MUSIC MASTER ALBUMS CATALOGUE

18TH EDITION

First published as the Music Master Record Catalogue in 1974.

This edition first published November, 1991.

Published by Music Master (a division of MBC Information Services Ltd) Music House, 1 De Cham Avenue, Hastings, East Sussex, England. TN37 6HE.

Advertising enquiries: Telephone: 071-490-0049. Fax: 071-608-1163.

Editorial enquiries: Telephone: (0424) 715181. Fax: (0424) 422805.

Book trade enquiries: Harrap Publishing Group Limited, Chelsea House, 26 Market Square, Bromley, Kent. BR1 1NA. Telephone: 081-313-3484. Fax: 081-313-0702.

Record trade enquiries: Music Master, Music House, 1 De Cham Avenue, Hastings, East Sussex. TN37 6HE. Telephone: (0424) 715181. Fax: (0424) 422805.

ISBN 0 904520 65 X

THE MUSIC MASTER TEAM: Production Manager: George Rankin. **Production Team:** Dave Kent, Jason Philpott, Clive Brown, Fiona Allman. **Editorial Team:** Pete Smith, Karen Blackman, Sylvia Davis, James Kent, Pam Brown, Jennifer Bellerose, Anita Ferrario. **Sales Team:** Tracy Dale, Anna Sperni, Marianne Hyne. **Product Development Manager:** Chris Spalding.

Printed and bound in Great Britain by BPCC Wheatons Limited, Exeter, Devon.

Cover artwork and design by Creatrix Design Partnership, Hastings, East Sussex.

MUSIC MASTER ALBUMS CATALOGUE

18TH EDITION

CONTENTS

INTRODUCTION

Welcome to the new-look Music Master Albums Catalogue - probably the most comprehensive guide to popular music records and cassettes ever published. In the following 1400 pages of this catalogue (previously the Music Master Record Catalogue), you will find gathered more information on LP's and cassettes than ever before - a veritable treasure trove of little known, yet vitally important facts about recorded popular music.

Whatever your musical tastes, the Music Master Albums Catalogue contains all the information on current and deleted products you could ever wish to know.

Within these pages you will find information on over 100,000 albums and cassettes, and over half a million tracks, plus full catalogue numbers - probably more than in any other music publication. Perfect for use by serious record collectors, trivia buffs, music lovers in general, or simply for settling arguments, the Music Master Albums Catalogue is an indispensible part of any record collection.

G & S MUSIC
THE FZ MAIL ORDER SPECIALISTS
0442 63287

HOW TO USE THIS CATALOGUE

The Music Master Albums Catalogue has been compiled in such a way as to make reference quick and easy for the reader, so the following guide should make this book even simpler to use!

The catalogue is put together in alphabetical sections and all the pages are numbered within each letter, for instance, section 'A' is numbered A1, A2, A3 and so on. The key to quick and easy reference in this book are the 'black strip' headings. These headings are normally the name of the artist or artists who have recorded the various albums or cassettes listed under their name, but in the case of Various artists recordings, the title will either be listed under the black strip heading of the recording or the musical genre.

To assist in identifying which record labels the various catalogue numbers refer to, a quick index is published at the back of this book. This index lists all the major catalogue number prefixes and indicates the record label to which these prefixes refer.

Black strip heading — **Track listing** — **Recording title** — **Catalogue number** — **Recording format**

Tauber, Richard

GOLDEN AGE OF RICHARD TAUBER.
Tracks: / We'll gather lilacs / One alone / English rose / Lover come back to me / One day when we were young / Long ago (and far away) / Sympathy / Dearly beloved / Can I forget you / Waltz song / Pedro, the fisherman / I knew that you must care / Love serenade / Sylvia / Largo (ombra maifu) / At the Balalaika / For this I pray / Serenade / Ave Maria / Serenade - Farewell my love - Farewell.
LP: .... GX 2504
MC: .... TCGX 2504

GOLDEN MELODIES.
Tracks: / Asleep in the deep / Viennese and italian songs / Land without music / Lockende ziel.
LP: .... GEMM 263

GOODNIGHT SWEETHEART.
LP: .... GEMM 231

GREAT VOICES OF THE CENTURY.
Tracks: / Prize song / Am stillen herd / Selig sind / Ach so fromm / Solo profugo / Ewig will lehdir gehoeren / Non plangere liu / Nessun dorma / Lug dursel lug / Addio fiorito asil / Lenski's aria / Adieu mignon / Di rigori armato / Flower song / Recondita armonia / Lucevan le stelle.
LP: .... GVC 502

OLD CHELSEA - A MUSICAL ROMANCE.
LP: .... SR 5007

PARADISE LOST, A (Tauber, Richard & Dajos Bela).
LP: .... REH 754
MC: .... ZCR 754

SONGS AND DUETS.
Tracks: / Love never comes too late / Nobody could love you more / Lovely as a night in June / Free and young (Frie un jung da bie) / Much has been written of love / Cup of tea with you, A / Love what has given you this magic power / Gianniana mia / Fascination / Rose Marie / Indian love call / Serenade / Will you remember / Waltz of my heart / Sweethearts.
LP: .... EG 2601861
MC: .... EG 2601864

THIS WAS RICHARD TAUBER.
LP: .... SRS 5065
MC: .... TCEXE 54

VOICE OF ROMANCE, THE.
LPS: .... ALBUM 43
MCSET: .... CASSETTE 43

Recording formats

The abbreviations for record formats used in this book are as follows:-

LP: Album. **2LP:** Double album. **LPS:** Album set. **LPPD:** Album picture disc. **MLP:** Mini LP. **MC:** Musicassette. **MCSET:** Cassette set.

NUMERICAL

1 To 1

FORWARD YOUR EMOTIONS.
Tracks: / Don't call it love / Angel in my pocket / Hearts and diamonds / Where's the answer / Forward your emotions / There was a time / Black on white / Love is blind / Boys will be boys / Tell me straight.
LP: **207 055**
MC: **407 055**

1'O Clock Gang

ONE O'CLOCK GANG.
Tracks: / Close your eyes / Innocent / Trigger happy / Friday's child / Whipping boy / Never let you burn / Closer to the angels / Giving in / Bitter end, The / Drill, The.
LP: **207121**
MC: **407121**

1st

FIRST IMPRESSIONS (Various artists).
LP: . . . . **NAGE 16**
MC: . . . . **NAGE 16C**

FIRST THINGS FIRST (Various artists).
Tracks: / True colours: *One Deaf Ear* / Everest: *Uncertain Trumpet* / First move, The: *Western Justice*/ American man: *Big Electric Pit* / Bread winner, The: *Donnelly Brothers* / Hung up and hung over: *Cut The* Bag / No joy: *Various artists* / Heart of shame: *Sonitcha* / Kings of nothing: *Violet Sky* / White sex: *Meantime In Czechoslavakia* / Fabulous love: *Red Circus* / Actors farewell, The: *Kaape*.
LP: . . . . **FIRST 1**

2 A.M.

WHEN EVERY SECOND COUNTS.
Tracks: / Never gonna let you escape / You're the one / Somebody, someday / Who will you run to? / Too late / Lost souls / Running with the same old crowd / Never feel this way again / Dreams and promises / Now you're leaving.
LP: . . . . **PL 71400**
MC: . . . . **PK 71400**

2 Bad

IDIOT TREE.
LP: . . . . **FULL 003**

2 Beggarmen

FLOWERS OF MANCHESTER (Two Beggarmen).
Tracks: / Flowers of Manchester / Hen's march / Calico printers clerk / Packet of biscuits, A / First flame / Knocker upper man / Dog fat / Ancoats pair / Pit boots / Gypsies rennies and things / Child of Merseyside / Bide awhile / Pomana.
LP: . . . . **SFA 109**

2 Belgen

2 BELGEN.
Tracks: / 2 Belgen.
MLP: . . . . **ANT 007**

SOULSMASKING.
Tracks: / Soulsmasking.
LP: . . . . **ANT 022**

SWEET AND SOUR.
Tracks: / Sweet and sour.
LP: . . . . **ANT 049**
LP: . . . . **DIL 3599**

2 Black 2 Strong

BURN BABY BURN.
LP: **4676881**
MC: **4676884**

2 Daughters

KISS THE CLOTH.
LP: . . . . **A+P 01**

2 Deep

HONEY THAT'S SHOWBIZZ.
LP: **75992617012**
MC: **75992617042**

2 Helens

REFLECTIONS IN RED.
LP: . . . . **TUFT 004**

2 In A Room

VOLUME 1.
LP: **INALP1**
MC: **INAMC1**

WIGGLE IT (ALBUM).
Tracks: / Wiggle it (radio mix) / She's got me going crazy / Hype stuff / House junkie (1990 version) / Got 'em on the run / Bring it on down / Body to body / Do what you want / Booty hump / Soul train / Rock bottom / Rock the house / She's got me going crazy (Todd Terry mix) / Wiggle it (David Morales mix) (CD only.).
LP: . . . . **SBKLP 11**
MC: . . . . **SBKTC 11**

2 Left Hands

MUSIC FOR THE LEFT-HANDED.
MC: . . . . **LEFTC 1**

2 Live Crew

AS CLEAN AS THEY WANNA BE.
LP: . . . . **XR 108**
MC: . . . . **CXR 108**

AS NASTY AS THEY WANNA BE.
LP: . . . . **XR 107**

2 Lost Sons

808 FEVER.
LP: . . . . **BLUNT 047**

2 Man Sound

DISCO SAMBA.
Tracks: / Disco samba / Que tel America / Samba samba / Brazil O Brazil / Vas-y-maman / Menina rainbow / Djin djin / Ritmocada.
LP: . . . . **OV 2001**

2 Minds Crack

VICTORY PARADE.
Tracks: / One sky above us / Walk on back / Hunger and greed / Fire / Find the key / Cry cry cry / Upside down / Love is in control / Live to die / Sense that never sleeps.
LP: **925517 1**
MC: **925517 4**

2 Nations

BOTH SIDES.
Tracks: / Any luck / Write me / Can this be love / Don't say your leaving / Independence / That's the way it feels / Evermore / Driving me wild / Who do you believe / Living in two nations.
LP: . . . . **DIX 44**
MC: . . . . **CDIX 44**

2 Nice Girls

LIKE A VERSION.
Tracks: / I feel (like makin') love / Bang bang / Top of the world / Speed racer / Cotton crown / I spent my last $10 (on birth control & beer).
MLP: . . . . **RTM 235**

TWO NICE GIRLS.
LP: . . . . **ROUGH 135**
MC: . . . . **ROUGHC 135**
LP: . . . . **US 59**

2 Rocks

WHEN SANITY IS ACTING KIND OF WILD.
LP: . . . . **WKFMLP 174**
MC: . . . . **WKFMMC 174**

2 Saints

IN NOMINE SOLIS.
LP: . . . . **YEAH-HUP 004**

ON BOURBON STREET.
Tracks: / On bourbon street.
LP: . . . . **YEAH-HUP 013**

2 Sisters

DESTINY.
LP: . . . . **XKHAN 502**

2 Ton Machine

CHINATOWN.
LP: . . . . **DA 103**

2 Tone Story

TWO TONE STORY, THE (Various artists).
LP: . . . . **CNW 8**
MC: . . . . **ZCNW 8**
LP: . . . . **CHRTT 5009**
MC: . . . . **ZCHRT 5009**

2 Tons O' Fun

TWO TONS O'FUN.
Tracks: / Do you wanna boogie huh? / Just us / Got the feeling / Gone away / Earth can be just like heaven / Make someone feel happy today / Taking away your space / One sided love affair.
LP: . . . . **FT 566**

2nd Communication

BRAIN THAT BINDS THE BODY, THE (see under Second Communication).

2nd Generation

SPY-CATCHER.
LP: . . . . **PHZA 22**

2nd Generation (USA)

STATE OF MIND.
Tracks: / Green hill mountain home / Something to be finding / Newsreel / Barstool blues / Favourite memory / Two by four / State of mind / Stitch in time / Goin' home in the rain / Old man (life cycled) / Living waters.
LP: . . . . **CMH 6208**
MC: . . . . **CMH 6208C**

2nd Power

DA SOUL MAN.
Tracks: / People / Get busy / Livin' like a gansta' / Da soul man / Side / Fonkay drunk ghetto bass / People B trippin' / Make it fonkay / Private freak / Don't rush my beat (Only on MC and CD.) / S.O.S. (same ole story) (Only on MC and CD.).
LP: . . . . **ICH 1102**
MC: . . . . **ICH 1102 MC**

2nd Street Dreads

PICK A DUB.
LP: . . . . **RU 1001**

3

3 BILLY GOATS GRUFF & OTHER FAVOURITE STORIES (for children aged 3-7) (Various artists).
MC: . . . . **VCA 607**

TO THE POWER OF THREE.
Tracks: / Talkin' about / Lover to lover / Chains / Desde la vida / Eight miles high / Runaway / You do or you don't / On my way home.
LP: . . . . **K 9241811**
MC: . . . . **K 9241814**

3 Amigos

THREE AMIGOS (Film soundtrack) (Various artists).
Tracks: / Ballad of the 3 Amigos: *Various artists* / Main title: *Various artists* / Big sneak, The: *Various artists* / My little buttercup: *Various artists* / Santa Poco: *Various artists* / Fiesta and flamenco: *Various* artists / El guapo: *Various artists* / Return of the Amigos: *Various artists* / Blue shadows on the trail: *Various artists* / Singing bush, The: *Various artists* / Amigos at the mission: *Various artists* / Capture: *Various artists* / El guapo's birthday: *Various artists* / Chase, The: *Various artists* / Amigo's, amigo's, amigo's: *Various artists* / Farewell: *Various artists* / End credits: *Various artists*.
LP: **925558 1**
MC: **925558 4**

3 D

HILLTOP HUSTLERS (3 D - Cool C).
LP: . . . . **CBLP 2**
MC: . . . . **CBMC 2**

ORIGINAL STYLING.
LP: . . . . **CBLP 3 F**
MC: . . . . **CBMC 3**

3 Degrees

3D.
Tracks: / Jump the gun / Red light / Set me free / Starlight / My simple heart / Without you / Bodycheck.
LP: **3D 1**

6 TRACK HITS.
Tracks: / Woman in love / Magic in the air / My simple heart / Jump the gun / Without you / Runner, The.
MC: **7SC 5005**

20 GOLDEN GREATS: THREE DEGREES.
LP: . . . . **SHM 3155**
MC: . . . . **HSC 3155**

BEST OF THE THREE DEGREES, THE.
Tracks: / When will I see you again / Year of decision / Toast of love / This is the house / Starlight / Love Train / Woman in love / Get your love back / Dirty ol' man / Without you / TSOP(the sound of Philadelphia) / My simple heart / Long lost lover / Heaven I need, The / I didn't know / Givin' up givin' in / Take good care of yourself / Golden lady / Love is the message / Distant lover / Jump the gun / Runner, The.
LP: **911182**
MC: **911205**
2LP: . . . . **VSOPLP 149**
MC: . . . . **VSOPMC 149**

COLLECTION OF THEIR 20 GREATEST HITS, A.
LP: . . . . **EPC 10013**

GOLD.
LP: . . . . **NE 1089**
MC: . . . . **CE 2089**
LP: **3D 2**

GOLD (EPIC).
Tracks: / Dirty ol' man / We're all alone / I didn't know / I like being a woman / What I did for love / Take good care of yourself / Year of decision / Another heartache / Can't you see what you're doing to me / Distant lover / Toast of love / Get your love back / When will I see you again / Long lost lover / Macaroni man / In love we grow / Gee baby / Standing up for love / T.S.O.P. / Free ride / Love train / Don't let the sun go down on me / Living for the city / For the love of money.
2LP: . . . . **EPC 22110**

GOLDEN HOUR OF THE THREE DEGREES.
Tracks: / You're the one / Love the one you're with / Who is she and what is she to you / Magic mirror / There's so much love all around me / Rose garden / Caught between two fires / Collage / Lonely man / Maybe / Ebb tide / Tradewinds / I do take you / If you must leave my life / Magic door / Stardust / You're the fool / Sugar on Sunday / MacArthur Park.
LP: . . . . **GH 881**

HITS HITS HITS.
Tracks: / Woman in love / My simple heart / We are family / Falling in love again / Givin' up, givin' in / Without you / Magic in the air / I'll never love this way again / Starlight / Jump the gun / You light up my life / Red light / Bodycheck.
LP: . . . . **SHM 3086**
MC: . . . . **HSC 3086**

NEW DIMENSIONS.
Tracks: / Givin' up, givin' in / Falling in love again / Looking for love / Runner / Woman in love / Magic in the air.
LP: . . . . **ARL 5012**
MC: . . . . **ZCARL 5012**

SATIN AND SOUL.
Tracks: / Woman in love / My simple heart / Golden lady / Without you / Set me free / Starlight / Runner, The / Givin' up, givin' in / Falling in love again / Bodycheck / Red light / Out of love again / Magic in the air / Jump the gun.
MC: **410.362**

TAKE GOOD CARE OF YOURSELF.
LP: . . . . **PIR 69137**

THREE DEGREES... AND HOLDING, THE.
Tracks: / Tie u up / Win, place or show / Make it easy on yourself / Lock it up / Vital signs / Tender lie, A / After the night is over / Are you that kind of guy.
LP: . . . . **ICH 1041**
MC: . . . . **ZCICH 1041**

THREE DEGREES, THE.
Tracks: / Jump the gun / Red light / Set me free / Bodycheck / Givin' up, givin' in / Starlight / My simple heart / Without you / Stardust / We are family.
LP: . . . . **PIR 32044**
MC: **40 32044**
LP: . . . . **MFP 50543**
MC: . . . . **TCMFP 50543**
LP: **65858**

TWENTY OF THEIR GREATEST HITS.
Tracks: / When will I see you again / Can't you see what you're doing to me / Toast of love / We're all alone / Long lost lover / Get your love back / I like being a woman / What I did for love / Standing up for love / Take good care of yourself / Dirty ol' man / Loving cup / Woman needs a good man, A / TSOP / Another heartache / Distant lover / Together / Here I am / Year of decision / Love train.
LP: . . . . **EPC 32478**
MC: **40 32478**

3 Musketeers

THREE MUSKETEERS, THE (see Dumas, Alexandre) (Unknown narrator(s)).

3 Mustaphas 3

FRIENDS, FIENDS AND FRONDS.
MC: . . . . **ORBC 070**

GOLDEN WORLD OF MUSTAPHA, THE.
Tracks: / Linda Linda / Vranjanski Ekspres / Chilling tale, A / Voulez vous danser / Shika shika / Mehmeteli / Kopanitsa / Besarabia / Si vous passez

par la / Shouffi Rhirou / Singe tema / Night off Beirut, A / Szegerely farewell.
MC: ORBC 027

HEART OF UNCLE.
Tracks: / Awara hoon / Mama O / Anapse to tsigaro / Yeni yol / Kaba mustafa / Taxi driver / Aj zajdi zajdi jasno sonce / Sitna Lisa / Ovcepolsko oro / Kem kem / Trois fois trois (city version) / Vi bist du geveyzn far prohibish'n / Benga taxi / Trois fois trois (country version).
MC: ORBC 043
LP: ORB 043

HEART OF UNCLE (see under 'Three Mustaphas Three').

L'ORCHESTRE "BAM" DE GRAND MUSTAPHA INT.& PARTY HITS.
Tracks: / Vranjanski ekspres / O Memetis / Hora lui marin / Besarabia / Niska banja / Ainy la la/ah ya assmar el lawn / Cabra.
LP: FEZ 002

BAM! MUSTAPHAS PLAY STEREO.
Tracks: / Lebedik un freilach / To tilephone tiszenitias / Singe tema / Chilling tale, A / Thalasso p'ola ta nera / Mehmeteli / Beltz.
LP: FEZ 001

SHOPPING.
Tracks: / Ljubav kraj izvora/zvezdanova (skupovo) kolo / Shika shika / Xamenh evtexia/Fiz'n / Musafir / Szegerely farewell / Night off Beirut, A / Selver / Shouffi rhirou / Valle e pogradecit / Darling, don't say 'no' (CD only) / Voulez vous danser.
LP: ORB 022
MC: ORBC 022

SOUP OF THE CENTURY.
LP: FEZLP 004
MC: FEZC 004

3 O'Clock

ARRIVE WITHOUT TRAVELLING.
LP: MIRF 1002
MC: MIRFC 1002

EVER AFTER.
Tracks: / Suzie's on the ball now / Look into your eyes / When we can / Penny girls, The / Follow him around / Warm aspirations / Step out of line / We are one / If you could see my way / Songs and gentle words.
LP: MIRF 1006
MC: MIRFC 1006

SIXTEEN TAMBOURINES.
LP: LOLITA 5008

VERMILLION.
Tracks: / Vermillion / Love explosion / To be where you are / When she becomes my girl / World on fire / Neon telephone / On paper / Ways of magic / Time is going slower / Love has no heart / Through the creepy town.
MC: 925717 4
LP: 925717 1

3 O'Clock High

THREE O'CLOCK HIGH (Film soundtrack) (Various artists).
LP: STV 81339
MC: CTV 81339

3 Wise Men

GB-BOYZ.
Tracks: / Urban hell / What it iz kuttin wittin / Hardcore lover / Cruising for a bruising / Refresh yourself / Hard bop / Return of the drunken master.
LP: LEFTLP 1
MC: LEFTC 6

3rd Bass

CACTUS ALBUM.
Tracks: / Stymie's theme / Sons of 3rd Bass / Russell Rush / Gas face, The / Monte hall / Oval office / Hoods / Soul in the hole / Triple stage darkness / M.C. Disagree / Wordz of wisdom / Product of the environment / Desert boots / Cactus, The / Jim Backus / Flippin' off the wall like Lucy Ball / Brooklyn Queens / Steppin' to the A.M. / Episode 3 / Who's on third.
LP: 4660031
MC: 4660034

DERELICTS OF DIALECT.
Tracks: / Merchant of grooves, The / Derelicts of dialect / Ace in the hole / French toast / Portrait of the artist as a hood / Pop goes the weasel / Sea vessel soliloquy / Daddy rich in the land of 1210 / Word to the third / Herbalz in your mouth / Al's a b cee'z / No master plan no master race / Come in / No static at all / Eye jammie / Microphone techniques / Problem child / 3 strikes 5000 / Kick 'em in the grill / Green eggs and swine / Check yourself (Only available on LP).
LP: 4683171
MC: 4683174

4 Hero

IN ROUGH TERRITORY.
LP: RIVETLP 001
MC: RIVETMC 001

4 Men & A Dog

BARKING MAD.
LP: CBMMC 001

4 Skins

FEW 4 SKINS MORE, VOL. 1, A.
LP: LINK LP 015

FEW 4 SKINS MORE VOL. 2, A.
LP: LINK LP 021

FISTFUL OF....FOUR SKINS, A.
LP: SYNLP 1

FROM CHAOS TO 1984.
LP: SYNLP 5

GOOD THE BAD AND THE 4 SKINS, THE.
Tracks: / Plastic gangster / Jealousy / Yesterday's heroes / Justice / Jack the lad / Remembrance day / Manifesto / Wonderful world / Sorry / Evil / I don't wanna die / A.C.A.B. / Chaos / One law for them.
LP: SEC 4

LIVE AND LOUD.
LP: LINKLP 090

WONDERFUL WORLD OF THE 4 SKINS.
Tracks: / Evil / One law for them / ACAB / Seems to me / Yesterdays heroes / Clockwork skinhead.
LP: LINKLP 002

5 Birds & A Monk

5 BIRDS & A MONK.
Tracks: / Billie's bounce / 'Round midnight / Confirmation / Yardbird suite / Relaxin' at Camarillo / Bloomdido.
LP: GXY 5134

5 TA

ANGEL.
MC: TCCRB 1096

KIND OF TRIUMPH, A.
Tracks: / Question of belief / Decadent and sexy / My brilliant career / We are the men / Heaven / Walking on the water / Fine day / Law of the jungle, The / Salt / Trinity / Trinity (highly strung mix) (Available on Cassette/Compact Disc only).
LP: 207983
MC: 407983

5th Dimension

6 TRACK HITS.
Tracks: / Puppet man / Never my love / One less bell to answer / Carpet man / Save the country / Last night I didn't get to sleep at all.
MC: 7SC 5025

HIGH ON SUNSHINE.
Tracks: / High on sunshine / Turn my love away / Everybody's got to give it up / Magic man / Children of tomorrow / Sway / Skyway / Can't get you / You're my star.
LP: STML 12106

6

SIX FAT DUTCHMAN Various artists (Various artists).
LP: PC 382

SIX NUMBER ONES Various artists (Various artists).
Tracks: / I love to love: *Charles, Tina* / When will I see you again?: *3 Degrees* / San Francisco: *McKenzie, Scott* / What's another year?: *Logan, Johnny* / Ob la di ob la da: *Marmalade* / Yellow river: *Christine (film)*.
MC: 7SC 5052

SIX SEQUENCES POUR ALFRED HITCHCOCK Various artists (Various artists).
Tracks: / Fear of incarceration: *Various artists* / Family plot: *Various artists* / Teenage heartthrob: *Various* artists / Cafe Mozart waltz: *Various artists* / OK: *Various artists* / Question de principe: *Various* artists / Audition, The: *Various artists* / Movie A: *Various artists* / Movie B: *Various artists*/ Pour un demi poulet: *Various artists*.
LP: NATO 304

SIX SWINGERS Various original artists (Various artists).
LP: SH 248

6 Fat Dutchmen

ENTER POLKA HALL OF FAME.
LP: PC 375

7th Avenue Stompers

FIDGETY FEET.
LP: WL 70509

8 & 1/2 (film)

EIGHT AND A HALF (1963 film soundtrack) (Various artists).
LP: NL 33210
MC: NK 33210

8 Dayz

EVERY DAY IS LIKE A NEW BEGINNING.
LP: WIND 3

8 Eyed Spy

EIGHT EYED SPY.
LP: FR 2003

LIVE: EIGHT EYED SPY (With Lydia Lunch).
MC: A 101

8th Day

EIGHTH DAY.
Tracks: / Call me up / It ain't funny no more / In the valley / Right mood / I've got my heart in the right place / Body buddy / Last night made my day / Hot on the heels of love / Don't blow it.
LP: AMLH 64942

8th Wonder

FEARLESS.
Tracks: / Cross my heart / When the phone stops ringing / Baby baby / Will you remember / Wild love / I'm not scared / Use me / Anything at all / My baby's heartbeat / Dress, The.
LP: 4606281
MC: 4606284

9 & 1/2 Weeks (film)

NINE & A HALF WEEKS (Film Soundtrack) (Various artists).
Tracks: / I do what I do: *Taylor, John* / Best is yet to come, The: *Luba* / Slave to love: *Ferry, Bryan*/ Black on black: *Dalbello* / Eurasian eyes: *Hart, Corey* / You can leave your hat on: *Cocker, Joe* / Bread and butter: *Devo* / This city never sleeps: *Eurythmics* / Cannes: *Copeland, Stewart* / Let it go: *Luba*.
LP: EST 2003
MC: TCEST 2003

9 to 5

9 TO 5 (Film soundtrack) (Various artists).
LP: T 627
MC: C 627

10 CC

10 CC.
Tracks: / Johnny don't do it / Sand in my face / Donna / Dean & I / Headline hustler / Speed kills / Rubber bullets / Hospital song / Ships don't disappear / Fresh air for my mama.
LP: UKAL 1005
LP: 6359014
LP: PRICE 7
MC: CLAMC 185
LP: CLALP 185

10 CC IN CONCERT.
Tracks: / Second sitting for the last supper / You've got a cold / Things we do for love, The / Art for arts sake / People in love / Wall Street shuffle / I'm Mandy, fly me / Marriage bureau rendezvous / Good morning Judge / Honeymoon with B-troop / Waterfall / I'm not in love.
LP: CN 2056
MC: CN4 2056

BEST OF 1975-77.
LP: 9279 567

BLOODY TOURISTS.
Tracks: / Dreadlock holiday / For you and I / Take these chains / Shock on the tube / Last night / Anonymous alcoholic / Reds in my bed / Life line / Tokyo / Old mister time / From Rochdale to Ocho Rios / Everything you've wanted to know about.
LP: 9102 503
LP: PRICE 6

BLOODY TOURISTS/THE ORIGINAL SOUNDTRACK (Two Great Pop Classics Series).
2LP: 8301851

CHANGING FACES - THE VERY BEST OF... (10 CC & Godley & Creme).
Tracks: / Dreadlock holiday / Wall Street shuffle, The / Under your thumb / Life is a minestrone / Englishman in New York / Art for art's sake / Donna / Snack attack / Cry / Things we do for love, The / Wedding bells / I'm Mandy, fly me / Good morning judge / Rubber bullets / Save a mountain for me / I'm not in love.
LP: TGCLP 1
MC: TGCMC 1

COLLECTION: 10CC.
2LP: CCSLP 214
MC: CCSMC 214

DECEPTIVE BENDS.
Tracks: / Good morning judge / Things we do for love / Marriage bureau / Rendezvous / People in love / Modern man blues / Honeymoon with B troop / I bought a flat guitar tutor / You've got a cold / Feel the benefit.
LP: 9102 502
LP: PRICE 5

DREADLOCK HOLIDAY.
LP: 814 655 1

GREATEST HITS: TEN CC 1972-78.
Tracks: / Rubber bullets / Donna / Silly love / Dean and I / Life is a minestrone / Wall Street shuffle / Art for art's sake / I'm Mandy, fly me / Good morning judge / Things we do for love / Dreadlock holiday / I'm not in love.
LP: 9102 504
MC: 7231 304
LP: UKAL 1012

HOW DARE YOU?.
Tracks: / Art for art's sake / Don't hang up / Head room / How dare you? / I wanna rule the world / Iceberg / I'm Mandy, fly me / Lazy ways / Rock 'n' roll lullaby.
LP: PRICE 60
MC: PRIMC 60
LP: 9102 501

LIVE AND LET LIVE.
Tracks: / Second sitting for the Last Supper, The / You've got a cold / Honeymoon with B troop / Art for art's sake / People in love / Wall Street shuffle, The / Ships don't disappear in the night / I'm Mandy, fly me / Good morning, judge / Feel the benefit / Things we do for love, The / Waterfall / I'm not in love (Seven-minute version.) / Modern man blues.
2LP: 6641 714
2LP: 6641 698

LOOK HEAR.
Tracks: / One, two, five / Welcome to the world / How'm I ever gonna say goodbye / Don't send we back / I took you home / It doesn't matter at all / Dressed to kill / Lovers anonymous / I hate to eat alone / L.A. inflatable.
LP: 9102 505
MC: 7231 305

NIGHTRIDING: TEN CC.
Tracks: / Rubber bullets / Donna / Silly love / Dean and I, The / Life is a minestrone / Wall Street shuffle, The / Good morning judge / Art for art's sake / I'm Mandy, fly me / Things we do for love, The / Dreadlock holiday / I'm not in love.
MC: KNMC 10012
LP: KNLP 10012

ORIGINAL SOUNDTRACK, THE.
Tracks: / Blackmail / Brand new day / Film of my love / Flying junk / I'm not in love / Life is a minestrone / Second sitting for the Last Supper, The / Une nuit a Paris / One night in Paris / Same night in Paris / Later the same night in Paris.
LP: PRICE 48
MC: PRIMC 48
LP: 9102 50 Q
LP: HS 9102 500

PROFILE: TEN CC.
LP: 6.24012
MC: CL4 24012

SHEET MUSIC.
Tracks: / Wall Street shuffle, The / Worst band in the world / Hotel / Old wild men / Clockwork creep / Silly love / Somewhere in Hollywood / Baron Samedi / Sacro-liac, The / Of effendi.
LP: PRICE 8
MC: PRIMC 8
LP: UKAL 1007
LP: 6310508
MC: CLAMC 186
LP: CLALP 186

SONGS WE DO FOR LOVE, THE.
LP: RJ 7437

TEN OUT OF TEN.
Tracks: / Don't ask / Overdraft on overdrive / Don't turn me away / Les nouveaux riches / Memories / Notell hotel / Action man in Motown suit / Listen with your eyes / Lying here with you / Survivor.
LP: 6359 048
MC: 7150 048

WINDOWS IN THE JUNGLE.
Tracks: / 24 hours / Feel the love / Here I am / American panorama.
LP: MERL 28
MC: MERLC 28

WORST BAND IN THE WORLD.
LP: UKPAL 001

10 Dance

10 DANCE RECORD, A (Various artists).
Tracks: / Tell me (how it feels) (M+M stylee): *52nd Street* / We don't have to take our clothes off: *Stewart, Jermaine*/ This house is haunted: *Arnold, P.P.* / Ain't that the truth: *Kelly, Frankie* / Keep on: *Mardis, Bobby*/ Warrior groove: *D.S.M.* / More than one night: *Roberts, Julie* / Galveston bay: *Hill, Lonnie* / Raise the roof: *Conway Brothers* / Good to the last drop: *C-Bank* (Featuring Eleanor Mills).

MC: TDRC 1

10 (film)

"10" (Film soundtrack) (Various artists).
Tracks: / Don't call it love: *Ten...* / He pleases me: *Ten...* / Keyboard harmony: *Ten...* / It's easy to say: *Various artists* / Something for Johnny: *Various artists* / Get it on: *Various artists* / Hot sound Mexican Band: *Various artists* / I have an ear for love: *Various artists* / Bolero: *Various artists.*
LP: K 56775
LP: BS 3399

10 x 12

10 BY 12 (Various artists).
Tracks: / Living in America: *Brown, James* / Alice, I want you just for me: *Full Force* / I wonder if I take you home: *Lisa Lisa/Cult Jam with Full Force* / House rocker: *Lovebug Starski* / Hot: *Ayers, Roy* / Saturday love: *Cherrelle & Alexander O'Neal* / Sugar free: *Juicy* / New York eyes: *Nicole with Tommy Thomas* / If I were here tonight: *O'Neal, Alexander* / Finest, The: *S.O.S. Band.*
LP: PRT 26920
MC: 40 26920

10th Anniversary...

TENTH ANNIVERSARY ANTHOLOGY VOL.1 (Various artists).
LP: AN 004
LP: BEDLP 8

11th Dream Day

BEET.
LP: LP 46
MC: MC 46

ELEVENTH DREAM DAY.
LP: FC 056

PRAIRIE SCHOOL FREAKOUT.
LP: ROSE 159

12

TWELVE X TWELVE Twelve megamixes (Various artists).
LP: INCH 1
MC: ZCINC 1

12 Carat Gold

TWELVE CARAT GOLD Reggae Hits (Various artists).
LP: MLP 12-217

12 Chairs

TWELVE CHAIRS (Original soundtrack) (Various artists).
LP: TER 1033

12 Commandments...

TWELVE COMMANDMENTS IN METAL (Various artists).
LP: RR 9799
MC: RR 49799

12 Drummers Drumming

WHERE THE WILD BUFFALO ROAMS.
Tracks: / I'll be there / Too much too soon / Rivers / Where the wild buffalo roams / Russian sun / Love, The / Love is a treasure / Just good friends / It takes a lot / Don't stop.
LP: MERH 127
MC: MERHC 127

12 Inches...

TWELVE INCHES OF PLEASURE VOL.2 (Various artists).
LP: PROTO 2

12" Tapes

TWELVE INCH TAPES - EXTENDED MIXES VOL.2 (Various artists).
Tracks: / All cried out: *Moyet, Alison* / Wherever I lay my hat: *Young, Paul* / Time after time: *Lauper, Cyndi* / Feels like heaven: *Fiction Factory* / Total eclipse of the heart: *Tyler, Bonnie.*
MC: 40 54879

TWELVE INCH TAPES - EXTENDED MIXES VOL.5 (Various artists).
Tracks: / Just the way you like it: *S.O.S. Band* / State of shock: *Jacksons* / It's raining men: *Weather Girls* / Doctor Beat: *Various artists* / Dancing in the streets: *Shalamar.*
MC: 40 54882

TWELVE INCH TAPES - EXTENDED MIXES (Various artists).
Tracks: / Billie Jean: *Jackson, Michael* / Let's hear it for the boy: *Williams, Deniece* / Just be good to me: *S.O.S. Band* / Slippery people: *Staple Singers* / Rock it: *Hancock, Herbie.*
MC: 40 54878

TWELVE INCH TAPES - EXTENDED MIXES VOL.3 (Various artists).
Tracks: / Club Tropicana: *Wham* / Love resurrection: *Moyet, Alison* / Love kills: *Mercury, Freddie* / Girls just want to have fun: *Lauper, Cyndi* / Dance hall days: *Wang Chung.*
MC: 40 54880

12th Night

ART AND ILLUSION.
Tracks: / Counterpoint / Art and illusion / C.R.A.B. / Kings and queens / First new day.
LP: MFN 36

COLLECTOR'S ITEM.
2LP: GRUB 18
MCSET: TGRUB 18

FACT AND FICTION.
Tracks: / We are sane / World without end / Creep show / Poet sniffs a flower / Human being / Love song / Fact and fiction.
LP: TN 006

LIVE AND LET LIVE (LIVE AT THE MARQUEE).
Tracks: / Ceiling speaks, The / Fact and fiction / End of the endless majority, The / Poet sniffs a flower, The / Sequences / We are sane.
LP: MFN 18

LIVE AT THE TARGET.
Tracks: / Fur helene (pt 1) / After the eclipse / East to west / Sequences.
LP: TN 002

SMILING AT GRIEF.
Tracks: / East of Eden / This city / Honeymoon is over, The / Creepshow / Puppets (intro) / Puppets / Make no sense / Three dancers, The / Fur helene (pt 2).
MC: TN 003

TWELFTH NIGHT Old Vic Company (Various artists).
LPS: D 159 D 3

TWELFTH NIGHT (see under Shakespeare, William) (Various artists).

TWELFTH NIGHT.
Tracks: / Last song, The / Pressure / Jungle / Craft, The / Blue powder monkey / Theatre / Shame / This is war / Take a look.
LP: CHC 72
MC: CHCMC 72
LP: CASG 1174

13 At Midnight

LAST TRUE FRIENDS.
LP: SURB 2

13 Days

THIRTEEN DAYS.
Tracks: / Future blues / Shot down in flames / Morphine Bill / Angel / Crazy Bill / Kennedy said / Garden of Eden / Houseparty / Lonesome prairie / Melanie.
LP: 083081

13 Engines

BEFORE OUR TIME.
Tracks: / Come back lover / End of your chain, The / Reunion, The / Cold pennies / It's easy to see / Annabelle Lee / Mothra / No more flowers.
LP: RES 339028

13 Problems (bk)

THIRTEEN PROBLEMS, THE (Agatha Christie) (Hickson, Joan (nar)).
MCSET: LFP 7312

13th Floor Elevators

BULL OF THE WOODS.
Tracks: / Livin' on / Barnyard blues / Till then / Never another / Rose and the thorn / Down by the river / Scarlet and gold / Street song / Doctor Boom / With you / May the circle remain unbroken.
LP: LIK 40

EASTER EVERYWHERE.
Tracks: / Slip inside this house / Slide machine / She lives in a time of her own / Nobody to love / It's all over now baby blue / Earthquake / Dust / I've got levitation / I had to tell you / Postures (leave your body behind).
LP: RAD 15
LP: LIK 28

ELEVATORS LIVE.
Tracks: / Before you accuse me / She lives in a time of her own / Tried to hide / You gotta take that girl / I'm gonna love you too / Everybody needs somebody to love (Russell/Burke/Wexler) / I've got levitation / You can't hurt me anymore / Roller coaster / You're gonna miss me.
LP: LIK 30

I'VE SEEN YOUR FACE BEFORE.
Tracks: / Fire engine / Tried to hide / Levitation / Don't fall down / Kingdom of heaven / You're gonna miss me / Reverberation / Monkey island / Splash / She lives in a time of her own / Roller coaster.
LP: WIK 82

PSYCHEDELIC SOUNDS OF..,THE.
Tracks: / You're gonna miss me / Roller coaster / Splash 1 / Reverberation (doubt) / Don't fall down / Fire engine / Thru the rhythm / You don't know / Kingdom of heaven / Monkey island / Tried to hide.
LP: LIK 19
LP: RAD 13

14

14 GREAT TRUCK HITS (See under Truck Hits) (Various artists).

14 Iced Bears

PRECISION.
LP: TBLP 002

WONDER.
LP: BORDLP 002

15 Flaming Groovies

15 FLAMING GROOVIES (Various artists).
MC: FIREMC 19

16

16 BLUEGRASS HITS (Various artists).
LP: SLP 3015
MC: GT 53015
LP: SLP 3022

16 FIDDLERS GREATEST HITS (Various artists).
LP: SLP 3014
MC: GT 53014

16 NO.1 HITS IN THE SUMMERTIME (Various artists).
LP: OCN 2013WL
MC: OCN 2013WK

16 TRUCK DRIVER GREATS (Various artists).
LP: SLP 3024
MC: GT 53024

16 Big Hits

16 BIG HITS OF THE SIXTIES (Various artists).
LP: MFP 50405
MC: TCMFP 50405

16 Classic Irish

16 CLASSIC IRISH HITS OF THE EIGHTIES (Various artists).
Tracks: / Bunch of thyme: *Foster & Allen* / Fields of Athenry: *Reilly, Paddy* / It's hard to be humble: *Dallas, T.R.* / Totus totus (totally yours): *Dana* / When you were: *Fureys & Davey Arthur* / Black sheep: *Foster, Mick* / Four country roads: *Big Tom* / When the sun says ...: *McCann, Susan* / Red rose cafe, The: *Fureys* & Davey Arthur / Flight of Earls: *Dublin City Ramblers* / Wait 'till the clouds: *Dolan, Joe* / Marino waltz, The: *Sheahan, John & Michael Howard* / Grace: *McCann, Jim* / Midnight to moonlight: *Durkin, Kathy* / Limerick you're a lady: *Allen, Dennis* / Tears on the telephone: *Curtin, Glen.*
LP: HM 059

16 Country...

16 NUMBER ONE COUNTRY HITS VOL.2 (Various artists).
Tracks: / D.I.V.O.R.C.E.: *Various artists* / Crazy arms: *Various artists* / El Paso city: *Various artists*/ Saginaw Michigan: *Various artists* / Just good ol' boys: *Various artists* / Almost persuaded: *Various artists*/ All the gold in California: *Various artists* / Take this job and shove it: *Various artists* / One piece at a time: *Various artists* / Rolling with the flow: *Various artists* / Games people play: *Various artists* / Door: *Various artists* / What a man my man is: *Various artists* / Candy kisses: *Various artists* / North to Alaska: *Various artists* / If you've got the money, I've got the time: *Various artists.*
LP: CBS 31805
MC: 40 31805

16 NUMBER ONE COUNTRY HITS VOL.1 (Various artists).
LP: CBS 31456
MC: 40 31456

16 Dynamite Reggae

16 GREATEST REGGAE HITS (Various artists).
Tracks: / Hurt so good: *Cadogan, Susan* / Monday morning feeling: *Simon, Tito* / Walk a mile in my shoes: *Note, Freddie/ Rudies* / No one-day love: *Groovy, Winston* / Give and take: *Pioneers* / After tonight: *Matumbi*/ Love of the common people: *Thomas, Nicky* / Country roads: *Toots & The Maytals* / Sideshow: *Biggs, Barry*/ Morning of my life: *Holt, John* / God bless the children: *Thomas, Nicky* / Eighteen with a bullet: *Harriott, Derrick* / Caribbean way: *Miller, Lloyd* / Je t'aime: *Judge Dread* / Oh Patricia: *Simon, Tito* / In the game: *Honey Boy.*
LP: TRLS 146

SIXTEEN DYNAMITE REGGAE HITS (Various artists).
LP: TRLS 231
MC: ZCTRL 231

16 Forever

HERE COME THE BOP BOYS.
LP: NISHI 213

16 Hits Of...

16 HITS OF THE SIXTIES (See under 60's) (Various artists).

16 Hot Bullets

16 HOT BULLETS (Various artists).
LP: SHM 3109
MC: HSC 3109

16 Hymns

16 HYMNS FROM NORTHERN IRELAND VOL 2 (Various artists).
LP: POL 815

16 Irish ...

16 IRISH PUB DRINKING SONGS (Various artists).
Tracks: / Reluctant patriot: *Various artists* / Little Armalite: *Various artists* / Barry's column: *Various artists* / Town I loved so well: *Various artists* / Four green fields: *Various artists* / Only our rivers run free: *Various artists* / Nation once again: *Various artists* / I'm a rover: *Various artists* / Many young men of twenty: *Various artists* / McAlphine's: *Various artists* / Galway races: *Various artists* / Spanish lady: *Various artists* / Orange and the green: *Various artists* / Big strong man: *Various artists* / Streams of Bunclody: *Various artists* / Paddy's green shamrock shore: *Various artists.*
LP: G 008

16 Orchestral...

16 ORCHESTRAL WORLD HITS PART 1 (Various artists).
LP: 824 320 1
MC: 824 320 2

16 ORCHESTRAL WORLD HITS PART 2 (Various artists).
LP: 824 392 1
MC: 824 392 4

16 Requested ...

16 REQUESTED BALLADS OF IRELAND (Various artists).
LP: HRL 178

16 Singing Men

KING IS COMING, THE.
Tracks: / King is coming / Chariots of clouds / Whatever he wants for me / Through it all / Yesterday, today and tomorrow / Happiness is the Lord / Love was when / Jesus is the friend of sinners / No more death / Jesus is coming.
LP: PC 842

16 Super Irish Hits

16 SUPER IRISH HITS (Various artists).
Tracks: / When you were sweet sixteen: *Woods, Pat* / Pal of my cradle days: *Breen, Ann* / Home town on the Foyle: *Coll, Brian* / Bunch of thyme: *Mitchell, Mark* / Cottage by the Lee: *Cunningham, Larry* / Galway shawl: *O'Brien, Dermot* / Cliffs of Dooneen: *Margo* / Four country roads: *Watt, John* / Green fields of France: *Woods, Pat* / Old flames: *Bell, Crawford* / Rare ould times: *Woods, Pat* / Old cross of Arboe: *Begley*, Philomena / Bunch of violets blue: *Shine, Brendan* / Among the Wicklow hills: *Ely, Pat* / Three leaf shamrock: *Kerr, John* / One day at a time: *Leon.*
LP: PHL 455
MC: CPHL 455

16 Tambourines

HOW GREEN IS YOUR VALLEY.
Tracks: / Bathed in the afterglow / April / Pokey town / If I should stay / England / Baby there is nothing going on / How green is your valley / Love like this, A / When lovers walk / This is not love.
LP: 210307
MC: 410307

16 Tearjerkers

16 TEARJERKERS VOL 2 (Various artists).
LP: SHM 3145
MC: HSC 3145

16 Tons

HEAD OUT.
LP: ABT 091
MC: ABT 091 CD

17 & 21st Lancers

DEATH OR GLORY BOYS, THE.
LP: PRD 2006

18th Emergency (bk)

EIGHTEENTH EMERGENCY, THE (Betsy Byars (auth)) (Aubery, James (nar)).
MC: 881387

19th Century...

19TH CENTURY AMERICAN BALLROOM MUSIC (Smithonian Social Orchestra).
LP: H 71313

20 4 7

ALL RECORDINGS (See under Twenty 4 Seven).

20 All Time...

20 ALL TIME JUNIOR HITS (Various artists).
Tracks: / Nellie the elephant: *Various artists* / Sun has got his hat on: *Various artists* / Laughing policeman, The: *Various artists* / Two little boys: *Various artists* / Puff the magic dragon: *Various artists* / Sing a rainbow: *Various artists* / Old King Cole: *Various artists* / Pink Panther scheme: *Various artists*/ Teddy bear's picnic: *Various artists* / How much is that doggy in the window: *Various artists* / All things bright and beautiful: *Various artists.*
LP: . . . . **MFP 50488**
MC: . . . . **TCMFP 50488**

20 ALL TIME VOCAL CHARTBUSTERS (Various artists).
LP: . . . . **MFP 5567**
MC: . . . . **TC MFP 5567**

20 Beach Boys Hits

20 BEACH BOY HITS (Various artists).
MC: . . . . **AIM 9**

20 Bluegrass..

20 BLUEGRASS INSTRUMENTALS (Various artists).
LP: . . . . **SLP 5027**
MC: . . . . **GT 55027**

20 Classic...

20 CLASSIC ROCK 'N' ROLL TRACKS (Various artists).
Tracks: / Be bop a lula: *Various artists* / Forty days: *Various artists* / Rumble: *Various artists* / Sheila: *Various artists* / Monkey's uncle: *Various artists* / Good rockin' tonight: *Various artists* / Tutti frutti: *Various artists* / Down at the in den: *Various artists* / We did it in '54: *Various artists*/ Reelin' and rockin': *Various artists* / Memphis earthquake: *Various artists* / All the way to the USA: *Various* artists / Wrapped up in rockabilly: *Various artists* / Lucille: *Various artists* / Rockabilly baby: *Various* artists / Maybelline: *Various artists* / Blue suede shoes: *Various artists* / Say mama: *Various artists*/ That's alright mama: *Various artists* / Disciple in blue suede shoes: *Various artists.*
LP: . . . . **MTB 001**
LP: . . . . **SMT 001**

20 Classic Tracks

TWENTY CLASSIC TRACKS (Various artists).
Tracks: / Here come's my baby: *Various artists* / Memphis earthquake: *Various artists* / Blue suede shoes: *Various* artists / Going down town: *Various artists* / Shake a tail feather: *Various artists* / Oh what a night: *Various* artists / Save the last dance for me: *Various artists* / Great pretender, The: *Various artists* / Ain't no sunshine: *Various artists* / When a man loves a woman: *Various artists* / For your love: *Various artists*/ Voices: *Various artists* / Carvan man: *Various artists* / Going to the river: *Various artists* / Blueberry hill: *Various artists* / I'm going home: *Various artists* / Be bop a lula: *Various artists* / Say mama: *Various artists* / Roll me baby: *Various artists* / Suzanne in the mirror: *Various artists.*
LP: . . . . **SMT 016**

20 Country...

20 CLASSIC COUNTRY TRACKS (Various artists).
Tracks: / Let's think about living: *Various artists* / You comb her hair: *Various artists* / Have I stayed away too long: *Various artists* / Building heartaches: *Various artists* / Rueben's train: *Various artists*/ Wings of a dove: *Various artists* / I've got to be somebody: *Various artists* / Gambler's guitar: *Various* artists / Snowbird: *Various artists* / Mental revenge: *Various artists* / Sticks and stones: *Various* artists / Follow me back to Louisville: *Various artists* / Sally was a good old girl: *Various artists* / So sad: *Various artists* / Love hurts: *Various artists* / Honky tonk angels: *Various artists* / Those other boys: *Various artists* / My kingdom for a car: *Various artists.*
LP: . . . . **SMT 003**
MC: . . . . **SMTC 003**

20 COUNTRY CLASSICS (Various artists).
Tracks: / Just someone I used to know: *Wagoner, Porter/Dolly Parton* / When you're hot you're hot: *Redd, Jerry*/ Would you hold it against me?: *West, Dottie* / Angels don't lie: *Reeves, Jim* / Then you can tell me goodbye: *Arnold, Eddy* / Please help me, I'm falling: *Locklin, Hank* / Cold hard facts of life, The: *Wagoner, Porter*/ I never once stopped loving you: *Smith, Connie* / Brown eyed handsome man: *Jennings, Waylon* / Lonesome number one: *Gibson, Don* / Five hundred miles: *Bare, Bobby* / Coat of many colours: *Parton, Dolly* / Amos Moses: *Reed, Jerry* / Big wind: *Wagoner, Porter* / End of the world: *Davis, Skeeter* / Taker, The: *Jennings, Waylon* / Mule skinner blues: *Parton, Dolly* / I won't come in while he's there: *Reeves, Jim* / Better move it on home: *Wagoner, Porter/Dolly Parton* / Country hall of fame: *Locklin, Hank.*
LP: . . . . **CBR 1022**
MC: . . . . **KCBR 1022**

20 COUNTRY GREATS (Various artists).
LP: . . . . **PLE 7018**
MC: . . . . **PLC 7018**

20 TRACKS OF COUNTRY HITS VOL.3 (Various artists).
MC: . . . . **CWGR 053**

20 TRACKS OF COUNTRY HITS VOL.2 (Various artists).
MC: . . . . **CWGR 052**

20 TRACKS OF COUNTRY HITS VOL.1 (Various artists).
MC: . . . . **CWGR 051**

20 Dancin' Hits

20 DISCO DANCIN HITS (Various artists).
LP: . . . . **PLE 7010**
MC: . . . . **PLC 7010**

20 Detroit

TWENTY DETROIT CHARTBUSTERS VOL.1 (Various artists).
LP: . . . . **MOTCLP 21**

20 Explosive Hits

20 EXPLOSIVE HITS (Various artists).
Tracks: / Rasta no pickpocket: *Byles, Junior* / Reggae makossa: *Dowe, Brent* / Crowded city: *Messengers*/ I'll be waiting: *Thomas, Nicky* / Ain't no sunshine: *Boothe, Ken* / I'll never find another you: *London, Jimmy* / Working on it night and day: *Aces* / World is falling down, The: *Seaton, B. B.* / It was written down: *Maytals* / Starting all over again: *Lewis, Hopeton* / Don't break your promise: *Holt, John* / Keep on moving: *Various artists* / Nice nice time: *Zap Pow.*
LP: . . . . **TRLS 81**

20 Favourite..

20 FAVOURITE HYMNS (From the royal naval college chapel, Grenwich) (Various artists).
Tracks: / Lead us heavenly Father, lead us: *20 Favourite Hymns* / All people that on Earth do dwell: *20 Favourite* Hymns / Immortal love forever full: *20 Favourite Hymns* / When I survey the wondrous cross: *20 Favourite Hymns*/ Ye holy Angels bright: *20 Favourite Hymns* / Allelujah, sing to Jesus: *20 Favourite Hymns* / Christ is made the sure foundation: *20 Favourite Hymns* / There is a green hill far away: *20 Favourite Hymns* / Just as I am: *20* Favourite Hymns / Love divine: *20 Favourite Hymns* / O God, our help in ages past: *20 Favourite Hymns* / Guide me o thou great Redeemer: *20 Favourite Hymns* / O worship the King: *20 Favourite Hymns* / Holy, holy, holy: *20 Favourite Hymns* / Lord, enthroned in Heavenly splendour: *20 Favourite Hymns* / Eternal Father, strong to save: *20* Favourite Hymns / Praise to the holiest in the heights: *20 Favourite Hymns* / Now thank we all our God: *20 Favourite* Hymns / Dear Lord and Father of mankind: *20 Favourite Hymns* / Day thou gavest, Lord is ended, The: *20 Favourite Hymns.*
LP: . . . . **MVP 826**
MC: . . . . **MVPC 826**

20 Golden...

20 GOLDEN MEMORIES (Various artists).
LP: . . . . **MA 16287**
MC: . . . . **MAMC 916287**

20 Golden ...

20 GOLDEN NUMBER ONES VOL.2 (Various artists).
Tracks: / Whiter shade of pale, A: *Procul Harum* / This is my song: *Clark, Petula* / Sweets for my sweet: *Searchers*/ Have I the right: *Honeycombs* / Always something there to remind me: *Shaw, Sandie* / Sunny afternoon: *Kinks*/ Michelle: *Overlanders* / Let the heartaches begin: *Baldry, Long John* / Blackberry Way: *Move* / If paradise is half as nice: *Amen Corner* / In the Summertime: *Mungo Jerry* / Baby, now that I've found you: *Foundations*/ Kung fu fighting: *Douglas, Carl* / Matchstalk men: *Brian & Michael* / Sad sweet dreamer: *Sweet Sensation*/ Out of time: *Farlowe, Chris* / Israelites: *Dekker, Desmond* / Mouldy old dough: *Lieutenant Pigeon* / Double barrel: *Collins, Dave & Ansel* / Everything I own: *Boothe, Ken.*
MC: . . . . **TCMFP 5898**

20 Jackpot

20 JACKPOT HITS (Various artists).
LP: . . . . **NSPL 28236**
MC: . . . . **ZCP 28236**

20 Mod Classics

20 MOD CLASSICS (Various artists).
LP: . . . . **STML 12125**
MC: . . . . **CSTML 12125**
LP: . . . . **ZL 72032**

20 MOD CLASSICS - VOL.2 (Various artists).
LP: . . . . **STML 12133**
MC: . . . . **CSTML 12133**
LP: . . . . **ZL 72033**

20 Of Another Kind

20 OF ANOTHER KIND VOL 2 (Various artists).
LP: . . . . **POLS 1012**

20 Oldies...

20 OLDIES BUT GOOD (Various artists).
LP: . . . . **FUN 9040**
MC: . . . . **FUNC 9040**

20 Pieces Of...

20 PIECES OF GOLD (Various artists).
MC: . . . . **AIM 68**

20 Songs To ...

20 SONGS TO REMEMBER (Various artists).
LP: **28030**
MC: **48030**

20's

1926 (Various artists).
LP: . . . . **NL 89464**
MC: . . . . **NK 89464**

1927 (Various artists).
LP: . . . . **NL 89465**
MC: . . . . **NK 89465**

1928 (Various artists).
LP: . . . . **NL 89466**
MC: . . . . **NK 89466**

CHARLESTON DAYS 1923-29 (Various artists).
Tracks: / Let's all go to Mary's house: *Whidden, Jay & His New Midnight Follies Band* / After I say I'm sorry: *Mackey,* Percival & His Band / Laugh, clown laugh: *Schubert, Adrian Dance Orchestra* / Charleston: *Bell, Edison & His Dance* Orchestra / I've never seen a straight banana: *Happiness Boys* / What did I tell ya?: *Savoy Orpheans* / Where's that rainbow?: *Baker, Edythe Piano* / How could Red Riding Hood?: *Royal Automobile Club Orchestra* / Chinese moon: *Douglas, Fred* / High up in the sky: *Maddison, Bert & Dance Orchestra* / Under the moon: *Radio Imps* / Latest dance hits of 1926: *Coliseum Dance Orchestra* / Julian: *Denza Dance Band* / Thanks for the buggy ride: *Mackey,* Percival & His Band / Breezing along with the breeze: *Revelers* / Hitch up the horses: *Savoy Orpheans* / If I had a talking picture of you: *Alfredo & His Band* / Russian lullaby: *Bidgood, Harry & His Broadcasters* / Seven and eleven: *Corona Dance Orchestra* / Dainty Miss: *Da Costa, Raie* / Molly: *Hylton, Jack & His Orchestra*/ My wife is on a diet: *Hudson, Harry Melody Men* / Barcelona: *Savoy Orpheans* / Electric flashes of 1926: *Munro, Ronnie & His Dance Orchestra.*
LP: . . . . **PAST 706**

CHICAGO IN THE TWENTIES 1926-28 (Various artists).
LP: . . . . **ARCADIA 2011**

DIAMOND DISCS (Hot dance music of the 20's) (Various artists).
Tracks: / Louisville: *Various artists* / Tessie stop teasin' me: *Various artists* / Nobody knows what a red-head mama can do: *Various artists* / Lonely and blue: *Various artists* / Sweet Georgia Brown: *Various artists*/ Isn't she the sweetest thing?: *Various artists* / Jig walk: *Various artists* / Sweet thing: *Various artists*/ Rosy cheeks: *Various artists* / What do I care what somebody said?: *Various artists* / Oh Doris where do you live?: *Various artists* / Anything to make you happy: *Various artists* / Mary Ann: *Various artists* / I'm riding to glory: *Various artists.*
LP: . . . . **SDL 342**
MC: . . . . **CSDL 342**

GOLDEN AGE OF THE CHARLESTON (Various artists).
Tracks: / Black bottom Charleston: *Various artists* / Mississippi mud: *Various artists* / Ain't she sweet?: *Various* artists / My pet: *Various artists* / Barcelona: *Various artists* / Everybody stomp: *Various artists*/ Painting the clouds with sunshine: *Various artists* / Miss Annabelle Lee: *Various artists* / Paddlin' Madelin' home: *Various artists* / Brown sugar: *Various artists* / Didn't I tell you?: *Various artists* / Kansas City Kitty: *Various artists* / All by yourself in the moonlight: *Various artists* / Charleston Charley: *Various artists.*
LP: . . . . **GX 2507**
MC: . . . . **TCGX 2507**
LP: . . . . **MFP 2507**

GREAT SOUNDS OF THE 1920'S (Various artists).
LPS: . . . . **AJAB 401**

HOT AIRE (American hot bands of the twenties) (Various artists).
Tracks: / Hot aire: *Olsen, George & His Music* / If I had a girl like you: *Seattle Harmony Kings* / Darktown shuffle: *Seattle Harmony Kings* / I'm goin' out if Lizzie comes in: *Romano, Phil & His Orchestra* / Keep on croonin'a tune: *Romano, Phil & His Orchestra* / Melancholy Lou: *Lanin, Howard/his Ben Franklin Dance Orchestra* / Don't wake me up, let me dream: *Lanin, Howard/his Ben Franklin Dance Orchestra* / Paddlin' Madelin' home: *White Kaufman & His Orchestra*/ Breezin' along with the breeze: *Seattle Harmony Kings* / How many times: *Seattle Harmony Kings* / Tiger rag: *Dornberger, Charles & His Orchestra* / Does she love me ? - positively, absolutely: *Garber, Jan & His Orchestra*/ What do I care what somebody said: *Garber, Jan & His Orchestra* / You don't like it, not much: *Garber, Jan & His* Orchestra / Swanee shore: *Crawford, Jack & His Orchestra* / Sugar babe I'm leavin': *Blue Steele & His Orchestra*/ When the morning glories wake up in the morning: *Renard, Jacques & His Cocoanut Grove Orchestra* (Full title: When the morning glories wake up in the morning (Them I'll k) / Baltimore: *Crawford, Jack & His Ochestra.*
MC: . . . . **CHAL 16**
LP: . . . . **HAL 16**

ORIGINAL SOUND OF THE TWENTIES (Various artists).
Tracks: / Blue room: *Venuti, Joe & His Blue Four* / St. Louis blues: *Armstrong, Louis & His Orchestra* / Varsity drag: *Hagan, Cass & His Park Central Hotel Orch.* / Alexander's ragtime band: *Lewis, Ted/his orchestra* / Black and blue: *Ethel Waters* / Am I blue: *Aunt Jemima (Tess Gardella)* / Bill: *Young, Victor* / Man I love, The: *Whiteman, Paul & His Orchestra* / Nobody's sweetheart: *Whiteman, Paul & His Orchestra* / Rhythm king: *Whiteman,* Paul & Rhythm Boys / Someone to watch over me: *Gershwin (Composer)* / Home on the range: *Sims, Lee* / Can't we be friends: *Various artists.*
LP: . . . . **CBS 32741**
MC: **40 32741**

PICCADILLY NIGHTS (British dance bands of the 1920's) (Various artists).
Tracks: / That girl over there: *Various bands* / Swing on the gait: *Various bands* / It's a million to one you're in love: *Various bands* / What'll you do?: *Various bands* / Make my cot where the cot-cot-cotton grows: *Various bands* / How long has this been going on?: *Various bands* / Miss Annabelle Lee: *Various bands* / Lila: *Various* bands / That's my weakness now: *Various bands* / Sunny skies: *Various bands* / Matilda, Matilda: *Various bands* / Saskatchewan: *Various bands* / There's a blue ridge round my heart Virginia: *Various bands* / S wonderful: *Various bands* / Crazy rhythm: *Various bands* / I'm a one man girl: *Various bands* / Spread a little happiness: *Various bands* / Out of the dawn: *Various bands* / Ida (sweet as apple cider): *Various bands* / I don't know why I do it but I do: *Various bands.*
LP: . . . . **HAL 17**
MC: . . . . **CHAL 17**

SHAKE THAT THING (America's top Bands of the 20's) (Various artists).
Tracks: / I wanna be loved by you: *Broadway Nitelites* / Shakin' the blues away: *Selvin, Ben/his orchestra* / Hello Swanee, hello: *Lentz, Al/his orchestra* / Mighty blue: *Waring's Pennsylvanians* / What a day: *Weems, Ted & His* Orchestra / Melancholy Lou: *Lanin, Howard/his Ben Franklin Dance Orchestra* / Confessin': *Lombardo, Guy*/ his Royal Canadians / Shake that thing: *Lyman, Abe/his California Orchestra* / Everything's made for love: *Lopez,* Vincent/his orchestra / Wabash blues: *Charleston Chasers* / Smile: *Whiteman, Paul & His Orchestra* / Let's misbehave: *Aaronson, Irving/his Commanders* / Just a night for meditation: *Shilkret, Nat/ Victor Orchestra* / Bugle call rag: *Lewis, Ted/his band* / S'posin': *Vallee, Rudy & His Connecticut Yankies* / He's the last word: *Bernie, Ben/his Hotel Roosevelt Orchestra.*
LP: . . . . **AJA 5002**
MC: . . . . **ZC AJA 5002**

SONGS AND SINGERS OF THE 1920'S (Various artists).

MC: .... NEO 945

20th All Time...

20TH ALL TIME CHRISTMAS HITS (Various artists).
MC: .... AMP 004

20th Anniversary

20TH ANNIVERSARY ALBUM (Various artists).
LP: .... EGLP 75

20TH ANNIVERSARY COLLECTION (See Under Alligator (Label)) (Various artists).

20TH ANNIVERSARY OF THE SUMMER OF LOVE (Various artists).
LP: .... SR 6787

20th Century Blues

TWENTIETH CENTURY BLUES.
Tracks: / In former times / Marathon / Study to be quiet / Four pieces / Twentieth century tutti / Life on the farm.
LP: .... MMC 002
MC: .... TCMMC 1002

20th Century Poetry

FOUR POETS OF THE TWENTIETH CENTURY (Various artists).
Tracks: / Old Possum's book of practical cats: *Eliot, T.S.* / In parenthesis (extracts): *Jones, David* / Anathemata (extracts): *Jones, David* / Poem: *Graves, Robert (aut)* / High windows: *Larkin, Philip.*
MCSET: 414 718-4
MCSET: .... ARGO 1067

20th Concord...

20TH CONCORD FESTIVAL ALL STARS.
Tracks: / Blues for Sam Nassi / Time after time / I wish I knew / Just a closer walk with thee / Sophisticated lady / Bye bye blackbird / I got it bad and that ain't good.
LP: .... CJ 366
MC: .... CJ 366C

21...

21 YEARS OF ALTERNATIVE RADIO 1 (See under Radio 1) (Various artists).

21st ...

21ST CENTURY DUB (Various artists).
MC: .... A 147

21ST CENTURY QUAKE MAKERS (Various artists).
LP: .... BBAT 2
MC: .... BBAT 2C

21ST CENTURY QUAKE MAKERS VOL 2 (Various artists).
Tracks: / Germany is burning: *Pankow* / Hacked (reprogrammed!!): *Clock DVA* / House is taking over: *Unique* & Dashan / Mr Walker: *Hard Sonic Bottoms Three* / Hit song, A (version): *Peron, Carlos* / Canraia canaria: *Santa B Boys* / King Kong dub rubber mix: *K.M.F.D.M.* / Devil does not the drugs: *Thrill Kill Kult* / Splash 2: *Shamen.*
MC: .... BBAT 005 C
LP: .... BBAT 005

21ST CENTURY SOUND (Various artists).
LP: .... VPRL 1059
MC: .... VPRC 1059

22 Pistepirkko

22 PISTEPIRKKO.
Tracks: / Don't play cello / Hong Kong king / Hank's TV set / Don't try to tease me / Frankenstein / Motorcycle man.
MLP: .... SONL 22

23 Skidoo

CULLING IS COMING.
Tracks: / Banishing / In vocation / Stifling / Healing for the strong / 9-2 contemplation / 5-matrix / Shrine / Mahakala.
LP: .... LAY 023

G.I. (See under 400 Blows).

JUST LIKE EVERYBODY.
Tracks: / Kundalini / Vegas el bandito / I Y / Just like everybody / Assassin / Coup / Urban gamelan act 1 / Congo do / Language dub / Drunkards reprise / Shrine / Porno base.
LP: .... BC 1

SEVEN SONGS.
LP: .... JAMS 47

URBAN GAMELAN.
LP: .... JAMS 40

24th Street Band

24TH STREET BAND.
LP: .... YX 7547

25...

TWENTY FIVE YEARS OF RECORDED SOUND (Various artists).
2LP: .... DARC 2100

27 Devils Joking

ACTUAL TOONS.
Tracks: / No compromise / Let's see some action / Where's Bo Diddley (when we need him) / Two headed dog / Actual toons / Make it quick (make it loud) / Indian Joe / Everything's goin' in the wrong ear / Danger within'. The.
LP: .... SAVE 048

SUCKING EFFECT.
LP: .... RAVE 018

28 Golden Rockers

28 GOLDEN ROCKERS (Various artists).
MC: 48058

29 Palms

FATAL JOY.
LP: .... EIRSA 1044
MC: .... EIRSAC 1044

29th Street Sax ...

UNDERGROUND (29th Street Sax Quartet).
MC: .... ANC 8759
LP: .... ANLP 8759

30 Years Of ...

30 YEARS OF NO 1 HITS (Various artists).
MCSET: .... DTO 10289
MCSET: .... DTOL 10289

30's

1930'S VOLUME 1, THE (Various).
Tracks: / Cowboy from Brooklyn / I'se a muggin' / Sing me a swing song / So long / Don't be that way / Interlude in B-flat / Blues / Shadrack / Nobody knows the trouble I've seen.
LP: .... AIRCHECK 1

1930'S:SMALL COMBOS (Various artists).
Tracks: / Dismal Dan: *Purvis, Jack* / Who's sorry now: *Rhythmakers* / Blues in E flat: *Norvo* / T'ain't no use: *Smith* / Wabash stomp: *Eldridge, Roy* / Jungle drums: *Bechet, Sidney* / Dee blues: *Chocolate* Dandies / There's a house in... / Isle of Capri: *Mannone, Wingie* / Shoe shine swing: *Jones-Smith INC* / There's no two ways...: *Newton, Frankie* / Royal Garden blues: *Kirby, John.*
LP: 4606094

1937 - ROCK IT FOR ME (Various artists).
Tracks: / One o'clock jump: *Basie, Count* / Sailboat in the moonlight, A: *Holiday, Billie & Her Orchestra* / I can't get started: *Berigan, Bunny* / Honeysuckle rose: *Hawkins, Coleman* / Boo hoo: *Lombardo, Guy* / When we're alone: *James, Harry* / Alabamy home: *Ellington, Duke* / Getting some fun out of life: *Holiday, Billie & Orchestra* With Barney, Kessel / Carry me back to old Virginney: *Armstrong, Louis* / Song of India: *Dorsey, Tommy*/ I can't give you anything but love: *Goodman, Benny* / Who's sorry now: *Crosby, Bob* / Loch Lomand: *Sullivan,* Maxine / Posin': *Lunceford, Jimmie* / I've got my love to keep me warm: *Norvo, Red* / Rock it for me: *Webb,* Chick / Whose babe: *Hampton* / I must have that man: *Wilson, Teddy* / Caravan: *Ellington, Duke* / Topsie: *Various artists.*
LP: .... PHONT 7663
MC: .... PHONT 8663

1938 - BEGIN THE BEGUINE (Various artists).
Tracks: / Begin the beguine: *Shaw, Artie* / Tisket a tasket, A: *Webb, Chick* / Ring dem bells: *Hampton*/ Sweet Georgia Brown: *Goodman, Benny Quartet* / I can't give you anything but love: *Armstrong, Louis* / Flat foot floogie: *Slim & Slam* / Music maestro please: *Dorsey, Tommy* / March of the bob cats: *Crosby, Bob* / When you're smiling: *Wilson, Teddy* / Swingin' the blues: *Basie, Count* / Louise: *Goodman, Benny* / Margie: *Lunceford, Jimmie* / Really the blues: *Ladnier, Tommy* / Little Joe from Chicago: *Kirk, Andy* / Back in your own back yard: *Holiday, Billie* / Back bay shuffle: *Shaw, Artie* / I let a song go out of my heart: *Ellington,* Duke / Jeepers creepers: *Krupa, Gene* / You must have been a beautiful baby: *Crosby, Bing* / Lullaby in rhythm: *James, Harry.*
LP: .... PHONT 7665
MC: .... PHONT 8665

1939 - AND THE ANGELS SING OVER THE RAINBOW (Various artists).
Tracks: / Jeepers creepers: *Armstrong, Louis* / Jive at five: *Basie, Count* / Undecided: *Webb, Chick*/ Zigeuner: *Shaw, Artie* / Moonlight serenade: *Miller, Glenn* / When lights are low: *Hampton, Lionel*/ Ain't she sweet: *Lunceford, Jimmie* / At the woodchoppers ball: *Herman, Woody* / I'm checkin' out, goo'm bye: *Ellington, Duke* / Body and soul: *Hawkins, Coleman* / And the angels sing: *Goodman, Benny* / I wish I could shimmy like my sister Kate: *Spanier, Muggsy* / Lady's in love with you, The: *Miller, Glenn* / Over the rainbow: *Garland, Judy* / Sugar: *Wilson, Teddy* / Lester leaps in: *Basie, Count* / I've got my eyes on you: *Dorsey,* Tommy / Opus 5: *Kirby, John* / Flyin' home: *Goodman, Benny* / Tain't what you do: *Lunceford, Jimmie*/ I'm coming, Virginia: *Shaw, Artie.*
LP: .... PHONT 7667
MC: .... PHONT 8667

CHICAGO IN THE 30'S (Various artists).
LP: .... M 8007

DANCE SOUNDS OF THE THIRTIES (Various artists).
Tracks: / Everything I have is yours: *Various artists* / Lonely lane: *Various artists* / Breeze, The: *Various* artists / I never had a chance: *Various artists* / Rosy come easy: *Various artists* / It's all forgotten now: *Various artists* / Straight from the shoulder: *Various artists* / When you've got a little springtime in your...: *Various artists.*
MC: .... NEO 958

MUSIC GOES ROUND AND ROUND THE 30'S, THE (see under swing collection) (Various artists).

RADIO DAYS - BRITISH 30'S RADIO (Various artists).
Tracks: / Radio Times: *Hall, Henry & BBC Dance Orchestra* / I don't do things like that: *Trinder, Tommy* / Scrimplethorp's talcum (commercial): *Long, Norman* / Coronation girls, The: *Waters, Elsie & Doris (Gert & Daisy)* / Tale of Hector Cramp, The: *Fletcher, Cyril* / Radio Baloni time signal: *Taunton, Peter* / Schnotzelheimer's suspenders (commercial): *Long, Norman* / All for ten shillings a year: *Stanelli/Norman Long* / There's a small hotel: *Daniels, Bebe* & Ben Lyon / Football commentary: *Keys, Nelson/Ivy St. Helier* / Little Betty Bouncer: *Flotsam & Jetsam (2)*/ British mother's big fight, A: *Desmond, Florence/Max Kester* / Ye B.B.C.: *Flanagan & Allen* / Hi de ho: *Revnell,* Ethel/Gracie West / Gritty granules (commercial): *Taunton, Peter* / In 1992: *Campbell, Big Bill & His Rocky Mountain* Rhythm / I know that sailors do care: *O'Shea, Tessie* / Radio Baloni close-down: *Taunton, Peter* / Ding dong bell: *Askey, Arthur* / Mr. and Mrs. Ramsbottom went off: *Holloway, Stanley (nar)* / We can't let you broadcast that: *Long, Norman* / Cricket commentary: *Clapham & Dwyer* / Jubilee baby: *Driver, Betty* / University motors (commercial): *Potter, Gillie* / On the good ship Ballyhoo: *Warner, Jack/Jeff Darnell* / Five-in-one radios: *Pola,Eddie* / The adventures of Lt. Featherston-Haugh DSO: *Taunton, Peter* / Mirror cleanser: *Fields, Gracie*/ Sing as we go: *Dixon, Reginald* / Sandy's own broadcasting station: *Powell, Sandy* / You'll never understand: *Bowlly, Al* / X (commercial): *Taunton, Peter* / We're frightfully BBC: *Western Brothers* / Let me call you sweetheart: *Oliver, Vic/Nellie Wallace* / Next week's film (commercial): *Formby, George* / Dromedary cigarettes (commercial): *Pola,Eddie* / About cruises: *Murgatroyd & Winterbottom* / Here's to the next time: *Hall, Henry & BBC Dance Orchestra.*
LP: .... CHD 163
MC: .... MCHD 163

RADIO PERSONALITIES OF THE THIRTIES (Various artists).
Tracks: / Where the arches used to be: *Flanagan & Allen* / Play the game you cads: *Western Brothers* / Ring your little bell: *Formby, George* / Huntin': *Waters, Elsie & Doris (Gert & Daisy)* / After all that: *Western Brothers*/ Fourth form at St. Michaels, The: *Hay, Will & his Scholars* / Move into my house: *Flotsam & Jetsam* / Sam, pick up tha' musket: *Holloway, Stanley (nar)* / Gert and Daisy and the tandem: *Waters, Elsie & Doris (Gert & Daisy)*/ Sport of kings, The: *Flanagan & Allen* / Miss Otis regrets: *Winn, Anona* / I've got a feeling I'm falling: *Layton &* Johnstone / Old school tie, The: *Western Brothers* / It ain't nobody's business what I do: *Formby, George*/ Goody goody: *Formby, George* / I like bananas: *Formby, George* / Life begins again: *Flanagan & Allen*/ Village blacksmith, The: *Flotsam & Jetsam* / Thomas a Becket and Winnie: *Hemsley, Harry.*
LP: .... JOYD 289

SONGS AND STARS OF THE THIRTIES (Various artists).
Tracks: / My melancholy baby: *Bowlly, Al* / I'm in the mood for love: *Hildegarde* / Night and day: *Astaire,* Fred / Blue moon: *Baker, Belle* / I only have eyes for you: *Derrickson & Brown* / Dancing on the ceiling: *Matthews, Jessie* / Let's face the music and dance: *Brown, Sam & The Rhythm Sisters* / Million dreams: *Ponce Sisters* / That old feeling: *Hall, Adelaide* / I've got my love to keep me warm: *Stanley, Aileen* / Stormy weather: *Langford, Frances* / These foolish things / As time goes by: *Hale, Binnie* / Hold me: *Small, Paul*/ I've got you under my skin: *Day, Frances* / There's a small hotel: *Daniels, Bebe & Ben Lyon* / Would you like to take a walk?: *Harris, Marion* / Try a little tenderness: *Williams, Frances* / Goodnight my love: *Vallee, Rudy* / Nearness of you, The: *Various artists.*
LP: .... SH 370
MC: .... TCSH 370

STARS OF THE 30'S (Various artists).
Tracks: / April showers: *Jolson, Al* / Things might have been different: *Boswell, Connie* / Little lady make believe: *Cantor, Eddie* / Moon song: *Smith, Kate* / I guess it had to be that way: *Crosby, Bing* / I got rhythm: *Hall, Adelaide* / Day you came along, The: *Crosby, Bing* / It's love again: *Etting, Ruth* / You are too beautiful: *Jolson, Al* / Baby: *Hall, Adelaide* / If you should ever need me: *Crosby, Bing* / Take my heart: *Etting, Ruth* / I'll never say "never again" again: *Boswell, Connie* / Rockabye your baby with a Dixie melody: *Jolson, Al* / Too darn fickle: *Hall, Adelaide* / Shine: *Crosby, Bing & The Mills Brothers* / You: *Etting, Ruth* / That's the kind of baby for me: *Cantor, Eddie.*
LP: .... RAL 501

STARS OF THE 30'S, VOL 2 (Various artists).
LP: .... RAL 505

SWINGING 30'S (Various artists).
Tracks: / Stratton Street strut: *Various artists* / More than somewhat: *Various artists* / Blue murder: *Various artists* / That's plenty: *Various artists* / Money for jam: *Various artists* / Mr. Polo takes a solo: *Various* artists / Home sweet home: *Various artists* / Three's company: *Various artists* / Let's go: *Various artists*/ No smoking: *Various artists* / Archer Street drag: *Various artists* / Rosetta: *Various artists* / You'll always be mine: *Various artists* / Penalty five pounds: *Various artists* / How many times: *Various artists*/ Jazz me blues: *Various artists* / Don't try your jive on me: *Various artists* / Mozeltov: *Various artists*/ If you were the only girl in the world: *Various artists* / Hitchy koo: *Various artists* / He's a rag-picker: *Various artists* / Back home in Tennessee: *Various artists* / Where the black eyed Susans grow: *Various artists*/ D'ye ken John Peel: *Various artists* / There is a tavern in the town: *Various artists* / Colonel Bogey: *Various* artists / Widdicombe Fair: *Various artists* / Drink to me only with thine eyes: *Various artists* / Early one morning: *Various artists* / Frankie and Johnnie: *Various artists* / Three of a kind: *Various artists.*
2LP: .... DDV 5013/4

THIRTIES GIRLS: ON THE AIR (Various).
Tracks: / Can't help it / I surrender dear / I've got a cousin in Milwaukee / Sittin' up, waitin' for you / When you love only one / Moanin' low / Body and soul / Lost my man / Pardon my southern accent / Time was / Dream ship / It's love I'm after / For sentimental reasons.
LP: .... TOTEM 1026

THREE T'S AT THE HICKORY HOUSE 1936-37 (Various artists).
LP: .... BR 106

38 Special

SPECIAL FORCES.
Tracks: / Caught up in you / Back door stranger / Back on the track / Chain lightnin' / Rough housin' / You keep running away / Breakin' loose / Take 'em out / Firestarter.
LP: .... AMLH 64888

STRENGTH IN NUMBERS.
Tracks: / Somebody like you / Like no other night / Last time, The / Once in a lifetime / Just a little love / Has there ever been a good goodbye? / One in a million / Heart's on fire / Against the night / Never give an inch.
LP: .... AMA 5115
MC: .... AMC 5115

TOUR DE FORCE.
Tracks: / If I'd been the one / Back where you belong / One time for old times / See me in your eyes / Twentieth Century Fox / Long distance affair / I oughta let go / One of the lonely ones / Undercover lover.
LP: .... AMLX 64971
MC: .... CXM 64971

WILD EYED SOUTHERN BOYS.
Tracks: / Hold on loosely / First time around / Wild eyed southern boys / Back alley Sally / Fantasy girl / Hittin' and running / Honky tonk dancer / Throw out the line / Bring it on.

LP: . . . . AMLH 64835

39 Nine Clocks

BLADES IN YOUR MASQUERADE.
Tracks: / Twist and shout / 78 soldiers dead / Louie Louie.
LP: . . . . SHARP 109

39 Steps (bk)

THIRTY-NINE STEPS, THE (John Buchan) (Waterston, Sam (nar)).
MCSET: 2098

THIRY NINE STEPS, THE (Powell, Robert (nar)).
MCSET: . . . . LFP 7379

40's

1940'S - SINGERS (Various artists).
Tracks: / What did I do wrong: Waters, Ethel / I'll be glad: Teagarden, Ted / Old yazoo: Boswell Sisters/ I'm crazy 'bout my baby: Lewis, Ted / Doin' what I please: Redman, Don / Frankie and Johnny: Bullock, Chick / Out where the blue begins / Rose of the Rio Grande: Ellington, Duke / Mama's gone, goodbye: Williams, Midge / Blue again: Armstrong, Louis / Dinah: Crosby, Bing & Mills Brothers / River's taking care: Boswell, Connie / All my life: Wilson, Teddy / My old man: Spirits Of Rhythm / Chasing shadows: Prima, Louis/ Lover come back to me: Bailey, Mildred / Mean to me: Wilson, Teddy.
LP: 4610951
MC: 4610954

1940'S SMALL GROUPS (New Directions) (Various artists).
Tracks: / Igor: Various artists / Four men on a horse: Various artists / Nero's conception: Various artists/ Pam: Various artists / I surrender, dear (take 2): Various artists / Dark eyes: Various artists / Stompin' at the Savoy: Various artists / Limehouse blues: Various artists/ Tuxedo Junction: Various artists/ Steps: Various artists / Fan it: Various artists / Lost weekend: Various artists / I surrender, dear: Various artists / Someday, sweetheart: Various artists / Body and soul: Various artists / Three men on third: Various artists / Pagan love song: Various artists.
LP: 4610941
MC: 4610944

1944 REVISITED (Various artists).
LP: . . . . GHB 196

BANDS OF THE 40'S (Various artists).
2LP: . . . . RDLD 42

FAVOURITES OF THE FORTIES (Various artists).
Tracks: / Begin the beguine: Heywood, Eddie / Tico tico: Smith, Ethel / You'll never know: Haymes, Dick/ Voodoo man: Cavallaro, Carmen / Green eyes: Dorsey, Jimmy / My happiness: Fitzgerald, Ella / Sweet Lorraine: Various artists / I wonder who's kissing her now: Weems, Ted/Perry Como / Hong Kong blues: Carmichael, Hoagy / Java jive: Ink Spots / So tired: Morgan, Russ / Yi, yi, yi, yi (I like you very much): Miranda, Carmen / Again: Jenkins, Gordon / Blues in the night: Lunceford, Jimmie / Till then: Mills Brothers/ Choo choo ch' boogie: Jordan, Louis.
LP: . . . . MFP 50553
MC: . . . . TCMFP 50553

GOLDEN HITS OF THE 40'S (Various artists).
2LP: . . . . BRLP 63/64
MCSET: . . . . BRMC 63/64

GOLDEN HITS OF THE 40'S (Various artists).
Tracks: / Rum and coca cola: Andrew Sisters / That lucky old sun: Armstrong, Louis / Old buttermilk sky: Carmichael, Hoagy / Moonlight becomes you: Crosby, Bing / Don't fence me in: Crosby, Bing & The Andrew Sisters / I hear a rhapsody: Dorsey, Jimmy / Baby it's cold outside: Fitzgerald, Ella / Time waits for no one: Forrest, Helen/ Trolley song, The: Garland, Judy / It might as well be spring: Haymes, Dick / I'm always chasing rainbows: Haymes, Dick & Helen Forrest / Blues in the night: Herman, Woody / Whispering grass: Ink Spots / Paper doll: Mills Brothers / Jingle jangle: Merry Macs / Anniversary song: Jolson, Al.
LP: . . . . MCM 5031
MC: . . . . MCMC 5031

MILLION SELLERS OF THE 40'S (Various artists).
Tracks: / In the mood: Miller, Glenn / Stardust: Shaw, Artie / On the sunny side of the street: Dorsey, Tommy / Blues in the night: Shore, Dinah / Little brown jug: Miller, Glenn / Begin the beguine: Shaw, Artie / There are such things: Dorsey, Tommy & Frank Sinatra / Chattanooga choo choo: Miller, Glenn / Tuxedo Junction: Miller, Glenn / Frenesi: Shaw, Artie / Boogie woogie: Dorsey, Tommy / Pennsylvania 6-5000: Miller, Glenn / Dance ballerina dance: Miller, Glenn / Marie: Dorsey, Tommy / Dancing in the dark: Shaw, Artie / I've got a gal in Kalamazoo: Miller, Glenn.
LP: . . . . MFP 5844
MC: . . . . TC-MFP 5844

SONGS AND STARS OF THE FORTIES (Various artists).
Tracks: / It's a lovely day tomorrow: Bowlly, Al / Only one who's difficult is you, The: Kirkwood, Pat / They call me a dreamer / Left hand side of Egypt, The: Formby, George / Our love affair: Lipton, Celia / I'm looking for a melody: Buchanan, Jack / If I should fall in love again: Fields, Gracie / There goes my dream: Layton, Turner / I'm going to see you today: Grenfell, Joyce / Pedro the fisherman: Tildesley, Vincent Master Singers/ I'll always love you: Clark, Petula / Clopin clopant: Guetary, Georges / Gipsy, The: Squires, Dorothy/ Hello to the sun: Askey, Arthur / Promises: Conway, Steve / Lady Spiv: Gynt, Greta / Powder your face with sunshine: Peters, Donald / Mia mantilla: Ray, Monte / You can't be true, dear: Gray, Dolores/ While the Angelus was ringing: Jones, Allan.
LP: . . . . EG 2602931
MC: . . . . EG 2602934

SWINGING 40'S (Various artists).
2LP: . . . . FUN 9005/6
MCSET: . . . . FUNC 9005/6

UNFORGETTABLE 40'S, THE Various artists (Various artists).
LP: . . . . SHM 3223
MC: . . . . HSC 3223

42nd Street

42ND STREET (See under swing collection) (Various artists).

42ND STREET (1980 Original Broadway cast) (Various artists).
Tracks: / Overture: Various artists / Audition: Various artists / Shadow waltz: Various artists / Young and healthy: Various artists / Go into your dance: Various artists / You're getting to be a habit with me: Various artists / Getting out of town: Various artists / We're in the money: Various artists / Dames: Various artists / Sunny side to every situation: Various artists / Lullaby of Broadway: Various artists/ About a quarter to nine: Various artists / Shuffle off to Buffalo: Various artists / 42nd Street: Various artists / Finale: Various artists / 42nd Street (reprise - bows): Various artists.
LP: . . . . BL 83891
MC: . . . . BK 83891

44 Magnum

DANGER.
LP: . . . . RR 9805

STREET ROCK 'N' ROLLER.
LP: . . . . RR 9816

44 Max

MAXIN' WITH A FULL CLIP.
Tracks: / Second without a pause / Code / Hole lotta nonsense / Tear the lid off / Rewind the future / Political frame-up / Measurement of the snucknose / Players rolling a stone / Both barrells / Dee / Watch my back / Push and shove (Only on MC and CD) / Confusion on the inside (Only on MC and CD).
LP: . . . . KEY 4104
MC: . . . . KEY 4104 MC

4-4 Sax

FOUR-FOUR SAX (Various artists).
Tracks: / I'll remember April: Konitz, Lee / Record shop suey: Konitz, Lee / Lee tchee: Konitz, Lee/ Young Lee: Konitz, Lee / You'd be so nice to come home to: Konitz, Lee / 4 p.m.: Konitz, Lee / Lost Henri: Konitz, Lee / Toot's suite: Sims, Zoot / Late Tiny Kahn, The: Sims, Zoot / Call it anything: Sims, Zoot / Zoot suite: Sims, Zoot / Once in a while: Sims, Zoot / Great drums: Sims, Zoot/ Escale a Victoria: Foster, Frank / Things we did last summer, The: Foster, Frank / Just 40 bars: Foster, Frank / My heart stood still: Foster, Frank / Fat shoes: Foster, Frank / I'll take romance: Foster, Frank / Eleanore: Jaspar, Bobby / Capri: Jaspar, Bobby / Schabozz: Jaspar, Bobby / Simplicity: Jaspar, Bobby / Up in Quincy's room: Jaspar, Bobby / Consultation: Jaspar, Bobby / Au tabour: Jaspar, Bobby / Expansion: Jaspar, Bobby.
LP: . . . . VJD 577

45 King

MASTER OF THE GAME.
LP: . . . . DRXLP 702
MC: . . . . DRXC 702

48...

WE KNOW NONSENSE.
LP: . . . . CHUG 4

48 Cameras

B SIDES ARE FOR LOVERS.
LP: 139K 001

48 Chairs

LIVE IN COGNITO.
LP: . . . . R 102

48 Hours

BOYS ARE BACK IN TOWN (See under Bus Boys).

49ers

49ERS.
Tracks: / Touch me / I need you / I will survive / Die walkure / Don't you love me / How longer / Shadows (remix) / Girl to girl.
MC: . . . . BRCA 547
LP: . . . . BRLP 547

50...

50 FAVOURITE NURSERY RHYMES (Bisco, Patsy).
LP: . . . . CF 12

50's

20 FAB NO.1'S OF THE 50'S (Various artists).
LP: . . . . MFP 415649-1
MC: . . . . TCMFP 415649-4

20 GOLDEN HITS OF 1957 (Various artists).
LP: . . . . MFP 415648 1
MC: . . . . TCMFP 415648 4

20 GOLDEN HITS OF 1958 (Various artists).
LP: . . . . MFP 50551
MC: . . . . TCMFP 50551

20 GOLDEN HITS OF 1959 (Various artists).
LP: . . . . MFP 50566
MC: . . . . TCMFP 50566

20 GOLDEN PIECES: 50'S AND 60'S (Various artists).
Tracks: / Problem child: Orbison, Roy / My pillow: Miller, Roger / I still remember: Freeman, Bobby/ Please love me: Everett, Betty / Cradle of my arms: Pitney, Gene / Not that you've gone: Brown, Maxine/ Such a mess: Price, Lloyd / Let it live: Mimms, Garnet / Dreaming dreams: Benton, Brook / Out here: Clovers / This is real: Four Seasons / Snow deer: Kramer, Floyd / No greater love: Dove, Ronnie/ Something a little bit different: Jan & Dean / Pony time: Covay, Don / Bonnie B: Lewis, Jerry Lee/ Set me free: Thomas, Irma / Come on and love me: Jackson, Chuck / Friendship ring: Burke, Solomon/ Just a dream: Clayton, Jimmy.
LP: . . . . BDL 2008

20 GREAT CRUISING FAVOURITES OF THE 50'S AND 60' (Various artists).
Tracks: / Lovers who wander: Dion / Rock everybody: Teen Queens / When will I be loved: Everly Brothers/ She said 'yeah': Williams, Larry / Hickory dickory dock: Myles, Big Boy & The Shaw Wees / Little star: Dion/ My boyfriend's back: Angels / One fine day: Chiffons / I cried a tear: Chordettes / Lawdy Miss Clawdy: Price, Lloyd / Mary Lou: Young Jessie / Lucille: Little Richard / Hey doll baby: Everly Brothers/ Forever: Cooke, Sam / My block: Four Pennies / Please don't tell me now: Dean & Jean / Little bitty pretty one: Day, Bobby / Buzz buzz buzz: Hollywood Flames / Hey boy, hey girl: McLollie, Oscar / Bama lama, bama loo: Little Richard.
LP: . . . . DROP 1016
MC: . . . . CROP 1016

20 GREAT CRUISING FAVOURITES OF THE 50'S AND 60' (Various artists).
Tracks: / Wanderer, The: Dion / Party girl: Carroll, Bernadette / Chattanooga choo choo: Fields, Ernie Orchestra / Dizzy Miss Lizzy: Williams, Larry / Rockin' robin: Day, Bobby / Angel baby: Rosie & The Originals / Sunday kind of love, A: Mystics / Will you love me tomorrow: Shirelles / Bandit of my dreams: Hodges, Eddie / Baby face: Little Richard / Denise: Randy & The Rainbows / Chantilly lace: Big Bopper / Pretty girls everywhere: Church, Eugene / No wheels: Chordettes / Problems: Everly Brothers/ Way you look tonight: Jarmels / It's my party / Heart: Chandler, Kenny / Rockin' Pneumonia: Neville, Art/ I got a feeling: Tillotson, Johnny.
LP: . . . . DROP 1015
MC: . . . . CROP 1015

20 GREAT CRUISING FAVOURITES OF THE 50'S AND 60' (Various artists).
Tracks: / Wake up little Susie: Everly Brothers / Nut rocker: B. Bumble & The Stingers / Lonely teenager: Dion/ Over and over: Day, Bobby / Church bells may ring: Cadets / In the mood: Fields, Ernie Orchestra/ Long tall Sally: Little Richard / Short fat Fanny: Williams, Larry / Tall Paul: Chordettes / Poetry in motion: Tillotson, Johnny / Runaround Sue: Dion / I'll come running back to you: Cooke, Sam / I cried a tear: Baker, Ruth / Tick tock: Marvin, Johnny / Girl of my dreams: Belvin, Jesse / Take a message to Mary: Everly Brothers / She say: Royal Olympics, The / He's so fine: Chiffons / Pink shoe laces: Chordettes / Tra la la la Suzy: Dean and Jean.
LP: . . . . DROP 1014
MC: . . . . CROP 1014

20 GREAT TEEN BALLADS OF THE 50'S AND 60'S (Various artists).
Tracks: / I can't help it (if I'm still in love with you): Tillotson, Johnny / Send me the pillow that you dream on: Tillotson, Johnny / Teenager in love, A: Dion & The Belmonts / I wonder if I care as much: Everly Brothers / Maybe tomorrow: Everly Brothers / Casual look, A: Cooper, Dolly / Love you so: Holden, Ron / (I love you) for sentimental reasons: Belvin, Jesse / Sixteen candles: Stewart, Skip / Why: Avalon, Frankie / Laurie Ann: Glenn, Glen / Way you look tonight, The: Lonely guys, The / Beggin' you please: Jive Five / Eddie my love: Teen Queens / I made a vow: Robins / Send me some lovin': Little Richard / Loveable: Cooke, Sam / Just to be with you: Passions / Whenever a teenager cries: Jeans.
LP: . . . . DROP 1012
MC: . . . . CROP 1012

20 NO. 1'S OF 50'S & 60'S (Various artists).
MCSET: . . . . DTO 10259

30 YEARS OF NUMBER 1'S VOL 2 (1958-61) (Various artists).
Tracks: / It's all in the game: Edwards, Tommy / It's only make believe: Twitty, Conway / Smoke gets in your eyes: Platters / Fool such as I, A: Presley, Elvis / Only sixteen: Douglas, Craig / Why: Newley, Anthony / Running bear: Preston, Johnny / Three steps to heaven: Cochran, Eddie / Please don't tease: Richard, Cliff / Apache: Shadows / Hoots mon: Lord Rockingham's XI / As I love you: Bassey, Shirley / Side saddle: Conway, Russ / Living doll: Richard, Cliff / What do you want: Ford, Emile / Poor me: Faith, Adam / Do you mind: Newley, Anthony / Good timin': Jones, Jimmy (singer) / Shakin' all over: Kidd, Johnny & The Pirates.
2LP: . . . . TYNOLP 101
MC: . . . . TYNOMC 101

30 YEARS OF NUMBER 1'S VOL 1 (1956-58) (Various artists).
Tracks: / Rock around the clock: Haley, Bill & The Comets / Memories are made of this: Martin, Dean / Why do fools fall in love: Lymon, Frankie / Singing the blues: Steele, Tommy / Cumberland Gap: Donegan, Lonnie/ All shook up: Presley, Elvis / That'll be the day: Holly, Buddy / Great balls of fire: Belafonte, Harry/ Story of my life: Holliday, Michael / Whole lotta woman: Rainwater, Marvin / Sixteen tons: Ford, Tennessee Ernie / Rock and roll waltz: Starr, Kay / Lay down your arms: Shelton, Anne / Garden of Eden: Vaughan, Frankie / Diana: Anka, Paul / Gamblin' man: Donegan, Lonnie / Mary's boy child: Belafonte, Harry/ Jailhouse rock: Presley, Elvis / Magic moments: Como, Perry.
2LP: . . . . TYNOLP 100
MC: . . . . TYNOMC 100

50 EASY LISTENING FAVOURITES (Various artists).
MCSET: . . . . TR 4115485
MCSET: . . . . TR 1548

50 FAVOURITES OF THE 50'S (Various artists).
MCSET: . . . . TR 1521
MCSET: . . . . MFP 4115215

50'S: JUKE JOINT BLUES, THE (Various artists).
Tracks: / 3 o'clock blues: King, B.B. / Long tall woman: James, Elmore / Ramblin' on my mind: Gilmore, Boyd / Gonna let you go: Turner, Babyface / Love my baby: Bland, Bobby & Junior Parker / Riding in the moonlight: Howlin' Wolf / 44 blues: Dudlow & Peck Curtis / Step back baby: Blair, Sunny / This is the end: Reed, James / Jake head boogie: Lightnin' Hopkins / Down in New Orleans: Smith, Little George / Monte Carlo: Dixie Blues Boys / Doin' the town: Dixon, Floyd / Just got in from Texas: Gordon, Roscoe / Big mouth: Nelson, Jimmy / Have you ever: Dee, Mercy / Sputterin' blues: Robertson, Walter / Prowling blues: Fuller, Johnny/ Going to New Orleans: Tanner, Kid / Good morning little angel: Louis, Joe Hill / Panic's on, The: McCracklin, Jimmy (Available on CD only) / What's the matter with you: Horton, Walter "Shakey" (Available on CD only).
LP: . . . . CHA 216
MC: . . . . CHC 216

50'S: R & B VOCAL GROUPS, THE (Various artists).

Tracks: / Rock bottom: Rams / Hold me, thrill me, chill me: Flairs / My darling, my sweet: Flairs/ I made a vow: Robins / Please remember my heart: Five Bells / My cutie pie: Five Bells / Girl in my dreams: Cliques / Even since you've been gone: Hawks (film) / It's all over: Hawks (film) / Please don't go: Chanters / Tick tock: Marvin & Johnny / Why did I fall in love: Jacks / Sweet thing: Maye, Arthur Lee & The Crowns / Hands across the table: Cadets / Hey Rube: Rocketeers / It won't take long/Native girl: Native Boys / Farewell: Relf, Bobby & the Laurels / At last: Berry, Richard & the Dreamers / Please, please baby: Five Hearts / Love me, love me, love me: Chimes (Available on CD only) / I love you, yes I do: Marvin, Johnny (Available on CD only).
LP: . . . . **CHA 212**
MC: . . . . **CHC 212**

50'S: ROCKABILLY FEVER, THE (Various artists).
Tracks: / I guess it's meant that way: Cupp, Pat / Long gone daddy: Cupp, Pat / Don't do me no wrong: Cupp, Pat / Everybody's movin': Glenn, Glen / If I had me a woman: Glenn, Glen / I don't know when: Harris, Hal / True affection: Johnson, Byron / Be boppin' daddy: Cole, Les & The Echoes / Rock little baby: Cole, Les & The Echoes / My big fat baby: Hall, Sonny & The Echoes / Rock my warriors rock: Jackson, Joe / Snake eyed mama: Cole, Don / Nuthin' but a nuthin': Stewart, Jimmy & his Nighthawks / Wild wild party: Feathers, Charlie / Pink cadillac: Todd, Johnny / Slipping and sliding: Davis, Link / All the time: La Beef, Sleepy / Go home letter: Barber, Glen / Boppin' wigwam Willie: Scott, Ray / I can't find the doorknob: Jimmy & Johnny / Jitterbop baby: Harris, Hal (Available on CD only) / Little bit more, A: La Beef, Sleepy (Available on CD only).
LP: . . . . **CHA 218**
MC: . . . . **CHC 218**

1950'S: SINGERS (Various artists).
Tracks: / Street of dreams: Wiley, Lee / Fine and mellow: Holiday, Billie / Easy to love: Mathis, Johnny/ Hey! bartender, give...: Williams, Joe / Flying: Gonzales, Babs/Griffin, Johnny / Charleston: Lambert, Hendricks & Annie Ross / Mack the knife: Various artists / Russian lullaby: Rushing, Jimmy / There ain't no flies on...: Hot Lips Page / Take the 'A' train: Ellington, Duke / Frenesi: Carter, Betty.
LP: **4606081**

AT THE HOP (15 rockin million sellers of the 50's) (Various artists).
Tracks: / At the hop: Danny & The Juniors / Peggy Sue: Holly, Buddy & The Crickets / See you later alligator: Haley, Bill & The Comets / When: Kalin Twins / Stagger Lee: Price, Lloyd / Come go with me: Del-Vikings/ That'll be the day: Holly, Buddy & The Crickets / Here comes summer: Keller, Jerry / I hear you knocking: Storm, Gale / Shake, rattle and roll: Haley, Bill & The Comets / Green door: Lowe, Jim / Jingle bell rock: Helms, Bobby / I'm gonna got married: Price, Lloyd / Maybe baby: Holly, Buddy & The Crickets / Rock around the clock: Haley, Bill & The Comets.
LP: . . . . **SHM 3210**
MC: . . . . **HSC 3210**

BALLAD HITS MID 50'S (Various artists).
Tracks: / Unchained melody: Hibbler, Al / Cool water: Laine, Frankie / Mangos: Clooney, Rosemary / Magic moments: Como, Perry / Look homeward angel: Ray, Johnnie / Big man: Four Preps / My prayer: Platters/ Memories are made of this: Martin, Dean / Passing strangers: Vaughan, Sarah/Billy Eckstein / We will make love: Hamilton, Russ / Island in the Sun: Belafonte, Harry / Wayward wind: Grant, Gogi / Twelfth of never: Mathis, Johnny / When I fall in love: Cole, Nat King.
LP: . . . . **OG 1016**
MC: . . . . **OG 2016**

CLASSIC POP HITS OF THE LATE 50'S (Various artists).
Tracks: / Living doll: Richard, Cliff / Sea of love: Wilde, Marty / Teenager in love: Dion & The Belmonts/ Lipstick on your collar: Francis, Connie / Oh, Carol: Sedaka, Neil / C'mon everybody: Cochran, Eddie/ Red river rock: Johnny & The Hurricanes / What do you wanna make those eyes at me for?: Ford, Emile & The Checkmates/ Here comes summer: Keller, Jerry / Till I kissed you: Everly Brothers / Come softly to me: Fleetwoods/ Susie Darlin: Lake, Robin / Three bells, The: Browns / It doesn't matter anymore: Holly, Buddy.
LP: . . . . **OG 1010**
MC: . . . . **OG 2010**

DO YOU WANNA DANCE? (Various artists).
Tracks: / 40 miles of bad road: Various artists / Tallahassee lassie: Various artists / Haunted house: Various artists / By the light of the silvery moon: Various artists / Rebel rouser: Various artists / Way down yonder in New Orleans: Various artists / Tossin' and turnin': Various artists / Baby face: Various artists/ Because they're young: Various artists / Do you wanna dance?: Various artists / Little darlin': Various artists / La Bamba: Various artists / Kansas City: Hawkins, Ronnie / Party doll: Knox, Buddy / Forty days: Hawkins, Ronnie / You don't know what you've done: Donner, Ral / Speedoo: Cadillacs / Honeycomb: Rodgers, Jimmie (2) / Woo hoo: Rock A Teens / Do you wanna dance?: Freeman, Bobby / Barbara Ann: Regents/ Teenage love: Lymon, Frankie & The Teenagers / Fannie Mae: Brown, Buster / Too young: Lymon, Frankie & The Teenagers / I need your lovin': Gardiner, Don & Dee Dee Ford / Poor boy: Royaltones.
LP: . . . . **TOP 147**
MC: . . . . **KTOP 147**
LP: . . . . **NCP 1002**

EAST COAST TEEN ROCK 1959-58 (Various artists).
LP: . . . . **CGB 1005**

EASYRIDING: MUSIC AFTER MIDNIGHT (Various artists).
Tracks: / What a difference a day made: Washington, Dinah / Endlessly: Benton, Brook / Misty: Vaughan, Sarah / Smoke gets in your eyes: Platters / Romance in the dark: Jo, Damita / I apologise: Eckstine, Billy / Unforgettable: Washington, Dinah / It's just a matter of time: Benton, Brook / Broken hearted melody: Vaughan, Sarah / Twilight time: Platters / You won't let me go: Jo, Damita / Guilty: Eckstine, Billy / I should have kissed him more: Vaughan, Sarah / I'm sorry: Platters / Cheek to cheek: Vaughan, Sarah/Billy Eckstein / Joanna: Walker, Scott / Softly: Washington, Dinah / Deep purple: Lawrence, Syd Orchestra / My prayer: Platters / Stardust: Lawrence, Syd Orchestra / Smoke gets in your eyes: Cascading Strings.
MC: . . . . **KNMC 11008**
LP: . . . . **KNLP 11008**

EVERGREEN (26 of your favourite ballads) (Various artists).
Tracks: / Forevermore: Damone, Vic / Laura: Damone, Vic / Strange enchantment: Damone, Vic / Bali Ha'i: Damone, Vic / Anyone who had a heart: Carr, Vikki / You don't have to say you love me: Carr, Vikki/ Can't take my eyes off you: Carr, Vikki / For once in my life: Carr, Vikki / Portrait of my love: Monro, Matt / Somewhere: Monro, Matt / From Russia with love: Monro, Matt / One day: Monro, Matt / Here, there and everywhere: Monro, Matt / More I see you, The: Cogan, Alma / Can't help falling in love: Cogan, Alma / I'm in the mood for love: Cogan, Alma / Yesterday: Cogan, Alma / Close to you: Hill, Vince/ Where do I begin: Hill, Vince / Maria: Hill, Vince / Somewhere my love: Hill, Vince / I've got you under my skin: Bassey, Shirley / Love is a many splendored thing: Bassey, Shirley / As long as he needs me: Bassey, Shirley / Let's fall in love: Bassey, Shirley / What kind of fool am I?: Bassey, Shirley.
2LP: . . . . **DL 1179**
MC: . . . . **TCDL 1179**

FABULOUS 50'S, THE (Various artists).
Tracks: / Mobile: Burns, Ray / Ricochet: Anthony, Billie / Bell bottom blues: Anthony, Billie / I still believe: Hilton, Ronnie / No other love: Hilton, Ronnie / Half as much: Cogan, Alma / You belong to me: Cogan, Alma / Story of my life: Holliday, Michael / Heart and soul: Carr, Carole / How much is that doggie in the window: Carr, Carole / White sports coat and a pink carnation: King Brothers / Hold me, thrill me, kiss me: Brereton, Gerry / Book, The: Brereton, Gerry / Let me go lover: Murray, Ruby / Heartbeat: Murray, Ruby / Oh my papa: Calvert, Eddie / Sky blue shirt and a rainbow tie: Ellington, Ray Quartet / Naughty lady of Shady Lane, The: Ellington, Ray Quartet / Little shoemaker, The: Boswell, Eve/ Shifting whispering sands, The - pt. 1: Andrews, Eamonn / Shifting whispering sands, The - pt. 2: Andrews, Eamonn/ Wanted: Brent, Tony / Happy days and lonely nights: Vaughan, Frankie / I lived when I met you: Howard, Les / Answer me: Campbell, Jean / Unsuspecting heart: Brown, Fay / Unchained melody: Carson, Jean/ St. Therese of the roses: Vaughan, Malcolm.
2LP: . . . . **DL 1167**
MC: . . . . **TCDL 1167**
MCSET: . . . . **KNMC 35002**

FABULOUS FIFTIES, THE (Various artists).
Tracks: / Secret love: Day, Doris / Just walking in the rain: Ray, Johnnie / Mambo Italiano: Clooney, Rosemary/ Woman in love: Laine, Frankie / Rock-a-billy: Mitchell, Guy / Such a night: Ray, Johnnie / On the street where...: Damone, Vic / I believe: Laine, Frankie / Strangers in paradise: Bennett, Tony / Singing the blues: Mitchell, Guy / Hey Joe: Laine, Frankie / Black hills of Dakota, The: Day, Doris / Hey there: Ray, Johnnie / Heart aches by the number: Mitchell, Guy / This ole house: Clooney, Rosemary / She wears red feathers: Mitchell, Guy / Answer me: Laine, Frankie / Yellow rose of Texas: Miles, Mitch / Yes tonight Josephine: Ray, Johnnie / Whatever will be, will be...: Day, Doris.
MCSET: . . . . **DTOL 10252**

FABULOUS FIFTIES VOL.2 (Various artists).
Tracks: / Look at the girl: Mitchell, Guy / If I give my heart...: Day, Doris / Look homeward angel: Ray, Johnnie / Where will the...: Clooney, Rosemary / Blowing wild: Laine, Frankie / Faith can move mountains: Ray, Johnnie / High noon: Laine, Frankie / Chicka boom: Mitchell, Guy / Affair to remember, An: Damone, Vic / Love me or leave me: Day, Doris / Cool water: Laine, Frankie / Having too much: Clooney, Rosemary/ Ready, willing and able: Day, Doris / Hernando's hideaway: Ray, Johnnie / Pretty little...: Mitchell, Guy / Diana: Anka, Paul / Sippin' soda: Mitchell, Guy.
MCSET: . . . . **DTO 10278**

FABULOUS FIFTIES VOL 3 (Various artists).
MCSET: . . . . **DTO 10294**

FAVOURITES OF THE FIFTIES (Various artists).
Tracks: / Walking to Missouri: Brent, Tony / May you always: Regan, Joan / China tea: Conway, Russ/ My thanks to you: Conway, Steve / Blue star: Boswell, Eve / Tammy: Lotis, Dennis / Naughty lady of Shady Lane: Ellington, Ray / Don't laugh at me: Wisdom, Norman / Robin Hood: James, Dick / Careless love: Abicair, Shirley / Mad, passionate love: Bresslaw, Bernard / Bells across the meadow: Ronalde, Ronnie/ Small talk: Yana / My boy Bill: Hockridge, Edmund / Yell for your mama: Beverley Sisters / Stranger in Paradise: Calvert, Eddie / Go now, for ever: Murray, Ruby / That's right: Deep River Boys / Bee song: Askey, Arthur / Ain't misbehavin': Laine, Cleo / Pink shoe laces: Cogan, Alma / On the street where you live: Hilton, Ronnie / Good luck, good health, God bless you: Holliday, Michael/Ruby Murray/Eddie Calvert/ Shifting, whispering sands: Andrews, Eamonn / Istanbul: Vaughan, Frankie / Narcissus: Wisdom, Norman & Joyce Grenfell / Manhattan spiritual: Delaney, Eric & His Band / Little red monkey: Nicholls, Joy/ Dick Bentley/Jimmy Edwards / Memories are made of this: Hill, Benny & The Coronets / Cumberland Gap: Vipers / Book of love: Mudlarks / Splish splash: Drake, Charlie / Li'l Liza Jane: Barber, Chris / Wake up little Susie: King Brothers / Six five special: Lang, Don.
2LP: . . . . **DL 41 1050 1**
MC: . . . . **TCDL 41 1050 4**

FIFTIES MEMORIES (Various artists).
LP: . . . . **NE 1370**
MC: . . . . **CE 2370**

FIFTIES NO. 1'S VOL 3 (OLD GOLD) (Various artists).
Tracks: / Just walking in the rain: Ray, Johnnie / Puttin' on the style: Donegan, Lonnie / Here comes summer: Keller, Jerry / It doesn't matter anymore: Holly, Buddy / Smoke gets in your eyes: Platters / Who's sorry now: Francis, Connie / What do you want to make those eyes at me for: Ford, Emile & The Checkmates / When: Kalin Twins / Whole lotta woman: Rainwater, Marvin / Garden of Eden: Vaughan, Frankie / Butterfly: Williams, Andy / Woman in love: Laine, Frankie / Young love: Hunter, Tab / Singing the blues: Mitchell, Guy.
LP: . . . . **OG 1516**
MC: . . . . **OG 2516**

FIFTIES VOLUME 1, THE (Various artists).
Tracks: / To know him is to love him: Teddy Bears / Born too late: Poni-Tails / It's all in the game: Edwards, Tommy / Great pretender, The: Platters / Tammy: Reynolds, Debbie / All I have to do is dream: Everly Brothers / Day the rains came, The: Morgan, Jane / Only sixteen: Douglas, Craig / Story of my life: Holliday, Michael / Remember you're mine: Boone, Pat / Young love: Hunter, Tab / It's only make believe: Twitty, Conway / Who's sorry now?: Francis, Connie / Donna: Valens, Ritchie.
LP: . . . . **OG 1001**
MC: . . . . **OG 2001**

FIFTIES VOLUME 2, THE (Various artists).
Tracks: / Bye bye love: Everly Brothers / Singing the blues: Mitchell, Guy / Yes tonight Josephine: Ray, Johnnie / Ninety-nine ways: Hunter, Tab / Butterfly: Williams, Andy / Don't forbid me: Boone, Pat/ Garden of Eden: Vaughan, Frankie / That'll be the day: Holly, Buddy & The Crickets / Diana: Anka, Paul/ At the hop: Danny & The Juniors / Little darlin': Diamonds / When: Kalin Twins / Whole lotta woman: Rainwater, Marvin / Ma, he's making eyes at me: Otis, Johnny Show.
LP: . . . . **OG 1005**
MC: . . . . **OG 2005**

GOLDEN GOODIES VOL 1 (Various artists).
LP: . . . . **XELLP 108**
MC: . . . . **XELMC 108**

GOLDEN HITS OF THE 50'S (Various artists).
Tracks: / Love is a many splendoured thing: Four Aces / Sweet old fashioned girl: Brewer, Teresa / Love letters in the sand: Boone, Pat / Eddie my love: Various artists / Little things mean a lot: Kallen, Kitty/ It's almost tomorrow: Dream Weavers / Unchained melody: Hibbler, Al / May you always: McGuire Sisters/ Mr. Wonderful: Lee, Peggy / Day the rains came, The: Morgan, Jane / Tammy: Reynolds, Debbie / Young love: Hunter, Tab / Rock around the clock: Haley, Bill & The Comets / When: Kallin Twins / Here comes summer: Keller, Jerry / Peggy Sue: Holly, Buddy.
LP: . . . . **MCM 5032**
MC: . . . . **MCMC 5032**

GOLDEN HITS OF THE 50'S (Various artists).
2LP: . . . . **BRLP 65/66**
MCSET: . . . . **BRMC 65/66**

GOLDEN YEARS '50'S VOL. 3 (Various artists).
MC: . . . . **PWKMC 4056P**

GOLDEN YEARS OF THE 50'S, VOL 3, THE (Various artists).
Tracks: / Only you (and you alone): Platters, The / My happiness: Francis, Connie / As I love you: Bassey, Shirley / Swedish rhapsody: Mantovani & His Orchestra / Endlessly: Benton, Brook / Nairobi: Steele, Tommy / Ko ko mo (I love you so): Crew Cuts / My prayer: Platters, The / Carolina moon: Francis, Connie/ Donna: Wilde, Marty / Little darlin': Diamonds, The / It's just a matter of time: Benton, Brook / No one but you: Eckstine, Billy / Ebb tide: Chacksfield, Frank & His Orchestra / Gum drop: Crew Cuts/ Twilight time: Platters, The.
MC: . . . . **PWKMC 4056P**

GREAT ENTERTAINERS, THE (Various artists).
Tracks: / When I fall in love: Cole, Nat King / I (who have nothing): Bassey, Shirley / Let me go lover: Martin, Dean / Dreamboat: Cogan, Alma / Spanish eyes: Martino, Al / Fever: Lee, Peggy / Portrait of my love: Monro, Matt / Falling in love with love: Shore, Dinah / I remember you: Ifield, Frank / Memories are made of this: Martin, Dean / Till there was you: Lee, Peggy / Walk away: Monro, Matt / As long as he needs me: Bassey, Shirley / Story of my life: Holliday, Michael / Softly softly: Murray, Ruby/ No other love: Hilton, Ronnie / Comes a-long-a-love: Starr, Kay / Let there be love: Cole, Nat King/ Wanted: Martino, Al (CD only.) / Bell bottom blues: Cogan, Alma (CD only.) / Rock 'n' roll waltz: Starr, Kay (CD only.) / Evermore: Murray, Ruby.
LP: . . . . **MFP 5852**
MC: . . . . **TCMFP 5852**

GREAT ENTERTAINERS, THE VOL. 2 (Various artists).
Tracks: / It's impossible: Como, Perry / On a slow boat to China: Crosby, Bing / Diamonds are a girl's best friend: Horne, Lena / Welcome to my world: Reeves, Jim / Polka dots and moonbeams: Sinatra, Frank & Tommy Dorsey / C'est si bon: Kitt, Eartha / It's a sin to tell a lie: Waller, Fats / Girl from Ipanema: Damone, Vic / Light my fire: Feliciano, Jose / If I were a carpenter: Belafonte, Harry / Don't let the stars get in your eyes (Willet): Como, Perry / It happened in Monterey: Crosby, Bing / People will say we're in love: Horne, Lena / I love you because: Reeves, Jim / How about you: Sinatra, Frank & Tommy Dorsey / Let's do it: Kitt, Eartha / Two sleepy people: Waller, Fats (CD only.) / Shadow of your smile: Damone, Vic (CD only.) / California dreamin': Feliciano, Jose (CD only.) / Homeward bound: Belafonte, Harry (CD only.).

LP: .... **MFP 5855**
MC: .... **TCMFP 5855**

GREAT GROUPS OF THE 50'S, VOL 2 (Various artists).
LP: .... **COL 5038**

GREAT GROUPS OF THE 50'S, VOL 1 (Various artists).
LP: .... **COL 5037**

GREAT GROUPS OF THE 50'S, VOL 3 (Various artists).
LP: .... **COL 5039**

GREAT HIT BALLADS OF THE 50'S (Various artists).
Tracks: / Beyond the stars: *Whitfield, David* / No other love: *Johnston Brothers* / Alone: *Southlanders* / More: *Young, Jimmy* / Happy days and lonely nights: *Miller, Suzi* / Mister Sandman: *Valentine, Dickie* / Memories are made of this: *King, Dave* / Blossom fell, A: *Valentine, Dickie* / Unchained melody: *Young, Jimmy* / Forget me not: *Lynn, Vera* / Prize of gold: *Regan, Joan* / Answer me: *Whitfield, David* / Finger of suspicion: *Valentine, Dickie* / When you lose the one you love: *Whitfield, David* / Eternally: *Young, Jimmy* / Maybe tomorrow: *Fury, Billy* / House with love in it, A: *Lynn, Vera* / Broken wings: *Stargazers* / My September love: *Whitfield, David* / Hey there: *Johnston Brothers* / Friends.....: *Cotton, Billy & His Band* / I dreamed: *Beverly Sisters* / My son my son: *Lynn, Vera*.
MCSET: .... **DTO 10288**

HEART THROBS (Various artists).
Tracks: / Why: *Avalon, Frankie* / Venus: *Avalon, Frankie* / De de dinah: *Avalon, Frankie* / Tiger: *Fabian* / Hound dog man: *Fabian* / More than I can say: *Vee, Bobby* / Rubber ball: *Vee, Bobby* / Night has a 1000 eyes, The: *Vee, Bobby* / Forget him: *Rydell, Bobby* / Wild one: *Rydell, Bobby* / Volare: *Rydell, Bobby*.
LP: .... **TOP 146**

HITS OF 1957 (Various artists).
Tracks: / White sports coat, A (and a pink carnation): *King Brothers* / In the middle of an island: *King Brothers* / I'm not a juvenile delinquent: *Lymon, Frankie & The Teenagers* / Baby baby: *Lymon, Frankie & The Teenagers* / I'm walkin': *Domino, Fats* / Ain't that a shame: *Domino, Fats* / School day (ring ring goes the bell): *Lang, Don & His Frantic 5* / Ma he's making eyes at me: *Johnny Otis Show* / You, me and us: *Cogan, Alma* / Whatever Lola wants (Lola gets): *Cogan, Alma* / Around the world: *Hilton, Ronnie* / Wonderful wonderful: *Hilton, Ronnie* / My special angel: *Vaughan, Malcolm* / Chapel of the roses: *Vaughan, Malcolm* / Wisdom of a fool: *Wisdom, Norman* / Party doll: *Knox, Buddy* / Be my girl: *Dale, Jim* / I'll take you home again Kathleen: *Whitman, Slim* / Man who plays the mandolino, The: *Martin, Dean* / When I fall in love: *Cole, Nat King* / He's got the whole world in his hands: *London, Laurie* / Any old iron: *Sellers, Peter* / Garden of Eden: *James, Dick* / Young love: *James, Sonny*.
MC: .... **HR 8185**

HITS OF 1959 (Various artists).
Tracks: / C'mon everybody: *Cochran, Eddie* / It's late: *Nelson, Red* / Last night on the back porch: *Cogan, Alma* / Living doll: *Richard, Cliff* / Guitar boogie shuffle: *Weedon, Bert* / Pub with no beer, A: *Dusty, Slim* / Side saddle: *Conway, Russ* / What do you want?: *Faith, Adam* / World outside, The: *Hilton, Ronnie* / Three bells, The: *Champagnons De La Chanson* / Only sixteen: *Douglas, Craig* / Come softly to me: *Fleetwoods* / May you always: *Regan, Joan* / Travellin' light: *Richard, Cliff* / Goodbye Jimmy goodbye: *Murray, Ruby* / Seven little girls sitting in the back seat: *Avons* / Teenager in love: *Douglas, Craig* / Tom Dooley: *Kingston Trio* / Roulette: *Conway, Russ* / Love game, The: *Mudlarks* / Something else: *Cochran, Eddie* / We got love: *Cogan, Alma* / Why should I be lonely: *Brent, Tony* / Please don't touch: *Kidd, Johnny & The Pirates* / Be my guest: *Domino, Fats* / Little drummer boy: *Flanders, Michael*.
MC: .... **HR 8171**

HITS OF THE 50'S (Various artists).
Tracks: / Whatever will be will be (medley): *Day, Doris* / I believe: *Laine, Frankie* / Cry: *Ray, Johnnie* / Stranger in paradise: *Bennett, Tony* / Swinging the blues: *Mitchell, Guy* / This ole house: *Clooney, Rosemary* / On the street where you live: *Damone, Vic* / Diana: *Anka, Paul* / How much is that doggie in the window: *Page, Patti* / Wonderful, wonderful: *Mathis, Johnny* / Man that got away, The: *Garland, Judy* / Rawhide: *Link Wray* / Yellow rose of Texas: *Miller, Mitch* / White sports coat: *Robbins, Marty* / We will make love: *Hamilton, Russ* / Secret love: *Day, Doris* / Little white cloud that cried, The: *Ray, Johnnie* / Answer me: *Various artists* / I walk the line: *Cash, Johnny* / Blue suede shoes: *Perkins, Carl* / Start movin': *Mineo, Sal* / Heart aches by the number: *Mitchell, Guy* / Battle of New Orleans: *Horton, Johnny* / Waterloo: *Jackson, Stonewall*.
2LP: .... **CCSLP 145**
MC: .... **CCSMC 145**

HITS OF THE 50'S (Various artists).
MC: .... **SPC 8558**

HITS OF THE 50'S (Various artists).
Tracks: / Petite fleur: *Barber, Chris Jazzband* / Young and foolish: *Hockridge, Edmund* / Venus: *Valentine, Dickie* / Lollipop: *Miller, Gary*.
MCSET: .... **DTO 10022**

IT'S SOMETHING ELSE (20 HITS FROM 50'S) (Various artists).
LP: **50079**

JUKE BOX COLLECTION - OH BOY (Sound of the 50's part 2) (Various artists).
Tracks: / Till I kissed you: *Everly Brothers* / Three bells, The: *Browns* / Making love: *Robinson, Floyd* / Mona Lisa: *Twitty, Conway* / Shape I'm in, The: *Restivo, Johnny* / Why baby why: *Boone, Pat* / Only sixteen: *Cooke, Sam* / Oh boy: *Holly, Buddy & The Crickets* / Last train to San Fernando: *Duncan, Johnny (1)* / My Dixie darlin': *Donegan, Lonnie* / Personality: *Price, Lloyd* / In the mood: *Fields, Ernie* / Butterfingers: *Steele, Tommy* / Island in the sun: *Belafonte, Harry*.
LP: .... **OG 1720**
MC: .... **OG 2720**

JUKE BOX COLLECTION - WHOLE LOTTA SHAKIN' .... (Juke box 50's) (Various artists).
Tracks: / Johnny B Goode: *Berry, Chuck* / Bring a little water Sylvie: *Donegan, Lonnie* / Stagger Lee: *Price, Lloyd* / Lucille: *Little Richard* / Razzle dazzle: *Haley, Bill & The Comets* / Not fade away: *Holly, Buddy & The Crickets* / Whole lotta shakin' goin' on: *Lewis, Jerry Lee* / Bird dog: *Everly Brothers* / Come on let's go: *Valens, Ritchie* / Pretend: *Mann, Carl* / Whispering bells: *Del-Vikings* / Reveille rock: *Johnny & The Hurricanes* / Danny: *Wilde, Marty* / Tallahassee Lassie: *Steele, Tommy*.
LP: .... **OG 1723**
MC: .... **OG 2723**

JUKE BOX COLLECTION - YOUNG LOVE (Sound of the 50's part 1) (Various artists).
Tracks: / To know him is to love him: *Teddy Bears* / All I have to do is dream: *Everly Brothers* / Donna: *Valens, Ritchie* / Come go with me: *Del-Vikings* / Where or when: *Dion & The Belmonts* / Lollipop: *Chordettes* / Susie darlin': *Lake, Robin* / Born too late: *Poni-Tails* / Seventeen: *Fontane Sisters* / Day that the rains came, The: *Morgan, Jane* / Friendly persuasion: *Boone, Pat* / Young love: *Hunter, Tab* / No other baby: *Helms, Bobby* / Volare: *Marini, Marino*.
LP: .... **OG 1715**
MC: .... **OG 2715**

LOVIN' FIFTIES (Baby Boomer Series) (Various artists).
Tracks: / Teenager in love: *Dion & The Belmonts* / Lonely boy: *Anka, Paul* / Come softly to me: *Fleetwoods* / Oh Carol: *Sedaka, Neil* / I'm in love again: *Domino, Fats* / Sixteen candles: *Crests* / Why do fools fall in love: *Lymon, Frankie & The Teenagers* / Bye bye love: *Everly Brothers* / Little darlin': *Diamonds* / It's all in the game: *Edwards, Tommy* / Donna: *Wilde, Marty* / Magic moments: *Como, Perry* / You always hurt the one you love: *Francis, Connie* / Smoke gets in your eyes: *Platters* / Fever: *Lee, Peggy* / Only sixteen: *Douglas, Craig*.
LP: .... **BOOMER 107**
MC: .... **BOOMERC 107**

LOVING FIFTIES (Baby Boomer Series) (Various artists).
Tracks: / Who's sorry now: *Francis, Connie* / Teen angel: *Dinning, Mark* / Only you: *Platters, The* / Mr. Sandman: *Chordettes* / As I love you: *Bassey, Shirley* / You got what it takes: *Johnson, Marv* / White sports coat, A: *Dene, Terry* / Unchained melody: *Young, Jimmy* / Blueberry Hill: *Domino, Fats* / Why: *Newley, Anthony* / It's only make believe: *Twitty, Conway* / Maybe tomorrow: *Fury, Billy* / All I have to do is dream: *Everly Brothers* / Singing the blues: *Steele, Tommy* / Story of my life: *Holliday, Michael* / Softly Softly: *Murray, Ruby*.
LP: .... **BOOMER 102**
MC: .... **BOOMERC 102**

MAGIC MOMENTS FROM THE 50'S (Various artists).
MC: .... **AIM 69**
MC: .... **AM 69**

MAY YOU ALWAYS (24 Golden hits 1952-59) (Various artists).
Tracks: / Twelfth of never: *Mathis, Johnny* / My happiness: *Francis, Connie* / End, The: *Grant, Earl* / May you always: *McGuire Sisters* / My special angel: *Helms, Bobby* / Love me forever: *Ryan, Marion* / Look homeward angel: *Ray, Johnnie* / Tammy: *Reynolds, Debbie* / Come prima: *Marini, Marino* / If only I could live my life again: *Morgan, Jane* / For a penny: *Boone, Pat* / My prayer: *Platters* / Answer me: *Whitfield, David* / Sugarbush: *Day, Doris & Frankie Laine* / Mr. Sandman: *Chordettes* / Love me or leave me: *Davis, Sammy Jnr.* / Mr. Wonderful: *Lee, Peggy* / Alone: *Kaye Sisters* / Sixteen tons: *Laine, Frankie* / Tea for two cha cha: *Dorsey, Tommy* / Finger of suspicion: *Valentine, Dickie* / Ivory towers: *Carr, Cathy* / Mangos: *Clooney, Rosemary* / With all my heart: *Clark, Petula*.
MCSET: .... **OG 2212**

MEMORIES OF THE 50'S (16 All Time Favourites) (Various artists).
LP: .... **PFP 1006**
MC: .... **PFC 1006**

MID-LATE FIFTIES BALLAD NUMBER ONES (OLD GOLD) (Various artists).
Tracks: / Magic moments: *Como, Perry* / Whatever will be will be: *Day, Doris* / It's almost tomorrow: *Dream Weavers* / Cherry pink and apple blossom white: *Prado, Perez* / On the street where you live: *Damone, Vic* / Little things mean a lot: *Kallen, Kitty* / Cara mia: *Whitfield, David* / Answer me: *Laine, Frankie* / Hold my hand: *Cornell, Don* / Mambo Italiano: *Clooney, Rosemary* / Unchained melody: *Young, Jimmy* / It's all in the game: *Edwards, Tommy* / Carolina moon: *Francis, Connie* / Rock and roll waltz: *Starr, Kay*.
LP: .... **OG 1501**
MC: .... **OG 2501**

MILLION SELLERS OF THE 50'S (Various artists).
2LP: .... **CR 034**
MCSET: .... **CRT 034**

MILLION SELLERS OF THE 50'S (Various artists).
Tracks: / Ricochet: *Brewer, Teresa* / Love letters in the sand: *Boone, Pat* / That'll be the day: *Crickets* / Young love: *Hunter, Tab* / Tammy: *Reynolds, Debbie* / Autumn leaves: *Williams, Roger* / When: *Kalin Twins* / Ain't that a shame: *Boone, Pat* / It's almost tomorrow: *Dream Weavers* / Sincerely: *Macguire Sisters* / It doesn't matter anymore: *Holly, Buddy* / Cherry pink and apple blossom white: *Dale, Alan* / Green door: *Lowe, Jim/High fires* / Moonglow: *Stoloff, Morris & his orchestra* / Chattanooga shoeshine boy: *Foley, Red* / Undecided: *Ames Brothers* / Till I waltz again with you: *Brewer, Teresa* / Three coins in the fountain: *Four Aces* / Shake, rattle and roll: *Haley, Bill* / Little things mean a lot: *Kallen, Kitty* / My heart is an open book: *Dobkins, Carl Jr.* / Deck of cards: *Martindale, Wink* / Puppy love: *Anka, Paul* / Personality: *Price, Lloyd* / Sweet nothin's: *Lee, Brenda* / Crying in the chapel: *Allen, Rex*.
MC: .... **GM 0205**

MILLION SELLERS OF THE 50'S VOL 2 (Various artists).
Tracks: / Third man, Theme from: *Lombardo, Guy* / Tell me why: *Four Aces* / Hold me, thrill me, kiss me: *Chandler, Karen* / April love: *Boone, Pat* / P.S. I love you: *Hilltoppers* / Hearts of stone: *Fontane Sisters & Billy Vaughan Orchestra* / Tear fell, A: *Brewer, Teresa* / At the hop: *Danny & The Juniors* / Come go with me: *Del-Vikings* / More and more: *Pierce, Webb* / Let me go, lover: *Brewer, Teresa* / Love is a many splendoured thing: *Four Aces* / I hear you knocking: *Storm, Gale* / I'll be home: *Boone, Pat* / I'm yours: *Cornell, Don* / Tea for two cha cha: *Covington, Warren* / Maybe baby: *Crickets* / Sugar time: *Macguire Sisters* / I'm sorry: *Lee, Brenda* / Wonderful time up there, A: *Boone, Pat* / Stranger in Paradise: *Four Aces*.
2LP: .... **CR 035**
MCSET: .... **CRT 035**

MILLION SELLING HITS OF THE 50'S (Various artists).
Tracks: / Mona Lisa: *Cole, Nat King* / That's amore: *Martin, Dean* / Blueberry Hill: *Domino, Fats* / Rock & roll waltz: *Starr, Kay* (CD only.) / Shotgun boogie: *Ford, Tennessee Ernie* (CD only.) / Mockin' Bird Hill: *Paul, Les & Mary Ford* / Unchained melody: *Baxter, Les* / Come softly to me: *Fleetwoods* / Shrimp boats: *Stafford, Jo* / You send me: *Cooke, Sam* / Fever: *Lee, Peggy* / Here in my heart: *Martino, Al* / On the street where you live: *Damone, Vic* / Oh mein papa: *Calvert, Eddie* / Vaya con dios: *Paul, Les & Mary Ford* / Sixteen tons: *Ford, Tennessee Ernie* / Wheel of fortune: *Starr, Kay* / Ain't that a shame: *Domino, Fats* / Return to me: *Martin, Dean* (CD only.) / Blossom fell, A: *Cole, Nat King*.
LP: .... **MFP 5847**
MC: .... **TCMFP 5847**

MUSIC AFTER MIDNIGHT PART 1 (Various artists).
Tracks: / What a difference a day made: *Various artists* / Unfortunately: *Washington, Dinah* / Endlessly: *Benton, Brook* / It's just a matter of time: *Benton, Brook* / Misty: *Vaughan, Sarah* / Broken hearted melody: *Vaughan, Sarah* / Smoke gets in your eyes: *Platters* / Twilight time: *Platters* / Romance in the dark: *Jo, Damita* / You won't let me go: *Jo, Damita* / I apologise: *Eckstine, Billy* / Guilty: *Eckstine, Billy*.
LP: **824 321-1**
MC: **824 321-4**

MUSIC AFTER MIDNIGHT PART 2 (Various artists).
Tracks: / I should have kissed him more: *Vaughan, Sarah* / I'm sorry, my prayer: *Platters* / Cheek to cheek: *Vaughan, Sarah/Billy Eckstein* / Joanna: *Walker, Scott* / Softly: *Washington, Dinah* / I'll come back for more: *Washington, Dinah* / Stardust - deep purple: *Lawrence, Syd Orchestra* / Smoke gets in your eyes: *Cascading Strings* / Danny boy: *Justis, Bill* / Party is over, The: *Raymonde, Ivor & His Orchestra*.
LP: **824 322-1**
MC: **824 322-4**

OH BOY (Various artists).
LP: .... **MFP 50462**

OH BOY (TV soundtracks) (Various artists).
LP: .... **PMC 1072**

OH BOY (Jack Good's TV Show) (Various artists).
LP: .... **NUTM 13**

OLD GOLD DECADES (1) (Various artists).
Tracks: / Young love: *Hunter, Tab* / Garden of Eden: *Vaughan, Frankie* / Day that the rains came down, The: *Morgan, Jane* / Don't forbid me: *Boone, Pat* / Story of my life: *Holiday, Michael*.
MC: .... **OG 5001**

OLD GOLD DECADES (2) (Various artists).
Tracks: / Here comes summer: *Keller, Jerry* / Only 16: *Douglas, Craig* / Teenager in love: *Dion & The Belmonts* / C'mon everybody: *Cochran, Eddie* / It doesn't matter anymore: *Holly, Buddy*.
MC: .... **OG 5002**

OLD GOLD DECADES (3) (Various artists).
Tracks: / At the hop: *Danny & The Juniors* / Little darlin': *Diamonds* / That'll be the day: *Crickets* / Bye bye love: *Everly Brothers* / Red River rock: *Johnny & The Hurricanes*.
MC: .... **OG 5003**

OLD GOLD DECADES (11) (Various artists).
Tracks: / All I have to do is dream: *Everly Brothers* / To know him is to love him: *Teddy Bears* / Donna: *Valens, Ritchie* / Born too late: *Poni-Tails* / Tammy: *Reynolds, Debbie*.
MC: .... **OG 5011**

OLD GOLD DECADES (12) (Various artists).
Tracks: / Girl can't help it, The: *Little Richard* / Great balls of fire: *Lewis, Jerry Lee* / Ain't that a shame: *Domino, Fats* / Be bop a lula: *Vincent, Gene* / Rave on: *Holly, Buddy*.
MC: .... **OG 5012**

OLD GOLD DECADES (13) (Various artists).
Tracks: / Tom Dooley: *Kingston Trio* / Sixteen tons: *Ford, Tennessee Ernie* / Love letters in the sand: *Boone, Pat* / When: *Kalin Twins* / Whole lotta woman: *Rainwater, Marvin*.
MC: .... **OG 5013**

ONE HIT WONDERS OF THE 50'S (Various artists).
Tracks: / Zambesi: *Busch, Lou & His Orchestra* / Buona sera: *Prima, Louis* / Unchained melody: *Baxter, Les*, his Chorus & Orchestra / Wayward wind: *Ritter, Tex* / Man with the Golden Arm, Theme from: *May, Billy & His Orchestra* / Say you're mine again: *Hutton, June* / Vaya con dios: *Paul, Les & Mary Ford* / Portuguese washerwoman: *Carr, Joe 'Fingers'* / Happy whistler, The: *Robertson, Don* / This ole house: *Anthony, Billie,Eric Jupp & his Orchestra* / Mad passionate love: *Bresslaw, Bernard* / Arrivederci darling: *Savage, Edna* / Poppa piccolino: *Decker*, Diana / He's got the whole world in his hands: *London, Laurie* / Bad penny blues: *Lyttelton, Humphrey Band* / Pickin' a chicken: *Boswell, Eve* (with Glen Somers & His Orchestra) / Pub with no beer, A: *Dusty, Slim* (with Dick Carr &

His Bushlanders.) / Happy wanderer, The: Obernkirchen Children's Choir (Sung in German and English).
LP: . . . . MFP 5802
MC: . . . . TCMFP 5802

POP HITS OF THE MID-LATE 50'S (Various artists).
Tracks: / Love Letters In The Sand: Boone, Pat (By Pat Boone) / Just walking in the rain: Ray, Johnnie (By Johnnie Ray) / Young Love: James, Sonny (By Sonny James) / Sixteen Tons: Ford, Tennessee Ernie (By Tennessee Ernie Ford) / Banana boat song: Belafonte, Harry / Fever: Lee, Peggy (By Peggy Lee) / Patricia: Prado, Perez (By Perez Prado) / Coma Prima: Marini, Marino (By Marino Marini) / Tom Dooley: Kingston Trio (By Kingston Trio) / Freight Train: Whiskey, Nancy & The Chas McDevitt Skiffle Group (By Nancy Whiskey & The Chas McDevitt Skiffle Group) / Lollipop: Chordettes (By Chordettes) / I Love You Baby: Anka, Paul (By Paul Anka) / Smoke Gets In Your Eyes: Platters (By The Platters) / Broken hearted melody: Vaughan, Sarah.
LP: . . . . OG 1011
MC: . . . . OG 2011

REMEMBERING THE 50'S (Radio Days) (Various artists).
Tracks: / Finger of suspicion: Valentine, Dickie / Handful of songs: Steele, Tommy / Limelight, Theme from: Chacksfield, Frank & His Orchestra / Alone: Southlanders / Willie can: Beverley Sisters / Hey there: Rosa, Lita / Ricohet: Regan, Joan / Auf wiederseh'n sweetheart: Lynn, Vera / I see the moon: Stargazers/ Poor people of Paris, The: Atwell, Winifred / Hernando's hideaway: Johnston Brothers / Cara mia: Whitfield, David / You need hands: Bygraves, Max / Moulin Rouge, Theme from: Mantovani & His Orchestra / Friends and neighbours: Cotton, Billy / Memories are made of this: King, Dave.
MC: . . . . PWKMC 4066P

ROCK 'N' ROLL YEARS 1959 (Various artists).
Tracks: / I kissed you: Everly Brothers / Never be anyone else but you: Nelson, Rick(y) / What do you want: Faith, Adam / Please don't touch: Kidd, Johnny & The Pirates / C'mon everybody: Cochran, Eddie / Teen beat: Nelson, Sandy / Sea of love: Wilde, Marty / Travellin' light: Richard, Cliff / What do you want to make those eyes at me for: Ford, Emile & The Checkmates / Lipstick on your collar: Francis, Connie / Three bells: Browns / It's only make believe: Twitty, Conway / Smoke gets in your eyes: Platters / Chantilly lace: Big Bopper / I go ape: Sedaka, Neil / Margie: Domino, Fats / Guitar boogie shuffle: Weedon, Bert / Teenager in love, A: Douglas, Craig / Petite fleur: Barber, Chris / Making love: Robinson, Floyd/ Venus: Avalon, Frankie / It's all in the game: Edwards, Tommy / Tomboy: Como, Perry / Battle of New Orleans: Donegan, Lonnie.
LP: . . . . YRNRLP 59
MC: . . . . YRNRMC 59

ROCK 'N' ROLL YEARS (1956-1959) (Various artists).
Tracks: / Rock around the clock: Haley, Bill & The Comets / Rock Island Line: Donegan, Lonnie / Great pretender, The: Platters / Be bop a lula: Vincent, Gene / Ain't that a shame: Domino, Fats / Tutti frutti: Little Richard / 6-5 Special: Lang, Don & His Frantic 5 / Diana: Anka, Paul / That'll be the day: Holly, Buddy & The Crickets / Singing the blues: Mitchell, Guy / Great balls of fire: Lewis, Jerry Lee / At the hop: Danny & The Juniors / When: Kalin Twins / Summertime blues: Cochran, Eddie / All I have to do is dream: Everly Brothers / Donna: Valens, Ritchie / Lipstick on your collar: Francis, Connie / Here comes summer: Keller, Jerry / Living doll: Richard, Cliff / Teenager in love: Wilde, Marty.
LP: . . . . REN 631
MC: . . . . ZCN 631

ROCK WITH THE CAVEMAN (Rediscover the 50's) (Various artists).
Tracks: / Rock-a-beatin' boogie: Haley, Bill & The Comets / Rock island line: Donegan, Lonnie / Giddy up a ding dong: Bell, Freddy & The Bellboys / Green door: Vaughan, Frankie / Start movin' (in my direction): Mineo, Sal / Sweet little sixteen: Berry, Chuck / Rock with the caveman: Steele, Tommy / Great pretender, The: Platters / Banana boat song: Belafonte, Harry / Freight train: McDevitt, Chas & Nancy Whisky / Patricia: Prado, Perez / We will make love: Hamilton, Russ / Little darlin': Diamonds / Maybe baby: Crickets/ Come on-a my house: Clooney, Rosemary / Love letters in the sand: Boone, Pat / You don't owe me a thing: Ray, Johnnie / Love makes the world go round: Como, Perry / Oh Carol: Sedaka, Neil / Lipstick on your collar: Francis, Connie / Broken hearted melody: Vaughan, Sarah / Battle of New Orleans: Horton, Johnny / Colette: Fury, Billy / Peggy Sue: Holly, Buddy.
MCSET: . . . . OG 2202

ROCKIN' FIFTIES VOL.2 (Baby Boomer Series) (Various artists).
Tracks: / Twenty flight rock: Cochran, Eddie / Rockin' robin: Day, Bobby / Hoot's mon: Lord Rockingham's XI / Party doll: Knox, Buddy / Western Movies: Olympics / Bony Moronie: Williams, Larry / Rock Island line: Donegan, Lonnie / Mona lisa: Twitty, Conway / Rebel rouser: Eddy, Duane / Bird dog: Everly Brothers / Bobby Day: Rockin' Robin / Blue jean bop: Vincent, Gene / I go ape: Sedaka, Neil / Tutti frutti: Little Richard / Teen beat: Nelson, Sandy / Kansas City: Harrison, Wilbert / Diana: Anka, Paul.
MC: . . . . BOOMER C 108
LP: . . . . BOOMER 108

ROCKING FIFTIES (Baby Boomer series) (Various artists).
Tracks: / Rock around the clock: Haley, Bill & The Comets / Something else: Cochran, Eddie / Willie and the hand jive: Otis, Johnny / Teenager in love: Wilde, Marty / Peggy Sue: Holly, Buddy / Running bear: Preston, Johnny / Whole lotta woman: Rainwater, Marvin / Chantilly Lace: Big Bopper / Ain't that a shame: Domino, Fats / Sweet little sixteen: Berry, Chuck / That'll be the day: Crickets / Be bop a Lula: Vincent, Gene / Let's have a party: Jackson, Wanda / Keep a knockin': Little Richard / Blue suede shoes: Perkins, Carl / High school confidential: Lewis, Jerry Lee.
LP: . . . . BOOMER 101
MC: . . . . BOOMERC 101

SENTIMENTAL JOURNEY THROUGH THE 50'S (Various artists).
Tracks: / From here to eternity: Brereton, Gerry / Bridge of sighs: Johnson, Teddy / Cross over the bridge: Brent, Tony & Billie Anthony / Why do fools fall in love: Cogan, Alma / St. Therese of the roses: Vaughan, Malcolm / This ole house: Anthony, Billie / Green door: Mason, Glen / Once: Savage, Edna / Look at that girl: Vaughan, Frankie / Arrivederci darling: Savage, Edna / Chapel of the roses: Vaughan, Malcolm/ Little things mean a lot: Johnson, Teddy / Give me your word: Lawrence, Lee / Happiness Street: Day, Jill/ No help wanted: Vaughan, Frankie / In the middle of the house: Cogan, Alma / Sugartime: Cogan, Alma/ Blossom fell, A: Hilton, Ronnie / Something's gotta give: Anthony, Billie / Wisdom of a fool: Wisdom, Norman / Blue star: Howard, Les / Teach me tonight: Anthony, Billie / Clouds will still roll by: Brent, Tony / True love: Boswell, Eve / Young and foolish: Hilton, Ronnie / I hear you knocking: Day, Jill/ Book, The: Brereton, Gerry / Where you are: Boswell, Eve / Wait till April: Warren, Alma / Hot diggity (dog ziggity boom): Mason, Glen / I still believe: Hilton, Ronnie / Young at heart: Warren, Alma.
2LP: . . . . DL 1116
MC: . . . . TCDL 1116

SIMON BATES - THE 50'S (Various artists).
Tracks: / Sweet little sixteen: Berry, Chuck / Rave on: Holly, Buddy & The Crickets / Bo Diddley: Diddley, Bo / Rock a beatin' boogie: Haley, Bill & The Comets / Born too late: Poni-Tails / Heartbeat: Holly, Buddy & The Crickets / Mabellene: Berry, Chuck / Rock'n'roll is here to stay: Danny & The Juniors / Oh boy: Holly, Buddy & The Crickets / Hey Bo Diddley: Diddley, Bo / Rockin' through the Rye: Haley, Bill & The Comets/ I'm gonna sit right down & write myself: Williams, Billy / Personality: Price, Lloyd / School days: Berry, Chuck.
MC: . . . . HSC 3289
LP: . . . . SHM 3289

SIMON BATES - THE 50'S (2) (Various artists).
Tracks: / Great pretender, The: Platters / Lipstick on your collar: Francis, Connie / Theme from Moulin Rouge: Mantovani / Giddy up a ding dong: Bell, Freddy & The Bellboys / Broken hearted melody: Vaughan, Sarah/ Whole lotta woman: Rainwater, Marvin / Margo: Fury, Billy / Sh boom: Crew Cuts / Limelight: Chacksfield, Frank / Singing the blues: Steele, Tommy / It's all in the game: Edwards, Tommy / Passing strangers: Eckstine, Billy & Sarah Vaughan / Rock Island line: Donegan, Lonnie / Memories are made of this: King, Dave / Maybe tomorrow: Fury, Billy / Teenager in love: Wilde, Marty / Earth angel: Crew Cuts / Stupid cupid: Francis, Connie / Chantilly lace: Big Bopper / Smoke gets in your eyes: Platters.
MC: CN4 2112
LP: . . . . CN 2112

SPOTLIGHT ON THE FABULOUS 50'S (Various artists).
LP: . . . . SPOT 1035
MC: . . . . ZCSPT 1035

STARLIGHT SERENADES (Various artists).
Tracks: / Coming home: Lynn, Vera / After a while: Lynn, Vera / Someone's rocking my dreamboat: Lynn, Vera/ Starlight serenade: Lynn, Vera / Maybe: Lynn, Vera / You'll never know: Lynn, Vera / I'm beginning to see the light: Lynn, Vera / I shall be waiting: Lynn, Vera / Wish me luck (as you wave me goodbye): Lynn, Vera / So-so in love: Peers, Donald / Tangerine: Peers, Donald / Don't sweetheart me: Peers, Donald/ I can't begin to tell you: Peers, Donald / You're in love: Peers, Donald / Maria Elena: Peers, Donald/ Amapola: Peers, Donald / By the river of roses: Peers, Donald / In a shady nook: Peers, Donald / Danger ahead: Dennis, Denny / After all: Dennis, Denny / Chi-baba chi-baba: Dennis, Denny / It's the bluest kind of blues my baby sings: Dennis, Denny / Stepping out with my baby: Dennis, Denny / Music stopped, The: Dennis, Denny / Judaline: Dennis, Denny / Lovely way to spend an evening, A: Dennis, Denny / I'd give a million tomorrows: Dennis, Denny / I just dropped in to say hello: Shelton, Anne / Let's keep it that way: Shelton, Anne / That's the moon my son: Shelton, Anne / Don't ever leave me: Shelton, Anne / How deep is the ocean: Shelton, Anne / Strangers in the dark: Shelton, Anne / I keep forgetting to remember: Shelton, Anne / There's a Moon over the ocean: Shelton, Anne / Lili Marlene: Shelton, Anne.
2LP: . . . . RECDL 3
MCSET: . . . . RECDC 3

STARS OF THE 50'S (Various artists).
Tracks: / Softly softly: Murray, Ruby / Heartbeat: Murray, Ruby / My special angel: Vaughan, Malcolm / Ev'ry day of my life: Vaughan, Malcolm / Stairway of love: Holliday, Michael / Starry eyed: Holliday, Michael / Dreamboat: Cogan, Alma / Never do a tango with an eskimo: Cogan, Alma / Around the world: Hilton, Ronnie / World outside, The: Hilton, Ronnie / Wake up little Susie: King Brothers / White sports coat: King Brothers / My thanks to you: Conway, Steve / Zambesi: Calvert, Eddie / Mandy: Calvert, Eddie / Pickin' a chicken: Boswell, Eve / Blue star: Boswell, Eve / Lollipop: Mudlarks / Tammy: Lotis, Dennis / Be my girl: Dale, Jim / China tea: Conway, Russ / Cindy Oh Cindy: Brent, Tony / Only sixteen: Douglas, Craig / Don't laugh at me: Wisdom, Norman.
MC: . . . . HR 8110
MC: . . . . HR 4181104

SUGARTIME (Rediscover the 50's) (Various artists).
Tracks: / Music! Music! Music!: Brewer, Teresa / I see the moon: Stargazers / Hernando's hideaway: Johnston Brothers / Secret love: Day, Doris / Little things mean a lot: Kallen, Kitty / Moonlight gambler: Laine, Frankie / Mambo italiano: Clooney, Rosemary / Mountain greenery: Torme, Mel / Chances are: Mathis, Johnny / Hey there: Ray, Johnnie / Cara mia: Whitfield, David / Faithful hussar, The: Heath, Ted/ Lay down your arms: Shelton, Anne / How much is that doggie in the window: Roza, Lita / Only you: Hilltoppers/ Island in the sun: Belafonte, Harry / Cindy oh Cindy: Fisher, Eddie / Love is a many splendoured thing: Four Aces / Unchained melody: Hibbler, Al / Round and round: Como, Perry / Jeepers creepers: Torme, Mel/ Naughty lady of Shady Lane, The: Ames Brothers / Ricochet: Regan, Joan.
MCSET: . . . . OG 2201

SUPER HITS: 1953 (Various artists).
LP: . . . . GT 0021

SUPER HITS: 1956 (Various artists).
LP: . . . . GT 0024

SUPER HITS: 1959 (Various artists).
LP: . . . . GT 0027

TESTAMENT OF ROCK, VOL 1 (Various artists).
Tracks: / Buena sera: Prima, Louis / Let's have a party: Jackson, Wanda / Be bop a lula: Vincent, Gene/ Loop de loop: Otis, Johnny / Medley: Prima, Louis / Stupid cupid: Jackson, Wanda / Ma he's making eyes at me: Otis, Johnny / Tweedle Dee: Jackson, Wanda / Woman love: Vincent, Gene / Pennies from Heaven: Prima, Louis / Telephone baby: Otis, Johnny / Over the rainbow: Vincent, Gene / Race the devil: Vincent, Gene / Rip it up: Jackson, Wanda / Hum ding a ling: Otis, Johnny / Nothing's too good for my baby: Prima, Louis / She she little Sheila: Vincent, Gene / Rock your baby: Jackson, Wanda / Willie and the hand jive: Otis, Johnny / Jump, jive and wail: Prima, Louis / Don'a wan'a: Jackson, Wanda / Five feet of lovin': Vincent, Gene / Three girls named Molly: Otis, Johnny / Banana split for my baby, A: Prima, Louis / Oh Marie!: Prima, Louis / Mumble Rosie: Otis, Johnny / Candy man: Jackson, Wanda / Little mama: Sands, Tommy / I ain't got nobody: Prima, Louis / Dance to the bop: Vincent, Gene / Kansas city: Jackson, Wanda / Maybelline: Vincent, Gene / When it's sleepy time down South: Prima, Louis / Such a night: Sands, Tommy / Long tall Sally: Jackson, Wanda / Blue jean bop: Vincent, Gene.
LP: 2M 126-5260/22

THIS IS THE FIFTIES (Various artists).
LP: . . . . THIS 13

THOSE FABULOUS 50'S (See under Those Fabulous 50's) (Various artists).

THOSE FABULOUS 50'S (Various artists).
Tracks: / High noon: Laine, Frankie / This ole house: Clooney, Rosemary / Singing the blues: Mitchell, Guy / Three coins in the fountain: Four Aces / Cry: Ray, Johnnie / How much is that doggie in the window: Page, Patti / Great pretender, The: Platters / Earth angel: Crew Cuts (Group) / Unchained melody: Hibbler, Al / Standing on the corner: Four Lads / Tennessee waltz: Page, Patti / Heartaches by the number: Mitchell, Guy / Jezebel: Laine, Frankie.
LP: . . . . OCN 2003WL
MC: . . . . OCN 2003WK

TRUE ROMANCES (Various artists).
Tracks: / Donna: True Romances / Tell Laura I love her: True Romances / Susie Darlin': True Romances/ Mr. Lee: True Romances / Teen girl: True Romances / Maybe: True Romances / Poetry in motion: True Romances / Mountain of love: True Romances / Sea of love: True Romances / At the hop: True Romances/ To know him is to love him: True Romances / Come softly to me: True Romances.
LP: . . . . TOP 162
MC: . . . . KTOP 162

UNCHAINED MELODIES - FOUR STARS OF THE 50'S (Various artists).
Tracks: / You make me feel so young: Young, Jimmy / You're getting to be a habit with me: Young, Jimmy / Eternally (limelight): Young, Jimmy / Hold me, thrill me, kiss me: Young, Jimmy / Isle of Innisfree: Young, Jimmy/ Faith can move mountains: Young, Jimmy / I'll never be the same: Young, Jimmy / Unchained melody: Young, Jimmy / Man from Laramie, The: Young, Jimmy / I'm walking behind you: Young, Jimmy / Secret love: Roza, Lita / P.S. I love you: Roza, Lita / Hey there: Roza, Lita / You've changed: Roza, Lita / Love is beautiful stranger: Roza, Lita / No one: Roza, Lita / Joey: Roza, Lita / Fools rush in: Roza, Lita / It could happen to you: Roza, Lita / Man in the raincoat, The: Roza, Lita / Kiss to build a dream on, A: Valentine, Dickie / Somebody loves me: Valentine, Dickie / It had to be you: Valentine, Dickie/ I can't give you anything but love: Valentine, Dickie / Sunday: Valentine, Dickie / There'll be some changes made: Valentine, Dickie / Don't leave me now: Valentine, Dickie / One I love belongs to somebody else, The: Valentine, Dickie / Clown who cried, The: Valentine, Dickie / I see you again every night: Valentine, Dickie / I'll close my eyes: Regan, Joan / Two kinds of tears: Regan, Joan / I know why (and so do you): Regan, Joan/ That old feeling: Regan, Joan / For all we know: Regan, Joan / Blue bells of broadway, The: Regan, Joan/ Till I waltz again with you: Regan, Joan / I know for sure: Regan, Joan / Someone else's roses: Regan, Joan / Tani: Regan, Joan.
2LP: . . . . RECDL 10
MC: . . . . RECDC 10

UNCHAINED MELODIES (PICKWICK) (Million selling love songs of the Fifties) (Various artists).
Tracks: / Unchained melody: Hibbler, Al / Love letters in the sand: Boone, Pat / Tear fell, A: Brewer, Teresa / Tell me why: Four Aces / Hearts of stone: Fontane Sisters / Hold my hand: Cornell, Don/ Don't forbid me: Boone, Pat / It doesn't matter anymore: Holly, Buddy / Moonglow & theme from 'Picnic': Stoloff, Morris & his orchestra / Hold me, thrill me, kiss me: Chandler, Karen / Crying in the chapel: Allen, Rex/ Autumn leaves: Williams, Roger / Sentimental me: Ames Brothers / P.S. I love you: Hilltoppers / Remember you're mine: Boone, Pat.
LP: . . . . SHM 3245
MC: . . . . HSC 3245

UNFORGETTABLE SOUND OF THE 50S, THE (Various artists).
LP: . . . . **NE 1217**
MC: . . . . **CE 2217**

52nd Street

CHILDREN OF THE NIGHT.
Tracks: / Tell me (how it feels) / Never give up on you / You're my last chance / Abandon love / Children of the night / Look I've heard / I can't let you go / Smiling eyes / I'm available / Let's celebrate.
LP: . . . . **XID 10**
MC: . . . . **CXID 10**

SOMETHING'S GOING ON.
LP: . . . . **DIX 60**
MC: . . . . **CDIX 60**

60

60 MINUTES PLUS Heavy metal compilation - Various artists (Various artists).
MC: . . . . **C 2001**

SIXTY YEARS OF MOTORING (60 Years Of Motoring).
LP: . . . . **Unknown**

60's

15 HEART BREAKERS (Various artists).
LP: . . . . **SHM 976**
MC: . . . . **HSC 358**

15 TEAR JERKERS (Various artists).
LP: . . . . **SHM 979**
MC: . . . . **HSC 360**

20 FAB NO. 1'S OF THE 60'S (Various artists).
Tracks: / Three steps to heaven: *Cochran, Eddie* / Poor me: *Faith, Adam* / Tell Laura I love her: *Valence, Ricky* / Shakin' all over: *Kidd, Johnny & The Pirates* / You don't know: *Shapiro, Helen* / Moon river: *Williams*, Danny / Nut rocker: *B. Bumble & The Stingers* / Lovesick blues: *Ifield, Frank* / You'll never walk alone: *Gerry & the Pacemakers* / Bachelor boy: *Richard, Cliff* / She loves you: *Beatles* / Bad to me: *Kramer*, Billy J. & The Dakotas / Dance on: *Shadows* / You're my world: *Black, Cilla* / World without love: *Peter &* Gordon / I'm alive: *Hollies* / Pretty flamingo: *Manfred Mann* / Good vibrations: *Beach Boys* / Where do you go to (my lovely): *Sarstedt, Peter* / Lily the pink: *Scaffold.*
LP: . . . . **MFP 41 5657 1**
MC: . . . . **MFP 41 5657 4**
LP: . . . . **MFP 5657**
MC: . . . . **TC MFP 5657**

20 FAB NO. 2'S OF THE 60'S (Various artists).
Tracks: / Please, please me: *Beatles* / Just one look: *Hollies* / Someone else's baby: *Faith, Adam* / Tell me what he said: *Shapiro, Helen* / If you gotta go, go now: *Manfred Mann* / Hippy hippy shake: *Swinging* Blue Jeans / You've lost that lovin' feeling: *Black, Cilla* / Sloop John B: *Beach Boys* / Excerpt from a teenage opera: *West, Keith* / Honey: *Goldsboro, Bobby* / I can't let go: *Hollies* / Do you want to know a secret: *Kramer, Billy J. & The Dakotas* / As long as he needs me: *Bassey, Shirley* / I'm telling you now: *Freddie* & The Dreamers / True love ways: *Peter & Gordon* / I'm the one: *Gerry & the Pacemakers* / It must be him: *Various artists* / Edelweiss: *Hill, Vince* / Stop stop stop: *Hollies* / God only knows: *Beach Boys.*
LP: . . . . **MFP 41 5658 1**
MC: . . . . **MFP 41 5658 4**
LP: . . . . **MFP 5658**
MC: . . . . **TCMFP 5658**

20 GOLDEN HITS OF 1960 (Various artists).
LP: . . . . **MFP 50535**
MC: . . . . **TCMFP 50535**

20 GOLDEN HITS OF 1961 (Various artists).
Tracks: / Rubber ball: *Vee, Bobby* / Baby I don't care: *Holly, Buddy* / Weekend: *Cochran, Eddie* / She she, little Sheila: *Vincent, Gene* / Piltdown rides again: *Piltdown Men* / Mountain's high, The: *Dick & Deedee*/ Let there be drums: *Nelson, Sandy* / Johnny will: *Boone, Pat* / You're sixteen: *Burnette, Johnny* / Exodus: *Ferrante & Teicher* / Theme for a dream: *Richard, Cliff* / I love how you love me: *Crawford, Jimmy*/ Kon Tiki: *Shadows* / Michael row the boat ashore: *Highwaymen* / Walkin' back to happiness: *Shapiro, Helen*/ You're driving me crazy: *Temperance Seven* / Moon river: *Williams, Danny* / African waltz: *Dankworth, John*/ 100 pounds of clay: *Douglas, Craig* / Johnny remember me: *Leyton, John.*
LP: . . . . **MFP 5573**
MC: . . . . **TCMFP 5573**

20 GOLDEN HITS OF 1962 (Various artists).
Tracks: / Nut rocker: *Bumble, B & The Stingers* / Speedy Gonzales: *Boone, Pat* / Reminiscing: *Holly, Buddy*/ Shelia: *Roe, Tommy* / Don't ever change: *Crickets* / Sealed with a kiss: *Hyland, Brian* / Drums are my beat: *Nelson, Sandy* / Jambalaya: *Domino, Fats* / Clown shoes: *Burnette, Johnny* / Sharing you: *Vee*, Bobby / James Bond theme: *Barry, John Seven & Orchestra* / Young ones, The: *Richard, Cliff* / Norman: *Deene*, Carol / As you like it: *Savile's Time Travels* / Up on the roof: *Lynch, Kenny* / I remember you: *Ifield*, Frank / Tell me what he said: *Shapiro, Helen* / Wonderful land: *Shadows* / When my little girl is smiling: *Douglas, Craig* / Doctor Kildare, Theme from: *Spence, Johnny & His Orchestra.*
LP: . . . . **MFP 5639**
MC: . . . . **TCMFP 5639**

20 GOLDEN HITS OF 1963 (Various artists).
Tracks: / She loves you: *Beatles* / How do you do it: *Gerry & the Pacemakers* / Do you want to know a secret: *Kramer, Billy J. & The Dakotas* / If you gotta make a fool of somebody: *Freddie & The Dreamers* / Stay: *Hollies*/ Hippy hippy shake: *Swinging Blue Jeans* / I'll never get over you: *Kidd, Johnny & The Pirates* / Hello little girl: *Fourmost* / Foot tapper: *Shadows* / Summer holiday: *Richard, Cliff* / Night has a thousand eyes, The: *Vee, Bobby* / Brown eyed handsome man: *Holly, Buddy* / My way: *Cochran, Eddie* / Fools rush in: *Nelson*, Rick(y) / My little girl: *Crickets* / All alone am I: *Lee, Brenda* / Folk singer, The: *Roe, Tommy*/ Red sails in the sunset: *Domino, Fats* / Take these chains from my heart: *Charles, Ray* / Surfin' USA: *Beach Boys.*
LP: . . . . **MFP 50541**
MC: . . . . **TCMFP 50541**

20 GOLDEN HITS OF 1964 (Various artists).
LP: . . . . **MFP 5620**
MC: . . . . **TCMFP 5620**

20 GOLDEN HITS OF 1965 (Various artists).
Tracks: / Help: *Beatles* / 3-2-1: *Barry, Len* / Look through any window: *Hollies* / You've lost that lovin' feeling: *Black, Cilla* / If you gotta go, go now: *Manfred Mann* / Yesterday: *Monro, Matt* / Little you, A: *Freddie & The Dreamers* / Minute you're gone, The: *Richard, Cliff* / All I really want to do: *Cher*/ Ferry 'cross the Mersey: *Gerry & the Pacemakers* / California girls: *Beach Boys* / Clapping song, The: *Ellis*, Shirley / Girls, girls, girls: *Fourmost* / Tears: *Dodd, Ken* / Don't make my baby blue: *Shadows*/ Hard day's night, A: *Sellers, Peter* / True love ways: *Peter & Gordon* / Trains and boats and planes: *Kramer, Billy J. & The Dakotas* / Maria: *Proby, P.J.* / I'll take you home: *Bennett, Cliff & The Rebel Rousers.*
LP: . . . . **MFP 41 5655 1**
MC: . . . . **MFP 41 5655 4**

20 GOLDEN HITS OF 1966 (Various artists).
Tracks: / Like a baby: *Barry, Len* / Michelle: *David & Jonathan* / Don't make me over: *Swinging Blue Jeans*/ Witches brew: *Jones, Janie* / Supergirl: *Bonney, Graham* / Alfie: *Black, Cilla* / Bang bang (my baby shot me down): *Cher* / Pretty flamingo: *Manfred Mann* / Monday, Monday: *Various artists* / To make a big man cry: *Proby, P.J.* / Paperback writer: *Beatles* / Bus stop: *Hollies* / Place in the sun, A: *Shadows*/ Got to get you into my life: *Bennett, Cliff & The Rebel Rousers* / God only knows: *Beach Boys* / Lady Godiva: *Peter & Gordon* / High time: *Jones, Paul* / No milk today: *Herman's Hermits* / Elusive butterfly: *Doonican, Val* / In the country: *Richard, Cliff.*
LP: . . . . **MFP 41 5679 1**
MC: . . . . **MFP 41 5679 4**

20 GOLDEN HITS OF 1967 (Various artists).
LP: **41 5707 1**
MC: **41 5707 4**

20 GOLDEN HITS OF 1968 (Various artists).
Tracks: / Little arrows: *Lee, Leapy* / Fire brigade: *Move* / Weight, (The): *Band* / Something's happening: *Herman's Hermits* / Dream a little dream of me: *Elliot, "Mama" Cass* / On the road again: *Canned Heat*/ Do it again: *Beach Boys* / Lily the pink: *Scaffold* / Me the peaceful heart: *Lulu* / With a little help from my friends: *Cocker, Joe* / McArthur Park: *Harris, Richard* / Ob la di ob la da: *Bedrocks* / I'm the urban spaceman: *Bonzo Dog Band* / Love is blue: *Beck, Jeff* / Rosie: *Partridge, Don* / Congratulations: *Richard, Cliff* / What a wonderful world: *Various artists* / Jennifer Eccles: *Hollies* / If I only had time: *Rowles, John* / Sabre dance: *Love Sculpture.*
LP: **415 725-1**
MC: **415 725-4**

20 GOLDEN HITS OF 1969 (Various artists).
Tracks: / Tracy: *Cuff Links* (Original sound recording made by MCA Records Inc.) / Breakaway: *Beach* Boys (Sound recording by Capitol Records Inc.) / Wonderful world, beautiful people: *Cliff, Jimmy* (Orig. sound recording by Trojan Recordings Ltd) / It's getting better: *Elliot,"Mama" Cass* / Delta lady: *Cocker, Joe* (Orig. sound recording by C/Era Records Ltd) / Wichita Lineman: *Campbell, Glen* / My sentimental friend: *Herman's Hermits* (Orig. sound recording by RAK Records Ltd.) / Melting Pot: *Blue Mink* (Orig. sound recording by Trojan Recordings Ltd.) / Surround yourself with sorrow: *Black, Cilla* (Orig. sound recording by EMI Records Ltd.) / Aquarius: *Jones, Paul* (Orig. sound recording by EMI Records Ltd) / Dizzy: *Roe, Tommy* (ABC Records Ltd. Inc. Orig. sound recording by MCA Records Inc. MCA Reco) / I'll never fall in love again: *Gentry, Bobbie* (Orig. sound recording by Capitol Records Ltd.) / Israelites: *Dekker, Desmond*(Orig. sound recording by Trojan Recordings Ltd.) / Blackberry Way: *Move* (Orig. sound recording by C/Era Records Ltd.) / Gin gan goolie: *Scaffold* (Orig. sound recordingby EMI Records Ltd.) / Where do you go to (my lovely): *Sarstedt*, Peter (Orig. sound recording by United Artists Ltd.) / Boom bang a bang: *Lulu* (Orig. sound recording by RAK Records Ltd.) / Going up the country: *Canned Heat* (Orig. sound recording by Liberty Records Inc., a division of Capitol Rec) / Return of Django: *Upsetters* (Orig. sound recording by Trojan Recordings Ltd.).
LP: . . . . **MFP 5791**
MC: . . . . **TC MFP 5791**

20 GOLDEN NUMBER ONES (Various artists).
Tracks: / Nut rocker: *B. Bumble & The Stingers* / I'm alive: *Hollies* / Bad to me: *Kramer, Billy J.* & The Dakotas / Poor me: *Faith, Adam* / Johnny remember me: *Leyton, John* / Do wah diddy diddy: *Manfred Mann*/ Kon-Tiki: *Shadows* / January: *Pilot* / See my baby jive: *Wizzard* / Anyone who had a heart: *Black*, Cilla / You're my world: *Black, Cilla* / I'll never find another you: *Seekers* / Tell Laura I love her: *Valence*, Ricky / You'll never walk alone: *Gerry & the Pacemakers* / World without love: *Peter & Gordon* / Lily the pink: *Scaffold* / Only sixteen: *Douglas, Craig* / Little children: *Kramer, Billy J. & The Dakotas* / What do you want: *Faith, Adam* / Pretty flamingo: *Manfred Mann.*
LP: . . . . **MFP 50491**
MC: . . . . **TCMFP 50491**

20 GREAT CRUISING FAVOURITES OF THE 50'S AND 60' (see under 50's) (Various artists).

20 GREAT HITS OF THE 60'S (Various artists).
Tracks: / Talk talk: *Music Machine* / I had too much to dream last night: *Nomad, Naz & The Nightmares* / For your love: *Christy, Charles & The Crystals* / Sha-la-la-lee: *Jades Of Fort Worth* / I wanna be your man: *Milkshakes*/ Are you a boy or are you a girl: *Barbarians* / I can't explain: *Maddens* / Try and stop me: *Radiators*/ In my room: *Christy, Charles & The Crystals* / I want candy: *Bishops* / Get me to the world on time: *Clapham* South Escalators / Don't bring me down: *Jades Of Fort Worth* / Sometimes good guys don't wear white: *Count Bishops*/ 96 tears: *Music Machine* / Hard time coming: *Stingrays* / You turn me on: *Whitcomb, Ian & Bluesville*/ I take what I want: *Bishops* / Little girl: *Jades Of Fort Worth* / Question of temperature, A: *Balloon Farm*/ Come see me (I'm your man): *Cannibals.*
LP: . . . . **DROP 1007**
MC: . . . . **CROP 1007**

20 ONE HIT WONDERS (Various artists).
Tracks: / Softly whispering I love you: *Congregation* / Super girl: *Bonney, Graham* / With a little help from my friends: *Young Ideal* / Baby sittin': *Angelo, Bobby & The Tuxedos* / Saturday night at the duck pond: *Cougars*/ Poison ivy: *Paramounts* / Blue girl: *Bruisers* / I should have known better: *Naturals* / I'm the urban spaceman: *Bonzo Dog Band* / Sabre dance: *Love Sculpture* / Games people play: *South, Joe* / Tell Laura I love her: *Valance, Ricky* / Doctor Kildare theme: *Spence, Johnny Orchestra* / Love at first sight: *Sound* Nice / Sweet dreams: *Sampson, Dave & The Hunter* / Lady Jane: *Merrick, Tony* / Rudi's in love: *Locomotive*/ Shame and scandal in the family: *Percival, Lance (nar)* / Ob la di ob la da: *Bedrocks* / Nut rocker: *Various artists.*
LP: . . . . **CM 111**

20 ONE HIT WONDERS - VOL.2 (Various artists).
Tracks: / I was Kaiser Bill's batman: *Various artists* / I can't let Maggie go: *Honeybus* / House of the Rising Sun: *Frijid Pink* / So much in love: *Mighty Avengers* / Birds and the bees, The: *Warm Sound* / She's not there: *MacArthur, Neil* / Can't you hear my heartbeat: *Goldie & The Gingerbreads* / I keep ringing my baby: *Soul* Brothers / Beggin': *Timebox* / Leaving here: *Birds* / Can't you hear my heart: *Rivers, Danny* / Can can '62: *Jay, Peter & The Jaywalkers* / Now we're thru: *Poets* / That's what I want: *Marauders* / Girl: *St. Louis Reunion* / Please stay: *Crying Shames (2)* / Walk with me my angel: *Charles, Don* / Not too little not too much: *Sanford, Chris* / More I see you, The: *Marshall, Joy* / Goin' out of my mind: *West, Dottie.*
LP: . . . . **CM 124**
LP: **C5-529**

20 SUPER HITS OF THE 60'S (Various artists).
LP: **2637237**

30 BRITISH HITS OF THE 60'S (Various artists).
LP: **818 398 1**
MC: **818 398 4**

30 YEARS OF NUMBER 1'S VOL 4 (1963-63) (Various artists).
Tracks: / You'll never walk alone: *Gerry & the Pacemakers* / Diane: *Bachelors* / Little children: *Kramer*, Billy J. & The Dakotas / Don't throw your love away: *Searchers* / House of the rising sun, The: *Animals* / Have I the right: *Honeycombs* / There's always something there to remind me: *Shaw, Sandie* / Go now: *Moody* Blues / Tired of waiting for you: *Kinks* / It's not unusual: *Jones, Tom* / Minute you're gone, The: *Richard*, Cliff / I'm alive: *Hollies* / Needles and pins: *Searchers* / Anyone who had a heart: *Black, Cilla*/ World without love, A: *Peter & Gordon* / Juliet: *Four Pennies* / Doo wah diddy diddy: *Manfred Mann*/ You really got me: *Kinks* / Yeh yeh: *Fame, Georgie/Blue Flames* / You've lost that loving feeling: *Righteous* Brothers / I'll never find another you: *Seekers* / Concrete and clay: *Unit 4+2* / Long live love: *Shaw, Sandie.*
2LP: . . . . **TYNOLP 103**
MC: . . . . **TYNOMC 103**

30 YEARS OF NUMBER 1'S VOL 3 (1961-63) (Various artists).
Tracks: / Sailor: *Clark, Petula* / You're driving me: *Temperance Seven* / You don't know: *Shapiro, Helen*/ Kon tiki: *Shadows* / Tower of strength: *Vaughan, Frankie* / Young ones, The: *Richard, Cliff* / Nut rocker: *B. Bumble & The Stingers* / Telstar: *Tornados* / Next time, The: *Richard, Cliff* / Diamonds: *Harris*, Jet & Tony Meehan / How do you do it: *Gerry & the Pacemakers* / Sweet for my sweet: *Searchers* / Blue moon: *Marcels* / Runaway: *Shannon, Del* / Johnny remember me: *Leyton, Johnny* / Walkin' back to happiness: *Shapiro*, Helen / Moon river: *Williams, Danny* / Wonderful land: *Shadows* / I remember you: *Ifield, Frank*/ Lovesick blues: *Ifield, Frank* / Dance on: *Shadows* / Summer holiday: *Richard, Cliff* / I like it: *Gerry & the Pacemakers* / Do you love me: *Poole, Brian & the Tremeloes.*
2LP: . . . . **TYNOLP 102**
MC: . . . . **TYNOMC 102**

30 YEARS OF NUMBER 1'S VOL 5 (1965-69) (Various artists).
Tracks: / Mr. Tambourine man: *Byrds* / Carnival is over, The: *Seekers* / You don't have to say you love me: *Springfield*, Dusty / Get away: *Fame, Georgie/Blue Flames* / Good vibrations: *Beach Boys* / Release me: *Humperdinck*, Engelbert / San Francisco: *McKenzie, Scott* / Baby now that I found you: *Foundations* / Ballad of Bonnie and Clyde: *Fame, Georgie* / Congratulations: *Richard, Cliff* / Young girl: *Puckett, Gary & The Union Gap*/ Albatross: *Fleetwood Mac* / Make it easy: *Walker Brothers* / Sun ain't gonna shine anymore: *Walker Brothers*/ Pretty flamingo: *Manfred Mann* / Out of time: *Farlowe, Chris/Thunderbirds* / Green green grass of home: *Jones*, Tom / Whiter shade of pale, A: *Procul Harum* / Massachusetts: *Bee Gees* / Let the heartaches begin: *Baldry*, Long John / Everlasting love: *Love Affair* / What a wonderful world: *Armstrong, Louis* / With a little help from my friends: *Cocker, Joe* / All or nothing: *Small Faces.*
2LP: . . . . **TYNOLP 104**
MC: . . . . **TYNOMC 104**

50 FAVOURITES OF THE 60'S (Various artists).

Tracks: / I like it: Gerry & the Pacemakers / Our favourite melodies: Douglas, Craig / Guitar tango: Shadows/ James Bond theme: Barry, John Seven & Orchestra / I'm the urban spaceman: Bonzo Dog Band / First time: Adam Faith & The Roulettes / Hello little girl: Fourmost / Yes I will: Hollies / I've been a bad bad boy: Jones, Paul / Stand by me: Lynch, Kenny / Pretty flamingo: Manfred Mann / World without love: Peter & Gordon/ Good golly Miss Molly: Swinging Blue Jeans / Walkin' back to happiness: Shapiro, Helen / I'll keep you satisfied: Kramer, Billy J. & The Dakotas / Hungry for love: Kidd, Johnny & The Pirates / House of the rising sun: Animals/ Pretty blue eyes: Douglas, Craig / Don't make my baby blue: Shadows / Walk don't run: Barry, John Seven/ I'll take you home: Bennett, Cliff & The Rebel Rousers / You're sixteen: Sherman, B & D / How can I tell her?: Fourmost / If you've gotta make a fool of somebody: Freddie & The Dreamers / Sabre dance: Love Sculpture/ High time: Jones, Paul / Here I go again: Hollies / Surfin' USA: Beach Boys / There's a kind of hush: Herman's Hermits / Little children: Kramer, Billy J. & The Dakotas / Shot of rhythm and blues, A: Kidd, Johnny & The Pirates / Supergirl: Bonney, Graham / Wonderful land: Shadows / One way love: Bennett, Cliff & The Rebel Rousers / Love of the loved: Black, Cilla / Kites: Dupree, Simon & The Big Sound / Message to Martha: Faith, Adam / I'm telling you now: Freddie & The Dreamers / I'm the one: Gerry & the Pacemakers/ Searchin': Hollies / I remember you: Ifield, Frank / If you gotta go, go now: Manfred Mann / I'm into something good: Herman's Hermits / Don't make me over: Swinging Blue Jeans / Boom bang a bang: Lulu/ Lily the pink: Scaffold / I'm a moody guy: Fenton, Shane / Tribute to Buddy Holly: Berry, Mike & The Outlaws/ Rubber ball: Avons.
MCSET: . . . . **TR 1563**

50 TOP TEN FAVOURITES OF THE 60'S (Various artists).
MCSET: . . . . **TR 1515**
MCSET: . . . . **MFP 4115155**

60'S CHART CLASSICS (See under Chart) (Various artists).

60'S COLLECTION (Various artists).
MCSET: . . . . **DTO 10307**

60'S FILE (Various artists).
2LP: . . . . **FILD 006**

60'S GREATEST HITS (Various artists).
Tracks: / You've got your troubles: Fortunes / Everlasting love: Love Affair / Silence is golden: Tremeloes/ Those were the days: Hopkin, Mary / Same old feeling: Pickettywitch / Crying game, The: Berry, Dave/ Somewhere: Proby, P.J. / Wild thing: Troggs / Hippy hippy shake: Swinging Blue Jeans / Hitchin' a ride: Vanity Fare / My old man's a dustman: Donegan, Lonnie / You'll never walk alone: Gerry & the Pacemakers/ Da doo ron ron: Crystals / He's so fine: Chiffons / Run to him: Vee, Bobby / Young girl: Puckett, Gary & The Union Gap / On Broadway: Drifters / When a man loves a woman: Sledge, Percy / Letter, The: Box Tops / Rebel rouser: Eddy, Duane / Zip-a-dee-doo-dah: Soxx, Bob B. & The Blue Jeans / Let's twist again: Checker, Chubby / Peppermint twist: Dee, Joey & The Starlighters / Yakety yak: Coasters.
LP: . . . . **WW 2006**
MC: . . . . **WW 20064**

60'S HITS PARTY MIX (Various artists).
LP: **8911 1**
MC: **8911 4**

60'S LOST AND FOUND (Various artists).
Tracks: / Say you don't mind: Laine, Denny / Ask the people: Laine, Denny / Somethin's got a hold on me: Brooks, Elkie / Hello stranger: Brooks, Elkie / Beyond the rising sun: Bolan, Marc / Wizard: Bolan, Marc/ Let the good times roll: Various artists / Make it better: Various artists / When love is true: Various artists / When the world was our own: Various artists / Good morning little schoolgirl: Stewart, Rod / I'm gonna move to the outskirts of town: Stewart, Rod / So called loving: Various artists / Never mind it's only love: Various artists / Silent sun: Genesis / In the wilderness: Genesis / Louie Louie go home: Jones, Davie & The King Bees / Liza Jane: Jones, Davie & The King Bees / Elf, The: Stewart, Al / Turn into earth: Stewart, Al / I'll cry instead: Cocker, Joe / Those precious: Cocker, Joe.
2LP: . . . . **DPA 3083**

60'S POP (Various artists).
LP: . . . . **KNLP 15005**
MC: . . . . **KNMC 15005**

60'S ROCK (See under Rock...) (Various artists).

60'S SOUL (See under Soul) (Various artists).

60'S SOUL CLUB (See under Soul) (Various artists).

100 FANTASTIC NO. 1 HITS FROM THE 60'S 1968/69 (Various artists).
MCSET: . . . . **AM 68/69**

100 FANTASTIC NO. 1 HITS FROM THE 60'S 1962/63 (Various artists).
MCSET: . . . . **AM 62/63**

100 FANTASTIC NO. 1 HITS FROM THE 60'S 1964/65 (Various artists).
MCSET: . . . . **AM 64/65**

100 FANTASTIC NO. 1 HITS FROM THE 60'S 1960/61 (Various artists).
MCSET: . . . . **AM 60/61**

100 MINUTES OF 60'S HITS (Various artists).
MC: . . . . **ZCTON 112**

ALL TIME HITS FROM THE SIXTIES (Various artists).
Tracks: / Young girl: Puckett, Gary & The Union Gap / Hippy hippy shake: Swinging Blue Jeans / Charlie Brown: Coasters / Let's twist again: Checker, Chubby / Wild thing: Troggs / Silence is golden: Tremeloes/ When a man loves a woman: Sledge, Percy / Those were the days: Hopkin, Mary / Da doo ron ron: Crystals/ My old man's a dustman: Donegan, Lonnie / You'll never walk alone: Gerry & the Pacemakers / Run to him: Vee, Bobby / You've got your troubles: Fortunes / Hold me: Proby, P.J. / Crying game, The: Berry, Dave/ I think of you: Merseybeats / That same old feeling: Pickettywitch / Everlasting love: Love Affair.
LP: . . . . **SHLP 153**
MC: . . . . **SHTC 153**

BACK TO THE 60'S (Various artists).
Tracks: / You've lost that lovin' feeling: Righteous Brothers / I get around: Beach Boys / Nowhere to run: Martha Reeves & Vandellas / I heard it through the grapevine: Gaye, Marvin / Stand by me: King, Ben E. / When a man loves a woman: Sledge, Percy / I got you babe: Sonny & Cher / Hey baby: Chanel, Bruce / Do you love me: Poole, Brian & the Tremeloes / Locomotion, The: Little Eva / Sunshine superman: Donovan / Hello Susie: Amen Corner / My generation: Who.
LP: . . . . **STAR 2348**
MC: . . . . **STAC 2348**

BLAST FROM THE PAST (Various artists).
Tracks: / Let's twist again: Checker, Chubby / Little darlin': Diamonds / Da doo ron ron: Crystals/ Build me up, Buttercup: Foundations / Young girl: Puckett, Gary / Dizzy: Roe, Tommy / Rescue me: Bass, Fontella / Single girl: Posey, Sandy / Good golly Miss Molly: Little Richard / Rockin' robin: Day, Bobby / Singing the blues: Mitchell, Guy / Chapel of love: Dixie Cups / Sweet talking guy: Chiffons/ Yakety yak: Coasters / Wipe out: Surfaris / It's my party: Gore, Lesley / Rubber ball: Vee, Bobby / I'm gonna make you mine: Christie, Lou / Only you: Platters / Leader of the pack: Shangri-Las.
LP: . . . . **CRX 16**
MC: . . . . **CRXC 16**

BOYFRIENDS AND LOVE (Girl Groups of the Sixties) (Various artists).
Tracks: / My boyfriend's back: Angels / Sally go round the roses: Jaynettes / Remember (walking in the sand): Shangri-Las / He's so fine: Chiffons / Party lights: Clark, Claudine / I wanna love him so bad: Jelly Beans / Chapel of love: Dixie Cups / Goodnight baby: Butterflys / Dedicated to the One I Love: Various artists / Will you love me tomorrow: Shirelles / Boy from New York City: Ad Libs / I Can't Let Go: Sands, Evie.
LP: . . . . **TOP 156**
MC: . . . . **KTOP 156**

BREAKING UP IS HARD TO DO (Million sellers of the swinging sixties) (Various artists).
Tracks: / I'm a believer: Monkees / Moon river: Williams, Andy / You've lost that lovin' feeling: Righteous Brothers.
LP: . . . . **SHM 3242**
MC: . . . . **HSC 3242**

BRITISH INVADERS (Various artists).
Tracks: / Do you want to know a secret: Kramer, Billy J. / I'm telling you now: Freddie & The Dreamers / Hello little girl: Fourmost / Sorrow: Merseys / Tobacco road: Nashville Teens / Hippy hippy shake: Swinging Blue Jeans / How do you do it: Gerry & the Pacemakers / Baby come back: Equals / Game of love: Fontana, Wayne / You've got your troubles: Fortunes / Baby now that I've found you: Foundations / In the Summertime: Mungo Jerry.
LP: . . . . **TOP 165**
MC: . . . . **KTOP 165**

BRITISH ROCK HISTORY (The very best of...) (Various artists).
Tracks: / Ferry 'cross the Mersey: Gerry & the Pacemakers / With a girl like you: Troggs / Wild thing: Troggs/ I understand: Freddie & The Dreamers / If you gotta make a fool of somebody: Freddie & The Dreamers / I'm telling you now: Freddie & The Dreamers / Here come's my baby: Tremeloes / Silence is golden: Tremeloes.
LP: . . . . **TN 806315**

CALIFORNIA DREAMIN' (Various artists).
Tracks: / California dreamin': Mamas & Papas / It ain't me babe: Surfaris / Sins of a family, The: Sloan, P.F. / Where were you when I needed you: Grassroots (bluegrass) / Monday, Monday: Mamas & Papas / You were on my mind: Surfaris / Eve of destruction: McGuire, Barry / Summer in the city: Celebration / I saw her again last night: Mamas & Papas / Take me for what I'm worth: Sloan, P.F. / Hey Joe where are you going: Surfaris / Lovin' things: Grassroots / Child of our times: McGuire, Barry / You baby: Mamas & Papas / Let's live for today: Grassroots / She belongs to me: McGuire, Barry / All I really want to do: Surfaris / Ballad of a thin man: Grassroots / Dedicated to the one I love: Mamas & Papas / Sloop John B.: McGuire, Barry / Halloween Mary: Sloan, P.F. / Concrete and clay: Surfaris / Creeque alley: Mamas & Papas / Only when you're lonely: Grassroots / It's all over now baby blue: McGuire, Barry / You tell me why: Surfaris / Mississippi: Phillips, John / Twelve thirty: Mamas & Papas / Like a rolling stone: Surfaris / California earthquake: Elliot, "Mama" Cass.
2LP: . . . . **MCLD 622**
MCSET: . . . . **MCLDC 622**

CALIFORNIA SOUND OF THE 60'S,THE (Various artists).
LP: . . . . **GH 83023**
MC: . . . . **GHC 83023**

CARATS, VOLS 3 & 4 (Various artists).
Tracks: / Wooly bully: Sam The Sham & The Pharaohs / Lipstick on your collar: Francis, Connie / Keep on dancing: Gentrys / Good timin': Jones, Jimmy (singer) / Whole lotta woman: Rainwater, Marvin / Purple people eater: Wooley, Sheb / Mona Lisa: Twitty, Conway / You've lost that lovin' feeling: Righteous Brothers/ Single girl: Posey, Sandy / Lonely blue boy: Twitty, Conway / It's all in the game: Edwards, Tommy/ You're my one and only love: Nelson, Rick(y) / Corina Corina: Peterson, Ray / Lightning strikes: Christie, Lou / Handy man: Jones, Jimmy (singer) / Teen angel: Dinning, Mark / It's only make believe: Twitty, Conway / Born a woman: Posey, Sandy / Sorry (I ran all the way): Impalas / Everyday I have a cry: Gentrys/ Unchained melody: Righteous Brothers / You're my soul and inspiration: Righteous Brothers / I've been hurt: Deal, Bill & The Rhondells / Angela Jones: Ferguson, Johnny / Hey little Lucy: Twitty, Conway / I take it back: Posey, Sandy / Li'l Red Riding Hood: Sam The Sham & The Pharaohs / Society's child: Ian, Janis/ Let it all hang out: Hombres.
MCSET: **3271 304**
2LP: **2624 037**

CHRISTMAS GIFT FOR YOU FROM PHIL SPECTOR, A (See under Christmas...) (Various artists).

CLASS OF '64 (Various artists).
LP: . . . . **BUDDY 001**
MC: . . . . **BUDDYC 001**

CLASSIC POP HITS MID 60'S (Various artists).
Tracks: / Barbara Ann: Beach Boys / Hi ho silver lining: Beck, Jeff / Have I the right: Honeycombs/ Stop stop stop: Hollies / Legend of Xanadu: Dave Dee, Dozy, Beaky, Mick & Tich / If you gotta go go now: Manfred Mann / I'm a believer: Monkees / 1-2-3: Barry, Len / Baby now that I've found you: Foundations/ Black is black: Los Bravos / Yesterday man: Andrews, Chris / Concrete and clay: Unit 4+2 / You've got your troubles: Fortunes / Elusive butterfly: Lind, Bob.
LP: . . . . **OG 1014**
MC: . . . . **OG 2014**

COLOUR DREAMS (14 Gonzoid wig lifters from the mid-sixties) (Various artists).
LP: . . . . **GONE 1**

CRUSIN' THE DRAG (Various artists).
LP: . . . . **RELIC 8011**

DANCIN' PARTY (Various artists).
Tracks: / Red river rock: Various artists / Twist, The: Various artists / Tell him: Various artists/ Stagger Lee: Various artists / Green door: Various artists / Bend me shape me: Various artists / Boy from New York City: Various artists / Save the last dance for me: Various artists / Do you wanna dance: Various artists / Do the bird: Various artists / Sweet pea: Various artists.
MCSET: . . . . **DTO 10014**

DO YOU REMEMBER? (20 Golden Hits of the 60's) (Various artists).
LP: . . . . **BRLP 25**
MC: . . . . **BRMC 25**

DO YOU REMEMBER? VOL.2 (Various artists).
LP: **1A 222-58170**
MC: **TC-1A 222-58170**

DOWN TO MIDDLE EARTH (Baubles Volume 1) (Various artists).
Tracks: / Things (goin' round in my mind): Fankhauser, Merrell & HMS Bounty / Anyway the wind blows: Sonics/ French girl, The: Daily Flash / Man who paints the pictures, The: Fever Tree / Tendency to be free: Mackay, Rabbit & the Somis Rhythm Boyze / You must be a witch: Lollipop Shoppe / Six feet down: Druids Of Stonehenge/ Down to middle earth: Hobbits / More than it seems: Salvation / Pale dream: Druids Of Stonehenge/ Forgotten man: Nova Local / Nightmare of percussion: Strawberry Alarm Clock / Visit with Ashiya, A: Fankhauser, Merrell & HMS Bounty / Full cycle: Ill Wind.
LP: . . . . **WIK 72**

DREAM BABIES (Girls and girl groups of the 60's) (Various artists).
Tracks: / He's got the power: Exciters / Usher boy: Clayton, Merry / In the morning: Crystal / Daddy, you just gotta let him in: Satisfactions / 'Cause I love you: Ray, Alder / Here's a heart: Thrills/ Dream baby: Cher / About my baby, (I could write a book): Pandoras / Till: Angels / What makes little girls cry: Victorians / All grown up: Exciters / Teenage Cleopatra: Dey, Tracey / Chico's girl: Girls/ When the right boy comes along: Crystals / It's in his kiss: Clayton, Merry / One you can't have: Honeys.
LP: . . . . **EG 2605731**
MC: . . . . **EG 2605734**

EARLY SIXTIES POP NUMBER ONES VOL.1 (OLD GOLD) (Various artists).
Tracks: / Are you lonesome tonight: Presley, Elvis / Johnny remember me: Leyton, John / Good timin': Jones, Jimmy (singer) / Poetry in motion: Tillotson, Johnny / Blue moon: Marcels / Running bear: Preston, Johnny / Runaway: Shannon, Del / Wooden heart: Presley, Elvis / Apache: Shadows / Sailor: Clark, Petula / On the rebound: Cramer, Floyd / Why: Newley, Anthony / Sweets for my sweet: Searchers/ Young ones, The: Richard, Cliff.
LP: . . . . **OG 1503**
MC: . . . . **OG 2503**
LP: . . . . **OG 1512**
MC: . . . . **OG 2512**

ELECTRIC SIXTIES (Baby Boomer Series) (Various artists).
Tracks: / On the road again: Canned Heat / This wheel's in fire: Driscoll, Julie & the Brian Auger Trinity / Evil ways: Santana / Flowers in the rain: Move / Fire: Brown, Arthur / All tomorrow's parties: Velvet Underground and Nico / Sunshine of your love: Cream / I got a line on you: Spirit / Eight miles high: Byrds/ Foxy lady: Hendrix, Jimi Experience / Well all right: Blind Faith / Marjorine: Cocker, Joe / Time has come today: Chambers Brothers / Black magic woman: Fleetwood Mac.
LP: . . . . **BOOMER 105**
MC: . . . . **BOOMERC 105**

ELECTROSHOCK- THE SIXTIES (Various artists).
Tracks: / Please let me love you: Beefeaters (Byrds) / Don't be long: Beefeaters (Byrds) / Been burnt: Luke & The Apostles / March of the mad duke's circus: Ars Nova / Black roses: Clear Light / Mr. Blue: Clear Light / Red sox are winning: Earth Opera / Home to you: Earth Opera / Nevertheless: Eclection/ I like Marijuana: Peel, David & The Lower East Side / In a gadda-da-vida: Wild Thing / Rock and roll circus: Roxy / Go back: Appleton, Crabby / Apricot brandy: Rhinoceros / I need love: Rhinoceros / Christing: Feat, Gulliver & Daryl Hall / Right on be free: Voices Of East Harlem / Someday: Delaney & Bonnie/ Get ourselves together: Delaney & Bonnie / Arthur comics: Stalk-Forrest Group / Frozen warnings: Nico/ East West: Butterfield Blues Band / Way back in the 1960's: Incredible String Band / My little red book: Love (band) / Hey Joe: Love

(band) / Signed D.C.: *Love (band)* / Seven and seven is: *Love (band)* / She comes in colours: *Love (band)* / Alone again or: *Love (band)* / Andmoreagain: *Love (band)* / Singing cowboy: *Love (band)* / Aren't you the girl: *Buckley, Tim* / Strange street: *Buckley, Tim* / Affair under blue: *Buckley, Tim* / I can't see you: *Buckley, Tim* / No man can find the war: *Buckley, Tim* / Pleasant Street: *Buckley, Tim* / Dream letter: *Buckley, Tim* / Morning glory: *Buckley, Tim* / Kick out the jams: *M.C.5*/ Come together: *M.C.5* / Motor city is burning: *M.C.5* / Ramblin' rose: *M.C.5* / Starship: *M.C.5*/ 1969: *Pop, Iggy & The Stooges* / I wanna be your dog: *Pop, Iggy & The Stooges* / No fun: *Pop, Iggy & The Stooges* / T.V. eye: *Pop, Iggy & The Stooges* / 1970: *Pop, Iggy & The Stooges* / Bird song: *Holy Modal Rounders.*
LPS: **9604031**

EPITAPH FOR A LEGEND (Various artists).
Tracks: / Night time: *Chaynes* / In my own time: *Patterns* / I tried so hard: *Chapparrals* / Part of you, A: *Thursday's Child* / If I were a carpenter: *Electric Rubayyat* / Poor planet earth: *Hall, Sonny*/ Communication breakdown: *Inner Scene* / Hurricane fighter plane: *Red Crayola* / Pink stainless tail: *Red* Crayola / Nickle niceness: *Red Crayola* / Vile vile grass: *Red Crayola* / Transparent radiation: *Red Crayola* / I want my woman: *Emperors* / 25 m.p.h.: *Lost & Found* / Breakfast in bed: *Big Walter* / C.C. rider: *Allen, Dave* / Saturday A.M. blues: *Allen, Dave* / Conversation with Lightnin' Hopkins: *Hopkins, Lightnin'* / Black ghost: *Hopkins, Lightnin'* / Interview with Roky Ksan: *Ksan, Roky* / Before you accuse me: *13th Floor Elevators* / I'm gonna love you too: *13th Floor Elevators* / Splash 1: *Roky/C.Hall* / Right track now: *Roky/ C.Hall* / Wait for my love: *13th Floor Elevators* / Radio spot for Bull Of The Woods LP: *13th Floor Elevators* / Fire engine: *13th Floor Elevators.*
2LP: . . . . **LIKD 52**

FABULOUS SOUNDS OF THE 60'S (16 Original Hits) (Various artists).
MC: . . . . **FUNC 9051**
LP: . . . . **FUNLP 9051**

FANTASTIC 60'S, THE (Various artists).
LP: . . . . **FUN 9039**
MC: . . . . **FUNC 9039**

FLASHBACK TO THE 60'S (Various artists).
Tracks: / I like it: *Gerry & the Pacemakers* / World without love: *Peter & Gordon* / Walkin' back to happiness: *Shapiro, Helen* / One way love: *Bennett, Cliff & The Rebel Rousers* / Kites: *Dupree, Simon & The Big Sound*/ Anyone who had a heart: *Black, Cilla* / Bad to me: *Kramer, Billy J. & The Dakotas* / Look through any window: *Hollies* / I'm telling you now: *Freddie & The Dreamers* / Kon-Tiki: *Shadows* / You're driving me crazy: *Temperance Seven* / Pretty Flamingo: *Manfred Mann* / Little loving, A: *Fourmost* / I'm the urban spaceman: *Bonzo Dog Band* / What do you want?: *Faith, Adam* / Surfin' USA: *Beach Boys* / I remember you: *Ifield*, Frank / House of the Rising Sun: *Animals* (Trad. arr: Price) / I'm into something good: *Herman's Hermits*/ Up on the roof: *Lynch, Kenny* / Lily the pink: *Scaffold* / I'm a tiger: *Lulu* / I'll never fall in love again: *Gentry, Bobbie* / I've been a bad bad boy: *Jones, Paul* (From the fil, 'Privilege', A Universal Release.).
2LP: . . . . **DL 1112**
MC: . . . . **TCDL 1112**

FRIDAY ON MY MIND 1964-1968 (Various artists).
Tracks: / For your love: *Yardbirds* / Colours: *Donovan* / Gin house: *Amen Corner* / Take a heart: *Sorrows*/ All day and all of the night: *Kinks* / Night of fear: *Move* / Louie Louie: *Kingsmen* / Wooly bully: *Sam The Sham & The Pharaohs* / I put a spell on you: *Price, Alan Set* / Homburg: *Procul Harum* / Daydream: *Lovin' Spoonful* / I fought the law: *Fuller, Bobby Four* / Lies: *Knickerbockers* / Delta lady: *Cocker*, Joe / Friday on my mind: *Easybeats* / Green tambourine: *Lemon Pipers* / Liar liar: *Castaways* / Dirty water: *Standells* / Out of time: *Farlowe, Chris* / Pushin' too hard: *Seeds* / Fire: *Crazy World of Arthur Brown.*
MCSET: . . . . **OG 2208**

GARAGE KINGS (& JUNKYARD ANGELS) (Various artists).
Tracks: / People who died: *Prowlers* / Fallen angel: *Radiation, Roddy & Tearjerkers* / I don't believe you: *Hooker*, Steve Shakers / Little girl: *Cannibals* / We love you: *Russian Roulette Jack* / Southern style: *Bad Losers*, The / Can you please...: *Johnson, Wilko* / Shazam: *Cobras* / She belongs to me: *Beatitudes* / Streak a lightning: *Thunderbolt, Johnny.*
MC: . . . . **WF 039C**
LP: . . . . **WF 039**

GARAGE MONSTERS: WILD 60'S PUNK TRAX (Various artists).
LP: . . . . **VAULT 3881**

GARAGE PUNK UNKNOWNS 1965-67 VOL. 1 (Various artists).
LP: . . . . **STONEAGE 661**

GARAGE ... VOL. 3 (Various artists).
LP: . . . . **STONEAGE 663**

GARAGE..VOL. 2 (Various artists).
LP: . . . . **STONEAGE 662**

GARAGE..VOL. 4 (Various artists).
LP: . . . . **STONEAGE 664**

GARAGE...VOL. 5 (Various artists).
LP: . . . . **STONEAGE 665**

GARAGE...VOL. 6 (Various artists).
LP: . . . . **STONEAGE 666**

GARAGE...VOL. 7 (Various artists).
LP: . . . . **STONEAGE 667**

GET PRIMITIVE (Best of Pebbles, Vol 2) (Various artists).
LP: . . . . **TAKE 2**

GOFFIN AND KING (Various artists).
Tracks: / Will you love me tomorrow: *Shirelles* / Some of your lovin': *Springfield, Dusty* / Chains: *Cookies*/ Pleasant Valley Sunday: *Monkees* / I can't hear you no more: *Everett, Betty* / One fine day: *Chiffons*/ Goin' back: *Byrds* / Hi de ho: *Blood, Sweat & Tears* / Don't say nothin': *Cookies* / I can't stay mad at you: *Davis, Skeeter* / Take good care of my baby: *Vee, Bobby* / Halfway to paradise: *Vinton, Bobby*/ Locomotion, The: *Little Eva* / Some kind of wonderful: *Jay & the Americans* / He's in town: *Rockin' Berries*/ Oh no not my baby: *Brown, Maxine* / Let's turkey trot: *Jan & Dean* / Just once in my life: *Righteous Brothers*/ Up on the roof: *Nyro, Laura* / It might as well rain until September: *King, Carole* / No easy way down: *DeShannon, Jackie* / I'd never find another you: *Fury, Billy* / Don't ever change: *Crickets* / You make me feel like: *Lee, Peggy.*
2LP: . . . . **VSOPLP 134**
MC: . . . . **VSOPMC 134**

GOLDEN DECCADE 1968-9 (Various artists).
Tracks: / Delilah: *Jones, Tom* / I want you to be my baby: *Davis, Billie* / Day the earth stood still: *Essex*, David / Was it yesterday?: *Peers, Donald* / Girl watcher: *White, Tam* / Don't stop the carnival: *Price*, Alan Set / Am I that easy to forget?: *Humperdinck, Engelbert* / Jesamine: *Casuals* / All along the watchtower: *Nashville Teens* / When you gotta go: *Forsyth, Bruce* / Young girl: *Harrison, Noel* / Reflections of my life: *Marmalade.*
LP: . . . . **SPA 481**

GOLDEN DECCADE, 1960-61 (Various artists).
Tracks: / Looking high, high, high: *Johnson, Bryan* / This place called home: *Squires, Dorothy* / Once in every lifetime: *Dodd, Ken* / Darktown strutters' ball: *Brown, Joe* / Tom Pillibi: *Andrews, Julie* / Fings ain't wot they used t'be: *Bygraves, Max* / Why?: *Various artists* / Never on Sunday: *Cornell, Lyn* / Halfway to Paradise: *Fury, Billy* / What a mouth: *Steele, Tommy* / As long as he needs me: *Brown, Georgia* / Well I ask you: *Kane, Eden.*
LP: . . . . **SPA 477**

GOLDEN DECCADE 1962-63 (Various artists).
Tracks: / Telstar: *Tornados* / Secret love: *Kirby, Kathy* / Just like Eddie: *Heinz* / Believe me I'm no fool: *Unknown artist(s)* / Wimoweh: *Denver, Karl* / Flash bang wallop: *Steele, Tommy* / Diamonds: *Harris*, Jet & Tony Meehan / Like I've never been gone: *Fury, Billy* / Memphis Tennessee: *Berry, Dave* / Tell him: *Davis, Billie* / Charmaine: *Bachelors* / Do you love me: *Poole, Brian & the Tremeloes.*
LP: . . . . **SPA 478**

GOLDEN DECCADE, 1964-65 (Various artists).
Tracks: / Concrete and clay: *Unit 4 + 2* / In thoughts of you: *Fury, Billy* / Walk tall: *Doonican, Val*/ Here comes the night: *Lulu* / Tell me when: *Applejacks* / It's not unusual: *Jones, Tom* / You've got your troubles: *Fortunes* / As tears go by: *Faithfull, Marianne* / Crying game, The: *Berry, Dave* / Let me go, lover: *Kirby, Kathy* / Diane: *Bachelors* / She's not there: *Zombies.*
LP: . . . . **SPA 479**

GOLDEN DECCADE 1966-67 (Various artists).
Tracks: / Black is black: *Los Bravos* / Angel of the morning: *Davis, Billie* / Elusive butterfly: *Doonican, Val* / Blessed: *Unknown artist(s)* / There goes my everything: *Humperdinck, Engelbert* / Simon Smith and his amazing dancing bear: *Price, Alan* / Call me: *Lulu* / Our love has gone: *Fortunes* / Mama: *Berry, Dave* / Goin' out of my head: *Zombies* / Biggest night of her life: *Harpers Bizarre* / Green green grass of home: *Jones, Tom.*
LP: . . . . **SPA 480**

GOLDEN HITS OF THE 60'S (Various artists).
2LP: . . . . **BRLP 67/68**
MCSET: . . . . **BRMC 67/68**

GOLDEN HITS OF THE 60'S VOLUME 2 (Various artists).
Tracks: / Speedy Gonzales: *Boone, Pat* / Sealed with a kiss: *Hyland, Brian* / All alone I am: *Lee, Brenda*/ Brown eyed handsome man: *Holly, Buddy* / Mr. Bass man: *Cymbal, Johnny* / Deck of cards: *Martindale, Wink*/ Pipeline: *Chantays* / Red sails in the sunset: *Domino, Fats* / Like a baby: *Barry, Len* / Dedicated to the one I love: *Mamas & Papas* / Bend me shape me: *American Breed* / What a wonderful world: *Armstrong*, Louis / Macarthur Park: *Harris, Richard* / Little arrows: *Lee, Leapy* / Dizzy: *Roe, Tommy* / Tracy: *Cuff Links.*
LP: . . . . **MCM 5034**
MC: . . . . **MCMC 5034**

GOLDEN HITS OF THE 60'S VOLUME 1 (Various artists).
Tracks: / Sweet nothin's: *Lee, Brenda* / Johnny will: *Boone, Pat* / Little bitty tear, A: *Ives, Burl*/ Ginny come lately: *Hyland, Brian* / Sheila: *Roe, Tommy* / Our day will come: *Ruby And The Romantics*/ Bo diddley: *Holly, Buddy* / Wipe out: *Surfaris* / Grazing in the grass: *Maskela, Hugh* / Clapping song, The: *Ellis, Shirley* / Eve of destruction: *McGuire, Barry* / 1-2-3: *Barry, Len* / Monday Monday: *Mamas & Papas* / If only I had time: *Rowles, John* / Midnight confessions: *Grassroots* / Born to be wild: *Steppenwolf.*
LP: . . . . **MCM 5033**
MC: . . . . **MCMC 5033**

GOLDEN HOUR OF HITS OF THE 60'S (Various artists).
MC: . . . . **KGHMC 160**

GOLDEN OLDIES (Various artists).
Tracks: / Dancin' party: *Various artists* / Reet petite: *Various artists* / Under the moon of love: *Various* artists / Love really hurts without you: *Various artists* / Donna: *Various artists* / Under the boardwalk: *Various artists* / When: *Various artists* / See you later alligator: *Various artists* / Spanish Harlem: *Various artists.*
MC: **510470.0**

GOLDEN OLDIES VOL 1 (Various artists).
Tracks: / Lucille: *Various artists* / Hitchin' a ride: *Various artists* / Young girl: *Various artists*/ Beautiful dreamer: *Various artists* / Ferry cross the Mersey: *Various artists* / Wild beautiful woman: *Various artists* / Hucklebuck, The: *Various artists* / Blues, The: *Various artists* / Charlie Brown: *Various artists*/ Ballad of the Green Berets: *Various artists* / Run to him: *Various artists* / Ruby baby: *Various artists.*
MC: **510406.8**

GOLDEN OLDIES VOL 2 (Various artists).
Tracks: / Rebel rouser: *Various artists* / Chapel of love: *Various artists* / Tequila: *Various artists*/ Runaway: *Various artists* / Leader of the pack: *Various artists* / Natural born boogie: *Various artists*/ If paradise is half as nice: *Various artists* / Friday on my mind: *Various artists* / Itchycoo park: *Various artists* / Donna: *Various artists* / Man of the world: *Various artists* / Painter man: *Various artists.*
MC: **510414.9**

GOLDEN OLDIES VOL 3 (Various artists).
Tracks: / Jukebox jive: *Various artists* / Game of love: *Various artists* / Night chicago died, The: *Various* artists / Tribute to Buddy Holly: *Various artists* / Candy man: *Various artists* / So fine: *Various artists*/ Yellow river: *Various artists* / Sorrow: *Various artists* / My old man's a dustman: *Various artists*/ Warm and tender love: *Various artists* / Baby come back: *Various artists* / Skinny Minnie: *Various artists.*
MC: **510455.6**

GOLDEN SIXTIES - INSTRUMENTALS ON PARADE (See under Instrumental...) (Various artists).

GOLDEN SOUL OF THE 60'S (See under Soul...) (Various artists).

GOLDEN YEARS OF THE 60'S, VOL. 3, THE (Various artists).
Tracks: / White room: *Cream* / Papa's got a brand new bag: *Brown, James* / Sorrow: *Merseys* / Only one woman: *Marbles* / Hey girl: *Small Faces* / Sunny: *Hebb, Bobby* / New York mining disaster 1941: *Bee* Gees / Walking in the rain: *Walker Brothers* / Unchained melody: *Righteous Brothers* / To love somebody: *Bee* Gees / Hang on to a dream: *Hardin, Tim* / Whatcha gonna do about it: *Small Faces* / Winchester Cathedral: *New Vaudeville Band* / I think of you: *Merseybeats* / Love is all around: *Troggs* / Sunshine of your love: *Cream.*
MC: . . . . **PWKMC 4057P**

GOOD TIMES (Various Original Hit Recordings) (Various artists).
Tracks: / Question: *Moody Blues* / World: *Bee Gees* / I'm gonna get me a gun: *Stevens, Cat* / I feel free: *Cream* / Rainbow: *Marmalade* / (You're my) soul and inspiration: *Righteous Brothers* / Saved by the bell: *Gibb, Robin* / San Francisco nights: *Burdon, Eric & The Animals* / Reflections of my life: *Marmalade*/ Strange brew: *Cream* / 98.6: *Keith* / Words: *Bee Gees* / Good times: *Burdon, Eric & The Animals*/ Midnight to six man: *Pretty Things* / Natural high: *Bloodstone* / Voices in the sky: *Moody Blues.*
MC: **CN4 2111**
LP: . . . . **CN 2111**

GREATEST HITS MEMORIES (Various artists).
LP: . . . . **MA 24287**
MC: . . . . **MAMC 924287**

GREATEST HITS OF 1960, THE (Various artists).
Tracks: / Poor me: *Faith, Adam* / Good timin': *Jones, Jimmy (singer)* / Apache: *Shadows* / Ain't misbehavin': *Bruce, Tommy & the Bruisers* / Mack the knife: *Fitzgerald, Ella* / Wonderful world: *Cooke, Sam* / Pistol packin' mama: *Various artists* / Voice in the wilderness, A: *Richard, Cliff* / Tell Laura I love her: *Valance*, Ricky / Three steps to heaven: *Cochran, Eddie* / Short'nin' bread: *Viscounts* / Do you mind: *Newley*, Anthony / Running bear: *Preston, Johnny* / On a slow boat to China: *Ford, Emile & The Checkmates* / Dreamin': *Burnette, Johnny* / Shakin' all over: *Kidd, Johnny & The Pirates* / Walking to New Orleans: *Domino, Fats*(CD only.) / Perfidia: *Ventures* (CD only.) / Man of mystery: *Shadows* (CD only.) / Someone else's baby: *Faith, Adam* (CD only.).
MC: . . . . **TCGH 1960**

GREATEST HITS OF 1961, THE (Various artists).
Tracks: / Halfway to paradise: *Fury, Billy* / Jealousy: *Fury, Billy* / Hello Mary Lou: *Nelson, Rick(y)*/ Kon-tiki: *Shadows* / Moon river: *Williams, Danny* / Michael row the boat ashore: *Highwaymen* / Rubber ball: *Vee, Bobby* / You're sixteen, you're beautiful: *Burnette, Johnny* / Walkin' back to happiness: *Shapiro*, Helen / Stranger on the shore: *Bilk, Acker* / Blue moon: *Marcels* / Time has come, The: *Faith, Adam*/ Are you sure: *Allisons* / Tower of strength: *Vaughan, Frankie* / War paint: *Brook Brothers* / When the girl in your arms: *Richard, Cliff* / I'm a moody guy: *Fenton, Shane & The Fentones* / F.B.I.: *Shadows*(CD only.) / She-she little Sheila: *Vincent, Gene* (CD only.) / You don't know: *Shapiro, Helen* (CD only.).
MC: . . . . **TCGH 1961**

GREATEST HITS OF 1962, THE (Various artists).
Tracks: / Next time, The: *Richard, Cliff* / Venus in blue jean: *Wynter, Mark* / Last night was made for love: *Fury, Billy* / Jezebel: *Wilde, Marty* / Wonderful land: *Shadows* / Let there be love: *Cole, Nat King*/ Tell me what he said: *Shapiro, Helen* / I remember you: *Ifield, Frank* / It might as well rain until September: *King, Carole* / Wimoweh: *Denver, Karl* / Bobby's girl: *Maughan, Susan* / Picture of you: *Brown, Joe* & The Bruvvers / V-A-C-A-T-I-O-N: *Francis, Connie* / Roses are red: *Carroll, Ronnie* / Island of dreams: *Springfields*/ Loco-motion, The: *Little Eva* / Go away little girl: *Wynter, Mark* (CD only.) / Nut rocker: *B. Bumble* & The Stingers (CD only.) / Don't ever change: *Crickets* (CD only.) / When my little girl is smiling: *Douglas, Craig*(CD only.).
MC: . . . . **TCGH 1962**

GREATEST HITS OF 1963, THE (Various artists).
Tracks: / Sweets for my sweet: *Searchers* / Sugar and spice: *Searchers* / You were made for me: *Freddie &* The Dreamers / Like I've never been gone: *Fury, Billy* / When will you say I love you: *Fury, Billy* / You'll never walk alone: *Gerry & the Pacemakers* / Bad to me: *Kramer, Billy J. & The Dakotas* / Do you want to know a secret: *Kramer, Billy J. & The Dakotas* / I only want to be with you:

Springfield, Dusty / Stay: *Hollies*/ I'll never get over you: *Kidd, Johnny & The Pirates* / Surfin' U.S.A.: *Beach Boys* / Secret love: *Kirby*, Kathy / Hippy hippy shake: *Swinging Blue Jeans* / It's all in the game: *Richard, Cliff* / Do you love me: *Poole, Brian & the Tremeloes* / Cruel sea, The: *Dakotas* (CD only.) / I'm telling you now: *Freddie & The Dreamers*(CD only.) / Hello little girl: *Fourmost* (CD only.) / How do you do it: *Gerry & the Pacemakers* (CD only.).
MC: . . . . **TCGH 1963**

GREATEST HITS OF 1964, THE (Various artists).
Tracks: / I just don't know what to do with myself: *Springfield, Dusty* / Needles and pins: *Searchers* / Yeh yeh: *Fame, Georgie* / Do wah diddy diddy: *Manfred Mann* / Juliet: *Four Pennies* / Tell me when: *Applejacks*/ Don't bring me down: *Pretty Things* / House of the rising sun: *Animals* / You really got me: *Kinks*/ Always something there to remind me: *Shaw, Sandie* / Little children: *Kramer, Billy J. & The Dakotas* / Downtown: *Clark, Petula* / Crying game, The: *Berry, Dave* / Shout: *Lulu and the Luvvers* / Tobacco Road: *Nashville* Teens / Hold me: *Proby, P.J.* / Don't throw your love away: *Searchers* (CD only.) / Wishin' and hopin': *Merseybeats*(CD only.) / Ferry 'cross the Mersey: *Gerry & the Pacemakers* (CD only.) / Just one look: *Hollies* (CD only.).
MC: . . . . **TCGH 1964**

GREATEST HITS OF 1965, THE (Various artists).
Tracks: / You've lost that lovin' feeling: *Righteous Brothers* / Tired of waiting for you: *Kinks* / Don't let me be misunderstood: *Animals* / Here comes the night: *Them* / My ship is coming in: *Walker Brothers* / Make it easy on yourself: *Walker Brothers* / It's not unusual: *Jones, Tom* / If you gotta go, go no: *Manfred* Mann / True love ways: *Peter & Gordon* / Little things: *Berry, Dave* / Game of love: *Fontana, Wayne &* the Mindbenders / Wooly Bully: *Sam The Sham & The Pharaohs* / I'm alive: *Hollies* / I'll never find another you: *Seekers* / You've got your troubles: *Fortunes* / Long live love: *Shaw, Sandie* / Funny how love can be: *Ivy League* (CD only.) / Baby please don't go: *Them* (CD only.) / Hang on Sloopy: *McCoys* (CD only.) / We've got to get out of this place: *Animals* (CD only.).
MC: . . . . **TCGH 1965**

GREATEST HITS OF 1966, THE (Various artists).
Tracks: / Sun ain't gonna shine anymore, The: *Walker Brothers* / All or nothing: *Small Faces* / You don't have to say you love me: *Springfield, Dusty* / Sunny afternoon: *Kinks* / Winchester Cathedral: *New Vaudeville Band*/ Bang bang (my baby shot me down): *Cher* / It's a man's man's man's world: *Brown, James* / Wild thing: *Troggs*/ Good vibrations: *Beach Boys* / Daydream: *Lovin' Spoonful* / Pretty flamingo: *Manfred Mann* / Sunshine superman: *Donovan* / Groovy kind of love: *Mindbenders* / I feel free: *Cream* / Out of time: *Farlowe*, Chris / Got to get you into my life: *Bennett, Cliff & The Rebel Rousers* / Hold tight: *Dave Dee, Dozy, Beaky*, Mick & Tich (CD only.) / Sha-la-la-la-lee: *Small Faces* (CD only.) / Summer in the city: *Lovin' Spoonful*(CD only.) / Dead end street: *Kinks*(CD only.).
MC: . . . . **TCGH 1966**

GREATEST HITS OF 1967, THE (Various artists).
Tracks: / Whiter shade of pale: *Procul Harum* / Let the heartaches begin: *Baldry, Long John* / Strange brew: *Cream*/ Kites: *Dupree, Simon & The Big Sound* / Flowers in the rain: *Move* / Mellow yellow: *Donovan* / Release me: *Humperdinck, Engelbert* / Massachusetts: *Bee Gees* / Waterloo sunset: *Kinks* / Itchycoo park: *Small* Faces / Matthew and Son: *Stevens, Cat* / Let's go to San Francisco: *Flowerpot Men* / Hi ho silver lining: *Beck, Jeff* / Zabadak: *Dave Dee, Dozy, Beaky, Mick & Tich* / Carrie Anne: *Hollies* / Heroes and villains: *Beach Boys* / Gin house blues: *Amen Corner* (CD only.) / New York mining disaster 1941: *Bee Gees* (CD only.) / San Franciscan nights: *Burdon, Eric* (CD only.) / Excerpt from a teenage opera: *West, Keith* (CD only.).
MC: . . . . **TCGH 1967**

GREATEST HITS OF 1968, THE (Various artists).
Tracks: / Fire: *Crazy World of Arthur Brown* / Lazy Sunday: *Small Faces* / Jennifer Juniper: *Donovan*/ Bend me, shape me: *Amen Corner* / Jesamine: *Casuals* / This wheel's on fire: *Driscoll, Julie & Brian Auger*/ Cinderella Rockefella: *Ofarim, Esther & Abi* / With a little help from my friends: *Cocker, Joe* / Blackberry way: *Move* / I've gotta get a message to you: *Bee Gees* / Sunshine of your love: *Cream* / Son of a preacher man: *Springfield, Dusty* / Do it again: *Beach Boys* / She wears my ring: *King, Solomon* / Jennifer Eccles: *Hollies* / On the road again: *Canned Heat* / Days: *Kinks* (CD only.) / Hurdy gurdy man: *Donovan*(CD only.) / Joanna: *Walker, Scott* (CD only.) / Weight, The: *Band* (CD only.).
MC: . . . . **TCGH 1968**

GREATEST HITS OF 1969, THE (Various artists).
Tracks: / If paradise is half as nice: *Amen Corner* / Something in the air: *Thunderclap Newman* / He ain't heavy, he's my brother: *Hollies* / Going up the country: *Canned Heat* / Badge: *Cream* / Oh happy day: *Hawkins*, Edwin Singers / Don't forget to remember: *Bee Gees* / Delta lady: *Cocker, Joe* / Where do you go to my lovely: *Sarstedt, Peter* / Israelites: *Dekker, Desmond* / My sentimental friend: *Herman's Hermits* / Nobody's child: *Young, Karen* / Melting pot: *Blue Mink* / I'll never fall in love again: *Gentry, Bobbie* / Saved by the bell: *Gibb, Robin* / Je t'aime...: *Birkin, Jane/ Serge Gainsbourgh* / White room: *Cream* (CD only.) / I can hear music: *Beach Boys* (CD only.) / Barabajagal: *Donovan & Jeff Beck Group* (CD only.) / Sorry Suzanne: *Hollies* (CD only.).
MC: . . . . **TCGH 1969**

GREATEST HITS: THE SIXTIES (Various artists).
Tracks: / You really got me: *Kinks* / Have I the right?: *Honeycombs* / Silence is golden: *Tremeloes*/ If paradise is half as nice: *Amen Corner* / Out of time: *Farlowe, Chris* / Needles and pins: *Searchers*/ Baby now that I've found you: *Foundations* / Sugar sugar: *Archies* / Go now: *Moody Blues* / Whiter shade of pale, A: *Procul Harum*.
MC: . . . . **THPA 1236**

HIT LOVE SONGS OF THE 60'S (Various artists).
Tracks: / Michelle: *Overlanders* / Don't sleep in the subway: *Clark, Petula* / Don't throw your love away: *Searchers*/ Girl don't come: *Shaw, Sandie* / Days: *Kinks* / Catch the wind: *Donovan* / He's in town: *Rockin'* Berries / When my little girl is smiling: *Justice, Jimmy* / Somewhere in my heart: *Paper Dolls* / Build me up buttercup: *Foundations* / Waterloo sunset: *Kinks* / Colours: *Donovan* / Let the heartaches begin: *Baldry, Long John* / Goodbye love: *Searchers* / Baby now that I've found you: *Searchers* / Where are you now my love: *Trent, Jackie* / This is my song: *Clark, Petula* / Spanish harlem: *Justice, Jimmy* / There's always something there to remind me: *Shaw, Sandie*.
MC: . . . . **HSC 3267**

HIT SONGS OF THE 60'S VOL.1 (Various artists).
Tracks: / My old man's a dustman: *Donegan, Lonnie* / When my little girl is smiling: *Justice, Jimmy* / Z cars (theme from): *Keating, Johnny Orchestra* / Swing on a star: *Irwin, Big Dee* / Dedicated follower of fashion: *Kinks*/ What do you want to make those eyes at me for: *Ford, Emile* / Sukiyaki: *Ball, Kenny & His Jazzmen* / Catch the wind: *Donovan* / Funny how love can be: *Ivy League* / Mr Blue: *MacBeth, David* / Mockingbird hill: *Migil* 5 / Sweets for my sweets: *Searchers* / Sucu sucu: *Johnson, Laurie Orchestra* / Picture of you, A: *Brown, Joe* & The Bruvvers / On a slow boat to China: *Ford, Emile & The Checkmates* / Warpaint: *Brook Brothers* / Be mine: *Fortune, Lance* / Venus in blue jeans: *Wynter, Mark* / Blue moon: *Marcels* / Have I the right: *Honeycombs* / Sailor: *Clark, Petula* / Goodbye cruel world: *Darren, James* / He's in town: *Rockin' Berries* / Ain't that funny: *Justice, Jimmy* / Tired of waiting for you: *Kinks*.
MCSET: . . . . **DTOL 10023**

HITS OF 1960 (Various artists).
Tracks: / Hit and miss: *Barry, John Seven* / Ain't misbehavin': *Bruce, Tommy & the Bruisers* / Someone else's baby: *Faith, Adam* / What do you want: *Faith, Adam* / Poor me: *Faith, Adam* / Shakin' all over: *Kidd*, Johnny & The Pirates / Starry eyed: *Holiday, Michael* / Seven little girls sitting in the back seat: *Avons*/ Tell Laura I love her: *Valence, Ricky* / Apache: *Shadows* / Please don't tease: *Richard, Cliff* / I love you: *Richard, Cliff* / Nine times out of ten: *Richard, Cliff* / Summer place, A (theme from): *Paramour*, Norrie Orchestra / Walk don't run: *Ventures* / Standing on the corner: *King Brothers* / Pistol packin' mama: *Vincent, Gene* / Three steps to heaven: *Cochran, Eddie* / Walking to New Orleans: *Domino, Fats* / As long as he needs me: *Bassey, Shirley* / Teen beat: *Nelson, Sandy* / McDonald's cave: *Piltdown Men* / Portrait of my love: *Monro, Matt* / Train of love: *Cogan, Alma* / Who could be bluer?: *Lordan, Jerry*.
MC: . . . . **HR 8124**
MC: . . . . **HR 4181244**

HITS OF 1961 (Various artists).
Tracks: / Rubber ball: *Vee, Bobby* / Weekend: *Cochran, Eddie* / She-she little Sheila: *Vincent, Gene*/ Piltdown rides again: *Piltdown Men* / Mountain's high: *Dick & Deedee* / Let there be drums: *Nelson, Sandy*/ You're sixteen: *Douglas, Craig* / I'm a moody guy: *Fenton, Shane & The Fentones* / You don't know: *Shapiro*, Helen / Walkin' back to happiness: *Shapiro, Helen* / Don't treat me like a child: *Shapiro, Helen* / Pasadena: *Temperance Seven* / You're driving me crazy: *Temperance Seven* / Easy going me: *Faith, Adam* / Lonely pup (in a christmas shop): *Faith, Adam* / F.B.I.: *Shadows* / Kon-Tiki: *Shadows* / My kind of girl: *Monro, Matt* / Theme for a dream: *Richard, Cliff* / I love how you love me: *Crawford, Jimmy* / Black stockings: *Barry*, John Seven / Tribute to Buddy Holly: *Berry, Mike* / Michael row the boat ashore: *Highwaymen* / Hundred pounds of clay: *Douglas, Craig* / African waltz: *Dankworth, John Orchestra* / Moon river: *Williams, Danny*.
MC: . . . . **HR 8121**
MC: . . . . **HR 4181214**

HITS OF 1962 (Various artists).
Tracks: / When my little girl is smiling: *Douglas, Craig* / Softly as I leave you: *Monro, Matt* / Right said Fred: *Cribbins, Bernard (nar)* / Cindy's birthday: *Fenton, Shane & The Fentones* / Little Miss Lonely: *Shapiro*, Helen / Guitar tango: *Shadows* / What now my love?: *Bassey, Shirley* / Lovesick blues: *Ifield, Frank*/ Hole in the ground: *Cribbins, Bernard (nar)* / Must be Madison: *Loss, Joe & His Orchestra* / Baby take a bow: *Faith, Adam* / Let's talk about love: *Shapiro, Helen* / Our favourite melodies: *Douglas, Craig* / Nut rocker: *Bumble, B & The Stingers* / Drums are my beat: *Nelson, Sandy* / Jambalaya: *Domino, Fats* / Clown shoes: *Burnette, Johnny* / Sharing you: *Vee, Bobby* / James Bond theme: *Barry, John Seven & Orchestra*/ Norman: *Deene, Carol* / As you like it: *Faith, Adam* / Up on the roof: *Lynch, Kenny* / I remember you: *Ifield, Frank* / Tell me what he said: *Shapiro, Helen* / Wonderful land: *Shadows* / Doctor Kildare, Theme from: *Spence, Johnny Orchestra*.
MC: . . . . **HR 8137**

HITS OF 1963 (Various artists).
Tracks: / How do you do it: *Gerry & the Pacemakers* / Do you want to know a secret: *Kramer, Billy J. & The Dakotas*/ If you've got make a fool of somebody: *Freddie & The Dreamers* / Stay: *Hollies* / Hippy, hippy shake: *Various* artists / I'll never get over you: *Kidd, Johnny & The Pirates* / Hello little girl: *Fourmost* / Foot tapper: *Shadows* / Night has a thousand eyes, The: *Vee, Bobby* / My way: *Cochran, Eddie* / My little girl: *Crickets*/ Surfin' USA: *Beach Boys* / Little town flirt: *Shannon, Del* / We are in love: *Faith, Adam* / Hungry for love: *Kidd, Johnny & The Pirates* / Searchin': *Hollies* / First time: *Faith, Adam & The Roulettes*/ Dance on: *Shadows* / Don't you think it's time": *Berry, Mike & The Outlaws* / I'll keep you satisfied: *Kramer*, Billy J. & The Dakotas / Confessin' (that I love you): *Ifield, Frank* / I like it: *Gerry & the Pacemakers*/ Bad to me: *Kramer, Billy J. & The Dakotas* / Cruel sea: *Dakotas* / I (who have nothing): *Bassey, Shirley*/ I'm telling you now: *Freddie & The Dreamers* / I'm in love: *Fourmost* / From Russia with love: *Monro, Matt*.
MC: . . . . **HR 8138**

HITS OF 1965 (Various artists).
Tracks: / Look through any window: *Hollies* / You've lost that lovin' feeling: *Black, Cilla* / If you gotta go, go now: *Manfred Mann* / Yesterday: *Monro, Matt* / Little you, A: *Freddie & The Dreamers* / Ferry 'cross the Mersey: *Gerry & the Pacemakers* / Girls, girls girls: *Fourmost* / Tears: *Dodd, Ken* / Don't make my baby blue: *Shadows, The* / Hard day's night, A: *Sellers, Peter* / True love ways: *Peter & Gordon* / I'll take you home: *Bennett, Cliff & The Rebel Rousers* / I'm alive: *Hollies* / Trains and boats and planes: *Kramer*, Billy J. & The Dakotas / Silhouettes: *Herman's Hermits* / Yes I will: *Hollies* / I'll be there: *Gerry* & the Pacemakers / Come tomorrow: *Manfred Mann* / Genie with the light brown lamp: *Shadows, The* / I've been wrong before: *Black, Cilla* / Don't let me be misunderstood: *Animals* / Wonderful world: *Herman's Hermits*/ Thou shalt not steal: *Freddie & The Dreamers* / Bring it on home to me: *Animals* / To know you is to love you: *Peter & Gordon*.
MC: . . . . **HR 8150**

HITS OF 1969 (Various artists).
Tracks: / He ain't heavy, he's my brother: *Hollies* / Sorry Suzanne: *Hollies* / Wichita lineman: *Campbell*, Glen / Where do you go to my lovely: *Sarstedt, Peter* / Surround yourself with sorrow: *Black, Cilla* / I can hear music: *Beach Boys* / Breakaway: *Beach Boys* / My sentimental friend: *Herman's Hermits* / I'll never fall in love again: *Gentry, Bobbie* / Going up the country: *Canned Heat* / Dick a dum dum: *O'Connor, Des*/ Aquarius: *Jones, Paul* / All I have to do is dream: *Campbell, Glen & Bobbie Gentry* / Boom bang a bang: *Lulu*/ Breakfast: *Partridge, Don* / Games people play: *South, Joe* / Little bluebird: *Hill, Vince* / Barabajagal: *Donovan & Jeff Beck Group* / Gin gan goolie: *Scaffold* / Love at first sight (Je t'aime...moi mon plus): *Sounds Nice*.
MC: . . . . **HR 8190**

HITS OF THE 60'S (Various artists).
LP: . . . . **CCSLP 188**
MC: . . . . **CCSMC 188**

HITS OF THE 60'S (Various artists).
Tracks: / Universal soldier: *Donovan* / Hold me: *Proby, P.J.* / Baby please don't go: *Them* / Crying game, The: *Berry, Dave* / Waterloo sunset: *Kinks* / America: *Nice* / Flowers in the rain: *Move*/ Itchycoo Park: *Small Faces* / Needles and pins: *Searchers* / She's not there: *Zombies* / First cut is the deepest: *Arnold, P.P.* / Homburg: *Procul Harum* / If paradise is half as nice: *Amen Corner* / Baby, now that I've found you: *Foundations* / Out of time: *Farlowe, Chris* / Go now: *Moody Blues* / Shakin' all over: *Kidd, Johnny & The Pirates* / Man of the world: *Fleetwood Mac* / I can't let Maggie go: *Honeybus*/ With a little help from my friends: *Cocker, Joe* / I like it: *Gerry & the Pacemakers* / Excerpt from a teenage opera: *West, Keith* / Do you want to know a secret: *Kramer, Billy J. & The Dakotas*.
2LP: . . . . **CCSLP 138**
MC: . . . . **CCSMC 138**

HITS OF THE 60'S (Various artists).
MC: . . . . **MCTC 028**

HITS OF THE 60'S (2) (Various artists).
Tracks: / Rubber ball: *Vee, Bobby* / Dizzy: *Roe, Tommy* / Baby come back: *Equals* / Let's twist again: *Checker, Chubby* / Love letters: *Lester, Ketty* / Poetry in motion: *Tillotson, Johnny* / But I do: *Henry*, Clarence 'Frogman' / Wooly bully: *Sam The Sham & The Pharaohs* / Will you love me tomorrow: *Shirelles* / Hey baby: *Channel, Bruce* / Lightning strikes: *Christie, Lou* / Little things: *Berry, Dave* / Young girl: *Puckett, Gary & The Union Gap* / If you gotta tell somebody: *Freddie & The Dreamers* / Wimoweh: *Denver, Karl Trio* / Games people play: *South, Joe*.
LP: . . . . **OCN 2008WL**
MC: . . . . **OCN 2008WK**

HITS OF THE 60'S AND 70'S (Various artists).
MCSET: . . . . **PDC 045**

HITS OF THE 60'S (BOX SET) (Various artists).
MCSET: . . . . **TCMFPBOX 2**

HITS OF THE SWINGING 60'S VOL.1 (Various artists).
Tracks: / Monday, monday: *Mamas & Papas* / Dizzy: *Roe, Tommy* / Woodstock: *Matthews Southern Comfort*/ Here comes that feeling: *Lee, Brenda* / Little arrows: *Lee, Leapy* / Johnny will: *Boone, Pat* / Brown eyed handsome man: *Holly, Buddy* / Ginny come lately: *Hyland, Bryan* / Heartaches: *Cline, Patsy* / As usual: *Lee, Brenda* / Hello dolly: *Armstrong, Louis* / Hush' not a word to Mary: *Rowles, John* / Folk singer, The: *Roe, Tommy* / Creeque alley: *Mamas & Papas* / Lady luck: *Price, Lloyd* / Sheila: *Roe*, Tommy / What a wonderful world: *Armstrong, Louis* / Red sails in the sunset: *Domino, Fats* / Bo Diddley: *Holly, Buddy* / Main attraction: *Boone, Pat* / 1-2-3: *Barry, Len* / When you ask about love: *Crickets* / Rock around the clock: *Haley, Bill & The Comets* / Speak to me pretty: *Lee, Brenda* / Deck of cards: *Martindale, Wink* / Sealed with a kiss: *Hyland, Brian*.
2LP: . . . . **CR 036**
MCSET: . . . . **CRT 036**

IDOLS (Various artists).
MC: . . . . **GM 0212**

IMMEDIATE ALTERNATIVE, THE (Collection of Immediate label rarities) (Various artists).
Tracks: / Circles: *Les Fleurs De Lys* / Goin' back: *Goldie* / She belongs to me: *Masterminds* / Baby don't you do it: *Poets* / Miranda: *Excelsior Spring* / In my lonely room: *Factotums* / Angeline: *Warm* Sounds / So much in love: *Dickens, Charles (Author)* / You stole my love: *Mockingbirds* / Tell me have you ever seen me: *Apostolic Intervention* /

Would you believe: *Nichols, Billy* / Girl don't tell me: *Rivers, Tony* & The Castaways / On the bombsite: *Browne, Duncan* / So come on: *Les Fleurs De Lys* / Sticks and stones: *Warm* Sounds / I'll come home: *Poets* / Great train robbery: *Outer Limits* / It: *Excelsior Spring* / Run in the green and tangerine flaked forest: *Factotums* (CD only.) / Our soul brothers: *Dickens, Charles* (CD only.) / Daytime girl: *Nichols, Billy* (CD only.) / Skit skat: *Mockingbirds* (CD only.) / Changing of the guard: *Marquis of* Kensington (CD only.) / Salt Lake City: *Rivers, Tony & The Castaways* (CD only.) / Taken my love: *Masterminds*(CD only.).
LP: . . . . **NEXLP 110**

IMMEDIATE STORY (Various artists).
LP: . . . . **V 2165**

IT HAPPENED THEN (Various artists).
Tracks: / What's the matter, baby?: *Wayne, Carl & The Vikings* / You can't sit down: *Beatmen* / Take a heart: *Sorrows* / Bye bye baby: *Jackson, Tony & The Vibrations* / Wake up my mind: *Uglys* / Aggravation: *Curtis, Chris* / Just a little bit: *Undertakers* / Wild side of life: *Quickly, Tommy & The Remo Four.*
MLP: . . . . **DOW 451**

IT'S MY PARTY (Hit Girls of the Sixties) (Various artists).
Tracks: / It's my party: *Gore, Lesley* / I close my eyes and count to ten: *Springfield, Dusty* / Shout: *Lulu*/ Locomotion, The: *Little Eva* / Wedding, The: *Rogers, Julie* / My boyfriends back: *Angels* / Where the boys are: *Francis, Connie* / Bobby's girl: *Maughan, Susan* / Single girl, The: *Posey, Sandy* / Can't you hear my heartbeat: *Goldie & The Gingerbreads* / I want you to be my baby: *Davies, Billie* / Lover please: *Vernons Girls* / V-A-C-A-T-I-O-N: *Francis, Connie.*
LP: . . . . **CN 2095**
MC: **CN4 2095**

IT'S MY PARTY - SIXTIES TEENAGE MEMORIES (Various artists).
Tracks: / Da doo ron ron: *Crystals* / He's so fine: *Chiffons* / Zip a dee doo dah: *Soxx, Bob B. & The Blue* Jeans / Baby it's you: *Shirelles* / Jimmy Mack: *Reeves, Martha* / Goin' out of my head: *Little Anthony* & The Imperials / Rhythm of the rain: *Cascades* / Leader of the pack: *Shangri-Las* / It's my party: *Gore,* Lesley / My boyfriends back: *Angels* / She cried: *Jay & the Americans* / Boy from New York City: *Ad Libs*/ Thousand stars, A: *Young, Kathy* / People say: *Dixie Cups* / Goin' out of my head: *Little Anthony* / Sally go round the roses: *Jaynettes.*
LP: . . . . **OCN 2006WL**
MC: . . . . **OCN 2006WK**

JUKE BOX COLLECTION - DOWN TOWN (Sound of the Sixties part 3) (Various artists).
Tracks: / Will you love me tomorrow: *Shirelles* / Rhythm of the rain: *Cascades* / Downtown: *Clark, Petula*/ He's so fine: *Chiffons* / Hey Paula: *Paul & Paula* / Swiss maid: *Shannon, Del* / When my little girl is smiling: *Justis, Jimmy* / Why?: *Avalon, Frankie* / I wanna go home: *Donegan, Lonnie* / When will I be loved?: *Everly Brothers* / Too good: *Little Tony* / Beatnik fly: *Johnny & The Hurricanes.*
MC: . . . . **OG 2705**
LP: . . . . **OG 1705**

JUKE BOX COLLECTION - EBONY EYES (Juke box 60's) (Various artists).
Tracks: / Ebony eyes: *Everly Brothers* / Ginny come lately: *Hyland, Brian* / Poor man's son: *Rockin' Berries*/ Little bitty tear, A: *Ives, Burl* / Shy girl: *Cascades* / I understand: *G-Clefs* / Folk singer, The: *Roe, Tommy* / Dr Kildare, Theme from: *Chamberlain, Richard* / Angela Jones: *Ferguson, Johnny* / Pretty blue eyes: *Lawrence, Steve* / Things: *Darin, Bobby* / Kelly: *Shannon, Del* / Our day will come: *Ruby & The Romantics* / I will: *Fury, Billy.*
LP: . . . . **OG 1724**
MC: . . . . **OG 2724**

JUKE BOX COLLECTION - FRIDAY ON MY MIND (Sound of the Sixties part 2) (Various artists).
Tracks: / Go now: *Moody Blues* / You really got me: *Kinks* / Have I the right?: *Honeycombs* / Black is black: *Los Bravos* / She'd rather be with me: *Turtles* / Death of a clown: *Davies, Dave* / Baby, now that I've found you: *Foundations* / Out of time: *Farlowe, Chris* / Red red wine: *James, Jimmy & The Vagabonds*/ Friday on my mind: *Easybeats* / Delta lady: *Cocker, Joe* / To whom it concerns: *Andrews, Chris.*
MC: . . . . **OG 2704**
LP: . . . . **OG 1704**

JUKE BOX COLLECTION - LEADER OF THE PACK (Sound of the Sixties part 6) (Various artists).
Tracks: / Wild wind: *Leyton, John* / Runaround Sue: *Dion* / Hey little girl: *Shannon, Del* / Counting teardrops: *Ford, Emile* / I'm gonna be strong: *Pitney, Gene* / Leader of the pack: *Shangri-Las* / Colours: *Donovan* / Needles and pins: *Searchers* / Everyone's gone to the moon: *King, Jonathan* / Lovers of the world unite: *David & Jonathan* / Pied piper: *St. Peters, Crispian* / Concrete and clay: *Unit 4+2.*
MC: . . . . **OG 2710**
LP: . . . . **OG 1710**

JUKE BOX COLLECTION - LET'S DANCE (Sound of the Sixties part 1) (Various artists).
Tracks: / Wanderer: *Dion* / Hats off to Larry: *Shannon, Del* / Hey baby: *Channel, Bruce* / Picture of you: *Brown, Joe* / Poetry in motion: *Tillotson, Johnny* / Johnny remember me: *Leyton, John* / Let's dance: *Montez, Chris* / Always something there to remind me: *Shaw, Sandie* / 24 hours from Tulsa: *Pitney, Gene*/ Catch the wind: *Donovan* / You were on my mind: *St. Peters, Crispian* / Yesterday man: *Andrews, Chris*/ Reveille rock: *Johnny & The Hurricanes.*
MC: . . . . **OG 2702**
LP: . . . . **OG 1702**

JUKE BOX COLLECTION - SUNNY AFTERNOON (Sound of the Sixties part 5) (Various artists).
Tracks: / Sunny afternoon: *Kinks* / Flowers in the rain: *Move* / Let's go to San Francisco: *Flowerpot Men*/ Eleanore: *Turtles* / Melting pot: *Blue Mink* / If paradise is half as nice: *Amen Corner* / Whiter shade of pale, A: *Procul Harum* / I put a spell on you: *Price, Alan Set* / Man of the world: *Fleetwood Mac*/ Pictures of matchstick men: *Status Quo* / Itchycoo Park: *Small Faces* / With a little help from my friends: *Cocker, Joe.*
MC: . . . . **OG 2709**
LP: . . . . **OG 1709**

JUKE BOX COLLECTION - SWEET TALKIN' GUY (Greats from 60's gals) (Various artists).
Tracks: / Soldier boy: *Shirelles* / Sweet talkin' guy: *Chiffons* / First cut is the deepest: *Arnold, P.P.*/ Sailor: *Clark, Petula* / Long live love: *Shaw, Sandie* / Terry: *Twinkle* / It's getting better: *Cass, Mama* / You don't own me: *Gore, Lesley* / Chapel of love: *Dixie Cups* / Walk on by: *Warwick, Dionne*/ Big hurt, The: *Fisher, Toni* / Bobby's girl: *Maughan, Susan* / Born a woman: *Posey, Sandy* / You don't have to say you love me: *Springfield, Dusty.*
LP: . . . . **OG 1712**
MC: . . . . **OG 2712**

JUKE BOX COLLECTION - TEEN BEAT (Sound of the Sixties part 4) (Various artists).
Tracks: / What'd I say?: *Lewis, Jerry Lee* / Teen beat: *Nelson, Sandy* / Lonely weekends: *Rich, Charlie*/ Nut rocker: *B. Bumble & The Stingers* / War paint: *Brook Brothers* / Some kinda fun: *Montez, Chris*/ Runaway: *Shannon, Del* / So, this is she: *Leyton, John* / It only took a minute: *Brown, Joe* / Rockin' goose: *Johnny & The Hurricanes* / Be mine: *Fortune, Lance* / Blue moon: *Marcels.*
MC: . . . . **OG 2708**
LP: . . . . **OG 1708**

JUKE BOX COLLECTION - WITH A GIRL LIKE YOU (Juke box 60's) (Various artists).
Tracks: / I love my dog: *Stevens, Cat* / Dedicated follower of fashion: *Kinks* / Girl don't come: *Shaw, Sandie*/ Bend me shape me: *Amen Corner* / Golden lights: *Twinkle* / So much in love: *Mighty Avengers* / Groovy kind of love: *Mindbenders* / Here comes the night: *Them* / Universal soldier: *Donovan* / Goodbye my love: *Searchers* / Tell him: *Davies, Billie* / With a girl like you: *Troggs* / Sh la la la lee: *Small Faces*/ You've got to hide your love away: *Silkie.*
LP: . . . . **OG 1722**
MC: . . . . **OG 2722**

JUKE BOX HITS (Various artists).
Tracks: / Let's twist again: *Checker, Chubby* / Save the last dance for me: *Various artists* / Letter, The: *Box* Tops / Then he kissed me: *Crystals* / Stand by me: *King, Ben E.* / In crowd, The: *Gray, Dobie* / At the hop: *Danny & The Juniors* / Lucille: *Little Richard* / Lightning strikes: *Christie, Lou* / He's so fine: *Chiffons.*
MCSET: . . . . **DTO 10012**
LP: . . . . **NE 1224**
MC: . . . . **CE 2224**
MC: . . . . **GM 0220**

LEGENDARY 60'S (Various artists).
LP: . . . . **FUN 9023**
MC: . . . . **FUNC 9023**

LOVIN' SIXTIES VOL 2 (Various artists).
Tracks: / Make it easy on yourself: *Walker Brothers* / Game of love: *Fontana, Wayne & the Mindbenders* / Oh no not my baby: *Manfred Mann* / Sorrow: *Merseys* / Delta lady: *Cocker, Joe* / Goodnight midnight: *Rodgers,* Clodagh / I'm leaving it all up to you: *Dale & Grace* / Run to him: *Vee, Bobby* / Angel of the morning: *Rush,* Merilee / Tired of waiting: *Kinks* / Catch the wind: *Donovan* / Here it comes again: *Fortunes* / I'm a believer: *Monkees* / I will follow him: *March, Little Peggy* / Maria Elena: *Los Indios Tabajaros.*
LP: . . . . **BOOMER 110**
MC: . . . . **BOOMERC 110**

LOVING SIXTIES (Baby Boomer Series) (Various artists).
Tracks: / Where do you go to my lovely: *Sarstedt, Peter* / With a little help from my friends: *Cocker, Joe* / Albatross: *Fleetwood Mac* / You've lost that lovin' feeling: *Righteous Brothers* / As tears go by: *Faithfull,* Marianne / Sun ain't gonna shine anymore, The: *Walker Brothers* / Let the heartaches begin: *Baldry, Long John*/ There's a kind of hush: *Herman's Hermits* / Nights in white satin: *Moody Blues* / I'll never find another you: *Seekers, The* / Turn, turn ,turn: *Byrds, The* / Will you love me tomorrow: *Shirelles* / I can't let Maggie go: *Honeybus* / You don't have to say you love me: *Springfield, Dusty* / San Francisco: *Mackenzie, Scott*/ You've got your troubles: *Fortunes.*
LP: . . . . **BOOMER 106**
MC: . . . . **BOOMERC 106**

MAYHEM AND PSYCHOSIS VOL. 1 (20 Psych punk classics from the 60's) (Various artists).
LP: . . . . **XSLP 100**

MAYHEM AND PSYCHOSIS VOL. 2 (20 Psych punk classics from the 60's) (Various artists).
LP: . . . . **XSLP 101**

MEANWHILE BACK AT THE GOGO (Various artists).
Tracks: / Hawaii five-O: *Ventures* / Breakaway: *Thomas, Irma* / You've got what it takes: *Johnson, Marv*/ Mother-in-law: *K-Doe, Ernie* / Papa-oom-mow-mow: *Rivingtons* / He's got the power: *Exciters* / When you walk in the room: *DeShannon, Jackie* / James Bond theme: *Barry, John* / Sixty minutes of your love: *Banks,* Homer / Mockingbird: *Foxx, Inez & Charlie* / Lurch, The: *Cassidy, Ted* / Livin' above your head: *Jay &* the Americans / It's too late: *Goldsboro, Bobby* / All about my girl: *McGriff, Jimmy* / Spooky: *Classics IV* / Cry baby: *Mimms, Garnet.*
LP: . . . . **KENT 040**

MEANWHILE BACK AT THE RANCH BIG DAN IS FIGHTING (Various artists).
LP: . . . . **MARX 075**

MEMORIES ARE MADE OF HITS (Various artists).
Tracks: / Personality: *Price, Lloyd* / Jimmy Dean: *Big Bad John* / My old man's a dustman: *Donegan, Lonnie*/ If I had a hammer: *Lopez, Trini* / You'll never walk alone: *Gerry & the Pacemakers* / Diane: *Bachelors*/ Stranger on the shore: *Bilk, Acker* / Those were the days: *Hopkin, Mary.*
LP: . . . . **DPA 3015**
LP: . . . . **OCN 2004WL**
MC: . . . . **OCN 2004WK**

MID SIXTIES POP NUMBER ONES (Various artists).
Tracks: / You've lost that lovin' feeling: *Righteous Brothers* / Always something there to remind me: *Shaw, Sandie*/ Tired of waiting for you: *Kinks* / Make it easy on yourself: *Walker Brothers* / I've gotta get a message to you: *Bee Gees* / All or nothing: *Small Faces* / I'm alive: *Hollies* / Yeh yeh: *Fame, Georgie* / It's not unusual: *Jones, Tom* / With a girl like you: *Troggs* / Whiter shade of pale, A: *Procul Harum* / Do it again: *Beach Boys* / Good, the bad and the ugly, The: *Montenegro, Hugo* / In the year 2525: *Zager/Evans.*
LP: . . . . **OG 1504**
MC: . . . . **OG 2504**
LP: . . . . **OG 1513**
MC: . . . . **OG 2513**

MILLION SELLING HITS OF THE 60'S (Various artists).
Tracks: / Next time, The: *Richard, Cliff* / I'm telling you now: *Freddie & The Dreamers* / Sloop John B: *Beach* Boys / Sealed with a kiss: *Hyland, Brian* / He ain't heavy he's my brother: *Hollies* / World of our own, A: *Seekers* / Tracy: *Cuff Links* / Michael row the boat ashore: *Highwaymen* / Wichita lineman: *Campbell,* Glen / Carrie Anne: *Hollies* / There's a kind of hush: *Herman's Hermits* / Don't let the sun catch you crying: *Gerry & the Pacemakers* / Little arrows: *Lee, Leapy* / Lucky lips: *Richard, Cliff* / You were made for me: *Freddie & The Dreamers* / Tears: *Dodd, Ken* / Monday Monday: *Mamas & Papas* / Carnival is over, The: *Seekers* / Little children: *Kramer, Billy J. & The Dakotas* (CD only.) / Anyone who had a heart: *Black, Cilla*(CD only.).
LP: . . . . **MFP 5821**
MC: . . . . **TCMFP 5821**

MONSTER HITS COLLECTION (Various artists).
Tracks: / I like it: *Various artists* / You'll never walk alone: *Various artists* / Somewhere: *Various artists*/ Deep purple: *Various artists* / Letter: *Various artists* / Lightnin' strikes: *Various artists* / Let's dance: *Various artists* / I fought the law: *Various artists* / Da doo ron ron: *Various artists* / Silence is golden: *Various artists* / Raindrops keep fallin': *Various artists* / Judy in disgrace: *Various artists*/ Indian reservation: *Various artists* / Rubber ball: *Various artists* / Rhythm of the rain: *Various artists*/ Chapel of love: *Various artists* / High time: *Various artists* / Louie Louie: *Various artists* / Hey Paula: *Various artists* / Wild thing: *Various artists* / Tom Dooley: *Various artists* / Wimoweh: *Various artists* / Rebel rouser: *Various artists* / My prayer: *Various artists* / My guy: *Various artists*/ He's so fine: *Various artists* / Runaway: *Various artists* / Blue moon: *Various artists* / Yakety yak: *Various artists* / Donna: *Various artists.*
2LP: . . . . **PDA 064**

MY GENERATION (Various artists).
Tracks: / My white bicycle: *Tomorrow* / Baby you got it: *Action* / Hand don't fit the glove, The: *Reid, Terry*/ Glendora: *Downliners Sect* / God only knows: *Rivers, Tony* / Baby's rich: *Gods* / Gin house: *Boston* Crabs / Mr. Armageddan: *Locomotive* / We are the moles: *Moles* / Long cigarette, The: *Roulettes*/ Light of the charge brigade: *Prince, Viv* / I could feel the whole world turn round: *Shotgun Express* / What shall I do: *Artwoods* / Stumble, The: *Love Sculpture* / Shake: *Stewart, Rod.*
LP: . . . . **NUT 4**

NIGHTS IN WHITE SATIN (Various artists).
Tracks: / Nights in white satin: *Moody Blues* / Matthew and son: *Stevens, Cat* / Wild thing: *Troggs*/ Bend me shape me / All or nothing: *Small Faces* / Sun ain't gonna shine anymore, The: *Walker Brothers* / Something in the air: *Thunderclap Newman* / Jackie: *Walker, Scott* / Hey Joe: *Hendrix, Jimi* / Badge: *Cream*/ My minds eye: *Small Faces* / Here comes the night: *Them.*
LP: . . . . **CN 2096**
MC: **CN4 2096**

NO PARTICULAR PLACE TO GO (Various artists).
Tracks: / No particular place to go: *Berry, Chuck* / Rescue me: *Bass, Fontella* / Lady Luck: *Price, Lloyd*/ Ginny come lately: *Hyland, Brian* / Like a baby: *Barry, Len* / Baby my heart: *Crickets* / Main attraction: *Boone, Pat* / Itsy bitsy teeny weeny yellow polka dot bikini: *Hyland, Brian* / Mr. Bass man: *Cymbal, Johnny*/ Hi heel sneakers: *Tucker, Tommy* / You never can tell: *Berry, Chuck* / When you ask about love: *Crickets*/ Johnny will: *Boone, Pat* / Nadine: *Berry, Chuck.*
MC: . . . . **HSC 3280**
LP: . . . . **SHM 3280**

NORTHERN BEAT, THE (22 classic hits from the 60's) (Various artists).
Tracks: / I'm into something good: *Herman's Hermits* / Groovy kind of love: *Mindbenders* / Do you want to know a secret?: *Kramer, Billy J. & The Dakotas* / I like it: *Gerry & the Pacemakers* / Just one look: *Hollies*/ Needles and pins: *Searchers* / You've got your troubles: *Fortunes* / Little things: *Berry, Dave* / Juliet: *Four Pennies* / Hello little girl: *Fourmost* / Shout: *Lulu and the Luvvers* / Ain't she sweet: *Beatles*/ Hippy hippy shake: *Swinging Blue Jeans* / House of the rising sun: *Animals* / If you gotta make a fool of somebody: *Freddie & The Dreamers* / Halfway to paradise: *Fury, Billy* / Game of love: *Fontana, Wayne* / I think of you / Anyone who had a heart: *Black, Cilla* / Sorrow: *Merseys* / Everything's alright: *Mojos* / Some other guy: *Big Three.*
MC: **840 968 4**
LP: **840 968 1**

NOT JUST BEAT MUSIC 1965-70 (Various artists).
Tracks: / Excerpt from a teenage opera: *West, Keith* / My white bicycle: *Tomorrow* / Skeleton and the roundabout: *Idle Race* / In the land of the few: *Love Sculpture* / Kites: *Dupree, Simon & The Big Sound* / Mr. Armageddan: *Locomotive* / You've got a habit of leaving: *Jones, Davy & The Lower Third* / Rumours: *Kippington*

Lodge / It's so nice to come home: *Lemon Tree* / Real love guaranteed: *Gods* / We are the Moles part 1: *Moles* / S F sorrow is born: *Pretty Things* / Baby loves that way: *Jones, Davy & The Lower Third* / Lady on a bicycle: *Kippington Lodge* / On a Saturday: *West, Keith* / Birthday, The: *Idle Race* / Strawberry fields forever: *Tomorrow* / She says good morning: *Pretty Things* / Yes sir, no sir: *Art Movement, The* / Hey bulldog: *Gods, The*.
LP: . . . . **CM 112**

OLD GOLD DECADES (4) (Various artists).
Tracks: / Young girl: *Puckett, Gary & The Union Gap* / San Francisco (be sure to wear flowers in your hair): *McKenzie, Scott* / Mr. Tambourine man: *Byrds* / California dreamin': *Mamas & Papas* / Let's go to San Francisco: *Flowerpot Men*.
MC: . . . . **OG 5004**

OLD GOLD DECADES (5) (Various artists).
Tracks: / House of the rising sun: *Animals* / You'll never walk alone: *Gerry & the Pacemakers* / Needles and pins: *Searchers* / Have I the right?: *Honeycombs* / Do wah diddy diddy: *Manfred Mann*.
MC: . . . . **OG 5005**

OLD GOLD DECADES (6) (Various artists).
Tracks: / Good vibrations: *Beach Boys* / Legend of Xanadu: *Dave Dee, Dozy, Beaky, Mick & Tich* / Hi ho silver lining: *Beck, Jeff* / Itchycoo Park: *Small Faces* / Massachusetts: *Bee Gees*.
MC: . . . . **OG 5006**

OLD GOLD DECADES (7) (Various artists).
Tracks: / Runaway: *Shannon, Del* / Runaround Sue: *Dion* / Take good care of my baby: *Vee, Bobby* / Will you love me tomorrow?: *Shirelles* / It might as well rain until September: *King, Carole*.
MC: . . . . **OG 5007**

OLD GOLD DECADES (14) (Various artists).
Tracks: / Sailor: *Clark, Petula* / Sealed with a kiss: *Hyland, Brian* / Run to him: *Vee, Bobby* / Rhythm of the rain: *Cascades* / Soldier boy: *Shirelles*.
MC: . . . . **OG 5014**

OLD GOLD DECADES (15) (Various artists).
Tracks: / Poetry in motion: *Tillotson, Johnny* / Locomotion, The: *Little Eva* / Let's dance: *Montez, Chris* / He's so fine: *Chiffons*.
MC: . . . . **OG 5015**

OLD GOLD DECADES (17) (Various artists).
Tracks: / How do you do it: *Gerry & the Pacemakers* / Do you want to know a secret: *Kramer, Billy J. & The Dakotas* / I'm into something good: *Herman's Hermits* / Hippy hippy shake: *Swinging Blue Jeans* / I'm alive: *Hollies*.
MC: . . . . **OG 5017**

OLD GOLD DECADES (18) (Various artists).
Tracks: / She's not there: *Zombies* / For your love: *Yardbirds* / All or nothing: *Small Faces* / Out of time: *Farlowe, Chris* / Go now: *Various artists*.
MC: . . . . **OG 5018**

OLD GOLD DECADES (19) (Various artists).
MC: . . . . **OG 5019**

OLD GOLD DECADES (20) (Various artists).
Tracks: / From a jack to a king: *Miller, Ned* / Green green grass of home: *Jones, Tom* / Release me: *Humperdinck, Engelbert* / She wears my ring: *King, Solomon* / Honey: *Goldsboro, Bobby*.
MC: . . . . **OG 5020**

OLD GOLD DECADES (21) (Various artists).
Tracks: / Where do you go to my lovely: *Sarstedt, Peter* / Nights in white satin / Whiter shade of pale, A: *Procul Harum* / Sloop John B: *Beach Boys* / Pretty flamingo: *Manfred Mann*.
MC: . . . . **OG 5021**

OLD GOLD DECADES (22) (Various artists).
Tracks: / I'm a believer: *Monkees* / Sugar sugar: *Archies* / Sweet talking guy: *Chiffons* / Baby, now that I've found you: *Foundations* / If paradise is half as nice: *Amen Corner*.
MC: . . . . **OG 5022**

OLDIES BUT GOLDIES 1 (Various artists).
Tracks: / All or nothing: *Small Faces* / Stairway of love: *Dene, Terry* / Little things: *Berry, Dave* / I wish I could dance: *Poole, Brian & the Tremeloes* / Thunderball: *Jones, Tom* / Put a ring on her finger: *Steele, Tommy* / Why: *Newley, Anthony* / As tears go by: *Faithfull, Marianne* / Here it comes again: *Fortunes* / In thoughts of you: *Fury, Billy* / I want you to be my baby: *Davis, Billie* / Going nowhere: *Los Bravos* / Memories are made of this: *Doonican, Val* / Dommage dommage (too bad too bad): *Engelbert* / Watcha gonna do about it: *Small Faces* / Mystic eyes: *Them*.
LP: **AQ6.25038**
MC: **CQ4 25038**

OLDIES BUT GOLDIES 2 (Various artists).
Tracks: / I can dance: *Poole, Brian & the Tremeloes* / Everything's alright: *Mojos* / Bye bye girl: *Applejacks* / Hey girl: *Small Faces* / Little love, a little kiss, A: *Denver, Karl* / Come and stay with me: *Faithfull, Marianne* / Ice cream man: *Tornados* / Besame mucho: *Harris, Jet* / Main title: *Harris, Jet* / Don't bring me your heartaches: *Ryan, Paul & Barry* / Elusive butterfly: *Doonican, Val* / Angel of the morning: *Davis, Billie* / Secret love: *Kirby, Kathy* / Last night was made for love: *Fury, Billy* / Get lost: *Kane, Eden* / Diane: *Bachelors*.
LP: **AQ6.25039**
MC: **CQ4 25039**

ON THE ROAD AGAIN Rock's new frontiers 1966/1970 (Various artists).
Tracks: / Dirty water: *Standells* / Time won't let me: *Outsiders* / Psychotic reaction: *Count Five* / Rollin' and tumblin': *Winter, Johnny* / On the road again: *Canned Heat* / Living in the USA / Green eyed lady: *Sugarloaf* / Who do you love: *Quicksilver Messenger Service* / Up on cripple creek: *Band* / Different drum: *Stone Poneys* / Mr. Bojangles: *Nitty Gritty Dirt Band* / Brownsville: *Joy Of Cooking* / Big Joe: *Stewart, John* / Power of love, The: *Hourglass* / Early morning rain: *Lightfoot, Gordon* / Games people play: *South, Joe*.
LP: . . . . **CGB 1011**
MC: . . . . **TC CGB 1011**

ONE HIT WONDERS OF THE 60'S (Various artists).
Tracks: / Nut rocker: *Bumble, B & The Stingers* / Games people play: *South, Joe* / I'm the urban spaceman: *Bonzo Dog Band* / Communication: *McCallum, David* / Baby sittin': *Angelo, Bobby* / Magnificent seven, The: *Caiola, Al* / Rudi's in love: *Locomotive* / Sabre dance: *Love Sculpture* / I should've known better: *Naturals* / Tell Laura I love her: *Valance, Ricky* / Poison ivy: *Paramounts* / I cried for you: *Stevens, Ricky* / Sakiyaki: *Sakamoto, Kyu* / With a little help from my friends: *Young Idea* / Old rivers: *Brennan, Walter* / Spooky: *Classics IV* / Shame and scandal in the family: *Percival, Lance (nar)* / Walking my cat named dog: *Tanega, Norma*.
LP: . . . . **MFP 5820**
MC: . . . . **TCMFP 5820**

OPEN TOP CARS AND GIRLS IN T-SHIRTS (Various artists).
LP: . . . . **STAR 2257**
MC: . . . . **STAC 2257**

PARTY TIME SIXTIES (Various artists).
Tracks: / Somebody to love: *Jefferson Airplane* / Cry like a baby: *Box Tops* / Light my fire: *Feliciano, Jose* / Bad to me: *Kramer, Billy J. & The Dakotas* / Chains: *Cookies, The* / Hey baby: *Channel, Bruce* / Sunny afternoon: *Kinks* / It's my party: *Gore, Lesley* / Working in a coalmine: *Dorsey, Lee* / I'm your puppet: *Purify, James & Bobby* / Don't throw your love away: *Searchers* / Pleasant valley sunday: *Monkees* / Sweet talking guy: *Chiffons* / Sunny: *Fame, Georgie* / Son of a preacher man: *Springfield, Dusty*.
LP: . . . . **BOOMER 112**
MC: . . . . **BOOMERC 112**

POP EXPLOSION VOL.1 (Various artists).
2LP: . . . . **CR 028**
MCSET: . . . . **CRT 028**

POP EXPLOSION VOL.2 (Various artists).
Tracks: / Still I'm sad: *Yardbirds* / I can never go home anymore: *Shangri-Las* / Folsom Prison blues: *Cash, Johnny* / Johnny B. Goode: *Lewis, Jerry Lee* / Cry for a shadow: *Beatles & Tony Sheridan* / Lucille: *Little Richard* / Matchbox: *Perkins, Carl* / Why: *Beatles & Tony Sheridan* / Iko iko: *Dixie Cups* / Evil hearted you: *Yardbirds* / It's in his kiss: *Everett, Betty* / Everybody's trying to be my baby: *Perkins, Carl* / High school confidential: *Lewis, Jerry Lee* / Shapes of things: *Yardbirds* / Give him a great big kiss: *Shangri-Las* / Lawdy Miss Clawdy: *Little Richard* / Harper Valley PTA: *Riley, Jeannie C.* / Heartful of soul: *Yardbirds* / Ya ya: *Beatles & Tony Sheridan* / Girl most likely, The: *Riley, Jeannie C.* / Whole lotta shakin' goin' on: *Various artists* / Raunchy: *Justis, Bill* / For your love: *Yardbirds*.
LP: . . . . **CBD 103**
MCSET: . . . . **CRT 103**

POP INSIDE THE SIXTIES (Various artists).
Tracks: / Somethings just stick in your mind: *Vashti* / Love hit me: *Orchids* / (Walking thru the) sleepy city: *Mighty Avengers* / You came along: *Warriors* / Don't make me blue: *Warriors* / Mirror mirror: *Pinkertons* Assorted Colours / Magic rocking horse: *Pinkertons Assorted Colours* / I can make it with you: *Douglas, Rob* & Dean / Now it's my turn: *Gunn, Jon* / I just made up my mind: *Gunn, Jon* / Till you say you'll be mine: *Newton-John*, Olivia / For ever: *Newton-John, Olivia* / Give her my regards: *Marriott, Steve* / Yes I do: *Wilson, Tony* / Lost without you: *Wilson, Tony* / Lovingly yours: *Mockingbirds* / Lost without Linda: *Essex, David* / Acapulco 1922: *Great, Johnny B* / Girl don't make me wait: *Timebox* / Yellow van: *Timebox*.
LP: . . . . **SEE 243**

POP SIXTIES (Baby Boomer Series) (Various artists).
Tracks: / Carrie Anne: *Hollies, The* / Young girl: *Puckett, Gary* / Mama told me not to come: *Three Dog Night* / Dedicated follower of fashion: *Kinks* / Lightning strikes: *Christie, Lou* / Concrete and clay: *Unit 4 + 2* / Boat that I row, The: *Lulu* / Everlasting love: *Love Affair* / Hippy hippy shake: *Swinging Blue Jeans* / Barbara Ann: *Beach Boys* / Hang on Sloopy: *McCoys* / Runaway: *Shannon, Del* / Take good care of my baby: *Vee, Bobby* / Monday Monday: *Mamas & Papas* / Bang bang (my baby shot me down): *Cher* / All I really want to do: *Byrds*.
LP: . . . . **BOOMER 103**
MC: . . . . **BOOMERC 103**

POP/ROCK GROUP HITS OF THE MID 60'S (OLD GOLD) (Various artists).
Tracks: / Here comes the night: *Them* (By Them) / Needles and pins: *Searchers* / You really got me: *Kinks* (By The Kinks) / She's not there: *Zombies* (By The Zombies) / Do wah diddy diddy: *Manfred Mann* (By Manfred Mann) / I'm alive: *Hollies* (By The Hollies) / Go now: *Moody Blues* (By The Moody Blues) / Hippy hippy shake: *Swinging* Blue Jeans (By The Swinging Blue Jeans) / House of the rising sun: *Animals* (By The Animals) / All or nothing: *Small* Faces (By The Small Faces) / Heart full of soul: *Yardbirds* (By The Yardbirds) / Tobacco Road: *Nashville Teens* (By The Nashville Teens) / I can't explain: *Who* (By The Who) / I feel free: *Cream* (By Cream).
LP: . . . . **OG 1013**
MC: . . . . **OG 2013**

PURPLE HEARTS FROM PASTURES GONE (Various artists).
Tracks: / Mockin' Bird Hill: *Migil 5* / Near you: *Migil 5* / Dedicated follower of fashion: *Kinks* / Sunny afternoon: *Kinks* / Wear it on our face: *Dells* / Don't mess up a good thing: *Bass, Fontella & Bobby* McClure / Entertainer, The: *Clarke, Tony* / It's growing: *James, Jimmy* / I can't turn you loose: *James*, Jimmy / Daydream: *Lovin' Spoonful* / Hi hi Hazel: *Washington, Geno* / Que sera sera: *Washington, Geno* / Jenny take a ride: *Ryder, Mitch/Detroit Wheels* / Long live love: *Shaw, Sandie* / Always something there to remind me (There's): *Shaw, Sandie* / Rescue me: *Bass, Fontella* / Recovery: *Bass, Fontella* / Rinky dink: *Cortez*, Dave 'Baby' / Lover's concerto: *Toys* / Swingin' on a star: *Irwin, Big Dee & Little Eva* / Baby now that I found you: *Foundations* / Soulful dress: *Sugar Pie Desanto* / Summertime: *Stewart, Billy* / High heel sneakers: *Little Tommy Tucker*.
LP: . . . . **PRCD 5641**
MC: . . . . **ZCPRD 5641**

QUICK BEFORE THEY CATCH US (See under Quick Before They Catch Us) (Various artists).

QUICK BEFORE THEY CATCH US (Pop Era Vol 1) (Various artists).
Tracks: / Quick before they catch us: *Klaus, Paddy & Gibson* / My world fell down: *Ivy League* / End of the season: *Uglys* / Pattern people: *Bystanders* / Tomorrow never comes: *Hellions* / Pink, purple, yellow, red: *Sorrows* / Here today: *Factotums* / Each time: *Searchers* / You gotta be with me: *Onyx, The* / Can't stop thinking about her: *Chapters* / Creeping Jean: *Davies, Dave* / Love hate revenge: *Episode Six* / Water is over my head, The: *Rockin' Berries* / I take it we're through: *Riot Squad* / Just you: *Thursday's Children* / Roses: *Downliners Sect* / Pay you back with interest: *Gillespie, Dana* (CD bonus track.) / Tracker, The: *Bernard*, Kenny & The Wranglers (CD bonus track.) / Lazy old sun: *Kinks* (CD bonus track.) / Man from the marriage guidance bureau, The: *Knack* (CD bonus track.) / Make me stay a little bit longer: *Status Quo* (CD bonus track.) / World wrapped around my neck, The: *Hammond, Steve* (CD bonus track.).
LP: . . . . **NEXLP 108**

RAIN AND TEARS (Hit Ballads of the Sixties) (Various artists).
Tracks: / Yesterday: *Faithfull, Marianne* / You've lost that lovin' feeling: *Righteous Brothers* / I just don't know what to do with myself: *Springfield, Dusty* / Rain and tears: *Aphrodite's Child* / Juliet: *Four Pennies* / I will: *Fury, Billy* / Jesamine: *Casuals* / Joanna: *Walker, Scott* / Someone, someone: *Poole, Brian* & the Tremeloes / Mama: *Berry, Dave* / Sitting in the park: *Fame, Georgie* / Stranger on the shore: *Bilk, Acker*.
LP: . . . . **CN 2094**
MC: **CN4 2094**

RAISED ON ROCK - 60'S ROCK UK (Various artists).
Tracks: / With a little help from my friends: *Cocker, Joe* / Here comes the night: *Them* / Pictures of matchstick men: *Status Quo* / For your love: *Yardbirds* / We've gotta get out of this place: *Animals* / I feel free: *Cream* / You really got me: *Kinks* / Out of time: *Farlowe, Chris* / Man of the world: *Fleetwood Mac* / America: *Nice* / Natural born bugie: *Humble Pie* / Got to get you into my life: *Bennet, Cliff* / Hi ho silver lining: *Beck, Jeff* / Fire: *Crazy World of Arthur Brown*.
LP: . . . . **RORLP 17001**
MC: . . . . **RORMC 17001**

RAISED ON ROCK - 60'S ROCK US (Various artists).
Tracks: / Mister Tambourine man: *Byrds* / Weight, The: *Band* / Summer in the city: *Lovin' Spoonful* / Letter, The: *Box Tops* / Dance to the music: *Sly & the Family Stone* / Happy together: *Turtles* / Bang bang (my baby shot me down): *Cher* / In the year 2525: *Zager/Evans* / Green tambourine: *Lemon Pipers* / Keep on: *Channel, Bruce* / Last train to Clarksville: *Monkees* / Hang on Sloopy: *McCoys* / You've made me so very happy: *Blood, Sweat & Tears* / On the road again: *Canned Heat*.
LP: . . . . **RORLP 17002**
MC: . . . . **RORMC 17002**

READY STEADY GO! (Various artists).
LP: . . . . **TAB 60**
MC: . . . . **KTBC 60**

READY STEADY WIN....PLUS (Various artists).
Tracks: / Hide and seek: *Thyrds, The* / I'll miss you: *Harbour Lights* / Bow Street runner: *Bow Street Runners* / Did you ever hear the sound: *Knight, Tony & The Livewires* / Lonely one, The: *Deltones with Tony Lane* / She loves to be loved: *Falling Leaves* / Our love feels new: *Echolettes* / You make me go 'oooh': *Dynamos* / Not guilty: *Falling Leaves* / And I just do what I want: *Bow Street Runners* / Tell me what you're gonna do: *Bow Street Runners* / I'm leaving you: *Royal, Jimmy & The Hawkes* / So much in love: *Planets* / Every time I look at you: *Five Aces* / Anytime: *Scene Five* / Ain't it a shame: *Vibrons* / Mistletoe love: *Fenda*, Jaymes & The Vulcans / Think of me: *Olympics* / You've come back: *Leasides* / Only girl, The: *Fenda, Jaymes & The Vulcans* / Get out of my way: *Bow Street Runners* / Baby never say goodbye: *Bow Street Runners*.
LP: . . . . **SEE 202**

RED BIRD STORY, THE (Various artists).
Tracks: / Chapel of love: *Dixie Cups* / I wanna love him so bad: *Jelly Beans* / People say: *Dixie Cups* / Remember (walking in the sand): *Shangri-Las* / Goodnight baby: *Butterflies* / Leader of the pack: *Shangri-Las* / Gee baby gee: *Dixie Cups* / Iko iko: *Dixie Cups* / Give him a great big kiss: *Shangri-Las* / Gee the moon is shining bright: *Dixie Cups* / I can never go home anymore: *Shangri-Las* / Boy from New York City: *Ad Libs* / Give us your blessing: *Shangri-Las* / He ain't no angel: *Ad Libs* / Past, present and future: *Shangri-Las* / I'm just a down home girl: *Ad Libs* / Down home girl: *Robinson, Alvin* / I hurt on the other side: *Barnes*, Sidney / Something you got: *Robinson, Alvin* / Bad as they come: *Hawkins, Sam* / Let the good times roll: *Hawkins, Sam* / Come on baby: *Hawkins, Sam* / Fever: *Robinson, Alvin* / Go now: *Banks, Bessie* / Bossa nova baby: *Tippie & the Clovers* / My heart said (the bossa nova): *Tippie & the Clovers* / I can't let go: *Sands, Evie* / Take me for a little while: *Sands, Evie* / Standing by: *Warwick, Dee Dee* / I don't think my baby's coming back: *Warwick, Dee Dee* / New Yorks a lonely town: *Tradewinds* / I know it's alright: *Jeff & Ellie*.

2LP: . . . . **CDX 15**
MC: . . . . **TCCDX 15**

RED BIRD STORY VOL.2, THE (Various artists).
Tracks: / Paradise: *Shangri-Las* / He cried: *Shangri-Las* / Dressed in black: *Shangri-Las* / I wonder: *Butterflys* / Gee baby gee: *Butterflys* / Dum dum ditty: *Goodees* / If there's anything else you want (let me know): *Joy, Roddie* / Welcome to my heart: *Bouquets* / Big bad world: *Saint, Cathy* / It sounds like my baby: *Banks, Bessie* / Searchin': *Robinson, Alvin* / How can I get over you: *Robinson, Alvin* / I'm gonna put some hurt on you: *Robinson, Alvin* / Bottom of my soul: *Robinson, Alvin* / Keep it up: *Soul* Brothers / Fugitive from love: *Jones, Linda* / It was a lie: *Bobby Moore & The Fourmosts* / You don't know: *Greenwich, Ellie* / Baby: *Greenwich, Ellie* / Another boy like mine: *Greenwich, Ellie* / Our love can still be saved: *Barry, Jeff* / I'll still love you: *Barry, Jeff* / Talk to me baby: *Mann, Barry* / Amy: *Mann, Barry* / Dressed in black: *Morton, Shadow* / Baby be mine: *Jelly Beans* / Kind of boy you can't forget, The: *Jelly Beans* / Chapel of love: *Jelly Beans* / Here she comes: *Jelly Beans* / Ain't love a funny thing: *Jelly Beans* / Whisper sweet things: *Jelly Beans* / Goodnight baby: *Jelly Beans* / Do wah diddy diddy: *Jelly Beans*.
2LP: . . . . **CDX 19**
MCSET: . . . . **TCCDX 19**

REMEMBER: A COLLECTION OF POP MEMORIES, VOL 1 (Various artists).
Tracks: / Sugar and spice: *Searchers* / Girl don't come: *Shaw, Sandie* / Downtown: *Clark, Petula* / Never my love: *Adrissi Brothers* / Bye bye baby: *Jackson, Tony* / Where are you now, my love?: *Trent, Jackie* / Rescue me: *Bass, Fontella* / Summer in the city: *Lovin' Spoonful* / Green tambourine: *Lemon Pipers* / Pictures of matchstick men: *Status Quo* / Tip of my tongue: *Quickly, Tommy & The Remo Four* / Love potion No.9: *Jackson, Tony* / Just a little bit: *Undertakers* / Fool number one: *Lee, Brenda* / Clapping song, The: *Ellis, Shirley* / California dreamin': *Mamas & Papas* / As usual: *Lee, Brenda* / I feel love comin' on: *Taylor, Felice* / Ain't got no....I got life: *Simone, Nina* / Hellraiser: *Sweet* / Oh Carol: *Sedaka*, Neil / Come back and shake me: *Rogers, Clodagh* / Walk on the wild side: *Reed, Lou* / Heart: *Pavone, Rita* / My coo ca choo: *Stardust, Alvin* / Lucy in the sky with diamonds: *John, Elton*.
2LP: . . . . **CR 070**
MCSET: . . . . **CRT 070**

REMEMBER THE PIRATES (Various artists).
Tracks: / Touch of velvet - A sting of brass, A: *Mood Mosaic* / I can't let go: *Hollies* / Little things: *Goldsboro*, Bobby / Don't turn your back: *DeShannon, Jackie* / Dead man's curve: *Jan & Dean* / Baby it's you: *Black*, Cilla / I'm into something good: *Herman's Hermits* / Excerpt from A teenage opera: *West, Keith* / You're so good to me: *Beach Boys* / Days of Pearly Spencer, The: *McWilliams, David* / Elusive butterfly: *Lind, Bob* / Livin' above your head: *Jay & the Americans* / Bang bang (my baby shot me down): *Cher* / It's my life: *Animals* / Somewhere: *Proby, P.J.* / Got to get you into my life: *Bennett, Cliff & The Rebel Rousers* / Reservations: *Dupree*, Simon & The Big Sound (CD only.) / Long cigarette, The: *Roulettes* (CD only.) / I ain't gonna eat out my heart anymore: *New York Public Library* (CD only.) / Don't make me over: *Swinging Blue Jeans* (CD only.).
LP: . . . . **GO 2027**
MC: . . . . **TCGO 2027**

RHYTHM & BLUE EYED SOUL (Various artists).
Tracks: / Need your loving: *Flirtations* / Whose little girl: *Williams, Danny* / Ask the lonely: *Fantastics* / I wanna know: *Paul, John E* / Bert's apple crumble: *Quick* / I want you to be: *Davis, Billie* / Crawling up a hill: *Mayall, John* / Air travel: *Farlowe, Chris* / Name it you got it: *Moonshine, Micky* / Only a fool: *McPhatter, Clyde* / Don't change it: *Fearns Brass Foundry* / Girl don't make me wait: *Timebox* / Blue beat: *Beazers* / Looking back: *Williams, Larry & Johnny Watson* / Keep you hand out: *Spann, Otis* / Can't let her go: *Hipster Image*.
LP: . . . . **KENT 086**

RHYTHM OF THE RAIN (16 hits of the 60's) (Various artists).
LP: . . . . **PFP 1004**
MC: . . . . **PFC 1004**

ROCK 'N' ROLL YEARS 1960 (Various artists).
Tracks: / Only the lonely: *Orbison, Roy* / Shakin' all over: *Kidd, Johnny & The Pirates* / Hit and miss: *Barry*, John Seven / Dreamin': *Burnette, Johnny* / Let it be me: *Everly Brothers* / Voice in the wilderness: *Richard*, Cliff / You got what it takes: *Johnson, Mary* / Three steps to heaven: *Cochran, Eddie* / Walk don't run: *Ventures* / Colette: *Fury, Billy* / Handy man: *Jones, Jimmy (singer)* / Rawhide: *Laine, Frankie* / Running bear: *Preston, Johnny* / El paso: *Robbins, Marty* / Heartaches by the number: *Mitchell, Guy* / Why: *Avalon*, Frankie / Someone else's baby: *Faith, Adam* / Man of mystery: *Shadows* / Among my souvenirs: *Francis*, Connie / Harbour lights: *Platters* / Summer place, Theme from: *Faith, Percy* / On a slow boat to China: *Ford, Emile & The Checkmates* / Bad boy: *Wilde, Marty* / I'll never fall in love again: *Ray, Johnnie*.
LP: . . . . **YRNRLP 60**
MC: . . . . **YRNRMC 60**

ROCK 'N' ROLL YEARS 1961 (Various artists).
Tracks: / Poetry in motion: *Tillotson, Johnny* / You're sixteen: *Burnette, Johnny* / Blue moon: *Marcels* / Are you sure: *Allisons* / Calendar girl: *Sedaka, Neil* / Wild wind: *Leyton, John* / Runaround Sue: *Dion* / Hats off to Larry: *Shannon, Del* / On the rebound: *Cramer, Floyd* / Weekend: *Cochran, Eddie* / What I'd say: *Lewis, Jerry Lee* / F.B.I.: *Shadows* / Hello Mary Lou: *Nelson, Rick(y)* / Take good care of my baby: *Vee, Bobby* / Sea of heart break: *Gibson, Don* / War paint: *Brook Brothers* / Theme for a dream: *Richard, Cliff* / Sailor: *Clark, Petula* / Who put the bop: *Viscounts* / Perfidia: *Ventures* / Don't treat me like a child: *Shapiro, Helen* / Counting teardrops: *Ford, Emile & The Checkmates* / You're the only good thing: *Reeves, Jim* / Have a drink on me: *Donegan, Lonnie*.
LP: . . . . **YRNRLP 61**
MC: . . . . **YRNRMC 61**

ROCK 'N' ROLL YEARS 1962 (Various artists).
Tracks: / Young ones, The: *Richard, Cliff* / Speedy gonzales: *Boone, Pat* / Loco-motion, The: *Little Eva* / (Dance with the) guitar man: *Eddy, Duane* / Sweet little sixteen: *Lewis, Jerry Lee* / Breaking up is hard to do: *Sedaka, Neil* / Let's dance: *Montez, Chris* / Bobby's girl: *Maughan, Susan* / Norman: *Deene, Carol* / Hey little girl: *Shannon, Del* / It might as well rain until September: *King, Carole* / Don't ever change: *Crickets* / Wonderful land: *Shadows* / Picture of you, A: *Brown, Joe* / Sealed with a kiss: *Hyland*, Bryan / Language of love: *Loudermilk, John D.* / Island of dreams: *Springfields* / Once upon a dream: *Fury, Billy* / Twistin' the night away: *Cooke, Sam* / Forget me not: *Kane, Eden* / Venus in blue jeans: *Wynter, Mark* / Love letters: *Lester, Ketty* / Adios amigo: *Reeves, Jim* / Moon river: *Williams, Danny*.
LP: . . . . **YRNRLP 62**
MC: . . . . **YRNRMC 62**

ROCK 'N' ROLL YEARS 1963 (Various artists).
Tracks: / Foot tapper: *Shadows* / Hippy hippy shake: *Swinging Blue Jeans* / I only want to be with you: *Springfield*, Dusty / Night has a thousand eyes, The: *Vee, Bobby* / Bad to me: *Kramer, Billy J.* / You'll never walk alone: *Gerry & the Pacemakers* / Do you love me?: *Poole, Brian* / Wipe out: *Surfaris* / It's my party: *Gore*, Lesley / You were made for me: *Freddie & The Dreamers* / First time: *Faith, Adam* / I'll never get over you: *Kidd, Johnny & The Pirates* / Diamonds: *Harris, Jet* / Tell him: *Davis, Billie* / Searchin': *Hollies* / Rhythm of the rain: *Cascades* / Hello little girl: *Fournotes* / Secret love: *Kirby, Kathy* / Brown eyed handsome man: *Holly, Buddy* / Good golly Miss Molly: *Lewis, Jerry Lee* / Mr Bass man: *Cymbal, Johnny* / Little town flirt: *Shannon, Del* / Welcome to my world: *Reeves, Jim* / End of the world: *Davis, Skeeter*.
LP: . . . . **YRNRLP 63**
MC: . . . . **YRNRMC 63**

ROCK 'N' ROLL YEARS 1964 (Various artists).
Tracks: / You really got me: *Kinks* / Shout: *Lulu and the Luvvers* / Yeh yeh: *Fame, Georgie* / Needles and pins: *Searchers* / Have I the right?: *Honeycombs* / I get around: *Beach Boys* / Do wah diddy diddy: *Mann, Manfred* / Always something there to remind me: *Shaw, Sandie* / Terry: *Twinkle* / He's in town: *Rockin' Berries* / You're no good: *Swinging Blue Jeans* / Downtown: *Clark, Petula* / World without love, A: *Peter & Gordon* / Little children: *Various artists* / Tell me when: *Applejacks* / I understand: *Freddie* & The Dreamers / I love you because: *Reeves, Jim* / Ferry 'cross the Mersey: *Gerry & the Pacemakers* / You're my world: *Black, Cilla* / I just don't know what to do with myself: *Springfield, Dusty* / I'm crying: *Animals* / Crying game, The: *Berry, Dave* / Mockin' Bird Hill: *Migil 5* / Juliet: *Four Pennies*.
LP: . . . . **YRNRLP 64**
MC: . . . . **YRNRMC 64**

ROCK 'N' ROLL YEARS 1965 (Various artists).
Tracks: / Make it easy on yourself: *Walker Brothers* / You've lost that loving feeling: *Righteous Brothers* / Don't let me be misunderstood: *Animals* / For your love: *Yardbirds* / Wooly bully: *Sam The Sham & The Pharaohs* / 1-2-3: *Barry, Len* / Tired of waiting for you: *Kinks* / Eve of destruction: *McGuire, Barry* / Catch the wind: *Donovan* / If you gotta go now: *Mann, Manfred* / In the middle of nowhere: *Springfield, Dusty* / It's not unusual: *Jones, Tom* / To know you is to love you: *Peter & Gordon* / I'll never find another you: *Seekers* / You've got your troubles: *Fortunes* / Game of love: *Fontana, Wayne & the Mindbenders* / Little things: *Berry*, Dave / Silhouettes: *Herman's Hermits* / I'm alive: *Hollies* / California girls: *Beach Boys* / Tossing and turning: *Ivy League* / Poor man's son: *Rockin' Berries* / Everyone's gone to the moon: *King, Jonathan* / Clapping song, The: *Ellis, Shirley*.
LP: . . . . **YRNRLP 65**
MC: . . . . **YRNRMC 65**

ROCK 'N' ROLL YEARS 1966 (Various artists).
Tracks: / Wild thing: *Troggs* / Shape of things: *Yardbirds* / Got to get you into my life: *Bennett, Cliff* / Working in a coal mine: *Dorsey, Lee* / Sun ain't gonna shine any more: *Walker Brothers* / It's a man's man's man's world: *Brown, James* / I feel free: *Cream* / Stop stop stop: *Hollies* / You don't have to say you love me: *Springfield, Dusty* / Sorrow: *Merseys* / All or nothing: *Small Faces* / Bang bang (my baby shot me down): *Cher* / Sunny afternoon: *Kinks* / California dreamin': *Mamas & Papas* / Pretty flamingo: *Mann, Manfred* / High time: *Jones, Paul* / No milk today: *Herman's Hermits* / Elusive butterfly: *Lind, Bob* / Michelle: *Overlanders* / God only knows: *Beach Boys* / Groovy kind of love: *Mindbenders* / Alfie: *Black, Cilla* / I couldn't live without your love: *Clark, Petula* / Bend it: *Dee, Dave*.
LP: . . . . **YRNRLP 66**
MC: . . . . **YRNRMC 66**

ROCK 'N' ROLL YEARS 1967 (Various artists).
Tracks: / Hey Joe: *Hendrix, Jimi Experience* / Strange brew: *Cream* / San Franciscan nights: *Burdon, Eric* & The Animals / Waterloo sunset: *Kinks* / Excerpt from a teenage opera: *West, Keith* / Kites: *Dupree*, Simon / I'm a believer: *Monkees* / Hi ho silver lining: *Beck, Jeff* / Ha ha said the clown: *Mann, Manfred* / Massachusetts: *Bee Gees* / I've been a bad bad boy: *Jones, Paul* / Baby now that I've found you: *Foundations* / Whiter shade of pale: *Harum, Procul* / Let the heartaches begin: *Baldry, Long John* / Death of a clown: *Davies*, Dave / Letter, The: *Box Tops* / Matthew and son: *Stevens, Cat* / Nights in white satin: *Moody Blues* / There's a kind of hush: *Herman's Hermits* / Let's go to San Francisco: *Flowerpot Men* / Dedicated to the one I love: *Mamas & Papas* / Zabadak: *Dee, Dave* / Carrie Ann: *Hollies* / Puppet on a string: *Shaw, Sandie*.
LP: . . . . **YRNRLP 67**
MC: . . . . **YRNRMC 67**

ROCK 'N' ROLL YEARS 1968 (Various artists).
Tracks: / All along the watchtower: *Hendrix, Jimi Experience* / Fire: *Crazy World of Arthur Brown* / Valleri: *Monkees* / Ice in the sun: *Status Quo* / Blackberry way: *Move* / Summertime blues: *Cochran, Eddie* / With a little help from my friends: *Cocker, Joe* / Mighty Quinn: *Mann, Manfred* / On the road again: *Canned* Heat / Weight, The: *Band* / Cry like a baby: *Box Tops* / This wheel's on fire: *Driscoll, Julie* / Legend of Xanadu: *Dave Dee, Dozy, Beaky, Mick & Tich* / Build me up buttercup: *Foundations* / Judy in disguise with glasses: *Fred, John & His Playboy Band* / Bend me shape me: *Corner, Amen* / Gimme little sign: *Wood*, Brenton / Urban spaceman: *Bonzo Dog Band* / I've gotta get a message to you: *Bee Gees* / Honey: *Goldsboro*, Bobby / I can't let Maggie go: *Honeybus* / Jesamine: *Casuals* / Jennifer Eccles: *Hollies* / White horses: *Jacky*.
LP: . . . . **YRNRLP 68**
MC: . . . . **YRNRMC 68**

ROCK 'N' ROLL YEARS 1969 (Various artists).
Tracks: / Suspicious minds: *Presley, Elvis* / Something in the air: *Thunderclap Newman* / Badge: *Cream* / Reflections of my life: *Marmalade* / Games people play: *South, Joe* / Dizzy: *Roe, Tommy* / In the year 2525: *Zager/Evans* / Aquarius: *5th Dimension* / Wonderful world beautiful people: *Cliff, Jimmy* / Delta lady: *Cocker, Joe* / Harlem shuffle: *Bob & Earl* / Barabajagal: *Donovan* / Je t'aime...: *Birkin*, Jane / Israelites: *Dekker, Desmond & The Aces* / Liquidator: *Harry J. All Stars* / Melting pot: *Blue* Mink / Something's happening: *Herman's Hermits* / Throw down a line: *Richard, Cliff* / Where do you go to my lovely: *Sarstedt, Peter* / I'll never fall in love again: *Gentry, Bobbie* / He ain't heavy he's my brother: *Hollies* / Wichita lineman: *Campbell, Glen* / Saved by the bell: *Gibb, Robin* / Move in a little closer: *Harmony Grass*.
LP: . . . . **YRNRLP 69**
MC: . . . . **YRNRMC 69**

ROCK 'N' ROLL YEARS (1960-1963) (Various artists).
Tracks: / What do you want: *Faith, Adam* / Apache: *Shadows* / Ain't misbehavin': *Bruce, Tommy & the Bruisers* / Good timin': *Beach Boys* / On the rebound: *Cramer, Floyd* / Runaway: *Shannon, Del* / Johnny remember me: *Leyton, John* / Walkin' back to happiness: *Shapiro, Helen* / Runaround Sue: *Dion* / Take good care of my baby: *Vee, Bobby* / Let's dance: *Montez, Chris* / Nut rocker: *Bumble, B & The Stingers* / Twistin' the night away: *Cooke, Sam* / Locomotion, The: *Little Eva* / How do you do it: *Gerry & the Pacemakers* / Surf city: *Jan & Dean* / Do you want to know a secret: *Kramer, Billy J. & The Dakotas* / Sugar and spice: *Searchers* / She loves you: *Beatles*.
LP: . . . . **REN 632**
MC: . . . . **ZCN 632**

ROCK 'N' ROLL YEARS (1964-1967) (Various artists).
Tracks: / Tobacco road: *Nashville Teens* / I'm in to something good: *Herman's Hermits* / You really got me: *Kinks* / House of the rising sun: *Animals* / Anyone who had a heart: *Black, Cilla* / Leader of the pack: *Shangri-Las* / Go now: *Moody Blues* / Here comes the night: *Them* / Little things: *Berry, Dave* / My generation: *Who* / River deep, mountain high: *Supremes* / Keep on running: *Davis, Spencer Group* / Sun ain't gonna shine anymore, The: *Walker Brothers* / Good vibrations: *Beach Boys* / I can't let go: *Webb, Marti* / Dedicated to the one I love: *Mamas & Papas* / Whiter shade of pale, A: *Procul Harum* / I'm a believer: *Monkees* / San Francisco: *Flowerpot Men* / All you need is love: *Beatles*.
LP: . . . . **REN 633**
MC: . . . . **ZCN 633**

ROCKIN' SIXTIES VOL.2 (Various artists).
LP: . . . . **BOOMER 109**
MC: . . . . **BOOMER C 109**

ROCKING SIXTIES (Baby Boomer Series) (Various artists).
Tracks: / My generation: *Who* / Fire brigade: *Move* / Hi ho silver lining: *Beck, Jeff* / Got to get you into my life: *Bennett, Cliff & The Rebel Rousers* / Spinning wheel: *Blood, Sweat & Tears* / Hold me: *Proby*, P.J. / Sha-la-la-la-lee: *Small Faces* / Feeling alright: *Cocker, Joe* / Purple haze: *Hendrix, Jimi* / Race with the devil: *Gun* / Stand: *Sly & the Family Stone* / I feel free: *Cream* / 5 4 3 2 1: *Manfred Mann* / Debora: *T. Rex* / Matthew & Son: *Stevens, Cat* / Xanadu: *Dave Dee, Dozy, Beaky, Mick & Tich*.
LP: . . . . **BOOMER 104**
MC: . . . . **BOOMERC 104**

SALUTE THE SIXTIES (Various artists).
LP: . . . . **CBS 85860**

SEALED WITH A KISS Million sellers of the swinging sixties (Various artists).
LP: . . . . **SHM 3220**
MC: . . . . **HSC 3220**

SEALED WITH A KISS 1959-1963 (see under Rediscover Series) (Various artists).

SEALED WITH A KISS 1959-1963 (Various artists).
Tracks: / Blue bayou: *Orbison, Roy* / Hey baby: *Channel, Bruce* / Bobby's girl: *Maughan, Susan* / Can't get used to losing you: *Williams, Andy* / Please help me, I'm falling: *Locklin, Hank* / Island of dreams: *Springfields* / Cathy's clown: *Everly Brothers* / Save the last dance for me: *Drifters* / Tell Laura I love her: *Peterson*, Ray / Beatnik fly: *Johnny & The Hurricanes* / Baby sittin' boogie: *Clifford, Buzz* / El Paso: *Robbins*, Marty / Telstar: *Tornados* / Breaking up is hard to do: *Sedaka, Neil* / Sealed with a kiss: *Hyland, Brian* / Venus: *Avalon, Frankie* / Roses are red: *Vinton, Bobby* / End of the world: *Davis, Skeeter* / Rawhide: *Laine, Frankie* / Beyond the sea: *Darin, Bobby* / Johnny get angry: *Summers, Joannie* / All alone am I: *Lee, Brenda* / He'll have to go: *Reeves, Jim* / Boy's cry: *Kane, Eden*.

MCSET: . . . . **OG 2207**

SENSATIONAL 60'S (BOX SET) (Various artists).
MCSET: . . . . **KNMC 35001**

SENSATIONAL SIXTIES,THE (Various artists).
Tracks: / Only the lonely: *Orbison, Roy* / I only want to be with you: *Springfield, Dusty* / Spinning wheel: *Blood*, Sweat & Tears / Somethings gotten hold of my heart: *Pitney, Gene* / You've got your troubles: *Fortunes* / Oh Carol: *Sedaka, Neil* / Lion sleeps tonight, The: *Tokens* / Yeh,Yeh: *Fame, Georgie* / Mr.Tambourine Man: *Byrds, The* / Make it easy on yourself: *Walker Brothers* / Young Girl: *Puckett, Gary & The Union Gap*/ Everlasting love: *Love Affair* / This wheels on fire: *Driscoll, Julie & the Brian Auger Trinity* / Daydream believer: *Monkees* / San Francisco: *Mackenzie, Scott* / Letter, The: *Box Tops* / Working in the coalmine: *Dorsey, Lee* / Crying game, The: *Berry, Dave* / Keep on: *Channel, Bruce* / Nights In White Satin: *Moody Blues*.
MC: . . . . **STDMC 34**

SENTIMENTAL HITS OF EARLY 60'S (Various artists).
Tracks: / Sailor: *Clark, Petula* / Soldier boy: *Various artists* / Michael: *Highwaymen* / Love letters: *Lester, Ketty* / Why: *Avalon, Frankie* / Breaking up is hard to do: *Sedaka, Neil* / Summer place, A theme from: *Faith, Percy Orchestra* / You don't know: *Shapiro, Helen* / Put your head on my shoulder: *Anka, Paul*/ Pretty blue eyes: *Douglas, Craig*/ Doctor Kildare theme: *Chamberlain, Richard* / Go away little girl: *Lawrence, Steve* / Last night was made for love: *Fury, Billy* / Next time, The: *Richard, Cliff*.
LP: . . . . **OG 1012**
MC: . . . . **OG 2012**

SHOT OF RHYTHM & BLUES, A The R&B Era Vol 1 (Various artists).
Tracks: / Country Line Special: *Davies, Cyril* / Fortune Teller: *Jackson, Tony* / I'm a lover not a fighter: *Brand*/ Milk cow blues: *Kinks* / You said: *Primitives (60's)* / Shot of rhythm and blues,A: *Sundowners* / Jump: *Riot Squad* / Turn on your lovelight: *Felders Orioles* / Baby: *Sorrows* / I'm a hog for you baby: *Grant Erky/Earwigs* / Let's make it pretty baby: *S.O.U.L. Agents* / Today, tonight and tomorrow: *Chosen Few* / I got my mojo working: *Sheffields* / I'm looking for a woman: *Powell, Jimmy* / Portland Down: *Gibson, Wayne*/ We didn't kiss: *Clique* / You can't sit down: *Beatmen* (CD only.) / All I want is you: *Van Dyke & The Bambis*(CD only.) / Gotta keep movin' baby: *Game* (CD only.) / Show you mean it too: *Me & Them* (CD only.) / I've seen such things: *Dangerfield,Tony* (CD only.) / If you don't come back: *Takers*.
LP: . . . . **NEXLP 106**

SIMON BATES - THE 60'S (Volume 1) (Various artists).
Tracks: / Delilah: *Jones, Tom* / Here it comes again: *Fortunes* / Little things: *Berry, Dave* / I only want to be with you: *Springfield, Dusty* / Do you love me: *Poole, Brian & the Tremeloes* / Tell me when: *Applejacks*/ You've got your troubles: *Fortunes* / It's not unusual: *Jones, Tom* / Crying game, The: *Berry, Dave*/ Yeh yeh: *Fame, Georgie & The Australian Blue Flames* / It's only make believe: *Fury, Billy* / Juliet: *Four Pennies*.
MC: **CN4 2103**
LP: . . . . **CN 2103**

SIMON BATES - THE 60'S (2) (Various artists).
Tracks: / Sha la le lee: *Small Faces* / I love my dog: *Stevens, Cat* / Lightnin' strikes: *Christie, Lou*/ In thoughts of you: *Fury, Billy* / What's new pussycat: *Jones, Tom* / Gin house blues: *Amen Corner*/ Candy man: *Poole, Brian & the Tremeloes* / Halfway to paradise: *Fury, Billy* / Get away: *Fame, Georgie/Blue* Flames / Stay awhile: *Springfield, Dusty* / It's a man's man's man's world: *Brown, James* / Girl from Ipanema, The: *Gilberto, Astrud & Stan Getz* / Any way that you want me: *Troggs* / Summer nights: *Faithfull, Marianne*/ Island of dreams: *Springfields* / Sunny: *Fame, Georgie*.
LP: . . . . **CN 2108**
MC: **CN4 2108**

SIXTIES BACKBEAT (Various artists).
Tracks: / She's my girl: *Shafto, Bobby* / Look at me: *Whirlwinds* / Marlena: *Federals* / Little people: *Three Quarters* / Hard times for young lovers: *Arlon, Deke* / Hold tight: *'N' Betweens* / Gotta get a good thing going: *Original Dyaks* / Ugly girl: *'N' Betweens With Kim Fowley* / I don't want to love you: *Show*, Barry Lee / Mr. Rainbow: *Flynn, Steve* / Teenage love: *Five Chesterons* / Pretty thing: *Kins, Danny*/ He's a good face, but he's down and out: *Ford, Dean And The Gaylords* / I'd rather be with the boys: *Toggery Five*/ Congratulations: *West Five* / Go home baby: *Bunch Of 5's* / Don't mind: *Fairies* / Angel face: *Andrews, Tim And Paul Korda* / Never my love: *Christian, Hans* / William Chaulker's time machine: *Lemon Tree*.
LP: . . . . **SEE 39**

SIXTIES BALLADS NUMBER ONES (Various artists).
Tracks: / You're my world: *Black, Cilla* / I remember you: *Ifield, Frank* / Can't help falling in love: *Various* artists / Moon river: *Williams, Danny* / Distant drums: *Reeves, Jim* / Carnival is over, The: *Seekers*/ Reach for the stars: *Bassey, Shirley* / Next time, The: *Richard, Cliff* / You don't know: *Shapiro, Helen*/ Michael: *Highwaymen* / I'll never fall in love again: *Gentry, Bobbie* / This is my song: *Clark, Petula*/ Michelle: *Overlanders* / Crying in the chapel: *Presley, Elvis*.
LP: . . . . **OG 1506**
MC: . . . . **OG 2506**

SIXTIES GROUP GOLD (Silence is Golden) (Various artists).
Tracks: / Silence is golden: *Tremeloes* / Sound of silence: *Bachelors* / Wild thing: *Troggs* / Surfin' safari: *Beach Boys* / Understand: *Freddie & The Dreamers* / Where have all the flowers gone: *Kingston Trio*/ Build me up buttercup: *Foundations* / Hitchin' a ride: *Vanity Fair*.
LP: . . . . **OCN 2012WL**
MC: . . . . **OCN 2012WK**

SIXTIES LOST AND FOUND - VOL 1 (1964-1969) (Various artists).
Tracks: / Blue ribbons: *Paramounts* / Bad time, The: *Roulettes* / What a sweet thing that was: *Sheridan*, Mike & The Nightriders / Where do you belong: *Viscounts* / Take my tip: *Manish Boys* / This boy always been true: *Herd* / Funny cos neither could I: *Shotgun Express* / La la la la la: *Persuasions* / You make me happy: *Bennett, Cliff* / It's getting better: *Jones, Paul* / What more can anyone do: *Faith, Adam* / Peculiar situation: *Young Idea* / Seagull: *Love Sculpture* / Day will come, The: *Stewart, Rod* / Bring your love back home: *Soulmates With The Jet Set*.
LP: . . . . **CM 113**

SIXTIES LOST AND FOUND - VOL 2 (Various artists).
Tracks: / I'll cry instead: *Cocker, Joe* / Good morning little schoolgirl: *Stewart, Rod* / That's a long time ago: *Nero & The Gladiators* / Woman: *Zombies* / Money: *Elliott, Bern & The Fenmen* / Don't you just know it: *Screaming Lord Such* / Buckle shoe stomp: *Snobs* / Baby please don't go: *Them* / Just one more chance: *Outer Limits* / London boys: *Bowie, David* / Sister morphine: *Faithfull, Marianne* / Say you don't mind: *Laine, Denny* / Will you be my lover tonight: *Bean, George* / Surprise surprise: *Lulu and the Luvvers*/ Now I know: *Beat Chics* / We love the Beatles: *Vernons Girls* / Like dreamers do: *Applejacks* / That's alright mama: *Gonks* / Uncle Willie: *Money, Zoot* / Long tall shorty: *Bond, Graham Organisation*.
LP: . . . . **CM 123**

SIXTIES LOST AND FOUND - VOL 3 (Various artists).
Tracks: / What's new pussycat: *Crying Shames (2)* / Please Mr. Postman: *Elliott, Bern & The Fenmen* / No response: *Hep Stars* / Elbow baby: *Habits* / Bow Street runner: *Bow Street Runners* / St. James infirmary: *Cops* & Robbers (bk) / You're on my mind: *Byrds* / Lonely weekends: *Beard, Dean* / Kansas City: *Jay, Peter &* The Jaywalkers / Long legged baby: *Bond, Graham Organisation* / Third time lucky: *Beat Boys* / My baby's crazy about Elvis: *Boyle, Billy* / Shang a doo lang: *Posta, Adrienne* / Yes I do: *McClain, Pete & The Clan*/ Caroline: *Fortunes* / Something better: *Faithfull, Marianne* / I've got you out of my mind: *Cristo, Bobby* & The Rebels / Country boy: *Heinz* / Really gonna shake: *Barry, Sandra & The Boys* / There you go: *Ryan, Paul & Barry*.
LP: . . . . **CM 126**

SIXTIES LOST AND FOUND VOLUME 4 (Various artists).
Tracks: / She's my girl: *Shafto, Bobby* / Look at me: *Whirlwinds* / Marlena: *Federals* / Little people: *Three Quarters* / Hard times for young lovers: *Arlon, Deke* / Hold tight: *'N' Betweens* / Gotta get a good thing going: *Original Dyaks* / Ugly girl: *'N' Betweens With Kim Fowley* / I don't want to love you: *Barry* Lee Show / Mr. Rainbow: *Flynn, Steve* / Teenage love: *Five Chestnuts* / Pretty thing: *King, Danny*/ I'd rather be with the boys: *Toggery Five* / He's a good face but he's down and out: *Ford, Dean* / Congratulations: *West Five* / Go home baby: *Bunch Of 5's* / Don't mind: *Fairies* / Angel face: *Andrews, Tim And Paul Korda* / Never my love: *Christian, Hans* / William Chaulker's time machine: *Lemon Tree*.
LP: . . . . **SEE 215**

SIXTIES MANIA (Various artists).
LP: . . . . **STAR 2287**
MC: . . . . **STAC 2287**

SIXTIES MIX 1 (Various artists).
Tracks: / Do wah diddy diddy: *Manfred Mann* / Hold tight: *Dave Dee, Dozy, Beaky, Mick & Tich* / Sugar sugar: *Archies*/ Shakin' all over: *Kidd, Johnny/ Pirates* / Loco-motion, The: *Little Eva* / 1-2-3: *Barry, Len* / Bend me, shape me: *Amen Corner* / It's my party: *Gore, Lesley* / You really got me: *Kinks* / Hippy hippy shake: *Swinging Blue Jeans* / Shout: *Lulu and the Luvvers* / Bobby's girl: *Maughan, Susan* / I get around: *Beach* Boys / Let's dance: *Montez, Chris* / Judy in disguise: *Fred, John & The Playboys* / It's not unusual: *Jones, Tom* / You were made for me: *Freddie & The Dreamers* / Working in a coalmine: *Dorsey, Lee* / Barefootin': *Parker, Robert* / It might as well rain until September: *King, Carole* / Good timin': *Jones, Jimmy (Handyman)* / Little loving, A: *Fourmost* / Do you love me: *Poole, Brian & the Tremeloes* / Do you wanna dance / Foot tapper: *Shadows, The* / Yeh yeh: *Fame, Georgie* / She's about a mover: *Sir Douglas Quintet* / For your love: *Yardbirds*/ Walkin' back to happiness: *Shapiro, Helen* / Let there be drums: *Nelson, Sandy* / Yesterday man: *Andrews*, Chris / Gimme little sign: *Wood, Brenton* / Baby, now that I've found you: *Foundations* / It's in his kiss: *Everett, Betty* / Rescue me: *Fontella Bass* / Sweets for my sweet: *Searchers* / I only want to be with you: *Springfield, Dusty* / Tobacco Road: *Nashville Teens* / You've got your troubles: *Fortunes* / F.B.I.: *Shadows* / Wooly Bully: *Sam The Sham & The Pharaohs* / Sha-la-la-la-lee: *Small Faces* / How do you do it: *Gerry & the Pacemakers* / Rubber Ball: *Vee, Bobby* / Barbara Ann: *Beach Boys* / Leader of the Pack: *Shangri-Las* / Sorrow: *Merseys* / On the road again: *Canned Heat* / She's not there: *Zombies*/ I'm alive: *Hollies* / Hi ho silver lining: *Beck, Jeff* / Don't ever change: *Crickets* / I'm into something good: *Herman's Hermits* / Sunshine superman: *Donovan* / You got what it takes: *Johnson, Mary* / Got to get you into my life: *Bennett, Cliff & The Rebel Rousers* / He's so fine: *Chiffons* / Sweet talking guy / Clapping song, The: *Ellis, Shirley* / High heel sneakers: *Tucker, Tommy*.
2LP: . . . . **SMR 733**
MCSET: . . . . **SMC 733**

SIXTIES MIX 2 (Various artists).
Tracks: / Flowers in the rain: *Move* / It's now or never: *Presley, Elvis* / World without love: *Peter & Gordon*/ Three steps to heaven: *Cochran, Eddie* / Poetry in motion: *Tillotson, Johnny* / Simon says: *1910 Fruitgum* Company / Please don't tease: *Richard, Cliff* / Dreamin': *Burnette, Johnny* / High time: *Jones, Paul*/ Good vibrations: *Beach Boys* / Happy birthday sweet sixteen: *Sedaka, Neil* / Tell me when: *Applejacks*/ Twistin' the night away: *Cooke, Sam* / Tell him: *Davis, Billie* / Night has a thousand eyes, The: *Vee, Bobby*/ Wild thing: *Troggs* / Green tambourine: *Lemon Pipers* / Game of love: *Fontana, Wayne & the Mindbenders*/ If paradise is half as nice: *Amen Corner* / Pretty flamingo: *Manfred Mann* / Wanderer: *Dion* / With a girl like you: *Troggs* / Harlem shuffle: *Bob & Earl* / All or nothing: *Small Faces* / Go now: *Moody* Blues / Carrie Anne: *Hollies* / When will I be loved: *Everly Brothers* / We gotta get out of this place: *Animals*/ Time is tight: *Booker T & The MGs* / Apache: *Shadows* / Return to sender: *Presley, Elvis* / One way love: *Bennett, Cliff & The Rebel Rousers* / High in the sky: *Amen Corner* / Matthew & Son: *Stevens, Cat*/ I'm gonna get me a gun: *Stevens, Cat* / On the rebound: *Cramer, Floyd* / Poor me: *Faith, Adam* / Everything's alright: *Mojos* / Boat that I row, The: *Lulu* / Bend it: *Dave Dee, Dozy, Beaky, Mick & Tich* / Diamonds: *Harris, Jet & Tony Meehan* / With a little help from my friends: *Cocker, Joe* / Delilah: *Jones, Tom* / Bang bang (my baby shot me down): *Cher* / I just don't know what to do with myself: *Springfield, Dusty* / Groovy kind of love: *Mindbenders* / Here comes the night: *Them* / Private number: *Clay, Judy & William Bell*/ Swinging on a star: *Irwin, Big Dee* / Light my fire: *Feliciano, Jose* / Daydream: *Lovin' Spoonful* / You're no good: *Swinging Blue Jeans* / Something's happening: *Herman's Hermits* / Natural born boogie: *Humble* Pie / Calendar girl: *Sedaka, Neil* / In the year 2525: *Zager/Evans* / Out of time: *Farlowe, Chris*/ Bad to me: *Kramer, Billy J. & The Dakotas* / I remember you: *Ifield, Frank* / Step inside love: *Black, Cilla*.
2LP: . . . . **SMR 855**
MCSET: . . . . **SMC 855**

SIXTIES MIX 3 (Various artists).
LP: . . . . **SMR 021**
MC: . . . . **SMC 021**

SIXTIES NO. 1'S VOL 4 (OLD GOLD) (Various artists).
Tracks: / Only the lonely: *Orbison, Roy* / Tower of strength: *Vaughan, Frankie* / Do you mind: *Newley, Anthony*/ Diamonds: *Harris, Jet & Tony Meehan* / Go now: *Moody Blues* / Have I the right?: *Honeycombs* / You don't have to say you love me: *Springfield, Dusty* / Do you love me?: *Poole, Brian & the Tremeloes* / Don't throw your love away: *Searchers* / Long live love: *Shaw, Sandie* / Oh pretty woman: *Orbison, Roy* / Concrete and clay: *Unit 4+2* / Ballad of Bonnie and Clyde: *Fame, Georgie* / Sugar sugar: *Archies*.
LP: . . . . **OG 1517**
MC: . . . . **OG 2517**

SIXTIES PARTY MEGAMIX ALBUM (Various artists).
Tracks: / Judy in disguise: *Fred, John & His Playboy Band* / Simon says: *1910 Fruitgum Company* / Lily the pink: *Scaffold, The* / Yummy yummy yummy: *Ohio Express* / Sugar sugar: *Archies* / Tracy: *Cuff Links*/ Sheila: *Roe, Tommy* / Brown eyed handsome man: *Holly, Buddy* / Iko iko: *Dixie Cups* / Speedy Gonzales: *Boone, Pat* / Dance on: *Shadows* / Shindig: *Shadows* / On the beach: *Richard, Cliff* / Sweets for my sweet: *Searchers* / When you walk in the room: *Searchers* / Baby now that I've found you: *Foundations*/ You really got me: *Kinks* / All day and all of the night: *Kinks* / Down the dustpipe: *Status Quo* / Ice in the sun: *Status Quo* / Have I the right: *Honeycombs* / Hello Susie: *Amen Corner* / To whom it may concern: *Andrews, Chris* / Hi lili hi lo: *Price, Alan* / Getaway: *Fame, George* / Candy man: *Poole*, Brian & the Tremeloes / I like it: *Gerry & the Pacemakers* / I'm the one: *Gerry & the Pacemakers* / Just one look: *Hollies* / Good golly Miss Molly: *Swinging Blue Jeans* / No particular place to go: *Berry, Chuck*/ I'll never: *Kidd, Johnny & The Pirates* / I'm telling...: *Freddie & The Dreamers* / Tell me what he said: *Shapiro*, Helen / Then I kissed her: *Beach Boys* / I can hear music: *Beach Boys* / Melting pot: *Blue Mink*/ Lazy Sunday: *Small Faces* / Running bear: *Preston, Johnny* / Xanadu: *Dave Dee, Dozy, Beaky, Mick & Tich*/ Zabadak: *Dave Dee, Dozy, Beaky, Mick & Tich* / Diamonds: *Harris, Jet & Tony Meehan* / Applejack: *Harris*, Jet & Tony Meehan / In the middle of nowhere: *Springfield, Dusty* / What's new pussycat: *Jones, Tom* / Puppet on a string: *Shaw, Sandie* / Long live love: *Shaw, Sandie* / Israelites: *Dekker, Desmond & The Aces* / That's nice: *Christian, Neil* / Return of Django: *Upsetters* / Working in a coalmine: *Dorsey, Lee* / Holy cow: *Dorsey, Lee* / Barefootin': *Parker, Robert*.
LP: . . . . **STAR 2307**
MC: . . . . **STAC 2307**

SIXTIES REVISITED (Various artists).
MC: . . . . **KMC 25005**

SIXTIES SMASHES (Various artists).
Tracks: / Heartaches by the number: *Mitchell, Guy* / Big bad John: *Dean, Jimmy* / All I really want to do: *Byrds*/ If I were a rich man: *Topol* / Day without love, A: *Love Affair* / Move over darling: *Day, Doris* / Can't take my eyes off you: *Williams, Andy* / Summer place, A (theme from): *Faith, Percy* / North to Alaska: *Horton*, Johnny / Dance to the music: *Sly & the Family Stone* / Rawhide: *Laine, Frankie* / Devil woman: *Robbins, Marty* / Just loving you: *Harris, Anita* / Rainbow valley: *Love Affair* / Boy named Sue, A: *Cash, Johnny*/ Can't get used to losing you: *Williams, Andy* / Son of Hickory Holler's...: *Smith, O.C* / Lady Willpower: *Puckett, Gary* / Like I do: *Evans, Maureen* / Race with the devil: *Gun*.
MCSET: . . . . **DTO 10292**
MCSET: . . . . **DTOL 10292**

SIXTIES SOUL STARS (See under Soul) (Various artists).

SIXTIES, THE (See under Motown ...) (Various artists).

SIXTIES VOLUME 1, THE (Various artists).
Tracks: / Wanderer: *Dion* / Run to him: *Vee, Bobby* / Will you love me tomorrow: *Shirelles* / Runaway: *Shannon, Del* / He's so fine: *Chiffons* / Sealed with a kiss: *Hyland, Bryan* / Island of dreams: *Springfields*/ Telstar: *Tornados* / Hey baby: *Channel, Bruce* / Three steps to Heaven: *Cochran, Eddie* / Poetry in motion: *Tillotson, Johnny* / Johnny

remember me: *Leyton, John* / Running bear: *Preston, Johnny* / Tell Laura I love her: *Valence, Ricky.*
LP: . . . . **OG 1002**
MC: . . . . **OG 2002**

SIXTIES VOLUME 2, THE (Various artists).
Tracks: / Young girl: *Puckett, Gary & The Union Gap* / San Francisco (be sure to wear flowers in your hair): *McKenzie, Scott* / Let's go to San Francisco: *Flowerpot Men* / Everlasting love: *Love Affair* / California Dreamin': *Mamas & Papas* / Pretty flamingo: *Manfred Mann* / Massachusetts: *Bee Gees* / Good vibrations: *Beach Boys* / Kites: *Dupree, Simon & The Big Sound* / Excerpt from a teenage opera: *West, Keith* / Mr. Tambourine man: *Byrds* / Something in the air: *Thunderclap Newman* / Waterloo sunset: *Kinks* / From the underworld: *Herd.*
LP: . . . . **OG 1003**
MC: . . . . **OG 2003**

SIXTIES VOLUME 3, THE (Various artists).
Tracks: / Walk right back: *Everly Brothers* / Save the last dance for me: *Drifters* / Handy man: *Jones, Jimmy* (singer) / Locomotion, The: *Little Eva* / Swiss maid: *Shannon, Del* / More than I can say: *Vee, Bobby* / It might as well rain until September: *King, Carole* / Halfway to Paradise: *Fury, Billy* / Sheila: *Roe, Tommy* / Rhythms of the rain: *Cascades* / Let's dance: *Montez, Chris* / Don't ever change: *Crickets* / Runaround Sue: *Dion.*
LP: . . . . **OG 1006**
MC: . . . . **OG 2006**

SIXTIES VOLUME 4, THE (Various artists).
Tracks: / Sun ain't gonna shine any more, The: *Walker Brothers* / Itchycoo Park: *Small Faces* / Whiter shade of pale, A: *Procul Harum* / Monday Monday: *Mamas & Papas* / Mighty Quinn, (The): *Manfred Mann* / Albatross: *Fleetwood Mac* / You've lost that lovin' feeling: *Righteous Brothers* / Sloop John B: *Beach Boys* / Sunny afternoon: *Kinks* / For your love: *Yardbirds* / With a girl like you: *Troggs* / Hang on Sloopy: *McCoys* / We've gotta get out of this place: *Animals* / Friday on my mind: *Easybeats.*
LP: . . . . **OG 1007**
MC: . . . . **OG 2007**

SIXTIES VOLUME 5, THE (Various artists).
Tracks: / Wedding, The: *Rogers, Julie* / Just loving you: *Harris, Anita* / This is my song: *Clark, Petula* / Last waltz, The: *Humperdinck, Engelbert* / Carnival is over, (The): *Seekers* / What a wonderful world: *Armstrong, Louis* / Edelweiss: *Hill, Vince* / Green green grass of home: *Jones, Tom* / Careless hands: *O'Connor, Des* / There must be a way: *Vaughan, Frankie* / It must be him: *Various artists* / Almost there: *Williams, Andy* / If only I had time: *Rowles, John* / She wears my ring: *King, Solomon.*
LP: . . . . **OG 1008**
MC: . . . . **OG 2008**

SLOW - ORIGINAL POP HITS (Various artists).
Tracks: / Great pretender, The: *Platters* / Only one woman: *Marbles* / My girl: *Fame, Georgie* / It's a man's man's man's world: *Brown, James* / I started a joke: *Bee Gees* / Rain and tears: *Aphrodite's Child* / Only you: *Platters* / Hey Paula: *Paul & Paula* / Unchained melody: *Righteous Brothers* / Massachusetts: *Bee Gees* / It's five o'clock: *Aphrodite's Child* / Hey Joe: *Hendrix, Jimi.*
LP: **819 309-1**
MC: **819 309-4**

SOME OTHER GUYS (32 Merseybeat Nuggets 1963-1966) (Various artists).
Tracks: / Farmer John: *Searchers* / Yes: *Sandon, Johnny* / Do the mashed potato: *Undertakers* / Come go with me: *Chants* / Boys: *Jeannie & The Big Guys* / Girl who wanted fame, The: *Wackers* / Some other guy: *Searchers* / You're a wonderful one: *Trends* / Needles and pins: *Searchers* / Just a little bit: *Undertakers* / I wanna know: *Klaus, Paddy & Gibson* / I pretend I'm with you: *Searchers* / Way you do the things you do, The: *Trends* / Stage door: *Jackson, Tony* / I know a girl: *Remo Four* / I could write a book: *Chants* / Stupidity: *Undertakers* / Wildside of life: *Quickly, Tommy* / Love or money: *Wackers* / Stand by me: *Searchers* / Lies: *Sandon, Johnny* / Peter Gunn: *Remo Four* / I'll go crazy: *Quickly, Tommy* / Everybody loves a lover: *Undertakers* / If you don't come back: *Takers* / She's mine: *Chants* / Hey Teresa: *Klaus, Paddy & Gibson* / Sticks and stones: *Jeannie & The Big Guys* / All my loving: *Trends* / I don't want to go on without you: *Searchers* / Aggravation: *Curtis, Chris* / Bye bye baby: *Jackson, Tony.*
2LP: . . . . **NEDLP 102**
MCSET: . . . . **NEDMC 102**

SOMETHING IN THE AIR (Rediscover the 60's) (Various artists).
Tracks: / Oh pretty woman: *Orbison, Roy* / Juliet: *Four Pennies* / When you walk in the room: *Searchers* / Memphis Tennessee: *Berry, Chuck* / She's not there: *Zombies* / Gloria: *Them* / Whatcha gonna do about it: *Small Faces* / That's what I want: *Marauders* / Matthew and son: *Stevens, Cat* / Heart full of soul: *Yardbirds* / Wrapping paper: *Cream* / Dead end street: *Kinks* / I'd rather go blind: *Chicken Shack* / Need your love so bad: *Fleetwood Mac* / My ship is coming in: *Walker Brothers* / Bringing on back the good times: *Love Affair* / San Fransiscan nights: *Burdon, Eric* / This wheels on fire: *Driscoll, Julie & Brian Auger* / Hey Joe: *Hendrix, Jimi* / Race with the devil: *Gun* / All I really want to do: *Byrds* / Morning dew: *Rose, Tim* / Born to be wild: *Steppenwolf* / Something in the air: *Thunderclap Newman.*
MCSET: . . . . **OG 2204**

SONGS LENNON AND MCCARTNEY GAVE AWAY (Various artists).
LP: . . . . **NUT 18**

SOUL OF BRITISH R'N'B 1962-1968 (Various artists).
Tracks: / Stop stop stop (or honey I'll be gone): *Gouldman, Graham* / Time it takes, The: *Dean, Alan & His Problems* / Midnight confession: *Kelly, Pete Solution* / Mary open the door: *Duffy's Nucleus* / Get on the right track baby: *Money, Zoot Big Roll Band* / Little girl: *Bond, Graham Organisation* / My love: *Jones, Ronnie* / Precious words: *Cocker, Joe* / Strut around: *Bond, Graham Organisation* / Sugar baby (part 1): *Powell, Jimmy* / Cross my heart: *Exotics* / If your love don't swing: *Kelly, Pete Solution* / I need your lovin': *Jones, Ronnie* & The Nightimers / Night time is the right time: *Korner, Alexis & Blues Inc* / Walking the dog: *Money, Zoot Big Roll Band* / Can you hear me: *Powerhouse* / Love is a beautiful thing: *Quick* / Ooh-la-la: *Exotics* / Sugar baby (part 2): *Powell, Jimmy* / Chain gang: *Powerhouse.*
LP: . . . . **SEE 67**

SOUL SOURCE (The soul era vol.1) (Various artists).
Tracks: / Emergency (dial 999): *Bown, Alan* / (Accept my) invitation: *Band Of Angels* / Hallelujah: *Revolution* / Questions: *Barry, Sandra* / Hey diddley dee dum dum: *James, Jimmy* / Neighbour, neighbour: *Spectres* / Down home girl: *Felders Orioles* / When you move you lose: *Keith & Billie* / Soul sauce: *Timebox* / Nevertheless: *Riot Squad* / You beat me to the punch: *Jackson, Tony* / Parchment farm: *Jay, Peter* / Every little bit hurts: *Clark, Petula* / Ain't no soul: *Bernard, Kenny* / I can't believe what you say: *McKenna, Val* / Michael: *Washington, Geno* / Ain't love good: *Cotton, Mike* (CD bonus track.) / It was easier to hurt her: *Powell, Keith* & The Valets (CD bonus track.) / Stay with me baby: *Baldry, Long John* (CD bonus track.) / Build me up buttercup: *Foundations* (CD bonus track.) / Agent double o soul: *Schroeder, John Orchestra* (CD bonus track.) / Ain't that peculiar: *Sounds Orchestral* (CD bonus track.).
LP: . . . . **NEXLP 109**

SOUND OF SUMMER, THE (Various artists).
Tracks: / Surf city: *Jan & Dean* / Surfin' safari: *Beach Boys* / Hey little cobra: *Regents* / Little Honda: *Hondells* / Tequila: *Cannon, Ace* / Indian lake: *Cowsills* / Ride the wild surf: *Jan & Dean* / Wipe out: *Surfaris* / Surfer girl: *Beach Boys* / Baby talk: *Jan & Dean* / GTO: *Regents* / Remember (walking in the sand): *Shangri-Las* / Summer song, A: *Chad & Jeremy* / Beach baby: *Regents* / Surfin: *Beach Boys* / Pipeline: *Chantays.*
LP: . . . . **ONE 1365**
MC: . . . . **OCE 1365**

SOUNDS OF THE 60'S (Various artists).
Tracks: / I'm a believer: *Monkees* / Sealed with a kiss: *Hyland, Bryan* / When you walk in the room: *Searchers* / Make me an island: *Dolan, Joe* / Waterloo sunset: *Kinks* / You don't have to say you love me: *Springfield, Dusty* / I'm sorry: *Lee, Brenda* / Runaway: *Shannon, Del* / Telstar: *Tornados* / Joanna: *Walker, Scott* / Flowers in the rain: *Move* / You really got me: *Kinks* / Save the last dance for me: *Drifters* / Monday, Monday: *Mamas & Papas* / Whiter shade of pale, A: *Procul Harum* / Let the heartaches begin: *Baldry, Long John* / Remember (walking in the sand): *Shangri-Las* / Itsy bitsy teeny weeny yellow polka dot bikini: *Hyland, Bryan* / Needles and pins: *Searchers* / One two three: *Barry, Len* / Running bear: *Preston, Johnny* / Soldier boy: *Shirelles* / Monkees theme: *Monkees* / With a girl like you: *Troggs* / California dreamin': *Various artists* / Under the boardwalk: *Drifters* / Poetry in motion: *Tillotson, Johnny* / Will you love me tomorrow: *Shirelles* / Blue moon: *Marcels* / With a little help from my friends: *Cocker, Joe.*
MCSET: . . . . **CRT 007**

SPOTLIGHT ON HITS OF THE SIXTIES Various artists (Various artists).
Tracks: / You really got me: *Kinks* / Mony mony: *James, Tommy & The Shondells* / Have I the right?: *Honeycombs* / No particular place to go: *Berry, Chuck* / Death of a clown: *Davis, Dave* / Pictures of matchstick men: *Status Quo* / I hear you knocking: *Edmunds, Dave* / Needles and pins: *Searchers* / In the Summertime: *Mungo Jerry* / Baby, now that I've found you: *Foundations* / Green tambourine: *Lemon Pipers* / Long live love: *Shaw, Sandie* / Get it on: *T. Rex* / Simon says: *1910 Fruitgum Company* / Take a heart: *Sorrows* / Tossin' and turning: *Ivy League* / I'm gonna make you mine: *Christie, Lou* / He's in town: *Rockin' Berries* / With a little help from my friends: *Cocker, Joe* / Blackberry way: *Move* / Daydream: *Lovin' Spoonful* / Catch the wind: *Donovan* / Michelle: *Overlanders* / Whiter shade of pale, A: *Procul Harum.*
2LP: . . . . **SPOT 1015**
MCSET: . . . . **ZCSPT 1015**

SPOTLIGHT ON THE SWINGIN' 60'S (Various artists).
LP: . . . . **SPOT 1034**
MC: . . . . **ZCSPT 1034**

STARS SING LENNON & MCCARTNEY (Various artists).
Tracks: / Do you want to know a secret: *Kramer, Billy J. & The Dakotas* / Hello little girl: *Fourmost* / Yesterday: *Monro, Matt* / World without love: *Peter & Gordon* / It's for you: *Black, Cilla* / Long and winding road, The: *Newton-John, Olivia* / With a little help from my friends: *Young, J* / Come together: *Turner, Ike & Tina* / Ob la di ob la da: *Marmalade* / Eight days a week: *Cogan, Alma* / I saw her standing there: *Richard, Cliff* / Day tripper: *Lulu* / Hard day's night, A: *Sellers, Peter* / Here, there and everywhere: *Hill, Vince* / Misery: *Lynch, Kenny* / She's leaving home: *David & Jonathan* / When I'm sixty four: *Cribbins, Bernard (nar)* / Back in the USSR: *Bennett, Cliff & His Band* / Help: *Deep Purple* / Hey bulldog: *God's Feat & Ken Hensley.*
LP: . . . . **MFP 5755**
MC: . . . . **TCMFP 5755**

SUMMER OF LOVE (DINO LABEL) (Various artists).
Tracks: / California dreamin': *Mamas & Papas* / Happy together: *Turtles* / Albatross: *Fleetwood Mac* / Let's go to San Francisco: *Flowerpot Men* / Eve of destruction: *McGuire, Barry* / Summer in the city: *Lovin' Spoonful* / She'd rather be with me: *Turtles* / Oh happy day: *Hawkins, Edwin Singers* / Sunshine of your love: *Cream* / Delta lady: *Cocker, Joe* / Mr Tambourine man: *Byrds* / Daydream: *Lovin' Spoonful* / San Franciso (be sure to wear some flowers): *McKenzie, Scott* / Green tambourine: *Lemon Pipers* / Ruby Tuesday: *Melanie* / Monday Monday: *Mamas & Papas* / Venus: *Shocking Blue* / Eight miles high: *Byrds* / Something in the air: *Thunderclap Newman* / Woodstock: *Matthews Southern Comfort.*
LP: . . . . **DINTV 10**
MC: . . . . **DINMC 10**

SUNNY AFTERNOON (Various artists).
LP: . . . . **IMP 2**
MC: . . . . **TCIMP 2**

SUNNY AFTERNOON, VOL 2 (Various artists).
Tracks: / I'm into something good: *Herman's Hermits* / Silhouettes: *Herman's Hermits* / Needles and pins: *Searchers* / Sweets for my sweet: *Searchers* / Do wah diddy diddy: *Manfred Mann* / Pretty flamingo: *Manfred Mann* / House of the Rising Sun: *Animals* / We've gotta get out of this place: *Animals* / Keep on running: *Davis, Spencer Group* / Somebody help me: *Davis, Spencer Group* / God only knows: *Beach Boys* / Good vibrations: *Beach Boys* / With a girl like you: *Troggs* / Love is all around: *Troggs* / I'm a believer: *Monkees* / Daydream believer: *Monkees* / Bend me, shape me: *Amen Corner* / If paradise is half as nice: *Amen Corner* / Go now: *Moody Blues* / Kites: *Dupree, Simon & The Big Sound.*
LP: . . . . **LPIMP 7**
MC: . . . . **TCIMP 7**

SUPER HITS: 1960 (Various artists).
LP: . . . . **GT 0028**

SUPER HITS: 1961 (Various artists).
LP: . . . . **GT 0029**

SUPER HITS: 1965 (Various artists).
LP: . . . . **GT 0033**

SWEET TALKING OLDIES (Oldies But Goodies) (Various artists).
Tracks: / Speedy Gonzales: *Boone, Pat* / Are you sure: *Allisons* / Up on the roof: *Drifters* / Picture of you: *Brown, Joe* / Crying game, The: *Berry, Dave* / Judy in disguise: *Fred, John & The Playboys* / Night has a thousand eyes, The: *Vee, Bobby* / Runaway: *Shannon, Del* / Twist, The: *Checker, Chubby* / What in the world: *Scott, Jack* / Do you wanna dance: *Freeman, Bobby* / He's a rebel: *Crystals* / Sweet talking guy: *Chiffons* / Indian reservation: *Fardon, Don* / You were on my mind: *St. Peters, Crispian.*
LP: . . . . **OCN 2009WL**
MC: . . . . **OCN 2009WK**

SWINGING SIXTIES (Various artists).
Tracks: / Telstar: *Tornados* / Sweets for my sweet: *Searchers* / You really got me: *Kinks* / Foot tapper: *Shadows* / House of the rising sun: *Animals* / How do you do it: *Gerry & the Pacemakers* / Do wah diddy diddy: *Manfred Mann* / Good vibrations: *Beach Boys* / Mr. Tambourine man: *Byrds, The* / I'm alive: *Hollies* / Albatross: *Fleetwood Mac* / I'm into something good: *Herman's Hermits* / All or nothing: *Small Faces* / Everlasting love: *Love Affair.*
LP: . . . . **HMA 264**
LP: . . . . **SMR 726**
MC: . . . . **SMC 726**
MC: . . . . **HSCM 264**

TEEN DREAMS (Various artists).
LP: . . . . **LRSLP 1003**
MC: . . . . **LRSK 1003**

TEENAGE LOVE (Various artists).
Tracks: / One fine day: *Chiffons* / He's so fine: *Chiffons* / I have a boyfriend: *Chiffons* / Out of this world: *Chiffons* / Love so fine: *Chiffons* / Sweet-talking guy: *Chiffons* / Nobody knows what's going on: *Chiffons* / Stop, look and listen: *Chiffons* / Oh my lover: *Chiffons* / Teenager in love: *Dion* & The Belmonts / No one knows: *Dion & The Belmonts* / I wonder why: *Dion & The Belmonts* / In the still of the night: *Dion & The Belmonts* / Don't pity me: *Dion & The Belmonts* / When you wish upon a star: *Dion* & The Belmonts / Where or when: *Dion & The Belmonts* / Runaround Sue: *Dion* / Lonely teenager: *Dion* / Little Diane: *Dion* / Love came to me: *Dion* / Wanderer: *Dion* / Sandy: *Dion* / Lovers who wander: *Dion* / Runaway girl: *Dion* / Denise: *Randy & The Rainbows* / Snoopy v the Red Baron: *Royal Guardsmen* / Little bit of soap, A: *Jarmels* / Hey Dean, hey Jean: *Dean & Jean* / Party girl: *Carol, Bernadette* / Little bit of soul: *Music Explosion* / I'm on my way: *Parrish, Dean* / Hush-a-bye: *Mystics.*
2LP: . . . . **CR 051**
MCSET: . . . . **CRT 051**

THAT WAS THE SWINGING 60'S VOL.1 (Various artists).
Tracks: / What do you want to make those eyes...: *Ford, Emile & The Checkmates* / Be mine: *Fortune, Lance* / Michael, row the boat ashore: *Donegan, Lonnie* / War paint: *Brook Brothers* / Venus in blue jeans: *Wynter, Mark* / Little bitty tear, A: *Miki & Griff* / Sugar and spice: *Searchers* / Sukiyaki: *Ball, Kenny & His Jazzmen* / Mocking Bird Hill: *Migil 5* / Downtown: *Clark, Petula* / Poor man's son: *Rockin' Berries* / Funny how love can be: *Ivy League* / Daydream: *Lovin' Spoonful* / Dedicated follower of fashion: *Kinks* / Flowers in the rain: *Move* / Puppet on a string: *Shaw, Sandie* / Build me up buttercup: *Foundations* / Mexico: *Baldry, Long John* / Oh happy day: *Hawkins, Edwin Singers* / Make me an island: *Dolan, Joe.*
MC: . . . . **TCMFP 5897**

THOSE WERE THE 60'S (Various artists).
LP: . . . . **BRLP 26**
MC: . . . . **BRMC 26**

THOSE WERE THE HITS OF 1960 (Various artists).
LP: **1A 022 1582831**
MC: **1A 222 1582834**

THOSE WERE THE HITS OF 1961 (Various artists).
LP: **1A 022 1582841**
MC: **1A 222 1582844**

THOSE WERE THE HITS OF 1962 (Various artists).
LP: **1A 022 1582851**
MC: **1A 222 1582854**

THOSE WERE THE HITS OF 1963 (Various artists).
LP: **1A 022 1582861**
MC: **1A 222 1582864**

THOSE WERE THE HITS OF 1964 (Various artists).
LP: **1A 022 1582871**
MC: **1A 222 1582874**

TOBACCO ROAD - THE SIXTIES EXPLOSION (Various artists).
Tracks: / How do you do it: *Gerry & the Pacemakers* / You were made for me: *Freddie & The Dreamers* / Hippy hippy shake: *Swinging Blue Jeans* / Little loving, A: *Fourmost* / Tobacco Road: *Nashville Teens* / Sorrow: *Merseys/* Game of love: *Fontana, Wayne* / Do you want to know a secret: *Kramer, Billy J. & The Dakotas* / Bad to me: *Kramer, Billy J. & The Dakotas* / Ferry 'cross the Mersey: *Gerry & the Pacemakers* / You're no good: *Swinging Blue Jeans.*
LP: . . . . **OCN 2007WL**
MC: . . . . **OCN 2007WK**

TOP TEN HITS OF THE 60'S (Various artists).
Tracks: / House of the rising sun: *Animals* / Do it again: *Beach Boys* / Got to get you into my life: *Bennett, Cliff &* The Rebel Rousers / Someone else's baby: *Faith, Adam* / Little loving, A: *Fourmost* / Ferry cross the Mersey: *Gerry & the Pacemakers* / Something is happening: *Herman's Hermits* / In the country: *Richard, Cliff* / Look through any window: *Hollies* / High time: *Jones, Paul* / I'm a tiger: *Lulu* / F.B.I.: *Shadows* / Hippy hippy shake: *Swinging Blue Jeans* / Pasadena: *Temperance Seven* / Twelfth of never: *Richard, Cliff* / Let's go to San Francisco: *Flowerpot Men* / Seven little girls sitting in the back seat: *Avons* / You were made for me: *Freddie & The Dreamers.*
LP: . . . . **MFP 5822**
MC: . . . . **TCMFP 5822**

TOP TEN HITS OF THE 60'S, 70'S, 80'S (Various artists).
MCSET: . . . . **TCMFPBOX 1**

TRANSFUSION - ANTHOLOGY (Various artists).
Tracks: / Keep a lovin' me: *Everly Brothers* / Sun keeps shining, The: *Everly Brothers* / Buddy Holly interview: *Various artists* / Down on the farm: *Downing, Big Al & The Poe Kats* / Oh babe: *Downing, Big Al & The Poe* Kats / Transfusion: *Nervous Norvous* / Dig: *Nervous Norvcus* / Come back Maybeline: *Greer, John/* Brand new Cadillac: *Taylor, Vince & Playboys* / Flat tyre: *Del-Vikings* / Rocky road blues: *Self, Ronnie/* Ain't I'm a dog: *Self, Ronnie* / Little red rooster: *Hawkins, Ronnie* / Going to the river: *Hawks (film)/* I need your lovin: *Twitty, Conway* / Born to sing the blues: *Twitty, Conway.*
LP: . . . . **UP 004**

TWENTY ONE HIT WONDERS (Various artists).
Tracks: / Softly whispering I love you: *Congregation, The* / Super girl: *Bonney, Graham* / With a little help from my friends: *Young Idea* / Baby sittin: *Angelo, Bobby & The Tuxedos* / Saturday night at the duckpond: *Cougars/* Poison ivy: *Paramounts* / Blue girl: *Bruisers* / I should have known better: *Naturals* / I'm the urban spaceman: *Bonzo Dog Band* / Sabre dance: *Love Sculpture* / Games people play: *South, Joe* / Tell Laura I love her: *Valence, Ricky* / Doctor Kildare theme: *Spence, Johnny & His Orchestra* / Love at first sight: *Sounds* Nice / Sweet dreams: *Sampson, Dave & The Hunter* / Lady Jane: *Merrick, Tony* / Rudi's in love: *Locomotive/* Shame and scandal in the family: *Percival, Lance (nar)* / Ob la di ob la da: *Bedrocks* / Nut rocker: *Bumble, B & The Stingers.*
LP: **C5-525**

ULTIMATE 60'S COLLECTION (Various artists).
2LP: . . . . **CTVLP 305**
MC: . . . . **CTVMC 305**

UNFORGETTABLE (Various artists).
Tracks: / Unforgettable: *Morton Music Machine* / Crazy music: *Morton Music Machine* / Uptight: *Morton Music* Machine / Get ready: *Morton Music Machine* / Jimmy Mack: *Morton Music Machine* / My guy: *Morton Music* Machine / I can't help myself: *Morton Music Machine* / Tears of a clown: *Morton Music Machine* / Reach out I'll be there: *Morton Music Machine* / Stop in the name of love: *Morton Music Machine* / Yellow River: *Christie/* How do you do it?: *Gerry/Pacemakers* / Here it comes again: *Fortunes* / You are everything: *Morton Music* Machine / Tobacco Road: *Nashville Teens* / In the Summertime: *Mungo Jerry* / Black is black: *Morton Music* Machine / I can't give you anything but love: *Morton Music Machine* / Singing in the rain: *Morton Music Machine/* Love grows where my Rosemary goes: *Edison Lighthouse* / If you gotta make a fool of somebody: *Freddie & The Dreamers/* Somewhere: *Proby, P.J.* / Tender trap, The: *Morton Music Machine* / Love and marriage: *Morton Music Machine/* Bobby's girl: *Maughan, Susan* / Hello, little girl: *Fourmost* / Hitchin' a ride: *Vanity Fair* / Goody goody: *Morton Music Machine* / Ain't she sweet?: *Morton Music Machine* / Great balls of fire: *Morton Music* Machine / Good golly Miss Molly: *Morton Music Machine* / Rock around the clock: *Morton Music Machine* / Baby, now that I've found you: *Foundations* / Wishin' and hopin': *Merseybeats* / Wild thing: *Troggs* / Witch Queen of New Orleans: *Morton Music Machine* / I'm telling you now: *Freddie & The Dreamers* / You don't have to be a baby to cry: *Caravelles* / Deep in the heart of Texas: *Morton Music Machine* / Manana: *Morton Music Machine/* Sugarbush: *Morton Music Machine* / Summertime blues: *Morton Music Machine* / You've got your troubles: *Fortunes/* With a girl like you: *Troggs* / Hold me: *Proby, P.J.* / Nice 'n' easy: *Morton Music Machine* / Witchcraft: *Morton Music Machine* / Peter Gunn: *Morton Music Machine* / Crying game, The: *Berry, Dave* / You'll never walk alone: *Gerry/Pacemakers.*
2LP: . . . . **STD 1**
MCSET: . . . . **STDK 1**

UNFORGETTABLE SOUND OF THE 60S, THE (Various artists).
LP: . . . . **NE 1213**
MC: . . . . **CE 2213**

WHAT'S SHAKIN' (Various artists).
Tracks: / Good time music: *Lovin' Spoonful* / Almost grown: *Lovin' Spoonful* / Spoon...: *Paul Butterfield* Blues Band, The / Off...: *Paul Butterfield Blues Band, The* / Can't keep from cryin': *Kooper, Al* / I want...: *Clapton, Eric & The Powerhouse* / Crossroads: *Clapton, Eric & The Powerhouse* / Lovin': *Paul Butterfield Blues* Band, The / Good: *Butterfield, Paul* / Steppin': *Clapton, Eric & The Powerhouse* / I'm in love again: *Rush, Tom* / Don't bank on it / Searchin': *Various artists* / One more...: *Paul Butterfield Blues Band, The.*
LP: . . . . **ED 249**

WILD WEEKEND 60's U.S.pop Vol.2 (Various artists).
Tracks: / Everyday I have to cry: *Alaimo, Steve* / Palisades Park: *Various artists* / Wild weekend: *Rockin'* Rebels / Surfin' bird: *Trashmen* / You baby: *Turtles* / Land of a thousand dances: *Cannibal & The Head* Hunters / Eleanore: *Turtles* / Judy in disguise: *Fred, John & His Playboy Band* / Last kiss, The: *Wilson,J.Frank & The Cavaliers* / Hey baby: *Channel, Bruce* / Hey Paula: *Paul & Paula* / Cry like a baby: *Box Tops.*
LP: . . . . **TOP 150**
MC: . . . . **KTOP 150**

YESTERDAY - THOSE ROMANTIC 60'S (Various artists).
Tracks: / Yesterday: *Mantovani & His Orchestra* / Sunny: *Aldrich, Ronnie, His Piano & The Festival Orchestra/* Almost there: *Mantovani & His Orchestra* / Somethin' stupid: *Aldrich, Ronnie & His Orchestra* / Love is blue: *Howard, Johnny Orchestra & Singers* / Softly as I leave you: *Aldrich, Ronnie & His Orchestra* / Leaving on a jet plane: *Mantovani & His Orchestra* / Moon river: *Chacksfield, Frank & His Orchestra* / Release me: *Aldrich,* Ronnie, His Piano & The Festival Orchestra / Strangers in the night: *Mantovani & His Orchestra* / I can't stop loving you: *Stapleton, Cyril & His Show Band* / Didn't we: *Aldrich, Ronnie, His Piano & The Festival Orchestra* / (I left my heart) in San Francisco: *Howard, Johnny Orchestra & Singers* / My cherie amour: *Aldrich, Ronnie, His Piano & The* Festival Orchestra / What now my love?: *Mantovani & His Orchestra* / Goin' out of my head: *Aldrich, Ronnie,* His Piano & The Festival Orchestra / What kind of fool am I?: *Mantovani & His Orchestra* / I'll never fall in love again: *Chacksfield, Frank & His Orchestra* / Joanna: *Howard, Johnny Orchestra & Singers* / Cherish: *Aldrich, Ronnie, His Piano & The Festival Orchestra.*
MC: **8440654**

60's Soul

6T'S SOUL EXPLOSION (Various artists).
Tracks: / Keep her guessing: *Alexander, Arthur* / Nobody knows what's goin' on in my mind but me: *Chiffons* / See you at the gogo: *Gray, Dobie* / Lover: *Hunt, Tommy* / Walkin' up a one way street: *Tee, Willie* / Haunted house: *Wilson, Jackie* / One more chance: *Joseph, Margie* / Drifter, The: *Pollard, Ray* / Just say goodbye: *Phillips, Esther* / If I had known: *Houston, Freddie* / Record, The: *Barnum, H.B.* / It's a sad thing: *Pollard, Ray* / Guess who loves you: *Daye, Eddie & Four Bars* / I'll pay the price: *Dillard, Moses.*
LP: . . . . **COD 22**

70's

15 MONSTER HITS (VOL 1) (Various artists).
LP: . . . . **SHM 984**
MC: . . . . **HSC 364**

15 MONSTER HITS (VOL 2) (Various artists).
LP: . . . . **SHM 986**
MC: . . . . **HSC 365**

16 NO.1'S OF THE 70'S (Various artists).
Tracks: / Heart of glass: *Blondie* / January: *Pilot* / Hey girl, don't bother me: *Tams* / When I need you: *Sayer, Leo* / Devil gate drive: *Quatro, Suzi* / Everything I own: *Boothe, Ken* / When you're in love with a beautiful woman: *Dr. Hook* / Angel fingers: *Wizzard* / Make me smile (come up and see me): *Harley,* Steve & Cockney Rebel / Oh boy: *Mud* / Woodstock: *Matthews Southern Comfort* / See my baby jive: *Wizzard/* Double barrel: *Collins, Dave & Ansel* / If: *Savalas, Telly* / Sunday girl: *Blondie* / Float on: *Floaters.*
LP: . . . . **MFP 41 5694 1**
MC: . . . . **MFP 41 5694 4**

18 SMASH HITS (Various artists).
LP: . . . . **NSPL 28227**

20 MORE ORIGINAL HITS OF THE 70'S (Various artists).
LP: . . . . **MFP 41 5698 1**
MC: . . . . **MFP 41 5698 4**

20 ORIGINAL HITS OF THE 70'S (1970-1974) (Various artists).
LP: . . . . **MFP 41 5695 1**
MC: . . . . **MFP 41 5695 4**

20 SUPER HITS OF THE 70'S (Various artists).
LP: **2636547**

30 YEARS OF NUMBER 1'S VOL 6 (1969-72) (Various artists).
Tracks: / Blackberry way: *Move* / If paradise is half as nice: *Corner, Amen* / Where do you go to my love: *Sarstedt, Peter* / Israelites: *Dekker, Desmond & The Aces* / Dizzy: *Roe, Tommy* / In the year 2525: *Zager/Evans/* I'll never fall in love again: *Gentry, Bobbie* / Sugar sugar: *Archies* / Love grows: *Edison Lighthouse/* Wand'rin' star: *Marvin, Lee* / In the Summertime: *Jerry, Mungo* / Woodstock: *Matthews Southern Comfort/* I hear you knocking: *Edmunds, Dave/* Baby jump: *Jerry, Mungo* / Hot love: *T. Rex* / Double barrel: *Collins, Dave & Ansel* / Knock three times: *Dawn* / Chirpy chirpy cheep cheep: *Middle Of The Road* / Get it on: *T. Rex* / Hey girl don't bother me: *Tams* / Coz I luv you: *Slade* / Without you: *Nilsson/* Metal guru: *T. Rex* / Vincent: *McLean, Don.*
2LP: . . . . **TYNOLP 105**
MC: . . . . **TYNOMC 105**

30 YEARS OF NUMBER 1'S VOL 9 (1977-80) (Various artists).
Tracks: / Name of the game: *Abba* / Up town top ranking: *Althia & Donna* (Not on CD) / Figaro: *Brotherhood* Of Man (Not on CD) / Take a chance on me: *Abba* / Wuthering heights: *Bush, Kate* / Dreadlock holiday / Rat trap: *Boomtown Rats* / Hit me with your rhythm stick: *Dury, Ian* / I will survive: *Gaynor, Gloria* / Ring my bell: *Ward, Anita* (Not on CD) / Are 'friends' electric: *Tubeway Army* / I don't like Mondays: *Boomtown* Rats / Cars: *Numan, Gary* / Video killed the radio star: *Buggles* / When you're in love with a beautiful woman: *Dr. Hook* / Too much too young: *Specials* / Coward of the country: *Rogers, Kenny* / Together we are beautiful: *Kinney, Fern* (Not on CD) / Going underground: *Jam* / Dreams of children: *Jam* / Call me: *Blondie/* Geno: *Dexy's Midnight Runners* / Crying: *McLean, Don* / Sunday girl: *Blondie.*
2LP: . . . . **TYNOLP 108**
MC: . . . . **TYNOMC 108**

30 YEARS OF NUMBER 1'S VOL 8 (1975-1977) (Various artists).
Tracks: / January: *Pilot* / Make me smile (come up and see me): *Harley, Steve & Cockney Rebel* / Bye bye baby: *Bay City Rollers* / Oh boy: *Mud* / Stand by your man: *Wynette, Tammy* / I'm not in love: *10 CC/* Tears on my pillow: *Nash, Johnny* / Give a little love: *Bay City Rollers* / Barbados: *Typically Tropical/* I can't give you anything but my love: *Stylistics* / Hold me close: *Essex, David* / Mama mia: *Abba/* December '63: *Four Seasons* / I love to love (but my baby loves to dance): *Charles, Tina* / Forever and ever: *Roussos, Demis* (The Roussos Phenomenon EP) / Dancing queen: *Abba* / Mississippi: *Pussycat* / Don't give up on us: *Soul, David* / Free: *Williams, Deniece* / Lucille: *Rogers, Kenny* / Show you the way to go: *Jacksons* / So you win again: *Hot Chocolate* / Silver lady: *Soul, David* / Yes sir, I can boogie: *Baccara.*
2LP: . . . . **TYNOLP 107**
MC: . . . . **TYNOMC 107**

30 YEARS OF NUMBER 1'S VOL 7 (1972 - 75) (Various artists).
Tracks: / You wear it well: *Stewart, Rod* / Mouldy old dough: *Lieutenant Pigeon* / Clair: *O'Sullivan, Gilbert/* Blockbuster: *Sweet* / See my baby jive: *Wizzard* / Can the can: *Quatro, Suzi* / Rubber bullets: *10 CC* / Welcome home: *Peters & Lee* / I'm the leader of the gang: *Glitter, Gary* / Angel fingers: *Wizzard/* Daydreamer: *Cassidy, David* / You won't find another fool like me: *New Seekers* / Tiger feet: *Mud* / Devil gate drive: *Quatro, Suzi* / Seasons in the sun: *Jacks, Terry* / Sugar baby love: *Rubettes* / Streak, The: *Stevens, Ray* / Always yours: *Glitter, Gary* / Kung fu fighting: *Douglas, Carl* / Sad sweet dreamer: *Sweet Sensation* / Everything I own: *Boothe, Ken* / You're the first, the last, my everything: *White, Barry/* Down down: *Status Quo* / Ms. Grace: *Tymes.*
2LP: . . . . **TYNOLP 106**
MC: . . . . **TYNOMC 106**

50 FAVOURITES OF THE 70'S (Various artists).
MCSET: . . . . **TR 1557**

60 MORE CLASSIC DANCE HITS OF THE 70'S (Various artists).
MC: . . . . **TMC 70**

'79 CHARTBUSTERS (Various artists).
MC: . . . . **AM 22**

AND THE BEAT GOES ON (34 Dance hits of the 70's) (Various artists).
Tracks: / Boogie wonderland: *Earth, Wind & Fire* / I will survive: *Gaynor, Gloria* / Young hearts run free: *Staton,* Candi / Lady marmalade: *Labelle* / Nutbush city limits: *Turner, Ike & Tina* / Car wash: *Rose Royce/* Love train: *O'Jays* / You're the first, the last, my everything: *White, Barry* / Ain't no stoppin' us now: *McFadden & Whitehead* / Show you the way to go: *Jacksons, The* / Don't take away the music: *Tavares* / Get down: *Chandler,* Gene / Baby don't change your mind: *Knight, Gladys & The Pips* / If I can't have you: *Elliman, Yvonne* / Streetlife: *Crusaders* / Ring my bell: *Ward, Anita* / Play that funky music: *Wild Cherry* / Best of my love: *Emotions* (group) / Dance, dance, dance: *Chic* / He's the greatest dancer: *Sister Sledge* / Contact: *Starr, Edwin/* I'm on fire: *5000 Volts* / Y.M.C.A.: *Village People* / Rock your baby: *McGrae, George* / Le freak: *Chic/* Disco stomp: *Bohannon (Hamilton)* / Hold back the night: *Trammps* / Everyone's a winner: *Hot Chocolate/* You bet your love: *Hancock, Herbie* / And the beat goes on: *Whispers.*
2LP: . . . . **STAR 2338**
MC: . . . . **STAC 2338**

BALLAD NO.1'S OF THE 70'S (Volume 2) (Various artists).
LP: . . . . **OG 1514**
MC: . . . . **OG 2514**

BALLAD NUMBER ONES OF THE 70'S VOL.1 (Various artists).
Tracks: / Wand'rin' star: *Marvin, Lee* / Daydreamer: *Cassidy, David* / Eye level: *Park, Simon Orchestra/* If: *Savalas, Telly* / Clair: *O'Sullivan, Gilbert* / Welcome home: *Peters and Lee* / Stand by me: *Wynette,* Tammy / I'd like to teach the world to sing: *New Seekers* / Wonder of you, The: *Presley, Elvis* / Without you: *Nilsson (Harry)* / Mississippi: *Pussycat* / Lucille: *Rogers, Kenny* / Fernando: *Abba* / Don't cry for me Argentina: *Covington, Julie.*
LP: . . . . **OG 1507**
MC: . . . . **OG 2507**

CONCERT FOR BANGLADESH, THE (Various artists).
Tracks: / Introduction: *Various artists* / Bangla dhun: *Various artists* / Wah-wah: *Various artists/* My sweet Lord: *Various artists* / Awaiting on you all: *Various artists* / That's the way God planned it: *Various* artists / It don't come easy: *Various artists* / Beware of darkness: *Various artists* / Introduction of the band: *Various artists* / While my guitar gently weeps: *Various artists* / Jumpin' Jack Flash/Youngblood: *Various* artists / Here comes the sun: *Various artists* / Hard rain's gonna fall, A: *Various artists* / It takes a lot to laugh, It takes a train to cry: *Various artists* / Blowin' in the wind: *Various artists* / Mr Tambourine man: *Various artists* / Just like a woman: *Various artists* / Something: *Various artists* / Bangladesh: *Various artists.*
MCSET: **4688354**

GOLDEN HITS OF THE 70'S (Various artists).
2LP: . . . . **BRLP 69/70**
MCSET: . . . . **BRMC 69/70**

GOLDEN HITS OF THE 70'S (Various artists).
Tracks: / Wand'rin' star: *Marvin, Lee* / When Julie comes around: *Cuff Links* / Hey girl don't bother me: *Tams*/ Mama told me: *Three Dog Night* / Woodstock: *Matthews Southern Comfort* / Gypsy woman: *Hyland, Brian*/ Walking in the rain with the one I love: *Love Unlimited* / Entertainer (The): *Hamlisch, Marvin* / If: *Savalas, Telly* / Don't cry for me Argentina: *Covington, Julie* / Float on: *Floaters* / Lonely girl: *Holman, Eddie*/ Morning dance: *Spyra Gyra* / I did what I did for Maria: *Christie, Tony* / Parisienne walkways: *Moore, Gary*/ You can do it: *Hudson, Al & The Partners*.
LP: . . . . **MCM 5035**
MC: . . . . **MCMC 5035**

GOLDEN SUPERSTARS (Various artists).
Tracks: / China grove: *Doobie Brothers* / Say you love me: *Fleetwood Mac* / Love is alive: *Wright, Gary*/ How sweet it is: *Taylor, James* / Wreck of Edmund Fitzgerald: *Lightfoot, Gordon* / Young hearts run free: *Staton, Candi* / December '63 (oh what a night): *Four Seasons* / I never cry: *Cooper, Alice* / This masquerade: *Benson, George* / Disco boy: *Zappa, Frank* / One of these nights: *Eagles* / Still the one: *Orleans* / Lonely boy: *Gold, Andrew* / That'll be the day: *Rondstadt, Linda* / Take it easy: *Browne, Jackson* / Attitude dancing: *Simon, Carly* / Cupid: *Orlando, Tony* / Cats in the cradle: *Chapin, Harry* / Send in the clowns: *Collins, Judy* / Riders on the storm: *Doors* / Rubberband man, The: *Spinners* / Pick up the pieces: *Average White Band* / I'd really love to see you tonight: *England Dan/John Ford Coley* / You are the woman: *Firefall*/ Hi jack: *Mann, Herbie* / Chanson d'amour: *Manhattan Transfer* / That's where the happy people go: *Trammps*/ I say a little prayer: *Franklin, Aretha* / There he still goes: *Akkerman, Jan* / Killing me softly with his song: *Flack, Roberta*.
LP: . . . . **K 68019**

GOLDEN YEARS OF THE 70'S, VOL. 3, THE (Various artists).
Tracks: / You're the first, the last, my everything: *White, Barry* / Don't let the sun go down on me: *John, Elton*/ Oh what a circus: *Essex, David* / Ladies night: *Kool & The Gang* / Get up offa that thing: *Brown, James*/ Oh no not my baby: *Stewart, Rod* / Lookin' after no. 1: *Boomtown Rats* / Hustle, The: *McCoy, Van & Soul City Symphony* / Let the music play: *White, Barry* / Hang on in there baby: *Bristol, Johnny* / Rocket man: *John, Elton* / You ain't see nothing yet: *Bachman-Turner Overdrive* / Maggie May: *Stewart, Rod* / I just wanna be your everything: *Gibb, Andy* / I don't like Mondays: *Boomtown Rats*.
MC: . . . . **PWKMC 4058P**

GREATEST HITS OF 1970, THE (Various artists).
Tracks: / In the summertime: *Mungo Jerry* / Rag mama rag: *Band* / Lola: *Kinks* / Down the dustpipe: *Status Quo* / Brontasaurus: *Move* / Whole lotta love: *CCS* / Black night: *Deep Purple* / Let's work together: *Canned Heat* / Voodoo chile: *Hendrix, Jimi* / Question: *Moody Blues* / Ride a white swan: *T. Rex*/ I hear you knocking: *Edmunds, Dave* / When I'm dead and gone: *McGuinness Flint* / Neanderthal man: *Hotlegs*/ I can't tell the bottom from the top: *Hollies* / Blame it on the Pony Express: *Johnson, Johnny & Bandwagon* / Love grows (where my Rosemary goes): *Edison Lighthouse* / Ruby Tuesday: *Melanie*.
MC: . . . . **TCGH 1970**

GREATEST HITS OF 1971, THE (Various artists).
Tracks: / Maggie May: *Stewart, Rod* / Get it on: *T. Rex* / Malt and barley blues: *McGuinness Flint* / Strange kind of woman: *Deep Purple* / Tonight: *Move* / Tap turns on the water: *CCS* / Coz I luv you: *Slade*/ Witch Queen of New Orleans: *Redbone* / Your song: *John, Elton* / Hot love: *T. Rex* / Double barrel: *Collins, Dave & Ansel* / Banner man: *Blue Mink* / Pushbike song: *Mixtures* / Something old, something new: *Fantastics* / I believe (in love): *Hot Chocolate* / If not for you: *Newton-John, Olivia* / Rose garden: *Anderson, Lynn* / Chestnut mare: *Byrds*.
MC: . . . . **TCGH 1971**

GREATEST HITS OF 1972, THE (Various artists).
Tracks: / Rocket man: *John, Elton* / You wear it well: *Stewart, Rod* / Rock 'n' roll (part 2): *Glitter, Gary*/ Metal guru: *T. Rex* / Ball pard incident: *Wizzard* / Gudby T'Jane: *Slade* / Hold your head up: *Argent*/ Family affair: *Sly & the Family Stone* / All the young dudes: *Mott The Hoople* / American pie: *McLean, Don*/ 10538 overture: *E.L.O.* / Telegram Sam: *T. Rex* / Mama were all crazee now: *Slade* / California man: *Move* / I didn't know I loved you (till I say you rock 'n' roll): *Glitter, Gary* / Brand new key: *Melanie*/ Say you don't mind: *Blunstone, Colin* / Sylvia's mother: *Dr. Hook*.
MC: . . . . **TCGH 1972**

GREATEST HITS OF 1973, THE (Various artists).
Tracks: / Caroline: *Status Quo* / Roll over Beethoven: *E.L.O.* / Whisky in the jar: *Thin Lizzy* / Do you wanna touch me (oh yeah): *Glitter, Gary* / Dance with the devil: *Powell, Cozy* / Can the can: *Quatro, Suzi* / Cum on feel the noize: *Slade* / All the way from Memphis: *Mott The Hoople* / 20th Century boy: *T. Rex* / I'm the leader of the gang (I'm am): *Glitter, Gary* / Nutbush city limits: *Turner, Ike & Tina* / See my baby jive: *Wizzard* / Rubber bullets: *10 CC* / One and one is one: *Medicine Head* / Rock on: *Essex, David* / If you don't know me by now: *Melvin, Harold & The Bluenotes* / Me and Mrs Jones: *Paul, Billy* / Daniel: *John, Elton*.
MC: . . . . **TCGH 1973**

GREATEST HITS OF 1974, THE (Various artists).
Tracks: / You ain't seen nothing yet: *Turner-Overdrive, Bachman* / Down down: *Status Quo* / Always yours: *Glitter, Gary* / Tiger feet: *Mud* / Sugar baby love: *Rubettes* / Wall Street shuffle: *10 CC* / Waterloo: *Abba*/ Far far away: *Saleh, Kumbi* / Gonna make you a star: *Essex, David* / You're the first, the last, my everything: *White, Barry* / Never can say goodbye: *Gaynor, Gloria* / Summer breeze: *Isley Brothers* / Most beautiful girl, The: *Rich, Charlie* / Candle in the wind: *John, Elton* / You make me feel brand new: *Stylistics*/ Rock your baby: *McCrae, George* / Judy Teen: *Harley, Steve & Cockney Rebel* / I can help: *Swann, Billy*.
MC: . . . . **TCGH 1974**

GREATEST LOVE OF ALL (Rediscover the 70's) (Various artists).
Tracks: / Daniel: *John, Elton* / Arms of Mary: *Sutherland Brothers & Quiver* / Forever autumn: *Hayward, Justin*/ All by myself: *Carmen, Eric* / Amoureuse: *Dee, Kiki* / Stay with me til dawn: *Tzuke, Judie* / Uptown, uptempo woman: *Edelman, Randy* / Africa: *Toto* / Free: *Williams, Deniece* / Like sister and brother: *Drifters*/ Too much, too little, too late: *Mathis, Johnny & Deniece Williams* / Greatest love of all, The: *Benson, George*/ Laughter in the rain: *Sedaka, Neil* / Woman in love: *3 Degrees* / Feelings: *Albert, Morris* / You're a lady: *Skellern, Peter* / Last farewell, The: *Whittaker, Roger* / Always on my mind: *Nelson, Willie*/ For the good times: *Como, Perry* / I have a dream: *Abba* / I recall a gypsy woman: *Williams, Don* / If you go away: *Jacks, Terry* / I'm not in love / Without you: *Nilsson (Harry)*.
MCSET: . . . . **OG 2205**

GUINNESS ALBUM OF HITS OF THE 70'S (Various artists).
Tracks: / Maggie May: *Stewart, Rod* / All right now: *Free* / Get it on: *T. Rex* / Gonna make you a star: *Essex, David* / In the Summertime: *Mungo Jerry* / I hear you knocking: *Edmunds, Dave* / Cum on feel the noize: *Slade* / Bye bye baby: *Bay City Rollers* / My sweet Lord: *Harrison, George* / I'm not in love / When I need you: *Sayer, Leo* / Air that I breathe, The: *Hollies* / Sylvia's mother: *Dr. Hook* / Vincent: *McLean, Don* / Clair: *O'Sullivan, Gilbert* / I'd like to teach the world to sing: *New Seekers* / Without you: *Nilsson (Harry)* / Love me for a reason: *Osmonds* / Night fever: *Bee Gees* / You're the one that I want: *Travolta, John & Olivia Newton John* / Hit me with your rhythm stick: *Dury, Ian & The Blockheads* / Dance away: *Roxy Music* / Don't give up on us: *Soul, David* / We don't talk anymore: *Richard, Cliff* / Don't go breaking my heart: *John, Elton & Kiki Dee* / Wuthering Heights: *Bush, Kate* / I don't like Mondays: *Boomtown Rats* / Dancing queen: *Abba* / Show you the way to go: *Jacksons* / Rock your baby: *McCrae, George*/ Band of gold: *Payne, Freda* / Tears on my pillow / When will I see you again?: *3 Degrees* / Free: *Williams, Deniece* / You make me feel brand new: *Stylistics*.
2LP: . . . . **CBS 10020**
MC: **40 10020**

HITS OF THE 70'S (Various artists).
LP: . . . . **OCN 2011WL**
MC: . . . . **OCN 2011WK**

HITS OF THE 70'S (Golden hour of) (Various artists).
MC: . . . . **KGHMC 152**

HITS OF THE 70'S (Various artists).
MC: . . . . **ARLC 1019**

JUKE BOX COLLECTION - HOT LOVE (Sound of the Seventies part 1) (Various artists).
Tracks: / Spirit in the sky: *Greenbaum, Norman* / Hot love: *T. Rex* / Devil's answer: *Atomic Rooster*/ Lola: *Kinks* / In a broken dream: *Jackson, Python Lee* / How long?: *Ace* / Baby jump: *Mungo Jerry*/ Paranoid: *Black Sabbath* / Radar love: *Golden Earring* / Conquistador: *Procul Harum* / Darlin': *Miller, Frankie* / I hear you knocking: *Edmunds, Dave*.
MC: . . . . **OG 2707**
LP: . . . . **OG 1707**

JUKE BOX COLLECTION - IN THE SUMMER TIME (Sound of the 70's part 2) (Various artists).
Tracks: / In the Summertime: *Mungo Jerry* / Jarrow song: *Price, Alan* / Crying, laughing, loving, lying: *Siffre, Labi* / Egyptian reggae: *Richman, Jonathan* / Everything I own: *Boothe, Ken* / Barbados: *Typically Tropical*/ Misty: *Stevens, Ray* / Something here in my heart: *Paper Dolls* / Popcorn: *Hot Butter* / It's a heartache: *Tyler, Bonnie* / I'll go where your music takes me: *James, Jimmy & The Vagabonds* / You to me are everything: *Real Thing* / Pepper box: *Peppers* / That same old feeling: *Pickettywitch*.
LP: . . . . **OG 1714**
MC: . . . . **OG 2714**

JUKE BOX COLLECTION - MUSIC (Sound of the 70's part 3) (Various artists).
Tracks: / Stuck in the middle with you: *Stealers Wheel* / Mama told me not to come: *Three Dog Night* / Standing in the road: *Blackfoot Sue* / Paper plane: *Status Quo* / Whisky in the jar: *Thin Lizzy* / Rubber bullets: *10 CC* / Music: *Miles, John* / Telegram Sam: *T. Rex* / Tomorrow night: *Atomic Rooster* / Who do you love: *Juicy Lucy* / Broken down angel: *Nazareth* / One and one is one: *Medicine Head* / Show me the way: *Frampton, Peter* / Rock mountain way: *Walsh, Joe*.
LP: . . . . **OG 1717**
MC: . . . . **OG 2717**

KNUCKLE SANDWICH (Various artists).
LP: . . . . **EMTV 18**

LOVE SONGS OF THE 70'S (Always & Forever) (Various artists).
Tracks: / Always and forever: *Heatwave* / Every night: *Snow, Phoebe* / Free: *Williams, Deniece* / Summer breeze: *Isley Brothers* / I don't believe in miracles: *Blunstone, Colin* / When will I see you again: *3 Degrees*/ I can see clearly now: *Nash, Johnny* / Most beautiful girl, The: *Rich, Charlie* / Me & Mrs Jones: *Paul, Billy* / Lovely day: *Withers, Bill* / Hurt: *Manhattans* / Highway of my life, The: *Isley Brothers*/ More than a feeling: *Boston* / That's what friends are for: *Williams, Deniece* / Love train: *O'Jays*/ Say you don't mind: *Blunstone, Colin* / Arms of Mary: *Sutherland Brothers* / Sylvia's mother: *Dr. Hook*.
MC: . . . . **PWKMC 4064**

OLD GOLD DECADES (8) (Various artists).
Tracks: / Whisky in the jar: *Thin Lizzy* / Layla: *Derek & The Dominoes* / Smoke on the water: *Deep Purple*/ Paranoid: *Black Sabbath* / Silver machine: *Hawkwind*.
MC: . . . . **OG 5008**

OLD GOLD DECADES (9) (Various artists).
Tracks: / I will survive: *Gaynor, Gloria* / I love the nightlife: *Bridges, Alicia* / I feel love: *Summer, Donna* / Contact: *Starr, Edwin* / Get down: *Chandler, Gene*.
MC: . . . . **OG 5009**

OLD GOLD DECADES (10) (Various artists).
Tracks: / Music: *Miles, John* / Make me smile (come up and see me): *Harley, Steve & Cockney Rebel* / 2 4 6 8 motorway: *Robinson, Tom* / Boys are back in town: *Thin Lizzy* / You ain't seen nothing yet: *Bachman-Turner Overdrive*.
MC: . . . . **OG 5010**

OLD GOLD DECADES (23) (Various artists).
Tracks: / You're my best friend: *Williams, Don* / Don't it make my brown eyes blue: *Gayle, Crystal* / Blanket on the ground: *Spears, Billie Jo* / I recall a gypsy woman: *Williams, Don* / Lucille: *Rogers, Kenny*.
MC: . . . . **OG 5023**

OLD GOLD DECADES (24) (Various artists).
Tracks: / Mississippi: *Pussycat* / Love is in the air: *Young, John Paul* / Seasons in the sun: *Jacks, Terry*/ All by myself: *Carmen, Eric* / Billy don't be a hero: *Paper Lace*.
MC: . . . . **OG 5024**

OLD GOLD DECADES (25) (Various artists).
Tracks: / When I'm dead and gone: *McGuinness Flint* / I hear you knocking: *Edmunds, Dave* / Spirit in the sky: *Greenbaum, Norman* / Lady Eleanor: *Lindisfarne* / Ride a white swan: *T. Rex*.
MC: . . . . **OG 5025**

ONE HIT WONDERS OF THE 70'S (Various artists).
Tracks: / Rock me gently: *Kim, Andy* / Float on: *Floaters* / Spanish archer: *Mink Deville* / Journey: *Browne, Duncan* / Rich kids: *Rich Kids* / Tired of toein' the line: *Burnette, Rocky* / Calendar song, The: *Trinidad Oil Company* / El bimbo: *Bimbo Jet* / Woodstock: *Matthews Southern Comfort* / Softy whispering I love you: *Congregation* / Boogie oogie oogie: *Taste Of Honey* / This will be: *Cole, Natalie* / What in the worlds come over you: *White, Tam* / My hearts symphony: *Lewis, Gary & The Playboys*.
LP: . . . . **MFP 5812**
MC: . . . . **TCMFP 5812**

PHIL SPECTOR 1974/1979 (Various artists).
LP: **2307 015**

PINK GREASE (Various artists).
LP: . . . . **ENGY 5**

RAISED ON ROCK - 70'S ROCK UK (Various artists).
Tracks: / I don't like Mondays: *Boomtown Rats* / Lola: *Kinks* / Rubber bullets / Hold your head up: *Argent*/ Paranoid: *Black Sabbath* / Take on the world: *Judas Priest* / Show me the way: *Frampton, Peter* / You wear it well: *Stewart, Rod* / Layla: *Derek & The Dominoes* / Question: *Moody Blues* / Roll away the stone: *Mott The Hoople* / Who do you love: *Juicy Lucy* / Bad bad boy: *Nazareth* / Part of the union: *Strawbs*.
LP: . . . . **RORLP 17003**
MC: . . . . **RORMC 17003**

RAISED ON ROCK - 70'S ROCK US (Various artists).
Tracks: / Voodoo Chile: *Hendrix, Jimi Experience* / Witch queen of New Orleans: *Redbone* / American: *Guess Who* / Rich girl: *Hall & Oates* / Baby come back: *Player* / Ramblin' man: *Allman Brothers* / Hold the line: *Toto* / You took the words right out of my mouth: *Meatloaf* / Let's work together: *Canned Heat*/ Miracles: *Jefferson Starship* / She's not there: *Santana* / Spooky: *Atlanta Rhythm Section* / Fooled around and fell in love: *Bishop, Elvin* / Devil Gate Drive: *Quatro, Suzi* / You ain't seen nothin' yet: *Bachman-Turner Overdrive*.
LP: . . . . **RORLP 17004**
MC: . . . . **RORMC 17004**

RARE GROOVE MIX (Various artists).
2LP: . . . . **SMR 863**
MCSET: . . . . **SMC 863**

REVIVAL 70'S, VOL 3 (Pop ballads of the early 70's) (Various artists).
Tracks: / Without you: *Various artists* / Summer (the first time): *Goldsboro, Bobby* / Seasons in the sun: *Jacks, Terry* / Vincent: *McLean, Don* / Rainbow: *Marmalade* / Blue guitar: *Hayward, Justin & John Lodge*/ All by myself: *Carmen, Eric* / Mandy: *Various artists* / Amoureuse: *Dee, Kiki* / Stay with me: *Blue Mink* / Laughter in the rain: *Sedaka, Neil* / Air that I breathe, The: *Hollies* / Candle in the wind: *John, Elton* / I'm not in love.
LP: . . . . **OG 1015**
MC: . . . . **OG 2015**

REVIVAL 70'S, VOL 4 (Great rock hits of the early 70's) (Various artists).
Tracks: / Ride a white swan: *T. Rex* / Lola: *Kinks* / You wear it well: *Stewart, Rod* / Let's work together: *Canned Heat* / Paper plane: *Status Quo* / Walk on the wild side: *Reed, Lou* / Sylvia: *Focus*/ Layla: *Derek & The Dominoes* / Smoke on the water: *Deep Purple* / American woman: *Guess Who* / You ain't seen nothing yet: *Bachman-Turner Overdrive* / Boys are back in town: *Thin Lizzy* / Radar love: *Golden Earring*/ Voodoo chile: *Hendrix, Jimi*.
LP: . . . . **OG 1017**
MC: . . . . **OG 2017**

REVIVAL 70'S, VOL 5 (Soft soul ballad hits of the 70's) (Various artists).
Tracks: / Hustle, The: *McCoy, Van* / Betcha by golly wow: *Stylistics* / Float on: *Floaters* / Drift away: *Gray, Dobie* / La la means I love you: *Delfonics* / Jack and Jill: *Raydio* / Loving you: *Riperton, Minnie* / Love's theme: *Love Unlimited Orchestra* / Just the way you are: *White, Barry* / Native New Yorker: *Odyssey* / Summer breeze: *Isley Brothers* / Wake

up everybody: *Melvin, Harold & The Bluenotes* / Whole town's laughing at me, The: *Pendergrass, Teddy* / Greatest love of all, The: *Benson, George.*
LP: . . . . **OG 1019**
MC: . . . . **OG 2019**

REVIVAL 70'S, VOL 6 (Late 70's dance greats) (Various artists).
Tracks: / Don't leave me this way: *Various artists* / Ain't no stoppin' us now: *McFadden & Whitehead* / September: *Earth, Wind & Fire* / Boogie nights: *Heatwave* / Boogie oogie oogie: *Taste Of Honey* / Ain't gonna bump no more: *Tex, Joe* / I will survive: *Gaynor, Gloria* / Best of my love: *Emotions (group)* / Heaven must be missing an angel: *Tavares* / Love really hurts without you: *Ocean, Billy* / Contact: *Starr, Edwin* / Get down: *Chandler, Gene* / Que sera mi vida: *Gibson Brothers* / I feel love: *Summer, Donna.*
LP: . . . . **OG 1020**
MC: . . . . **OG 2020**

ROCK 'N' ROLL YEARS 1970 (Various artists).
Tracks: / I hear you knocking: *Edmunds, Dave* / Young gifted and black: *Bob and Marcia* / Na na hey hey (kiss him goodbye): *Steam...* / Get up, I feel like a sex machine: *Brown, James* / Groovin' with Mr Bloe: *Mr. Bloe* / Let's work together: *Canned Heat* / Lola: *Kinks* / Woodstock: *Matthews Southern Comfort* / Mama told me not to come: *Three Dog Night* / I can't tell the bottom from the top: *Hollies* / Love of the common people: *Thomas, Nicky* / Rainbow: *Marmalade* / Black night: *Deep Purple* / American woman: *Guess Who* / Down the dustpipe: *Status Quo* / Whole lotta love: *CCS* / Question / You can get it if you really want: *Dekker, Desmond & The Aces* / In the Summertime: *Mungo Jerry* / Montego Bay: *Bloom, Bobby* / Love grows: *Edison Lighthouse* / Black pearl: *Faith, Horace* / Neanderthal man: *Hotlegs* / Julie do ya love me: *White Plains.*
LP: . . . . **YRNRLP 70**
MC: . . . . **YRNRMC 70**

ROCK 'N' ROLL YEARS 1971 (Various artists).
Tracks: / Maggie May: *Stewart, Rod* / Hot love: *T. Rex* / Hey girl don't bother me: *Tams* / I just can't help believing: *Presley, Elvis* / Didn't I (blow your mind this time): *Delfonics* / Co-co: *Sweet* / I'd like to teach the world to sing: *New Seekers* / Knock three times: *Dawn* / Chirpy chirpy cheep cheep: *Middle Of The Road* / Your song: *John, Elton* / I believe (in love): *Hot Chocolate* / Jig a jig: *East Of Eden* / Resurection shuffle: *Ashton Gardener & Dyke* / Tap turns on the water: *CCS* / When I'm dead and gone: *McGuinness* Flint / Burundi black: *Black, Burundi Stephenson* / He's gonna step on you again: *Kongos, John* / Joy to the world: *Three Dog Night* / Coz I luv you: *Slade* / Oh you pretty thing: *Noone, Peter* / Let your yeah be yeah: *Pioneers* / Freedom come freedom go: *Fortunes* / Black and white: *Greyhound* / Double barrel: *Collins, Dave & Ansel.*
LP: . . . . **YRNRLP 71**
MC: . . . . **YRNRMC 71**

ROCK 'N' ROLL YEARS 1972 (Various artists).
Tracks: / All the young dudes: *Mott The Hoople* / Layla: *Derek & The Dominoes* / Family affair: *Sly & the* Family Stone / Rocket man: *John, Elton* / Backstabbers: *O'Jays* / Say you don't mind: *Blunstone, Colin* / Rock'n'roll: *Glitter, Gary* / Little willy: *Sweet* / Mama weer all crazee now: *Slade* / Oh babe what would you say: *Smith, Hurricane* / Silver machine: *Hawkwind* / 10538 overture: *E.L.O.* / You wear it well: *Stewart, Rod* / Suzanne beware of the devil: *Livingstone, Dandy* / In a broken dream: *Jackson, Python Lee* / Hold your head up: *Argent* / Hallelujah freedom: *Campbell, Junior* / Without you: *Nilsson* / Sylvia's mother said: *Dr. Hook* / You're a lady: *Skellern, Peter* / Son of my father: *Chicory Tip* / Oh Carol: *Sedaka, Neil* / Storm in a teacup: *Fortunes* / It's four in the morning: *Young, Faron.*
LP: . . . . **YRNRLP 72**
MC: . . . . **YRNRMC 72**

ROCK 'N' ROLL YEARS 1973 (Various artists).
Tracks: / Nutbush city limits: *Turner, Ike & Tina* / Walk on the wild side: *Reed, Lou* / All the way from Memphis: *Mott The Hoople* / Rock on: *Essex, David* / Love train: *O'Jays* / Oh no, not my baby: *Stewart, Rod* / Rubber bullets / Blockbuster: *Sweet* / See my baby jive: *Wizzard* / Leader of the gang: *Glitter, Gary* / Can the can: *Quatro, Suzi* / Gudbuy t'Jane: *Slade* / Goodbye yellow brick road: *John, Elton* / Born to be with you: *Edmunds, Dave* / Roll over Beethoven / Caroline: *Status Quo* / Always on my mind: *Presley,* Elvis / Like sister and brother: *Drifters* / Me and Mrs Jones: *Paul, Billy* / That lady: *Isley Brothers* / Brother Louie: *Hot Chocolate* / Gonna make you an offer you can't refuse: *Helms, Jimmy* / Monster mash: *Pickett, Bobby Boris & Krypt Kickers* / Whiskey in the jar: *Thin Lizzy.*
LP: . . . . **YRNRLP 73**
MC: . . . . **YRNRMC 73**

ROCK 'N' ROLL YEARS 1974 (Various artists).
Tracks: / Waterloo: *Abba* / Never can say goodbye: *Gaynor, Gloria* / Roll away the stone: *Mott The Hoople* / Wall street shuffle: *10 CC* / I shot the sheriff: *Clapton, Eric* / Candle in the wind: *John, Elton* / Down down: *Status Quo* / Tiger feet: *Mud* / Dance with the devil: *Powell, Cozy* / Sugar baby love: *Rubettes* / Shang-a-lang: *Bay City Rollers* / Devil gate drive: *Quatro, Suzi* / Summer breeze: *Isley Brothers* / When will I see you again: *3 Degrees* / Rock the boat: *Hues Corporation* / Kissin' in the back row of the movies: *Drifters* / Judy teen: *Harley, Steve & Cockney Rebel* / Everyday: *Slade* / Sad sweet dreamer: *Sweet* Inspiration / Kung fu fighting: *Douglas, Carl* / Everything I own: *Boothe, Ken* / You make me feel brand new: *Stylistics* / Seasons in the sun: *Jacks, Terry* / Gonna make you a star: *Essex, David.*
LP: . . . . **YRNRLP 74**
MC: . . . . **YRNRMC 74**

ROCK 'N' ROLL YEARS 1975 (Various artists).
Tracks: / Ms. Grace: *Tymes* / You ain't seen nothing yet: *Bachman-Turner Overdrive* / Make me smile (come up and see me): *Harley, Steve & Cockney Rebel* / There goes my first love: *Drifters* / Lady Marmalade: *Labelle* / Loving you: *Ripperton, Minnie* / You're the first, the last, my everything: *White, Barry* / Have you seen her: *Chi-lites* / Higher and higher: *Wilson, Jackie* / I can help: *Swan, Billy* / SOS: *Abba* / I'm not in love / Promised land: *Presley, Elvis* / Angie baby: *Reddy, Helen* / Hold me close: *Essex, David* / Hustle: *McCoy, Van* / Barbados: *Typically Tropical* / Tears on my pillow: *Cash, Johnny* / Can't give you anything but my love: *Stylistics* / Hurts so good: *Cadogan, Susan* / Help me make it through the night: *Holt, John* / January: *Pilot* / Give a little love: *Bay City Rollers* / Bump, The: *Kenny.*
LP: . . . . **YRNRLP 75**
MC: . . . . **YRNRMC 75**

ROCK 'N' ROLL YEARS 1976 (Various artists).
Tracks: / Wide eyed and legless: *Fairweather-Low, Andy* / Let's do the latin hustle: *M & O Band* / Show me the way: *Frampton, Peter* / Dr Kiss Kiss: *5000 Volts* / I love to love: *Charles, Tina* / Arms of Mary: *Sutherland* Brothers / Fernando: *Abba* / Sunshine day: *Osibisa* / We do it: *Stone, R & J* / You to me are everything: *Real Thing* / Uptown uptempo woman: *Edelman, Randy* / Midnight train to Georgia: *Knight, Gladys & The Pips* / Love really hurts without you: *Ocean, Billy* / Play that funky music: *Wild Cherry* / Now is the time: *James,* Jimmy & The Vagabonds / I'm your puppet: *Purify, James & Bobby* / You see the trouble with me: *White, Barry* / Misty blue: *Moore, Dorothy* / Boys are back in town: *Thin Lizzy* / Glass of champagne: *Sailor* / You don't have to go: *Chi-lites* / You'll never find another love: *Rawls, Lou* / This is it: *Moore, Melba* / Music: *Miles, John.*
LP: . . . . **YRNRLP 76**
MC: . . . . **YRNRMC 76**

ROCK 'N' ROLL YEARS 1977 (Various artists).
Tracks: / Red light spells danger: *Ocean, Billy* / Peaches: *Stranglers* / All around the world: *Jam* / Looking after no. 1: *Boomtown Rats* / Year of the cat: *Stewart, Al* / Torn between two lovers: *McGregor,* Mary / 2 4 6 8 motorway: *Robinson, Tom* / Spanish stroll: *Deville, Mink* / Boogie nights: *Heatwave* / Native New Yorker: *Odyssey* / Free: *Williams, Deniece* / Way down: *Presley, Elvis* / Rockin' all over the world: *Status Quo* / Don't believe a word: *Thin Lizzy* / Knowing me knowing you: *Abba* / Good morning judge / Baby don't change your mind: *Knight, Gladys & The Pips* / Don't leave me this way: *Melvin, Harold* / Romeo: *Mr. Big* / She's not there: *Santana* / They shoot horses don't they: *Racing Cars* / Black Betty: *Ram Jam* / Ain't gonna bump no more: *Tex, Joe* / When I need you: *Sayer, Leo.*
LP: . . . . **YRNRLP 77**
MC: . . . . **YRNRMC 77**

ROCK 'N' ROLL YEARS 1978 (Various artists).
Tracks: / Denis: *Blondie* / Don't fear the reaper: *Blue Oyster Cult* / Fantasy: *Earth, Wind & Fire* / More than a woman: *Tavares* / Love is in the air: *Young, John Paul* / Take a chance on me: *Abba* / Forever autumn: *Hayward, Justin* / In the bush: *Musique* / Lay your love on me: *Racey* / I lost my hearey: *Baccara* / Grease: *Valli, Frankie* / 5 minutes: *Stranglers* / If you can't give me love: *Quatro, Suzi* / Run for home: *Lindisfarne* / Rat trap: *Boomtown Rats* / Every one's a winner: *Hot Chocolate* / Baker street: *Rafferty, Gerry* / Darlin': *Miller, Frankie* / Sorry I'm a lady: *Baccara* / I lost my heart to a starship trooper: *Brightman, Sarah.*
2LP: . . . . **YRNRLP 78**
MC: . . . . **YRNRMC 78**

ROCK 'N' ROLL YEARS 1979 (Various artists).
Tracks: / Bat out of hell: *Meatloaf* / I will survive: *Gaynor, Gloria* / Living on an island: *Status Quo* / Oliver's army: *Costello, Elvis* / Ain't no stoppin' us now: *McFadden & Whitehead* / When you're in love with a beautiful woman: *Various artists* / I don't wanna lose you: *Kandidate* / Can you feel the force: *Real Thing* / Some girls: *Racey* / Gangsters: *Specials* / Milk and alcohol: *Dr. Feelgood* / I don't like Mondays: *Boomtown Rats* / Eton rifles: *Jam* / My Sharona: *Knack* / On my radio: *Selector* / Are 'friends' electric: *Tubeway Army* / Ring my bell: *Ward, Anita* / Angel eyes: *Abba* / Hold the line: *Toto* / Teen: *Regents* / Cars: *Numan, Gary* / You bet your love: *Hancock, Herbie.*
LP: . . . . **YRNRLP 79**
MC: . . . . **YRNRMC 79**

SENSATIONAL SEVENTIES, THE (Various artists).
Tracks: / So you win again: *Hot Chocolate* / Everyday hurts: *Sad Cafe* / Tragedy: *Bee Gees* / Fantasy: *Earth, Wind & Fire* / Don't leave: *Melvin, Harold* / She's not there: *Santana* / Boogie nights: *Heatwave* / I don't like Mondays: *Boomtown Rats* / See my baby jive: *Wizzard* / Cum on feel the noize: *Slade* / Blockbuster: *Sweet* / All the young dudes: *Mott The Hoople* / 2-4-6-8 motorway: *Robinson Band, Tom* / January: *Pilot.*
LP: . . . . **SMR 727**
MC: . . . . **SMC 727**

SEVENTIES NO. 1'S VOL 3 (OLD GOLD) (Various artists).
Tracks: / I can't give you anything but love: *Stylistics* / You won't find another fool like me: *New Seekers* / Gonna make you a star: *Essex, David* / Love grows (where my Rosemary goes): *Edison Lighthouse* / Don't go breaking my heart: *John, Elton & Kiki Dee* / How can I be sure: *Cassidy, David* / Yellow river: *Christie* / Tie a yellow ribbon round the old oak tree: *Dawn* / I love you love me love: *Glitter, Gary* / Sunday girl: *Blondie* / Bye bye baby: *Bay City Rollers* / When a child is born: *Mathis, Johnny* / Mama mia: *Abba* / Ms. Grace: *Tymes.*
LP: . . . . **OG 1518**
MC: . . . . **OG 2518**

SEVENTIES NO. 1'S VOL 4 (OLD GOLD) (Various artists).
Tracks: / Spirit in the sky: *Greenbaum, Norman* / Telegram Sam: *T. Rex* / Baby jump: *Mungo Jerry* / I hear you knocking: *Edmunds, Dave* / Maggie May: *Stewart, Rod* / Voodoo chile: *Hendrix, Jimi Experience* / Hot love: *T. Rex* / Woodstock: *Matthews Southern Comfort* / Rubber bullets: *10 CC* / I'm the leader of the gang (I am): *Glitter, Gary* / Down down: *Status Quo* / Heart of glass: *Blondie* / I don't like Mondays: *Boomtown Rats.*
LP: . . . . **OG 1519**
MC: . . . . **OG 2519**

SEVENTIES POP NUMBER ONES (OLD GOLD) (Various artists).
Tracks: / Son of my father: *Chicory Tip* / In the Summertime: *Mungo Jerry* / Blockbuster: *Sweet* / Knock three times: *Dawn* / Seasons in the sun: *Jacks, Terry* / Sugar baby love: *Rubettes* / Waterloo: *Abba* / When will I see you again: *3 Degrees* / Rivers of Babylon: *Boney M* / When I need you: *Sayer, Leo* / I'm not in love: *10 CC* / Night fever: *Bee Gees* / Show you the way to go: *Jacksons* / Barbados: *Typically Tropical.*
LP: . . . . **OG 1505**
MC: . . . . **OG 2505**

SEVENTIES VOL.2, THE (Various artists).
Tracks: / Spirit in the sky: *Greenbaum, Norman* / Horse with no name, A: *America (Group)* / Hot love: *T. Rex* / Maggie May: *Stewart, Rod* / I hear you knocking: *Edmunds, Dave* / Woodstock: *Matthews Southern* Comfort / When I'm dead and gone: *McGuinness Flint* / Whisky in the jar: *Thin Lizzy* / Black night: *Deep* Purple / Mama told me not to come: *Three Dog Night* / Hold your head up: *Argent* / Devil's answer: *Atomic Rooster* / Witch Queen of New Orleans: *Redbone* / Meet me on the corner: *Lindisfarne.*
LP: . . . . **OG 1009**
MC: . . . . **OG 2009**

SIMON BATES - THE 70'S (Various artists).
Tracks: / Hallelujah freedom: *Campbell, Junior* / Sugar baby love: *Rubettes* / One and one is one: *Medicine* Head / I'm on fire: *5000 Volts* / United we stand: *Brotherhood Of Man* / Walkin' miracle, A: *Limmie &* Family Cooking / Don't stay away too long: *Peters & Lee* / You're a lady: *Skellern, Peter* / Juke box jive: *Rubettes* / You can do magic: *Limmie & Family Cooking* / Montego Bay: *Bloom, Bobby* / Dancing with the captain: *Nicholas, Paul* / High fly: *Miles, John* / Rising sun: *Medicine Head* / My baby loves lovin': *White Plains* / Welcome home: *Peters & Lee.*
MC: **CN4 2099**
LP: . . . . **CN 2099**

SIMON BATES' - THE 70'S (Various artists).
Tracks: / Rat trap: *Boomtown Rats* / Angel: *Stewart, Rod* / Love's theme: *Love Unlimited Orchestra* / I'm your puppet: *Purify, James & Bobby* / Reunited: *Peaches & Herb* / Uptown, uptempo woman: *Edelman, Randy* / Standing in the road: *Blackfoot Sue* / What am I gonna do: *White, Barry* / You wear it well: *Stewart, Rod* / Crocodile rock: *John, Elton* / Like clockwork: *Boomtown Rats* / Radancer: *Marmalade* / Shuffle, The: *McCoy, Van* / Betcha by golly wow: *Stylistics* / I got the music in me: *Dee, Kiki* / Giving it all away: *Daltrey, Roger.*
MC: **CN4 2110**
LP: . . . . **CN 2110**

SOUND OF THE 70'S (Various artists).
2LP: . . . . **NE 1172 AB**
MCSET: . . . . **CE 2172 AB**

SOUNDS OF THE 70'S (Various artists).
2LP: . . . . **CR 087**
MCSET: . . . . **CRT 087**

SOUNDS OF THE 70'S VOL.2 (Various artists).
2LP: . . . . **CR 136**
MCSET: . . . . **CRT 136**

SOUNDS OF THE SEVENTIES (VIDEO) (See under Seventies for details) (Various artists).

SPOTLIGHT ON HITS OF THE SEVENTIES (Various artists).
LP: . . . . **SPOT 1026**
MC: . . . . **ZCSPT 1026**

TOP TEN GROUPS OF THE SEVENTIES (Various artists).
LP: . . . . **CN 2078**
MC: **CN4 2078**

TOP TEN HITS OF THE 70'S (Various artists).
Tracks: / Wuthering heights: *Bush, Kate* / American pie: *McLean, Don* / Baker Street: *Rafferty, Gerry* / Roll over Beethoven: *E.L.O.* / Tap turns on the water: *CCS* / 2-4-6-8 motorway: *Robinson, Tom* / You sexy thing: *Hot Chocolate* / Angie baby: *Reddy, Helen* / Air that I breathe, The: *Hollies* / Make me smile (come up and see me): *Harley, Steve & Cockney Rebel* / Let's work together: *Canned Heat* / Some girls: *Racey* / Heaven must be missing an angel: *Tavares* / 48 crash: *Quatro, Suzi* / Cottonfields: *Beach Boys* (CD only.) / Cat crept in, The: *Mud* (CD only.) / Little bit more, A: *Dr. Hook* (CD only.) / Years may come years may go: *Herman's Hermits* (CD only.).
LP: . . . . **MFP 5875**
MC: . . . . **TCMFP 5875**

WIG WAM GLAM (Various artists).
LP: . . . . **CE 2455**

YOU AIN'T SEEN NOTHIN' YET (Various artists).
Tracks: / Classical gas: *Williams, Mason* / Frankenstein: *Winter, Edgar* / Vicious: *Reed, Lou* / Rocky mountain way: *Walsh, Joe* / Schools out: *Cooper, Alice* / Hold your head up: *Argent* / Pinball wizard: *John, Elton* / Free electric band: *Hammond, Albert* / Ballroom blitz: *Sweet* / Caroline: *Status Quo* / Sweet home Alabama: *Skynyrd, Lynyrd* / Jessica: *Allman Brothers Band* / Don't fear the reaper: *Blue Oyster* Cult / Baby I love your way: *Frampton, Peter* / In a broken dream: *Python Lee Jackson* / Why did you do it: *Stretch* / My oh my: *Sad Cafe* / Bat out of hell: *Meatloaf* / Life's been good: *Walsh, Joe* / Jane: *Jefferson Starship* / Closer to the heart: *Rush* / You ain't seen nothin' yet: *Bachman-Turner Overdrive* / Slow down: *Miles, John* / Hotel California: *Eagles.*
MCSET: . . . . **OG 2211**

75...

75 MILLION SELLERS (Various artists).
Tracks: / Honky cat: *John, Elton* / I feel like making love: *Flack, Roberta* / Rock on: *Essex, David* / Hold your head up:

Argent / Spinning wheel: *Blood, Sweat & Tears* / (Sittin' on) the dock of the bay: *Redding*, Otis / Soul man: *Sam & Dave* / Streak, The: *Stevens, Ray* / I never loved a man: *Franklin, Aretha*/ Behind closed doors: *Rich, Charlie* / Harper Valley PTA: *O'Riley, Jeannie* / Blue suede shoes: *Perkins, Carl* / San Francisco: *McKenzie, Scott* / I can see clearly now: *Various artists.*
LP: . . . . **IMP 75**
MCSET: . . . . **IMPC 75**

77's

ALL FALL DOWN.
LP: . . . . **ER 0007**
MC: . . . . **TC ER 0007**

80's

30 YEARS OF NUMBER 1'S VOL 11 (1983-1986+) (Various artists).
Tracks: / Give It: *K.C. & The Sunshine Band* / Karma Chameleon: *Culture Club* / Only You: *Flying Pickets*/ 99 red balloons: *Nena* / Wake me up before you go go: *Wham* / I feel for you: *Khan, Chaka* / I should have known better: *Diamond, Jim* / I want to know what love is: *Foreigner* / 19: *Hardcastle, Paul* / Frankie: *Sister Sledge* / Good heart, A: *Sharkey, Feargal* / Sun always shines on TV, The: *A-Ha* / Rock me Amadeus: *Falco* / Spirit in the sky: *Dr. & the Medics* (Not on CD) / Every loser wins: *Berry, Nick* (Not on CD) / Final countdown, The: *Europe* / Reet petite: *Wilson, Jackie* (Not on CD) / Stand by me: *King, Ben E.*/ Nothing's gonna stop us now: *Starship* / Never gonna give you up: *Astley, Rick* / You win again: *Bee Gees*/ I think we're alone now: *Tiffany* (Not on CD) / Perfect: *Fairground Attraction* / Orinoco Flow: *Enya.*
2LP: . . . . **TYNOLP 110**
MC: . . . . **TYNOMC 110**

30 YEARS OF NUMBER 1'S VOL 10 (1980-1983) (Various artists).
Tracks: / Use it up and wear it out: *Odyssey* (Not on CD) / Start: *Jam* / Feels like I'm in love: *Marie*, Kelly / Tide is high, The: *Blondie* / Green door: *Stevens, Shakin'* / Japanese boy: *Aneka* (Not on CD) / Tainted love: *Soft Cell* / Prince Chaming: *Adam & The Ants* / Land of make believe: *Bucks Fizz*(Not on CD) / Model, The: *Kraftwerk* / Seven Tears: *Goombay Dance Band* / My camera never lies: *Bucks Fizz*(Not on CD) / House of fun: *Madness* / Goody two shoes: *Adam & The Ants* / Happy Talk: *Captain Sensible*/ Fame: *Cara, Irene* / Come on Eileen: *Dexy's Midnight Runners & Emerald Express* / Do you realy want to hurt me: *Culture Club* / I don't wanna dance: *Grant, Eddy* / Down under: *Men At Work* / Too shy: *Kajagoogoo*/ Total eclipse of the heart: *Tyler, Bonnie* / Is there something I should know: *Duran Duran* / True: *Spandau Ballet.*
2LP: . . . . **TYNOLP 109**
MC: . . . . **TYNOMC 109**

80'S REVISITED VOL.2, THE (Hit City) (Various artists).
Tracks: / Total eclipse of the heart: *Tyler, Bonnie* / Goody two shoes: *Ant, Adam* / Love and pride: *King*/ Pretty in pink: *Psychedelic Furs* / (Feels like) Heaven: *Fiction Factory* / Don't talk to me about love: *Altered* Images / Take it on the run: *REO Speedwagon* / One rule for you: *After The Fire* / Down Under: *Men At* Work / Kings of the wild frontier: *Adam & The Ants* / Dog eat dog: *Adam & The Ants* / I could be happy: *Altered* Images / Who can it be now: *Men At Work* / Alone without you: *King* / January February: *Dickson, Barbara*/ Keep on loving you: *REO Speedwagon* / Susanna: *Art Company* / Holding out for a hero: *Tyler, Bonnie.*
MC: . . . . **PWKMC 4063**

80'S, THE (The album of the decade) (Various artists).
Tracks: / Another brick in the wall (part 2): *Pink Floyd* / Brass in pocket: *Pretenders* / Call me: *Blondie*/ Eye of the tiger: *Survivor* / Come on Eileen: *Dexy's Midnight Runners* / House of fun: *Madness* / Red red wine: *UB40* / Every little thing she does is magic: *Police* / Jealous guy: *Roxy Music* / Ebony and ivory: *McCartney, Paul & Stevie Wonder* / Careless whisper: *Michael, George* / Freedom: *Wham* / Is there something I should know?: *Duran Duran* / Karma chameleon: *Culture Club* / Wherever I lay my hat (that's my home): *Young, Paul* / True: *Spandau Ballet* / Do they know it's Christmas?: *Band Aid* / West End girls: *Pet* Shop Boys / Good heart, A: *Sharkey, Feargal* / When the going get's tough, the tough get going: *Ocean, Billy*/ Chain reaction: *Ross, Diana* / Never gonna give you up: *Astley, Rick* / Pump up the volume: *M/A/R/R/S*/ 19: *Hardcastle, Paul* / I should be so lucky: *Minogue, Kylie* / Only way is up, The: *Yazz & The Plastic* Population / Theme from S Express: *S. Express* / Don't turn around: *Aswad* / With a little help from my friends: *Wet Wet Wet* / Perfect: *Fairground Attraction* / Orinoco flow: *Enya* / Something's gotten hold of my heart: *Almond, Marc/Gene Pitney.*
2LP: . . . . **EMTVD 48**
MCSET: . . . . **TCEMTVD 48**

BEST OF SMASH HITS (Various artists).
Tracks: / House of fun: *Madness* / Do you really want to hurt me: *Culture Club* / Africa: *Toto* / Down under: *Men At Work* / Chariots of fire: *Vangelis* / Rock the boat: *Forrest* / She means nothing to me: *Richard, Cliff* / Arthur's theme: *Cross, Christopher.*
MC: . . . . **AIM 107**

BEST OF SMASH HITS OF 1981 (Various artists).
MC: . . . . **AIM 49**

BEST OF SMASH TRACKS FROM THE 80'S (Various artists).
MC: . . . . **AIM 70**

CLASSIC HITS OF '84 (Various artists).
2LP: . . . . **STAR 2006**
MCSET: . . . . **STAC 2006**

DIE NEUE DEUTSCHE WELLE IST DA DA DA (Various artists).
LP: . . . . **HERE 1**
MC: **7133 205**

DINDISC 1980 (Various artists).
Tracks: / Waiting for the man: *O.M.D.* / Messages: *O.M.D.* / Electricity: *O.M.D.* / Motorbike beat: *Revillos*/ Where's the boy for me: *Revillos.*
LP: . . . . **DONE 1**
MC: . . . . **DONE C1**

DIRECT HITS (Various artists).
Tracks: / Someone, somewhere in summertime: *Simple Minds* / Night porter: *Japan* / Harry's game (theme from): *Clannad* / Annie get your gun: *Squeeze* / Be proud, be loud, be heard: *Toyah* / Maneater: *Hall &* Oates / Reap the wild wind: *Ultravox* / Best years of our lives: *Modern Romance* / Back on the chain gang: *Pretenders* / Holy Joe: *Haysi Fantayzee* / Mannequin: *Kids From Fame.*
LP: . . . . **STAR 2226**
MC: . . . . **STAC 2226**

ELECTRIC EIGHTIES, THE (Various artists).
Tracks: / Planet Earth: *Duran Duran* / Eloise: *Damned* / True: *Spandau Ballet* / Golden brown: *Stranglers*/ Love plus one: *Haircut 100* / Lunatics, The: *Fun Boy Three* / Ghost town: *Specials* / Tide is high, The: *Blondie* / Night to remember, A: *Shalamar* / Love take over: *Five Star* / Doctor doctor: *Thompson Twins* / Too shy: *Kajagoogoo* / Only you: *Yazoo* / Geno: *Dexy's Midnight Runners.*
LP: . . . . **SMR 728**
MC: . . . . **SMC 728**

ELECTRO SHOCK VOLTAGE ONE (Various artists).
Tracks: / Blowin' your mind: *Various artists* / Survivin' in the 80s: *Various artists* / Get tough: *Various artists* / Out come the freaks: *Various artists* / That's the way I like it: *Various artists* / Rockit: *Various artists* / Jungle rock: *Various artists* / Autodrive: *Various artists.*
LP: . . . . **VOLT 1**
MC: . . . . **VOLT 40 1**

GIANT (Various artists).
LP: . . . . **LONLP 35**
MC: . . . . **LONC 35**

GIRLS, GIRLS, GIRLS (Various artists).
MC: . . . . **ASK 792**

GREATEST HITS OF 1985 (Various artists).
Tracks: / Do they know it's Christmas?: *Band Aid* / Love and pride: *King* / I feel love: *Bronski Beat & Marc* Almond / You spin me round (like a record): *Dead or Alive* / White wedding: *Idol, Billy* / Wide boy: *Kershaw*, Nik / That ole devil called love: *Moyet, Alison* / Suddenly: *Ocean, Billy* / There must be an angel (playing with my heart): *Eurythmics* / Cherish: *Kool & The Gang* / Move closer: *Nelson, Phyllis* / Could it be I'm falling in love?: *Grant, David & Jaki Graham* / Rhythm of the night: *DeBarge* / Clouds across the moon: *Rah* Band / Live is life: *Opus* / 19: *Hardcastle, Paul* / We close our eyes: *Go West* / Slave to love: *Ferry, Bryan* / Everything she wants: *Wham* / Feel so real: *Arrington, Steve* / Say I'm your number one: *Princess* / Nightshift: *Commodores* / I want to know what love is: *Foreigner* / Things can only get better: *Jones, Howard* / Axel F: *Faltermeyer, Harold* / Everything must change: *Young, Paul* / Since yesterday: *Strawberry Switchblade* / Ghostbusters: *Parker, Ray Jnr.* / Last kiss, The: *Cassidy, David* / I know him so well: *Paige, Elaine & Barbara Dickson.*
2LP: . . . . **STAR 2269**
MCSET: . . . . **STAC 2269**

GREATEST HITS OF 1986 (Various artists).
LP: . . . . **STAR 2286**
MC: . . . . **STAC 2286**

GREATEST HITS OF 1987 (Various artists).
Tracks: / Pump up the volume: *M/A/R/R/S* / Lies: *Butler, Jonathan* / Crush on you: *Jets (American)* / Star trekkin': *Firm* / House nation: *Housemaster Boyz* / Another step (closer to you): *Wilde, Kim & Junior*/ Let's dance: *Rea, Chris* / Jive talkin': *Boogie Box High* / Can't be with you tonight: *Boucher, Judy*/ Victim of love: *Erasure* / Toy boy: *Sinitta* / Looking for a new love: *Watley, Jody* / Real wild child: *Pop, Iggy* / Strange love: *Depeche Mode* / I found lovin': *Fatback (Band)* / Jack mix II: *Mirage*/ Just don't want to be lonely: *McGregor, Freddie* / Respectable: *Mel & Kim* / Male stripper: *Man 2 Man meets* Man Parrish / I love my radio: *Taffy* / Let it be: *Ferry Aid* / Let's wait awhile: *Jackson, Janet*/ No more the fool: *Brooks, Elkie* / Nothing's gonna stop me now: *Fox, Samantha* / Circus, The: *Erasure*/ Roadblock: *Stock/ Aitken/Waterman* / Cars (E reg model): *Numan, Gary* / Once bitten, twice shy: *Williams, Vesta.*
LP: . . . . **STAR 2309**
MC: . . . . **STAC 2309**

GREATEST HITS OF 1988 (Story Of The Year) (Various artists).
Tracks: / I think we're alone now: *Tiffany* / Together forever: *Astley, Rick* / Love will save the day: *Houston*, Whitney / Cross my broken heart: *Sinitta* / That's the way it is: *Mel & Kim* / Candle in the wind: *John*, Elton / Don't turn around: *Aswad* / Perfect: *Fairground Attraction* / Crash: *Primitives* / Little respect, A: *Erasure* / Tell it to my heart: *Dayne, Taylor* / Loadsamoney: *Enfield, Harry* / Doctorin' the Tardis: *Time Lords* / Nothing can divide us: *Donovan, Jason.*
2LP: . . . . **STAR 2334**
MCSET: . . . . **STAC 2334**

GREATEST HITS OF 1989 (Story Of The Year) (Various artists).
MCSET: . . . . **STAC 2389**
2LP: . . . . **STAR 2389**

HIT SINGLES 1980-1988 (Various artists).
Tracks: / Rose, The: *Midler, Bette* / Waiting for a girl like you: *Foreigner* / Gloria: *Branigan, Laura*/ I want to know what love is: *Foreigner* / Self control: *Branigan, Laura* / Two hearts: *Stacey Q* / St. Elmo's fire: *Parr, John* / Shake your love: *Gibson, Debbie* / I can't wait: *Nu Shooz* / Foolish beat: *Gibson, Debbie.*
LP: . . . . **K 781 921 1**
MC: . . . . **K 781 921 4**

JIVE JUKE BOX (Various artists).
Tracks: / Nothing's gonna stop me now: *Fox, Samantha* / I can't help myself: *Real Thing* / Summer in the city: *Fresh* / Only the strong survive: *Wilson, Precious* / Time code: *Louie Louie.*
LP: . . . . **HOP 219**

JUST 17 (Heartbeats) (Various artists).
Tracks: / Can't stay away: *Estefan, Gloria* / She's like the wind: *Swayze, Patrick* / Suddenly: *Anderson*, Angry / Nothing's gonna change my love for you: *Medeiros, Glenn* / Say a little prayer: *Bomb The Bass* / Hold me in your arms: *Astley, Rick* / First time: *Beck, Robin* / Baby I love your way/Freebird: *Will to Power*/ Cat among the pigeons: *Bros* / Fine time: *Yazz* / Looking for Linda: *Hue & Cry* / Be my twin: *Brother Beyond* / Nathan Jones: *Bananarama.*
LP: . . . . **FARE 1**
MC: . . . . **FAREC 1**

KICK UP THE 80'S VOL.1 (Various artists).
Tracks: / Fields of fire: *Country* / Senses working overtime: *XTC* / Town called malice, A: *Jam* / Our lips are sealed: *Fun Boy Three* / It must be love: *Madness* / Ghost town: *Specials* / Labelled with love: *Squeeze* / Reward: *Teardrop Explodes* / Look of love, The: *ABC* / Joan of Arc: *O.M.D.* / Living on the ceiling: *Blancmange* / Just can't get enough: *Depeche Mode* / Only you: *Yazoo* / Fade to grey: *Visage.*
LP: . . . . **OG 1520**
MC: . . . . **OG 2520**

KICK UP THE 80'S VOL.2 (Go Wild in the Country) (Various artists).
Tracks: / Hand in glove: *Smiths* / Modern girl: *Meatloaf* / Go wild in the country: *Bow Wow Wow* / Start: *Jam* / Come on Eileen: *Dexy's Midnight Runners* / First picture of you, The: *Lotus Eaters* / Communication: *Spandau Ballet* / I'm still standing: *John, Elton* / Reap the wild wind: *Ultravox* / Enola Gay: *O.M.D.*/ Damned don't cry: *Visage* / Einstein a go go: *Landscape* / Poison arrow: *ABC* / Doctor doctor: *Thompson Twins* / Don't go: *Yazoo* / Christian: *China Crisis.*
LP: . . . . **OG 1521**
MC: . . . . **OG 2521**

KICK UP THE 80'S VOL.3 (Love and Pride) (Various artists).
Tracks: / Maneater: *Hall & Oates* / Down under: *Men At Work* / Break my stride: *Wilder, Matthew* / Human touch: *Springfield, Rick* / Karma chameleon: *Culture Club* / My oh my: *Slade* / 99 red balloons: *Nena*/ Love and pride: *King* / Don't talk to me about love: *Altered Images* / Japanese boy: *Aneka* / Land of make believe: *Bucks Fizz* / Feels like I'm in love: *Marie, Kelly* / Fantasy island: *Tight Fit* / Favourite waste of time: *Paul, Owen* / Let's hear it for the boy: *Williams, Deniece* / Ghostbusters: *Parker, Ray Jnr..*
LP: . . . . **OG 1522**
MC: . . . . **OG 2522**

KICK UP THE 80'S VOL.4 (Various artists).
Tracks: / Pretty in pink: *Psychedelic Furs* / Heaven knows I'm miserable now: *Smiths* / Love on a farmboy's wages: *XTC* / Rip it up: *Orange Juice* / Walk out to winter: *Aztec Camera* / I'm in love with a German film star: *Passions* / 7 teen: *Regents* / Soul train: *Swansway* / New life: *Depeche Mode* / Black man Ray: *China Crisis* / Talking loud and clear: *O.M.D.* / Night porter: *Japan* / Doot doot: *Freur* / Da da da: *Trio* / (Feels like) heaven: *Fiction Factory* / Der Kommissar: *After The Fire.*
LP: . . . . **OG 1523**
MC: . . . . **OG 2523**

KICK UP THE 80'S VOL.5 (Various artists).
LP: . . . . **OG 1524**
MC: . . . . **OG 2524**

KICK UP THE 80'S VOL.6 (Various artists).
LP: . . . . **OG 1525**
MC: . . . . **OG 2525**

LET'S BEAT IT (Various artists).
Tracks: / Say say say: *McCartney, Paul & Michael Jackson* / Girls just want to have fun: *Lauper, Cyndi* / You might think: *Cars* / Queen of the broken hearts: *Lover Boy* / Separate ways: *Journey (Group)* / Heat of the moment: *Asia* / Cum on feel the noize: *Quiet Riot* / Human nature: *Jackson, Michael* / 99 luftballons: *Nena* / Down under: *Men At Work* / Every breath you take: *Police* / Love is a battlefield: *Benatar, Pat* / Maneater: *Hall & Oates* / Language of love: *Fogelberg, Dan.*
LP: . . . . **EPC 26345**
MC: **40 26345**

LIVE A WEEK AT THE BRIDGE E16 (Various artists).
LP: . . . . **BHLP 001**

LIVE FOR LIFE (Various artists).
Tracks: / Love lessons: *Various artists* / Lively up yourself: *Various artists* / Ages of you: *Various artists*/ Howling wind: *Various artists* / Amy: *Various artists* / I been down so long: *Various artists* / Hero takes a fall: *Various artists* / Take your medicine: *Various artists* / We got the beat: *Various artists*/ Tempted: *Various artists.*
LP: . . . . **MIRF 1013**
MC: . . . . **MIRFC 1013**

LIVE-IN WORLD (Anti heroin project) (Various artists).
Tracks: / Smack: *Welch, Lizzie & the Anti Smack band* / Cold turkeying: *Miles, Sarah* / Hot line: *Sutton*, Chris / End of the rainbow, The: *Costello, Elvis* / Live-in world: *Anti-Heroin Project* / It's not easy: *Tyler*, Bonnie / Don't use drugs: *Jonno & Dennis* / Needle and the damage done: *Icicle Works & Pete Wylie* / Freak street: *Foskett, C* / Suspended pool: *Mills, Hayley & Dave Evans* / Something better: *Wilson, P#K. Wilde#D.* Pandy#B. Whitlock / You know it makes sense: *Starr, Ringo* / Waiting in the dark: *Wilson, Precious* / World spins so slow, The: *Stewart, Dave & Barbara Gaskin* / Slay the dragon: *Johnson, Holly* / Simple as that: *McCartney*, Paul / Naughty atom bomb: *Various artists* / Candles: *Rea, Chris* / Head full of shadows: *Boon* / Aqua: *Eurythmics* / We came here to rock: *Saxon* / Heroin: *Various artists* / Little bit of snow: *Jones*, Howard / Never never: *Sharkey, Feargal* / Hooked on love: *Bananarama* / Man's too strong, The: *Various* artists / Blue (armed with love): *Wham* / Something better: *Various artists* / On the street: *Henry, Lenny* / Magical: *Bucks Fizz* / She's gonna love you to death: *Parr, John.*
2LP: . . . . **AHPLP 1**
MCSET: . . . . **TCAHPLP 1**

MERIDIANS TWO (Various artists).
MC: . . . . **T 3**

MODERN LOVE (Various artists).
LP: . . . . **NE 1286**
MC: . . . . **CE 2286**

MONSTER HITS (Various artists).
Tracks: / Cherish: Madonna / Ride on time: Black Box / Numero uno: Starlight / Oye mi canto: Estefan, Gloria / Lambada: Kaoma / All around the world: Stansfield, Lisa / Real wild house: Orellana, Raul/ Sun rising, The: Beloved / I feel the earth move: Martika / Don't ask me why: Eurythmics / Road to Hell: Rea, Chris / If I could turn back time: Cher / Love in an elevator: Aerosmith / Poison: Cooper, Alice / Head on: Jesus & Mary Chain / Walking on thin ice: Fuzzbox / You've got it: Simply Red/ Never too much (89 remix): Vandross, Luther / Don't make me over: Sybil / I need your lovin': Williams, Alyson / Partyman: Prince / Secret rendezvous: White, Karyn / Love's about to change my heart: Summer, Donna / Losing my mind: Minnelli, Liza / That's what I like / My love: London Boys / Blame it on the boogie: Big Fun / Chocolate box: Bros / After all: Dees, Sam / Git on up: Fast Eddie / Hey DJ/I can't dance to that music: Beatmasters feat. Betty Boo / Pacific 707: 808 State.
LP: . . . . **HITS 11**
MC: . . . . **HITSC 11**

NICE PRICE SAMPLER ALBUM (Various).
Tracks: / Eye of the tiger / Love my way / Hold the line / Rock 'n' roll rebel / If you want my love / It's a mistake / Lady marmalade / Sexual healing / European female / Honesty / Breakaway / America / Lady lynda / Keep on loving you / If you leave me now.
LP: . . . . **XPR 1313**

NOW - SMASH HITS 32 swingorilliant hits of the 80's (Various artists).
Tracks: / Down to earth: Curiosity Killed The Cat / If you let me stay: D'Arby, Terence Trent / Respectable: Mel & Kim / Labour of love: Hue & Cry / Rain or shine: Five Star / West End girls: Pet Shop Boys/ Happy hour: Housemartins / Holding back the years: Simply Red / Take on me: A-Ha / You spin me round (like a record): Dead or Alive / There must be an angel (playing with my heart): Eurythmics / Everybody wants to rule the world: Tears For Fears / Wake me up before you go go: Wham / Smalltown boy: Bronski Beat/ Master and servant: Depeche Mode / Careless whisper: Michael, George / True: Spandau Ballet / Red red wine: UB40 / Hold me now: Thompson Twins / Love cats, The: Cure / Come on Eileen: Dexy's Midnight Runners & Emerald Express / Look of love, The: ABC / Do you really want to hurt me?: Culture Club / Save a prayer: Duran Duran / Under pressure: Queen & David Bowie / One day in your life: Jackson, Michael(Not on CD) / Favourite shirts (Boy meets girl): Haircut 100 / Ghost town: Specials / Going underground: Jam/ Baggy trousers: Madness / Ant music: Adam & The Ants / Atomic: Harry, Debbie.
2LP: . . . . **NOSH 1**
MCSET: . . . . **TCNOSH 1**

NOW THAT'S WHAT I CALL MUSIC VOL.15 (Various artists).
Tracks: / I want it all: Queen / Kick it in: Simple Minds / Good thing: Fine Young Cannibals / Americanos: Johnson, Holly / Baby I don't care: Transvision Vamp / Mystify: INXS / Look, The: Roxette/ Rooms on fire: Nicks, Stevie / My brave face: McCartney, Paul / Ferry 'cross the Mersey: Marsden, Gerry & Paul McCartney / Song for whoever: Beautiful South / Days: MacColl, Kirsty / Second summer of love, The: Danny Wilson / Cry: Waterfront / Violently: Hue & Cry / Best of me, The: Richard, Cliff / Back to life (however do you want me): Soul II Soul/Caron Wheeler / Manchild: Cherry, Neneh / Every little step: Brown, Bobby (1) / Do you love what you feel: Inner City / It is time to get funky: D Mob featuring LRS/ Joy and pain: Allen, Donna / Licence to kill: Knight, Gladys / Miss you like crazy: Cole, Natalie/ It's alright: Pet Shop Boys / Swing the mood: Jive Bunny & The Mastermixers / You on my mind: Swing Out Sister / Cruel Summer '89: Bananarama / Say no go: De La Soul / Blame it on the bassline: Cook, Norman & MC Wildski / Just keep rockin': Double Trouble Feat. Rebel MC / Lullaby: Cure.
2LP: . . . . **NOW 15**
MCSET: . . . . **TCNOW 15**

NOW THAT'S WHAT I CALL MUSIC VOL.1 (Various artists).
Tracks: / You can't hurry love: Collins, Phil / Is there something I should know?: Duran Duran / Red red wine: UB40 / Only for love: Limahl / Temptation: Heaven 17 / Give it up: K.C. & The Sunshine Band/ Double Dutch: McLaren, Malcolm / Total eclipse of the heart: Tyler, Bonnie / Karma chameleon: Culture Club / Safety dance: Men Without Hats / Too shy: Kajagoogoo / Moonlight shadow: Oldfield, Mike/ Down under: Men At Work / Hey you (the Rock Steady Crew): Rock Steady Crew / Baby Jane: Stewart, Rod/ Wherever I lay my hat: Young, Paul / Candy girl: New Edition / Big Apple: Kajagoogoo / Let's stay together: Turner, Tina / Fascination: Human League / New song: Jones, Howard / Please don't make me cry: UB40 / Tonight, I celebrate my love: Bryson, Peabo & Roberta Flack / They don't know: Ullman, Tracey/ Kissing with confidence: Powers, Will / That's all: Genesis / Love cats, The: Cure / Waterfront: Simple Minds / Sun and the rain, The: Madness / Victims: Culture Club.
2LP: . . . . **NOW 1**
MCSET: . . . . **TCNOW 1**

NOW THAT'S WHAT I CALL MUSIC VOL.9 (Various artists).
Tracks: / Reet petite: Wilson, Jackie / Live it up: Mental As Anything / Right thing, The: Simply Red/ Sometimes: Erasure (Not on CD) / C'est la vie: Nevil, Robbie / You sexy thing: Hot Chocolate / It doesn't have to be this way: Blow Monkeys / Caravan of love: Housemartins (Not on CD) / Everything I own: Boy George / Rat in mi kitchen: UB40 / Big fun: Gap Band (Not on CD) / Stay out of my life: Five Star/ Heartache: Pepsi & Shirlie / Trick of the night, A: Bananarama (Not on CD) / Take my breath away: Berlin/ Great pretender, The: Mercury, Freddie / Stand by me: King, Ben E.E. / Down to earth: Curiosity Killed The Cat / So cold the night: Communards (Not on CD) / Jack your body: Hurley, Steve 'Silk' (Not on CD) / I love my radio: Taffy (Not on CD) / Loving you is sweeter than ever: Kamen, Nick (Not on CD) / Manhattan skyline: A-Ha (Not on CD) / Sonic boom boy: Westworld (Not on CD) / Livin' on a prayer: Bon Jovi (Not on CD) / Land of confusion: Genesis / Final countdown, The: Europe (Not on CD) / Over the hills and far away: Moore, Gary (Not on CD) / Cross that bridge: Ward Brothers (Not on CD) / Hymn to her: Pretenders.
2LP: . . . . **NOW 9**
MCSET: . . . . **TCNOW 9**

NOW THAT'S WHAT I CALL MUSIC VOL.14 (Various artists).
Tracks: / Something's gotten hold of my heart: Almond, Marc/Gene Pitney / Two hearts: Collins, Phil / Stop: Erasure / Help: Bananarama & Lananeeneenoonoo / Looking for Linda: Hue & Cry / Fine time: Yazz/ Four letter word: Wilde, Kim / Stop: Brown, Sam / You got it: Orbison, Roy / She drives me crazy: Fine Young Cannibals / Need you tonight: INXS / Burning bridges (on and off and on again): Status Quo/ Big area: Then Jerico / Last of the famous international playboys, The: Morrissey / Every rose has it's thorn: Poison / Belfast child: Simple Minds / Buffalo stance: Cherry, Neneh / Good life: Inner City/ Hey music lover: S. Express / Blow the house down: Living In A Box / Promised land: Style Council/ Respect: Adeva / Wild thing: Tone Loc / I live for your love: Cole, Natalie / First time: Beck, Robin / Straight up: Abdul, Paula / I only wanna be with you: Fox, Samantha / Be my twin: Brother Beyond/ Love like a river: Climie Fisher / All she wants is: Duran Duran / Tracie: Level 42 / Love changes everything: Ball, Michael.
2LP: . . . . **NOW 14**
MCSET: . . . . **TCNOW 14**

NOW THAT'S WHAT I CALL MUSIC VOL.4 (Various artists).
Tracks: / No more lonely nights (Arthur Baker remix): McCartney, Paul / Together in electric dreams: Moroder & Oakey/ Why: Bronski Beat / Never ending story: Limahl / Warning sign: Heyward, Nick / Missing you: Waite, John / Farewell my summer love: Jackson, Michael / Hello: Richie, Lionel / War song: Culture Club/ Passengers: John, Elton / Too late for goodbyes: Lennon, Julian / Shout to the top: Style Council/ Doctor doctor: Thompson Twins / Sunset now: Heaven 17 / Respect yourself: Kane Gang / Private dancer: Turner, Tina / It's a hard life: Queen / Wanderer: Status Quo / East of Eden: Big Country (group)/ Pride (in the name of love): U2/ Listen to your father: Sharkey, Feargal / Tesla girls: O.M.D. / Second time, The: Wilde, Kim / Human racing: Kershaw, Nik / Ghostbusters: Parker, Ray Jnr. / If it happens again: UB40 / Jump: Pointer Sisters / Hot water: Level 42 / Sexcrime (1984): Eurythmics/ Somebody's watching me: Rockwell / Madame Butterfly: McLaren, Malcolm / Gotta get you home tonight: Wilde, Eugene.
2LP: . . . . **NOW 4**
MCSET: . . . . **TCNOW 4**

NOW THAT'S WHAT I CALL MUSIC VOL.8 (Various artists).
Tracks: / Showing out (get fresh at the weekend): Mel & Kim / We don't have to take our clothes off: Stewart, Jermaine(Not on CD) / Step right up: Graham, Jaki / What have you done for me lately: Jackson, Janet (Not on CD) / Human: Human League (Not on CD) / I wanna wake up with you: Gardiner, Boris (Not on CD) / Dont give up: Gabriel, Peter & Kate Bush / Think for a minute: Housemartins (Not on CD) / (Waiting for) the ghost train: Madness/ In the army now: Status Quo (Not on CD) / Stuck with you: Lewis, Huey & The News / One great thing: Big Country (group) (Not on CD) / Greetings to the new brunette: Bragg, Billy (Not on CD) / (I just) died in your arms: Cutting Crew (Not on CD) / You keep me hangin' on: Wilde, Kim / Calling all the heroes: It Bites / Waterloo: Various artists / French kissin' in the USA: Harry, Debbie / I didn't mean to turn you on: Palmer, Robert / Wizard, The: Hardcastle, Paul (Not on CD) / Close to you: Guthrie, Gwen (Not on CD) / Every loser wins: Berry, Nick (Not on CD) / (Forever) live and die: O.M.D. / Notorious: Duran Duran / Suburbia: Pet Shop Boys / Walk this way: Run D.M.C. / Don't leave me this way: Communards (Not on CD) / Breakout: Swing Out Sister / Higher love: Winwood, Steve (Not on CD) / In too deep: Genesis / Word up: Cameo/ I'm not perfect (but I'm perfect for you): Jones, Grace.
2LP: . . . . **NOW 8**
MCSET: . . . . **TCNOW 8**

NOW THAT'S WHAT I CALL MUSIC VOL.6 (Various artists).
Tracks: / One vision: Queen / When a heart beats: Kershaw, Nik / Good heart, A: Sharkey, Feargal / There must be an angel (playing with my heart): Eurythmics / Alive and kicking: Simple Minds / Its only love: Adams, Bryan & Tina Turner / Empty rooms: Moore, Gary / Lavender: Marillion / Nikita: John, Elton/ Running up that hill: Bush, Kate / Something about you: Level 42 / We don't need another hero: Turner, Tina / Don't break my heart: UB40 / I got you babe: UB40/Chrissie Hynde / She's so beautiful: Richard, Cliff / Separate lives: Collins, Phil & Marilyn Martin / Election day: Arcadia / Blue: Fine Young Cannibals/ If I was: Ure, Midge / Cities in dust: Siouxsie & Banshees / Uncle Sam: Madness / Lost weekend: Cole, Lloyd & The Commotions / You are my world: Communards / Just for money: Hardcastle, Paul / Miami vice theme: Hammer, Jan / Body rock: Vidal, Maria / Tarzan boy: Baltimora / Body and soul: Mai Tai / Single life: Cameo / Mated: Graham, Jaki & David Grant.
MCSET: . . . . **TCNOW 6**
2LP: . . . . **NOW 6**

NOW THAT'S WHAT I CALL MUSIC VOL.13 (Various artists).
Tracks: / Only way is up, The: Yazz & The Plastic Population / Teardrops: Womack & Womack / Little respect, A: Erasure / Harvest for the world: Christians / Ordinary angel: Hue & Cry / Breakfast in bed: UB40/Chrissie Hynde / She makes my day: Palmer, Robert / Hands to heaven: Breathe / Groovy kind of love: Collins, Phil / Don't worry, be happy: McFerrin, Bobby / Kiss: Art Of Noise & Tom Jones / Let's stick together: Ferry, Bryan / You came: Wilde, Kim / Don't make me wait: Bomb The Bass / Harder I try, The: Brother Beyond/ He ain't heavy, he's my brother: Hollies / Twist, The (yo twist): Fat Boys & Chubby Checker / Wee rule: Wee Papa Girl Rappers / Twist and shout: Salt 'N' Pepa / Race, The: Yello / Big fun: Inner City/Kevin Saunderson/ We call it acieed: D-Mob/Gary Haisman / Burn it up: Beatmasters with P.P.Arnold / Girl you know it's true: Milli Vanilli / Heaven in my hands: Level 42 / Rush hour: Wiedlin, Jane / I'm gonna be (500 miles): Proclaimers / Secret garden: T'Pau / I want your love: Transvision Vamp / I don't want your love: Duran Duran / Love is all that matters: Human League / Martha's harbour: All About Eve.
2LP: . . . . **NOW 13**
MCSET: . . . . **TCNOW 13**

NOW THAT'S WHAT I CALL MUSIC VOL.10 (Various artists).
Tracks: / Barcelona: Mercury, Freddie & Montserrat Caballe / Rent: Pet Shop Boys / Never can say goodbye: Communards/ Pump up the volume: M/A/R/R/S / Labour of love: Hue & Cry / Real thing, The: Jellybean featuring Steven Dante / I don't want to be a hero: Johnny Hates Jazz / Wanted: Style Council / China in your hand: T'Pau/ Alone: Heart / Crazy crazy nights: Kiss / Mony mony: Idol, Billy / Here I go again (USA remix): Whitesnake/ Rain in the summertime: Alarm / Sugar mice: Marillion / Sweet little mystery: Wet Wet Wet / Misfit: Curiosity Killed The Cat / La bamba: Los Lobos / Wipe out: Fat Boys & The Beach Boys / Love in the first degree: Bananarama / My pretty one: Richard, Cliff / Hey Matthew: Fialka, Karel / Crockett's theme (Instrumental new mix): Hammer, Jan / My baby just cares for me: Simone, Nina / Circus, The (remix): Erasure/ Build: Housemartins / It's over (Remix): Level 42 / When Smokey sings: ABC / Hourglass: Squeeze/ Fairytale of New York: Pogues with Kirsty MacColl.
2LP: . . . . **NOW 10**
MCSET: . . . . **TCNOW 10**

NOW THAT'S WHAT I CALL MUSIC VOL.11 (Various artists).
Tracks: / Always on my mind: Pet Shop Boys / Heaven is a place on earth: Carlisle, Belinda / Get outta my dreams, get into my car: Ocean, Billy / Say it again: Stewart, Jermaine / Gimme hope Jo'anna: Grant, Eddy / C'mon everybody: Cochran, Eddie / Suedehead: Morrissey / Candle in the wind: John, Elton / Angel eyes (home and away): Wet Wet Wet / Turn back the clock: Johnny Hates Jazz / Hot in the city: Idol, Billy/ Mandinka: O'Connor, Sinead / Tower of strength: Mission / Give me all your love: Whitesnake / Valentine: T'Pau / I should be so lucky: Minogue, Kylie / That's the way it is: Mel & Kim / Come into my life (Radio): Sims, Joyce / Who found who: Jellybean & Elisa Fiorillo / I can't help it: Bananarama / Oh l'amour: Dollar / Joe le taxi: Paradis, Vanessa / Stutter rap (no sleep til bedtime): Morris Minor & The Majors / Beat dis: Bomb The Bass / Doctorin' the house: Cold Cut featuring Yazz & The Plastic Population/ House arrest: Krush / Jack that house built, The: Jack 'n' Chill / Rock da house: Beatmasters, featuring The Cookie Crew / Tired of getting pushed around: 2 Guys, A Drum Machine.. / Rise to the occasion: Climie Fisher.
2LP: . . . . **NOW 11**
MCSET: . . . . **TCNOW 11**

NOW THAT'S WHAT I CALL MUSIC VOL.12 (Various artists).
Tracks: / With a little help from my friends: Wet Wet Wet / Circle in the sand: Carlisle, Belinda / Wild world: Priest, Maxi / Give a little love: Aswad / Love changes (everything): Climie Fisher / I don't wanna go on with you like that: John, Elton / Oh Patti (don't feel sorry for loverboy): Scritti Politti / In the air tonight (88 remix): Collins, Phil / Don't go: Hothouse Flowers / Everyday is like Sunday: Morrissey/ Mary's prayer: Danny Wilson / Heart of gold: Johnny Hates Jazz / Don't call me baby: Voice Of The Beehive/ Can I play with madness: Iron Maiden / These dreams: Heart / I will be with you: T'Pau / Doctorin' the tardis: Time Lords / Boys (summertime love): Sabrina / I want you back: Bananarama / I think we're alone now: Tiffany / Who's leaving who: Dean, Hazell / There's more to love: Communards / Get lucky: Stewart, Jermaine / Nothing's gonna change my love for you: Medeiros, Glenn / Theme from S.Express: S. Express/ Push it: Salt 'N' Pepa / Bad young brother: Derek B. / Payback mix: Brown, James / Car wash: Rose Royce / Pink cadillac: Cole, Natalie / Just a mirage: Jellybean & Adele Berte / Love supreme, A (radio mix): Downing, Will.
2LP: . . . . **NOW 12**
MCSET: . . . . **TCNOW 12**

NOW THAT'S WHAT I CALL MUSIC VOL.2 (Various artists).
Tracks: / Radio Ga Ga: Queen / Wouldn't it be good: Kershaw, Nik / Hold me now: Thompson Twins / Get out of your lazy bed: Matt Bianco / More more more: Carmel / Michael Caine: Madness / Only you: Flying Pickets / 99 Red balloons: Nena / Girls just want to have fun: Lauper, Cyndi / My guy's mad at me: Ullman, Tracey / Break my stride: Wilder, Matthew / Breakin' down: Julia & Company / That's livin' alright: Fagin, Joe / I gave you my heart (didn't I): Hot Chocolate / Bird of Paradise: Snowy White / Relax: Frankie Goes To Hollywood / Here comes the rain again: Eurythmics / What is love: Jones, Howard / What difference does it make: Smiths / Feels like heaven: Fiction Factory / Politics of dancing, The: Re-Flex / Hyperactive: Dolby, Thomas / Wishful thinking: China Crisis / Modern love: Bowie, David / It's a miracle: Culture Club / Undercover of the night: Rolling Stones / Wonderland: Big Country (group) / Run runaway: Slade/ New moon on Monday: Duran Duran / Pipes of peace: McCartney, Paul.
2LP: . . . . **NOW 2**
MCSET: . . . . **TCNOW 2**

NOW THAT'S WHAT I CALL MUSIC VOL.3 (Various artists).
Tracks: / Reflex, The: *Duran Duran* / I won't let the sun go down on me: *Kershaw, Nik* / Thinking of you: *Sister Sledge* / Locomotion, The: *O.M.D.* / Dancing with tears in my eyes: *Ultravox* / Pearl in the shell: *Jones*, Howard / Don't tell me: *Blancmange* / Against all odds: *Collins, Phil* / Two tribes: *Frankie Goes To...* / White lines (don't don't do it): *Grandmaster Melle Mel* / Nelson Mandela / Love wars: *Womack & Womack* / You're the best thing: *Style Council* / One love / People get ready / Smalltown boy: *Bronski Beat* / I want to break free: *Queen* / Time after time: *Lauper, Cyndi* / Love resurrection: *Moyet, Alison* / Young at heart: *Bluebells*/ Robert De Niro's waiting: *Bananarama* / Doctor Mabuse: *Propaganda* / What's love got to do with it: *Turner*, Tina / When you're young and in love: *Flying Pickets* / Wake me up before you go go: *Wham* / You take me up: *Thompson Twins* / It's raining men: *Weather Girls* / Dance me up: *Glitter, Gary* / Susanna: *Art Company*/ One better day: *Madness* / Red guitar: *Sylvian, David*.
2LP: . . . . **NOW 3**
MCSET: . . . . **TCNOW 3**

NOW THAT'S WHAT I CALL MUSIC VOL.7 (Various artists).
Tracks: / Sledgehammer: *Gabriel, Peter* / Sing our own song: *UB40* / Let's go all the way: *Sly Fox* / Lessons in love: *Level 42* / Opportunities (Lets make lots of money): *Pet Shop Boys* / Sinful!: *Wylie, Pete*/ Camouflage: *Ridgway, Stan* / Paranoimia: *Art Of Noise With Duane Eddy* / Lady in red: *De Burgh, Chris*/ Absolute beginners: *Bowie, David* / Invisible touch: *Genesis* / All the things she said: *Simple Minds*/ Happy hour: *Housemartins* / Look away: *Big Country (group)* / Brilliant mind: *Furniture* / Call of the wild: *Various artists* / Edge of heaven: *Wham* / My favourite waste of time: *Paul, Owen* / Too good to be forgotten: *Amazulu* / Spirit in the sky: *Dr. & The Medics* / New beginning (Mamba Seyra): *Bucks Fizz*/ Hunting high and low (Remix): *A-Ha* / Holding back the years: *Simply Red* / When the going gets tough (the tough get going): *Ocean, Billy* / Set me free: *Graham, Jaki* / I can't wait: *Nu Shooz* / (Bang zoom) Let's go go: *Real Roxanne with Hitman Howie Tee* / Amityville (house on the hill): *Lovebug Starski* / Headlines: *Midnight Star* / You and me tonight: *Aurra* / On my own: *Patti La Belle and Michael McDonald*.
2LP: . . . . **NOW 7**
MCSET: . . . . **TCNOW 7**

NOW THAT'S WHAT I CALL MUSIC VOL.16 (Various artists).
Tracks: / Sowing the seeds of love: *Tears For Fears* / Leave a light on: *Carlisle, Belinda* / Drama: *Erasure*/ I wan't that man: *Harry, Debbie* / If only I could: *Youngblood, Sydney* / Name and number: *Curiosity Killed* The Cat / You keep it all in: *Beautiful South* / Sweet surrender: *Wet Wet Wet* / Breakthru: *Queen*/ Best, The: *Turner, Tina* / Born to be sold: *Transvision Vamp* / Waterfall '89: *Wendy & Lisa* / Sensual world, The: *Bush, Kate* / I'm not the man I used to be: *Fine Young Cannibals* / Sugarbox: *Then Jerico*/ Room in your heart: *Living In A Box* / Right here waiting: *Marx, Richard* / Girl I'm gonna miss you: *Milli Vanilli* / Street tuff: *Rebel MC & Double Trouble* / On our own: *Brown, Bobby (1)* / Pump up the jam: *Technotronic* featuring Felly / French kiss / I thank you: *Adeva* / C'mon and get my love: *D Mob featuring Cathy Dennis*/ Eye know: *De La Soul* / Whatcha gonna do with my lovin': *Inner City* / Can't shake the feeling: *Big Fun*/ I just don't have the heart: *Richard, Cliff* / Comment te dire adieu: *Somerville, Jimmy/June Miles Kingston*/ Drive on: *Brother Beyond*.
2LP: . . . . **NOW 16**
2LP: **793 673 1**
MCSET: . . . . **TCNOW 16**
MCSET: **793 672 4**

NOW THAT'S WHAT I CALL MUSIC VOL.5 (Various artists).
Tracks: / View to a kill, A: *Duran Duran* / Word girl, The: *Scritti Politti* / Axel F: *Faltermeyer, Harold*/ Johnny come home: *Fine Young Cannibals* / In too deep: *Dead or Alive* / Icing on the cake: *Duffy, Stephen* "Tin Tin" / Cherish: *Kool & The Gang* / Every time you go away: *Young, Paul* / Kayleigh: *Marillion*/ Slave to love: *Ferry, Bryan* / This is not America: *Bowie, David/Pat Metheny Group* / Don't you (forget about me): *Simple Minds* / Get it on: *Power Station* / Black man Ray: *China Crisis* / One more night: *Collins*, Phil / Frankie: *Sister Sledge* / History: *Mai Tai* / Money's too tight to mention: *Simply Red* / Feel so real: *Arrington, Steve* / Round and around: *Graham, Jaki* / Turn it up: *Conway Brothers* / Magic Touch: *Loose Ends* / N-n-nineteen not out: *Commentators* / Unforgettable fire, The: *U2* / Walls come tumbling down: *Style Council* / Walking on sunshine: *Katrina & The Waves* / Out in the fields: *Moore, Gary & Phil Lynott*/ Shadow of love: *Damned* / Life in one day: *Jones, Howard* / Love don't live here anymore: *Nail, Jimmy*.
2LP: . . . . **NOW 5**
MCSET: . . . . **TCNOW 5**

NOW THAT'S WHAT I CALL MUSIC VOL. 19 (Various artists).
Tracks: / Should I stay or should I go: *Clash* / She's a woman: *Scritti Politti feat. Shabba Ranks* / You got the love: *Source Featuring Candi Staton* / 3 a.m. eternal: *KLF featuring Children Of The Revolution* / Gonna make you sweat: *C & C Music Factory* / (I wanna give you) devotion: *Nomad feat. MC Mikee Freedom* / I believe: *EMF*/ In yer face: *808 State* / Unfinished sympathy: *Massive* / Pray: *M.C. Hammer* / G.L.A.D.: *Appleby*, Kim / What do I have to do: *Minogue, Kylie* / Stonk, The: *Hale & Pace & The Stonkers* / Wiggle it: *2 In A Room* / Play that funky music: *Vanilla Ice* / Bow down mister: *Jesus Loves You* / Sadness part 1: *Enigma* (90's) / Only you: *Praise...* / Get here: *Adams, Oleta* / Cry for help: *Astley, Rick* / Mercy mercy me/I want you: *Palmer, Robert* / I've had the time of my life: *Medley, Bill & Jennifer Warnes* / You've lost that lovin' feelin': *Righteous Brothers* / Crazy: *Seal* / This is your life: *Banderas* / Because I love you: *Stevie B* / Auberge: *Rea, Chris* / Blue hotel: *Isaak, Chris* / All right now (Bob Clearmountain remix): *Free* / Disappear: *INXS* / Summer rain: *Carlisle, Belinda* / Every beat of the heart: *Railway Children*/ Love walked in: *Thunder* / Innuendo: *Queen*.
2LP: . . . . **NOW 19**
MCSET: . . . . **TCNOW 19**

NOW-THE SUMMER ALBUM (Various artists).
Tracks: / Groovin': *Young Rascals* / Summer breeze: *Isley Brothers* / Do it again: *Beach Boys* / Lovely day: *Withers, Bill* / Dreadlock holiday: *10 CC* / Girl from Ipanema: *Gilberto, Astrud* / Summer (The first time): *Goldsboro, Bobby* / Summer holiday: *Richard, Cliff* / California girls: *Beach Boys* / Summertime blues: *Cochran, Eddie* / Sunny afternoon: *Kinks* / Under the boardwalk: *Drifters* / California dreamin': *Mamas & Papas* / San Francisco (be sure to wear flowers in your hair): *McKenzie, Scott* / All you need is love: *Beatles* / Sun goes down (living it up). The: *Level 42* / Walking on sunshine: *Katrina & The Waves*/ Give it up: *K.C. & The Sunshine Band* / Fantastic day: *Haircut 100* / Island girl: *John, Elton* / Echo beach: *Martha & The Muffins* / Summer fun: *Barracudas* / Here comes the sun: *Beatles* / Day I met Marie, The: *Richard, Cliff* / In the Summertime: *Various artists* / Daydream: *Various artists* / Daydream believer: *Monkees* / Here comes summer: *Keller, Jerry*.
LP: . . . . **SUMMER 1**
MC: . . . . **TC SUMMER 1**

OUT NOW: 28 HOT HITS (Various artists).
Tracks: / Everybody wants to rule the world: *Tears For Fears* / Heat is on, The: *Frey, Glenn* / Could it be I'm falling in love: *Grant, David & Jaki Graham* / Do what you do: *Jackson, Jermaine* / Fresh: *Kool & The Gang*/ Move closer: *Nelson, Phyllis* / Love is a battlefield: *Benatar, Pat* / We close our eyes: *Go West* / I feel love: *Bronski Beat & Marc Almond* / Riddle, The: *Kershaw, Nik* / Thinking of you: *Colourfield*/ Last kiss, The: *Cassidy, David* / Change your mind: *Sharpe & Numan* / Lay your hands on me: *Thompson Twins*/ Grimly fiendish: *Damned* / Let's go together: *Change* / Don't come around here no more: *Petty, Tom*/ Cry: *Godley & Creme* / Cool it now: *New Edition* / Rage to love: *Wilde, Kim* / Between the wars: *Bragg*, Billy / Love like blood: *Killing Joke* / Piece of the action: *Meatloaf* / Don't worry, baby: *Los Lobos*/ Music and you: *Solo, Sal* / Got a little heartache: *Stardust, Alvin* / Gun law: *Kane Gang*.
2LP: . . . . **OUTV 1**
MC: . . . . **ZOUTV 1**

OUT NOW: VOL 2 (Various artists).
Tracks: / Money for nothing: *Dire Straits* / If I was: *Ure, Midge* / Don't stop the dance: *Ferry, Bryan*/ White wedding: *Idol, Billy* / I can dream about you: *Hartman, Dan* / Brand new friend: *Cole, Lloyd*/ Knock on wood: *Stewart, Amii* / Say I'm your number one: *Princess* / Don Quixote: *Kershaw, Nik* / Power of love, The: *Lewis, Huey & The News* / Lodgers, The: *Style Council* / Excitable: *Amazulu* / I'll be good: *Rene & Angela* / Don't mess with Doctor Dream: *Various artists* / Rebel yell: *Idol, Billy* / Do not disturb: *Bananarama* / Hot fun: *7th Heaven* / Two rivers: *Adventures* / Trapped: *Abrams, Colonel* / Oh Sheila: *Ready For The World* / Obession: *Animotion* / Goodbye girl: *Go West* / Is it a dream: *Damned*/ Strength: *Alarm* / I wish he didn't trust me so much: *Womack, Bobby* / Romeo where's Juliet: *College*/ When it's over: *Bertei, Adele* / Shadows of the night: *Benatar, Pat*.
2LP: . . . . **OUTV 2**
MC: . . . . **ZOUTV 2**

OVERLOAD (Various artists).
LP: . . . . **RTL 2079**
MC: **4CRTL 2079**

P.I. PRIVATE INVESTIGATIONS (Various artists).
Tracks: / City of shadows: *Spence, Brian* / Something about you: *Level 42* / Loving of a stranger, The: *Brady*, Paul / Wanted dead or alive: *Bon Jovi* / Hold the heart: *Big Country (group)* / Layla: *Derek & The Dominoes*/ River of people: *Love & Money* / Do the dinosaur: *Was Not Was* (Previously unreleased version of the hit 'Walk The Dinosaur') / Mothers talk (US mix): *Tears For Fears* / Long white car: *Hipsway* / Running away: *Lone Prey*/ True confessions: *Bananarama* / Ghost town: *Munro, Murray*.
LP: . . . . **MERH 107**
MC: . . . . **MERHC 107**
LP: **816 463-1**
MC: **816 463-4**

RAIDERS OF THE POP CHARTS (Various artists).
LP: . . . . **RTL 2088**

RAISED ON ROCK - '80S UK ROCK (Various artists).
Tracks: / Come on Eileen: *Dexy's Midnight Runners* / Night games: *Bonnet, Graham* / Killer on the loose: *Thin Lizzy* / Wanderer, The: *Status Quo* / Shot in the dark: *Osbourne, Ozzy* / Take that situation: *Heyward*, Nick / Holding out for a hero: *Tyler, Bonnie* / Unchain my heart: *Cocker, Joe* / Garden party: *Marillion*/ I want candy: *Bow Wow Wow* / Wild boys: *Duran Duran* / Love and pride: *King* / Breaking the law: *Judas Priest* / Golden brown: *Stranglers*.
MC: . . . . **RORMC 17005**

RAISED ON ROCK - '80S US ROCK (Various artists).
Tracks: / Rosanna: *Toto* / Modern girl: *Meatloaf* / If you let me stay: *D'arby, Terence Trent* / Broken wings: *Mr. Mister* / Keep on loving you: *REO Speedwagon* / Dreamtime: *Hall, Daryl* / Bette Davis eyes: *Carnes, Kim* / We built this city: *Starship* / I can't go for that: *Hall & Oates* / Rockit: *Hancock*, Herbie / Living in America: *Brown, James* / Talk to me: *Nicks, Stevie* / Let's groove: *Earth, Wind & Fire* / Walking on sunshine: *Katrina & The Waves*.
MC: . . . . **RORMC 17006**

ROCK 'N' ROLL YEARS 1980 (Various artists).
Tracks: / Tide is high, The: *Blondie* / I can't stand up for falling down: *Costello, Elvis & The Attractions*/ Too much too young: *Specials* / Geno: *Dexy's Midnight Runners* / Winner takes it all: *Abba* / Babooshka: *Bush, Kate* / Let's go round again: *Average White Band* / Use it up and wear it out: *Odyssey* / Oops up side your head: *Gap Band* / Groove: *Franklin, Rodney* / Funky town: *Lipps Inc.* / Bourgie bourgie: *Knight*, Gladys / Going underground: *Jam* / Modern girl: *Easton, Sheena* / No doubt about it: *Hot Chocolate*/ Celebration: *Kool & The Gang* / Never knew love like this before: *Mills, Stephanie* / Jane: *Jefferson Starship*/ Ant music: *Adam & The Ants* / Turning Japanese: *Vapors* / January February: *Dickson, Barbara* / All out of love: *Air Supply* / Suicide is painless (Theme from M*A*S*H): *M.A.S.H.* / Wednesday week: *Undertones*.
LP: . . . . **YRNRLP 80**
MC: . . . . **YRNRMC 80**

ROCK 'N' ROLL YEARS 1981 (Various artists).
Tracks: / Good year for the roses, A: *Costello, Elvis & The Attractions* / Bette Davis eyes: *Carnes, Kim* / Ghost town: *Specials* / It's gonna happen: *Undertones* / Favourite shirts (boy meets girl): *Haircut 100* / Chant no.1 (I don't need this pressure on): *Spandau Ballet* / I want to be free: *Toyah* / Absolute beginners: *Jam*/ Kids in America: *Wilde, Kim* / Rock this town: *Stray Cats* / Wedding bells: *Godley & Creme* / Let's groove: *Earth, Wind & Fire* / Keep on loving you: *REO Speedwagon* / One of us: *Abba* / How 'bout us: *Champaign*/ Japanese boy: *Aneka* / Hucklebuck, The: *Coast To Coast* / Star: *Dee, Kiki* / Happy birthday: *Altered* Images / Stand and deliver: *Adam & The Ants* / For your eyes only: *Easton, Sheena* / Runaround Sue: *Racey*/ Reward: *Teardrop Explodes* / Fade to grey: *Visage*.
LP: . . . . **YRNRLP 81**
MC: . . . . **YRNRMC 81**

ROCK 'N' ROLL YEARS 1982 (Various artists).
Tracks: / Golden brown: *Stranglers* / Poison arrow: *ABC* / Sexual healing: *Gaye, Marvin* / Island of lost souls: *Blondie* / Message, The: *Grandmaster Flash & The Furious Five* / View from a bridge: *Wilde, Kim*/ It started with a kiss: *Hot Chocolate* / Fame: *Cara, Irene* / Go wild in the country: *Bow Wow Wow* / Town called Malice, A: *Jam* / Ever so lonely: *Monsoon* / Harry's Game, Theme from: *Clannad* / Dead ringer for love: *Meatloaf* / Inside out: *Odyssey* / Centrefold: *Geils, J. Band* / T'aint what you do: *Fun* Boy Three & Bananarama / Lion sleeps tonight, The: *Tight Fit* / Seven tears: *Goombay Dance Band* / Get down on it: *Kool & The Gang* / Drowning in Berlin: *Mobiles* / Starmaker: *Kids From Fame* / Goody two shoes: *Ant, Adam* / Oh Julie: *Stevens, Shakin'* / Just what I always wanted: *Wilson, Mari*.
LP: . . . . **YRNRLP 82**
MC: . . . . **YRNRMC 82**

ROCK 'N' ROLL YEARS 1983 (Various artists).
Tracks: / Family man: *Hall & Oates* / Africa: *Toto* / True: *Spandau Ballet* / Down under: *Men At Work* / Tonight I celebrate my love: *Bryson & Flack* / Heartbreaker: *Warwick, Dionne* / Marguerita time: *Status Quo* / Love town: *Newbury, Booker* / Give it up: *K.C. & The Sunshine Band* / We are detectives: *Thompson Twins* / White lines: *Grandmaster Flash & Melle Mel* / Sun goes down, The (living it up): *Level 42* / Total eclipse of the heart: *Tyler, Bonnie* / In a big country: *Big Country (group)* / What kinda boy you looking for (girl): *Hot Chocolate* / Rockit: *Hancock, Herbie* / Garden party: *Marillion* / Sign of the times: *Belle Stars* / Too shy: *Kajagoogoo* / Dancing tight: *Galaxy and Phil Fearon* / Boxerbeat: *Joboxers* / Rip it up: *Orange Juice* / Only for love: *Limahl* / Don't talk to me about love: *Altered Images*.
LP: . . . . **YRNRLP 83**
MC: . . . . **YRNRMC 83**

SATURDAY SUPERSTORE - REPLAY SELECTION (Various artists).
Tracks: / Young guns (go for it): *Wham* / Mad world: *Tears For Fears* / Run for your life: *Bucks Fizz*/ Get the balance right: *Depeche Mode* / Don't talk to me about love: *Altered Images* / Lies: *Thompson Twins*/ I don't wanna dance: *Grant, Eddy* / Butterfly ball: *Sgt. Frog* / Too shy: *Kajagoogoo* / Sweet dreams (are made of this): *Eurythmics* / High life: *Modern Romance* / Living on the ceiling: *Blancmange* / Down under: *Men At Work* / Shiny shiny: *Haysi Fantayzee* / Ooh la la la (let's go dancing): *Kool & The Gang*/ Let's get this straight: *Rowland, Kevin & Dexy's Midnight Runners* / Total eclipse of the heart: *Tyler, Bonnie*.
LP: . . . . **REB 489**
MC: . . . . **ZCF 489**

SATURDAY SUPERSTORE SELECTION REPLAY, VOL 2 (Various artists).
Tracks: / Wake me up before you go go: *Wham* / Dancing girls: *Kershaw, Nik* / People are people: *Depeche Mode* / New song: *Jones, Howard* / I'm falling: *Bluebells* / Lament: *Ultravox* / Move over, darling: *Ullman, Tracey* / Love of the common people: *Young, Paul* / One better day: *Madness* / Nelson Mandela: *Special AKA* / Get out of your lazy bed: *Matt Bianco* / I feel like Buddy Holly: *Stardust, Alvin* / Sixteen: *Musical Youth* / Love worth waiting for, A: *Stevens, Shakin'*.
LP: . . . . **CDL 1494**
MC: . . . . **ZCDL 1494**

SECOND SUITE (Various artists).
Tracks: / Zaius: *Various artists* / Magic number, The: *Various artists* / Orange express: *Various artists*/ I ain't jivin': *Various artists* / I'm jammin': *Various artists* / Coming to you (live): *Various artists*/ Give peace a chance: *Various artists* / I want you for myself: *Various artists* / You're a star: *Various* artists / Wild dog: *Various artists* / Sign of the times: *Various artists* / Hill Street blues: *Various* artists / Home made jam: *Various artists* / First light of the morning: *Various artists* / Live to love: *Various* artists / Dreamin': *Various artists* / So much more: *Various artists* / Yuma: *Various artists* / Go away little boy: *Various artists*.
LP: . . . . **CBS 88566**

SMASH HITS OF '88 (Various artists).
LP: . . . . **CHR 1691**
MC: . . . . **ZCHR 1691**

SMASH HITS PARTY '88 (Various artists).
LP: . . . . **ADD 5**
MC: . . . . **ZDD 5**

SMASH HITS PARTY 89 (Various artists).
Tracks: / Especially for you: *Minogue, Kylie & Jason Donovan* / My prerogative: *Brown, Bobby (1)* / Stand up for your love rights: *Yazz* / She drives me crazy: *Fine Young Cannibals* / You'll never stop: *Sonia* / Blame it on the boogie: *Big Fun* / Help: *Bananarama & Lananeeneenoonoo* / Straight up: *Abdul, Paula* / Back to life (however do you want me): *Soul II Soul* / Good life: *Inner City* / Say no go: *De La Soul* / Blow the house down: *Living In A Box* / Cuddly toy: *Roachford* / Wages day: *Deacon Blue* / Looking for Linda: *Hue & Cry* / Can't stay: *Estefan, Gloria/Miami Sound Machine* / Buffalo stance: *Cherry, Neneh* / Stop: *Erasure* / Cat among the pigeons: *Bros* / Requiem: *London Boys* / Time warp (PWL mix): *Damian* / Pink sunshine: *Fuzzbox* / Baby don't forget my number: *Milli Vanilli* / Warning: *Adeva* / Hey music lover: *S. Express* / Grandpa's party: *Love, Monie* / Love train: *Johnson, Holly* / Baby I don't care: *Transvision Vamp* / You got it: *Orbison, Roy* / Song for whoever: *Beautiful South*.
LP: . . . . **CHR 1736**
MC: . . . . **ZCHR 1736**
2LP: . . . . **ADD 8**
MCSET: . . . . **ZDD 8**

SUPER HITS OF THE 80'S (Various artists).
MC: . . . . **BBM 141**

SUPERCHART : 83 (Various artists).
LP: . . . . **STAR 2236**
MC: . . . . **STAC 2236**

SUPERHITS, 1 & 2 (Various artists).
Tracks: / Love action (I believe in love): *Human League* / Cover plus - we're all grown up: *O'Connor, Hazel* / Back to the sixties (part 1): *Tight Fit* / This ole house: *Various artists* / New life: *Depeche Mode* / Swords of a thousand men: *Tenpole Tudor* / Feeding time: *Look* / Stat cat strut: *Stray Cats* / Something on the side: *Groovy, Winston* / Going back to my roots: *Odyssey* / Body talk: *Imagination* / Dancing on the floor: *Third World* / Razzamatazz: *Jones, Quincy* / It's a love thing: *Whispers* / Throw away the key: *Lynx* / Good thing going: *Minott, Sugar* / Jitterbuggin': *Heatwave* / Japanese boy: *Aneka* / Wunderbar: *Tenpole Tudor* / I wanna be free: *Toyah* / Grey day: *Madness* / Love song: *Simple Minds* / Love you, yes I love you: *Grant, Eddy* / Keep on loving you: *REO Speedwagon* / Live a life: *Black Slate* / Beach boy gold: *Gidea Park* / Stars on 45: *Starsound* / Super trouper: *Abba* / How 'bout us: *Champaign* / Will you?: *O'Connor, Hazel* / Rock 'n' roll dreams: *Steinman, Jim* / More than in love: *Robbins, Kate* / Piece of the action: *Bucks Fizz* / Stay the way you are: *Q-Tips* / Star: *Dee, Kiki*.
2LP: . . . . **RTL 2058 A/B**
MCSET: . . . . **4CRTL 2058 A/B**

TEMPLE OF TERPSICHORE (Various artists).
LP: . . . . **EMS 1004**

TOGETHER (Various artists).
Tracks: / There'll be sad songs (to make you cry): *Ocean, Billy* / Should've known better: *Diamond, Jim* / Tender love: *Force M.D.'s* / Zoom: *Fat Larry's Band* / Power of love,The: *Rush, Jennifer* / Amoureuse: *Dee, Kiki* / I'm in love baby: *Turner, Ruby* / You're everything to me: *Gardiner, Boris* / Move closer: *Nelson, Phyllis* / My favourite waste of time: *Paul, Owen* / Starting together: *Pollard, Su (aut)* / Only love: *Mouskouri, Nana* / Anyone who had a heart: *Dickson, Barbara* / If you don't know me by now: *Melvin, Harold & The Bluenotes* / Me and Mrs Jones: *Paul, Billy* / Secret Lovers: *Atlantic Starr*.
LP: . . . . **NE 1345**
MC: . . . . **CE 2345**
LP: . . . . **CBS 54679**
MC: **40 54679**

TOP 10 (Various artists).
LP: . . . . **MXLP 234**
MC: . . . . **MXMC 234**

TOP TEN HITS OF THE 80'S (Various artists).
Tracks: / Girls on film: *Duran Duran* / Running up that hill: *Bush, Kate* / Geno: *Dexy's Midnight Runners* / Golden brown: *Stranglers* / Kids in America: *Wilde, Kim* / Harder I try, The: *Brother Beyond* / Bette Davis eyes: *Carnes, Kim* / Tonight I celebrate my love: *Bryson, Peabo & Roberta Flack* / Kayleigh: *Marillion* / Set me free: *Graham, Jaki* / Model, The: *Kraftwerk* / Too shy: *Kajagoogoo* / Turning Japanese: *Vapors* / Searchin': *Dean, Hazell* / Walking on sunshine: *Katrina & The Waves* / Tarzan boy: *Baltimora* / Election day: *Arcadia* (CD only.) / Sexy eyes: *Dr. Hook* (CD only.) / No doubt about it: *Hot Chocolate* (CD only.) / Let's go all the way: *Sly Fox* (CD only.).
MC: . . . . **TCMFP 5893**

TRUELOVE (Various artists).
Tracks: / Hold me now: *Logan, Johnny* / No more the fool: *Brooks, Elkie* / Lies: *Butler, Jonathan* / Shake 'em on down: *Abbott, Gregory* / Weak in the presence of beauty: *Moyet, Alison* / Just to see her: *Robinson, Smokey* / I get the sweetest feeling: *Wilson, Jackie* / I just don't want: *McGregor, Freddie* / Loving you again: *Rea, Chris* / Goodbye girl: *Go West* / True: *Spandau Ballet* / Lorraine: *Jones, Oran "Juice"* / I'd rather go blind: *Turner, Ruby* / Endless love: *Ross, Diana/Richie, Lionel* / You caught my eye: *Boucher, Judy* / Come softly to me: *Fleetwoods*.
LP: . . . . **NE 1359**
MC: . . . . **CE 2359**

TURBO TRAX (Various artists).
LP: . . . . **NE 1176**
MC: . . . . **CE 2176**

TWENTY WITH A BULLET (Various artists).
LP: . . . . **EMTV 32**

VIDEO STARS Various Artists (Various artists).
LP: . . . . **NE 1066**
MC: . . . . **CE 2066**

WHAT Q SAID (Various artists).
Tracks: / Intervention: *Hudson, Lavine* / Dream kitchen: *Frazier Chorus* / All I wanted: *In Tua Nua* / In my heart and in my house: *Senators* / What'll you do 'til Sunday baby: *Win* / Out of the dark: *Jazz Devils* / Dear darling: *O'Hara, Mary Margaret* / I don't care about the past: *Senators* / Some things never change: *In* Tua Nua / Censored feelings: *Jazz Devils* / Body's in trouble: *O'Hara, Mary Margaret* / Sugar high: *Frazier Chorus* / Create in me a clean heart: *Hudson, Lavine* / Thokozile: *Mahlathini*.
MC: . . . . **TCQ 2**

ZANG TUUM TUMB SAMPLED (Various artists).
Tracks: / Closing: *Art of Noise* / Disneyland: *Frankie Goes To...* / Femme fatale: *Propaganda* / Intermission: *Pigalle, Anne* / Swamp out: *Instinct* / Egypt: *Art of Noise* / Object is a hungry wolf: *Poppy, Andrew* / P machinery: *Propaganda* / Looking for love: *Pigalle, Anne* / Time for fear, A: *Art of Noise* / Born to run: *Frankie Goes To...* / Object is a hungry wolf (extract no.2): *Poppy, Andrew*.
LP: **1Q 6**
MC: **1QC 6**

ZE-A CHRISTMAS RECORD Various artists (Various artists).
Tracks: / It's a holiday: *Various artists* / Things fall apart: *Various artists* / Christmas wrapping: *Various artists* / Christmas time in the motor city: *Various artists*.
LP: . . . . **ILPS 7017**
MC: . . . . **ICT 7017**

80's Colours

EIGHTIES COLOURS, VOL.2.
LP: . . . . **EELP 007**

84 Charing Cross

84 CHARING CROSS ROAD (1987 film soundtrack) (Various artists).
Tracks: / Fanfare maintitle (the journey): *Various artists* / Book of love poems: *Various artists* / Marks and co: *Various artists* / Dear speed: *Various artists* / Christmas gift, 1949: *Various artists* / Nora writes: *Various artists* / Church sonata in A: *Corelli (Composer)* / Pilgrimage - Helene and Frank: *Various artists* / Wedding, The: *Various artists* / Subway, The: *Various artists* / Love between friends: *Various artists* / Tred softly: *Various artists* / Helen's first letter: *Various artists* / Business as usual: *Various artists* / Festival of Britain conga: *Various artists* / Daydream: *Various artists* / Meeting Ginny and Ed: *Various artists* / Move, The, 1958/9: *Various artists* / New year, 1960 (Auld lang syne): *Various artists* / Hopes fade: *Various artists* / Love between friends (reprise): *Various artists* / 84 Charing Cross Road (closing credits): *Various artists*.
LP: . . . . **TER 1129**
MC: . . . . **ZCTER 1129**

86 (Band)

MINUTES IN A DAY.
Tracks: / Minutes in a day / Gems / Floating / Waiting / Smile / Just one.
LP: . . . . **HOLY 004**

PROVOCATION.
Tracks: / New pair of eyes / City, The / Shade of black / Seven weeks and one day / King's mountain / Eyeless / Sonambo / Wondering / Inside / Getaway / Wheel of confusion.
LP: . . . . **SAVE 047**
LP: . . . . **TRO 10**

9.0

TOO FAR GONE.
LP: . . . . **RR 93441**
MC: . . . . **RR 93444**

90 Degrees

FIRE OVER YONDER.
LP: . . . . **ICEL 1005**

90 Minutes...

NINETY MINUTES OF SUSPENSE (McConnell, Jean).
MC: . . . . **SOUND 38**

90's

GREATEST HITS 1990 (Various artists).
LP: . . . . **STAR 2439**
MC: . . . . **STAC 2439**

MONSTER HITS 2 (Snap! it up) (Various artists).
Tracks: / Treat me good: *Yazz* / I still haven't found what I'm looking for: *Chimes* / Hold on: *En Vogue* / Hello: *Beloved* / Black velvet: *Myles, Alannah* / Mona: *Mc Lachlan, Craig & Check One Two* / Crying scene: *Aztec Camera* / Downtown train: *Stewart, Rod* / Lily was here: *Stewart, David A & Candy Dulfer* / Softly whispering I love you: *Young, Paul* / Love thing: *Pasadenas* / Star: *Erasure* / Everybody, everybody: *Black Box* / Infinity: *Guru Josh* / Venus: *Don Pablo's Animals* / Hear the drummer (get wicked): *Jackson, Chad* / What did I do to you?: *Stansfield, Lisa* / I'm still waiting (remix): *Ross, Diana* / Free style (megamix): *Brown, Bobby (1)* / Ghetto heaven: *Family Stand* / Love shack: *B-52'S* / Birdhouse in your soul: *They Might Be Giants* / Celebrate: *An Emotional Fish* / Angel: *Eurythmics* / Here we are: *Estefan, Gloria* / Could have told you so: *Halo James* / You've got a friend: *Big Fun & Sonia* / Touched by the hand of god: *Pop* Will Eat Itself / World in motion: *England New Order* / Doin' the doo: *Boo, Betty* / Ooops up: *Snap* / Only rhyme that bites: *M.C. Tunes Vs 808 State*.
2LP: . . . . **HITS 12**
MCSET: . . . . **HITSC 12**

NOTHING COMPARES TO THIS (Various artists).
LP: . . . . **PMLP 5020**
MC: . . . . **PMMC 5020**

NOW THAT'S WHAT I CALL MUSIC 17 (Various artists).
Tracks: / Blue Savannah: *Erasure* / Better world: *Rebel MC* / Opposites attract: *Abdul, Paula* / Dub be good to me: *Beats International, featuring Lindy Layton* / Kingston town: *UB40* / Strawberry fields forever: *Candy Flip* / I don't wanna lose you: *Turner, Tina* / I wish it would rain down: *Collins, Phil* / He's gonna step on you again: *Happy Mondays* / Loaded: *Primal Scream* / Enjoy the silence: *Depeche Mode* / Real real real: *Jesus Jones* / This is how it feels: *Inspiral Carpets* / Shine on: *House Of Love* / From out of nowhere: *Faith No More* / Hey you: *Quireboys* / This beat is Technotronic: *Technotronic featuring MC* Eric / Happenin' all over again: *Gordon, Lonnie* / Don't you love me: *49ers* / Read my lips (enough is enough): *Somerville, Jimmy* (Available on CD and cassette.) / Stronger than that: *Richard, Cliff* / Another day in paradise: *Jamtronik* / Moments in soul: *J T & The Big Family* / Got to have your love: *Mantronix featuring Wondress* / Don't miss the partyline: *Bizz Nizz* / Everything starts with an 'E': *E Zee Possee* (Featuring MC Kinky.) / Put your hands together: *D Mob featuring Nuff Juice* / Killer: *Adamski* / Chime: *Orbital* / Tomorrow: *Tongue 'N' Cheek* / Talking with myself: *Electribe 101* / I'd rather go blind: *Youngblood, Sydney*.
2LP: . . . . **NOW 17**
MCSET: . . . . **TCNOW 17**

NOW THAT'S WHAT I CALL MUSIC VOL.18 (Various artists).
Tracks: / Little time, A: *Beautiful South* / Joker, The: *Miller, Steve Band* / Sacrifice: *John, Elton* / It must have been love: *Roxette* / Something happened on the way to heaven: *Collins, Phil* / Hold on: *Wilson* Phillips / Nothing compares 2U: *O'Connor, Sinead* / Unchained melody: *Righteous Brothers* / (We want) the same thing: *Carlisle, Belinda* / Anniversary waltz (part 1): *Status Quo* / Suicide blonde: *INXS* / Don't ask me: *Public Image Ltd (PIL)* / It's my life: *Talk Talk* / There she goes: *La's* / Be tender with me baby: *Turner, Tina* / I'll be your baby tonight: *Palmer, Robert/UB 40* / So hard: *Pet Shop Boys* / Fascinating rhythm: *Bass-O-Matic* / Missing you: *Soul II Soul featuring Rose Windrush* / Tom's diner: *DNA and Suzanne* Vega / Englishman in New York: *Sting* / Close to me: *Cure* / I've got you under my skin: *Cherry, Neneh* / Little brother: *Blue Pearl* / Step back in time: *Minogue, Kylie* / Don't worry: *Appleby, Kim* / Megamix: *Technotronic* / Itsy bitsy teeny weeny yellow polka dot bikini: *Bombalurina* / Where are you baby: *Boo, Betty* / Dirty cash (money talks): *Adventures Of Stevie V* / Have you seen her: *M.C. Hammer* / To love somebody: *Somerville, Jimmy*.
2LP: . . . . **NOW 18**
MCSET: . . . . **TCNOW 18**

SMASH HITS 1990 (Various artists).
Tracks: / U can't touch this: *M.C. Hammer* / Power, The: *Snap* / Naked in the rain: *Blue Pearl* / Rockin' over the beat: *Technotronic featuring Ya Kid K* / Doin' the do: *Boo, Betty* / Happenin' all over again: *Gordon,* Lonnie / Opposites attract: *Abdul, Paula* / Blue savannah: *Erasure* / Itsy bitsy teeny weeny yellow polka bot bikini: *Bombalurina* / Turtle power: *Partners In Kryme* / Mona: *McLachlan, Craig* / Tears on my pillow: *Minogue, Kylie* / Rhythm of the rain: *Donovan, Jason* / Could have told you so: *Halo James* / King of wishful thinking: *Go West* / End of the world: *Sonia* / Nothing compares 2 U: *O'Connor, Sinead* / Enjoy the silence: *Depeche Mode* / Groovy train: *Farm* / Step on: *Happy Mondays* / Only rhyme that bites, The: *M.C. Tunes Vs 808 State* / This is how it feels: *Inspiral Carpets* / Strawberry fields forever: *Candy Flip* / Dub be good to me: *Beats International, featuring Lindy Layton* / Poison: *Bell Biv Devoe* / It's a shame (my sister): *Love, Monie* / I'm free: *Soup Dragons* / Hello: *Beloved* / Silly games: *Layton, Lindy* / I still haven't found what I'm looking for: *Chimes*.
2LP: . . . . **ADD 18**
MCSET: . . . . **ZDD 18**

94 East

MINNEAPOLIS GENIUS.
Tracks: / If you feel like dancin' / Lovin' cup / Just another sucker / Dance to the music of the world / One man jam.
LP: . . . . **CLALP 132**
MC: . . . . **CLAMC 132**

100 Best Classics

TOP 10 OF YOUR 100 BEST CLASSICS (Volume 2) (Various artists).
LP: . . . . **AVM 1025**
MC: . . . . **AVMC 1025**

TOP 10 OF YOUR 100 BEST CLASSICS (Volume 1) (Various artists).
LP: . . . . **AVM 1016**
MC: . . . . **AVMC 1016**

100 Best Tunes

20 OF YOUR HUNDRED BEST TUNES (Various artists).
Tracks: / Fingal's cave: *Maag, Peter & The London Symphony Orchestra* / Abridged: *Goodman, Roy & The Choir of Angels* College, Cambridge / Sheep may safely graze: *Boult, Sir Adrian & The Orchestra of the Royal Opera House* / Elizabethan serenade: *Mortimer, Harry & Massed Brass Bands* / 1812 overture: *Alwyn, Kenneth & London Symphony Orchestra & Band* of the ... (...Grenadier Guards) / Blue Danube: *Dorati, Antal & London Philharmonic Orchestra* / Meditation: *Agoult,* Raymond & New Symphony Orchestra of London / Largo (xerxes): *Siell, George & London Symphony Orchestra* / Nessun dorma: *McKellar, Kenneth with Robert Sharples Orchestra* / Op 42 Toccata (Organ symphony no 5): *Britico, Windor* / K525 1st Met (Eine Kleine Nachtmusik): *Boskovsko, Wilh & The Vienna Mozart Ensemble* / Easter hymn: *Sulotis, Elan with Silvo* Varviso & Orchestra Coro di Roma / Fantasia on Greensleeves: *Marriner, Neville & Academy of St Martin in the Field* / Barcarolle: *Guirand, Carre, Sutherland, Tourangean,Bonynge & Orchestra..* (...De La Susse Romande) / Toccata and fugue in D Minor: *Richter, Karl* / Arrival of the Queen of Sheba, The: *Marriner, Neville & Academy of St Martin in the Field* / Elijah: *Ferrier, Kathleen with Boyd Neel & Orchestra* / Symphony No 7, (2nd movement) (Beethoven): *Schmudt-Isserstedt,* Hans & Vienna Philharmonic / Abide with me: *Burrows, Stuart & The Ambrosian Singers* / Dance of the sugar plum fairy: *Von Karajan, Herbert*.
2LP: . . . . **CCSLP 132**
MC: . . . . **CCSMC 132**

WORLD OF YOUR 100 BEST TUNES VOL 8 (Various artists).
MC: . . . . **KCSP 356**
LP: . . . . **SPA 356**

WORLD OF YOUR 100 BEST TUNES VOL 1 (Various artists).
LP: . . . . **SPA 112**
MC: . . . . **KCSP 112**

WORLD OF YOUR 100 BEST TUNES VOL 10 (Various artists).
MC: KCSP 400
LP: SPA 400

WORLD OF YOUR 100 BEST TUNES VOL 9 (Various artists).
LP: SPA 373
MC: KCSP 373

WORLD OF YOUR 100 BEST TUNES VOL 2 (Various artists).
LP: SPA 155
MC: KCSP 155

WORLD OF YOUR 100 BEST TUNES VOL 4 (Various artists).
LP: SPA 264
MC: KCSP 264

WORLD OF YOUR 100 BEST TUNES VOL 6 (Various artists).
MC: KCSP 316
LP: SPA 316

WORLD OF YOUR 100 BEST TUNES VOL 7 (Various artists).
LP: SPA 355
MC: KCSP 355

WORLD OF YOUR 100 BEST TUNES VOL 3 (Various artists).
LP: SPA 205
MC: KCSP 205

WORLD OF YOUR 100 BEST TUNES VOL 5 (Various artists).
LP: SPA 299
MC: KCSP 299

WORLD OF YOUR 100 BEST TUNES(NEW CHART) (Various artists).
LP: SPA 491
MC: KCSP 491

YOUR HUNDRED BEST TUNES (Various artists).
LPS: 16BB 22332
MC: K4M 18 PART 1
MC: K4M 19 PART 2

100 Minutes

100 MINUTES OF POPULAR CLASSICS (Various artists).
MC: ZCTON 127

100 Ton & A Feather

ONE HUNDRED TON & A FEATHER.
Tracks: / It only takes a minute / Rag doll / Learning the game / Skyline pigeon / Sisters of mercy / When a child is born / Sweet surrender / Don't forget me when you're on your island / Two lovers / One tin soldier / Easy loving / Precious few / Love around.
LP: UKAL 1025

101

100 ALL TIME CLASSIC DANCE HITS OF THE 1970'S (See Under 70's) (Various artists).

100 DANCE HITS OF THE 80'S (See Under Dance ...) (Various artists).

100 GREATEST CLASSICS VOL 1 (Various artists).
LP: TRX 144
MC: TRXC 144

100 GREATEST CLASSICS VOL 2 (Various artists).
LP: TRX 145
MC: TRXC 145

100 GREATEST CLASSICS VOL 3 (Various artists).
LP: TRX 146
MC: TRXC 146

100 GREATEST CLASSICS VOL 4 (Various artists).
LP: TRX 147
MC: TRXC 147

100 GREATEST CLASSICS VOL 5 (Various artists).
LP: TRX 148
MC: TRXC 148

100 GREATEST CLASSICS VOL 6 (Various artists).
LP: TRX 149
MC: TRXC 149

100 GREATEST CLASSICS VOL 7 (Various artists).
LP: TRX 150
MC: TRXC 150

100 GREATEST CLASSICS VOL 8 (Various artists).
LP: TRX 151
MC: TRXC 151

ONE HUNDRED AND ONE DALMATIANS (spoken word) (Rogers, Anton).
MC: Unknown

101 Club

101 CLUB - BEYOND THE GROOVE.
LP: 247 814 0

101 Dalmations

101 DALMATIONS (Film Soundtrack) (Various artists).
Tracks: / Playful melody: *Various artists* / Kanine krunchies kommercial: *Various artists* / Cruella De Ville: *Various artists* / Dalmation plantation: *Various artists.*
LP: WD 017
MC: WDC 017

101 DALMATIONS (Various artists).
LP: ST 3934
LP: REC 544
MC: ZCM 544

101 Strings

DOWN DRURY LANE TO MEMORY LANE.
LP: GGL 0061

GRAND CANYON SUITE.
LP: GGL 0048

GYPSY CAMPFIRES.
LP: GGL 0009

110 in the Shade

110 IN THE SHADE (Original Broadway Cast) (Various artists).
Tracks: / 110 in the shade (overture): *Various artists* (CD only.) / Gonna be another hot day: *Various artists*/ Lizzie's comin' home: *Various artists* / Love, don't turn away: *Various artists* / Poker polka: *Various* artists / Hungry moon: *Various artists* / Rain song: *Various artists* / You're not foolin' me: *Various* artists / Raunchy: *Various artists* / Man and a woman, A: *Various artists* / Old maid: *Various artists*/ Everything beautiful happens at night: *Various artists* / Melisande: *Various artists* / Simple little things: *Various artists* / Little red hat: *Various artists* / Is it really me?: *Various artists* / Wonderful music/Rain song finale: *Various artists.*
MC: GK 81085

200 Days

200 DAYS & 200 WAYS (Various artists).
LP: ZOO FOUR

2-4-2

2-4-2.
LP: RODNEY 1

24-7 Spyz

GUMBO MILLENIUM.
Tracks: / John Connelly's theory / New super hero worship / Deathstyle / Dude u knew / Culo posse / Don't push me / Spyz on piano / Valdez 27 million / Don't break my heart / We'll have power / Racism / Heaven and hell / We got a date / Dome defenders memories.
LP: 4671201
MC: 4671204

HARDER THAN YOU.
Tracks: / Grandma dynamite / Juni'z jam / Sypz dope / Social plague / I must go on / Ballots not bullets / Jungle boogie / Spill my guts / Sponji reggae / Tango skin polka / Pillage / New drug.
LP: 828 167 1
MC: 828 167 4

250

250 DISCO JINGLES (Various artists).
LP: R 108
MC: C 104

2.99

TWO NINETY NINE (Various artists).
LP: ASS 10

306 Album

3:06 ROOTS ALBUM FOR LIVERPOOL (Various artists).
LP: HILL 306

400 Blows

GOOD CLEAN ENGLISH FIST, THE.
Tracks: / Movin (extented remix 12" version) / Declaration of intent / Pressure / Jive 69 / Them thar hills / Groove jumping / Return of the dog, The / Breakdown / Conscience / For Jackie M..
LP: DOJOLP 14
MC: DOJOTC 14

IF I KISSED HER I'D HAVE TO KILL HER FIRST.
LP: JAMS 42

LOOK.
LP: AMA 27

NEW LORDS ON THE BLOCK.
LP: CPRODLP 008

YESTERDAY, TODAY, TOMORROW, FOREVER.
LP: CPRODLP 006

4-2-4

4-2-4 (The El football scrapbook) (Various artists).
Tracks: / Nice one Cyril: *Various artists* / I'm forever blowing bubbles: *Various artists* / Onward Sexton soldiers: *Various artists* / Canaries, The: *Various artists* / Football football: *Various artists* / World cup Willie: *Various artists* / Good old Arsenal: *Various artists* / Back home: *Various artists* / We are Wimbledon: *Various artists* / Belfast boy: *Various artists* / We are the owls: *Various artists* / Hibernian: *Various artists* / Going back to Derby: *Various artists* / Boys in blue: *Various artists* / Viva el Fulham: *Various artists* / Sunderland: *Various artists.*
LP: ACME 19

500

500 FANTASTIC NO. 1 HITS FROM THE 60'S 1960 - 1969 (Various artists).
MCSET: AM 60/69

801

801 LIVE.
LP: 2302 044
LP: ILPS 9444

808 State

EX.EL.
LP: ZTT 6
MC: ZTT 6C

EX.EL (DOUBLE) (Limited edition).
2LP: ZTT 6D

NEW BUILD.
LP: CREED 001

NINETY.
LP: ZTT 2
MC: ZTT 2C

QUADRASTATE.
LP: STATE 004

999

13TH FLOOR MADNESS.
LP: AS 8502
MC: CAS 8502
LP: LILP 400073

999.
LP: FC 026
LP: UAG 30199

999 SINGLES ALBUM.
Tracks: / Nasty, nasty / No pity (in the naked city) / Me and my desire / Crazy / Emergency / My street stinks / Feeling alright with the crew / Titanic (my over) reaction / You can't buy me / Homicide / Soldier / I'm alive / Quite disappointing / Waiting / Action.
LP: SOS 999

CONCRETE.
LP: ALLP 400017

FACE TO FACE.
LP: LABLP 1000

GREATEST HITS: 999.
LP: ALB 118
MC: CALB 118

IN CASE OF EMERGENCY.
Tracks: / Homicide / Nasty nasty / Public enemy no.1 / Silent anger / Emergency / High energy plan / Li'l Red Riding Hood / Me and my desire / Obsessed / Feeling alright with the crew / Break it up / Titanic (my over) reaction.
LP: DOJOLP 31

LUST, POWER AND MONEY.
Tracks: / Inside out / Hit me / Don't you know I need you / White crash / Feeling alright with the crew / Obsessed / On the line / Let's face it / Emergency / English wipe out / Nasty nasty / Homicide / Lust, power and money / My street stinks.
LP: ABCLP 11
MC: ABCK 11

SEPARATES.
LP: FC 027

1000...

GOD BLESS THE PRINCE OF WALES (One Thousand English Voices).
Tracks: / Drink to me only / John Peel / Morte Christe / Pilgrims' chorus (from 'Tannhauser') / God bless the Prince of Wales / Iona / Cavalry of the Steppes / Soldiers' chorus / Close thine eyes / Jerusalem / For brass / Royal Doulton march / Bacio, (Il) / Nimrod / Little suite for brass / Thunder and lightning polka / National anthem / Sweet lass of Richmond Hill.
LP: LBRD 004
MC: LBTD 004

1000 Mexicans

CHINESE WHISPERS.
MC: C 1000

DANCE LIKE AMMUNITION.
LP: FIRELP 1

1000 Violins

HEY MAN THAT'S BEAUTIFUL.
Tracks: / All aboard the love mobile / Place to surf, A / Hey man that's beautiful / Halcyon days / Thanks for nothing / Locked out of the love in / Let me charm the pants off your world / If only words (could let me conquer you) / Start digging my grave sugar / On-one was saving the world.
LP: IMMACLP 1

1000 Welsh Male Voices

ALL OF US ONE.
LP: REC 343
MC: ZCM 343

AT THE ROYAL ALBERT HALL 1979.
LP: BM 27

AT THE ROYAL ALBERT HALL 1980.
LP: BM 38

AT THE ROYAL ALBERT HALL 1982.
LP: BM 71

GOING HOME.
Tracks: / Entrance and march of the Peers / Drinking song / Going home / Song of the jolly roger / Nidaros / O, Isis and Osiris / Praise ye, praise ye God the Lord / Swansea town / We'll keep a welcome in the hills / Myfanwy / Llanfair / Tydi a roddaist.
LP: REC 404
MC: ZCM 404

WE'LL KEEP A WELCOME.
LP: SM 395

14-18

GOOD-BYE-EE (20 great hits from the war years).
LP: MAG 4001

1776

1776 (Original Broadway Cast) (Various artists).
LP: JS 3310

1812

1812 & OTHER RUSSIAN POPS (Various artists).
MC: TC2MOM 107

TRUTH ABOUT 1812, THE.
Tracks: / Bernard's motor car / 1812 overture / Nurse / She was poor but she was honest / Two little chaps / Girlfriends / Effluent society / Nudist colony.
LP: SFA 023

1900 (film)

1900 (Film Soundtrack) (Various artists).
LP: NL 43738
MC: NK 43738

1919

MACHINE.
LP: REDLP 25

1927

IF I COULD.
Tracks: / If I could / Not talking / All the people (Only on CD and 12") / Willing and able (Only on CD and 12") / If I could (version).
MCSET: YZ 402C

OTHER SIDE, THE.
LP: WX 360
MC: WX 360 C

1949

1949 CARNEGIE HALL CONCERT (See under Carnegie Hall) (Various artists).

1969 (film)

1969 (Film Soundtrack) (Various artists).
LP: 837 362-1
MC: 837 362-4

1983

1983 BRASS BAND FESTIVAL Various bands (Various artists).
Tracks: / March brilliant: *Various bands* / Sorcerer's apprentice, The: *Various bands* / Mermaid's song, The: *Various bands* / Ballet for band: *Various bands* / Resurgam: *Various bands* / Jerusalem: *Various bands.*
LP: BBRD 1023
MC: BBTD 1023

1984

1984 - FOR THE LOVE OF BIG BROTHER (Film soundtrack) (See under Eurythmics) (Eurythmics).

1985

1985 MASTER MEGAHITS VOL 2 (Various artists).
LP: J 003

1990

1990 MUSIC MASTER TOP 10 VOL.2 (See under Music Master for details) (Various artists).

1992

1992 (Various artists).
LP: KK 018

2001... (bk)

2001: A SPACE ODYSSEY (Arthur C Clarke).
MC: CDL 51504

2001: A SPACE ODYSSEY (Arthur C Clarke).
MC: 001042475

2001... (film)

2001: A SPACE ODYSSEY Film soundtrack (Various artists).
Tracks: / Also sprach Zarathustra: *Various artists* / Requiem for soprano, mezzo soprano, 2 mixed choirs and ...: *Various* artists (Full title:... and orchestra) / Blue Danube: *Various artists* / Gayne ballet suite: *Various artists*/ Atmospheres: *Various artists* / Blue Danube: *Various artists* (Reprise) / Also sprach Zarathustra (reprise): *Various artists*.
LP: . . . . **CBS 70275**
LP: . . . . **MCA 39049**
MC: . . . . **MCAC 39049**
LP: . . . . **CBS 61772**

2010

2010: ODYSSEY TWO (Clarke, Arthur C (aut)).
MC: **1709**

2010: ODYSSEY TWO (Film Soundtrack) (Various artists).
LP: . . . . **AMA 5038**
MC: . . . . **AMC 5038**

20/20

20/20.
Tracks: / Sky is falling / Yellow pills / 7/ 79 / Cheri / Out of this time / Tell me why / Tonight we fly / Remember the lightning / She's an obsession / Leaving your world behind / Backyard guys / Jet lag / Action now.
LP: . . . . **PRT 83898**

10,000 Maniacs

BLIND MAN'S ZOO.
LP: . . . . **EKT 57**
MC: . . . . **EKT 57 C**

HOPE CHEST (The Fredonia Recordings 1982-83).
LP: . . . . **EKT 79**
MC: . . . . **EKT 79C**

HUMAN CONFLICT NUMBER FIVE.
LP: . . . . **P 2010**

IN MY TRIBE.
Tracks: / What's the matter here? / Hey Jack Kerouac / Like the weather / Cherry tree / Painted desert / Don't talk / Peace train / Gun shy / My sister Rose / Campfire song, A / City of angels / Verdi cries.
LP: . . . . **EKT 41**
MC: . . . . **EKT 41C**

SECRETS OF THE I-CHING.
Tracks: / Grey victory / Pour de chicico / Death of Manolete / Tension / Daktari / Pit viper / Katrina's fair / Latin one, The / My mother the war.
LP: . . . . **P 3001**

TEN THOUSAND MANIACS: INTERVIEW PICTURE DISC.
LPPD: . . . . **BAK 2156**

WISHING CHAIR, THE.
Tracks: / Can't ignore the train / Just as the tide was flowing / Scorpio rising / Lilydale / Maddox table / Everyone a puzzle lover / Arbor day / Back o' the moon / Tension makes a tangle / Among the Americans / Grey victory / Cotton Alley / My mother the war.
LP: . . . . **EKT 14**
MC: . . . . **EKT 14C**

20,000

20,000 LEAGUES UNDER THE SEA (see also under Verne, Jules) (Mason, James (nar)).

5,4,3,2,1 Go!

5,4,3,2,1 GO! (Countdown compilation) (Various artists).
LP: . . . . **DREW 1**
MC: . . . . **CDREW 1**

1,000,000 Bulgarians

TERAZ ALBO NIGBY.
LP: . . . . **GP 0489**

4,000,000 Telephones

4,000,000 TELEPHONES.
LP: . . . . **BUNK 001**

MOST CAREFUL, THE.
Tracks: / It's dark / If it's not quite rite / Most careful, The / This time / No / French girls / Miracle worker / Each minute / She's there / Wait.
LP: . . . . **SUML 001**

A2L

A2L IN WONDERLAND.
LP: 080 770

A/10

SEX GOD WAR - CONTRIBUTIONS AND REWARDS.
LP: DMM 88009

A B Sounds

A B SOUNDS NEW BEAT - TAKE 3 (Various artists).
LP: SUB 054
MC: SUB 054 MC

A B SOUNDS NEW BEAT - TAKE 4 (Various artists).
LP: SUB 064
MC: SUB 064C

NEW BEAT TAKE 2.
LP: SUB 044

A Bones

FREE BEER FOR LIFE.
LP: 206

A Certain Ratio

ACR.
Tracks: / Spirit dance / BTTW 90 / Good together / Tribeca / Won't stop loving you / Be what you wanna be / Funky heaven / Repercussions live.
LP: 3970571
MC: 3970574

FORCE.
Tracks: / Only together / Bootsy / Fever 103 degrees / Naked and white / Mickey way / And then she smiled / Take me down / Anthem / Si fermi o gredo (Available on CD and cassette only).
LP: FACT 166
MC: FACT 166C

GOOD TOGETHER.
Tracks: / Your blue eyes / Your little world / Big E, The / God's own girl / Love is the way / Backs to the wall / River's edge / Every pleasure / Coldest days / Good together / Repercussions / 2000 AD.
LP: AMA 9008
MC: AMC 9008

GRAVEYARD AND THE BALLROOM, THE.
MC: FACT 16 C

I'D LIKE TO SEE YOU AGAIN.
LP: FACT 65

LIVE IN AMERICA.
Tracks: / Sounds like something dirty / Fox, The / Shack up / Life's a scream / Wild party / Flight / And then again / Touch / Knife slits water / Si fermi o gredo.
LP: DOJOLP 47

OLD AND THE NEW, THE.
LP: FACT 135
MC: FACT 135 C

A from Antler

A FROM ANTLER Compilation (Various artists).
LP: ANT 028

A House

I WANT TOO MUCH.
Tracks: / Talking / Shivers up my spine / I give you you / I think I'm going mad / Manstrong / You'll cry when I die / I want too much / Patron Saint of Mediocrity, The / Marry me / Now that I'm sick / Bring down the beast / Keep the home fires burning / Small talk.
LP: BYN 22
MC: BYNC 22

ON OUR BIG FAT MERRY-GO-ROUND.
Tracks: / Call me blue / I'll always be grateful / Don't ever think you're different / Love of the eighties / Love quarry / Stone the crows / I want to kill something / My little lighthouse / That's not the truth / Violent love / Clump of trees.
LP: BYN 18
MC: BYNC 18

A II Z

WITCH OF BERKELEY, THE.
Tracks: / No fun after midnight / Lay down / Walking the distance / Glastonbury massacre / Danger UXB / Witch of Berkeley / Last stand / Romp / King is dead, The.
MC: 3170 587

A R B

HARD AND SOFT, THE.
Tracks: / New Jack City / All or nothing / Crank it up / Night life / Just music / Jack to this / Make you sweat / Somebody workit / Cuttin' like Jason / Bump-n-grind / X marks the spot / It's a woman's thang (Cassette & CD only).
LP: ZL 72738
MC: ZK 72738

A Split Second

KISS OF FURY.
LP: AS 5014

Aaak

BUILDINGSCAPE BEAT.
LP: SCAM 003
MC: SCAM 003C

Aaberg, Philip

HIGH PLAINS.
LP: 371037 1
MC: 371037 4

OUT OF THE FRAME.
Tracks: / Walking through walls / Out of the frame / Nevertheless hello / Swoop / Call and response / Before barbed wire / Words over water / Full court pickup / Surround / Blue horses / Wedding, The.
LP: 37 1069 1
MC: 37 1069 4

Aag

FIRE.
LP: OZ 1002
MC: OZ 0102

Aardvark

PUT THAT IN YOUR PIPE AND SMOKE IT.
Tracks: / Copper sunset / Very nice of you to call / Many things to do / Greencap, The / I can't stop / Outing-yes, The / Once upon a hill / Put that in your pipe and smoke it.
LP: SEE 43

Aaron, Lee

CALL OF THE WILD.
Tracks: / Rock me all over / Running from the fire / Champion / Barely holding on / Burning love / Beat 'em up / Paradise / Evil game / Danger zone / Hot to be rocked / Line of fire.
LP: DIX 46
MC: CDIX 46
MC: RR 49780
LP: XID 24

LEE AARON.
Tracks: / Powerline / Hands are tied / Only human / Empty heart / Number one / Don't rain on my parade / Going off the deep end / If this is love / Eye for an eye / Heartbeat of the world / Dream with me.
LP: DIX 49
MC: CDIX 49

LEE AARON PROJECT, THE.
LP: RR 9842

METAL QUEEN.
Tracks: / Metal Queen / Lady of the darkest night / Head above water / Got to be the one / Shake it up / Deceiver / Steal away your love / Hold out / Breakdown / We will be rockin'.
LP: DIX 47
MC: CDIX 47
LP: RR 9861
LP: XID 25

Aaron Slick From ...

AARON SLICK FROM PUMPKIN CRICK/SATIN & SPURS (Various artists).
LP: MPT 4

Aaronson

THROUGH THE FIRE (See under Hagar, Sammy) (Aaronson, Hagar, Schon, Shrieve).

Aaronsrod

ILLUSIONS KILL.
Tracks: / Do me in / I wanna take you higher / She say...no way / Never cry wolf / Russian roulette / Hard as stone / Deceiving eyes / Mirage / Roll the dice / Khoram's blade.
LP: RR 9690

Abattoir

ONLY SAFE PLACE, THE.
LP: N 0045

VICIOUS ATTACK.
LP: RR 9788

Abba

ABBA (ALBUM).
LP: EPC 32052
MC: 40 32052
LP: EPC 80835

ABBA LIVE.
LP: POLH 29
MC: POLHC 29

ABSOLUTE ABBA.
Tracks: / Fernando / Name of the game / Thank you for the music / Angel eyes / Waterloo / Knowing me, knowing you / Summer night city / Lay all your love on me / Winner takes it all, The / Super trouper / Money, money, money / Voulez vous / Head over heels / Mamma mia / S.O.S. / I have a dream.
LP: STAR 2329
MC: STAC 2329

ALBUM, THE.
Tracks: / Eagle / Take a chance on me / One man one woman / Name of the game / Move on / Hole in your soul / Girl with the golden hair, The / 3 scenes from a mini musical.
LP: EPC 32321
MC: 40 32321
LP: EPC 86502
LP: 2315180
MC: 3199180

ARRIVAL.
Tracks: / My love my life / When I kissed the teacher / Dancing queen / Dum dum diddle / Knowing me, knowing you / Money money money / That's me / Why did it have to be me / Tiger / Arrival.
LP: EPC 32320
MC: 40 32320
LP: EPC 86108
LP: 2344058
MC: 3226058

BOXED SET.
LPS: ABBA 26

COLLECTION: ABBA.
Tracks: / Waterloo / Name of the game / Winner takes it all, The / Dancing queen / Super trouper / Fernando / Gimme gimme gimme / S.O.S. / I have a dream / Does your mother know / Voulez vous / Angel eyes / Ring ring / Day before you came, The / Head over heels / Thank you for the music / I do, I do, I do / Under attack / Arrival / Honey honey / Visitors, The / Rock me / Eagle / Dance (while the music still goes on).
MC: CCSMC 176
2LP: CCSLP 176

COLLECTION: ABBA VOL 2.
Tracks: / Dancing queen / Take a chance on me / I have a dream / Does your mother know / Chiquitita / Ring ring / Another town another train / Disillusion / People need love / I saw it in the mirror / Nina, pretty ballerina / Thank you for the music / Two for the price of one / Fernando / Gimme gimme gimme / Super trouper / Waterloo / Love isn't easy / Me and Bobby and Bobby's brother / He is your brother / I am just a girl / Rock 'n' roll band.
2LP: CCSLP 198
MC: CCSMC 198

GREATEST HITS: ABBA, VOL.1.
Tracks: / Fernando / S.O.S. / He is your brother / Hasta manana / Dance (while the music still goes on) / Another town, another train / Mamma mia / Waterloo / I do, I do, I do / Honey honey / People need love / Ring ring / Bang-a-boomerang / Nina, pretty ballerina / So long.
LP: EPC 32571
MC: 40 32571
LP: EPC 62918

GREATEST HITS VOL.2.
Tracks: / Take a chance on me / Gimme gimme gimme / Money money money / Rock me / Eagle / Angel eyes / Dancing queen / Does your mother know / Chiquitita / Summer night city / I wonder / Name of the game / Thank you for the music / Knowing me, knowing you.
LP: 4509151
MC: 4509154
LP: 2344145
MC: 3100533
LP: EPC 10017

HITS BOX, THE.
MCSET: BOX C1

HITS, THE.
Tracks: / Waterloo / S.O.S. / Dancing queen / Knowing me, knowing you / Lay all your love on me / Super trouper / Take a chance on me / I do, I do, I do / Honey honey / Hasta manana / Visitors, The / Mamma mia / Winner takes it all, The / King has lost his crown, The / Dance (while the music still goes on) / Gimme gimme gimme / Head over heels / Rock me / I have a dream.
LP: SHM 3215
MC: HSC 3215

HITS, THE (2).
Tracks: / Name of the game / Ring ring / Arrival / Summer night city / Happy New Year / Angel eyes / Kisses of fire / Fernando / Day before you came, The / Money, money, money / Andante andante / Voulez vous / When I kissed the teacher.
LP: SHM 3229
MC: HSC 3229

HITS, THE (3).
LP: SHM 3241
MC: HSC 3241

LOVE SONGS, THE.
Tracks: / Under attack / Slippin' through my fingers / Should I laugh or cry / Gonna sing you a love song / Lovers (live a little longer) / Lovelight / I've been waiting for you / My love my life / One man, one woman / Tropical loveland / Another town, another train / When all is said and done / If it wasn't for the night / So long.
LP: SHM 3297
MC: HSC 3297

MOST OF ABBA, THE.
LP: VBTV 08

RING RING.
LP: PMP 1018

SINGLES - THE FIRST 10 YEARS, THE.
Tracks: / Ring ring / Waterloo / So long / I do, I do, I do / S.O.S. / Mama Mia / Fernando / Dancing queen / Money money money / Knowing me, knowing you / Name of the game / Take a chance on me / Summer night city / Chiquitita / Does your mother know / Voulez vous / Gimme gimme gimme / I have a dream / Winner takes it all, The / Super trouper / One of us / Day before you came, The / Under attack.
2LP: ABBA 10
MCSET: ABBA 40/10
2LP: 2612040
MC: 8500134

SOUNDS LIKE ABBA VOL. 1 (Various artists).
MC: VCA 011

SUPER TROUPER.
Tracks: / Super trouper / Winner takes it all, The / On and on and on / Andante Andante / Me and I / Happy New Year / Our last summer / Piper, The / Lay all your love on me / Way old friends do, The.
LP: EPC 10022
MC: 40 10022
MC: 3100578
LP: 2344162

THANK YOU FOR THE MUSIC.
Tracks: / My love, my life / I wonder / Happy new year / Slipping through my fingers / Fernando / One man, one woman / Eagle / I have a dream / Our last summer / Day before you came, The / Chiquitita / Should I laugh or cry / Old way friends do, The / Thank you for the music.
LP: EPC 10043
MC: 40 10043

VISITORS, THE.
Tracks: / Visitors, The / Head over heels / When all is said and done / Soldiers / I let the music speak / One of us / Two for the price of one / Slipping through my fingers / Like an angel / Passing through my room / Eagle.
LP: EPC 10032
MC: 40 10032
MC: 8000 011 4
LP: 2311 122

VOULEZ VOUS.
Tracks: / As good as new / Voulez vous / I have a dream / Angel eyes / King has lost his crown, The / Does your mother know / If it wasn't for the night /

Chiquitita / Lovers (like a little longer) / Kisses of fire.
LP: EPC 32322
MC: 40 32322
LP: EPC 86086
LP: 2344136
MC: 3100510

WATERLOO.
Tracks: / Waterloo / Watch out / King Kong song / Hasta manana / My mama said / Dance (while the music still goes on) / Honey honey / Watch out / What about Livingstone / Gonna sing you a love song / Suzy hang around / Ring ring.
MC: 40 32009
LP: EPC 80179
LP: 32009

Abba, Dimi Mint

MOORISH MUSIC FROM MAURITANIA (See under Eide, Khalifa Ould) (Abba, Dimi Mint & Khalifa Ould Eide).

Abbey Radar

THING, THE.
LP: IRI 5005

Abbott, Gregory

I'LL PROVE IT TO YOU.
Tracks: / Back to stay / Prisoner of love / I'll prove it to you / Runaway / Unfinished business / Crazy over you / Let me be your friend / Take me back / Two of a kind / She's an entertainer.
LP: 4606911
MC: 4606914

SHAKE YOU DOWN.
Tracks: / I got the feelin' / Say you will / Shake you down / You're my angel / Magic / Wait until tomorrow / Rhyme and reason / I'll find a way.
LP: 450061 1
MC: 450061 4
LP: 4609501
MC: 4609504

Abbott, Russ

I LOVE A PARTY.
LP: ONE 1313
MC: OCE 2313

RUSS ABBOTT'S MADHOUSE.
LP: RTL 2096

ABC

ABRACADABRA.
Tracks: / Love conquers all / Unlock the secrets of your heart / Answered prayer / Spellbound / Say it / Welcome to the real world / Satori / All that matters / This must be magic.
LP: PCS 7355
MC: TCPCS 7355

ABSOLUTELY ABC (The greatest hits).
Tracks: / Poison arrow / Look of love, The / All of my heart / Tears are not enough / That was then but this is now / S.O.S. / How to be a millionaire / Be near me / When Smokey sings / Night you murdered love, The / King without a crown / One better world / Look of love, The (1990 remix) (Only on CD and cassette.) / When Smokey sings (12" remix) (Only on CD and cassette.) / Be near me (12" remix) (Only on CD and cassette.) / One better world (12" remix) / Ocean blue (Only on CD and cassette.).
MC: 842967-4
LP: 842967-1

ALPHABET CITY.
Tracks: / Avenue A / When Smokey sings / Night you murdered love, The / Think again / Rage and then regret / Arkangel / King without a crown / Bad blood / Jealous lover / One day / Avenue Z.
LP: NTRH 4
MC: NTRH C 4

BEAUTY STAB.
Tracks: / That was then but this is now / Love's a dangerous language / If I ever thought you'd be lonely / Power of persuasion / Beauty stab / By default, by design / Hey citizen / King money / Bite the hand / Unzip / S.O.S. / United Kingdom.
LP: VOG 13332
LP: NTRL 2

HOW TO BE A ZILLIONAIRE.
Tracks: / A to Z / How to be a millionaire / Tower of London / So hip it hurts / Between you and me / Fear of the world / Be near me / Vanity kills / Ocean blue / 15 story halo.
LP: NTRH 3

LEXICON OF LOVE, THE.
Tracks: / Show me / Poison arrow / Many happy returns / Tears are not enough / Valentine's day / Look of love, The (part 1) / Date stamp / All of my heart / 4 ever 2 gether / Look of love, The.
LP: NTRS 1
MC: NTRSC 1

UP.
Tracks: / Never more than now / Real thing, The / One better world / Where is the Heaven? / Greatest love of all, The / I'm in love with you / Paper thin.
LP: 838 646 1
MC: 838 646 4

ABC (Alphabet)

ABC.
MC: DIS 014

ABC (THE ALPHABET HUNT).
MC: STK 023

ABC Rhymes

ABC RHYMES (Various artists).
MC: PLB 258

Abdul, Paula

FOREVER YOUR GIRL.
Tracks: / Way that you love me, The / Knocked out / Opposites attract (Duet with the Wild Pair) / State of attraction / I need you / Forever your girl / Straight up / Next to you / Cold hearted / One or the other.
LP: SRNLP 19
MC: SRNMC 19

SHUT UP AND DANCE (THE DANCE REMIXES).
2LP: VUSLP 28
MC: VUSMC 28

SPELLBOUND.
MC: VUSMC 33
LP: VUSLP 33

Abdulai, Alhaji

MASTER DRUMMERS OF DAGBON.
LP: ROUNDER 5016
MC: ROUNDER 5016C

Abel, Eric

I'VE GOT WHAT I WANTED.
LP: STOFF 005

Abercrombie, John

ANIMATO.
Tracks: / Right now / Single moon / Agitato / First light / Last light / For hope of hope / Bright reign / Ollie Mention.
LP: ECM 1411

CURRENT EVENTS.
Tracks: / Clint / Alice in Wonderland / Ralph's piano waltz / Lisa / Hippityville / Killing time / Still.
LP: ECM 1311

GETTING THERE.
Tracks: / Sidekick / Upon a time / Getting there / Remember hymn / Thalia / Furs on ice / Chance / Labour day.
LP: ECM 1321

JOHN ABERCROMBIE TRIO (Abercrombie, John Trio).
Tracks: / Furs on ice / Alice in Wonderland / Innerplay / Drum solo / Samurai hee-haw / Stella by starlight / Beautiful love / Light beam / Four on one / Haunted heart.
LP: ECM 1390

M (Abercrombie Quartet).
LP: ECM 1191

NIGHT.
Tracks: / Etherreggae / Night / 3 East / Look around / Believe you me / Four on one.
LP: ECM 1272

SARGASSO SEA (see Towner, Ralph) (Abercrombie, John & Ralph Towner).

SOLAR (See Scofield, John) (Abercrombie, John & John Scofield).

WORKS: JOHN ABERCROMBIE.
Tracks: / Red and orange / Night / Ralph's piano waltz / Backward glance / Nightlake / Dreamstalker / Isla / Sing song.
LP: 8372751

Aberdeen, Angus

10 SOLO.
Tracks: / Jet plane / Cracklin' Rosie / For the good times.
LP: ERON 011 LP
MC: ERON 011 CA

Aberjaber

ABERJABER.
LP: SAIN 1340 M

Abie

WHILE THE FEELINGS GOOD.
Tracks: / While the feelings good / My mother's eyes / From a Jack to a King / Funny, familiar forgotten feelings / Vincent / Unchained melody / 500 miles away from home / If I had my life to live over / Blueberry Hill / Funny how time slips away / This a story of a starry night / Somewhere.
LP: KLP 44
MC: ZCKLP 44

Abiodun, Dele

ADAWA SUPER SOUND.
LP: SHAN 43032

CONFRONTATION.
LP: MWKS 3002

IT'S TIME FOR JUJU MUSIC.
LP: ASLP 05

Able Tasmans

CUPPA TEA, A.
LP: FNE 18

Abnormals

SKINS 'N' PUNKS VOL 4 (Abnormals & Barbed Wire).
Tracks: / Wales today / New generation / Holocaust / Here we go again / Girl on a train / Local copper / We've got the sus / Football sons / Stealing babiez / Face don't fit / Killing time / Don't let the bastards beat u / Hark (I hear no angels sing) / Christmas song, The.
LP: OIR 010

Abomination

TRAGEDY STRIKES.
LP: NB 050

Abou-Khalil, Rabih

BETWEEN DUSK AND DAWN.
LP: MMP 170886

BUKRA.
LP: MMP 170889

NAFAS.
LP: ECM 1359

ROOTS AND SPROUTS.
Tracks: / Remembering Machghara / Walking on air / Nida / Revelation / Wordless / Sweet tain / Outlook / Caravan / Dreams of a dying city.
LP: MMP 170890
MC: MMP 170890MC

About Last Night

ABOUT LAST NIGHT (Film Soundtrack) (Various artists).
Tracks: / So far so good: *Easton, Sheena* / Shape of things to come: *Hall & Oates* / Natural love: *Easton, Sheena* / Words into action: *Jackson, Jermaine* / Step by step: *Seger, J.D.* / Living inside my heart: *Seger, Bob* / Trials of the heart: *Shanks, Nancy* / Till you love somebody: *Henderson, Michael* / If we can get through the night: *Davis, Paul* / True love: *Del Lords* / If anybody had a heart: *Waite, John.*
LP: AML 3109
MC: TCAML 3109
MC: E41E46560

About Love

ABOUT LOVE (Various artists).
LP: SHM 3101
MC: HSC 3101

Above The Law

LIVIN' LIKE HUSTLERS.
Tracks: / Livin' like hustlers / Murder rap / Untouchable / Another execution / Menace to society / Just kickin' lyrics / Ballin' freedom of speech / Flow on (Move me to mountain) / Last song, The.
LP: 046041
LP: 4667601
MC: 4667604

Abracadabra

ABRACADABRA (Various artists).
LP: 1212011

Abracadaver... (bk)

ABRACADAVER - A SERGEANT CRIBB MYSTERY (Lovesey, Peter).
MCSET: CAB 294

Abraham, Ivan

TAKE UP THY CROSS.
Tracks: / Stone was rolled away / Beneath the willow / Gathering flowers for the master's bouquet / Whiskey is the devil / Hold fast to the right / Men with broken hearts / Take up thy cross / Old account / Let me walk with you Jesus / From the manger to the cross / There is a hand that's a waitin' / On a tree at Calvary.
LP: POL 833

THREE RUSTY NAILS.
Tracks: / Three rusty nails / Pastor absent on vacation / I dreamed about mama last night / If Jesus came to your house / What then / Be careful of stones that you throw / Pink bouquet / Gunman's prayer / Are all the children in / Trouble in the Amen Corner / Old country church / Beyond the sunset.
LP: POL 830

Abrahams, Chris

PIANO.
LP: HOT 1014

Abrahams, Doris

LABOR OF LOVE.
LP: PH 1034

Abrahams, Mick

ALL SAID AND DONE.
Tracks: / Roadroller / Watch your step / Billy the kid / Black night / All tore down / Redway of Milton Keynes / Long gone / Rock me right / So much trouble / Dear Jane / I wonder who / All said and done / Cats squirrel / Let me love you baby.
MC: ELITE 007 MC

AT LAST.
LP: ED 335

Abrahams, Mike

HAVE FUN LEARNING THE GUITAR.
LP: SRT 73313

Abrams, Colonel

ALBUM, THE.
Tracks: / Truth, The / Specualtion / Never change / Picture me in love with you / Trapped / I'm not gonna let / Over and over / Margaux / Table for two.
LP: MCG 6001
MC: MCGC 6001

YOU AND ME EQUALS US.
Tracks: / How soon we forget / We live a memory / Nameless / Can't stay away / Soon you'll be gone / You and me equals us / Caught in the middle / When a man loves / Running / Fame and fantasy.
LP: MCF 3388
MC: MCFC 3388

Abrams, Muhal Richard

1-0 QA + 19.
LP: BSR 0017

DUET WITH AMINA CLAUDINE MYERS.
LP: BSR 0051

LEVELS & DEGREES OF LIGHT.
LP: DS 413

SIGHT SONG.
LP: BSR 003

YOUNG AT HEART.
LP: DS 423

Abrasive Wheels

BLACK LEATHER GIRL.
LP: CLAYLP 9

WHEN THE PUNKS GO IN.
LP: CITY 001

Abravanel, Maurice

FANTASIA (see under Vaughan Williams).

Abril, Anton Garcia

ANTON GARCIA ABRIL CONDUCTS HIS FILM MUSIC (Orquesta Sinfonica De Madrid).
LP: VND 1034

CONDUCTS THE MUSIC OF JOAQUIN TURINA (Orquesta Sinfonica De Madrid).
Tracks: / El abanderado / Luis candelas / Eugenia de montijo / Noche en blanco.
LP: VND 1035

Absent Friends

HERE'S LOOKING UP YOUR ADDRESS.
Tracks: / Hullabaloo / Mean streak / Sister / Hallelujah / Everybody up / I don't wanna be with nobody but you / Come clean / Water is wide, The / Harmony / I had a premonition / Pomona's place / Clemency / Here's lookin up your address / Thank you goodnight.
LP: 842828 1
MC: 842828 4

Abshire, Nathan

CAJUN LEGEND, A (Best of Nathan Abshire).
LP: 6061
MC: 6061 TC

CAJUN TRADITION, A.
LP: 139

CAJUN TRADITION, A-VOL. 2.
LP: 144
MC: 144 TC

CAJUNS VOL 1 (Abshire, Nathan & Balfa Brothers).
Tracks: / Acadian two step / Mamou hot step / Ce voulait separe / Le valse de la prison / Johnny ne pas danse / Apres du midi / Mon chapeau / Lacassine special / Les veuves de Basile / Pinegrove blues / J'ai passe devant ta porte / La valise de grand bois.
LP: SNTF 643

GOOD TIMES ARE KILLING ME (Abshire, Nathan & Balfa Brothers).
LP: 6023
MC: 6023 TC
LP: SNTF 776

NATHAN ABSHIRE & OTHER CAJUN GEMS.
LP: ARHOOLIE 5013
MC: C 5013

NATHAN ABSHIRE & THE PINEGROVE BOYS (Abshire, Nathan And The Pinegrove Boys).
Tracks: / Popcorn blues / Chere petite blonde / Jolie catin / Gabriel waltz / Good time two step / Pinegrove stomp /

Dans grand bois / La la blues, The / French two step.
LP: FLY 535

PINEGROVE BLUES.
Tracks: / Pinegrove blues / Sur le courteblue / Musicians's life, A / Choupique two step / Off shore blues / La valse de bayou teche / Games people play / Lemonade song / Tramp sur la rue / I don't hurt anymore / Phil's waltz / Service blues / Maison lafayette two step / French blues / La valse de holly beach / Shamrock.
LP: 6014
LP: CHD 217
MC: 6014 TC

Absolute

ABSOLUTE REGGAE (see under Reggae) (Various artists).

ABSOLUTE ROCK'N'ROLL (see under Rock 'n' Roll) (Various artists).

Absolute Beginners

ABSOLUTE BEGINNERS (Complete soundtrack) (Various artists).
Tracks: / Absolute beginners: *Bowie, David* / Killer blow: *Sade* / Have you ever had it blue?: *Style Council* / Quiet life: *Davies, Ray* / Va va voom: *Evans, Gil* / That's motivation: *Bowie, David* / Having it all: *8th Wonder* / Roderigo Bay: *Working Week* / Selling out: *Gaillard, Slim* / Riot city: *Dammers, Jerry* / Boogie stop shuffle: *Evans, Gil* / Ted ain't dead: *Tenpole Tudor* / Volare: *Bowie, David* / Napoli: *Langer, Clive* / Little cat (you've never had it so good): *Jonas* / Absolute beginners (slight refrain): *Evans, Gil* / Better git it in your soul: *Evans, Gil* (The hot and the cool) / Landlords and tenants: *Aitken, Laurel* / Santa Lucia: *Abban, Ekow* / Cool Napoli: *Evans, Gil* / So what?: *Smiley Culture* / Absolute beginners: *Evans, Gil*.
2LP: VD 2514
MC: TCVD 2514

ABSOLUTE BEGINNERS (Film Soundtrack Highlights) (Various artists).
Tracks: / Absolute beginners: *Bowie, David* / Killer blow: *Sade* / Have you ever had it blue?: *Style Council* / Quiet life: *Davies, Ray* / Va va voom: *Evans, Gil* / That's motivation: *Bowie, David* / Having it all: *8th Wonder* / Roderigo Bay: *Working Week* / Selling out: *Gaillard, Slim* / Riot city: *Dammers, Jerry* / Boogie stop shuffle: *Evans, Gil* / Ted ain't dead: *Tenpole Tudor* / Volare: *Bowie, David* / Napoli: *Jonas* / Little cat you've never had it so good: *Jonas* / Better git it in your soul: *Evans, Gil* / So what: *Smiley Culture* / Absolute beginners (refrain): *Bowie, David*.
LP: OVED 225
MC: OVEDC 225
LP: V 2386
MC: VVIPC 112

ABSOLUTE BEGINNERS (THEME FROM) (See under Bowie, David).

Absolute Elsewhere

HOLIDAY.
Tracks: / Miniature / Tin man / Another try / Lonely people / Glad to see you / Mad dog / Hollywood / Baby it's up to you / Old man took / You / What does it matter / In the country.
LP: K 56045

IN SEARCH OF ANCIENT GODS.
Tracks: / Earthbound / Future Past / Miracles of the Gods / El Enladrillado / Legend of Santa Cruz / Pyramids of Teotihuacan / Temple of The Inscriptions / Gold of the gods / Toktela / Chariots of Gods / Return to the stars / Moon city.
LP: K 56192

Absurd Take Away

ABSURD TAKE AWAY (Various artists).
LP: TAYK 1

Abuse

ABUSE (Various artists).
LP: SD 003

Abuser

SONGS OF SEX AND NOT OF WAR.
LP: MEAT 1

Abwarts

DER WESTERN IST EINSAM (Film Soundtrack).
LP: 6435 155

Abyss (film)

ABYSS, THE (Film soundtrack) (Various artists).
LP: VS 5235
MC: VSC 5235

Abyssinians

ARISE.
Tracks: / Oh Lord / Land is for everyone / Mightiest of all / Meditation / Wicked men / Jah loves / Dem a come / South African enlistment / Hey you / Let my days be long.
MC: FLC 9010

FORWARD.
Tracks: / Forward jah / Prophecy / This is not the end / Satta a masagana / Mabrak / Forward on to Zion / Praise him / Peculiar number / Peculiar dub / Jerusalem.
LP: AL 101148

FORWARD TO ZION.
Tracks: / Declaration of rights / Good Lord / Forward on to Zion / Know Jah today / Abondico / Yi mas gan / Black man strain / I and I / Africa race / Satta a masagana.
LP: AL 27888

A.C. Marias

ONE OF OUR GIRLS HAS GONE MISSING.
Tracks: / Trilby's couch / Just talk / There's a scent of rain in the air / Our dust / So soon / Give me / To sleep / Looks like / Sometime / One of our girls has gone missing / Time was.
LP: STUMM 68
MC: CSTUMM 68

AC Temple

BLOWTORCH.
LP: FU 6 LP

SONGS OF PRAISE.
LP: FU 1

SOURPUSS.
Tracks: / Sundown pet corner / Miss Sky / Stymied / Mother tongue / Crayola / Devil you know / Horsetrading / Mouthful, A / Faith is a windsock / Ringpiece / (Dirty) weekend.
LP: BFFP 45
MC: BFFP 45C

Academy

ACADEMY.
Tracks: / On the beach / Pushing / Lies / Stranded / King (one more bridge) / Stand up / Keep quiet / You are in my system / 15 years / Tonight (the world keeps swinging).
LP: PL 70976

Academy Award Winners

ACADEMY AWARD WINNERS (Various artists).
Tracks: / Continental, The: *Various artists* / Lullaby of Broadway: *Various artists* / Way you look tonight, The: *Various artists* / Sweet Leilani: *Various artists* / Thanks for the memory: *Various artists* / Over the rainbow: *Various artists* / When you wish upon a star: *Various artists* / Last time I saw Paris, The: *Various* artists / White Christmas: *Various artists* / You'll never know: *Various artists* / Swinging on a star: *Various* artists / It might as well be spring: *Various artists* / On the Atchison, Topeka and Santa Fe: *Various artists* / Zip-a-dee-doo-dah: *Various artists*.
LP: MTLP 1010

Academy Chamber

CLARINET QUINTET / OBOE QUARTET / HORN QUINTET (MOZART) (See under Mozart (composer)).

Academy Collection

ACADEMY COLLECTION (Various artists).
LP: AR 102

Academy Of London

PIANO CONCERTI NO.12/22 (See under Mozart) (Academy Of London/Neil Rutman).

Academy Of St. Martin...

30TH ANNIVERSARY JUBILEE EDITION (See under St Martin ...) (St. Martin-in-the-Field).

YOUNG PERSON'S GUIDE TO THE ORCHESTRA (Academy Of St.Martin In The Field).
LP: ASD 1436281
MC: TCASD 1436284

Academy Urchins

WHY AS A CHILD.
MC: BH 8908 C

Acadian Two Step

ACADIAN TWO STEP (Cajun 1940's) (Various artists).
LP: FLY 610

Acapella

BEST OF ACAPPELLA, VOLUME 7 (Various artists).
LP: RELIC 109

Acapella Gospel

ACAPELLA GOSPEL SINGING (Various artists).
LP: FL 9045

Acceleration

ACCELERATION.
LP: ECM 1357

Accelerators

DREAM TRAIN.
LP: FILER 404
MC: FILERCT 404

Accept

ACCEPT.
Tracks: / Lady Lou / Tired of me / Seawinds / Take him in my heart / Sounds of war / Free me now / Glad to be alone / That's rock'n'roll / Hell driver / Street fighter.
LP: METAL 103
LPPD: METALP 101
LP: 0060 188

BALLS TO THE WALL.
Tracks: / Balls to the wall / London leatherboys / Fight it back / Head over heels / Losing more than you've ever had / Love child / Turn me on / Losers and winners / Guardian of the night / Winter dreams.
LP: PRT 25791
MC: 40 25791

BALLS TO THE WALL/ METAL HEART.
2LP: PRT A 241

BEST OF ACCEPT.
Tracks: / Burning / Restless and wild / Son of a bitch / Breaker / Do it / I'm rebel / China lady / No time to lose / Princess of the dawn / Lady Lou.
LP: 811 994 1
MC: 811 994 4

BREAKER.
Tracks: / Starlight / Breaker / Run if you can / Can't stand the night / Son of a bitch / Burning / Feelings / Midnight highway / Breaking up again / Down and out.
LP: 1060 390

BREAKER/I'M A REBEL.
2LP: TFOLP 23
MC: TFOMC 23

EAT THE HEAT.
Tracks: / X-T-C / Love sensation / Stand 4 what U R / Generation clash / Hellhammer / Prisoner / Chain reaction / D-train / Turn the wheel / Mistreated.
LP: 4652291
MC: 4652294

HUNGRY YEARS.
Tracks: / Fast as a shark / Burning / Son of a bitch / Princess of the dawn / I'm a rebel / Breaker / Restless and wild / King, The / Midnight highway.
LP: METALP 119

I'M A REBEL.
Tracks: / I'm a rebel / Save us / No time to lose / Thunder and lightning / China lady / I wanna be no hero / King, The / Do it.
LP: 0060 389
LP: 1025

KAISOKU-BAN.
Tracks: / Metal heart / Screaming for a love bite / Up to the limit / Head over heels / Love child / Living for tonight.
LP: PRT 54916
MC: 40 54916

METAL HEART.
Tracks: / Metal heart / Midnight mover / Up to the limit / Wrong is right / Screaming for a love bite / Too high to get it right / Dogs on leads / Teach us to survive / Living for tonight / Bound to fail.
LP: PRT 26358
MC: 40 26358

METAL MASTERS.
LP: RAZD 11
MC: RAZDK 11

RESTLESS AND WILD.
Tracks: / Fast as a shark / Restless and wild / Demons night / Ahead of the pack / Shake your hands / Neon nights / Get ready / Flash rockin' man / Don't go stealing my soul away / Princess of the dawn.
LP: PRT 32804
MC: 40 32804
LP: HMILP 6
MC: HMIMC 6
LPPD: HMIPD 6

RUSSIAN ROULETTE.
Tracks: / T.V. war / Monsterman / Russian roulette / It's hard to find a way / Aiming high / Heaven is hell / Another second to be / Walking in the shadow / Man enough to cry / Stand tight.
LP: PRT 26893
MC: 40 26893

Accident

CLOCKWORK LEGION, A.
LP: SHARP 016

CRAZY.
Tracks: / Crazy / Get ready / Valerie / Camouflage / And the band played on / Get ready (dub) / Sherwood rangers / Bad co. / Leaders / Sorry / Man on the wall / Respectable / Twisted mind / Cue the dead.
LP: LINK LP 012

Accidental Tourist

ACCIDENTAL TOURIST, THE (Film Soundtrack) (Various artists).
LP: K 925846 1
MC: K 925846 4

Acclaim

ACCLAIM (Great classical performers) (Various artists).
LP: SHM 3216
MC: HSC 3216

Accordion

20 GRANDS VEDETTES DE L'ACCORDEON (Various artists).
LP: VG 404507

ACCORDEON DE CAMERA (Various artists).
LP: LP 3008

ACCORDION A LA CARTE (Various artists).
MC: AM 29

ACCORDION ALBUM VOL.1 (Various artists).
MC: CWGR 023

ACCORDION ROUND THE ANTIPODES (THE) (Various artists).
Tracks: / Hoki mai: *Various artists* / Jolly Caballero: *Various artists* / Jeepers creepers: *Various artists* / Paris skies: *Various artists* / Spanish medley: *Various artists* / Vocal medley: *Various artists* / Pokarekareana: *Various artists* / Schneewaltzer: *Various artists* / Coucou: *Various artists* / Marriage of Figaro: *Various artists* / Accordionisin' on the Swanee: *Various artists* / Yugoslav medley: *Various artists* / Chanson d'amour: *Various artists* / Maori farewell: *Various artists*.
LP: AFA 801

ACCORDIONS OF SCOTLAND (Various artists).
Tracks: / My love is like a red red rose: *Various artists* / Flowers of Edinburgh: *Various artists* / Lucky Scaup: *Various artists* / Wee dug Tim, The: *Various artists* / Jessie the flower of Dunblane: *Various artists* / Ye banks and braes: *Various artists* / Will ye gang to Kelvinside: *Various artists* / Jacqueline waltz: *Various* artists / My heart is fair: *Various artists* / Auld Scots sangs, The: *Various artists* / Nameless lassie, The: *Various artists* / Annie Laurie: *Various artists* / Laird of Drumblair, The: *Various artists* / Masons apron: *Various artists* / Miss Delicia Chisholm: *Various artists* / Gay Gordons: *Various artists* / Dark Lochnagar: *Various artists* / My ain folk: *Various artists* / Corn rigs: *Various artists* / My love she's but a lassie yet: *Various artists* / High laddie: *Various artists* / There was a lad: *Various artists* / Eriogal cree: *Various artists* / Jessie's hornpipe: *Various artists* / Kirk's hornpipe: *Various artists* / Drumlees: *Various artists* / Cuckoo, The: *Various artists* / Tocherless lass, The: *Various artists* / Leaving Stornoway: *Various artists*.
LP: LOCLP 1030
MC: ZCLOC 1030

ACCORDIONS OF SCOTLAND VOL.2 (Various artists).
Tracks: / Scotch on the rocks: *Various artists* / Campbeltown Loch: *Various artists* / Tom Burns polka: *Various* artists / Scalloway Voe: *Various artists* / Bonnie wells o' Wearie: *Various artists* / Ballochmyle: *Various* artists / Masons apron: *Various artists* / Bluebells of Scotland: *Various artists* / Star o' Rabbie Burns, The: *Various artists* / Scots wha' hae: *Various artists* / Annie Laurie: *Various artists* / Bonnie Charlie: *Various artists* / Rothesay bay: *Various artists* / Come by the stream: *Various artists*.
LP: LOCLP 1037
MC: ZCLOC 1037

ALL SCOTLAND ACCORDION FESTIVAL 1978/9 (Various artists).
LP: GES 1205

BACH TO BERNSTEIN (Accordion Orchestra).
Tracks: / Praefugium no.1 / Marsch in B / Black bolero / Nina / Danza Siziliana / West Side story / Tango Della Marquesa / Western swing / Praefugium no.3.
LP: HR 690

BEST OF ACCORDION/FIDDLE (Scottish box and fiddle) (Various artists).
LP: LILP 5115
MC: LICS 5115

ELMER SCHEID STORY, THE (Various artists).

2LP: PC 384

HOP SCOTCH (see under Carmichael, John).

HUGO HERMANN WETTBEWERB 1977 Various Artists (Various artists).
LP: 099 065
LP: 099 076

INTERNATIONAL VIRTUOSOS OF THE ACCORDION (Various artists).
LP: NEA LP 37

IT'S ALL ACCORDION TO WHAT YOU LIKE (Various artists).
Tracks: / Dizzy fingers: *Various Midlands artistes* / Musetta: *Various Midlands artistes* / For the good times: *Various Midlands artistes* (Polish waltzes.) / Bavaian waltzes: *Various Midlands artistes* / Simonentta Ibiza: *Various Midlands artistes* / Georgia: *Various Midlands artistes* / Blues impromptu: *Various Midlands artistes*/ Moonglow: *Various Midlands artistes* / C minor and ad lib: *Various Midlands artistes* / Autumn breezes: *Various* Midlands artistes / Funiculi: *Various Midlands artistes* / Polish: *Various Midlands artistes* / Bavarian: *Various Midlands artistes* / French: *Various Midlands artistes* / Telstar: *Various Midlands artistes*/ Tulips from Amsterdam: *Various Midlands artistes* / Quando: *Various Midlands artistes*.
LP: AFA 791

LARS EK PLAYS FROSINI (Various artists).
Tracks: / That's a plenty: *Various artists* / Limehouse blues: *Various artists* / St. Louis blues: *Various* artists / Hot accordeon: *Various artists* / Tiger rag: *Various artists* / Carnival of Venice: *Various* artists / Chinka bazara: *Various artists* / Hasttrav: *Various artists* / O silenzo: *Various artists*/ Swedish-Italian mazurka: *Various artists* / Silver moon waltz: *Various artists* / Frosini symphonic march: *Various artists*.
LP: EKLP 8101

LARS EK X 2 (Various artists).
Tracks: / King Cotton: *Various artists* / Temptation rag: *Various artists* / Honeysuckle rose: *Various artists*/ Nobody's sweetheart: *Various artists* / Chinatown: *Various artists* / Brospannet: *Various artists* / Snokangan: *Various artists* / qornuddsvalsen: *Various artists* / A malva rosa: *Various artists* / Fancy twister: *Various artists* / L'etna: *Various artists* / Karlekstankar: *Various artists* / Latta fingrar: *Various artists* / Vals fran dreviken: *Various artists*.
LP: EKLP 8201

LAUGHING ACCORDIAN (Various artists).
MC: AIM 72

MUSIC FOR ACCORDION ORCHESTRA NO. 5 (Various artists).
LP: HS 064

MUSIC FOR ACCORDION ORCHESTRA NO 6 (Various artists).
LP: HS 068

ORIGINAL MUSIC FOR ACCORDION NO.3 (Various artists).
LP: 10A 03

PIANOS WITH BRACES (The Garlic & Gauloises World Of The French Acco (Various artists).
Tracks: / L'accordeoniste: *Bonel, Marc* (Singer: Edith Piaf.) / Balajo: *Privat, Jo* / Quand on s'promene au bord de l'eau: *Deprince, Adolphe* (Singer: Jean Gabin. Film: La Belle Equipe) / Polka: *Deprince, Adolphe* (Singer: Joli Pinson.) / Tout change dans la vie: *Various artists* (Singer: Frehel) / L'ame des poetes/ accordion musette: *Huard*, Albert Jr. / C'etait bien (au petit bal perdu): *Lorin, Etienne* (Singer: Bourvil) / Swing valse: *Viseur, Gus*/ La Seine: *Alexander, Maurice* (Singer: Denise Ascain) / La fete des as: *Azzola, Marcel* / La guinguette a ferme ses volets: *Damia* (With Pierre Chagnon & His Orchestra) / Vents d'automne: *Carrara, Emile* / Le plus beau tango du monde: *Sims, Alibert & Gaby* (With George Sellers & His 'Marseilles Jazz'.) / Song of the Moulin Rouge: *Azzola*, Marcel / Dede de Montmartre: *Prejean, Albert* / Joyeux canari: *Roussel, Gilbert* / Une robe valsait: *Paris* Accordion Quartet (Includes Marcel Azzola, Andre Astier, Andre & Louis Damergue.) / Boum: *Vaissade, Jean* / Boum: *Vaissade*, Jean / Sous les toits de Paris: *Alexander, Maurice* / Le diable de la Bastille: *Bonel, Marc* (Singer: Edith Piaf.).
LP: EMS 1400
MC: TCEMS 1400

PRESERVATION OF SWEDISHNESS (Various artists).
LP: TPLP 33

RICHARD GALLIANO (Various artists).
Tracks: / Prelude du tombeau de couperin, image no.1: *Various artists* / Children's corner (Image no.2 De Galliano): *Various artists*.
LP: RG 66

ROCKIN' ACCORDIAN (Various artists).
LP: FLY 622

SCANDANAVIAN EVERGREENS (Various artists).
LP: ALP 111

UNIVERSITY OF MISSOURI KANSAS CITY ACCORDION ORC (Various artists).
LP: SR 8683

WARSAW ACCORDION QUINTET (Various artists).
LP: SX 1148

Accordion & Fiddle

ACCORDION & FIDDLE CLUB JAMBOREE '79 (Various artists).
LP: GES 1209

Accursed

AGGRESSIVE PUNK.
LP: ACC 1

LAUGHING AT BREAKAGE.
LP: ACC 4

UP WITH THE PUNKS.
LP: ACC 2

Accused

GRINNING LIKE AN UNDERTAKER.
LP: JUST 17

MARTHA SPLATTERHEAD'S MADDEST STORIES EVER TOLD.
LP: WEBITE 43

MORE FUN THAN AN OPEN CASKET FUNERAL.
Tracks: / Halo of flies / W.C.A.L.T. / Rape / Lifeless zone / Scotty / Devil woman / Bethany home / Mechanized death / Take no prisoners / Splatter rock / Septi-child / I'll be glad when you're dead, you rascal you.
LP: JUST 11

RETURN OF MARTHA SPLATTERHEAD, THE.
LP: 88561-8197-1
LP: GURT 017
LP: MOSH 1

Accuser

CONVICTION, THE.
LP: ATOMH 003

EXPERIMENTAL ERRORS.
LP: ATOMH 006

WHO DOMINATES WHO.
LP: ATOMH 008

AC/DC

AC/DC: INTERVIEW PICTURE DISC.
LPPD: CT 1016
LPPD: BAK 2030

BACK IN BLACK.
Tracks: / Back in black / Hell's bells / Shoot to thrill / Give the dog a bone / What do you do for money honey? / Rock 'n' roll ain't noise pollution / Let me put my love into you / You shook me all night long / Shake a leg / Have a drink on me.
LP: K 50735
MC: K4 50735

BLOW UP YOUR VIDEO.
Tracks: / Heatseeker / That's the way I wanna rock 'n' roll / Meanstreak / Go zone / Kissin' dynamite / Nick of time / Some sin for nuthin' / Ruff stuff / Two's up / This means war.
LP: WX 144
MC: WX 144 C

BOX SET, 2.
LPS: AC/DC 2

BOX SET: AC/DC.
LPS: AC/DC 1

DIRTY DEEDS DONE DIRT CHEAP.
Tracks: / Dirty deeds done dirt cheap / Love at first feel / Big balls / Rocker / Problem child / There's gonna be some rockin' / Ain't no fun waiting round to be a millionaire / Ride on / Squealer.
LP: K 50323
MC: K4 50323

FLICK OF THE SWITCH.
Tracks: / Rising power / Badlands / Brain shake / Flick of the switch / Deep in the hole / Landslide / Guns for hire / Bedlam in Belgium.
LP: 780 100-1
MC: 780 100-4

FLY ON THE WALL.
Tracks: / Fly on the wall / Shake your foundations / First blood / Danger / Sink in pink / Playing with the girls / Stand up / Hell or high water / Back in business / Send for the man.
LP: 781 263-1
MC: 781 263-4

FOR THOSE ABOUT TO ROCK (WE SALUTE YOU).
Tracks: / For those about to rock (we salute you) / Put the finger on you / Let's get it up / Inject the venom / Snowballed / Evil walk / C.O.D. / Breaking the rules / Night of the long knives / Spellbound.
LP: K 50851
MC: K4 50851

HIGH VOLTAGE.
Tracks: / It's a long way to the top / Rock and roll singer / Jack, The / T.N.T / Can I sit next to you girl / Little lover / She's got balls / High voltage / Live wire.
LP: K 50257
MC: K4 50257

HIGHWAY TO HELL.
Tracks: / Highway to hell / Girls got rhythm / Touch too much / Beating around the bush / Shot down in flames / Get it hot / If you want blood (you've got it) / Love hungry / Night prowler.
LP: K 50628
MC: K4 50628

IF YOU WANT BLOOD YOU'VE GOT IT.
Tracks: / Riff raff / Hell ain't a bad place to be / Bad boy boogie / Jack, The / Problem child / Whole lotta Rosie / Rock 'n' roll damnation / High voltage / Let there be rock / Rocker.
LP: K 50532
MC: K4 50532

LET THERE BE ROCK.
Tracks: / Go down / Dog eat dog / Let there be rock / Bad boy boogie / Overdose / Crapsody in blue / Hell ain't a bad place to be / Whole lotta Rosie.
LP: K 50366
MC: K4 50366

MUSIC AND MEDIA INTERVIEW PICTURE DISC.
LPPD: MM 1210
LPPD: AC 1001

POWERAGE.
Tracks: / Gimme a bullet / Down payment blues / Gone shootin' / Riff raff / Sin city / Up to my neck in you / What's next to the Moon / Cold hearted man / Kicked in the teeth.
LP: K 50483
MC: K4 50483

RAZOR'S EDGE, THE.
Tracks: / Thunderstruck / Fire your guns / Money talks / Razors edge, The / Mistress for Christmas / Rockyour heart out / Are you ready? / Got you by the balls / Shot of love / Let's make it / Goodbye and good riddance to bad luck / If you dare.
LP: WX 364
MC: WX 364C

WHO MADE WHO (Film Soundtrack for Maximum Overdrive).
Tracks: / Who made who / You shook me all night long / D.T. / Sink the pink / Ride on / Hell's bells / Shake your foundations / Chase the ace / For those about to rock (we salute you).
LP: WX 57
MC: WX 57 C

AC/DC Blues...

AC/DC BLUES GAY JAZZ REISSUES (Various artists).
LP: ST 106

Ace

BEST OF ACE, THE.
Tracks: / How long / I'm a man / Ain't gonna stand for this no more / Rock 'n' roll runaway / Real feeling, The / Rock and roll singer / You're all that I need / 24 hours / Crazy world / No future in your eyes / Tongue tied / Time ain't long / Sail on my brother / I think it's gonna last.
LP: SEE 214

FIVE-A-SIDE.
Tracks: / Sniffin about / Rock and roll runaway / How long / Reel feeling, The / 24 hours / Why? / Time ain't long / Know how it feels / Satellite / So sorry baby.
LP: CSAP 103
MC: CSAPC 103
LP: ANCL 2001
MC: TCANCL 2001

SIX A SIDE.
Tracks: / Sniffin' about / Why / How long / I'm a man / Tongue tied / Does it hurt / You / Rock 'n' roll singer / Sail on brother / You're all that I need / I'm not takin' it out on you / No future in your eyes / C'est la vie.
LP: 2478 159

Ace, Johnny

EARL FOREST & THE BEALE STREETERS (See under Forest, Earl) (Ace, Johnny/Bobby Bland/Earl Forest).

MEMORIAL ALBUM FOR JOHNNY ACE.
Tracks: / Pledging my love / Ace's wild / Anymore / Yes baby / My song / Never let me go / Clock, The / No money / Angel / Follow the rule / Burley cutie / Please forgive me / You've been gone so long.
LP: CH 40

Ace Of Clubs

ACE OF CLUBS (Various artists).
Tracks: / You'll never know: *Various artists* / Very last drop: *Various artists* / You can handle it: *Various* artists / Give it to me: *Various artists* / Little bit of Jazz, A: *Various artists* / Hot summer nights: *Various* artists / Searching to find the one: *Various artists* / Dyin' to be dancin': *Various artists* / Who's been kissing you: *Various artists* / Inch by inch: *Various artists*.
LP: EPC 85450
MC: 40 85450

Ace Story

ACE STORY VOL 1, THE (Various artists).
LP: CH 11

ACE STORY VOL 2, THE (Various artists).
LP: CH 12

ACE STORY VOL 3, THE (Various artists).
Tracks: / Boppin' with Sonny: *Williamson, Sonny Boy* / Saturday night fish fry: *Blue Notes* / Everybody's whalin': *Smith, Huey & His Rhythm Aces* / Marked deck: *Smith, Huey & His Rhythm Aces* / Snake eyes: *Tyler, Alvin 'Red'* / I'm so glad you're mine: *Scott, Albert* / Don't take your love from me: *Marchan, Bobby* / Somebody told it: *Smith*, Huey & The Clowns / Don't leave me here to cry: *Supremes* / She's tough: *McCain, Jerry* / For cryin' out loud: *Smith, Huey & The Clowns* / My love for you: *Gordon, Junior* / Sahara: *Rebennack, Mac & His Orchestra* / Such a mess: *Price, Lloyd* / Rock 'n' roll baby: *Baby, Mercy* / Steady: *McCain, Jerry*.
LP: CH 55

ACE STORY VOL 4, THE (Various artists).
Tracks: / Teenage wedding: *Angel, Johnny* / Tee nah nah: *Williams, Dicky* / Walk on: *Tyler, Alvin & The Gyros* / I wanna know why: *Cooke, Roland* / Wherever you may be: *Joe & Ann* / Free single and disengaged: *Smith*, Huey "Piano" / Charlie Brown got expelled: *Tex, Joe* / Scald dog: *Smith, Huey "Piano"* / Can I have a word: *Brown, Floyd* / Can't let you go I love you so: *Scott, Albert* / Yum yum yum: *Tex, Joe* / Mothers advice: *Tex, Joe* / I'll keep on trying: *Bo, Eddie* / Walking with Frankie: *Sims, Frankie Lee*.
LP: CH 98

ACE STORY VOL 5, THE (Various artists).
Tracks: / Well I never get tired: *Fairchild, Johnny* / Educated fool: *Smith, Huey "Piano"* / Let's get it: *Blanchard*, Edgar / Hey hey baby come home: *Scott, Albert* / Baby say you will: *Jesse Allen* / Somebody else is taking my place: *Webb, Bobby* / Roll on train: *Anderson, Elton* / Well goodbye baby: *Sims, Frankie Lee* / Doin' the rock 'n' roll: *Spears, Calvin* / Classy lassie: *Tyler, Alvin 'Red'* / Love is my business: *Woods, Bobby*/ Packin' up: *King, Earl* / Something keeps dragging me on: *Ronnie & The Delinquents* / Love's like a river: *Brown, Charles* / Who can I turn to: *Big Boy Myles* / Roll 'em back: *Bo, Eddie*.
LP: CH 113

Acetate Sessions

ACETATE SESSIONS, THE (See under Rockabilly) (Various artists).

Achanak

NACHURALLY.
LP: MUT 1097
MC: CMUT 1097

PANACHE.
MC: CMUT 1156

Achwgha Ney Wodei

TRYPTIQUE.
2LP: NIR 872

Acid

DON'T LOSE YOUR DREAMS.
Tracks: / Drivin' / All through the night / Draw the line / Memories / Die by order / Up to the neck / Fine / Don't lose your dreams / To the edge of the world / Dark voices.
LP: 080604

MANIAC.
LP: MEGATON 007

Acid Amigo

ACID AMIGO (Various artists).
LP: ACIDLP 2
MC: ZCACID 2

Acid Beats

ACID BEATS VOL 1 (Various artists).
LP: . . . . **WRLP 003**

ACID BEATS VOL 2 (Various artists).
LP: . . . . **WRLP 004**

Acid Drinkers

ARE YOU A REBEL.
Tracks: / Del Rocca / I mean acid (do you like it) / L.O.V.E. machine / I am the mystic / Megalopolis / Moshin' in the nite / Barmy army / Waitin' for the hair / Fu** the violence (I'm sure I'm right) / Women with the dirty feet / Nagasaki baby / Mike Cwel.
LP: . . . . **FLAG 45**
MC: . . . . **TFLAG 45**

DIRTY MONEY - DIRTY TRICKS.
LP: . . . . **FLAG 59**
MC: . . . . **TFLAG 59**

Acid House

ACID HOUSE (Various artists).
LP: . . . . **DOT 1**
MC: . . . . **ZCDOT 1**

ACID HOUSE VOLUME.1 (Various artists).
LP: . . . . **BPLP 001**

NEW ACID HOUSE TECHNO BEAT (See under New Acid House) (Various artists).

Acid Jazz

ACID JAZZ AND OTHER ILLICIT GROOVES VOL.2 (Freedom Principle) (Various artists).
LP: **837 925-1**
MC: **837 925-4**

ACID JAZZ AND OTHER ILLICIT GROOVES (Various artists).
Tracks: / Introduction: *Ace Of Clubs* / Ace of clubs: *Ace Of Clubs* / Jalal: *Jalal* / Push: *Traffic*/ Shaft in action: *Acid Jazz* / Galliano: *Six Sharp Fists* / And now we have rhythm: *Night Trains* / Doin' it naturally: *Rhythm Blades* / Jazz renegades: *Various artists*.
LP: . . . . **URBLP 16**
MC: . . . . **URBMC 16**

ACID JAZZ VOL.1 (Various artists).
Tracks: / Better half: *Funk Inc* / Got myself a good man: *Pucho* / Houston Express, The: *Houston Person*/ Grits and gravy: *Kloss, Eric* / Hoochie coo chickie: *Jones, Ivan "Boogaloo Joe"* / Lady Mama: *Ammons, Gene*/ Hip shaker: *Spencer, Leon* / Psychedelic Sally: *Various artists*.
LP: . . . . **BGP 1015**

ACID JAZZ VOL.2 (Various artists).
Tracks: / Super bad: *Muhammad, Idris* / Cold sweat: *Purdie, Bernard* / Wildfire: *Bryant, Rusty* / Hot barbecue: *McDuff, Jack* / Reelin' with the feelin': *Kynard, Charles* / Spinky: *Earland, Charles* / Who's gonna take the weight: *Sparks, Melvin*.
LP: . . . . **BGP 1017**

ACID JAZZ VOL.3 (Various artists).
Tracks: / I want you back: *Mabern, Harold* / Psychedelic Pucho: *Pucho* / Zebra walk: *Kynard, Charles*/ Akilah: *Sparks, Melvin* / What it is: *Jones, Ivan "Boogaloo Joe"* / Bad Montana: *Parker, Maynard* / Dig on it: *Smith, Johnny "Hammond"* / Bowlegs: *Funk Inc*.
LP: . . . . **BGP 1025**

ACID JAZZ VOL.4 (Various artists).
Tracks: / Soul dance: *Person, Houston* / Sing a simple song: *Earland, Charles* / Twang thang, The: *Butler, Billy* / Shaft, Theme from: *Purdie, Bernard* / Sure 'nuff, sure 'nuff: *Phillips, Sonny* / Mamblues: *Tjader, Cal & Bernard Purdie* / Haw right now: *Rushen, Patrice* / Life is funky: *Round Robin Monopoly*.
LP: . . . . **BGP 1029**

BEST OF ACID JAZZ, THE (Various artists).
Tracks: / Chicken lickin': *Funk Inc* / Zebra walk: *Kynard, Charles* / Reelin' with the feelin': *Kynard, Charles*/ Dig on it: *Smith, Johnny "Hammond"* / Got myself a good man: *Pucho* / Super bad: *Muhammad, Idris* / Who's gonna take the weight: *Sparks, Melvin* / Sure 'nuff, sure 'nuff: *Phillips, Sonny* / Cold sweet: *Purdie, Bernard* / Psychadelic Sally: *Jefferson, Eddie* / Soul dance: *Houston Person* / Houston Express, The: *Houston Person* / Smokin' at Tiffany's: *Funk Inc*.
MC: . . . . **BGPC 921**

Acid Mix

ACID MIXES VOL 1 (Various artists).
LP: . . . . **UKDOT 1**
LP: . . . . **ERELP 1**
MC: . . . . **EREMC 1**

Acid Reign

FEAR, THE.
Tracks: / You never know / Insane ecstasy / Blind agression / Lost in solitude / Reflection of truths / Humanoia / Life in form s.
LP: . . . . **FLAG 31**
MC: . . . . **TFLAG 31**

MOSHKINSTEIN.
LP: . . . . **MFLAG 20**

OBNOXIOUS.
LP: . . . . **FLAG 39**

Acid Trance

ACID TRANCE VOL 1 (Various artists).
LP: . . . . **BLUEACLP 1**

Acid Trax

ACID TRAX (Various artists).
Tracks: / Face the nation: *M.D./Tyree* / Personal problems: *M.D./Tyree* / Yo body: *Nexus 1/Steve Simmons*/ So smooth: *Smooth, Joe* / Touch me: *Scrappy* / I am: *Tyree* / House express: *Mix Masters* / Move your acid: *Professor Funk* / Microdot: *Smooth, Joe* / Afro acid: *Power, Wonder & Love*.
LP: . . . . **ACIDLP 1**
MC: . . . . **ZCACID 1**

ACID TRAX 1 (Various artists).
Tracks: / House this house: *Mr. Lee* / Get the hole: *Townsell* / Cool and...: *Frost, Jack* / Shout: *Frost, Jack* / Downfall: *Armando* / Get the bug: *Phuture Fantasy Club* / Tom tom: *Frost, Jack* / Two the max: *Frost, Jack*.
LP: . . . . **BRUTAL 1**
MC: . . . . **ZCBRUT 1**

ACID TRAX 2 (Various artists).
Tracks: / Art of acid: *Mr. Lee* / Slam: *Phuture Fantasy Club* / That shit's wild: *Various artists* / City hall: *Six Brown Brothers* / Box energy: *D.J. Pierre* / Jackin' tall: *Townsell, Lidell* / Feels good: *Mr. Lee* / Hello lover: *VL & The Porch Monkeys* / Bango acid: *Wilson, Mike 'Hitman'* / I got a big dick: *Joshua, Maurice* / Never gonna change: *Mr. Lee* / Hot hands: *Hot Hanas Hula* / I'll make you dance: *Townsell*, Lidell / Feel the mood: *Joshua, Maurice* / Spank spank: *Phuture Fantasy Club* / 70th and King Drive: *Hot Hanas Hula*.
2LP: . . . . **DRUG 2**
MC: . . . . **ZCUG 2**
2LP: . . . . **BRUTAL 2**
MC: . . . . **ZCBRUT 2**

ACID TRAX MEGAMIX VOL.1 (Various artists).
LP: . . . . **DUIX 1**
MC: . . . . **ZCIX 1**

ACIDTRAX 1 (Various artists).
LP: . . . . **WDRLP 002**
MC: . . . . **ZCWDR 002**

ACIDTRAX 2 (Various artists).
LP: . . . . **WDRLP 003**
MC: . . . . **ZCWDR 003**

Acid Vision

ACID VISION VOL II (Various artists).
LP: . . . . **VOXX 200054**

Acid Visions

ACID VISIONS (Various artists).
LP: . . . . **VOXX 200008**

Ackah, Jewel

SUPA PAWA.
LP: . . . . **KYK 005-A**

Ackerman, Bob

HEART SONG (See under Purvis, Pam for details) (Ackerman, Bob & Pam Purvis).

Ackerman, Will

CONFERRING WITH THE MOON.
LP: **371050-1**
MC: **371050-4**
LP: . . . . **WHA 1050**

PASSAGE.
Tracks: / Remedios / Processional / Independing death of the virgin spirit / Pacific I / Bricklayer's beautiful daughter, The / Hawk circle / Annie's song / Passage.
LP: **371014-1**
MC: **371014-4**

PAST LIGHT.
LP: **371028-1**
MC: **371028-4**
LP: . . . . **WHA 1028**

WILL ACKERMAN.
LP: **371 078 1**
MC: **371 078 4**

Acklin, Barbara

FROM THE TEACHER TO THE PREACHER (See under Chandler, Gene) (Acklin, Barbara & Gene Chandler).

GROOVY IDEAS.
Tracks: / I'll bake me a man / I call it trouble / I'm living with a memory / It's a groovy idea / I did it / Portrait of a broken heart / Seven days of night / More ways than one / Love makes a woman / Be by my side / Just ain't no love / Here is a heart / I've got you baby / After you / Am I the same girl / Come and see my baby.
LP: . . . . **KENT 072**

Acoustic Alchemy

BACK ON THE CASE.
Tracks: / Alchemist, The / Jamaica heartbeat / Georgia Peach / Playing for time / When lights go out / Clear air for miles / Fire of the heart / Freeze frame / On the case / Break for the border.
MC: . . . . **GRP 96484**

BLUE CHIP.
LP: . . . . **IMCA 6291**
MC: . . . . **IMCAC 6291**

NATURAL ELEMENTS.
LP: . . . . **IMCA 42125**
MC: . . . . **IMCAC 42125**

RED DUST AND SPANISH LACE.
Tracks: / Mr. Chow / Ricochet / Stone circle / Rideout, The / Girl with a red carnation / Colonel and the ashes, The / One for the road / Sarah Victoria / Red dust and Spanish lace.
LP: . . . . **IMCA 5816**
MC: . . . . **IMCAC 5816**

REFERENCE POINT.
Tracks: / Reference point / Missing your touch / Take five / Same road, same reason / Make my day / Caravan of dreams / Homecoming / Cuban heels / Lullaby for the first born.
LP: . . . . **GRP 96141**
MC: . . . . **GRP 96144**

Acoustic Rock

ACOUSTIC ROCK (Various artists).
LP: . . . . **STAR 2399**
MC: . . . . **STAC 2399**

Acres For Cents

ACRES FOR CENTS (Various artists).
LP: . . . . **ZNIP 501**

Acridity

FOR FREEDOM I CRY.
LP: . . . . **PROPH 2/1**

Acrophet

CORRUPT MINDS.
Tracks: / Intro to corruption / Lifeless image / Crime for loving / Holy spirit / Ceremonial slaughter / Forgotten faith / Corrupt minds / Slaves of sin / From the depths / Living in today / Warped illusions / Victims of the holocaust.
LP: . . . . **RR 9523 1**

Across 110th Street

ACROSS 110TH STREET (Film Soundtrack) (Various artists).
Tracks: / Across 110th street: *Womack, Bobby & Peace* / If you don't want my love: *Womack, Bobby & Peace* / Quicksand: *Womack, Bobby & Peace* / Do it right: *Womack, Bobby & Peace* / Hang on in there: *Womack, Bobby & Peace*/ Across 110th street (pt 2): *Womack, Bobby & Peace* / Harlem clavinette: *Johnson, J J & His Orchestra* / Hang on in there: *Johnson, J J & His Orchestra* / Harlem love theme: *Johnson, J J & His Orchestra* / Across 110th street: *Johnson, J J & His Orchestra* / If you don't want my love: *Johnson, J J & His Orchestra*.
LP: . . . . **UAS 29451**

Act (group)

LAUGHTER, TEARS AND RAGE.
Tracks: / Absolutely immune / Chance / Laughter / I can't escape from you / Under the nights of Germany / Gestures / Friendly warning, A / Certified / Where love lies bleeding / Snobbery and decay.
LP: . . . . **ZQLP 1**
MC: . . . . **ZQMC 1**

Act (show)

ACT ,THE (Original Broadway Cast with Liza Minnelli) (Various artists).
Tracks: / Shine it on: *Various artists* / It's the strangest thing: *Various artists* / Bobo's: *Various artists*/ Turning: *Various artists* / Little do they know: *Various artists* / Arthur in the afternoon: *Various artists*/ Money tree: *Various artists* / City lights: *Various artists* / There when I need him: *Various artists*/ Hot enough for you?: *Various artists* / Little do they know (reprise): *Various artists* / My own space: *Various artists* / Walking papers: *Various artists*.
LP: . . . . **MRS 701**
MC: . . . . **MRSC 701**
LP: . . . . **DRG 6101**
MC: . . . . **DRGC 6101**

Action

PIECE OF THE ACTION, A.
Tracks: / In my dreams / Come around / I've got something to say / Love is all / Icarus / Strange roads / Things you cannot see / Brain / Climbing up the wall to see you see me / It really doesn't matter / I'm a stranger here myself / Follow me / In my dreams (demo version).
LP: . . . . **LIK 44**

ULTIMATE ACTION, THE.
Tracks: / I'll keep holding on / Harlem shuffle / Never ever / Twenty fourth hour / Since I lost my baby / My lonely room / Hey sah-lo-ney / Shadows and reflections / Something has hit me / Place, The / Cissy, The / Baby you got it / I love you (yeah) / Land of a thousand dances.
LP: . . . . **ED 101**

Action (2)

ACTIONS SPEAK LOUDER THAN.
Tracks: / Only dreaming / Dustbin full of rubbish / Understanding love, An / My favourite day / Saying for today, A.
LP: . . . . **DOJOLP 3**

Action Force (tv)

FLINT'S HOLIDAY (For Ages 7-12).
MC: . . . . **PLBA 226**

RETURN OF THE DINOSAURS (For Ages 7-12).
MC: . . . . **PLBA 227**

Action Jackson

ACTION JACKSON (Film Soundtrack) (Various artists).
Tracks: / He turned me out: *Pointer Sisters* / Action Jackson: *Madam X* / For the love of money: *Levert*/ Undress: *Vanity* / Building up Action Jackson: *Various artists* / Keeping good loving: *Sister Sledge*/ Shotgun: *Vanity & David Koz* / Faraway eyes: *Vanity* / Lover's celebration: *SKYY* / To protect and serve: *Jam, M.C. & Pee Wee Jam*.
LP: **790 886 1**
MC: **790 886 4**

Action Pact

MERCURY THEATRE: ON THE AIR.
LP: . . . . **FALL LP 013**
MC: . . . . **FALL CLP 013**

SURVIVAL OF THE FATTEST.
LP: . . . . **FALL LP 030**

Action Replay

ACTION REPLAY (Various artists).
LP: . . . . **REH 441**

Action Songs

ACTION SONGS (Various artists).
MC: . . . . **PLB 270**

Action Tracks

ACTION TRACKS (Various artists).
LP: . . . . **NE 1162**
MC: . . . . **CE 2162**

Activity Box

CHRISTMAS.
MC: . . . . **TATAB 2**

NURSERY RHYMES.
MC: . . . . **TATAB 1**

Acts Of Madmen

DREAM, THE.
Tracks: / Dream, The.
LP: . . . . **DS 5464**

Acuff, Roy

BEST OF ROY ACUFF, THE.
MC: **4XL 9371**

FLY, BIRDIE, FLY 1939 - 41 (Acuff, Roy & His Smokey Mountain Boys).
LP: . . . . **SS 024**
MC: . . . . **CSS 24**

GREAT ROY ACUFF, THE.
Tracks: / Sunshine special / Is it love or is it lies / I closed my heart's door / Don't judge your neighbour / Thief upon the tree,The / Rushing around / Sweep around your own back door / I'm planting a rose / Oh those tombs / Swamp lily / Please daddy forgive / Little Moses.
LP: . . . . **HAT 3055**
MC: . . . . **HATC 3055**

GREATEST HITS: ROY ACUFF VOL.1.
Tracks: / Wabash cannonball / Blue eyes crying in the rain / Great speckled bird, The / We live in two different worlds / Wreck on the highway / Jole Blon / Pins and needles / Precious jewel / Fireball mail / Back in the country / Story of the violin / Smokey Mountain memories / Take me home, country roads / End of memory lane / Rolling in my sweet baby's arms / That's the man I'm looking for / Precious memories / Will the circle be unbroken / Turn your radio on / I saw the light.
2LP: . . . . **K 62023**

GREATEST HITS, VOL 2.
LP: . . . . **K 62029**

SONGS OF THE SMOKEY MOUNTAIN (Acuff, Roy & His Smokey Mountain Boys).
LP: . . . . **HAT 3038**
MC: . . . . **HATC 3038**

STEAMBOAT WHISTLE BLUES.
Tracks: / Yes Sir that's my baby / Red lips / Steamboat whistle blues / You've

gotta see mama every night / Sad memories / Smokey mountain rag / Shout on Lulu / Old three room shack, An / Charming Betsy / One old shirt / Automobile of life / Honky tonk mamas.
LP: SS 23
MC: SSC 23

TWO DIFFERENT WORLDS.
Tracks: / Wabash cannonball / Blue eyes crying in the rain / Great speckled bird, The / Two different worlds / Wreck on the highway / Jole blon / Pins and needles / Precious jewel, The / Fireball mail / Back in the country.
LP: SDLP 028

AD

ART OF THE STATE.
LP: KRR R 5401
MC: KRR C 5401

PRIME MOVER.
LP: SP R 1181
MC: SP C 1181

RECONSTRUCTIONS.
LP: KRR R 5406
MC: KRR C 5406

Adagio

ADAGIO (Various artists).
2LP: LPCEL 6428271
MC: MCCEL 6428271

Adams, Bob

BOB ADAMS' EARLY TIMES SHOW BAND (Adams, Bob Early Times Show Band).
LP: CLP 23

Adams, Bryan

BRYAN ADAMS.
Tracks: / Hidin' from love / Win some lose some / Wait and see / Give me your love / Wastin' time / Don't ya say it / Remember / State of mind / Try to see it my way.
LP: 393 100-1
MC: CS 69902
LP: AMLH 64800

CUTS LIKE A KNIFE.
Tracks: / Only one, The / Take me back / This time / Straight from the heart / Cuts like a knife / I'm ready / What's it gonna be / Don't leave me lonely / Best was yet to come, The.
LP: AMLH 64919
MC: CAM 64919

CUTS LIKE A KNIFE/RECKLESS.
Tracks: / Only one, The / Take me back / This time / Straight from the heart / Cuts like a knife / I'm ready / What's it gonna be / Don't leave me lonely / Best was yet to come, The / One night love affair / She's only happy when she's dancin' / Run to you / Heaven / Somebody / Summer of '69 / Kids wanna rock / It's only love / Long gone / Ain't gonna cry.
MC: AMC 24101

INTO THE FIRE.
Tracks: / Heat of the night / Into the fire / Victim of love / Another day / Native son / Only the strong survive / Rebel / Remembrance day / Hearts on fire / Home again.
LP: AMA 3907
MC: AMC 3907

RECKLESS.
Tracks: / One night love affair / She's only happy when she's dancin' / Run to you / Heaven / Somebody / Summer of '69 / Kids wanna rock / It's only love / Long gone / Ain't gonna cry.
LP: AMA 5013
MC: AMC 5013

WAKING UP THE NEIGHBOURS.
LP: 397164 1
MC: 397164 4

YOU WANT IT, YOU GOT IT.
Tracks: / Lonely nights / One good reason / Don't look now / Coming home / Fits ya good / Tonight / Jealousy / You want it you got it / Last chance / No one makes it right.
LP: AMLH 64864
MC: CAM 64864

Adams, Cliff

100TH SING SOMETHING SIMPLE.
Tracks: / Moonlight bay / When I grow too old to dream / Moonlight and roses / September song / Song sung blue / Love's old sweet song / Roses of Picardy / You are the sunshine of my life / Together / Singing in the rain / Down by the old mill stream / Way we were.
LP: REH 373
MC: ZCR 373

SING SOMETHING DISNEY (Adams, Cliff Singers).
Tracks: / Sing something Disney / Magic song, The / Little April showers / With a smile and a song / La la lu / Let's go fly a kite / Casey the pride of them all / Who's afraid of the big bad wolf / When you wish upon a star / Spoonful of sugar, A / Supercalifragilisticexpialidocious / Unbirthday song, The / Love is a song / He's a tramp / Siamese cat song / Ev'rybody wants to be a cat / Never smile at a crocodile / Ballad of Davy Crockett, The / Feed the birds / Some day my prince will come / Lavender blue / When I see an elephant fly / Chim chim cheree / Heigh-ho / Zip-a-dee-doo-dah / Make mine music.
LP: REH 574
MC: ZCR 574

SING SOMETHING SILVER (Adams, Cliff Singers).
LP: REH 546
MC: ZCR 546

SING SOMETHING SIMPLE (Adams, Cliff Singers).
Tracks: / I don't want to walk without you / Can't smile without you / Mandy / If I had a hammer / Down by the riverside / He's got the whole world in his hands / Marianne / I can give you the starlight / Love is my reason / Someday my heart will awake / We'll gather lilacs / Singing the blues / Truly fair / Feet up / Chicka boom / My love is like a red, red rose / Liverpool Lou / Little children / How do you do it / Ferry cross the Mersey / Little bit of heaven, A / Irish lullaby / If you're Irish come into the parlour / It's a great day for the Irish / I want a girl / My mothers eyes / Mother.
MC: HSC 660

SING SOMETHING SIMPLE (Adams, Cliff Singers).
LP: MPL 28013
LP: GGL 0150

SING SOMETHING SIMPLE '76 (Adams, Cliff Singers).
2LP: WW 5016/17

SING SOMETHING SIMPLE (100 GOLDEN GREATS) (Adams, Cliff Singers).
2LP: RTD 2087
MCSET: 4CRTD 2087

SOMETHING OLD, SOMETHING NEW (Adams, Cliff Singers).
Tracks: / Tumbling tumbleweeds / 76 trombones / Shepherd of the hills / Back in your own back yard / Exodus / I'm an airman / Me and Jane in a plane / When I take my sugar to tea / Get happy / If I had a talking picture of you / Moonglow.
LP: OU 2163

SONGS TO REMEMBER (50 OLD TIME FAVOURITES) (Adams, Cliff Singers).
2LP: RONLP 7
MCSET: CRON 7

VERY BEST OF SING SOMETHING SIMPLE, THE (Adams, Cliff Singers).
MC: HSC 656

Adams, Dave

DANCING IN MY SLEEP.
Tracks: / Tars / Dancing in my sleep / Love love love / Something's happening / What do you say / Fighting / Tea and symphony / Where do we go from here / Shattering.
LP: 9604831
MC: 9604834

Adams, Deroll

SONGS OF THE BANJOMAN.
LP: FF 4016

Adams, Don

DON ADAMS MEETS THE ROVING REPORTER.
LP: GNPS 91

Adams, Douglas (aut)

HITCH-HIKER'S GUIDE TO THE GALAXY (See Under Hitch-hikers Guide...) (Moore, Stephen (nar)).

LIFE, THE UNIVERSE AND EVERYTHING (See under Life, the Universe...) (Moore, Stephen (nar)).

RESTAURANT AT THE END OF THE UNIVERSE (See under Restaurant at... (bk) (Moore, Stephen (nar)).

SO LONG, AND THANKS FOR ALL THE FISH (See under So Long & Thanks... (bk)) (Moore, Stephen (nar)).

Adams, Elliott

PLAYS THE BUFFALO RAG.
LP: SOS 1198

Adams Family

SOMETIMES I WONDER.
LP: SPIV 3

Adams, Faye

I'M GONNA LEAVE YOU.
Tracks: / You ain't been true / I'm gonna leave you / Johnny Lee / Shake a hand / It hurts me to my heart / Look around / I'm so happy / Cry you crazy heart.
LP: RB 110

SHAKE A HAND.
Tracks: / Witness to the crime / Teenage heart / Takin' you back / Don't forget to smile / Tag along / Angels tell me / Your love (has my heart burnin') / Anything for a friend / Shake a hand / I've gotta leave you / Everyday / I'll be true / Say a prayer / Hurts me to my heart / I owe my heart to you / Love ain't nothing to play with.
LP: OFF 6027

Adams, Gayle

GAYLE ADAMS.
Tracks: / Baby I need your loving / Don't blame it on me / You don't owe me nothing / Let's go all the way / Love fever / I can't get enough of you / Don't jump to conclusions / I loved every minute of it.
LP: EPC 85687

Adams, George

ALL THAT FUNK (Adams, George & Don Pullen).
Tracks: / Alfie / Intentions / Big Alice.
LP: PAL 15002

CITY GATES (Adams, George & Don Pullen Quartet).
Tracks: / Mingus metamorphosis / Samba for now / Thank you very much Mr. Monk / Nobody knows the trouble I've seen / City gates.
LP: SJP 181

EARTH BEAMS (Adams, George & Don Pullen Quartet).
Tracks: / Magnetic love / Dionysus / Saturday nite in the cosmos / More flowers / Sophisticated Alice.
MC: SJP 1147
LP: SJP 147

GEORGE ADAMS AND THE DON PULLEN QUARTET (Adams, George & Don Pullen Quartet).
LP: SFP 154

LIVE AT MONTMARTRE (Adams, George & Don Pullen Quartet).
LP: SJP 219

LIVE AT VILLAGE VANGUARD (Adams, George & Don Pullen Quartet).
Tracks: / Necessary blues, The / Solitude / Intentions / Diane.
LP: SN 1094

MELODIC EXCURSIONS.
Tracks: / Calling, The / God has smiled on me / Kahji / Playground uptown and downtown / Decisions / Reflexions inward / Resolution of conflicts.
LP: SJP 166

MORE FUNK (Adams, George & Don Pullen).
Tracks: / Metamorphosis for Charles Mingus.
LP: PAL 15003

MORE SIGHTINGS (Adams, George, Hannibal & friends).
LP: ENJA 4084

NIGHTINGALE.
Tracks: / Bridge over troubled water / What a wonderful world / Nightingale sang in Berkley Square, A / Moon River / Precious Lord, take my hand / Ol' man river / Going home.
LP: B1 91984

PARADISE SPACE SHUTTLE (Adams, George Quintet).
Tracks: / Paradise space shuttle / Intentions / Send in the clowns / Metamorphosis for Mingus / City of peace / Funk-roonie-pea cock.
LP: JSP 127

SONG EVERLASTING (see under Pullen, Don) (Adams, George Quartet/ Don Pullen).

Adams, Greg

RUNAWAY DREAMS.
Tracks: / Leave me / Too late to love you / Need to be right / If you think I can / Lonely girl / We're in it together / Way we love / Lady Liberty / Can't get over you / Runaway dreams.
LP: EPC 83752

Adams, John

CHAIRMAN DANCES, THE.
Tracks: / Chairman dances, The / Christian zeal and activity / Two fanfares for orchestra / Tromba lontana / Short ride in a fast machine / Common tones in simple time.
LP: K 979144 1
MC: K 979144 4

FEARFUL SYMMETRIES (Wound dresser).
LP: 9792181
MC: 9792184

HARMONIE LEHRE.
LP: 979115-1

HARMONIUM.
Tracks: / Negative love (part one) / Because I could not stop for death - Wild nights (part 2) / Negative love (Poem by John Donne) / Because I could not stop for death (Poem by Emily Dickinson) / Wild nights / Why do I / Laughin' and clownin' / If I ever had a good time / Scarred knees / Your love is so doggone good / We don't see eye to eye / Road block / Teach me to forget.
LP: ECM 1277

MUSIC FROM NIXON IN CHINA.
LP: 979193 1
MC: 979193 4

NIXON IN CHINA.
LPS: 979177 1
MCSET: 979177 4

Adams, Johnny

AFTER DARK.
LP: REU 1008

AFTER DARK.
LP: ROUNDER 2049
MC: ROUNDER 2049C

CHRISTMAS IN NEW ORLEANS.
Tracks: / Silent night / O little town of Bethlehem / Lord's prayer, The / Silver bells / Christmas song, The / Little boy that Santa Claus forgot, The / This Christmas / Lonesome Christmas / Bells of St. Mary's / White Christmas / Please come home for Chr istmas.
LP: 1023
MC: 1023 TC

FROM THE HEART.
Tracks: / I feel like breaking up somebody's home / Why do I / Laughin' and clownin' / If I ever had a good thing / Scarred knees / From the heart / Your love is so doggone good / We don't see eye to eye / Roadblock / Teach me to forget.
LP: FIEND 26
LP: OLD 3
LP: ROUNDER 2044
MC: ROUNDER 2044C

ROOM WITH A VIEW OF THE BLUES.
Tracks: / Room with a view / I don't want to do wrong / Not trustworthy / Neither one of us / Body and fender man / I owe you / Wished I'd never loved you at all / Hunt is on, The / World I never made, A.
LP: FIEND 111
LP: ROUNDER 2059
MC: ROUNDER 2059 C

TAN NIGHTINGALE, THE.
Tracks: / Release me / You made a new man out of me / How can I prove I love you / You depend on me / Real live living hurtin' man / I won't cry / Losing battle, A / I have no one / Love me now / Proud woman / Reconsider me / Something worth leaving for / Let me be myself / It's got to be something / Hell yes, I cheated.
LP: CRB 1058

WALKING ON A TIGHTROPE.
LP: ZS 89

Adams, Linda & Paul

AMONG THE OLD FAMILIAR MOUNTAINS.
Tracks: / Witch of the Westmorlands, The / Fall of the leaf, The / Fine hunting day / Banks of red roses, The / Copshawholme fair / Keswick bonny lassies / Rosie Nell / Long Meg and her daughters / Horn of the hunter / Female drummer / Dowie dens of Yarrow, The / Caroline and her young sailor bold / Swarthfell rocks / My miner lad / Farewell to the fells.
LP: FE 006

COUNTRY HIRINGS.
Tracks: / Songs of Cumbria and the Border / Country hirings / Wellington disaster / Shepherds life / Lark in the morning, The / Bonnie Maisry / Tups / John Peels lament / Blackthorn stick / Widow of the Westmorlands daughter / Saddle the pony / Parton Colliers lament / Beagle Inn / Philipsons curse / Walney Cockfighting song / Eskdale and Ennerdale hunt song, The / North Country lass.
LP: SFA 053

FAR OVER THE FELL.
Tracks: / Keswick driver, The / German clockwinder, The / Jimmy's enlisted / Brisk young sailor, A / Jolly boys song, The / King Dunmail / Lament of the border widow, The / Tarry Woo / Sun shines fair on Carlisle wall, The / Paul Jones / Farewell to the miner / Witch of the Westmorlands, The.
LP: SFA 027

Adams, Oleta

CIRCLE OF ONE.
Tracks: / Rhythm of life / Get here / Circle of one / You've got to give me room / I've got to sing my song / I've got a right / Will we ever learn / Everything must change.
LP: 8427441
MC: 8427444
MC: 8487404

Adams, Pepper

10 TO 4 AT THE 5-SPOT (Adams, Pepper Quintet).
LP: OJC 031

EPHEMERA.
Tracks: / Ephemera / Bouncing with Bud / Civilization and it's discontents / Jitterbug waltz / Quiet lady / Patrice / Hellure.
LP: SPJ LP 6

JULIAN.
LP: ENJA 2060

MASTER, THE.
Tracks: / Enchilada / Chelsea Bridge / Bossallegro / Rue Serpente / Lovers of their time / My shining hour.
LP: MR 5213

PURE PEPPER.
LP: WL 70514

REFLECTORY.
Tracks: / Reflectory / Sophisticated lady / Etude diabolique / Claudette's way / I carry your heart / That's all.
LP: MR 5182

TWELFTH AND PINGREE.
LP: ENJA 2074

URBAN DREAMS.
LP: PA 8009
MC: PAC 8009

Adams, Richard (aut)

WATERSHIP DOWN (See under Watership Down) (Dotrice, Roy (nar)).

Adams, Rusty (Ko Ko)

BEYOND THE SUNSET.
Tracks: / Beyond the sunset / Long black veil / I never heard the music / I'll quit truck driving / Burning memories / They left their memory in good hands / Till I lose you (all the way) / Somebody's always leaving / Fools advice, A / Little Rosa / I'm so lonesome I could cry.
MC: BRC 1001

Adams, Shirley

GOD'S TIME (Adams, Shirley & The Adams Singers).
LP: MIR 5009
MC: ZCMIR 5009

Adams, Suzie

SONGBIRD (Adams, Suzie & Helen Watson).
LP: DIN 327

Adams, Trevor

COUNTRY CLASSICS.
LP: BSS 178

I BELIEVE IN COUNTRY MUSIC.
LP: BSS 124

Adamski

DOCTOR ADAMSKI MUSICAL PHARMACY.
LP: MCG 6107
MC: MCGC 6107

LIVE AND DIRECT.
Tracks: / N-R-G (parts 1 & 2) / I dream of you / Tekno krisna / Bassline changed my life, The / In your face / Magik piano / You. Me. House / Brand new house, A / M 25 / I love teknology (pt 1) / Rap you in sound / Into orbit / Love and life.
LP: MCG 6078
MC: MCGC 6078

Adamson, Barry

DELUSION.
LP: IONIC 004
MC: CIONIC 004

MOSS-SIDE STORY.
LP: STUMM 53
MC: CSTUMM 53

Adamson, Dierdre

DIERDRE'S FANCY.
LP: DA 8809

OFF SHE GOES.
LP: SM 003

SWINGING ALONG.
LP: DA 8601

Adamson, Joy (aut)

BORN FREE (See under Born Free) (McKenna, Virginia).

ADC Band

BROTHER LUCK.
Tracks: / Brother luck / Celebrate / Waiting for you / Nothing you can do / Superfreak / Hot box / Nuclear funk out / Our thought (lovers and friends).
LP: K 50795

ROLL WITH THE PUNCHES.
LP: SD 5232

Adcock, Eddie

2ND GENERATION, THE (Adcock, Eddie & Martha).
Tracks: / Old man / Bound to ride / Make me a pallet on the floor / Eddie's matchbox blues / Wayward wind, The / Foggy lady / Remember me / Sugarfoot rag / High hill, The / Singer, The / Scream theme.
LP: CMH 6263
MC: CMH 6263 C

ACOUSTIC COLLECTION, THE.
Tracks: / Good ol' Sallie Gooden (inst) / Where will I shelter my sheep / I'll go steppin' too / Emotions (inst) / Loose talk / Love and wealth / I'd rather die young / Limehouse blues (inst) / (There'll be) peace in the valley for me / No letter in the mail today / I can hear Kentucky calling me / Eddie on the high ground / Gathering flowers from the hillside / Heartaches (inst) / Before I met you / (I'll pawn my) gold watch / Waiting for the sunrise (inst) / Go down yonder Moses / Mom and Dad's waltz / Meet Mister Callaghan (inst) / Next Sunday is my birthday / Where could I go (but to the Lord) / Come in stranger / Freight train (inst).
2LP: CMH 9039

EDDIE ADCOCK & HIS GUITAR.
Tracks: / Guitar echoes / Sun fall 1988 / Under the double eagle / Love is blue / Bluegrass boogie / Sunshine / Exodus (Theme from) / Sugarfoot rag / Eddie's love theme / Birth of the blues / Silver blue / Guitar rag / Bump and jump / Strollin'.
LP: CMH 6265
MC: CMH 6265C

GUITAR ECHOES.
Tracks: / Guitar echoes / Wild blackberries / Orange blossom overture / Eddie's love theme / Bird lips and banana juice / Sun fall / Freewheelin' boogie / Jamagination / Birth of the blues.
LP: CMH 6236

Adderley, Cannonball

ACCENT ON AFRICA (Adderley, Cannonball Quintet).
Tracks: / Ndo Lima / Hamba nami / Dikhutsana / Up and at it / Gumba Gumba / Marabi / Gun-Jah / Lehadima.
LP: AFF 148
MC: TCAFF 148

AFRICAN WALTZ.
Tracks: / African waltz / Barefoot sunday blues / Kelly blue.
LP: OJC 258

ALABAMA/AFRICA.
Tracks: / African waltz / Kelly blue / Smoke gets in your eyes / West Coast blues / Letter from home / Something different / Blue brass groove / I'll close my eyes / Stockholm sweetnin / Uptown, The / This here / John Benson Brooks / Alabama concerto (in four movements).
2LP: M 47059

ALTO GIANT.
Tracks: / Scavenger / Sweet Emma / Ballads medley / This here / Manha De Carnaval / Walk tall.
LP: LOP 14 070

CANNONBALL ADDERLEY.
LP: M 47029

CANNONBALL ADDERLEY COLLECTION VOL. 3 (Jazz Workshop Revisited).
Tracks: / Pimitiva / Jessica's day / Unit 7 / Jive samba / Marney / Mellow buno / Lillie.
LP: LLP 1303
MC: LMC 1303

CANNONBALL ADDERLEY COLLECTION VOL. 4 (The Poll Winners).
Tracks: / Chant / Azule serape / Heart alone / Lolita / Au privave / Never will I marry.
LP: LLP 1304
MC: LMC 1304

CANNONBALL ADDERLEY COLLECTION VOL. 5 (At The Lighthouse).
Tracks: / Sack o'woe / Azule serape / Our delight / Big 'P' / Blue Daniel / Exodus / What is this thing called love?.
LP: LLP 1305
MC: LMC 1305

CANNONBALL ADDERLEY COLLECTION VOL. 7 (Cannonball In Europe).
Tracks: / P. Bouk / Gemini / Work song / Trouble in mind / Dizzy's business.
LP: LLP 1307
MC: LMC 1307

CANNONBALL ADDERLEY COLLECTION VOL. 1 (Them Dirty Blues).
Tracks: / Dat dere / Del sasser / Soon / Work song / Jeannine / Easy living / Them dirty blues.
LP: LLP 1301
MC: LMC 1301

CANNONBALL ADDERLEY COLLECTION VOL. 2 (Cannonball's Bossa Nova) (Adderley, Cannonball & The Bossa Rio Sextet).
Tracks: / Clouds (take 7) / Groovy samba / Joyce's samba / Corcovado / Sambop / Batida differente / Once I loved / Minha Suadade / Clouds.
LP: LLP 1302
MC: LMC 1302

CANNONBALL ADDERLEY COLLECTION VOL. 6 (Cannonball Takes Charge).
Tracks: / If this isn't love / I guess I'll hang my tears out to dry / Serenata / I've told every little star / Barefoot Sunday blues / Poor butterfly / I remember you.
LP: LLP 1306
MC: LMC 1306

CANNONBALL AND EIGHT GIANTS.
2LP: ML 47001

CLEANHEAD AND CANNONBALL (See under Vinson, Eddie) (Vinson, Eddie & Cannonball Adderley).

COAST TO COAST.
Tracks: / This hare / Spontaneous combustion / High fly / Straight no chaser / You got it / Gemini / Planet earth / Dizzy's business / Syn anthesia / Scotch and water / Cannonball's theme.
2LP: M 47039

COMPACT JAZZ.
MC: 8429304

EASE IT (See Chambers, Paul) (Adderley, Cannonball/Paul Chambers).

JUST FRIENDS (See under Chambers, Paul) (Adderley, Cannonball/Paul Chambers).

KNOW WHAT I MEAN.
Tracks: / Arriving soon / Well, you needn't / New Delhi / Winetone star eyes / Lisa / Waltz for Debby / Goodbye / Who cares? / Elsa / Toy / Nancy / Venice / Know what I mean?.
2LP: M 47053
2LP: OJC 105

MERCY, MERCY, MERCY.
LP: IC 048 50710

NAT & JULIAN CANNONBALL ADDERLEY (see Adderley, Nat).

RADIO NIGHTS.
LP: VNLP 2
MC: VNTC 2

SOMETHIN' ELSE (Adderley, Cannonball & Miles Davis).
Tracks: / Autumn leaves / Love for sale / Something else / One for Daddy O / Dancing in the dark / Alison's uncle.
LP: BST 81595
MC: TCBST 81595
LP: BNS 40036

SOMETHING ELSE (see Davis, Miles) (Adderley, Cannonball & Miles Davis).

SPONTANEOUS COMBUSTION.
Tracks: / Still talkin' to ya / Little taste, A / Caribbean cutie / Bohemia after dark / Chasm / Willow weep for me / Late entry / Spontaneous combustion / Flamingo / Hear me talkin' to ya / With apologies to Oscar / We'll be together again.
2LP: WL 70531
MCSET: WK 70531
LP: SJL 2206

STICKS AND SOUL.
Tracks: / Sticks / Games / I'm on my way / Mercy mercy mercy / Mini man / Why am I treated so bad / Walk tall (baby that's what I need) / Country preacher.
LP: AFF 162

THINGS ARE GETTING BETTER (Adderley, Cannonball with Milt Jackson).
LP: RSLP 286

WHAT IS THIS THING CALLED SOUL? (Adderley, Cannonball Quintet).
Tracks: / Azule serape / Big 'p' / One for daddy-o / Chant / What is this thing called love? / Cannonball's theme.
LP: 230 8238
MC: K 08 238

Adderley, Nat

ART FORD'S JAZZ PARTY (August 1958).
Tracks: / Body and soul / Cootie's blues / I got it bad and that ain't good / Fine and dandy / Bugle call rag / Airmail special.
LP: AFJP 5

BLUE AUTUMN (Adderley, Nat Quintet).
LP: TR 122

DON'T LOOK BACK.
LP: SCS 1059

NAT & JULIAN CANNONBALL ADDERLEY (Adderley, Nat & Julian Cannonball Adderley).
Tracks: / Stay on it / Autumn leaves / This here / Prelude / Gemini.
LP: KLJ 20024

NOBLE AND NAT (See under Watts, Noble 'Thin Man' (Adderley, Nat & Noble 'Thin Man' Watts).

SAYIN' SOMETHING/THAT'S JAZZ.
LP: K 50246

THAT'S NAT.
LP: WL 70506

WE REMEMBER CANNON.
Tracks: / I'll remember April / Unit 7 / Talkin' about you, Cannon / Work song / Soul eyes / Stella by starlight.
LP: 70121

WORK SONG.
Tracks: / Work song / Pretty memory / I've got a crush on you / Mean to me / Fallout / Sack o' woe / My heart stood still / Violets for your furs / Scrambled eggs.
LP: RSLP 318

YOKOHAMA CONCERT, THE (See under Johnson, J.J.) (Adderley, Nat & J.J. Johnson).

Addictive

PITY OF MAN.
LP: RAT 508

Addis Rockers

ADDIS ROCKERS.
LP: WAFLP 1

ENTER ADDIS ABABA.
LP: WAFLP 2

Addotta, Kip

LIFE IN THE SLOW LANE.
LP: RNLP 70826

Addrisi Brothers

ADDRISI BROTHERS.
Tracks: / Ghost dancer / Last chance for romance / Lady broke my heart / Streetlight love / As long as the music keeps playing / So you are love / Look, but don't touch / Loretta.
LP: K 50676

Addy, Mustapha Tettey

MASTER DRUMMER FROM GHANA.
LP: TGS 113
LP: LLST 7250
MC: LLCT 7250

MUSTAPHA TETTEY ADDY-VOL.2.
LP: TGS 139

PERCUSSIONS DU GHANA, LES.
Tracks: / Rythmes du culte Igari / Rythmes bambaya / Gongs ga / Solo de calebasses / Frafra / Gigbo waka.
LP: ARN 33574

Ade, King Sunny

AURA.
LP: ILPM 9746
MC: ICM 9746

EXPLOSION.
LP: SALPS 40

GRATITUDE (Ade, King Sunny & Mo Dupe).
LP: SALPS 44

IJINLE ODU.
LP: SALPS 32

JU JU MUSIC.
MC: ICT 9712
LP: ILPS 9712

KING SUNNY ADE VOL.1.
MC: TCAS 8006

KING SUNNY ADE VOL.4.
MC: TC AS 8010

LIVE JUJU.
LP: RACS 0047

MERCIFUL.
Tracks: / Merciful God, The / E bi mi ra-ba-ba-ba / Ori adi lori mi / Ko ma ro / Da mi lola / Enti ohwan da lejo / Ewuju to lohun yio fa ope tu / Kaja ma mu lo / Pagidar igi da / Peregede.
LP: APLPS 5

SAVIOUR.
LP: SALPS 48

SWEET BANANA.
LP: APLPS 1

SYNCHRO SYSTEM (Ade, King Sunny & His African Beats).
LP: ILPS 9737
MC: ICT 9737

TOGETHERNESS.
LP: SALPS 42

TRUTH, THE (Ade, King Sunny & Otito).
LP: SALPS 46

VINTAGE KING SUNNY ADE.
LP: KOO 1LP

Ade Liz

DEKA.
LP: KL 052

Adebambo, Jean

OFF KEY LOVING.
LP: . . . . AJO 124

Adeva

ADEVA.
Tracks: / Respect / I thank you / In and out of my life / I don't need you / Musical freedom / Treat me right / So right / Warning / Promises.
MC: . . . . ZCTLP 13
LP: . . . . CTLP 13

RING MY BELL (See under Love, Monie) (Monie Love Vs Adeva).

Adewale, Segun

CASH AND CARRY.
LP: . . . . IVR 003

OJO JE (NIGERIA).
Tracks: / Ojo Je / Bobo / Gbe mi leke / Atewo / Lara / Ka tepa mo se / E ma fi lle iwe sere.
LP: . . . . STERNS 1009
LP: . . . . ROUNDER 5019
MC: . . . . ROUNDER 5019C

PLAY FOR ME.
Tracks: / Yo-pop music / Oshogbo oroki / Odaran kan to sa / Adewale play for me / Kole sori apata / Sise alafe / Peko o gbodo gbin / Gbin.
LP: . . . . STERNS 1003
LP: . . . . ROUNDER 5015
MC: . . . . ROUNDER 5015C

Adicts

FIFTH OVERTURE.
LP: . . . . FALL LP 042

LIVE AND LOUD (Official Bootleg).
Tracks: / Sensitive / Easy way out / Joker in the pack / Chinese takeaway / How sad / Hurt / Tango / Viva la revolution / Just like me / Numbers / Steamroller / Too young / Straight jacket / Let's go.
LP: . . . . LINK LP 010

ROCKERS IN RAGS (Live in Alabama).
LP: . . . . FALL LP 046

SKINS'N'PUNKS VOL 5 (Adicts/Press).
Tracks: / World gone mad / Wanna be an Adict / Kids of a nation / Is it any wonder? / A.S.A.P. / Revolution now / 21 guitar suite / No place like home / Rebel sound / Revolution city / Shut your mouth / Try / Crackdown / It's not what I want.
LP: . . . . OIR 015

SONGS OF PRAISE.
Tracks: / England / Hurt / Just like me / Tango / Telepathic people / Mary Whitehouse / Distortion / Get addicted / Viva la revolution / Calling calling / In the background / Dynasty / Peculiar music numbers / Sensitive / Songs of praise.
LP: . . . . FALL LP 006
LPPD: . . . . FALL LP 006P

SOUND OF MUSIC.
LP: . . . . RAZ 2

THIS IS YOUR LIFE (1978 -1980).
LP: . . . . FALL LP 021

Adioa

SOWETO MAN.
Tracks: / Jiggen bu nul / Sama yone / Toubab bile / Soweto man / Reggae musik / N'deye loye joy / Freedom for the black people / Buma done yene.
MC: . . . . MCT 1013
LP: . . . . MLPS 1013

Adjroud, Ahcene

ADOUNITH.
Tracks: / Wine ihamjabe / Achhal ayagui isnadhi / Athamourthiou / Attane / Adounith / Thayrime themouth / Amele / Thefaghdh iwabridhe / Almakhtouve.
LP: . . . . ORB 031

Adkins, Hasil

CHICKEN WALK.
Tracks: / Shake that thing / Ugly woman / Let's slop tonight / Chicken walk / She's mine / Tell me baby / If you want to be my baby / Big fat mama / Get out of my car / Donnio boogie / Walk and talk with me / I need your head / Roll roll train / I don't want nobody the way I want you.
LP: . . . . BB 2043

OUT TO HUNCH.
LP: 201

ROCK 'N' ROLL TONIGHT.
Tracks: / I could never be blue / I want some lovin' / Jenny Lou / Let me go / Rock the blues / I don't love you / Rock 'n' roll tonight / Shake with me / Miami kiss / Hunch, The / Duncens / No more hot dogs / Truly ruly / Is that right.
LP: . . . . BB 2044

SHE SAID.
Tracks: / She said / My baby loves me / D.P.A. on the moon / Baby rock / Let's make it up / Louise wait for me / I'm in misery / Comin' home to you / We got a date / Reagun blues / Chicken twist / W.P.A / Fast run / You're my baby / Turn my coat tails loose .
LP: . . . . WIK 34

WILD MAN, THE.
LP: 203

Adkins, Wendell

I CAN'T LET YOU BE A MEMORY.
Tracks: / Shotgun rider / What'll I do / I can't let you be a memory / Trying to survive loving / Too far gone / Feeling about you, A / Call the breeze / Falling for you / Back in you dreams / Missing the kid / I wish I was single again.
LP: . . . . SDLP 058
MC: . . . . SDC 058

IF THAT AIN'T COUNTRY.
Tracks: / Rodeo cowboys / Back to back / Bright morning light / If that ain't country / Lonesome, on'ry and mean / I came here to party / What a way to go / Willie, Waylon and me / Funny how time slips away / Crazy / Night life.
LP: . . . . SDLP 029
MC: . . . . SDC 029

Adler, Danny

DANNY ADLER STORY, THE.
LP: . . . . RIDE 2

GUSHA GUSHA MUSIC.
LP: . . . . ARM 8

ROOGALATOR YEARS, THE.
Tracks: / Zero hero / Tasty too / Cincinnati fatback / Water / Sweet mama Kundalini / Sock it to my pocket / All abroad / Humanitation / Change.
LP: . . . . CRB 1130
MC: . . . . TCCRB 1130

Adler, Larry

GOLDEN AGE OF LARRY ADLER.
LP: . . . . GX 41 2539 1
MC: . . . . GX 41 2539 4

LARRY ADLER WORKS FOR HARMONICA AND ORCHESTRA (Adler, Larry & Royal Philharmonic).
Tracks: / Blues / Lullaby time / Merry Andrew / Harmonica concerto / Morton Gould Orchestra, The / Romance / Harmonica concerto / Suite for harmonica & Orchestra.
LP: . . . . GL 42747

MUSIC OF GERSHWIN, ARLEN, RODGERS ETC. (Adler, Larry & Morton Gould Orchestra).
Tracks: / Perfume of love / Three quarter blues / My best love / Merry Andrew / Love for two / Happy with the blues / Lullabye time / Tonight I love you more / Once in a million moons / Night walk.
LP: . . . . NL 70421

Admiral Tibet

COME INTO THE LIGHT.
LP: . . . . LALP 18

TIME IS GOING TO COME, THE.
LP: . . . . GPLP 001

WAR IN A BABYLON.
LP: . . . . RAS 3028

WAR IN BABYLON.
MC: . . . . RASC 3028

Adni, Daniel

FAVOURITE DEBUSSY (See under (Debussy (Composer).

Adolescents

ADOLESCENTS, THE.
Tracks: / I hate children / Who is who / Wrecking crew / L.A. girl / Self destruct / Kids of the black hole / No way / Amoeba / Word attack / Rip it up / Democracy / No friends / Creatures.
LP: . . . . WS 32

BALBAO FUN ZONE.
LP: . . . . RR 9494 1

BRATS IN BATTALIONS.
LP: . . . . SOS 1001
LP: 083604

Adrenalin O.D.

CRUISING WITH ELVIS IN BIGFOOTS' UFO.
Tracks: / If this is Tuesday / Swindel / My mother can't drive / Second to none / Imaginary midget western, Theme from / Flip side unclassified / Bulimic food fight / Stew / Something about... Amy Carter / Baby elephant walk.
LP: . . . . JUST 12M

HUMONGOUSFUNGUSAMONGUS.
Tracks: / AOD VS son of Godzilla / Office building / Yuppe / Answer / Pope - on a rope / Fishin' musician / Pizza 'n' beer / Bugs / Youth blimp / Commercial cuts / Survive / Masterpiece / Crowd control / Velvet Elvis / F**k the neighbours / Surfin' Jew / Bruces lament / Nice song, The.
LP: . . . . JUST 5

WACKY HI JINKS OF.
LP: . . . . BOR 12002

Adrian Mole (bk)

SECRET DIARY OF ADRIAN MOLE AGED 13 & 3/4 (Sue Townsend).
MC: . . . . TTC/K 11

SECRET DIARY OF ADRIAN MOLE (PART 2) (Sue Townsend) (Lowe, Alex).
MC: . . . . TTC/K 02

SECRET DIARY OF ADRIAN MOLE (PART 1) (Sue Townsend) (Lowe, Alex).
MC: . . . . TTC/K 01

Adult Fantasies

EIGHT NEO PATHETIC SCENES.
LP: . . . . ANT 086

Adult Net

HONEY TANGLE, THE.
Tracks: / Take me / Waking up in the sun / Sad / Honey tangle / Tomorrow morning daydream / August / Spin this web / Where were you / Tiffany Tuesday / It's the way.
LP: 8381251
MC: 8381254

Advance Kusugar

ADVANCE KUSUGAR (Various artists).
LP: . . . . AFRILP 06
MC: . . . . AFRIZZ 06

Adventurers (Film)

ADVENTURERS (Film Soundtrack) (Various artists).
Tracks: / Main title: *Various artists* / Children's games: *Various artists* / Rome montage: *Various artists*/ Bolero/ Dax rides: *Various artists* / Dax and Amparo (love theme): *Various artists* / Cortequay: *Various* artists / Long trek: *Various artists* / Search for Amparo: *Various artists* / That old black magic: *Various* artists / Bitter victory: *Various artists* / El lobo's band: *Various artists* / Bed of flowers for Sue Ann: *Various artists.*
LP: . . . . SPFL 260

Adventures

SEA OF LOVE, THE.
Tracks: / Drowning in the sea of love / Broken land / You don't have to cry / Trip to bountiful, The / Heavens knows which way / Hold me now / Sound of Summer, The / When your heart was young / One step from heaven.
LP: . . . . EKT 45
MC: . . . . EKT 45C

THEODORE AND FRIENDS.
Tracks: / Always / Feel the raindrops / Send my heart / Two rivers / Don't tell me / Another silent day / When the world turns upside down / Love in chains / Hollywood / These children.
LP: . . . . CHR 1488
MC: . . . . ZCHR 1488

TRADING SECRETS WITH THE MOON.
LP: . . . . EKT 63
MC: . . . . EKT 63C
LP: . . . . K 960 871 2
MC: . . . . K 960 871 4
LP: 7559608711
MC: 7559608714

Adventures in the Mist

ADVENTURES IN THE MIST (Rubble Eleven) (Various artists).
Tracks: / Wind of change: *Accent* / Wooden spoon: *Poets* / Cheadle peace: *Felius Andromeda* / Looking for the sun: *Plague* / Listen to many cry: *Fairy Tale* / Treacle toppy world: *Fire* / Colours of my mind: *Attack* / Follow me: *Californians* / Guess I was dreaming: *Fairy Tale* / Meditations: *Felius Andromeda*/ Dream machine: *Sauterelles* / Lady orange peel: *Attack* / In your tower: *Poets* / Woodstock: *Turquoise*/ Fade away Maureen: *Cherry Smash* / Iceman: *Ice.*
LP: . . . . KIRI 069

Adventures Of Stevie V

ADVENTURES OF STEVIE V.
LP: 8469661
MC: 8469664

Adventures of...(bk)

ADVENTURES OF BARON MUNCHAUSEN (Film soundtrack) (Various artists).
LP: . . . . K 9258261
MC: . . . . K 9258264

ADVENTURES OF CREAMCAKE AND COMPANY (Zabel, Jennifer) (Stubbs,Una).
MC: . . . . TBC 9509

ADVENTURES OF DOCTOR SNUGGLES (Craven, John (nar)).
MC: . . . . TBC 9507

ADVENTURES OF DUSTY AND THE DINOSAURS (Newman, Nannette (nar)).
MC: . . . . TBC 9508

ADVENTURES OF FIREMAN SAM, THE (See under Fireman Sam) (Alderton, John (nar)).

ADVENTURES OF FORD FAIRLINE SOU (Film soundtrack) (Various artists).
LP: . . . . EKT 74
MC: . . . . EKT 74 C

ADVENTURES OF GOODNIGHT AND LOVING, THE (Leslie Thomas) (Barron, Keith (nar)).
MC: 0600560546

ADVENTURES OF HEGGARTY HAGGERTY (Cole, George (nar)).
LP: . . . . STMP 9033
MC: STMP4 9033

ADVENTURES OF MARY MOUSE (see under Blyton, Enid (aut)) (Kent, Cindy (nar)).

ADVENTURES OF MILLY-MOLLY-MANDY (Rayne, Janie (nar)).
LP: . . . . STMP 9026
MC: STMP4 9026

ADVENTURES OF MR MEN: MR CHATTERBOX (Percival, Lance (nar)).
MC: . . . . TTS 9806

ADVENTURES OF MR MEN: MR GREEDY (Percival, Lance (nar)).
MC: . . . . TTS 9819

ADVENTURES OF MR MEN: MR MESSY (Percival, Lance (nar)).
MC: . . . . TTS 9823

ADVENTURES OF MR MEN: MR NOISY (Percival, Lance (nar)).
MC: . . . . TTS 9805

ADVENTURES OF MR MEN: MR SILLY (Percival, Lance (nar)).
MC: . . . . TTS 9824

ADVENTURES OF MR MEN: MR SMALL (Percival, Lance (nar)).
MC: . . . . TTS 9820

ADVENTURES OF MR MEN: MR SNEEZE (Percival, Lance (nar)).
MC: . . . . TTS 9822

ADVENTURES OF MR MEN: MR TICKLE (Percival, Lance (nar)).
MC: . . . . TTS 9821

ADVENTURES OF MR. PINKWHISTLE (Bennett, Clive (nar)).
LP: . . . . STMP 9022
MC: STMP4 9022

ADVENTURES OF NAUGHTY AMELIA JANE (Pollard, Su).
LP: . . . . STMP 9021
MC: STMP4 9021

ADVENTURES OF ORLANDO (The Marmalade Cat) (Various artists).
Tracks: / Orlando buys a farm: *Various artists* / Orlando & the water cats: *Various artists.*
MC: . . . . TS 311
MC: . . . . TS 315

ADVENTURES OF PORTLAND BILL (Rossington, Norman (nar)).
LP: . . . . STMP 9032
MC: . . . . STMP 49032

ADVENTURES OF ROBIN HOOD (Film Soundtrack) (Utah Symphony Orchestra).
Tracks: / Prologue / Banquet at Nottingham Castle / Robin enters the great hall / Escape from the castle / Robin meets Little John / Oath and black arrow / Robin and Friar Tuck / Ambush in Sherwood / Feast in the forest / Robin and Marion / Archery tournament / Escape from the gallows / Love scene / Dagger fight/King Richard in Sherwood / Duel, victory and epilogue / Coronation process ion.
LP: . . . . TER 1066
MC: . . . . ZCTER 1066

ADVENTURES OF ROBIN HOOD Sound book (Various artists).
MC: . . . . SBC 109

ADVENTURES OF ROBIN HOOD (Original soundtrack) (Various artists).
MC: . . . . C 704.180

ADVENTURES OF ROBINS (Various artists).
MC: . . . . FILMC 705

ADVENTURES OF SHERLOCK HOLMES, THE (see under Sherlock Holmes (bk)).

ADVENTURES OF SINBAD THE SAILOR (Various artists).
MC: . . . . TS 312

ADVENTURES OF TEDDY ROBINSON (Aitken, Tony).
LP: . . . . STMP 9027
MC: STMP4 9027

ADVENTURES OF THE SECRET SEVEN (Castle, Roy).
MC: . . . . PTB 606

ADVENTURES OF TOM SAWYER (Mark Twain) (Crosby, Bing).
MCSET: . . . . SAY 31
MCSET: . . . . ARGO 1166

ADVENTURES OF VICTORIA PLUM (Rippon, Angela (nar)).
LP: STMP 9024
MC: STMP4 9024

ADVENTURES OF WORZEL GUMMIDGE, THE (Pertwee, Jon).
MC: PTB 604

MORE ADVENTURES OF MILLY - MOLLY - MANDY (Harris, Anita).
MC: TBC 9511

MORE ADVENTURES OF TEDDY ROBINSON (Various artists).
MC: TBC 9510

Adventurous Four (bk)

ADVENTUROUS FOUR, THE (See under Blyton, Enid (aut)) (Schofield, Philip (nar)).

Adverse, Anthony

RED SHOES.
LP: ACME 11

SPIN.
Tracks: / Paradise lost / Best friend / Wednesday's child / Cold winds / Centre of your world / Good girl / Night and day / No sweet surrender / Wastelands of your soul / Spin.
LP: ACME 22

Adversity

LOST IT ALL.
Tracks: / Wasted life / Jester / Destinized / Religions for sale / No more wars / Smash the odds / Lost it all / Total extremes / Metaphysics / Fight back / Angel of bread.
LP: ACHE 13

Adverts

CAST OF THOUSANDS.
Tracks: / Cast of thousands / Adverts / My place / Male assault / Television's over / Fate of criminals / Love songs / I surrender / I looked at the sun / I will walk you home.
LP: PL 25246

CROSSING THE RED SEA.
LP: ALSO 002
LP: BRL 201

LIVE AT THE ROXY.
LP: RRLP 136
MC: RRLC 136

Advise & Consent

ADVISE AND CONSENT (Original soundtrack) (Various artists).
LP: LOC 1068

A.D.X.

WEIRD VISIONS.
Tracks: / Weird visions / King of pain / Lost generation / Sacrifice in the ice / Mystical warfare / Fortunetelling / Behind the mirror / Sign of the time / Trouble / Invasion.
LP: NUK 161
MC: ZCNUK 161

Aengus

AENGUS.
LP: TARA 2001
MC: 4TA 2001

Aer Lingus Singers

ON WINGS OF SONG.
Tracks: / Hannigan's hooley / Harp that once through Tara's hall, The / Roisin dubh.
LP: ARAL 1003

Aerial Shots

AERIAL SHOTS (Various artists).
MC: AIRFORCE 1

Aero (2)

MASQUELERO.
LP: ECM 1367

Aerobics

AEROBIC EXERCISE MUSIC (with subliminal suggestions) (Various artists).
MC: C 308

AEROBICISE (The California Exercise Craze) (Various artists).
LP: RTL 2092
MC: 4 CRTL 2092

ARNOLD SCHWARZENEGGER'S TOTAL BODY WORKOUT (Various artists).
LP: CBS 26022

AS YOUNG AS YOU FEEL WITH EILEEN FOWLER (Various artists).
LP: REC 195
MC: MRMC 007

COMPLETE FITNESS COURSE, THE (With Simon Ward & Al Murray) (Various artists).
LP: LEG 11

DANCE KEEP FIT & SLIM TO MUSIC (with Eileen Fowler) (Various artists).
Tracks: / Warm-up: *Various artists* / Tangotime: *Various artists* / Ragtime swing: *Various artists* / Criss cross: *Various artists* / Beguine: *Various artists*.
LP: REC 382
MC: ZCM 382

ENJOY YOUR SLIMMING WITH EILEEN FOWLER (Various artists).
LP: REC 284
MC: ZCM 284

EX 'N' DANS (Various artists).
MC: TDS 012

FAMILY KEEP FIT WITH EILEEN FOWLER (Various artists).
LP: REC 174

GET FIT WITH THE GREEN GODDESS (Moran, Diana).
Tracks: / Introduction - Breakfast time / Morning dance (Legs and ankles.) / Wake up everybody (the great stretch) / Chi Mai (Neck and shoulders) / Hill Street blues / I heard it through the grapevine (Boobs, Chest & Underarms) / (They long to be) close to you / Daybreak (Hips) / I'm not in love (Back.) / Rise / Whiter shade of pale, A / Green goddess, The / In the Summertime (exercises for legs) / Who pays the ferryman? ((back and leg exercises)) / Relax.
LP: REH 479
MC: ZCR 479

KEEP IN SHAPE SYSTEM (Arlene Phillips) (Various artists).
LP: SUP 1
MC: ZCSUPS 1

KEEP IN SHAPE, VOL.2 (Arlene Phillips) (Various artists).
LP: SUP 2
MC: ZCSUP 2

PRIME TIME WORKOUT WITH JANE FONDA (Various artists).
LP: 9603821

SHAPE UP FOR MOTHERHOOD (Various artists).
LP: LEG 6
MC: LEGC 6

SLIM TO RHYTHM WITH EILEEN FOWLER (Various artists).
LP: REC 132

Aerosmith

AEROSMITH.
LP: PC 32005

AEROSMITH: INTERVIEW PICTURE DISC.
LPPD: BAK 2091

ANTHOLOGY - AEROSMITH.
Tracks: / Toys in the attic / Sweet emotion / Walk this way (live) / No more no more / You see me crying / Bright light fright / Lord of the thighs / Back in the saddle (live) / Sick as a dog / Critical mass / Bite the hand that feeds / Sight for sore eyes / Mother popcorn / Train kept a rollin' / S.O.S. / Rock in a hard place / Jailbait / Push comes to shove / Rats in the cellar / Bone to bone / Dream on.
LP: RAWLP 037
MC: RAWTC 037

CLASSICS LIVE 1..
Tracks: / Train kept a rollin' / Kings and Queens / Sweet emotion / Dream on.
LP: FC 40329
MC: FCT 40329
LP: CBS 26901
MC: 40 26901
LP: 4672971
MC: 4672974

CLASSICS LIVE 2..
Tracks: / Back in the saddle / Walk this way / Movin' out / Draw the line / Same old song and dance / Last child / Let the music do the talking / Toys in the attic.
LP: FC 40855
MC: FCT 40855

DONE WITH MIRRORS.
Tracks: / Let the music do the talking / My fist your face / Shame on you / Reason a dog, The / Shela / Gypsy boots / She's on fire / Hop, The / Darkness (Extra track on cassette only.).
LP: GEF 26695
MC: 4026695
LP: 924091 1
MC: 924091 4
MC: GEFC 24091

DRAW THE LINE.
Tracks: / Draw the line / Kings and queens / Sight for sore eyes / Milk cow blues.
LP: PC 34856
LP: 4667291
MC: 4667294

GEMS.
LP: 4632241
MC: 4632244

GET YOUR WINGS.
Tracks: / Same old song and dance / Lord of the thighs / Women of the world / Train kept a rollin'.
LP: PC 32847
LP: 4667321
MC: 4667324

GREATEST HITS: AEROSMITH.
Tracks: / Dream on / Same old song and dance / Sweet emotion / Walk this way / Remember (walking in the sand) / Back in the saddle / Draw the line / Kings and queens / Come together / Last child.
LP: 4607031
MC: 4607034
LP: CBS 84704
LPPD: 4607038

LIVE BOOTLEG.
Tracks: / Back in the saddle / Sweet emotion / Lord of the thighs / Toys in the attack / Last child / Come together / Walk this way / Sick as a dog / Dream on / Mama kin / S.O.S. / Train kept a rollin' / Sight for sore eyes / Chip away the stone / I ain't got you / Mother popcorn.
2LP: CBS 88325
2LP: CG 35564
MC: CGT 35564

NIGHT IN THE RUTS.
Tracks: / No surprises / Chiquitita / Remember (walking in the sand) / Cheesecake / Three mile smile / Reefer headwoman / Bone to bone (Coney Island white fish boy) / Mia / Think about it.
LP: PC 36050
LP: 83681
LP: 4667201
MC: 4667204

PERMANENT VACATION.
Tracks: / Hearts done time / Magic touch / Rag doll / Simoriah / Dude (looks like a lady) / St. John / Hangman jury / Girl keeps comin' apart / Angel / Permanent vacation / I'm down / Movie, The.
LP: WX 126
MC: WX 126C
MC: GEFC 24162
LP: GEF 24162

PUMP.
Tracks: / Young lust / F.I.N.E / Love in an elevator / Monkey on my back / Janie's got a gun / Other side, The / My girl / Don't get mad, get even / Voodoo medicine man / What it takes.
LP: WX 304
MC: WX 304C
MC: GEFC 24254
LP: GEF 24254

ROCK IN A HARD PLACE.
Tracks: / Jailbait / Bitches brew / Cry me a river / Jig is up / Push comes to shove / Lightning strikes / Bolivian ragamuffin / Prelude to Joanie / Joanie's butterfly / Rock in a hard place.
LP: PC 38061
LP: 4667191
MC: 4667194

ROCKS.
Tracks: / Back in the saddle / Last child / Rats in the cellar / Combination / Sick as a dog / Nobody's fault / Get the lead out / Lick and a promise / Home tonight.
LP: PC 34165
MC: PCT 34165

TOYS IN THE ATTIC.
LP: PC 33479
MC: PCT 33479
LP: CLALP 135X
MC: CLAMC 135X
MC: 4606984

Aesop...

AESOP FABLES (Simak, Clifford (nar)).
MC: CP 1649

AESOP IN FABLELAND (Lowe, Arthur with the London Symphony Orchestra).
LP: MFP 50538
MC: TCMFP 50538
LP: FOUR 2

AESOP'S FABLES (Karloff, Boris (nar)).
Tracks: / Ant and the grasshopper, The / Oak and the reed, The / Mice in council, The / Lion in love, The.
MC: 1221

AESOP'S FABLES BOOK 1 (For Ages 7-12).
MC: PLB 114

AESOP'S FABLES BOOK 2 (For Ages 7-12).
MC: PLB 128

Afflicted Man

AFFLICTED MAN'S MUSICAL BOX (Various artists).
LP: UD 013

Afghan Whigs

UP IN IT.
LP: GR 0092

Afghanistan

FOLK MUSIC OF AFGHANISTAN VOL.2 (Various artists).
LP: LLST 7231

FOLK MUSIC OF AFGHANISTAN VOL.1 (Various artists).
LP: LLST 7230

INSIDE AFGHANISTAN (Various artists).
Tracks: / National dance music: *Various artists* (Atan) / Nomad dance: *Various artists* (Atan) / Nomad tribal song of separation: *Various artists* / Marching music of the Kochi tribe: *Various artists* / Caravan song: *Various artists* / Ai delbari khamosh: *Various artists* / Song from Herat: *Various artists* / Love song: *Various artists* / Rabab: *Various artists* / Uzbek folk melody: *Various artists* (Dambura).
LP: ALM 4003

LE LUTH AFGHAN (Kassimi, Essa/ Nazir Khan).
LP: ARN 33471

MUSIC FROM KABUL (Various artists).
LP: LLST 7259

Afraid Of Mice

AFRAID OF MICE.
LP: CAS 1155

Africa

AFRICA CALLING (Various artists).
LP: RRTG 7734

AFRICA DANCE (Various artists).
LP: A 366
MC: C 366

AFRICA ROOTS VOL.4 (Various artists).
LP: F 37986

AFRICAN ACOUSTIC VOL.1 (Various artists).
MC: OMA 108C

AFRICAN HORNS (Various artists).
Tracks: / Next stop Soweto: *Various artists* / Tshona: *Various artists* / Black and brown cherries: *Various artists* / Tegeni: *Various artists* / Msunduza: *Various artists* / Mafuta: *Various artists*.
LP: KAZ LP 8
MC: KAZ MC 8

AFRICAN MAGIC (Various artists).
LP: RK 17

AFRICAN MOVES (Various artists).
2LP: STERNS 1015/6
MC: STC 1015/6

AFRICAN MOVES VOL.2 (Various artists).
Tracks: / Pole mama: *Somo Somo* / Amilo: *Tabu Ley* / Boya ye: *M'Bilia Bell* / Sanza Misato: *Orchestra* Africa / Mon couer balance: *Daouda* / Gbebe mi: *Obey, Ebenezer* / Segun Adewale: *Adewale, Segun*/ Yeme breoo: *African Brothers*.
MC: STC 1029
LP: STERNS 1029

AFRICAN MUSEUM SELECTION (Various artists).
LP: HB 19

AFRICAN REGGAE (Various artists).
Tracks: / Le telephone sonne: *Various artists* / Sir Victor Uwaifo & his melody: *Various artists* / Ekassa: *Maestros*/ Ready, aim, fire: *Moses, Pablo* / Ndito isong emana nyin: *Ulaeto, Martha* / Onu kwulunjo: *Moses, Pablo*/ Mo fe mu yan: *Various artists* / In the future: *Moses, Pablo* / Let them say: *Nico Mbarga, Prince* / Igede: *Ukwu, Celestine* / What is it?: *Moses, Pablo* / Obiako nnwam: *Ejeagha, Mike* / Odindu nyuliba: *Osiat, Stephen* / Who?: *Moses, Pablo*.
MC: 822 810 4

AFRICAN RHYTHMS AND INSTRUMENTS, VOL. 3 (Morocco, Algeria, Tunisia, Libya) (Various artists).
LP: LLST 7339
MC: LLCT 7339

AFRICAN RHYTHMS AND INSTRUMENTS, VOL. 1 (Mali, Niger, Ghana, Nigeria, Upper Volta, Senegal, Liberia) (Various artists).
LP: LLST 7328
MC: LLCT 7328

AFRICAN RHYTHMS AND INSTRUMENTS, VOL. 2 (Tanzania, Kenya, Zimbabwe, Congo Brazzanville, Chad) (Various artists).
LP: LLST 7338
MC: LLCT 7338

AFRICAN SUNSET (Various artists).
Tracks: / Kugara Nekugara: *Indi Brothers* / Shungu iwe: *Shasha, Jethro* / Ngotsotsi: *Masuka, Dorothy*/ Alouis na jane: *Shasha, Jethro* / Honayi toenda: *Indi Brothers* / Gona ramachingura: *Masuka, Dorothy*/ Pasi: *Dango, Stan* / Ndiudzeyi: *Dango, Stan* / Musi watunya:

Sando, Tanga / Nhema musasa: *Zambezi, Coco* / Ruva rangu ndiwe chete: *Pied Pipers* / Torera unzwe mwanangu: *Munyaka, Adois.*
LP: . . . . **CSLP 5000**
MC: . . . . **ZCSLC 5000**

AFRICAN TYPIC COLLECTION (Various artists).
Tracks: / African typic collection: *Thomas, Sam Fan* / Noa: *Thomas, Sam Fan* / Zouk en avant: *Tam Tam 2000*/ Dikom lam la mota: *Mbango, Charlotte* / Si tcha: *Thomas, Sam Fan* / Nelson Mandela: *Ateba, Koko.*
LP: . . . . **EWV 12**
MC: . . . . **TCEWV 12**

ANGOLAN BORDER, THE (Musicians of the Tshokwe of Angola and Zaire) (Various artists).
LP: . . . . **LLST 7311**

ANTICHI CANTI AFROCUBANI (Various artists).
LP: . . . . **VPA 8400**
MC: . . . . **VC 1932**

BRAVOS DEL RITMO (Various artists).
LP: . . . . **LTLA 192 E**

BRINGING IT DOWN- SOUTH AFRICAN SAX JIVE (Various artists).
LP: . . . . **TWLP 002**

BULLETS WON'T STOP US NOW (Various artists).
LP: . . . . **K 031 102**

CANTI EL RITMI (Various artists).
LP: . . . . **VPA 8175**

CASSETTE D'AFRIQUE (African dance compilation) (Various artists).
Tracks: / Adjani Muana Kini: *Various artists* / Tyole: *Various artists* / Masquereau: *Various artists*/ Sane-mamadou: *Various artists* / Lascar Pa Kapi: *Various artists* / Izia: *Various artists* / Le bon samaritan: *Various artists.*
MC: . . . . **ORBC 907**

CHURCHICAL CHANTS OF THE NYABINGI (Live field recordings) (Various artists).
LP: . . . . **HB 20**

COLLECTION OF SOUTH AFRICAN MUSIC (Various artists).
LP: . . . . **ROUNDER 5009**
MC: . . . . **ROUNDER 5009C**

COMPILATION.
LP: . . . . **ROUGH 37**

GOODBYE SANDRA (Various artists).
LP: . . . . **AFRILP 05**
MC: . . . . **AFRIZZ 05**

GUITAR AND THE GUN (Various artists).
Tracks: / Momma mo akoma ntutu: *Genesis Gospel Singers* / Mama shile oga: *Salam's cultural Imani Group* / Ye beko yesu: *Kuntum 13* / Nyameco: *Kenya, F* / Noko nya m'akire: *African Internationals* / Mmra ye tiaseyi moma yen sum: *Supreme Xian Singers* / Awurade yesu: *Baptist Disciple Singers* / Oh papa: *Kenya, F.*
LP: . . . . **ADRY 1**

GUITAR PARADISE OF EAST AFRICA (Various artists).
LP: . . . . **EWV 21**
MC: . . . . **TCEWV 21**

HEARTBEAT OF SOWETO (Various artists).
Tracks: / Nwana wamina: *Chauke, Thomas* / Thathezakho: *Mlokothwa* / Jabula mfana: *Emvelo, Amaswazi* / Nsati wa wina: *Shirinda, M.D. & Family* / Siyoklishaya kusasa: *Elimnyama, Kati* / Waqala Ngowendlala: *Usuthu*/ Mashama: *ChiJumane, Arando Bila* / Xumaxilovile: *Chauke, Thomas & Shinyori* / Yithinamhlaje: *Mlokothwa*/ Bumnandi utshwala bakho: *Elimnyama, Kati* / Kamakhalawana: *ChiJumane, Arando Bila* / Ndzi Hkensa: *Shirinda, M.D. & Family.*
LP: . . . . **SERLP 5**
MC: . . . . **SERC 5**

HIGHLIFE (Various artists).
Tracks: / Ekassa 24: *Various artists* / Obiako nnwam onu kwulujo: *Various artists* / Five days a week love: *Various artists* / Ewa tomuno bo ibro ma: *Various artists* / Odindu nyuliba: *Various artists* / Let them say: *Various artists* / Igede: *Various artists* / Mo fe mu'yan: *Various artists* / Ndito isong emana nyin: *Various artists.*
LP: **814 480 1**

HOMELAND (Collection of Black South African Music) (Various artists).
Tracks: / Ngayishela: *Various artists* / Ea nyoloha khanyapa: *Various artists* / Maraba start 500: *Various artists* / Ntlela a tingangeni: *Various artists* / Nginbonile ubaba: *Various artists* / Sayishayinduku: *Various artists* / Khutsana: *Various artists* / Umuntu: *Various artists* / Mti wa ngwenda: *Various artists*/ Ntate bereng: *Various artists* / Yashimizi: *Various artists* / Nayintombi ibaleka: *Various artists.*
LP: . . . . **GREL 2002**
MC: . . . . **GREEN 2002**

INDESTRUCTIBLE BEAT OF SOWETO (Various artists).
LP: . . . . **EMW 5502**
MC: . . . . **SHANC 43033**
LP: . . . . **SHAN 43033**

INDESTRUCTIBLE BEAT OF SOWETO VOL.1 (Various artists).
Tracks: / Awungilobolele: *Udokotela Shange Namajaha* / Sobabamba: *Udokotela Shange Namajaha* / Qhude manikinki: *Nabo, Umahlathini* / Qhwayilahle: *Mchunu, Moses* / Sini lindile: *Nganeziyamfisa* / Johce No. 2: *Mkhalali*, Johnson / Holotelani: *Sedibe, Nelcy* / Indoda yejazi: *Emvelo, Amaswazi* / Emthonjeni: *Mahlathini & the* Mahotella Queens / Thul'ulalele: *Embelo, Amaswazi* / Ngicabange: *Mahlathini & the Mahotella Queens* / Nansi imali: *Ladysmith Black Mambazo.*
LP: . . . . **EWV 14**
MC: . . . . **TCEWV 14**

INDESTRUCTIBLE BEAT VOL.2 (Thunder Before Dawn) (Various artists).
Tracks: / Utshwala begazati: *Emvelo, Amaswazi & Mahlathini* / Thuto ke senotlolo: *Mahlathini* / Amazimuzimu: *Dilika*/ Wakwami: *Abafakasi* / Sunshine boots: *Mkhalali, Johnson* / Phumani Endlini: *Jozi* / Kwa volondiya: *Mahlathini*/ Vula bops: *Makgona Tsohle Band* / Jabula Mfana: *Emvelo, Amaswazi* / Siwuhambile umhlaba: *Emvelo, Amaswazi* & Mahlathini / Ngasebenza ngedwa: *Mahlathini* / Motshile: *Malombo* / Thandaza: *Nganeziyamfisa* (CD only).
LP: . . . . **EWV 1**
MC: . . . . **TCEWV 1**
LP: . . . . **SSW 1**
MC: . . . . **SSWC 1**

JIVE HITS OF THE TOWNSHIPS (Various artists).
Tracks: / Umqombothi: *Chaka Chaka, Yvonne* / Together as one: *Lucky Dube* / Kazet: *Mahlathini & the Mahotella* Queens / Sharp as a razor: *Stimela* / We miss you Mandela: *Melodi, Chicco* / Yalla: *Mahlathini & the* Mahotella Queens / Whispers in the deep: *Stimela* / Slave: *Lucky Dube* / Waya waya all the way down: *Teaspoon*/ African salad: *Peto.*
LP: **841 470 1**
MC: **841 470 4**

JIVE HITS OF THE TOWNSHIPS (See Under Urban Africa) (Various artists).

KINGS AND QUEENS OF TOWNSHIP JIVE, THE (Various artists).
LP: . . . . **EWV 20**
MC: . . . . **TCEWV 20**

LET THEIR VOICES BE HEARD in South Africa (Various artists).
LP: . . . . **ROUNDER 5024**
MC: . . . . **ROUNDER 5024C**

MBUBE! (Zulu men's singing competition) (Various artists).
LP: . . . . **ROUNDER 5023**
MC: . . . . **ROUNDER 5023C**

MUSIC FROM BURUNDI (Various artists).
LP: . . . . **VPA 8137**

MUSIC OUT OF AFRICA VOL.1 (Various artists).
LP: . . . . **SNTF 1013**

MUSIC OUT OF AFRICA VOL.2 (Various artists).
LP: . . . . **SNTF 1014**

MUSICA NERA DI BAHIA (Various artists).
LP: . . . . **VPA 8318**
MC: . . . . **VC 4818**

MUSICA POPOLARE VOL 2 (Various artists).
LP: . . . . **VPA 8449**
MC: . . . . **VC 4983**

MUSIQUE ET CHANTS (Various artists).
MC: . . . . **G 4511**

REMEMBER SOWETO (Various artists).
LP: . . . . **K 032 102**

RHYTHM OF RESISTANCE (South Africa collection) (Various artists).
LP: . . . . **SHAN 43018**
MC: . . . . **SHANC 43018**

RHYTHMS OF RESISTANCE (Various artists).
Tracks: / U mama uyajabula: *Mlangeni, Babsy* / Ke ya le leboha: *Mlangeni, Babsy* / Perefere: *Malomba*/ Pampa madiba: *Malomba* / Jesu otsoile: *Mparanyana & The Cannibals* / Umthombowase golgota: *Ladysmith Black* Mambazo / Yinhleleni: *Ladysmith Black Mambazo* / Inkunzi ayi hlabi ngokusima: *Johnny & Sipho* / Igula lamasi: *Mahotella Queens* / Ubu gowelle: *Baseqhudeni, Abafana.*
LP: . . . . **OVED 58**
MC: . . . . **OVEDC 58**

ROOTS AFRICAN DRUMS (See under Kenya) (National Percussion Group of Kenya).

SANZA AND GUITAR (Music of the Bena Lulawa of Angola & Zaire) (Various artists).
LP: . . . . **LLST 7313**

SOUND D' AFRIQUE (Various artists).
Tracks: / Me bowa ya: *Various artists* / Masoua Mo: *Various artists* / Dounougnan: *Various artists* / Bo mbanda: *Various artists* / Jalo: *Various artists.*
LP: . . . . **ISSP 4003**
MC: . . . . **ICT 4003**

SOUNDS OF SOWETO (Various artists).
2LP: . . . . **EN 5006**
MCSET: . . . . **TCEN 5006**

SOUNDS OF SOWETO VOL 1 (Various artists).
LP: . . . . **TUS 8001**
MC: . . . . **ZCTUS 8001**

SOWETO NEVER SLEEPS (Various artists).
LP: . . . . **SHAN 43041**
MC: . . . . **SHANC 43041**

SOWETO STREET MUSIC - THE DEFINITIVE COLLECTION (Various artists).
LP: . . . . **ATXLD 04**
MC: . . . . **ZCADX 04**

SOWETO STREET MUSIC VOL 1 (Various artists).
LP: . . . . **MODEM 1017**
MC: . . . . **MODEMC 1017**

SOWETO STREET MUSIC VOL 2 (Various artists).
LP: . . . . **MODEM 1018**
MC: . . . . **MODEMC 1018**

SPIRITS OF AFRICA VOL.1 (Various artists).
LP: . . . . **MALP 02**

TAARAB 4 (Various artists).
LP: . . . . **ORBD 041**

TOGO: MUSIC OF WEST AFRICA (Various artists).
LP: . . . . **ROUNDER 5004**

TRADITIONAL MUSIC OF BURUNDI (Various artists).
LP: **558 511**
MC: **4559 003**

TRADITIONAL PERCUSSION STRUCTURE (Various artists).
LP: . . . . **G 1038**
MC: . . . . **G 4038**

URBAN AFRICA (See under Urban Africa) (Various artists).

WOMEN OF AFRICA (Various artists).
Tracks: / Kuteleza si kwanguka: *Lady Isa* / Sawura wako: *Chiweshe, Stella & The Earthquake* / Lomfana ngi yamithanda: *Africa, Patience & Pedlers* / Tsiketa kuni barassara: *Dulce & Orchestra Marrabenta* / True love: *Ilanga* & Busi Ncube / Ukuthokoza kwami: *Mabokela, Sarah* / Mahlalela: *Ncube, Doreen* / Qagala: *Mahotella Queens*/ Kangela: *Mhuriro, Maggie* / I'm like this: *Masuka, Dorothy* / Uyai mose: *Mabokela, Sarah* / A vassati va lomo: *Mingas & Orchestra Marrabenta.*
LP: . . . . **CSLP 5003**
MC: . . . . **ZCSLC 5002**

ZULU CHORAL MUSIC FROM SOUTH AFRICA (Mbube Roots) (Various artists).
Tracks: / Jim takata kanjan: *Bantu Glee Singers* / Hewul kwaqaqamba amathambo: *Crocodiles* / Ina na wala: *Fear* No Harm Choir / Kuyek: *African Zulu Male Voice Choir* / Nga: *Solomomn, Linda & Evening Birds* / Aoku: *Solomomn*, Linda & Evening Birds / Yek emagumeni: *Shooting Stars* / Mbube: *Solomomn, Linda & Evening Birds* / Izindaba: *Morning Light Choir* / Hamba: *Dundee Wandering Singers* / Ngl-e-kaya: *Natal Champions* / Akasangibhaleli: *Durban Crocodiles* / Cothoza Mfana: *Scorpions* / Mus' ukuqubuda: *King Star Brothers* / Umama lo: *Ladysmith Black Mambazo.*
LP: . . . . **ROUNDER 5025**
MC: . . . . **ROUNDER 5025C**

ZULU JIVE (Various artists).
LP: . . . . **EMW 5503**
MC: . . . . **EC 01**
LP: . . . . **CGLP 4410**
MC: . . . . **CGC 4410**

Africa 70

ZOMBIE (see Kuti, Fela) (Africa 70 & Fela Kuti).

African Brothers

MADAM FO PA WUO.
LP: . . . . **AB 006**

ME MAANE.
LP: . . . . **AB 005**

ME POMA.
Tracks: / Me poma / Getty / Yemo breoo / Gye mani / Me bisa.
LP: . . . . **STERNS 1004**
LP: . . . . **ROUNDER 5018**
MC: . . . . **ROUNDER 5018C**

African Connexion

WELCOME.
LP: . . . . **MUSALP P88**
MC: . . . . **MUCAFF 088**

African Dawn

JALI.
LP: . . . . **AD 400**
MC: . . . . **ADC 400**

African Disciples

PLACE CALLED EARTH, A.
LP: . . . . **Unknown**

African Head Charge

DRASTIC SEASON.
LP: . . . . **ONULP 27**

ENVIRONMENTAL STUDIES.
LP: . . . . **ONULP 19**

MY LIFE IN A HOLE ON THE GROUND.
Tracks: / Elastic dance / Family doctoring / Steberu's theme / Crocodile shoes / Stone charge / Far away chant / Primal one drop / Hole in the roof.
LP: . . . . **ONULP 13**

OFF THE BEATEN TRACK.
MC: . . . . **ONULP 40C**
LP: . . . . **ONULP 40**

African Jazz Pioneers

AFRICAN JAZZ PIONEERS.
Tracks: / Nonto sangoma / Yeka yeka / Hellfire / Hosh / Mzabalazo (hometown) / Ten ten special / Riverside special / Mbombela.
LP: . . . . **KAZLP 14**
MC: . . . . **KAZMC 14**

African Journey

AFRICAN JOURNEY VOL 1.
Tracks: / Kelefa ba / Alfayaya / Jola dance / Kedo / Mandingo street drumming / Bowdi / Fula procession, A / Almami samari tour ay.
LP: . . . . **SNTF 666**

AFRICAN JOURNEY VOL 2.
LP: . . . . **SNTF 667**

Africka Korps

GOD, IT'S THEM AGAIN.
LP: . . . . **ROSE 125**

Africolor

AFRICOLOR (Various artists).
MC: **795244**

Afrika Bambaataa

HIP HOP FUNK DANCE CLASSICS 1.
LP: . . . . **SPOCK 3**

Afro Charanga

AFRO CHARANGA VOL 2.
LP: . . . . **JS 21480**

Afro International

EFFACER LE TABLEAU.
LP: . . . . **EVVI 23**

Afro Latino

AFRO LATINO (Live from the Bass Cleff, London) (Various artists).
LP: . . . . **WAVE LP 28**

Afrobeat 2000

N.E.P.A. (see Allen, Tony).

Afro-Cuba

EARLY AFRO CUBAN SONGS (Various artists).
LP: . . . . **VPA 8445**
MC: . . . . **VC 4932**

ECLIPSE DE SOL.
Tracks: / Eclipse de sol / Carousel / Carnival Humanoide / Tornado / Lo Dije Antes / Mahatma.
LP: . . . . **JHR 004**

OH MELANCOLIA (see under Rodriguez, Silvio) (Afro-Cuba/Silvio Rodriguez).

Afros

KICKIN' AFROLISTICS.
Tracks: / Afro like a mutha / Better luck next time / Phoenix / Coolin' with the Fros / Hoe cakes / On the Fro farm / This jams for you / Causin' destruction / Afros in the house / Why do I wear my fro / Afros and afrettes / Jump / Smokin' / Federal offence / Straight from the penal / Kickin' afrolistics.

LP: 4675711
MC: 4675714

After 7

AFTER 7.
Tracks: / Don't cha think / In the heat of the moment / Can't stop / My only woman / Love's been so nice / One night / Ready or not / Sayonara.
LP: . . . . VUSLP 7
MC: . . . . VUSMC 7

After Dark

AFTER DARK (The Party Album) (Various artists).
Tracks: / Flowers in the rain: *Move* / All right now: *Free* / Ride a white swan: *T. Rex* / Down the dustpipe: *Status Quo* / Black night: *Deep Purple* / Lola: *Kinks* / When I'm dead and gone: *McGuinness Flint*/ Resurrection shuffle: *Ashton Gardener & Dyke* / Silver machine: *Hawkwind* / Whisky in the jar: *Thin Lizzy*/ See my baby jive: *Wizzard* / Roll over Beethoven: *E.L.O.* / Walk on the wild side: *Reed, Lou* / Fox on the run: *Sweet* / Make me smile (come up and see me): *Harley, Steve & Cockney Rebel* / This town ain't big enough for the both of us: *Sparks* / You to me are everything: *Real Thing* / Shotgun wedding: *C, Roy* / Nutbush city limits: *Turner, Ike & Tina* / Israelites: *Dekker, Desmond* / Everything I own: *Boothe, Ken* / How long: *Ace* / Sad sweet dreamer: *Sweet Sensation* / Rock me gently: *Kim, Andy* / Baby love: *Supremes*/ Reach out I'll be there: *Four Tops* / What becomes of the broken hearted?: *Ruffin, Jimmy* / Yester-me, yester-you, yesterday: *Wonder, Stevie* / Tears of a clown: *Robinson, Smokey & The Miracles* / This old heart of mine: *Isley Brothers* / Don't leave me this way: *Houston, Thelma*.
2LP: . . . . IMDP 2
MC: . . . . IMPDK 2

After Dusk

AFTER DUSK (Various artists).
MC: 2641

After Eight

AFTER EIGHT (Various artists).
Tracks: / Fantasia on greensleeves: *Various artists* / Cavatina: *Various artists* / Gymnopedie no.3: *Various* artists / Belladonna: *Various artists* / Fool on the hill: *Various artists* / Rachmaninov 18th variation: *Various artists* / Tonight: *Various artists* / Send in the clowns: *Various artists* / Morning - Peer Gynt suite No. 1: *Various artists* / Barcarolle: *Various artists* (Fro6 "Gaite parisienne") / Clair de lune: *Various* artists / Fur Elise: *Various artists* / Swan, The: *Various artists* / Mack the knife: *Various artists*/ Bess, you is my woman now: *Various artists* / Man in love, The: *Various artists*.
LP: . . . . MP 39777
MC: . . . . MPT 39777

After Henry (tv)

AFTER HENRY (Various artists).
MCSET: . . . . CAB 290
MCSET: . . . . ZBBC 1030

After Hours

AFTER HOURS.
MC: . . . . AFT 001

TAKE OFF.
Tracks: / Love attack / Better late than never / Stay by my side / Take off / Game, The / Another lonely night / Paint it black / Without you.
LP: . . . . WKFMLP 89
MC: . . . . WKFMMC 89
LPPD: . . . . WKFMPD 89

After the Dance

AFTER THE DANCE (Various artists).
LP: . . . . STAR 2501
MC: . . . . STAC 2501

After The Fire

80F.
Tracks: / 1980-F / Love will always make you cry / Can you face it? / Who's gonna love you / Starflight / Wild west show / Billy, Billy / It's high fashion / Why can't we be friends / Joanne.
LP: . . . . EPC 84545

AFTER THE FIRE.
LP: . . . . RR 001

BATTERIES NOT INCLUDED.
Tracks: / Short change / Frozen rivers / Sometimes / Sailing ship / I don't understand your love / Stranger, The / Carry me home / Dancing in the shadows / Space walking / Gina / Stuck in Paris (nowhere to go) / Bright lights.
LP: . . . . CBS 32440
MC: 40 32440
LP: . . . . CBS 85566

DER KOMMISSAR.
Tracks: / Der Kommissar / Who's gonna love you? / Frozen rivers / Joy / Dancing in the shadows / Billy / 1980-F / Rich boys / Starlight / Laser love / Love wll always make you cry / One rule for you / Sailing ship.
MC: 40 25527
LP: . . . . CBS 25227

LASER LOVE.
Tracks: / Laser love / Joy / Take me higher / Life in the city / Suspended animation / Like the power of a jet / One rule for you / Time to think / Timestar / Check it out.
LP: . . . . CBS 83795

ONE RULE FOR YOU (OLD GOLD) (see under Fiction Factory - Feels like heaven).

After the Fox (film)

AFTER THE FOX (Original soundtrack) (Various artists).
LP: . . . . MCA 25132
MC: . . . . MCAC 25132

After the Hop

AFTER THE HOP (Various artists).
Tracks: / There'll be no teardrops tonight: *McVoy, Carl* / Oochie Koochie: *Burgess, Sonny* / Sally's got a sister: *Pinkney, Bill* / You're just my kind: *Mercer, Will* / High school rock: *Pinkney, Bill* / After the hop: *Pinkney, Bill* / Cattywampus: *Cannon, John 'Ace'* / Bo Diddley: *Van Eaton, Jimmy* (Inst.) / Willie Brown: *Self, Mack* / Crazy baby: *Cooke, Ken* / Ooh wee: *Suggs, Brad* / Hey good lookin': *Cash, Eddie*/ College man: *Riley, Billy Lee* / Stagger Lee: *Various artists* / No teardrops tonight: *McVoy, Carl*.
LP: . . . . SUN 1037

After the Hurricane

AFTER THE HURRICANE (Various artists).
LP: . . . . CHR 1750
MC: . . . . ZCHR 1750

After Tonite

POLISH MAN WHO SITS IN THE CORNER, THE.
Tracks: / Ain't gonna stand for it / Big mouth / Strut / Do you really care / Break down the door / Here is the news / Thin line / Put your money where your mouth is / Summer song / This generation / Standing in the queue / Times in life / 365.
LP: . . . . BGP 1010
MC: . . . . BGPC 1010

Aftermath

DON'T CHEER ME UP.
LP: 20001

Against All Odds

AGAINST ALL ODDS (Film soundtrack) (Various artists).
Tracks: / Against all odds: *Collins, Phil* / Violet and blue: *Nicks, Stevie* / Walk through the fire: *Gabriel*, Peter / Balcony: *Big Country (group)* / Making a big mistake: *Rutherford, Mike* / My male curiosity: *Kid Creole* & The Coconuts / Search, The (main title): *Carlton, Larry & Michel Colombier* / El solitario: *Carlton*, Larry & Michel Colombier / Rock and roll jaguar: *Carlton, Larry & Michel Colombier* / For love alone: *Carlton, Larry* / Race, The: *Carlton, Larry* / Murder of a friend: *Carlton, Larry*.
LP: . . . . V 2313
MC: . . . . TCV 2313
LP: . . . . OVED 155
MC: . . . . OVEDC 155

Agajanian, Dennis

WHERE ARE THE HEROES.
LP: . . . . BIRD 155
MC: . . . . TC BIRD 155

Agapeland

MUSIC MACHINE MEDLEY.
Tracks: / Land called love / Music machine, The / Whistle song / Smile / String song, The / Patience / Gentleness / Joy / Peace / Self control / Goodness / Music machine, The (Reprise) / Nathaniel the grublet / Diddle daddle day / Nathaniel's song / Sunshine / Sir Oliver's Song.
LP: . . . . WING 516
MC: . . . . TC WING 516

Agata, Rich

PARADE OF TEARS.
LP: 609205

Agathocles/Drudge

SPLIT LP.
Tracks: / Fake friend / Gorgonized dorks / Purified by death / Use the mincer / Lay off me / Deceased / Big 1 / Teachers / Majesty of fools / Squeeze anton / Introtyl / Christianity means tyrany / Fog.
LP: . . . . DEAF 001

Age Of Chance

1000 YEARS OF TROUBLE.
Tracks: / We've got trouble / Don't get mad get even / Ready or not here we come / Shut up and listen / Big bad noise / Take it / This is crush collision / Learn to pay / Hold on.
LP: . . . . V 2473
MC: . . . . TCV 2473

CRUSH COLLISION.
LP: . . . . AGE 9

MECCA.
Tracks: / 4 more years / Higher than heaven / Joyride / Refuse to lose / Snowblind / Mecca / Time's up / You can run but you can't hide / Playing with fire / What's happening.
MC: . . . . TCV 2564
LP: . . . . V 2564

Agee, James

LET US NOW PRAISE FAMOUS MEN (Various artists).
MC: 1324

Agee, Ray

BLACK NIGHT IS GONE.
Tracks: / Black night is gone / I brought it all on myself / Love's limit / It's bed time baby / My lonesome days are gone / No more blue shadows falling / I can't find my way / One I love, The / Deep trouble / Brought it all on myself / Without a friend / I need you / Till death do us part / Devils Angels,The / Dream queen / My silent prayer / One too many.
LP: . . . . RB 105

I'M NOT LOOKING BACK.
Tracks: / True lips / Rock head / Lookit them eyes / Tijuana / Monkey on my back, The / Tragedy / I'm not looking back / Baby's coming home / I'm out to get you baby / Count the days I'm gone / Keep smiling / Doing it good for you / Love is a gamble / Somebody messed up / Soul of a man / It's hard to explain.
LP: . . . . RB 1003

TIN PAN ALLEY.
LP: . . . . DD 4301

Agent Steel

SKEPTICS APOCALYPSE.
Tracks: / Calling, The / Taken by force / Bleen for the Godz / 144.000 gone / Back to reign / Agents of steel / Evil eye / Children of the sun / Guilty as charged.
LP: . . . . RR 9759

UNSTOPPABLE FORCE.
LP: . . . . MFN 66
MC: . . . . TMFN 66

Ages Of Man

AGES OF MAN (Gielgud, Sir John (nar)).
Tracks: / As you like it speech / Merchant of Venice speech / Tempest speech / Romeo and Juliet speech / Measure for measure speech / Henry IV parts 1 & 2 speech / Richard II speech / Richard III speech / Julius Caesar speech / Hamlet speech / King Lear speech / Sonnets 18. 73, 116, 130 and 138 speech.
2LP: . . . . SRS 200
2LP: . . . . CBS 61830

Aggrovators

DUB JACKPOT.
LP: . . . . ATLP 111

DUB JUSTICE.
LP: . . . . ATLP 110

JAMMIES IN THE LION DUB STYLE.
LP: . . . . LAP 004

JOHNNY IN THE ECHO CHAMBER.
LP: . . . . ATLP 106

KAYA DUB.
LP: . . . . TWS 939

Agnes of God (film)

AGNES OF GOD (Film soundtrack) (Various artists).
LP: . . . . TER 1108
MC: . . . . CTV 81257
MC: . . . . ZCTER 1108

Agnes Strange

STRANGE FLAVOUR.
Tracks: / Give yourself a chance / Alberta / Loved one / Failure / Children of the absurd / Odd man out / Highway blues / Granny don't like rock 'n' roll / Interference.
LP: . . . . BRL 9000

Agnostic Front

CAUSE FOR ALARM.
LP: . . . . JUST 3

LIBERTY AND JUSTICE (FOR ALL).
LP: . . . . JUST 8

VICTIM IN PAIN.
LP: 88561-8181-1

A-Going to the Fair

A-GOING TO THE FAIR (Songs of Diversion) (Various artists).
Tracks: / Widdicombe fair: *Various artists* / Brian-O-Linn: *Various artists* / Counting song: *Various artists*/ Crocodile: *Various artists* / Dame Durden: *Various artists* / Frog and the mouse, The: *Various artists*/ Hawk and the crow: *Various artists* / Herring song: *Various artists* / Farmyard song: *Various artists*/ Mallard: *Various artists* / Acre of land: *Various artists* / Old daddy fox: *Various artists* / Old King Cole: *Various artists* / Ram song, The: *Various artists* / Soldier soldier: *Various artists* / Men went a-hunting: *Various artists* / Three scamping rogues: *Various artists* / Tom Pearce: *Various artists* / Was you ever see: *Various artists* / When I was a boy: *Various artists* / Wild man of borneo: *Various artists*/ Wim wim waddles: *Various artists*.
MC: 60-027

Agony

FIRST DEFIANCE, THE.
Tracks: / Hey Suze / Falling rain / Discipline / Chasing dreams / Ah-ha / Sailors on the sea / Stalk the girls / Dream girl / Strung out on you / Country girl / Goodnight darling.
LP: . . . . FLAG 19

Agony Agony

AGONY AGONY (Various artists).
LP: . . . . GAZLP 004

Agressor

DESTINY.
LP: . . . . NUK 154
MC: . . . . ZCNUK 154

A-Grumh

BLACK VINYL UNDER COVER.
Tracks: / Bach catalogue / Hammam / Generation / R.L.P.K. / Bumf, The (we know what life is) / Control / Yesterday / Drive, The / M.D.A. / Island called....
LP: . . . . BIAS 072

HARD DAY'S KNIGHT, A HARD KNIGHT'S DAY, A.
LP: . . . . BIAS 140

MIX YOURSELF.
LP: . . . . MFACE 009

NO WAY OUT.
LP: . . . . FACE 019

REBEARTH.
LP: . . . . FACE 14

Aguilar, Freddie

CHILD OF THE REVOLUTION.
MC: C2CS 001

Agyeman, Eric

WONKO MENKO.
LP: . . . . EBLS 7111

A-Ha

A-HA: INTERVIEW PICTURE DISC.
LP: . . . . TT 1002

A-HA: INTERVIEW PICTURE DISC.
LPPD: . . . . BAK 2031

EAST OF THE SUN, WEST OF THE MOON.
Tracks: / Crying in the rain / I call your name / East of the sun / Waiting for her / Way we talk, The / Seemingly nonstop July / Early mornings / Slender frame / Sycamore leaves / Cold river / Rolling thunder.
LP: . . . . WX 378
MC: . . . . WX 378C

HUNTING HIGH AND LOW.
Tracks: / Take on me / Train of thought / Hunting high and low / Blue sky, The / Living a boy's adventures tale / Sun always shines on TV, The / And you tell me / Love is reason / Dream myself alive / Here I stand and face the rain.
LP: . . . . WX 30
MC: . . . . WX 30C

SCOUNDREL DAYS.
Tracks: / Scoundrel days / Swing of things, The / I've been losing you / October / Manhattan skyline / Cry wolf / Looking for the whales / Weight of the wind, The / Maybe maybe / Soft rains of April.
LP: . . . . WX 62
MC: . . . . WX 62C

STAY ON THESE ROADS.
Tracks: / Blood that moves the body, The / Touchy / This alone is love / Hurry home / Living daylights, The / There's never a forever thing / Out of blue comes green / You are the one / You'll end up crying / Stay on these roads.
LP: . . . . WX 166
MC: . . . . WX 166 C

Ahead of his Time

AHEAD OF HIS TIME (Film soundtrack) (See under Zachariah) (Various artists).

A-Heads

FORGOTTEN HERO.
LP: . . . . FISH 3

Ahlberg, Allan (aut)

VARIOUS RECORDINGS (See under Title of Book).

Ahlberg, Janet (aut)
VARIOUS RECORDINGS (See under Title of Book).

Ahmed, Abdullah Mussa
TAARAB MUSIC OF ZANZIBAR VOL 1 (Ahmed, Abdullah Mussa/Seif Salim).
Tracks: / Taksim in hijaz mode / Wawili Tunapedani / Taksim in nihawad mode / Nur el nujum / Taksim in sabah mode / Ulimwengu una visa / Taksim in sikka mode / Mpenzi wagu hawesi / Shada la maua / Safaa.
LP: ORBD 032

Ahmed, Mahmoud
ERE MELA MELA.
LP: CRAM 047

Ahvenainen, Veikko
ACCORDION VARIETY CONCERT.
Tracks: / Granada / Preludio and fugue / Ritual fire dance / Idyll Finlandia / La mariposita / Dizzy fingers / Gershwin melodies / Cuckoo, The / Midsummer night waltz / Sakkjarven polkka.
LP: ALP 107

BACH, HANDEL.
Tracks: / Organ concerto no. 14 - A major / Largo / Allegro / Adante / Grave / Bach prelude and fugue E minor / Toccata and fugue in D minor.
LP: ALP 114

CELEBRATION CONCERT.
Tracks: / Preludi ja fugga / Sontaine / Sonsati d-duuri / La campanella idyll op 27 no.1 / Polkka balettisarjasta no.1 / Kesaillan valssi / Al, al / Sorja sinisimapoika / Valssi fantasia / La mariposita / Dizzy fingers.
LP: NEA 42

OLD DANCE MUSIC OF FINLAND.
LP: ALP 108

OLD FINNISH DANCE MUSIC.
Tracks: / Taikayo / Nikkelimarkka / Kenosen polkka / Mandshurian kukkuloilla / Talikkalan markkinoila / Raatikkoon / Rantakoivun alla / Kyllikki valssi / Kulkurin kaiho / Karjalan polkka / Amalia armas / Kulkurin masurkka / Hulivili polkka / Soita humupekka .
LP: ALP 101

Aida
AIDA (See under Verdi) (Various artists).

Aida & Cooper Terry
FEELIN' GOOD.
LP: AP 032

Aide Memoire.....
AIDE MEMOIRE, FOLKMUSIC & SONATY SLAVICKLOVE (Various artists).
LP: RR 22

AIDS
AIDS - THE FACTS (Tedder, Dr. Richard (nar)).
MC: AIDS 3

Aiken, Joan (author)
KINGDOM UNDER THE SEA, THE (See under Kingdom Under the...).

MORTIMER'S CROSS (See under Mortimer's Cross) (Bennett, Judy (nar)).

WOLVES OF WILLOUGHBY CHASE, THE.
MC: 1540

Ailana
MYSTERIOUS PLANET.
LP: HNBL 1324
MC: HNBC 1324

NEW ORCHESTRA, THE.
LP: HNBL 1314

Aililiu, Seinn
NOIRIN NI RIAIN.
LP: CEF 067

Aimer Gates
AIMER GATES (Garner, Alan (nar)).
LP: ZDSW 726

Aimless Device
DOG DAYS.
LP: ABR 017

HARD TO BE NICE.
LP: ABR 012

Ainsworth, Alyn
THEMES AND DREAMS (See under Moonlight Moods Orchestra).

TRUE LOVE (Ainsworth, Alyn Orchestra).
Tracks: / Never knew love like this before / Little in love, A / Do that to me one more time / Woman / One day in your life / Woman in love / Suddenly / Lately / One day I'll fly away / Take me as I am / With you I'm born again / Keep on loving you / When he shines / More than I can say / Crying / All out of love / More than a lover / Winner takes it all, The / After the love has gone / You've lost that lovin' feeling / Just as I am / Power of love, The / I can't let go / After all / I wanna hold you tonight / When the time is right / Sandy / Great pioneer / Black and blue / Sunset / Never fade away.
LP: SHM 3103
MC: HSC 3103

Ain't Gonna Rain No
AIN'T GONNA RAIN NO MORE (Various artists).
LP: ROUNDER 2016

Ain't Misbehavin'
AIN'T MISBEHAVIN' (original cast) (Various artists).
Tracks: / Lookin' good but feelin' bad: *Various artists* / Squeeze me: *Various artists* / Handful of keys: *Various artists* / How ya baby: *Various artists* / Ladies who sing with the band: *Various artists* / Yacht club swing: *Various artists* / Fat and greasy: *Various artists* / Black and blue: *Various artists* / I'm gonna sit right down and write myself a letter: *Various artists* / Two sleepy people: *Various artists* / I can't give you anything but love: *Various artists* / It's a sin to tell a lie: *Various artists* / Find out what they like: *Various artists* / T'ain't nobody's bizness if I do: *Various artists* / I've got my fingers crossed: *Various artists*/ Jitterbug waltz: *Various artists* / Lounging at the Waldorf: *Various artists* / When the nylons bloom again: *Various artists* / Cash for your trash: *Various artists* / That ain't right: *Various artists* / Mean to me: *Various artists* / Your feet's too big: *Various artists* / Keepin' out of mischief now: *Various artists*/ Joint is jumpin': *Various artists* / Spreadin' rhythm around: *Various artists* / Vipers drag: *Various artists*/ Honeysuckle rose: *Various artists* / Ain't misbehavin: *Various artists* / I've got a feeling I'm falling: *Various artists* / Off time: *Various artists*.
2LP: RL 82965
2LP: BL 82965
MC: RK 82965

Air
AIR SONG.
LP: PA 7120

Air America (film)
AIR AMERICA (Original Soundtrack) (Various artists).
LP: MCG 6112
MC: MCGC 6112

Air Supply
AIR SUPPLY.
Tracks: / Just as I am / Power of love, The / I can't let go / After all / Wanna hold you tonight / Make it right / When the time is right / Sandy / Great pioneer / Black and blue / Sunset / Never fade away.
LP: 207039
MC: 407039

LONELY IS THE NIGHT.
Tracks: / Every woman in the world (On 12" only) / All out of love (On 12" only) / It's not too late / Lonely is the night / Put love in your life / One more chance / Stars in your eyes / My heart's with you / I'd die for you / You're only in love / Time for love, A / Heart and soul / Hope springs eternal.
LP: 207891
MC: 407891

LOST IN LOVE.
Tracks: / Lost in love / All out of love / Every woman in the world / Just another woman / Having you near me / American hearts / Chances / Old habits die hard / I can't get excited / My best friend.
LP: SPART 1138
MC: TCART 1138
LP: 209045
MC: 409045

MAKING LOVE...THE BEST OF AIR SUPPLY.
Tracks: / Lost in love / Even the nights are better / One that you love, The / Every woman in the world / Two less lonely people in the world / Chances / Making love out of nothing at all / All out of love / Here I am / Sweet dreams / Keeping the love alive / Now and forever.
LP: 205545
MC: 405545
LP: 210757
MC: 410757

NOW AND FOREVER.
Tracks: / Now and forever / Even the nights are better / Young love / Two less lonely people in the world / Taking the chance / Come what may / One step closer / Don't be afraid / She never heard me call / What kind of girl.
LP: 204718
MC: 404718

ONE THAT YOU LOVE, THE.
Tracks: / Don't turn me away / Here I am / Keeping the love alive / One that you love, The / This heart belongs to me / Sweet dreams / I want to give it all / I'll never get enough of you / Tonite / I've got your love.
LP: SPART 1169
MC: TCART 1169
LP: 209061
MC: 409061

Airbridge
PARADISE MOVES.
Tracks: / Round dance / Paradise moves / With the turning of the centuries / Better times / To absent friends / Wave length / Night and silence / More than just to win / Visitation.
LP: CU 3

Aircraft Sounds
GREAT BRITISH AIRCRAFT (British aircraft).
MC: AC 115

Aird, Catherine (aut)
LATE PHOENIX, A (See under Late Phoenix, A (bk)) (Bailey, Robin (nar)).

Aire, Jane
JANE AIRE & BELVERDERES (Aire, Jane & The Belverderes).
Tracks: / Breaking down the walls of heartache / No more cherry icing / Driving / When you can't be loved / Take it to the next wave / Duke of love / Come see about me / Life after you / Wind up / Love is a fire.
MC: TCV 2134
LP: V 2134

Airplay
AIRPLAY (Various artists).
LP: RALP 6048

Airport (film)
AIRPORT (Original soundtrack) (Various artists).
LP: 255 086.1

Airrace
SHAFT OF LIGHT.
Tracks: / I don't care / Promise to call / First one over the line / Open your eyes / Not really me / Brief encounter / Caught in the game / Do you want my love again / Didn't want to lose ya / All i'm asking.
LP: 790 219-1

Airs Of Ireland
AIRS OF IRELAND (Various artists).
LP: SOLP 1035

Airspace
AIRSPACE II (The Sequel) (Various artists).
LP: BREAKLP 003

Airwaves
NEXT STOP.
Tracks: / Ain't got love / If you'd only talk to me / Love on the run / Mailman / Next stop / Now / Steal it / Talkin' to myself / Under your spell / You've got it.
LP: 9109625

Aisha
HIGH PRIESTESS.
Tracks: / Evil spirits / Tribulation / Creator, The / Hi tech / Prophecy / Downpressor / Love is so simple / This battle.
LP: ARILP 029

Aitken, Joe
IF YE'VE NEVER BEEN TAE KIRRIE.
MC: SPRC 1027

Aitken, Laurel
EARLY DAYS OF BLUE BEAT, SKA AND REGGAE (Aitken, Laurel & Friends).
LP: BRMLP 025

IT'S TOO LATE.
LP: PHZA 53

POTATO 5 MEET LAUREL AITKEN (Aitken, Laurel & The Potato 5).
Tracks: / Tear up / Jesse Jackson / Spin on your head / Big city / Western special / Sally Brown / Mad about you / Sahara / Long time I've been watching you.
LP: GAZLP 001

RISE AND FALL.
LP: PHZA 48

SALLY BROWN.
LP: PHZA 54

Ajao, Y.K. Professor
MAKOSSA SERIES 1.
LP: AR 001

Ajax
ONE WORLD (LP).
LP: WAX 113

AK Band
MANHOLE KIDS.
LP: RCALP 5024
MC: RCAK 5024

Akabu
AKABU.
LP: VV 003

Akaoldren, Viv
I'LL CAN YOU SOMETIME.
LP: VIVAK 001

VIVIAN'S FOUNTAIN.
LP: RES 339027

WITNESS.
Tracks: / Witness.
LP: R 33 8818

Akash
NACH NACH.
LP: SSRLP 5093
MC: SC 5093

Akendengue
AFRIKA OBOTA/NANDIPO.
LP: CELC 4112

MANDO.
Tracks: / Epunguzu / Okuwa / Mando / Evogamanga / Ewaka / Ekuru / Okongo / Ilumbu / Imbunga / Vigego.
LP: CBS 25355
MC: 40 25355

Akimbo
AKIMBO.
LP: FORWARD 001

Akiyoshi, Toshiko
COLLECTION (Akiyoshi, Toshiko and Lew Tabackin).
Tracks: / Studio j / American ballad / Quadrille, anyone ? / Children in the temple ground / First night / Kogun / Since Perry/ Yet another tear / Road time shuffle.
MC: NK 83106

INSIGHTS (Akiyoshi, Toshiko and Lew Tabackin).
LP: PL 45363

INTERLUDE.
Tracks: / Interlude / I know who loves you / Blue and sentimental / I ain't gonna ask no more / Pagliacci / Solitude / So in love / You stepped out of a dream.
LP: CJ 324
MC: CJC 324

LIVE AT NEWPORT '77.
LP: NL 70579

SUMI-E (Akiyoshi, Toshiko and Lew Tabackin).
LP: PL 37537

Akkerman, Jan
CAN'T STAND NOISE.
Tracks: / Pietons / Everything must change / Back to the factory / Journey (a real elegant gypsy) / Heavy treasure / Just because / Who knows.
LP: CR 30250

COLLAGE COLLECTION (See under Thielemans, Toots) (Akkerman, Jan & Toots Thielemans).

FORCEFIELD III (see under Bonnet, Graham) (Akkerman, Jan/Graham Bonnet/Cozy Powell/Ray Fenwick).

GOLDEN HIGHLIGHTS OF AKKERMAN & OGERMAN (Akkerman & Ogerman).
LP: 54730
MC: 40 54730

IT COULD HAPPEN TO YOU.
Tracks: / Old tennis shoes / Come closer / Funkology / It could happen to you.
LP: CR 30246

JAN AKKERMAN 3.
LP: K 50664

NOISE OF ART, THE.
Tracks: / Prima Donna / Akkerman's sombrero / Quiet storm / You can't keep a bad man up / Shame on you / Having fun / My pleasure / Trojan horse / Bonnaville / Prelude - friend's always.
LP: EIRSA 1026
MC: EIRSAC 1026

PLEASURE POINT.
Tracks: / Valdez / Heavy pleasure / Cool in the shadow / Visions of blue / C.S. / Bird Island.
LP: LIK 13
MC: TCLIK 13

PROFILE: JAN AKKERMAN.
LP: 5C 038 24707

Akkordeon Orchester
AKKORDEON ORCHESTER.
LP: LKLP 6260

Akron Compilation
AKRON COMPILATION (Various artists).
LP: GET 3

Al Munzer, Ihsan
BELLY DANCE.
LP: VOS 10042

DISCO BELLY DANCE.
LP: . . . . VOS 10045

Alaap

BEST OF ALAAP.
MC: . . . . CMUT 001

CHAM CHAM NACHDI PHIRAN.
LP: . . . . MUT 1121
MC: . . . . CMUT 1121

DANCE WITH ALAAP.
Tracks: / Lak patia patang / Dupatta be-imman ho gaya / Kade na billo bolt hus ke / Ay sharaab ay sharaab / Ve vanjareya / Bhabhiyie nee Bhabhiyie / Eh zindgani eh jawani / Gidhe wich deven jadon gera balliya / Ve vanjareya.
LP: . . . . CON LP100

GOLD.
MC: . . . . CMUT 1122

NACH MUNDEYA.
LP: . . . . MUT 1035
MC: . . . . CMUT 1035

PATTAKA.
Tracks: / You can't catch me / I didn't mean to be mean / Crossing, The / Loretta.
LP: . . . . MUT 1055
MC: . . . . CMUT 1055
LP: . . . . BHANGRA 4LP

PATTAUA.
MC: . . . . CMUT 1054

WITH LOVE FROM ALAAP.
LP: . . . . MUT 1014
MC: . . . . CMUT 1014

Alabama

ALABAMA JUG AND STRING BANDS (Various artists).
LP: . . . . BD 2028

Alabama Blues

ALABAMA BLUES (1927-31) (Various artists).
LP: . . . . L 1006

ALABAMA BLUES (1927-51) (Various artists).
LP: . . . . HK 4004

ALABAMA COUNTRY BLUES (Various artists).
LP: . . . . RL 325

Alabama (Group)

ALABAMA.
Tracks: / My homes in Alabama / Feels so right / Love in the first degree / Why lady why / Getting over you / I wanna come over / Fantasy / Old flame / Tennessee River / Some other place, some other time / Can't forget about you / Get it while it's hot / Woman back home / See the embers, feel the flame / I'm stoned.
LP: . . . . PL 89247
MC: . . . . PK 89247

FEELS SO RIGHT.
Tracks: / Feels so right / Love in the first degree / Burn Georgia burn / Ride the train / Fantasy / Hollywood / Old flame / Woman back home / See the embers feel the flame / I'm stoned.
LP: . . . . RCALP 5025

FORTY HOUR WEEK.
Tracks: / As right now / If it ain't Dixie / Nobody but me / Forty hour week / Can't keep a good man down / There's no way / Down on longboat key / Lousiana moon / I want to know you before we make love / Fire works.
LP: . . . . PL 85339
MC: . . . . PK 85339

GREATEST HITS: ALABAMA.
Tracks: / She and I / Mountain music / Feels so right / Old flame / Tennessee river / Love in the first degree / Forty hour week (for a livin') / Why lady why / Fans, The / My home's in Alabama.
LP: . . . . PL 87170
MC: . . . . PK 87170

JUST US.
Tracks: / Tar top / I can't stop / I saw the time / You're my explanation for living / Face to face / I wish it could always be 55 / Old man / If I could just see you now / Falling again.
LP: . . . . PL 86495
MC: . . . . PK 86495

MOUNTAIN MUSIC.
Tracks: / Mountain music / Close enough to perfect / Words at twenty paces / Changes comin' on / Green river / Take me down / You turn me on / Never be one / Loving you is killing me / Gonna have a party.
LP: . . . . PL 84229
MC: . . . . PK 84229

MY HOME'S IN ALABAMA.
Tracks: / My home's in Alabama / Hanging up my travelling shoes / Why lady why / Getting over you / I wanna come over / Tennessee river / Some other place / Can't forget about you / Get it while it's hot / Keep on dreamin'.
MC: . . . . NK 89966
LP: . . . . NL 89966
LP: . . . . PL 13644

TOUCH, THE.
Tracks: / Cruisin' / Touch me when we're dancing / Let's hear it for the girl / It's all coming back to me now / I taught her everything she knows / Pony express / You've got the touch / Vacation / True true housewife / Is this how love begins?.
LP: . . . . PL 85649
MC: . . . . PK 85649

Alabama Harmonica

ALABAMA HARMONICA KINGS 1927-30.
LP: . . . . WSE 127

Alabama Kids

WHAT GOES DOWN.
LP: . . . . SCHEMER 9009

Alabama Rocks

ALABAMA ROCKS (Various artists).
Tracks: / I've gotta find someone: *Tiny Tim* / Lonesome man: *Tiny Tim* / Teenage lover: *Tiny Tim* / Kisses and fire: *Tiny Tim* / Foolish way: *Bowman, Leon* / I love you: *Bowman, Leon* / Carnival in town: *Bowman*, Leon / Don't knock no more: *Cook, Johnny* / One little baby: *Salvo, Sammy* / Sweet shop doll: *Moore*, Ronnie / Romp, The: *Epics* / Strange feeling: *Villian, Jesse* / Mr. Songwriter: *Holder, Jimmy* / What'd I say?: *Holder, Jimmy*.
LP: . . . . WLP 8873

Alabama Singers

NEGRO SPIRITUAL MUSIC.
Tracks: / Battle of Jericho, The / Poor pilgrim of sorrow / Talk about Jesus / Jesus met the woman at the well / Daniel saw the stone / He'll never let go your hand / Come home / Yes indeed / Go down, Moses / I could do better than that / Soldier's plea / Motherless child / I remember the time / Walk around.
LP: . . . . SM 3342

Alabama Soul

ALABAMA SOUL (Various artists).
LP: . . . . RPL 113

Aladdin... (bk)

ALADDIN (for ages 7-12).
MC: . . . . PLB 129

ALADDIN AND ALI BABA (Graham, John (nar)).
MC: . . . . TS 326

ALADDIN AND HIS LAMP (Lee, Dennis (nar)).
MC: 1250

ALADDIN AND HIS MAGIC LAMP (And other Favourite Stories for Children Aged 5.
MC: . . . . VCA 611

ALADDIN AND THE WONDERFUL LAMP (Jones, Terry (nar)).
MC: . . . . LP 214

ARABIAN NIGHTS: ALADDIN (Jones, Terry (nar)).
MC: . . . . LPMC 214

Aladdin (show)

ALADDIN (Original London cast) (Various artists).
Tracks: / Spell, The: *Various artists* / Aladdin: *Various artists* / Hang chow: *Various artists* / Proclamation, The: *Various artists* / Tuang kee po: *Various artists* / It is written in the sands: *Various artists*/ There and then: *Various artists* / Love's a luxury: *Various artists* / Dream about me: *Various artists*/ Song of the genie of the ring: *Various artists* / Song of the genie of the lamp: *Various artists* / Chopsticks: *Various artists* / All I did: *Various artists* / Wicked: *Various artists* / Dirge: *Various artists*/ Life in the laundry: *Various artists* / Give him the old Kung Fu: *Various artists* / Aladdin (reprise): *Various artists*.
LP: . . . . PTLS 1072

ALADDIN AND HIS LAMP (Various artists).
Tracks: / Aladdin and his lamp: *Various artists* / Deer and the jaguar, The: *Various artists* / Beef tongue of Orula, The: *Various artists* / Uncle Bookie: *Various artists* / Balsam tree, The: *Various artists* / Soupstone, The: *Various artists*.
MC: . . . . ANV 653

Alaimo, Steve

EVERY DAY I HAVE TO CRY.
Tracks: / Every day I have to cry / I don't want to cry / My heart cries for you / I cried all the way home / Cry me a river / I wake up crying / Cry / She cried / Don't cry / Cry of the wild goose / Cry myself to sleep / Don't let the sun catch you crying.
LP: . . . . GCH 8100

Alamo Bay (film)

ALAMO BAY (Film soundtrack) (Various artists).
Tracks: / Alamo Bay, Theme from: *Various artists* / Gooks on Main Street: *Various artists* / Too close: *Various* artists / Klan meeting: *Various artists* / Sailfish evening: *Various artists* / Last stand: *Various artists*/ Quatro vicios: *Various artists* / Search and destroy: *Various artists* / Glory: *Various artists*.
LP: . . . . SLAP 7
MC: . . . . SMAC 7

Alamo (Film)

ALAMO, THE (Film soundtrack) (Various artists).
LP: . . . . PC 8358

Alamshan, Bill

IN THE DARK.
LP: . . . . ARCADIA 2014

Alarm

ALARM, THE.
Tracks: / Stand, The / Across the border / Marching on / Lie of the land / For freedom.
MLP: . . . . ILP 25573

CHANGE.
Tracks: / Sold me down the river / Rock, The / Devolution working mans blues / Love don't come easy / Hardland / Change 11 / No frontiers / Scarlet / Where a town once stood / Black sun / Prison without prison bars / How the mighty fall / Rivers to cross / New South Wales, A.
LP: . . . . EIRSAX 1020
MC: . . . . EIRSAC 1020

DECLARATION.
Tracks: / Declaration / Marching on / Where were you when the storm broke? / Third light / Sixty eight guns / We are the light / Shout to the devil / Blaze of glory / Tell me / Deceiver / Stand (prophecy) / Howling wind.
LP: . . . . IRSA 7044
MC: . . . . IRSC 7044

ELECTRIC FOLKLORE.
Tracks: / Rescue me / Rain in the summertime / Permanence in change / Strength / Spirit of '76.
MLP: . . . . MIRM 5001
MC: . . . . MIRMC 5001

EYE OF THE HURRICANE.
Tracks: / Rain in the summertime / Newtown Jericho / Hallowed ground / One step closer to home / Shelter / Rescue me / Permanence in change / Presence of love / Only love can set me free / Eye of the hurricane.
LP: . . . . MIRG 1023
MC: . . . . MIRGC 1023

RAW.
Tracks: / Raw / Rockin' in the free world / God save somebody / Moments in time / Hell or high water / Lead me through the darkness / Wind blows away my words, The / Let the river run its course / Save your crying / Wonderful world.
LP: . . . . EIRSA 1055
MC: . . . . EIRSAC 1055

STANDARDS.
LP: . . . . EIRSA 1043
MC: . . . . EIRSAC 1043

STRENGTH.
Tracks: / Knife edge / Strength / Dawn chorus / Spirit of '76 / Day the ravens left the tower / Deeside / Father to son / Only the thunder / Walk forever by my side.
LP: . . . . MIRF 1004
MC: . . . . MIRFC 1004

Alaska

HEART OF THE STORM.
LP: . . . . MFN 23

PACK, THE.
LP: . . . . MFN 41

Alba

ALBA.
Tracks: / Glen Rinnes / Jig of slurs, The / Overgate, The / King's favourite / Van Diemans land / Mermaid's song, The / John Murray of Lochlee / Pipe Major George Allan / Blacksmith's reel, The / Star of Munster, The / Fear a bhata / Drummond Castle / Paddy's leather breeches / Captain Ward / Gartan mothers lullaby / Geese in the bog, The / Doctor McInnes' fancy.
LP: . . . . RUB 021
MC: . . . . RUBC 021

Albam, Manny

JAZZ WORKSHOP, THE.
Tracks: / Anything goes / Headstrong / Black bottom / Changing scene, The / Turning point / Charmaine / Diga diga doo / Royal Garden blues / Swingin' on a star / Intermezzo / Ferris wheel urbanity.
2LP: . . . . PM 43551

MANNY ALBAM AND THE GREATS OF OUR TIME VOL 1.
Tracks: / Blues for neither coast / Latined fracture / Poor Doctor Millmoss / Minor matters / My sweetie went away / All too soon / See here Miss Bromley.
LP: . . . . JASM 1010

WEST SIDE STORY (Albam, Manny/his Jazz Greats).
Tracks: / Prologue and jet song / Something's coming (could be) / Cool / Maria / Tonight / I feel pretty / Somewhere / Finale.
LP: . . . . JASM 1003

Albania (country)

FOLK MUSIC OF ALBANIA (Various artists).
LP: 12T 154

FOLKLORE OF ALBANIA, THE (Various artists).
LP: . . . . CEL 010
MC: . . . . MC CEL 010

Albania (group)

ARE YOU ALL MINE.
Tracks: / So O.K. / Albania / Addicts of the first night / Take it away / French farewell / Cold light of day / Great Zambesi / Kaytie King / Men in a million / Deathwatch.
LP: . . . . CWK 3016

Albany

EAST - WEST, HAME'S BEST.
Tracks: / Grand march / Fagail liosmor / Cuckoo waltz / Singing bird / March/ Strathspey/Reel / Mo mhathair / Bonnie lass o' Fyvie / Bheir mi o / Crags of tumbledown mountain / Silver darlings / Balkin hills, The / Nuair a bha mi og / Tribute to the late Hugh Kirk.
LP: . . . . LAP 114
MC: . . . . LAP 114 C

Albany, Joe

AT HOME: JOE ALBANY.
Tracks: / What's new / You're blase / Why was I born / Jitterbug waltz / Night and day / What are you doing the rest of your life / Barbados / Can't we be friends / Everything happens to me / You've changed / Birdtown birds / Isn't it romantic.
LP: . . . . SPJ JA1

BIRD LIVES.
LP: . . . . IP 7723

PORTRAIT OF AN ARTIST.
Tracks: / Autumn in New York / Guess I'll hang my tears out to dry / For the little guy / They say it's wonderful / Too late now / Confirmation / Ruby, my dear.
LP: . . . . K 52390

PROTO-BOPPER.
Tracks: / When lights are low / Our love affair is over / You don't know what love is / For heaven's sake / Getting sentimental over you / Yardbird suite / Imagination / Like someone in love / C.C. rider / You're blase / Suddenly it's spring.
LP: . . . . SPJ JA3

RIGHT COMBINATION, THE.
Tracks: / Daahoud / I love you / It's you or no one / Nearness of you, The / Angel eyes / Body and soul / All the things you ar e.
LP: . . . . RSLP 270

Albee, Edward (author)

DELICATE BALANCE, A (Various artists).
MCSET: 0360

Albert Herring

ALBERT HERRING (VIDEO) (see under Britten (composer)) (Various artists).

Albert, Trigger

TRIGGER HAPPY!.
LP: . . . . FS 108

Alberto Y Los Trios...

WORST OF THE BERTS (Alberto Y Los Trios Paranoias).
Tracks: / Juan Lopez / Mother Superior / Teenage paradise / Wholefood love / 23 / God is mad / Anarchy in the UK / Kill / Gobbin' on life / Snuffin' in a Babylon / Heads down no nonsense mindless boogie / Death of rock'n'roll.
LP: . . . . MOGO 4008

Albion Band

1990.
LP: . . . . 12 TS 457
MC: . . . . KTSC 457

BATTLE OF THE FIELD.
LP: . . . . CGLP 4420

CHRISTMAS PRESENT, A.
LP: . . . . FUN 003
MC: . . . . FUN 003 C

GIVE ME A SADDLE AND I'LL TRADE YOU A CAR.
LP: . . . . 12 TS 454

MC: .... KTSC 454

LARK RISE TO CANDLEFORD (See under Folk) (Various artists).

LIGHT SHINING.
LP: .... ALB 001

RISE UP LIKE THE SUN.
LP: .... SHSP 4092
LP: .... CGLP 4431
MC: .... CGC 4431

SHUFFLE OFF.
LP: .... SPIN 103

UNDER THE ROSE.
LP: .... SPIN 110

Albright, Gerald

BERMUDA NIGHTS.
Tracks: / When you say you love me / In the mood / Bermuda nights / Hook, The / Feeling inside / Still in love / Truth / Too co ol.
LP: .... K 781 919 1
MC: .... K 781 919 4

JUST BETWEEN US.
Tracks: / New girl on the block / Trying to find a way / So amazing / King Boulevard / Come back to me / You're my no. 1 / Just between us / You don't even know / Softly at sunrise.
LP: 781 813-1
MC: 781 813-4

Alcapone, Dennis

BELCH IT OFF.
LP: .... AT 1005

MY VOICE IS INSURED FOR 1/2 MILLION DOLLARS.
LP: .... TRLS 272

Alcatrazz

DISTURBING THE PEACE.
Tracks: / God blessed video / Mercy / Will you be home tonight / Wire and wood / Desert diamond / Stripper, The / Painted lover / Lighter shade of green / Sons and lovers / Sky fire / Breaking the heart of the city.
LP: .... EJ 2402991
MC: .... EJ 2402994

LIVE SENTENCE - NO PAROLE FROM ROCK'N'ROLL.
Tracks: / Island in the sun / General hospital / Jet to jet / Hiroshima mon amour / Kree nakoorie / Incubus / Too young to die, too drunk to live / Big foot / Starcarr Lane / Suffer me.
LP: .... PL 83263
MC: .... PK 83263
LP: .... SLAM 11

RADIO 5.
Tracks: / Blinded / Blame it on the night / Long time no love / Halfway there / Short change / Think it over / Communication / Save my heart / So hard / Miles away.
LP: .... RCALP 3066
MC: .... RCAK 3066

YOUNG BLOOD.
Tracks: / Rockin' high / Young blood / Maybe tomorrow / Late news, The / Deadline / Crazy dancer / Give it all away / Live fast, die hard / You and the night / Run wild.
LP: .... RCALP 5023
MC: .... RCAK 5023

Alcock, Gary

GARY ALCOCK AND MIDLAND ALL STARS BIG BAND.
LP: DROY5001

Alcock, Vivien

CUCKOO SISTER, THE (See under Cuckoo Sister (bk)) (Hayman, Carole (nar)).

Alcorn, Alvin

ALVIN ALCORN & HIS NEW ORLEANS JAZZ BAND (Alcorn, Alvin & His New Orleans Jazz Band).
LP: .... NOR 7205

Alcott, Louisa May

LITTLE WOMEN (See under Little Women) (Jackson, Glenda).

Alda Reserve

LOVE GOES ON.
Tracks: / Some get away / Dressed for love / Cure me / Pain is mine / Overnite jets / Ancient lies / That was summertime / Whiter than white / Love goes on.
LP: .... SRK 6079

Aldbrickham Band

ALDBRICKHAM BAND.
MC: .... ACS 004

Aldeberts

LOS ANGELES.
Tracks: / Toi et moi samba / Life's mockinbird / In the middle of the night / Mandarin me / La fiesta / Los Angeles / Without a friend / When you know / It happens every day / When we go to San Francisco.

LP: .... TR 533

Alden Barrett Quintet

ABQ SALUTES BUCK CLAYTON, THE.
Tracks: / Chocolate chip / Winter light / Candi / Abbotsford Road / Mink Avenue / Way down yonder in New Orleans / Love jumped out / Switch hitter / In a Parisian mood / C minor swing / Beaujolais (on CD only) / Dickie's dream / Claytonia / Beautiful yesteryear, A.
MC: .... CJ 395C

SWING STREET.
Tracks: / Lullaby in rhythm / Black sheep blues / Front and centre / Lord's prayer, The / Wonderful words of life / Fun city swinger / I may be wrong / Cottontail / Guide me o thou great Jehovah / How great thou art.
LP: .... CJ 349
MC: .... CJ 349 C

Alden, Howard

13 STRINGS (Alden, Howard & George Van Eps).
Tracks: / Just you, just me / My ideal / I hadn't anyone till you / Beautiful friendship, A / Touch of your lips, The / Ain't misbehavin' / Too marvellous for words / Love walked in / Queerology / How long has this been going on? / Mine / Embraceable you / Emaline.
MC: .... CJ 464 C

HOWARD ALDEN TRIO (Alden, Howard, Trio).
Tracks: / You showed me the way / Where are you / Love theme No. 1 / Reflections / Your love has faded / Alice blue gown / Purple gazelle / Douce ambiance / Back home blues / Tears / Keep a song in your soul.
LP: .... CJ 378
MC: .... CJ 378C

SNOWY MORNING BLUES (Alden, Howard, Trio).
Tracks: / One morning in May / I'm through with love / Bye-ya / Melancholia / Sleepy time gal / Le sucrier velours (Only on CD) / Dancers in love (Only on CD) / Snowy morning blues / Ask me now / You leave me breathless / Swing 39.
MC: .... CJ 424 C

Alderton, John (nar)

FIREMAN SAM SERIES (See under Fireman Sam).

Aldiss, Brian W. (aut)

BEST SCIENCE FICTION OF BRIAN W. ALDISS.
MCSET: .... LISF 0003/0004

Aldrich, Ronnie

28 GREAT PIANO CLASSICS (Aldrich, Ronnie & His Orchestra).
Tracks: / As time goes by / Stardust / Barefoot in the park / Old fashioned way, The / People / You are the sunshine of my life / Hey Jude / Bewitched / My cherie amour / Shadow of your smile / Unforgettable / Ode to Billy Joe / Tie a yellow ribbon / You made me feel brand new / MacArthur Park / Wave / Man and a woman, A / Something / Candy man / Autumn leaves / Somewhere my love / Onedin line / Way we were, The / Love is blue / Michelle / Summer of '42 / Bridge over troubled water / Sound of silence, The.
2LP: .... SIV 100
MC: .... CSIV 100

FOCUS ON RONNIE ALDRICH.
Tracks: / Way we were, The / By the time I get to Phoenix / What are you doing the rest of your life / Old fashioned way, The / Chim chim cheree / MacArthur Park / Autumn leaves / Scarborough fair / More / Concierto de Aranjuez / Entertainer, The / It's impossible / Summer of '42 / Sun dance / Felicidade / She / Wave / Amazing grace / In the gentle hours / Man and a woman, A / Whiter shade of pale, A / Tie a yellow ribbon / This guy's in love with you / Love story.
2LP: .... FOS 13/14
MC: .... KFOC 28047

FOR ALL SEASONS (Aldrich, Ronnie, His Piano & The Festival Orchestra).
Tracks: / April in Paris / Spring song / It might as well be Spring / Summertime / Solway in Summer / Summer wind / Early Autumn / September song / Forever Autumn / When Winter comes / Winter world of love / June in January.
LP: .... MFP 5800
MC: .... TCMFP 5800

FOR THE ONE YOU LOVE (Aldrich, Ronnie & His Orchestra).
Tracks: / You needed me / Main event, The / Fight / She believes in me / Just when I needed you most / Can't smile without you / I know I'll never love this way again / Gypsomania / Reunited / Just the way you are / You take my breath away / You're the only one / After the love has gone.
LP: .... SKL 5319
MC: .... KSKC 5319

GREAT TUNES FROM THE CLASSICS.
Tracks: / Mozart 40 / Meditation / Serenade / None but the lonely heart / Vocalise / Barcarolle / Nocturne / Serenade / Air on a G string / Mozart piano concerto No. 21 theme.
LP: .... DGSR 9

HOUR OF RONNIE ALDRICH, AN (Aldrich, Ronnie His Piano and Orchestra).
Tracks: / La mer / Hello / Bermuda triangle / Sound of the sea, The / Last farewell, The / Calypso / Stranger on the shore / Sailing / Trade winds / Begin the beguine / Arthur's theme / Memory (from 'Cats') / Hill Street blues / Chariots of fire / Nights birds / Albareda / Stay / For Liza.
MC: .... HR 8147

NIGHT BIRDS (Aldrich, Ronnie & His Two Pianos).
Tracks: / Begin the beguine / Arthur's theme / Memory / Santa Catalina / Hill Street blues / Chariots of fire / Night birds / Have you ever been in love / Little peace, A / Albareda / Stay / For Liza.
LP: .... MFP 5586
MC: .... TCMFP 5586

ONE FINE DAY.
Tracks: / Woman in love / One fine day / Shadow waltz / Fame / On Broadway / Stand by me / Reminiscing / Autumn tears / Magic / Romeos tune.
LP: .... SKL 5324
MC: .... KSKC 5324

SEA DREAMS (Aldrich, Ronnie & His Two Pianos).
Tracks: / La mer / Hello / Sailing by / Bermuda triangle / Sound of the sea, The / Last farewell, The / Calypso / Stranger on the shore / Sailing / Trading winds / To all the girls I've loved before / How deep is the ocean.
LP: .... MFP 41 5686-1
MC: .... MFP 41 5686 4

SILVER BELLS.
LP: .... HDY 1920
MC: .... ZCHDY 1920

SOFT AND WICKED (Aldrich, Ronnie & His Two Pianos).
Tracks: / Last tango in Paris / You're so vain / Tie a yellow ribbon / Call me (come back home) / Good time Charlie's got the blues / Oh babe what would you say / Last song, The / Love theme / It never rains in Southern California.
LP: .... JASM 2208
MC: .... JASMC 2208

TENDER LOVE...TENDER MOMENTS (Aldrich, Ronnie & His Orchestra).
Tracks: / Cavatina / Light my fire / My one and only love / United we stand / Ruby / What are you doing the rest of your life / For once in my life / Don't cry for me Argentina / Clair / Save your kisses for me / Amazing grace / I left my heart in San Francisco / Summer of 42, Theme from / Summer knows, The / Can't smile without you / I wish you love.
LP: .... CN 2049
MC: CN4 2049

UNFORGETTABLE SOUND OF RONNIE ALDRICH AND HIS TWO PIANOS.
Tracks: / Bewitched / Stardust / Look of love, The / Windmills of your mind / Sound of silence, The / How deep is the ocean / I didn't know what time it was / Mas que nada / Entertainer, The / Amazing grace / Imagine / Long and winding road, The / Adaigo / Way we were, The / Embraceable you / Things you are, The / Bridge over troubled water / Both sides now / Impossible dream, The / Love is blue / Where or when / Spanish harlem / When I fall in love / If you leave me now / Love me tonight / How deep is your love / Memories are made of this.
2LP: .... UNKNOWN

WINTER WONDERLAND.
LP: .... AFEMP 1028

WITH LOVE AND UNDERSTANDING.
LP: .... PFS 4406
MC: .... KPFC 4406

Aldridge, Michael

ALAN AYCKBOURN DOUBLE BILL (See under Ayckbourn, Alan) (Aldridge, Michael/Nicky Henson).

Aleanna

IRISH TRADITIONAL MUSIC.
LP: .... INC 7421

Aleem

CASUALLY FORMAL.
Tracks: / Love's on fire / Two faces / Confusion / Stay / More than a million / Think / Fine young tender / Dance to the groove.
LP: 781 622-1
MC: 781 622-4

Aless, Tony

LONG ISLAND SUITE.
LP: .... FS 121

Alessi

LONG TIME FRIENDS.
Tracks: / Jagged edge / You got the way / As far as I'm concerned / Rise up / I'm gonna tell her tonight / Put away your love / What a way to go / Still in love / How long how much / Forever / Long time friends.
LP: .... K 56999

OH LORI (OLD GOLD) (See under Sandpipers/Gutanamera).

Alexa

ALEXA.
Tracks: / I can't shake you / Dance the night away / Cry away, A / Heart to heart / From now on / We don't remember why / Wanderlust / Cool wind / Spookey.
LP: .... LPVAG 911
MC: .... CASVAG 911

Alexander, Alger

TEXAS TROUBLESOME BLUES.
LP: .... AB 2009

Alexander, Arthur

ARTHUR ALEXANDER.
Tracks: / I'm comin' home / Go home girl / Burning love / Lover please / Down with the back roads / Come along with me / Thank God he came / It hurts to want it so bad / In the middle of it all / Rainbow Road / Love's where life begins / Call me honey / Call me in Tahiti / They'll do it every time.
LP: .... CH 270

SHOT OF RHYTHM & SOUL, A.
Tracks: / Anna / Sally Sue Brown / You're the reason / Dream girl / Go home girl / Shot of rhythm and blues, A / Pretty girls everywhere / I wonder where you are tonight / You better move on / Girl that radiates that charm, The / Black night / Soldiers of love / I hang my head and cry / Where have you been / You don't care / Old John Amos.
LP: .... CH 66
MC: .... CHC 166

SOLDIER OF LOVE.
Tracks: / Don't you know / Call me lonesome / Detroit City / After you / Love letters / Keep her guessing / Hey baby / Soldiers of love / All I need is you / Whole lot of trouble / In the middle of it all / Funny how time slips away / Without a song / Love me warm and tender.
LP: .... CH 207

Alexander, Ashley

PLAYS FRANK MANTOOTH (Alexander, Ashley Big Band).
Tracks: / Secret love / Prelude to a kiss / Stone lizard / Outside St. Louis / Spring can really hang you up the most / Mixolydiasn soul frog / Latin schizophrenia.
LP: .... AM 12

SEEMS LIKE OLD TIMES (Alexander, Ashley Big Band).
LP: .... CMD 8005

Alexander Brothers

ALEXANDER BROTHERS COLLECTION.
Tracks: / Boys of Killybegs / Rose of Allandale / Typewriter, The / Marriage / Carnival is over, The / Auld meal mill, The / Old rustic bridge / I have a dream / Happy hours / Village where I went to school / All my life / Alpine Express / Through the eyes of a child / Teuchter music.
LP: .... LIDL 6011
MC: .... LIDC 6011
LP: .... LILP 6011

FLOWER OF SCOTLAND.
Tracks: / Scotland the brave / Skye boat song / Campbeltown loch / Road and the miles to Dundee, The / Northern lights of old Aberdeen, The / My ain folk / Mari's wedding / Scottish soldier, A / Amazing grace / Heilan lassie / Rowan tree, The / Wild rover, The / Cock o' the north / Tunes of glory / How are things in Glocca Morra / Flower of Scotland, The / These are my mountains (CD only.) / Two highlands lads (CD only.) / When you and I were young Maggie (CD only.) / Ballad of Glencoe (CD only.).
MC: .... TCMFP 5889

GLORIOUS NORTH, THE.
Tracks: / Glorious North, The / Caledonia / Hill o'Benachie, The / Lass o'bon accord, The / Oil rigger, The / Northern lights of old Aberdeen / Dark island / Lonely scapa flow / Jigs medley / Farewell my love / McGinty's meal and ale.

LP: . . . . NCP 701
MC: . . . . ZCNCP 701

LEGENDS OF SCOTLAND.
Tracks: / Lass o'bon accord, The / Road to Dundee, The / Flying Scotsman / Wild side of life / All along Loch Long / Nobody's child / Flower of Scotland / Northern lights of old Aberdeen / Dark island / These are my mountains / Blackboard of my heart / My big Kilmarnock bunnet / Soor milk cairt / Johnnie lad.
MC: . . . . ZCLLS 703

MY ISLAND TOO.
Tracks: / Tunes of glory / Old fashioned waltz, The / My island too / Swiss polka, The / Teenie fae troon / Isle of Innisfree / Hiking medley / She's called Nova Scotia / Lily McNally McNair / Dream of Olwen / Mary Mack / Forty shades of green / Cuckoo waltz, The / Sing along melody.
LP: . . . . LIDL 6023
MC: . . . . LIDC 6023

NOW.
Tracks: / Welcome medley / Nobody's child / Old button box, The / Pistonette / Gentle Annie / Inverary Inn / Daisy a day / Dark island / Doon in the wee room / Maggie / Sing along medley / Way old friends do / Home from the sea / On the rebound / Goodnight Bobby / Mary mack / Could I have this dance / Glencoe / Flying Scotsman, The / Bunch of thyme / Catch me if you can / Flower of Scotland.
LP: . . . . LIDC 8010

SCOTLAND FOR ME.
Tracks: / Bunch of thyme / Old flames / Slangeva / Song of the mira / Dark Lochnagar / Always Argyll / Down in the wee room / Gentle Annie / Wee china pig / Inverary inn / Dark island / Daisy a day / Could I have this dance / Glasgow Dan / There's a tree in the meadow.
LP: . . . . LIDL 6007
MC: . . . . LIDC 6007

SINCERELY YOURS.
Tracks: / All on a summer's day / Gentle Annie / Wee china pig / Floral dance / Could I have this dance / Inverary Inn / Lord of the dance / There's a tree in the meadow / Daisy a day / Dark Island / Juggin' pig / Glasgow Dan / Farewell my love.
LP: . . . . LIDL 6016
MC: . . . . LIDC 6016

THESE ARE MY MOUNTAINS.
LP: . . . . GGL 0375

TOM AND JACK.
MC: . . . . ZCP 18560

TRIBUTE TO SIR HARRY LAUDER.
Tracks: / Wedding of Lauchie McGraw, The / End of the road / Killiecrankie / There is somebody waiting for me / I love you / It's nice to get up in the morning / Wee hoose among the heather / Waggle o' the kilt, The.
MC: . . . . ZCSMPS 8929

VERY BEST OF ALEXANDER BROTHERS, THE.
MC: . . . . ZCPKB 5559

WAY OLD FRIENDS DO, THE.
Tracks: / Catch me if you can / Caledonia / Le manege / Kingdom I call home / Music box dancer / Mary Milne / Golden days / Way old friends do, The / Kilt song,The / Bilitis / Do you want yer oul lobby washed down / On the rebound / La di da di da / Scotland forever.
LP: . . . . LIDL 6004
MC: . . . . LIDC 6004

WELCOME THE ALEXANDER BROTHERS.
Tracks: / Auld Scots sangs, The (medley) / Hundred thousand welcomes, A / Lass o'leven vale, The / Jacqueline waltz (Accordion Solo.) / Dancing in Kyle / Dark lochs of Scotland,The / Ballad of Glencoe / Let's have a ceilidh / Two highland lads / Flying Scotsman / Nobody's child / Rose of Allendale / When you and I were young Maggie / Lily McNally McNair / Rowan tree / Reine de musette (Accordion solo.) / Flower of Scotland / Calin mo ruin sa / Waters of Kylesku / These are my mountains / All along Loch Long / High level hornpipe (Accordion solo.) / Tillietudlem castle / Old Scots mother mine / Haste ye back.
2LP: . . . . COMP 4
MCSET: . . . . ZCCOM 4

WELCOME THE ALEXANDER BROTHERS - VOL.2.
Tracks: / Caledonia (Wild rose of the mountain) / Lass o'bon accord, The / Jolly Caballero (Accordion Solo.) / He bought my soul at Calvary / Friendly folk O' the border / Auld Scots sangs, The / Rowan tree / Auld hoose, The / Forty shades of green / Whistling Rufus (Accordion solo.) / Scotland, Scotland (Based on "She was one of the early birds".) / Road to Dundee, The / Let's have one more / One day at a time / Amazing Grace / Jim Johnstone / Colonel,The / Kilwaughter house (Accordion solo.) / Poor little rich boy / Tartan, The / Star o' Rabbie Burns, The / Mull of Kintyre / Whiskey on a Sunday / Dance of the comedians (Accordion solo.) / Old Shep / Here's to the Gordons / My big Kilmarnock Bunnet / Soor milk cairt / Johnnie lad / Scotland the brave / Auld Scots sangs, The (medley).
2LP: . . . . COMP 7
MC: . . . . ZCCOMP 7

WORDS AND MUSIC OF ALEXANDER BROTHERS.
Tracks: / Hiking songs / There's nae toon / Lest we forget / Burns trilogy / My ain folk / Come by the hills / Cornkisters / Auld Scots sangs, The / Marching home / Jolly caballer / Whistlin' Rufus / Last date / El relicario / Oil rigger / Dance of the comedians / Rumbango.
2LP: . . . . PKD 2005
MC: . . . . ZCPKD 2005

Alexander, Dave

DIRT ON THE GROUND.
LP: . . . . ARHOOLIE 1071

RATTLER, THE.
LP: . . . . ARHOOLIE 1067

Alexander, David

DAVID ALEXANDER.
Tracks: / Anyone who isn't me tonight / For no reason at all / Can't stop lovin' you / Sylvia's mother / She thinks I still care / Answer to everything, The / I know / Lay down beside me / Love or something like it / For the first time in my life / Funny face / You and the looking glass.
LP: . . . . OU 2230

Alexander, Larry

RIVERBOAT MAN.
Tracks: / Hey riverboat / Greenville woman / Tadpole Simpson / Sunday morning woman / Mighty fine picker / River song, The / Shady was a lady from Louisville / P-nut song, The / Take things when you can / Johnny Walker.
LP: . . . . FIEND 139

Alexander, Monty

CARIBBEAN DUET (See under Sardaby, Michel) (Alexander, Monty/ Micel Sardaby).

COBILIMBO.
LP: . . . . MPS 68 188

DUKE ELLINGTON SONG BOOK.
Tracks: / I let a song go out of my heart / Sophisticated lady / Things ain't what they used to be / Love you madly / Eastside Westside / In a mellow tone / In a sentimental mood / C jam blues.
LP: 8211511

FULL STEAM AHEAD.
Tracks: / Freddie freeloader / Once I loved / Ray's idea / Because you're mine / Satisfaction / Happy talk / Estate / Hi-fly / Just friends.
LP: . . . . CJ 287
MC: . . . . CJC 287

JAMBOREE.
LP: . . . . CJP 359
MC: . . . . CJPC 359

JAMENTO (Alexander, Monty Seven).
Tracks: / Accompong / Slippery / Sugar loaf at twilight / Weekend in L.A. / Jamento / Mango rengue.
LP: 231 0826
MC: K10 826

MONTREUX ALEXANDER.
Tracks: / Nite mist blues / Feelings / Satin doll / Work song / Drown in my own tears / Battle hymn of the Republic.
LP: . . . . MPS 68 170

MONTY ALEXANDER IN TOKYO.
Tracks: / Broadway / Just in time / Sweet lady / Tricrotism / Never let me go / Montevideo / Pawnbroker / See see rider.
LP: 231 0836
MC: K10 836

MONTY STRIKES AGAIN.
LP: . . . . MPS 68 044

OVERSEAS SPECIAL.
Tracks: / But not for me / Time for love, A / Orange in pain / F S R / For all we know / C.C. rider.
LP: . . . . CJ 253

PERCEPTION.
LP: . . . . MPS 68 042

RAY BROWN THREE, A (See under Brown, Ray).

REUNION IN EUROPE (Alexander, Monty Quartet).
Tracks: / Two bass hit / Got my mojo working / Smile / Yesterdays / Blues for Stephanie / Love you madly / Ben / Eleuthra / That's why.
LP: . . . . CJ 231

RIVER, THE.
Tracks: / Stand up, stand up for Jesus / River, The / Serpent, The / Ave Maria / David danced / Renewal / Ain't gonna study war no more (Only on CD) / Holy Holy Lord God Almighty / What a friend we have in Jesus / How great thou art.
MC: . . . . CJ 422 C

SATURDAY NIGHT (Alexander, Monty Quartet).
LP: . . . . MLP 024

SOUL FUSION (See under Jackson, Milt).

SPONTANEOUS COMBUSTION (See under Kessel, Barney) (Kessel, Barney & Monty Alexander Trio).

TRIO (Alexander / Brown / Ellis).
LP: . . . . CJ 136

TRIPLE TREAT (Alexander, Monty/ Ray Brown/ Herb Ellis).
Tracks: / Flintstones, The / Body and soul / Small fry / When lights are low / Triple treat blues / Fungi mama / Sweet lady / But not for me.
LP: . . . . CJ 193

TRIPLE TREAT II (Alexander, Monty/ Ray Brown/ Herb Ellis).
Tracks: / Lined with a groove / Straighten up and fly right / It might as well be Spring / Seven come eleven / Smile / I'll remember April / Polka dots and moonbeams / Lester leaps in.
LP: . . . . CJ 338
MC: . . . . CJC 338

TRIPLE TREAT III (Alexander, Monty/ Ray Brown/ Herb Ellis).
Tracks: / I told you I love you, now get out / In the wee small hours of the morning / Renewal / My one and only love / There will never be another you / Secret love / High heel sneakers / I love you / Corcovado (quiet nights).
MC: . . . . CJ 394C

WAY IT IS, THE.
LP: . . . . MPS 68 223

Alexander, Peter

ROCKY TOCKY BABY.
Tracks: / Rocky tocky baby / O Josefin, die nacht in Napoli / Hol Den Peter / Titino tinn / Immer zieht es mich zu ihr / Der himmel uber der prarie / Missouri cowboy / Ich zahle taglich meine sorgen / Wunderbares madchen / Mandolinen und mondschein / Bimbombey / Der gitarrentramp / Das schone spiel / Komm bald wieder / Bist du einsam heut nacht (Are you lonesome tonight) / Und... Wilma Lucini / Ja, ich einsam heut'nacht.
LP: . . . . BFX 15120

Alexander, Ray

CLOUD PATTERNS.
Tracks: / Cloud patterns / I can't get started / Softly as in a morning sunrise / My foolish heart / Green Dolphin Street / Refections / Ray's blues.
LP: . . . . NERUS 4477
MC: . . . . NERUSC 4477

Alexander, Texas

TEXAS ALEXANDER VOL 1 (1927-28).
Tracks: / Range in my kitchen blues / Long lonesome day blues / Corn bread blues / Section gang blues / Levee camp moan blues / Mama I heard you brought it right back home / Farm hand blues / Evil woman blues / Sabine River blues / Death bed blues / Yellow girl blues / West Texas blues / Bantam rooster blues / Deep blue sea blues / No more woman blues / Don't you wish your baby was built up like mine / Bell cow blues.
LP: . . . . MSE 206

TEXAS ALEXANDER VOL 2.
Tracks: / Sittin' on a log / Mam's bad luck child / Bo hog blues / Work ox blues / Risin' sun,The / Penitentiary moan blues / Blue devil blues / Tell me woman blues / Frisco train blues / St. Louis fair blues / I am calling blues / Double crossing blues / Ninety-eight degree blues / Some day baby your troubles is gonna be like mine / Water bound blues / Awful moaning blues (part 1 & 2).
LP: . . . . MSE 214

TEXAS ALEXANDER VOL 3 (1929-30).
Tracks: / Gold tooth blues / Johnny Behren's blues / Rolling mill blues / Broken yo yo / Texas special, The / When you get to thinking / Thirty day blues / Peaceful blues / Days is lonesome / Last stage blues / See better days / Stealing to her man / She's so fair / Rolling and stumbling blues / Frost Texas tornado blues / Texas troublesome blues.
LP: . . . . MSE 220

TEXAS ALEXANDER VOL 4 (1934-50).
LP: . . . . MSE 224

Alexander the Great

ALEXANDER THE GREAT (History for Ages 8+).
MC: . . . . PLBH 98

Alexander the Great

ALEXANDER THE GREAT (Various artists).
Tracks: / Alexander the great: *Various artists* / Turkish magician, The: *Various artists.*
MC: . . . . ANV 617

ALEXANDER THE GREAT (Original soundtrack) (Various artists).
LP: . . . . MG 20148

Alexander, Van

SAVOY STOMP.
Tracks: / Let's get together / Chant of the weed / Until the real thing comes along / Uptown rhapsody / Stompin' at the Savoy / Undecided / I would do anything for you / Tisket a tasket, A / East St. Louis toodle-oo / Organ grinder's swing / Christopher Columbus / Ride, red, ride.
LP: . . . . PM 154 767 1

SWING GOES ON VOL 2.
Tracks: / Get me to the church on time / Way down yonder in New Orleans / In a mellow tone / Ol' man river / Say it isn't so / Blues in twos / Uptown rhapsody / Let's get together / Chant of the weed / Lulu's back in town / Until the real thing comes along / Tisket a tisket, A / Christopher Columbus / Ride, red, ride.
LP: . . . . IC 054 52711

Alexander, Willie

AUTRE CHOSE (Alexander, Willie 'Loco').
LP: . . . . ROSE 13

DRAGONS ARE STILL OUT, THE (Alexander, Willie 'Loco').
LP: . . . . ROSE 152

GIRL LIKE YOU, A (Alexander, Willie 'Loco').
LP: . . . . ROSE 15

GREATEST HITS: WILLIE LOCO ALEXANDER.
LP: . . . . FC 013

MEANWHILE... BACK IN THE STATES (Alexander, Willie 'Loco').
Tracks: / Mass Avenue / Modern lovers / You looked so pretty when / Pass the Tabasco / Melinda / Hitchhiking / R.A. baby / Sky queen / Bring your friend / For old times sake.
LP: . . . . MCF 2876

SOLO LOCO (Alexander, Willie 'Loco').
LP: . . . . ROSE 3

TAP DANCING ON MY PIANO (Alexander, Willie 'Loco').
LPPD: . . . . ROSE 106

Alexandria, Lorez

BAND SWINGS LOREZ.
Tracks: / You're my thrill / Don't blame me / Ain't misbehavin' / What is this thing called love / Dancing on the ceiling / Love is just around the corner / I'm gonna sit right down / Just you, just me / All the things you are / Thrill is gone, The / My baby just cares for me.
LP: . . . . SING 657

HOW WILL I REMEMBER YOU?.
Tracks: / Make someone happy / You light up my life / Greatest love of all, The / Until its time for you to go / While we're yo ung.
LP: . . . . DS 782
MC: . . . . DSC 782

LOREZ SINGS PRES (Late session at an intimate club).
Tracks: / Fine and dandy / Fooling myself / D.B. blues / You're driving me crazy / Easy living / Polka dots and moonbeams / This year's kisses / There will never be another you / No eyes blues / Jumpin' with symphony Sid.
LP: . . . . SING 565

SINGS THE SONGS OF JOHNNY MERCER VOL.I (Alexandria, Lorez & The Mike Wofford Quartet).
Tracks: / I remember you / My shining hour / Days of wine and roses / I thought about you / Early Autumn / Dearly beloved / Travellin' light / When a woman loves a man / Fools rush in.
LP: . . . . DS 826

SINGS THE SONGS OF JOHNNY MERCER VOL.II (Harlem butterfly) (Alexandria, Lorez / Gildo Mahones Quintet).
Tracks: / Lazy mood / This time the dream's on me / Mandy is two / Come rain or come shine / Harlem butterfly / Skylark / P.S. I love you / Too marvellous for words.
LP: . . . . DS 905
MC: . . . . DSC 905

STANDARDS WITH A SLIGHT TOUCH OF JAZZ.
Tracks: / Just one of those things / Then I'll be tired of you / Lush life / Sometimes I'm happy / Long ago and far away / But beautiful / I'm beginning to see the light /

I can't believe that you're in love with me / Spring is here / Angel eyes / Better luck next time / I didn't know what time it was.
LP: . . . . **SING 676**

TANGERINE (Alexandria, Lorez / Gildo Mahones Quintet).
Tracks: / Bittersweet / I'm old fashioned / When the world was young / Any place I hang my hat is home / That old black magic / Namely you / Midnight sun / I'm building up to an awful let-down / Day in, day out / Days of wine and roses / Travellin' light / When a woman loves a man / I remember you / My shining hour.
LP: . . . . **TR 538**

Alexiades, Minas

INTEGRA.
LP: . . . . **GM 1001**

Alfie (film)

ALFIE (THEME FROM) (See under Black, Cilla).

Algerie Eternelle

ALGERIE ETERNELLE (Various artists).
Tracks: / La touchia: *Various artists* / Poete et sa flute: *Various artists* / Musique de fete: *Various artists*/ Le berger solitaire: *Various artists* / La zorna: *Various artists* / Chant du Sahara: *Various artists*/ Prelude a la fantasia: *Various artists* / Danse de tiaret: *Various artists* / Mariage Algerois: *Various artists* / Danse des Aures: *Various artists* / Chant de Biskra: *Various artists* / Chant Algerois: *Various artists* / Fantasia: *Various artists.*
LP: . . . . **ARN 33417**
MC: . . . . **ARN 433417**

Alhambra

ART OF JUDEO-SPANISH SONG.
MC: . . . . **GVMMC 127**

PERFORM JUDEO-SPANISH SONGS.
MC: . . . . **GVMMC 108**

Ali Baba

ALI BABA.
MC: . . . . **HA 5**

ALI BABA AND THE FORTY THIEVES (Classic Tales).
MC: . . . . **PLBC 139**

ALI BABA AND THE FORTY THIEVES (And other favourite stories).
MC: . . . . **VCA 609**

ALI BABA AND THE FORTY THIEVES (Lee, Dennis (nar)).
MC: **1251**

ALI BABA AND THE FORTY THIEVES.
Tracks: / Ali Baba and the forty thieves / Not yours to yours / Camlet flower, The / Judgement of Karakoush / King John and the Abbot of Canterbury / Snake and the dreams, The / King's tower, The / Why the parrot repeats men's words.
MC: . . . . **ANV 654**

Ali Baba 85

KAI HABA.
LP: . . . . **SAS 056**

Ali, Salamat

NAZAKAT AND SALAMAT ALI (See under Nazakat) (Ali, Salamat/Nazakat).

Alias

ALIAS.
Tracks: / Say what I wanna say / Haunted heart / Waiting for love / Power, The / Heroes / What to do / After all the love is gone / More than words can say / One more chance / True emotion / Standing in the darkness.
LP: . . . . **EMC 3587**
MC: . . . . **TCEMC 3587**

Alibi

FRIENDS.
Tracks: / Move it / Million years / Friends / If you want some more / Brighter by the day / Easy street / Up until midnight / Custom made / Hands off / In too deep.
LP: . . . . **MAGL 5034**

Alice Donut

MULE.
LP: . . . . **VIRUS 82**

Alice In Chains

FACE LIFT, A.
Tracks: / We die young / Man in the box / Sea of sorrow / Bleed the freak / I can't remember / Love, hate, love / It ain't like that / Sunshine / Put you down / Confusion / I know somethin' (bout you) / Real thing.
LP: **4672001**
MC: **4672004**

Alice In Wonderland

ALICE IN WONDERLAND (See under Carroll, Lewis).

ALICE IN WONDERLAND (Various artists).
Tracks: / All on a golden afternoon: *Various artists* / Readin, riting and rithmetic: *Dotrice, Karen* / Decisions: *Connor, Kenneth* / Speak roughly to your little boy: *Reid, Beryl/Dorothy Squires* / Lobster quadrille, The: *Howerd, Frankie* / Beautiful soup: *Howerd, Frankie/Harry H. Corbett/ Karen Dotrice* / Mad hatters tea party, The: *Forsyth, Bruce/Karen Dotrice/ Fenella Fielding/Tommy Cooper* / Ceremonial march: *Dotrice, Karen/ Peggy Mount/Arthur Haynes* / Love makes the world go round: *Reid, Beryl (nar)* / I'll have you executed on the spot: *Haynes, Arthur/Peggy Mount/* I remember the incident: *Connor, Kenneth* / All on a golden afternoon (reprise): *Various artists.*
2LP: . . . . **MFP 1013**
MCSET: . . . . **TCMFP 1013**

ALICE THROUGH THE LOOKING GLASS (see under Carroll, Lewis).

ALICE'S ADVENTURES IN WONDERLAND (see Carroll, Lewis).

Alice's Adventures...

ALICE'S ADVENTURES IN WONDERLAND (Film Soundtrack) (Various artists).
Tracks: / Overture: *Various artists* / Curiouser and curiouser: *Various artists* / You've gotta know when to stop: *Various artists* / Royal procession: *Various artists* / Last word is mine: *Various artists* / Dum and Dee dance, and nursery rhyme: *Various artists* / Pun song: *Various artists* / I've never been this far before: *Various artists* / Me I never knew: *Various artists* / Lobster quadrille: *Various artists* / Will you walk a little faster: *Various artists* / They told me you have been to her: *Various artists* / Me I never knew: *Various artists* / Playout music: *Various artists.*
LP: . . . . **K 56009**

Alice's Restaurant

ALICE'S RESTAURANT (Film soundtrack) (Guthrie, Arlo).
Tracks: / Alice's restaurant massacre / Chilling of the evening / Ring around a rosy rag / Now and then I'm going home / Motorcycle song, The / Highway in the wind.
LP: . . . . **K 44045**
LP: . . . . **RSLP 6267**

Alien Earth

ALIEN EARTH, THE (see Elder, Michael) (Elder, Michael).

Alien (Film)

ALIEN (Film soundtrack) (National Philharmonic Orchestra).
Tracks: / Alien (main title) / Face hugger, The / Breakaway / Acid test / Landing, The / Droid, The / Recovery, The / Alien planet, The / Shaft, The.
LP: . . . . **FILM 003**
MC: . . . . **FILMC 003**
LP: . . . . **CT 593**

Alien (Group)

SPACE FANTASY.
LP: . . . . **NOISE 103**

Alien Sex Fiend

ACID BATH.
Tracks: / In God we trust / Dead and reburied / She's a killer / Hee-haw (here come the bone people) / Smoke my bones / Breakdown and cry (lay down & die goodbye) / E.S.T. (trip to the moon) / Attack + 2 / Boneshaker baby / I'm a product (Only available on CD.) / 30 second coma (Only available on CD.).
LP: . . . . **GRAM 18**
MCSET: . . . . **CGRAM 18**

ALL OUR YESTERDAYS (The Singles Collection 1983-87).
Tracks: / Ignore the machine / Lips can't go / R.I.P. / Dead and buried / E.S.T. (trip to the moon) / Drive my rocket (up Uranus) / I'm doing time in a maximum security twilight home / I walk the line / Smells like shit / Hurricane fight plane.
LP: . . . . **GRAM 34**
MC: . . . . **CGRAM 34**

ANOTHER PLANET.
Tracks: / Bun ho / Everybody's dream / Radiant city / Spot your lucky warts / Sample my sausage / Outer limits / Instant Karma Sutra / So much to do - so little time / Alien / Wild green fiendy liquid / Nightmare zone / Another planet / Silver machine (On cassette only.).
LP: . . . . **GRAM 38**
MC: . . . . **CGRAM 38**

CURSE.
Tracks: / Katch 22 / Now I'm feeling zombiefied / Stress / Blessings / Eat eat eat (an eye for an eye) / Ain't got no time to bleed / Bleeding reprise (Not on LP) / Dalisms / Burger bar baby / I think I / Mad daddy drives a UFO (Not on LP) / Wuthering wind (Not on LP) / Radio Jimi (Not on LP) / Hand of the silken (Not on LP) / Blessing in disguise (Not on LP).
LP: . . . . **GRAM 46**
MC: . . . . **CGRAM 46**

HERE CUM GERMS.
Tracks: / Here cum germs / Here cum germs (ravi mix) / Here cum germs (dub mix) / Camel camel / Impossible mission / Here cum germs (ravi mix 9) / Isolation / My brain is in the cupboard above the kitchen sink / You are soul / Death / Boots on!.
LP: . . . . **GRAM 31**
MC: . . . . **CGRAM 31**
LP: . . . . **ANT 067**

IT.
Tracks: / It / Smells like shit / Manic depression / Believe it or not / April showers / Wop bop / Get into it / Lesson one / Do it right / To be continued.
LP: . . . . **ANT 048**
LP: . . . . **GRAM 26**

IT/MAXIMUM SECURITY.
Tracks: / Smells like shit / Manic depression / Believe it or not / April showers / Wop-bop / Get into it / Lesson one / Do it right / To be continued / I'm doing time in a maximum security twilight home / Mine's full of maggots / Do you sleep / In and out of my mind / Spies / Fly in the ointment / Seconds to nowhere / Beaver destroys forests, The / Do you sleep (version) / Depravity Lane
MC: . . . . **CGRAM 26**

LIQUID HEAD IN TOKYO.
Tracks: / R.I.P. / E.S.T. (trip to the moon) / Dead and buried / In God we trust / Back to the egg / Attack / Lips can't go / Wild women.
LP: . . . . **GRAM 22**

MAXIMUM SECURITY.
Tracks: / I'm doing time in a maximum security twilight home / Mine's full of maggots / Do you sleep / In and out of my mind / Spies / Fly in the ointment / Seconds to nowhere / Beaver destroys forests, The / Depravity Lane / Maximum security.
LP: . . . . **GRAM 24**
LP: . . . . **ANT 037**

TOO MUCH ACID.
Tracks: / It lives again / I walk the line / Nightmare zone / Get into it / E.S.T. (trip to the moon) / So much to do so little time (bun ho) / Haunted house / Smells like shit / Hurricane fighter plane / Sample my sausage / Boneshaker baby.
2LP: . . . . **GRAM 41**
MC: . . . . **CGRAM 41**

WHO'S BEEN SLEEPING IN MY BRAIN.
Tracks: / Wish I woz a dog / Wild women / I'm not mad / New christian music / Wigwam wipeout / I'm her frankenstein / I am a product / Ignore the machine / Lips can't go / Black rabbit.
LP: . . . . **GRAM 10**

WHO'S BEEN SLEEPING IN MY BRAIN (USA VERSION).
LP: . . . . **EMC 8002**

Aliens (film)

ALIENS (Film soundtrack) (London Symphony Orchestra).
Tracks: / Going after newt / Sub-level 3 / Ripley's rescue / Atmosphere Station / Futile escape / Dark discovery / Bishop's countdown / Resolution / Hyperspace.
LP: . . . . **TER 1115**
MC: . . . . **ZCTER 1115**

Alive Down Your Prong

ALIVE DOWN YOUR PRONG.
MC: **45-401**

Alive in the...

ALIVE AT THE LIVING ROOM (Various artists).
LP: . . . . **CRELP 001**

ALIVE IN THE LIVING ROOM (Various artists).
LP: . . . . **CRE 01**

All...

ALL NIGHT DANCING (Various artists).
LP: . . . . **PL 70497**
MC: . . . . **PK 70497**

ALL YOU NEED IS LOVE (Various artists).
LP: **9199 995**

All About Dragons (bk)

ALL ABOUT DRAGONS.
MCSET: . . . . **DTO 10565**

All About Eve

ALL ABOUT EVE.
Tracks: / Flowers in our hair / Gypsy dance / In the clouds / Martha's harbour / Every angel / Shelter from the rain / She moved through the fair / Wild hearted woman / Never promise / What kind of fool.
LP: . . . . **MERH 119**
MC: . . . . **MERHC 119**

ALL ABOUT EVE: INTERVIEW PICTURE DISC.
LPPD: . . . . **BAK 2087**

SCARLET AND OTHER STORIES.
Tracks: / Road to your soul / Dream now / Gold and silver / Scarlet / December / Blind lemon Sam / More than the blues / Tuesday's child / Empty dancehall, The / Only one reason / Pearl fishermen, The.
LP: **838 965 1**
MC: **838 965 4**

TOUCHED BY JESUS.
Tracks: / Strange way / Farewell Mr. Sorrow / Wishing the hours away / Touched by Jesus / Dreamer, The / Rhythm of life / Mystery we are, The / Hide child / Ravens / Are you lonely / Share it with me (Only on MC and CD.).
LP: **510 146 1**

All About My...

ALL ABOUT MY NAUGHTY LITTLE SISTER (see Edwards, Dorothy) (Kendall, Felicity (nar)).

All American...

ALL AMERICAN ROCK VOL.1 (Various artists).
LP: **33.8017**

ALL AMERICAN ROCK VOL.2 (Various artists).
LP: . . . . **UNKNOWN**

ALL AMERICAN ROCK VOL.3 (Doo Wop Style) (Various artists).
LP: **33.8026**

ALL AMERICAN ROCK VOL.4 (Rockin' Recorded Hop) (Various artists).
LP: **33.8027**

ALL AMERICAN SWING GROUPS VOL. 5 (Various artists).
LP: . . . . **RARITIES 61**

All By Myself

ALL BY MYSELF (Various artists).
LP: . . . . **CHR 1756**

ALL BY MYSELF (Various artists).
Tracks: / Feelings: *Albert, Morris* / Crying game, The: *Berry, Dave* / Alone again (naturally): *O'Sullivan, Gilbert* / Little love, A: *Becaud, Gilbert* / All by myself: *Carmen, Eric* / I will wait for you: *Walker, Scott* / Good life: *Distel, Sacha* / One less bell to answer: *5th Dimension* / Don't throw it all away: *Benson, Gary* / As tears go by: *Faithfull, Marianne* / Last night I didn't get to sleep at all: *5th Dimension* / I'm not in love.
LP: . . . . **SHM 3121**
MC: . . . . **HSC 3121**

ALL BY MYSELF (K-TEL) (Various artists).
2LP: . . . . **NE 1273**
MC: . . . . **CD 2273**

ALL BY MYSELF VOL. 1 (Various artists).
Tracks: / All by myself: *Carmen, Eric* / Every time we say goodbye: *Simply Red* / Suddenly: *Ocean, Billy*/ (Sittin' on) the dock of the bay: *Redding, Otis* / Room in your heart: *Living In A Box* / She's gone: *Hall* & Oates / Without you: *Nilsson* / Blue eyes: *John, Elton* / Waiting for a girl like you: *Foreigner*/ Move closer: *Nelson, Phyllis* / Greatest love of all, The: *Benson, George* / Temptation: *Wet Wet Wet*/ Fool (if you think it's over): *Rea, Chris* / You've lost that loving feeling: *Righteous Brothers* / Gold: *Spandau Ballet* / Only the love: *Stokes, Graham.*
LP: . . . . **ADD 12**
MC: . . . . **ZDD 12**

ALL BY MYSELF VOL. 2 (Various artists).
Tracks: / Will you still love me tomorrow: *Shirelles* / Everywhere: *Fleetwood Mac* / Chocolate girl: *Deacon* Blue / I can see clearly now: *Nash, Johnny* / Go now: *Moody Blues* / Vincent: *McLean, Don* / Couldn't say goodbye: *Jones, Tom* / King of wishful thinking: *Go West* / She makes my day: *Palmer, Robert* / It must have been love: *Roxette* / Save a prayer: *Duran Duran* / Take it to the limit: *Eagles* / So sad (to watch good love go bad): *Everly Brothers* / Midnight at the Oasis: *Muldaur, Maria* / Cry for help: *Astley, Rick* / Waiting for a star to fall: *Boy Meets Girl* / Little time, A: *Beautiful South* / Reason to believe: *Stewart, Rod.*
LP: . . . . **ADD 23**
MC: . . . . **ZDD 23**

All for Art...

ALL FOR ART AND ART FOR ALL (Various artists).
LP: . . . . **BIG 8**
MC: . . . . **BIG 9**

All Girl Startracks

ALL GIRL STARTRACKS (Various artists).

Tracks: / Midnight at the Oasis: *Muldaur, Maria* / Music speaks louder than words: *Staton, Candi* / I never loved a man: *Franklin, Aretha* / Feel like makin' love: *Flack, Roberta* / Track of the cat: *Warwick, Dionne*/ Stay with me baby: *Ellison, Lorraine* / Desperado: *Rondstadt, Linda* / Lotta love: *Larson, Nicolette*/ Luxury liner: *Harris, Emmylou* / Nights on Broadway: *Staton, Candi* / Reverend Lee: *Flack, Roberta*/ Natural woman, A: *Franklin, Aretha* / If my friends could see me now: *Clifford, Linda* / It's so easy: *Ronstadt*, Linda / Three time loser: *Raitt, Bonnie* / Coldwater Canyon: *Previn, Dory* / Danger of a stranger, The: *Parton*, Stella / Never together but close sometimes: *Carter, Carlene* / Piece of my heart: *James, Etta* / Bridge over troubled water: *Nolan Sisters*.
LP: K4 58038

All (Group)

ALLROY FOR PREZ.
LP: CRZ 004
MC: CRZ 004 CA

ALLROY SAVES.
LP: CRZ 011
MC: CRZCA 011

ALLROY SEZ....
LP: CRZ 001
MC: CRZ 001 CA

ALLROY'S REVENGE.
LP: CRZ 006
MC: CRZ 006CA

JUST PERFECT.
Tracks: / Just perfect.
LP: CRZ 003

SHE'S MY EX.
LP: CRZ 005
MC: CRZ 005 C

TRAILBLAZER.
MC: CRZMC 010
LP: CRZLP 010

All Guitars

ALL GUITARS (Various artists).
LP: BFFP 21/22

All Ireland Pipe Band

ALL IRELAND PIPE BAND CHAMPIONSHIP (Various artists).
Tracks: / Field Marshall Montgomery: *Various artists* / Eden: *Various artists* / Seven towers: *Various artists*/ McNeillstown: *Various artists* / St. Laurence O Toole: *Various artists* / Upper crossgare: *Various artists*/ Graham memorial: *Various artists* / Ravara: *Various artists* / Cullybackey: *Various artists* / Massed pipes and drums: *Various artists*.
LP: LRIR 3003
MC: LRIC 3003

All Jolly Fellows

ALL JOLLY FELLOWS (Songs of Country Life) (Various artists).
Tracks: / Jolly thresher, The: *Various artists* / Keepers and poachers: *Various artists* / Merry haymakers: *Various* artists / Months of the year, The: *Various artists* / Muckin' o' Geordie's byre: *Various artists* / Northamptonshire poacher: *Various artists* / Old fat buck: *Various artists* / Roving ploughboy, The: *Various artists* / Turnip-hoer, The: *Various artists* / Van Dieman's land: *Various artists* / We'll all go a-hunting today: *Various artists* / Life of a man, The: *Various artists*.
MC: 60-023

All New Leeds...

ALL NEW LEEDS TOP OF THE ICEBERG (Various artists).
Tracks: / On the ground: *Various artists* / This girl: *Various artists* / I wanna be loved by you: *Various* artists / Lights of Tokyo: *Various artists* / I've got some: *Various artists* / It's hard to believe it: *Various artists* / All the night: *Various artists* / War of the world: *Various artists* / Crimson red: *Various* artists / Colours turn to grey: *Various artists* / Dreaming the night away: *Various artists* / Misplaced Ideals: *Various artists* / Live by the sword: *Various artists* / Berlin nuns: *Various artists* / Imagine by a song: *Various artists* / Tramp: *Various artists*.
MC: BOMB 003

All Night Garage

ALL NIGHT GARAGE SERVICE (Various artists).
LP: WF 029
MC: WF 029C

All Of My...

ALL OF MY APPOINTED TIME:40 YEARS OF ACAPPELLA (see under Forty Years...) (Various artists).

All on the Same...

ALL ON THE SAME RHYTHM (Various artists).
LP: RASSO 9002
MC: RASSOC 9002

All Our Own Work

ALL OUR OWN WORK (Various artists).
LP: SH 273

All Our Tomorrows (bk)

ALL OUR TOMORROWS (Ted Allbeury) (Davenport, Nigel (nar)).
MC: LFP 41 7188 5

All Platinum

ALL PLATINUM (Various artists).
LP: CXMP 2001

BEST OF ALL PLATINUM (Various artists).
Tracks: / Shame shame shame: *Shirley & Company* / Suspicious minds: *Staton, Candi* / Where did our love go: *Elbert*, Donnie / Love on a two way street: *Moments, The* / It won't rain in my backyard: *Moments, The* / Girls: *Moments* & Whatnauts / Dolly my love: *Moments, The* / Jack in the box: *Moments, The* / Pillow talk: *Sylvia*/ 7654321 (blow your whistle): *Rimshots, The* / Sending out an S.O.S.: *Young, Retta* / We got the funk: *Positive Force*.
LP: BLATLP 3
MC: BLATMC 3

All Round Cowboys

ALL ROUND COWBOYS (Various artists).
Tracks: / Lorne Green: *Various artists* / Cool water: *Various artists* / Reno: *Various artists* / Jesse James: *Various artists* / Old Doc Brown: *Various artists* / My adobe hacienda: *Various artists* / That palomino pal of mine: *Various artists* / Gunslinger's prayer: *Various artists* / Rancho Grande: *Various artists*/ Fools Paradise, A: *Various artists* / Cattle call: *Various artists* / Last gunfighter ballad, The: *Various* artists / Hang the key on the bunkhouse door: *Various artists* / Marshal of Silver City, The: *Various artists*/ When the work's all done this fall: *Various artists* / She's in love with a rodeo man: *Various artists* / Pinto pal, A: *Various artists* / Strawberry roan, The: *Various artists* / Streets of Laredo: *Various artists*/ Bandit, The: *Various artists*.
LP: NL 89416
MC: NK 89416

All Seasons...

ALL SEASONS VOL 1 (Various artists).
Tracks: / Have I sinned: *Lee, Hubert* / Oh what a night: *Lee, Hubert* / Anniversary: *Lee, Hubert* / First time I met you, The: *Hazel & Lee* / I won't cry: *Sewell, Hazel* / Change got to come: *Parker, Ken* / C.C. rider: *Lindo, Willie / Ossie Scott* / New moon: *Decosta, Glen / David Madden* / Still still: *Lindo / Hammond / Wilson* / In my heart: *Scott, Ossie / Deadly Headley* / What a dream: *Frazer, Dean / Willie Lindo*.
LP: CMLP 002

All Souls' Orchestra

CROWN HIM (Prom praise from Wembley) (All Souls' Orchestra/Choir).
LP: WST R 9693
MC: WST C 9693

HYMNS FOR TODAY'S CHURCH (All Souls' Orchestra/Choir).
MC: LANG C 002

KENDRICK COLLECTION, THE (All Souls' Orchestra/Choir).
Tracks: / Lord is King, The / Servant King, The / Such love / Burn on / Fighter / May our worship be acceptable / May the fragrance of Jesus / Meekness and majesty.
LP: LANG R 003
MC: LANG C 003

PROM PRAISE AT THE ALBERT HALL (All Souls' Orchestra/Choir).
LP: LANG R 001
MC: LANG C 001

SING A NEW SONG (All Souls' Orchestra/Choir/Congregation).
Tracks: / Sing a new song to the Lord / Blessed is the man / Lord is King, The / Stand up, O God / O righteous Lord / O Lord I love you / May God be gracious / Mary sang a song / Safe in the shadow of the Lord / Fool has been gracious, The / O praise God / Angels praise Him / Sing a song / Listen to my prayer, Lord / God of gods, we sound His praises.
LP: WST 9586
MC: WC 9586

SONGS OF WORSHIP (All Souls' Orchestra/Singers).
Tracks: / My Lord of light / Canticle of the gift, The / We come as guests / Make me a channel of thy peace / We have a gospel to proclaim / Freedom song / Jubilate everybody / Come, Christians, join to sing / He gave His life / Calypso carol / Jesus is Lord / O lamb of God / Alleluia, alleluia, give thanks to the Risen Lord / Lord of all hopefulness.
LP: WST 9590
MC: WC 9590

All Star Six

MY BABY LIKE TO BE BOP.
LP: ESQ 337

All Star Swing Band

SWING FEVER.
Tracks: / In the swing / Swingin' easy / Swing's the thing / Swing with swing / Swing, swing, swing, swing and sway / Swing with the king.
LP: CBS 25042

All That Jazz

ALL THAT JAZZ (Film soundtrack) (Various artists).
Tracks: / On Broadway: *Benson, George* / Michelle: *Burns, Ralph* / Take off with us: *Bergman, Sandahl & Chorus* Vavaldi / Ponte vecchio: *Burns, Ralph* / Everything old is new again: *Allen, Peter* / South Mt Sinai parade: *Burns, Ralph* / After you've gone: *Palmer, Leland* / There'll be some changes made: *Reinking, Ann* / Who's sorry now?: *Burns, Ralph* / Some of these days: *Foldi, Erzsebet* / Going home now: *Burns, Ralph* / Bye bye love: *Vereen, Ben & Roy Scheider* / Vivaldi concerti in G: *Burns, Ralph*.
LP: 912 804 5
LP: 822 869.1
MC: 822869.4
LP: NBLP 7198
MC: 7268 030

All That Jazz (Group)

ALL THAT JAZZ.
LP: V 2470
MC: TCV 2470

All Time Greats

ALL TIME GREATS (Various artists).
Tracks: / Puttin' on the ritz: *Various artists* / No man is ever going to worry me: *Various artists* / April showers: *Various artists* / That's the kind of baby for me: *Various artists* / Eadie was a lady: *Various artists*/ Please: *Various artists* / I got rhythm: *Various artists* / Solitude: *Various artists* / Crazy feet: *Various artists* / You are too beautiful: *Various artists* / Canoe song: *Various artists* / Tisket a tasket, A: *Various artists* / Change partners: *Various artists* / Somebody stole Gabriel's horn: *Various artists*/ I come from a musical family: *Various artists* / Man I love, The: *Various artists* / Rockabye your baby with a Dixie melody: *Various artists* / It never rains but it pours: *Various artists* / I used to be colour blind: *Various* artists / Gotta pebble in my shoe: *Various artists* / Washing the blues from my soul: *Various artists* / Little lady make believe: *Various artists* / Bob White: *Various artists*.
MCSET: DTO 10312

Alla Blues

ALLA BLUES(CALIFORNIA 1947-54) (Various artists).
LP: MUSKADINE 103

Allah, Ras

SHOWCASE.
LP: STLP 1030

Allair, John

LARKSPUR.
Tracks: / Rockin' the joint / My back went out / Ravel / Since I fell for you / Mess around / Sugar mama / Evil woman / Go to the high place in your mind / Baby what you want me to do / Long legs / Stack-o-lee / Mendelsson / Ives.
LP: MMC 007
MC: TCMMC 1007

Allan, Johnnie

1959-1960'S (Allan, Johnnie & The Crazy Cats).
Tracks: / I'll be waiting / My baby is gone / Tell me do you love me so / Lonely days lonely nights / Rubber dolly / Letter of love / Family rules / Prisoner's song / One more chance / Give me more of your kisses / Crying over you / Please accept my love / You got me whistling / Nobody's darlin' but mine.
LP: KK 792

ANOTHER MAN'S WOMAN.
LP: JIN 9015

CAJUN COUNTRY.
MC: JIN 9022 TC

DEDICATED TO YOU.
LP: JIN 9006

GOOD TIMIN' MAN.
LP: FLY 551

JOHNNIE ALLAN SINGS.
LP: JIN 9002

JOHNNIE ALLAN SINGS CAJUN NOW.
LP: 6069
MC: 6069 TC

JOHNNIE ALLAN'S GREATEST HITS.
LP: JIN 9017

LOUISIANA SWAMP FOX.
LP: JIN 9019

PORTRAIT OF JOHNNIE ALLAN.
LP: JIN 9012

SOUTH TO LOUISIANA.
Tracks: / Promised land / Cajun man / I'll never love again / Let's do it / Talk to me / Convict and the rose, The / South to Louisiana / Just a little bit / This life I live / Whatcha do / Nights of misery / Love me all the way / Do you love me so / Your picture.
LP: JIN 4001
LP: CH 145

THANKS FOR THE MEMORIES.
LP: JIN 9026
MC: JIN 9026 TC

Allanson, Susie

SUSIE.
Tracks: / While I was makin' love to you / Something different / Just when I was beginning to like it / You never told me about goodbye / Home again / Step right up / Dance the two step / Michael / That's all I want from you / Just between the two of us / I'm born again.
LP: LBG 30335

Allbeury, Ted (author)

ALL OUR TOMORROWS (See under All Our Tomorrows) (Davenport, Nigel (nar)).

NO PLACE TO HIDE (See under No Place to Hide) (Nettles, John (nar)).

PAY ANY PRICE (See under Pay Any Price) (Harte, Jerry).

Alldis, Dominic

NIGHT MUSIC.
MC: LUMCA 4

Alldred, Bill

SWING THAT MUSIC (Alldred, Bill Goodtime Jazz Band).
LP: BEAR 31
MC: BEARMC 31

Alleluja

ALLELUJA (Various artists).
LP: DOVE 11

Alleman, Oscar

SWING GUITAR LEGEND.
LP: RAMBLER 106

Allen, Annisteen

GIVE IT UP.
Tracks: / Hard to get along / Cloudy day blues / Lies, lies, lies / Too long / Bittersweet, The / Bluest blues / My baby keeps rollin' / Trying to live without you / My brand of loving / Wanted / I don't want no substitute / Down by the river / I want a man (who's gonna do me right) / I've got big bulging eyes (for you) / She lost her be-bop / Give it up.
LP: OFF 6051

Allen, Bishop H. H.

JUNKIE.
LP: MIR 5015
MC: MIR 5015MC

Allen Brothers

ALLEN BROTHERS, THE.
LP: OT 115

CLARA'S BOYS.
LP: ROUNDER 0154

SWEET RUMOURS.
LP: ROUNDER 0079

Allen, Chris

WE'RE HAVING A PARTY (Allen, Chris Orchestra).
Tracks: / Having a party / Sweeney, The / Love me / Save your kisses for me / Honey pie / Una paloma blanca / United we stand / Don't give up on us baby / Get ready / Beautiful noise / Highway affair / Hawaii five-O / Little bit more, A / Y viva Espana.
LP: GRS 1058

Allen, Daevid

AUSTRALIAN YEARS.
LP: VP 101

BANANA MOON.
Tracks: / Time of your life / Memories / All I want is out of here / Fred the fish / White neck blooze / Stoned innocent Frankenstein / His adventures in the land of Flip / I am a bowl.
LP: CL 30165

DAEVID ALLEN PLAYBOX 80.
Tracks: / When / Well / Bell / Boon / Dab / Gay / Rude / Disguise / Pearls /

Bodygas / Froghello / Fast-father / Smile.
LP: CR 30218

DEATH OF ROCK AND OTHER ENTRANCES, THE.
LP: HAI 201

EX-STOP/DON'T.
Tracks: / Do / Eat / Work / Dinosaur / What they say.
LP: HAI 202

GOOD MORNING.
Tracks: / Children of the New World / Good morning / Spirit / Song of satisfaction / Have you seen my friend / French garden / Wise man in your heart / She doesn't she... / Enterpe gratitude piece (Only on CD.).
LP: V 2054

MOTHER TONGUE (See under Gong) (Allen, Daevid/Gong).

N'EXISTE PAS.
LP: CRL 5015

NOW IS THE HAPPIEST TIME.
Tracks: / Flamenco zero / Why do we treat ourselves like we do / Tally & Orlando / Meet the cockpot pixie / See you on the moontower / Poet for sale / Only make love if you want to / I am / Deya Goddess.
LP: AFF 3

SHE.
LP: DMLP 1025

Allen, Dave

COLOR BLIND.
Tracks: / Terp / How can you be so cold / Baby please don't try to tell me what to do / Daves blues / Lord have mercy / Goin' back to Houston / Poor soul / Livin' in a world of darkness / Bone's home / Midnight hour blues / Goin' to St Louis.
LP: LIK 60

Allen, Dennis

LIMERICK, YOU'RE A LADY & OTHER FAVOURITES.
LP: BT 301
MC: BTC 301

Allen, Dolly

DOLLY ALLEN SOLO ALBUM.
LP: BRO 129
MC: KBRO 129

Allen, Donna

HEAVEN ON EARTH.
Tracks: / Can we talk / Come for me / Heaven on Earth / Joker's wild / Hot seat (of my car) / We're smokin' now / You move, you lose / Joy and pain / Renew the love / Make it my night.
LP: 910 281
MC: 910 284
LP: BCM 260LP
MC: BCM 260MC

PERFECT TIMING.
Tracks: / Serious / Sweet somebody / Satisfied / Daydreams / Wild nights / Perfect timing / Bit by bit / Another affair / Bad l ove.
LP: 450888 1
MC: 450888 4
MC: AVAC 10
LP: AVAL 10

Allen, Doris

THEM CHANGES (See under Hamilton, John/Doris Allen) (Allen, Doris & John Hamilton).

Allen, Fred

FRED ALLEN: ON THE AIR.
LP: LP 1002

Allen, Geri

HOME GROWN.
LP: MM 004

IN THE YEAR OF THE DRAGON (Allen, Geri/ Charlie Haden/ Paul Motian).
Tracks: / Oblivion / For John Malachi / Rollano / See you at per tutti's / Last call / No more Mr. Nice Guy / Invisible / First song / In the year of the dragon.
LP: 8344281

OPEN ON ALL SIDES IN THE MIDDLE.
LP: MM 1013

PRINTMAKERS.
LP: MM 001

TWYLIGHT.
LP: MM 1014

Allen, Henry 'Red'

1933-34 (see under Hawkins, Coleman) (Allen, Henry 'Red'/Coleman Hawkins/ Horace Hender).

AND FRIENDS VOL. 1 (1932-56).
Tracks: / Swingin' at the Lido / Swingin' at the Lido (2nd try) / Swingin' at the Lido (3rd try) / Havin' a ball / Havin' a ball (4th try) / Sheridan square, A / Travelin' light / Ride, red, ride / Riffin' / Dark eyes / Sweet Lorraine / Indiana / Frankie and Johnny / Maryland, my, Maryland.
LP: MERITT 26

ART FORD'S JAZZ PARTY (November 1958).
Tracks: / Runnin' wild / Stompin' at the Savoy / Somebody loves me / True blue Lou / Charleston / China boy / Memphis blues.
LP: AFJP 8

AT NEWPORT FESTIVAL 1957 (Allen, Henry Red / Kid Ory & Jack Teagarden).
Tracks: / Struttin' with some barbecue / St. James infirmary / China boy / Basin Street blues / Muskrat ramble / High society.
LP: 8177 921

BLUEGRASS COUNTRY.
LP: SAVE 029

COLLEGE CONCERT, THE (see Russell, Pee Wee) (Allen, Red & Pee Wee Russell).

HENRY 'RED' ALLEN.
Tracks: / That's a plenty / Tin roof blues / Royal garden blues / Way down yonder in New Orleans / Beale Street blues / Muskrat ramble / I've found a new baby / Basin street blues / Wolverine blues.
LP: JR 161

HENRY 'RED' ALLEN 1933-41.
2LP: MERITT 13-14

HENRY 'RED' ALLEN 1939/41.
LP: E 1000

HENRY 'RED' ALLEN AND MILLS BLUE RHYTHM BAND (Allen, Henry 'Red' & Mills Blue Rhythm Band).
LP: GAPS 170

HENRY 'RED' ALLEN AND ORCHESTRA (Allen, Henry 'Red' & his Orchestra).
LP: CC 13

HENRY 'RED' ALLEN AND ORCHESTRA, VOL. 5 (1932-7).
LP: CC 55

HENRY 'RED' ALLEN AND ORCHESTRA, VOL. 3 (1936) (Allen, Henry 'Red' & his Orchestra).
LP: CC 51

JAZZ CLASSICS IN DIGITAL STEREO.
Tracks: / Lookin' good but feelin' bad / New call of the freaks, The / Doggin' that thing / Singing pretty songs / I fell in love with you / Jersey lightning / Feeling the spirit / Roamin' / Patrol wagon blues / Bugle call rag / Sweet sorrow blues / Minnie the moocher's wedding day / Whose honey are you ? / Yes yes / Sweet Sue / Get goin' / Ride, Red, Ride / Barrel house.
LP: REB 685
MC: ZCF 685

LIVE 1965 (Allen, Red Quartet).
Tracks: / Canal Street blues / Mack the knife / Blue spruce boogie / Muskrat ramble / Crazy blues / Lover, come back to me / St.Louis blues / Caravan / Pleasin' Paul / Hello Dolly / Memphis blues / Satin doll / Never on Sunday / New Orleans medley.
LP: MERITT 27

NICE.
Tracks: / Theme / Red jump / Ride red, ride / Dark eyes / Dear old southland / Get the mop / Just a feeling / Wild man blues / Rosetta / Memphis blues / Yellow dog blues / Cherry / Fidgety feet.
LP: LP 24

RED ALLEN (Allen, Henry 'Red'/James P Johnson).
LP: MERITT 5

RED ALLEN AND BLUES SINGERS (Vol. 1) (Allen, Henry 'Red' & The Blues Singers).
LP: JA 47

RED ALLEN AND GEORGE LEWIS (Allen, Henry 'Red'/George Lewis Quartet).
LP: HSLP 1002

RED ALLEN AND THE BLUES SINGERS (Allen, Henry 'Red' & The Blues Singers).
LP: JA 46

RED ALLEN MEETS KID ORY (Allen, Red & Kid Ory).
LP: 2304 544

STANDARDS AND WARHORSES (See under Hawkins, Coleman) (Allen, Red & Coleman Hawkins).

TRUMPET ALBUM Vol. 1 (Allen, Henry 'Red' & Mills Blue Rhythm Band).
LP: MERITT 8

VERY GREAT HENRY 'RED' ALLEN (VOL 2).
Tracks: / Peoria / Basin Street blues / St. James Infirmary blues / Wolverine blues / Savoy blues / Tin roof blues / That's a plenty / Aunt Hagar's blues / Panama rag / At the Jazz Band Ball.
LP: RARITIES 60

VERY GREAT HENRY 'RED' ALLEN-VOL.1.
Tracks: / Sometimes I'm happy / Ol' man river / Siesta at the Fiesta / Jack the bellboy / Ride, red ride / Dark eyes / Dear old Southland / Red jump / Crawl,The / Buzz me / Drink hearty / Get the mop / Count me out / Check up / If it's love you want / Let me miss you.
LP: RARITIES 14

WE'VE GOT RHYTHM (see Ory, Kid) (Allen, Henry Red / Kid Ory & Jack Teagarden).

WORLD ON A STRING.
LP: NL 92497
MC: NK 92497

Allen, Jerry

ANKLE DEEP IN BITTER (Allen, Jerry & Friend).
LP: GMX 5028

HANDS OF JERRY ALLEN.
LP: AL 1003

PARTY TIME.
LP: AL 1001

Allen, Jules

WHEN I WAS A COWBOY (Allen, Jules & Carl Sprague).
LP: MS 45008

Allen, Lee

DENNY DENNIS AND LEE ALLEN (see Dennis, Denny) (Allen, Lee & Denny Dennis).

DOWN ON BOURBON STREET (Allen, Lee & His Band).
LP: NOLA LP 16

LEE ALLEN'S RHYTHM & BLUES BAND.
MC: TC 023

Allen, Linda

WOMEN'S WORK.
LP: FF 458

Allen, Marcus

BREATHE (See under Bernoff, John/ Marcus Allen) (Allen, Marcus / John Bernoff).

PETALS (Allen, Marcus / John Bernoff / Dallas Smith / Eja Bell).
LP: LP 8009
MC: CAS 8009

Allen, Milt

DON'T BUG ME BABY.
Tracks: / Don't bug me baby / Jamboree / One love too many / Half loved / (In the) land of tomorrow / It's simply grand / Youthfull lover / Love a love a lover / Just look, don't touch, she's mine / It's love and it's real / Half loved (part 2).
LP: BFX 15357

Allen, Patrick (nar)

COLDITZ STORY, THE (see under Colditz Story (bk)).

Allen, Pete

DIXIE DATE (Allen, Pete Band).
Tracks: / Clarinet marmalade / At the Devil's ball / Sailing down Chesapeake Bay / St. Phillip street breakdown / Fidgety feet / Mama's gone / Do you know what it means to miss New Orleans? / There's yes yes in your eyes / I found a new baby.
LP: BLM 51107

DOWN IN HONKY TONK TOWN.
Tracks: / Royal Garden blues / Black and tan fantasy / Down in honky tonk town / South Rampart Street parade / I'm gonna sit right down and write myself a letter / Cornet chop suey / Rent party blues / Ole miss rag / Black lion rag / Riverboat shuffle.
LP: BLP 12185

GONNA BUILD A MOUNTAIN (Allen, Pete Jazz Band).
Tracks: / Gonna build a mountain / Livery stable blues / I ain't gonna give nobody none of my jelly roll / Seagull strut / My little bimbo / Louisiana / Chimes blues / Snake rag / I've got a feeling I'm falling / Potato head blues / I'm slapping Seventh Avenue with the sole of my shoe / T'ain't no sin to take off your skin (Full title: T'ain't no sin to take off your skin and dance around in you) / West End blues / 1919 march.
LP: PAJB 1
MC: TC PAJB 1

JAZZIN' AROUND II (Allen, Pete Band).
LP: ARB 853

MARTINIQUE (Allen, Pete Jazz Band).
LP: ARB 831

ONE FOR THE ROAD (Allen, Pete Jazz Band).
Tracks: / Honeysuckle rose / Hiding place, The / Drop me off in Harlem / Sensation rag / Potato rag / Potato head blues.
LP: PAR 187 S
MC: PAR 187

TURKEY TROT (Allen, Pete Jazz Band).
LP: BLP 12174

WHILE WE DANCED AT THE MARDI GRAS (Allen, Pete Jazz Band).
LP: JLP 5501

WILD CAT BLUES (Allen, Pete Jazz Band).
Tracks: / Hiawatha rag / Chips are down, The / Apex blues / Tea for two / Sweet Georgia Brown / Petite fleur / Wild cat blues / Until the real thing comes along / Sentimental journey / Froggie Moore / I'm putting all my eggs in one basket / Concord blues.
LP: PAR 288

Allen, Peter

BI-COASTAL.
Tracks: / One step over the borderline / Fly away / Bi-coastal / I don't go shopping / Hit in the heart / I could really show you around / Simon / Somebody's angel / Pass this time / When this love affair is over.
LP: AMLH 64825

I COULD HAVE BEEN A SAILOR.
Tracks: / I could have been a sailor / Don't wish too hard / Two boys / Angels with dirty faces / Don't cry out loud / If you were wondering / Don't leave me now / I'd rather leave while I'm in love / We've come to an understanding / Paris at 21.
LP: AMLH 64739
MC: CAM 64739

NOT THE BOY NEXT DOOR.
Tracks: / Just another make-out song / Not the boy next door / You'll always get your way / You and me (we had it all) / Fade to black / Somebody's got your love / You haven't heard the last of me / Easy on the weekend / Once before I go.
LP: 205198

TAUGHT BY EXPERTS.
Tracks: / Puttin' out roots / She loves to hear the music / Back doors crying / I go to Rio / Planes / Quiet please, there's a lady on stage / This time around / More I see you, The / Harbour / I've been taught by experts / Six-thirty Sunday morning / New York, I don't know about you.
LP: AMLH 64584

Allen, Rex

BONEY KNEED, HAIRY LEGGED COWBOY SONGS.
Tracks: / Little Joe / Wrangler, The / Moonshine steer / Fireman cowboy, The / Braggin' / Drunk from Wilcox / Fiddling medley / Tyin' knots in the devil's tail / Droop ears / Windy Bill / When the work's all done this fall / Streets of Laredo.
LP: BFX 15024

HAWAIIAN COWBOY.
Tracks: / Texas tornado / Queen of the rodeo / Teardrops in my heart / Loaded pistol / Arizona waltz / Hawaiian cowboy / Who shot that hole in my sombrero / Wind is my woman / Cowpoke / Cattle call / Chime bells / Tennessee tears / Song of the hills / Slap her down again, Paw / Miranda Doakes / Lord protect my darlin'.
LPPD: BDP 15192

MISTER COWBOY.
Tracks: / Cindy / Sweet Betsy from Pike / Sleep with Moses / Cowboy's dream / Alla en el rancho grande / Softly and tenderly / Lonesome valley / Hoosen Johnny / Curtains of the night / Rarin' to go / Old Joe Clark / On top of old smokey / Feeling bad / Prayer of the frontier doctor.
MC: HATC 3034
LP: HAT 3034

UNDER WESTERN SKIES.
Tracks: / Trail of the lonesome pine / Nothin' to do / Last round-up, The / Last frontier, The / Rocky mountain lullaby / Ole faithful / Twilight on the trail / Railroad corral / I'm a young cowboy / At the rainbows end / Sky boss / Too-lee Roll-um.
LP: HAT 3001
MC: HATC 3001

Allen, Rodney

HAPPY SAD.
LP: SUBORG 002

Allen, Steve

ALL STAR JAZZ CONCERT VOL 1.
Tracks: / I want to be happy / Sweet Georgia Brown / I can't get started / Big noise from Winnetka / Love me or leave me / Swing that music / Big town boogie / That's a plenty / Long gone.
LP: JASM 1030

ALL STAR JAZZ CONCERT VOL 2.

Tracks: / When the saints / Blues / Basin Street blues / Lover / St James Infirmary / At sundown / Whistling cow blues / Only man blues / South Rampart Street parade.
LP: . . . . **JASM 1042**

JAZZ FOR TONIGHT.
Tracks: / S'posin I should fall in love with you / Chicken wire blues / Body and soul / I thought about you / Limehouse blues / Tea for two / Lover man / Poor butterfly.
LP: . . . . **JASM 1018**

STEVE ALLEN AT THE ROUNDTABLE.
LP: . . . . **FS 253**

Allen, Terry

AMERASIA - THE SOUNDTRACK.
LP: **FETE4**

BLOODLINES.
LP: . . . . **SPIN 114**

BLOODLINES.
LP: **FETE3**

JUAREZ.
LP: . . . . **FETE 1**
LP: . . . . **FETE 1394**

LUBBOCK (ON EVERYTHING).
2LP: . . . . **SPD 1007/8**
MC: . . . . **SPDC 1007**

SMOKIN' THE DUMMY.
LP: . . . . **FPSS 1002**

Allen, Thomas

SCHUMANN: LEIDER RECITAL (Allen, Thomas & Roger Vignoles).
MC: . . . . **VC 7907874**

SONGS OF NORTHUMBRIA (Allen, Thomas & Sheila Armstrong).
LP: . . . . **MWM SP 9**
MC: . . . . **MWM CSP 9**

Allen, Tony

N.E.P.A. (Allen, Tony / Afrobeat 2000).
LP: . . . . **MWKS 3001**

Allen, Woody

NIGHTCLUB YEARS (1964-1968) (see under EMI Comedy Classics).

Alleycat

ALLEYCAT.
LP: . . . . **CHILLP 5**
MC: . . . . **ZCCHIL 5**

Allez Allez

PROMISES.
LP: . . . . **V 2256**
MC: . . . . **TCV 2256**

Allies

LONG WAY FROM PARADISE.
LP: . . . . **DAY R 4174**
MC: . . . . **DAY C 4174**

SHOULDER TO SHOULDER.
LP: . . . . **DAY R 4164**
MC: . . . . **DAY C 4164**

VIRTUES.
LP: . . . . **LS R 7092**
MC: . . . . **LS C 7092**

Alligator (Label)

20TH ANNIVERSARY COLLECTION (Various artists).
Tracks: / Give me back my wig: *Various artists* / No cuttin' loose: *Various artists* / Black cat bone: *Various* artists / Big chief: *Various artists* / That's why I'm crying: *Various artists* / Double eyed whammy: *Various* artists / I'm free: *Various artists* / These blues is killing me: *Various artists* / Rain: *Various artists*/ Look, but don't touch: *Various artists* / Fannie Mae: *Various artists* / Serves me right to suffer: *Various* artists / Leaving: *Various artists* / Born in Louisiana: *Various artists* / Leaving your town: *Various* artists / Drowning on dry land: *Various artists* / If I hadn't been high: *Various artists* / Trouble in mind: *Various artists* / Brick: *Various artists* / Pussycat moan: *Various artists* / You don't exist anymore: *Various artists* / Second hand man: *Various artists* / I've got dreams to remember: *Various artists* / Going down to Big Mary's: *Various artists* / 300 pounds of heavenly joy: *Various artists* / Going back home: *Various* artists / Strike like lightning: *Various artists* / Middle aged blues boogie, The: *Various artists* / Eyeballin': *Various artists* / Full moon on Main Street: *Various artists* / Crow Jane blues: *Various artists* / I'm the Zydeco Man: *Various artists* / You don't know what love is: *Various artists* / Blues after hours: *Various artists* / Boot Hill: *Various artists*.
MCSET: . . . . **AC 1056**

ALLIGATOR SHOES (Various artists).
LP: . . . . **SNTF 894**

Alligator Swing

ALLIGATOR SWING (Various artists).
Tracks: / I love you: *Anderson, Elton* / Crazy over Daisy: *Nelson, Jay & His Jumpers* / Raise some sand: *Nelson, Jay & His Jumpers* / Clema: *Morris, Jerry* / Silly filly: *Nelson, Jay & His Jumpers* / I gotta leave: *Campbell*, Ray / Only one I love: *Nelson, Jay & His Jumpers* / Lost my lover: *Morris, Jerry* / He's got 'em: *Morris*, Jerry / Cool down baby: *Morris, Jerry* / Uncle John: *Campbell, Ray* / Little Lizzie: *Campbell, RayS2]*.
LP: . . . . **GCL 116**

Allin, G.G.

DIRTY LOVE SONGS.
LP: . . . . **FC 032**

HATED IN THE NATION.
MC: . . . . **A 148**

Allingham, Margery

CAMPION (See under Campion).

MORE WORK FOR THE UNDERTAKER (See under More Work for the... (Matthews, Francis (nar)).

Allison, Clay

CLAY ALLISON.
LP: . . . . **ROUGH 73**

Allison, David

REPORTING.
Tracks: / Birnam oak, The / Dreamdays / Excuse me / Ceuta / Chinese whispers / Ishka / Spiral / Journey / Something more comfortable / Forgive, forget... / Border, The / Going home.
LP: . . . . **DUN 007**
MC: . . . . **DUNC 007**

Allison, Luther

LET'S HAVE A NATURAL BALL.
Tracks: / You're all I need / Let's have a natural ball / Sit and talk / Funkin' it / I have the same old blues / Get out of my life / You're gonna need my help / Let me love you baby.
LP: . . . . **JSP 1077**

LOVE ME MAMA.
LP: . . . . **DS 625**
LP: . . . . **DL 625**

POWER WIRE BLUES.
Tracks: / Dust my broom / I got worries / You don't love me / Going down / I'm gonna leave you alone / Sweet home Chicago.
LP: . . . . **CRB 1105**

RICH MAN.
Tracks: / Chicago / Rich man / Love is free / Cold as ice / Freedom / Fight / Big mistake / Get down / Cry (crying for peace).
LP: . . . . **CRB 1227**

SERIOUS.
LP: **BP-2287**

SOUTH SIDE SAFARI.
Tracks: / Strokes / You're gonna need me / You upset me baby / Movin on up / Thrill is gone, The / Cat blues / Messin with the kid.
LP: . . . . **RL 036**

Allison, Mose

BACK COUNTRY SUITE.
Tracks: / Back country suite / New ground / Train / Warm night / Blues / Saturday / Scamper / January / Promised land / Spring song / Highway 49 / Blueberry Hill / I thought about you / In Salah / You won't let me go / One room country shack.
LP: . . . . **OJC 075**

EVER SINCE THE WORLD ENDED.
Tracks: / Ever since the world ended / Top Forty / Puttin' up with me / Josephine / I looked in the mirror / Gettin' there / Tai chi life / What's you movie / Trouble in mind / I'm alive / Tumblin' tumbleweeds.
LP: . . . . **BLJ 48015**

LESSONS IN LIVING.
Tracks: / Lost mind / Wild man on the loose / Your mind is on vacation / You are my sunshine / Seventh son / Everybody is cryin' mercy / Middle class white boy / I don't worry about a thing / Night club.
LP: **9602371**

MOSE ALIVE.
Tracks: / Smashed / Seventh son / Fool's paradise / I love the life I live / Since I fell for you / Love for sale / Baby please don't go / That's alright / Parchman farm / Tell me somethin' / Chaser.
LP: . . . . **ED 153**
LP: **587-007**

MOSE ALLISON SINGS THE SEVENTH SON.
Tracks: / Seventh son / Eyesight to the blind / Do nothing till you hear from me / Lost mind / I got a right to cry baby / Baby let me hold your hand / Parchman farm / If you live / Don't get round much anymore / One room country shack / I hadn't anyone till you / Young man, A / That's alright.
LP: . . . . **PR 7279**
MC: . . . . **PRC 7279**
LP: . . . . **OJC 3003**

MY BACKYARD.
Tracks: / Ever since I stole the blues / Big brother / Stranger in my hometown / Gettin' paid waltz, The / That's your red waltz / Sleepy lagoon / You call it joggin' / Sentimental fool / Was / Dr. Jekyll and Mr. Hyde / Long song / My backyard.
LP: **B1 93840**

Allisons

ALLISONS SING CHRISTMAS, THE.
Tracks: / Deck the hall / Good King Wenceslas / Mister Father Christmas / First Noel, The / Holly and the ivy, The / Angels from the realms of glory / Tinkerbell / O Come all ye faithful / Twelve days of Christmas, The / Wee three kings / O Christmas tree / Jingle bells / Golden carol / Ding dong merrily on high / Silent night / We wish you a merry Christmas.
MC: . . . . **CHV 112**

ARE YOU SURE (OLD GOLD) (See under Maughan, Susan/Bobby's girl(Old Gold).

INSIDE AND OUT.
Tracks: / Heat lightning / Inside and out / Are you sure / In the middle of nowhere / No go situation / Who am I this time / Breaking up the act / Great indoors, The / I hate you / Roses are red, people are blue / Little by little / Uninvited guest, The.
LP: . . . . **VCLP 009**
MC: . . . . **ZCVCL 009**

SINGS CHRISTMAS.
Tracks: / White Christmas / Jingle bells / Rudolf the red nosed reindeer / Sleigh ride / Sleigh bells / Winter wonderland / Mister Father Christmas / Here comes Santa Claus / Golden carol / Holly and the ivy, The / O Little town of Bethlehem / Marys boy child / Twelve days of Christmas / Silent night / Once in Royal David's City / Deck the hall / O Come all ye faithful / While shepherds watched / Ding dong merrily on high / Away in a manger / We wish you a merry Christmas.
MC: . . . . **AM 55**

Allman Brothers

BEST OF ALLMAN BROTHERS.
Tracks: / Ramblin' man / Dreams I'll never see / Midnight rider / Southbound / Melissa / Little Martha / Jessica / Win lose or draw / Standback / Blue sky / Crazy love / Statesboro blues.
LP: **242 919 8**

BROTHERS AND SISTERS.
Tracks: / Wasted words / Ramblin man / Come and go blues / Jelly jelly / Southbound / Jessica / Pony boy.
LP: **2482 504**
LP: . . . . **K 47507**
LP: . . . . **MID 1008**

BROTHERS OF THE ROAD.
Tracks: / Brothers of the road / Leaving / Straight from the heart / Heat is on, The / Maybe we can go back to yesterday / Judgement / Two rights / Never knew how much I needed you / Things you used to do / I beg of you.
LP: . . . . **SPART 1176**

DREAMS.
LPS: **839 417 1**
MCSET: **839 417 4**

ENLIGHTENED ROGUES.
Tracks: / Crazy love / Can't take it with you / Pegasus / Need your love so bad / Blind love / Try it one more time / Just ain't easy / Sail away.
LP: . . . . **POLD 5016**

LIVE AT LUDLOW GARAGE (1970).
MCSET: **8432604**

NIGHTRIDING: ALLMAN BROTHERS.
Tracks: / Ramblin' man / Pegasus / Revival / Midnight rider / Melissa / I don't want you no more / It's not my cross to bear / Statesboro' blues / Jessica.
MC: . . . . **KNMC 10004**
LP: . . . . **KNLP 10004**

REACH FOR THE SKY.
Tracks: / Hell and high water / Mystery woman / From the madness of the West / I got a right to be wrong / Angeline / Famous last words / So long.
LP: . . . . **SPART 1146**

ROAD GOES ON FOREVER.
LP: **2637 101**

SEVEN TURNS.
Tracks: / Good clean fun / Low down dirty mean / Let me ride / Shine it on / Loaded dice / Seven turns / Gamblers roll / True gravity / It ain't over yet.
LP: **4668501**
MC: **4668504**

SHADES OF TWO WORLDS.
Tracks: / End of the line / Bad rain / Nobody knows / Desert blues / Get on with your life / Midnight man / Kind of bird / Come on in the kitchen.
LP: **4685251**
MC: **4685254**

WIPE THE WINDOWS, CHECK THE OIL, DOLLAR GAS.
Tracks: / Wasted words / Southbound / Ramblin' man / In memory of Elizabeth Reed / Ain't wastin' time no more / Come and go blues / Can't lose what you never had / Don't want you no more / It's not my cross to bear / Jessica.
2LP: **2637 103**

Allman, Duane

BEST OF DUANE ALLMAN.
Tracks: / Sweet little angel / It's my own fault / How blue can you get / No money down / Been gone too long / Mean old world / Midnight rider / Happily married man / Dimples / Don't keep me wondering / Going down slow.
LP: **2429187**

Allman, Greg

I'M NO ANGEL.
Tracks: / I'm no angel / Anything goes / Evidence of love / Yours for the asking / Things that might have been / Can't keep running / Faces without names / Lead me on / Don't want you no more / It's not my cross to bear.
LP: **4503921**
MC: **4503924**

JUST BEFORE THE BULLETS FLY.
Tracks: / Demons / Slip away / Ocean awash the gunwale / Island / Every hungry woman / Before the bullets fly / Thorn and a wild rose / Can't get over you / Night games.
LP: **4624771**
MC: **4624774**

TWO THE HARD WAY (See under Cher) (Allman, Greg/Cher).

Allnighters

ALL NIGHTERS (Various artists).
LP: **649 802 5**

Allons au Fais Do-Do

ALLONS AU FAIS DO-DO (Various artists).
LP: **6009**
MC: . . . . **6009 TC**

All's Well That Ends

ALL'S WELL THAT ENDS WELL (see under Shakespeare, William) (Various artists).

All-Time Comedy...

ALL-TIME COMEDY MUSIC HALL (Aba Daba) (Various artists).
Tracks: / On Mother Kelly's doorstep: *Baker, Kent* / Out in the cold, cold snow: *Bishop, Diana* / Musical saw, The: *Robinson, Geoffrey* / Your baby has gone down the plughole: *Holland, Elaine & John Heawood* / Laziest girl in town: *Bishop, Diana* / Sister Sarah: *McManus, Jim* / Los campos patheticos: *Ranger, Jeanette & Christopher* Lillicrap / Yip-I-addy-I-ay: *Heawood, John* / Alice blue gown: *Holland, Elaine* / It's been a long long time: *Lillicrap, Christopher* / Frankie and Johnny: *Ranger, Jeanette* / Swimmin' with women: *Baker, Kent*.
MC: . . . . **TT 002**

Allyn, David

I ONLY HAVE EYES FOR YOU.
Tracks: / Get out of town / You go to my head / You're laughing at me / When you're lover has gone / Soon / Heart and soul.
LP: . . . . **DS 803**

IN THE BLUE OF THE EVENING.
Tracks: / Remind me / It's a pity to say goodnight / It all comes back to me now / That ole devil called love / All through the day / Dream a little dream of me / Cocktails for two / Down with love.
LP: . . . . **DS 794**

SINGS JEROME KERN.
Tracks: / Sure thing / Dearly beloved / I'm old fashioned / Lovely to look at / Way you look tonight / Folks who live on the hill, The / Long ago and far away / I've told every little star / All in fun / In love in vain.
LP: . . . . **DS 900**
MC: . . . . **DSC 900**

SOFT AS A SPRING.
LP: . . . . **AP 155**

YOURS SINCERELY (Allyn, David & The Bill Holman Orchestra).
Tracks: / Hooray for love / You send me / Impossible / I like the likes of you / Sitting on top of the world / They all laughed / Let's face the music and dance.
LP: . . . . **DS 916**

Almanac

ALMANAC (Various artists).
LP: . . . . **IAI 373851**

Almario, Justo

FAMILY TIME.
Tracks: / Seventh Avenue / Jugando / Abrazos y besos / Quiet wind / Welcome / Morning goodness / To the max / Smiles ahead / Ru mbon.
LP: . . . . **MCA 6271**

FOREVER FRIENDS.
LP: . . . . **MLR 7003**
MC: . . . . **MLC 7003**

PLUMBLINE.
LP: . . . . **MLR 7017**
MC: . . . . **MLC 7017**

Almeida, Laurindo

ARTISTRY IN RHYTHM (Almeida, Laurindo Trio).
Tracks: / Chariots of fire / Astronauta / Andante / Te amo / Artistry in rhythm / Always on my mind / Slaughter on Tenth Avenue / Up where we belong / Almost a farewell / Liza / Puka shells in a whirl.
LP: . . . . **CJ 238**

BRAZILIAN SOUL (Almeida, Laurindo & Charlie Byrd).
LP: . . . . **CJP 150**

LATIN ODYSSEY (Almeida, Laurindo & Charlie Byrd).
Tracks: / Memory / Zum and ressurection / El nino / Gitanerias / Adios / El cavilan / Estrellita / Turbilhao / Intermezzo malin conico.
MC: . . . . **CJPC 211**

NEW DIRECTIONS OF VIRTUOSO GUITAR.
Tracks: / Stuff like that / Feels so good / Just the way you are / What are you doing the rest of your life / Copacabana / Tomorrow / You needed me / All my love (Only on CD) / Yesterday (Only on CD) / Jazz-tuno at the mission (Only on CD) / Late last night (Only on CD) / I write the songs (Only on CD) / Hey Jude (Only on CD).
LP: . . . . **CCS 8007**

SELECTED CLASSICAL WORKS FOR GUITAR AND FLUTE (Almeida, Laurendo / Bud Shank).
LP: . . . . **CC 2003**

TANGO (Almeida, Laurindo & Charlie Byrd).
Tracks: / Orchids in the moonlight / Blue tango / Jalousie / Los enamorados / La Rosita / Tanog alegre / La cumparsita / Moon was yellow, The / Hernando's hideaway / Tanguero.
LP: . . . . **CJP 290**
MC: . . . . **CJPC 290**

VIRTUOSO GUITAR.
LP: . . . . **CCS 8001**

Almighty

BLOOD, FIRE AND LIVE.
Tracks: / Full force lovin' machine / Lay down the law / Destroyed / Resurrection mutha / You've gone wild / Blood, fire and love / Wild and wonderful / You ain't seen nothin' yet.
LP: **8413471**
MC: **8413474**
LP: **8471071**
MC: **8471074**

SOUL DESTRUCTION.
MC: **8479614**
LP: **8479611**

Almond, Marc

ENCHANTED.
Tracks: / Madame de la Luna / Waifs and strays / Desperate hours, The / Toreador in the rain / Widow weeds / Lover spurned, A / Death's diary / Sea still sings, The / Carnival of life / Orpheus in red velvet.
LP: . . . . **PCS 7344**
LP: **794 404 1**
MC: . . . . **TCPCS 7344**
MC: **794 404 4**

JACQUES.
LP: . . . . **BREL 001**
MC: . . . . **BRELC 001**

MARC ALMOND: INTERVIEW PICTURE DISC.
LPPD: . . . . **BAK 2147**

MEMORABILIA - THE SINGLES (See under Soft Cell) (Almond, Marc & Soft Cell).

MOTHER FIST AND HER FIVE DAUGHTERS.
Tracks: / Mother fist / There is a bed / St. Judy / Room below, The / Angel in her kiss / Mr. Sad / Melancholy rose / Sea says, The / Champ, The / Ruby red / Hustler, The.
LP: . . . . **FAITH 2**
MC: . . . . **TFTH 2**

SINGLES '84-'87.
Tracks: / Boy who came back, The / You have / Tenderness is a weakness / Stories of Johnny / Love letters / House is haunted, The / Woman's story, a / Ruby red / Melancholy rose / Mother fist.
LP: . . . . **FAITH 3**
MC: . . . . **TFTH 3**

STARS WE ARE, THE.
Tracks: / Stars we are, The / These my dreams are yours / Bittersweet / Only the moment / Your kisses burn / Frost comes tomorrow, The (Cassette & CD only.) / Very last pearl, The / Tears run rings / Something's gotten hold of my heart / Sensualist, The / She took my soul in Istanbul / Kept boy (Cassette & CD only.).
MC: . . . . **TCPCS 7324**
LP: . . . . **PSC 7324**
LP: . . . . **PCSX 7324**
MC: . . . . **TCPCSX 7324**

STORIES OF JOHNNY.
Tracks: / Traumas, traumas, traumas / Stories of Johnny / House is haunted, The / Love letters / Flesh is willing, The / Always / Contempt / I who never / My candle burns / Love and little white lies / Love letters (CD & cassette only-with Westminster City School Choir).
MC: . . . . **TFTH 1**
LP: . . . . **FAITH 1**

TUESDAY IN NEW YORK (see under Mark, Jon) (Almond, Marc/Jon Mark).

VERMINE IN ERMINE.
Tracks: / Shining sinners / Hell was a city / You have / Crime sublime / Gutter hearts / Ugly head / Boy who came back, The / Solo adultos / Tenderness is a weakness.
LP: . . . . **BIZL 8**
MC: . . . . **BIZLC 8**

Almost Perfect Affair

ALMOST PERFECT AFFAIR, AN (Film soundtrack) (Various artists).
LP: . . . . **STV 81132**

Almost Summer (film)

ALMOST SUMMER (Original soundtrack) (Various artists).
LP: . . . . **MCF 2840**
MC: . . . . **TC MCF 2840**

Almost There

ALMOST THERE (A Collection of British no.2 Hits) (Various artists).
Tracks: / Little arrows: *Lee, Leapy* / Ride a white swan: *T. Rex* / Jeepster: *T. Rex* / Rocket man: *John, Elton* / My coo ca choo: *Stardust, Alvin* / Come back my love: *Darts* / Boy from New York City: *Darts*/ It's raining: *Darts* / Love is a many splendoured thing: *Four Came Home* / Tear fell, A: *Brewer, Theresa*/ Tammy: *Reynolds, Debbie* / Baby face: *Little Richard* / I'm gonna be strong: *Pitney, Gene* / Heartful of soul: *Yardbirds* / Wild thing: *Troggs* / Night of fear: *Move* / Nobody needs your love: *Pitney, Gene* / I can't control myself: *Troggs* / Flowers in the rain: *Move.*
2LP: . . . . **CR 120**
MCSET: . . . . **CRT 120**

Alms House Business

ALMS HOUSE BUSINESS (Various artists).
LP: . . . . **GALP 004**

Aloha Hawaii

ALOHA HAWAII (Various artists).
LP: . . . . **SM 4126**
MC: . . . . **MC 4126**

Alomar, Carlos

DREAM GENERATOR.
Tracks: / Hallucination / Siamese dreams / Global alpha / Winkin' blinkin' and nod / Insomniac / Dream generator / R.E.M. / Feline lullaby (Sam's song).
LP: **209.964**
MC: **409.964**

Alondra

CHANTS SEPHARADES - CHANTS JUDEO-ESPAGNOLS.
Tracks: / Canto de seder / Escuchiz Senor Soldado / Una matica de ruda / Dieciocho anos tengo / Una pastora yo ami / Poverata muchachica / Dise la nuestra novia / En este mundo tuve un deseo / La historia de Zimbolucha / Mi suegra, la negra / El Rey de Francia / Morena me llaman / Morenica me llaman / Nani nani.
LP: . . . . **ARN 33711**

Aloopa

ALOOPA (Devon childrens' rhyme games) (Various artists).
MC: **30 201**

Alper, Greg

FAT DOGGIE (Alper, Greg Band).
LP: . . . . **AD 5009**

Alperin, Mikhail

WAVES OF SORROW (Alperin, Mikhail/ Arkady Shilkloper).
Tracks: / Song / Poem / Wave of sorrow / Toccata / Unisons / Introduction and dance / Short storey / Prelude in B minor / Miniature / Epilogue.
LP: . . . . **ECM 1396**

Alpert, Herb

40 GREATEST (Alpert, Herb / Tijuana Brass).
LP: . . . . **NE 1005**

AMERICA (Alpert, Herb / Tijuana Brass).
LP: . . . . **AMLB 1000**

BEAT OF THE BRASS (Alpert, Herb / Tijuana Brass).
LP: . . . . **AMLS 916**

BEYOND.
Tracks: / Kamalie / Continental / Reach for the stars / Interlude / Red hot / Beyond / That's the way of the world / Keep it go ing.
LP: . . . . **AMLK 63717**

BLOW YOUR OWN HORN.
Tracks: / Red hot / True confessions / Blow your own horn / Gently / Midnight tango, The / Garden party / Paradise cove / Latin lady / Oriental eyes / Sundown.
LP: . . . . **AMLX 64949**
MC: . . . . **CXM 64949**

BRASS ARE COMIN' THE (Alpert, Herb / Tijuana Brass).
LP: . . . . **AMLS 962**

BULLISH.
Tracks: / Bullish / Always have a dream / Make a wish / Maniac / Struttin on five / Love without words / Passion play / Life is my song.
LP: . . . . **AMLX 65022**
MC: . . . . **CXM 65022**

CLOSER YOU GET.
LP: . . . . **PL 84663**
MC: . . . . **PK 84663**

DOWN MEXICO WAY (Alpert, Herb / Tijuana Brass).
LP: . . . . **AMLS 974**

FANDANGO.
Tracks: / Fandango / Margarita / Push and pull / California blues / Quiereme tal como soy / Route 101 / Coco loco / Aria / Angel / Sugarloaf / Latin (medley) / Bahia / Moliando cafe.
LP: . . . . **AMLK 63731**
MC: . . . . **CKM 63731**

GOING PLACES (Alpert, Herb / Tijuana Brass).
LP: . . . . **NPL 28065**

GREATEST HITS:HERB ALPERT (Alpert, Herb / Tijuana Brass).
Tracks: / Lonely bull, The / Spanish flea / My favourite things / If I were a rich man / Up Cherry Street / Marjorine / Wade in the water / Cabaret / Taste of honey, A / Tijuana taxi / Hello Dolly / A banda / Lollipops and roses / So whats new / Zorba the Greek.
LP: . . . . **AMID 111**
MC: . . . . **CMID 111**
LP: . . . . **SHM 3143**
MC: . . . . **HSC 3143**
LP: . . . . **AMLS 980**

KEEP YOUR EYE ON ME.
Tracks: / Keep your eye on me / Our song / Hot shot / Pillow / Diamonds / Stranger on the shore / Traffic jam / Rocket to the moon / Making love in the rain.
LP: . . . . **AMA 5125**
MC: . . . . **AMC 5125**

MAGIC MAN.
Tracks: / Magic man / Manhattan melody / I get it from you / Secret garden / Besame mucho / This one's for me / Fantasy island / You smile, the song begins.
MC: . . . . **CKM 63728**
LP: . . . . **AMLK 63728**

MAIN EVENT (LIVE) (Alpert, Herb/ Hugh Masekela).
Tracks: / Foreign natives / People make the world go 'round / Besame mucho / I'm comin' home / She-been / Kalahari nights / Shame the devil / Mama way.
LP: . . . . **AMLH 64727**

MY ABSTRACT HEART.
LP: **395 273-1**
MC: **395 273-4**
LP: . . . . **AMA 5273**
MC: . . . . **AMC 5273**

NINTH (Alpert, Herb / Tijuana Brass).
LP: . . . . **AMLS 905**

NORTH ON SOUTH STREET.
LP: **3953451**
MC: **3953454**

RISE.
Tracks: / 1980 / Rise / Behind the rain / Rotation / Street life / Love is / Angelina / Aranjuez (mon amour).
LP: . . . . **SHM 3163**
MC: . . . . **HSC 3163**
LP: . . . . **AMLH 64790**

SOUNDS LIKE HERB ALPERT (Alpert, Herb / Tijuana Brass).
LP: . . . . **AMLS 900**

S.R.O.
LP: . . . . **NSPL 28088**

THIS GUY'S IN LOVE WITH YOU (ALBUM).
LP: . . . . **MFP 50432**

UNDER A SPANISH MOON.
Tracks: / Fragile / My song / I need you / Under a Spanish moon / Rumba flamenca / Lamento / Pachanga / Ancient source / Zamba / Hidden angel.
LP: . . . . **AMA 5209**
MC: . . . . **AMC 5209**

VERY BEST OF HERB ALPERT.
LP: **397165 1**
MC: **397165 4**

WARM (Alpert, Herb / Tijuana Brass).
LP: . . . . **AMLS 937**

WHAT NOW MY LOVE (Alpert, Herb / Tijuana Brass).
LP: . . . . **NPL 28077**

WHIPPED CREAM AND OTHER DELIGHTS (Alpert, Herb / Tijuana Brass).
LP: . . . . **NPL 28058**

WILD ROMANCE.
Tracks: / "8" ball / You are the one / Lady love / It's all for you / Catch me / African flame / Dancin' in the light / No time for time.
LP: . . . . **AMA 5082**
MC: . . . . **AMC 5082**

Alpha Band

ALPHA BAND.
LP: . . . . **ARTY 143**

INTERVIEWS (Alpha Band/T-Bone Burnett).
Tracks: / Interviews / Cheap perfume / Ten figures / Dogs, The / Last chance to dance / East of East / You angel you / Spark in the dark / Rich man / Mighty man / Back in my baby's arms again.
LP: . . . . **EDLP 272**

Alpha Blondy

APARTHEID IS NAZISM.
Tracks: / Afrika / Jah houphouet / Apartheid is nazism / Idjidja / Sahel / Sebe allah y'e / Kiti / Come back Jesus / Djinamory.
LP: . . . . **STERNS 1017**

Alpha Omega (show)

ALPHA OMEGA (West End cast) (Various artists).
2LP: . . . . **UAR 101**
MCSET: **2TCK 101**

ALPHA OMEGA (Film soundtrack) (Various artists).
LP: . . . . **MYR R 1210**
MC: . . . . **MYR C 1210**

DANIEL IN THE LIONS DEN.
LP: . . . . **SO 001**

Alphaville

AFTERNOONS IN UTOPIA.
Tracks: / I A O / Fantastic dream / Jerusalem / Dance with me / Afternoons in Utopia / Sensations / 20th century / Voyager, The / Carol Masters / Universal daddy / Lassie come home / Red rose / Lady bright.
LP: **240948 1**
MC: **240948 4**

BREATHTAKING BLUES, THE.
Tracks: / Summer rain / She fade away / Ariana / For a million / Patricia's park / Romeo's / Mysteries of love / Heaven or hell / Middle of the riddle / Anyway.
LP: **2448551**
MC: **2448554**

FOREVER YOUNG.
Tracks: / Victory of love / Summer in Berlin / Big in Japan / To Germany with love / Fallen angel / Forever young / In the mood / Sounds like a melody / Jet set, The / Lies.
LP: **240 536-1**
MC: **240 536-4**

Alphonso, Roland

PHOENIX CITY (see under Emperor Rosko).

ROLL ON.
LP: . . . . **W 2451**

Alsop, Peter

ASLEEP AT THE HELM.
LP: . . . . **FF 034**

DRAW THE LINE.
LP: . . . . **FF 223**

FAN CLUB FAVORITES.
LP: **FF 396**

UNIFORMS.
LP: **FF 256**

WHA'D' YA WANNA DO?.
LP: **FF 298**

Alston, Gerald

GERALD ALSTON.
Tracks: / Take me where you want to / Stay a little while / I come alive when I'm with you / Let's try love again / Midnight angel / You laid your love on me / I can't tell you why / I've waited all night / Activated / We've only just begun / Still in love with loving you (Only on cassette and CD.) / You laid your love on me (extended version) (Only on cassette and CD.).
LP: **ZL 72651**
MC: **ZK 72651**

OPEN INVITATION.
Tracks: / Slow motion / Getting back into love / Don't you know how I feel / I'll go crazy / Nothing can change (the love we shared before) / Never give up / Tell me this night won't end / Open invitation / Still in love / Any day now / Almost there.
LP: **ZL 72725**
MC: **ZK 72725**

Alta Moda

ALTA MODA.
Tracks: / Train / Cool love / Julian / Wait / Push / Back to back / Classique / No town (in particular) / Draw a straight line / My millionaire / Cool love (cooler re-mix) / Push (push push in the mix).
LP: **PTLS 1096**
MC: **PTLC 1096**

Altan

ALTAN.
Tracks: / Highlandman, The / An Seanchaileach Gallda / Ta mo Chleamhnas a Dheanamh / Cat that ate the candle, The / Ceol A'Phiobaire / Tommy Peoploe's loch Altan / Danny Meehan's / Rogha an Ghabha / Sunset, The / Thug me Ruide / Humours of whiskey / Jimmy Lyon's Les / Citi na cumann / Con Cassidy's highland.
LP: **SIF 1078**
MC: **CSIF 1078**

HORSE WITH A HEART.
LP: **SIF 1095**
MC: **CSIF 1095**

Altar Boys

AGAINST THE GRAIN.
Tracks: / Fallen world / Kids are on the run / Heart lost in nowhere / Broken / Where's the new world / Against the grain / Take control / Shout louder / Human sound, The / Count on love.
LP: **RO 9023**
MC: **CO 9023**

SOUL DESIRE.
LP: **60491 B**

Altena, Maarten

MIERE (Altena, Maarten Quartet).
Tracks: / Monks measure / London 72 / Something / Miere / Amsterdam 83 / Ciao.
LP: **NATO 235**

Altenburg (Composer)

TRUMPET CONCERTOS AND FANFARES (See under Trumpet Music - Classical) (Philharmonia Orchestra).

Alterations

MY FAVOURITE ANIMALS.
Tracks: / Sleeping beauty / Segue to my heart / Adios half cow-boy / Up in the paint cards / Ca n'est pas mon chat / Thru and thru / Cat's whiskers / Calamity Joan / Emus in the zone / Nopan kissa / Horse with no hooves, A / Hank's pantry / Old coffity pot, The / Burning rosebush, The / Yes sir.
LP: **NATO 280**

Altered Images

BITE.
Tracks: / Bring me closer / Another lost look / Love to stay / Now that you're here / Don't talk to me about love / Stand so quiet / Change of heart / Thinking about you.
LP: **EPC 25413**

COLLECTED IMAGES.
LP: **EPC 25973**
MC: **40 25973**

HAPPY BIRTHDAY.
Tracks: / Happy birthday / Love and kisses / Real toys / Idols / Legionaire / Faithless / Beckoning strings / Midnight / Day's wait / Leave me alone / Insects.
LP: **EPC 84893**
LP: **EPC 32355**

PINKY BLUE.
Tracks: / Pinky blue / See those eyes / Forgotten / Little brown head / See you later / Song sung blue / Funny funny me / Think that it might / I could be happy / Jump jump / Goodnight and I wish.
LP: **EPC 85665**

Altered States (Film)

ALTERED STATES (Film soundtrack) (Various artists).
Tracks: / Altered states (main title and 1st hallucination): *Various artists* / Love theme: *Various artists* / Second hallucination: *Various artists* / First transformation: *Various artists* / Primeval landscape: *Various* artists / Second transformation: *Various artists* / Ape man sequence, The: *Various artists* / Religious memories and fathers death: *Various artists* / Laboratory experiment, The: *Various artists* / Jessup's transformation: *Various* artists / Collapse of the laboratory: *Various artists* / Whirlpool and journey to another dimension, The: *Various artists* / Return to reality: *Various artists* / Final transformation, The: *Various artists.*
LP: **AGL 1 5066**
MC: **AGK 1 5066**
MC: **GK 83983**

Altered States (group)

IS ANYONE OUT THERE.
Tracks: / Twin obsession / Is anyone out there / What is left / Everything / Them / Cathy / Those voices / Low life / Walls and fences / Final chapter.
LP: **CALCLP 031**

Alternative Cabaret

ALTERNATIVE CABARET.
LP: **ORA 007**
MC: **TORA 007**

Alternative Radio

FIRST NIGHT (SINGLE).
LP: **COLDLP 001**
MC: **COLDTC 001**

Alternative TV

IMAGE HAS CRACKED, THE.
LP: **DLP 01**

LIVE AT THE RAT CLUB 77.
LP: **CLP 01**

PEEP SHOW.
Tracks: / Chrissie's dream / Let's sleep now / River, The / Tumbletime / My baby's laughing / Scandal / White walls / Animal.
LP: **GRAM 32**

SCARS ON SUNDAY (Alternative TV/ Good Missionaries).
MC: **WEIRD 001**

SPLITTING IN TWO.
Tracks: / Action time vision / Love lies limp / Life / How much longer / Another coke / Still life / You bastard / Nasty little lonely / Why don't you do me right / Facing up to the facts / Lost in room / Force is blind / Slitting in two.
LP: **GRAM 40**

STRANGE KICKS.
Tracks: / Ancient rebels / Strange kicks / Communicate / Mirror boys / Anye is back / My hand is still wet / Fun city / T. V. operator / There goes my date with Doug / Cold rain / Who are they / Sleep in dub.
LP: **SP 70023**

VIBING UP THE SENILE MAN (PART 1).
LP: **DLP 03**

WHAT YOU SEE IS WHAT YOU ARE.
LP: **DLP 02**

Alternatives

BUZZ.
Tracks: / Pudgy / Sex face / Black hole / 1/2 cheek sneek / Nubbing.
LP: **SST 245**
MC: **SSTC 245**

Alternatives To ...

ALTERNATIVES TO MARRIAGE (Rogers, Carol).
MC: **PT 28**

Altissimo

ALTISSIMO.
LP: **WW 019**

Altman, Laurie

FOR NOW AT LEAST (Altman, Laurie Quintet).
Tracks: / Song for Charles Mingus / Often enough / Lonely woman (elusive form) / Song for Oliver / Pirate, The / Salut, ma femme / Colour me.
LP: **PRO 7066**

Altogether Now

ALTOGETHER NOW (Various artists).
MC: **ANC 484**

ALTOGETHER NOW (SING-ALONG PARTY PACK) (Various artists).
LP: **JBLP 303**

Alton, Roy

CARNIVAL DISCO.
LP: **TAK LP 006**

CARNIVAL IN LADBROKE GROVE.
LP: **TAK LP 001**

DON'T STOP THE CARNIVAL.
LP: **TAK LP 004**

IN THE GROVE.
LP: **TAK LP 002**

WE SHALL OVERCOME.
MC: **TC PRCV 122**

Altschul, Barry

BRAHMA (Altschul, Barry, Trio).
LP: **3023**

YOU CAN'T NAME YOUR OWN TUNE.
LP: **MR 5124**

Alvin, Dave

EVERY NIGHT ABOUT THIS TIME.
Tracks: / Every night about this time / Fourth of July / Long white cadillac / Romeo's escape / Brother (on the line) / Jubilee train / Border radio / Fire away / New tattoo / You got me / I wish it were Saturday night.
LP: **FIEND 90**
MC: **FIENDCASS 90**

Alvin Lives In Leeds

ALVIN LIVES IN LEEDS (Various artists).
LP: **CLANG 4**

Alvin, Phil

UNSUNG STORIES.
Tracks: / Somebody stole Gabriel's horn / Next week sometime / Ballad of Smoky Joe, The / Death in the morning / Old man of the mountain, The / Daddy rollin' stone / Titanic blues / Brother can you spare a dime / Collins cave / Gangsters blues.
LP: **SLAP 12**

Always

ALWAYS (Various artists).
LP: **NE 1377**
MC: **CE 2377**

ALWAYS (Berlin, Irving).
MC: **835 450 4**

Always August

BLACK PYRAMID.
Tracks: / Freedom flight / Interrogation / Pan's lament / Swim with me / Spacin' out / On my mind / Soweto / Half the time.
LP: **SST 078**

Always Catching...

ALWAYS CATCHING SNOT IN THE WIND (Various artists).
LP: **HA 001**

Always (Film)

ALWAYS (Film soundtrack) (Various artists).
Tracks: / Smoke gets in your eyes: *Various artists* / Cowboy man: *Various artists* / Fool in love, A: *Various* artists / Follow me: *Various artists* / Saying goodbye: *Various artists* / Return, The: *Various artists*/ Seeing Dorinda: *Various artists* / Promise to Hap: *Various artists* / Dorinda solo flight: *Various artists*/ Boomerang love: *Various artists* / Give me your heart: *Various artists* / Among the clouds: *Various artists*/ Pete in heaven: *Various artists* / Pete and Dorinda: *Various artists* / Rescue operation: *Various artists*/ Intimate conversation: *Various artists* / Old timer's shack, The: *Various artists.*
LP: **MCG 6085**
MC: **MCGC 6085**

Always & Forever

ALWAYS AND FOREVER (Various artists).
Tracks: / Still: *Commodores* / Lovely day: *Withers, Bill* / Heartbreaker: *Warwick, Dionne* / If you don't know me by now: *Melvin, Harold & The Bluenotes* / You make me feel brand new: *Stylistics* / You'll never find another love like mine: *Rawls, Lou* / Touch me in the morning: *Ross, Diana* / Three times a lady: *Commodores*/ Jack and Jill: *Raydio* / Me and Mrs. Jones: *Paul, Billy* / Tears on my pillow / How 'bout us: *Champagne*/ Always and forever: *Heatwave* / Do you know where you're going to: *Ross, Diana.*
LP: **LPIMP 4**
MC: **TCIMP 4**
LP: **STAR 2301**
MC: **STAC 2301**

ALWAYS AND FOREVER (20 Soulful Hits) (Various artists).
Tracks: / That lady: *Isley Brothers* / You're love is king: *Sade* / I don't love you anymore: *Pendergrass, Teddy* / Rain or shine: *Five Star* / Best of my love: *Emotions* / I will survive: *Gaynor, Gloria*/ Jack and Jill: *Raydio* / It's a man's man's man's world: *Brown, James* / Inside out: *Odyssey* / If you were here tonight: *O'Neal, Alexander* / September: *Earth, Wind & Fire* / Used ta be my girl: *O'Jays* / Hold on to my love: *Ruffin, Jimmy* / Like sister and brother: *Drifters* / Friends: *Stewart, Amii* / Always and forever: *Heatwave* / Heartbreaker: *King, Evelyn "Champagne"* / I'm your puppet: *Purify, James & Bobby*/ Night I fell in love, The: *Vandross, Luther* / Greatest love of all, The: *Benson, George.*
MC: **STDMC 31**

Always (group)

LOOKING FOR MR WRIGHT.
LP: **SOH 005**

Always Rockin'

ALWAYS ROCKIN' (Various artists).
Tracks: / Come along, baby: *Astronauts* / Raymond's beat: *McArthur, Ray Stoppers* / Rowdy Mae is back in town again: *Caldwell, Joe* / What are little girls made of?: *Witter, Jimmy* / Rhythm feet: *Pegues, Carroll*/ I can't do without you: *Zack, Jimmy* / Evil ways: *Zack, Jimmy* / Walking in circles: *Henderson, Wayne*/ Roll that rig: *Little Ben* / I've had it, I'm through: *Davis, Gene* / No doubt about it: *Doggett, Ray*/ That's alright mama: *Murphy, Jim* / Surrounders, The: *McCoys* / I'll tear your playhouse down: *Free, Billy*/ Gone, gone, gone dreams: *Towers, Bobby.*
LP: **WLP 8882**

AM 4

AND SHE ANSWERED.
LP: **ECM 1394**

Am I Cool Or What

AM I COOL OR WHAT (See under Garfield) (Various artists).

Amadeus

AMADEUS (Film soundtrack) (Various artists).
2LP: **LONDP 6**
MCSET: **LONDC 6**

Amalgam

INNOVATION.
LP: **TGS 121**

Amampondo

HEARTBEAT OF AFRICA.
LP: **BIG 004**

Amaphisi

CITY SHOES, RURAL BLUES (Amaphisi & Uthwalofu Namankentshane).
LP: **BIG 005**

Amaro, Eugene

OWL, THE (Amaro, Eugene Quartet).
LP: **JC 0002**

Amaswazi

HAMBA DRIVER.
Tracks: / Hamba driver / Lomuntu ngiyamsiza / Ungakhali ngisaya ekhaya / Ohlatshwayo / Sithwele kanzima / Bayokubona abanamehlo / Bamthwesa isiphambano / Umsebenzi ophelile.
LP: **TUS 8007**
MC: **TUS 8007MC**

Amayenge

AMAYENGE.
LP: **MON 003**

Amazing Grace

AMAZING GRACE (Various artists).
LP: **NE 1218**
MC: **CE 2218**

AMAZING GRACE (Gotham gospel vol.3) (Various artists).
LP: **KK 836**

AMAZING GRACE AND OTHER SCOTTISH FAVOURITES (Various artists).
MC: **HR 8198**

Amazing Grace & Chuck

AMAZING GRACE &...(FILM) (Film soundtrack) (Various artists).
LP: **STV 81312**
MC: **CTV 81312**

Amazing Monsters (bk)

AMAZING MONSTERS (Jarvis, Martin (nar)).
MC: **CDSC 1**

Amazing Rhythm Aces

AMAZING RHYTHM ACES.
LP: **ABCL 5267**

BURNING THE BALLROOM DOWN.
LP: **ABCL 5244**

STACKED DECK.
LP: **ABCL 5152**

TOO STUFFED TO JUMP.
LP: **ABCL 5160**

TOUCAN DO IT TOO.
LP: **ABCL 5219**

Amazing Spiderman

AMAZING SPIDERMAN, THE (Various artists).
LPPD: . . . . **FUNPD 001**

Amazones

AU COEUR DE PARIS.
LP: . . . . **SLP 76**

Amazulu

BEST OF AMAZULU.
Tracks: / Too good to be forgotten / Excitable / After tonight / All over the world / Things the lonely do / Montego Bay / Don't you just know it / Cairo / Moonlight romance / Upright forward.
LP: . . . . **ILPS 9851**
MC: . . . . **ICT 9851**

Ambassadeurs

AMBASSADEURS FEATURING SALIF KEITA (Ambassadeurs and Salif Keita).
LP: . . . . **CEL 6716**

BEST OF AMBASSADEUR.
LP: . . . . **CEL 6640**

DANCE MUSIC FROM WEST AFRICA.
LP: . . . . **ROUNDER 5013**
MC: . . . . **ROUNDER 5013C**

MANDJOU (Ambassadeur International).
LP: . . . . **CEL 6721**

Ambassador Orchestra

WHEN YOU WISH.
LP: **BH4.409**

Ambassadors Male

IT IS WELL WITH MY SOUL.
Tracks: / Worthy is the lamb / It is well / Song and melody I bring / Purer in heart / Behold the wonderous love / Crown of thorns / I am so glad that Jesus loves me / Ring the bells of Heaven / When I think / Saviour with me, The / Yes he did / Then the Lord stood by me / This love of mine / He set me free.
LP: . . . . **WST 9602**
MC: . . . . **WC 9602**

Ambassadors Of Funk

MONSTER JAM.
LP: . . . . **NOMIS 1**
MC: . . . . **NOMIS 1 C**

Ambel, Eric

ROSCOE'S GANG.
Tracks: / If you gotta go, go now / Total destruction to your mind / Girl that ain't got, The / Forever came today / 30 days in the workhouse / Power lounger theme / Don't wanna be your friend / I waited for you / Next to the last waltz / Loose talk / You must have we confused / Vampire blues.
LP: . . . . **FIEND 157**

Ambient House

AMBIENT HOUSE (Various artists).
LP: . . . . **BCM 422**
MC: . . . . **BCM 422 MC**

Ambitious Lovers

GREED.
Tracks: / Love overlap / Admit it / Steel wool / Para nao contrariar / Privacy / Caso / Too far / Copy me / King / Omotesando / Quasi you / It only has to happen once / Dot stuff.
LP: . . . . **V 2545**
MC: . . . . **TCV 2545**

LUST.
MC: **7559609814**

Ambrose

1929 SESSIONS (Ambrose & His Orchestra).
MC: . . . . **CHAL 19**
LP: . . . . **HAL 19**

AMBROSE 1928-1932 (Ambrose & His Orchestra).
LP: . . . . **SHB 21**

AMBROSE AND HIS ORCHESTRA (Ambrose & His Orchestra).
LP: . . . . **MES 7032**
LP: . . . . **GNPS 9020**

AMBROSE AND HIS ORCHESTRA 1936/38.
Tracks: / My red letter day / Head over heels / There's a small hotel / Until the real thing comes along / On your toes / Swing patrol / Rhythm's OK in Harlem / With plenty of money and you / Music maestro please / Blue skies are round the corner.
LP: . . . . **SCS D-02**

AMBROSE (HARLEQUIN) 1935-37 (Ambrose & His Orchestra).
Tracks: / Hors d'ouvres / B'wanga / Did you mean it / Night rides / Wood and ivory / Power house / Organ grinder's swing / Caravan / Embassy stomp / My red letter day / Swing patrol / Cotton picker's congregation / Bye bye baby / Champagne cocktail / Cuban Pe te.
LP: . . . . **HQ 3016**

AMBROSE (LIVING ERA) (Ambrose & His Orchestra).
Tracks: / Don't let that moon get away / Says my heart / Love bug will bite you, The / Two sleepy people / Rhythm's OK in Harlem / Blue skies are round the corner / Goodnight to you all / I've got a pocketful of dreams / Sailor, where art thou? / While a cigarette was burning / Lord and Lady Whoozis / Moon or no moon / Lambeth Walk / Chestnut tree, The / I may be poor but I'm honest / Oh, they're tough, mighty tough, in the West / Ten pretty girls / Organ, the monkey and me, The / In a little French casino / Fifty million robins can't be wrong / Smile when you say goodbye / Sympathy.
LP: . . . . **AJA 5066**
MC: . . . . **ZC AJA 5066**

BODY & SOUL (Ambrose & His Orchestra).
Tracks: / Stormy weather / There's a cabin in the pines / You've got me crying again / Punch and Judy show, The / Lazybones / I can't remember / Body and soul / Goodnight but not goodbye / Cupid / It's the talk of the town / Stay as sweet as you are / Last round-up, The / College rhythm / Willow weep for me / I couldn't be mean to you / Who's been polishing the sun.
LP: . . . . **CHD 124**
MC: . . . . **MCHD 124**

CHAMPAGNE COCKTAIL (Ambrose & His Orchestra).
LP: . . . . **GNPS 9005**

FAITHFULLY YOURS 1930-1932 (Ambrose & His Orchestra).
Tracks: / Please / I'm just wearing out my heart for you / Have a little faith in me / If they ever had an income, take on love / Till tomorrow / Livin' in the sunlight, lovin' in the moonligh / For you, just you my baby (28/7/32) / Laughing at the rain / Little girl / Just like in a story book / Loving you the way I do / Hummin' to myself / Kiss by kiss / Love, you funny thing / I'm in the market for you / What good am I without you / One little raindrop / Here lies love / Faithfully yours.
LP: . . . . **SVL 159**
MC: . . . . **CSVL 159**

GOLDEN AGE OF AMBROSE AND HIS ORCHESTRA, THE (Ambrose & His Orchestra).
Tracks: / I don't know why (I just do) / Dancin in the dark / Soft lights and sweet music / When Yuba plays the rumba on the tuba / Isn't it romantic / Pu-leeze Mr. Hemingway / Too many tears / Let's put out the lights / Leven thirsty Saturday night / Cryin' for the Carolines / Free and easy / Stardust / Blue again / Bye bye blues / Yes yes (my baby says yes) / Whistling in the dark.
LP: . . . . **GX 41 2525 1**
MC: . . . . **GX 2525 4**

HAPPY DAYS, 1929-30 (Ambrose & His Orchestra).
Tracks: / Precious little thing called love / You're the cream in my coffee / Breakaway / Makin' whoopee / Love me or leave me / For the likes of you and me / L.O.V.E / Who cares / If I had a talking picture of you / You want lovin' / Little by little / I'll be getting along / Blondy / Happy days are here again / High and low / I don't want your kisses / One I love just can't be bothered with me / I'm following you / Mona / I'm on a diet of love.
LP: . . . . **SVL 147**
MC: . . . . **CSVL 147**

HITS OF 1931 (Ambrose & His Orchestra).
Tracks: / Wrap your troubles in dreams / On a little balcony in Spain / I surrender dear / When your lover has gone / Out of nowhere / It must be true / Just one more chance / I'm an unemployed sweetheart / You can't stop me from lovin' you / For you / Smile darn ya smile / Nevertheless / You forgot your gloves / Love letters in the sand / Cuban love song / Longer that you linger in Virgin ia.
LP: . . . . **SH 419**
MC: . . . . **TC SH 419**

I ONLY HAVE EYES FOR YOU (Ambrose & His Orchestra).
Tracks: / It's an old Southern custom / According to the moonlight / Top hat, white tie and tails / Isn't this a lovely day / How could we be wrong / Because it's love / Tick tock town / Stars fell on Alabama / I travel alone / Lost in a fog / I only have eyes for you / Dames / Winter wonderland / If I had a million dollars / If I love again / London on a rainy night / Maracas / Copenha gen.
LP: . . . . **OLD 9**
MC: . . . . **COLD 9**

LOVE IS THE SWEETEST THING (Ambrose & His Orchestra).
Tracks: / Love is the sweetest thing / Marching along together / At eventide / Low down / Don't say goodbye / Just friends / When mother played the organ (and daddy sang a hymm) / Let's put out the lights / Please / Here lies love / You're the one / All of me / Nicolette / I still get a thrill thinking of you / Livin' in the sunlight / Lovin' in the moonlight / Big Ben's saying goodnig ht.
LP: . . . . **JOYD 280**

MAKIN' WHOOPEE (Ambrose & His Orchestra).
2LP: . . . . **SVLD 007**
MC: . . . . **CSVLD 007**

MIDNIGHT IN MAYFAIR (Ambrose & His Orchestra).
LP: . . . . **SVL 207**
MC: . . . . **CSVL 207**

NIGHT RIDE (Ambrose & His Orchestra).
Tracks: / Champagne cocktail / Caravan / Embassy stomp / Night ride / Deep Henderson / Cotton pickers congregation / Copenhagen / Hors D'oeuvres.
MC: . . . . **CMOIR 301**

RECOLLECTIONS (Ambrose & His Orchestra).
Tracks: / If I didn't care / What do we care / I'm in love for the last time / Let there be love / You made me care / No mama no / Two sleepy people / Continental, The / I threw a kiss in the ocean / My own / I have eyes / Sympathy / How about you / Cinderella / Sweetheart / I got love / That lovely weekend / Scatterbrain / Apple for teacher, An.
LP: . . . . **RFL 10**

'S WONDERFUL (Ambrose & His Orchestra).
Tracks: / 'S wonderful / Roll away, clouds / Louise / Old Italian love song / I'll see you again / If love were all / Singin' in the rain / Too wonderful for words / Ain't misbehavin' / Am I blue / Love is a dreamer / Thought never entered my head, The / She's such a comfort to me / How am I to know / My sweeter than sweet / Piccolo Pete / Just you - just me / My love parade / Little kiss each morning a little kiss each night / Lucky me, lovable me.
LP: . . . . **SVL 181**
MC: . . . . **CSVL 181**

SOFT LIGHT AND SWEET MUSIC (Ambrose & His Orchestra).
Tracks: / I'll guess I'll have to change my plan / Moon / You brought a new kind of love to me / After tonight we say goodbye / You forgot your gloves / When mother played her organ / I don't want to go to bed / Let's all sing like the birdies sing / Lullaby of the leaves / I'm an unemployed sweetheart / I'm gonna get you / You rascal you / Trees / All of me / Aboard the lugger.
LP: . . . . **JOYD 271**

SUN HAS GOT HIS HAT ON, THE (Ambrose & His Orchestra).
Tracks: / I can't believe it's true / After tonight we say goodbye / Sun has got his hat on, The / Day by day / At eventide / Clouds will soon roll by, The / Streamline strut / Dames / Big Ben is saying goodnight / Memphis blues / I only have eyes for you / Who's been polishing the Sun / La cucaracha / Home James and don't spare the horses / Yip Neddy / I'm gonna wash my hands of you / Stay as sweet as you are / No, no, a thousand times no.
LP: . . . . **BUR 002**
MC: . . . . **4 BUR 002**

SWING IS IN THE AIR (Ambrose & His Orchestra).
Tracks: / Jeepers creepers / Too marvellous for words / Woe is me / They can't take that away from me / No mama no / Careless / Lost my rhythm, lost my music, lost my man / Arm in arm / I'm all in / Swing is in the air / Let's call the whole thing off / Hurry home / I promise / Life begins when you're in love / Three little fishes / Lord and lady whoozles / Beer barrel polka / When day is done.
LP: . . . . **RFL 35**

TRIBUTE TO COLE PORTER (Ambrose & His Orchestra).
Tracks: / Night and day / I get a kick out of you / I've got my eyes on you / Thank you so much, Mrs Lowsborough / Begin the beguine / After you / Anything goes / I've got you on my mind / Easy to love / I've got you under my skin / Just one of those things / My heart belongs to daddy / You're the top / You'd be so nice to come home to.
LP: . . . . **JASM 2017**

Ambrose Slade

BEGINNINGS.
MC: **8491854**

Ambrosetti, Franco

CLOSE ENCOUNTER.
LP: . . . . **ENJA 3017**

HEART BOP.
LP: . . . . **ENJA 3087**

WINGS.
LP: . . . . **ENJA 4068**

Ambrosia

ROAD ISLAND.
Tracks: / For openers / Still not satisfaction / Kid no more / Feeling alive again / How can you love me / Fool like me / Ice age / Endings.
LP: . . . . **K 56968**

Amebix

ARISE.
LP: . . . . **VIRUS 46**

MONOLITH.
Tracks: / Monolith / Nobody's driving / Power remains, The / Time bomb / Last will and testament, The / I.C.B.M. / Chain reaction / Fallen from grace / Coming home.
LP: . . . . **HMRLP 99**
MC: . . . . **HMRMC 99**

NO SANCTUARY.
LP: . . . . **SDL 14**

Ameling, Elly

AFTER HOURS (classic 20th century popular songs).
Tracks: / Embraceable you / I got rhythm / With a song in my heart / Man I love, The / Body and soul / My cousin in Milwaukee.
LP: **6514 284**
MC: **7337 284**

Amen Corner

EXPLOSIVE COMPANY.
LP: . . . . **IMSP 023**

GREATEST HITS: AMEN CORNER.
LP: . . . . **IML 2004**

HIGH IN THE SKY.
Tracks: / High in the sky / Hello Suzie / Weight, The / Sanitation / So fine / Our love is in the pocket / Gin house blues / Welcome to the club / Things ain't what they used to be / Proud Mary.
LP: . . . . **SHLP 159**
MC: . . . . **SHTC 159**

RETURN OF THE MAGNIFICENT SEVEN.
LP: . . . . **IML 1004**

ROUND AMEN CORNER.
Tracks: / Bend me, shape me / Judge Rumpel Crassila / Love me tender / Our love (is in the pocket) / Something you got / I am an angel / Expressway (to your heart) / Good time / Let the good times roll - feel so good / Can't get used to losing you / Lost and found / Gin house blues / Nema / I know / Satisnek the job's worth / World of broken hearts, The / I don't wanna discuss it.
LP: . . . . **SML 1021**

America...

AMERICA - FOLK/WESTERN/ SPIRITUAL (Various artists).
2LP: . . . . **SM 3767/2**

BLACK CONVICT WORKSONGS FROM TEXAS (Various artists).
LP: . . . . **ROUNDER 2013**

CARRY IT ON-SONGS OF AMERICA'S WORKING CLASS (Various artists).
LP: . . . . **FF 104**

COUNTRY NEGRO JAM SESSIONS (Various artists).
LP: . . . . **ARHOOLIE 2018**

HONOR THE EARTH POWWOW (Songs of the Great Lakes Indians) (Various artists).
Tracks: / Grand entry song: *Little Otter Singers* / Intertribal dance song: *LCO Soldiers' Drum* / We're the people: *Smokeytown Singers* / Sneak up dance song: *Bad River Singers* / Winnebago army song: *Winnebago Sons* / Intertribal dance song: *Bearclaw Singers* / Ojibway Airforce song: *LCO Soldiers' Drum* / Intertribal dance song: *Bad River Singers* / Intertribal dance song: *Three Fires Society Drum* / Intertribal dance song: *Little Otter Singers*.
MC: . . . . **RACS 0199**

LEGENDARY SONGS OF THE OLD WEST (Various artists).
LPS: **P4-15542**

MINSTRELS & TUNESMITHS (Roots of American music 1902-23) (Various artists).
LP: . . . . **JEMF 109**

MUSICA DEL SIOUX/NAVAJO (Various artists).
LP: . . . . **VPA 8441**

ONE MOMENT IN TIME (American Olympic theme) (Various artists).

LP: 209299
MC: 409299

PLAINS OF ALBERTA (Cowboy songs) (Various artists).
LP: HLP 8007

ROOTS OF AMERICAN'S MUSIC (Various artists).
2LP: ARHOOLIE 2001-2

SONGS OF THE CIVIL WAR (Various artists).
Tracks: / I wish I was in Dixies' land: *Various artists* / All quiet along the Potomac tonight: *Various artists*/ We are coming, Father Abra'am: *Various artists* / Mother, is the battle over?: *Various artists* / Drummer boy of Shiloh, The: *Various artists* / Beauregards's retreat from Shiloh: *Various artists* / Jeff in petticoats: *Various artists* / Weeping, sad and lonely: *Various artists* / It's a gold old rebel: *Various artists*.
LP: NW 202

America (Group)

ALIBI.
LP: IC 064 826201

AMERICA.
Tracks: / Riverside / Sandman / Three roses / Children / Here / I need you / Rainy day / Never found the time / Clarice / Donkey jaw / Pigeon song.
LP: K 46093

AMERICA LIVE.
MC: K4 56434

HARBOR.
MC: K4 56351

HAT TRICK.
Tracks: / Muskrat love / Wind wave / She's gonna let you down / Rainbow song / Submarine ladies / It's life / Hat trick / Molten love / Green monkey / Willow tree lullaby / Goodbye.
LP: K 56016

HEARTS.
Tracks: / Daisy Jane / Half a man / Midnight / Bell Tree / Old Virginia / People in the valley / Company / Woman tonight / Story of a teenager / Sister golden hair / Tomorrow / Seasons.
LP: K 56115

HIDEAWAY.
Tracks: / Lovely night / Amber cascades / Don't let it get you down / Can't see you / Watership down / She's beside you / Hideaway (part 1) / She's a liar / Letter / Today's the day / Jet boy blue / Who loves you / Hideaway (part 2).
LP: K 56236

HISTORY - AMERICA'S GREATEST HITS.
Tracks: / Horse with no name, A / I need you Sandman / Ventura highway / Don't cross the river / Only in your heart / Muskrat love / Tin man / Lonely people / Sister golden hair / Daisy Jane / Woman tonight.
LP: K 56169
MC: K4 56169

HOMECOMING.
Tracks: / Ventura highway / To each his own / Don't cross the river / Moon song / Only in your heart / Till the sun comes up again / Cornwall blank / Head and heart / California revisited / Saturn nights.
LP: K 46180

SILENT LETTER, THE.
Tracks: / Only game in town, The / All around / Tall treasures / 1960 / And forever / Foolin' / All night / No fortune / All my life / One morning / High in the city.
LP: FA 4130781
MC: TCFA 41 30784
LP: EST 11950

VIEW FROM THE GROUND.
Tracks: / You can do magic / Never be lonely / You girl / Inspector Mills / Love on the vine / Desperate love / Right before your eyes / Jody / Sometimes lovers / Even the score.
LP: EST 12209
MC: TC EST 12209

YOUR MOVE.
Tracks: / My kinda woman / She's a runaway / Cast the spirit / Loves worn out again / Border / Your move / Honey / My dear / Tonight is for dreamers / Don't let me be lonely / Someday woman.
LP: EST 712 277 1

American...

AMERICAN MUSICOLOGICAL SOCIETY PRESENTS.. (Various artists).
Tracks: / Balkan fantasy solo: *Various artists* / Greek dancerama: *Various artists* / Variations on twinkle star: *Various artists* / Russian pear tree: *Various artists* / Variations on Father John: *Various artists* / You'll never know just how much I love you: *Various artists* / Sunny side of the street: *Various artists* / Poinciana: *Various artists* / This is a lovely way to spend an evening: *Various artists* / Twilight time: *Various artists*/ All the things you are: *Various artists*.
LP: AAMS 3

GREAT AMERICAN COMPOSERS, THE (Various artists).
2LP: ADL 521
MCSET: ADK 521

American Anthem

AMERICAN ANTHEM (Film soundtrack) (Various artists).
Tracks: / Two hearts: *Parr, John* / Run to her: *Mr. Mister* / Same direction: *INXS* / Battle of the dragon: *Nicks, Stevie* / Wings to fly: *Nash, Graham* / Take it easy: *Taylor, Andy* / Wings of love: *Taylor, Andy* / Love and loneliness: *Thompson, Chris* / Angel eyes: *Taylor, Andy* / Arthur's theme: *Various a rtists*.
LP: 781 661-1
MC: 781 661-4

American Authentic...

AMERICAN AUTHENTIC SQUARE DANCES (See under Folk...) (Various artists).

American Blues...

AMERICAN BLUES LEGENDS 75 (Various artists).
LP: BEAR 8

AMERICAN BLUES LEGENDS 79 (Various artists).
Tracks: / Love with you baby: *Various artists* / Look what you've done: *Various artists* / High rise blues: *Various artists* / 480 pounds: *Various artists* / I wish I had somebody: *Various artists* / I'm goin' home where women got meat on their bones: *Various artists* / Buzzard luck: *Various artists* / Conjured: *Various artists*/ Don't throw your love on me so strong: *Various artists* / All your love: *Various artists* / I'm trying: *Various artists* / No peace: *Various artists*.
LP: BEAR 23

American Blues (group)

DOIN' THEIR THING.
Tracks: / You were so close to me / Wonder man / Just plain Jane / Shady / Captain Fire / Chocolate ego / Nightmare of a wise man / Dreams / Softly to the sun.
LP: SEE 99

American Dances

AMERICAN DANCES (Various artists).
LP: UD 301513

American Dreams

AMERICAN DREAMS (Various artists).
Tracks: / Song for America: *Kansas* / Joker, The: *Miller, Steve Band* / Read 'em and weep: *Meatloaf*/ Born to be wild: *Steppenwolf* / Stage fright: *Band* / Keep on loving you: *REO Speedwagon* / Do you believe in love: *Lewis, Huey & The News* / Foolish heart: *Parry, Steve* / She's not there: *Santana* / White rabbit: *Jefferson Airplane* / More than a feeling: *Boston* / Heart like a wheel: *Ronstadt, Linda* / Even the nights are better: *Air Supply* / We belong: *Benatar, Pat* / I can't hold back: *Survivor* / American Woman: *Guess Who* / Don't stop believing: *Journey (Group)* / She's gone: *Hall & Oates* / Sylvia's mother: *Dr. Hook*/ Trouble: *Buckingham, Lindsey* / Missing you: *Waite, John* / Rosanna: *Toto* / Because the night: *Smith, Patti* / Miracles: *Jefferson Starship* / Nobody but you: *Loggins & Messina* / Freebird: *Lynyrd Skynyrd*/ Feels so right: *Alabama (Group)* / Here comes that feeling: *Asia*.
2LP: SLTD 12
MCSET: SLTK 12

AMERICAN DREAMS (Various artists).
Tracks: / Windy: *Association* / In crowd, The: *Various artists* / Bend me shape me: *American Breed* / Lightning strikes: *Christie, Lou* / Traces: *Classics IV* / Louie Louie: *Kingsmen* / Little old lady from Pasadena: *Jan & Dean* / Letter, The: *Box Tops* / Little honda: *Hondells* / Then he kissed me: *Crystals*/ Stay: *Williams, Maurice* / Where have all the flowers gone: *Kingston Trio* / It's my party: *Gore, Lesley*/ I fought the law: *Fuller, Bobby* / Deadman's curve: *Jan & Dean* / Runaway: *Shannon, Del* / Night has a thousand eyes, The: *Vee, Bobby* / Donna: *Valens, Ritchie* / Tell Laura I love her: *Peterson, Ray* / Spooky: *Classics IV* / Lady Willpower: *Puckett, Gary* / Venus in blue jeans: *Clayton, Jimmy* / Let's dance: *Montez, Chris* / Wipe out: *Surfaris* / Dedicated to the one I love: *Various artists* / Pipeline: *Chantays*/ Lover's concerto: *Toys* / La bamba: *Valens, Ritchie* / Rhythm of the rain: *Cascades* / He's a rebel: *Crystals*.
2LP: SSD 8033

AMERICAN DREAMS 50'S VOL 1 (Various artists).
Tracks: / My heart cries for you: *Shore, Dinah* / Be my love: *Lanza, Mario* / Slow poke: *King, Pee Wee*/ C'est si bon: *Kitt, Eartha* / Cherry pink and apple blossom white: *Prado, Perez* / Cattle call: *Arnold, Eddy* / Rock and roll waltz, The: *Starr, Kay* / Heartbreak hotel: *Presley, Elvis* / Banana boat song: *Belafonte*, Harry / Melodie d'amor: *Ames Brothers* / Lazy man: *Monte, Lou* / Oh lonesome me: *Gibson, Don* / Send me the pillow you dream on: *Locklin, Hank* / Guess who: *Belvin, Jesse* / Making love: *Robinson, Floyd*/ Three bells, The: *Browns* / Oh Carol: *Sedaka, Neil* / He'll have to go: *Reeves, Jim*.
MC: NK 90370

AMERICAN DREAMS 50'S VOL 2 (Various artists).
Tracks: / I'm movin' on: *Snow, Hank* / Thing, The: *Harris, Phil* / I get ideas: *Martin, Tony* / Because you're mine: *Lanza, Mario* / Oh my papa: *Fisher, Eddie* / Crying in the chapel: *Valli, June* / Naughty lady of Shady Lane: *Ames Brothers* / Hot diggety (dog ziggety boom): *Como, Perry* / Canadian sunset: *Winterhalter*, Hugo / Don't be cruel: *Presley, Elvis* / Love is strange: *Mickey & Sylvia* / Mama look a boo boo: *Belafonte*, Harry / Four walls: *Reeves, Jim* / Patricia: *Prado, Perez* / Diary, The: *Sedaka, Neil* / Wonder of you, The: *Peterson, Ray* / Battle of Kookamonga, The: *Homer & Jethro* / Don't know you: *Reese, Della*/ Shout: *Isley Brothers*.
MC: NK 90371

AMERICAN DREAMS 60'S VOL 1 (Various artists).
Tracks: / Tell Laura I love her: *Peterson, Ray* / It's now or never: *Presley, Elvis* / Chain gang: *Cooke*, Sam / Last date: *Cramer, Floyd* / I just don't understand: *Ann-Margaret* / Lion sleeps tonight, The: *Tokens*/ Love me warm and tender: *Anka, Paul* / Breaking up is hard to do: *Sedaka, Neil* / End of the world: *Davis*, Skeeter / I will follow him: *March, Little Peggy* / Maria Elena: *Los Indios Tabajaros* / 500 miles away from home: *Bare, Bobby* / Java: *Hirt, Al* / Baby the rain must fall: *Yarbrough, Glen* / Make the world go away: *Arnold, Eddy* / Somebody to love: *Jefferson Airplane* / Light my fire: *Feliciano, Jose* / These eyes: *Guess Who* / Grazing in the grass: *Friends Of Distinction* / Romeo and Juliet, Love theme from: *Mancini, Henry*.
MC: NK 90372

AMERICAN DREAMS 60'S VOL 2 (Various artists).
Tracks: / Old lamplighter, The: *Browns* / Please help me, I'm falling: *Locklin, Hank* / On the rebound: *Cramer*, Floyd / Funny how time slips away: *Elledge, Jimmy* / Twistin' the night away: *Cooke, Sam* / Steel guitar and a glass of wine: *Anka, Paul* / Dance with the guitar man: *Eddy, Duane* / Detroit City: *Bare, Bobby* / Abilene: *Hamilton, George IV* / Hello heartache, goodbye love: *March, Little Peggy* / I can't stay mad at you: *Davis, Skeeter* / We'll sing in the sunshine: *Garnett, Gale* / Ringo: *Greene, Lorne* / Ballad of the Green Berets: *Sadler, Sgt. Barry* / My cup runneth over: *Ames, Ed* / Good, the bad and the ugly, The: *Montenegro*, Hugo / In the year 2525: *Zager/Evans* / Let's get together: *Youngbloods* / Everybody's talkin': *Nilsson (Harry)* / Suspicious minds: *Presley, Elvis*.
MC: NK 90373

AMERICAN DREAMS 70'S VOL 1 (Various artists).
Tracks: / Love or let me be lonely: *Friends Of Distinction* / American woman: *Guess Who* / Amos Moses: *Reed*, Jerry / It's impossible: *Como, Perry* / Without you: *Nilsson (Harry)* / Troglodyte (caveman): *Castor*, Jimmy Bunch / Everybody plays the fool: *Main Ingredient* / Burning love: *Presley, Elvis* / My Maria: *Stevenson*, B.W. / Rock the boat: *Hues Corporation* / You little trustmaker: *Tymes* / Life is a rock (but the radio rolled me): *Reunion* / Lady: *Styx* / Miracles: *Jefferson Starship* / Turn the beat around: *Robinson, Vicki* Sue / Rich girl: *Hall & Oates* / Here you come again: *Parton, Dolly* / Shame: *King, Evelyn "Champagn e"*.
MC: NK 90374

AMERICAN DREAMS II (Various artists).
Tracks: / Bat out of hell: *Meatloaf* / Don't fear the reaper: *Blue Oyster Cult* / You ain't seen nothing yet: *Bachman-Turner Overdrive* (Not available on CD.) / American woman: *Guess Who* (Not available on CD.) / Something in the air: *Thunderclap Newman* (Not available on CD.) / Two hearts: *Parr, John* (Not available on CD.) / Hold on: *Santana* / St. Elmos Fire: *Parr, John* / Carry on wayward son: *Kansas* / So you want to be a rock'n'roll star: *Byrds* / Ramblin' man: *Allman Brothers* (Not available on CD.) / Jessica: *Allman Brothers* / White rabbit: *Jefferson Airplane* (Not available on CD.) / All along the watchtower: *Hendrix, Jimi* / Don't look back: *Boston* / Summertime blues: *Blue Cheer* (Not available on CD.) / Walk this way: *Aerosmith* (Not available on CD.) / Foolish heart: *Perry, Steve* / Miracles: *Jefferson Starship* / Promise you made, The: *Cock Robin*/ That's what love is all about: *Bolton, Michael* (Not available on CD.) / Eye of the tiger: *Survivor* / Take it on the run: *REO Speedwagon* / Kiss on my list: *Hall & Oates* / Layla: *Derek & The Dominoes* / Jessie's girl: *Springfield, Rick* / Don't stop believin': *Journey (Group)* / Hymn: *Barclay James Harvest* (Not available on CD.).
2LP: STDLP 26
MC: STDMC 26

American Flyer

AMERICAN FLYER.
LP: UAG 29991

American Gigolo (film)

AMERICAN GIGOLO (Film soundtrack) (Various artists).
LP: POLS 1018
MC: POLSC 1018
LP: 813632.1
MC: 813632.4
LP: 2391 447

CALL ME (See under Blondie).

American Girls

AMERICAN GIRLS.
Tracks: / American girls / Androgynous zone / Last prayer / Stay with me / Out on my own / Goodbye, Amen / Blind ambition / Take the night / Sharkskin suit / Practice (what you preach).
LP: MIRF 1009
MC: MIRFC 1009

American Gothic

AMERICAN GOTHIC (Various artists).
LP: EFA 15551

American Graffiti

AMERICAN GRAFFITI VOL.1 (Various artists).
Tracks: / Rock around the clock: *Haley, Bill & The Comets* / Sixteen candles: *Crests* / Runaway: *Shannon, Del* / Why do fools fall in love: *Lymon, Frankie & The Teenagers* / That'll be the day: *Holly, Buddy & The Crickets*/ Maybe baby: *Holly, Buddy & The Crickets* / Fannie Mae: *Brown, Buster* / At the hop: *Flash Cadillac & The* Continental Kids / She's so fine: *Flash Cadillac & The Continental Kids* / Goodnight well it's time to go: *Spaniels*/ See you in September: *Tempos* / Surfin' safari: *Beach Boys* / All summer long: *Beach Boys* / He's the great imposter: *Fleetwoods* / Almost grown: *Berry, Chuck* / Johnny B. Goode: *Berry, Chuck* / Smoke gets in your eyes: *Platters* / Only you: *Platters* / Great pretender, The: *Platters* / Little darlin': *Diamonds*/ Stroll, The: *Diamonds* / Peppermint twist: *Dee, Joey & The Starlighters* / Ya, Ya: *Dorsey, Lee* / Ain't that a shame: *Domino, Fats* / I only have eyes for you: *Flamingos* / Get a job: *Silhouettes* / To the aisle: *Five Satins* / Do you wanna dance: *Freeman, Bobby* / Party doll: *Knox, Buddy* / Come go with me: *Del-Vikings* / You're sixteen: *Burnette, Johnny* / Love potion No.9: *Clovers* / Since I don't have you: *Skyliners* / Chantilly lace: *Big Bopper* / Teen angel: *Dinning, Mark* / Crying in the chapel: *Till*, Sonny & The Orioles / Thousand miles away: *Heartbeats* / Heart and soul: *Cleftones* / Green onions: *Booker T & The MGs* / Barbara Ann: *Regents* / Book of love: *Monotones*.
2LP: MCSP 253
MCSET: MCSPC 253
2LP: MCLD 617
MCSET: MCLDC 617

AMERICAN GRAFFITI VOL.2 (Various artists).
Tracks: / See you later alligator: *Haley, Bill & The Comets* / Maybe: *Chantels* / Bony Moronie: *Williams*, Larry / Shoop shoop song: *Everett, Betty* / Teenager in love: *Dion & The Belmonts* / Ready Teddy: *Little* Richard / Tutti frutti: *Little Richard* / Stagger Lee: *Price, Lloyd* / Gee: *Crows* / My heart is an open book: *Dobkins, Carl Jr.* / Oh boy: *Holly, Buddy & The Crickets* / Happy happy birthday baby: *Tune* Weavers / Louie Louie: *Kingsmen* / It might as well rain until September: *King, Carole* / Peggy Sue: *Holly*, Buddy / Locomotion, The: *Little Eva* / He will break your heart: *Butler, Jerry* / Twilight time: *Platters*/ Will you love me tomorrow: *Shirrelles, The* / Could this be magic: *Dubs* / Poison ivy: *Coasters* / I'm sorry: *Lee, Brenda* / Speedo: *Cadillacs* / Duke of Earl: *Chandler, Gene* / One summer night: *Dan leers*.
2LP: MCLD 618

MCSET: . . . . MCLDC 618
2LP: . . . . MCSP 303

AMERICAN GRAFFITI VOL.3 (Various artists).
Tracks: / Surfer girl: *Beach Boys* / Lucille: *Little Richard* / Good golly Miss Molly: *Little Richard*/ At my front door: *Eldorados* / For your precious love: *Butler, Jerry* / Endless sleep: *Reynolds, Jody*/ Wake up little Susie: *Everly Brothers* / Bye bye love: *Everly Brothers* / You talk too much: *Jones, Joe*/ Mary Lou: *Hawkins, Ronnie* / Poetry in motion: *Tillotson, Johnny* / Donna: *Valens, Ritchie* / La bamba: *Valens, Ritchie* / Honeycomb: *Various artists* / Since I fell for you: *Welch, Lenny* / Kansas City: *Harrison,* Wilbert / Hey little one: *Burnette, Dorsey* / To know him is to love him: *Teddy Bears* / Thousand stars, A: *Young, Kathy* / Alley oop: *Hollywood Argyles* / Shimmy shimmy ko ko bop: *Little Anthony* / Western movies: *Olympics* / Mule skinner blues: *Fendermen* / Rave on: *Holly, Buddy & The Crickets* / Birds and the bees, The: *Atkins, Jewel* / Let's dance: *Montez, Chris* / My special angel: *Helms, Bobby* / Mountain of love: *Dorman, Harold* / Baby, what you want me to do?: *Reed, Jimmy* / Big hurt, The: *Fisher, Toni* / Surfin': *Beach Boys.*
2LP: . . . . MCLD 619
MCSET: . . . . MCLDC 619

AMERICAN GRAFFITI VOL.4 (Various artists).
Tracks: / Heatwave: *Reeves, Martha* / Moon river: *Williams, Andy* / Mr. Tambourine man: *Byrds, The* / My boyfriend's back: *Angels* / Sound of silence, The: *Simon & Garfunkel* / Season of the witch: *Donovan*/ Stop in the name of love: *Ross, Diana & The Supremes* / Strange brew: *Cream* / Just like a woman: *Dylan, Bob* / Respect: *Franklin, Aretha* / She's not there: *Zombies* / 96 tears: *Question Mark & The Mysterians*/ Pipeline: *Chantays* / Since I fell for you: *Welch, Lenny* / Beachwood 4-5789: *Marvelettes* / Mister lonely: *Various artists* / Cool jerk: *Capitols* / I feel like I'm fixin' to die rag: *Country Joe & The Fish*/ Ballad of the Green Berets: *Sadler, Barry* / My guy: *Wells, Mary* / I'm a man: *Sahm, Doug* / Hang on Sloopy: *McCoys* / When a man loves a woman: *Sledge, Percy* / Like a rolling stone: *Dylan, Bob.*
2LP: . . . . MCLD 620
MCSET: . . . . MCLDC 620

American Greats

100 MINUTES OF AMERICAN GREATS (Various artists).
MC: . . . . ZCTON 113

American Heart...

AMERICAN HEART AND SOUL (Various artists).
Tracks: / Jaguar skies: *Lost Patrol* / Your eyes reflect: *Mod Fun* / Trains, The: *Nashville Ramblers*/ My guilty pleasure: *Lost Patrol* / What's happening today: *Key* / Nashville ramblin': *Nashville Ramblers*/ Open your eyes: *Mod Fun* / Live today: *Modest Proposals* / New song: *Manual Scan* / My girl: *Rumble*/ When you're up: *J-Walkers* / After you: *Modest Proposals* / Trendy girl: *Rumble* / Give it up: *]J-Walkers.*
LP: . . . . LO 6

American Heartbeat

AMERICAN HEARTBEAT (Various artists).
Tracks: / Eye of the tiger: *Various artists* / American heartbeat: *Various artists* / Rosanna: *Various artists*/ Africa: *Various artists* / Hold the line: *Various artists* / Who's crying now?: *Various artists* / Don't fear the reaper: *Various artists* / Babe: *Various artists* / Take it on the run: *Various artists* / Keep on loving you: *Various artists* / Dance hall days: *Various artists* / More than a feeling: *Various artists*/ Harden my heart: *Various artists* / Carry on wayward son: *Various artists* / I got you: *Various artists*/ Heat of the moment: *Various artists.*
LP: . . . . EPC 10045
MC: 40 10045

American Heroes (film)

AMERICAN HEROES (Film soundtrack) (Various artists).
LP: . . . . AHLP 1
MC: . . . . AHC 1

American Hot Dance

AMERICAN HOT DANCE BANDS (1925-1928) (Various artists).
MC: . . . . NEO 946

American Hot Wax

AMERICAN HOT WAX (Film soundtrack) (Various artists).
2LP: . . . . AMLM 66500

American In Paris

AMERICAN IN PARIS/LES GIRLS (Film soundtracks) (Various artists).
Tracks: / 'S wonderful: *Various artists* / Love is here to stay: *Various artists* / I'll build a stairway to paradise: *Various artists* / I got rhythm: *Various artists* / American in Paris Ballet, An: *Various artists* / Les Girls: *Various artists* / You're just too, too: *Various artists* / Ca c'est l'amour: *Various artists*/ Ladies in waiting: *Various artists* / Why am I so gone (about that girl): *Various artists.*
LP: . . . . CBS 70286
MC: 40 70286
LP: 2353 068
MC: 3110 007

GIGI/AN AMERICAN IN PARIS (See under Gigi) (film soundtracks) (Various artists).

American Indian...

AMERICAN INDIAN DANCE THEATRE.
LP: 824311
MC: 824314

American Legends

AMERICAN LEGENDS VOL.1 (Laine, Frankie/Guy Mitchell/Johnny Ray).
MCSET: . . . . DTO 10300

AMERICAN LEGENDS VOL.2 (Various artists).
MCSET: . . . . DTO 10309

American Military Band

SOUSA MARCHES.
Tracks: / Hands across the sea / Bells of Chicago, The / Thunderer, The / Stars and stripes forever / Semper Fidelis / Crusader / Gladiators, The / Washington post march / High school cadets / El captain / King cotton.
LP: . . . . SOLP 351
MC: . . . . BK 351

American Music Club

CALIFORNIA.
Tracks: / Firefly / Somewhere / Laughing stock / Lonely / Pale skinny girl / Blue and grey shirt / Bad liquor / Now you're defeated / Jenny / Western sky / Highway 5 / Last harbor.
LP: . . . . FIEND 134

ENGINE, THE.
Tracks: / Big night / Outside this bar / At my mercy / Gary's song / Night watchman / Lloyd / Electric light / Mom's TV / Art of love / Asleep / This year.
LP: . . . . ZONG 020

UNITED KINGDOM.
Tracks: / Here they roll down / Dreamers of the dream / Never mind / United Kingdom / Dream is gone / Heaven of your hands / Kathleen / Hula maiden, The / Animal pen / California (Available on CD only).
LP: . . . . FIEND 151

American Pop (film)

AMERICAN POP (Original soundtrack) (Various artists).
Tracks: / Hell is for children: *Benatar, Pat* / Summertime: *Big Brother & The Holding Company* / California dreamin': *Mamas & Papas* / Turn me loose: *Fabian* / This train: *Peter, Paul & Mary* / Somebody to love: *Levy,* Marcy / Purple haze: *Hendrix, Jimi* / Take five: *Brubeck, Dave Quartet* / You send me: *Cooke, Sam*/ People are strange: *Doors.*
LP: . . . . MCF 3118

American Ram Jam

AMERICAN RAM JAM.
LP: . . . . EPC 82215

American Samoa...

AMERICAN SAMOA (American Samoa Arts Choir).
LP: . . . . VP 360

American School Choir

SAVE THE ANIMALS.
LP: . . . . KMR 390
MC: . . . . ZCKMR 390

American Spring

SPRING...PLUS.
Tracks: / Tennessee waltz / Thinkin' 'bout you baby / Mama said / Superstar / Awake / Sweet mountain / Everybody / This whole world / Forever / Good time / Now that everything's been said / Down home / Shyin' away / Fallin' in love / It's like Heaven / Had to phone ya.
LP: . . . . SEE 269

American Standard Band

AMERICAN STANDARD BAND.
Tracks: / Got what it takes / You never get over heartbreak / Questions and answers / Make it last / So far away / Fallin' in love again / Take it easy on me / Dance with me forever / Take me away my friend / Children's island.
LP: . . . . ILPS 9540

American Tail (film)

AMERICAN TAIL, AN (Film soundtrack) (Various artists).
Tracks: / American tail, An: *Persoff, Nehemiah/John Guarncieri/Warren Hays* / Cossack cats, The: *Persoff, Nehemiah/John* Guarncieri/Warren Hays / There are no cats in America: *Persoff, Nehemiah/John Guarncieri/ Warren Hays* / Storm, The: *Plummer, Christopher/Phillip Glasser* / Give me your tired, your poor: *Plummer, Christopher/Phillip Glasser* / Never say never: *Plummer, Christopher/Phillip Glasser* / Market place, The: *Glasser, Phillip/Betsy Cathcart* / Somewhere out there: *Ronstadt, Linda & James Ingram* / Releasing the secret weapon: *Deluise, Dom/Phillip Glasser*/ Duo, A: *Deluise, Dom/Phillip Glasser* / Great fire: *London Symphony Orchestra* / Reunited: *London Symphony* Orchestra / Flying away: *London Symphony Orchestra* / End credits: *London Symphony Orchestra* / Somewhere out there (instrumental): *Glasser, Phillip/Betsy Cathcart.*
LP: . . . . MCF 3367
MC: . . . . MCFC 3367

AMERICAN TAIL, AN (Film soundtrack) (Horner, James).
LP: MCA39096
MC: MCAC39096

American Youth Report

AMERICAN YOUTH REPORT (Various artists).
LP: . . . . LBOM 2

America's Greatest

AMERICA'S GREATEST HITS (Various artists).
Tracks: / Goodnight, Irene: *Jenkins, Gordon & His Orchestra* / Cry: *Ray, Johnnie* / Vaya con dios: *Paul,* Les & Mary Ford / Rock around the clock: *Haley, Bill & The Comets* / Memories are made of this: *Martin, Dean*/ Great pretender, The: *Platters* / Blueberry Hill: *Domino, Fats* / Singing the blues: *Mitchell, Guy*/ It's not for me to say: *Mathis, Johnny* / Love letters in the sand: *Boone, Pat* / Bye bye love: *Everly Brothers*/ Whole lotta shakin' goin' on: *Lewis, Jerry Lee* / At the hop: *Danny & The Juniors* / It's all in the game: *Edwards,* Tommy / Battle of New Orleans: *Horton, Johnny* / Summer place, A (theme from): *Faith, Percy Orchestra* / Twist, The: *Checker, Chubby* / Tossin' and turnin': *Lewis, Bobby* / I get around: *Beach Boys* / Where did our love go?: *Supremes* / Mr. Tambourine man: *Byrds* / California dreamin': *Mamas & Papas* / I'm a believer: *Monkees* / Respect: *Franklin, Aretha* / Letter, The: *Box Tops* / I heard it through the grapevine: *Gaye,* Marvin / Raindrops keep falling on my head: *Thomas, B.J.* / Close to you: *Carpenters* / I'll be there: *Jackson 5* / First time ever I saw your face, The: *Flack, Roberta* / Tie a yellow ribbon: *Dawn* / Love will keep us together: *Captain & Tennille* / Rhinestone cowboy: *Cambell, Glen* / You light up my life: *Boone, DebbieS2].*
2LP: . . . . BEDP 013

Americathon (film)

AMERICATHON (Film soundtrack) (Various artists).
LP: . . . . CBS 70172

Amhrain, Ceol Agus

RANN NA FEIRSTE.
LP: . . . . CEF 036

Amina

YALIL.
Tracks: / Le cercle rouge / Yalil / Embrasse-moi / Ma lisane soul / Belly dancer / Gallouli / Neila / Mektoubi.
LP: 8386091
MC: 8386094

Amir, Mr.

NO PLACE TO GO.
LP: . . . . PP 11

Amis, Kingsley (aut)

LUCKY JIM (See under Lucky Jim) (Courtenay, Tom (nar)).

Ammons, Albert

ALBERT AMMONS VOL 1 (King of the blues and boogie woogie).
LP: . . . . OL 2807

ALBERT AMMONS VOL 2 (King of the blues and boogie woogie).
LP: . . . . OL 2822

BOOGIE WOOGIE AND THE BLUES (Ammons, Albert & His Rhythm Kings).
Tracks: / Bugle boogie / Revelle boogie / Blues in the groove / Breaks, The / Jammin the boogie / Bottom blues / Albert's special boogie / Boogie rocks, The / Blues on my mind.
LP: 6 24297

BOOGIE WOOGIE BOYS (Ammons, Albert/Pete Johnson/Meade Lux Lewis).
LP: . . . . SLP 229

BOOGIE WOOGIE CLASSICS (Ammons, Albert & Pete Johnson).
LP: . . . . BLP 1209

BOOGIE WOOGIE WOOGIE PIANO STYLINGS.
Tracks: / Swanee River boogie / Boogie woogie at the Civic Opera / S.P.Blues / Sheik of Araby, The / St. Louis Blues / You are my sunshine / Shufflin' the boogie / Twelfth St. boogie.
LP: 6336 326

GIANTS OF BOOGIE WOOGIE (Ammons, Albert/Pete Johnson/Meade Lux Lewis).
Tracks: / St. Louis blues / Mecca flat blues / Bass goin' crazy / Closing hour blues / Messin' around / Deep fives / Blues de luxe / Let 'em jump / Pete's blues / B and O blues.
LP: . . . . SM 3094

KING OF BOOGIE WOOGIE.
LP: . . . . BC 27

Ammons, Gene

ALL STARS SESSIONS (Ammons, Gene All Stars).
LP: . . . . OJC 014

BOSS TENOR.
Tracks: / Hittin' the jug / Close your eyes / My romance / Canadian Sunset / Blue Ammons / Confirmation / Savoy.
LP: . . . . PR 7180
MC: . . . . PRC 7180

EARLY VISIONS.
Tracks: / Swinging for Xmas / Talk of the town / Battle, The / Jam for boppers / Do you really mean it? / Bless you / Stuffy / Once in a while / Pennies from Heaven / Cha bootie / More moon / Last mile, The / Goodbye / Ten or eleven / It's you or no one / My foolish heart / Jug head ramble / You go to my head / Baby won't you please say yes / Don't do me wrong / Prelude to a kiss / Can anyone explain? / You're not the kind / Happiness is a thing called Joe.
2LP: . . . . CXJD 6701
MC: . . . . ZCCJD 6701
2LP: . . . . GCH 2-6031

GENE AMMONS.
LP: . . . . JR 150

GENE AMMONS STORY - ORGAN COMBOS.
Tracks: / Twisting the jug / Born to be blue / Satin doll / Moten swing / Stormy Monday blues / Down the line / Velvet soul / In Sid's thing / Blue room / Water jug / Angel eyes / Gettin' around.
2LP: . . . . PR 24071

HAPPY BLUES, THE (Ammons, Gene All Stars).
LP: . . . . OJC 7039

HAPPY BLUES, THE (Ammons, Gene All Stars).
LP: . . . . OJC 013

IN SWEDEN.
LP: . . . . ENJA 3093

JAMMIN' WITH GENE (Ammons, Gene All Stars).
LP: . . . . OJC 211

JUG & SONNY (Ammons, Gene & Sonny Stitt).
Tracks: / You're not that kind of girl / I cover the waterfront / Full moon / Jam for boppers / Don't do me wrong / Don't worry about me / Baby won't you please say yes / Cha bootie / Tenor eleven / Last mile, The.
LP: . . . . GCH 8091
MC: . . . . GCHK 78091

JUGANTHOLOGY.
2LP: . . . . PR 24036

JUGGIN' AROUND (Ammons, Gene and Benny Green).
Tracks: / Juggin' around / Sermonette / Swinging for Benny / Little ditty / Going South / Jim dog.
LP: . . . . ATS 1
MC: . . . . KATS 1

PUNKY.
Tracks: / Pint size / Punky / Stella by starlight / King size.
LP: . . . . OJC 244

UP TIGHT.
Tracks: / Breeze and I / Moonglow / Five o'clock whistle / Lester leaps in / I sold my heart to the junkman / Uptight / Jug's blue blues.
LP: . . . . PR 7208

Ammy Coco

DJAGURA.
LP: . . . . S 1834

Amnesia

HYSTERIA.
LP: . . . . LP 3625

MC: MC 3625

UNKNOWN ENTITY.
LP: WADES 3
MC: WADES 3MC

Amnesty International

CONSPIRACY OF HOPE (See under Conspiracy of Hope) (Various artists).

Amoah, Charles

FREE ME.
LP: KAM 1001

IT'S A LOVE STORY.
Tracks: / It's a love story / Change your style / Cotton love / Have some fun.
LP: LC 18957

Amon Duul

AIRS ON A SHOESTRING.
Tracks: / Hymn for the hardcore / Pioneer / One moment of anger is two pints of blood / Marcus Lied / Olaf.
LP: THBL 043
MC: THBC 043

ANTHOLOGY - AMON DUUL (Amon Duul II).
Tracks: / Soap shock rock / Burning sister / Halluzination guillotine / Gulp a sonata / Flesh coloured anti-aircraft alarm / Kanaan / Trap / Phallus dei / Yeti (improvisation) / Wolf city / C.I.D. in Uruk / Morning excuse / Apocalyptic bore / Jailhouse frog.
LP: RAWLP 032

DIE LOSUNG (Amon Duul & Bob Calvert).
Tracks: / Big wheel / Urban Indian / Adrenalin Rush / Visions of fire / Drawn to the flame / They call it home / Die Losung / Drawn to the flame (part 2).
LP: DMLP 1015

FOOL MOON.
Tracks: / Who who / Tribe, The / Tik tok song, The / Haupmotor / Hymn for the hardcore.
LP: DMLP 1013

HAWK MEETS PENGUIN,VOL.1.
Tracks: / One moment of anger is two pints of blood / Meditative music from the third o before the p (part 1) / Meditative music from the third o before the p (part 2).
LP: DM 004
LP: JAMS 24

MEETINGS WITH MENMACHINES IN GLORIOUS HEROES OF THE PAST.
LP: JAMS 27

MEETINGS WITH MENMACHINES UNREMARKABLE HEROES OF THE PAST.
Tracks: / Pioneer / Old one, The / Marcus lied / Song, The / Things aren't always what they seem / Burundi drummer's nightmare.
LP: DM 006

MINNELIED.
Tracks: / Ein wunderhubsches Madchen traumt von Sandosa / Kaskados Minnelied / Mama Duul und ihre Sauerkrautband spielt auf / Im garten Sandosa / Der garten Sandosa im morgentau / Bitterlings verwandlung.
LP: 0040 149

YETI.
2LP: DT6 28521
2LP: DT6 28521
2LP: LSP 101

Among The...

AMONG THE NORTHUMBRIAN HILLS (Various artists).
LP: VRSS 001

Amoreuse

AMOREUSE - THE FEMININE TOUCH (Various artists).
Tracks: / How can I be sure: *Springfield, Dusty* / Loving and free: *Dee, Kiki* / Answer me: *Dickson, Barbara*/ I can't get you out of my mind: *Elliman, Yvonne* / September in the rain: *Washington, Dinah* / I put a spell on you: *Simone, Nina* / Je t'aime...: *Birkin, Jane/ Serge Gainsbourgh* / Amoreuse: *Dee, Kiki* / It may be Winter outside: *Love Unlimited* / Some of your lovin': *Springfield, Dusty* / Love me: *Elliman, Yvonne*/ Here I go again: *Twiggy* / Stay with me till dawn: *Tzuke, Judie*.
MC: CN4 2097

Amos, Adam

ADAM AMOS & NOEL ROCKS (Amos, Adam & Noel Rocks).
LP: CM 011

CASUAL ON THE BALCONY (Amos, Adam & Noel Rocks).
LP: CM 026

Ampage

CHAMPAGNE & CAVIAR.
LP: IW 1026

D-DAY.
LP: IW 1025

Amram, David

AT HOME AROUND THE WORLD.
LP: FF 094

DAVID AMRAM'S LATIN-JAZZ CELEBRATION.
Tracks: / En memoria de chano pozo / New York charanga / Andes breeze / Take the 'A' train / Blue bomba / Brazilian memories / Celebration / Song of the rain forest / Interview with David Amram.
LP: 9601951

HAVANA/NEW YORK.
LP: FF 057

NO MORE WALLS.
MC: FC 27752

TRIPLE CONCERTO.
MC: FC 27751

Amrouche, Taos

CHANTS BERBERES DE LA MEULE ET DU BERCEAU.
Tracks: / Meditation sur tes parents / O mon frere, que tu es pale / Source des bucherons no.1 et no.2 / Un palmier dans le desert / Penche sur un tombe nouvelle / Je me suis promis de dire la verite / Berceuse de Zahoua / Berceuse au clair de lune.
LP: ARN 34278

CHANTS DE L'ATLAS.
Tracks: / Genies de montagnes de neige / Le hors-la-loi / Le pecher du champ / Chant de procession de l'oncle Rameau d'oranger / Chant des bellesmeres / Chant de la bru / O tante malh'a / La fille au yeux bleus / Qu'on aimerait suivre les ames / Danseuse inconnue / Complainte de la femme abandonnee / Ma chere, connais-tu la nouvelle.
LP: ARN 30103
MC: ARN 430 103

CHANTS ESPAGNOLS ARCHAIQUES DE LA ALBERCA.
Tracks: / Calores, la del rio / Albo ada de bodas / La del molinero / Eleonor, no me olvides, no chalaneru / La de San Antonio / La de la nina / La colombiana / La del molinero / La del capotino / La del pastor / Alborada sagrada de Santa Agueda / Petenera muy antigua.
LP: ARN 34170

INCANTATIONS.
Tracks: / J'ai dit ma peine / Chant des pelerins du village des Aghribs / Preperation a la priere / Pretresses de la joie / Danse sacree des Amariens / Procession de l'oncle Mahmoud no.1 et no.2 / Des adeptes du prophete, Une / Allah le dispensateur / Alaouilia / Danse sacree des Aissaouas / Le cheminement de la mort / Voici le jour ou ils creusent ma tombe / Grande procession.
LP: ARN 34233

Amstell, Billy

SESSION AFTER MIDNIGHT (Amstell, Billy, Dixielanders).
Tracks: / Blues in B flat / British grenadiers, The / Tishomingo blues / Paradise / Free'n'easy / Don't fuss / Washington and Lee sing / Tootin' around / My old Kentucky home / Sue, Sue / My bonnie lies over the ocean / Royal garden blues.
LP: ZR 1010

Amsterdam Loeki...

EXTRA TIME (Amsterdam Loeki Stardust Quartet).
Tracks: / Misty / Fugue (Bach) / Batalla famossa / Loeki the lion on the trail of the Pink Panther / Shadow of your smile / Michelle / Allegro and rondo grazioso (Bach) / Concerto in D (Vivaldi) / Nocturne (Rimsky-Korsakov) / When shall the sun shine / Scrapple from the apple / Aan de Amsterdamse Grachten / Tango fur Elise (Beethoven).
MC: 4252224

Amy, Curtis

KATANGA (Amy, Curtis & Dupree Bolton).
LP: AFF 128

An Emotional Fish

AN EMOTIONAL FISH.
Tracks: / Celebrate / Blue / Julian / Change / That demon jive / Grey matter / Lace Virginia / All I am / Colours / Brick it up.
LP: WX 359
MC: WX 359 C

An Teallach

DROPS OF BRANDY (An Teallach Ceilidh Band).
LP: SPR 1028
MC: SPR 1028C

PLOUGH AND THE STARS, THE (An Teallach Ceilidh Band).
LP: SPR 1018

Anaamika

ANONYMOUS.
LP: SSRLP 5090
MC: SC 5090

Anacrusis

MANIC IMPRESSIONS.
LP: ZORRO 23

REASON.
Tracks: / Stop me / Not forgotten / Silent crime / Afraid to feel / Vital / Terrified / Wrong / Misshapen intent / Child inside / Quick to doubt.
LP: ATV 90

SUFFERING HOUR.
LP: AXISLP 4

Anastasia Screamed

LAUGHING DOWN THE LIMEHOUSE.
LP: NECK LP 2

Anastasia (tv series)

ANASTASIA (Film soundtrack) (Munich Philharmonic Orchestra).
Tracks: / Main title (part 1) / Ballroom, The / Siberia / Sled, The / Family only/ The cellar / Berlin bridge / Confronting Sophie / After the interview / Railroad car / Main title (part 2) / Denial / Shopping spree / Romanoffs, The / At the Astor / Russian antiques / Darya says no / Luncheonette, The / Anna and Erich / Ekaterinburg / Back to Europe.
LP: SLIM 10
MC: SLIMC 10
LP: STV 81125

ANASTASIA: THE MYSTERY OF ANNA (TV soundtrack) (Various artists).
Tracks: / Main title (part 1): *Various artists* / Ballroom, The: *Various artists* / To Siberia: *Various artists*/ Sied, The: Ekaterinberg: *Various artists* / Family only/The cellar: *Various artists* / Berlin Bridge: *Various* artists / Confronting Sophie: *Various artists* / After the interview: *Various artists* / Railroad car, The: *Various artists*.
LP: FILM 010
MC: FILMC 010

Anastasio

ANASTASIO/HOLLY & HICKS (Anastasio/Holly & Hicks).
LP: ARHOLIE 5032

Anchors Aweigh (film)

ANCHORS AWEIGH (Film soundtrack) (Various artists).
LP: CC 100/17

ANCHORS AWEIGH (Film soundtrack) (Various artists).
LP: SH 2024

Ancient Beatbox

ANCIENT BEATBOX.
Tracks: / Laride / Raining (my eyes are filled with clouds) / Wooden box / I'll wait for you / Bouree a pichon / Diamond / Many lives of Diana, The / All we live for.
LP: COOK 021
MC: COOKC 021

Ancient Evenings (bk)

ANCIENT EVENINGS (Mailer, Norman).
MC: 2091

Ancient Future

NATURAL RHYTHMS.
LP: PH 9006
MC: PH 9006C

Ancient Ways...

ANCIENT WAYS TO NEW FREEDOM (Doris Lessing (aut)).
MC: SS 102

And All Because...

AND ALL BECAUSE THE LADY LOVES... (Various artists).
Tracks: / My cherie amour: *Wonder, Stevie* / You are everything: *Ross, Diana & Marvin Gaye* / Up where we belong: *Cocker, Joe & Jennifer Warnes* / Tonight I celebrate my love: *Flack, Roberta & Peabo Bryson* / Wonderful tonight: *Clapton, Eric* / Give me a chance: *Carrack, Paul* / Let's stay together: *Turner, Tina* / Miss you nights: *Richard, Cliff* / True: *Spandau Ballet* / Slave to love: *Ferry, Bryan* / When I need you: *Sayer, Leo*.
2LP: ADD 6
MC: ZDD 6

And All Because The

ANYTHING BUT A SOFT CENTRE.
LP: RED 003

And Also The Trees

AND ALSO THE TREES.
LP: LEX 1

FAREWELL TO THE SHADE.
Tracks: / Prince Rupert / Nobody Inn, The / Lady D'Arbanville / Pear tree, The / Horse fair, The / MacBeth's head / Belief in the rose / Misfortunes / Ill omen.
LP: LEX 10
MC: MC LEX 10

MILLPOND YEARS, THE.
LP: LEX 9

NIGHT OF THE 24TH,THE.
Tracks: / Room lives in Lucy, A / Twilight pool / Vincent Crane / Wallpaper dying / Shantell / Gone like the swallows / Headless clay woman / Slow pulse boy / Virus meadow / So this is silence.
LP: LEX 8

VIRUS MEADOW.
Tracks: / Slow pulse boy / Maps in her wrists and arms / Dwelling place, The / Vincent Crane / Jack / Headless clay woman / Gone like the swallows / Virus meadow.
LP: LEX 6

And the Bands Played

AND THE BANDS PLAYED ON (Various artists).
Tracks: / My kind of music: *Various artists* / Champagne cocktail: *Various artists* / I've got my love to keep me warm: *Various artists* / Let's put out the lights: *Various artists* / What a perfect combination: *Various* artists / Nobody's sweetheart: *Various artists* / Tiger rag: *Various artists* / What a little moonlight can do: *Various artists* / Dancing in the dark: *Various artists* / Easy come, easy go: *Various artists* / Crazy rhythm: *Various artists* / You're my everything: *Various artists* / White jazz: *Various artists*/ We're tops on Saturday night: *Various artists* / Alone: *Various artists* / Snakehips: *Various artists*/ Limehouse blues: *Various artists* / You've got me crying again: *Various artists*.
LP: MOR 529
MC: KMORC 525
2LP: DDV 5001/2

And The Ship ...

AND THE SHIP SAILS ON (Film soundtrack) (Various artists).
Tracks: / Convoi funebre: *Various artists* (From Il Carro Funebre.) / Le depart: *Various artists* (From La Partenza.) / De la cuisine au salon: *Various artists* (From Dalla cucina al salone.) / Le cygne: *Various artists* (From Il Ciagno.) / Pas de trois: *Various artists* (From Passo a tre.) / L'escalier d'honneur: *Various artists* (From Lo scalone d'onore.) / Valse de l'archiduchesse: *Various artists* (Walzer per l'arciduca) / Glass-concertino: *Various* artists (F Schubert-G Plenizio.) / Clair de lune: *Various artists* (C Debussy G Pleizio.) / Kolo vlah: *Various artists* (From G Plenizio.).
LP: A 228
MC: C 228

And Why Not

MOVE YOUR SKIN.
Tracks: / Rhythm money / Shame / Cage, The / Something you got / Restless days / Face, The / Move your skin / Standing there / Correct me if I'm wrong / Speak the word.
MC: ICT 9935
LP: ILPS 9935

Andante

ANDANTE (Various artists).
2LP: LP 1635186
MC: MC 1635186

Anders, Bob

DANCING A-GO-GO..IN STRICT TEMPO RHYTHM.
LP: NR 1005

Anders, Christoph

ES HERRSCHT UHU IM LAND (Anders, C/H.Goebels/A.Harth/P.Lovens/ R.Riehm/A.M.Roelofs).
LP: JAPO 60037

Andersen, Arild

BANDE A PARTE (Andersen, Arild Quintet).
Tracks: / 3 for 5 / Natt / Sort of / Vanilje / Bali / Tutte / No soap / Nyl.
LP: ECM 1319

LIFELINES.
LP: ECM 1188

MOLDE CONCERT, A.
LP: ECM 1236

Andersen, Eric

BEST OF ERIC ANDERSEN.
LP: VNP 5316
MC: VNP 6316

GHOSTS UPON THE ROAD.
Tracks: / Belgian bar / Spanish steps / It starts with a lie / Trouble in Paris / Listen to the rain / Ghosts upon the road / Too many times (I will try) / Carry me away / Six senses of darkness / Irish lace.
LP: VGC 14
MC: TCVGC 14

Andersen, Hans

HANS ANDERSEN (Various artists).
MC: . . . . STC 003

HANS ANDERSEN.
Tracks: / Emperor's new clothes, The / Tinder box / Nightingale, The / Princess and the pea.
LP: . . . . KPM 7008

HANS C. ANDERSEN FAIRY TALES.
MC: . . . . BBMLB 6

HANS CHRISTIAN ANDERSEN 1.
MC: . . . . VCA 104

HANS CHRISTIAN ANDERSEN 2.
MC: . . . . VCA 105

HANS CHRISTIAN ANDERSEN FAIRY TALES (Craig, Wendy (nar)).
MC: . . . . TC LFP 7105

TALES OF HANS CHRISTIAN ANDERSEN (Redgrave, Sir Michael).
Tracks: / Tinder box, The / Steadfast tin soldier, The.
MC: 1073

VARIOUS RECORDINGS (See under Title of Recording).

Andersen, Lale

DREI ROTE ROSEN.
LP: . . . . IC 178 31341/42

HAFENTRAUME.
Tracks: / Hafentraume / In Hamburg sind die nachte lang / Weisse move, komm bald wieder / Matrosen, matrosen / Hafen harmonika / Friesenlied (Wo die Nordseewellen...) / Au revoir, Marcel / Ich wunsch dir eine gute Fahrt / Geh'nicht zuruck auf's Meer / Ein fremder Mann / Ein Schiff wird kommen / Sommerwind / Ein bisschen Sehnsucht in den Augen / Blaue nacht am Hafen / Blue Hawaii / Moonlight and roses.
LP: . . . . BFX 15354

SUPERGOLD.
LP: . . . . IC 134 29762/63

Anderson, Alistair

ALISTAIR ANDERSON PLAYS ENGLISH CONCERTINA.
LP: . . . . LER 2074

CONCERTINA WORKSHOP.
Tracks: / Dancing tailor / O'Carolan's fancy / Blarney pilgrim / Barrington hornpipe, The / Cliff hornpipe, The / Recruited colliers, The / Sir Sydney Smith's march / Flannel jacket, The / Scholar, The / Joe Burke's hornpipe / Fairy queen, The / Jenny Lind polka / One horned sheep, The / Turnpike side / Sunbeam / Admiral Cole / Derwentwater's farewell / Jimmy Allen / Herd on the hill / King's favourite / Tipsy sailor, The / Aith rant, The / Framm upon him / Da south end / Fateful head, The / Randy wives of Greenlaw, The / John McNeil's reel / Kick the world before you / Come upstairs with me / Malt man comes on Monday.
LP: 12FRS 501

CORBY CRAG.
Tracks: / Hawk polka, The / Thrunton woods / Keelman's petition, The / Tipp staff, The / La fille de Lyon / Cotillon des marionettes / Blakes hornpipe / President Garfield's hornpipe / Bonnie broom hill / Felton lonnin / Kirden fair / Tich Richardson's favourite / Hey to the camp / Brosehill / Alistair Anderson's favourite / Old french / Belfast hornpipe / Prize potato, The / Trip to Carlisle, The / Corby crag / Ali Anderson / Henry Atkinson / Blayton flats / Whittingham games / James Brown / Derwent water's bonny lord / Bride's favourite, The / Remember me / Left handed fiddler, The / Geld him lasses, geld him / Uncle John / Darkening, The.
LP: 12TS 371

GRAND CHAIN, THE (With Steel Skies Band, Joe Hutton etc.).
LP: . . . . CRO 216
MC: . . . . CROC 216

LOOKIN' FOR APPLES.
Tracks: / Culloden day / Kaspar's rant / New moon, The / Curds and cream / Crooked bawbee / Carrick hornpipe / Weddings shoes / Number 28 / Highland reel / West Indian, The / Stage hornpipe, The / Johnson's hornpipe / White meadow, The / Simonside reel, The / Wedderburn's cave / Lookin' for apples / Mayday / Penicuick hornpipe / Silver tassle / Flowers of the forest / Hold on / Miss Fenwick's reel / Lads of Leith / Up and run away / Whittle dean hornpipe / Pet of the pipers / Bob Johnson's reel / Miss Soutar of Plains / Great Eastern reel / Jack's getting a wife / New way of gettin' bairns, A / Carding and spinning / Polly the lass.
LP: 12TS 402

PLAYS TRADITIONAL MUSIC ON THE ENGLISH CONCERTINA.
LP: 12TS 501

STEEL SKIES.
Tracks: / First light / Rhymeside 1 / Mountain stream, The / Rhymeside 3 / Road to the North, The / Clennel Street / Franklin river, The / Air of Maurice Ogg, The / Jumping Jack / Green ginger / Ironbridge, The / Eynhallow / In trim / Mount Hooley / Lemington bank / Kestral, The / High force / Dog leap stairs / Hot rivets / Seven gate road, The / When the frosts are setting in / East winds / Millstream, The / Centenary pack / Rhymeside 2.
LP: 12TS 427
LP: . . . . FF 288

Anderson, Anders

HELP ME MAKE IT THROUGH THE NIGHT.
MC: . . . . CHV 319

Anderson, Andy

ANDY ANDERSON'S TRIBE.
LP: . . . . WEBITE 44

ONE MAN'S ROCK AND ROLL.
Tracks: / Johnny Valentine / I-I-I love you / You shake-a me up / Way she smiled, The / Tough, tough, tough / Gimme lock a yo hair / Promise me / Sit right down and cry over you / Chop suey / Deep in the heart of Texas rock / All by myself / Mustang Kid / Big game hunter / Sad notes / So long.
LP: . . . . UP 006

Anderson, Angry

BEATS FROM A SINGLE DRUM.
LP: . . . . GRUB 11
MC: . . . . TGRUB 11

BLOOD FROM STONE.
LP: . . . . MFN 21
MC: . . . . MFNT 21

Anderson, Bill

BEST OF BILL ANDERSON.
Tracks: / Still / Happiness / I get the fever / Golden guitar / Quits / Sometimes / Wild weekend / Peanuts and diamonds / Walk out backwards / World of make believe / Don't she look good / Head to tow / Mama sang a song / I still feel the same about you / Po' folks / Liars one, believers zero / For loving you / My life / 8 X 10 / Every time I turn the radio on.
LP: . . . . MCF 2865

BILL ANDERSON STORY.
Tracks: / Bright lights and country music / No one's gonna hurt you anymore / I get the fever / Mama sang a song / I love you drops / Tip of my fingers, The / Po' folks / City lights / Get while the getting's good / 8 x 10 / That's what it's like to be lonesome / For loving you / Still / Easy come - easy go / Once a day / I can do nothing alone / Cincinnati / Golden guitar / Wild weekend / Think I'll go somewhere and cry myself to sleep / Ninety nine / Papa / Happiness / Five little fingers.
2LP: . . . . IMCA 24001

BRIGHT LIGHTS AND COUNTRY MUSIC (Anderson, Bill & The PO Boys).
Tracks: / Bright lights and country music / Wild side of life / Golden guitar / Wine / How the other half lives / Good ole mountain dew / Truck driving man / I'll go down swinging / Stranger's story, The / Sittin' in an all nite cafe / Cocktails / I'm walking the dog.
LP: . . . . HAT 3005
MC: . . . . HATC 3005

GOLDEN GREATS: BILL ANDERSON.
Tracks: / Mama sang a song / Still / I get the fever / My life / 8 x 10 / Wild weekend / Happy state of mind / But you know I love you / Tip of my fingers, The / For loving you / I love you drops / Five little fingers / Get while the getting's good / Love is a something thing / Bright lights and country music / Three AM.
LP: . . . . MCM 5017
MC: . . . . MCMC 5017

GREATEST HITS: BILL ANDERSON.
Tracks: / I get the fever / Tip of my fingers, The / Bright lights and country music / Mama sang a song / Easy come - easy go / Still / I love you drops / 8 x 10 / Po' folks / Five little fingers / Three A.M. / Golden guitar.
LP: . . . . IMCA 13

LADIES CHOICE.
Tracks: / Trust me / One more sexy lady / This is a love song / Remembering the good / Ladies get lonesome too / I can't wait any longer / Kiss you all over / Doubles / Married lady / Stay with me / Three times a lady.
LP: . . . . BDL 4001

PLACE OUT IN THE COUNTRY, A.
Tracks: / Place out in the country, A / Once more / No ordinary memory / Unicorn / Your eyes / Sheet music / Fathers and sons / I wonder where you are tonight / Maybe go down / Mr. Peepers / Family reunion / We may never pass this way again.
LP: . . . . BDL 1061

Anderson, Billy

BILLY BOY AND MARY LOU (Anderson, Billy & Mary Lou Turner).
Tracks: / Country lay on my mind / I'm way ahead of you / What we're taking here tonight / Just enough to make me want it all / I've been lovin' you too long / Building fires / Children / We made love (but where's the love we made) / Where are you going, Billy boy / Sad ol' shade of grey / Sometimes / Circle in a triangle / Gone at last / Come walk with me / Can we still be friends / That's what made me love you / Without / Charlie, Mary and us / I can't sleep with you / Let me take you away.
LP: . . . . BDL 4000

SCOTLAND NOW (Albany) (Anderson, Billy Band & Margaret Macleod).
Tracks: / Bonnie Highlanders, The / Joan C. Mackenzie / Dark island / Mull of the cool high bens / Thady you gander / Cobbler, The / Drops of brandy / Queen's Maries, The / Galway shawl / Blackbird, The / Nickels and dimes / Till the end of the day / Orange blossom special / Bernera barn dance, The / Fire hose reel, The / Albany reel, The / Boatie rows, The / Household Brigade, The / Nead na circe fraoiche / Carson Carson a Mhorag Bheag / Fear an duin' Mhor / Mingulay boat song, The / Aodann Strathbhain.
LP: . . . . ALM 4008
MC: . . . . ZC ALM 4008
LP: . . . . LAP 120

TRAVELLIN' SCOTS.
Tracks: / Scottish medley / Kalinka / Act naturally / Gaelic waltzes / Magnificent seven, The / You're my best friend / Beer barrel polka / Blue Danube / Good hearted woman / March, strathspey and reel / Lara's theme / Me and Bobby McGee / Mull of the cool high bens / Granada.
LP: . . . . SBE 194

Anderson, Bruford, ...

ANDERSON, BRUFORD, WAKEMAN, HOWE (Anderson, Bruford, Wakeman, Howe).
Tracks: / Sound / Second attention / Soul warrior / Fist of fire / Brother of mine / Big dream / Nothing can come between us / Long lost brother of mine / Birthright / Meeting, The / I wanna learn / She gives me love / Who was the first / I'm alive / Teakbois / Order of the universe / Order theme / Rock gives courage / It's so hard to grow / Universe, The / Let's pretend.
LP: 209970
MC: 409970

Anderson, Carl

ABSENCE WITH OUT LOVE.
LP: . . . . FE 38063

CARL ANDERSON.
Tracks: / Friends and lovers / C'est la vie / First time on a ferris wheel / Buttercup / Can't stop this feeling / Mr. V.J. / You are my shining star / Just a little love / Woman in love.
LP: 4500811
MC: 4500814

PIECES OF A HEART.
Tracks: / My love will / Baby my heart / How deep does it go / You're the reason / Hot coffee / Pieces of a heart / If I could / Children of a lesser god / Life's lessons / Dance of the seven veils / Maiden voyage.
LP: . . . . GRP 96121
MC: . . . . GRP 96124

PROTOCOL.
Tracks: / Can't stop this feeling / Let's talk / Still thinking of you / What will happen now / Buttercup / Somebody up there likes me / One more time with feeling / Love on ice / Girl I won't take no / Saving my love for you.
LP: . . . . EPC 26591
MC: 40 26591

Anderson, Cat

CAT ANDERSON AND LES FOUR BONES.
LP: 80715

PARIS - 1958 AND 1964 (Anderson, Cat & The Duke Ellington All Stars).
LP: . . . . SW 8412

Anderson, C.W.

BILLY AND BLAZE (See under Billy & Blaze) (Cassidy, David).

Anderson, Ernestine

BE MINE TONIGHT.
Tracks: / Sunday in New York / In a mellow tone / I'm comin' home again / Christopher Columbus / London by night / Little bird / Be mine (tonight) / Lend me your life / Sack full of dreams.
LP: . . . . CJ 319
MC: . . . . CJC 319

BIG CITY.
Tracks: / All I need is you / 59th Street Bridge song / Spring is here / I'll never pass this way again / Big city / All blues / Welcome to the club / I didn't know what time it was.
LP: . . . . CJ 214
MC: . . . . CJC 214

BOOGIE DOWN (Anderson, Ernestine & Clayton Hamilton Jazz Orch).
Tracks: / Boogie down / That Sunday that Summer / Love walked in / Only trust your heart / Day by day / Nothing ever changes my love for you / Wait till you see him / One mint julep / Le blues (instrumental).
MC: . . . . CJ 407C

LIVE AT THE 1990 CONCORD JAZZ FESTIVAL (3RD SET).
Tracks: / Blues in the closet / I let a song go out of my heart / I should care / There is no greater love / Skylark / On my own / Never make your move too soon.
MC: . . . . CJ 454 C

MISS ERNESTINE ANDERSON.
Tracks: / Let's get away from it all / End of a love affair, The / So nice / Funny how time slips away / Talk to me baby / Tears have to fall / Big spender / What did I have that I don't have / On a clear day / I fall in love too easily / Feeling good / Make it another old fashioned please.
LP: . . . . EMS 1141
MC: . . . . TCEMS 1141

NEVER MAKE YOUR MOVE TOO SOON.
Tracks: / Never make your move too soon / What a difference a day made / As long as I live / Old folks / Just one more chance / My shining hour / Why did I choose you / Poor butterfly.
LP: . . . . CJ 147

WHEN THE SUN GOES DOWN.
Tracks: / Someone else is steppin' in / In the evening / I love being here with you / Down home blues / I'm just a lucky so and so / Alone on my own / Mercy, mercy, mercy / Goin' to Chicago blues.
LP: . . . . CJ 263
MC: . . . . CJC 263

Anderson, Gladstone

GLADY UNLIMITED.
Tracks: / Sound in symphony / It's not easy / You're welcome / Rock the drift / Yours to remember / Everybody knows / Sad sweet dreamer / This is the day / Love is gone.
LP: . . . . HM 109

IT MAY SOUND SILLY.
Tracks: / It may sound silly / Mad mad ivy / Portrait of Inga / Crazy skank / Reggae delight / Feel like dancing / Glady's workshop / Leaving Rome / Mudie's groove / Black beat.
LP: . . . . HM 103

Anderson, Ian

CONTINUOUS PREACHING BLUES (see Cooper, Mike) (Cooper, Mike & Ian Anderson).

WALK INTO LIGHT.
Tracks: / Fly by night / Made in England / Walk into light / Trains / End game / Black and white television / Toad in the hole / Looking for Eden / User friendly / Different Germany.
LP: . . . . CDL 1443
MC: . . . . ZCDL 1443

Anderson, John

GREATEST HITS:JOHN ANDERSON.
Tracks: / Swingin' / I just came home to count the memories / 1959 / She just started likin' cheatin' songs / Chicken truck / I'm just an old chunk of coal / Would you catch a falling star / Wild and blue / Your lying blue eyes / Black sheep.
LP: 925169 1
MC: 925169 4

I JUST CAME HOME TO COUNT THE MEMORIES.
Tracks: / I just came home to count the memories / Would you catch a falling star / One of those old things / Girl, for you / When lady is cloudin' your vision / Stop in the road / I danced with the San Antone Rose / Don't think twice / Jessie Clay & the 12.05 / Trail of time.
LP: . . . . K 56977

LET'S DANCE (Anderson, John Band).
Tracks: / Glenn Miller Medley, The / Abba medley / Scots medley / Neil Diamond medley / Irish medley / Tamla Motown medley / Rock and roll medley / Seventies medley / States medley / Tequila cocktail / Charleston.
LP: . . . . MODLP 1
MC: . . . . MODC 1

SWING THE MOOD (Anderson, John Band).
LP: MODLP 2
MC: MODMC 2

TOO TOUGH TO TAME.
LP: UVL 76008

Anderson, Jon

ANIMATION.
Tracks: / Olympia / Animation / Surrender / All a matter of time / Unlearning / Boundaries / Pressure point / Much better reason / All God's children.
LP: POLD 5044

IN THE CITY OF ANGELS.
Tracks: / Hold on to love / If it wasn't for love / Is it me / In a lifetime / For you / Top of the world / Hurry home / New civilisation / It's on fire / Betcha.
LP: 4606931
MC: 4606934

OLIAS OF SUNHILLOW.
Tracks: / Ocean song / Meeting / Sound out the galleon / Dance of Ranyart Olias / Qoquaq en transic / Solid space / Moon ra chords song of search / To the runner / Naon / Transic to.
LP: K 50261

SONG OF SEVEN.
Tracks: / For you for me / Some are born / Don't forget / Heart of the matter / Hear it / Everybody loves you / Take your time / Days / Song of seven.
LP: K 50756
MC: K4 50756

THREE SHIPS.
Tracks: / Three ships / Forest of fire / Ding dong merrily on high / Save all your love / Holly and the ivy, The / Day of days / 2,000 years / Where were you / Oh holy night / How it hits you / Jingle bells / Easier said than done.
LP: EKT 22

Anderson, Laurie

BIG SCIENCE.
Tracks: / From the air / Big science / Sweaters / Walking and falling / Born never asked / O superman / Example 22 / Let X=X / It tango.
MC: K4 57002
LP: K 57002

HOME OF THE BRAVE (Original soundtrack).
Tracks: / Smoke rings / White lily / Late show, The / Talk normal / Language is a virus from outer space / Radar / Sharkey's night / Credit racket.
LP: 925400 1
MC: 925400 4

MISTER HEARTBREAK.
Tracks: / Sharkey's day / Langue d'armour / Gravity's angel / Blue lagoon / Excellent birds / Sharkey's night.
LP: 925077 1
MC: 925077 4

STRANGE ANGELS.
LP: WX 258
MC: WX 258C

UNITED STATES LIVE.
LPS: 925192 1

Anderson, Leroy

CONDUCTS LEROY ANDERSON (Leroy Anderson & His Orchestra).
LP: MCL 1690

Anderson, Lew

ALL AMERICAN BIG BAND.
LP: SB 2032

Anderson, Lynn

BEST OF LYNN ANDERSON.
LP: NE 1196
MC: CE 2196
MC: GM 0219

COLLECTION: LYNN ANDERSON.
LP: MA 04484
MC: MAMC 94484

COUNTRY GIRL.
LP: CBS 31486
MC: HSC 3401

COUNTRY GIRL (DITTO).
MCSET: DTO 10099

COUNTRY STORE: LYNN ANDERSON.
Tracks: / Rose garden / Sweet talking man / Honey come back / For the good times / Sea of heartbreak / I love how you love me / You're my man / Cry / Killing me softly with his song / Top of the world / It's only make believe / Stay there 'til I get there / Snowbird / Even cowgirls get the blues / Love me tonight / Sunday morning coming down / Bedtime story.
LP: CST 25
MC: CSTK 25

EVEN COWGIRLS GET THE BLUES.
Tracks: / Even cowgirls get the blues / Poor side of town / Shoulder to shoulder / Give you up to get you back / Lonely hearts cafe / Blue baby blue / You thrill me / See through me / Love me tonight / Louisiana 1927.
LP: CBS 84634

GREATEST HITS: LYNN ANDERSON (IMPORT).
Tracks: / Midnight train to Georgia / Rose garden / You don't have to say you love me.
LP: FUN 9036
MC: FUNC 9036

GREATEST HITS:LYNN ANDERSON.
Tracks: / Rose garden / Cry / Can I unlove you / Stay there 'til I get there / That's what loving you has meant to me / Listen to a country song / You're my man / No love at all / Don't say things you don't mean / I'm gonna write a song / Nothing between us.
LP: CBS 32771
MC: 40 32771

HER TOP HITS.
MC: 805

LISTEN TO A COUNTRY SONG.
Tracks: / Listen to a country song / It don't do no good to be a good girl / If you can't be your woman / Fool me / That's what your loving has mean't to me / Take me to your world / There's a party going on / Reason to believe / You're everything / Everybody's reaching out for someone.
LP: SHM 991
MC: HSC 369

LYNN ANDERSON.
Tracks: / Rose garden / I still belong to you / Another lonely night / It's only make believe / Your sweet love lifted me / You're my man / Help me make it through the night / I'm gonna write a song / Cry, cry again / I might as well be here alone / Flying ma chine.
MCSET: DTO 10041

OUTLAW IS JUST A STATE OF MIND.
Tracks: / Isn't it always love / I love how you love me / Child with you tonight / This night won't last forever / I am alone / Say you will / Outlaw is just a state of mind / Come as you are / Come running / Sea of heartbreak.
LP: CBS 83611

ROSE GARDEN.
LP: CBS 64333
MC: 2604044

Anderson, Marian

MARIAN ANDERSON (Bach, Brahms, Schubert).
MC: GK 87911

Anderson, Moira

20 SCOTTISH FAVOURITES.
Tracks: / Dark island / Farewell my love / Soft lowland tongue of the border / Loch Lomond / Always Argyll / John Anderson my Jo / Rowan tree / O Waly Waly / Isle of Mull / Sleeps the noon / O lovely land of Canada / Eriskay love lilt / Way old friends do, The / Ye banks and braes / Durisdeer / Glencoe / Ae fond kiss / My ain folk / Calling me home / Amazing Grace.
MC: LIDC 6031

FAVOURITE SCOTTISH SONGS.
LP: GLN 1015

FOCUS ON MOIRA ANDERSON.
MC: KFOC 28077

GOLDEN MEMORIES (Anderson, Moira & Harry Secombe).
LP: WW 5107
MC: WW 4 5107

LAND FOR ALL SEASONS, A (My Scotland).
Tracks: / Come by the hills / Road to the Isles / Leaving Lismore / Flowers of the forest / Mull of Kintyre / These are my mountains / Mhari's wedding / Loch Maree / De ye mind lang syne / Uist tramping song / Dancing in Kyle / Skye boat song / Wild mountain th yme.
LP: LIDL 6022
MC: LIDC 6022

LOVE OF GOD, THE.
LP: WRD R 3025
MC: WRD C 3025

MOIRA ANDERSON.
MCSET: DTO 10241

MOIRA - IN LOVE.
Tracks: / Time after time / Love is the sweetest thing / You light up my life / Shadow of your smile / Here's that rainy day / And I love you so / More I see you, The / Until it's time for you to go / Nearness of you, The / I won't last a day without you / I just fall in love again / Sometimes when we touch / If (Only on CD.) / I'll walk alone (Only on CD.) / You needed me (Only on CD.) / Somewhere my love (Only on CD.).
LP: DLCL 104
MC: DLCT 104

SCOTTISH SONGS.
MC: TC GLN 1015

SINGS OPERETTA.
Tracks: / Laughing song, The / Don't be cross / Chambre separee / Vilia / Though they say that love is blind / On my lips every kiss is like wine / Letter song, The / My hero / Some day I'll find him.
LP: FBLP 8078
MC: ZCFBL 8078

STAR FOR SUNDAY, A.
LP: MFP 50424
MC: TCMFP 50424

THESE ARE MY SONGS.
LP: SKL 5016

THIS IS MY LOVELY DAY (see Secombe, Harry) (Anderson, Moira & Harry Secombe).

WORLD OF MOIRA ANDERSON VOLUME 2.
MC: KCSP 346

WORLD OF MOIRA ANDERSON VOLUME 5.
MC: KCSP 354

WORLD OF MOIRA ANDERSON VOLUME 1.
MC: KCSP 345

WORLD OF MOIRA ANDERSON VOLUME 4.
MC: KCSP 353

Anderson, Pink

CAROLINA BLUES MAN VOL.1.
Tracks: / My baby left me this morning / Baby please don't go / Mama where did you stay last night / Big house blues / Meet me in the bottom / Weeping willow blues / Baby I'm going away / I had my fun / Everyday in the week.
LP: OBC 504

Anderson, Ray

WHAT BECAUSE.
Tracks: / Alligatory crocodile / Let's fall in love / Warm up, The / I'm just a lucky so-and-so / What because / Off peak / Raven a ning / Waltze for Phoebe.
LP: GV 794531

Anderson, Roshell

NATURES WAY.
LP: ICH 1021
MC: ZCICH 1021

OUTLAWWH CASANOVA, THE.
Tracks: / Wild thang in the rain / Groove thang / Outlawwh Casanova, The / I'm still in love with you / I love you more than you'll ever know / Sunshine lady / Shell shockin' body / Eye for eye.
LP: ICH 1113
MC: ICH 1113MC

STEPPING OUT.
Tracks: / Twilight state / Bodies talking / Peace / Victim of a system / Better love / Passionate transition / Stepping out / Broken heart.
LP: ICH 1053
MC: MCICH 1053

SWEET 'N' SOUR RHYTHM 'N' BLUES.
Tracks: / Come on back / Leaving me / Chokin' kind, The / Grapevine will lie sometimes / Dearest darling / What do you expect from me / You wouldn't believe / Stop doggin' me.
LP: ICH 1035
MC: ZCICH 1035

Anderson, Stuart

ACCORDIONLY YOURS.
Tracks: / Dream valley of Glendaruel, The / Oil rigger, The / Beer barrel polka / Sheen A' Vaan / Captain Carswell / Chariots of fire / Maxwell's rant / Jig of slurs, The / Il silenzio / Jolly beggarman / John Drummond of the Binns / We man fae Skye / Hoe down / March hare, The.
MC: PAS 2643

ON TOP OF THE WORLD.
Tracks: / Millbank cottage etc. / Hawaii tattoo / John MacFadyen of Melfort / Dumfries polka etc, The / Horee Horro etc. / Brig'Motel etc, The / Bandboys / Reine de musette / Heroes of Kohima / Pipers weird crying time & On top of the world / Eight men of Moidart / Donald Maclean's farewell to Oban, etc..
LP: LILP 5080

REUNION.
Tracks: / Accordion polka / My home / Morag of Dunvegan / San Antonio Rose / Flowers of Edinburgh / Jamie Shearer / Cradle song / Millbrae / Linda's wedding / Lochaber gathering / Pottinger's reel / Swiss polka / Swing of the kilt / South Georgia whaling s ong.
LP: GLN 1008

STUART ANDERSON.
Tracks: / Orange blossom special / Mist covered mountains / My own land / Diggy liggy lo / Norman's telly tune / Jaqueline waltz / Happy accordion / Shetland two-step / Lord Lovat's lament / Losefalter's / Mr. A. Spink Snr. / Dancing fingers / Mary of Skye / Circassian circle.
LP: BGC 262
MC: KBGC 262

STUART ANDERSON PLAYS SCOTTISH FAVOURITES.
MC: KITV 418

STUART ANDERSON'S PARTY.
Tracks: / Doon in the wee room / Bonnie Wee Jeannie McCall / Donald where's your troosers / Stuart's song / Marriage / Coulters candy / Ghostie, The / Catch me if you can / Wee kirkcudbright centiped / Come to the Ceilidah.
MC: KITV 502
LP: ITV 502

STUART ANDERSON'S WELCOME.
Tracks: / Donald Ian Rankine, etc. / My Florence / Captain Lumsden / Skyline of Skye / Spanish eyes / Cuckoo waltz / Flett from flotta / Helen Black of Inveran / Triumph march / Mingulay boat song / Crusader's march etc. / Double eagle / Harvest home / Mull of the coal / High Bens.
LP: LILP 5037

Anderson, Tom

RINGING STRINGS (FIDDLE MUSIC OF NORWAY) (see under Buen, Hauk) (Anderson, Tom/Hauk Buen/Vidar Lande/Knut Buen).

SHETLAND FOLK FIDDLING VOL 1 (see under Bain, Aly) (Anderson, Tom & Aly Bain).

SHETLAND FOLK FIDDLING VOL 2 (see Bain, Aly & Tom Anderson) (Anderson, Tom & Aly Bain).

Andersons

TIN PAN ALLEY.
Tracks: / Love me forever / Thanks for the memory / Talking in your sleep / Boogie woogie bugle boy / Reason to believe / Tin pan alley / Daddy / Baby come back / You never done it like that / We don't make each other laugh anymore / It won't be easy / Show me the way to go home.
LP: PRX 23

Andersson, Krister

KRISTER ANDERSSON AND FRIENDS.
LP: DRLP 113

Andes

INTI RAYMI (MUSIC OF THE ANDES) (See Under Inti Raymi) (Inti Raymi).

INTI RAYMI (MUSIC OF THE ANDES) (Various artists).
LP: TUMIR 009
MC: TUMIC 009

MUSIC OF THE ANDES (60'S - 80'S) (Various artists).
LP: ARHOOLIE 3025

Andi Sex Gang

ARCO VALLEY.
LP: FREUD 24
MC: FREUDC 24

BLIND.
LP: JAMS 48

Andi, Su

PROFILE.
MC: BIP 602

SOLILOQUY.
MC: BIP 601

Andreou, Petros

CLASSIC BOUZOUKI, THE.
LP: MSBCR 1

Andrews, Catherine

FRUITS.
LP: PURRLP 2

Andrews, Chris

20 GOLDEN PIECES: CHRIS ANDREWS.
Tracks: / Yesterday man / To whom it concerns / Pretty Belinda / Something on my mind / Stop that girl / I love you / Whatcha gonna do now / Long live love / They've all got their eyes on you / First time / Brown eyes / Silver lining / Sugar daddy / Lazy days / Carole O.K. / Too bad you don't want me / Message understood / Lady oh lady / It's all coming back to me / I'll walk to you.
LP: BDL 2052

Andrews, Elaine

AMAZING ELAINE ANDREWS, THE.
Tracks: / Dark Lochnagar / White rose of Athens / Don't cry for me Argentina / No regrets / My ain folk / Holy city, The / Nobody's child / Amazing grace / Contentment / Lord's my shepherd / Flower of Scotland / In the beginning.
MC: ZCKLP 09
LP: KLP 09

Andrews, Ernie

FROM THE HEART.
Tracks: / On Broadway / Don't let the sun catch you crying / I cover the waterfront / If you could see me now / Again.
LP: . . . . DS 825

TRAVELIN' LIGHT.
LP: . . . . GNPS 10008

Andrews, Harry (nar)

END OF THE TETHER, THE (see under End Of The... (bk).

Andrews, Harvey

25 YEARS ON THE ROAD.
LP: . . . . HYLP 200 105

BRAND NEW DAY.
Tracks: / Friends of mine / We in Berning'm / Unaccompanied / Lullaby / Gift of a brand new day / Song for Phil Ochs / Volendam / Margarita / Boothferry Bridge / Sundays / Long ago, far away.
LP: 2388 595

FRIENDS OF MINE.
LP: . . . . LBEE 003
MC: . . . . KLBEE 003

MARGARITA.
Tracks: / My little boy / Dear Miss Allyson / Lot 204 / Margarita / Long ago, far away / Pinball / Able baker / Hey, old friend .
LP: . . . . LBEE 001
MC: . . . . KLBEE 001

OLD MOTHER EARTH.
LP: . . . . LBEE 004
MC: . . . . KLBEE 004

PG.
Tracks: / Bruges / Cheeky young lad / Yesterday's bread / Songs that Harry wrote / Take a little time / Please don't get on the plane / Room service / She saw him smile / First you lose the rhyming / PG / Binges.
LP: . . . . LBEE 005
MC: . . . . KLBEE 005

WRITER OF SONGS.
LP: . . . . LBEE 002
MC: . . . . KLBEE 002

Andrews, Inez

IF JESUS CAME TO YOUR TOWN TODAY.
Tracks: / Holding on with a smile / People get ready / If Jesus came to town / Joy / No place but up / Praise the Lord / We've got work to do / Mind made up.
LP: . . . . MIR 5004
MC: . . . . ZCMIR 5004

Andrews, Julie

BROADWAY'S FAIR.
LP: 32415
MC: 4032415

JULIE ANDREWS AND CAROL BURNETT AT LINCOLN CENTRE (Andrews, Julie & Carol Burnett).
LP: . . . . AS 31153
MC: . . . . BT 31153

LOVE JULIE.
Tracks: / Out of this world / Love / How deep is the ocean / Island, The / So in love / What are you doing? / Come rain or come shine / Tea for two / My lucky day / Soundsketch, A / Where or when / Nobody does it better.
LP: . . . . PREC 5000
MC: . . . . ZPREC 5000

LOVE ME TENDER.
Tracks: / Crazy / Some days are diamonds / See the funny little clown / When I dream (hey won't you play) / Another somebody done somebody wrong song / You don't bring me flowers / I wish I could hurt that way again / Valley that time forgot, The / Blanket on the ground / Love is a place where two people fall / We love each other / Lyin' in my arms.
LP: . . . . JULIE 1
LP: . . . . SPALP 7550
MC: . . . . ZCSPL 7550

SOUND OF CHRISTMAS, THE.
Tracks: / Hark the herald angels sing / In the bleak mid winter / See, amid the winter's snow / It came upon a midnight clear / O little town of Bethlehem / What child is this / Silent night / Holy boy, The / Away in a manger / Rockin' / I wonder as I wander / O come all ye faithful / Patapan / Secret of Christmas, The.
LP: C5-511
MC: C5K-511
LP: . . . . CBS 31522
MC: . . . . PWKMC 4035

Andrews, June (nar)

SWEET ROSEMARY (see under Sweet Rosemary (bk)).

Andrews, Lucilla

FLOWERS FROM THE DOCTOR (See under Flowers From the...) (Clarke, Marie).

Andrews, Mark

BIG BOY (Andrews, Mark & The Gents).
Tracks: / West one / Say it's all right / Talking with your body / Don't let go / Big boy / Laid on a plate / Born to be wild / Does it get to you / Show me / Let yourself go / In a jam.
LP: . . . . AMLH 68513

Andrews, Ruby

KISS THIS.
Tracks: / I want to rock with you baby no.2 / Since I met you / Que pasa / To the other woman (I'm the other woman) / Kiss this / Lovey dovey / Throw some more dirt on me (the shacking song) / Loving you no.44 / I got what I want at home / As in always....
LP: . . . . ICH 1104
MC: . . . . ICH 1104 MC

Andrews Sisters

16 ORIGINAL HITS.
MC: . . . . MC 1634

20 GREATEST HITS: ANDREWS SISTERS.
LP: . . . . N 22006
MC: 42006

ANDREWS SISTERS.
Tracks: / Begin the beguine / I'll be with you in apple blossom time / Roll out the barrel / Don't sit under the apple tree / Don't bring Lulu.
LP: . . . . AWE 4
LP: 022-58097
MC: 1A 222-58097

AT THE MICROPHONE.
LP: . . . . TT 305

BEAT ME DADDY EIGHT TO THE BAR.
Tracks: / Beat me daddy, eight to the bar / Boogie woogie bugle boy / I'll be with you in apple blossom time / Beer barrel polka / I can dream, can't I / Pennsylvania polka / Hold tight / Oh Johnny, oh Johnny oh / Rum and coca cola / Down in the valley / Bei mir bist du schon / Shrine of St Cecilia / Rhumboogie / Joseph Joseph / South American way / Strip polka.
LP: . . . . MFP 50556
MC: . . . . TCMFP 50556

BEI MIR BIST DU SCHON.
LPPD: . . . . AR 30054

BEST OF THE ANDREWS SISTERS, THE.
Tracks: / Joseph, Joseph / South American way / Oh Johnny, oh Johnny oh / Rum and coca cola / Strip polka / Sonny boy / Beat me daddy, eight to the bar / Well all right / Pennsylvania polka / Beer barrel polka / Bei mir bist du schon / Tico tico / Oh ma ma / Don't sit under the apple tree / Hold tight / Ti-pi-tin / Boogie woogie bugle boy / I can dream, can't I / I'll be with you in Apple Blossom time / Rhumboogie / Say si si / Yes, my darling daughter / I wanna be loved / There will never be another you.
2LP: . . . . MCLD 604

BING CROSBY, JUDY GARLAND AND THE ANDREWS SISTERS (see under Crosby, Bing) (Andrews Sisters/Bing Crosby/Judy Garland).

CHRISTMAS WITH THE ANDREWS SISTERS.
Tracks: / Winter wonderland / Jingle bells / Twelve days of Christmas, The.
LP: . . . . SHM 3253
MC: . . . . HSC 3253

EARLY YEARS, 1937-42.
Tracks: / Just a simple melody / Why talk about love / I married an angel / Love is where you find it / When a Prince of a fella meets a Cinderella / Chico's love song / Let's have another one / I want my mama / Oh he loves me / I wish I had a dime / Music makers / Sleepy serenade / Why don't we do this more often / Honey / What to do / Zoot suit, A.
LP: . . . . OFF 12005
MC: . . . . OFF 412005

EARLY YEARS, VOL.2.
Tracks: / Where have we met before? / It's easier said than done / From the land of the sky blue water / Oh, faithless maid / Lullaby to a little jitterbug / Goodbye, goodbye / You don't know how much you can suffer / Rock, rock, rock-a-bye baby / Cock-eyed mayor of Kaunakakai, The / Let's pack our things and trek / Hit the road / Sweet Molly Malone / Mean to me / Jack of all trades / Nickel serenade, The / He said, she said.
LP: . . . . OFF 12011

GOLDEN GREATS: ANDREWS SISTERS.
Tracks: / Boogie woogie bugle boy / Bei mir bist du schon / Don't sit under the apple tree / Rum and coca cola / Beat me daddy, eight to the bar / Boogie woogie piggy, The / Rhumboogie / House of blue lights / Say si si / Oh Johnny, oh Johnny oh / Beer barrel polka / South American way / Shoo shoo baby / Strip polka / I'll be with you in apple blossom time / Hold tight.
LP: . . . . MCM 5015
MC: 1CMC 5015

GREATEST HITS: ANDREWS SISTERS.
LP: 27019
MC: 47019

GREATEST HITS: ANDREWS SISTERS (IMPORT).
Tracks: / Beer barrel polka / I can dream, can't I / When the midnight choo choo leaves for Alabama.
LP: . . . . FUN 9004
MC: . . . . FUNC 9004

HOLD TIGHT IT'S THE ANDREWS SISTERS.
LP: . . . . DBD 12
MC: . . . . DBDC 12

JUMPIN' JIVE.
Tracks: / Jumpin' jive (jim, jam' jump), The / Tu-li-tulip time / Ooooo-boom / Tuxedo Junction / Johnny Peddler / Daddy / Coffee song, The / Straighten up and fly right / Three little sisters / I'll pray for you / Pennsylvania 6-5000 / Rainy night in Rio, A / Mister five by five / Money is the root of all evil / Rancho pillow / Massachusetts.
LP: . . . . MCL 1789
MC: . . . . MCLC 1789

SAYS MY HEART.
Tracks: / Says my heart / Why talk about love? / Love is where you find it / It's easier said than done / Ooo Oo-oh boom / Oh faithless maid / Lullaby to a little jitterbug / Joseph Joseph / Tu-li-tulip time / Shortenin' bread / Bei mir bist du schon / Just a simple melody / Billy boy / Where have we met before / Ti-pi-tin / From the land of sky-blu water / Sha sha / Oh mama / Hold tight / Goodbye, goodbye.
LP: . . . . CHD 161
MC: . . . . MCHD 161

SING... AND WIN.
Tracks: / Any bonds today? / You're a lucky fellow, Mr. Smith / Yi, yi, yi, yi / At Sonya's cafe / Helena / Boolie boolie boon / Hummingbird, The / East of the rockies / Here comes the navy / I've got a guy in Kalamazoo / When Johnny comes marching home / There'll be a jubilee / Great day / Smile, smile, smile / Welcome song, The / Put that ring on my finger.
LP: . . . . OFF 12008
MC: . . . . OFF 412008

SING, SING, SING.
Tracks: / Beat me daddy, eight to the bar / I'll be with you in apple blossom time / Oh Johnny, oh Johnny oh / Bei mir bist du schon / Sing, sing, sing / Pennsylvania 6-5000 / Joseph Joseph / In the mood / Boogie woogie bugle boy / Don't sit under the apple tree / Hold tight / I can dream, can't I / I got a girl in Kalamazoo / Coffee song, The / Lullaby of Broadway / Elmer's tune / Alexander's ragtime band (CD only.) / Don't be that way (CD only.) / Yes my darling daughter (CD only.) / Say si si (CD only.).
LP: . . . . MFP 5841
MC: . . . . TCMFP 5841

SING THE DANCING 20'S.
Tracks: / Last night on the back porch / When Francis dances with me / Back in your own back yard / Keep your skirts down / Mary Ann / Japanese Sandman / Show me the way to go home / Don't bring Lulu / Me too / That naughty waltz / Smile will go a long long way, A / Barney Google / Collegiate.
LP: . . . . ED 2604171
MC: . . . . ED 2604174

UNFORGETTABLE: ANDREWS SISTERS (16 Golden Classics).
Tracks: / I'll be with you in apple blossom time / Woody Woodpecker / Near you / Shoo shoo baby / Underneath the arches / Ferryboat serenade / Toolie oolie doolie / East of the sun / In the mood / I wanna be loved / Civilization / Rumours are flying / Strip polka / You call everybody darling / She wore a yellow ribbon / Don't be that way / Sing, sing, sing / If I had a boy like you / Piccolo Pete / Don't sit under the apple tree.
LP: . . . . UNLP 025
MC: . . . . UNMC 025

VERY BEST: ANDREWS SISTERS.
MC: . . . . HSC 3234
LP: . . . . SHM 3234

VERY BEST OF THE ANDREWS SISTERS.
Tracks: / Boogie woogie piggy, The / Beat me daddy, eight to the bar / Rhumboogie / House of blue lights / Say si si / Oh Johnny, oh Johnny oh / Boogie woogie bugle boy / Don't sit under the apple tree / Rum and coca cola / Beer barrel polka / South American way / Bei mir bist du schon / Shoo shoo baby / Strip polka / I'll be with you in apple blossom time / Hold tight.
LP: . . . . MCL 1635
MC: . . . . MCLC 1635

Andrews, William

CLASSICS OF IRISH PIPING VOL 2 (Andrews, William & Liam Walsh).
Tracks: / Portlaw reel, The / Faithful brown cow, The / Billy Taylor's fancy / Garden of daisies, The / Bank of the Suir, The / Mountain lark, The / Dan McCarthy's fancy / Cliffs of Moher, The / Saddle the pony / Yellow John / Kitty's rambles / Speed the plough / Johnny Gorman / Two single jigs / May Day / Cuckoo's nest, The / Smash the windows / Rocky road to Dublin / Bonnie Kate / First house in Connaught, The / Munster buttermilk.
LP: 12T 262

Andreyev, V

SUITE (Andreyev, V & Russian Folk Orchestra).
LP: . . . . C 010667-8

Andromeda Strain

ANDROMEDA STRAIN, THE (Original soundtrack) (Various artists).
LP: . . . . KRS 5513

Andrzej Wajda Trilogy

ANDRZEJ WAJDA TRILOGY (see "Canal 'Canal/Ashes and diamonds/ Gen.X'") (Various artists).

Andy, Bob

BOB ANDY'S DUB BOOK AS REVEALED TO MAD PROFESSOR.
LP: . . . . AV 007 STLP

FREELY.
LP: . . . . AV 006 STLP

FRIENDS.
LP: . . . . AV 001 STLP

LOTS OF LOVE AND I.
LP: . . . . SKYLP 15

MUSIC INSIDE ME, THE.
Tracks: / Make mine music / Nyah / Let them say / Hell and go broke loose / Desperate lover / Music inside me / Check it out / Fire burning / Rock it down / Feeling soul.
LP: . . . . TSL 1003

REALLY TOGETHER (Andy, Bob & Marcia Griffiths).
LP: . . . . AV 003 STLP

RETROSPECTIVE.
LP: . . . . AV 002 STLP
MC: . . . . AV 002 STC
LP: . . . . HB 32

SONG BOOK.
LP: . . . . SOL 1121

Andy Capp (show)

ANDY CAPP (London Stage Cast, with Tom Courtenay) (Various artists).
Tracks: / On my street: *Various artists* / I ought to be ashamed of myself: *Various artists* / We're waiting: *Various artists* / Good evening: *Various artists* / Good old legs: *Various artists* / I have a dream: *Various artists* / Oh gawd men...beasts: *Various artists* / Point of view: *Various artists* / Spend, spend, spend: *Various artists* / Don't tell me that again: *Various artists* / Frozen moments: *Various artists*/ I could not have dreamed him: *Various artists* / Hermione: *Various artists* / Goin' to Barcelona: *Various* artists / When you've lived in love with someone: *Various artists* / Mr. Scrimmett: *Various artists* / Trouble with people: *Various artists* / It's better to be in simple harmony: *Various artists* / Wedding: *Various artists*.
LP: . . . . KEY 4
MC: . . . . KEYC 4

Andy, Horace

BEST OF HORACE ANDY.
Tracks: / Serious thing / Live of a woman / Something on my mind / Just say who / Skylarking / You are my angel / Ain't no sunshine / No man is an island / Bless you / Man to man / Forward home.
LP: . . . . VSLP 5009

BIG BAD MAN, THE.
LP: . . . . HR 001

CLASH OF THE ANDYS (Andy, Horace & Patrick).
LP: . . . . Unknown

CONFUSION.
LP: . . . . MHLP 001

DANCE HALL STYLE.

LP: W 1383

EARTH MUST BE HELL (See under Wailers) (Wailers, The).

ELEMENTARY (LP) (Andy, Horace & The Rhythm Queen).
LP: ROUGH 82

EXCLUSIVELY.
LP: SGL 107

FRESH.
LP: BW 104

HAUL AND JACK UP.
LP: LALP 14

REGGAE SUPERSTAR'S MEET (see under Brown,Dennis).

SHAME AND SCANDAL.
LP: MRLP 8801

SHOWCASE.
LP: VSLP 2005

THINGS FOR YOU AND I.
LP: TSL 107

Andy Pandy...

ANDY PANDY AND TEDDY AT THE ZOO (Churchman, Ysanne (nar)).
MC: LL 41 8022 4

ANDY PANDY AND THE BADGER (Churchman, Ysanne (nar)).
MC: LL 41 8021 4

ANDY PANDY AND THE DOVECOT (Various artists).
MC: LL 41 8007 4

ANDY PANDY AND THE DUCKLINGS (Various artists).
MC: LL 41 8012 4

ANDY PANDY AND THE RED MOTOR CAR (Various artists).
MC: LL 41 8008 4

ANDY PANDY AND THE SPOTTED COW (Various artists).
MC: LL 41 8010 4

ANDY PANDY AND THE WILLOW TREE (Various artists).
MC: LL 41 8011 4

Andy, Patrick

SHUTDOWN VOLUME 7 (Also see Smith Wayne) (Andy, Patrick & Wayne Smith).
LP: JJ 193

TWO NEW SUPERSTARS (Andy, Patrick & Frankie Jones).
Tracks: / What a hell / Not in this race / Vision / You are my special lady / Little girl / Run come / Gee pee / Your love / Nice like she / Get out of my life.
LP: BS 1065

Andy & The Bey ...

'ROUND MIDNIGHT (Andy & The Bey Sisters).
Tracks: / Love is just around the corner / Squeeze me / Hallelujah I love her so / Round midnight / Feeling good / God bless the child / Tammy / Everybody loves my baby / Solitude / Every time we say goodbye.
LP: PR 7411

Aneka

ANEKA.
Tracks: / Ooh shooby doo doo lang / Tu whit tu whoo / Japanese boy / Put out the light / Come back to me / Ahiriman / It'll be alright / Be my only Karma / I was free / Little lady.
LP: HANLP 3
MC: ZCHAN 003

Aneke, Aster

ASTER.
LP: TERRA 107
MC: TERRAC 107

Angel

SINFUL.
Tracks: / Don't take your love / L.A. lady / Just can't take it / You can't buy love / Bad time / Waited a long time / I'll bring the whole world to your door / I'll never fall in love again / Wild and hot / Lovers live on.
LP: CAL 2046

Angel City

DARKROOM.
Tracks: / No secrets / Ivory stairs / Wasted sleepless nights / Darkroom / Face the day / Night comes early / Straightjacket / Moment / Poor baby / Devil's gate.
LP: EPC 84502

FACE TO FACE.
Tracks: / Take a long line / Marseilles / After the rain / Am I ever gonna see your face again / Shadow boxer / Comin' down / Out of the blue / Can't shake it / Waiting for the world / No exit.
LP: EPC 84253

NIGHT ATTACK.
Tracks: / Long night / Living on the outside / Back on you / Fashion and fame / Night attack / City out of control / Talk about you / Runnin' wild / Nothin' to win / Storm the Bastille.
LP: EPC 85480

Angel Corpus Christi

ACCORDION POP VOL 1.
LP: STIM 001

EIGHTIES, THE.
LP: NBT 007

I LOVE NEW YORK.
LP: CRIMLP 128

WAKE UP AND CRY.
LP: CRIMLP 137

Angel Heart (film)

ANGEL HEART (Film soundtrack) (Various artists).
Tracks: / Harry Angel: *Jones, Trevor and Courtney Pine* / Honeymoon blues: *Smith, Bessie* / Nightmare: *Jones,* Trevor and Courtney Pine / Girl of ...: *Gray, Glen & The Casa Loma Orchestra* / I got this thing about chickens: *Jones,* Trevor and Courtney Pine / Right key but the wrong keyhole: *Various artists* / Rainy rainy day: *McGhee, Brownie*/ Looking for Johnny: *Jones, Trevor and Courtney Pine* / Soul on fire: *Baker, Laverne* / Bloodmare: *Jones, Trevor and Courtney Pine* / Johnny Favourite: *Jones, Trevor and Courtney Pine*.
LP: AN 8709
MC: ANC 8709
MC: ICM 2025
LP: ILPM 2025

Angel & The Soldier

ANGEL AND THE SOLDIER BOY, THE (Film Soundtrack) (Clannad & Tom Conti).
Tracks: / Dream in the night, A / Pirates, The / Soldier boy, The / Angel, The / Flies, The / Spider, The / Cat, The / Jolly Rodger, The / Into the picture / Pirates merrymaking / Finding the key / Pirates on the island / Sea and storm / Love theme, The / Chase, The / Toys, The / Rescue, The / Back to the book / Dream in the night (instrumental).
LP: PL 74328
MC: PK 74328

Angel Voices

NEW DAY.
Tracks: / You are the new day / Orinoco flow / Pie Jesu / San Damiano / Always there (Howard's Way theme) / One voice / Adoramus te / Bright eyes / Song of joy / Sailing / Amazing grace / One day.
LP: 211280
MC: 411280

Angel Witch

ANGEL WITCH.
Tracks: / Angel Witch / Gorgon / Atlantis / White witch / Confused / Sorceress / Sweet danger / Free man / Angel of death / Devil's tower.
LP: BRON 532
MC: BRONC 532
MC: CLAMC 239
LP: CLALP 239

DOCTOR PHIBES.
Tracks: / Angel Witch / Atlantis / White Witch / Confused / Sorceress / Loser / Doctor Phibes / Gorgon / Sweet danger / Free man / Angel of death / Devil's tower / Suffer.
LP: RAWLP 025

FRONTAL ASSAULT.
Tracks: / Frontal assault / Dream world / Rendezvous with the blade / Religion (born again) / Straight from hell / She don't lie / Take to the wing / Something wrong / Undergods.
LP: KILP 4003

LIVE.
Tracks: / Angel of death / Confused / Gorgon / Extermination day / Flight 19 / White Witch / Sweet danger / Sorceress / Baphamet / Atlantis / Angel Witch.
LP: ZORRO 1
MC: TZORRO 1

SCREAMIN' 'N'BLEEDIN'.
Tracks: / Who's to blame / Child of the night / Evil games / Afraid of the dark / Screamin' n' bleedin' / Reawakening / Waltz the night / Goodbye / Fatal kiss / UXV.
LP: KILP 4001

Angelic Gospel Singers

40 YEARS.
LP: MAL 04398

I'VE GOT VICTORY.
LP: MAL 04407

OUT OF THE DEPTHS.
LP: MAL 4424

Angelic Upstarts

ANGEL DUST (THE COLLECTED HIGHS).
Tracks: / Murder of Liddel Towers, The / Police oppression / I'm an upstart / Teenage warning / Never 'ad nothin' / Last night another soldier / Two million voices / Kids on the street / England / Hearts lament / Shotgun solution / Never say die / Woman in disguise / Solidarity / Lust for glory / Never give up / Waiting, hating / Reason why? / Nobody was saved / Geordies wife / Loneliness of the long distance runner / 42nd Street / Burglar, The / Five flew over the cuckoo's nest / As the passion / Young punk, A / Where we started.
LP: GRAM 07
MC: CGRAM 07

BLOOD ON THE TERRACES.
LP: LINK LP 019

BOOTLEGS AND RARITIES.
Tracks: / Kids on the street / Stick's diary / Last night another soldier / I'm an upstart / Student power / Teenage warning / Liddle towers / We are the people / Tommy, never again / Box on / Solidarity (Polish folk song.) / Tut tut shuffle, The / Gonna be a st ar.
LP: DOJOLP 7

LAST TANGO IN MOSCOW.
LP: PIK 004
LP: RAZ 31

LIVE ANGELIC UPSTARTS.
Tracks: / Teenage warning / Never had nothing / Four words / Last night another soldier / Guns for the Afghan rebels / Mr. Politician / Shotgun solution / Pride without prejudice / England / Police oppression / Kids on the street / I understand / You're nicked / Two million voices / I'm an upstart.
LP: ZEM 102

LIVE IN YUGOSLAVIA.
LP: HCLP 002M
LP: RAZM 32

POWER OF THE PRESS.
LP: GAS 4012
LP: CLINK 006

STILL FROM THE HEART.
Tracks: / Never say die / Flames of Brixton / Action man / Wasted / Here comes trouble / Theme for lost souls / I stand accused / Black knights of the 80's / Cry wolf / Soldier.
LP: ZONO 106

TEENAGE WARNING.
Tracks: / Teenage warning / Student power / Young ones, The / Never again / We are the people / Liddle towers / I'm an upstart / Small town small mind / Youth leader / Do anything / Let's speed / Leave me alone.
LP: K 56717
MC: K4 56717

TWO MILLION VOICES.
Tracks: / Two million voices / Ghost town / You're nicked / England / Heath's lament / Guns for the Afghan rebels / I understand / Mensi's marauders / Mr. Politician / Kids on the street / Jimmy / We're gonna take the world / Last night another soldier / I wish.
LP: ZONO 104

WE GOTTA GET OUT OF THIS PLACE.
Tracks: / Never 'ad nothin' / Police oppression / Lonely man of spandau / Their destiny is coming / Shotgun solution / King coal / Out of control / Ronnie is a rocker / Listen to the steps / Can't kill a legend / Capital city / We gotta get out of this plac e.
LP: K 56806
MC: K4 56806

Angelo, Bobby

BABY SITTIN' (OLD GOLD) (See Valence, Ricky-Tell Laura I love her).

Angelo, Don

CLASH (see under Saw, Tenor) (Angelo, Don/ Tenor Saw).

GOLDEN HEN, THE (see under Saw, Tenor) (Angelo, Don/ Tenor Saw).

Angels

BEYOND SALVATION.
LP: CHR 1677
MC: ZCHR 1677

LIVE FROM ANGEL CITY.
LP: ACE 001

Angels Are Coming

ANGELS ARE COMING (Various artists).
MC: SGC 1

Anger, Darol

CHIAROSCURO (Anger, Darol & Mike Marshall).
Tracks: / Dolphins / Saurian's farewell / Beneath the farewell / Beloved infidel / Placenza / Coming back / Dardanelles / Spring gesture.
LP: 371043-1
MC: 371043-4
LP: WHA 1043

DUO, THE (Anger, Darol & Mike Marshall).
LP: ROUNDER 0168
MC: ROUNDER 0168C

FIDDLISTICS.
LP: K 8

JAZZ VIOLIN CELEBRATION: RECORDED LIVE.
LP: F 22
MC: C 22

LIVE AT MONTREUX: DAROL ANGER (Anger, Darol/Barbara Higbie Quintet).
LP: 371036-1
MC: 371036-4
LP: WHA 1036

TIDELINE (Anger, Darol & Barbara Higbie).
Tracks: / Tideline / Movie / Above the fog / Keep sleeping / Onyame / True story / Fortunate / Gemini / Gualala / Lifeline.
LP: 371021-1
MC: 371021-4
LP: WHA 1021

Angkor Wat

CORPUS CHRISTI.
LP: ZORRO 5

WHEN OBSCENITY BECOMES THE NORM...AWAKE.
LP: RO 94571

Anglaspel

LAPPLAND.
LP: DRLP 112

Angola Prisoner's

ANGOLA PRISONER'S BLUES (Various artists).
LP: ARHOOLIE 2011

Angola-Bonga

NOIR TON PAY.
LP: PS 890

Angrum, Steve

WITH KID SHEIK'S STORYVILLE RAMBLERS.
LP: JCE 16

Angst

CRY FOR HAPPY.
LP: SST 206
MC: SSTC 206

MYSTERY SPOT.
Tracks: / Outside my window / Back in January / It's mine / What's the difference / Looking for a reason / Colours / Mind average / One life (out of 9) / Wallee Street / I remember / Ah, the morning / Red wing.
LP: SST 111

Angus

TRACK OF DOOM.
LP: MEGATON 0017

WARRIOR OF THE WORLD.
Tracks: / Warriors of the world / Moving fast / Leather and lace / Money satisfies / Black despair / 2086 / Freedom fighter / I'm in love with love / If Gods in heaven.
LP: MEGATON 020

Angus Strathspey ...

ANGUS STRATHSPEY AND REEL SOCIETY (Angus Strathspey & Reel Society).
Tracks: / March strathspey and reel / Hornpipes / Reels / Slow air / Two step / Strathspey and reels / Marches / Reels (2) / March strathspey and reel (2) / Jigs / Marches (2) / Slow air (2) / March strathspey and reel (3) / Slow air, strathspey and reel / Reels (3).
MC: CWGR 136

Anhrefn

RASTA.
LP: PLAY LP 7

SHEEP SKATEBOARDS AND WELLIES.
Tracks: / Menthyg wal / Pres am gi / Malu pem / Defaid / Dagrau / Cornel / Pryna si / Dawns y dawlau / Dyfodol disglair.
LP: PLAY LP 1

UNTITLED WORKERS PLAYTIME.
LP: PLAY LP 5

Animal Alphabet

ANIMAL ALPHABET, THE (Well Loved Tales Up to Age 9).
MC: PLB 204

Animal Fairyland

ANIMAL FAIRYLAND (Various artists).
MC: STC 010

Animal House

ANIMAL HOUSE (Film soundtrack) (Various artists).
Tracks: / Faber College theme: *Berstein, Elmer* / Louie Louie: *Belushi, John* / Twistin' the night away: *Belushi,*

John / Tossin' and turnin': *Lewis, Bobby* / Shama lama ding dong: *Various artists* / Hey Paula: *Paul* and Paula / Animal house: *Bishop, Stephen* / Money (that's what I want): *Belushi, John* / Let's dance: *Montez*, Chris / Dream girl: *Bishop, Stephen* / (What a) wonderful world: *Cooke, Sam* / Shout: *Various artists*/ Intro: *Various artists*.
LP: **MCF 2868**
LP: **MCL 1867**
MC: **MCLC 1867**

Animal (label)

ANIMAL SAMPLER (Various artists).
Tracks: / Run through the jungle: *Gun Club* / Dancing in heaven: *Steding, Walter* / Pantherman: *Panther Burns*/ Horse song, The: *Pop, Iggy* / Like calling up thunder: *Gun Club* / I'm on this rocket: *Panther Burns*/ Villagers, The: *Pop, Iggy* / All the way: *Steding, Walter* / I don't know samba: *Tate, Snuky* / Twitch: *White, James & The Blacks* / Babylon under pressure: *Tate, Snuky* / Irresistible impulse: *White, James & The Blacks*.
LP: **CAGED 1**
MC: **ZCAGED 1**

Animal Liberation

ANIMAL LIBERATION (Various artists).
Tracks: / Don't kill the animals: *Hagen/ Lovich* / Monkey in a bin: *Attrition* / Skin: *Siouxsie & Banshees*/ Silent cry: *Chris & Cosey* / Supernature: *Lovich, Lene* / Cruel circus: *Colourfield* / Hunter, The: *Van Acker, Luc* / Hanging fire: *Shriekback* / Assault and battery: *Jones, Howard* / Meat is murder: *Smiths, The*.
LP: **WAXUK 025**

Animal Logic

ANIMAL LOGIC.
Tracks: / There's a spy (in the house of love) / Someday we'll understand / Winds of Santa Ana / I'm through with love / Someone to come home to / As soon as the sun goes down / I still feel for you / Elijah / Firing up the sunset gun / I'm sorry baby (I want you in my life).
LP: **V 2590**
MC: **TCV 2590**

Animal Nightlife

LUSH LIFE.
Tracks: / Why couldn't your black heart tell a white lie / Always your humble slave / T.V. scene / Sweet smell of success, The / Boys with the best intentions / Luck / Month / Last hotel in the world / Breakaway / War I lost, The.
LP: **DIX 71**
MC: **CDIX 71**

SHANGRI-LA.
LP: **ILPS 9830**
MC: **ICT 9830**

Animal Tales

ANIMAL TALES (Various artists).
MC: **ST 3636**

Animals

ALL TIME GREATEST HITS.
Tracks: / I'm crying / House of the rising sun / Boom boom / I'm mad again / Bring it on home to me / We've gotta get out of this place / Story of Bo Diddley / How you've changed / Bright lights big city / Road runner / Worried life blues / It's my life / Bury my body / I've been around / Dimples / I'm in love again / Girl can't help it, The / For Miss Caulker / Talkin' about you / She said yeah.
2LP: **IC 148 50290/91**

ANIMAL TRACKS.
Tracks: / Mess around / How you've changed / Hallelujah / I love her so / I believe to my soul / Worried life blues / Roberta / I ain't got you / Bright lights big city / Let the good times roll / For Miss Caulker / Road runner.
LP: **FA 41 3110 1**
MC: **FA 41 3110 4**
LP: **33SX 1708**

ANIMALISMS.
LP: **LK 4797**

ANIMALS GOLDEN DECADE.
MC: **KNMC 10013**

ANIMALS, THE.
LP: **33SX 1669**

ANIMALS WITH SONNY BOY WILLIAMSON (Animals/Sonny Boy Williamson).
Tracks: / Sonny's slow walk / Pontiac blues / My babe / I don't care no more / Baby don't you worry / Night time is the right time / I'm gonna put you down / Fattening frogs for snakes / Nobody but you / Bye bye Sonny bye bye / Coda.
LP: **LIK 45**

ARK.
Tracks: / Loose change / Love is for all time / My favourite enemy / Prisoner of the light / Being there / Hard times / Night / Trying to get to you / Just can't get enough / Melt down / Gotta get back to you / Crystal nights.
LP: **SP 70037**

BEFORE WE WERE SO RUDELY INTERRUPTED.
Tracks: / Last clean shirt / It's all over now, baby blue / Fire on the sun / As the crow flies / Please send me someone to love / Many rivers to cross / Just a little bit / Riverside County / Lonely avenue / Fool, The.
LP: **2486 266**
MC: **3186 095**
LP: **231 410 4**

BEST OF THE ANIMALS, THE.
LP: **RMB 5638**

COMPLETE ANIMALS, THE.
Tracks: / Boom boom / Talking 'bout you / Blue feeling / Dimples / Baby let me take you home / Gonna send you back to Walker / Baby what's wrong / House of the rising sun, The / F-E-E-L / I'm mad again / Right time, The / Around and around / I'm in love again / Bury my body / She said yeah / I'm crying / Take it easy / Story of Bo Diddley, The / Girl can't help it, The / I've been around / Memphis Tennessee / Don't let me be misunderstood / Club a gogo / Roadrunner / Hallelujah I love her so / Don't want much / I believe to my soul / Let the good times roll / Mess around / How you've changed / I ain't got you / Roberts / Bright lights big city / Worried life blues / Bring it on home to me / For Miss Caulker / I can't believe it / We gotta get out of this place / It's my life / I'm gonna change the world.
2LP: **EM 1367**
MCSET: **TCEM 1367**

EP COLLECTION, THE: ANIMALS.
Tracks: / House of the rising sun / Gonna send you back to Walker / I'm crying / Baby let me take you home / Boom boom / Around and around / Dimples / I've been around / I'm in love again / Bury my body / I'm mad again / She said yeah / Bring it on home to me / Don't let me be misunderstood / We've gotta get out of this place / Club a gogo / Now you've changed / I believe to my soul / Let the good times roll / Worried life blues.
LP: **SEE 244**
MC: **SEEK 244**

ERIC BURDON & THE ANIMALS (see under Burdon, Eric).

GREATEST HITS LIVE: ANIMALS.
Tracks: / It's too late / House of the rising sun / It's my life / Don't bring me down / Don't let me be misunderstood / I'm crying / Bring it on home to me / O lucky man / Boom boom / We've gotta get out of this place.
LP: **IRSA 7043**
MC: **IRSC 7043**

HOUSE OF THE RISING SUN.
Tracks: / House of the rising sun / Don't let me be misunderstood / I'm crying / It's my life.
LP: **048 CRY 50731**
MC: **248 CRY 50731**
LP: **1916691**
MC: **1916694**

HOUSE OF THE RISING SUN (3LP SET).
LPS: **PM 155 153 3**

INSIDE LOOKING OUT.
Tracks: / Inside looking out / Outcast / Don't bring me down / Cheating / Help me girl / See see rider / One monkey don't stop now show / Maudie / Sweet little sixteen / You're on my mind / Clapping / Gin house blues / Squeeze her, tease her / What am I living for? / I put a spell on you / That's all I am to you / She'll return it / Mama told me not to come / I just wanna make love to you / Boom boom / Big boss man / Pretty thing.
2LP: **NEDLP 153**
MCSET: **NEDMC 153**

LIVE AT THE CLUB A-GO-GO, NEWCASTLE.
Tracks: / Let it rock / Gotta find my baby / Bo Diddley / Almost grown / Dimples / Boom boom (out goes the light) / C jam blues .
LP: **LIK 46**

MOST OF THE ANIMALS.
LP: **MFP 5218**
MC: **TCMFP 5218**
LP: **33SX 6035**
LP: **RVLP 05**

NEWCASTLE DECEMBER 1963 (Animals/Sonny Boy Williamson).
Tracks: / Sonny's slow walk / Pontiac blues / My babe / I don't care no more / Baby don't you worry / Night time is the right time / I'm gonna put you down / Fattening frogs for snakes / Nobody but you / Bye bye sonny / Bye bye coda.
LP: **CR 30199**

TRACKIN' THE HITS.
LP: **LIK 72**
MC: **TCLIK 72**

Animals of

ANIMALS OF FARTHING WOOD (Colin Dann) (Gordon, Hannah (nar)).
MCSET: **LFP 7505**

Animashaun, Akanni

AKANNI DE ALAWIYE DRIN.
LP: **SHAN 43022**

Animotion

ANIMOTION.
LP: **837 314-1**
MC: **837 314-4**

OBSESSION.
Tracks: / Obsession / Let him go / Everything's leading / Turn around / Fun fun fun / Tremble / Holding you / Run to me / Open door.
LP: **MERH 70**
MC: **MERHC 70**

STRANGE BEHAVIOUR.
Tracks: / I want you / I engineer / Strange behaviour / Stealing time / Anxiety / Out of control / Stranded / Essence / One step ahead / Staring down the demons.
LP: **MERH 88**
MC: **MERHC 88**

Anita

ANITA.
LP: **RD 009**

Anka, Paul

3 GREAT GUYS (see under Cooke, Sam) (Anka, Paul/Sam Cooke/Neil Sedaka).

21 GOLDEN HITS.
Tracks: / Diana / Put your head on my shoulder / Lonely boy / Time to cry / Puppy love / I love you in the same old way / You are my destiny / Crazy love / Don't you ever leave me / Summer's gone / Adam and Eve / Don't gamble with love / I'm still waiting here for you / I love you baby / It doesn't matter anymore / Tonight my love, tonight / My home town / Cinderella / Love land / Dance on little girl / Longest dance.
LP: **INTS 5048**
MC: **INTK 5048**

BEST OF PAUL ANKA.
Tracks: / My way / Yesterday my life / Do I love you / That's what living's about / We make it happen / Les filles de paris / She's a lady / Jubilation / Something good is coming / Love is / Let me be the one.
LP: **252 211-1**
MC: **252 211-4**

BEST OF PAUL ANKA (RHINO).
Tracks: / My way / Yesterday my life / Do I love you? / That's what living's about / We make it happen / Les filles de Paris / She's a lady / Jubilation / Something good is coming / Love is / Let me be the one.
LP: **RNLP 70220**

DIANA.
Tracks: / Diana / Put your head on my shoulder / Lonely boy / Time to cry / I love you in the same old way / You are my destiny / Crazy love / I love you baby / Adam and Eve / Tonight my love, tonight.
LP: **MFP 5773**
MC: **TCMFP 5773**

GOLDEN HIGHLIGHTS OF PAUL ANKA.
LP: **54738**
MC: **40 54738**

GRAFFITI COLLECTION.
MC: **GRMC 12**

GREATEST HITS: PAUL ANKA.
LPPD: **AR 30044**

GREATEST HITS: PAUL ANKA(IMPORT).
LP: **BRLP 17**
MC: **BRMC 17**

HEADLINES.
Tracks: / Headlines / As long as we keep believing / Andi / Never get to know you / Learning to love again / I can't get over you / Together again / Life song / Leave it all to me.
LP: **PL 13382**

ITALIANO.
LP: **CRESCENT 10130**

MY WAY.
LP: **CDS 1134**
MC: **ORC 011**
MC: **4XLL 9035**
MC: **2604054**

ORIGINAL HITS OF PAUL ANKA, THE.
Tracks: / Diana / Put your head on my shoulder / Crazy love / I love you baby / Puppy love / My home town / Cinderella / Lonely boy / Adam and Eve / You are my destiny / Loveland / Tonight my love / Just young / Dance on little girl.
LP: **CBS 32370**
MC: **40 32370**

PAUL ANKA AT HIS BEST.
Tracks: / You're having my baby / Times of your life / I don't like to sleep alone / Everybody ought to be in love / It doesn't matter anymore / My best friend's wife / One man woman, one woman man / There's nothing stronger than our love / She's a lady / Let me try again / My way.
LP: **UAG 30216**

PAUL ANKA IN CONCERT - 16 HITS.
LP: **MA 61285**
MC: **MAMC 961285**

PAUL ANKA LIVE.
LP: **GNPS 2175**
MC: **GNP5 2175**

SONGS.
LP: **CL. 42110**

WALK A FINE LINE.
Tracks: / Second chance / Hold me 'til the morning comes / Darlin' darlin' / No way out / Walk a fine line / Take me in your arms / This is the first time / Gimme the world / Golden boy, The.
LP: **CBS 25259**
MC: **40 25259**

Ann & Sonia

FROM MY HEART.
LP: **BBLP 0012**

Anna (film)

ANNA (Film Soundtrack) (Various artists).
LP: **STV 81353**

Anna G

ON A MISSION.
LP: **781 946-1**
MC: **781 946-4**

Anna of the Five Towns

ANNA OF THE FIVE TOWNS (Arnold Bennett) (Jeffrey, Peter (nar)).
MCSET: **418 150-4**

Annabella

FEVER.
Tracks: / School's out / Under the gun / Desire / Nightmare / Magdalen / War boys / High powered girl / Fever / Marry for love / Wild in me.
LP: **PL 70890**
MC: **PK 70890**

Annabouboula

GREEK FIRE.
MC: **SHMC 64027**

HAMAN.
LP: **V 2556**
LP: **209 246**

Annals Of The Parish

ANNALS OF THE PARISH (See under Galt, John) (Sheddon, John).

Annapolis Brass

BYRD & BRASS (See under Byrd, Charlie).

Anne of Green Gables

ANNE OF GREEN GABLES (See under Montgomery, L.M.).

Anne, Shirley

PEACE ON EARTH.
LP: **HAD LP 1**
MC: **HAD MC 1**

Anneix, Christian

DANSE DE BRETAGNE (See under Baron, Jean) (Anneix, Christian & Jean Baron).

Annie Get Your Gun

ANNIE GET YOUR GUN (Original soundtrack) (Various artists).
Tracks: / Doin' what comes naturally: *Various artists* / Moonshine lullaby: *Various artists*/ You can't get a man with a gun: *Various artists* / I'm an Indian too: *Various artists* / They say it's wonderful: *Various artists* / Anything you can do: *Various artists* / I got lost in his arms: *Various artists* / I got the sun in the morning: *Various artists* / Girl that I marry, The: *Various artists* / My defences are down: *Various artists* / Who do you love I hope: *Various artists* / There's no business like show business: *Various artists*.
LP: **MCL 1660**
MC: **MCLC 1660**

ANNIE GET YOUR GUN (Original soundtrack) (Various artists).
LP: **SH 2053**
MC: **CSH 2053**

ANNIE GET YOUR GUN (Studio cast) (Various artists).
LP: **PS 2360**
MC: **PST 2360**

ANNIE GET YOUR GUN (London revival cast) (Various artists).
Tracks: / Annie get overture: *Various artists* / Colonel Buffalo Bill: *Various artists* / I'm a bad bad man: *Various artists* / Doin'

what comes natur'lly: *Various artists* / Girl that I marry, The: *Various artists* / You can't get a man with a gun: *Various artists* / There's no business like show business: *Various artists* / They say it's wonderful(plus reprise): *Various artists* / Moonshine lullaby: *Various artists* / My defenses are down: *Various artists* / Wild horse ceremonial dance: *Various artists* / I'm an indian too: *Various artists* / I got lost in his arms: *Various artists* / I got the sun in the morning: *Various artists* / Old fashioned wedding: *Various artists* / Anything you can do: *Various artists* / Finale: *Various artists*.
MC: . . . . **CASTC 4**
LP: . . . . **CAST 4**

SEVEN BRIDES FOR SEVEN BROTHERS/ANNIE GET YOUR GUN (see under Seven brides for seven brothers) (Various artists).

Annie (musical)

ANNIE - BROADWAY (Original Broadway cast) (Various artists).
MC: **40 70157**

ANNIE - FILM (Film soundtrack) (Various artists).
Tracks: / Tomorrow: *Various artists* / It's the hard-knock life: *Various artists* / Maybe: *Various artists*/ Dumb dog: *Various artists* / Sandy: *Various artists* / I think I'm gonna like it here: *Various artists*/ Little girls: *Various artists* / We got Annie: *Various artists* / Let's go to the movies: *Various artists*/ Sign: *Various artists* / You're never fully dressed without a smile: *Various artists* / Easy street: *Various artists* / Tomorrow reprise: *Various artists* / Finale: *Various artists*.
LP: . . . . **CBS 70219**
MC: **40 70219**
LP: **4676081**
MC: **4676084**

ANNIE - LONDON (Original London cast) (Various artists).
Tracks: / Annie overture: *Various artists* / Maybe: *Various artists* / Hard knock life, The: *Various artists*/ Tomorrow: *Various artists* / We'd like to thank you: *Various artists* / Herbert Hoover: *Various artists*/ Little girls: *Various artists* / I think I'm gonna like it here: *Various artists* / NYC: *Various artists*/ Easy street: *Various artists* / You won't be an orphan for long: *Various artists* / You're never fully dressed without a smile: *Various artists* / Tomorrow, reprise: *Various artists* / Something was missing: *Various artists*/ I don't need anything but you: *Various artists* / Annie: *Various artists* / New deal for Christmas, A: *Various artists*.
MC: **40 70160**

ANNIE - STORY (Original childrens soundtrack and story) (Various artists).
Tracks: / Tomorrow: *Various artists* / Hard knock life, The: *Various artists* / Maybe: *Various artists*/ Sandy: *Various artists* / I think I'm gonna like it here: *Various artists* / We got Annie: *Various artists*/ You're never fully dressed without a smile: *Various artists* / Easy street: *Various artists* / Maybe (reprise): *Various artists* / Finale: *Various artists*.
LP: . . . . **CBS 32239**

Annihilator

ALICE IN HELL.
Tracks: / Crystal Ann / W.T.Y.D. / Burns like a buzzsaw blade / Schizos (are never alone) (parts 1 & 2) / Human insecticide / Alison Hell / Wicked mystic / Word salad / Ligeia.
LP: . . . . **RR 9488 1**
MC: . . . . **RR 9488 4**

ANIALATOR.
LP: . . . . **WRR 006**

CREATED IN HATE.
LP: . . . . **VOV 668**
MC: . . . . **VOV 668C**

NEVER NEVER LAND.
LP: . . . . **RR 93741**
MC: . . . . **RR 93744**

ULTIMATE DESECRATION, THE.
LP: . . . . **VOV 675**

Anniversary

ANNIVERSARY (Various artists).
LP: . . . . **XAN 201**

Anonyma

BURNT FEATHERS.
Tracks: / Quiet people, The / Moth / Fill fill / A-ruin o / Cathy loves a priest / Song to the siren / Stone circles / Seagull / How to stand still / Fionnuala's song / Icarus / Cassandra.
LP: . . . . **FE 059**
MC: . . . . **FE 059C**

Another 48 Hours

ANOTHER 48 HOURS (Various artists).
Tracks: / Boys are back in town: *Various artists* / I just can't let it end: *Various artists* / Courthouse: *Various artists* / King Mei shootout: *Various artists* / I'll never get out: *Various artists* / Give it all you got: *Various artists* / I've got my eye on you: *Various artists* / Another 48 hours: *Various artists* / Birdcage battle: *Various artists*.
LP: **846 872-1**
MC: **846 872-4**

Another Bad Creation

COOLIN' AT THE PLAYGROUND.
Tracks: / Parents / Playground / Mental (so pay attention) / Interlude / Little soldiers / My world / Lesha / Spydermann / That's my girl / Jealous girl / A.B.C. / Lesha (after hours mix) (Only on CD and Cassette).
LP: . . . . **ZL 72737**
MC: . . . . **ZK 72737**

Another Bloody Tour

ANOTHER BLOODY TOUR.
MCSET: **0600558479**

Another Saturday Night

ANOTHER SATURDAY NIGHT (Various artists).
Tracks: / Before I grow too old: *McLain, Tommy* / Cajun fugitive: *Belton, Richard* / Try to find another man: *McLain, Tommy & Clint West* / Jole blon: *Bruce, Vin* / I cried: *Cookie and the cupcakes* / Oh Lucille: *Belton, Richard* / Who needs you so bad: *Walker, Gary* / Don't mess with my man: *White, Margo* / Another Saturday night: *White, Margo* / Un auter soir d'ennui: *Belton, Richard* / Promised land: *Allan, Johnnie*/ Two steps de bayou teche: *Pitre, Austin* / Sweet dreams: *McLain, Tommy* / Breaking up is hard to do: *Cookie & The Cupcakes* / Laisser les cajuns dancer: *Belton, Richard* / Downhome music: *Jangeaux, Rufus*.
LP: . . . . **OVLP 506**
LP: . . . . **CH 288**
MC: . . . . **CHC 288**

Another Shot

ANOTHER SHOT, VOL. 2 (Various artists).
MC: . . . . **BSIC 25**

Another Spark Number 1

ANOTHER SPARK NUMBER 1 (Various artists).
MC: . . . . **AS 001**

Another Ten Years

ANOTHER 10 YEARS OF OFFSHORE RADIO (Various artists).
2LP: . . . . **R 117/118**
MCSET: . . . . **C 117/118**

Anselm Gets His Chance

ANSELM GETS HIS CHANCE (See under Wodehouse, P.G.) (Carlton, Timothy).

Anson

KNOCK YOU OUT (Anson & the Rockets).
LP: . . . . **SPIN 202**

Ant, Adam

ANTICS IN THE FORBIDDEN ZONE.
Tracks: / Zerox / Whip in my valise / Car trouble / Kick / Kings of the wild frontier / Ant music / Dog eat dog / Los Rancheros / Killer in the home / Stand and deliver / Beat my guest / Prince Charming / Ant rap / Desperate but not serious / Place in the country / Friend or foe / Goody two shoes / Strip / Puss 'n' boots / Apollo 9 / Vive le rock.
MC: **4687624**

DIRK WEARS WHITE SOX.
Tracks: / Car trouble / Nine plan failed / Catholic day / Idea, The / Never trust a man (with egg on his face) / Animals and men / Family of noise / Table talk / Day I met God, The.
LP: . . . . **RIDE 3**
LP: **25361**

FRIEND OR FOE.
Tracks: / Friend or foe / Something girls / Place in the country / Desperate but not serious / Here comes the grump / Hello I love you / Goody two shoes / Crackpot history and the right to lie / Made of money / Cajun twisters / Try this for sighs / Man called Marco.
LP: . . . . **CBS 25040**

HITS.
Tracks: / Kings of the wild frontier / Dog eat dog / Ant music / Stand and deliver / Prince Charming / Ant rap / Goody two shoes / Friend or foe / Desperate but not serious / Puss 'n' boots / Strip / Apollo 9 / Vive le rock.
LP: **4500741**
MC: **4500744**
LP: **4669441**
MC: **4669444**

KINGS OF THE WILD FRONTIER.
Tracks: / Dog eat dog / Antmusic / Feed me to the lions / Los rancheros / Ants invasion / Killer in the home / Kings of the wild frontier / Magnificent five / Don't be square / Jolly Roger / Making history / Human beings.
LP: . . . . **CBS 84549**

MANNERS AND PHYSIQUE.
Tracks: / Room at the top / If you keep on / Can't set rules about love / Bright lights black leather / Young dumb and full of it / Rough stuff / Manners and physique / U.S.S.A. / Piccadilly / Anger Inc..
LP: . . . . **MCG 6068**
MC: . . . . **MCGC 6068**

PEEL SESSIONS: ADAM & THE ANTS (Adam & The Ants).
LP: . . . . **SFRLP 115**
MC: . . . . **SFRMC 115**

PRINCE CHARMING.
Tracks: / Prince Charming / Scorpios / Picasso visita el planeta de los Simios / Five guns west / That voodoo / Stand and deliver / Mile high club / Ant rap / Mowhok / S.E.X..
LP: . . . . **CBS 85268**

STRIP.
Tracks: / Baby let me scream at you / Libertine / Spanish games / Vanity / Puss 'n' boots / Playboy / Strip / Montreal / Naval to neck / Amazon.
LP: . . . . **CBS 25705**

VIVE LE ROCK.
Tracks: / Vive le rock / Miss thing / Razor keen / Rip down / Scorpio rising / Apollo 9 / Hell's eight acres / Mohair lockeroom pin-up boys / No zap / P.O.E. / Human bondage den (Available on cassette only).
LP: . . . . **CBS 26583**
MC: **40 26583**

Ant Bee

ANT BEE.
LP: . . . . **VOXX 200056**

Antarctica

ANTARCTICA (See under Vangelis).

Antena, Isabelle

CAMINO DEL SOL.
LP: . . . . **TWI 114**

DE L'AMOUR ET DES HOMMES.
Tracks: / De l'amour et des hommes / Le cinema.
LP: . . . . **TWI 874**

EN CAVALE.
LP: . . . . **TWI 610**

HOPING FOR LOVE.
Tracks: / Des Calins, Des Caresses / Laying on the sofa / Naughty, naughty / Sweet boy / La tete contre les murs / Le poisson des mers du sud / Quand le jazz entre en lice melodie / L'ideal / Musique de 4 a 6 / Toutes les etoiles de tunisie / Otra bebera.
LP: . . . . **TWI 759**

JOUEZ LE CINQ.
LP: . . . . **TWI 882**

TOUS MES CAPRICES.
LP: . . . . **TWI 842**

Anthem

GYPSY WAYS.
Tracks: / Gypsy ways (win, lose or draw) / Bad habits die hard / Cryin' heart / Midnight sun / Final risk / Love in vain / Legal killing / Silent child / Shout it out / Night stalker.
LP: . . . . **MFN 103**

HUNTING TIME.
Tracks: / Juggler, The / Evil touch / Sleepless night / Let your heart beat / Hunting time / Tears for the lovers / Jailbreak / Bottle bottom.
LP: . . . . **MFN 104**

NO SMOKE WITHOUT FIRE.
Tracks: / Shadow walk / Blinded pain / Love on the edge / Power and blood / Night we stand, The / Hungry soul / Do you understand / Voice of thunderstorm / Fever eyes.
LP: . . . . **MFN 101**
MC: . . . . **TMFN 101**

Anthem de Danann

ANTHEM DE DANANN (Various artists).
Tracks: / Wren's nest, The: *Various artists* / Let it be: *Various artists* / Johnstone hornpipe: *Various artists* / Connie from Constantinople: *Various artists* / Johnny I hardly knew ye: *Various artists* / Ril and Spideal: *Various artists* / Anthem for Ireland: *Various artists* / Jimmy Byrnes and Dinkies: *Various artists*/ Diglake fields: *Various artists* / Duo in G: *Various artists* / Paddy's lamentation: *Various artists2]*.
LP: . . . . **DARA 013**
MC: . . . . **DARAC 013**

Anthems

ANTHEMS 4 (Various artists).
LP: . . . . **MUSIC 12**
MC: . . . . **ZCMUS 12**

ANTHEMS 6 (Various artists).
Tracks: / Dance, dance, dance: *Chic* / Contact: *Starr, Edwin* / Young hearts run free: *Staton, Candi*/ Hi tension: *Hi Tension* / Get down: *Chandler, Gene* / Keep your body working: *Kleeer* / Dancer: *Soccio, Gino* / Tuch me: *Rae, Fonda*.
LP: . . . . **MUSIC 14**
MC: . . . . **ZCMUS 14**

Anthology Of...

SOME PEOPLE WHO PLAY (Various artists).
LP: . . . . **KM 104**

Anthology - Poetry...

ANTHOLOGY - POETRY READINGS (see under Burton, Richard) (Burton, Richard).

Anthony, CJ

LUV'S INVITATION (IMPORT).
MC: . . . . **KMALPC 4**

Anthony, John

GUITAR GOES TRAVELLING.
Tracks: / Maria Elena / Zorba's dance / South of the border / Stairway to the sea / Don't cry for me Argentina / Summertime in Venice / Have naguila / African sunset / Shenandoah / Annie's song / Tokyo melody.
LP: . . . . **PRX 9**

GUITAR TALK.
Tracks: / Main theme (Star wars) / Evergreen / Somewhere my love / Albatross / James Bond theme / Granada / Speak softly / Just a little note / Rodrigo's guitar concerto de aranjuez / Catari.
LP: . . . . **PRX 7**

MIDNIGHT GUITAR SERENADE.
MCSET: . . . . **DTO 10082**

Anthony, Julie

I DREAMED A DREAM.
LP: . . . . **GNPS 2195**
MC: **GNP5 2195**

Anthony, Nigel (nar)

FUN FOR THE SECRET SEVEN (see under Blyton, Enid (aut)) (Sheridan, Sue (nar) & Nigel Anthony (nar)).

GOOD WORK SECRET SEVEN (see under Blyton, Enid (aut)) (Sheridan, Sue (nar) & Nigel Anthony (nar)).

SECRET SEVEN WIN THROUGH (see under Blyton, Enid (aut) (Sheridan, Sue (nar) & Nigel Anthony (nar)).

THREE CHEERS SECRET SEVEN (see under Blyton, Enid (aut)) (Sheridan, Sue (nar) & Nigel Anthony (nar)).

Anthony, Pad

HELL IN THE DANCE (Anthony, Pad/ Frankie Jones).
Tracks: / Long run short catch / Love just a fool / Flash it mash it / She's in love with me / Way dem a do fe we / Me a know / Run come / Hell in the dance / Stay on your corner / Niceness.
LP: . . . . **CSLP 21**

P A MEETS K E (Anthony, Pad & King Everald).
LP: . . . . **UNKNOWN**

Anthony, Ray

1988 & ALL THAT JAZZ (Anthony, Ray & His Orchestra).
LP: . . . . **RA 1030**
MC: . . . . **RAC 1030**

ARTHUR MURRAY DANCE PARTY (Dances from waltz to tango).
Tracks: / Swing / Shuffle my boogie / Guantanamera / Bunny hop cha cha / New York, New York / Last cheater's waltz, The / Don't cry for me Argentina / Coffee song, The / Riviera rumba / Tango, anyone?.
LP: . . . . **RA 1009**
MC: . . . . **RAC 1009**

BIG BAND JAZZ.
Tracks: / Baby but you did / Roll 'em around / South Dakota / This may be the time / Every dog has his day / Why should I worry? / Why don't you want to come home? / You gotta get lucky sometime / Mr. Moon / Indubitably / You're the one for me / Lavender mood, A.
LP: . . . . **RA 998**
MC: . . . . **RAC 998**

BIG BAND SINGER.
Tracks: / Swing dance / Just hooked on dancing / Singing in the rain / Moonlight saving time / Candy and cake / I've never been in love before / I let a song go out of my heart / Young at heart / Gloria / Jean / Your eyes / Count every star.
LP: . . . . **RA 1021**
MC: . . . . **RA 1021C**

BRASS GALORE.
Tracks: / Annie Laurie / Deep river / Reuben, Reuben / Camptown races /

Mockingbird / Bluebells of Scotland / Kerry dance, The / Dry bones / Comin' thro' the rye / American patrol / Swing low, sweet chariot / Chopsticks.
LP: RA 997
MC: RA 997C

DANCERS' CHOICE.
Tracks: / Anonimo Veneziano / Country bumpkin / Touch dancing / Cotton-eyed Joe / Country blues / Bunny hop disco / Chaputin / Early morning love / Leroy's back / Shadows, The / Fun dancers / Malibu sunset.
LP: RA 1006

DANCERS IN LOVE (Anthony, Ray & His Orchestra).
LP: MOIR 210
MC: CMOIR 210

DANCING ALONE TOGETHER.
Tracks: / My funny valentine / Guess I'll hang my tears out to dry / To love and be loved / I should care / Party's over, The / Here's that rainy day / What's new / Misty / Like someone in love / Alone together / All the way.
LP: EMS 1156
MC: TCEMS 1156

DANCING IN THE DARK.
Tracks: / Dancing in the dark / True blue Lou / Begin the beguine / Cheek to cheek / Dancing on the ceiling / I wonder what's become of Sally / Continental, The / You and the night and the music / Taking a chance on love / You're the cream in my coffee / It's de-lovely / I get a kick out of you.
LP: RA 995
MC: RA 995C

DREAM DANCING AROUND THE WORLD.
Tracks: / My way / Love story / Girl from Ipanema / Yesterday / Wonderland by night / It's impossible / Snowbird / To be the one you love / Japanese love song, A / Dreamtime for Jedda / Shadows, The / Royal Hawaiian sunset.
LP: RA 1007

DREAM DANCING MEDLEY.
Tracks: / As time goes by / Soon / Where am I? / I'll string along with you / Of thee I sing / It had to be you / Auf wiedersehen, my dear / Can't we be friends? / Heaven can wait / Too marvellous for words / When your lover has gone / Love nest, The / Dancing on the ceiling / Sweet madness / 'S wonderful / With a song in my heart / Very thought of you, The / Boulevard of broken dreams / Autumn in New York / Man I love, The / Tis' autumn / Please be king / Ev'ry day / If there is someone lovelier than you / September in the rain / My heart stood still / Dancing in the dark / Something to remember you by / Oh you crazy moon / Mine.
LP: ED 2604311
MC: ED 2604314

FOR DANCERS ONLY (Cheek to cheek) (Anthony, Ray & His Orchestra).
MC: 4XL 57009

GLENN MILLER - THEN AND NOW (Anthony, Ray & His Orchestra).
LP: RA 1011
MC: RAC 1011

HITS OF RAY ANTHONY.
Tracks: / Slaughter on Tenth Avenue / Man with the horn, The / Mr. Anthony's boogie / Oh mein papa / Bunny hop, The / Thunderbird / Dragnet / At last / Harlem nocturne / Stardust / Peter Gunn / Tenderly / When the saints go marching in.
LP: RA 999
MC: RA 999C

HOOKED ON BIG BANDS - LIVE FROM RADIO PROGS.
LP: RA 1012
MC: RAC 1012

HOUSEPARTY HOP.
Tracks: / I get a kick out of you / Houseparty hop / Begin the beguine / Perdido / Bunny hop, The / Darktown strutters' ball / Dinah / Sentimental journey / My blue Heaven / Wagon wheels / Rockin' in rhythm / Bandstand matinee.
LP: EG 2606011
MC: EG 2606014

I GET THE BLUES WHEN IT RAINS.
LP: R 8082

I REMEMBER GLENN MILLER.
Tracks: / Tuxedo Junction / Chattanooga choo choo / Serenade in blue / Elmer's tune / Sunrise serenade / Song of the Volga boatmen / In the mood / I know why (and so do you) / Sweet as apple cider / At last / Little Brown jug / Moonlight serenade.
LP: 2C 068 86544

LET'S DANCE AGAIN.
LPS: RA 1020
MCSET: RAC 1020

LET'S GO DANCING.
Tracks: / All of me / Ain't misbehavin' / Always / Sleepy lagoon / Spaghetti rag / Swing dance / Similau / Al di la / Skokiaan / Tango for two / Petard mambo.
LP: RA 1028
MC: RAC 1028

MORE DREAM DANCING.
Tracks: / April in Paris / Blue Hawaii / There's a small hotel / I cover the waterfront / Meet me tonight in dreamland / Venezuela / East of the sun / Along the Santa Fe trail / Palm Springs / Home Monika / Dream while you dance.
LP: 2C 068 54570
MC: PM 154 570 4

MUSIC OF YOUR MEMORIES.
Tracks: / What's new? / Here's that rainy day / Like someone in love / My funny valentine / To love and be loved / All the way / Misty / I should care / I'm through with love / Guess I'll hang my tears out to dry / Alone together / Party's over, The.
LP: RA 1019
MC: RA 1019C

PLAYS FOR DREAM DANCING.
Tracks: / This love of mine / Dream dancing / I'll never smile again / Out of nowhere / I only have eyes for you / Embraceable you / Street of dreams / Stars fell on Alabama / I don't know why (I just do) / Laura / Moonlight in Vermont / September song.
LP: CAPS 2600011
MC: TCCAPS 2600014

RAY ANTHONY.
LP: ENT LP 13015
MC: ENT MC 13015

SAMPLER, THE.
Tracks: / Mr. Anthony's boogie / Man with the horn, The / Dancing in the dark / Cheek to cheek / Baby but you did / Roll 'em around / Swingin' at the Tower / How high the moon / Country bumpkin / Leroy's back / Annie Laurie / Deep river.
LP: RA 1000

SHOW AND DANCE AND PARTY.
LPS: RA 1027
MCSET: RA 1027C

SWEET AND SWINGIN' (1949-53).
LP: CLP 96

SWING.
Tracks: / Swing / Swing machine / Big band blast / Swing along / Swinger, The / Movin' / Swing thing / Shuffle my boogie / Boogie on down / Heat Ray / Swingin' affair, A / Fanfare boogie.
LP: RA 1010
MC: RA 1010C

SWING GOES ON VOL 10.
Tracks: / What can I say / I wonder what's become of Sally / Idaho / Blue moon / Dancing over the waves / It's de-lovely / Man with the horn, The / For dancers only / Jeepers creepers / My blue Heaven / Amor / Dinah / Sentimental journey / Begin the beguine / I get a kick out of you / Houseparty hop.
LP: IC 054 52719

SWINGIN' AT THE TOWER.
Tracks: / Flying home / Night train / How high the moon / Perdido / One o'clock jump / Swingin' at the Tower.
LP: RA 996
MC: RAC 996

SWINGIN' ON CAMPUS.
Tracks: / What can I say after I say I'm sorry / On the Alamo / I've found a new baby / Chloe / At sundown / Pick yourself up / Ain't misbehavin' / Lady is in love with you, The / Am I blue / If I had you / Undecided / Swing on campus.
LP: EMS 1137
MC: TCEMS 1137

TOUCH DANCING.
Tracks: / Touch dancing / Too much, too little, too late / Just a gigolo / How deep is your love? / Feelings / Closer I get to you, The / Dancing close together / Come dance with me / My way / Yesterday / Love story / It's impossible.
LP: RA 1008
MC: RA 1008C

Anthony, Richard

DISQUE D'OR.
Tracks: / J'entends siffler le train / Donne-moi ma chance / C'est ma fete / A present, tu peux t'en aller / Ce monde / Je me suis souvent demande / Le deserteur / Sunny / Arranguez, mon amour / Les mains dans les poches / Il faut croire aux etoiles / L'ete / Les ballons / Le sirop typhon.
LP: 2C 070 72022

Anthony & The Camp

SUSPENSE.
Tracks: / Little closer to me, A / Suspense / Don't forget your way to my love / I take chances / Thought I could handle it / Who do you love (what's it gonna be) / What I like / Touch and go girl.
LP: K 925648 1
MC: K 925648 4

Anthrax

AMONG THE LIVING.
LPPD: PILPS 9865
LP: ILPS 9865
MC: ICT 9865

ANTHRAX: INTERVIEW PICTURE DISC.
LPPD: CT 1021

ANTHRAX: INTERVIEW PICTURE DISC (BAKTABAK).
LPPD: BAK 2134

ARMED AND DANGEROUS.
LP: MRS05
LPPD: MRS05P

ATTACK OF THE KILLER B'S.
LP: ILPS 9980
MC: ICT 9980

FISTFUL OF METAL.
Tracks: / Deathrider / I'm eighteen / Subjagator / Howling furies (American remix) / Death from above / Across the river / Metal thrashing mad / Panic / Soldiers of metal (American remix) / Soldiers of metal / Anthrax / Howling furies.
LPPD: MFN 14P
LP: MFN 14
2LP: MFN 14DM
MC: TMFN 14

MUSIC AND MEDIA INTERVIEW PICTURE DISCS.
LPPD: MM 1254

PERSISTENCE OF TIME.
LP: ILPS 9967
MC: ICT 9967
LPPD: ILPSP 9967

SPREADING THE DISEASE.
LP: MFN 62
MC: TMFN 62
MC: ICM 9806

STATE OF EUPHORIA.
MC: ICT 9916
LP: ILPS 9916
LP: 910041
LPPD: PILPS 9916

Anti Group

AUDIOPHILE.
LP: SAX 030
LPS: SBX 030

TESE TONES.
LP: SER 12

Anti Heros

THAT'S RIGHT.
LP: LINK LP 020

Anti Pasti

ANTI PASTI.
LP: ABOUT 13

CAUTION IN THE WIND.
Tracks: / Caution in the wind / One Friday night / X affair / Get out now / Mr. Mystery / East to the West / See how they run / Hate circulation / Agent ABC / Best of us, The / Guinea pigs / Beyond belief.
MC: CARB 7

DON'T LET 'EM GRIND YOU DOWN (EP) (See under Exploited) (Exploited & Anti Pasti).

LAST CALL, THE.
Tracks: / No government / Brew your own / Another dead soldier / Call the army (I'm alive) / City below / 24 hours / Night of the war cry / Freedom row / St. George (get's his gun) / Last call / Ain't got me / Truth and justice / Hell / I wanna be your dog.
LP: ABOUT 5
MC: CARB 5

Anti Social Workers

PUNKY REGGAE PARTY (Positive Style).
LP: ARILP 008

Anti-Choc

ANTI-CHOC.
LP: STERNS 1022

Anti-Cimex

NOTHING LEFT BUT SILENCE.
LP: UNKNOWN

Antietam

ANTIETAM.
LP: HMS 025

MUSIC FROM ELBA.
LP: HMS 068

Antigua

ANTIGUA (Various artists).
Tracks: / Calypso non-stop: *Steel Band* / Love story: *Steel Band* / Never on Sunday: *Steel Band* / Valse: *Steel Band* / Rondeau: *Steel Band.*
LP: PS 804
MC: PS 9804

Antilles

FETE CREOLE AUX ANTILLES (Various artists).
Tracks: / Monsieur Leonard: *Various artists* / Bande zaoua: *Various artists* / La ronde des cuisinieres: *Various* artists / Serpent maigre: *Various artists* / Ernestine attention: *Various artists* / Guitare des Antilles: *Various artists* / L'ete en pyjama: *Various artists* / Ba moin un tibo, doudou: *Various artists* / Maladie d'amour: *Various artists* / Ce les Antilles: *Various artists* / Oh, pepe: *Various artists* / Dis adieu: *Various artists.*
LP: ARN 30087
MC: ARN 430087

LES ANTILLES (Various artists).
Tracks: / Ernestine, attention: *Various artists* / Ce les Antilles: *Various artists* / Ba moin un tibo, doudou: *Various artists* / Mr. Leonard: *Various artists* / Bande Zaoua: *Various artists* / La ronde des cuisinieres: *Various artists* / Serpent maigre: *Various artists* / L'ete en pyjama: *Various artists* / Maladie d'amour: *Various artists* / Guitare des Antilles: *Various artists* / Le rocher: *Various artists* / Oh pere: *Various* artists / Ninon, merengue, merengue: *Various artists* / Danse de gros ca: *Various artists* / Guyane, o Guyana: *Various artists* / Sans chemise, sans pantalon: *Various artists* / Maman, maman: *Various artists* / Biguine a Henri: *Various artists* / Aye Tumbaye: *Various artists* / Roro: *Various artists* / Madiana: *Various* artists / Papillon vole: *Various artists* / Adieu foulard: *Various artists* / Adieu madras: *Various artists.*
LP: ARN 33320
MC: ARN 433320

MARIAGE CREOLE AUX ANTILLES (Various artists).
Tracks: / Je t'aime, tu m'aimes: *Various artists* / Dis la verite: *Various artists* / Aime-moi: *Various artists*/ Doudou passou ka pati: *Various artists* / La ronde du mariage: *Various artists* / Eloi pas aime la loi: *Various* artists / Maye le ka roule: *Various artists* / Cette nuit: *Various artists* / Ou ka danse mal: *Various* artists / Un jour chevalier St Georges: *Various artists* / Demaye moin: *Various artists* / Quadrille antillais: *Various artists.*
LP: ARN 33596
MC: ARN 433596

Anti-Nowhere League

LIVE AND LOUD.
LP: LINKLP 120

LONG LIVE THE LEAGUE.
Tracks: / For you / We will survive / Out on the wasteland / On the waterfront / Queen and country / We're the league / Streets of London / So what / Let's break the law / Ballad of JJ Decay, The / Woman / Snowman / Wreck a nowhere / Let the country feed you / Going down / I hate people.
LP: DOJOLP 15

PERFECT CRIME, THE.
Tracks: / Crime / On the waterfront / Branded / I don't believe this is my England / Johannesburg / Shining / Working for the company / System / Curtain.
LP: GWLP 12
MC: GWTC 12

WE ARE...THE LEAGUE.
Tracks: / Roll on world war three / So what / Wreck a nowhere / Let's break the law / Woman / Streets of London / For you.
LP: NOSE 6
LP: LMNOP 1
LP: LMNOPC 1

WE ARE...THE LEAGUE (Live in Yugoslavia).
LP: NOSE 36
LP: NOSE 3

Antisect

IN DARKNESS THERE IS NO CHOICE.
LP: SDL 15

Anti-System

LOOK AT LIFE, A.
LP: RECONCILE 4

NO LAUGHING MATTER.
LP: RECONCILE 1

Antix

GET UP GET HAPPY.
LP: HMASP 42

Antobal's Cubans

ANTOBAL'S CUBANS (1936-37).
Tracks: / Conga karabalicero / Let's be gay / Said the monkey / Say si si / Whoa,

Nellie whoa / Les trois loups / Songo songo / Cuban belle / El maraquero.
LP: . . . . **HQ 2081**

Antoine, Fe La

THIS HOUSE IS SMOKIN'.
Tracks: / This house is smokin' / This party (is for everybody) / Fad (This ain't no..) / Heartbreak / Beat freaks, The / Nasty, The / Daddio / Beatin' around the bush / Hop til you drop / Desperate people.
LP: . . . . **ICH 1059**
MC: . . . . **ICH 1059MC**

Antolini, Charly

SPECIAL DELIVERY.
LP: . . . . **MPS 68 256**

Antonia

RESTLESS FINGERS.
Tracks: / Cin cin polka / Cubalero, The / Caprice / Marsala bella / Simple et musette / Samba polka / Restless fingers / Luci e ombre dark eyes / Interrogation / Bouquet / Valse des as.
LP: . . . . **CA 103**

Antony & Cleopatra

ANTONY AND CLEOPATRA (Film soundtrack) (Various artists).
Tracks: / Antony and Cleopatra (main title): *Various artists* / Give me to drink Mandragora (Cleopatra's theme): *Various* artists / Confrontation with Pompey: *Various artists* / Antony and Octavia (Caesar's sister): *Various artists*/ Barge she sat in: *Various artists* / One will tear the other: *Various artists* / Battle of Actium: *Various* artists / Prelude to part 2 (love theme): *Various artists* / Whither hast thou led me Egypt: *Various artists*/ Death of Enobarbus: *Various artists* / He goes forth gallantly: *Various artists* / Sometimes we see a cloud that's dragonish: *Various artists* / Death of Antony (love theme): *Various artists* / Pretty worm of Nilus: *Various artists* / She shall be buried by her Antony (end titles): *Various artists.*
LP: **2383 109**
MC: **3170 056**

Antony & Cleopatra

ANTONY AND CLEOPATRA (see under Shakespeare, William) (Various artists).

Antrobus, Frosdsham

STEP IN WILD HORSE (Soul Caring).
MC: **60-107**

Ants' Hillvania

ANTS' HILLVANIA (Various artists).
Tracks: / Work song: *Various artists* / Independ-ant's song: *Various artists* / All it really is: *Various* artists / Mr. Worm: *Various artists* / Seeds: *Various artists* / Choice is up to you, The: *Various artists*/ Toast of the town, The: *Various artists* / Riddle, The: *Various artists* / Repentants song: *Various artists*/ Come on home: *Various artists* / Ants' hillvania: *Various artists.*
LP: . . . . **BW R 2030**
MC: . . . . **TC BWR 2030**

Anvil

BACKWAXED.
LP: . . . . **RR 9776**

FORGED IN FIRE.
LP: . . . . **LAT 1170**
MC: . . . . **CAT 1170**
LP: . . . . **RR 9927**

HARD AND HEAVY.
LP: . . . . **LAT 1100**
MC: . . . . **CAT 1100**

METAL ON METAL.
LP: . . . . **LAT 1130**
MC: . . . . **CAT 1130**

PAST AND PRESENT LIVE.
Tracks: / Concrete jungle / Toe jam / Motorneount / Forged in fire / Blood on the ice / March of the crabs / Jack hammer / Metal on metal / Winged assassins / 666 / Mothra.
LP: . . . . **RO 94531**

STRENGTH OF STEEL.
Tracks: / Strength of steel / Concrete jungle / 9-2-5 / I dreamed it was the end of the world / Flight of the bumble beast / Cut loose / Mad dog / Straight between the eyes / Wild eyes / Kiss of death / Paper general.
LP: . . . . **RR 9618**

Anvil Bitch

RISE TO OFFEND.
LP: . . . . **NRR 13**
MC: . . . . **NRC 13**

Anxiety, Annie

SOUL POSSESSION.
LP: . . . . **CHRIST ITS 10**

Any Kind A Man

ANY KIND A MAN (1934-1938 Unissued Titles & Takes) (Various artists).
LP: . . . . **TM 8811**

Any Old Time

LADIES' CHOICE.
LP: . . . . **BAY 217**

PHOENIX.
LP: . . . . **DARA 025**

Any Old Time String

ANY OLD TIME STRING BAND.
LP: . . . . **ARHOOLIE 4009**

Any Trouble

ANY TROUBLE.
Tracks: / I'll be your man / Please don't stop / Touch and go / Foundations / Party in the streets / Northern soul / Man of the moment / Time does not heal / You'd better go home / Falling in love with you again.
LP: . . . . **AML 4991791**

LIVE AT THE VENUE.
LP: **6 25967**

WHEELS IN MOTION.
Tracks: / Trouble with love / Open fire / As lovers do / Walking in chains / Dimming of the day / Another heartache / To be a King / Power cut / Eastern promise / Sun never sets, The.
LP: . . . . **SEEZ 37**

WHERE ARE ALL THE NICE GIRLS.
Tracks: / Second choice / Playing Bogart / No idea / Foolish pride / Nice girls / Turning up the heat / Romance / Hurt, The / Girls are always right / Growing up / Honolulu / (Get you off) the hook.
LP: . . . . **SEEZ 25**
MC: . . . . **ZSEEZ 25**

WRONG END OF THE RACE.
Tracks: / Open fire / Old before your time / Lover's moon / Lucky day / Coming of age / Baby, now that I've found you / All the time in the world / Wheels in motion / Turning up the heat / Yesterday's love.
LP: . . . . **AMLS 2401203**

Any Which Way

ANY WHICH WAY YOU CAN (Original soundtrack) (Various artists).
Tracks: / Beers to you: *Various artists* / Any which way you can: *Various artists* / You're the reason God made Oklahoma: *Various artists* / Whiskey heaven: *Various artists* / One too many women in your life: *Various artists*/ Cow Patti: *Various artists* / Acapulco: *Various artists* / Anyway you want me: *Various artists* / Cotton eyed Clint: *Various artists* / Orangutan hall of fame: *Various artists* / Too loose: *Various artists*/ Good guys and the bad guys: *Various artists.*
LP: . . . . **HS 3499**
LP: . . . . **K 56884**

Anyone Can Whistle

ANYONE CAN WHISTLE (Original Cast Recording) (Various artists).
MC: . . . . **PST 02480**
LP: . . . . **AS 32608**
MC: . . . . **BT 32608**

Anyone for Dennis

ANYONE FOR DENNIS (Original London Cast) (Various artists).
LP: . . . . **RCALP 6006**
MC: . . . . **RCAK 6006**

Anyone's Daughter

ADONIS.
LP: **0060 186**

Anything Goes

ANYTHING GOES (1988 Revival Cast with Patti Lupone) (Various artists).
LP: . . . . **RL 87769**
MC: . . . . **RK 87769**

ANYTHING GOES (Revival 1969 London cast) (Various artists).
Tracks: / Overture(anything goes): *Various artists* / You're the top: *Various artists* / Bon voyage: *Various* artists / It's delovely: *Various artists* / Heaven hop: *Various artists* / Friendship: *Various artists*/ Let's do it: *Various artists* / Anything goes: *Various artists* / Public enemy number one: *Various artists*/ Let's step out: *Various artists* / Let's misbehave: *Various artists* / Blow, Gabriel, blow: *Various artists*/ Be like the bluebird: *Various artists* / All through the night: *Various artists* / Take me back to Manhattan: *Various artists* / I get a kick out of you: *Various artists* / Finale: *Various artists.*
LP: . . . . **TER 1080**
MC: . . . . **ZCTER 1080**

ANYTHING GOES (1988 Revival cast with Patti LuPone) (Various artists).
LP: **7769.1**
MC: **7769.4**

ANYTHING GOES (New 89 Studio version) (Various artists).
Tracks: / Anything goes overture: *Various artists* / I get a kick out of you: *Various artists* / Bon voyage: *Various artists* / All through the night: *Various artists* / There'll always be a lady fair: *Various artists* / Where are the men: *Various artists* / You're the top: *Various artists* / You're the top (Encore): *Various artists*/ There'll always be a lady fair (reprise): *Various artists* / Anything goes: *Various artists* / Anything goes finale: *Various artists* / Entr'acte: *Various artists* / Public enemy No. 1: *Various artists* / What a joy to be young: *Various artists* / Blow, Gabriel, blow: *Various artists* / Be like the bluebird: *Various* artists / Buddie beware: *Various artists* / Gypsy in me, The: *Various artists* / Finale ultimo: *Various* artists / There's no cure like travel: *Various artists* / Kate the great: *Various artists* / Waltz down the aisle: *Various artists.*
LP: . . . . **EL 7498481**
MC: . . . . **EL 7498484**

ANYTHING GOES (Various artists).
Tracks: / Anything goes prelude: *Various artists* / There's no cure like travel: *Various artists* / You're the top: *Various artists* / I want to row on the crew: *Various artists* / Friendship: *Various artists* / Anything goes: *Various artists* / Public enemy No. 1: *Various artists* / Goodbye, little dream, goodbye: *Various artists*/ All through the night: *Various artists* / Buddie beware: *Various artists* / I get a kick out of you: *Various* artists / Bon voyage: *Various artists* / Easy to love: *Various artists* / Sailor's chantey: *Various artists*/ It's de lovely: *Various artists* / Entracte: *Various artists* / Blow Gabriel, blow: *Various artists*/ Be like the bluebird: *Various artists* / Gypsy in me, The: *Various artists* / I get a kick out of you: *Various artists.*
LP: . . . . **CAST 18**
MC: . . . . **CASTC 18**

ANYTHING GOES (1962 Revival cast) (Various artists).
LP: . . . . **FLS 15100**

ANYTHING GOES/BANDWAGON (Original cast recordings) (Various artists).
LP: . . . . **AML 4751**

ANYTHING GOES/PANAMA HATTIE (Original soundtracks) (Various artists).
LP: . . . . **SH 2043**

AOA

SATISFACTORY ARRANGEMENT.
LP: . . . . **EDRLP 2**

UNLIMITED GENOCIDE (AOA & Oi Polloi).
LP: . . . . **GURT 12**

AOR

MUSIC FOR THE MIRACLE (Various artists).
Tracks: / Heart and soul: *Lewis, Huey & The News* / Run to you: *Adams, Bryan* / Out of touch: *Hall & Oates*/ Running with the night: *Richie, Lionel* / Careless whisper: *Wham* / Smooth operator: *Sade* / Cover me: *Springsteen, Bruce* / I'm so excited: *Pointer Sisters* / She bop: *Lauper, Cyndi* / Everybody wants to rule the world: *Tears For Fears* / Can't fight this feeling: *REO Speedwagon* / Everytime you go away: *Young, Paul.*
LP: . . . . **EPC 26973**
MC: **40 26973**

AP50

I'VE GOT AN AP50 AND I'M GONNA THRASH IT.
LP: . . . . **AP 50612**

Apache

APACHE.
Tracks: / Please don't stop the music / And you know / Cold fire / Suzanne / Working man / J.B.'s open house / Marathon / Down on the corner / Born to raise hell / Children of the night.
LP: . . . . **K 50826**

Apache Moon

APACHE MOON (Horne, David (nar)).
MC: . . . . **SOUND 5**

Apartment Zero (film)

APARTMENT ZERO (Film soundtrack) (Various artists).
Tracks: / Buenos Aires Capriccio - Main title: *Various artists* / Jack's appearance: *Various artists* / Deal, The: *Various artists* / Crime in the night: *Various artists* / Rescue: *Various artists* / Friendship: *Various artists* / Victim number 13: *Various artists* / Air of love: *Various artists* / Suspicions: *Various* artists / Cambalache: *Various artists* / Training Jack: *Various artists* / Invaded by neighbours: *Various* artists / Capriccio 2: *Various artists* / Touch of death: *Various artists* / Lament: *Various artists*/ Farewell to Laura/hell: *Various artists* / Fight, The: *Various artists* / Last supper, The: *Various artists*/ Apartment zero - End title: *Various artists.*
LP: . . . . **MOMENT 120**
MC: . . . . **MOMENTC 120**

Apartments

EVENING VISITS, THE.
LP: . . . . **ROUGH 88**

APB

CURE FOR THE BLUES.
LP: . . . . **YTHANLP 4**

SOMETHING TO BELIEVE IN (LP).
LP: . . . . **YTHANLP 005**

Apetrea, Costa

BLUE RAIN (See under Tolonen, Jukka).

Apex Jazz Band

SPREADING JOY.
Tracks: / Spreading joy / Chant / Just a closer walk with thee / Fish seller (soprano sax solo) / Sing on / One sweet letter from you / Burgundy Street blues / Give me your telephone number / Someday, sweetheart / Cheek to cheek.
LP: . . . . **PHL 498**
MC: . . . . **CPHL 498**

Apfelbaum, Peter

SIGNS OF LIFE.
MC: . . . . **ANC 8764**

Aphrodite's Child

666.
Tracks: / Aegean sea / All the seats were occupied / Altomont / Babylon / Battle of the beast / Beast, The / Break / Capture of the beast / Do it / Four horsemen / Hic-et-nunc / Infinity / Lamb, The / Lament / Loud loud / Marching beast,The / Ofis / Seven trumpets / Seventh seal, The / System, The / Tribulation / Wakening beast, The / Wedding of the lamb,The.
2LP: **6673 001**
MC: **7528 001**

APHRODITE'S CHILD (Greatest hits).
LP: **6420 006**
MC: **7240 955**
LP: **6886 650**

Apocalypse

APOCALYPSE.
MC: . . . . **TFLAG 23**
LP: . . . . **FLAG 23**

Apocalypse 84

APOCALYPSE 84 (Various artists).
Tracks: / Gimme more: *Kiss* / Cold sweat: *Thin Lizzy* / Out for blood: *Ford, Lita* / Don't talk to strangers: *Dio* / Analog kid, The: *Rush* / Trashed: *Black Sabbath* / Trop fou pour yoi: *Satan Jokers* / Devil made me do it, The: *Golden Earring* / Don't say make me: *Coney Hatch* / Whipping boy: *Nazareth.*
LP: **818 601 1**
MC: **818 601 4**

Apocalypse Now (film)

APOCALYPSE NOW (Film Soundtrack) (Various artists).
LP: . . . . **K 62025**

Apochrypha

EYES OF TIME.
LP: . . . . **RR 9507 1**

FORGOTTEN SCROLL, THE.
Tracks: / Penance / Lost children of hope / Holy wars (only lock the doors) / Fall of the crest / Tablet of destiny / Look to the sun / Riding in the night / Distorted reflections / Broken dreams.
LP: . . . . **RR 95681**

Apollo

APOLLO.
Tracks: / Apollo / Right in front of you / Astro disco / Never learn / Happiness / Hungry eyes / Space cannibals / Do you love me.
LP: . . . . **STML 1210**

Apollo 100

CLASSICAL GAS.
Tracks: / Joy / William Tell / In the hall of the mountain king / Swan lake.
LP: . . . . **MFP 50526**
MC: . . . . **TCMFP 50526**

TELSTAR.
Tracks: / Apache / Hang on Sloopy / Orange blossom special / Talk back / I will return / Walk in the Black Forest / Amazing grace / Tidal wave / Valleys / Matthew and son / Telstar / Lady Madonna / Soul coaxing / Rock 'n' reel / Besame mucho / Cast your fate to the wind / Exodus / Custer's last stand / Popcorn / Nut rocker.
LP: . . . . **MFP 5574**

Apollo Audition

ACAPELLA ALBUM.
LP: . . . . **RELIC 5075**

Apollo Saturday Night

APOLLO SATURDAY NIGHT (Various artists).
LP: . . . . **SD 33159**

Apollonia

APOLLONIA.
Tracks: / Since I fell for you / Synchronize / Victima / Same dream, The / Am I growin' on you / Mismatch / Beat of my heart / For your love / Help wanted / I yi yi.
LP: . . . . K 925594 1
MC: . . . . K 925594 4

Apollonia 6

APOLLONIA 6.
Tracks: / Happy birthday, Mr. Christian / Sex shooter / Blue limousine / Million miles, A / Ooo she she wa wa / Some kind of lover / In a Spanish villa.
LP: 925108 1

Apology (film)

APOLOGY (Film soundtrack) (Various artists).
LP: . . . . STV 81284

Apostles

LIVES AND TIMES OF THE APOSTLES, THE.
LP: . . . . GURT 11

PUNK OBITUARY.
LP: . . . . MORT 23

Appalachia ...

APPALACHIA-THE OLD TRADITIONS (Blue Ridge Mountain Music) (Various artists).
LP: . . . . LP 002

Appalachian Express

EXPRESS TRACKS.
Tracks: / I'm old Kentucky bound / Cabin of love / Have I loved you too late / Express lane / Water's so cold, The / It takes one to know one / Cabin on the mountain / Blue mountain memories / Going home / Two in the morning / When the bees are in the hive / Tiny doll.
LP: . . . . REBEL 1674
MC: . . . . REBELMC 1674

I'LL MEET YOU IN THE MORNING.
LP: . . . . UNKNOWN
MC: . . . . UNKNOWN

Appice, Carmine

CARMINE APPICE.
LP: . . . . RVLP 15

Applause (show)

APPLAUSE (Original Broadway Cast) (Various artists).
Tracks: / Overture: *Various artists* / Backstage babble/ First nighters: *Various artists* / Think how it's gonna be (when we're gonna...): *Various artists* / But alive: *Various artists* / Best night of my life: *Various* artists / Who's that girl: *Various artists* / Applause: *Various artists* / Hurry back: *Various artists*/ Fasten your seat belts: *Various artists* / Welcome to the theatre: *Various artists* / Good friends: *Various* artists / One halloween: *Various artists* / Something greater: *Various artists* / Finale: *Various ar tists.*
LP: . . . . MCL 1724
LP: . . . . SPB 1055

Apple Jack

BEATLES MAGIC.
LP: . . . . DS 030

Appleby, Kim

KIM APPLEBY.
Tracks: / Don't worry / Mama / If you cared / Downtown clown / I'll be there / G.L.A.D. / Hey you / What did I do wrong? / Dodgy people / Teach me.
LP: . . . . PCS 7348
LP: 795 467 1
MC: . . . . TCPCS 7348
MC: 795 467 4

Applejacks

TELL ME WHEN (OLD GOLD) (See under Heinz - Just like Eddie).

Appollon, Dave

MANDOLIN VIRTUOSO.
LP: . . . . L 1066

Appropriate Noise

DECEPTION.
MC: . . . . DHC 4

April Fools Day (film)

APRIL FOOLS DAY (Original soundtrack) (Various artists).
LP: . . . . STV 81278

April In Managua

APRIL IN MANAGUA (Various artists).
MC: . . . . MSC 001

April Sixteenth

SLEEP WALKING.
LP: . . . . HD 032

April Wine

ANIMAL GRACE.
Tracks: / This could be the right one / Sons of the pioneers / Without your love / Rock tonite / Hard rock kid / Money talks / Gimme that thing called love / Last time I'll ever sing the blues.
LP: . . . . EST 2400831
MC: . . . . TC EST 2400834

HARDER FASTER.
Tracks: / I like to rock / Say hello / Tonight / Ladies man / Before the dawn / Babes in arms / Better do it well / 21st century schizoid man.
LP: . . . . EST 12013

NATURE OF THE BEAST.
Tracks: / All over town / Tellin' me lies / Sign of the gypsy queen / Just between you and me / Wanna rock / Caught in the crossfire / Future tense / Big city girls / Crash and burn / Bad boys / One more time.
LP: . . . . EST 12125

POWER PLAY.
Tracks: / Anything you want you get it / Enough is enough / If you see Kay / What if we fall in love / Waiting on a miracle / Doin' it right / Ain't got your love / Blood money / Tell me why / Runners in the night.
LP: . . . . EST 12218

Aquai

SHADES OF MOODS.
Tracks: / Mabra / Daben / Odo, mewu ama wo.
LP: . . . . AQ 1002

Aquarian Dream

AQUARIAN DREAM.
Tracks: / Phoenix / Once again / Treat me like the one you love / Guitar talk / East 6th Street / Let me be the one / Look ahead / I'll always love you.
LP: . . . . DISC 08

Aquino, Leo

LEO AQUINO.
Tracks: / Carnival of Venice / Brave matador, The / Florrette / Dizzy accordion / Mazurka / Hot points / Olive blossoms / Internal patrol / Jolly Caballero / Comedians, The / Presto / Malaguena / Gitanerias / La cumparsita / Acquarelli Cubani / Waltz.
MC: . . . . TAPE 1

LEO AQUINO II.
Tracks: / Dance of the swans / Clair de lune / Prayer hora staccato / Sleeping beauty waltz / Hungarian rhapsody no. 2 / Dizzy fingers / Valse arabesque / Flight of the bumble bee / Wine women and song / Pizzicato polka / Impromptu EF1 / Perpetual motion / Rondo capriciosso.
MC: . . . . TAPE 2

LEO AQUINO III.
Tracks: / Glocca morra / Dizzy fingers / Nola / Miglia vacca / Flight of the bumble bee / Fiddle faddle / Wooden soldiers / Sole mio / Torna a surriento / Funiculi / Barber of Seville / Carnival of Venice / Summer night / Anitra's dance / March of the dwarf s.
MC: . . . . TAPE 3

Ar Bras, Dan

ACOUSTIC.
LP: . . . . FLVM 3062

ALLEZ DIRE A LA VILLE.
LP: 883021

MUSIQUES POUR LES SILENCE A VENIR.
LP: . . . . RS 30063
MC: . . . . KMMC 02

TERRE NOUVELLE.
LP: 883009

A.R. Kane

69.
LP: . . . . ROUGH 119
MC: . . . . ROUGHC 119

I.
Tracks: / Hello / Crack up / What's all this then / Off into space / Yeti / Honeysuckle swallow / In a circle / Miles apart / Mars / Sugar wings / Down / Insect love / Catch my drift / Love from outer space / Timewind / Snow joke / And I say / Conundrum / Long body / Fast ka / Pop / Spook / Back home / Super vixons / Sorry / Challenge.
LP: . . . . ROUGH 139

REMIXES, THE.
MLP: . . . . RTD 171
MC: . . . . RTCMC 171

Ar Marh Dall

AR MARH DALL (LE CHEVAL AVEUGLE) Cantate sur des motifs celtiques (Various artists).
Tracks: / Salud dit va bro: *Various artists* / Douaret eo bet: *Various artists* / Buan eo bet gwerzet peb tra: *Various artists* / Med bez ez eus 'n eun tu bennag: *Various artists* / Gwisket a peus: *Various artists*/ Rod an istor: *Various artists* / Et out da get: *Various artists* / Ha setu te: *Various artists* / Setu te war bord an hent: *Various artists* / Kouezet oun: *Various artists* / Med al labous war da skoaz: *Various* artists / Dalh da alan: *Various artists* / Dalh sonj: *Various artists* / N'out ket mouget: *Various artists*/ Hag e tihun: *Various artists* / Gwelet'm eus ar vugale: *Various artists* / Dihun ta, sao da benn: *Various artists.*
LP: . . . . ARN 34556
MC: . . . . ARN 434556

Arabesque

TRADITIONAL ARABIC MUSIC (Film Soundtrack) (Various artists).
Tracks: / Longa: *Various artists* / Taksim hussayni: *Various artists* / Ansam (Breezes): *Various artists*/ Redile guelbi (Give me back my heart): *Various artists* / Hiwar (dialogue): *Various artists* / Sama'I thaqil: *Various artists* / Sidi blal: *Various artists* / Cerga: *Various artists* / Alway mizan: *Various artists*/ Bab arraja (The door of hope): *Various artists.*
MC: . . . . CSDL 387

Arabesque (film)

ARABESQUE (Film soundtrack) (Various artists).
LP: . . . . NL 43757

Arabesque, Hassan

NIKRIZ (See under Erraji, Hassan) (Erraji, Hassan & Hassan Arabesque).

Arabia

ARAB MUSIC VOL. 1 (Various artists).
LP: . . . . LLST 7186

ARAB MUSIC VOL. 2 (Various artists).
LP: . . . . LLST 7198
MC: . . . . LLCT 7198

EXOTIC MUSIC FOR THE OUD (Various artists).
LP: . . . . LLST 7303

FANTASIE ARABE (Various artists).
LP: . . . . LLST 7318
MC: . . . . LLCT 7318

MUSIC OF THE NILE VALLEY (Various artists).
LP: . . . . LLST 7355
MC: . . . . LLCT 7355

OUD, THE (Various artists).
LP: . . . . LLST 7160
MC: . . . . LLCT 7160

TRADITIONAL ARABIC MUSIC (Various artists).
MC: D58002

Arabia (group)

VENGEANCE.
LP: 4364371
MC: 4634374

Arabian Nights

ALADDIN AND HIS LAMP (See under Aladdin... (bk)) (Lee, Dennis (nar)).

ALI BABA AND THE FORTY THIEVES (See under Ali Baba) (Lee, Dennis (nar)).

ARABIAN NIGHTS: ALADDIN (See under Aladdin... (bk)) (Jones, Terry (nar)).

SINBAD THE SAILOR (See under Sinbad the Sailor) (Lee, Dennis (nar)).

TALE OF SCHEHEREZADE (See under Tale of Scheherezade) (Lee, Dennis (nar)).

VOYAGES OF SINBAD (See under Sinbad the Sailor) (Jones, Terry (nar)).

Arabic

ARABIC (See under Language Courses).

Aragon

DON'T BRING THE RAIN.
LP: . . . . ARAMLP 001

Araiza, Francisco

FIESTA MEXICANA.
Tracks: / Granada / Te quiero kijiste / Mexico lindo / La golondrina / Fiesta Mexicana / Gratia plena.
LP: 4191931

Aram, Vikki

SINGS AND PLAYS THE GREAT SONGS (Aram, Vikki Plus Her All Star Band).
LP: . . . . ZR 1013

Aranbee Symphony ...

ARANBEE POP SYMPHONY ORCHESTRA, THE (Under the Direction of Keith Richard) (Aranbee Symphony Orchestra).
Tracks: / There's a place / Rag doll / I got you babe / We can work it out / Play with fire / Mother's little helper / In the midnight hour / Take it or leave it / Sittin' on a fence / I don't want to go on without you.
LP: C5-522
MC: C5K-522

Arase, Randy

HOLLYWOOD FANTASIA.
Tracks: / There will never be another you / Someone to watch over me / Three coins in the fountain / Foggy day, A / Boy next door, The / Hollywood fantasia / American in Japan, The / Sonata di bravura.
LP: . . . . NEO 102-A

Arawaks

CARIBBEAN EXPERIENCE (Arawaks & Friends).
LP: . . . . CBLP 1001

Arbereshe Di Lungro

CHANTS DES ALBANAIS DE CALABRE.
Tracks: / Lule Lule / Ajiret / Vjershe / Vemi na vemi / Tarentelle / Ajiri piruks / Ti vasharele / Bini tosk / Pieces instrumen tales.
LP: . . . . ARN 33714

Arcadia

SO RED THE ROSE.
Tracks: / Election day / Keep me in the dark / Goodbye is forever / Flame / Missing / Rose arcana / Promise, The / El diablo / Lady Ice.
LP: . . . . PCSD 101

Arcadians

MAD MAD WORLD.
LP: . . . . IM 012

Arcane Device

ENGINES OF MYTH.
LP: . . . . RER 35

Arcansiel

STILL SEARCHING.
LP: . . . . CONTE 143

Arceneaux, Fernest

FROM THE HEART OF THE BAYOUS (Arceneaux, Fernest & his Louisiana French band).
Tracks: / Mother's love / Last night / It's alright / You don't have to go / I don't want nobody / Mean woman blues / London zydeco / Everyday I have the blues / Chains of love / Reconsider, baby.
LP: . . . . JSP 1064

GUMBO SPECIAL (Arceneaux, Fernest & Thunders).
LP: . . . . SCH 104

ZYDECO STOMP (Arceneaux, Fernest & Thunders).
LP: . . . . JSP 1029

Arch

MESSIER ALBUM, THE.
LP: . . . . AS 5008

STRANGE POINT OF VIEW.
LP: . . . . ABR 020

Archangel, Natalie

NATALIE ARCHANGEL.
Tracks: / Mr. Perfect for me / I can't reach you / Diamonds in the rough / Lets make love / What I'd do / Never be the same / Pledge my time / It was us / La vie continue / Never let me down again.
LP: 4509941
MC: 4509944

Archer, Jeffrey (aut)

LOOPHOLE, THE (And Other Stories From 'A Twist In The Tale') (Havers, Nigel).
MCSET: . . . . LFP 7400

MATTER OF HONOUR, A (Jarvis, Martin (nar)).
MCSET: . . . . LFP 7280

NOT A PENNY MORE, NOT A PENNY LESS (Daneman, Paul (nar)).
MCSET: . . . . LFP 7274
MCSET: . . . . TCLFP 7274

NOT A PENNY MORE, NOT A PENNY LESS (Various artists).
MCSET: . . . . ZBBC 1040

PERFECT MURDER, A (And Other Stories From a Twist in the Tale) (Jarvis, Martin & Rosalind Ayres).
MCSET: . . . . LFP 7382

QUIVER FULL OF ARROWS (Schofield, Paul (nar)).
MCSET: . . . . LISF 0005/0006

QUIVER FULL OF ARROWS, A VOL. 1 (Jarvis, Martin (nar)).
MC: . . . . TTDMC 408

QUIVER FULL OF ARROWS, A VOL. 2 (Jarvis, Martin (nar)).
MC: . . . . TTDMC 410

Archer, Robyn

LADIES' CHOICE.
LP: . . . . PLR 045

TAKE YOUR PARTNERS FOR...
LP: . . . . LRF 023

WILD GIRL IN THE HEART, THE.

LP: . . . . LRF 027

Archers (Group)

STAND UP.
Tracks: / Only His love / We're all gonna leave here / Fool's paradise / Moments with you / Stand up / Blame it on the one I love / More (so much more) / Livin' in your love / God loves you / Picking up the pieces.
LP: . . . . LS 7055
MC: . . . . LC 7055

Archers (radio)

VINTAGE ARCHERS (Various artists).
MCSET: . . . . ZBBC 1036

VINTAGE ARCHERS 2 (Various artists).
MCSET: . . . . ZBBC 1080

WEDDING, THE.
MCSET: . . . . ZBBC 1206

Archibald

BALLIN' WITH ARCHIE (Complete New Orleans Sessions 1950-52).
Tracks: / Great big eyes / Early morning blues / Ballin' with Archie / Little Miss Muffet / Stack-a-lee / Crescent city bounce / Shake baby shake / Soon as I go home / House party blues / My gal / She's scattered everywhere.
LP: . . . . KK 7409

Archie

LISTEN TO WHAT ARCHIE SEZ!.
LP: KIX4U 2224
LP: . . . . PLAT 2224

Archies

20 GREATEST HITS: ARCHIES.
LP: 2636261
MC: 2636264

Archy & Mehitabel

ARCHY & MEHITABEL (Original Broadway cast) (Various artists).
LP: . . . . AOL 4963

Arco Iris

PEACE PIPES.
LP: . . . . PJ 88037

Ardelles

TRIBUTE TO THE POLICE, A.
MC: . . . . ZCFPA 1024

Arden, John (nar)

DRAMATIST SPEAKS, THE (See under Dramatist Speaks).

Ardkore

NAPALM STIX TO KIDZ.
LP: . . . . VOV 671

Ardley, Neil

HARMONY OF THE SPHERES.
Tracks: / Upstarts all / Leap in the dark / Glittering circles / Fair mirage / Soft stillness and the night / Headstrong, headlong / Toward tranquility.
LP: . . . . TXSR 133

KALEIDOSCOPE OF RAINBOWS.
Tracks: / Prologue / Rainbow one / Rainbow two / Rainbow three / Rainbow four / Rainbow five / Rainbow six / Rainbow seven / Ep ilogue.
LP: . . . . GULP 9077

Ardoin, Boisec

LA MUSIQUE CREOLE.
LP: . . . . ARHOOLIE 1070

Ardoin Family

COUPLE OF CAJUNS (Ardoin Family Orchestra/Dewey Balfa).
Tracks: / La Cucaracha / Grande mamou / La valse de gros garcon / Valse de meche / La valse fonce / Cher toute toute.
LP: . . . . SNTF 873

Ardoin, Lawrence

ZYDECO (Ardoin, Lawrence 'Black' & his French band).
LP: . . . . ARHOOLIE 1091
MC: . . . . C 1091

Area

AGATE LINES.
LP: . . . . TMLP 59

FRAGMENTS OF THE MORNING.
LP: . . . . CLM 031
MC: . . . . CLM 031MC

PERFECT DREAM.
Tracks: / 25 / I'll gather flowers / Sympathy / Vigilant / Tunnel / With Louise / Surrender to the wheel / Why should I worry / Thread / As thick as thieves.
LP: . . . . TMLP 28

Argent

ALL TOGETHER NOW.
LP: . . . . EPC 64962

ANTHOLOGY - ARGENT (Best of Argent).
Tracks: / School girl / It's only money / Pleasure / Hold your head up / Thunder and lighting / Liar / God gave rock 'n' roll to you / Keep on rolling.
LP: . . . . EPC 32517
MC: 40 32517

ARGENT.
LP: . . . . BGOLP 110

IN DEEP.
LP: . . . . EPC 65475

MUSIC FROM THE SPHERES.
Tracks: / Music from the spheres / I don't believe in miracles / I am the dance of ages / Keep on rolling / Time of the season / Celebration / Tragedy / Man for all reasons / Like honey / High wire / Dance in the smoke / It's only money (part 2) / Sweet Mary / Chained / Rejoice / Pleasure.
MC: . . . . ELITE 004 MC

Argent, Christopher

JESUS COLLEGE CHOIR, CAMBRIDGE (See under Jesus College) (Argent, Christopher/JesusCollege choirCambridge/GeraintBowen).

Argent, Rod

MOVING HOME.
Tracks: / Silence / Home / I'm in the mood / Summer / Number 1 / Well well well / Tenderness / Pastorius mentioned / Smiling / Recollection.
LP: . . . . MCL 1695

RED HOUSE.
Tracks: / Teenage years / Salvation song / 4th gymnopedie, A / Helpless / Sweet Russian / In memory / Baby don't you cry no more / First touch / Suite T / Spirits.
LP: . . . . LPMMC 1012
MC: . . . . TCMMC 1012

SHADOWSHOW (Argent, Rod/Barbara Thompson).
LP: . . . . TM 3
MC: . . . . ZCTM 3

Argentina (Country)

ARGENTINE FOLK MUSIC Chaqueonos in song and dance - magic rituals (Various artists).
LP: . . . . LLST 7254

CLASSIC GUITAR, THE (Various artists).
LP: . . . . LLST 7299

GUITAR OF THE PAMPAS, THE (Various artists).
LP: . . . . LLST 7253
MC: . . . . LLCT 7253

INDIANS OF THE GRAN CHACO, THE (Various artists).
LP: . . . . LLST 7295

Argo Treasury Of..

ARGO TREASURY OF COMIC & CURIOUS VERSE (Various artists).
MCSET: 418 189-4

ARGO TREASURY OF ENGLISH POETRY (1) (Chaucer to Shakespeare) (Various artists).
MCSET: 417 931-4

ARGO TREASURY OF ENGLISH POETRY (2) (Donne to Gray) (Various artists).
MCSET: 417 934-4

ARGO TREASURY OF ENGLISH POETRY (3) (Hardy to Elliot) (Various artists).
MCSET: 417 928-4

ARGO TREASURY OF JOHN MILTON (Various artists).
MCSET: 418 021-4

ARGO TREASURY OF LOVE POEMS (Various artists).
MCSET: 418 216-4

ARGO TREASURY OF READINGS FROM LONGER POEMS (Various artists).
MCSET: 418 012-4

ARGO TREASURY OF RELIGIOUS VERSE (Various artists).
MCSET: 418 195-4

ARGO TREASURY OF ROMANTIC VERSE (Various artists).
MCSET: 418 015-4

ARGO TREASURY OF VICTORIAN POETRY (Various artists).
MCSET: 418 009-4

Arguelles, Steve

ARGUELLES.
Tracks: / Redman / Don't tell me now / Lucky star / Dis at ease / Cherry waltz / Blessed light / Elderberries / My heart belongs to Daddy / Guara / Hermana guapa / Tin tin / Trimmings.
MC: . . . . AHUM 0074

Argyle Arms Ceilidh,

ARGYLE ARMS CEILIDH, THE (Various artists).
LP: . . . . LAP 110
MC: . . . . LAP 110C

Argyll & Sutherland...

ROAD TO THE ISLES (Argyll & Sutherland Highlanders).
Tracks: / Road to the Isles / Impressions of a Scottish air / Pantomime / A Moorside suite / Garb of Old Gaul / Thin red line, The / Through bolts and bars / Mistral's daughter / Tartan tuba / Pavanne in blue / Fascinating drums / Nightingale sang in Berkley square, A / Kalinka / Tocatta in D minor.
LP: . . . . BND 1034
MC: . . . . ZC BND 1034

Arhelger, Jerry

LONDON LADY.
Tracks: / Travellin' on / No heart to go home to / Never lonely again / You don't have very far to go / Moanin' the blues / London lady / I like winning / It's been that kind of night / For all the lonely hearts / Do you wanna / Beside you, beside me / Tell me who / Nashville without Jesus.
LP: . . . . SDLP 064

Aria (film)

ARIA (Film soundtrack) (Various artists).
LP: . . . . BL 86587
MC: . . . . BK 86587

Arian Aquarians

MEET THEIR WATERLOO.
LP: . . . . LAY 029

Ariel

ARIEL.
LP: . . . . MVLP 8

Arima, Susumu

SUPER TOUCH.
LP: . . . . SGS 4

Aristocats (bk)

ARISTOCATS.
MC: . . . . DIS 012

Aristocats (film)

ARISTOCATS, THE (Film soundtrack) (Various artists).
LP: . . . . WD 020
MC: . . . . WDC 020

Aristocrats Of...

FLORIDA BLUES (Aristocrats Of Dixieland).
LP: . . . . AP 129

Ariwa

ARIWA HITS '89 (Various artists).
Tracks: / I'm in love with a dreadlock: *Kofi* / At the dance: *Simmonds, Leroy* / Don't sell your body: *B, Macka* / You'll never get to Heaven: *Annette B* / Let's make a baby: *Tajah, Paulette* / Midnight train to Georgia: *McLean,John* / Stop chat: *Lorna, G* / On my mind: *Intense* / Best friend's man: *Cross, Sandra* / Sheba's verandah: *King, Allan.*
LP: . . . . ARILP 050
MC: . . . . ARIMC 050

ARIWA POSSE (Various artists).
LP: . . . . ARILP 012

Arizona

ARIZONA.
Tracks: / Sweet fantasy / Let go yer lowdowns / So hard living without you / Dance if you wanna dance / Strugglin' singers / Gamblin' man / Johnny O / Tomorrow's picture / Don't it feel good / Mary's waltz (if you believe in me) / Too late to begin.
LP: . . . . SF 8465

LOW DOWN.
Tracks: / Low down music / Like can turn to love / Got no business (bein' that funky) / Wind wishin' / Music ship / Aberration / Go down town / Love take over / Play a little music / Don't let it get you down.
LP: . . . . PL 25103

Arizona Colt (film)

ARIZONA COLT (Film soundtrack) (Various artists).
LP: . . . . SP 8060

Arizona Dranes

BARREL HOUSE PIANO 1926-28.
LP: . . . . HERWIN 210

Arizona Smoke Revue

ARIZONA SMOKE REVUE (Arizona Smoke Revue featuring Bill Zorn).
Tracks: / Take me back to my last life / January second / Football Phil / In the real old style / Same old man / Good morning stranger / Avalon town / No-one to blame but yourself / Pardon me while I smoke / Stockade / Prison / Sweet home.
LP: . . . . AVA 110

THUNDERING ON THE HORIZON, A.
Tracks: / Last day of July / Rain / Feeling lazy / It's the pits / All fall down / Further along / Factory / Good idea at the time / He settles down / Border song.
LP: . . . . R 006LP

Ark Royal

LAST FAREWELL, THE.
Tracks: / Hearts of oak / Sailing / Yellow submarine / Back home / Swing low sweet chariot / Wombling song / Green green grass of home / Land of hope and glory / Last farewell, The / Ram it / All the nice girls love a sailor / Zulu warrior / Holy ground / Ob la di, ob la da / You'll never walk alone.
LP: . . . . REH 357
MC: . . . . ZCR 357

Arkansas Blues

ARKANSAS BLUES VOL.1 (Keep it yourself) (Various artists).
LP: . . . . R 7605

Arkhangelsk

ARKHANGELSK.
LP: . . . . LR 135

Arkin, Alan

CATCH 22.
MC: . . . . LFP 41 7204 5

Arkle, Phyllis (aut)

RAILWAY CAT, THE (See under Railway Cat) (Branch, Andrew (nar)).

Arky's Toast

FROM THE HALF MOON TO THE RISING SUN.
Tracks: / From the half moon to the rising sun / Summer sketch / Arky's people / April / Cold's the wind / Child's dream, A / Tree I love best, The / Merry haymakers / Acrobats / Sir Marmaduke / Balaclave charge, The / Hunting song / Village pub / Plastic's all the go / Arky's toast.
LP: . . . . GVR 212

Arlen, Harold

HAROLD ARLEN IN HOLLYWOOD.
Tracks: / Out of this world / It's only a paper moon / Accentuate the positive / Last night when we were young / This time the dream's on me / That old black magic / Medley "The Wizard of Oz" / Now I know / Let's fall in love / What's good about goodbye / One for my baby / Rusty Dedrick and the winds of change.
LP: . . . . MES 6918

PLAYS HARRY RESER.
LP: . . . . SOS 1200

SINGS HAROLD ARLEN.
Tracks: / Blues in the night / Ding dong the witch is dead / Sleepin' bee / In the shade of the new apple tree / Hit the road to dreamland / Accentuate the positive / My shining hour / Today I love everybody / House of flowers / For every man there's a woman / That's a fine kind of freedom.
LP: 32311

SONGS WITH A FRIEND (Arlen, Harold/Barbra Streisand).
LP: . . . . AOS 2920
MC: . . . . BT 2920

Arlington Street

HONOUR THY WOMANSELF (Arlington Street Women's Caucus).
LP: . . . . ROUNDER 4006

Ar-Log

AR-LOG I.
Tracks: / Rali twm sion / Y blewyn glas / Difyrrwch crbet on ynys Maenggwyn / Ymdaith Caerffili / Ar lan y mor / Dainty Davey / Ygwcw fach / Hafoty fraichddu / Yn harbwr Corc / Breuddwyd y Frenhines / Cerdd y gog Lwydlas / Clychau Aberdyfi / Ffidl ffadl / Tra bo dau / Glan bran.
LP: . . . . DIN 305

AR-LOG II.
LP: . . . . DIN 310

AR-LOG III.
LP: . . . . DIN 315

MEILLIONEN (The Clover).
LP: . . . . DID 715

PEDAWAR.
LP: . . . . RAL 001

Arlott, John (nar)

TALKS CRICKET.
LP: . . . . CAS 1157
MC: . . . . CASMC 1157

VOICE OF CRICKET, THE (See under Voice of Cricket).

WORLD OF THE COUNTRYSIDE.
LP: . . . . SPA 304

Arm The Insane

REMEMBER.
LP: . . . . CLP 224

Armada Orchestra

DISCO ARMADA.
Tracks: / Do me right / Tell me what you want / It's the same old song / Classical bump / Hustle, The / Drifter, The / Cochise band / Band of gold / You want it you got it.
LP: . . . . CLP 528

PHILLY ARMADA.
Tracks: / Philly Armada / I love music / You make me feel brand new / I'll always love my mama / Love I lost, The / Let me make love to you / For the love of money / Philly Armada Part 2.
LP: . . . . CLP 536

Armatrading, Joan

BACK TO THE NIGHT.
Tracks: / No love for free / Travelled so far / Steppin' out / Dry land / Cool blue stole my heart / Get in touch with Jesus / Body to dust / Back to the night / So good / Let's go dancing / Come when you need me.
LP: . . . . SHM 3153
MC: . . . . HSC 3153
LP: . . . . AMID 112

GOLDEN HOUR OF JOAN ARMATRADING.
MC: . . . . KGHMC 112

HEARTS AND FLOWERS.
Tracks: / More than one kind of love / Promise land / Can't let go / Something in the air tonight / Good times / Hearts and flowers / Someone's in the background / Free / Always / Power of dreams, The.
LP: 3952981
MC: 3952984

JOAN ARMATRADING.
Tracks: / Down to zero / Help yourself / Water with the wine / Love and affection / Save me / Join the boys / People / Somebody who loves you / Like fire / Tall in the saddle.
LP: . . . . AMLH 64588
MC: . . . . CAM 64588

KEY, THE.
Tracks: / I love it when you call me names / Foolish pride / Drop the pilot / Key, The / Everybody gotta know / Tell tale / What do boys dream / Game of love / Dealer / Bad habits / I love my baby.
LP: . . . . AMLX 64912
MC: . . . . CXM 64912

ME, MYSELF, I.
Tracks: / Me, myself, I / Ma-me-o-beach / Friends / Is it tomorrow yet / Turn out the light / When you kissed me / All the way from America / Feeling in my heart (for you) / Simon / I need you.
LP: . . . . AMLH 64809
MC: . . . . CAM 64809

ME, MYSELF, I. (TRACK RECORD).
MC: . . . . AMC 24107

MEAN OLD MAN.
LP: . . . . PLP 34
MC: . . . . PMC 34

REPLAY OF JOAN ARMATRADING.
LP: . . . . FEDB 5005
MC: . . . . CFEDB 5005

SECRET SECRETS.
Tracks: / Temptation / Moves / Talking to the wall / Love by you / Thinking man / Friends not flowers / One night / Secret secrets / Strange / Persona grata.
LP: . . . . AMA 5040
MC: . . . . AMC 5040

SHOUTING STAGE, THE.
Tracks: / Devil I know, The / Living for you / Did I make you up / Stronger love / Shouting stage, The / Words / Straight talk / Watch your step / All a woman needs / Dark truths / Innocent request (extra track on CD only.).
LP: . . . . AMA 5211
MC: . . . . AMC 5211

SHOW SOME EMOTION.
Tracks: / Woncha come on home / Show some emotion / Warm love / Never is too late / Peace in mind / Opportunity / Mama mercy / Get in the sun / Willow / Kissin' and a hugging.
LP: . . . . AMLH 68433
MC: . . . . CAM 68433

SLEIGHT OF HAND.
Tracks: / Kind words (and a real good heart) / Killing time / Reach out / Angel man / Laurel and the rose / One more chance / Russian roulette / Jesse / Figure of speech / Don Juan.
LP: . . . . AMA 5130
MC: . . . . AMC 5130

STEPPIN' OUT.
Tracks: / Mama mercy / Cool blue stole my heart / How cruel / Love song / Love and affection / Steppin' out / You rope you tie me / Kissin' and a hugging / Tall in the saddle.
LP: . . . . AMLH 64789
MC: . . . . CAM 64789
LP: . . . . SHM 3176
MC: . . . . HSC 3176

TO THE LIMIT.
Tracks: / Barefoot and pregnant / Your letter / Am I blue for you / You rope you tie me / Baby I / Bottom to the top / Taking my baby uptown / What do you want / Wishing / Let it last.
LP: . . . . AMLH 64732
MC: . . . . CAM 64732

TRACK RECORD.
Tracks: / Drop the pilot / I love it when you call me names / Frustration / When I get it right / I'm lucky / Me, myself, I / Weakness in me, The / Heaven / Down to zero / Love and affection / Show some emotion / Willow / Rosie.
LP: . . . . JA 2001
MC: . . . . JAC 2001

VERY BEST OF JOAN ARMATRADING.
LP: 3971221
MC: 3971224

WALK UNDER LADDERS.
Tracks: / I'm lucky / When I get it right / Romancers, The / I wanna hold you / Weakness in me, The / No love / At the hop / I can't lie to myself / Eating the bear / Only one, The.
LP: . . . . AMLH 64876
MC: . . . . CAM 64876

WHATEVER'S FOR US.
Tracks: / My family / City girl / Spend a little time / Whatever's for us / Child star / Visionary mountains / It could have been better / Head of the table / Mister remember me / Gave it a try / Alice / Conversation / Mean old man / All the king's gardens.
LP: . . . . HIFLY 12
MC: . . . . ZCFLY 12
LP: . . . . CLALP 143
MC: . . . . CLAMC 143

Armed Force

ARMED FORCE.
LP: . . . . IW 1009

Armenia

KAMANCHEH D'ARMENIA (Various artists).
Tracks: / Dunen guiken: *Armenia* / Siretzhi yaris taran: *Armenia* / Improvisation aremenienne: *Armenia* / Valayati delkash: *Armenia* / Marush: *Armenia* / Chanson populaire d'Azerbaidjan: *Armenia*.
LP: . . . . ARN 33665

Armored Saint

DELIRIOUS NOMAD.
Tracks: / Long before I die / Nervous man / Over the edge / Laugh, The / Conqueror, The / For the sake / Aftermath / In the hole / You're never alone / Released.
LP: . . . . CHR 1516
MC: . . . . ZCHR 1516

MARCH OF THE SAINTS.
Tracks: / March of the saint / Can U deliver / Mad house / Take a turn / Seducer, The / Mutiny on the world / Glory hunter / Stricken by fate / Envy / False alarm.
LP: . . . . CHR 1479
MC: . . . . ZCHR 1479

RAISING FEAR.
Tracks: / Raising fear / Saturday night special / Out on a limb / Isolation / Chemical euphoria / Frozen will / Human vulture / Book of blood / Terror / Underdogs / Legacy.
LP: . . . . CHR 1610
MC: . . . . ZCHR 1610

SAINTS WILL CONQUER.
Tracks: / Raising fear / Nervous man / Book of blood / Can U deliver / Mad house / No reason to live.
LP: . . . . RR 9520 1
LP: . . . . ZORRO 26
MC: . . . . TZORRO 26

SYMBOL OF SALVATION.
LP: . . . . ZORRO 20
MC: . . . . TZORRO 20

Armour, Matt

ON THE MORNING TIDE.
Tracks: / Trawlerman, The / On the morning tide / Isle of May / Wild white rose, The / Greytown / Harvest home, The / Deep sea fishermen, The / Lammasfair, The / Reyjavic / Head for home / Shores of the Forth, The / Hills of Caithness, The.
LP: . . . . SFA 102

Armoury Show

WAITING FOR THE FLOODS.
Tracks: / Castles in Spain / Kyrie / Feeling, A / Jungle of cities / We can be brave again / Higher than the world / Glory of love / Waiting for the floods / Sense of freedom / Sleep city sleep / Avalanche.
LP: . . . . ARM 1
MC: . . . . TCARM 1

Armpit Jug Band

LAUGHING AT LIFE.
LP: . . . . WR 008

LIVE AT THE LAUGHING ACADEMY.
Tracks: / I'm satisfied with my gal / Christopher Columbus / Wild about my lovin' / Blues my naughty sweetie gives to me / Borneo / Last night in Memphis / Take your fingers off it / All worn out / Never swat a fly / My gal / Fishin' blues / Somebody stole my gal.
LP: . . . . COT 121

Armstrong, Billy

BILLY, DON'T SELL YOUR FIDDLE.
Tracks: / Fraulein / Truck driving man / San Antonio medley / Kind of love I can't forget, The / Six days on the road / Roly poly / Last letter, The / Take me back to Tulsa / Liberty.
LP: . . . . WRS 135

MR. FIDDLE.
LP: . . . . WRS 104

Armstrong, Craig

WINNERS AND LOSERS (See under Grantham, Leslie) (Armstrong, Craig/ Leslie Grantham).

Armstrong, Frankie

FRANKIE ARMSTRONG.
Tracks: / Little Duke Arthur's nurse / Pitmen's union, The / Lady Diamond / Lament for the Hull trawlers / Month of January, The / Three drunken maidens / Jack the lad / Whore's lament, The / Little musgrave / Collier lass, The / Female drummer.
LP: 12TS 273

I HEARD A WOMAN SINGING.
LP: . . . . CF 389
LP: . . . . FF 332

LOVELY ON THE WATER.
Tracks: / Tarry trousers / Green valley, The / Low down in the broom / Cruel mother / Crafty maid's policy, The / Maid on the shore / Frog and the mouse, The / Lovely on the water / Brown girl, The / Young girl cut down in her prime, The / Unquiet grave, The / Saucy sailor / Two sisters, The.
LP: 12TS 216

OUT OF LOVE, HOPE AND SUFFERING.
LP: . . . . BAY 206

TAM LIN (Armstrong, Frankie/Brian Pearson/Blowzabella/Jon Gillespie).
LP: . . . . PLR 063

WAYS OF SEEING.
MC: . . . . HARC 009

Armstrong, Herbie

BACK AGAINST THE WALL.
Tracks: / Josie / Horses of steam / Friday's child / Heaven only knows / You take me up / Back against the wall / Losing you / Let it run / Save the last dance for me / Coming in from the rain.
LP: . . . . MMC 006
MC: . . . . TCMMC 1006

Armstrong, Jack

CELEBRATED MINSTREL.
LP: . . . . SDL 252

Armstrong, Lil

B AND W MASTERS (See under Jackson, Cliff) (Armstrong, Lil/Cliff Jackson).

BORN TO SWING 1936-37.
LP: . . . . HQ 2069

LIL ARMSTRONG AND UNA MAE CARLISLE (Armstrong, Lil & Una Mae Carlsile).
LP: . . . . HQ 2076

Armstrong, Louis

20 GOLDEN PIECES: LOUIS ARMSTRONG.
Tracks: / Someday you'll be sorry / Heebie Jeebies / I can't give you anything but love baby / Muskrat ramble / Dear old Southland / That lucky old sun / Black and blue / Panama / Royal Garden blues / Chinatown my Chinatown / Swing that music / Tiger rag / Baby won't you please come home / Storyville blues / Jeepers creepers / Do you know what it means to miss New Orleans / Old rockin' chair / Way down yonder in New Orleans / I'm not so rough.
LP: . . . . BDL 2007
MC: . . . . BDC 2007

20 GREATEST HITS: LOUIS ARMSTRONG.
LP: 20123
MC: 40123

20 UNFORGETTABLE HITS (Armstrong, Louis & His Allstars).
MC: 40191

1924: DOC COOK (Cook, Doc's Dreamland Orchestra/Louis Armstrong/ Freddie Kepp).
Tracks: / Everybody loves my baby / Texas moaner blues / Of all the wrongs you've done to me / Terrible blues / Santa Claus blues / Nobody knows the way I feel this morning / Early every morn / Cake walkin' babies from home / Scissor grinder Joe / Lonely little wallflower / So this is Venice / Moanful man / Memphis maybe man, The / One I love belongs to somebody else, The / Stockyards strut / Salty dog.
LP: . . . . S 804

1940-47.
LP: . . . . LPJT 64

1944-45.
Tracks: / Blues in the night / Pretty girl is like a melody, A / Baby don't you cry / Coquette / Dear old Southland / Lazy river / I've got a gal in Kalamazoo / Ain't misbehavin' / Is you is or is you ain't my baby / Perido / Accentuate the positive / Alway s.
LP: . . . . SM 3082

1944-51.
Tracks: / Blues in the night / Pretty girl is like a melody, A / Baby don't you cry / Coquette / Dear old Southland / Lazy river / I've got a gal in Kalamazoo / Ain't misbehavin' / Is you is or is you ain't my baby / Perdido / Accentuate the positive / Always / Back o' town blues / Basin Street blues / Black and blue / Do you know what it means to miss New Orleans / I got a right to sing the blues / I'm confessin' / You rascal you / Someday you'll be sorry / Panama / Struttin' with some barbecue.
2LP: . . . . SM 3764/2

ALL STARS VOL II.
Tracks: / High society / I cried for you / Whispering / Me and Brother Bill / Don't fence me in / Basin Street blues / I gotta right to sing the blues / Jack Armstrong blues / Mop mop.
LP: . . . . UJ 17

AMBASSADOR SATCH.
LP: 21121
MC: 40-21121

ARMED FORCES RADIO SERVICE (Armstrong, Louis & His Orchestra).
LP: . . . . D 1021

AT HIS RAREST OF ALL RARE PERFORMANCES VOL 2.
LP: . . . . KLJ 20026

AT THE EDDIE CONDON FLOOR SHOW.
Tracks: / When it's sleepy time down South / Them there eyes / St. James infirmary / Sweets on parade / Do you know what it means to miss New Orleans / Struttin' with some barbecue / Sweet Georgia Brown / After you've gone / Royal Garden blues / Back o' town blues / Me and Brother Bill / Blues in B flat.
LP: . . . . QU 010

AT THE EDDIE CONDON FLOOR SHOW VOL 2.
LP: . . . . QU 011

BACK O' TOWN BLUES.
Tracks: / Someday you'll be sorry / Sweethearts on parade / Jelly roll blues / Chimes blues / Dippermouth blues / Snake rag / New Orleans stomp / Bye and bye / Back o' town blues / I want a big butter and egg man.
LP: 2400591

BASIN STREET BLUES.
LP: 2M 056 78139
MC: 2M 256 78139
LP: . . . . BLP 60128

BEAUTIFUL AMERICAN, THE.
MC: 771501

BEST LIVE CONCERT 1965.
MC: 302002

BEST OF LOUIS ARMSTRONG.
Tracks: / What a wonderful world / Hello Dolly / C'est si bon / Skokiaan.
LP: 1A 022-58256
MC: 1A 222-58256

BEST OF SATCHMO.
Tracks: / On the sunny side of the street / Lazy river / Georgia on my mind / I surrender dear / Exactly like you / Some of these days / Kiss to build a dream on, A / La vie en rose / Blueberry Hill / Whiffenpoof song, The / Shadrack / When it's sleepy time down South / I can't give you anything but love / If I could be with you one hour tonight / When you're smiling.
LP: . . . . MCL 1600
MC: . . . . MCLC 1600

BIG BANDS 1928-1930.
LP: . . . . SW 8450

BIG BANDS, THE.
LP: . . . . S 1253

BING AND LOUIS LIVE (See under Crosby, Bing) (Armstrong, Louis/Bing Crosby).

BLOW THAT HORN.
Tracks: / Ain't misbehavin' / I ain't got nobody / I'm confessin' / St. James Infirmary / Gut bucket blues / You can depend on me / Peanut vendor / You rascal you / Body and soul / Drop that sack / West End blues / Heebie jeebies / Up a lazy river / Dinah / Muskrat ramble / Struttin' with some barbecue / Mahogany Hall stomp / Got no blues / Georgia on my mind / Cornet chop suey / Knockin' on jug / Ory's creole trombone / Chinatown my Chinatown / You're lucky to me.
MCSET: . . . . **DTO 10310**

BLUES 'N' MORE.
Tracks: / St. Louis blues / Ain't hater's blues / Yellow dog blues / Loveless dove / Black and blue / Ain't misbehavin' / Memphis blues, The / Squeeze me / Hesitating blues / Beale Street blues / Chantez...les bas / Atlanta blues / Blue turning grey over you / Long gone.
MC: . . . . **ELITE 013 MC**

BUNNY BERIGAN, LOUIS ARMSTRONG AND MILLS BROTHERS 1937 (See under Berigan, Bunny) (Armstrong, Louis/Bunny Berigan/Mills Brothers).

CARNEGIE HALL CONCERT (February 8th, 1947).
Tracks: / New Orleans function / Free as a bird / Oh didn't he ramble? / Dippermouth blues / Mahogany Hall stomp / Muskrat ramble / St. Louis blues / Rockin' chair / Tiger rag / Black and blue / I'm confessin' / Struttin' with some barbecue / Up a lazy river / You rascal you / Save it, pretty mama / Ain't misbehavin'.
LP: . . . . **CR 520**
LP: . . . . **SM 3614**
LP: . . . . **KLJ 20001**

CHEEK TO CHEEK (Armstrong, Louis/ Ella Fitzgerald).
LP: . . . . **ENT 13023**

CHICAGO CONCERT 1956.
Tracks: / Memphis blues, The / Frankie and Johnny / Tiger rag / Do you know what it means to miss New Orleans / Basin Street blues / Black and blue / West End blues / On the sunny side of the street / Struttin' with some barbecue / Manhattan / When it's sleepy time down South / Indiana / Gypsy, The / Faithful hussar, The / Rockin' chair / Bucket's got a hole in it / Perdido / Clarinet marmalade / Mack the knife / Tenderly / You'll never walk alone / Stompin' at the Savoy / Margie / Mama's back in town / That's my desire / Kokomo / I love you so.
2LP: **22106**
MCSET: **40 22106**

CHICAGO JAZZ (1923-1929) (Armstrong, Louis/Johnny Davis).
LP: . . . . **S 818**

CHINATOWN MY CHINATOWN.
LP: **20073**
MC: **40073**

CLASSIC LOUIS ARMSTRONG.
MCSET: . . . . **WW 6039**

CLASSICS.
LP: . . . . **BD 3001**

COLLECTION : LOUIS ARMSTRONG (20 Golden Greats).
Tracks: / Hello Dolly / Cabaret / Tiger rag / When it's sleepy time down South / Indiana / Muskrat ramble / Mack the knife / Blueberry Hill / St. James' Infirmary / Kiss to build a dream on, A / When the saints go marching in / Jeepers creepers / On the sunny side of the street / Ain't misbehavin' / Panama rag / Black and blue / Dear old Southland / Basin Street blues / Lazy river / Struttin' with some barbecue.
LP: . . . . **DVLP 2007**
MC: . . . . **DVMC 2007**

COLLECTION: LOUIS ARMSTRONG AND HIS ALLSTARS (Armstrong, Louis & His Allstars).
LP: . . . . **LPJT 78**
MC: . . . . **MCJT 78**

COMPLETE LOUIS ARMSTRONG.
MC: . . . . **NK 89279**

COMPLETE TOWN HALL CONCERT, THE.
Tracks: / Cornet chop suey / Our Monday date / Dear old Southland / Big butter and egg man / Tiger rag / Struttin' with some barbecue / Sweethearts on parade / St. Louis blues / Pennies from Heaven / On the sunny side of the street / I can't give you anything but love / Back o' town blues / Ain't misbehavin' / Rockin' chair / Muskrat ramble / Save it pretty mama / St. James Infirmary / Royal Garden blues / Do you know what it means to Miss New Orleans? / Jack Armstrong blues.
2LP: . . . . **NL 89746**
MC: . . . . **NK 89746**

COUNTDOWN.
Tracks: / Way down yonder in New Orleans / Won't you come home Bill Bailey / Avalon / Honeysuckle rose / On the sunny side of the street / Sweet Georgia Brown / Bourbon Street parade / Muskrat ramble / I got rhythm / Tiger rag / Jeepers creepers / Someday you'll be sorry.
LP: . . . . **COUNT 7**
MC: . . . . **ZC CNT 7**

DO YOU KNOW WHAT IT MEANS TO MISS NEW ORLEANS?.
LP: **837 919-1**
MC: **837 919-4**

ELLA AND LOUIS (see under Fitzgerald, Ella) (Armstrong, Louis/Ella Fitzgerald).

ELLA AND LOUIS AGAIN, (VOL. 1) (Armstrong, Louis/Ella Fitzgerald).
Tracks: / Don't be that way / Makin' whoopee / They all laughed / Comes love / Autumn in New York / Let's do it / Stompin' at the Savou / I won't dance / Gee baby ain't I good to you.
LP: **2304 501**
LP: **837 442 1**

ELLA AND LOUIS AGAIN, (VOL. 2) (Armstrong, Louis/Ella Fitzgerald).
Tracks: / Let's call the whole thing off / These foolish things / I've got my love to keep me warm / I'm puttin' all my eggs... / Fine romance, A / I'll wind / Love is here to stay / I get a kick out of you / Learnin' the blues.
LP: **837 443 1**

ELLA FITZGERALD AND LOUIS ARMSTRONG (Armstrong, Louis/Ella Fitzgerald).
Tracks: / When the saints go marching in / West End blues / Jeepers creepers / On the sunny side of the street / Ain't misbehavin' / Swing that music / Undecided / Tisket a tasket, A / Got a pebble in my shoe / You'll have to swing it / Chew, chew, chew, chew (your bubble gum) / I found my yellow basket.
LP: . . . . **SM 3099**

ELLA FITZGERALD AND LOUIS ARMSTRONG (2) Compact/Walkman jazz (see under Fitzgerald, Ella (Fitzgerald, Ella & Louis Armstrong).

ESSENCE OF LOUIS ARMSTRONG, THE.
LP: . . . . **NOST 7662**

ESSENTIAL LOUIS ARMSTRONG, THE.
Tracks: / Bourbon Street parade / Washington and Lee swing / Avalon / New Orleans / That's a plenty / Just a closer walk with thee / Dixie / Sheik of Araby / Wolverine blues / Sweet Georgia Brown / Limehouse blues / Back o' town blues / Sweethearts on parade / Sugar foot stomp / Canal Street blues / Bill Bailey won't you please come home / Someday you'll be sorry / Struttin' with some barbecue / I ain't gonna give nobody none of my jelly roll / Cornet chop suey / My bucket's got a hole in it.
2LP: . . . . **AFESD 1042**
MC: . . . . **ZCAFD 1042**

ESSENTIAL, THE.
MC: **4671454**

EVENING WITH LOUIS ARMSTRONG.
MC: . . . . **ZCVJD 538**
2LP: . . . . **GNPS 2-11001**
MCSET: **GNP5 2-11001**

EVENING WITH LOUIS ARSTRONG VOL. II, AN.
LP: . . . . **GNPS 9050**
MC: **GNP5 9050**

FABULOUS PARIS CONCERT VOL. 1 (March 2, 1948) (Armstrong, Louis & His Allstars).
LP: . . . . **TFD 5.003**

FABULOUS PARIS CONCERT VOL. 2 (March 2, 1948) (Armstrong, Louis & His Allstars).
LP: . . . . **TFD 5.004**

FATS WALLER LAST TESTAMENT 1943 (Louis Armstrong in the 30's).
MC: . . . . **UMK 99005**

FIRST RECORDED CONCERT 1932/ 1933.
Tracks: / I cover the waterfront / Tiger rag / My Chinatown / You rascal you / On the closest / Dinah / Harlem stomp / When it's sleepy time down South.
LP: . . . . **JA 5223**

FROM THE BIG BAND TO THE ALL STARS.
Tracks: / Long long journey / Linger in my arms a little longer baby / Back o' town blues / Where the blues were born in New Orleans / I believe / You don't learn that in school / Rockin' chair / I never saw a better day / Hobo you can't ride this train.
LP: . . . . **NL 89279**

GEORGIA ON MY MIND.
LP: . . . . **DBD 17**
MC: . . . . **DBDC 17**

GIANTS, 3 (See under Ellington, Duke) (Armstrong, Louis/Duke Ellington/Billie Holiday).

GOLDEN GREATS: LOUIS ARMSTRONG.
Tracks: / What a wonderful world / Hello Dolly / Cabaret / On the sunny side of the street / Lazy river / Georgia on my mind / I surrender dear / Exactly like you / Some of these days / Kiss to build a dream on, A / La vie en rose / Blueberry Hill / Whiffenpoof song, The / Shadrack / When it's sleepy time down South / I can't give you anything but love / If I could be with you one hour tonight / When you're smiling.
LP: . . . . **MCM 5013**
MC: . . . . **MCMC 5013**

GOLDEN HIGHLIGHTS.
LP: . . . . **CBS 54720**

GREAT ENTERTAINER, THE.
Tracks: / Hello Dolly / Gone fishin' / Cabaret / Lazybones / High society / Basin Street blues / Confessin' / Skokiaan / Swing that music (CD only.) / Lazy river (CD only.) / Pretty little missy (CD only.) / I love jazz (CD only.) / What a wonderful world / Everybody loves my baby / When you're smiling / On the sunny side of the street / Ain't misbehavin' / Blueberry Hill / Shadrack / Among my souvenirs.
LP: . . . . **MFP 5857**
MC: . . . . **TCMFP 5857**

GREAT REUNION (Armstrong, Louis/ Duke Ellington).
2LP: **400505**

GREAT REUNION, THE (Armstrong, Louis/Duke Ellington).
Tracks: / It don't mean a thing / Solitude / Don't get around much anymore / I'm beginning to see the light / Just squeeze me / I got it bad and that ain't good / Azalea.
LP: . . . . **ROU 1008**
2LP: **400505**

GREATEST CONCERT, THE.
Tracks: / Rose room / Back o' town blues / C'est si bon / Way down yonder in New Orleans / Stardust / Rockin' chair / Where did you stay last night / Baby it's cold outside / C jam blues / Stompin' at the Savoy / I used to love you / La vie en rose / Lover / That's my desire / Royal Garden blues / Ain't misbehavin' / Love me or leave me / How high the moon / Tea for two / Hucklebuck, The.
LP: . . . . **ALB 154**

GREATEST HITS: LOUIS ARMSTRONG.
LP: **33001**
MC: **63001**

GREATEST HITS: LOUIS ARMSTRONG VOL 2.
LP: **33002**
MC: **63002**

GREATEST HITS: LOUIS ARMSTRONG(IMPORT).
LP: . . . . **FUN 9018**
MC: . . . . **FUNC 9018**

GREATEST HITS:LOUIS ARMSTRONG.
Tracks: / Mack the Knife / Back o' town blues / Black and blue / Ain't misbehavin' / Basin Street blues / Cabaret / Honeysuckle Rose / When it's sleepy time down South / All of me / West End blues / Struttin' with some barbecue / Indiana / Tin roof blues.
LP: . . . . **CBS 21058**
MC: **40 21058**
LP: . . . . **CBS 32030**
MC: **40 32030**
LP: . . . . **NE 1306**
MC: . . . . **CE 2306**

HALL OF FAME.
Tracks: / When it's sleepy time down south / Indiana / Hello Dolly / St.James infirmary / Blueberry hill / Mack the knife / Cabaret / That's my desire / Ole miss / Kiss to build a dream on, A.
LP: . . . . **BLPS 20155**

HELLO DOLLY.
LP: . . . . **HAR 8190**

HIGH SOCIETY.
Tracks: / Someday you'll be sorry / Dippermouth blues / Do you know what it means to miss New Orleans? / Honeysuckle rose / Panama / Save it, pretty mama / High society / Rockin' chair / Back o' town blues / Tin roof blues / You can depend on me.
LP: . . . . **BLM 52035**

HIS IMMORTAL CONCERT SERIES.
Tracks: / Back o' town blues / Do you know what it means to miss New Orleans / Black and blue / Basin Street blues / I gotta right to sing the blues / I'm confessin' / You rascal you / Lazy river / Someday you'll be sorry / Panama / Struttin' with some barbec ue.
LP: . . . . **SM 3133**

HIS LAST RECORDINGS - 1970.
Tracks: / Boy from New Orleans / What a wonderful world / Mood indigo / Give peace a chance / My one and only love / Everybody's talkin' / His father wore long hair / This black cat has nine lives / We shall overcome.
LP: . . . . **PL 43553**

HOT FIVE (1925-1926).
LP: . . . . **S 1230**

HOT FIVE AND HOT SEVEN (GIANTS OF JAZZ) (1926-1928).
LP: . . . . **LPJT 15**

HOT FIVE AND SEVEN (SWAGGIE) (1927-1928).
LP: . . . . **S 1236**

HOT FIVE (SWAGGIE) (1928).
LP: . . . . **S 1239**

HOT FIVES AND SEVEN (1926-27).
Tracks: / Lonesome blues / Sweet little papa / Jazz lips / Skid-dat-de-dat / I want a big butter and egg man / Sunset cafe stomp / You made me love you / Irish black bottom / Willie the weeper / Wild man blues / Chicago breakdown / Alligator crawl / Potato head blues / Melancholy blues / Weary blues / Twelfth street rag.
LP: . . . . **S 1233**

HOT FIVES AND SEVENS (CBS).
Tracks: / My heart / I'm in the barrel / Gut bucket blues / Come back sweet papa / Georgia grind / Heebie jeebies / Cornet chop suey / Oriental strut / You're next / Muskrat ramble / Don't forget to mess around / I'm gonna gitcha / Droppin' sucks / Whosit / King of the Zulus, The / Big fat Ma and skinny Pa.
LP: **4608211**
MC: **4608214**
LP: **4608211**
MC: **4608214**

HOT FIVES AND SEVENS (CBS).
Tracks: / Lonesome blues / Jazz lips / Big butter and egg man / You made me love you / Willie the weeper / Alligator crawl / Melancholy / Twelfth St. rag / Sweet little papa / Skid dat de dat / Sunset cafe stomp / Irish black bottom / Wild man blues / Potato head blues / Weary blues / Keyhole blues.
LP: **4630521**
MC: **4630524**

HOT FIVES AND SEVENS (CBS).
LP: **4651891**
MC: **4651894**

HOT FIVES AND SEVENS (RETROSPECT) (Complete (2)).
Tracks: / My heart / Yes I'm in the barrel / Gut bucket blues / Come back sweet papa / Georgia grind / Heebie jeebies / Cornet chop suey / Oriental strut / You're next / Muskrat ramble / Don't forget to mess around / I'm gonna getcha / Dropping shucks / Who's it? / King of the Zulus, The / Big fat ma and skinny pa / Lonesome blues / Sweet little papa / Jazz lips / Skid dat de dat / Big butter and egg man / Sunset cafe stomp / You made me love you / Irish black bottom / Willie the weeper / Wild man blues / Chicago breakdown / Alligator crawl / Potato head blues / Melancholy blues / Weary blues / Twelfth St. rag / Keyhole blues / SOL blues / Gully low blues / That's when I'll come back to you / Put 'em down blues / Ory's Creole trombone / Last time, The / Struttin' with some barbecue / Got no blues / Once in a while / I'm not rough / Hotter than that / Savoy blues / Fire works / Skip the gutter / Monday date, A / Don't jive me / West End blues / Sugar foot strut / Two deuces / Squeeze me / Kneedrops / Symphonic raps / Savoyagers' stomp / No papa no / Basin Street blues / No one else but you / Bean koo jack / Save it, pretty mama / Weather bird / Muggles / Heah me talkin' to ya / St. James' Infirmary / Tight like this / Knockin' a jug.
LPS: . . . . **SH 405**

HOT FIVES AND SEVENS (RETROSPECT) (Complete - Set of 4).
LPS: . . . . **SHB 69**

I GOT RHYTHM.
Tracks: / I got rhythm / Honeysuckle rose / Jeepers creepers / Tiger rag / Muskrat ramble / Way down yonder in New Orleans / When the saints go marching in / Body and soul / Sweet hearts on parade / You're driving me crazy / Just a gigolo / Ain't misbehavin' / Back o town blues / C'est si bon / Stompin' at the Savoy / Shine / On the

sunny side of the street / La vie en rose / Hucklebuck, The / Memories of you.
MC: . . . . HSC 3308

IN CONCERT.
2LP: 426014

IN EAST EUROPE.
LP: . . . . SM 3864

IN NEW YORK.
LP: 22018
MC: 42018

IN SWEDEN (1959).
LP: . . . . CAH 4000

INTEGRAL NICE CONCERT 1948 - VOLUME 1.
Tracks: / Panama / Black and blue / Velma's blues / Monday date / Royal Garden blues / Someday / Muskrat ramble / I cried last night.
LP: . . . . JA 5154

JACK ARMSTRONG BLUES (Armstrong, Louis/Allstars).
LP: . . . . JJ 601

JAZZ CLASSICS.
LP: . . . . AH 7

JAZZ CLASSICS IN DIGITAL STEREO (Louis Armstrong 1923-1931) (Armstrong, Louis Hot Five & Hot Seven).
LP: . . . . REB 597
MC: . . . . ZCF 597

JAZZ GREATS.
Tracks: / St. Louis blues / Do you know what it means to miss New Orleans / Swing you cats.
2LP: . . . . NL 45217

JAZZ POTPOURRI.
LP: . . . . MERITT 19

JAZZ TIME VOL.6.
LP: 502706

JULY 4, 1900 - JULY 6, 1971.
Tracks: / (You so and so) You'll wish you'd never been / Hustlin' and bustlin' for baby / Sittin' in the dark / He's a son of the South / Some sweet day / Honey don't you love me anymore / Mississippi basin / Tomorrow night / Dusky stevedore / Song was born, A / Lovely weather we're having / Please stop playing that blues, boy / Ain't misbehavin' / Pennies from Heaven / Save it, pretty mama / Rain, rain / I never saw a better day / I wonder who / Don't play me cheap / Linger in my arms a little longer baby / Whatta ya gonna do / Joseph 'n' his brudders / No variety blues / Blues in the South / I want a little girl / Sugar (that sugar baby o' mine) / Blues are brewin' / Endie / I believe / Why doubt my love / You don't learn that in school / Fifty fifty blues / Some day you'll be sorry.
2LP: . . . . DPM 2017
2LP: 26 28109

KING OLIVER'S JAZZ BAND WITH LOUIS ARMSTRONG (see under King Oliver) (Armstrong, Louis & King Oliver's Jazzband).

LA VOCE DEL JAZZ (Armstrong, Louis & His Allstars).
LP: 2MJP 1056

L'ART VOCAL VOLUME 2: LA SELECTION 1926-1938 (See Under L'Art Vocal).

LAUGHIN' LOUIS.
Tracks: / That's my home / Hobo, you can't ride this train / Medley of Armstrong hits (part 2) / When you're smiling (the whole world smiles) / St James infirmary / Dinah / Medley of Armstrong hits (part 1) / I'll be glad when you're dead you rascal you / When it's sleepy time down south / Nobody's sweetheart / I've got the world on a string / I gotta right to sing the blues / High society / Basin Street blues / Mahogany Hall stomp / Laughin' Louis / Dusky stevedore / There's a cabin in the pines / Sweet Sue, just you / Don't play me cheap / St. Louis blues.
LP: . . . . NL 90404
MC: . . . . NK 90404

LEGEND (Armstrong, Louis Hot Five & Hot Seven).
Tracks: / My heart / Yes!I'm in the barrel / Gut bucket blues / Come back sweet papa / Georgia grind / Heebie jeebies / Cornet chop suey / Oriental strut / You're next / Muskrat rumble / Don't forget to mess around / I'm gonna gitcha / Dropping shucks / Who'sit / King of the Zulus, The / Big fat ma and skinny pa.
LP: . . . . SH 404

LEGENDARY LOUIS ARMSTRONG, THE.
MCSET: . . . . M 10224

LEGENDARY PERFORMER, A.
Tracks: / What a wonderful world / I gotta right to sing the blues / When you're smiling / St. James infirmary / Dinah / Basin Street blues / Mahogany Hall stomp / High society / Do you know what it means to miss New Orleans / Rockin' chair / Ain't misbehavin' / Some day you'll be sorry / You rascal you / When it's sleepytime down south / Nobody's sweetheart / St. Louis blues / Some sweet day.
LP: . . . . PL 12659
MC: . . . . PK 12659

LIVE AND AT HIS BEST.
LP: 2273262
MC: 2173262

LIVE FROM HOLLYWOOD 1949.
LP: . . . . SWH 2

LIVE IN YOKOHAMA.
Tracks: / When it's sleepy time down South / Indiana / Kiss to build a dream on, A / Tea for two / My bucket's got a hole in it / Margie / Velma's blues / C'est si bon / Stompin' at The Savoy.
LP: . . . . QU 032

LOUIS AND FRIENDS.
LP: . . . . MCL 1772

LOUIS ARMSTRONG (Compact/ Walkman jazz).
Tracks: / I gotta right to sing the blues / Moon song / Don't get around much anymore / Let's fall in love.
MC: 833 293-4
LP: 833 293-1

LOUIS ARMSTRONG (1935-38).
Tracks: / I'm in the mood for love / You are my lucky star / Thanks a million / Dipper mouth / Alexander's ragtime band / Sunny side of the street / Satchel mouth swing / Struttin' with some barbecue / Let that be a lesson to you.
MC: . . . . NEO 853

LOUIS ARMSTRONG ALL STARS PHILADEPHIA (August 7 and 9, 1949).
LP: . . . . JC 005

LOUIS ARMSTRONG ALL STARS VOL 2 1948-1949 (Armstrong, Louis & His Allstars).
LP: . . . . JC 110

LOUIS ARMSTRONG AND ALL STARS (Armstrong, Louis & His Allstars).
LP: . . . . SM 3863

LOUIS ARMSTRONG AND DUKE ELLINGTON VOL 1.
LP: . . . . JR 133

LOUIS ARMSTRONG AND FLETCHER HENDERSON (1924-25) (Armstrong, Louis/Fletcher Henderson Orchestra).
LP: . . . . VLP 60

LOUIS ARMSTRONG AND GUESTS.
MC: . . . . ENT MC 13041
LP: . . . . ENT LP 13041

LOUIS ARMSTRONG AND HIS ALL STARS (1947-50) (Armstrong, Louis & His Allstars).
LP: 99002

LOUIS ARMSTRONG AND HIS ALL STARS.
2LP: . . . . SM 3806/2

LOUIS ARMSTRONG AND HIS ALL STARS (1961-2).
LP: . . . . SLP 4012
MCSET: . . . . DTO 10234

LOUIS ARMSTRONG AND HIS ALL STARS, VOL. 1 (Armstrong, Louis & His Allstars).
Tracks: / Sleepy time down south / Indiana / Someday / Ole miss / Tin roof blues / My bucket's got a hole in it / Perdido / Dar danella.
LP: . . . . JR 110

LOUIS ARMSTRONG AND HIS ALL STARS.
MC: . . . . CSWH 2

LOUIS ARMSTRONG AND HIS ALL STARS (Armstrong, Louis & His Allstars).
LP: . . . . SFR DP 692

LOUIS ARMSTRONG AND HIS ALL STARS (Armstrong, Louis & His Allstars).
Tracks: / When it's sleepy time down South / Hello Dolly / Blueberry Hill / Volare / St. James' Infirmary / Girl from Ipanema / Indiana / Muskrat ramble / Mack the knife / I love Paris / Time after time / Cabaret / Tiger rag / When the saints go marching in / This could be the start of something big / Please don't talk about me when I'm gone / Stompin' at the Savoy / That's my desire / Closer walk with thee, A / Them there eyes / Avalon / Kiss to build a dream on, A / Ole miss.
LP: . . . . SLP 4095

LOUIS ARMSTRONG AND HIS ALL STARS (Armstrong, Louis & His Allstars).
LPS: . . . . C 65/4 BOX 4

LOUIS ARMSTRONG AND HIS ORCHESTRA (1931-32) (Armstrong, Louis/his orchestra).
LP: . . . . S 1403

LOUIS ARMSTRONG AND HIS ORCHESTRA (1929-31) (Armstrong, Louis/his orchestra).
LP: . . . . S 1402

LOUIS ARMSTRONG AND HIS ORCHESTRA (1929-49) (Armstrong, Louis & His Orchestra).
LP: . . . . LPJT 53

LOUIS ARMSTRONG AND HIS ORCHESTRA (1935-1944) (Armstrong, Louis/his orchestra).
LP: . . . . S 702

LOUIS ARMSTRONG AND JACK TEAGARDEN (Armstrong, Louis/Jack Teagarden).
LP: . . . . SM 3873

LOUIS ARMSTRONG AND JACK TEAGARDEN (Armstrong, Louis/Jack Teagarden).
LP: . . . . EJLP 07

LOUIS ARMSTRONG AND KING OLIVER.
Tracks: / Just gone / Canal Street blues / Mandy Lee blues / I'm going to wear you off my mind / Chimes blues / Weather bird rag / Dipper mouth blues / Froggie Moore / Snake rag / Alligator hop / Zulu's ball / Working man blues / Krooked blues / Mabel's dreams (take 1) / Mabel's dreams (take 2) / Southern stomps (take 1) / Southern stomps (take 2) / Riverside blues / King Oliver / Jelly Roll Morton (King Porter stomp) / Tom cat blues / Terrible blues / Santa Claus blues / Texas moaner blues / Of all the wrongs you've done to me / Nobody knows the way I feel this morning / Early every morn / Cake walkin' babies from home.
2LP: . . . . M 47017

LOUIS ARMSTRONG AND LUIS RUSSELL 1929-1930.
LP: . . . . S 1267

LOUIS ARMSTRONG AND THE ALL STARS (Philadelphia 1948).
Tracks: / Just you, just me (Recorded Philadelphia, June 2nd. 1948) / Boogie woogie on St. Louis blues (Recorded Philadelphia, June 2nd. 1948) / Struttin' with some barbecue (Recorded Philadelphia, June 4th. 1948) / St. Louis blues (Recorded Philadelphia, June 4th. 1948) / Someday (Recorded Philadelphia, June 5th. 1948) / Together (Recorded Philadelphia, June 5th. 1948) / That's a plenty (Recorded Philadelphia, June 12th. 1948) / East of the sun (Recorded Philadelphia, June 12th. 1948) / St. James' Infirmary (Recorded Philadelphia, Sept. 6th. 1948) / Panama (Recorded Philadelphia, Sept.18th. 1948) / Maybe you'll be there (Recorded Philadelphia, Sept.18th. 1948) / Lazy river (Recorded Philadelphia, Sept.18th. 1948) / Muskrat ramble (Recorded Philadelphia, Sept.18th. 1948) .
LP: . . . . QU 19

LOUIS ARMSTRONG (AUDIO FIDELITY).
MC: . . . . ZCGAS 725

LOUIS ARMSTRONG (CAMBRA).
Tracks: / Hello Dolly / Sit down you're rockin' the boat / I'm confessin' / Jeepers creepers / Swing that music / On the sunny side of the street / When the saints go marching in / Cabaret / Heebie jeebies / I'll string along with you / West End blues / Down by the riverside / Among my souvenirs / 'S wonderful / Georgia on my mind / What a wonderful world / High society / Mahogany Hall stomp / Carry me back to old Virginny / When you're smiling / I can't give you anything but love / Alexander's ragtime band / Blueberry Hill / Naturally / That lucky old sun / Dippermouth blues / Ain't misbehavin' / Basin Street blues / When it's sleepy time down South.
MCSET: . . . . CRT 010

LOUIS ARMSTRONG (ENTERTAINERS).
Tracks: / Cabaret / Mack the knife / Ramona / Gypsy, The / Only you / Blueberry hill / Hello Dolly.
LP: . . . . ENT LP 13007
MC: . . . . ENT MC 13007

LOUIS ARMSTRONG IN THE 1930'S.
LP: . . . . CC 26

LOUIS ARMSTRONG LEGEND.
LP: . . . . P 42

LOUIS ARMSTRONG LEGEND, THE (1926-27).
Tracks: / Lonesome blues / Sweet little Papa / Jazz lips / Skid dat de dat / I want a big butter and egg man / Sunset cafe stomp / You made me love you / Irish black bottom / Willie the weeper / Wild man blues / Chicago breakdown / Alligator crawl / Potato head blues / Melancholy / Weary blues / Twelfth St. rag.
LP: . . . . EG 2604581
MC: . . . . EG 2604584

LOUIS ARMSTRONG LEGEND, THE (1927-1928) (Hot Fives & Sevens vol. 3).
Tracks: / Put 'em down blues / Ory's creole trombone / Last time, The / Struttin' with some barbecue / Got no blues / Once in a while / I'm not rough / Hotter than that / Savoy blues / Fire works / Skip the gutter / Monday date, A / Don't jive me / Keyhole blues / SOL blues / Gully low blues / That's when I'll come back to you.
LP: . . . . SH 406

LOUIS ARMSTRONG LEGEND, THE (1928-1929) (Hot Fives & Sevens complete vol. 4).
Tracks: / West end blues / Sugar foot strut / Two deuces / Squeeze me / Kneedrops / Symphonic raps / Savoyagers' stomp / No papa, no / Basin street blues / No one else but you / Beau koo Jack / Save it pretty mam / Weather bird / Muggles / Heah me talkin to ya / St. James infirmary / Tight like this / Knockin' a jug.
LP: . . . . SH 407
MC: . . . . TC SH 407

LOUIS ARMSTRONG -- LIVE (February 24, 1962).
LP: . . . . SG 8008

LOUIS ARMSTRONG LIVE IN PARIS.
LP: . . . . A 553
MC: . . . . AC 553

LOUIS ARMSTRONG (LOTUS).
LP: . . . . LOP 14,030

LOUIS ARMSTRONG MEETS OSCAR PETERSON (See also under Peterson, Oscar) (Armstrong, Louis/Oscar Peterson).
Tracks: / That old feeling / I'll never be the same / How long has this been going on / I was doing all right / Moon song / There's no you / Sweet Lorraine / Let's fall in love / Blues in the night / What's new / Just one of those things / You go to my head.
LP: 2304 422

LOUIS ARMSTRONG STORY, THE.
LP: 66427

LOUIS ARMSTRONG STORY, THE.
Tracks: / When you're smiling / Some of these days / On the sunny side of the street / Solitude / When the saints go marching in / Ain't misbehavin' / Jeepers creepers / I want a little girl / Someday you'll be sorry / Lazy river / I love jazz / Mack the knife / Muskrat ramble / Tiger rag / When it's sleepy time down South / Cabaret / Volare / Indiana / Kiss to build a dream on, A / Hello Dolly / Blueberry hill / St. James Infirmary / Tenderly / You'll never walk alone / Mop mop.
MCSET: . . . . DVREMC 04

LOUIS ARMSTRONG VOL.1 (1925-26).
MC: . . . . NEO 704

LOUIS ARMSTRONG VOL.2 (1926-27) (NEOVOX).
MC: . . . . NEO 715

LOUIS ARMSTRONG VOL 1 (Muskrat Ramble).
Tracks: / My heart / Yes, I'm in the barrel / Gut bucket blues / Come back sweet Papa / Georgia grind / Heebie jeebies / Cornet chop suey / Oriental Strut / You're next / Muskrat ramble / Don't forget to mess around / I'm gonna gitcha.
LP: . . . . SM 3742

LOUIS ARMSTRONG, VOL 2 (Irish Black Bottom).
Tracks: / Droppin' sucks / Who's it / Big fat ma and skinny pa / Lonesome blues / Sweet little papa / Jazz lips / King of the Zulus, The / Skid dat de dat / Big butter and egg man / Sunset Cafe stomp / You made me love you / Irish black bottom.
LP: . . . . SM 3743
LP: . . . . JR 129

LOUIS ARMSTRONG, VOL 3 (Potato Head Blues).
Tracks: / Willie the weeper / Wild man blues / Chicago breakdown / Alligator crawl / Potato head blues / Melancholy blues / Weary blues / Twelfth St. rag / Keyhole blues / SOL blues / Gully low blues / That's when I'll come back to you.
LP: . . . . SM 3744

LOUIS ARMSTRONG, VOL 4 (Savoy Blues).
Tracks: / Put 'em down blues / Ory's Creole trombone / Last time, The / Struttin' with some barbecue / Got no blues / Once in a while / I'm not rough / Hotter than that / Savoy blues / Fire works / Skip the gutter / Monday date / Don't jive me.
LP: . . . . SM 3745

LOUIS ARMSTRONG, VOL 5 (West End Blues).
Tracks: / West End blues / Sugarfoot strut / Kneedrops / Two deuces / Squeeze me / Symphonic raps / Savoyagers' stomp / No papa no / Basin Street blues / No one else but you / Beau Koo Jack / Save it, pretty mama / Weather bird / Muggles.
LP: . . . . **SM 3746**

LOUIS ARMSTRONG, VOL 6 (Savoy Ballroom Five and Louis Armstrong Orchestra).
Tracks: / Hear me talkin' to ya / St. James' Infirmary / Tight like this / Ain't misbehavin' / Black and blue / That rhythm man / Sweet Savanah Sue / Some of these days / When you're smiling / After you've gone.
LP: . . . . **SM 3747**

LOUIS ARMSTRONG, VOL 7 (Orchestra, 1929-30).
Tracks: / I ain't got nobody / Dallas blues / St. Louis blues / Rockin' chair / Song of the islands / Bessie couldn't help it / Blue turning grey over you / Dear old Southland / My sweet / I can't believe that you're in love with me / Indian cradle song / Exactly like you / Dinah / Tiger rag.
LP: . . . . **SM 3748**

LOUIS ARMSTRONG, VOL 8 (Sebastian New Cotton Club Orchestra).
Tracks: / I'm a ding dong daddy / I'm in the market for you / I'm confessin' / If I could be with you / Body and soul / Memories of you / You're lucky to me / Sweethearts on parade / You're driving me crazy / Peanut vendor / Just a gigolo / Shine.
LP: . . . . **SM 3749**

LOUIS ARMSTRONG VOL 9: ORCH 1931.
Tracks: / Walkin' my baby back home / I surrender dear / When it's sleepy time down South / Blue again / Little Joe / You rascal you / Them there eyes / When your lover has gone / Lazy river / Chinatown, my Chinatown / Wrap your troubles in dreams / Stardus t.
LP: . . . . **SM 3750**

LOUIS ARMSTRONG VOL 10: ORCH 1931.
Tracks: / You can depend on me / Georgia on my mind / Lonesome road / I got rhythm / Between the devil and the deep blue sea / Kicking the gong around / Home / All of me / Love, you funny thing / New tiger rag, The / Keepin' out of mischief now / Lawd, you made the night too long.
LP: . . . . **SM 3751**

LOUIS ARMSTRONG VOL 11: ORCH. 1932-33.
Tracks: / That's my home / Hobo you can't ride this train / I hate to leave you now / You'll wish you'd never been born / I've got the world on a string / I've got a right to sing the blues / Hustling and bustling for baby / Sittin' in the dark / High society / He's a son of the South.
LP: . . . . **SM 3752**

LOUIS ARMSTRONG VOL 12: ORCH. 1933.
Tracks: / Basin street blues / Honey do / Snowball / Mahogany Hall stomp / Swing, you cats / Honey, don't you love me anymore / Mississippi basin / Laughing Louis / Tomorrow night / Dusky Stevedore / There's a cabin in the sky / Mighty river / Sweet Sue / I wonder who / St. Louis blues / Don't play me cheap.
LP: . . . . **SM 3753**

LOUIS ARMSTRONG VSOP SERIES (Volumes 3/4).
MC: **40 88002**

LOUIS ARMSTRONG VSOP SERIES (Volumes 5/6).
MC: **40 88003**

LOUIS ARMSTRONG/SIDNEY BECHET (Armstrong, Louis/Sidney Bechet).
Tracks: / On the sunny side of the street / King Porter stomp* (*Featuring Sidney Bechet & Dutch Swing College Band) / Dutch Swing College blues (featuring Sidney Bechet & Dutch Swing College Band) / St. Louis blues / Tiger rag / Pretty little missy / Bye'n'bye / Tyree's blues / Short but sweet / Tin roof blues / Circle of your arms, The / When the saints go marching in.
LP: **6499 355**

LOUIS' BLUES.
LP: **20074**
MC: **40074**

LOUIS IN LOS ANGELES.
LP: . . . . **S 1265**

LOUIS' LOVE SONGS.
Tracks: / Among my souvenirs / I'm confessin' / It's all in the game / Only you (and you only) / I'll string along with you / I'm in the mood for love / Dream a little dream of me / You are my lucky star / Gypsy, The / Be my life's companion / Your cheatin' heart / I guess I'll get the papers and go home / Ramona / April in Portugal / Them there eyes / Ain't misbehavin'.
LP: . . . . **MCL 1822**
MC: . . . . **MCLC 1822**

MAHOGANY HALL STOMP.
Tracks: / Blueberry Hill / That's my desire / Dear old Southland / Struttin' with some barbecue / Jeepers creepers / St. Louis blues / Hello Dolly / Tiger rag.
LP: . . . . **BLM 52015**

MAHOGANY HALL STOMP (2).
Tracks: / Mahogany Hall stomp / I can't give you anything but love / Ain't misbehavin' / That rhythm man / Sweet Savannah Sue / Rockin' chair / Song of the islands / Blue, turning grey over you / I can't believe that you're in love with me / I'm in the market for you / Confessin' / Body and soul / You're driving me crazy / Them there eyes / Wrap your troubles in dreams / Star dust / I got rhythm / Between the devil and the deep blue sea.
LP: . . . . **SVL 198**
MC: . . . . **CSVL 198**

MAHOGANY HALL STOMP (LIVING ERA).
Tracks: / Mahogany Hall stomp / Rockin' chair / Savoy blues / Sweethearts on parade / Swing that music / Lyin' to myself / Thankful / I come from a musical family / Eventide / Red nose / If we never meet again / Peanut vendor / You're lucky to me / St. James Infirmary / You rascal, you / Lazy river / I ain't got nobody / Ain't misbehavin'.
LP: . . . . **AJA 5049**
MC: . . . . **ZC AJA 5049**

MASTERS OF JAZZ.
LP: . . . . **CL 42327**

MASTERS OF JAZZ VOL.1.
LP: . . . . **SLP 4101**

MEMORIAL.
LP: **500 816**

MET. OPERA HOUSE 1944 (Armstrong, Louis/Esquire All Stars).
2LP: . . . . **AA 522/523**

MORE FUN (Armstrong, Louis/Bing Crosby).
LP: . . . . **SR 5010**
MC: . . . . **JAS C2526**

MUSIC FOR THE MILLIONS.
Tracks: / Stompin' at the Savoy / Do nothing till you hear from me / Just one of those things / Foggy day, A / Uncle Satchmo's lullaby / When the saints go marching in / Someday you'll be sorry / Nobody knows the trouble I've seen / Top hat, white tie and tails / Blues in the night.
LP: **245 9406**
MC: **319 2596**

NEW ORLEANS DAYS (See under Bechet, Sidney) (Armstrong, Louis/ Sidney Bechet).

NEW ORLEANS FUNCTION.
Tracks: / When it's sleepy time down South / Indiana / Give me a kiss to build a dream on / My bucket's got a hole in it / Mack the knife / Ole Miss / C'est si bon / La vie en rose / New Orleans function / Free as a bird / Oh didn't he ramble?.
LP: . . . . **BLM 52005**
LP: . . . . **SM 3965**

NEW ORLEANS JAZZ AT NEWPORT.
LP: . . . . **WJS 1003**

NEW ORLEANS MASTERS VOLUME 2.
LP: . . . . **SWH 44**
MC: . . . . **CSWH 44**

NOONE 1941.
LP: . . . . **S 1210**

ON STAGE.
Tracks: / Jubilee / Do you know what it means / I'm confessin' / Panama rag stomp / Struttin' with some barbecue / Muskrat ramble / High society / Basin street blues.
LP: . . . . **BLJ 8041**

OREGON STATE FAIR 1960 (Armstrong, Louis/Allstars).
LP: . . . . **IAJRC 29**

ORIGINAL RECORDINGS 1936-39.
Tracks: / Swing that music / Dippermouth blues / I've got a heart full of rhythm / On the sunny side of the street / Struttin' with some barbecue / When the Saints go marching in / Flat foot floogie / Ain't misbehavin' / Jeepers creepers / What is this thing called swing? / Savoy blues / West End blues.
LP: . . . . **SM 3052**
MC: . . . . **MC 3052**

PASADENA CIVIC AUDITORIUM, THE.
LP: **500 206**

PASADENA CONCERT.
Tracks: / Someday / Ole Miss / Tin roof blues / My bucket's got a hole in it / Dardanella / Gypsy, The / Undecided / Blues / That's my desire / Didn't he ramble / Sleepy time down south (2 takes) / Indiana.
LPS: **000201**

PLAYS W.C.HANDY.
LP: **4509811**
MC: **4509814**

PORGY AND BESS (Armstrong, Louis/ Ella Fitzgerald).
Tracks: / Summertime / I got plenty o' nuttin' / My man's gone now / Bess, you is my woman now / It ain't necessarily so / There's a boat that's leaving shortly for New York / Bess, oh where's my Bess? / I'm on my way / I loves you, Porgy / Woman is a sometime thing.
LP: **2632 052**
MC: **3507 034**
LP: **171 110 5**
MC: **100 7016**
LP: **827 475 1**
MC: **350 150**

RARE LOUIS ARMSTRONG VOLUME 3 (The Big Band 1943-44).
Tracks: / I can't give you anything but love / If I could be with you one hour tonight / I'm confessin' / In the mood / I never knew / What's the good word / Lost my sugar in Salt Lake City / Lazy river / On the sunny side of the street / King Porter stomp / It's love love love / Ain't misbehavin' / Barrelhouse Bessie from Basin Street / Peanut vendor / Slender, tender and tall / Co quette.
LP: . . . . **RARITIES 50**

RARE PERFORMANCES OF THE 50'S AND 60'S.
Tracks: / T'aint what you do (it's the way that you do it) / Back o' town blues / Mack the knife / Mack the knife (instrumental) / Indiana / Six foot four / When the red, red robin comes bob, bob, bobbin' along / Way down yonder in New Orleans / Blueberry Hill / Tin roof blues / My bucket's got a hole in it / Whispering / Bugle blues / Kokomo / Basin Street blues / Mahogany hall stomp / St. Louis blues / Rockin' chair / On the sunny side of the street / Nomad / Lonesome / You swing baby / Canal Street blues.
LP: . . . . **CBS 88669**

REMINISCIN' WITH LOUIS.
Tracks: / Ain't misbehavin' / When the saints go marching in / I cried for you / Boogie woogie on St. Louis blues / When it's sleepy time down South / I cried last night / Steak face.
LP: . . . . **QU 004**

REPLAY ON LOUIS ARMSTRONG.
LP: . . . . **FEDB 5028**
MC: . . . . **CFEDB 5028**

REUNION CONCERT (See Ellington, Duke) (Armstrong, Louis/Duke Ellington).

ROCKIN' CHAIR (Armstrong, Louis & His Allstars).
Tracks: / Rockin' chair / Where did you stay last night / Baby, it's cold outside / C Jam Blues / Stompin' at the Savoy / I used to love you / La vie en rose / Lover / I love the guy / That's my desire / Royal Garden blues / Ain't misbehavin' / Back o' town blues / Rose room / C'est ci bon / Way down yonder in New Orleans / Stardust.
LP: . . . . **TOP 119**
MC: . . . . **KTOP 119**

SATCH PLAYS FATS.
Tracks: / Honeysuckle rose / Blue turning grey over you / I'm crazy 'bout my baby / I've got a feeling I'm falling / Keepin' out of mischief now / All that meat and no potatoes / Squeeze me / Black and blue / Ain't misbehavin'.
LP: **21103**
MC: **40 21103**
LP: **4509801**
MC: **4509804**

SATCHMO.
Tracks: / What a wonderful world / Cabaret / Hello Dolly / Jeepers creepers / Georgia on my mind / Lazy river / When you're smiling / Wiffenpoof song, The / Blueberry Hill / La vie en rose / I can't give you... / I surrender dear / On the sunny side of the street / Some of these days / Exactly like you.
LP: . . . . **VS 3404**
MC: . . . . **VSK 3404**

SATCHMO IN STOCKHOLM.
Tracks: / When it's sleepy time down South / Indiana / Tin roof blues / Basin street blues / Sweet Georgia Brown / Struttin' with some barbecue / Gipsy, The / Pretty little missy / When the saints go marching in.
LP: . . . . **QU 053**

SATCHMO MEETS BIG T (Armstrong, Louis/Jack Teagarden).
LP: . . . . **LPJT 69**

SATCHMO (PICKWICK).
Tracks: / Back o' town blues / I want a big butter and egg man / Back home again in Indiana / Tiger rag / Jelly roll blues / C'est si bon / St. James Infirmary / When the Saints go marching in / Someday you'll be sorry / Sweethearts on parade / (What did I have to do to get) black and blue / Chimes blues / Dipper mouth blues / Snake rag / New Orleans stomp / Bye and bye.
MC: . . . . **HSC 3272**

SATCHMO PLAYS KING OLIVER.
LP: . . . . **AFLP 1930**

SATCHMO STYLE.
LP: . . . . **SW 8451**

SATCHMO - WHAT A WONDERFUL WORLD.
LP: **835 895-1**
MC: **835 895-4**
MC: **837 786-4**

SATCHMO'S GREATEST HITS.
Tracks: / I gotta right to sing the blues / High society / When you're smiling / St. James Infirmary / Dinah / Basin Street blues / You rascal you / Sleepy time down south / Nobody's sweetheart / Mahogany hall stomp / Do you know what it means to Miss New Orleans? / St. Louis blues / Sweet Sue / Back o' town blues / Jack Armstrong blues / Where the blues were born in New Orleans.
LP: . . . . **CL 89799**
MC: . . . . **CK 89799**

SINGIN' N' PLAYIN'.
Tracks: / Hello Dolly / Mack the knife / Muskrat ramble / Blueberry Hill / That's my desire / Ole Miss / When it's sleepy time down South / Kiss to build a dream on ,A / St. James infirmary / Indiana.
MC: . . . . **MC 7685**

SPECIAL MAGIC (Armstrong, Louis/ Ella Fitzgerald).
MC: **3113 190**

SPECIAL MAGIC OF BING AND SATCHMO, THE (see Crosby, Bing) (Armstrong, Louis/Bing Crosby).

ST. LOUIS BLUES.
Tracks: / Tiger rag / Maine / So long dearie / Cheesecake / Pretty little miss / Short and sweet / When the saints go marching in / St. Louis blues / Circle of your arms, The / Tin roof blues / Tyrees blues / Bye'n'bye / On the sunny side of the street / Black and blue / I'm confessin' / Struttin' with some barbecue / Up a lazy river / Save it pretty mama / Ain't misbehavin' / St. Louis blues / Rockin' chair / Dippermouth blues / Mahogany hall stomp / Muskrat ramble.
LP: . . . . **INT 127 035**
MC: . . . . **CAS 427 035**

ST. LOUIS BLUES (1960'S).
Tracks: / Tiger rag / Maine / So long dearie / Cheesecake / Pretty little miss / Short and sweet / When the saints go marching in / St. Louis blues / Circle of your arms, The / Tin roof blues / Tyrees blues / Bye'n'bye / On the sunny side of the street.
LP: **9279 254**
MC: **7259 154**

ST. LOUIS BLUES (CBS).
LP: **54612**
MC: **40 54612**

ST. LOUIS BLUES VOL.6.
MC: **4679194**

STRUTTIN' WITH SOME BARBECUE.
Tracks: / Struttin' with some barbecue / What is this thing called swing? / Jeepers creepers / Lyin' to myself / Shoe shine boy / I hope Gabriel likes my music / Perdido street blues / 2.19 blues / Swing that music / Down in honky tonk town / Coal cart blues / Eventide / Dippermouth blues / Solitude / Jubilee / Mahogany hall stomp.
LP: . . . . **AFS 1024**

THAT RHYTHM MAN.
Tracks: / All of me / Knockin' a jug / I'm confessin' / Dinah / St. Louis blues / St. James infirmary / Mahogany hall stomp / Chinatown / No papa no / Hear me talkin' to ya / New tiger rag / I ain't got nobody / Kicking the gong around / Blue turning grey over you / That rhythm man / I'm in the market for you / After you've gone / Some of these days.
LP: . . . . **RAL 507**

TOGETHER FOR THE FIRST TIME (Armstrong, Louis/Duke Ellington).
Tracks: / Duke's place / I'm just a lucky so and so / Cottontail / Mood indigo / Do nothin' till you hear from me / Beautiful American, The / Black and tan fantasy / Drop me off at Harlem / Mooche, The / In a mellow tone.

LP: ROU 1007

TOWN HALL CONCERT PLUS.
Tracks: / Rockin' chair / Ain't misbehavin' / Back o' town blues / Long long journey / I want a little girl / Mahogany hall stomp / Pennies from Heaven / St. James Infirmary / Save it pretty mama / Someday you'll be sorry / Sugar / Snafu.
LP: NL 80419
MC: NK 89419
LP: INTS 5070

TWELFTH STREET RAG.
Tracks: / Baby it's cold outside / On the sunny side of the street / Gypsy, The / Mame / Old man Mose / 2.19 blues / I can't give you anything but love / Twelfth St. rag / Faithful hussar, The / After you've gone / What a wonderful world.
LP: BLM 52045

UNFORGETTABLE LOUIS ARMSTRONG.
LP: UNLP 009
MC: UNMC 009

V DISC ALL STARS (Armstrong, Louis/ Jack Teagarden).
LP: PUMPKIN 103

VERY BEST OF LOUIS ARMSTRONG.
LP: WW 5512

WHAT A WONDERFUL WORLD (PLATINUM).
Tracks: / What a wonderful world / Jeepers creepers / Georgia on my mind / On the sunny side of the street / Cabaret / Hello Dolly / Lazy river / When you're smiling / Whiffenpoof song, The / Blueberry Hill / La vie en rose / Can't give you anything but love / When it's sleepy time down South / Surrender dear / Some of these days / Exactly like you.
LP: PLAT 304
MC: PLAC 304

WHAT A WONDERFUL WORLD (STATESIDE).
LP: SSL 10247

WHEN THE SAINTS GO MARCHING IN.
Tracks: / St. James' Infirmary / When the saints go marching in / I'm confessin' / Royal Garden blues / Black and blue / Up a lazy river / I'll be glad when you're dead, you rascal you / Ain't misbehavin' / Basin Street blues.
LP: BLM 52025

WONDERFUL WORLD OF LOUIS ARMSTRONG, THE.
LP: MFP 5584
MC: TCMFP 5584

YOUNG LOUIS ARMSTRONG (1930-1933).
Tracks: / Blue yodel no. 9 (Standing on the corner) / That's my home (2 takes) / Hobo, you can't ride this train / I hate to leave you now (2 takes) / You'll wish you'd never been born / When you're smiling / St. James' Infirmary / Dinah / You rascal, you / When it's sleepy time down South / Nobody's sweetheart / I've got the world on a string / I gotta right to sing the blues / Hustlin' and bustlin' for baby / Sittin' in the dark / High Society / Basin Street blues / He's a son of the South / Some sweet day / Honey do / Snowball / Mahogany hall stomp / Swing, you cats / Honey don't you love me anymore? / Mississippi basin / Laughing Louis / Tomorrow night / Dusky stevedore / There's a cabin in the pines / Mighty river / Sweet Sue / I wonder who / St. Louis blues / Don't play me cheap.
2LP: NL 89747
MCSET: NK 89747
2LP: PM 43269

YOUNG LOUIS ARMSTRONG (1930-1933).
2LP: PM 43269

Armstrong, Robert

RAMS AT FERGUS ROCK (Armstrong, Robert Memorial Band).
MC: CHRL 102
LP: HRL 102

Armstrong, Sheila

SONGS OF NORTHUMBRIA (See under Allen, Thomas) (Armstrong, Sheila & Thomas Allen).

Armstrong Twins

HILLBILLY MANDOLIN.
LP: OT 118

JUST COUNTRY BOYS.
LP: ARHOOLIE 5022

Armstrong, Vanessa

FOLLOWING JESUS.
LP: MSSG 8001

TRUE LOVE NEVER FAILS (See Butler, Jonathan).

VANESSA BELL ARMSTRONG.
LP: HIP 52
MC: HIPC 52

WONDERFUL ONE.
LP: HIP 78
MC: HIPC 78
MC: 12004 J

Arne, Thomas

INSTRUMENTAL WORKS (Le Nouveau Quatuor).
MC: CSAR 42

Arnez, Chico

FROM CHICO WITH LOVE (Arnez, Chico & His Orchestra).
LP: LR 2001

LET'S GO LATIN (Arnez, Chico & His Orchestra).
Tracks: / This is Chico / Soul limbo / Do the salsa / Wave / Aquarius / Cherry pink and apple blossom white / Girl from Rio, The / Quiet nights / Jezebel / La paloma / You only live twice / Temptation / Spanish eyes / Miserlou / Eo beso / Mambo No.5 / Bim bam bom / This was Chico.
LP: PYL 4005
MC: PYM 4005

Arnold, Billy Boy

BLOW THE BACK OFF IT.
Tracks: / I'm sweet on you baby / You got to love me baby / I wish you would / I was fooled / Don't stay out all night / I ain't got you / Hello stranger / Here's my picture / You've got me wrong / My heart is crying / Kissing at midnight / Prisoners plea / Rockinits.
LP: RL 012

CHECKIN' IT OUT.
Tracks: / Dirty mother fucker / Don't stay out all night / 1-2-99 / Riding the el / Just to know / Christmas time / I wish you would / Ah'w baby / Sweet Miss Bea / Blue and lonesome / Eldorado Cadillac / Mary Bernice.
LP: RL 024

CRYING AND PLEADING.
LP: CRB 1016

JOHNNY JONES AND BILLY BOY ARNOLD (See under Jones, Johnny) (Arnold, Billy Boy & Johnny Jones).

MORE BLUES ON THE SOUTH SIDE.
Tracks: / School time / You don't love me no more / Oh baby / I love only you / I'll forget about you / You better cut that out / Going by the river / You're my girl / Evalena / Two drinks of wine / Billy Boy's blues / Get out of here.
LP: CH 253

SINNER'S PRAYER.
Tracks: / I was fooled / High heel sneakers / Back door friend / Tomorrow night / Annie Lee / Ooh wee / Blues in A natural / I'm gonna move / Sinner's prayer.
LP: RL 014

Arnold, Buddy

WAILING.
LP: FS 231

Arnold, Dave

CONJURING IMAGES.
MC: DHC 10

FOR ALL AND SUNDRY.
MC: DHC 14

FRUSTRATION OF ECONOMY.
MC: DHC 13

I'M A NATURAL CANDIDATE FOR THE TORTURED ARTISTS.
MC: DHC 8

SPOTLIGHT ON DAVE ARNOLD.
MC: 00178

Arnold, Eddy

20 OF THE BEST: EDDY ARNOLD.
Tracks: / Make the world go away / Cattle call / Just call me lonesome / What's he doing in my world / I really don't want to know / I want to go with you / Somebody like me / Lonely again / Turn the world around / Then you can tell me goodbye / I'll hold you in my heart / Bouquet of roses / Anytime / Just a little lovin' / Don't rob another man's castle / I'm throwing rice at the girl I love / There's been a change in me / Kentucky waltz / I wanna play house with you / Eddy's song.
LP: NL 89316
MC: NK 89316

ALL-TIME FAVOURITES.
Tracks: / Moonlight and roses / Missouri waltz, The (Hush-a-bye, my baby) / I'm gonna lock my heart / You always hurt the one you love / I'm thinking tonight of my blue eyes / It makes no difference now / I'm waiting for ships that never come in / I'm gonna sit right down and write myself a letter / When your hair has turned to silver / Angry / Prisoner's song / Seven years with the wrong woman.
LP: NL 90004
MC: NK 90004

ANYTIME.
Tracks: / Bouquet of roses / That's how much I like you / Rockin' alone in an old rocking chair / I'll hold you in my heart / Anytime / Will the circle be unbroken / It's a sin / Don't rob another man's castle / Molly darling / Heart full of love, A / Texarkane baby / Who at my door is standing.
LP: HAT 3086
MC: HATC 3086

MAKE THE WORLD GO AWAY (OLD GOLD) (See under Davis, Skeeter/End of the world).

Arnold, Jimmy

RAINBOW RIDE.
LP: REBEL 1603
MC: REBELMC 1603

SOUTHERN SOUL.
Tracks: / Jesse James / Georgia moon / Rebel soldier, The / Southern comfort / Night they drove old Dixie down, The / Sail away ladies / General Lee / My home's across the blue ridge mountains / Dixon line, The / Bonaparte's retreat / Arkansas soldier / Lorena / Southern soul / Heroes / Sally Ann.
LP: REBEL 1621
MC: REBELMC 1621

Arnold, Kokomo

KOKOMO ARNOLD AND CASEY BILL WELDON (Arnold, Kokomo & Casey Bill Weldon).
LP: L 1049

KOKOMO ARNOLD - MASTER OF THE BOTTLENECK GUITAR 1930-38.
LP: DLP 512

PEETIE WHEATSTRAW AND KOKOMO ARNOLD (See under Peetie Wheatstraw) (Arnold, Kokomo & Peetie Wheatstraw).

Arnold, Lloyd

MEMPHIS -- ROCK 'N' ROLL CAPITAL, VOL 7.
Tracks: / Red coat, green pants & red suit shoes / Hangout / Dixie doodle / Half my fault / Great speckled bird, The / School days / Cold duck blues / I got the blues / 'Cause I love you / Gonna love my baby / Schooldays, Part 2 / Tennessee twist / Go go go / Sugaree / Don't care blues.
LP: WLP 8921

Arnold, Pete

DRUMS OF CHILDHOOD DREAMS, THE.
Tracks: / Drums of child dreams / Fitzroy girl, The / Time was / Leinster fusilier / Easy come mornings / Remembrance day / Night of the Robinson's ball, The / Echoing still / For the children of the dust / I remember Mary / Cobblestone days / Ghost days / Ghost trains / Lady Mary.
LP: MHK LPA 501
MC: MHK LPC 501

Arnold, P.P.

ANGEL.
LP: SHLP 157
MC: SHTC 157

BURN IT UP (See under Beatmasters) (Arnold, P.P./Beatmasters).

DREAMING (See under Pressure Point) (Arnold, P.P. & Pressure Point).

GREATEST HITS: P P ARNOLD.
Tracks: / First cut is the deepest / Dreaming / Would you believe / To love somebody / Born to be together / Eleanor Rigby / Angel of the morning / As tears go by / Am I still dreaming / Though it hurts me badly / Speak to me / If you think you're groovy.
LP: IML 2006

KAFUNTA - THE FIRST LADY OF IMMEDIATE.
Tracks: / (If you think you're) groovy / Something beautiful happened / Born to be together / Am I still dreaming / First cut is the deepest / Everything is gonna be alright / Treat me like a lady / Would you believe / Speak to me / God only knows / Eleanor Rigby / Yesterday / Angel of the morning / It'll never happen again / As tears go by / To love somebody / Dreamin' / If you see what I mean / Though it hurts me badly (Available on CD only) / Welcome home (Available on CD only) / Life is but nothing (Available on CD only) / Time has come, The (Available on CD only).
LP: SEE 235

Aroma Di Amore

DESKEER VAN GROTE BAGEN.
LP: BIAS 010

HARDE FEITEN.
LP: ABR 015

KOUDVUUR.
LP: ABR 019

Around The World

AROUND THE WORLD, VOL. 1 (Various artists).
LP: ADL 522
MC: ADK 522

Around The World In 80

AROUND THE WORLD IN 80 DAYS (Plummer, Christopher).
LP: TC 1553
MC: 1553

Arpeggio

LOVE AND DESIRE.
Tracks: / Love and desire / Let the music play / Play the music / I wanna tango / Runaway / Desire / Spellbound.
LP: 2310 656
MC: 3100 504

Arpin, John

CREOLE RAGS.
LP: JCE 94

Arran, John

CASTLES OF SPAIN.
LP: RES 803

Arriba D.F.

BARCELONA CUIDAD.
LP: PUT 8

Arrin

SPIRIT OF ARRIN.
MC: HI 002

Arrington, Steve

DANCIN' IN THE KEY OF LIFE.
Tracks: / Feel so real / Dancin' in the key of life / She just don't know / Willie Mae / Gasoline / Stand with me / Brown baby boy / Turn up love.
LP: 781 245-1
MC: 781 245-4

HALL OF FAME.
Tracks: / Nobody can be you / You meet my approval / Last nite-nite before / Strange / Speak with your body / Week at the knees / Way out.
LP: A 0049

JAM PACKED.
Tracks: / Jam packed (at the wall) / Stone love / Let it loose / True love always / I just wanna be with you / Kelly 16-33 / Never take your love / Trouble / What I do for you.
LP: MTL 1015
MC: TCMTL 1015
LP: MTL 46903

JAMMIN' NATIONAL ANTHEM, THE.
Tracks: / Jammin' National Anthem, The / Holiday / Teenage jazz / One of a kind / Paradise / Everybody's got to be free / Home boy / Like it loud / Have a heart.
LP: WX 58
MC: WX 58 C

POSITIVE POWER.
Tracks: / 15 rounds / Money on it / Sugar momma baby / What do you want from life / Young and ready / Mellow as a cello / Hump to the bump / Positive power.
LP: 780 127-1

Arrogance

RUMOURS.
Tracks: / We love to play / Sunday feeling / Final nickel / Two good legs / Dying to know / Open window / Why do you love me / Lady luck and luxury / Pitchin' woo.
LP: VSD 79369

Arrow

DEADLY.
LP: ARROW 025

HEAVY ENERGY.
LP: ARROW 028

HOT HOT HOT (ALBUM).
Tracks: / Pirates / Pulling bull / Hot, hot, hot / Party hopping / Money, money / Menu.
LP: CHR 1434
MC: ZCHR 1434

KNOCK 'EM DEAD.
Tracks: / Groove master / More arrow / Rhumba again / Tiny winey / Tell mama / As you see me gimme / Dance sister dance / Big b ig.
MC: ICT 9809
LP: ILPS 9809
LP: ARROW 029

MASSIVE.
LP: ARROW 031

O' LA SOCA.
Tracks: / O' la soca / Crazy mama / Pump it up / Man must live / Hey Pocky away / Little extra, A / Dancin' mood / London city.
MC: MCT 1009
LP: MLPS 1009

SOCA DANCE PARTY.

Tracks: / Zouk me / Limbo calypso / Good wine / Don't force it / Fire / Easy dancing / Dance party / Bills (interpolating 'bust ed').
LP: . . . . MLPS 1057
MC: . . . . MCT 1057

SOCA SAVAGE.
Tracks: / Long time / Columbia rock / Hot, hot, hot.
LP: . . . . DY 3447
LP: . . . . LONLP 9

Arrow To The Heart

ARROW TO THE HEART (See under Murray, Jill) (Mitchell, Nancy).

Arroyo, Joe

FIRE IN MY MIND.
Tracks: / La noche / Si si gole / Fuego en mi mente / Mi dios todd le dero, A / En barranquilla me quedo / Las cajas / Por ti no morire / Quien lo sabe baila.
MC: . . . . MCT 1020
LP: . . . . MLPS 1020

REBELLION.
LP: . . . . WCB 012
MC: . . . . WCC 012

SOMO SKRES.
Tracks: / Somo skres / Todo de ti / Pa'l bailador / La cocha / Suave Bruta / Centurion de la noche / Simula tibula / La aidea del cocoreque.
LP: . . . . MLPS 1037
MC: . . . . MCT 1037
LP: 846 439 1
MC: 846 439 4

Arsen Gardens

UNDER TOWERS.
LP: . . . . COMM 39011

Arsenal

FACTORY SMOG IS A SIGN OF PROGRESS.
LP: . . . . BFFP 51

Arsenal F.C.

ARSENAL CENTENNIAL ALBUM.
LPPD: . . . . GBFA 001

ARSENAL RAP (See under A-Team (Football)) (A-Team (Football)).

Arsenic & Old Lace

KIND HEARTS AND CORONETS/ ARSENIC AND OLD LACE (See under 'Kind hearts & coronets') (Powell, Robert (nar)).

Art Barbeque

FEET HACKED RAILS.
LP: . . . . ST 7506

Art Bears

WINTER SONGS.
LP: . . . . RE 0618

Art Company

GET IT OUT OF YOUR HEAD (LP).
Tracks: / Get it out of your head / I don't wanna be without you / Susanna / Marianne / Life like yours / I can see a future / Maybe tomorrow / She's there / 17th floor / Simon.
LP: . . . . EPC 26027

Art Deco Orchestra

THERE IS ALWAYS A PLACE FOR THE PAST.
Tracks: / Tin Lizzie / Romance in the night / Harry's happy now / There is always a place for the past / Moon over Rio / Come dance with me / Hunky-dory / When you are near / Put on those dancing shoes / You're for me / Tango Helene / So debonair.
LP: . . . . RRS 102

Art Ensemble of

A.A.C.M: GREAT BLACK MUSIC, A JACKSON IN YOUR...
Tracks: / Waltz / Ericka / Song for Charles / Jackson in your house, A (Only on CD.) / Get in line.
LP: . . . . AFF 9

AMONG THE PEOPLE.
LP: . . . . CM 103

FANFARE OF THE WARRIORS.
Tracks: / Illistrum / Barnyard scuffel shuffel / Nonaah / Fanfare for the warriors / What's to say / Tnoona / Key, The.
LP: . . . . K 50304

KABBALABA LIVE AT MONTREUX.
LP: . . . . AECO 004

LES STANCES A SOPHIE.
LP: . . . . N 4

LIVE: ART ENSEMBLE OF CHICAGO.
2LP: . . . . AFFD 46

MESSAGE TO OUR FOLKS.
Tracks: / Old time religion / Dexterity / Rock out / Brain for the Seine.
LP: . . . . AFF 77

PARIS SESSION, THE.
Tracks: / Tutankhamun / Ninth room that evening the sky fell through / Toro / Lori song / Tthinitthedalen / Spiritual freedom.
2LP: . . . . FLP 41106/7

PEOPLE IN SORROW.
LP: . . . . N 3

REESE AND THE SMOOTH ONES.
LP: . . . . AFF 22

THIRD DECADE.
LP: . . . . EXM 1273

TUTANKHAMUN.
LP: . . . . FLP 40122

URBAN BUSHMEN.
LP: . . . . ECM 1211
MC: 7579037

Art In The Dark

IN COLOUR.
Tracks: / Tell me / In colour / Calling anyone / Answer.
LP: . . . . P 2013

Art Of...

ART OF SELECTIONS (Various artists).
LP: . . . . HOOT LP 2

ART OF SURVIVAL (Various artists).
LP: . . . . SURLP 009

ART OF THE MUSICAL BOX Various works and composers (Various artists).
LP: . . . . ARN 36461

Art Of Mechanical

GAVIOLI ORGAN AT THE THRONE FAIRGROUND (Various artists).
LP: . . . . ARN 36410

Art Of Noise

AMBIENT COLLECTION, THE.
Tracks: / Opus 4 / Nothing was going to stop them / Island / Ode to Don Jose / Roundabout 727/Ransom in the sand / Robinson Crusoe / Art of love / Opus for 4 / Crusoe / Camilla / Counterpoint / Eye of a needle / Nation rejects, A.
LP: 8434031
MC: 8434034

BELOW THE WASTE.
Tracks: / Yebo / Promenade 1 / Island / Chain gang / Back to back / Spit / Catwalk / Dilemma / Dan dare / Promenade 2 / Flashback / Finale.
LP: 8394041
MC: 8394044

BEST OF THE ART OF NOISE.
Tracks: / Beat box / Moments in love / Close (to the edit) / Peter Gunn / Paranoimia / Legacy / Dragnet '88 / Kiss / Something always happens / Opus 4.
LP: 8373671
MC: 8373674
MC: . . . . WOLMC 1010

IN NO SENSE I NONSENSE.
Tracks: / Galleons of stone / Dragnet / Fin du temps / How rapid? / Opus for four / Debut / E.F.L. / Ode to Don Jose / Day at the races, A / Counterpoint / Roundabout 727 / Ransom on the sand / Roller 1 / Nothing was going to stop them then, anyway / Crusoe / One earth.
LP: . . . . WOO 4
MC: . . . . ZWOO 4
MC: . . . . WOLMC 1017

INTO BATTLE WITH THE ART OF NOISE.
LP: . . . . ZTTIQ 2
MC: . . . . ZCIQ 2

INVISIBLE SILENCE.
Tracks: / Opus for four / Paranoimia / Eye of a needle / Legs / Slip of the tongue / Backbeat / Instruments of darkness / Peter Gunn / Camilla / Chameleon's dish.
LP: . . . . WOL 2
MC: . . . . ZWOL 2
MC: . . . . WOLMC 1016

MOMENTS IN LOVE.
Tracks: / Moments in love / Love beat.
MC: . . . . CTIS 109

RE-WORKS OF ART OF NOISE.
Tracks: / Paranoimia / Legacy / Peter Gunn / Legs / Hammersmith to Tokyo and back.
LP: . . . . WOLD 2

WHO'S AFRAID OF THE ART OF NOISE.
Tracks: / Time for fear / Beat box / Snapshot / Close / Who's afraid / Moments in love / Memento / Hard to kill / Realisation / Liquid sky.
LP: . . . . ZTTIQ 2

Artery

AFTERWARDS.
MC: . . . . PS 011

LIVE IN AMSTERDAM.
LP: . . . . GDLP 2

OCEANS.
LP: . . . . RFM 4

TERMINAL.
LP: . . . . GDLP 1

Artful Dodger

HONOUR AMONG THIEVES.
LP: . . . . PC 34273

Arthey, Johnny

SENTIMENTAL JOURNEY (Arthey, Johnny Orchestra).
LP: . . . . WH 5005
MC: . . . . WH 6005

Arthur, Charline

WELCOME TO THE CLUB.
Tracks: / Welcome to the club / Burn that candle / What about tomorrow / Honey bun / Kiss the baby goodnight / Just look, don't touch, she's mine / How many would there be / Later on / I heard about you / Anything can happen / Looking at the moon and wishing on a star / I'm having a party all by myself / Leave my man alone / Please darlin' please / Heartbreak ahead / I was wrong / Count your blessings / Real love / Nobody walks in L.A. / How does it fit / Relations / What becomes of love / Way ahead / 10th round.
LP: . . . . BFX 15234

Arthur, Dave & Toni

HARKEN TO THE WITCHES RUNE.
LP: . . . . LER 2017

LARK IN THE MORNING, THE.
Tracks: / All frolicking I'll give over / Death of Queen Jane, The / Creeping Jane / Merchant's daughter of Bristol, The / Bold dragoon, The / Cold blows the Winter's wind / Lark in the morning, The / Poor old horse / Hey John Barleycorn / Bedlam / Admiral Benbow / Father father build me a boat / Press gang, The / Six jolly miners.
LP: 12T 190

Arthur (film)

ARTHUR (1980 film) (Various artists).
LP: . . . . BS 3582

ARTHUR 2: ON THE ROCKS (Film Soundtrack) (Various artists).
Tracks: / Love is my decision: *Various artists* / Gravity: *Various artists* / Secret: *Various artists*/ Speed of light: *Various artists* / Boys night out: *Various artists* / Best of times, The: *Various artists*/ Locomotion, The: *Various artists* / Reflections: *Various artists* / Devotion: *Various artists* / Arthur love theme: *Various artists.*
LP: 393 916-1
MC: 393 916-4

ARTHUR 2: ON THE ROCKS (Original film score) (Various artists).
LP: . . . . SP 3916
MC: . . . . CS 3916

Arthur & The Belly...

ARTHUR AND THE BELLY BUTTON DIAMOND (See under Coren, Alan).

Arthur, Toni

TONI ARTHUR'S MUSIC BOX.
MC: . . . . BILL 1CA

Artillery

ARTILLERY 3.
LP: . . . . NEAT 1046

BY INHERITANCE.
Tracks: / 7-00 from Tashkent / Beneath the clay / Bombfood / Life in bondage / Razamanaz / Khomaniac / By inheritance / Don't believe / Equal at first / Back in the trash.
LP: . . . . RO 93971
MC: . . . . RO 93974

FEAR OF TOMORROW.
Tracks: / Time has come / Almighty, The / Show you hate / King thy name is slayer / Out of the sky / Into the universe / Eternal war / Deed of darkness.
LP: . . . . NEAT 1030
MC: . . . . NEATC 1030

TERROR SQUAD.
Tracks: / Challenge, The / In the trash / Terror squad / Let there be sin / Hunger and greed / Therapy / At war with science / Decapitation of deviants.
LP: . . . . NEAT 1038
MC: . . . . NEATC 1038

Artisan

DRIVING HOME.
LP: . . . . FESTIVAL 4
MC: . . . . FESTIVAL 4C

SEARCHING FOR YORLADALE.
LP: . . . . FESTIVAL 1

SEASON OF HOLLY AND IVY.
Tracks: / God rest ye merry gentlemen / Three kings are here / Little Blakenham carol, The / Here we come a wassailing / Season of holly and ivy, The / Angel Gabriel, The / We three kings / Herod and the cock / Lullay my liking / Torches / Sans day carol / Veni veni Emmanuel / Gallery carol, A (Rejoice and be merry) / Grampound wassail, The / I saw three ships / Patapan / In the bleak mid winter / While shepherds watched.
MC: . . . . BHC 9011

THREE PIECE SWEET.
MC: . . . . ARTI 001

Artists

ARTISTS VOL.1, THE (Various artists).
LP: . . . . ARTIS 1
MC: . . . . ZCART 1

ARTISTS VOL.2, THE (Various artists).
LP: . . . . ARTIS 2
MC: . . . . ZCART 2

ARTISTS VOL.4, THE (Various artists).
LP: . . . . ARTIS 4
MC: . . . . ZCART 4

Artists for Animals

LIBERATOR (Various artists).
LP: . . . . DELTLP 3
MC: . . . . DELTMC 3

Artists United

SUN CITY (Artists United Against Apartheid).
LP: . . . . MTL 1001
MC: . . . . TCMTL 1001

Artman, Gilbert

URBAN SAX 2.
LP: . . . . CEL 6739

Artphag

GODS OF GRUNGE.
LP: . . . . SUK 004

INSTANT VENTRIL.
LP: . . . . RES 339131

Artwoods

100 OXFORD STREET.
Tracks: / Sweet Mary / If I ever get my hands on you / Goodbye sisters / Oh my love / I take what I want / Big city / She knows what to do / I'm looking for a saxophonist / Keep looking / I keep forgettin' / I feel good / One more heartache / Down in the valley / Be my lady / Stop and think it over / Don't cry no more.
LP: . . . . ED 107

Artzt, Alice

GLORY OF THE GUITAR.
LP: . . . . AVM 1007
MC: . . . . AVMC 1007

VARIATIONS, PASSACAGLIAS AND CHACONNES.
MC: . . . . KH 88026

Arvo Part

TABULA RASA.
Tracks: / Fratres / Cantus in memory of Benjamin Britten / Tabula rasa.
LP: . . . . ECM 1275
MC: 8177644

A's

A'S.
Tracks: / After last night / C.I.A. / Words / Parasite / Five minutes in a hero's life / Artificial love / Who's gonna save the world / Teenage jerk off / Grounded / Twist and shout / Nothing wrong with falling in love.
LP: . . . . NEW 3

As Time Goes By

AS TIME GOES BY (A Collection of Timeless Love Songs) (Various artists).
Tracks: / Way I want to touch you, The: *Captain & Tennille* / Dedicated to the one I love: *Mamas & Papas* / Sad sweet dreamer: *Sweet Sensation* / Hey there lonely girl: *Holman, Eddie* / You keep me steady: *Howard, John*/ So sad the song: *Various artists* / Tired of being alone: *Green, Al* / Can't get by without you: *Real Thing*/ Two people in the morning: *Howard, John* / I wanna get next to you: *Rose Royce* / Best thing that ever happened to me, The: *Knight, Gladys & The Pips* / Let's stay together: *Green, Al* / Suspicious minds: *Jennings, Waylon* & Jessi Colter / I feel love comin' on: *Taylor, Felice* / Nobody needs your love: *Pitney, Gene* / Stardust: *Damone, Vic* / Melodie d'amour: *Ames Brothers* / On the street where you live: *Fisher, Eddie* / My heart cries for you: *Shore, Dinah* / Never my love: *Addrissi Bros.* / Arriverderci, my love: *Damone, Vic.*
2LP: . . . . CR 078
MCSET: . . . . CRT 078

As You Like It (ply)

AS YOU LIKE IT (see under Shakespeare, William) (Suzman, Janet & John Stride).

A.S.A.P.

SILVER AND GOLD (ALBUM).
Tracks: / Lion, The / Silver and gold / Down the wire / You could be a King / After the storm / Misunderstood / Kid gone astray / Fallen heroes / Wishing your life away / Blood on the ocean.
LP: . . . . EMC 3566
MC: . . . . TCEMC 3566

LP: .... EMCG 3566

Ash, Daniel

COMING DOWN.
LP: .... BEGA 114
MC: .... BEGC 114

Ashadu

SOLUTION.
Tracks: / Solution / Funky reggae / Uchafunga / Cholera / Walking against the wind / U and I.
LP: .... TUS 8004
MC: .... TUS 8004MC

Ashby, Christofer

RENAISSANCE.
MC: .... C 106

Ashby, Harold

CANDY (Ashby, Harold / Don Friedman / George Mraz/Ronnie Bedford).
Tracks: / Candy / Quickie / There is no greater love / Dainty / Over the rainbow / Pleading / Days of wine and roses / Cous cous.
LP: .... PRO 7040

Ashby, Irving

MEMOIRS.
LP: .... AP 133

Ashby, Sue

CLOSE RELATIONS (See under Okines, Ken) (Ashby, Sue / Ken Okines).

Ashcroft, Dame Peggy

CANTERBURY TALES, THE (see under Chaucer, Geoffrey (aut)).

WORLD OF, THE (Ashcroft, Peggy/Sir John Geilgud).
LP: .... SPA 573

Ashdown, Doug

WINTER IN AMERICA.
MC: .... KTXCR 125

Asher D

RAGAMUFFIN HIP-HOP (Asher D & Daddy Freddy).
MC: .... ASHER 1C
LP: .... ASHER 1

STILL KICKIN'.
LP: .... ASHER 22
MC: .... ASHER 22C

Asher, James

AQUARIAN SYMPHONY.
MC: .... C 117

GREAT WHEEL, THE.
MC: .... LUMCA 1

Asher, Jane (nar)

ALICE IN WONDERLAND & THROUGH THE LOOKING GLASS (See under Carroll, Lewis) (Asher, Jane & Margaretta Scott).

EMPERORS NEW CLOTHES (See under Emperors New Clothes).

TINDER BOX, THE (See under Tinder Box).

Ashes

ASHES 1948-1981, THE (Bradman to Botham) (Various artists).
MCSET: .... ZBBC 1172

Ashes & Diamonds...

ASHES AND DIAMONDS, GENERATION A, CANAL (See under Canal) (Various artists).

Ashford, Geoff

SYLVANTONE SHOWCASE, THE (See under Goodacre, Tony).

Ashford & Simpson

COME AS YOU ARE.
Tracks: / It'll come, it'll come, it'll come / One more try / Believe in me / Caretaker / Somebody told a lie / Tell it all / Sell the house / It came to me.
LP: .... K 56159

COMPOSER SERIES: ASHFORD & SIMPSON (See under Great Songs) (Various artists).

DO YOU KNOW WHO I AM (See under Vidal, Maria - Body rock).

GREATEST SONGS WRITTEN BY ASHFORD & SIMPSON (See Under Motown...) (Various artists).

HIGH RISE.
Tracks: / High rise / Side effect / Experience / It's a rush / My kinda pick me up / I'm not that tough / It's much deeper / Still such a thing.
LP: .... EST 712 282 1

IS IT STILL GOOD TO YA.
LP: .... K 56547
MC: K4 56547

LOVE OR PHYSICAL.
Tracks: / Love or physical / I'll be there for you / Comes with the package / 'Till we get it right / Something to you / In your arms / Cookies and cake / Timing.
LP: .... EST 2085
MC: .... TCEST 2085
LP: C1 46946

MUSICAL AFFAIR, A.
Tracks: / Love don't make it right / Rushing to / I ain't asking for your love / Make it to the sky / We'll meet again / You never left me alone / Get out your handkerchief / Happy ending.
MC: K4 56840

REAL LOVE.
Tracks: / Count your blessings / Real love / Nobody walks in L.A. / How does it fit / Relations / What becomes of love / Way ahead / Tenth round.
LP: .... EST 2019
MC: .... TCEST 2019

SOLID.
Tracks: / Solid / Jungle / Honey I love you / Babies / Closest to love / Cherish forever more / Tonight we escape (we make love) / Outta the world.
LP: .... EJ 2402501
MC: .... EJ 2402504
LP: .... SASH 1

STAY FREE.
Tracks: / Found a cure / Stay free / Dance forever / Nobody knows / Crazy / Finally got to me / Follow your heart.
LP: .... K 56703

STREET OPERA.
LP: .... EST 12207

Ashkenazy, Vladimir

ASHKENAZY - LIVE IN MOSCOW (see under Royal Philharmonic Orchestra for deta (Royal Philharmonic Orchestra).

Ashlaw, Ted

ADIRONDACK WOODS SINGER.
LP: .... PH 1022

Ashley, Steve

FAMILY ALBUM, THE.
LP: .... WWM 002

MYSTERIOUS WAYS.
LP: .... LHO 100-4

SPEEDY RETURN.
Tracks: / None can tell / Don't forget / Well, well, well / Good enemies / Lazy lament / Speedy return / Old John England / Cynical Sam / Travelling through the night / Broken wing / Well at the world's end / Duke of Cambridge / First thing.
LP: .... GULP 1012

STROLL ON.
Tracks: / Fire and wine / Finite time / Silly Summer games / Spring song / Monkey puzzle tree / Farewell green leaves / Morris Minor / Candlemass carol / John Donne song / Lord Bateman / Follow on.
LP: .... GULP 1003

Ashoka Group

BHANGRA SENSATION.
Tracks: / Dhol walia o dagha dhol te lagee / Kori kori chaati wich - Boliyan / Boliyan - rock 'n' roll / Bhabhiyie nee Bhabhiyie / Menoon tere naal tyar gaya no / Meri gut saprni wal khawe / Chuk lae ghund mukhre toon / Giddhe de riwaaj ho gaya.
LP: .... SSRLP 5087
MC: .... SC 5087

Ashra

BLACK OUTS.
Tracks: / 77 slightly delayed / Midnight on Mars / Don't trust the kids / Blackouts / Shuttle cock / Lotus (part 1) / Lotus (part 2) / Lotus (part 3) / Lotus (part 4).
LP: .... OVED 193

BLACKOUTS (AMBIENT BOX SET) (See under Ambient).

CORRELATIONS.
Tracks: / Ice train / Club cannibal / Oasis / Bamboo sands / Morgana da capo / Pas de trois / Phantasus.
LP: .... V 2117

NEW AGE OF EARTH.
Tracks: / Sunrain / Ocean of tenderness / Deep distance / Nightdust.
LP: .... OVED 45

WALKIN' THE DESERT.
Tracks: / First movement / Second movement / Third movement / Fourth movement.
LP: .... THBL 086

Ashton, Mark

SOLO.
Tracks: / Dancing in the street / Blue blue night / That's the way it is / One more chance / In the street / So many do / Down to you boy / Thinking of you / One road at a time / When I'm out West.
LP: .... ARL 5023

Ashton, Tony

MALICE IN WONDERLAND (See under Paice Ashton Lord) (Paice, Ashton, Lord).

Asia

ALPHA.
Tracks: / Don't cry / Smile has left your eyes, The / Never in a million years / My own time (I'll do what I want) / Heat goes on, The / Eye to eye / Last to know, The / True colours / Midnight sun / Open your eyes.
LP: 9040081
MC: 9040084
LP: .... GEF 25508
MC: .... GEFC 04008

ASIA.
Tracks: / Go / Voice of America / Hard on me / Wishing / Rock and roll dream / Countdown to zero / Love now till eternity / Too late / Suspicion / After the war / Heat of the moment / Only time will tell / Sole survivor / Time again / One step closer / Wildest dreams / Without you / Cutting it fine / Here comes the feeling.
LP: 9020081
MC: 9020084
LP: .... GEF 85577
MC: .... GEFC 02008

ASTRA.
Tracks: / Go / Voice of America / Hard on me / Wishing / Rock and roll dream / Countdown to zero / Love now till eternity / Too late / Suspicion / After the war.
LP: .... GEF 26413
MC: 4026413

COMPILASIAN NO.1 (Various artists).
Tracks: / Govinda's house: *Sons Of Arqa* / Pump up the bhangra: *New Paradesi Music Machine* / One: *Chandra, Sheila* / Yeh naina yaad hai: *Bhosle, Asha* / Tootak, tootak, tootak: *Singh, Malkit* / Habiba: *Lahiri*, Bappi / Ghoom charakhana: *Ahktar, Najma* / Gidha pa nikiye: *Premi* / Sajne ve: *Radhashiri, Nishi*/ Hai mohabbat: *Mangeshkar, Lata* / Calling, The (part 1): *Ganges Orchestra* / Orissa: *Amok*.
MC: .... INDMC 1

THEN AND NOW.
Tracks: / Only time will tell / Wildest dreams / Smile has left your eyes, The / Prayin' 4 a miracle / Summer (can't last too long) / Heat of the moment / Don't cry / Days like these / Am I in love? / Voice of America.
LP: 7599242981
MC: 7599242984
MC: .... GEFC 24298

Asimov, Isaac (aut)

FOUNDATION - PSYCHOHISTORIANS (See under Foundation - Psychohistorians) (Shatner, William (nar)).

FOUNDATIONS EDGE.
MC: 1710

MULE, THE (See under Mule (bk)).

ROBOTS OF DAWN, THE (See under Robots Of Dawn (bk)).

Askey, Arthur

GOLDEN AGE OF ARTHUR ASKEY, THE.
Tracks: / Bee song / Chirrup / Only a glass of champagne / Ding dong bell / All to specification / Turn on the old music box / Proposal, The / Sarah Sarah / Cuckoo, The / Give a little whistle / Talking shop / She was very very shy / Destiny waltz / Rachmaninov prelude in C sharp major / September in the rain / Now is the moment.
LP: .... GX 41 2548
MC: .... TCGX 2548

Aslan

FEEL NO SHAME.
Tracks: / Loving me lately / Pretty thing / This is / Been so long / Hunger, The / Heat of the cell / Please don't stop / Down on me / Sands of time / Feel no shame / Book of life (on CD only.).
LP: .... EMC 3541
MC: .... TCEMC 3541

Asleep At The Wheel

COLLISION COURSE.
LP: .... EST 11726

COMIN' RIGHT AT YA'.
Tracks: / Take me back to Tulsa / Daddy's advice / Before you stopped loving me / Drivin' nails in my coffin / I'll never get out of this world alive / Space buggy / Cherokee boogie / Hillbilly nut / Your down home is uptown / I'm the fool / I've been everywhere / Sun shines down on me.
LP: .... ED 187
MC: .... CED 187

FRAMED.
Tracks: / Midnight in Memphis / Lonely Avenue revisited / Slow dancing / Cool as a breeze / You wanna give me a lift / Don't get caught out in the rain / Whatever it takes / Fiddle funk - corn fusion / Up up up / Musical talk.
LP: .... IMCA 742

JUMPING AT THE WOODSIDE.
LP: .... ED 169

PASTURE PRIME.
Tracks: / Across the valley from the Alamo / Switchin' in the kitchen / Write your own song / Cotton-eyed Joe / Baby / Shorty / That chick's too young to fry / Big beaver / This is the way we make a broken heart / Deep water / Natural thing to do, The / Liar's moon / That's your red wagon.
LP: .... FIEND 44
MC: .... FIENDCASS 44

SERVED LIVE.
Tracks: / Choo choo ch' boogie / Last meal / God bless the child / Jumpin' at the Woodside / Am I high? / Route 66 / Baby, you've got what it takes / Too many bad habits / Miles and miles of Texas / Will the circle be unbroken.
LP: .... EST 11945

TEN.
Tracks: / Way down Texas way / Tulsa straight ahead / Coast to coast / House of blue lights / Blowin' like a bandit / I want a new drug / Big foot stomp / Boogie back to Texas / String of pars / Blues stay away from me.
LP: 4506291
MC: 4506294

VERY BEST OF ASLEEP AT THE WHEEL.
Tracks: / Cherokee boogie / I'll never get out of this world alive / Space buggy / Letter that Johnny Walker read, The / Let me go home whiskey / Trouble in mind / Runnin' after fools / Miles and miles of Texas / Route 66 / My baby thinks she's a train / Am I high? / Ragtime Annie / Somebody stole his body / When love goes wrong / Louisiana 1927 / Ain't nobody here but us chickens / One o'clock jump.
LP: .... SEE 81

WESTERN STANDARD TIME.
Tracks: / Chattanooga choo choo / Don't let go / Hot rod Lincoln / That's what I like about the South / That lucky old sun / Walk on by / San Antonio rose / Roly poly / Sugarfoot rag / Walking the floor over you.
LP: 4609851
MC: 4609854

WHEEL, THE.
LP: .... EST 11620

Asmus Tietchens

ABFLEISCUNG.
LP: .... HAM 25

LITIA.
LP: .... SKY 087

SEUCHENGBIETE.
LP: .... PROV 18:14

Asmussen, Svend

AS TIME GOES BY (See under Hampton, Lionel) (Asmussen, Svend/ Lionel Hampton).

DANISH JAZZ VOL.6.
LP: .... SLP 415

JUNE NIGHT.
Tracks: / June night / Sweet Georgia Brown / Lazy River / Ladja / Blue prelude / Just a gigolo / Careless love / Pretty girl is like a melody, A / When day is done / Hush-a-bye.
LP: .... ASLP 803
MC: .... ZCAS 803

PRIZE WINNERS (See Under Drew, Kenny) (Asmussen, Svend/ Drew/ Pedersen/ Asmussen/ Thigpen).

STRING SWING.
Tracks: / East St. Louis toodle-oo / Two guitars / Nadja / Prelude in C minor / Mooche / Dark eyes / Vipers dream / Peacocks.
LP: .... SNTF 902

TWO OF A KIND (Asmussen, Svend/ Stephane Grappelli).
LP: .... SLP 4088

YESTERDAY AND TODAY (See under Thielemans, Toots) (Asmussen, Svend/ Toots Thielemans).

Aspects of Love (show)

ASPECTS OF LOVE (Various artists).
Tracks: / Love changes everything: *Various artists* / Seeing is believing: *Various artists* / Chason d'enfante: *Various artists* / She's far better off without you: *Various artists* / Leading lady: *Various artists*/ There's more to love: *Various artists* / First man you remember, The: *Various artists* / Falling: *Various* artists / Anything but lonely:

Various artists / Cafe, The: *Various artists* / Memory of a happy moment, The: *Various artists* / Everybody loves a hero: *Various artists* / Stop wait please: *Various artists*/ Other pleasures: *Various artists* / Mermaid song: *Various artists* / Journey of a lifetime: *Various artists*/ Hand me the wine and the dice: *Various artists*.
LP: **841 126 1**
MC: **841 126 4**

FIRST MAN YOU REMEMBER, THE (See under Ball, Michael) (Various artists).

LOVE CHANGES EVERYTHING (See under Ball, Michael) (Various artists).

Aspey, Gary

FROM THE NORTH (Aspey, Gary & Vera).
Tracks: / From the North / Parting, The / Coal picking / Three foot seam / Mill girls lullaby / King Cotton / Auntie Ketyll / Cum t'thi tay / Cradle song / Roving navvy / Ship canal song, The / Hailey go / Tuppence on the rope / Bit of a sing, A.
LP: **12TS 255**

NIGHTSHIFT ARMY (Aspey, Gary & Vera).
LP: . . . . **DIN 333**

SEEING DOUBLE (Aspey, Gary & Vera).
Tracks: / Seeing double / My goodlooking man / Miss Tickle Toby / Dowie dens of Yarrow, The / Cruise of the Calibar / Hounds and horn together / Bolinder boatman, The / Testimony of Patience Kershaw, The / July wakes / Knocker upper man / Price of coal, The / Coal and Albert Berry, The.
LP: **12TS 407**

STORIES,SONGS & HUMOUR (Aspey, Gary & Vera).
LP: . . . . **DIN 325**

TASTE OF HOTPOT, A (Aspey, Gary & Vera).
Tracks: / Eskdale and Ennerdale hunt song, The / Weepin' an' wailin' away / Shuttle kissing song, The / Foddered me yowes / Nightingale, The / Don't get married girl / Kids songs / Coal hole cavalry, The / Morning stands on tiptoe.
LP: **12TS 299**

Aspey, Vera

BLACKBIRD, THE.
Tracks: / Blackbird, The / Owd Betty Barlow / Ladybird / Maypole Inn, The / Pit brow lassies, The / My Johnny was a shoemaker / Coal black faces / Highwayman / Shule agra / Aggie Bell / Sprig of thyme.
LP: **12TS 356**

DON'T GET MARRIED GIRL (see under Aspey, Gary & Vera) (Aspey, Gary & Vera).

Asphyxia

EXIT - REALITY.
Tracks: / Capital punishment / Violence first / Slice of death / Health for sale / Paranoia time / One who minds the worm, The / One big family / Where shadows are dark / No thanks.
LP: . . . . **RUMLP 1005**

Assad, Sergio Odair

BRAZILIAN GUITAR MUSIC FOR 2 GUITARS.
LP: **9791161**

Assassin

INTERSTELLAR EXPERIENCE.
LP: **087519**
MC: **087520**

UPCOMING TERROR.
LP: **081895**

Assassins Of God

JUPITER OX REVEALED, THE.
LP: . . . . **EFA 15292**

Associates

AFFECTIONATE PUNCH, THE.
Tracks: / Logan time / Paper house / Deeply concerned / Even dogs in the wild / Transport to central / Amused as always / Affectionate punch, The / Matter of gender, A / Would I ....bounce back.
LP: . . . . **SPELP 33**
MC: . . . . **SPEMC 33**
LP: . . . . **FIXD 5**

FOURTH DRAWER DOWN.
Tracks: / White car in Germany / Girl named property, A / Kitchen person / Q quarters / Tell me Easter's on Friday / Associate, The / Message oblique speech / Even whiter car, An.
LP: . . . . **BEGA 43**
MC: . . . . **BEGC 43**

PERHAPS.
Tracks: / Those first impressions / Waiting for the loveboat / Perhaps / Schampout / Helicopter helicopter / Breakfast / Thirteen feelings / Stranger in your voice, The / Best of you, The / Don't give me that I told you so look.
LP: . . . . **WX 9**
MC: . . . . **WX 9C**

SULK.
Tracks: / It's better this way / Party fears two / Club country / Love hangover / 18 carat love affair / Arrogance gave him up / No / Skipping / White car in Germany / Gloomy Sunday / Associate, The.
LP: **2400 005 1**
MC: **2400 005 4**
LP: . . . . **ASCL 1**

WILD AND LONELY.
Tracks: / Fire to ice / People we meet / Just can't say goodbye / Calling all around the world / Glamour chase, The (Only on CD.) / Where there's love / Something's got to give / Strasbourg Square / Ever since that day / Wild and lonely / Fever in the shadows (Only on CD.).
MC: . . . . **CIRC 11**
LP: . . . . **CIRCA 11**

Association

ASSOCIATION AND THE KINGSTON TRIO (Association/Kingston Trio).
MC: **803**

ASSOCIATION, THE.
Tracks: / Time it is today, The / Everything that touches you / Like always / Never my love / Requiem for the masses / Along comes Mary / Enter the young / No fair at all / Time for living / We love / Cherish / Windy / Six man band.
LP: . . . . **K 26012**
MC: **K4 26012**

GOLDEN HEEBIE JEEBIES.
Tracks: / Along comes Mary / Enter the young / Your own love / Remember / Changes / I'm the one / Memories of you / You hear me call your name / Pandora's golden heebie jeebies / Come to me / Windy / When love comes to me / On a quiet night / Not fair at all / Wantin' ain't gettin'.
LP: . . . . **ED 239**

Assoluto Naturale

ASSOLUTO NATURALE (Film soundtrack) (Various artists).
LP: . . . . **C'BUS 112**

Assumpaco, Itamar

INTERCONTINENTAL.
LP: **15990**

Astaire

BORN TO DANCE.
Tracks: / Born to dance / Shame / Love trap / In the name of love / Keep movin' / Get that girl / Feelings for me / Lazy days, magical nights / You were made to love me / Treat me like a fool / Creatures of the night / Because we've got the love / Dancing my way to the top / Living as one.
LP: . . . . **PAPX 101**

Astaire, Fred

BEST OF FRED ASTAIRE.
LP: . . . . **MCA 25985**
MC: . . . . **MCAC 25985**
LP: . . . . **MCL 1706**

CBS YEARS, THE.
LP: **4655981**
MC: **4655984**

CHANTE SES PLUS GRANDES SUCCESS.
LP: **24204**

CLASSIC YEARS IN DIGITAL STEREO (Shall We Dance - Fred Astaire 1926-1937).
Tracks: / Shall we dance / Fascinating rhythm / Crazy feet / Puttin' on the Ritz / Night and day / No strings / Top hat / Cheek to cheek / Pick yourself up / Way you look tonight / Fine romance, A / Slap that bass / Beginner's luck / Let's call the whole thing off / They can't take that away from me / Shall we dance-finale.
LP: . . . . **REB 665**
MC: . . . . **ZCF 665**

CRAZY FEET.
Tracks: / Night and day / My one and only / Fascinating rhythm / New sun in the sky / Louisiana / Swiss miss / I'd rather Charleston / High hat / Whichness of the whatness, The / I've got you on my mind / Puttin' on the Ritz / White heat / Dancing in the dark / Hang on to me / Oh gee, oh gosh / Not my girl / Half of it dearie blues, The / Babbitt and the bromide, The / I love Louisa / Funny face / Crazy feet.
LP: . . . . **AJA 5021**
MC: . . . . **ZC AJA 5021**

EASY TO DANCE WITH.
Tracks: / So near and yet so far / Dream dancing / Since I kissed my baby goodbye / Wedding cake walk, The / You're so easy to dance with / I can't tell a lie / Wedding in the spring / I'm old fashioned / Dearly beloved / You were never lovelier / On the beam / Shorty George / If swing goes I go too / This heart of mine / One for my baby / Oh my achin' back / Puttin' on the Ritz.
LP: . . . . **MCL 1858**
MC: . . . . **MCLC 1858**

EVENING WITH....
2LP: . . . . **N 22007/8**

FRED ASTAIRE (Original recordings 1935-40).
LP: **66316**

FRED ASTAIRE.
MC: . . . . **MRT 40036**

FRED ASTAIRE AND GINGER ROGERS STORY, THE (Astaire, Fred & Ginger Rogers).
Tracks: / Half of it dearie blues, The / High hat / My one and only / Not my girl / Crazy feet / Night and day / I've got you on my mind / Fine romance, A / Music makes me / Out for no good / I won't dance / I got a new lease of life / Puttin' on the ritz / Cheek to cheek / You'll be reminded of me / I used to be colour blind / I can't be bothered now / Wedding cake walk, The / If swing goes I go too / They can't take that away from me / Weekend in the country, A / You'll never know / By myself / Something's gotta give / Before the parade passes by.
MCSET: . . . . **DVREMC 09**

FRED ASTAIRE COLLECTION (20 Golden Greats).
Tracks: / Night and day / My one and only / Fascinating rhythm / Puttin' on the Ritz / White heat (medley) / Hang on to me / Continental, The / Funny face / Louisiana / Swiss miss / High hat / I can't be bothered now / Change partners / I've got you on my mind / Not my girl / Babbitt and the bromide, The / Half of it dearie blues, The / Crazy feet / Cheek to cheek / This is a fine romance.
LP: . . . . **DVLP 2022**
MC: . . . . **DVMC 2022**

FUNNY FACE (Astaire, Fred & Adele).
LP: . . . . **WRCSH 144**

GOLDEN AGE OF FRED ASTAIRE.
Tracks: / Top hat, white tie and tails / Fine romance, A / Cheek to cheek / I wanna be a dancin' man / They can't take that away from me / One for my baby / Night and day / Something's gotta give / Foggy day, A / Isn't this a lovely day / They all laughed / That's entertainment.
LP: . . . . **MFP 5827**
MC: . . . . **TC MFP 5827**
LP: . . . . **GX 2511**

GOLDEN AGE OF FRED ASTAIRE VOL.2.
LP: . . . . **GX 41 2538 1**
MC: . . . . **GX 41 2538 4**

GREAT MGM STARS: FRED ASTAIRE.
Tracks: / Steppin' out with my baby / It only happens when I dance with you / Oops! / Bachelor's dinner song / Baby doll / Seeing's believing / I wanna be a dancin' man / Ev'ry night at seven / I left my hat in Haiti / You're all the world to me / How could you believe me when I said I loved you (when you know I've been a liar all my life.) / Fated to be mated / Paris loves lovers / Ritz roll and rock, The / Nevertheless / Where did you get that girl / Three little words / Shine on your shoes, A / By myself / Triplets / I love Louisa / That's entertainment / All of you.
LP: . . . . **LPMGM 28**
LP: **795 853 1**
MC: . . . . **TCMGM 28**
MC: **795 853 4**

NICE WORK (Fred Astaire Sings Gershwin).
Tracks: / Hang on to me / Fascinating rhythm / Half of it dearie blues, The / I'd rather Charleston / Funny face / Babbitt and the bromide, The / High hat / My one and only / They can't take that away from me / They all laughed / I've got beginner's luck / Let's call the whole thing off / Shall we dance? / Slap that bass / Foggy day, A / Things are looking up / Nice work if you can get it / I can't be bothered now.
LP: . . . . **SVL 199**
MC: . . . . **CSVL 199**

NOW.
Tracks: / Change partners / Isn't this a lovely day / Foggy day, A / Girl on the magazine cover, The / I love to quarrel with you / Along came Ruth / Afterbeat, The / They can't take that away from me / They all laughed / I'll walk alone / One for my baby / Oh lady be good / Puttin' on the Ritz / Top hat, white tie and tails / Lady of the evening / Something's gotta give.
LP: . . . . **OFF 12010**

PUTTIN' ON THE RITZ.
LP: **2245712**
MC: **2145712**

SOUNDTRACKS, VOICES AND THEMES (Astaire, Fred & Gene Kelly).
LP: . . . . **MRS 509**

SPECIAL MAGIC OF FRED ASTAIRE.
LP: . . . . **SPELP 61**
MC: . . . . **SPEMC 61**

SPECIAL MAGIC OF FRED ASTAIRE VOL.2.
MC: **3177 262**

STARRING FRED ASTAIRE (DOUBLE ALBUM).
Tracks: / No strings / Isn't this a lovely day / Top hat, white tie and tails / Cheek to cheek / Piccolino, The / We saw the sea / Let yourself go / I'd rather lead a band / I'm putting all my eggs in one basket / Let's face the music and dance / I'm building up to an awful let-down / Pick yourself up / Way you look tonight / Waltz in swing time, The / Fine romance, A / Bojangles of Harlem / Never gonna dance / Slap that bass / Beginner's luck / They all laughed / Let's call the whole thing off / They can't take that away from me / Shall we dance / I can't be bothered now / Things are looking up / Foggy day in London town, A / Nice work if you can get it / I used to be colour blind / Change partners / Yam, The.
2LP: **VS2LP 32472**
MCSET: **VS2C 32472**

STARRING FRED ASTAIRE (SINGLE ALBUM).
LP: **4601271**
MC: **4601274**

STEPPING IN PARADISE.
LP: . . . . **ENT LP 13037**
MC: . . . . **ENT MC 13037**

THREE EVENINGS WITH FRED ASTAIRE (2).
2LP: . . . . **DARC 11107**

THREE EVENINGS WITH FRED ASTAIRE (2).
LPS: . . . . **SL 5181**
MCSET: . . . . **SLC 5181**

TOP HAT, WHITE TIE AND TAILS.
Tracks: / Night and day / After you-who / Flying down to Rio / Music makes me / Cheek to cheek / No strings / Isn't this a lovely day / Top hat white tie and tails / Piccolino, The / Let's face the music and dance / I'm putting all my eggs in one basket / We saw the sea / I'm building up to an awful let down / Let yourself go / I'd rather lead a band / Way you look tonight / Never gonna dance / Pick yourself up / Fine romance, A / Bojangles of Harlem.
LP: . . . . **SVL 184**
MC: . . . . **CSVL 184**

Aster, Andre

BALLADE EN QUERCY (Aster, Andre & Andre Roques).
Tracks: / Bon vin de cahors / Quercy mon beau pays / Les filles de Montauban / Querca querla / Lapelleto / De Mauriac a rodez / Plaisirs de quercy / Le grand pere / Potpourri de valses / Aio de rosta / Chez la mere Antoine a pas legers / Bourees / Polka pi quee.
MC: . . . . **ILD 742012**

Asterisks

SOCA FUSION VOL.4.
Tracks: / Is thunder? / She wants me to sing in she party / She wants me to sing in she party (DJ mix) / Say say / Curry tabanca / International boops.
LP: . . . . **GS 2275**

SOCA FUSION VOL.5.
LP: . . . . **GS 2285**

SOCA FUSION VOL.6.
LP: . . . . **GS 2304**
MC: . . . . **GSC 2304**

Asterix...

ASTERIX AND THE MAGIC CARPET (Rushton, Willie (nar)).
MCSET: . . . . **LFP 7370**

ASTERIX IN BRITAIN Goscinny (Rushton, Willie (nar)).
MCSET: . . . . **LFP 7294**

ASTERIX THE GAUL (Rushton, Willie (nar)).
MCSET: . . . . **LFP 7493**

ASTERIX THE GLADIATOR (Rushton, Willie (nar)).
MCSET: . . . . **LFP 7238**
MCSET: . . . . **LFP 4172385**

Astier, Jean-Yves

JEAN-YVES ASTIER ET SERIE LIMITEE.
LP: . . . . **DFG 8413**

Astley, John

COMPLEAT ANGLER, THE.
Tracks: / But is it commercial / Put this love to the test / I'll show you bastards / I dream about you (but I cannot sleep) / Menu, The / Been there, done that

(what's next mix) / Welcome to the circus / Fire the editor / Don't talk to strangers.
LP: . . . . K 781 882 1
MC: . . . . K 781 882 4

EVERYONE LOVES THE PILOT EXCEPT THE CREW.
Tracks: / Jane's getting serious / Lip service / Target practice / Suffering fools / Animal, The / Jumping in the deep end / Better never than later / I want to dance / Disclaimer / Emperor, The.
LP: 781 740-1
MC: 781 740-4

Astley, Rick

FREE.
Tracks: / In the name of love / Cry for help / Move right out / Be with you / Really got a problem / Is this really love (Track on cassette/ CD only.) / This must be Heaven / Never new love / Bottom line / Wonderful you / Behind the smile.
LP: . . . . PL 74896
MC: . . . . PK 74896

HOLD ME IN YOUR ARMS.
Tracks: / She wants to dance with me / Take me to your heart / I don't want to lose her / Giving up on love / Ain't too proud to beg / Put yourself in my place / Till then (time stands still) / Dial my number / I'll never let you down / I don't want to be your lover / Hold me in your arms.
LP: . . . . PL 71932
MC: . . . . PK 71932

LEARNING TO LIVE (WITHOUT YOUR LOVE) (See under Brown, O'Chi) (Astley, Rick & O'Chi Brown).

RICK ASTLEY: INTERVIEW PICTURE DISC.
LPPD: . . . . BAK 2085

WHENEVER YOU NEED SOMEBODY.
Tracks: / Never gonna give you up / Whenever you need somebody / Together forever / It would take a strong, strong man / Love has gone, The / Don't say goodbye / Slipping away / No more looking for love / You move me / When I fall in love.
LP: . . . . PL 71529
MC: . . . . PK 71529

Astley, Virginia

FROM THE GARDENS WHERE WE FEEL SECURE.
LP: . . . . ROUGH 58

HOPE IN A DARKENED HEART.
Tracks: / Some small hope / Father / So like Dorian / I'm sorry / Tree top club / Charm / Love's a lonely place to be / Summer long since passed / Darkness has reached it's end.
LP: . . . . WX 78

PROMISE NOTHING.
LP: . . . . TWI 194

Aston, John

YOU TAKE THE BLAME FOR THE ROSES.
LP: . . . . MMLP 1017

Aston Manor School

DAVID.
LP: . . . . PC 439

JERUSALEM JOY (Aston Manor School (Easter Cantata)).
Tracks: / To Jerusalem / Palm Sunday / In the temple / Let's get rid of him / Last supper, The / Gethsemane / Peter's denial / Trial, The / Don't let him go / Crucifixion / It is over now / He's not here (for He is risen) / David, you're gonna be King / Samuel, we're waiting for you / Lord's my shepherd, The / David and Goliath / Look out, David / I will bless the Lord / David and Jonathan / Mighty are fallen, The / David is the one / Praise the Lord.
LP: . . . . KLPS 56

STARGAZERS, THE.
Tracks: / Let's take a trip / Farewell home / Riding high / Are we in the right place / Bethlehem (that's the place) / Look here, wise guys / In search of love / Look at the star / Jesus, baby Jesus / Just you / As with gladness men of old / Psalm 100 / How sweet the name.
LP: . . . . KLPS 62

Astor, Peter

SUBMARINE.
LP: . . . . CRELP 065

Astorians

GUFFAW.
LP: . . . . PD 19008

Astronauts (3)

IT'S ALL DONE WITH MIRRORS.
LP: . . . . MAD 5

Aswad

ASWAD.
LP: . . . . ILPS 9399

DISTANT THUNDER.
Tracks: / Message, The / Don't turn around / Set them free / Smokey Blues / I can't get over you / Give a little love / Tradition / Feelings / International melody / Bittersweet / Justice.
LP: . . . . ILPS 9895
MC: . . . . ICT 9895
MC: . . . . RRCT 27

DON'T BITE THE HAND (See under Osbourne, Johnny) (Aswad & Johnny Osbourne).

HULET.
Tracks: / Behold / Sons of criminals / Judgment day / Not guilty / Can't walk the street / Corruption / Playing games / Hulet.
LP: . . . . ILPS 9611

JAH SHAKA MEETS ASWAD IN ADDIS ABABA STUDIO.
LP: . . . . SHAKA 850 LP

LIVE AND DIRECT.
Tracks: / Not guilty / Not satisfied / Your recipe / Roots rocking drum and bass line / African children / Soca rumba / Rockers medley / Love fire.
LP: . . . . IMA 6
MC: . . . . IMC 6
MC: . . . . ICM 2002
MC: 818 040 4

NEW CHAPTER.
Tracks: / African children / Natural progression / Ways of the Lord / I will keep on loving you / He gave the sun to shine / Tuff we tuff / Didn't know at the time / Zion / In a your rights / Candles / Love fire.
LP: . . . . CBS 32473
MC: 40 32473
LP: . . . . CBS 85336
MC: . . . . ICM 2001
MC: . . . . ICT 9711
MC: 842 929 4

NEW CHAPTER/NOT SATISFIED.
2LP: . . . . AW 241
MCSET: . . . . AW 40241

NOT SATISFIED.
Tracks: / Drum and bass line / Not satisfied / Reality / African children (part 2) / Pass the cup / I need your love / No more living a lie / Down the line / Your recipe / Girl's got to know.
LP: . . . . CBS 32564
MC: 40 32564
LP: . . . . CBS 85666

PROMISED LAND (See under Brown,Dennis) (Aswad/Dennis Brown).

PUSHING UPWARD.
LP: . . . . ILPS 9780
MC: . . . . ICT 9780
MC: . . . . ICM 2003
MC: 824 006 4

RENAISSANCE.
Tracks: / Don't turn around / Set them free / 54 46 (was my number) (88 remix) / Hooked on you / Roots rockin' / Gimme the dub / Need your love (each and every day) (88 remix) / Warrior charge / Kool noh / Smokey blues (88 remix) / Give a little love / Bubbling / Chasing for the breeze (88 remix) / Rainbow culture / Back to Africa / African children (live) / Dub fire / Three Babylon / It's not our wish / Pull up.
LP: . . . . SMR 866
MCSET: . . . . SMC 866

TO THE TOP.
LP: . . . . SIMBALP 2
MC: . . . . SIMBALC 100
MC: . . . . MCTM 1017
LP: . . . . MLPM 1017
MC: . . . . ICM 2004
MC: 842 349 4

TOO WICKED.
LP: . . . . MLPS 1054
MC: . . . . MCT 1054

Aswyn, Freya

FRUITS OF YGGDRASILL, THE (Aswyn, Freya/ Sixth Comm).
LP: . . . . EYAS 006

LEAVES OF YGGDRASILL (Aswyn, Freya/ Sixth Comm).
MC: . . . . CENCB 6

Asylum

WE WILL BE FREE (Asylum/ Stalag 17/ Toxic Waste).
LP: . . . . WARZONE 1

Asylum Party

BORDERLINE.
LP: . . . . ARTY 8

At The Drop Of...

AT THE DROP OF A HAT (See under Flanders & Swann) (Flanders & Swann).

AT THE DROP OF A HAT (ORIGINAL ISSUE) (London cast) (Various artists).
LP: . . . . PMC 1033

At the Party

AT THE PARTY (16 Rompin' Stompin' Lease Breakin' Tunes) (Various artists).
LP: . . . . CANDY 001

At the Rockhouse

AT THE ROCKHOUSE VOL.10 (Various artists).
LP: . . . . EAGLE 320

At War

ORDERED TO KILL.
LP: . . . . GWD 90550
MC: . . . . GWC 90550

At Your Request

AT YOUR REQUEST: ANNE ROBINSON (Most Requested Tracks) (Various artists).
Tracks: / Blanket on the ground: *Spears, Billie Jo* / It's impossible: *Como, Perry* / I recall a gypsy woman: *Williams, Don* / I'm not in love / Snowbird: *Murray, Anne* / I love you because: *Reeves, Jim* / Enough of each other: *Fricke, Janie* / Words of love: *Holly, Buddy* / Rose garden: *Anderson, Lynn* / Living doll: *Richard, Cliff* / We're all alone: *Coolidge, Rita* / Crystal chandeliers: *Pride, Charley* / You make me feel brand new: *Stylistics* / El Paso: *Robbins, Marty* / When I dream: *Gayle, Crystal* / Heart on my sleeve: *Gallagher & Lyle*.
LP: . . . . REN 733
MC: . . . . ZCN 733

AT YOUR REQUEST: DAVID JACOBS (Most Requested Tracks) (Various artists).
Tracks: / One morning in May: *Monro, Matt* / Bring him home: *Cantible* / Me and my shadow: *Lee, Peggy*/ Pretty butterfly: *Damone, Vic* / Man and a woman, A: *Williams, Andy* / Autumn in New York: *Mathis, Johnny*/ Second time around, The: *Torme, Mel* / Very thought of you, The: *Bennett, Tony* / You and me against the world: *Reddy, Helen* / Everything's coming up roses: *Bassey, Shirley* / Fancy meeting you here: *Crosby, Bing & Rosemary* Clooney / Days of wine and roses: *Mancini, Henry* / If I were a bell: *Day, Doris* / I concentrate on you: *Horne, Lena* / Dancing in the dark: *Manuel & The Music of the Mountains*.
LP: . . . . REN 711
MC: . . . . ZCN 711

AT YOUR REQUEST: JIMMY YOUNG (Most Requested Tracks) (Various artists).
LP: . . . . REN 712
MC: . . . . ZCN 712

AT YOUR REQUEST: KEN BRUCE (Most Requested Tracks) (Various artists).
Tracks: / Oh pretty woman: *Orbison, Roy* / Devil woman: *Robbins, Marty* / Most beautiful girl in the world: *Rich,* Charlie / Someday soon: *Collins, Judy* / Boy named Sue, A: *Cash, Johnny* / Save the last dance for me: *Drifters*/ Here, there and everywhere: *Harris, Emmylou* / I only want to be with you: *Springfield, Dusty* / Sundown: *Lightfoot,* Gordon / Half the way: *Gayle, Crystal* / Cathy's clown: *Everly Brothers* / City of New Orleans: *Nelson,* Willie / Wedding bells: *Godley & Creme* / You might need somebody: *Crawford, Randy* / Things we do for love: *10 CC* / Always there: *Webb, Marti*.
LP: . . . . REN 710
MC: . . . . ZCN 710

AT YOUR REQUEST: RAY MOORE (Most Requested Tracks) (Various artists).
Tracks: / Singin' the blues: *Mitchell, Guy* / 99 miles from LA: *Hammond, Albert* / That Sunday that Summer: *Cole,* Nat King / Affair to remember, An: *Damone, Vic* / Sad sweet dreamer: *Sensations* / Is that all there is: *Lee,* Peggy / For no one: *Black, Cilla* / For all we know: *Conniff, Ray* / Bog eyed jog: *Moore, Ray* / Orchard Road: *Sayer, Leo* / Diane: *Bruce, Ed* / Here, there and everywhere: *Leander, Mike* / Good things in life, The: *Bennett, Tony* / Highway to Spain: *Magna Carta* / Fool if you think it's over: *Brooks, Elkie*/ Gone gone gone: *Mathis, Johnny* / Wichita linesman: *Campbell, Glen* / Oh my father had a rabbit: *Moore, Ray*.
LP: . . . . REN 713
MC: . . . . ZCN 713

Atari-Sci/Fi

ATARI-SCI-FI ADVENTURES IN SOUND (Various artists).
MC: . . . . PTB 637

Atavistic

VANISHING POINT.
LP: . . . . DEAF 03

A-Team (tv prog)

A-TEAM, THE (Original Score) (Various artists).
Tracks: / A team: *Various artists* / Young Hannibal: *Various artists* / B. A. 's ride: *Various artists*/ A Team in New York City, The: *Various artists* / Bandits: *Various artists* / Taxi chase: *Various artists*/ A Team escape, The: *Various artists* / A Team prepare for war, The: *Various artists* / Showtime: *Various* artists / Move sucker: *Various artists* / Let's get busted: *Various artists* / Murdock's "face": *Various artists* / Helicopters: *Various artists* / More bandits: *Various artists*.
LP: 41 5733 1
MC: 41 5733 4

MUSIC FROM THE A-TEAM (Various artists).
MC: . . . . FILMC 701

Atheist

PIECE OF TIME.
Tracks: / Piece of time / Unholy war / Room with a view / On they slay / Beyond / I deny / Why brother / Life / No truth.
LP: . . . . ATV 8

UNQUESTIONABLE PRESENCE.
LP: . . . . ATV 20
MC: . . . . TATV 20

Athena (film)

ATHENA (Original soundtrack) (Various artists).
LP: . . . . MPT 2

Athenians

12 OF THE MOST POPULAR SYRTAKIS.
LP: . . . . EULP 1058
MC: . . . . EUMC 1058

ALEXIS SORBAS.
LP: . . . . EULP 1057
MC: . . . . EUMC 1057

ATHENIANS LIFE.
LP: . . . . EULP 1036

BEST OF GREECE.
LP: . . . . EULP 1091
MC: . . . . EUMC 1091

CANTO GENERAL.
LP: . . . . EULP 1027
MC: . . . . EUMC 1027

GREEK POPULAR MUSIC.
LP: . . . . EULP 1024
MC: . . . . EUMC 1024

REMBETIKO.
LP: . . . . EULP 1063
MC: . . . . EUMC 1063

Athens, G.A. (film)

ATHENS, G.A.- INSIDE OUT (Original soundtrack) (Various artists).
LP: . . . . IRS 6185
MC: . . . . IRSC 6185

Athletico Spizz 80

DO A RUNNER.
Tracks: / Touched / New species / Intimate / Effortless / European heroes / Energy / Red and black / Rhythm inside / Person impersonator / Clocks are big / Airships.
LP: . . . . AMLE 68514

Atkin, Pete

CLIVE JAMES/PETE ATKIN SONGBOOK, THE (1967-74) (See under James, Clive) (James, Clive & Pete Atkin).

Atkins

ATKINS.
LP: . . . . BSK 3659

Atkins, Chet

20 OF THE BEST: CHET ATKINS.
Tracks: / Yakety axe / Yankee doodle Dixie / Galloping on the guitar / Walkin' on strings / You're just in love / In the mood / Whispering / Summer place, Theme from / Hidden charms / Heartaches / When you wish upon a star / Over the rainbow / Music to watch girls by / Siboney / El relicario / Early dawn (La madrugada) / Steeplechase Lane / Funky junk / Cascade / Black mountain rag.
LP: . . . . NL 89849
MC: . . . . NK 89849

BEST OF CHET ATKINS.
LP: . . . . CDS 1217
MC: . . . . CAM 1217

BEST OF CHET ATKINS AND FRIENDS (Atkins, Chet & Friends).
Tracks: / Terry on the turnpike / Sail along silv'ry moon / Sweet Georgia Brown / Avalon / Sugarfoot rag / Battle of New Orleans / Do I ever cross your mind / Frog kissin' / Twichy / Fiddlin' around / Poison love / I'll see you in my dreams.
LP: . . . . MFP 5766
MC: . . . . TCMFP 5766
LP: . . . . PL 11985

BEST OF CHET ATKINS (RCA).

Tracks: / Teensville / Boo boo stick beat / One mint julep / Jitterbug waltz / Peanut vendor / Django's castle / Blue ocean echo / Yankee doodle Dixie / Swedish rhapsody / Vanessa / Trombone / Malaguena / Meet Mr. Callaghan / Main street breakdown / Country gentleman / Yakety axe.
LP: INTS 5051
MC: INTK 5051

CARIBBEAN GUITAR.
LP: RD 7519

CHESTER AND LESTER (Atkins, Chet & Les Paul).
Tracks: / It's been a long, long time / Moonglow and theme from Picnic / Caravan / It had to be you / Out of nowhere / Avalon / Birth of the blues / Someday, sweetheart / Deed I do / Lover come back to me.
LP: LSA 3290

CHET ATKIN'S GUITAR WORKSHOP.
LP: RD 27214

EAST TENNESSEE CHRISTMAS.
Tracks: / Jingle bell rock / White Christmas / Let it snow, let it snow, let it snow / Winter wonderland / Christmas song, The / I'll be home for Christmas / East Tennessee Christmas / Do you hear what I hear? / Little drummer boy / God rest ye merry gentlemen / Silent night / Away in a manger.
MC: 40 25735
LP: CBS 25735

FAMOUS COUNTRY MUSIC MAKERS.
Tracks: / Yakety axe / Walkin' on strings / Bells of St. Mary's / Corina Corina / Amazing grace / Third man, Theme from / Little bit of blues, A / Dill pickle rag / Country style / Django's castle / Glow worm / Stephen Foster medley / Trombone / Remembering / Prisoner's song / Country gentleman / Oh by jingo, oh by gee / Will the circle be unbroken / Greensleeves / Windy and warm / Arkansas traveller / Squirrelly / Red wing / Twelfth St. Rag / Get on with it / Little Rock getaway / South / When you wish upon a star / Whispering / Halacious / Main street breakdown.
2LP: DPS 2063

FIRST NASHVILLE GUITAR QUARTET.
Tracks: / Carolina shout / Londonderry air / Love song of Pepe Sanchez / Skirts of Mexico / You needed me / Bound for Boston / Washington post / Someday my prince will come / Rings of grass / Concierto de Aranjuez / Brandenburg.
LP: PL 13302

GUITAR MONSTERS (Atkins, Chet & Les Paul).
Tracks: / Limehouse blues / I want to be happy / Over the rainbow / Meditacao / Lazy river / I'm your greatest fan / It don't mean a thing / I surrender dear / Brazil / Give my love to Nell / Hot toddy.
MC: PK 12786
LP: PL 12786

GUITAR PICKIN' MAN.
Tracks: / Swedish rhapsody / Liza / Tiger rag / In the mood / Mountain melody / Heartaches / Glow worm / Malaguena / Hot mocking bird / Rainbow / I know that you know / Hello bluebird / Siesta / Country style / Show me the way to go home / Goofus / Petite waltz / Gavotte in D / Jitterbug waltz / Tara's theme / Downhill drag / Portuguese washerwoman / Unchained melody / Backwoods / Country gentleman / Summers place, Theme from / Slinky / Jessie / Rhythm guitar / Poor people of Paris, The / Dizzy fingers.
2LP: CR 062
MCSET: CRT 062

IN THREE DIMENSIONS.
LP: HAT 3083

LEGENDARY PERFORMER VOL 1, THE.
Tracks: / Ain'tcha tired of makin' me blue / I've been working on the guitar / Barber shop rag / Chinatown, my Chinatown / Oh, by jingo, oh by gee (you're the only girl) / Tiger rag / Jitterbug waltz / Little bit of blues, A / How's the world treating you / In the pines (medley) / Michelle: Chet's tune.
LP: PL 12503
MC: PK 12503

MAN AND HIS GUITAR, A.
LP: NL 89160
MC: NK 89160

ME AND MY GUITAR.
Tracks: / Cascade / West Memphis serenade / Long long ago / All thumbs / Vincent / Me and my guitar / Struttin' / You'd be nice to come home to / David's dance / Song for Anna, A (Chanson pour Anna) / My little waltz.
LP: PL 12405

NASHVILLE GOLD.
LP: 26 21233

NECK AND NECK (Atkins, Chet & Mark Knopfler).
Tracks: / Poor boy blues / Sweet dreams / There'll be some changes made / Just one time / So soft / Your goodbye / Yakety axe / Tears / Tahitian skys / I'll see you in my dreams / Next time I'm in town, The.
LP: 4674351
MC: 4674354

OTHER CHET ATKINS, THE.
LP: RD 27194

PICKS ON THE BEATLES.
Tracks: / I feel fine / Yesterday / If I fell / Can't buy me love / I'll cry instead / Things we said today / Hard day's night, A / I'll follow the sun / She's a woman / And I love her / Michelle / She loves you.
LP: NL 12002

SAILS.
Tracks: / Sails / Why worry / Sometime, someplace / Up in my treehouse / Waltz for the lonely / Laffin' at life / On a roll / My song / Wobegon (the way it used to be).
LP: 4505041
MC: 4505044

SOLID GOLD GUITAR.
Tracks: / White silver sands / Never on Sunday / Freight train / Wheels / Banana boat song / Tammy / Vaya con dios / Blowin' in the wind / Spanish Harlem / Yesterday / Hard day's night, A / And I love her / Things we said today / Love letters / I love how you love me / Sleepwalk / Calcutta / Exodus / Summers place, Theme from) / Stranger on the shore.
MC: INTK 9008

STAY TUNED.
Tracks: / Sunrise / Please stay tuned / Quiet eyes / Mouse in the house, A / Some leather and lace / Cricket ballet, The / Cosmic square dance / Boot and the stone, The / Tap room / If I should lose you.
LP: CBS 26265
MC: 40 26265

STREET DREAMS (Atkins, Chet C.G.P.).
Tracks: / Spat 'n' hats / Crystal in the light, The / Official beach music, The / Street dreams / Stay a little longer (if you'll) / Classical gas / Last farewell, The / Alisha / Homecoming anthem, The / Honolulu blues.
LP: CBS 26855
MC: 40 26855

WORK IT OUT.
Tracks: / Warm up medley / Grandfather's clock / Jubilo / Swanee river/Humoresque / Climbing up the golden stairs / Goodnight Irene / Walk me home / Strolling medley / Bicycle built for two / Farewell blues / Bye bye blues / Bouree / Streak / Walk don't run / Chase, The / In the good old summertime / Tara's theme / Cross country medley / Take me home country roads / Jersey bounce / On the street where you live / Physical / Army Air Corp song, The / Harlequin romance.
LP: CBS 24345

Atkins, Pete

ESSENTIAL PETE ATKINS.
Tracks: / Thirty year man / Master of the revels / Sunlight gate / Between us there is nothing / Girl on the train / Faded mansion on the hill, The / Wristwatch for a drummer / I see the joker / Perfect moment / Sessionman's blues / Thief in the night / Screen freak / Flowers and the wine.
LP: PL 25041

Atkinson, Lisle

MIDNIGHT CREEPER (See Simmons,Norman/Lisle Atkinson/Al Harewood) (Atkinson, Lisle/Norman Simmons/Al Harewood).

Atkinson, Rowan

LIVE IN BELFAST.
Tracks: / Man in seat 23c / Sir Marcus Browning MP / Mary Jane / I hate the French / Interval announcement / Do bears sha la la / Senator Brea / Devil, The / Impatient man in queue behind student / Joke / Wedding / Station announcement.
LP: SPART 1150
MC: TCART 1150

NOT JUST A PRETTY FACE.
Tracks: / Gobble D. Gook / Tom, Dick and Harry / Vicar's point / Perkins intro / Fatal beatings / 37-0 / I believe / Indian waiter / Madonna / Awards / Zak / Fish / CND / Peace camp / Perkins outro / Cana / Nasty end, A.
LP: POLD 5217
MC: POLDC 5217

VERY BEST OF ROWAN ATKINSON, THE (LIVE).
MC: LAFFC 1

Atkinson, 'Sweet Pea'

DON'T WALK AWAY.
MC: 842 684 4
LP: 842 684 1

Atlain

LIVING IN THE DARK.
LP: SKULL 8365

Atlan, Pierre

HOTTER THAN THAT (Atlan, Pierre & Piccadilly Revellers).
LP: SOS 1181

Atlanta

ATLANTA.
Tracks: / Can't you hear that whistle blow / She will / Dancin' on the Bayou / Long ago shoes / We're history / Why not tonight / She's the best friend I've ever had / One jump ahead of the storm / My sweet-eyed Georgia girl / Good time chariot.
LP: IMCA 5576

PICTURES.
Tracks: / Dixie dreaming / Wishful drinkin' / Pictures / Sweet was our rose / Blue side of the grey / Atlanta burned again last night / Sweet country music / But Alabama (nothing left between us) / You are the wine / Long cool woman in a black dress.
LP: IMCA 5463
LP: MCF 3216
MC: MCFC 3216

Atlanta Blues...

ATLANTA BLUES 1933 (Various artists).
LP: JEMF 106

Atlanta Brass ...

SONIC FIREWORKS V1 (See under Morris, Richard) (Atlanta Brass Ensemble/Richard Morris).

SONIC FIREWORKS V2 (See under Morris, Richard) (Atlanta Brass Ensemble/Richard Morris).

Atlanta Gospel

ATLANTA GOSPEL (Various artists).
Tracks: / I don't...: *Peach, Georgia & Reliables* / Open up: *Reliable Jubilee Singers* / God shall wipe all tears away: *Reliable Jubilee Singers* / On Mount Olive: *National Independent Gospel Singers* / I got it right: *National* Independent Gospel Singers / Evening sun: *Echoes Of Zion* / Keep still: *Echoes Of Zion* / Awful day will...: *Starlight Spiritual Singers* / Tone the bell easy: *Five Trumpets* / I can see: *Five Trumpets* / Ten commandments: *Five Trumpets* / Bread of heaven: *Five Trumpets* / My chains fell off: *Five Trumpets* / Servant's prayer: *Five Trumpets* / Stand by me: *Five Trumpets* / How I got over: *Five Trumpets.*
LP: HT 312

Atlanta Rhythm Section

BEST OF THE ATLANTA RHYTHM SECTION.
Tracks: / So in to you / Imaginary lover / Angel / Spooky / Doraville / Cocaine Charlie / Georgia rhythm / I'm not gonna let it bother me tonight / Do it or die.
LP: 2391 535
MC: 3177 535
LP: 2391 533

BOYS FROM DORAVILLE.
Tracks: / Cocaine Charlie / Next year's rock and roll / I ain't much / Putting my faith in love / Rough at the edges / Silver eagle / Pedestal / Try my love / Strictly rock and roll.
LP: 2391 467

QUINELLA.
Tracks: / Homesick / Quinella / Alien / Higher / You're so strong / Outlaw music / Pretty girl / Southern exposure / Going to Shangri La.
LP: CBS 85230

RED TAPE.
LP: 2391 223

UNDERDOG.
Tracks: / Do it or die / Born ready / I hate the blues / Let's go get stoned / Indigo passions / While time is left / It's only music / Spooky / My song.
LP: 2391 398

Atlantic 1

ATLANTIC 1 (Various artists).
LP: HRLP 705

Atlantic City (film)

ATLANTIC CITY (Film soundtrack) (Various artists).
LP: DRG 6104
MC: DRGC 6104
LP: SL 6104

Atlantic Family

ATLANTIC FAMILY LIVE AT MONTREUX, THE (Various artists).
Tracks: / Bahia (na baixa do sapateiro): *Various artists* / Jadoo: *Various artists* / Everything must change: *Various artists* / McEwans export: *Various artists* / One to one: *Various artists* / Pick up the pieces: *Various artists.*
LP: K 60136

Atlantic (Label)

AGE OF ATLANTIC, THE (Various artists).
Tracks: / Comin' home: *Delaney & Bonnie* / Tonight: *M.C.5* / Black hearted woman: *Allman Brothers* / Survival: *Yes* / I'm a good woman: *Cold Blood* / Whole lotta love: *Led Zeppelin* / Termination: *Iron* Butterfly / Last time, The: *Dada* / Communication breakdown: *Led Zeppelin* / Wash mama wash: *Dr. John*/ Need love: *Vanilla Fudge* / Broken arrow: *Buffalo Springfield.*
LP: K 20011

ATLANTIC BLUES (Various artists).
LP: K 781 713 1
MC: K 781 713 4

ATLANTIC BLUES: GUITAR (Various artists).
Tracks: / Broke down engine: *McTell, Blind Willie* / Shake 'em on down: *McDowell, Mississippi Fred* / My baby don't love me: *Hooker, John Lee* / Tall pretty woman: *McGhee, Stick* / Blues rock: *Brown, Texas Johnny*/ There goes the blues: *Brown, Texas Johnny* / Bongo boogie: *Brown, Texas Johnny* / Two bones and a pick: *Walker,* T-Bone / Mean old world: *Walker, T-Bone* / Let me know: *Norris, Chuck* / It hurts to love someone: *Guitar* Slim / Down through the years: *Guitar Slim* / Okie dokie stomp: *Dupree, Cornell* / Blues nocturne: *Dupree,* Cornell / T.V. mama: *Turner, Big Joe* / Reconsider baby: *King, Al* / Midnight midnight: *Baker, Mickey*/ I smell trouble: *Turner, Ike & Tina* / Why I sing the blues: *King, Albert* / Crosscut saw: *King, Albert*/ Angels of mercy: *King, Albert* / Can't be satisfied: *Hammond, John* / Flood down in Texas: *Vaughan, Stevie Ray.*
LP: UNKNOWN

ATLANTIC BLUES: PIANO (Various artists).
Tracks: / Yancey special: *Yancey, Jimmy* / Talkin' boogie: *Montgomery, Little Brother* / Mournful blues: *Yancey,* Jimmy / Farish street jive: *Montgomery, Little Brother* / Salute to pinetop: *Yancey, Jimmy* / Vicksburg blues: *Montgomery, Little Brother* / Shave 'em dry: *Yancey, Jimmy* / Frankie and Johnny: *Walker, T-Bone* / T B blues: *Walker, T-Bone* / Strollin': *Walker, T-Bone* / Boogie woogie: *Professor Longhair* / Tipitina: *Professor Longhair* / Blue sender: *Walls, Van* / After midnight: *Walls, Van* / Roll 'em Pete: *Turner,* Big Joe / Fore day rider: *McShann, Jay* / Cherry red: *Turner, Big* / My chile: *McShann, Jay* / Cow cow blues: *Atlantic...* / Albert's blues: *Lewis, Meade Lux* / Honky tonk train blues: *Lewis, Meade Lux*/ Ray's blues: *Charles, Ray* / Low society: *Charles, Ray* / Bit of soul, A: *Charles, Ray* / Hey bartender: *Dixon, Floyd* / Floyd's blues: *Dixon, Floyd* / After hours blues: *Brown, Texas Johnny* / Junco partner: *Jordan, Louis* / I don't know: *Mabon, Willie.*
LP: UNKNOWN

ATLANTIC BLUES: VOCALISTS (Various artists).
Tracks: / You got to know how: *Wallace,* Sippie / Suitcase blues: *Wallace, Sippie* / Mighty tight woman: *Wallace,* Sippie / How long blues: *Witherspoon, Jimmy* / In the evening: *Witherspoon, Jimmy* / Gimme a pigfoot and a bottle of beer: *Various artists* / Make me a pallet on the floor: *Yancey, Mama* / St. Louis blues: *Turner,* Big Joe / Oke-she-moke-she-pop: *Turner, Big Joe* / I've got that feeling: *Green, Lil* / Destination love: *Harris, Wynonie* / Tell a whale of a tale: *Harris, Wynonie* / Rain is a bringdown: *Brown, Ruth* / R.B. blues: *Brown, Ruth* / I don't want to be president: *Mayfield, Percy* / Nothing stays the same: *Mayfield, Percy*/ River's invitation: *Taylor, Ted* / Just like a fish: *Phillips, Esther* / Pouring water on a drowning man: *Clay, Otis* / Did you ever love a woman: *Thomas, Rufus* / Baby girl (parts 1 & 2): *Turner, Titus* / Ain't that lovin' you: *Bland, Bobby* / It's my own tears that's being wasted: *Copeland, Johnny* / Cheatin' woman: *Holmes, Eldridge*/ I had a dream: *Various artists* / Takin' another mans place: *Franklin, Aretha* / It's a hang up baby: *Hill, Z.Z.* / Home ain't home at suppertime: *Hill, Z.Z..*
LP: UNKNOWN

ATLANTIC HONKERS (Various artists).
LP: 81666

ATLANTIC JAZZ (Various artists).
Tracks: / Bourbon Street Parade: *Barbarin, Paul* / Burgundy Street Blues:

Lewis, George / My bucket's got a hole in it: *Robinson, Jim* / Cielito Lindo: *De Paris, Wilbur* / Salty dog: *Lewis, George* / Eh la bas: *Barbarin,* Paul / Maple leaf rag: *Murphy, Turk* / Eureka brass band, The: *Avery, Joe's Blues* / Nobody knows the way I feel this morning: *Miller, Ernest 'Punch'* / Shreveport Stomp: *De Paris, Wilbur* / Sing on: *Barbarin, Paul* / Shake it and break it: *Pierce, Joseph 'De De'* / Tiger rag: *Miller, Ernest 'Punch'* / You're driving me crazy: *Turner, Big Joe* / Lamp is low, The: *Dickenson, Vic* / Hootie blues: *McShann, Jay* / E flat boogie: *Smith,* Buster / Confessin' the blues: *McShann, Jay* / Jumpin' at the woodside: *McShann, Jay* / Until the real thing comes along: *Turner, Big Joe* / Undecided: *McShann, Jay* / Evenin': *Walker, T-Bone* / Buster's tune: *Smith,* Buster / Piney Brown blues: *Turner, Big Joe* / Our love is here to stay: *Turner, Big Joe* / Evidence: *Blakey, Art/Jazz* Messengers/Thelonious Monk / Bebop: *Blakey, Art/Jazz Messengers/ Thelonious Monk* / Koko: *Stitt, Sonny*/ Salt peanuts: *Jones, Philly Joe* / Almost like me: *Roach, Max* / Allen's alley: *Roach, Max* / Sa-Frantic: *Safranski, Eddie* / Not really the blues: *Rogers, Shorty* / Paradox: *Montrose, Jack* / Cheremoya: *Candoli,* Conte / Blues way up high: *Rogers, Shorty* / Song is you, The: *Giuffre, Jimmy* / Topsy: *Giuffre, Jimmy*/ Triplin' awhile: *Mitchell, Red & Harold Land* / You name it: *Manne, Shelly* / I'll be seeing you: *Fruscella,* Tony / Ain't misbehavin': *Charles, Ray* / Stuffy: *Hawkins, Coleman & Milt Jackson* / Django: *Hawkins,* Coleman & Milt Jackson / Daphne: *Grappelli, Stephane* / Perdido: *Ellington, Duke* / Embraceable you: *Farmer,* Art / Four brothers: *Herman, Woody* / Everything happens to me: *Sullivan, Ira* / Speedy reeds: *Clarke-Boland* Big Band / Lydian M-1: *Tentet, Charles 'The Teddy'* / I can't get started: *Konitz, Lee* / Bag's groove: *MJQ* with Sonny Rollins, The / This 'n' that: *Jazz Modes, The* / Giant steps: *MJQ with Sonny Rollins, The* / Sister salvation: *Slide Hampton Octet, The* / White sand: *Freeman, Von* / Misty: *Hubbard, Freddie* / Thoroughbred: *Evans, Gil* / Hard times (no one knows better than I): *Charles, Ray* / I want a little girl: *Turner, Big*/ T'aint nobody's business if I do: *De Paris, Wilbur* / Have you met Miss Jones: *Monney, Joe* / Empty bed blues: *Various artists* / I can dream, can't I: *Brown, Ruth* / Any time: *Coleman, Earl* / Crazy he calls me: *Hunter, Lurean* / Love is a word for the blues: *Richards, Ann* / Your mind is on vacation: *Various artists*/ Whisper not: *Hunter, Lurean* / T'aint nobody's business if I do: *Harrow, Nancy* / Desafinado: *Gilberto,* Joao / Good life: *Carter, Betty* / Salty papa blues: *Redd, Vi* / Confessin' the blues: *Phillips, Esther*/ There's no you: *Coleman, Earl* / I got it bad and that ain't good: *McRae* / Do nothing till you hear from me: *Hibbler, Al & Kirk Roland* / Moody's Mood: *Franklin, Aretha* / Don't let me be lonely tonight: *Lee, Peggy*/ Something: *Vaughan, Sarah* / Lonely woman: *Syms, Sylvia* / Sing joy Spring: *Manhattan Transfer* / Way you look tonight: *Garner, Erroll* / In the purple grotto: *Williams, Mary Lou* / Line up: *Tristano, Lennie*/ Celia: *Newborn, Phineas Jr.* / Sweet sixteen bars: *Charles, Ray* / In walked Bud: *Blakey, Art/Jazz Messengers/Thelonious* Monk / Delaunay's dilemma: *Lewis, John* / One for fun: *Taylor, Billy* / Night in Tunisia: *Hanna, Sir* Roland / Lazy bird: *Tyner, McCoy* / Nirvana: *Mann, Herbie* / Blues for five reasons: *Weston, Randy*/ Young soul: *Mitchell, Dwike* / My one and only love: *Zawinul, Joseph* / Sweet Georgia Brown: *Mance, Junior*/ Ein bahn strasse: *Hancock, Herbie* / Blues 2: *Bryant, Ray* / Pardon my rags: *Jarrett, Keith* / Koto song: *Brubeck, Dave* / Last year's lies and tomorrow's promises: *Pullen, Don* / Acorn: *Jamal, Ahmad* / State trooper: *Wright, Leo* / Think: *Scott, Shirley J.* / Twist city: *Griffin, Johnny* / Broasted or fried: *Wheeler, Clarence* / Wade in the water: *McDuff, Brother Jack* / How long blues: *Charles, Ray* / Comin' home baby: *Mann, Herbie* / Russell and Eliot: *Lateef, Yusef* / Burnin coal: *McCann, Les* / Listen here: *Ponty, Jean-Luc* / Compared to what: *McCann, Les* / You're the one: *Crawford, Hank* / Jive samba: *Adderley,* Nat / Money in the pocket: *Zawinul, Joseph* / Memphis soul stew: *Curtis, King* / Wednesday night prayer meeting: *Mingus, Charles* / Eventually: *Coleman, Ornette* / Cherryco: *Coleman, Ornette* / Countdown: *Coleman,* Ornette / Inflated tear, The: *Various artists* / Nonaah / Yoruba: *Laws, Hubert* / Tones for Joan's bones: *Corea, Chick* / In a silent way: *Zawinul, Joseph* / Standing outside: *Zawinul, Joseph* / Chega De Saudade: *Burton, Gary* / Fortune smiles: *Burton, Gary* / Freedom jazz dance: *Vitous, Miroslav* / Beaux J. Pooboo: *McCann, Les* / Quadrant 4: *Cobham, Billy* / Beneath the earth: *Mouzon, Alphonse* / Homunculus: *Passport*/ Egocentric molecules: *Ponty, Jean-Luc.*
LPS: . . . . **K 781 712 1**
MCSET: . . . . **K 781 712 4**

ATLANTIC MASTERS STARTRACKS, PART 1 (Various artists).
LP: . . . . **K 50732**

ATLANTIC MASTERS STARTRACKS, PART 2 (Various artists).
LP: . . . . **K 50733**

ATLANTIC R & B (1947-1974) (Various artists).
LPS: **781 620-1**
MCSET: **781 620-4**

BLACK ATLANTIC 45'S 1965-67 (Various artists).
Tracks: / Record, The: *King, Ben E.* / I'm gonna run away from you: *Lynn, Tammi* / Outside world, The: *Drifters*/ Just say goodbye: *Phillips, Esther* / Scratchy: *Wammack, Travis* / Philly dog: *Mar Keys* / Smokey Joe's la-la: *Rene, Googie* / Love makes the world go round: *Jackson, Deon* / Can't you see you're losing me: *Wells, Mary* / There's no place to hide: *King, Ben E.* / Candy: *Astors* / Dear lover: *Wells, Mary.*
LP: . . . . **ATLM 123**

HIT SINGLES 1958-1977 (Various artists).
Tracks: / Splish splash: *Darin, Bobby* / Mack the knife: *Darin, Bobby* / Deep purple: *Tempo, Nino & April* Stevens / Good lovin': *Rascals* / Groovin': *Rascals* / Ride captain ride: *Blues Image* / Love the one you're with: *Stills, Stephen* / Lion sleeps tonight, The: *John, Robert* / Smokin' in the boys room: *Brownsville* Station / Pick up the pieces: *Average White Band* / Beat goes on: *Sonny & Cher* / For what it's worth: *Buffalo* Springfield / People got to be free: *Rascals* / I'd really love to see you tonight: *England Dan/John Ford Coley*/ Angel in your arms: *Hot....*
LP: . . . . **K 781 920 1**
MC: . . . . **K 781 920 4**

Atlantic R & B

ATLANTIC RECORDS HISTORY OF R&B VOCAL GROUPS (Various artists).
Tracks: / Sh'boom: *Chords* / Come back my love: *Cardinal (film)* / Devil or angel: *Clovers, The* / She's mine all mine: *Royal Jokers, The* / Adorable: *Drifters* / Smokey Joe's cafe: *Robins, The* / Ruby baby: *Drifters* / Fools fall in love: *Drifters* / Yes sir that's my baby: *Sensations featuring Yvonne Mills, The*/ Please me disc jockey: *Sensations featuring Yvonne Mills, The* / Mr. Lee: *Bobbettes* / Down in Mexico: *Coasters, The.*
LP: **790 132-1**

Atlantic Soul

ATLANTIC SOUL BALLADS (Various artists).
Tracks: / Try a little tenderness: *Redding, Otis* / I say a little prayer: *Franklin, Aretha* / Save the last dance for me: *Drifters* / I'm in love: *Pickett, Wilson* / Warm and tender love: *Sledge, Percy* / Patches: *Carter,* Clarence / Thin line between love and hate: *Persuaders* / Spanish Harlem: *King, Ben E.* / When something is wrong with my baby: *Sam & Dave* / My girl: *Redding, Otis* / Love won't let me wait: *Harris, Major* / On Broadway: *Drifters* / Baby I'm yours: *Lewis, Barbara* / Rainy night In Georgia: *Benton, Brook* / Hey Jude: *Pickett, Wilson.*
LP: . . . . **WX 98**
MC: . . . . **WX 98 C**

ATLANTIC SOUL CLASSICS (Various artists).
Tracks: / Sweet soul music: *Conley, Arthur* / In the midnight hour: *Pickett, Wilson* / Knock on wood: *Floyd,* Eddie / Soul man: *Sam & Dave* / Respect: *Franklin, Aretha* / See-saw: *Convoy, Don* / Everybody needs somebody to love: *Burke, Solomon* / Soul finger: *Bar-Kays* / Stand by me: *King, Ben E.* / B-A-B-Y: *Thomas,* Carla / Under the boardwalk: *Drifters* / Tramp: *Redding, Otis & Carla Thomas* / Green onions: *Booker* T & The MGs / When a man loves a woman: *Sledge, Percy* / Tribute to a king, A: *Bell, William* / (Sittin' on) the dock of the bay: *Redding, Otis.*
LP: . . . . **WX 105**
MC: . . . . **WX 105 C**

Atlantic Starr

ALL IN THE NAME OF LOVE.
Tracks: / One lover at a time / You belong with me / Females / Don't take me for granted / Always / Let the sun in / Thankful / All in the name of love (Only on 12" version.) / My mistake / Interlude.
LP: . . . . **WX 115**
MC: . . . . **WX 115 C**

AS THE BAND TURNS.
Tracks: / Freak-a-ristic / Cool, calm, collected / One love / In the heart of passion / If your heart isn't in it / Silver shadow / Let's start it over / Secret lovers / Thank you.
LP: . . . . **AMA 5019**
MC: . . . . **AMC 5019**

BEST OF ATLANTIC STARR, THE.
Tracks: / Circles / Silver shadow / Send for me / Secret lovers / Love me down / Stand up / When love calls / Am I dreaming / Touch a four leaf clover / One love / Gimme your lovin' / If your heart isn't in it.
LP: . . . . **AMA 5141**
MC: . . . . **AMC 5141**

BRILLIANCE.
LP: . . . . **AMLH 64883**

RADIANT.
Tracks: / When love calls / Does it matter / Think about that / Send for me / Mystery girl / Am I dreaming? / Under pressure / My turn now.
LP: . . . . **AMLH 64833**

STRAIGHT TO THE POINT.
Tracks: / Rock'n'roll / Kissin' power / Let the spirit move ya / Straight to the point / Bullseye / What'cha feel inside / Fallin' in love with you / Losin' you.
LP: . . . . **AMLH 64764**

YOURS FOREVER.
Tracks: / Yours forever / Four leaf clover / More more more / I want your love / Second to none / Island dreams / Who could love you better / More time for me / Trying.
LP: . . . . **AMLX 64948**
MC: . . . . **CXM 64948**

Atlantis

ATLANTIS.
LP: **6360 609**
MC: **7149 002**

Atmosfear

FIRST/FOURMOST.
LP: . . . . **ATM 33**

Atmospheres

ATMOSPHERES Software compilation (Various artists).
LP: **26795**
MC: **40 26795**

Atom Gods

WOW.
LP: . . . . **GWLP 30**

Atom Kraft

CONDUCTORS OF NOIZE.
Tracks: / Requiem / Total metal / Queen of death / Vision of Belshazzar / Foliage / Rich bitch / Tutonic pain / Demolition.
LP: . . . . **NEAT 1041**

FUTURE WARRIORS.
Tracks: / Future warriors / Starchild / Dead man's hand / Total metal / Pour the metal in / Death valley / Warzones / Burn in hell / Heat and pain / This planet's burning.
LP: . . . . **NEAT 1028**

Atom Seed

GET IN LINE.
LP: . . . . **HMRLP 163**
MC: . . . . **HMRMC 163**

Atomic Cafe (film)

ATOMIC CAFE (Film Soundtrack) (Various artists).
LP: . . . . **ROUNDER 1034**
MC: . . . . **ROUNDER 1034C**

Atomic Rooster

ATOMIC ROOSTER.
Tracks: / They took control of you / She's my woman / He did it again / Where's the show? / In the shadows / Do you know who's looking for you / Don't lose your mind / Watch out I can't stand it / Lost in space.
LP: . . . . **CHC 58**
LP: . . . . **CAS 1010**
LP: . . . . **EMC 3341**

BEST OF AND THE REST OF, THE.
Tracks: / Banstead / Winter / Breakthrough / Decision/ Indecision / Devil's answer / Spoonful of bromide helps the pulse rate go down, A / Black snake / Head in the sky / Tomorrow night / Break the ice.
MC: . . . . **ARLC 1001**

BEST OF ATOMIC ROOSTER.
LP: . . . . **DMLP 1020**

DEATH WALKS BEHIND YOU.
Tracks: / Death walks behind you / Vug / Tomorrow night / 7 streets / Sleeping for years / I can't take no more / Nobody else / Gershatzer.
LP: . . . . **CAS 1026**

DEVIL HITS BACK, THE.
LP: . . . . **DMLP 1023**

DEVILS' ANSWER.
LP: . . . . **RRLD 003**

HEADLINE NEWS.
Tracks: / Hold your fire / Headline news / Taking a chance / Metal minds / Land of freedom / Machine / Dance of death / Carnival / Time.
LP: . . . . **TOWLP 004**
MC: . . . . **ZCTOW 004**

HOME TO ROOST.
Tracks: / Death walks behind you / V.U.G. / Seven streets / Sleeping for years / Can't take no more / Nobody else / Friday the 13th / And so to bed / Broken wings / Before tomorrow / Banstead / Winter / Breakthrough / Decision/ Indecision / Devils answer / Black snake / Head in the sky / Spoonful of bromide helps the pulse rate go down, A / Tomorrow night / Break the ice.
2LP: . . . . **RAWLP 027**
MCSET: . . . . **RAWTC 027**
2LP: . . . . **CRD 2**

IN HEARING OF ATOMIC ROOSTER.
Tracks: / Breakthrough / Break the ice / Decision/ Indecision / Spoonful of bromide, A / Helps the pulse rate go down / Devil's answer / Black snake / Head in the sky / Rock, The / Price, The.
LP: . . . . **PEG 1**
LP: . . . . **EKS 74109**

Atra

ATRA 10 TRACK (Various artists).
LP: . . . . **ATRA 1010**

Atrocity

HALLUCINATIONS.
LP: . . . . **NB 038**

INFECTED.
LP: . . . . **CORE 3**

Atrophy

SOCIALIZED HATE.
LP: . . . . **RR 9518 1**

VIOLENT BY NATURE.
Tracks: / Puppies and friends / Violent by nature / In their eyes / Too late to change / Slipped through the cracks / Forgotten but not gone / Process of elimination / Right to die / Things change.
LP: . . . . **RO 9450 1**
MC: . . . . **RO 9450 4**

A.T.'s

A.T.'S.
Tracks: / Sand in my face / Heart moves / Me and Rio / It's over / Thirty wasted years / Crime of passion / Leaving lonely / Hot shot / Come 'ere / Action man / Go / Too young girl / Way of the world / 54/ 46 (was my number) / One more for the road.
LP: . . . . **ALTO 104**

Attack

ATTACK.
Tracks: / Don't wind me up / Time slipped away / Maybe I've been fooling / Take 'em back / Girl it's you / I'm in danger / If only I could find a way / Don't you believe in magic / Stay / Why can't we talk it over / Don't let the world run out of love.
LP: . . . . **LIMLP 1**

ZOMBIES.
LP: . . . . **PUNK 6**

Attack From ...

ATTACK FROM DOWNUNDA (Various artists).
LP: . . . . **RRLP 103**
MC: . . . . **RRLC 103**

Attack of the...

ATTACK OF THE KILLER B'S (32 Stinging Classics from the Archives of Pop) (Various artists).
Tracks: / Ready teddy: *Little Richard* / R.O.C.K.: *Haley, Bill* / My blue heaven: *Domino, Fats* / It'll be me: *Lewis, Jerry Lee* / Words of love: *Holly, Buddy* / Cut across Shorty: *Cochran, Eddie* / Let it rock: *Berry, Chuck* / You can't judge a book: *Diddley, Bo* / Ebony eyes: *Everly Brothers* / Bachelor boy: *Richard, Cliff* / Walkin' with my angel: *Vee, Bobby* / Kelly: *Shannon, Del* / As long as I live: *Sedaka,* Neil / Midnight: *Shadows* / Gloria: *Them* / My colouring book: *Springfield, Dusty* / Only love can break a heart: *Pitney, Gene* / I don't want to go on without you: *Drifters* / Love potion No. 9: *Searchers*/ Where have all the good times gone: *Kinks* / Talkin' 'bout you: *Animals* / Time is on my side: *Moody Blues*/ Silence is golden: *Four Seasons* / Can't you hear my heartbeat: *Herman's Hermits* / I'm not your stepping stone: *Monkees* / Hey Gyp, dig the slowness: *Donovan* / Wouldn't it be nice: *Beach Boys* / Intro and the outro, The: *Bonzo Dog Band* / Still I'm sad: *Yardbirds* / My girl: *Mamas & Papas* / Night they drove old Dixie down: *Band* / Girl of my best friend: *Presley, Elvis.*
2LP: . . . . **REQ 739**

MCSET: ZCF 739

Attacker

BATTLE AT HELMS DEEP.
LP: RR 9750

Attaco Decente

BABY WITHIN US MARCHES ON.
Tracks: / Will of one, The / Fear of freedom / Don't join their army / Bully, The / Natural anger / Dad was God / There comes a time / Middle ages, The / Rose grower, The / Baby within us marches on, The.
LP: AON 002
MC: AONC 002

UNITED KINGDOM OF AMERICA.
LP: AON 001

Attar, Bachir

IN NEW YORK (Attar, Bachir & Elliot Sharp).
LP: EMY 114

Atte

SONDELA.
LP: CC 25
MC: 4CC 25

Atterson, Alex

PUSHING THE BUSINESS ON.
Tracks: / Johnny Alleluia / Three masts / O Billy do you hear that bell / Nelson Gardens / Hawthorn white / Billy medal's / Two corbies, The / Reaper, The / Wimbledon wag / In the wee midnight hour / Pass the bottle round.
LP: PLR 005

Attila The Stockbroker

LIBYAN STUDENTS FROM HELL.
Tracks: / Libyan students / I'm so miserable / Ballad of Comrade Enver, The / Rapping mole / Radio rap / Airstrip 1 / Green fields of France / Another country / Glanzende's empire.
LP: PLASLP 009

RANTING AT THE NATION.
Tracks: / Night I slept with seething wells, The / Contributory negligence / Nigel wants to go to C&A's / Albanian football / Perils of stealing half a bottle of wine, The / They must be Russians / Russians in the DHSS / Russians in MacDonalds / Oracle, The / Death in Bromley / Bang and a Wimpey, A / Nigel wants to go and see Depeche Mode / Russians at the Henley Regatta / Russians on the centre court / Fifth column / Fall of King Zog, The / Holiday in Albania / Burn it down / England are back (Luxembourg where are you) / Where you goin' with that flounder? / Hands off our halibuts / Flappin' in the wind / Gentlemen o' the wrist / Eros products commercial / Spencer's croft cat, The (dead cat strut) / Very silly East European propaganda station / Fall of King Zog, The (reprise) / Aw ayday.
LP: ARED 46

SAWDUST AND EMPIRE.
Tracks: / March of the Levellers / Sawdust and empire / Alone in the Sidco / Recession / Spare a thought / Nigel's revenge / Holiday in Albania (GJI Rokastra folk festival version.) / Boadicea uber alles / Factory gods / Midas the grand / Ghosts of the leveller s.
LP: GRAM 13

SCORNFLAKES.
LP: PROBE 20

Attilla & The Huns

UNDER THE BODHI TREE.
LP: MMLP 028

Attitude

GOOD, THE BAD AND THE OBNOXIOUS, THE.
LP: WEBITE 28
LP: 601261

KEIN SCHLAF BIS DEUTSHLAND.
LP: WEBITE 21
LP: 601240

Attitude Adjustment

AMERICAN PARANOIA.
Tracks: / Grey world / Dope friend / Hunger and poverty / Fu*k Chuck / Dead serious / Johnny / Attitude adjustment / DSFA / American paranoia / Warfear / Streetwise / Working class pride / In the centre / Bombs / Rambo / Incredible end.
LP: PUS 0012-11

NO MORE MR. NICE GUY.
LP: FACE 12

Attitudes

GOOD NEWS.
Tracks: / Being here with you / Drink my water / Sweet Summer music / Let's talk turkey / Foster frees / Turning in space / Change / In a stranger's arms / Manual dexterity / Promise me the moon / Good news.

LP: K 56385

Attractions

MAD ABOUT THE WRONG BOY.
Tracks: / Arms race / Damage / Little Miss Understanding / Straight jacket / Mad about the wrong boy / Motorworld / On the third stroke / Slow patience / La la la la loved you / Single girl / Lonesome little town / Taste of poison / High rise housewife / Talk about me / Sad about girls / Camera, camera.
LP: FIEND 25
MC: XXC 8
LP: XXLP 8

Attrition

ACTION AND REACTION.
MC: ARR 012

AT THE FIFTIEST GATE.
LP: ANT 078

ATTRITION OF REASON, THE.
Tracks: / Day I was born / Behind innocence, lies / Redoubt of light, The / Decline, The / You will remember nothing / Prayer for the head / Beast of burden / Prayer for the head (version).
LP: TMLP 6

DEATH HOUSE.
MC: ARR 011
LP: HAM 18

IN THE REALM OF THE ANGRY GHOSTS.
Tracks: / Vigil / Into the waves / In your band / Surge and sun / Marianne's dream / Dream sleep / Last refuge, The / Beginning of the end.
LP: TMLP 14

SMILING, AT THE HYPOGANDA CLUB.
Tracks: / Look out, Hedonist / Game is up, The / Feel the backlash / Mind drop / Pendulum turns / Fusillade (part 1) / Fusillade (part 2) / Hallucinator / My eyes / Fate is smiling.
LP: TMLP 13

Atwell, Winifred

AROUND THE WORLD OF WINIFRED ATWELL IN EIGHTY TUNES.
MC: KCSP 256

IT'S RAGTIME.
Tracks: / Raggin' the scale / Entertainer, The / Kitten on the keys / Glad rag / Russian rag / Jubilee rag / Doll dance / Maple leaf rag / Black and white rag / Down yonder / Hunting rag / Flirtation rag / South Rampart Street parade / Grizzly bear rag / Dizzy fingers / Vamp, The / Rialto ripples / Steamboat rag / Flapper rag / Temptation rag.
LP: NL 70258
MC: NK 70258
LP: INTS 5119

PIANO PARTY.
Tracks: / Poor people of Paris, The / Plink plank plunk / Flirtation waltz / Maple leaf rag / Britannia rag / Left bank / Cross hands boogie / Twelfth St. Rag / Coronation rag / Jubilee rag / Port au Prince / Summer of the seventeenth doll / Dixie boogie / Black and white rag / Piano party.
LP: TAB 80

SEVEN RAGS, SEVEN BOOGIES.
LP: ECS 2176

WINIFRED ATWELL.
Tracks: / Cross hands boogie / Dixie boogie / Tattoo samba / Swanee River boogie / Big Ben boogie / Bounce the boogie / Bumble boogie / Hamp's boogie woogie.
LP: 6495 125
MC: 7195 125

WINIFRED ATWELL PLAYS 50 ALL-TIME GREATS.
Tracks: / On your toes / It's de-lovely / I won't dance / Goody goody / Shall we dance / April in Portugal / Wish you were here / C'est magnifique / I talk to the trees / Cherry pink and apple blossom white / Bewitched / I couldn't sleep a wink last night / Bill / Can't help lovin' dat man / Californ-I-Ay / Falling in love with love / It's a grand night for singing / Best things in life are free, The / Look for the silver lining / Lady is a tramp, The / I love Paris / My heart belongs to daddy / How high the moon / I whistle a happy tune / People will say we're in love / Bluebird of happiness / Harry Lime theme / Life is just a bowl of cherries / Blueberry hill / It might as well be spring / Young and foolish / Room 504 / Sea, The / Darn ya smile, The / Smoke gets in your eyes / Lovely to look at / Long ago (and far away) / Dearly beloved / Good morning / June is bustin' out all over / Pedro the fisherman / We'll gather lilacs / Make believe / How are things in Glocca Morra / This is my lovely day / Some enchanted evening.
LP: PLE 508
MC: TC-PLE 508

WINIFRED ATWELL'S PIANO PARTY.
Tracks: / Carolina in the morning / Get out and get under the moon / Sleepy time gal / Chicago / Cecilia / My sweetie went away / Sweet Georgia Brown / Broadway melody / Lullaby of Broadway / Bye bye blues / Let's fall in love / After you've gone / I cried for you / By the light of the silvery moon / I'm sorry I made you cry / Darktown strutters' ball / Alexander's ragtime band / Bill Bailey won't you please come home? / My blue Heaven / Am I blue? / Some of these days / It had to be you / I'm sitting on top of the world / Crying for the Carolines / Tiptoe through the tulips / Me and my shadow / Them there eyes / Five foot two, eyes of blue / Dinah / Tisket a tasket, A / If you were the only girl in the world / I don't know why.
LP: FBLP 8088
MC: ZCFBL 8088

WINNIE'S PIANO PARTY.
Tracks: / Make it a party (medley) / Cross hands boogie / Bumble boogie / Johnson rag / Serenata (Moszkowski) / Make it a party (medley part 2) / Plink plank plunk / Let's have a ball (medley) / At the woodchopper's ball / Let's have a ball (medley part 2) / Let's rock 'n' roll (medley) / Black and white rag / Twelfth Street rag (Bowman) / Hamp's boogie woogie / Lazy train / Let's rock 'n' roll (medley part 2) / Brazillian rhapsody / I'll remember April / Britannia rag / Bewitched.
LP: PLE 531
MC: TC-PLE 531

Atwood, Margaret

POETRY AND VOICE OF MARGARET ATWOOD.
MC: CDL 51537

Au Bal Antillais

FRANCO-CREOLE BIGUINES FROM MARTINIQUE 1929-32.
LP: FL 9050

Au Pairs

LIVE IN BERLIN.
LP: AKA 6

PLAYING WITH A DIFFERENT SEX.
LP: HUMAN LP 1

SENSE AND SENSUALITY.
LP: KAM 010

Au Revoir Les...

AU REVOIR LES ENFANTS (Film soundtrack) (Various artists).
LP: 704.430
MC: C 704.430

Aubery, James (nar)

EIGHTEENTH EMERGENCY, THE (see under Eighteenth Emergency).

Aubrey, John (aut)

BRIEF LIVES (See under Brief Lives) (Dotrice, Roy (nar)).

Auburn Aires

BEDTIME STORIES.
LP: ROSE 164

ROOMFUL OF MONKEYS.
LP: ROSE 136

Auckland Dorian Choir

BLUEBIRD.
Tracks: / Bluebird / Be merry / Little road to Bethlehem, The / Holy boy, The / Behold the greater creator / Our lady's lullaby / My spirit sang all day / I praise the tender flower / I'll aye cai'in by yon toun / Feller from fortune / Ca' the yowes / I love my love / Bushes and briars / Oh what a beautiful city.
LP: SLC 145

Auclair, Philippe

THEME FORM OCEANONOX (See under 'Oceanonox').

Auden, W.H. (aut)

FOUR TWENTIETH CENTURY POETS (See under Four Twentieth (bk)) (Lewis, C. Day (nar)).

W.H. AUDEN READING.
MC: 1019

Audience

HOUSE ON THE HILL, THE.
Tracks: / Jackdaw / You're not smiling / I had a dream / Raviole / Eye to eye / I put a spell on you / House on the hill / Nanc y.
LP: CHC 4
MC: CHCMC 4

LUNCH.
Tracks: / Stand by the door / Seven sore bruises / Hula girl / Ain't the man you need / In accord / Barracuda Dan / Thunder and lightning / Party games / Trombone gulch / Buy me an island.
LP: CHC 36
MC: CHCMC 36

Audio 80's

AUDIO 80'S (Various artists).
Tracks: / I second that emotion: *Japan* / First picture of you, The: *Lotus Eaters* / You only left your picture: *Fashion* / Sister of mercy: *Thompson Twins* / Brilliant mind: *Furniture* / Hand on my heart: *Shriekback*/ Wicked ways: *Blow Monkeys* / Favourite shirts (boy meets girl): *Haircut 100* / Just got lucky: *Joboxers*/ John Wayne is big leggy: *Haysi Fantayzee* / I want candy: *Bow Wow Wow* / Freak: *Foxton, Bruce* / Silver mac: *Westworld* / Dance hall days: *Huang Chung* / My world: *Secret Affair.*
MC: 411299

Audio Two

WHAT MORE CAN I SAY.
Tracks: / Top billin' / What more can I say / When the two is on the mic / I like cherries / I don't care / Giz starts buggin' / Make it funky / Hickeys around my neck / Put it 2 music / Top billin' (inst) / Questions, The.
LP: K 790 907 1
MC: K 790 907 4

Audion Sampler

AUDION SAMPLER (Various artists).
LP: SYN 105
MC: SYNC 105

Audio/Visual

AUDIO/VISUAL (Abstract no.6) (Various artists).
LP: SAM 006

Auerbach, Loren

AFTER THE LONG NIGHT (Auerbach, Loren/Bert Jansch with Presence).
Tracks: / Rainbow man / Frozen beauty / Christabel / So lonely / Journey of the moon through sorrow.
LP: CRL 001
MC: CRL 001C

PLAYING THE GAME.
Tracks: / Carousel / Weeping willow blues / Give me love / I can't go back / Smiling faces / Yarrow / Playing the game / Is it real / Sorrow / Days and nights.
LP: CRL 002
MC: CRL 002C

Auf Wiedersehn Pet

AUF WIEDERSEHN PET (TV soundtrack) (Various artists).
LP: AUF 1
MC: ZCAUF 1

Aufray, Hughes

CHANTE DYLAN.
LP: 80553

Auger, Arleen

SONGS OF THE AUVERGNE (Arr. Joseph Canteloube) (Auger, Arleen/Yan Pascal Tortelier & ECO).
Tracks: / L'aio de rotso (part 1 of trois bourees) / Ound' onoren gorda (part 2 of trois bourees) / Obal, din lou limouzi (part 3 of trois bourees) / Pastourelle / Lou coucut / Jou l'pount d'o mirabel / Chut, chut / Lo folaire / La delaissado / Oi ayai / La pastrouletta e lou chibalie / Bailero / Postouro, se tu m'aymo / Brezairola / Lou boussu / Uno jionto postouro / Te l'co te / Malurous qu'o uno fenno.
LP: VC 7907141
MC: VC 7907144

Auger, Brian

ENCORE (Auger, Brian & Julie Tippetts).
Tracks: / Spirit / Don't let me be misunderstood / Git up / Freedom highway / Future pilot / Rope ladder to the moon / No time to live / Nothing will be as it was / Lock all the gates.
LP: K 56458

HAPPINESS HEARTACHES (Auger, Brian Oblivion Express).
Tracks: / Backstreet bible class / Spice Island / Gimme a funky break / Never gonna come down / Happiness heartaches / Got to be born again / Paging Mr. McCoy.
LP: K 56326

HERE AND NOW.
Tracks: / Hurricane / Call me / Happiness is just around the bend / Downtown hookup / Seeker, The / They say nothing lasts forever / Let's keep this love together / Heart of the hunter.
LP: 823 753-1
MC: 823 753-4

JAM SESSION (see under Page, Jimmy) (Auger, Brian/Jimmy Page/Sonny Boy Williamson).

LONDON 1964-1967 (Auger, Brian & Julie Driscoll).
Tracks: / I know you love me not / I don't to have to do it / If you should ever leave me / I don't know where you are / Shadows of you / Kiko / Foolkiller / Let's

do it tiger / Come back to Croydon / Own up Lady Astor.
LP: . . . . **CR 30019**

August, Joseph

ROCK MY SOUL (August, Joseph 'Mr. Google Eyes').
Tracks: / Rough and rocky road / No wine, no women / Life can be a hard road to travel / Love me / Play the game / For you my love / Strange things happening in the dark / Poppa stoppa's be bop blues / Young boy / Rock my soul / I'm glad you're comin' home / Oh what a fool / Rough and rocky road / I cried / Boogie with calypso.
LP: . . . . **KIX 32**

Aukauldren, Viv

OLD BAGS AND PARTY RAGS.
Tracks: / Life expectancy / Tanzil / As you wish / Flooding crowd space / Lost / Censored / Null / Catabolic blues.
LP: . . . . **R 33/8604**

Auld, Georgie

BY GEORGE - 1949 (Auld, Georgie & His Orchestra).
Tracks: / So what's new / Sweet thing / Nashooma / Lullaby in rhythm / They didn't believe me / Blues for me / Flying home / So what can be new? / You got me jumpin' / No no.
LP: . . . . **SWH 25**
MC: . . . . **CSWH 25**

GEORGIE AULD AND HIS ORCHESTRA, VOL.1 (1945).
LP: . . . . **MVS 501**

GEORGIE AULD AND HIS ORCHESTRA, VOL.2 (Auld, Georgie & His Orchestra/Sarah Vaughan).
Tracks: / You're blase / I don't know why / Just you, just me / Blue moon / Route 66 / Hundred years from today / Canyon passag e.
LP: . . . . **MVS 509**

HOMAGE.
LP: . . . . **XAN 190**

I'VE GOT YOU UNDER MY SKIN.
Tracks: / I've got you under my skin / S'posin / I cover the waterfront / I didn't know what time it was / Stairway to the stars, A / Body and soul / I don't stand a ghost of a chance with you / Take care / Smoke gets in your eyes / All the things you are / Someone to watch over me.
LP: . . . . **JASM 1006**

JUMP GEORGIE JUMP.
Tracks: / Short circuit / Mandrake root / Poinciana / Jivin with the jug / Yesterdays / I'll always be in love with you / Stompin' at the Savoy / Sentimental journey / Jump Georgie jump / I'm always chasing rainbows / I can't get started / Taps Miller / Concerto for tenor.
LP: . . . . **HEP 27**

Auld Meal Mill

AULD MEAL MILL (Various artists).
Tracks: / Buchan vet, The: *Lovie, Robert* / March strathspey and reel: *Geddes, Graham & His Band* / Duchess tree, The: *Mearns, John* / Auld maid in a garret, An: *Little Lynda* / Lewisvale waltz: *Geddes, Graham & His Band*/ After all these years: *Geddes, Graham* / Rathlin island: *Miller, Ina* / Jigs: *Geddes, Graham & His Band*/ Yellow on the broom, The: *Lovie, Robert* / Iain MacPhail's welcome to Scotland: *Geddes, Graham & His Band* / Valley where the Leven flows, The: *Little Lynda* / Village where I went to school: *Lovie, Robert* / When I grow too old to dream: *Geddes, Graham* / Jacqueline waltz: *Geddes, Graham & His Band* / Div ye mind?: *Miller, Ina*/ Tam's hunting horn: *Geddes, Graham & His Band* / Lassie lives by yonder burn, A: *Mearns, John*.
LP: . . . . **WGR 044**
MC: . . . . **CWGR 044**

AULD MEAL MILL, 1989 (Various artists).
Tracks: / Auld meal mill, The: *Mearns, John* / Gleniffer polka: *Geddes, Graham & His Band* / Cottage in the country: *Miller, Ina* / Touch of a master's hand: *Mearns, John* / Far o'er struie: *Turriff & District Pipe Band*/ Colin's cattle: *Turriff & District Pipe Band* / Pair o' nicky tams: *Turriff & District Pipe Band* / I'm lookin' for a bonnie lass tae love me: *Lovie, Robert* / Scapa flow: *Geddes, Graham* / Crags of tumbledown mountain: *Turriff &* District Pipe Band / J. K. Cairns: *Turriff & District Pipe Band* / Scotland the brave: *Turriff & District Pipe* Band / Rita's waltz: *Geddes, Graham & His Band* / Long island, The: *Miller, Ina* / Turkey in the straw: *Geddes,* Graham & His Band / Chicken reel: *Geddes, Graham & His Band* / Auchmithie: *Louie, Robert* / Sleep tight: *Mearns,* John / Earl of Errol: *Geddes, Graham & His Band* / Woo'ed, married and a': *Geddes, Graham & His Band* / Marchioness of Huntly's Jig, The: *Geddes, Graham & His Band* / Jim Kennedy's jig: *Geddes, Graham & His Band* / Trawler song, The: *Geddes, Graham* / Leaving Port Askaig: *Turriff & District Pipe Band* / Tenth Bn H.L.I.: *Turriff & District* Pipe Band / Crossing the Rhine: *Turriff & District Pipe Band* / Farewell to the creeks: *Turriff & District Pipe Band*.
MC: . . . . **CWGR 133**

Auld Reekie Dance Band

CAPITAL REELS.
Tracks: / Dashing white sergeant / Dashing white sergeant (encore) / Eightsome reel / Foursome reel / Scottish waltz / Hamilton House (jig) / Hamilton House (encore) / Duke of Perth, The (Broun's reel) / Duke of Perth, The (encore) / Strip the willow (jig) / Strip the willow (encore) / Duke and Duchess of Edinburgh, The (reel) / Duke and Duchess of Edinburgh, The (encore) / Gay Gordons / Scottish reform (jig) / Scottish reform (encore) / Reel of the 51st division / Reel of the 51st division (encore).
LP: . . . . **LILP 5190**
MC: . . . . **LICS 5190**

Auld Triangle

AULD TRIANGLE.
Tracks: / Old miner, The / Do you love an apple / Wee room, The / No man's land / Saturday's cowboys / Ryebuck shearers / Coal black faces / Now I'm easy / May, and might never / Leaving Nancy / B.U.D.G.I.E..
LP: . . . . **CAS LP 008**

Auldridge, Coleman

HIGH TIME (See Under Auldridge, Reid).

Auldridge, Mike

AN OLD DOG.
LP: . . . . **FLY 0004**

DOBRO.
Tracks: / Hillbilly hula / Tennessee stud / It's over / Pickaway / Rolling fog / Dobro island train 451-2 / Take me / Greensleeves / Silver threads / Rockbottom / Jamboree / House of the rising sun.
LP: . . . . **SNTF 657**

EIGHT STRING SWING.
Tracks: / Little rock getaway / Redskin rag / Bethesada / Swing scene / Caravan / Almost to Tulsa / Bluegrass boogie / Eight string swing / Brown's baggin' / Pete's place / Crazy red top.
LP: . . . . **SH 3725**
MC: . . . . **SH 3725 MC**

MIKE AULDRIDGE.
LP: . . . . **FLY 0003**
LP: . . . . **FF 029**

MIKE AULDRIDGE AND OLD DOG.
LP: . . . . **FF 054**

SLIDIN' SMOKE (Auldridge, Mike & Jeff Newman).
LP: . . . . **FF 080**

Auldridge, Reid

HIGH TIME (Auldridge, Reid & Coleman).
LP: . . . . **SH 3776**
MC: . . . . **SH 3776C**

Aungier, Cliff

FULL MOON.
LP: . . . . **ALP 001**

Auracle

AURACLE.
LP: . . . . **CHR 1172**
MC: . . . . **ZCHR 1172**

CITY SLICKERS.
LP: . . . . **CHR 1210**
MC: . . . . **ZCHR 1210**

Aural Wax

AURAL WAX (Various artists).
LP: . . . . **BAUL 601**

Aurra

DREAM.
Tracks: / Too much / Who are you / When I come home / In the mood / You're the only one / Got to get my lady back.
LP: . . . . **SALP 3**

LIKE I LIKE IT.
Tracks: / You and me tonight / Keep on dancing / Hooked on you / Talking in your sleep / Bedtime story / Like I like it (remixed version) / Living inside yourself / Happy feelings (remixed version) / I'll keep waiting / I love myself.
LP: . . . . **XID 7**
MC: . . . . **CXID 7**
LP: . . . . **DIX 12**

LIVE AND LET LIVE.
Tracks: / Live and let live / Such a feeling / Coming to get you / Undercover lover / Baby love / You can't keep on walking / One more time / Positive.
LP: . . . . **SA 8559**

SEND YOUR LOVE.
Tracks: / Nasty disposition / Send your love / Kingston lady / Forever / Are you single / Keep doin' it / Living too fast / Party time.
LP: . . . . **SALP 6**

Ausberg Orchestra

ACCORDION IN CONCERT (Ausberg Orchestra - Leader Marianne Probst).
Tracks: / Sinfonietta concertante / Dorische suite / Scherzino / Sinfonietta / Burleske auf eine speilmannweise.
LP: **099/027**

Ausgang

MANIPULATE.
LP: . . . . **WKFMLP 52**

Aussiebilly

AUSSIEBILLY (Various artists).
LP: . . . . **NERD 022**

Austen, Jane (Author)

EMMA (Scales, Prunella (nar)).
MCSET: . . . . **SAY 27**
MCSET: . . . . **ARGO 1109**

EMMA (Lapotaire, Jane).
MCSET: **CC/014**

EMMA VOL. 1 (Rees, Angharad (nar)).
MCSET: . . . . **ZBBC 1077**

EMMA VOL. 2 (Rees, Angharad (nar)).
MCSET: . . . . **ZBBC 1079**

MANSFIELD PARK (O'Brien, Maureen (nar)).
MCSET: **CC/036**

PERSUASION (Massey, Anna (nar)).
MCSET: **CC/022**

PERSUASION (Scales, Prunella (nar)).
MCSET: . . . . **ARGO 1178**

PRIDE AND PREJUDICE (Sutcliffe, Irene (nar)).
MCSET: **CC/001**

PRIDE AND PREJUDICE (Bloom, Claire (nar)).
MC: **1595**

PRIDE AND PREJUDICE (Johnson, Celia (nar)).
MCSET: . . . . **LFP 7224**
MCSET: . . . . **LFP 4172245**

SENSE AND SENSIBILITY (Badel, Sarah (nar)).
MCSET: **CC/033**

SENSE AND SENSIBILITY (Bloom, Claire (nar)).
MC: **1627**

Austin, Charles

MIAMI.
Tracks: / Moods / To Shoenberg / Motions in blue and red / Michelle / Compositions for our peers / Absolute end, almost, The / Birds, The / Tuning fork / Reflective thinking, (part 1) / Little train / Speedway / Reflective thinking, (part 2).
LP: . . . . **IRI 5004**

Austin, Claire

1954 (Austin, Claire (with Kid Ory)).
LP: . . . . **HSLP 1001**

Austin, Dean

SHARE MY MUSIC.
Tracks: / Country comfort / Change places with me / Old Shep / Home to Emma Jane / Three good reasons / Greyhounds and trailways / She's free but she's not easy / Working in the diner / Before this day ends / Heartbreak hotel.
LP: . . . . **KO 1009**

Austin, Derek

HARMAGEDDON/CHINA FREE FALL (See under Emerson, Keith) (Emerson, Keith/Derek Austin).

Austin, Lonnie

LONNIE AUSTIN AND NORMAN WOODLEIFF (See under Woodleiff, Norman) (Austin, Lonnie & Norman Woodleiff).

Austin, Lovie

BLUE SERENADERS.
LP: **22019**
MC: **42019**

LOVIE AUSTIN'S BLUES SERENADERS 1924-26 (Austin, Lovie & His Blue Serenaders).
LP: . . . . **FJ 105**

Austin, Patti

BABY COME TO ME (OLD GOLD) (See under Ingram, James/Yah mo be there).

BODY LANGUAGE.
Tracks: / Body language / Another nail in my heart / S.O.S. / We've got tonite / He's killing me / I can't stop / Love me again / Soar me like an eagle flies / People in love / I want you tonight.
LP: **240 601 3**

END OF A RAINBOW.
Tracks: / Say you love me / You don't have to say you're sorry / In my life / More today than yesterday / Give it time / There is no time / What's at the end of the rainbow / This side of heaven / Sweet Sadie the saviour.
LP: . . . . **CTI 5001**

EVERY HOME SHOULD HAVE ONE.
Tracks: / Do you love me / Love me to death / Way I feel, The / Every home should have one / Baby, come to me / Genie / Stop look listen / Symphony of love / Oh no, Margerita / Island, The.
LP: . . . . **K 56931**
MC: **K4 56931**

GETTIN' AWAY WITH MURDER.
Tracks: / Talking about my baby / Big bad world / Heat of heat, The / If I believe / Honey for the bees / Anything can happen here / Only a breath away / Summer is the coldest time of year.
LP: **925276 1**
MC: **925276 4**

LIVE AT THE BOTTOM LINE.
MC: . . . . **CTK 9501**
MC: **4679224**

LOVE IS GONNA GETCHA.
Tracks: / Through the test of time / Too soon to know / In my life / Love is gonna getcha / Ooh-whee (the carnival) / Believe the children / Good in love / Wait for me / First time love / In my dream / Girl who used to be me, The (Available on CD only).
LP: . . . . **GRP 96031**
MC: . . . . **GRP 96034**

PATTI AUSTIN.
Tracks: / It's gonna be special / Rhythm of the street / All behind us now / Hot in flames of love / Change your attitude / Shoot the moon / I've got my heart set on you / Fine fine fella / Starstruck / Any way you can.
LP: **923974 1**
MC: **923974 4**

REAL ME, THE.
Tracks: / I can cook too / Stockholm sweetnin' / Smoke gets in your eyes / True love / Across the valley from the Alamo / How long has this been going on / Mood indigo / Cry me a river / Someone is standing outside / Spring can really hang you up the most.
LP: . . . . **K 925696 1**
MC: **925696 4**

Australia (country)

ABORIGINNES OF NORTH AUSTRALIA Song and dance music (Various artists).
Tracks: / Dingo: *Various artists* / Birruck: *Various artists* / Lumbuck: *Various artists* / Djetberdi: *Various artists* / Galkau: *Various artists* / Le pivert: *Various artists* / Le cacatoes blanc: *Various* artists / Kookaburra: *Various artists* / Miparra: *Various artists* / Laitj laitj: *Various artists*/ Bidjurrdu: *Various artists* / Ancien chant tradition du centre de l'Arnhem: *Various artists* / La creation de la terre: *Various artists* / Budbal: *Various artists* / Karrbarde: *Various artists* / Brolga: *Various artists* / Mook mook: *Various artists* / Danse des ombres: *Various artists* / Danse des esprits - Mimi: *Various artists* / Didjeridou: *Various artists*.
LP: . . . . **ARN 33553**

AUSTRALIA (Come listen to Australia) (Various artists).
Tracks: / Didjeridu solo: *Various artists* / No more boomerang: *Various artists* / Captain Cook: *Various* artists / Girls fron the Shamrock Shore, The: *Various artists* / Tent poles are rotten, The: *Various artists*/ Teams, The: *Various artists* / Come listen: *Various artists* / 1,000 miles away: *Various artists* / Australia Square: *Various artists* / Mullimbmy madness: *Various artists* / Wimmins ball, The: *Various artists*/ F1 11: *Various artists* / Aussie medley: *Various artists* / Red dust: *Various artists* / Million are: *Various artists*.
LP: **6 30127**

AUSTRALIA: 20 SONGS OF THE COUNTRY (Various artists).
LP: . . . . **PLAT 22**
MC: . . . . **PLAC 22**

AUSTRALIA DOWN UNDER COUNTRY (Various artists).
LP: . . . . **ALR 1**
MC: . . . . **ALC 1**

MAN OF THE EARTH (Songs of the Australian Mining Industry) (Various artists).
LP: . . . . **LRF 01**

NAVVY ON THE LINE (Various artists).
LP: . . . . **LRF 09**

SONGS OF THE ABORIGINES (Various artists).
LP: . . . . **LLST 7331**

MC: . . . . LLCT 7331

Australian...

AUSTRALIAN ROCK 84 (Various artists).
LP: . . . . EPC 26000
MC: 40 26000

Australian Army

AUSTRALIAN ARMY TOUR (Australian Army, Band of).
LP: . . . . SPVP 161
MC: . . . . SPVP 161 C

Australian Crawl

SEMANTICS.
Tracks: / Boys light up / Errol / Indisposed / Looking for cool / Reckless / Lakeside / White limbo / Things don't seem / Night / Unpublished critic.
LP: . . . . GEF 25934

SONS OF BEACHES.
Tracks: / Run-away girls / Daughters of the Northern Coast / Mid-life crisis / Shut down / King Sap / Letter from Zimbabwe / Downhearted / Live now, pay later / Dianne / Grinning bellhops / Waiting / Happy song for problem children.
LP: . . . . EMC 3423

Australian TV's ...

AUSTRALIAN TV'S GREATEST HITS (Original Television Themes) (Various artists).
Tracks: / Neighbours: *Various artists* / Prisoner cell block H (theme from): *Various artists* / Sullivans, The: *Various artists* / Sons and daughters: *Various artists* / Anzacs: *Various artists* / Skippy: *Various* artists / Paul Hogan show, The: *Various artists* / Young doctors, The: *Various artists* / Chopper squad: *Various artists* / Country practice, A: *Various artists* / Carsons law: *Various artists.*
LP: . . . . FILM 028
MC: . . . . FILMC 028

Austria (Country)

AUSTRIAN FOLK MUSIC East provinces vol. 1 (Various artists).
LP: . . . . ARHOOLIE 3001

AUSTRIAN FOLK MUSIC Western provinces vol. 2 (Various artists).
LP: . . . . ARHOOLIE 3003

AUSTRIAN FOLKLAW (Various artists).
LP: 12C 052 33262
MC: 12C 252 33262

Ausweis

DUB ACTION.
LP: . . . . DANMLP 005

Auto Suggestion

HYPNOSIS TAPES - SELECTION (see under 'Sutphen, Dick').

Autograph

SIGN IN PLEASE.
Tracks: / Send her to me / Turn up the radio / Nineteen and non-stop / Cloud 10 / Deep end / My girlfriend's boyfriend isn't me / Thrill of love / Friday in the night / All I'm gonna take.
LP: . . . . PL 89495
MC: . . . . PK 89495

Automatic Diamini

D IS FOR DRUM, THE.
Tracks: / Unhappy marriage / Cover girl fall over boy / Me and my conscience / Crazy supper / Your idea of heaven drove love away / I've never been that colour anywhere... / Black and white / I don't know you but... / Strings from the heart.
LP: . . . . IDEALP 001

Automatic Instruments

PIPES, BARRELS AND PINS (Various artists).
Tracks: / That certain party: *Various artists* / Ramona: *Various artists* / Auld lang syne: *Various artists*/ Bedelia: *Various artists* / Bye, bye, blackbird: *Various artists* / Annie Laurie: *Various artists* / Last rose of summer: *Various artists.*
MC: . . . . CSDLB 271

Automatic Slim

HE AIN'T HEAVY, HE'S THE SINGER.
LP: . . . . SQUARE 30

SLIM LIVE.
LP: . . . . SQUARE 020

Autopilot

RAPID EYE MOVEMENTS.
Tracks: / Weather and closedown / George goes solo / Pictures on a video screen / New terrain / Why do I feel so good / Face, The / Woman in the fair, The / Midnight sun / Hiding to nothing, A / Place with no emotion, A / Approach to the city / Ears of the city, The / Won't give in / George rides again / Something in the shadows / Escaping from a maze.
2LP: . . . . CTY 1309
MCSET: . . . . ZCTY 1309

Autopsy

SEVERED SURVIVAL.
LP: . . . . VILE 012
MC: . . . . VILEC 012

Autosalvage

AUTOSALVAGE.
Tracks: / Autosalvage / Burglar song / Rampant generalities / Our life as we lived it / Good morning blues / Ancestral wants / Hundred days, A / Land of their dreams / Parahighway / Great brain robbery / Glimpses of the next world's world.
LP: . . . . ED 286

Autry, Gene

20 GOLDEN PIECES: GENE AUTRY.
Tracks: / Dixie cannonball / My old Kentucky home / Down in the valley / Cowboy blues / Boy from Texas, a girl from Tennesse, A / West a nest and you, The / Don't bite the hand that's feeding you / Missouri waltz / There's no back door to heaven / Kentucky babe / You're the only good thing / When day is done / You are my sunshine / I hang my head and cry / San Antonio rose / Goodbye little darling / Trouble in mind / Lonely river / You're the only star in my blue heaven / Tweedle-o-twill.
LP: . . . . BDL 2013
MC: . . . . BDC 2013

BACK IN THE SADDLE AGAIN (22 Cowboy Classics).
MC: . . . . PLAC 25

BEST OF GENE AUTRY.
MC: 16-21

GENE AUTRY.
Tracks: / Tumbling tumbleweeds / I'll go riding down that old Texas trail / It makes no difference now / There's a new Moon over my shoulder / Amapola / Ridin' down the canyon / Deep in the heart of Texas / Same old fashioned hoedown / Don't fence me in.
LP: . . . . CBS 25016

GENE AUTRY 50TH ANNIVERSARY.
2LP: . . . . RLP 6022 9001

LIVE FROM MADISON SQUARE GARDENS.
Tracks: / Down yonder / Anytime / My lazy day / Someday you'll want me to want you / Silver haired daddy of mine / Last letter, The / Let me cry on your shoulder / Half as much / Blue Canadian Rockies / I was just walking out the door / Rounded up in glory / There's a goldmine in the sky.
LP: . . . . BDL 1024
MC: . . . . BDC 1024

SINGS SOUTH OF THE BORDER.
Tracks: / El rancho grande / You belong to my heart / In a little Spanish town / My adobe hacienda / Under fiesta stars / Vaya con dios / Gay ranchero, A / It happened in Monterey / Rancho pillow / Mexicali rose / Serenade of the bells / South of the border.
LP: . . . . BDL 1021

YELLOW ROSE OF TEXAS, THE.
Tracks: / Yellow rose of texas / Cattle ranch house on the old Circle B, The / Louisiana moon / Cowboy's heaven / Kentucky lullaby / Black bottom blues / That ramshackle shack / Back home in the blue ridge mountain / Do right daddy blues / Money ain't no use anyway / That's how I got my start / Bear cat papa blues / Don't do me that way / High steppin' mama / There's a good gal in the mountains / My dreaming of you.
LPPD: . . . . BDP 15204

Autumn Leaves

AUTUMN LEAVES (Various artists).
MCSET: . . . . WW 6033

Autumn Records Story

AUTUMN RECORDS STORY (Various artists).
Tracks: / C'mon and swim pt.1: *Freeman, Bobby* / S-W-I-M: *Freeman, Bobby* / Scat swim: *Stewart, Sly*/ Buttermilk: *Stewart, Sly* / Somebody to love: *Great Society* / Free advice: *Great Society* / She's my baby: *Mojo Men* / Jerk, The: *Beau Brummels & B.Freeman Band* / Sad little girl: *Beau Brummels* / No 1: *Charlatans* / Anything: *Vejetables* / Pay attention to me: *Tikis.*
LP: . . . . ED 145
MC: . . . . CED 145

Autumns

1980S DOO-WOP ALBUM, THE (Autumns & Infernos).
LP: 2001

Avada Band

AVADA BAND.
LP: . . . . AM 54

Avalanche

PRAY FOR THE SUMMER.
LP: . . . . RR 9740

Avalanche Express

AVALANCHE EXPRESS (Norgate, Clifford).
MC: . . . . IAB 88092

Avalon

HEAVY HEARTS.
Tracks: / Litany / Anton the fox / Heavy hearts / On the field of broken dreams / Candy row / Sea link / Knerbs of Bettur, The / Sound of Mull / Flotterstone jig / Dode's reel / So still the scene / Silver and steel / Just between friends / Sandgate lass.
LP: . . . . LIFL 7015
MC: . . . . LIFC 7015

ROCKY ROADS.
Tracks: / Overture / Jack in irons / Traveller's tale / Greenpeace / Bruntsfield link / Leith walk / Open roads / Ballrooms of romance / Another encore / Blue highways / Road to Dingwall/Arran more.
LP: . . . . LIFL 7013
MC: . . . . LIFC 7013

Avalon, Frankie

BEST OF FRANKIE AVALON.
MC: 16-13

BOBBY SOX TO STOCKINGS.
Tracks: / Teacher's pet / Just ask your heart / Gingerbread / Blue Betty / Ooh la la / Why / Dede Dinah / Venus / Don't throw away all those teardrops / Bobby sox to stockings / Don't make fun of me / Boy without a girl / I'll wait for you / You are mine / Don't let love pass me by.
LP: . . . . CHA 121

COLLECTION: FRANKIE AVALON.
MC: . . . . CCSMC 240

FABULOUS FRANKIE AVALON, THE.
MC: . . . . FABC 007

FRANKIE AVALON.
LP: . . . . CHL 5001

GRAFFITI COLLECTION.
MC: . . . . GRMC 09

TEEN KINGS (See under Fabian & Frankie Avalon).

Avant Gardeners

CHURCH OF THE INNER COSMOS.
LP: . . . . AP 027

Avante-Garde

COMPANY VOL.1 (Various artists).
LP: . . . . INCUS 21

COMPANY VOL.2 (Various artists).
LP: . . . . INCUS 23

COMPANY VOL.5 (Various artists).
LP: . . . . INCUS 28

COMPANY VOL.6 (Various artists).
LP: . . . . INCUS 29

COMPANY VOL.7 (Various artists).
LP: . . . . INCUS 30

Avenger

BLOOD SPORTS.
Tracks: / Enforcer / You'll never make me (alive) / Matriarch / Warfare / On the rocks / Rough ride / Victims of force / Death race 2000 / Night of the jackal.
LP: . . . . NEAT 1018

KILLER ELITE.
Tracks: / Revenge attack / Run for your life / Brand of torture / Steel on steel / Right to rock, The / Hard times / Under the hammer / Face to the ground / Dangerous games / Yesterday's hero / M.M.85 / Saw mill.
LP: . . . . NEAT 1026

Avengers...

AVENGERS (TV SERIES) (See under Johnson, Laurie) (Johnson, Laurie).

AVENGERS/NEW AVENGERS/ PROFESSIONALS (TV Soundtracks) (Johnson, Laurie).
LP: . . . . ASV 95003

Avengers (group)

AVENGERS, THE.
LP: . . . . CD 007
LP: . . . . LPL 8901

CADILLACS AND LINCOLNS.
LP: . . . . ROCK 8901

Avenue

THREE CHEERS.
LP: . . . . BR 4

Average White Band

AFTER SHOCK.
Tracks: / Spirit of love, the / Aftershock / I'll get over you / Let's go all the way / Stocky sachoo a shun / Sticky situation / Love at first sight / Later we'll be greater / We're in too deep.
LP: 839 466 1
MC: 839 466 4

AVERAGE WHITE BAND.
Tracks: / You got it / Got the love / Pick up the pieces / Person to person / Nothing you can do / Work to do / Just want to love you tonight / Keepin' it to myself / I just can't give you up / There's always someone waiting.
LP: . . . . FA 3157
MC: . . . . TCFA 3157
LP: . . . . K 50058
LP: . . . . INTS 5049

BENNY AND US (Average White Band & Ben E. King).
Tracks: / Get it up for love / Fool for your anyway / Star in the ghetto, A / Message, The / What is soul / Someday we'll be free / Imagine / Keepin' it to myself.
LP: . . . . K 50384
MC: K4 50384

BEST OF THE AVERAGE WHITE BAND.
Tracks: / Pick up the pieces / Cut the cake / Queen of my soul / Love of your own, A / Person to person / I heard it through the grapevine / Walk on by / You got it / Cloudy / Work to do / Atlantic Avenue / When will you be mine.
LP: . . . . NL 89091
MC: . . . . NK 89091

CUPID'S IN FASHION.
Tracks: / You're my number one / Easier said than done / You wanna belong / Cupids in fashion / Theatre of excess I believe / Is it love that you're running from / Reach out I'll be there / Isn't it strange / Love's a heartache.
LP: . . . . RCALP 6052
MC: . . . . RCAK 6052

CUT THE CAKE.
Tracks: / Cut the cake / School boy crush / It's a mystery / Groovin' the night away / If I ever lose this heaven / Why / High flyin' woman / Cloudy / How sweet can you get / When they bring down the curtain.
LP: . . . . K 50146

FEEL NO FRET.
Tracks: / When will you be mine / Please don't fall in love / Walk on by / Feel no fret / Stop the rain / Atlantic Avenue / Ace of hearts / Too late to cry / Fire burning / Cut the cake / School boy crush / It's a mystery / Groovin' the night away / If I ever lose this heaven / Why / High flyin' woman / Cloudy / How sweet can you get / When they bring down the curtain.
LP: . . . . INTS 5140
MC: . . . . INTK 5140
LP: . . . . XL 13063

PERSON TO PERSON.
Tracks: / Person to person / Cut the cake / If I ever lose this heaven / Cloudy / T.L.C. / I'm the one / Pick up the pieces / Love you life / School boy crush / I heard it through the grapevine.
2LP: . . . . K 60127
MCSET: K4 60127

PUT IT WHERE YOU WANT IT.
LP: . . . . MCL 1650

SHINE.
Tracks: / Catch me / Let's go round again / Whatch' gonna do for me / Help is on the way / Shine / For you, for love / Into the night / Our time has come / If love only lasts for one night.
LP: . . . . XL 13123

SHOW YOUR HAND.
Tracks: / Jugglers, The / This world has music / Twilight zone / Put it where you want it / Show your hand / Back in '67 / Reach out / T.L.C..
LP: . . . . FA 3062
MC: . . . . TCFA 3062
LP: . . . . MCF 2514

SOUL SEARCHING TIME.
Tracks: / Overture / Love your life / I'm the one / Love of your own, A / Queen of my soul / Soul searching / Going home / Everybody's darling / Would you stay / Sunny days / Digging deeper.
LP: . . . . INTS 5058
MC: . . . . INTK 5058
LP: . . . . K 50272

WARMER COMMUNICATIONS.
Tracks: / Your love is a miracle / Same feeling, different song / Daddy's all gone / Big city lights / She's a dream / Sweet and sour / One look over my shoulder (is this really).
LP: . . . . XL 13053
MC: . . . . XK 13053

Averi, Peter

20 GOLDEN HYMNS VOL.1.
LP: . . . . SPVP 157
MC: . . . . SPVP 157C

20 GOLDEN HYMNS VOL.2.
Tracks: / Glorious things of Thee are spoken / Soldiers of Christ arise / Praise my soul the King of Heaven / Thy kingdom come O God / O God our help in ages past / Fight the good fight / O God

of Bethel / Love divine all loves excelling / King of love my shepherd is, The / All people that on earth do dwell.
LP: SPVP 164

20 GOLDEN HYMNS VOL.3.
Tracks: / Hark a thrilling voice is sounding / Lo, He comes with clouds descending / Great and mighty wonder, A / O little town of Bethlehem / Of the Father's heart / Earth has many a noble city / What star is this / Forty days and forty nights / O sacred head / When I survey the wondrous cross / Ye choirs of New Jerusalem / Jesus Christ is risen today / Come, down O love divine / Holy, holy, holy / O God unseen yet ever near / Jesu, gentlest saviour / Come ye thankful people, come / Spirit of Jesus who didst move / Who are these, like stars appearing / For all the saints.
LP: SPVP 170

Averill, Esther (aut)

JENNY AND THE CAT CLUB/JENNY'S FIRST PARTY (See under Jenny & the Cat (bk)) (Grimes, Tammy (nar)).

WHEN JENNY LOST HER SCARF/ JENNY'S ADOPTED BROTHER (See under When Jenny Lost (bk)) (Grimes, Tammy (nar)).

Avery, John

JESSICA IN THE ROOM.
LP: TEK 003

NIGHTHAWKS.
LP: FIB 002

Avia (film)

AVIA (Original soundtrack) (Various artists).
Tracks: / Wake up and sing out: *Avia (film)* / Spring song of the masses: *Avia (film)* / Russian lesson part 1 (goodbye): *Avia (film)* / Night watch, The: *Avia (film)* / I don't love you: *Avia (film)* / Russian lesson part 2 (home): *Avia (film)* / Celebration: *Avia (film)* / Aviavial: *Avia (film)* / Semaphore: *Avia (film)*.
LP: 602 760 500 7
LP: HNBL 1358
MC: HNBC 1358

Aviator

AVIATOR.
Tracks: / Front line / Back on the street / Don't turn away / Wrong place, wrong time / Never let the rock stop / Comeback / Magic / Can't stop / Too young / Every schoolboy knows / Through the night.
LP: PL 89934
MC: PK 89934

TURBULENCE.
Tracks: / Way of the world / American / Turbulence / Ovation / Fallen star / Track eleven / Get your rocks off / Strange worlds .
LP: SHSP 4107

Aviator (Film)

AVIATOR, THE (Film soundtrack) (Various artists).
LP: STV 81240

Aviva

LIFE OF A SONGS SINGER.
LP: EULP 1025

Avon Calling

AVON CALLING (Various artists).
LP: HB 1

Avon Cities Jazz Band

BLUE FUNK.
Tracks: / Stevedore stomp / Blue funk / Aquarius / Machine gun Kelly / Midnight sleighride / Pata pata / Godspell / Road to the Isles / Mercy mercy mercy / Superstar.
LP: JOYS 249

CURRENT A/C.
Tracks: / Brazilian bounce / Fuse blues / Wabash blues / Ritual fire dance / Life raver / Doctor Caligari / Louisiana / Little three-quarters for God and Co, A / Delta dawn.
LP: JOYS 262

SILVER COLLECTION.
Tracks: / St. Thomas / El Condor Pasa / Sometime later / Bourbon Street parade / We believe in music / Heliotrope bouquet / Hi de ho / South / Tsar Paul.
LP: JOYS 261

Avons

THREE RIVERS REACH.
LP: LETHLP 1

Avsenik, Slavko

SPIEL UNS EINS.
MC: CT4 23522

Awaken Your Power

AWAKEN YOUR POWER (New Frontiers Bible week) (Various artists).
Tracks: / Praise the Lord with all your heart: *Various artists* / Come let us sing for the joy of the Lord: *Various artists* / We extol you: *Various artists* / Father in Heaven how we love you: *Various artists* / Glorious Father: *Various artists* / Hear O shepherd: *Various artists* / Lord the light of Your love: *Various artists* / I will worship You, Lord: *Various artists* / Jehovah Jireh: *Various artists* / Give thanks: *Various artists*/ Thank you for the cross: *Various artists* / It's Your blood that cleanses me: *Various artists* / Jesus, You are the power: *Various artists* / I want to serve the purpose of God: *Various artists*.
LP: SOP R 2019
MC: SOP C 2019

Awakening

INTO THY HANDS.
LP: RRA R 0035
MC: RRA C 0035

Awakening (Film)

AWAKENING, THE (Film soundtrack) (Bolling, Claude).
LP: ERS6520

Awakenings (film)

AWAKENINGS (Film soundtrack) (Newman, Randy).
MC: 7599264664

Awatinas, Los

AWATKIPASIPXANANAKASATAKI (Bolivian).
LP: GAMM 48156

Awdry, Rev. W.

FURTHER RAILWAY STORIES (See under Railway Stories) (Rushton, Willie (nar)).

MORE RAILWAY STORIES (1) (See under Railway Stories) (Rushton, Willie (nar)).

RAILWAY STORIES (See under Railway Stories) (Rushton, Willie (nar)).

Awesome

AWESOME (Various artists).
Tracks: / Ice ice baby: *Vanilla Ice* / Wiggle it: *2 In A Room* / 3 a.m. eternal: *KLF featuring Children Of The Revolution* / Hippychick: *Soho* / There she goes: *La's* / All together now: *Farm* / International bright young thing: *Jesus Jones* / X Y & Zee: *Pop Will Eat Itself* / My definition of a bombastic jazz style: *Dream Warriors* / Can I kick it?: *Tribe Called Quest* / Crazy: *Seal* / Fantasy: *Black Box* / Forget me nots: *Tongue 'N' Cheek* / U can't touch this: *M.C. Hammer* / Don't worry: *Appleby, Kim* / It's alright now: *Beloved* / Cubik: *808 State* / Situation (remix): *Yazoo* / Dressed for success: *Roxette* / Little time, A: *Beautiful South*.
LP: EMTV 58
MC: TCEMTV 58

Awful Truth

AWFUL TRUTH.
Tracks: / It takes so long / I should have known all along / Ghost of heaven / Drowning man / Circle of pain / Higher / No good reason / Mary.
MC: TZORRO 3

Axe

NEMESIS.
Tracks: / Heat in the street / Young hearts / All through the night / I'll think you'll remember tonight / She's had the power / Girls, girls, girls / Eagle flies alone / Keep playing that rock 'n' roll / Foolin' your mama again / Let the music come back / Masquerade.
LP: 790 099-1

OFFERING.
Tracks: / Rock 'n' roll party in the streets / Video inspiration / Steal another fantasy / Jennifer / I got the fire / Burn the city down / Now or never / Holdin' on / Silent soldiers.
LP: K 50895

Axe Attack

AXE ATTACK (See under Heavy Metal) (Various artists).

Axe Attack (Group)

NIGHTMARE.
LP: AXE 7024

Axe Victims

ANOTHER VICTIM.
LP: SKULL 8334
MC: TAPE 78334

Axegrinder

RISE OF THE SERPENT MEN, THE.
Tracks: / Never ending winter / Life chain / Evilution / Final war, The / Hellstorm / War machine / Rise of the serpent men.
LP: VILE 007
MC: DEAF 0102 MC

Axelrod, Dan

NEW AXE.
Tracks: / Unnatural axe / Lime / Namely you / Stranger in paradise / Three little words / Love letters / Tristeza / Meteor.
LP: PHOENIX 1003

Axemaster

BLESSING IN THE SKIES.
LP: A 33

Axewitch

LORD OF THE FLIES.
LP: FINGLP 101

VISIONS OF THE PAST.
Tracks: / Visions of the past / Give them hell / Tonight / Hot lady / Stand up / Heading for a storm / Born in hell / Time to live.
LP: NEAT 1025

Axidentals

AXIDENTALS WITH THE KAI WINDING TROMBONES.
Tracks: / Day in, day out / I will come back / You don't know what love is / Gypsy in my soul / Close to you / No moon at all / Waiting for the Robert E. Lee / Walkin' / Rockaby bluebird / Flamingo / Out of this world / You gotta wail.
LP: JASM 1507

Axis, Jon Butcher

JON BUTCHER AXIS.
Tracks: / Life takes a life / It's only words / Ocean in motion / Can't be the only fool / Sentinel / New man / Fairlight / Send one care of / Walk like this / We will be as one.
LP: POLS 1084

Axis Point

AXIS POINT.
Tracks: / Moving the night away / First drink of the day / Women of the world / Black ice / Fire it up / Slow down / Westbound for glory / Eugene / Newman Street.
LP: PL 30039

BOAST OF THE TOWN.
Tracks: / Boast of the town / Home made wine / Empty sky / Rock and roll circus / My love / Red hot and blue / Manyana / Fire mountain / Trouble / Drinking song.
LP: PL 25277

Axton, Hoyt

20 GREATEST HITS: HOYT AXTON.
LP: FUN 9048
MC: FUNC 9048

EVERYBODY'S GOIN' ON THE ROAD.
Tracks: / Everybody's goin' on the road / Betty La Rue / Boozers are losers / Politicians / You do not tango / Smile as you go by / Where did the money go / Some people ride / Midnight in Memphis / Ease your pain / Battle of New Orleans / House song.
LP: YB LP 120

ROAD SONGS.
Tracks: / No no song / Boney fingers / In a young girl's mind / Telephone booth / Paid in advance / Lion in the winter / I love to sing / When the morning comes / Lay, lady, lay / Sweet misery / Flash of fire / Less than the song.
LP: AMLH 64669

RUSTY OLD HALO, A.
Tracks: / Rusty old halo / Della and the dealer / Hotel Ritz / So hard to give it all up / Evangelina / Torpedo / Viva Pancho Villa / Wild bull rider / In a young girl's mind / Gotta keep rollin'.
LP: MFP 50520
MC: TCMFP 50520
MC: YBC 800
LP: YBLP 800

SNOWBLIND FRIEND.
Tracks: / You're the hangnail in my life / Little white moon / Water for my horses / Funeral of the King / I light this candle / Never been to Spain / You taught me how to cry / Snowblind friend / Poncho and lefty / Seven come / I don't know why I love you.
LP: IMCA 647

Axxess

NOVELS FOR THE MOONS.
LP: LMGLP 1000
MC: ZCLMC 1000

Axxis

KINGDOM OF THE NIGHT.
Tracks: / Living in a world / Kingdom of the night / Never say never / Fire and ice / Young souls / Singing for a song / Love is like an ocean / Moon, The / Tears of the trees / Just one night / Kings made of steel / Living in a world (Ext. version) (CD only.).
LP: PCS 7334
LP: 791 829 1
MC: TCPCS 7334
MC: 791 829 4

Ayala, Bob

RESCUED.
LP: BIRD R 188
MC: BIRD C 188

Ayckbourn, Alan (aut)

ALAN AYCKBOURN DOUBLE BILL (Relatively Speaking & Season's Greetings) (Aldridge, Michael/Nicky Henson).
MCSET: ZBBC 1043

Ayers, Kevin

AS CLOSE AS YOU THINK.
LP: AMA 25

BANANA PRODUCTIONS (Best of Kevin Ayers).
Tracks: / Butterfly dance / Girl on a swing / Soon soon soon / Sweet deceiver / Caribbean moon / Decadence (Album only.) / Irreversible neural damage / Gemini child / Lady Rachel, The / Toujours le voyage (Album only.) / Stranger in blue suede shoes / There is loving / Clarietta rag / Reinhardt and Geraldine / Stars / Don't let it get you down / Hat song / Singing a song in the morning / Ballad of a salesman who sold himself / Clarence in wonderland / Diminished but not finished / Blue (Album only.) / Song from the bottom of a well / Among us / Colores para Dolores.
MC: TCEM 2032
2LP: EM 2032

BANANAMOUR.
Tracks: / Don't let it get you down / Shouting in a bucket blues / When your parents go to sleep / Interview / International anthem / Decadence / Oh, wot a dream / Hymn / Beware of the dog.
LP: SHVL 807
LP: EMS 1124
MC: TCEMS 1124

CONFESSIONS OF DR DREAM.
LP: BGOLP 86

DIAMOND JACK AND THE QUEEN OF PAIN.
Tracks: / Madame Butterfly / Lay lady lay / Who's still crazy / You keep me hangin' on / You are a big girl / Steppin out / My speedin' heart / Howling man / Give a little bit / Champagne and valium.
LP: CR 30224

FALLING UP.
Tracks: / Saturday night (in Deya) / Flying start / Best we have, The / Another rolling stone / Do you believe? / That's what we did / Nightfighters / Am I really Marcel?.
LP: V 2510
MC: TCV 2510

JOY OF A TOY.
Tracks: / Joy of a toy continued / Clarietta rag / Song for insane times / Eleanor's cake which ate her / Oleh oleh bandu bandong / Town feeling / Girl on a swing / Stop this train / Lady Rachel, The / All this crazy gift of time.
LP: BGOLP 78

JOY OF A TOY/SHOOTING AT THE MOON.
Tracks: / Joy of a toy / Town feeling / Clarietta rag / Girl on a swing / Song for insane times / Stop this train again doing it / Eleanor's cake which ate her / Lady Rachel, The / Oleh oleh bandu bandong / All this crazy gift of time / Shooting at the moon / May I / Rheinhardt and Geraldine / Colores para Dolores / Lunatics lament / Pisser dans un violon / Oyster and the flying fish, The / Underwater / Red, green and you blue / Shooting at the moon.
2LP: SHDW 407

KEVIN AYERS.
LP: BGOLP 11

KEVIN AYERS COLLECTION.
Tracks: / Lady Rachel, The / May I / Puis-je / Stranger in blue suede shoes / Caribbean moon / Shouting in a bucket blues / After the show / Didn't feel lonely till I thought of you / Once upon an ocean / City waltz / Blue star / Blaming it all on love / Strange song / Miss Hanaga / Money, money, money.
LP: CM 117

RAINBOW TAKEAWAY.
Tracks: / Blaming it all on love / Ballad of a salesman who sold himself / View from the mountain, A / Rainbow takeaway / Waltz for you / Beware of the dog / Strange song / Goodnight, goodnight / Hat song.
LP: SHSP 4085

SHOOTING AT THE MOON (Ayers, Kevin & The Whole World).
Tracks: / May I / Colores para dolores / Lunatics lament / Underwater / Red green and you blue / Rheinhardt and Geraldine / Pisser dans un violon / Oyster and the flying fish / Clarence in Wonderland / Shooting at the moon.

LP: . . . . BGOLP 13

SOPORIFICS (June 1, 1974) (Ayers, Kevin, John Cale, Nico & Eno).
Tracks: / Driving me backwards / Baby's on fire / Heartbreak hotel / End, The / May I / Shouting in a bucket blues / Stranger in blue suede shoes / Everybody's sometime and some people's all the time / Two goes into four.
LP: . . . . ILPS 9291

WHATEVER SHE BRINGS WE SING.
Tracks: / There is loving / Among us / Margaret oh my / Song from the bottom of a well / Whatever she brings we sing / Stranger in blue suede shoes / Champagne cowboy blues / Lullaby.
LP: . . . . SHVL 800

Ayers, Roy

2000 BLACKS (See under Kuti, Fela) (Ayers, Roy & Fela Kuti).

AFRICA, CENTER OF THE WORLD.
Tracks: / Africa, center of the world / River Niger / I'll just keep trying / Destination motherland / Third eye / Land of fruit and honey / Mo nise si E / There's a master plan.
LP: 2391 517

BEST OF ROY AYERS.
Tracks: / Heat of the beat / Can't you see me / Fever / Love will bring us back together / Running away / Get on up, get on down / Freaky deaky / You send me.
MC: 3177 429
LP: 2391 429

CRYSTAL REFLECTIONS (Ayers, Roy & B.Williams).
LP: . . . . MR 5101

DRIVE.
LP: . . . . ICH 1028
MC: . . . . ZCICH 1028

DRIVIN' ON UP.
Tracks: / Drive / Everybody / And then we were one / Black family / Chicago.
LP: . . . . UMLP 2

EASY MONEY (Live At Ronnie Scott's).
Tracks: / Spirit of do do / I wanna touch you / Everybody loves the sunshine / Fast money / Battle of the vibes / Can't you see me / Running away / Don't stop the feeling.
MC: . . . . ESMMC 017

EVERYBODY LOVES THE SUNSHINE.
Tracks: / Hey u / Golden rod, The / Keep on walking / You and me my love / Third eye, The / It ain't your sign / People and the world / Everybody loves the sunshine / Tongue power / Lonesome cowboy.
LP: . . . . UMID 1
MC: . . . . UMIDC 1

FEELIN' GOOD.
Tracks: / Our time is coming / Fire up the funk / Let's stay together / Ooh / Turn me loose / Knock knock / Stairway to the stars / Feeling good.
LP: 2391 539

FEVER.
Tracks: / Love will bring us back together / Simple and sweet / Take me out to the ball game / I wanna feel it (I wanna dance) / Fever / Is it too late to try / If you love me / Leo.
LP: . . . . UMID 2
MC: . . . . UMIDC 2
LP: 2391396

I'M THE ONE (FOR YOUR LOVE TONIGHT).
Tracks: / I'm the one / Don't you ever turn away / Blue summer / I once had your love (and I can't let go) / I really want to be with you / Let me love you / Marion / Word / Crack attack.
LP: 4505971
MC: 4505974
LP: . . . . FC 40423

IN THE DARK (ALBUM).
Tracks: / In the dark / Sexy, sexy, sexy / I can't help it / Compardre / Goree Island / Poo poo la la / Blast the box / Love is in the feel.
LP: 26199

LET'S DO IT.
Tracks: / Let's do it / Melody maker / When is real real / Sweet tears / You came into my life / Freaky deaky / Kiss.
LP: . . . . UMID 4
MC: . . . . UMIDC 4

LOVE FANTASY.
Tracks: / Rock your roll / Betcha gonna / Sometimes believe in yourself / Love fantasy / Sigh / Baby Buba.
LP: . . . . UMID 6
MC: . . . . URBMC 6
LP: 2391 492

NO STRANGER TO LOVE.
Tracks: / Don't stop the feeling / What you won't do for love / Shack up, pack up / It's up / Slyde / No stranger to love / Don't let our love slip away / Don't hide your love.
LP: 2391 438
MC: 3177 438

PRIME TIME (Ayers, Roy/Wayne Henderson).
Tracks: / You make me feel like / Thank you thank you / Weekend lover / Tell me what you want / Can you dance / It ain't your sign / Have your way / Million dollar baby.
LP: 2391 455

RARE.
Tracks: / Evolution / Love from the sun / Magic lady / Fikisha (to help somebody arrive) / 2000 black / Mystic voyage / Tear to a smile, A / For real / Change up the groove / Time and space / It's so sweet / Life is just a moment / Show us a feeling / Des nude soul.
LP: 841 416 1
MC: 841 416 4

RARE VOLUME II.
Tracks: / Brother Louie / Don't you worry about a thing / When is real, real? / Ebony blaze / Funky motion / Sensitize / Ain't got time / Ain't no sunshine / Sweet tears / Red, black and green / Hummin' / Feel like makin' love / Wee bit, A / Raindrops keep falling / On my head.
LP: 8437581
MC: 8437584

SILVER VIBRATIONS.
LP: . . . . UMLP 1
MC: . . . . UMC 1

STEP INTO OUR LIFE.
LP: . . . . POLS 1004

VIBRATIONS (Ayers, Roy Ubiquity).
Tracks: / Domelo (give it to me) / Baby I need your love / Higher / Memory, The / Come out and play / Better days / Searching / One sweet love to remember / Vibrations / Moving, grooving / Baby you give me a feeling.
LP: . . . . UMID 5
MC: . . . . UMIDC 5
LP: 2391 256

WAKE UP.
Tracks: / Midnight after dark / Suave / Sweet talk / Spirit of dodo '89 / Crack is in the mirror (wake up) / You've got the power / Mystic vibrations.
LP: . . . . ICH 1040
MC: . . . . ZCICH 1040

YOU MIGHT BE SURPRISED.
Tracks: / Hot / Programmes for love / Virgo / You might be surprised / Night flyte / Can I see you ? / For you / Slip 'n' slide .
LP: . . . . CBS 26653
MC: 40 26653

YOU SEND ME.
Tracks: / You send me / I wanna touch you baby / Can't you see me / Get on up, get on down / Every time I see you / Rhythm / And don't you say no / It ain't your sign / It's your mind.
LP: 2391 365
LP: . . . . UMID 3
MC: . . . . UMIDC 3

Ayinla, Kollington

IJO YO YO.
LP: . . . . KRLP 35

Ayler, Albert

ALBERT AYLER.
LP: . . . . ESP 1020

ALBERT AYLER IN GREENWICH VILLAGE.
LP: . . . . AS 9155
MC: . . . . ASC 9155

AT SLUG'S SALOON (Ayler, Albert Quintet).
LP: . . . . BASE 3031

AT SLUG'S SALOON VOL.2, MAY 1ST 1966 (Ayler, Albert Quintet).
LP: . . . . BASE 3032

FIRST RECORDINGS, THE.
Tracks: / I'll remember April / Rollin's tune / Tune up / Free.
LP: . . . . SNTF 604
LP: . . . . GNPS 9022

LIVE IN GREENWICH VILLAGE.
Tracks: / For John Coltrane / Change has come / Truth is marching in / Our prayer.
LP: . . . . JAS 70
LP: . . . . MCA 39123

NEW YORK EYE AND EAR CONTROL.
LP: . . . . ESP 1016

NUITS DE LA FONDATION.
2LP: . . . . SHAN 83503/4

PROPHECY.
LP: . . . . ESP 3030

SPIRITUAL UNITY (Ayler, Albert Trio).
LP: . . . . ESP 1002

VIBRATIONS (Ayler, Albert & Don Cherry).
Tracks: / Ghosts / Children / Holy spirit / Vibrations / Mothers.
LP: . . . . FLP 41000

WITCHES AND DEVILS.
LP: . . . . FLP 41018

Ayler, Don

IN FLORENCE, VOL. 1 1981.
LP: . . . . RF 2001

IN FLORENCE, VOL. 2 1981.
LP: . . . . RF 2002

IN FLORENCE, VOL. 3 1981.
LP: . . . . RF 2003

Ayres, Pam

SOME MORE OF ME POEMS AND SONGS.
LP: . . . . GAL 6010
MC: . . . . GALC 6010

SOME OF ME POEMS AND SONGS.
Tracks: / Battery hen / Oh I wish I looked after my teeth / Minnie Dyer / In fear of the butcher / Like you would / Hegg / Time / Embarrassing experience with the parrot / Don't sell our Edgar no more violins / Not you Basil / In defence of hedgehogs / Stuffed horse / Bike / I'm a starling, me darling / Fling another chair leg on the fire mother / Father dear father / Goodwill to men, give us your money / Oh no, I got a cold.
LP: . . . . MFP 50461
MC: . . . . TCMFP 50461
LP: . . . . GAL 6003

THOUGHTS OF A LATE NIGHT KNITTER.
LP: . . . . SCX 6595

WILL ANYBODY MARRY ME.
LP: . . . . EMC 3216

Ayres, Rosalind (nar)

PERFECT MURDER, A (See under Archer, Jeffrey (aut)) (Jarvis, Martin & Rosalind Ayres).

Ayrshire Fiddle...

BOWING THE STRINGS (Ayrshire Fiddle Orchestra).
MC: . . . . KITV 506

FIDDLERS GATHERING (Ayrshire Fiddle Orchestra).
Tracks: / Annie's reel / Jean Kirk Patrick's fancy / Irish washerwoman, The / Sorry to part / Lament for the death of the Rev Archie Beaton / Steamboat hornpipe / Miss Cayton's hornpipe / Musette / Callum MacLeuan of Barra / Petronella / Northlands and fire hose reel / Teviot Brig / Mary Bain's wedding / Hundred pipers, The / Bush aboon Traquair / Hen's march / Memory / Frank Jamieson two step / Scottish salute.
MC: . . . . KITV 462

Azaad

DRUM 'N' DHOL.
LP: . . . . MUT 1078
MC: . . . . CMUT 1078

JUGNI.
MC: . . . . CMUT 1152

NACHDI JAWANI.
Tracks: / Gurdh nalo ishq mitah / Banh ghut te rumaal / Teri husan di gal / Punjaban jati / Gal sunja / Choudvin da chand / Terian khiyalan wich / Kar gai jat sharabi / Duron akhian milaveh / Nachdi jawani.
LP: . . . . MUT 1016
MC: . . . . CMUT 1016

Azala

MARRUTXIPI.
LP: . . . . ELKAR 104

Azikmen

ABORIGINES.
LP: . . . . BM 118

Aziz El Mubarak, Abdel

SOUNDS OF SUDAN VOL. 2 Songs from the city.
LP: . . . . WCB 004

Azizi

TROUBLE.
Tracks: / Midnight lover (young girl) / Don't say that it's over / Sweet thing / Evermore / Don't make me wait / Trouble / Free / Things are not the way / I betcha / (They long to be) close to you.
LP: 211685
MC: 411685

Aznavour, Charles

30 CARATS.
LP: 2C 070 72000

1980...A L'OLYMPIA.
LPS: 1092 073

AZNAVOUR SINGS AZNAVOUR VOL.3.
LP: 80472

BEST OF CHARLES AZNAVOUR.
LP: 91017

BEST OF SAMPLER.
LP: 920491

CHARLES AZNAVOUR COLLECTION 1.
Tracks: / Old fashioned way, The / Women of today / Love is new everyday / Between us / How sad Venice can be / Town, The / It will be my day / Yesterday when I was young / Ciao, always ciao / All those pretty girls / What makes a man.
LP: . . . . BALP 1
MC: . . . . KBAMC 1
LP: . . . . TAB 36

CHARLES AZNAVOUR COLLECTION 2.
Tracks: / She / Sunday is not my day / Happy anniversary / C'est fini / I live for you / Sound of your name, The / After loving you / From today / My hand needs your hand / You've got to learn / Slowly / La boheme (en Francais).
LP: . . . . BALP 2
MC: . . . . KBAMC 2

COMME ILS DISENT.
LP: 90242

DESRMAIS.
LP: 90240

EMMEZ MOI.
LP: 90239

FACE AU PUBLIC.
LP: 90250

HIER ENCORE.
LP: 90252

HIS GREATEST LOVE SONGS.
LP: . . . . NE 1078
MC: . . . . CE 2078

IL FAUT SAVOIR.
LP: 90233

IN TIMES TO BE.
Tracks: / I'll be there / In your room / Hold back the night / To be a soldier / I didn't see the time go / In times to be / Somewhere out of town / We / Daydreaming / I act as if.
MC: . . . . KBAMC 3
LP: . . . . BALP 3

JE M'VOYAIS DEJA.
LP: 90231

JE N'AI PAS VU LE TEMPS PASSER.
LP: 90055

LA BOHEME.
LP: 90237

LA MAMA.
LP: 90232

LE TEMPS.
LP: 90235

LES GRANDS SUCCESS.
LP: 90251

MY CHRISTMAS ALBUM.
Tracks: / Very private Christmas / Christmas calypso / Tell me who was born / Christmas Eve in a gambling town / Ave Maria / My own child for Christmas from you / I don't understand / Goodbye Christmas past / Snowball / Hosanna.
LP: . . . . SHM 3081
MC: . . . . HSC 3081

NON JE N'AI RIEN OUBLIE.
LP: 90241

PARIS AU MOIS D'AOUT.
LP: 90056

PLEIN FEU SUR AZNAVOUR.
LP: 90253

PRIVATE CHRISTMAS, A.
Tracks: / Very private Christmas, A / Christmas calypso / Tell me who was born / Christmas Eve in a gambling town / My own child for Christmas from you / Ave Maria / I don't understand / Goodbye Christmas past / Snowball / Hosanna.
LP: . . . . MAMLP 5002

QUI.
LP: 90234

RESTE.
LP: 90236

SHE.
MC: . . . . TC MFP 50298
LP: . . . . MFP 50298

TAPESTRY OF DREAMS.
LP: 90003

UNE PREMIERE DANSE.
Tracks: / Une premiere dnase / La legende de stenka razine.
LP: 1200 421
MC: 1300 421

VISAGES DE L'AMOUR.
LP: 90243

WE WERE HAPPY THEN.
Tracks: / Let's turn out the light.
LP: . . . . SL 5189

Azrie, Abed

EPIC OF GILGAMESH.
2LP: . . . . **SHAN 83519/20**

Aztec Camera

HIGHLAND, HARD RAIN.
Tracks: / Oblivious / Boy wonder / Walk out to Winter / We could send letters / Bugle sounds again, The / Pillar to post / Release / Lost outside the tunnel / Back on board / Down the dip.
LP: . . . . **ROUGH 47**

KNIFE.
Tracks: / Just like the USA / Head is happy (heart's insane) / Backdoor to heaven / All I need is everything / Backwards and forwards / Birth of the true / Knife / Still on fire.
LP: . . . . **WX 8**
MC: . . . . **WX 8C**

LOVE.
Tracks: / Deep and wide and tall / How men are / Everybody is a number one / More than a law / Somewhere in my heart / Working in a goldmine / One and one / Paradise / Killermont street.
LP: . . . . **WX 128**
MC: . . . . **WX 128 C**

STRAY.
LP: . . . . **WX 350**
MC: . . . . **WX 350C**

Azumah

LONG TIME AGO.
Tracks: / Emigodini yasegoli / Nkombose / Woza woza / Inkonjane mnyama / Saphelisizwe / Zamadlozi / Intombenjant / Nyamsoro / African unite.
MC: . . . . **KAZ MC 15**

Azure

AZURE (Various artists).
LP: . . . . **PMC 001**

Azymuth

AZYMUTH '85.
Tracks: / Adios lony / Dream - lost song / Who are you / Breathtaking / Potion 1 / February daze / Til bakeblikk / Potion 2.
LP: . . . . **ECM 1298**

DEPART (Azymuth with Ralph Towner).
LP: . . . . **ECM 1163**

FLAME.
LP: . . . . **M 9128**

JAZZ CARNIVAL - BEST OF AZYMUTH.
Tracks: / Jazz carnival / Dear Limmertz / Estreito de taruma / Cascade of the seven waterfalls / Missing doto / Maracana / Samba da barra / Textile factory, The / Turma do samba / Papaia / Partido alto / Pantanal il swamp.
LP: . . . . **BGP 1007**
MC: . . . . **BGPC 1007**

OUTUBRO.
Tracks: / Papsong / 500 miles high / Pantanal / Dear Limmertz / Carta pro airto / Outubro / Maracana / Un amigo.
LP: . . . . **M 9097**

RAPID TRANSIT.
Tracks: / Make mine guarana / Afternoon / Missing doto / Somewhere in Brazil / I'm just looking around / Montreux / Gate of tim e.
LP: . . . . **M 9118**

TUDO BEN.
LP: . . . . **ENVLP 533**

Azzola, Marcel

TROIS TEMPS POUR BIEN FAIRE (See under Caratini, Patrice) (Azzola, Marcel/ Patrice Caratini).

B

B-52'S

B-52'S.
Tracks: / Planet Claire / 52 Girls / Dance this mess around / Rock lobster / Lava / There's a Moon in the sky (called Moon) / Hero worship / 6060-842 / Downtown.
LP: ILPM 9580
MC: ICM 9580
LP: ILPS 9580
MC: 842 444 4

BOUNCING OFF THE SATELLITES.
Tracks: / Summer of love / Girl from Ipanema goes to Greenland / Housework / Detour thru your mind / Wig / Theme for a nude beach / Juicy jungle / Communicate / She brakes for rainbows.
LP: ILPS 9871
MC: ICT 9871
MC: ICM 2010
MC: 842 480 4

COSMIC THING.
Tracks: / Cosmic thing / Deadbeat club / Junebug / Bushfire / Topaz / Dry county / Love shack / Roam / Channel Z / Follow your bliss.
LP: WX 283
MC: WX 283C

DANCE THIS MESS AROUND (Best of the B-52's).
Tracks: / Party out of bounds / Dirty back road / Wig / Rock lobster / Give me back my man / Planet Claire / Devil in my car / 6060 842 / Dance this mess around / Strobe light / Song for a future generation.
MC: ICT 9959
LP: ILPS 9959
MC: 846238-4
LP: 846238-1

MESOPOTAMIA.
Tracks: / Loveland / Mesopotamia / Throw that beat in the garbage can / Deep sleep / Cake / Nip it in the bud.
LP: ISSP 4006
MC: ICT 4006
MC: ICM 2013
MC: 846 239 4

PARTY MIX.
Tracks: / Party out of bounds / Private Idaho / Give me back my man / Lava / Dance this mess a-round / 52 girls.
LP: IPM 1001
MC: ICT 1001
MC: ICM 2012
MC: 846 044 4

WHAMMY!.
Tracks: / Legal tender / Whammy kiss / Song for a future generation / Butterbean / Trism / Queen of Las Vegas / Don't worry / Big bird / Work that skirt.
LP: ILPS 9759
MC: ICT 9759
MC: ICM 2011
MC: 842 445 4

WILD PLANET.
Tracks: / Party out of bounds / Dirty back road / Running around / Give me back my man / Private Idaho / Quiche Lorraine / Strobelight / 53 miles West of Venus / Devils in my car, The.
LP: ILPS 9622
MC: ICT 9622
MC: ICM 2009
MC: 842 436 4

B B & Q Band

ALL NIGHT LONG.
Tracks: / All night long / Imagination / Things we do in love / Desire / Hanging out / Hard to get around / It's over / Children of the night.
LP: EST 12212

GENIE.
Tracks: / Genie / Main attraction / Won't you be with me tonight? / Don't force it / Minutes away / On the shelf / Dreamer / Riccochet.
LP: CHR 1509
MC: ZCHR 1509

B. B. Queen

IN THE MOOD (FOR SOMETHING GOOD).
Tracks: / I'm in the mood (for something good) / Now love me / Blueshouse (radio mix) / Try to find me back / No time to hesitate / We gonna rock this house / Love you nights / I wanna be next to you / Soultrain / Hey B. B. Be careful out there in the jungle / Blueshouse ballad.
LP: EMC 3591
MC: TCEMC 3591

B & G Party

B & G PARTY (Various artists).
Tracks: / Rock Creek Park: *Blackbyrds* / Glide: *Pleasure* / Straight to the bank: *Summers, Bill* / I've learned from my burns: *Spyders Webb* / Keep that same old feeling: *Side Effect* / Ghettos of the mind: *Pleasure*/ Sister Jane: *Funk Inc.*
LP: BGP 1006

B & R Brass Band

IN A CLASSICAL MOOD.
Tracks: / Radetsky march / Sonata pathetique / Troika / In the hall of the mountain king / Melody in F / Sabre dance / Russian dance / Waltz in A flat / Farandole / Easter hymn / 1812 overture / Moonlight sonata.
MC: ASK 770
LP: MTRA 2017

B. Troop

EUROPEANS.
LP: JAMS 6

Baa Baa Black Sheep

BAA BAA BLACK SHEEP (Various artists).
MC: STC 018
MC: STC 309B

Baal

BAALS' HYMN (See under Bowie, David).

Babaou

AFRIK DANCE.
LP: BA 15

Babar The Elephant

STORY OF BABAR (see De Brunhoff, Jean) (De Brunhoff, Jean (Author)).

Babatunde

DANCE TO THE BEAT OF MY DRUM (Featuring Carlos Santana).
Tracks: / Beat of my drum, The / Loyin, loyin / Ife l'oju l'aiye / Akiwowo / Se eni a fe l'amo - kere kere.
LP: BLU 706

Babbacombe Lee...

BABBACOMBE LEE AND WIDDICOMBE FAIR (Various artists).
Tracks: / Farmyard song: *Various artists* / Farmer's boy: *Various artists* / Counting song: *Various artists*/ House that Jack built, The: *Various artists* / Steamboat and Devonshire hornpipes: *Various artists* / Stag-hunting ballad: *Various artists* / Tedburn Hill: *Various artists* / Toll the bell: *Various artists* / Green grass grew all round: *Various artists* / Mallard: *Various artists* / Morty unlucky old chap: *Various artists*/ Game of all fours, The: *Various artists* / Three sons o'rogues: *Various artists* / Ladies breast knot: *Various* artists / Last sheaf of harvest: *Various artists* (Spoken word) / Schottisch: *Various artists* / Health to the barley mow: *Various artists.*
MC: 60-086

Babe Ruth

BEST OF BABE RUTH.
Tracks: / Wells Fargo (single version) / Ain't that livin' / For a few dollars more (theme from) / Private number (single version) / Joker / Dancer / Duchess of Orleans The / Black dog / If heaven's on beauty's side / Lady / Jack O'Lantern.
MC: WKFMMC 81
LP: WKFMLP 81

FIRST BASE.
LP: SHSP 4022

Babel 17

CALEANO FRAGMENTS.
LP: ARTY 025

Babes In Arms

BABES IN ARMS (Original soundtrack) (Various artists).
LP: SH 2077

BABES IN ARMS (Studio cast) (Various artists).
LP: AOS 2570
MC: BT 2570

BABES IN ARMS/BABES ON BROADWAY (Various artists).
2LP: CC 100/6-7

Babes In Toyland

SPANKING MACHINE.
LP: 891831

Babes On Broadway

BABES ON BROADWAY (See under Babes in arms) (Various artists).

Babette's Feast

BABETTE'S FEAST (Original Soundtrack) (Various artists).
LP: A 333
MC: C 333

Babs, Alice

DUKE ELLINGTON WITH ALICE BABS AND NILS LINDBERG (See Under Ellington, Duke) (Babs, Alice with Duke Ellington & Nils Lindberg Orchestras).

FAR AWAY STAR (Babs, Alice with Duke Ellington & Nils Lindberg Orchestras).
Tracks: / Far away star / Serenade to Sweden / Spaceman / Jeep's blues / Daydream / Is God a three-letter word for love? / Jump for joy / Warm valley / Blues for the maestro.
LP: PHONT 7511
MC: PHONT 8511

Babson, Marian (aut)

REEL MURDER (See under Reel Murder) (Leach, Rosemary (nar)).

Baby Boomer

ELECTRIC 70'S (Baby Boomer classics) (Various artists).
LP: BOOMER 117
MC: BOOMERC 117

LOVIN' 70'S (Baby Boomer classics) (Various artists).
LP: BOOMER 115
MC: BOOMERC 115

MELLOW 70'S (Baby Boomer classics) (Various artists).
LP: BOOMER 116
MC: BOOMERC 116

POP 70'S (Baby Boomer Classics) (Various artists).
LP: BOOMER 118
MC: BOOMERC 118

ROCKIN' 70'S (Baby Boomer classics) (Various artists).
Tracks: / Crocodile rock: *John, Elton* / Rock on: *Essex, David* / Long tall woman in a black dress: *Hollies*/ Tokoloshe man: *Kongos, John* / Toulaine: *Gibbons, Steve* / See my baby jive: *Wizzard* / You ain't seen nothin' yet: *Bachman-Turner Overdrive* / Sky high: *Jigsaw* / I shot the sheriff: *Clapton, Eric* / Your mama don't dance: *Loggins & Messina* / Black night: *Deep Purple* / Dancing on a Saturday night: *Blue, Barry*/ Up on Cripple Creek: *Band* / Witch queen of New Orleans: *Redbone* / Mississippi Queen: *Mountain* / Devil gate drive: *Quatro, Suzi* / Nutbush city limits: *Turner, Ike & Tina.*
LP: BOOMER 114
MC: BOOMERC 114

ROLLIN' 70'S (Baby Boomer classics) (Various artists).
LP: BOOMER 113
MC: BOOMERC 113

Baby Flies

COLORFUL VIEW, A.
Tracks: / Let it fall / Washing over me / Colorful view, A / Chains / Where the creatures call / Coming back to haunt you / Just the begining / Only one, The / Searching everyday / Give me the light.
LP: 338 922

RAIN.
LP: R 33/8815

Baby Ford

FORD TRAX.
Tracks: / I love it / Oochy koochy / Crashing New York / My innersence / Chikki chikki ahh ahh / Flowers / Reprise.
LP: BFORD 003
MC: BFORD 003 C

OOO - THE WORLD OF BABY FORD.
Tracks: / Place of dreams and magic, A / Milky tres / Hi, Mr. Logan / Let's talk it over / Change your words / Children of the revolution / Poem for Wican / Beach bump / World is in love, The.
LP: BFORD 5
MC: BFORD 5C

Baby Grand

BABY GRAND IN CONCERT.
Tracks: / Baby grand / Purdy purdy / Parole song / Pip pip / La pipe / Neuter suitor / Be my turpentine / I remember Albert Einstein / Myfanwy / Constable of course / Hard on the rich / Haute cuisine / Piles magic / Wop doo wop.
LP: MOR 520

Baby Lemonade

ONE THOUSAND SECRETS.
LP: DISPLP 22

Baby Let's Rock

BABY LET'S ROCK (Various artists).
LP: RR 2013

Baby Love

BABY LOVE (Original soundtrack to Lemon Popsicle 5) (Various artists).
Tracks: / Take good care of my baby: *Vee, Bobby* / Summertime blues: *Cochran, Eddie* / Teen beat: *Nelson, Sandy* / You send me: *Cooke, Sam* / Sweet little sixteen: *Berry, Chuck* / Dream lover: *Darin, Bobby*/ Rescue me: *Bass, Fontella* / Locomotion, The: *Little Eva* / Maybellene: *Berry, Chuck* / Sixteen candles: *Crests* / Splish splash: *Darin, Bobby* / He's so fine: *Chiffons* / Keep a knockin': *Little Richard*/ Crazy love: *Anka, Paul* / Apache: *Cherokees* / What a wonderful world: *Cooke, Sam* / Multiplication: *Darin, Bobby* / Pretty little angel eyes: *Lee, Curtis* / Speedy Gonzales: *Boone, Pat* / Wanderer: *Dion*/ Girl can't help it, The: *Little Richard* / Raunchy: *Justis, Billy* / Twilight time: *Platters* / Who put the bomp: *Mann, Barry* / Rhythm of the rain: *Cascades* / Only sixteen: *Cooke, Sam* / Silence is golden: *Tremeloes* / Ginny come lately: *Hyland, Brian* / Tiger: *Fabian* / End of the world: *Davis, Skeeter*/ Bend me shape me: *Amen Corner* / Wipe out: *Surfaris* / Sixteen candles: *Crests.*
2LP: RBMD 8571
MCSET: ZCRBM 8571

BABY LOVE (1) (Various artists).
LP: RONLP 11
MC: CRON 11

Baby (show)

BABY (Original Broadway cast) (Various artists).
Tracks: / Opening: *Various artists* / We start today: *Various artists* / What could be better?: *Various artists* / Plaza song: *Various artists* / Baby, baby, baby: *Various artists* / I want it all: *Various artists* / At night she comes home to me: *Various artists* / Fatherhood blues: *Various artists* / Romance: *Various artists* / I chose right: *Various artists* / Story goes on: *Various artists* / Ladies singing their song: *Various artists* / Patterns: *Various artists* / Romance 2: *Various artists* / Easier to love: *Various artists* / Romance 3: *Various artists* / Two people in love: *Various artists* / With you: *Various artists* / And what if we had loved like that?: *Various artists* / Birth: *Various artists* / Finale: *Various artists.*
LP: TER 1089
MC: ZCTER 1089

Baby Snakes

SWEET HUNGER.
Tracks: / Moonlight / Walk on water / Save me / Sixties, The / Prophet, The / Looking for strange / Sweet hunger.
LP: FOAD 7

Baby Soother

BABY SOOTHER, THE. (Various artists)
MC: JG 1

BABY SOOTHER TAPE (Various artists).
MC: ZCLUL 1

Baby Tuckoo

FIRSTBORN.
Tracks: / Hot wheels / Things aren't always what they seem / Holdin' on / Mony mony / A.W.O.L. / Baby's rocking tonight / Broken heart / Sweet rock'n'roll.
LP: CLALP 115
MC: CLAMC 115
LP: ULTRA 2

FORCE MAJEURE.
LP: MFN 56
MC: TMFN 56

Babyface

LOVERS.
LP: . . . . **ST 72552**

TENDER LOVER.
Tracks: / It's no crime / Tender lover / Let's be romantic / Can't stop my heart / My kinda girl / Where will you go (prelude) / Whip appeal / Soon as I get home / Given a chance / Sunshine / Where will you go.
LP: . . . . **MCG 6064**
MC: . . . . **MCGC 6064**
LP: **4657621**
MC: **4657628**

TENDER LOVER (IMPORT).
LP: . . . . **FZ 45288**
MC: . . . . **FZT 45288**

Babylon A Fall Down

BABYLON A FALL DOWN (See under reggae for details) (Various artists).

Babylon A.D.

BABYLON A.D..
Tracks: / Bang go the bells / Hammer swings down / Caught up in the crossfire / Desperate / Kid goes wild / Shot o'love / Maryanne / Back in Babylon / Sweet temptation / Sally danced.
LP: **210313**
MC: **410313**

Babylon (film)

BABYLON (Original soundtrack) (Various artists).
Tracks: / Deliver me from my enemies: *Yabby U* / Turn me loose: *Prophet, Michael* / Free Africa: *Yabby U*/ Whap 'n' bap 'n': *Roy, I.* / Beefy's tune: *Bovell, Dennis* / Thank you for the many things you've done: *Cassandra*/ Hey jay children: *Aswad* / Manhunter: *Bovell, Dennis* / Jazterpiece: *Bovell, Dennis* / Warrior charge: *Aswad.*
LP: . . . . **CHR 1294**
MC: . . . . **ZCHR 1294**

Babys

BABYS.
Tracks: / Looking for love / If you've got the time / I believe in love / Wild man / Laura / I love how you love me / Rodeo / Over and over / Read my stars / Dying man.
LP: . . . . **CHR 1129**
MC: . . . . **ZCHR 1129**

BABY'S ANTHOLOGY, THE.
Tracks: / Head first / Isn't it time / Midnight rendezvous / Money / Back on my feet again / Give me your love / Turn and walk away / Everytime I think of you / If you've got the time / Sweet 17.
LP: . . . . **CHR 1351**
MC: . . . . **ZCHR 1351**

BROKEN HEART.
Tracks: / Wrong or right / Give me your love / Isn't it time / And if you could see me fly / Golden mile / Broken heart / I'm falling / Rescue me / Silver dream / Piece of the action.
LP: . . . . **CHR 1150**
MC: . . . . **ZCHR 1150**

HEAD FIRST.
Tracks: / Love don't prove I'm right / Everytime I think of you / I was one / White lightning / Run to Mexico / Head first / You (got it) / Please don't leave me here / California.
LP: . . . . **CHR 1195**
MC: . . . . **ZCHR 1195**

ON THE EDGE.
Tracks: / Turn and walk away / Sweet 17 / She's my girl / Darker side of town / Rock'n'roll is / Downtown / Postcard / Too far gone / Gonna be somebody / Love won't wait.
LP: . . . . **CHR 1305**

UNION JACKS.
Tracks: / Back on my feet again / True love true confession / Union jacks / In your eyes / Anytime / Jesus are you there / Turn around in Tokyo / Love is just a mystery.
LP: . . . . **CHR 1267**

Babysitters

BABYSITTERS, THE.
Tracks: / Can you hear it / American toys / No particular place / Beard song, The / I wanna be on the T.V. / Pickin' the blues / Old L.A. / Give us a loan / Everybody loves you when you're dead / Tel Aviv / Rock 'n' roll chicken / Alright O.K..
LP: . . . . **HMRLP 35**
MC: . . . . **HMRMC 35**

Baccara

BACCARA.
Tracks: / Yes sir, I can boogie / Love you till I die / Granada / Gimme more / Koochie koo / Sorry, I'm a lady / Cara mia / Feel me / Can't help falling in love / Number one / Don't play me a symphonie.
LP: . . . . **PL 28316**
MC: . . . . **PK 28316**

COLOURS.
Tracks: / Ay sailor / For you / One, two, three, that's life / I'll learn to fly tonight / By 1999 / Body talk / Roses in the snow / Boomerang / Groovy kinda lovin' / Sing our love a lullaby.
LP: . . . . **PL 28380**

Bach, C.P.E.

FLUTE CONCERTOS (see under Dingfelder, Ingrid) (Dingfelder, Ingrid/ English Chamber Or./Sir Charles Mackerras).

TRIO SONATAS (C.P.E.BACH) (Nuovo Quatuor).
MC: . . . . **CSAR 44**

Bach, Cwrw

AWST 1AF.
Tracks: / Awst 1af.
MC: . . . . **POPDY CP3**

Bach, George

CONSTRUCTIVE ANGER.
MC: . . . . **PT 25**

Bach, J.S. (composer)

BACH (Various artists).
MC: . . . . **DLCMC 202**

BACH CONCERTOS.
MC: . . . . **RK 87991**

BRANDENBURG CONCERTOS, THE (Orchestra Of The Age Of Enlightenment).
Tracks: / Concerto no. 1 in F major / Concerto no. 2 in F major / Concerto no. 3 in G major / Concerto no. 4 in G major / Concerto no. 5 in D major.
2LP: . . . . **VCD 7907471**
MCSET: . . . . **VCD 7907474**

CHROMATIC (Cole, Maggie).
Tracks: / Chromatic fantasia and fugue in D minor / Partita no. 1 in B flat / Praleludium / Allemande / Corrente / Sarabande / Gigue / Toccata / Adagio.
LP: . . . . **VC 7907121**
MC: . . . . **VC 7907124**

COMPLETE CANTATAS V26 (BACH, JS) (Various artists).
Tracks: / Cantata BWV 103 (Bach, JS): *Various artists* / Cantata BWV 104: *Various artists* / Cantata BWV 105: *Various artists* / Cantata BWV 106: *Various artists.*
2LP: **6.35558**

COMPLETE CANTATAS V27 (BACH, JS) (Various artists).
Tracks: / Cantata BWV 107: *Various artists* / Cantata BWV 108: *Various artists* / Cantata BWV 109: *Various artists* / Cantata BWV 110: *Various artists.*
2LP: **6.35559**

COMPLETE CANTATAS V28 (BACH, JS) (Various artists).
Tracks: / Cantata BWV 111: *Various artists* / Cantata BWV 112: *Various artists* / Cantata BWV 113: *Various artists* / Cantata BWV 114: *Various artists.*
2LP: **6.35573**

COMPLETE CANTATAS V29 (BACH, JS) (Various artists).
Tracks: / Cantata BWV 115: *Various artists* / Cantata BWV 116: *Various artists* / Cantata BWV 117: *Various artists* / Cantata BWV 118: *Various artists* / Cantata BWV 119: *Various artists.*
2LP: **6.35577**

COMPLETE CANTATAS V30 (BACH, JS) (Various artists).
Tracks: / Cantata BWV 120: *Various artists* / Cantata BWV 121: *Various artists* / Cantata BWV 122: *Various artists* / Cantata BWV 123: *Various artists.*
2LP: **6.35578**

COMPLETE CANTATAS V31 (BACH, JS) (Various artists).
Tracks: / Cantata BWV 125: *Various artists* / Cantata BWV 124: *Various artists* / Cantata BWV 126: *Various artists* / Cantata BWV 127: *Various artists.*
2LP: **6.35602**

COMPLETE CANTATAS V32 (BACH, JS) (Various artists).
Tracks: / Cantata BWV 128: *Various artists* / Cantata BWV 129 (Bach, JS): *Various artists* / Cantata BWV 130: *Various artists* / Cantata BWV 131: *Various artists.*
2LP: **6.35606**

COMPLETE CANTATAS V33 (BACH, JS) (Various artists).
Tracks: / Cantata BWV 132: *Various artists* / Cantata BWV 133: *Various artists* / Cantata BWV 134: *Various artists* / Cantata BWV 135: *Various artists.*
2LP: **6.35607**

COMPLETE LUTE SUITES, THE (Isbin, Sharon).
MC: . . . . **VC 7907174**

FANTASIEN (Staier).
MC: . . . . **RK 77039**

FLUTE SONATAS (Kuijken, Sigiswald).
MC: . . . . **RK 77026**

GOLDBERG VARIATIONS (Various artists).
MC: . . . . **VETC 6516**
LP: . . . . **ECM 1395**
MC: **8396224**

JESU, JOY OF MANS DESIRING (Various artists).
MC: . . . . **VETC 6517**

MASS IN B MINOR (Herreweghe, Philippe).
Tracks: / Kyrie eleison / Gloria in excelsis / Gratias agimus / Patrem omnipotentem.
LPS: . . . . **VCD 7907571**
MCSET: . . . . **VCD 7907574**

MOTETS (Kammler).
MC: . . . . **RK 77031**

ORGAN CONCERTI (Various artists).
MC: . . . . **VETC 6515**

ORGAN MUSIC - TOCCATA & FUGUE, PASSACAGLIA (Koopman).
MC: **4278014**

PIANO WORKS - BACH, DEBUSSY, CHOPIN (See under Perlemuter, Vlado) (Perlemuter, Vlado).

SONATAS FOR VIOLIN AND KEYBOARD, THE (Various artists).
Tracks: / Sonata no.1 in B minor: *Various artists* / Sonata no.2 in A minor: *Various artists* / Sonata no.3 in E major: *Various artists* / Sonata no.4 in C minor: *Various artists* / Sonata no.5 in F minor: *Various artists*/ Sonata no.6 in G major: *Various artists.*
2LP: **5VCD 7907411**
MCSET: **5VCD 7907414**

VIOLIN CONCERTOS.
MC: **426 075-4**

Bach, Othello

LILLY, WILLY AND THE MAIL-ORDER WITCH.
MC: . . . . **CDL 51725**

WHOEVER HEARD OF A FIRD? (Performed by Joel Grey).
MC: **1735**

Bach, Richard (aut)

ILLUSIONS (See under Illusions (bk)).

JONATHAN LIVINGSTONE SEAGULL (See under Jonathan Livingstone Seagull).

Bacharach, Burt

BURT BACHARACH'S GREATEST HITS.
Tracks: / I'll never fall in love again / What the world needs now is love / (They long to be) close to you / This guy's in love with you / Wives and lovers / Reach out for me / Look of love, The / I say a little prayer / Raindrops keep falling on my head / Make it easy on yourself / Alfie / Living together growing together.
LP: . . . . **AMID 113**
MC: . . . . **CMID 113**

GREATEST HITS: BURT BACHARACH.
MCSET: . . . . **DTO 10077**

HIT MAKER - BURT BACHARACH.
LP: . . . . **HAR 8233**

IN CONCERT (Bacharach, Burt & His Orchestra).
Tracks: / Alfie / Way to San Jose / Walk on by / Come touch the sun / Raindrops keep falling on my head / Look of love / This guy's in love with you / I'll never fall in love again / Close to you / Bond Street / House is not a home, A / What the world needs now / Promises promises.
LP: . . . . **MFP 50442**

PORTRAIT IN MUSIC.
LP: . . . . **AMLS 2010**

REACH OUT.
LP: . . . . **AMLS 908**

WOMAN (Bacharach, Burt & Houston Symphony Orchestra).
Tracks: / Summer of '77 / Woman / Riverboat / Magdalena / New York lady / There is time / Dancing fool / I live in the woods.
LP: . . . . **AMLK 63709**

Bacharach & David

BURT BACHARACH/HAL DAVID SONGBOOK, THE (Various artists).
Tracks: / I say a little prayer: *Warwick, Dionne* / What the world needs now is love: *DeShannon, Jackie* / Alfie: *Black, Cilla* / Message to Michael: *Warwick, Dionne* / I just don't know what to do with myself: *Springfield,* Dusty / Do you know the way to San Jose: *Warwick, Dionne* / Twenty four hours from Tulsa: *Pitney, Gene* / (They long to be) close to you: *Monro, Matt* / You'll never get to heaven: *Warwick, Dionne* / Anyone who had a heart: *Black, Cilla* / I'll never fall in love again: *Gentry, Bobbie* / Walk on by: *Van Dyke, Leroy* / Story of my life: *Holliday, Michael* / What's new pussycat: *Jones, Tom* / This guy's in love with you: *Distel,* Sacha / Trains and boats and planes: *Kramer, Billy J.* / Make it easy on yourself: *Walker Brothers* / House is not a home, A: *Bassey, Shirley* / There's always something there to remind me: *Shaw, Sandie* / Look of love, The: *Warwick, Dionne* / Raindrops keep falling on my head: *Distel, Sacha* / Wishin' and hopin': *Merseybeats*/ Only love can break a heart: *Yuro, Timi* / Promises, promises: *Warwick, Dionne.*
2LP: . . . . **VSOPLP 128**
MC: . . . . **VSOPMC 128**

THEY WROTE THE SONGS (Various artists).
Tracks: / Walk on by: *Warwick, Dionne* / I say a little prayer: *Franklin, Aretha* / I just don't know what to do with myself: *Springfield, Dusty* / Make it easy on yourself: *Walker Brothers* / Do you know the way to San Jose?: *Warwick, Dionne* / House is not a home, A: *Vandross, Luther* / There's always something there to remind me: *Shaw,* Sandie / What the world needs now is love: *De Shannon, Jackie* / Windows of the world: *Pretenders* / I'll never fall in love again: *Gentry, Bobbie* / You'll never get to Heaven if you break my heart: *Stylistics* / Look of love, The: *Springfield, Dusty* / Trains and boats and planes: *Kramer, Billy J. & The Dakotas* / Reach out for me: *Warwick, Dionne* / (They long to be) Close to you: *Hayes, Isaac* / Anyone who had a heart: *Vandross, Luther*/ Arthur's theme: *Cross, Christopher* / This guy's in love with you: *Bacharach, Burt.*
LP: . . . . **DINTV 16**
MC: . . . . **DINMC 16**

Bachdenkel

LEMMINGS.
LP: . . . . **IRC 001**

STALINGRAD.
Tracks: / With the whole world looking over my shoulder / After the fall / Seven times tomorrow / For you to live with me / Tournament, The / Easy to be hard / Xenophon / Stalingrad (1) / Stalingrad (2).
LP: . . . . **IRC 002**

Bachelor Pad

TALES OF HOFMAN.
LP: . . . . **ILLUSION 009**

Bachelor Party (film)

BACHELOR PARTY (Original soundtrack) (Various artists).
Tracks: / American heartbeat '84: *Various artists* / Something isn't right: *Various artists* / Crazy over you: *Various artists* / Little demon: *Various artists* / Wind out: *Various artists* / Bachelor party: *Various* artists / What kind of hell: *Various artists* / Alley oop: *Various artists* / Why do good girls like bad boys: *Various artists* / Dream of the West: *Various artists* / Translation: *Various artists* / Equals: *Various* artists / Appointment with the master, An: *Various artists* / Settlement song, The: *Various artists* / Long time living: *Various artists* / Stranger still: *Various artists* / Come all ye faces: *Various artists.*
LP: . . . . **IRSA 7051**

Bachelors

6 TRACK HITS: BACHELORS.
Tracks: / Sound of silence, The / Marie / Hello Dolly / Me with all your heart / Marta / Mame.
MC: **7SC 5021**

25 GOLDEN GREATS.
LP: . . . . **WW 5068**

BACHELORS AND 16 GREAT SONGS.
LP: . . . . **LK 4614**

BACHELORS' GIRLS.
LP: . . . . **LK 4827**

BEST OF THE BACHELORS, THE.
Tracks: / Diane / Impossible dream, The / Edelweiss / With these hands / Charmaine / When the saints go marching in / No arms can ever hold you / Marie / Whispering grass / I wouldn't trade you for the world / Ramona / By the light of the silvery moon.
LP: . . . . **TAB 27**
MC: . . . . **KTBC 27**

CHARMAINE.
Tracks: / Charmaine / I'm yours / I wouldn't trade you for the world / You're breaking my heart / I wish you love / Ramona / Diane / I believe / Heartaches / Mistakes / No arms could ever hold you / Whispering.
LP: . . . . **SPR 8511**

MC: SPC 8511

COLLECTION: BACHELORS.
Tracks: / Cecilia / Gonna build a mountain / Walk with faith in your heart / Marie / Well respected / Sound of silence, The / Elusive butterfly / Chapel in the moonlight / You'll never walk alone / Mame / Marta / My foolish heart.
MCSET: DTO 10004

FOCUS ON BACHELORS.
Tracks: / Cabaret / Gonna build a mountain / Love is all / Homeward bound / Michael row the boat ashore / Wand'rin star / Climb every mountain / Ramona / With these hands / Diane / All I do is dream of you / Last thing on my mind / Scarlet ribbons / Unicorn / Mame / Hello / Dolly / Answer me / Sunrise, sunset / Sound of silence / Where the blue of the night / Phil the fluter / Love me with all your heart / 3 o'clock Flamingo Street / Well respected man / No arms can ever hold you / Charmaine / Colours of love / You'll never walk alone.
2LP: FOS 59/60

GOLDEN ALL-TIME HITS.
LP: SKL 4849

HITS OF THE SIXTIES.
LP: TXL 102

MORE GREAT SONG HITS FROM THE BACHELORS.
LP: LK 4721

WORLD OF THE BACHELORS, THE.
Tracks: / Charmaine / If ever I would leave you / Mame / My foolish heart / Marie / Love isn't love / Diane / No arms can ever hold you / He's got the whole world in his hands / You were meant for me / Sound of silence, The / Unicorn.
LP: SPA 2
MC: KCSP 2

WORLD OF THE BACHELORS, THE VOL.2.
LP: SPA 22

Bachman-Turner

B T O.
Tracks: / For the weekend / Just look at me now / My sugaree / City's still growin' / Another fool / Lost in a fantasy / Toledo / Service with a smile.
LP: CLTLP 353
MC: ZCCLT 353

BEST OF (SO FAR).
Tracks: / Blue collar / Gimme your money please / Hey you / Let it ride / Lookin' out for no.1 / Roll on down the highway / Stayed awake all night / Take it like a man / Takin' care of business / You ain't seen nothing yet.
LP: 9100 026

GREATEST HITS: BACHMAN TURNER OVERDRIVE.
Tracks: / Lookin' out for no. 1 / Hey you / Taking care of business / You ain't seen nothin' yet / Flat broke love / Rock and roll nights / Roll on down the highway / Freeways / Down down / Let it ride / Can we all come together / Jamaica.
LP: 6430 151
MC: 7420 043

LIVE FOR LIFE.
LP: IMCA 5760
MC: IMCAC 5760

NIGHTRIDING: BACHMAN-TURNER OVERDRIVE.
Tracks: / Roll on down the highway / Hey you / Freeway / Takin' care of business / Down down / You ain't seen nothing yet / Let it ride / Flat broke love / Can we all come together / Rock and roll nights / Jamaica / Looking after no. 1.
MC: KNMC 10008
LP: KNLP 10008

NOT FRAGILE.
LP: 9100 007

STREET ACTION.
LP: 9100 051

YOU AIN'T SEEN NOTHING YET.
Tracks: / Four wheel drive / She's a devil / You ain't seen nothing yet / Gimme your money please / Free wheelin' / Not fragile / Roll on down the highway / My wheels won't turn / Take it like a man.
LP: PRICE 46
MC: PRIMC 46

YOU AIN'T SEEN NOTHING YET (OLD GOLD) (See under Thin Lizzy/Boys are back in town).

Bach's Greatest Hits

BACH'S GREATEST HITS (Various artists).
MC: 40 79019

Back Door

ANOTHER FINE MESS.
Tracks: / I'm gonna stay a long, long time / Blakey Jones / T B blues / Candles round your hat / Detroit blues / Spoiler, The / Shaken by love / Streamline guitar / Manager's shirt / Dashing white sergeant.
LP: K 56098

BACK DOOR.
Tracks: / Vienna breakdown / Plantagenets, The / Lieutenant loose / Askin' the way / Turning point / Slivadiv / Jive grind / Human bed / Catcoke rag / Waltz for a wollum / Folk songs / Back door.
LP: K 46231

EIGHTH STREET NITES.
Tracks: / Roberta / It's nice when it's up / One day you're down / Walkin' blues / Bed creaks louder, The / Adolphus Beal / Linin' track / Forget me Daisy / His old boots / Country blues no.1 / Dancin' in the van.
LP: K 46265

Back From The Grave

BACK FROM THE GRAVE (Rockin' sixties punkers) (Various artists).
LP: LP 001

BACK FROM THE GRAVE VOL.3 (Mid-60's garage punkers) (Various artists).
LP: LP 003

BACK FROM THE GRAVE VOL.4 (Mid-60's garage punk screamers) (Various artists).
LP: LP 004

BACK FROM THE GRAVE VOL.5 (Crunchin' mid-60's garage punkers) (Various artists).
LP: LP 005

BACK FROM THE GRAVE VOL.6 (Wild Mid-60's garage punkers) (Various artists).
LP: LP 007

BACK FROM THE GRAVE VOL.7 (Various artists).
LP: CRYPT 013

Back in the Saddle

BACK IN THE SADDLE AGAIN (Various artists).
Tracks: / Old Chisholm trail, The: *McClintock, Harry'Haywire Mac'* / Pot wrassler, The: *Jackson, Harry* / Goldurned wheel, The: *Holyoak, Van* / When the work's all done this fall: *Sprague, Carl T.* / Streets of Laredo: *Prude, John G.* / Sioux Indians: *Williams, Marc* / Dying cowboy, The: *Allen, Jules Verne* / Tyin' knots in the devil's tail: *Jack, Powder River & Kitty Lee* / Strawberry Road: *Arizona Wranglers* / Lone star trail, The: *Maynard, Ken* / Ridge runnin' road: *Rice, Glen & His Beverly Hill Billies* / Whoopie ti yi yo: *White, John* / Cowhand's last ride, The: *Various artists* / Little old log shack I always call my home: *Carter, Wilf (Montana Slim)* / A-ridin' old paint: *Ritter, Tex* / I want to be a cowboy's sweetheart: *Montana, (Duchess) Patsy* / Cattle call: *Owens, Tex* / One more ride: *Sons Of The Pioneers* / Dim narrow trail: *Ruby, Texas* / I want to be a real cowboy girl: *Girls Of The Golden West* / Back in the saddle again: *Autry, Gene* / My dear old Arizona home: *Allen, Rex* / Cowboy stomp: *Various artists* / D-Bar-2 horse wrangler: *Critchlow, Slim* / City boarders: *Agins, Sam* / Cowboys, The: *Ohrlin, Glenn* / Rusty spurs: *Doux, Chris Le* / Cowboy song: *Riders In The Sky.*
2LP: NW 314/315

Back in the USA

BACK IN THE USA (Various artists).
MC: KNMC 15009

Back O' Benachie

BACK O' BENACHIE (Songs and ballads from the lowland East of Scotland) (Various artists).
Tracks: / Forfar soldier, The: *Various artists* / Bogieside: *Various artists* / Tarves rant, The: *Various* artists / Back O'Benachie: *Various artists* / Guise o'tough, The: *Various artists* / Bonnie hoose o' Airlie: *Various artists* / Billy Taylor: *Various artists* / I canna wah: *Various artists* / Willie Graham: *Various* artists / Orange and blue: *Various artists* / Lothian hairst: *Various artists* / Mill o'tiftys Annie: *Various artists.*
LP: 12T 180

Back On...

BACK ON THE RIGHT TRACK BABY (Various artists).
Tracks: / Walking up a one way street: *Tee, Willie* / See-saw: *Covay, Don* / Candy: *Astors* / Someday we're gonna love again: *Lewis, Barbara* / Get on the right track baby: *Charles, Ray* / Soul man: *Sam & Dave* / (Ain't that) just like me: *Coasters* / It's in his kiss: *King, Ramona* / Comin' home baby: *Torme, Mel* / Here I go again: *Bell, Archie & The Drells* / Respect: *Redding, Otis* / Last night: *Mar Keys* / Stupidity: *Burke, Solomon* / Tramp: *Redding, Otis & Carla Thomas* / Beat goes on: *Sonny & Cher* / Stay with me (baby): *Ellison, Lorraine.*
LP: KENT 091
MC: KENC 091

Back on the Road

BACK ON THE ROAD (Various artists).
Tracks: / All right now: *Free* / All along the watchtower: *Hendrix, Jimi* / Living in the past: *Jethro Tull* / Hocus pocus: *Focus* / Eight miles high: *Byrds, The* / Rainbow chaser: *Nirvana* / America (2nd Amendment): *Nice* / Northern sky: *Drake, Nick* / On the road again: *Canned Heat* / Paranoid: *Black Sabbath* / White rabbit: *Jefferson Airplane* / Mona: *Quicksilver Messenger Service* / My white bicycle: *Tomorrow* / Love really changed me: *Spooky Tooth* / Race with the devil: *Gun* / 10.30 returns to the bedroom: *Soft Machine* / Silver machine: *Hawkwind* / Meet on the ledge: *Fairport Convention* / Fire: *Crazy World of Arthur Brown* / Woodstock: *Matthews Southern Comfort* / Paper sun: *Traffic* / Do it: *Pink Fairies* / Tom Tiddler's ground: *Harper, Roy* / Black night: *Deep Purple* / Out demons out: *Broughton, Edgar Band* / Love like a man: *Ten Years After* / Venus in furs: *Velvet Underground* / Fresh garbage: *Spirit* / One and one is one: *Medicine Head* / Change song: *Blodwyn Pig* / Something in the air: *Thunderclap Newman.*
2LP: SMR 854
MCSET: SMC 854

Back Street Crawler

2ND STREET.
Tracks: / Selfish lover / Blue soul / Stop doing what you're doing / Raging river / Some kind of happy / Sweet beauty / Just for you / On your life / Leaves in the wind.
LP: K 50267

Back to Buchan

BACK TO BUCHAN (Various artists).
MC: CJR 002

Back to School

BACK TO SCHOOL/ PEE WEE'S BIG ADVENTURE (See under 'Pee Wee's big adventure') (Various artists).

Back to Sing...

BACK TO SING FOR FREE AGAIN (Various artists).
MC: 1

Back to the Alley

BACK TO THE ALLEY (Various artists).
LP: LTD 601

Back to the Future

BACK TO THE FUTURE (Film soundtrack) (Various artists).
Tracks: / Johnny B. Goode: *McFly, Marty & the Starlighters* / Power of love, The: *Lewis, Huey & The News* / Time bomb town: *Buckingham, Lindsey* / Back to the future: *Silvestri, Alan* / Heaven is one step away: *Clapton, Eric* / Back in time: *Lewis, Huey & The News* / Back to the future overture: *Silvestri, Alan* / Wallflower (dance with me, Henry): *James, Etta* / Night train: *Berry, Marvin & the Starlighters* / Earth angel: *Berry, Marvin & the Starlighters.*
LP: MCF 3285
MC: MCFC 3285

BACK TO THE FUTURE II (Film Soundtrack) (Various artists).
Tracks: / Back to the future II (main theme): *Various artists* / Hoverboard chase: *Various artists* / My father: *Various artists* / If they ever did: *Various artists* / Book, The: *Various artists* / Burn the book: *Various* artists / Western union: *Various artists* / Future, The: *Various artists* / Flying delorean, A: *Various* artists / Alternate 1985: *Various artists* / Pair of Docs: *Various artists* / Tunnel chase: *Various artists* / Back to the future II (end title): *Various artists.*
LP: MCG 6072
MC: MCGC 6072

BACK TO THE FUTURE PART III (Various artists).
Tracks: / Back to the future part III (main title): *Various artists* / It's Clara: *Various artists* / Train, The (part II): *Various artists* / Hill Valley: *Various artists* / Hanging, The: *Various artists* / At first sight: *Various artists* / Indians: *Various artists* / Goodbye Clara: *Various artists* / Doc returns: *Various artists* / Point of no return: *Various artists* / Future isn't written, The: *Various artists* / Showdown, The: *Various artists* / Doc to the rescue: *Various artists* / Kiss, The: *Various artists* / We're out of gas: *Various artists* / Wake up juice: *Various artists* / Science experiment: *Various artists* / Doubleback: *Various artists* / Back to the future part III (end credits): *Various artists.*
LP: VS 5272
MC: VSC 5272

Backhouse, Miriam

GYPSY WITHOUT A ROAD.
LP: MUM 1203

Backlash (film)

BACKLASH (Film soundtrack) (Various artists).
LP: CRIMP 126
LP: PLAY 002

Backroom Joys

BACKROOM JOYS (London 1951-52) (Various artists).
LP: S 1290

Backsliders

NATIONAL NIGHTMARE.
Tracks: / National nightmare / Gotta be right / Undertaker / Hear me howlin / Did you no wrong / Do it again / I blow my head away / I just wanna play / Snakeskin cowboys / Fighting, riding, having fun.
LP: HMILP 103
MC: HMIMC 103

Backstage

BACKSTAGE.
Tracks: / Tell me / Movin' on / This kind of blues / Keep on lovin' / I'll never get there / Let your daddy role / You get me like you want / Cold water flat blues / That's wrong / Going back on the road / Boogie woogie.
LP: SNTF 852

Backstreet (film)

BACKSTREET (Original soundtrack) (Various artists).
LP: DL 79097

Backtrack Blues Band

KILLIN' TIME.
Tracks: / Killin' time / Heavy built woman / Cruesin' for a bluesin' / Like it or not / Work to do / Babe oh babe / Come on to me mama / Don't need nobody / I make my home in Florida / You'll come back someday.
LP: ICH 9005
MC: ICH 9005MC

Backus, Gus

DAMALS.
Tracks: / Wooden heart / Sieben susse girls (seven little girls) / Hatt' ich dock ein girl (if I had a girl) / Brauner Bar und weisse Taube (running bear) / Ab und zu (a fool such as I) / Das ist viel zu schon, um wahr zu sein / Baby deine beine (lyin' kisses) / Ich bin traurig, wenn du gehst (have you ever / Damals (your love) / Wein' nicht mehr (teenage tears) / Blue boy / Ich leibe dich so sehr (a story of my love) / Ich steh' an der Bar und habe kein geld (a pub / Da sprach der alte hauptling / Big Willie broke jail tonight / Short on love.
LP: BFX 15052

Backwoods Band

JES' FINE.
LP: ROUNDER 0128

Bacon Fat

GREASE ONE FOR ME.
LP: OLLP 5309

Bad Beach

CORNUCOPIA.
Tracks: / Morgan Le Fey / Armageddon son / Bad beach / Septa salina / Beach patrol / Dionysus / Bad trip / Blind fate / Purple indian / Level 45 / It's always better / Victim of society / All systems go / Zero is born, A / Puppy killer, The / End of the day.
LP: ACHE 04

CUT IT OFF.
Tracks: / Cut it off / Widey's County / You are in me / Big whole, The / Self destruct / Cut me up / Inside / Fat American, The / Slagheap / Skull rise / Push and pull.
LP: K 044/122

Bad Boy Orchestra

STILL BUGGIN'.
LP: TAILP 4444

Bad Brains

BAD BRAINS.
MC: A 106

BAD BRAINS LIVE.
LP: SST 160 LP
MC: SST 160 CA

I AGAINST I.
LP: SST 065

QUICKNESS.
Tracks: / Soul craft / Voyage into infinity / Messengers, The / With the quickness / Gene machine / Don't bother me / Don't blow bubbles / Sheba / Yout juice / No conditions / Silent tears / Prophets eye, The / Endtro.
LP: CARLP 4
MC: CARC 4

ROCK FOR LIGHT.
LP: . . . . PVC 8933
MC: . . . . PVCC 8933
LP: . . . . CARLP 12
MC: . . . . CARC 12

YOUTH ARE GETTING RESTLESS, THE (Live at the Paradiso, Amsterdam 1987).
Tracks: / I / Rock for light / Right brigade / House of suffering / Day tripper / She's a rainbow / Coptic times / Sacred love / Re-ignition / Let me help / Youth are getting restless, The / Banned in DC / Sailin' on / Fearless vampire killer / At the movies / Revolution (dub) / Pay to cum / Big takeover.
MC: . . . . CARC 8
LP: . . . . CARLP 8

Bad Company

10 FROM 6.
Tracks: / Can't get enough / Feel like makin' love / Run with the pack / Shooting star / Movin' on / Bad Company / Rock 'n' roll fantasy / Electric land / Ready for love / Live for the music.
MC: . . . . WX 31 C
LP: . . . . WX 31

BAD COMPANY.
LP: . . . . ILPS 9279
MC: . . . . ICT 9279

BURNIN' SKY.
LP: . . . . ILPS 9441

DANGEROUS AGE.
Tracks: / One night / Shake it up / No smoke without fire / Bad man / Dangerous age / Dirty boy / Rock of America / Something about you / Way it goes, The / Love attack.
LP: . . . . K 781 884 1
MC: . . . . K 781 884 4

DESOLATION ANGELS.
Tracks: / Rock 'n' roll fantasy / Crazy circles / Gone, gone, gone / Evil wind / Early in the morning / Lonely for your love / Oh, Atlanta / Take the time / Rhythm machine / She brings me love.
LP: . . . . SSK 59408
MC: SK4 59408

FAME AND FORTUNE.
Tracks: / Burning up / This love / Fame and fortune / Long walk / Valerie / Hold on my heart / That girl / When we made love / If I'm sleeping / Tell it like it is.
LP: . . . . WX 69
MC: . . . . WX 69 C

HOLY WATER.
LP: 7567 91371 1
MC: 7567 91371 4

ROUGH DIAMONDS.
Tracks: / Electric land / Untie the knot / Nuthin' on the TV / Painted face / Kickdown / Ballad of the band / Cross country boy / Old Mexico / Downhill ryder / Racetrack.
LP: . . . . SSK 59419

RUN WITH THE PACK.
Tracks: / Live for the music / Simple man / Honey child / Love me somebody / Run with the pack / Silver blue and gold / Young blood / Do right by your woman / Sweet lil' sister / Fade away.
LP: . . . . ILPS 9346
MC: . . . . ICT 9346

STRAIGHT SHOOTER.
Tracks: / Good lovin' gone bad / Feel like makin' love / Weep no more / Shooting star / Deal with the preacher / Wild fire women / Anna / Call on me.
LP: . . . . ILPS 9304
MC: . . . . ICT 9304

Bad Dooleys

BAD DOOLEYS.
LP: KIX4U 3344
LP: . . . . ROCK 3344

SHARK ATTACK.
LP: KIX4U 2226
LP: . . . . PLAT 2226

Bad Dream Fancy Dress

CHOIRBOYS GAS.
Tracks: / Supremes, The / Lemon tarts / Choirboys gas / Where have all the schoolboys gone / Foreign muck / Discotheque / Kick in the teeth / Dali's diet / Leigh-On-Sea / Curry crazy / Colour problem / Rave up.
LP: . . . . ACME 18

Bad Dreams (film)

BAD DREAMS (Film soundtrack) (Various artists).
LP: 704.560

Bad Dress Sense

GOODBYE...IT WAS FUN.
Tracks: / G C B / Could I ever / Truth / Cynical smile / Life's demand / Never mine / Always away / Need to love.
LP: . . . . SOL 4

Bad English

BAD ENGLISH.
Tracks: / Best of what I got / Heaven is a 4 letter word / Possession / Forget me not / When I see you smile / Tough times don't last / Ghost in your heart / Price of love / Ready when you are / Lay down / Restless ones, The / Rockin' horse / Don't walk away.
LP: 4634471
MC: 4634474

B.A.D. II

GLOBE, THE.
LP: 4677061
MC: 4677064

Bad Influence (film)

BAD INFLUENCE (Film Soundtrack) (Various artists).
LP: . . . . MLPS 1067
MC: . . . . MCT 1067

Bad Karma Beckons

MUTATE AND SURVIVE.
Tracks: / Mutate and survive.
LP: . . . . MB 15

Bad Lizard

POWER OF DESTRUCTION.
LP: . . . . RR 9728

Bad Luck 'N' Trouble

BAD LUCK 'N TROUBLE (Various artists).
LP: . . . . ARHOOLIE 1018

Bad Manners

ANTHOLOGY - BAD MANNERS.
LP: . . . . BBSLP 014
MC: . . . . BBSMC 014

BEST OF BAD MANNERS.
Tracks: / Lip up fatty / Special brew / Lorraine / Just a feeling / Can can / My girl lollipop / Walking in the sunshine / Skaville U.K. / This is ska / Midnight rider / You fat ... / Christmas time again / Gonna get along without you now.
LP: . . . . BBSLP 010
MC: . . . . BBSMC 010

CAN CAN.
Tracks: / Can can / My girl lollipop / Walking in the sunshine / Special brew / Runaway / Echo / El pussy cat / Here comes the major / Lip up fatty / Lorraine / Under sea adventures of Ivor the Engine / Tequila / Never will change.
LP: . . . . SHM 3138
MC: . . . . HSC 3138

FORGING AHEAD (IV FOR ENTERTAINMENT).
Tracks: / Salad bar / Tonight is your night / Samson and Delilah / Exodus / Got no brains / Rose of Italy / My girl lollipop / Falling out of love / Seventh heaven.
LP: . . . . MAGL 5050
MC: . . . . ZCMAG 5050

GOSH IT'S BAD MANNERS.
Tracks: / Walking in the sunshine / Dansetta / Can-can / Weeping and wailing / Casablanca / Don't be angry / Ben. E. Wriggle / Runaway / Never change / Only funkin' / End of the world / Gherkin.
LP: . . . . MAGL 5043
MC: . . . . ZCMAG 5043

HEIGHT OF BAD MANNERS, THE.
Tracks: / Special brew / Ne ne na na na na nu nu / Lip up fatty / Wooly bully / Lorraine / Just a feeling / Inner London violence / Buona sera / Walking in the sunshine / Can can / Samson and Delilah / My girl lollipop / Got no brains / Elizabethan reggae / Falling out of love / That'll do nicely.
LP: . . . . STAR 2229
MC: . . . . STAC 2229

LIVE AND LOUD.
LP: . . . . LINK LP 07

LOONEE TUNES.
Tracks: / Echo / Just a feeling / El pussy cat / Doris / Spy I / Tequila / Lorraine / Echo gone wrong / Suicide / Under sea adventures of Ivor the Engine / Back in '60 / Just pretending.
LP: . . . . MAGL 5038
MC: . . . . ZCMAG 5038

RETURN OF THE UGLY.
Tracks: / Skaville UK / Sally Brown / Since you've gone away / Rosemary / Bonanza ska / Return of the ugly / Hey little girl / Buffalo ska / Memory train / This is ska / Gonna get along without you now.
LP: . . . . BBSLP 002
MC: . . . . BBSMC 002

SKA 'N' B.
Tracks: / Ne ne na na na na nu nu / Here comes the major / Fattie fattie / King ska fa / Monster mash / Calonia / Magnificent seven, The / Wooly bully / Lip up fatty / Special brew / Inner London violence.
LP: . . . . MAGL 5033
MC: . . . . ZCMAG 5033

Bad News

BAD NEWS.
Tracks: / Hey hey Bad News / Warriors of Ghengis Khan / Bohemian rhapsody / Bad News / Masturbike / Drink till I die.
LP: . . . . EMC 3535
MC: . . . . TCEMC 3535

BOOTLEG.
Tracks: / Bad dreams / AGM / Double entendre / Locked in / Aids / O levels / Wedding / H.M. farmer / Masturbike / Cashing in on Christmas (dub).
LP: . . . . EMC 3542
MC: . . . . TCEMC 3542

Bad Religion

AGAINST THE GRAIN.
LP: . . . . E 864091

Bad River Band

WHISTLE STOP.
MC: . . . . VCA 043

Bad Seed

J-BECK STORY, THE.
LP: . . . . EVA 12034

Bad Steve

KILLING THE NIGHT.
LP: . . . . SKULL 8370

Bad & the Beautiful

BAD AND THE BEAUTIFUL (1952 Film Soundtrack) (Various artists).
MC: 422 385 4

Badalmenti, Angelo

MUSIC FROM TWIN PEAKS.
LP: 7599263161
MC: 7599263164

Badarou, Wally

BACK TO SCALES TONIGHT.
LP: 1091 065

ECHOES.
Tracks: / Keys / Hi life / Mambo / Voices / Canyons / Endless race / Chief inspector / Waltz / Jungle / Rain.
LP: . . . . ILPS 9822
MC: . . . . ICT 9822

KISS OF THE SPIDER WOMAN (See under Kiss of the spider woman).

WORDS OF A MOUNTAIN.
MC: . . . . ICT 9897
LP: . . . . ILPS 9897
MC: . . . . ICM 2008

Baddeley, John (nar)

MYSTERY OF TALLY-HO COTTAGE, THE (see under Blyton, Enid (aut)) (Morgan, Liz & John Baddeley (nars)).

MYSTERY OF THE BURNT COTTAGE, THE (see under Blyton, Enid (author)) (Morgan, Liz & John Baddeley (nars)).

MYSTERY OF THE STRANGE MESSAGES, THE (see under Blyton, Enid (author)) (Morgan, Liz & John Baddeley (nars)).

Baddoo International

TROUBLE AT HOME.
LP: . . . . BDD 001

Badel, Sarah (nar)

SENSE AND SENSIBILITY (See under Austen, Jane).

Badfinger

AIRWAVES.
Tracks: / Airwaves / Look out California / Lost inside your love / Love is gonna come at last / Sympathy / Winner, The / Dreamer, The / Come down hard / Sail away.
LP: . . . . K 52129

DAY AFTER DAY (LIVE).
LP: . . . . ESSLP 135
MC: . . . . ESSMC 135

MAGIC CHRISTIAN MUSIC.
Tracks: / Come and get it / Crimson ship / Dear Angie / Fisherman (version 2) / Midnight sun / Beautiful and blue / Rock of all ages / Carry on till tomorrow / I'm in love / Walk out in the rain / Angelique / They're knocking down our home / Give it a try / Maybe tomorrow / Storm in a teacup / Arthur.
2LP: . . . . SAPCOR 12
MC: . . . . TCSAPCOR 12

SHINE ON.
Tracks: / I miss you / Song for a lost friend / Lonely you / Andy Norris / Just a chance / Dreamin' / Shine on / Why don't we talk / Island / In the meantime, some other time / Know one knows.
LP: . . . . ED 302

Badgeman

KINGS OF THE DESERT.
Tracks: / Secret diary of Jim Morrison's bastard / Sean's seen the light / Cupid's exploding harpoon / King of the desert / Montezuma's revenge / My flash on you / Crystals / Extraordinary girl / False yellow eyes / Make me feel / Going sane gain / P.A.F.
LP: . . . . PAPLP 003

Badlands

BADLANDS.
LP: 781 966-1
MC: 781 966-4

VOODOO HIGHWAY.
MC: 7567822512
LP: 7567822511

Badowski, Henry

LIFE IS A GRAND.
Tracks: / My face / Henry's in love / Swimming with the fish in the sea / Inside out / Life is a grand / Silver trees / This was meant to be / Anywhere else / Baby sign here with me / Rampant.
LP: . . . . AMLH 68527

Baerwald, David

BEDTIME STORIES.
Tracks: / All for you / Dance / Best inside you / Sirens in the city / Walk through fire / In the morning / Good times / Hello Mary / Young anymore / Liberty lies / Colette / Stranger.
LP: 3952891
MC: 3952894

Baez, Joan

100 MINUTES OF JOAN BAEZ.
MC: . . . . ZCTON 106

ANY DAY NOW.
Tracks: / Love minus zero / No limit / You ain't goin' nowhere / Drifter's escape / I pity the poor immigrant / Tears of rage / Sad eyed lady of the Lowlands / Love is just a four letter word / I dreamed I saw St. Augustine / Walls of red wing, The / Dear landlord / One too many mornings / I shall be released / Boots of Spanish leather / Walkin' down the line / Restless farewell.
2LP: . . . . VSD 79306/7
MCSET: . . . . CVSD 79306/7

BALLAD BOOK VOL.1, THE.
LP: . . . . VFLP 5106
MC: . . . . VFTC 6106

BALLAD BOOK VOL 2, THE.
LP: . . . . VFLP 5108
MC: . . . . VFTC 6108

BAPTISM.
LP: . . . . VFLP 5103
MC: . . . . VFTC 6103

BEST OF JOAN BAEZ.
Tracks: / Diamonds and rust / Prison trilogy (Billy Rose) / Never dreamed you'd leave in summer / Please come to Boston / Sweeter for me / Gracias a la vida / Forever young / Simple twist of fate / Love song to a stranger / Children and all that jazz / Imagine / Night they drove old Dixie down, The.
MCSET: . . . . DTO 10078
LP: . . . . SHM 3173
MC: . . . . HSC 3173

BLESSED ARE....
Tracks: / Blessed are / Night they drove old Dixie down, The / Salt of the earth / Three horses / Brand new Tennessee waltz / Last lonely and wretched / Lincoln freed me today / Outside the Nashville City Limits / San Francisco Mabel Joy / When time is stolen / Heaven help us all / Angeline / Help me make it through the night / Let it be / Put your hand in the hand / Gabriel / And me / Milanese waltz / Marie Flore / Hitchhikers song, The / 33rd of August, The / Fifteen months.
2LP: . . . . VSD 6570/1

CONTEMPORARY BALLAD BOOK.
Tracks: / North country blues / It ain't me babe / Children of darkness / E'era un ragazzo che come me amaya / Beatles E I Rolling stones / I am a poor way faring stranger / Birmingham Sunday / San Francisco Mabel Joy / Be not too hard / Restless farewell / Rangers command / Long black veil / Hickory wind / Lady came from Baltimore, The / I dreamed I saw St. Augustine / Tramp on the street / Saigon bride / Donna Donna / Song in the blood / Magic wood, The / Babe I'm gonna leave you.
2LP: . . . . VSD 49

COUNTRY MUSIC.
Tracks: / Take me back to the sweet sunny South / Hickory wind / Will the circle be unbroken / Tramp on the street / Carry it on / Gospel ship / Little Moses / Banks of the Ohio / Engine 143 / Pal of mine / Night they drove old Dixie down / Brand new Tennessee waltz / Outside the Nashville city limits / Ghetto, The / My home's across the Blue Ridge Mountains / Rock salt and nails / Help me make it through the night / Long black veil / I still miss someone / San Francisco Mabel Joy.
2LP: . . . . VSD 105

2LP: . . . . VSD 79200

DIAMONDS AND RUST IN THE BULLRING.
Tracks: / Diamonds and rust / No woman no cry / Swing low sweet chariot / El preso numero nuevo / Txoria txori / Gracias a la vida / Ain't gonna let nobody turn me round / Famous blue raincoat / Let it be / Llego con tres heridas / Ellas danzan solas (cueca sola) / No nos moveran.
MC: . . . . TCVGC 9
LP: . . . . VGC 9
MC: . . . . OVEDC 387

EUROPEAN TOUR.
Tracks: / Boxer, The / Don't cry for me Argentina / Cracias a la vida / Rose / Donna Donna / Diamonds and rust / Jari ya hamoude / Cambodia / Soyuz druzyei / Here's to you / Blowin' in the wind.
LP: . . . . PRT 84790

FIRST TEN YEARS.
Tracks: / Ghetto, The / If I were a carpenter / Silver dagger / Love is just a four letter word / There but for fortune / Will the circle be unbroken / John Riley / You ain't goin' nowhere / Mary Hamilton / Carry it on / Manha de carnaval / If I knew.
2LP: . . . . VSD 6560/1

FIRST TEN YEARS.
LP: 6635 003

HITS GREATEST AND OTHERS.
Tracks: / Night they drove old Dixie down, The / Dangling conversation, The / Help me make it through the night / Blessed are / Eleanor Rigby / Let it be / There but for fortune / Brand new Tennessee waltz / I pity the poor immigrant / Love is just a four letter word / Heaven help us all.
LP: . . . . VSD 79332

HONEST LULLABY.
Tracks: / Let your love flow / No woman, no cry / Light a light / She sings at the end of the movie / Before the deluge / Honest lullaby / Michael / For Sasha / For all we know / Free at last.
LP: . . . . PRT 83474

JOAN BAEZ.
Tracks: / Silver dagger / East Virginia / Ten thousand miles / House of the rising sun / All my trials / Wildwood flower / Donna Donna / John Riley / Rake and the rambling boy / Little Moses / Mary Hamilton / Henry Martin / El preso numero nuevo.
LP: . . . . VSD 79073
LP: . . . . TFL 6002

JOAN BAEZ BALLAD BOOK, THE.
Tracks: / East Virginia / Henry Martin / All my trials / Old blue / House of rising son / Wagoner's lad / Black is the colour of my true love's hair / Lily of the west / Silkie / House carpenter / Trees they do grow high, The / 10,000 miles / Barbara Allen / Jackaroe / John Riley / Matty Groves / Queen of hearts / Fe-nario / Go way from my window / Railroad boy / Mary Hamilton / Once I had a sweetheart / Silver dagger.
2LP: . . . . VSD 41-2

JOAN BAEZ IN CONCERT.
Tracks: / Babe / I'm gonna leave you / Geordie / Copper kettle / Kubaya / What have they done to the rain / Black is the colour of my true love's hair / Danger water / Gospel ship / House carpenter / Pretty boy Floyd / Lady Mary / Ate amanha / Matty Groves.
LP: . . . . VSD 79112

JOAN BAEZ IN CONCERT.
2LP: . . . . VSD 23007/8

JOAN BAEZ IN CONCERT VOL.2.
Tracks: / Once I had a sweetheart / Jackaroe / Don't think twice / We shall overcome / Portland Town / Queen of hearts / Manha de carnaval / Te ador / Long black veil / Fennario / Ne belle cardillo / With God on our side / Three fishers / Hush little baby / Battle Hymn of the republic.
LP: . . . . VSD 79113
LP: . . . . TFL 6033

JOAN BAEZ ON VANGUARD.
LP: . . . . SVXL 100

JOAN BAEZ VOL.5.
Tracks: / There but for fortune / Stewball / It ain't me babe / Death of Queen Jane, The / Child No.170 / Bachianas Brasileires No.5 -Aria / Go 'way from my window / I still miss someone / When you hear them cuckoos hollerin' / Birmingham Sunday / So we'll go no more a- roving / O'Cangaceiro / Unquiet grave, The / Child No. 78.
LP: . . . . VSD 79160
LP: . . . . TFL 6043

LIVE EUROPE '83'.
LP: 206.742
MC: 205 742

LOVE SONGS: JOAN BAEZ.
Tracks: / Come all ye fair and tender maidens / No limit / Sweet Sir Galahad / Love is just a four letter word / Wild mountain thyme / Lass from the low country, The / Sad eyed lady of the lowlands / Plaisir d'amour.
2LP: . . . . VSD 79
MC: . . . . ZC VSD 79

NIGHT THEY DROVE OLD DIXIE DOWN.
Tracks: / Night they drove old dixie down, The / Brand new Tennessee waltz / Outside the Nashville City limits / Ghetto, The / My home's across the blue ridge mountains / Rock salt and nails / Help me make it through the night / Long black veil / I still miss someone / San Francisco Mabel Joy.
MC: . . . . VFTC 6104
LP: . . . . VFLP 5104

NOEL.
LP: . . . . VFLP 5107
MC: . . . . VFTC 6107

ONE DAY AT A TIME.
Tracks: / Sweet Sir Galahad / No expectations / Long black veil / Ghetto, The / Carry it on / Take me back to the sweet sunny south / Seven bridges road / Jolie blonde / Joe Hill / Song for David / One day at a time.
LP: . . . . VSD 79310

RECENTLY.
Tracks: / Brothers in arms / Recently / Asimbonanga / Moon is a harsh mistress, The / James and the gang / Let us break bread together / MLK / Do right woman, do right man / Biko.
LP: . . . . VGC 1
MC: . . . . TCVGC 1
MC: . . . . OVEDC 354
LP: . . . . OVED 354

SPEAKING OF DREAMS.
Tracks: / China / Warriors of the sun / Carrickfergus / Hand to mouth / Speaking of dreams / El Salvador / Rambler gambler / Whispering bells / Fairfax county / A mi manera (Only on CD and MC.).
MC: . . . . TCVGC 12
LP: . . . . VGC 12
MC: . . . . OVEDC 371

SPOTLIGHT ON JOAN BAEZ.
Tracks: / There but for fortune / Lady came from Baltimore, The / Suzanne / Don't think twice / All my trials / We shall overcome / It's all over now baby blue / Farewell Angelina / It ain't me babe / If I were a carpenter / Joe Hill / Long black veil / Love's just a four letter word / Love minus zero / No limit / Blessed are / What have they done to the rain / I shall be released / Sagt Mir wo die blumen sind / Night they drove old Dixie down, The / Eleanor Rigby / Donna Donna / Colours / Let it be / Hush little baby.
2LP: . . . . SPOT 1008
MC: . . . . ZCSPT 1008

VERY EARLY JOAN.
Tracks: / Last night I had the strangest dream / Willie Moore / She's a trouble maker / Tears in my eyes / Somebody got lost in a storm / Water is wide, The / Man of constant sorrow / Freight train / Lady Gay / Johnny Cuckoo / Lonesome valley / Riddle song, The / Streets of Laredo / Railroad Bill / My good old man / Little darlin' / In the pines / Pilgrim of sorrow / Where have all the flowers gone / Rambler gambler / Come all ye fair and tender maidens / Hallowed be thy name / Twelve gates to the city / Silver dagger.
2LP: . . . . VSD 79436
MCSET: . . . . ZCVS 79436

WHERE ARE YOU NOW MY SON.
LP: . . . . AMLS 64390

Bag Of Sleepers

FRIDAY NIGHT VOL 1 (1927-32).
LP: . . . . ARCADIA 2003

HOT LICKS VOL 2 (1927-30).
LP: . . . . ARCADIA 2004

SPIKED BEER VOL 3 (1927-30).
LP: . . . . ARCADIA 2005

Bagatelle

ARE WE KEEPING YOU UP.
LP: 2904 024

BAGATELLE.
Tracks: / Second violin / Trump card / Love is the reason.
LP: 2904 023
LP: . . . . POLS 1047

CRY AWAY THE NIGHT.
2LP: . . . . HM 029D

GOLD: BEST OF BAGATELLE.
Tracks: / Summer in Dublin / Love is the reason / Is it raining in Paris tonight? / Jersey girl / Lesson street lady / Rock 'n' roll fantasy / Outrageous / Second violin / Trump card / Johnny set 'em up tonight / Baby's looking good tonight / I need you / Hurting inside / All fall down Philadelphia.
LP: 827 223-1
MC: 827 223-4

Baghdad Cafe (film)

BAGHDAD CAFE (Film soundtrack) (Various artists).
Tracks: / Calling you: *Steele, Jevette* / Zwifach: *Blasmusik, Deihinger* / C major prelude: *Flagg, Darron*/ Calling you: *Telson, Bob* / Blues harp: *Galison, William* / Brenda, Brenda: *Steele, Jevette* / Calliope: *Telson, Bob.*
MC: . . . . ICT 18
LP: . . . . ISTA 18
MC: . . . . ICM 2005
MC: 842 817 4

Bagley, Desmond (aut)

FLYAWAY (BOOK) (See under Flyaway (book)) (Barron, Keith (nar)).

JUGGERNAUT (See under Juggernaut) (Marinker, Peter (nar)).

RUNNING BLIND (See under Running Blind) (Jarvis, Martin (nar)).

SNOW TIGER, THE (See under Snow Tiger) (Davenport, Nigel (nar)).

Baglin, Lyndon

BEST OF BRASS (Baglin, Lyndon group).
Tracks: / Marching the blues / Child's play / Capriol suite / Endearing young charms / Dance of the Russian sailors / Little serenade / Fantasia on 'Tico tico' / Walkabout / Landscape / Cheeky little charleston / Brass bandinerie / Summer knows, The / Una paloma blanca / Dance of the tumblers / Li'l darlin' / Lezghinka.
LP: . . . . SDL 347
MC: . . . . CSDL 347

Bahumutsi

BUSANG MEROPA (Bring Back the Drums).
LP: . . . . SFB 001A
MC: . . . . SFB 001C

Bailey, Admiral

BORN CHAMPION.
LP: . . . . DSR 4817

UNDISPUTED.
MC: . . . . DSRC 1078

Bailey, Benny

BIG BRASS.
LP: . . . . CS 9011

EAST OF ISAR (Bailey, Benny/Sal Nistico).
LP: . . . . EGO 4010

FOR HEAVEN'S SAKE (Bailey, Benny Quintet).
Tracks: / Little jazz / Blues East / Peruvian nights / Mood indigo / For heaven's sake / One for Wilton / No mo blues.
LP: . . . . HH 1006
MC: . . . . HHMC 1006

ISLANDS.
LP: . . . . ENJA 2082

SERENADE TO A PLANET.
LP: . . . . EGO 4004

Bailey Brothers

JUST AS THE SUN WENT DOWN.
LP: . . . . ROUNDER 0056

TAKE ME BACK TO HAPPY VALLEY.
LP: . . . . ROUNDER 0030

Bailey, Buster

ALL ABOUT MEMPHIS.
Tracks: / Bear wallow / Hatton Avenue and Gayoso Street / Sunday parade / Beale street blues / Memphis blues / Chicasaw bluff / Hot water ba you.
LP: . . . . AFF 170

COMPLETE RECORDINGS 1934-1940.
Tracks: / Call of the Delta / Shanghai shuffle / Afternoon in Africa / Dizzy debutante / Planters punch / Sloe jam fizz / Chained to a dream / Light up / Man with a horn goes berzerk / Should I / Blue room / April in Paris / Am I blue / Seems like a month of Sundays / Fable of the rose / Pinetop's boogie woogie / Eccentric rag.
LP: . . . . RARITIES 17

VARSITY SESSIONS VOL.1, THE (Bailey, Buster & His Orchestra).
LP: . . . . SLP 701

Bailey, Chris

CASABLANCA.
LP: . . . . ROSE 20

WHAT WE DID ON OUR HOLIDAYS.
LP: . . . . ROSE 30

Bailey, Dave

DAVE BAILEY AND HIS FRIENDS.
Tracks: / Snake rag / Isle of Capri / Lily of the valley / Blues for pop / Darkness on the delta / Sweet Georgia Brown / Ice cream / Rose room / New Orleans hula / Over the rainbow / Burgundy Street blues / Four leaved clover / St. Phillipe St. Breakdown.
MC: . . . . CMJMC 004

Bailey, Deford

HARMONICA SHOWCASE (Bailey, Deford & D.H. 'Bert' Bilbro).
LP: . . . . MSE 218

Bailey, Derek

COMPANY 3 (Bailey, Derek & Hans Bennink).
LP: . . . . INCUS 25

COMPANY 4 (See under Lacy, Steve).

CONCERT... (See under Honsinger, Tristan) (Bailey, Derek & Tristan Honsinger).

DROPS (Bailey, Derek & Andrea Centazzo).
LP: . . . . INCUS 3

ISKRA 1903 (See under Rutherford, Paul) (Bailey, Derek/Paul Rutherford/ Barry Guy).

LIVE FROM VERITY'S PLACE (Bailey, Derek & Hans Bennink).
LP: . . . . INCUS 9

LONDON CONCERT (Bailey, Derek & Evan Parker).
LP: . . . . INCUS 16

LOT 74-SOLO IMPROVISATIONS.
LP: . . . . INCUS 12

ROYAL VOL 1 (See Braxton, Anthony) (Bailey, Derek & Anthony Braxton).

SOLO.
LP: . . . . INCUS 2

Bailey, Don

NO ADMITTANCE, NO EXIT / THE WILLOUGHBY OBSESSION (Don Bailey & Milo Ringham) (Various artists).
MC: . . . . NF 8

Bailey, Michael

RUFF STUFF (See under Luchi) (Luchi and Michael Bailey).

Bailey, Mildred

ALL OF ME.
LP: . . . . MES 6814

HARLEM LULLABY.
Tracks: / Georgia on my mind / Concentratin' / Harlem lullaby / Junk man / Ol' Pappy / Squeeze me / Downhearted blues / Porter's love song to a chambermaid, A / Smoke dreams / Rockin' chair / Moon got in my eyes, The / It's the natural thing to do / Worried over you / Thanks for the memory / More than ever / Please be kind / I let a song go out of my heart / Rock it for me / My melancholy baby / Lonesome road, The.
LP: . . . . AJA 5065
MC: . . . . ZC AJA 5065

MILDRED BAILEY WITH THE PAUL BARONS ORCHESTRA 1944 (Bailey, Mildred & The Paul Barons Orchestra).
Tracks: / Please don't talk to me when I'm gone / I'll never be the same / St. Louis blues / Man I love, The / I'll get by / I dream of you / Someday sweetheart / Four in a bar / From the land of the sky blue water / Lover come back to me / I didn't know / I never knew / China boy / Evelina / Body and soul / It had to be you.
LP: . . . . HMP 5056

MILDRED BAILEY 1938/39.
LP: . . . . VA 7996

MILDRED BAILEY COLLECTION (20 Golden Greats).
Tracks: / Georgia on my mind / Stop the sun, stop the moon / Rockin' chair / Smoke dreams / Heaven help this heart of mine / Don't be that way / Old folks / Thanks for the memory / St. Louis blues / I thought about you / Gulf Coast blues / Ghost of a chance / There'll be some changes made / I'm nobody's baby / More than you know / Squeeze me / Honeysuckle rose / Summertime / I'll close my eyes / Lover come back to me.
LP: . . . . DVLP 2106
MC: . . . . DVMC 2106

PAUL WHITEMAN YEARS 1931-1932.
LP: TJ6002

RAREST OF ALL RARE PERFORMANCES VOL 1.
LP: . . . . KLJ 20035

UNCOLLECTED MILDRED BAILEY, THE (CBS Radio Show).
Tracks: / Please don't talk about me / St. Louis blues / I'll get by / Someday, sweetheart / From the land of the sky blue water / Body and soul / China boy / It had to be you / I'll never be the same / Man I love, The / I dream of you / Four in

a bar / Lover come back to me / I didn't know / Evelina / I never knew.
LP: . . . . HSR 133

Bailey, Pearl

COME ON LET'S PLAY WITH PEARLIE MAE.
Tracks: / Small world / Let me entertain you / Woman's work is never done, A / Lady never forgets she's a lady, A / Put on your old grey bonnet / You gotta dance / Come on let's play with Pearlie Mae / Goodbye song, The / Please don't talk about me when I'm gone / Am I blue / Poor butterfly / Go back where you stayed last night.
LP: . . . . ROU 1006

LENA HORNE & PEARL BAILEY.
LP: . . . . GP 706

ROULETTE YEARS, THE: PEARL BAILEY.
Tracks: / Diamonds are a girl's best friend / Satin and silk / Around the world with me / Easy to love / I hate men / Always true to you in my fashion / Love for sale / Hey there / Takes two to tango / Since I became a hussy for my husband / Good little girls / You came a long way from St. Louis / She had to go and lose it at the Astor / You brought me more sunshine (than I can use) / Pushin' forty / My handy man / Confession (I'm confessin' that I love you) / Memories of you / I left my heart in San Francisco / St. Louis blues / I got rhythm / I got plenty o' nuttin' / Bill Bailey, won't you please come home.
MC: . . . . TCROU 1032

Bailey, Philip

CHINESE WALLS.
Tracks: / Photogenic memory / I go crazy / Walking on the Chinese wall / For every heart that's been broken / Go / Easy lover / Show you the way to love / Time is a woman / Woman / Children of the ghetto.
LP: 4500891
MC: 4500894
LP: . . . . CBS 26161

CONTINUATION.
Tracks: / I know / It's our time / Desire / I'm waiting for your love / Vaya (go with love) / Good guys are supposed to get the girl / Your boyfriend's back / Trapped.
LP: . . . . CBS 32680
MC: 40 32680
LP: . . . . CBS 25550
MC: 40 25550

FAMILY AFFAIR.
LP: . . . . MYRR 6877
MC: . . . . MYRC 6877

INSIDE OUT.
Tracks: / Welcome to the club / State of the heart / Long distance love / Echo my heart / Don't leave me baby / Special effect / Because of you / Back it up / Take this with you / Day will come, The.
LP: . . . . CBS 26903
MC: 40 26903

TRIUMPH.
Tracks: / All soldiers / Thank you / Love of God, The / Marvellous / Same way (you've always been), The / Other side, The / Bring it to Jesus / Triumph / Came before his presence.
LP: . . . . MYR R 1226
MC: . . . . MYR C 1226

WONDERS OF HIS LOVE, THE.
Tracks: / I will no wise cast you out / I want to know you / God is love / Sing a new song / Safe in God's love / I am gold / He don't lie / Make us one / Wonders of his love.
LP: . . . . MYR 1181
MC: . . . . MC 1181

Bailey, Razzy

FEELIN' RIGHT.
Tracks: / She left love all over me / I've had my limit (of two timing women) / Blaze of glory / Travellin' time / Night life / Bad news look / Everytime you cross my mind (you break my heart) / Sittin' here wishing (I was someplace else) / I loved 'em all / Your momma and daddy sure did something right.
LP: . . . . INTS 5216
MC: . . . . INTK 5216

MAKIN' FRIENDS.
Tracks: / Friend's too far gone and much too close to you / Scratch my back and whisper in my ear / Best kept secret in town, The / Spending my nights with you / Midnight hauler / Blind faith and the naked truth / Anywhere there's a duke box / Old no Homer / Late night honky tonk country song.
LP: . . . . RCALP 5051
MC: . . . . RCAK 5051

RAZZY BAILEY.
Tracks: / What time do you have to be back to heaven / If love had a face / Too old to play cowboy / True life country music / There's really nothing to it / What's a little love between friends / Wifey / Is it over / I ain't got no business today / Tonight she's gonna love me / Loving up a storm / I can't get enough of you / Let's go find some country music / I keep coming back / That's the way a cowboy rocks and rolls / 9,999,999 tears.
LP: . . . . PL 43482

STILL GOING STRONG.
Tracks: / Still going strong / Suzie Q / Mona Lisa / Loki / Lover please come back / Let the good times roll / Linda Lu / Pretend / Sunshine / High heel sneakers.
LP: . . . . SDLP 049

Bailey, Richard

FIREDANCE.
LP: . . . . MML 890077

Bailey, Robin (nar)

CLASSIC TALES OF MYSTERY AND THE SUPERNATURAL (see under Classic Tales... (bk).

LATE PHOENIX, A (See under Late Phoenix (bk).

Bailey, Roy

FREEDOM PEACEFULLY.
LP: . . . . CF 386

HARD TIMES.
LP: . . . . CF 382

IF I KNEW WHO THE ENEMY WAS... (Bailey, Roy/Leon Rosselson).
LP: . . . . CF 284

LEAVES FROM A TREE.
LP: . . . . CF 394

LOVE, LONELINESS, LAUNDRY (Bailey, Roy/Leon Rosselson).
LP: . . . . CF 271

NEW BELL WAKE.
LP: . . . . CF 262

ROY BAILEY.
LP: . . . . LER 3021

THAT'S NOT THE WAY IT'S GOT TO BE (See under Rosselson, Leon) (Bailey, Roy & Leon Rosselson).

WHY DOES IT HAVE TO BE ME.
LP: . . . . CF 396

Baillies Mills...

50 YEARS OF BAILLIES MILLS ACCORDION BAND (Baillies Mills Accordion Band).
Tracks: / I'm getting married in the morning / When you're smiling / Roll out the barrel / Bonnie Dundee / Lochnagar / Soldier's dream / Hills of Lorne, The / Yellow bird / Spanish eyes / Never on a Sunday / Sweet forget-me-not / Rose of Allendale / Marching through Georgia / Camptown races / Swanee / Count your blessings / Wide wide as the ocean / Love lifted me / And can it be / Love divine / Guide me o thou great Jehovah / Now Israel may say / Who is on the Lord's side / What a friend we have in Jesus / Just a closer walk with thee / Rescue the perishing / My best rock of ages.
MC: . . . . CHRL 223

ONE HUNDRED THOUSAND WELCOMES TO IRELAND (Baillies Mills Accordion Band).
Tracks: / It's a long way to Tipperary / Pack up your troubles in your old kit bag / Keep the home fires burning / My bonnie / Daisy, Daisy / Bunch of violets blue / If you're Irish / With my shillelagh under me arm / MacNamara's Band / My love is like a red red rose / Rowan tree / Ballad of Glencoe / Bonnie lass o' Fyvie / Scotland the brave / I love a lassie / Home on the range / Tulips from Amsterdam / When it's springtime in the Rockies / Hiking song, The / Mitchell march, The / Westering home / Doonaree / When Irish eyes are smiling / Morningtown ride / World of our own, A / Carnival is over, The / Dark island / Northern lights, The / I belong to Glasgow / Dancing in the Clyde / Green glens of Antrim / Boys from County Armagh / Mountains of Mourne / Will ye no come back again? / Shepherd's boy / Nut brown maiden.
LP: . . . . HRL 208
MC: . . . . CHRL 208
MC: . . . . CHRL 176

TO GOD BE THE GLORY (Baillies Mills Accordion Band).
Tracks: / Jesus I will trust thee / Saviour again / Rest in the Lord / Hark, hark my soul / Whispering hope / Lead me to Calvary / At the cross / Onward Christian soldiers / Stand up, stand up for Jesus / Abide with me / My hope is built on nothing less / To God be the glory / Song of the soldiers / Tell me the old old story / Deep harmony / When the roll is called / Mine eyes have seen the glory / I need thee every hour / Work for the night is coming / If I come to Jesus / There shall be showers of blessing / There is a name / Precious memories / Before I met you.
LP: . . . . POL 829

Bain, Alec

SCOTTISH FIDDLE FAVOURITES (Bain, Alec with Hugh Melvin).
Tracks: / Pastoral air / Slow air / Slow Strathspey / Reels.
MC: . . . . CJW 010

Bain, Aly

ALY BAIN.
LP: . . . . WHIRLIE 001
MC: . . . . WHIRLIE 001 C

ALY BAIN AND FRIENDS (Various artists).
Tracks: / Waiting for the federals: *Bain, Aly/Cunningham, Phil* / Donald MacLeans farewell to Oban: *Bain, Aly/Cunningham, Phil* / Sands of Burness, The: *Bain, Aly/Cunningham, Phil* / Miller's reel: *Bain, Aly/Cunningham, Phil* / Dean Cadalan Samhach: *Capercaillie* / Kerryman's daughter: *Boys Of The Lough* / O'Keefe's plough: *Boys Of The Lough*/ Sligo maid, The: *Boys Of The Lough* / Humours of Ballinahinch: *Boys Of The Lough* / Gravel walk: *Boys Of The Lough* / Out by East Da Vong: *Boys Of The Lough* / Maiden's prayer: *Junior Daugherty* / Jimmy Mann's reel: *Hunter, Willie* / Aly's sound: *Hunter, Willie* / It's all just talk: *Gregson, Clive & Christine Collister*/ Pearl, The: *Cunningham, Phil* / Floggin', The: *Bain, Aly/Tulloch, Violet/ John* / Chimes at midnight: *Bain, Aly* / Humours of Tulla: *O'Connor, Martin* / Fox Hunter's reel: *O'Connor, Martin* / St. Anne's reel: *O'Connor, Martin* / New road under my wheels: *Junior Daugherty* / Anne's tune: *Moore, Hamish/Lee, Dick* / Love of the islands: *Hunter, Willie* / Compliments to Dan R. MacDonald: *Hunter, Willie* / Marie MacLennan's reel: *Hunter, Willie* / Bonjour Tristesse: *Queen Ida & The Bon Temps Zydeco Band.*
LP: . . . . TRAX 026
MC: . . . . CTRAX 026

ALY MEETS THE CAJUNS.
Tracks: / Midland two step / My friend / Mazuka / Jongle a moi / Sassy on step / Jolie blonde / La contre danse a perepere / Water pump, The / J'ai ete zau bal / Paper in my shoe / La vie est pas donne / Back door / Chere toute toute / Rosa majeur / Devant ta porte / When I was poor.
LP: . . . . LIFL 7017
MC: . . . . LIFC 7017

MIKE WHELLANS AND ALY BAIN (See under Whellans, Mike) (Bain, Aly & Mike Whellans).

SHETLAND FIDDLERS VOL.1 (Silver bow) (Bain, Aly & Tom Anderson).
Tracks: / Jack broke da prison door / Donald blue / Sleep soond ida morning / Lasses trust in providence / Day dawn, The / Cross reel / Shive her up / Da silver bow / Auld foula reel / Wynadepla / Da slockit light / Smith O'Couster / Da grocer / Da galley watch / Kair and knock it corn / Da auld restin' chair / Hamnavoe polka / Maggies reel / Unst bridul march / Da bride is a boanie ting / Jack is yet alive / Auld clettenroe / Da mill / Aoon da rooth / Pit hame da borrowed claes / Wha'll dance wi wattie / Bush below da gairden / Soldier's joy / Shetland moods / De'il stick da minister / Taste da green / Dean brig o' Edinburgh, The / Banks hornpipe.
LP: 12TS 281
MC: . . . . KTSC 281

SHETLAND FOLK FIDDLING VOL 2 (Bain, Aly & Tom Anderson).
LP: 12TS 379
MC: . . . . KTSC 379

Baines, Murray

TOGETHER FOREVER (Baines, Murray & George Faith).
Tracks: / Together forever.
LP: . . . . LCLP 1001

Bairds

WELCOME TO IRELAND (Bairds & The Caern Folk Trio).
Tracks: / Two recruiting sergeants / Four strong winds / High level, The / Creggan white hare / Honey and wine / Peggy Gordon / Jolly beggar man / Orange maid of Sligo / Bottles of ... / Ballinderry / Flight / German / I know my love / Guns and drums / Ball O'Yarn / I'm a rover.
MC: . . . . 4 HOM 004

Baiza, Joe

CERTAIN WAY (Baiza, Joe & The Universal Congress).
Tracks: / Certain way / Chasing.
LP: . . . . SST 109

Baker, Anita

AIN'T NO NEED TO WORRY (See under Winans) (Winans with Anita Baker).

COMPOSITIONS.
Tracks: / Talk to me / Whatever it takes / Lonely / More than you know / Fairy tales / Perfect love affair / Soul inspiration / No one to blame / Love you to the letter.
LP: . . . . EKT 72
MC: . . . . EKT 72C

GIVING YOU THE BEST THAT I GOT (ALBUM).
Tracks: / Priceless / Lead me into love / Giving you the best that I got / Good love / Rules / Good enough / Just because I love you / You belong to me.
LP: . . . . EKT 49
MC: . . . . EKT 49C

RAPTURE.
Tracks: / Sweet love / You bring me joy / Caught up in the rapture / Been so long / Mystery / No one in the world / Same ole love / Watch your step.
LP: . . . . EKT 37
MC: . . . . EKT 37 C

SONGSTRESS.
LP: . . . . BG 10002
MC: . . . . BGC 10002

Baker, Arthur

MERGE (Baker, Arthur & The Backbeat Disciples).
Tracks: / Talk it over / Willin' to be chillin' / Last thing on my mind / Mythical girl / I believe in love / Message is love, The / Walk away / It's your time / Count to ten / 2 x 1 / All I ever wanted / Silly games.
LP: . . . . AMA 5262
MC: . . . . AMC 5262

Baker, B

B. BAKER CHOCOLATE CO (Baker, B Chocolate Co).
Tracks: / Snow blower / Carousel / Dreamer / Spirit level / Higher and higher / High and mighty / It's where you're coming from.
LP: . . . . TKR 83367

Baker, Carroll

ALL FOR THE LOVE OF A SONG.
Tracks: / It's snowing outside / Brand new tears / Time you're the healer / Breaking and entering / Here I am / It's only make believe / Burning up your memory / Still falling in love / This is it / Ev'ry good song is a bad song.
LP: . . . . RCALP 5012

AT HOME IN THE COUNTRY.
Tracks: / Death and taxis / Slowly / Such a true love / You've lost that lovin' feeling / If you only knew / I fall for that feeling / She's in love with the radio / First comes the fire / As long as we both shall live / Dreamin' ain't cheatin'.
LP: . . . . TMT 4333
MC: . . . . TMK 4333

CARROLL BAKER.
Tracks: / You've never been this far before / Hungry fire of love, The / Picture in my mind / One is one too many (and a thousand's not) / Why me / One night of cheatin' (ain't worth reapin') / Tonight with love / Gone, gone, gone (travelling man) / Why I had to pass this way / Like you touched me.
LP: . . . . PL 10171

HEARTBREAK TO HAPPINESS.
Tracks: / I found a l-i-e in the middle of believe / I'm an old rock'n'roller (dancin' to a different beat) / Too late for the two of us / You are my everything / Arms that love (hearts that don't) / It always hurts like the first time / Star in momma's eyes, A / You still excite me / I'm taking care of myself / If you can't stand the heat don't light the fi / Anything but hearts.
LP: . . . . TMB 109
MC: . . . . TMBC 109

HOLLYWOOD LOVE.
Tracks: / My turn / It wasn't me / Second time around / Fooling my senses / Hollywood love / I know I can / Play your steel guitar for me / God I'm sorry / Tarnished wedding band / Deeper than the eye can see / I'll live in dreams / Just a closer walk with thee / How great Thou Art.
LP: . . . . PL 43061

IF IT WASN'T FOR YOU.
Tracks: / If it wasn't for you / Me and Bobby McGhee / Hooked on a feeling / Born winner / We got nothin' / Don't touch me / I'm getting high remembering / Let me be your woman / I'm so lonesome I could cry / Build my life around you.
LP: . . . . PL 42770

SWEET SENSATION.
Tracks: / It's my party / Portrait in the window / I can't stop loving you / Love's

golden rule / It's late (and I have to go) / Who's gonna love me when the morning comes / Morning after baby let me down, The / Slow / Sweet sensation / I might as well believe (I'll live forever).
LP: . . . . PL 43414
MC: . . . . PK 43414

Baker, Chet

ALL TOGETHER (Baker, Chet, Lee Konitz & Keith Jarrett).
LP: . . . . JC 113

AS TIME GOES BY.
Tracks: / You and the night and the music / As time goes by / My melancholy baby / I'm a fool to want you / When she smiles / Sea breeze / You have been here all along / Angel eyes / You'd be so nice to come home to / Round midnight.
2LP: . . . . SJP 251/252

BALLADS FOR TWO.
LP: . . . . SMP 2102

BEST OF GERRY MULLIGAN WITH CHET BAKER (see under Mulligan, Gerry).

BLUES FOR... (Feat. Warne Marsh) (Baker, Chet Quartet).
LP: . . . . CRISS 1010

CALIFORNIA CONCERTS VOL. 1 (See under Mulligan, Gerry) (Mulligan, Gerry & Chet Baker).

CALIFORNIA CONCERTS VOL. 2 (See under Mulligan, Gerry) (Mulligan, Gerry & Chet Baker).

CANDY.
LP: . . . . SNTF 946

CHET.
Tracks: / Alone together / How high the moon / It never entered my mind / 'Tis Autumn / If you could see me now / September song / You'd be nice to come home to / Time on my hands / You, the night and the music.
LP: . . . . OJC 087

CHET BAKER.
LP: . . . . AMLJ 726

CHET BAKER (Walkman Jazz).
Tracks: / Summertime / Girl from Greenland, The / Anticipated blues / Chet / I'll remember april / Every time we say goodbye / Halfbreed Apache / That ole devil called love / Don't explain / Baby breeze / This is the thing / Pamela's passion / Comin' down / I wish you love / Touch of your lips, The.
MC: 840 632 4

CHET BAKER AND STRINGS: FEATURING ZOOT SIMS.
Tracks: / You don't know what love is / I'm through with love / Love walked in / You better go now / I married an angel / Love / I love you / What a difference a day made / Why shouldn't I? / Little duet, A / Wind, The / Trickledidlier.
LP: . . . . CBS 21142
MC: 40 21142

CHET BAKER BIG BAND (Baker, Chet Big Band).
LP: . . . . FS 89

CHET BAKER IN CONCERT (Baker, Chet & Lee Konitz).
LP: . . . . IN 1052

CHET BAKER IN TOKYO.
LP: . . . . K 28P6495

CHET BAKER INTRODUCES JOHNNY PACE (Baker, Chet & Johnny Pace).
LP: . . . . RLP 292

CHET BAKER SEXTET AND QUARTET (UP INTERNATIONAL) (Baker, Chet Sextet & Quartet).
Tracks: / Ladybird / Cheryl / Tune up / Line for Lyons / Pent up house / My old flame / Indian Summer / Look for the silver lining.
LP: . . . . LPUP 5116
LP: . . . . SM 3910

CHET BAKER SINGS AGAIN.
LP: . . . . SJP 238

CHET IN PARIS (1955-6/Barclay Years).
LPS: . . . . FSBOX 1

CHET IN PARIS - VOL 3.
LP: 80711

CHET IS BACK.
Tracks: / Well you needn't / Pent up house / Barbados.
LP: . . . . CL 31649
LP: . . . . NL 70578

CHET'S CHOICE (Baker, Chet Trio).
LP: . . . . CRISS 1016

COMPACT JAZZ (see under Blakey, Art) (Blakey, Art/Chet Baker/Anita O'Day/Memphis Slim).

COOL BLUES (Unissued Live Recordings Vol.2) (Baker, Chet Quintet).
LP: . . . . RR 2

COOL CAT.
Tracks: / Swift shifting / Round midnight / Caravelle / For all we know / Blue moon / My foolish heart.
MC: . . . . MCSJP 262

COOLS OUT (Baker, Chet Quintet).
Tracks: / Extra mild / Halema / Jumpin' off a cliff / Route / Lucius lou / Pawnee junction.
LP: . . . . BOP 013

DAYBREAK.
LP: . . . . SCS 1142

DIANE (Baker, Chet/Paul Bley).
LP: . . . . SCS 1207

EVERYTHING HAPPENS TO ME.
MC: . . . . SJP 1192

EXITUS (Unissued Live Recordings Vol.1) (Baker, Chet Quintet).
LP: . . . . RR 1

FOUR.
Tracks: / Four / Arborway / Seven steps to heaven / I'm a fool to want you / For all we know / Broken wings.
LP: K28P 6495
MC: . . . . KIMC 6281

GERRY MULLIGAN QUARTET WITH CHET BAKER (See under Mulligan, Gerry) (Mulligan, Gerry & Chet Baker).

GERRY MULLIGAN-CHET BAKER (see under Mulligan, Gerry).

HEART OF THE BALLAD (Baker, Chet & Enrico Pieranunzi).
LP: 214W 20

IN NEW YORK.
LP: . . . . OJC 207

ITALIAN MOVIES.
LP: . . . . IRS 00631LP

ITALIAN SESSIONS, THE.
Tracks: / Well you needn't / These foolish things / Barbados / Star eyes / Somewhere over the rainbow / Pent-up house / Ballata in forma di blues / Blues in the closet.
LP: . . . . NL 82001
MC: . . . . NK 82001

JAMES DEAN STORY, THE (Baker, Chet & Bud Shank).
LP: . . . . FS 110

JAZZ AT ANN ARBOR (Baker, Chet Quartet).
LP: . . . . FS 26

KIRK LIGHTSEY TRIO AND CHET BAKER (Baker, Chet & Kirk Lightsey Trio).
LP: . . . . SJP 176

LET'S GET LOST (Film soundtrack).
Tracks: / Moon and sand (motivo di raggio di luna) / Imagination / You're my thrill / For heaven's sake (Only on the CD.) / Every time we say goodbye / I don't stand a ghost of a chance with you / Daydream / Zingaro a/k/a/ portrait in black and white / Blame it on my youth / My one and only love / Almost blue / Everything happens to me (Only on CD.).
LP: . . . . PL 83054
MC: . . . . PK 83054

LET'S GET LOST (2) (Best of Chet Baker Sings).
Tracks: / Thrill is gone, The / But not for me / Time after time / I get along without you very well / There will never be another you / Look for the silver lining / My funny valentine / I fall in love too easily / Daybreak / Just friends / I remember you / Let's get lost / Long ago (and far away) / You don't know what love is.
LP: B1 92932
LP: 792 932 1

LIVE AT NICK'S.
LP: . . . . CRISS 1027

LIVE AT ROSENHEIMER.
LP: . . . . SJP 233

LIVE FROM THE MOONLIGHT (Baker, Chet Trio).
2LP: 214W 10-11

LIVE IN PARIS 1960 & NICE 1975.
LP: . . . . FC 123

LIVE IN SWEDEN.
Tracks: / Lament / My ideal / Beatrice / You can't go home again / But not for me / Ray's idea / Milestones.
LP: . . . . DRLP 56

MEMORIES.
Tracks: / For minors only / Almost blue / My funny valentine / Portrait in black and blue / Stella by starlight.
LP: K28P 6491
MC: . . . . KIMC 6270

MR B.
Tracks: / Dolphin dance / Ellen and David / Strollin' / In your own sweet way / Mister B.
LP: . . . . SJP 192

MULLIGAN-BAKER (see under (Pacific Jazz II collection) (Mulligan, Gerry & Chet Baker).

MY FAVOURITE SONGS.
LP: . . . . ENJA 5097 1
MC: . . . . ENJA 5097 4

NEW BLUE HORNS (Baker, Chet/ Kenny Dorham).
LP: . . . . OJC 256

NIGHTBIRD (Live at Ronnie Scott's).
Tracks: / But not for me / Arboway / If I should loose you / My ideal / Nightbird / Love for sale / Shifting down / You can't go home again / Send in the clowns.
MC: . . . . ESMMC 015

PEACE.
LP: . . . . ENJA 4016

PLAYBOYS (Baker, Chet & Art Pepper).
Tracks: / For minors only / Original Pepper / Resonant emotions / Tynan time / Pictures of Heath / For miles and miles / C.T.A..
LP: . . . . BOP 003

QUARTET: RUSS FREEMAN AND CHET BAKER (See under Freeman, Russ) (Baker, Chet/Russ Freeman).

REUNION (see under Mulligan, Gerry).

SINGS.
LP: . . . . FS 87

TOUCH OF YOUR LIPS, THE.
LP: . . . . SCS 1122

WHEN SUNNY GETS BLUE.
LP: . . . . SCS 1221
MC: . . . . SCM 51221

WITCH DOCTOR (Baker, Chet & Lighthouse All Stars).
Tracks: / Loaded / I'll remember April / Winter wonderland / Pirouette / Witch doctor.
LP: . . . . COP 033

WITH STRINGS.
MC: 4669684

Baker, Duck

FINGER STYLE JAZZ GUITAR.
Tracks: / Tintiyana / Summertime / White with foam / Take the 'A' train / Yes, yes / Sweet and lovely / Wishes / Plain as the winter / Stompin' at the Savoy / Southern Cross / Everything that rises must converge / Good intentions / In a sentimental mood / You're a lady.
LP: . . . . SNKF 154

KING OF BONGO BONG, THE.
Tracks: / New righteous blues / Crazy rhythm / I found a new baby / No love / There'll be some changes made / See you in my dreams / I ain't got nobody / Mama's getting younger / Papa's getting older each day / Immaculate conception rag / River blues / Chicken ain't nothin' but a bird, A / King of bongo bong / Business as usual.
LP: . . . . SNKF 137

THERE'S SOMETHING FOR EVERYONE IN AMERICA.
Tracks: / Jackson stomp, The / Mission street blues, The / Allegheny county / Matty powell / Zebra blues / Wolverine blues / Melancholy baby / Take me out to the ball game (Medley (a)) / America (Medley (b)) / Temperence reel / Pineapple rag / Hicks farewell / Doctor jazz / Old folks polka, The / There'll be a happy meeting / Wreck of the old '97.
LP: . . . . SNKF 116

WHEN YOU WORE A TULIP.
Tracks: / You took advantage of me / Grace street / Was / Liza (all the clouds will roll away) / Boys from Blue Hill / Back home again in Indiana / Rapid transit blues / Two cats with new shoes / Plymouth rock / Honeysuckle rose / Cousin / Lazy river / Drunken wagoner / When you wore a tulip / Thou swell / Angeline the baker.
LP: . . . . SNKF 123

Baker, Earl

LEGENDARY EARL BAKER CYLINDERS, THE.
LP: . . . . JA 43

Baker, George

BEST OF BAKER, THE (Baker, George Selection).
Tracks: / Paloma blanca / Love me like I love you / Manana / Superstar / Wildbird / Morning sky / Beautiful rose / As long as the sun will shine / Marja / Silver / Fly away little paraguayo / Fisherman.
LP: . . . . K 56446

PALOMA BLANCA (Baker, George Selection).
Tracks: / Paloma blanca / Song for you, A / As long as the sun will shine / Fisherman / Seagull / African dream / Superstar / Send me the pillow that you dream on / Israel / Take me home / Morning sky.
LP: . . . . K 56136

RIVER SONG (Baker, George Selection).
Tracks: / Silver / You're my brightest star / If you understand / Annie you're the woman that I love / River song / Gone by the wind / Wild bird / All I have to do is dream / Libertad / I look for the sun / For Esther.
LP: . . . . K 56282

SUMMER MELODY (Baker, George Selection).
Tracks: / Summer melody / Beautiful rose / Movie lovers / Manana daughter of mine / Jimmy / Let my son / Sunshine / Old man / Love will be the answer / Marja / In the morning.
LP: . . . . K 56395

Baker, Ginger

AFRICAN FORCE.
LP: . . . . ITM 0017

ELEVEN SIDES OF (Baker, Ginger & Friends).
Tracks: / Ginger man / Candlestick maker / High life / Don Dorango / Little bird / N'kon kini n'kon n'kon / Howlin' Wolf / Ice cream dragon / Winner / Pampero / Don't stop the carnival.
LP: . . . . TOPC 5005

FELA KUTI AND GINGER BAKER LIVE (See under Kuti, Fela) (Kuti, Fela & Ginger Baker).

FROM HUMBLE ORANGES (Baker, Ginger & Band).
Tracks: / Eleventh hour, The / Too many apples / It / Under the sun / On the road to Granma's house / Land of Mordor, The / This planet / Sore head in the morning blues / Wasting time / Lament.
LP: . . . . INT 20303
MC: 30INT 20303

GINGER BAKER IN CONCERT.
Tracks: / Chemical babies / Perfect nation / Everything I say / Wheelchair dance festival / Lost in space / Where are you?.
LP: . . . . ONS 2

GINGER BAKER'S AIRFORCE (Baker, Ginger/Airforce).
LP: 2662 001

PALANQUIN'S POLE (Baker, Ginger/ African Force).
LP: . . . . ITM 0033

Baker, Glen

BRIEF ENCOUNTER.
LP: . . . . STAND 3

Baker, Janet

SEA PICTURES (see under Du Pre, Jacqueline).

Baker, Josephine

DIS MOI JOSEPHINE BAKER?.
Tracks: / J'ai deux amours / Le petite tonkinoise / Voulez vous de la canne a sucre? / Dis moi Josephine / You're driving me crazy / My fate is in your hands / Si j'etais blanche / Sans amour / Madiana / Haiti / C'est lui (pour moi y qu'un homme dans Paris) / Vous faites partie de moi / C'est un nid charmant / I'm feelin' like a million / Message from the man in the moon, A / Zelli's dream / Loveliness of you, The / De temps en temps / Brazil / Piel canela.
LP: . . . . SH 511
MC: . . . . TCSH 511

FIFTY YEARS OF SONG.
LP: 2C 178 14987/8

JOSEPHINE BAKER.
Tracks: / J'ai deux amours / Dis moi Josephine / Voulez vous de la canne a sucre / Haiti / C'est un nid charmant / Pardon si je t'importune / La petite tonkinoise / Piel canela / Dans mon village / Sur deux notes / Demain (Una casa in cima al mondo.) / La vie en rose / Hello Dolly / Quand je pense a ca.
LP: 1152761
MC: 1152764
LP: . . . . MES 7023

JOSEPHINE BAKER AT TIVOLI.
Tracks: / Avec / Make believe / You are my lucky star / Quand tu m'embrasses / Quando, quando, quando / La Seine / Hello, young lovers / Bill / Enamorada / I got a feeling you're fooling / La novia / Je pars.
LP: . . . . SM 3237

JOSEPHINE BAKER COLLECTION (20 golden greats).
Tracks: / Suppose / J'ai deux amours / Love is a dreamer / Sans amour / Ram pam pam / You're driving me crazy / J'etais blanche / My fate is in your hands / Confessin' / Haiti / C'est si facile de vous aimer / Vous faites partie de moi / London Town / De temps en temps / Sur deux notes / Mon coeur est un oiseau des isles / Brazil / Paris cheri / Zoubida / Besame mucho.
LP: . . . . DVLP 2097

MC: DVMC 2097

Baker, Kenny (1)

BAKERS DOZEN, A.
LP: CO 730

DARKNESS ON THE DELTA (Featuring Buck White and Allen Shelton) (Baker, Kenny & Bob Hicks).
LP: CO 782
MC: CO 782 MC

DRY AND DUSTY.
LP: CO 744

FARMYARD SWING.
Tracks: / Lost indian / Bean blossom / Chickens under the back porch / Blue mountain waltz / Old Kentucky home / Dailey's reel / Indian creek / Arkansas traveller / Georgianna moon / Smokey mountain / Rag / Farmyard swing / Paddy on the turnpike.
LP: CO 775
MC: CO 775 MC

FROST ON THE PUMPKIN.
LP: CO 770
MC: CO 770 MC

GRASSY FIDDLE BLUES.
LP: CO 750
MC: CO 750 MC

HIGH COUNTRY (Baker, Kenny & Joe Greene).
LP: CO 714

HIGHLIGHTS.
Tracks: / Tom and Jerry / A and E reel / Rooster dog / Beautiful dreamer / Nova Scotia breakdown / Gold rush / Tee totaler's reel / Bobby Van's hornpipe / Call of the shepherd / Last train to Durham / Whispering hope / Tune for Andy.
LP: CO 785
MC: CO 785 MC

KENNY BAKER COUNTY.
LP: CO 736

PLAYS BILL MONROE (Featuring Bill Monroe).
LP: CO 761
MC: CO 761 MC

PORTRAIT OF A BLUE GRASS FIDDLER.
LP: CO 719

RED APPLE RAG (Baker, Kenny & Howdy Forrester).
LP: CO 784

Baker, Kenny (2)

BAKER'S JAM (Baker, Kenny All Stars).
LP: 77 S 56

DATE WITH THE DOZEN.
LP: DM 9

KENNY BAKER HALF DOZEN (Baker, Kenny featuring George Chisolm).
Tracks: / How's this / Love me or leave me / If I could be with you / Keepin' out of mischief now / How can you face me / Puttin' on the ritz / Mr. Paganini / Doodee / St. Louis blues / Honolulu blues.
LP: DMLP 19

Baker, Laverne

HITS AND RARITIES.
Tracks: / Jim Dandy / Tweedle dee / So high so low / Soul on fire / Romance in the dark / Tomorrow night / Humpty dumpty heart / Manana / Harbour lights / Fool that I am / I can't love you enough / I'm living my life for you / I can't hold out any longer / I'll do the same for you / Game of love / Help each other romance, A.
LP: OFF 6042

I'M GONNA GET YOU.
Tracks: / Love is ending / Born to lose / I need you so / Play it fair / Baby / One monkey don't stop no show / Batman to the rescue / Think twice / Call me darling / Nothing like being in love / I'm gonna get you / Pledging my love to you / Let me belong to you / I'm the one to do it / Baby don't you do it / Please dont hurt me.
LP: C5-510
MC: C5K-510

LAVERNE BAKER SINGS BESSIE SMITH/THAT'S JAZZ.
Tracks: / Gimme a pigfoot and a bottle of beer / Baby doll / On revival day / Money blues / I ain't gonna play no second fiddle / Back water blues / Empty bed blues / There'll be a hot time in the old town tonight / Nobody knows you when you're down and out / After you've gone / Young woman's blues / Preaching the blues.
LP: K 50241

REAL GONE GAL.
Tracks: / How can you leave a man like this / Jim Dandy / My happiness for ever / Fee fi fo fum / Jim Dandy got married / Substitute / Whipper snapper / Voodoo voodoo / I cried a tear / He's a real gone guy / I waited too long / Tiny Tim / Shake a hand / Bumble bee / Hey Memphis / See see rider.
LP: CRB 1072
MC: TCCRB 1072

Baker, Marilyn

CLOSE TO HIS HEART.
LP: WST R 9688
MC: WST C 9688

EVENING WITH MARILYN BAKER, AN.
Tracks: / He's my saviour, my friend and my Lord / What a great day / Jesus is alive in me / Rest in my love.
LP: WRD R 3028
MC: WRD C 3028

MARILYN BAKER.
LP: WST R 9670
MC: WST C 9670

Baker, Mickey

BLUES AND JAZZ GUITAR.
Tracks: / Corina corina / Zanzie / Belzona blues / Got the blues / Spoonful / Lord ,have mercy / Hello world / Stack O'Lee / Baby please don't go / Town's East end, The / Juicy Lucy / Love in vain.
LP: SNKF 127

JAZZ ROCK GUITAR.
LP: SNKF 145
LP: KM 140

TAKE A LOOK INSIDE.
Tracks: / Make your bed up mamma / Take a look inside / Blues fell this morning / Diggin' my potatoes / Playing with danger / I'll always be in love with you / She brings out the animal / New York, New York / Tight ropes and bumpy roads / Bewildered.
LP: BEAR 5

WILDEST GUITAR, THE.
LP: SD8035

Baker, Richard

KID ON THE MOUNTAIN (Baker, Richard Royal).
Tracks: / Wicklow hornpipe, The / Proudlock's hornpipe / Blind Mary / Blarney pilgrim / Duke of Fife's welcome to Deeside / Sir Sidney Smith's march / Bantry Bay / Morgan Magan / Kid on the mountain, The / Rights of man, The / Fanteladda boys of Ballisodore / Elsie Marley / Sheebeg sheemore / Lament of Limerick.
LP: SNKF 167

LET'S BEGIN AGAIN (See Kings Singers).

RICHARD BAKER'S MUSICAL MENAGERIE.
LP: KPM 7014
MC: UKC 7014

WIND IN THE WILLOWS AND THE RELUCTANT DRAGON (See Kings Singers) (Baker, Richard & Kings Singers).

Baker, Sam

BRINGING YOU SOME SOUL.
Tracks: / Coming to bring you some soul / Hold back girl / I love you / I can't breakaway / Let me come on home / Sometimes you have to cry / What did sister do / Don't feel rained on / Sugarman / I believe in you / I'm number one / It's all over / Strange sensation / Something tells me / You can't see the blood / Sunny.
LP: CRB 1137

Baker, Shorty

SUMMER CONCERT 1960 (Baker, Shorty & Bud Freeman).
LP: JA 38

Baker, Susan

FIDDLES AND FOLLIES.
Tracks: / Waterman's hornpipe / Wonder / Slingby's allamande / Vicar of Bray / London Bridge / Lulle ne beyond thee / Cuckolds all in a row / Lord of Carnavon's jig / Watkins ale / Kettle drum / Walking song / Sleigh ride / Beggarman, The / Sonata / Variations for violins / Stars fell on Alabama / Plaisir d'amour / Largo / Minuet and trio / Wolsey's wilde / Sonatina for mandolina / Harry Lime theme / Here comes the hurdy gurdy / Czardas / My fiddle is my sweetheart.
LP: ZK 86

Baker, Tony

ACADEMY AWARD WINNERS (Baker, Tony & His Orchestra).
Tracks: / Continental, The / Lullaby of Broadway / Way you look tonight / Sweet Leilani / Thanks for the memory / Over the rainbow / When you wish upon a star / Last time I saw Paris, The / White Christmas / You'll never know / Swingin' on a star / It might as well be Spring / On the Atchison, Topeka and the Santa Fe / Zip a dee doo dah / Buttons and bows / Baby, it's cold outside / Mona Lisa.
MC: HSC 655

ACADEMY AWARD WINNERS VOL.2 (Baker, Tony & His Orchestra).
Tracks: / In the cool, cool, cool of the evening / High noon / Screen love / Three coins in my fountain / Love is a many splendoured thing / What ever will be will be (Que sera sera) / All the way / Gigi / High hopes / Never on a Sunday / Moon river / Days of wine and roses / Call me irresponsible / Chim chim cheree / Shadows of your smile, The / Born free / Talk to the animals.
MC: HSC 661

Baker-Gurvitz Army

BAKER-GURVITZ ARMY.
LP: 9103 201

Bakerloo

BAKERLOO.
LP: SHVL 762

Bakerloo Junction

IRISH SONGS AND BALLADS.
Tracks: / When I grow too old to dream / Lassie from sweet Aghalee / Isle of Innisfree / Girl I left behind me, The / Shimna, The / Green fields of France / Dunmurry Mill / Wild mountain thyme / Farewell to you my lovely rose / Dark island / I'll tell me ma / Reap the wild harvest.
LP: GES 1231
MC: KGEC 1231

MY LAGAN SOFTLY FLOWING.
Tracks: / Grey Belfast lough / Off to school / Belfast street songs / Harland and Wolff / Winds of change / Cruise of the Calibar / James 'Foo' Young / Black velvet band / My Lagan softly flowing / Wee Willie / Somme, The / Mary of Dungloe / I remember / Flowers of Manchester.
LP: GES 1219
MC: KGEC 1219

Bakers Dozen...

BAKERS DOZEN FROM VINDALOO (Various artists).
Tracks: / Rockin' with Rita: *Vindaloo Summer Special* / Let's surf: *Nightingales* / XX Sex: *We've Got A Fuzzbox* & We're Gonna Use It / Open up she said: *Bumbites* / Driving down the road: *Chippington, Ted* / Down in the dumps: *Nightingales* / Aaarrrggghhh: *We've Got A Fuzzbox & We're Gonna Use It* / Keep lying I love it: *Bob* & Vi / She loves you: *Chippington, Ted* / Buck up: *Bumbites* / Fever: *We've Got A Fuzzbox & We're Gonna Use It* / At the end of the day: *Nightingales* / Rockin' with Rita: *Chippington, Ted.*
LP: YUS 8
MC: YUSC 8

Baker's Wife

BAKER'S WIFE, THE (London Cast) (Various artists).
2LP: TER2 1175
MC: ZCTED 1175
LP: THT 772

Balaam & The Angel

DAYS OF MADNESS.
Tracks: / Don't want your love / I took a little / She really gets to me / Body and soul / Heartbreaker / Tender loin / Two days of madness / Did he fall / Goodbye forever / I am the only one / Stop messin' around.
LP: V 2598
MC: TCV 2598

GREATEST STORY EVER TOLD, THE.
Tracks: / New kind of love / Don't look down / She knows / Burn me down / Light of the world / Slow down / Wave, The / Warm again / Her end / Nothing there at all / Walk away (CD only) / Day and night (CD only).
LP: V 2377
MC: TCV 2377
LP: OVED 250
MC: OVEDC 250

LIVE FREE OR DIE.
Tracks: / I'll show you something special / I love the things you do to me / Big city fun time girl / On the run / It goes on / Live free or die / Long time loving you / Would I die for you / I won't be afraid / Running out of time / You took my soul (CD only) / Let it happen (CD only) / You're in the way of my dreams (CD only) / As tears go by (CD only) / I feel love (CD & cassette only).
LP: V 2476
MC: TCV 2476

SUN FAMILY.
LP: CHAPLP 4

Balalaika

BALALAIKA, THE (Various artists).
LP: LDX 74804
MC: K 298

KALAKOLTSCHIK.
LP: EULP 1064
MC: EUMC 1064

KALINKA.
LP: EULP 1054
MC: EUMC 1054

SONGS FROM THE TAIGA.
LP: EULP 1050
MC: EUMC 1050

Balalaika Trio

TRIANGLE.
Tracks: / Katusha / Song of the plains / Moscow nights romance / If I were a rich man / Brightly shines the moon / Narybalke / Kalinka / Cliff on Volga / In the garden / Ochi chorniye / Play my pipes / Kasbek.
LP: EER 030

Balancing Act

THREE SQUARES AND A ROOF.
LP: ILP 023

Balcony (bk)

BALCONY, THE (Jean Genet).
MCSET: 0316

PORTRAIT: BALCONY.
MC: BAL 1

Balcony Dogs

BALCONY DOGS.
MC: ICT 9922
LP: ILPS 9922

TRIP.
LP: ILPS 9922

Bald-Headed End

BALD-HEADED END OF THE BROOM (Songs of uneasy wedlock) (Various artists).
Tracks: / Bald headed end of the broom: *Various artists* / Bargain with me: *Various artists* / Birmingham boys: *Various artists* / Crabfish: *Various artists* / Cunning cobbler, The: *Various artists* / Deserted husband: *Various artists* / Gamecock: *Various artists* / German musician: *Various artists* / Grat for gruel: *Various* artists / He comes down our alley: *Various artists* / Wish to be single: *Various* artists / Linen song: *Various* artists / Molecatcher: *Various artists* / Never wed a' auld man: *Various artists* / Old woman of blighter town: *Various artists* / One thing or the other: *Various artists* / Poor old maid: *Various artists* / Rap-tap-tap: *Various artists* / Rocking the cradle: *Various artists* / Scolding wife: *Various artists*/ Wearing of the britches, The: *Various artists* / Young and growing: *Various artists* / All jolly fellows that follow the plough: *Various artists* / Barnyards of Delgaty: *Various artists* / Bold Reynard the fox: *Various* artists / Brisk and bonny lass: *Various artists* / Contented countryman: *Various artists* / Echoing horn: *Various artists* / Farmers boy: *Various artists* / Gallant poacher: *Various artists* / Keepers lie sleeping: *Various artists* / Ground for the floor: *Various artists* / Innocent hare, The: *Various artists* / Joe Bowman: *Various artists.*
MC: 60-019

Baldry, Long John

BALDRY'S OUT.
Tracks: / Baldry's out / Stealer / Lonely nights / You've lost that lovin' feelin' / Come and get your love / Find you / Like a dog / Thrill's a thrill / So sad / Darling.
LP: AML 3002

EVERYTHING STOPS FOR TEA.
LP: MQCLP 4
MC: MQCMC 4

GOLDEN HOUR OF LONG JOHN BALDRY, A.
MC: KGHMC 127

LET THE HEARTACHES BEGIN (Best of John Baldry).
LP: PYL 4008
MC: PYM 4008

LOOKING AT LONG JOHN.
LP: BGOLP 2

WELCOME TO THE CLUB CASABLANCA.
LP: MQCLP 5
MC: MQCMC 5

Baldursson

MELODY OF LIFE (Baldursson, Hurdle and Ricotti).
MC: C 104

Baldwin, Bob

DREAM, THE.
LP: MJ 1501
MC: MJC 1501

Baldwin, Luke

TATTOO ON MY CHEST, THE.
LP: FF 039

Baldwin, Stephen

ENGLISH VILLAGE FIDDLER.
LP: LED 2068

Balearic Beats

BALEARIC BEATS VOL 1 (Various artists).
Tracks: / Jibaro: *Electra* / Drop the deal: *Code 61* / Sure beats workin': *Beats Workin'* / Blackout: *Enzo Avitable* / Mandy's theme (I just can't wait): *Smith, Mandy* / Kaw-liga: *Residents* / Why why why: *Woodentops* (live) / Join in the chant: *Nitzer Ebb* / De testimony: *Fini Tribe* / Jesus on the payroll: *Thrashing Doves*.
LP: FFRLP 5
MC: FFRMC 5

Bales, Bert

NEW ORLEANS RAGTIME.
LP: ESR 1210

Balfa Brothers

ARCADIAN MEMORIES.
Tracks: / 'Tit galop pour mamou / Drunkars's sorrow waltz / Lacassine special / Indian on a stomp / T'ai petite et t'ai meon / Two step a Hadley / Valse de Balfa / Pealez nous a boure / Two step de l'anse a Paille / Enterre moi pas / La valse de grand bois / T'en as eu mais t'en n'auras plus / Je suis Orphelin / J'ai passe devant ta porte / Madeleine / La danse de Mardi Gras.
LP: CHD 183
MC: CHDC 183

CAJUN DAYS.
LP: SNTF 813

CAJUNS VOL. 1 (See under Abshire, Nathan) (Abshire, Nathan & Balfa Brothers).

J'AI VU LE LOUP, LE RENARD ET LA BELETT.
LP: ROUNDER 6007
MC: ROUNDER 6007C

LOUISIANA CAJUN MUSIC.
LP: ARHOOLIE 5019
MC: C 5019

MORE TRADITIONAL CAJUN MUSIC.
LP: 6019
MC: 6019 TC

NEW YORK CONCERTS, THE.
LP: 6037
MC: 6037 TC

TRADITIONAL CAJUN MUSIC.
LP: 6011
MC: 6011 TC

Balfa, Dewey

COUPLE OF CAJUNS (see Ardoin Family Orchestra) (Balfa, Dewey/Ardoin Family Orchestra).

FAIT A LA MAIN (Balfa, Dewey & Friends).
LP: 6063
MC: 6063 TC

SOUVENIRS.
LP: 6056
MC: 6056 TC

Balham Alligators

BALHAM ALLIGATORS, THE.
Tracks: / Balham 2 step / Hey, hey, ho, ho / Malheureuse / Sugar bee / Tennessee blues / Johnny B. Goode / Oh Siobhan let's dance / Louisiana / Scotland / Allons a Lafayette / Tacos / Little Liza Jane / Hobo blues / Balham 2 step (reprise).
LP: SPD 1002
MC: SPDC 1002

LIFE IN THE BUS LANE.
Tracks: / Cajun walk / It's my own business / Diggy liggy lo / Fine fine fine / Love has no pride / Alligators grinning / Big mamou / What've you got to lose / I don't wanna be in love / Feel like a fool.
LP: SPD 1018
MC: SPDC 1018

Bali

BALI ETERNEL (Various artists).
Tracks: / Le lelong: *Various artists* / Baris: *Various artists* / Oleg tambulilingan: *Various artists* / Raja pala: *Various artists* / Tari tenun: *Various artists* / Panji semirang: *Various artists* / Le ramayana: *Various artists* / Prelude: *Various artists* / Pendet: *Various artists* / Kriss transe a Kuta: *Various artists*.
LP: ARN 33544

BALI - LES CELEBRES GAMELANS (Various artists).
Tracks: / Rayamanat ballet: *Various artists* / Barung: *Various artists* / Defile des offrandes: *Various artists* / Ketjak: *Various artists* / Gender wayang: *Various artists* / Pendent: *Various artists* / Legong: *Various artists*.
LP: ARN 30130
MC: ARN 430130

GAMELAN ENSEMBLE OF BATUR (Various artists).
LP: 558 510
MC: 4559 002

GAMELAN MUSIC OF BALI (Various artists).
LP: LLST 7179
MC: LLCT 7179

SCINTILLATING SOUNDS OF BALI (Various artists).
LP: LLST 7305

Bali (Group)

KHATRA.
LP: MUT 1087
MC: CMUT 1087

Balkan Rhythm Band

JAZZIEST BALKAN DANCE BAND AROUND, THE.
LP: FF 314

Balkana

MUSIC OF BULGARIA, THE.
MC: HNBC 1335
LP: HNBL 1335

Ball

BALL 4 - HARDBALL.
Tracks: / Hard ball / She's always driving / Timmy the toad man / Mary Jane / Road to Heaven, The / Ball four prelude / Ball one / Ball two / Ball three / Ball four / R.I.P..
LP: SDE 9018

BIRD.
Tracks: / When is a man / If I breakdown / Love was the end / Burning wood / Another straight line / It don't come easy / Just like the last time / Drink on it / Dylan side, The / Eye / Scene's over / Bird / Charm / Long ago / Buick McKane / Wildest thing, The / Spit shine / Wah wah / Shelter / Swim this way / Bangla Desh.
LP: SD 8803
LP: SHIMMY 014
LP: SDE 8803LP

PERIOD (ANOTHER AMERICAN LIE).
LP: SR 0388
LP: SHIMMY 006

TROUBLE DOLL.
Tracks: / Should brother kill / Never meant to say / Trouble world / This is war / Little Tex in trouble / Trash man / Trouble momma / I could always be with you / Cracked life of a cracked man, The / Flowers grow on the wall / French, The / When is a man / Bird / Charm / My T.V. is broken / King will never die, The / If I breakdown / It don't come easy / Love was the end / Just like the last time / Buick McKane / Little Tex's prelude (CD only.) / Reagans bush is on fire (CD only.) / Amazon (CD only.) / Trouble baby (CD only.) / TX-five (CD only.) / African sunset (CD only.) / Everywhere (CD only.) / Trouble finale (CD only.).
LP: SDE 8909LP
LP: SHIMMY 022

Ball, Chris

GIRL FROM GALWAY TOWN, THE.
MC: GTDC 074

IRISH COLLECTION, THE.
MC: GTDC 099

MY LOVELY ROSE OF CLARE.
Tracks: / My lovely Rose of Clare / Noreen Bawn / Catch me if you can / Let us try again / Three leaf shamrock / Village of Astee, The / Blacksmith / Golden jubilee / True love never dies / I'll take you home again, Kathleen.
LP: DOLS 2012
MC: DOCS 2012

Ball, Dave

IN STRICT TEMPO.
Tracks: / Mirrors / Sincerity / Passion of a primitive / Strict tempo / Man in the man / Only time / Life of love / Rednecks / American stories.
LP: BIZL 5
MC: BIZLC 5

Ball, E.C.

E.C. BALL WITH ORMA BALL (Ball, E.C./Orma Ball/Friendly Gospel Singers).
LP: ROUNDER 0026

Ball, Kenny

AT THE MOVIES.
Tracks: / Raiders of the Lost Ark / Mrs. Robinson / As time goes by / Arthur's theme / I love you, Samantha / Cavatina / March of the Siamese children / Mona Lisa / When you wish upon a star / Hello, Dolly / Green leaves of summer / Ben / Bare necessities / I wanna be like you.
LP: MFP 5803
MC: TCMFP 5803

BEST OF BARBER, BALL & BILK (Barber, Chris/Kenny Ball/Acker Bilk).
LP: GGL 0131

COLLECTION, THE.
Tracks: / Midnight in Moscow / Alexander's ragtime band / Casablanca / Muskrat ramble / Samantha / Gavotte and rondo / Green leaves of summer / Wonderful world / Saturday night / From Russia with love / Someday / When the saints go marching in / March of the Siamese children / So do I / Cabaret / Pay off, The / Ace in the hole / Hello Dolly / Sukiyaki / When I'm sixty four / Acapulco 1922 / I still love you all / Maple leaf rag / I shall not be moved.
MC: CCSMC 258

COTTON CLUB.
Tracks: / Minnie the moocher / Midnight in Moscow / I wanna be like you / Scorpio blues / March of the Siamese children / You are my sunshine / Sailing / Samantha / Eyes / It's life / So do I / One night stand / Annie's song / Is that the human thing to do.
LP: CFRC 510
MC: MCFRC 510

DIXIE (Ball, Kenny & His Jazzmen).
Tracks: / Aura Lee / Sophie's rag / Sunshine time / Nicole / Lighting up the town / Stepping along to the beat / Frankie and Johnny / My home town / Down Dixie way / Southland blue / Kibbutz girl / Honky stonkin'.
MC: HSC 3269

GOLDEN HITS: KENNY BALL (Ball, Kenny & His Jazzmen).
Tracks: / Midnight in Moscow / So do I / March of the Siamese children / Someday you'll be sorry / 55 Days at Peking / Rondo alla turk / Sukiyaki / I still love you all / Green leaves of Summer / I love you Samantha.
LP: FBLP 8104
MC: ZCFBL 8104

GOLDEN HOUR: KENNY BALL (Ball, Kenny & His Jazzmen).
MC: ZCGH 512

GOLDEN HOUR OF KENNY BALL & HIS JAZZ MEN, A (Ball, Kenny & His Jazzmen).
Tracks: / I love you Samantha / Someday (you'll be sorry) / March of the Siamese children / Midnight in Moscow / So do I / Sukiyaki / Rondo / I still love you all / From Russia with love / When I'm sixty four / Green leaves of Summer / 55 days at Peking / At the jazz band ball / Bourbon Street parade / Muskrat ramble / I shall not be moved / Ace in the hole / Georgia swing / Maple leaf rag / When the saints go marching in.
MC: KGHMC 131

GOLDEN HOUR OF KENNY BALL VOL.2.
MC: KGHMC 141

GREENSLEEVES (Ball, Kenny & His Jazzmen).
Tracks: / Flow gently sweet Afton / Nobody knows you (when you're down and out) / I got rhythm / Ostrich walk / I shall not be moved / St. Louis blues / Greensleeves / My mother's eyes / I wanna be like you / Mood indigo / Them there eyes / Old folks / Sweet Georgia Brown.
LP: TTD 505
MC: TTD 5505

HELLO DOLLY.
LP: GH 636

IMAGES: KENNY BALL.
Tracks: / Green leaves of summer / 1919 march / Tie a yellow ribbon round the old oak tree / Tin roof blues / 55 days at Peking / From Russia with love / High society / Midnight in Moscow / Blue turning grey over you / Old miss rag / Sukiyaki / Rondo / Livery stable blues / March of the Siamese children.
MC: KNMC 16009

KENNY BALL IN CONCERT (Ball, Kenny & His Jazzmen).
LP: NEVLP 139

KENNY BALL PLAYS BRITISH.
Tracks: / White cliffs of Dover / Eton boating song / Lincolnshire poacher / Men of Harlech / We'll keep a welcome in the hillside / British grenadiers, The / Ilkley Moor / Lambeth walk / Danny boy (Londonderry air) / When Irish eyes are smiling / Scarborough Fair / Sweet Afton / Scotland the brave / Greensleeves / English country garden (CD only.).
LP: MFP 5864
MC: TCMFP 5864

KENNY BALL'S GOLDEN HITS.
LP: GGL 0209

KENNY IN CONCERT IN THE USA VOL.2.
LP: J 66

KENNY IN CONCERT IN THE USA VOL.1.
LP: J 65

LIGHTING UP THE TOWN (Ball, Kenny & His Jazzmen).
LP: ISST 199

LIVE AT THE ROYAL FESTIVAL HALL (Ball, Barber & Bilk).
2LP: CR 5152
MCSET: CRT 5152

MIDNIGHT IN MOSCOW (2) (Ball, Kenny & His Jazzmen).
MCSET: DTO 10209

ON STAGE.
Tracks: / Midnight in Moscow / Rondo / Saturday night / Someday / I still love you all / Sukiyaki / Payoff, the / When I'm sixty four / Samantha / Green leaves of summer / So do I / Casablanca / Acapulco 1922 / 55 days at Peking / March of the Siamese children / Hello dolly.
LP: STOL 102
MC: STOC 102

SATURDAY NIGHT AT THE MILL.
Tracks: / Saturday night at the mill / Sunday / Sweet painted lady / Feline stomp / Them there eyes / You can't get to Heaven by livin like hell / Lady of Spain / I got plenty o' nuttin' / Bess, you is my woman now / T'aint what you do (it's the way that you do it) / Lili Marlene / Down by the river.
LP: SPJ 9000

SINGLES COLLECTION, THE (Ball, Kenny & His Jazzmen).
Tracks: / Midnight in Moscow / Rondo / Saturday night / Someday you'll be sorry / I still love you all / Sukiyaki / Pay off, The / When I'm sixty four / Samantha / Green leaves of summer / So do I / Casablanca / Acapulco 1922 / 55 days at Peking / March of the Siamese children / Hello Dolly.
LP: PYL 6029
MC: PYM 6029

SOAP.
MC: AMILP 101

ULTIMATE, THE (See under Barber, Chris) (Barber, Chris/Acker Bilk/Kenny Ball).

WAY DOWN YONDER (Ball, Kenny & His Jazzmen).
LP: NEVLP 161
MC: NEVC 161

Ball, Marcia

DREAMS COME TRUE (See Under Barton, Lou Ann) (Ball, Marcia, Lou Ann Barton & Angela Sterhli).

HOT TAMALE BABY.
LP: REU 1012
LP: ROUNDER 3095
MC: ROUNDER 3095C

SOULFUL DRESS.
LP: ROUNDER 3078
MC: ROUNDER 3078C

Ball, Patrick

CELTIC HARP VOL.1.
Tracks: / Carolan's quarrel with the landlady / Maurice O' Connor / Blind Mary / Carolan's receipt for drinking / Carolan's ramble to cashel / Carolan's welcome / Young William Plunkett / George Brabazon / Give me your hand / Lady Maxwell / Derriott O'Dowd / Mrs. Judge / Carolan's farewell to music / Sheebeg sheemore.
LP: LPFOR 005
MC: MCFOR 005

CELTIC HARP VOL.2.
Tracks: / Come live with me and be my love / Greensleeves / Blackthorn stick / Down by the sea / John O' Connor / Grenadier and the lady, The / Londonderry air / Three ravens / Munster cloak, The / Star of the County Down / Ode to whiskey / Doctor John Hart / Caitlin trial / Ash Grove, The.
MC: MCFOR 11
LP: LPFOR 11

CELTIC HARP VOL 3.
LP: LPFOR 029
MC: MCFOR 029

O'CAROLANS DREAM.
LP: LPFOR 17061
MC: MCFOR 17061

Ball, Tom

BLOODSHOT EYES (Ball, Tom & Kenny Sultan).
LP: FF 386

Ball, William J.

BANJO GALAXY, A.
LP: ROUNDER 3005

Ballad of Reading Gaol

BALLAD OF READING GAOL (Oscar Wilde) (Mason, James (nar)).
MC: 1473

Ballad of the Irish...

BALLAD OF THE IRISH HORSE (See under Chieftans) (Chieftans).

Ballads

50 FAVOURITE BALLADS (Various artists).
MCSET: TR 4115545
MCSET: TR 1554

GOLDEN BALLADS (Various artists).
MC: . . . **BRC 2511**

Ballads in Blue

BALLADS IN BLUE (Big Sounds for the Small Hours) (Various artists).
Tracks: / Child is born, A: *Turrentine, Stanley* / Since I fell for you: *Morgan, Lee* / Guess I'll hang my tears out to dry: *Gordon, Dexter* / Autumn leaves: *Adderley, Cannonball Quintet* / I'm old fashioned: *Coltrane,* John / Cry me not: *Hubbard, Freddie* / Bouquet: *Hutcherson, Bobby* / Lazy afternoon: *la Roca, Pete*/ Easy living: *Brown, Clifford* / Nature boy: *Quebec, Ike* / You taught my heart to sing: *Tyner, McCoy.*
MC: . . . **B4 96098**

Ballads of...

BALLAD OF THE BLACK COUNTRY (Various artists).
Tracks: / John Hobbs: *Various artists* / Nine times a night: *Various artists* / All bells of paradise: *Various* artists / Brave collier lads: *Various artists* / John Wilkinson: *Various artists* / Wedgebury cocking: *Various* artists / Funny rigs of good and tender hearted masters, The: *Various artists* / Tommy note: *Various artists*/ Nailmakers strike, The: *Various artists* / Jews they crucified him, The: *Various artists* / Brave Dudley boys, The: *Various artists* / Souling, clemency, gooding: *Various artists* / Oxford and Hampton railway, The: *Various artists* / Perry Croft's bull-bait: *Various artists* / Song of the Staffordshire men, The: *Various artists.*
LP: . . . **BRO 116**
MC: . . . **KBRO 116**

BALLADS OF BRITAIN AND IRELAND VOL.3 (Classic ballads) (Various artists).
MC: . . . **90-503**

BALLADS OF BRITAIN AND IRELAND VOL.1 (Classic ballads, vol 1-nos 2-84) (Various artists).
MC: . . . **90-501**

BALLADS OF BRITAIN AND IRELAND VOL.2 (Classic ballads, vol 2-nos 85-215) (Various artists).
MC: . . . **90-502**

Ballads & Songs

BALLADS AND SONGS (Various artists).
LP: . . . **OT 102**

Ballamy, Iain

BALLOON MAN.
Tracks: / Mode forbode / Remember / Rahsaan / Strawberries / Albert / Balloon man / Jumble sale / All I ask of you.
LP: . . . **EGED 63**
MC: . . . **EGEDC 63**

Ballantyne, R.M. (aut)

CORAL ISLAND (See under Coral Island) (Heller, Martin (nar)).

DOG CRUSOE, THE (see under Dog Crusoe) (Boland, Arthur).

Ballard, Hank

HANK BALLARD & THE MIDNIGHTERS (Ballard, Hank & The Midnighters).
LP: . . . **BID 8003**

LIVE AT THE PALAIS (Ballard, Hank & The Midnighters).
Tracks: / Lucille (Instrumental) / Hoochie coochie coo, The / Work with Annie / Tore up over you / Teardrops on your letter / Look at little sister / Annie had a baby / My girl / Girl's alright with me, The / You're all I need to get by / I'll try something new / Stand by me / Hold on I'm coming / Soul man / Sky is crying, The / Sugaree / It's love baby / Sexy ways / Deep blue sea / Baby workout / Your love keeps lifting me higher and higher / Christmas time for everyone but me / Finger poppin' time / Let's go, let's go, let's go / Twist (The).
2LP: . . . **CDX 16**
MC: . . . **TCCDX 16**

ONE AND ONLY, THE.
Tracks: / Sugaree / Rain down tears / Cute little ways / House with no windows / Everybody does wrong some time / So good to be home / Kansas city / I'll keep you happy / I'm crying mercy, mercy / She's got a whole lot of soul / I'll pray for you / Move, move, move.
LP: . . . **SING 674**

SINGIN' AND SWINGIN' (Ballard, Hank & The Midnighters).
Tracks: / Teardrops on your letter / Ring-a-ling-a-ling / Let me hold your hand / Don't say your last goodbye / Whatsoever you do / Stingy little thing / Ashamed of myself / Twist, The / That house on the hill / Sweet mama do right / Ooh ooh baby / Tell them / Rock and roll wedding / I'll be home someday.
LP: . . . **SING 618**

THEIR GREATEST JUKE BOX HITS (Ballard, Hank & The Midnighters).
Tracks: / Work with me Annie / Moonrise / Sexy ways / Get it / Switchie witchie titchie / It's love baby / Annie had a baby / She's the one / Annie's Aunt Fannie / Crazy loving / Henry's got flat feet / Tore up over you.
LP: . . . **SING 541**

TWENTY ORIGINAL HITS:HANK BALLARD (Ballard, Hank & The Midnighters).
LP: . . . **K 5003**

WHAT YOU GET WHEN THE GOING GETS GOOD (Ballard, Hank & The Midnighters).
Tracks: / Sexy ways / Don't change your pretty ways / Rock and roll wedding / Open up the back door / Rock, granny, roll / Tore up over you / Is your love for real? / Twist, The / Teardrops on your letter / Kansas City / Sugaree / Finger poppin' time / Let's go, let's go, let's go / What is this I see / I'm gonna miss you / Work with me Annie.
LP: . . . **CRB 1090**
MC: . . . **TCCRB 1090**

Ballard, J.G. (aut)

EMPIRE OF THE SUN (See under Empire of the Sun (bk) (Irons, Jeremy (nar)).

Ballard, Russ

FIRE STILL BURNS, THE.
Tracks: / Once a rebel / Omen, The / Hey Bernadette / Searching / Time / Your time is gonna come / Dream on / Fire still burns, The.
LP: . . . **EJ 2403671**
MC: . . . **EJ 2403674**

INTO THE FIRE (Ballard, Russ & Barnet Dogs).
Tracks: / Rock and roll lover / Breakdown / Where do we go from here / Guilty / Don't go to Soho / Tonight / Madman / Strangers / Here comes the hurt / I will be there.
LP: . . . **EPC 84806**

RUSS BALLARD.
Tracks: / I can't hear you no more / In the night / Two silhouettes / Voices / Woman like you, A / Day to day / Playing with fire / Last time, The.
LP: . . . **EJ 2401331**
MC: . . . **EJ 2401334**

Ballet

BEST OF BALLET (Various artists).
LP: . . . **TRX 163**
MC: . . . **TRXC 163**

WORLD OF BALLET VOL 1 (Various Orchestras).
LP: . . . **SPA 55**

WORLD OF BALLET VOL 2 (Various Orchestras).
LP: . . . **SPA 97**
MC: . . . **KCSP 97**

Ballet Shoes

BALLET SHOES (Noel Streatfeild) (Shearer, Moira (nar)).
MCSET: . . . **SAY 110**
LPS: . . . **ZDSW 715/7**

BALLET SHOES (Noel Streatfelid) (Francis, Jan (nar)).
MCSET: . . . **LFP 7286**

Ballistic Breakouts

BALLISTIC BREAKOUTS (Various artists).
LP: . . . **SAM 102**

Ballistic Kisses

TOTAL ACCESS.
Tracks: / Whose mama is this / Recipe for revolt / Workaholic / Five o'clock world / Black and broke / Domestic servants / Body rhymes / Tough shit / Samurai toys.
LP: . . . **X 15**

WET MOMENTS.
LP: . . . **X 19**

Balliu, Rudy

RUDY BALLIU'S SOCIETY SERENADERS (Balliu, Rudy & the Society Serenaders).
LP: . . . **GHB 223**

Balloons

BALLOONS (Various artists).
LP: . . . **CRD 2000**

Ballou Canta

BOLINGO SONIA (Ballou Canta & Soukous Stars).
LP: . . . **S 1829**
MC: . . . **S 1829C**

Ballou, Classie

ALL NIGHT MAN.
LP: . . . **KK 800**

Ballou, Monte

THEY'RE MOVING WILLIE'S GRAVE (Ballou, Monte & His New Castle Jazz Band).
LP: . . . **GHB 155**

Ballroom

GOLDEN HOUR OF STRICT TEMPO (Various artists).
MC: . . . **KGHMC 118**
MC: . . . **KGHMC 126**

QUICKSTEPS AND FOXTROTS (Various artists).
MC: . . . **CPK 1**

SPOTLIGHT ON SEQUENCE (Various artists).
Tracks: / Three o'clock in the morning: *Cole, Bobby* / My wonderful one: *Selley, Graham* (Medley) / Till we meet again: *Selley, Graham* (Medley) / Let us be sweethearts over again: *Selley, Graham* (Medley) / I'll be your sweetheart: *Selley, Graham* (Medley) / All I do is dream of you: *Selley, Graham* (Medley) / It might as well rain until September: *Roberts,* Paul / Boom / Big brass band from Brazil: *Roberts, Paul* (Medley) / Moonlight on the Nile: *Roberts, Paul* (Medley) / Home: *Roberts, Paul* (Medley) / Little man you've had a busy day: *Cole, Bobby* / How are things in Glocca Morra: *Cole, Bobby* / Say has anybody seen my sweet Gypsy Rose: *Cole, Bobby* / Whistle while you work: *Cole, Bobby*(Medley) / Give a little whistle: *Cole, Bobby* (Medley) / Ja da: *Roberts, Paul* (Medley) / Oh Johnny: *Roberts,* Paul (Medley) / When Joanna loved me: *Roberts, Paul* / Do that to me one more time: *Smith, Jimmy (USA)* (Medley) / When you wish upon a star: *Smith, Jimmy (USA)* (Medley) / Fine romance, A: *Smith, Jimmy (USA)* (Medley) / Patricia: *Smith, Jimmy (USA)* (Medley) / You are always in my heart: *Selley, Graham* / Song of the rose: *Roberts, Paul.*
LP: . . . **SUS 528**

STRICT TEMPO VOL. 6 (Golden hour of) (Various artists).
MC: . . . **KGHMC 158**

TEACH YOURSELF TO: CHA-CHA (Various artists).
MC: . . . **BKK 1502**

TEACH YOURSELF TO: QUICKSTEP (Various artists).
MC: . . . **BKK 1503**

TEACH YOURSELF TO: WALTZ (Various artists).
MC: . . . **BKK 1501**

WE'RE DANCING (STRICT DANCE TEMPO) VOLUME 6 (Various artists).
LP: . . . **2491 556**
MC: . . . **3195 187**

WE'RE DANCING (STRICT DANCE TEMPO) VOLUME 4 (Various artists).
LP: . . . **2491 548**
MC: . . . **3195 168**

WE'RE DANCING (STRICT DANCING TEMPO) VOLUME 5 (Various artists).
LP: . . . **2491 549**
MC: . . . **3195 169**

Ballroom Kings

MORE BALLROOM KINGS (Various artists).
Tracks: / Beauty is as beauty does: *King, Pee Wee* / Rag mop: *King, Pee Wee* / Honey honey mine: *Pine, Hal* Lone / Hadacol boogie: *Rogers, Jesse* / Jaw jaw yap yap yap: *Robertson, Texas Jim* / Waxahachie boogie woogie dishwasher boy: *Boyd, Jim* / You played on my piano: *Penny, Hank* / Let me be: *Wills, Johnny Lee* / Idaho red: *Ray, Wade* / It'd surprise you: *Allen, Rosalie* / I feel the blues coming on: *Britt, Elton* / Child psychology: *Homer & Jethro* / I don't think I'm gonna like it: *Hill, Eddie* / Old Mcdonald's boogie: *Tyler, Johnny.*
LP: . . . **DT 33005**

Bally

FROM BALLY WITH LOVE.
LP: . . . **LPL 004**

Ballyclare Male Voice

BALLYCLARE MALE VOICE CHOIR.
Tracks: / How great thou art / Speed your journey.
LP: . . . **SGOL 112**

Ballycoan Pipe Band

PIPES AND DRUMS.
MC: . . . **CGL 001**

WORLD CHAMPIONS (Pipes and Drums).
LP: . . . **G 001**
MC: . . . **CGL 001**

Ballykeigle...

FIFTY YEARS OF MARCHING (Ballykeigle Accordion Band).
Tracks: / Waveney / Under the double eagle / Erman / Officer of the day / Lest we forget / Le reve passe / How great thou art / Blades of steel / Aurella / Nazareth / True and trusty / Standard / Old rugged cross.
LP: . . . **STOL 140**

Ballymena...

VARIOUS SONGS OF PRAISE (Ballymena West Church Choir).
Tracks: / Jubilate / Childin a manger / With a vice of singing / In the bleak mid winter / Thou wilt keep him in perfect peace / Ye servants of God / Down by the riverside / Psalm 23 / Round me falls the night / Come, o holy ghost / Three kings / Infant king, The / Love devine / Jubilate jazz.
LP: . . . **POL 827**

Balogh, Meta

GYPSY MUSIC FROM HUNGARY.
LP: . . . **EULP 1073**
MC: . . . **EUMC 1073**

Baltazar, Gabe

GABE BALTAZAR.
LP: . . . **ST 3005**

Baltimora

LIVING IN THE BACKGROUND.
Tracks: / Tarzan boy / Pull the wires / Living in the background / Woody boogie / Chinese restaurant / Running for your love.
LP: . . . **EJ2404261**

Bam Bam

KING OF THE UNDERGROUND.
LP: . . . **LUVLP 7**

Bama Band

BAMA BAND.
LP: . . . **DFG 8402**

Bambaataa, Afrika

BEWARE (THE FUNK IS EVERYWHERE).
Tracks: / Funk jam party / Funk you / Bionic kats / What time is it / Beware (the funk is everywhere) / Bambaataa's theme / Tension / Rock America / Kick out the jams.
LP: . . . **253092 1**
MC: . . . **253092 4**

DEATH MIX THROWDOWN.
Tracks: / Deathmix parts 1 and 2 / Afrika Bambaata / Zulu nation throwdown parts 1 and 2 / Ninny.
LP: . . . **BLATLP 2**
MC: . . . **BLATMC 2**

LIGHT, THE (Bambaataa, Afrika & Family).
Tracks: / Light, The / Reckless / Radical music, revolutionary dance / Something he can feel / Clean up your act / Zouk your body / World racial war / Shout it out / Sho nuff funky / All I Want.
LP: . . . **EMC 3545**
MC: . . . **TCEMC 3545**
LP: . . . **EMCX 3545**

Bambi (bk)

BAMBI.
MC: . . . **DIS 005**

BAMBI (Felix Salter) (Kendall, Felicity (nar)).
MC: . . . **PTB 632**

Bambi (film)

BAMBI (Various artists).
Tracks: / Main title: *Various artists* / Little April shower: *Various artists* / Gallop of the stags: *Various artists* / Love is a song: *Various artists* / Wintry winds: *Various artists* / Let's sing a gay little spring song: *Various artists* / Looking for romance (I bring you a song): *Various artists* / Finale: *Various artists.*
MC: . . . **D 7DC**
LP: . . . **D 3903**
LPPD: . . . **D 3108**
LP: . . . **DQ 1203**

BAMBI (Film soundtrack) (Various artists).
Tracks: / Love is a song: *Various artists* / Little April showers: *Various artists* / Let's sing a gay little Spring song: *Various artists* / Looking for romance (I bring you a song): *Various artists.*
LP: . . . **REC 541**
MC: . . . **ZCM 541**

Bambi Slam

BAMBI SLAM.
Tracks: / Ba ba ba boom / Long time coming / Now / Outa my head / Thinkin' 'bout chu / Summer smilin' / Take me with you / I'm left wonderin' / We can't let go or mellowdrama / Awful flute song, The.
LP: . . . **BYN 17**
MC: . . . **BYNC 17**

IS....
LP: . . . **EXPROD 20**

Bamboo Fringe

LIFE AND TIMES OF THE BAMBOO FRINGE.
LP: . . . . **SAW 002**

Bamboola

BAMBOOLA.
LP: . . . . **PLASLP 005**

Banana Blush

BANANA BLUSH (see under Betjeman, Sir John) (Betjeman, Sir John).

Bananarama

BANANARAMA.
LP: . . . . **RAMA 2**
MC: . . . . **KRAMC 2**

BANANARAMA (12" TAPE).
Tracks: / Venus / More than physical / Robert de Niro's waiting / Na na hey hey (kiss him goodbye) / Cruel summer.
MC: **6509164**

BANANARAMA: INTERVIEW PICTURE DISC.
LPPD: . . . . **BAK 2107**

DEEP SEA SKIVING.
Tracks: / He was really saying something / Boy trouble / What a shambles / Young at heart / Na na hey hey (kiss him goodbye) / Shy boy.
LP: . . . . **RAMA 1**
MC: . . . . **KRAMC 1**

GREATEST HITS: BANANARAMA.
Tracks: / Venus / I heard a rumour / Love in the first degree / I can't help it / I want you back / Love, truth and honesty / Nathan Jones / Really saying something / Shy boy / Robert De Niro's waiting / Cruel summer / It ain't what you do / Na na hey hey (kiss him goodbye) / Rough justice.
LP: . . . . **RAMA 5**
MC: . . . . **KRAMC 5**
LP: . . . . **RAMR 5**
MC: . . . . **KRAMR 5**

POP LIFE.
Tracks: / Preacher man / Long train running / Only your love / What colour R the skies where U live? / Is your love strong enough / Ain't no cure / Outta sight / Megalomaniac / I can't let you go.
LP: **8282461**
MC: **8282464**

T'AINT WHAT YOU DO (IT'S THE WAY THAT YOU DO IT) (See under Fun Boy Three) (Bananarama & Fun Boy 3).

TRUE CONFESSIONS.
Tracks: / True confessions / Ready or not / Trick of the night, A / Dance with a stranger / In a perfect world / Venus / Do not disturb / Cut above the rest / Promised land / More than physical / Hooked on love.
LP: . . . . **RAMA 3**
MC: . . . . **KRAMC 3**

WOW.
Tracks: / I can't help it / I heard a rumour / Some girls / Once in a lifetime / Strike it rich / Bad for me / Come back / Nathan Jones / I want you back.
MC: . . . . **KRAMC 4**
LP: . . . . **RAMA 4**
LP: . . . . **RAMG 4**
LP: . . . . **RAMAG 4**
MC: . . . . **KRAM 4**

Bananas

BANANAS (Various artists).
LP: . . . . **RODNEY 001**

Banchory Strathspey...

BANCHORY STRATHSPEY & REEL SOCIETY (Banchory Strathspey & Reel Society).
LP: . . . . **BGC 358**
MC: . . . . **KBGC 358**

IN CRATHE'S CASTLE VOL 2 (Banchory Strathspey & Reel Society).
MC: . . . . **KITV 445**

Banco

BANCO.
Tracks: / Chorale (from Traccia's theme) / L'albero del pane / Metamorphosis / Outside / Leave me alone / Nothing's the same / Traccia II.
LP: . . . . **K 53507**

Bancroft, Armsbee

CINEMA ORGAN ENCORES.
LP: . . . . **DEROY 1425**

Band

ANTHOLOGY - BAND (VOL.1).
Tracks: / Weight, The / Chest fever / I shall be released / Rag mama rag / Night they drove old Dixie down, The / Up on Cripple Creek / King harvest (has surely come) / Stage fright / Shape I'm in, The / Daniel and the sacred harp.
MC: **3C 254 85684**
2LP: . . . . **ESTSP 19**

ANTHOLOGY - BAND (VOL.2).
Tracks: / Life is a carnival / When I paint my masterpiece / Wheel's on fire, The / Great pretender, The / Mystery Train / Ophelia / It makes no difference / Acadian Driftwood / Right as rain / Living in a dream.
MC: **3C 254 85685**
2LP: . . . . **ESTSP 20**

BAND, THE.
Tracks: / Across the great divide / Rag mama rag / Night they drove old Dixie down, The / When you awake / Up on cripple creek / Whispering pines / Jemima surrender / Rockin' chair / Look out Cleveland / Jawbone / Unfaithful servant / King harvest (has surely come).
LP: . . . . **EMS 1192**
MC: . . . . **TCEMS 1192**
LP: . . . . **ATAK 87**
MC: . . . . **TCATAK 87**
LP: . . . . **EST 132**

BEFORE THE FLOOD (Band & Bob Dylan).
LP: . . . . **IDBD 1**

BEST OF THE BAND.
Tracks: / Weight / Up on cripple creek / Shape I'm in / Rag mama rag / Life is a carnival / Time to kill / Twilight / Ain't got no home / I shall be released / Stage fright / Ophelia / Night they drove old Dixie down, The.
LP: . . . . **FA 3016**

CAHOOTS.
Tracks: / Life is a carnival / When I paint my masterpiece / Last of the blacksmiths / Where do we go from here / 4% pantomime / Shoot out in Chinatown / Moon struck one, The / Thinkin' out loud / Smoke signal / Volcano / River hymn.
LP: . . . . **GO 2015**
LP: . . . . **EAST 651**

ISLANDS.
Tracks: / Right as rain / Street walker / Let the night fall / Ain't that a lot of love / Christmas must be tonight / Islands / Saga of Pepote Rouge, The / Georgia on my mind / Living in a dream / Knockin' lost John.
LP: . . . . **EST 11602**

LAST WALTZ, THE (Film soundtrack).
Tracks: / Last waltz, The / Up on Cripple Creek / Who do you love / Helpless / Stage fright / Coyote / Dry your eyes / It makes no difference / Such a night / Night they drove old Dixie down / Mystery train / Mannish boy / Further on up the road / Shape I'm in, The / Down South in New Orleans / Ophelia / Tura lura larai (That's an Irish lullaby) / Caravan / Life is a carnival / Baby let me follow you down / I don't believe you (she acts like we never have met) / Forever young / I shall be released / Last waltz suite, The / Well, The / Evangeline / Out of the blue / Weight, The.
2LP: . . . . **K 66076**
MCSET: **K4 66076**

MOONDOG MATINEE.
Tracks: / Ain't got no home / Holy cow / Share your love with me / Mystery train / Third man theme, The / Promised land, The / Great pretender, The / I'm ready / Saved / Change is gonna come, A.
LP: **5C 038 81539**

MUSIC FROM BIG PINK.
Tracks: / Tears of rage / To Kingdom come / In a station / Caledonia mission / Weight, The / We can talk / Long black veil / Chest fever / Lonesome Suzie / This wheels on fire / I shall be released.
LP: . . . . **GO 2001**
MC: . . . . **TC GO 2001**

ROCK OF AGES.
Tracks: / Gentle method, The / Don't do it / King harvest (has surely come) / Caledonia mission / Get up, Jake / W.S. Walcott medicine show, The / Stage fright / Night they drove old Dixie down, The / Across the great divide / This wheel's on fire / Rag mama rag / Weight, The / Shape I'm in, The / Unfaithful servant / Life is a carnival / Chest fever / Hang up my rock 'n' roll shoes.
2LP: **3C 154 81188/9**
MCSET: **3C 254 81188/9**
2LP: **1C 188 81188/9**

STAGE FRIGHT.
Tracks: / Strawberry wine / Sleeping / Just another whistle stop / All la glory / Shape I'm in, The / W.S. Walcott medicine show, The / Daniel and the sacred harp / Stage fright / Rumor, The / Time to kill.
LP: . . . . **GO 2003**
LP: . . . . **EA SW 425**

TO KINGDOM COME.
Tracks: / Back to Memphis / Tears of rage / To kingdom come / Long black veil / Chest fever / Weight, The / I shall be released / Up on Cripple Creak / Lovin you is sweeter than ever / Rag mama rag / Night they drove old Dixie down, The / Unfaithful servant / King harvest (has surely come) / Shape I'm in, The / W.S. Walcott medicine show, The / Daniel and the sacred harp / Stage fright / Don't do it (baby don't you do it) / Life is a carnival / When I paint my masterpiece / 4% pantomime / River hymn, The / Mystery train / Endless highway / Get up Jake / It makes no difference / Ophelia / Acadian driftwood / Christmas must be tonight / Saga of pepote rouge, The / Knockin' lost John.
LP: . . . . **EN 5010**
MC: . . . . **TCEN 5010**

Band AKA

BAND AKA.
Tracks: / Funkdown / Grace / When you believe in love / Steppin' out / Homeward bound / New beginning / Funny kind of love.
LP: . . . . **EPC 85887**

MEN OF THE MUSIC.
Tracks: / If you want to know / Joy / Men of the music / Work me all over / You got it all / It must be love / It's you that I need (loneliness made me realise).
LP: . . . . **EPC 25415**
MC: **40 25415**

Band Apart

BAND APART.
LP: . . . . **CRAM 012**

MARSEILLE.
LP: . . . . **CRAM 022**

Band of Angels (Film)

BAND OF ANGELS (Film soundtrack) (Various artists).
Tracks: / Band of angels: *Various artists* / Death of a scoundrel: *Various artists* / Charge of the light brigade: *Various artists* / Four wives: *Various artists* / Searchers, The: *Various artists* / Stolen life, A: *Various artists.*
LP: . . . . **ERM 6003**

Band Of Blacky

BAND OF BLACKY RANCHETTE.
LP: . . . . **ROSE 62**

HEARTLAND.
Tracks: / Heartland / Moon over Memphis / All done in / Badlands / Roof's on fire / Underground train / Nowhere / Steadfast / One way ticket / Changing heart.
LP: . . . . **ZONG 014**

SAGE ADVICE.
Tracks: / Loving cup / Burning desire / Trouble man / Dreamville, New Mexico / Indiosa / Wild dog waltz / Sage advice / Outside an angel's reach (3 6ixes) / Shards of time / Still too far / Blanket of stars / You are my sunshine.
LP: . . . . **FIEND 181**

Band Of Gold

LOVE SONGS ARE BACK AGAIN.
Tracks: / Love songs are back again / Let's put it all together / Betcha by golly wow / Sideshow / Have you seen her / Reunited / You make me feel brand new / Kiss and say goodbye / Just to say / In love again.
LP: . . . . **PL 70602**
MC: . . . . **PK 70602**

THIS IS OUR TIME.
Tracks: / This is our time / Love songs are back again / In love again / Lovers are / Just to say i love you.
LP: . . . . **PL 70790**

Band Of Holy Joy

BIG SHIP SAILS, THE.
LP: . . . . **HARP 1**

DEVIL AND THE DEEP BLUE SEA, THE.
LP: . . . . **CFC 003**

MANIC, MAGIC AND MAJESTIC.
Tracks: / Bride / What the Moon saw / Blessed boy / Baubles, bangles, emotional tangles / Manic, magic, majestic / You're not singing anymore / Route to love.
LP: . . . . **ROUGH 125**
MC: . . . . **ROUGHC 125**

MORE TALES FROM THE CITY.
LP: . . . . **HARPLP 1**

POSITIVELY SPOOKED.
LP: . . . . **ROUGH 155**
MC: . . . . **ROUGHC 155**

WHEN STARS COME OUT TO PLAY.
LP: . . . . **BYEBYE 1**

Band Of Joy

24 K.
Tracks: / 3 a.m. in the city / Woman / Overseer / So cold / Live bait / Like a river / Please call home / She's the one / Shock house.
LP: . . . . **THBL 003**

Band Of Outsiders

UP THE RIVER.
LP: . . . . **SHARP 028**

Band Of Susans

HOPE AGAINST HOPE.
Tracks: / Not even close / Learning to sin / Throne of blood / Elliott Abrams in hell / All the wrong reasons / I, the jury / No God / You were an optimist / Ready to bend / Hope against hope.
LP: . . . . **FU 005**
MC: . . . . **FU 005C**

LOVE AGENDA.
LP: . . . . **BFFP 43**
MC: . . . . **BFFP 43 C**

Band, Richard

REANIMATOR, THE.
LP: . . . . **VS 1018**

Band Y Betws

TWMPATH DAWNS.
LP: . . . . **SAIN 1357 D**

Bandera Rockabillies

BANDERA ROCKABILLIES (Various artists).
LP: . . . . **JSP 1005**

HYPE YOU INTO SELLING YOUR HEAD.
LP: . . . . **JSP 1018**

Banderas

RIPE.
Tracks: / This is your life / Comfort of faith, The / May this be your last sorrow / First hand / Why aren't you in love with me? / She sells / Too good / Don't let that man / It's written all over my face / Never too late.
LP: **828 247 1**
MC: **828 247 4**

Bandez, Annie

JACKAMO.
Tracks: / As I lie in your arms / Bastinado / Chasing the dragon down Broadway / Jackamo / One mourning / Jak yo mama / Rise.
LP: . . . . **TBLP4 B**

Bandit

BANDIT.
LP: . . . . **ARTY 149**

PARTNERS IN CRIME.
Tracks: / Don't you worry / Change of heart / Memories of you / Love song / Best of you, The / High on your love / One way love / Visions of you / Stick around / Rocker.
LP: . . . . **ARL 5010**

Banditi A ...

BANDITI A ORGOSOLO/CRONACA FAMILIARE (Original soundtrack) (Various artists).
LP: . . . . **IM 014**

Band'its at Ten

BAND'ITS AT TEN O'CLOCK (Various artists).
LP: **2384 116**

Bandoggs

BANDOGGS (Various artists).
LP: . . . . **LTRA 504**

Bandolero (Film)

BANDOLERO (1968 Film soundtrack) (Various artists).
Tracks: / Trap, The: *Various artists* / El jefe: *Various artists* / Bait, The: *Various artists* / Ambushed: *Various artists* / Sabinas: *Various artists* / Dee's proposal: *Various artists* / Across the river: *Various artists* / Bad day for a hanging, A: *Various artists* / Better way, A: *Various artists.*
LP: . . . . **TCS 1001.1**

Bandstand Grand

BANDSTAND GRAND (Various artists).
Tracks: / Greensleeves: *Various bands* / Spitfire prelude: *Various bands* / Cockles and mussels: *Various* bands / Trumpet voluntary: *Various bands* / Sullivan at sea: *Various bands* / Spirt of pageantry: *Various* bands / Farandole: *Various bands* / Yeoman of the guard, The (overture): *Various bands* / Tannhauser grand march: *Various bands* / Birdie's song: *Various bands* / Caesar' camp: *Various bands* / Policeman's holiday: *Various bands* / Concerto for two trumpets: *Various bands* / Musical joke, A: *Various bands* / Pique dame: *Various bands* / Great war medley: *Various bands* / Skye boat song: *Various bands* / Frensham: *Various bands.*
2LP: . . . . **CR 090**
MCSET: . . . . **CRT 090**

Bandwagon (film)

BANDWAGON (Original soundtrack) (Various artists).
Tracks: / Overture: *Various artists* / Sweet music: *Various artists* / High and low: *Various artists* / Hoops: *Various artists* / Confessions: *Various artists* / New sun in the sky: *Various artists* / I

love Louisa: *Various artists* / Ballet music: *Various artists* / Beggars waltz: *Various artists* / White heat: *Various artists* / I've got you on my mind: *Various artists* / Maybe I love you too much: *Various artists*/ My temptation: *Various artists* / Heart of stone: *Various artists* / Gold diggers song: *Various artists*.
LP: . . . . **MCA 25015**
MC: . . . . **MCAC 25015**
LP: . . . . **LSA 3082**

BANDWAGON/SHOWBOAT (See under Showboat) (Various artists).

Bandy, Moe

CHAMP, THE.
Tracks: / Champ, The / Cowboy's a kitten at home, The / Wild side of life / Beethoven was before my time / Giver took all she could stand, The / Yesterday once more / I just can't leave those honky tonks alone / She took out the outlaw in me / Like some good ol' boy / Accidentally on purpose tonight.
LP: . . . . **CBS 84426**
MC: **40 84426**

COUNTRY STORE: MOE BANDY.
Tracks: / Champ, The / Yesterday once more / You're gonna lose her / She's not really cheatin' / Wild side of life, The (Only on CD.) / My woman loves the devil out of me (Only on CD.) / Where's the dress / Jambalaya / Still on a roll / Don't sing me no songs about Texas / Your cheatin' heart (Only on CD.) / Hank and Lefty raised my country soul (Only on CD.).
LP: . . . . **CST 29**
MC: . . . . **CSTK 29**

DEVOTED TO YOUR MEMORY.
Tracks: / Let's get over them together / One more port / Devoted to your memory / Don't sing me no songs about Texas / You're gonna lose her like that / Bar-room is my battleground tonight / Country side / Someone like you / She's looking good.
LP: . . . . **CBS 25552**

FOLLOWING THE FEELING.
Tracks: / Following the feeling / Today I almost stopped loving you / Would you mind if I just called you Julie / Mexico winter / Liquor emotion / My woman loves the devil out of me / It's you and me again / I've got your love all over me / If I lay down the bottle / It's better than being alone.
LP: . . . . **CBS 84891**

GOOD OL' BOYS - ALIVE AND WELL, THE (Bandy, Moe & Joe Stampley).
Tracks: / Where's the dress / He's back in Texas / Honky tonk money / Wild and crazy guys / We've got our moe-joe workin' / Boy's night out / Daddy's honky tonk / Wildlife sanctuary / Alive and well / Still on a roll.
LP: . . . . **CBS 26068**
MC: **40 26068**

HEY JOE, HEY MOE (Bandy, Moe & Joe Stampley).
Tracks: / Honky tonk queen / Girl don't ever get lonely / I'd rather be a pickin' / Drinkin' dancin' / Drunk front / Hey Joe, hey Moe / Country boys / Let's hear it for the workin' man / Get off my case / Two beers away.
LP: . . . . **CBS 84966**

I CAN STILL LOVE YOU IN THE SAME OL' WAY.
Tracks: / I can still love you in the same ol' way / I took a princess home with me / City boy / One lonely heart lead to another / Early Nancy / I lost her to a Dallas cowboy / What Chicago took from me / Leave the honky tonks alone / Drivin' my love back to you / Monday night cheatin'.
LP: . . . . **CBS 25296**

I LOVE COUNTRY.
Tracks: / Barroom is my battleground tonight, The / Wound time can't erase, A / Barroom roses / There's nobody home on the range / You can't close to cheatin' as I came / Yippi cry yi / Yesterday once more / Two lonely people / Soft lights and Hard Country Music / Jambalaya / One of a kind / Barstool mountain / It's a cheating situation / Would you mind if I just called you Julie / My woman loves the devil out of me / I cheated me right out of you.
LP: **4504291**
MC: **4504294**

IT'S A CHEATING SITUATION.
Tracks: / It's a cheating situation / Barstool mountain / Cheaters never win / Conscience where were you / Try my love on for size / To cheat or not to cheat / She stays in the name of love / It just helps to keep the hurt from hurtin' / When my working girl comes home / They haven't made the drink.
LP: . . . . **CBS 83552**

JUST GOOD OL' BOYS (Bandy, Moe & Joe Stampley).
Tracks: / Just good ol' boys / Make a little love each day / Tell Ole I ain't here, he better get on home / Honky tonk man / Partner's in rhyme / Holding the bag / Bye bye love / Only the names have been changed / When it comes to cowgirls / Thank goodness it's Friday.
LP: **84012**

LIVE FROM BAD BOB'S (Bandy, Moe & Joe Stampley).
Tracks: / We've got our moe joe working / Hey joe / Daddy's honky tonk / Holding the bag / Boy's night out / Tell ole i ain't here he better get on home / Where's the dress / Your cheatin' heart / Still on a roll / Just good ol' boys.
LP: . . . . **CBS 26364**

LOVE IS WHAT LIFE IS ALL ABOUT.
Tracks: / Love is what life is all about / Ghost of a chance / I guess I had a real good time last night / Bic flicking baby / For tears to come / Two lonely people / Jambalaya / Mom and dad's waltz / I never miss a day / Yippy cry yi.
LP: . . . . **CBS 83174**

MOTEL MATCHES.
Tracks: / Motel matches / Woman your love / Beauty lies in the eyes of the beholder / Don't start me cheatin' again / That horse that you can't ride / It took a lot of drinkin' / Lovin' it up / In Mexico / Your memory always finds it's way home / Texas Saturday night.
LP: . . . . **CBS 25927**

ONE OF A KIND.
Tracks: / I cheated me right out of you / One of a kind / Gonna honky tonk right out on you / Bitter with the sweet / We start the fire / In the middle of losing you / Tell her it's over / Sweet Kentucky woman / Honky tonk merry go round / Man of means.
LP: . . . . **CBS 84145**

SHE'S NOT REALLY CHEATIN' (SHE'S JUST GETTIN' EVEN).
Tracks: / She's not really cheatin' / He's taking my place at your place / Can I pick you up / Hank and Lefty raised my country soul / All American dream, The / Only if there is another you / Our love could burn Atlanta down again / Your memory is showing all over me / Angel like you, An / Jesus in a Nashville jail.
LP: . . . . **CBS 85868**

SINGS 20 GREAT SONGS OF THE AMERICAN COWBOY.
Tracks: / Home on the range / I'm an old cowhand / Back in the saddle again / Streets of Laredo / Old faithful / Don't fence me in / San Antonio rose / Deep in the heart of Texas / Oklahoma hills / When it's springtime in the rockies / Take me back to Tulsa / Red river valley / Cool water / Sioux City Sue / Tumbling tumbleweeds / Bury me not on the lone prairie / High noon / Good old paint / Strawberry roan, The / Old Chisholm trail, The.
MC: . . . . **PLAC 3907**

TWENTY GREAT SONGS OF THE AMERICAN COWBOY.
Tracks: / Springtime in the rockies / Red river valley / Take me back to Tulsa / Bury me not on the lone prairie / Don't fence me in / Tumbling tumbleweeds / San Antonio rose / I'm an old cowhand / Oklahoma hills / Old faithful / Home on the range / Sioux City Sue / Deep in the heart of Texas / Cool water / Good old paint / Back in the saddle again / Streets of Laredo / High noon / Strawberry roan, The / Old Chisholm trail, The.
LP: . . . . **WW 5118**
MC: . . . . **WW 4 5118**

YOU HAVEN'T HEARD THE LAST OF ME.
Tracks: / One man band / I forgot that I don't live here anymore / Sunny side of you, The / Times I tried to love you, The / You can't straddle the fence anymore / Till I'm too old to die young / Ridin' her memory down / Between us / You haven't heard the last of me / Rodeo Song.
LP: . . . . **IMCA 5914**
MC: . . . . **IMCAC 5914**

Bandzilla

BANDZILLA.
Tracks: / Slave to the rhythm / For you / Don't touch / Brief encounter / Breakout / Will power / Alligator stomp / Never too late / Blue movies.
LP: . . . . **BAND 1**
MC: . . . . **BAND C1**

Bane

WHAT HAPPENS NEXT.....
MC: . . . . **JIMP 1C**

Banera Force

BANERA FORCE (Various artists).
LP: . . . . **MUT 1090**

Banerjee, Nikhil

RGS. SOHENI/MEGH.
LP: . . . . **EASD 1377**
MC: . . . . **TC 2405**

Bang Bang Bazooka

BANG BANG BAZOOKA.
LP: . . . . **ROCK 4**

Bang on a Drum

BANG ON A DRUM (Various artists).
Tracks: / Early in the morning: *Various artists* / Brush, brush, brush: *Various artists* / Sunbeams play: *Various artists* / I am here: *Various artists* / Caterpillars only crawl: *Various artists* / Wheels keep turning: *Various* artists / I like peace, I like quiet: *Various artists* / Building up my house: *Various artists* / Israeli boat song, The: *Various artists* / One potato, two potato: *Various artists* / Bang on a drum: *Various artists*/ Jump: *Various artists* / Paper song, The: *Various artists* / Down on the farm: *Various artists* / Fidget: *Various artists* / Come to the shops: *Various artists* / What do we do with this and that: *Various artists*/ Circus is coming, The: *Various artists* / Build it up: *Various artists* / I think I've got a cold: *Various artists* / You can stamp your feet: *Various artists* / Playaway: *Various artists*.
LP: . . . . **REC 242**
MC: . . . . **MRMC 004**

BANG ON A DRUM AGAIN (Various artists).
Tracks: / Head and shoulders, knees and toes: *Various artists* / How do you feel today: *Various artists* / Paddle your own canoe: *Various artists* / Hey you: *Various artists* / Elephants on a piece of string: *Various artists*/ Hokey cokey: *Various artists* / Spells: *Various artists* / Wiggle my ears: *Various artists* / Stand up sit down: *Various artists* / Zoom: *Various artists* / Step aside: *Various artists* / How high does a fly fly: *Various artists* / Well Jemima, let's go shopping: *Various artists* / Share: *Various artists*/ Wouldn't it be funny: *Various artists* / Rain makes all things beautiful, The: *Various artists*.
LP: . . . . **REC 474**
MC: . . . . **ZCM 474**

Bang Tango

DANCIN' ON COALS.
LP: . . . . **MCA 10196**
MC: . . . . **MCAC 10196**

PSYCHO CAFE.
LP: . . . . **MCG 6048**
MC: . . . . **MCGC 6048**

Bang The Party

BACK TO PRISON.
LP: . . . . **WAFLP 4**
MC: . . . . **WAFTC 4**

Bangers & Mash (tv)

CHIMPS AT WORK.
MC: . . . . **STK 029**

EGGS IS EGGS.
MC: . . . . **PLBM 273**

GHOST BOAST.
MC: . . . . **PLBM 272**

SNITCHNOSE SWITCH.
MC: . . . . **STK 030**

Bangles

12" TAPE: BANGLES.
MC: **6509074**

ALL OVER THE PLACE.
Tracks: / Hero takes a fall / Live / James / All about you / Dover beach / Tell me / Restless / Going down to Liverpool / He's got a secret / Silent treatment / More than meets the eye.
LP: **4500911**
MC: **4500914**
LP: . . . . **CBS 26105**

BANGLES: INTERVIEW PICTURE DISC.
LPPD: . . . . **BAK 2131**

BANGLES - THE 12" TAPE.
Tracks: / If she knew what she wants / Walking down your street / In your room / Manic Monday / Walk like an Egyptian.
MC: **4689884**

DIFFERENT LIGHT.
Tracks: / Manic Monday / In a different light / Walking down your street / Walk like an Egyptian / Standing in the hallway / Return post / If she knew what she wants / Let it go / September girl / Angels don't fall in love / Following / Not like you.
LP: . . . . **CBS 26659**
MC: **40 26659**
LP: **465581**
MC: **465584**

EVERYTHING.
Tracks: / In your room / Complicated girl / Bell jar / Something to believe in / Eternal flame / Be with you / Glitter years / I'll set you free / Watching the sky / Some dreams come true / Make a play for her now / Waiting for you / Crash and burn.
LP: **4629791**
MC: **4629794**

GREATEST HITS.
Tracks: / Hero takes a fall / Going down to Liverpool / Manic monday / If she knew what she wants / Walk like an Egyptian / Walking down your street / Following / Hazy shade of winter / In your room / Eternal flame / Be with you / I'll set you free / Everything I wanted / Where were you when I needed you.
LP: **4667691**
MC: **4667694**

MUSIC AND MEDIA INTERVIEW PICTURE DISC.
LPPD: . . . . **BAN 1018**

REAL WORLD, THE.
LP: . . . . **ILS 6509616**

SUSANNA, VIKKI, MICHAEL, DEBBI INTERVIEW.
LP: . . . . **EGYPT 10**

Bangor

TERRAS BANGKOK.
LP: . . . . **BANG 01**

Bangor Parish...

CAROLS BY CANDLELIGHT (Bangor Parish Church Choir).
Tracks: / O little town of Bethlehem / Adam lay ybounden / Ding dong merrily on high / Gabriel's message / Away in a manger / Blessed son of God / As with gladness men of old / Sussex carol / We've been awhile a wondering / Still still still / As I outrode this endless night / Tender shoot, A / Stille nacht / Chester carol / Joseph and the angel / Lute book lullaby / Psallite unigenito / O come all ye faithful / Over the hills / While shepherds watched their flocks by night.
LP: . . . . **APS 341**

Bangsters

ESCAPE FROM BUBBLEGUM LAND.
LP: . . . . **ROSE 43**

SCARLET PLAGUE.
LP: . . . . **ROSE 61**

Banim, Al

AL BANIM.
MC: . . . . **LNMC 7017**

Banjo...

BANJO PICKIN' GIRLS (Various artists).
LP: . . . . **ROUNDER 1029**

BANJO'S GREATEST HITS (Various artists).
LP: . . . . **PO 236**

FIVE STRING BANJO WITH 12 STRING GUITAR (Various artists).
LP: . . . . **GNPS 98**

THEY ALL PLAYED BANJO (Various artists).
LP: . . . . **FG 403**

Banjo Dan

HIGH TIME (Banjo Dan & The Midnight Ploughboys).
LP: . . . . **FR 129**

Banjo in the Hills

BANJO IN THE HILLS (Various artists).
LP: . . . . **SLP 104**
MC: . . . . **GT 5104**

Banjo Man (film)

BANJO MAN (Original soundtrack) (Various artists).
Tracks: / Lonesome Ruben: *Scruggs, Earl* / Battle of New Orleans: *Nitty Gritty Dirt Band* / You ain't goin' nowhere: *Baez, Joan* / Freight train boogie: *Watson, Doc & Merle* / T for Texas: *Scruggs, Earl* / Roll over Beethoven: *Byrds* / Me and Bobby McGee: *Elliot, Ramblin' Jack* / Mr. Tambourine man: *Byrds* / Black mountain rag: *Watson, Doc & Merle* / Night they drove old dixie down, The: *Baez, Joan* / Diggy liggy lo: *Nitty Gritty Dirt* Band / Blowin' in the wind: *Baez, Joan* / Foggy mountain breakdown: *Scruggs, Earl* / Billy Fehr: *Elliot, Ramblin' Jack*.
LP: . . . . **SRK 6026**

Bank Statement

BANK STATEMENT.
Tracks: / Throwback / Queen of darkness / Raincloud / Big man / More I hide it, The / I'll be waiting / That night / Border, The / House needs a roof, A / Thursday the twelfth.
LP: . . . . **V 2600**
MC: . . . . **TCV 2600**

Banks, Bishop Jeff

CAUGHT UP IN THE RAPTURE.
LP: . . . . **SL 14787**
MC: . . . . **SC 14787**

Banks, Buddy

HAPPY HOME BLUES.
Tracks: / I need it bad / Bank's boogie / Voo-it, voo-it / Cryin' blues / Fluffy's debut / Bank's boogie / Hi-jinks blues / Name it and claim it / Goin' for the okey-doke / Roses of Picardy / East side boogie / '686' blues / Maybe some rainy day / Be fair with me / Happy home blues / Nite is fading too soon, The.
LP: . . . . **OFF 6050**

Banks, Tony

CURIOUS FEELING, A.
Tracks: / From the undertow / Lucky me / Lie, The / After the lie / Curious feeling, A / Forever morning / You / Somebody else's dream / Waters of Lethe, The / For a while / In the dark.
LP: . . . . **CHC 42**
MC: . . . . **CHCMC 42**
LP: . . . . **CAS 1148**

DEAF FUGITIVE.
Tracks: / This is love / Man of spells / And the wheels keep turning / Say you'll never leave me / Thirty three's / By you / At the edge of night / Charm / Moving under.
MC: . . . . **CHCMC 43**
LP: . . . . **CHC 43**
LP: . . . . **TBLP 1**

SOUNDTRACKS.
Tracks: / Shortcut to somewhere / Smilin' Jack Casey / Quicksilver suite / You call this victory / Lion of symmetry / Redwing suite.
LP: . . . . **CAS 1173**
MC: . . . . **CASMC 1173**
LP: . . . . **CHC 82**
MC: . . . . **CHCMC 82**

STILL.
LP: . . . . **V 2658**
MC: . . . . **TCV 2658**

Bannatyne, Donald

GREAT WESTERN HIGHWAY.
MC: . . . . **MR 1019**

Banquet Scene

BANQUET SCENE, THE (From Dune, by Frank Herbert).
MC: . . . . **CDL 1555**

Banshee

CRY IN THE NIGHT.
LP: . . . . **RR 9525 1**

Banton, Evans

GENTLEMEN PREFER BLUES (See under Jackson, Banton, Evans) (Banton, Evans, Jackson).

Banton, George

YOU'RE ALL I NEED.
LP: . . . . **LLT 1105**

Banton, Lloyd

YOU WILL BE MY LOVE.
LP: . . . . **BS 039**

Banton, Pato

NEVER GIVE IN.
Tracks: / Absolute perfection / My opinion / Don't Worry / Handsworth riot / Gwarn / Pato and Roger come again / Never give in / Don't sniff coke / Sattle Satan / King step / Hello Tosh.
LP: . . . . **GREL 108**
MC: . . . . **GREEN 108**

PROFESSOR CAPTURES PATO BANTON (See Mad Professor) (Banton, Pato & Mad Professor).

RECAPTURED.
LP: . . . . **ARILP 043**

TAKE YOUR TIME (See Cross, Sandra) (Banton, Pato/Sandra Cross).

WIZE UP (NO COMPROMIZE).
Tracks: / From now on / Situation crazy / Don't stop the music / I'm addicted / Celebrate (Mandela's freedom) / Give a little love / Wize up / Niceness / All drugs out / Spirits in the material world.
LP: . . . . **EIRSA 1034**

Bantu

BANTU (Various artists).
2LP: . . . . **CIC 8401/2**

Bap

KRISTALLNACHT.
Tracks: / Alexandra, nit nur do / Bahnhofskino / Drei wunsch frei / Sendeschlub / Kristallnaach / Diess nach ess alles drin / Deshalv'spill' mer he / Zofall un'e janz klei bessje glock / Do kanns zaubere.
LP: . . . . **EJ 2403411**
LP: . . . . **BAP 1**

Baptist Beat

BAPTIST BEAT (Various artists).
Tracks: / Rev. Moses: *Donaldson, Lou* / Jody grind, The: *Horace Silver Quintet* / Turn around: *Patton, John* / Fungii mama: *Smith, Jimmy (USA)* / Baptist beat, A: *Mobley, Hank* / Sara's dance: *Turrentine, Stanley* / Party time: *Roach, Freddie* / Good gracious: *Donaldson, Lou.*
LP: . . . . **BNSLP 3**
MC: . . . . **TCBNSLP 3**

Baptiste, Mona

ES LIEGT WAS IN DER LUFT.
Tracks: / Es liegt was in der luft / Wenn es heut' nochware liebe gibt / Dixie doodle rag / O Jackie Joe / Ich habe solche Angst / Ja, da Kussen (ja, ja) / Wo ist der Eine? / Turn the key / An der Ecke (gib mir einen Kuss) / Wer mich kusst, ist gerfangen / Polly dolly du / Ach komm' doch zurueck (I cry more) / Halt, halt (halt doch deinen Mann fest) / Rumbango / You're wrong all wrong / No, no, no.
LP: . . . . **BFX 15336**

Bar B Q Killers

COMELY.
Tracks: / Sarcophag / Greatneck / Weird shit / Larger than large / Dookie tingue / Bovine viewfinder / Jose O Dingleberry / They / Fitsula / Crowd, not me, The / Her shit on his dick.
LP: . . . . **SAVE 056**

Bar Mitzvah Boy (show)

BAR MITZVAH BOY (Original cast recording) (Various artists).
Tracks: / Overture: *Various artists* / Why?: *Various artists* / If only a little bit sticks: *Various artists* / Bar mitzvah of Elliot Green: *Various artists* / This time tomorrow: *Various artists* / Thou shalt not: *Various* artists / Harolds of this world: *Various artists* / We've done alright: *Various artists* / Simchas: *Various* artists / You wouldn't be you: *Various artists* / Rita's request: *Various artists* / Sun shines out of your eyes: *Various artists* / Where is the music coming from: *Various artists* / I've just begun: *Various artists.*
LP: . . . . **CBS 70162**
MC: **40 70162**

Barabbas (film)

BARABBAS (1962 Film soundtrack) (Various artists).
LP: . . . . **CT 7034**

Baraka, Imamu Amiri

NEW YORK QUARTET AND IMAMU AMIRI BARAKA (See under New York Quartet/Imamu Amiri Baraka) (Baraka, Imamu Amiri/New York Quartet).

Baranco, Wilbert

GROOVIN' HIGH (See under Wilson, Gerald) (Baranco, Wilbert/Gerald Wilson/Jimmy Mundy).

Barb

BOUQUET OF BARBS.
LP: . . . . **MAGL 5060**
MC: . . . . **ZCMAG 5060**

Barbarin, Paul

STREETS OF THE CITY (Barbarin, Paul & His New Orleans Band 1950).
LP: . . . . **LPS 9**
MC: . . . . **TCS 9**

Barbary Coast

CLEAN UP.
Tracks: / Last ride, The / Rollin' on / Take me home truck / Toe the line / Many roads I ride / Truck driver's blues / Trucker's life, A / God bless the trucker's bike / Rockabilly trucker / Breaker's blues.
LP: . . . . **KO 1013**
MC: . . . . **TC KO 1013**

COASTLINES.
Tracks: / Did it rain / Fool such as I, A / Leave them with a smile / Living on sunshine / Give my love to Rose / If this is just a game / Blowin' away / You only live once in a while / Old five and dimers like me / Long gone.
LP: . . . . **KO 1004**

FISTFUL OF ROSES.
LP: . . . . **BSS 184**

LONG VEHICLE.
Tracks: / Son of a son of a trucker / Ridin' rubber / Move on down the road / Don's cafe / Keep those wheels a rollin' / High rollin' lonesome / Truck stop woman / Queen of the road / Joe's rig road / Reversing song, The / Pedal to the metal.
LP: . . . . **KO 1008**
MC: . . . . **TC KO 1008**

Barbecue Bob

BROWN SKIN GAL.
LP: . . . . **AB 2001**

REMAINING TITLES, THE 1927-30.
Tracks: / Good time rounder / Yo yo blues / Darktown gamblin' / Easy rider don't you deny my name / Cold wave blues.
LP: . . . . **MSE 1009**

Barbed Wire

AGE THAT DIDN'T CARE, THE.
LP: . . . . **OIR 006**

SKINS 'N' PUNKS VOLUME 4 (See also Adnormals) (Barbed Wire & Adnormals).

Barbee, John Henry

BLUES LIVE (Barbee, John Henry/ Sleepy John Estes).
LP: . . . . **SLP 4074**

Barber, Chris

BARBER'S BEST.
Tracks: / Bobby Shaftoe / Martinique, The / Chimes blues / Merry down rag / Skokiaan / St. Louis blues / It's tight like that / Ice cream / Oh, didn't he ramble / Storyville blues / World is waiting for the sunshine, The / Reckless blues.
LP: . . . . **JASM 2028**

BARBER'S CHOICE.
LP: **6 28491**

BARBICAN BLUES.
Tracks: / Bourbon Street parade / Mary had a little lamb / Perdido street blues / Spanish castles / Barbican blues / Bugle boy march / Good Queen Bess / Wild cat blues / Rose room / Basin Street blues / Ice cream.
2LP: . . . . **BLM 61003/4**

BEST OF BALL, BARBER & BILK (See under 'Ball, Kenny' for details) (Barber, Chris/Acker Bilk/Kenny Ball).

BEST OF BARBER AND BILK VOL.1 (Barber, Chris/Acker Bilk/Kenny Ball).
LP: . . . . **GGL 0075**

BEST OF BARBER AND BILK VOL.2 (Barber, Chris/Acker Bilk/Kenny Ball).
LP: . . . . **GGL 0096**

BEST OF CHRIS BARBER.
Tracks: / Bobby Shaftoe / Rock Island line / New Orleans / John Henry / Stevedore stomp / Merrydown blues / I'd love it / Storyville blues / Girls go crazy, The / I hate a man like you / Alution march / Weeping willow blues.
LP: . . . . **TAB 86**
LP: . . . . **ACL 1037**
MC: . . . . **KTBC 86**

BEST OF CHRIS BARBER (PRT).
Tracks: / Petite fleur / One sweet letter from you / Wabash blues / Texas moaner / Old rugged cross, The / Olga / Papa de da da / Thriller rag / When you and I were young, Maggie / Tishomingo blues / Sweet Georgia Brown / Big house blues / Just a closer walk with thee / Ugly child / Careless love.
LP: . . . . **PYL 6031**
MC: . . . . **PYM 6031**

CAN'T WE GET TOGETHER (Barber, Chris Jazz & Blues Band).
Tracks: / Holiday / Double check stomp / Here come my blackbird / I wish I could shimmy like my sister Kate / Over the waves / Everybody love my baby / Whistling Rufus / Can't we get together / Good time tonight / High Society / Bobby Shaftoe / New Orleans Ceremony / Just a little while to stay here / Oration by Chris Barber / Just a closer walk with thee / When the saints go marching in / At the jazz band ball / Good Queen Bess / Easter Parade / Isle of Capri / Wabas blues / Sheik of Araby, The / Going home / Old rugged cross, The / Too busy.
2LP: . . . . **TTD 517/18**
MCSET: . . . . **TTD 5517/18**

CHOO CHOO CH' BOOGIE (See under Jordan, Louis) (Barber, Chris & Louis Jordan).

CHRIS BARBER BAND BOX NO.2.
LP: **33SCX 3277**

CHRIS BARBER IN NEW ORLEANS.
Tracks: / Shake it or break it / Eh la bas / It's right here for you / High society / You can't depend on me / Hindustan / Mama's in the racket / Billies' boogie / Gulf coast blues / Dippermouth blues / Billie's blues / All of me / Love song of the Nile.
LP: . . . . **HJ 106**

CHRIS BARBER STORY VOL.1 (In the beginning).
Tracks: / Gatemouth / Mama's gone, goodbye / Sing on / How long blues / Martinique / Bobby Shaftoe / Stevedore stomp / Yellow dog blues / Original Charleston strut / Jazz lips / Over in the gloryland / Tiger rag / Baby won't you please come home / Doctor jazz.
LP: . . . . **BLM 51003**

CHRIS BARBER STORY VOL.2.
Tracks: / When things go wrong with you / Highway to heaven / High society / I'm gonna move to the outskirts of town / Help me / Drat that fratle rat / Bone and bread / Just a sittin' and a rockin' / Couldn't keep it to myself / Mooche / Jenny's ball.
LP: . . . . **BLM 51004**

CHRIS BARBER STORY VOL.3.
Tracks: / Everybody knows / Cortina run / Oro / I think it's going to rain today / Watcha gonna do / Jazz me blues / Give me an old fashioned swing in the evening / Shout 'em Aunt Tillie / I'm slapping Seventh Avenue with the sole of my shoe.
LP: . . . . **BLM 51005**

CLASSICS CONCERT IN BERLIN 1959.
Tracks: / Climax rag / Gotta travel on / Chimes blues / Just a little white to stay here / S'wonderful / Lord, Lord, Lord / Revival.
2LP: . . . . **CBJBD 4002**
MC: . . . . **ZCBJB 4002**

COME FRIDAY (Barber, Chris Jazz & Blues Band).
Tracks: / Alligator hop / St. Louis blues / Wild cat blues / Come Friday / Sweet Sue / Stevedore stomp.
LP: . . . . **BLM 51008**

CONCERT FOR THE BBC (Barber, Chris Jazz & Blues Band).
2LP: . . . . **TTD 509/510**

CREOLE LOVE CALL (Barber, Chris Band).
Tracks: / Stevedore stomp / Come Friday / Sweet Sue / Wild cat blues / St. Louis blues / Alligator hop / Queen Bess / Creole love call / South Rampart street parade / Snag it / Easter parade.
2LP: . . . . **TTD 502/503**

DOCTOR JOHN & CHRIS BARBER (See under Doctor John) (Barber, Chris & Dr John).

ECHOES OF ELLINGTON VOL 1 (Barber, Chris Jazz & Blues Band).
Tracks: / Stevedore stomp / Jeep's blues / I'm slapping Seventh Avenue with the sole of my shoe / In a mellow tone / Prelude to a kiss / Second line / Perdido / Moon indigo / Shout 'em Aunt Tilly.
MC: . . . . **MCTTD 555**

ECHOES OF ELLINGTON VOL 2 (Barber, Chris Jazz & Blues Band).
Tracks: / Squatty roo / Blues for Duke / Take the 'A' train / Warm valley / Caravan / Sophisticated lady / It don't mean a thing / Just squeeze me / Mooche, The / Jeep is jumpin'.
MC: . . . . **MCTTD 556**

ECHOES OF HARLEM.
LP: . . . . **DM 8**

ELITE SYNCOPATIONS.
LP: **33SX 1245**

ESSENTIAL CHRIS BARBER (Featuring Ottilie Patterson & Monty Sunshine).
Tracks: / Panama rag / Petite fleur / Savoy blues / Sister Kate / Sweet Georgia Brown / Thriller rag / Beale Street blues / Bill Bailey won't you please come home / Bourbon Street parade / New blues / Trombone cholly / Texas moaner / Willie the weeper / Careless love / Everybody loves my baby / High society / Jailhouse blues / Make me a pallet opn the floor / One sweet letter from you / Tishomingo blues / Trouble in mind / When you and I were young / Whistling Rufus / Wildcat blues.
MC: . . . . **KAZMC 13**

GET YOURSELF TO JACKSON SQUARE (Barber, Chris Jazz & Blues Band & Dr John).
Tracks: / Down on the bayou / They took my money / Oh didn't he ramble / Black widow / Battersea rain dance / Waiting for a train.
LP: . . . . **SNTF 1018**
MC: . . . . **ZCSN 1018**

GETTING AROUND (Barber, Chris Jazz & Blues Band).
Tracks: / Isle of Capri / Freight train blues / Magnolia's wedding day / I love my baby / Tishomingo blues / Strange things / See see rider / Tight like that / When my sugar walks down the street / Bonsoir mes souvenirs / Mack the knife / How to survive / Army song / Useless song / Great bear, The / O sole mio.
LP: . . . . **SLP 423**

ICE CREAM.
Tracks: / Wild cat blues / Old rugged cross, The / Over in the gloryland / Canal Street blues / Muskrat ramble / High society / Jazz me blues / New Orleans wiggle / London blues / Ice cream.
LP: . . . . **INT 127 029**
MC: . . . . **CAS 427 029**

IN BUDAPEST.
Tracks: / Lord lord lord / Mood indigo / Whistling Rufus / Some of these days /

Mama he treats your daughter mean / Trad tavern.
LP: SLP 4085

JAZZ HOLIDAY (Meets Rod Mason's Hot Five) (Barber, Chris/Rod Mason's Hot Five).
LP: TTD 524

JUBILEE ALBUM.
Tracks: / Savoy blues / Doctor jazz / Baby won't you please come home / Star of the County Down / Bill Bailey won't you please come home / Please don't talk about me when I'm gone / Oro / Give me an old fashioned swing in the evening / It's tight like that / New Orleans wiggle / I'm slapping Seventh Avenue with the sole of my shoe / I think it's going to rain today / Jazz me blues / Whatcha gonna do? / Canal Street blues / Muskrat ramble / Ice cream / Goodbye, goodbye, goodbye.
LP: INT 182 010

LIVE 54/55 (Barber, Chris Jazzband).
LP: 8208781

LIVE IN '85 (Barber, Chris Jazz & Blues Band).
LP: TTD 527

MARDI GRAS AT THE MARQUEE (Barber, Chris & Dr John).
LP: TTD 546
MC: TTD 5546

MUSIC FROM THE LAND OF DREAMS.
Tracks: / Music from the land of dreams / Goin' up the river / Nobody knows you (when you're down and out) / New Orleans Louisiana / Big bass drum (on a Mardi Gras day) / Beg, steal or borrow / Whose blues / New York town / Second line saints.
LP: SNTF 962
MC: ZCSN 962

PETITE FLEUR.
MCSET: DTO 10226

REUNION.
Tracks: / Bourbon Street parade / Saturday night function / Martinique, The / Isle of Capri / Hush-a-bye / It's tight like that / Fairfield reunion blues / Bobby Shaftoe / On a Monday / Bury my body / Long gone lost John / Jenny's ball / Chimes blues / Whistling Rufus / Jazz me blues / Just a sittin' and a rockin' / Stevedore stomp / Jack-ass blues / New Orleans stomp / Maryland my Maryland / When you wore a tulip / Panama rag.
LP: INT 182 014

SPECIAL.
Tracks: / Dardanella / Jazz lips / Original Charleston strut / Lonesome Road / Eh La bas / I wish I could shimmy like my sister Kate / Makin' whoopee / Clarinet Marmalade / Precious lord, take my hand / Colla voce / High society / I'm looking for a four leaf clover / Panama rag / From me to you / Money can't buy me love / Over in the gloryland / Tiger rag / South Rampart Street parade / Easter parade / All my loving.
2LP: INT 157 004

STAR PORTRAIT: CHRIS BARBER.
Tracks: / Down by the riverside / Burgundy Street blues / Phil's late / Sweet Lorraine / Blueberry Hill / When the saints go marching in / Whistling Rufus / Lazy River / St. George's rag / Creole song / Gonna build a mountain / Stevedore stomp / Ice cream / Baby won't you please come home / I can't escape from you / Canal Street blues / Running wild / Just a closer walk with thee / Muskrat ramble / Savoy blues / When you and I were young, Maggie / Bourbon Street parade / Oh didn't he ramble / Goodbye, goodbye, goodbye.
2LP: INT 156 502

STARDUST (Barber, Chris Jazz & Blues Band).
LP: TTD 537
MC: TTD 5537

SWING IS HERE (Barber, Chris with John Lewis & Trummy Young).
Tracks: / Home folks / Time / Mood indigo / T'aint what you do (it's the way that you do it) / Georgia / Someday you'll be sorry / Muskrat ramble / When the saints go marching in.
LP: BLP 12182

TAKE ME BACK TO NEW ORLEANS (Barber, Chris & Dr John).
Tracks: / Take me back to New Orleans / Ti-pi-ti-na / Perdido street blues / New Orleans, Louisiana / Decatur drive / New Orleans / Meet me on the Levee / Harlem rag / Ride on / Big bass drum (on a mardi gras day) / At the cemetery / Concert on Canal Street / Bourbon Street scene / Basin Street / Just a little while to stay here / Oration by Dr. John / What a friend we have in Jesus / When the Saints go marching in / Concert in Canal Street / When the saints go marching in / Buddy Bolden's blues / South Rampart Street Parade / Burgandy Street Blues / Canal Street Blues / Bourbon Street Parade / Do you know what it means to miss New Orleans / Professor Longhair's tip / Brass band blues / Basin Street blues.
2LP: BLM 61001/2
2LP: INT 157 007

THREE B'S, THE (See under Bilk, Acker) (Barber, Chris/Acker Bilk/Sandy Brown).

TIMELESS TRADITIONAL JAZZ FESTIVAL (Barber, Chris/Acker Bilk/Kenny Ball).
2LP: TTD 522-23

ULTIMATE, THE (Barber, Chris/Acker Bilk/Kenny Ball).
Tracks: / I love you Samantha / Panama rag / Midnight in Moscow / Nobody knows you (when you're down and out) / Avalon / I wanna be like you / Christopher Columbus / Spanish harlem / That da da strain / Them there eyes / Stranger on the shore / That's my home / Good Queen Bess / Perdido street blues / Harlem rag / Mood indigo / Mary had a little lamb / When the saints go marching in / St. Louis blues / So do I / Muskrat ramble / Auf wiedersehen.
2LP: KAZ LP 4
MCSET: KAZ MC 4

WHEN IT'S THURSDAY NIGHT IN EGYPT (Barber, Chris Band).
Tracks: / When it's Thursday night in Egypt / I'm beginning to see the light / Sweet Sue / Under the bamboo tree / Lonesome Road / Goodnight sweetheart / All our tomorrows / Memphis blues / We'll meet again / One sweet letter again / Georgia on my mind / Just once for all time.
LP: SNTF 996

Barber (Composer)

SAMUEL BARBER (London Symphony Orchestra/Tedd Joselson).
Tracks: / Piano concerto / Medea's meditation / Dance of vengeance / Adagio for strings.
LP: DCA 534
MC: ZC DCA 534

Barber, Frank

BARBER CUTS.
Tracks: / James Bond medley / If only I could talk to you / Michel Le Grand medley / Charlie Chaplin medley / Richard Rodgers medley / Henry Mancini medley / I know I'm lucky / John Williams medley / Where are you now / Dicing with disco / Bond medley.
LP: N 149
MC: ZCN 149

BIG BANDS ARE BACK.
Tracks: / One o'clock jump / 9.20 special / Jumpin' at the Woodside / Li'l darlin' / Lester leaps in / Swingin' the blues / Li'l darlin' / Song on India / Marie / At the Fat Man's / Liebestraum / Chloe / Tuxedo Junction / String of pearls / When Johnny comes marching home / Serenade in blues / Song of the volga boatmen / On the Atchison, Topeka and Santa Fe / Woodchopper's ball / Four brothers / Your father's moustache / Good earth, The / Northwest passage / Skyliner / Cherokee / Redskin rhumba / Pompton turnpike / Skyliner (reprise) / Artistry in rhythm / Intermission riff / Southern scandal / Eager beaver / Painted rhythm.
LP: N 144
MC: ZCN 144

MEDDLIN' WITH MILLER (Barber, Frank & His Orchestra).
Tracks: / In the mood / Pennsylvania 6 5000 / I've got a gal in Kalamazoo / Moonlight serenade / Little brown jug / Chattanooga choo choo / At last / American patrol / Perdido / Take the 'A' train / C jam blues / Satin doll / Things ain't what they used to be / I'm beginning to see the light / Begin the beguine / Back bay shuffle / What is this thing called love / Frenesi / My heart stood still / Johnson rag / Tangerine / So rare / I'm getting sentimental over you / On the sunny side of the street / Opus one / Hello dolly / When it's sleepy time down South / What a wonderful world / Struttin' with some barbecue / Rockin' chair / Mack the knife / Sing, sing, sing / Stompin' at the Savoy / Don't be that way / Jersey bounce / Christopher Columbus / And the angels sing.
LP: N 143
MC: ZCN 143

Barber Of Seville

BARBER OF SEVILLE (Glyndebourne Festival Opera).
2LP: CFPD 4704
MCSET: TCCFPD 4704

BARBER OF SEVILLE, THE (See under Rossini).

BARBER OF SEVILLE (VIDEO) (see under Rossini for information) (Various artists).

Barber, Tony

SOME DAY ... NOW.
LP: REBEL 1008

Barbershop

BARBERSHOP CONVENTION Caister, 1978 (Various artists).
LP: SDL 295

BEST OF BRITISH BARBERSHOP (Various artists).
Tracks: / I'd give a million tomorrows: *Various artists* / Darkness on the delta: *Various artists* / Berkeley Square: *Various artists* / Let the rest of the world go by: *Various artists* / Muskrat ramble: *Various artists*/ Carolina in the morning: *Various artists* / Sam, the old accordion man: *Various artists* / What a wonderful world: *Various artists* / Don't bring Lulu: *Various artists* / Sweet and lovely: *Various artists* / Over the rainbow: *Various artists* / Do you remember: *Various artists* / Born free: *Various artists* / I believe: *Various artists* / 76 trombones: *Various artists* / Wonderful guy: *Various artists* / Oh Susannah: *Various* artists / Swing low sweet chariot: *Various artists* / Daddy sang bass: *Various artists* / Pollution: *Various artists.*
LP: MWM 1010

Barbican Lovers

FATAL EMBRACE.
LP: AUL 736

Barbie

DREAM GLOW COLLECTION, THE (For Ages 7-12).
MC: PLBB 192

GIRL WITH THE GOLDEN HAIR (For Ages 7-12).
MC: PLBB 193

ISLAND ADVENTURE (For Ages 7-12).
MC: PLBB 209

MOUNTAIN KIDNAP (For Ages 7-12).
MC: PLBB 208

Barbieri, Gato

APASSIONADO.
Tracks: / Latin lovers / Que pasa / Last tango in Paris / Terra me siente / Angel / Tiempo buono / Habanera.
LP: 815 585-1
MC: 815 585-4

CHAPTER FOUR - ALIVE IN NEW YORK.
Tracks: / Milonga triste / La China Leioncia arreo la / Baihia / Lluvia azul.
LP: JAS 54
MC: JAS C54

CHAPTER ONE - LATIN AMERICA.
Tracks: / Encuentros / La China Leioncia arreo la / To be continued / India / Nunca mas.
LP: MCA 39124

CHAPTER THREE.
LP: ASD 9279
MC: ASCD 9279

CONFLUENCE (Barbieri, Gato & Dollar Brand).
Tracks: / Aloe and the wild rose, The / Hamba khale / To Elsa / Eighty first street.
LP: BLM 52010

EL GATO.
LP: PL 13816

EUPHORIA.
Tracks: / Sophia / Carnavalito / Lions also cry / Firepower / Gods and astronauts / Secret fiesta / Speak law.
LP: AMLH 64774

GATO...PARA LOS AMIGOS!.
Tracks: / Llamerito tango / Carnavalito / Brazil / Viva Emilliano Zapata / Encuentros / Latino America / El arriero / Bolivia / Finale (medley).
LP: ASLD 851
MC: ZCASD 851

HAMBA KHALE (Barbieri, Gato & Dollar Brand).
Tracks: / Hamba khale / Aloe and the wild rose, The / To Elsa / 81st Street.
LP: AFF 39

IN SEARCH OF THE MYSTERY.
LP: ESP 1049

OBSESSION.
LP: AFF 12

UNDER FIRE.
Tracks: / El parana / Yo le canto a la luna / Antonico / Maria Domingas / El sertao.
LP: 632 111 6

VIVA EMILIANO ZAPATA.
LP: AS 9279

Barbosa-Lima, Carlos

IMPRESSIONS.
Tracks: / Sicilienne / Gymnopedie no.3 / Girl with the flaxen hair, The / Three pieces from'childrens corner' / Pavane pour une infante defunte / New York rush / Lost child / Kerry morn / Prelude - introduction / Sentimental melody / Baa-too-kee-al almeida.
LP: CC 2009

PLAYS LUIZ BONFA AND COLE PORTER.
Tracks: / Amor fascinante (love fascination) / Manha de carnaval / Xango / Sambolero / Na sombra da mangue - ira (in the shade of the / Passeio no Rio (a walk in Rio) / It's a lovely day / Where or when / Begin the beguine / Let's do it / Still of the night, The / Night and day / Love for sale.
LP: CC 2008

PLAYS THE ENTERTAINER AND OTHERS BY SCOTT JOPLIN.
Tracks: / Entertainer, The / Heliotrope bouquet / Weeping willow / Solace / Maple leaf rag / Sugar cane / Chrysanthemum / Pleasant moments / Easy winners / Cascades, The.
LP: CC 2006

RHAPSODY IN BLUE/WEST SIDE STORY (Barbosa-Lima, Carlos/Sharon Isbin).
Tracks: / I feel pretty / Scherzo/ Somewhere / Cha-cha / Something's coming / Maria / America / Cool / Tonight / I have a love/Finale / Jasbo brown evenings / Liza / Prelude No.3 / Rhapsody in blue.
LP: CC 2012
MC: CC 2012C

Barbour, Freeland

FIRE IN THE HEARTH.
LP: REL 462
MC: REC 462

KILLIEKRANKIE.
Tracks: / Glorious revolution, The / White rose, The / House of Stewart, The / Bluidy clavers / Cameronians march, The / Lands beyond forth, The / Tremble false Whigs / Band at distance, The ("Bonnie Dundee") / Dudhope / Green field of Dalcomera,The / Blair Castle / Braes of Glen Roy,The / Murray's siege / Mackay's advance / Men from Lochaber,The / Am feasgair samhraidh (the summer evening) / Allt Girnaig / Thickets of Raon Ruaraidh, The / Battle of Killiecrankie, The / MacBean's Chase / Flight and Pursuit / Urrard House / South to Dunkeld / Fiery cross, The / Battle of Dunkeld, The / Thanksgiving / There is no enemy in sight / Old Blair / Killiecrankie.
LP: LAP 126
MC: LAP 126C

NO LONG FAREWELL.
LP: LAP 105
MC: LAP 105 C

Barchester Towers (bk)

BARCHESTER TOWERS (Anthony Trollope) (West, Timothy (nar)).
MCSET: CC/035

BARCHESTER TOWERS (Anthony Trollope) (Hawthorne, Nigel (nar)).
MCSET: SAY 92
MCSET: ARGO 1265

Barclay, Bill

ALMOST LIVE.
Tracks: / Introduction / Railway porter, The / American tour '72 / Camp in the country / Bookie, The / Epsom races / Mr. Sax / Does your hair hang low / Language barrier, The / Jelly piece song, The / Two wee hard men, The / Twelve days of Christmas, The / In which Bill Barclay bids farewell.
LP: GML 1016

HALF ALIVE.
LP: BOOB 1

VERY BEST OF BILL BARCLAY, THE.
Tracks: / Ghost train/The Falkland island / Blood bats / Plague of moths, A / Rockin' yule / Does your hair hang low / My old man lays carpets / Sporting section, The / Travel agent / The Scottish GI / Polly had a poodle / Chapati junction/The polis / Twelve days of Christmas, The.
MC: CTRAX 035

VIVA DUNBAR.
Tracks: / Ah Bisto / Bill and Ben / Siamese twins / Viva Dunbar / Fokkers / Five foot two / Dishes in the sink / Glassknickers / Doctor's surgery / Rooster bee sting / Irishman / Tall tale / Barnyards of Delgatay / Scottish knock / Neighbours / D-day dodgers / Doctor and the girl / Polly had a poodle / Concert in the rain / Hebridean evening / Bye bye blackbird.
LP: PKL 5555

Barclay, Eddie

ET VOILA!.
LP: . . . . FS 159

Barclay James Harvest

ALONE WE FLY.
Tracks: / Crazy city / Mockingbird / Our kid's kid / Loving is easy / Rock 'n' roll lady / Fifties child / Blow me down / He said love / Rock 'n' roll star / On the wings of love / For no one / Hymn / Berlin / Love on the line / Shades of B hill / Waiting for the right time / Sideshow / Guitar blues / Poor boy blues / You need love.
2LP: . . . . VSOPLP 140
MC: . . . . VSOPMC 140

AND OTHER SHORT STORIES.
LP: . . . . SHVL 794

BABY JAMES HARVEST.
Tracks: / Moonwater / Crazy (over you) / Delph Town Morn / Summer soldier / Thank you / One hundred thousand smiles out.
LP: . . . . FA 3172
MC: . . . . TCFA 3172
LP: . . . . ATAK 8
MC: . . . . TCATAK 8

BARCLAY JAMES HARVEST LIVE.
2LP: 2683 052
LP: . . . . VSOPLP 164
MC: . . . . VSOPMC 164

BEST OF BARCLAY JAMES HARVEST 1.
Tracks: / Medicine man / Iron Maiden / Moonwater / Ursula / Brother thrush / Poor wages / Child of man / Joker, The / Rock 'n' roll woman / Good love child / Mockingbird / Galadriel.
MC: . . . . TCSHSM 2013
LP: . . . . SHSM 2013
LP: . . . . ATAK 95
MC: . . . . TCATAK 95

BEST OF BARCLAY JAMES HARVEST 2.
Tracks: / Early morning / She said / Lady loves / Crazy (over you) / When the city sleeps / Medicine man / Mother dear / Vanessa Simmons / One hundred thousand smiles out / Mr. Sunshine / Taking some time on / Breathless.
LP: . . . . SHSM 2023
MC: . . . . TCSHSM 2023

COLLECTION: BARCLAY JAMES HARVEST.
LP: . . . . IC 028 07533

CONCERT FOR THE PEOPLE (BERLIN), A.
Tracks: / Berlin / Loving is easy / Mockingbird / Sip of wine / Nova lepidopter / In memory of the martyrs / Life is for living / Child of the universe / Hymn.
LP: . . . . POLD 5052
MC: . . . . POLDC 5052

EARLY MORNING ONWARDS.
Tracks: / Early morning / Poor wages / Brother thrush / Mr. Sunshine / Taking some time on / Mother dear / Mockingbird / Song with no meaning / I'm over you / Child of man / After the day.
LP: . . . . CRY 048 50798

EVERYONE IS EVERYBODY ELSE.
LP: . . . . SPELP 11
MC: . . . . SPEMC 11

EYES OF THE UNIVERSE.
Tracks: / Alright get down boogie / Capricorn / Love on the line / Play to the world / Rock and roll lady / Skin flicks / Song they love to sing, The / Sperratus / Child of the Universe / Negative earth / Paper wings / Great 1974 mining disaster, The / Crazy city / See me, see you / Poor boy blues / Mill boys / For no one.
LP: . . . . POLD 5029
MC: . . . . POLDC 5029

FACE TO FACE.
Tracks: / Prisoner of your love / He said love / Alone in the night / Turn the key / Guitar blues / You need love / Kiev / African / Following me / All my life / Panic.
LP: . . . . POLD 5209
MC: . . . . POLDC 5209

GLASNOST.
Tracks: / Poor man's moody blues / Alone in the night / Hold on / African / On the wings of love / Love on the line / Berlin / Medicine man / Kiev / Hymn / Turn the key / He said love.
LP: . . . . POLD 5219
MC: . . . . POLDC 5219

GONE TO EARTH.
Tracks: / Hymn / Love is like a violin / Friend of mine, A / Poor man's moody blues / Hard hearted woman / Sea of Tranquility / Spirit on the water / Leper's song / Taking me higher.
LP: 2442 148
MC: 3170 460

HARVEST YEARS, THE.
Tracks: / Early morning / Mr. Sunshine / Pools of blue / I can't go on without you / Eden unobtainable / Brother thrush / Poor wages / Taking some time on / When the world was woken / Good love child / Iron maiden / Dark now my sky / She said / Song for dying / Galadriel / Mocking bird / Vanessa Simmons / Happy old world (quad mix) / Ball and chain / Medicine man / Ursula (The Swansea song) / Someone there you know / Poet, The/After the day / I'm over you / Child of man / Breathless / When the city sleeps / Summer soldier / One hundred thousand smiles out / Moonwater / Joker, The.
LPS: . . . . EN 5014
MCSET: . . . . TCEN 5014

JAMES HARVEST BARCLAY.
LP: . . . . SHVL 770

LIVE TAPES.
Tracks: / Child of the universe / Rock and roll star / Poor man's Moody Blues / Mockingbird / Hard hearted woman / One night / Taking me higher / Suicide / Crazy city / Jonathan / For no one / Polk Street rag / Hymn.
2LP: . . . . PODV 2001
MCSET: . . . . PODVC 2001

MOCKINGBIRD (Early years, The).
Tracks: / Mockingbird / Joker, The / Rock and roll woman / 100,000 miles out / Thank you / Medicine man / Ursula / Song for dying / Crazy / She said / Galadriel.
LP: . . . . IC 064 07236

OCTOBERON.
Tracks: / World goes on, The / May day / Ra / Rock and roll / Star / Polk street rag / Believe in me / Suicide.
LP: . . . . SPELP 13
MC: . . . . SPEMC 13
LP: 2442 144

ONCE AGAIN.
Tracks: / She said / Happy old world / Song for dying / Galadriel / Mockingbird / Vanessa Simmons / Ball and chain / Lady loves.
LP: . . . . FA 3073
MC: . . . . TCFA 3073

RING OF CHANGES.
Tracks: / Fifties child / Looking from the outside / Teenage heart / High wire / Midnight drug / Waiting for the right time / Just a day away / Paraiso des cavalos / Ring of changes.
LP: . . . . POLH 3

TIME HONOURED GHOSTS.
LP: . . . . SPELP 12
MC: . . . . SPEMC 12
LP: 2383 361

TURN OF THE TIDE.
Tracks: / Waiting on the borderline / How do you feel now / Back to the wall / Highway for fools / Echoes and shadows / Death of a city / I'm like a train / Doctor doctor / Life is for living / In memory of the martyrs.
LP: . . . . POLD 5040
MC: . . . . POLDC 5040
LP: . . . . POLD 5006

VICTIMS OF CIRCUMSTANCE.
Tracks: / Sideshow / Hold on / Rebel woman / Say you'll stay / For your love / Victims of circumstance / Inside my nightmare / Watching you / I've got a feeling.
LP: . . . . POLD 5135

WELCOME TO THE SHOW.
MC: 841 751 4
LP: 841 751 1

XII.
Tracks: / Loving is easy / Tale of two sixties, A / Turning in circles / Closed shop / In search of England / Sip of wine / Harbour / Nova lepidopter / Giving it up / Streets of San Francisco, The.
LP: . . . . POLD 5006

Barde

IMAGES: BARDE.
LP: . . . . FF 217

Bardens, Pete

HEART TO HEART.
Tracks: / Julia / Doing the crab / Slipstream / Raining all over the world / Jinked / After dark / Slow motion / Tune for Des / Heart to heart.
LP: . . . . SPART 1108

SEEN ONE EARTH.
Tracks: / Seascape / Man alive / Seen on earth / Home thoughts / Prelude / In dreams / Stargate, The / Many happy returns.
LP: . . . . EST 2044
MC: . . . . TCEST 2044

SPEED OF LIGHT.
Tracks: / Westward ho / Black elk / Gold / This could be paradise / Afterthought / Speed of light / Whisper in the wind / Heartland / Columbine / Gold (reprise).
LP: . . . . EST 2076
MC: . . . . TCEST 2076

Bardot

ROCKING IN RHYTHM.
Tracks: / Africa / Julie / Sympathy's no good / No-one else cries / Hero's reward / Rocking in a rhythm / Ouled nail / Eagle road / Witchfire / Mountainside.
LP: . . . . PL 25121
MC: . . . . PK 25121

Bardot, Brigitte

LE DISQUE D'OR (La cassette d'or).
Tracks: / Harley Davidson / Mister Sun / David B / Saint Tropez / Oh qu'il est villain / Je reviendrai toujours vers toi / Le diable est Anglais / Contact / Marseillaise generique / Ay que viva la sangria / Gang gang / Port grimaud / Paris / On demenage / Ce n'est pas vrai.
LP: 103561
MC: 103564
LP: . . . . AZ 2356
MC: . . . . C 2356

Bards

BARDS, THE.
LP: . . . . TA 3018
MC: 4TA 3018
LP: 2904 041
LP: 3188 120

DIARMUID O'LEARY AND THE BARDS LIVE (Bards & Diarmuid O'Leary).
MC: . . . . KMC 200
LP: . . . . KLP 200

OLDEST SWINGER IN TOWN, THE.
Tracks: / Matt Hyland / Old Dungarvan Oak / John O'Dreams / Castle of Dromore / Wandering dream / Oldest swinger in town, The / Rose, The / Shaney boy / Sailin' ships / Blind Mary / Leaving Nancy / Little shirt that my mother made for me, The.
LP: 8217191
MC: 8217194

Bards Of The

WHEN GRANDMA USED....
LP: . . . . BMR 101

Bare, Bobby

20 OF THE BEST: BOBBY BARE.
Tracks: / All American boy / Detroit City / 500 miles away from home / Four strong winds / Millers cave / It's alright shame on me / Streets of Baltimore / Come kiss me love / Charleston railroad tavern / Have I stayed away too long / Piney wood hills / Find out what's happening / You know who / I hate goodbyes / Winner, The / Singing in the kitchen / Daddy what if / Where'd I come from.
LP: . . . . NL 89332
MC: . . . . NK 89332
LP: . . . . INTS 5187
MC: . . . . INTK 5187

AIN'T GOT NOTHIN' TO LOSE.
Tracks: / Ain't got nothin' to lose / Candle in the wind / Old swimmin' hole / Isn't that just like love / Goodnight Irene / Golden memories / I've been rained on too / Cold day in hell / So good to so bad / Praise the lord and send me the money.
LP: 85504

AS IS.
Tracks: / Dollar pool fool / Learning to live again / Call me the breeze / Take me as I am / Let him roll / New cut road / She is gone / Dropping out of sight / Summer wages / White freight liner blues.
LP: . . . . CBS 84989

BEST OF BOBBY BARE.
LP: . . . . COLT 2001
MC: . . . . COLTK 2001

BIGGEST HITS OF BOBBY BARE.
Tracks: / Tequila Shelia / Till I gain control again / Learning to live again / Let him roll / Greasy grit gravy / Numbers / Take me as I am / Big Dupree / New cut road / Goin' back to Texas / Sleep tight goodnight man / Too many nights alone / Healin' / Food blues / Willie Jones / Dropping out of sight.
LP: . . . . CBS 32303

BOBBY BARE (I Love Country).
Tracks: / Gambler, The / Jogger, The / Last time, The / Numbers / Tequila Sheila / Let him roll / Goin' up's easy, comin' down's harder / Praise the Lord and send the money / Goodnight Irene / I've never gone to bed with an ugly woman / Food blues / Desperados waiting for the train / Three legged man / Finger on the button / Greasy grit gravy / Big dupree / Yard full of rusty cars / Too many nights alone / Childhood hero / February snow / This guitar is for sale / Sing for the song.
LP: . . . . CBS 54950
MC: 40 54950
LP: . . . . CBS 32095
MC: 40 32095

CITY BOY.
Tracks: / Fool / Fallen star, A / Hello darlin' / Lonely street / Under it all / Crazy arms / Alabama rose / High and dry / City boy country born / New York City snow / Leaving on a jet plane.
2LP: . . . . CR 5153
MCSET: . . . . CRT 5153

COUNTRY STORE: BOBBY BARE.
Tracks: / Way I feel tonight, The / Gambler, The / Goodnight Irene / If you ain't got nothing / Jogger, The / Till I gain control again / Drinkin' from the bottle / Desperados waiting for the train (Only on CD.) / Call me the breeze (Only on CD.) / Take me as I am or let me go / Tequila Sheila / Too many nights alone / I'm not a candle / Numbers / She is gone / Praise the Lord and send the money / New cut road (Only on CD.) / Some days are diamonds (Only on CD.).
LP: . . . . CST 28
MC: . . . . CSTK 28

DETROIT CITY.
LP: 26.21212

DOWN AND DIRTY.
Tracks: / Good for nothing blues / Numbers / Some days are diamonds / Tequila Sheila / Rock star's lament / Crazy again / Tecumseh Valley / Blind Willie Harper / Rough on the living / Down to my last come and get me / Qualudes again / Goin' back to Texas / I can't watch the movie anymore.
LP: . . . . CBS 84132

DRINKIN' FROM THE BOTTLE....
Tracks: / Jogger, The / Easy as dreaming / Rodeo queen / Me and Jimmy Rodgers / Three legged man / Diet song / Jennifer Johnson and me / Drinkin' from the bottle / Some place to come when it rains / Stacy Brown got two / Time.
LP: 25470

DRUNK AND CRAZY.
Tracks: / Drunk & crazy / Food blues / World's last truck drivin' man / I can almost see Houston from here / If that ain't love / Rock and roll hotel / Song of the south / Appaloosa rider / Bathroom tissue paper letter / Willie Jones / Gotta get rid of this band / I've never gone to bed with an ugly woman / Desperados waiting for the train.
MC: 40 84643
LP: . . . . CBS 84643

FAMOUS COUNTRY MUSIC MAKERS.
Tracks: / Daddy what if / Sunday mornin' down / You made a believer out of me / Dropkick me Jesus (through the goalposts of life) / Wonderful soup stone, The / Bird named yesterday, A / Vegas / High plains jamboree / They covered up the old swimmin' hole / Woman in every man's life, The / Up against the wall / If you think I'm crazy / Amarillo highway / Great snowman, The / Red-neck hippie / Don't turn out the light / Somebody bought my old home town / Chester / (There was a) tall oak tree / Ride me down easy / Salt Lake City / Marie Laveau / Faster horses / Long black veil / Vince / Old gang's gone, The / Put a little lovin' on me / Little bit later on down the line / Hillbilly hell / Jackson / Back home in Huntsville again / I've got a thing about trains / Last dance at the Texas Moon / One among the three of us / Singer of sad songs / Wilma Lou / Cowboys and daddies / Alimony / Air conditioner song, The.
2LP: . . . . PL 42958

LULLABYS, LEGENDS AND LIES.
Tracks: / Lullabys, legends and lies / Paul / Marie Laveau / Daddy what if / Winner, The / In the hills of Shiloh / She's my ever lovin' machine / Mermaid, The / Rest awhile / Bottomless well / Wonderful soup stone, The / True story / Sure hit songwriters pen / Rosalie's good eats cafe.
LP: . . . . NL 89998
MC: . . . . NK 89998

MORE TUNES FOR TWO (Bare, Bobby & Skeeter Davis).
Tracks: / Your husband my wife / Before the sunrise / True love you'll never find, A / I'm so afraid of losing you again / Dream baby / My elusive dreams / Let's make love not war / I got you / Jackson / There was never a time.
LP: . . . . INTS 5055

SLEEPER WHEREVER I FALL.
Tracks: / Sleep tight, goodnight man / Hot afternoon / What did it get me / Goin' up's easy, comin' down's harder / Way I feel tonight / Healin' / Love is a cold wind / I'll feel a whole lot better / Last time, The / On a real good night.
LP: . . . . CBS 83533

THIS IS BARE.
2LP: 26 28046

TUNES FOR TWO (Bare, Bobby & Skeeter Davis).

Tracks: / Dear John letter, A / Too used to being with you / In the misty moonlight / We'll sing in the sunshine / I don't care / True love / Love you / (We must have been) Out of our minds / Let it be me / Together again / That's all I want from you / Invisible tears.
LP: . . . . LSA 3252

Bare Bones

BARE BONES (Various artists).
Tracks: / Rakes of mallow: *Various artists* / Ewe, The: *Various artists* / Earl's chair, The: *Various artists*/ Boys around Tantaragee: *Various artists* / Cork hornpipe, The: *Various artists* / Limerick slides: *Various* artists / Wearing of the britches, The: *Various artists* / My love is in America: *Various artists* / Pigeon on the gate: *Various artists* / Tramps and hawkers: *Various artists* / Charlie Chaplin: *Various artists*/ Musical priest, The: *Various artists* / Sailor on the rock, The: *Various artists* / Union, The: *Various* artists / Navvy on the line: *Various artists* / Maggie in the wood: *Various artists* / Tralee jail: *Various* artists / Four hand reel: *Various artists* / Delahunty's hornpipe: *Various artists* / Girl I left behind me, The: *Various artists* / Sporting races of Galway, The: *Various artists*.
LPS: . . . . GVR 202

Bare Necessities

ENGLISH COUNTRY DANCES.
MC: . . . . VR 013C
LP: . . . . VR 013

Barefoot Bill's...

BAREFOOT BILL'S HARD LUCK BLUES (Various artists).
LP: 3812

Barefoot, Jerry

WATCHING TV.
LP: . . . . TAKE 2

Barely Works

BIG BEAT, THE.
Tracks: / White cockade / Bonaparte's retreat / Flop eared mule / Byker Hill / Big old road / Let's have a good time / Liberty / Blackberry blossom / Cuckoo's nest, The / It's not that bad anymore / Inventor, The / As a Thoiseach / Tropical hot dog night / Growing old man and woman.
LP: . . . . COOK 024
MC: . . . . COOKC 024

DON'T MIND WALKING.
LP: . . . . COOK 045
MC: . . . . COOKC 045

Barenberg, Russ

BEHIND THE MELODIES.
LP: . . . . ROUNDER 0176
MC: . . . . ROUNDER 0176C

CALYPSO COWBOY.
LP: . . . . ROUNDER 0111
MC: . . . . ROUNDER 0111C

MOVING PICTURES.
LP: . . . . ROUNDER 0249
MC: . . . . ROUNDER 0249C

Barflies

DOWN TO THE BONE.
MLP: . . . . FB 501

Bargepole

SODBUSTER.
Tracks: / Building site / Schwartz yorren / Please God we should only meet at Simchas museum / Terry's all gold / Cost of living / Clinic / Ambulance / It's a fair cop, guv / Now I've released the urge.
LP: . . . . CALCLP 041

Barham, Ronnie

BRAND NEW MAN.
Tracks: / Glad / Brand new man / No measure / Rejoice / Loved / Picking up the pieces / Meltdown / Now is the time / Power for life / Thank you Jesus.
MC: . . . . ROJOC 1010

Barinov, Valeri

TRUMPET CALL, THE (Musical rock gospel show) (Various artists).
MC: . . . . MYR C 1217

Barish, Jesse

JESSE BARISH.
Tracks: / Count on me / Feeling for a song / Power of love / Love that's right / You / Grand illusion / Kiss made the world begin, A / Winds away / Lovers leap / Way to love.
LP: . . . . PL 12555
MC: . . . . PK 12555

Bark

BARK (Various artists).
LP: . . . . SAX 025

Barkays

AS ONE.
Tracks: / Boogie body land / Say it through love / Work it out / Bodyfever / Take the time to love somebody / Open your heart / Deliver us / As one.
LP: . . . . SRM 13844
LP: 6337 108

BANGING THE WALL.
LP: 824 727-1
MC: 824 727-4

BAR-KAYS.
MC: . . . . SRC 14028

CONTAGIOUS.
LP: 8303051
MC: 8303054

DANGEROUS.
Tracks: / Dangerous / Dirty dancer / Make believe lover / Dance party / Freakshow on the dance floor / Lovers should never fall in love / Loose talk / Sexomatic.
LP: 818 478 1

MONEY TALKS.
Tracks: / Holy ghost / Feeling alright / Monster / Money talks / Mean mistreater.
LP: . . . . STX 3023

MONEY TALKS (RE-ISSUE).
Tracks: / Holy ghost / Feeling alright / Monster / Money talks / Mean mistreater / Holy ghost (reborn).
LP: . . . . SXE 023

PROPOSITIONS.
Tracks: / Propositions / Tripping out / Anticipations (busted) / Do it (let me shake you) / She talks to me with her body / I can't believe you're leaving me / You made a change in my life.
LP: 6337 257
LP: . . . . SRM 14065
LP: 6447 257

Barker, Clive (aut)

BODY POLITIC, THE (See under Body Politic).

Barker, Dave

CRUISIN' (see Rush, Barbara) (Barker, Dave & Barbara Rush).

Barker, Guy

HOLLY J (Barker, Guy Quintet).
Tracks: / Life is a beach / It never entered my mind / Mr. Talbot / Three minutes away / How about it / Holly J..
LP: . . . . MM 078

Barker, Les

DOGMATIC.
LP: . . . . AVA 111

DOGOLOGUES.
LP: . . . . DOG 002
MC: . . . . DOG 002C

EARWIGO.
LP: . . . . DOG 004
MC: . . . . DOG 004 C

MRS ACKROYD - SUPERSTAR.
LP: . . . . FRR 015

MRS.ACKROYDS ROCK'N'ROLL SHOW.
LP: . . . . DOG 001

Barker, Ronnie

TWO RONNIES (Barker, Ronnie & Ronnie Corbett).
LP: . . . . RED 257
MC: . . . . RMC 4054

TWO RONNIES VOL 2 (Barker, Ronnie & Ronnie Corbett).
LP: . . . . REB 300
MC: . . . . ZCF 300

Barker, Sally

IN THE SPOTLIGHT.
LP: . . . . PUP 1

RHYTHM IS MINE, THE.
LP: . . . . HNBL 1356
MC: . . . . HNBC 1356

Barking Tribe

SERPENT GO HOME.
Tracks: / Pretty in print / Two important Pauls / White man's mind / Hide a prize / Breakaway / God knows what to do / Dammit to hell / Four fuses / Complain / With cretins as friends / Ain't as many girls as there used to be / Running down on my luck / City streets.
MC: . . . . RACS 0200

Barklem, Jill

SECRET STAIRCASE, THE/THE HIGH HILLS (See under Brambly Hedge (bks)).

Barkleys Of Broadway

BARKLEYS OF BROADWAY, THE (Film soundtrack) (Various artists).
LP: . . . . STK 116

Barkmarket

1-899-GODHOUSE.
LP: . . . . PURGE 025

EASY LISTENING RECORD.
LP: . . . . OUT 101

Barley

REMEMBER REMEMBER.
LP: . . . . SRTM 75348

Barley Bree

SPEAK UP FOR IRELAND.
LP: . . . . SHAN 52016

Barley Mow

BARLEY MOW (Songs of good company) (Various artists).
Tracks: / Barley mow, The: *Various artists* / Billy Johnson's ball: *Various artists* / Black ram: *Various* artists / Punch ladle: *Various artists* / Campbell the rover: *Various artists* / Drink old England dry: *Various* artists / Ewie wi' the crookit horn: *Various artists* / Farewell to whiskey: *Various artists* / Good ale: *Various artists* / Irish familie: *Various artists* / John Barleycorn: *Various artists* / Jug of punch: *Various artists* / Penny wager, the: *Various artists* / Rosin the beau: *Various artists* / Rothesay-o: *Various artists* / Thousands or more: *Various artists* / Good companion: *Various artists* / Twanky dillo: *Various artists* / When Jones's ale was new: *Various artists* / Wild rover: *Various artists*.
MC: 60-025

Barleycorn

FIELDS OF ATHENRY.
LP: . . . . DOLM 5034

FOLK'S SAKE, THE.
LP: . . . . DOLM 5016

IRISH REBEL SONG.
LP: . . . . CSDBL 514

LIVE IN NEW YORK.
LP: . . . . DOLM 5022

MY LAST FAREWELL.
MC: . . . . DOCX 9010

SONG FOR IRELAND, A.
Tracks: / Song for Ireland, A / Cavan Ireland / Portland Town / Dublin in my tears / Roseville fair / Long before your time / Over my mountains / Charlie on the M.T.A / Mary's song / Lakes of Coolfin.
LP: . . . . DOLX 9004
MC: . . . . DOCX 9004

WINDS ARE SINGING FREEDOM.
LP: . . . . DOLM 5011

Barlow, Charles

24 BALLROOM DANCING FAVOURITES (Barlow, Charles & His Orchestra).
Tracks: / Yankee doodle dandy / Godfather, The / Thanks for the memory / Blackpool tango / Carnival / Coffee song, The / Y viva Espana / No other love / Shake, rattle and roll.
LP: . . . . NTS 192
LP: . . . . CF 260

COME CLOSER TO ME (Barlow, Charles & His Orchestra).
LP: . . . . NTS 174

DANCE ON AND ON (Barlow, Charles & His Orchestra).
Tracks: / Bring me sunshine (Quickstep) / All my loving (Quickstep) / When Irish eyes are smiling (Waltz) / Cavatina (Waltz) / Rockin' chair (Foxtrot) / As time goes by (Foxtrot) / Remordimiento (Tango) / Super trouper (Cha cha cha) / Chacharini (Cha cha cha) / Caprice (Samba) / I'll never love this way again (Slow rhumba) / All the things you are, are mine (Slow rhumba) / Exotica (Paso doble) / On and on (Jive).
LP: . . . . ALM 4005

GOLDEN YEARS, THE (Barlow, Charles & His Orchestra).
LP: . . . . DS 074

MEMORIES (Barlow, Charles & His Orchestra).
Tracks: / Sing, sing, sing / Perdido / Lester leaps in / Back home in Tennessee / Play fiddly play / Thorn birds / Don't tell a soul / Hold me / Annientamento / Shy serenade / Sam baba / Memory / Woman in love / Here comes the toreador.
LP: . . . . DS 067

NEARNESS OF YOU (Barlow, Charles & His Orchestra).
Tracks: / Calcutta / Idaho / Roses of Picardy / Kiss waltz / Nearness of you / Love walked in / Corrida real / Yes, we have no bananas / Sunny / I yi yi yi yi / La playa / Long ago / Chihuahua / Tequila.
LP: . . . . EMS 1066881

STEPPIN' OUT (Barlow, Charles & His Orchestra).
LP: . . . . S 6422

Barlow, Eric

BALLROOM FAVOURITES.
MC: . . . . LTOT CF 260

BALLROOM MAGIC (Eric Barlow plays the wonder Wurlitzer).
LP: . . . . LTOT 8218

Barlow, Randy

ARRIVAL.
LP: . . . . JULEP 5

FALL IN LOVE WITH ME.
Tracks: / No sleep tonight / Our honeymoon has never ended / Singing the blues / One more time / One of the great love affairs / Fall in love with me tonight / It should've been me / Burning bridges / Little bird fly home / Slow and easy.
LP: . . . . SHU 8526

Barmy Army

ENGLISH DISEASE, THE.
LP: . . . . ONULP 48

Barnabas

FEEL THE FIRE.
LP: . . . . LS 7074
MC: . . . . LC 7074

Barnard, Bob

AT BIX FESTIVAL 1976 (Barnard, Bob & His Australian Jazz Band).
LP: . . . . BBMS 8

BIG BOB, LITTLE BEN.
LP: . . . . EAGLELP 1

BUD FREEMAN WITH THE BOB BARNARD JAZZBAND (see Freeman, Bud).

COUNT 'EM (Barnard, Bob, Jazz Orchestra).
LP: . . . . S 1353

FIRST UP (1975-76) (Barnard, Bob & His Jazz Band).
LP: . . . . S 1369

NED KELLY JAZZ SUITE (Barnard, Bob & Friends).
LP: . . . . S 1374

RIVERBOAT DAYS (Barnard, Bob & Friends).
LP: . . . . S 1366

WITH GEORGE CHISHOLM AND KENNY BAKER (Barnard, Bob/George Chisholm/Kenny Baker).
LP: . . . . EAGLE 1

Barnard, Len

LEN BARNARD'S FAMOUS JAZZ BAND (The naked dance).
LP: . . . . S 1287

Barnard, Robert (aut)

BODIES (See under Bodies) (Midgeley, Richard (nar)).

Barnbrack

BELFAST.
Tracks: / Unicorn / Jug of punch / Home boys home / Coortin' in the kitchen / As I roved out / Postman Pat / I'll take you home again Kathleen / Star of the County Down / Mother's love's a blessing, A / Goodbye Johnny dear / Gentle mother / Will you go Lassie go / Whiskey on a Sunday / Belfast.
LP: . . . . PHL 480
MC: . . . . CPHL 480

CHILDRENS PARTY.
Tracks: / Teddy bears' picnic / Mickey Marley's roundabout / Yellow submarine / Matchstalk men and matchstalk cats and dogs / Old MacDonald had a farm / When I was a lad / Postman Pat / Puff the magic dragon / Big rock candy mountain / Unicorn / Big ship sails on the alley alley o, The / Mama will you buy me a banana / Happy wanderer, The.
LP: . . . . DHL 172
MC: . . . . CDHL 172

CHILDREN'S SING-SONG.
Tracks: / Puff the magic dragon / Old McDonald had a farm / Big rock candy mountain / When I was a lad / Yellow submarine / Happy wanderer, The / Teddy bears' picnic / Matchstick men / Mickey Marley's roundabout / Postman Pat / Unicorn / Big ship sails on the alley alley o, The / Ma ma will you buy me a banana.
LP: . . . . DHL 712

FEAST OF IRISH FOLK SONGS VOL.2.
Tracks: / Westmeath bachelor / If you're Irish / Dear oul Donegal / Blacksmith / Old flames / Doonaree / Butcher boy / Green glens of Antrim / Boys from County Armagh / Irish eyes are smiling / Nancy Spain / Leaving of Liverpool / Mursheen Durkin / Belfast mill / Boston burglar / Moonshine / Hills of Connemara / Mountains of Mourne / Three counties meet / My Eileen is waiting for me / Homes of Donegal / My aunt Jane / Al lammas fair / Gentle Annie

/ Spancil hill / Village where I went to school / Any dream will do / Mickey Marley's roundabout.
LP: . . . . PHL 474
MC: . . . . CPHL 474

IRISH FOLK PUB SING-A-LONG.
Tracks: / Whiskey in the jar / I'll tell me ma / Wild colonial boy / Catch me if you can / Golden Jubilee / When you and I were young Maggie / Galway shawl / Slievenamon / Love is teasin' / Green fields of France / Cliffs of Dooneen / Weel a weel a waile / Do you want yer oul lobby washed down / Bunch of thyme / Old maid in a garret / Bold O'Donaghue / Peggy Gordon / Black velvet band / Holy ground / McAlpines fusiliers / When you were sweet sixteen.
LP: . . . . HRL 199
MC: . . . . CHRL 199

IRISH PARTY SING-A-LONG.
Tracks: / Irish rover, The / Goodbye Mick, goodbye Pat / Banana song / Green glens of Antrim / Boys from County Armagh / Irish eyes are smiling / Nancy Spain / Leaving of Liverpool / Mursheen Durkin / Alley alley O / Uncle Nobby's steamboat / My Aunt Jane / Aul Lammas fair / Gentle Annie / Mother's love's a blessing, A / Good-bye Johnny dear / Gentle mother / Phil the fluter / Paddy Reilly / Slattery's mounted fut / Three counties meet / My Eileen is waiting / Homes of Donegal / Westmeath bachelor / If you're Irish / Dear oul Donegal / B for Barney / Doffer, The / Boston burglar / Moonshiner / Hills of Connemara / Home boys home / Courtin' in the kitchen / As I roved out.
LP: . . . . PHL 494
MC: . . . . CPHL 494

MEMORY LANE.
LP: . . . . ERTV 5

MICKEY MARLEY'S ROUNDABOUT.
Tracks: / Westmeath bachelor / If you're Irish / Dear oul Donegal / Blacksmith / Old flames / Doonaree / Butcher boy / Green glens of Antrim / Boys from County Armagh / Irish eyes are smiling / Nancy Spain / Leaving of Liverpool / Mursheen Durkin / Belfast mill / Boston burglar / Moonshiner / Hills of Connemara / Mountains of Mourne / Three counties meet / My Eileen is waiting for me / Homes of Donegal / My Aunt Jane / Aul Lammas fair / Gentle Annie / Spancil Hill / Village where I went to school / Any dream will do / Mickey Marley's roundabout.
LP: . . . . TVPHL 474

MUSIC AND CRACK.
2LP: . . . . HM 027D

MY THANKS TO YOU.
Tracks: / My thanks to you / When I was a lad / Wedding prayer, The / Phil the fluter / Come back Paddy Reilly to Ballyjamesduff / Slattery's mounted fut / Postman Pat / Martha / Unicorn / More than yesterday / Love is teasin' / Mickey Marley / Home boys home / Courtin' in the kitchen / As I roved out / Punch and Judy man / Will you go lassie go / Belfast.
MC: . . . . CPHL 503

WORLD OF BARNBRACK.
Tracks: / Irish rover, The / Goodbye Mick, goodbye Pat / Mama will you buy me a banana / Punch and Judy / Moon behind the hill / Alley alley O / Uncle Nobby's steamboat / Love's old sweet song / Swallow (La golondrina), The / Wedding prayer, The / B for Barney / Doffer, The / My lovely Irish rose / More than yesterday / Love is teasin' / Phil the fluter / Come back Paddy Reilly to Ballyjamesduff / Slattery's mounted fut.
LP: . . . . DHL 709
MC: . . . . CDHL 709

Barnes, Alan

AFFILIATION (Barnes, Alan Quartet).
Tracks: / Fried bananas / Affiliation / You go to my head / Alice B / Easy does it / You don't know what love is / Pickles / Top flat / Straight life.
LP: . . . . MM 002

Barnes, Buddy

MAGIC TIME, THE.
LP: . . . . AP 139

Barnes, Emile

EMILE BARNES AND DOC PARLIN'S NEW ORLEANS JAZZ BAND (Barnes, Emile & Doc Parlin).
LP: . . . . JCE 23

N.O.-THE LEGENDS LIVE (Barnes, Emile & His New Orleans Music).
LP: . . . . JCE 34

Barnes, George

GEORGE BARNES, 1946 (Barnes, George & His Octet).
Tracks: / I can't give you anything but love / South side blues / Somebody loves me / Smoke gets in your eyes / Zebra's derby / September in the rain / Chicago / Undecided / Aren't you glad you're you / Starlight interlude / Kilroy was here / Priority on a moonbeam / Something to remember you by / At the jazz band ball / Imagination.
LP: . . . . HSR 106

GUITARS, ANYONE? (Barnes, George/ Carl Kress).
LP: . . . . AP 87

PLAYS GERSHWIN (See under Braff, Ruby) (Barnes, George & Ruby Braff).

RODGERS AND HART (See under Braff, Ruby) (Barnes, George & Ruby Braff).

TWO GUITARS (See under Kress,Carl/ George Barnes) (Barnes, George/Carl Kress).

TWO GUITARS AND A HORN.
LP: . . . . ST 228

Barnes, James

DETROIT HOUSE PARTY PIANO BLUES (Barnes, James & Emmet Brooks).
LP: . . . . JSP 1041

WORLD OF BUDDY BOLDEN, THE (See under Lyttleton, Humphrey) (Barnes, J/Humphrey Lyttelton/etc.).

Barnes, Jimmy

BODYSWERVE.
LP: . . . . RML 53138

FOR THE WORKING CLASS MAN.
2LP: . . . . RML 53196/7

FREIGHT TRAIN HEART.
Tracks: / Driving wheels / Seven days / Too much ain't enough love / Lessons in love / Waitin' for the heartache / Last frontier, The / I'm still on your side / Do or die / I wanna get started with you / Walk on.
MC: 9241464
LP: 9241461

JIMMY BARNES.
Tracks: / No second prize / I'd die to be with you tonight / Working class man / Promise me you'll call / Boys cry out for war / Paradise / Without your love / American heartbeat / Thick skinned / Ride the night away / Daylight.
LP: 9240891
MC: 9240894

TWO FIRES.
LP: 756 782 141 1
MC: 756 782 141 4

Barnes, J.J.

GROOVESVILLE MASTERS, THE.
Tracks: / Baby please come back home / Your love is gone / Chains of love / I need a change / To an early grave / Time has come, The / Now I got you back / Sweet sherry / Help me / Welcome to the club / Cloudy days.
LP: . . . . CLP 520

SARA SMILE.
Tracks: / Errol Flynn / Sara smile / She's mine / If you move I'll fall / Errol Flynn (reprise) / Let me feel the funk / We can't hide it any more / How long / I'm the one who loves you / Let me feel the funk (reprise).
LP: . . . . CLP 604

Barnes, John

FANCY OUR MEETING.
Tracks: / Samba rossi / Blue horizon / Boko's bounce / Hawk, The / Moonlight becomes you / Fascinating rhythm / Falling in love with you.
LP: . . . . CLGLP 019
MC: . . . . ZCLG 019

Barnes, Johnny

JAZZ MASTERS (Barnes, Johnny & Bruce Turner).
LP: . . . . SGC 1005

Barnes, Kathy

BODY TALKIN'.
Tracks: / I'm in it for the love / Paradise island / Something's burning / When I need you / I'm in love with you / Off / Your eyes give you away / Loving arms / After you / It's not the spotlight / You make me feel it again.
LP: . . . . SHU 8525

Barnes, Max D.

PIECES OF MY LIFE.
LP: . . . . DBWLP 1005

Barnes, Paul

PAUL BARNES QUARTETS (Barnes, Paul Quartets).
MC: . . . . TC 017
LP: . . . . NOLA LP 17

PAUL "POLO" BARNES, INTERNATIONAL JAZZ BAND.
LP: . . . . CLPS 1013

PORTRAIT OF A NOR CLARINET PLAYER.
LP: . . . . CLPS 1010

VIOLET AND THE VINE, THE (Barnes, Paul & His Polo Players).
LP: . . . . JCE 15

Barnes, Roosevelt

HEARTBROKEN MAN, THE (Barnes, Roosevelt & The Playboys).
LP: . . . . BEDLP 17

Barnes, Walter

WALTER BARNES AND ROYAL CREOLIANS (1928-29) (Barnes, Walter & His Royal Creolins).
LP: . . . . Unknown

WALTER BARNES AND ROYAL CREOLIANS (1927-29) (Barnes, Walter & His Royal Creolins).
LP: . . . . FJ 125

WALTER BARNES/GEORGE E. LEE (Barnes, Walter/George E. Lee).
LP: . . . . Unknown

Barnes, William

BLACKMORE BY THE STOUR (Poems of William Barnes) (Various artists).
MC: . . . . FTC 6020

LYDLINCH BELLS (Poems of William Barnes) (Various artists).
MC: . . . . FTC 6021

Barnes-Bocage ...

BARNES-BOCAGE BIG FIVE (Barnes-Bocage Big Five).
LP: . . . . NOLA LP 9

Barnet, Charlie

AIRCHECKS/RHYTHMAKERS (See under Goodman, Benny) (Barnet, Charlie & Benny Goodman).

APRIL 1938 (Barnet, Charlie & His Orchestra).
Tracks: / Make believe ballroom time / Lullaby in rhythm / Stop, look and listen / In a jam / Prelude in C sharp minor / Chatterbox / Blue turning grey over you / Undecided / Harmony in Harlem / I let a song go out of my heart / You go to my head / Rock it for me / Prelude to a kiss / Ya got me / Jump jump's here.
LP: . . . . BLJ 8008

CHARLIE BARNET (Barnet, Charlie Orchestra).
LP: . . . . BO 706

CHARLIE BARNET AND HIS ORCHESTRA 1941 (Barnet, Charlie & His Orchestra).
LP: . . . . CLP 65

CHARLIE BARNET AND HIS ORCHESTRA (Barnet, Charlie & His Orchestra).
LP: . . . . FH 17
LP: . . . . GELP 15015

CHARLIE BARNET AND HIS ORCHESTRA 1945/47.
LP: . . . . FH 12

CHARLIE BARNET AND ORCHESTRA 1944-45 (Barnet, Charlie Orchestra).
LP: . . . . LP 38-138

CHARLIE BARNET BIG BAND 1967 (Barnet, Charlie Big Band).
LP: . . . . ST 1056

CHARLIE BARNET ON THE AIR VOL 1 (Barnet, Charlie & His Orchestra).
Tracks: / Poor little rich girl / Very thought of you, The / E-bob-o-lee-bob / Trolley song, The / I didn't know about you / Right idea, The / Flying home / Ring dem bells / Rockin' in rhythm / Dream / More and more / Skyliner / Story of two cigarettes, The / Dear old Southland.
LP: . . . . AIRCHECK 5

CHARLIE BARNET ON THE AIR VOL 2 (Barnet, Charlie & His Orchestra).
Tracks: / Smiles / Nobody knows the trouble I've seen / Everyday of my life / I can't get started / I like to riff / Keep the home fires burning / Cherokee / Until my baby comes back to me / Skyliner / Share croppin' blues / Blue skies / Washington whirligig / Cottontail.
LP: . . . . AIRCHECK 30

CHARLIE BARNET VOL 16 1942/3.
LP: . . . . AJAX 140

CHARLIE BARNET VOL 17 1944.
LP: . . . . AJAX 147

CHARLIE BARNET VOL 18.
LP: . . . . AJAX 155

DANCE BASH.
Tracks: / Jubilee jump / Charleston alley / Gal from Joe's, The / Deep purple / Blue Lou / Southern fried / Cherokee / Skyliner / Fur trappers boogie / Wosie posie / Let's blow the blues / Rhubarb / St. Louis blues / Swinging down the lane / Who's sorry now.
LP: 2304 541

DANCE DATE - 1959 (Barnet, Charlie & His Orchestra).
Tracks: / Blue juice / One for my baby / Jubilee jump / Easy living / For heavens sake / Bang tail / Smiles / Serenade to May / Skyliner / My old flame / Southern fried / Moten swing / Habanera.
LP: . . . . SWH 6
MC: . . . . CSWH 6

DUKE'S IDEAS 1939/41 VOL 1.
LP: . . . . PM 42041

FILM TRACKS OF..., THE.
LP: . . . . JLP 3001

IN DISCO ORDER VOL 1.
LP: . . . . AJAX 104

IN DISCO ORDER VOL 2.
LP: . . . . AJAX 106

INDISPENSABLE CHARLIE BARNET (VOLS.3 & 4) (1940-42).
Tracks: / Comanche war dance / Tappin' at the Tappa / Southland shuffle / Lover's lullaby / Leapin' at the Lincoln / Wanderin' blues / Shake, rattle and roll / Lament for May / Flyin' home / No name jive, part 1&2 / Reverie of a moax,The (Oh Claire the goon) / It's the last time I'll fall in love / Rockin' in rhythm / Pompton turnpike / Ring dem bells / Sgt was shy, The / Wild Mab of the fishpond / Night and day / Redskin rhumba / Lumby / Phyllysee / Blue juice / Charleston alley / Little John ordinary / Haunted town / Merry-go-round / Birmingham breakdown / Ponce de leon / Little dip / Harlem speaks / I can't get started.
2LP: . . . . NL 89483
MCSET: . . . . NK 89483

INDISPENSABLE CHARLIE BARNET VOLS.1 & 2 (1935-39).
Tracks: / Echoes of Harlem / Scotch and soda / Miss Annabelle Lee / Lazy bug / Midweek function / I never knew / Ebony rhapsody / Lament for a lost love / Cherokee / All-night record man, The / Last jump, The / Duke's idea, The / Count's idea, The / Ogoun badagris / Oh what you said / Wrong idea, The / Right idea, The / Night glow / Between 18th and 19th on Chestnut Street / Clap hands here comes Charlie / Growlin' / Nagasaki / On a holiday / Always / I'm praying humble / Tin roof blues / Knocking at the famous door / Gal from Joe's, The / Jump session / Swing street strut / Night song / Some like it hot / Only a rose.
2LP: . . . . NL 89743
MCSET: . . . . NK 89743

LIVE AT BASIN ST. EAST.
LP: . . . . HEP 2005

MAKE BELIEVE BALLROOM, 1936-41 (Barnet, Charlie & His Orchestra).
LP: . . . . BS 7123

ON STAGE WITH CHARLIE BARNET ORCHESTRA.
LP: . . . . BO 719

ONE FOR MY BABY.
MC: 40180

REDSKIN RHUMBA.
LP: . . . . FS 333

SHOWCASE.
Tracks: / Cherokee / Makin' whoopee / Victory walking / Everything but you / Haunted town / Tulip or turnip.
LP: . . . . FH 44

SKYLINER (Big band bounce and boogie) (Barnet, Charlie & His Orchestra).
Tracks: / Skyliner / Flat top flips his lid / Andy's boogie / Gulf coast blues / E-bob-o-lee-bob / Pow wow / Drop me off in Harlem / Xango / Washington whirligig / Moose / Sharecroppin' blues / Thing's ain't what they used to be / West End blues / Great lie, The / Strollin' / Just a sittin' and a rockin'.
LP: . . . . AFS 1012

Barnett, Janice

JANICE.
Tracks: / Wake up smiling / Goody two shoes / Told you so / Take me away / Him / If I had known (I'd be gone) / Love on the line / You're letting me go / I should have left you.
LP: . . . . MPF 4523

Barnett, Sue

FIT FOR LIFE.
LP: . . . . WRD 3005
MC: . . . . TCWRD 3005

FIT FOR LIFE VOL. 2.
MC: . . . . WRD C 3019

Barnum (show)

BARNUM (Original London stage cast) (Various artists).
Tracks: / Sucker born every minute, A: *Various artists* / Museum song: *Various artists* / Prince of humbug: *Various* artists / Colours of my life: *Various artists* / Join the circus: *Various artists* /

Come follow the band: *Various artists* / One brick at a time: *Various artists* / Black and white: *Various artists* / Love makes such fools of us all: *Various artists* / I like your style: *Various artists* / Bigger isn't better: *Various artists* / At least I tried: *Various artists* / Thank God I'm old: *Various artists*.
LP: CDL 1348
MC: ZCDL 1348

BARNUM (Original Broadway Cast) (Various artists).
MC: PST 36576
LP: JS 36576

Barnwell, Bobbie
BOBBIE.
LP: WRS 130

Barod Am Roc
BAROD AM ROC.
LP: SAIN 1311 H

Baron
PARTY FUSION.
LP: JWBA 019

Baron, Don
YOUNG, GIFTED AND BLACK.
Tracks: / Funky reggae / Spanish fly / Let's dance / Western style / Action / D J Imitators / Mike Chanter / Fast talk man / Girl's Irie, The.
LP: MCF 3430
MC: MCFC 3430

Baron, Jean
BOMBARDE, OCARINA ET ORGUE (Baron, Jean & Michel Ghesquiere).
Tracks: / La Derobee / Airs gallos / La drolette / Silvestric / An dro / Suite vannetaise / Laride / Bolom koz / La guedaine / Melodie de Ploemel / La quenouille / La vache a Biron.
LP: ARN 33591
MC: ARN 433591

BOMBARDE, OCARINA ET ORGUE EN PAYS GALLO (Baron, Jean & Michel Ghesquiere).
Tracks: / C'est entre nous les jeunes filles / En avant deux / Sa mere lui avait dit un jour / Suite de polkas / Jeune fille amoureuse / Belle, nous irons dans ton grand pre / L'hirondelle / Rond de Saint-Vincent / Caressons la bouteille / La trompeuse et la violette / Goasdoue / Pile menu: revenez a moi, ma blonde.
LP: ARN 33697

Baron, Joey
MINATURE (Baron,Joey/Tim Berne/ Hank Roberts).
Tracks: / Ethiopian boxer / Circular prairie song / Hong Kong sad song / Lonely mood / Narlin' / Peanut / Abeetah / Sanctuary.
LP: 834423-1

Baron, Paul
ONE DEEP BREATH.
LP: SWH 13

Baron Rojo
BARON AL ROJO VIVI.
LP: BALLS 83454

BRUTAL VOLUME.
LP: SKULL 8327

LARGA VIDA AL ROCK AND ROLL.
LP: SKULL 8328

METAL MORFOSIS.
LP: SKULL 8322

VOLUMEN ROJO (SPANISH VERSION).
LP: SKULL 8326

Barone Brothers
BLUES AND OTHER HAPPY MOMENTS.
LP: PA 8004

Barone, Richard
COOL BLUE HALO.
Tracks: / Bullrushes, The / I belong to me / Visit, The / Tangled in your web / Silent symphony / Flew a falcon / Cry baby cry / Sweet blue cage / Man who sold the world, The / Love is a wind that screams / Number with wings.
LP: PB 6058
MC: PBC 6058
LP: ROSE 171

Barone-Burghardt
MAIDEN SWITZERLAND.
LP: DS 790

Baroness Orczy (aut)
SCARLET PIMPERNEL, THE (See under Scarlet Pimpernel (bk)) (Powell, Robert (nar)).

Barooga Bandit
COME SOFTLY.
Tracks: / Marianne / Solo / Come softly / Turn to me / Good day sunshine / Speak now / Lovin' queen / Holiday / Music man / You are the fire.
LP: EST 11924

Baroque...
BAROQUE (Various artists).
MC: TC2MOM 103

BAROQUE BEATLES BOOK,THE (Baroque Ensemble of the Merseyside).
LP: H 7306

COLLECTION: BAROQUE (Various artists).
MC: 4277234

TRUMPET MUSIC (Trompeten Consolet).
MC: RK 77027

Barr, Bert
UPTOWN LOWDOWN JAZZBAND.
LP: GHB 149

Barr, Walt
ARTFUL DANCER.
LP: MR 5238

Barracudas
BIG GAP,THE.
LP: COR 022

DROP OUT WITH THE BARRACUDAS.
Tracks: / I can't pretend / We're living in violent times / Don't let go / Codine / This ain't my time / I saw my death in a dream last night / Somewhere outside / Summer fun / His last summer / Somebody / Campus tramp / On the strip / California lament / I wish it could be 1965 again.
LP: ZONO 103
MC: TC ZONO 103
LP: VOXX 200009

ENDEAVOUR TO PERSEVERE.
LP: CL 09

GARBAGE DUMP TAPES.
LP: YEAHHUP 006

LIVE 1983.
LP: COR 021

MEANTIME.
Tracks: / Grammar of misery / Bad news / I ain't no miracle worker / Be my friend again / Shades of today / Dead skin / Middle class blues / You've come a long way / Ballad of a liar / When I'm gone / Eleventh hour, The / Hear me calling.
LP: CL 001

WORLD'S A BURN,THE.
LP: MINITRUST 001
LP: BLUNT 044

Barratt Band
PLAYING IN THE CITY.
Tracks: / Only one, The / Not the way / Your love / Playing in the city / Coming of the man / Bad mean world / My spirit's free / Voice in the night / Never seen your face.
LP: CLS 8005
MC: TC CLS 8005

VOICE.
Tracks: / Descender / Stereo / Computer failure / Loud silence / Play my guitar / Exit through exit / Being alive / Voice.
LP: CLS 8015
MC: TC CLS 8015

Barratt, Norman
ROCK FOR ALL AGES.
LP: CLS 8017
MC: TC-CLS 8017

Barrel Organ...
PARRY'S BARREL ORGAN.
Tracks: / Devil among the tailors / Speed the plough / Stowe Lodge / Chartreuse.
MC: CSDL 234

Barrelhouse...
BARRELHOUSE BLUES AND BOOGIE PIANO 1927-30 (Various artists).
LP: BD 2033

BARRELHOUSE BLUES AND STOMPS VOL.5 (Various artists).
LP: ESR 1204

BARRELHOUSE BLUES AND STOMPS-VOL.4 (Various artists).
LP: ESR 1205

Barrelhouse Boogie
BARRELHOUSE BOOGIE (Various artists).
Tracks: / Honky tonk train blues: *Lewis, Meade Lux* / Whistlin' blues: *Lewis, Meade Lux* / Yancy stomp: *Yancy, Jimmy* / State Street special: *Yancy, Jimmy* / Tell 'em about me: *Yancy, Jimmy* / Five o'clock blues: *Yancy, Jimmy* / Slow and easy blues: *Yancy, Jimmy* / Mellow blues, The: *Yancy, Jimmy* / Crying in my sleep: *Yancy, Jimmy* / Death letter blues: *Yancy, Jimmy* / Yancy's bugle call: *Yancy, Jimmy* / 35th and dearborn: *Yancy, Jimmy* / Boogie woogie man: *Johnson, Pete/Albert Ammons* / Boogie woogie jump: *Johnson, Pete/Albert Ammons* / Barrelhouse boogie: *Johnson, Pete/ Albert Ammons* / Cuttin' the boogie: *Johnson, Pete/Albert Ammons* / Walkin' the boogie: *Johnson, Pete/Albert Ammons* / Foot pedal boogie: *Johnson, Pete/Albert Ammons* / Sixth Avenue express: *Johnson, Pete/Albert Ammons* / Pine Creek: *Johnson, Pete/Albert Ammons* / Movin' the boogie: *Johnson, Pete/Albert Ammons*.
MC: NK 88334
LP: NL 88334

Barrelhouse Jazz Band
DRIVING HOT JAZZ FROM THE 20'S.
LP: GHB 49

Barrelhouse Mob
MAKIN' WHOOPEE.
LP: DS 071

TICKLED PINK.
Tracks: / Tickled pink / True love / Always / Together / Carolina moon / Singin' in the rain / Goodnight Vienna / Margie / Baby face / You were meant for me / Diane / Ramona / Charmaine / Harry Lime theme / You'll never know / Sally / Peg o' my heart.
LP: DS 068

Barrelhouse Piano...
BARRELHOUSE PIANO (Various artists).
LP: JP 5007

BARRELHOUSE PIANO 1927-36 (Various artists).
LP: L 1028

Barrelhouse Women
BARRELHOUSE WOMEN (Various artists).
LP: PY 449

Barren Cross
ATOMIC ARENA.
LP: MFN 84

HOTTER THAN HELL.
Tracks: / Imaginary music / Killers of the unborn / Going nowhere / Opus to the third heaven / In the eye of the fire / Light the flame / King Jesus and blues jam / Dying day / Close to the edge / Dead lock / King of Kings / Rock for the king / Terrorist child / Give your life.
LP: MD 93831

STATE OF CONTROL.
LP: ENVLP 530
MC: TCENV 530

Barrere, Paul
ON MY OWN TWO FEET.
Tracks: / Sweet coquette / High roller / Fool for you, A / Love sweet love / Who knows for sure / She lays down the beat / Fortune cookie / Along this lane.
MC: U 00 934

Barreta
BARRETA.
LP: BSS 212

Barrett, Al Linemen
DEEP WATER.
Tracks: / Miles of Texas / Heart, The / Rodeo clown man / Drifter / Faded love / Pure love / Sweet dreams / Why ask why / Deep water / Desperation.
MC: TC KO 1006

DON'T GET AROUND MUCH ANYMORE.
Tracks: / Rollin' with the flow / Do you right tonight / When loves goes wrong / Don't get around much anymore / Harder times / Vincent / I changed everything but my mind / Two dollars in the jukebox.
LP: KO 1012
MC: TC KO 1012

OPEN COUNTRY.
Tracks: / Muddy Mississippi line / Take me / I still miss someone / Hawaiian wedding song / Everything a man could ever need / Break my mind / Dear God / I fall to pieces / Truck driving man / Twelfth of never / Last thing on my mind / Crazy / Try a little kindness / Buckaroo.
LP: SFA 026

OPEN COUNTRY - VOL.2.
Tracks: / See you in the windshield / Drinking again / Corina Corina / Streets of Laredo / Pop a top / I forget you everyday / Streets of Baltimore / Drinking champagne / Back of my hand / Games people play / Every fool has a rainbow / Where love used to live.
LP: SFA 045

Barrett Brothers
MACKA DUB.
LP: LPCT 0018
MC: LPCTC 0018

Barrett, Dan
STRICTLY INSTRUMENTAL (Barrett, Dan Octet).
LP: CJ 331
MC: CJC 331

Barrett, Emma
SWEET EMMA BARRETT AND HER NEW ORLEANS MUSIC.
LP: GHB 141

Barrett, Jack
CEILI TIME IN IRELAND.
LP: HARP 6

Barrett, Sean (aut)
PERFUME - THE STORY OF A MURDERER (See under Perfume - The Story ...) (Suskind, Patrick (nar)).

Barrett Sisters
PRECIOUS LORD.
LP: AV 4907
MC: AV 5907

Barrett, Syd
BARRETT.
Tracks: / Baby lemonade / Love song / Dominoes / It is obvious / Rats / Maisie / Gigolo aunt / Waving my arms in the air / Wined and dined / Wolfpack / Effervescing elephant / I never lied to you.
LP: SHSP 4007
MC: TCSHSP 4007

MADCAP LAUGHS/BARRETT.
Tracks: / Terrapin / No good trying / Love you / No man's land / Here I go / Dark globe / Octopus / Golden hair / Long gone / She took a long cool look / Feel / If it's in you / Late night.
LP: SHVL 765
MC: SHDW 404

OPEL.
Tracks: / Opel / Clowns and jugglers (Octopus) / Rats / Golden hair (vocal) / Dolly rocker / Word song / Wined and dined / Swan Lee (Silas Lang) / Birdie hop / Let's split / Lanky (part 1) / Wouldn't you miss me / Milky way / Golden hair (Inst.).
LP: SHSP 4126
MC: TCSHSP 4126

TRIBUTE TO SYD BARRETT (See under Beyond The Wildwood) (Various artists).

Barrett & Weeks
SPACE BETWEEN, THE.
LP: RRA 007
MC: RRAMC 007

Barrett, Wild Willie
CALL OF THE WILD.
Tracks: / Late night lady / Temptation / Heartbeat of the city / Let's play schools / Close encounters / Song / Nigel Pringle / Eye of a hurricane / Take me back / Ole slewfoot / I did it Otway.
LP: 2383541

DEEP AND MEANINGLESS (See under Otway, John) (Barrett, Wild Willie & John Otway).

JOHN OTWAY AND WILD WILLIE BARRETT (See under Otway, John) (Barrett, Wild Willie & John Otway).

KRAZY KONG ALBUM.
LP: EYE 001

ORGANIC BONDAGE (Barrett, Wild Willie & Stephen Two Names).
LP: DIP 1
LP: DIPW 1

Barretto, Ray
BEST OF RAY BARRETTO.
LP: 530 260

HANDPRINTS.
Tracks: / Tercer oja / Blues for Leticia / Dancing winds / Kwanza / Handprints / Brandy / Triangle / Santa Cruz / Caribena / Jamprints.
MC: CJP 473C

HARD HANDS.
Tracks: / Mirame de frente / Oye la noticia / Indestructible / Abidjan / No me paren la salsa / Tumbao Africano / Acid / Hard hands.
LP: HOT 109
MC: TCHOT 109

LA CUNA.
Tracks: / La cuna / Dolorosa / Mambotango / Old castle / Pastime paradise.
MC: CTK 9502
LP: CTI 9002

LIVE IN NEW YORK CITY.
Tracks: / Intro / Vaya / Ahora si que vamo a gozar / Bab ban quere / Guarare / Night Flowers (flores de noche) / Slo flo / Cocinando / Que viva la misica.
2LP: 1115948

QUE VIVA LA MUSICA.
LP: SLP 00427

RITMO DE LA VIDA.
LP: SLP 605

TODO SE VA PODER.
LP: JM 633

VIVA WATUSI.
LP: . . . . WS 4058

Barrie, James

DREAMIN'.
Tracks: / I just fall in love again / I hear you talking / In love with you / Oshawa man / I'll have to say I love you in a song / Million miles away / Where's the reason / You look like an angel / Walk away from me.
LP: . . . . PL 25208

Barrie, J.J

CALL MY NAME.
Tracks: / Call my name / Why did you have to go and do it / Say goodbye to my life / Lady singer with a country music band / First goodnight, The / Save me / While the feeling's good / Sunday morning blues / Deanna Yates / I don't love you anymore.
LP: . . . . PL 25161
MC: . . . . PK 25161

ESPECIALLY FOR YOU.
LP: . . . . JJB 1
MC: . . . . ZCJJB 1

FORTY AND FADING.
LP: . . . . MAGIC 10

LOVE 'N' COUNTRY.
LP: . . . . MON LP 027

MY SON.
Tracks: / Why did you have to go and do it.
LP: . . . . MAGIC LP 3
MC: . . . . MAGIC C 3

SINGS SONGS FROM FRAGGLE ROCK.
LP: . . . . PIPLP 712
MC: . . . . ZCPIP 712

YOU CAN'T WIN 'EM ALL.
Tracks: / You can't win 'em all / I'll have to say I love you in a song / Where's the reason / I just fall in love again / Walk away from me / Bottle of gin / You look like an angel.
LP: . . . . PL 25294

Barrie, J.M. (aut)

PETER PAN (Original play and music) (Various artists).
MCSET: . . . . ZBBC 1085

PETER PAN (See under Peter Pan (bk)).

Barrie, Ken (nar)

POSTMAN PAT (See under Postman pat).

Barrie, Mike

DANCE TIME WITH THE ORGAN (Spotlight on Sequence).
Tracks: / I do, I do, I do / It's a pity to say goodnight / I do (reprise) / You were never lovelier / Somewhere along the way / You stepped out of a dream / Paper doll / It's a lovely day tomorrow / Best things for you, The / You keep coming back like a song / Girl that I marry, The / Mother of mine / Meet me in my dreams tonight / Story of Tina / Meet me tonight in dreamland / Boy next door, The / Sisters / Out of town / Take me in your arms and hold me / Tree in the meadow, A / Shepherd of the hills / I'm walking behind you / Man without love, A / Count your blessings instead of sheep / Let it be me / Count your blessings (reprise) / Love bells / You always hurt the one you love / Carnival / Be careful it's my heart.
LP: . . . . SUS 529

GIRLS.
Tracks: / Second hand Rose / Sweet Lorraine / Pretty girl is like a melody, A / Louise / Lady they call the gypsy, The / Ramona / Irene / Dance my darlings / Sweetheart of all my dreams / I'm thinking tonight of my blue eyes / No no Nanette / Waltz for Sarah / Emily / Mary Rose / Barbara Allen / Josephine / When Joanna left me / Woman in love / Laura / Rio Rita / Darlin' / Anastasia.
LP: . . . . SUS 516

GOLDEN SOUVENIRS.
Tracks: / Pick yourself up / So do I / Have you met Miss Jones / I've got my eyes on you / Take me to the dance / I apologise / Isle of my golden dreams / Sleepy lagoon / Silence is golden / Golden souvenirs / Cherie amour / You make me feel brand new / I'm beginning to see the light / Sentimental journey / Apple for teacher, An / Yes we have no bananas / El cumbanchero / Nice work if you can get it / Camptown races / Nic-nac-paddy-wac / Lady be good / 12th Street rag.
LP: . . . . SUS 524

MY SOUVENIRS (Barrie, Mike With The Starlight Sound).
Tracks: / Canadian capers / 57 Chevrolet / Tears / Among my souvenirs / Danke schon / My baby just cares for me / Daddy's little girl / Sweet heart land / Mistakes / Always there / Mam'selle / All I ask of you / Habanera / Who can I turn to / Tales from the Vienna Woods / Lili / Strauss theme / Little boxes / Cuckoo waltz / Till the time when you're with me / Consider yourself / Round the Marble Arch / Two little boys / Susan slept here / I love the way you say goodnight / Shores of Ballachulish / Loch Lomond.
LP: . . . . SUS 520

PARADISE.
Tracks: / So in love / You do something to me / When the poppies bloom again / We just couldn't say goodbye / It looks like rain in Cherry Blossom lane / You are my sunshine / If I should fall in love again / Paradise waltz / When my sugar walks down the street / Met a gal in Calico / Stranger in paradise / Mind if I make love to you / Latin touch-down / Suagr, sugar / Bambino de los playa.
LP: . . . . SUS 511

SAY IT WITH FLOWERS.
Tracks: / Three little words / Oh what a beautiful morning / Apple blossom time / We'll gather lilacs / Moonlight and roses / Lambeth walk / This is my lovely day / Red roses for a blue lady / Rose in a garden of weeds, A / Edelweiss / I got the sun in the morning / Cherry / I won't send roses / Say it with flowers / Lavender blue / Where have all the flowers gone / Begin the beguine / Azalae delicado / Orchids in the moonlight / Oh Rosalita.
LP: . . . . SUS 506

Barrington, Hugo

PRESENTING HUGO.
LP: . . . . MMLP 12

Barron, Blue

BLUE BARRON (1946) (Barron, Blue & His Orchestra).
LP: . . . . CLP 24

BLUE BARRON, 1938-41.
Tracks: / Sometime's I'm happy / Love is where you find it / Heart and soul / That's right I'm wrong / At long last love / You're the only star in my blue heaven / Don't cross your fingers / Garden in the rain / I heard bluebirds / Ida / I guess I'll have to dream the rest / Do you care / Blues my naughty sweetie gives to me / Things I love, The / Fancy meeting you / Maria Elena / You are my sunshine / Yesterday and today.
LP: . . . . HSR 110
LP: . . . . HMP 5047

UNCOLLECTED BLUE BARRON, THE - VOL.2 1938-39.
Tracks: / Teacher's pet / Garden of the moon / Yam, The / Love of my life / No wonder / Somebody nobody knows / That's right, I'm wrong / Roller skating on a rainbow / Goody goodbye / Does your heart beat for me / Scatterbrain / Faithful forever / I wanna wrap you up / Make with the kisses / I'm fit to be tied / It's a whole new thing.
LP: . . . . HSR 137

Barron, Keith (nar)

ADVENTURES OF GOODNIGHT AND LOVING, THE (See under Adventures of...).

FLYAWAY (BOOK) (See under Flyaway (book)).

Barron, Kenny

1+1+1+1.
LP: . . . . BKH 50601
MC: . . . . BKHMC 50601

GOLDEN LOTUS.
LP: . . . . MR 5220

IN TANDEM (Barron, Kenny & Ted Dunbar).
LP: . . . . MR 5140

LUCIFER.
Tracks: / Spirits / Firefly / Ethereally Yours / Hellbound / Lucifer / Oleo.
LP: . . . . MR 5070

RED BARRON DUO, THE (Barron,Kenny & Red Mitchell Trio).
LP: . . . . SLP 4137

SPIRAL.
LP: . . . . EWIND 709

SUNSET TO DAWN.
Tracks: / Sunset / Flower / Swamp demon / Al-Kifha / Delores St. S.F. / Dawn.
LP: . . . . MR 5018

TOGETHER (see Flanagan, Tommy) (Barron, Kenny & Tommy Flanagan).

Barron Knights

BARRON KNIGHTS.
Tracks: / Call up the groups / Pop go the workers / Under new management / Come to the dance / Round the world / Rhythm and blues / Return my love / Big girls don't cry / Sphinx won't tell, The / She's a woman / Merry minuet / Knock knock / Let her go.
LP: . . . . CN 2052
MC: CN4 2052

BEST OF THE BARRON KNIGHTS.
2LP: . . . . WW 5128/9
MCSET: . . . . WW 4 5128/9

FUNNY IN THE HEAD.
Tracks: / Buffalo Bill's last scratch / Funny in the head / Keep fat / He's everywhere / I was 'Itler's 'orse / Du' wot ? / Full circle / Grandfathers clock / Eye of the hurricane / Waste of time / Micky Burt / Prawns in the game.
LP: . . . . EPC 25709

I'D LIKE TO TEACH THE WORLD TO LAUGH.
LP: . . . . SPR 8555
MC: . . . . SPC 8555

JUST A GIGGLE.
Tracks: / Never mind the presents / Oh Miami / Masochistic and sadistic hospital song / Space invaders / Mind de doors / African humoresque / Sit song, The / We know who done it / Swindon cowboys / Hello mother, hello father / Fads and crazes / Barron's fun 40 / It's hard to be humble.
LP: . . . . EPC 84550

KNIGHTS OF LAUGHTER.
Tracks: / Ballad of Frank Spencer / You know what / Cold in my nose / Couldn't spell / Popumentry '71 / 1358 into beetroot song / Green knickers / I'm a nut / Head tucked underneath her arm.
LP: . . . . SHM 981
MC: . . . . HSC 361

LIVE IN TROUBLE.
Tracks: / Live in trouble / You make me feel like dancing / Angelo / D.I.V.O.R.C.E. / Lucille / Float on / Telephone man / Ernie (the fastest milkman in the west) / Clair / Amazing Grace / 1358 number song / Linking - Incidental music / Space oddity / Autograph hunter / Loving you / What is a pop star? / Three finger picker / Any old iron.
LP: . . . . SPR 8510
MC: . . . . SPC 8510

NIGHT GALLERY.
Tracks: / Get down Shep / Boozy nights / Little white bum / Lazy fitter / Big V-asectomy / Chapel lead is missing / Taste of aggro / Rivers of Babylon / Smurfs song / Matchstalk men / My will / Hand on the ear folk song / Awful seance / Boy scouts out camping.
LP: . . . . EPC 83221

TEACH THE WORLD TO LAUGH.
Tracks: / Food for thought / Evolution / Telephone line / Herbie the head / Fleetwood bus / Mr. Tambourine man / Topical song / Nanu nanu / Arthur Clark / Preservation / Farewell to punk / Busker / Heaving on a jet plane / Here here.
MC: 40 83891
LP: . . . . EPC 83891

TWISTING THE KNIGHTS AWAY.
Tracks: / Blackboard jumble / Prince Charming / Wired for sound / This 'ole house / Mademoiselle from Armentiers / Mr. Rubik / Spaghetti Betty / San Andreas fault / Rise / Gobbledegook / Centrefold / Taste of aggro / Little white bum / Chapel lead is missing / Heaving on a jet plane / Live in trouble / Sit song.
LP: . . . . EPC 85319

TWO SIDES OF BARRON KNIGHTS, THE.
Tracks: / Ballad of Frank Spencer / You know what / Cold in my nose / Couldn't spell / Popumentry '71 (Part 1) / Banner man / Grandad / Did you ever / 1358 into Beetroot song / Green knickers / I'm a nut / Head tucked underneath her arm / Popumentry '71 (Part 2) / Chirpy chirpy cheep cheep / Resurrection shuffle / Knock three times / You're all I need / Before you leave / Bottle on the shelf / Lonely / You know what I mean / Don't let it die / Turning my back on you / Oh little girl / To the wood / Peaceful life.
2LP: . . . . SSD 8037
MCSET: . . . . SSDC 8037

TWO SIDES OF YOU.
MC: C5K 572

Barron, Ronnie

BON TON ROULETTE.
Tracks: / Bon ton roulet / Carry on / Fever / Bony Moronie / Rock and roll dream / Lights out / Life is just a struggle / Pixie / Maybellene / Cha dooky-doo.
LP: . . . . CH 79

Barroso, Jose

SONGS OF THE LATIN AMERICAN PEOPLE (Barroso, Jose & Emilio).
LP: . . . . LRF 185

Barrow Poets

ISLANDS OF THE MOON.
Tracks: / Aloysius Barley and the music of the spheres / When it's night time in Italy / That that / Riddle / Twiner / Un cordier / Lay of the mouthpiece / Mr. Finney's turnip / Man of words / Soldier's dance / Row / Juggler's wife / Cake walk, The / Tale of the Leprechauney man / Magic train / Flea / Frog / Antelope song / Thomas cat / Galloping cat / Terrific legend of the Kilkenny cats / In an island of the moon / Trip tomorrow / Punch brother punch / Three limericks / Dinah / White mouse / Poem for Lorna to keep away foxes / Hairy toe / Winkle and the pin.
LP: . . . . ASW 6001

Barry, Carl

HOLDING ON (Barry, Carl & Joanne).
LP: . . . . ST 236

Barry, Claudja

I, CLAUDJA.
Tracks: / Down and counting / Can't you feel my heartbeat / Dance for your life / Give me a sign / Hot to the touch / Dead or alive (I don't know if you are) / Secret affair / You've got me jumpin' / Change of heart / Show me another way.
LP: 4510451
MC: 4510454

I WANNA BE LOVED BY YOU.
Tracks: / Boogie tonight / Cold fire / Dancin' shoes / Down by the water / Give it up / Heavy makes you happy / I wanna be loved by you / Love of the hurtin' kind / Nobody but you / Way you are dancing.
LP: 630 610 7

Barry, Harry

OLD WAYS NEW BEGINNINGS.
Tracks: / Symphony of love / In Winter / Lonely in the night / All I need is you / Give your love a chance / Your cheatin' heart / God bless you / See what we can do / Building a wall / It doesn't matter anymore / Happy in love again.
LP: . . . . OKLP 3003
MC: . . . . ZCOK 3003

Barry, John

BEAT GIRL (SOUNDTRACK) (Various artists).
Tracks: / Off beat, The: *Barry, John* / Lindon Home rock: *Barry, John* / Time out: *Barry, John* / Sharks, The: *Barry, John* / City 2000 AD, The: *Barry, John* / Stripper, The: *Barry, John* / Car chase: *Barry, John* / Chicken: *Barry, John* / Blues for beatniks: *Barry, John* / Immediate pleasure, The: *Barry, John*/ Blondie's strip: *Barry, John* / End shot: *Barry, John* / I did what you told me: *Faith, Adam* / Beat girl: *Faith, Adam* / Cave, The/Beat girl/Kids stuff: *Faith, Adam* / Made you: *Faith, Adam* / It's legal: *Field, Shirley Anne* / Slaughter in Soho: *Barry, John.*
LP: . . . . WIK 31
LP: 33SX 1225

BEST OF JOHN BARRY.
Tracks: / Thunderball / 007 / We have all the time in the world / Curiouser and curiouser / Strip drive / Diamonds are forever / Dolls house / Goldfinger / Love among the ruins / Adventurer / Yesternight suite / Midnight cowboy.
LP: 2384 120

BEST OF THE JOHN BARRY SEVEN & ORCHESTRA (Barry, John Seven & Orchestra).
Tracks: / Hit and miss / Big guitar / Rodeo / Big fella / Walk, don't run / Bee's knees / Ev'ry which way / Beat girl / Human jungle / I'm movin' on / Zapata / Like waltz / Black stockings / James Bond theme / Lost patrol / Magnificent seven, The / Hideaway / Menace / Never let go / Sharks.
LP: . . . . NUTM 21

BIG SCREEN HITS OF JOHN BARRY, THE.
Tracks: / Thunderball / Born free / Persuaders, The / Midnight cowboy / Ipcress file, The / We have all the time in the world / Lion in Winter, The / Goldfinger / You only live twice / Girl with the sun in her hair, The / More things change, The / Fun city / James Bond theme.
MC: 40 31862
LP: . . . . CBS 31862

BLACK HOLE (See under Black Hole for details).

BORN FREE (See under Born Free for details).

DANCES WITH WOLVES (See under Dances With Wolves).

HIGH ROAD TO CHINA (See under High Road To China).

HIT AND MISS (Barry, John Seven & Orchestra).
Tracks: / Hit and miss / Big guitar / Rodeo / Big fella / Walk don't run / Bees' knees / Ev'ry which way / Beat girl / Human jungle, The / I'm movin' on / Zapata / Like waltz / Black stockings /

James Bond theme / Lost patrol / Magnificent seven, The / Hideaway / Menace / Never let go / Sharks.
LP: . . . . CM 110
MC: . . . . CMK 110
MC: C5K-516
LP: C5-516

JOHN DUNBAR THEME, THE (See Under Dances With Wolves).

KNACK, THE (FILM SOUNDTRACK) (See under Knack, The).

LAST VALLEY, THE (See under Films).

LET THINGS HAPPEN.
LP: . . . . ISST 200

MUSIC FROM THE BIG SCREEN.
Tracks: / James Bond / Whisperers / Mr. Kiss Kiss Bang / King rat / You only live twice / Thunderball / Ipcress file, The / Chase dutchman / From Russia with love / On her Majesty's secret service / Fun city / Knack / We have all the time in the world / Born free / Midnight cowboy / Girl with the sun in her hair, The / Wrong box / More things change / Goldfinger.
MCSET: . . . . DTO 10229

MUSIC OF JOHN BARRY.
Tracks: / Born free / You only live twice / Goldfinger / Whisperers / From Russia with love / Wednesday's child / Quiller memorandum / Space march (capsule in space) / Girl with the sun in her hair, The / Thunderball / Wrong box, The / James Bond theme / 007 / Mister kiss kiss bang bang / Chase, The / King rat / Seance on a wet afternoon / Ipcress file, The / Midnight cowboy / Romance for guitar & orchestra, Theme from / On Her Majesty's secret service / Appointment, Theme from / Lion in Winter, The.
2LP: . . . . CBS 22014

STRINGBEAT.
Tracks: / It doesn't matter anymore / Sweet talk / Moody river / There's life in the old boy yet / Handful of songs / Like waltz / Rodeo / Donna's theme / Star fire / Baubles, bangles and beads / Zapata / Rum-de-dum-de-da / Spanish Harlem / Man from Madrid / Challenge, The.
LP: . . . . BRED 51

VERY BEST OF JOHN BARRY.
Tracks: / 007 / Thunderball / Diamonds are forever.
MC: 3192 627
LP: . . . . MID 1009

Barry, Len

MORE FROM THE 1-2-3 MAN.
Tracks: / Bob, Carol, Ted and Alice / Christopher Columbus / Now I'm alone / Spread it on like butter / This old world / Funky nite / Put out the fire / You're my Picasso baby / In my present state of mind / Wouldn't it be beautiful / Keem-o-sabe.
LP: . . . . BDL 1013

Barry, Margaret

HER MANTLE SO GREEN (Barry, Margaret & Michael Gorman).
LP: 12T 123

IRELAND'S OWN STREET SINGER.
LP: . . . . SOLP 1029
MC: . . . . COX 1029

SHE MOVES THROUGH THE FAIR.
Tracks: / Blarney stone, The / Factory girl / Moses ri-tooral-i-ay / Kathleen / Where Lagan streams / Gradh mo chroidhe / Banjo tune / Galway shawl / Let Mr. Maguire sit down / Mantle so green / Turfman from Ardee / Bard of Armagh, The / Cycling champion: Eddie Richardson, The / Martha of Strabane / Wild colonial boy.
MC: 60-070

Barry, Sheila

I'M A PUSHOVER FOR A COUNTRY SONG.
LP: . . . . RBA 112

Barry Sisters

WHEN THE BOAT COMES IN.
Tracks: / Dance ti thi daddy / O heh ye seen wor Jimmy / Cushie butterfield / Water o' Tyne, The / Amble feast, The / Blaydon races / Bobby Shaftoe / Lambton worm, The / Sally Gee / Barn dance hustle, The / Cullercoats fish lass / This old hat / Adam Buckamo / Wherever ye gan / Molly Dunn / Hi canny man / Keep your feet still / Wor Nanny's a mazer / Keel row, The / Ma bonny lad.
LP: . . . . MWM 1021
MC: . . . . MWMC 1021

Barrymore, John

JOHN BARRYMORE: FROM MATINEE IDOL TO BUFFOON.
MC: . . . . FACET 8112

Barstow, Josephine

JOSEPHINE BARSTOW SINGS VERDI ARIAS.
LP: . . . . VIR 8307
MC: . . . . ZCVIR 8307

Barth, Bobby

TWO HEARTS-ONE BEAT.
Tracks: / Stop in the name of love / Sara / Knifes edge / I don't want to be alone tonight / Burn me once, burn me twice / Once in a lifetime / Dangerous games / Don't come to me.
LP: 790 502-1
MC: 790 502-4

Bartholomew, Dave

CLASSIC NEW ORLEANS R'N'B BAND, THE.
Tracks: / Country gal / Who drank my beer while I was in the rear / Carnival day / When the saints go marching in boogie / Snatchin' back / Jump children / No more black nights / Little girl sing ting-a-ling / Monkey, The / Shout, sister, shout / Another mule / Old cow hand from a blues band / Love no more / Can't take it no more / Yeah yeah / Portrait of a drummer, A.
LP: . . . . SSL 6036
MC: . . . . TCSSL 6036

JUMP CHILDREN.
LP: . . . . PM 1546601

MONKEY,THE.
LP: . . . . PM 156 1331

MY DING A LING.
Tracks: / In the alley / Sweet home blues / Bad habit / Twins / Golden rule, The / High flying woman / I'll never be the same / Mother knows best / Stormy weather / Lawdy lawdy Lord (part 1) / Lawdy lawdy Lord (part 2) / My ding-a-ling.
LP: . . . . SING 1158

Bartle, Peter

PLAYS SIMPLY HAMMOND.
LP: . . . . GRS 1060

Barto, Tzimon

RHAPSODY IN BLUE.
Tracks: / Rhapsody in blue / Piano concerto no.2 / Piano concerto in G.
LP: . . . . EL 749 495 1
MC: . . . . EL 749 495 4

Bartok (composer)

MIRACULOUS MANDARIN, THE (See under Stravinsky (composer) Petrushka) (Vienna Philharmonic Orchestra).

MUSIC FOR STRINGS, PERCUSSION & CELESTE DIVERTIMENTO (Various artists).
MC: 4303524

STRING QUARTET NO.6- PIANO QUINTET (Chilingirian String Quartet).
LP: . . . . ABRD 1346
MC: . . . . ABTD 1346

STRING QUARTETS 3.4.5 (Chilingirian String Quartet).
LP: . . . . ABRD 1323
MC: . . . . ABTD 1323

STRING QUARTETS NO.1 & 2 (BARTOK) (Chilingirian String Quartet).
Tracks: / String quartet no.1 op.7 (Bartok) / String quartet no.2 op.17 (Bartok).
LP: . . . . ABRD 1280
MC: . . . . ABTD 1280

Barton, Edward

HERE IS MY SPOON.
LP: . . . . WOOD 008

Barton, Lou Ann

DREAMS COME TRUE (Barton, Lou Ann/Marcia Ball/Angela Strehli).
Tracks: / Fool in love, A / Good rockin' daddy / It hurts to be in love / Love sweet love / Gonna make it / You can if you think you can / I idolize you / Dreams come true / Bad thing / Turn the lock on love / Something's got a hold on me / Snake dance.
MC: . . . . ANTMC 14

READ MY LIPS.
LP: . . . . ROSE 190

Barton, Tony

STONED (Live at the Belvedere).
Tracks: / Blueberry Hill / He'll have to go / Green green grass of home / When I fall in love / Ernie / Last one home (Mr.Toad), The / Dave, Stones bitter & me.
LP: . . . . PRX 27
MC: . . . . TC-PRX 27

Bartz, Jim

PICTURES OF EARTH AND SPACE.
LP: . . . . SYN 311
MC: . . . . SYNC 311

Base, Rob

INCREDIBLE BASE, THE.
LP: . . . . FILER 285
MC: . . . . FILERCT 285

IT TAKES TWO (ALBUM) (Base, Rob & D.J. E-Z Rock).
Tracks: / Get on the dancefloor / It takes two / Joy and pain / Check this out.
LP: . . . . PRO 1267
LP: . . . . SU 4
MC: . . . . ZCSU 4
LP: 33008

Baselli, Joss

CLASSIC JAZZ (Baselli, Joss & His Quartet).
Tracks: / March turque (Mozart) / Albino adagio / Choral de veilleur (Bach) / Menuet (Mozart) / Mazurka (Chopin) / Danse d'anitra (Grieg) / Sonate (Mozart) / Italian concerto / Adante and Presto (1st movement) / De falla danse du feu.
MC: . . . . UNKNOWN
LP: . . . . CBS 25848

INOUBLIABLE.
Tracks: / Geraldine / Mazureva / Minousette / Marquisette / La corsette / Belinda / Basquaise la rivale / La galliniere / Corisette / Lori Lori / L'oiseleur.
MC: . . . . UNKNOWN
LP: . . . . ILD 42047

LES DOIGTS D'OR.
Tracks: / Piccolo rag / Multi faces / La polka Suedoise / La balocharde / Rock minuer / Passy musette / Les doigts d'or / Via Rio / L'avigonnaise / Campans de fiesta / Pour une valse / Accordion rag.
LP: . . . . ILD 42020
MC: . . . . UNKNOWN

PERLES D'ACCORDEON.
Tracks: / Feu vert / Pietro's return / La migliavacca / Perles de cristal / Aubade d'oiseaux / Mille accordeon / Jeanette les troilets / Brazil accordeon / Indifference / Croma duet / Perles d'accordeon / Boutade / Roba / Accordeon holiday / Electro ballade.
LP: . . . . CBS 54899
MC: . . . . UNKNOWN

Basement 5

1965-1980.
Tracks: / Riot / No ball games / Hard work / Immigration / Heavy traffic / Last white Christmas / Union games / Too soon / Omega man.
LP: . . . . ILPS 9641

Basement Boys

BLUE NOTES IN THE BASEMENT.
LP: . . . . WX 410
MC: . . . . WX 410C

Basement Walls

BASEMENT WALLS (14 US oil slickers & garage mechanics) (Various artists).
LP: . . . . GONE 2

Bash 'N' The Code

BIG MOUTH.
LP: . . . . MYR R 6860
MC: . . . . MYR C 6860

MORE THAN ENOUGH.
LP: . . . . SS R 8130
MC: . . . . SS C 8130

Bashful Brother Oswald

BASHFUL BROTHER OSWALD.
LP: . . . . SLP 192
MC: . . . . GT 5192

BROTHER OSWALD.
LP: . . . . ROUNDER 0013

DON'T SAY ALOHA.
LP: . . . . ROUNDER 0080
MC: . . . . ROUNDER 0080C

OZ AND CHARLIE (Bashful Brother Oswald & Charlie Collins).
Tracks: / Mountain dew / Indian killed the woodcock / Homestead on the farm / Hilo march / Nobody's darling but mine / Stoney point / Black smoke / Oswald's special / Polly wolly doodle / Hills of old Kentucky / Snowflake reel / Mother, the queen of my heart / Loo Loo's nest / What a friend we have in Jesus.
LP: . . . . ROUNDER 0060
MC: . . . . ROUNDER 0060C

THAT'S COUNTRY (Bashful Brother Oswald & Charlie Collins).
LP: . . . . ROUNDER 0041
MC: . . . . ROUNDER 0041C

Bashville (group)

BASHVILLE (Original Cast Recording) (Various artists).
Tracks: / Prelude: *Various artists* / Fancy Free: *Various artists* / Lydia: *Various artists* / 8-9-10: *Various artists* / One pair of hands: *Various artists* / Gentleman's true to his code,A: *Various artists*/ Because I love her: *Various artists* / Take the road to the ring: *Various artists* / Entr'acte: *Various* artists / Hymn to law and order: *Various artists* / Blackman's burden: *Various artists* / He is my son: *Various artists* / Bashville: *Various artists* / Boats are burned: *Various artists* / Finale: *Various artists.*
LP: . . . . TER 1072
MC: . . . . ZCTER 1072

Basia

LONDON, WARSAW, NEW YORK.
Tracks: / Cruising for a bruising / Best friends / Brave new hope / Baby you're mine / Ordinary people / Reward / Until you come back to me / Copernicus / Not an angel / Take him back Rachel.
LP: 4632821
MC: 4632824

TIME AND TIDE.
Tracks: / Promises / Run for cover / Time and tide / Freeze thaw / From now on / New day for you / Prime time TV / Astrud / How dare you / Miles away / Forgive and forget (Extra track on cassette and Compact Disc.).
LP: 450263 1
MC: 450263 4

Basic Black

BASIC BLACK.
Tracks: / She's mine / Give your love to me / What ever it takes / Nothing but a party / Special kind of fool / It's a man's thang / Don't make me fall in love / Baby can we talk / Now or never / Stupid.
LP: . . . . ZL 72723
MC: . . . . ZK 72723

Basie, Count

14 CLASSICS.
Tracks: / Hollywood jump / I never knew / Tickle toe / Let me see / Blow top / What's your number / Five o'clock whistle / Broadway / Stampede in G minor / Rockin' the blues / Wiggle woogie / Jitters / Tuesday at ten / I do mean you.
LP: . . . . CBS 21133
MC: 40 21133

20 GOLDEN PIECES: COUNT BASIE.
Tracks: / One o'clock jump / Motem swing / Study in brown, A / Dinah / Good morning blues / Lady be good / Flat foot floogie / Every tub / Boogie woogie blues / Lullaby of Birdland / Summertime / These foolish things / One note samba / Makin' whoopee / April in Paris / Jumpin' at the woodside / Ain't misbehavin' / Shake, rattle and roll / I got it bad (and that ain't good) / Lester leaps in.
LP: . . . . BDL 2020
MC: . . . . BDC 2020

88 BASIE STREET (Basie, Count & His Orchestra).
Tracks: / Bluesville / 88 Basie Street / Contractor's blues / Blues machine, The / Katy / Sunday at the Savoy.
LP: 231 0901
MC: K10 901

1946.
LP: . . . . FH 22
MC: . . . . CFH 22

AFRIQUE.
Tracks: / Step right up / Hobo flats / Gypsy queen / Love flower / Afrique / Kilimanjaro / African sunrise / Japan.
LP: . . . . ASLP 809
MC: . . . . ZCAS 809

AIN'T IT THE TRUTH (Basie, Count & His Orchestra).
Tracks: / In case you didn't know / These foolish things / Peter Pan / Ain't it the truth / Ingin' the Ooh / Confessin'.
LP: . . . . BLM 51009

AMERICANS IN SWEDEN 1954.
2LP: . . . . AA 526/527

ANYTHING GOES (See under Bennett, Tony) (Basie, Count Big Band).

AT SAVOY BALLROOM 1937-44.
Tracks: / Moten swing / Shout and feel it / Me and you that used to be, The / Count steps in, The / I'll always be in love with you / When my dreamboat comes home / Swing brother swing / Down for double / Rockin' the blues / Wiggle woogie / Andy's blues / I've found a new baby / Basie boogie.
LP: . . . . SM 3083

AT SOUTHLAND CAFE, BOSTON (Basie, Count/Chick Webb).
LP: . . . . CC 11

AT THE BLUENOTE (Basie, Count & His Orchestra).
Tracks: / Fancy meeting you (Recorded at the Chicago Bluenote during August 1955) / Basie English (Recorded at the Chicago Bluenote during January 1956) / Everyday (Recorded at the Chicago Bluenote during January 1956) / Basses loaded (Recorded at the Chicago Bluenote during January 1956) / April in Paris (Recorded at the Chicago Bluenote during August 1955) / Peace pipe (Recorded at the Chicago Bluenote during August 1955) / Cherry point (Recorded at the Chicago Bluenote during August 1955) / Smack dab in the middle (Recorded at the Chicago Bluenote during January 1956) / Jumpin' at the woodside (Recorded at the Chicago Bluenote during January 1956)

/ Teach me tonight (Recorded at the Chicago Bluenote during August 1955) / How high the moon (Recorded at the Chicago Bluenote during August 1955).
LP: . . . . AWE 24
MC: . . . . CAWE 24

AT THE MONTREUX JAZZ FESTIVAL, 1975.
Tracks: / Jam session / Billie's bounce / Festival blues / Lester leaps in.
LP: 231 0750
MC: K10 750

ATOMIC MR BASIE, THE (PRT) (Basie, Count & His Orchestra).
MC: . . . . ZCNFP 5503
LP: . . . . NFP 5503

ATOMIC MR BASIE, THE (ROULETTE) (Basie, Count & His Orchestra).
Tracks: / Kid from Red Bank, The / Duet / After supper / Flights of the foo birds / Double O / Teddy the toad / Whirly bird / Midnite blue / Splanky / Fantail / Li'l darlin'.
LP: . . . . ROU 1005
LP: 793 273 1

ATOMIC MR BASIE, THE (VOGUE) (Basie, Count & His Orchestra).
LP: 500 001
MC: 700 788

ATOMIC MR CHAIRMAN, THE.
Tracks: / Kid from Red Bank, The / Duet / After supper / Flights of the foo birds / Double-O / Teddy the toad / Whirly-bird / Midnite blue / Splanky / Fantail / Li'l darlin' / Blues in Hoss's flat / H.R.H. / Segue in C / Kansas City shout / Speaking of sounds / T.V. time / Who, me? / Deacon, The / Half Moon Street / Mutt and Jeff.
2LP: . . . . VJD 517
MCSET: . . . . ZCVJD 517

ATOMIC PERIOD, THE (Basie, Count Orchestra).
Tracks: / Shiny stockings / HRH / Bag of bones / Deacon, The / Whirly bird / In a mellow tone / Midgets, The / Basie boogie / Ol' man river / Sisteen men a'swinging.
LP: . . . . RARITIES 52

AUTUMN IN PARIS (Basie, Count & His Orchestra).
Tracks: / Whirlybird / Little pony / Corner pocket / Lovely baby / Blee blop blues / Nails / Kid from Red Bank, The / Spring is here / Why not? / Well, alright, OK, you win / Roll 'em / Ol man river / Duet / Gee, baby ain't I good to you / One o'clock jump.
LP: . . . . AWE 13
MC: . . . . CAWE 13

AVENUE C (1944) (Basie, Count & Lester Young).
LP: . . . . JJ 604

BACK WITH BASIE.
LP: 500022

BASIC BASIE.
Tracks: / Idaho / Blues in my heart / I don't stand a ghost of a chance / Red roses for a blue lady / Moonglow / Ma he's making eyes at me / M-squad / Sweet Lorraine / Ain't misbehavin' / Don't worry 'bout me / As long as I live / I've got the world on a string.
LP: 8212911

BASIE AND ZOOT (Basie, Count & Zoot Sims).
Tracks: / I never knew / Its only a paper moon / Blues for Nat Cole / Captain Bligh / Honeysuckle rose / Hardav / Mean to me / Surrender dear.
LP: 2310 745
MC: K10 745

BASIE AT BIRDLAND.
LP: 500020

BASIE BIG BAND.
Tracks: / Front burner / Freckle face / Orange sherbert / Soft as velvet / Heat's on, The / Midnight freight / Give 'em time / Wind machine, The / Tall cotton.
LP: 231 0756
MC: K10 756

BASIE BLUES.
LP: 2M 056 64865
MC: 2M 256 64865

BASIE BOOGIE (Basie, Count & His Orchestra).
Tracks: / One o'clock jump / Basie boogie / Taps Miller / Red bank boogie / mad boogie / King / Hob nail boogie / Wild bill's boogie / Little pony / Hozit / Beaver junction / Nails / Squeeze me / Boone's blues / Jumping at the woodside.
LP: . . . . CBS 21063
MC: 40 21063

BASIE DOUBLE.
Tracks: / Rat race / Five o'clock in the morning / Easin' it / Blue on blue / Good time blues / Meetin' time / Counter block / Let's have a taste / Not now, I'll tell you when / Swingin' at the Waldorf / Vine Street rumble / Quince / Square at the round table / Brotherly shove / Blue five jive / Rare butterfly / Jackson County jubilee / Big walk, The.
2LP: . . . . VJD 509
2LP: 400614

BASIE IN SWEDEN.
LP: 500023

BASIE JAM NO.2.
Tracks: / Mama don't wear no drawers / Doggin' around / Kansas City line / Jump.
LP: 231 0786
MC: K10 786
LP: 2335 748

BASIE JAM NO.3.
Tracks: / Bye bye blues / Moten swing / I surrender, dear / Song of the islands.
LP: 231 0840
MC: K10 840

BASIE - ONE MORE TIME (Music from the Pen of Quincy Jones).
Tracks: / For Lena and Lennie / Rat race / Quince / Meet B B / Big walk, The / Square at the round table, A / I needs to be bee'd with / Jessica's day / Midnite sun never sets, The / Muttnik.
LP: 500006

BASIE PIANO.
LP: . . . . RD 9

BASIE PLAYS HEFTI.
LP: 500002

BASIE RIDES AGAIN.
LP: 2304 410

BASIE SPECIAL, THE (Basie, Count Orchestra).
LP: . . . . EV 3004

BASIE'S BASEMENT (Basie, Count & His Orchestra).
Tracks: / Bill's mill / Swingin' the blues / Basie's basement / I never knew / Sugar / South / Seventh Avenue express / Your red wagon / Just a minute / Bye bye baby / Shoutin' blues / Rat race.
LP: . . . . CL 89802
MC: . . . . CK 89802

BENNETT AND BASIE (see under Bennett, Tony) (Basie, Count & Tony Bennett).

BEST OF BASIE VOL.1.
LP: 500014

BEST OF BASIE VOL.2.
LP: 500015

BEST OF COUNT BASIE (The Roulette years) (Basie, Count & His Orchestra).
Tracks: / Kid from red bank, The / Late late show, The / Flight of the foo birds / Jive at five / Blue and sentimental / Lullabye of birdland / Cute / Seque in C (wess) / Topsy / Jumpin at the woodside / Broadway / Tickle toe / Scoot / For Lena and Lennie / Whirly bird / Down and double / Easy money / Turnabout / Taps miller / Old man river.
MC: . . . . TCROU 1046

BEST OF COUNT BASIE.
Tracks: / Tree frog / Swee' pea / Ticker / Flirt / Blues for Alfy / Billie's bounce / Festival blues / Jumpin' at the Woodside / Blue and sentimental / Red bank boogie / Shorty George / Rockabye Basie / Every tub / Swingin' the blues / Sent for you yesterday / Boogie woogie / Broadway / Texas shuffle / Tickle toe / Doggin' around / Dickie's dream / Topsy / Lester leaps in / Out the window.
LP: 2310 852
MC: K10 852

BEST OF THE BASIE BIG BAND.
Tracks: / Blues for Alfy / Heat's on, The / C.B. express / Swee'pea / Way out Basie / Featherweight / Katy / Prime time / Mr. Softie.
LP: . . . . PEM 002
MC: . . . . PEMC 002

BIG BAND, VOL 1 (See under Jackson, Milt) (Basie, Count & Milt Jackson).

BIG BAND, VOL 2 (See under Jackson, Milt) (Basie, Count & Milt Jackson).

BIG BASIE.
Tracks: / Avenue C / Tess torch song / Jumpin' at The Woodside / I'm gonna sit right down and write myself a letter / Rockabye Basie / Dance of the gremlins / When they ask about you / I've found a new baby / Slender, tender and tall / Do nothing till you hear from me / Basie boogie / Havard blues.
LP: . . . . QU 025

BING 'N' BASIE (See under Crosby, Bing) (Basie, Count & Bing Crosby).

BIRDLAND ERA VOL.1, THE (Basie, Count & His Orchestra).
LP: . . . . D 1013

BIRDLAND ERA VOL.2, THE (Basie, Count & His Orchestra).
Tracks: / One o'clock jump / Why not? / Out of nowhere / How high the moon / Hobnail boogie / Jumpin' at The Woodside / Blee blop blues / Basie blues / Every tub / You're not the kind / Paradise squat / Lullaby of Birdland.
LP: . . . . D 1018

BLUES BY BASIE.
Tracks: / Tootie / How long blues / Way back blues / Blues / Harvard blues / Bugle blues / Take me back baby / Golden bullet / Nobody knows / Royal garden blues / I'm gonna move to the outskirts of town / Bluebird blues.
LP: . . . . CBS 54304

BOARD OF DIRECTORS, THE (Basie, Count & Mills Brothers).
Tracks: / Up a lazy river / I may be wrong but I think you're wonderful / Release me / I want to be happy / Down down down / Whiffenpoof song, The / I dig rock 'n' roll music / Tiny bubbles / December / Let me dream / April in Paris.
LP: . . . . MOIR 201
MC: . . . . CMOIR 201

BOSSES, THE (Basie, Count & Joe Turner).
Tracks: / Honeydripper / Honey hush / Cherry red / Night time is the right time / Blues around the clock / Since I fell for you / Flip flop and fly / Wee baby blues / Good morning blues / Roll 'em Pete.
LP: 231 0709
MC: K10 709

BRAND NEW WAGON (Basie, Count & His Orchestra).
Tracks: / Bill's mill / Brand new wagon / One o'clock boogie / Swingin' the blues / St. Louis boogie / Basie's basement / Backstage at Stuff's / My buddy / Shine on harvest moon / Sugar / House rent boogie / South / Don't you want a man like me / Seventh Avenue express / Sophisticated swing / Your red wagon / Money is honey / Just a minute / Robbin's nest / Hey, pretty baby / Bye, bye baby.
LP: . . . . NL 82292
MC: . . . . NK 82292

BREAKFAST DANCE AND BARBECUE.
LP: 500009

BROADCASTS 1944/45 (Basie, Count & His Orchestra).
Tracks: / Basie blues / One o'clock jump / Basie boogie / I'm gonna sit right down and write myself a letter.
LP: 20806

C. WEBB & HIS ORCHESTRA 1936 (Basie, Count & His Orchestra).
MC: . . . . UMK 99007

CAFE SOCIETY UPTOWN (Vol. 2).
LP: . . . . JU 5

CAFE SOCIETY UPTOWN (Vol. 1).
LP: . . . . JU 4

CARNEGIE HALL CONCERT.
LP: 509168

CATERINA '86 (See under Valente, Caterina) (Valente, Caterina & Count Basie Orchestra).

CHAIRMAN OF THE BOARD.
LP: 33SX 1209

CHAIRMAN, THE.
LP: 500007

CHAPTER FIVE (Basie, Count Orchestra).
Tracks: / Fiesta in blue / Tom Thumb / My old flame / Take me back, baby / Something new / Platterbrains / All of me / Feather merchant / Down for double / More than you know / Havard blues / Coming-out party / Blue shadows and white gardenias.
LP: . . . . QU 034

CHAPTER FOUR (Basie, Count Orchestra).
Tracks: / Nobody knows / How long blues / Blues (I still think of her) / Who am I? / I'll forget / Beau Brummel / Jump the blues away / Tuesday at ten / Undecided blues / Down, down, down / Tune town shuffle / One two three O'Leary / Diggin' for Dex.
LP: . . . . QU 033

CHAPTER SIX (Basie, Count Orchestra).
Tracks: / Basie blues / Outskirts of town / I didn't know / Blue skies / Jivin' for Johnson / High tide / Queer Street / Lazy lady blues / Hobnail boogie / Danny boy / Goodbye baby / Wild Bill's boogie / Fla-ga-la-pa / Baby don't be mad at me / I've only myself to blame / It's Monday every day.
LP: . . . . QU 035

CHAPTER THREE (Basie, Count Orchestra).
Tracks: / Don't worry 'bout me / And the angels sing / If I didn't care / Lonesome Miss Pretty / You can count on me / You and your love / Apple jump, The / Volcano / Louisiana / You can't run around / World is mad, The / All or nothing at all / Moon fell in the river, The / Five o'clock whistle / My wandering man.
LP: . . . . QU 022
LP: . . . . QUEEN 022

CHICAGO (See under Bennett, Tony) (Basie, Count & Tony Bennett).

CLASS OF '54.
LP: . . . . BLP 60924

CLASSY PAIR, A (See under Fitzgerald, Ella) (Basie, Count & Ella Fitzgerald).

COUNT BASIE (1939-41).
LP: . . . . QUEEN 015

COUNT BASIE (Compact/Walkman Jazz).
Tracks: / Shiny stockings / Down for the Count / Corner pocket / Blues backstage / April in Paris / One o'clock jump / I'm shouting again / Count 'em / Nasty magnus / St. Louis Blues / All of me / Doodle oodle.
MC: 831 364 4

COUNT BASIE (1940).
LP: . . . . EV 3006

COUNT BASIE (1944).
LP: . . . . CLP 60

COUNT BASIE (1938-39).
LP: . . . . JA 41

COUNT BASIE, 1940-44.
LP: . . . . AA 512

COUNT BASIE AND HIS ORCHESTRA 1946-56 (Basie, Count & His Orchestra).
Tracks: / What am I here for / Jive at five / Hob nail boogie / Softly, with feeling / Blee blop blues / Mutton leg / Paradise squat / Seventh avenue express / April in Paris / Basie talks / There's a small hotel / Did you ever see Jackie Robinson hit that ball / Mad boogie / Beaver junction / King, The / Wild Bill's boogie.
LP: . . . . LPJT 89

COUNT BASIE AND HIS ORCHESTRA 1956-59 (Basie, Count & His Orchestra).
Tracks: / Moten swing / Li'l darlin' / Kid from Red Bank, The / After supper / Duet / Double-O / Stompin' and jumpin' / One O'Clock jump / Fantail / Flight of the Foo Birds / Midnight blue / Whirly bird / Who me / Blues in Hoss's flat.
LP: . . . . LPJT 92

COUNT BASIE AND HIS ORCHESTRA (ECHO JAZZ) (Basie, Count Orchestra).
LP: . . . . EJLP 03
MC: . . . . EJMC 03

COUNT BASIE AND HIS ORCHESTRA (HINDSIGHT).
LP: . . . . HSR 224

COUNT BASIE AND HIS ORCHESTRA (JAZZ ARCHIVES) (Basie, Count & His Orchestra).
LP: . . . . JA 16

COUNT BASIE AND HIS ORCHESTRA (JOKER (USA)) (Basie, Count & His Orchestra).
Tracks: / Moten swing / Bugle call rag / Lady be good / Darn that dream / Sent for you yesterday / I'm gonna sit right down and write myself a letter / Jumpin' at the woodside / 9.20 Special / Avenue C / Blue Lou / One o'clock jump.
LP: . . . . SM 3109

COUNT BASIE AND HIS ORCHESTRA VOL.3.
Tracks: / Little pony / Plymouth Rock / Backwater blues / Who me / April in Paris / Blues backstage / Good time blues / Peace pipe.
LP: . . . . JR 146

COUNT BASIE AND JOE WILLIAMS (Compact/Walkman Jazz) (Basie, Count & Joe Williams).
Tracks: / Every day (I have the blues) / Fine romance, A / Amazing love / Too close for comfort / Please send me someone to love / I'm beginning to see the light / In the evening / Smack dab in the middle / I can't believe that you're in love with me / Teach me tonight / Party blues / Come rain or come shine / Roll 'em Pete / Comeback, The / Thou swell / Alright, okay, you win.
MC: 835 329 4

COUNT BASIE AND JOE WILLIAMS (Basie, Count & Joe Williams).
2LP: . . . . VJD 553

COUNT BASIE AND ORCHESTRA.
LP: . . . . SM 3970-2

COUNT BASIE AND THE 16.
LP: . . . . TAX 8029

COUNT BASIE AND THE KANSAS CITY SEVEN (JASMINE) (Basie, Count & The Kansas City Seven).
Tracks: / Lady be good / Secrets / I want a little girl / Shoeshine boy / Count's place / Senator Whitehead / Tally-ho Mr Basie / What'cha talkin'.
LP: . . . . JAS 3

MC: . . . . **JAS C3**

COUNT BASIE AND VOICES.
2LP: **400012**

COUNT BASIE BIG BAND.
Tracks: / Heat's on, The / Freckle face / Splanky / More I see you, The / Night in Tunisia / Hittin' twelve / Bag of dreams / Things ain't what they used to be / I needs to be'd with / Li'l darlin' / Jumpin' at the Woodside / One o'clock jump.
LP: **2308 207**
MC: . . . . **K 08 207**

COUNT BASIE COLLECTION (20 Golden Greats).
Tracks: / One o'clock jump / Moten swing / Count steps in, The / Basie boogie / Shout and feel it / Andy's blues / Down for double / Study in brown, A / I've found a new baby / Lady be good / Good morning blues / Swing, brother, swing / Me and you that used to be, The / Dinah / Every tub / Boogie woogie blues / I'll always be in love with you / Swingin' the blues / 9:20 Special / Jumpin' at The Woodside.
LP: . . . . **DVLP 2009**
MC: . . . . **DVMC 2009**

COUNT BASIE (IMPORT).
Tracks: / Moten swing / Shout & feel it / Me and you that used to be, The / Count steps in, The / I'll always be in love with you / When my dreamboat comes home / Swing brother swing / Down for double / Rockin' the blues / Wiggle woogie / Andy's blues / I've found a new baby / Basie boogie / Fare thee honey, fare thee well / What's your number? / Draftin' blues / It's square but it rocks / You lied to me / Music makers / 9/20 special / Feedin' the bean / H and J / Goin' to Chicago blues / You betcha my life / Down, down, down / King Joe.
LP: . . . . **QU 015**
LP: . . . . **PHX 1010**

COUNT BASIE JAM.
Tracks: / Bookie blues / She's funny that way / These foolish things / Kidney stew / Trio blues / I got it bad and that ain't good / Jumpin' at the Woodside.
LP: **2308 209**
MC: . . . . **K 08 209**

COUNT BASIE & ORCHESTRA (Basie, Count & Orchestra).
LP: . . . . **LPJT 4**

COUNT BASIE ORCHESTRA.
Tracks: / Good morning blues (Recorded 9/8/37) / What comes up, must come down (Recorded 19/3/39) / Baby don't tell on me (Recorded 19/3/39) / Sub dab blues (Recorded 24/6/39) / Moonlight serenade (Recorded 4/8/39) / I can't believe that you're in love with me (Recorded 4/8/39) / Between the devil and the deep blue sea (Recorded 7/11/39) / Let's make hay (Recorded 19/3/40) / Blow top (Recorded 31/5/40) / Gone with "what" wind (Recorded 31/5/40) / Do I mean you? (Recorded 10/4/41) / When the sun goes down (Recorded 26/1/39) / Royal flush (Recorded 31/12/41) / I got rhythm (Recorded 16/1/42) / How long blues (Recorded 24/7/42) / Farewell blues (Recorded 24/7/42).
LP: . . . . **QU 008**

COUNT BASIE PLAYS, JOE WILLIAMS SINGS (Basie, Count & Joe Williams).
MC: **833774 4**

COUNT BASIE SWINGS - TONY BENNETT SINGS (Basie, Count & Tony Bennett).
Tracks: / Life is a song / With plenty of money and you / Jeepers creepers / Are you having any fun? / Anything goes / Strike up the band / Chicago / I've grown accustomed to her face / Poor little rich girl / Growing pains / I guess I'll have to change my plans / After supper (CD only.).
LP: . . . . **ROU 1009**
LP: **793 899 1**

COUNT BASIE (VERVE) (Walkman Jazz).
Tracks: / Chicago / Lady is a tramp, The / Day in day out / I didn't know what time it was / Hey, jealous lover / Saturday night / I thought about you / Come fly with me / On the road to Mandalay / All of me / Idaho / Blues in my heart / I don't stand a ghost of a chance with you / Moonglow / Sweet Lorraine / Ain't misbehavin / As long as I live / I've got the world on a string.
MC: **841 197 4**

COUNT BASIE VOL.1.
MC: . . . . **ZCRP 785**

COUNT BASIE VOL.1 (Count and the President).
Tracks: / Shoe shine boy / Evenin' / Boogie woogie / Oh lady be good / I ain't got nobody / Goin' to Chicago blues / Live and love tonight / Love me or leave me / What goes up must come down / Rockabye Basie / Baby don't you tell on me / If I could be with you / One house tonight / Taxi war dance / Don't worry 'bout me / Jump for me / And the angels sing / If I didn't care / Twelfth St. rag / Miss Thing (Part 1) / Miss Thing (Part 1) / Lonesome & pretty / Bolero at the Savoy / Nobody knows / Pound cake / You can count on me / You and your love / How long blues / Sub-deb blues.
2LP: . . . . **CBS 88667**
MC: **40 88667**

COUNT BASIE VOL.1.
Tracks: / Rat race / Five o'clock in the morning / Easin' it / Blue on blue / Peppermint pipes / Good time blues / Meetin' time / Counter block / Let's have a taste.
LP: . . . . **JR 121**

COUNT BASIE VOL.2 (Lester Leaps In).
Tracks: / Moonlight serenade / Song of the islands / I can't believe that you're in love with me / Clap hands here comes Charlie / Dickie's dream / Lester leaps in / Apple jump, The / I left my baby / Riff interlude / Volcano / Between the devil and the deep blue sea / Ham 'n' eggs / Hollywood jump / Someday, sweetheart / I never knew / Tickle toe / Let's make hay / Louisiana / Easy does it / Let me see / Blues (still think of her) / Somebody stole my gal / Blow top / Gone with "what" wind / Super chief / You can't run around / Evenin'.
2LP: . . . . **CBS 88668**
MC: **40 88668**

COUNT BASIE VOL.2.
Tracks: / Not now, I'll tell you when / Swingin' at the Waldorf / Quince / Vine Street rumble / Square at the Round table / Brotherly shove / Blue five jive / Rare butterfly / Jackson County Jubilee / Big walk, The.
LP: . . . . **JR 138**

COUNT BASIE VOL.2 1978 (See under Jackson, Milt) (Basie, Count & Milt Jackson).

COUNT BASIE VOL.2 1937/8.
LP: . . . . **AJAX 129**

COUNT BASIE VOL.3 (Don for Prez).
Tracks: / World is mad, The (part 1) / World is mad, The (part 2) / Moten swing / It's torture / I want a little girl / All or nothing at all / Moon fell in the river, The / What's your number / Draftin' blues / Five o'clock whistle / Love jumped out / My wandering man / Broadway / It's the same old South / Stampede in G minor / Who am I? / Rockin' the blues / It's square but it rocks / I'll forget / I'll forget-2 / You lied to me / Wiggle woogie / Beau Brummel / Music makers / Jump the blues away / Deep in the blues / Jitters / Tuesday at ten / Undecided blues / I do mean you / 9.20 Special / H and J.
2LP: . . . . **CBS 88672**
MC: **40 88672**

COUNT BASIE VOL.3 1938.
LP: . . . . **AJAX 137**

COUNT BASIE VOL.4 (One O'Clock Jump).
Tracks: / Goin' to Chicago blues / You betcha my life / Down down down / Tune town shuffle / I'm tired of waiting for you / One two three O'Leary / Basie boogie / Fancy meeting you / Diggin' for Dex / My old flame / Fiesta in blue / Tom Thumb / Take me back baby / King Joe / King Joe (part 2) / Moon nocturne / Something new / I struck a match in the dark / Platterbrains / All of me / Feather merchant / Down for double / More than you know / Havard blues / Coming out party / One o'clock jump / Blue shadows and white gardenias / Ay now / Basie blues.
2LP: . . . . **CBS 88673**
MC: **40 88673**

COUNT BASIE VOL.4 1938/9.
LP: . . . . **AJAX 143**

COUNT BASIE VOL.5.
2LP: . . . . **CBS 88674**
MC: **40 88674**

COUNT BASIE VOL.5 1939.
LP: . . . . **AJAX 149**

COUNT BASIE VOL.6.
2LP: . . . . **CBS 88675**
MC: **40 88675**

COUNT BASIE VOL.6 1939.
LP: . . . . **AJAX 157**

COUNT BASIE VOL.7 1939.
LP: . . . . **AJAX 163**

COUNT DOWN.
MC: **771503**

COUNT ON THE COAST, VOL. 1 (1958) (Basie, Count & Joe Williams).
LP: . . . . **PHONT 7555**

COUNT ON THE COAST VOL. 3.
LP: . . . . **PHONT 7575**
MC: . . . . **PHONT 8575**

DANCE ALONG WITH BASIE.
LP: **500011**

DECEMBER 1962 (Basie, Count & His Orchestra).
Tracks: / Just before midnight / Comin' thro' the rye / Sometimes I feel like a motherless child / Evil weevil / Basically blue / Splash / Danny boy / Wash / Clementine Annie Laurie / Swing low sweet chariot.
LP: . . . . **JV 102**

DIGITAL III AT MONTREUX (See under Fitzgerald, Ella) (Basie, Count/Ella Fitzgerald/Joe Pass).

DOCUMENT.
Tracks: / Moten swing / One o'clock jump / I can't get started / Study in brown, A / Rhythm in my nursery rhymes / John's idea / Good morning blues / Dinah / Every tub / Song of the wanderer / Flat foot floogie / Boogie woogie blues.
LP: . . . . **NOST 7640**

DOWN FOR TROUBLE.
Tracks: / Something new / I struck a match in the dark / Platterbrains / All of me / Feather merchant / Down for double / My old flame / Fiesta in blue / Tom Thumb.
LP: . . . . **SHLP 105**
MC: . . . . **SHTC 105**

EASIN' IT.
LP: **500019**

ELLA AND BASIE (See under Fitzgerald, Ella) (Basie, Count & Ella Fitzgerald).

ESSENTIAL COUNT BASIE VOL.1, THE.
Tracks: / Lady be good / Goin' to Chicago Blues / Love tonight / Live and love tonight / Love me or leave me / Rockabye basie / Baby don't tell on me / If I could be with you one more hour tonight / Taxi war dance / Jump for me / Twelfth St. rag / Miss thing (part 1) / Miss thing (part 2) / Pound cake / How long blues.
LP: **4600611**
MC: **4600614**

ESSENTIAL COUNT BASIE VOL.2, THE.
Tracks: / I can't believe that you're in love with me / Clap hands, here comes Charlie / Dickie's dream / Lester leaps in / Apple jump, The / I left my baby / Volcano / Between the devil and the deep blue sea / I never knew / Tickle toe / Louisiana / Easy does it / Let me see / Blow top / Gone with "what" wind / Super chief.
LP: **4608281**
MC: **4608284**

ESSENTIAL COUNT BASIE VOL.3, THE.
Tracks: / World is mad, The (part 1) / Moten swing / What's your number / Broadway / Rockin' the blues / Jitters / Undecided blues / 9.20 special / World is mad, The (part 2) / I want a little girl / Love jumped out / Stampede in G minor / Jump the blues away / Tuesday at ten / I do mean you / Feedin' the bean.
LP: **4610981**
MC: **4610984**

ESSENTIAL, THE.
MC: **4671434**

EVERYDAY I HAVE THE BLUES.
LP: **500010**

FANCY PANTS (Basie, Count & His Orchestra).
Tracks: / Put it right there / By my side / Blue chip / Fancy pants / Hi five / Time stream / Samantha / Strike up the band.
LP: **231 0920**
MC: **K10 920**

FIRST RECORDS HE EVER MADE, THE.
LP: . . . . **SH 2017**

FIRST TIME COUNT MEETS DUKE.
Tracks: / Battle royal / To you / Take the 'A' train / Until I met you / Wild man / Segue in C / B.D.B. / Jumpin' at the woodside.
LP: **4505091**
MC: **4505094**

FIRST TIME WITH DUKE ELLINGTON.
LP: **84417**
MC: **40 84417**

FOR THE SECOND TIME (Basie, Count /Kansas City 3).
Tracks: / Sandman / If I could be with you one hour tonight / Draw / On the sunny side of the street / One I love belongs to somebody else, The / Blues for Eric / I surrender dear / Racehorse.
LP: **2310 878**
MC: **K10 878**

GIFTED ONES, THE (Basie, Count & Dizzy Gillespie).
Tracks: / Back to the land / Constantinople / You got it / St. James Infirmary / Follow the leader / Ow.
LP: **231 0833**
MC: **K10 833**

GOLDEN YEARS, VOL.1, THE 1937.
Tracks: / Shout and feel it / You and me that used to be, The / Count steps in, The / They can;t take that away from me / I'll always be in love with you / When my dreamboat comes home / Swing, brother, swing / Bugle blues / I got rhythm / One o'clock jump / I can't get started / Study in brown, A / Rhythm in my nursery rhymes / John's idea / Good morning blues / Dinah.
LP: . . . . **FDC 5502**

GOLDEN YEARS, VOL.2, THE 1938.
Tracks: / Allez oop / Blues with Helen / I ain't got nobody / Don't be that way / Song of the wanderer / Mortgage stomp / Every tub / Song of the wanderer / Flat foot floogie / Lady be good / Boogie woogie / One o'clock jump / I let a song go out of my heart / King Porter stomp / I haven't changed a thing.
LP: . . . . **FDC 5510**

GOLDEN YEARS, VOL.3, THE 1940/44.
Tracks: / One o'clock jump / Ebony rhapsody / Riff interlude / Darn that dream / Take it, pres / Baby, don't you tell on me / One hour / I got rhythm / Do nothing till you hear from me / Sent for you yesterday / Basie boogie / I've found a new baby / Rock-a-bye Basie / Swing shift / Red band boogie / Dinah / Baby, won't you please come home.
LP: . . . . **FDC 5521**

GOOD MORNIN' BLUES (See under Rushing, Jimmy & The Count Basie Band) (Rushing, Jimmy & The Count Basie Band).

GOOD MORNIN' BLUES (Big Band Bounce and Boogie) (Basie, Count/ Jimmy Rushing).
Tracks: / Good morning blues / Listen my children / Exactly like you / London Bridge is falling down / Stop beatin' around the mulberry bush / Now, will you be good? / Boo hoo / Blues I like to hear, The / Blues in the dark / Pennies from Heaven / Boogie woogie / Evil blues / Don't you miss your baby? / Georgianna / I keep remembering / Do you wanna jump, children?.
LP: . . . . **AFS 1002**

GREAT CONCERT OF COUNT BASIE AND HIS ORCHESTRA (Basie, Count & His Orchestra).
Tracks: / All of me / Flight of the foo birds / Boone blues / Stormy Monday blues / Magic flea, The / Wee baby blues / In a mellow tone / Whirly bird / Night in Tunisia / Hittin' twelve / Cherokee / Midnight sun will never set, The / Blues for Eileen / Jumpin' at the woodside / April in Paris / I got rhythm / I needs to be'd with / Li'l darlin' / All heart / One o'clock jump.
2LP: . . . . **ALB 231**

HALL OF FAME: COUNT BASIE.
Tracks: / One o'clock jump / Study in brown / Rhythm in my nursery rhymes / Good morning blues / Shout and feel it / I'll always be in love with you / Count steps in, The / I got rhythm / When my dreamboat comes home / Bugle blues.
LP: . . . . **BLPS 20153**

HELLO DOLLY (See under Sinatra, Frank) (Basie, Count & Frank Sinatra).

I GOT RHYTHM.
LP: . . . . **AFF 48**

IN DISCO ORDER VOL.1.
LP: . . . . **AJAX 126**

IN PERSON (See under Bennett, Tony) (Basie, Count & Tony Bennett).

INDISPENSABLE COUNT BASIE, THE.
Tracks: / Bill's mill / Brand new wagon / One o'clock boogie / Futuile frustration / Swingin' the blues / St. Louis boogie / Basie's basement / Backstage at Stuff's / My buddy / Shine on harvest moon / Lopin' / I never knew / Sugar / Jungle king / I ain't mad at you / After you've gone / House rent boogie / South / Don't you want a man like me / Seventh Avenue express / Sophisticated swing / Guest in a nest / Your red wagon / Money is honey / Just a minute / Robbin's nest / Hey pretty baby / Bye bye baby / Just an old manuscript / She's a wine-o / Shoutin' blues / Wonderful thing / Mine too / Walking slow behind you / Normania / Rat race / Sweets.
2LP: . . . . **PM 43688**

IT MIGHT AS WELL BE SWING (See under Sinatra, Frank) (Basie, Count & Frank Sinatra).

JAZZ LEGENDS (Holiday, Billie & Count Basie).
MCSET: . . . . **DTO 10256**

JAZZ TIME VOL.18.
LP: 502718

JITTERS - 1939/41, THE.
LP: . . . . M 8027

JOE WILLIAMS AND COUNT BASIE (See under Williams, Joe) (Basie, Count & Joe Williams).

JUBILEE 1904-1984.
LP: . . . . VS 3407
MC: . . . . VSK 3407

JUMPIN' WITH BASIE.
LP: 500071
LP: . . . . JL 71

JUST THE BLUES (Basie, Count & Joe Williams).
LP: 500017

KANSAS CITY 5.
Tracks: / Jive at five / One o'clock jump / No special thing / Memories of you / Frog's blues / Rabbit / Perdido / Timekeeper / Mean to me / Blues for Joe Turner.
LP: 231 2126
MC: . . . . K 12 126

KANSAS CITY 6.
Tracks: / Walking the blues / Blues for little jazz / Vegas drag / Wee baby / Scooter / St. Louis blues / Opus six.
LP: 2310 871
MC: K10 871

KANSAS CITY 7.
Tracks: / Oh lady be good / Secrets / I want a little girl / Shoe shine boy / Count's place / Senator Whitehead / Tally ho Mr. Basie! / What'cha talkin'?.
LP: 231 0908
MC: K10 908

KANSAS CITY 8 (Get Together).
Tracks: / Ode to Pres / Basie's bag / Swinging on the cusp / Like it used to be / My main men / Pretty time / I can't get started / What will I tell my heart / Talk of the town / I can't give you anything but love / I'm confessin'.
LP: 231 0924
MC: K10 924

KANSAS CITY SHOUT (Basie, Count, Joe Turner, Eddie Vinson).
Tracks: / My jug & I / Cherry red / Apollo daze / Standing on the corner / Stormy Monday / Signifying / Just a dream on my mind / Blues for Joe Turner / Blues for Joel / Everyday I have the blues / Blues au four.
LP: . . . . D 2310 859
MC: K10 859

KANSAS CITY STYLE.
Tracks: / Aces and faces / Don't cry baby / Just an old manuscript / One o'clock jump (partial) / Mad boogie / One o'clock jump / You for me / Bubbles / You're not the kind / Jonesy / Two for the blues / Cleep, clop blues / Yesterdays / Perdido.
LP: . . . . GOJ 1004
MC: . . . . GOJC 1004
LP: . . . . AFM 1-5180

KANSAS CITY SUITE.
LP: 500018

KANSAS CITY SUITE (2) (Basie, Count & His Orchestra).
Tracks: / Vine Street rumble / Katy-do / Miss Missouri / Jackson County jubilee / Sunset glow / Wiggle walk, The / Meetin' time / Paseo promenade / Blue five jive / Rompin' at the Reno.
LP: . . . . ROU 1013
LP: 794 575 1

KING OF SWING.
LP: 837 433-1
MC: 837 433-4

LA CABARET CASINO BAHAMAS (Live Stereo - 1969) (Basie, Count Band).
Tracks: / All of me / Frankie and Johnny / Cute / Lonely Street / Cherokee / Does anyone ever win ? / Night in Tunisia, A / Little darlin' / Blues in Hoss's flat.
LP: . . . . EB 405

LAST DECADE, THE.
2LP: . . . . AR 2 107

LE DOUBLE DISQUE D'OR.
2LP: 400525

LEGEND, THE.
LP: 500021

LESTER LEAPS IN VOL.2 (Basie, Count & His Orchestra).
Tracks: / Dickie's dream / Lester leaps in / Song of the islands / Riff interlude / Volcano / Hollywood jump / Someday sweetheart / Tickle toe / Superchief.
2LP: 88668

LESTER MEETS BASIE (Air Shots Birdland, Jan. 1953) (Basie, Count & Lester Young).
Tracks: / Theme & prevue / Jingle bells / Why not? / Hob nail boogie / Perdido / Fancy meeting you / Basie kicks / Jumpin' at the Woodside / Bread / Smooth sailing.
LP: . . . . UJ 04

LESTER MEETS BASIE VOL.2 (Air Shots Birdland, Jan. 1953) (Basie, Count Orchestra).
Tracks: / Basie English / Basie blues / Paradise squat / Every tub.
LP: . . . . UJ 05

LET'S JUMP - 1943/44 (Basie, Count & His Orchestra).
LP: . . . . GELP 15033

LIFE IS A SONG (See under Bennett, Tony) (Basie, Count & Tony Bennett).

LISTEN, YOU SHALL HEAR (1938) (Basie, Count & His Orchestra).
Tracks: / Honeysuckle rose / Pennies from Heaven / Swingin' at the daisy chain / Roseland shuffle / Exactly like you / Boo hoo / Glory of love / Boogie woogie (I may be wrong) / Smarty (you know it all) / One o clock jump / Listen my children / John's idea / Good morning blues / Our love was meant to be / Time out.
LP: . . . . HEP 1025

LIVE AT THE SAVOY BALLROOM.
LP: 20076
MC: 40076

LIVE FROM BIRDLAND.
LP: . . . . VJD 568

LIVE IN ANTIBES 1968.
Tracks: / Vine Street rumble / Pleasingly plump / Cherokee / Good times blues / Lonely Street / Night in Tunisia / Goin' to Chicago blues / I got rhythm / In a mellow tone / Basie's / Li'l darlin' / Blues in Hoss's flat / Everyday I have the blues / Wee baby blues / Stormy Monday blues / Magic flute / Jumpin' at the woodside.
LP: . . . . FC 112

LIVE IN JAPAN '78.
Tracks: / Heat's on, The / Freckle face / Ja da / Things ain't what they used to be / Bit of this and a bit of that, A / All of me / Shiny stockings / Left hand funk / John the III / Basie / Black velvet / Jumpin' at the Woodside.
LP: 230 8246
MC: . . . . K 8246

LIVE IN NASSAU (Basie, Count Band).
LP: . . . . EB 414

LIVE IN PERSON (Basie, Count Orchestra).
LP: NAT:ORG:7002

LIVE IN STOCKHOLM (Feb, 1959) (Basie, Count Orchestra).
LP: . . . . AWE 15

LONG LIVE THE CHIEF (Basie, Count & His Orchestra).
Tracks: / You got it / April in Paris / Misunderstood blues / Autumn leaves / Foggy day, A / Hey, see you over there / Li'l darlin' / Bus dust / Corner pocket / Doctor Feelgood / Four five six / Shiny stockings.
MC: . . . . CC 11

MASTERS OF JAZZ.
LP: CL.42113

MEMORIAL.
LP: . . . . FH 55
MC: . . . . CFH 55

MEMORIES AD LIB.
LP: 500004

MOSTLY BLUES AND SOME OTHERS (Basie, Count Kansas City Seven).
Tracks: / I'll always be in love with you / Snooky / Blues for Charlie Christian / Jaws / I'm confessin' / I want a little girl / Blues in C / Brio.
MC: K10 919
LP: 231 0919

MY KIND OF GIRL (See under Sinatra, Frank) (Basie, Count & Frank Sinatra).

NIGHT RIDER (Basie, Count & Oscar Peterson).
Tracks: / Night rider / Memories of you / 9.20 Special / Sweet Lorraine / It's a wonderful world / Blues for Pamela.
LP: 231 0843
MC: K10 843

NOT NOW, I'LL TELL YOU WHEN.
LP: 500016

ON THE ROAD.
Tracks: / Wind machine, The / Blues for Stephanie / John the III / There'll never be another you / Bootie's blues / Splanky / Basie / What happens / Work song / In a mellow tone.
LP: 231 2112
MC: . . . . K 12 112

ON THE SUNNY SIDE OF THE STREET (see Fitzgerald, Ella) (Basie, Count & Ella Fitzgerald).

ONE O'CLOCK JUMP.
Tracks: / One o'clock jump / When my dreamboat comes home / I got rhythm / John's idea / Good morning blues / Dinah / Shout and feel about / I'll always be in love with you / Count steps in, The / I got rhythm / Study in brown, A / Bugle blues.
MC: 40177

OUR SHINING HOUR (Basie, Count & Sammy Davis Jnr.).
LP: 837 446 1
MC: 837 446 4

PERDIDO (Basie, Count & Sarah Vaughan).
LP: 500012

PERFECT MATCH, A (See under Fitzgerald, Ella) (Fitzgerald, Ella/Count Basie).

PLAYS BENNY CARTER'S KANSAS CITY SUITE.
Tracks: / Vine Street rumble / Katy-do / Miss Missouri / Jackson County Jubilee / Sunset glow / Wiggle walk / Meetin' time / Paseo promenade / Blue five jive / Rompin' at the Reno / Trot, The / Easy money / Amoroso / Goin' on / Swizzle / Legend, The / Who's blues / Turnabout.
LP: . . . . VJD 569
MC: . . . . ZCVJD 569

RHYTHM MEN.
LP: . . . . SWH 23
MC: . . . . CSWH 23

ROCK-A-BYE BASIE.
Tracks: / Jumping at the Woodside / Blue and sentimental / Red Bank boogie / Sent for you yesterday / Yesterday / Shorty George / Rockabye Basie / Every tub / Jive at five / Down for trouble / Boogie woogie / Taps Miller / Swinging the blues / Broadway / Texas shuffle / Tickle toe / Doggin' around / Dickie's dream / Topsy / Lester leaps in / Time out / 9.20 special / Avenue C / Out the window.
LP: . . . . VJD 503
LP: . . . . SWH 41

SARAH VAUGHAN/COUNT BASIE (See under Vaughan, Sarah) (Basie, Count & Sarah Vaughan).

SATCH AND JOSH (See under Peterson, Oscar) (Basie, Count & Oscar Peterson).

SATCH AND JOSH AGAIN (See under Peterson, Oscar) (Basie, Count & Oscar Peterson).

SEND IN THE CLOWNS (See under Vaughan, Sarah) (Basie, Count & Sarah Vaughan).

SINATRA AT THE SANDS (See under Sinatra, Frank) (Basie, Count & Frank Sinatra).

SINATRA-BASIE (See under Sinatra, Frank) (Basie, Count & Frank Sinatra).

SING ALONG WITH BASIE.
LP: 500003

SING ALONG WITH BASIE (2) (Basie, Count & His Orchestra).
Tracks: / Jumpin' at the woodside / Goin' to Chicago blues / Tickle toe / Let me see / Every tub / Shorty George / Rusty dusty blues / King, The / Swingin' the blues / Li'l darlin'.
LP: . . . . ROU 1023
LP: 795 332 1

SOUTHLAND CAFE (Basie, Count Orchestra & Chick Webb Orchestra).
Tracks: / One o'clock jump / Ebony rhapsody / Riff interlude / Take it Prez / Baby don't you tell on me / Breakin' 'em down / If I didn't care / Stars and stripes forever / My wild Irish rose / Chew, chew, chew, chew (your bubble gum).
LP: . . . . SM 3084

STANDING OVATION - THREE ERAS OF BASIE.
Tracks: / Down for trouble / Li'l darlin' / Broadway / Jive at five / Cherry Point / Jumpin' at the Woodside / One o'clock jump / Shiny stockings / Blue and sentimental / Every rub / Corner pocket / Ki$ from Red Bank, The.
LP: . . . . JAS 30
MC: . . . . JAS C30

STEREO SOUND OF COUNT BASIE, THE.
LP: . . . . BO 702

STORMY MONDAY BLUES (Basie, Count & Billy Eckstine).
LP: 500008

STRIKE UP THE BAND (Basie, Count & Tony Bennett).
LP: 500005

SWINGIN' AT THE DAISY CHAIN.
Tracks: / Swingin' at the Daisy Chain / Glory of love / My heart belongs to daddy / Cherokee / How long how long blues / Dirty dozens / Honeysuckle rose / Thursday / One o'clock jump / Sing for your supper / Your red wagon / Smarty (you know it all) / Dark rapture / Dupree blues / When the sun goes down / Roseland shuffle.
LP: . . . . AFS 1019

SWINGIN' THE BLUES (Big Band Bounce and Boogie) (Basie, Count & His Orchestra).
Tracks: / Swinging the blues / John's idea / Blue and sentimental / Texas shuffle / Panassie stomp / Sent for you yesterday / You can depend on me / Every tub / Jumpin' at the woodside / Time out / Jive at five / Oh lady be good / Shorty George / Out of the window / Topsy / Doggin' around.
LP: . . . . AFS 1010
MC: . . . . TCAFS 1010

SWINGIN' THE BLUES (1937-1945) (Basie, Count & His Orchestra).
LP: . . . . SM 3968
MC: . . . . MC 3968

SWINGING IN THE FIFTIES (Basie, Count/Horace Henderson).
LP: . . . . IAJRC 27

THIS AND THAT (Very Best of Count Basie, The).
Tracks: / Basie boogie / Sent for you yesterday / Gotta be this or that / Old manuscript, An / Just sittin' and rockin' / I ain't mad at you / My silent love / Lady be good / Theme / Move / One o'clock jump / One golden bullet, Theme from / Andy's blues.
LP: . . . . SWH 29
MC: . . . . CSWH 29

TOPSY (1937-1945) (Basie, Count & His Orchestra).
LP: . . . . SM 3969
MC: . . . . MC 3969

V DISCS VOL. 2.
Tracks: / Rhythm man / G.I. Stomp / Dance of the gremlins / Yeah man / Harvard blues / San Jose / Jammin' on a v-disc / B Glat blues / Sweet Lorraine / High tide / Jimmy's boogie woogie / Tippin' on the QT / Sent for you yesterday / Lady be good.
LP: . . . . AA 506
LP: . . . . OFF 3046

V-DISCS VOL.1.
Tracks: / Basie strides again / Gee baby ain't I good to you / Circus in rhythm / Beaver junction / Kansas City stride / Aunt Hagar's country home / Taps miller / Old manuscript / Playhouse no 2 stomp / On the upbeat / Jimmy's blues / Take me back baby.
LP: . . . . AA 505
LP: . . . . OFF 3038

WARM BREEZE.
Tracks: / C.B. express / After the rain / Warm breeze / Cookie / Flight to Nassau / How sweet it is to be loved by you / Satin doll.
LP: . . . . D 2312 131
MC: . . . . K 12 131

YES SIR THAT'S MY BABY (Basie, Count & Oscar Peterson).
Tracks: / Blues for Roy / Teach me tonight / Joe Turner blues / Blues for cat / Yes sir that's my baby / After you've gone / Tea for two / Poor butterfly.
LP: 2310923
MC: . . . . K 10923

Basil, Toni

TONI BASIL.
LP: . . . . UNKNOWN
MC: . . . . UNKNOWN

WORD OF MOUTH.
Tracks: / Nobody / Hanging around / Thief on the loose / Time after time / Mickey / Little red book / Be stiff / Space girls / You gotta problem.
LP: . . . . BASIL 1
MC: BASC1
LP: . . . . OVED 148
MC: . . . . OVEDC 148

Basile, John

VERY EARLY... (Basile, John & Friends).
LP: . . . . SB 2024

Basin Street Boys

I SOLD MY HEART TO THE JUNK MAN.
Tracks: / Jumping at the Jubilee / Nothing ever happens to me / Vootnay on the Vootnay / I sold my heart to the junk man / I need a knife fork spoon / This is the end of a dream / I want to love and be loved / Changes / I'm gonna write a letter to my baby / Josephine / I'll get along somehow / Exactly like you / Summertime gal / Satchel mouth baby / You're mine forever / Near to you.
LP: . . . . OFF 3034

Basin Street Six

BONAPARTES RETREAT (Basin Street Six & Pete Fountain).
Tracks: / Waiting for Robert E Lee / South Rampart Street parade / Angry /

Bonaparte's retreat / Land of dreams / Milenburg joys / I'm going home / Margie.
LP: . . . . LPS 16

Basque Country

BASQUE COUNTRY VOL 1 Biaritz & Pamplona (Various artists).
MC: 60-606

Basque Songs ...

BASQUE SONGS AND DANCES (Various artists).
LP: . . . . LLST 778

Bass Contra Bass

BASS CONTRA BASS (Various artists).
LP: . . . . SLP 4084

Bass Dance

LOUD.
LP: . . . . REVLP 161
MC: . . . . REVMC 161

Bass, Fontella

NEW LOOK, THE.
Tracks: / Our day will come / How glad I am / Oh no,not my baby / Rescue me / Gee whiz / I'm a woman / Since I fell for you / Impossible / You've lost that lovin' feelin' / Soul of the man / Come and get these memories / I know.
LP: . . . . GCH 8048
MC: . . . . GCHK 78048

Bass Is

BASS IS.
LP: . . . . ENJA 2018

Bass Talk

BASS TALK (Various artists).
Tracks: / Answering machine: *Eckhardt, Kai & Torsten De Win* / Southpaw rag: *Hodgkinson, Colin* / Profilaxe: *Itt, Frank* / Browns: *Cottle, Laurence* / Kick No. Two: *Wolfhound's Kick* / Four miles to Ulm: *Hattler & Kraus* / Heart ascends: *Clarke, Kim* / Waves: *Foster, Mo* / Jazz los: *Hullenkremer, Benjamin* / Big bass boom: *Berliner Bass Ballet* / Li'l sweetheart: *Hattler, Hellmut* / Lonesome bass: *Domling, Norbert* / Gavotte in D major: *Burns, Robert (aut).*
LP: . . . . HOT 8901 L

Bass Tone Tap

TRAPPING.
LP: . . . . BTT 1

Bass Wingates Band

SPARKLING BRASS.
Tracks: / Woodhouse lane / Tameside overture / Symphony of marches / Bramwyn / Myfanwy / Paragon / Swing low / Misty / Festive prelude, A.
LP: . . . . LKLP 7060
MC: . . . . LKLC 7060

Bassa Bassa

BASSA BASSA.
LP: . . . . PROP 005

Bassey, Shirley

20 GOLDEN SHOWSTOPPERS.
Tracks: / Far away / Come back to me / He loves me / So in love / Somewhere / Party's over / You'll never walk alone / As long as he needs me / Something wonderful / Who can I turn to / If I were a bell / Where or when / People / One of those songs.
LP: . . . . NTS 187

21 HIT SINGLES.
Tracks: / I (who have nothing) / As long as he needs me / My special dream / Kiss me honey honey kiss me / Tonight / Banana boat song / With these hands / What now my love / Climb every mountain / As I love you / I'll get by / Gone / Fire down below / No regrets / Ave Maria / You'll never know / Far away / Goldfinger / What kind of fool am I / Reach for the stars / You you Romeo.
LP: . . . . EMTC 105
MC: . . . . TCEMTC 105

25TH ANNIVERSARY ALBUM: SHIRLEY BASSEY.
Tracks: / Fire down below / As I love you / Banana boat song / You you Romeo / Kiss me honey honey kiss me / With these hands / As long as he needs me / Reach for the stars / You'll never know / I'll get by / Climb every mountain / Far away / Ave Maria / What now my love / Tonight / What kind of fool am I / I (who have nothing) / My special dream / Gone / Goldfinger / No regrets / Big spender / Does anybody miss me / This is my life / Something / Fool on the hill, The / Diamonds are forever / Where do I begin / For all we know / And I love you so / Make the world a little younger / Never never never / Nobody does it like me / Send in the clowns / Emotion / Good bad but beautiful / Way we were, The / What I did for love / Feelings / If I never sing another song.
2LP: . . . . SBTV 60147
MCSET: . . . . TC-SB 1100

AND I LOVE YOU SO.
LP: . . . . UAS 29385

AS I LOVE YOU.
Tracks: / Kiss me honey honey kiss me / As I love you.
LP: . . . . TIME 11
MC: . . . . TIMEC 11

AS LONG AS HE NEEDS ME.
Tracks: / As long as he needs me / What now my love / In the still of the night / Moon river / Come back to me / Who can I turn to / With these hands / Tonight / Somewhere / Let there be love / What kind of fool am I / I'll get by / I who have nothing / You'll never know / Goldfinger / All of me / I get a kick out of you / He loves me / You'll never walk alone / People / Don't rain on my parade / Every time we say goodbye.
MC: . . . . TC IDL 5

AS TIME GOES BY.
Tracks: / Big spender / It must be him / As time goes by / I'll never fall in love again / If you go away / Funny girl / On a clear day / Look of love, The / It's impossible / Bridge over troubled water / My way / Impossible dream, The / Hold me thrill me kiss me / You made me love you / Time after time / Softly as I leave you / For all we know / Breakfast in bed / One less bell to answer / That's life.
LP: . . . . MFP 50494
MC: . . . . TCMFP 50494

BEST OF SHIRLEY BASSEY.
LP: . . . . BRLP 60
MC: . . . . BRMC 60
LP: 1A 022 58085
MC: 1A 222 58085

BIG SPENDER.
LP: . . . . SLS 50262

BORN TO SING THE BLUES.
Tracks: / As I love you / Stormy weather / Night and day / You, you Romeo / Tonight my heart she is crying / Blues in the night / Kiss me honey honey kiss me / Gypsy in my soul / From this moment on / Puh-leeze Mister Brown / How about you / I've got you under my skin / Born to sing the blues / Love for sale / After the lights go down low / Wayward wind, The / My funny valentine / Fire down below / Banana boat song / Crazy rhythm / If I had a needle and thread / Take my love, take my love / Basin Street blues / Sex.
2LP: . . . . VSOPLP 110
MC: . . . . VSOPMC 110

EMOTIONS.
LP: . . . . PLP 46
MC: . . . . PMC 46

FABULOUS SHIRLEY BASSEY, THE.
Tracks: / Foggy day in London town, A / I've got you under my skin / Cry me a river / April in Paris / I've never been in love before / Man that got away, The / She's wonderful / I'll remember April / Easy to love / No one ever tells you / They can't take that away from me / Party's over, The.
LP: . . . . PM 154 768 1
LP: 33SX 1178
LP: . . . . MFP 1398

GOLDEN HITS: SHIRLEY BASSEY.
Tracks: / Who can I turn to / As long as he needs me / Goldfinger / I (who have nothing) / You'll never know / What now my love / What kind of fool am I / Once in a lifetime / Climb every mountain / Till / Reach for the stars / Party's over, The / With these hands / No regrets.
MC: . . . . TCSCX 6294
LP: . . . . SCX 6294

GOOD BAD BUT BEAUTIFUL.
Tracks: / Emotion / Send in the clowns / Good bad but beautiful / Sing / Way we were, The / I'll be your audience / Feel like makin' love / All in love is fair / Run on and on and on / Other side of me, The / Jesse / Living.
LP: . . . . UAS 29881
MC: . . . . TCK 29881

HER FAVOURITE SONGS.
LP: 1A 022 1583471
MC: 1A 222 1583474

I AM WHAT I AM.
Tracks: / Gold finger / I (who have nothing) / As long as he needs me / Big spender / Something / For all we know / Send in the clowns / What know my love.
LP: . . . . TOWLP 7

I CAPRICORN.
LP: . . . . UAS 29246

I'M IN THE MOOD FOR LOVE.
Tracks: / What now my love / Moon river / Fools rush in / No regrets / I wish you love / Liquidator / Nearness of you, The / This love of mine / Where are you / If love were all / There will never be another you / Days of wine and roses / People / Second time around / Tonight / Strange how love can be / I'm in the mood for love / I get a kick out of you / Angel eyes / To be loved by a man / Hold me tight / I believe in you / Let's start all over again / I'm a fool to want you.
2LP: . . . . MFP 1024
MCSET: . . . . TCMFP 1024

IT'S MAGIC.
LP: . . . . SRS 5082

I'VE GOT A SONG FOR YOU.
LP: . . . . ULP 1142

I'VE GOT YOU UNDER MY SKIN.
LPPD: . . . . AR 30040

KISS ME HONEY, HONEY KISS ME.
Tracks: / Kiss me honey, honey kiss me / Let me sing and I'm happy / I've got a song for you / You can have him / All or nothing at all / Sound of music / Shadow of your smile / You're gonna hear from me / Strangers in the night.
LP: . . . . SHM 967

LA MUJER.
Tracks: / La pasion que nos devora / Sin ti (without you) / Volveras / No me hablas mas de amor / Nadie mas te quiso (como you) / Asi sola yo (out here on my own) / No fingire / Hoy no tengo nada (I who have nothing) / Vallas (rivals) / Si yo te quiero mas.
LP: 838 033 1
MC: 838 033 4

LET ME SING AND I'M HAPPY.
Tracks: / Send in the clowns / Don't cry for me Argentina / Can't help falling in love / Spinning wheel / That's life / Until it's time for you to go / On a clear day / Something / Feel like makin' love / Shadow of your smile / Let me sing and I'm happy / Diamonds are forever / Alone again (naturally) / Killing me softly with his song / Fool on the hill, The / Yesterday when I was young.
LP: . . . . EMS 1290
MC: . . . . TCEMS 1290

LET'S FACE THE MUSIC.
Tracks: / Let's face the music and dance / I should care / Let's fall in love / Second time around, The / Imagination / All the things you are / I get a kick out of you / Everything I have is yours / Spring is here / All of me / I can't get you out my mind.
LP: 33SX 1454
MC: . . . . CMOIR 512
LP: . . . . MOIR 512

LIVE AT THE TALK OF THE TOWN.
LP: . . . . UAS 29095

LOVE ALBUM, THE.
Tracks: / Something / What now my love / Where do I begin (Love story) / Tonight / As long as he needs me / Time after time / As time goes by / With these hands / You'll never know / It must be him / Look of love, The / You made me love you / Softly as I leave you / I wish you love / Who can I turn to / Party's over, The / I'll never fall in love again (CD only.) / If you go away (Ne me quitte pas) (CD only.) / I get a kick out of you (CD only.) / Nearness of you, The (CD only.).
LP: . . . . MFP 5879
MC: . . . . TCMFP 5879

LOVE, LIFE AND FEELINGS.
LP: . . . . UAS 29944

LOVE SONGS: SHIRLEY BASSEY.
Tracks: / All by myself / This masquerade / If and when / He's out of my life / New York state of mind / Can you read my mind / Only when I laugh / Solitare / New York medley / We don't cry out loud.
LP: . . . . APKL 1163
MC: . . . . APKC 2163

MAGIC IS YOU, THE.
Tracks: / This is my life / Better off alone / You never done it like that / Don't cry for me Argentina / As we fall in love once more / Night moves / Anyone who had a heart / Magic is you / How insensitive / Greatest love of all, The.
LP: . . . . UATV 30230

MOTIVE SERIES.
LP: 6381 076
MC: 7215 076

NEVER NEVER NEVER.
LP: . . . . UAG 29471

PLAYING SOLITAIRE.
Tracks: / All by myself / Masquerade, The / If and when / He's out of my life / New York state of mind / Can you read my mind / Only when I laugh / Solitaire / New York, New York / Don't cry out loud.
LP: . . . . PRCV 117
MC: . . . . TC PRCV 117

PORTRAIT OF A SONG STYLIST.
Tracks: / Every time we say goodbye / Shadow of your smile, The / Moon river / Send in the clowns / It's impossible / You are the sunshine of my life / Bridge over troubled water / If you go away / Killing me softly with his song / Cry me a river / And I love you so / Way we were, The / Softly as I leave you / People.
MC: . . . . HARMC 114

SHIRLEY.
LP: 33SX 1286

SHIRLEY BASSEY.
LP: . . . . DINTV 21
MC: . . . . DINMC 21

SHIRLEY BASSEY.
Tracks: / Let me sing and I'm happy / And I love you so / You're gonna hear from me / Strangers in the night / Where do I begin / Way a woman loves, The / Without you / Light of my life / Sound of music, The / I've never been a woman before / Baby I'm a want you / Killing me softly with his song / Yesterday I heard the rain / And we were lovers / You are the sunshine of my life / Spinning wheel.
LP: . . . . SHM 3094
MC: . . . . HSC 3094
LP: 33SX 1382

SHIRLEY BASSEY AT THE PIGALLE.
LP: 33SX 1787

SHIRLEY BASSEY COLLECTION, THE.
2LP: . . . . UAD 60013/14

SHIRLEY BASSEY: THE SINGLES.
Tracks: / Something / Were do I begin? / Diamonds are forever / Fool on the hill, The / Make the world a little younger / Big spender / Never never never / When you smile / If you go away / And I love you so / Does anybody miss me? / For all we know / Goldfinger / No regrets / I (who have nothing) / What kind of fool am I?.
LP: 1A 024 15838
MC: 1A 224 15838
LP: . . . . MFP 5729
MC: . . . . TCMFP 5729
LP: . . . . MFP 415 729 1
MC: . . . . MFP 415 729 4
LP: . . . . UAS 29728
MC: . . . . TCK 29728

SHIRLEY BASSEY (TWIN CASSETTE).
MCSET: . . . . DTO 10076

SING THE SONGS FROM THE SHOWS.
Tracks: / Moon river / People / Tonight / If love were all / Days of wine and roses / I believe in you / I've never been in love before / Long ago and far away / Lady is a tramp, The / Somewhere / It might as well be spring / Don't rain on my parade / I get a kick out of you / Just one of those things / As long as he needs me / Where or when / 'S wonderful / Everything's coming up roses / He loves me / If ever I would leave you / You'll never walk alone.
MC: . . . . HR 8101
MC: . . . . HR 4181014

SOMETHING.
LP: . . . . UAS 29100

SOMETHING ELSE.
LP: . . . . UAG 29149

SUPERSTAR.
Tracks: / All by myself / Solitaire / Can you read my mind / He's out of my life / New York state of mind / If and when / Only when I laugh / This masquerade / New York, New York / Don't cry out loud.
MC: . . . . HSC 3270

THIS IS.
Tracks: / When you smile / Something / I get a kick out of you / In other words / Sing / Lady is a tramp, The / Don't rain on my parade / Other side of me, The / I've got you under my skin / On a wonderful day like today / Somewhere / Lot of livin' to do, A / Once in a lifetime / Nobody does it like me / Goldfinger / As long as he needs me / Just one of those things / I (who have nothing) / Easy to love / Climb every mountain / Send in the clowns / Every time we say goodbye / Let there be love / What kind of fool am I / Everything's coming up roses / With these hands / Party's over, The / Tonight (CD set only) / Where do I begin (CD set only) / What now my love (CD set only) / No regrets (CD set only) / Big spender (CD set only) / Diamonds are forever (CD set only).
2LP: . . . . DL 1140
MC: . . . . TC-DL 1140

THIS IS MY LIFE.
LP: 022 58085
MC: 222 58085
LP: 1A 022 58085
MC: 1A 222 58085
MC: . . . . MCTC 038

THIS IS SHIRLEY BASSEY.
Tracks: / Climb every mountain / House is not a home, A / He loves me / I'll get by / Till / Everything's coming up roses / In the still of the night / Once in a lifetime / Tonight / Lady is a tramp, The / Don't rain on my parade / Reach for the stars / Every time we say goodbye / Somewhere / Fools rush in / People / With these hands / Moon river / Lot of livin' to do / You'll never know.

LP: THIS 15

THOUGHTS OF LOVE.
Tracks: / Send in the clowns / Killing me softly with his song / Feelings / What are you doing the rest of your life / What I did for love / All that love went to waste / Way we were, The / If you go away / Alone again (naturally) / Jesse / I won't last a day without you / You are the sunshine of my life.
LP: UAS 30011
MC: TCK 30011

TONIGHT.
Tracks: / Tonight / On a wonderful day like today / You'll never know / Who can I turn to / As long as he needs me / Party's over, The / Cry me a river / Goldfinger / I (Who have nothing) / I'll get by / You'd better love me / Imagination / All of me / Climb every mountain / What now my love / Second time around.
LP: MFP 41 5682-1
MC: MFP 41 5682-4

TWELVE OF THOSE SONGS.
LP: SCX 6204

VERY BEST OF SHIRLEY BASSEY, THE.
Tracks: / Goldfinger / Fly me to the moon / Let there be love / What now my love / I've got you under my skin / No regrets / You'll never walk alone / What kind of fool am I / I wish you love / Who can I turn to / Party's over, The / Just one of those things / I get a kick out of you / I (who have nothing) / Love is a many splendoured thing / Days of wine and roses / Easy to love / If you love me / Liquidator / As long as he needs me.
LP: SCX 6569
MC: TC SCX 6569

WHAT I DID FOR LOVE.
Tracks: / What I did for love / Shadow of your smile / Does anybody miss me / You take my heart away / Time after time / What are you doing the rest of your life.
LP: UAG 30280

WHAT NOW MY LOVE.
LP: MFP 5230

YOU TAKE MY HEART AWAY.
LP: UAS 30037

Bassment Noize

BASSMENT NOIZE (Various artists).
LP: CELLAR 1

Basso, Gianni

LUNET (Basso, Gianni European Quartet).
LP: SPLASCH 101

Bass-O-Matic

SET THE CONTROLS FOR THE HEART OF THE BASS.
LP: V 2641
MC: TCV 2641

Bastard Kestrel

BASTARD.
Tracks: / Tharn / Semtex sandwich / Motofry / Ten / Surf pink baby / Love story / Ulrich / (Born) brain stupid / Sheep dip / Skitzersister / Bruising / Slob / Dooby bloody do.
LP: KESTREL LP

OH SPLENDID MUSHROOM.
LP: WIIIJLP 2

Basti

B.
LP: WAY 009

Bastow, Geoff

TALK TO ME.
LP: ISST 187

Bastro

BASTRO DIABLO GUAPO.
LP: HMS 132 1
MC: HMS 132 4

RODE HARD AND PUT UP WET.
LP: HMS 111
MC: HMS 111C

Bat 21 (film)

BAT 21 (Film soundtrack) (Various artists).
LP: VS 5202
MC: VSC 5202

Bat Cave

BAT CAVE YOUNG LIMBS AND NUMB HYMNS (Various artists).
Tracks: / Dead man's auto chop: *Specimen* / Sex beat: *Sex Beat* / Shockwork: *Test Department* / Eyes shine kaleidoscope: *Pursey, James T.* / Meat of youth: *Meat of youth* / Coming up for the downstroke: *Brilliant*/ R.I.P.: *Alien Sex Fiend* / Dance of death: *Venomettes*.
LP: CAVE 1
MC: KCAVE 1

Bataan, Joe

MISTIZO.
Tracks: / Mistizo / Rap o, clap o / Sadie / Latin lover / Rock me all night long / I see your hiney / Rap o, dance o / Always and forever.
LP: SALP 1

MR. NEW YORK.
Tracks: / Purto rico me lllama / Special girl / Muneca / What good is a castle (part 1) / Magic rose / Subway Joe / Chilli beans / Young gifted and black / Uptown / Auguanta la lengua / Mambo de Bataan / My opera / Riot (it's a good feeling) / Gypsy woman / Shaft, Theme from / What good is a castle (part 2).
MC: TCHOT 122
LP: HOT 122

Bate, Seldiy

PAGAN EASTER (Bate, Seldiy/Nigel Bourne).
LP: TOPY 24

Batera, Chico

CABANA COCKTAIL.
MC: LUMCA 3

Bates, Blaster

BLASTER BATES VOL 1 (Laughter With a Bang).
LP: BB 00 01
MC: BBMC 00 01

BLASTER BATES VOL 2 (1001 Gelignites).
LP: BB 00 03
MC: BBMC 00 03

BLASTER BATES VOL 3 (TNT For Two).
LP: BB 00 05
MC: BBMC 00 05

BLASTER BATES VOL 4 (Watch Out For the Bits).
LP: BB 00 07
MC: BBMC 00 07

BLASTER BATES VOL 5 (Lift Off).
LP: BB 00 09
MC: BBMC 00 09

BLASTER BATES VOL 6 (Gellybabe).
LP: BB 00 11
MC: BBMC 00 11

BLASTER BATES VOL 7 (Blastermined).
LP: BB 00 13
MC: BBMC 00 13

BLASTER BATES VOL 8 (Hunting and Shooting Stories).
LP: BB 00 15
MC: BBMC 00 15

Bates, Martyn

LETTERS WRITTEN.
Tracks: / Morning singing / Cut like sunset / In June / Mirrored in me / Overflowing look / Aftertaste of old / Jagged tears of words / Letters from yesterday / Calls of birds / Hungry like sharp desire.
LP: T RED 38

LOVE SMASHED ON A ROCK.
LP: IR 2
LP: INT 002

RETURN OF THE QUIET.
LP: BRED 81

STARS COME TREMBLING.
LP: IR 011

Batey, Derek

WORDS AND MUSIC FOR EVERY MR. AND MRS..
Tracks: / Mr. and Mrs. / Play the game - at home / High hopes / Swinging on a star / What a wonderful world / Tie a yellow ribbon / Day's end, The / Music hall medley / Sing / Funny thing happened, A / King of the road / You are the sunshine of my life / Everything is beautiful / Marriage lines / Mr. and Mrs. (reprise).
LP: LKLP 6444
MC: LK 6444

Batfinks

LIVE 'N' ROCKIN'.
LP: LINKLP 122

WAZZED 'N' BLASTED.
LP: LINK LP 082

Batfish Boys

BATFISH BREW.
LP: GWLP 28
MC: GWTC 28

GODS HATE KANSAS, THE.
LP: USS 102

HEAD.
LP: USS 106

Bathers

SWEET DECEIT.
MC: ICT 9953
LP: ILPS 9953

LP: CGT1 1 1
MC: CGTI 4 1

UNUSUAL PLACES TO DIE.
Tracks: / Perpetual adoration / Latta's dream / Fancy dress / Time regained / Take me back to the Brooklands / Candide / Ju ju peach / Unusual places to die / Isn't she shining? / Fortuny.
LP: AGOLP 10
MC: ZGOLP 10

Bathory

BATHORY.
Tracks: / Hades / Reaper / Necromancy / Sacrifice / In conspiracy with Satan / Armageddon / Raise the dead / War.
LP: FLAG 8

BLOOD FIRE DEATH.
Tracks: / Odens ride over wordland / Golden wall of heaven, The / Pace 'til death / Dies irae / Fine day to die, A / Holocaust / For all those who died / Blood fire death.
LP: FLAG 26
MC: TFLAG 26

HAMMERHEART.
LP: NUK 153
MC: ZCNUK 153

RETURN, THE.
Tracks: / Total destruction / Born for burning / Wind of mayhem / Bestial lust / Possessed / Rite of darkness, The / Reap of evil, The / Son of the dammed / Sadist / Return of the darkness and evil, The.
LP: FLAG 9

UNDER THE SIGN OF THE BLACK MARK.
MC: TFLAG 11
LP: FLAG 11

Batida

TERRA DO SUL.
LP: SJP 245

Batimbos

MAITRES-TAMBOURS DU BURUNDI.
Tracks: / Arrivee et salut a l'assistance / Offrande / Appel / Suite de danses rituelles / Suite de danses et d'appels rituels.
LP: ARN 33682
MC: ARN 433682

Batish, Ashwin

SITAR POWER.
LP: SHAN 64004

Batish Family

NORTH INDIAN FOLK AND CLASSICAL MUSIC.
Tracks: / Northwest frontier dance / Kashmiri hill song / Punjabi love song / Punjabi lyrical song / Urban folksong / Punjabi women's song / Central Indian melody / Raga pat multani / Raga todi / Raga shudh sarang / Raga khamaj.
LP: 12T 191

Batlord

BLOOD SURE DEATH.
Tracks: / Leprosy / Forgotten past / Pull the plug / Primitive ways / Born dead / Left to die / Open casket / Choke on it.
LPPD: FLAG 24P

Batman

BATMAN (FILM) (See under Prince) (Various artists).

BATMAN IN RHYMES, RIDDLES & RIOTS (Various artists).
MC: 415 716-4

Batman (bk)

FUNHOUSE OF FEAR (Batman).
MC: PLBB 265

WARHAWK, THE.
MC: PLBB 264

Batmobile

BAIL WAS SET AT $6,000,000.
Tracks: / Kiss me now / Magic word called love / Can't find my way back home / Mystery Street / Calamity man / Shoot shoot / Gorilla rock / Gates of heaven / Girls, girls, girls / Hang on / 100 pounds of trouble / Ace of spades.
LP: NERD 035

BAMBOO LAND.
LP: ROCK 1

BATMOBILE.
LP: KIX4U 2222
LP: PLAT 2222

BURIED ALIVE.
LP: ROCK 3

Baton Rouge Blues

BATON ROUGE BLUES (Various artists).
Tracks: / I'm a kingbee: *Anderson, Jimmy* / It's half past midnight: *Anderson, Jimmy* / Draft board blues: *Anderson, Jimmy* / Sittin' here wonderin': *Hogan, Silas* / Cigarettes: *Harpo, Slim* / G.I. blues: *Slim, Lightning*/ Cold chills: *Grey, Henry* / I'm a lucky man: *Grey, Henry* / Hoodoo party: *Thomas, Tabby* / Bloodstains: *Lazy Lester* / Oh baby: *Dotson, Jimmy* / I need your love: *Dotson, Jimmy* / I don't know why: *Jack, Boogie*.
LP: FLY 607

Baton Rouge Harmonicas

BATON ROUGE HARMONICAS (Various artists).
Tracks: / Tell me pretty baby: *Various artists* / Whoa now: *Various artists* / Sad city blues: *Various artists*/ Courtroom blues: *Various artists* / One more day: *Various artists* / I'm getting tired: *Various artists*/ My poor heart in pain: *Various artists* / Keep on naggin': *Various artists* / In the dark in the park <Anderson>: *Various artists* / Baby let's burn: *Various artists* / Looking for my baby: *Various artists* / Frankie and Johnnie: *Various artists* / Angel please: *Various artists* / I wanna boogie: *Various artists*.
LP: FLY 614

Bators, Stiv

DISCONNECTED.
LP: LILP 400174

Bats

DADDY'S HIGHWAY.
LP: FNE 23

Batstone, Bill

ONE BY ONE (See under Howard, Tom).

Batt, Mike

CHILDREN OF THE SKY.
LP: EPC 57023
MC: 40 57023

DREAM STONE, THE (See under Dream Stone).

SCHIZOPHONIA.
Tracks: / Walls of the world, The / Berber's prayer.
LP: S EPC 82001

SIX DAYS IN BERLIN (Parts 1-6).
LP: EPC 85149

TAROT SUITE.
Tracks: / Journey of a fool / Imbecile / Plainsong / Lady of the dawn / Valley of swords / Losing your way in the rain / Tarota / Night of the dead / Dead of the night / Run like the wind.
LP: EPC 86099

URPNEY SONG, THE (See under Connolly, Billy) (Connolly, Billy/Bruno, Frank/Osbourne, Ozzy/Batt, Mike).

WAVES.
Tracks: / Winds of change / Portishead radio / Mona / Conga reel / Buenos dias, captain / Lobsterissimus bumbicissimus / Fishing for the moon / Echo foxtrot / Sierra tango / Waiting for a wave.
LP: EPC 846 17

ZERO ZERO.
Tracks: / Introduction (The birth of No 17) / System 605 / Love makes you crazy / Delirium / Whispering fools / Zero zero / Dance of the neurosurgeons / No lights in my eyes / Love makes you crazy (instrumental reprise).
LP: EPC 25201
MC: 40 25201

Batteries Not Included

BATTERIES NOT INCLUDED (Film soundtrack) (Various artists).
LP: MCA 6225
MC: MCAC 6225

Battering Ram

BATTERIN' RAM, THE (Various artists).
LP: HRL 150
MC: CHRL 150

IRISH REBEL SONGS.
LP: ROUNDER 4002

Battin, Skip

DON'T GO CRAZY.
LP: AP 034

NAVIGATOR.
LP: AP 014

Battin' the Boogie

BATTIN' THE BOOGIE (Various artists).
Tracks: / One note boogie: *Restum, Willie* / Good morning Mary: *Restum, Willie* / What'd he say: *Restum,* Willie / Rock-a-beatin' boogie: *Restum, Willie* / Kiss me: *Restum, Willie* / Off and on: *Restum, Willie*/ Do it easy: *Restum, Willie* / Restum in peace blues: *Restum, Willie* / Save me a boogie: *Johnson, Marvin*/ Hello: *Williams, Paul* / You're breaking my heart no more: *Williams, Paul* / It's over: *Williams, Paul*/ Rock it Davy Crockett: *Williams, Paul* / Battin' the boogie: *Johnson, Joshua* / Ramblin' woman: *Johnson, Joshua* / Your love has me rockin' and reelin': *Valentine, Billy*.
LP: CRB 1127

Battisti, Lucio

GREATEST HITS:LUCIO BATTISTI.
LP: . . . . NL 70148
MC: . . . . NK 70148

IMAGES.
Tracks: / To feel in love / Song to feel alive / Only thing I've lost, The / Keep on cruising / Sun song, The / There's never been a moment / Only.
LP: . . . . PL 31839
MC: . . . . PK 31839

Battle Bratt

BATTLE BRATT.
LP: . . . . US 015

Battle, Kathleen

CHRISTMAS CELEBRATION, A.
Tracks: / O come all ye faithful / O holy night / Un flambeau, Janette, Isabelle / Fum, fum, fum / How a rose e'er blooming / Gesu bambino / I saw three ships / First Noel, The / Holly and the ivy, The / Away in a manger / Hark the herald angels sing / Marie Weigenlied / Zither carol / I wonder as I wander / Mary had a baby / Rise up shepherd / What child is this? / Ave Maria / Veni, veni, Emanuelle / It came upon a midnight clear / O little town of Bethlehem / Silent night.
LP: . . . . EL 2705391
MC: . . . . EL 2705394

PLEASURE OF THEIR COMPANY (Battle, Kathleen/Christopher Parkening).
LP: . . . . EL 270 307 1
MC: . . . . EL 270 307 4

Battle of...

BATTLE OF WATERLOO (A Guards live recording) (Various artists).
LP: . . . . LR 101

Battle of Britain

BATTLE OF BRITAIN (Various artists).
2LP: . . . . AFP 131
MCSET: . . . . AFP 131T

BATTLE OF BRITAIN (Film 1969) (Various artists).
LP: . . . . SLS 50407

BATTLE OF BRITAIN (Music from film plus others) (Various artists).
Tracks: / Battle of Britain: *Various artists* / Aces high: *Various artists* / Lull before the storm, The: *Various* artists / Work and play: *Various artists* / Death and destruction: *Various artists* / Briefing and the Luftwaffe: *Various artists* / Prelude to battle: *Various artists* / Victory assured: *Various artists* / Defeat: *Various* artists / Hitler's headquarters: *Various artists* / Return to base: *Various artists* / Threat: *Various* artists / Civilian tragedy: *Various artists* / Offensive build-up: *Various artists* / Attack: *Various* artists / Personal tragedy: *Various artists* / Battle in the air: *Various artists* / Absent friends: *Various* artists / Battle of Britain (end title): *Various artists* / Operation crossbow (theme): *Various artists* / Monte Carlo or bust (theme): *Various artists* / Trap, The (theme): *Various artists* / Those magnificent men in their flying machines: *Various artists.*
LP: . . . . LPMGM 21
LP: 794 865 1
MC: . . . . TCMGM 21
MC: 794 865 4

Battle Of Bubble...

BATTLE OF BUBBLE AND SQUEAK, THE (Pearce, Philippa (nar)).
MCSET: 086 222 0490

Battle of Dune (bk)

BATTLE OF DUNE (Frank Herbert).
MC: . . . . CDL 51601

Battle Of Neretva

BATTLE OF NERETVA (Film soundtrack) (Various artists).
Tracks: / Prelude: *Various artists* / Retreat, The: *Various artists* / Separation: *Various artists* / From Italy: *Various artists* / Chetnik's march: *Various artists* / Farewell: *Various artists* / Partisan march: *Various artists* / Pastorale: *Various artists* / Turning point, The: *Various artists* / Death of Danica, The: *Various artists* / Victory: *Various artists.*
LP: . . . . SCAR 5005

Battle of the Bands

BATTLE OF THE BANDS (Various artists).
LP: . . . . RCALP 3067
MC: . . . . RCAK 3067
LP: . . . . RCALP 5015

Battle of the Big

BATTLE OF THE BIG BANDS 1 (Various artists).
LP: . . . . BO 720

BATTLE OF THE BIG BANDS 2 (Various artists).
LP: . . . . BO 721

Battleaxe

BURN THIS TOWN.
LP: . . . . MFN 8

POWER FROM THE UNIVERSE.
LP: . . . . MFN 25

Battlefield

WE COME TO FIGHT.
LP: . . . . TRC 011

Battlefield Band

ANTHEM FOR THE COMMON MAN.
LP: . . . . TP 015

AT THE FRONT.
Tracks: / Lady Carmichael / South of the Grampians / Mickie Ainsworth / Bachelor, The / Ge do theid mi do m'leabradh / Battle of harlaw, The / Jenny Nettles / Grays of tongside, The / Tae the beggin' / Tamosher, The / Blackbird and the thrush, The / Moray club, The / Lang Johnnie More / Brown milkmaid, The / Dunnottar castle / Maid of Glengarrysdale / Disused railways / Lady Leroy, The / Stirling castle / Earl of Mansfield.
LP: 12TS 381

BATTLEFIELD BAND.
Tracks: / Silver spear / Humours of Tulla / Shipyard apprentice, The / Crossing the Minch / Minnie Hynd / Glasgow gaelic club / Brisk young lad / Birnie bouzle / Compliments of the band / A.A. Cameron's strathspey / Scott Skinner's compliments to Dr MacDonald / Bonnie Jean / Paddy Fahey's / Joseph's fancy / Hog's reel, The / It was all for our rightful king / Inverness gathering, The / Marquis of Huntley's strathspey / John MacNeil's reel / Miss Margaret Brown's favourite / Deserts of Tulloch / Cruel brother, The.
LP: 12TS 313

CELTIC HOTEL.
Tracks: / Conway's farewell / Andy Renwick's Ferrett / Short coated Mary / Seacoalers / Return To Kashmagiro / Cuddly with the wooden leg, The / Jack the can / Rovin' dies hard, The / Muineira sul sacrato della chiesa / Hyoy Frwynen / E kostez an hebont / Celtic Hotel, The / Left handed fiddler, The / Floating crowbar, The / Ships are sailing, The / Lucy Campbell / June apple / We work the black seam / Tail o' the bank, The / Cran Tara / Madadh Ruadh.
LP: . . . . TP 027
MC: . . . . CTP 027

FAREWELL TO NOVA SCOTIA.
LP: . . . . SB 349
LP: . . . . BUR 806

HOME GROUND.
LP: . . . . TP 034
MC: . . . . CTP 034

HOME IS WHERE THE VAN IS.
LP: . . . . TP 005
LP: . . . . FF 250
MC: . . . . CTP 005

ON THE RISE.
LP: . . . . TP 021
MC: . . . . CTP 021

STAND EASY.
Tracks: / Miss Drummond of Perth / Fiddler's joy / Trad reels, parts 3 & 4 / Shetland fiddler, The / Seven braw gowns / Miss Drummond of Perth's favourite Scotch measure / Miss MacLeod's minuet / My last farewell to Stirling / Cuidich'n righ / I hae a herrin' in salt / My wife's a wanton wee thing / Banks of Allan, The / Battle of Falkirk Muir / John D. Burgess / Braemar gathering, The / I hae nae with I hae nae kin / Miss Lyall / Small coals for nailers / Bleaton gardens / Christ has my hart ay / Joe McGann's fiddle / Center's bonnet.
LP: 12TS 404

STORY SO FAR..., THE.
LP: . . . . TP 007
LP: . . . . FF 274
MC: . . . . CTP 007

THERE'S A BUZZ.
LP: . . . . TP 010
LP: . . . . FF 299
MC: . . . . CTP 010

WAES ME FOR PRINCE CHARLIE.
LP: . . . . SB 358
LP: . . . . BUR 807

WINTERFOLK 80.
LP: . . . . MU 7475

Battlestar Galactica

BATTLESTAR GALACTICA (Film Soundtrack) (Various artists).
LP: . . . . MCF 2860
MC: . . . . MCFC 2860
LP: 252 602 1

Bauer, Billy

ANTHOLOGY.
LP: . . . . IP 8603

Bauerle, Dick

DICK BAUERLE GROUP (Bauerle, Dick Group).
LP: . . . . IMCA 5874
MC: . . . . IMCAC 5874

Baughen, Simon

THIEF OF NEW YORK, THE (Baughen, Simon & The Extremists).
LP: . . . . DES 002

Bauhaus

BAUHAUS 1979-1983.
Tracks: / Kick in the eye / Hollow hills / In fear of fear / Ziggy Stardust / Silent hedges / Lagartija Nick / Third uncle / Spirit / All we ever wanted was everything / She's in parties / Sanity assassin, The / Crowds / Double dare / In the flat field / Stigmata martyr / Bela Lugosi's dead / Telegram Sam / St.Vitas dance / Spy in the cab, The / Terror couple kill colonel / Passions of lovers / Mask.
2LP: . . . . BEGA 64
MC: . . . . BEGC 64

BAUHAUS: INTERVIEW PICTURE DISC.
LPPD: . . . . BAK 2072

BURNING FROM THE INSIDE.
LP: . . . . BEGA 45
MC: . . . . BEGC 45
LP: . . . . BBL 45
MC: . . . . BBLC 45

IN THE FLAT FIELD.
LP: . . . . CAD 13

MASK.
Tracks: / Hair of the dog / Passion of lovers / Of lilies and remains / Hollow hills / Dancing / Kick in the eye / Muscle in plastic / In fear of fear / Man with the X-ray eyes, The / Mask.
LP: . . . . BEGA 29
MC: . . . . BEGC 29
LP: . . . . BBL 29
MC: . . . . BBLC 29

PRESS THE EJECT AND GIVE ME THE TAPE.
Tracks: / In the flat field / Rosegarden funeral of sores / Dancing / Man with the X-ray eyes, The / Bela Lugosi's dead / Spy in the cab, The / Kick in the eye / In fear of fear / Hollow hills / Stigmata martyr / Dark entries.
LP: . . . . BEGA 38
MC: . . . . BEGC 38
LP: . . . . BBL 38
MC: . . . . BBLC 38

SKY'S GONE OUT, THE.
Tracks: / Third uncle / Silent hedges / In the night / Swing the heartache / Spirit / Three shadows (part 1) / Three shadows (part 2) / Three shadows (part 3) / All we ever wanted was everything / Exquisite corpse.
MC: . . . . BEGC 42
LP: . . . . BEGA 42
LP: . . . . BBL 42
MC: . . . . BBLC 42

SWING THE HEARTACHE.
Tracks: / Hair of the dog / Telegram Sam / Double dare / Terror couple kill colonel / Ziggy Stardust / Third uncle / Silent hedges / Three shadows (pt. 2) / Party of the first part / Poison pen / Departure / Nightime / She's in parties / God in an alcove / In the flat field / In fear of fear / Swing the heartache / St. Vitus dance.
2LP: . . . . BEGA 103
MC: . . . . BEGC 103

Baumann, Peter

REPEAT REPEAT.
Tracks: / Repeat repeat / Home sweet home / Deccadance / Real times / M.A.N. series two / Brain damage / Kinky dinky / Daytime logic / Playland pleasure / What is your use?.
LP: . . . . V 2214
LP: . . . . OVED 199
MC: . . . . OVEDC 199

ROMANCE 76.
Tracks: / Bicentennial present / Romance / Phase by phase / Meadow of infinity part 1 / Glass bridge, The / Meadow of infinity part 2.
LP: . . . . V 2069
LP: . . . . OVED 197
MC: . . . . OVEDC 197

TRANS-HARMONIC NIGHTS.
LP: . . . . V 2124
LP: . . . . OVED 198
MC: . . . . OVEDC 198

Bavan

AT NEWPORT '63 (See under Lambert) (Bavan/Lambert/Hendricks).

HAVIN' A BALL AT THE VILLAGE GATE (See under Lambert) (Bavan/Lambert/Hendricks).

Bavaria

BAVARIAN FOLK MUSIC (Various artists).
LP: DP6 28014

BAVARIAN MUSIC (24 GOLDEN FOLK SONGS - WINE SONG (Various artists).
MC: 822 400-4

BAVARIAN MUSIC (ALPINE SONGS & BRASS MUSIC) (Various artists).
MC: 822 396-4

BAVARIAN MUSIC (ALPINE SONGS ON A ZITHER) (Various artists).
MC: 822 391-4

BAVARIAN MUSIC (BEER FESTIVAL SONGS) (Various artists).
MC: 822 390-4

BAVARIAN MUSIC (BRASS MUSIC) (Various artists).
MC: 822 389-4

BAVARIAN MUSIC (EDELWEISS ACCORDION PLAYERS-SNOW (Various artists).
MC: 822 397-4

BAVARIAN MUSIC (FOLK SONGS FROM THE EGER COUNTRY (Various artists).
MC: 822 392-4

BAVARIAN MUSIC (GOLDEN SOUNDS FROM THE LAND OF C (Various artists).
MC: 822 388-4

BAVARIAN MUSIC (SCHUPLATTEN MUSIC-KNEE SLAPPING (Various artists).
MC: 822 399-4

BAVARIAN MUSIC (YODELLING SONGS FROM THE ALPS) (Various artists).
MC: 822 393-4

KINGS OF BRASS MUSIC (Bavarian Brass Bands).
LP: 816 334-1
MC: 816 334-4

Bavarian ...

BAVARIAN MUSIC (Songs from the October Festival) (Various artists).
LP: 816 347-1
MC: 816 347-4

OOMPAH STRIKES BACK, THE (Bavarian Steinswingers).
Tracks: / Radetzky march / Russian medley / Wooden heart / Stars on 33 medley / Wunderbar Bavaria / Sailing / Trumpet echo / Cuckoo waltz medley / Sea shanties / Chanson d'amour / Magnificent men in their flying machines / MacNamara's Band.
LP: . . . . AFA 831

Bavarian Oompah Band

BAVARIAN OOMPAH BAND.
LP: . . . . OAK R 105

Bavarian Symphony

MUSIC OF CHARLIE CHAPLIN.
MC: . . . . TRXC 156
LP: . . . . TRX 156

Bawden, Nina (aut)

CARRIE'S WAR (See under Carrie's War) (Clarke, Zela (nar)).

Baxter, Bruce

POP GUITAR EXTRAVAGANZA (Baxter, Bruce Orchestra).
Tracks: / Alone again (naturally) / Let it be / Don't give up on us / Yesterday / Little bit more, A / Sailing / Don't cry for me Argentina / Tie a yellow ribbon / Stand by your man / You are the sunshine of my life / Save your kisses for me / Summer of '42.
MCSET: . . . . DTO 10029

Baxter, Les

AFRICAN BLUE.
LP: . . . . GNPS 2047

BRAZIL NOW.
LP: . . . . GNPS 2036
MC: GNP5 2036

LOVE IS BLUE.
LP: . . . . GNPS 2042

Baxter, Olive (aut)

FORGIVING HEART (see under Forgiving Heart) (Donald, Sheila (nar)).

Baxters

ERA BUFFET.
Tracks: / Worlds too small / Long way home / Generation / Bend in the river / I won't bite / Lifetime / Tears come down / Beer theme / Cliches / Bare burden / We all need sleep / Goin' nowhere fast.
LP: . . . . P 4011
MC: . . . . P 4411

Bay Area...

BAY AREA BLUES BLASTERS (Various artists).

LP: .... CHD 224

BAY AREA GOSPEL -SAN FRANSISCO (Various artists).
LP: .... HT 314

Bay City Rollers

DEDICATION.
LP: .... SYBEL 8005

IT'S A GAME.
LP: .... SPARTY 1009

ONCE UPON A STAR.
LP: .... SYBEL 8001

ROLLIN'.
LP: .... BELLS 244

WOULDN'T YOU LIKE IT.
LP: .... SYBEL 8002

Bayard, Eddie

OWLS HOOT 1925-7, THE (Bayard, Eddie & Nor Classic Jazz Orch).
LP: .... SOS 1145

Bayer Sager, Carole

CAROLE BAYER SAGER.
Tracks: / Come in from the rain / Until the next time / Don't wish too hard / Sweet alibis / Aces / I'd rather leave while I'm in love / Steal away again / You're moving out today / Shy as a violet / Home to myself.
LP: .... K 52059
MC: .... K 452059

SOMETIMES LATE AT NIGHT.
Tracks: / I won't break / Just friends / Tell her / Somebody's been lying again / On the way to the sky / You and me / Sometimes late at night / Wild again / Easy to love again / Stronger than before / You don't know me.
LP: .... EPC 85110

TOO.
Tracks: / To make you smile again / It's the falling in love / Peace in my heart / Shadows / You're interesting / There's something about you / It doesn't add up / I don't wanna dance no more / One star shining / I'm coming home again.
LP: .... K 52093

Bayless, John

BACH MEETS THE BEATLES.
LP: .... PAD 211

Bayne, Pam

BORDER COUNTRY (Bayne, Pam & Phil).
LP: .... NA 104
MC: .... NC 104

Bayou...

BAYOU BEAT (Various artists).
LP: .... FLY 581

BAYOU BOOGIE (Various artists).
LP: .... FLY 557

BAYOU DRIVE (Various artists).
Tracks: / Big wheel: *Chenier, Clifton* / Baby please: *Chenier, Clifton* / Where can my baby be: *Chenier,* Clifton / My soul: *Chenier, Clifton* / Bayou drive: *Chenier, Clifton* / Now is the time: *Chenier, Clifton*/ Bad luck and trouble: *Boogie Jake* / Early morning blues: *Boogie Jake* / Bad feeling blues: *Lightning Slim*/ Lightning boogie: *Lightning Slim* / School boy jump: *Lightning Slim* / Station blues: *Lightning Slim*/ Good understanding: *Talbert,Henry* / Shake it baby: *Talbert,Henry.*
LP: .... GCH 8122

BAYOU RHYTHM & BLUES SHUFFLE (Various artists).
Tracks: / Washing: *Various artists* / Catch that train: *Anderson, Elton* / Let me hold your hand: *Big Chenier*/ I'm goin': *Dunaway, Shelton & The Boogie Ramblers* / Keep livin': *Dunaway, Shelton & The Boogie Ramblers* / Bayou shuffle: *Cookie & The Boogie Ramblers* / One life to live: *Miller, Tal* / Please try to release: *Big Chenier*/ Honey bee: *Left Hand Charlie* / Emmagene: *Stevens, Duke* / I wants you: *Savoy, Ashton* / I been your fool: *Stevens, Duke* / You wanta do me wrong: *Smith, Al.*
LP: .... GCL 111

BAYOU RHYTHM & BLUES SHUFFLE VOL 3 (Various artists).
Tracks: / Shed so many tears: *Various artists* / You went away: *Various artists* / I hear someone: *Various* artists / Good rockin' Bob: *Various artists* / Take it easy Katie: *Various artists* / B-a-b-y: *Various artists* / San Antonio: *Various artists* / Flim flam night: *Various artists.*
LP: .... GCL 120

BAYOU RHYTHM & BLUES SHUFFLE VOL 2 (Various artists).
Tracks: / Little Miss Peggy and the Bill: *Various artists* / Yellow pants and blues: *Various artists* / Suede shoes: *Various artists* / Too much: *Various artists* / Such as love: *Various artists* / Sweet potato: *Various artists* / Only sixteen: *Various artists* / If I don't see you: *Various artists.*
LP: .... GCL 199

Bayou Brothers

COME ON HOME (see Aspeys with Bayou Brothers) (Bayou Brothers/ Aspeys).

Baysal, Salih

MYTH, THE.
Tracks: / Maya / Ilk Aksamdan Meyhanede / Telegrafin Telleri / Kabagin Koneiyim / Pinar basi / Hakim Hanim / Lingo / Findil serdim Harmana / Nonno / Sut ictim dilim Yandi / Yesil ordek / Kacma Guzel / Kurt Ali / Onyun Havasi / Oyali Yazma Basinda / Yol Havasi.
LP: .... SNTF 739

Bazar, Thereze

BIG KISS, THE.
LP: .... MCF 3293
MC: .... MCFC 3293

Bazooka Joe

VIRTUAL WORLD.
LP: .... BIAS 165

BB Allstars...

BB ALLSTARS SUPERHITS VOLUME 1 (Various artists).
LP: .... BBLP 008

BBC...

BBC 1922-1972 (TV and Radio extracts) (Various artists).
LP: .... BBC 50

BBC CHILDREN'S TV THEMES (See under TV Themes) (Various artists).

BBC COMEDY THEMES (See under TV Themes) (Various artists).

BBC SPACE THEMES (See under TV Themes) (Various artists).

BBC SPORTING THEMES (See under TV Themes) (Various artists).

BBC'S FOLK ON 2 PRESENTS NORTHUMBRIAN FOLK (See under Folk) (Various artists).

BEST OF BBC TV THEMES (Various artists).
Tracks: / Singing detective, The: *Various artists* / Tender is the night: *Various artists* / Dr Who: *Various* artists / Dallas: *Various artists* / Howards' Way: *Various artists* / Bergerac: *Various artists*/ My family and other animals: *Various artists* / Ski Sunday: *Various artists* / Eastenders: *Various artists*/ Miss Marple: *Various artists* / Mastermind: *Various artists* / Neighbours: *Various artists* / Tomorrow's world: *Various artists* / Star cops: *Various artists* / Shoestring: *Various artists* / Knots Landing: *Various artists* / Whicker's world: *Various artists* / Life and loves of a she devil, The: *Various artists*/ Flight of the condor: *Various artists* / Fawlty Towers: *Various artists* / Who pays the ferryman?: *Various artists* / Life and times of David Lloyd George, The: *Various artists* / Fortunes of war: *Various artists.*
MC: .... HSC 645

DOWN AT THE OLD PEBBLE MILL (Various artists).
LP: .... REC 306

BBC Concert Orchestra

ASPECTS OF ANDREW LLOYD WEBBER.
Tracks: / Music of the night / Memory / Variations / Don't cry for me Argentina / Anything but lonely / Tell me on a Sunday / Jellicle ball, The / Loves changes everything / I only want to say / Pie Jesu / Close every door / Buenos Aires / I don't know how to love him / Aspects of Andrew.
LP: .... REB 750
MC: .... ZCF 750

BATTLE OF BRITAIN - 50TH ANNIVERSARY.
Tracks: / Speedbird salutes the few / Mars / Winston Churchill speech / Fighter command / Highflight / Spitfire prelude and fuge / Lie in the dark / Last enemy, The / O peaceful England / Washing on the siegfried line / We'll meet again / Armed forces medley / American hoedown / Speedbird salutes the few (theme).
LP: .... PZA 005 A
MC: .... PZA 005 C

FRIDAY NIGHT IS MUSIC NIGHT.
LP: .... REH 583
MC: .... ZCR 583

BBC Radiophonic

21 YEARS.
Tracks: / Quatermass and the pit / Artist speaks / Time beat / Know your car / Dr. Who / Environmental studies / Mysterioso / Merry go round / Newton / For love or money.
LP: .... REC 354

LIVING PLANET, THE (Music From the Television Series).
LP: .... REB 496
MC: .... ZCF 496

SOUND HOUSE.
Tracks: / Radiophonic rock, The / Lascaux / Computers in the real world / Seascape / Whale, The / Rallyman / Catch the wind / Believe it or not / Planet earth / Dawn / Mainstream / Unseeing eye / Fancy fish / Brighton pier / Amagideon war games / Yellow moon / Radio Blackburn / Macrocosm / Land and people / Housin's musical box / Ghost in the water / Milonga, The.
LP: .... REC 467
MC: .... ZCM 467

BBC Symphony Orchestra

LAST NIGHT OF THE PROMS.
LP: .... REH 290
MC: .... ZCR 290
LP: .... SFM 23033

LAST NIGHT OF THE PROMS '82.
LP: .... NE 1198
MC: .... CE 2198

MIDNIGHT.
Tracks: / You stepped out of a dream / What are you doing the rest of your life / Smoke gets in your eyes / Midnight at the Mermaid / If / I'll be seeing you / As time goes by / Easy to love / Misty morning / That lovely weekend / Where or when / Fools rush in / King Cole / Candlelight lovers / Laura / Nuages / These foolish things / Sun flower / Thanks for the memory.
MC: .... HSC 652

SYMPHONY NO.3 (BRIAN HAVERGAL) (Bell, Adrian & Julian Jacobson).
MC: .... KA 66334

BBC Welsh Chorus

VOICES FROM THE HOLY LAND (see under Jones, Aled) (BBC Welsh Chorus with Aled Jones).

BBC Welsh Orch.

CARDIFF SINGERS OF THE WORLD, THE.
LP: .... REGL 581
MC: .... ZCF 581

B.Boy (label)

B.BOY BOOGIE DOWN SAMPLER (See under Dance) (Various artists).

B.BOY BOOGIE DOWN SAMPLER VOL.2 (See under Dance...) (Various artists).

Be Thankful...

BE THANKFUL - AN ATTACK SAMPLER (See under Reggae for details) (Various artists).

Beach Bastards

SON OF A BEACH.
LP: .... DIST 1

Beach Boys

15 BIG ONES.
Tracks: / Rock and roll music / It's OK / Had to phone ya / Chapel of love / Everyone's in love with you / Talk to me / That same song / T M song / Palisades Park / Susie Cincinnati / Casual look, A / Blueberry hill / Back home / In the still of the night / Just once in my life.
LP: .... K 54079
MC: 4683464

16 ORIGINAL HITS (Beach Boys/Jan & Dean).
MC: .... MC 1635

20 GOLDEN GREATS: BEACH BOYS.
Tracks: / Surfin' USA / Fun,fun,fun / I get around / Don't worry baby / Little deuce coupe / When I grow up (to be a man) / Help me Rhonda / California girls / Barbara Ann / Sloop John B. / You're so good to me / God only knows / Wouldn't it be nice / Good vibrations / Then I kissed her / Heroes and villains / Darlin' / Do it again / I can hear music / I break away.
LP: .... EMTV 1
MC: .... TC EMTV 1

40 GREATEST HITS.
Tracks: / Surfin' safari / 409 / 10 little indians / Surfin' USA / Shut down / Farmer's daughter, The / Hawaii / Surfer girl / Little deuce coupe / Be true to your school / In my room / Fun,fun,fun / I get around / Don't worry baby / When I grow up (to be a man) / Wendy / Little Honda / Dance, dance, dance / Do you wanna dance? / Please let me wonder / Help me Rhonda / California girls / Little girl / Barbara Ann / Sloop John B. / Wouldn't it be nice / God only knows / You're so good to me / Good vibrations / Then I kissed her / Heroes and villains / Gettin' hungry / Wild honey / Darlin' / Friends / Do it again / Bluebirds over the mountain.
2LP: 1A 152 85750/1

20/20.
LP: .... EST 133

ALL SUMMER LONG.
Tracks: / I get around / All summer long / Hush-a-bye / Little Honda / We'll run away / Carl's big chance / Wendy / Do you remember? / Girls on the beach / Drive-in / Our favourite recording session / Don't back down.
LP: .... EMS 1176
MC: .... TCEMS 1176
LP: .... ATAK 80
MC: .... TCATAK 80

BEACH BOYS.
LP: 4673631
MC: 4673634

BEACH BOYS (AUDIO FIDELITY).
MC: .... ZCGAS 720

BEACH BOYS (CAMBRA).
Tracks: / Surfin' USA / Then I kissed her / I can hear the music / Fun fun fun / Don't worry baby / Cottonfields / Dance, dance, dance / Barbara Ann / You're so good to me / Good vibrations / Little deuce coupe / Surfer girl / When I grow up to be a man / In my room / Do you wanna dance / God only knows / Do it again / Wendy / California girls / You still believe in me / Help me Rhonda / Breakaway / I get around / Wouldn't it be nice / Darlin' / Here today / Sloop John B / Surfing safari / Good to my baby / Heroes and villains.
MCSET: .... CRT 009

BEACH BOYS (CAPITOL).
MC: 4XL 8350

BEACH BOYS (CARIBOU).
Tracks: / Getcha back / It's gettin' late / Crack at your love / Maybe I don't know / She believes in love again / California calling / Passing friend / I'm so lonely / Where I belong / I do love you / It's just a matter of time.
MC: 40 26378
LP: .... CRB 26378

BEACH BOYS CONCERT.
Tracks: / Fun fun fun / Little old lady from Pasadena / Little deuce coupe / Long tall Texan / In my room / Monster mash / Let's go trippin' / Papa oom mow mow / Wanderer / Hawaii / Graduation day / Johnny B. Goode.
MC: .... TC GO 2005
LP: .... GO 2005

BEACH BOYS CONCERT & BEACH BOYS '69 (Beach Boys Live in London).
Tracks: / Fun, fun, fun / Little old lady from Pasadena, The / Little deuce coupe / Long tall Texan / In my room / Monster mash / Let's go trippin' / Papa-oom-mow-mow / Wanderer, The / Hawaii / Graduation day / I get around / Johnny B. Goode / Darlin' / Wouldn't it be nice / Sloop John B / California girls / Do it again / Wake the world / Aren't you glad / Bluebirds over the mountain / Their hearts were full of spring / Good vibrations / God only knows / Barbara Ann / Don't worry baby / Heroes and villains.
MC: C4 93695

BEACH BOYS IN CONCERT, THE.
Tracks: / Sail on sailor / Sloop John B / Trader, The / You still believe in me / California girls / Darlin' / Marcella / Caroline / No / Leaving this town / Heroes and villains / Funky pretty / Let the wind blow / Help me, Rhonda / Surfer girl / Wouldn't it be nice / We got love / Don't worry baby / Surfin' USA / Good vibrations / Fun fun fun.
LP: .... K 84001
MC: 4683454

BEACH BOYS LOVE YOU, THE.
Tracks: / Let us go on this way / Roller skating child / Mona / Johnny Carson / Good time / Honkin' down the highway / Din dang / Solar system / Night was so young / I'll bet he's nice / Let's put our hearts together / I wanna pick you up / Airplane / Love is a woman.
LP: .... K 54087

BEACH BOYS PARTY.
Tracks: / Baby hully gully / I should have known better / Tell me why / Papa oom mow mow / Mountain of love / You've got to hide your love away / Devoted to you / Alley oop / There's no other (like my baby) / I get around / Little deuce coupe / Times they are a-changin' / Barbara Ann.
LP: .... EMS 1177
MC: .... TCEMS 1177
LP: .... ATAK 81
MC: .... TCATAK 81
LP: .... T 2398

BEACH BOYS PARTY/STACK-O-TRACKS.
Tracks: / Hully gully / I should have known better / Tell me why / Papa-oom-mow-mow / Mountain of love / You've got to hide your love away / Devoted to you / Alley oop / There's no other like my

baby / Times they are a-changin' / Barbara Ann / Darlin' / Salt Lake City / Sloop John B / In my room / Catch a wave / Wild honey / Little Saint Nick / Do it again / Wouldn't it be nice / God only knows / Surfer girl / Little honda / Here today / You're so good to me / Help me Rhonda / California girls / Our car club.
MC: **C4 93698**

BEACH BOYS RARITIES.
Tracks: / With a little help from my friends / Letter, The / I was made to love her / You're welcome / Lord's prayer, The / Bluebirds over the mountain / Celebrate the news / Good vibrations / Land ahoy / In my room / Cottonfields / All I want to do / Auld lang syne.
LP: . . . . **ATAK 6**
MC: . . . . **TC ATAK 6**
LP: . . . . **EST 7122931**

BEACH BOYS TODAY.
LP: . . . . **T 2269**

BEACH BOYS TODAY/SUMMER DAYS AND SUMMER NIGHTS.
Tracks: / Do you wanna dance / Don't hurt my little sister / Help me Rhonda / Please let me wonder / Kiss me baby / In the back of my mind / Girl from New York City, The / Then I kissed her / Girl don't tell me / Let him run wild / Summer means new love / And your dreams come true / I'm so young (alternate take) / Graduation day (studio version) / Good to my baby / When I grow up (to be a man) / Dance, dance, dance / I'm so young / She knows me too well / Bull session with Big Daddy / Amusement Parks USA / Salt Lake City / California girls / You're so good to me / I'm bugged at my ole man / Little girl I once knew, The / Let him run wild (alternate take) / Help me, Rhonda (LP version) / Dance, dance, dance (alt. take).
MC: **C4 93694**

BEACH BOYS (WORLD RECORDS).
Tracks: / Getcha back / It's gettin' late / Crack at your love / Maybe I don't know / She believes in love again / California calling / Passing friend / I'm so lonely / Where I belong / I do love you / It's just a matter of time / Add some music to your day / Roller skating child / Disney girls / It's a beautiful day / California saga / Won't cha come out tonight / Marcella / Rock and roll music / Goin' on / It's ok / Cool cool water / San Miguel / School day / Good timin' / Sail on sailor / Darlin' / Lady Lynda / Sea cruise / Trader, The / This whole world / Don't go near the water / Surf's up / Come go with me / Diedre / She's got rhythm / River song / Long promised road / Feel flow's / Till I die / Surfin' USA / Then I kissed her / I can hear music / Fun, fun, fun / Don't worry baby / Cottonfields / Dance, dance, dance / Barbara Ann / Good vibrations / You're so good to me / Little deuce coupe / Surfer girl / When I grow up (to be a man) / In my room / Do you wanna dance / God only knows / Do it again / California girls / You still believe in me / Wendy / Help me Rhonda / Breakaway / Wouldn't it be nice / I get around / Here today / Sloop John B / Surfing safari / Good to my baby / Heroes and villains.
LPS: . . . . **ALBUM 65**
MCSET: . . . . **CASSETTE 65**

BEST OF THE BEACH BOYS.
Tracks: / Barbara Ann / Sloop John B / Cottonfields / Good vibrations / I can hear music / Heroes and villains.
LP: **1A 022 58080**
MC: **1A 222 58080**
LP: . . . . **T 20865**

BEST OF THE BEACH BOYS VOL.2.
LP: . . . . **ST 20965**

BEST OF THE BEACH BOYS VOL.3.
LP: . . . . **ST 21142**

BUSTIN' SURFBOARDS (Beach Boys/ Dick Dale/Neil Norman).
LP: . . . . **GNPS 2152**
MC: **GNP5 2152**

CAPITOL YEARS, THE: BEACH BOYS.
LP: . . . . **PM 1551803**

CARL AND THE PASSIONS, SO TOUGH.
Tracks: / You need a mess of help to stand alone / Here she comes / He come down / Marcella / Hold on dear brother / Make it good / All this is that / Cuddle up.
LP: . . . . **K 44184**
MC: **4683494**

COLLECTION: BEACH BOYS.
LP: . . . . **IC 038 80184**
LP: **1C 038 85459**

DISQUE D'OR.
Tracks: / I get around / Fun fun fun / Surfin' USA / Shut down / Little deuce coupe / Dance, dance, dance / California girls / Barbara Ann / Then I kissed her / Sloop John B. / God only knows / Good vibrations / Do it again / I can hear music.
LP: **2C 070 85014**

DO IT AGAIN.
Tracks: / Warmth of the sun / 409 / Catch a wave / Lonely sea / Do it again / Long tall Texan / Wild honey / Darlin' / Please let me wonder / Let him run wild / Country air / I know there's an answer / Friends / Heroes and villains.
LP: . . . . **MFP 5763**
MC: . . . . **TC MFP 5763**

DON'T WORRY BABY (See under Everly Brothers) (Beach Boys & Everly Brothers).

ENDLESS SUMMER.
Tracks: / Surfin' safari / Surfer girl / Catch a wave / Warmth of the sun / Surfin' USA / Be true to your school / Little deuce coupe / In my room / Shut down / Fun fun fun / I get around / Girls on the beach / Wendy / Let him run wild / Don't worry baby / California girls / Girl don't tell me / Help me Rhonda / You're so good to me / All summer long / Good vibrations.
LP: . . . . **MFP 50528**
MC: . . . . **TCMFP 50528**

FRIENDS.
LP: . . . . **ST 2895**

FRIENDS/20-20.
Tracks: / Meant for you / Friends / Wake the world / Be here in the morning / When a man needs a woman / Passing by / Anna Lee, the healer / Little bird / Be still / Busy doing nothing / Diamond head / Transcendental meditation / Do it again / I can hear music / Bluebirds over the mountain / Be with me / All I want to do / Nearest faraway place, The / Cottonfields (the cotton song) / I went to sleep / Time to get alone / Never learn not to love / Our prayer / Cabinessence / Breakaway / Celebrate the news / We're together again / Walk on by / Old folks at home/Ol' man river.
MC: **C4 93697**

GIRLS ON THE BEACH.
Tracks: / Girls on the beach / In my room / Hush-a-bye / We'll run away / California girls / Surfer girl / God only knows / Caroline no / You still believe in me / Warmth of the sun / Wouldn't it be nice / Lonely sea / Don't worry / Baby / Don't talk / Keep an eye on summer / Then I kissed her.
MC: . . . . **TC CAPS 1037**
LP: . . . . **CAPS 1037**

GOOD VIBRATIONS.
LP: . . . . **CGB 1010**
MC: . . . . **TC CGB 1010**

GREATEST HITS: BEACH BOYS.
LP: . . . . **ST 21628**

HOLLAND.
Tracks: / Sail on sailor / Steamboat / California saga / Big surf / Beaks of eagles / California / Trader, The / Leaving this town / Only with you / Funky pretty / I'm the pied piper / Better get back in bed / Magic transistor radio / Radio king dom.
LP: . . . . **K 54008**
MC: **4678374**

KEEPIN' THE SUMMER ALIVE.
Tracks: / Keepin' the summer alive / Oh darlin' / Some of your love / Livin' with a heartache / School day / Goin' on / Sunshine / When girls get together / Santa Anna winds / Endless harmony.
LP: . . . . **CRB 86109**
MC: **4683504**

L.A. (LIGHT ALBUM).
Tracks: / Good timin' / Lady Lynda / Full sail / Angel come home / Love surrounds me / Sumahama / Here comes the night / Baby blue / Going South / Shortnin' bread.
LP: . . . . **CRB 32806**
MC: **40 32806**
LP: . . . . **CRB 86081**

LITTLE DEUCE COUPE.
Tracks: / Little deuce coupe / Ballad of 'ole Betsy / Be true to your school / Car crazy cutie / Cherry cherry coupe / 409 / Shut down / Spirit of America / Our car club / No-go showboat / Young man is gone, A (Melody from 'Their hearts were full of spring'-B Troup) / Custom machine.
LP: . . . . **EMS 1174**
MC: . . . . **TCEMS 1174**
LP: . . . . **ATAK 78**
MC: . . . . **TCATAK 78**
LP: . . . . **GO 2025**

LITTLE DEUCE COUPE/ALL SUMMER LONG.
Tracks: / Little deuce coupe / Ballad of ole' Betsy / Be true to your school / Car crazy cutie / Cherry, cherry coupe / 409 / Shut down / Spirit of America / Our car club / No-go showboat / Young man is gone, A / Custom machine / I get around / All summer long / Hushabye / Little honda / We'll run away / Carl's big chance / Wendy / Do you remember? / Girls on the beach / Drive-in / Our favourite recording sessions / Don't back down / Be true to your school (single version) / All dressed up for school / Don't back down (alt. take).
MC: **C4 93693**

LOVE YOU.
Tracks: / Let us go on this way / Roller skating child / Mona / Johnny Carson / Good time / Honkin' down the highway / Ding dang / Solar system / Night was so young, The / I'll bet he's nice / Let's put our hearts together / I wanna pick you up / Airplane / Love is a woman.
MC: **4683474**

MADE IN THE USA.
Tracks: / Surfin' safari / 409 / Surfin' U.S.A. / Be true to your school / Surfer girl / Dance, dance, dance / Fun fun fun / I get around / Help me Rhonda / Don't worry baby / California girls / When I grow up to be a man / Barbara Ann / Good vibrations / Heroes and villains / Wouldn't it be nice / Sloop John B / God only knows / Caroline no / Do it again.
2LP: . . . . **EN 5005**
MC: . . . . **TCEN 5005**

M.I.U..
Tracks: / She's got rhythm / Come go with me / Hey little tomboy / Kona Coast / Peggy Sue / Wontcha come out tonight / Sweet Sunday kinda love / Belles of Paris / Pitter patter / My Diane / Match point of our love / Winds of change.
LP: . . . . **K 54102**
MC: **4683484**

PET SOUNDS.
Tracks: / Caroline no / Wouldn't it be nice / You still believe in me / That's not me / Don't talk / I'm waiting for the day / Let's go away for awhile / Sloop John B / God only knows / I know there's an answer / Here today / I just wasn't made for these times / Pet sounds / Hang on to your ego (CD only.) / Unreleased background (CD only.) / Trombone dixie (CD only.).
LP: . . . . **EMS 1179**
MC: . . . . **TCEMS 1179**
LP: . . . . **ATAK 83**
MC: . . . . **TCATAK 83**
LP: . . . . **FA 3018**
LP: . . . . **GO 2002**
MC: **C4 48421**

PROFILE: BEACH BOYS.
Tracks: / Surfin' safari / Judy / 409 / Beach boy stomp / What is a young girl / Surfer girl / Barbi / Ludy / Surfin' / Little deuce coupe.
LP: **6.25056**
MC: **CL4 25056**

SHUTDOWN VOL 2 (Surfin' Girl).
Tracks: / Fun fun fun / Don't worry baby / In the parkin' lot / Cassius love vs Sonny Wilson / Warmth of the sun / This car of mine / Why do fools fall in love / Pom pom play girl / Keep an eye on summer / Shut down (part II) / Louie Louie / Denny's drums.
LP: **C5-535**

SMILEY SMILE.
LP: . . . . **ST 9001**

SMILEY SMILE/WILD HONEY.
Tracks: / Heroes and villains / Vegetables / Fall breaks and back to winter / She's goin' bald / Little pad / Good vibrations / With me tonight / Wind chimes / Gettin' hungry / Wonderful / Whistle in / Wild honey / Aren't you glad / I was made to love her / Country air / Thing or two, A / Darlin' / I'd love just once to see you / Here comes the night / Let the wind blow / How she boogalooed it / Mama says / Heroes and villains (alt. take) / Good vibrations (various sessions) / Good vibrations (early take) / You're welcome / Their hearts were full of spring / Can't wait too long.
MC: **C4 93696**

STACK O'TRACKS.
Tracks: / Darlin' / Salt Lake city / Sloop John B / In my room / Catch a wave / Wild honey / Little Saint Nick / Do it again / Wouldn't it be nice / God only knows / Surfer girl / Little Honda / Here today / You're so good to me / Let him run wild.
LP: . . . . **EST 24009**

STILL CRUISIN'.
Tracks: / Still cruisin' (From Lethal Weapon 2.) / Somewhere near Japan / Island girl / In my car / Kokomo (From Cocktail.) / Wipe out / Make it big (From Troop Beverly Hills.) / I get around (From Good Morning Vietnam.) / Wouldn't it be nice (From The Big Chill) / California girls (From Soul Man.).
LP: . . . . **ESTU 2107**
MC: . . . . **TCESTU 2107**

SUMMER DAYS (AND SUMMER NIGHTS).
Tracks: / Girl from New York City, The / Amusement parks U.S.A. / Then I kissed her / Salt Lake City / Girl don't tell me / Help me Rhonda / California girls / Let him run wild / You're so good to me / Summer means new love / I'm bugged at my ol' man / And your dreams come true.
LP: . . . . **EMS 1178**
MC: . . . . **TCEMS 1178**
LP: . . . . **ATAK 82**
MC: . . . . **TCATAK 82**
LP: . . . . **T 2354**

SUMMER DREAMS.
Tracks: / I get around / Surfin' U.S.A. / In my room (Not on CD.) / Fun fun fun / Little deuce coupe / Warmth of the sun, The (Not on CD.) / Surfin' safari / Help me Rhonda / Good vibrations / Sloop John B / You're so good to me / God only knows / Then I kissed her / Wouldn't it be nice / Heroes and villains / Wild honey / California girls / Don't worry baby / All summer long (Not on CD.) / Wendy (Not on CD.) / When I grow up (to be a man) / Dance, dance, dance / Little girl I once knew, The / Barbara Ann / Do it again / Friends / Darlin' / Bluebirds over the mountain / I can hear music / Breakaway / Cottonfields / California dreamin'.
2LP: . . . . **EMTVD 51**
MC: . . . . **TCEMTVD 51**
2LP: **794 620 1**
MC: **794 620 4**
MC: **4XL 8351**

SUNFLOWER.
Tracks: / Slip on through / This whole world / Add some music to your day / Got to know the woman / Deirdre / It's about time / Tears in the morning / All I want to do / Forever / Our sweet love / At my window / Cool, cool water.
LP: . . . . **SSL 8251**
LP: . . . . **CBS 32086**
LP: . . . . **CRB 31773**
MC: **4678364**

SUPERGOLD.
2LP: . . . . **IC 134 81675/6**

SURFER GIRL.
Tracks: / Surfer girl / Catch a wave / Surfer moon, The / South bay surfer / Rocking surfer, The / Little deuce coupe / In my room / Hawaii / Surfer's rule / Our car club / Your summer dream / Boogie woogie / Surfin' / Barbi / Karate / Luan / Surfer's stomp / Balboa blue / Surfin' safari / What is a young girl / Wipe out / Don't go near the water.
LP: . . . . **EMS 1175**
MC: . . . . **TCEMS 1175**
LP: . . . . **TOP 109**
MC: . . . . **KTOP 109**
LP: . . . . **ATAK 79**
MC: . . . . **TCATAK 79**
LP: . . . . **T 1981**

SURFER GIRL/SHUT DOWN VOL. 2.
Tracks: / Surfer girl / Catch a wave / Surfer moon, The / South bay surfer / Rocking surfer / Little deuce coupe / In my room / Hawaii / Surfers rule / Our car club / Your summer dream / Boogie woogie / Fun, fun, fun / Don't worry baby / In the parkin' lot / "Cassius" Love vs "Sonny" Wilson / Warmth of the sun, The / This car of mine / Why do fools fall in love / Pom, pom play girl / Keep an eye on summer / Shut down part II / Louie Louie / Denny's drum / Fun, fun, fun - single version / In my room - German version / I do.
MC: **C4 93692**

SURFIN' SAFARI.
Tracks: / Sufin' safari / County fair / Ten little indians / Little girl / 409 / Chug a lug / Heads you win - tails I lose / Summertime blues / Moon dawg / Shif.
LP: . . . . **GO 2014**

SURFIN' SAFARI/SURFIN' USA.
Tracks: / Surfin' safari / County fair / Ten little indians / Chug-a-lug / Little girl / 409 / Surfin' / Heads you win - tails I lose / Summertime blues / Cuckoo clock, The / Moon dawg / Shift, The / Surfin' U.S.A. / Farmer's daughter, The / Misirlou / Stoked / Lonely sea / Shut down / Noble surfer / Honky tonk / Lana / Surf jam / Let's go trippin' / Finders keepers / Cindy oh Cindy / Baker man, The / Land ahoy.
MC: **C4 93691**

SURFIN' USA.
LP: . . . . **T 1890**

SURF'S UP.
Tracks: / Long promised road / Take a load off your feet / Disney girls / Students demonstration time / Feel flows / Lookin' at tomorrow / Day in the life of a tree, A / Till I die / Surf's up / Don't go near the water.
LP: . . . . **CRB 32085**
LP: . . . . **CBS 31774**
MC: **4678354**

SURF'S UP (CAPITOL).

Tracks: / Surfin' USA / Help me Rhonda / Little deuce coupe / Don't worry baby / Surfin' / Barbara Ann / All summer long / You're so good to me / Do you wanna dance.
MC: **4XL-9053**

TEN YEARS OF HARMONY.
Tracks: / Add some music to your day / Roller skating child / Disney girls / It's a beautiful day / California saga / California / Won't cha come out tonight / Marcella / Rock and roll music / Goin' on / It's OK / Cool, cool water / San Miguel / School day / Good timin' / Sail on sailor / Darlin' / Lady Lynda / Sea cruise / Trader, The / This whole world / Don't go near the water / Surf's up / Come go with me / Deirdre / She's got rhythm / River song / Long promised road / Feel flows / Till I die.
2LP: . . . . **CBS 22178**
MCSET: **40 22178**
2LP: . . . . **CRB 88553**

VERY BEST OF THE BEACH BOYS.
Tracks: / Surfin' safari / Surfin' USA / Shut down / Little deuce coupe / In my room / Fun,fun,fun / I get around / Don't worry baby / When I grow up (to be a man) / Wendy / Little Honda / Dance, dance, dance / All summer long / Do you wanna dance / Help me Rhonda / California girls / Little girl I once knew, The / Barbara Ann / You're so good to me / Then I kissed her / Sloop John B / God only knows / Wouldn't it be nice / Here today / Good vibrations / Heroes and villains / Wild honey / Darlin' / Country air / Here comes the night / Friends / Do it again / Bluebirds over the mountain / I can hear music / Breakaway / Cottonfields.
LPS: . . . . **BBTV 1867193**
MCSET: . . . . **TC BBTV 186719**
LPS: . . . . **BBTV 1**
MCSET: . . . . **TC BBTV 1**

WILD HONEY.
LP: . . . . **ST 2859**

WIPE OUT.
Tracks: / Balboa blue / Wipe out / Surfers stomp / Surfin' safari / Luan / Karate / Surfin' / What a young girl is made of / Surfer girl / Barbi.
LP: . . . . **MTM 022**

Beachcomber

BEACHCOMBER - BY THE WAY (Various artists).
MCSET: . . . . **ZBBC 1101**

Beaches (film)

BEACHES (See under Midler, Bette) (Midler, Bette).

Beacon, Kim

RAVENNA.
Tracks: / My blues have gone / Baltimore / Nightbird / Ooh child / Imagine / Minute by minute / It takes time to find love / Ravenna / Lonely.
LP: . . . . **TENOR 103**

TALKING TO MYSELF.
Tracks: / Don't tell me / Destiny / Hurt inside / Third time / Don't let it show / Crossfire / Honest man / If I had you / Foolish isle / Back again.
LP: . . . . **TENOR 105**
MC: . . . . **ZCTEN 105**

Beadle, Rob

ROB AND HIS MUSIC.
Tracks: / At the woodchoppers ball / Try a little tenderness / Lady be good / Somebody loves me / Lady is a tramp, The / Don't get around much anymore / Sunny side of the street / Time after time / I'll string along with you / Whiffenpoof song, The / Umbrella man / Around the world / Whispering / Yours / Can't buy me love / All my loving / Hello Dolly / It's de-lovely / Mame / Cabaret / New York, New York / I don't want to set the world on fire / I'm always chasing rainbows / Amor amor amor / Brazil / What I did for love / I left my heart in San Francisco / We'll meet again.
LP: . . . . **GRS 1135**

Beagles

DEAD CICADA (see under Boring Songs - Hee Bee Gee Bees).

Beaker, Norman

MODERN DAYS, LONELY NIGHTS (Beaker, Norman Band).
LP: . . . . **JSP 1120**

Beal, David

BIG PICTURE, THE (See Shrieve, Michael) (Beal, David & Michael Shrieve).

Beal, Jeff

LIBERATION.
MC: . . . . **ANC 8704**
LP: . . . . **AN 8704**

Beaman, Lottie

LOTTIE BEAMAN/LUELLA MILLER (1924-26/1928) (Beaman, Lottie/Luella Miller).
LP: . . . . **WSE 124**

Beamer, Kapono

DAYDREAMS.
LP: . . . . **ISST 159**

SILENT CROSSING.
LP: . . . . **ISST 183**

Bean, Billy

BEAN BAG (An Album of Adult Humour).
LP: . . . . **CLIB 1**
MC: . . . . **CLIC 1**

Beanyman

TEN YEAR OLD WONDER D J, THE.
LP: . . . . **JUSLP 003**

Bear (film)

BEAR, THE (Film soundtrack) (Various artists).
LP: **209446**
MC: **409446**

Bear, Richard T

RED HOT AND BLUE.
Tracks: / Blues power / Heart's a lonely hunter / Lay your head against my pillow / Suicide / Pain in my heart / Bring on the night / If you really want my love / Speed on / Susannah '73 / Sunshine Hotel.
LP: . . . . **PL 12927**

Bearburger

BEARBURGER.
MC: . . . . **U 018 MC**

Beard, Joe

NO MORE CHERRY ROSE.
Tracks: / When I get drunk / Cancel my reservation / Something's on my baby's mind / Heaven of my own / Let me love you / Highway 49 / No more cherry rose / Have you ever wanted someone / Papa's little girl / New York woman.
LP: . . . . **KIN 4040**
MC: . . . . **KIN 4040MC**

Beargarden

ALL THAT FALL.
LP: . . . . **CLP 9**

Bearman, Louisa

POEMS IN THE LANCASHIRE DIALECT.
LP: . . . . **BB 00 06**

Bears

BEAR ESSENTIALS.
Tracks: / He's gonna get me / Back to the drawing board / Happy go lucky / Newsman / Quiet one, The / Anorak city / Cruising down the Rhine / Roundabout romeoes / Whistling in the dark / Donny Rimshott / Blood will run / I like dogs / After eights / Putting on the style.
LP: . . . . **OKLP 3001**
MC: . . . . **ZCOK 3001**

BEARS, THE.
Tracks: / None of the above / Fear is never boring / Honey bee / Man behind the curtain / Wavelength / Trust / Raining / Superboy / Meet me in the dark / Figure it out.
LP: . . . . **MIRF 1026**
MC: . . . . **MIRFC 1026**

INSANE.
LP: . . . . **GROWL 001**

RISE AND SHINE.
Tracks: / Rise and shine.
LP: . . . . **ILP 026**

Bears' Christmas

BEARS' CHRISTMAS AND OTHER STORIES, THE (See Berenstain, Stan & Jan) (Berenstain, Stan & Jan).

Bears' Picnic (bk)

BEARS' PICNIC AND OTHER STORIES, THE (Berenstain, Stan & Jan).
MC: **1549**

Beasley, Jimmy

JIMMY'S HOUSEPARTY.
Tracks: / Don't feel sorry for me / Harbour lights / I'm so blue / She's good to me / Rhumba rock / No love for me / Coquette / Near you / Thinking of you / I want my baby / My happiness / Moonlight / Johnny's houseparty / You were only fooling / I'm not free / We three.
LP: . . . . **CH 190**

Beasley, Paul

MY SOUL IS FREE.
LP: . . . . **MYR 1157**
MC: . . . . **MC 1157**

Beasley, Walter

I'M SO HAPPY.
Tracks: / I'm so happy / On the edge / Call me / Jump on it / Back in love again / Tenderness / Nothin' but a thang / Where / I'm so happy (12" remix).
LP: . . . . **URBLP 6**
MC: . . . . **URBMC 6**

JUST KICKIN' IT.
Tracks: / Just kickin' it / Good love / I would never go / Get loose / Don't say goodbye / You are the one / Muriel's lament / In time / Have you seen my girl / Mancy.
LP: **838 912 1**
MC: **838 912 4**

Beast

BEAST HAS ARRIVED, THE.
LP: . . . . **FLAME 001**

CARNIVAL OF SOULS.
LP: **084600**

Beast (Film)

BEAST, THE (Original Soundtrack) (Various artists).
LP: . . . . **SP 3919**
MC: . . . . **C 3919**

Beastie Boys

BEASTIE BOYS: INTERVIEW PICTURE DISC.
LPPD: . . . . **BAK 2048**

LICENSED TO ILL.
Tracks: / Rhymin and stealin' / New style / She's crafty / Posse in effect / Slow ride / Girls / (You gotta) Fight for your right / No sleep till Brooklyn / Paul Revere / Hold it, now hit it / Brass monkey / Slow and low / Time to get ill.
LP: **4500621**
MC: **4500624**
LP: **4609491**

PAUL'S BOUTIQUE.
Tracks: / To all the girls / Shake your rump / Johnny Ryall / Egg man / High plains drifter / Sounds of science / 3 minute rule / Hey ladies / 5 piece chicken dinner / Looking down the barrel of a gun / Car thief / What comes around / Shadrach / Ask for Janice / B boy bouillabaisse.
LP: . . . . **EST 2102**
LP: **791 743 1**
MC: . . . . **TCEST 2102**
MC: **791 743 4**

Beastmaster (film)

BEASTMASTER, THE (Original soundtrack) (Various artists).
LP: . . . . **STV 81174**
MC: . . . . **CTV 81174**

Beasts Of Bourbon

AXEMAN'S JAZZ.
LP: . . . . **HYBLP 1**

Beat

I JUST CAN'T STOP IT.
Tracks: / Mirror in the bathroom / Hand's off... she's mine / Two swords / Twist and crawl / Rough rider / Click click / Big shot / Wine and grine / Stand down Margaret / Noise in this world / Can't get used to losing you / Best friend / Jackpot.
LP: . . . . **BEAT 1**
MC: . . . . **TCBT 1**
LP: . . . . **FA 413091-1**
MC: . . . . **TCFA 41 40914**

SPECIAL BEAT SERVICE.
Tracks: / I confess / Jeanette / Sorry / Sole salvation / Spar wid me / Rotating head / Save it for later / She's going / Ago talk / Sugar and stress / End of the party / Ackee 123.
LP: . . . . **BEAT 5**
MC: . . . . **TCBT 5**

WHA'PPEN.
Tracks: / Door of your heart / All out to get you / Monkey murders / I am your flag / French toast / Drowning / Dreamhome in N-Z / Walk away / Over and over / Cheated / Get a job / Limits we set, The.
LP: . . . . **BEAT 3**
MC: . . . . **TCBT 3**

WHA'PPEN/I JUST CAN'T STOP IT.
Tracks: / Mirror in the bathroom / Hand's off... she's mine / Two swords / Twist and crawl / Rough rider / Click click / Big shot / Whine and grine / Stand down Margaret / Noise in this world / Can't get used to losing you / Best friend / Jackpot / Doors of your heart / All out to get you / Monkey murders / I am your flag / French toast / Drowning / Dreamhome in NZ / Walk away / Over and over / Cheated / Get a job / Limits we set, The.
MC: . . . . **XTWO 23**

WHAT IS BEAT? (Best of the Beat).
Tracks: / Tears of a clown / Hand's off... she's mine / Mirror in the bathroom / Stand down Margaret / Twist and crawl / Doors of your heart / Save it for later / Too nice to talk to you / I confess / Best friend / Drowning / Ackee 1-2-3 / Can't get used to losing you / Ranking full stop / Twist and crawl / Too nice to talk to / Psychedelic rockers (Not on LP.) / March of the swivelheads (Not on LP.) / Save it for later (extended) (Not on LP.) / Doors of your heart (extended) (Not on LP.) / Drowning (extended) (Not on LP.) / I confess (extended) (Not on LP.).
LP: . . . . **BEAT 6**
MC: . . . . **TCBT 6**

Beat Apartheid

BEAT APARTHEID (Various artists).
LP: . . . . **PIR 22001**

Beat Direction

LONG DISTANT BEAT.
LP: . . . . **HIS 006**

Beat Farmers

GLAD 'N' GREASY.
Tracks: / Powder finger / Death train / Beat generation / Glad,n,greasy / Delayed reaction / Big rock candy mountain.
LP: . . . . **VEX 5**

PURSUIT OF HAPPINESS, THE.
Tracks: / Hollywood hills / Ridin' / Dark light / Make it last / Key to the world / God is here tonight / Big big man / Elephant day parade / Rosie / Texas / Big river.
LP: . . . . **ZL 71545**
MC: . . . . **ZK 71545**

TALES OF THE NEW WEST.
Tracks: / Bigger stones / There she goes again / Reason to believe / Lost weekend / California kid / Never goin' back / Goldmine / Showbiz / Lonesome hound / Where do they go / Selfish heart.
LP: . . . . **FIEND 39**

VAN GO.
Tracks: / Riverside / Deceiver / Powder finger / Seven year blues / Blue Chevrolet / I want you too / Road of ruin / Buy me a car / Gun sale at the church / Bigger fool than me / Big ugly wheels.
LP: . . . . **MCF 3326**
MC: . . . . **MCFC 3326**

Beat Generation...

BEAT GENERATION AND THE ANGRY YOUNG MEN, THE (Various artists).
Tracks: / That's what I want: *Long Tall Sally* / Underground: *Small Arrows* / I'll make you mine: *Purple Hearts* / Frustration: *Les Elite* / I do: *Long Tall Sally* / Dangerous Man: *Merton Parkas* / Get a job: *Les Elite* / Weekend dancers: *Directions* / Concrete mixer: *Purple Hearts* / Career girl: *Les Elite* / All by Myself: *Long Tall Sally* / It may be too late: *Directions* / You say you will: *Merton Parkas* / Kid: *Small Hours* / Hurry darkness: *Purple Hearts*.
LP: . . . . **NIXON 3**
LP: . . . . **SUSS 1**

BEAT GENERATION, THE (double cassette) (Various artists).
MCSET: . . . . **DTO 10260**

Beat Girl (film)

BEAT GIRL (FILM SOUNDTRACK) (See under Barry, John) (Barry, John).

Beat Happening

BEAT HAPPENING.
LP: . . . . **ROUGH 105**

BLACK CANDY.
LP: . . . . **ROUGH 145**

JAMBOREE.
LP: . . . . **AGAS 002**
LPPD: . . . . **AGAS 002F**

THREE TEA BREAKFAST.
MC: . . . . **KC 001**

Beat In Time

DOG FIGHT.
LP: . . . . **WHOS 044**

Beat Master Clay D.

YOU BE YOU AND I BE ME.
LP: . . . . **VR 3304**

Beat Poets

TOTALLY RADIO.
LP: . . . . **ILLUSION 015**

Beat Rodeo

HOME IN THE HEART OF THE BEAT.
Tracks: / Twin home towns / Everything I'm not / New love / It could happen here / (I have) everything I need / I'm not afraid (doesn't matter to me) / In the Summertime / Home in the heart of the beat / Song for an angry young man / It's been too long / While we're apart.
LP: . . . . **MIRF 1019**
MC: . . . . **MIRFC 1019**

STAYING OUT LATE WITH THE BEAT RODEO.
LP: . . . . **ZSUK 01**

Beat Runs Wild

BEAT RUNS WILD (Various artists).
LP: . . . . **WILD 1**

Beat Street (film)

BEAT STREET (Film soundtrack) (Various artists).
Tracks: / Beat street: *Grandmaster Melle Mel & The Furious Five* / Baptize the beat: *System* / Strangers in a strange world: *Burton, Jenny & Patrick Jude* / Frantic situation: *Beatstreet* / Beat street strut: *Juicy*/ Us girls: *Green, Sharon, Lisa Counts & Debbie D* / This could be the night: *Mizelle, Cindy* / Breaker's revenge: *Baker, Arthur* / Tu carino - Carmen's theme: *Blades, Ruben*.
LP: 780 154-1
MC: 780 154-4

BEAT STREET VOLUME 2 (Original soundtrack) (Various artists).
Tracks: / Son of beat street: *Jazzy Jay* / Give me all: *Jazzy Jay* / Nothin's gonna come easy: *B, Tina (See* under Tina B) / Santa's rap: *Various artists* / It's alright by me: *Various artists* / Battle cry: *Various artists* / Phony four MC's-wappin': *Various artists* / Into the night: *Various artists*.
LP: 780 158-1
MC: 780 158-4

Beat Temptation

BEAT TEMPTATION.
LP: HMS 053

Beat the Street

BEAT THE STREET (Various artists).
Tracks: / Beat the street: *Redd, Sharon* / Never give you up: *Redd, Sharon* / Straight ahead: *Redd, Sharon*/ Walk on by: *D-Train* / Contagious: *Strikers*.
LP: PRL 32253

Beat This

BEAT THIS (Various artists).
MLP: LEFTLP 16

Beating Hearts

LOVE BEAT KID.
MC: SRT 005

RETROSPECTIVE JEALOUSY.
MC: SRT 004

Beating the Meat

BEATING THE MEAT (Various artists).
LP: ODD 001

Beatles

3-D 'THE BRITISH ARE COMING'.
LP: ULS 1920V

20 GOLDEN HITS: BEATLES.
Tracks: / She loves you / I want to hold your hand / Can't buy me love / Hard day's night, A / Ticket to ride / Help / Something / We can work it out / Michelle / Hey Jude / All you need is love / Penny Lane / With a little help from my friends / Lady Madonna / Paperback writer / Ob la di ob la da / Yesterday / Get back / Here comes the sun / Let it be.
LP: 2C 070 07030
LP: 2C 266 07030

1960-1962.
LP: MA 141285
MC: MAMC 9141285

1962-1966.
Tracks: / Love me do / Please please me / From me to you / She loves you / I want to hold your hand / All my loving / Can't buy me love / Hard day's night, A / And I love her / Eight days a week / I feel fine / Ticket to ride / Yesterday / Help / You've got to hide your love away / We can work it out / Day tripper / Drive my car / Norwegian wood / Nowhere man / Michelle / In my life / Girl / Paperback writer / Eleanor Rigby / Yellow Submarine.
2LP: PCSP 717
MC: TC2 PCSP 717
2LP: PCPS 7231
MCSET: TCPCSP 7231

1967-1970.
Tracks: / Strawberry Fields forever / Penny Lane / Sgt. Pepper's lonely hearts club / With a little help from my friends / Lucy in the sky with diamonds / Day in the life, A / All you need is love / I am the walrus / Hello goodbye / Fool on the hill, The / Magical mystery tour / Lady Madonna / Hey Jude / Revolution / Back in the U.S.S.R. / While my guitar gently weeps / Ob la di ob la da / Get back / Don't let me down / Ballad of John and Yoko / Old brown shoe / Here comes the sun / Come together / Something / Octopus's garden / Let it be / Across the universe / Long and winding road, The.
2LP: PCSP 718
MCSET: TC2 PCSP 718
MCSET: TCPCSP 7241
2LP: PCSP 7241

ABBEY ROAD.
Tracks: / Come together / Something / Maxwell's silver hammer / Oh darling / Octopus's garden / I want you (she's so heavy) / Here comes the sun / Because / You never give me your money / Sun king / Mean Mr Mustard / Polythene Pam / She came in through the bathroom window / Golden slumbers / Carry that weight / End Her Majesty, The.
LP: PCS 7088
MC: TCPCS 7088

BEATLES '65.
Tracks: / She's a woman / I'm a loser / I feel fine.
LP: 1C 072 04201
MC: 1C 472 04201

BEATLES '65 (IMPORT).
LP: ST 2228

BEATLES AT THE HOLLYWOOD BOWL, THE.
Tracks: / Twist and shout / She's a woman / Dizzy Miss Lizzy / Ticket to ride / Can't buy me love / Things we said today / Roll over Beethoven / Boys / Hard day's night, A / Help / All my loving / She loves you / Long tall Sally.
LP: MFP 41 5676 1
MC: MFP 41 5676 4
LP: EMTV 4
LP: MFP 5676
MC: TCMFP 5676

BEATLES BALLADS.
Tracks: / Yesterday / Norweigan wood / Do you want to know a secret / For no one / Michelle / You've got to hide your love away / Across the universe / Here comes the sun / Blackbird / And I love her / She's leaving home / Here, there and everywhere / Let it be me.
LP: PCS 7214
MC: TCPCS 7214

BEATLES BEAT.
Tracks: / She loves you / Thank you girl / From me to you / I'll get you / I want to hold your hand / Hold me tight / Can't buy me love / You can't do that / Roll over Beethoven / Till there was you / Money / Please Mr. Postman.
LP: IC 072 04363

BEATLES BOX.
LPS: ALBUM 70
MCSET: CASSETTE 70

BEATLES BOX SET.
LPS: BC 13
MCSET: TCBC 13

BEATLES FOR SALE.
Tracks: / No reply / I'm a loser / Baby's in black / Rock and roll music / I'll follow the sun / Mr. Moonlight / Kansas City / Eight days a week / Words of love / Honey don't / Don't want to spoil the party / What you're doing / Everybody's trying to be my baby.
LP: PCS 3062
LP: PMC 1240
MC: TCPMC 1240
MC: TCPCS 3062

BEATLES GREATEST HITS.
Tracks: / Love me do / From me to you / She loves you / I want to hold your hand / Can't buy me love / Hard day's night, A / I feel fine / Ticket to ride / Help / Day tripper / We can work it out / Paperback writer / Yellow Submarine / Eleanor Rigby / All you need is love / Hello goodbye / Lady Madonna / Hey Jude / Get back / Ballad of John and Yoko.
LP: PCTC 260
MC: TCPCTC 260

BEATLES IN ITALY.
LP: 1A 062 04632

BEATLES: INTERVIEW PICTURE DISC (Beatles Conquer the USA).
LPPD: BAK 2114

BEATLES: INTERVIEW PICTURE DISC (Beatles II).
LPPD: BAK 2108

BEATLES' STORY, THE.
2LP: STB 02222

BEATLES TALK DOWN UNDER VOL. 1 (Australia 1964).
LP: GP 5001
MC: GMC 5001
LPPD: PGP 5001
MC: MBAK 6022

BEATLES TALK DOWN UNDER VOL. 2.
LPPD: VBAK 3006
MC: MBAK 6023

BEATLES TAPES (David Wigg Interviews 69-73).
Tracks: / Interview (part I) June 1969 / Give peace a chance / Interview (Part 2) June 1969 / Imagine / Interview (Part 3) June 1969 / Come together / Interview October 1971 / Interview (Part 1) March 1970 / Because / Interview (Part 2) March 1970 / Hey Jude / Interview (Part 1) March 1969 / Here comes the sun / Interview (Part 2) March 1969 / Something / Interview December 1968 / Interview July 1970 / Interview (Part 1)December 1973 / Octopus's Garden / Interview (Part 2) December 1973 / Yellow Submarine.
MCSET: TWOMC 7
2LP: 2683 068
2LP: TWOLP 7
MCSET: 847 185-4

BEATLES, THE (The White Album).
Tracks: / Back in the U.S.S.R / Dear Prudence / Glass onion / Ob la di ob la da / Wild honey pie / Continuing story of bungalow Bill / While my guitar gently weeps / Happiness is a warm gun / Martha my dear / I'm so tired / Blackbird / Piggies / Rocky raccoon / Don't pass me by / Why don't we do it in the road / I will / Julia / Yer blues / Mother nature's son / Everybody's got something to hide except me and my monkey / Sexy Sadie / Helter skelter / Long long long / Revolution 1 / Honey pie / Savoy truffle / Cry baby cry / Revolution 9 / Goodnight.
2LP: PCS 7067/8
MC: TC2 PCS 4501
2LP: PMC 7067/8

BEATLES THE - THE ULTIMATE BOX SET.
Tracks: / I saw her standing there / Anna / Chains / Boys / Please please me / Love me do / P.S. I love you / There's a place / Baby it's you / Taste of honey, A / Twist and shout / It won't be long / All my loving / Till there was you / Please Mr. Postman / Roll over Beethoven / Hard day's night, A / I'm happy just to dance with you / Can't buy me love / And I love her / Baby's in black / I'm a loser / No reply / Eight days a week / You've got to hide your love away / Act naturally / Help / Yesterday / You won't see me / Drive my car / Michelle / Girl / In my life / Taxman / Eleanor Rigby / Here, there and everywhere / Yellow submarine / For no one / Sgt. Pepper's lonely hearts club band / Lucy in the sky with diamonds / She's leaving home / Lovely Rita / Day in the life, A / Magical mystery tour / Fool on the hill / I am the walrus / Your mother should know / Hello goodbye / Strawberry fields forever / Penny Lane / All you need is love / While my guitar gently weeps / Ob la di ob la da / Revolution 1 / Revolution 9 / Maxwell's silver hammer / Here comes the sun / Across the universe / Let it be / Long and winding road, The / Get back / I'll get you / Thank you girl / This boy / She loves you / From me to you / I call your name / I feel fine / Long tall Sally / Yes it is / I'm down / She's a woman / Day tripper / We can work it out / Paperback writer / Hey Jude / Lady Madonna / Revolution / Don't let me down / Ballad of John and Yoko.
LPS: BBX 1
MCSET: TCBBX 1

BEATLES VOL I.
MC: ZCGAS 701

BEATLES VOL II.
MC: ZCGAS 702

BEATLES VOL III.
MC: ZCGAS 731

BEATLES VOL IV.
MC: ZCGAS 741

BEATLES VOL VI.
LP: ST 2358

CASSETTE SINGLES COLLECTION, THE.
Tracks: / Love me do / P.S. I love you / From me to you / Thank you girl / Please please / Ask me why / She loves you / I'll get you / I want to hold your hand / This boy / Can't buy me love / You can't do that / Hard day's night, A / Things we said today / I feel fine / She's a woman / Ticket to ride / Yes it is / Help / I'm down / We can work it out / Day tripper / Paperback writer / Rain / Yellow submarine / Eleanor Rigby / Strawberry fields forever / Penny Lane / All you need is love / Baby you're a rich man / Hello goodbye / I am the walrus / Lady Madonna / Inner light, The / Hey Jude / Revolution / Get back / Don't let me down / Ballad of John and Yoko / Old brown shoe / Something / Come together / Let it be / You know my name.
MCSET: TCBSC 1

COLLECTION: BEATLES.
LP: Unknown

COLLECTION OF BEATLES OLDIES.
Tracks: / She loves you / From me to you / We can work it out / Help / Michelle / Yesterday / I feel fine / Yellow submarine / Can't buy me love / Bad boy / Hard day's night, A / Ticket to ride / Paperback writer / Eleanor Rigby / I want to hold your hand.
LP: FA 413081-1
MC: TCFA 41 3084
LP: PMC 7016
LP: FA 3081
MC: TCFA 3081

COMPLETE SILVER BEATLES, THE.
Tracks: / Three cool cats / Crying, waiting, hoping / Besame mucho / Searchin' / Sheik of Araby, The / Money / To know him is to love him / Take good care of my baby / Memphis / Sure to fall / Till there was you / September in the rain.
LP: AFELP 1047
MC: ZCALP 1047

DAY TRIPPER (See under We Can Work It Out for details).

DECCA SESSIONS (1/1/62).
Tracks: / Three cool cats / Memphis / Besame mucho / Sheik of Araby, The / Till there was you / Searchin' / Sure to fall in love with / Take good care of my baby / Money / To know him is to love him / September in the rain / Crying, waiting, hoping.
LP: TOP 181
MC: KTOP 181

DOWNUNDER, VOL 1.
LP: RVLP 1012

DOWNUNDER, VOL 2.
LP: RVLP 1013

EARLY BEATLES, THE.
Tracks: / Love me do.
LP: ST 2309

EARLY BEATLES VOL 1.
Tracks: / I saw her standing there / Roll over Beethoven / Hippy hippy shake / Sweet little shake / Gotta go home / Twist and shout / Mr. Moonlight / Taste of honey, A / Besame mucho / Reminiscing.
LP: PHX 1004

EARLY BEATLES VOL 2.
Tracks: / Ain't nothing shakin' / To know her is to love her / Little Queenie / Falling in love again / Ask me way / Red sails in the sunset / Everybody's trying to be my baby / You ain't no friend / Talking about you / Shimmy shake.
LP: PHX 1005

EASY LISTENING BEATLES (See under Easy Listening Beatles) (Various artists).

GEORGE MARTIN TALKS ABOUT THE BEATLES (Martin, George).
LP: STUD 10

GOLDEN BEATLES (INTERVIEWS).
LP: SM 10015

GREATEST.
Tracks: / I want to hold your hand / Twist and shout / Hard day's night, A / 8 day's a week / I should have known better / Long tall Sally / She loves you / Please Mr. Postman / I feel fine / Rock and roll music / Ticket to ride / Please please me / It won't be long / From me to you / Can't buy me love / All my loving.
LP: IC 038 04207

GREATEST HITS, VOL 1: BEATLES.
LP: PCS 07533

GREATEST HITS, VOL 2: BEATLES.
Tracks: / Hard day's night, A / I feel fine / Ticket to ride / Help / Daytripper.
LP: PCS 07534

HAMBURG 1961 (See under 'Tony Sheridan featuring the Beatles') (Beatles & Tony Sheridan).

HARD DAY'S NIGHT, A (Film Soundtrack).
Tracks: / I should have known better / If I fell / I'm happy just to dance with you / And I love her / Tell me why / Can't buy me love / Hard day's night, A / Anytime at all / I'll cry instead / Things we said today / When I get home / You can't do that / I'll be back.
LP: PCS 3058
LP: PMC 1230
MC: TCPMC 1230
MC: TCPCS 3058

HARRISON TRACKS.
LP: UXP 829V

HEAR THE BEATLES TELL ALL (A Unique Collectors Item).
LP: CRV 202

HELP (Film Soundtrack).
Tracks: / Help / Night before, The / You've got to hide your love away / I need you / Another girl / You're going to lose that girl / Ticket to ride / Act naturally / It's only love / You like me too much / Tell me what you see / I've just seen a face / Yesterday / Dizzy Miss Lizzy.
LP: PCS 3071
LP: PMC 1255
MC: TCPCS 3071

HEY JUDE.
Tracks: / Can't buy me love / I should have known / Rain / Lady Madonna / Hey Jude / Old brown shoe / Don't let me down.
LP: PCS 7184
MC: TCPCS 7184

HISTORY OF THE BEATLES.
LP: MA 161285
MC: MAMC 9161285

INTERVIEWS.
Tracks: / Newscast and interview Feb 1966 / Press conference (Recorded at the Astor Hotel, Chicago) / Newscast concerning John Lennon / Red Robinson talks / Press conference (Recorded at Empire Stadium, Vancouver).
LP: . . . . **CBR 1008**
MC: . . . . **KCBR 1008**

INTERVIEWS VOLUME 2.
LP: . . . . **CBR 1047**
MC: . . . . **KCBR 1047**

INTROSPECTIVE.
LP: . . . . **LINT 5004**
MC: . . . . **MINT 5004**

LENNON TRACKS.
LP: . . . . **UXP 827V**

LET IT BE.
Tracks: / Two of us, The / Dig a pony / Across the universe / I me mine / Dig it / Let it be / Maggie Mae / I've got a feeling / One after 909 / Long and winding road, The / Get back.
LP: . . . . **PCS 7096**
MC: . . . . **TCPCS 7096**
LP: . . . . **PXS 1**

LIVE AT THE STAR CLUB, HAMBURG.
Tracks: / I saw her standing there / Roll over Beethoven / Hippy hippy shake / Sweet little sixteen / Lend me your comb / Your feets too big / Twist and shout / Mr. Moonlight / Taste of honey, A / Besame mucho / Reminicising / Kansas city / Hey hey hey / Ain't nothing shakin / To know her is to love her / Little Queenie / Falling in love again / Ask me why / Be bop a lula / Hallelujah I love her so / Red sails in the sunset / Everybody's trying to be my baby / Matchbox / Talking about you / Shimmy shake / Long tall Sally / I remember you.
2LP: . . . . **LNL 1**

LIVE BEATLES - NIPPON BUDOKAN HALL, TOKYO, THE.
LP: . . . . **BGLP 002**

LIVE: BEATLES VOL.1.
Tracks: / I'm gonna sit right down and cry over you / Roll over Beethoven / Hippy hippy shake / Sweet little sixteen / Lend me your comb / Your feets too big / Where have you been all my life / Mr. Moonlight / Taste of honey, A / Besame mucho / Till there was you / Kansas City / Hey hey hey.
LP: . . . . **SHLP 130**
MC: . . . . **SHTC 130**

LIVE: BEATLES VOL.2.
Tracks: / Ain't nothing shakin' / To know her is to love her / Little Queenie / Falling in love again / Sheila / Be bop a lula / Hallelujah I love her so / Red sails in the sunset / Everybody's trying to be my baby / Match box / Talking about you / Shimmy shake / Long tall sally / I remember you.
LP: . . . . **SHLP 131**
MC: . . . . **SHTC 131**

LIVE RECORDINGS (1962).
2LP: . . . . **LTAB 5001**
MC: . . . . **MTAB 5001**

LOVE SONGS: BEATLES.
Tracks: / Yesterday / I'll follow the sun / I'll get by / Girl in my life / Words of love / Here, there and everywhere / Something / I love her / If I fell / I'll be back / Tell me what you see / Yes it is / Michelle / It's only love / You're going to lose that girl / Every little thing I do / For no one / She's leaving home / Long and winding road, The / This boy / Norwegian wood / You've got to hide your love away / I will / P.S. I love you.
2LP: . . . . **PCSP 721**
MC: . . . . **TC 2PCSP 721**

MAGICAL MYSTERY TOUR.
Tracks: / Magical mystery tour / Fool on the hill / Flying / Blue jay way / Your mother should know / I am the walrus / Hello goodbye / Strawberry fields forever / Penny Lane / Baby you're a rich man / All you need is love.
LP: . . . . **PCTC 255**
MC: . . . . **TCPCS 3077**
LP: . . . . **SMAL 2835**

PAST MASTERS (Volumes 1 and 2).
Tracks: / Love me do / From me to you / Thank you girl / She loves you / I'll get you / I want to hold your hand / This boy / Komm gib mir deine hand / Sie liebt dich / Day tripper / We can work it out / Paperback writer / Rain / Lady Madonna / Inner light, The / Hey Jude / Revolution / Get back / Don't let me down / Ballad of John and Yoko / Old brown shoe / Across the universe / Let it be / You know my name (Look up the number).
2LP: . . . . **BPM 1**
MCSET: . . . . **TVBPM 1**

PLEASE PLEASE ME.
Tracks: / Taste of honey, A / I saw her standing there / Misery / Anna / Chains / Boys / Ask me why / Please please me / Love me do / I love you / Baby it's you / Do you want to know a secret / There's a place / Twist and shout.
LP: . . . . **PCS 3042**
LP: . . . . **PMC 1202**
MC: . . . . **TCPMC 1202**
MC: . . . . **TCPCS 3042**

RARE BEATLES.
Tracks: / Be bop a lula / Long tall Sally / Your feets too big / I'm gonna sit right down and cry over you / Where have you been all of my life? / Sheila / Hallelujah, I love her so / Till there was you / Kansas City / Hey hey hey / I remember you.
LP: . . . . **PHX 1011**

RARITIES.
Tracks: / Across the universe / Yes it is / This boy / Inner light, The / I'll get you / Thank you girl / Komm, gib mir deine Hand / You know my name / Sie liebt dich / Rain / She's a woman / Matchbox / I call your name / Bad boy / Slow down / I'm down / Long tall Sally.
LP: **2C 070 07291**
LP: . . . . **PCM 1001**

REEL MUSIC.
Tracks: / Hard day's night, A / I should have known better / Can't buy me love / And I love her / Help / You've got to hide your love away / Ticket to ride / Magical mystery tour / I am the walrus / Yellow submarine / All you need is love / Let it be / Get back / Long and winding road, The.
LP: . . . . **PCS 7218**
MC: . . . . **TCPCS 7218**

REVOLVER.
Tracks: / Taxman / Eleanor Rigby / I'm only sleeping / Love you to / Here, there and everywhere / Yellow submarine / She said she said / Good day sunshine / And your bird can sing / For no one / Doctor Robert / I want to tell you / Got to get you into my life / Tomorrow never knows.
LP: . . . . **PCS 7009**
LP: . . . . **PMC 7009**
MC: . . . . **TCPCS 7009**

ROCK 'N' ROLL (1).
Tracks: / Twist and shout / I saw her standing there / You can't do that / I call your name / Boys / Long tall Sally / Anytime at all / Drive my car / Everybody's trying to be my baby / Night before, The / I'm down / Revolution / Be bop a lula / Stand by me / Ready Teddy / Rip it up / You can't catch me / Ain't that a shame / Do you wanna dance? / Sweet little sixteen / Rock and roll music / Slow down / Money (that's what I want) / Bad boy / Matchbox / Roll over, Beethoven / Back in the USSR / Helter skelter / Taxman / Got to get you into my life / Hey bulldog / Birthday / Get back / Slippin' and slidin' / Peggy Sue / Bring it on home to me / Save me some lovin' / Bony Moronie / Ya ya / Just because / I wanna be your man / Kansas City.
LPS: **4M1 285 4084/6**

ROCK 'N' ROLL MUSIC (Original Release).
LP: . . . . **PCSP 719**

ROCK 'N' ROLL MUSIC VOL. 1.
Tracks: / Roll over, Beethoven / Dizzy Miss Lizzy / Anytime at all / Drive my car / Everybody's trying to be my baby / Night before, The / I'm down / Revolution / Back in the USSR / Helter skelter / Taxman / Got to get you into my life / Hey bulldog / Birthday / Get back.
LP: . . . . **MFP 50507**
MC: . . . . **TC MFP 50507**

ROCK 'N' ROLL MUSIC VOL. 1.
Tracks: / Twist and shout / I saw her standing there / You can't do that / I wanna be your man / I call your name / Boys / Long tall Sally / Rock'n'roll music / Slow down / Kansas City / Money (that's what I want) / Bad boy / Matchbox / Roll over Beethoven.
LP: . . . . **MFP 50506**
MC: . . . . **TCMFP 50506**

RUBBER SOUL.
Tracks: / Drive my car / Norwegian wood / You won't see me / Nowhere man / Think for yourself / Word, The / Michelle / What goes on / Girl / I'm looking through you / In my life / Wait / If I needed someone / Run for your life.
LP: . . . . **PCS 3075**
LP: . . . . **PMC 1267**
MC: . . . . **TCPCS 3075**

SAVAGE YOUNG BEATLES, THE.
Tracks: / Why? / Cry for a shadow / Let's dance / Ya ya / What'd I say / Ruby baby / Take out some insurance / Sweet Georgia Brown.
LP: . . . . **CFM 701**

SGT.PEPPER'S LONELY HEARTS CLUB BAND.
Tracks: / Sgt.Pepper's lonely hearts club band / With a little help from my friends / Lucy in the sky with diamonds / Getting better / Fixing a hole / She's leaving home / Being for the benefit of Mr. Kite / Within you without you / When I'm sixy four / Lovely Rita / Good morning good morning / Day in the life, A.
LP: . . . . **PCS 7027**
LP: . . . . **PMC 7027**
MC: . . . . **TCPCS 7027**
LP: . . . . **PEPPER 1**
MC: . . . . **TCPEPPER 1**

SILVER BEATLES.
LPPD: . . . . **AR 30003 C**
LPPD: . . . . **AR 30003 B**

SOMETHING NEW.
LP: . . . . **IC 072 04600**

SOMETHING NEW (IMPORT).
LP: . . . . **ST 2108**

SONGS OF THE BEATLES (See under Songs Of The..) (Various artists).

SWEET GEORGIA BROWN (See under Sheridan, Tony) (Sheridan, Tony & The Beatles).

TIMELESS.
LPPD: **10004**

TIMELESS II.
LPPD: . . . . **UPS 352V**

TONY SHERIDAN FEATURING THE BEATLES.
Tracks: / Why / Cry for a shadow / Let's dance / Ya ya / What'd i say / Ruby baby / Take out some insurance / Sweet Georgia Brown.
LP: . . . . **CN 2007**
MC: **CN4 2007**
LP: . . . . **TOP 108**

WHITE ALBUM, THE (See under Beatles, The).

WHY (See under Sheridan, Tony) (Sheridan, Tony & The Beatles).

WITH THE BEATLES.
Tracks: / It won't be long / All I've got to do / All my loving / Don't bother me / Little child / Till there was you / Please Mr. Postman / Roll over Beethoven / Hold me tight / You really got a hold on me / I wanna be your man / Devil in her heart / Not a second time / Money.
LP: . . . . **PCS 3045**
LP: . . . . **PMC 1206**
MC: . . . . **TCPMC 1206**
MC: . . . . **TCPCS 3045**

WORDS AND MUSIC.
2LP: . . . . **CR 5149**
MCSET: . . . . **CRT 5149**

YEAH, YEAH, YEAH.
LP: **3C 06404145**
MC: **3C 26404145**

YELLOW SUBMARINE (Film Soundtrack).
Tracks: / Yellow Submarine / Only a northern song / All you need is love / Hey bulldog / It's all too much / All together now / Pepperland / Sea of time / Sea of holes / Sea of monsters / March of the meanies / Pepperland laid to waste / Yellow submarine in Pepperland.
LP: . . . . **PCS 7070**
MC: . . . . **TCPCS 7070**
LP: . . . . **PCM 7070**

YELLOW SUBMARINE (VIDEO) (See Under Yellow Submarine).

Beatles Songs

GOLDEN HOUR OF THE BEST OF THE BEATLES' SONGS (Various artists).
Tracks: / Michelle: *Overlanders* / Eleanor Rigby: *London Pops Orchestra* / Yesterday: *Stapleton, Cyril* / Let it be: *George, John* / Yellow submarine: *Knight, Peter* / World without love: *Stapleton, Cyril* / Nowhere man: *Settlers* / Something: *Four Pianos of Drex Nelson, The* / Ob la di ob la da: *Stapleton, Cyril* & His Show Band / Hey Jude: *Hatch, Tony and the satin brass* / When I'm sixty four: *Ball, Kenny & His Jazzmen* / Long and winding road, The: *London Pops Orchestra* / Ticket to ride: *Stapleton, Cyril* / Fool on the hill, The: *Hatch, Tony & Jackie Trent* / Maxwells silver hammer: *London Pops Orchestra* / She loves you: *Stapleton, Cyril* / Norwegian wood: *Hatch, Tony Orchestra, The* / Goodnight: *Stapleton, Cyril*.
LP: . . . . **GH 523**

Beatmasters

ANYWAYAWANNA.
Tracks: / Who's in the house / Hey DJ/I can't dance to that music you're play / Burn it up (on the groove trip) / Warm love / Ska train / Rok da house (w.e.f.u.n.k.) / Make me feel / Don't stop the beat / Midnight girl / Sarayet-sayam sembtae (pt.1) / Rok da house (7" original) (CD only.) / Burn it up (7" radio edit) (CD only.).
LP: . . . . **LEFT 010**
MC: . . . . **LEFTC 010**

Beatnigs

BEATNIGS.
LP: . . . . **VIRUS 65**
MC: . . . . **VIRUS 65C**

Beatnik Flies

BEHIND THESE WALLS.
LP: . . . . **ROSE 154**

FROM PARTS UNKNOWN.
LP: . . . . **ROSE 86**

Beatniks

BEATNIKS.
LP: . . . . **STAT LP 13**

Beatons of Mabou

BEATONS OF MABOU, THE.
LP: . . . . **ROUNDER 7011**

Beats International

LET THEM EAT BINGO.
LP: **842 196 1**
MC: **842 196 4**

Beattie, Johnny

TRIBUTE TO THE KINGS OF SCOTTISH COMEDY.
LP: . . . . **KLP 67**
MC: . . . . **ZCKLP 67**

WELCOME TO THE CEILIDH.
LP: . . . . **NEVLP 164**
MC: . . . . **NEVC 164**

Beau Brummels

AUTUMN IN SAN FRANCISCO.
Tracks: / Laugh laugh / Just a little / You tell me why / Don't talk to strangers / In good time / Sad little girl / Still in love with you baby / Stick like glue / That's if you want me to / Can it be / When it comes to your love / Gentle wanderin' ways / I grow old / Lonely man / She sends me.
LP: . . . . **ED 141**

BRADLEY'S BARN.
Tracks: / Turn around / Added attraction, An / Deep water / Long walking down to misery / Little bird / Cherokee girl / I'm a sleeper / Loneliest man in town / Love can fall a long way down / Jessica / Bless you California.
LP: . . . . **ED 151**

Beau, Heinie

HEINIE BEAU AND HIS HOLLYWOOD JAZZ QUARTET (Beau, Heinie & His Hollywood Jazz Quartet).
LP: . . . . **HRC 101**

Beau, Toby

MORE THAN A LOVE SONG.
Tracks: / Dream girl / It must have been the moonlight / Then you can tell me goodbye / You and I should be forever / Look for the light / High roller / I just wanna love you / Boogie woogie melody / She used to be mine / All right now.
LP: . . . . **PL 13119**

TOBY BEAU.
Tracks: / Moonshine / California / Same ole line / Into the night / My angel baby / Westbound train / Buckaroo / Watching the world go by / Bulldog / Wink of an eye / Broken down cowboy.
LP: . . . . **PL 12771**
MC: . . . . **PK 12771**

Beaujolais Band

MIND HOW YOU GO.
Tracks: / Banda llego / Ain't no sunshine / Descarga na'ma' / Waterfalls / Fine vintage / Old hat, new hat / Mount Kashima / So much for that.
LP: . . . . **JAZIDLP 024**

Beaumont, Howard

AS TIME GOES BY VOL 1.
LP: . . . . **GRS 1142**

AS TIME GOES BY VOL. 2 (Beaumont, Howard & John Taylor).
LP: . . . . **GRS 1166**

CHRISTMAS MAGIC.
Tracks: / Sleigh ride / Mary's boy child / In dulci jubilo / Winter wonderland / Let it snow, let it snow, let it snow / Good King Wenceslas / Jingle bells / Rudolph the red nosed reindeer / Frosty the snowman / Christmas carols / Hark the herald angels sing / Away in a manger / Once in Royal David's city / While shepherds watched their flocks by night / Silent night / Ding dong merrily on high / When a child is born / I saw mommy kissing Santa Claus / Christmas melody / Holly and the ivy, The / Joy to the world / God rest ye merry gentlemen / Christmas song, The / Ave Maria.
LP: . . . . **GRS 1068**

ELECTRIFYING.
Tracks: / Without a song / Bermuda triangle / You needed me / Dallas hoedown - Turkey in the straw / Jambalaya / Juliet Bravo, Theme from / Hungry years / String of pearls / Continental, The / Piccolino, The / Somewhere over the rainbow /

Romance / Superman love theme / Just the way you are / Star wars (Vido toccato.).
LP: GRS 1101

EMINENT ARTISTRY.
Tracks: / Skyliner / Arthur's theme / Tomorrow / Waltz / Makin' whoopee / They can't take that away from me / Ease on down the road / Lonely shepherd / Easier said than done / Chopin nocturne op 27 no.2 / We're all alone / Samba / Cavaquinho / Wedding samba, The / Zambesi / To hell with him / Boomerang / Ride like the wind / Let it run / Love party / Listen to your heart / Kiss it and make it better / I saw him first.
LP: GRS 1123
MC: KGRS 1123

FASCINATING RHYTHM.
Tracks: / Fascinating rhythm / Crazy rhythm / I got rhythm / Way you look tonight / Time was / I'm gonna wash that man right out of my hair / Cock-eyed optimist / Many a newday / Whisper not / Our love is here to stay / Perdido / Undecided / Amazing grace / Best of times, The / I am what I am / Other side of me, The / Early Autumn / Poor butterfly / Harlem nocturne / Triste / Quiet nights / Days of wine and roses / Just for you.
MC: KGRS 1195

HOWARD BEAUMONT PLAYS....
LP: GRS 1061

IT TAKES TWO TO TEMPO (Beaumont, Howard & John Taylor).
LP: GPR 22

MOONLIGHTING (Plays Kawai SR6).
MC: KGRS 1202

PLAY THE WURLITZER AT COTTON (Beaumont, Howard/Bryan Jones).
LP: GRS 1174

REAL HAMMOND SOUND, THE.
LP: GRS 1158

SOUNDS NEW.
MC: KGRS 1170

Beausoleil

ALLONS A LAFAYETTE.
LP: ARHOOLIE 5036
MC: C 5036

BAYOU BOOGIE.
Tracks: / Zydeco gris gris / Fais pas ca / It's you I love / Dimanche apres-midi / Madame Bozo / Kolinda / Maman Rosin Boudreaux / Chez Seychelles / Jongle a moi / Flame will never die, The / La vaise de malchanceaux / Beausoleil boogie.
LP: REU 1027
LP: ROUNDER 6015
MC: ROUNDER 6015C

HOT CHILI MAMA (Beausoleil & Michael Doucet).
LP: ARHOOLIE 5040
MC: C 5040

SPIRIT OF CAJUN MUSIC.
LP: 6031
MC: 6031 TC

ZYDECO GRIS GRIS.
LP: 6054
MC: 6054 TC

Beautiful Bend

BEAUTIFUL BEND.
Tracks: / That's the meaning / Boogie motion / Make that feeling come again / Ah-do it.
LP: TKR 82548

Beautiful Dreams

BEAUTIFUL DREAMS (Various artists).
Tracks: / My way: *Various artists* / Whiter shade of pale, A: *Various artists* / Greensleeves: *Various artists*/ My funny valentine: *Various artists* / Plaisir d'amour: *Various artists* / I'll never fall in love again: *Various artists* / Yesterday: *Various artists* / Vergib mein nicht: *Various artists* / Nearness of you: *Various artists* / Santa Lucia: *Various artists* / Fur elise: *Various artists* / You stepped out of a dream: *Various artists.*
LP: 2872 166
MC: 3472 166
LP: 2872 166

Beautiful Happiness

BEAUTIFUL HAPPINESS (Various artists).
LP: HAPPY 001

Beautiful Music

BEAUTIFUL MUSIC (Various artists).
2LP: CR 005
MCSET: CRT 005

BEAUTIFUL MUSIC (1) (Various artists).
LP: ABM 750
MC: ZC ABM 750

BEAUTIFUL MUSIC (2) (Various artists).
MC: ZC ABM 751
LP: ABM 751

BEAUTIFUL MUSIC, BEAUTIFUL WORDS (Various artists).
Tracks: / Autumn leaves: *Various artists* / Summer knows: *Various artists* / If I ruled the world: *Various* artists / Sweet gingerbread man: *Various artists* / Isn't she lovely: *Various artists* / If ever I would leave you: *Various artists* / Love story: *Various artists* / Annie's song: *Various artists* / Misty: *Various artists* / Raindrops keep falling on my head: *Various artists.*
2LP: RIM 7001/3

IMAGES.
MC: KNMC 16016

MORE BEAUTIFUL MUSIC (Various artists).
Tracks: / Born free: *Various artists* / Love letters: *Various artists* / My cherie amour: *Various artists*/ Very thought of you, The: *Various artists* / Aquarius: *Various artists* / I'll be seeing you: *Various artists*/ This is the song: *Various artists* / For once in my life: *Various artists* / Bridge over troubled water: *Various* artists / Mrs. Robinson: *Various artists* / By the time I get to Phoenix: *Various artists* / Love me tonight: *Various artists* / Impossible dream, The: *Various artists* / Raindrops keep falling on my head: *Various artists*/ Alfie: *Various artists* / Man in love, A: *Various artists* / Moulin Rouge: *Various artists* / Good morning starshine: *Various artists* / Exodus: *Various artists* / More: *Various artists* / People: *Various* artists / Sunny: *Various artists* / I have dreamed: *Various artists* / Girl from Ipanema: *Various artists*/ Lawrence of Arabia: *Various artists.*
2LP: CR 080
MCSET: CRT 080

Beautiful Pea Green

GET RELIGION.
Tracks: / Powerhouse / Hammers of Islam / Screw, The / Vase, The / Too much / Nostalgia / Among the ruins.
LP: TMLP 26

OBSESSIONS.
LP: TMLP 20

Beautiful South

CHOKE.
Tracks: / Tonight I fancy myself / Let love speak up itself / I've come for my award / I think the answer's yes / Mother's pride / Rising of Grafton Street, The / My book / Should've kept my eyes shut / Lips / Little time, A / I hate you (but you're interesting).
LP: 8282331
MC: 8282334

WELCOME TO THE BEAUTIFUL SOUTH.
Tracks: / Song for whoever / Have you ever been away? / From under the covers / I'll sail this ship alone / Girlfriend / Straight in at 37 / You keep it all in / Woman in the wall / Oh Blackpool / Love is / I love you (but you're boring).
LP: AGOLP 16

Beauty

BEAUTY (Various artists).
LP: PINKY 15

Beauty & The Beast

BEAUTY AND THE BEAST.
MC: HA 2

BEAUTY AND THE BEAST (Well Loved Tales Age Up to 9).
MC: PLB 58
MC: TS 323

OF LOVE AND HOPE (Music & poetry from Beauty & The Beast) (Various artists).
Tracks: / Beauty and the beast: *Various artists* / Acquainted with the night: *Various artists* / Laura's theme: *Various artists* / Margaret's theme-longing: *Various artists* / On her own-she walks in beauty: *Various artists*/ Night of beauty: *Various artists* / Single night, A: *Various artists* / Angel's theme: *Various artists*/ Devin's theme-I arise from the dreams of thee: *Various artists* / Promise remembered, A: *Various artists* / Journey's end - Sonnet - CXVI: *Various artists* / Dancing light - Sonnet - XXIX: *Various artists* / Quest, The - Letters to a young poet (excerpt): *Various artists* / Fear: *Various artists* / You darkness: *Various artists*/ Father remembers - composed on Westminster Bridge: *Various artists* / Intimations of immortality: *Various artists*/ To cast all else aside: *Various artists* / Riches, not gold: *Various artists* / Catherine's lullabye: *Various* artists / Somewhere I have never travelled: *Various artists* / First time I loved forever, The: *Various artists*/ Happy life: *Various artists* / This is the creature: *Various artists* / Return, The: *Various artists*/ Broken dreams-ode: *Various artists.*
LP: EST 2115
MC: TCEST 2115

Beauty the Beat...

BEAUTY THE BEAT ON BROADWAY (Various artists).
LP: BEAUT 1
MC: BEAUTC 1

Beauvoir, Jean

DRUMS ALONG THE MOHAWK.
Tracks: / Feel the heat / Never went down / Missing the young days / Rockin' in the street / Sorry I missed your wedding day / Drive you home / Sam's songs play on and on / This is our house / If I was me / Nina.
LP: OVED 222
MC: OVEDC 222
LP: V 2370
MC: TCV 2370

JACKNIFED.
Tracks: / Jacknifed / Standing on my own feet / Gamblin' man / Alone again / Searching for a light / Dyin' at your door / Spend your life with me / Find my way home / If love could only / Jimmy.
LP: V 2511
MC: TCV 2511

Beaver & Krause

GANDHARVA.
Tracks: / Soft / White / Saga of the blue beaver / Nine Moons In Alaska / Walkin' by the river / Gandharva / By Your Grace / Good places / Short film for David / Bright shadows.
LP: K 46130

Beaver Towers (bk)

BEAVER TOWERS.
MCSET: DTO 10562

Bebb, Richard (nar)

WIFE OF BATH'S TALE (see under Chaucer, Geoffrey (aut)) (Scales, Prunella (nar) & Richard Bebb (nar)).

Bebey, Francis

AKWAABA.
MC: OMA 105C

Bebo

BEBO IN A DUB STYLE.
LP: BB 097

Be-Bop...

ANTHOLOGY - BEBOP BOYS (Various artists).
Tracks: / Bebop in pastel: *Various artists* / Fool's fancy: *Various artists* / Bombay: *Various artists*/ Ray's idea: *Various artists* / Serenade to a square: *Various artists* / Good kick: *Various artists*/ Seven up: *Various artists* / Blues in bebop: *Various artists* / For heckler's only: *Various artists*/ Smokey hollow jump: *Various artists* / Boppin' the blues: *Various artists* / Moody speaks: *Various artists*/ Tropicana: *Various artists* / Blues to a debutante: *Various artists* / Scene changes, The: *Various artists*/ Mean to me: *Various artists* / Baby I'm coming home: *Various artists* / Way you look tonight: *Various artists*/ Ornithology: *Various artists* / Get out of that bed: *Various artists* / Body and soul: *Various artists*/ Birdland story, The: *Various artists* / I got the blues: *Various artists* / Honeysuckle rose: *Various artists*/ Wee dot: *Various artists* / Solitude: *Various artists* / Lion roars: *Various artists* / On the house: *Various artists* / Dinky: *Various artists* / Leo's bells: *Various artists* / Sweet talkin' Leo: *Various artists* / Swingin' for lowe: *Various artists.*
2LP: SJL 2225

BE BOP BOOGIE (Various artists).
Tracks: / River rock: *Hager, Don & The Hot Tots* / Be bop boogie: *Hager, Don & The Hot Tots* / Liza Jane bop: *Hager, Don & The Hot Tots* / I love you dear: *Hager, Don & The Hot Tots* / Boppin' the blues: *Rockin' Ronnie*/ Little heart attacks: *Johnson, Glenn* / Sweet thing: *Green, Bobby & Sportsmen* / Putting it together: *Johnson,* Glenn & Acorns / Run here honey: *Johnson, Glenn & Acorns* / Heart trouble: *Callicutt, Dudley* / Saturday night: *Deloacher Sisters* / Ramble: *Go Boys.*
LP: KK 826

BE-BOP (Various artists).
LP: 509170

BE-BOP 61 (From the East Coast 1960-62)) (Various artists).
LP: MC5 87

BE-BOP BE-BOP (Various artists).
Tracks: / Congo blues: *Norvo, Red & His Selected Sextet* / You're not the kind: *Vaughan, Sarah/Tadd Dameron's Orchestra*/ Shaw 'nuff: *Gillespie, Dizzy All Star Quintet* / Parkers mood: *Parker, Charlie All Stars* / Things to come: *Gillespie, Dizzy & His Orchestra* / Relaxin' at Camarillo: *Parker, Charlie & His New Stars* / Embraceable you: *Parker, Charlie Quintet* / Koko: *Parker, Charlie Reboppers* / Lemon drop: *Herman, Woody & His Orchestra*/ Un poco loco: *Powell, Bud Trio* / Jahbero: *Dameron, Tadd Septet* / Misterioso: *Monk, Thelonious Quartet*/ What is this thing called love: *Roach, Max Quintet* / Stop time: *Silver, Horace Quintet.*
LP: NW 271

BE-BOP BOOGIE (Various artists).
LP: RR 2025

BE-BOP ERA (Various artists).
Tracks: / Epistrophy: *Williams, Cootie* / Good bait: *Gillespie, Dizzy* / Keen and peachy: *Herman, Woody*/ Disc jockey jump: *Krupa, Gene* / Lemon drop: *Krupa, Gene* / Donna Lee: *Thornhill, Claude* / Yardbird suite: *Thornhill, Claude* / Godchild: *Jackson, Chubby* / Elevation: *Lawrence, Elliot* / Double date: *Metronome* All Star Band / No figs: *Metronome All Star Band* / Don't blame me: *Davis, Miles/Tadd Dameron* / Ornithology: *Parker, Charlie* / 'Round midnight: *Parker, Charlie.*
LP: 4610961
MC: 4610964

BE-BOP IS WHERE IT'S AT VOL 1 (Various artists).
LP: HD 6609

BE-BOP IS WHERE IT'S AT VOL 2 (Various artists).
LP: HD 6610

BE-BOP KEYBOARD MASTERS (Various artists).
Tracks: / Fairyland: *Various artists* / Woody'n you: *Various artists* / Just one of those things: *Various* artists / Honeysuckle rose: *Various artists* / Star eyes: *Various artists* / N.Y.: *Various artists*/ Day in Paris, A: *Various artists* / Yardbird suite: *Various artists* / Taboo: *Various artists* / Mighty like a rose: *Various artists* / 'S wonderful: *Various artists* / Just you and me: *Various artists* / Moon was yellow, The: *Various artists* / 'Round about midnight: *Various artists* / Embraceable you: *Various artists*/ Scotch blues: *Various artists* / Confirmation: *Various artists* / Darn that dream: *Various artists*/ They can't take that away from me: *Various artists* / Wait and see: *Various artists* / Perdido: *Various* artists / Dream a little dream of me: *Various artists* / Wade Legge's blues: *Various artists* / Swedish folk song, A: *Various artists* / Dance of the infidels: *Various artists* / Aren't you glad you're you: *Various artists* / These foolish things: *Various artists* / Why don't you believe me: *Various artists.*
2LP: VJD 574

BE-BOP REVOLUTION (Various artists).
Tracks: / Night in Tunisia, A: *Gillespie, Dizzy* / 52nd Street theme: *Gillespie, Dizzy* / Epistrophy: *Clarke,* Kenny & His 52nd Street Boys / Boppin' the blues: *Thompson, Lucky* / Two base hit: *Gillespie, Dizzy* / Cubana be, Cubana bop: *Gillespie, Dizzy* / Manteca: *Gillespie, Dizzy* / Guarachi guaro: *Gillespie, Dizzy* / Royal roost (rue capital): *Clarke, Kenny* / Jumpin' with Symphony Sid: *Gillespie, Dizzy* / Anthropology: *Gillespie,* Dizzy / Allen's alley: *52nd Street All Stars* / Half step down please: *Hawkins, Coleman* / Woody 'n you: *Gillespie,* Dizzy / Good bait: *Gillespie, Dizzy* / Oop bop sh bam: *Clarke, Kenny* / Dizzier and dizzier: *Gillespie, Dizzy.*
LP: NL 82177
MC: NK 82177

BE-BOP VOCALS (Various artists).
Tracks: / I don't want love: *Various artists* / Bye bye blackbird: *Various artists* / Sugar Ray: *Various* artists / Cool whalin': *Various artists* / But beautiful: *Various artists* / Gambler's blues: *Various* artists / Let there be love: *Various artists* / But beautiful (2): *Various artists* / Bless my soul: *Various* artists / Beautiful memories: *Various artists* / I'll remember April: *Various artists* / Gone with the wind: *Various artists* / Oop-pop-a-da: *Various artists* / Especially to you: *Various artists* / Nobody knows: *Various artists* / Searching blues: *Various artists* / Nightingale: *Various artists.*
LP: SPJ 135

Be-Bop DeLuxe

AXE VICTIM/FUTURAMA.
Tracks: / Axe victim / Love is swift arrows / Jet silver and the dolls of Venus / Third floor heaven / Night creatures / Rocket cathedrals / Adventures in a Yorkshire landscape / Jets at dawn / No trains to heaven / Darkness / Stage whispers / Love with the madman / Maid in heaven / Sister seagull / Sound track /

Music in dreamland / Jean Cocteau / Between the worlds / Swan song.
2LP: . . . . **EDP 154 6793**

BE BOP DELUXE SINGLES A'S & B'S.
Tracks: / Jet silver and the dolls of Venus / Between the worlds / Maid in heaven / Ships in the night / Kiss of light / Japan / Panic in the world / Electrical language / Third floor heaven / Lights / Crying to the sky / Shine / Futurist manifesto / Blue as a jewel / Surreal / Estate.
LP: . . . . **SHSM 2034**
MC: . . . . **TCSHSM 2034**

BOP TO THE RED NOISE.
Tracks: / Ships in the night (1976) / Life in the air age (1976) / Maid in heaven (1975) / Jean Cocteau (1975) / 3rd floor heaven (1974) / Rocket cathedrals (1974) / No trains to heaven (1974) / Orphans of Babylon (1976) / Modern music (1976) / New precision (1978) / Don't touch me (1979) / For young moderns (1979).
LP: . . . . **DOJOLP 42**

DRASTIC PLASTIC.
Tracks: / Electrical language / New precision / New mysteries / Surreal estate / Love in flames / Panic in the world / Dangerous stranger / Superenigmatix / Visions of endless hopes / Possession / Islands of the dead / Blimps / Lovers are mortal / Lights.
LP: . . . . **SHSP 4091**

LIVE - IN THE AIR-AGE.
Tracks: / Life in the air age / Ships in the night / Piece of mind / Fair exchange / Mill Street junction / Adventures in a Yorkshire landscape / Blazing apostles / Shine / Sister seagull / Maid in heaven.
2LP: . . . . **SHVL 816**

MODERN MUSIC.
Tracks: / Orphans of Babylon / Twilight capers / Kiss of light / Bird charmer's destiny, The / Gold at the end of my rainbow, The / Bring back the spark / Modern music / Dancing in the moonlight (all alone) / Honeymoon on Mars / Lost in the neon world / Dance of the Uncle Sam humanoids / Modern music (reprise) / Forbidden lovers / Down on terminal street / Make the music magic / Futurist manifesto / Quest for the harvest of the stars / Autosexual.
LP: . . . . **SHSP 4058**

RAIDING THE DIVINE ARCHIVES (Best of Be Bop Deluxe).
Tracks: / Jet Silver and the Dolls of Venus / Adventures in a Yorkshire landscape / Maid in Heaven / Ships in the night / Life in the air age / Kiss of light / Sister Seagull / Modern music / Japan / Panic in the world / Bring back the spark / Forbidden lovers / Electrical Language / Fair exchange (CD only.) / Sleep that burns (CD only.) / Between the worlds (CD only.) / Music in dreamland (CD only.).
LP: . . . . **EMS 1130**
MC: . . . . **TCEMS 1130**

SUNBURST FINISH.
Tracks: / Fair exchange / Heavenly homes / Ships in the night / Crying to the sky / Sleep that burns / Beauty secrets / Life in the air age / Like an old blues / Crystal gazing / Blazing apostles / Shine (CD only.) / Speed of the wind (CD only.) / Blue as a jewel (CD only.).
LP: . . . . **REV LP 71**
MC: . . . . **REV MC 71**
LP: . . . . **SHSP 4053**
LP: . . . . **FA 3004**

Be-Bop Preservation...

PIED PIPER OF HAMELIN SUITE (Be-Bop Preservation Society).
Tracks: / Hamelin / Council cakewalk / Rats / Pied piper / Mayor's got the blues / Little boy lost / Town band birthday.
LP: . . . . **SPJ 500**

Becaud, Gilbert

AL'OLYMPIA.
Tracks: / Y'a pas d'lapin dans le chapeau / So far away from Courbevoie / Viens nous aider / C'est en Septembre / Toi et moi / Credo / Chaque enfant qui nait, A / Les tantes Jeanne / Quand Jules est au violin / Le pommier a pommes / L'orange / Le pianiste de Varsovie.
LP: **2C 068 72267**

DISQUE D'OR VOL. 1.
Tracks: / Le train de la vie / C'est en Septembre / Un peu d'amour et d'amitie / Charlie, t'iras pas au paradis / L'important c'est la rose / Mademoiselle Lise / Nathalie / Et maintenant / Le jour ou la pluie viendra / Les marches de provence / La corrida / Alors raconte... / Quand tu dances / Viens.
LP: **2C 070 72002**

DISQUE D'OR VOL. 2.
Tracks: / Mes mains / Le pianiste de Varsovie / L'absent / Quand Jules est au violin / Les tantes Jeanne / T'es venu de loin / Quand il est mort le poete / Les petites mad'maselles / Je reviens te chercher / Les cerisier's sont blancs / La vente aux encheres / La solitude, ca n'existe pas / Chante / Et le spectacle continue / Jaloux de tout / Ballade pour un fou / Souffrir par toi n'est pas souffrir / Juste comme un enfant / C'est une Andalouse / Terre de France / Le partiner / Le coeur volcan / 4 heures du matin / Le petit vieillard qui chantait mal / Des jours entiers a t'aimer / Ivanovitch.
LP: **2C 070 72015**

GILBERT BECAUD.
LP: **2C 068 72189**

L' IMPORTANT C'EST LA ROSE.
MC: **2526244**

LITTLE LOVE AND UNDERSTANDING, A.
Tracks: / Little love and understanding, A / Masquerade, The / Something missing / If only I could live my life again / It's wonderful to be alive / What now my love / Importance of your love, The / Mexican singing bird, The / Sand and sea / Days the rains came, The / My pretty summer princess / Living / Let it be me (CD only.) / Merry go round (CD only.) / Summertime's the time for love (CD only.) / My love don't say a word (CD only.) / L'amour (CD only.) / That's all (CD only.).
LP: . . . . **SKLR 5209**
MC: . . . . **KSKC 5209**

MOI JE VEUX CHANTER.
LP: **2C 070 14856**

MON COPAIN.
LP: **S2L 5199**

Bechet Legacy

ODE TO BECHET (see under Wilber, Bob) (Bechet Legacy/Bob Wilber).

ON THE ROAD (see under Wilber, Bob) (Bechet Legacy/Bob Wilber).

Bechet, Sidney

1947: SIDNEY BECHET (See under Manone, Wingy) (Bechet, Sidney & Wingy Manone).

1939-44.
LP: . . . . **LPJT 65**

BACK TO MEMPHIS (Bechet, Sidney & Sammy Price's Bluesicians).
LP: **500053**

BECHET.
LP: . . . . **GNPS 9012**

BECHET VOLUME 5 (1941-43) (The Panassie Session) (Bechet, Sidney, Mezzrow & T. Ladnier).
Tracks: / Mood indigo (pt.1) / Mood indigo (pt.2) / Rose room / Lady be good / Lady be good (pt 2) / What is this thing called love? / After you've gone / Bugle call rag / Ole miss rag / St. Louis blues / Revolutionary blues / Comin' on with the come on (pt.1) / Comin' on with the come on (pt.2) / Careless love (swingin' for Mezz) / Careless love (swingin' for Mezz) (pt.2) / Royal Garden blues (part 1) / Royal Garden blues (part 2) / Everybody loves my baby (part 1) / Everybody loves my baby (part 2) / I ain't gonna give nobody none of my jelly roll (pt.1) / I ain't gonna give nobody none of my jelly roll (pt.2) / If you see me comin' (pt1) / If you see me comin' (pt2) / Gettin' together (pt.1) / Gettin' together (pt.2) / Rosetta / Minor jive / World is waiting for the sunrise, The / Who? / Blues my baby gave to me, The / Rompin'.
2LP: . . . . **NL 89751**
MCSET: . . . . **NK 89751**

BECHET-SPANIER BIG FOUR (Bechet, Sidney & Muggsy Spanier Big Four).
Tracks: / Sweet Lorraine / Lazy river / China boy / Four or five times / That's plenty / If I could be with you / Squeeze me / Sweet Sue.
LP: . . . . **SM 3090**

BIG FOUR WITH MUGGSY SPANIER 1940.
LP: . . . . **S 1392**

BLUEBIRD SESSIONS 1932-1943, THE.
Tracks: / Sweetie dear / I want you tonight / I've found a new baby / Lay your racket / Maple leaf rag / Shag / Ja da / Really the blues / When you and I were young Maggie / Weary blues / Oh, didn't he ramble / High society / I thought I heard Buddy Bolden say / Winin' boy blues / Indian Summer / One o'clock jump / Preachin' blues / Sidney's blues / Shake it and break it / Old man blues / Nobody knows the way I feel this morning / Wild man blues / Make me a pallet on the floor / St. Louis blues / Blues in thirds / Blue for you, Johnny / Ain't misbehavin' / Save it pretty mama / Stompy Jones / Muskrat ramble / Coal black shine / Egyptian fantasy / Baby won't you please come home / Slippin' and slidin' / Sheik of Araby, The / Blues of Bechet / Swing parade / I know that you know and you know that I know / When it's sleep-time down South / I ain't gonna give nobody none of my jelly / I'm coming Virginia / Limehouse blues / Georgia cabin / Texas moaner blues / Strange fruit / You're the limit / Rip up the joint / Suey / Blues in the air / Mooche, The / Laughin' in rhythm / 12th Street rag / Mood indigo / Rose room / Oh lady be good / What is this thing called love / After you've gone / Bugle call rag / Old Miss Blues.
LPS: . . . . **NL 90317**
MCSET: . . . . **NK 90317**

BLUES IN PARIS.
2LP: **400672**

BOSTON 1945 (Bechet/Bunk).
LP: . . . . **JA 48**

BRUSSELS WORLD FAIR CONCERT 1958.
LP: **500203**

BRUXELLES 1954.
LP: **502012**

COMPLETE SIDNEY BECHET 1 & 2 (1932 - 1941).
Tracks: / One o'clock jump / Preachin' blues / Old man blues / Blues in thirds / Ain't misbehavin' / Save it pretty mama / Stomp Jones / Muskrat ramble / Coal black shine / Sweetie dear / Lay your racket / Maple leaf rag / Ja da / Really the blues / Weary blues / Indian Summer / I want you tonight / I've found a new baby / When you and I were young Maggie / Maggie / Sidney's blues / Shake it and break it / Wild man blues / Nobody knows the way I feel this morning / Make a pallet on the floor / St. Louis blues / Blues for you / Johnny / Egyptian fantasy.
2LP: . . . . **NL 89760**
MCSET: . . . . **NK 89760**
2LP: . . . . **PM 42409**

COMPLETE SIDNEY BECHET 3 & 4 (1941).
Tracks: / I'm coming Virginia (take 1) / I'm coming Virginia (take 2) / Limehouse blues / Geogia cabin (take 1) / Geogia cabin (take 2) / Texas moaner (take 1) / Texas moaner (take 2) / Strange fruit / You're the limit (take 1) / You're the limit (take 2) / Rip up the joint / Suey (take 1) / Suey (take 2) / Blues in the air (take 1) / Blues in the air (take 2) / Mooche, The / Mooche, The (take 2) / Laughin' in rhythm / 12th Street rag (take 1) / 12th Street rag (take 2) / I know that you know (take 3) / Egyptian fantasy / Baby won't you please come home? / Slippin' and slidin' / Sheik of Araby, The / Blues of Bechet / Swing parade (take 1) / Swing parade (take 2) / I know that you know (take 1) / I know that you know (take 2) / When it's sleepy time down South / I ain't gonna give nobody none of my jelly roll (take 1) / I ain't gonna give nobody none of my jelly roll (take 2).
2LP: . . . . **NL 89759**
MCSET: . . . . **NK 89759**
2LP: . . . . **PM 43262**

DEUX GEANTS DU JAZZ (Bechet, Sidney & Django Reinhardt).
Tracks: / Roses de Picardie / Dardanella / Petite fleur / Onge d'automne / Willow weep for me / Laura / Down by the old mill stream / Gypsy love song / Stormy weather / Folie amphion / Lover man / Improvisation sur une danse Norvegienne / Melodie au crepuscule / I can't give you anything but love.
LP: **429010**
MC: **829010**

FABULOUS SIDNEY BECHET, THE.
Tracks: / Original Dixieland one-step / Blues my naughty sweetie gives to me / That's a plenty / Ballin' the Jack / Avalon / Rose of the Rio Grande / Black and blue / Sweet Georgia Brown / All of me / Ding dong daddy.
LP: . . . . **BLP 1207**

GIANT OF JAZZ VOL.1.
LP: . . . . **BLP 1203**
MC: . . . . **TCBST 12034**

HIS WAY 1951.
LP: . . . . **PUMPKIN 102**

HOLD TIGHT 1938-46.
LP: . . . . **JJ 603**

IN PHILADELPHIA VOL.2.
LP: . . . . **JA 37**

IN THE GROOVE.
MC: **771506**

INEDITS.
LP: **502001**

INEDITS 1939-42.
LP: **502013**

INEDITS (DOUBLE).
2LP: **406503**

JAZZ AT STORYVILLE.
LP: . . . . **BLP 60902**

JAZZ CLASSICS IN DIGITAL STEREO (Sidney Bechet 1924-1938).
Tracks: / Okey doke / Early every morn / Shag / Polka dot rag / Viper mad / Black stick / Sweet patootie / I've found a new baby / Characteristic blues / Mandy make up your mind / Maple leaf rag / Ja da / Really the blues / When you and I were young Maggie / Weary blues / When the sun sets down south.
LP: . . . . **REB 700**
MC: . . . . **ZCF 700**

JAZZ CLASSICS VOL.1.
Tracks: / Blue horizon / Weary blues / Summer time / Blame it on the blues / Milenberg joys / Days beyond recall / Salty dog / Dear old Southland / Weary way blues.
LP: . . . . **BLP 1201**

JAZZ CLASSICS VOL.2.
Tracks: / St. Louis blues / Up in Sidney's flat / Lord let me in the lifeboat / Pounding heart blues / Changes made / High society / Jackass blues / Jazz me blues / Blues for Tommy Ladnier / Old stack o'lee blues.
LP: . . . . **BLP 1202**

JAZZ NOCTURNE VOL.1.
LP: **502007**

JAZZ TIME VOL.9.
LP: **502709**

JAZZ TIME VOL.20 (Bechet, Sidney & Django Reinhardt).
LP: **502720**

KING JAZZ VOL.5 (See under Mezzrow-Bechet) (Bechet-Mezzrow Quintet#Septet).

LA GRANDE PARADE.
2LP: **400001**

LA MUSIQUE C'EST MA VIE.
2LP: **430329**

LE DISQUE D'OR.
LP: **509001**

LE DOUBLE DISQUE D'OR VOL.1.
2LP: **416001**

LE DOUBLE DISQUE D'OR VOL.2.
2LP: **416033**

LE SOIR OU..L'ON CASA L'OLYMPIA.
2LP: **400316**

LEGENDARY SIDNEY BECHET, THE.
Tracks: / Maple leaf rag / I've found a new baby / Weary blues / Really the blues / High society / Indian Summer / Sidney's blues / Shake it and break it / Wild man blues / Save it, pretty mama / Stompy Jones / Muskrat ramble / Baby, won't you please come home / Sheik of Araby, The / When it's sleepy time down South / I'm coming Virginia / Strange fruit / Blues in the air / Mooche, The / Twelfth St. rag / Mood indigo / What is this thing called love?.
LP: . . . . **NL 86590**
MC: . . . . **NK 86590**

LEGENDARY SIDNEY BECHET, THE (2).
LP: . . . . **GNPS 9037**

LIVE IN NEW YORK.
LP: **2M 056 64846**
MC: **2M 256 64846**

LOUIS ARMSTRONG/SIDNEY BECHET (see under Armstrong, Louis).

MASTERS OF JAZZ VOL.4.
LP: . . . . **SLP 4104**

MEMORIAL SET VOL.1.
Tracks: / House party / Perdido street stomp / Minor swoon / Sheik of Araby, The / Breathless blues / Really the blues(Parts 1 & 2) / Ole miss / Blowin' the blues away / I'm gonna give nobody to my Jelly Roll / Perdido street stomp / Old school / Gone away blues / De luxe stomp / Out of the Gallion.
LP: . . . . **SM 3078**

MEMORIAL SET VOL.2.
Tracks: / Groovin' the minor / Where am I? / Tommy's blues / Revolutionary blues / I want some / I'm speaking my mind / Kaiser's last break / Funky butt / Delta mood / Blues of the roaring twenties.
LP: . . . . **SM 3079**

NEW ORLEANS DAYS (Bechet, Sidney & Louis Armstrong).
LP: **500093**

NEW ORLEANS, LOUISIANA.
LP: **509071**

NEW ORLEANS STYLE OLD AND NEW (Bechet, Sidney & Bob Wilber).
Tracks: / Jelly roll blues / At a Georgia camp meeting / National emblem march / Hindustan / I'll take New Orleans music / Willie the weeper / Willie the weeper no.2 / Mabel's dream / Mabel's dreams (take 2) / Wild cat blues / Wild cat blues no.2 / Blues for Fowler / Blues for Fowler no.2.
LP: **6.25492**

ORIGINALS, THE.
MC: **714003**

PARISIAN ENCOUNTER (Bechet, Sidney & Teddy Buckner).
Tracks: / Bravo / Aubergines / I can't get started / Souvenirs / Blue festival / Weary blues / Ain't misbehavin' / Sugar / Who's sorry now / All of me.
LP: **500113**

PLATINUM FOR....
Tracks: / Petite fleur / Promenade aux Champs D'Elysee / A-tu le cafard / Passport to paradise / Marchand de poissons / Si tu vois ma mere / Ce mossieu qui parle / Bechet creole blues / Madame Becassine / Blues in Paris / Moulin a cafe / Sobbin' and cryin' / Les oignons / Premier bal / Egyptian fantasy / Temperamental / Buddy Bolden story / Dans les rue's d'Antibes.
LP: **522 008**
MC: **722 008**

RAREST OF ALL RARE PERFORMANCES VOL 1.
LP: . . . . **KLJ 20033**

REED ALBUM VOL 1.
LP: . . . . **MERITT 10**

REFRESHING TRACKS -1958 VOL.1.
Tracks: / I only have eyes for you / Man I love, The / Exactly like you / These foolish things / Jeepers creepers / I never knew / All the things you are / All of me / Embraceable you / Wrap your troubles in dreams / Rose room / I don't mean a thing / Pennies from Heaven / Rosetta / Once in a while / Sweet Georgia Brown / St. Louis Blues / On the sunny side of the street / Sister Kate / I'm coming Virginia.
2LP: . . . . **VJD 541**

REFRESHING TRACKS VOL.2.
2LP: . . . . **VJD 552**

SIDNEY BECHET.
LP: . . . . **ENT LP 13027**
MC: . . . . **ENT MC 13027**

SIDNEY BECHET 1923/38.
LP: . . . . **LPJT 52**

SIDNEY BECHET: 1945-51.
LP: . . . . **LPJT 76**
MC: . . . . **MCJT 76**

SIDNEY BECHET AND FRIENDS (Bechet, Sidney & Friends).
Tracks: / High society / On the sunny side of the street / Honeysuckle rose / I can't believe that you are in love with me / Wrap your troubles in dreams / It had to be you / Baby won't you please come home / Please don't talk about me when I'm gone / Ooh boogie / After you've gone / I'm goin' way down home / Margie / Dutch swing college blues / King Porter stomp / Weary way blues / Panama / Tiger rag / Texas moaner blues / That's a plenty / Swanee river / Limehouse blues / Black stick / Les oignons.
MC: **8406334**

SIDNEY BECHET AND NEW ORLEANS JAZZ BAND.
LP: . . . . **MERITT 2**

SIDNEY BECHET AND THE NEW ORLEANS FEETWARMERS VOL.2 (Bechet, Sidney & New Orleans Feetwarmers).
Tracks: / Blues for you / Ain't misbehavin' (part 1) / Save it pretty mama / Coal black shine / Egyptian fantasy / Baby won't you please come home / Slippin' and slidin' / Sheik of Araby, The / Blues of bechet / Swing parade / I know that you know / When it's sleepy time down South / I ain't gonna give nobody none of my Jellyroll / Ain't misbehavin' (part 2).
LP: . . . . **SM 3572**

SIDNEY BECHET AND THE NEW ORLEANS FEETWARMERS VOL.1 (Bechet, Sidney & New Orleans Feetwarmers).
Tracks: / Sweetie dear / I want you tonight / I've found a new baby / Lay your racket / Maple leaf rag / Shag / Indian Summer / One o'clock jump / Sidney blues / Shake it and break it / Old man blues / Wild man blues / Nobody knows the way I feel this morning / Make me a pallet on the floor / Blues in thirds.
LP: . . . . **SM 3571**

SIDNEY BECHET AND THE NEW ORLEANS FEETWARMERS VOL. 3 (Bechet, Sidney & New Orleans Feetwarmers).
Tracks: / I'm coming Virginia / Limehouse blues / Georgia cabin / Texas moaner / Strange fruit / You're the limit / Rip up the joint / Blues in the air / Mooche, The / Laughin' in rhythm / Twelfth St. rag / Mood indigo / Rose room / Oh lady be good / What is this thing called love?.
LP: . . . . **SM 3573**

SIDNEY BECHET COLLECTION (20 Golden Greats).
Tracks: / Jelly roll blues / National emblem march / Hindustan / At a Georgia camp meeting / I'll take New Orleans music / Ain't misbehavin' / Sheik of Araby, The / Cindy blues / Wild cat blues / Blues for you / I'm coming, Virginia / Coal black shine / Suey / You're the limit / Kansas City man blues / Summertime / Baby won't you please come home? / St. Louis blues / Polka dot stomp rag / I know that you know.
LP: . . . . **DVLP 2066**
MC: . . . . **DVMC 2066**

SIDNEY BECHET JUBILEE & CLAUDE LUTER (C.Luter et Son Orchestre) (Bechet, Sidney & Claude Luter).
2LP: **400011**

SIDNEY BECHET LEGACY.
LP: **502608**

SIDNEY BECHET SESSIONS (With Mezzrow and Joe Sullivan) (Bechet, Sidney, Mezzrow & Joe Sullivan).
LP: . . . . **SLP 4028**

SIDNEY BECHET VOL.1.
Tracks: / Petite fleur / Marchand de poissons / Temperamental / Promenade aux Champs-Elysses / A moi d'payer / Les oignons / Dans les rues d'Antibes / Premier bal / Si tu vois ma mere / Passport to Paradise / As-tu le cafard / Au secours.
LP: . . . . **JR 145**

SIDNEY BECHET WITH.....
Tracks: / Blues, The / Baby won't you please come home / Charleston / I know that you know / That's a plenty / Black and blue / You are some pretty doll / Farewell blues / Summertime / Sensation rag.
LP: . . . . **JA 44**
LP: . . . . **KLJ 20004**

SIDNEY BECHET WITH EDDIE CONDON ALL STARS (Bechet, Sidney/ Eddie Condon).
Tracks: / Buddy Bolden stomp / Black and blue / Summertime / Honeysuckle Rose / Argone stomp / High society / Blues in my heart / Sweet Georgia Brown / September song / Just one of those things / Blues / Ole Miss.
LP: . . . . **QU 029**

SIDNEY'S BLUES.
Tracks: / Sweetie dear / Maple leaf rag / Shag / Ja da / Really the blues / Indian Summer / Sidney's blues / Blues in thirds / Blues in the air / Suey / Mooche, The / Mood indigo.
LP: . . . . **CL 89800**
MC: . . . . **CK 89800**

SISSLE AND HIS SIZZLING SYNCOPATORS (See under Sissle, Noble) (Bechet, Sidney/Sissle, Noble).

SOME OF THESE DAYS.
LP: . . . . **30 CV 952**

SUPERB SIDNEY.
LP: **54613**
MC: **40 54613**

THIRTIES, THE.
Tracks: / Black stick / Loveless love / Basement blues / Roll on, Mississippi, roll on / Viper mad / When the sun sets down South / Sweet patootie / Uncle Joe / Freight train blues / My daddy rocks me / You can't live in Harlem / T'ain't a fit night out for man or beast / Rhythm of Broadway moon / Polka dot rag.
LP: . . . . **AFS 1025**

TROPICAL MOOD, 1931-39.
LP: . . . . **ST 1014**

WHEN A SOPRANO MEETS A PIANO (Bechet, Sidney & Solal Martial).
LP: **500087**

Beck, Bogert, Appice

BECK, BOGERT, APPICE (see Beck, Jeff).

Beck, Elder Charles

COMPLETE ELDER CHARLES BECK.
LP: . . . . **ELE 2-200**

Beck Family

DANCIN' ON THE CEILING.
Tracks: / Can't shake the feeling / Dancin' on the ceiling / Words and music / Nobody but you / Falling in love again / Can you feel it / Butterflies / Love-a-thon.
LP: . . . . **SHE 8534**

Beck, Gordon

MUSIC MAKERS (see under Merrill, Helen) (Beck, Gordon/ Helen Merrill).

NEW WORLD (see Lockwood, Didier etc.) (Beck, Gordon/Didier Lockwood/ Tony Williams/Niels Pedersen).

Beck, Jack

O LASSIE, LASSIE.
Tracks: / Birnie Bouzie / Matt Hyland / Twa corbies / Kilbowie Hill / Bleacher lass o' Kelvinhaugh / Bound to be a row / Ned of the hill / Jolly beggar, The / Love is teasin' / Merchant's son, The.
LP: . . . . **TRAX 027**
MC: . . . . **CTRAX 027**

Beck, Jeff

ANTHOLOGY.
LP: . . . . **MA 14185**
MC: . . . . **MAMC 914185**

BECK, BOGERT, APPICE (Beck, Bogert, Appice).
Tracks: / Black cat moan / Lady / Oh to love you / Superstition / Sweet sweet surrender / Why should I care about you / Lose myself with love / Livin' alone / I'm so proud.
LP: . . . . **EPC 32491**
MC: **40 32491**
LP: . . . . **EPC 65455**
LP: . . . . **ESSLP 011**
MC: . . . . **ESSMC 011**

BECKOLA.
LP: **2C 062 90496**
LP: . . . . **SCX 6351**

BEST OF JEFF BECK (1967-69) (Featuring Rod Stewart).
Tracks: / Shapes of things / Morning dew / You shook me / I ain't superstitious / All shook up / Jailhouse rock / Plynth (water down the drain) / Hi ho silver lining / Tallyman / Love is blue / I've been drinking / Rock my plimsoul / Beck's bolero / Rice pudding.
LP: . . . . **FA 41 3125 1**
MC: . . . . **FA 41 3125 4**

BLOW BY BLOW.
Tracks: / It doesn't really matter / She's a woman / Constipated duck / Air blower / Scatterbrain / Cause we've ended as lovers / Thelonious / Freeway jam / Diamond dust.
LP: . . . . **EPC 32367**
MC: **40 32367**

COSA NOSTRA BECK-OLA.
Tracks: / All shook up / Spanish boots / Girl from Mill Valley / Jailhouse rock / Plynth (water down the drain) / Hangman's knee / Rice pudding.
LP: . . . . **ED 2606001**
MC: . . . . **ED 2606004**

FLASH.
Tracks: / Ambitious / Gets us all in the end / Escape / People get ready / Stop, look and listen / Get workin' / Ecstacy / Night after night / You know, we know.
LP: . . . . **EPC 26112**
MC: **40 26112**

JEFF BECK'S GUITAR SHOP.
Tracks: / Guitar shop / Behind the veil / Where were you / Day in the house / Sling shot / Savoy / Big block / Stand on it / Two rivers.
LP: **4634721**
MC: **4634724**

LIVE: JEFF BECK (Beck, Jeff with Jan Hammer Group).
Tracks: / Freeway jam / Earth (still our only home) / She's a woman / Full moon boogie / Darkness earth in search of a sun / Scatterbrain / Blue wind.
LP: . . . . **EPC 32297**
MC: **40 32297**

ROCK GIANTS.
LP: **544 51**

ROUGH AND READY.
Tracks: / Got the feeling / Situation / Short business / Max's tune / I've been used / New ways / Train train / Jody.
LP: **32037**
MC: **40 32037**

ROUGH AND READY/JEFF BECK GROUP.
Tracks: / Ice cream cakes / Glad all over / Tonight I'll be staying here with you / Sugar cane / I can't give back the love I feel for you / Going down / I gotta have a song / Highways / Definitely maybe / Got the feeling / Situation / Max's tune / I've been used / New ways / Short business / Jody.
2LP: . . . . **TFOLP 19**
MC: . . . . **TFOMC 19**

THERE AND BACK.
Tracks: / Star cycle / Too much to lose / You never know / Pump / El Becko / Golden road / Space boogie / Final peace.
LP: . . . . **EPC 83288**
LP: . . . . **EPC 32197**
MC: **40 32197**

TRUTH.
Tracks: / Shapes of things / Let me love you / Morning dew / You shook me / Ol' man river / Greensleeves / Rock my plimsoul / Beck's bolero / Blues de luxe / I ain't superstitious.
LP: . . . . **FA 3155**
MC: . . . . **TCFA 3155**
LP: . . . . **ATAK 42**
MC: . . . . **TC ATAK 42**

TRUTH/BECKOLA (Beck, Jeff Group).
Tracks: / Shapes of things / Let me love you / Morning dew / You shook me / Ol' man river / Greensleeves / Rock my plimsoul / Beck's bolero / Blues deluxe / I ain't superstitious / All shook up / Spanish boots / Girl from Mill Valley / Jailhouse rock / Plynth (water down the drain) / Hangman's knee / Rice pudding.
MC: . . . . **TCEMS 1379**

WIRED.
Tracks: / Led boots / Come dancing / Goodbye pork pie hat / Head for backstage pass / Blue wind / Sophie / Play with me / Love is green.
LP: . . . . **EPC 32067**
MC: **40 32067**
LP: **86012**

Beck, Robin

TROUBLE OR NOTHING.
Tracks: / Hide your heart / If you were a woman (and I was a man) / Save up all your tears / Tears in the rain / Sleepin' with the enemy / Don't lose any sleep / Hold back the night / In a crazy world like this / Heart for you, A / First time.
LP: **838 768 1**
MC: **838 768 4**

Becker, David

LONG PETER MADSEN.
Tracks: / Long Peter Madsen / Pepe / Struttin' down Hollywood Boulevard / Bop du bu bop / Days of wine and roses / Reconnaissance / Nazareth / Pictures of the past.
LP: . . . . **IMCA 5865**
MC: . . . . **IMCAC 5865**

Becker, Ernest

EVERYDAY HEROICS OF LIVING & DYING (see under Everyday Heroics of...).

Becker, Jason

PERPETUAL BURN.
Tracks: / Altitudes / Perpetual blues / Mabel's fatal fable / Temple of the absurd / Eleven blue Egyptians / Dweller in the cellar / Opus pocus.
LP: . . . . **RR 9528 1**

Becker, Margaret

NEVER FOR NOTHING.
LP: . . . . **BIRD R 190**
MC: . . . . **BIRD C 190**

RECKONING, THE.
LP: . . . . **SP R 1161**
MC: . . . . **SP C 1161**

Becker, Randy

KISSES (See under Das Pferd) (Becker, Randy & Das Pferd).

Becker, Walter

COLLECTION: BECKER/FAGEN (Becker, Walter & Donald Fagen).
Tracks: / Brain tap shuffle / Brooklyn / Mock turtle song / Yellow peril / Soul ram / Ida Lee / Any world (that I'm welcome to) / You go where I go / This seat's been taken / Berry Town / More to come / Little with sugar, A / Take it out on me / Android warehouse / Roaring of the lamb / Charlie Free / Sun mountain / Horse in town / Stone piano / Parker's band / Oh wow, it's you.
2LP: . . . . **CCSLP 193**
MC: . . . . **CCSMC 193**

Beckers, Chris

HIGH TENSION.
Tracks: / Blow back, buddy / Seven star motel / Gentle grande / Funky red shoes / Metal bass / Cafe solo (por dos) / South Avenue.
LP: . . . . **CCR 016**
MC: . . . . **MCCR 016**

Becket

TENTH ANNIVERSARY.
LP: . . . . **PT 0700**

VINCYMAS.
LP: . . . . **SBLP 07**

YUH SWEET.
LP: . . . . **PYF 0080**

Becket (Film)

BECKET (Original soundtrack) (Various artists).
LP: . . . . **DL 79117**
LP: **254 883 1**

Becket House

BECKET HOUSE (Various artists).
Tracks: / Still: *Brighter* / Strange: *All Over the Place* / Hacienda sweat: *Synchro System* / Prototype: *Durutti Column* / One way mind: *Cunningham, John* / Morning dew: *Telescopes* / Electra: *Becketts*/ Time to time: *Pooh Sticks* / Drop the mic: *Breaking The Illusion* / I can wait: *Are You Mr. Riley.*

LP: PHEW 002

Beckett, Chris

20 COUNTRY AND WESTERN HITS (Beckett, Chris and the Sandpipers).
Tracks: / Crying time / Together again / Burning bridges.
LP: HRL 106

Beckett, Harry

LIVE VOL 2. (Beckett, Harry & Courtney Pine).
LP: WW 2030

PICTURES OF YOU.
Tracks: / What's the secret / Pictures of you / One step ahead / In case you hadn't heard Mrs Smith is here / Chosen one, The.
LP: PAL 2

Beckett, Samuel (plrt)

MACGOWRAN SPEAKING BECKETT (MacGowran, Jack (nar)).
LP: CCT 3

SAMUEL BECKETT (Cusack, Cyril (nar)).
MC: 1169

Becketts

LUST.
MLP: BG2L MLP 002
MC: BG2L MMC 002

Beckford, Keeling

COMBINATION.
LP: SSPL 20

STAY TUNED.
LP: KRV 190

Beckingham, Keith

TWO SIDES OF KEITH BECKINGHAM.
Tracks: / Show business / Dancing years, The / Girl from Ipanema / Thoroughly modern Millie / Cherokee / Mr. Lucky / Yeh, yeh / Ebb tide / Makin' whoopee / Song that I sing, The / Cuckoo waltz / Tico tico.
MC: AC 165

Bedford, David

ODYSSEY, THE.
Tracks: / Penelope's shroud / King Aeolus / Penelope's shroud (2) / Phaeacian games, The / Penelope's shroud (3) / Sirens, The / Scylla and Charybois / Penelope's shroud (4) / Circe's island / Penelope's shroud completed / Battle in the hall, The.
LP: OVED 153

RIGEL 9.
Tracks: / Forest, The (part 1 of overture : Scene 1) / Anders' capture (part 3 of overture ; scene 1) / City, The (part 1 of scene 2) / Anders and the red one (part 2 of scene 2) / Kapper and Lee in the forest (part 1 of scene 3) / Death of the orange one, The (part 2 of scene 3) / Funeral procession, The (part 3 of scene 3) / Anders alone in the city (part 1 of scene 4) / Ritual song / Anders flight through the forest (part 3 of scene 4) / At the ship : countdown & lift-off (part 4 of scene 4) / Finale.
LP: CHC 77
MC: CHCMC 77

RIME OF THE ANCIENT MARINER, THE.
Tracks: / Rime of the ancient mariner, The.
LP: OVED 152

Bedknobs & ... (film)

BEDKNOBS AND BROOMSTICKS (Studio cast) (Various artists).
Tracks: / Old home guard: *Various artists* / Step in the right direction: *Various artists* / Age of not believing: *Various artists* / With a flair: *Various artists* / Eglantine: *Various artists* / Portobello Road: *Various* artists / Beautiful briny: *Various artists* / Substitutiary locomotion: *Various artists* / Old home guard: *Various artists* / Reprise: *Various artists*.
LP: DQ 1326

Bedlam Rovers

FROTHING GREEN.
LP: HEY 017 1
MC: HEY 017 4

Bedlem

BEDLEM.
Tracks: / I believe in you (fire in my body) / Hot lips / Sarah / Sweet sister Mary / Seven long years / Beast, The / Whiskey and wine / Lookin' through love's eyes / Putting on the flesh / Set me free.
LP: METALP 104

Bednarczyk, Stefan

LIVE AT THE MORGUE.
Tracks: / Pusillanimity / 'Sunny View Rest Home' commercial / Taboo / N.W.3 / Gold day of youth / Seance humoresque / Visual aids / Dinosaur can-can / Champagne aria, The / With a charm that is all your own / Valentine's song / Twelve days of warning / Young executives square dance / Children's action workshop (When Santa kissed the fairy on the Christmas tree).
LP: ALA 3005
MC: ZC ALA 3005

Bedroom Window (film)

BEDROOM WINDOW (Original soundtrack) (Various artists).
LP: STV 81307

Bedtime For Bonzo

HAVE A NICE DAY.
LP: FACE 12

ULTIMATE REFRESHMENT.
LP: SWING 001

Bedtime Stories

BEDTIME STORIES (Various artists).
MC: 0600560902

Bee, Celi

FLY ME ON THE WINGS OF LOVE.
Tracks: / Fly me on the wings of love / Higher and higher / Love, look what you've done to me / Midnight passion / Epilogue / Boomerang / Can't let you go / For the love of my man / You're the best thing.
LP: TKR 83351

Bee Gees

1967-70.
Tracks: / Massachusetts / Don't forget to remember / Words / Lonely days / August October / Spicks and specks / I.O.I.O. / To love somebody / I can't see nobody / World / I've gotta get a message to you / New York mining disaster 1941.
LP: 825 748-1
MC: 825 748-4
LP: 2872 242
MC: 3472 242

BEST OF THE BEE GEES.
LP: 6886 553
LP: 583-063

BEST OF THE BEE GEES VOL.1.
Tracks: / Holiday / I've gotta get a message to you / I can't see nobody / Words / I started a joke / Spicks and specks / First of May / World / Massachusetts / To love somebody / Every christian lion-hearted man / New York mining disaster 1941.
LP: SPELP 83
MC: SPEMC 83

BEST OF THE BEE GEES VOL.2.
Tracks: / How can you mend a broken heart / I.O.I.O. / Don't wanna live inside myself / Melody fair / My world / Let there be love / Saved by the bell / Lonely days / Morning of my life / Don't forget to remember / And the sun will shine / Run to me / Man for all seasons / Alive.
LP: 2394 106
MC: 3216 005
LP: SPELP 90

CUCUMBER CASTLE.
Tracks: / If I only had my mind on something else / Then you left me / I was the child / Sweetheart / My thing / Turning tide / I.O.I.O. / Lord, The / I lay down and die / Bury me down by the river / Chance of love, The / Don't forget to remember.
LP: 2383-010

EARLY DAYS, THE.
Tracks: / Where are you / Spicks and specks / Playdown / Big chance / Glass house / How many birds / Secondhand people / I don't know why I bother with myself / Monday's rain / Tint of blue / Jingle jangle / Born a man.
MCSET: DTO 10008

EARLY DAYS VOL. 3.
Tracks: / I was a lover, a leader of men / Follow the wind / Claustrophobia / Jamie McPheeters / Everyday I have to cry / Take hold of that star / Could it be / To be or not to be / Three kisses of love / Cherry red / All of my life / Don't say goodbye.
LP: SHM 982

E.S.P..
Tracks: / E.S.P. / You win again / Live or die / Giving up the ghost / Longest night / This is your life / Angela / Overnight / Crazy for your love / Backtafunk.
LP: WX 83
MC: WX 83 C

FIRST.
Tracks: / Close another door / Craise Frinton Kirk-Royal Academy of Arts / Cucumber Castle / Every christian lion-hearted man / I can't see nobody / I close my eyes / In my own time / New York mining disaster 1941 / One minute woman / Please read me / Red chair fade away / To love somebody / Turn of the century.
LP: SPELP 56
MC: SPEMC 56
LP: 2479 133
LP: 583 012

GREATEST HITS: BEE GEES.
Tracks: / Child of the world / Don't throw it all away / Fanny / How deep is your love / If I can't have you / Jive talkin' / Love me / Love so right / Love you inside out / More than a woman / Night fever / Nights on Broadway / Rest of your love on me / Spirits (having flown) / Stayin' alive / Too much heaven / Tragedy / Wind of change / You should be dancing / You stepped into my life.
LP: RSDX 001
MC: RSDXC 001

GREATEST HITS: BEE GEES VOL.1.
Tracks: / Massachusetts / To love somebody / Holiday / I can't see nobody / Don't forget to remember / Words / I started a joke / Saved by the bell / World / New York mining disaster 1941 / I've gotta get a message to you / Tomorrow, tomorrow / First of May / How can you mend a broken heart / My world / Lonely days.
LP: 8152 211
MC: 8152 224

HERE AT LAST - BEE GEES LIVE.
Tracks: / I've gotta get a message to you / Love so right / Edge of the universe / Come on over / Can't keep a good man down / New York mining disaster 1941 / Run to me / World / Holiday / Can't see nobody / I started a joke / Massachusetts / How can you mend a broken heart / To love somebody / You should be dancing / Boogie child / Down the road / Words / Wind of change / Nights on Broadway / Jive talkin' / Lonely days.
MCSET: 3517 013

HORIZONTAL.
LP: 582-020

IDEA.
Tracks: / Let there be love / In the Summer of his years / Down to earth / I've gotta get a message to you / When the swallows fly / I started a joke / Swan song / Kitty can / Indian gin and whisky dry / Such a shame / Idea / I have decided to join the airforce / Kilburn towers.
LP: 583-086

I'VE GOTTA GET A MESSAGE TO YOU.
Tracks: / To love somebody / I've gotta get a message to you / My life has been a song / I am the world / World one million years / It doesn't matter much to me.
LP: CN 2028
MC: CN4 2028

LIVING EYES.
Tracks: / Living eyes / He's a liar / Paradise / Don't fall in love with me / Soldiers / I still love you / Wild flower / Nothing could be good / Cryin' every day / Be who you are.
LP: SPELP 22
MC: SPEMC 22
LP: RSBG 002

MAIN COURSE.
LP: SPELP 111
MC: SPEMC 111

MASSACHUSETTS.
LP: CN 2002
MC: CN4 2002

MUSIC FOR THE MILLIONS.
Tracks: / Holiday / I can't see nobody / I started a joke / First of May / Massachusetts / Every Christian lionhearted man / New York mining disaster 1941 / I've gotta get a message to you / Words / Turn of the century / World / To love somebody.
LP: 2479 303
MC: 3215 080

ODESSA.
Tracks: / Odessa (city on the Black Sea) / You'll never see my face again / Marley Purt Drive / Black diamond / Melody fair / Suddenly / Whisper whisper / Lamplight / Sound of love / Give your best / Seven sea symphony / With all nations (international anthem) / Laugh in your face / Never say never again / First of May / British opera,The / Edison.
2LP: 2674 012
MC: 825 451-4
2LP: 583-049/50

ONE.
Tracks: / Ordinary lives / Bodyguard / Tears / Flesh and blood / House of shame / One / It's my neighbourhood / Tokyo nights / Wish you were here / Will you ever let him.
LP: WX 252
MC: WX 252C

SPIRITS HAVING FLOWN.
Tracks: / Tragedy / Too much heaven / Love you inside out / Reaching out / Spirits (having flown) / Living together / I'm satisfied / Until.
LP: SPELP 48
MC: SPEMC 48
LP: RSBG 001

TALES FROM THE BROTHERS GIBB (A History in Song).
MCSET: 843911 4

THEIR MOST BEAUTIFUL SONGS.
LP: BRLP 45
MC: BRMC 45

VERY BEST OF THE BEE GEES.
Tracks: / You win again / How deep is your love / Night fever / Tragedy / Massachusetts / I've gotta get a message to you / You should be dancing / New York mining disaster 1941 / World / First of May / Don't forget to remember / Saved by the bell / Run to me / Jive talkin' / More than a woman / Stayin' alive / Too much heaven / Ordinary lives / To love somebody (CD and cassette only.) / Nights on Broadway (CD and cassette only.).
LP: 847 339 1
MC: 847 339 4

WORDS (OLD GOLD) (See under Gibb, Robin/Saved By the Bell).

Beecher, Melody

SUGAR CANDY.
LP: JUSLP 09

Beeching, Jenny

NO MORE SAD GOODBYES.
LP: AP 029

Beef

LIVING IN A HEE HEE HAY.
LP: LOS 002

Beefeater

HOUSE BURNING DOWN.
LP: DISCHORD 23

PLAYS FOR LOVERS.
LP: DISCHORD 17

Beer, Mark

DUST ON THE ROAD.
LP: TAO 001

Beer, Phil

MANDOLIN.
Tracks: / Dan Tucker / Morning sky / Banks of the Bann / Three pretty maidens / Good King Arthur's days / Green rag / Up to the rigs / Buddy can you spare a dime.
LP: GVR 206

Beerdrop Explodes

BEERDROP EXPLODES (Various artists).
LP: BEER 1

Beethoven (composer)

BEETHOVEN (Various artists).
MC: DLCMC 206

BEETHOVEN: PIANO SONATAS OP.109-111 (Serkin).
MC: 4274984

BEETHOVEN QUARTETS (Delme string quartet).
MC: KH 88032

BEETHOVEN QUARTETS (Smithson Quartet).
MC: RK 77029

BEETHOVEN SEXTETS (Swiss Chamber Players).
MC: MCE 75544

BEETHOVEN'S GREATEST HITS (Various artists).
MCSET: 40 79017

DAS KONZERT (Berlin Philharmonic Orchestra).
Tracks: / Symphony no.1 / Piano concerto no.1.
MC: 404 580 3

END GAMES (see under Brodsky Quartet) (Brodsky Quartet).

FIDELO Includes Mozart's Zauberflote highlights. (Various artists).
MC: 4277134

HEART OF BEETHOVEN Conducted by Wyn Morris (London Symphony Orchestra).
Tracks: / Piano concerto No. 5 in E flat, Opus 73a / Symphony No. 3 in E flat, Opus 55 'Eroica' / Trio for piano, violin & cello in B flat Op 97 / Symphony No. 5 in C minor, Opus 67 / Bagatelle in A minor, Wo 58 'Fur elise' / Sonata No. 14 in C sharp minor, Opus 27 No. 2 / Overture: the creatures of prometheus Opus 43 / Sonata for violin & piano No.5 in F, Opus 24 / Symphony No. 6 in F 'Pastoral', Opus 68.
LP: DUET 25

MOONLIGHT PIANO SONATAS (Hungerford, Bruce).
MC: VETC 6519

PIANO CONCERTO NO. 5 IN E MAJOR OP 73, 'EMPOROR' (Israel Philharmonic Orchestra).
MC: 4250254

PIANO CONCERTOS NOS 3 & 4 (BEETHOVEN) (BBC Symphony Orchestra).
MC: 426 062-4

PIANO SONATAS NOS. 14 ETC (Barenboim).
MC: 4278034

PIANO SONATAS NOS 15, 21 & 26.
MC: 426 068-4

STRING QUARTETS OP127 & 135 (Quartetto Italiano).
MC: 422 840-4

SYMPHONIES NOS 4 AND 8 (Concertgebouw Orchestra Amsterdam).
MC: 420 539-4
LP: 420 539-1

SYMPHONY NO.1 (BEETHOVEN) (in C) (London Symphony Orchestra).
Tracks: / Symphony No. 1 in C, Opus 21 (Beethoven) / Symphony No. 2 in D, Opus 36 (Beethoven).
MC: . . . . CIMPC 929

SYMPHONY NO.1/NO.3 (BEETHOVEN) (Schroder).
MC: . . . . RK 77030

SYMPHONY NO.1/NO.8 (BEETHOVEN) (Halle Orchestra).
Tracks: / Symphony no.1 op.21 (Beethoven) / Symphony no.8 op.93 (Beethoven).
LP: . . . . ALH 917
MC: . . . . ZC ALH 917

SYMPHONY NO.2/NO.4 (BEETHOVEN) (Halle Orchestra).
Tracks: / Symphony no.2 op.36 (Beethoven) / Symphony no.4 op.60 (Beethoven).
LP: . . . . ALH 909
MC: . . . . ZC ALH 909

SYMPHONY NO.3 (BEETHOVEN) Eroica (Northern Sinfonia of England).
Tracks: / Symphony no.3 op.55 (Beethoven).
LP: . . . . ALH 946
MC: . . . . ZC ALH 946

SYMPHONY NO.3 (BEETHOVEN) Eroica (Halle Orchestra).
Tracks: / Symphony no.3 op.55 (Beethoven).
LP: . . . . ALH 901
MC: . . . . ZC ALH 901

SYMPHONY NO.5 (BEETHOVEN) (Halle Orchestra).
Tracks: / Symphony no.5 op.67 (Beethoven) / Coriolan overture op.62.
LP: . . . . ALH 908
MC: . . . . ZC ALH 908

SYMPHONY NO.6 (BEETHOVEN) Pastoral (Halle Orchestra).
Tracks: / Symphony no.6 op.68 (Beethoven).
LP: . . . . ALH 902
MC: . . . . ZC ALH 902

SYMPHONY NO.6 (BEETHOVEN) (Unknown).
Tracks: / Symphony No.6 / Leonora overture.
MC: 4217734
LP: 4217731

SYMPHONY NO.9 (BEETHOVEN) (City Of Birmingham Symphony Orchestra).
Tracks: / Symphony no.9 (Beethoven).
LP: . . . . ABRD 1389
MC: . . . . ABTD 1389

SYMPHONY NO.9 (BEETHOVEN) Choral (Vienna Philharmonic Orchestra).
MC: 4278024

SYMPHONY NO 3 (BEETHOVEN) Eroica (Concertgebouw Orchestra Amsterdam).
MC: 426 066-4

SYMPHONY NO 6 (BEETHOVEN) Pastoral.
MC: 426 061-4

SYMPHONY NO. 9 'CHORAL' (See under Solti, Sir George) (Chicago Symphony Orchestra).

VIOLIN CONCERTO (BEETHOVEN) Violin romances 1 & 2 (New Philharmonia Orchestra).
MC: 426 064-4

Beetlejuice (film)

BEETLEJUICE (Film soundtrack) (Various artists).
Tracks: / Day o: *Belafonte, Harry* / Jump in the line: *Belafonte, Harry* / Beetlejuice (maintitle): *Various* artists / Travel music: *Various artists* / Book, The: *Various artists* / Enter..."The family"/Sand worm planet: *Various artists* / Fly, The: *Various artists* / Lydia discovers?: *Various artists* / In the model: *Various* artists / Juno's theme: *Various artists* / Beetle-snake: *Various artists* / Sold: *Various artists*/ Flyer, The: *Various artists* (Track includes: Lydia's pep talk.) / Incantation: *Various artists* / Lydia strikes a bargain: *Various artists* / Showtime: *Various artists* / Laughs: *Various artists* / Wedding, The: *Various artists* / Aftermath: *Various artists* / Beetlejuice (end credits): *Various artists.*
LP: 9242021
MC: 9242024

Beetles, Chris

PINK MEDICINE ALBUM (Beetles, Chris & Rob Buckman).
LP: . . . . SCX 6616

B.E.F.

MUSIC OF QUALITY AND DISTINCTION (Various artists).
Tracks: / Ball of confusion: *Turner, Tina* / Secret life of Arabia, The: *MacKenzie, Billy* / There's a ghost in my house: *Jones, Paul* / These boots are made for walking: *Yates, Paula* / Suspicious minds: *Glitter, Gary*/ You keep me hangin' on: *Nolan, Bernie* / Wichita lineman: *Gregory, Glen* / Anyone who had a heart: *Shaw, Sandie* / Perfect day: *Gregory, Glen* / It's over: *MacKenzie, Billy.*
LP: . . . . OVED 86
MC: . . . . OVEDC 86

Beggar & Co

MONUMENT.
Tracks: / You need love / Laughing on / Somebody help me out / Mule (chant no.2) / Break it up / Got to get away / Bahia de palma / I tried to write a song / That's life / Keep on writing.
LP: . . . . RCALP 6024
MC: . . . . RCAK 6024

Beggars Mantle

HOME THAT I LOVE.
Tracks: / Home that I love / Gentle Annie / All God's creatures / Broom o'the Cowdenknowes / Friends of mine / Carrick hills / Beggar's mantle / Whiskey on a Sunday / Rantin' rovin' Robin / Love's the rising sun / Rolling hills of the borders / Will ye no come back again.
LP: . . . . LOCLP 1036
MC: . . . . ZCLOC 1036

MILESTONE.
Tracks: / Barnyards of Delgaty / Massacre of Glencoe / Roses of Prince Charlie / Jock O'Hazeldean / Wee china pig / Loch Lomond / Wee Scots lad / My wee laddie / Aye waukin' o / Braes o' mar / No man's land / Mingulay boat song / Staying alive.
LP: . . . . LOCLP 1015
MC: . . . . ZCLOC 1015

Beggar's Opera

ACT ONE.
Tracks: / Poet and peasant / Passacaglia / Memory / Raymond's road / Light cavalry.
LP: 6360018

Beggars & Thieves

BEGGARS AND THIEVES.
LP: 7567821131
MC: 7567821134

Beggars Velvet

LADY OF AUTUMN.
LP: . . . . DRGN 901

Begin The Beguine 1938

BEGIN THE BEGUINE 1938 (Various artists).
LP: . . . . NOST 7665

Begley, Philomena

BEST OF PHILOMENA BEGLEY.
LP: . . . . RITZLP 0021
MC: . . . . RITZLC 0021
MC: . . . . RITZSC 406

BLANKET ON THE GROUND.
LP: . . . . TSLP 82
MC: . . . . TSC 82

COUNTRY SCENES.
LP: . . . . KLP 110

COUNTRY SCOTS 'N' IRISH.
Tracks: / Big wheel cannonball / Flower of Scotland / Rose of Mooncoin / Way old friends do, The / Mummy and daddy's little girl / Making love to you is just like eating peanuts / Cliffs of Dooneen / Come by the hills / I'm crying my heart out over you / Mull of Kintyre / That's what your love means to me / Cottage on the hill / Everything I touch turns to sugar / Scotland again.
LP: . . . . ITV 476
MC: . . . . KITV 476

COUNTRY STARS (Begley, Philomena & Ray Lynam).
Tracks: / You're the one I can't live without / Papa's wagon / You never were mine / My elusive dreams / Truck driving woman / Door is always open, The / You and me, her and him / What's your mamma's name child / I can't believe that you stopped loving me / Jeannie's afraid of the dark / Gypsy Joe and Me / Here today and gone tomorrow.
LP: . . . . PHL 409
MC: . . . . CPHL 409

DUET ALBUM (Begley, Philomena & Mick Flavin).
MC: . . . . RITZLC 0061

IRISH COUNTRY QUEEN.
Tracks: / 41st St. Lonely Hearts Club / Irish eyes / Grandma whistled / Can I sleep in your arms / County Tyrone / Once around the dancefloor / How great thou art / My Mother's home / Medals for mothers / Lonesome end of the line / Tipperary town / Light in the window.
LP: . . . . TSLP 90
MC: . . . . CSLP 90
LP: . . . . RITZLP 0019
MC: . . . . RITZLC 0019
MC: . . . . RITZSC 404

LIVE IN CONCERT.
MC: . . . . RITZRC 502

MORE ABOUT LOVE.
Tracks: / That's more about love / Grandpa / Mama she's crazy / Standing in line / Another chance / Sailor / Captured by love / It only hurts for a little while / I'll be faithful to you / Memories are made of this / One love at a time / Real men don't make quiche.
LP: . . . . RITZLP 0040
MC: . . . . RITZSC 040

NASHVILLE COUNTRY.
LP: . . . . TSLP 110

PHILOMENA.
LP: . . . . RITZLP 0018
MC: . . . . RITZLC 0018

PHILOMENA'S COUNTRY.
Tracks: / Triangle song, The / Foolin' around / Faded love / Everything I've always wanted / Okie from Muskogee / God if only I could write your love song / If this is what love's all about / I don't believe I'll fall in love today / One night of cheating / Daydreams about night things / I can't keep my hands off you / Sweet baby Jane.
MC: . . . . RITZSC 403

QUEEN OF THE SILVER DOLLAR.
LP: . . . . TSLP 86
MC: . . . . BTC 305

REFLECTIONS.
MC: . . . . OCE 2471

SILVER ANNIVERSARY ALBUM.
Tracks: / Keys in the mailbox, The / Here today and gone tomorrow / Rose of my heart / Behind the footlights / Jeannie's afraid of the dark / Red is the rose / Dark island / Leavin' on your mind / Queen of the silver dollar / Blanket on the ground / Truck drivin' woman / One is one too many / Galway Bay / Old arboe.
LP: . . . . RITZLP 0046
MC: . . . . RITZLC 046

SIMPLY DIVINE (Begley, Philomena & Ray Lynam).
Tracks: / You don't know love / Simply divine / Together alone / Near you / Don't cross over an old love / Making plans / Sweetest of all / I'll never need another you / She sang the melody / As long as we're dreaming / Hold on / Fire of two old flames.
LP: . . . . RITZLP 0028
MC: . . . . RITZLC 028

TOGETHER AGAIN (Begley, Philomena & Ray Lynam).
LP: . . . . BRL 4057

TRUCK DRIVING WOMAN.
Tracks: / Never again / Truck driving woman / I'll be all smiles / I really think I'm crying / How can I face tomorrow / Here today and gone tomorrow / Ramblin' man / Darling are you ever coming home / Philadelphia lawyer / Village in County Tyrone / My little son (England's motorway) / Old Arboe.
MC: . . . . CPHL 405
LP: . . . . PHL 405

TRUCKIN' QUEEN.
Tracks: / Big wheel cannonball / Highwayman / In God I trust / Long legged truckdrivers / Ravishing Ruby / Truckin' queen / Route 65 to Nashville / Truck driving mother / Old Ben / Big Mack / Roll on Big Mama.
LP: . . . . TSLP 98
MC: . . . . RITZLC 0020
LP: . . . . RITZLP 0020
MC: . . . . RITZSC 405

YOU'RE IN MY HEART.
LP: . . . . RITZLP 0026
MC: . . . . RITZLC 0026
MC: . . . . RITZSC 415

Behan, Dominic

EASTER WEEK AND AFTER.
LP: 12T 44

IRISH ROVER, THE.
LP: . . . . 77 FLEUT 2

STREETS OF SONG (Behan, D./Ewen MacColl).
LP: 12T 41

Beiderbecke Affair

BEIDERBECKE AFFAIR, THE (see under Plater, Alan).

Beiderbecke, Bix

1924: BIX BEIDERBECKE.
LP: . . . . S 802

1924-30.
LP: . . . . LPJT 25

BEIDERBECKE FILE, THE.
Tracks: / Flock o' blues / I'm glad / Toddin' blues / Davenport blues / Three blind mice / Clarinet marmalade / Singin' the blues / Ostrich walk / Riverboat shuffle / I'm coming Virginia / Way down yonder in New Orleans / Lonely melody / San / At the jazz band ball / Jazz me blues / Goose pimples / Sorry / Somebody stole my gal / Margie / Deep down south.
LP: . . . . SVL 201
MC: . . . . CSVL 201

BIX AND HIS GANG (1927 - 28).
LP: . . . . S 1271

BIX AND TRAM (1927) (Beiderbecke, Bix & Frankie Trumbauer).
LP: . . . . S 1242
MC: . . . . NEO 713

BIX BEIDERBECKE AND THE CHICAGO CORNETS.
Tracks: / Fidgety feet / Jazz me blues / Oh baby / Copenhagen / Riverboat shuffle / Susie / Royal garden blues / Tiger rag / I need some pettin' / Sensation / Lazy daddy / Tia Juana / Big boy / I'm glad / Flovk o' blues / Toddlin' blues / Davenport blues / Prince of Wails / When my sugar walks down the street / Steady roll blues / Mobile blues / Really a pain / Chicago blues / Hot mittens / Buddy's habits.
2LP: . . . . M 47019

BIX BEIDERBECKE AND THE WOLVERINES (Beiderbecke, Bix & the Wolverines).
LP: . . . . JT 1003
LP: . . . . OLYMPIC 7130
LP: . . . . FS 317

BIX BEIDERBECKE COLLECTION (20 Golden Greats).
Tracks: / Riverboat shuffle / Clementine / Way down yonder in New Orleans / Royal Garden blues / Tiger rag / Davenport blues / I'm comin', Virginia / Three blind mice / Ol' man river / Coquette / Dardanella / Georgia on my mind / Strut Miss Lizzie / Singing the blues / Ostrich walk / Sorry / Sugar / Georgie Porgie / Felix the cat / Is it gonna be long?.
LP: . . . . DVLP 2049
MC: . . . . DVMC 2049

BIX BEIDERBECKE JAZZ FESTIVAL, IOWA, 1975 (Various artists).
2LP: . . . . BBMS 6/7

BIX BEIDERBECKE JAZZ FESTIVAL, IOWA, 1976 (Various artists).
2LP: . . . . BBMS 9/10

BIX BEIDERBECKE JAZZ FESTIVAL, IOWA, 1974 (Various artists).
2LP: . . . . BBMS 3/4

BIX BEIDERBECKE JAZZ FESTIVAL, IOWA, 1972 (Various artists).
2LP: . . . . BBMS 1/2

BIX BEIDERBECKE STORY, THE.
Tracks: / Riverboat shuffle / Tiger rag / Davenport blues / I'm looking over a four leaf clover / Trumbology / Clarinet marmalade / Ostrich walk / Way down yonder in New Orleans / Three blind mice / Clementine / Royal Garden blues / Coquette / When / Lovable / Is it gonna be long? / Oh, you have no idea! / Felix, the cat / 'Tain't so, honey, 'tain't so / I'd rather cry over you / Louisiana / Futuristic rhythm / Raisin' the roof / Rockin' chair / Strut Miss Lizzie / Georgia on my mind.
LPS: 66367
MCSET: . . . . DVREMC 14

BIX BEIDERBECKE VOL.1 (Riverboat Shuffle).
Tracks: / Jazz me blues / Fidgety feet / Oh babe / Copenhagen / Riverboat shuffle / Susie (take 1) / Susie (take 2) / I need some pettin' / Royal garden blues / Tiger rag / Sensation / Lazy daddy (take 1) / Lazy daddy (take 2) / Tia Juana / Big boy.
LP: . . . . SM 3557

BIX BEIDERBECKE VOL.2 (Davenport Blues).
Tracks: / Flock o' blues / I'm glad I didn't know / Toddling blues / Idolizing / Hush-a-bye / I'd rather be the girl in your arms /

Sunday / Cover me up with sunshine / Just one more kiss.
LP: . . . . **SM 3558**

BIX BEIDERBECKE VOL.3 (My Pretty Girl).
Tracks: / I'm proud of a baby like you / I'm looking over a four leaf clover / I'm gonna meet my sweetie now / Hoosier sweetheart / Look at the world and smile / My pretty girl / Sunny disposish / Lane in Spain, A.
LP: . . . . **SM 3559**

BIX BEIDERBECKE VOL.4 (Singin' the Blues).
Tracks: / Trumbology / Clarinet marmalade / Singing the blues / Slow river / Ostrich walk / Riverboat shuffle / I'm coming Virginia / Way down yonder in New Orleans / For no reason at all in 'C' / In my merry oldsmobile / Three blind mice / Blue river / There's a cradle in Caroline.
LP: . . . . **SM 3560**
MC: **40179**
LP: **20179**

BIX BEIDERBECKE VOL.5 (In a mist).
Tracks: / In a mist / Blue river / Clementine / Wringin' and twistin' / Humpty dumpty / Krazy kat / Baltimore / There ain't no land like dixieland / There's a candle Caroline / Just an hour of love / I'm wondering who / At the jazz band ball / Royal garden blues / Jazz me blues.
LP: . . . . **SM 3561**

BIX BEIDERBECKE VOL.6 (A Good Man is Hard to Find).
Tracks: / Three blind mice / Clorinda / I'm more than satisfied / Goose pimples / Sorry / Crying all day / Good man is hard to find, A / Since my best gal turned me down.
LP: . . . . **SM 3562**

BIX BEIDERBECKE VOL.7 (Lonely Melody).
Tracks: / Washboard blues / Changes / Mary (who are you waiting for) / Lonely melody / Smile / There'll come a time / Jubilee / Ol' man river / San 6 / San 7.
LP: . . . . **SM 3563**

BIX BEIDERBECKE VOL.8 (Mississippi Mud).
Tracks: / Mississippi mud / Smile / Make believe / Dardanella / There ain't no sweet man that's worth the salt of my tears / Back in your own back yard / Love nest, The / From Monday to Mississippi mud / From Monday on.
LP: . . . . **SM 3564**

BIX BEIDERBECKE VOL.9 (Showboat).
Tracks: / Why do I love you / Can't help lovin' dat man / You are my love / Make believe / Coquette / When / Metropolis / Lovable / Our bungalow of dreams / Lila.
LP: . . . . **SM 3565**

BIX BEIDERBECKE VOL.10.
LP: . . . . **SM 3566**

BIX BEIDERBECKE VOL.11 (Ol' Man River).
Tracks: / My melancholy baby / Is it gonna be long / Get out and get under the moon / Oh you have no idea / Felix the cat / T'aint so honey / I'd rather cry over you / That's my weakness now / Georgie porgie / Because my baby don't mean "Maybe" now / Out of town gal / Bless your sister / Dusty Stevedore / Ol' man river / Wa-da-da.
LP: . . . . **SM 3567**

BIX BEIDERBECKE VOL.12 (Rhythm King).
Tracks: / Concerto in F (2nd movement pt 1) / Gipsy / Sweet Sue / Take your tomorrow / Love affairs / Rhythm king / Louisiana / Margie / Love nest, The / Japanese sandman / High upon a hilltop / Sentimental baby.
LP: . . . . **SM 3568**

BIX BEIDERBECKE VOL.13 (Futuristic rhythm).
Tracks: / Futuristic rhythm / Raisin' the roof / Louise / Wait till you see ma cherie / Baby won't you please come home / No one can take your place / I like that / When my dreams come true / Reaching for someone (and not finding anyone there) / China boy / Oh miss Hannah / Waiting at the end of the road / When you're counting the stars alone.
LP: . . . . **SM 3569**

BIX BEIDERBECKE VOL.14 (Georgia on My Mind).
Tracks: / Rockin' chair / Barnacle Bill the sailor / Loved one / Loved one (take 2) / Deep harlem / Strut Miss Lizzie / Deep South (take 1) / I don't mind walking in the rain / I'll be a friend with pleasure (take 3) / Georgia on my mind / One night in Havana / Bessie couldn't help it (Take 1) / Deep South (take 2) / I'll be a friend with pleasure (take 2) / Bessie couldn't help it (Take 2).
LP: . . . . **SM 3570**

BIX LIVES (Various artists).
Tracks: / Clementine: *Goldkette, Jean & His Orchestra* / Proud (of a baby like you): *Goldkette, Jean & His Orchestra* / Changes: *Whiteman, Paul & His Orchestra* / What are you waiting for Mary: *Whiteman, Paul & His Orchestra* / Lonely melody: *Whiteman, Paul & His Orchestra* / San: *Whiteman, Paul & His Orchestra* / Smile: *Whiteman, Paul & His* Orchestra / Back in your own back yard: *Whiteman, Paul & His Orchestra* / There ain't no sweetman that's worth the salt: *Whiteman, Paul & His Orchestra* / Dardanella: *Whiteman, Paul & His Orchestra* / Love nest, The: *Whiteman,* Paul & His Orchestra / From Monday on: *Whiteman, Paul & His Orchestra* / Sugar coquette: *Whiteman, Paul & His* Orchestra / When (take 2): *Whiteman, Paul & His Orchestra* / When (take 3): *Whiteman, Paul & His Orchestra* / Loveable: *Whiteman, Paul & His Orchestra* / My pet: *Whiteman, Paul & His Orchestra* / Forget me not: *Whiteman,* Paul & His Orchestra / Louisiana: *Whiteman, Paul & His Orchestra* / You took advantage of me: *Whiteman, Paul & His* Orchestra / Deep down South: *Beiderbecke, Bix & His Gang* / I'll be friend with pleasure: *Beiderbecke, Bix & His Gang.*
LP: . . . . **NL 86845**
MC: . . . . **NK 86845**

BIX 'N' BING (Beiderbecke, Bix/Bing Crosby/Paul Whiteman Orchestra).
Tracks: / Changes / Mary (what are you waiting for?) / There ain't no sweet man that's worth the salt of my tears / Sunshine / Mississippi mud / High water / From Monday on / Loveable / My pet / Louisiana / Do I hear you saying "I love you"? / You took advantage of me / That's my weakness now / Because my baby don't mean maybe now / I'm in the seventh heaven / Reaching for someone (and not finding anyone there) / Oh, Miss Hannah / Your mother and mine / Waiting at the end of the road / T'ain't so honey, t'ain't so.
LP: . . . . **AJA 5005**
MC: . . . . **ZC AJA 5005**

FIDGETY FEET.
Tracks: / Fidgety feet / Jazz me blues / Copenhagen / Riverboat shuffle / Oh baby / Susie / Sensation rag / Lazy daddy / Tiger rag / Big boy / Tia juana.
LP: . . . . **SM 3087**
LP: . . . . **LPJT 25**
MC: . . . . **MCJT 25**

GOLDEN AGE OF BIX BEIDERBECKE.
Tracks: / Singing the blues / Riverboat shuffle / I'm coming Virginia / Way down yonder in New Orleans / There ain't no land like Dixieland to me / I'm wondering who / At the jazz band ball / Sorry / Crying all day / Since my best gal turned me down / Royal garden blues / Humpty Dumpty / In a mist / Trumbology.
LP: . . . . **MFP 5828**
MC: . . . . **TC MFP 5828**
LP: . . . . **GX 2513**

INDISPENSABLE BIX BEIDERBECKE (1924-30).
Tracks: / I didn't know / Idolizing / Sunday / I'm proud of a baby like you / I'm looking over a four leaf clover / I'm gonna meet my sweetie now / Hoosier sweetheart / My pretty girl / Slow river / In my merry Oldsmobile / Clementine / Washboard blues / Changes / Mary / Lonely melody / San / Back in your own back yard / There ain't no sweet man that's worth the salt of my tears / Dardanella / From Monday on / Mississippi mud / Sugar / Coquette / When / Lovable / My pet / Forget me not / Louisiana / You took advantage of me / Rockin' chair / Barnacle Bill the sailor / Deep down south / I don't mind walking in the rain / I'll be a friend with pleasure / Georgia on my mind / Bessie couldn't help it.
2LP: . . . . **NL 89572**
MCSET: . . . . **NK 89572**

JAZZ CLASSICS IN DIGITAL STEREO (Bix Beiderbecke 1924-1930).
Tracks: / Take your tomorrow / Goose pimples / Wa-da-da / Rhythm King / Since my best gal turned me down / There'll come a time / Barnacle Bill the sailor / Deep Harlem / Rockin' chair / I like that / Jazz me blues / At the jazz band ball / Copenhagen / Royal garden blues / Mississippi mud / Sorry.
MC: . . . . **ZCF 601**
LP: . . . . **REB 601**

LEGENDARY BIX BEIDERBECKE, THE.
LP: **22020**
MC: **42020**
MC: . . . . **MRT 40048**

RARE BIX, 1927-29, THE.
LP: . . . . **S 1218**

STUDIO BANDS 1928.
Tracks: / Sugar / Jubilee / Mississippi mud / Ol' man river / Lila / Borneo / My pet / Thou swell / Dusky stevedore / Take your tomorrow / Love affairs.
LP: . . . . **SH 415**

STUDIO BANDS 1928-1938.
Tracks: / Rhythm king / Louisiana / Margie / Love nest / Japanese sandman / Futuristic rhythm / Louise / Baby won't you please come home / I like that / Loved one / Deep Harlem.
LP: . . . . **SH 416**

STUDIO GROUPS 1927.
Tracks: / Trumbology / Clarinet marmalade / Singing the blues / Ostrich walk / Riverboat shuffle / I'm coming Virginia / Way down yonder in New Orleans / For no reason at all in C / Three blind mice / Blue river / There's a cradle in Carolina / In a mist / Wringin' and twistin' / Humpty Dumpty / Krazy kat / Baltimore.
LP: . . . . **EG 2605271**
MC: . . . . **EG 2605274**
LP: . . . . **SH 413**

STUDIO GROUPS LATE 1927 VOL.2.
Tracks: / There ain't no land like Dixieland / There's a cradle in Carolina / Just an hour of love / I'm wondering who / At the jazz band ball / Royal Garden blues / Jazz me blues / I'm more than satisfied (take 1) / I'm more than satisfied (take 2) / Clorinda (take 1) / Clorinda (take 2) / Three blind mice (take 1) / Three blind mice (take 2) / Goose pimples / Sorry / Crying all day / Good man is hard to find, A / Since my best gal turned me down.
LP: . . . . **SH 414**
MC: . . . . **TCSH 414**

TRUMPET ALBUM (Vol 2) (Beiderbecke, Bix/Various Artists).
LP: . . . . **MERITT 9**

UNHEARD BIX (Beiderbecke, Bix/ Various Artists).
LP: . . . . **BWY 102**

YOUNG MAN WITH A HORN.
Tracks: / Jazz me blues / Louisiana / Sorry / Thou swell / Ol' man river / Somebody stole my gal / Royal garden blues / At the jazz band ball / Since my best gal turned me down / Wa-da-da (everybody's doin' it now) / Goose pimples / Rhythm King / Singing the blues / Clarinet marmalade / Way down yonder in New Orleans / Mississippi mud / For no reason at all in C / There'll come a time / I'm comin', Virginia / Ostrich walk / Good man is hard to find, A / Wringin' and twistin' / Crying all day / Riverboat shuffle.
2LP: . . . . **CBS 22179**
MC: **40 22179**

Beiderbecke Tapes (bk)

BEIDERBECKE TAPES, THE (Alan Plater) (Bolam, James (nar)).
MCSET: . . . . **LFP 7439**

Beirach, Richie

COMMON HEART.
LP: . . . . **OWLL 048**
MC: . . . . **OWLL 748**

DOUBLE EDGE (Beirach, Richie/ Liebman, David).
LP: . . . . **SLP 4091**

Bel Airs

NEED ME A CAR.
LP: **BP-1684**

Bel Canto

WHITE OUT CONDITION.
LP: . . . . **CRAM 057**

Bel, M'Bilia

BA GERANTS YA MABALA.
LP: . . . . **GEN 110**

BAMELI SOY.
LP: . . . . **SHAN 43025**
MC: . . . . **SHANC 43025**
MC: . . . . **SHMC 43025**

BEYANGA.
LP: . . . . **GEN 120**

BOYA YE (ZAIRE).
Tracks: / Boya ye / Maeta vi / Shawuri yako / Tonton skoll.
LP: . . . . **STERNS 1012**
MC: . . . . **C 2011**

ESWI YO WAPI.
MC: . . . . **C 2001**

FAUX PAS.
LP: . . . . **GEN 105**
MC: . . . . **C 2003**

Belafonte, Harry

16 ORIGINAL HITS: HARRY BELAFONTE.
MC: . . . . **MC 1633**

24 HITS.
2LP: **26 28056**

ALL TIME GREATEST HITS: HARRY BELAFONTE.
Tracks: / Day-O / Don't ever love me / Mama look a boo boo / Jump in the line / Scarlet ribbons / Michael row the boat ashore / Island in the sun / John Henry / Abraham, Martin and John / Hallelujah I love her so / Coconut woman / Mary's boy child / Hold 'em Joe / Jamaica farewell.
MC: . . . . **NK 90366**
LP: . . . . **NL 90366**

BANANA BOAT SONG.
LP: . . . . **ENT LP 13016**
MC: . . . . **ENT MC 13016**

BELAFONTE SINGS OF LOVE.
Tracks: / By the time I get to Phoenix / Annie love / Sleep late, my lady friend / Once in my lifetime / Your time / In the beginning / Day in the life of a fool, A / When Spring comes around / In the name of love / First day of forever / Each day (I look for yesterday).
LP: . . . . **PL 42176**

COLLECTION: HARRY BELAFONTE (20 golden greats).
Tracks: / Darlin' Cora / Day O (Banana boat song) / Matilda, Matilda / Shenandoah / Come back, Liza / Sylvie / Mama look a boo boo / Man piaba / Take my mother home / Jump down, spin around / Jamaica farewell / Windin' road / In my Father's house / All my trials / Allelujah, I love her so / Fox, The / In that great gettin' up morning / Turn around / Shake that little foot / La bamba.
LP: . . . . **DVLP 2003**
MC: . . . . **DVMC 2003**

COLLECTION: HARRY BELAFONTE.
Tracks: / Island in the sun / Day O (Banana boat song) / Son of Mary, The / There's a hole in my bucket / Don't stop the carnival / Michael row the boat ashore / Annie love / John Henry / Round the Bay of Mexico / By the time I get to Phoenix / Matilda, Matilda / Danny boy / Mama look a boo boo / Shenandoah / Hava nagila / Come back Liza / Angelina / La bamba / When spring comes round (my love my love) / Long long time / Walking on the moon / Marching saints, The / Sylvie / Brown skin gal.
MC: . . . . **CCSMC 186**
2LP: . . . . **CCSLP 186**

EVENING WITH BELAFONTE, AN.
Tracks: / My moon (fenagari moo) / Dream / If you are thirsty / Train, The / In the small boat / Town crier, The / Walking on the moon / Baby snake, The / Wide sea, The / Irene.
LP: . . . . **LSA 3031**

EVENING WITH BELAFONTE & MAKEBA, AN (Songs from Africa) (Belafonte, Harry & Miriam Makeba).
Tracks: / Train song / In the land of the Zulus / Hush, hush / To those we love / Give us our land / Beware Verwoerd / Gone are my children / Hurry, mama, hurry / My angel / Cannon / Lullaby / Show me the way / My brother.
LP: **26 21029**

FABULOUS, THE.
Tracks: / Day O / Island in the sun / Fox, The / Come back Liza / Wedding song, The / Jump down, spin around / Man piaba / John Henry / Soldier, soldier / Shenandoah / Scratch, scratch / Jamaica farewell / Matilda, Matilda / Judy drowned / Turn around / Mama look a boo boo / Danny boy / Try to remember / Coconut woman / Scarlet ribbons / Man smart (woman smarter) / Abraham, Martin and John.
2LP: . . . . **CR 046**
MCSET: . . . . **CRT 046**

FOLK SONGS.
2LP: **26 28024**

GOLDEN RECORDS.
Tracks: / Banana boat song / Angelina / Coconut woman / Mama look a boo boo / Mary's boy child / Haiti cherie / Island in the sun / Matilda, Matilda / Jamaica farewell / Jump in the line / Round the bay of Mexico / Marching saints, The / Come back Liza / Star-O.
LP: . . . . **SF 8397**

GOLDEN RECORDS VOL 2.
Tracks: / Merci bon dieu / Hava nagila / Danny boy / La bamba / Man smart (woman smarter) / Take my mother home / Shenandoah / Man piaba / Hene ma tov / Cu-cu-rru-cu-cu-paloma / There's a hole in the bucket / Scarlet ribbons (for her hair).
LP: . . . . **SF 8441**

GREATEST HITS: HARRY BELAFONTE.
LPPD: . . . . **AR 30048**

GREATEST HITS: HARRY BELAFONTE.
LP: **32001**
MC: **62001**

GREATEST HITS: HARRY BELAFONTE(IMPORT).
Tracks: / Banana boat song / Island in the sun / Angelina / Matilda, Matilda.
LP: . . . . FUN 9047
MC: . . . . FUNC 9047

HARRY B & MIRIAM M (Belafonte, Harry & Miriam Makeba).
LP: . . . . NL 89253
MC: . . . . NK 89253

HARRY BELAFONTE.
LP: . . . . ENT 13016

LEGENDARY PERFORMER, A.
Tracks: / Day-O (banana boat song) / Mama look a boo boo / Matilda, Matilda / Jump down, spin around / Jamaica farewell / John Henry / Shenandoah / Hava nagila / Danny boy / Scarlet ribbons for her hair / All my trials / When the saints go marching in.
LP: . . . . PL 12469
MC: . . . . PK 12469

LOVING YOU IS WHERE I BELONG.
Tracks: / Something to hold onto / Mary makes magic / Rose / I told you / Streets of London / Loving you is where I belong / Forever young / I don't need her / Did you know / Genuine imitation life.
LP: . . . . CBS 85254

MIDNIGHT SPECIAL, THE.
Tracks: / Midnight special / Crawdad song / Memphis Tennessee / Gotta travel on / Did you hear about Jerry / On top of Old Smokey / Muleskinner / Makes a long time man feel bad / Michael row the boat ashore.
LP: . . . . INTS 5029
MC: . . . . INTK 5029
LP: . . . . NL 82324
MC: . . . . NK 82324

PARADISE IN GAZANKULU.
Tracks: / We are the wave / Paradise in Gazankulu / Skin to skin / Amandla / Kwela (listen to the man) / Monday to Monday / Global carnival / Capetown / Sisiwami (sweet sister) / Move it.
LP: . . . . MTL 1024
MC: . . . . TCMTL 1024

THIS IS HARRY BELAFONTE.
Tracks: / Mr. Bojangles / Maniia de carnival / Play me / Shenandoah / By the time I get to Phoenix / Coconut woman / La bamba / Put your tears away / Unchained melody / Scarlet ribbons / Angelina / Oh Linda / Morningside (for the children) / Matilda, Matilda / Brown skin gal / And I love you so.
LP: . . . . MFP 5851
MC: . . . . TC-MFP 5851

TO WISH YOU A MERRY CHRISTMAS.
LP: . . . . NL 89108
MC: . . . . NK 89108

TOGETHER (Belafonte, Harry & Miriam Makeba).
MC: 495592

VERY BEST OF HARRY BELAFONTE, THE.
Tracks: / Banana boat song / Island in the sun / Scarlet ribbons / Mary's boy child / Shenandoah / Jamaica farewell / Mama look a boo boo / Danny boy / Matilda, Matilda / Swing dat hammer / There's a hole in my bucket / Angelina / Unchained melody / Coconut woman / Waltzing Matilda / Michael row the boat ashore / Boat, The.
LP: . . . . PL 89192
MC: . . . . PK 89192
LP: . . . . RCALP 3056

Belew, Adrian

MR MUSIC HEAD.
Tracks: / Oh daddy / One of those days / Bad days / Hot zoo / Bumpity bump / 1967 / House of cards / Coconuts / Peaceable kingdom / Motor bungalow / Bird in a box.
LP: . . . . K 781 959 1
MC: . . . . K 781 959 4

TWANG BAR KING.
LP: . . . . ILPS 9768
MC: . . . . ICT 9768

YOUNG LIONS.
Tracks: / Young lions / Heartbeat / I am what I am / Men in helicopters / Phone call from the moon / Pretty pink rose / Looking for A.U.F.O. / Not alone anymore / Small world / Gunman.
LP: 7567820991
MC: 7567820994

Belfast Cowboys

RELIEF.
LP: . . . . SWFMLP 011

Belfegore

BELFEGORE.
Tracks: / All that I wanted / Questions / Love / Wake up the sirens / Seabird seamoan / Don't you run / Comic with rats now / Into the dungeon / Belfegore.
LP: 9603781

Belgian.....

BELGIAN ASSOCIABILITY (Various artists).
LP: . . . . PETC 013

Belgian Beat

SIX PACK.
LP: . . . . SUB 058

Belgian New Beat

BELGIAN NEW BEAT (See under Best Of..) (Various artists).

Belgian Six Pack

BELGIAN SIX PACK (Various artists).
LP: . . . . SUB 58

Believer

SANITY OBSCURE.
LP: . . . . RC 93121
MC: . . . . RC 93124

Believers (film)

BELIEVERS, THE (Film soundtrack) (Various artists).
LP: . . . . STV 81328

Belizaire- The Cajun

BELIZAIRE- THE CAJUN (See under Doucet, Michael) (Doucet, Michael).

Bell, Alan

ALAN BELL FOLK BAND AND POULTON SILVER PRIZE (Bell, Alan Folk Band).
LP: . . . . TSR 039

MINSTREL, THE.
Tracks: / All in our north country / Windmills / Good shepherd / Two thousand years ago / Alice White / Band in the park / Ballad of a working man / Gypsy laddie, The / Bread and fishes / Weaver's song, The / Packman, The / Minstrel's song, The.
LP: . . . . FHR 103
MC: . . . . CFHR 103

Bell, Archie

ARTISTS SHOWCASE: ARCHIE BELL.
LP: . . . . MUSIC 8
MC: . . . . ZCMUS 8

I NEVER HAD IT SO GOOD.
Tracks: / Don't wait for the world / Anytime is right / I never made love I never had it so good / Why didja do me / Good guys / Harder and harder / Without you.
LP: . . . . BKLP 1002

WHERE WILL YOU GO WHEN THE PARTY'S OVER? (Bell, Archie & The Drells).
Tracks: / Don't let love get you down / Where will you go when the party's over / Right here is where I want to be / Dancin' man / Everybody have a good time / I swear you're beautiful / Nothing comes easy / I bet I can do that dance you're doing.
LP: . . . . PRT 57121
MC: 40 57121

Bell Biv Devoe

POISON (ALBUM).
Tracks: / Dope / B.B.D. (I thought it was me) / Let me know something / Do me / Ronnie, Bobby, Ricky, Mike / Ralph and Johnny (word to the Mutha) / Poison / Ain't nut'in changed / When will I see you smile / Again / I do need you.
LP: . . . . MCG 6094
MC: . . . . MCGC 6094

WBBD - BOOT CITY.
LP: . . . . MCA 10345
MC: . . . . MCAC 10345

Bell, Book & Candle

BELL, BOOK AND CANDLE (Film soundtrack) (Duning, George).
LP: . . . . CT 6006

Bell, Carey

BIG WALTER HORTON WITH CAREY BELL (See under Horton, Big Walter) (Bell, Carey & Walter Horton).

CAREY BELL'S BLUES HARP.
LP: . . . . DL 622

GAMBLIN' WOMEN (see under Sumlin, Hubert) (Bell, Carey & Hubert Sumlin).

GOIN' ON MAIN STREET (Bell, Carey Blues Harp Band).
LP: . . . . LR 42.051

MY LIFE WITH CAREY BELL (see under Louisiana Red) (Bell, Carey & Louisiana Red).

SON OF A GUN (Bell, Carey & Lurrie).
LP: . . . . R 2617

STRAIGHT SHOOT (Bell, Carey & Lurrie & Junkyard Angels).
LP: . . . . BSW 001

Bell, Charles

CHARLES BELL TRIO IN CONCERT (Bell, Charles Trio).
LP: . . . . FS 211

Bell, Clive

KUROKAMI - THE MUSIC OF JAPAN (See under Yanagisawa, Rie) (Yanagisawa, Rie/Clive Bell).

Bell, Crawford

ANOTHER TEXAS SONG.
Tracks: / (When you're in love) everything's a waltz / Learning to live again / Lullabies, legends and lies / Three / Another Texas song / Stay a little longer / Queen bee / Texas when I die / Some days are diamonds.
LP: . . . . PHL 442
MC: . . . . CPHL 442

BEST OF CRAWFORD BELL.
MC: . . . . CPHL 483

C.B. COUNTRY.
Tracks: / Molly darlin' / Mama sang a song / Saginaw, Michigan / Mother country music / Real thing, The / Good morning darling / Mama's waiting / God only knows / Too late / Silver medals and sweet memories / Lightning express.
LP: . . . . PHL 419
MC: . . . . CPHL 419

COWBOY SINGER.
Tracks: / Union mare and confederate grey / Ozark mountain / Tequila Sheila / Cowboy singer, The / Old flames / Angelina / Hard to be humble / Littlest cowboy rides again, The / Mississippi you're on my mind / Leaving Louisiana in the broad daylight / Evangeline / Mother of a wandering boy.
LP: . . . . PHL 428
MC: . . . . CPHL 428

HYMNS AND SONGS FROM THE FAMILY ALBUM.
Tracks: / Where the soul never dies / Softly and tenderly / Let the lower lights be burning / Tell mother I'll be there / Angel band / In the garden / Life's railway to Heaven / Jesus tender shepherd / He's the one / Jesus hold my hand / Precious memories / At the end of the day / Another bridge to burn / I dreamed I saw our country on her knees / Peace of mind.
LP: . . . . PHL 466
MC: . . . . CPHL 466

STAR SPANGLED BANNER.
Tracks: / There's a star spangled banner waving somewhere / Have I stayed away too long / Down the trail of aching hearts / Sioux city Sue / Vaya con dios / Molly darling / Blue moon of Kentucky / Down in the little green valley / Can I sleep in your arms / Lamplighting time in the valley / Sweetheart of the valley / Three little bells.
LP: . . . . PHL 452
MC: . . . . CPHL 452

Bell, Dee

LET THERE BE LOVE (Bell, Dee with Stan Getz & Eddie Duran).
Tracks: / There's a lull in my life / Let there be love / This life we've led / Waltz for Debbie / You must believe in Spring / Give me one more chance / Reminiscin' in tempo / Living inside my mind / Just because we're kids.
LP: . . . . CJ 206

ONE BY ONE (Bell, Dee & Eddie Duran).
Tracks: / What a little moonlight can do / This time the dream's on me / One by one / Please / Estate / Don't be that way / All my tears / Wonder why / Let's fall in love / Zingaro.
LP: . . . . CJ 271
MC: . . . . CJC 271

Bell, Delia

BILL GRANT AND DELIA BELL (See under Grant, Bill) (Bell, Delia & Bill Grant).

BLUER THAN MIDNIGHT.
Tracks: / Bluer than midnight / God gave you to me / My Kentucky Mountain home / Heartless / I want to be loved / Broken heart, a wedding band, A / Dirt you throw, The / Roses in the snow / Come walk with me / Oklahoma bluegrass blues / My last request / Come back and get these memories.
LP: . . . . CO 768
MC: . . . . CO 768 MC

CHEER OF THE HOMEFIRES (Bell, Delia & Bill Grant).
Tracks: / Dreaming / Cheer of the home fires, The / Fields of flowers / Wall, The / Where did we go wrong / Heartbreak express / Thinking of the old days / Sad situation / It'll be me / There'll be no teardrops tonight / Shadows of my mind / Don't let me cross over.
LP: . . . . ROUNDER 0187
MC: . . . . ROUNDER 0187C

FEW DOLLARS MORE, A (Bell, Delia & Bill Grant).
Tracks: / Foggy mountain home / Silver tongue and gold plated lies / Don't worry about me / Love's turned you to stone / Red clay Georgia / Few dollars more, A / I'll get by / Night flyer / Lonely violet / Louisa / Cold hard facts of life, The / Jack and Lucy.
LP: . . . . ROUNDER 0217
MC: . . . . ROUNDER 0217C

FOLLOWING A FEELING (Bell, Delia & Bill Grant).
Tracks: / If I had my life to live over / No one mends a broken heart like you / Following a feeling / They'll soon pay the price / Two lonely hearts / Could this have been the man / Fiddler, The / Beggin' to you / Flame in my heart / Love you've the teacher / River, The / Won't you come and sing for me.
LP: . . . . ROUNDER 0257
MC: . . . . ROUNDER 0257C

ROLLIN' (See under Grant, Bill) (Bell, Delia & Bill Grant).

Bell, Derek

CAROLAN'S FAVOURITE (Music of Carolan, Vol 2).
LP: . . . . CC 28
MC: 4CC 28
LP: . . . . SHAN 79020

CAROLAN'S RECEIPT.
MC: 4CC 18
LP: . . . . CC 18
LP: . . . . SHAN 79013

DEREK BELL'S MUSICAL IRELAND.
LP: . . . . CC 35
MC: 4CC 35

Bell, Eja

PETALS (see Allen, Marcus) (Bell, Eja/ Marcus Allen).

Bell For Adano

BELL FOR ADANO Hersey, John (Marshall, E.G.).
MC: 0503

Bell, Freddy

ROCK 'N' ROLL ALL FLAVOURS (Bell, Freddy & The Bellboys).
LP: . . . . MG 20289

Bell, Graeme

CZECHOSLOVAK JOURNEY.
LP: . . . . S 1394

GRAEME BELL ALL STARS.
LP: . . . . J 75

GRAEME BELL AND HIS AUSTRALIAN JAZZ BAND (London, 1951).
LP: . . . . S 1291

GRAEME BELL AND HIS AUSTRALIAN JAZZ BAND (1947-51) (Bell, Graeme & his Australian Jazz Band).
MC: . . . . S 1411

GRAEME BELL AND HIS AUSTRALIAN JAZZ BAND (1949-52).
LP: . . . . S 1397

GRAEME BELL AND HIS AUSTRALIAN JAZZ BAND (1948-49).
LP: . . . . S 1396

GRAEME BELL AND HIS AUSTRALIAN JAZZ BAND (1949-50).
LP: . . . . S 1224

GRAEME BELL AND HIS AUSTRALIAN JAZZ BAND (1949).
LP: . . . . S 1268

IN CZECHOSLOVAKIA (Bell, Graeme & His Dixieland Jazz Band).
LP: . . . . DC 12002

PARIS (1948).
LP: . . . . S 1395

Bell & James

BELL & JAMES.
Tracks: / Livin' it up / Three way love affair / Just can't get enough / Ask Billie / You never know what you've got / I need you / Don't let the man get you / I love the music.
LP: . . . . AMLH 64728

Bell, Jimmie

STRANGER IN YOUR TOWN.
LP: . . . . JSP 1007

Bell, J.S. (author)

WEE MACGREEGOR (see under Wee MacGreegor) (Copeland, James (nar)).

Bell, Lurrie

CHICAGO'S YOUNG BLUES GENERATION (Bell, Lurrie & Billy Branch).
LP: . . . . LR 42.049

Bell, Madelaine

RUBADUB-POP GOES THE NURSERY RHYMES (Bell, Madelaine & John Telfer).
LP: . . . . DUBLP 1

THIS IS ONE GIRL.
LP: . . . . NSPL 18483

Bell, Maggie

HOLD ME (See under Robertson, BA) (Bell, Maggie & BA Robertson).

Bell Notes

I'VE HAD IT.
LP: . . . . TLP 202

Bell, Paddie

IN RETROSPECT (Bell, Paddie & Corrie Folk Trio).
Tracks: / Greenland fisheries, The / Uist tramping song / Lord Gregory / My love she's but a lassie yet / Cherry tree carol, The / Bonnie lass o' Fyvie / Johnny lad / Fear a bhata / Killiecrankie / Christ was born in Bethlehem / Singing games, The / Blow ye winds in the morning.
LP: . . . . STAL 5005

Bell Ringing

SPARKLING BRONZE (English handbell ringing) (Various artists).
Tracks: / Cubley Brook: *Various artists* / Old Comrades: *Various artists* / Gay Gordons: *Various artists*/ Under the double eagle: *Various artists* / Nights of gladness: *Various artists* / Colonel Bogey: *Various* artists / Happy wanderer, (The): *Various artists* / Christmas medley: *Various artists* / Mexican march: *Various artists* / Waltz (Iolanthe): *Various artists.*
LP: . . . . GRS 1059

Bell, Roger

MAPLE LEAF RAG.
LP: . . . . S 1351

Bell & Shore

LITTLE MOVIES.
LP: . . . . FF 460

Bell Sisters

HIS BANNER OVER ME IS LOVE.
Tracks: / Dust on the bible / Whispering hope / His banner over me is love / Why me Lord / Old rugged cross / Learning to be free / What a friend we have in Jesus / Freedom / When the Saviour calls / Singing for my Lord / Help me / Medley of light.
LP: . . . . HRL 158
MC: . . . . CHRL 158

Bell, Teja

SUMMER SUITE (Bell, Teja/Dallas Smith/John Bernoff).
LP: . . . . LP 8007
MC: . . . . CAS 8007

Bell, Tony

JOGGER, THE (See under Wynne-Jones, Tim - The Thinking Room) (Various artists).

Bell, William

DO RIGHT MAN.
Tracks: / You don't miss your water / Any other way / I'm waiting on you / Somebody mentioned your name / I'll show you / Don't stop now / Crying all by myself / Share what you got / Never like this before / Everybody loves a winner / Do right woman, do right man / Then you can tell me goodbye / Eloise / It's happening all over / Everyday will be like a holiday / Tribute to a king, A.
LP: . . . . CRB 1076
MC: . . . . TCCRB 1076

ON A ROLL.
Tracks: / Getting out of your bed / If you don't use it / I need your love so bad / When you've got the best / On a roll / I'm ready / I can do it / Short circuit / Holding on to love.
LP: . . . . WIL 3007
MC: . . . . WIL 3007MC

PASSION.
LP: . . . . LPLUTE 1
MC: . . . . LUTEC 1
LP: . . . . WIL 3001

SOUL OF WILLIAM BELL.
LP: . . . . SD 07719

Bellamy Brothers

BEAUTIFUL FRIENDS.
Tracks: / Slippin' away / Make me over / Bird dog / My shy Anne / It's just the gypsy in your soul / Let's give love a go / Wild honey / Tumbleweed and Rosalie / Mornin' mockingbird / When the music plays.
LP: . . . . K 56485

BEST OF THE BELLAMY BROTHERS, THE.
LP: . . . . MCF 3248
MC: . . . . MCFC 3248

GREATEST HITS: BELLAMY BROTHERS VOL.2.
Tracks: / Feeling the feeling / When I'm away from you / Old hippie / I'd lie to you for your love / Too much is not enough / Forget about me / World's greatest lover / I need more of you / Strong weakness / I love her mind.
LP: . . . . IMCA 5812
MC: . . . . IMCAC 5812

HOWARD & DAVID.
Tracks: / Wheels / Season of the wind / Single man and his wife, The / I'm gonna hurt her on the radio / Feeling the feeling / You're my favourite waste of time / Lie to you for your love / Old hippie / Everybody's somebody's darling / Jeannie Rae.
LP: . . . . IMCA 5586

LET YOUR LOVE FLOW.
Tracks: / Satin sheets / Nothin' heavy / Rainy, windy, sunshine / Rodeo Road / Let fantasy live / Highway 2-18 (hang on to your dreams) / Living in the west / I'm the only sane man left alive / Inside of my guitar / Hell cat / Let your love flow.
LP: . . . . K 56242

PLAIN AND FANCY.
Tracks: / You made me / Tiger Lily lover / Memorabilia / Maybe by then / Cross fire / Misunderstood / If it's so easy / Hard rockin' / Can somebody hear me now.
LP: . . . . K 56357

RESTLESS.
Tracks: / Forget about me / World's greatest lover / Down to you / We're having some fun now / Rockabilly / Restless / I love it / Diesel cafe / Tragedy / I need more of you.
LP: . . . . IMCA 5489

SONS OF THE SUN.
Tracks: / Lovers live longer / Do you love as good as you look / It's hard to be a cowboy these days / Dancin' romance / Endangered species / Givin' in to love again / Honey, we don't know no one in Nashville / Spiders and snakes / Classic case of the blues / Illusions of love.
LP: . . . . K 56872
MC: 456872

YOU CAN GET CRAZY.
Tracks: / Dancin' cowboys / Sugar daddy / Foolin' around / Comin' back for more / I could be makin' love to you / Dead aim.
LP: . . . . K 56777

Bellamy, Peter

BOTH SIDES THEN.
Tracks: / Barbaree / Trees they do grow high, The / Lord will provide, The / Gallant frigate Amphitite, The / Roving on a winter's day, The / Derry gaol / Long time travelling / Shepherd of the downs / House carpenter / When I die / Edmund in the lowlands / Around Cape Horn / Turfman from Ardee / Amazing grace.
LP: . . . . 12 TS 400

FOX JUMPS OVER THE PARSON'S GATE, THE.
Tracks: / Spotted cow, The / Two pretty boys (the two brothers) / Female drummer / Here's adieu, sweet lovely Nancy / Ghost's song, The (the cruel ship's carpenter) / Carnal and crane, The / Little black horse, The (penny wager) / Barley and the Rye, The / Turkish lady, The / Warlike seamen / Blackberry fold / St. Stephen / Rigs of London town, The / Fox jumps over the parson's gate, The.
LP: 12T 200

KEEP ON KIPLING.
Tracks: / Pilgrims way, A / Cuckoo song, The / Blue roses / Ford O'kabul river / Land, The / Dayspring mishandled / Roll down to Rio / Liner she's a lady, The / Anchor song / Minesweepers / My lady's law / Coiner, The / My boy Jack / Follow me home / Cities and thrones and powers.
LP: . . . . FE 032
MC: . . . . FE 032 C

SECOND WIND.
LP: . . . . EF 002

SINGS THE BARRACK ROOM BALLADS OF RUDYARD KIPLING.
LP: . . . . FRR 014

TELL IT LIKE IT WAS.
LP: . . . . LER 2089

TRANSPORTS, THE.
2LP: . . . . FRR 021/022

Belle, Lulu & Scotty

SWEETHEARTS OF COUNTRY MUSIC.
LP: . . . . SLP 206
MC: . . . . GT 5206

SWEETHEARTS STILL.
LP: . . . . SLP 351
MC: . . . . GT 5351

Belle of New York

BELLE OF NEW YORK (Film soundtrack) (Various artists).
Tracks: / Baby doll: *Various artists* / Oops: *Various artists* / Seeing is believing: *Various artists*/ I wanna be a dancing man: *Various artists* / Bachelor dinner song: *Various artists* / Naughty but nice: *Various artists* / Belle of New York: *Various artists* / Let a little love come in: *Various artists.*
LP: . . . . DS 15004
MC: . . . . TCDS 15004

BELLE OF NEW YORK/2 WEEKS WITH LOVE (Original soundtracks) (Various artists).
LP: . . . . MCA 39082
MC: . . . . MCAC 39082

BELLE OF NEW YORK/GOOD NEWS/ RICH YOUNG & PRETTY (Various artists).
Tracks: / When I'm out with the belle of New York: *Various artists* / Oops!: *Astaire, Fred* / Naughty but nice: *Ellis, Anita* / Bachelor's dinner song: *Astaire, Fred* / Baby doll: *Astaire, Fred* / Bride's wedding day, A: *Ellis, Anita* / Seeing's believing: *Astaire, Fred* / I wanna be a dancin' man: *Astaire, Fred* / Good news: *McCracken, Joan* / He's a ladies man: *Lawford, Peter* / Lucky in love: *Marshall, Pat/Peter Lawford/June* Allyson / French lesson, The: *Allyson, June/Peter Lawford* / Best things in life are free, The: *Allyson, June/Peter* Lawford / Pass that peace pipe: *McCracken, Joan* / Just imagine: *Allyson, June* / Varsity drag, The: *Allyson,* June/Peter Lawford / Wonder why?: *Powell, Jane* / Dark is the night: *Powell, Jane* / Paris: *Lamas, Fernando*/ We never talk much: *Darrieux, Danielle* / There's danger in your eyes, cherie: *Darrieux, Danielle.*
LP: . . . . LPMGM 23
LP: 794 869 1
MC: . . . . TCMGM 23
MC: 794 869 4

Belle, Regina

ALL BY MYSELF.
Tracks: / Show me the way / Take your love away / Please be mine / After the love has lost its shine / Intimate relations / You got the love / How could you do it to me / Gotta give it up / So many tears.
LP: 4509981
MC: 4509984
LP: 4670171
MC: 4670174

STAY WITH ME.
Tracks: / Baby come to me / When will you be mine / Dream lover / What goes around / Make it like it was / Good livin' / It doesn't hurt / This is love / (It's gonna take) all our love / Someday we'll all be free / Save the children.
LP: 4651321
MC: 4651324

WITHOUT YOU (See under Bryson, Peabo) (Belle, Regina & Peabo Bryson).

Belle (show)

BELLE OR THE BALLAD OF DR CRIPPEN (Original London cast) (Various artists).
Tracks: / Ain't it a shame?: *Various artists* / Ballad of Dr Crippen, The: *Various artists* / Belle: *Various artists* / Bird of paradise: *Various artists* / Bravest of men,The: *Various artists* / Coldwater: *Various* artists / Michigan: *Various artists* / Devil's bands man, The: *Various artists* / Colonies: *Various artists*/ Dit dit song, The: *Various artists* / Don't ever leave me: *Various artists* / Fairy godmother: *Various artists*/ Fifty years ago: *Various artists* / I can't stop singing: *Various artists* / Lovely London: *Various artists*/ Meet me at the strand: *Various artists* / Mr Lasherwood and mighty Mick: *Various artists* / Minstrel song, The: *Various artists* / Pils, pils, pils: *Various artists* / Pint of wallop, A: *Various artists* / Policemans song: *Various artists* / Song of our future: *Various artists* / Waltzing with you: *Various artists* / You are mine: *Various artists* / You can't beat a British crime: *Various artists.*
MC: . . . . ZCTER 1048
LP: . . . . TER 1048

Belle Stars

BELLE STARS.
Tracks: / Sign of the times / Ci ya ya / Clapping song, The / Indian Summer / Harlem Shuffle / Reason, The / Iko Iko / Baby I'm yours / Mockingbird / Snake, The / Burning / Needle in a haystack.
LP: . . . . SEEZ 45

Bellis, Arthur D.

500 AS ONE.
LP: . . . . DKA 8316

Bellow, Roger

SUCCESS STREET (Bellow, Roger & The Drifting Troubadors).
LP: . . . . FF 504

Bellow, Saul (aut)

HERZOG (see under Herzog).

Bells

CHANGE RINGING ON HANDBELLS (Various).
Tracks: / Stedman cinques / Spliced surprise major / London surprise royal / Little Bob 20-in / Gransire caters / Treble Bob 16-in / Stedman triples / Bristol surprise maximus.
LP: . . . . SDL 310
MC: . . . . CSDL 310

Bells Are ...

BELLS ARE RINGING (Original Broadway Cast) (Various artists).
Tracks: / Overture: *Various artists* / Bells are ringing: *Various artists* / It's a perfect relationship: *Various* artists / On my own: *Various artists* / It's a simple little system: *Various artists* / It is a crime: *Various* artists / Hello, hello there: *Various artists* / I met a girl: *Various artists* / Long before I knew you: *Various artists* / Mu-cha-cha: *Various artists* / Just in time: *Various artists* / Drop that name: *Various* artists / Party's over, The: *Various artists* / Saltzburg: *Various artists* / Midas touch, The: *Various artists* / I'm goin' back: *Various artists.*
LP: . . . . CBS 32254
MC: 40-32254
MC: . . . . JST 02006
LP: . . . . AOS 2006
MC: PST2006

BELLS ARE RINGING (Film soundtrack) (Various artists).
MC: 92060 4

Bell's Cellar

BELL'S CELLAR OF SOUL 89 (Various artists).
Tracks: / She shot a hole in my soul: *Curry, Clifford* / Don't you know a true love: *O'Jays* / Sock it to em: *Moss, Bill* / I'm just an average guy: *Masqueraders* / Believe in me: *Henley, Floyd* / Love bug: *Davis,* Melvin / On the other side: *Jones, Lee* / Choice, The: *O'Jays* / I miss you: *O'Jays* / Love that never ...: *Tig & Co* / I ain't got love: *Williams/Weston* / Don't be afraid: *Henley, Floyd* / Love bug got a bear hug: *Davis, Melvin.*
LP: . . . . CRB 1221

Bellson, Louis

BIG BAND EXPLOSION LIVE.
Tracks: / Spacin' home / Intrigue / Groove blues / Spanish gipsy / I remember Duke / Time check.
LP: . . . . N 127

BIG BAND JAZZ FROM THE SUMMIT.
LP: . . . . FS 83

COOL, COOL BLUE.
Tracks: / Tapooze don / If we were in love / Wanderlust / Boss / Cool cool blue / Long ago / Third 'I'.
LP: 2310 899

EAST SIDE SUITE (Bellson, Louis & His Jazz Orchestra).
Tracks: / Tenor time / What makes Moses run.
LP: . . . . CIJD 40161W

ECUE (Bellson, Louis & Walfredo De Los Reyes).
Tracks: / Javille / Sentifo en seis (six feeling) / Para buenos bailarines (for good dancers) / Salsa en cinco (salsa in five) / Ecue (folder sleeve).
LP: 2310807
MC: K10 807

HOT (Bellson, Louis & His Jazz Orchestra).
Tracks: / Caravan / Ode to a friend / Peaceful poet, The / Together we rise / Hot / Hookin' it / Waltzing at Denison / Walkin' with Buddy.
MC: . . . . CIJD 260160ZX
LP: . . . . CIJD 460160ZY

LIVE AT JAZZ SHOWCASE (Bellson, Louis Four).
Tracks: / Sonny side / Duke's blues / 3 p.m. / I hear a rhapsody / Jam for your bread / Warm alley / Cherokee.
LP: . . . . CJ 350
MC: . . . . CJC 350

LONDON CONCERT, THE (see Peterson, Oscar) (Bellson, Louis/Oscar Peterson/John Heard).

LONDON GIG, THE (Bellson, Louis & Big Band).
Tracks: / Sing a song of love / My mother / Drum squad / Blues for Fred / Jus fer us / We've come a long way together / Put it right here / Santos.
LP: 2310 880
MC: K10 880

LONDON SCENE (Bellson, Louis & Big Band).
LP: . . . . CJ 157

LOUIS BELLSON AND HIS JAZZ ORCHESTRA (Bellson, Louis & His Jazz Orchestra).
Tracks: / It don't mean a thing / Fascinating rhythm / Latin affair, A.
LP: . . . . MMD 20120 A
MC: . . . . MMC 40120 Z

LOUIS BELLSON BIG BAND.

Tracks: / Intimacy of the bands / Quiet riots / Carnaby Street / Beyond category / Chameleon / Open your window / Movin' on / Groove blues / La banda grande.
LP: 2310 755
MC: K10 755

LOUIS BELLSON JAM.
Tracks: / Melody for Thelma / Stein on vine / Shave tail / Gonga din / I wonder why / Ballad medley-All the way home / Time to ride a moonbeam / Bye bye to all the birds / Blue invasion / Gush of periwinkles, A.
LP: 2310 838
MC: K10 838

MATTERHORN.
Tracks: / Matterhorn suite for drums, The / Knuf brothers, The / Conversations / Then and now / War bird.
LP: 2310 834
MC: K10 834

ORIGINALS (Bellson, Louis/Malach/Pizzapelli/Jones).
LP: ST 205

SIDE TRACK.
LP: CJ 141

SUNSHINE ROCK (Bellson, Louis & The Explosion Orchestra).
Tracks: / Sunshine swing / Mid-eastern spango / Night birds / Feels so good / Hawk talks, The / Rich outing / Niles blues / Numero uno.
LP: 2310 851
MC: K10 851

THUNDERBIRD.
Tracks: / Thunderbird / Little pixie / Nails / Serenade in blues.
LP: JAS 40
MC: JAS C40

WITH BELLS ON!.
Tracks: / Who's who / Cool / Amoroso / Prelude / Gumshoe / Blitzen / St. Louis / Moon is low / Doozy / Lou's blues / With bells on / Diplomat speaks, The / Mighty two, The / Paradiddle song / Rolls a la bossa nova / More flams / Swinging the rudiments / Que sticks / Two in one / Rhythmic excursion / Slides and hides.
LP: VJD 564

Belly Dance Nights

BELLY DANCE NIGHTS VOL. 1 (Layale burg el haman) (Various artists).
MC: TC GVDL 262

BELLY DANCE NIGHTS VOL 2 (Layale burg el haman) (Various artists).
MC: TC GVDL 263

Belly Of An... (film)

BELLY OF AN ARCHITECT (Film Soundtrack) (Various artists).
LP: FACT 195
MC: FACT 195C

Belmonde, Pierre

THEMES FOR DREAMS.
LP: ONE 1077

Beloved

BLISSED OUT.
Tracks: / Up, up and away (happy sexy mix) / Wake up soon (something to believe in) / Pablo (special K dub) / It's alright now (back to basics) / Hell (honky tonk) / Time after time (muffin mix) / Sun rising (Norty's spago mix), The / Your love takes me higher.
LP: WX 383
MC: WX 383C

HAPPINESS.
Tracks: / Hello / Your love takes me higher / Time after time / Don't you worry / Scarlet beautiful / Sun rising, The / I love you more / Wake up soon / Up, up and away / Found.
LP: WX 299
MC: WX 299C

WHERE IT IS.
LP: HARPLP 2

Beloved Screen Music

BELOVED SCREEN MUSIC (Various artists).
Tracks: / Over the rainbow: *Various artists* / Gonna fly now: *Various artists* / Speak softly love: *Various* artists / Ben Hur love theme: *Various artists* / Raindrops keep falling on my head: *Various artists* / Summertime in Venice: *Various artists* / East of Eden: *Various artists* / Tara's theme: *Various artists* / From Russia with love: *Various artists* / Plein soleil: *Various artists* / Love is many splendored thing: *Various artists*.
LP: SX 7008

Beltane Fire

DIFFERENT BREED.
Tracks: / Captain Blood / Fortune favours the brave / Night fishing / Poacher, The / Excalibur / King Arthur's cave / Different breed / Run (light the Beltane Fire).

LP: CBS 26582
MC: 40 26582

Belton, Richard

AT HIS BEST.
LP: 6043
MC: 6043 TC

GOOD 'N' CAJUN.
LP: 6021
MC: 6021 TC

LOUISIANA CAJUN MUSIC.
LP: 6032
MC: 6032 TC

MODERN SOUNDS IN CAJUN MUSIC.
LP: 6010

MODERN SOUNDS IN CAJUN MUSIC VOL. 2.
LP: 6013
MC: 6013 TC

Belvin, Jesse

HANG YOUR TEARS OUT TO DRY.
Tracks: / Dream girl / Hang your tears out to dry / I'm only a fool / Betty my darling / Trouble and misery / Hum de dum / Dear heart / Little darlin' / This is my love / My satellite / Baby, don't go / Let me dream / Where's my girl / Deacon Dan Tucker / Beware / One little blessing / Sugar doll.
LP: JD 900

JUST JESSE BELVIN.
Tracks: / Secret love / Love is here to stay / Ol man river / Now you know / Zing went the strings of my heart / Guess who / Witchcraft / Funny / Take me back to the island / Masquerade is over / My funny valentine / Alright okay you win.
LP: NL 89458
MC: NK 89458

MEMORIAL ALBUM.
Tracks: / Goonight my love, pleasant dreams / You send me / Let me love you tonight / Senorita / I'm in love (with a girl) / Girl of my dreams / My desire / (I love you) for sentimental reasons / Dream house / Just to say hello / I wanna know why / Sad and lonesome / I need you so / I'll mess you up.
LP: CH 96

MR EASY.
LP: FS 41

Bembeya Jazz

MOUSSOKORO.
LP: ESP 8430

TELEGRAMME.
LP: ESP 8418
MC: C 1011

YEKEKE.
LP: ESP 8431

Beme Seed

FUTURE IS ATTACKING.
Tracks: / Future is attacking.
LP: BFFP 50

Ben Hur (film)

BEN HUR (Original Soundtrack Musical Highlights) (Various artists).
Tracks: / Prelude: *Various artists* / Adoration of the Magi, The: *Various artists* / Roman march: *Various* artists / Friendship: *Various artists* / Love theme on Ben Hur: *Various artists* / Burning desert, The: *Various* artists / Rowing of the gallery slaves: *Various artists* / Naval battle: *Various artists* / Return to Judea: *Various artists* / Victory parade: *Various artists* / Mother's love: *Various artists* / Lepers search for the Christ: *Various artists* / Procession to Calvary: *Various artists* / Miracle and finale: *Various artists*.
LP: 2353 030

BEN HUR (1) (Film soundtrack) (Rome Symphony Orchestra).
Tracks: / Prelude / Miracle and finale, The / Procession to Calvary / Lepers search for the Christ / Mother's love, The / Victory parade / Return of Judea / Naval battle / Rowing of the galley slaves / Burning desert, The / Ben Hur love theme / Roman march / Adoration of the Magi, The.
LP: CBS 70276
MC: 40 70276

BEN HUR (2) (1925 Film Soundtrack) (Davis, Carl/Liverpool Philharmonic Orch).
Tracks: / Ben Hur (Opening titles) / Nativity / Esther and the young prince / Roman march and disaster / Galley slave / Pirates / Iras the Egyptian / Chariot race / Ben Hur's return / Via Dolorosa / Earthquake / New dawn.
MC: FILMC 043
LP: FILM 043

BEN HUR (ORIGINAL ISSUE) (Film soundtrack) (Various artists).
LP: MGM C 802

BEN-HUR (See under Rozsa, Miklos) (National Philharmonic Orchestra).

BEN-HUR (Film Soundtrack) (Rozsa, Miklos/National Phil.Orch.).
Tracks: / Fanfare to prelude / Star of Bethlehem and adoration of the Magi / Friendship / Burning desert, The / Arrius / Rowing of the galley slaves / Parade of the charioteers / Mother's love, The / Return to Judea / Ring for freedom / Lepers search for the Christ / Procession to Calvary / Miracle and finale.
LP: PFS 4394
MC: 4178494

Ben, Jorge

BEN-VINDA AMIZADE.
MC: CELC 7608

DADIVA.
Tracks: / Eu quero ver a rainha / Energia bom bom / Daviva da da / Taj Mahal / Filho maraviha / Pais tropical / A lobo comeu o canario / Ana tropicana / Conquero / Rio babilonia / No reino encantado do mar.
LP: 409 6274

SONSUAL.
LP: 7700

Ben, Mohammed

AFRICAN FEELING (GHANA) (Ben, Mohammed Malcolm).
Tracks: / Preservation of humanity / Zimbabwe / Turn me loose / Reconciliation.
LP: STERNS 1001

Benatar, Pat

BEST SHOTS.
Tracks: / Hit me with your best shot / Love is a battlefield / We belong / We live for love / Sex as a weapon / Invincible / Shadows of the night / Heartbreaker / Fire and ice / Treat me right / If you think you know how to love me / You better run.
LP: PATV 1
MC: ZPATV 1
LP: TAT V 1
MC: ZTAT V 1

CRIMES OF PASSION.
Tracks: / Treat me right / You better run / Never wanna leave you / Hit me with your best shot / Hell is for children / Prisoner of love / Out a touch / Little paradise / I'm gonna follow you / Wuthering heights.
LP: CHR 1275
MC: ZCHR 1275

GET NERVOUS.
Tracks: / Shadows of the night / I want out / Looking for a stranger / Anxiety (get nervous) / Fight it out / Victim, The / Little too late / I'll do it / Tell it to her / Silent partners.
LP: CHR 1386
LPPD: PCHR 1386
MC: ZCHR 1386

IN THE HEAT OF THE NIGHT.
Tracks: / Heartbreaker / I need a lover / If you think you know how to love me / In the heat of the night / My clone sleeps alone / We live for love / Rated X / Don't let it show / No you don't / So sincere.
LP: CHR 1236
MC: ZCHR 1236

IN THE HEAT OF THE NIGHT/CRIMES OF PASSION.
Tracks: / Heartbreaker / I need a lover / If you think you know how to love me / In the heat of the night / My clone sleeps alone / We live for love / Rated X / Don't let it show / No you don't / So sincere / Treat me right / You better run / Never wanna leave you / Hit me with your best shot / Hell is for children / Prisoner of love / Outa touch / Little paradise / I'm gonna follow you / Wuthering heights.
MCSET: ZCDP 108

LIVE FROM EARTH.
Tracks: / Looking for a stranger / I want out / We live for love / Hell is for children / Hit me with your best shot / Promises in the dark / Heartbreaker / Love is a battlefield / Lipstick lies / Fire and ice.
LP: CHR 1451
MC: ZCHR 1451
LPPD: CHRP 1451

PAT BENATAR: INTERVIEW PICTURE DISC.
LPPD: BAK 2111

PRECIOUS TIME.
Tracks: / Promises in the dark / Fire and ice / Just like me / Precious time / It's a tuff life / Take it any way you want it / Hard to believe / Helter skelter / Evil genius.
LP: CHR 1346
MC: ZCHR 1346

SEVEN THE HARD WAY.
Tracks: / Sex as a weapon / Le bel age / Walking in the underground / Big life / Red version / 7 rooms of gloom / Run between the raindrops / Invincible / Art of letting go, The.
LP: CHR 1507
MC: ZCHR 1507

TROPICO.
Tracks: / Diamond field / We belong / Painted desert / Temporary heroes / Love in the ice age / Ooh ooh song / Outlaw blues / Suburban king / Crazy world like this, A / Takin' it back.
MC: ZCHR 1471
LP: CHR 1471

TRUE LOVE.
Tracks: / Bloodshot eyes / Payin' the cost to be the boss / So long / I've got papers on you / I feel lucky / True love / Good life / Evening / I get evil / Don't happen no more / Please come home for Christmas.
LP: CHR 1805
MC: ZCHR 1805

WIDE AWAKE IN DREAMLAND.
Tracks: / All fired up / One love / Let's stay together / Don't walk away / Too long a soldier / Cool soldier / Cerebral man / Lift 'em on up / Suffer the little children / Wide awake in dreamland.
LP: CDL 1628
MC: ZCDL 1628

Benbow, Steve

SONGS OF IRELAND (Benbow, Steve & The Strawberry Hill Boys).
Tracks: / O'Reilly's daughter / Banks of roses / Boul thady quill / Little beggar man / Mush, mush / Spanish lady / I'm a rambler / Holy ground / Irish rover, The / She moved through the fair / Finnegan's wake / Green grows the laurel / Brennan on the moor / Hot asphalt / Brian O'Linn / Wild colonial boy.
LP: BDL 1020

Benchenet, Cheb

LA BLONDA.
LP: KAN 1986

Benchley, Robert

BEST OF BENCHLEY.
MC: CDL 51731

Benders

DISTANCE.
LP: HOT 1015

Bendeth, David

ADRENALIN.
Tracks: / Breakdown / Easy ridin' / Lock stock and barrel / Doctor Dimento / Feel the real / Copycat / Bozonoknowz / Adrenalin / Count me out / Turbo charger / Calm.
LP: SWK 2004

JUST DESSERT.
Tracks: / Make it pop / Goldmine / I was there / Love collects / Rollin' / Feel the real (again) / Colourful dream, A / Risque rock / Better believe it / Acapulco.
LP: ENVY 502
MC: ENCAS 502

Bendix, Ralf

SING ROCK 'N' ROLL.
Tracks: / Wirfahr'n nach San Fernando / Weit von Alaska / Hotel zur einsamkeit / Mona Lisa / Hey Joe / Heute geh ich nicht nach haus / 99 Jahr' (Geht meine post jetzt nach sing sing) / Rock-a-beatin' boogie / See you later alligator / Shake, rattle and roll (medley) / Ich liebe ein Hassliches madchen / Sputnick rock / At the hop / So geht das jede nacht / Babysitter boogie / Du bist ja so schon / Minne haha / Buona sera.
LP: BFX 15078

Bene Jesserit

FASHION IS A DIRTY WORD.
Tracks: / Gloria / I had taken a few minutes to go... / Kidnapping, The / I could feel a pulse hammering in... / No rule for a dream: Peking (with rain) / Room had faded from her mind / Words / Il serait peu t'etre judicieux / You can dance if you want it... / Band was playing some unfamiliar... / La chanson d'ugly / Joyeux poeme / This guy was so mad he stuttered as... / Femmes aux yeux d'argile / She was never so beautiful as then / So far from Asia / Watching watching the world move / Derisoire / She had faded blondish hair... / Be happy / Little lady.
LP: DMC 021

Benediction

GRAND LEVELLER.
LP: NB 048
LPPD: NB 048PD

SUBCONCIOUS TERROR.
LP: 082971
MC: NB 033MC
LPPD: NB 033PD

Beneke, Tex

BENEKE ON BROADWAY (Beneke, Tex & The Glenn Miller Sound).
Tracks: / More I see you, The / Hello Dolly / I left my heart in San Francisco / My favourite things / Lemon tree / I wish

you love / On a clear day / Walk right in / Stranger on the shore / I've grown accustomed to her face / Tonight.
LP: . . . . BDL 1037
MC: . . . . AJKL 1037

HI THERE TEX (Beneke, Tex & Miller Orchestra).
LP: . . . . SWS 3

LOOSE LIKE (Beneke, Tex Orchestra).
LP: . . . . HEP 29

MEMORIES.
LP: . . . . FH 33
MC: . . . . CFH 33

RAMBLIN' AROUND.
Tracks: / Sleepy time gal / Put 'em in a box / Do you ever think of me / Don't blame me / Rainy afternoon / My romance / Ramblin' around.
LP: . . . . AWE 33
MC: . . . . CAWE 33

SALUTES GLENN MILLER (Beneke, Tex Orchestra).
LP: . . . . GELP 15093

SHOOTING STAR (1948) (Beneke, Tex & His Orchestra).
Tracks: / Shooting star / Now is the hour / Over the rainbow / Whistler, The / Dream lullaby / 18th century drawing room / Thoughtless / Things ain't what they used to be / Rhapsody in blue / That feathery feeling / Sabre dance / Pianissimo / Saturday date / Body and soul / Cherokee canyon / Dreamy lullaby / Beyond the sea / All the things you are.
LP: . . . . AWE 8
MC: . . . . CAWE 8

TEX BENEKE AND ORCHESTRA, 1949 (Beneke, Tex Orchestra).
LP: . . . . GELP 15050

TEX BENEKE AND THE GLENN MILLER ORCHESTRA (Beneke, Tex & The Glenn Miller Sound).
LP: . . . . EB 416

UNDER THE RAINBOW.
LP: . . . . ART 004
MC: . . . . CART 004

WITH NO STRINGS (Beneke, Tex Orchestra).
Tracks: / What can you do / What's new / Begin the beguine / Devil and the deep blue sea / Blue moon / Cock-a-doodle-doo / Way you look tonight / Java junction / Look up / La Rosita / Castle rock / Horses / Dancer's delight / Hop scotch / Baby o / World on a string.
LP: . . . . HEP 8

Benet, Stephen Vincent

DEVIL AND DANIEL WEBSTER, THE (see under Devil & Daniel... (bk)) (Hingle, Pat (nar)).

Benford, Mac

BACKWOOD BANJO.
LP: . . . . ROUNDER 0115

Bengal Minstrel

MUSIC OF THE BAULS.
LP: . . . . H 72068

Bengal Tigers

METAL FETISH.
LP: . . . . HMILP 19

Benjamin, Sathima Bea

MEMORIES AND DREAMS.
Tracks: / Liberation suite.
LP: . . . . EKAPA 003

Benjamin, Tony

AFRICAN REBEL.
LP: . . . . ARILP 009

Bennato, Eduardo

ABBI DUBBI.
Tracks: / Sogni / La luna / La chitarra / Stasera o mai / Mergellina / Viva la mamma / Abbt dubbt / Vendo bagnoli / Ma quale ingenuita / Zen.
MC: . . . . TCV 2617
LP: . . . . V 2617

Bennett, Alan (nar)

FORTY YEARS ON/A WOMAN OF NO IMPORTANCE (see under Forty Years On) (Gielgud, Sir John/Patricia Routledge (nars)).

TALKING HEADS (Original TV Cast) (Various artists).
MCSET: . . . . ZBBC 1097

Bennett, Arnold (aut)

ANNA OF THE FIVE TOWNS (See under Anna of the Five Towns) (Jeffrey, Peter (nar)).

OLD WIVE'S TALE, THE (Calvert, Phyllis).
MCSET: 418 198-4

Bennett, Billy

ALMOST A GENTLEMAN.
Tracks: / Nell / My mother doesn't know I'm on the stage / Mandalay / I'll be thinking of you / Ogul mogul - a kanakanese love lyric / No power on earth / She was poor but she was honest / Family secrets / Please let me sleep on your doorstep tonight / Christmas day in the cookhouse / Club raid, The / Mottoes / Green tie on the little yellow dog, The.
LP: 12T 387

Bennett, Boyd

SEVENTEEN (Bennett, Boyd & His Rockets).
Tracks: / Seventeen / Click clack / Banjo rock and roll / Little ole you-all / Tennessee rock 'n' roll / Hit that jive jack / Cool disc jockey / My boy flat top / Move / Rabbit-eye pink and charcoal black / Right around the corner / Blue suede shoes / Boogie at midnight / High school hop.
LP: . . . . SING 1160

Bennett, Brian

CHANGE OF DIRECTION/ ILLUSTRATED LONDON NOISE.
Tracks: / Slippery Jim De Grize / Canvas / Whisper not / Memphis / Tricycle / Sunshine superman / On Broadway / Sunny afternoon / Little old lady / 98.6 / Con Alma / Change of direction / Love and occasional rain / I heard it through the grapevine / Chameleon / Just lookin' / Rocky raccoon / Ticket to ride.
LP: . . . . SEE 205

RUTH RENDELL MYSTERIES.
Tracks: / Sleeping life, A / No crying he makes / Guilty thing surprised, A / Shake hands for ever / Ruth Rendell mysteries theme.
LP: . . . . SHM 3286
MC: . . . . HSC 3286

RUTH RENDELL MYSTERIES VOL.II.
MC: 847 524 4
LP: 847 524 1

VOYAGE.
Tracks: / Voyage / Solstice / Chain reaction / Pendulum force / Air quake / Ocean glide.
MC: . . . . DJH 40532
LP: . . . . DJF 20532

Bennett, Cliff

DRIVIN' ME WILD.
LP: . . . . MFP 1121

GOT TO GET YOU INTO MY LIFE (Bennett, Cliff & The Rebel Rousers).
Tracks: / Use me / Hold on I'm coming / C.C. rider / One way love / Beautiful dreamer / Ain't that loving you baby / Ain't love good, ain't love proud? / Got to get you into my life / I take what I want / Back in the USSR / Three rooms with running water / I'll take good care of you / Said I weren't gonna tell nobody / It's all right / I'll take you home / Barefootin' / Hurting inside / That's what I said / I'm in love with you / You got what I like.
LP: . . . . CM 108
MC: . . . . CMK 108

SLOW DOWN (Bennett, Cliff & The Rebel Rousers).
LP: . . . . ED 148

Bennett, Clive (nar)

ADVENTURES OF MR. PINKWHISTLE (See under Adventures of...).

LIVE AT THE STAR CLUB (See under Live At ...) (Various artists).

Bennett, Elinor

WELSH HARP.
LP: . . . . SAIN 1331 D

Bennett, Joe

JOE BENNETT AND THE SPARKLETONES (Bennett, Joe & The Sparkletones).
LP: 33.7281

Bennett, Judy (nar)

ALL FAMOUS FIVE RECORDINGS (see under Blyton, Enid (aut)) (Bennett, Judy (nar) & Charles Collingwood (nar)).

FAVOURITE RUPERT STORIES (See under Rupert Bear).

FIVE ON A HIKE TOGETHER (See under Blyton, Enid) (Bennett, Judy (nar) & Charles Collingwood (nar)).

MORTIMER'S CROSS (See under Mortimer's Cross).

Bennett, Louise

YES M'DEAR.
Tracks: / Long time gal / Caribbean rhythm / Jamaica language / Buggy Bruck / Street cries / Balanci / Colonizing in reverse / Jamaicans coming home for vacation / Noh lickle twang / Dry foot bwoy / Funny names / Praises / Hosanna / Ring ding / Rhythm games / Coconut tree / Heaby load / Jamaica woman / Oman a bread winner / Chi chi bud / Gay Paree / Walk good.
MC: . . . . ICT 9740
LP: . . . . ILPS 9740

Bennett, Max

MAX BENNETT.
LP: . . . . FS 149

MAX BENNETT PLAYS.
LP: . . . . FS 203

Bennett, Pinto

BIG IN WINNEMUCCA (Bennett, Pinto & The Motel Cowboys).
Tracks: / Wood and steel / Winnemucca / Bad girl / First door to the wrong / Hard core cowboy / Honky tonk asshole / Two waltzing mice / Dream lover / Wine me up / Ol' blue / Jack Tarr the sailor.
LP: . . . . PTLP 003
MC: . . . . PTLC 003

FAMOUS MOTEL COWBOY SONGS (Bennett, Pinto & The Motel Cowboys).
Tracks: / Valuable time / Shelter / Pardner I know / More or less / Moonlight at the oasis / Carolina morning / Only in my dreams / She almost reminds me of you / She wouldn't take nothing / What the hell am I doin' here.
LP: . . . . PTLP 001
MC: . . . . PTLC 001

PURE QUILL (Bennett, Pinto & The Motel Cowboys).
Tracks: / You cared enough to lie / Livin' and dyin' for love / Peaceful woman / I ain't in it for the money / True lovin' daddy / No sweat / Stranger in the mirror / Prarie blues / Ballad of Hai-Sing, The / Different ways to sing the blues / Pure quill.
LP: . . . . PTLP 007
MC: . . . . PTLC 007

Bennett, Richard

HAROLD ARLEN'S SONGS.
LP: . . . . AP 168

I GOT RHYTHM (Music of George Gershwin).
Tracks: / I got rhythm / Swanee / Nobody but you / So it again / I'll build a stairway to paradise / Three preludes / Fascinating rhythm / Lady be good / Promenade / Man I love, The / Somebody loves me / Jazzbo Brown blues / That certain feeling / Sweet and lowdown / Merry Andrew / Clap yo' hands / Do do do / Impromptu in two keys / My one and only / S'wonderful / Two waltzes in C / Strike up the band / Liza / Three quarter blues / Who cares.
LP: . . . . ED 2913471
MC: . . . . ED 2913474
LP: . . . . EMD 5538

LITTLE JAZZ BIRD.
Tracks: / Nobody else but me / Up with the lark / Folks who live on the hill, The / Little jazz bird / Bess, oh where's my Bess? / Sleeping bee / I had myself a true love / My romance / Nobody's heart belongs to me / Wait till you see her / I didn't know what time it was / Miss Otis regrets / What is this thing called love? / After you.
LP: . . . . EMD 1077011

PUTTIN' ON THE RITZ (see Montgomery, Marion & R.R.Bennett).

SURPRISE SURPRISE (see Montgomery, Marion & R.R.Bennett).

TAKE LOVE EASY.
LP: . . . . AP 206

TOWN AND COUNTRY (see under Montgomery, Marian).

Bennett, Sam

GREENWOOD SIDE-I-O (See Under Costello, Cecilia) (Bennett, Sam & Cecilia Costello).

Bennett, Steve

COMEDY.
Tracks: / Comedy / Bright lights / Lost weekend / Broken heart / Empty / Watching TV / Delhi / Puppets / Throwback / Don't let go.
LP: . . . . SMV 001

Bennett, Tony

ALL TIME GREATEST HITS.
Tracks: / Something / Where do I begin / Maybe this time / Just in time / For once in my life / Firefly / Shadow of your smile / Put on a happy face / Love look away / Rags to riches.
LP: . . . . CBS 22176

ALL TIME GREATEST HITS.
Tracks: / Something / (Where do I begin) love story / Maybe this time / Just in time / For once in my life / (I left my heart) in San Francisco / Because of you / Boulevard of broken dreams, The / Stranger in paradise / I wanna be around / Time for love, A / Who can I turn to (when nobody needs me) / This is all I ask / Smile / Sing, you sinners / Firefly / Shadow of your smile, The / Put on a happy face / Love look away / Rags to riches.
LP: 4688434

ANYTHING GOES (Bennett, Tony & The Count Basie Big Band).
Tracks: / I guess I'll have to change my plan / Chicago / With plenty of money and you / Anything goes / Life is a song / I've grown accustomed to her face / Jeepers creepers / Growing pains / Poor little rich girl / Are you having any fun?.
LP: . . . . BDL 1054
MC: . . . . BDC 1054

ART OF EXCELLENCE, THE.
Tracks: / Why do people fall in love / Moments like this / What are you afraid of? / When love was all we had / Everybody has the blues / How do you keep the music playing? / City of the angels / Forget the woman / I got lost in her arms / Day you leave me, The.
LP: . . . . CBS 26990
MC: 40 26990

ASTORIA - PORTRAIT OF THE ARTIST.
Tracks: / When do the bells ring for me / I was lost, I was drifting / Little street where old friends meet, A / Girl in love, The / It is like reaching for the moon / Speak low / Folks that live on the hill, The / Antonia / Waver of dreams / There will never be another you / Body and soul / Where do you go from love / Boulevard of broken dreams / Where did the magic go / We've come home again.
LP: 4660051
MC: 4660054

BENNETT AND BASIE (Bennett, Tony & Count Basie).
Tracks: / Strike up the band / I guess I'll have to change my plan / Chicago / With plenty of money and you / Life is a song / Anything goes / Are you having any fun? / Jeepers creepers / Growing pains / Poor little rich girl / I've grown accustomed to her face.
LP: . . . . JR 149

BENNETT/BERLIN.
Tracks: / They say it's wonderful / Isn't this a lovely day / All of my life / Now it can be told / Song is ended, The / When I lost you / Cheek to cheek / Let yourself go / Let's face the music and dance / Shakin' the blues away / Russian lullaby / White Christmas.
LP: 4604501
MC: 4604504

BEST OF TONY BENNETT.
MC: 16-19

CHICAGO (Bennett, Tony & Count Basie).
LP: 20029
MC: 40029

COLLECTION: TONY BENNETT (20 golden greats).
Tracks: / Stranger in Paradise / Fascinating rhythm / I left my heart in San Francisco / Climb every mountain / April in Paris / Sunday / Ol' man river / Sometimes I'm happy / Always / Solitude / Just in time / All the things you are / Our love is here to stay / Lullaby of Broadway / Anything goes / Blue velvet / Love look away / My heart tells me / It amazes me / I'm just a lucky so and so.
LP: . . . . DVLP 2026
MC: . . . . DVMC 2026

COUNT BASIE SWINGS - TONY BENNETT SINGS (see under Basie, Count) (Bennett, Tony & Count Basie).

FOR ONCE IN MY LIFE.
LP: . . . . SBPG 63166

GRAFFITI COLLECTION.
MC: . . . . GRMC 17

I LEFT MY HEART IN SAN FRANCISCO.
Tracks: / I left my heart in San Francisco / Once upon a time / Tender is the night / Smile / Love for sale / Taking a chance on love / Candy kisses / Have I told you lately that I love you / Rules of the road, The / Marry young / I'm always chasing rainbows / Best is yet to come, The.
LP: . . . . CBS 32732
MC: 40 32732
LP: . . . . BPG 62201

IN PERSON (Bennett, Tony & Count Basie).
Tracks: / Just in time / When I fall in love / Taking a chance on love / Without a song / Fascinating rhythm / Solitude / Pennies from Heaven / Lost in the stars / Firefly / There will never be another you / Lullaby of Broadway / Ol' man river.
LP: . . . . CBS 32373
LP: . . . . BGP 62250

JAZZ.
Tracks: / I can't believe that you're in love with me / Don't get around much anymore / Stella by starlight / On Green Dolphin Street / Let's face the music and dance / I'm through with love / Solitude / Lullaby of Broadway / Dancing in the dark / I let a song go out of my heart / When lights are low / Just one of those

things / Crazy rhythm / Judy / Give me the simple life / Street of dreams / Love scene / While the music plays on / Close your eyes / Out of this world / Just friends / Have you met Miss Jones? / Danny boy / Sweet Lorraine.
LP: 4504651
MC: 4504654

LIFE IS A SONG (Bennett, Tony & Count Basie).
Tracks: / I've grown accustomed to her face / Jeepers creepers / Growing pains / Poor little rich girl / Are you having any fun? / I guess I'll have to change my plans / Chicago / With plenty of money and you / Anything goes / Life is a song.
LP: . . . . TOP 115
MC: . . . . KTOP 115

MAGIC OF TONY BENNETT, THE.
Tracks: / What is this thing called love / Love for sale / I'm in love again / Easy to be so nice to come home to / Easy to love / It's alright by me / Night and day / Dream dancing / I've got you under my skin / Get out of town / Experiment / One / This funny world / Lost in the stars / As time goes by / I used to be colour blind / Mr. Magic.
LP: . . . . YU 106
MC: . . . . CYU 106

MY HEART SINGS.
LP: . . . . FS 168

PORTRAIT OF A SONG STYLIST.
Tracks: / Shadow of your smile, The / Who can I turn to / When Joanna loved me / Don't worry 'bout me / It had to be you / Where or when / Ain't misbehavin' / Dancing in the dark / Second time around / Old devil moon / My funny valentine / Autumn leaves / Taste of honey, A / I left my heart in San Francisco / Toot toot tootsie / September song / Moment of truth / I'll be around.
LP: . . . . HARLP 105
MC: . . . . HARMC 105

RODGERS AND HART COLLECTION.
Tracks: / Thou swell / Most beautiful / Small hotel / I've got five dollars / You took advantage of me / I wish I were in love again / This funny world / My heart stood still / My romance / Mountain greenery / This can't be love / Blue moon / Lady is a tramp, The / Lover / Manhattan / Spring is here / Have you met Miss Jones / Isn't it romantic / Wait 'till you see her / I could write a book.
LP: . . . . YU 108
MC: . . . . CYU 108

RODGERS AND HART SONGBOOK.
Tracks: / This can't be love / Blue moon / Lady is a tramp, The / Lover / Manhattan / Spring is here / Have you met Miss Jones? / Isn't it romantic / Wait 'till you see her / I could write a book / Thou swell / Most beautiful girl in the world, The / There's a small hotel / I've got five dollars / You took advantage of me / I wish I were in love again / This funny world / My heart stood still / My romance / Mountain greenery.
MCSET: . . . . DARC 2C 2102
2LP: . . . . DARC 22102

SAN FRANCISCO.
Tracks: / I left my heart in San Francisco / Taking a chance on love / Have I told you lately that I love you / Candy kisses / I'm always chasing rainbows / MacArthur Park / Little green apples / Eleanor Rigby / My cherie amour / Look of love, The / Something.
MCSET: . . . . DTO 10040

SNOWFALL.
Tracks: / Snowfall / My favourite things / Christmas song, The / Santa Claus is coming to town / We wish you a merry Christmas / Silent night, holy night / O come all ye faithful / Jingle bells / Where is love / Christmasland / I love the winter weather / I've got my love to keep me warm / White Christmas / Winter wonderland / Have yourself a merry little Christmas.
LP: 4604681
MC: 4604684

STRIKE UP THE BAND (See Basie, Count) (Bennett, Tony & Count Basie).

STRING OF TONY'S HITS, A.
LP: . . . . DP 66010

TO MY WONDERFUL ONE.
Tracks: / Wonderful one / Till / September song / Suddenly / I'm a fool to want you / We mustn't say goodbye / Autumn leaves / Laura / April in Paris / Speak low / Tenderly / Just in time / When I fall in love / Taking a chance on love / Without a song / Fascinating rhythm / Solitude / Pennies from Heaven / Lost in the stars / Firefly / There will never be another you / Lullaby of Broadway / Ol' man river.
MC: 40 22184
LP: 22184

TOGETHER AGAIN (Bennett, Tony & Bill Evans).
Tracks: / Child is born, A / Make someone happy / Bad and the beautiful / Lucky to be me / You're near me / Two lonely people / You don't know what love is / Maybe September / Lonely girl / You must believe in spring.
LP: . . . . MRS 901
MC: . . . . MRSC 901
MC: . . . . CSIV 1122

TONY BENNETT AND FRIENDS MAKE MAGNIFICENT MUSIC.
LP: . . . . MRS 910
MC: . . . . MRSC 910

TONY MAKES IT HAPPEN.
LP: . . . . SBPG 63055

TONY'S GREATEST HITS.
LP: . . . . SBPG 62821

UNFORGETTABLE: TONY BENNETT (16 Golden Classics).
Tracks: / There'll be some changes made / Blue moon / Lady is a tramp, The / Lover / Manhattan / Spring is here / I could write a book / Child is born, A / Make someone happy / Life is beautiful / Maybe September / Lonely girl / You don't know what love is / Thou swell / There's a small hotel / As time goes by.
LP: . . . . UNLP 019
MC: . . . . UNMC 019

VERY BEST OF TONY BENNETT (20 greatest hits).
LP: . . . . PA 5021

Bennington, Billy

BARFORD ANGEL, THE.
LP: . . . . EAL 1

Bennink, Hans

COMPANY 3 (See Bailey, Derek) (Bennink, Hans & Derek Bailey).

LIVE FROM VERITY'S PLACE (see Bailey, Derek & Hans Bennink) (Bennink, Hans & Derek Bailey).

Benno, Marc

LOST IN AUSTIN.
Tracks: / Hotfoot blues / Chasin' rainbows / Me and a friend of mine / New romance / Last train / Lost in Austin / Splish splash / Monterrey pen / Drifter / Hey there senorita.
LP: . . . . AMLH 64767

Benns, Jon

BENNS' MEAN LAFFS.
Tracks: / Mr. Average / Windmills of your mind / Orchestra story / Saturday night / Super Janner / Typewriter song / Goodnight / Dreams of a frustrated folk singer.
LP: . . . . AVA 106

Benny, Jack

BING CROSBY WITH PEGGY LEE, JACK BENNY, GARY COOPER (See under Crosby, Bing) (Benny, Jack/ Bing Crosby/ Peggy Lee/ Gary Cooper).

Benoit, Bernard

LUTUNN NOZ - MUSIQUE CELTE POUR GUITARE.
Tracks: / Aet kuit an ankou / Lost an diaoul / Soizig / Fidandoue kernevad / Lutunn noz / Jig izelbriz / L'heritiere de Keroulaz / Tom an aven / Riviere du Huelgoat / La folle de Toujane, Theme de.
LP: . . . . ARN 33306

Benoit, Cedric

CAJUN CAJUN CAJUN.
LP: 6074
MC: . . . . 6074 TC

Benoit, David

EVERY STEP OF THE WAY.
Tracks: / Every step of the way / Shibuya Station / Key to you, The / Remembering what you said / Painted desert / ReBach / Sao Paulo / No worries / I just can't stop loving you / Once running free.
LP: . . . . GRP 91047
MC: . . . . GRPM 91047

FREEDOM AT MIDNIGHT.
Tracks: / Freedom at midnight / Along the Milky Way / Kei's song / Man with the panama hat, The / Pieces of time / Morning sojourn / Tropical breeze / Passion walk / Del sasser / Last goodbye (On CD Only).
LP: . . . . GRP 91035
MC: . . . . GRPM 91035

INNER MOTION.
Tracks: / M.W.A. (musicians with attitude) / Coconut Roads / Every corner of the world / 6 string poet / Houston / Along love's highway / Deep light / El camino real / South East Quarter / Last request, A.
LP: . . . . GRP 96211
MC: . . . . GRP 96214

THIS SIDE UP.
Tracks: / Beach trails / Stingray / Land of the loving / Linus and Lucy / Sunset Island / Hymn for Aquino / Santa Barbara / Waltz for Debbie.
LP: . . . . GRP 91031

URBAN DAYDREAMS.
Tracks: / Sailing through the city / Urban daydreams / Snow dancing / Wild kids / Seattle morning / Cloud break / When the winter's gone / Safari / Looking back / As if I could reach rainbows.
LP: . . . . GRP 95871
MC: . . . . GRP 95874

WAITING FOR SPRING.
LP: . . . . GRP 95951

Benson, Clifford

MUSIC FOR CLARINET AND PIANO -2 (See under King, Thea) (King, Thea & Clifford Benson).

Benson, Cy

CY BENSON & FAIRWIND.
LP: . . . . BLP 008

Benson, E.F (aut)

MAPP AND LUCIA (Scales, Prunella (nar)).
MC: 0600560481

QUEEN LUCIA (Various artists).
MCSET: . . . . ZBBC 1120

Benson & Farrell

BENSON AND FARRELL.
LP: . . . . CTI 6069

Benson, Gary

DON'T THROW IT ALL AWAY.
Tracks: / To kill another day / This house the concert / Best thing I can do, The / No guarantee / Don't throw it all away / Playing in the band / Let her in / Help me get through / Quiet man / Forever lady / You.
LP: . . . . ETAT 3

GARY BENSON STORY.
Tracks: / Don't throw it all away / No guarantee / To kill another day / Let her in / You / Comedy world / Like I've never been gone / Actor, The / After all this time / Can't let you go / Sharing you / New world.
LP: . . . . ETMP 2

NEW WORLD.
Tracks: / Like I've never been gone / After all this time / River, The / Sharing you / Background music / Comedy world / Heart of stone / Actor, The / All the time in the world / Can't let you go / Love me like the first time / New world.
LP: . . . . ETAT 10

Benson, George

20/20.
Tracks: / No one emotion / Please don't walk away / I just wanna hang around you / Nothing's gonna change my love for you / La mer / New day / You are the love of my life / Hold me / Stand up / 20/20 / Shark bite.
LP: 925178 1
MC: 925178 4

BEST OF GEORGE BENSON.
Tracks: / White rabbit / Somewhere in the East / Body talk / Take five / California dreamin' / Full compass.
LP: . . . . AMID 115
MC: . . . . CMID 115

BIG BOSS BAND (Featuring The Count Basie Orchestra).
Tracks: / Without a song / How do you keep the music playing? / Baby workout / Portrait of Jennie / Skylark / Ready now that you are / On Green Dolphin Street / I only have eyes for you / Walkin' my baby back home / Basie's rag.
LP: 7599262951
MC: 7599262954

BLUE BENSON.
Tracks: / Billie's bounce / Low down and dirty / That lucky old sun / Thunder walk / Doobie, doobie blues / What's new / I remember Wes.
LP: 2486 272
MC: 3186 098

BODY TALK.
MC: . . . . CTK 9503

BREEZIN'.
Tracks: / This masquerade / Six to four / Breezin' / So this is love / Lady / Affirmation.
LP: . . . . K 56199
MC: K4 56199

COLLABORATION (Benson, George/ Earl Klugh).
Tracks: / Mt. Airy road / Mimosa / Brazilian stomp / Dreamin' / Since you're gone / Collaboration / Jamaica / Romeo and Juliet love theme.
LP: . . . . WX 91
MC: . . . . WX 91 C

COLLECTION: GEORGE BENSON.
LP: . . . . DVLP 2076
MC: . . . . DVMC 2076

DETROIT'S GEORGE BENSON.
LP: . . . . PARKWOOD 107

EARLY YEARS.
Tracks: / White rabbit / Somewhere in the East / Take five / California dreamin' / Body talk / Full compass.
LP: . . . . SPELP 53
MC: . . . . SPEMC 53
LP: . . . . CTI 2409219

ELECTRIFYING GEORGE BENSON, THE (Benson, George Quartet).
Tracks: / All the things you are / Love for sale / Oleo / All blues / Masquerade is over, The / Invitation / Li'l darlin'.
2LP: . . . . AFFD 140
MC: . . . . MCCL 091764
LP: . . . . CL 001764

EXCLUSIVE BENSON.
Tracks: / I am the walrus / You make me feel like a natural woman / Doobie doobie blues / Along comes Mary / Billie's bounce / Groovin' / Sunny / I remember Wes / Low down and dirty / Sack o' woe / Walk on by / Julie / What's new? / That lucky old sun / Giblet gravy / Windmills of your mind / People get ready / Thunder walk / Song for my father / Carnival joys.
2LP: . . . . VSOPLP 109
MC: . . . . VSOPMC 109

GENIUS OF GEORGE BENSON.
Tracks: / California dreamin' / Shell of a man / Summer knows, The / Summertime / Cast your fate to the wind / No sooner said than done / Changing world / Take five.
LP: . . . . SHM 3129
MC: . . . . HSC 3129

GEORGE BENSON (Compact/Walkman jazz).
Tracks: / Billie's bounce / What's new / Thunder walk / Low down and dirty / That lucky old sun / Song for my father / Sack o' woe / Doobie doobie blues / Tuxedo Junction / I remember Wes.
MC: 833 292-4

GEORGE BENSON AND JACK MCDUFF (Benson, George & Jack McDuff).
Tracks: / Shadow dancers, The / Sweet Alice blues, The / I don't know / Just another Sunday / Will you still be mine / Easy living / Rock a bye / Hot barbecue / Party's over, The / Briar patch / Hippy dip / 601 1/2 No. Poplar / Cry me a river / Three day thang, The.
2LP: . . . . PR 24072

GEORGE BENSON COLLECTION, THE.
Tracks: / Turn your love around / Love all the hurt away / Give me the night / Cast your fate to the wind / Love ballad / Nature boy / Last train to Clarksville / Livin' inside your love / Never give up on a good thing / On Broadway / White rabbit / This masquerade / Here comes the sun / Breezin' / Moody's mood / We got the love / Greatest love of all, The.
2LP: . . . . K 66107
MC: K4 66107

GEORGE BENSON IN CONCERT.
Tracks: / Love for sale / Witch craft / Love walked in / Dahlin's delight (on cassette only) / Masquerade is over, The / All the things you are / There will never be another you / All blues (on cassette only).
LP: . . . . CBR 1029
MC: . . . . KCBR 1029

GEORGE BENSON LIVE IN CONCERT.
LP: . . . . DELD 309
MC: . . . . CELD 309

GIVE ME THE NIGHT.
Tracks: / What's on your mind? / Dinorah Dinorah / Love dance / Star of the story / Midnight love affair / Turn out the lamplight / Love x love / Off Broadway / Moody's mood / Give me the night.
LP: . . . . K 56823
MC: K4 56823

GRAFFITI COLLECTION.
MC: . . . . GRMC 05

IN CONCERT - CARNEGIE HALL.
LP: . . . . CTI 6072

IN FLIGHT.
Tracks: / Nature boy / Wind and I, The / World is a ghetto, The / Gonna love you more / Valdez in the country / Everything must change.
LP: . . . . K 56327
MC: K4 56327

IN YOUR EYES.
Tracks: / Feel like makin' love / Inside love (so personal) / Lady love me (one more time) / Love will come again / In your eyes / Never too far to fall / Being with you / Use me / Late at night / In search of a dream.

LP: 923744 1
MC: 923744 4

IT'S UPTOWN/GEORGE BENSON COOKBOOK.
Tracks: / Clockwise / Summertime / Ain't that peculiar? / Jaguar / Willow weep for me / Foggy day, A / Hello birdie / Bullfight / Stormy weather / Eternally / Myna bird blues / Cooker, The / Benny's back / Bossa rocka / All of me / Big fat lady / Benson's rider / Ready and able / Borgia stick, The / Return of the prodigal son / Jumpin' with symphony Sid.
2LP: . . . . CBS 22187
MCSET: 40 22187

LIL' DARLIN'.
Tracks: / Witchcraft / Blue bossa / Oleo / Li'l darlin'.
LP: . . . . THBL 078

LIVIN' INSIDE YOUR LOVE.
Tracks: / Before you go / Welcome into my world / Love is a hurtin' thing / You're never too far from me / Love ballad / Change is gonna come, A / Prelude to fall / Soulful strut / Nassau day / Hey girl.
2LP: . . . . K 66085
MC: K4 66085

LOVE FOR SALE.
LP: . . . . CL 91784
MC: . . . . CLMC 91784

LOVE SONGS: GEORGE BENSON.
Tracks: / Give me the night / Lady love me (one more time) / Love X love / New day / Feel like makin' love / 20/20 / Never give up on a good thing / Inside love (so personal) / No one emotion / In your eyes / Turn your love around / Greatest love of all, The.
LP: . . . . NE 1308
MC: . . . . CE 2308

LOVE WALKED IN.
Tracks: / All the things you are / Invitations / Love walked in / Dahlin's delight.
LP: . . . . PLP 36
MC: . . . . PMC 36

MASQUERADE.
Tracks: / Love for sale / Masquerade is over, The / There will never be another you / All blues.
LP: . . . . THBL 072

REPLAY ON GEORGE BENSON.
LP: . . . . FEDB 5019
MC: . . . . CFEDB 5019

SPACE.
Tracks: / Hold on I'm coming / Summertime / Son of sky dive / Gone / Octane.
LP: . . . . CTI 7085

STORMY WEATHER.
Tracks: / Clockwise / Big fat lady / Hammond's bossa nova / Stormy weather / Slow scene / Jumpin' with symphony Sid / Cooker, The / Push push / Bullfight / Ready 'n' able / Bossa rocka / Flamingo.
LP: 31689
MC: 40 31689

SUMMERTIME.
LP. . . . . EPC 32191
MC: 40 32191

TENDERLY.
LP: . . . . WX 263
MC: . . . . WX 263 C
LP: 9259071

TWICE THE LOVE.
Tracks: / Twice the love / Starting all over / Good habit / Everybody does it / Living on borrowed love / Let's do it again / Stephanie / Tender love / You're still my baby / Until you believe.
LP: . . . . WX 160
MC: . . . . WX 160 C

WEEKEND IN LA.
Tracks: / Greatest love of all, The / Down here on the ground / Ode to a Kudu / We as love / California pm / Lady blue / We all remember Wes / Windsong / On Broadway / It's all in the game / Weekend in LA.
2LP: . . . . K 66074
MC: K4 66074

WHILE THE CITY SLEEPS.
Tracks: / Shiver / Love is here tonight / Teaser / Secrets in the night / Too many times / Did you hear the thunder / While the city sleeps / Kisses in the moonlight.
LP: . . . . WX 55
MC: . . . . WX 55 C

WONDERFUL YEARS, THE.
LP: . . . . PENALP 2

Benson, Ivy

IVY BENSON AND HER ORCHESTRA (Benson, Ivy & Her Orchestra).
LP: . . . . LIB 3333

Benson, Jo Jo

SOUL SHAKE (see under Scott, Peggy) (Benson, Jo Jo/Peggy Scott).

Bensusan, Pierre

MUSIQUES.
LP: . . . . ROUNDER 3038

SOLILAI.
Tracks: / Nice feeling / Bamboule / Au jardin d'amour / Santa Monica / Suite flamande aux pommes / Milton / Solilai / Doa tea.
LP: . . . . ROUNDER 3068
LP: 4650851
MC: 4650854

SPICES.
Tracks: / Femme cambree / Mille vallees / Le bateau fiction / Shi big, shi mhor / Agadiramadan / La cour interieure / Last pint, The / Les voiles catalanes / Montsegur / Four am.
LP: 4608551
MC: 4608554

Bent Back Tulips

LOOKING THROUGH.
LP: . . . . ROSE 205

Bentick, Anna

FLUTES IN ZANIBAR.
MCSET: . . . . MRC 1030

Bentine, Michael

BEST OF BENTINE.
LP: . . . . REH 492
MC: . . . . ZCR 492

SQUARE BASHING.
Tracks: / March on / Concert / Freedom of the airways / What the public thinks / Tragedy at the National Gallery / Lady at the door / Conversation in a train / Welcome stranger / Toast master / Music for Michael Bentine's square dance / Utter end.
LP: . . . . INTS 5054
MC: . . . . INTK 5054

Bentley, Gladys

COMPLETE BLUES SESSIONS (Bentley, Gladys/Mary Dixon).
LP: . . . . CC 52

Bentley, John

BENTLEY AND THE BEAR (Bentley, John & Guy Richards).
LP: . . . . ESR 1214

JOHN BENTLEY & HIS BUDDIES Various artists (Bentley, John & His Buddies).
LP: . . . . ESR 1211

Benton, Brook

20 GOLDEN PIECES: BROOK BENTON.
Tracks: / Bayou baby / Sunshine / Endlessly / Old-fashioned strut / Soft / Trust me to do what you want me to do (and I'll do it) / Pulling me down / Makin' love is good for you / Love is best of all / Tribute to "Mamam" / Let the sun come out / We need what we need / Better times / Lover's question / Let me in your world / I love her / Lord, you know how men are / Till I can't take it anymore / I keep thinking to myself / There's still a little love left for me.
LP: . . . . BDL 2039

20 GREATEST HITS (MASTERS (HOLLAND)).
LP: . . . . MA 20983
MC: . . . . MAMC 20983

BEST OF BROOK BENTON.
Tracks: / Fools rush in / Kiddio / Hotel happiness / Sill waters run deep / Shadrack / Think twice / Frankie and Johnny / Rockin' good way, A / Hit record / Boll weevil / Revenge / Endlessly / Lie to me / So many ways / It's just a matter of time / Walk on the wild side / Baby (you've got what it takes).
LP: . . . . TIME 01
MC: . . . . TIMEC 01
MC: . . . . GM 0229

BEST OF BROOK BENTON, VOL 1.
Tracks: / It's just a matter of time / Kiddio / Same one, The / It's just a house without you / My true confession / Fools rush in / Think twice / Hotel happiness / Thank you pretty baby / Boll weevil.
LP: . . . . PHX 1019

BROOK BENTON.
MC: . . . . ZCGAS 722

BROOK BENTON SINGS THE STANDARDS.
Tracks: / Hey there / That old feeling / Nightingale sang in Berkeley Square, A / Love is a many splendoured thing / Once in love with Amy / Try a little tenderness / Call me irresponsible / Blue moon / Second time around / Moon river / Hawaiian wedding song / More / There, I've said it again / I only have eyes for you / Unforgettable / There goes my heart.
LP: . . . . NL 89092
MC: . . . . NK 89092

DINAH WASHINGTON/BROOK BENTON (see Washington, Dinah) (Benton, Brook & Dinah Washington).

ENDLESSLY.
Tracks: / It's just a matter of time / Boll weevil / Baby you've got what it takes / Lie to me / So many ways / Hotel happiness / Kiddio / Endlessly / Revenge / Same one, The / Think twice / Rockin' good way, A.
LP: . . . . TOP 158
MC: . . . . KTOP 158
MC: . . . . GM 0208

HIS GREATEST HITS.
LP: 822321 1
MC: 822321 4

HIS TOP HITS.
MC: 808

INCOMPARABLE BROOK BENTON, THE.
Tracks: / It's just a matter of time / Kiddio / Same one, The / It's just a house without you / My true confession / Fools rush in / Think twice / Hotel happiness / Thank you pretty baby / Boll weevil / Rainy night in Georgia / So close / Frankie and Johnny / Revenge / Lie to me / So many ways / I got what I wanted / Ties that bind, The / Shadrack / For my baby.
LP: . . . . AFEMP 1024

MAGIC MOMENTS WITH BROOK BENTON.
Tracks: / That old feeling / My darling, my darling / Nightingale sang in Berkeley Square, A / Love is a many splendoured thing / Once in love with Amy / Try a little tenderness / Hey there / Call me irresponsible / Peg o' my heart / Blue moon / Second time around, The / Moon river / While there's life (there's still hope) / Mother Nature, Father Time / I still wanna be with you (everywhere you go) / Life is too short (for me to stop loving you) / You're so wonderful / It's a crime / Boy I wish I was in your place / Since you've been gone / Song I heard last night, The (play it again) / Foolish enough to try / You're mine (and I love you) / More time to be with you.
MC: . . . . NK 89623

PORTRAIT OF A SONG STYLIST.
MC: . . . . HARMC 109

RAINY NIGHT IN GEORGIA, A.
MC: 260 422 4

SONGS I LOVE TO SING.
Tracks: / Moonlight in Vermont / It's been a long long time / Lover come back to me / If you are but a dream / Why try to change me now / September song / Oh what it seemed to be / Baby won't you please come home / They can't take that away from me / I'll be around / I don't know enough about you / Fools rush in.
LP: . . . . MOIR 112
MC: . . . . CMOIR 112

SPOTLIGHT ON BROOK BENTON.
2LP: 6612 116

TWO OF US, THE (See Washington, Dinah) (Benton, Brook & Dinah Washington).

UNFORGETTABLE: BROOK BENTON (16 Golden Classics).
Tracks: / Kiddio / It's just a matter of time / My true confession / Frankie and Johnny / Think twice / Hotel happiness / Thank you pretty baby / Boll weevil / Rainy night in Georgia / Lie to me / Revenge / So many ways / I got what I wanted / Ties that bind, The / Shadrack / For my baby.
LP: . . . . UNLP 010
MC: . . . . UNMC 010

WHERE FOOLS RUSH IN (See Washington, Dinah) (Benton, Brook & Dinah Washington).

Benton, Buster

BLUESBUSTER.
Tracks: / Spider in my stew / Born with the blues / Sweet 94 / Love like I wanna / Leave me alone / Sorry / Funny about my money / Lonesome for a dime / Do it in the rain / Disco blues.
LP: . . . . RL 026

FIRST TIME IN EUROPE.
LP: 33722

MONEY'S THE NAME OF THE GAME.
Tracks: / Sweet 94 / You accuse me / Sit your fine self down / Money's the name of the game / As the years go passing by / Come and see about me / Sweet sixteen / Lean on me.
LP: . . . . ICH 1046
MC: . . . . ICH 1046 MC

WHY ME?.
LP: . . . . ICH 1023
MC: . . . . ZCICH 1023

Benton, Marv

BEST OF MARV BENTON.
LP: . . . . REBEL 1005

Benton, Walt

WALT BENTON (Benton, Walt & The Diplomats).
Tracks: / Big wheel / Hang loose / Stuck up / Summer school blues / Janis / Kansas city / Do it again / I'm gonna leave you / True fine mama / No, no honey / When my blue moon turns to gold again / My baby left me.
LP: . . . . BB 2013

Bentzon, Adrian

DANISH JAZZ VOL.7.
LP: . . . . SLP 416

Beowulf

LOST MY HEAD....
Tracks: / Muy bonita / Flare / Plastic people / Fuzzy princess / Hippy liquor / Once chance / Done got caught / You get me off / Winer diner / Where you from / Lost my head / Cruisin'.
LP: . . . . CARLP 2
MC: . . . . CARC 2

SLICE OF LIFE, A.
Tracks: / Slice of life, A / Ain't gettin' any younger / Fantasy / London woman / Hideaway / Getaway / Social champ / Thanks to you / Half a number / Hounds of tindalos, The.
LP: . . . . MORRHYTHM 20

Berenstain, Stan & Jan

BEARS' CHRISTMAS AND OTHER STORIES.
MC: 1573

BEARS' PICNIC AND OTHER STORIES, THE (See under Bears' Picnic).

Beresford

BEOWULF AND OTHER OLD ENGLISH POEMS (Various artists).
MCSET: . . . . SAY 73

Beresford Band

YORKSHIRE DALES DANCE NIGHT.
LP: . . . . LEA 2069

Beresford, Steve

DANCING THE LINE (See under Beretta, Ann Marie) (Beresford, Steve/Ann Marie Beretta).

DEADLY WEAPONS (Beresford, Steve/David Topp/John Zorn/Tonie Marshall).
LP: . . . . NATO 950

ELEVEN SONGS FOR DORIS DAY.
Tracks: / I was there / Secret love / Let it ring / Serenade in blue / Sentimental journey / Black hills of Dakota, The / It's magic / Que sera sera / At last / I'm beginning to see the light / Back in Cincinnati.
LP: . . . . CHABADA 07

TEA TIME.
LP: . . . . INCUS 15

Beretta, Anne Marie

DANCING THE LINE (Beretta, Anne Marie & Steve Beresford).
Tracks: / Comfortable gestures / Ata 82 / Gift of linen / Horse tail / Tendance / Sand from the desert / Hiver 83/84 / Lover of paradox / Snap / Un aimant vivant / Altitude / Clins d'oeil.
LP: . . . . NATO 565

Berg, Bob

CYCLES (Berg, Bob/Mike Stern/Don Grolnick).
Tracks: / Bruze / Back home / Pipes / Diamond method, The / Company B / Mayumi / So far so / Someone to watch over me.
LP: . . . . INLP 804
MC: . . . . CC 72745

EASTERN REBELLION VOL.2 (See Under Walton, Cedar) (Berg, Bob, Cedar Walton, Sam Jones & Billy Higgins).

FLAME WITHIN, THE (See Under Drew, Kenny Jr) (Drew, Kenny Jr. Featuring Bob Berg).

SHORT STORIES.
Tracks: / Friday night at the Cadillac Club / Words / Snakes / Kalimba / Search, The / Maya / That's the ticket / Junior.
MC: . . . . CC 21

STEPPIN - LIVE IN EUROPE.
LP: . . . . VPA 178

Berg, Jorg Maria

SUGAREE.
Tracks: / Kewpie doll / You're my baby doll / Tip top mama / Kisses sweeter than wine / Take a message to Mary / Devoted to you / Young love / Return to me / Smoke along the track.
LP: . . . . BFX 15135

Berg, Matraca

LYING TO THE MOON.
Tracks: / Things you left un-done / I got it bad and that ain't good / Lying to the moon / I must have been crazy / You are the storm / Calico plains / Appalachian rain / Baby, walk on / Alice in the looking glass / Dancin' on the wire (Only on CD).
MC: . . . . **PK 90532**
LP: . . . . **PL 90532**

Bergalli, Gustavo

GUSTAVO BERGALLI QUINTET (Bergalli, Gustavo Quintet).
LP: . . . . **DRLP 119**

SOUL TRAIN (see under Janson, Claes) (Bergalli, Gustavo/Janson, Claes).

Bergcrantz, Anders

OPINIONS (Bergcrantz, Anders Quintet).
LP: . . . . **DRLP 97**

Berger, Bengt

BITTER FUNERAL BEER BAND.
Tracks: / In a Balinese bar / Two ewe songs / Upper region / Twisted pattern / Ammasu / Pire for Palme / Dar-Kpen: Gan da Yina / Praise drumming for ANC.
LP: . . . . **DRLP 142**
LP: . . . . **ECM 1179**

Berger, Karl

ALL KINDS OF TIME (Berger, Karl & David Holland).
Tracks: / Simplicity / Perfect love / Fragments / Beginning, The / Now is / D'accord / All kinds of time / We are.
LP: **3010**

WITH SILENCE.
LP: . . . . **ENJA 2022**

Berger, Terry (aut)

BLACK FAIRY TALES (see under Black Fairy Tales (bk)) (McNeil, Claudia (nar)).

Bergeyk Van, Ton

FAMOUS RAGTIME GUITAR SOLOS.
Tracks: / Buffalo rag / Atlanta rag / Felicity rag / Blake's breakdown / Grizzly bear / Ragtime nightmare / Silver swan, The / King Porter stomp / Pineapple rag / Smokey mokes / Powder rag / Original rags / Harlem rag / American beauty rag.
LP: . . . . **SNKF 106**

FROM SOUP TO NUTS.
Tracks: / Junk man rag / Mustard swing / Zither melodies / From soup to nuts / Kansas City stomp / Rondo caprice / Ragtime melody / Bantam step / Springtime rag / Wabash blues / Notoriety / If I had you / Moonlight serenade / Jazz me blues / Divertissment / Georgia grind / Coconut dance / Florida rag.
LP: . . . . **SNKF 114**

I GOT RHYTHM.
Tracks: / I got rhythm / Sophisticated slide / Jubilee stomp / Take it easy / Somewhere over the rainbow / Sugar / Cat and the dog, The / Who's that knocking at my door? / Frog-I-more rag / Dirty dozens / Ain't misbehavin' / Stumbling / Ballin' the jack / These foolish things / Anno 1926 / Under the moon.
LP: . . . . **SNKF 125**

LULU'S BACK IN TOWN (Hot guitar solos).
Tracks: / Georgia on my mind / Black and tan fantasy / Nobody's sweetheart / Mexican bonito / Boogie dance, The / Rockin' chair / Between the lines / We're all alone / Fabulous Rosina, The / Blue monk / Cry me a river / Hombre mio / Lulu's back in town / Rosa De Castella / Lady Madonna / March of the hoodlums.
LP: . . . . **SNKF 166**

Bergin, Mary

FEADOGA STAIN.
LP: . . . . **CEF 071**

Bergland, Bond

UNEARTH.
LP: . . . . **PTF 8607**

Berglund, Paavo

PAAVO BERGLUND AND STOCKHOLM PHILHARMONIC ORCH (Berglund, Paavo/Stockholm Philharmonic Orchestra).
Tracks: / Rachmaninov; symphony no.3 in A minor (op.44) / Rock, The - fantasy for orchestra (op.7).
MC: . . . . **RK 87902**

Bergman, Bill

MIDNIGHT SAX.
LP: . . . . **PJ 88022**
MC: . . . . **PJC 88022**

Bergman, Ingemar

MAGIC FLUTE (VIDEO) (See under Magic Flute).

Bergman, Ingrid (nar)

HUMAN VOICE, THE (see under Human Voice (bk)).

ON THE RADIO.
LP: . . . . **MR 1154**

SMALL WOMAN, THE (see under Small Woman).

Berigan, Bunny

1936 VOLUME 1.
Tracks: / It's been so long / I'd rather go blind / Let yourself go / Swing Mister Charlie / Melody from the sky, A / I can't get started / Rhythm saved the world / Little bit later on, A / If I had my own way / When I'm with you / Just to be in Carolina / It ain't nobody's biz'ness.
LP: . . . . **CAH 3000**

BUNNY BERIGAN.
Tracks: / Shanghai shuffle / Devils holiday / Sing you sinners / Sunday / 'Taint so honey, 'taint so / I'll always be in love with you / Frankie and Johnny / Flat foot floogie / Peg o' my heart / Mahogany hall stomp / Wearing of the green, The / Dardanella (blues).
LP: . . . . **ATS 7**
MC: . . . . **KATS 7**

BUNNY BERIGAN 1931.
Tracks: / I can't get Mississippi off my mind / I apologise / Beggin' for love / Parkin' in the moonlight / In the merry month of maybe / How the time can fly / At your command / When Yuba plays the rhumba on the tuba / Bubbling over with love / You're in my arms / Fiesta / Have you forgotten / Dancing with the daffodils / Love is like that / When the moon comes over the mountains / Nevertheless.
LP: . . . . **SS 115**

BUNNY BERIGAN 1937/40 VOL.2.
Tracks: / Tommy Dorsey theme / My ghost goes to town / Head over heels in love / Maria / Dark eyes / Fable of the rose / What can I say, after I say I'm sorry? / I can't get started with you / My melancholy baby / Deed I do / Savoy jump / Sugar foot stomp / Linger awhile / Sunday / China boy.
LP: . . . . **SS 101**

BUNNY BERIGAN AND HIS ORCHESTRA (Berigan, Bunny & His Orchestra).
Tracks: / Theme / Intro / Started / Stompin' at the Savoy / Mr. Paganini / Sing me a sweet song / Copper coloured gal / There's a small hotel / Closing theme / St. Louis blues / Swing for sale / Pennies from Heaven / Skeleton in closet, The / Started / Organ grinders swing / You turned the tables on me.
LP: . . . . **JA 11**

BUNNY BERIGAN BAND 1938/9 (Berigan, Bunny & His Orchestra).
Tracks: / I can't get started with you / Round my old deserted farm / Old straw hat, An / You took the words right out of my heart / Kiss me again / Moonshine over Kentucky / Heigh-ho / Prisoner's song / Shanghai shuffle / In a mist / Little gate's special / Livery stable blues.
LP: . . . . **SS 100**

BUNNY BERIGAN, LOUIS ARMSTRONG & MILLS BROTHERS (Berigan, Bunny/Louis Armstrong/Mills Brothers).
LP: . . . . **SS 103**

BUNNY BERIGAN WITH 1936 STUDIO BANDS.
Tracks: / Moonburn / My heart and I / It's been so long / Sing an old fashioned song / Whose big baby are you / Much too much / Garbo green / You hit the spot / Oh Susannah / Just because / Deep Elem blues / If I could be with you one hour tonight / Ja da / I can't get started with you / I can pull a rabbit out of a hat.
LP: . . . . **SS 106**

BUNNY BERIGAN WITH HAL KEMP & HIS ORCHESTRA 1930 Vol.1 (Berigan, Bunny & Hal Kemp).
Tracks: / Give yourself a pat on the back (take 1) / I remember you from somewhere / If I had a girl like you (take 1) / Washin' the blues from my soul (take 1) / Medley of Southern College songs / She loves me just the same (take 1) / Them there eyes / Give yourself a pat on the back (take 2) / If I had a girl like you (take 2) / Washin' the blues from my soul (take 2) / She loves me just the same (take 2).
LP: . . . . **SS 110**

COMPLETE BUNNY BERIGAN VOL 3, THE.
Tracks: / Ten easy lessons / When a prince of a fella meets Cinderella / Livery stable blues / Let this be a warning to you / Why doesn't somebody tell me these things / High society / Father dear father / Simple and sweet / Button, button / I won't tell a soul I love you / Rockin' rollers' jubilee / Sobbin' blues / I cried for you / Jelly roll blues / 'Deed I do / In a mist / Flashes / Davenport blues / Candlelights / In the dark / Walkin' the dog / Patty cake, patty cake / Jazz me blues / Ya had it comin' to ya / There'll be some changes made / Little Gate's special / Gangbuster's holiday / Peg o my heart / Night song / Ain't she sweet / Ay ay ay.
2LP: . . . . **NL 90439**
MCSET: . . . . **NK 90439**

INDISPENSABLE BUNNY BERIGAN (1937-39) (RCA UK) (Berigan, Bunny & His Orchestra).
Tracks: / Swanee river / Frankie and Johnnie / Study in brown, A / I can't get started / Prisoner's song / Black bottom / Azure / Russian lullaby / High society / Sobbin' blues / In a mist / Flashes / Candlelights / In the dark / Blue Lou / Jazz me blues / Night song / Honeysuckle rose / Blues / 'Cause my baby says so / All God's chillun got rhythm / Mahogany Hall stomp / Turn on that red hot heat / Wearing of the green, The / Livery stable blues / Rockin' rollers' jubilee / Jelly roll blues / Davenport blues / Walking the dog / Blues, The / There'll be some changes made / Little gates special / Ain't she sweet.
MCSET: . . . . **NK 89744**
2LP: . . . . **NL 89744**

INDISPENSABLE BUNNY BERIGAN, THE (1937-1939) (RCA France).
Tracks: / Honeysuckle rose / Blues / 'Cause my baby says so / Swanee river / All God's chillun got rhythm / Frankie and Johnny / Mahogany hall stomp / Turn on that red hot heat / Study in brown, A / I can't get started / Prisoner's song / Mama, I wanna make rhythm / Black bottom / Russian lullaby / Azure / Wearing of the green, The / Livery stable blues / High society / Rockin' rollers jubilee / Sobbin' blues / Jelly roll blues / In a mist / Flashes / Davenport blues / Candlelights / In the dark / Walking the dog / Blue Lou / Be some changes made / Little gate's special / Peg o'my heart / Night song / Ain't she sweet.
2LP: . . . . **PM 43689**

LEADER AND SIDEMEN.
LP: . . . . **MERITT 504**

LEE WILEY & BUNNY BERIGAN (See Wiley, Lee) (Berigan, Bunny & Lee Wiley).

PORTRAIT OF BUNNY BERIGAN.
Tracks: / Me minus you / She reminds me of you / Troubled / Plantation moods / In a little Spanish town / Solo hop / Nothin' but the blues / Squareface / King Porter stomp / Buzzard, The / Tillie's downtown now / You took advantage of me / Chicken and waffles / I'm coming Virginia / Blues / Swing Mister Charlie / Blue Lou / Marie / Black bottom / Prisoner's song / I can't get started.
LP: . . . . **AJA 5060**
MC: . . . . **ZC AJA 5060**

SATURDAY NIGHT SWING CLUB 1936 (Berigan, Bunny & The Original Dixieland Jazz Band).
LP: . . . . **JASM 2524**
MC: . . . . **JASMC 2524**

UNKNOWN BAND 1939.
LP: . . . . **NOST 7638**
LP: . . . . **MERITT 501**

Berk, Dick

BIG JAKE (Berk, Dick & The Jazz Adoption Agency).
Tracks: / Raving lunatic / Message, The / if I were a bell / Groovin' / Metamorphosis / Juxtaposition / Bewitched, bothered and bewildered / Big Jake / Force to hang.
LP: . . . . **DS 890**

RARE ONE (Berk, Dick & The Jazz Adoption Agency).
Tracks: / Dizzy's business / Lament for Brad / I didn't know what time it was / Kadee Van Browne / Fun at sea / Rare one / Commissioner / Theme.
LP: . . . . **DS 877**

Berk, Lotte

LOTTE BERK EXERCISE RECORD - GET PHYSICAL.
LP: . . . . **WW 5122**
MC: . . . . **WW 4 5122**

Berkeley Blues

BERKELEY BLUES FESTIVAL (Various artists).
LP: . . . . **ARHOOLIE 1030**

Berkeley Rhythm

BERKELEY RHYTHM.
LP: . . . . **BR 1**

Berkshire Bell Ringers

BELLS OF CHRISTMAS, THE.
LP: . . . . **HDY 1922**
MC: . . . . **ZCHDY 1922**

Berlin

COUNT THREE AND PRAY.
Tracks: / Will I ever understand you / You don't know / Like flames / Heartstrings / Take my breath away / Trash / When love goes to war / Hideaway / Sex me, talk me / Pink & velvet.
LP: . . . . **MERH 101**
MC: . . . . **MERHC 101**

LOVE LIFE.
Tracks: / When we make love / Touch / Beg, steal or borrow / Now it's my turn / Dancing in Berlin / Rumour of love / Pictures of you / In my dreams / No more words / List in a crowd / For all tomorrow's lies / Fall.
LP: **818 329 1**
LP: . . . . **MERL 41**

PLEASURE VICTIM.
Tracks: / Tell me why / Pleasure victim / Sex (I'm a...) / Masquerade / Metro, The / World of smiles / Torture.
LP: **6302 236**

Berlin Affair (film)

BERLIN AFFAIR, THE (Film soundtrack) (Various artists).
LP: . . . . **A 286**
MC: . . . . **C 286**

Berlin Alexanderplatz

BERLIN ALEXANDERPLATZ (Original soundtrack) (Various artists).
LP: . . . . **STV 81217**

Berlin Blondes

BERLIN BLONDES.
Tracks: / Framework / Astro / Science / Romance / Trail to Istanbul / Secret days / Mannequin / Neon probe / Zero song.
LP: . . . . **EMC 3346**

Berlin Blues (film)

BERLIN BLUES (Film soundtrack) (Various artists).
LP: . . . . **A 357**

Berlin by Night

BERLIN BY NIGHT (Various artists).
Tracks: / Ungarwein (gipsy wine): *Von Geczy, Barnabas & His Orchestra* / Ich tanze mit dir in den himmel hinein: *Harvey*, Lilian & Willi Fritsch / Gruss und kuss Veronika: *Die Weintraubs* (Vocal: Eva Bisch) / Regentropfen: *Ruth, Ludwig* Orchestra & Metropol Vocalists / Musik! Musik! Musik!: *Stenzel, Otto Dance Orchestra* (Vocal: Wilfried Sommer.) / Arpanetta: *Gaden, Robert Orchestra* / Abends in der taverne: *Strienz, Wilhelm* / Du hast gluck bei den frau'n bel ami: *Waldmuller*, Lizzi / Wochenend' und sonnenschein: *Comedy Harmonists* / Liebling, mein herz lasst dich grussen: *Harvey, Lilian* & Willi Fritsch / Rosamunde: *Glahe, Will Orchestra* / Liebe is ein geheimnis: *Hildebrand, Hilde with Orchestra*/ O mia bella Napoli: *Schuricke, Rudi* / Lili Marlene: *Andersen, Lale* / Schones wetter heute: *Zacharias*, Helmut / Sing "Nachtingall, sing": *Kunneke, Evelyn* / Liebe, kleine schaffnerin: *Carl, Rudolf* / Es geht alles voruber, es geht alles vorbei: *Andersen, Lale* / Das alte spinnrad: *Groh, Herbert Ernst & Odeon-Kunstler Orchester*/ Sag' beim abschied leise "servus": *Forst, Willi.*
LP: . . . . **EMS 1395**
MC: . . . . **TCEMS 1395**

Berlin Contemporary

BERLIN CONTEMPORARY JAZZ ORCHESTRA (Conducted by Alexander Von Schlippenbach) (Berlin Contemporary Jazz Orchestra).
LP: . . . . **ECM 1409**

Berlin Filmharmonic

BERLIN FILMHARMONIC CONCERTS, THE (Rias Youth Orchestra).
2LP: . . . . **ACH 037/038**

Berlin, Irving

A CENTURY OF IRVING BERLIN (Face the Music) (Various artists).
Tracks: / Always: *Various artists* / Russian lullaby: *Various artists* / Cheek to cheek: *Various artists.*
MC: . . . . **MMD 20147 H**
LP: . . . . **MMC 40147 F**

ALWAYS (See under Always).

CENTENARY- A CELEBRATION (See under Centenary- a celebration).

CENTENARY- A CELEBRATION (Various artists).
MC: . . . . **HSC 3233**
LP: . . . . **SHM 3233**

FACE THE MUSIC (A CENTURY OF IRVING BERLIN) (See under Face The Music).

GOLDEN AGE OF IRVING BERLIN,THE (Various artists).

Tracks: / Me: *Various artists* / Say it isn't so: *Various artists* / How deep is the ocean: *Various artists*/ Maybe it's because I love you so much: *Various artists* / Heatwave: *Various artists* / Easter parade: *Various* artists / Piccolino, The: *Various artists* / Cheek to cheek: *Various artists* / Isn't this a lovely day: *Various* artists / Let yourself go: *Various artists* / Let's face the music and dance: *Various artists* / On the avenue - selection part 1: *Various artists* / Slumming on Park Avenue: *Various artists* / You're laughing at me: *Various* artists / He ain't got rhythm: *Various artists* / On the avenue - selection part 2: *Various artists* / This year's kisses: *Various artists* / I've got my love to keep me warm: *Various artists* / Girl on the police gazette, The: *Various artists* / Alexander's ragtime band: *Various artists* / Now it can be told: *Various artists*/ Everybody's doing it now: *Various artists* / I used to be colour blind: *Various artists* / Change partners: *Various artists*.
LP: . . . . **GX 41 2518-1**
MC: . . . . **GX 41 2518-4**

GREAT BRITISH DANCE BANDS PLAY THE MUSIC OF IRVING BERLIN (See under Dance Bands...) (Various artists).

GREAT STARS SALUTE IRVING BERLIN (Various artists).
LP: . . . . **CHD 166**

IRVING BERLIN SHOWCASE, AN (See Under Irving Berlin Showcase) (Various artists).

IRVING BERLIN SONGBOOK, THE (See under Irving Berlin Songbook).

MILESTONE OF MEMORY (See under Milestone Of Memory) (Various artists).

MUSIC OF IRVING BERLIN (see under Dance Bands) (Various artists).

SAY IT WITH MUSIC (1923-1933) (See under Say It With Music) (Various artists).

SONG IS...IRVING BERLIN (Various artists).
Tracks: / Alexander's Ragtime Band: *Various artists* / All alone: *Various artists* / Because I love you: *Various* artists / Blue skies: *Various artists* / Cheek to cheek: *Various artists* / He ain't got rhythm: *Various* artists / Heat wave: *Various artists* / I never had a chance: *Various artists* / I'm putting all my eggs in one basket: *Various artists* / I've got my love to keep me warm: *Various artists* / Let me sing and I'm happy: *Various artists* / Let yourself go: *Various artists* / Let's face the music and dance: *Various artists*/ Marie: *Various artists* / Piccolino, The: *Various artists* / Pretty girl is like a melody, A: *Various artists*/ Slumming on Park Avenue: *Various artists* / This year's kisses: *Various artists* / Top hat, white tie and tails: *Various artists* / We saw the sea: *Various artists* / White Christmas: *Various artists* / You keep coming back like a song: *Various artists*.
LP: . . . . **AJA 5068**
MC: . . . . **ZC AJA 5068**

VINTAGE IRVING BERLIN (See Under Vintage Irving Berlin) (Various artists).

Berlin, Jeff

CHAMPION (Berlin, Jeff & Vox Humana).
LP: . . . . **PJ 88004**
MC: . . . . **PJC 88004**

PUMP IT.
LP: . . . . **PJ 88017**
MC: . . . . **PJC 88017**

Berlin Philharmonic

BEATLES IN CLASSIC, THE (Berlin Philharmonika Cellists (12)).
Tracks: / Yellow submarine / Let it be / Something / Fool on the hill, The / Help / Yesterday / Michelle / Hard day's night, A / Norwegian wood / Here, there and everywhere / Can't buy me love / Hey Jude.
LP: **6.25579**
MC: **425579**

EINSTEIN IN EDEN.
LP: **2372117**
MC: **3151117**

SYMPHONIES NO'S 31'PARIS',40,41'JUPITER',38 & 39 (see under Mozart (composer)).

Berlin Soloists

VIENNESE TALES (Waltz transcriptions) (Berlin Soloists/Elisabeth Leonskaja/Philip Moll).
Tracks: / Gypsy baron / Treasure waltz / Roses from the South / Wine, women and song / Wiener gemuts waltz / Steyrische tanze / Till Eulenspiegel.
MC: **244 925-4**

Berlin Symphony

UPPSALA RHAPSODY (see under Alfven (composer)).

Berlin Tattoo

MUSICAL HIGHLIGHTS OF THE BERLIN TATTOO (Various artists).
Tracks: / All hail to the chief - a king is crowned: *Various artists* / Massed pipes and drums marching display: *Various* artists / Prince Charles Edward Stuart arrives: *Various artists* / The King's troop, royal horse: *Various artists*/ Massed band, The: *Various artists* / Kevock choir, The: *Various artists* / Music for Scottish dancing: *Various artists* / Gathering of the clans, The (finale): *Various artists*.
2LP: . . . . **LCDM 8006**

Berline, Byron

B-C-H (Berline, Byron & Dan Crary & John Hickman).
LP: . . . . **SH 3755**
LP: . . . . **SH 3720**
MC: . . . . **SH 3720 MC**
MC: . . . . **SH 3755 MC**

BYRON BERLINE & L.A. FIDDLE BAND.
Tracks: / Roanoke / Dixie hoedown / I'll just stay around / All the good times / Jack rabbit / Sitting on top of the world / Red haired boy / Don't put it away / On and on / Brown county breakdown / Uncle pen.
LP: . . . . **SH 3716**

DAD'S FAVORITES.
Tracks: / Coming down from Denver / New broom / Grey eagle / B & B rag / Redbird / Ragtime Annie / Limerock / Stones rag / Millers reel / Arkansas traveller / Sweet memories waltz / Birmingham fling.
LP: . . . . **ROUNDER 0100**
MC: . . . . **ROUNDER 0100C**

DOUBLE TROUBLE (Berline, Byron & John Hickman).
LP: . . . . **SH 3750**
MC: . . . . **SH 3750MC**

FIDDLER'S DREAM (Berline, Byron & Sundance).
LP: . . . . **AP 043**

NIGHT RUN (Berline, Byron & Dan Crary & John Hickman).
LP: . . . . **SH 3739**
MC: . . . . **SH 3739 MC**

NOW THERE ARE FOUR (Berline, Byron & Dan Crary & John Hickman).
LP: . . . . **SH 3773**
MC: . . . . **SH 3773 MC**

OUTRAGEOUS.
LP: . . . . **FF 227**

Berliner, Paul

SUN RISES LATE HERE, THE (Berliner, Paul & Kudu).
LP: . . . . **FF 092**

Berlioz (composer)

SYMPHONIE FANTASTIQUE (See under Solti, Sir George) (Chicago Symphony Orchestra).

SYMPHONY 'FANTASTIQUE' (Vienna State Opera Orchestra).
MC: . . . . **VETC 6507**

Berlitz

DUTCH FOR TRAVEL.
MC: . . . . **BCP 003**

DUTCH LANGUAGE BASICS.
MC: . . . . **BMC 004**

FRANCE TRAVEL KIT.
MC: . . . . **BTK 003**

FRENCH FOR TRAVEL.
MC: . . . . **BCP 004**

FRENCH LANGUAGE BASICS.
MC: . . . . **BMC 005**

GERMAN FOR TRAVEL.
MC: . . . . **BCP 005**

GERMAN LANGUAGE BASICS.
MC: . . . . **BMC 003**

GERMANY TRAVEL KIT.
MC: . . . . **BTK 004**

GREEK FOR TRAVEL.
MC: . . . . **BCP 006**

GREEK LANGUAGE BASICS.
MC: . . . . **BMC 006**

ITALIAN FOR TRAVEL.
MC: . . . . **BCP 012**

ITALIAN LANGUAGE BASICS.
MC: . . . . **BMC 008**

ITALY TRAVEL KIT.
MC: . . . . **BTK 007**

PORTUGUESE FOR TRAVEL.
MC: . . . . **BCP 011**

PORTUGUESE LANGUAGE BASICS.
MC: . . . . **BMC 011**

SPAIN TRAVEL KIT.
MC: . . . . **BTK 010**

SPANISH FOR TRAVEL.
MC: . . . . **BCP 013**

SPANISH LANGUAGE BASICS.
MC: . . . . **BMC 009**

TURKISH FOR TRAVEL.
MC: . . . . **BCP 015**

TURKISH LANGUAGE BASICS.
MC: . . . . **BMC 014**

Berman, Shelley

INSIDE SHELLEY BERMAN.
LP: . . . . **CLP 1300**

Berman, Sonny

CONFIRMATION (See Gillespie, Dizzy) (Berman, Sonny & Dizzy Gillespie).

JAZZ IMMORTAL 1946.
LP: . . . . **FS 195**

Bermuda Triangle

BERMUDA TRIANGLE (Various artists).
LP: . . . . **RL 12885**

Bernadette

BACK ON THE ROAD AGAIN.
Tracks: / Both sides now / Wild mountain thyme / Come kiss me, love / Alastair John / You're the nearest thing to Heaven / Riding a plane to happiness / First time ever I saw your face, The / Back on the road again / Twelfth of never / Seasons / Four Maries, The / Some day I'll go back to Arizona / Four strong winds / Many a day / Water is wide, The.
LP: . . . . **LIDL 6010**
MC: . . . . **LIDC 6010**
LP: . . . . **LILP 6010**

Bernard, Bob

CLASS.
Tracks: / I cried for you / My foolish heart / Mamas gone goodbye / Linger awhile / My melancholy baby.
LP: . . . . **CLGLP 017**

Bernard, Len

TAKE ME TO THE CIRCUS.
LP: . . . . **S 1329**

Bernard, Rod

BOOGIE IN BLACK & WHITE (Bernard, Rod & Clifton Chenier).
LP: . . . . **JIN 9014**
MC: . . . . **JIN 9014 TC**

COUNTRY LOVIN'.
LP: . . . . **JIN 9008**
MC: . . . . **JIN 9008 TC**

NIGHT LIGHTS AND LOVE SONGS.
LP: . . . . **JIN 9010**

ROD BERNARD.
LP: . . . . **JIN 4007**

THIS SHOULD GO ON FOREVER.
Tracks: / Pardon Mr. Gordon / Colinda forgive / Fais do do / I might as well / Who's gonna rock my baby / Diggy liggy lo / Loneliness / My joile blonde / Congratulations to you / Cajun honey / Take her back / Boss man's son.
LP: . . . . **CH 143**

Berne, Tim

MINATURE (See Under Baron, Joey) (Baron,Joey/Tim Berne/Hank Roberts).

SANCTIFIED DREAMS.
Tracks: / Velcho man / Hip doctor / Elastic lad / Blue alpha (for alpha) / Mag's groove / Terre haute.
LP: **4606761**
MC: **4606764**

THEORETICALLY (Berne, Tim & Bill Frisell).
LP: . . . . **MM 008**

Bernelle, Agnes

FATHER'S LYING DEAD ON THE IRONING BOARD.
Tracks: / Homecoming / Chansonette / Bertha de Sade / Hafen-kneipe / Tootsies / Horse, The / Girl with brown mole / Night elegy / Ballad of the poor child / Hurdy gurdy / Nightingale, The.
LP: . . . . **FIEND 35**

MOTHER IN THE WARDROBE.
LP: . . . . **UNKNOWN**

Bernhard, Sandra

WITHOUT YOU I'M NOTHING.
LP: . . . . **ENVLP 528**
MC: . . . . **TCENV 528**

Bernhardt, Clyde

CLYDE BERNHARDT & THE HARLEM BLUES JAZZ BAND.
LP: . . . . **VLP 7402**

MORE BLUES AND JAZZ FROM HARLEM.
LP: . . . . **BARON 400**

Bernie & Monica

TONGS BY THE FIRE.
MC: . . . . **GTDC 091**

Bernoff, John

BREATHE (Bernoff, John/Marcus Allen).
LP: . . . . **LP 8008**
MC: . . . . **CAS 8008**

PETALS (see Allen, Marcus).

SUMMER SUITE (see Bell, Teja).

Bernsen, Randy

MUSIC FOR PLANETS, PEOPLE AND WASHING MACHINES.
Tracks: / Conehead bop / Olde hats / My funny valentine / I Shot the sheriff / Steppin' / Sir yellow bird / Sundance (abra dance) / Windsong.
LP: . . . . **IZEB 5756**
MC: . . . . **IZEBC 5756**

Bernstein, Elmer

BUCCANEER, THE (See under Buccaneer, The).

GREAT ESCAPE, THE (Film soundtrack) (See under Great Escape) (Various artists).

GRIFTERS, THE (Original Soundtrack).
LP: . . . . **VS 5290**
MC: . . . . **VSC 5290**

MIDAS RUN, THE (Film soundtrack).
LP: . . . . **CT 6016**

MISE EIRE (Bernstein, Elmer & Sean O'Riada).
LP: . . . . **CEF 134**

Bernstein, Ira

TEN TOE PERCUSSION.
MC: . . . . **GVMMC 307**

Bernstein, Leonard

BERNSTEIN CONDUCTS BERNSTEIN.
Tracks: / Ballet (fancy free) / Overture(Candide) / Three dance episodes(On the town) / Prelude,fugue and riffs(On the town).
LP: . . . . **CBS 61816**

BERNSTEIN ON BROADWAY (Various artists).
Tracks: / West side story:prologue: *Various artists* / Somethings coming: *Various artists* / Maria: *Various* artists / Tonight: *Various artists* / Cool: *Various artists* / One hand one heart: *Various artists*/ I feel pretty: *Various artists* / Somewhere: *Various artists* / Subway ride: *Various artists* / Some other time: *Various artists* / Simple song,A: *Various artists* / Pax: *Various artists* / Communion (secret songs): *Various artists*.
LP: . . . . **FM 39535**
MC: . . . . **FMT 39535**

BERNSTEIN'S AMERICA.
Tracks: / Rhapsody in blue / Great lover, The / Lonely town: Pas de deux / Times Square: 1944 / Appalachian spring / Overture to Candide / Symphonic dances from West Side Story / America / Adagio for strings (From Platoon) / On the waterfront.
2LP: . . . . **LBTV 1**
MCSET: . . . . **LBTVC 1**

BERNSTEIN'S GREATEST HITS (Various artists).
Tracks: / (Candide) Overture: *Various artists* / Three dances: *Various artists* / Wonderful Town: Introduction: *Various artists* / Wrong note rag: *Various artists* / Little bit in love, A: *Various artists* / Quite girl, A: *Various artists* / My darlin' Eileen: *Various artists* / Ohio: *Various artists* / Christopher Street: *Various artists* / I feel pretty: *Various artists* / Maria: *Various artists* / Something's coming: *Various artists* / Tonight: *Various artists* / One hand One heart: *Various artists* / America: *Various* artists / Simple song,A: *Various artists* / Somewhere: *Various artists* / Pax: *Various artists* / Communion (secret songs): *Various artists* / New York, New York: *Various artists*.
MC: . . . . **GK 89792**
LP: . . . . **GL 89792**

GREATEST HITS: LEONARD BERNSTEIN (Various artists).
LP: . . . . **GL 89792**

MUSIC OF BERNSTEIN (Slatkin, Leonard).
Tracks: / (Candide) Overture / Fancy free / Facsimile / On the town - three dance episodes.
LP: . . . . **EL 2705101**
MC: . . . . **EL 2705104**

SYMPHONIC DANCES (See under Duffy, John).

Beroard, Jocelyne

SIWO.
LP: . . . . **GREL 2004**
LP: . . . . **GD 036**

MC: GREEN 2004

Berry, Benny

SOME THINGS NEVER CHANGE.
MC: HAWC 171

Berry, Bill

SHORTCAKE.
Tracks: / Avalon / Betty / Bloose / I didn't know about you / Royal Garden blues / Moon song / I'm getting sentimental over you / I hadn't anyone till you....
LP: CJ 75

Berry, Chuck

20 GOLDEN GREATS: CHUCK BERRY.
LP: HMR 9003

20 GREATEST HITS: CHUCK BERRY.
LP: FUN 9012
LP: MA 16983
MC: FUNC 9012
MC: MAMC 91683

20 SUPER HITS: CHUCK BERRY.
LP: 6 24372
MC: 4 24372

100 MINUTES OF CHUCK BERRY.
MC: ZCTON 114

AFTER SCHOOL SESSION.
LP: 515030

BACK IN THE U.S.A..
LPPD: PD 50009

BACK TO BACK (see under Domino, Fats) (Berry, Chuck/Fats Domino).

BERRY IS ON TOP.
Tracks: / Almost grown / Carol / Maybelline / Sweet little rock and roller / Anthony boy / Johnny B Goode / Little Queenie / Jo Jo Gunne / Roll over Beethoven / Around and around / Hey Pedro / Blues for Hawaiians.
LP: GCH 8043
MC: GCHK 78043

BEST OF CHUCK BERRY.
MC: 16-2

BEST OF CHUCK BERRY VOL.1 1955-1957.
MC: 771100

BEST OF CHUCK BERRY VOL.2 1958-1960.
MC: 771101

BEST OF CHUCK BERRY VOL.3 1960-1965.
MC: 771102

BIO.
Tracks: / Bio / Hello little girl / Goodbye / Woodpecker / Rain eyes / Aimlessly driftin' / Got it and gone / Talkin' about my buddy.
LP: GCH 8046
MC: GCHK 78046

CHESS MASTERS.
Tracks: / Maybellene / Wee wee hours / You can't catch me / Downbound train / No money down / Brown eyed handsome man / Roll over Beethoven / Too much monkey business / Havana moon / School days / La Juanda / Rock and roll music / Oh baby doll / Sweet little sixteen / Johnny B. Goode / Round and round / Carol / Jo Jo Gunne / Beautiful Delilah / House of blue lights / Memphis / Sweet little rock 'n' roller / Johnny B. Goode / Nadine / Hail, hail rock'n'roll / My ding a ling.
2LP: CXMD 4016

CHESS MASTERS:CHUCK BERRY.
Tracks: / No particular place to go / Maybellene / You can't catch me / School days / Roll over Beethoven / Sweet little sixteen / Round and round / Sweet little rock 'n' roller / Nadine / Rock and roll music / Old baby doll / Johnny B. Goode / Reelin' and rockin' / Memphis Tennessee / Carol / Come on.
2LP: SMR 848
MCSET: SMC 848

CHESS YEARS, THE.
LP: MFC 076

CHICAGO GOLDEN YEARS (Golden decade Vol.2).
2LP: 427009

CHICAGO GOLDEN YEARS (Golden decade Vol.3).
2LP: 427010

CHICAGO GOLDEN YEARS (Golden decade Vol.1).
2LP: 427008

CHUCK BERRY.
LP: SM 3989-2
LP: CXMP 2011

CHUCK BERRY.
LPPD: AR 30013
MC: ZCGAS 726
LP: NPL 28024

CHUCK BERRY BOX SET.
LPS: CH 68001
MCSET: CHC 68001

CHUCK BERRY BOX SET.
LPS: BOX 256
MCSET: TCBOX 256

CHUCK BERRY ON STAGE.
LP: NPL 28027

CHUCK BERRY'S ROCK 'N' ROLL PARTY.
LP: C 7788

COLLECTION: CHUCK BERRY (20 rock 'n' roll greats).
Tracks: / Maybellene / Carol / Johnny B. Goode / Roll over Beethoven / Hoochie coochie man / Brown eyed handsome man / Oh baby doll / Around and around / Hail, hail rock'n'roll / Thirty days / Sweet litle sixteen / Memphis / Reelin' and rockin' / Too much monkey business / You can't catch me / In the wee wee hours / Rock and roll music / Havana moon / No particular place to go / Little Queenie.
LP: DVLP 2068
MC: DVMC 2068

COLLECTION: CHUCK BERRY (2).
Tracks: / Sweet little sixteen / Johnny B. Goode / Back in the USA / Maybellene / Too much monkey business / Rock and roll music / Reelin' and rockin' / No particular place to go / Roll over Beethoven / You never can tell / Nadine / Carol / School days / My ding a ling / Almost grown / Let it rock / Little Queenie / Promised land / Memphis / Sweet little rock 'n' roller / Thirty days / Brown eyed handsome man / Run Rudolph run / Merry Christmas baby.
2LP: CCSLP 194
MC: CCSMC 194

DECADE '55-'65.
Tracks: / School days / Maybellene / Sweet little sixteen / Roll over Beethoven / Too much monkey business / Memphis / Let it rock / Little Queenie / Carol / Almost grown / Nadine / Johnny B. Goode / No particular place to go / Promised land / Back in the USA / Rock and roll music.
LP: PLAT 24
MC: PLAC 24

DUCK WALK.
LP: ENT LP 13046
MC: ENT MC 13046

DUCKWALKING.
Tracks: / School days / No particular place to go / Promised land / Reelin' and rockin' / Sweet little sixteen / Memphis Tennessee / Nadine / You never can tell.
LP: DOW 14
MC: ZCDOW 14

EP COLLECTION, THE: CHUCK BERRY.
MC: SEEK 320
LP: SEE 320

GRAFFITI COLLECTION.
MC: GRMC 03

GREATEST HITS: CHUCK BERRY.
Tracks: / Sweet little sixteen / Carol / Route 66 / Back in the USA / No particular place to go / Nadine / Roll over Beethoven / Too much monkey business / Sweet little rock 'n' roller / Reelin' and rockin' / Johnny B. Goode / Promised land / Maybellene / Rock and roll music / School days / Little Queenie.
LP: SHLP 136
MC: SHTC 136

GREATEST HITS: CHUCK BERRY.
LP: 2636801
MC: 2636804

GREATEST HITS LIVE: CHUCK BERRY.
Tracks: / Johnny B. Goode / Sweet little sixteen / In the wee wee hours / Rock and roll music / Maybellene / Too much monkey business / Hail, hail rock'n'roll / My ding a ling.
LP: SPR 8512
MC: SPC 8512

HAIL, HAIL, ROCK & ROLL.
Tracks: / Maybelline / Thirty days / No money down / Roll over Beethoven / Brown eyed handsome man / Too much monkey business / You can't catch me / School day (ring ring goes the bell) / Rock and roll music / Sweet little sixteen / Reelin' and rockin' / Johnny B Goode / Around and around / Beautiful Delilah / Carol / Sweet little rock and roller / Almost grown / Little Queenie / Back in the U.S.A. / Memphis Tennesse / Too pooped to pop / Let it rock / Bye bye Johnny / I'm talking about you / Come on / Nadine (is it you) / No particular place to go / You never can tell / Little Marie / Promised land / Tulane / My ding-a-ling.
2LP: DETD 207

HAIL, HAIL, ROCK'N'ROLL (Film soundtrack).
Tracks: / Maybellene / Around and around / Sweet little sixteen / Brown eyed handsome man / Memphis, Tenessee / Too much monkey business / Back in the USA / Wee wee hours / Johnny B. Goode / Little Queenie / Rock and roll music / Roll over Beethoven / I'm through with love.
LP: MCF 3411
MC: MCFC 3411

HIS LATEST AND GREATEST.
LP: NPL 28037

LET IT ROCK.
LP: CHECKMATE 1955

LIVE: CHUCK BERRY.
Tracks: / No particular place to go / Hail, hail rock'n'roll / In the wee wee hours / Johnny B. Goode / Promised land / Hoochie coochie man / Sweet little sixteen / Memphis tennessee / My ding a ling.
LP: CBR 1007
MC: KCBR 1007

LONDON CHUCK BERRY SESSIONS,THE.
Tracks: / Let's boogie / Mean old world / I will not let you go / London Berry blues / I love you / Reelin' and rockin' / My ding a ling / Johnny B Goode.
LP: 515 035
LP: CH 9295

LONG LIVE ROCK 'N' ROLL (Berry, Chuck & Little Richard).
MCSET: M 10154

MAYBELLENE.
LP: SM 3984

MORE CHUCK BERRY.
LP: NPL 28028

MOTIVE SERIES.
Tracks: / Louis to Frisco / Sweet little rock 'n' roller / Roll over Beethoven / Back to Memphis / Wee baby blues / Johnny B. Goode / Club nitty gritty / Sweet little sixteen / School days / Feeling it / Let it rock / Carol.
LP: 6463 129
MC: 7145 129

MOTORVATIN' (Greatest hits live).
Tracks: / Maybellene / Carol / Johnny B. Goode / Roll over Beethoven / Hoochie coochie man / Brown eyed handsome man / Oh baby doll / Around and around / Hail, hail rock'n'roll / Thirty days / Sweet little sixteen / Memphis Tennessee / Reelin' and rockin' / Too much monkey business / You can't catch me / In the wee wee hours / Rock and roll music / Havana moon / No particular place to go / Little queenie.
LP: SMT 009
LP: 9288 690

MR ROCK 'N' ROLL.
LP: 509075

NEW JUKE BOX HITS.
Tracks: / I'm talking about you / Diploma for two / Thirteen question method / Away from you / Don't you lie to me / The way it was before / Little star / Route 66 / Sweet sixteen / Run around / Stop and listen / Rip it up.
LP: GCH 8008
MC: GCHK 78008
LP: 515032

ONE DOZEN BERRYS.
LP: 515031

PROFILE: CHUCK BERRY.
MC: CL4 25472
LP: 6.25472

REELIN' AND ROCKIN' (LIVE).
Tracks: / Reelin' and rockin' / School days / My ding a ling / Too much monkey business / Memphis / Maybellene / Nadine.
LP: MFM 017

REELIN' AND ROCKIN' (TOPLINE).
Tracks: / Bonsoir cherie / Carol / Hail, hail rock'n'roll / Hoochie coochie man / In the wee wee hours / Johnny B. Goode / Johnny B. Goode (encore) / Maybellene / Sweet little sixteen / Too much monkey business.
LP: TOP 117
MC: KTOP 117

REELING, ROLLING & ROCKING.
Tracks: / Memphis Tennessee / Too much monkey business / My ding a ling / Reelin' & rockin' / Johnny B. Goode / Maybellene / Nadine / Hail, hail rock'n'roll / Sweet little sixteen.
LP: BDL 1051
MC: BDC 1051

ROCK AND ROLL MUSIC (INSTANT).
Tracks: / Maybelline / School days / Rock and roll music / Sweet little sixteen / Johnny B. Goode / Memphis Tennessee / Come on / Let it rock / Reelin' and rockin' / Nadine / No particular place to go / You never can tell / Promised land / My ding a ling.
MC: TCINS 5002
LP: INS 5002

ROCK 'N' ROLL HITS.
Tracks: / Johnny B. Goode / Rock and roll music / School days / Maybellene / Back in the USA / Sweet little sixteen / Memphis / Roll over Beethoven / Forty days / Carol / Club nitty gritty.
LP: 9279 138
MC: 7259 138

ROCK 'N' ROLL RARITIES (CHESS).
Tracks: / Rock'n'roll music (demo) / Rock'n'roll music / Sweet little sixteen (demo) / Sweet little sixteen / Reelin' and rockin' / Johnny B Goode / Beautiful Delilah / Oh yeah / House of blue lights / Time was / Sweet little rock'n'roller / Run Rudolph run / Little Queenie / Betty Jean / County line / Bye bye Johnny / I got to find my baby / Down the road a piece / Route 66 / I'm talking about you / Come on / Go go go / Brown eyed handsome man / Nadine (is that you) / You never can tell / Promised land / No particular place to go / I want to be your driver / Little Marie / My Mustang Ford / Ain't that just like a woman / It wasn't me.
2LP: DETD 206
MCSET: DETDK 7206
2LP: 427018

ROCKIN' AT THE HOPS.
Tracks: / Bye bye Johnny / Worried life blues / Down the road a piece / Confessin' the blues / To pooped to pop / Mad lad / I got to find my baby / Betty Jean / Childhood sweetheart / Broken arrow / Driftin' blues / Let it rock.
LP: GCH 8041
MC: GCHK 78041
LP: 515033

ROCKING WITH CHUCK BERRY.
LP: 9279 140
MC: 7259 140

ROCKIT.
Tracks: / Move it / Oh what a thrill / I need you baby / If I were / House lights / I never thought / Havana moon / Pass away.
LP: MFLP 065
LP: K 50648

ROLL OVER BEETHOVEN.
LP: SM 3983

ROLL OVER BEETHOVEN.
MC: OCN 2033WK
LP: OCN 2033WL

SPOTLIGHT ON CHUCK BERRY.
Tracks: / School days / Sweet little sixteen / Carol / Route 66 / Back in the USA / Rock and roll music / Promised land / Let it rock / Brown eyed handsome man / Maybellene / Round and round / Run Rudolph run / No particular place to go / You never can tell / Nadine / Roll over Beethoven / Too much monkey business / Go go go / Reelin and rockin / Memphis / Johnny B. Goode / Tulane / Come on / My ding a ling.
2LP: SPOT 1003
MCSET: ZCSPT 1003

ST LOUIS TO FRISCO TO MEMPHIS (Berry, Chuck & Steve Miller band).
LP: 2872 103
MC: 3472 103

ST. LOUIS TO LIVERPOOL.
Tracks: / Little Marie / Our little rendezvous / No particular place to go / You two / Promised land / You never can tell / Go bobby soxer / Thing's I used to do / Liverpool drive / Night beat / Merry christmas baby / Brenda Lee.
LP: GCH 8007
MC: GCHK 78007
LP: 515034

SWEET LITTLE ROCK 'N' ROLLER.
LP: 661 9039
MC: 758 1340

TWO GREAT GUITARS (Diddley Bo/ Chuck Berry).
LP: 515023

YOU NEVER CAN TELL.
LP: NPL 29039

Berry, Connie

WOULD YOU FOR A BIG RED APPLE?.
LP: CLP 33

Berry, Dave

CRYING GAME.
Tracks: / Memphis, Tennessee / You better move on / Crying game, The / In your life / Baby, it's you / Sticks and stones / My baby left me / Little things / Tossin' and turnin' / Mama / This strange effect / One heart between you / Round and around / Not fade away.
LP: TAB 69

HOSTAGE TO THE BEAT.
Tracks: / Searchlight / Love from Johnny / Heart of stone / Love is a killer / Bring my cadillac back / God bless the child / Mountains of the moon / On the waterfront / My baby left me / For a knight to win his spurs / Boppin' the blues / Tracks of my tears.

LP: . . . . BUTT 007

THIS STRANGE EFFECT.
Tracks: / I love you babe / Go on home / You're gonna need somebody / Don't gimme no lip child / My baby left me / Memphis Tennessee / Hoochie coochie man / St. James infirmary / Diddley daddy / Alright baby / Same game / One heart between two / I'm gonna take you there / Mama / This strange effect / Forever / Crying game, The / Baby it's you / Little things / Picture me gone.
LP: . . . . CM 122

Berry, Heidi

BELOW THE WAVES.
LP: . . . . CRELP 048

FIREFLY.
LP: . . . . CRELP 023

LOVE.
LP: . . . . CAD 1012
MC: . . . . CADC 1012

Berry, Len & Barbara

LEN & BARBARA BERRY.
LP: . . . . GVR 229

Berry, Leon Chu

CALLOWAY YEARS, THE 1937.
2LP: . . . . MERITT 21-22

DENTISTRY IN RHYTHM (VOL. 3) (Fillin' the Chu gaps) (Berry, Leon Chu with Cab Calloway).
LP: . . . . TFD 5.009

DENTISTRY IN RHYTHM (VOL. 4) (Fillin' the Chu gaps).
LP: . . . . TFD 5.011

GIANT OF THE TENOR SAX, A (with Little Jazz Ensemble 1938 & 1941).
Tracks: / Blowin' up a breeze (2) / On the sunny side of the street / On the sunny side of the street (2) / Monday at Minton's / Monday at Minton's (2) / Gee baby ain't I good to you / Gee baby ain't I good to you (2) / Sittin' in (2 takes) / Stardust / Body and soul / Forty six west fifty two / Forty six west fifty two (2) / Blowin' up a breeze.
LP: AG6 24293

INDISPENSABLE, THE.
LP: . . . . NL 89481

LEON CHU BERRY.
LP: . . . . MERITT 12

RAREST...,THE 1037/40.
LP: . . . . E 1002

TENOR TRIUMVERATE (see Hawkins, Coleman) (Berry, Leon Chu/Coleman Hawkins/Lester Young).

Berry, Mike

BUDDY (see Chas & Dave/Mike Berry) (Berry, Mike/Chas'n'Dave).

MEMORIES.
Tracks: / What'll I do / Love letters / Whispering / Blue skies / Your lover, a friend and a lady / Memories / Crying in the rain / White dove / Like a fool / Funny the things we do / Heartaches / Till we meet again.
MC: . . . . POLSC 1054
LP: . . . . POLS 1054

ROCK 'N' ROLL BOOGIE.
Tracks: / I'm a rocker / Don't fight it / Love rocket / Don't ever change / Stay close to me / Hard times / Take me high / It's a hard hard world / Tribute to Buddy Holly / Boogaloo dues / Midnight train / Hey Joe / One by one / Rebel without a cause / Take a heart / Dial my number / New Orleans / Wake up little Suzy / Think it over (Available on CD only) / Don't be cruel (Available on CD only) / Hey baby (Available on CD only) / Low country woman (Available on CD only) / Baby boy (Available on CD only).
LP: C5-541

SOUNDS OF THE SIXTIES.
Tracks: / My baby doll / Set me free / Will you love me tomorrow / Tribute to Buddy Holly / What's the matter / It's just a matter of time / Little boy blue / Every little kiss / Don't you think it's time / How many times / Loneliness / My little baby / You'll do it, you'll fall in love / It really doesn't matter / Try a little bit harder.
LP: . . . . ROLL 2016

SUNSHINE OF YOUR SMILE.
Tracks: / If I could only make you care / Anniversary song / Billy Tyler / Near you / Words / Sunshine of your smile, The / My blue heaven / Special dream / Goodbye California / Heart of a clown / One more love story / I'm as old as Paul McCartney.
LP: 2383 592

SUNSHINE OF YOUR SMILE, THE / MEMORIES.
Tracks: / If I could only make you care / Anniversary song / Billy Tyler / Near you / Words / Sunshine of your smile, The / My blue Heaven / Special dream / Goodbye California / Heart of a clown / One more love story / I'm as old as Paul McCartney / What'll I do? / Love letters / Whispering / Blue skies / Your lover a friend and a lady / Memories / Crying in the rain / White dove / Like a fool / Funny the things we do / Heartaches / Till we meet again.
MCSET: . . . . TWOMC 4

TRIBUTE TO BUDDY HOLLY.
LP: . . . . CMJ 100
MC: . . . . ZCCMJ 100
LP: . . . . DLP 505

Berry, Nick

NICK BERRY.
LP: . . . . REB 618
MC: . . . . ZCF 618

Berry, Richard

GET OUT OF THE CAR.
Tracks: / Mad about you / Angel of my life / Yama yama pretty mama / Next time / Rockin' man / Oh, oh, get out of the car / Crazy lover / I'm still in love with you / Jelly roll / Big John / One little prayer / Big break, The.
LP: . . . . CH 59

LOUIE LOUIE.
LP: . . . . JD 901

Berry, Steve

TRIO (Berry, Steve Trio).
LP: . . . . LTLP 007

Berryhill, Cyndi Lee

NAKED MOVIE STAR.
LP: . . . . AWL 1016
MC: . . . . AWT 1016

WHO'S GONNA SAVE THE WORLD.
LP: . . . . RUE 001

Berryman, Pete

PETE BERRYMAN.
LP: . . . . FLLP 509

Bert, Eddie

KALEIDOSCOPE.
LP: . . . . SJL 1186

LET'S DIG BERT.
LP: . . . . FS 189

Bertei, Adele

LITTLE LIVES BIG LOVES.
LP: . . . . CHR 1634
MC: . . . . ZCHR 1634

Bertha

BERTHA (Children's TV series) (Various artists).
Tracks: / Bertha: *Various artists* / Mrs. Tupp: *Various artists* / Packing and stacking: *Various artists*/ Flying bear, The: *Various artists* / Mr. Duncan: *Various artists* / Turning wheels: *Various artists*/ Tom the robot: *Various artists* / Isn't it nice: *Various artists* / Mr. Willmake: *Various artists* / Tracy's robot song: *Various artists* / Spottiswood march: *Various artists* / Roy the apprentice: *Various artists.*
LP: . . . . REH 585
MC: . . . . ZCR 585

Bertha (bk)

BERTHA (Kinnear, Roy & Sheila Walker).
MC: . . . . 00 103457 X

Bertles, Bob

YOU MUST BELIEVE IN SPRING.
LP: . . . . LRF 147

Bertoncini, Gene

O GRANDE AMOR (Bertoncini, Gene & Michael Moore).
LP: . . . . ST 258

STROLLIN (Bertoncini, Gene & Michael Moore).
LP: . . . . ST 272

Bertsen, Rock

KELPERS AFTER ALL (Songs of a Falkland islander).
LP: . . . . FT 3017

Berwick Speedway Club

COLORADO.
MC: . . . . CTT 105

Beserkley (label)

BESERKLEY CHARTBUSTERS VOL.1 (Various artists).
Tracks: / Friday on my mind: *Earthquake* / All the right reasons: *Kihn, Greg* / Gorilla: *Rubinoos* / New teller, The: *Richman, Jonathan* / Road runner: *Richman, Jonathan* / Tall order for a short guy: *Earthquake*/ Mr. Security: *Earthquake* / Government centre: *Richman, Jonathan* / It will stand: *Richman, Jonathan*/ Mood mood number: *Kihn, Greg* / Madness: *Earthquake.*
LP: . . . . BZ 044
LP: . . . . BSERK 6
MC: . . . . BSERC 6

Besir, Jova

BLOW, BESIR, BLOW (Besir, Jova Stojiljkovic).
Tracks: / Sampionski cocek / Safetov cocek / Vranjsko kolo / Izrael oirijent / Cifteteli / Jovino kolo / Durak I srecko / Djokino cocek / Beogradska cocek / Ekstra cocek / Romski cocek.
LP: . . . . ORB 038

Besses Boys Band

OUR BOY'S WILL SHINE TONIGHT.
Tracks: / Our boys will shine tonight / Last farewell, The / Allelu'ia / Trombola / Margam Stones / Rollercoaster shepherd's song / Concert variations / 12th Street rag / Pink panther / Torramawakefield / Aces high / Drummers delight.
LP: . . . . LKLP 7039
MC: . . . . LKLC 7039

Besses o' Th' Barn

ALEX OWEN 60TH ANNIVERSARY.
Tracks: / Chorus / Duo concertante / Overture, Ruy Blas / Overture, Richard III / Ride of the Valkyries / Angels guard thee.
LP: . . . . BBR 1009
MC: . . . . BBT 1009

BESSES IN AUSTRALIA.
Tracks: / Iolanthe overture / David of the White Rock / Dublin's fair city / Annie Laurie / Famous British marches / Australian fantasy / Zanette / Colonial song / Down under / March around the world.
LP: . . . . BBR 1002
MC: . . . . BBT 1002

ENGLISH BRASS, VOL.1.
LP: . . . . TB 3012

ENGLISH BRASS, VOL.2.
LP: . . . . TB 3016

GORDON HIGGINBOTTOM & FRIENDS (Roy Newsome; Goff Richards).
Tracks: / Sylvia / Swan, The / Evergreen / Higgyjig / Masquerade / Georgia / Rhapsody no. 1 / Holy City, The / Carousel.
LP: . . . . PRL 028D
MC: . . . . CPRL 028D

HYMNS AND THINGS.
Tracks: / Praise my soul the King of heaven / Eventide / Aberystwyth / Dem bones / Jerusalem the golden / Old hundredth / Ave Maria / Simple gifts / Nun's chorus.
LP: . . . . BBRD 1016
MC: . . . . BBTD 1016

SHOWCASE FOR BRASS.
Tracks: / Three figures / In memoriam R.K. / Summer scherzo / Belmont variations / Northwest passage.
LP: . . . . BBRD 1020
MC: . . . . BBTD 1020

Bessinger, J.B (nar)

CANTERBURY TALES, THE (see under Chaucer, Geoffrey (aut)).

Best Foot Forward

BEST FOOT FORWARD (Original off-Broadway Cast) (Various artists).
LP: . . . . DS 15003

Best Friends

BEST FRIENDS (Various artists).
Tracks: / I believe in you: *Various artists* / You needed me: *Various artists* / Most beautiful girl, The: *Rich,* Charlie / Blanket on the ground: *Various artists* / When you're in love with a beautiful woman: *Various artists*/ Silver threads and golden needles: *Various artists* / Ode to Billy Joe: *Various artists* / Galveston: *Various* artists / Don't it make my brown eyes blue: *Various artists* / You're my best friend: *Various artists* / Snowbird: *Various artists* / Behind closed doors: *Various artists* / 57 Chevrolet: *Various artists* / Stand by your man: *Various artists* / You were always on my mind: *Various artists* / If not you: *Various artists* / Give me back that old familiar feeling: *Various artists* / Wrong road again: *Various artists.*
LP: . . . . LP IMP 1
MC: . . . . TC IMP 1

Best From McTavish...

BEST FROM MCTAVISH'S KITCHENS various original artists (Various artists).
2LP: . . . . VARD 5958

Best Little... (film)

BEST LITTLE WHOREHOUSE IN TEXAS (original cast) (Various artists).
Tracks: / 20 fans: *Various artists* / Li'l ole bitty pissant country place, A: *Various artists* / Girl you're a woman: *Various artists* / Watch dog theme: *Various artists* / Texas has a whorehouse in it: *Various artists*/ Twenty hour of lovin': *Various artists* / Doatsy Mae: *Various artists* / Aggie song, The: *Various artists*/ Bus from Amarillo, The: *Various artists* / Sidestep, The: *Various artists* / No lies: *Various artists*/ Good old girl: *Various artists* / Hard candy Christmas: *Various artists* / Finale: *Various artists.*
LP: . . . . MCF 3093
MC: . . . . MCFC 3093

BEST LITTLE WHOREHOUSE IN TEXAS (Original soundtrack) (Various artists).
LP: . . . . MCA 37218
MC: . . . . MCAC 37218

Best Loved Classics

BEST LOVED CLASSICS VOL. 1 (Various artists).
Tracks: / Toccata and fugue: *Various artists* / Hornpipe: *Various artists* / Scherzo: *Various artists*/ William Tell overture: *Various artists* / Toreador's song: *Various artists* / Dance of the Sugar Plum Fairy: *Various artists.*
LP: . . . . LZ 762 500 4

BEST LOVED CLASSICS VOL. 2 (Various artists).
Tracks: / Arrival of the Queen of Sheba, The: *Various artists* / 4th horn concerto: *Various artists* / Violin concerto (Adante): *Various artists* / Karelia (Alla Marcia): *Various artists* / Ride of the Valkyries: *Various artists* / Spartacus (Adagio): *Various artists.*
LP: . . . . LZ 762 501 4

BEST LOVED CLASSICS VOL. 3 (Various artists).
Tracks: / Four seasons (Spring): *Various artists* / Sheep may safely graze: *Various artists* / Symphony No. 40 (1st movement): *Various artists* / Fingal's cave: *Various artists* / Barcarolle: *Various artists* / Greensleeves: *Various artists.*
MC: . . . . LZ 762 502 4

BEST LOVED CLASSICS VOL. 4 (Various artists).
Tracks: / Carmina burana (O'fortuna): *Various artists* / Air on a G string: *Various artists* / Eine kleine nachtmusik (1st movement): *Various artists* / Hallelujah chorus: *Various artists* / Blue Danube: *Various artists*/ Flight of the bumble bee: *Various artists* / Nimrod: *Various artists.*
LP: . . . . LZ 762 503 4

BEST LOVED CLASSICS VOL. 5 (Various artists).
Tracks: / Trumpet voluntary: *Various artists* / Jesu, joy of man's desiring: *Various artists* / Morning: *Various* artists / Celeste aida: *Various artists* / Prelude a l'aprews-midi d'un faune: *Various artists* / Adagio: *Various artists.*
MC: . . . . LZ 762 504 4

BEST LOVED CLASSICS VOL. 6 (Various artists).
Tracks: / Canon: *Various artists* / Minuet: *Various artists* / Wedding march: *Various artists* / Tales from the Vienna woods: *Various artists* / Dance of the little swans: *Various artists* / Adagio: *Various artists*/ Piano concerto (1st movement): *Various artists.*
MC: . . . . LZ 762 505 4

BEST LOVED CLASSICS VOL. 7 (Various artists).
Tracks: / Adante cantabile: *Various artists* / In the hall of the mountain king: *Various artists* / New World symphony (Largo): *Various artists* / Piano concerto No. 2 (1st movement): *Various artists* / Vilja (Merry widow): *Various artists.*
MC: . . . . LZ 762 506 4

BEST LOVED CLASSICS VOL. 8 (Various artists).
Tracks: / Sleigh ride: *Various artists* / Moonlight sonata (Adagio): *Various artists* / Concierto de Aranjuez: *Various artists* / Rhapsody in blue: *Various artists* / Carnival of the animals: *Various artists* / Bolero: *Various artists.*
MC: . . . . LZ 762 507 4

Best Loved Verse (bk)

BEST LOVED VERSE (Watson, Gwen (nar) & Richard Pasco (nar)).
MCSET: . . . . LFP 7520

Best, Martin

ART OF MINSTREL (Best, Martin & E. Flower).
LP: . . . . GRS 1013

DESDEMONALISA.
Tracks: / Desdemonalisa / Whatever happened to Dionne Warwick / She was beautiful / Ever ready / Galliard / Precious memories / St. Tropez / Here, there and everywhere / Stopwatch song / Maudie / So we'll go no more a-roving / Do you remember '69.
LP: . . . . EMC 3281

KNIGHTS ON THE ROAD.
Tracks: / American dream / Cambric shirt / Elfin knight, The / Love death / Banks of the Ohio / Close up the gate /

Yesterday / Knight on the road / Peace of mind / City is a woman / Weary man / Two ravens / Ballad of the dead man.
LP: EMC 3185

Best of...

BEST OF A SWINGING ERA (Various artists).
LP: PL 42381
MC: PK 42381

BEST OF ABBA (Various artists).
MC: AIM 15

BEST OF BIG BANDS (See under Big Bands) (Various artists).

BEST OF PIETRO FROSINI (see under Frosini, Peter) (Various artists).

Best of British...

BEST OF BRITISH (Various artists).
Tracks: / Too different: *Various artists* / Walking on a highwire: *Various artists* / Top of the mountain: *Various* artists / Burn the Kings Road: *Various artists* / Nights of long shadow: *Various artists* / Maybe someday: *Various artists* / Antigua: *Various artists* / Whitefire: *Various artists* / We got the edge: *Various artists* / Broken heart: *Various artists.*
MC: COLM 1
LP: ZEB 5

BEST OF BRITISH (2) (Various artists).
Tracks: / Imperial march: *Various artists* (Opus 32) / Pomp and circumstance march no.4: *Various artists* / Nimrod: *Various artists* (No. 4 of the 'Enigma' Variations Op. 36.) / Land of hope and glory: *Various artists* (No. 4 of the Coronation Ode Op. 44.) / Coronation march: *Various artists* (1911.) / Rule Britannia: *Various artists* / British Grenadiers, The: *Various artists* (Patrol march.) / Spitfire prelude and fugue: *Various artists* / Orb and sceptre - Coronation march: *Various artists* (1953.) / Coronation march: *Various artists* (1937.) / Dambusters: *Various artists* / I was glad when they said unto me: *Various artists* / RAF march past: *Various artists.*
MC: TC2MOM 105
MC: LZ 762 528 4

Best Of Chess...

BEST OF CHESS, CHECKER, CADET ROCKABILLIES (Various artists).
Tracks: / Tall dark handsome man: *Various artists* / Suzy Q: *Various artists* / Cool off baby: *Various artists* / True love: *Various artists* / Sweet talk: *Various artists* / Save it: *Various artists* / Why did you leave me?: *Various artists* / Just go wild over rock 'n' roll: *Various artists* / Roses are blooming: *Various* artists / Pardon Mr. Gordon: *Various artists* / Sugaree: *Various artists* / Jet tone boogie: *Various* artists / Rock yea: *Various artists* / Go go go: *Various artists* / Vacation's over: *Various artists* / Are you with me: *Various artists* / All night long: *Various artists* / Nothing's shaking: *Various artists* / Love me: *Various artists* / Look out Mabel: *Various artists.*
LP: CXMP 2054

BEST OF CHESS JAZZ, THE (Various artists).
Tracks: / I'm in the mood for love: *Moody, James* / More moon: *Ammons,Gene Sextet* / Candy: *Terry, Clark* / Man I love, The: *Sims, Zoot Quartet* / Poinciana: *Jamal, Ahmad* / Benny rides again: *Goodman, Benny & Orchestra* / Lover man: *Stitt, Sonny* / It ain't necessarily so: *Farmer, Art & Benny Golson Jazztet* / Well you need'nt: *Burrell,* Kenny Trio / Wade in water: *Lewis, Ramsey* / Willow weep for me: *Bryant, Ray* / Soul station: *Kirk,Roland* & Ira Sullivan / Transfiguration: *Blakey, Art/Jazz Messengers* / Hobo flats: *Nelson, Oliver* / Come rain or come shine: *Johnson, Buddy Quartet* / Let my people go: *McDuff, Jack* / Like young: *Jacquet, Illinois* / Here comes the child: *Klemmer, John.*
2LP: GCH 2-6025
MCSET: GCHK 2-6025

BEST OF CHESS RHYTHM & BLUES, THE (Various artists).
Tracks: / Please send me someone to love: *Moonglows* / Bad girl: *Miracles* / Walk, The: *McCracklin, Jimmy* / Smokey places: *Corsairs* / Watusi, The: *Vibrations* / But I do: *Henry, Clarence 'Frogman'* / Searching for my love: *Moore,Bobby & The Rhythm Aces* / Mama didn't lie: *Bradley, Jan* / I do love you: *Stewart, Billy* / We're gonna make it: *Little Milton* / Summertime: *Stewart, Billy* / Entertainer, The: *Clarke, Tony* / I had a talk with my man: *Collier, Mitty* / Voice your choice: *Radiants* / Stay in my corner: *Dells* / Rescue me: *Bass, Fontella* / In crowd, The: *Lewis, Ramsey Trio* / Soulful dress: *Desanto, Sugar Pie* / Selfish one: *Ross, Jackie* / Tell mama: *James, Etta.*
2LP: GCH 2-6022
MCSET: GCHK 2-6022

BEST OF CHESS ROCK 'N' ROLL, THE (Various artists).
Tracks: / Maybellene: *Berry, Chuck* / Bo Diddley: *Diddley, Bo* / Rocket 88: *Brenston, Jackie* / See you later alligator: *Charles, Bobby* / Susie Q: *Hawkins, Dale* / Johnny B Goode: *Berry, Chuck* / Sincerely: *Moonglows* / Ain't got no home: *Henry, Clarence 'Frogman'* / I'll be home: *Flamingos* / Who do you love: *Diddley, Bo* / Happy happy birthday baby: *Tune Weavers* / I'm so young: *Students* / Book of love: *Monotones* / Teardrops: *Andrews, Lee & The Hearts* / Ten commandments of love: *Harvey & The Moonglows* / Let me in: *Sensations* / Over the mountain,across the sea: *Johnnie & Joe* / Hi heel sneakers: *Tucker, Tommy* / Rinky dink: *Cortez, Dave 'Baby'* / Sally go round the roses: *Jaynetts.*
2LP: GCH 2-6024
MCSET: GCHK 2-6024

Best Of Chicago Blues

BEST OF CHICAGO BLUES (Various artists).
Tracks: / Love me or leave me: *Various artists* / Next time you see me: *Various artists* / Rocket 88: *Various* artists / Vietcong blues: *Various artists* / When my baby left me: *Various artists* / Spann's stomp: *Various* artists / Twisted snake: *Various artists* / One room country shack: *Various artists* / Sweet little angel: *Various artists* / I had a dream last night: *Various artists* / Somebody been talkin': *Various artists* / Mule kicking in my stall: *Various artists* / Blues is a botheration: *Various artists* / S.P. blues someday: *Various* artists / Blues keep falling, The: *Various artists* / Rockin' my boogie: *Various artists* / Five long years: *Various artists* / Checking on my baby: *Various artists* / Tobacco road: *Various artists* / Money (that's all I want): *Various artists* / Stealin' back: *Various artists.*
LP: VSD 1
2LP: VSD L

Best Of Country

BEST OF COUNTRY (See Under Country...) (Various artists).

Best Of Italo

BEST OF ITALO-DISCO VOL.1 (Various artists).
2LP: 70 001

BEST OF ITALO-DISCO VOL.2 (Various artists).
2LP: 70 002

BEST OF ITALO-DISCO VOL.3 (Various artists).
2LP: 70 003

BEST OF ITALO-DISCO VOL.4 (Various artists).
2LP: 70 004

BEST OF ITALO-DISCO VOL.5 (Various artists).
2LP: 70 005

BEST OF ITALO-DISCO VOL.9 (Various artists).
LP: ZYX 7009

Best of the Best

BEST OF THE BEST (Various artists).
LP: FMOVILP 144
MC: FMOVIMC 144

BEST OF THE BEST (2) (Various artists).
Tracks: / Memories are made of this: *Martin, Dean* / Story of my life, The: *Holliday, Michael* / Cry me a river: *London, Julie* / Stranger in paradise: *MacRae, Gordon* / It must be him: *Carr, Vikki* / Buttons and bows: *Shore, Dinah* / Softly softly: *Murray, Ruby* / Shrimp boats: *Stafford, Jo* / Dreamboat: *Cogan, Alma* / Yellow rose of Texas: *Freberg, Stan* / Born free: *Monro, Matt* / Fever: *Lee, Peggy* / On the street where you live: *Damone, Vic* / Sugarbush: *Boswell, Eve* / No other love: *Hilton, Ronnie* / Over the rainbow: *Garland, Judy* / Vaya con dios: *Paul, Les & Mary Ford* / How high the moon: *Christy, June* / Istanbul: *Vaughan, Frankie* / My thanks to you: *Conway, Steve.*
LP: EMS 1391
MC: TCEMS 1391

Best Party Album...

BEST PARTY ALBUM IN THE WORLD (Various artists).
LP: NE 1258
MC: CE 2258

Best Shot (film)

BEST SHOT (Film soundtrack) (Various artists).
Tracks: / Best shot: *Various artists* / You did good: *Various artists* / Coach stays, The: *Various artists* / Pivot, The: *Various artists* / Get the ball: *Various artists* / Town meeting: *Various artists* / Finals, The: *Various artists.*
LP: TER 1141
MC: ZCTER 1141

Best, Tony

BY REQUEST.
Tracks: / San Antonio rose / You're my best friend / Words / One day at a time / I don't want to cry / Turn out the light (love me tonight) / Old rugged cross, The / Love or something like it / Legend in my time, A / Today I started loving you again / Crazy / Some broken hearts never mend / Nobody's child / China doll.
LP: KZ 1002 LS

DOING WHAT I LIKE DOING.
Tracks: / Doing what I like doing / Mansion on the hill / Great El Tigre, The / Let's keep it that way / Some days are diamonds / Angelean / Jimmy Brown song, The / Do what you do do well / Catfish John / Who were you thinking of / Drinking them beers / Smooth sailing.
LP: WW1003

Best Years Of.. (film)

BEST YEARS OF OUR LIVES, THE (Film Soundtrack) (Various artists).
Tracks: / Best years of our lives, The (Main title): *Various artists* / Homecoming: *Various artists* / Elevator, The: *Various artists* / Boone City: *Various artists* / Peggy: *Various artists* / Fred and Peggy: *Various* artists / Nightmare, The: *Various artists* / Fred asleep: *Various artists* / Neighbours: *Various artists* / Homer goes upstairs: *Various artists* / Citation, The: *Various artists* / Exit music: *Various artists.*
LP: EDP 8101

Bethel

BETHEL (Various artists).
MC: BETHEL 1

Betjeman, Sir John

BANANA BLUSH.
Tracks: / Indoor games near Newbury / Business girls / Agricultural caress / Youth and age on Beaulieu River Hants / Arrest of Oscar Wilde at the Cadogan Hotel / Lenten thoughts / Cockney amorist, The / Longfellow's visit to Venice / Flight from Bootle, The / Shropshire lad, A / On a portrait of a deaf man / Child ill, A.
LP: CHC 26

BETJEMAN READS BETJEMAN.
Tracks: / Middlesex / Harrow-on-the-hill / Upper Lambourne / Wantage bells / Trebetherick / Heart of Thomas Hardy, The / Arrest of Oscar Wilde at the Cadogan Hotel / I.M.Walter Ramsden / Devonshire Street W.1. / In a Bath tea shop / Attempt, The / Irish unionist's farewell, The / Lincolnshire church, The / Potpourri from a Surrey garden / Henley-on-Thames / Diary of a church mouse / In the public gardens / Eunice / Last of her order, The / Matlock bath.
MCSET: SAY 59
MCSET: ARGO 1037

BETJEMAN'S BRITAIN.
Tracks: / Hunter trials / Autumn 1964 / Subaltern's love song, A / Seaside golf / Upper Lambourne / Death of King George V / Middlesex / South London 1844 / South London 1944 / Harrow-on-the-Hill / City / Parliament hill fields.
LP: CHC 28

BETJEMAN'S BRITAIN/VARSITY RAG.
Tracks: / Hunter trials / Autumn 1964 / Subaltern's love song, A / Seaside golf / Upper Lambourne / Death of King George V / Middlesex / South London 1844 / South London 1944 / Harrow-on-the-Hill / City / Parliament hill fields / Varsity students' rag, The / Beaumaris / Costa Blanca she / Costa Blanca he (5 years later) / Peggy Purey-cust / Death in Leamington / Slough / Christmas / County / In a Bath tea shop / Exeter / North coast recollections (extract).
MCSET: CASMC 100

LATE FLOWERING LOVE.
Tracks: / Narcissus / Olympic girl, The / Invasion exercise on a poultry farm / Licorice fields at Pontefract, The / Russell flint, A / Station syren / Myfanwy and Myfanwy at Oxford / In the public gardens / Eunice / Senex / Late flowering lust / Sun and fun.
LP: CHC 27

LATE FLOWERING LOVE/BANANA BLUSH.
Tracks: / Narcissus / Olympic girl, The / Invasion exercise on a poultry farm / Licorice fields at Pontefract, The / Russell flint, A / Station syren / Myfanwy and Myfanwy at Oxford / In the public gardens / Eunice / Senex / Late flowering lust / Sun and fun / Indoor games near Newbury / Business girls / Agricultural caress / Youth and age on Beaulieu River Hants / Arrest of Oscar Wilde at the Cadogan Hotel, The / Lenten thoughts / Cockney amorist, The / Longfellow's visit to Venice / Flight from Bootle, The / Shropshire lad, A / On a portrait of a deaf man / Child ill, A.
MCSET: CASMC 101

READING A SELECTION OF HIS POEMS.
MC: TTC/PS 01

SIR JOHN BETJEMAN READING HIS POETRY.
MC: 1557
LP: TC 1557

VARSITY RAG.
Tracks: / Varsity students' rag, The / Beaumaris / Costa Blanca she / Costa Blanca he (5 years later) / Peggy Purey-cust / Death in Leamington / Slough / Christmas / County / In a Bath tea shop / Exeter / North coast recollections (extract).
LP: CHC 29

Betjemania (show)

BETJEMANIA (Original London cast) (Various artists).
LP: TER 1002

Betmead, Jon

VISION OF HEAVEN, A.
LP: PLR 004

Beton Combo

THANKS.
LP: SQ 001

Betrayal

RATTLESNAKE WALTZ.
Tracks: / Made / Magenta man / Dead man's hand / Rattlesnake waltz / Hall of mirrors / No smoke without desire / Respect / Independence day / Fraud franchise / No big thing / Ordinary day / End.
LP: PROBE 17

Betrayed (film)

BETRAYED (Film Soundtrack) (Conti, Bill).
Tracks: / Main title / Way, The / Shoot the horse / Bank robbery, The / Kill me Kathy / To the bank / Riding to work / Guns / Passing time / End title.
MC: ZCTER 1163
LP: VS 70470
MC: VSC 70470

Better An Old Demon...

BETTER AN OLD DEMON THAN A NEW GOD (Various artists).
LP: GPS 033

Better Mousetrap

BETTER MOUSETRAP, A.
LP: TUFFER 1

Betts, Dickey

PATTERN DISRUPTIVE (Betts, Dickey Band).
Tracks: / Rock bottom / Stone cold heart / Time to roll / Blues ain't nothin', The / Heartbreak line / Duane's tune / Under the guns of love / C'est la vie / Far cry / Loverman.
LP: FE 44289

Betty Blue (film)

BETTY BLUE (Film soundtrack) (Yared, Gabriel).
Tracks: / Betty et Zorg / Des orages pour la nuit / Cargo voyage / La poubelle cuisine / Humecter la monture / Le petit Nicolas / Gyneco zebre / Comme les deux doigts de la main / Zorg et Betty / Chili con carne / C'est le vent, Betty / Un coucher de soleil accroche dans les arbres / Lisa rock / Le coeur en skai mauve / Bungalow zen / 37'2 le matin / Maudits maneges.
LP: V 2396
MC: TCV 2396

Between

CONTEMPLATION.
LP: WER SM 1012

DHARANA.
LP: WER SM 1011

HESS BETWEEN MUSIC.
LP: WER SM 1015

Between The Woods...

BETWEEN THE WOODS AND THE WATERFRONT (see Patrick Leigh Fermor).

Bevan, Bob

ONE FLEW OVER THE BAR - SIX FLEW INTO THE NET.
LP: BUSLP 1002

Beverley Minster

SOUNDS OF BEVERLEY MINSTER (Beverley Minster Choir).
Tracks: / Rejoice in the Lord alway / Benedictus (Little organ mass) / There is no rose / Salutation carol, The /

Pastricchio (Organ Book No X) / Tues petrus / Ave verum corpus / Exsultate deo / Let all the world in every corner sing / Hail, gladdening light / Lord is my shepherd (Psalm 23) / This is the record of John / Saraband (in modo elegiaco) / Steal away to Jesus / Teach me, O Lord / Rejoice in the Lord alway.
MC: . . . . HAC 842

Beverley Sisters

SPARKLE.
LP: . . . . ONE 1315
MC: . . . . OCE 2315

TOGETHER.
Tracks: / Together / Hold me / English muffins and Irish stew / We have to be so careful / Green fields / Skye boat song / Oh wishing star / Water or the wine, The / Sultan, The / Sphinx won't tell, The / I never was loved by anyone / Undecided / Teasin' / Yell for your mama / String along / I wish I wuz / Wheel of fortune / Poor whip - poor will / For you / In the wee small hours of the morning / Once in a while / When the boys talk about the girls / I'm always chasing rainbows / No one but you / Mother never told me (it was anything like this) / Goodnight my someone / Nearness of you, The / Tammy / It takes so long (to say goodbye) / Beneath the lights of home / It's no sin / Wyoming lullaby.
2LP: . . . . DL 41 1066 3
MC: . . . . DL 41 1066 9

Beverly, Frankie

CAN'T GET OVER YOU (See under Maze) (Maze featuring Frankie Beverly).

LIFELINES VOL. 1 (See under Maze) (Maze featuring Frankie Beverly).

LIVE IN LOS ANGELES (See under Maze) (Maze featuring Frankie Beverly).

LIVE IN NEW ORLEANS (See under Maze) (Maze featuring Frankie Beverly).

Beverly Hills Cop

BEVERLY HILLS COP (Film soundtrack) (Various artists).
Tracks: / New attitude: *Labelle, Patti* / Don't get stopped in Beverly Hills: *Shalamar* / Do you really (want my love)?: *Junior* / Emergency: *Robbins, Rockie* / Neutron dance: *Pointer Sisters* / Heat is on, The: *Frey, Glenn* / Gratitude: *Elfman, Danny* / Stir it up: *Labelle, Patti* / Rock 'n' roll me again: *System*/ Axel F: *Faltermeyer, Harold.*
LP: . . . . MCF 3253
MC: . . . . MCFC 3253
MC: . . . . MCLC 1870
LP: . . . . MCL 1870

BEVERLY HILLS COP II (Film soundtrack) (Various artists).
Tracks: / Shakedown: *Seger, Bob* / Be there: *Pointer Sisters* / In deep: *Sexton, Charlie* / Hold on: *Hart, Corey* / I want your sex: *Michael, George* / Better way: *Ingram, James* / Love/Hate: *Pebbles* (Singer) / Cross my broken heart: *Jets (American)* / 36 lovers: *Ready For The World* / I can't stand it: *Sue Ann* / All revved up: *Jackson, Jermaine.*
LP: . . . . MCF 3383
MC: . . . . MCFC 3383

Bevis Frond

ACID JAM.
LP: . . . . W 006

ANY GAS FASTER.
Tracks: / Lord Plentiful reflects / Rejection day (am) / Ear song (olde world) / This corner of England / Legendary / When you wanted me / Lost rivers / Somewhere else / These dark days / Head on a pole / Your mind's gone grey / Old sea dog / Rejection day (pm) / Good old fashioned pain / Olde worlde.
LP: . . . . RECK 18

AUNTIE WINNIE ALBUM, THE.
LP: . . . . RECK 17

BEVIS THROUGH THE LOOKING GLASS.
2LP: . . . . RECKD 9

INNER MARSHLAND.
LP: . . . . W 003
LP: . . . . RECK 14

MAGIC EYE (See under Twink) (Bevis Frond & Twink).

MIASMA.
LP: . . . . RECK 13

TRIPTYCH.
LP: . . . . W 008
LP: . . . . RECK 15

Bevis Marks Synagogue

SEPHARDI MELODIES LIVE.
MC: . . . . S 004 171C

Bevoir, Paul

HAPPIEST DAY OF YOUR LIFE, THE.
LP: . . . . WORK 2

Bewitched

BRAIN ERASER.
LP: . . . . KAR 007

Beyond

CRAWL.
Tracks: / Sacred garden / Empire / Sick / Day before tomorrow / One step too far / Second sight / Great indifference, The / Eve of my release, The / No more happy ever afters / Lead the blind / Dominoes.
LP: . . . . SHSP 4128
MC: . . . . TCSHSP 4128

EPISCENE.
LP: . . . . CHIME 25

Beyond Possession

IS BEYOND POSSESSION.
LP: . . . . RR 9663

Beyond The Calico Wall

BEYOND THE CALICO WALL (Various artists).
LP: . . . . VOXX 200051

Beyond The Fringe

BEYOND THE FRINGE (Broadway 1962) (Various artists).
MC: 92055.4

BEYOND THE FRINGE (see also under EMI Comedy Classics) (Various artists).

BEYOND THE FRINGE (ORIGINAL ISSUE) (London cast) (Various artists).
LP: . . . . PMC 1145

Beyond The Pale (bk)

BEYOND THE PALE (Austin Clarke).
LP: . . . . CCT 2

Beyond The Planets

BEYOND THE PLANETS (Various artists).
Tracks: / Waves: *Various artists* / Journey, The: *Various artists* / Mars, the bringer of war: *Various artists*/ Venus, the bringer of peace: *Various artists* / Mercury, the winged messenger: *Various artists* / Jupiter, the bringer of jollity: *Various artists* / Circles: *Various artists* / Saturn, The bringer of old age: *Various* artists / Uranus, the magician: *Various artists* / Neptune, the mystic: *Various artists* / Heavens reply, The: *Various artists* / Beyond: *Various artists.*
LP: . . . . STAR 2244
MC: . . . . STAC 2244

Beyond The Rainbow

BEYOND THE RAINBOW (Original London cast) (Various artists).
Tracks: / Come join us at the table: *Various artists* / Pity: *Various artists* / Ding dong song: *Various* artists / Throw it away: *Various artists* / Time for love: *Various artists* / Tiny ant: *Various artists*/ San Crispino: *Various artists* / Consolation: *Various artists* / Love according to me: *Various artists*/ I want you: *Various artists* / Clementine: *Various artists.*
LP: . . . . MCF 2874
MC: . . . . MCFC 2874

Beyond The River

BEYOND THE RIVER (Various artists).
LP: . . . . OD 001

Beyond The Southern

BEYOND THE SOUTHERN CROSS (Various artists).
2LP: . . . . INK 4D

Beyond The Valley

BEYOND THE VALLEY OF THE DOLLS (Film Soundtrack) (Various artists).
Tracks: / Beyond the valley of the dolls: *Various artists* / Come with the gentle people: *Various artists* / Look on up at the bottom: *Various artists* / Girl from the city: *Various artists* / In the long run: *Various artists*/ Beyond the valley of the dolls: *Various artists* / Sweet talkin' candy man: *Various artists* / Find it: *Various* artists / Ampersand: *Various artists* / Once I had love: *Various artists* / I'm coming home: *Various artists* / Beyond the valley of the dolls: *Various artists.*
LP: . . . . SSL 10311

Beyond The Wildwood

BEYOND THE WILDWOOD (Tribute to Syd Barrett) (Various artists).
LP: . . . . ILLUSION 001

Beyond Therapy (film)

BEYOND THERAPY (Film soundtrack) (Various artists).
LP: . . . . A 301
MC: . . . . C 301

Beytelman

LA BORDONA (Beytelman, Caratini, Mosalini).
Tracks: / La bordona / El choclo / Cardo y malvon / Nocturna / La cumparsita / Inspiracion / Palomita blanca / Contrajeando la cumparsita / Inspiracion (2) / Palomita blanca (2).

LP: . . . . CARA 004

BFG

BLUE.
LP: . . . . ATT 007

FATHOMS.
Tracks: / In fields of sleep / Higher than heaven / Maluria summer / Laughing tigers / Fathoms / Coming home / Southern belle / Another island / Unsure she said / Mako.
LP: . . . . ATT 004

B.F.M.

CITY OF DOPE.
Tracks: / City of dope / Go amazen' (do yo' thang) / Can't slow down / Am I black enough? / Let yourself go / Why ya "p" ain't tight / Gimme a bottle / Larceny / Give it up / Pass the joint.
LP: . . . . ICH 1118
MC: . . . . ICH 1118MC

Bhamra, Mohinder Kaur

PUNJABI DISCO.
Tracks: / Disco wich aa / Par Toon Ki Janay / Pyar mainu kar / Ve toon jaldi jaldi a / Aye Diwane / Chum chum dil nal / Mainu apne dyar wich / Nainan da pyar degaya / Sohnia Mukh Tera.
MC: . . . . ECSD 2907

PUNJABI FOLK DANCE SONGS (Bhamra, Mohinder Kaur & Bawa Charanjit).
Tracks: / Giddha pao haan dio / Lutley toon jindri / Kurhi patli patang wargi / Dil kadke toon baliye / Hogya ni chit chor / Kurhi southall di / Ton patli patang / Chardi umar jawani / Maan kari na / Is joban de din char / Terian dil jani / Aari aari aari.
LP: . . . . IRHLP 1001

PUNJABI GEET (Bhamra, Mohinder Kaur & K.Deep).
Tracks: / Rahia Ve Haria / Hara ni koi kario chara / Mere Nach Di Jawani / Mach gai dohai / Kuri Ne Sawaya / Ve sadi sajnan tu yard / Papoo Diay Amma / Dhand mere eun hassde / Kurti Sawaday Kutmi / Toon Vidah Hoaya / Menu Tilley Dar Jutti / Raatan Chhad De Ve.
LP: . . . . BR 1

Bhangra...

BHANGRA FEVER (Various artists).
LP: . . . . ARI 1005
MC: . . . . ARI 0105

BHANGRA FEVER 2 (Various artists).
LP: . . . . ARI 1008

BHANGRA FORCE (Various artists).
MC: . . . . CMUT 1090

BHANGRA NOW (Various artists).
Tracks: / Soniyae ni Soniaye: *Shoring* / Gurdh nalo ishq mitah: *Azaad* / Rail Gaddi / Jago aye: *Premi*/ Ik pathli jehi mutyaar: *Sahotas* / Saun Rabdi Mauj lag javey: *Kapoor, Mahendra* / Paliey Punjean Waliey: *Premi*/ Sanu Roki Na Kar: *Sidhu, Amarjit* / Giddh wich nachdi de: *Manak, Kuldip* / Kar Gai Jat Sharabi: *Azaad*/ Giddha Penda: *Various artists* / Bhangra rap: *Sidhu, Amarjit.*
LP: . . . . BHANGRA 2LP
MC: . . . . BHANGRA 2MC

BHANGRA POWER (Various artists).
Tracks: / Bhangra Paa Ni..: *Sidhu, Amarjit* / Bhabi gal na kari: *Kapoor, Mahendra* / Sachi Muchi: *Sachi Muchi*/ Ek Sohni Jahe Mutiyear: *Paaras* / Aa Kudiye: *D.C.S.* / Yaar pooch de yaaran nu / Nachdi di gooth khulgaye: *Premi*/ Tere husan di gal: *Azaad* / Akh mar ghider vich: *Sahotas* / O mere yaaro: *Paaras* / Giddhe Wich Nach Patia: *Sachi Muchi* / Nachdi pitho da: *Premi.*
LP: . . . . BHANGRA 1LP
MC: . . . . BHANGRA 1MC

BHANGRA TOP 10 (VOL 2) (Various artists).
LP: . . . . SSRLP 5103

BHANGRA TOP TEN (Various artists).
LP: . . . . S 5101
MC: . . . . SC 5101

BHANGRA WEDDING SONGS (Various artists).
MC: . . . . BHANGRA 3MC

EXTRA HOT ONE- BHANGRA REMIXES (Various artists).
MC: . . . . CMUT 1139

EXTRA HOT TWO (Various artists).
MC: . . . . CMUT 1144

Bhatt, Krishna

RASA (See under Stecher, Jody (Bhatt, Krishna & Jody Stecher).

Bhlongo, Geo

LOCOMOTIVE ARRIVE.
LP: . . . . AR 1013

Bhowani Junction

BHOWANI JUNCTION.
MCSET: . . . . ZBBC 1105

Bhujhangy Ra

BHUJHANGY RA.
LP: . . . . KEDAL 1
MC: . . . . KEDA 1

Bhundu Boys

LIVE AT KING TUT'S WAH WAH HUT.
LP: . . . . AFRILP 09

PAMBERI.
LP: . . . . WX 321
MC: . . . . WX 321C

SHABINI.
LP: . . . . AFRILP 02
MC: . . . . AFRIZC 02
LP: . . . . AFRILP 02X

TRUE JIT.
Tracks: / Jit jive / My foolish heart / Chemedzevana / Rugare / Vana (the children) / Wonderful world / Ndoitasei / Susan / African woman / Happy birthday / Jekesa / I don't think that man should sleep alone / Over you / Loving you / You shoulda kept a spare / Past, The / You make my nature dance / Perfect lovers / After midnite / I love your daughter / After dark.
LP: . . . . WX 129
MC: . . . . WX 129 C

TSVIMBO-DZE-MOTO (Sticks on Fire).
LP: . . . . AFRILP 03
MC: . . . . AFRIZZ 03

Biafra, Jello

HIGH PRIEST OF HARMFUL MATTER.
2LP: . . . . VIRUS 66

LAST SCREAM OF THE MISSING NEIGHBORS (Biafra, Jello & DOA).
LP: . . . . VIRUS 78

NO MORE COCOONS.
LP: . . . . VIRUS 59

SKY IS FALLING, THE (Biafra, Jello & No Means No).
LP: . . . . VIRUS 085
MC: . . . . VIRUS 085C

Bianco, Bonnie

STAY.
Tracks: / Sail / Stage, The / Just a friend / Our love / Circus / Sky / Stay / My first love / Six ways / My gipsy wanderer / Too young / No tears anymore.
LP: 6.26494
MC: 4.26494

Bibb, Eric

APRIL FOOLS (Bibb, Eric & Bert Deivert).
LP: . . . . OP 7914

GOLDEN APPLES OF THE SUN.
LP: . . . . OP 8109

RAINBOW PEOPLE.
LP: . . . . OP 7703

RIVER ROAD (Bibb, Eric & Bert Deivert).
LP: . . . . OP 8017

Bibi Den's Tshibayi

BEST AMBIANCE, THE.
LP: . . . . ROUNDER 5012
MC: . . . . ROUNDER 5012C

Bible

BEST OF THE BIBLE, THE.
LP: . . . . CHR 1732
MC: . . . . ZCHR 1732

BIBLE STORIES (Various artists).
Tracks: / Good Samaritan, The: *Various artists* / Great flood, The: *Various artists* / Joseph's coat: *Various artists.*
MC: . . . . AC 110

BIBLE SUNDAY (Various artists).
MC: . . . . MMC 0216

BIBLE, THE.
Tracks: / Graceland / Crystal Palace / Honey be good / Skeleton crew / Red Hollywood / Abraham, Martin and John / Skywriting / Glorybound / Up in smoke / Blue shoes stepping / Cigarette girls / Golden mile.
LP: . . . . CHEN 12
MC: . . . . ZCHEN 12

EUREKA.
Tracks: / Skywriting / Honey be good / Skeleton crew / November brides / Cigarette girls / Crystal Palace / Wishing game, The / Red Hollywood / Tiny lights / Blue shoes stepping.
LP: . . . . CHR 1646
MC: . . . . ZCHR 1646

READINGS FROM THE BIBLE -THE AUTHORISED VERSION (Various artists).
MCSET: . . . . SAY 85

WALKING THE GHOST BACK HOME.
LP: . . . . NCHLP 8

Bible Stories

BIBLE STORIES (see under Kossoff, David (nar)) (Kossoff, David (nar)).

Biblioni, Juan

FOR A FUTURE SMILE.
LP: . . . . TET 7
MC: . . . . CTET 7

Bibs & Vanya

RUSSIAN BALALAIKA.
LP: . . . . BCLP 5

Bicat, Nick

IRISH RM (THEME) (See under Irish R. M.) (Various artists).

Bickert, Ed

BORDER CROSSING.
Tracks: / For all we know / Man I love, The / Goodnight my love / My funny valentine.
LP: . . . . CJ 216

BYE BYE BABY.
Tracks: / You're in love with someone / Bye bye baby / Barbados / It's time / Nobody else but me / Things are getting better / Flower is a lovesome thing / Pensativa / Keeping myself for you.
LP: . . . . CJ 232

DANCE TO THE LADY (Bickert, Ed & Don Thompson).
Tracks: / Bluesette / Ruby my dear / Solar / Dance to the lady / Take five / Blue monk.
LP: 4010

FROM CANADA WITH LOVE.
LP: . . . . PM 011

I WISHED ON THE MOON (Bickert, Ed Quartet).
Tracks: / CTA / Easy street / Somewhere along the way / Blues for Tommy / Blues my naughty sweetie gives to me / Handful of stars, A / I wished on the moon / I'll never stop loving you.
LP: . . . . CJ 284

IN CONCERT AT THE GARDEN PARTY (Bickert, Ed & Don Thompson).
Tracks: / Alone together / Face like yours, A / You are too beautiful / What is this thing called love? / Who can I turn to? / Walkin' my baby back home / Please be kind.
LP: 4005

RUBY BRAFF WITH THE ED BICKERT TRIO (see Braff, Ruby).

THIRD FLOOR RICHARD (Bickert, Ed Trio).
Tracks: / Band call / Together / Louisiana / I know why and so do you / One moment worth years / Tonite I shall sleep / I got a right to sing the blues / Circus / Third floor Richard / I surrender dear / This can't be love.
LP: . . . . CJ 380
MC: . . . . CJ 380 C

THIS IS NEW (Bickert, Ed & Lorne Lofsky).
Tracks: / This is new / Elsa / Twisted blues (Only on CD.) / Maybe you'll be there / Ecaroh / Namely you / Ah leu cha / Peau douce (Only on CD.) / Cold comfort / Star crossed lovers, The / Estate / Ugetsu.
MC: . . . . CJ 414 C

Biddu

NIRVANA.
LP: . . . . HEAV 1
MC: . . . . HEAVTC 1

Biddu Orchestra

SERENADE FOR LOVERS.
Tracks: / Un homme et une femme / Rain forest / Girl you'll be a woman soon / Summer of '42 / Lover's serenade / Blue eyed soul / Couldn't we be friends / I could have danced all night / Bionic boogie / Journey to the moon / Blacker the berry / Soul coaxing.
LP: . . . . SHM 3054
MC: . . . . HSC 3054

Bieler, Ernie

EINE REISE INS GLUCK.
Tracks: / Wenn die glocke der liebe erklingt / Lollipop / Eine reise ins gluck / My happiness / Mauerblumchen / Stardust / Johnny guitar / O dio mio / Sag wann kommst du Kitty Sisters / Oho noch ein kuss / Das ist das ende vom lied / So wie eine melodie / Lass die welt daruber reden / Heisse kusse / Bleib fur immer bei mir / Ich freu much auf heut abend / Seit ich dich gesehn.
LP: . . . . BFX 15227

Biff Bang Pow

ACID HOUSE ALBUM, THE.
LP: . . . . CRELP 046

GIRL WHO RUNS THE BEAT HOTEL.
Tracks: / Someone stole my wheels / Love's going out of fashion / She never understood / He don't need that girl / She shivers inside / Beat hotel, The / Happiest girl in the world, The / If I die / Five minutes in the life of Greenwood / Whole world is turning Brouchard, The / There must be a better life / Lost your dreams / Love and hate / Chocolate elephant man, The / Water bomb / Colin Dobbins / Wouldn't you? / I wish I could drink like Jeff Barrett.
MCSET: . . . . C-CRE 015
LP: . . . . CRELP 015

LOVE IS FOREVER.
LP: . . . . CRELP 029

ME.
LP: . . . . CRELP 071
MC: . . . . CCRE 071

OBLIVION.
LP: . . . . CRELP 020

PASS THE PAINTBRUSH HONEY.
LP: . . . . CRELP 004

SONGS FOR THE SAD EYED GIRL.
LP: . . . . CRELP 058
MC: . . . . CCRELP 058

Big Apple Boogie

BIG APPLE BOOGIE (Various artists).
LP: . . . . BLP 112

Big Audio Dynamite

KOOL AID.
LP: 4674661
MC: 4674664

MEGATOP PHOENIX.
Tracks: / Start / Rewind / All mink and no manners / Union? Jack / Contact / Dragon town / Baby don't apologise / Is yours working yet / Around the girl in 80 ways / James Brown / Everybody needs a holiday / Mick's a hippie burning / House arrest / Green lady, The / London Bridge / Stalag 123 / End.
LP: 4657901
MC: 4657904

NO. 10 UPPING STREET.
Tracks: / C'mon every beatbox / Beyond the pale / Limbo the law / Samba drome / V13 / Ticket / Hollywood Boulevard / Dial a hitman / Sightsee M.C. / Ice cool killer (On cassette & cd only.) / Big V, The.
LP: 4501371
MC: 4501374
LP: 4633981
MC: 4633984

THIS IS BIG AUDIO DYNAMITE.
Tracks: / Medicine show / Sony / E = MC2 / Bottom line / Sudden impact / Stone Thames / B.A.D. / Party.
LP: . . . . CBS 26714
MC: 40 26714
LP: 4629991
MC: 4629994

TIGHTEN UP VOL. 88.
Tracks: / Rock non stop (all night long) / Other 99 / Funny names / Applecart / Esquerita / Champagne / Mr. Walker said / Battle of All Saints Road / Battle of New Orleans / Duelling banjos / Hip neck and thigh / Two thousand shoes / Tighten up vol. 88 / Just play music.
LP: 4611991
MC: 4611994

Big Bam Boo

FUN, FAITH AND FAIRPLAY.
Tracks: / Fell off a mountain / If you could see me now / Justice / Brazilian waltz / Haven't got the time / Shooting from my heart / What's bigger than life / Dream song / Wicked love / Tender skin.
LP: . . . . MCF 3431
MC: . . . . MCFC 3431

Big Band Commotion

BIG BAND COMMOTION.
Tracks: / One mint julip / Moonlight in Vermont / Basie 'C' / Feelings / Pompton turnpike / Hangin' out / Huntington beach / How deep is the ocean / Sudden Sam / Sugar blues / Rock around the clock / Goodnight sweetheart / I'll see you in my dreams / Dream.
LP: . . . . MORRHYTHM 25

Big Bands

100 MINUTES OF BIG BAND MEDLEYS (Various artists).
MC: . . . . ZCTON 8175

BIG BAND JAZZ VOL.2 (Various artists).
Tracks: / Uskadara: *Various artists* / Easy: *Various artists* / Procrastination: *Various artists* / Just the way you are: *Various artists* / All stops: *Various artists* / Glad Hamp: *Various artists.*
LP: . . . . MAN 5024

BIG BANDS, VOL.3 (Various artists).
LP: . . . . VDL 1011

ESSENTIAL BIG BANDS, THE (See under Essential Big Bands) (Various artists).

ESSENTIAL BIG BANDS, THE (Various artists).
MC: 4671504

GOLDEN GREATS: 20 BIG BANDS (Various artists).
Tracks: / Skyliner: *Various artists* / Undecided: *Various artists* / South rampart street parade: *Various* artists / Flying home: *Various artists* / I get a kick out of you: *Various artists* / One o'clock jump: *Various* artists / Moonlight bay: *Various artists* / T.D.'s boogie woogie: *Various artists* / Comanche war dance: *Various* artists / Washington whirligig: *Various artists* / Woodchoppers ball: *Various artists* / In the mood: *Various* artists / When the saints go marching in: *Various artists* / Gambler's blues: *Various artists* / Liza: *Various* artists / Organ grinder's swing: *Various artists* / John Silver: *Various artists* / Wednesday night hop: *Various artists* / Casa loma stomp: *Various artists* / Down south camp meeting: *Various artists.*
LP: . . . . MCM 5025
MC: . . . . MCMC 5025

GOLDEN HOUR OF SOUNDS OF THE BIG BANDS, A (Various artists).
MC: . . . . KGHMC 124

GREAT BIG BANDS (Various artists).
Tracks: / Jumpin' at The Woodside: *Basie, Count* / Sandman: *Basie, Count* / I found a new baby: *Basie, Count* / Take the 'A' train: *Ellington, Duke* / Tea for two: *Ellington, Duke* / Black and tan fantasy: *Ellington,* Duke / Honeydripper: *Calloway, Cab* / Let's go, Joe: *Calloway, Cab* / Jumpin' jive: *Calloway, Cab* / Body and soul: *Lunceford, Jimmie* / For dancers only: *Lunceford, Jimmie* / Blues in the night: *Lunceford,* Jimmie / Artistry in rhythm: *Kenton, Stan* / Harlem folk dance: *Kenton, Stan* / Tampico: *Kenton, Stan* / Etude for saxophone: *Kenton, Stan* / Goof and I, The: *Herman, Woody* / Baby I need you: *Herman, Woody* / My pal Gonzales: *Herman, Woody* / In the mood: *Miller, Glenn* / Moonlight serenade: *Miller, Glenn* / Tuxedo Junction: *Miller, Glenn* / Moten swing: *Goodman, Benny* / Clap hands, here comes Charlie: *Goodman, Benny* / Begin the beguine: *Goodman, Benny.*
2LP: . . . . ALB 371

LEGENDARY BIG BANDS (Various artists).
LP: . . . . RTL 2047

SWING TO THE 30'S & 40'S (Various artists).
LP: . . . . MCM 1001

THEME SONGS OF THE BIG BANDS (Various artists).
LP: . . . . BO 725

THEMES SONGS OF THE BIG BANDS (Various artists).
LP: . . . . GELP 15026

THIS IS THE BIG BAND ERA (Various artists).
Tracks: / South: *Moten, Bennie Kansas City Orchestra* / Song of India: *Dorsey, Tommy & His Orchestra* / Sing, sing, sing: *Goodman, Benny & His Orchestra* / I can't get started: *Berigan, Bunny & His Orchestra* / Don't be that way: *Goodman, Benny & His Orchestra* / Begin the beguine: *Shaw, Artie & His Orchestra* / And the angels sing: *Elman, Ziggy* & His Orchestra / Twelfth Street rag: *Hampton, Lionel & His Orchestra* / Cherokee: *Barnet, Charlie & His* Orchestra / In the mood: *Miller, Glenn & His Orchestra* / Boogie woogie on St. Louis blues: *Hines, Earl 'Fatha'* & His Orchestra / Frenesi: *Shaw, Artie & His Orchestra* / After hours: *Hawkins, Erskine & His Orchestra* / Pompton turnpike: *Barnet, Charlie & His Orchestra* / Take the 'A' train: *Ellington, Duke And His Orchestra* / String of pearls, A: *Miller, Glenn & His Orchestra* / Opus one: *Dorsey, Tommy & His Orchestra* / Tippin' in: *Hawkins,* Erskine & His Orchestra / Mister Roberts' roost: *Basie, Count & His Orchestra* / Study in brown: *Clinton, Larry & His Orchestra.*
2LP: 26 28037

UNCOLLECTED BIG BANDS VOL 1, THE (Various artists).
Tracks: / Dipsey doodle, The: *Clinton, Larry* / Imagination: *Dorsey, Jimmy* / My baby just cares for me: *James,* Harry / Serenade in blue: *Spivak, Charlie* / Meet me tonight in dreamland: *Gray, Glen* / I've got my love to keep me warm: *Brown, Les* / Somebody else is taking my place: *Nelson, Ozzie* / I'm making believe: *Brown,* Les / Exactly like you: *Herman, Woody* / Contrasts: *Dorsey, Jimmy* / Heart and soul: *Barron, Blue* / I didn't know what time it was: *Cavallaro, Carmen.*
LP: . . . . HSR 301

UNCOLLECTED BIG BANDS VOL 2, THE (Various artists).
Tracks: / Blue Lou: *James, Harry* / April in Paris: *Rey, Alvino* / After you've gone: *Gray, Glen* / Three little words: *Brown, Les* / I didn't know: *Bailey, Mildred* / Apple honey: *Herman, Woody* / Take the 'A' train: *Ellington, Duke* / Lazy river: *James, Harry* / Dancing on the ceiling: *Gray, Glen* / To each his own: *Howard, Eddy* / Does your heart beat for me: *Barron, Blue* / Honeysuckle rose: *Busse, Henry.*
LP: . . . . HSR 302

UNCOLLECTED BIG BANDS VOL 3, THE (Various artists).
Tracks: / One o'clock jump: *Ellington, Duke* / Fools rush in: *Dorsey, Jimmy* / Royal garden blues: *Herman,* Woody / I couldn't sleep a wink last night: *James, Harry* / I can't believe that you're in love with me: *Brown,* Les / Little brown jug: *Gray, Glen* / Stardust: *Spivak, Charlie* / Deed I do: *Thornhill, Claude* / Maybe: *Gray, Glen* / Ain't misbehavin': *Herman, Woody* / Harbour lights: *Jurgens, Dick* / Dark eyes: *Foster, Chuck.*
LP: . . . . HSR 303

UNCOLLECTED BIG BANDS VOL 4, THE (Various artists).
Tracks: / Between the devil and the deep blue sea: *Rey, Alvino* / I cover the waterfront: *James, Harry* / Just squeeze me: *Ellington, Duke* / Hindustan: *Gray, Glen* / Sometimes I'm happy: *Brown, Les* / Begin the beguine: *Kenton, Stan* / Indiana: *James, Harry* / I'm stepping out with a memory tonight: *Dorsey, Jimmy* / Jones Beach Head: *Herman, Woody* / Adios: *Thornhill, Claude* / I let a song go out of my heart: *Jurgens, Dick* / Do you ever think of me: *Garber, Jan.*
LP: . . . . HSR 304

UNCOLLECTED BIG BANDS VOL 5, THE (Various artists).
Tracks: / It's only a paper moon: *Brown, Les* / Just about this time last night: *Thornhill, Claude* / Sometimes I'm happy: *Gray, Glen* / Glen Island hop: *Clinton, Larry* / Laura: *Spivak, Charlie* / Shine on Harvest moon: *Dorsey, Jimmy* / Should I: *Rey, Alvino* / Hour of parting: *Kenton, Stan* / Someday sweetheart: *Herman,* Woody / You are my sunshine: *Barron, Blue* / Whispers in the dark: *Jurgens, Dick* / Zing went the strings of my heart: *Cavallaro, Carmen.*
LP: . . . . HSR 305

UNCOLLECTED BIG BANDS VOL 6, THE (Various artists).
Tracks: / April showers: *Brown, Les* / If I love again: *Gray, Glen* / Ain't she sweet: *James, Harry* / Nearness of you, The: *Dorsey, Jimmy* / Jersey bounce: *Nelson, Ozzie* / Arkansas traveller: *Kenton, Stan* / Let's go home: *Spivak, Charlie* / You go to my head: *Clinton, Larry* / Lover come back to me: *Barron, Paul Orchestra* / Maria Elena: *Barron, Blue* / Because of you: *Garber, Jan* / Hot lips: *Busse, Henry.*
LP: . . . . HSR 306

UNCOLLECTED BIG BANDS VOL 7, THE (Various artists).
Tracks: / Song is ended, The: *Brown, Les* / Royal garden blues: *Ellington, Duke* / My old flame: *James, Harry* / Basie's basement: *Herman, Woody* / Wrap your troubles in dreams: *Gray, Glen* / Carolina in the morning: *Dorsey,* Jimmy / Old man river: *Kenton, Stan* / Body and soul: *James, Harry* / I'll get by: *Barron, Paul Orchestra* / I've got a pocketful of dreams: *Jurgens, Dick* / It's a wonderful world: *Garber, Jan* / When my dreamboat comes home: *Howard, Eddy.*
LP: . . . . HSR 307

UNCOLLECTED BIG BANDS VOL 8, THE (Various artists).
Tracks: / Perdido: *Ellington, Duke* / Dardanella: *Rey, Alvino* / Them there eyes: *Brown, Les* / All of me: *James, Harry* / Mean to me: *Spivak, Charlie* / Eager beaver: *Kenton, Stan* / Idaho: *Nelson, Ozzie* / You turned the tables on me: *James, Harry* / Feeling like a dream: *Clinton, Larry* / Don't take your love from me: *Gray, Glen* / Puttin' and takin': *Thornhill, Claude* / Bumble boogie: *Rey, Alvino.*
LP: . . . . HSR 308

UNCOLLECTED BIG BANDS VOL 9, THE (Various artists).
Tracks: / Red top: *Herman, Woody* / Kiss to remember, A: *Brown, Les* / Tuxedo junction: *Gray, Glen* / Girl of my dreams: *James, Harry* / Polka dots and moonbeams: *Thornhill, Claude* / Remember: *Clinton, Larry* / Ida, sweet as apple cider: *Barron, Blue* / You must have been a beautiful baby: *Howard, Eddy* / Rose room: *Garber,* Jan / Music, maestro please: *Jurgens, Dick* / Little bit south of North Carolina, A: *Foster, Chuck* / Just one of those things: *Cavallaro, Carmen.*
LP: . . . . HSR 309

UNCOLLECTED BIG BANDS VOL 10, THE (Various artists).
Tracks: / 9.20 special: *Ellington, Duke* / On the alamo: *Brown, Les* / No name jive: *Gray, Glen* / Sweet Lorraine: *Herman, Woody* / Central Avenue

shuffle: *Nelson, Ozzie* / Liza: *Kenton, Stan* / Blue Lou: *Dorsey, Jimmy* / I'll be around: *James, Harry* / I used to love you: *Spivak, Charlie* / Dreamers holiday: *Howard, Eddy* / Scatterbrain: *Barron, Blue* / Whispering: *Garber, Jan.*
LP: . . . . **HSR 310**

UNCOLLECTED BIG BANDS VOL 11, THE (Various artists).
Tracks: / Stardust: *Shaw, Artie* / On the sunnyside of the street: *James, Harry* / Baby won't you please come home: *Kenton, Stan* / Nice work if you can get it: *James, Harry* / Blueberry Hill: *Dorsey, Jimmy* / Leap frog: *Brown, Les* / Swamp fire: *Ellington, Duke* / Poor butterfly: *Kenton, Stan* / Opus 1: *James, Harry* / Out of nowhere: *Shaw, Artie* / Elegie: *Kenton, Stan* / I've had this feeling before: *James, Harry*/ Tea for two: *Ellington, Duke* / Is you is or is you ain't my baby: *Herman, Woody* / Just you, just me: *Shaw, Artie* / Sentimental journey: *Brown, Les.*
LP: . . . . **HSR 311**

UNCOLLECTED BIG BANDS VOL 12, THE (Various artists).
Tracks: / Garden in the rain: *Barron, Blue* / It's delovely: *Cavallaro, Carmen* / Ballin' the jack: *Howard, Eddy* / I guess I'll have to dream the rest: *Barron, Blue* / Shuffle off to buffalo: *Kemp, Hal* / I hear a rhapsody: *Garber, Jan* / Moonlight and shadows: *Morgan, Russ* / Gone with the wind: *Jurgens, Dick* / You've got me crying again: *Kemp, Hal* / I married an angel: *Jurgens, Dick* / I'll see you in my dreams: *Garber, Jan* / I guess I'll have to change my plans: *Kemp, Hal* / I'm gonna lock my heart: *Jurgens, Dick* / I've got you under my skin: *Cavallaro, Carmen* / Boo hoo: *Morgan, Russ* / Our love is here to stay: *Howard, Eddy.*
LP: . . . . **HSR 312**

Big Barn Orchard

TOPPING THE ORCHARD.
LP: . . . . **RES 339300**

Big Beat Beach Party

BIG BEAT BEACH PARTY (Various artists).
Tracks: / Peter Gunn locomotion: *Delmonas* / Melanie: *Prisoners* / Love is a beautiful thing: *Larry & The* Blue Notes / Tricksters, The: *Thee Mighty Caesars* / Tracking the dog: *Screaming Blue Messiahs* / Clucaracha taco: *Carrasco, Joe 'King'* / Tommy's blue valentine: *Pride Of The Cross* / Surf taboo: *Surfin' Lungs*/ Down at the 'B' club: *Surfin' Lungs* / Bitter tears: *Lariat, Lash* / Mr Blues: *Restless* / Rumba chile: *Ford, Sugar Ray* / I'm in misery: *Adkins, Hasil* / Dynamite: *Legendary Stardust Cowboy* / Dragstar: *Tall Boys* / Come on kid: *Stingrays* / Feel the purple hills: *Turkey Bones & The Wild Dogs.*
LP: . . . . **WIKM 39**

Big Beautiful Guitars

BIG BEAUTIFUL GUITARS (Various artists).
LP: . . . . **PELVIS 001**

Big Ben Banjo Band

BIG BEN BANJO BAND.
Tracks: / It's a hap-hap-happy day / Good old bad old days / Entertainer, The / Doh re mi / I want to be happy / Harry Lime theme / Those lazy hazy crazy days of summer / Who wants to be a millionaire / Wheels / Ramling rose / Tie a yellow ribbon / Say has anybody seen my sweet gypsy rose / Hello Dolly.
MCSET: . . . . **DTO 10024**

BIG BEN BANJO BAND.
MC: . . . . **TCIDL 104**

DANCIN' BANJOS.
Tracks: / Roll out the barrel / Paddlin' Madelin' home / Ma (he's making eyes at me) / Who's sorry now / Tiptoe through the tulips / Painting the clouds with sunshine / Moonlight bay / My sweetie went away / I'll string along with you / When you wore a tulip / Jeepers creepers / I want a girl / I'm forever blowing bubbles / Let me call you sweetheart / I wonder who's kissing her now / Three little words / Who's baby are you / I wonder where my baby is tonight / Exactly like you / Pasadena / On the sunny side of the street / Shine on harvest moon / Pretty baby / You made me love you / Deep in the heart of Texas / You are my sunshine / Put on your old grey bonnet / Let bygones be bygones / I'll be your sweetheart / Let the rest of the world go by / Little white lies / Ain't that a grand and glorious feeling / I ain't got nobody / I lift up my finger and say tweet tweet / Nobody's sweetheart / Smile, darn you, smile.
LP: . . . . **SH 107 821 1**
MC: . . . . **TCSH 107 821 4**

MORE MINSTREL MELODIES.
LP: **33SX 1254**

RAGS AND TATTERS.
LP: . . . . **NSPL 18575**

RAGTIME (see Paramor, Norrie) (Big Ben Banjo Band/Norrie Paramor).

SING-A-LONG PARTY HITS.
Tracks: / It's a hap-hap-happy day / Entertainer, The / I want to be happy / Those lazy hazy crazy days of summer / Wheels / Tie a yellow ribbon round the old oak tree / Hello Dolly / Ma, he's making eyes at me / Alabama jubilee / Everything is beautiful / Thank heaven for little girls / Cabaret / Old fashioned way, The / Summer holiday / Sidesaddle / Charley my boy / Good old bad old days / Do-re-mi / Eye level / Who wants to be a millionaire / Rambling rose / Say has anybody seen my sweet gypsy rose / Who's in the strawberry patch / Harry Lime theme / Give me the moonlight / Charleston / Stumbling / Raindrops keep falling on my head / Twelfth Street rag / You won't find another fool like me / Black and white rag / One of those songs.
MC: . . . . **KGHMC 105**

Big Ben Hawaiian Band

BIG BEN HAWAIIAN BAND.
MC: . . . . **TC IDL 17**

Big Big Sun

STOP THE WORLD.
LP: . . . . **K 7819641**
MC: . . . . **K 7819644**

Big Black

ATOMISER.
LP: . . . . **BFFP 11**
LP: . . . . **HMS 043**

BIG BLACK: LIVE.
LP: . . . . **BFFP 49**
MC: . . . . **BFFP 49C**

HAMMER PARTY.
LP: . . . . **HMS 044**

HEADACHE.
LP: . . . . **BFFP 14**
MC: . . . . **BFFP 14C**

RACER X.
LP: . . . . **HMS 007**

SONGS ABOUT FUCKING.
LP: . . . . **BFFP 19**
MC: . . . . **BFFP 19C**

SOUND OF IMPACT.
LP: . . . . **NOT 2**

Big Blue (film)

BIG BLUE, THE (Film soundtrack) (Various artists).
Tracks: / Big Blue overture, The: *Various artists* / Rescue in a wreck: *Various artists* / Huacracocha: *Various* artists / Remembering a heart beat: *Various artists* / Homo delphinus: *Various artists* / Virgin Islands: *Various artists* / For Enzo: *Various artists* / My lady blue: *Various artists* / Deep blue dream: *Various* artists / In raya: *Various artists* / Between the sky scrapers: *Various artists* / Let them try (instrumental): *Various artists* / Synchronised instant: *Various artists* / Monastery of Amorgos, The: *Various artists*/ Leaving the world behind: *Various artists.*
LP: . . . . **V 2541**
MC: . . . . **TCV 2541**
LP: **70609**
MC: **50609**

BIG BLUE,THE (COMPLETE) (Serra, Eric).
2LP: **60065**
MCSET: **40065**

BIG BLUE,THE VOL. 2 (Serra, Eric).
LP: **70667**
MC: **50667**

Big Bob

WE'VE MADE MEMORIES (Big Bob & The Fugitives).
Tracks: / I love you forever and forever / Old flames / All my cloudy days are gone / Cold windy city of Chicago / We've made memories / I've news for you / If those lips could only speak / Foolin' around / Ashes of love / Tears on the roses / Perfect strangers / I love the country way of life / Don't let your sweet love die / Charleston railroad tavern / Happy anniversary / Pearly shells / On the beach at Waikiki / There's nobody home at the range.
MC: . . . . **ARDV 002**

Big Bopper

CHANTILLY LACE.
LP: **6463 057**
MC: **7245 057**
LP: **832 902-1**

CHANTILLY LACE (OLD GOLD) (See under Bell, Freddie/Giddy up a ding dong).

Big Boy...

1930-36 (Big Boy Teddy Edwards).
LP: . . . . **LE 300.002**

Big Broadcast Of 1932

BIG BROADCAST OF 1932, THE (Film soundtrack) (Various artists).
LP: . . . . **SH 2007**
LP: . . . . **STK 101**

Big Brother

CHEAPER THRILLS (Big Brother & The Holding Company).
Tracks: / Let the good times roll / I know you rider / Moanin' at midnight / Hey baby / Down on me / Whisperman / Women is losers / Blow my mind / Ball and chain / Coo-coo / Gutra's garden / Harry.
LP: . . . . **ED 135**

JOSEPH'S COAT (Big Brother & Holding Co.).
Tracks: / Keep on / Joseph's coat / Home on the strange / Someday / Mr. Natural / Funkie Jim / Be a brother / How hard it is / You've been talking 'bout me baby / House on fire / Nu boogaloo jam / Maui / Buried alive in the blues.
LP: . . . . **ED 170**

Big Chill (film)

BIG CHILL, THE (Film soundtrack) (Various artists).
Tracks: / I heard it through the grapevine: *Gaye, Marvin* / My girl: *Temptations* / Good lovin': *Rascals*/ Tracks of my tears: *Robinson, Smokey* / Joy to the world: *Three Dog Night* / Ain't too proud to beg: *Temptations*/ (You make me feel like) a natural woman: *Franklin, Aretha* / I second that emotion: *Robinson, Smokey* / Whiter shade of pale, A: *Procul Harum.*
LP: . . . . **STMR 9021**
MC: . . . . **CSTMR 9021**
LP: . . . . **ZL 72138**
MC: . . . . **ZK 72138**

Big Country (Film)

BIG COUNTRY (Film soundtrack) (Philharmonia Orchestra).
Tracks: / Big country / Old thunder, The / Waltz, The / War party / Stalking, The / Welcoming / Mackay's triumph / Big Muddy / Death of Buck Hannassey.
LP: . . . . **FILM 030**
MC: . . . . **FILMC 030**
DAT: . . . . **FILMDT 030**

BIG COUNTRY, THE (Film soundtrack) (Various artists).
Tracks: / Big country, The: *Various artists* / Welcoming, The: *Various artists* / Old thunder: *Various artists*/ McKay's triumph: *Various artists* / Waltz: *Various artists* / Old waltz, The: *Various artists* / Big muddy: *Various artists* / War party gathers, The: *Various artists* / McKay in Blanco Canyon: *Various artists*/ Death of Buck Hannassey: *Various artists* / Stalking, The: *Various artists.*
LP: . . . . **SHM 968**
MC: . . . . **HSC 343**

BIG COUNTRY/HOW THE WEST WAS WON (Various artists).
Tracks: / Big country, The: *Various artists* (Big Country.) / Welcoming, The: *Various artists* (Big Country.) / Old thunder: *Various artists* (Big Country.) / McKay's triumph: *Various artists* (Big Country.) / Waltz, The: *Various artists* (Big Country.) / Old house, The: *Various artists* (Big Country.) / Big muddy: *Various artists*(Big Country.) / War party gathers, The: *Various artists* (Big Country.) / McKay in Blanco Canyon: *Various artists*(Big Country.) / Death of Buck Hannery, The: *Various artists* (Big Country.) / Stalking, The: *Various artists*(Big Country.) / Big country, The: *Various artists* (Big Country.) / How the west was won (main title): *Various artists*(How The West Was Won.) / Home in the meadow: *Reynolds, Debbie* (How The West Was Won.) / Cleve and the mule: *Various* artists (How The West Was Won.) / Raise a ruckus: *Reynolds, Debbie/Ken Darby Singers* (How The West Was Won.) / Come share my life: *Various artists* (How The West Was Won.) / Marriage proposal, The: *Various artists* (How The West Was Won.) / Cheyennes: *Various artists* (How The West Was Won.) / He's Linus' boy: *Various artists* (How The West Was Won.) / Climb a higher hill: *Various artists* (How The West Was Won.) / What was your name in the States?: *Reynolds, Debbie* (How The West Was Won.) / No goodbye: *Various artists* (How The West Was Won.) / How the west was won (finale): *Darby, Ken Singers* (How The West Was Won.).
LP: . . . . **LPMGM 12**
LP: **791 927 1**
MC: . . . . **TCMGM 12**
MC: **791 927 4**

Big Country (group)

BIG COUNTRY: INTERVIEW PICTURE DISC.
LPPD: . . . . **BAK 2122**

CROSSING, THE.
Tracks: / In a big country / Inwards / Chance / Thousand stars, A / Storm, The / Harvest home / Lost patrol / Close action / Fields of fire / Porroh man.
LP: . . . . **MERH 27**
MC: . . . . **MERHC 27**

NO PLACE LIKE HOME.
Tracks: / We're not in Kansas / Republican party reptile / Dynamite lady / Keep on dreaming / Beautiful people / Hostage speaks, The / Beat the devil / Leap of faith / Ships / Into the fire.
LP: **5102301**
MC: **5102304**

PEACE IN OUR TIME.
Tracks: / King of emotion / Broken hearts / Thousand yard stare / From here to eternity / Everything I need / Peace in our time / Time for leaving / River of hope / In this place.
LP: . . . . **MERH 130**
MC: . . . . **MERHC 130**

SEER, THE.
Tracks: / Eiledon / Hold the heart / Look away / One great thing / Remembrance day / Red fox, The / Sailor, The / Seer, The / Teacher, The / I walk the hill.
LP: . . . . **MERH 87**
MC: . . . . **MERHC 87**

STEELTOWN.
Tracks: / East of Eden / Steeltown / Where the rose is sown / Come back to me / Tall ships go / Girl with grey eyes / Rain dance / Great divide, The / Just a shadow.
LP: . . . . **MERH 49**
MC: . . . . **MERHC 49**

THROUGH A BIG COUNTRY (Greatest Hits).
Tracks: / In a big country / Fields of fire / Chance / Wonderland / Where the rose is sown / Just a shadow / Look away / King of emotion / East of Eden / One great thing / Teacher, The / Broken heart (thirteen valleys) / Peace in our time / Eiledon (Only on CD & cassette.) / Seer, The (Only on CD & cassette.) / Harvest home (Only on CD & cassette.).
LP: **846 022-1**
MC: **846 022-4**

Big Daddy

BIG DADDY.
Tracks: / I write the songs / Bette Davis eyes / Super freak / Star wars / Whip it / Ebony and ivory / Rose, The / You don't bring me flowers / Hit me with your best shot / Just what I needed / Hotel California / Eye of the tiger / Dancing in the dark.
LP: . . . . **SPRAY 101**
MC: . . . . **CSPRAY 101**

Big Daddy Kane

IT'S A BIG DADDY THING.
Tracks: / It's a Big Daddy thing / Another victory / Mortal combat / Children are the future / Young gifted and black / Smooth operator / Calling Mr Welfare / I get the job done / Ain't no stoppin' us now / Pimpin' ain't easy / Big Daddy's theme / To be your man / House that Cee built, The / On the move.
LP: . . . . **WX 305**
MC: . . . . **WX 305C**

LONG LIVE THE KANE.
Tracks: / Long live the kane / Raw / Set it off / Day you're mine, The / On the bugged tip / Ain't no half steppin' / I'll take you there / Just rhymin' with biz / Mister Cee's master plan / Word to the mother.
LP: . . . . **K 925731 1**
MC: . . . . **K 925731 4**

TASTE OF CHOCOLATE.
LP: **7599263031**
MC: **7599263034**

Big Daddy Sun

BIG DADDY SUN AND THE OUTER PLANETS (Big Daddy Sun & The Outer Planets).
LP: . . . . **NERD 012**

Big Dave

ARTHUR MURRAY ROCK'N'ROLL.
LP: . . . . **PM 1561341**

Big Dipper

BOO-BOO.
Tracks: / Faith healer / San Quentin, CA / What's In Sam hill..? / Wrong in the charts / Ancers / Loch Ness Monster.
LP: . . . . **HMS 077**

CRAPS.
Tracks: / Meet the witch / Ron Klaus wrecked his house / Insane girl, The / Semjase / Stardom because / Bonnie /

Hey Mr. Lincoln / Bells of love / Song to be beautiful, A.
LP: FIEND 132
LP: HMS 122
MC: HMS 122 C

HEAVENS.
Tracks: / She's fetching / Man o'war / Easter eve / Humason / Lunar module / All going out together / Younger bums / When men were trains / Wet weekend / Mr Woods.
LP: FIEND 136

Big Dish

CREEPING UP ON JESUS.
Tracks: / Life / Waiting for the parade / Faith healer / Burn / Swansong / European rain / Jean / Monday / Wishing time / Where do you live? / Can't stand up (CD only).
LP: V 2540
MC: TCV 2540

SATELLITES.
LP: WX 400
MC: WX 400 C

SWIMMER.
Tracks: / Prospect Street / Christina's world / Slide / Big new beginning / Another people's palace / Swimmer, The / Loneliest man in the world, The / Jealous / Her town / Beyond the pale / Second swimmer.
LP: V 2374
MC: TCV 2374
LP: OVED 248
MC: OVEDC 248

Big Drill Car

ALBUM/TAPE/CD TYPE THING.
LP: CRZ 008
MC: CRZ 008 CA

SMALL BLOCK.
LP: VAR 001

Big Easy (film)

BIG EASY, THE (Original Soundtrack) (Various artists).
Tracks: / Iko iko: *Dixie Cups* / Tipitina: *Professor Longhair* / Ma 'tit fille: *Buckwheat Zydeco* / Colinda: *Newman, Jimmy C.* / Tell it like it is: *Neville, Aaron & the Neville Bros* / Zydeco gris gris: *Beausoleil*/ Oh yeah: *Simien, T & the mallet playboys* / Hey hey: *Wild Tchoupitoulas* / Closer to you: *Quaid, Dennis*/ Savour, pass...: *Swan Silvertones.*
LP: ISTA 14
MC: ICM 2006
MC: 846 000 4
MC: ICT 14

Big Ed

BINGO (Big Ed & The Rockin' Rattlesnakes).
LP: INCMLP 11

Big Eighteen

SWING COLLECTION, THE.
Tracks: / Tuxedo junction / Easy does it / Hors d'oeuvre / Blues on parade / Liza (all the clouds'll roll away / Five o clock drag / March of the toys / I'm prayin' humble / Campbells are swinging / Summit ridge drive / Parade of the milk bottle caps / Swingtime in the rockies / Feet draggin' blues / Okay for baby / Quaker city jazz / Celery stalks at midnight / Skyliner / Organ grinder's swing / Ton o'rock bump.
2LP: DPS 2058

Big F

BIG F, THE.
Tracks: / Killing time / Why / Doctor vine / Monkey boy 2 kill / Biz about brains / Kill the cowboy / Here's to the good life / Power pig / Alpert tango / Good God (shot dead at Honk King).
LP: EKT 70

Big Fun

POCKETFUL OF DREAMS, A.
LP: FUN 1
MC: FUNC 1

Big Heat

BURNING.
MC: DRSCS 100
LP: DRSLP 100

Big Hits ...

BIG HITS OF THE 40'S & 50'S (One For The Road) (Various artists).
Tracks: / Buttons and bows: *Crosby, Bing* / Don't sit under the apple tree: *Andrew Sisters* / Making believe: *Reeves, Jim* / Song of India: *Dorsey* / Choo choo ch' boogie: *Jordan, Louis.*
MC: CONE 5

BIG HITS OF THE 40'S AND 50'S (Various artists).
Tracks: / Open the door, Richard: *Basie, Count* / Hey ba ba re bop: *Beneke, Tex* / Mona Lisa: *Day, Dennis*/ I'll never smile again: *Dorsey, Tommy* / Lady of Spain: *Fisher, Eddie* / Rag mop: *Flanagan, Ralph* / This ole house: *Hamblen, Stuart* / Cocktails for two: *Jones, Spike* / Don't fence me in: *Kaye, Sammy*/ Slow poke: *King, Pee Wee* / C'est si bon: *Kitt, Eartha* / I've got a lovely bunch of coconuts: *Martin, Eddy*/ Stranger in paradise: *Martin, Tony* / White cliffs of Dover, The: *Miller, Glenn* / Dance ballerina dance: *Monroe, Vaughn* / Happy wanderer, The: *Rene, Henri* / Ballad of Davy Crockett, The: *Schuman, Walter* / My heart cries for you: *Shore, Dinah* / Peg o' my heart: *Three Suns* / Naughty lady of Shady Lane: *Ames Brothers.*
MC: INTK 9010

Big Ivan

MOTHER LIKE MINE, A.
Tracks: / She's in love with a rodeo man / Old mud cabin on the hill / Mother like mine, A.
LP: HRL 174
MC: CHRL 174

Big Jim

BIG JIM.
Tracks: / Wooden heart / Funny face / Arms full of empty / Dust on mother's Bible / Nobody's child / Anniversary song / Wild side of life / I can't stop loving you / Behind the footlights / Gonna change everything / How great Thou art / Little bitty tear, A.
LP: PHL 449
MC: CPHL 449

BIG JIM'S LITTLE SIX.
LP: GHB 185

FAVOURITES.
MC: UNKNOWN

REQUESTS.
Tracks: / Sweet forget me not / Amazing grace / She wears my ring / Did your mother come from Ireland / I will love you all my life / Jerusalem / When your old wedding ring was new / Way love's supposed to be, The / Old pals of yesterday / Baby blue / Veil of white lace / Mother of mine.
LP: PHL 489
MC: CPHL 489

Big John's Yoppers

YOPPER'S DREAM.
MC: JTN 132

Big Maceo

BIG MACEO.
MC: C 210

KING OF CHICAGO BLUES PIANO, VOLUME 2.
LP: BC 29

KING OF CHICAGO BLUES PIANO, VOLUME 1.
LP: BC 28

Big Maybelle

OKEH SESSIONS, THE.
Tracks: / Just want your love / So good to my baby / Gabbin blues / My country man / Rain down rain / Way back home / Stay away from my Sam / Jinny Mule / Maybelle's blues / I've got a feeling / You'll never know / No more trouble out of me / My big mistake / Ain't no use / I'm getting 'long alright / You'll be sorry / Hairdressin' women / One monkey don't stop no show / Don't leave poor me / Ain't to be played with / New kind of mambo / Whole lotta shakin' goin' on.
MC: TCCDX 27
2LP: CDX 27

ROOTS OF ROCK'N'ROLL AND EARLY SOUL.
LP: SJL 1143

Big One Compilation

BIG ONE COMPILATION (Various artists).
LP: BIGA 002
MC: BIGC 002

Big Pancake

BIG PANCAKE, THE (Well Loved Tales up to Age 9).
MC: PLB 95

Big Pig

BONK.
Tracks: / Breakaway / Hungry town / Iron lung / Fine thing / Money god / Boy wonder (Only available on CD) / Hellbent heaven (Only available on CD) / Breakaway (version) (Available only on CD) / Hungry town (version) (Available only on CD).
LP: AMA 5185
MC: AMC 5185

Big Pop Nightmare

BIG POP NIGHTMARE (Various artists).
LP: TEC 2

Big River (show)

BIG RIVER - ADVENTURES OF HUCKLEBERRY FINN (Original Broadway cast) (Various artists).
Tracks: / Big River - Overture: *Various artists* / Do you wanna go to heaven?: *Various artists* / Boys, The: *Various artists* / Waitin' for the light to shine: *Various artists* / Guv'ment: *Various artists* / Hand for the hog: *Various artists* / I, Huckleberry, me: *Various artists* / Muddy water: *Various artists* / Crossing, The: *Various artists* / River in the rain: *Various artists* / When the sun goes down in the south: *Various artists*/ Entracte: *Various artists* / Royal nonesuch, The: *Various artists* / Worlds apart: *Various artists*/ Arkansas: *Various artists* / How blest we are: *Various artists* / You oughta be here with me: *Various artists*/ Leavin's not the only way to go: *Various artists* / Waitin' for the light to shine (reprise): *Various artists*/ Free at last: *Various artists* / Muddy water (reprise): *Various artists.*
LP: MCF 3304

Big Rumble

BIG RUMBLE, THE (Various artists).
LP: F 100

Big Self

STATELESS.
LP: RKLP 2

Big Shoulders

BIG SHOULDERS.
LP: AM 1013

Big Sky Mudflaps

SENSIBLE SHOES.
LP: FF 293

Big Sleep (bk)

BIG SLEEP, THE (Raymond Chandler) (Massey, Daniel (nar)).
MCSET: LFP 7113

Big Soul Sound

BIG SOUL SOUND (Various artists).
MC: CE 2216
LP: NE 1216

Big Sound Authority

INWARD REVOLUTION.
Tracks: / Call me soulman / Be true to yourself / Moving heaven and earth / My hell shaped room / This is the day / I'm stronger now / This house (is where your love stands) / Bad town, A / Loverama / Let's hold together / When things fall apart.
LP: MCF 3279
MC: MCFC 3279

Big Sound For...

BIG SOUND FOR A SMALL WORLD (Various artists).
Tracks: / Reach for the sky: *Various artists* / Prisoner of romance: *Various artists* / Play with fire: *Various* artists / Love sick: *Various artists* / Yellow light: *Various artists* / Whole world: *Various artists*/ Instant karma: *Various artists* / Rescue me: *Various artists* / Bad boy: *Various artists* / All grown up: *Various artists* / Wonder: *Various artists* / Love like yours: *Various artists* / Grow yourself up: *Various artists* / To know him is to love him: *Various artists.*
LP: SHY 8527

Big Star

BIG STARS 3RD/SISTERS LOVER.
LP: PVC 8917
MC: PVCC 8917

NO.1 RECORD.
Tracks: / Feel / Ballad of El Goodo, The / In the street / Thirteen / Don't lie to me / India song, The / When my baby's beside me / My life is right / Give me another chance / Try again / Watch the sunrise / St 100/6.
LP: WIK 53

RADIO CITY.
Tracks: / Oh my soul / Life is white / Way out west / What's goin ahn / You get what you deserve / Mod lang / Back of a car / Daisy glaze / She's a mover / September gurls / Morpha too / I'm in love with a girl.
MC: WIKC 54
LP: WIK 54

SISTERS LOVER.
Tracks: / Stroke it Noel / Downs / Femme fatale / Thank you friends / Holocaust / Jesus Christ / Blue moon / Dream lover / You can't have me / Big black car / Kizza me / For you / O Dana / Nightime / Whole lotta shakin' goin' on / Kangaroo / Take care.
LP: DOJOLP 55

Big Stick

CRACK 'N' DRAG.
LP: BFFP 25
MC: BFFP 25C

Big Three

CAVERN STOMP.
Tracks: / Some other guy / I'm with you / Let true love begin / By the way / Cavern stomp / Peanut butter / Bring it on home to me (Live) / What'd I say / Don't start running away / Zip-a-dee-doo-dah / Reelin' and rockin' / You've got to keep her under hand / Bring it on home to me (Studio).
LP: ED 111

I FEEL LIKE STEPPIN' OUT (Big Three Trio, The).
Tracks: / Signifying monkey, The / Reno blues / After while / No more sweet potatoes / Ebony rhapsody / My love will never die / Big three boogie / You sure look good to me / I feel like steppin' out / Lonesome / I'll be right someday / Blue because of you / Violent love / Evening / Appetite blues.
LP: H 804

Big Time

BIG TIME COMPILATION (Various artists).
Tracks: / Land and life: *Lucy Show* / Alone: *Dumptruck* / Now I ride alone: *Dream Syndicate* / Quiet lives: *Eider, Max* / Boy's town work song: *Christmas* / Chilli part two: *Love Tractor* / Juice squeezer: *Alisa* / Love is you: *Redd Kross.*
LP: WL 71275
MC: WK 71275

Big Tiny Little

GOLDEN PIANO HITS.
LP: GNPS 2113

PIANO MEMORIES.
LP: GNPS 2120

Big Tom

20 GREATEST HITS: BIG TOM.
MC: KMC 55

ALL TIME HITS OF.... (Big Tom & The Mainliners).
Tracks: / Gentle mother / Sunset years of life, The / Please mama please / Tears on a bridal bouquet / Old log cabin for sale, An / Bunch of violets blue / Old rustic bridge / Flowers for Mama / I'll settle for old Ireland / Wheels fell off the wagon again, The.
LP: GES 1051
MC: KGEC 1051

AROUND IRELAND WITH BIG TOM.
LP: DNV 16

BLUE WINGS/FOUR COUNTRY ROADS.
MC: DNVC 14

I'LL SETTLE FOR OLD IRELAND.
LP: GES 1102

KING OF COUNTRY MUSIC, VOLUME 6.
LP: BT 6

KING OF COUNTRY MUSIC, VOLUME 5.
LP: BT 5

KING OF COUNTRY MUSIC, VOLUME 3.
LP: BT 3

KING OF COUNTRY MUSIC, VOLUME 4.
LP: BT 4

KING OF COUNTRY MUSIC, VOLUME 2.
LP: BT 2

KING OF COUNTRY MUSIC, VOLUME 1.
LP: BT 1

LITTLE BIT OF COUNTRY & IRISH (Big Tom & The Mainliners).
Tracks: / Isle of Innisfree / Don't be angry / My world's come down / Guess things happen that way / Back in my babys arms / Tears on a bridal bouquet / She's gone / Cold hard facts of life / Before (I met you) / Gentle mother.
LP: BER 004
MC: KBER 004

TEARDROPS IN THE SNOW.
LP: DNV 15

Big Tony

BUST THE BEAT (Big Tony & The T.F. Crew).
LP: RTT 3

Big Town (Film)

BIG TOWN (Film soundtrack) (Various artists).
Tracks: / Fever: *John, Little Willie* / Ruby baby: *Drifters* / Drown in my own tears: *Charles, Ray* / Home of the blues: *Cash, Johnny* / Mack the knife: *Darin, Bobby* / Since I met you baby: *Hunter, Ivory Joe*/ Shake, rattle and roll: *Turner, Big Joe* / Goodnight my love: *Belvin, Jesse* / Jim Dandy: *Baker, Laverne*/ Big town: *Self, Ronnie.*
LP: K 781 769 1
MC: K 781 769 4

Big Town Playboys

NOW APPEARING.
Tracks: / Hungry man / Who showed my baby / Baby please / Drinkin' beer / You must be foolin' / In the middle of the night

/ I'm so satisfied / Wobble, The / Blues came rollin' / Doopin / Mellow saxophone / What a shame.
LP: . . . . BLUH 010

PLAYBOY BOOGIE.
Tracks: / Hurry baby / Chicken shack boogie / Happy pay day / Walkin' / She walked right in / What more do you want me to do ? / Playboy boogie / Come on / Down the road apiece / I done it / Shake your hips / Roomin' house boogie / Driftin'.
LP: . . . . SPIN 203

Big Trouble

BIG TROUBLE.
Tracks: / When the love is good / Say yes / One more arrow / Cool jerk / What about you and me / Dangerous / Crazy world / Trains and boats and planes / I like it / Lipstick.
LP: 4604891
MC: 4604894

Big Trouble In..(film)

BIG TROUBLE IN LITTLE CHINA (Film Soundtrack) (Coup De Villes).
Tracks: / Big trouble in little China / Coup de villes / Pork chop express / Alley, The / Here comes the storm / Lo Pan's Domain / Escape from wing kong / Into the spirit path / Great Arcade, The / Final escape, The.
MC: . . . . FILMC 008
LP: . . . . FILM 008

Big Twist

BIGGER THAN LIFE (Live from Chicago) (Big Twist & the Mellow Fellows).
LP: . . . . SNTF 989

ONE TRACK MIND (Big Twist & the Mellow Fellows).
Tracks: / Living it up / I wouldn't treat a dog the way you treated me / Cold woman / Give up what you want / Lo and behold / Rescue me / Wait till the time is right / Real thing, The / I got the blues.
LP: . . . . RL 040
LP: . . . . FF 268

PLAYING FOR KEEPS (Big Twist & the Mellow Fellows).
Tracks: / 300 pounds of heavenly joy / Flip flop / I want your love / Pork salad Annie / Pouring water on a drowning man / I've got a problem / I brought the blues on myself / We're gonna make it / Just one woman.
LP: . . . . SNTF 907
MC: . . . . AC 4732

Big Vern

LULLABIES FOR LAGER LOUTS.
LP: . . . . PRKA 2
MC: . . . . PRKC 2

Big Walter

BOOGIES FROM COAST TO COAST.
Tracks: / I don't know / Walking across Texas / It had to be / Bloodstains on the wall / Long way to go / I won't lie to you anymore / Clock on the motel wall / I want to be your chauffeur / Darkest hour is just before dawn, The / I thought I heard my baby cry / Someone who don't understand / Walter's boogie.
LP: . . . . CHD 246

JOHNNY YOUNG AND BIG WALTER (See Young, Johnny) (Big Walter/ Johnny Young).

Big Western Film

BIG WESTERN FILM THEMES (Various artists).
Tracks: / High noon: *Various artists* / True grit: *Various artists* / Good, the bad and the ugly, The: *Various* artists / Magnificent seven, The: *Various artists* / Man from Laramie, The: *Various artists* / Hang 'em high: *Various artists*.
MC: . . . . AIM 118

Big Wheels Of Motown

BIG WHEELS OF MOTOWN (Various artists).
Tracks: / I heard it through the grapevine: *Gaye, Marvin* / Too busy thinking about my baby: *Gaye, Marvin* / Tears of a clown: *Robinson, Smokey & The Miracles* / Tracks of my tears: *Robinson, Smokey & The Miracles* / My guy: *Wells, Mary* / I can't help myself: *Four Tops* / Reach out I'll be there: *Four Tops* / Get ready: *Temptations*/ I'm still waiting: *Ross, Diana* / I want you back: *Jackson Five* / Jimmy Mack: *Reeves, Martha* / Dancing in the street: *Reeves, Martha* / Yester-me, yester-you, yesterday: *Wonder, Stevie* / I'm gonna make you love me: *Ross, Diana & The Supremes & The Temptations* / Stoned love: *Supremes* / For once in my life: *Wonder, Stevie*/ Help me make it through the night: *Knight, Gladys* / What becomes of the broken hearted?: *Ruffin, Jimmy* / This old heart of mine: *Isley Brothers* / Where did our love go: *Ross, Diana & The Supremes*.
LP: . . . . MTV 12
MC: . . . . CMTV 12
LP: . . . . ZL 72006
MC: . . . . ZK 72006

Big Youth

A LUTA CONTINUA.
LP: . . . . HB 28
MC: . . . . HBC 28

CHANTING DREAD INNA FINE STYLE.
Tracks: / My time / Skyjuice / African daughter / My buddy / All nations bow / Salvation light / Dread inna Babylon / Mama look / Streets in Africa / Jah Jah shall guide / Jah Jah love them / Jah Jah golden jubilee / Golden dub / Who laughed last.
LP: . . . . BMLP 024
MC: . . . . BMC 024
LP: . . . . HB 08

DREADLOCKS DREAD.
Tracks: / Train to Rhodesia / House of dreadlocks / Lightning flash / Weak heart / Natty dread she want / Some like it dread / Marcus Garvey / Big Youth special / Dread organ / Blackman message / You don't care / Moving away.
LP: . . . . VX 1009
MC: . . . . FLC 9006

EVERYDAY SKANK (Best of Big Youth).
Tracks: / S.90 / One of these fine days / Pride & joy rag / So we stay / Cool breeze / Can you keep a secret / Screaming target / Killer / Give praises / Hell is for heroes / Natty / Cultural dread / 10 against.
LP: . . . . TRLS 189

HIT THE ROAD JACK.
Tracks: / What's going on / Hit the road Jack / Wake up everybody / Get up stand up / Jah man of Syreen / Ten against one / Hotter fire / Way of the light, The / Dread high ranking / Dread is the best.
LP: . . . . TRLS 137

LIVE AT THE REGGAE SUNSPLASH.
LP: . . . . VSLP 8905

MANIFESTATION.
Tracks: / No nukes / Love fighting so / Turn me on / Mr. Right / Like it like that / Conqueror, The / Spiderman meet the Hulk / No way to treat a lady.
LP: . . . . HB 46
MC: . . . . HBC 46

NATTY CULTURAL DREAD.
Tracks: / Wolf in sheep's clothing / Natty cultural dread / Hell is for heroes / Jim Squashey / Touch me in the morning / Every nigger is a star / I love the way you love.
LP: . . . . TRLS 123

REGGAE PHENOMENON.
LP: . . . . TRLD 411
MC: . . . . ZCTRD 411

SCREAMING TARGET.
Tracks: / Screaming target / Pride and joy rock / Be careful / Tippertone rock / One of these fine days / Screaming target (Vers 2) / Killer / Solomon A Gunday / Honesty / I am alright / Lee a low / Concrete jungle.
LP: . . . . TRLS 61

SOME GREAT BIG YOUTH.
Tracks: / World war III / Living / Roots foundation / Get on up / Dancing mood / Time alone will tell / Suffering / Love Jah with all of my heart / Green bay killing / We can work it out.
LP: . . . . BMLP 015
LP: . . . . HB 03

Bigard, Barney

BARNEY BIGARD 37-40 (Goin' easy).
LP: . . . . TAX 8026

BARNEY BIGARD & THE PELICAN TRIO (Bigard,Barney & The Pelican Trio).
LP: . . . . CJP 5

MY BUCKET'S GOT A HOLE IN IT.
Tracks: / I'll be back / My bucket's got a hole in it.
LP: . . . . DS 211

Bigfoot & The

BIGFOOT & THE HENDERSONS (Film soundtrack) (Various artists).
LP: . . . . MCF 3416
MC: . . . . MCFC 3416

Bigga

EARTH PEOPLE.
LP: . . . . VR 3306

Biggest Band...

BIGGEST BAND SPECTACULAR IN THE WORLD (1985 Military Musical Pageant Wembley Stadium) (Various artists).
Tracks: / General salute and opening fanfare: *Various artists* / By beat of drum: *Various artists* / Light of foot: *Various artists* / Pipes and drums: *Various artists* / Queen's guards, The: *Various artists* / Massed band, The: *Various artists* / Royal military band of The Netherlands: *Various artists* / War and peace: *Various artists* / Finale: *Various artists*.
2LP: . . . . BNC 3003
MCSET: . . . . ZC BNC 3003

Biggins, Christopher

BILLY BUNTER GETS THE BOOT (see under Billy Bunter...(bk)).

Biggles

BIGGLES (Original soundtrack) (Various artists).
Tracks: / Do you want to be a hero: *Andrews, Jon* / Chock's away: *Andrews, Jon* / Big hot blues: *Chakk*/ Knocking on your back door: *Deep Purple* / Knock 'em dead kid: *Motley Crue* / No turning back: *Immortals*/ Music soundtrack: *Various artists* / Ariel pursuit: *Syrewicz, Stanislas* / Discovery: *Syrewicz, Stanislas*/ Biggles theme: *Syrewicz, Stanislas* / Maria's theme: *Syrewicz, Stanislas*.
LP: . . . . MCF 3328
MC: . . . . MCFC 3328

Biggles (bk)

BIGGLES (Capt. W.E Johns) (York, Michael (nar)).
MC: . . . . TCLFP 417136 5

Biggs, Barry

BARRY BIGGS & THE INNER CIRCLE.
Tracks: / Stoned in love with you / Sideshow / Westbound train / Your kiss is sweet / Burial / Love grows / Why must you cry / Got to be mellow / Natty dread / Forward jah jah children / One bad apple / T.S.O.P..
LP: . . . . TRLS 142

SIDESHOW (OLD GOLD) (See under Cadogan, Susan (Hurt so good)).

SO IN LOVE.
LP: . . . . SDLP 915

WHAT'S YOUR SIGN GIRL? (ALBUM).
Tracks: / What's your sign girl? / It's my house / Don't know why I love you / Took the show on the road / Love on a two way street / Precious / Too much heaven / Give me a call / Surely / Test of time / Killing me softly / I like to sing.
LP: . . . . DYLP 3015

Biggun, Ivor

MORE FILTH DIRT CHEAP.
Tracks: / Cockerel song, The / My shirt collar (it won't go stiff) / Southern breeze / Burglars holler, The / Gums and plums / John Thomas Allcock / I have a dog his name is Rover / My brothers magazine / Richard the third / Walking your blues away / Are mice electric / I can be the hot dog and you can be the bun / I wanna be a bear / I woke up dis moanin' / Terrific Teddy sings the blues / Ah feel so bad / Other educated monkey.
LP: . . . . BOPA 3
MC: . . . . BOPAC 3
LP: . . . . BBL 3
MC: . . . . BBLC 3

PARTNERS IN GRIME (Biggun, Ivor and Ivors Jivers).
Tracks: / Hide the sausage / Nobody does it like the ukelele man / Chantilly lace / Halfway up Virginia / Pussy song, The / Probing Andromeda / Majorca song, The / Sixty minute man / Toolbag Ted from Birkenhead / Where did the lead in my pencil go / Cue for a song / I've got a monster.
LP: . . . . BIGG 1
MC: . . . . BIGG C1
LP: . . . . BBL 79
MC: . . . . BBLC 79

WINKERS ALBUM, THE.
Tracks: / I've parted / Great grandad John / My brother's got files / Oh oh oh / Cucumber number / Underground music / Winker's paradise, The / Charabanc.
LP: . . . . BOPA 1
LP: . . . . BBL 1
MC: . . . . BBLC 1

Bigshot Mixes

BIGSHOT MIXES (Various artists).
LP: . . . . DBLP 506
MC: . . . . DBMC 506

Bihary, Jean-Claude

AKOW MAJIK.
LP: . . . . AKA 010

Bikaye, Zazou

GUILTY.
LP: . . . . CRAM 062

MR. MANAGER.
LP: . . . . CRAM 039

Bilbro, D.H. 'Bert'

HARMONICA SHOWCASE (see Bailey, Deford & D.H. 'Bert' Bilbro).

Bilbrough, Dave

DAVE BILBROUGH & FRIENDS.
LP: . . . . DOVE 58

Bileams Asna

BILEAMS ASNA.
LP: . . . . SLP 550

Bilezikjian, John

ART OF THE OUD, THE.
LP: . . . . TR 513

NEO-CLASSICAL OUD, THE.
Tracks: / Sonata 14 in C sharp minor Opus 27 / No.2 / Ave Maria / La fille aux cheveux de lin / Le minuet / Malaguena / Eastern fantasy.
LP: . . . . DS 201

Bilitis (film)

BILITIS (Film soundtrack) (Lai, Francis).
Tracks: / Bilitis / Promenade / Les deux nudites / Spring time ballet / L'abre / I need a man / Melissa / La campagne / Scene d'amour / Rainbow / Bilitis.
LP: . . . . UAS 30161
MC: . . . . TCK 30161
LP: . . . . WB 56412

Bilk, Acker

100 MINUTES OF ACKER BILK.
MC: . . . . ZCTON 107

ACKER.
LP: 33SX 1248

ACKER BILK AND THE PARAMOUNT JAZZ BAND (Bilk, Acker & His Paramount Jazz Band).
Tracks: / St. Philip breakdown / All the girls / Gladiolus rag / East coast trot / Bei mir bist du schon / Bye and bye / St. Louis blues / Breeze / Old rugged cross.
LP: . . . . TTD 543-4
LP: . . . . BD 3006

ACKER BILK IN HOLLAND.
Tracks: / I can't believe that you're in love with me / Clarinet marmalade / Mood indigo / Them there eyes / Take the 'A' train / World is waiting for the sunshine, The / Just a closer walk with thee / Jeepers creepers / Lover man / Watermelon man / I don't want to set the world on fire / St. Thomas / Georgia / Senora Signora / Blues walks / Stranger on the shore / Nobody's sweetheart / Once in a while / Old music master, The.
2LP: . . . . TTD 506/7
MCSET: . . . . TTD 5506

ACKER BILK PLAYS LENNON & MCCARTNEY.
LP: . . . . GNPS 2191
MC: GNP5 2191

ACKER BILK SAGA, THE.
Tracks: / Perdido street blues / Papa dip / South / Summerset / Snag it / Should I / Acker's personal jungle / Royal Garden blues / Blues for this year / Blues for last year / Acker raga / La paloma / Soho blues / Bustamento / Adios mi chaparita / Too-ra-loo-ra-loo-ra / Petite fleur / Honeysuckle rose / Basin Street blues / Georgia on my mind / Creole love call / Dinah / Stranger on the shore.
2LP: 2668 020
MC: 3577 348

ACKER BILK'S OMNIBUS.
LP: . . . . NJL 22

ACKER'S CHOICE.
2LP: DP6 28490

AFTER MIDNIGHT.
Tracks: / Stranger on the shore / Right here waiting / Room in your heart / Smack a Latin, A / Another day in paradise / Don't know much / After midnight / Don't wanna lose you / How am I supposed to live without you / I'm not in love / Best of me, The / Anything for you / Disney girls / If leaving is easy / When summer comes / Traces of dreams.
MC: . . . . PWKMC 4019

BEST OF ACKER BILK, HIS CLARINET AND STRINGS.
Tracks: / Aria / Canio's tune / Pachelbel canon / You are the sunshine of my life / Miss you nights / First of spring, The / Evergreen / Aranjuez mon amour / Stranger on the shore / Chi mai / Spanish Harlem / Up in the world / Cavatina / Without you / Chariots of fire / Don't cry for me Argentina.
LP: . . . . PYL 6030
MC: . . . . PYM 6030
LP: . . . . GNPS 2116
MC: GNP5 2116
MC: . . . . PYC 6030

BEST OF ACKER BILK VOLUME 2.
Tracks: / Aria / Sugar / Windmills of your mind / Swan Lake Theme / Dancing in the dark / Clair / When / Honeysuckle Rose / Canio's tune / Hundred years from today / Shepherds song / Wolverine blues / Sailing / Missing you / Fire and rain / Snow Goose Themes /

Feeling / Rose of the Rio Grande / Homecoming.
LP: .... GH 667
LP: .... GNPS 2171
MC: GNP5 2171

BEST OF BALL, BARBER & BILK (See under 'Ball, Kenny' for details) (Bilk, Acker/Kenny Ball/Chris Barber).

BEST OF BARBER AND BILK VOL.1 (See under 'Barber, Chris' for details) (Bilk, Acker/Chris Barber).

BEST OF BARBER AND BILK VOL.2 (See under 'Barber, Chris' for details) (Bilk, Acker/Chris Barber).

COLLECTION: ACKER BILK.
2LP: 11PP 605
2LP: .... CCSLP 209
MC: .... CCSMC 209

DREAMING IN THE SUN (Bilk, Acker & Norman Candler).
LP: .... ISST 130

EVERGREEN.
LP: .... PW 5045

EXTREMELY LIVE IN STUDIO 1.
MC: .... ZCP 18569

FINEST MOMENTS.
Tracks: / Stranger on the shore / Send in the clowns / Night that made me forget,The / Red haired girl / August evening / Fond memories / Just for you / Birchtree road / Aria / Fool on the hill / Autumn evening / Goodbye / You won't see a tear / Western farm / Dusk / Windharp.
LP: .... SHLP 138
MC: .... SHTC 138

FREE.
MC: .... ZCP 41056

GOLDEN HOUR OF ACKER BILK.
MC: .... KGHMC 117

GOLDEN HOUR OF ACKER BILK VOLUME 2.
Tracks: / Sugar (that sugar baby of mine) / Windmills of your mind / Swan lake (theme from) / Dancing in the dark / Clair / When / Honeysuckle rose / Canio's tune / Hundred years from today, A / Shepherd's song, The / Wolverine blues / Sailing / Missing you / Fire and rain / Snow goose (theme from) / Feelings / Rose of the Rio Grande / Homecoming.
MC: .... KGHMC 139

GOLDEN HOUR OF THE BEST OF ACKER BILK.
MC: .... ZCGH 624

GOLDEN TREASURY OF BILK.
LP: 33SX 1304

HIS CLARINET & STRINGS LOVE SONGS.
Tracks: / Evergreen / Miss you nights / (They long to be) close to you.
LP: .... SHM 3239
MC: .... HSC 3239

HITS, BLUES AND CLASSICS (Bilk, Acker & His Paramount Jazz Band).
Tracks: / Louisian-i-ay / Black and tan fantasy / My baby just cares for me / Papa dip / That's my home / Sempre fidelis / Basin St.Blues / White cliffs of Dover, The / Blaze away / Nairobi / Sleepytime down South / Savoy blues / Just a closer walk with thee / South / Mood indigo / Buona sera / Ain't misbehavin' / Aria / Beale Street blues / Stranger on the shore.
2LP: .... KAZ LP 10
MCSET: .... KAZ MC 10

I LIKE BEER (See under Bygraves, Max) (Bygraves, Max & Acker Bilk).

I'M IN THE MOOD FOR LOVE.
Tracks: / Stranger on the shore / Frenesi / I'm in the mood for love / La paloma / Petite fleur / Scarlet ribbons / Georgia on my mind / Taste of honey, A / Greensleeves / Non dimenticar / Nature boy / Perhaps, perhaps perhaps / Meravigliose labbra / Moon river.
LP: 9279 608
MC: 7259 608

IMAGES: ACKER BILK.
Tracks: / Petite fleur / Scarlet ribbons / La mer / Greensleeves / Moon river / Nature boy / Stranger on the shore.
MC: .... KNMC 16002

IMAGINE.
Tracks: / Mull of Kintyre / Norwegian wood / Sailing / Send in the clowns / Stranger on the shore / Yesterday / Windmills of your mind / You are the sunshine of my life / Aranjeuz mon amour / Aria / Ebony and ivory / Feelings / Fool on the hill / Imagine / Michelle / Missing you.
MC: .... PLS MC 511

INVITATION.
MC: .... ZCP 41054

IT LOOKS (Bilk, Acker & Ken Colyers Jazzmen).
LP: .... SOS 1119

JOHN, PAUL AND ACKER (Bilk, Acker, His Clarinet & Strings).
Tracks: / Norwegian wood / With a little luck / Imagine / Michelle / World without love / Mull of Kintyre / Fool on the hill / Ebony and ivory / Nowhere man / Yesterday / She's leaving home / Here, there and everywhere / Pipes of peace.
LP: .... N 6561
MC: .... ZCN 6561
LP: .... PYL 2
MC: .... PYM 2

LOVE ALBUM, THE.
Tracks: / When I fall in love / Groovy kind of love / Silvery nights / Could've been / My love / He ain't heavy he's my brother / Good times / One moment in time / Till I loved you / Candle in the wind / Tune for melody / Take my breath away / Love changes everything / Sweet crystal / Lady in red / Every time we say goodbye.
LP: .... SHM 3282
MC: .... HSC 3282

LOVE SONGS MY WAY.
Tracks: / Let it be me / First time ever I saw your face, The / Rose, The / My way / Hey Jude / Never my love / Ramblin' rose / We've only just begun / Morning has broken / I can't stop loving you / Stranger on the shore / (Eres Tu) touch the wind.
LP: .... TOP 160
MC: .... KTOP 160

MADE IN HUNGARY.
Tracks: / Victors theme / New summer / Needing someone / Berolina / From night to night / Mama please / Love is different / Summer song / Miracle / Heartbreak / Fly high / Fancy / How many evenings / Those were beautiful.
MC: .... ZCN 124
LP: .... N 124

MAMA TOLD ME SO (Bilk, Acker & His Paramount Jazz Band).
Tracks: / Mama told me so / Chips are down, The / Gee baby ain't I good to you / Time's a wastin' / Bloodshot eyes / Um / Liza / Someday you'll be sorry / Gospel truth.
LP: .... FBLP 8092
MC: .... ZCFBL 8092
MC: .... ZCN 128
LP: .... N 128

MOMENT I'M WITH YOU, THE.
Tracks: / Norwegian wood / Colours of my life / Bilitis / Little green apples / How does it feel / Imagine / Chi mai / Spanish harlem / First of spring, The / Moment I'm with you, The / Chariots of fire / Pechel canon / Missing you ain't easy / Love letters / For the good times / Soap.
LP: .... N 141
MC: .... ZCN 141
LP: .... PRT N141

MR. ACKER BILK COLLECTION.
LP: .... MA 3686
MC: .... MAMC 93686

ON STAGE.
Tracks: / Aria / Canio's tune / Pachelbel canon / You are the sunshine of my life / Miss you nights / First of spring, The / Evergreen / Aranjuel mon amour / Stranger on the shore / Chi mai / Spanish harlem / Up in the world / Cavatina / Without you / Chariots of fire / Don't cry for me Argentina.
LP: .... STOL 101
MC: .... STOC 101

ONE FOR ME, THE.
MC: .... ZCP 41052
LP: .... NSPX 41052

RELAXIN'.
Tracks: / Verde / One more time / Minuetto / Stay / Cavatina / I'm happy when I'm dancing with you / Volveras / On Sunday / Incredible Hulk, Theme from / Piccolino / Back to you / Summer never came / Aranjuez mon amour / Best out of me, The.
MC: .... ZCN 138
LP: .... N 138

SEVEN AGES OF ACKER.
LP: 33SX 1304

SHEER MAGIC.
LP: .... WW 5028

SOME OF MY FAVOURITE THINGS.
Tracks: / Stranger on the shore / What are you doing the rest of your life / Folks who live on the hill, The / Makin' Whoopee / Misty / Close to you / Raindrops keep falling on my head / This guy's in love with you / Sugar / What a wonderful world / Hundred years from today / Going home / Summer knows, The.
LP: .... NSPL 41022
MC: .... CDNSPL 4102

SPOTLIGHT ON ACKER BILK.
Tracks: / Verde / Universe / Incontro / Volveras / Canio's tune / Swan Lake, Theme from / Stranger on the shore / Bridge over troubled water / Fool on the hill / Close to you / Clair / Way we were, The / Aria sailing / Amazing grace / We're all alone / Fire and rain / Aranjuez mon amour / Cavatina / Where do I begin / Miss you nights / Don't cry for me Argentina / Song I wrote to you, The / I don't want to talk about it.
2LP: .... SPOT 1005
MC: .... ZCSPT 1005

SPOTLIGHT ON ACKER BILK VOL.2.
LP: .... SPOT 1024
MC: .... ZCSPT 1024

STRANGER ON THE SHORE.
Tracks: / When I need you / Amazing grace / Down in nempnett thrumbwell / If / Together we are beautiful / Stranger on the shore / Fool on the hill / Up in the world / First of spring, The / Norwegian wood / You are the sunshine of my life / On Sunday.
LP: .... FBLP 8099
MC: .... ZCFBL 8099
MC: 3192 615
LP: 2482 489
LP: 33SX 1407

TASTE OF HONEY, A.
LP: 33SX 1493

THREE B'S, THE.
LP: .... ESQ 333

TOGETHER (See under Bygraves, Max) (Bilk, Acker & Max Bygraves).

TWOGETHER (Bilk, Acker & Max Bygraves).
Tracks: / You say something nice about everybody / Who wants to be a millionaire / I like beer / Harmonize / Wait till the sun shines Nellie / Down by the old mill stream / Goodnight ladies / Civilization / Hometown / Movies / Crazy / Stranger on the shore / Guilty / Prisoner / Dreaming my dreams / Tonight you belong to me.
MC: .... ZCN 133
LP: .... N 133

UNISSUED ACKER.
Tracks: / Dauphine street blues / Corina Corina / Gloryland / Trouble in mind / Travelling blues / Salutation march / Monday date / King Joe / Lou-easy-an-i-a / Darkness on the delta / Careless love / Deep bayou blues.
LP: .... HQ 3004

VERY BEST OF ACKER BILK.
Tracks: / Stranger on the shore / Way we were, The / Feelings / Send in the clowns / You are the sunshine of my life / What a wonderful world / Aria / Windmills of your mind, The / This guy's in love with you / Folks who live on the hill, The / Wichita lineman / Bridge over troubled water.
LP: .... HMA 262
MC: .... HSCM 262

WERELDSUCCESSEN.
Tracks: / Stranger on the shore / Petite fleur / Summer set / White cliffs of Dover, The.
2LP: 6641 954
MC: 7599 449

Bill & Ted's Excellent

BILL AND TED'S EXCELLENT ADVENTURE (Film soundtrack) (Various artists).
Tracks: / Play with me: *Extreme* / Boys and girls are doing it: *Vital* / Not so far away: *Burtnick, Glenn*/ Dancing with a gypsy: *Tora Tora* / Father time: *Shark Island* / I can't breakaway: *Big Pig* / Dangerous: *Shark Island* / Walk away: *Bricklin* / In time: *Robb, Robbie* / Two heads are better than one: *Power Tools*.
LP: .... AMA 391
MC: .... AMC 391
MC: 3939154

Bill The Galactic Hero

BILL THE GALACTIC HERO (Various artists).
LP: .... REC 532
MC: .... ZCM 532

Billberg, Rolf

RARE DANISH RECORDINGS.
LP: .... SLP 419

Billion Dollar..(film)

BILLION DOLLAR BRAIN (Film soundtrack) (Various artists).
LP: .... MCA 25091
MC: .... MCAC 25091

Billy Barnes (show)

BILLY BARNES IN LA (Original cast recordings) (Various artists).
LP: .... AEI 1134

BILLY BARNES SINGS MOVIE STAR (Original cast recordings) (Various artists).
LP: .... AEI 1142

Billy & Blaze

BILLY AND BLAZE (C.W. Anderson) (Cassidy, David).
MC: 1737

Billy Boyo

BUSHMASTER CONNECTION (See under Little John).

JANET SINCLAIR (See under Little John) (Billy Boyo & Little John).

Billy Bunter..(bk)

BILLY BUNTER GETS THE BOOT (see under Richards, Frank (aut) (Biggins, Christopher (nar)).

Billy The Kid (film)

BILLY THE KID (Film soundtrack) (See under Dylan, Bob) (Dylan, Bob).

Bim Skala Bim

BOSTON BLUEBEAT.
LP: .... SKAR 002

TUBA CITY.
Tracks: / Gopher rodeo / Native / Fathead / Let me in / Sunshine of your love / Bangin' / Groucho go ska / Hung up / Vin's latin ska.
LP: .... SKAR 008

Binchy, Kate (nar)

DUBLIN 4 (see under Dublin 4 (bk)).

Binchy, Maeve (aut)

DUBLIN 4 (see under Dublin 4 (bk)) (Binchy, Kate (nar)).

Bingert, Hector

EL ENCUENTRO (Bingert, Hector & Don Menza).
LP: .... FLC 5064

JARDINS.
LP: .... SNTF 976

Biograph Girl (film)

BIOGRAPH GIRL (Film soundtrack) (Various artists).
LP: .... TER 1003
MC: .... ZCTER 1003

Biohazard

BIOHAZARD.
LP: 084650

Bionic Boogie

HOT BUTTERFLY.
Tracks: / Hot butterfly / Chains / Paradise / Cream / Fess up to the boogie.
LP: 239 137 3

Biota

RACKABONES.
2LP: .... DYS 12/13

TINCT.
LP: .... RRC 31

Bird, John

COLLECTED BROADCASTS OF IDI AMIN.
Tracks: / Gunboat dipperlomacy / Star gittin' born / Time check / Findin' de lady / Public announcement / Way to de stars / Costa Uganda / S.O.S. / Up for grabs / Amazin' man / Weather forecast / De collected works of Idi Amin.
LP: .... TRS 111
MC: .... KTRS 111

Bird Nest Roy

BIRD NEST ROY.
LP: .... FNE 19

Bird Songs

BIRD SONGS (CASSETTE BOX 1) (BBC/Swedish Radio Production) (Various).
MCSET: .... SRMK 5021/4

BIRD SONGS (CASSETTE BOX 2) (BBC/Swedish Radio Production) (Various).
MCSET: .... SRMK 5025/8

BIRD SONGS (CASSETTE BOX 3) (BBC/Swedish Radio Production) (Various).
MCSET: .... SRMK 5029/32

BIRD SONGS (CASSETTE BOX 4) (BBC/Swedish Radio Production) (Various).
MCSET: .... SRMK 5033/6

BIRD SONGS (VOL.1) (BBC/Swedish Radio Production) (Various birds).
LP: .... RFLP 5001

BIRD SONGS (VOL.2) (BBC/Swedish Radio Production) (Various birds).
LP: .... RFLP 5002

BIRD SONGS (VOL.3) (BBC/Swedish Radio Production) (Various birds).
LP: .... RFLP 5003

BIRD SONGS (VOL.4) (BBC/Swedish Radio Production) (Various birds).
LP: .... RFLP 5004

BIRD SONGS (VOL.5) (BBC/Swedish Radio Production) (Various birds).
LP: . . . . RFLP 5005

BIRD SONGS (VOL.6) (BBC/Swedish Radio Production) (Various birds).
LP: . . . . RFLP 5006

BIRD SONGS (VOL.7) (BBC/Swedish Radio Production) (Various birds).
LP: . . . . RFLP 5007

BIRD SONGS (VOL.8) (BBC/Swedish Radio Production) (Various birds).
LP: . . . . RFLP 5008

BIRD SONGS (VOL.9) (BBC/Swedish Radio Production) (Various birds).
LP: . . . . RFLP 5009

BIRD SONGS (VOL.10) (BBC/Swedish Radio Production) (Various birds).
LP: . . . . RFLP 5010

BIRD SONGS (VOL.11) (BBC/Swedish Radio Production) (Various birds).
LP: . . . . RFLP 5011

BIRD SONGS (VOL.12) (BBC/Swedish Radio Production) (Various birds).
LP: . . . . RFLP 5012

BIRD SONGS (VOL.13) (BBC/Swedish Radio Production) (Various birds).
LP: . . . . RFLP 5013

BIRD SONGS (VOL.14) (BBC/Swedish Radio Production) (Various birds).
LP: . . . . RFLP 5014

BIRD SONGS (VOL.15) (BBC/Swedish Radio Production) (Various birds).
LP: . . . . RFLP 5015

BIRD SPOT (British Wild Birds...).
Tracks: / Some large birds in the woods / Collared dove and owls / Woodpeckers, The / Swallow tribe and skylark, The / Farm crows / Some small birds of the woods / Thrushers of the woods and farms / Nightingale and warblers / Two hole nesters / Finch tribe.
LP: . . . . REC 438
MC: . . . . ZCM 438

BRITISH BIRD SONGS AND CALLS (Various birds).
MCSET: . . . . NSA C5/6

BRITISH WILD BIRDS IN STEREO (see under British Wild Birds...) (Various).

BRITISH WILD BIRDS IN STEREO (Various).
MC: . . . . RMC 4008
LP: . . . . REC 197

SOUND GUIDE TO BRITISH WADERS (Various).
LP: . . . . REC 545
MC: . . . . ZCM 545

YOUR FAVOURITE BIRD SONGS (Various birds).
LP: . . . . REC 511
MC: . . . . ZCM 511

Bird With The.. (film)

BIRD WITH THE CRYSTAL PLUMAGE (Film soundtrack) (Various artists).
LP: . . . . C'BUS 108

Birdcrash

BIRDCRASH (Various artists).
MC: . . . . KC 009

Birdhouse

BURNIN' UP.
LP: . . . . SOL 3

Birdland

BIRDLAND.
LP: . . . . LAZY 25
MC: . . . . LAZY 25C

Birdmen Of Alcatraz

FROM THE BIRDCAGE.
LP: . . . . CONTE 114

GLIDING OFF.
LP: . . . . EES 011

Birds

LONDON BOYS (See under London Boys) (Birds/Small Faces/David Bowie/ Dobie Gray).

THESE BIRDS ARE DANGEROUS.
LP: . . . . WEST 901

Birds, Beasts &

BIRDS, BEASTS & FLOWERS (Princess Grace of Monaco & Richard Pasco).
LP: . . . . NIMBUS 4112

Birdy (Film)

BIRDY (See under Gabriel, Peter) (Gabriel, Peter).

Birgitta & Swante

UP WHERE WE BELONG.
LP: . . . . WST 9685
MC: . . . . WC 9685

WHAT A DIFFERENCE.
Tracks: / We owe it all to you / What a difference you've made / Take my life / It wouldn't be joy / Mother prays, A / How many more / Jesus is here in my heart / Highest praise, The / My love song / Be exalted / Majesty.
LP: . . . . WST 9614
MC: . . . . WC 9614

Birkett, Stewart

STEWART BIRKETT PLAYS ORGAN AND DRUM.
LP: . . . . MTS 24

Birmingham Sessions

BIRMINGHAM SESSIONS, 1937 (Various artists).
LP: . . . . OT 1209

Birth Control

LIVE '79.
Tracks: / Titanic, The / Saturday special / Seems like it's confusion / Fight for you / Work is done.
LP: 0060 240

Birth Of A Nation

BIRTH OF A NATION, THE (Original soundtrack) (Various artists).
Tracks: / Bringing the African to America: *Various artists* / Abolitionists, The: *Various artists* / Austin Stoneman: *Various artists* / Elsie Stoneman: *Various artists* / Old Southland: *Various artists* / Boys at play: *Various artists* / Cottonfields: *Various artists* / Love strain: *Various artists* / Stoneman library: *Various artists* / Lydia Brown: *Various artists.*
2LP: . . . . LXDR 701-2

Birthday Concert

BIRTHDAY CONCERT FOR MY GRANDMOTHER, A (Various artists).
Tracks: / Albion polka: *Various artists* / Romanza for cello and small orchestra (David Matthews): *Various artists*/ Wagon (passes), The (Edward Elgar): *Various artists* / Suite for solo violin & chamber orchestra (Patrick Gowers): *Various* artists / Elizabeth of Glamis (Eric Coates): *Various artists* / Thistle and the rose, The (Patrick Doyle): *Various artists.*
LP: . . . . QM 90
MC: . . . . TCQM 90

Birthday Party

DRUNK ON THE POPE'S BLOOD (See under Lydia Lunch).

FIRST ALBUM, THE.
LP: . . . . LINK 7

IT'S STILL LIVING (LIVE).
LP: . . . . ING 009

JUNKYARD.
Tracks: / She's hit / Dead Joe / Dim locator / Hamlet pow pow pow / Several sins / Big Jesus trash can / Kiss me black / Six inch gold blade / Kewpie doll / Junkyard.
LP: . . . . CAD 207
MC: . . . . CADC 207
LP: . . . . LINK 21

Biscoe, Chris

LITTLE WESTBROOK MUSIC, A (see Westbrook, Kate & Mike) (Biscoe, Chris/ Kate & Mike Westbrook).

Biscuit, Karl

FATAL REVERIE.
LP: . . . . CRAM 043

REGRET ETERNELS.
LP: . . . . CRAM 035

Bishop, Debby

NO CHOIR OF ANGELS (see Amoo,Chris & Debby Bishop).

Bishop, Ed (aut)

BREAKHEART PASS (see under Breakheart Pass (bk)) (MacLean, Alistair (aut)).

Bishop, Elvin

BEST OF ELVIN BISHOP.
Tracks: / Travelin' shoes / Yes sir / Struttin' my stuff / Give it up / Fooled around and fell in love / Juke joint jump / Spend some time / Good times roll / Change is gonna come, A / Bring it on home / Love medley.
LP: 2429189

BIG FUN.
LP: . . . . AL 4767

DON'T LET THE BOSSMAN GET YOU DOWN.
Tracks: / Fannie Mae / Don't let the bossman get you down / Murder in the first degree / Kissing in the dark / My whiskey head buddies / Stepping up in class / You got to rock 'em / Come on in this house / Soul food / Rollin' with my blues / Devil's slide / Just your fool.
MC: . . . . AC 4791

HOMETOWN BOY MAKES GOOD.
Tracks: / Sugar dumplin' / Sidelines / Twist & shout / Yes sir / Spend some time / Give it up / Keep it cool / Graveyard blues / Once in a lifetime / D.C. strut.
LP: 2429 147

Bishop, Randy

UNDERDOG.
LP: . . . . AUL 730

Bishop, Stephen

BISH.
Tracks: / If I only had a brain / Losing myself in you / Looking for the right one / Everybody needs love / Fool at heart, A / What love can do / Vagabond from heaven / Bish's hideaway / Only the heart within you / Recognised / I've never known a nite like this / When I was in love.
LP: . . . . MCL 1846
MC: . . . . MCLC 1846
MC: . . . . CAB 5252
LP: . . . . ABCL 5252

BOWLING IN PARIS.
LP: . . . . K 781970 1
MC: . . . . K 781970 4

CARELESS.
Tracks: / Never letting go / Careless / Sinking in an ocean of tears / Madge / Every minute / Little Italy / One more night / Save it for a rainy day / Rock and roll slave / Same old tears on a new background, The / On and on.
LP: . . . . FA 3033
MC: . . . . TCFA 3033
LP: . . . . MCL 1616
MC: . . . . MCLC 1616
LP: . . . . ABCL 5201

RED CAB TO MANHATTAN.
Tracks: / Big house / Don't you worry / Thief in the night / Send a little love my way (like always) / Let her go / Little moon / Story of a boy in love, The / Living in the land of Abe Lincoln / Red cab to Manhattan / Sex kittens go to college / City girl / My clarinet.
LP: . . . . K 56853
MC: K4 56853

Bishop, Walter Jr.

CUBICLE.
Tracks: / My little suede shoes / Valley land / Those who chant / Summertime / Now, now that you've left me / Cubicle.
LP: . . . . MR 5151

HOT HOUSE.
Tracks: / Sophisticated lady / Dahoud / Time for love, A / Hot house / Move / My little suede shoes / Wave / All god's children.
LP: . . . . MR 5183

JUST IN TIME.
LP: . . . . IP 8605

MILESTONES.
LP: . . . . BLP 60109

SOUL VILLAGE.
Tracks: / Soul turnaround / Valerie / Sweet Rosa Rosa / Philadelphia bright / Coral keys / Soul village.
LP: . . . . MR 5142

SPEAK LOW.
Tracks: / Blues in the closet / Green Dolphin street / Alone together / Milestones / Speak low / Sometimes I'm happy.
LP: . . . . MR 5066

VALLEY LAND.
Tracks: / Sam's blues / You stepped out of a dream / Invitation / Lush life / Valley land / Killer Joe / Make someone happy.
LP: . . . . MR 5060

Bishops

CROSSCUTS.
Tracks: / I take what I want / Could you would you / What's your number / Your daddy don't mind / Good times / Too much too soon / Rolling man / I want candy / Somebody's gonna get their head kicked in ... / Hands on the wheel / Don't start me talkin' / These arms of mine / No lies / Mr. Jones.
LP: . . . . CWK 3009

Bisiker & Romanov

BISIKER AND ROMANOV.
Tracks: / Wey and Arun canal, The / Hungarian dance / When the wind blows / Kid on the mountain, The / Angus Campbell / Fox, The / Josika / Down the moor / Jarrow march / Czardas / Eve's end, The.
LP: . . . . FE 068
MC: . . . . FE 068C

Bisio, Michael

IN SEATTLE (Bisio, Michael Quartet).
LP: . . . . SHLP 107

Bit Of A Do (bk)

BIT OF A DO, A (John Rowe).
MCSET: . . . . ZBBC 1132

Bitch

BITCH IS BACK.
Tracks: / Do you wanna rock / Hot and heavy / Me and the boys / Storm raging up / Bitch is back, The / Head banger / Fist to face / Turns me on / Skullcrusher.
LP: . . . . RR 9627

Bitch Magnet

STAR BOOTY.
LP: . . . . GOESON 27
LP: . . . . EFA 08128

UMBER.
LP: . . . . GOES ON 35
LP: . . . . EFA 08129

Bitches Brue

WE MIGHT NOT BE AMERICAN BUT STILL WE FK.**
LP: . . . . HMRLP 131
MC: . . . . HMRMC 131

Bitches Sin

INVADERS.
LP: . . . . OTH 14

PREDATOR.
LP: . . . . HMRLP 4

Bite The Bullet

BITE THE BULLET.
Tracks: / Change of heart / Finished with love / Edge of the rain / Faith healing / Cold surprise / Running to stand still / Dark age / Playing at love / Big mountain / Sailor's song.
LP: 465089 1
MC: 465089 4

Biting Tongues

FEVERHOUSE (1985 Film Soundtrack).
LP: . . . . FACT 105

LIBREVILLE.
LP: . . . . VIRTUE 1

RECHARGE.
LP: . . . . CUT 90LP 2

Bitter Suite

BITTER SUITE (Various artists).
Tracks: / In the centre: *Various artists* / To prove my love: *Various artists* / Brazilian love affair: *Various* artists / Palos: *Various artists* / Just around the corner: *Various artists* / Mysteries of the world: *Various* artists / Together again: *Various artists* / First love: *Various artists* / New Killer Joe rap: *Various* artists / New Killer Joe: *Various artists* / Strawberry letter 23: *Various artists* / Family: *Various* artists / Odyssey: *Various artists* / You are the reason: *Various artists* / Sara smile: *Various artists*/ To touch you again: *Various artists* / Lady blue: *Various artists* / Kari: *Various artists* / All about love: *Various artists.*
2LP: . . . . CBS 22140

Bitter Sweet (film)

BITTER SWEET (Film soundtrack) (Various artists).
Tracks: / Opening: *Various artists* / That wonderful melody: *Various artists* / Call of life, The: *Various* artists / If you could only come with me: *Various artists* / I'll see you again: *Various artists* / Polka: *Various artists* / What is love?: *Various artists* / Last dance: *Various artists* / Finale: *Various* artists / Opening chorus (Life in the morning): *Various artists* / Ladies of the town: *Various artists* / If love were all: *Various artists* / Dear little cafe: *Various artists* / Bittersweet waltz: *Various artists*/ Officer's chorus (we wish to order wine): *Various artists* / Tokay: *Various artists* / Bonne nuit, merci: *Various* artists / Kiss me: *Various artists* / Ta-ra-ra-boom-de-ay: *Various artists* / Alas, the time is past: *Various* artists / We all wear a green carnation: *Various artists* / Zigeuner: *Various artists* / Finale: *Various artists.*
2LP: TER2 1160
MCSET: . . . . ZCTER 1160

Biz Markie

BIZ NEVER SLEEPS, THE.
LP: . . . . K 9260031
MC: . . . . K 9260034

GOIN' OFF.
Tracks: / Pickin' boogers / Albee square mile / Biz is goin' off / Return of the biz dance / Make the music with your mouth biz / Biz dance / This is something for the radio / Cool V's tribute to scratching / Nobody beats the biz.
LP: . . . . K 925675 1
MC: . . . . K 925675 4

Bizarre

BIZARRE.
Tracks: / Get up / Don't move / Hot Hollywood nights / You make my life so beautiful / Let me fill your world with love / Take the money and run.
LP: 2385553

Bizarre Beauties

BIZARRE BEAUTIES, THE (Various artists).
LP: . . . . FAB 13

Bizarre Inc.

TECHNOLOGICAL.
LP: . . . . BLUE TEC 1

Bizet (Composer)

BIZET: ORCHESTRAL WORKS 1 (Royal Philharmonic Orchestra).
LP: . . . . DCA 596
MC: . . . . ZC DCA 596

BIZET: ORCHESTRAL WORKS 2 (Royal Philharmonic Orchestra).
LP: . . . . DCA 620
MC: . . . . ZC DCA 620

BIZET: ORCHESTRAL WORKS 3 (Royal Philharmonic Orchestra).
Tracks: / Symphony in C (Bizet) / Roma suite (Bizet).
LP: . . . . DCA 696
MC: . . . . ZC DCA 696

CARMEN (OPERA) (Various artists).
LPS: 422 366-1
MCSET: 422 366-4

CARMEN (OPERA) (Various artists).
LP: 426 040-1
MC: 426 040-4

CARMEN & TOSCA HIGHLIGHTS (Various artists).
MC: 4277194

Bjerg, Svend

FJAND.
LP: . . . . SHD 3

Bjoerling, Jussi

FABULOUS RADIO PERFORMANCES (20th Anniversary tribute 1911-60).
LP: . . . . GL 8006

Bjorn J

ATLANTIS (see under Lindh, Son) (Bjorn J/Lindh, Son).

Bjornstad, Ketil

PRELUDE.
LP: . . . . U 025

BKA

CLEVER.
LP: . . . . FILER 405
MC: . . . . FILERCT 405

Black

BLACK.
LP: 3971261
MC: 3971264

COMEDY.
Tracks: / Big one, The / I can laugh about it now / Whatever people say you are / You're a big girl now / Let me watch you make love / Hey / I was right, you were wrong / All we need is the money / You don't always do what's best for you / Now you're gone / No-one done nothing / It's not over yet (Available on CD only) / Paradise lost (Additional track available on CD only.).
LP: . . . . AMA 5222
MC: . . . . AMC 5222

WONDERFUL LIFE (ALBUM).
Tracks: / Ravel in the rain / Sixteens (Only on CD.) / Leave yourself alone (Extra track available on CD only.) / It's not you Lady Jane (Available on CD only) / Hardly star crossed lovers / Wonderful life / Everything's coming up roses / Sometimes for the asking / Finder / Paradise / I'm not afraid / I just grew tired / Blue / Just making memories / Sweetest smile.
LP: . . . . AMA 5165
MC: . . . . AMC 5165

Black Ace

BLACK ACE AND HIS STEEL GUITAR.
LP: . . . . ARHOOLIE 1003

Black Alice

ENDANGERED SPECIES.
LP: . . . . STLP 004

Black, Andrea

ANDREA BLACK.
LP: . . . . GWLP 32
LP: . . . . AKR 32
MC: . . . . AKRC 32

Black Angels

KICK DOWN.
LP: . . . . GULP 1041

Black Bands

ON FILM 1928-1935.
LP: . . . . HQ 2038

Black Beauty (bk)

BLACK BEAUTY (Anna Sewell) (Black Beauty).
MC: . . . . CBB 1

BLACK BEAUTY (Anna Sewell) (Davis, David (nar)).
MC: . . . . P 90006

BLACK BEAUTY (Anna Sewell).
MC: . . . . PLBC 197

BLACK BEAUTY (Anna Sewell) (Black Beauty).
MCSET: . . . . DTO 10571

BLACK BEAUTY (Anna Sewell) (Rippon, Angela (nar)).
MCSET: . . . . SAY 10

BLACK BEAUTY (Anna Sewell) (Mills, Hayley).
MCSET: . . . . LFP 7162
MCSET: . . . . LFP 4171625

BLACK BEAUTY & OTHER FAVOURITE STORIES (Black Beauty).
MC: . . . . VCA 602

Black Belly Of..(film)

BLACK BELLY OF THE TARANTULA (Original soundtrack) (Various artists).
LP: . . . . C'BUS 116

Black, Bill (1)

FIRST YEAR, THE (see Presley, Elvis) (Black, Bill/Elvis Presley/Scotty Moore).

UNTOUCHABLE SOUND OF BILL BLACK'S COMBO.
Tracks: / White silver sands / Smokie part 2 / Movin' / Monkey-shine / Don't be cruel / Little Queenie / Josephine / Willie / Turn on your lovelight / Memphis, Tennessee / Hearts of stone / Twist-her / Honky train / Little Jasper / Do it-rat now / So what.
LP: . . . . HIUKLP 410

Black, Bill (2)

BACK WHERE I BELONG.
Tracks: / Back where I belong / Wild side of life / These are my mountains / Things / When you and I were young Maggie / Forty shades of green / Can't help falling in love / It hurts so much / Teddy bear / This world is not my home / Wooden heart / Glencoe.
MC: . . . . KABOO 1

COAST TO COAST (Black, Bill & His Scottish Dance Band).
MC: . . . . SPRC 1023

SHEPHERD'S CHOICE, THE (Black, Bill & His Scottish Dance Band).
Tracks: / Loch Ruan / Lady Mary Stopford / Sporty boys / Eilean Donan castle / Old St Paul's / Doctor Ross' 50th welcome to the Argyllshire gathering / Duke of Perth / Scholar, The / Kenneth MacDonald's jig / Chilliwack barn dance / Hills of Moffat / Dark Lochnagar.
LP: . . . . SPR 1008
MC: . . . . SPRC 1008

Black, Bobby

LADIES ON THE STEAMBOAT.
Tracks: / Ladies on the steamboat / Monroe's blues / Jerusalem ridge / Star of the county down / Staten Island hornpipe / Nervous breakdown / Limerock / Saratoga blues / Flight to DC / Over the waterfall / Flowers of Edinburgh / Little black moustache.
LP: . . . . RRR 0018

Black Bottom Stompers

BLACK BOTTOM STOMPERS.
Tracks: / Weatherbird rag / Shout 'em Aunt Tillie / Wild man blues / Cornet chop suey / Sidewalk blues / Garittin' with some barbeque / Hiawatha rag / Blue blood blues / Mahogany hall stomp / Where did you stay last night / Potato head blues / Alligator hop.
LP: . . . . SOS 1045
MC: . . . . VC 10

FOUR O'CLOCK BLUES.
LP: . . . . SOS 1130

Black Box

DREAMLAND.
Tracks: / Everybody everybody / I don't know anybody else / Open your eyes / Fantasy / Dreamland / Ride on time / Hold on / Ghost box / Strike it up.
LP: . . . . PL 74572
MC: . . . . PK 74572

Black Boy Shine

BLACK BOY SHINE 1936-37 (Various artists).
LP: . . . . BD 2039

Black Britain

OBVIOUS.
Tracks: / Night People / Obvious / Baby baby / Black Britain man / Funky Nassau / Ain't no rockin' (in a police state) / It's not material / Freetown boy / Real life / Runaway.
LP: . . . . DIX 30
MC: . . . . CDIX 30

Black Cat Bone

DELTA BLUES.
Tracks: / Treat me right / Ain't doing too bad / Reconsider baby / Hachch'n a maij, A / Larry is back / Just a fool / Delta blues.
LP: . . . . MMLP 99004

Black Cauldron (film)

BLACK CAULDRON (Film soundtrack) (Various artists).
LP: . . . . CST 8009
LP: . . . . REH 578
MC: . . . . ZCR 578
LP: . . . . STV 81253
MC: . . . . CTV 81253

Black, Cilla

25TH ANNIVERSARY ALBUM: CILLA BLACK.
Tracks: / Love of the loved / Every little bit hurts / One two three / Love letters / Ol' man river / It's for you / Sing a rainbow / This empty place / Anyone who had a heart / You'd be so nice to come home to / Baby it's you / I am a woman / In a woman's eyes / Step inside love / Suddenly you love me / Something's gotten hold of my heart / You're my world / Aquarius / Right one is left, The / Words / Work is a four letter word / Abyssinian secret / Time / World I wish for you, The / Something tells me (something's gonna happen) / Child of mine / He was a writer / I wanted to call it off / Alfie Darling / You you you / Easy in your company.
2LP: . . . . DL 1134
MC: . . . . TC-DL 1134

BEST OF CILLA BLACK.
LP: . . . . PCS 7065

BEST OF THE EMI YEARS: CILLA BLACK.
Tracks: / You're my world (Il mio mondo) / Anyone who had a heart / Love of the loved / It's for you / You've lost that lovin' feelin' / I've been wrong before / Goin' out of my head / Love's just a broken heart / Alfie / Fool am I, A (Dimmelo parlami) / Sing a rainbow / Don't answer me / When I fall in love / Yesterday / Make it easy on yourself / What good am I / I only live to love you / Step inside love / Where is tomorrow? / What the world needs now is love / Conversatikons / Surround yourself with sorrow / If I thought you'd ever change your mind / Something tells me (something's gonna happen tonight) / Liverpool lullaby / Baby we can't go wrong.
MC: . . . . TCEMS 1410

CILLA.
LP: . . . . PMC 1243

CILLA SINGS A RAINBOW.
LP: . . . . PMC 7004

SHER-OO.
LP: . . . . PCS 7041

SURPRISINGLY CILLA.
Tracks: / I know him so well / One more night / Step inside love / You're my world / Surprise surprise / There's a need in me.
LP: . . . . TOWLP 14
MC: . . . . ZCTOW 14

SWEET INSPIRATION.
LP: . . . . PCS 7103

VERY BEST OF CILLA BLACK.
Tracks: / Love of the loved / Anyone who had a heart / You're my world / It's for you / You've lost that lovin' feeling / I've been wrong before / Love's just a broken heart / Alfie / Don't answer me / Fool am I, A / What good am I / I only live to love you / Step inside love / Where is tomorrow / Surround yourself with sorrow / Conversations / If I thought you'd ever change your mind / Something tells me / Baby we can't go wrong / Liverpool lullaby.
LP: . . . . MFP 41 5653 1
MC: . . . . MFP 41 5653 4
LP: . . . . EMTV 38

YESTERDAY.
Tracks: / Yesterday / Shy of love / Just for you / Is it love? / I don't want to know / I've been wrong before / Night time is here / Baby I'm yours / When I fall in love / There I go / He won't ask me / Don't answer me / You've lost that loving feeling / Suffer now I must.
LP: C5-547

Black, Clint

KILLIN' TIME.
Tracks: / Straight from the factory / Nobody's home / You're gonna leave me again / Winding down / Live and learn / Better man, A / Walkin' away / I'll be gone / Killin' time.
MC: . . . . PK 90443
LP: . . . . PL 90443

PUT YOURSELF IN MY SHOES.
Tracks: / Put yourself in my shoes / Gulf of Mexico, The / One more payment / Where are you now / Old man, The / This nightlife / Loving blind / Heart like mine, A / Goodnight-loving, The.
LP: . . . . PL 90544
MC: . . . . PK 90544

Black Country...

BEST OF THE BLACK COUNTRY NIGHT OUT SHOW (Various artists).
LP: . . . . LJES 001
MC: . . . . KLJES 001

BLACK COUNTRY NIGHT OUT, VOL.1 (Various artists).
LP: . . . . BRO 120
MC: . . . . KBRO 120

BLACK COUNTRY NIGHT OUT, VOL.2 (Various artists).
LP: . . . . BRO 122
MC: . . . . KBRO 122

BLACK COUNTRY NIGHT OUT, VOL.3 (Various artists).
LP: . . . . BRO 132
MC: . . . . KBRO 132

Black Crowes

SHAKE YOUR MONEY MAKER.
Tracks: / Twice as hard / Jealous again / Sister luck / Could I've been so blind / Seeing things / Hard to handle / Thick 'n' thin / She talks to angels / Struttin' blues / Stare it cold.
LP: 842 515 1
MC: 842 515 4

Black Crucial

MR. SUNNY.
LP: . . . . J 006

Black Diamond

PLAY TED HEATH HITS (Big Bands Vol.2).
MC: . . . . BBM 146

Black, Dick

AYE ON THE ROAD (Black, Dick & His Band).
MC: . . . . ZCKBP 513

BY YON BONNIE BORDER BURN (Black, Dick & His Band).
MC: . . . . ZCKBP 508

COME SEQUENCE DANCING.
MC: . . . . ZCKBP 510

COME TO THE BARN DANCE.
LP: . . . . DB 2
MC: . . . . ZCKBP 512

DANCING TIME, MODERN SEQUENCE (Black, Dick & His Band).
MC: . . . . ZCKBP 514

KEEP ON DANCING (Black, Dick & His Dance Band).
MC: . . . . ZCKBP 506

LET'S DANCE (Black, Dick & His Dance Band).
MC: . . . . ZCKBP 507

MODERN SEQUENCE DANCING (Black, Dick & His Dance Band).
MC: . . . . ZCKBP 505

SCOTTISH DANCE TIME (Black, Dick & His Band).
MC: . . . . ZCKBP 509

SOUND OF THE LOTHIANS (Black, Dick & His Dance Band).
Tracks: / La-va / Tom burns polka / Blue violets / New high level / Scotland well / By yon bonnie border burn / Mormond braes / Fitba crazy / North lands, The / Old rustic bridge.
MC: . . . . ZCKBP 503

Black, Donald

DANCING HAZARDS.
Tracks: / Highland laddie / Glenlogie / Hornpipes / Slow air / 2/4 march and reels / Eppie morrie / Braemar poacher / Lady Mary Ann / Jigs / Slow air and reel / Two Scottishes.
LP: . . . . LILP 7008
MC: . . . . LIFC 7008

Black Dyke Mills Band

BEST OF THE BLACK DYKE MILLS BAND.
Tracks: / Joyeuse march / Drink to me only with thine eyes / La danza / Fantasy on British sea songs / British Grenadiers, The / All through the night / Best foot forward / Brilliant march / Concorde / Colonel Bogey / Blaydon races / Marching with Sousa / Greensleeves / Girl I left behind me, The.
LP: . . . . PL 5025
MC: . . . . PK 5025

BLACK DYKE IN DIGITAL.
Tracks: / Overture, Les Francs juges / Three Haworth impressions / Norwegian carnival / Czardas der geist des woiwoden / Shadow of your smile / Knight templar / Czardas no.1 / Goose fair from Nott'num Town.
LP: . . . . BBRD 1012
MC: . . . . BBTD 1012

BLACK DYKE KINGS OF BRASS.
Tracks: / Hungarian rhapsody no. 2 / Carnival of Venice / Scherzo from Borodin's symphony no.2 / Serenade /

Les millions d'arlequin / Finale from Richard Strauss' horn concerto no.1 / Le roi d'ys overture.
MC: . . . . BBT 1007
LP: . . . . BBR 1007

BLACK DYKE PLAYS LANGFORD.
Tracks: / Sinfonietta in three movements / Rhapsody for trombone / Prelude and fugue / Billy boy / Pavane / Waltzing Matilda / Irish washerwoman, The / Sullivan fantasy, A.
LP: . . . . LSA 3270
MC: . . . . MPK 253

BLACK DYKE PLAYS ROSSINI.
Tracks: / La scala di seta / Tancredi / William Tell / La cenerentola (Cinderella) / Barber of Seville / Largo al factotum / Tarantella Napolitana - La Danza.
LP: . . . . BBRD 1021
MC: . . . . BBTD 1021

BLACK DYKE PLAYS WINGS.
Tracks: / Mull of Kintyre / Band on the run / Love awake / Let 'em in / Big barn bed / With a little luck / London Town / Jet / My love / Listen to what the man said.
LP: . . . . BBR 1001
MC: . . . . BBT 1001

BLITZ.
Tracks: / Blitz / Pageantry / Journey into freedom / Tam O'Shanter's ride.
LP: . . . . BBRD 1014

BRASS TO THE FORE.
Tracks: / Joyeuse march / Daughter of the regiment / Tales of Hoffmann, The / Festival music - romance / Espana / Fantasy on British sea songs / Greensleeves / Two tunes for trumpet / North countrie fantasy.
LP: . . . . LSA 3088

CHAMPIONS, THE.
LP: . . . . GSGL 10410

CHRISTMAS FANTASY.
Tracks: / We wish you a merry Christmas / Christmas festival (overture) / Joy to the world / Deck the halls / God rest ye merry gentlemen / Good King Wenceslas / Hark the herald angels sing / Silent night / Jingle bells / O come, all ye faithful / Nativity carol / Farandole / Shepherd's farewell, The / Ring out wild bells.
LP: . . . . RS 1083
MC: . . . . PK 11748

COMPLETE CHAMPIONS.
Tracks: / Contest music / Royal parks / Salute to youth / Cloudcatcher fells.
LP: . . . . BBRD 1032

CONCERT SOUND OF THE BLACK DYKE MILLS BAND.
Tracks: / Die fiedermaus overture / Marche militaire / La danza / Plantagenets, The / Rule Britannia / Concorde / Second rhapsody on negro spirituals.
LP: . . . . LSA 3254

EUROPEAN BRASS.
Tracks: / Bartered bride, The / Thievish magpie, The / Russalka's song to the moon / Entry of the huntresses / Miniature overture / Siciliana and Giga / Rhapsody on sea shanties / Cloud / Pomp and circumstance march No. 1.
LP: . . . . PL 25117
MC: . . . . PK 25117

GREAT BRITISH TRADITION, THE.
Tracks: / Endeavour / West country fantasy / North country fantasy / Sir Roger De Coverley / Sally in our alley / On Ilkley Moor baht'at / Fifth of August / Lincolnshire poacher / Carnival of the animals suite / Carmen fantasy.
LP: . . . . BBRD 1024
MC: . . . . BBTD 1024

JAMES COOK - CIRCUMNAVIGATOR.
Tracks: / Bantock / Prometheus unbound / Variations for brass band / James Cook circumnavigator / New world fantasy.
LP: . . . . LSA 3213

LIFE DIVINE.
Tracks: / Labour and love / Kenilworth / Life divine / Three musketeers, The.
LP: . . . . BBRD 1030
MC: . . . . BBT 1030

LION AND THE EAGLE, THE.
Tracks: / Yeomen of the guard, The / Phil the fluter's ball / Land of my fathers / Fantasia on the dargason / Scottish lament, A / Will ye no come back again / Auld lang syne / Pomp and circumstance march No. 4 / Stars and stripes forever, The / Rhapsody on negro spirituals / Go down, Moses / Peter, go ring dem bells / Ev'ry time I feel de spirit / I'm a rollin' through an unfriendly world / Stephen Foster fantasy, A / Camptown races / My old Kentucky home / Beautiful dreamer / Jeanie with the light brown hair / Old folks at home, The / Oh Suzanna / Old black Joe / Strike up the band / Embraceable you / They can't take that away from me / Someone to watch over me / Oh lady be good / Rhapsody in blue / Man I love, The.
LP: . . . . PL 25089
MC: . . . . PK 25089

MARCHING TO THE BLACK DYKE MILLS BAND.
Tracks: / Under the double eagle / Coronation march / Brilliant march / Onward Christian soldiers / Torch of freedom / Spirit of pageantry / Best foot forward / New colonial, The / Pacemakers, The / Colonel Bogey / Marching with Sousa / Dambusters march.
LP: LFL1 5071

MORE OF THE WORLD'S MOST BEAUTIFUL MELODIES.
Tracks: / Your tiny hand is frozen / Celeste Aida / Skye boat song / Bruch and Mendelssohn violin concerto themes / Flower song / Holy city, The / I hear you calling me / Ave Maria.
LP: . . . . BBRD 1033
MC: . . . . BBTD 1033

OVERTURES.
Tracks: / Beautiful galathea / Merry wives of Windsor / Italian girl in Algiers / Light cavalry / Daughter of the regiment / Black domino / Oberon.
LP: . . . . BBRD 1036
MC: . . . . BBTD 1036

RUSSIAN FESTIVAL, A.
Tracks: / Festival overture / Vocalise / Gopak / Scheherazade love theme / Montagues and Capulets from "Romeo and Juliet" / Russian and Ludmilla overture / Nocturne / Khovantschina prelude / Little Russian, The.
LP: . . . . BBR 1011
MC: . . . . BBT 1011

THEMES FROM FILMS,TV & STAGE.
Tracks: / Last of the summer wine / Galloping home / Hustle, The / Country canter / Pink panther, Theme from / Washington behind closed doors / Star Wars (Luke Skywalker.) / Ben Kenobi / Princess Leia's theme / Rebel spaceship / Down the throne room / Alla marcia (From Karelia Suite) / Adagio (From Spartacus and Phrygia.) / Don't cry for me Argentina / Eagle has landed, The / Clayhanger / Good word / King and I, The / Getting to know you / I have dreamed / I whistle a happy tune / March of the Siamese children / Finale.
LP: . . . . PL 25220

TRADITIONALLY BRITISH.
Tracks: / Blaydon races / Drink to me only / British Grenadiers, The / Jerusalem / Charlie is my darling / My love is like a red red rose / Loch Lomond-comin' throu' the rye / Girl I left behind me, The / Minstrel boy / Gentle maiden, The / Ash grove, The / All through the night / Men of Harlech.
LP: . . . . NL 70130
MC: . . . . NK 70130
LP: . . . . LSA 3186

TRIPLE CHAMPIONS 1977.
Tracks: / Connotations for brass band / Diadem of gold / Vivat regina / Suite for brass band, Opus 75 / Harmonious variations on a theme of Handel.
LP: . . . . PL 25143
MC: . . . . PK 25143

TRIUMPHANT BRASS.
LP: . . . . GSGL 10489

VOLCANO.
Tracks: / Volcano / Symphonic music / John O'Gaunt / Introduction Elegy and Caprice / Connotations.
LP: . . . . BBR 1004
MC: . . . . BBT 1004

WORLD CHAMPION BRASS.
Tracks: / Prelude for an occasion / Allegro from bassoon concert / Pageantry / Suite for brass band / Ballet suite No 2 from Pineapple Poll / Cornet roundabout / Trio for cornets / Recitative and romance / Overture: Benvenuto Cellini.
LP: . . . . GSGL 10477

WORLD FAMOUS MARCHES.
Tracks: / Cossack / Punchinello / Australasian, The / North star, The / Irresistible / Black knight / Flying eagle / Gruss und thuringen / Auf heimatlicher erde / Nec aspera terrent / Jubelsturm / Unter kaisers fahnen / Jugendfruhling.
LP: . . . . PL 25165
MC: . . . . PK 25165

Black Dynamites

READY TO ROCK WITH THE BLACK DYNAMITES.
LP: . . . . REDITA 123

Black Eagle Jazz Band

AT SYMPHONY HALL.
LP: . . . . PH 1086
MC: . . . . PH 1086C

BLACK EAGLE JAZZ BAND 1981 (with Rudi Balliu & Butch Thompson) (Black Eagle Jazz Band/B.Thompson).
LP: . . . . SOS 1048

DON'T MONKEY WITH IT.
LP: . . . . SOS 1147

MOUNT GRETNA WEEKEND.
LP: . . . . SOS 1092

TIGHT LIKE THIS (Black Eagle Jazz Band/B.Thompson).
LP: . . . . SOS 1054

Black Earth

BLACK EARTH, THE.
Tracks: / Momma's boy / Prisoner of your love / If I said I was sorry / Cold in the silence / Every minute of the day / There'll never be another day / Colours / Lady friend / Dead man proud / Tonight.
LP: . . . . PTLS 1091
MC: . . . . PTLC 1091

FEELING, THE.
Tracks: / Never stop loving you / Too touch / You made my night / Madelaine / Too late / Next man / Marianne / How can I? / Feeling, The / Paradise / Going kind of crazy.
LP: . . . . PTLS 1103

Black Eyed Biddy

GUID NEIBOURS.
LP: . . . . BNK 1
MC: . . . . BNKC 1

Black Fairy Tales (bk)

BLACK FAIRY TALES (Terry Berger) (McNeil, Claudia (nar)).
MC: 1425

Black Family

BLACK FAMILY, THE.
Tracks: / Broom o'the Cowdenknowes / Colannon / Motorway song, The / Tomorrow is a long time / Donkey riding / Will ye gang, love / Bramble and the rose, The / Ploughboy lad, The / Warlike lads of Russia, The / Dark and roving eye / James Connolly / Wheel the perambulator.
LP: . . . . DARA 023
MC: . . . . DARAC 023

BLACK FAMILY'S FAVOURITES, THE.
LP: . . . . C 1002

TIME FOR TOUCHING HOME.
LP: . . . . DARA 035
MC: . . . . DARAC 035

Black Flag

FAMILY MAN.
LP: . . . . SST 026

FIRST FOUR YEARS, THE.
LP: . . . . SST 002
MC: . . . . SST 002 C
LP: . . . . SST 021

IN MY HEAD.
LP: . . . . SST 045

LIVE 84.
Tracks: / Process of weeding out / My ghetto / Jealous again / I love you / Swinging man / Three nights / Nothing left inside / Black coffee.
MC: . . . . SST 030

LOOSE NUT.
LP: . . . . SST 035

MY WAR.
LP: . . . . SST 023

SLIP IT IN.
LP: . . . . SST 029

WASTED...AGAIN.
Tracks: / Wasted / T.V. party / Six pack / I don't care / I've had it / Jealous again / Slip it in / Annihilate this week / Loose nut / Gimmie gimmie / Louie Louie / Drinking and driving.
LP: . . . . SST 166

Black Girls

HAPPY.
Tracks: / Happy / In the room / Cathedral / Car / Charleston / Talk / Letter / Fat / Thunder / I love you song, The / Tell you everything / Smart man / Mother.
LP: . . . . HNBL 1365
MC: . . . . HNBC 1365

PROCEDURE.
LP: . . . . HNBL 1348
MC: . . . . HNBC 1348

Black Hole (film)

BLACK HOLE (Film soundtrack) (Various artists).
LP: . . . . D 381
MC: . . . . D 25DC
LP: . . . . SHM 3017
MC: . . . . HSC 3017

Black, Ika

SPECIAL LOVE.
LP: . . . . KM 004
MC: . . . . KMC 004

Black Ivory

BLACK IVORY.
Tracks: / Big apple rock / Get down / Peace and harmony / Mainline / Rest inside my love / Hustlin' / You turned my whole world around.
LP: . . . . BDLP 4060

Black Lace

16 GREATEST HITS : BLACK LACE.
LP: . . . . LACELP 1
MC: . . . . LACEC 1

20 ALL TIME PARTY FAVOURITES.
Tracks: / Agadoo / Hands up / Atmosphere / D.I.S.C.O. / We danced we danced / Wig wam bam / I just called to say I love you / Viva Espana / I am the music man / Dancing in the street / Superman / Simon says / Birdie song, The / Brown girl in the ring / Soaking up the sun / Let's twist again / Sailing / Hokey cokey.
LP: . . . . BLPFLP 1
MC: . . . . BLPFMC 1

PARTY CRAZY.
LP: . . . . STAR 2288
MC: . . . . STAC 2288

PARTY PARTY.
Tracks: / Agadoo / Hands up / Ob la di ob la da / Birdie song, The / Locomotion, The / This ole house / Dancing party / Rock around the clock / Wig wham bam / Do the conga / Knock three times / Super man / Hi ho silver lining / Simon says / Bump, The / Fiddling / Let's twist again / Sailing / You'll never walk alone.
LP: . . . . STAR 2250
MC: . . . . STAC 2250

PARTY PARTY 2.
Tracks: / Y.M.C.A. - In the navy / Brown girl in the ring / Rivers of Babylon / Hooray hooray it's a holi holiday / D.I.S.C.O. / Ghostbusters / Come on Eileen / Let's dance / Leap up and down (wave your knickers in the air) / Y viva Espana / Hokey cokey / Atmosphere / Dancing in the street / Do wah diddy / Hippy hippy shake / Good golly Miss Molly / Twist and shout / Do you love me / Clapping song, The / I speaka da lingo / Can can (Medley.) / Knees up Mother Brown (Medley.).
LP: . . . . STAR 2266
MC: . . . . STAC 2266

Black Lace (USA)

GET IT WHILE IT'S HOT.
LP: . . . . SKULL 8380

UNLACED.
LP: . . . . SKULL 8348

Black Magic

BLACK MAGIC (Various artists).
2LP: . . . . PLD 8000

BLACK MAGIC (Various artists).
2LP: . . . . SMR 619
MCSET: . . . . SMC 619

Black, Mary

BY THE TIME IT GETS DARK.
Tracks: / By the time it gets dark / Schooldays over / Once in a very blue moon / Farewell farewell / Sparks might fly / Katy / Leaving the land / There is a time / Jamie / Leaboy's lassie / Trying to get the balance right.
LP: . . . . DARA 027
MC: . . . . DARAC 027

COLLECTED.
Tracks: / Mo Ghile Mear / Fare thee well my own / True love / Men of worth / She moved through the fair / Love's endless war / Both sides of the Tweed / My youngest son came / Home today / Isle of St. Helena / Don't explain / Everything that touches me.
LP: . . . . DARA 010
MC: . . . . DARAC 010

MARY BLACK.
Tracks: / Rose of Allendale / Loving you / Loving Hannah / My Donald / Crusader / Anachie Gordon / Home / God bless the child / Rare's hill.
LP: . . . . DARA 002
MC: . . . . DARAC 002

NO FRONTIERS.
LP: . . . . DARA 032
MC: . . . . DARAC 032

WITHOUT THE FANFARE.
Tracks: / There's a train that leaves tonight / State of heart / Night time / Crow on the cradle, The / Greatest dream / Water is wilde, The / Ellis island / Strange thing / Without the fanfare / As I leave behind Neidin / Diamond days / Going gone.
LP: . . . . DARA 016
MC: . . . . DARAC 016

Black Music

CAPITOL BLACK MUSIC 82 (see under Capitol (label) (Various artists).

CHARLY BLACK MUSIC SAMPLER (See under Charly (label)) (Various artists).

Black Music in Britain

BLACK MUSIC IN BRITAIN 1 (The early fifties - Port of Spain shuffle) (Various artists).
Tracks: / Underground train: *Kitchener, Lord* / Dollar and the pound, The: *Beginner, Lord* / General election: *Beginner, Lord* / Iere: *Blake, Cyril Calypso Band* / Man smart (woman smarter): *Blake, Cyril Calypso Band*/ Federation: *Beginner, Lord* / Port of Spain shuffle: *Calypso Rhythm Kings* / Ugly woman: *Lion, The*/ Tick' tick' (the story of the lost watch): *Lion, The* / King Porter stomp: *Lyttelton, Grant Paseo Jazz Band*/ Fat Tuesday: *Lyttelton, Grant Paseo Jazz Band* / Daddy gone: *Rogers, Bill* / London blues: *Lyttelton, Grant* Paseo Jazz Band / Sightseeing in the UK: *Rogers, Bill* / Mam'selle Josephine: *Lyttelton, Grant Paseo Jazz Band*(Trad. arr, Grant Lyttelton/Preston) / Linstead Market: *Johnson, Tony*.
LP: . . . . NC 005

BLACK MUSIC IN BRITAIN 2 (The early fifties - Caribbean Connections) (Various artists).
Tracks: / Nora: *Kitchener, Lord* / I will die a bachelor: *Beginner, Lord* / Rum more rum: *Beginner, Lord*/ Breakaway: *Calypso Rhythm Kings* / Mary Ann: *Lion, The* / Weed woman: *Rogers, Bill* / Calypso be: *Young Tiger* / Mattie rag: *Jackson, Tony* / Massa Johnnie: *Verona, Lili* (Trad. arr. Samuel.) / Fire fire: *Keane, Shake* (Trad. arr. S. Keane.) / Trinidad land of calypso: *Lipton, Celia* / Trouble in Arima: *Trinidad All Stars* Steel Band / Trinidad: *Browne, George* / Mikes Tangana: *Lyttelton, Grant Paseo Jazz Band* / Baionga: *Keane, Shake Highlifers* / Kalenda march: *Lion, The*.
LP: . . . . NC 006

Black Oak Arkansas

10 YEAR OVERNIGHT SUCCESS.
Tracks: / When the band was singin' 'shakin' all over' / Pretty, pretty / Can't blame it on me / Television indecision / Back it up / Bad boy's back in school / Love comes easy / You can't keep a good man down / Fireball.
LP: . . . . MCF 2784

BLACK ATTACK IS BACK (Black Oak Arkansas/Jim Dandy).
LP: . . . . HMUSA 63
MC: . . . . HMAMC 63

Black Orpheus (film)

BLACK ORPHEUS (ORFEU NEGRO) (Original soundtrack) (Various artists).
LP: 8124 731
MC: 8124 734

Black Out

BLACK OUT (Various artists).
LP: . . . . REVLP 166
MC: . . . . REVMC 166

Black, Pablove

CHARCOAL CHARLIE.
LP: . . . . TWLP 1015

Black, Peter

CHAMELEON.
LP: . . . . PBCLP 001
MC: . . . . ZCPBC 001

Black Radical Mk II

UNDILUTED TRUTH, THE.
MC: . . . . MCT 1070
LP: . . . . MLPS 1070

Black Rain (film)

BLACK RAIN (Film soundtrack) (Various artists).
LP: . . . . V 2607
MC: . . . . TCV 2607
MC: . . . . OVEDC 363
LP: . . . . OVED 363

Black Religious...

BLACK RELIGIOUS SINGERS 1927-42 (Various artists).
LP: . . . . HK 4008

Black Riders

CHOSEN FEW.
LP: . . . . GILP 555

Black Rock Coalition

HISTORY OF OUR FUTURE.
Tracks: / Son talking (intro) / H.O.P.E / Make it my world / Bluestime in America / Tough times / MLK... Check / It will all / Think twice / Didn't live long / Hustler man / Son talkin' / Dadahdoodahda / Royal pain / Good guys, The / Michael Hill's Bluesband / Jupiter / Blue print / JJ jumpers / Blackasaurus mex / PBR Streetgang / Shock counsel.
MC: . . . . RACS 0211

Black Rock & Ron

STOP THE WORLD.
LP: . . . . SU 5
MC: . . . . ZCSU 5

Black Roots

ALL DAY ALL NIGHT.
Tracks: / Realize / Pin in the ocean / Release the food / Freedom / Poor children / Spare the rod / Conman / Seeing your face / All day all night / Suffer me not / Mighty lion / Childless mother.
LP: . . . . NRLP 01
MC: . . . . NRTC 01

BLACK ROOTS.
LP: . . . . KIK 002
LP: . . . . REC 554
MC: . . . . ZCM 554

FRONT LINE (T.V. soundtrack).
LP: . . . . REC 555
MC: . . . . ZCM 555
LP: . . . . KICLP 06

IN SESSION.
Tracks: / Confusion / Survival / Juvenile delinquent / What them a do / Move on / Opportunity / Tribal war / Africa / Father, The / Chanting for freedom.
LP: . . . . REC 570
MC: . . . . ZCM 570

LIVE POWER.
LP: . . . . NRLP 02

NATURAL REACTION.
LP: . . . . NRLP 6
MC: . . . . NRCT 6

Black Rose

BOYS WILL BE BOYS (LP).
LP: . . . . BULP 3

WALK IT HOW YOU TALK IT.
Tracks: / California USA / Ezly / Don't fall in love / Bright lights burnin' / Walk it how you talk it / Shout it out / I honestly love you / Part animal / Want you love.
LP: . . . . NEAT 1034
MC: . . . . NEATC 1034

Black Russian

BLACK RUSSIAN.
Tracks: / Move together / 'Cause I love you / Love's enough / Leave me now / Mystified / New York City / Life is too short / Emptiness.
LP: . . . . STML 12142

Black Sabbath

BACKTRACKIN'.
Tracks: / Paranoid / Iron man / Black Sabbath / Killing yourself to live / Snowblind / Sweet leaf / Into the void / Electric funeral / Sabbra cadabra / St. Vitus dance / Fairies wear boots / Superstarz / Children of the grave / Sabbath bloody Sabbath / Nib / Symptom of the universe / Planet caravan / War pigs / Rat salad / Am I going insane (radio) / Megalomania / Wizard, The / Cornucopia / Hole in the sky.
2LP: . . . . TRKLP 103
MCSET: . . . . TRKMC 103

BEST OF BLACK SABBATH.
LP: . . . . STAR 301

BLACK SABBATH.
Tracks: / Black Sabbath / Wizard, The / Behind the walls of sleep / N.I.B. / Evil woman / Sleeping village / Warning.
LP: . . . . NEL 6002
MC: . . . . NELMC 6002
LP: . . . . VO 6
LP: . . . . CLALP 196
MC: . . . . CLAMC 196

BLACK SABBATH 1970-1987.
LP: 831 188-1

BLACK SABBATH: INTERVIEW PICTURE DISC.
LPPD: . . . . BAK 2075

BLACK SABBATH VOL 4.
Tracks: / Wheels of confusion / Tomorrow's dream / Changes / FX / Supernaut / Snowblind / Cornucopia / Laguna sunrise / St. Vitas dance / Under the sun.
LP: . . . . NEL 6005
MC: . . . . NELMC 6005
LP: 6360 071
LP: . . . . CLALP 199
MC: . . . . CLAMC 199

BLACKEST SABBATH.
Tracks: / Black Sabbath / Paranoid / Iron man / Snowblind / Sabbath bloody Sabbath / Hole in the sky / Rock'n'roll doctor / Never say die / Lady evil / Turn up the night / Sign of the southern cross, The / Heaven and hell (live) / Children of the sea / Digital bitch / Seventh star / Born to lose.
2LP: 838 818 1
MC: 838 818 4

BORN AGAIN.
Tracks: / Trashed / Stonehenge / Disturbing the priest / Park / Hot line / Zero the hero / Digital bitch / Born again / Keep it warm.
LP: . . . . VERL 8

COLLECTION: BLACK SABBATH.
Tracks: / Paranoid / Behind the walls of sleep / Sleeping village / Warning / Warpigs / Hand of doom / Planet caravan / Electric funeral / Rat salad / Iron man / After forever / Supernaut / St.Vitas dance / Wheels of confusion / Snowblind / Killing yourself to live / Sabbra cadabra / Writ, The.
2LP: . . . . CCSLP 109
MC: . . . . CCSMC 109

ETERNAL IDOL, THE.
Tracks: / Shining / Ancient warrior / Hard life to love / Flory ride / Born to lose / Scarlet Pimpernel / Lost forever / Eternal idol.
LP: . . . . VERH 51
MC: . . . . VERHC 51

GREATEST HITS: BLACK SABBATH.
Tracks: / Paranoid / Changes / Sabbath bloody Sabbath / Iron man / Black Sabbath / War pigs / Laguna sunrise / Tomorrow's dream / Sweet leaf / N.I.B..
LP: . . . . NEL 6009
MC: . . . . NELMC 6009
LP: . . . . CLALP 200
MC: . . . . CLAMC 200

HEADLESS CROSS (ALBUM).
Tracks: / Gates of hell / Headless cross / Devil and daughter / When death calls / Kill in the spirit world / Call of the wild / Black moon / Nightwing.
LP: . . . . EIRSA 1002
MC: . . . . EIRSAC 1002

HEAVEN AND HELL.
Tracks: / Neon knights / Children of the sea / Lady evil / Heaven and hell / Wishing well / Die young / Walk away / Lonely is the world / Tomorrow's dream.
LP: . . . . PRICE 10
MC: . . . . PRIMC 10
LP: 9102 752

LIVE AT LAST.
Tracks: / Tomorrow's dreams / Sweet leaf / Killing yourself to live / Cornucopia / War pigs / Laguna sunrise / Paranoid / Wicked world.
MC: . . . . NELMC 001
LP: . . . . NEL 001
LP: 832 704 1
LP: . . . . BS 001
MC: . . . . BSMC 001
LP: . . . . CLALP 203
MC: . . . . CLAMC 203

LIVE EVIL.
Tracks: / E 5 150 / Neon knights / N.I.B. / Children of the sea / Voodoo / Black Sabbath / War pigs / Iron man / Mob rules / Heaven and hell / Sign of southern cross / Paranoid / Children of the grave / Fluff.
2LP: . . . . PRID 11
MCSET: . . . . PRIDC 11
2LP: . . . . SAB 10

MASTER OF REALITY.
Tracks: / Sweet leaf / After forever / Embryo / Children of the grave / Lord of this world / Solitude / Into the void / Orchid.
LP: . . . . NEL 6004
LP: 6360 050
LP: 832 707 1
MC: 832 707 2
MC: . . . . NELMC 6004
LP: . . . . CLALP 198
MC: . . . . CLAMC 198

MOB RULES.
Tracks: / Turn up the night / Voodoo / Sign of the Southern Cross / E 5150 / Mob rules / Country girl / Slippin' away / Falling off the edge of the world / Over and over.
LP: . . . . PRICE 77
MC: . . . . PRIMC 77
LP: 6302 119

NEVER SAY DIE (Live in concert).
Tracks: / Black Sabbath / Dirty women / Rock and roll doctor / Electric funeral / Children of the grave / Paranoid / Snowblind / Never say die / Johnny Blade / Junior eyes / Hard road / Shockwaves / Air dance / Over to you / Breakout / Swinging the chain.
LP: . . . . PRICE 9
MC: . . . . PRIMC 9
LP: 9102 750

OZZY OSBOURNE YEARS.
Tracks: / Black Sabbath / Wizard, The / Behind the wall of sleep / N.I.B. / Evil woman / Sleeping woman / Warning / War pigs / Paranoid / Planet Caravan / Iron man / Hand of doom / Fairies wear boots / Electric funeral / Sweet leaf / After forever / Embryo / Lord of the world / Solitude / Into this void / Wheels of confusion / Tomorrow's dream / Changes / Supernaut / Snowblind / Cornucopia / St. Vitus dance / Under the sun / Sabbath bloody Sabbath / National acrobat, A / Sabbra cadabra / Killing yourself to live / Who are you / Looking for today / Spiral architect / Hole in the sky / Symptom of the universe / Am I going insane (radio) / Thrill of it all / Meglomania / Writ, The.
LPS: . . . . ESBLP 142

PARANOID.
Tracks: / War pigs / Planet caravan / Iron man / Electric funeral / Hand of doom / Rat salad / Fairies wear boots / Wicked world / Paranoid.
LP: . . . . NEL 6003
MC: . . . . NELMC 6003
LP: 6360 011
LP: 832 7011
MC: 832 7012
LP: . . . . CLALP 197
MC: . . . . CLAMC 197

PRESENTATION BOX SET.
LPS: . . . . BS 01BOX

SABBATH BLOODY SABBATH.
Tracks: / Sabbath bloody sabbath / National acrobat, A / Fluff / Sabbra Cadabra / Killing yourself to live / Who are you / Looking for today / Spiral architect.
LP: . . . . NEL 6017
MC: . . . . NELMC 6017
LP: . . . . WWA 005
LP: 832 700 1
MC: 832 700 2
LP: . . . . CLALP 201
MC: . . . . CLAMC 201

SABBATH BLOODY SABBATH/ BLACK SABBATH.
Tracks: / Sabbath bloody sabbath / National acrobat, A / Fluff / Sabbra cadabra / Killing yourself to live / Who are you / Looking for today / Spiral architect / Black Sabbath / Wizard, The / Behind the walls of sleep / N.I.B. / Evil woman / Sleeping village / Warning.
MC: . . . . TFOMC 10
2LP: . . . . TFOLP 10

SABOTAGE.
Tracks: / Hole in the sky / Don't start (too late) / Symptom of the universe / Megalomania / Thrill of it all / Superzar / Am I going insane / Writ, The.
LP: . . . . NEL 6018
MC: . . . . NELMC 6018
LP: 9119 001
LP: 832 706 1
MC: 832 706 2
LP: . . . . CLALP 202
MC: . . . . CLAMC 202

SEVENTH STAR.
Tracks: / In for the kill / No stranger to love / Turn to stone / Sphinx (The guardian) / Seventh star / Danger zone / Heart like a wheel / Angry heart / I memory....
LP: . . . . VERH 29
MC: . . . . VERHC 29

TECHNICAL ECSTASY.
Tracks: / All moving parts / Backstreet kids / Dirty woman / Gypsy / It's alright / Rock and roll doctor / She's gone / You won't change me.
LP: . . . . PRICE 40
MC: . . . . PRIMC 40

TYR.
LP: . . . . EIRSA 1038
MC: . . . . EIRSAC 1038

WE SOLD OUR SOUL FOR ROCK'N'ROLL.
Tracks: / Black Sabbath / Wizard, The / Warning / Paranoid / Wicked world / Tomorrow's dream / Fairies wear boots / Changes / Sweat leaf / Children of the grave / Sabbath bloody sabbath / Am I going insane (radio) / Laguna sunrise / Snowblind.
2LP: . . . . RAWLP 017
MC: . . . . RAWTC 017
2LP: . . . . NELD 101
2LP: 6641 335
2LP: . . . . CCSLP 249
MC: . . . . CCSMC 249

Black Scorpio

BLACK SCORPIO ALL STARS VOL 2.
LP: . . . . BSCLP 07

Black Sea

AN EARLY FALL.
LP: . . . . KAR 004

Black Sheep

BLACK SHEEP.
LP: . . . . MACH 2

WOLF IN SHEEPS CLOTHING, A.
LP: 8483681
MC: 8483684

Black Shepherd

IMMORTAL AGRESSION.
Tracks: / Immortal agression / State of decay / Make love war / Corbes / Preacher of death / Trash / Another day to die / Kill the priest / Animal / Lord of darkness / I'm god / Evil revenge.
LP: . . . . PETC 12

Black Slate

AMIGO (LP).
Tracks: / Amigo / Mind your notion / Reggae music / Sticks man 80 / Freedom time / Boom boom / Losing game / Romans / Thin line between love and hate / Legalise collie herb.
LP: . . . . **ENVY 15**

BLACK SLATE.
LP: . . . . **FEDL 100**
MCSET: . . . . **CFEDL 100**

SIRENS IN THE CITY.
Tracks: / Sirens in the city / Live a life / I love you still / Reggae everytime / Message to Mr Sus Man / Dread in the house / Winners / Rocker's palace / Zion.
LP: . . . . **ENVY 505**
MC: . . . . **ENCAS 505**

SIX PLUS ONE.
LP: . . . . **TRY IT 1**

Black Sorrows

HARLEY AND ROSE.
Tracks: / Harley and Rose / Never let me go / Love goes wild / Hold it up to the mirror / Angel Street / Soul on fire / Carried by the light / House of light / Tears for the bride / Cannonball Cafe.
LP: **4673521**
MC: **4673524**

HOLD ON TO ME (ALBUM).
Tracks: / Chosen ones, The / Crack up, The / Chained to the wheel / In the hands of the enemy / Raise that lantern / Hold on to me / Glorybound / Fire down below / Sleep through the hurricane / Story never changes, The / One driver / Before the shooting starts (Only on cassette.) / Kiss the motherlode (Only on cassette.) / Safe in the arms of love (Only on cassette.) / Waiting for the rain (Only on cassette.) / Mercenary heart (Only on cassette.).
LP: **4628911**
MC: **4628914**

Black Stalin

MOVING UP.
LP: . . . . **BSRBA 085**

Black Stallion (film)

BLACK STALLION (Film soundtrack) (Various artists).
LP: . . . . **UAG 30306**
LP: . . . . **LT 10279**
MC: **L4T 10279**

Black, Stanley

DIGITAL MAGIC (Black, Stanley and His Orchestra).
Tracks: / Chiquitita / California suite / Bilitis / Tomorrow / Just when I needed you most / I will survive / Here's that rainy day / Way we were, The / Cavatina.
LP: . . . . **TXDS 501**

EPIC, THE (London Festival Orchestra and Chorus).
Tracks: / Exodus: Ari's theme / Lawrence of Arabia / Cleopatra / Magnificent Seven, The / Alamo, The / Doctor Zhivago:Lara's theme / Stagecoach / For whom the bell tolls / Patton / Sea hawk / Doctor Zhivago:Revolution.
MC: **4178454**

GREAT LOVE STORIES (Black, Stanley & LSO).
Tracks: / Casablanca / Man and a Woman, A / Intermezzo / Blood and sand / La strada / Love Story / Gone with the wind.
MC: **4178504**

ITV THEMES (Black, Stanley & LSO).
Tracks: / Upstairs downstairs / Black Beauty / Hill Street blues / L.A. law / Minder / Professionals, The.
LP: . . . . **SHM 3247**
MC: . . . . **HSC 3247**

SPAIN (Black, Stanley and His Orchestra).
Tracks: / Valencia / Ay ay ay / Malaguena / Bulerias / Ritual fire dance / Granada / Estrelita / Macarenas / Sevillanas / Carmen fantasy.
LP: . . . . **DGS 11**

S'WONDERFUL.
Tracks: / Memories are made of this / Holiday for strings / Blue tango / April in Portugal / S'wonderful / Poor people of Paris / Summer place, A (Theme from) / Limelight / Malaguena / Brazil / Hand in hand / Breeze and I / Girl from Ipanema, The / Granada / That old devil moon / Melodie d'amour / Soon / But not for me / On the street where you live / La cumparsita.
LP: . . . . **PLE 527**
MC: . . . . **TCPLE 527**

Black Star

NYOTA (Black Star & Lucky Star Musical Clubs).
Tracks: / Amana / Mpende anaekupenda / Nimekuja pasi haya / Chozi lanitoka / Hisani nakuusiya / Enyi wanadamu / Nazi / Duniani / Mnazi mkinda / Nini dawa ya mahaba / Bunduki / Rehema.
LP: . . . . **ORB 044**

Black State Choir

HARDSHELL PREACHER.
LP: . . . . **SCAM 002**
MC: . . . . **SCAM 002C**

Black Steel

JUNGLE WARRIOR.
Tracks: / Defending your roots / Garden of Eden / Celestrial rock / Jungle spirit / Roots and culture rise again / Flame of light / Tribute to Peter Tosh / Defending your dub / Garden of dub / Celestial dub / Jungle (dub) / Roots and dub / Flame of dub / Peter's dub.
LP: . . . . **ARILP 041**

Black Sun Ensemble

BLACK SUN ENSEMBLE.
Tracks: / Sapphire sky symphony / Dove of the desert / Hurricane Isis / Bleeding heart / Golden rays / X Y Z / Clear yellow days / Raga del sol / Dove of the desert (2) / Bleeding heart 2.
LP: . . . . **RECK 6**

LAMBENT FLAME.
LP: . . . . **RECK 11**
MC: . . . . **TCRECK 11**

TRAGIC MAGIC.
LP: . . . . **AGO 1994**
MC: . . . . **AGO 1994MC**

Black Swing Tradition

BLACK SWING TRADITION (Various artists).
LP: . . . . **SJL 2246**

Black Symbol

BLACK SYMBOL PRESENTS HANSWORTH EXPLOSION VOL 2.
LP: . . . . **BS 007**

Black Task

LONG AFTER MIDNIGHT.
LP: . . . . **AXE 7025**

Black UA Singles

FROM MOTOR CITY TO CENTRAL PARK (Various artists).
Tracks: / Tell him: *Exciters* / Cry baby: *Mimms, Garnet/Enchanters* / I love the way you love: *Johnson, Marv*/ Bells, The: *Marcels* / Who's that lady: *Isley Brothers* / You're so fine: *Falcons* / Everybody's going: *Holland, Eddie* / You got what it takes: *Johnson, Marv* / Love potion No.9: *Clovers* / Masquerade is over, The (I'm afraid): *Pinkney, Bill & The Originals* / Wonder of it all, The: *Little Anthony & The Imperials* / I'll take good care of you: *Mimms, Garnet* / Till the end: *Five Satins* / Come to me: *Johnson, Marv.*
LP: . . . . **SSL 6031**
MC: . . . . **TCSSL 6031**

Black Uhuru

ANTHEM.
Tracks: / What is life / Party next door / Try it / Black Uhuru anthem / Botanical roots / Somebody's watching you / Bull in the pen / Elements.
LP: . . . . **ILPS 0773**

BAD GIRL.
LP: . . . . **WAR 140**

BLACK SOUNDS OF FREEDOM.
Tracks: / I love King Selassie / Satan Army Band / Time to unite / Natural mystic / Edan out deh / Love crisis / African love / Hard ground / Willow tree / Sorry for the man.
LP: . . . . **GREL 23**
MC: . . . . **GREEN 23**

BLACK UHURU.
Tracks: / Shine eye girl / Leaving to Zion / General penitentiary / Guess who's coming to dinner / Abortion / Natural reggae beat / Plastic smile.
LP: . . . . **VX 1004**
MC: . . . . **TCVX 1004**

BRUTAL.
Tracks: / Let us pray / Dread in the mountain / Brutal / City vibes / Great train robbery / Uptown girl / Vision / Reggae with you / Conviction or fine / Fit you haffe fit.
LP: . . . . **RAS 3015**
MC: . . . . **RASC 3015**

BRUTAL DUB.
Tracks: / Let us dub / Dub in the mountain / Brutalize me with dub / City dub / Dub you haffe dub / Robbery dub / Uptown dub / Visions of dub / Dub it with you / Conviction or a dub.
LP: . . . . **RAS 3020**
MC: . . . . **RASC 3020**

CHILL OUT.
Tracks: / Darkness / Youths of Eglington.
LP: . . . . **ILPS 9701**
MC: . . . . **ICT 9701**

DUB EXTRAVAGANZA, A (Black Uhuru & Johnny Osbourne).
Tracks: / Mystic mix / His imperial majesty / Weeping willow / Bad girls dub / Tonight is the night / Firehouse special / African culture / Crisis dub / Dancing dub / Soundman style / Loving tonight / Jah is with you / Pumping dub / Double trouble / See no evil / Pure is the soul / Rise up / Reggae stylee / Eden dub.
MCSET: . . . . **ZCSAP 100**
2LP: . . . . **CSAP 100**

DUB FACTOR, THE.
LP: . . . . **MLPS 9756**
MC: . . . . **RRCT 28**

ELEMENTS.
LP: . . . . **ILPS 9773**

GUESS WHO'S COMING TO DINNER.
LP: . . . . **HB 18**
MC: . . . . **HBC 18**

LIVE IN NEW YORK.
MC: . . . . **RBUC 88000**
LP: . . . . **RBU 88000**

NOW.
MC: . . . . **R 479021**

POSITIVE.
Tracks: / Positive / Dry weather house / I create / Concept / Cowboy town / Fire city / Space within my heart / Pain.
LP: . . . . **RAS 3025**
MC: . . . . **RASC 3025**

POSITIVE DUB.
Tracks: / Cowboy town / Firecity / Positive / My concept / Space within my heart / Dry weather house / Pain / Create.
MC: . . . . **RASC 4025**
MC: . . . . **A 159**
LP: . . . . **RAS 4025**

RED.
Tracks: / Youth of Eglington / Sponji reggae / Sistren / Journey / Utterance / Puff she puff / Rockstone / Carbine.
LP: . . . . **ILPS 9625**
MC: . . . . **RRCT 18**

REGGAE GREATS.
Tracks: / Happiness / World in Africa / Sponji reggae / Youth of Eglington / Darkness / What is life? / Bull in the pen / Elements / Push push / Right stuff, The.
LP: . . . . **IRG 13**
MC: . . . . **IRGC 13**
MC: . . . . **ICM 2014**
MC: **824 694 4**

SINSEMILLA.
Tracks: / Happiness / World is Africa / Push push / There is fire / No loafing / Sinsemilla / Every dreadlocks / Vampire.
LP: . . . . **ILPS 9593**
MC: . . . . **ICT 9593**
MC: . . . . **RRCT 12**

TEAR IT UP.
Tracks: / Shine eye gal / Guess who's coming to dinner / I love King Selassie.
LP: . . . . **ILPS 9696**
MC: . . . . **ICT 9696**

Black Velvet Band

WHEN JUSTICE CAME.
LP: . . . . **EKT 65**
MC: . . . . **EKTC 65**

Black Voices

NO ADDITIVES.
LP: . . . . **QUARTZLP 002**

Black Watch Band

BAND AND PIPES AND DRUMS (Black Watch Military Band).
Tracks: / Ceremonial occasion / All the blue bonnets are over the border / March past by companies / Scotland on the march / Morag of Dunvegan / Gairloch / Salute to the British forces / Concorde / Salute to the three nations / Last post.
LP: . . . . **RKLB 1004**

ON THE MARCH, VOL 3 (Black Watch Military Band).
LP: . . . . **DR 34**
MC: . . . . **CDR 34**

ON THE MARCH, VOL 4 (Black Watch Military Band).
Tracks: / Glorious victory / Action front / Gridiron club, The / Under the banner of victory / Festjubel / Argancab bavarda / Army of the Nile.
LP: . . . . **DR 43**
MC: . . . . **CDR 43**

ON THE MARCH, VOL 5 (Black Watch Military Band).
LP: . . . . **DR 45**

ON THE MARCH, VOL 6 (Black Watch Military Band).
Tracks: / Punchinello / Hanoverian, The / Army and marine / Colonel Bogey / Espana / Bravura / San Lorenzo / Sylvia / Valley Forge / Sons of the brave / Washington Post.
LP: . . . . **DR 50**
MC: . . . . **CDR 50**

ON THE MARCH, VOL 7 (Black Watch Military Band).
Tracks: / Liberty bell / Graf Zeppelin / Radetzky march / St. Julien / Ambassador, The / Laridah.
LP: . . . . **DR 51**
MC: . . . . **CDR 51**

RED HACKLE, THE (Black Watch Military Band).
Tracks: / Hundred pipers / Caller herrin' / Ye banks and braes / Will ye no come back again / Road to Dundee / Oh why I left my hame / Charlie is my darling / Afton water / Auld hoose, The / Robin Adair / Bluebells of Scotland / Skye boat song.
LP: . . . . **RKLP 1001**

SANDS OF TIME (ALBUM) (Black Watch Military Band).
LP: . . . . **GNPS 2160**
MC: **GNP5 2160**

SCOTCH ON THE ROCKS (Black Watch Military Band).
Tracks: / Scotch on the rocks / Dance of the cuckoos.
LP: . . . . **SRLM 503**
MC: . . . . **ZCSM 503**

SPIRIT OF THE ISLES (Black Watch Military Band).
Tracks: / Spirit of the Isles / Ob la di ob la da / Country roads / Africana / Our gracious Queen / Banner man / Jigger of whiskey / Miller Cha's in the mood / Chattanooga choo choo / Hackle red / Blueberry Hill / Put your hand in the hand / Soul finger.
LP: . . . . **RKLP 5001**

STRIKE UP THE BAND (Black Watch Military Band).
LP: . . . . **SRLM 504**

Black Way

BLACK WAY, THE (Various artists).
2LP: . . . . **ESC 398/9**

Black & White

DON'T KNOW YET.
LP: **7819671**
MC: **7819674**

Black & White Blues

BLACK & WHITE BLUES (Various artists).
LPS: **DS6 28537**

Black & White

DOWN MEMORY LANE (See Mitchell, George Minstrels).

FROM THE BLACK AND WHITE MINSTREL SHOW (See under Mitchell, George for details).

Black Widow

SACRIFICE.
LP: **63948**

Blackbeard

STRICTLY DUBWISE.
LP: . . . . **LBR 1013**

Blackbird

BLACKBIRD.
LP: . . . . **SAVE 089**

Blackbyrds

BEST OF THE BLACKBYRDS VOL.1.
Tracks: / Do it fluid / Love don't strike twice / Walking in rhythm / Mysterious vibes / Baby, The / Gut level / Funkie junkie / Dreaming about you.
LP: . . . . **BGP 1012**
MC: . . . . **BGPC 918**

BEST OF THE BLACKBYRDS VOL.2.
Tracks: / Rock creek park / Time is movin' / Don't know what to say / Blackbyrds' theme / Happy music / Supernatural feeling / Soft and easy.
LP: . . . . **BGP 1014**

BETTER DAYS.
Tracks: / Dancin' dancin' / Lonelies for your love / Better days / Do it girl / Without your love / Do you wanna dance / Love don't strike twice / What's on your mind / Don't know what to say / What we have is right.
LP: . . . . **F 9602**

BLACKBYRDS: GREATEST HITS.
Tracks: / Happy music / Gut level / Walking in rhythm / Do it fluid / Rock Creek Park / Supernatural feeling / Soft and easy.
LP: . . . . **FT 555**

UNFINISHED BUSINESS.
Tracks: / Time is movin' / In life / Enter in / You've got that something / Party land / Lady / Unfinished business.
LP: . . . . **FTA 3007**

Blackcountrymen

FIRST TIME OUT.
Tracks: / Cradley Heath song / Slap bum tailor, The / Arthur McBride / Perry Croft's bull-bait / John O'Dreams / Cuckoo's nest, The / Can't find Brummagen / July wakes / Y viva Morris / Gornal nailmakers carol / Spotted cow, The / Punk folkers / I don't belong to Glasgow.
LP: . . . . **FHR 102**

Blackeyed Susan

ELECTRIC RATTLEBONE.
Tracks: / Electric rattlebone / Satisfaction / None of it matters / Sympathy / Ride with me / Old lady snow / Don't bring me down / Indica / She's so fine / How long / Best of friends / Holiday / Heart of the city.
LP: **848 575-1**
MC: **848 575-4**

Blackfoot

HIGHWAY SONG (Blackfoot live).
Tracks: / Gimme, gimme, gimme / Every man should know / Good morning / Dry county / Rollin' and tumblin' / Road fever / Trouble in mind / Train train / Highway song / Howay the lads.
LP: . . . . **K 50910**

MARAUDER.
Tracks: / Good morning / Paying for it / Diary of a working man / Too hard to hand / Fly away / Dry county / Fire of the dragon / Rattlesnake rock 'n' roller / Searchin'.
LP: . . . . **K 50799**
MC: **K4 50799**

MEDICINE MAN.
Tracks: / Doin' my job / Stealer, The / Sleazy world / Not gonna cry any more / Runnin', Runnin' / Chilled to d'bone / Guitar slingers song and dance.
LP: . . . . **MFN 106**
MC: . . . . **TMFN 106**

SLIGO.
Tracks: / Send me an angel / Crossfire / Heart's grown cold / We're goin' down / Teenage idol / Goin' in circles / Run for cover / White man's land / Sail away / Drivin' fool.
LP: . . . . **B 0080**
LP: **790 081 0**

STRIKES.
Tracks: / Road fever / I got a line on you / Left turn on a red light / Pay my dues / Baby blue / Wishing well / Run and hide / Train train / Highway song.
LP: . . . . **K 50603**
MC: **K4 50603**

TOMCATTIN'.
Tracks: / Warped / On the run / Dream on / Street fighter / Gimme gimme gimme / Every man should know / In the night / Reckless daughter / Spendin' cabbage / Fox chase, The.
LP: . . . . **K 50702**
MC: **K4 50702**

VERTICAL SMILES.
Tracks: / Morning dew / Living in the limelight / Ride with you / Get it on / Young girl summer days / Legend never dies, A / Heartbeat and heels / In for the kill.
LP: **790 218-1**
MC: **790 218-4**

Blackfoot, J.

CITY SLICKER.
Tracks: / Way of the city, The / Taxi / Street girl / One of those parties / Where is love? / I stood on the sidewalk / City slicker / All because of what you did to me / Can you hang?.
LP: . . . . **ALE 5602**
MC: . . . . **ZCALE 5602**

Blackhouse

HOLY WAR.
Tracks: / I make a choice / Fight, The / Whispers of love / Satan and his demons / Rhythmus II / Remember who / Took the fall / Power and wisdom / Repent / Holy war.
LP: . . . . **RRR 017**

WE WILL FIGHT BACK.
LP: **081109**

Blackjack

BLACKJACK.
Tracks: / Love me tonight / Heart of stone / Night has me calling for you / Southern ballad / Fallin' / Without your love / Countin' on you / I'm aware of your love / For you / Heart of mine.
LP: **2391411**
MC: **8433354**

Blacklight Chameleon

INNER MISSION.
Tracks: / Theme / Reverse, The / Poison arrow / Yeah you / Fired up / Surf wizards, The / Thirteen miles to midnight / Love is a mystery / Getting down under / Cross that bridge / Tehru.
LP: **R33/8812**
LP: . . . . **RES 338812**

Blackman, Honor

EVERYTHING I'VE GOT.
Tracks: / Kinky boots / Everything I've got / Darling, je vous aime beaucoup / Men will decieve you / I wish I'd never loved you / Den of iniquity / World without love / Remind me / To keep my love alive / C'est drole / I wouldn't walk across the street / Tomorrow is my turn / I want a fair and square man.
LP: . . . . **BRED 49**

KINKY BOOTS (LP).
Tracks: / Kinky boots / Everything I've got / Darling, je vous aime beaucoup / Men will deceive you / I wish I'd never loved you / Den of iniquity / World without love / Remind me / To keep my love / C'est drole / I wouldn't walk across the street / Tomorrow is my turn / I want a fair and square man.
MC: **8840574**
LP: **8840571**

Blackmore, George

GOODBYE (see Shepherd, David) (Blackmore, George & David Shepherd).

Blackmore, R.H. (aut)

LORNA DOONE (see under Lorna Doone (bk)) (Gilmore, Peter (nar)).

LORNA DOONE (see under Lorna Doone (bk)).

Blackmore, Ritchie

ROCK PROFILE VOL 1 (Various artists).
Tracks: / Return of the outlaws: *Outlaws (Group)* / Texan spiritual: *Outlaws (Group)* / If you gotta pick a baby: *Collins, Glenda* / Big fat spider: *Heinz* / Doo dah day: *Outlaws (Group)* / Thou shalt not steal: *Collins,* Glenda / I'm not a bad guy: *Heinz* / Ritchie Blackmore interview: *Blackmore, Ritchie* / Been invited to a party: *Collins, Glenda* / Shake with me: *Outlaws (Group)* / Movin' in: *Heinz* / Keep a knockin': *Outlaws* (Group) / I shall be released: *Boz* / Playground: *Deep Purple* / Wring that neck: *Deep Purple* / Why didn't Rosemary: *Deep Purple* / Living wreck: *Deep Purple* / Guitar job: *Blackmore, Ritchie* / No, no, no: *Deep Purple* / Highway star: *Deep Purple* / A 200: *Deep Purple* / Gypsy: *Deep Purple*/ Hold on: *Deep Purple* / Show me the way to go home: *Blackmore, Ritchie.*
2LP: . . . . **RPVSOPLP 143**
MC: . . . . **RPVSOPMC 143**

ROCK PROFILE VOL 2.
2LP: . . . . **RPVSOPLP 157**

Black'n'Blue

BLACK'N'BLUE.
Tracks: / Strong will rock, The / School of hard knocks / Autoblast / Hold onto 18 / Wicked bitch / Action / Show me the night / One for the money / I'm the king / Chains around heaven.
LP: . . . . **GEF 26020**
MC: **4026020**

IN HEAT.
Tracks: / Rock on / Sight for sore eyes / Heat it up burn it out! / Suspicious / Snake, The / Live it up / Gimme your love / Get wise to the rise / Stranger / Great guns of fire.
LP: . . . . **K 9241801**
MC: . . . . **K 9241804**

NASTY NASTY.
Tracks: / Nasty nasty / I want it all / Does she or doesn't she / Kiss of death / 12 o'clock high / Do what you wanna do / I'll be there for you / Rules / Best of the West.
LP: **9241111**
MC: **9241114**

Blacksmiths

MERRILY KISSED THE QUAKER.
LP: . . . . **ISLE 3010**

Blackstock, Wayne

BLACK STAR LINER (Various artists).
LP: . . . . **HB 16**

Blackstone, Eddie

LIGHT AND SHADE OF EDDIE BLACKSTONE, THE.
Tracks: / After dark / 1643 Pennsylvania Boulevard / Spencer Walker Rose / Dolly McGraw / Never let a dream go by / Blues for a weirdo / You never left me side / Turn back the years / Lay my feet down on the street / Hero of the dreamers.
LP: . . . . **PROP 5**

Blackstones

TAKE ANOTHER LOOK AT LOVE.
LP: . . . . **ARKLP 1**

Blackthorn

BLACKTHORN.
LP: . . . . **HRL 118**
MC: . . . . **CHRL 118**

FOLK SONGS OF IRELAND.
Tracks: / Paddy's green shamrock shore / Cliffs of Dooneen / Peggy Gordon / Paddy lie back / Hi for the beggarman / Dingle regatta / Follow me up to Carlow / Morrison's jig / Raglan road / Man from the Daily Mail / High Germany / Kelly the boy from Killane / Lid of me granny's bin.
LP: . . . . **G 011**

LID OF ME GRANNY'S BIN, THE.
LP: . . . . **CDBL 502**

PADDY LIE BACK, KATIE LIE OVER.
LP: . . . . **G 005**

Blackwell

TRIBUTE TO BLACKWELL (See under Tribute To ...) (Various artists).

Blackwell, Ed

OLD AND NEW DREAMS (Blackwell, Ed, Don Cherry & Redman).
LP: . . . . **BSR 0013**

Blackwell, Jill

ADVENTURES OF NOTION (Blackwell, Jill & Bernard).
Tracks: / Hesleyside reel / Hunting a loaf / Edwin in the lowlands / Paddy Maloney / Botany bay / Sitting on top of the world / Sweet Hesleyside / Bonnie Cragside / Blessed quietness / Standing stones / Too much of a good thing / Green grows the laurel.
LP: . . . . **FE 056**

Blackwell, Otis

SINGIN' THE BLUES.
LP: . . . . **FLY 575**

Blackwell, Scrapper

BLUES.
LP: . . . . **AB 2008**

GREAT PIANO AND GUITAR DUETS 1929-35 (see Carr, Leroy) (Blackwell, Scrapper & Leroy Carr).

SCRAPPER'S BLUES.
Tracks: / Goin' where the moon crosses the yellow dog / 'A' blues / George Street blues / Little boy blue / Penal farm blues / Nobody knows you (when you're down and out) / Little girl blue / Blues before sunrise / Shady lane.
LP: . . . . **CH 255**

VIRTUOSO GUITAR OF SCRAPPER BLACKWELL.
LP: . . . . **L 1019**

Blackwych

OUT OF CONTROL.
LP: . . . . **METALP 111**

Blade Runner

BACK STREET LADY.
LP: . . . . **EBON 26**

WARRIORS OF ROCK.
LP: . . . . **EBON 35**

Blade Runner (Film)

BLADE RUNNER (Film soundtrack) (Various artists).
LP: . . . . **K 99262**
MC: **K4 99262**

Blades

LAST MAN IN EUROPE, THE.
Tracks: / Last man in Europe, The / Downmarket / That's not love / Talk about listening / Got soul / Chance to stop / Don't break the silence / Those were the days / Pride / Boy one / Waiting.
LP: . . . . **RKLP 1**
MC: . . . . **RKMC 1**

RAYTOWN REVISITED.
LP: . . . . **RKLP 3**

Blades, Ruben

AGUA DE LUNA.
Tracks: / Isobel / No te Duermas / Blackaman / Ojos de Perro Azul / Claro Oscuro / Laura Farina / La cita / Agua de luna.
LP: **9607211**
MC: **9607214**

ANTECEDENTE (Blades, Ruben Y Son Del Solar).
Tracks: / Juana mayo / 'Tas caliente / La marea / Contrabando / Patria / Noches del ayer / Nuestro adios / Nacer de ti / Plaza herrera.
LP: **960 795 1**
MC: **960795 4**

BUSCANDO AMERICA (SEARCHING FOR AMERICA).
Tracks: / Decisions / G D B D / Desapariciones / Todos Vuelven / Caminos verdes / El Padre Antonio y el Monaguillo Andres / Buscando America.
LP: **960 452 1**
LP: **115924**

EL QUE LA HACE LA PAGA.
LP: . . . . **SLP 624**

ESCENAS.
Tracks: / Cuentas del alma / Tierra dura / La cancion del final del mundo / La sorpresa / Caina / Silencois / Muevete.
LP: . . . . **EKT 29**
MC: . . . . **EKT 29C**

METIENDO MANO (Blades, Ruben/ Willie Colon).
Tracks: / Pablo pueblo / Segun el color / Le maleta / Plantacion adentro / La mora / Lluvia de tucielo / Fue varon / Pueblo.
MC: . . . . **TCHOT 103**
LP: . . . . **HOT 103**

MUCHO MEJOR.
LP: . . . . **JM 630**

NOTHING BUT THE TRUTH.
Tracks: / Hit, The / I can't say / Hopes on hold / Miranda syndrome, The / Letters to the Vatican / Calm before the storm / In Salvador / Letter, The / Chameleons / Ollie's doo-wop / Shamed into love.
LP: . . . . **K 9607541**
MC: . . . . **K 9607544**

RUBEN BLADES LIVE.
LP: **7559608681**
MC: **7559608684**

SCENES.
LP: **115937**

Blaffen, Mensen

RAVEN.
Tracks: / Over de lijn / Maree d'envie / Barbaar / Raven / L'angoissee / Tournesol / Snijdzucht / La griffe / Eclat / E-blues / Modderman.
LP: . . . . **CR 802**

Blaggers

ON YER TOEZ.
Tracks: / On yer toez / Crazy / Bronco bullfrog / Nice one blaggers / Britain's dreams / Young blaggers / Weekend warriors / Save your hate / Jailhouse doors.
LP: . . . . **OIR 014**

Blah

BLAH.... OR WHAT.
Tracks: / Ominous elements / Stranded / Mad man, The / Big vern / Russian roulette / She got / Evil daze / Anytime pal / Always high.
MC: . . . . **ACLMC 5**

Blah Blah Blah

BLAH BLAH BLAH.
LP: . . . . **TV 1**

Blair, Alex

ESPECIALLY FOR YOU.
Tracks: / What you gonna do / Changes of the world / Monologue 1 / Especially for you / Monologue II / Dreams come and go away / Monologue III / Enchanted place.
LP: . . . . **YX 7549**

Blair, Douglas

CELTOLOGY.
LP: . . . . **RED 1**

Blair, Lionel

AEROBIC DANCING.
LP: . . . . **CFR 104**
MC: . . . . **MCFR 104**
LP: **33104**

Blair, Robert

SING WITH THE ANGELS (Blair, Robert/ Fantastic Violinaires).
LP: . . . . **MAL 04415**

Blair, Sally

SQUEEZE ME.
LP: . . . . **FS 233**

Blair, Terry

ULTRA MODERN NURSERY RHYMES.
Tracks: / Ultra modern nursery rhyme / Missing / Fishbones and scaredy cats / Lucky in luv' / Day like today / Sweet September sacrifice / Beautiful people / Three cool catz / Happy families / Just go.
LP: . . . . **CHR 1701**
MC: . . . . **ZCHR 1701**

Blak, Kristian

DEN YDERSTE O (Blak, Kristian/William Heinesen).
LP: . . . . **HJF 12**

HARRAR PAETUR OG ELINBORG.
MC: . . . . **FKT 2 MC**

KINGOLOG.
LP: . . . . **HJF 16**

RAVNATING.
LP: . . . . **HJF 13**

Blake Babies

EARWIG.
LP: . . . . **MR 0016**

SLOW LEARNER.
LP: . . . . **UTIL 006**

Blake, Betty

SINGS IN A TENDER MOOD.
LP: . . . . **FS 154**

Blake, Dorothy

MEMORIES OF OSBORNE.
LP: SDL 285
MC: CSDL 285

Blake, Eubie

EIGHTY SIX YEARS, THE.
LP: CBS 22223

LIVE CONCERT.
LP: ST 130

RAGS TO RICHES.
LP: ST 128

Blake, Howard

GRANPA (See under Brightman, Sarah).

SNOWMAN, THE (see under Snowman).

Blake, John

MAIDEN DANCE.
Tracks: / Caravan of dreams / Movin' up / Beautiful love / Other side of a world, The / Maiden dance / For tomorrow / Todos mis ninos.
LP: GR 8309
MC: GRC 8309

TWINKLING OF AN EYE.
LP: GR 8501

Blake, Karl

PREHENSILE TALES, THE.
LP: NORMAL 131

Blake, Maxine

WILL YOU BE READY FOR THE BRIDEGROOM? (Blake, Maxine & The Seeds Of Faith Singers).
Tracks: / Will you be ready for the bridegroom? / He changed me / Are you living in vain? / New creature, A / Come on in / I'll let my light shine / Praise Him / I can't leave him alone.
LP: MIR 5020
MC: MIR 5020MC

Blake, Nancy

GRAND JUNCTION.
LP: ROUNDER 0231
MC: ROUNDER 0231C

NATASHA'S WALTZ (See under Blake, Norman) (Blake, Norman & Nancy).

Blake, Norman

BLACKBERRY BLOSSOM.
Tracks: / Are you from Dixie? / Right of a man, The / Hornpipe / Highland light, The / Railroad blues / Foggy valley / Lonesome Jenny / Blackberry blossom / D medley / Jerusalem ridge.
LP: FLY 0005
LP: FF 047

BLAKE AND RICE (Blake, Norman & Tony Rice).
LP: ROUNDER 0233
MC: ROUNDER 0233C

BLIND DOG (Blake, Norman & Nancy).
LP: ROUNDER 0254
MC: ROUNDERC 0254

FIELDS OF NOVEMBER.
LP: FF 004

FULL MOON ON THE FARM (Featuring Nancy Blake and James Bryan).
LP: ROUNDER 0144
MC: ROUNDER 0144C

HOME IN SULPHUR SPRINGS.
LP: ROUNDER 0012
MC: ROUNDER 0012C

LIGHTHOUSE ON THE SHORE.
LP: ROUNDER 0211
MC: ROUNDER 0211C

NASHVILLE BLUES.
LP: ROUNDER 0188
MC: ROUNDER 0188C

NORMAN BLAKE AND TONY RICE (Blake, Norman & Tony Rice).
LP: ROUNDER 0266
MC: ROUNDERC 0266

NORMAN BLAKE & JETHRO BURNS (Blake, Norman/Jethro Burns).
LP: HDS 701

OLD AND NEW.
Tracks: / Widow's creek / Bristol in the bottle / Billy Gray / Forked deer / Rubagfre / Cuckoo's nest, The / Witch of the wave / My old home on the mountainside / Miller's reel / Dry grass on the high fields / Harvey's reel / Railroad days, The / Valley head / Sweet heaven / Sally in the garden / Ajimina / Flat rock.
LP: FF 010

ORIGINAL UNDERGROUND MUSIC FROM MYSTERIOUS SOUTH (Blake, Norman & Other Mandolin Pickers).
LP: ROUNDER 0166
MC: ROUNDER 0166C

RISING FAWN STRING ENSEMBLE (Featuring Nancy Blake and James Bryan).
LP: ROUNDER 0122
MC: ROUNDER 0122C

WHISKEY BEFORE BREAKFAST.
Tracks: / Hand me down my walking cane / Under the double eagle / Six white horses / Salt river / Old grey mare / Down at Mylow's house / Sleepy eyed Joe / Indian creek / Arkansas traveller / Girl I left in Sunny Tennessee, The / Mistrel boy to war has gone, The / Ash grove, The / Church Street blues / Macon rag / Fiddler's dream / Whiskey before breakfast / Slow train through Georgia.
LP: ROUNDER 0063
MC: ROUNDER 0063C

Blake, Peter

FOX (TV soundtrack).
Tracks: / Fox / King Billy / Not quite strangers, not quite friends / Fathers and songs / Foxes kill / Empty sum / Midnight spider / Two up for trouble / Madam Manhattan / Of course it was raining / New York / Car park.
LP: EMC 3325

TWO UP FOR TROUBLE (See under Old Pals Act) (Old Pals Act).

Blake, Ran

BREAKTHRU (Solo piano).
LP: IAI 373842

DUKE DREAMS, THE LEGACY OF STRAYHORN-ELLINGTON.
LP: SN 1027

Blake, Roger (nar)

ENORMOUS CROCODILE, THE (see under Enormous Crocodile (bk)).

MOUNTAIN OF ADVENTURE (see under Blyton, Enid (aut)) (Blake, Roger (nar) & Elizabeth Lindsay (nar)).

SHIP OF ADVENTURE, THE (see under Blyton, Enid (aut)) (Blake, Roger (nar) & Elizabeth Lindsay (nar)).

TOUGH TED (See Simon Bond).

Blake, Tim

BLAKE'S NEW JERSUALEM.
LP: CLAY 7005

CRYSTAL MACHINE.
LP: 900545

NEW JERUSALEM.
LP: 90288

Blake, Tommy

TOMMY BLAKE & GENE WYATT (Blake, Tommy & Gene Wyatt).
Tracks: / Rock 'n' roll guitar / One love / Like last night / Baby, I know what I wanna do / Your cheatin' heart / Love fever / Loverboy / Greenback bucks / Boo hoo / Little girl / Campus queen / Prettiest girl at the dance / Koolit / Folding money / Kool alligator / I'll be free.
LP: WLP 8874

Blake, William

POETRY OF WILLIAM BLAKE (Richardson, Sir Ralph (nar)).
MC: 1101

Blakey, Art

AIN'T LIFE GRAND? (Blakey, Art Big Band & Quintet).
Tracks: / Midriff / Ain't life grand? / Tippin' pristine / El toro valiente / Kiss of no return / Late date / Outer world.
LP: AFF 106

ALBUM OF THE YEAR.
Tracks: / Cheryl / Ms. BC / In case you missed it / Little man / Witch hunt / Soulful Mister Timmons.
LP: SJP 155

ALL STAR JAZZ MESSENGER, THE.
LP: PL 45365

AND THE JAZZ MESSENGERS (Blakey, Art/Jazz Messengers).
Tracks: / A la mode / Invitation / Circus / You don't know what love is / I hear a rhapsody / Gee baby ain't I good to you.
LP: JAS 72

ART BLAKEY IN SWEDEN 1959.
LP: DRLP 137

ART BLAKEY & THE JAZZ MESSENGERS (Blakey, Art/Jazz Messengers).
Tracks: / This here / April jammin' / Dat dere / Along came Betty.
LP: KLJ 20023

ART BLAKEY & THE JAZZ MESSENGERS (RCA) (Blakey, Art/Jazz Messengers).
LP: CL 42789

ART'S BREAK (Blakey, Art/Jazz Messengers).
LP: LPPS 111 13
LP: LOP 14 071

AT THE CAFE BOHEMIA VOL.1 (Blakey, Art/Jazz Messengers).
Tracks: / Soft winds / Theme / Minors holiday / Alone together / Prince Albert / Ladybird / What's new / Decifering the message.
MC: 4BN 81507
LP: BST 81507

AT THE CAFE BOHEMIA VOL.2 (Blakey, Art/Jazz Messengers).
Tracks: / Like someone in love / Yesterdays / Avila and Tequila / Sportin'crowd / I waited for you / Just one of those things* / Hanks symphony / Gone with the wind / Soft winds / Theme / Minor's holiday / Alone together / Prince Albert.
LP: BST 81508

BACKGAMMON (Blakey, Art/Jazz Messengers).
Tracks: / Uranus / Whisper not / Backgammon / Blues march / Georgia on my mind / Third world express / Namefully / I can't get started.
LP: RLP 1007

BEST OF ART BLAKEY (Blakey, Art/Jazz Messengers).
Tracks: / Moanin' / Blues march / Lester's left town / Night in Tunisia, A / Dat dere / Mosaic (CD only.) / Free for all (CD only.).
LP: B1 93205
LP: 793 205 1

BIG BEAT.
Tracks: / It's only a paper moon / Chess players / Sakeena's vision / Politely / Dat dere / Lester left town / It's only a paper moon (alternate take).
MC: 4BN 84029
LP: BST 84029

BIRDLAND 21ST FEB. 1954 (See under Brown, Clifford) (Blakey, Art & Clifford Brown).

BLUE NIGHT (Blakey, Art/Jazz Messengers).
Tracks: / Two of a kind / Blue minor / Blue night / Body and soul / Mr. Combinated.
LP: SJP 217

BLUES BAG (Blakey, Art/Buddy de Franco).
Tracks: / Blues bag / Rain dance / Straight no chaser / Cousin Mary / Blues connotation / Kush / Twelve tone blues.
LP: ATS 4
MC: KATS 4
LP: AFF 55
MC: TCATS 4

BLUES MARCH (Blakey, Art/Jazz Messengers).
Tracks: / Blues march / Uranus / Whisper not / Backgammon / Georgia on my mind / Third world express / Nam fulay / I can't get started.
LP: 520235

BUHAINA (The Continuing Message) (Blakey, Art/Jazz Messengers).
Tracks: / For minors only / Right down front / Leo-x / Sweet sakeena / For miles and miles / Krafty / Late spring.
LP: AFF 113

CARAVAN (Blakey, Art/Jazz Messengers).
LP: NL 70244

CHICAGO GOLDEN YEARS (Blakey, Art/Max Roach).
2LP: 427002

CHILD'S DANCE (Blakey, Art/Jazz Messengers).
Tracks: / C.C. / Child's Dance / Song for a lonely woman / I can't get started.
LP: PR 10047
MC: PRC 10047

COMPLETE DEBUT SESSION '53 (Blakey, Art/Mingus, Charles/Bley, Paul).
LP: FC 5014

DAY WITH, A (VOLUME 2).
Tracks: / Night in Tunisia / Nelly Bly / Dat Dere / Round about midnight / Night in Tunisia.
LP: EWIND 708

DRUM SOUNDS (Blakey, Art/Jazz Messengers).
Tracks: / New world / Angel eyes / Slide No.2 / Theme.
LP: SJAZZ 9
MC: SJAZZC 9

DRUM SUITE.
Tracks: / Sacrifice / Cubano chant / Oscalypso / Nica's tempo / D's dilemma / Just for Marty.
LP: CBS 21067
MC: 40 21067

FEEL THE WIND (Blakey, Art/Freddie Hubbard).
LP: SJP 307

FREE FOR ALL (Blakey, Art/Jazz Messengers).
Tracks: / Free for all / Hammerhead / Core, The / Pensativa.
LP: BST 84170
MC: TCBST 84170

GYPSY FOLK TALES.
LP: 520292

HARD BOP.
Tracks: / Cranky spanky / Stella by starlight / My heart stood still / Little Melonae / Stanley's stiff chickens.
LP: CBS 54302

HARD CHAMPION.
LP: K 28P 6472

I GET A KICK OUT OF BU (Blakey, Art/Jazz Messengers).
LP: 1211551

IN MY PRIME VOL.1 (Blakey, Art/Jazz Messengers).
LP: SJP 114

IN MY PRIME VOL.2 (Blakey, Art/Jazz Messengers).
Tracks: / Hawkman / People who laugh / Time will tell / Ronnie's a dynamite lady.
LP: SJP 118

IN SWEDEN (Blakey, Art/Jazz Messengers).
Tracks: / Webb city / How deep is the ocean / Skylark / Gypsy folk tales.
LP: AMLP 839

IN WALKED SONNY (See under Stitt, Sonny) (Blakey, Art/Jazz Messengers/ Sonny Stitt).

INDESTRUCTIBLE (Blakey, Art/Jazz Messengers).
Tracks: / Egyptian, The / Sortie / Calling Miss Khadija / When love is new / Mr. Jin.
LP: BST 84193
MC: 4BN 84193

JAZZ MESSAGE.
Tracks: / Cafe / Just knock on my door / Summertime / Blues back / Sunday / Song is you, The.
LP: JAS 76

JAZZ MESSENGER, THE.
MC: 4679024

JAZZ MESSENGERS (That's Jazz) (Blakey, Art/Thelonious Monk).
Tracks: / Evidence / In walked Bud / Blue Monk / I mean you / Rhythm a ning / Purple shades.
LP: K 50248
LP: MCA 5886

JAZZ TIME VOL.19.
LP: 502719

KILLER JOE (Blakey, Art/George Kawaguchi).
LP: SLP 4100

LIAISONS DANGEREUSES, 1960, (LES) (Blakey, Art/Jazz Messengers).
Tracks: / No problem / No hay problems / Prelude in blue / Valmontana / Miguel's party / Weehawken mad pad.
LP: 8120 171
MC: 8120 174

LIKE SOMEONE IN LOVE (Blakey, Art/Jazz Messengers).
Tracks: / Like someone in love / Johnny's blue / Noise in the attic / Sleeping dancer sleep on / Giants / Sleeping dancer sleep on (alt. take) (CD only.).
LP: B1 84245

LIVE: ART BLAKEY (Blakey, Art/Jazz Messengers).
LP: 64513

LIVE AT BUBBA'S (Blakey, Art/Jazz Messengers).
Tracks: / Moanin' / My funny valentine / Soulful Mister Timmons / Au privave / Free for all.
LP: GATE 7003
MC: CGATE 7003

LIVE AT KIMBALL'S (Blakey, Art/Jazz Messengers).
Tracks: / Second thoughts / I love you / Jody / Old folks / You and the night and the music / Polka dots and moonbeams / Doctor Jekyll.
LP: CJ 307
MC: CJC 307

LIVE AT MONTREUX & NORTHSEA (Blakey, Art/Jazz Messengers).
Tracks: / Minor thesis / Wheel within a wheel, A / Bit a bittadose / Stairway to the stars / Linwood.
LP: SJP 150

LIVE AT RONNIE SCOTTS.
Tracks: / On the Ginza / Dr.Jeckyll / Two of a kind / I want to talk about you.
MC: ESMMC 014

LIVE AT SWEET BASIL (Blakey, Art/Jazz Messengers).
Tracks: / Jodie / Blues march / Mr. Babe / Moanin'.
LP: K 28P 6357
LP: GNPS 2182
MC: GNP5 2182

MESSAGES (Blakey, Art/Jazz Messengers).
Tracks: / Woody'n you / Sakeena / Short / Dawn on the desert / From bird / Blues for M.F. / East of the sun / No smiles please / Afternoon outing.
LP: VJD 557

MESSAGES (Blakey, Art/John Handy III).
2LP: 421004

MOANIN'.
Tracks: / Moanin' / Moanin' (alt. take) / Are you real / Along came Betty / Drum thunder suite, The / Blues march / Come rain or come shine.
LP: BST 84003
LP: BNS 40012
LP: BLJ 84003

MOSAIC (Blakey, Art/Jazz Messengers).
Tracks: / Mosaic / Down under / Children of the night / Arabia / Crisis.
LP: BST 84090

NEW YEAR'S EVE AT SWEET BASIL (Blakey, Art/Jazz Messengers).
Tracks: / Hide and seek / Little man / New York / I want to talk about you.
LP: K 28P 6426

NEW YORK SCENE.
Tracks: / Oh by the way / It's easy to remember / Who cares / Controversy / Tenderly / Falafel.
LP: CJ 256
MC: CJC 256

NIGHT AT BIRDLAND, VOL 1 (Blakey, Art Quintet).
Tracks: / Split kick / Once in a while / Quicksilver / Wee-dot / Blues / Night in Tunisia / Mayreh.
LP: BLP 1521
MC: 4BN 81521
LP: BST 81521
LP: BNS 40007

NIGHT AT BIRDLAND, VOL 2 (Blakey, Art Quintet).
Tracks: / Wee dot / If I had you / Quicksilver / Now's the time / Confirmation.
MC: 4BN 81522
LP: BST 81522
LP: BNS 40008
LP: BLP 1522

NIGHT IN TUNISIA, A (Blakey, Art/Jazz Messengers).
Tracks: / Night in Tunisia / Sincerely Diana / So tired / Yama / Kozo's waltz.
LP: BST 84049
MC: BSC 840494
LP: B1 84049

OH BY THE WAY (Blakey, Art/Jazz Messengers).
Tracks: / Oh by the way / Duck soup / Tropical breeze / One by one / Sudan blue / My funny valentine / Alicia.
LP: SJP 165

ONE BY ONE (Blakey, Art/Jazz Messengers).
Tracks: / One by one / Rhapsody in blue / Summertime / It ain't necessarily so / Someone to watch over me / Man I love, The / Song is you, The / Moanin'.
LP: PAL 15005

ORGY IN RHYTHM, VOL 1.
LP: BST 81554

PARIS JAM SESSION (Blakey, Art/Jazz Messengers).
Tracks: / Dance of the infidels / Bouncing with Bud / Midget, The / Night in Tunisia.
LP: 8326921
MC: 8326924

PERCUSSION DISCUSSION (Blakey, Art/Max Roach).
Tracks: / Scotch blues / Flight to Jordan / Transfiguration / Exhibit A / Gershwin medley / Crackle hut / Speculate / That ole devil called love / Audio blues / CM / Four - X.
2LP: CXJD 6703
MCSET: ZCCJD 6703
2LP: GCH 2-6028

REFLECTIONS IN BLUE (Blakey, Art/Jazz Messengers).
Tracks: / Reflections in blue / E.T.A. / Say, Dr J / Mishima / My foolish heart / My one and only love / Chelsea Bridge / In a sentimental mood / Stretching.
LP: SJP 128

STRAIGHT AHEAD.
Tracks: / Falling in love with love / My romance / Webb city / How deep is the ocean / E.T.A. / Theme, The.
LP: CJ 168
MC: CJ 168 C

UGETSU.
Tracks: / One by one / Ugetsu / Time off / Ping pong / I didn't know what time it was / On the ginza.
LP: OJC 090

Blakley, Ronee

WELCOME.
Tracks: / American beauty / I was born to love you / Please / Young Man / Idaho home / She lays it on the line / Nobody's Bride / If I saw you in the morning / Tapedeck / Need a new sun rising / Locked behind my true love's door / Welcome.
LP: K 56174

Blame it on Rio (film)

BLAME IT ON RIO (Film soundtrack) (Various artists).
LP: STV 81210

Blanchard, Jean

ACCORDEON DIATONIQUE.
LP: SB 367

Blanchard, Terence

DISCERNMENT (Blanchard, Terence & Donald Harrison).
Tracks: / Worth the pain / When the saints go marching in / When I fall in love / Directions / Discernment / Are you sleeping? / Akira / Dorchester House.
LP: GW 3008
MC: GWC 3008

NEW YORK SECOND LINE (Blanchard, Terence & Donald Harrison).
Tracks: / New York second line / Oliver Twist / I can't get started / Duck steps / Doctor Drums / Isn't it so? / Subterfuge.
LP: GW 3002

Blancmange

BELIEVE YOU ME.
Tracks: / Lose your love / What's your problem? / Paradise is / Who don't they leave things alone? / 22339 / Don't you love it all? / Believe / Lorraine's my nurse / Other animals / No wonder they never made it back / John.
LP: LONLP 10
MC: LONC 10

HAPPY FAMILIES.
Tracks: / I can't explain / Feel me / I've seen the world / Wasted / Living on the ceiling / Waves / Kind / Sad days / Cruel / God's kitchen.
LP: SH 8552
MC: KSAC 8552
LPPD: SHPD 8552

MANGE TOUT.
Tracks: / Don't tell me / Blind vision / That's love that it is / Day before you came, The.
LP: SH 8554
MC: KSAC 8554
LPPD: SHPD 8554

SECOND HELPINGS (Best of Blancmange).
Tracks: / God's kitchen / I've seen the world / Feel me / Living on the ceiling / Waves / Game above my head / Blind vision / That's love that it is / Don't tell me / Day before you came, The / What's your problem.
LP: 8280431
MC: 8280434

Bland, Billy

BLUES CHICKEN, FRIENDS AND RELATIVES.
Tracks: / Fat man / Chicken in the basket / Oh, you for me / I Had A Dream / If I could be your man / What's That / Grandma give a party / Uncle Bud / Little boy / Chicken hop / My hearts on fire / Flo, open the door / Momma stole the chicken / Bug, The.
LP: CH 222

Bland, Bobby

AFTER ALL.
LP: MALP 009

AIN'T NOTHING YOU CAN DO.
LP: DL 78

ANGELS IN HOUSTON: LEGENDARY DUKE BLUES.
LP: ROUNDER 2031
MC: ROUNDER 2031C

BAREFOOT ROCK (Bland, Bobby & Junior Parker).
LP: DL 72

BEST OF BOBBY BLAND.
Tracks: / Cry cry cry / I pity the fool / Turn on your lovelight / Stormy Monday blues / That's the way love is / Ain't nothing you can do / Too far gone / Good time Charlie / That did it / Rockin' in the same old boat / Chains of love / Do what you set out to do / This time I'm gone for good / It's not the spotlight / Ain't no love in the heart of the city / Yolanda / Love to see you smile / Soon as the weather breaks.
LP: MCL 1673
MC: MCLC 1673

BLUES IN THE NIGHT.
Tracks: / Blue moon / If I hadn't called you back / Ask me 'bout nothing but the blues / Jelly, jelly / When you put me down / Blind man / Chains of love / Fever / Blues in the night / Loneliness hurts / Feeling is gone, The / I'm too far gone / Black night / Share your love with me.
LP: CH 132
MC: CHC 132

BLUES YOU CAN USE.
LP: MAL 7444

BOBBY BLAND.
LP: MALP 7439

CALIFORNIA ALBUM.
Tracks: / This time I'm gone for good / Up and down world / It's not the spotlight / (If loving you is wrong) I don't wanna be right / Going down slow / Right place at the right time, The / Help me through the day / Where baby went / Friday the 13th child / I've got to use my imagination.
LP: BGOLP 64

CALL ON ME.
LP: DL 77

COME FLY WITH ME.
LP: ABCL 5249

DREAMER.
LP: BGOLP 63

EARL FOREST & THE BEALE STREETERS (See under Forest, Earl) (Bland, Bobby/Earl Forest/Johnny Ace).

FOOLIN' WITH THE BLUES.
Tracks: / You got me (where you want me) / Loan me a helping hand / I pity the fool / Who will the next fool be? / Two steps from the blues / Reconsider, baby / Bobby's blues / Cry cry cry / Touch of the blues, A / You're worth it all / Don't cry no more / I'm not ashamed / I'll take care of you / 36-22-36 / Ain't no telling / Yield not to temptation.
LP: CRB 1049

HERE'S THE MAN.
LP: DL 75

INSTRUMENTAL ALBUM.
LP: LP 8502

INTROSPECTIVE OF THE EARLY YEARS.
LP: DL 92

LIKE 'ER RED HOT.
LP: DL 73

MEMBERS ONLY.
Tracks: / Members only / In the ghetto / I've just got to know / Straight / From the shoulder / Sweet woman's love / Can we make love tonight / Sweet surrender / I need your love so bad / Heart open up again.
LP: MAL 7429
LP: MALP 004
MC: MALC 7429

MIDNIGHT RUN.
LP: MALP 7450
MC: MALC 7450

REFLECTIONS IN BLUE.
LP: ABCL 5196

SOUL OF THE MAN, THE.
LP: DL 79

SOUL WITH A FLAVOUR.
Tracks: / Wishing well / St. James' infirmary / Ain't that lovin' you / Turn on your lovelight / You're the one (that I adore) / Stormy Monday blues / Your friends / Honky tonk / That's the way love is / These hands (small, but mighty) / Poverty / Driftin' blues / Sad feeling / Rockin' in the same old boat / Gotta get to know you / Soon as the weather breaks / You'd be a millionaire / Soul with a flavour / Real woman is what it takes, A / Try me I'm real / Recess in heaven / You're about to win / Is this the blues / Just because I love you / Looking back.
2LP: CDX 30
MC: TCCDX 30

SOULFUL SIDE OF BOBBY BLAND, THE.
Tracks: / Getting used to the blues / Yum yum tree / These hands (small, but mighty) / Back in the same old bag again / Keep on loving me / Honey child / Wouldn't you rather have me / Call on me / Dear Bobby / How does a cheating woman feel / I ain't myself anymore / That did it / Ain't doing too bad / Love with a reputation / Good time Charlie / Ain't nothing you can do.
LP: KENT 044

SPOTLIGHTING THE MAN B.B..
LP: DL 89

TELL MR. BLAND.
LP: MCF 3181

TOGETHER AGAIN - LIVE (Bland, Bobby & B.B. King).
Tracks: / Let the good times roll / Strange things happen / Feel so bad / Mother in law blues / Mean old world / Everyday (I have the blues) / Thrill is gone, The / I ain't gonna be the first to cry.
LP: IMPL 8027
LP: IMCA 27012

TOGETHER FOR THE FIRST TIME - LIVE (See under King, BB) (Bland, Bobby & B.B. King).

TOUCH OF THE BLUES.
LP: DL 88

TWO STEPS FROM THE BLUES (Bland, Bobby & B.B. King).
Tracks: / Cry, cry, cry / I pity the fool / I'll take care of you.
LP: DL 74
LP: MCA 27036
LP: MCA 4160

WOKE UP SCREAMING.
Tracks: / No blow, no show / Wise man blues / Army blues / Lost lover blues / It's my life baby / Honey bee / Time out / Little boy blue / Woke up screaming / You've got bad intentions / I can't put you down / I smell trouble / Don't believe / I learned my lesson / Farther up the road.
LP: CH 41

Blank, Stu

NO FAT ON THE BONE (Blank, Stu & His Nasty Habits).
LP: MVLP 18

Blarney Boys

IRISH PARTY TIME SINGALONG.
LP: UNKNOWN

Blarney Lads

FOLK SONGS FROM THE EMERALD ISLE.
LP: OAK 102

Blasmusik, Deinnger

CALLING YOU (See under Steele, Jvetta).

Blasphemy

FALLEN ANGEL OF DOOM.
LP: WRE 9011

Blast

BLAST (Various artists).
LP: CRIMLP 140

Blast, C.L.

BOOMERANG LOVE.
LP: CRB 1145

I WANNA GET DOWN.
Tracks: / I wanna get down / If I had loved you more / I've got to make it on my own / Our love will last / Let's do something different tonight / If I could feel that old feeling again / Share your love with me / Love don't feel like love no more / Beautiful lover.
LP: TRPL 111

Blast (Group)

IT'S IN MY BLOOD.
LP: SST 106

POWER OF EXPRESSION, THE.
LP: RR 9713

Blaster Bates

ALL RECORDINGS (See Under Bates, Blaster).

Blasters

BLASTERS.
Tracks: / Marie Marie / No other girl / I'm shakin' / Border radio / American music / So long baby goodbye / Hollywood bed / Never no more blues / This is it / Highway 61 / I love you so / Stop the clock.
LP: XXLP 15

HARD LINE.
LP: SLAP 5
MC: SMAC 5

OVER THERE.
Tracks: / High school confidential / Rock boppin' baby / Keep a knockin' / I don't want to / Go go go / Roll 'em Pete.
LP: 9237351

Blasting Concept

BLASTING CONCEPT VOL 1 (Various artists).
LP: SST 013

BLASTING CONCEPT VOL 2 (Various artists).
LP: SST 043

Blasts of Bourbon

BLACK MILK.
LP: RED 012

Blaze

25 YEARS LATER.
Tracks: / Get up / So special / Miss my love / You don't really love me / Anything for your lovin' / We all must live together / I wonder / Gonna make it work / All that I should know / Missing you / Loverman (Only on cassette.) / Love is forever (CD & cassette only.) / Broad and market / NWK (CD & cassette only.) / Hope song, The / Mission (CD & cassette only.).
LP: ZL 72713

MC: ZK 72713

Blaze, Edwin

MUSIC FOR TREBLE VOICE (Blaze, Edwin/Stephen Lomas).
Tracks: / Oh had I Jubal's lyre / Drop, drop slow tears / O mysterium ineffabile / Voice of joy, The / Ave Maria / I know that my Redeemer liveth / Hymn to God the Father / I got me flowers / Love bade me welcome / Call, The / Benedictus (from Little Organ Mass) / Turn thee to me / I will lift up my eyes / Abide with me.
LP: APS 365

Blaze (Film)

BLAZE (Film soundtrack) (Various artists).
Tracks: / Blaze main title: *Various artists* / One night: *Various artists* / Next time you see me: *Various* artists / Drive to the general store: *Various artists* / Sho bar: *Various artists* / When the Saints go marching in: *Various artists* / Fine day for a walk: *Various artists* / To the couch and beyond: *Various artists*/ Precious Lord: *Various artists* / Louisiana 1927: *Various artists*.
LP: AMA 3932
MC: AMC 3932

Blaze Foley

IF ONLY I COULD FLY.
LP: HLD 011

Blazing Aces

BLAZING ACES.
LP: 4705

Blazing Redheads

BLAZING REDHEADS.
LP: RR 26

CRAZED WOMEN.
LP: RR 41

Bleak House (bk)

BLEAK HOUSE (See under Dickens, Charles (aut)).

BLEAK HOUSE (See under Dickens, Charles (aut)).

Bleasdale, Alan (aut)

BOYS FROM THE BLACKSTUFF (see under Boys From the ...) (Hill, Bernard (nar)).

Blechreitz

WHO NAPPED J.B. (Blechreitz (Black Rights)).
LP: RUDELP 009

Bleeched Black

BLEECHED BLACK.
LP: 88561-8151-1

Bleeps & Booster

BLEEPS AND BOOSTER (Various artists).
LP: TOVE 1

Blegvad, Peter

DOWNTIME.
LP: RER 34

KEW RHONE (Blegvad, Peter & John Greaves).
Tracks: / Good evening / Twenty two proverbs / Exhuming the first American (Seven scenes from the above painting) / Kew Rhone / Pipeline / Catalogue of fifteen objects and their titles / One footnote (to Kew Rhone) / Three tenses onanism / Nine mineral emblems / Apricot / Gegenstand.
LP: OVED 171

KING STRUT AND OTHER STORIES.
Tracks: / King Strut / Gold / Meantime / On obsession / Not weak enough / Swim / Northern lights / Chicken / Real slap in the face / Shirt and comb / Stranger to myself / King Strut (reprise).
LP: ORELP 511
MC: OREC 511

KNIGHTS LIKE THIS.
Tracks: / Special delivery / Face off / Let him go / Incinerator / Pretty U and ugly I / Always be new to me / Last man / Meet the rain / Wooden pyjamas, The / Marlene.
LP: OVED 188
LP: V 2352
MC: TCV 2352

NAKED SHAKESPEARE, THE.
Tracks: / How beautiful you are / Karen / Lonely too / First blow struck / Weird monkeys / Naked Shakespeare / Irma / Like a baby / Powers in the air / You can't miss it / Vermont / Blue eyed William.
LP: V 2284
LP: OVED 174

Blenner, Serge

LA DIMENSION PROCHAINE.
LP: SKY 110

PLAISIR ARDENT.
LP: SKY 099

Bless

GUMS.
LP: DT 26
MC: DT 26MC

Bless Me Father (bk)

BLESS ME FATHER (Wheeler, Peter (nar)).
MC: SOUND 30

Bless The

BLESS THE BEASTS AND CHILDREN (Film Soundtrack) (Various artists).
Tracks: / Bless the beasts and children: *Various artists* / Botton's dream: *Various artists* / Down the line: *Various artists* / Bless the beasts and children: *Various artists* / Lost: *Various artists* / Bless the beasts and children: *Various artists* / Down the line: *Various artists* / Journey's end: *Various artists*/ Stampede: *Various artists* / Free: *Various artists* / Requiem: *Various artists*.
LP: AMLS 64322

Blessing

PRINCE OF THE DEEP WATER.
LP: MCA 10070
MC: MCAC 10070

Bleu, Mikki

I PROMISE.
Tracks: / I promise / Lock-n-key / Something real / Every little thing / Knocks me off my feet / Move your feet (let's dance) / Nothin' but the best / Until / Can he rock you like this / Stand.
LP: MTL 1047
LP: 791 171 1
MC: TCMTL 1047
MC: 791 171 4

Bley, Carla

DINNER MUSIC.
MC: 7200191

DUETS (Bley, Carla & Steve Swallow).
Tracks: / Baby baby / Walking batteriewoman / Utviklingssang / Ladies in Mercedes / Romantic notions / Remember / Ups and downs / Reactionary tango parts 1/2/3 / Soon I will be done with the troubles of this world (CD only.).
LP: WATT 20

ESCALATOR OVER THE HILL.
LPS: 2641802

FLEUR CARNIVORE.
LP: WATT 21

HEAVY HEART.
Tracks: / Light or dark / Talking hearts / Joyful noise / Ending it / Starting again / Heavy heart.
LP: WATT 14
MC: 818 862 4

I HATE TO SING.
LP: WATT 12

LIVE: CARLA BLEY.
Tracks: / Blunt object / Lord is listenin' to ya,hallelujah, The / Time and us / Still in the room / Real life hits / Song sung long.
MC: 3103112

MORTELLE RANDONNEE.
Tracks: / Musique mecanique / Whistling palomino / Morning / Death rolls / Los Palominos / Sad paloma / Paloma, La / Some dirge / Teenage Paloma / Grown up Paloma / Blunt object.
LP: 812 097- 1
MC: 812 097-4

MUSIQUE MECANIQUE.
MC: 7200151
LP: WATT 9

NIGHT-GLO.
Tracks: / Pretend you're in love / Night-glo / Rut / Crazy with you / Wildlife (Horn-paws with out claws - sex with birds).
LP: WATT 16

SEXTET.
Tracks: / More Brahms / Houses and people / Girl who cried champagne, The / Brooklyn Bridge / Lawns / Healing power.
LP: WATT 17

SOCIAL STUDIES.
LP: WATT 11

VERY BIG CARLA BLEY BAND, THE.
Tracks: / United States / Strange arrangements / All fall down / Who will rescue you? / Lo ultimo.
LP: WATT 23

Bley, Paul

ALONE AGAIN.
LP: IAI 37 3840

BALLADS (Bley, Paul, Altschul & Peacock).
LP: ECM 1010

DIANE (See under Baker, Chet) (Baker, Chet/Paul Bley).

FRAGMENTS.
LP: ECM 1320

JAPAN SUITE.
LP: IAI 373849

LIVE AGAIN.
LP: SCS 1230

PAUL BLEY, CHARLES MINGUS AND ART BLAKELY (1953) (Bley, Paul/ Charles Mingus/Art Blakey).
LP: RARETONE 5014

PAUL BLEY QUARTET (Bley, Paul Quartet).
LP: ECM 1365

QUIET SONG (Bley, Paul, Connors & Guiffre).
LP: IAI 373839

RAMBLING.
LP: AFF 37

RIGHT TIME RIGHT PLACE (See under Burton, Gary) (Burton, Gary & Paul Bley).

SOLEMN MEDITATION.
LP: GNPS 31

SONOR.
Tracks: / Little bell / Landscape / Speed / Recollection / Joined / Sonor / Waltz / Set / Darkness / Tightrope.
LP: SN 1085

TURNING POINT (Bley, Paul & various artists).
LP: IAI 373841

VIRTUISI (Bley, Paul, Altschul & Peacock).
LP: IAI 373844

Blind Blake

1926-29: THE REMAINING TITLES.
LP: MSE 1003

ACCOMPIANIST, THE 1926-31.
LP: WSE 133

BLIND BLAKE.
2LP: YAZOO 1068

BLIND BLAKE AND PAPA CHARLIE JACKSON (Blind Blake/Papa Charlie Jackson).
LP: CC 6

BOOTLEG RUM DUM BLUES.
Tracks: / Come on boys / Let's do that messin' around / Skeedle loo doo blues / Bucktown blues / Black dog blues / Bad feeling blues / That will never happen no more / Brownskin man / Hey hey daddy blues / Low down loving girl / Bootleg rum dum blues / Paying policy blues / Righteous blues.
LP: BMLP 1044

RAGTIME GUITAR'S FOREMOST FINGERPICKER.
2LP: L 1068

Blind Date (Film)

BLIND DATE (1987 Film soundtrack) (Various artists).
Tracks: / Simply meant to be: *Morris, Gary & Jennifer Warnes* / Let you get away: *Vera, Billy* / Oh what a nite: *Vera, Billy* / Anybody seen her: *Vera, Billy* / Talked about lover: *L'Neire, Keith* / Crash, band, boom: *Tubbs, Hubert* / Something for Nash: *Various artists* / Treasures: *Jordan, Stanley*.
LP: FILM 016
MC: FILMC 016

BLIND DATE (1983 Film soundtrack) (Various artists).
LP: ATXLP 01
MC: ZCATX 01

Blind Faith

BLIND FAITH.
Tracks: / Had to cry today / Can't find my way home / Well alright / Presence of the Lord / Sea of joy / Do what you like.
LP: SPELP 14
MC: SPEMC 14
LP: 583-059
MC: 825 094-4

Blind Fury

OUT OF REACH.
LP: RR 9814

Blind Idiot God

BLIND IDIOT GOD.
LP: SST 104
MC: SST 104C

UNDERTOW.
LP: EMY 107

Blind Illusion

SANE ASYLUM, THE.
Tracks: / Sane asylum, The / Vengeance is mine / Kamikaze / Vicious vision / Bloodshower / Death noise / Smash the crystal / Metamorphosis of a monster.
LP: FLAG 18

Blind Mice

SOMETHING'S WRONG.
LP: DLLP 14

Blinding Tears

BLINDING TEARS.
LP: RVLP 20
MC: ZCRV 20

Blipvert Big Top

NORTH POLE.
LP: EARL 22

Bliss

CHANGE IN THE WEATHER, A.
Tracks: / Crash into the ocean / I don't want to hurry / Only you / Gotta give up / Spirit of the man / Keep me in mind / Watching over me / Ain't that just the way / Open up the skies / Inviting my soul / Life don't let me down / Be together.
LP: PCS 7352
MC: TCPCS 7352

LOVE PRAYER.
Tracks: / I hear you call / How does it feel the morning after / Good love / Your love meant everything / Won't let go / Lovin' come my way / Light and shade / May it be on this earth / All across the world / I walk alone / Better take care (CD only.) / Further from the truth (CD only.).
LP: PCS 7329
MC: TCPCS 7329

Bliss, Don

ORGAN MOODS.
LP: GNPS 2085
MC: GNP5 2085

Blistering Moments

THERAPEUTIC DREAMS.
LP: DMC 010

Blitz

BLITZ 1 (Various artists).
Tracks: / Shout: *Tears For Fears* / Lady writer: *Dire Straits* / Hot water: *Level 42* / Come to Milton Keynes: *Style Council* / Now those days are gone: *Bucks Fizz* / Robin (The hooded man): *Clannad* / I will be your friend: *Sade* / I'm your man: *Wham* / Mad world: *Tears For Fears* / Twisting by the pool: *Dire* Straits / Sun goes down (living it up), The: *Level 42* / Have you ever had it blue: *Style Council* / Land of make believe: *Bucks Fizz* / Harry's game, Theme from: *Clannad* / Hang on to your love: *Sade* / Different corner, A: *Michael, George*.
LP: SHM 3206
MC: HSC 3206

BLITZ 2 (Various artists).
MC: HSC 3527

Blitz (group)

ALL OUT ATTACK.
Tracks: / All out attack / 4Q / Time bomb / Criminal damage / Razors in the night / Attack / Escape / Never surrender / Nation on fire / Warriors / Someone's gonna die / 45 revolutions / Fight to live / Youth / I don't need you / Propaganda / Closedown.
LP: LINK LP 029

KILLING DREAM, THE.
Tracks: / Killing dream, The / Overdrive / Intermission 1 / Intermission 2 / Thrown away / Lady Anne / Fade / All you want / Empire fall / Those days / Final hour / Don't care / Walkaway.
LP: SKUNKLP 002

SECOND EMPIRE JUSTICE.
LP: FL 1

VOICE OF A GENERATION.
Tracks: / Warriors / Propaganda / Time bomb / Criminal damage / F**k you / We are the boys / Bleed / I don't need you / Your revolution / Moscow / Voice of a generation / T.O.? / Vicious / Nation on fire / Scream / 4.Q. / Escape / Closedown.
LP: PUNK 1

Blitz (Show)

BLITZ (ORIGINAL ISSUE) (London cast) (Various artists).
LP: CLP 1569

Blitzkrieg

READY FOR ACTION.
LP: RR 9743

TIME OF CHANGES, A.
Tracks: / Ragnarok / Inferno / Blitzkreig / Pull the trigger / Armageddon / Hell to pay / Vikings / Time of changes, A / Saviour.
LP: NEAT 1023

Blixen, Karen (aut)

OUT OF AFRICA (see under Out Of Africa (bk)) (James, Geraldine (nar)).

Bloch, Robert (aut)

PSYCHO (see under Psycho (bk)) (McCarthy, Kevin (nar)).

Block, Max

MAX BLOCK.
LP: . . . . FN 71

Block, Rory

BLUE HORIZON.
LP: . . . . ROUNDER 3073
MC: . . . . ROUNDER 3073C

HIGH HEELED BLUES.
LP: . . . . ROUNDER 3061
MC: . . . . ROUNDER 3061C

HOUSE OF HEARTS.
LP: . . . . ROUNDER 3104
MC: . . . . ROUNDER 3104C

I'M IN LOVE.
LP: . . . . BG 2022

I'VE GOT A ROCK IN MY SOCK.
LP: . . . . ROUNDER 3097
MC: . . . . ROUNDER 3097C

RHINESTONE AND STEEL STRINGS.
LP: . . . . ROUNDER 3085
MC: . . . . ROUNDER 3085C

TURNING POINT.
LP: . . . . SPD 1038
MC: . . . . SPDC 1038

YOU'RE THE ONE.
Tracks: / You're the one / Askin' for more / Someone like you / I can't believe in you no more / Please put out the fire / Love at first sight / If I can't have good love / Movin' up / Movin' out.
LP: . . . . CHR 1233

Blodwyn Pig

AHEAD RINGS OUT.
Tracks: / It's only love / Sing me a song that I know / Up and coming / Change song, The / Dear Jill / Modern alchemist, The / Leave it with me / Ain't ya coming home, babe?.
LP: . . . . BGOLP 54
LP: . . . . ILPS 9101

GETTING TO THIS.
LP: . . . . ILPS 9122
LP: . . . . BGOLP 81

Blonde On Blonde

AND HOW.
Tracks: / Whole lotta love / Shut down / Love in the afternoon / Who's on the line / Hold on, I'm coming / Past, present and future / Letter, The / Woman is free.
LP: . . . . N 7120

Blondel (musical)

BLONDEL (Original Soundtrack) (Rice, Tim).
Tracks: / Monk's introduction / Blondel and Fiona / Ministry of Reudal affairs, The / Last of my troubles, The / Lionheart / No rhyme for Richard / Trio / Assassins song / Running back for more / Blondel in Europe / Saladin days / I can't wait to be King / Inn at Salzburg, The / Blondel's search / Duke of Austria's quarters, The / Cell, The / Westminster Abbey / I'm a monarchist.
LP: . . . . DBL 1
MC: . . . . DBLC 1

Blondell, Joan

BING CROSBY AND JOAN BLONDELL (See under Crosby, Bing) (Blondell, Joan/Bing Crosby).

SHE LOVES ME NOT (NOVEMBER 8, 1937) (See under Crosby, Bing) (Blondell, Joan/Bing Crosby).

Blondie

AUTOAMERICAN.
Tracks: / Europa / Live it up / Here's looking at you / Tide is high, The / Angels on the balcony / Go through it / Do the dark / Rapture / Faces / T-Birds / Walk like me / Follow me.
LP: . . . . CDL 1290
MC: . . . . ZCDL 1290

BEST OF BLONDIE.
Tracks: / Denis / Tide is high, The / In the flesh / Sunday girl / I'm always touched by your presence dear / Dreaming / Hanging on the telephone / Rapture / Picture this / Union city blue / Call me / Atomic / Rip her to shreds / Heart of glass.
LP: . . . . CDLTV 1
MC: . . . . ZCLTV 1

BLONDIE.
Tracks: / X offender / Rifle range / Look good in blue / In the sun / Shark in jets clothing, A / Man overboard / Rip her to shreds / Little girl lies / In the flesh / Kung fu girls / Attack of the giant ants, The.
LP: . . . . SHM 3119
MC: . . . . HSC 3119
LP: . . . . MFP 41 5696 1
MC: . . . . MFP 41 5696 4
LP: . . . . CHR 1165

BLONDIE: INTERVIEW PICTURE DISC.
LP: . . . . BLO 1019

COMPLETE PICTURE, THE (See under Harry, Debbie) (Harry, Deborah & Blondie).

EAT TO THE BEAT.
Tracks: / Dreaming / Hardest part, The / Union city blue / Shayla / Eat to the beat / Accidents never happen / Die young stay pretty / Slow motion / Atomic / Sound asleep / Victor / Living in the real world.
LP: . . . . CDL 1225
MC: . . . . ZCDL 1225

HIT COLLECTION: BLONDIE.
LP: 840 261
MC: 840 264

HUNTER, THE.
Tracks: / Orchid club / Island of lost souls / Dragonfly / For your eyes only / Beast, The / War child / Little Caesar / Danceway / Can I find the right words (to say) / English boys / Hunter gets captured by the game, The.
LP: . . . . CDL 1384
MC: . . . . ZCDL 1384
LPPD: . . . . PCDL 1384

ONCE MORE INTO THE BLEACH.
Tracks: / Denis / Heart of glass / Call me / Rapture / Rapture (bonus beats) / Tide is high, The / Jam was moving / In love with love / Rush rush / French kissin' in the USA / Feel the spin / Backfired / Sunday girl (french version).
LP: . . . . CJB 2
MC: . . . . ZCJB 2
LP: 209 556

PARALLEL LINES.
Tracks: / Fade away / Hanging on the telephone / One way or another / Picture this / Pretty baby / I know but I don't know / 11.59 / Will anything happen / Sunday girl / Heart of glass / I'm gonna love you too / Just go away.
LP: . . . . FA 41 3089 1
MC: . . . . FA 41 3089 4
LP: . . . . CDL 1192
MC: . . . . ZCDL 1192
LP: . . . . FA 3089
MC: . . . . TCFA 3089

PLASTIC LETTERS.
Tracks: / Fan mail / Denis / Bermuda triangle / Youth nabbed as sniper / Contact in Red Square / (I'm always touched by your) presence dear / I'm on / I didn't have the nerve to say no / Love at the pier / No imagination / Kidnapper / Detroit 442 / Cautious lip.
LP: . . . . CHR 1166
MC: . . . . ZCHR 1166

Blondy, Alpha

BEST OF ALPHA BLONDY.
MC: . . . . SHANC 43075

COCODY ROCK.
Tracks: / Cocody rock / Tere / Super powers / Interplanetary revolution / Fangandan kameleba / Bory samory.
LP: . . . . SGLP 1
MC: . . . . SGLC 1

JAH GLORY (Blondy, Alpha & The Natty Rebels).
LP: . . . . DFK 8710

JERUSALEM (Blondy, Alpha & The Wailers).
Tracks: / Jerusalem / Politique / Bloodshed in Africa / I love Paris / Kalachnikor love / Travailler c'est trop dur / Mina / Poultevard de la mort / Dji.
LP: . . . . STERNS 1019
MC: . . . . STC 1019
LP: . . . . SHAN 43054

Blonker

HOMELAND.
Tracks: / African kalimba / Morning breeze / Sleepwalk / Perpetuum motion / Blue horizon / Here, there and everywhere / Alhambra / Maria Elena / Homeland / When a man loves a woman.
LP: 8129 081
MC: 8129 084

Blood

FALSE GESTURES FOR A DEVIOUS PUBLIC.
Tracks: / Done some brain cells last night / Degenerate / Gestapo khazi / Well sick / Sewer brain / Sucker / Mesrine / Rule 43 / Joys of noise / Waste of flesh and bones / Throttle you blue.
LP: . . . . NOYZLP 1

FULL TIME RESULT (Blood/Gonads).
Tracks: / Stark raving normal / Meglomania / Such fun / Alconaut / Napalm job / Drunk addict / Coffin dodgers / Go mad with the gonads / I lost my love to a UK sub / Sandra Bigg really big / Got any Wrigleys John? / Punk rock will never die / Drinking song / Jobs not jails.
LP: . . . . LINK LP 024

SICK KICKS FOR SHOCK ROCKERS.
LP: . . . . QUEST 3

Blood Brothers (band)

HONEY AND BLOOD.
Tracks: / Replica / Building it up again / True force / Gasoline / Goodbye / Vanilla girl / Justine / Raise high the roof / Evita the crown / Take the pain.
LP: . . . . HIP 66
MC: . . . . HIPC 66

Blood Brothers (show)

BLOOD BROTHERS (See under Dickson, Barbara) (Various artists).

Blood Feast

CHOPPING BLOCK BLUES.
LP: . . . . FLAME 1016

FACE FATE.
MLP: . . . . NRR 35
MC: . . . . NRC 35
LPPD: . . . . NRPD 35

KILL FOR PLEASURE.
LP: . . . . NRR 16
MC: . . . . NRC 16

Blood, James

TALES OF CAPTAIN BLACK.
LP: . . . . AH 7

Blood On The Cats

BLOOD ON THE CATS (VIDEO) (See under Psychobilly) (Various artists).

BLOOD ON THE CATS/REVENGE OF THE KILLER PUSSIES (See under Psychobilly) (Various artists).

Blood On The Roq

BLOOD ON THE ROQ (Various artists).
LP: . . . . QLP 3

Blood On The Saddle

BLOOD ON THE SADDLE.
LP: . . . . NAR 15

FRESH BLOOD.
LP: . . . . ROSE 126

POISON LOVE.
LP: . . . . PETE 1
LP: . . . . ROSE 88

Blood On The Sun(film)

BLOOD ON THE SUN (Film soundtrack) (Various artists).
LP: . . . . CT 6031

Blood & Roses

ENOUGH IS NEVER ENOUGH.
LP: . . . . SIN 1

LIFE AFTER DEATH.
MC: 96 10

Blood Simple (film)

BLOOD SIMPLE/RAISING ARIZONA (See under Raising Arizona) (Various artists).

Blood, Sweat & Tears

BLOOD, SWEAT & TEARS.
LP: . . . . BGOLP 28
LP: 63504

BLOOD, SWEAT & TEARS 3.
LP: 64024

CHALLENGE, THE.
LP: 20140
MC: 40140

CHILD IS FATHER TO THE MAN.
LP: 63296

CLASSIC BLOOD SWEAT & TEARS.
Tracks: / You've made me so very happy / I can't quit her / Go down gamblin' / Hi de ho / Sometimes in the winter / Without her / When I die / Spinning wheel / Lisa / Listen to me / Smiling phases / I love you more than you'll ever know / Lucretia MacEvil / God bless the child.
LP: . . . . CBS 31824

GREATEST HITS: BLOOD, SWEAT & TEARS.
Tracks: / Spinning wheel / I can't quit her / Go down gamblin' / God bless the child / Hi de ho.
LP: . . . . CBS 32159

LATIN FIRE.
LP: . . . . PLP 25
MC: . . . . PMC 25

MIDNIGHT CONCERT.
LP: . . . . MA 25884
MC: . . . . MAMC 925884

NUCLEAR BLUES.
Tracks: / Agitato / Nuclear blues / Manic depression / I'll drown in my own tears / Fantasy stage / Spanish wine / Latin fire / Challenge, The / Duel, The / Amor.
LP: . . . . MCF 3061
LP: 2215235
MC: 2115235

SMILING PHASES.
Tracks: / Smiling phases / More and more / Fire and rain / Lonesome Susie / Somethin' comin' on / Cowboys and Indians / High on a mountain / Take me in your arms (rock me a little while) / Down in the flood / Touch me / Alone / Morning glory / Without her / Just one smile / Roller coaster / Rosemary / Back up against the wall / Velvet.
MC: . . . . ELITE 005 MC

Blood Uncles

LIBERTINE.
Tracks: / Beathag / Let's go crazy / Under your heel / Crash / Danny's favourite game / Caravan / Shake / Scars in the morning / Never happy man / Breakdown express / Speaker / Broken town (CD & Cassette only).
LP: . . . . V 2437
MC: . . . . TCV 2437
LP: . . . . OVED 265
MC: . . . . OVEDC 265

Bloodcum

HARDCORE DEMO SERIES, THE.
LP: . . . . WRR 002

Bloodfire Posse

ARE YOU READY.
Tracks: / Are you ready / Rub-a-dub soldier / Pink panther / Nuclear weapons / Every posse get flat / Suddenly / Coconut water / Be / I should have known better.
LP: 4502091
MC: 4502094
LP: . . . . SYNC 01

Bloodgood

DETONATION.
LP: . . . . RO 9019
MC: . . . . CO 9019

ROCK IN A HARD PLACE.
Tracks: / Shakin' it / Presence, The / What have I done / Heaven on Earth / Do or die / She's gone / World, The / Seven.
LP: . . . . RO 9036
MC: . . . . CO 9036

Bloodied Sword

BLOODIED SWORD (Langdown, Maxwell/Ure, Midge/Chris Cross).
Tracks: / Sword's theme, The / Sword speaks / Gun / Propaganda machine / Seer / Haunting, The / Warnings / Confrontation / Mercy / Alliance / Oceana's theme / One with man / Damnation / Threats / Propaganda / Jester's theme, The / Pageant, The / Soliloquy / Sword's theme (part 2), The.
LP: . . . . CDL 1424
MC: . . . . ZCDL 1424

Bloodline (film)

BLOODLINE (Film soundtrack) (Various artists).
LP: . . . . STV 81131

Bloodlust

GUILTY AS SIN.
LP: . . . . RR 9744

TERMINAL VELOCITY.
LP: . . . . WRR 005

Bloodshed & Butchery

BLOODSHED AND BUTCHERY (Various artists).
LP: . . . . CRIMLP 105

Bloodstone

BLOODSTONE.
LP: . . . . TXS 110

DON'T STOP.
Tracks: / Don't stop / I'm just doing my job / Throw a little bit of love my way / It's all been said before / She wants to hear the words / Just wanna get the feel of it / You bring out the best in me / It's been a long time.
LP: . . . . STML 12097

NATURAL HIGH (OLD GOLD) (See under Albert, Morris/Feelings(Old Gold).

Bloody Marys

STAIN.
Tracks: / Stain / Suspicion.
LP: . . . . JOSS 2

Bloody Six

IN THE NAME OF BLOOD.
LP: . . . . SKULL 8390

Bloom, Claire (nar)

JANE EYRE (see under Jane Eyre (bk)).

PRIDE AND PREJUDICE (See under Austen, Jane).

SECRET GARDEN, THE (see under Secret Garden).

SENSE AND SENSIBILITY (See under Austen, Jane).

SILVER SKATES, THE (See under Silver Skates (bk)).

WUTHERING HEIGHTS (see under Wuthering Heights (bk)).

Bloom, Ken

KEN BLOOM.
LP: . . . . FF 051

Bloom, Luka

LUKA BLOOM.
LP: . . . . **MRLP 008**

RIVERSIDE.
LP: **926 092 1**
MC: **926 092 4**

Bloom, Rube

SEVEN HOT AIR MEN.
LP: . . . . **VLP 41**

Bloomer Girl (film)

BLOOMER GIRL (Original Broadway cast) (Various artists).
LP: . . . . **MCA 1536**
MC: . . . . **MCAC 1536**

Bloomfield (film)

BLOOMFIELD (Film Soundtrack) (Various artists).
Tracks: / Opening theme (Nimrod's theme): *Various artists* / Loner: *Various artists* / Nimrod's exit from Eirad: *Various artists* / Love theme: *Various artists* / Title theme: *Various* artists / Swinging Greek: *Various* artists / Eitan's salty drive: *Various artists* / Homing in on the next trade wind: *Various artists* / Eitan pays the penalty: *Various artists* / Eight in the arena: *Various artists* / Hail the conquering hero: *Various* artists / Closing love theme: *Various artists* / Eitan does his net: *Various artists* / Hello my life: *Various artists* / On top of the world: *Various artists* / Distraction: *Various artists*.
LP: . . . . **NSPL 18376**

Bloomfield, Mike

AMERICAN HERO.
Tracks: / Hully gully / Wings of an angel / Walking the floor / Don't you lie to me / Junko partner / Knockin' myself out / Women lovin' each other / Cherry red / RX for the blues / You must have Jesus.
LP: . . . . **THBL 1.009**

ANALINE.
Tracks: / Peepin' an' amoaning / Mr. Johnson and Mr.Dunn / Frankie and Johnny / At the cross / Big C blues / Hilo waltz / Effinonna rag / Mood indigo / Analine.
LP: . . . . **SNTF 749**

BETWEEN A HARD PLACE AND THE GROUND.
Tracks: / Eyesight to the blind / Linda Lou / Kansas City blues / Darktown strutters ball / Mop mop / Call me a dog / I'm glad I'm jewish / Great gifts from heaven / Lo, though I am with thee / Jockey blues / Between a hard place and the ground / Uncle Bon's barrelhouse blues / Wee wee hours / Vamp in C / One of these days.
LP: . . . . **THBL 076**

BLOOMFIELD.
Tracks: / I got my Mojo working / Born in Chicago / Texas / Groovin' is easy / Killing floor / You don't realise / Wine / Albert's shuffle / Stop / I wonder who / You're killing my love / Goofers / It hurts me too / Relaxin' blues / Blues for Jimmy Yancey / Sunnyland Slim and Otis Spann / Woodyard Street / Midnight on my radio / Why, Lord, oh why? / Easy rider.
2LP: . . . . **CBS 22164**
MCSET: **40 22164**

BLOOMFIELD AND HARRIS (Bloomfield, Mike/Woody Harris).
LP: . . . . **SNKF 164**

CRUISING FOR A BRUISING.
Tracks: / Cruising for a bruising / Linda Lu / Papa mama rompah stompah / Junkers blues / Midnight / It'll be me / Motorized blues / Mathilda / Winter moon / Snowblind.
LP: . . . . **SNTF 860**

FATHERS AND SONS (See under Waters, Muddy) (Bloomfield, Mike/ Muddy Waters).

IF YOU LOVE THESE BLUES....
Tracks: / Hey foreman / India / Death cell rounder blues / City girl / Kansas City / Mama lion / Thrift shop rag / Death in my family / East Colorado blues / Blue ghost blues / Train is gone, The / Altar song, The.
LP: . . . . **SNTF 726**

I'M WITH YOU ALWAYS.
Tracks: / Eyesight to the blind / Frankie And Johnny / I'm with you always / Jockey blues / Some of these days / Don't you lie to me / Hymn tune / Darktown strutters' ball / Stagger Lee / I'm glad I'm Jewish / A flat boogaloo.
LP: . . . . **FIEND 92**

LIVE ADVENTURES OF MIKE BLOOMFIELD AND AL COOPER (Bloomfield, Mike/Al Cooper).
Tracks: / Opening speech / 59th Street bridge song / I wonder why / Her holy modal highness / Weight, The / Mary Ann / Together / That's alright / Green onions.
2LP: . . . . **DED 261**

LIVING IN THE FAST LANE.
LP: . . . . **DAMP 100**

TRIUMVIRATE (Bloomfield, Mike/John Hammond/Doctor John).
Tracks: / Cha dooky-doo / Last night / I yi yi / Just to be with you / Baby let me kiss you / Sho' 'bout to drive me wild / It hurts me too / Rock me baby / Ground hog blues / Pretty thing.
LP: . . . . **ED 228**

Bloomfield, Steve

ROCKABILLY ORIGINALS.
Tracks: / Hurricane / Rockin' rhythm / Sure fire way / Blues in my shoes / Over the hill / Anything I can do / Take my boots off / Hot potato / Who's gonna be your daddy? / I can't get on / There ain't no one to talk to / Fresh outa love / Country girl / Bobcat.
LP: . . . . **CR 30159**
LP: . . . . **LP 7810**

Bloomsday

FORTUNY.
LP: . . . . **ILPS 9972**
LP: **846 964 1**
MC: . . . . **ICT 9972**
MC: **846 964 4**

Bloss, Rainer

AMPSY.
Tracks: / Oracle, The / From long ago / Energy / Adoring multitudes, The / Psyche / I'm the heat / He's an angel / Who the hell is she / Lights out baby / Love is a beginning.
LP: . . . . **THBL 032**
LP: . . . . **ID 20007**

APHRICA (See under Schulze, Klaus) (Bloss, Rainier/Klaus Schulze/Ernst Such).

DRIVE INN (See under Schulze,Klaus) (Bloss, Rainer/Klaus Schulze).

Blossom Toes

COMPLETE, THE.
Tracks: / Look at me, I'm you / I'll be late for tea / Remarkable saga of the frozen dog, The / Telegram Tuesday / Love is / What's it for / People of the Royal Parks / What on Earth / Mrs. Murphy's budgerigar / I will bring you this and that / Mr. Watchmaker / When the alarm clocks ring / You / Postcard / Everyone's leaving me now / Peace lovin' man / Kiss of confusion / Listen to the silence / Love bomb / Billy Boo - The gun man / Indian Summer / Just above my hobby horse's head / Wait a minute.
2LP: . . . . **LIKD 43**
MCSET: . . . . **TCLIKD 43**

COMPLETE, THE/ THIRD (Blossom Toes/ Soft Machine).
MC: . . . . **TCAD 23**

Blossom Toes II

NEW DAY (Blossom Toes II Aka B.B. Blunder).
Tracks: / Sticky living / You're so young / Lost horizons / Research / Rocky yagbag / Seed / Put your money where your mouth is / Rise / Moondance / New day.
LP: . . . . **LIK 48**
MC: . . . . **TCLIK 48**

Blount, Chris

CHRIS BLOUNT'S NEW ORLEANS JAZZBAND (Blount, Chris New Orleans Jazz Band).
LP: . . . . **GHB 234**

LIVE AT THE KENDAL JAZZ FESTIVAL 1987.
Tracks: / Hindustan / Wabash blues / Lily of the valley / Just a closer walk with thee / Collegiate / My old kentucky home / Take my hand / Precious Lord / Old grey bonnet / In the upper garden / I can't escape from you / Red wing.
LP: . . . . **LA 5009**
MC: . . . . **LA 5009C**

MAYBE ANOTHER DAY (Blount, Chris New Orleans Jazz Band).
Tracks: / Bugle boy march / Honey swat blues / My life will be sweeter / Eyes of Texas, The / Does Jesus care / It's a sin to tell a lie / I ain't gonna give nobody none of my jelly roll / Plaisir d'amour / Yaaka hula hickey dula / Franklin St blues / If I had my life to live over / Ole miss rag.
LP: . . . . **LA 5005**
MC: . . . . **LA 5005C**

OLD RUGGED CROSS, THE (Blount, Chris New Orleans Jazz Band).
Tracks: / Mary wore a golden chain / Amazing grace / Lord, Lord, Lord / Only a look / Royal telephone / Old rugged cross / In the sweet bye and bye / Hands of God / Lead me saviour / It is no secret / Walking with the king / Evening prayer, An / Yes Lord, I'm crippled / His eye is on the sparrow / End of a perfect day.
MC: . . . . **LA 5016/C**

TELL ME YOUR DREAMS (Blount, Chris New Orleans Jazz Band).
LP: . . . . **RSL 142**

Blow By Blow

HARMONICA ANTHOLOGY.
LP: . . . . **SG 709-01**

Blow Fly

ELECTRIC BANANA (X-RATED).
LP: . . . . **RL 054**

Blow It 'Till You ...

BLOW IT 'TILL YOU LIKE IT (See under Blues) (Various artists).

Blow, Kurtis

AMERICA.
Tracks: / America / America (dub mix) / Super sperm / AJ meets Davy mix / Hello baby / If I ruled the world / Respect to the king / Summertime groove MC lullaby / Don"t cha feel like making love.
LP: **826 141-1**
MC: **826 141-4**

BEST RAPPER IN TOWN, THE.
Tracks: / Party time / Do the do / Boogie blues / Breaks, The / One two five / Throughout your years.
LP: **822 283 1**
MC: **822 283 4**

EGO TRIP.
Tracks: / Eight million stories / AJ Scratch / Basketball / Under fire / I can't take it no more / Ego trip / Falling back in love again.
LP: **8224201**
MC: **8224204**

KINGDOM BLOW.
Tracks: / Street rock / Bronx / Unity party jam / Sunshine / Magilla Gorilla / I'm chillin' / Kingdom blow / Reasons for wanting you.
LP: . . . . **JABH 22**
MC: . . . . **JABHC 22**

KURTIS BLOW.
Tracks: / Rappin' blow / Breaks, The / Way out West / Throughout your years / Hard times / All I want in this world / Takin' care of business.
LP: **6337137**

TOUGH.
Tracks: / Tough / Juice / Daydreaming / Boogie blues / Baby you've got to go.
LP: . . . . **MX 1505**
MC: **M4X 1505**

Blow Monkeys

ANIMAL MAGIC.
Tracks: / Digging your scene / Animal magic / Wicked ways / Sweet murder / Aeroplane city lovesong / I nearly died laughing / Don't be scared of me / Burn the rich / I backed a winner (in you) / Forbidden fruit / Heaven is a place I'm moving to.
LP: . . . . **PL 70910**
MC: . . . . **PK 70910**

CHOICES (The Singles Connection).
Tracks: / Wait / Choice / Slaves no more / Celebrate the day (after you) / Wicked ways / Digging your scene / It doesn't have to be this way / Out with her / This is your life / It pays to belong / Wait (extended) (on cassette and CD only) / Choice (extended) (on cassette and CD only) / Man from Russia (on CD only) / Atomic lullaby (on CD only) / Wildflower / Forbidden fruit.
LP: . . . . **PL 74191**
MC: . . . . **PK 74191**

LIMPING FOR A GENERATION.
Tracks: / He's shedding skin / Wild flower / Atomic lullaby / Fat cat Bolsha / Go public / Professor Supercool / Man from Russia / Waiting for Mr. Moonlight / Limping for a generation / Trashtown incident.
LP: . . . . **NL 71495**
MC: . . . . **PK 70395**
MC: . . . . **NK 71495**

SHE WAS ONLY A GROCER'S DAUGHTER.
Tracks: / It doesn't have to be this way / Some kind of wonderful / Out with her / How long can a bad thing last / Man at the end of his tether / Rise above / Day after you, The / Checking out / Don't give it up / Cash / Beautiful child / This is the way it has to be (Available only on Casette/Compact Disc) / Grantham grizzler, The (Available only on Cassette/Compact Disc).
LP: . . . . **PL 71245**
MC: . . . . **PK 71245**
LP: . . . . **NL 74741**
MC: . . . . **NK 74741**

SPRINGTIME FOR THE WORLD.
Tracks: / In too deep / Vibe alive / Be not afraid / La passionara / Fruits of the earth / Checking out / Springtime for the world / Reflections '89 / If you love somebody / Let the people dance / As the dust settles / Other side of you, The.
MC: . . . . **PK 74359**
LP: . . . . **PL 74359**

WHOOPS, THERE GOES THE NEIGHBOURHOOD.
Tracks: / At home / This is your life / No woman is an island / Squareville / Sweet talking rapist / Zebs emigrate / Wait / It pays to belong / Come on down / Bombed into the stoneage.
LP: . . . . **PL 71858**
MC: . . . . **PK 71858**

Blow The Wind

BLOW THE WIND SOUTHERLY (Various artists).
LP: . . . . **VRW 002**

Blow Up

AMAZON EYEGASM.
Tracks: / Somersault sunrise / Fly me across the ocean / World / Thorn of crowns / Caterpillar song / Just sin / She fades away / Different sounding sighs / Across me today.
LP: . . . . **BRED 91**

IN WATERMELON SUGAR.
Tracks: / Own world waiting / Heaven tonight / Sweet skin / Beauty lies / Forever holiday / Baby superstar / What is in your mind? / I / Todd / Wish / Honker's cha cha (Only on CD.) / Lovescene (Only on CD.) / Slip into something (Only on CD.) / Little fool 52 (Only on CD.).
LP: . . . . **BRED 85**
MC: . . . . **CBRED 85**

ROLLERCOASTER.
LP: . . . . **MD 7918**

Blowzabella

BLOWZABELLA.
LP: . . . . **PLR 038**

BLOWZABELLA IN COLOUR.
LP: . . . . **PLR 051**

BLOWZABELLA SOUND, THE.
LP: . . . . **PLR 074**
MC: . . . . **PLC 074**

BOBBITYSHOOTY.
LP: . . . . **PLR 064**

PINGHA FRENZIE.
LP: . . . . **BIGH 001**
LP: . . . . **BIGHOK 422**

RICHER DUST, A.
LP: . . . . **PLR 080**
MC: . . . . **PLC 080**

TAM LIN (See under Armstrong, Frankie) (Blowzabella/Frankie Armstrong/Brian Pearson/Jon Gillaspie).

VANILLA.
LP: . . . . **SPD 1028**
MC: . . . . **SPDC 1028**

Blu, Peggi

BLU BLOWIN'.
Tracks: / Tender moments / Love's just a mystery / Once had your love (and I can't let go) / All the way with you (Duet with Bert Robinson.) / Over and over / Mesmorize me / Feels good to me / All and all / Two can play at that game / I believe in you.
LP: . . . . **ESTV 2033**
MC: . . . . **TCESTV 2033**

Blubbery Hellbellies

CAFE BLUR.
LP: . . . . **BLUNT 034**

FLABBERGASTED.
LP: . . . . **UPLP 8**
MC: . . . . **UPLM 8**

Bludgeoned

BLUDGEONED (Various artists).
LP: . . . . **BLUD 1**
MC: . . . . **BLUDGE 1**

Blue

FOOLS PARTY.
Tracks: / Blue nights / Danger sign / Fools party / How beautiful / I don't want to leave her / Long enough / Love sings / Mexico / Mona / Stranger's town / Victim / Without you.
LP: . . . . **TRAIN 4**

Blue Aeroplanes

BEATSONGS.
Tracks: / Huh! / Your own world / Angelwords / Fun / Cardboard box / My hurricane / Aeroplanes blues / Jack leaves and black Spring / Colour me / Streamers / Boy in the bubble, The / Sixth continent.
LP: . . . . **CHEN 21**
MC: . . . . **ZCHEN 21**

BOP ART.
LP: . . . . **ABT 009**
LP: . . . . **PART 001RV**

FRIENDLOVERPLANE.
2LP: . . . . **FIRELP 15**

SPITTING OUT MIRACLES.
Tracks: / Spitting out miracles.

LP: FIRELP 10

SWAGGER.
Tracks: / Jacket hangs / World view blues / Weightless / ...And stones / Love come around / Your ages / Applicant, The / What it is / Anti-pretty / Careful boy / Picture framed / Cat-scan hist'ry.
LP: CHEN 13
MC: ZCHEN 13

TOLERANCE.
LP: FIRELP 3

Blue Angel

BLUE ANGEL.
Tracks: / Maybe he'll know / I had a love / Fade / Anna blue / Can't blame me / Late / Cut out / Take a chance / Just the other day / I'm gonna be strong / Lorraine / Everybody's got an angel.
LP: 2391 486

Blue Bandanna Country

COUNTRY BLUES.
MC: C 1

Blue, Barry

BEST OF AND THE REST OF, THE.
Tracks: / Do you wanna dance / Dancin' on a Saturday night / Don't wanna be blue / Ooh i do / Kalamazoo / Pay at the gate / Queen of hearts / One way ticket (to the blues) / Tip of my tongue / Don't put your money on my horse / Miss hit and run / School love / Hi-cool woman / Hotshot / Mona / Rosetta stone.
MC: ARLC 1003

Blue Bay

BLUE BAY (Various artists).
LP: MESSAROUND 001

Blue Beard (bks)

BLUE BEARD (Various artists).
Tracks: / Blue beard: *Various artists* / Peter and the golden bird: *Various artists* / Golden goose, The: *Various artists* / Allskin: *Various artists* / Jack and Jill: *Various artists.*
MC: ANV 615

Blue Beard (Film)

BLUE BEARD (1972 Film soundtrack) (Various artists).
LP: C'BUS 105

Blue, Bill

GIVING GOOD BOYS A BAD NAME.
LP: AD 4118

SING LIKE THUNDER (Blue, Bill Band).
LP: AD 4109

Blue Bird

MOST UNIQUE MUSICAL EXPERIENCE, A (Blue Bird Society Orch).
LP: ST 268

Blue Blood

BLUE BLOOD.
LP: SNTF 615

Blue Blud

BIG NOISE, THE.
LP: MFN 93
MC: TMFN 93

Blue Bossa

BLUE BOSSA (See under Jazz) (Various artists).

Blue Box

CAPTURED DANCE FLOOR.
LP: 807 801

Blue Boy

BLUE FEVER.
LP: CH 001

Blue Caps

BLUE CAPS UNLEASHED.
Tracks: / Wrapped up in rockabilly / Baby blue / Yes I love you baby / I got a baby / Blue cap man / I lost an angel / Silly song / Lotta lovin / Say mama / Down at the den / Dance to the bop / Johnny's boogie / Be bop a lula / Rap, The.
LP: MFLP 019

ON THE ROAD AGAIN.
Tracks: / Lotta lovin' / Dance to the bop / I got it / Yes I love you baby / Little lover / Git it / Rollin' Danny / Teenage partner / Dance in the street / Baby blue / Lovely Loretta / Who's pushing your swing / Right now / Be-bop-boogie boy / I got a baby / Say mama / Be bop a lula.
LP: MFLP 1020

Blue Cats

BLUE CATS.
LP: LPL 8011
LP: CR 30204

EARLY DAYS VOL1.
LP: NERD 010

EARLY DAYS VOL 2.
LP: NERD 011

EARLY DAYS: VOLUMES 1 AND 2.
2LP: NERD 010-011

FIGHT BACK.
LP: LPL 8111

Blue Cheer

BEST OF BLUE CHEER.
LP: 6463 142
MC: 7145 142

BLITZKRIEG OVER NUREMBERG.
Tracks: / Babylon / Girl next door / Ride with me / Just a little bit / Summertime blues / Out of focus / Doctor please / Hunter, The.
LP: THBL 091

HIGHLIGHTS AND LOWLIGHTS.
LP: 23010413
MC: THBC 125

Blue Chip Orchestra

BLUE CHIP ORCHESTRA.
LP: IRS 949 166

Blue City (film)

BLUE CITY (See under Cooder, Ry) (Cooder, Ry).

Blue Diamonds

RAMONA.
LP: 022 58193
MC: 222 58193

Blue Eyed Soul

BLUE EYED SOUL (See under Soul) (Various artists).

Blue Feather

FEATHER FUNK.
LP: 6423 530

Blue Flame Stringband

BLUE FLAME STRINGBAND.
LP: FF 275

Blue For Two

BLUE FOR TWO.
LP: CALCLP 008

Blue Geranium (bk)

BLUE GERANIUM AND MORE STORIES (Agatha Christie) (Hickson, Joan (nar)).
MCSET: LFP 7340

Blue Grass Cardinals

CARDINAL CLASS.
LP: SH 3731
MC: SH 3731 MC

CARDINAL SOUL.
Tracks: / Low and lonely / Nothing can my loving you / With half a heart / Blue is the color of lonesome / I feel good / Gift of love / Don't give up on me / 32 acres / Old man in the park, The / I've had a time / Mountain Laurel.
LP: CMH 6235
MC: CMHC 6235

HOME IS WHERE THE HEART IS.
Tracks: / Be good as my little girl / Rebel's last request / I don't believe you've met my baby / Home is where the heart is / Wicked path of sin / Slowly / Five days in heaven / Slowly getting you out of the way / It rained / Tiny broken heart / Colarado / It's mighty dark to travel.
LP: SH 3741

LIVIN' IN THE GOOD OLD DAYS.
Tracks: / I think we're livin' in the good old days / Knee deep in loving you / Dedication to Lester Flatt / What's good for you (should be alright for me) / Darling is it too late now? / Sweet hour of prayer / On down the line / I wonder where you are tonight / First one to love you, The / Greener pastures / You took all the ramblin' out of me / Uncle Billy play your fiddle for me.
LP: CMH 6229
MC: CMHC 6229

SHINING PATH, THE.
LP: SH 3751
MC: SH 3751 MC

SUNDAY MORNIN' SINGIN'.
LP: CMH 6247
MC: CMHC 6247

WELCOME TO VIRGINIA.
LP: ROUNDER 0097
MC: ROUNDER 0097C

WHERE RAINBOWS TOUCH DOWN.
LP: CMH 6259
MC: CMHC 6259

Blue in Heaven

ALL THE GODS MEN.
Tracks: / Sometimes / Big beat, The / It's Saturday / Old Ned / All you fear / Julie cries / Like a child / In your eyes / Slowly.
LP: BIH 1
MC: BIHC 1

EXPLICIT MATERIAL.
Tracks: / Change your mind / Tell me / Just another day / Sister / Be your man / I just wanna / Close your eyes / Rolling in the crowd / Hope to God.
LP: ILPS 9838
MC: ICT 9838

Blue, Jimmy

FAVOURITE SCOTTISH DANCE MUSIC VOL.1 (Blue, Jimmy & His Scottish Band).
Tracks: / Duke of Perth / Original / Back o'Benachie / Ailsa's fancy / Scottish ramble / Doon the burn / David lad / Broom hill / Morpeth rant / Jack's delight / Don hornpipe / Military two step / Frank Jamieson / Gay Gordons / Bonnie hoose o' Airlie / Bobs shaggy dog / Flowers of Edinburgh / Waverly steps / Donald McLeod / Dashing white sergeant / Reconciliation / C T S express / Hamilton house / Family pride / Malcolm Ross / Scottish waltz / Bonnie lass o' Scotland / Aviemore / Lovely glens of Angus, The / Maxwells' rant / Dancing the baby / Snouts ears / Highland Schottische / Pipe Major William McLean / Strip the willow / Rock and wee pickle tow, The / John Grumlie / Nellie Wemyess / Jig of slurs, The.
LP: NL 70129
MC: NK 70129
LP: NL 25215
LP: INTS 5245

HIS SCOTTISH DANCE BAND - VOL.1 (Blue, Jimmy & His Scottish Dance Band).
MC: ZCPKB 5562

SATURDAY BARN DANCE (Blue, Jimmy Band & Various artists).
MC: ZCPKB 5565

Blue Lagoon (film)

BLUE LAGOON, THE (Film soundtrack) (Various artists).
Tracks: / Blue lagoon (love theme): *Various artists* / Fire: *Various artists* / Island, The: *Various artists*/ Sands of time, The: *Various artists* / Paddy's death: *Various artists* / Children grow, The: *Various artists*/ Lord of the lagoon: *Various artists* / Underwater courtship: *Various artists* / Kiss, The: *Various artists.*
LP: TKR 70195

Blue, Little Joe

BLUE'S BLUE'S.
Tracks: / Right there where you left it / Little Joe Blue / Sometime tomorrow / Encourage me baby / Don't stop loving me / Fool is what you wanted, A / Southern country boy / Just love won't do / If you'd only let me love you / I'm not your first love / Loose me / Gonna walk on / If there's a better way / Fool is what you wanted, A.
LP: CRB 1150

I'M DOING ALL RIGHT AGAIN.
Tracks: / I'm doing all right again / As meaning as I've been good / Who / I'm not blind / Me and my woman / Devil in disguise / My tomorrow / You keep my nose to the grinding stone.
LP: EJR 4009
MC: MCEJR 4009

Blue Magic

BLUE MAGIC.
Tracks: / Sideshow / Look me up / What's come over me / Just don't want to be lonely / Stop to start / Welcome to the club / Spell / Answer to my prayer / Tear it down.
LP: K 40532

FROM OUT OF THE BLUE.
Tracks: / It's like magic / Couldn't get to sleep last night / Secret lover / We're gonna make it / I heard you're going away / From out of the blue / Romeo and Juliet / We ain't new to this / There's a song in my head / Tuesday heartbreak / More I get, The / Take a long last look / Break it out / Dancin' to the flag.
LP: 4633921
MC: 4633924

GREATEST HITS: BLUE MAGIC.
Tracks: / Sideshow / Stop to start / Spell / What's come over me / Three ring circus / Tear it down / Look me up / Welcome to the club / Chasin' rainbows / Just don't want to be lonely / Summer snow / Where have you been.
LP: XXHAN 508

Blue Max (film)

BLUE MAX (Film soundtrack) (Various artists).
Tracks: / Dream machine: *Various artists* / Sing song blues: *Various artists* / Bad bad amigo: *Various artists*/ Hangman: *Various artists* / Need your love: *Various artists* / Flying to Moscow: *Various artists* / Paid assassin: *Various artists* / Camera, camera: *Various artists* / Photographing gold: *Various artists*/ Murder at the movies: *Various artists* / I know you're there: *Various artists* / Wait for the new one: *Various artists.*
LP: CT 6008
LP: CAS 1142
LP: CT 7007

Blue Mercedes

RICH AND FAMOUS.
LP: MCF 3403
MC: MCFC 3403

Blue, Mikki

I PROMISE (IMPORT).
MC: E 491171

Blue Mink

BEST OF AND THE REST OF, THE.
Tracks: / Melting pot / Randy / Gimme reggae / Good morning freedom / Can you feel it baby / By the devil (I was tempted) / Our world / Gasoline alley bred / Get up / Stay with me / Banner man / Sunshine of my life.
MC: ARLC 1004

COLLECTION: BLUE MINK.
Tracks: / Melting Pot / Randy / Gimme reggae / Good morning freedom / Can you feel it baby / By the devil (I was tempted) / Ock world / Gasoline Alley bred / Get up / Stay With Me / Banner Man / Sunshine of my life.
LP: ARLP 108
MC: ZCAR 108

HIT MAKING SOUNDS.
Tracks: / Melting pot / Can you feel it / Our world / We have all been saved / Cat house / Gasoline Alley bred / Good morning freedom / Bang bang Johnny's gang is after me / World (you're closing in on me) / Gimme reggae / Gap, The / Jubilation.
LP: GULM 500

Blue Monday

BLUE MONDAY (See under Blues) (Various artists).

Blue Moon Boys

MAKE THAT ROCKABILLY ROLL.
LP: ROCK 8905

Blue Moon (film)

BLUE MOON (See under Moebius) (Moebius (film)).

Blue Murder

BLUE MURDER.
Tracks: / Riot / Valley of the kings / Blue murder / Billy / Black hearted woman / Sex child / Jelly roll / Out of love / Vtolemy.
LP: WX 245
MC: WX 245C

BLUE MURDER AT HOME.
Tracks: / Settle down / Let's go / Not so sure anymore / Isabella / Start all over again / Straight to hell / Winter blues / Zabriskie Point / Ryu's song / Walk home my guitar.
LP: EM 9604

ENERGISE.
LP: BM 003

Blue Nile

HATS.
Tracks: / Downtown lights, The / Over the hillside / Let's go out tonight / Headlights on the parade / From a late night train / Seven am / Saturday night.
LP: LKH 2
MC: LKHC 2

WALK ACROSS THE ROOFTOPS, A.
Tracks: / Walk across the rooftops, A / Tinsel Town in the rain / From rags to riches / Stay / Easter parade / Heatwave / Automobile noise.
LP: LKH 1
MC: LKHC 1

Blue Note Jazzband

BLUE NOTE JAZZBAND.
LP: SDL 288

Blue Orchids

GREATEST HITS: BLUE ORCHIDS.
LP: ROUGH 36

Blue Oyster Cult

AGENTS OF FORTUNE.
Tracks: / This ain't the summer of love / True confessions / Don't fear the reaper / E.T.I. (Extra Terrestrial Intellegence) / Revenge of Vera Gemini / Sinful love / Tattoo vampire / Morning final / Tenderloin / Debbie Denise.
LP: CBS 32221
LP: CBS 81385

BLUE OYSTER CULT.
Tracks: / Transmission MC / I'm the lamb but I ain't no sheep / Then came the last days of May / Stairway to the stars / Before the kiss / Redcap, A / Screams / She's as beautiful as a foot / Cities on flame / Workshop of the telescopes / Redeemed.
LP: CBS 32025

CAREER OF EVIL.
Tracks: / Cities on flame / Red and the black, The / Hot rails to hell / Dominance and submission / 7 screaming Diz-

Busters / Me 262 / ETI (Extra Terrestrial Intellegence) / Beat 'em up / Black blade / Harvester of eyes, The / Flaming telepaths / Godzilla / (Don't fear) The reaper.
LP: 4659291
MC: 4659294

CLUB NINJA.
Tracks: / White flags / Dancin' in the ruins / Rock not war / Perfect water / Spy in the house of the night / Beat 'em up / When the war comes / Shadow warrior / Madness to the method.
LP: . . . . CBS 26775
MC: 40 26775

CULTOSAURUS ERECTUS.
Tracks: / Black blade / Monsters / Divine wind / Deadlines / Marshall plan, The / Hungry boys / Fallen angel / Lips in the hills / Unknown tongue.
LP: . . . . CBS 86120

E.T.I..
Tracks: / Dominance and submission / Cities on flame / Doctor Music / Red and the black, The / Joan Crawford / Burnin' for you / Roadhouse blues / Black blade / Hot rails to Hell / Godzilla / Veteran of the psychic wars / E.T.I. (Extra Terrestrial Intelligence) / Don't fear the Reaper.
2LP: . . . . CBS 22203

FIRE OF UNKNOWN ORIGIN.
Tracks: / Fire of unknown origin / Burnin' for you / Veteran of the psychic wars / Sole survivor / Heavy metal / Black and silver vengeance / After dark / Joan Crawford / Don't turn your back.
LP: 85137

IMAGINOS.
Tracks: / I am the one you warned me of / Les invisibles / In the presence of another world / Del Rio's song / Siege and investiture of Baron von Frankenstein's castle / Astronomy / Magna of illusion / Blue Oyster Cult / Imaginos.
LP: 4600361
MC: 4600364
LPPD: 4600360

MIRRORS.
Tracks: / Doctor Music / Great sun jester / In thee / Mirrors / Moon crazy / Vigil / I am the storm / You're not the one / Lonely teardrops.
LP: . . . . CBS 86087

ON YOUR FEET OR ON YOUR KNEES.
Tracks: / Subhuman / Harvester of eyes / Hot rails to hell / Red and the black, The / 7 screaming diz-busters / Buck's boogie / Then came the last days of May / Cities on flame / Me 262 / Before the kiss / I ain't got you / Born to be wild.
LP: 4601131
MC: 4601134

REVOLUTION BY NIGHT.
Tracks: / Take me away / Eyes on fire / Shooting shark / Veins / Shadow of California / Feel the thunder / Let go / Dragon lady / Light years of love.
LP: . . . . CBS 25686

SOME ENCHANTED EVENING.
Tracks: / R U ready 2 rock / ETI (Extra Terrestrial Intellegence) / Astronomy / Kick out the jams / Godzilla / Don't fear the reaper / We gotta get out of this place.
LP: . . . . CBS 86074
MC: 40 86074

SPECTRES.
Tracks: / Godzilla / Golden age of leather / Death valley nights / Searchin' for Celine / Fire works / R.U. ready / Rock / Celestial the queen / Going through the motions / I love the night / Nosferatu.
LP: . . . . CBS 32715
MC: 40 32715
LP: . . . . CBS 86050

Blue Pearl

NAKED.
MC: . . . . BLRMC 4
LP: . . . . BLRLP 4

Blue Print (label)

BLUE PRINT SAMPLER (Various artists).
LP: . . . . BLUSP 1

Blue, Rabbi Lionel

RABBI LIONEL BLUE.
MCSET: . . . . ZBBC 1178

Blue Ribbon Boogie

BLUE RIBBON BOOGIE (Various artists).
Tracks: / Paper boy boogie: *Various artists* / Barbershop boogie: *Various artists* / Blue ribbon boogie: *Various artists* / Cherokee boogie: *Various artists* / Long John boogie: *Various artists* / Big bear boogie: *Various* artists / All nite boogie: *Various artists* / Elevator boogie: *Various artists* / Too hot to handle: *Various* artists / Juke joint Johnny: *Various artists* / I'm a ding dong daddy: *Various artists* / Baby you should live so long: *Various artists* / I ain't got time: *Various artists* / Bloodshot eyes: *Various artists*.
LP: . . . . CR 30244

Blue Riddim Band

ALIVE IN JAMAICA.
LP: . . . . FF 325

RESTLESS SPIRIT.
LP: . . . . FF 255

Blue Ridge Corn

ERNEST V. STONEMAN AND BLUE RIDGE CORN SHUCKERS (See under Stoneman, Ernest V./Blue etc.) (Blue Ridge Corn Shuckers/Ernest V. Stoneman).

Blue Ridge Rangers

BLUE RIDGE RANGERS.
Tracks: / Blue Ridge Mountain blues / Somewhere listening (for my name) / You're the reason / Jambalaya / She thinks I still care / California blues / Workin' on a building / Please help me I'm falling / Have thine own way / I ain't never / Hearts of stone / Today I started loving you again.
LP: . . . . FACE 506
MC: . . . . FACC 506
LP: 5C 038 94373

Blue River Show Band

TOGETHER AGAIN.
Tracks: / All my cloudy days are gone / Four country roads / Oslo waltz / Love me tonight / Blue eyes / Dark island / Blanket on the ground / Scottish waltz / Before I met you / Together again / Gay Gordons / Old rugged cross, The.
MC: . . . . BRP 0002

Blue Rodeo

CASINO.
LP: 9031727701
MC: 9031727704

DIAMOND MINE.
Tracks: / God and country / Love and understanding / Diamond mine / House of dreams / Fall in line / Florida / Ballad of the dime store greaser / How long / Girl of mine / Now and forever / Nice try / One day / Fuse.
LP: . . . . WX 271
MC: . . . . WX 271C
LP: 256268 1

OUTSKIRTS.
Tracks: / Heart like mine, A / Rose coloured glasses / Rebel / Joker / Pirahna pool / Outskirts of life / Underground / 5'll get you 6 / Try / Floating.
LP: . . . . K 254718-1
MC: . . . . K 254718-4

Blue Rondo A La Turk

BEES KNEES AND CHICKENS ELBOWS.
Tracks: / Samba no pe / Slipping into daylight / Manifesto / Smoking dynamite / Masked moods / And then rain came / Hot corner / Are you satisfied.
LP: . . . . V 2311
LP: . . . . OVED 146
MC: . . . . OVEDC 146

CHEWING THE FAT.
Tracks: / Change / I spy for the FBI / Coco / Heavens are crying, The / Method, The / They really don't / Sarava / Klactoveesedstein / Carioca.
LP: . . . . OVED 90
MC: . . . . OVEDC 90

TOO SOON TO COME.
Tracks: / Carioca / Change / I spy for the FBI / Klactoveesedstein / Masked Moods / Slipping into daylight / Coco / Me & Mr. Sanchez / Hot corner / Are you satisfied / Heavens are crying, The.
LP: . . . . OVED 172
MC: . . . . OVEDC 172

Blue Rose

BLUE ROSE.
LP: . . . . SH 3768

Blue, Ruby

ALL RECORDINGS (See under Ruby Blue).

Blue Ruin

FLAME.
LP: . . . . MLRR 027

Blue Skies (film)

BLUE SKIES (Film soundtrack) (Various artists).
LP: . . . . SH 2095

Blue Sky Boys

BLUE SKY BOYS, BILL AND EARL BOLICK.
Tracks: / Don't this road look rough and rocky / Green grow the lilacs / Lawson family, The / Tragedy / You could be a millionaire / Curly headed baby / If I could hear my mother pray again / Tramp on the street / Searching for a soldier's grave / Unloved and unclaimed / Let me be your salty dog / My ma in trail / What does the deep sea say / When I take my vacation in heaven.
LP: . . . . ROUNDER 0052

IN CONCERT 1964.
LP: . . . . ROUNDER 0236
MC: . . . . ROUNDERC 0236

PRESENTING THE BLUE SKY BOYS.
LP: . . . . JEMF 104

SUNNY SIDE OF LIFE.
LP: . . . . ROUNDER 1006
MC: . . . . ROUNDER 1006C

Blue Steele

NO MORE LONELY NIGHTS.
LP: . . . . INS 2011

Blue Suede Shoes

BLUE SUEDE SHOES (VIDEO) (See under Rock 'n' Roll) (Various artists).

Blue Tears

BLUE TEARS.
LP: . . . . MCG 6111
MC: . . . . MCGC 6111

Blue Thunder (film)

BLUE THUNDER (Film soundtrack) (Various artists).
LP: . . . . MCA 6122
MC: . . . . MCAC 6122
LP: . . . . MCF 3183

Blue Tones

KNOCKOUT (See under Sugar Ray).

Blue Up

NOW.
LP: . . . . SANE 3

Blue Velvet (film)

BLUE VELVET (Film soundtrack) (Various artists).
Tracks: / Night streets/Sandy and Jeffrey: *Various artists* / Frank Jeffrey's dark side: *Various artists* / Mysteries of love(2 versions): *Various artists* / Frank returns: *Various artists* / Blue velvet: *Vinton, Bobby* / Lumberton USA/Going down to Lincoln: *Various artists* / Akron meets the blues: *Various artists* / In dreams: *Orbison, Roy* / Honky tonk: *Doggett, Bill* / Love letters: *Lester, Ketty* / Mysteries of love: *Various artists* / Blue star: *Various artists*.
LP: . . . . TER 1127
MC: . . . . ZCTER 1127

Blue Yonder

BLUE YONDER.
Tracks: / Windsong / House of love / When grace is falling / In the rain / Still I love / Long haul, The / Something for the pain / Indigo / Secret miracle.
LP: . . . . K 781 686 1
MC: . . . . K 782 686 4

Blue Zoo

TWO BY TWO.
Tracks: / Cry boy cry / John's lost / Far cry / Count on me (you can) / In love and in life / Love moves in strange ways / Somewhere in the world there's a cowboy smiling / Forgive and forget / I'm your man / Open up / Can't hold me down / Something familiar.
LP: . . . . MAGL 5051
MC: . . . . ZCMAG 5051

Bluebell & The...

BLUEBELL AND THE SHAMROCK (See under Ireland) (Various artists).

Bluebells

SISTERS.
Tracks: / Everbody's somebody's fool / Young at heart / I'm falling / Will she always be waiting / Cath / Red guitars / Syracuse University / Learn to love / Patriots game / South Atlantic way.
LP: . . . . LONLP 1
MC: . . . . LONC 1

Bluebird (label)

BLUEBIRD SAMPLER 1990 (Various artists).
Tracks: / St. Louis blues: *Armstrong, Louis & His Orchestra* / Moten swing: *Basie, Count & Bernie Moten's Kansas City* Orchestra / Indian Summer: *Bechet, Sidney & New Orleans Feetwarmers* / Georgia on my mind: *Carmichael, Hoagy* & His Orchestra / Ill wind: *Hawkins, Coleman & Ben Webster, Benny Carter & Orchestra* / All the things you are: *Desmond*, Paul & Gerry *Mulligan* / We'll git it: *Dorsey, Tommy & His Orchestra* / Caravan: *Ellington, Duke & His Famous Orchestra*/ Body and soul: *Ellington, Duke/Jimmy Blanton* / Night in Tunisia, A: *Gillespie, Dizzy & His Orchestra* / Tuxedo junction: *Hawkins, Erskine & His Orchestra* / Hocus pocus: *Henderson, Fletcher & His Orchestra* / What is this thing called love: *Horne, Lena* / Honky tonk train blues: *Lewis, Meade Lux* / Sunrise serenade: *Miller, Glenn* & His Orchestra / Struggle buggy: *Oliver, King & his Orchestra* / After you've gone: *Reinhardt, Django* / Now's the time: *Rollins, Sonny & co.* / Grabtown grapple, The: *Shaw, Artie & His Gramercy Five* / St James infirmary: *Teagarden, Jack & Louis Armstrong* / All that meat and no potatoes: *Waller, Fats & His Rhythm* / Boogie misterioso: *Williams, Mary Lou.*
LP: . . . . NL 82192
MC: . . . . NK 82192

Bluegrass...

20 BLUEGRASS ORIGINAL HYMNS (Various artists).
LP: . . . . SLP 5030
MC: . . . . GT 55030

20 BLUEGRASS ORIGINALS (Various artists).
LP: . . . . SLP 5028
MC: . . . . GT 55028

20 BLUEGRASS ORIGINALS VOL.2 (Various artists).
LP: . . . . SLP 5029
MC: . . . . GT 55029

ALL AROUND BLUEGRASS (Various artists).
Tracks: / On the southbound: *Various artists* / Chalk up another one: *Various artists* / Blue moon of Kentucky: *Various artists* / You can't go in the red playing bluegrass: *Various artists* / Carolina breakdown: *Various* artists / Have you come to say goodbye: *Various artists* / It's only a phonograph record: *Various artists*/ I'll go steppin' too: *Various artists* / Windy mountain: *Various artists* / Save it, save it: *Various artists*/ Cuttin the grass: *Various artists*/ Corn cob blues: *Various artists* / Kentucky rigerunner: *Various artists*/ Bringin' in the Georgia mail: *Various artists* / I won't be hanging around: *Various artists* / Nashville grass breakdown: *Various artists* / Kentucky: *Various artists* / Special: *Various artists* / When it's peach pickin' time in Georgia: *Various artists* / Williams Lake stampede: *Various artists*.
LP: . . . . NL 89139
MC: . . . . NK 89139
LP: . . . . INTS 5188

BARREL OF FUN (Various artists).
LP: . . . . ROUNDER 0033

BLUEGRASS ALBUM (Various artists).
Tracks: / Blue ridge cabin home: *Various artists* / We can't be darlings anymore: *Various artists* / Molly and tenbrooks: *Various artists* / I believe in you darling: *Various artists* / Model church: *Various artists*/ On my way back to the old home: *Various artists* / Gonna settle down: *Various artists* / Toy heart: *Various* artists / Pain in my heart: *Various artists* / Chalk up another one: *Various artists* / River of death: *Various artists*.
LP: . . . . ROUNDER 0140
MC: . . . . ROUNDER 0140C

BLUEGRASS ALBUM VOL. 2 (Various artists).
LP: . . . . ROUNDER 0164
MC: . . . . ROUNDER 0164C

BLUEGRASS ALBUM VOL. 3 (Various artists).
LP: . . . . ROUNDER 0180
MC: . . . . ROUNDER 0180C

BLUEGRASS ALBUM VOL. 4 (Various artists).
Tracks: / Age: *Various artists* / Cheyenne: *Various artists* / Cora is gone: *Various artists* / Old home town, The: *Various artists* / Talk it all over with him: *Various artists* / Head over heels: *Various artists*/ Nobody loves me: *Various artists* / When you are lonely: *Various artists* / I might take you back again: *Various artists* / Lonesome wind blues: *Various artists*.
LP: . . . . ROUNDER 0210
MC: . . . . ROUNDER 0210C

BLUEGRASS ALBUM VOL. 5 (Sweet Sunny South) (Various artists).
Tracks: / Rock hearts: *Various artists* / Big black train: *Various artists* / Thinking about you: *Various* artists / Out in the cold war: *Various artists* / On the old Kentucky shore: *Various artists* / Preaching, praying, singing: *Various artists* / Someone took my place with you: *Various artists* / Foggy mountain rock: *Various* artists / My home's across the Blue Ridge Mountains: *Various artists* / Along about daybreak: *Various artists*/ Sweet sunny South: *Various artists*.
LP: . . . . ROUNDER 0240
MC: . . . . ROUNDER 0240C

BLUEGRASS HALL OF FAME (Various artists).
LP: . . . . SLP 181
MC: . . . . GT 5181

BLUEGRASS: THE WORLD'S GREATEST SHOW (Various artists).
LP: . . . . SH 2201

MC: . . . . ZCSH 2201

CONFEDERATION (Bluegrass Instrumentals & Vocals) (Various artists).
LP: . . . . LAB 8

EARLY DAYS OF BLUEGRASS 1 (Various artists).
LP: . . . . ROUNDER 1013

EARLY DAYS OF BLUEGRASS 2 (Various artists).
LP: . . . . ROUNDER 1014

EARLY DAYS OF BLUEGRASS 3 (Various artists).
LP: . . . . ROUNDER 1015

EARLY DAYS OF BLUEGRASS 4 (Various artists).
LP: . . . . ROUNDER 1016

EARLY DAYS OF BLUEGRASS 5 (Various artists).
LP: . . . . ROUNDER 1017

EARLY DAYS OF BLUEGRASS 6 (Various artists).
LP: . . . . ROUNDER 1018

EARLY DAYS OF BLUEGRASS 7 (Various artists).
LP: . . . . ROUNDER 1019

EARLY DAYS OF BLUEGRASS 8 (Various artists).
LP: . . . . ROUNDER 1020

EARLY DAYS OF BLUEGRASS 9 (Various artists).
LP: . . . . ROUNDER 1022

EAST VIRGINIA: NEW SOUNDS, NEW SEASONS (Various artists).
LP: . . . . ROUNDER 0114

EAST VIRGINIA: PATHWAYS OF TRADITION (Various artists).
LP: . . . . ROUNDER 0134

LIBRARY OF CONGRESS BANJO COLLECTION, VOL. 1 1937-1946 (Various artists).
LP: . . . . ROUNDER 0237
MC: . . . . ROUNDER 0237C

MELODIC CLAWHAMMER BANJO-CHIEF O'NEILL'S FAVORIT (Various artists).
LP: . . . . SNKF 132

MUSIC FROM SOUTH TURKEY CREEK (Various artists).
LP: . . . . ROUNDER 0065

NEW ACCOUSTIC MUSIC SAMPLER (Various artists).
LP: . . . . AN 02
MC: . . . . ANC 02

NEW ENGLAND TRADITIONAL FIDDLING 1926-1975 (Various artists).
LP: . . . . JEMF 105

THIRTY YEARS OF BLUEGRASS (Various artists).
2LP: . . . . GTV 101

Blues

20 GREAT BLUES RECORDINGS OF THE 50'S AND 60'S VOL. 2 (Various artists).
Tracks: / Long tall woman: *James, Elmore* / Cotton picker: *Higgins, Chuck With Geechie Howard* / Trouble makin' woman: *Hawkins, Roy* / It's all right: *Egan, Willie* / Oh baby: *Watson, Johnny 'Guitar'* / Down now: *King, B.B.* / Don't take it out on me: *Sims, Frankie Lee* / Keep what you got: *Howlin' Wolf* / Sittin' and wonderin': *King, Earl* / Mercy's blues: *Baby, Mercy* / Love me tonight: *Littlefield, Little Willie* / Love me baby: *Bland, Bobby "Blue"* / Change your way of loving: *Crayton, Pee Wee* / It's time: *Kirkland, Eddie* / Lonesome trail blues: *Slim, Bumble Bee* / Just tell me baby: *Merriweather, Big Maceo* / Cold chills: *Louis, Joe Hill*/ Sweet little woman: *Jones, Little Johnny* / Romp and stomp blues: *Dee, Mercy* / Black cat bone: *Harris, Peppermint.*
LP: . . . . DROP 1010
MC: . . . . CROP 1010

20 GREAT BLUES RECORDINGS OF THE 50'S AND 60'S (Various artists).
Tracks: / Rolling and rolling: *Hopkins, Lightnin'* / Drifting: *Bland, Bobby* / Gone with the wind: *Sykes*, Roosevelt / Me and my chauffeur: *Thornton, Big Mama* / No rollin' blues: *Witherspoon, Jimmy* / No nights by myself: *Williamson, Sonny Boy* / Cool little car: *Hooker, John Lee* / Dark and dreary: *James, Elmore*/ Ain't drunk: *Turner, Ike's Rhythm Kings* / Crying at daybreak: *Howlin' Wolf* / Three hours past midnight: *Watson*, Johnny 'Guitar' / Talking woman: *Fulson, Lowell* / Moon is rising, The: *Littlefield, Little Willie* / Tease me baby: *Hooker, John Lee* / Dedicating the blues: *Crayton, Pee Wee* / Ten years long: *King, B.B.* / Beer drinking woman: *McCracklin, Jimmy* / Sunnyland: *James, Elmore* / Cow town: *Dixon, Floyd* / Heartache baby: *Louis, Joe Hill.*
LP: . . . . DROP 1005

MC: . . . . CROP 1005

24 GEANTS DU BLUES (Various artists).
2LP: 400037

50'S: JUKE JOINT BLUES, THE (See under 50's) (Various artists).

100 MINUTES OF BLUES (Various artists).
MC: . . . . ZCTON 128

100 MINUTES OF BLUES (Various artists).
MC: . . . . ZCTON 117

AFTER HOUR BLUES (Various artists).
Tracks: / Hard work boogie: *Various artists* / Your evil ways: *Various artists* / I sit up all night: *Various* artists / State Street blues: *Various artists* / When I was young (take 1): *Various artists* / When I was young (take 2): *Various artists* / Vicksburg blues: *Various artists* / A and B blues: *Various artists*/ After hour blues: *Various artists* / Little brother stomp: *Various artists* / No special rider: *Various artists.*
LP: . . . . BMLP 1067

ALL NIGHT LONG THEY PLAY THE BLUES (Various artists).
Tracks: / Part time love: *Various artists* / Country boy: *Various artists* / I know you hear me calling: *Various* artists / Little green house: *Various artists* / Hey hey baby's gone: *Various artists* / I'm serving time: *Various artists* / Life goes on: *Various artists* / Mama Rufus: *Various artists.*
LP: . . . . FT 563

ALLEY SPECIAL (Various artists).
Tracks: / Good road blues: *Holmes, Wright* / Alley special: *Holmes, Wright* / Quinsella: *Johnson, Sonny Boy*/ Drove from home blues: *Holmes, Wright* / Ardelle: *McKinley, David* / Little girl: *Hammond, Stick Horse*/ Truck 'em: *Hammond, Stick Horse* / Mean red spider: *Waters, Muddy* / Nervy woman blues: *Warren, Baby Boy*/ My special friend blues: *Warren, Baby Boy* / Angel of mercy: *Harris, W.* / Low down dirty shame: *Harris, W.* / Untitled blues: *Burns, Eddie* / Shreveport blues: *McKinley, David.*
LP: . . . . KK 820

ATLANTIC BLUES (See under Atlantic (label)) (Various artists).

ATLANTIC BLUES: CHICAGO (Various artists).
Tracks: / Chicago blues: *Jones, Johnny* / Hoy hoy: *Jones, Johnny* / Play on little girl: *Walker, T-Bone*/ T-Bone blues special: *Walker, T-Bone* / Poor man's plea: *Guy, Buddy & Junior Wells* / My baby she left me: *Guy*, Buddy & Junior Wells / T-Bone shuffle: *Guy, Buddy & Junior Wells* / I wonder why: *King, Freddie* / Play it cool: *King, Freddie* / Woke up this morning: *King, Freddie* / Gambler's blues: *Rush, Otis* / Feel so bad: *Rush, Otis* / Reap what you sow: *Various artists* / Highway 49: *Various artists* / Honey bee: *Waters*, Muddy / Wang dang doodle: *Taylor, Koko* / Dust my broom: *Shines, Johnny* / Going down: *King, Freddie*/ Please send me someone to love: *Allison, Luther* / Walking the dog: *Allison, Luther* / Feel so good: *Hutto, J.B.*.
LP: . . . . UNKNOWN

BATTLE OF THE BLUES Vol. 3 (Various artists).
Tracks: / Person to person: *Various artists* / I'm weak but willing: *Various artists* / Somebody done stole my cherry red: *Various artists* / Queen bee: *Various artists* / Featherbed mama: *Various artists* / I trusted you baby: *Various artists* / No good woman: *Various artists* / Ashes on my pillow: *Various artists* / JW: *Various artists* / Last mile, The: *Various artists* / 24 sad hours: *Various artists* / Blues in trouble: *Various artists* / Sad life: *Various artists* / Don't tell me now: *Various artists* / Foolish prayer: *Various artists* / Highway to happiness: *Various artists* / I done told you: *Various artists.*
LP: . . . . SING 634

BEST OF CHESS BLUES (Various artists).
Tracks: / Recession blues: *King, B.B.* / Don't keep me waiting: *King, B.B.* / Tickle britches: *King, B.B.*/ Don't break your promise: *Burnett, Chester* / You can't put me out: *Burnett, Chester* / Gettin' late: *Burnett*, Chester / Rockin daddy: *Burnett, Chester* / I didn't know: *Burnett, Chester* / I better go now: *Burnett*, Chester / New crawlin' king snakes: *Burnett, Chester* / My mind is ramblin': *Burnett, Chester* / Tail dragger: *Burnett, Chester* / Poor wind that never changes: *Burnett, Chester* / Stick around: *Guy, Buddy* / Gully hully: *Guy, Buddy* / That's it: *Guy, Buddy* / American Bandstand: *Guy, Buddy* / Untitled instrumental: *Guy, Buddy* / My love is real: *Guy, Buddy* / Moanin': *Timmons, Bobby* / Down home special: *Taylor*, Hound Dog / Watch out: *Taylor, Hound Dog* / Scrappin': *Taylor, Hound Dog* / Sittin' here alone: *Taylor*, Hound Dog / Hound dog: *Taylor, Hound Dog* / Little village: *Williamson, Sonny Boy* / Unseen eye: *Williamson, Sonny Boy.*
2LP: . . . . CMXD 4055

BEST OF CHESS BLUES, THE (Various artists).
Tracks: / Rollin' stone: *Waters, Muddy* / Black angel blues: *Nighthawk, Robert* / 24 hours: *Boyd, Eddie*/ Seventh son: *Mabon, Willie* / Reconsider baby: *Fulson, Lowell* / Hoochie coochie man (I'm your): *Waters*, Muddy / Smokestack lightnin': *Howlin' Wolf* / Juke: *Little Walter* / Eisenhower blues: *Lenoir, J.B.*/ Walking by myself: *Rogers, Jimmy* / Back door man: *Howlin' Wolf* / Madison blues: *James, Elmore* / Your funeral my trial: *Williamson, Sonny Boy* / So many roads,so many trains: *Rush, Otis* / My time after a while: *Guy*, Buddy / Bring it on home: *Williamson, Sonny Boy* / One bourbon one scotch one beer: *Hooker, John Lee* / Baby what you want me to do: *James, Etta* / Stormy Monday: *Little Milton* / Wang dang doodle: *Taylor, Koko.*
2LP: . . . . GCH 2-6023
MCSET: . . . . GCHK 2-6023

BEST OF CHICAGO BLUES, THE (Various artists).
LP: . . . . VNP 5312
MC: . . . . VNP 6312

BEST OF THE BLUES (Various artists).
LP: . . . . SLP 4023

BEST OF THE BLUES AND JAZZ (Various artists).
Tracks: / On the sunny side...: *Various artists* / Oh lady be good: *Basie, Count* / I smell trouble: *Bland*, Bobby / Mood indigo: *Ellington, Duke* / Tisket a tasket, A: *Fitzgerald, Ella* / How high the moon: *Hampton*, Lionel / Quintessence: *Jones, Quincy* / Blue room: *Rollins, Sonny* / Sweet little angel: *King, B.B.* / My home is on the delta: *Spann, Otis* / Cherry red: *Turner, Joe* / I wonder why: *Hooker, John Lee* / Poor man: *McGhee,Brownie/ Sonny Terry* / Stormy Monday: *Walker, T-Bone* / I don't know why: *Witherspoon, Jimmy*/ I ain't from Chicago: *Reed, Jimmy* / Sent for you yesterday: *Rushing, Jimmy.*
LP: . . . . MCL 1862
MC: . . . . MCLC 1862

BEST OF THE BLUES SINGERS VOLUME 2 (Various artists).
MC: . . . . MC 9007

BLUE MONDAY (Various artists).
Tracks: / They want money: *Various artists* / Driving wheel: *Various artists* / Creeper: *Various artists*/ 8 men, four women: *Various artists* / Things that I used to do: *Various artists* / Bad luck: *Various artists*/ More bad luck: *Various artists* / Born under a bad sign: *Various artists* / Blues, what a feeling: *Various artists* / Married woman: *Various artists* / I wonder: *Various artists* / Blue Monday: *Various artists*/ After hours: *Various artists.*
LP: . . . . STX 3015

BLUES - A REAL SUMMIT MEETING, THE (Various artists).
Tracks: / Little red rooster: *Thornton, Big Mama* / Ball and chain: *Thornton, Big Mama* / Clean head blues: *Vinson*, Eddie "Cleanhead" / Back door blues: *Vinson, Eddie "Cleanhead"* / Kidney stew: *Vinson, Eddie "Cleanhead"*/ That's alright mama: *Crudup, Arthur 'Big Boy'* / Honkey tonk train blues: *Glen, Lloyd* / After hours: *Glen*, Lloyd / Pinetop's boogie woogie: *Glen, Lloyd* / Long distance call: *Waters, Muddy* / Wheres my woman been: *Waters, Muddy* / Got my mojo working: *Waters, Muddy* / Drifter, The: *Brown, Clarence* / Please Mr. Nixon: *Brown, Clarence* / Outside help: *King, B.B.* / Smooth sailing: *McShann, Jay* / Confessin' the blues: *McShann, Jay.*
MC: . . . . TCCDX 34
2LP: . . . . CDX 34

BLUES AND SOUL POWER (Various artists).
LP: . . . . KENT 068

BLUES ANTHOLOGY VOL. 1 (Memphis Blues) (Various artists).
LP: . . . . ECB 801

BLUES ANTHOLOGY VOL. 2 (More Memphis Blues) (Various artists).
LP: . . . . ECB 802

BLUES ANTHOLOGY VOL. 3 (Real Chicago Blues) (Various artists).
LP: . . . . ECB 803

BLUES ANTHOLOGY VOL. 4 (More from Chicago) (Various artists).
LP: . . . . ECB 804

BLUES ANTHOLOGY VOL. 5 (Blues from St. Louis) (Various artists).
LP: . . . . ECB 805

BLUES AS BIG AS TEXAS, VOL 1 (Various artists).
LP: . . . . HCS 106
MC: . . . . HCS 106 TC

BLUES BALLADS VOL 2 (Various artists).
LP: 01434022
MC: 01434021

BLUES CAME DOWN FROM MEMPHIS (Various artists).
Tracks: / Boogie disease: *Doctor Ross* / Juke box boogie: *Doctor Ross* / Come back baby: *Doctor Ross*/ Chicago breakdown: *Doctor Ross* / Cotton crop blues: *Cotton, James* / Baker shop boogie: *Nix, Willie*/ Seems like a million years: *Nix, Willie* / Bear cat: *Thomas, Rufus* / Tiger man: *Thomas, Rufus* / Take a little chance: *Deberry, Jimmy* / Time has made a change: *Deberry, Jimmy* / I feel so worried: *Lewis, Sammy & Willie Johnson* / So long baby goodbye: *Lewis, Sammy & Willie Johnson.*
LP: . . . . CR 30125

BLUES DELUXE (Various artists).
Tracks: / Clouds in my heart: *Blues Deluxe* / Hey bartender: *Taylor, Koko* / Wang dang doodle: *Dixon, Willie*/ Sweet home Chicago: *Brooks, Lonnie* / Don't throw your love on me so strong: *Seals, Son* / You too might need a friend: *Young, Mighty Joe.*
LP: . . . . SNTF 859

BLUES EXPERIENCE, VOL.1 (Various artists).
LP: . . . . RRB 301

BLUES FOR A BIG TOWN (Various artists).
Tracks: / Walkin' the boogie: *Hooker, John Lee* / Blues for a big town: *Hooker, John Lee* / Big fine woman: *Hooker*, John Lee / Blues for Christmas: *Hooker, John Lee* / Lily Mae: *Frazier, Calvin* / Have blues will travel: *Frazier*, Calvin / Trying to get you off my mind: *Watkins,Katie* / Biscuit baking mama: *Big Ed & His Combo* / Superstition: *Big Ed & His Combo* / Democrat man: *Jenkins,Bobo* / Bad luck and trouble: *Jenkins,Bobo* / Treat me like I treat you: *Burns, Eddie* / Don't cha leave me baby: *Burns, Eddie* / Black snake blues: *Texas Red & Jimmy.*
LP: . . . . GCH 8119

BLUES FOR COLTRANE (A Tribute) (Various artists).
LP: . . . . MCA 42122

BLUES FROM BIG BILL'S COPACABANA (Various artists).
LP: 515041

BLUES FROM GEORGIA (Various artists).
LP: . . . . RL 309

BLUES FROM SOUTH CAROLINA AND GEORGIA 1924/32 (Various artists).
Tracks: / Boogie lovin': *Various artists* / Thirty days in jail: *Various artists* / Ding dong ring: *Various* artists / Pick and shovel captain: *Various artists* / Six months ain't no sentence: *Various artists* / Hard times hard times: *Various artists* / Trouble ain't nothin' but ....: *Various artists* / Down in the chain gang: *Various artists* / Prison bound blues: *Various artists* / Georgia chain gang: *Various artists* / Gonna leave from Georgia: *Various artists* / Black woman: *Various artists* / Shootin' craps and gamblin': *Various artists* / Nobody knows my name: *Various artists* / Been pickin' and shovellin': *Various artists.*
LP: . . . . HT 304

BLUES FROM ST. LOUIS 1929-30 (Various artists).
LP: . . . . BD 2017

BLUES FROM THE FIELDS TO THE TOWNS VOL. 2 (Various artists).
Tracks: / Noted rider: *Leadbelly* / I bought you a brand new home: *Hooker, John Lee* / I believe I'll lose my mind: *Hooker, John Lee* / Worried life blues: *McGhee, Brownie & Sonny Terry* / Going down slow: *McGhee, Brownie* & Sonny Terry / C.C. rider: *Davis, Blind John* / Love 'n' trouble: *Johnson, Luther* / Love without jealousy: *Johnson, Luther* / This is a good time to write a song: *Various artists* / Three women blues: *Various artists*/ Excuse me baby: *Various artists* / Mud in your ear: *Various artists.*
LP: . . . . F 90134
MC: . . . . MF 990134

BLUES FROM THE FIELDS TO THE TOWNS VOL. 3 (Various artists).
Tracks: / Dekalb woman: *Leadbelly* / Teasin' me: *Hooker, John Lee* / Time is

marching: *Hooker, John Lee*/ Right now: *McGhee, Brownie & Sonny Terry* / That good old jelly roll: *McGhee, Brownie & Sonny Terry* / How long blues: *Davis, Blind John* / I'm so glad: *Johnson, Luther* / Evil: *Johnson, Luther* / El capitan: *Various* artists / Two of a kind: *Various artists* / Long distance call: *Various artists* / Sting it: *Various artists*.
LP: . . . . **F 90142**
MC: . . . . **MF 90142**

BLUES FROM THE FIELDS TO THE TOWNS VOL. 1 (Various artists).
Tracks: / John Henry: *McGhee, Brownie & Sonny Terry* / Take this hammer: *Sonny Terry & Brownie McGhee* / Snake: *Johnson, Luther* / Chicken shack: *Johnson, Luther* / Hobo blues: *Hooker, John Lee* / C.C. rider: *Hooker,* John Lee / Everyday I have the blues: *Davis, Blind John* / Bertha May: *Various artists* / Diggin' my potatoes: *Various artists* / Watch dog: *Various artists*.
LP: . . . . **F 90099**
MC: . . . . **MF 990099**

BLUES FROM THE WESTERN STATES 1947-49 (Various artists).
LP: . . . . **L 1032**

BLUES GIRLS FROM THE '40'S (Various artists).
LP: . . . . **PM 1561421**

BLUES GUITAR ALBUM (Various artists).
Tracks: / Girl you're nice and clean: *Guy, Buddy* / I'm a stranger: *Kirkland, Eddie* / Garbage man blues: *Guy,* Phil / Blues stomp: *Hound Dog Taylor* / One room country shack: *Left Hand Frank* / Honky tonk: *Left Hand Frank* / Lonesome blues: *Granderson, John Lee* / I was wrong: *Davis, Bobbay Trio*.
LP: . . . . **JSP 1016**
LP: . . . . **JSP 1055**

BLUES GUITAR ALBUM (Various artists).
2LP: **400027**

BLUES GUITAR BLASTERS (Various artists).
Tracks: / After hours: *Nolan, Jimmy* / Killing floor: *King, Albert* / You threw your love on me too strong: *King,* Albert / Talkin' woman: *Fulson, Lowell* / Everytime it rains: *Fulson, Lowell* / Early in the morning: *King,* B.B. / Talkin' the blues: *King, B.B.* / Dust my blues: *James, Elmore* / Elmo's shuffle: *James, Elmore*/ Hawaiian boogie: *James, Elmore* / Jumpin' in the heart of town: *Thomas, Lafayette* / Certainly all: *Guitar* Slim / Things that I used to do, The: *Guitar Slim* / Twistin' the strings: *Turner, Ike* / 3 hours past midnight: *Watson, Johnny 'Guitar'* / Twinky: *Crayton, Pee Wee* / Mistreated so bad: *Crayton, Pee Wee* / Hey hey baby: *Walker, T-Bone* / I had a good girl: *Hooker, John Lee*.
LP: . . . . **CHA 232**

BLUES GUITAR BOX (Various artists).
Tracks: / Tell me what's the reason: *Walker, T-Bone* / Steppin' out: *Mayall,John Bluesbreakers* / Who's gonna be your sweet man: *Waters, Muddy & Rory Gallagher* / She's into something: *Cray, Robert/Albert Collins/ Johnny Copeland*/ If you have to know: *Mack, Lonnie & Stevie* / Greeny: *Mayall,John Bluesbreakers* / Dimples: *Hooker,* John Lee / Statesboro blues: *Allman Brothers Band* / There's my baby: *King, B.B.* / Blues for Barry and Michael: *Goldberg, Barry and Mike Bloomfield* / Big bird: *Cropper, Steve and Albert King* / Pete's blues: *Buchanan,* Roy / Gate walks to the board: *Brown, Clarence 'Gatemouth'* / So many roads: *Rush, Otis* / Oh pretty woman: *Mayall,John Bluesbreakers* / All your love: *Magic Sak* / Fake 10: *Collins, Albert* / Long distance call: *Waters, Muddy* / Worried blues: *Guy, Buddy* / Little red rooster: *Howlin' Wolf* / Don't take advantage of me: *Winter, Johnny* / Meanstreak: *Funderburgh, Anson & Sam Myers* / Reconsider baby: *Fulson, Lowell*/ Black Jack: *Cray, Robert/Albert Collins/Johnny Copeland* / Steelin': *Beck, Jeff* / Going down: *King, Freddie*/ Prancin': *Turner, Ike* / I'll play the blues for you: *King, Albert* / Stick around: *Radcliff, Bobby*/ Walking the backstreets and crying: *Little Milton* / Score, The: *Cray, Robert* / Freight loader: *Page, Jimmy* and Eric Clapton / Side: *Taylor, Hound Dog & The House Rockers* / Takin' off: *Murphy, Matt* / Stumble, The: *Mayall,John Bluesbreakers* / Outside help: *King, B.B.* / Shame shame shame: *Reed, Jimmy* / Sun is shining, The: *James, Elmore* / City of angels: *Walker, Joe Louis* / Madison blues: *Thorogood, George and The Destroyers*/ Texas flood: *Robinson, Fenton* / Tired out: *Collins, Albert* / I'm ready: *King, Freddie*.
LPS: . . . . **TBBLP 47555**
MCSET: . . . . **TBBMC 47555**

BLUES GUITAR WORKSHOP (Various artists).
Tracks: / Black monk: *Various artists* / Cat's squirrel: *Various artists* / How come you do me like you do: *Various* artists / Buck dance: *Various artists* / Turnaround: *Various artists* / I just want to make love to you: *Various* artists / Always: *Various artists* / Panic room blues: *Various artists* / Morning star blues: *Various* artists / Forty ton parachute: *Various artists* / When I've been drinking: *Various artists* / Stroll: *Various artists* / Blake's rag: *Various artists* / Keep a bootin': *Various artists* / Clown: *Various artists*.
LP: . . . . **SNKF 159**
LP: . . . . **KM 141**

BLUES IN D NATURAL - ANTHOLOGY (Various artists).
Tracks: / Crying won't help you: *Nighthawk, Robert* / Moon is rising, The: *Nighthawk, Robert* / Hawaiian boogie: *James, Elmore* / Early in the morning: *James, Elmore* / Hidden charms: *Clarke, Charles* / Row your boat: *Clarke, Charles* / Woman I love, The: *Homesick James* / Blues in D natural: *Hooker, Earl* / Tanya: *Hooker, Earl* / She likes to boogie real low: *Sims, Frankie Lee* / Southern woman: *Brown, Tommy* / Remember me: *Brown, Tommy* / I believe in a woman: *Williams, Sly* / Boot Hill: *Williams, Sly*.
LP: . . . . **RL 005**

BLUES IN THE BOTTLE (Various artists).
Tracks: / Blues in the bottle: *Holy Modal Rounders* / Baby please don't go: *Rush* / Pretty boy Floyd: *Elliott*/ Sometimes I feel like a motherless child: *Van Ronk, Dave* / House of Carpenter, The: *Van Ronk, Dave* / Junco partner: *Holy Modal Rounders* / Duncan Brady: *Rush* / Candy man: *Nelson, Tracy* / Death letter blues: *Van Ronk, Dave* / Barbara Allen: *Rush* / So long it's been good to know: *Elliott* / Long John: *Van Ronk,* Dave / Down on me: *Schmidt (composer)* / Alabamy bound: *Rush* / Cuckoo, The: *Elliott* / Good gin blues: *Muldair*.
LP: . . . . **WIK 71**

BLUES IS ALRIGHT VOL. 1 (Various artists).
Tracks: / Down home blues: *Hill, Z.Z.* / Blues is alright, The: *Little Milton* / Your husband is cheatin' on us: *Lasalle, Denise* / End of the rainbow, The: *Mitchell, McKinley* / Misty blue: *Moore, Dorothy* / Lady, my whole world is you: *Lasalle, Denise* / Down home blues (x-rated): *Lasalle, Denise* / Two steps from the blues: *Bland, Bobby* / I'm a bluesman: *Hill, Z.Z.* / Bad risk: *Latimore*.
LP: . . . . **MAL 7430**

BLUES IS ALRIGHT VOL. 2 (Various artists).
LP: . . . . **MALP 010**

BLUES IS ALRIGHT VOL. 3 (Various artists).
LP: . . . . **MALP 7449**
MC: . . . . **MALC 7449**

BLUES IS KILLING (Various artists).
LP: . . . . **JUKE JOINT 1501**

BLUES JAM IN CHICAGO (Various artists).
Tracks: / Watch out: *Various artists* / South Ooh baby: *Various artists* / South Indiana: *Various artists*/ Last night: *Various artists* / Red hot jam: *Various artists* / I'm worried: *Various artists* / I held my baby last night: *Various artists* / Madison blues: *Various artists* / I can't hold out: *Various artists*/ I need your love: *Various artists* / I got the blues: *Various artists* / World's in a tangle, The: *Various* artists / Talk with you: *Various artists* / Like it this way: *Various artists* / Someday soon baby: *Various artists* / Hungry country girl: *Various artists* / Black Jack blues: *Various artists* / Rockin' boogie: *Various artists* / Sugar mama: *Various artists* / Home work: *Various artists*.
2LP: . . . . **EPC 88591**

BLUES LEGEND VOL. 1 (Various artists).
LP: . . . . **SM 3947**
MC: . . . . **MC 3947**

BLUES LEGEND VOL. 1 (Various artists).
Tracks: / Little wheel: *Hooker, John Lee* / I'm in the mood: *Hooker, John Lee* / Hobo blues: *Hooker, John Lee* / Crawling king snake: *Hooker, John Lee* / Blues before sunrise: *Hooker, John Lee* / Want ad blues: *Hooker,* John Lee / My first wife left me: *Hooker, John Lee* / Wednesday evening blues: *Hooker, John Lee* / Maudie: *Hooker, John Lee* / Time is marching: *Hooker, John Lee* / Short-haired woman: *Hopkins, Lightnin'* / Bottle it up and go: *Hopkins, Lightnin'* / Long time: *Hopkins, Lightnin'* / Foot race is on, The: *Hopkins, Lightnin'*/ Prison blues come down on me: *Hopkins, Lightnin'* / Bunion stew: *Hopkins, Lightnin'* / Mama and Papa Hopkins: *Hopkins, Lightnin'* / Get off my toe: *Hopkins, Lightnin'* / Trouble in mind: *Hopkins, Lightnin'* / Gonna pull a party: *Hopkins, Lightnin'* / Till the rain runs out: *Hopkins, Lightnin'* / When the saints go marching in: *Hopkins, Lightnin'* / Bourgeois blues: *Leadbelly* / Looky looky yonder: *Leadbelly* / Black Betty: *Leadbelly*/ Yellow woman's doorbells: *Leadbelly* / Poor Howard: *Leadbelly* / Green corn: *Leadbelly* / Gallis pole, The: *Leadbelly* / Dekalb woman: *Leadbelly* / Noted rider: *Leadbelly* / Big fat woman: *Leadbelly*/ Burrow Love & Co: *Leadbelly* / Bring a little water Sylvie: *Leadbelly* / Julie Ann: *Leadbelly* / Line 'em: *Leadbelly* / Whoe black buck: *Leadbelly* / John Hardy: *Leadbelly* / El capitan: *Various artists*/ This is a good time to write a song: *Various artists* / I'm so alone: *Various artists* / Two of a kind: *Various* artists / Big city girl: *Various artists* / Three and one boogie: *Various artists* / Bertha May: *Various artists* / Celeste boogie No 2: *Various artists*.
LPS: **F4 50031**

BLUES LEGEND VOL. 2 (Various artists).
Tracks: / I bought you a brand new home: *Hooker, John Lee* / I believe I'll lose my mind: *Hooker, John Lee* / Teasin' me: *Hooker, John Lee* / My cryin' days are over: *Hooker, John Lee* / Sittin' here thinkin': *Hooker,* John Lee / Mean mistreatin': *Hooker, John Lee* / How long? how many more years?: *Hooker, John Lee* / C.C. rider: *Hooker, John Lee* / Sad and lonesome: *Hooker, John Lee* / Can't you see what you're doing to me?: *Hooker,* John Lee / My own boogie: *Davis, Blind John* / Everyday I have the blues: *Davis, Blind John* / Texas Tony: *Davis, Blind John* / Trouble in mind: *Davis, Blind John* / If I had a listen: *Davis, Blind John* / St. Louis blues: *Davis, Blind John* / After hours: *Davis, Blind John* / How long blues: *Davis, Blind John*/ Everybody's boogie: *Davis, Blind John* / Memphis blues: *Davis, Blind John* / Rockin' chair boogie: *Davis,* Blind John / House of blue lights: *Davis, Blind John* / Run away boogie: *Davis, Blind John* / Pinetop: *Davis,* Blind John / You hear me talkin': *Terry, Sonny & Brownie McGhee* / Going down slow: *Terry, Sonny & Brownie McGhee*/ Raise a ruckus tonight: *Terry, Sonny & Brownie McGhee* / Right now: *Terry, Sonny & Brownie McGhee* / Worried life blues: *Terry, Sonny & Brownie McGhee* / John Henry: *Terry, Sonny & Brownie McGhee* / Crawdad hole: *Terry,* Sonny & Brownie McGhee / Down by the riverside: *Terry, Sonny & Brownie McGhee* / Take this hammer: *Terry, Sonny* & Brownie McGhee / That good old jelly roll: *Terry, Sonny & Brownie McGhee* / Diggin' my potatoes: *Waters, Muddy*/ Watchdog: *Waters, Muddy* / Sting it: *Waters, Muddy* / Why d'you do me?: *Waters, Muddy* / Natural wig: *Waters, Muddy* / Mud in your ear: *Waters, Muddy* / Excuse me baby: *Waters, Muddy* / Sad day uptown: *Waters,* Muddy / Top of the boogaloo: *Waters, Muddy* / Long distance call: *Waters, Muddy* / Cindy Cindy: *Terry, Sonny & Brownie McGhee*.
LPS: **F4 90098**

BLUES LEGEND VOL. 3 (Various artists).
Tracks: / Bourgeois blues: *Leadbelly* / Whoe black buck: *Leadbelly* / John Henry: *Terry, Sonny & Brownie* McGhee / Take this summer: *Terry, Sonny & Brownie McGhee* / Hobo blues: *Hooker, John Lee* / C.C. rider: *Hooker,* John Lee / Everyday I have the blues: *Davis, Blind John* / Bertha May: *Various artists* / Diggin' my potatoes: *Waters, Muddy* / Mini dress: *Johnson, Luther with the Muddy Waters Blues Band* / Remember me: *Johnson, Luther* with the Muddy Waters Blues Band / Snake: *Johnson, Luther with the Muddy Waters Blues Band* / Comin' home baby: *Johnson,* Luther with the Muddy Waters Blues Band / Blues for hippies: *Johnson, Luther with the Muddy Waters Blues Band* / Chicken shack: *Johnson, Luther with the Muddy Waters Blues Band* / Love 'n' trouble: *Johnson, Luther with the Muddy Waters* Blues Band / I'm so glad: *Johnson, Luther with the Muddy Waters Blues Band* / Love without jealousy: *Johnson,* Luther with the Muddy Waters Blues Band / Evil: *Johnson, Luther with the Muddy Waters Blues Band* / Easy riding gal: *Charles, Ray* / Ray's blues: *Charles, Ray* / Here I am: *Charles, Ray* / Blow my baby back home: *Charles, Ray* / Blues is my middle name: *Charles, Ray* / I'm just a lonely boy: *Charles, Ray* / Going down slow: *Charles,* Ray / St. Pete blues: *Charles, Ray* / Late in the evening: *Charles, Ray* / Mercy on me: *Dupree, Champion* Jack / Sleeping in the street: *Dupree, Champion Jack* / I'm a gamblin' man: *Dupree, Champion Jack* / I hate to be alone: *Dupree, Champion Jack* / Door-to-door blues: *Dupree, Champion Jack* / When I've been drinking: *Dupree,* Champion Jack / Cold ground is my bed, The: *Dupree, Champion Jack* / Lonesome bedroom blues: *Dupree, Champion Jack* / Good woman is hard to find, A: *Dupree, Champion Jack* / I'm growing older every day: *Dupree, Champion Jack*.
LPS: **F4 90111**

BLUES (LES PLUS GRANDS ...) (Various artists).
MC: **4671774**

BLUES MEETING IN CHICAGO (Various artists).
LP: . . . . **SRLP 010**

BLUES 'N' TROUBLE 1 (Various artists).
LP: . . . . **ARHOOLIE 1006**

BLUES 'N' TROUBLE 2 (Various artists).
LP: . . . . **ARHOOLIE 1012**

BLUES ON 2 (BBC Radio) (Various artists).
LP: . . . . **REN 610**
MC: . . . . **ZCN 610**

BLUES PROJECT (Various artists).
Tracks: / Fiin' to die: *Ray, David* / Blow whistle blow: *Schmidt Von Eric* / My little woman: *Koerner, John*/ Ginger man: *Muldaur, Geoff* / Bad dream blues: *Van Ronk, Dave* / Winding boy: *Buchanan Ian* / I'm troubled: *Kalb Danny* / France blues: *Spoelstra Mark* / Don't leave me here: *Van Ronk, Dave* / Devil got my woman: *Muldaur, Geoff* / Southbound train: *Koerner, John* / Slappin' on my black cat Bone: *Ray, David* / She's gone: *Spoelstra Mark* / Hello baby blues: *Kalb Danny*.
LP: . . . . **ED 248**

BLUES RARITIES (Various artists).
Tracks: / Recession blues: *King, B.B.* / Don't keep me waiting: *King, B.B.* / Tickle britches: *King, B.B.*/ Don't break your promise: *King, B.B.* / You can't put me out: *Howlin' Wolf* / Gettin' late: *Howlin' Wolf*/ Rockin' daddy: *Howlin' Wolf* / I better go now: *Howlin' Wolf* / New crawlin' king snake: *Howlin' Wolf*/ My mind is ramblin': *Howlin' Wolf* / Tail dragger: *Howlin' Wolf* / Poor wind that never change: *Howlin'* Wolf / Stick around: *Guy, Buddy* / Gully hully: *Guy, Buddy* / That's it: *Guy, Buddy* / American Bandstand: *Guy, Buddy* / Untitled instumental: *Guy, Buddy* / My love is real: *Guy, Buddy* / Moanin': *Guy, Buddy*/ Down home special: *Taylor, Hound Dog* / Watch out: *Taylor, Hound Dog* / Scrappin': *Taylor, Hound Dog*/ Sittin' here alone: *Taylor, Hound Dog* / Hound dog: *Taylor, Hound Dog* / Little village: *Williamson, Sonny Boy* / Unseen eye: *Williamson, Sonny Boy*.
2LP: . . . . **GCH 2-6035**

BLUES ROOTS (Various artists).
LP: . . . . **TOM 2-7006**

BLUES ROOTS VOL. 1 (Mississippi Blues) (Various artists).
LP: . . . . **SLP 4035**

BLUES ROOTS VOL. 2 (Blues all Around My Bed) (Various artists).
LP: . . . . **SLP 4036**

BLUES ROOTS VOL. 3 (I Ain't Gonna Pick No More Cotton) (Various artists).
LP: . . . . **SLP 4037**

BLUES ROOTS VOL. 4 (Dirty Dozen, The) (Speckled Red).
LP: . . . . **SLP 4038**

BLUES ROOTS VOL. 5 (Ramblin' and Wanderin' Blues) (Williams, Big Joe).
LP: . . . . **SLP 4039**

BLUES ROOTS VOL. 6 (I'm Growing Older Everyday) (Various artists).
LP: . . . . **SLP 4040**

BLUES ROOTS VOL. 7 (Good Morning Mr. Blues) (Spann, Otis).
LP: . . . . **SLP 4041**

BLUES ROOTS VOL. 8 (Swingin' with Lonnie) (Various artists).
LP: . . . . **SLP 4042**

BLUES ROOTS VOL. 9 (Sad & Lonesome Blues) (Various artists).
LP: . . . . **SLP 4043**

BLUES ROOTS VOL. 10 (I'm so alone) (Various artists).
LP: . . . . **SLP 4044**

BLUES ROUND MIDNIGHT (Various artists).
Tracks: / Three o'clock blues: *Davis, Larry* / Old man blues: *Copeland, Johnny* / Something about you: *Davis,* Larry / Blues around midnight: *Fulson, Lowell* / Love will lead you right: *Walker, T-Bone* / You're breaking my heart: *King, B.B.* /

Down now: *King, B.B.* / Shattered dreams: *Fulson, Lowell* / T-99 Blues: *Nelson*, Jimmy (Available on CD and cassette only) / I'm wonderin' and wonderin': *Charles, Ray* (Available on CD and cassette only) / Secondhand fool: *Nelson, Jimmy* / Quit hanging around: *King, Saunders* / Dragnet blues: *Ervin, Frankie*/ Crazy with the blues: *Jones Marti* / Love is here to stay: *Holden, Lorenzo* / I need somebody: *Witherspoon*, Jimmy / Gee baby ain't I good to you: *Witherspoon, Jimmy* / Picture of you: *Green, Vivianne* / Playing the numbers: *Ervin, Frankie* / It just wasn't true: *Jones Marl*.
LP: . . . . **CH 235**
MC: . . . . **CHC 235**

BLUES SAMPLER (Walkman/Compact jazz) (Various artists).
Tracks: / Saint Louis blues: *Various artists* / Sun is going down: *Various artists* / Caldonia: *Various artists*/ St James infirmary: *Various artists* / Funky mama: *Various artists* / How long has that train been gone: *Various* artists / When Buddy comes to town: *Various artists* / Le blues de la vache a lait: *Various artists* / Mr Sykes blues: *Various artists* / Jelly, jelly: *Various artists* / Going back to Tennessee: *Various artists*/ Sweet home Chicago: *Various artists* / They call me Doctor Professor Longhair: *Various artists* / When I was young: *Various artists* / John Henry: *Various artists*.
MC: **839 393 4**

BLUES SINGERS (Various artists).
LP: . . . . **WBJ 003**

BLUES SINGERS OF THE 20'S SERIES 3 (Various artists).
MC: **047**

BLUES SOUTHSIDE CHICAGO (Various artists).
Tracks: / Can't help myself: *Horton, Shakey* / One more time: *Young, Johnny* / Every time I get to drinking: *Sunnyland* Slim / I won't be happy: *Poor Bob* / Where you belong: *Boyd, Eddie* / Merry Christmas: *Nighthawk, Robert*/ Crutch and cane: *Homesick James* / Little girl: *Young, Johnny* / Sun is rising, The: *Poor Bob* / Got to move: *Homesick James* / I got to get to my baby: *Sunnyland Slim* / J.F. Kennedy's reservation: *Mitchell, Ronda & Mrs.Lovell* / Lula Mae: *Nighthawk, Robert* / Losing hand: *Boyd, Eddie*.
LP: . . . . **TAB 63**
LP: . . . . **FLY 521**

BLUES STORY, THE (Various artists).
LP: . . . . **MA 5686**
MC: . . . . **MAMC 95686**

BLUES VOL 1, THE (Various artists).
Tracks: / Don't start me to talkin': *Williamson, Sonny Boy* / First time I met the blues: *Guy, Buddy* / Worried life blues: *Berry, Chuck* / My baby: *Little Walter* / Juke: *Little Walter* / Walkin' the boogie: *Hooker*, John Lee / Hoochie coochie man: *Waters, Muddy* / Just make love to me: *Waters, Muddy* / Reconsider baby: *Fulson, Lowell* / Smokestack: *Howlin' Wolf* / Spoonful: *Howlin' Wolf* / When the lights go out: *Witherspoon, Jimmy*.
LP: . . . . **GCH 8027**
MC: . . . . **GCHK 78027**

BLUES VOL 2, THE (Various artists).
Tracks: / Thirty days: *Berry, Chuck* / Wee wee hours: *Berry, Chuck* / Sugar mama: *Hooker, John Lee* / Evil: *Howlin' Wolf* / Got my mojo working: *Waters, Muddy* / I'm a man: *Diddley, Bo* / Key to the highway: *Little Walter* / Ten years ago: *Guy, Buddy* / So many roads: *Rush, Otis* / It ain't no secret: *Witherspoon, Jimmy*.
LP: . . . . **GCH 8035**
MC: . . . . **GCHK 78035**

BLUES VOL 3, THE (Various artists).
LP: . . . . **BDUB 1**

BLUES VOL 4, THE (Various artists).
Tracks: / I've been down so long: *Various artists* / Every jug stands on its own bottom: *Various artists* / I wish you would: *Various artists* / Fool is what you wanted, A: *Various artists* / Chicken head: *Various artists*/ Seems like a million years: *Various artists* / Gamblin' man: *Various artists* / Make your bed up mamma: *Various* artists / I'm a root man: *Various artists* / I can't lose with the stuff I use: *Various artists* / Letter dressed in red, A: *Various artists* / Leaving Kansas City: *Various artists* / New York, New York: *Various* artists / Hazel: *Various artists* / Dangerous woman: *Various artists* / I feel so fine: *Various artists*/ Blue midnight: *Various artists* / Sloppy drunk: *Various artists* / You're never too old to boogie: *Various* artists / Crossroads: *Various artists* / Hard luck blues: *Various artists* / Bury me back in the USA: *Various artists* / After hours: *Various artists* / Sassy: *Various artists*.
LP: . . . . **BDUB 2**

BLUES WOMEN (Various artists).
LP: . . . . **KK 793**

BLUESMAN SONGSTERS (1929-33) (Various artists).
LP: . . . . **BD 2016**

BLUES/ROCK AVALANCHE (Various artists).
Tracks: / I hear you knocking: *McDaniel, Elias* / You can't judge a book by the cover: *Dixon, Willie* / Diddley daddy: *McDaniel, Elias* / Early in the morning: *Morganfield, McKinley* / Baby what you want me to do?: *Reed*, Jimmy / Wang dang doodle: *Dixon, Willie* / I got what it takes: *Dixon, Willie* / Wrinkles: *Leake, Lafayette*/ Swiss boogie: *Leake, Lafayette* / County jail: *Morganfield, McKinley* / Trouble no more: *Morganfield, McKinley*/ Got my mojo working: *Morganfield, McKinley* / Stormy Monday: *Walker, Aaron T-Bone* / She says she loves me: *Walker, Aaron T-Bone & Jane Jarest*.
2LP: . . . . **CXMD 4056**
2LP: . . . . **GCH 2-6033**

BLUESSCENE USA VOL. 1 (Louisiana Blues) (Various artists).
LP: . . . . **SLP 177**

BLUESSCENE USA VOL 2 (Rhythm & Blues of Chicago) (Various artists).
LP: . . . . **SLP 840**

BLUES-THE BRITISH CONNECTION (Various artists).
MC: . . . . **KTBC 88**
LP: . . . . **TAB 88**

BLUESVILLE (Various artists).
LP: . . . . **GRLP 7774**

BLUESVILLE VOL. 1 (Various artists).
Tracks: / Judge Boushay blues: *Lewis, Furry* / Country girl blues: *B, Memphis Willie* / Big road blues: *Douglas*, K.C. / Levee camp blues: *Williams, Big Joe* / Catfish: *Smith, Robert Curtis* / San Quentin blues: *Maiden*, Sidney / Big fat mama: *Walton, Wade* / Grievin' me: *Franklin, Pete* / Dyin' crapshooters blues, The: *McTell*, Blind Willie / Fine booze and heavy dues: *Johnson, Lonnie* / Blues before sunrise: *Blackwell, Scrapper* / You got to move: *Davis, Rev. Gary* / Brown skinned woman: *Eaglin, Snooks* / Pawn shop: *McGhee, Brownie & Sonny* Terry / T-model blues: *Hopkins, Lightnin'* / You is one black rat: *Quattlebaum, Doug* / Highway 61: *B, Memphis Willie* (Available on CD and cassette only) / Shake 'em on down: *Lewis, Furry* (Available on CD and cassette only) / Hand-me-down baby: *Maiden, Sidney* (Available on CD and cassette only) / Alberta: *Eaglin, Snooks* (Available on CD and cassette only) / See what you have done: *Tate, Baby* (Available on CD and cassette only) / Goin' where the moon crosses the yellow dog: *Blackwell, Scrapper* (Available on CD and cassette only).
LP: . . . . **CH 247**
MC: . . . . **CHC 247**

BLUESVILLE VOL. 2 (Various artists).
Tracks: / Train done gone: *Kirkland, Eddie* / Down on my knees: *Kirkland, Eddie* / Homesick's blues: *Homesick* James / Stones in my passway: *Homesick James* / Rack 'em back Jack: *Memphis Slim* / Happy blues for John Glenn: *Hopkins, Lightnin'* / Devil jumped the black man: *Lightnin' Hopkins* / My baby done gone: *Terry, Sonny*/ School time: *Arnold, Billy Boy* / Big legged woman: *Johnson, Lonnie* / I have to worry: *Curtis, King*/ Calcutta: *Sykes, Roosevelt* / Show down: *Lucas, Buddy* / How long how long blues: *Witherspoon, Jimmy*/ You better cut that out: *Arnold, Billy Boy* (Available on CD and cassette only) / Driving wheel: *Sykes, Roosevelt*(Available on CD and cassette only) / It's a lonesome old world: *Witherspoon, Jimmy* (Available on CD and cassette only) / Jelly roll baker: *Johnson, Lonnie* (Available on CD and cassette only).
LP: . . . . **CH 250**
MC: . . . . **CHC 250**

BOPPIN' THE BLUES (Various artists).
LP: . . . . **RR 2022**

BULL CITY BLUES (Various artists).
LP: . . . . **PY 1812**

CALIFORNIA JUMP BLUES (Various artists).
Tracks: / Rockola: *Lutcher, Joe* / Take a ride: *Lutcher, Joe* / Mardi gras: *Lutcher, Joe* / Rag mop: *Lutcher, Joe* / Wino: *Tanner, Kid & His Orchestra* / Have you ever been in love: *Tanner, Kid & His Orchestra*/ K.C. limited (part 2): *Enois, Lucky Quintet* / Rampart Street blues: *Davis, Ramp* / Mary Sue: *Davis, Ramp*/ Bayou bounce: *Davis, Ramp* / Blues have got me, The: *Davis, Ramp* / I want to rock 'n' roll: *Scatman*/ Flirting blues: *Agee, Ray* / K.C. limited (part 1): *Enois, Lucky Quintet*.
LP: . . . . **CH 71**

CAN'T SIT DOWN (Hot blues guitar) (Various artists).
LP: . . . . **JSP 1097**

CAP'N YOU'RE SO MEAN Negro songs of protest vol.2 (Various artists).
LP: . . . . **ROUNDER 4013**

CAROLINA BLUES GUITAR 1936-1951 (Various artists).
LP: . . . . **OT 1211**
LP: . . . . **HK 4006**

CENTRAL AVENUE BLUES (Various artists).
LP: . . . . **ACE OF SPADES 101**

CENTRAL MISSISSIPPI BLUES (Various artists).
LP: . . . . **WSE 130**

CHESS CHICAGO BLUES (Various artists).
LP: . . . . **CXMD 4013**

CHICAGO BLUES (Various artists).
Tracks: / Tough times: *Brim, John* / Be careful: *Brim, John* / Anna Lee: *Nighthawk, Robert* / Jackson town gal: *Nighthawk, Robert* / So glad I found you: *Shines, Johnny* / Having fun: *Memphis Slim* / Goin' away baby: *Rogers, Jimmy* / Chicago bound: *Rogers, Jimmy* / Dark road: *Jones, Floyd* / You can't live long: *Jones, Floyd* / Dust my broom: *James, Elmore* / I see my baby: *James, Elmore* / Eisenhower blues: *Lenoir, J.B.* / Korea blues: *Lenoir, J.B.* / By myself: *Broonzy, Big Bill/Washboard Sam* / Murmur low: *Spires, Big Boy* / I can't stop: *Rush, Otis* / You know my love: *Rush, Otis* / Third degree: *Boyd, Eddie* / Ten years ago: *Guy, Buddy* / My time after a while: *Guy, Buddy*.
LP: . . . . **NL 89588**
MC: . . . . **NK 89588**

CHICAGO BLUES 60'S STYLE (Various artists).
Tracks: / You're only a woman: *Anderson,Jessie* / True love express: *Anderson,Jessie* / So much loving for you baby: *Thompson, Johnny* / Bell bottom Sue: *Thompson, Johnny* / One sunny day: *Brooks, Lonnie* / Let it all hang out: *Brooks, Lonnie* / You mean everything to me: *Detroit Junior* / Too poor: *Detroit Junior*/ Much too much: *Rush, Bobby* / Sock boo ga loo: *Rush, Bobby* / I'm happy now: *Little Mac* / I've been a fool: *Tucker, Tommy* / Must I holler: *Thomas,Jamo* / Like a gentleman oughta: *Williams, Larry* / My heart beats like a hammer: *Little Joe Blue* / Me and my hammer: *Various artists*.
LP: . . . . **GCH 8114**

CHICAGO BLUES 1937-41 (Various artists).
LP: . . . . **HK 4007**

CHICAGO BLUES ANTHOLOGY (Various artists).
Tracks: / Tough times: *Brim, John* / Anna Lee: *Nighthawk, Robert* / So glad I found you: *Shines, Johnny*/ Having fun: *Various artists* / Goin' away baby: *Rodgers, Jimmie (1)* / I don't know: *Mabon, Willie*/ Dark road: *Jones, Floyd* / Dust my broom: *James, Elmore* / Eisenhower blues: *Lenoir, J.B.* / By myself: *Broonzy, Big Bill* / Murmur low / Rattlesnake: *Brim, John* / I see my baby: *James, Elmore* / Korea blues: *Lenoir, J.B.* / You can't live long: *Jones, Floyd* / I can't stop: *Rush, Otis* / Third degree: *Boyd*, Eddie / Ten years ago: *Guy, Buddy* / Be careful: *Brim, John* / Jackson Town gal: *Nighthawk, Robert* / World's in a tangle, The: *Rodgers, Jimmie (1)* / You know my love: *Rush, Otis* / My time after awhile: *Guy, Buddy* / Chicago bound: *Guy, Buddy*.
LP: . . . . **CXMD 4053**

CHICAGO BLUES AT HOME (Various artists).
LP: . . . . **ADVENT 2806**

CHICAGO BLUES - EARLY 50'S (Various artists).
LP: . . . . **BC 8**

CHICAGO BLUES LIVE (Various artists).
LP: . . . . **WOLF 120.287**

CHICAGO BLUES (RED LIGHTNIN') (Various artists).
Tracks: / We're ready: *Guy, Buddy & Junior Wells* / First time I met the blues: *Guy, Buddy & Junior Wells* / Country girl: *Guy, Buddy & Junior Wells* / Hoodoo man: *Guy, Buddy & Junior Wells* / In my younger days: *Guy, Buddy* & Junior Wells / Driving wheel: *Young, Johnny* / Walking groundhog: *Young, Johnny* / She's 19 years old: *Waters*, Muddy / Hoochie coochie man: *Waters, Muddy* / I got my mojo working: *Waters, Muddy* / Why you want to hurt me: *Young, Mighty Joe* / Wang dang doodle: *Taylor, Koko* / Speak my mind: *Hutto, J.B.* / Come on back home: *Hutto, J.B.* / You're gonna miss me: *Lewis, Johnny* / Uncle Sam: *Lewis, Johnny* / Hobo blues: *Lewis, Johnny*.
2LP: . . . . **RL 0055**

CHICAGO BLUES ROOTS VOL 1 1937-38 (Various artists).
LP: . . . . **DLP 573**

CHICAGO BLUES ROOTS VOL. 2 (Various artists).
LP: . . . . **DLP 574**

CHICAGO BLUES ROOTS VOL. 3 (1934-36) (Various artists).
LP: . . . . **DLP 578**

CHICAGO BLUES SESSION 2 (Various artists).
LP: . . . . **WOLF 120 848**

CHICAGO BLUES SESSION 3 (Various artists).
LP: . . . . **WOLF 120 849**

CHICAGO BLUES SESSION 8 (Various artists).
LP: . . . . **WOLF 120 854**

CHICAGO BLUES TEARDROPS JAM (Various artists).
LP: . . . . **WOLF 120.855**

CHICAGO BLUESMASTERS, VOL.1 (Various artists).
Tracks: / Combination boogie: *Various artists* / Now she's gone: *Various artists* / Pet cream man: *Various artists* / Dim lights: *Various artists* / Loving you: *Various artists* / Price of love, The: *Various artists*/ Things are so slow: *Various artists* / Judgement day: *Various artists* / Someone to love me: *Various artists*/ You tried to ruin me: *Various artists* / Nervous wreck: *Various artists* / No more love: *Various artists*/ Just can't stay: *Various artists* / All by myself: *Various artists*.
LP: . . . . **CRB 1042**

CHICAGO BLUESMASTERS, VOL.2 (Ain't times hard) (Various artists).
Tracks: / Schooldays on my mind: *Various artists* / Floyd's blues: *Various artists* / Any old lonesome day: *Various* artists / Delta Joe: *Various artists* / 4 o'clock blues: *Various artists* / I cried: *Various artists*/ Johnnie Mae: *Various artists* / Lonesome ole train: *Various artists* / Whisky headed woman: *Various artists*/ Williamson boogie: *Various artists* / I had a dream: *Various artists* / My baby's gone: *Various artists*/ Can't eat, can't sleep: *Various artists* / Hesitatin blues: *Various artists*.
LP: . . . . **CRB 1047**

CHICAGO BLUESMASTERS, VOL.3 (Goin' back home) (Various artists).
Tracks: / Goin' back home: *Various artists* / My baby left me: *Various artists* / King's Highway: *Various* artists / Eula Mae: *Various artists* / About to lose my mind: *Various artists* / Which one do I love: *Various* artists / Silver haired woman: *Various artists* / Fat mouth: *Various artists* / That's alright: *Various* artists / Just keep loving her: *Various artists* / Talkin' boogie: *Various artists* / Miss Lorraine: *Various* artists / I love to boogie: *Various artists* / Graveyard blues: *Various artists* / 609 boogie: *Various artists* / Road trouble: *Various artists*.
LP: . . . . **CRB 1067**

CHICAGO BLUESMASTERS, VOL.4 (Chills & fever) (Various artists).
LP: . . . . **CRB 1080**

CHICAGO BREAKDOWN (Various artists).
Tracks: / Minglewood town: *Granderson, John Lee* / Chicago breakdown: *Ross, Dr.Isiah* / I feel so worried: *Williams*, Big Joe / V-8 Ford blues: *Cotton, James* / Cryin' won't make it stay: *Maxwell Street Jimmy* / Michigan water: *Montgomery, Little Brother* / Good morning little schoolgirl: *Granderson, John Lee* / Hobo blues: *Ross, Dr.Isiah*/ Stack o'dollars: *Williams, Big Joe* / Polly put the kettle on: *Cotton, James* / Five long years: *Boyd, Eddie*.
LP: . . . . **SNTF 863**

CHICAGO CALLING (Various artists).
Tracks: / How long can this go on: *Various artists* / Oh Mama: *Various artists* / Mean cop: *Various artists*/ Win the dance: *Various artists* / Remember the time: *Various artists* / Off the hook: *Various artists*/ Lotta lovin: *Various artists* / My man is a lover: *Various artists* / Apache war dance: *Various artists*/ That ain't right: *Various artists* / Bright sound, The: *Various artists* / Early in the morning: *Various* artists / That man: *Various artists* / Will my man be home tonight: *Various artists* / I stay mad: *Various artists* / Cut you loose: *Various artists*.

LP: CRB 1135

CHICAGO PIANO BLUES 1947-1956 (Various).
Tracks: / I'm leaving you / I'm in love with you baby / It must have been the devil / Five spot / I declare that ain't right tks 2+4 / Matchbox blues / Big town playboy / Selby country blues / Wandering lover / Rumba dust / I found out / Lima beans / Johnson machine gun / Fly right little girl.
LP: GCH 8105

CHICAGO SLICKERS 1948-53 VOL 1 (Various artists).
LP: NH 102

CHICAGO SLICKERS 1948-55 VOL 2 (Various artists).
LP: NH 107

CINCINNATI BLUES 1928-36 (Various artists).
LP: BD 2021

COMIN' HOME TO THE BLUES (Various artists).
Tracks: / She's into something: *Cray, Robert* / You can't judge a book: *Buchanan, Roy* / Two fisted mama: *Webster*, Katie / Blues overtook me, The: *Musselwhite, Charlie* / Don't you call that boogie: *Hopkins, Lightnin'* / That woman is poison: *Thomas, Rufus* / Everyday I have the blues: *Memphis Slim* / Sonny's whoopin' the doop: *Terry, Sonny* / I think I got the blues: *Dixon, Willie* / What am I living for: *Brown, Clarence 'Gatemouth'* / Don't take advantage of me: *Winter, Johnny* / Who's lovin' you tonite: *Eaglin, Snooks* / Moon is full, The: *Collins*, Albert / Jump for joy: *Taylor, Koko* / Whole lotta lovin': *Professor Longhair* / Drinkin' wine spo-dee-o-dee: *Otis, Johnny*.
MC: MCTC 016

COMIN' HOME TO THE BLUES, VOL. 3 (Various artists).
MC: MCTC 044

COPULATIN' BLUES VOL.2 (Various artists).
LP: ST 122

COPULATION BLUES (Various artists).
Tracks: / Preachin' blues: *Bechet, Sidney & New Orleans Feetwarmers* / Stavin' chain: *Smith, Bessie* / Do your duty: *Various artists* / New rubbin' on the darned old thing: *Various artists* / Press my button (ring my bell): *Various artists* / Don't make me high: *Various artists* / You stole my cherry: *Various artists* / I need a little sugar in my bowl: *Various artists* / Get off with me: *Various artists* / My daddy rocks me: *Tampa* Red Hokum Jug Band / Keep your hands of my mojo: *Tampa Red Hokum Jug Band* / Winnin' boy: *Morton, Jelly Roll* / Shave 'em dry: *Bogan, Lucille* / Barbeque Bess: *Jackson, Bessie* / I'll keep sittin' on it if I can't sell it: *Various artists*.
LP: ST 101
MC: STAC 101

CRUISIN' AND BLUESIN' (Various artists).
LP: CHD 284

CRYIN' IN THE MORNING (Various artists).
Tracks: / Got a get a gettin': *Edwards, Frank* / Pig 'n' whistle red: *Edwards, Frank* / A to Z blues: *McTell*, Blind Willie / She don't treat me good no more: *Weaver, Curley* / Poor little angel girl: *McMillan, Dennis* / You're gonna weep & moan: *Wylie, David* / When my wife quit me: *Hooker, John Lee* / Kidman blues: *Memphis* Minnie / I'm a country boy: *Hughes Pee Wee* / Cryin' in the morning: *Tate, Blind Billy* / Trying to change my ways: *Jimmy, St. Louis* / Orphan boy blues: *Sunnyland Slim* / Ooh wee baby: *Tate, Blind Billy*.
LP: MR 5212

CUTTIN' THE BOOGIE (Various artists).
Tracks: / Chicago stomp: *Blythe, Jimmy* / Mr. Freddie blues: *Blythe, Jimmy* / Suitcase blues: *Thomas, Hersal* / Pinetop's boogie woogie: *Smith, Clarence Pinetop* / Jump steady blues: *Smith, Clarence Pinetop* / Honky tonk train blues: *Lewis, Meade Lux* / Yancey special: *Lewis, Meade Lux* / Mr. Freddie blues: *Lewis, Meade Lux* / Boogie woogie stomp: *Ammons, Albert* / Bass goin' crazy: *Ammons, Albert* / Mellow blues, The: *Yancey, Jimmy* / Tell 'em about me: *Yancey, Jimmy* / Climin' and screamin': *Johnson, Pete* / Blues on the downbeat: *Johnson, Pete* / Kaycee on my mind: *Johnson, Pete* / Cuttin' the boogie: *Ammons, Albert* (With Pete Johnson on piano and James Hoskins on drums.).
LP: NW 259

DELTA BLUES Volume 2 (29-39) (Various artists).
LP: DLP 533

DELTA BLUES (Various artists).
LP: RL 339

DELTA EXPERIMENTAL PROJECTS COMPILATION VOL 1 (Various artists).
LP: FC 044

DETROIT BLUES-EARLY 50'S (Various artists).
LP: BC 12

DETROIT GHETTO BLUES 1948-54 recordings (Various artists).
LP: NH 104

DEVIL WITH THE DEVIL (Various artists).
Tracks: / Right key but the wrong keyhole: *Bruners, Cliff Texas Wanderers* / Gimme my dime back: *Blue Ridge Playboys* / They go wild over me: *Tune Wranglers* / Gulf coast blues: *Light Crust Doughboys* / I can't dance: *Newman, Roy/his boys* / Cats are bad luck: *Revard, Jimmie & His Oklahoma Playboys* / When my baby comes to town: *Modern* Mountaineers / Easy ridin' papa: *Brown, Milton & The Brownies* / I'm wild about that thing: *Tune Wranglers* / I ain't gonna give nobody none of this jelly roll: *Bruners, Cliff Texas Wanderers* / Wonder stomp: *Texas Wanderers* / Devil with the devil: *Newman, Roy/his boys* / Cake eatin' man: *Revard, Jimmie & His Oklahoma Playboys* / Jig: *Boyd, Bill & his cowboys*.
LP: RAMBLER 102

DEVIL'S MUSIC, THE (Various artists).
Tracks: / Stop and listen: *Chatmon, Sam* / Highway 49: *Williams, Big Joe* / Cool drink of water: *Stackhouse* / Sam's rag: *Chatmon, Sam* / Watergate blues: *Williams, Big Joe* / Who gonna love you tonight: *Chatmon, Sam* / Aberdeen Mississippi blues: *White, Bukka* / When you got rid of my mule: *Vinson, Mose* / One room country shack: *Blake, Sonny* / Bring it on home to me: *Blake, Sonny* / Mr. Downchild: *Wilkins, Joe Willie* / Mean red spider: *Stackhouse, Houston* / Bugle call blues: *Vinson, Mose* / Take a little walk with me: *Aces* / Somebody help me: *Arnold, Billy Boy* / Somebody loan me a dime: *Robinson, Fenton* / Don't start me to talkin': *Good* Rockin' Charles / You don't know what love is: *Robinson, Fenton* / It hurts me too: *Carter, Joe* / She fooled me: *Arnold, Billy Boy* / Blue shadows: *Aces* / Shake your boogie: *Good Rockin' Charles* / Vicksburg Blues: *Little Brother Montgomery* / Yankee doodle blues: *Wilson, Edith* / I ain't got no special rider now: *Little Brother Montgomery*.
2LP: RL 033

DOWN SOUTH (Various artists).
LP: RL 313

DOWNHOME BLUES (Various artists).
LP: JSP 1068

DOWNHOME BLUES- 1ST LP (Various artists).
LP: MMLP 55001

DOWNHOME DELTA BLUES 1949-1952 (Various artists).
LP: NH 109

EASIN' IN: WOMEN SING THE BLUES 1924/41 (Various artists).
LP: MUSKADINE 105

EAST COAST BLUES (Various artists).
Tracks: / So many days: *Willis, Ralph* / That gal's no good: *Willis, Ralph* / Foolin' me: *Quattlebaum, Doug* / Don't be funny baby: *Quattlebaum, Doug* / Goin' to Chattanooga: *Willis, Ralph* / New goin' down slow: *Willis,* Ralph / Number writer: *Pickett, Dan* / Laughing blues: *Pickett, Dan* / Somebody changed the lock: *Slim,* Tarheel / You're a little too slow: *Slim, Tarheel* / Driving that thing: *Pickett, Dan* / I can shake it: *Willis, Ralph* / I will never love again: *Willis, Ralph* / No love blues: *Terry, Sonny* / Lizzie Lou: *Quattlebaum, Doug*.
LP: KK 824

EAST COAST BLUES 1924-37 (Various artists).
LP: L 1013
LP: BD 2038

EAST COAST STATES VOL.1 (Various artists).
LP: RL 318

EAST COAST STATES VOL.2 (Various artists).
LP: RL 326

ESSENTIAL BLUES (Various artists).
MC: 2644

FEMALE BLUES 1940/42 (Various artists).
LP: DLP 548

FEMALE COUNTRY BLUES VOL.2 (20's into the 30's) (Various artists).
LP: BD 2076

FESTIVAL OF BLUES (Recorded in Europe) (Various artists).
LP: SLP 214

FROM NEW ORLEANS TO CHICAGO Vol. 3 (Various artists).
LP: SM 3949

GAZ'S ROCKIN' BLUES (Various artists).
Tracks: / Gonna boogie: *Hooker, John Lee* / Shake holler and run: *Hooker, John Lee* / Who's been jivin with you: *Witherspoon, Jimmy* / She's dynamite: *King, B.B.* / Whoopin and hollerin: *Stevens, Preach* / Strange kinda feeling: *James, Elmore* / Texas hop: *Crayton, Pee Wee* / Good rockin' daddy: *James, Etta* / Mary Lou: *Young Jessie* / Open the door: *Tex, Joe* / Oh oh get out of the car: *Berry, Richard* / Yama yama pretty mama: *Berry, Richard* / Tough lover: *James, Etta* / Have mercy Miss Percy: *Long Tall Marvin*.
LP: CH 43

GEORGIA BLUES (Various artists).
LP: ROUNDER 2008

GEORGIA BLUES 1924-35 (Various artists).
LP: HK 4005

GEORGIA BLUES 1927-33 (Various artists).
LP: L 1012

GEORGIA BLUES GUITARS 1926-35 (Various artists).
LP: BD 2015

GEORGIA BLUES TODAY (Various artists).
LP: FLY 576

GET YOUR ASS IN THE WATER AND SWIM LIKE ME (Various artists).
LP: ROUNDER 2014

GOIN' UP THE COUNTRY (Various artists).
LP: ROUNDER 2012

GOING AWAY BLUES 1926-35 (Various artists).
LP: L 1018

GOING BACK ON THE FARM CHICAGO BLUES 1940-1942 (Various artists).
LP: TM 809

GOING BACK TO NEW ORLEANS (Various artists).
LP: SNTF 5021

GOOD MORNING BLUES (Var God Droj) (Various artists).
Tracks: / Good morning blues: *Various artists* / Riding in the moonlight: *Various artists* / Breaking up is hard to do: *Various artists* / Little by little: *Various artists* / Everyday I have the blues: *Various artists* / Almost grown: *Various artists* / Hard times got me: *Various artists* / I got my mojo working: *Various artists* / That's alright mama: *Various artists* / Sporting life: *Various artists*.
LP: PHONT 7507

GREAT BLUES GUITARISTS - STRING DAZZLERS (Various artists).
MC: 4678944

GREAT BLUES SINGERS & MEZZROW-BECHET SEPTET (Various artists).
Tracks: / Blood on the moon: *Various artists* / Levee blues: *Various artists* / Layin' my rules in blues: *Various* artists / Bad bad baby blues: *Various artists* / Sawmill man blues: *Various artists* / Baby, I'm cuttin' out: *Various artists* / Evil gal blues: *Various artists* / Fat mama blues: *Various artists* / You gotta give it to me: *Various artists* / Hey daddy blues: *Various artists* / Whoop this wolf away from my door: *Various artists* / You can't do that to me: *Various artists*.
LP: SM 3076

GREAT BLUESMEN (Various artists).
Tracks: / Midnight boogie: *Williams, Robert Pete* / Levee camp blues: *Williams, Robert Pete* / My baby done changed the lock on the door: *Terry, Sonny & Brownie McGhee* / Tupelo: *Hooker, John Lee* / Bus station blues: *Hooker,* John Lee / Son's blues: *House, Son* / Death letter blues: *House, Son* / Pony blues: *House, Son* / Mailman blues: *Estes, Sleepy John* / Clean up at home: *Estes, Sleepy John* / Hey rattler: *Reese, Dock* / Oh my Lord: *Reese, Dock* / Sliding Delta: *Hurt, Mississippi John* / Trouble, I've had it all my days: *Hurt,* Mississippi John / Hard times: *James, Skip* / Killing floor blues: *James, Skip* / Cherry ball blues: *James,* Skip / Illinois blues: *James, Skip* / Death don't have no mercy: *Davis, Rev. Gary* / Catfish blues: *Doss,* Willie / I had a woman: *Doss, Willie* / I'm going down south: *McDowell, Mississippi Fred* / If the river was whisky: *McDowell, Mississippi Fred* / Cottonfield blues: *Hopkins, Lightnin'* / Shake that thing: *Hopkins, Lightnin'*.
2LP: VSD 77

GREAT BLUESMEN: VOL 2 (Various artists).
Tracks: / Candy man: *Various artists* / Highway '61: *Various artists* / Death letter: *Various artists* / Midnight boogie: *Various artists* / My baby done gone changed to lock my door: *Various artists* / I had a woman: *Various artists* / Sporting life blues: *Various artists* / Bus station blues: *Various artists* / Clean up at home: *Various artists* / Shake that thing: *Various artists* / Death don't have no mercy: *Various artists* / Cotton crop blues: *Various artists* / Burning fire: *Various artists* / Poison ivy: *Various artists* / I can't quit you baby: *Various artists* / Messing with the kid: *Various artists* / I got mine in time: *Various* artists / Please help: *Various artists* / Set a date: *Various artists* / Dynaflow blues: *Various artists* / Everyday: *Various artists*.
MC: ZCGH 879
LP: GH 879

GREAT BLUESMEN/NEWPORT (Various artists).
MC: CVSD 77/78

GREAT BRITISH BLUES 1962-68 (Various artists).
LP: TAB 53

GREAT HARP PLAYERS (1927-30) (Various artists).
Tracks: / John Henry blues: *Francis, William & Richard Sowell* / Roubin' blues: *Francis, William & Richard Sowell* / Pot licker blues: *Watson, El* / Narrow gauge blues: *Watson, El* / El Watson's fox chase: *Watson, El* / Bay rum blues: *Watson, El* / Sweet bunch of daisies: *Watson, El* / One sock blues: *Watson, El* / Lost boy blues: *McAbee, Palmer* / McAbee's railroad piece: *McAbee, Palmer* / Railway blues: *Stowers, Freeman* / Texas wild cat chase: *Stowers, Freeman* / Medley of blues: *Stowers, Freeman* / Sunrise on the farm: *Stowers,* Freeman / Mean low blues: *Blues Birdhead* / Harmonica blues: *Blues Birdhead* / Mississippi swamp moan: *Lewis, Alfred* / Friday moan blues: *Lewis, Alfred*.
LP: MSE 209

GREAT VOCALISTS Vol. 6.
LP: SM 3952

GREATEST IN COUNTRY BLUES (Various artists).
LPS: BD 01

GUITAR IN MY HANDS (Texas blues guitar 49-66) (Various artists).
LP: BLP 104

GUITAR IN MY HANDS VOL 2 (Various artists).
LP: BLP 110

HI RECORDS: THE BLUES SESSIONS (Various artists).
Tracks: / I'm so glad: *Hines, Don* / Tell it like it is: *Hines, Don* / Stormy monday: *Hines, Don* / Please accept my love: *Hines, Don* / You had to pay: *Hines, Don* / Trouble is my name: *Hines, Don* / He won't bite me twice: *Patton, Big Amos* / Move with me baby: *Patton, Big Amos* / Going to Vietnam: *Patton, Big Amos* / I'm gone: *Patton, Big Amos* / Dog man: *Patton, Big Amos* / You're too young: *Patton, Big Amos* / Stop arguing over me: *Carter, Big Lucky* / Miss Betty Green: *Carter, Big Lucky* / Goofer dust: *Carter, Big Lucky* / I've been hurt: *Carter, Big Lucky* / Please don't leave me: *Carter, Big Lucky* / You'd better mind: *Carter,* Big Lucky / Please Mr. Foreman: *Carter, Big Lucky* / As the years go passing on: *Carter, Big Lucky* / Let me know: *Carter, Big Lucky* / Don't turn your back on me: *Bryant, Don* / Call of distress, The: *Bryant, Don* / Is that asking too much: *Bryant, Don* / There is something on your mind: *Bryant, Don* / Prayer meeting: *Mitchell,* Willie / I was wrong: *Miller, Gene* / What do you mean: *Miller, Gene* / Aretha, sing one for me: *Jackson, George*.
2LP: DHIUKLP 427

HOUSTON GHETTO BLUES (Various artists).
LP: FLY 527

I DIDN'T GIVE A DAMN IF WHITES BOUGHT IT, VOL.5 (Various artists).
Tracks: / Dirty old man: *Jackson, Lee* / Take my love: *Gibson, Lacy* / Lee's boogie: *Jackson, Lee* / Ship made of paper: *Magic Slim* / Soft and mellow Stella: *Sunnyland Slim* / Mayor Daley's blues: *Clearwater,* Eddy / Depression blues: *Sunnyland Slim* / Bobby's rock: *Carter, Joe* / Smile on my face: *Sunnyland Slim* / Juanita: *Jackson, Lee*.
LP: RL 057

I DIDN'T GIVE A DAMN IF WHITES BOUGHT IT, VOL.3 (Various artists).
LP: RL 052

I DIDN'T GIVE A DAMN IF WHITES BOUGHT IT, VOL.4 (Various artists).

Tracks: / Showing off my car: Williams, Willie / I had it so hard: Sunnyland Slim / Pleading for love: Jackson, Lee / Came up the hard way: Clearwater, Eddy / That ain't right: Magic Slim / Things I used to do, The: Johnson, Jimmy / Chicago woman: Jackson, Lee / Every time I get to drinking: Sunnyland Slim / Bessie Mae: Sunnyland Slim / Rocks is my pillow: Jackson, Lee.
LP: . . . . **RL 056**

I DIDN'T GIVE A DAMN IF WHITES BOUGHT IT,VOL.1 (Various artists).
LP: . . . . **RL 050**

I GOT RHYTHM (Anthology) (Various artists).
LP: . . . . **KM 132**

I HAVE TO PAINT MY FACE (Various artists).
LP: . . . . **ARHOOLIE 1005**

INSTANT BLUES (Various artists).
Tracks: / Truck load of lovin': King, Albert / If you're thinkin' what I'm thinkin': Cray, Robert / Boom boom: Hooker, John Lee / Dust my broom: James, Elmore / Recession blues: King, B.B. / Juke: Little Walter/ Hung down head: Fulson, Lowell / Shame, shame, shame: Reed, Jimmy / Messin' with the kid: Wells, Junior/ Still a fool: Muddy Waters / Down in the bottom: Howlin' Wolf / All your love: Rush, Otis / That evening train: Walker, T-Bone / Let me love you baby: Guy, Buddy.
LP: . . . . **INS 5011**
MC: . . . . **TCINS 5011**

IT'S YOUR VOODOO WORKING (Various artists).
LP: . . . . **FLY 60**

JACKSON BLUES (1928-38) (Various artists).
LP: . . . . **L 1007**
MC: . . . . **YAZMC 1007**

JAILHOUSE BLUES Women's acappella songs from Parchman Penitentia (Various artists).
LP: . . . . **RR 1316**

JERICHO ALLEY BLUES FLASH, VOL. 1 (Various artists).
LP: . . . . **DD 4312**

JERICHO ALLEY BLUES FLASH, VOL. 2 (Various artists).
LP: . . . . **DD 4313**

JSP SAMPLER (CONTEMPORARY BLUES) (Various artists).
LP: . . . . **JSP 1072**

JUG, JOOK AND WASHBOARD BANDS (Various artists).
LP: . . . . **BC 2**

JUG & WASHBOARD BANDS VOL.1 (Various artists).
LP: . . . . **BD 2023**

JUG & WASHBOARD BANDS VOL.2 (Various artists).
LP: . . . . **BD 2024**

JUICY HARMONICA (Various artists).
LP: . . . . **CG 709-06**

JUKE JOINT BLUES (Various artists).
LP: . . . . **BC 23**

JUST BLUES (Various artists).
2LP: **416037**

KINGS OF THE BLUES (ACE LABEL) (Various artists).
Tracks: / Sweet little angel: King, B.B. / She moves me: Watson, Johnny 'Guitar' / I'll get along somehow: Sims, Frankie Lee / Blues serenade: Turner, Babyface / On my way back home: Flash Terry / Odds against me: Hooker, John Lee / Sitting here thinking: Walker, T-Bone / Problem child: Dee, Mercy / Lonesome old feeling: Slim, Bumble Bee / I tried: Young Wolf / Cotton picker: Higgins, Chuck & The Melotones / Wild hop: Crayton, Pee Wee / Worried about my baby: Howlin' Wolf / Tavern lounge boogie: Burns, Eddie 'guitar' / Believe I'll change towns: Hogg, Smokey / Too many rivers: Fulson, Lowell / Yesterday: Chenier, Clifton / Lonesome dog blues: Lightnin' Hopkins / Hard times: Fuller, Johnny / Riding mighty high: Dixon, Floyd / Please find my baby: James, Elmore.
LP: . . . . **CH 276**
MC: . . . . **CHC 276**

KINGS OF THE BLUES (CHARLY LABEL) (Various artists).
LPS: . . . . **BOX 250**
MCSET: . . . . **TCBOX 250**

KINGS OF THE BLUES (TOPLINE LABEL) (Various artists).
Tracks: / Dust my broom: James, Elmore ((James)) / I wish you would: Arnold, Billy Boy ((b)) / San-ho-zay: King, Freddie ((c)) / Open up baby: Butler, George 'Wild Child' ((d)) / My back scratcher: Frost, Frank ((d)) / Thug: Fulson, Lowell ((d)) / I love you honey: Hooker, John Lee ((b)) / Loose me: Blue, Little Joe((d)) / Born under a bad sign: King, Albert ((f)) / Hide away: Otis, Shuggie ((g)) / I ain't got you: Reed, Jimmy ((b)) / Somebody loan me a dime: Robinson, Fenton ((h)) / Part time love: Taylor, Little Johnny ((d)) / I need your love so bad: Taylor, Ted ((d)) / Crawl, The: Guitar Junior / Honky tonk: McCain, Jerry.
LP: . . . . **TOP 180**
MC: . . . . **KTOP 180**

LADIES SING THE BLUES VOLUME 1 (Various artists).
LP: . . . . **SJL 2233**

LADIES SING THE BLUES VOLUME 2 (Various artists).
LP: . . . . **SJL 2256**

LEGACY OF THE BLUES (Various artists).
Tracks: / Funky malaguena: Eaglin, Snooks / Found my baby gone: Dupree, Champion Jack / Wishy washy woman: Young, Mighty Joe / I'm a bluesman: Bonner, Juke Boy / Black gal you're sure looking warm: Williams, Big Joe / Long time gone: Memphis Slim / Stary crown blues: Shore, J D / I'm going to have myself a ball: Williams, Robert Pete / Cannonball: Boyd, Eddie / She's so mellow: Sunnyland Slim / Please help poor me: Hopkins, Lightnin'.
LP: . . . . **SNTX 1**

LEGACY OF THE BLUES (Various artists).
LP: . . . . **SNTD 202**

LEGACY OF THE BLUES SAMPLER (Various artists).
2LP: . . . . **GNPSX 10010**
LP: . . . . **GNPS 10010**
MC: **GNP5 10010**

LEGENDS OF THE BLUES VOL.1 (Various artists).
MC: **4672454**

LEGENDS OF THE BLUES, VOL. 1 (See under Legends of the Blues) (Various artists).

LISTEN TO DR. JIVE (Various artists).
LP: . . . . **KK 780**

LIVE AT NEWPORT (Various artists).
Tracks: / Outside help: Various artists / Little red rooster: Various artists / Ball and chain: Various artists / Long distance call: Various artists / Where's my woman been: Various artists / Got my mojo working: Various artists.
LP: . . . . **BMM 002**

LIVE AT SMALL'S PARADISE (Various artists).
Tracks: / Loose it: Various artists / Mannish boy: Various artists / Everything's gonna be alright: Various artists / That's alright: Various artists / Ode to Billy Joe: Various artists / Pee wee's texas boogie: Various artists / Louella brown: Various artists / My little girl: Various artists / Blues after hours: Various artists.
LP: . . . . **BMLP 1029**

LIVE CHICAGO BLUES - VOL.1 (Various artists).
LP: . . . . **SNTF 784**

LIVE CHICAGO BLUES - VOL.2 (Various artists).
LP: . . . . **SNTF 285**

LIVE CHICAGO BLUES - VOL.3 (Various artists).
LP: . . . . **SNTF 786**

LIVING CHICAGO BLUES, VOL.1 (Various artists).
Tracks: / Your turn to cry: Various artists / Serves me to right to suffer: Various artists / Ain't that just like a woman: Various artists / Feel like breaking up somebody's home: Various artists / It's alright: Various artists / Out of bad luck: Various artists / Stoop down baby: Various artists / Sitting on top of the world: Various artists / My baby's so ugly: Various artists / Come home, darling: Various artists / Blues won't let me be: Various artists / One room country shack: Various artists / Linda Lu: Various artists/ Too late: Various artists / Laundromat blues: Various artists / One day: Various artists / Woman in trouble: Various artists.
LP: . . . . **SNTF 784**

LIVING CHICAGO BLUES, VOL.2 (Various artists).
Tracks: / Don't answer the door: Various artists / Two headed man: Various artists / Cold, lonely nights: Various artists / Move over, little dog: Various artists / Would you, baby: Various artists / Worry, worry: Various artists / Sunnyland blues: Various artists / Cry, cry darling: Various artists / Stranded on the highway: Various artists / Dirty mother for you: Various artists / Spider in my stew: Various artists / Don't say that no more: Various artists / Take it easy, baby: Various artists / Blues after hours: Various artists / Little angel child: Various artists / How much more longer: Various artists.
LP: . . . . **SNTF 785**

LIVING CHICAGO BLUES, VOL.3 (Various artists).
LP: . . . . **SNTF 786**

LIVING CHICAGO BLUES, VOL.4 (Various artists).
Tracks: / Hard times: Reed, A.C. & The Spark Plugs / She's fine: Reed, A.C. & The Spark Plugs / Moving out of the ghetto: Reed, A.C. & The Spark Plugs / Going to New York: Reed, A.C. & The Spark Plugs / Big legged woman: Scotty & The Rib Tips / Careless without love: Scotty & The Rib Tips / Road block: Scotty & The Rib Tips/ Poison ivy: Scotty & The Rib Tips / I dare you: Lee, Lovie & Carey Bell / Nobody knows my troubles: Lee, Lovie & Carey Bell / Sweet little girl: Lee, Lovie & Carey Bell / Nap town: Lee, Lovie & Carey Bell.
LP: . . . . **SNTF 840**

LIVING CHICAGO BLUES, VOL.5 (Various artists).
Tracks: / Drown in my own tears: Various artists / Crying for my baby: Various artists / I feel so bad: Various artists / Wish me well: Various artists / Blues for a real man: Various artists / Thirteen years in prison: Various artists / Country boy: Various artists / My life ain't the same: Various artists / You don't know: Various artists / Morning noon and night: Various artists / Two years: Various artists.
LP: . . . . **SNTF 841**

LIVING CHICAGO BLUES, VOL.6 (Various artists).
Tracks: / If I hadn't been high: Detroit Junior / Some nerve: Detroit Junior / Somebody to shack: Detroit Junior / I got money: Detroit Junior / Somebody have mercy: Johnson, Luther "Guitar Junior" / Got to have money: Johnson, Luther "Guitar Junior" / Just like mama said: Johnson, Luther "Guitar Junior" / Look what you've done: Johnson, Luther "Guitar Junior" / Going upstairs: Embry, Queen Sylvia / Blues this morning: Embry, Queen Sylvia / Tired of being pushed around: Embry, Queen Sylvia / Please let me stay: Embry, Queen Sylvia.
LP: . . . . **SNTF 842**

LONESOME ROAD BLUES (15 years in the delta) (Various artists).
LP: . . . . **L 1038**

LOW BLOWS (An anthology of Chicago harmonica blues) (Various artists).
LP: . . . . **R 7610**

LOWDOWN MEMPHIS HARMONICA JAM (1950-1955 recordings) (Various artists).
LP: . . . . **NH 103**

L&R BLUES SAMPLER (Various artists).
LP: . . . . **LR 42.006**

MAMA LET ME LAY IT ON YOU (Various artists).
LP: . . . . **L 1040**

MASTERS OF THE BLUES VOL. 5 (Various artists).
LP: . . . . **CC 29**

MASTERS OF THE BLUES VOL. 12 (Various artists).
LP: . . . . **CC 38**

MEMPHIS BLUES 1927-37 (Various artists).
LP: . . . . **HK 4002**

MEMPHIS BLUES (KRAZY KAT) (Various artists).
Tracks: / Last time, The: Various artists / Cat squirrel: Various artists / That's all right: Various artists/ Black snake boogie: Various artists / 44: Various artists / Outside friends: Various artists / Sittin' on top of the world: Various artists / High (but high): Various artists / Peg leg baby: Various artists/ Ooowee baby: Various artists / Stay with me: Various artists / Baby I'm off that stuff: Various artists/ All alone: Various artists / Blues jumped a rabbit, The: Various artists / Hello pretty baby: Various artists / Phineas boogie: Various artists / Joint is jumping, The: Various artists.
LP: . . . . **KK 7427**

MEMPHIS BLUES (RCA) (Various artists).
Tracks: / How long?: Stokes, Frank / 'T'ain't nobody's business if I do: Stokes, Frank (part 2) / It won't be long now: Stokes, Frank / Right now blues: Stokes, Frank / I'm wild about my lovin': Jackson, Jim / I'm gonna move to Louisiana: Jackson, Jim (parts 1 & 2) / This mornin' she was gone: Jackson, Jim / Casey Jones: Lewis, Furry (part 1) / Dry land blues: Lewis, Furry / I will turn your money green: Lewis, Furry / Mistreatin' mama: Lewis, Furry / Jailhouse blues: Wilkins, Robert / Rolling stone: Wilkins, Robert(parts 1 & 2) / I do blues: Wilkins, Robert / Sun brimmer blues: Memphis Jug Band / Snitchin' gambler blues: Memphis Jug Band / Peaches in the Springtime: Memphis Jug Band / Black woman is like a black snake, A: Memphis Jug Band / Dirty butter: Wallace, Minnie / Old folks started it, The: Wallace, Minnie / Won't you be kind to me?: Hart, Hattie / You wouldn't would you Papa?: Hart, Hattie / Big railroad blues: Cannon's Jug Stompers/ Feather bed: Cannon's Jug Stompers / Viola Lee blues: Cannon's Jug Stompers / Bring it with you when you come: Cannon's Jug Stompers / I'm going back home: McCoy & Johnson / I never told a lie: McCoy & Johnson/ Don't want no woman: McCoy & Johnson / Georgia skin: McCoy & Johnson.
2LP: . . . . **NL 89276**
MC: . . . . **NK 89276**

MEMPHIS BLUES VOL.1 (Various artists).
LP: . . . . **RL 323**

MEMPHIS BLUES VOL.2 (Various artists).
LP: . . . . **RL 329**

MEMPHIS GIRLS 1929-35 (Various artists).
LP: . . . . **BD 2029**

MEMPHIS HARMONICA KINGS (Various artists).
Tracks: / Chickaway special: Lewis, Noah/Beale Street Rounders/Jed Davenport / Devil in the woodpile: Lewis, Noah/Beale Street Rounders/Jed Davenport / Like I want to be: Lewis, Noah/Beale Street Rounders/Jed Davenport / Ticket agent blues: Lewis, Noah/Beale Street Rounders/Jed Davenport / New minglewood blues: Lewis, Noah/Beale Street Rounders/Jed Davenport / Selling the jelly: Lewis, Noah/Beale Street Rounders/Jed Davenport / Bad luck's my buddy: Lewis, Noah/Beale Street Rounders/Jed Davenport / I'm sitting on top of the world: Lewis, Noah/Beale Street Rounders/Jed Davenport/ Talking 'bout yo-yo: Lewis, Noah/Beale Street Rounders/Jed Davenport / How long how long blues: Lewis, Noah/Beale Street Rounders/Jed Davenport / Cow cow blues: Lewis, Noah/Beale Street Rounders/Jed Davenport / Beale Street breakdown: Lewis, Noah/Beale Street Rounders/Jed Davenport / You ought to move out of town: Lewis, Noah/Beale Street Rounders/Jed Davenport / Dirty dozen, The: Lewis, Noah/Beale Street Rounders/Jed Davenport / Jug blues: Lewis, Noah/Beale Street Rounders/Jed Davenport / Save me some: Lewis, Noah/Beale Street Rounders/Jed Davenport / Piccolo blues: Lewis, Noah/ Beale Street Rounders/Jed Davenport.
LP: . . . . **MSE 213**

MEMPHIS JAMBOREE 1927-36 (Various artists).
LP: . . . . **L 1021**

MERCURY NEW ORLEANS SESSIONS, THE (1950) (Various artists).
Tracks: / Hey now baby: Byrd, Roy / Bald head: Byrd, Roy / Her mind is gone: Byrd, Roy / Oh well: Byrd, Roy / Hadacol bounce: Byrd, Roy / Longhair stomp: Byrd, Roy / Been foolin' around: Byrd, Roy / Between the night and day: Byrd, Roy / Byrd's blues: Byrd, Roy / Her mind is gone (2): Byrd, Roy / Hadacol bounce (2): Byrd, Roy / Between the night and day (2): Byrd, Roy / Longhair stomp (2): Byrd, Roy / Miss lollipop's confession: Mondy, Alma / Love troubles: Mondy, Alma / Still my angel child: Mondy, Alma / Baby get wise: Mondy, Alma / Just as soon as I get home: Mondy, Alma / No stuff for me: Mondy, Alma / Street walkin' daddy: Mondy, Alma / Job for a jockey, A: Mondy, Alma / Miss lollipop's confession (2): Mondy, Alma / Love troubles (2): Mondy, Alma / Just as soon as I get home (2): Mondy, Alma / Mercury boogie: Craven, Dwight / New way of lising: Craven, Dwight / She won't leave no more: Gaines, Little Joe/ Snuff dipper: Gaines, Little Joe / I walk in my sleep: Johnson, Theard / Lost love: Johnson, Theard/ Boogies the thing: Miller, George / Bat Lee swing: Miller, George / Bat Lee swing (2): Miller, George.
2LP: . . . . **BFD 15308**

MISSISSIPPI BLUES (Various artists).
LP: . . . . **HK 4001**

MISSISSIPPI BLUES 1927-41 (Various artists).
LP: . . . . **L 1001**

MISSISSIPPI BLUES GUITAR 1926-35 (Various artists).
LP: . . . . **BD 2014**

MISSISSIPPI BLUES VOL.1 (Various artists).
LP: . . . . **RL 302**

MISSISSIPPI BLUES VOL.2 (Various artists).
LP: . . . . **RL 303**

MISSISSIPPI BLUES VOL.3 (Various artists).
LP: . . . . **RL 314**

MISSISSIPPI COUNTRY BLUES VOL.2 (Various artists).
LP: . . . . **DLP 520**

MISSISSIPPI COUNTRY BLUES VOL.1 (Various artists).
LP: . . . . **DLP 519**

MISSISSIPPI DELTA BLUES (VOL.1) (Various artists).
LP: . . . . **ARHOOLIE 1041**

MISSISSIPPI DELTA BLUES (VOL.2) (Various artists).
LP: . . . . **ARHOOLIE 1042**

MISSISSIPPI GIRLS 1928-31 (Various artists).
LP: . . . . **BD 2018**

MISSISSIPPI LEGENDS (Music of New Orleans) (Various artists).
LPS: **FXM3 7242**

MISSISSIPPI MOANERS 1927-42 (Various artists).
LP: . . . . **L 1009**

MISSISSIPPI STRING BANDS 1928-36 (Various artists).
LP: . . . . **BD 2043**

MISTER CHARLIES BLUES (Old Timey anthology) (Various artists).
LP: . . . . **L 1024**

MODERN NEW ORLEANS MASTERS (Various artists).
LP: . . . . **ROUNDER 2072**
MC: . . . . **ROUNDER 2072C**

MORE DEVIL MUSIC (Various artists).
Tracks: / Crossroads: *Various artists* / Pony blues: *Various artists* / Mistake in life: *Various artists*/ Evil is going on: *Various artists* / Hold that train: *Various artists* / Forty four: *Various artists*/ Providence help the poor people: *Various artists* / Tears came rolling down: *Various artists* / Sloppy drunk: *Various artists* / Wave my hands bye bye: *Various artists* / Meet me at the bottom: *Various artists*.
LP: . . . . **RL 038**

MORE WEST COAST WINNERS (Various artists).
LP: . . . . **BLP 115**

NASTY BLUES (Various artists).
Tracks: / Strokin': *Carter, Clarence* / Trudy sings the blues: *Lynn, Trudy* / I want to play with your poodle: *Willis, Chick* / Rainy day: *White, Artie* / One eyed woman: *Coleman, Gary B. B.* / I want a big fat woman: *Willis, Chick* / Ugly man: *Taylor, Little Johnny* / Watch where you stroke: *Coleman, Gary B. B.* / Two heads are better than one: *Haddix, Travis* / Why do I stay here and take all this shit: *Carter, Clarence*.
LP: . . . . **ICH 1048**
MC: . . . . **ICH 1048 MC**

NASTY BLUES 2 (Various artists).
Tracks: / Jack you up: *Willis, Chick* / Come back pussy: *Williams, Dicky* / Cook me: *Legendary Blues Band*/ Grandpa can't fly his kite: *Carter, Clarence* / Let me funk with you: *Blues Boy Willie* / Tittie man: *Drink* Small / Nuts for sale: *Willis, Chick* / Don't pet my dog: *White, Artie* / Lemon squeezin' Daddy: *Brown, Nappy* / Kiss you all over: *Carter, Clarence*.
LP: . . . . **ICH 1066**
MC: . . . . **ICH 1066 MC**

NATIONAL DOWNHOME BLUES FESTIVAL VOL 3 (Various artists).
LP: . . . . **SLP 23**

NATIONAL DOWNHOME BLUES FESTIVAL VOL.2 (Various artists).
LP: . . . . **SLP 22**

NATIONAL DOWNHOME BLUES FESTIVAL VOL. 4 (Various artists).
LP: . . . . **SLP 24**

NATIONAL DOWNHOME BLUES FESTIVAL VOL 1 (Various artists).
LP: . . . . **SLP 21**

NEGRO RELIGIOUS MUSIC VOL.1 Sanctified singers I (Various artists).
LP: . . . . **BC 17**

NEW BLUEBLOODS (Various artists).
LP: . . . . **SNTF 984**

NEW YORK BLUES VOL. 1 (Various artists).
Tracks: / Shake baby shake: *Dupree, Champion Jack* / Daisy: *McGhee, Brownie* / Candied yams: *Brown, B & His* Rockin' McVouts / Drunk again: *Dupree, Champion Jack* / Doggin' my heart around: *Terry, Sonny* / My baby left me: *Brown, B & His Rockin' McVouts* / Number nine blues: *Dupree, Champion Jack* / Harmonica hop: *Terry, Sonny*/ Fannie Mae is back: *Brown, B & His Rockin' McVouts* / Highway blues: *Dupree, Champion Jack* / Don't dog your woman: *McGhee, Brownie* / Stumbling block blues: *Dupree, Champion Jack* / Hardworking man: *Brown, B & His Rockin' McVouts* / Shim sham shammy: *Dupree, Champion Jack*.
LP: . . . . **CRB 1207**

NEW YORK BLUES VOL. 2 (Various artists).
Tracks: / Angel child: *Myers, Sammy* / Little girl: *Myers, Sammy* / You don't have to go: *Myers, Sammy*/ Sad sad lonesome day: *Myers, Sammy* / Rockin' with B: *Brown, B & His Rockin' McVouts* / Pleasure is all mine, The: *Long, Bobby* / I'm tired of it: *Doctor Horse* / I go into orbit: *Acey, Johnny*.
LP: . . . . **CRB 1208**

NEW YORK KNOCKOUTS, THE (Various artists).
LP: . . . . **BLP 111**

NEW YORK NOTABLES (Various artists).
LP: . . . . **BLP 105**

NEWPORT (Various artists).
MCSET: . . . . **MCCVSD 78**

OAKLAND BLUES (Various artists).
LP: . . . . **ARHOOLIE 2008**

OKEH CHICAGO BLUES (Various artists).
2LP: . . . . **EPC 22123**
MC: **40 22123**

OLD TIME BLUES VOL.1 (Various artists).
Tracks: / Chicken hop: *Various artists* / Climbing on top of the hill: *Various artists* / Uncle Bud: *Various artists* / Slider: *Various artists* / She loves so easy: *Various artists* / I need a woman: *Various artists*/ Confusing: *Various artists* / Crazy 'bout you baby: *Various artists* / Love's a disease: *Various artists*/ Sweet sweet woman: *Various artists* / Reap what you sew: *Various artists* / Word out: *Various artists*/ Sweet little girl: *Various artists* / Playboy: *Various artists* / Hard luck baby: *Various artists* / Let the doorbell ring: *Various artists*.
LP: . . . . **CH 180**

ORIGINAL MEMPHIS BLUES BROTHERS, THE (Various artists).
Tracks: / Good lovin': *Bland, Bobby* / Dry up baby: *Bland, Bobby* / Crying all night long: *Bland, Bobby*/ Drifting from town to town (take 1): *Bland, Bobby* / Drifting from town to town (take 2): *Bland, Bobby* / Love me baby: *Bland, Bobby & Junior Parker* / You're my angel: *Parker, Junior & the Blue Flames* / Bad women: *Parker*, Junior & the Blue Flames / Whole heap of mama: *Forrest, Earl* / I wronged a woman: *Forrest, Earl* / Sad and lonely: *Forrest, Earl* / Trouble and me: *Forrest, Earl* / I can't forgive you: *Forrest, Earl* / Rumpus romp: *Forrest, Earl* / Midnight hours journey: *Ace, Johnny* / I cried: *Ace, Johnny*.
LP: . . . . **CHD 265**

OUT OF BAD LUCK Chicago blues 1961-66 (Various artists).
Tracks: / Out of bad luck: *Magic Sam* / Every night about this time: *Magic Sam* / Blue light boogie: *Magic* Sam / It's like Heaven to me: *Taylor, Koko* / Honky tonk: *Taylor, Koko* / I swing 'em the way I feel: *Lenoir, J.B.* / I feel so good: *Lenoir, J.B.* / Heavy heart beat: *Fortune, Jesse* / Good things: *Fortune, Jesse*/ Too many cooks: *Fortune, Jesse* / Crossroads: *Homesick James* / My baby's sweet: *Homesick James* / Ouch: *Allen, Ricky* / I'd rather fight than switch: *Reed, A.C.*.
LP: . . . . **FLY 590**

PACKIN' UP MY BLUES (BLUES FROM THE DEEP SOUTH) (Various artists).
LP: . . . . **MUSKADINE 102**

PHILADELPHIA BOOGIE (Various artists).
Tracks: / Bobbie town boogie: *Brown, Lee* / She's alright: *Terry, Dossie* / Let me be your coalman: *Carter*, James / New blow top blues: *Groner, Duke* / Ain't nothin' to it: *Variety Chocolate Bars* / Philadelphia boogie: *McCall, Len* / Broad bottom boogie: *Dial, Harry* / Creepin' and peepin': *Price, Jesse* / Just before sunrise: *Price, Jesse* / Welcome home: *Davis, Maxwell* / Get out: *Davis, Maxwell* / Cold blooded blues: *Great "Gates"* / Come back home: *Great "Gates"* / Frank Bull's boogie: *Grissom, Jimmie*.
LP: . . . . **KK 834**

PIANO BLUES 1927-30 (Various artists).
LP: . . . . **HK 4010**

PIANO BLUES AND BOOGIE WOOGIE 1929-35 (Various artists).
LP: . . . . **BD 2034**

PIANO BLUES LEGENDS (Various artists).
Tracks: / P L bounce: *Various artists* / Seasick and waterbound: *Various artists* / With you on my mind: *Various* artists / Mother Fuyer: *Various artists* / Going down slow: *Various artists* / St. Louis blues: *Various* artists / T 99: *Various artists* / Bloodstains on the wall: *Various artists* / Why should I cry: *Various artists* / Blues ain't nothing but a botheration: *Various artists* / I got a gal: *Various artists*.
LP: . . . . **JSP 1056**

PIANO BLUES VOL.1 The Twenties 1923-30 (Various artists).
LP: . . . . **DLP 513**

PIANO BLUES, VOL.1: PARAMOUNT 1929-30 (Whip it to a Jelly) (Various artists).
LP: . . . . **PY 4401**

PIANO BLUES VOL.2 (Thirties 1930-39) (Various artists).
LP: . . . . **DLP 514**

PIANO BLUES, VOL.2: BRUNSWICK 1928-30 (Nothing But a Worried Mind) (Various artists).
LP: . . . . **PY 4402**

PIANO BLUES, VOL.3: VOCALION 1928-30 (Shake Your Wicked Knees) (Various artists).
Tracks: / Back in the alley: *Various artists* / Cow cow blues: *Various artists* / Slum gullion stomp: *Various artists* / Texas shout: *Various artists* / Michigan River blues: *Various artists* / You can't come in: *Various artists* / I'm so glad: *Various artists* / Mexico bound blues band: *Various artists*.
LP: . . . . **PY 4403**

PIANO BLUES, VOL.4: THE THOMAS FAMILY 1925-29 (Give it to me Good Mr. Hersal) (Various artists).
LP: . . . . **PY 4404**

PIANO BLUES, VOL.5: POSTSCRIPT 1927-33 (Hot Box on my Mind) (Various artists).
LP: . . . . **PY 4405**

PIANO BLUES, VOL.6: WALTER ROLAND 1933-35 (Take Your Big Legs Off) (Various artists).
LP: . . . . **PY 4406**

PIANO BLUES, VOL.7: LEROY CARR 1930-35 (Don't Cry When I'm Gone) (Various artists).
LP: . . . . **PY 4407**

PIANO BLUES, VOL.8: TEXAS SEAPORT 1934-37 (Stomp the Grinder Down) (Various artists).
LP: . . . . **PY 4408**

PIANO BLUES, VOL.9: LOFTON/ NOBLE 1935-36 (What's the Use of Gettin' Sober) (Various artists).
LP: . . . . **PY 4409**

PIANO BLUES, VOL.10: TERRITORY BLUES 1934-41 (That's Where I Was Born) (Various artists).
LP: . . . . **PY 4410**

PIANO BLUES, VOL.11: TEXAS SANTA FE 1934-37 (There's a Train Leavin' Houston) (Various artists).
LP: . . . . **PY 4411**

PIANO BLUES, VOL.12: BIG FOUR 1933-41 (Will You Satisfy My Mind) (Various artists).
LP: . . . . **PY 4412**

PIANO BLUES, VOL.13: CENTRAL HIGHWAY 1933-41 (Pull Up Your Dress Babe) (Various artists).
LP: . . . . **PY 4413**

PIANO BLUES, VOL.14: THE ACCOMPANIST 1933-41 (Play It For Me) (Various artists).
LP: . . . . **PY 4414**

PIANO BLUES, VOL.15: DALLAS 1927-29 (Elm Street's Paved in Brass) (Various artists).
LP: . . . . **PY 4415**

PIANO BLUES, VOL.16: CHARLIE SPAND 1929-31 (Soon This Morning) (Various artists).
LP: . . . . **PY 4416**

PIANO BLUES, VOL.17: PARAMOUNT, VOL.2 1927-32 (Raised in the Alley) (Various artists).
LP: . . . . **PY 4417**

PIANO BLUES, VOL.19: BARRELHOUSE WOMEN 1925-33 (Play it With Your Mama) (Various artists).
LP: . . . . **PY 4419**

PIANO BLUES, VOL.20: BARRELHOUSE YEARS 1928-33 (Some Piano Player, I'll Tell You That) (Various artists).
LP: . . . . **PY 4420**

PIANO BLUES, VOL.21: UNISSUED BOOGIE 1938-45 (Jump For Joy) (Various artists).
LP: . . . . **PY 4421**

PIANO BOOGIE & THE BLUES (Various artists).
Tracks: / If things don't get better: *Various artists* / G.R. boogie: *Various artists* / You ain't had no blues: *Various artists* / Boogie express: *Various artists* / Mr. Black man: *Various artists* / Blues boogie: *Various artists* / G.R. blues: *Various artists* / Rhapsody boogie: *Various artists* / Canal Street boogie woogie: *Various artists* / It was so good: *Various artists* / Hen house boogie: *Various artists* / Don't stop now: *Various artists* / Chocolate: *Various artists* / Man shortage blues: *Various artists* / Honky tonk train blues: *Various artists*.
LP: . . . . **KK 802**

PLAY ME THE BLUES (Various artists).
MC: . . . . **PBMC 101**

PRESTIGE BLUES SWINGERS (Various artists).
LP: **1902117**

PROFESSOR'S BLUES REVUE (Various artists).
LP: . . . . **DS 650**

RADAR BLUES (Various artists).
LP: . . . . **KLP 1050**
MC: . . . . **GT 51050**

RARE BLUES (Various artists).
Tracks: / Good morning little schoolgirl: *Ross, Dr.Isiah* / Alberta: *Maxwell Street Jimmy* / I ain't got nobody: *Williams, Big Joe* / Preachin' the blues: *House, Son* / I wish I was in heaven sitting down: *Wilkins, Rev* Robert / Pleadin' blues: *Little Brother Montgomery* / Lend me your love: *Sunnyland Slim* / Two trains running: *Maxwell Street Jimmy* / Whistling pines: *Williams, Big Joe* / Oh Lord I want you to help me: *Wilkins, Rev Robert*.
LP: . . . . **SNTF 853**

RARE BLUES GIRLS FROM KING (Various artists).
Tracks: / He's gone: *Ellis, Dorothy* / Grandpa can boogie too: *Greenwood, Lil* / Portrait of a faded love: *Young*, Helen / Please be good to me: *Hampton, Aletra* / Climb the wall: *Hunter, Fluffy* / You're gonna suffer baby: *Champion, Mickey* / I need you now: *McLawler, Sarah* / I dreamed the blues: *Carr, Valerie* / No more in life: *Anderson, Mildred* / Undecided: *Abernathy, Marion* / I'm on the outside lookin' in: *Garvin, Flo*/ Let me keep you warm: *Garvin, Flo* / You can't have me now: *Lester, Lorraine* / It's a sad, sad feeling: *Ryan, Cathy* / Slowly going out of your mind: *Ellis, Dorothy* / Please be true: *Ellis, Dorothy* / Sugar pie: *Ellis, Dorothy*.
LP: . . . . **SING 1159**

RAUNCHY BUSINESS - HOT NUTS AND LOLLIPOPS (Various artists).
MC: **4678894**

REAL BLUES, THE (Various artists).
LP: . . . . **LP 8011**

RECORDS WAS CHEAP TO MAKE THEN (Cadillac Records) (Various artists).
Tracks: / My baby's gone: *Homesick James* / My kind of woman: *Homesick James* / 3.38 woman: *Williams, Willie*/ Somebody changed the lock: *Williams, Willie* / Worried all the time: *McMahon, Andrew* / Potato diggin' man: *McMahon*, Andrew / Trouble no more: *Little Mac* / I'm tore up: *Little Mac* / Help me: *Little Mac* / Mother-in-law: *Little Mac* / Little girl: *Sunnyland Slim* / She got that jive: *Sunnyland Slim* / I done you wrong song: *Sunnyland Slim*.
LP: . . . . **RL 019**

REEFER MADNESS (Various artists).
Tracks: / Bea foote weed: *Various artists* / Cocaine: *Justice, Dick* / Willie the chimney sweeper: *Rodgers*, Ernest / Reefer head woman: *Various artists* / Reefer madness: *Davenport, Cow Cow* / Mess is here, The: *Various* artists / Pipe dream blues: *Various artists* / Willie the weeper: *Various artists* / Cocaine blues: *Various* artists / Save the roach for me: *Various artists* / Muggles: *Various artists* / Kokey Joe: *Various artists*/ Sendin' the vipers: *Various artists* / Viper's drag: *Various artists* / Vipers dream: *Various artists*/ Chant of the weed: *Various artists* / Blue reefer blues: *Various artists*.
LP: . . . . **ST 119**

ROCKIN' THE BLUES (Various artists).
Tracks: / Red house: *Various artists* / Blues power: *Various artists* / Evil

woman blues: *Various artists*/ Stormy Monday: *Various artists* / I got my mojo working: *Various artists* / Good morning little schoolgirl: *Various* artists / Unlucky boy: *Various artists* / Bringing it back: *Various artists* / Louisiana blues: *Various* artists / Ramblin' on my mind: *Various artists* / Bell bottom blues: *Various artists* / Statesboro blues: *Various artists* / Crossroads: *Various artists* / Six days on my mind: *Various artists* / Baby please don't go: *Various artists* / Lies: *Various artists* / Lonely years: *Various artists* / Highway blues: *Various artists* / Outside woman blues: *Various artists* / Dust my broom: *Various artists*.
2LP: . . . . **CCSLP 191**
MC: . . . . **CCSMC 191**

ROOMFUL OF BLUES (Various artists).
LP: . . . . **VR 035**

ROOTS OF THE BLUES (Various artists).
Tracks: / Louisiana: *Ratcliff, Henry* / Field song from Senegal: *Bakari Badji* / Po' boy blues: *Dudley, John*/ Katy left Memphis: *Tangle Eye* / Berta berta: *Miller, Leyroy & A Group Of Prisoners* / Old original blues: *McDowell*, Fred and Miles Pratcher / Jim and John: *Young, Ed & Lonnie Young* / Emmaline, take your time: *Askew, Alec*/ Buttermilk: *Pratcher, Miles & Bob* / Mama Lucy: *Gary, Leroy* / I'm gonna live, anyhow till I die: *Pratcher*, Miles & Bob / No more my lord: *Tangle Eye & A Group Of Prisoners* / Lining hymn and prayer: *Rev Crenshaw & Congregation*/ Death comes a creepin' in my room: *McDowell, Fred* / Church house moan: *Congregation Of New Brown's Chapel* / Beggin the blues: *Jones, Bessie* / Rolled and tumbled: *Hemphill, Rose & Fred McDowell* / Goin' down to the races: *McDowell, Fred, Miles Pratcher and Fannie Davis* / You gotta cut that out: *Forest City Joe*.
LP: . . . . **NW 252**

ROUGH DRIED BLUES (Various artists).
Tracks: / Bowlegged woman, knock kneed man: *Rush, Bobby* / I don't know: *Rush, Bobby* / Count the days I'm gone: *Agee, Ray* / What you're looking for: *King, Al* / High cost of living: *King, Al* / I can't understand: *King, Al* / Raining in my heart: *Harris, Peppermint* / Lonesome as can be: *Harris, Peppermint* / I've been up the mountain: *Turner, Big* / I found something better: *Griffin, Curtis* / Rough dried woman part 1: *Big Mac* / Food stamp blues parts 1&2: *Lang, Eddie* / Stoop down: *McCall, Cash* / Go on help yourself: *Washington, Albert* / Nicki Hoeky: *Rush, Bobby*.
LP: . . . . **CRB 1149**

RURAL BLUES 1949-53 (Roosevelt Sykes etc.) (Various artists).
LP: . . . . **MB 904**

RURAL BLUES PIANO 1927-35 (Various artists).
LP: . . . . **BD 2073**

RURAL BLUES - SACRED (Various artists).
LP: . . . . **HERWIN 206**

SAN DIEGO BLUES (Various artists).
LP: . . . . **ADVENT 2804**

SANCTIFIED JUG BANDS 1928-30 (Various artists).
LP: . . . . **MSE 222**

SHOUTIN' SWINGIN' AND MAKIN' LOVE (Various artists).
Tracks: / Jimmy's blues: *Various artists* / Lonesome daddy blues: *Rushing, Jimmy* / Clothespin blues: *Rushing, Jimmy* / Wigglin' blues: *Rushing, Jimmy* / Going down slow: *Witherspoon, Jimmy* / I can make love to you: *Witherspoon, Jimmy* / Everything but you: *Witherspoon, Jimmy* / Comeback, The: *Harris, Wynonie* / Buzzard luck: *Harris*, Wynonie / Conjured: *Harris, Wynonie* / It don't mean a thing: *Hibbler, Al* / My little brown book: *Hibbler, Al* / Fat and forty: *Hibbler, Al*.
LP: . . . . **GCH 8106**

SLIDE GUITAR - BOTTLES, KNIVES AND STEEL, THE (Various artists).
MC: **4672514**

SLOPPY HENRY (Various artists).
LP: . . . . **BD 2063**

SOME PEOPLE PLAY GUITAR LIKE A LOTTA PEOPLE DON' Various artists (Various artists).
Tracks: / Tell me, baby: *Grossman, Stefan* / Good gal: *Mann, Woody* / Old devil: *Mann, Woody* / Crosstown blues: *Mann, Woody* / Bad luck blues: *Bookbinder, Roy* / Delta swing: *Sandberg, Larry* / I got mine: *Bookbinder*, Roy / Bye bye baby blues: *Bookbinder, Roy* / Swingin' blues: *Davis, Rev. Gary* / Darktown strutters' ball: *Davis, Rev. Gary* / Who's been here?: *Mann, Woody* / Good morning little schoolgirl: *Grossman, Stefan*.
LP: . . . . **SNKF 102**

SONGSTERS & SAINTS VOL.1 various blues & gospel artists (Various artists).
2LP: . . . . **MSEX 2001/2**
2LP: . . . . **MSE 2001/2**

SONGSTERS & SAINTS VOL.2 various blues & gospel artists (Various artists).
2LP: . . . . **MSEX 2003/4**
2LP: . . . . **MSE 2003/4**

SOUL OF TEXAS BLUES WOMEN (Various artists).
LP: . . . . **HM 108**
MC: . . . . **HCS 108 TC**

SOUNDS OF MEMPHIS 1933-39 (Various artists).
LP: . . . . **BD 2006**

SOUTH MISSISSIPPI BLUES Original various artists (Various artists).
LP: . . . . **ROUNDER 2009**

SOUTH SIDE BLUES - CHICAGO: LIVING LEGENDS Various artists (Various artists).
Tracks: / Mississippi sheiks: *Various artists* / Mama Yancey, little brother Montgomery: *Various artists* / Henry Benson: *Various artists*.
LP: . . . . **OBC 508**

SOUTHSIDE SCREAMERS Chicago blues 1948-58 (Various artists).
LP: . . . . **STG 1003**

ST LOUIS BLUES 1929-35 (Various artists).
LP: . . . . **L 1030**

ST LOUIS JIMMY ODEN (Various artists).
LP: . . . . **BD 2068**

STAX BLUES MASTERS, VOL 1: BLUE MONDAY (Various artists).
Tracks: / They want money: *Little Sonny* / Driving wheel: *King, Albert* / Creeper, The: *Robinson, Freddie*/ Eight men, four women: *Little Milton* / Things that I used to do: *Little Sonny* / Bad luck: *King, Albert*/ More bad luck: *King, Albert* / Born under a bad sign: *King, Albert* / Blues with a feeling: *Little Sonny*/ Married woman: *Little Milton* / I wonder: *Robinson, Freddie* / Blue Monday: *Little Milton* / After hours: *Robinson, Freddie*.
LP: . . . . **STAXL 5005**

ST.LOUIS PIANO BLUES 1929-54 (Various artists).
LP: . . . . **DLP 529**

STORY OF THE BLUES (Various artists).
2LP: . . . . **CBS 22135**
MCSET: **40 22135**

STORY OF THE BLUES VOL.1 (Various artists).
LPS: . . . . **CBS 66426**

STREETWALKING BLUES (Various artists).
LP: . . . . **ST 117**

SUN RECORDS HARMONICA CLASSICS (Various artists).
LP: . . . . **SS 29**

SUN RECORDS - THE BLUES YEARS (Various artists).
LPS: . . . . **SUN BOX 105**

SUPER BLUES (Various artists).
LP: . . . . **BRP 2012**

SWEET HOME CHICAGO (Various artists).
LP: . . . . **DS 618**

SWINGIN' THE BLUES (Various artists).
LP: . . . . **BD 2077**

TASTE OF HARP, THE (Various artists).
LP: . . . . **BLP 102**

TEXAS BLUES (Various artists).
LP: . . . . **ARHOOLIE 2006**

TEXAS BLUES (Dallas 1928) (Various artists).
LP: . . . . **FB 305**

TEXAS BLUES-1950S (Various artists).
LP: . . . . **BC 16**

TEXAS BLUES, 1927-35 (Various artists).
LP: . . . . **DLP 558**

TEXAS BLUES 1927-52 (Various artists).
LP: . . . . **PL 102**

TEXAS BLUES 1928-29 (Various artists).
LP: . . . . **HK 4003**

TEXAS BLUES VOL.2 (Various artists).
LP: . . . . **ARHOOLIE 1017**

TEXAS LOVERS (Various artists).
Tracks: / Love whip: *Various artists* / All walks of life: *Heat, Reverend Horton* / Mean, mean man: *Stauber*, Beverly / Side tracked: *Brown, Hash and his Texas Tweeds* / Drink, dance and boogie: *Weebads* / Border jump: *Pollock, Mark* / I want to love you: *Nulisch, Darrell & Mark Pollock* / Texas love: *Pollock, Mark* / I'll kick your booty: *Orta, Paul & The Kingpins* / Nine below zero: *Orta, Paul & The Kingpins* / Exception to the rule: *Kathy & The Electrifying Kilowatts* / Just a fool for you: *Kathy & The Electrifying Kilowatts*.
LP: . . . . **RL 072**

TEXAS PIANO BLUES, 1929-48 (Various artists).
LP: . . . . **BD 2059**

TEXAS PIANO STYLES (1929-37) (Various artists).
LP: . . . . **WSE 132**

THIRTIES, THE with Pigmeat Terry (Various artists).
LP: . . . . **DLP 214**

THIS IS BLACK TOP (Various artists).
Tracks: / I can't stop loving you: *Funderburgh, Anson & Sam Myers* / Iron cupid: *King, Earl* / That certain door: *Eaglin, Snooks* / Woman's gotta have it: *Neville Brothers* / Stick around: *Radcliff, Bobby* / Can't call you no: *Sumlin, Hubert & Mighty Sam* / Lemonade: *Funderburgh, Anson & Sam Myers* / Young girl: *Eaglin, Snooks*/ If I don't get involved: *Medwick, Joe & Grady Gaines* / Hello sundown: *Davis, James "Thunderbird"* / Party in Nogales: *Levy, Ron*.
LP: . . . . **BTS 1**

THIS IS THE BLUES (24 Electric Blues Hits) (Various artists).
MC: . . . . **PLAC 3909**

THREE SHADES OF THE BLUES (Various artists).
LP: . . . . **RELIC 8003**

TRIBUTE TO FAHEY (Various artists).
LP: . . . . **KM 158**

TRYING TO MAKE A LIVING Meat & gravy from Cadillac baby vol.3 (Various artists).
Tracks: / Don't come back: *Little Mac* / Times are getting tougher: *Little Mac* / I'm your fool: *Little Mac*/ Dynamite: *Hooker, Earl* / Trying to make a living: *Saxton, Bobby* / All the way: *Boyd, Eddie* / Where you belong: *Boyd, Eddie* / Nit wit: *McKinley, L.C.* / You got to reap what you sow: *Boyd, Eddie* / Come home: *Boyd, Eddie* / Thank you baby: *Boyd, Eddie* / Red lips: *Hankins, Tall Paul* / It's you I'm going to miss: *Hudson, Willie*.
LP: . . . . **RL 021**

TWO GREENS MAKE A BLUES (Various artists).
LP: . . . . **RL 0087**

TWO WHITE HORSES STANDIN' IN LINE (Various artists).
LP: . . . . **SDM 265**

TWO WHITE HORSES STANDING IN LINE (Texas 1939) (Various artists).
LP: . . . . **FLY 264**

ULTIMATE BLUES COLLECTION, THE (Various artists).
Tracks: / Hoochie coochie man: *Waters, Muddy* / Smokestack lightning: *Howlin' Wolf* / Dust my broom: *James*, Elmore / Dimples: *Hooker, John Lee* / Don't start me talkin': *Williamson, Sonny Boy* / Juke: *Little Walter*/ Outside help: *King, B.B.* / All your love: *Mayall,John Bluesbreakers* / I got my mojo working: *Korner, Alexis* & Colin Hodgkinson / Black magic woman: *Fleetwood Mac* / I'd rather go blind: *Chicken Shack* / Train to nowhere: *Brown, Savoy* / Catfish blues: *Hendrix, Jimi* / Good morning little schoolgirl: *Winter, Johnny* / Leaving trunk: *Taj Mahal* / Stormy Monday: *Allman Brothers Band* / Who do you love: *Thorogood, George* / New walkin' blues: *Butterfield Blues Band* / Smoking gun: *Cray, Robert Band* / Tribute to Elmore: *Clapton, Eric* / Mannish boy: *Waters, Muddy* / King of the blues: *Moore, Gary* / I'm in the mood: *Raitt, Bonnie/John Lee Hooker*/ Ghost blues: *Gallagher, Rory*.
2LP: . . . . **CTVLP 206**
MC: . . . . **CTVMC 206**

UNAMERICAN BLUES ACTIVITIES VOL.1 (Various artists).
LP: . . . . **BEDLP 9**

UP & DOWN THE MISSISSIPPI (Various artists).
LP: . . . . **RL 319**

UPTOWN BLUES (Various artists).
LP: . . . . **L 1042**

URBAN BLUES Various original artists 1940's/50's (Various artists).
Tracks: / Rockin' boogie: *Lutcher, Joe & His Society Cats* / Life is a card game: *Turner, Big* / I can't lose with the stuff I use: *Williams, Lester & His Band* / Bachelor blues, The: *Mayfield, Percy & His Orchestra* / Please Mr. Jailer: *Carr, Wynona & The Bumps Blackwell Band* / Ooh ee ooh ee: *Dixon, Floyd* / When the clock strikes twelve: *Smith, Eddie & His Orchestra* / Please don't go: *Dixon, Floyd* / I need love so bad: *Mayfield, Percy & His* Orchestra / If you knew how much I love you: *Williams, Lester & His Band* / After 'while you'll be sorry: *Turner, Big* / Something's goin' on in my room: *Daddy Cleanhead & The Chuck Higgins Band*.
LP: . . . . **SNTF 5023**

VEE JAY BLUES (Various artists).
Tracks: / Dimples: *Various artists* / No more doggin': *Various artists* / Big boss man: *Various artists*/ Rolling and rolling: *Various artists* / Going home tomorrow: *Various artists* / Onions: *Various artists*/ Odds and ends: *Various artists* / Hands off: *Various artists* / Bright lights: *Various artists* / Frisco blues: *Various artists* / Mary Lou: *Various artists* / Messin' around: *Various artists* / I ain't got you: *Various artists* / Blues get off my shoulder: *Various artists* / Big soul: *Various artists* / Baby what you want me to do: *Various artists*.
LP: . . . . **CRB 1089**

VINTAGE BLUES (Various artists).
Tracks: / Kid man blues: *Various artists* / Cheating and lying blues: *Various artists* / Who's been fooling you: *Various artists* / War is over: *Various artists* / Whisky headed buddies: *Various artists* / Some day baby: *Various artists* / My love is down: *Various artists* / Sober: *Various artists* / My story blues: *Various artists* / My heart belongs to you: *Various artists* / Farewell little girl: *Various artists*/ Broke and hungry: *Various artists* / Bobby sox blues: *Various artists* / Her little machine: *Various artists*/ Give me mine now: *Various artists* / Better leave my man alone: *Various artists* / Drop down blues: *Various artists* / Wanita: *Various artists* / We got to win: *Various artists* / Sonny boys jump: *Various artists*.
LP: . . . . **NL 89418**
MC: . . . . **NK 89418**
LP: . . . . **INTS 5099**

VOICE OF THE BLUES (Bottleneck masterpieces) (Various artists).
LP: . . . . **L 1046**

WALKING BLUES (Various artists).
LP: . . . . **FLY 541**

WEIRD CUSTOM, WEIRD CULTURE (Various artists).
LP: . . . . **WCWC 001**

WEST COAST BLUES (Texas country blues 1948-52) (Various artists).
LP: . . . . **KK 7445**

WEST COAST GUITAR GREATS (Various artists).
LP: . . . . **BLP 108**

WHEN WOMEN SANG THE BLUES (Various artists).
LP: . . . . **BC 26**

WHITE BOY BLUES VOL.1 (Various artists).
Tracks: / Snake drive: *Clapton, Eric* / West Coast idea: *Clapton, Eric* / Choker: *Clapton, Eric & Jimmy Page*/ I'm your witch doctor: *Mayall,John Bluesbreakers* / Tribute to Elmore: *Clapton, Eric* / Freight loader: *Clapton*, Eric & Jimmy Page / Miles road: *Clapton, Eric & Jimmy Page* / Telephone blues: *Mayall,John Bluesbreakers*/ Draggin' my tail: *Clapton, Eric & Jimmy Page* / Down in the boots: *All Stars & Jimmy Page* / Stealin': *All* Stars & Jeff Beck / Chuckles: *All Stars & Jeff Beck* / L.A. breakdown: *All Stars & Jimmy Page* / Piano shuffle: *All Stars & Nicky Hopkins* / Some day baby: *Davies, Cyril & The All Stars* / Porcupine juice: *Santa Barbara* Machine Head / Rubber monkey: *Santa Barbara Machine Head* / Albert: *Santa Barbara Machine Head* / Who's knocking: *Spencer, Jeremy* / Look down at my woman: *Spencer, Jeremy*.
2LP: . . . . **CCSLP 103**
MC: . . . . **CCSMC 103**

WHITE BOY BLUES VOL.2 (Various artists).
Tracks: / Tried: *Savoy Brown Blues Band* / Cold blooded woman: *Savoy Brown Blues Band* / Can't quit you baby: *Savoy Brown Blues Band* / True blue: *Savoy Brown Blues Band* / I feel so good: *Kelly, Joanne* / Ain't gonna cry no more: *McPhee, Tony* / You don't love me: *McPhee, Tony* / When you got a good friend: *McPhee, Tony*/ Someone to love me: *McPhee, Tony* / Dealing with the devil: *Dharma Blues Band* / Roll 'em Pete: *Dharma Blues* Band / Water on my fire: *Lee, Albert* / Crosstown link: *Lee, Albert* / Flapjacks: *Masonry, Stones*/ Not fade away: *Davis, Cyril & The All Stars* / So much to say: *Stewart, Rod* / On top of the world: *Mayall,John* Bluesbreakers (featuring Eric Clapton.) / Hideaway:

Mayall,John Bluesbreakers (featuring Eric Clapton.) / Supernatural, The: *Mayall,John Bluesbreakers* / Standing at the crossroads: *Ten Years After* / I want to know: *Ten Years After* / Next milestone,The: *Lee, Albert.*
2LP: . . . **CCSLP 142**
MC: . . . **CCSMC 142**

WILD, WILD YOUNG WOMEN (Various artists).
LP: . . . **ROUNDER 1031**
MC: . . . **ROUNDER 1031C**

WINDY CITY BLUES 1935-1953 (Various artists).
LP: . . . **NH 101**

WIZARDS FROM THE SOUTHSIDE (Various artists).
Tracks: / Hate to see you go: *Little Walter* / Mellow down easy: *Little Walter* / I ain't superstitious: *Howlin' Wolf* / Down in the bottom: *Howlin' Wolf* / Evil: *Howlin' Wolf* / She's mine,she's fine: *Diddley, Bo*/ I'm a man: *Diddley, Bo* / Just to be with you: *Waters, Muddy* / Mannish boy: *Waters, Muddy* / Rollin'n'tumblin': *Waters, Muddy* / Still a fool: *Evans Shuffle* / Bring it on home: *Williamson, Sonny Boy* / Walkin' the boogie: *Hooker, John Lee.*
LP: . . . **GCH 8001**
MC: . . . **GCHK 78001**

WOMEN, WHISKY AND WAILIN' (Various artists).
Tracks: / Bloodshot eyes: *Harris, Wynonie* ((A)) / Good morning judge: *Harris, Wynonie* ((A)) / Sittin' on it all the time: *Harris, Wynonie* ((A)) / Boogie at midnight: *Brown, Roy* ((A)) / My girl from Kokomo: *Brown,* Roy ((A)) / Fannie Brown got married: *Brown, Roy* ((A)) / My gal: *Moonglows* ((B)) / Pedal pushin' papa: *Dominoes* ((A)) / My baby's 3-D: *Dominoes* ((A)) / South Shore drive: *Watts, Nobie* ((B)) / Just a gigolo: *Prima, Louis* ((C)) / I ain't got nobody: *Prima, Louis* ((C)) / Jump, jive and wail: *Prima,* Louis ((C)) / Buona sera: *Prima, Louis* ((C)) / Hucklebuck with Jimmy: *Five Keys* ((D)) / Too much boogie: *Pomus, Doc* ((E)) / Ain't that just like a woman: *Flowers, Pat* ((E)).
LP: . . . **CRB 1141**

WOMEN'S GUITAR WORKSHOP (Various artists).
LP: . . . **SNKF 149**
LP: . . . **KM 139**

WORLD OF BLUES VOL 1 (Various artists).
LP: . . . **2C 068 83300**

Blues Band

BACK FOR MORE.
Tracks: / Normal service / Victim of love / Not me / Blue collar / Can't get my ass in gear / Great crash, The / When I itches I scratch / Don't buy the potion / Bad boy / Down in the bottom / Leaving.
LP: . . . **210.095**
MC: . . . **410.095**

BRAND LOYALTY.
Tracks: / Seemed like a good idea at the time / Rolling log / I want to be loved / Might as well be / What do you want / Big fine girl / Sure feels good / Little baby / Grits ain't groceries / Funny money / Take me home / Oo-oo-ee / So bad (Extra track on reissue.) / Ain't it tough (Extra track on reissue.).
LP: . . . **204922**
MC: . . . **404922**
LP: . . . **211319**
MC: . . . **411319**

BYE BYE BLUES.
Tracks: / Hey hey little girl / Death letter / Grits ain't groceries / Flat foot Sam / Don't lie to me / Can't hold on much longer / It might as well be me / Nadine / Big boss man / Maggie's farm / Treat her right.
LP: . . . **205256**
MC: . . . **404256**

FAT CITY.
Tracks: / Fat city / Longing for you baby / Help me / I can't tell it all / Down to the river / Country blues (take 48) / Cold emotions, frozen hearts / Killing me by degrees / Duisburg blues, The / So lonely / Too bad you're no good / Long time gone.
LP: . . . **PL 75100**
MC: . . . **PK 75100**

ITCHY FEET.
Tracks: / Talkin' woman blues / Who's right who's wrong / Rock 'n' roll radio / Itchy feet / Ultimatum time / So lonely / Come on / Turn around / I can't be satisfied / Got to love you baby / Nothin' but the blues / Let your bucket down.
LP: . . . **BB 3**
MC: . . . **MC BB 3**
LP: . . . **210 697**
MC: . . . **410 697**

OFFICIAL BLUES BAND BOOTLEG ALBUM.
Tracks: / Talk to me baby / Flatfoot Sam / Two bones and a pick / Someday baby / Boom boom (out go the lights) / Come in / Death letter / Going home / I don't know / Diddy wah diddy.
LP: . . . **210497**
MC: . . . **410497**
LP: . . . **FA 3059**
MC: . . . **TCFA 3059**
LP: . . . **BBBP 101**

READY.
Tracks: / Twenty nine ways / I'm ready / Hallelujah I love her so / Sus blues / Noah Lewis blues / Treat her right / Lonely Avenue / Find yourself another fool / Hey hey little girl / Green stuff / Can't hold on / Cat, The / That's allright (On CD & cassette only.) / Nadine (On CD & cassette only.).
LP: . . . **BB 2**
MC: . . . **TCBB 2**
LP: . . . **210498**
MC: . . . **410498**

Blues Bastards

FRIENDSHIP.
Tracks: / Gee baby ain't I good to you / Next time you see me / Green and blue / Too late / Who's been talking / Who's who / Breaking up somebody's home / Down...down / Life goes on.
LP: . . . **CR 30225**

Blues Bianco

HARD TO GET BY.
LP: . . . **BS 4702**

Blues Boy Willie

BE WHO.
Tracks: / Why are you cheatin' on me / Same ol' fishing hole / Crack up / Stealing your love tonight / Let me funk with you / Can we talk before we separate / Highway blues / Be who.
LP: . . . **ICH 1064**
MC: . . . **ICH 1064 MC**

BE WHO, VOL. 2.
Tracks: / Party all night / I still care / Break away / Rest of my life, The / Where is Leroy / Love darling love / Let's get closer / Be who, two.
LP: . . . **ICH 1119**
MC: . . . **ICH 1119MC**

STRANGE THINGS HAPPENING.
Tracks: / Leroy / Blues in this town / On more mile / Fly, The / Sweet home Chicago / Fishing trip / Let's go, let's go, let's go / Strange things happening.
LP: . . . **ICH 1038**
MC: . . . **ZCICH 1038**

Blues Brothers

BEST OF THE BLUES BROTHERS.
Tracks: / Expressway / Everybody needs somebody to love / I don't know / She caught the Katy / Soul man / Rubber biscuit / Goin' back to Miami / Gimme some lovin' / B movie / Box car blues / Flip flop fly.
LP: . . . **K 50858**
MC: . . . **K 250858**

BRIEFCASE FULL OF BLUES.
Tracks: / I can't turn you loose / Hey bartender / Messin' with the kid / I got everything I need / Shot gun blues / Rubber biscuit / Groove me / Soul man / Flip flop and fly / B movie / Boxcar blues.
LP: . . . **K 50556**
MC: . . . **K 450556**

LIVE AT MONTREUX.
LP: . . . **903176131**
MC: . . . **903176134**

MADE IN AMERICA.
Tracks: / Soul finger / Funky Broadway / Who's making love / Do you love me / Guilty / Perry Mason (theme from) / Riot in cell block 9 / Green onions / I ain't got you / From the bottom / Going to Miami.
LP: . . . **K 50768**
MC: . . . **K4 50768**

Blues Brothers (Film)

BLUES BROTHERS (Film soundtrack) (Various artists).
Tracks: / Shake a tail feather: *Charles, Ray* / Think: *Franklin, Aretha* / Minnie the moocher: *Calloway,* Cab / Rawhide: *Blues Brothers* / Jailhouse rock: *Blues Brothers* / She caught the Katy: *Blues Brothers*/ Gimme some lovin': *Blues Brothers* / Old landmark: *Blues Brothers* / Sweet home Chicago: *Blues Brothers*/ Peter Gunn: *Blues Brothers* / Everybody needs somebody to love: *Blues Brothers.*
LP: . . . **K 50715**
MC: . . . **K4 50715**

Blues Bunch

LOOPED (Live at Peewees).
LP: . . . **JUMP 1**

Blues Burglars

BREAKIN' IN.
Tracks: / Feels so good / Up and down the avenue / Sugar Mama / Shake your moneymaker / Built for comfort / Hoochie coochie man / Trouble no more / Don't start me to talking / Mojo working / Spaced out / Evening / Walkin' / Whoppin.
LP: . . . **RL 070**

Blues Busters

ACCEPT NO SUBSTITUTE.
LP: . . . **LM LP 1009**
MC: . . . **LMC 1009**

PHILLIP AND LLOYD.
LP: . . . **DYLP 3007**

THIS TIME.
LP: . . . **LD 1014**

TOP OF THE POPS.
Tracks: / Monkey man / How sweet it is to be loved by you / Nice time.
LP: . . . **VSLP 2001**

TRUTH.
LP: . . . **SARGE 001**

Blues Caravan

BLUES CARAVAN.
LP: . . . **GNPS 2178**
MC: . . . **GNP5 2178**

Blues Giants

MASTERS OF JAZZ.
LP: . . . **CL 42858**

Blues In The... (film)

BLUES IN THE NIGHT (Original London Cast) (Various artists).
LP: . . . **SCENE 9**
MC: . . . **SCENEC 9**

Blues Project (Group)

BLUES PROJECT.
LP: . . . **SPELP 104**
MC: . . . **SPEMC 104**

Blues & Royals Band

QUEEN'S LIFE GUARD.
Tracks: / Knightsbridge march / Horse guards / Black horse / Triumphal march / Crown of joy / Royal salute / Regimental slow march / Trumpet march / Fehrbelliner reitermarsch / Coburg / To your guard / Regimental quick march / Galliard / Air (rinaldo) / Minuet (water music) / Salut d'amour / Prelude to Richard III.
LP: . . . **BND 1007**
MC: . . . **ZC BND 1007**

SOVEREIGNS ESCORT.
Tracks: / Coronation bells / Ceremonial march 'Aida / Radetsky march / Rose of England / Irish medley / Triple crown / Fanfare / Blues and royals / Trots / Canters / Marches and regimental quick march.
LP: . . . **GES 1017**

Bluesiana II

BLUESIANA II.
Tracks: / Fonkalishus / Doctor Blooze / Cowan woman / For art's sake / Skoshuss / Love's parody / Santa Rosalia / San Antone / Montana Banana / Tribute to Art.
MC: . . . **101334**

Bluesiana Triangle

BLUESIANA TRIANGLE.
Tracks: / Heads up / Life's one way ticket / Shoo fly don't bother me / Need to be loved / Next time you see me / When the saints go marchin' in / For all we know.
MC: . . . **WT 0125**

Blues'n'Trouble

BLUES 'N' TROUBLE.
LP: . . . **BNTLP 1**

HAT TRICK.
Tracks: / I got your number / Why / Cherry peaches / Travelling light / When the lights go down / Comin' home / What's the matter / Be mine tonight / Rockin' with you Jimmy / T.N.T / See my baby shake it / Don't need no doctor.
LP: . . . **BLUH 001**

LIVE.
Tracks: / Clock on the wall / Cherry peaches / BNT blues / Why? / Honey pot / See my baby shake it / Lying on the kitchen floor / Born in Chicago / Sugar coated love / What's the matter? / Travelling light / Driftin' blues / Madison blues.
LP: . . . **SKITE 002**
MC: . . . **SKITEC 002**

NO MINOR KEYS.
LP: . . . **BNTLP 2**
MC: . . . **BNTC 2**

THANK YOU AND GOODNIGHT.
LP: . . . **BNTLP 3**

WITH FRIENDS LIKE THESE.
LP: . . . **BRAVE 11**

Bluestein Family

SOWIN' ON THE MOUNTAIN.
LP: . . . **FR 141**

Bluiett, Hamiet

RESOLUTION (see under Pullen, Don) (Bluiett, H/Don Pullen).

Blume, Judy (aut)

DEENIE (see under Deenie (bk)) (Braden, Kim (nar)).

IGGIE'S HOUSE (see under Iggie's House (bk)) (Fellows, Susannah (nar)).

Blumenthal, Daniel

RHAPSODY IN BLUE.
Tracks: / Rhapsody in blue / Piano concerto in F / American in Paris, An.
LP: . . . **CFP 4144131**
MC: . . . **CFP 4144134**
LP: . . . **CFP 4413**
MC: . . . **TCCFP 4413**
MC: . . . **TCCFP 4144134**

Blunstone, Colin

COLIN BLUNSTONE SINGS HIS GREATEST HITS.
Tracks: / Say you don't mind / Old and wise / Caroline goodbye / Andora / I don't believe in miracles / She's not there / Tell her so / Time of the season / What becomes of the brokenhearted / Tracks of my tears / Still burning bright / Don't feel no pain.
LP: . . . **ESSLP 139**
MC: . . . **ESSMC 139**

I DON'T BELIEVE IN MIRACLES.
Tracks: / I don't believe in miracles / Caroline goodbye / Misty roses / Shadow of doubt / Wonderful / Beginning / Keep the curtains closed today / Say you don't mind / Let me come closer to you / Time's running out / Though you are far away / I want some more / Every sound I heard / Beware / How could we dare to be wrong.
LP: . . . **EPC 32192**
LP: . . . **CBS 31760**

Blur

LEISURE.
Tracks: / She's so high / Bang / Slow down / Reptition / Bad day / Sing / There's no other way / Fool / Come together / High cool / Birthday / War me down.
LP: . . . **FOODLP 6**
MC: . . . **FOODTC 6**

Blurt

BODY-LIVE, THE.
LP: . . . **EFA 15081**

IN BERLIN.
LP: . . . **ARM 6**

KENNY ROGERS GREATEST HITS: TAKE 2.
LP: . . . **TBLP 666**

POPPYCOCK.
LP: . . . **TBL 002**

Blush (label)

BLUSH ON BLACK (Various artists).
LP: . . . **BLUSH 1**

Blyth Power

ALNWICK AND TYNE.
LP: . . . **CHIME 0102**

BARMAN AND OTHER STORIES, THE.
LP: . . . **CHIME 0036S**

LITTLE TOUCH OF HARRY IN THE MIDDLE OF THE NIGHT, A.
MC: . . . **96 15**

PONT AU DESSUS DE LA BRUE.
LP: . . . **CHIME 0042S**
LP: . . . **CHIME 0042**

WICKED MEN, WICKED WOMEN AND WICKET KEEPERS.
Tracks: / Goodbye General / Stand into danger / Bricklayers arms / Smoke from Cromwell's time / John O'Grant / Hurling time / Probably going to rain / Caligula / Probably won't be easy / Marius moves / Ixion / Some of Shelley's hang-ups.
LP: . . . **MADLP 006**

Blythe, Arthur

BASIC BLYTHE.
Tracks: / Autumn in New york / Lenox Avenue breakdown / Heart to heart / As of yet / Ruby my dear / Faceless woman.
LP: . . . **4606771**
MC: . . . **4606774**

BLYTHE SPIRIT.
Tracks: / Contemplation / Faceless woman / Reverence / Stike up the band / Misty / Spirits in the field / Just a closer walk with thee.
LP: . . . **CBS 85194**

BUSH BABY.
LP: . . . **ECJ 404**

DA-DA.
Tracks: / Odessa / Spain thang / Esquinas / Crescent / Break tune / After Paris.
LP: . . . **CBS 26888**
MC: . . . **40 26888**

ELABORATION.
Tracks: / Elaboration / Metamorphosis / Sister Daisy / One mint julep / Shadows / Lower Nile.
LP: CBS 85980

GRIP, THE.
LP: IN 1029

IN THE TRADITION.
Tracks: / Jitterbug waltz / In a sentimental mood / Breaktune / Caravan / Hip dripper / Naima.
LP: CBS 84152

LENNOX AVENUE BREAKDOWN.
Tracks: / Down San Diego way / Slidin' through / Lennox Avenue breakdown / Odessa.
LP: CBS 83350

LIGHT BLUE.
Tracks: / We see / Light blue / Off minor / Epistrophy / Coming on the Hudson / Nutty / Tumalumah / Put sunshine in it / Uptown strut / Silhouette / 15 / Sentimental walk.
LP: CBS 25397
MC: 40 25397

PUT SUNSHINE IN IT.
Tracks: / Tumalumah / Put sunshine in it / Uptown strut / Silhouette / 15 / Sentimental walk.
LP: CBS 26098
MC: 40 26098

Blythe, Jimmy

STOMP YOUR STUFF (1927-31).
LP: S 1324

Blyton, Enid (aut)

ADVENTURES OF MARY MOUSE) (Kent, Cindy (nar)).
LP: STMP 9023
MC: STMP 49023

ADVENTURES OF NAUGHTY AMELIA JANE (See under Adventures of...) (Pollard, Su (aut)).

ADVENTUROUS FOUR, THE (Schofield, Philip (nar)).
MCSET: LFP 7328

CASTLE OF ADVENTURE, THE (Cribbins, Bernard (nar)).
MCSET: LFP 7478

ENID BLYTON - 15 MINUTE TALES.
MC: PTB 635

FIRST TERM AT MALORY TOWERS.
MCSET: DTO 10502

FIVE GET INTO A FIX (Newman, Nanette (nar)).
MCSET: 418 201-4

FIVE GET INTO TROUBLE (Enid Blyton) (Bennett, Judy (nar) & Charles Collingwood (nar)).
MC: 0 00 102259 8

FIVE GO ADVENTURING AGAIN (Unknown narrator(s)).
LP: STMP 9028
MC: STMP 49028

FIVE GO OFF IN A CARAVAN (Bennett, Judy (nar) & Charles Collingwood (nar)).
MC: 0 00 102256 3

FIVE GO OFF TO CAMP (Bennett, Judy (nar) & Charles Collingwood (nar)).
MC: 0 00 102254 7

FIVE GO TO BILLYCOCK HILL (Newman, Nanette (nar)).
MCSET: 418 213-4

FIVE GO TO DEMON'S ROCK (Newman, Nanette (nar)).
MCSET: 418 210-4

FIVE GO TO MYSTERY MOOR (Greene, Sarah (nar)).
MCSET: LFP 7248
MCSET: TCLFP 7248

FIVE HAVE A WONDERFUL TIME (Newman, Nanette (nar)).
MCSET: 418 207-4

FIVE HAVE PLENTY OF FUN (Bennett, Judy (nar) & Charles Collingwood (nar)).
MC: 0 00 102258 X

FIVE ON A HIKE TOGETHER (Bennett, Judy (nar) & Charles Collingwood (nar)).
MC: 0 00 102255 5

FIVE ON A SECRET TRAIL (Newman, Nanette (nar)).
MCSET: 418 204-4

FIVE ON A TREASURE ISLAND (Francis, Jan (nar)).
MCSET: LFP 7418

FIVE ON FINNISTON FARM (Greene, Sarah (nar)).
MCSET: LFP 7300

FIVE ON KIRRIN ISLAND AGAIN (Bennett, Judy (nar) & Charles Collingwood (nar)).
MC: 0 00 102257 1

FUN FOR THE SECRET SEVEN (Sheridan, Sue (nar) & Nigel Anthony (nar)).
MC: 0 00 102266 0

GOOD WORK SECRET SEVEN (Sheridan, Sue (nar) & Nigel Anthony (nar)).
MC: 0 00 102260 1

ISLAND OF ADVENTURE (Davison, Peter (nar)).
MCSET: LFP 7216

MOUNTAIN OF ADVENTURE (Blake, Roger (nar) & Elizabeth Lindsay (nar)).
MC: 0 00 102263 6

MR PLOD AND LITTLE NODDY (Burden, Ernest (nar)).
LP: CMCR 802
MC: CMC 802

MYSTERY OF TALLY-HO COTTAGE, THE (Morgan, Liz & John Baddeley (nars)).
MC: 0 00 102267 9

MYSTERY OF THE BURNT COTTAGE, THE (Morgan, Liz & John Baddeley (nars)).
MC: 0 00 102268 7

MYSTERY OF THE STRANGE MESSAGES, THE (Morgan, Liz & John Baddeley (nars)).
MC: 0 00 102265 2

NODDY AND THE TOOTLES (Burden, Ernest (nar)).
MC: CMC 804

NODDY GOES TO SEA (Burden, Ernest (nar)).
LP: CMCR 801
MC: CMC 801

NODDY HAS AN ADVENTURE (Burden, Ernest (nar)).
LP: CMCR 800
MC: CMC 800

SECRET ISLAND, THE (Francis, Jan (nar)).
MCSET: LFP 7514

SECRET SEVEN FIREWORKS.
MCSET: DTO 10511

SECRET SEVEN VOL. 1, THE.
MCSET: DTO 10501

SECRET SEVEN VOL. 2, THE.
MCSET: DTO 10527

SECRET SEVEN WIN THROUGH (Sheridan, Sue (nar) & Nigel Anthony (nar)).
MC: 0 00 102261 X

SHADOW THE SHEEPDOG (Timothy, Christopher (nar)).
MCSET: LFP 7409

SHIP OF ADVENTURE, THE (Blake, Roger (nar) & Elizabeth Lindsay (nar)).
MC: 0 00 102264 4

SHOCK FOR THE SECRET SEVEN.
MCSET: DTO 10532

TALE OF THE CUDDLY TOYS, THE (Burden, Ernest (nar)).
LP: CMCR 803
MC: CMC 803

THREE CHEERS SECRET SEVEN.
MC: 0 00 102262 8

WELL DONE THE SECRET SEVEN.
LP: STMP 9029
MC: STMP4 9029

B-Movie

DEAD GOOD TAPES.
LP: WAXLP 1
LPPD: WAXLP 1P

FOREVER RUNNING.
Tracks: / Forever running / Heart of gold / My ship of dreams / Just an echo in the valley / Remembrance day / Switch on switch off / Blind allegiance / Arctic Summer / Nowhere girl.
LP: 925272 1
MC: 925272 4

BMX Bandits

C86.
LP: CLICKLP 001

TOTALLY GROOVY LIVE EXPERIENCE.
LP: ONLYLP 007

Bo, Eddie

CHECK MR POPEYE.
Tracks: / Check Mr. Popeye / Now let's Popeye / It must be love / Dinky doo / I'll do anything for you / Warm daddy / Roamin itis / Hey there baby / I need someone / Tell it like it is / You got your mojo working / Ain't you ashamed / Baby I'm wise / Every dog has his day.
LP: ED 259
MC: ROUNDER 2077C
LP: ROUNDER 2077

VIPPIN' AND VOPPIN'.
Tracks: / Our love will never falter / All I ask of you / Skate it out / Let our love begin / Solid foundation / If I had to do it over / From this day on / Something working / S.G.B. / What you gonna do / Just friends / Fence of love / Falling in love again / You're with me / Lover and friend / I just keep rolling.
LP: CRB 1195

Boa, Philip

ARISTOCRACIE (Boa, Philip & The Voodoo Club).
Tracks: / Don't pour my whole life away / For what bastards / When my mother comes back / Empire's Burning / My sweet devil in the sky / Boy Scout / Clean eyes for dirty faces / I dedicate my soul to you / Make you see the world.
LP: RF 52

COPPERFIELD (Boa, Philip & The Voodoo Club).
LP: 835 237 1

HAIR (Boa, Philip & The Voodoo Club).
LP: 837 852-1
MC: 837 852-4

PHILISTRINES.
LP: RF 50

Boardman, Harry

BALLADS, SONGS AND RECITATIONS.
Tracks: / Lancashire mon, The / T spinners tale / Radcliffe otter hunt, The / Victoria bridge on a Saturday night / Kitty and Robin / Saddleworth buck rabbit / Whoam brewed / Warrikin fair / Spinning shoddy / To the begging / Beltane song, The / Garland, The / Owdham on a Saturday night / Nine times a night.
LP: 12TS 236

Boardman-Hillery

TRANS-PENNINE.
Tracks: / Scarborough sands / I'll have a collier for my sweetheart / Forty miles / Tommy Stroo's ghost / Cowd stringy pie / Tha's welcome, little bonny brid / Nellie o'bobs o't' crowtrees / Weaver's song, The / Happy Sam / Manchester canal, The / T'auld wife of coverdill / Lass O'Dallo gil / My love, my love / Cockfight, The / Haley paley / With Henry Hunt we'll go / Ensilver song, The.
LP: 12TS 215

Boat (film)

BOAT, THE (Original Soundtrack) (Various artists).
LP: K 58366

Boat To Progress

BOAT TO PROGRESS (Various artists).
LP: GREL 602
MC: GREEN 602

Boateng, Kwabena

ME DOFO WUO.
LP: AMP 1001

Boatman, Tooter

FOR TOOTER BOATMAN FANS ONLY.
Tracks: / Whole lotta shakin' goin' on / Susie's house / Big deal / They won't let me in / Pirate lover / Just going / Echo of your footsteps, The / Heartship of a broken love / Things / Thunder and lightning / I'm with you / Will of love, The / Gonna come a time / Depression blues / Heaven for broken hearts / I don't know / Lonesome old blues.
LP: WLP 8895

TOOTER BOATMAN AND FRIENDS.
Tracks: / Susie's house / Thunder and lightning / Hey little missy / When the party's over / More and more (I love you) / Will of love, The / I'm with you / Let's make a block / Isabella / Modern romance / Baby make a move / Big deal / Teenage hangout, take 1 / Teenage hangout, take 3.
LP: WLP 8863

TOOTER BOATMAN SOUND, THE.
Tracks: / Life begins at four o'clock / They won't let me in / Wayward wind / Other me, The / Gonna come a time / Stagger Lee / Depression blues / Who that? / Magic guitar.
LP: WLP 8879

Boatmen

STRAIGHT FROM THE TUNNEL'S MOUTH.
Tracks: / Waterways lament / Poor old 'orse / Orrible trip, The / Tommy Note / Boatie boatie spit in the cut / Lass of Coventry / Single bolinder / Girl on the cut / Winson Green jail / Dudley Tunnel / Hard working boater / Tom Beech's last trip / Tipton slasher, The / Humber belle, The.
LP: SFA 018

Bob

SWAG SACK.
LP: SOMBRERO 5

Bob & Carol,...(film)

BOB & CAROL, TED & ALICE (1969 film soundtrack) (Various artists).
LP: BD 1013

Bob Dylan Songbook

BOB DYLAN SONGBOOK (Various artists).
MC: VSOPMC 158

Bob & Earl

HARLEM SHUFFLE.
LP: OLLP 5160

Bob Hope To Die

LIVING EMBODIEMENT OF JIMI HENDRIX.
LP: NCHLP 10

SHITE.
LP: NCHMLP 7

Bob & Lucille

CANADIAN SWEETEARTS.
LP: LP 100

Bob & Marcia

CLASSIC TRACKS (See under Cliff, Jimmy) (Bob & Marcia/Jimmy Cliff).

Bobbidazzler

BOBBIDAZZLER.
Tracks: / Where love should've been / Rock and roll / Tumblin' down / Gypsy girl / Sunrise / City, city / You are my love / Road to Louveciennes / Beverly Hills / Who? you.
LP: PL 12196

Bobby & The Midnites

WHERE THE BEAT MEETS THE STREET.
Tracks: / (I want to live in) America / Where the beat meets the street / She's gonna win your heart / Ain't that peculiar / Lifeguard / Rock in the 80's / Lifeline / Falling / Thunder and lightning / Gloria Monday.
LP: CBS 26046

Bobbysocks

BOBBYSOCKS.
Tracks: / Adios / Cross over the bridge / I don't wanna break my heart / Go on shakin' / Boogie woogie piggy, The / Let it swing / Midnight rocks / Radio / Don't bring lulu / Little by little / Shoo shoo baby.
LP: PL70764

Bobcats

CAT'S GOT YOUR TONGUE.
Tracks: / Do it / I need you / Best in the west / Linda / She wanted to share her lovin' / I'm serious / Come with me / Clubbin' / Cat got ya tongue / Mob, The.
LP: 210011
MC: 410011

MOURNIN' BLUES (see under Crosby, Bob) (Bobcats & Bob Crosby).

Bobo, Willie

HELL OF AN ACT TO FOLLOW.
Tracks: / Always there / Keep that same old feeling / Together / Pisces / Dindi / Snort of green / Fairy tales for two / Sixty two fifty.
LP: CBS 83160

Bobs

NU-WAVE A CAPPELLA.
LP: TAN 7014
LP: F 18
MC: C 18

Bocage, Peter

AT SAN JACINTO HALL (Bocage, Peter with George Lewis/Louis Nelson).
LP: JCE 29

NEW ORLEANS- THE LEGENDS LIVE (Bocage, Peter & His Creole Serenaders).
LP: JCE 33

Boccherini (Composer)

CELLO CONCERTOS (See under Haydn for full details) (English String Orchestra, conducted by William Boughton).

Bocquet, Didler

PICTURES OF LIFE.
LP: PULSE 008

Bodast

BODAST TAPES, THE.
Tracks: / Do you remember / Beyond winter / Once in a lifetime / Black leather gloves / Tired towers / Mr. Jones / 1,000 years / Nether street.
LP: BRED 12

Boddy, Ian

CLIMB, THE.
LP: SIGNAL 1

SPIRIT.
LP: NMW 01

BoDeans

BLACK AND WHITE.
LP: 8282451
MC: 8282454

HOME.
Tracks: / Hand in hand / Far far away from my heart / Red river / When the love is good / Fire in the hole / No one / World's away / Brand new / Beaujolais / Beautiful rain / Good work / You don't get much.
LP: 828 161 1
MC: 828 161 4

LOVE AND HOPE AND SEX AND DREAMS.
Tracks: / She's a runaway / Fade away / Still the night / Rickshaw riding / Angels / Misery / Strangest kind, The / Say you will / Ultimately fine / That's all / Lookin' for me somewhere.
LP: . . . . SLMP 11
MC: . . . . SMMC 11
LP: . . . . SLAP 11

OUTSIDE LOOKING IN.
Tracks: / Dreams / Pick up the pieces / Take it tomorrow / Say about love / Don't be lonely / Only love / What it feels like / Ballad of Jenny Rae, The / Forever young / Someday / Runaway love / I'm in trouble (Only on cassette and CD.).
LP: 256291
LP: . . . . SLAP 22
MC: . . . . SMAC 22

Bodgers Mate

BRIGHTER THAN USUAL.
Tracks: / Brighter than usual / Fine young girl / T stands for Thomas / Road to Lisdoonvarna, The / Little drummer / Planxty Urwin / Matty Groves / Dunphy's hornpipe / Trumpet hornpipe / Sligo fancy / Blackthorn stick / Peter street / Swallows tail reel / Merry blacksmith.
LP: . . . . COT 521

Bodie, Ian

PHOENIX.
LP: . . . . SER 001

Bodies (bk)

BODIES (Robert Barnard) (Midgeley, Richard (nar)).
MCSET: . . . . CAT 4026

Bodine

THREE TIMES RUNNING.
Tracks: / Shout / Battlefield / Black star rising / Below the belt / Force / Hard times / Rampage / Free kick.
LP: 2402561

Bodines

PLAYED.
Tracks: / Shakin' queens (1000 times) / What you want / Scar tissue / Tall stories / Clear / Untitled / Therese / Slip slide / Back door / William Shatner.
LP: . . . . WX 197
MC: . . . . WX 197 C
LP: . . . . BODL 2001
MC: . . . . ZCBOD 2001

Bodley, Seoirse

GIRL, A (Bodley, Seoirse & Bernadette Greevy).
LP: . . . . CEF 085

Bodner, Phil

FINE AND DANDY.
LP: . . . . ST 214

Body (film)

BODY, THE (see under Waters, Roger) (Waters, Roger & Ron Geesin).

Body Politic (bk)

BODY POLITIC, THE (Clive Barker) (Peck, Bob (nar)).
MCSET: 0600558568

Body Snatcher

BODY SNATCHER, THE (see Stevenson, Robert Louis) (Sheddon, John).

Bodywork

BODYWORK (See Stilgoe, Richard) (Stilgoe, Richard).

Bofill, Angela

ANGEL OF THE NIGHT.
Tracks: / I Try / People make the world go round / Angel of the night / Rainbow child / What I wouldn't do / Feeling's love, The / Love to last / Voyage, The.
LP: . . . . SPART 1113

ANGIE.
Tracks: / Under the moon and over they sky / This time I'll be sweeter / Baby I need your love / Rough times / Only thing I would wish for, The / Summer days / Share your love / Children of the world united.
LP: . . . . SPART 1084

BEST OF ANGELA BOFILL.
Tracks: / I try / This time / I'll be sweeter / What I wouldn't do / Still in love / I'm on your side / Time to say goodbye / Something about you / Let me be the one / Tonight I give in / Call of the wild / Break it to me gently / Angel of the night.
LP: 207829
MC: 407829

BEST OF ANGIE, THE (Next Time I'll Be Sweeter).
Tracks: / This time I'll be sweeter / People make the world go round / Still in love / I'm on your side / Break it to me gently / Song for a rainy day / Holdin' out for love / I try / Tonight I give in / Stop look listen / Ain't nothing like the real thing / Tropical love / What I wouldn't do (for the love of you) / Something about you / Time to say goodbye.
MC: 411516

INTUITION.
Tracks: / Love is in your eyes / Intuition / I just wanna stop / Long gone / For you and I / Fragile handle with care / In your lovers eyes / Lover overtime / Festival / Special lover / Everlasting love.
LP: . . . . EST 2077
MC: . . . . TCEST 2077

SOMETHING ABOUT YOU.
Tracks: / Something about you / Break it to me gently / On and on / Tropical love / You should know by now / Only love / Holdin' out for love / Stop look listen / I do love you / Three blind mice / Time to say goodbye.
LP: . . . . SPART 1179

TELL ME TOMORROW.
Tracks: / Generate love / Tell me tomorrow / Midnight shine / I don't wanna come down / First time / This change of yours / Still in love / Woman' intuition / If you wanna love me, you're on..
LP: 207443
MC: 407443

TOO TOUGH.
Tracks: / Too tough / Ain't nothing like the real thing / Tonight I give in / You could come take me home / Love you too much / Is this a dream / Song for a rainy day / I can see it in your eyes / Accept me / Rainbow inside my heart.
LP: 205273
MC: 405273

Bogaert, Joe

NONE OF THEM ARE GREEN.
LP: . . . . W 9302

Bogan, Lucille

BESSIE JACKSON 1923-35.
LP: . . . . BD 2046

LUCILLE BOGAN & WALTER ROLAND (Bogan, Lucille & Walter Roland).
LP: . . . . RL 317
LP: . . . . L 1017

WOMAN WON'T NEED NO MAN.
LP: . . . . AB 2005

Bogan, Martin

BARNYARD DANCE (Bogan, Martin & Armstrong).
LP: . . . . ROUNDER 2003

Bogarde, Dirk

LYRICS FOR LOVERS.
Tracks: / Foggy day, A / Way you look tonight / Our love affair / You go to my head / Can't we be friends / Smoke gets in your eyes / Just one of those things / Get out of town / I get along without you very well / These foolish things / Where or when / As time goes by.
LP: . . . . MOR 531

Bogey Boys

JIMMY DID IT.
Tracks: / Word is out / Blind eye / Who's sorry now / Bang bang / Never let up / Lone grey mare / Do the buzz / Trouble / Emigrant / Stop messin' around.
LP: . . . . CHR 1298

Bogguss, Suzy

MOMENT OF TRUTH, A.
Tracks: / Under the gun / My side of the story / Moment of truth / All things made new again / Wild horses / Fear of flying / As if I didn't know / Blue days / Burning down / Friend of mine.
MC: C4 92653
MC: 792 653 4

Boghall & Bathgate ...

RUBIK CUBE, THE (Boghall & Bathgate Caledonia).
Tracks: / 2/4 marches / Hornpipes / March strathspey & reel / Slow air and 9/8 jigs / Selection / Reels / Hornpipe and jig / March and strathspey and reel / Slow air and 6/8 jigs / Strathspeys and reels / 6/8 marches / Jigs.
LP: . . . . LILP 5181
MC: . . . . LICS 5181

Bogle, Eric

DOWN UNDER.
LP: . . . . ALLP 220

ERIC BOGLE IN CONCERT.
LP: . . . . LRF 160
MC: . . . . TC-LRF 160

ERIC BOGLE SONGBOOK.
Tracks: / Reason for it all, A / Nobody's moggy now / Hard hard times / Scraps of paper / If wishes were fishes / Front row cowboy / And the band played waltzing Matilda / Little Gomez / Aussie Bar-b-q, The / When the wind blows.
LP: . . . . TRAX 028
MC: . . . . CTRAX 028

IN PERSON.
LP: . . . . ALLP 211

NOW I'M EASY.
LP: . . . . PLR 042
LP: . . . . LRF 041

PLAIN AND SIMPLE (Bogle, Eric/John Munro).
LP: . . . . PLR 033

PURE.
LP: . . . . ALLP 253

SCRAPS OF PAPER.
LP: . . . . PLR 046
LP: . . . . LRF 104
LP: . . . . FF 311

SINGING THE SPIRIT HOME.
Tracks: / Old song, An / Lifeline / Singing the spirit home / Twenty years ago / All the fine young men / Leaving the land / Australian through and through / Lancelot and Guinevere / Silo / Shelter.
LP: . . . . SNTF 983
LP: . . . . LRF 186
MC: . . . . LRF 186C

SOMETHING OF VALUE.
LP: . . . . SNTF 1004
LP: . . . . LRF 220

VOICES IN THE WILDERNESS.
Tracks: / Peace has broken out / Lily and the poppy, The / Blues for Alex / What kind of man / Wilderness / Feed the children / Amazon / Silly slang song / Fences and walls / It's only Tuesday / Gift of years, The.
MC: . . . . CTRAX 040

WHEN THE WIND BLOWS.
LP: 12TS 437
LP: . . . . FF 354

Bognermay

BERGPREDICT (Bognermay/ Zuschrader).
LP: 625590

Bogshed

BRUTAL.
LP: . . . . SHELF 4

STEP ON IT BOGSHED.
LP: . . . . SHELF 2

Bogside Volunteers

IRELAND'S FIGHT FOR FREEDOM.
LP: . . . . CSDBL 505

Bogus Order

ZEN BRAKES.
LP: . . . . ZEN 1

Bohannon (Hamilton)

BOHANNON DRIVE.
Tracks: / Rock your body / Wake up / Running from yourlove / Do it goo / Lets start the dance III / Tell me you'll wait / Enjoy your day.
LP: . . . . CLTLP 3

CUT LOOSE.
Tracks: / At nightfall / Beat / Cut loose / Let me see how you do it / Mighty groovy / That's the way it goes.
LP: 9100061

IT'S TIME TO JAM.
LP: . . . . SEW 033
MC: . . . . SEWC 033

MAKE YOUR BODY MOVE.
Tracks: / Make your body move / Wrong number / Don't leave me / B.T. is doing the reggae / School girl / Funkville / Come back my love / Make your body move (instrumental).
LP: . . . . CLTLP 1

Bohemian Girl

BOHEMIAN GIRL (Various artists).
LP: . . . . CSD 3651

Bohmerwald, Tief

GOLDEN BOHEMIAN BRASS VOL 3.
LP: . . . . ISST 186

Bohn, Rudi

PERCUSSIVE OOMPAH.
Tracks: / Liechtensteiner polka / Goodbye / Trink' trink' / Too fat folka / O du liber Augustin / Pennsylvania polka / Mack the knife / Accordion Joe / Happy wanderer, The / Beer barrel polka / In Munchen steht ein hofbrauhaus / Auf wiederseh'n sweetheart.
LP: . . . . DGS 13

Bohren, Spencer

BORN IN A BISCAYNE.
LP: 11019
MC: . . . . 11019 TC

Boiarsky, Andrew

PLAYS SOUTH THE BORDER.
Tracks: / Sudam / Despidiendome de ti (sleeping on the beach) / Ritmo da ruas (street rhythm) / Latinum plus / Durmiendo en la playa / Chapter one / Feijoada.
LP: . . . . SPJ LP 18

Boiled In Lead

FROM THE LADLE TO THE GRAVE.
Tracks: / Pinch of snuff / Cuz Mapfumo / Shopetski dopanitsa / Sher / Stop stop stop / My son John / Madman Mora blues / Step it out, Mary / Micro organism, The / Bahcevance (O Ya) / Guns of the magnificent seven, The / Spanish lady (CD only.) / Dilley Delaney's - Cherish the ladies (CD only.) / Pig dog daddy (CD only.).
LP: . . . . COOK 015
MC: . . . . COOKC 015

ORB.
LP: . . . . COOK 037
MC: . . . . COOKC 037

Boilers

ROCKIN' STEADY.
Tracks: / Outta control / Ice in her eyes / Under pressure / Straight road curving / In this time / Coeur a voil / Twisted step / Trouble me / So much I would leave you / Boiled potato.
LP: . . . . SKAR 005

Boiling Point

BOILING POINT VOL 1 (Various artists).
LP: . . . . BPLP 1

Boine Persen, Mari

GULA GULA.
LP: RWLP13
MC: . . . . RWMC 13

Bolam Children

CHILDREN'S CHRISTMAS.
Tracks: / Jingle bells / I saw three ships / Away in a manger / We three Kings of Orient are / Happy Christmas / Mary's boy child / Christmas is coming / Rudolph the red nosed reindeer / All I want for Christmas is my two front teeth / When Santa got stuck up the chimney / Little Jack Horner / We wish you a merry Christmas.
MC: . . . . PT 231

NELLIE THE ELEPHANT AND OTHER FAVOURITE SONGS.
MC: . . . . PT 233

Bolam, James (nar)

BEIDERBECKE TAPES, THE (see under Beiderbecke Tapes).

Bolan, Bernard

LIVELINESS OF THE LONG PLAYING..., THE.
LP: . . . . LRF 042

PASSAGE OF TIME.
LP: . . . . LRF 162

Bolan, Marc

ACROSS THE AIRWAVES.
Tracks: / Misty coast of Albany / Icariot / Once upon the seas of Abyssinia / Misty mist / Chariots of silk / Scenescof / Girl / Life's a gas / Jeepster / Beltane walk / Jewel / Sailors of the highway / Suneye / Daye laye, A / Wind cheetah / By the light of the magical moon / Hot love / First heart might dawn dart / Summertime blues / Pavillions of sun / Ride a white swan.
LP: . . . . ICS 1004

BEGINNING OF DOVES, THE.
Tracks: / Jasper C. Debussy / Beyond the rising sun / Observations / You got the power / Sarah / Rings of fortune / Beginning of doves, The / Pictures of purple people / Jasmine '49 / Misty mist cat / Lunacy's back / Black and white incident / Eastern spell / Hippy gumbo / Crazy child / Hot rod Momma / Mustang Ford / One inch rock / Charlie / Black Sally was an angel.
LP: . . . . MEDIA 2
MC: . . . . MEDIAC 2

BEST OF THE 20TH CENTURY BOY (Bolan, Marc & T.Rex).
Tracks: / Groover, The / Jeepster / Dreamy lady / Get it on / I love to boogie / One inch rock / Sunken rags / Telegram Sam / Deborah / Laser love / Summertime blues / Light of love / New York City / Soul of my suit, The / 20th century boy / By the light of the magical moon / Truck on (tyke) / Ride a white swan / Zip gun boogie / Teenage dream / Hot love / King of the rumbling spires /

Children of the revolution / London boys / Jitterbug love / Metal guru / Solid gold easy action / Cosmic dancer.
LP: NE 1297
MC: CE 2297

BEYOND THE RISING SUN.
2LP: CR 115
MCSET: CRT 115

BILLY SUPER DUPER.
LP: MARCL 500
MC: MARCK 500

BOLAN'S ZIP GUN.
Tracks: / Light of love / Solid baby / Precious star / Spaceboss / Token of my love / Think zinc / Till dawn / Girl in the thunderbolt suit / Golden belt / I really love you baby / Zip gun boogie.
LP: MARCL 506
MC: MARCK 506

CHILDREN OF RARN SUITE.
LP: A BOLAN 2

CROWN OF JEWELS, A (Bolan, Marc & T.Rex).
Tracks: / Slider, The / Buick McKane / Country honey / Mad Donna / Chance / Liquid gang / Token of my love / I really love you babe / My little baby / Dawn storm / Visions of Domino / Teen riot structure / Depth charge / Dance in the midnight.
LP: DOJOLP 12
MC: DOJOTC 12

DANCE IN THE MIDNIGHT.
LP: MARCL 501
MC: MARCK 501

DANDY IN THE UNDERWORLD.
Tracks: / Dandy in the underworld / Crimson moon / Universe / I'm a fool for you girl / I love to boogie / Visions of domino / Jason B Sad / Groove a little / Soul of my suit, The / Hang-ups / Pain and love / Teen riot structure.
LP: RAP 508
MC: RAPC 508
LPPD: RAPD 508
LP: BLN 5005
LP: MARCL 508
MC: MARCK 508

MARC BOLAN: INTERVIEW PICTURE DISC.
LPPD: VBAK 3001

MARC SHOWS, THE.
Tracks: / Sing me a song / I love to boogie / Jeepster / New York city / Ride a white swan / Groove a little / Let's dance / Hot love / Endless sleep / Dandy in the underworld / Celebrate summer / Get it on / Deborah / Laser love / Dandy in the underworld (part 2).
LP: MARCL 513
MC: MARCK 513

SLIDER, THE.
Tracks: / Metal guru / Mystic lady / Rock on / Slider, The / Baby boomerang / Spaceball ricochet / Buick McKane / Telegram Sam / Rabbit fighter / Baby strange / Ballrooms of Mars / Chariot choogle / Main man.
LP: MARCL 503
MC: MARCK 503
LP: BLN 5001

SOLID GOLD BOOGIE BOY (Bolan, Marc & T.Rex).
Tracks: / Hot love / Ride a white swan / Deborah / Motivator, The / Beltane walk / Woodland rock / Summertime blues / Telegram Sam / Solid gold easy action / 20th century boy / I love to boogie / Chariot choogle / Tenement lady / Casual agent.
LP: WW 2007
MC: WW 20074
LP: NUT 5

SOLID GOLD EASY ACTION (Bolan, Marc & T.Rex).
MCSET: DTO 10261

STAND BY ME (Bolan, Marc & T.Rex).
Tracks: / Groover, The / Think zinc / Tenement lady / Rock on / Free angel / Telegram Sam / Stand by me / Country honey / Teen riot structure / Solid gold easy action / Truck on (Tyke) / Pain and love / Children of the revolution / 20th century boy / I really love you babe / Visions of Domino / Teenage dream / Metal guru / Casual agent / Tame my tiger / Precious star / Chariot choogle / Leopards featuring gardenia and the mighty slug, The.
2LP: VSOPLP 100
MC: VSOPMC 100

TANX (Bolan, Marc & T.Rex).
Tracks: / Tenement lady / Rapids / Mister mister / Broken hearted blues / Shock rock / Country honey / Electric slim and the factory man.
LP: RAP 504
MC: RAPC 504
LPPD: RAPD 504
LP: MARCL 504
MC: MARCK 504

TILL DAWN (Bolan, Marc & T.Rex).
LP: MARCL 509
MC: MARCK 509

ULTIMATE COLLECTION, THE (Bolan, Marc & T.Rex).
MC: STAC 2539
LP: STAR 2539

VERY BEST OF VOLUME 1, THE (Bolan, Marc & T.Rex).
Tracks: / Metal guru / Cadillac / New York City / To know you is to love you / London boys / Think zinc / Light of love / Midnight / Children of the revolution / Lady / 20th century boy / Sunken rags / Spaceball ricochet / Ride my wheels / Truck on (tyke) / Dandy in the underworld.
LP: SHM 3204
MC: HSC 3204

WORDS AND MUSIC OF MARC BOLAN (1947-1977).
Tracks: / Afghan woman / One inch rock / Stacey grove / Eastern spell / Salamanda palaganda / Cat black (the wizard's hat) / She was born to be my unicorn / Warlord of the royal crocodiles / Woodland bop, The / By the light of the magical moon / Great horse / Elemental child / Cosmic dancer / King of the rumbling spires / Beltane walk / Ride a white swan / Hot love / Get it on / Jeepster / Frowning atahuallpa (my inca love) / Children of Rarn.
LP: HYFLD 1

ZINC ALLOY AND THE HIDDEN RIDERS OF TOMORROW (Bolan, Marc & T.Rex).
Tracks: / Venus loon / Sound pit / Explosive mouth / Galaxy / Change / Nameless wildness / Teenage dream / Liquid gang / Carsmile Smith and the old one / You got to live to stay alive / Interstellar soul / Painless persuasion v the meathawk imm / Avengers, The / Leopards featuring gardenia and the mighty slug, The.
LP: RAP 505
MC: RAPC 505
LPPD: RAPD 505
LP: BLNA 7751
LP: MARCL 505
MC: MARCK 505

Boland, Francy

AT HER MAJESTY'S PLEASURE (see Clarke, Kenny) (Boland, Francy Big Band & Kenny Clarke).

DOING TIME (See under Clarke, Kenny) (Clarke, Kenny & Francy Boland Big Band).

OPEN DOOR.
Tracks: / New box / A Rose Negra / Duas rosas / Milkshake / Open door / Dia blues / Total blues.
LP: MR 5056

Bolcom, William

OTHER SONGS BY LIEBER AND STOLLER (See under Morris, Joan) (Bolcom, William & Joan Morris).

RAGTIME BACK TO BACK (Bolcom, William & William Albright).
MC: MMC 40002

SILVER LININGS (See under Morris, Joan) (Bolcom, William & Joan Morris).

SONGS BY IRA AND GEORGE GERSHWIN (See under Morris, Joan) (Bolcom, William & Joan Morris).

Bold

SPEAK OUT.
Tracks: / Talk is cheap / Nailed to the X / Now or never / Clear / Accept the blame / Change within / Search.
LP: 8856182391

Bold Navigators

BOLD NAVIGATORS (Various artists).
LP: TSR 019

Bolden, Buddy

BUDDY BOLDEN STOMP.
LP: OP 7910

Bolduc, Madame Edouard

LA BOLDUC.
LP: PH 2009

Bole, Andy

RAMSHACKLE PIER.
LP: LL 101

Bo-Lero (film)

BO-LERO (Film soundtrack) (Various artists).
LP: STV 81228
MC: C 266

Bolger, Ray

LAND OF OZ.
MC: CDL 51618

Bolin, Tommy

PRIVATE EYES.
Tracks: / Bustin' out of Rosey / Sweet burgundy / Post toastee / Shake the devil / Gypsy soul / Someday we'll bring our love home / Hello again / You told me that you loved me.
LP: CBS 81612

RETROSPECTIVE.
LP: K 924248 1
MC: K 924248 4

TEASER.
Tracks: / Grind / Homeward / Strut / Dreamer savannah woman / Teaser / People people / Marching powder / Wild dogs / Lotus.
LP: K 50208

ULTIMATE TOMMY BOLIN, THE.
Tracks: / Sail on / See my people come together / Alexis / Spanish lover / Quadrant four / Time to move on / Nitroglycerin / Owed to 'G' / Wild dogs / People, people / Sweet burgundy / Brother brother / Cross the river / Showbizzy / Standing in the rain / Do it / Train / Golden rainbows / Gettin' tighter / You keep moving / Dreamer / Teaser / Shake the devil.
LPS: GHS 24248
LPS: 9242481
MCSET: 9242484

Bolivia

MUSIC FROM BOLIVIA (Wayra, Pukaj).
LP: LLST 7361

Boll Weevils

FARM BLUES BOSSMEN & BOLL WEEVILS (See under Farm Blues Bossmen)

Bolland

DOMINO THEORY.
LP: INL 3618

Bolling, Claude

CLAUDE BOLLING.
Tracks: / California suite / Suite for flute & jazz piano.
LP: RL 25348

CONCERTO FOR CLASSIC GUITAR AND JAZZ PIANO.
LP: EMD 5535
LP: CBS 73651

JAZZ A LA FRANCAIS (Bolling, Claude Trio).
Tracks: / A La Francaise / Gamerama / Bach to swing / Not this time / Etude in blue / Blue kiss from Brazil / Fiancees en folie.
LP: FM 39244
MC: FMT 39244

LIVE AT THE MERIDIEN (Bolling Claude, Big Band).
LP: FM 39245

NUANCES (Bolling, Claude & his French All-stars).
LP: SL 5201

PLAYS ELLINGTON VOL 1.
Tracks: / Stomp, look and listen / Blue serge / Koko / Echoes of Harlem / Sepia panorama / Cottontail / Sophisticated lady / It don't mean a thing / Magenta haze / In a mellow tone / Rockin' in rhythm.
LP: FM 42474
MC: FMT 42474

Bollock Brothers

77, 78, 79.
LP: KOMA 788011

FOUR HORSEMEN OF THE APOCALYPSE, THE.
Tracks: / Legend of the snake / Woke up this morning and found myself dead / Mistress of the macabre / Faith healer / King Rat / Four horsemen of the apocalypse, The / Return to the garden of Eden / Loud loud loud / Seventh seal.
LP: BOLL 103

LAST SUPPER, THE.
Tracks: / Horror movies / Enchantment / Reincarnation of Bollock Brothers / Save our souls / Face in the mirror / Last supper, The / Act became real / Gift, The.
LP: BOLL 100

LIVE - IN PUBLIC IN PRIVATE.
Tracks: / Woke up this morning / Drac's back / Four horsemen of the Apocalypse / Count Dracula where's yar troosers / King Rat / Midnight Moses / Faith healer / Rock and roll.
LP: BOLL 104

LIVE PERFORMANCES (Official Bootleg).
Tracks: / Slow removal of Vincent Van Gogh's left ear / Loose / Horror movies / Bunker, The / Last supper, The / Reincarnation of Bollock Brothers / New York / Holidays in the sun / Problems / Vincent / Pretty vacant / God save the queen.
2LP: BOLL 102

MYTHOLOGY.
LP: 083 543

NEVER MIND THE BOLLOCKS '83.
Tracks: / Holidays in the sun / Problems / No feelings / God save the queen / Pretty vacant / Submission / New York / Seventeen / Anarchy in the UK / Liar / Bodies / E.M.I..
LP: BOLL 101

ROCK 'N' ROLL SUICIDE.
LP: JUNK 788010

Bollox To The Gonads

BOLLOX TO THE GONADS-HERE'S THE TESTICLES (Various artists).
Tracks: / Mau Maus: *Various artists* / Anti-system: *Various artists* / Xtract: *Various artists* / Repulsive alien: *Various artists* / Skeptix: *Various artists* / Legion of parasites: *Various artists* / Savage circle: *Various artists.*
LP: PAX 14

Bolo, Yami

JAH MADE THEM ALL.
LP: GREL 140
MC: GREEN 140

RANSOM.
Tracks: / Ransom of a man's life, The / Take time to know / What make the world taste good / Definately / Memories / She loves me so / World of confusion / Jah is life / Star time - fun time / One has to be real strong.
LP: GREL 125

Bolshoi

BIGGER GIANTS.
LP: SITL 15

FRIENDS.
Tracks: / Away / Modern man / Someone's daughter / Sunday morning / Looking for a life to lose / Romeo in clover / Books on the bonfire / Pardon me / Fat and jealous / Waspy.
LP: BEGA 76
MC: BEGC 76
LP: BBL 76
MC: BBLC 76

GIANT.
LP: SITUM 15

LINDY'S PARTY.
Tracks: / Auntie Jean / Please / Crack in smile / Swings And Roundabouts / She don't know / T.V. Man / Can you believe it / Rainy Day / Barrowlands / Lindy's Party.
LP: BEGA 86
MC: BEGC 86
LP: BBL 86
MC: BBLC 86

Bolshoi Ballet

CINDERELLA (VIDEO) (See under Cinderella).

IVAN THE TERRIBLE (VIDEO) (see also under Rimsky Korsakov composer)).

Bolstertone Choir

MALE VOICE CHOIR.
LP: LKLP 7900

VILLAGE OF SONG, THE (Bolstertone Male Voice Choir).
Tracks: / Morning has broken / Llanfair / With catlike tread / Go down Moses / Mull of Kintyre / When a child is born / Sound an alarm / Uist tramping song / Sunrise, sunset / John Peel / Kalinka / Old woman, The / Stout hearted men / Gwahoddiad.
LP: LKLP 6356

Bolt From The Black

BOLT FROM THE BLACK (See under Heavy Metal) (Various artists).

Bolt Thrower

IN BATTLE THERE IS NO LAW.
LP: SOL 11

REALM OF CHAOS.
Tracks: / Eternal war / Through the eye of terror / Dark millenium / All that remains / Lost souls domaine / Plague bearer / World eater / Drowned in torment / Realm of chaos.
LP: MOSH 13
LPPD: MOSH 13 P
MC: MOSH 13 MC
LP: MOSH 13

WAR MASTER.
LP: MOSH 29
MC: MOSH 29 MC

Bolten, Hattie

BLUE LADIES VOL. 2 1934-36.
LP: DLP 580

Bolton, Dupree

KATANGA (See under Amy, Curtis) (Bolton, Dupree and Curtis Amy).

Bolton, Michael

EVERYBODY'S CRAZY.
Tracks: / Everybody's crazy / Save our love / Can't turn it off / Call my name / Everytime / Desperate heart / Start breaking my heart / You don't want me bad enough / Don't tell me it's over.
MC: 4666624

HUNGER, THE.
Tracks: / Hot love / Wait on love / (Sittin' on) the dock of the bay / Gina / That's what love is all about / Hunger, The / You're all I need / Take a look at my face / Walk away.
LP: . . . . BFC 40473
LP: 4601631
MC: 4601634

MICHAEL BOLTON.
Tracks: / Fool's game / She did the same thing / Home town hero / Can't hold on / Can't let go / Fighting for my life / Paradise / Back in my arms again / Carrie / I almost believed you.
LP: . . . . CBS 25342

SOUL PROVIDER.
Tracks: / Soul provider / Georgia on my mind / It's only my heart / How am I supposed to live without you / How can we be lovers / You wouldn't know love / When I'm back on my feet again / From now on / Love cuts deep / Stand up for love.
LP: 4653431
MC: 4653434

TIME, LOVE AND TENDERNESS.
Tracks: / Love is a wonderful thing / Time, love and tenderness / Missing you now / Forever isn't long enough / Now that I found you / When a man loves a woman / We're not makin' love anymore / New love / Save me / Steel bars.
LP: 4678121
MC: 4678124

Bolton, Polly

NO GOING BACK.
LP: . . . . SPIN 134
MC: . . . . SPIC 134

Bomans, Godfried

GODFRIED BOMANS.
LP: 022 58153
MC: 222 58153

Bomb

LUCY IN THE SKY WITH DESI.
Tracks: / Power of suggestion, The / Madness / B.E.A.F.A.G. / Because Tiffany feels / Bigger than fun / Spoked feet / Vagrant vampires / Lucy in the sky with Desi / Smile and pose.
LP: . . . . TUPLP 13

Bomb, Adam

PURE SEX.
LP: . . . . WKFMLP 140
MC: . . . . WKFMMC 140

Bomb Disneyland

BOMB EVERYTHING.
Tracks: / Faster bastard / World no.3 IOU / Wa'as sapennin / To the moon / Blood fuck / New one / Live in Grimsby / Hickory dickory death / Suicide 999 / Killer City / Fat pig / Bomb Disneyland / Prostitution / Woman / Blind faith.
LP: . . . . EFA 1711208

Bomb Drugs

DRUGS.
LP: . . . . ABT 014

Bomb Everything

GUESS WHAT.
LP: . . . . SOL 23

Bomb Party

FISH.
LP: . . . . NORMAL 103

LAST SUPPER, THE.
LP: . . . . ABT 016

LIBERACE RISING.
LP: . . . . PLAY LP 2

Bomb The Bass

INTO THE DRAGON.
LP: . . . . DOOD LP1
MC: . . . . DOOD MC1

UNKNOWN TERRITORY.
Tracks: / Throughout the entire world / Switching channels / Love so true / Winter in July / You see me in 3D / Liquid metal / Run baby run / Dune buggy attack 1991 / Understand this / Air you breath, The / Kannible / Moody / Pressure point.
LP: 4687741
MC: 4687744

Bombalurina

HUGGIN' AND A KISSIN'.
Tracks: / Splish splash / Kiss me honey honey kiss me / Speedy Gonzales / Down come the rain / Moots mon / My boomerang won't come back / Sweet nothin's / Lollipop / Baby sittin' boogie / She taught me how to yodel / Three balls / They're coming to take me away ha-haaa / Itsy bitsy teeny weeny yellow polka dot bikini / Seven little girls sitting in the back seat.
LP: 847 648 1
MC: 847 648 4

HUGGIN' AND A KISSIN' (Karaoke Version).
Tracks: / Itsy bitsy teeny weeny yellow polka dot bikini / Splish splash / Kiss me honey honey kiss me / Speedy Gonzales / Down came the rain / Hoots mon / My boomerang won't come back / Seven little girls (Sittin' in the back seat) / Lollipop / Sweet nothin's / Baby sittin' boogie / She taught me how to yodel / Three bells.
LP: 847 671 1
MC: 847 671 4

HUGGIN' AND A KISSIN' (Non Stop Party Mixes).
Tracks: / Itsy bitsy teeny weeny yellow polka dot bikini / Kiss me honey honey kiss me / Speedy Gonzalez / My boomerang won't come back / She taught me how to yodel / Lollipop / Seven little girls (Sitting in the back seat) / Three bells / Splish splash / Bay sittin' boogie / Hoots mon.
LP: 847 672 1
MC: 847 672 4

Bombay Ducks

DANCE MUSIC.
LP: . . . . UD 005

Bomber

FROM BURUNDI.
Tracks: / You die / B.O.W. / Brain rape / Change of life / Fist f**k / Screams / Free beer / Unmodified / Dunk my head / Extreme astute / Hit 'em / Don't ask me / Butcher.
LP: 087 600

Bomphray, Clint

LATE SPECIAL/WILDCATS (Dramatised by Otto Lowy) (Various artists).
MC: . . . . NF 7

Bon Jovi

7800 DEGREES FAHRENHEIT.
Tracks: / In and out of love / Price of love, The / Only lonely / King of the mountain / Silent night / Tokyo road / Hardest part is the night / Always run to you / To the fire / Secret dreams.
LP: . . . . VERL 24
MC: . . . . VERLC 24

BON JOVI.
Tracks: / Runaway / She didn't know me / Shot through the heart / Love lies / Burning for love / Breakout / Come back / Get ready.
LP: . . . . VERL 14
MC: . . . . VERLC 14

BON JOVI: INTERVIEW PICTURE DISC.
LPPD: . . . . BAK 2022

BON JOVI: INTERVIEW PICTURE DISC, VOL 2.
LPPD: . . . . BAK 2106

CHRIS TETLEY INTERVIEWS BON JOVI.
LPPD: . . . . CT 1001

NEW JERSEY.
Tracks: / Lay your hands on me / Bad medicine / Born to be my baby / Living in sin / Blood on blood / Stick to your guns / Homebound train / I'll be there for you / 99 in the shade / Love for sale / Wild is the wind / Ride cowboy ride.
LP: . . . . VERH 62
MC: . . . . VERHC 62
LPPD: . . . . VERHP 62

SLIPPERY WHEN WET.
Tracks: / Let it rock / You give love a bad name / Livin' on a prayer / Social disease / Wanted dead or alive / Raise your hands / Without love / I'd die for you / Never say goodbye / Wild in the streets.
LP: . . . . VERH 38
MC: . . . . VERHC 38
LPPD: . . . . VERHP 38

Bon Jovi, Jon

BLAZE OF GLORY (Inspired by the film Young Guns II).
Tracks: / Billy get your guns / Blaze of glory / Santa Fe / Never say die / Bang a drum / Guano City / Miracle / Blood money / Justice in the barrel / You really got me now / Dyin' ain't much of a livin'.
LP: 846 473 1
MC: 846 473 4

Bonano, Sharkey

SHARKEY & HIS KINGS OF DIXIELAND (Sharkey & His Kings of Dixieland).
LP: . . . . GHB 122

WITH HIS NEW ORLEANS BOYS & SHARKS OF RHYTHM (Bonano, Sharkey & His New Orleans Boys & Sharks of Rhythm).
MC: . . . . HM 09

Bond, Eddie

CAUTION EDDIE BOND MUSIC IS....
Tracks: / Caution / Traitor / It's wonderful / Another man's shoes / That glass / Whatever makes you happy / Before the next teardrop falls / Somebody that won't lie / Time / Free / Devil is a woman.
LP: . . . . MFLP 057

EARLY YEARS, THE.
Tracks: / Monkey and the baboon, The / Jukejoint Johnny / Cliff Finch train, The / When the jukebox plays / Hey Joe / It's been so long darling / Standing in your window / Blues got me, The / Here comes that train / Someday I'll sober up / Rockin' daddy / You don't miss your water / Boo bop da caa caa / You'll never be a stranger to me / Big boss man / My buckets got a hole in it / I'll step aside / Can't win for losing / Doody do right.
LP: . . . . SJLP 574

EDDIE BOND (Original Early Recordings).
Tracks: / Rockin' daddy / I got a woman / Baby, baby / Hershey bar / Backslidin' / Love, love, love / Double duty lovin' / Talkin' off the wall / Flip flop mama / Slip, slip, slippin' in / Boppin' Bonnie / You're a part of me / They say we're too young / Lovin' you, lovin' you / Love makes a fool / Your eyes.
LP: . . . . WLP 8876

EDDIE BOND SINGS COUNTRY GOSPEL HITS.
LP: 33.1962.01

NIGHT TRAIN TO MEMPHIS.
LP: . . . . RLP 002

ROCKIN' DADDY FROM MEMPHIS VOL.2.
LP: . . . . LP 8406
LP: . . . . LPL 8406

ROCKIN' DADDY FROM MEMPHIS VOL.1.
LP: . . . . LP 8206

Bond, Graham

BEGINNING OF JAZZ-ROCK.
Tracks: / Wade in the water / Big boss man / Early in the morning / Person to person blues / Spanish blues / First time I met the blues / Stormy Monday / Train time / What'd I say?.
LP: . . . . CR 30198

HOLY MAGIC.
LP: . . . . BGOLP 35

LIVE AT KLOOKS KLEEK.
Tracks: / Wade in the water / Big boss man / Early in the morning / Person to person blues / Spanish blues / Introduction by Dick Jordan / First time I met the blues, The / Stormy Monday / Train time / What's I say.
LP: . . . . LIK 47

SOLID BOND.
LP: . . . . WS 3001

SOUND OF '65/THERE'S A BOND BETWEEN US (Bond, Graham Organisation).
Tracks: / Hoochie coochie man / Baby make love to me / Neighbour neighbour / Early in the morning / Spanish blues / Oh baby / Little girl / I want you / Wade in the water / Got my mojo working / Train time / Baby be good to me / Half a man / Tammy / Who's afraid of Virginia Woolfe / Hear me calling your name / Night time is the right time / Walking in the park / Last night / Baby can it be true / What'd I say / Dick's instrumental / Don't let go / Keep-a drivin' / Have you ever loved a woman / Camels and elephants.
2LP: . . . . DED 254

WE PUT OUR MAGICK ON YOU.
LP: . . . . BGOLP 73

Bond, Jane

POLITICALLY CORRECT (Bond, Jane & the Undercover Men).
LP: . . . . BIG 1

Bond, Johnny

BEST OF JOHNNY BOND.
LP: . . . . SLP 954
MC: . . . . GT 5954

SINGS THE GREAT SONGS OF THAT WILD WICKED BUT WONDERFUL WEST.
Tracks: / Pass, The / Fool's paradise, The / Bully, The / Night noon / At dawn I die / Empty saddles / Conversation with a gun / Sadie was a lady / Wanderers of the wasteland / Long tall shadow, The / Deadwood stage, The / Carry me back to the lone prairie / Dusty skies / Belle star.
LP: . . . . OFF 9000

Bond, Joyce

CALL ME.
LP: . . . . OLP 33
MC: . . . . OLC 33

NICE TO HAVE YOU BACK AGAIN.
Tracks: / Nice to have you back again / Nothing ever comes easy / Love me and leave me / Lonesome Road / You've been gone too long / If I ever fall in love again / No other one is sweeter than you.
LP: . . . . OLP 026
MC: . . . . OLC 026

YOU TOUCH MY HEART.
LP: . . . . OLP 31
MC: . . . . OLC 31

Bond, Michael (author)

PADDINGTON BEAR (See under Paddington Bear).

Bond, Peter

IT'S ALL RIGHT FOR SOME.
Tracks: / Baron and the busker, The / Afrika '65 / Category D / Some you win, some you lose / Letter from Sunderland / Birthday cake city / No coals off / Lark across the vapour train, The / Let it be on your mind / It's all right for some / Joe Peel / Joker, The.
LP: . . . . LER 2108

SEE ME UP SEE ME DOWN.
LP: . . . . SHY 7008

Bond, Simon (aut)

TOUGH TED (see under Tough Ted) (Blake, Roger (nar)).

Bondi Beat Poets

BALTIMORE - BEHOLD THE PRECIOUS STUPA.
LP: . . . . BRED 60

WHITE LIGHT.
LP: . . . . DMC 011

Bonds, Gary U.S.

DANCE TIL QUARTER TO THREE WITH....
LP: . . . . LG 1002

DEDICATION.
Tracks: / Jole Blon / This little girl / Your love / Dedication / Daddy's come home / It's only love / Pretender / Way back when / From a Buick 6 / Just like a child.
LP: . . . . ED 2606951
MC: . . . . ED 2606954
LP: . . . . FA 4130751
MC: . . . . TCFA 41 30754
LP: . . . . AML 3017

GARY U.S. BONDS.
MCSET: . . . . GM 0230

GARY U.S. BONDS MEETS CHUBBY CHECKER.
LP: 2C 068 64431

GREATEST HITS: GARY U.S. BONDS.
Tracks: / New Orleans / Quarter to three / Not me / Dear lady twist / Mixed up faculty / School is out / School is in / Having so much fun / Twist twist senora / Where did that naughty girl go? / I dig this station / Take me back to New Orleans.
LP: . . . . ENGY 506
MC: . . . . ENCAS 506

GREATEST HITS: GARY U.S. BONDS (2).
LP: . . . . TRLG 100
MC: . . . . TRLGCX 100

ON THE LINE.
Tracks: / Hold on / Out of work / Club soul city / Soul deep / urn the music down / Love's on the line / Rendezvous / Angelyne / All I need / Bring her back / Last time, The.
LP: 1A 064 400099
LP: . . . . AML 3022

STANDING IN THE LINE OF FIRE.
LP: . . . . SPRAY 103
MC: . . . . CSPRAY 103

TWIST UP CALYPSO.
Tracks: / Calypso / Scratch me back / Coconut woman / Day O / Twist twist senora.
LP: 6.24794

U.S. BONDS GREATEST HITS.
LP: . . . . LPS 1001

WARNING.
LP: . . . . LG 1004

Bonds, Sons

COMPLETE RECORDINGS 1934-41 (Bonds, Sons/Sleepy John Estes/Hammie Nixon).
LP: . . . . WSE 129

Bone Orchard

JACK.
Tracks: / Jack.
LP: . . . . FREUD 06

PENTHOUSE POULTRY.
LP: . . . . VAXLP 1

Bone, Richard

BRAVE TALES.
LP: . . . . **SURLP 005**

EXSPECTABLE.
LP: . . . . **SURB 3**

Bonediggers

BONE DIGGIN'.
LP: . . . . **RMT 023**

Boneless Ones

SKATE FOR THE DEVIL.
LP: . . . . **BR 05**

Bones, Elbow

NEW YORK AT DAWN (Bones, Elbow & Racketeers).
Tracks: / Night in New York / Other guys / Happy times / Our love will always stand / Happy birthday baby / Mama's in love again / I got you / I call it like I see it / I belong to you / You got me high.
LP: . . . . **AML 7171031**

Bones, Frankie

DANCE, MADNESS AND THE BROOKLYN GROOVE (Bones, Frankie & Tommy Musto).
Tracks: / Call it techno (Brooklyn new beat mix) / Frankie Bones / Rock and boogie down (Lenny does London mix) / Li'l DJ Anthony acid, The / This is the dance (the paradise mix) / Eden's paradise / This is the sound of house music / Bluejean / Nightmare (it's over for you), The (club mix) / Lake Eerie / Call it techno (technocolour dub) / Feel it in my heart (UK house mix) / Stacey Paris (Only on cassette and CD.) / Why cry (N.Y. club mix) / Midnight fantasy / Get the hoe (Dino B.89 mix) / Gangsters of freestyle, The / Give me the energy (hyper club mix) / Pink noise / Listen to the rhythm flow (notice the bass mix / Break boys, The / Bluejean.
LP: . . . . **PL 74346**
MC: . . . . **PK 74346**

LOONEY TUNES VOL.1 (Bones, Frankie & Lenny Dee).
LP: . . . . **XLEP 102**

LOONEY TUNES VOL.2 (Bones, Frankie & Lenny Dee).
LP: . . . . **NG 050**

Bonestructure

BONESTRUCTURE (Various artists).
Tracks: / Dolphin Street: *Various artists* / Vatican roulette: *Various artists* / Modal t: *Various artists*/ Lush life: *Various artists* / Doodlin': *Various artists* / Bone idle rich, The: *Various artists.*
LP: . . . . **CLGLP 020**
MC: . . . . **ZCLG 020**

Boney M

BEST OF TEN YEARS.
Tracks: / Daddy cool / Ma Baker / Rivers of Babylon / Belfast / Rasputin / Brown girl in the ring / Sunny / Happy song.
2LP: . . . . **SMR 621**
MCSET: . . . . **SMC 621**

BOONOONOONOOS.
Tracks: / Boonoonoonoos / Silly confusion / African moon / Ride to Agadir / Consuela Biaz / Sad movies / We kill the world / Jimmy / Breakaway / Malaika / Homeland Africa / Goodbye my friend.
LP: . . . . **K 50852**
MC: **K4 50852**

EYE DANCE.
LP: . . . . **CAL 223**
MC: . . . . **CAC 223**

GREATEST HITS OF ALL TIME - REMIX.
Tracks: / Sunny / Daddy Cool / Rasputin / Ma Baker / Take the heat off me / Hooray hooray, it's a holi holiday / Rivers of Babylon / No woman no cry / Brown girl in the ring / Gotta go home / Painter man / Mary's boy child (Oh my Lord).
LP: **209.476**
MC: **409.476**

LOVE FOR SALE.
Tracks: / Ma Baker / Love for sale / Belfast / Have you seen the rain / Gloria / Can you waddle / Plantation boy / Motherless child / Silvent lover / Woman can change a man, A / Still I'm sad.
LP: . . . . **K 50385**
MC: **K4 50385**

MAGIC OF BONEY M.
Tracks: / Daddy cool / Rivers of Babylon / Sunny / Belfast / El lute / No woman no cry / Rasputin / Painter man / Ma baker / Gotta go home / My friend Jack / I see a boat on the river / Brown girl in the ring / Mary's boy child / Bahama mama / I'm born again / Oceans of fantasy / Ribbons of blue / Still I'm sad / Hooray hooray it's a holi holiday.
LP: . . . . **BMTV 1**
MC: **BMTV4 1**

NIGHTFLIGHT TO VENUS.
Tracks: / Nightflight to Venus / Rasputin / Painter man / He was a Steppenwolf / King of the road / Rivers of Babylon / Voodoonight / Brown girl in the ring / Never change / Lovers in the middle of the night / Heart of gold.
LP: . . . . **K 50498**
MC: **K4 50498**

OCEANS OF FANTASY.
Tracks: / Let it all be music / Gotta go home / Bahama mama / Hold on I'm coming / Bye bye bluebird / Two of us / Ribbons of blue / El lute / No more chain gang / No time to los / I'm born again / Calendar song, The / Oceans of fantasy.
LP: . . . . **K 50610**
MC: **K4 50610**

TAKE THE HEAT OFF ME.
Tracks: / Daddy Cool / Take the heat of me / Sunny / Help help / No woman no cry / Fever / Got a man on my mind / Lovin' or leavin'.
LP: . . . . **K 50314**
MC: **K4 50314**

Bonfa, Luiz

JAZZ SAMBA ENCORE (see Getz, Stan) (Bonfa, Luiz/Stan Getz).

Bonfire

FIRE WORKS.
Tracks: / Ready 4 reaction / Never mind / Sleeping all alone / Champion / Don't get me wrong / Sweet obsession / Rock me now / American nights / Fantasy / Give it a try / Cold days (Extra track on CD only.).
LP: . . . . **ZL 71518**
MC: . . . . **ZK 71518**

POINT BLANK.
Tracks: / Bang down the door / Waste no time / Hard on me / Why is it never enough / Tony's roulette / Minestrone / You're back / Look of love / Price of loving you.
LP: . . . . **ZL 74249**
MC: . . . . **ZK 74249**

Bonga

MARIKA.
Tracks: / Marika / Makongo / Espende / NH'Guvulu / Cambomborinho / Lamento de garina / Camin longe / Oma.
LP: . . . . **PS 609**

Bongos

BONGOS.
LP: . . . . **FR 2004**

TIME AND RIVER.
LP: . . . . **FR 2009**

Bongwater

BREAKING NO NEW GROUND.
LP: . . . . **SHIMMY 002**

DOUBLE BUMMER.
LP: . . . . **SHIMMY 011**
MC: . . . . **SDE 8801**

TOO MUCH WATER.
LP: . . . . **SDE 9017**

Bonham

DISREGARD OF TIME KEEPING, THE.
LP: **465 693 1**
MC: **465 693 4**

Bonham, Debbie

FOR YOU AND THE MOON.
LP: . . . . **CAL 216**
MC: . . . . **CAC 216**

Boni, Raymond

CHANTENAY 80 (See under Horsthuis, Maurice) (Boni, Raymond/Maurice Horsthuis/Lol Coxhill).

Bonn, Issy

BLESS YOU.
Tracks: / That lovely weekend / My little sailor man / Bless you / Someday / My Yiddishe Momma / Every night about this time / If I had my way / Shrine of St Cecilia.
LP: . . . . **RFL 48**

PAL FOREVER, A.
Tracks: / Here in my heart / My mother's lullaby / Pal must be a pal forever, A / Who knows / As sure as there's a heaven / My-na shay-na ty-ra(my sweet & dear one) / Bells of home, The / Humble people / Somewhere, someone (is saying a prayer) / Mom-e-le / My friend / I went to my mother / When you're home with the ones you love / Little boy that Santa Claus forgot, The / Home for Christmas.
LP: . . . . **SH 423**
MC: . . . . **TC SH 423**

WHISPERING GRASS (See under Carless, Dorothy) (Bonn, Issy/Dorothy Carless/Benny Lee/Adelaide Hall).

Bonnay, Max

ACCORDEON.
Tracks: / Fantaisie et fugue en sol mineur pour orgue monastere / Meditation no.9 / Petrouschka.
LP: **1001**

ACCORDEON CLASSIQUE.
Tracks: / Suite gothique / Espiegle / De profundis / Choral en si mineur / Mobile / Valeur de la transcription.
LP: . . . . **PIZ 62 012**

Bonnel, Jean

JEAN FRANCOIS BONNEL & LYTTELTON & COHEN.
LP: . . . . **SOS 1104**

WHAT A DREAM.
LP: . . . . **SOS 1131**

Bonner Brothers

NOW AND FOREVER.
Tracks: / 1-2-3-4 / All we've got is each other / Rivers of Babylon / Y viva Espana / Now and forever / Knock on my door / Anyway you want me / Mull of Kintyre / Brown girl in the ring / Nobody / Beautiful Sunday / Song for Guy.
LP: . . . . **PRX 8**

Bonner, Joe

LIFESAVER, THE.
Tracks: / Bonner's bounce / Tattoo / Little chocolate boy / Lifesaver, The / Native son / Observer.
LP: . . . . **MR 5065**

NEW BEGINNINGS.
Tracks: / Soft breezes / Revolution, The / Child is born, A / New beginnings / Primal scream / Ode to trane.
LP: . . . . **TR 125**

Bonner, Juke Boy

GOING BACK TO THE COUNTRY.
LP: . . . . **ARHOOLIE 1036**

LEGACY OF THE BLUES VOL. 5 (See under Legacy of the Blues).

ONE MAN TRIO, THE.
LP: . . . . **FLY 548**

STRUGGLE, THE.
LP: . . . . **ARHOOLIE 1045**

THEY CALL ME JUKE BOY.
Tracks: / Best way to lose the blues, The / Distant feel, A / Nowhere to run / Don't ever get down / It don't take too much / Shame, shame, shame / Boone's farm / What the blues has done to me / Texas zydeco / Nothing but a child / European tour / Live my troubles on down / Loving arms / Gettin' low down.
LP: . . . . **CHD 269**

Bonner, Les

STRICTLY INSTRUMENTAL (Farfisa Coronet Organ).
Tracks: / Sing / Long ago and far away / Madrugada / Music maestro please / Affair to remember, An / What I did for love / Honeysuckle rose / Sweet Georgie Fame / One morning in May / Cavatina / Nature boy.
LP: . . . . **GRS 1063**

Bonnet, Graham

FORCEFIELD III (To Oz and back) (Bonnet, Graham/Cozy Powell/Ray Fenwick/Jan Akkerman).
Tracks: / Hit and run / Always / Stay away / Desire / Tokyo / Who'll be the next in line? / Wings on my feet / Firepower / Hold on / Rendezvous.
LP: . . . . **PTLS 1100**
MC: . . . . **PTLC 1100**

HERE COMES THE NIGHT.
LP: . . . . **PTLS 114**
MC: . . . . **PTLC 1114**

LINE-UP.
Tracks: / Night games / S.O.S / I'm a lover / Be my baby / That's the way that it is / Liar / Anthony boy / Dirty hand / Out on the water / Don't stand in the open / Set me free.
LP: **6302 151**

Bonnett, Caroline

CAROLINE BONNETT.
LP: . . . . **WHA R 1253**
MC: . . . . **WHA C 1253**

Bonney, Barbara

SYMPHONY NO.2 (MENDELSSOHN) (see under Mendelssohn (Composer)) (Bonney, Barbara/Leipzig Gewandhaus Orch/Leipzig Radio Chorus).

Bonnie Prince Charlie

BONNIE PRINCE CHARLIE (History for Ages 8+).
MC: . . . . **PLBH 148**

Bonnie Scotland

BONNIE SCOTLAND (See under Scotland) (Various artists).

Bonny Lass...

BONNY LASS COME O'ER THE BURN (See under Scotland) (Various artists).

Bonny North Tyne

BONNY NORTH TYNE (Various artists).
LP: **12TS 239**
MC: . . . . **KTSC 239**

Bonoff, Karla

NEW WORLD.
Tracks: / How long / New world / Tell me why / All my life / Goodbye my friend / Way of the heart, The / Best part of you / Still be getting over you / Oh Mary / All walk alone.
LP: . . . . **VGC 6**
MC: . . . . **TCVGC 6**

RESTLESS NIGHTS.
Tracks: / Trouble again / Restless nights / Letter / When you walk in the room / Only a fool / Baby don't go / Never stop her heart / Loving you / Water is wide.
LP: . . . . **CBS 83587**

WILD HEART OF THE YOUNG.
Tracks: / Personally / Please be the one / I don't want to miss you / Even if / Just walk away / Gonna be mine / Wild heart of the young / It just takes one / Dream.
LP: . . . . **CBS 85173**

Bonsall, Joe

CAJUN JAMBOREE.
LP: **6008**

CAJUN JAMBOREE VOL 2.
LP: **6012**

JOE BONSALL'S GREATEST HITS.
LP: **6049**
MC: . . . . **6049 TC**

Bonucci, Rodolfo

FAURE VIOLIN CONCERTO (see under Faure (composer)) (Orquesta Filarmonica de la Ciudad de Mexico).

Bonzo Dog Band

BESTIALITY OF BONZO DOG BAND.
Tracks: / Intro and the outro, The / Canyons of your mind / Trouser press / Postcard / Mickey's son and daughter / Sport (the odd boy) / Tent / I'm the urban spaceman / Mr. Apollo / Shirt / Bad blood / Readymades / Rhinocratic oaths / Can blue men sing the whites? / Mr Slater's parrot / Strain, The / We are normal / My pink half of the drainpipe / Jazz, delicious hot, disgusting cold / Big shot / Jollity farm / Humanoid boogie.
LP: . . . . **EMS 1335**
MC: . . . . **TCEMS 1335**

DOUGHNUT IN GRANNY'S GREENHOUSE.
Tracks: / We are normal / Postcard / Beautiful Zelda / Can blue men sing the whites / Hello Mabel / Kama Sutra / Humanoid boogie / Trouser press, The / My pink half of the drain pipe / Rockaliser baby / Rhinocratic oaths / Eleven mustachioed daughters.
LP: . . . . **XED 209**
LP: . . . . **LBS 83158**

GORILLA.
Tracks: / Cool Britannia / Equestrian statute, The / Jollity farm / I left my heart in San Francisco / Look out there's a monster coming / Jazz delicious hot disgusting cold / Death cab for a cutie / Narcissus / Intro and the outro, The / Mickey's son and daughter / Big shot / Music for head ballet / Piggy bank love / I'm bored / Sound of music, The.
LP: . . . . **LBR 1019**
LP: . . . . **BGOLP 82**

HISTORY OF BONZOS.
Tracks: / Sport (the odd boy) / Noises for the leg / King of scurf / Labio dental fricative / Hello Mabel / Look at me, I'm wonderful / Canyons of your mind / Jollity farm / You done my brain in / My pink half of the drain pipe / Mr. Apollo / Hunting tigers out in India / Suspicion / Mr. Slater's parrot / Narcissus / I'm the urban spaceman / Bad blood / I left my heart in San Francisco / Tent / Can blue men sing the whites / 9-5 pollution blues / Big shot / Release me / We are normal / Sound of music, The / Kama Sutra / Rhinocratic oaths / Straight from my heart / Mickey's son and daughter / Blind date / Trouser press, The / Slush.
LP: . . . . **UAD 60071**

KEYNSHAM.
Tracks: / You done my brain in / Keynsham / Quiet talks and summer walks / Tent / We were wrong / Joke shop man / Bride stripped bare by 'bachelors', The / What do you do? / Mr. Slater's parrot / Sport / I want to be with you / Noises for the leg / Busted.
LP: . . . . **XED 235**
LP: . . . . **LBR 1041**

LET'S MAKE UP AND BE FRIENDLY.
Tracks: / Strain / Turkeys / King of scurf / Waiting for the wardrobe / Straight from my heart / Rusty / Rawlinson end / Fresh wound / Slush / Bad blood.
LP: . . . . **AWL 1004**
MC: . . . . **AWT 1004**

TADPOLES.
Tracks: / Hunting tigers out in India / Shirt / Tubas in the moonlight / Doctor Jazz / Monster mash / I'm the urban

spaceman / Ali Baba's camel / Laughing blues / By a waterfall / Mr. Apollo / Canyons of your mind.
LP: . . . . **ED 186**
LP: . . . . **LBS 83257**

VERY BEST OF BONZO DOG DOO DAH BAND.
Tracks: / I'm the urban spaceman / Jollity farm / Mr. Apollo / Can blue men sing the whites / Death cab for a cutie / Trouser press, The / We are normal / Look out there's a monster coming / Intro and the outro, The / Hunting tigers out in Africa / Canyons of your mind / Equestrian statute, The / Mickey's son and daughter / Humanoid boogie / Monster mash / My pink half of the drain pipe.
LP: . . . . **MFP 5680**
MC: . . . . **TCMFP 5680**

Boo, Betty

BOO-MANIA.
LP: . . . . **LEFT LP 12**
MC: . . . . **LEFT C 12**

Boogie Box High

OUTRAGEOUS.
LP: . . . . **SBKLP 1**
MC: . . . . **SBKTC 1**

Boogie Brothers

BAR BY BAR.
LP: . . . . **BB 333**
MC: . . . . **4 BUR 003**

Boogie Bus

BOOGIE BUS (Various artists).
LP: **9198174**

Boogie Down

BY ALL MEANS NECESSARY.
Tracks: / My philosophy / Ya slippin' / Stop the violence / Illegal business / Nervous / I'm still no.1 / Part time success / Jimmy / P'Cha / Necessary.
LP: . . . . **HIP 63**
MC: . . . . **HIPC 63**
LP: . . . . **1097 1 J A**

CRIMINAL MINDED.
LP: . . . . **BB 4787**

EDUTAINMENT.
Tracks: / Exhibit A / Blackman in effect / Ya know the rules / Exhibit B / Beef / House nigga's / Exhibit C / Love's gonna get'cha (material love) / 100 guns / Ya strugglin' / Breath control II / Exhibit D / Edutainment / Homeless / Original lyrics / Racist, The / Kenny Parker Show, The / Exhibit F.
LP: . . . . **HIP 100**
MC: . . . . **HIPC 100**

GHETTO MUSIC: THE BLUE PRINT OF HIP HOP.
Tracks: / Style you haven't done yet / Blueprint, The / Jah rulez / Who protects us from you / Hip hop rules / Gimme day (woy) / World peace / Why is that / Jack of spades / Breath control / You must learn / Bo bo bo / Ghetto music.
LP: . . . . **HIP 80**
MC: . . . . **HIPC 80**

Boogie Kings

BLUE EYED SOUL.
LP: **109**
MC: . . . . **109 TC**

BOOGIE KINGS.
LP: **104**
MC: . . . . **104 TC**

CLINT WEST & THE BOOGIE KINGS (see West, Clint) (Boogie Kings/Clint West).

LIVE AT THE BAMBOO HUT.
LP: **111**

Boogie Tunes

BOOGIE TUNES 1 (Various artists).
Tracks: / Boogie times: *Derrick* / Can't you feel it: *Michele* / Work that body: *Gardner, Taana* / Keep it up: *Wright, Milton* / Rappin' Duke: *Rappin' Duke* / Hustlin' (you gotta be...): *Black Ivory* / Standing right here: *Moore, Melba.*
LP: . . . . **LIPS 2**
MC: . . . . **TCLIPS 2**

BOOGIE TUNES 2 (Various artists).
Tracks: / Girl you need a change of mind: *Brooklyn Express* / Love design: *Kinsman Dazz* / Body fusion: *Starvue*/ Main thing: *Shot* / Got to get your love: *Alexander, Clyde* / Can't get away: *Williams, Carol* / All about the paper: *Dells.*
LP: . . . . **LIPS 3**
MC: . . . . **TCLIPS 3**

Boogie With A Bullet

BOOGIE WITH A BULLET.
LP: . . . . **REDITA 109**

Boogie Woogie

BOOGIE BLUES (Women sing and play the Boogie Woogie) (Various artists).
LP: . . . . **RR 1309**

BOOGIE WOOGIE (Various artists).
LP: . . . . **SLP 4006**

BOOGIE WOOGIE A LA PARISIENNE (Various artists).
LP: . . . . **PM 1552601**

BOOGIE WOOGIE BOYS VOL.1 (Various artists).
LP: . . . . **SLP 4094**

BOOGIE WOOGIE FEVER (Various artists).
Tracks: / Barracuda: *Stone, Cliffie* / Catfish boogie: *Ford, Tennessee Ernie* / Jukebox boogie: *Dolan, Ramblin' Jimmie* / Louisiana boogie: *Travis, Merle* / I'm a do right daddy: *Chappel, Leon* / Blackberry boogie: *Ford, Tennessee Ernie* / Cash on the barrelhead: *Louvin Brothers* / Downtown boogie: *Milo Twins* / Boogie woogie fever: *O'Quin, Gene* / Shotgun boogie: *Ford, Tennessee Ernie* / Hot rod race: *Dolan, Ramblin' Jimmie*/ Texas boogie: *O'Quin, Gene* / Honky tonkin' all the time: *Willard, Jess* / Baby buggy boogie: *Milo Twins*/ Slow down sweet mama: *Chappel, Leon* / Jump rope boogie: *Stone, Cliffie.*
LP: . . . . **CR 30215**

BOOGIE WOOGIE HITS (Various artists).
Tracks: / Yancey stomp: *Yancey, Jimmy* / Roll 'em: *Goodman, Benny* / Boogie woogie man: *Various artists*/ Barrelhouse boogie: *Ammons, Albert & Pete Johnson* / Boogie woogie: *Dorsey, Tommy* / Boogie woogie on St. Louis blues: *Hines, Earl* / Whisky and gin blues: *Memphis Slim* / One o'clock boogie: *Basie, Count* / Chicago breakdown: *Maceo, Big* / Rooming house boogie: *Calloway, Cab* / Hey ba ba re bop: *Hampton, Lionel* / Hamp's boogie woogie: *Hampton, Lionel.*
LP: . . . . **CL 89803**
MC: . . . . **CK 89803**

BOOGIE WOOGIE KINGS VOL. 1 (Various artists).
LP: . . . . **ESR 1208**

BOOGIE WOOGIE MASTERS (Big Band Bounce and Boogie) (Various artists).
Tracks: / Cow cow blues: *Davenport, Cow Cow* / State street jive: *Davenport, Cow Cow* / Pinetop's blues: *Smith, Pine Top* / Pinetop's boogie woogie: *Smith, Pine Top* / Jump steady blues: *Smith, Pine Top* / Detroit rocks: *Taylor, Montana* / Dirty dozen, The: *Perryman, Rufus* / Right string baby but the wrong yoyo: *Perryman, Rufus*/ Honky tonk train blues: *Lewis, Meade Lux* / Yancey special: *Lewis, Meade Lux* / Celeste blues: *Lewis, Meade Lux* / Boogie woogie stomp: *Ammons, Albert* / Mr. Freddie blues: *Williams, Mary Lou* / Boogie woogie: *Basie, Count* / Basement boogie: *Johnson, Pete* / Death ray boogie: *Johnson, Pete.*
LP: . . . . **AFS 1005**
MC: . . . . **TCAFS 1005**

BOOGIE WOOGIE MASTERSPIECES (Various artists).
LP: . . . . **OFF 3031**

BOOGIE WOOGIE REVIVAL (Various artists).
LP: . . . . **SM 4083**

GREAT PIANISTS MEET BOOGIE WOOGIE, THE (Various artists).
LP: . . . . **SM 4084**

GREAT VOCALISTS MEET BOOGIE WOOGIE, THE (Various artists).
LP: . . . . **SM 4085**

GREATEST BOOGIE WOOGIE 1 (Various artists).
MC: **64028**

GREATEST BOOGIE WOOGIE 2 (Various artists).
MC: **64029**

GREATEST HITS: BOOGIE WOOGIE (Various artists).
LP: . . . . **BW 1000**

GROOVIE BOOGIE WOOGIE BOY (Various artists).
LP: . . . . **RR 2014**

HEAVY TIMBRE (Chicago boogie piano) (Various artists).
LP: . . . . **SIREN S 102**

I WANT TO BOOGIE WOOGIE (Various artists).
LP: . . . . **RR 2021**

PIONEERS OF BOOGIE WOOGIE (Vol. 1) (Various artists).
LP: . . . . **SM 4081**

Boogie Woogie Red

RED HOT.
LP: **BP-003**

Book Of Beasts

BOOK OF BEASTS/THE FIERY DRAGON (see under Nesbitt, E (Fiery dragon) (Various artists).

Book Of Love

BOOK OF LOVE.
LP: **925355 1**

LULLABY.
Tracks: / Tubular bells / Pretty boys and pretty girls / Sea of Tranquility / Melt my heart / With a little love / Witchcraft / You look through me / Champagne wishes / Oranges and lemons / Lullaby.
LP: **925 700-1**
MC: **925 700-4**

Bookbinder, Roy

GOING BACK TO TAMPA.
LP: . . . . **FF 098**

RAGTIME MILLIONAIRE.
LP: . . . . **BG 2023**

ROY BOOKBINDER.
MC: . . . . **ROUNDER 3107C**
LP: . . . . **ROUNDER 3107**

TRAVELLIN' MAN.
LP: . . . . **AD 1017**

Booker, Bob

WHEN YOU'RE IN LOVE THE WHOLE WORLD IS JEWISH (Film Soundtrack) (Booker, Bob & George Foster).
Tracks: / Would you believe it / Hobby, The / My husband, the monster / Ballad of Irving / Shoe repair shop / Divorce, kosher style / Voyage to the bottom of the sea / Things might have been different / Call from Greenwich Village, A / Great bank robbery, The / Discussion in the airplane / Miami beach / Schtick / Kidnapping, The / Bar mitzvah / When your in love the whole world is jewish.
LP: . . . . **MCL 1670**
MC: . . . . **MCLC 1670**

YOU DON'T HAVE TO BE JEWISH (Film Soundtrack) (Booker, Bob & George Foster).
Tracks: / Call from Long Island / Home from the office / Reading of the will / Quickies / Jury, The / Presidents, The / Cocktail party / Final discussion / More quickies / Convicts, The / Housewarming, The / Luncheon, The / Still more quickies / Conversation in the hotel lobby / Agony and the ecstasy / My son, the captain / Secret agent / Enough already with the quickies / Goldstein.
LP: . . . . **MCL 1681**
MC: . . . . **MCLC 1681**
LP: . . . . **CDL 8502**

Booker, Chuckii

CHUCKII.
LP: . . . . **K 781947-1**
MC: . . . . **K 781947-4**

Booker, James

BOOGIE WOOGIE AND RAGTIME PIANO CONTEST.
LP: . . . . **GOLD 11055**

CLASSIFIED.
Tracks: / All around the world / One for the highway / King of the road / Bald head Tipitina / Baby face / Swedish rhapsody / Classified / Lawdy Miss Clawdy / Angel eyes / Hound dog / If you're lonely / Three keys.
LP: . . . . **FIEND 7**
LP: . . . . **ROUNDER 2036**
MC: . . . . **ROUNDER 2036C**

JUNCO PARTNER.
LP: . . . . **HELP 26**

KING OF THE NEW ORLEANS KEYBOARD.
Tracks: / How do you feel / Going down slow / Classified / One hell of a nerve / Blues rhapsody / Rockin' pneumonia / Please send me someone to love / All by myself / Ain't nobody's business / Something you got / Harlem in Hamburg.
LP: . . . . **JSP 1083**

KING OF THE NEW ORLEANS KEYBOARD VOL 2.
LP: . . . . **JSP 1086**

MR MYSTERY.
LP: . . . . **CG 709-09**

NEW ORLEANS PIANO WIZARD: LIVE.
LP: . . . . **ROUNDER 2027**
MC: . . . . **ROUNDER 2027C**

Booker, Steve

DREAMWORLD.
Tracks: / This side of heaven / Poet stone / Everytime you walk away / Running and hiding / Homeland / Shades of grey (CD only.) / Wedding day / I will be there / When the fire burns out / Songs from the river / Lay me down.
LP: . . . . **PCS 7347**
LP: **795 201 1**
MC: . . . . **TCPCS 7347**
MC: **795 201 4**

Booker T & The MG's

BEST OF BOOKER T AND THE MGS.
Tracks: / Green onions / Slim Jenkins place / Hip hug her / Soul dressing / Summertime / Bootleg / Jellybread / Tic-tac-toe / Can't be still / Groovin' / Mo' onions / Red beans and rice.
LP: . . . . **K 40072**
MC: **K4 40072**

BOOKER T AND THE MG'S.
Tracks: / Green onions / Rinky dink / I got a woman / Mo' onions / Twist and shout / Behave yourself / Stranger on the shore / Lonely avenue / One who really loves you / You can't sit down / Woman, a lover, a friend / Comin' home baby.
LP: . . . . **SHM 3031**

BOOKER T SET, THE.
Tracks: / Love child / Lady Madonna / Horse, The / Sing a simple song / Mrs. Robinson / This guy's in love with you / Light my fire / Michelle / You're all I need / I've never found a girl / It's your thing.
MC: . . . . **MPS 58531**
LP: . . . . **MPS 8531**
LP: . . . . **SXE 026**

GREEN ONIONS.
LP: . . . . **HAK 8182**

MCLEMORE AVENUE.
Tracks: / Golden slumbers / Here comes the sun / Come together / Because / Mean Mr Mustard / She came in through the bathroom window / Carry that weight / End, The / Something / You never give me your money / Polythene Pam.
LP: . . . . **SXE 016**
LP: . . . . **SXATS 1031**

SOUL LIMBO.
Tracks: / Be young, be foolish, be happy / Hang 'em high / Over easy / Eleanor Rigby / Sweet sweet baby / Foxy lady / La la means I love you / Willow weep for me / Soul limbo / Heads or tails / Born under a bad sign.
LP: . . . . **SXE 009**
LP: . . . . **SX 009**

TIME IS TIGHT (LP).
Tracks: / Time is tight / Hip hug her / Mrs. Robinson / Soul clap / Slum baby / Hang 'em high / Soul limbo / Sugar cane / Melting pot / Soul man / I'd rather drink muddy water / Heads or tails / Crop dustin' / Jive man / Way I feel tonight / Funky Broadway / One with sugar / Land of a thousand dances.
LP: . . . . **STX 3007**

UNIVERSAL LANGUAGE.
Tracks: / Sticky stuff / Grab bag / Space nuts / Love wheels / Moto cross / Last tango in Memphis / MG's salsa / Tie stick / Reincarnation.
LP: . . . . **K 53057**

UPTIGHT.
Tracks: / Johnny, I love you / Cleveland now / Children don't get weary / Tank's lament / Blues in the gutter / We've got Johnny Wells / Down at Ralph's joint / Deadwood Dick / Run tank run / Time is tight.
LP: . . . . **SXE 024**

Books

EXPERTISE.
Tracks: / Spillane / Metaphysic / Hirohito / Osterreich / Rain / Expertise / Ballroom debut / Dusters / I'll be your friend.
LP: . . . . **VOLUME 1**

Boom, Barry

LIVING BOOM, THE.
LP: . . . . **FADLP 016**

Boom Boom Room

STRETCH.
Tracks: / Julie / Love your face / Piece of the times / Here comes the man / Hurting serenade / Lisa eyes / Uncertain feeling / Big chance / Take your time / Future king.
LP: **4601581**
MC: **4601584**

Boom Crash Opera

BOOM CRASH OPERA.
Tracks: / Gap that opened / Hands up in the air / Love me to death / City flat / Her charity / Sleeping time / Great wall / Bombshell / Caught between two towns / Too hot to think.
LP: . . . . **K 925636 1**
MC: . . . . **K 925636 4**

THESE HERE ARE CRAZY TIMES.
LP: **7599261601**
MC: **7599261604**

Boom, Taka

BOOMERANG.
Tracks: / To hell with him / Boomerang / Ride like the wind / Let it burn / Love party / Listen to your heart / Kiss it and make it better / I saw him first.

MC: . . . . ZCCAB 1008
LP: . . . . CABLP 1008

MIDDLE OF THE NIGHT.
LP: 827 613-1
MC: 827 613-4

Boomerang

BOOMERANG.
Tracks: / Boomerang fanfare / Boomerang / These boots are made for walking / When the phone stops ringing / Night train / Guess you'll know I'll be around / Baby I'm back in love again / In the darkness / Money, men and make-up / Stowaway.
LP: 781 652-1
MC: 781 652-4

Boomtown Rats

BOOMTOWN RATS.
Tracks: / Close as you'll ever be / Do you in / I can make it if you can / Joey / Kicks / Looking after no. 1 / Mary of the 4th form / Neon heart / Never bite the hand that feeds.
LP: . . . . PRICE 57
MC: . . . . PRIMC 57
LP: . . . . ENVY 1

FINE ART OF SURFACING.
Tracks: / Having my picture taken / Nothing happened today / I don't like Mondays / Someone's looking at you / Diamond smiles.
LP: . . . . PRICE 73
MC: . . . . PRIMC 73
LP: . . . . ENROX 11

IN THE LONG GRASS.
Tracks: / Hold of me / Drag me down / Dave / Over again / Another sad story / Tonight / Hard times / Lucky / Icicles in the sun / Up or down.
LP: . . . . MERL 38

MONDO BONGO.
Tracks: / Mood mambo / Straight up / This is my room / Another piece of red / Go man go / Under their thumb / Please don't go / Fall down / Elephant's graveyard, The / Banana republic / Hurts hurt.
LP: 6359 042

TONIC FOR THE TROOPS.
Tracks: / Like clockwork / Blind date / I never loved Eva Braun / Living in an island / Don't believe what you read / She's so modern / Me and Howard Hughes / Can't stop / Watch out for the normal people / Rat trap.
LP: . . . . PRICE 58
MC: . . . . PRIMC 58
LP: . . . . ENVY 3

V DEEP.
Tracks: / Never in a million years / Bitter end / Talking in code / He watches all / Storm breaks / House on fire / Up all night / Skin on skin / Little death, The / House burned down.
MC: 7150 082
LP: 6359 082

Boone Creek

BOONE CREEK.
Tracks: / Dixieland / Dark is the night / Walkin' in Jerusalem / Gonna settle down / Drifting too far from the shore / White house blues / Boone Creek / Memory of your smile, The / Intro / Satisfy my mind / Sugar daddy / Ain't nobody gonna miss me.
LP: . . . . SDLP 017
LP: . . . . ROUNDER 0081
MC: . . . . ROUNDER 0081C

ONE WAY TRACK.
Tracks: / One way rider / Head over heels / Little community church / Mississippi queen / In the pines / Can't you hear me callin' / No mother or dad / Blue and lonesome / Daniel prayed / Sally Goodun.
LP: . . . . SH 3701
MC: . . . . SH 3701 MC

Boone, Daniel

BEAUTIFUL SUNDAY (OLD GOLD) (See under Shocking Blue/Venus (Old Gold)(CD).

I'M ONLY LOOKING.
Tracks: / Man on the other side of the moon / Street fighters / One more night / Sanctuary / Total reaction / VCR's and space invaders / Trouble in the family / I'm only looking (LP version) / Lifeline / Not me / Sweet conversation / Why not.
LP: . . . . BOON 1

Boone, Debbie

CHOOSE LIFE.
LP: . . . . LLR 3008
MC: . . . . LLC 3008

FRIENDS FOR LIFE.
MC: . . . . C 03011
LP: . . . . R 03011

SURRENDER.
LP: . . . . LLR 3001
MC: . . . . LLC 3001

Boone Girls

HEAVENLY LOVE.
Tracks: / Heavenly love / He lives / My sisters and brothers / Praise the Lord / No I've never / Because I love him / You came softly / No I can't stop / Your love / Fairest Lord Jesus.
LP: . . . . LL 2021
MC: . . . . LLC 2021

Boone, Larry

SWINGING DOORS, SAWDUST FLOORS.
Tracks: / I just called to say goodbye / It's our year to see the bluebird / Under a love star moon / Blue collar dollar / I'm not fool enough to fool around / Ten times Texas.
LP: 836 710-1
MC: 836 710-4

Boone, Lelly

I'VE REALLY GOT YOU (See under Boone, Daniel) (Boone, Lelly/Daniel Boone).

Boone, Pat

16 CLASSIC TRACKS: PAT BOONE.
Tracks: / April love / Don't forbid me / I almost lost my mind / At my front door / Friendly persuasion / Sugar moon / Moody river / I'll be home / Love letters in the sand / Gospel boogie / Remember you're mine / Ain't that a shame / Main attraction / It's too soon to know / Why baby why? / Speedy Gonzales.
LP: . . . . MCL 1676
MC: . . . . MCLC 1676
LP: . . . . MFP 50549

20 BEST LOVED GOSPEL SONGS - PAT BOONE.
Tracks: / Down from his glory / He touched me / Whispering hope / It's free / Answer, The / I'm coming home / Thank you / Woman at the well / Do Lord / Lord's prayer, The / There's a song in my heart / Face to face / Saved by grace / Man called Billy, A / Yesterday, today and tomorrow / How great thou art / Heaven is my home / Lead the way Lord / My wish my prayer.
LP: . . . . SHARON 323

20 GOLDEN PIECES: PAT BOONE.
LP: . . . . BDL 2053
MC: . . . . BDC 2053

ALL THE HITS.
Tracks: / Speedy Gonzales / Ain't that a shame / Love letters in the sand / Johnny Will / April love / I'll be home / Moody river / Don't forbid me / Remember you're mine / I almost lost my mind / Why baby why / Wonderful time up there, A.
LP: . . . . TOP 154
MC: . . . . KTOP 154

ALL-TIME FAVOURITES.
MC: . . . . GM 0218

BABY OH BABY.
Tracks: / Baby, oh baby / Rose Marie / Baby sonnenschein / Wie eine lady / Ein goldener stern / Komm zu mir wenn du einsam bist / Oh lady / Nein nein valentina / Mary Lou / Wo find ich meine traume / Que pasa contigo / Y te quiero / Recuerdame siempre / Amor al reves / En cualquier lugar / Cartas en la arena / Tu che non hai amato mai / E fuori la pioggia cade / Se tu non fossi qui.
LP: . . . . BFX 15185

BEST OF PAT BOONE.
LP: . . . . WW 5089
MC: . . . . WW 4 5089

COME TOGETHER (see under Owens, Jimmy & Carol) (Boone, Pat/Jimmy & Carol Owens).

FRIENDLY PERSUASION.
Tracks: / Ain't that a shame / I'll be home / I almost lost my mind / Friendly persuasion / No other arms / Gee Whittakers / Love letters in the sand / Spring rain / Don't forbid me / Wonderful time up there, A / Cherie I love you / Moody river / Long tall Sally / Why baby why? / Mona Lisa / It's too soon to know / Are you lonesome tonight / Deep purple / When I fall in love / Speedy Gonzales / Tutti frutti / Johnny will / When the swallows come back to Capistrane / Fools hall of fame / Wang dang taffy apple, The / I'll see you in my dreams / Bernadine.
2LP: . . . . CR 042
MCSET: . . . . CRT 042

GOLDEN GREATS: PAT BOONE.
Tracks: / I'll be home / Love letters in the sand / Friendly persuasion / Speedy Gonzales / April love / Don't forbid me / I almost lost my mind / At my front door / Sugar moon / Moody river / Gospel boogie / Remember you're mine / Ain't that a shame / Main attraction / It's too soon to know / Why baby why.
LP: . . . . MCM 5006
MC: . . . . MCMC 5006

GOLDEN HITS: PAT BOONE.
LP: . . . . MA 81285
MC: . . . . MAMC 981285

GREATEST HITS:PAT BOONE.
LPPD: . . . . AR 30043

HIS TOP HITS.
MC: 802

HOME.
MC: . . . . C 03012
LP: . . . . R 03012

HYMNS WE HAVE LOVED.
LP: . . . . HAD 2228

HYMNS WE LOVE.
LP: . . . . HAD 2092

JIVIN' PAT.
Tracks: / Good rockin' tonight / For my good fortune / Flip flop and fly / Shotgun boogie / Hoboken baby / Fat man / Tutti frutti / Two hearts / Rock boll weevil / Honey hush / Bingo / Rock around the clock / I'm in love with you / Money honey / Wonderful time up there, A / Ain't nobody here but us chickens.
LP: . . . . BFX 15230

LOVE LETTERS IN THE SAND.
LP: . . . . ENT LP 13030
MC: . . . . ENT MC 13030

LOVE SONGS: PAT BOONE.
Tracks: / Who's sorry now / It's a sin to tell a lie / True in my dreams / True love / Secret love / I'm in the mood for love / I'll see you in my dreams / Deep purple / Ebb tide / Stardust / Send me the pillow that you dream on / Blue moon / Misty / Night and day / Yesterday / He'll have to go / Are you lonesome tonight / Love letters in the sand.
LP: . . . . MFP 5758
MC: . . . . TCMFP 5758

PAT BOONE ORIGINALS.
2LP: . . . . ABSD 301

STARDUST.
LP: . . . . HAD 2127

SUGAR MOON.
Tracks: / Beach girl / Anastasia / Exodus / Dear John / Welcome new lovers / 500 miles / Blueberry Hill / For a penny / Candy sweet / Sugar moon / Ten lonely guys / Twixt 12 and 20 / At my front door.
MCSET: . . . . CRT 012

UNFORGETTABLE: PAT BOONE (16 Golden Classics).
Tracks: / I'll be home / Ain't that a shame / Speedy Gonzales / Yesterday / Exodus / Misty / By the time I get to Phoenix / Who's sorry now / April love / Quando, quando, quando / Johnny will / Friendly persuasion / Love letters in the sand / Wonderful time up there, A / I'll see you in my dreams / Words / Walking the floor over you / At my front door / No other arms.
LP: . . . . UNLP 023
MC: . . . . UNMC 023

VERY BEST OF PAT BOONE.
Tracks: / Love letters in the sand / Speedy Gonzales / April love / I'll be home / Gospel boogie / Johnny will / Sugar moon / Ain't that a shame / Don't forbid me / Remember you're mine / I almost lost my mind / It's too soon to know / Moody river / Main attraction / There's a goldmine in the sky / Friendly persuasion.
MC: . . . . HSC 3279

WHAT I BELIEVE.
Tracks: / Old rugged cross, The / Softly and tenderly / Onward christian soldiers / Wonderful words of life / How a firm foundation / It was his love / People need the Lord / Let me live / What I believe.
LP: . . . . LLR 3004
MC: . . . . LLC 3004

WHISPERING HOPE.
Tracks: / Whispering hope / Mine eyes have seen the glory / Yield not to temptation / I love to tell the story / Have thine own way / Take the name of Jesus with you / He (can turn the tide) / I walked today where Jesus walked / Saviour like a shepherd lead us / It is no secret / How great thou art / Sofly and tenderly / Abide with me / Let the lower lights be burning / Old rugged cross, The / Blessed assurance / Jesus is mine / I believe / What a friend we have in Jesus / God be with you till we meet again / Will the circle be unbroken.
LP: . . . . TWE 6008
MC: . . . . TC TWE 6008

Boot That Thing

FLORIDA 1935.
LP: . . . . FLY 258

Bootfare

WHERE'S LONDON.
LP: . . . . BUZZLP 1

Booth, John

AUTOGRAPH.
LP: . . . . OAK 004

Booth, Webster

GOLDEN AGE OF WEBSTER BOOTH, THE.
Tracks: / Roses of Picardy / Vienna, city of my dreams / Drink to me only with thine eyes / Sweethearts (From the film 'Sweethearts') / On the wings of song / Nirvana / Fairy song, The (From 'The Immortal Hour') / Perfect day / Serenade (From'The Student Prince') / Passing by / Everywhere I go (From the album'Four Pastorales') / Come into the garden Maud / Eleanore / Song of the vagabonds (From'The Vagabond King') / I leave my heart in an English garden (Theme from'Dear Miss Phoebe') / At the end of the day.
LP: . . . . GX 41 2547
MC: . . . . TCGX 2547

Boothe, Ken

BLOOD BROTHERS.
LP: . . . . TRLS 148

DON'T YOU KNOW.
LP: . . . . TZLP 1002

EVERYTHING I OWN.
Tracks: / Everything I own / Crying over you / (It's the way) nature planned it.
LP: . . . . TRLS 95

IMAGINE.
LP: . . . . PHLP 006

KEN BOOTHE COLLECTION.
LP: . . . . TRLS 249
MC: . . . . ZCTRL 249

REGGAE FOR LOVERS.
Tracks: / This love of ours / reggae steady / King and Queen / I am in love / Hello sunshine / Time of decision / I know it, I've got to be there / Good woman / No more war.
LP: . . . . TOPS 128

WHO GETS YOUR LOVE?.
Tracks: / Who get's your love? / You're no good / African lady.
LP: . . . . TRLS 164

Boothill Foot Tappers

AIN'T THAT FAR FROM BOOTHILL.
Tracks: / Love and affection / Jealousy / Pride takes a fall / Nothing ventured / Feelings / Sunday evening / Get your feet out of my shoes / Have you got the confidence for the trick / Stand or fall / What's the matter / There's no way / Too much time.
LP: . . . . MERH 76

Boots & His Buddies

SAN ANTONIO JAZZ 1935-36.
LP: . . . . M 8002

Bootsy's Rubber Band

AHH.. THE NAME IS BOOTSY.
Tracks: / Ahh the name is Bootsy, baby / Pinocchio theory, The / Rubber dickie / Preview side too / What's a telephone bill / Munchies for your love / Can't stay away / We want Bootsy (reprise).
LP: . . . . K 56302

JUNGLE BASS.
Tracks: / Jungle bass / Disciples of funk / Interzone / Jungle bass (House of bass mix).
MLP: . . . . BRLM 550

STRETCHIN' OUT.
Tracks: / Stretchin' out (In a rubber band) / Psychotic bum school / Another point of view / I'd rather be with you / Love vibes / Physical love / Vanish in our sleep.
LP: . . . . K 56200

THIS BOOT IS MADE FOR FONK-N.
Tracks: / Under the influence of a groove / Bootsy get live / O boy gorl / Jam fan / Chug-a-lug / Shejam / Reprise.
LP: . . . . K 56615

Booty, Charlie

BOOGIE WOOGIE 8-TO-THE-BAR.
LP: . . . . JCE 88

Boo-Ya T.R.I.B.E.

NEW FUNKY NATION.
Tracks: / Six bad brothers / Don't mess / Once upon a drive by / Psyko funk / R.A.I.D. / Riot pump / Rated R / New funky nation / Walk the line / Pickin' up metal / T.R.I.B.E..
MC: . . . . BRCA 544
LP: . . . . BRLP 544
MC: . . . . ICM 2063
LP: . . . . ILPM 2063

Boozoo Chavis

BOOZOO ZYDECO (See under Chavis, Boozoo).

Bop Baby Bop

BOP BABY BOP (See under Rock 'n' Roll) (Various artists).

Bop Boogie In...

BOP BOOGIE IN THE DARK (See under Rock 'n' Roll) (Various artists).

Bop City

BOP CITY (See under Jazz) (Various artists).

Bop Fathers In Paris

BOP FATHERS IN PARIS (See under Jazz) (Various artists).

Bop Harvey

BREAD AND CIRCUSES.
LP: **4676877**
MC: **4676871**

Bop Stop Rock

BOP STOP ROCK (see under Jazz) (Various artists).

Bop, Stroll, Roll

BOP, STROLL, ROLL (Various artists). Tracks: / Antmusic: *Various artists* / Dancing on the floor: *Various artists* / Stars on 45 (Beatles medley): *Various artists* / Attention to me: *Various artists* / This ole house: *Various artists* / Lay all your love on me: *Various artists* / You drive me crazy: *Various artists* / Stars on 45 (Abba medley): *Various artists*/ Gangsters of the groove: *Various artists* / You'll never know: *Various artists* / How bout us: *Various artists*/ Keep on loving you: *Various artists* / Everlasting love: *Various artists*.
LP: . . . . **CBS 85440**

Bop That Never...

VOL 1 - BOP THAT NEVER STOPPED (Various artists).
Tracks: / Mean mistreater: *Powers, Johnny* / I walk: *Powers, Johnny* / Rock crazy baby: *Adams, Art* / You'll never change me: *Allen, Lonnie* / Born unlucky: *Smith, Tommy* / Gee whiz: *Dazzlers* / Untrue: *Vidone*, Bob / Wa chic ka noka: *Holmes, Tommy* / Lobo Jones: *Gotroe, Jackie* / Money honey: *Engel, Gary* / Bad, bad boy: *Lollar, Bobby* / Old black Joe: *Adams, Jerry*.
LP: . . . . **BB 2000**

VOL 2 - BOP THAT NEVER STOPPED (Various artists).
Tracks: / Treat me right: *Powers, Johnny* / Somebody's gonna hurt you: *Powers, Johnny* / Something baby: *Dazzlers*/ Milkcow blues boogie: *Hepcat, Harry* / Rock 'n' roll with mom and dad: *Davenport, Bill* / Rockin' country fever: *Bros, Morris* / Indian Joe: *Adams, Art* / Hillbilly rock: *Tyndall, Carl E.* / Go girls: *Country G-J's*/ Ball tonight, A: *Campbell, Ray* / Folsom Prison blues: *Tidwell, Billy* / Frankie and Johnny: *Vidone, Bob*.
LP: . . . . **BB 2001**

VOL 3 - BOP THAT NEVER STOPPED (Various artists).
Tracks: / Red coat, green pants and red suit shoes: *Arnold, Lloyd* / Hang out: *Arnold, Lloyd* / Speed limit: *Lam*, Tommy / Little bitty mama: *Foley, Webb* / Heartbreak hotel: *Love, Buddy* / Rockin' in the graveyard: *Morningstar, Jackie*/ Crazy talk: *Loafers* / It's rock and roll: *Winston, Jack* / Poor gal: *Chaperrals* / One more chance: *Rock-A-Tones* / Mean and cruel: *Richardson, Murle* / Rockin' the blues: *Andrews, Gary*.
LP: . . . . **BB 2005**

VOL 4 - BOP THAT NEVER STOPPED (Various artists).
Tracks: / Alaska rock: *Rebelaires* / Satellite rock: *Rebelaires* / Spinner hub caps: *Davis, Pat* / Rock a bayou baby: *Moonlighters* / Saturday ball-slippin' and slidin': *Thompson, Tennessee* / Tell me baby: *Nash*, Cliff / Music to my ears: *Speck & Doyle* / I've met my one and only: *Etris, Barry* / There'll be a rockin' party: *Volk, Val* / Granny went rockin': *Lester, Jimmy* / Hurtin' and cryin': *Ryan, Mike*.
LP: . . . . **BB 2006**

VOL 5 - BOP THAT NEVER STOPPED (Various artists).
Tracks: / Jennie Lou: *Nash, Cliff* / No time for sister: *Nash, Cliff* / Joy ride: *Robbins, Mel* / Baby moon: *Smith, Herbie* / Oh yeah: *Wally, Jeffery* / That'll get it: *Imps* / Shake um up rock: *Cliff*, Benny / Mean mama blues: *Ray, Ronnie* / Born to lose: *Deckelman, Sonny* / I've got love: *Deckelman, Sonny*/ It's a lonely world: *Deckelman, Sonny* / Summer school: *Bucky & Premiers*.
LP: . . . . **BB 2007**

VOL 6 - BOP THAT NEVER STOPPED (Various artists).
Tracks: / Spinning my wheel: *Brooks, Chuck* / Don't hang around me anymore: *Ford, Jim* / You're gonna be sorry: *Ford, Jim* / Gotta have you: *Lee, Curtis* / I never knew what love could do: *Lee, Curtis* / You're always late: *Williams, Jimmy* / I belong to you: *Williams, Jimmy* / Going strong: *Head, Don* / Bo Peep rock: *Cheek-O-Vass* / Queen bee: *Orbits* / Story untold, A: *Hunt, Dennis* / Teenage boogie: *Wayne, Dennis*.
LP: . . . . **BB 2008**

VOL 7 - BOP THAT NEVER STOPPED (Various artists).
Tracks: / You lied to me honey: *Gravley, Junior* / Rockin' along: *Three Clicks* / Rock, baby rock: *Hicks*, Bob / Baby sittin' all the time: *Hicks, Bob* / Pony tail girl: *Garrison, Glen* / At the jamboree: *Ferguson*, Troy / Cool baby cool: *Edwards, Vern* / Satellite rock: *Copeland, James (nar)* / Rockin' teens: *Puckett, Dennis* / Bye bye blues: *Puckett, Dennis* / Rockin' daddy: *Dorn, Lee* / Freeloaders: *Carter, Fred*.
LP: . . . . **BB 2009**

VOL 8 - BOP THAT NEVER STOPPED (Various artists).
Tracks: / Daddy o rock: *Daniels, Jeff* / Foxy Dan: *Daniels, Jeff* / Get with it: *Glenn, Don* / Right now: *Montgomery, Gray* / Pitch black: *Jeffries, Linc* / Dancing girl: *Eay, Eddie* / Sugaree: *Diaz*, Carlos / Rock all night with me: *Tacker, D.* / Canteen baby: *Groves, Carl* / King fool: *Lane, Jack*/ 38 slug: *Three Clicks* / Ho key po key rock: *Goode, B.*.
LP: . . . . **BB 2010**

VOL 9 - BOP THAT NEVER STOPPED (Various artists).
Tracks: / Let's rock tonight: *Grubbs, Jimmy* / Swinging boogie: *Smith, Ray* / Gone baby gone: *Smith, Ray*/ Eeny meeny miney mo: *Walker, Lanie* / No use knocking on my door: *Walker, Lanie* / Teenage baby: *Anderkin*, Lonnie / Tell 'em: *Anderkin, Lonnie* / Crawdad song: *Moore, Red* / Rock and roll Dot: *Neighbors, Tex*/ Young Long John: *Barclay, Phil* / Little heart attacks: *Green, Bobby* / Slow boogie rock: *Harp, Lloyd*.
LP: . . . . **BB 2011**

VOL 10 - BOP THAT NEVER STOPPED (Various artists).
Tracks: / Screamin' Mimi Jeanie: *Hawks, Mickey* / Rock and roll rhythm: *Hawks, Mickey* / Bip bop boom: *Hawks*, Mickey / Hi di hi di hi di: *Hawks, Mickey* / Cottin' pickin': *Hawks, Mickey* / I'm lost: *Hawks, Mickey*/ Come back baby: *Wiley, Chuck* / I wanna dance all night: *Wiley, Chuck* / Why worry about me: *Wiley, Chuck*/ Right by my side: *Wiley, Chuck* / It's L-O-V-E: *Wiley, Chuck* / If you've ever been in love: *Wiley, Chuck*.
LP: . . . . **BB 2012**

VOL 11 - BOP THAT NEVER STOPPED (Various artists).
Tracks: / Rock the bob: *Martin, Jimmie* / Red bobby socks: *Martin, Jimmie* / Gonna rock'n'roll tonight: *Mann*, Carl / How I love you: *Speck, Darrell* / Proof of love: *Mayberry, Howard* / Raised on rock and roll: *Goetroe*, Jackie / She's my baby now: *Looper, Charles* / Broken hearted baby: *Lee, Alan* / River rock: *Hager, Don*/ Liza Jane bop: *Hager, Don* / Try me out and see: *Hager, Don* / Little heart attacks: *Johnson, Glenn*/ Run here honey: *Johnson, Glenn*.
LP: . . . . **BB 2014**

VOL 12 - BOP THAT NEVER STOPPED (Various artists).
Tracks: / Rockin' baby: *McCoy, Ray* / I need it: *McCoy, Ray* / Wiggling blonde: *Ford, Bubba* / Froggy: *Dell, Danny* / Rockin' and a boppin': *Newman, Carl* / Hoochie coochie man: *Long, Curtis* / Hep cat: *Terry*, Larry / Honey don't: *Schmidling, Tyrone* / It makes no difference: *Killen, Billie.J.* / I wonder: *Killen, Billie.J.* / Hot road Kelly: *Stringer, Jimmy* / Broken heart: *Moonlighters*.
LP: . . . . **BB 2015**

VOL 13 - BOP THAT NEVER STOPPED (Various artists).
Tracks: / Yes baby, I'm scared: *Gaida, Bill* / Take this message darling: *Gaida, Bill* / Rockin' romance: *Gaida*, Bill / Little Alice: *Moods* / Let me have your love: *Moods* / Rockin' Santa Claus: *Moods* / I'm gonna rock with my baby tonight: *McIntyre, Chester* / When my baby passes by: *Glenn Band* / Mean Gene: *Glenn Band*/ Won't tell you her name: *Urban, Al* / Gonna be better times: *Urban, Al* / Looking for money: *Urban, Al*/ No love in you: *Boaze-Man, Harmon* / Everybody rock: *Stone, Jeff*.
LP: . . . . **BB 2016**

VOL 14 - BOP THAT NEVER STOPPED Various artists (Various artists).
Tracks: / Tornado: *Jiants* / She's my woman: *Jiants* / Lou Ann: *Miller, Arlie* / Rock me baby: *Prowlers*/ Two timer: *Gray, Jimmy* / Sleigh bell rock: *Three Aces & A Joker* / Rock at the hop: *Dusters* / Cat, The: *Willis, Rod* / For you: *McCormack, Keith* / Can't see why: *Hammond, Wayne* / Live it up: *Burgett, Jim* / Come on baby: *Kirkland, Jimmy*.
LP: . . . . **BB 2017**

VOL 15 - BOP THAT NEVER STOPPED (Various artists).
Tracks: / Rockin' party: *Maddy Bros* / Hey little girlie: *Maddy Bros* / Baby I'll never let you go: *Love* Brothers / Umm: *Ken & Roy* / So wild: *Pete & Jimmy* / Night club rock and roll: *James, Kimbley* / She's mine: *Dusters* / Stella got a fella: *Fireflies* / Shakin' time: *Billy & Mickey* / Tree top: *Doell, Jerry* / Honey doll: *Dell, Don* / Put a nickel in the jukebox: *Godson, Willie*.
LP: . . . . **BB 2018**

VOL 16 - BOP THAT NEVER STOPPED (Various artists).
Tracks: / Ever'body's tryin': *Ross, Jerry* / Small little girl: *Ross, Jerry* / Dancing girl: *Adams, Art*/ She don't live here no more: *Adams, Art* / Tom Dooley rock and roll: *Hobock, Curtis* / Hey everybody: *Hobock*, Curtis / I love you baby: *Starr, Andy* / Just a walking: *Starr, Andy* / My hot mama: *Sabres* / Puppet: *Sabres* / One mile: *Dugosh, Eddie* / Strange kinda feeling: *Dugosh, Eddie*.
LP: . . . . **BB 2019**

VOL 17 - BOP THAT NEVER STOPPED (Various artists).
Tracks: / Spring fever: *Craig, Vilas* / So glad you're mine: *St. John, Frankie* / Full racing cam: *Ringo*, Eddie / Real soon: *Davis, Hank* / One way track: *Davis, Hank* / Rock and roll blues: *Teen Tones*/ Chicken session: *Rieux, Larry De* / Cajun queen: *Roberts, Bill* / Oh what love is: *Baley, Jack* / Pretty baby rock: *Mayo, Danny* / Baby of mine: *Dorsam, Tom* / One way love affair: *Dempsey, Jimmy*.
LP: . . . . **BB 2020**

VOL 18 - BOP THAT NEVER STOPPED (Various artists).
Tracks: / Blue swingin' mama: *Rock-A-Tones* / Bop hop: *Dempsey, Jimmy* / My Rosa Lee: *Orbits* / Eye'n you up: *Darro, George* / Somebody's been rocking my baby: *Willis, Rod* / I'm leaving town, baby: *Len & Judy*/ Satellite fever: *Miley, Lonnie* / Place called love, A: *Vee, Joey* / I'll be leaving you: *Moore, Turner*/ Uncle Sam's call: *Woodall, Jimmy* / You gotta show me: *Lane, Ralph* / Ready to rock: *Morrison, Jim*.
LP: . . . . **BB 2021**

VOL 19 - BOP THAT NEVER STOPPED (Various artists).
Tracks: / Good gosh Gerty: *Nelson, Darwin* / Mary Sue: *Nelson, Darwin* / Lazy Lu: *Nelson, Darwin* / Butterball: *Taro, Frankie* / I'm in love: *Talbot, Gus* / Rock away: *Sexton, Orden* / Jungle boogie: *Ronny & Johnny*/ Massacre: *Ronny & Johnny* / Cheer me up: *Plez Gary Man* / I like to go: *Mack, Floyd* / Nite spot rock: *Pollard, Bill* / Take a ride with me: *Reed, Johnny*.
LP: . . . . **BB 2023**

VOL 20 - BOP THAT NEVER STOPPED (Various artists).
Tracks: / Snaggle tooth Ann: *Norman, Gene* / Long gone night train: *Norman, Gene* / What have they got: *Horlick*, Maynard / Do the bop bop bop: *Horlick, Maynard* / Rollin' down the street: *Horlick, Maynard* / Betty Lou: *Bowman, Bob* / Mama's little girl: *Warfield, Joe* / Jenny Lou: *Nash, Cliff* (1st version) / Rampage: *Rockaways*/ Bye bye blackbird: *Conville, Johnny* / Goodbye train: *Foley, Jim* / Blues in the morning: *Foley, Jim*.
LP: . . . . **BB 2024**

VOL 21 - BOP THAT NEVER STOPPED (Various artists).
Tracks: / Tick tock: *Callaway, Bob* / What's the matter with me: *Callaway, Bob* / Love me, love me: *Faucett*, Ed / Sally Ann: *Wayne, Bobby* / War paint: *Wayne, Bobby* / Cherokee rock: *Wheeler, Chuck* / Rockin' on a reindeer: *Lee, Harry* / Kiss an Eskimo: *Lee, Harry* / Stampede: *Lee, Harry* / Pin ball baby: *Lee, Harry* / She's gone: *Pedigo Bros* / Wrong line: *Owens, Kenny*.
LP: . . . . **BB 2025**

VOL 22 - BOP THAT NEVER STOPPED (Various artists).
Tracks: / Midnight express: *Dawnbeats* / Undecided: *Parsons, Jerry* / Don't need no job: *Parsons, Jerry*/ Jukebox rock: *Seaton, Dick* / Rock while we ride: *Dockery, Chuck* / Baby let's dance: *Dockery, Chuck*/ Grandpa's rock: *Darden, Ray* / Dry run: *Cunningham, Parker* / Lord made a woman, The: *Powell, Doug*/ Jeannie with the dark blue eyes: *Powell, Doug* / Prom, The: *Runabouts* / Train: *Runabouts*.
LP: . . . . **BB 2026**

VOL 23 - BOP THAT NEVER STOPPED (Various artists).
Tracks: / Bomp bop, A: *Fern, Mike* / Cranberry blues: *Williams, Robert* / Wiggle walkin' baby: *Moss, Roy*/ Yes, Juanita's my name: *Moss, Roy* / Baby I don't care: *Scott, Rodney* / Granny went rockin': *Scott, Rodney*/ Going rockin' tonight: *Qual, Rex* / Tranquiliser boogie: *Qual, Rex* / Call me Shorty: *Childs, Billy*/ Latch on to your baby: *Lamberth, Jimmy* / Kentucky home rock: *Lamberth, Jimmy* / Rockin' and reelin': *Lamberth, Jimmy*.
LP: . . . . **BB 2027**

VOL 24 - BOP THAT NEVER STOPPED (Various artists).
Tracks: / Rock 'n' roll riot: *Stoltz Brothers* / Frog pond boogie: *Spurling, Hank* / Box car blues: *Spurling*, Hank / Baby doll: *Spurling, Hank* / I'm in debt: *Spurling, Hank* / Ninety one pounds of lovin': *Wilburn*, Dave / Can I go on loving you: *McMakin, Bill* / Hi lift: *Dotson, James* / Baby, I'm lonesome: *Earls, Jay* / Early every morning: *Walker, Lanie* / Jumping the gun: *Walker, Lanie* / Trot, The: *Dixieland Drifters*.
LP: . . . . **BB 2028**

VOL 25 - BOP THAT NEVER STOPPED (Various artists).
Tracks: / Betty Lou: *Kepler, Paul & The Cool Notes* / Phone me baby: *Woods, Bill* / Go crazy man: *Woods*, Bill / Bop: *Woods, Bill* / Great pretender, The: *Alley, Jim* / Dig that rock'n'roll: *Alley, Jim*/ Only two, me and you: *Goodspeed, Skip* / Weeping willow rock: *Hi Tombs* / Sweet rockin' mama: *Hi Tombs*/ Rock bottom blues: *Griffin, Curley* / Got rockin' on my mind: *Griffin, Curley* / Pete's blues: *Concillo, Peter & The Cool Notes*.
LP: . . . . **BB 2029**

VOL 26 - BOP THAT NEVER STOPPED (Various artists).
Tracks: / Rompin' stompin': *Lewis, Grady* / Flip flop and fly: *Nantz, Pete* / Jukebox pearl: *Nantz, Pete*/ I got a woman: *Miller, Buddy & The Rockin' Ramblers* / Rock 'n' roll Irene: *Miller, Buddy & The Rockin' Ramblers*/ Take up the slack daddy o: *Sabres* / Spider walk: *Sabres* / Tell me baby: *Smith, Billy* / Presley on her mind: *Hart, Don* / I'm a real glad daddy: *Potter, Curtis* / We're buggin' out: *Boyles, Tommy* / Gonna work: *Richard Brothers*.
LP: . . . . **BB 2030**

VOL 27 - BOP THAT NEVER STOPPED (Various artists).
Tracks: / Blond haired woman: *Lee, Harold* / Daddy loves mommy o: *Duncan, Tommy* / She's a devil: *Fackler*, Bob / Roberta, stanky woman: *Welch, Kenny* / Doin' my time: *Moore, Lucky* / You're gone, I'm left: *Schmidling*, Tyrone / Cape Canaveral: *Mead, Monte* / War chant boogie: *Elmore, Johnny* / Rock with the mambo: *Fraser, Johnny* / All about cha, babe: *Irwin, Kim* / Put my mind at ease: *Lando, Jerry*.
LP: . . . . **BB 2031**

VOL 28 - BOP THAT NEVER STOPPED (Various artists).
Tracks: / You shake me up: *Anderson, Andy & The Dawnbreakers* / Gimme lock a yo hair: *Anderson, Andy & The Dawnbreakers*/ Tough, tough, tough: *Anderson, Andy & The Dawnbreakers* / I'm gonna sit right down and cry over you: *Anderson, Andy* & The Dawnbreakers / Deep in the heart of Texas rock: *Anderson, Andy & The Dawnbreakers* / Promise, The: *Anderson*, Andy & The Dawnbreakers / Stone cold mama: *Carl, Steve & The Jags* / Blacksmith blues: *Carl, Steve & The Jags*/ You're for me: *Carl, Steve & The Jags* / Lonely road: *Carl, Steve & The Jags* / Curfew: *Carl, Steve & The Jags* / Eighteen year old blues: *Carl, Steve & The Jags*.
LP: . . . . **BB 2032**

VOL 29 - BOP THAT NEVER STOPPED (Various artists).
Tracks: / Holiday hill: *Waters, Wallace* / Keep me in your charms: *Waters, Wallace* / Rock it to the moon: *Gotroe*, Jackie / Cool guitar: *Blue Echoes* / It's witchcraft: *Blue Echoes* / King of rock 'n' roll: *Brian, Russ*/ Hillbilly's rock: *Brian, Russ* / I'm a real glad daddy: *Potter, Curtis* / Time is hanging heavy on my hands: *Beard, Dean* / Sing, sing, sing: *Beard, Dean* / Rebel yell: *Crowns* / Waiting for you to call: *Mack, Bobby*.
LP: . . . . **BB 2033**

VOL 30 - BOP THAT NEVER STOPPED (Various artists).
Tracks: / Rock 'n' roll mister moon: *Shulters, Harold* / Baby fan the flame: *Shulters, Harold* / Bunny honey: *Shulters, Harold* / Blues of a broken heart: *Shulters, Harold* / Party doll: *Shulters, Harold* / Come in world: *Shulters, Harold* / Half of me: *Shulters, Harold* / Blue fire: *Shulters, Harold* / Ramblin' rock: *Reed, Johnny* ((Previously unissued)) / Rockin' with Ruby: *Reed, Johnny* ((Previously unissued)) / Rockin' Peg: *Reed, Johnny* ((Previously unissued)) / Bubblegum: *Reed, Johnny* ((Previously unissued)) / Wall eyed shake: *Reed, Johnny* ((Previously unissued)) / Big black

ribbon: *Reed, Johnny* ((Previously unissued)) / Lost love blues: *Reed, Johnny* ((Previously unissued)) / I flipped my top: *Reed, Johnny.*
LP: . . . . **BB 2034**

VOL 31 - BOP THAT NEVER STOPPED
(Various artists).
Tracks: / What a dolly: *Berry, Red & Lou & The Berry Bros* / Hot rod: *Berry, Red & Lou & The Berry Bros* / Bobby Jean: *Bonny, Billy* / Bootleg rock: *Bonny, Billy* / Bull moose: *Clark, Vern* / Too young: *Clark, Vern* / I sez baby: *Wray, Link* / Johnny bom bonny: *Wray, Link* / Rockin' chair rock: *Dorn, Jerry*/ Laura Lee: *Giroy, Gil* / Venus rock: *Rollettes* / Back off: *Rollettes & The Ray Titze* / Mean mama blues: *Murphy, Don* / Truck driver's special: *Lillie, Lonnie.*
LP: . . . . **BB 2037**

VOL 32 - BOP THAT NEVER STOPPED
(Various artists).
Tracks: / You're the one: *Staggs, Jimmy & The Jay Rockers* ((Takes 1&2)(Previously unissued)) / Boppin' the stroll: *Welz, Joey & The Rock A Billies* / Shore party: *Welz, Joey & The Rock A Billies* / Mystery of love: *Welz, Joey & The Rock A Billies* / Scat cat cutie: *Various artists* ((Previously unissued)) / Gang's house: *Beckham, Tommy*/ Crazy mixed up baby: *Cook, Ross & The Jay Rockers* ((Previously unissued)) / Drag strip baby: *Roane, Johnny*/ Little girl: *Everhart, Bobby* / All messed up: *Hooper, Jess* / Sleepy time blues: *Hooper, Jess* / Baby please come home: *Runyon, Al* / Hungry: *Runyon, Al.*
LP: . . . . **BB 2038**

VOL 33 - BOP THAT NEVER STOPPED
(Various artists).
Tracks: / What is your technique: *Speaks, Ronnie* / Please wait for me: *Speaks, Ronnie* / Eleven o'clock: *Rainier*, Chris / Pull it man: *Earl, Johnny* / Daddy Joe: *Ciolino, Pete* / I've got a feeling: *Lewis, Grady*/ Tom Dooley rock & roll: *Brooks, Clinton* / Drivin': *Strawn, Ron* / Jungle rock: *Lee, Tommy* / Giggle wiggle: *Tennent, Jimmie* / She's gonna be mine: *Robbie & Joe* / Get hot or get home: *Kerby, John.*
LP: . . . . **BB 2041**

VOL 34 - BOP THAT NEVER STOPPED
(Various artists).
Tracks: / Radio boogie: *Smith, L.C.* / Corina corina: *Smith, L.C.* / She's my baby: *Holmes, Leon* / Swing it, little Kittie: *Owens, Clyde* / High class baby: *Arnold, Jerry* / Race for time: *Arnold, Jerry* / Little moon men, The: *George, Lee* / Kool it: *Blake, Tommy* / Ice cold baby: *Mitchell, Marion* / Shake it over sputnik: *Hogan, Billy* / If you don't like my apples: *Gentleman Jim* / Walking shoes: *Ray, Nelson.*
LP: . . . . **BB 2042**

VOL 35 - BOP THAT NEVER STOPPED
(Various artists).
Tracks: / Georgia Lee Brown: *Cochran, Jackie Lee* / Baby do: *Cochran, Jackie Lee* / I wanna see you: *Cochran*, Jackie Lee / Don't be long: *Cochran, Jackie Lee* / Pity me: *Cochran, Jackie Lee* / Cats were jumping: *Worthman*, John / Strange woman love too too many: *Worthman, John* / Evalina Malony: *Worthman, John* / Baby, I'll never let you go: *Love Brothers* / Flyin' saucers rock 'n' roll: *Love Brothers* / Baby, let's play house: *Love Brothers*/ I'm gonna get right down: *Love Brothers* / Baby, baby, baby: *Love Brothers.*
LP: . . . . **BB 2045**

VOL 36 - BOP THAT NEVER STOPPED
(Various artists).
Tracks: / Gee whiz Liz: *Jackson, Marvin* / Peek a boo: *Jackson, Marvin* / Pink shoes: *Matts, Merle* / Shake with me baby: *Matts, Merle* / Tennessee baby: *Matts, Merle* / Boot Hill rock'n'roll: *Rockinettes*/ Puppy dog love: *Branam, Ronnie* / Pink pedal pushers: *Viratones* / Rock rock rocket ship: *Rockers* / Diggety wiggety Wally: *Coates, Don* / Beau cheated: *Kirk, Larry* / Fragil heart: *Dean, Al* / Queen of rock: *Dean, Al* / Spinning my wheel: *Coates, Don.*
LP: . . . . **BB 2046**

VOL 37 - BOP THAT NEVER STOPPED
(Various artists).
Tracks: / Can't go dancin': *Bradley, Teray Ray* / Highway robbery: *Bradley, Teray Ray* / Live it up: *Moon*, Joe / She's gone: *Moon, Joe* / It's rough: *Brink, James* / I'm gonna tell on you: *Henry, John* / Ducks flying backwards: *Volk Brothers* / Rock house: *Jerome, Ralph* / Indian rock and roll: *Jerome, Ralph*/ Heartaches of love untrue: *Morris, Melvin* / Don't let love break your heart: *Rice, Eldon* / Go baby go: *Davis, Al* / Bermuda shorts: *Mitchell, Marlon* / Bubblegum boogie: *McBride, J..*
LP: . . . . **BB 2047**

VOL 38 - BOP THAT NEVER STOPPED
(Various artists).
Tracks: / That's what I call a ball: *Donn, Larry* / Honey bun: *Donn, Larry* / Brake Jake: *Fern, Mike*/ Head hunter: *Fern, Mike* / Restricted: *Haunchey, Donald* / Just because: *Elks, Jim* / Riding down the canyon: *Elks, Jim* / Left behind: *Stovall, Laverne* / Playtoy: *Cushman, Mike* / Me and my guitar: *Cushman*, Mike / I'm lonesome baby: *Philmon, Hiram* / Ronnie's night home: *Pearlecents* / Keen teen baby: *Martin, Leroy* / Chicken bop: *Force, Truit.*
LP: . . . . **BB 2048**

VOL 39 - BOP THAT NEVER STOPPED
(Various artists).
Tracks: / Willie was a bad boy: *Gentry, Ray* / Loverboy: *Dove, Ronnie* / Little drummer: *Rockets* / Emanons rock: *Emanons* / Come paddle footin' down: *Skyles, Johnny* / Never, never, never: *Moonlighters* / Brand new rock'n'roll: *Sanders, Curley* / Turned on the ice: *Baker, Bop* / That kind of carrying on: *Burden, Ray*/ Every time: *Darrow, Ken* / Do the fly: *Roving Gamblers* / Short stuff: *Jenkins, Gene* / Solid rock: *John, Jimmy* / Rains: *Edgar, Jim.*
LP: . . . . **BB 2051**

VOL 40 - BOP THAT NEVER STOPPED
(Various artists).
Tracks: / You tear me up: *Miller, Arlie* / I've heard: *Miller, Arlie* / Don't tease me: *Miller, Arlie*/ I got a girl: *Miller, Arlie* / Big black train: *Miller, Arlie* / Lou Ann: *Miller, Arlie* / Boppin' bug: *Neaville, Arlie* / Don't just stand there: *Neaville, Arlie* / Lucky day: *Neaville, Arlie* / Lovebug itch: *Neaville, Arlie* / Candy kisses: *Neaville, Arlie* / Twistin' Joe's: *Neaville, Arlie* / Mary Sue: *Neaville, Arlie* / Rockin' star: *Neaville, Arlie* / Sixteen tons: *Neaville, Arlie.*
LP: . . . . **BB 2052**

VOL 41 - BOP THAT NEVER STOPPED
(Various artists).
Tracks: / Mazie: *Phelps, Willie* / Nursery rhyme: *Phelps, Willie* / Don't stop baby: *Phelps, Willie*/ I'm leaving Lulabell: *Phelps, Willie* / Red headed Ruby: *Bevens, Earne* / Rock 'n' roll Anna: *Bevens, Earne*/ Devil or angel: *Montana, Tex* / Rock 'n' roll angel: *Chevalier, Jay* / Billy Cannon: *Chevalier, Jay*/ Blue baby boogie: *Simpson, Gene* / Shiver and shake: *Huften, Jim* / Brown eyed Beaulea: *Huften, Jim*/ Blast off: *Holloway, Alden* / Swinging the rock: *Holloway, Alden* / Loving is my business: *Holloway, Alden.*
LP: . . . . **BB 2053**

VOL 42 - BOP THAT NEVER STOPPED
(Various artists).
Tracks: / King of rock 'n' roll: *Bowman, Bob* / Let's paint the town red: *Sweatt, Al* / I hate myself: *Sweatt*, Al / Honey talk: *Hodges, Ralph* / Lazy Lu: *Nelson, Darwin* / Maggie: *Andy & The Live Wires* / You've done it again: *Andy & The Live Wires* / Hocus pocus: *Raiders* / Yoo hoo: *Raiders* / Black knee socks: *Palm, Tommy & The Rockers* / Linda Lee: *Dee, Johnny & The El Dorados* / Mary, Mary, Mary Jane: *Williams, Skeet*/ Go Jenny: *Martindale, Donnie* / How bad can bad luck be: *Miller, June.*
LP: . . . . **BB 2055**

VOL 43 - BOP THAT NEVER STOPPED
(Various artists).
Tracks: / Catalina push: *Catalinas* / Gotta get you off my mind: *Benson, Jackie* / Darn dem bones: *Hale*, Rex / Down at big mama's house: *Hale, Rex* / My rock and roll daddy: *Grimes, Jerry* / You're gonna reap what you sow: *Strong, Ray* / Witchapoo: *Cathey, Frank* / Susy Ann: *Taro, Frankie* / Pretty moon: *Winters*, Don / Be my baby, baby: *Winters, Don* / Alone and cryin': *Fortune, Johnny* / Crawdad song: *Jumper, Adron*/ Ghost train: *Swanks* / Run you down: *Ramirez, Joe.*
LP: . . . . **BB 2056**

VOL 44 - BOP THAT NEVER STOPPED
(Various artists).
Tracks: / Jo Jo rock'n'roll: *Martin, Bobby* / Back to school rock: *Martin, Bobby* / Dood it: *Martin, Bobby*/ Give your heart to me: *Martin, Bobby*/ Sleepy time blues: *Martin, Bobby* / Uh huh: *Bowman, Leroy* / Graveyard: *Bowman, Leroy* / She told a lie: *Mishoe, Watson* / Say mama: *Dean, Buddy* / My my: *Castain*, Jody / Jody's beat: *Castain, Jody* / Hep: *Manis, George* / School bus ride: *Sandy & The Uniques*/ Rock out of this world: *Norris, Joe.*
LP: . . . . **BB 2057**

VOL 45 - BOP THAT NEVER STOPPED
(Various artists).
Tracks: / Rock & roll fever: *B, Graham* / Treehouse: *Alexander, Bob* / You're wrong: *Garmon, Johnny*/ Willadean: *Louis, Jimmy* / Race track boogie: *Veluzat, Renaud* / Your excellency: *Veluzat, Renaud* / Don't wait: *Thomas, Dale* / Crocodile hop: *Thomas, Dale* / Rattlesnake: *Porter, Bruce* / Kaw-liga: *Porter*, Bruce / Misery: *Rockin' Sidney* / Pretty baby: *Pruitt, Lewis* / Don't be suprised: *Davis, Dean* / Down the road apiece: *Baker, Bob.*
LP: . . . . **BB 2058**

VOL 46 - BOP THAT NEVER STOPPED
(Various artists).
Tracks: / Be my baby: *Johnson, F. Dee* / But in a million years: *Ritchie, George* / My queen and me: *Lenny* & The Star Chiefs / Warpath: *Lenny & The Star Chiefs* / Too many girlfriends: *Bledsoe, Steve* / Little chick: *Wagoner, Lee* / Rockin' heart: *Wild childs* / Come on 'n' rock: *Sparkles* / Cute chick: *Odermatt, Titus* / When I'm gone: *Seals, Wayland* / Angel's rock: *Carnations* / Why oh why: *Titzie Brothers.*
LP: . . . . **BB 2059**

VOL 47 - BOP THAT NEVER STOPPED
(Various artists).
Tracks: / Rock on baby: *Sherrell, Bill* / Rock and roll teenager: *Sherrell, Bill* / Kool kat: *Sherrell, Bill*/ Yes, no or maybe: *Sherrell, Bill* / Don't you rock me daddy-o: *Sherrell, Bill* / Rockin' on the moon: *Deacon & The Rock & Rollers* / Wake me up: *Witcher, Norman* / What am I: *Williams, Brock* / Pretty Linda: *Owens*, Rudy & The Ravens / Mad at love: *Temptations* / I love you: *Temptations* / Cherokee stomp: *Tidwell, Bobby*/ Jo Jo rock'n'roll: *Greer, Amon.*
LP: . . . . **BB 2061**

VOL 48 - BOP THAT NEVER STOPPED
(Various artists).
Tracks: / That ain't nothing but right: *Castle, Joe* / Rock and roll daddy o: *Castle, Joe* / Somebody's been rocking my boat: *Witcher, Norman* / Flea circus: *Baxter, Bobo* / Sugar rock: *Day, Linden* / Craw fished: *Morris*, Gene / Look what you've done to me: *Blades, Emory* / Rock and roll carpenter: *Blades, Emory* / Crazy blue jeans: *Worthan, John* / So glad you're mine: *Hargett, Mackey* / What will the answer be: *Smith, Dayton*/ Teenage hop: *Slaughter, Lee* / Rock and roll world: *Slaughter, Lee* / Coal miner's blues: *Cole, Gene.*
LP: . . . . **BB 2062**

VOL 49 - BOP THAT NEVER STOPPED
(Various artists).
Tracks: / G.I. blues: *Knull, Ronnie* / Come along with me: *Parker, Malcom* / Gonna find some lovin': *Booth*, Charlie / Avalanche: *Don & The Galaxies* / Sundown: *Don & The Galaxies* / Don't go away: *Kent, Bobby*/ I don't wanna leave: *Deacon & The Rock & Rollers* / Parking lot: *McCrory, Jim* / School time: *McCrory, Jim*/ Pretty baby: *McCrory, Jim* / Rock and roll baby: *Billy & Mickey* / Wake up little boy blue: *Calloway, Bob*/ Wild man rock: *Watts, Hunter* / Big daddy rock: *Watts, Hunter* / St. James infirmary: *Sargent, Don.*
LP: . . . . **BB 2065**

VOL 50 - BOP THAT NEVER STOPPED
(Various artists).
Tracks: / Red headed woman: *Rebel Rousers* / Dark road: *Rebel Rousers* / Uh, mmm: *Billy & Mickey* / Two step: *Niswonger, Larry* / What did he say: *Terry & The Pirates* / Talk about the girl: *Terry & The Pirates*/ Fingertips: *Fisher, Brien* / Marianne: *Coachmen* / Let the black cat hop: *Sabres* / Little Miss Ivey: *Sabres* / Rock a baby: *Sabres* / Come over Rover: *Mooney, Glenn* / Big surf, The: *Mooney, Glenn.*
LP: . . . . **BB 2066**

VOL 51 - BOP THAT NEVER STOPPED
(Various artists).
Tracks: / We're gonna rock all night: *Gale, Jimmy* / Dandy Sandy: *Gale, Jimmy* / Thing called love, A: *Hardin*, Wesley / Anyway: *Hardin, Wesley* / Rockin' with Rosie: *Deane, Wally* / It should've been me: *Deane, Wally*/ Drag on: *Deane, Wally* / I'm tellin' ya baby: *Deane, Wally* / Kitten: *Voytek, Jimmy* / Sweetest gal in town: *Voytek, Jimmy* / I was a teenage cave man: *Luck, Randy* / I was doing it too: *Roxters* / My baby don't rock me: *Westberry, Kent* / No place to park: *Westberry, Kent.*
LP: . . . . **BB 2067**

VOL 52 - BOP THAT NEVER STOPPED
(Various artists).
Tracks: / Let's dance: *Gray, Bobby* / You're so nice: *Gray, Bobby* / She's mine: *Roxters* / So long: *Roxters* / No time for heartaches: *Spurlin, Tommy* / Hang loose: *Spurlin, Tommy* / Heart throb: *Spurlin*, Tommy / Blue's keep knockin', The: *Buck Trail* / Knocked out joint on Mars, The: *Buck Trail* / Reel kool cat: *Thomas, Dale* / Little bitty girl: *Bell, Bill* / Fearless: *Four Unknowns* / Get with it: *Austin, Donel* / Oh Pattie: *Kaye, Johnnie.*
LP: . . . . **BB 2068**

VOL 53 - BOP THAT NEVER STOPPED
(Various artists).
Tracks: / Ella Rea: *Leon & James* / Teenage blues: *Walton, Charles* / Four four time: *Walton, Charles*/ Teenage ball: *White, Buddy* / Tutti frutti: *Shaul, Lawrence* / Four o'clock baby: *Rhodes, Darrell* / Runnin' and chasin': *Rhodes, Darrell* / Can I be the one: *Rhodes, Darrell* / Lonesome old jail: *Blankenship* Brothers / Miami boogie: *Meyers, Berdine* / Whiplash: *Riki & The Rickatones* / Money, money, money: *Smith, T.N.T Don* / Rock moon rock: *James, Daniel.*
LP: . . . . **BB 2069**

VOL 54 - BOP THAT NEVER STOPPED
(Various artists).
Tracks: / Nervous wreck: *King, Jesse Lee* / Rock'n'roll rover: *King, Jesse Lee* / Old King Cole: *King, Jesse* Lee / Won't you be my baby: *Banes, Jerry* / Miss Mary: *Lee, Bobby* / Dancing Dan: *Jerry & The Capris*/ Sometimes: *Utah Carl* / Whiskey, women and wild women: *Pedigo, Tommy* / Red headed woman: *Pedigo, Tommy*/ Birds'n'bees: *Temptations* / Rang dang do: *Chieftones* / Hut hurp: *Patton, Jimmy* / Walking and talking: *Wainwright, Happy* / It goes without saying: *Kennington, Ken.*
LP: . . . . **BB 2070**

VOL 55 - BOP THAT NEVER STOPPED
(Various artists).
Tracks: / Hang out: *McCollough, Lloyd* / Do you love me: *McCollough, Lloyd* / He's a wild old man: *Little* Man Henry / Wailin' wildcat: *Little Man Henry* / Teen rock: *Teen Rockers* / Once a fool: *Raven, Eddy*/ Japanese rhumba: *Roberts, Wayne* / Martin boogie, The: *Frankie & Margie* / Jungle jive: *Puckett, Dennis*/ You're just that kind: *Jones, Little Montie* / My fragile heart: *Jeff & P.J.* / Twistin' with you: *Osborn, Dave* / Sandstorm: *Mic's Masters.*
LP: . . . . **BB 2071**

VOL 56 - BOP THAT NEVER STOPPED
(Various artists).
Tracks: / It makes no difference: *Mache, Billy* / Down at Big Mary's house: *Brown, Bobby (1)* / Mule skinner blues: *Jones, Rocky* / Little more lovin': *Comer, Chuck* / Please please baby: *Brown, Bobby (1)* / That's the way: *Clendening, Jimmy*/ *Keetie Kats* / Honey baby: *Miller, Buddy* / Frankie and Johnny: *Dean, Donnie* / Date on the corner: *Feger, Don* / Lucinder: *Derek, Tommy* / Nite beat: *Edwards, Slim* / Little Bo Pete: *Miller, Buddy* / Don't be mad: *Feger, Don.*
LP: . . . . **BB 2072**

VOL 57 - BOP THAT NEVER STOPPED
(Various artists).
Tracks: / Teenage party: *Bobbie & Bobbie* / Love just a little: *Carpenter Bros.* / I had a date: *Carpenter* Bros. / Don't cry little darling: *Carpenter Bros.* / Party line: *Senders* / Sugar booger: *Marcus Bros.*/ Caveman hop: *Coulston, Jerry* / Bon bon baby: *Coulston, Jerry* / Woman I love, The: *Terry, Gene* / Mixed up rhythm and blues: *Taylor, Johnny* / Nursery rock: *Allen, Ira* / Night club blues: *Conrad, Charlie*/ Suds: *Gale, J..*
LP: . . . . **BB 2073**

VOL 58 - BOP THAT NEVER STOPPED
(Various artists).
Tracks: / Red headed woman: *Worley, Wayne & Worley Birds* / Let's make it real: *Bryan, Dave* / I know why: *Clard*, Billy / Natalie: *Jones, Charles* / It's good to know: *Mann, Glenn* / Skip hop and wobble: *Artie & The* Mustangs / I'm a mean mean daddy: *Various artists* / Little Suzanne: *Jerry & The Del-Fi's* / Honky tonk stomp: *Payne, Hal* / Whoo oee: *Jones, Charles* / Sock bop: *Nighthawks* / I've got a baby: *Smedley, Jack*/ Nuthin' but a nuthin': *Stewart, Jimmy.*
LP: . . . . **BB 2074**

Bopcats

BLACK STOCKING ROCK.
Tracks: / Rockin' shoes / Mystery train / Big feet boogie / Let's rock / Shotgun boogie / I'm a big boy now / Brand new Cadillac / Cajun stomp / Tennesee girl / Jamso / Black stocking rock / Skippin' in.
LP: . . . . **MFLP 021**

BOP CATS, THE.
LP: . . . . **LAT 1113**

ROCK 'N' ROLL GRAFFITI.
Tracks: / Tennessee border / Rock it Pete / Bobpcat boogie / Night riding / M.T's boogie / Good rockin boogie / Doodle eye bop bop / Tore up / Doctor rock 'n' roll / Rockin daddy / Down on the line.
LP: . . . . **MFLP 001**

Bop'n'Roll Party

BOP'N'ROLL PARTY (See under Rock 'n' Roll) (Various artists).

Bopol

CA C'EST QUOI.
LP: . . . . CEL 6749

HELENA.
LP: . . . . SYLL 8310

SERREZ CEINTURE.
LP: . . . . CEL 8729

Boppin' Hillbilly

BOPPIN' HILLBILLY (See under Rockabilly) (Various artists).

Boppin' Rock'n'Roll

BOPPIN' ROCK'N'ROLL (See under Rock 'n' Roll) (Various artists).

Boppin' The Blues

BOPPIN' THE BLUES (See under Blues) (Various artists).

Borbetomagus & Friends

INDUSTRIAL STRENGTH.
LP: . . . . LR 113

Border Dance Band

BORDER COUNTRY DANCE BAND, THE (Border Country Dance Band).
Tracks: / Trip to Bavaria / Bill Sutherland / Caddam Woods / Kenmay house / Denis Murphy's / Athlone, The / Sherlock's / Davy's brae / Iain's hunting horn / 19th hole, The / Donald Ian Rankine / Dancing fingers / Braes of Breadalbane, The / Campbeltown kiltie ball / Capt. Home / Maguire / Rattigan / Jackie Coleman's reel / Mr. & Mrs. Mac Rogerson / Pig that shakes the piggery, The / Mr. & Mrs. T. M. Robertson / Bratch bana / Highland Donald / Black bear, The / Airlie Bobbies / Lassie come and dance with me / Hot potato / Morpeth rant / Miss K Rose / Miss C M Barfour / New high level / When you and I were round / Maggie dear / Castle, The.
LP: . . . . FE 007

BORDER DANCE BAND AT GRETNA HALL, THE.
LP: . . . . FE 020

Border (film)

BORDER, THE (Film Soundtrack) (Various artists).
LP: . . . . MCF 3133

Border Strathspey

RINGING STRINGS OF THE BORDER (Border Strathspey & Reel Society).
MC: . . . . SPRC 1010
LP: . . . . SPR 1010

Border Town Jive

BORDER TOWN JIVE (See under Rhythm & Blues) (Various artists).

Borders, Alan

ACROSS THE BORDER.
MC: . . . . ZCPREC 795

Boredoms

SOUL DISCHARGE.
LP: . . . . SHIMMY 035

Borge, Victor

AT HIS BEST.
Tracks: / Night and day / Happy birthday to you / Chopsticks / Hungarian rhapsody / Folk song / Russian opera / Borge on Bach, Beethoven and Handel.
2LP: . . . . COMP 5

BORGERING ON GENIUS.
Tracks: / Charmaine / Inflationary language / Blue Danube / Fascination / British Grenadiers, The / Anchors aweigh / Summertime / Tea for two / Cheek to cheek / I could have danced all night.
LP: 2354 029
MC: 3140 107

CAUGHT IN THE ACT.
Tracks: / Requests / Malaguena / Stardust / Nola / Trees / One fine day / Tales from the Vienna Woods / Third man, Theme from / Nocturne / Family background / Phonetic punctuation / Tea for two / Blue Danube.
LP: . . . . CBS 32502
MC: 40 32502

COMEDY IN MUSIC.
Tracks: / Happy birthday to you / Alexander's Ragtime Band / Medley of popular songs / Warsaw concerto.
LP: . . . . CBS 32372
MC: 40 32372

LIVE AT THE LONDON PALLADIUM.
Tracks: / Night and day / Happy birthday to you / Chopsticks / Hungarian rhapsody / Folk song, The / Russian opera, The.
LP: . . . . NSPL 18394

MY FAVOURITE THINGS (Excerpts).
Tracks: / Borge on Bach and Beethoven / Borge on Handel / Borge on Mozart and Offenbach / Borge on Rossini.
LP: . . . . NSPD 502

Borghesia

ESCORTS AND MODELS.
Tracks: / Am I? / In black / Naked lunch / Toxido / Rugged city / Naked, uniformed, dead / A.P.R. / Beat and scream / Forgot.
LP: . . . . BIAS 094

WE ARE EVERYWHERE.
LP: . . . . BIAS 058

Borgias (T.V.)

BORGIAS (Various artists).
LP: . . . . REP 428
MC: . . . . ZCH 428

Boris Gudunov

BORIS GUDUNOV (see under Prokofiev (composer)) (Various artists).

Borka & Other Stories

BORKA AND OTHER STORIES (Burningham, John).
MC: . . . . TS 329

Born Bad

BORN BAD VOL.3 (Various artists).
LP: . . . . BB 003

Born Free (bk)

BORN FREE (Joy Adamson) (McKenna, Virginia).
MCSET: . . . . LFP 7258

Born Free (film)

BORN FREE (Film Soundtrack) (Various artists).
Tracks: / Born free: *Monro, Matt* / Hunt: *Barry, John* / Elsa at play: *Barry, John* / Death of Pati: *Barry, John* / Waiting for joy: *Barry, John* / Killing at Kiunga: *Barry, John* / Born free: *Barry, John* / Holiday with Elsa: *Barry, John* / Flirtation: *Barry, John* / Warthog: *Barry, John* / Fight of the lioness: *Barry, John* / Reunion: *Barry, John* / Born free: *Barry, John.*
LP: 2315 031

Born On The Bayou

BORN ON THE BAYOU (See under Soul) (Various artists).

Born On The...(film)

BORN ON THE 4TH OF JULY (Film soundtrack) (Various artists).
Tracks: / Hard rain's gonna fall: *Brickell, Edie* / Brown eyed girl: *Morrison, Van* / My girl: *Temptations* / Venus: *Avalon, Frankie* / Prologue: *Various artists* / Shooting of Wilson, The: *Various artists* / Homecoming: *Various artists* / Born on the Bayou: *Broken Homes* / American pie: *McLean, Don* / Soldier boy: *Shirelles* / Moon river: *Mancini, Henry* / Early days, Massapequa, 1957, The: *Various artists* / Cua Viet River, Vietnam 1968: *Various artists* / Born on the fourth of July: *Various artists.*
LP: . . . . MCG 6079
MC: . . . . MCGC 6079
MC: . . . . MCAC 6340
LP: . . . . MCA 6340

Born to Dance (film)

BORN TO DANCE (1936 film soundtrack) (Various artists).
LP: . . . . CIF 3001

BORN TO DANCE (Film soundtrack) (Various artists).
LP: . . . . SH 2088

Borneo

ASIAN TRADITIONAL MUSIC VOL 6.
LP: . . . . PS 33506

Borobudur

BOROBUDUR (Various artists).
LP: . . . . LA DI DA 009

Borodin (composer)

PRINCE IGOR (Sofia Festival Orchestra).
LPS: 44878
MCSET: 4044878

SYMPHONY NO.2/PRINCE IGOR EXCERPTS (Mexican State Symphony Orchestra).
Tracks: / Symphony no.2 (Borodin) / Prince Igor overture / Polovtsian dances (Prince Igor).
MC: . . . . ZC QS 6018

Borofsky, Johnathan

RADICAL SONGBIRDS OF ISLAM (Borofsky, Johnathan & Ed Tomney).
MC: . . . . A 149

Borrelly, Jean Claude

PARIS COLLECTION VOL,4.
MC: . . . . MODEMC 1025

PARIS COLLECTION VOL.5.
MC: . . . . MODEMC 1026

Borroughs, William S.

DOCTOR IS ON THE MARKET, THE.
Tracks: / Twilight's last gleaming / Doctor is on the market / Green nun, The / From here to eternity / Meeting of international conference of technical... / Ah pook is here / Junkie / Towers open fire.
LP: . . . . IM 003

Borrowed Plumes

BORROWED PLUMES (see Milne, Roseleen) (Derby, Brown).

Borsalino (film)

BORSALINO (Film Soundtrack) (Various artists).
Tracks: / Generique: *Various artists* / La reussite: *Various artists* / Arts deco: *Various artists* / Tango Marseillais: *Various artists* / Les roses: *Various artists* / Escalade: *Various artists* / Theme Borsalino: *Various artists* / Les annees folles: *Various artists* / Prends moi matelot: *Various artists*/ Lola tango: *Various artists* / Exoticana: *Various artists* / La plangue: *Various artists* / Borsalino blues: *Various artists.*
LP: . . . . SPFL 263

Borsig, Alexander Von

ZUDEN ANDERSON GEROLT (see Hiroshima).

Boru, Brian

IN AN IRISH DANCING MOOD (Boru, Brian Ceili Band).
Tracks: / Jig / Pride of Erin / Irish Marches / Irish waltz / Hornpipe / Reel / Jigs / Military two step / Set dance / Slip jig / Irish barn dance / Marches / Victory waltz / Polka.
MC: . . . . 4 HOM 005

Bosbettes

MR. LEE.
Tracks: / Mr. Lee / Come-a come-a speedy / Look at the stars / Um bow bow / Dream, The / Rock and ree-ah-zole / Zoomy / Don't say goodnight / You are my sweetheart / I shot Mr. Lee / Untrue love / Billy / Dance with me Georgie / Have mercy baby.
LP: . . . . OFF 6055

Bosc Bub Eugen

REGEM IM PARK.
LP: . . . . ORG 086-5

Boscastle Breakdown

BOSCASTLE BREAKDOWN (Various artists).
LP: 12T 240

Bose, Miguel

MADE IN SPAIN.
Tracks: / Fuego / Sin ton ni son / La chula / Septiembra / Panama connection / Snack bar / Por un amor relampago / Te quiero amor / Los ojos del miedo / Twenty three horas al dia.
LP: . . . . S 25496
MC: 40 25496

SALAMANDRA.
Tracks: / Heaven / Up to the up / Living on the wire / You live in me / Amazonas / Over / Town of gold / Catch the season / Amapola besame.
LP: 242082 1
MC: 242082 4

XXX.
Tracks: / Big city / Eighth wonder / Lay down on me / Big fun / New tracks in the dust / Want you more / My perfect lover / Seems like it's midnight forever / Over my head / Hurt party, The.
LP: . . . . WX 153
MC: . . . . WX 153 C

Bosho

BOSHO.
LP: . . . . ST 7531

Boss Vocal Groups...

BOSS VOCAL GROUPS OF THE 60'S (See under Rhythm & Blues) (Various artists).

Bossa Nova

BEST OF BOSSA NOVA (Compact/ Walkman jazz) (Various artists).
Tracks: / Desafinado: *Getz, Stan & Joao Gilberto* / O Barquinho: *Wanderley, Walter* / Agua De Beber: *Jobim,* Antonio Carlos / Chega: *Getz, Stan/Gary McFarland Orchestra* / Tristeza: *Powell, Baden* / Baia: *Getz, Stan & Charlie Byrd.*
MC: 833 289-4

GIRLS FROM IPANEMA, THE (Best of Bossa Nova) (Various artists).
2LP: 841 396 1
MCSET: 841 396 4

Bostic, Earl

14 ORIGINAL GREATEST HITS:EARL BOSTIC.
LP: . . . . K 5010

16 SWEET TUNES OF THE 50'S.
LP: . . . . SLP 3022
MC: . . . . GT 53022

ALTO MAGIC IN HI-FI.
Tracks: / Twilight time / Stairway to the stars / Rockin' with Richard / Be my love / Pinkie / Goodnight sweetheart / Over the waves rock / Jer-on-imo / C jam blues / Wee-gee board / Wrecking rock, The / Home sweet home rock.
LP: . . . . SING 597

BEST OF BOSTIC.
Tracks: / Flamingo / Always / Deep purple / Smoke rings / What no pearls / Jungle drums / Serenade / I can't give you anything but love / Seven steps / I'm gettin' sentimental over you / Don't you do it / Steamwhistle jump.
LP: . . . . SING 500

BLOWS A FUSE.
Tracks: / Night train / 8.45 stomp / That's the groovy thing / Special delivery stomp / Moonglow / Mambostic / Earl blows a fuse / Harlem nocturne / Who snuck the wine in the gravy / Don't you do it / Disc jockey's nightmare / Flamingo / Steam whistle jump / What, no pearls / Tuxedo Junction.
LP: . . . . CRB 1091
MC: . . . . TCCRB 1091

BOSTIC FOR YOU.
Tracks: / Sleep / Moonglow / Velvet sunset / For you / Very thought of you, The / Linger awhile / Cherokee / Smoke gets in your eyes / Memories / Embraceable you / Wrap your troubles in dreams / Night and day.
LP: . . . . SING 503

BOSTIC ROCKS.
LP: . . . . ST 1022
LP: . . . . SC 1022

DANCE MUSIC FROM THE BOSTIC WORKSHOP.
Tracks: / Third man theme / Key, The / Does your heart beat for me / El choclo cha cha / Gondola / Sweet pea / Ducky / Sentimental journey / Barcarolle / Who cares / Rose Marie / Up there in orbit.
LP: . . . . SING 613

DANCE TIME.
Tracks: / Harlem nocturne / Where or when / Sweet Lorraine / Poems / You go to my head / Off shore / Moon is low, The / Ain't misbehavin' / Sheik of Araby, The / I hear a rhapsody / Roses of picardy / Melancholy serenade.
LP: . . . . SING 525

EARL BOSTIC.
LP: . . . . BID 8010

LET'S DANCE.
Tracks: / Lover come back to me / Merry widow waltz, The / Cracked ice / Song of the islands / Danube waves / Wrap it up / Blue skies / Ubangi stomp / Cherry bean / Earl's imagination / My heart at thy sweet voice / Lieberstraum.
LP: . . . . SING 529

SAX 'O' BOOGIE.
LP: . . . . OL 8007

THAT'S EARL BROTHER.
LP: . . . . SPJ 152

Boston

BOSTON.
Tracks: / More than a feeling / Peace of mind / Foreplay (long time) / Rock and roll band / Smokin' / Hitch a ride / Something about you / Let me take you home tonight.
MC: 40 32038
LP: . . . . EPC 32038
MC: 40 22155

DON'T LOOK BACK.
Tracks: / Journey / It's easy / Man I'll never be / Feeling satisfied / Part / Used to bad news / Don't be afraid.
LP: . . . . EPC 32048
MC: 40 32048
LP: . . . . EPC 86057

THIRD STAGE.
Tracks: / Amanda / We're ready / Launch, The / Cool the engines / My destination / New world, A / To be a man / I think I like it / Can'tcha say / Still in love / Hollyann.
LP: . . . . MCG 6017
MC: . . . . MCGC 6017

Boston, Lucy M.

CASTLE OF YEW, THE (see under Castle of Yew) (Goodland, David).

Boston Pops Orchestra

AISLE SEAT (See under Williams, John) (Boston Pops Orchestra/John Williams).

AMERICA, THE DREAM GOES ON.
Tracks: / American salute / America the beautiful / New York, New York / Lonely town / When the saints go marching in / Battle hymn of the Republic / This land is your land / America the dream goes on / Hoe down / Fanfare for the common man / America / Prayer of thanksgiving.
LP: 412 627 1

BACHARACH AND DAVID SONGBOOK.
Tracks: / Bond Street / Look of love, The / Promises, promises / Alfie / Wives and

lovers / What the world needs now is love / This guy's in love with you / Raindrops keep falling on my head / I'll never fall in love again / Make it easy on yourself / Do you know the way to San Jose.
LP: 2482 327

OUT OF THIS WORLD (see Williams,John) (Boston Pops Orchestra/ John Williams).

POPS IN SPACE.
Tracks: / Superman march / Superman love theme / Empire strikes back, The (excerpts) / Star Wars (Excerpts from.) / Close Encounters of the Third Kind suite.
LP: 9500921

POPS ON THE MARCH.
Tracks: / St.Louis blues / Coronation blues / 76 trombones / Orb and sceptre / Strike up the band / Pomp and circumstance No.4 / Midway march / Under the double eagle / South Rampart Street parade / Conquest.
LP: 6302 082

SATURDAY NIGHT FIEDLER.
Tracks: / Saturday night fever medley / Stayin' alive / Night fever / Manhattan skyline / Night on disco mountain / Disco inferno / Bachmania.
LP: 2310688

STOMPIN' AT THE SAVOY (See also Williams, John) (Boston Pops Orchestra/ John Williams).

TWO SOUNDS OF FIEDLER, THE.
Tracks: / Polonaise / Star wars / Send in the clowns / Jaws / Evergreen / Love will keep us together / Slavonic dance No. 7 / Wedding march / Pantomime / Aida ballet music.
LP: MOR 527

Boston Symphony

MER; FAUNE (See under Debussy (Composer)).

PANUFINIK : SINFONIA VOTIVA (SYMPHONY NO.8) Seiji Ozawa : conductor.
LP: LPA 66050
MC: KA 66050

Bostonians (film)

BOSTONIANS (1984 Film soundtrack) (Various artists).
Tracks: / River charles, The: *Various artists* / Bostonians, The: *Various artists* / Bostonians:opening titles(variations on America): *Various artists* / At Miss Birdseye's meeting: *Various artists* / Verena's education: *Various* artists / Annabelle Lee: *Various artists* / Faith healing: *Various artists* / Getting ready for Basil: *Various* artists / In Henry Burrage's rooms: *Various artists* / Verena's debut: *Various artists* / Wednesday club, The: *Various artists* / In Central park: *Various artists* / July 4th celebrations: *Various artists* / Summer days at Marmion: *Various artists* / By the sea: *Various artists* / Bostonians: End titles: *Various artists.*
LP: ATXLP 02
MC: ZCATX 02

Boswell, Connie

BING AND CONNIE BOSWELL (See under Crosby, Bing).

BOSWELL, CONNIE: ON THE AIR (Boswell, Connie & Boswell Sisters).
Tracks: / Object of my affection, The / Dinah / If love came wrapped in cellophane / Don't forget / I can't give you anything but love / When I'm with you / These foolish things / Until the real thing comes along / Silver threads among the gold / Manhattan / I hear a rhapsody / Amapola / Gay ranchero, A / Time was / Maria Elena.
LP: TOTEM 1025

IT'S THE GIRLS (see Boswell Sisters & Connie Boswell) (Boswell, Connie & Boswell Sisters).

ON THE AIR 1939.
Tracks: / Heaven can wait / Little skipper / And the Angels sing / Lullaby in rhythm / Wishing will make it so / Snug as a bug in a rug / Masquerade is over, The / Sing a song of sunbeams / Sunrise serenade / Lady's in love with you, The / Begin the beguine / Guess I'll go back home / Ain't cha comin' out.
LP: TOTEM 1043

SAND IN MY SHOES.
Tracks: / Top hat, white tie and tails / Cheek to cheek / I'm gonna sit right down and write me a letter / Music goes round and around, The / Let yourself go / I'm putting all my eggs in one basket / Between 18th and 19th on Chestnut Street / Yes indeed / Trust in me / Mama don't allow / Martha ah so pure / Fare thee, honey, fare thee well / Sand in my shoes / I hear a rhapsody / I let a song go out of my heart / That old feeling / Mr. Freddie blues / Sunrise serenade / Home on the range / Blueberry Hill.
LP: MCL 1689
MC: MCLC 1689

SINGING THE BLUES.
Tracks: / Singin' the blues / You need some lovin' / I'm gonna sit right down / Heebie jeebie blues / I gotta right to sing the blues / Right kind of man, The / Someday, sweetheart / Baby, won't you please come home / My little nest of heavenly blues / If I give my heart to you / How important can it be? / Begin the beguine / Believe it beloved / Fill my heart with happiness / I compare you / Main Street on Saturday night.
LP: OFF 12004

SWING ME A LULLABY.
Tracks: / Panic is on, The / I let a song go out of my heart / Is it love or infatuation? / Heart and soul / Loveliness of you, The / There's something about an old love / I'm glad for your sake (but I'm sorry for mine) / I hadn't anyone till you / Life is a song / If it rains, who cares? / On the beach at Bali-Bali / I can't give you anything but love, baby / I'm away from it all / Whispers in the dark / Outside of Paradise / Where are you? / Am I in love? / Chasing shadows / Blossoms on Broadway / Swing me a lullaby.
LP: CHD 159
MC: MCHD 159

Boswell, Eric

LEFT TO WRITE (Boswell, Eric & Various artists).
Tracks: / Golden voice of Bobby, The / Welcome to Geordieland / You'll never find a woman like me / North of the Tyne / Sweet waters of Tyne / Take me up the Tyne / I've got a little whippet / First footin' song / They don't write songs like these / Ballad of George Washington, The / Bird fly high / No one else for me / Wi me pit claes on / There's more to life than women and beer.
LP: MWM 1022

Boswell, Eve

EMI YEARS, THE: EVE BOSWELL (Best of Eve Boswell).
Tracks: / Sugarbush / Everything I have is yours / Little shoemaker, The / Hi lili hi lo / Bridge of sighs / Skokiaan / Young and foolish / Amor / Pickin' a chicken / Blue star / Romany violin / Tika tika tok / Here in my heart / If you love me (I don't care) / Bewitched / I believe.
LP: EMS 1330
MC: TCEMS 1330

SENTIMENTAL JOURNEY (Boswell, Eve with Reg Owen orchestra).
LP: CFRC 520
MC: MCFRC 520

Boswell Sisters

BOSWELL SISTERS, THE.
LPS: 59892

IT'S THE GIRLS (Boswell Sisters & Connie Boswell).
Tracks: / It's the girls / That's what I like about you / Heebie jeebies / Concentratin' on you / Wha'd ja do to me? / I'm all dressed up with a broken heart / When I take my sugar to tea / Don't tell him what happened to me / Roll on, Mississippi, roll on / I'm gonna cry (cryin' blues) / This is the missus / That's love / Life is just a bowl of cherries / My future just passed / What is it? / Shine on, harvest moon / Gee, but I'd like to make you happy / We're on the highway to Heaven / Time on my hands / Nights when I'm lonely / Shout, sister, shout! / It's you!.
LP: AJA 5014
MC: ZC AJA 5014

MUSIC GOES ROUND AND ROUND, THE.
LP: HDL 118
MC: CHDL 118

OKAY AMERICA!.
LP: JASS 1

ON THE AIR (see Boswell, Connie & Boswell Sisters) (Boswell Sisters & Connie Boswell).

THREE SYNCOPATIN' BOSWELL SISTERS.
Tracks: / I've lost you / Sharing / Poor little Cinderella Brown / If my friends find you they'll steal you from me / Abscence makes the heart grow fonder for someo / Livin' in the sunlight, Lovin' in the moonlight / Crazy people / Nothing is sweeter than you / Cheek to cheek / Top hat / I'm gonna sit right down and write myself a letter / Way back home / I'll never say "never again" again / Dinah.
LP: TOTEM 1042

YOU OUGHTA BE IN PICTURES.
Tracks: / Alexander's ragtime band (Recorded 23/5/35 (New York)) / You oughta be in pictures (Recorded 23/5/35 (New York)) / Doggone I've done it (Recorded 17/6/32 (New York)) / I hate myself (Recorded 23/3/34 (New York)) / Going home (Recorded 27/4/34 (New York)) / Louisiana hayride (Recorded 27/11/32 (New York)) / If I had a million dollars (Recorded 4/10/34 (Los Angeles)) / Object of my affection, The (Recorded 10/12/34 (Los Angeles)) / Old Yazoo (Recorded 29/6/32 (New York)) / Sentimental gentleman from Georgia (Recorded 13/9/32 (New York)) / It don't mean a thing (Recorded 22/11/32 (New York)) / Rock & roll (Recorded 4/10/34 (Los Angeles)) / Minnie the moocher's wedding day (Recorded 22/11/32 (New York)) / If it ain't love (Recorded 9/4/32 (New York)) / Lonesome road (Recorded 27/4/34(New York)) / There'll be some changes made (Recorded 21/3/32(New York)) / Stop the Sun, stop the Moon (Recorded 24/2/32(New York)) / Mood indigo (Recorded 9/1/33(New York)).
LP: CHD 136
MC: MCHD 136

Both Sides Of The

BOTH SIDES OF THE DOWNS (KENT & SUSSEX) (Various artists).
Tracks: / Lord Thomas and fair Ellen: *Various artists* / Sheep stealer, The: *Various artists* / William Bowmaneer: *Various artists* / Rigs o' Rye: *Various artists* / Fiddlers green: *Various artists.*
LP: ERON 002 LP
MC: ERON 002 CA

Botham, Ian

TAKE TIME TO CARE (See Buck, Bobby) (Botham, Ian/Bobby Buck).

Bothen, Christer

MOTHER EARTH (Bothen, Christer & Bolon Bata).
LP: DRLP 160

Bothy Band

AFTERHOURS.
Tracks: / Kesh jig / Butterfly / Casadh an tsugain / Farewell to Erin / Heathery hills of Yarrow / Queen Jane / Pipe on the hob / Mary Willies / How can I live at the top of a mountain / Rosie Finn's favourite / Green groves of Erin, The.
LP: 2383530
MC: 3170530

BEST OF THE BOTHY BAND.
Tracks: / Salamanca, The / Banshee / Sailor's bonnet, The / Petty peg / Craig's pipes / Blackbird, The / Maids of Mitchelstown, The / Casadh ant sugain / Music in the glen / Fionnghuala / Old hag you have killed me / Do you love an apple / Rip the calico / Death of Queen Jane, The / Green groves of Erin, The / Flowers of Red Hill, The.
LP: LUN 041
MC: CLUN 41
LP: 2383 583

BOTHY BAND.
Tracks: / Kesh jig / Give us a drink of water / Flowers of the flock / Famous Ballymote / Green groves of Erin, The / Flowers of Red Hill, The / Do you love an apple / Julia Delaney / Patsy Geary's / Coleman's cross / Is trua nack bhfuil me in Eirinn / Navvy on the line / Rainy day, The / Tar road to Sligo, The / Paddy Clancy's jig / Martin Wynn's / Lonford tinker, The / Pretty peg / Craigs pipes / Hector the hero / Laird of Drumblair, The / Traveller, The / Humors of Lissade, The / Butterfly / Salamanca, The / Banshee / Sailor's bonnet, The.
LP: 2383 379

BOTHY BAND 1975.
MC: CLUN 002

FIRST ALBUM.
LP: SIF 3011

OLD HAG YOU HAVE KILLED ME.
MC: CLUN 007

OUT OF THE WIND INTO THE SUN.
LP: SIF 3013

Bothy Greats

BOTHY GREATS (Various artists).
LP: SPR 1014
MC: SPRC 1014

Bottcher, Gerd

DEINE ROTEN LIPPEN.
Tracks: / Writing on the wall / Poetry in motion / Jambalaya / Just a closer walk with thee / Cielito lindo / Surrender / Now or never / Johnny will / She's not you / Tonight's so right for love / Goodbye / Loddy Lo / Tower of strength.
LP: BFX 15053

Botticelli Orchestra

TIE A YELLOW RIBBON.
Tracks: / Tie a yellow ribbon / My love / Killing me softly with her song / It never rains in Southern California / Day by day / Mammy blue / Song sung blue / You're so vain / Never never never / Looking through the eyes of love.
LP: DGS 15

Bottler

BOTTLER RIDES AGAIN.
MC: BOCAS 1316

YOUSE ALL LOOKIN' AT ME.
MC: BOCAS 1314

Boucher, Judy

CAN'T BE WITH YOU TONIGHT.
LP: OLP 024

Boudet, Michele

MULTIFACES.
Tracks: / Emotion / Monsieur Baselli / Ca marche / Chatoyante / Le marin a casquette / En Java / Multifaces / 1st of Mai / Caresse Andalouse / Bric-a-brac / Super favourite / Cristaline, Cristaline.
LP: 742029
MC: UNKNOWN

Bouffard, Patrick

MUSIC FOR HURDY GURDY FROM AUVERGNE.
MC: 4560007

Boughton (Composer)

RUTLAND BOUGHTON: SYMPHONY NO.3 B MINOR (Royal Philharmonic Orchestra).
MC: KA 66343

Boukman Experyans

VODOU ADJAE.
MC: MCT 1072
LP: MLPS 1072

Boulaye, Patti

PATTI BOULAYE.
Tracks: / Stop it I like it / I'm not going to put my shirt on you / I should have told him yesterday / Any time anywhere / Kiss and make up time / I'm hooked on you / Red alert / Without my man inside / Funky love / People some people choose to love / Don't get hooked on me.
LP: KY 102

YOU STEPPED INTO MY LIFE.
Tracks: / Every time you touch me / You stepped into my life.
LP: POLS 1009

Boulevard Of Broken

IT'S THE TALK OF THE TOWN.
LP: HNBL 1345
MC: HNBC 1345

Boulle, Pierre (aut)

BRIDGE ON THE RIVER KWAI (see under Bridge on the River Kwai) (Hardy, Robert (nar)).

Boulton, Andy

AIN'T MISBEHAVIN' (Boulton, Andy/ Tokyo Blade).
Tracks: / Heartbreaker / Too much too soon / Watch your step / Movie star / Hot for love / Tokyo city / Love and hate / Don't walk away / Ain't misbehavin'.
LP: 805336

Bouncing In The Red

BOUNCING IN THE RED (Various artists).
Tracks: / Biko's kindred lament: *Various artists* / Forty million: *Various artists* / Let go: *Various artists*/ Clinically dead: *Various artists* / Small wonder: *Various artists* / 25%: *Various artists* / Sunny day: *Various artists* / Rio: *Various artists* / Wait a minute baby: *Various artists* / Cruising: *Various artists* / I don't want to die young: *Various artists* / In the night: *Various artists.*
LP: EMC 3343

Bounty Hunters

THREADS A TEAR.
LP: CRELP 51

Bounty Killer (film)

BOUNTY KILLER, THE (Film Soundtrack) (Various artists).
LP: PHCAM 011

Bourbon Street Boogie

BOURBON STREET BOOGIE (Various artists).
LP: BLP 116

Bourbonese Qualk

BOURBONESE QUALK.
LP: NIR 871

HOPE.
LP: LOOSE 7

LAUGHING AFTERNOON.
LP: LOOSE 4

MY GOVERNMENT.
LP: EFA 04534

PREPARING FOR POWER.
LP: LOOSE 010

SPIKE, THE.
LP: ST 7504

Bourelly, Jean-Paul

JUNGLE COWBOY.
Tracks: / Love line / Tryin' to get over / Drifter / Hope you find your way / Jungle cowboy / No time to share / Can't get enough / Parade / Mother Earth / Groove with me.
LP: 8344091

Bourgeois Tagg

YOYO.
Tracks: / Best of all possible worlds, The / Cry like a baby / Pencil and paper / Out of my mind / 15 minutes in the sun / Waiting for the world to turn / I don't mind at all / What's wrong with this picture / Stress / Coma.
LP: . . . . ILPS 9890
MC: . . . . ICT 9890

YOYO (IMPORT).
LP: 906381

Bourne, Nigel

PAGAN EASTER (See Bate, Seldiy) (Bourne, Nigel/Seldiy Bate).

Bourvil

C'ETAIT BIEN.
2LP: 2C 178 14997/9

Boustedt, Christer

PLAYS THELONIOUS MONK.
Tracks: / Trinkle tinkle / Pannonica / Straight, no chaser / Reflections / Gallop's gallop / Ruby my dear / Well you needn't.
LP: . . . . DRLP 38

Boutte, Lillian

BIRTHDAY PARTY (Boutte, Lillian & Her Music Friends).
LP: . . . . ML 123

FINE ROMANCE, A (Boutte, Lillian & Thomas l'Etienne).
LP: . . . . GHB 206

I SING BECAUSE I'M HAPPY.
LP: . . . . JC 11003

LET THEM TALK (Boutte, Lillian & Thomas l'Etienne).
Tracks: / Tennessee waltz / Let them talk / I still get jealous / He's funny that way / Bugle call rag / Love / I surrender dear / Who rolled the stone away / Nobody knows the trouble I've seen / Traveller's tune.
LP: . . . . SLP 439

LILLIAN BOUTTE WITH HUMPHREY LYTTLETON AND BAND (Boutte, Lillian/Humphrey Lyttelton & His Band).
Tracks: / Back in your own back yard / Miss Otis regrets / Squiggles / I double dare you / Lillian.
LP: . . . . CLGLP 018
MC: . . . . ZCLG 018

MUSIC IS MY LIFE (Boutte, Lillian & Her Music Friends).
LP: . . . . JC 11002

Bouw Kool

MERRY CHRISTMAS (see under Funk Masters).

Bouzouki At The Bridge

BOUZOUKI AT THE BRIDGE (Various artists).
MC: 00681

Bovell, Dennis

AUDIO ACTIVE.
LP: . . . . MTLP 008
MC: . . . . MTLP 008C

BRAIN DAMAGE.
Tracks: / Brain damage / Bettah / After tonight / Our tune / Run away / Heaven / Bah-be-lon / Bertie / Aqua dub / Frea stoil / Smouche / El Passoah / Chief inspector / Eying / Dutty / Cabbage.
LP: 6627001

I WAH DUB.
Tracks: / Electrocharge / Steadie / Jazzz / Reflections / Blaubart / Oohkno / Nough / Binoculars.
LP: . . . . RDC 2002

Bow Wow Wow

BEST OF BOW WOW WOW, THE.
LP: . . . . RRLP 116

I WANT CANDY.
Tracks: / I want candy / Cowboy / Louis Quatorze / Mile high club / W.O.R.K. (nah no no my daddy don't) / Fools rush in / I want my baby on Mars / Gold he said / Sexy Eiffel towers / Radio G-string / C30, C60, C90 go / Sun, sea and privacy / Uomo sea al apache / Giant sized baby thing / C30, C60, C90 go.
LP: . . . . PG 25436
MC: . . . . PK 25463
LP: . . . . EMC 3416
LP: . . . . PIPLP 021
MC: . . . . PIPMC 021

SEE JUNGLE, SEE JUNGLE,.
Tracks: / Jungle boy / Chihuahua / Sinner sinner sinner / Mickey put it down / I'm a TV savage / Elimination dancing / Golly golly / Go buddy / King Kong / Go wild in the country / I am not a know it all / Why are babies so wise? / Orang-utan / Hello hello daddy.
LP: . . . . RCALP 3000
MC: . . . . RCAK 3000
LP: . . . . PIPLP 013
MC: . . . . PIPMC 013

WHEN THE GOING GETS TOUGH, THE TOUGH GET GOING.
Tracks: / Aphrodisiac / Do you wanna hold me / Roustabout / Lonesome tonight / Love me / What's the time / Mario (your own way to paradise) / (Arrows in my) quiver / Man mountain, The / Rikki Dee / Tommy Tucker / Love, peace and harmony.
LP: . . . . RCALP 6068
MC: . . . . RCAK 6068
LP: . . . . PIPLP 022
MC: . . . . PIPMC 022

Bowater, Chris

DO SOMETHING NEW LORD.
LP: . . . . SOP R 2009
MC: . . . . SOP C 2009

HIGHEST HONOUR, THE.
LP: . . . . SOP R 2030
MC: . . . . SOP C 2030

PROCLAIMING JESUS.
LP: . . . . SOP R 2014
MC: . . . . SOP C 2014

Bowden, John

MOTTY DOWN, A (see Shepherd, Vic & John Bowden) (Bowden, John & Vic Shepherd).

Bowen, Geraint

JESUS COLLEGE CHOIR, CAMBRIDGE (see under Jesus College) (Bowen, Geraint/JesusCollege choirCambridge/ChristopherArgent).

Bowen, Jimmy

JIMMY BOWEN.
LP: . . . . R 25004

Bowens, Bobby

GOTTA KEEP REACHING FOR THE TOP (Bowens, Bobby & The Shades Of Magic).
LP: . . . . MVLP 16

Bowers, Bryan

BY HEART.
LP: . . . . FF 313

VIEW FROM HOME, THE.
LP: . . . . FF 037

Bowie, David

1966: DAVID BOWIE.
Tracks: / I'm not losing sleep / I dig everything / Can't help thinking about me / Do anything you say / Good morning girl / And I say to myself.
MLP: . . . . PYL 6001
MC: . . . . PYM 6001
LPPD: . . . . PYX 6001
MLP: . . . . CLALP 154
MC: . . . . CLAMC 154

ALADDIN SANE.
Tracks: / Watch that man / Aladdin Sane / Drive in Saturday / Panic in Detroit / Cracked actor / Time / Prettiest star, The / Let's spend the night together / Jean Genie, The.
LP: . . . . NL 83890
MC: . . . . NK 83890
LPPD: . . . . BOPIC 1
LP: . . . . RS 1001
LP: . . . . INTS 5067
MC: . . . . PK 2134
LP: . . . . EMC 3579
LP: 794 768 1
MC: . . . . TCEMC 3579
MC: 794 768 4

ANOTHER FACE.
Tracks: / Rubber band / London boys / Gospel according to Tony Day, The / There is a happy land / Maid of Bond Street / When I live my dream / Liza Jane / Laughing gnome, The / In the heat of the morning / Did you ever have a dream / Please Mr. Gravedigger / Join the gang / Love you till Tuesday / Louie Louie go home.
LP: . . . . TAB 17
MC: . . . . KTAB 17
MC: . . . . TBC 17

BEST OF BOWIE.
LP: . . . . NE 1111

CHANGESBOWIE.
Tracks: / Space oddity / John, I'm only dancing / Changes / Ziggy Stardust / Suffragette City / Jean Genie, The / Diamond dogs / Rebel rebel / Young Americans / Fame 90 (remix) / Golden years / Heroes / Ashes to ashes / Fashion / Let's dance / China girl / Modern love / Blue Jean / Starman (CD only.) / Life on mars (CD only.) / Sound and vision (CD only.).
2LP: . . . . DBTV 1
MC: . . . . TCDBTV 1

CHANGESONEBOWIE.
Tracks: / Space oddity / John, I'm only dancing / Changes / Ziggy Stardust / Suffragette city / Jean Genie, The / Diamond dogs / Rebel rebel / Young Americans / Fame / Golden years.
LP: . . . . PL 81732
MC: . . . . PK 81732
LP: . . . . RS 1055
MC: . . . . PK 11727

CHANGESTWOBOWIE.
Tracks: / Aladdin Sane / Oh you pretty things / Starman / 1984 / Ashes to ashes / Sound and vision / Fashion / Wild is the wind / John, I'm only dancing again / D.J..
LP: . . . . PL 84082
MC: . . . . PK 84082
LP: . . . . BOW LP 3

CHRISTIANE F.WIR KINDER VOM BAHNOF ZOO.
Tracks: / V-2 Schneider / TVC-15 / Heroes / Helden / Boys keep swinging / Sense of double / Station to station / Look back in anger / Stay / Warszawa.
LP: . . . . RCALP 3074
MC: . . . . RCAK 3074

COLLECTION: DAVID BOWIE.
Tracks: / Laughing gnome, The / Rubber band / Love you till Tuesday / Maid of Bond Street / Sell me a coat / In the heat of the morning / Maka man / Please Mr. Gravedigger / London boys / She's got medals / Silly boy blue / Join the gang / Did you ever have a dream / Gospel according to Tony Day, The / I'm not losing sleep / I dig everything / Can't help thinking about me / Do anything you say / Good morning girl / And I say to myself.
2LP: . . . . CCSLP 118
MC: . . . . CCSMC 118

DAVID BOWIE.
Tracks: / Uncle Arthur / Sell me a coat / Rubber band / Love you till Tuesday / There is a happy land / We are hungry men / When I live my dream / Little bombardier / Silly boy blue / Come and buy my toys / Join the gang / She's got medals / Maid of Bond street / Please Mr. Gravedigger.
LP: . . . . DOA 1

DAVID BOWIE: INTERVIEW PICTURE DISC.
LPPD: . . . . BAK 2165

DAVID LIVE.
2LP: 26 28107

DAVID LIVE (At Tower Theatre Philadelphia).
Tracks: / 1984 / Rebel rebel / Moonage daydream / Sweet thing / Changes / Suffragette city / Aladdin Sane / All the young dudes / Cracked actor / Rock 'n' roll with me / Watch that man / Knock on wood / Diamond dogs / Big brother / Width of a circle, The / Jean Genie, The / Rock 'n' roll suicide / Band introduction (EMI release only.) / Here today, gone tomorrow (EMI release only.) / Time (EMI release only.).
2LP: . . . . PL 80771
MC: . . . . PK 80771
2LP: APL2 0771
MC: . . . . DPTK 5013
2LP: . . . . DBLD 1
MCSET: . . . . TCDBLD 1

DIAMOND DOGS.
Tracks: / Future legend / Diamond dogs / Sweet thing / Candidate / Rebel rebel / Rock 'n' with me / We are the dead / 1984 / Big brother / Chant of the ever circling skeletal family / Dodo (EMI release only.) / Candidate (EMI release only.).
LP: . . . . NL 83889
MC: . . . . NK 83889
LPPD: . . . . BOPIC 5
LP: APL1 0576
LP: . . . . INTS 5068
MC: APK1 0576
LP: . . . . EMC 3584
MC: . . . . TCEMC 3584

DON'T BE FOOLED BY THE NAME.
Tracks: / I'm not losing sleep / Dig everything / Can't help thinking about me / I do anything you say / Good morning girl / And I say to myself.
LP: . . . . DOW 1
MC: . . . . ZCDOW 1

EARLY YEARS.
Tracks: / Watch that man / Aladdin Sane / Drive-in Saturday / Panic in Detroit / Cracked actor / Time / Prettiest star, The / Let's spend the night together / Jean Genie, The / Lady grinning soul / Width of a circle, The / All the madmen / Black country rock / After all / Running gun blues / Saviour machine / She shook me cold / Man who sold the world, The / Supermen, The / Changes / Oh you pretty things / Eight line poem / Life on Mars / Kooks / Quicksand / Fill your heart / Andy Warhol / Song for Bob Dylan / Queen bitch / Bewlay Brothers, The.
LPS: . . . . NL 89494
MC: . . . . NK 89494

FASHION (IMPORT).
LP: . . . . PC 09638

GOLDEN YEARS.
Tracks: / Fashion / Red sails / Look back in anger / I can't explain / Ashes to ashes / Golden Years / Joe the lion / Scary monsters (and super creeps) / Wild is the wind.
LP: . . . . BOWLP 004
MC: . . . . BOWK 004

HEROES.
Tracks: / Beauty and the beast / Joe the lion / Sons of the silent age / Blackout / V-2 Schneider / Sense of doubt / Moss garden / Neukoln / Secret life of Arabia, The / Heroes / Abdulmajid (Only on EMI re-issues) / Joe the lion (1991 remix) (Only on EMI re-issues).
LP: . . . . NL 13857
LP: . . . . PC 09281
LP: . . . . NL 83857
MC: . . . . NK 83857
LP: . . . . PL 12522
LP: . . . . INTS 5066
MC: . . . . PK 12522
LP: . . . . EMD 1025
MC: . . . . TCEMD 1025

HUNKY DORY.
Tracks: / Changes / Oh you pretty things / Eight line poem / Life on Mars / Kooks / Quicksand / Fill your heart / Andy Warhol / Song for Bob Dylan / Queen bitch / Bewlay Brothers, The.
LP: . . . . NL 83844
MC: . . . . NK 83844
LPPD: . . . . BOPIC 2
LP: . . . . SF 8244
LP: . . . . INTS 5064
MC: . . . . PK 1850

HUNKY DORY (2).
Tracks: / Changes / Oh you pretty things / Eight line poem / Life on mars / Kooks / Quicksand / Fill your heart / Andy Warhol / Song for Bob Dylan / Queen bitch / Bewlay Brothers, The / Bombers / Supermen (alt. version) / Quicksand (demo version) / Bewlay Brothers, The (Alt. mix).
LP: . . . . EMC 3572
MC: . . . . TCEMC 3572

IMAGES: DAVID BOWIE.
Tracks: / Rubber band / Maid of Bond Street / Sell me a coat / Love you till Tuesday / There is a happy land / Laughing gnome, The / Gospel according to Tony Day, The / Did you ever have a dream / Uncle Arthur / We are hungry men / When I live my dream / Join the gang / Little bombardier / Come and buy my toys / Silly boy blue / She's got medals / Please Mr. Gravedigger / London boys / Karma man / Let me sleep beside you / In the heat of the morning.
2LP: . . . . DPA 3017/8

INTROSPECTIVE: DAVID BOWIE.
LP: . . . . LINT 5001
MC: . . . . MINT 5001

LABYRINTH (see under Films).

LET'S DANCE.
Tracks: / Modern love / China girl / Let's dance / Without you / Ricochet / Criminal world / Cat people (putting out fire) / Shake it.
LP: . . . . AML 3029
MC: . . . . TCAML 3029
LPPD: . . . . AMLP 3029

LODGER.
Tracks: / Fantastic voyage / African night flight / Move on / Yassassin / Red sails / D.J. / Look back in anger / Boys keep swinging / Repitition / Red money / I pray ole (On EMI reissues only.) / Look back in anger (1988 version) (On EMI reissues only.).
LP: . . . . NL 84234
MC: . . . . NK 84234
LP: . . . . BOW LP 1
LP: . . . . INTS 5212
LP: . . . . EMD 1026
MC: . . . . TCEMD 1026

LONDON BOYS (See under London Boys for details) (Bowie, David/Small Faces/Byrds/Dobie Gray).

LOVE YOU TILL TUESDAY.
Tracks: / Love you till Tuesday / London boys / Ching-a-ling / Laughing gnome, The / Liza Jane / When I'm five / Space oddity / Sell me a coat / Rubber band / Let me sleep beside you / When I live my dream.
LP: . . . . BOWIE 1
MC: . . . . BOWMC 1
MC: 8200834

LOW.
Tracks: / Speed of life / Breaking glass / What in the world / Sound and vision /

Always crashing in the same car / Be my wife / New career in a new town, A / Warszawa / Art decade / Weeping wall / Subterraneans / Some are (On EMI reissues only.) / All saints (On EMI reissues only.) / Sound and vision (1991 remix) (On EMI reissues only.).
LP: NL 83856
MC: NK 83856
LP: PL 12030
LP: INTS 5065
MC: PK 12030
LP: EMD 1027
MC: TCEMD 1027

MAN WHO SOLD THE WORLD.
Tracks: / Width of a circle, The / All the madmen / Black country rock / After all / Running gun blues / Saviour machine / She shook me cold / Man who sold the world, The / Supermen, The.
LP: 26 21100
MC: Unknown
LP: LSP 4816
LP: INTS 5237
MC: PK 2103

MAN WHO SOLD THE WORLD (2).
Tracks: / Width of a circle, The / All the madmen / Black country rock / After all / Running gun blues / Saviour machine / She shook me cold / Man who sold the world, The / Supermen, The / Lightning frightening ((Previously unreleased outtake)) / Holy holy ((Original 1971 single version)) / Moonage daydream / Hang onto yourself.
LP: EMC 3573
MC: TCEMC 3573

MUSIC AND MEDIA INTERVIEW PICTURE DISC.
LPPD: DB 1010

NEVER LET ME DOWN.
Tracks: / New York's in love / Too dizzy / Bang bang / Day in, day out / Time will crawl / Beat of your drum / Never let me down / Zeroes / Glass spider / Shining star (making my love) / Time will crawl (Extended dance mix.) / 87 and cry / Never let me down (7" version) / Time will crawl (ext. dance mix) / Day in, day out (Groucho mix).
LP: AMLS 3117
MC: TCAMLS 3117

PEACE ON EARTH (see Crosby, Bing) (Bowie, David/Bing Crosby).

PIN UPS.
Tracks: / Rosalyn / Here comes the night / I wish you would / See Emily play / Everything's alright / I can't explain / Friday on my mind / Sorrow / Don't bring me down / Shapes of things / Anyway anyhow anywhere / Where have all the good times gone / Growin' up (EMI releases only.) / Amsterdam (EMI releases only.).
LP: RCALP 3004
LPPD: BOPIC 4
MC: RCAK 3004
LP: RS 1003
LP: INTS 5236
MC: PK 11669
LP: EMC 3580
MC: TCEMS 3580

PORTRAIT OF A STAR.
LPS: PL 89078
LPS: PL 37700

RARE.
LP: PL 45406

RARE TRACKS.
Tracks: / I'm not sleeping / I dig everything / Can't help thinking about me / Do anything you say / Good morning girl / And I say to myself.
LP: SHLP 137
MC: SHTC 137

RISE AND FALL OF ZIGGY STARDUST AND THE SPIDERS FROM MARS.
Tracks: / Five years / Soul love / Moonage daydream / Starman / It ain't easy / Lady Stardust / Star / Hang onto yourself / Ziggy Stardust / Suffragette city / Rock 'n' roll suicide.
LP: NL 83843
MC: NK 83843
LPPD: BOPIC 3
LP: SF 8287
LP: INTS 5063
MC: PK 1932

RISE AND FALL OF ZIGGY STARDUST AND THE SPIDERS FROM MARS.
Tracks: / Five years / Soul love / Moonage daydream / Starman / It ain't easy / Lady Stardust / Star / Hang onto yourself / Ziggy Stardust / Suffragette city / Rock 'n roll suicide / John, I'm only dancing / Velvet goldmine / Sweet head / Ziggy Stardust (demo).
LP: EMC 3577
MC: TCEMC 3577

ROCK GALAXY.
Tracks: / Changes / Oh, you pretty things / Eight line poem / Life on Mars? / Kooks / Quicksand / Fill your heart / Andy Warhol / Song for Bob Dylan / Queen bitch / Bewlay brothers, The / Five years / Soul love / Moonage dream / Starman / It ain't easy / Lady Stardust / Star / Hang onto yourself / Ziggy stardust / Suffragette city / Rock 'n' roll suicide.
2LP: NL 43593
MCSET: TC NL 43593

SCARY MONSTERS.
Tracks: / It's no game / Up the hills backwards / Scary monsters and super creeps / Ashes to ashes / Fashion / Teenage wildlife / Scream like a baby / Kingdom come / Because you're young / It's no game (no.2).
LP: PL 83647
MC: PK 83647
LP: BOW LP 2

SECOND FACE.
Tracks: / Let me sleep beside you / Sell me a coat / She's got medals / We are hungry men / In the heat of the morning / Karma man / Little bombardier / Love you till Tuesday / Come and buy my toys / Silly boy blue / Uncle Arthur / When I live my dream.
LP: TAB 71

SPACE ODDITY.
Tracks: / Space oddity / Unwashed and somewhat slightly dazed / Letter to Hermione / Cygnet committee / Janine / Wild eyed boy from Freecloud, The / God knows I'm good / Memory of a free festival / Occasional dream, An.
LP: PL 84813
MC: PK 84813
LP: LSP 4813
MC: PK 2101

SPACE ODDITY (2).
Tracks: / Space oddity / Unwashed and somewhat slightly dazed / Don't sit down / Letter to Hermione / Cygnet committee / Janine / Occasional dream, An / Wild eyed boy from freecloud / God knows I'm good / Memory of a free festival / Conversation piece / Memory of a free festival part I / Memory of a free festival part II.
LP: EMC 3571
MC: TCEMC 3571

STAGE.
Tracks: / Hang onto yourself / Ziggy Stardust / Five years / Soul love / Star / Station to station / Fame / TVC 15 / Warszawa / Speed of life / Art decade / Sense of doubt / Breaking glass / Heroes / What in the world / Blackout / Beauty and the beast.
2LP: PL 02913
MCSET: PK 02913
2LP: PL 89002

STATION TO STATION.
Tracks: / Station to station / Golden years / Word on a wing / TVC-15 / Stay / Wild is the wind / Word on a wing (live) (EMI release only.) / Stay (live) (EMI release only.).
LP: PL 81327
MC: PK 81327
LP: APL1 1327
MC: PK 11678
LP: EMD 1020
MC: TCEMD 1020

TONIGHT.
Tracks: / Loving the alien / Don't look down / God only knows / Tonight / Neighbourhood threat / Blue Jean / Tumble and twirl / I keep forgettin' / Dancing with the big boys.
LP: EL 2402271
MC: EL 2402274
LP: DB 1
MC: TCDB 1

UNDER PRESSURE (see under Queen & David Bowie) (Bowie, David & Queen).

WORLD OF DAVID BOWIE, THE.
Tracks: / Uncle Arthur / Love you till Tuesday / There is a happy land / Little bombardier / Sell me a coat / Silly boy blue / London boys / Karma man / Rubber band / Let me sleep beside you / Come and buy my toys / She's got medals / In the heat of the morning / When i live my dream.
LP: SPA 58
MC: KCSP 58

YOUNG AMERICANS.
Tracks: / Young Americans / Win / Fascination / Right / Somebody up there likes me / Across the universe / Can you hear me / Fame / Who can I be now? (EMI release only) / It's gonna be me (EMI release only) / John I'm only dancing again (EMI release only).
LP: PL 80998
MC: PK 80998
LP: RS 1006
MC: PK 11677
LP: EMD 1021
MC: TCEMD 1021

ZIGGY STARDUST THE MOTION PICTURE (Original soundtrack).
Tracks: / Watch that man / Moonage daydream / Suffragette city / Changes / Time / All the young dudes / Space oddity / White light, white heat / My death / Wild eyed boy from Freecloud, The / Oh you pretty things / Hang onto yourself / Ziggy Stardust / Cracked actor / Width of a circle, The / Let's spend the night together / Rock 'n' roll suicide.
2LP: PL 84862
MCSET: PK 84862

Bowie, Lester

ALL THE MAGIC.
LP: ECM 1246

AVANT POP (Bowie, Lester, Brass Fantasy).
LP: ECM 1326

DUET (Bowie, Lester & Philip Wilson).
LP: IAI 373854

DUET (Bowie, Lester & Nobuyoshi Ino).
LP: K 28P 6367

FAST LAST.
LP: MR 5055

FIFTH POWER, THE (Bowie, Lester with Various artists).
LP: BSR 0020

GREAT PRETENDER.
LP: ECM 1209

I ONLY HAVE EYES FOR YOU.
LP: ECM 1296

NOS. 1 & 2.
LP: N 1

ROPE-A-DOPE.
LP: MR 5081

TWILIGHT DREAMS (Bowie, Lester, Brass Fantasy).
Tracks: / I am with you / Personality / Duke's fantasy / Thriller / Night time (is the right time) / Vibe waltz / Twilight dreams.
LP: VE 2
MC: TCVE 2

WORKS: LESTER BOWIE.
Tracks: / Charlie M / Rose drop / B funk / When the spirit returns / Let the good times roll.
LP: 8372741

Bowie, Pat

FEELIN' GOOD (Bowie, Pat & Charles McPherson).
Tracks: / Baby won't you please come home / They can't take that away from me / Summertime / Wonder why / Lonesome road / Since I fell for you / You don't know what love is / Why don't you do right / I wanna be loved / Feeling good.
LP: PR 7437

Bowler, Belinda

TURNING POINT.
Tracks: / I thought I was a child / Millworker / Baby I'm fallin' / Come down in time / How can I keep from singing? / Turning point / Lovin' arms / For Holden / Whitebark / Weakness in me.
LP: PTLP 006

Bowlly, Al

20 GOLDEN PIECES OF AL BOWLLY.
LP: OLM 2
MC: COLM 2

AL BOWLLY AND PHYLLIS ROBINS (Bowlly, Al/Phyllis Robins).
Tracks: / What do your know about love / Hey gypsy, play gypsy / South of the border / Dark eyes / Moon love / Au revoir but not goodbye / Man and his dream, A / Ridin' home / That's what I like about you / What are you thinkin' about baby? / It's a hap-hap-happy day / Over the rainbow / Scatterbrain / Oh, Johnny / Chatterbox / Sing for your supper.
LP: SH 307

AL BOWLLY CIRCLE, THE.
Tracks: / Cuddle up close - You'll never understand / Torn sails / Moon / Gone forever / If you were only mine / Call it a day / Sweepin' the clouds away / Who'll buy an old ring / Foolish facts / Eleven more months and ten more days / Minnie the moocher's wedding day / Roy Fox's commentary on the wedding reception / Lazy Louisiana moon / Moonlight on the Colorado (Duet with Les Allen.) / Dark clouds / Save the last dance for me.
LP: JOY'D 281
MC: TC JOY'D 281

AL BOWLLY IN NEW YORK.
Tracks: / Say When (Copyright Control.) / When love comes singing along (Copyright Control.) / Be still my heart / My melancholy baby / St. Louis blues / Way back home / If I had a million dollars / You and the night and the music / You were there / Little white gardenia, A / Piccolino, The / Everything's been done before / Little gypsy tearoom, A / Red sails in the sunset / Dinner for one please James.
LP: JOY'D 288

AMBASSADOR OF SONG.
Tracks: / Fancy our meeting / My canary has circles under his eyes / Judy / I'm through with love / Be still, my heart / Roll on, Mississippi, roll on / Heartaches / Maria, my own / If I had a million dollars / Miss Elizabeth Brown / If anything happened to you / Got a date with an angel / There's rain in my eyes / Night and day / Brother, can you spare a dime.
LP: ACL 1204

AU REVOIR (BUT NOT GOODBYE) (Bowlly, Al & Jim Mesene).
Tracks: / Make love with a guitar / When I dream of home / Over the rainbow / Careless / Make believe island / Woodpecker song, The / What do you know about love / Old pal of mine / Only forever / It was a lover and his lass / Dreaming / I'm stepping out with a memory tonight / I haven't time to be a millionaire / Turn your money in your pocket / I'll never smile again / We'll go smiling along / Walkin' thru Mockin' Bird Lane / Let the curtain come down / When you wear your Sunday blue / Ferry boat serenade, The / Moon love / Nicky the Greek (has gone) / Au revoir (but not goodbye) / You made me care / When that man is dead and gone.
LP: C5-542
MC: C5K-542

CLASSIC YEARS IN DIGITAL STEREO (Al Bowlly with Ray Noble 1931-1934) (Bowlly, Al with Ray Noble & His Orchestra).
Tracks: / Brighter than the sun / Pied piper / Makin' wickey wackey down in waikiki / Hold my hand / Lady of Spain / Shout for happiness / My Hat's On The Side Of My Head / Got A Date With An Angel / Time On My Hands / I'll Do My Best To Make You Happy / Love Is The Sweetest Thing / What More Can I Ask / Very thought of you, The / On The Other Side of Lover's Lane / Love Locked Out / It's time to say goodnight.
LP: REB 649
MC: ZCF 649

DANCE BAND DAYS, THE.
Tracks: / Time on my hands / Can't get Mississippi off my mind / Tell me (you love me) / Moon / Linda / I'm glad I waited / Heartaches / Goodnight sweetheart / Waltz you saved for me, The / Life is meant for love / We've got the Moon and sixpence / Longer that you linger in Virginia, The / Roll on, Mississippi, roll on / Lady play your mandolin / Time alone will tell / Can't we be friends / Girl in the upstairs flat, The / Trusting my luck / I'm saving the last waltz for you / Somebody's thinking of you tonight / Louisiana hayride / It's a long way to your heart / There's a goldmine in the sky / Proud of you / Souvenir of love / Waves of the ocean are whisp'ring goodnight / Little lady make believe / Fare thee well / Sweet Genevieve / Because it's love / In my little red book / In a shelter from a shower / I won't tell a soul / Riding on a haycart home / Say goodnight to your old fashioned mother.
LP: RFLD 46

FLOWERS FOR MADAME 1935-37.
Tracks: / I can dream, can't I / Basin Street blues / Carelessly / My melancholy baby / Flowers for madame / Sweet is the word for you / You opened my eyes / In a blue and pensive mood / Half moon on the Hudson / On a little dream ranch / I wished on the moon / Blue Hawaii / Why the stars come out at night / Where am I? / Blazin' the trail / Why dream.
LP: HQ 3024

GERALDO & AL BOWLLY (Bowlly, Al & Geraldo).
MC: CHAL 12

GOLDEN AGE OF AL BOWLLY, THE.
Tracks: / Love is the sweetest thing / Bei mir bist du schon (Means that you're grand) / Marie / In my little red book / Something to sing about / Walkin' thru Mockin' Bird Lane / My melancholy baby / Blow, thou winter wind / It was a lover and his lass / Have you ever been lonely? / You're a sweetheart / I'll string along with you / Only forever / Goodnight sweetheart.
LP: GX 2512
MC: TCGX 2512

GOODNIGHT SWEETHEART (1931 Sessions).
Tracks: / I'm telling the world she's mine / Goodnight sweetheart / Lazy day / Hang out the stars in Indiana / There's a ring around the Moon / Goodnight Vienna / I'll do my best to make you happy / Love is the sweetest thing /

Wanderer / Maybe I love you too much / Shadow waltz / I've got to sing a torch song / Close your eyes / Unless / Who walks in when I walk out? / Very thought of you, The / I'll string along with you / Grinzing / Dreaming a dream / Sing as we go / Don't say goodbye / I'm glad I waited.
LP: . . . . **SH 502**
MC: . . . . **TCSH 502**

GOODNIGHT SWEETHEART (2).
Tracks: / Time on my hands / What are you thinking about, baby? / Guilty / Take it from me (I'm taking to you) / Oh Rosalita / Time alone will tell / Thank your father / Would you like to take a walk / I'll keep you in my heart always / That's what I like about you / Bubbling over with love / Just one more chance / Dance hall doll / By the river Sainte Marie / You didn't have to tell me / By my side / Song of happiness / Lady play your mandolin / Smile, darn ya, smile / Goodnight, sweetheart.
LP: . . . . **SVL 150**
MC: . . . . **CSVL 150**

HMV SESSIONS, THE (See under Noble, Ray) (Bowlly, Al & the Ray Noble Orchestra).

LEGENDARY, THE.
MC: . . . . **MRT 40042**

LONDON SESSIONS, THE 1928-30.
Tracks: / Just imagine / Wherever you are / If I had you / Misery farm / I'm sorry Sally / When the lilac blooms again / Up in the clouds / After the sun's kissed the world goodbye / If anything happened to you / Happy days are here again / On the sunny side of the street / Sweepin' the clouds away / Dancing with tears in my eyes / Adeline / Beware of love / Frankie and Johnnie / By the old oak tree / Never swat a fly / Sunny days / Roamin' through the roses.
LP: . . . . **SVL 148**
MC: . . . . **CSVL 148**

MILLION DREAMS, A.
Tracks: / Moonstruck / Maria my own / Love locked out / There's a cabin in the pines / Night and day / Learn to croon / I'm getting sentimental over you / I'll follow you / Million dreams, A / My romance / Keep your last goodnight for me / Goodnight but not goodbye / Wherever you are / I'll do my best to make you happy / So ashamed / Glorious Devon / That's all that matters to me / You must believe me / Fancy our meeting / Lover come back to me.
LP: . . . . **SVL 163**
MC: . . . . **CSVL 163**

MY SONG GOES ROUND THE WORLD (Bowlly, Al & Ray Noble).
Tracks: / Wanderer / Just an echo in the valley / Can't we meet again / When you've fallen in love / Let me give my happiness to you / Hustling and bustling for my baby / Waltzing in a dream / It's within your power / Hiawatha's lullaby / Couple of fools in love, A / On the other side of lover's lane / It's bad for me / Dinner at eight / Experiment / Weep no more / Thanks / Oceans of time / On a steamer coming over / Did you ever see a dream walking / My song goes round the world.
MC: . . . . **CHAL 18**
LP: . . . . **HAL 18**

ON THE SENTIMENTAL SIDE (Bowlly, Al & Geraldo).
LP: . . . . **SH 516**
MC: . . . . **TC SH 516**
LP: . . . . **EG 2604621**
MC: . . . . **EG 2604624**

ONE AND ONLY.
Tracks: / I've had my moments / I'm so used to you now / I'm for you a hundred per cent / Whispering / Dark clouds / You didn't know the music / When we're alone / It was so beautiful / Ending with a kiss / Melody in Spring / Faded summer love, A / Tell me you are from Georgia / Beat o' my heart / What a perfect night for love / Rose Mia / You are my heart's delight / Dinah / Leave the rest to nature.
LP: . . . . **RFL 1**

PROUD OF YOU.
Tracks: / Marie / Sweet someone / Colorado sunset / Is that the way to treat a sweetheart? / When Mother Nature sings her lullaby / Two sleepy people / Sweet as a song / Goodnight angel / Any broken hearts to mend? / Al Bowlly remembers (medley) / Very thought of you, The / You're as pretty as a picture / Proud of you / True / Summer's end / There's rain in my eyes / Bei mir bist du schon / When the organ played 'O promise me' / While the cigarette was burning / Penny serenade.
LP: . . . . **AJA 5064**
MC: . . . . **ZC AJA 5064**

RAY NOBLE & AL BOWLLY, NO 1 (see Noble, Ray) (Bowlly, Al & Ray Noble & His Orchestra).

RAY NOBLE & AL BOWLLY, NO 6 (see Noble, Ray) (Bowlly, Al & Ray Noble & His Orchestra).

SENTIMENTAL SIDE (2) (Bowlly, Al & Geraldo).
Tracks: / My heart is taking lessons / On the sentimental side / Small fry / Never break a promise / When Mother Nature sings her lullaby / Penny serenade / Heart and soul / Two sleepy people / Is that the way to treat a sweetheart / Colorado sunset / While a cigarette was burning / Any broken hearts to mend? / Summers end / My own / You're as pretty as a picture / They say / If ever when we were young / I'm in love with Vienna.
2LP: . . . . **DDV 5009/10**

SENTIMENTALLY YOURS.
Tracks: / Madonna mine / I'm getting sentimental over you / Judy / Everything I have is yours / Glorious Devon / Isle of Capri / Lover come back to me / There's a cabin in the pines / If I had a million dollars / True / It's all forgotten now / That's me without you / Fancy our meeting / Learn to croon / Night & day / Love locked out / Be still my heart.
LP: . . . . **CHD 127**
MC: . . . . **MCHD 127**

SOMETHING TO SING ABOUT.
Tracks: / Home town (Recorded date 17.7.37.) / Grandma said (Recorded date 3.2.39.) / Deep in a dream (Recorded date 3.2.39.) / You're a sweet little headache (Recorded date 3.2.39.) / I'm madly in love with you (Recorded date 8.2.39.) / Same old story (With Geraldo and his Orchestra. Recorded date 7.3.39.) / Could be (With Geraldo and his Orchestra. Recorded date 7.3.39.) / Between a kiss and a sigh (With Geraldo and his Orchestra. Recorded date 7.3.39.) / To mother with love (With Geraldo & his Orchestra. Recorded date 4.3.39.) / Thanks for everything (With Geraldo & his Orchestra. Recorded date 4.3.39.) / I miss you in the morning (With Geraldo & his Orchestra. Recorded date 4.3.39.) / Small town (With Reginald Williams & his Futurists. Recorded date 5.5.39.) / What do you know about love (With Reginald Williams & his Futurists. Recorded date 5.5.39.) / Moon love (By Al Bowlly & his Orchestra. Recorded date 5.10.39.) / Au revoir but not goodbye (By Al Bowlly & his Orchestra. Recorded date 5.10.39.) / Vieni, vieni (Recorded date 17.7.37.) / Le touquet (Recorded date 17.7.37.) / Smile when you say goodbye (Recorded date 17.7.37.) / Something to sing about (Recorded date 4.3.38.) / In my little red book (Recorded date 4.3.38.).
LP: . . . . **SH 501**
MC: . . . . **TCSH 501**

SWEET AS A SONG.
Tracks: / Carelessly / On a little dream ranch / Blue Hawaii / Sweet is the word for you / Bei mir bist du schon / Marie / You're a sweetheart / Pretty little patchwork quilt, The / Sweet as a song / Sweet someone / Goodnight angel / When the organ played 'O promise me' (Full title: When the organ played 'O promise me (intro 'I love you truly) / Romany / Lonely / I miss you in the morning / Violin in Vienna / What do you know about love / Hey gypsy, play gypsy / South of the border / Dark eyes.
LP: . . . . **EG 2604571**
MC: . . . . **EG 2604574**

TIME ON MY HANDS.
2LP: . . . . **SVLD 003**
MC: . . . . **CSVLD 003**

VERY THOUGHT OF YOU, THE.
Tracks: / Little white gardenia, A / Very thought of you, The / By the fireside / Close your eyes / Love is the sweetest thing / I'll do my best to make you happy / Rock your cares away / Don't say goodbye / Marching along together / Got a date with an angel / Good evening / Echo of a song, The / Bedtime story / I was true / Living in clover / Goodnight Vienna / Shout for happiness / Goodnight sweetheart.
LP: . . . . **BUR 003**
MCSET: . . . . **DTO 10219**

VERY THOUGHT OF YOU, THE (EMI).
Tracks: / Time on my hands (New Mayfair Dance Orchestra directed by Ray Noble.) / Goodnight sweetheart (Novelty Orchestra.) / Sweet and lovely / Pied Piper of Hamlin, The (Ray Noble and The New Mayfair Dance Orchestra.) / By the fireside (Ray Noble and The New Mayfair Dance Orchestra.) / Love is the sweetest thing (Ray Noble and The New Mayfair Dance Orchestra.) / How could we be wrong? (Ray Noble And His Orchestra.) / Weep no more my baby (Ray Noble And His Orchestra.) / Love locked out (Ray Noble And His London Orchestra.) / You ought to see Sally on Sunday (Ray Noble And His Orchestra.) / One morning in May (Ray Noble And His Orchestra.) / Very thought of you, The (Ray Noble And His Orchestra.) / Isle of Capri (Ray Noble And His Orchestra.) / Blue Hawaii / In my little red book / Penny serenade / They say / South of the border / Over the rainbow / Somewhere in France with you (Orchestra conducted by Ronnie Munro.) / When you wish upon a star / Who's taking you home tonight / Blow, blow, thou winter wind / It was lover and his lass.
LP: . . . . **SH 518**
MC: . . . . **TCSH 518**

Bowman, Gill

CITY LOVE.
Tracks: / Your average woman / Very good year, A / Verses / Ballad of the four Mary's / Make it good / City love / Psychics in America / Story today, A / Lang-a-growing / Different game, A / If I didn't love you.
MC: . . . . **FE 080C**
LP: . . . . **FE 080**

Bowman, Priscilla

ORIGINAL ROCK 'N' ROLL MAMA, AN.
LP: . . . . **SG 5008**

Bown, Alan

KICK ME OUT.
Tracks: / My friend / Strange little friend / Elope / Perfect day / All I can do / Friends in St Louis / Still as stone / Prisoner The / Kick me out / Children of the night / Gypsy girl / Wrong idea, The.
LP: . . . . **SEE 42**

Bown, Andy

GOOD ADVICE.
Tracks: / Another shipwreck / Good advice / Sophie / Lifeline / Crazy girl / Kix / One more chance / Lions and eagles / Rock and roll baby blues / Money on my mind / Another night without you.
LP: . . . . **EMC 3283**

Bowyer, Brendan

HOME AND ABROAD.
MC: . . . . **HACS 7073**

LIVE AT CLONTARF CASTLE.
LP: . . . . **HM 043**

Box

GREAT MOMENTS IN BIG SLAM.
Tracks: / Walls come down / Flatstone, The / Big slam / Stop / Low line / Breaking stream / Small blue car / Still in the woodwork.
LP: . . . . **VFM 5**
MC: . . . . **ZVFM 5**

MUSCLE OUT.
LP: . . . . **DVR P3**

SECRETS OUT.
LP: . . . . **VFM 4**

Box & Banjo Band

AT THE MOVIES.
LP: . . . . **LILP 5154**
MC: . . . . **LICS 5154**

BOUNCING IN THE BALLROOM.
LP: . . . . **LILP 5155**
MC: . . . . **LICS 5155**

CHRISTMAS CRACKERS.
LP: . . . . **LILP 5176**
MC: . . . . **LICS 5176**

COULD I HAVE THIS DANCE.
Tracks: / Quick step 1 / Foxtrot 1 / Waltz 1 / Tango 1 / Madison 1 / Rumba 1 / Old time waltz (pride of Erin) 1 / Blues 1 / Quick step 2 / Foxtrot 2 / Waltz 2 / Tango 2 / Madison 2 / Rumba 2 / Old time waltz (pride of Erin) 2 / Blues 2.
LP: . . . . **LILP 5168**
MC: . . . . **LICS 5168**

GO DANCING.
Tracks: / Bye bye, blackbird / Darktown strutters' ball / Alexander's ragtime band / You made me love you / Oh, you beautiful doll / On the sunny side of the street / When Irish eyes are smiling / Lilly McNally McNair / Too-ra-loo-ra-loo-ra / Let's twist again / Birdie dance / I love a lassie / Roamin' in the gloamin' / Stop your ticklin' Jock / Just a wee deoch and doris / Anniversary song / Bicycle built for two / I'll be your sweetheart / Alley cat / El Cumbanchero / Charleston / I wonder where my baby is tonight / Yes sir, that's my baby / Side by side / Lily of Laguna / Carolina in the morning / Me and my gal / Isle of Capri / Jealousy / O sole mio / Camptown races / Steamboat Bill / Oh Susannah / Beautiful Sunday / Una paloma blanca / Amarillo / California here I come / Waiting for the Robert E. Lee / Baby face / Swanee / Come back to Sorrento / Edelweiss / Lara's theme / Quickstep / Breakaway blues / Pride of Erin / Twist and tweet / Gay Gordons / Old time waltz / Samba / Madison, The / Foxtrot / Alley cat / Tango / Barn dance / Slosh / Mississippi dip / Modern waltz.
LP: . . . . **LILP 5138**
MC: . . . . **LICS 5138**

GO SEQUENCE DANCING.
Tracks: / Quickstep (1) / Quickstep (2) / Cha cha (1) / Cha cha (2) / Foxtrot (1) / Foxtrot (2) / Tango (1) / Tango (2) / Rhumba (1) / Rhumba (2) / Old tyme waltz (1) / Old tyme waltz (2) / Quickstep (1) / Quickstep (2) / Waltz (1) / Waltz (2) / Madison (1) (Only on CD.) / Madison (2) (Only on CD.) / Blues (1) (Only on CD) / Blues (2) (Only on CD).
LP: . . . . **LILP 5186**
MC: . . . . **LICS 5186**

GREAT SCOTTISH SINGALONG.
Tracks: / Come in come in / Scottish soldier / Mull of Kintyre / Crying time / Down in the glen / Gordon for me / Amazing grace / Red yo yo / Always Argyll / Nobody's child / Westering home.
LP: . . . . **LILP 5144**
MC: . . . . **LICS 5144**

HUNDRED THOUSAND WELCOMES, A.
Tracks: / Hundred thousand welcomes, A / Thistle of Scotland, The / Scotland the brave / Northern lights, The / Rowan tree / These are my mountains / Wee cooper of Fife. The / I'm no comin' oot the noo / Soor milk cairt, The / Skye boat song, The / My love is like a red red rose / Ye banks and braes / Old rosin the bow / Muckin' o Geordie's byre, The / Atholl highlanders / Sailing up the Clyde / Doon in the wee room / Barras, The / Annie Laurie / Bonnie Mary of Argyle / Bonnie lass o' Ballochmyle / Star of Rabbie Burns, The / Tartan, The / Scots wha ha'e / Dark island / Rothesay Bay / Come by the hills / Lassie come and dance with me / Saturday dance, The / Ten wee wimmin / Auld hoose, The / Granny's Hieland hame / Sing tae me the old Scots songs / Barren rocks of Aden, The / Dornoch links / Black bear, The / Cock o' the North / Wachin' hame / Mairi's wedding / Ulst tramping song / Bonnie Dundee / Marching through the heather / Wi a hundred pipes / Auld lang syne / Guid new year, A.
LP: . . . . **LILP 5172**
MC: . . . . **LICS 5172**

Box Of Frogs

BOX OF FROGS.
LP: . . . . **EPC 25996**
MC: **40 25996**

STRANGE LAND.
Tracks: / Get it while you can / You mix me up / Average / House on fire / Hanging from the wreckage / Heart full of soul / Asylum / Strange land.
LP: . . . . **EPC 26375**
MC: **40 26375**

Box Tops

BEST OF THE BOX TOPS.
Tracks: / Letter, The / Neon rainbow / I pray for rain / Door you closed to me, The / Cry like a baby / Deep in Kentucky / Fields of clover / You keep me hangin' on / Choo choo train / I can dig it / Yesterday where's my mind / Soul deep / I shall be released / Together / I must be the devil / Sweet cream ladies forward march / Happy song.
LP: . . . . **LIK 41**

Boxcar Willie

20 GREAT HITS.
Tracks: / I've got a bad case of feeling sorry for me / Lord made a hobo out of me, The / Blue eyed girl of Berlin / Six pound fish / Fragrance of her perfume, The / Daddy was a railroad man / Day Elvis died, The / Hot box blues / I'm going back to Texas / I can't help it (if I'm still in love with you) / I'm so lonesome I could cry / Lonesome whistle / Waiting for a train / T B blues / Cold windy city of Chicago / Take me home / I wake up every morning with a smile on my face / Trouble / Train medley.
LP: . . . . **BRA 1012**
MC: . . . . **BRC 1012**

BEST LOVED FAVOURITES VOL.1.
Tracks: / Blue moon of Kentucky / Crazy arms / In the jailhouse now / I won't get over you / Six days on the road / Wings of a dove / Pistol packin' mama / Half as much / Whistle ain't made of gold / Almost persuaded / Louisiana Saturday night.
LP: . . . . **NL 71946**
MC: . . . . **NK 71946**

BEST LOVED FAVOURITES VOL.2.
Tracks: / This ole house / Good hearted woman / Mom and dad's waltz / I'm thinking tonight of my blue eyes / Fraulein / I'll fly away / Goodnight Irene / Cold cold heart / L.A. lady / Lovesick blues / Don't pretend.
MC: . . . . **NK 74210**

LP: . . . . **NL 74210**

BEST OF BOXCAR WILLIE.
Tracks: / Waitin' for a train / From a Rolls to the rails / Lord made a hobo out of me / Take me home / I wake up every morning with a smile / I came so close to calling you last night / I'm so lonesome I could cry / Lonesome whistle / Daddy was a railroad man / Hot box blues / I can't help it / Day Elvis died, The / Hank, you still make me cry / Train medley.
LP: . . . . **SHM 3117**
MC: . . . . **HSC 3117**

BOXCAR WILLIE.
Tracks: / Songs of songs / Dreary days / Gypsy lady and the hobo / Honey I love you / Cheating wife / Boxcar's my home / My hearts deep in the heart of Texas / Hobo heaven / Big freight train carry me home / Ain't gonna be your day.
LP: . . . . **MCF 3309**
MC: . . . . **MCFC 3309**
LP: . . . . **BRA 1001**

COLLECTION: BOXCAR WILLIE.
2LP: . . . . **CCSLP 159**
MC: . . . . **CCSMC 159**

COLLECTION: BOXCAR WILLIE (2).
Tracks: / Lost highway / We made memories / S.U.C.K.E.R. / Living it up in Washington D.C. / Blue blue days, blue blue nights / Tennessee rain / Atomic bum / I was kind of in the neighbourhood / Streamline cannon ball.
LP: . . . . **SPLP 005**
MC: . . . . **SPLC 005**

COUNTRY STORE: BOXCAR WILLIE.
Tracks: / Gotta travel on / Wayward wind / If you've got the money, I've got the time / When my blue moon turns to gold again / I love you because / Have I told you lately that I love you / Packy / Jambalaya / Movin' on / Walking the floor above you / Mama tried / Rock island line / Baby we're really in love / Will the circle be unbroken.
LP: . . . . **CST 26**
MC: . . . . **CSTK 26**

DADDY WAS A RAILROAD MAN.
LP: . . . . **BRA 1004**
MC: . . . . **BRC 1004**

FIREBALL MAIL (See under Acuff, Roy for details) (Boxcar Willie/Roy Acuff).

FREIGHT TRAIN BLUES.
Tracks: / Last train to heaven / Bummin' around / Bad news / Keep on rollin' down the line / Freight train blues / Lonesome blues / We made memories / You got the kind of love that grabs a hold / To my baby I'm a big star all the time / Don't blame me for what happened last night / There's nothing like a good ol' country song / Lefty left us lonely.
LP: . . . . **N 23001**

GOOD OL' COUNTRY SONGS.
Tracks: / Bummin' around / Bad news / That sinking feeling / Keep on rollin' down the line / Freight train blues / Lefty left us lonely / Eagle / Lonesome Joe / Alligator song, The / To my baby I'm a big star all the time / You got the kind of love that grabs a hold... / We made memories / Dearest darling / Don't blame me for what happened last night / There's nothing like a good ol' country song.
LP: . . . . **NE 1168**
MC: . . . . **CE 2168**

GREAT TRACKS.
LP: **2630041**
MC: **2630044**

GREATEST HITS: BOXCAR WILLIE.
LP: **2230025**
MC: **2130025**

KING OF THE ROAD.
Tracks: / King of the road / Warbash cannonball / You are my sunshine / Boxcar blues / Don't let the stars get in your eyes / Your cheatin' heart / I saw the light / Wreck of the old '97 / Hank and the hobo / Peace in the valley / Mule train / Hey good lookin' / Kaw-liga / Move it on over / London leaves / Rolling in my sweet baby's arms / Divorce me C.O.D. / Red river valley / Heaven / San Antonio rose.
MC: **43004**
LP: . . . . **N 23004**
LP: . . . . **PLAT 23**
MC: . . . . **PLAC 23**
LP: . . . . **WW 5084**

LIVE IN CONCERT.
Tracks: / Wreck of the old 97 / Mule train / Cold cold heart.
LP: . . . . **SHM 3137**
MC: . . . . **HSC 3137**

MARTY MARTIN SINGS COUNTRY.
Tracks: / Boxcar Willie / Mississippi river queen / This kind of man / Change of heart / Picture of you and me / River thru Reno / Living loving angel / Speed limit's thirty / I hope your world don't end / Was it all in fun / You and a fool / Hey doctor man.
LP: . . . . **WRS 161**

NO MORE TRAINS TO RIDE.
Tracks: / Man I used to be, The / Not on the bottom yet / Watching a new love grow / I just gotta go / Luther / Whine whistle / Daddy played over the waves / It ain't no record / Hobo's lament / Mister can you spare a dime / No more trains to ride.
LP: . . . . **N 23002**

SINGS HANK WILLIAMS AND JIMMIE RODGERS.
LP: . . . . **BRA 1006**
MC: . . . . **BRC 1006**

TAKE ME HOME.
Tracks: / Train medley / From a boxcar door / Take me home / Cold windy city of Chicago / Hank, you still make me cry / Country music nightmare / I can't help it (if I'm still in love with you) / I love the sound of a whistle / Blue blue days, blue blue nights / Six pound fish / 'T' for Texas.
LP: . . . . **N 23003**
LP: . . . . **BRA 1011**
MC: . . . . **BRC 1011**

Boxer

ABSOLUTELY.
Tracks: / Everybody's a star (so what's in a name) / Can't stand what you do.
LP: . . . . **S EPC 82151**

Boy George

HIGH HAT.
LP: . . . . **V 2555**
MC: . . . . **TCV 2555**

SOLD.
Tracks: / Sold / I asked for love / Keep me in mind / Everything I own / Freedom / Just ain't enough / Where are you now? / Little ghost / Next time / We've got the right / To be reborn.
LP: . . . . **V 2430**
MC: . . . . **TCV 2430**

TENSE NERVOUS HEADACHE.
Tracks: / Don't cry / You are my heroin / I go where I go / Girl with combination skin / Whisper / Something strange called love / I love you / Kipsy / Mama never knew / What becomes of the broken hearted? (Only on CD and cassette.) / American boys (Only on CD and cassette.) / Happy family (Only on CD and cassette.).
LP: . . . . **V 2546**
MC: . . . . **TCV 2546**

Boy Growing Up (poems)

BOY GROWING UP, A (Dylan Thomas) (Williams, Emlyn (nar)).
Tracks: / Introduction / Memories of childhood / Who do you wish was with us / Fight, The / Outing, The / Reminiscence of a schoolmaster / Just like little dogs / Self portrait / Adventures in the skin trade / Child's Christmas, A / Visit to America, A / Visit to grandpa's, A.
MCSET: . . . . **SAY 48**

Boy In Khaki

BOY IN KHAKI, A (Various).
Tracks: / Boy in khaki - a girl in lace / Salt water cowboy / Sam's got his / My wonderful / I've got 10 bucks and 24 hours to leave / One girl and two boys / Don't sit under the apple tree / Little guy who looks like you, The / Story of Private Joe / When your GI guy comes marching home / Don't worry.
MC: . . . . **K 1006**

Boy Meets Boy (show)

BOY MEETS BOY (Los Angeles Cast) (Various artists).
LP: . . . . **AEI 1102**

Boy Meets Girl

REEL LIFE.
Tracks: / Bring down the moon / Stormy love / Stay forever / One street dream / Restless dreamer / Waiting for a star to fall / Is anybody out there / If you run / No apologies / Someone's got to send out love.
LP: . . . . **PL 88414**
MC: . . . . **PK 88414**

Boy On The... (film)

BOY ON THE DOLPHIN (Original soundtrack) (Various artists).
LP: . . . . **STV 81119**

Boy Who Could...(film)

BOY WHO COULD FLY, THE (Film soundtrack) (Various artists).
LP: . . . . **STV 81299**
MC: . . . . **CTV 81299**

Boy Who Grew ...

BOY WHO GREW TOO FAST, THE (Opera soundtrack) (Various artists).
LP: . . . . **TER 1125**
MC: . . . . **ZCTER 1125**

Boy With Goldfish

BOY WITH GOLDFISH (Various artists).
LP: . . . . **VCDM 1000-30**

Boyce, Kim

KIM BOYCE.
LP: . . . . **MYR R 1233**
MC: . . . . **MYR C 1233**

TIME AND AGAIN.
LP: . . . . **MYR R 6861**
MC: . . . . **MYR C 6861**

Boyce, Mark

ACCORDION MAGIC.
LP: . . . . **UNKNOWN**

Boyce, Max

FAREWELL TO THE NORTH ENCLOSURE (See under EMI Comedy Classics).

I KNOW COS I WAS THERE.
LP: . . . . **MAX 1001**

IN TOUCH WITH MAX BOYCE.
LP: . . . . **OU 2500**
MC: . . . . **TCOU 2500**

INCREDIBLE PLAN, THE.
Tracks: / It's over / Sospan Fach / Hymns and arias / Pontypool front row, The / Asso asso yogishi / Divine intervention, The / Ode to Barry Island / Incredible plan, The (Interpolating Convoy march, Cardiff Arms.) / Gypsy, The / What does she know about music / Morning star / Bugail Aberdyfi / One hundred thousand million green bottles / French trip, The (Interpolating The Stripper.).
LP: . . . . **MFP 5580**
MC: . . . . **TCMFP 5580**
LP: . . . . **MB 102**

IT'S GOOD TO SEE YOU.
Tracks: / Fiddlers green / Mingulay boat song / Margarita / Liverpool Lou / Carrickfergus / Y deryn du ai blifym sidan / It's good to see you / You're my best friend / Hiraeth / Bonnie Brid / Love is teasing / Old Carmarthen oak / I loved a lassie / Bonnie Charlie.
LP: . . . . **MAX 1004**

LIVE AT TREORCHY.
Tracks: / 9-3 / Scottish trip, The / Ballad of Morgan the moon / Outside-half factory, The / Asso asso yogishi / Duw it's hard / Ten thousand instant Christians / Did you understand? / Hymns and arias.
LP: . . . . **OU 2033**
MC: . . . . **TC OU 2033**
LP: . . . . **MFP 41 5699 1**
LP: . . . . **OU 54053**

MAX BOYCE IN CONCERT.
LP: . . . . **SPR 8569**
MC: . . . . **SPC 8569**

ME AND BILLY WILLIAMS.
Tracks: / Day we lost to England / Paul Ringer's song / Tarquin's letter / Two soldiers / Y deryn pur / Me and Billy Williams / Dowlais top / Morgan and Rhys / Oggie song / Eli Jenkin's prayer.
LP: . . . . **MAX 1003**

NOT THAT I'M BIASED.
Tracks: / I think it's a spring onion / 27-3 / One night in Oldham / When we walked to Merthyr Tydfil / Young Davy / Mae ngahariad in Fenws / Seagulls of Llandudno / El teribie / There but for Johnny Walters / I don't like cabbage / Coats on the bed / How fast was Gerald Davies, Dad? / Collier lad / Ben Thomas and Mr Pocock / There were many babies born.
LP: . . . . **MAX 1002**

ROAD AND THE MILES, THE.
LP: . . . . **MB 103**

TROUBADOUR.
Tracks: / Peace will be mine / Old men and children / In the morning (morning of my life) / Railway hotel / Seth Davey (whiskey on a Sunday) / Tiger Bay / Bunch of thyme / Maggie / Winter too late, A / John O'Dreams.
LP: . . . . **PYL 0001**
MC: . . . . **PYM 0001**

WE ALL HAD DOCTORS PAPERS.
LP: . . . . **MB 101**

Boyd, Carole (nar)

BRIDE AT WHANGATAPU (see under Bride at Whangatapu (bk).

CANDLES FOR THE SURGEON (see under Candles for the... (bk)).

CASTLE OF THE MIST (see under Castle of the Mist (bk).

CHEQUERED SILENCE, A (see under Chequered Silence).

DANDELION SEED, THE (see under Dandelion Seed (bk).

MORE FROM TEN IN A BED (See under More From Ten... (bk)).

OBSESSION (see under Obsession (bk)).

PASSIONATE DECEPTION (see under Passionate Deception).

RELUCTANT PARAGON (see under Reluctant Paragon).

SAVAGE INTERLUDE (see under Savage Interlude).

SURGEON'S AFFAIR (see under Surgeon's Affair).

TALES FROM TEN IN A BED Spoken Word.
MC: . . . . **TS 337**

VIRTUOUS LADY (see under Virtuous Lady).

Boyd, Eddie

EDDIE BOYD & HIS BLUES BAND FEAT.PETER GREEN (Boyd, Eddie & His Blues Band/Peter Green).
Tracks: / Too bad / Dust my broom / Unfair lovers / Key to the highway / Vacation from the blues / Steakhouse rock / Letter missin' blues / Ain't doing too bad / Blue coat man / Save her doctor / Rack 'em back / Too bad (part 2) / Big bell / Pinetop's boogie woogie / Night time is the right time / Train is coming.
LP: . . . . **CCR 1002**

FIVE LONG YEARS.
LP: . . . . **LR 42.005**

LEGACY OF THE BLUES VOL. 10 (See under Legacy of the Blues).

LIVE.
LP: . . . . **SLP 268**

LOVER'S PLAYGROUND.
Tracks: / My idea / I will step aside / Black slacks / Brotherhood / Number nine / My lady / Sweet Leila / Steakhouse rock / Nothing / Lover's playground.
LP: . . . . **RJ 204**

RATTIN' AND RUNNIN' AROUND.
Tracks: / Rosa Lee swing / You got to love that gal / Edie's blues / Baby, what's wrong with you / Four leaf clover / Picture in the frame / Drifting / Don't / Blue Monday blues / What makes these things happen to me / Chicago is just that way / Rattin' and running around / Tickler, The / Nightmare is over, The / Please help me / Life gets to be a burden.
LP: . . . . **IG 400**

Boyd, Jimmy

TELL ME A STORY (See also Laine, Frankie) (Boyd, Jimmy & Frankie Laine).

Boyd, Kay

FIRST SLICE.
Tracks: / This could be the start of something / Love is here to stay / For once in my life / I'm gonna sit right down and write myself a letter / My way / Sometimes when I'm happy / When I fall in love / Teach me tonight / My funny Valentine.
LP: . . . . **SPJ LP 24**

Boyd, Liona

PERSONA.
LP: . . . . **FM 42120**

Boyd, William (aut)

MY GIRL IN SKIN TIGHT JEANS (see under My Girl In..) (Jarvis, Martin (nar)).

Boyens, Phyllis

I REALLY CARE.
Tracks: / Have you ever / Mean papa blues / One night stand / Truck driving man / Last old shovel / Coal tattoo / Here I am / Don't sell daddy no more whiskey / Hewed out of the mountain / To hell with the land / Old fashioned cheatin' / I really care for you.
LP: . . . . **ROUNDER 0162**

Boyer, Lucienne

50 YEARS OF SONG.
2LP: **2C 178 15312/13**

Boyfriend (musical)

BOYFRIEND, THE (1984 London revival cast) (Various artists).
Tracks: / Boyfriend overture: *Various artists* / Perfect young ladies: *Various artists* / Boyfriend: *Various* artists / Won't you Charleston with me?: *Various artists* / Fancy forgetting: *Various artists* / I could be happy with you: *Various artists* / Sur la plage: *Various artists* / Room in Bloomsbury, A: *Various artists* / It's nicer in Nice: *Various artists* / You-don't-want-to-play-with-me blues: *Various artists* / Safety in numbers: *Various artists* / Riviera, The: *Various artists* / It's never too late to fall in love: *Various artists* / Poor little Pierette: *Various artists* / Finale: *Various artists*.
LP: . . . . **TER 1095**
MC: . . . . **ZCTER 1095**

BOYFRIEND, THE (1971 Film soundtrack) (Various artists).
LP: . . . . MCA 39069
MC: . . . . MCAC 39069

BOYFRIEND, THE (1954 musical show) (Various artists).
Tracks: / Overture, The: *Various artists* / Perfect young ladies: *Various artists* / Boyfriend: *Various artists*/ Won't you Charleston with me: *Various artists* / Fancy forgetting: *Various artists* / I could be happy with you: *Various artists* / Sur la plage: *Various artists* / Room in Bloomsbury, A: *Various artists* / You-don't-want-to-play-with-me blues, The: *Various artists* / Safety in numbers: *Various artists* / Riviera, The: *Various artists* / It's never too late to fall in love: *Various artists* / Carnival tango: *Various artists* / Poor little Pierrette: *Various artists* / Finale, The: *Various artists*.
MC: . . . . GK 60056

BOYFRIEND, THE (MCA) (Original Broadway Cast) (Various artists).
LP: . . . . MCA 1537
MC: . . . . MCAC 1537

BOYFRIEND, THE (T.E.R.) (1967 London Revival Cast) (Various artists).
Tracks: / Boyfriend overture: *Various artists* / Perfect young ladies: *Various artists* / Boyfriend: *Various* artists / Won't you Charleston with me?: *Various artists* / Fancy forgetting: *Various artists* / I could be happy with you: *Various artists* / Sur le plage: *Various artists* / Room in Bloomsbury, A: *Various artists*/ It's nicer in Nice: *Various artists* / You-don't-want-to-play-with-me blues: *Various artists* / Safety in numbers: *Various artists* / Riviera, The: *Various artists* / It's never too late to fall in love: *Various artists*/ Poor little Pierette: *Various artists* / Finale: *Various artists*.
LP: . . . . TER 1054
MC: . . . . ZCTER 1054

BOYFRIEND, THE/GOODBYE MR. CHIPS (Various artists).
Tracks: / Overture, The: *Various artists* (The Boyfriend. Hortense with boys & girls.) / Perfect young ladies: *Various* artists (The Boyfriend. Hortense & the girls: Maisie/Fay/Nancy/Dulcie.) / I could be happy with you: *Various artists*(The Boyfriend. Polly & Tony.) / Fancy forgetting: *Various artists* (The Boyfriend. Percy & Mme. Dubonnet.) / Sur la plage: *Various artists* (The Boyfriend. Hortense & The Company.) / You are my lucky star: *Various artists* (The Boyfriend. Polly.) / It's never too late to fall in love: *Various artists* (The Boyfriend. Max & Fay.) / Won't you charleston with me?: *Various artists*(The Boyfriend. Tony/Maisie/The Boys & Girls.) / You-don't-want-to-play-with-me-blues, The: *Various* artists (The Boyfriend. Mme Dubonnet/Percy & The Girls.) / Room in Bloomsbury, A: *Various artists* (The Boyfriend. Polly & Tony.) / It's nicer in Nice: *Various artists* (The Boyfriend. Hortense & The Company.) / All I do is dream of you: *Various artists* (The Boyfriend. Polly.) / Safety in numbers: *Various artists* (The Boyfriend. Maisie & The Boys: Tommy/Peter/ Michael/Alphonse.) / Poor little pierrette: *Various artists* (The Boyfriend. Polly & Mme. Dubonnet.) / Riviera, The - The Boyfriend chorus (finale): *Various artists* (The Boyfriend. The Company.) / Goodbye Mr. Chips (overture): *Various* artists (Goodbye Mr. Chips.) / London is London: *Clark, Petula* (Goodbye Mr. Chips.) / And the sky smiled: *Clark, Petula* (Goodbye Mr. Chips.) / When I am older: *Various artists* (Goodbye Mr. Chips.) / Walk through the world: *Clark, Petula* (Goodbye Mr. Chips.) / Schooldays: *Clark, Petula & Boys* (Goodbye Mr. Chips.) / When I was younger: *O'Toole*, Peter (Goodbye Mr. Chips.) / You and I: *Clark, Petula* (Goodbye Mr. Chips.) / Fill the world with love: *O'Toole, Peter & Boys* (Goodbye Mr. Chips.).
LP: . . . . LPMGM 20
LP: 794 291 1
MC: . . . . TCMGM 20
MC: 794 291 4

Boyle, Maggie

REACHING OUT.
Tracks: / Proud man, The / Quiet land of Erin, The / Joe's in bed / Mountain streams where the moorcocks / October song / Lowlands of Holland, The / Has sorrow thy young days shaded / Busk busk bonnie lassie / Pancake Tuesday / Reaching out / Road to Ballinamuck.
LP: . . . . RRA 003

Boyle, Neil

MOVING CLOUDS, THE.
MC: 60-170

Boyo, Billy

D.J.CLASH VOL. 2 (Boyo, Billy & Little Harry).
Tracks: / Jessat promotion / Jah Jah made me a M.C. / Harry on the go / Billy Boyo in the area / Leggo mi Queen / Going back to school / Wicked and wild / Check in / Rougher than rough / Look how she fat.
LP: . . . . GREL 50

Boyoyo Boys

BACK IN TOWN.
Tracks: / Back in town / Maraba start 500 / Dayeyton special / Duba duba / Mapetla / Pulukwani centre / Brakpan no.2 / Dube station / Arcie special / Vezunyawo.
LP: . . . . GREL 2003
MC: . . . . GREEN 2003
LP: . . . . ROUNDER 5026
MC: . . . . ROUNDER 5026C

TJ TODAY.
Tracks: / Funny face / T.J. special / Gikeleza / Empty box / Tsou tsou / Boston special / Eloff street no.2 / Sofia / Nkosi / American jive.
LP: . . . . GREL 2005
MC: . . . . ROUNDER 5036C
LP: . . . . ROUNDER 5036

Boys

ALTERNATIVE CHARTBUSTERS.
LP: . . . . NEL 6015

BOYS ONLY.
LP: . . . . BOYS 4

BOYS, THE.
LP: . . . . NEL 6001

LIVE AT THE ROXY.
LP: . . . . RRLP 135
MC: . . . . RRMC 135

TO HELL WITH THE BOYS.
LP: . . . . 1-2 BOYS

Boy's Brigade Band

BOY'S BRIGADE CENTENARY ALBUM (1883-1983).
Tracks: / Anchor song / Lord bless the BB / Highland laddie / Scotland the brave / Old hundredth / Melrose / Battle hymn of the republic / Will your anchor hold / Onward Christian soldiers.
LP: . . . . LIDL 6006
MC: . . . . LIDC 6006

Boy's Choir of Vienna

CHRISTMAS VOICES AND BELLS.
LP: . . . . HDY 1918
MC: . . . . ZCHDY 1918

Boys Don't Cry

12" MEGAMIX ALBUM.
LP: . . . . LLM 3005

BOYS DON'T CRY.
LP: . . . . LLP 105
MC: . . . . LLK 105

Boys From Beersheba

BOYS FROM BEERSHEBA, THE (Various artists).
Tracks: / Boys from Beersheba, The: *Various artists* / Boy Jesus, The: *Various artists* / Joha the silly boy: *Various artists* / Hannah and the patriarch: *Various artists* / St. George: *Various artists* / Selim and the frog: *Various artists* / Fisherman: *Various artists* / Slave king, The: *Various artists* / Prince's robe, The: *Various artists* / Jesus and the dog: *Various artists*.
MC: . . . . ANV 657

Boys From Brazil

BOYS FROM BRAZIL (Film soundtrack) (Various artists).
LP: . . . . AMLH 64731

Boys From Syracuse

BOYS FROM SYRACUSE (1963 London Cast) (Various artists).
Tracks: / Boys from Syracuse: Overture: *Various artists* / I had twins: *Various artists* / Dear old Syracuse: *Various artists* / What can you do with a man?: *Various artists* / Falling in love with love: *Various artists*/ Shortest day of the year, The: *Various artists* / This can't be love: *Various artists* / Ladies of the evening: *Various artists* / He and she: *Various artists* / You have cast your shadow on the sea: *Various artists*/ Come with me: *Various artists* / Sing for your supper: *Various artists* / Oh! Diogenes: *Various artists*/ Boys from Syracuse: Finale: *Various artists*.
LP: . . . . TER 1078
MC: . . . . ZCTER 1078

BOYS FROM SYRACUSE, THE (Studio cast with Jack Cassidy) (Various artists).
LP: . . . . COS 2580

Boys from the... (bk)

BOYS FROM THE BLACKSTUFF (Alan Bleasdale) (Hill, Bernard (nar)).
MCSET: . . . . LFP 7487

Boys Next Door

DOOR, DOOR.
LP: . . . . L 36931

Boys Of The Lough

BOYS OF THE LOUGH.
Tracks: / Da Lerwick lasses / Da Scalloway lasses / Da underhill / Da valley watch / An goirtin eornan / Sally Monroe / Patsy C Campbell / Gravel walk / Lough erne / Gold ring, The / Halting march / Lovely Nancy / Merrily kiss the quakers wife / Padriac O'Keefe / Yow cam tir wir door yarmin / Christmas day Ida moarning / Lass with the bonny brown hair / Lowrie Tarrell / Masons apron / Lovesick soul.
LP: . . . . LER 2086
LP: . . . . SHAN 79002

FAR FROM HOME.
Tracks: / Far from home / Ballydesmond polka, The / Da slockit light / Pettitcoat loose / Barrowburn reel, The / Gates of the yellow town / Hanged man's reel, The / Mason's apron / For Ireland I'd not tell her name.
LP: . . . . AUK 001
MC: . . . . AUK 001C

FAREWELL AND REMEMBER ME.
LP: . . . . LOUGH 002
MC: . . . . LOUGHC 002

GOOD FRIENDS GOOD MUSIC.
LP: . . . . PH 1051
MC: . . . . PH 1051C

IN THE TRADITION.
Tracks: / Out on the ocean / Padeen O'Rafferty / Isabelle Blackley / Kiss her under the coverlet / Lads of Alnwick, The / Road to Cashel / Paddy Kelly's brew / Lord Gregory / Dark woman of the glen / L.O. Forbes Esq. of Corse / Hawk / Charles Sutherland / Eddie Kelly's / Green fields of Glentown / Eclipse / Tailor's twist / Biddy from Sligo / Sunset / Peoples / Padraig O'Keefe's / Con Cassidy's highland / Sea apprentice / Miss McDonald / For Ireland I'd not tell her name.
MC: . . . . KTSC 422
LP: . . . . 12 TS 422
LP: . . . . FF 263

LIVE AT CARNEGIE HALL.
MC: . . . . SA 001 C

LIVE AT PASSIM.
LP: . . . . PH 1026

LOCHABER NO MORE.
LP: . . . . PH 1031
MC: . . . . PH 1031C

OPEN ROAD.
Tracks: / Calliope house / Jerry O'Connor's jig in A / Harvest home-toss the feathers / Clay of Kilcreggan / On Raglan Road / Dying year-Madame Vanoni / Big Terry McAloon's-Tommy Peoples'-Jenny Dang the weaver / Flower of the quern etc / Trotting to the Larne-Spey in spate / Black cock of Whickham / Lough erne / Gates of the yellow town / Petticoat loose etc..
LP: 12TS 433
MC: . . . . KTSC 433
LP: . . . . FF 310

PIPER'S BROKEN FINGER.
LP: . . . . PH 1042
MC: . . . . PH 1042C

REGROUPED.
Tracks: / Star of munster / Owen Hackett's jig / King's favourite / Rocking chair / Willie O / Bamboo flute / Albert House / Annalese Bain / Castle / Mulqueen's / Anac cuain / Humours of Ballinahinch / Floggin' / I'll buy boots for Maggie / O'Connor's polka / Moorlough Mary / City of Savannah / Acrobat / Off to California / Da tushker / Susan Cooper / Millbrae / Jog along till shearing / Cup of tea set.
MC: . . . . KTSC 409
LP: 12TS 409
LP: . . . . FF 225

SECOND ALBUM.
LP: . . . . LER 2090
LP: . . . . ROUNDER 3006

SWEET RURAL SHADE.
Tracks: / Out on the ocean / Forest flower / Maro snaps / Hills of Donegal / Todd's sweet rural shade / Once I loved / Tim O'Leary's waltz / Captain Carswell.
LP: . . . . LOUGH 003
MC: . . . . LOUGH 003C
MC: . . . . LOUGHC 003

WELCOMING PADDY HOME.
Tracks: / When sick is it tea you want / Cape Breton wedding reel no 1 / Teelin march, The / Welcoming Paddy home / Miss Rowan Davies / Eugene Stratton / Antrim rose, The / Alexander's / Rose of Ardee, The / Tonbigbee waltz, The / Irish washerwoman, The.
LP: . . . . LOUGH 001
MC: . . . . LOUGHC 001
LP: . . . . SHAN 79061
MC: . . . . SHANC 9061

WISH YOU WERE HERE.
LP: . . . . FF 070

Boys (Soul)

BOYS, THE.
Tracks: / Dear fans (intro) / Crazy / Thing called love / Compton (interlude) / Funny / My love / What's for dinner (reprise) / I had a dream / Got to be there / Interview (interlude) / Sir Nose (interlude) / Thanx 4 the funk / Hey clown (interlude) / Bush, The / See ya! / Strings'n'things (On CD only.).
LP: . . . . ZL 72718
MC: . . . . ZK 72718

MESSAGES FROM THE BOYS.
Tracks: / Dial my heart / Lucky charm / Little romance, A / Sunshine / Love gram / Just for the fun of it / Personality / Be my girl / Happy / Let's dance.
LP: . . . . ZL 72648
MC: . . . . ZK 72648

Boys Wonder

RADIO WONDER.
LP: . . . . OUTA 002

Boystown Gang

CAST OF THOUSANDS, A.
Tracks: / Good man is hard to find, A / Brand new me / In and out of love / Here I am waiting for you / I just can't help believing / Dance trance medley / Yester-me, yester-you, yesterday / When will I see you again.
LP: . . . . RNF 7260
MC: . . . . ZCRNF 7260

CRUISIN' THE STREETS.
Tracks: / Remember me / Ain't no mountain high enough / Reprise / Finale / Cruisin' the streets / Cruisin' / Rejected / Pick up / Busted.
LP: . . . . BTG 231
LP: . . . . K 231

DISCHARGE.
LP: . . . . ERCLP 101
MC: . . . . ZCERC 101

Boyz II Men

COOLEYHIGHARMONY.
Tracks: / Please don't go / Lonely heart / This is my heart / Uhh ahh / It's so hard to say goodbye to yesterday / Motownphilly / Under pressure / Sympin' / Little things / Your love.
LP: . . . . ZL 72739
MC: . . . . ZK 72739

Boyzz

TOO WILD TO TAME.
Tracks: / Too wild to tame / Hoochie koochie / Wake it up, shake it up / Shady lady / Back to Kansas / Destined to die / Lean'n'mean / Dianne / Good life shuffle.
LP: . . . . EPC 82995

Boze, Calvin

CHOO CHOO'S BRINGIN' MY BABY HOME.
Tracks: / My friend told me / Good time Sue / Stinkin' from drinkin' / Blow man blow / Fish.
LP: . . . . KIX 35

HAVIN' A BALL (Boze, Calvin & His All Stars).
LP: . . . . BLP 113

B.P.I. Awards

B.P.I. AWARDS, THE (Various artists).
LP: . . . . STAR 2346
MC: . . . . STAC 2346

B.P.I. BRITS AWARDS 90 (Various artists).
Tracks: / All around the world: *Stansfield, Lisa* / Fine time: *Yazz* / My prerogative: *Brown, Bobby (1)*/ Sowing the seeds of love: *Tears For Fears* / Best, The: *Turner, Tina* / My one temptation: *Paris, Mica*/ Eye know: *De La Soul* / Sensual world, The: *Bush, Kate* / Girl I'm gonna miss you: *Milli Vanilli* / Bamboleo: *Gipsy Kings* / Best of me, The: *Richard, Cliff*.
MCSET: . . . . STAC 2386
2LP: . . . . STAR 2386

B.P.I. BRITS AWARDS 91 (Various artists).
LP: . . . . STAR 2481
MC: . . . . STAC 2481

B.P.M.

B.P.M. VOL 2 (Various artists).
LP: . . . . CAL 220
MC: . . . . CAC 220

Brace, Brent

VALLEY GIRL JAZZ.
LP: . . . . PRO 7071

Braces

PRIME CUT.
LP: . . . . PHZA 30

Bracey, Ishmael

COMPLETE RECORDINGS 1928-30.
LP: . . . . WSE 105

Bracey, Osiman

JOHNNY JOHNSTON & OSIMAN BRACEY (See Johnston, Johnny).

Brackeen, Charles

BANNAR (Brackeen, Charles Quartet).
LP: . . . . SHLP 105

Brackeen, Joanne

AFT.
Tracks: / Haiti B / Charlotte's dream / Dreamers / Aft / Winter is here / Green voices of play air.
LP: . . . . SJP 115

FI-FI GOES TO HEAVEN.
Tracks: / Estilo magnifico / Stardust / Fi Fi goes to heaven / Zingaro / I hear a rhapsody / Cosmonaut / Doctor Chang.
LP: . . . . CJ 316
MC: . . . . CJC 316

HAVIN' FUN (Brackeen, Joanne Trio).
Tracks: / Thinking of you / I've got the world on a string / Emily / Just one of those things / This is always / Everything she wants / Manha de carnaval / Day by day.
LP: . . . . CJ 280

INVITATION.
LP: . . . . FLP 41044

LIVE AT MAYBECK RECITAL HALL VOL.1.
Tracks: / Thou swell / Dr Chu Chow / Yesterdays / Curved space / My foolish heart / Calling Carl / I'm old fashioned / Strike up the band / Most beautiful girl in the world, The (Available on CD only) / It could happen to you (Available on CD only) / African Aztec (Available on CD only).
MC: . . . . CJ 409C

NEW TRUE ILLUSION (Brackeen, Joanne & Clint Houston).
Tracks: / Steps what was / Search for peace / New true illusion / My romance / Freedent / Solar.
LP: . . . . SJP 103

SPECIAL IDENTITY.
LP: . . . . AN 1001

TRINKETS AND THINGS (Brackeen, Joanne & Ryo Kawaski).
Tracks: / Trinkets & things / Showbrook air / Winnie & Woodstock / Fair weather / Whim within / Spring of things / Haiti B.
LP: . . . . SJP 123

Bracken Lads

ON THE BURGHEAD SAND.
LP: . . . . UNKNOWN

Brad Is Sex

GENTLEMEN START YOUR SHEEP.
LP: . . . . MARI 074

Bradbury, Colin

VIRTUOSO CLARINETTIST, THE (Bradbury, Colin/Oliver Davies).
Tracks: / Variations (Weber) / Morceau de salon (Kalliwoda) / Fantasia and variations on a theme of Danzi (Spohr) / Fantasia on Verdi's 'La Traviata' (Lovreglio) / Studio primo (Donizetti) / Il Convegno (Ponchielli) (also Donald Watson (clarinet)) / Cujus animam (from Stabat Mater) (Rossini) / Ballabile con variazioni (Panizza) / Morceau de concert (Waterson) / Solo de concours (Messager).
MC: . . . . ZC DCA 701

Bradbury, Ray (aut)

ILLUSTRATED MAN, THE (see under Illustrated Man (bk)) (Nimoy, Leonard).

MARTIAN CHRONICLES, THE (see under Martian Chronicles) (Nimoy, Leonard).

SMALL ASSASSIN, THE (See under Small Assassin).

Braddeley, John (nar)

WIND IN THE WILLOWS (see under Wind in the Willows).

Braden, Kim (nar)

DEENIE (see under Deenie (bk)).

Bradfield, Ray

ON PAROLE.
LP: . . . . STFC 002

Bradford

BRADFORD.
LP: . . . . CHIME 0043M

SHOUTING QUIETLY.
LP: . . . . FOUND 001
MC: . . . . FOUND 001C

Bradford, Bobby

SECRETS (see Carter, John).

Bradford, Geoff

MAGNOLIA.
Tracks: / South / Rockin' pneumonia / Brother can you spare a dime / Crippled Clarence says / Maggie's farm / My credit didn't go through / Magnolia / Winnin' boy / Red's piece / Everybody loves my baby / Drowning on dry land / Rockin' chair.
LP: . . . . CRL 004

ROCKIN' THE BLUES.
Tracks: / Leaving trunk / Forty days and forty nights / I'm gonna move to the outskirts of town / That bone thing / Drop down mama / St. Thomas / Little security / Back at the chicken shack.
LP: . . . . BLP 12142

Bradley, Hank

MUSIC OF THE POISON COYOTE KID.
LP: . . . . BAY 303

Bradley, Martyn

TIME CAN'T STAND STILL.
Tracks: / Burkes jig / Hardiman / Paddy be easy / Sligo fair / Helas medame / Humors of tullacreen / Rakes of Brandenburg / Spot the tune rag / McKinnons march / Lord Mayo / Sonata in F major (Handel) / South wind / Planxty hewlet / Playfords / Empty days.
LP: . . . . GVR 205

Bradley, Owen

BIG GUITAR.
Tracks: / Big guitar / Cannonball / Rumble / Ramrod / Tequila / Tricky / Raunchy / Blueberry Hill / Honky Tonk / Five o'clock jump / Hound dog / Stroll, The / Cool daddy / Funky.
LP: . . . . CR 30234

Bradley, Tommie

1930-32 (Bradley, Tommie/James Cole Group).
Tracks: / Mama keep your yes ma'am clean / Everybody got somebody / Adam and Eve / Runnin' wild / Sweet Lizzie / Pack up your trunk blues / Undertaker blues / Mistreated the only friend you had / Nobody's business if I do / Window pane blues / Where you been so long / When you're down and out / Please don't act that way / I love my Mary / Four day blues.
LP: . . . . MSE 211

Bradley, Will

1941 Featuring Ray McKinley (Bradley, Will & Orchestra).
LP: . . . . CLP 88

BASIN STREET BOOGIE 1941 - 42 (Bradley, Will & His Orchestra).
LP: . . . . BS 7110

FIVE O'CLOCK WHISTLE 1939 - 41 (Bradley, Will & His Orchestra).
LP: . . . . BS 7101

IN DISCO ORDER VOL 1.
LP: . . . . AJAX 112

IN DISCO ORDER VOL 2.
LP: . . . . AJAX 115

IN DISCO ORDER VOL 3.
LP: . . . . AJAX 119

ROCK-A-BYE THE BOOGIE 1940-41 (Bradley, Will & His Orchestra).
LP: . . . . BS 7112
MC: . . . . BS 7112C

WILL BRADLEY & RAY MCKINLEY, 1940-41 (Bradley, Will & Ray McKinley).
Tracks: / Fatal fascination / Cherry / I guess I'll have to dream the rest / Just a little bit south of North Caralina / I went out of my way / Be I bi / Song of the islands / Booglie wooglie piggy, The / This little icky went to town / Flying home / All the things you are / Wham / King Calypso / 'S wonderful / It's a wonderful world / Starlight hour, The / Hallelujah.
LP: . . . . AIRCHECK 15

WILL BRADLEY - VOL 4, 1940.
LP: . . . . AJAX 131

WILL BRADLEY - VOL 5, 1940-41.
LP: . . . . AJAX 136

WILL BRADLEY - VOL 6, 1941.
LP: . . . . AJAX 142

WILL BRADLEY - VOL 7, 1941.
LP: . . . . AJAX 150

WILL BRADLEY - VOL 8, 1941-46.
LP: . . . . AJAX 158

WILL BRADLEY & WINGY MANONE (Bradley, Will & Wingy Manone).
LP: . . . . HQ 2037

WINGY MANONE & WILL BRADLEY (see under Manone, Wingy) (Bradley, Will & Wingy Manone).

WOODCHOPPERS' BALL/ AT THE FAMOUS DOOR (See under Herman, Woody) (Bradley, Will & Woody Herman).

Bradman, Donald

BRADMAN - THE DON DECLARES.
MCSET: . . . . ZBBC 1089

Bradshaw, Tiny

BREAKING UP THE HOUSE.
Tracks: / Breaking up the house / Walk that mess / Train kept a rollin' / T 99 / Bradshaw boogie / Walking the chalk line / Mailman's sack / Snaggle tooth Ruth / Rippin' and runnin' / Blues came pouring down, The / Two dry bones on the pantry shelf / Brad's blues / Boodie green / Well oh well / Newspaper boy blues / One,two,three, kick blues.
LP: . . . . CRB 1092
MC: . . . . TCCRB 1092

I'M A HIGH BALLIN' DADDY.
Tracks: / I've been around / Straighten up and fly again / Salt Lake City bounce / School day blues / After you've gone / Bradshaw bounce / These things are love / Butterfly / I'm a high ballin' daddy / Pompton turnpike / Lay it on the line / If I had a million dollars / Spider web / If you don't love me tell me so / Overflow / Strange.
LP: . . . . JB 621

STOMPING ROOM ONLY.
Tracks: / Walk that mess / Bradshaw boogie / T 99 / Breaking up the house / Well oh well / Train kept a rollin' / Cat fruit / Stomping room only / Gravy train / Newspaper boy blues / I'm gonna have myself a ball / Long time baby / Mailman's sack / Blues came pouring down, The / Heavy juice / Cat nap.
LP: . . . . KK 419

TINY BRADSHAW 1934/TEDDY HILL 1935-1936 (Bradshaw, Tiny/Hill, Teddy).
Tracks: / Shout Sister Shout / Mister will you serenade / Darktown strutters ball / Sheik of Araby / Ol' man river / I ain't got nobody / I'm a ding dong daddy from Dumas / She'll be coming round the mountain / Lookie lookie lookie here comes Cookie / Got me doin' things / When the robin sings his song again / When love knocks at your heart / Uptown rhapsody / At the rug cutter's ball / Blue rhythm fantasy / Passionette.
2LP: . . . . HQ 2053

TRIBUTE TO THE LATE TINY BRADSHAW, A.
Tracks: / Soft / Off and on / Heavy juice / Well oh well / Free for all / Choice / Bushes / Stack of dollars / Later / Powder stuff / South of the Orient / Train kept a-rollin', The / Light / Ping pong / Come on / Cat fruit.
LP: . . . . SING 653

Bradshaws

BRADSHAWS VOL. 1 (In Their Own Words).
Tracks: / What was it like in olden days / Monkey with the funny coloured bum, The / God's spy 'ole / Mam's fys / 2 wheeler, influence and wee, The / Ragbone & dad's brown mac / Marbses / Fixin the window / Bonfire night / Fog an' dad's bike lamp, The / Can I 'ave a budgie / Dad's coat and the scruffy dog.
MC: . . . . ZW 26

BRADSHAWS VOL. 2 (In Their Own Voices).
Tracks: / Tooth fairy, The / Split the kipper / Taking plaster off / Hiccups / Are you in a good mood or a bad mood / Runaway / Wot's your belly button for / Old tin bath, The / Chapped legs / Will you fix me roller skate / Dad's black eye / Snowball, The.
MC: . . . . ZV 27

BRADSHAWS VOL. 3 (In Their Own Backyard).
Tracks: / Empty bottles / Bent cigs and corn dog / Politics and beans / Clubman cometh, The / Tea-time / Whit walks / Love letters / Pickles / Man's 'eadache and rickers / Heaster heggs / Fun at the fair / Two balls.
MC: . . . . ZB 28

Brady, Paul

BACK TO THE CENTRE.
LP: . . . . MERH 86
MC: . . . . MERHC 86

FULL MOON.
Tracks: / Hard station / Not the only one / Take me away / Busted loose / Dance the romance / Crazy dreams / Helpless heart / Steel claw / Tootsies.
LP: . . . . FIEND 34

HARD STATION.
Tracks: / Crazy dreams / Road to the promised land / Busted loose / Cold cold night / Hard station / Dancer in the fire / Night hunting time / Nothing but the same old story.
LP: . . . . POLS 1072
MC: . . . . POLSC 1072
MC: . . . . PRIMC 122
LP: . . . . PRICE 122
LP: . . . . K 58312
MC: K4 58312
LP: 834 996-1
MC: 834 996-4

HIGH PART OF ROAD.
MC: 4TA 29003

MOLLOY, BRADY, PEOPLES (Brady, Paul/Matt Molloy/Tommy Peoples).
Tracks: / Creel of turf, The / Tom Billys / Crosses of Annagh, The / McFaddens handsome daughter / Newport lass, The / Rambling pitchfork, The / Shamrock shore, The / Munster buttermilk / Connaught man's rambles, The / Speed the plough / Toss the feathers / Limerick lasses, The / Foxhunters, The / Mick Finns / Blackthorn / Fergal O'Gara / Cloon, The / Mulqueeney's / Out in the ocean / Rainy day, The / Grand canal, The / Scotsman over the border, The / Killavil, The / John Brennans / Drag her round the road / Graf spee, The.
LP: . . . . LUN 17
MC: . . . . CLUN 17

PRIMITIVE DANCE.
Tracks: / Steal your heart away / Soul commotion, The / Paradise is here / It's gonna work out fine / Awakening, The / Eat the peach / Don't start knocking / Just in case of accidents / Game of love.
LP: . . . . MERH 106
MC: . . . . MERHC 106

TRICK OR TREAT.
LP: 8484541
MC: 8484544

TRUE FOR YOU.
Tracks: / Great pretender, The / Let it happen / Helpless heart / Dance the romance / Steel claw / Take me away / Not the only one / Interlude / Trouble round the bend.
LP: . . . . POLD 5091
MC: . . . . POLDC 5091
LP: 810893-1
MC: 810893-4

WELCOME HERE KIND STRANGER.
LP: . . . . LUN 024
MC: . . . . CLUN 024

WORDS AND MUSIC OF SEAN O'CASEY (Brady, Paul & John Kavanagh).
LP: . . . . STAL 8012

Brady, Phil

LIVERPOOL SOUNDS.
LP: . . . . SFA 034

Brady, Sean

THATCHER SONG.
LP: . . . . CRULP 001
MC: . . . . CRUC 001
LP: . . . . IHLP 481
MC: . . . . IHMC 481

Braff, Ruby

AMERICA THE BEAUTIFUL (Braff, Ruby & Dick Hyman).
Tracks: / When it's sleepy time down South / When my sugar walks down the street / When I fall in love / As long as I live / America the beautiful / Louisiana / High society / I'll be with you in apple blossom time / I ain't got nobody / This is all I ask.
LP: . . . . GW 3003

BEST I'VE HEARD.
Tracks: / Our love is here to stay / On the sunny side of the street / It don't mean a thing / It don't mean a thing / You're a lucky guy / Struttin' with some barbecue / Rockin' in rhythm / Body and soul / Sugar.
LP: . . . . VJD 519
MC: . . . . ZC VJD 519

BRAFF PLAYS BING.
LP: . . . . PIZZA 5501
MC: . . . . PIZZA C5501

BRAVURA ELOQUENCE (Braff, Ruby Trio).
Tracks: / Ol' man river / Smile (who'll buy my violets) / Lonely moments (Only on CD) / Here's Cari / God bless the child / It's bad for me / I've grown accustomed to her face / Make sense (Only on CD) / I'm shooting high / Orange / Persian rug (Only on CD) / Trav'lin light / Royal Garden blues / Judy medley.
MC: . . . . CJ 423 C

EASY NOW.
Tracks: / My walking stick / Willow weep for me / When my sugar walks down the street / Song is ended, The / Give my regards to broadway / This is my lucky day / Someday you'll be sorry / Yesterdays / For now / I just couldn't take it baby / Little man, you've had a busy day / Swinging on a star / Old folks / Did you ever see a dream walking / Pocketful of dreams / Moonlight becomes you / Pennies from Heaven / Go fly a kite / Please / All alone / You're sensational / Too-ra-loo-ra-loo-ra / White Christmas.
LP: . . . . PL 45140

FINE MATCH, A (Braff, Ruby & Scott Hamilton).
Tracks: / Romance in the dark / When a woman loves a man / Rockin' chair / Dinah / All my life / Shine / If you were mine (Part of medley) / I wished on the moon** (**=Part of medley) / Bugle blues** (**=Part of medley).

LP: . . . . CJ 274

HEAR ME TALKIN'.
Tracks: / You've changed / Hear me talkin' to ya / Don't blame me / No one else but you / Nobody knows you (when you're down and out) / Buddy Bolden's blues / Mean to me / Where's Freddy?.
LP: . . . . BLP 30110

HUSTLIN' AND BUSTLIN'.
Tracks: / Hustlin' & bustlin' / There's a small hotel / What's the reason / 'S wonderful / When it's sleepy time down South / Flaky / Fine and mellow / Ad lib blues.
LP: . . . . BLP 60908

MANHATTAN JAZZ (See under Hyman, Dick) (Braff, Ruby & Dick Hyman).

ME, MYSELF AND I (Braff, Ruby Trio).
Tracks: / Muskrat ramble / You've changed / Honey / Me, myself and I / When I fall in love / That's my home / Let me sing and I'm happy / You're a lucky guy / No one else but you / When you're smiling / Swan lake / Jubilee.
LP: . . . . CJ 381
MC: . . . . CJ 381C

MIGHTY BRAFF, THE.
Tracks: / When you're smiling / Easy living / Pullin' through / You're a lucky guy / Blue room / I can't get started / This can't be love / Flowers for a lady / Foolin' myself / I'll be around / It's easy to blame the weather / Struttin' with some barbeque / Mean to me / Ellie / You're a sweetheart / Blue and sentimental.
LP: . . . . AFF 98

MUSIC FROM MY FAIR LADY (Braff, Ruby & Dick Hyman).
Tracks: / Wouldn't it be loverly / With a little bit of luck / I'm an ordinary man / Rain in Spain, The / I could have danced all night / Ascot gavotte / On the street where you live / Show me / Get me to the church on time / Without you / I've grown accustomed to her face.
MC: . . . . CJ 393C

MUSIC FROM SOUTH PACIFIC (Braff, Ruby & Dick Hyman).
Tracks: / Bali Ha'i / Some enchanted evening / Cock-eyed optimist / Wonderful guy, A / Happy talk / Dites-moi / This nearly was mine / There is nothing like a dame / Honeybun / Younger than Springtime / Bali Ha'i (final version).
MC: . . . . CJ 445C

ON SUNNIE'S SIDE OF THE STREET (Braff, Ruby & Ralph Sutton).
LP: . . . . BAJC 501

PRETTIES.
Tracks: / Nancy with the laughing face / Love me or leave me / Tangerine / S'posin'.
LP: . . . . SNTF 777

RUBY BRAFF.
Tracks: / Dancing in the dark / Blue prelude / Why was I born / Blue / If I could be you / I'm crazy about my baby / Louisiana / It's wonderful / Almost like being In love / Love come back to me / I must have that man.
LP: . . . . JASM 1043

RUBY BRAFF & SCOTT HAMILTON (Braff, Ruby & Scott Hamilton).
LP: . . . . PHONT 7568

RUBY BRAFF WITH THE ED BICKERT TRIO (Braff, Ruby & the Ed Bickert Trio).
Tracks: / True love / I've got a feeling I'm falling / This year's kisses / World is waiting for the sunrise, The / Very thought of you, The / After a while / What is there to say / My funny valentine / Song is ended, (The) / When I fall in love.
LP: 3022

RUBY BRAFF/MARSHALL BROWN SEXTET (Braff, Ruby/Marshall Brown Sextet).
LP: . . . . FS 142

RUBY GOT RHYTHM.
LP: . . . . BLP 30188

SAILBOAT IN THE MOONLIGHT (Braff, Ruby & Scott Hamilton).
Tracks: / Lover come back to me / Where are you? / Deed I do / When lights are low / Jeepers creepers / Milkman's matinee, The / Sweethearts on parade / Sailboat in the moonlight.
LP: . . . . CJ 296
MC: . . . . CJC 296

SWING THAT MUSIC (Braff, Ruby & Red Norvo).
2LP: . . . . AFFD 45

THEM THERE EYES.
Tracks: / Swinging on a star / Same old South / Yesterdays / Medley: I'm pulling through / It's the little things that mean so much / Them there eyes / I've grown accustomed to her face / Why was I born / Dream dancing / Love lies / Tea for two.
LP: . . . . SNTF 713
MC: . . . . ZCSN 713

Bragg, Billy

BACK TO BASICS.
Tracks: / Milkman of human kindness, The / To have and have not / Richard / Lovers town revisited / New England, A / Man in the iron mask, The / Busy girl buys beauty, The / It says here / Love gets dangerous / From a Vauxhall Velox / Myth of trust, The / Saturday boy, The / Island of no return, The / This guitar says sorry / Like soldiers do / St. Swithins day / Strange things happen / Lover sings, A / Between the wars / World turned upside down, The / Which side are you on.
2LP: . . . . AGODP 8
MCSET: . . . . ZGODP 8

BREWING UP WITH BILLY BRAGG.
Tracks: / It says here / Love gets dangerous / Myth of trust, The / From a vauxhall velox / Saturday boy, The / Island of no return, The / St. Swithin's day / Like soldiers do / This guitar says sorry / Strange things happen / Lover sings, A.
LP: . . . . AGOLP 4
MC: . . . . ZGOLP 4

INTERNATIONALE, THE.
LP: . . . . UTIL 011
MC: . . . . UTILC 011

LIFE'S A RIOT WITH SPY VS. SPY.
Tracks: / Milkman of human kindness, The / To have and have not / New England, A / Man in the iron mask, The / Busy girl buys beauty, The / Lovers town revisited / Richard.
LP: . . . . UTIL 1
MC: . . . . UTILC 1

SAVE THE YOUTH OF AMERICA.
MLP: . . . . AGOMLP 1
MC: . . . . ZAGOMLP 1

TALKING WITH THE TAXMAN ABOUT POETRY.
Tracks: / Greetings to the new brunette / Train train / Marriage, The / Ideology / Levi Stubbs tears / Honey I'm a big boy now / There is power in a union / Help save the youth of America / Wishing the days away / Passion, The / Warmest room, The / Home front, The.
LP: . . . . AGOLP 6
MC: . . . . ZGOLP 6
LP: . . . . LILP 400237

WORKERS PLAYTIME.
Tracks: / She's got a new spell / Must I paint you a picture / Tender comrade / Price I pay, The / Little time bomb / Rotting on remand / Valentine's day is over / Life with the lions / Only one, The / Short answer / Waiting for the great leap forwards.
LP: . . . . AGOLP 15
MC: . . . . ZGOLP 15

Brahem, Anouar

BARZAKH.
Tracks: / Raf raf / Barzakh / Sadir / Ronda / Hou / Sarandib / Souga / Parfum de Gitane / Bou naouara / Kerkenah / La nuit des yeux / Le belvedera assiege / Oaf.
LP: . . . . ECM 1432
MC: 8475404

Brahms (composer)

BRAHMS (Various artists).
MC: . . . . DLCMC 220

BRAHMS CLARINET TRIO AND SONATAS (Hacker, Alan/Jennifer Ward Clarke/Richard Burnett).
Tracks: / Trio in A minor (Brahms) (Opus 114. Allegro/Adagio/Andantino Grazioso/Allegro.) / Sonata no.1 (F minor) (Opus 120) (Brahms) (Allegro Appassionato/Andante un poco adagio/ Allegretto Grazioso/Vivace) / Sonata no.2 (E flat major) (Brahms) (Allegro amabile/Appassionato, ma n troppo allegro/Andante con moto Alleg).
MC: . . . . CSAR 37

BRAHMS SYMPHONY NO.3 (Davis, Sir Colin).
MC: . . . . RK 60118

BRAHMS VIOLIN CONCERTO (See Under Kennedy, Nigel) (Kennedy, Nigel).

PIANO CONCERTO NO.1 (BRAHMS) Variations on a theme of Schumann (Vienna Philharmonic Orchestra).
MC: 4251104

PIANO TRIO NO.3 Cello sonata no 2 (Various artists).
MC: 4254234

SYMPHONY NO.1 (BRAHMS) (Los Angeles Philharmonic Orchestra).
MC: 4278044

SYMPHONY NO. 4 IN E MINOR (See under Solti, Sir George) (Chicago Symphony Orchestra).

TRIPLE CONCERTO/DOUBLE CONCERTO (See under Beethoven) (Serkin & Larado & Parnas).

Braille Party

WELCOME TO MARYLAND.
LP: . . . . FOY 011

Brainiac 5

WORLD INSIDE, THE.
LP: . . . . RECK 1

Brains

BRAINS.
Tracks: / Treason / See me / Raeline / Girl I wanna / In the night / Money changes everything / Scared kid / Sweethearts / Girl in a magazine / Gold dust kids.
LP: 633 710 3

DANCING UNDER THE STREETLIGHTS.
Tracks: / Dancing under the streetlights / Danya / Read my mind / Don't give yourself away.
LP: . . . . LM 1201

Brainstorm

FUNKY ENTERTAINMENT.
Tracks: / Hot for you / Case of the boogie / Popcorn / Funky entertainment / You put a charge in my life / Don't let me catch you with your groove down.
LP: . . . . TBU 83736

Brainstorm (Film)

BRAINSTORM (Film Soundtrack) (Various artists).
Tracks: / Brainstorm: Main Theme: *Various artists* / Lilian's heart attack: *Various artists* / Gaining access to the tapes: *Various artists* / Michael's gift to Karen: *Various artists* / First playback: *Various artists*/ Race for time: *Various artists* / Final playback/End titles: *Various artists.*
LP: . . . . TER 1074
MC: . . . . CTV 81197

Braithwaite, Daryl

EDGE.
Tracks: / As the days go by / You could be wrong / All I do / Let me be / Sugar train / It's all in the music / One summer / Up out - all the same / Pretending to care / Down down (Only on cassette and CD.) / In my life (Only on cassette and CD.) / I don't remember (Only on cassette and CD.) / Edge (instrumental) (Only on CD.).
LP: 4626251
MC: 4626254

Brakes

FOR WHY YOU KICKA MY DONKEY?.
Tracks: / What am I gonna do? / I don't know nothing about Hollywood / Doing life / Who's that in the Brakes / Like a rolling stone / Blame it on the Brakes / Way I see it / Last man at the station / Strange man in the city / Yesterday's arrival / It's a shame.
LP: . . . . MAGL 5029

Brambles, Jaki

JAKI BRAMBLES PRESENTS THE MEGA VIDEO HITS OF 19 (See Under Jaki Brambles) (Various artists).

Brambly Hedge (bks)

SECRET STAIRCASE, THE/THE HIGH HILLS (Jill Barklem).
MC: 00 104 1282

Brammer, Junior

CRUISIN' (see under Kenton,Janet's "I need your loving').

HOLD YOUR LOVER.
LP: . . . . LLLP 26

TELEPHONE LINE.
LP: . . . . JDLP 003

Brammer, Phil

MUSIC BY NUMBERS.
LP: . . . . PLUCK 3

Branca, Glenn

SYMPHONY NO.1 (GLENN BRANCA).
MC: . . . . A 125

SYMPHONY NO.6 (Devil Choirs at the Gates of Heaven).
Tracks: / First movement / Second movement / Third movement / Fourth movement / Fifth movement.
LP: . . . . BFFP 39
MC: . . . . BFFP 39C

Brancaster Musicale

DREAMS.
Tracks: / Greensleeves / London by night / Songs of the seas / Irish prelude / Strawberry fair / English country / Dream of the isles / My love is like a red red rose / David of the white rock / Banks of the Cam / Scarborough fair / Ash grove, The / To a wild rose / Cornish floral, The / Windmills of your mind / Hunting the hare / Winter melody, A / Blowing in the wind / Dawn chorus / Watermill, The / September, song / Oranges and lemons / Elvira Madigan / Lark in the clear air / How deep is the ocean / Ship of dreams / Stratford on Avon / Ebb tide.
2LP: . . . . CR 067
MCSET: . . . . CRT 067

Brancaster Symphony...

WARM AND TENDER MOMENTS (Brancaster Symphony Orchestra).
Tracks: / All the love in the world / Begin the beguine / Can't smile without you / One more night / Crying / I made it through the rain / Imagine / Lately / Do that to me one more time / First time ever I saw your face, The / Hello / If you leave me now / I write the songs / Just when I needed you most / Lara's theme / More than a lover / One day i'll fly away.
LP: . . . . SHLP 151
MC: . . . . SHTC 151

Branch, Andrew (nar)

RAILWAY CAT, THE (See under Railway Cat).

SELECTED STORIES FOR UNDER 5'S (see under Selected Stories) (Branch, Andrew & Heather Tobias).

Branch, Billy

CHICAGO'S YOUNG BLUES GENERATION (see under Bell, Lurrie) (Branch, Billy & Lurrie Bell).

Brand, Dollar

AFRICA - TEARS AND LAUGHTER (Brand, Dollar Quartet).
LP: . . . . ENJA 3039

AFRICAN DAWN.
LP: . . . . ENJA 4030

AFRICAN PIANO.
Tracks: / Bra Joe from Kilimanjaro / Selby that the eternal spirit / Is the only reality / Moon, The / Xaba / Sunset in the blue / Kippy / Jabulani / Tintinyana.
LP: . . . . JAPO 60002

AFRICAN PORTRAITS.
Tracks: / Cherry / Bra Joe from Kilimanjaro / Blues for Hughie / Kipoie gafsa / Life is for the living / Death is for us all / Gwangwa / Little boy / Easter joy / Jabulani / Xaba.
LP: 3009

AFRICAN SKETCH BOOK.
LP: . . . . ENJA 2026

AFRICAN SPACE PROGRAMME.
LP: . . . . ENJA 2032

AFRICAN SUN.
Tracks: / African sun / Bra Joe from Kilimanjaro / Rollin' / Memories of you / Sathima / African herbs / Nobody knows the trouble I've seen / Blues for B / Gwidza / Kamalie.
2LP: . . . . KAZ LP 102
MCSET: . . . . KAZ MC 102

ANCIENT AFRICA.
Tracks: / Bra Joe from Kilimanjaro / Mamma / Tokai / Ilanga / Cherry / African sun / Tintinyana / Xaba / Peace-Salaam air.
LP: . . . . JAPO 60005

ANTHEM FOR THE NEW NATION.
Tracks: / Anthem of the New Nations / Biral / Liberation dance / Trial, The / Cape Town / Wedding suite, The / Wedding, The / Lovers / I surrender dear / One day when we were young / Thaba nchu.
LP: . . . . YX 7537

BLUES FOR A HIP KING.
Tracks: / Ornette's cornet / All day and all night long / Sweet Basil blues / Blue monk / Tsakwe here comes the postman / Blues for a hip king / Blues for B / Mysterioso / Just you just me / Eclipse at dawn / King Kong / Khumbula Jane / Boulevarde East (not on CD).
2LP: . . . . KAZ LP 104
MCSET: . . . . KAZ MC 104

CHILDREN OF AFRICA.
LP: . . . . ENJA 2070

CONFLUENCE (See under Barbieri, Gato) (Brand, Dollar & Gato Barbieri).

DUET (See under Shepp, Archie) (Brand, Dollar & Archie Shepp).

ECHOES FROM AFRICA.
LP: . . . . ENJA 3047

EKAYA.
Tracks: / Ekaya / Sotho blue / Ntyilo, Ntyilo / Bra timing from Phomolong / Ek se ou windhoek toe nou / Cape Town.
LP: . . . . EKAPA 005

GOOD NEWS FROM AFRICA (Brand, Dollar Duo).
LP: . . . . ENJA 2048

LIVE AT MONTREUX: DOLLAR BRAND.
LP: . . . . ENJA 3079

LIVE AT SWEET BASIL (Brand, Dollar & Carlos Ward).

Tracks: / Dream, The / And find me a shelter in the storm / Mummy / For Coltrane II / New York City / Anthem for the new nations / Gwangwa / King Kong, Theme from / Black lightning / Gwidza / Strides, The / Soweto.
LP: . . . . **EKAPA 004**

MINDIF.
LP: . . . . **ENJA 5073**
MC: . . . . **ENJA 45073**

ODE TO DUKE ELLINGTON.
Tracks: / Impressions on a caravan / Ode to Duke / What really happened in the cornfield / Rose got it bad in Harlem / Solitude / In a sentimental mood / Two spirituals.
LP: . . . . **WW 020**

REFLECTIONS.
Tracks: / Honeysuckle rose / Resolution / Knight's night / Mood indigo / Don't get around much anymore / Take the A train / Monk's mood / You are too beautiful / Little Niles / Pye R squared / On the banks of Allen Waters / Reflections / Which way.
LP: . . . . **BLP 60127**

ROUND MIDNIGHT AT MONTMARTRE.
LP: . . . . **BLP 60111**

SANGOMA (VOLUME 1).
LP: **3006**

THIS IS DOLLAR BRAND.
Tracks: / Little Niles / Resolution / Which way? / On the banks of Allen Waters / Knight's night / Pye R squared / Mood indigo / Don't get around much anymore / Take the 'A' train.
LP: . . . . **BLP 30139**

TINTINYANA.
Tracks: / Soweto is where it's at / Tintinyana / Little boy / Cherry / Bra Joe from Kilimanjaro / Shrimp boats / Salaam / Just a song.
LP: . . . . **KAZ LP 103**
MC: . . . . **KAZ MC 103**

VOICE OF AFRICA.
Tracks: / Black lightning / Little boy / Black and brown cherries / Ntyilo, Ntyilo / Mannenberg / Pilgrim, The.
2LP: . . . . **KAZ LP 101**
MC: . . . . **KAZ MC 101**

ZIMBABWE.
LP: . . . . **ENJA 4056**

Brand, Max (aut)

MAX BRAND'S BEST WESTERN STORIES (Edited by William F.Sloan).
MCSET: . . . . **CAB 254**

Brand New Heavies

BRAND NEW HEAVIES, THE.
LP: . . . . **JAZIDLP 023**
MC: . . . . **JAZIDMC 023**

Brand Nubian

ALL FOR ONE.
LP: **7559609461**
MC: **7559609464**

Brand, Oscar

BILLY THE KID IN SONG & STORY.
LP: . . . . **TC 1552**

Brand, Philippe

TIME AND COLORS (Brand, Philippe Trio).
LP: . . . . **SPJ 530**

Brand X

IS THERE ANYTHING ABOUT.
Tracks: / Ipanaemia / Longer April / Modern, noisy and effective / Swan song / Is there anything about / Tmiu'atga.
LP: **85967**

LIVESTOCK.
Tracks: / Nightmare patrol / Ish / Euthanasia waltz / Isis mourning (Parts 1 & 2) / Malaga virgen.
LP: . . . . **CLASS 5**

MASQUES.
Tracks: / Poke, The / Masques / Black moon / Deadly nightshade / Earth dance / Access to data / Ghost of Mayfield Lodge, The.
LP: . . . . **PB 9829**

MOROCCAN ROLL.
Tracks: / Sun in the night / Why should I lend you mine (when you've broken yours off) / Maybe I'll lend you mine after all / Hate zone / Collapsar / Disco suicide / Orbits / Malaga virgen / Machocosm.
LP: . . . . **CHC 45**
LP: . . . . **CAS 1126**

PRODUCT.
Tracks: / Don't make waves / Dance of the illegal aliens / Soho / Not good enough - see me / Algon / Rhesus perplexus / Wal to wal / And so to f... / April.
LP: . . . . **CHC 3**
MC: . . . . **CHCMC 3**

UNORTHODOX BEHAVIOUR.
Tracks: / Nuclear burn / Euthanasia waltz / Born ugly / Smacks of euphoric hysteria / Unorthodox behaviour / Running on three / Touch wood.
LP: . . . . **PB 9819**
MC: . . . . **PBC 9819**
LP: . . . . **CHC 44**

UNORTHODOX BEHAVIOUR/ MOROCCAN ROLL.
Tracks: / Nuclear burn / Euthanasia waltz / Born ugly / Smacks of euphoric hysteria / Unorthodox behaviour / Running on three / Touch wood / Sun in the night / Why should I lend you mine (when you've broken yours off) / Maybe I'll lend you mine after all / Hate zone / Collapsar / Disco suicide / Orbits / Malaga virgen / Macrocosm.
MCSET: . . . . **CASMC 109**

XTRAX (BEST OF).
LP: . . . . **PB 6054**
MC: . . . . **PBC 6054**

Brandenburg, Helmuth

BABYLON.
LP: . . . . **ISST 114**

Brandes, Will

KING CREOLE.
Tracks: / Wunderbares madchen / Wach auf little Susie / Ahoi-ohe / O Judy / Komm / Marina / Ich mocht mit dir traumen / Kiss me, honey honey, kiss me / King Creole / Die musik ist gut / Die boys und die girls von heute / Teenager melodie / Du bist schon / In Toni's pizzeria / Was war das alles ohne dich.
LP: . . . . **BFX 15117**

Branduardi, Angelo

FABLES AND FANTASIES.
Tracks: / Dust and ashes / Il ciliegio / Enchanted lake / By appointment / Lady / Merry we will be / Stolen bride / Hare in the moon / Mustapha's tale.
LP: . . . . **ARLH 5031**

HIGHDOWN FAIR.
Tracks: / Highdown fair / Herons / Old men and butterflies / Lullaby to Sarah / Song of eternal numbers / Stag / Funeral / Man and the cloud / Under the lime tree / Song of regret.
LP: . . . . **ARL 5016**

Brandy & Pope

GETTIN' HIGH WITH BRANDY & POPE.
Tracks: / I've been loving you so long / Evangeline / Kate and Edith / Everybody sings the blues / Idol of the band / Honky tonk heroes / Gettin' high, by, and strange / Train of life / Heaven is my woman's love / Hello darlin' / Me and Paul / I'll break out again tonight.
LP: . . . . **FHR 087**

Branigan, Laura

BRANIGAN 1.
Tracks: / All night with me / Gloria / Lovin' you baby / Living a lie / If you loved me / Please stay, go away / I wish I could be alone / Down like a rock / Maybe I love you.
LP: . . . . **K 50772**
MC: **K4 50772**

BRANIGAN 2.
Tracks: / Solitaire / Deep in the dark / Close enough / Lucky / Squeeze box / Gloria / How am I supposed to live with you / I'm not the only one / Mama / Find me / Don't show your love.
LP: . . . . **A 0066**
MC: . . . . **A 0066 4**

HOLD ME.
Tracks: / Hold me / Maybe tonight / Foolish lullaby / Spanish Eddie / Forever young / When i'm with you / I found someone / Sanctuary / Tenderness / When the heart hits the streets.
LP: **781 265-1**
MC: **781 265-4**

LAURA BRANIGAN.
Tracks: / Moonlight on water / Never in a million years / Let me in / Unison / Reverse psychology / Bad attitude / Smoke screen / Turn the beat around / No promise, no guarantee / Best was yet to come, The.
LP: **7567820861**
MC: **7567820864**

SELF CONTROL.
Tracks: / Lucky one / Self control / Ti amo / Heart / Will you love me tomorrow / Satisfaction / Silent partners / Breaking out / Take me / With every beat of my heart / Self control.
LP: **780 147-1**

TOUCH.
Tracks: / Over love / Shadow of love / Angels calling / Meaning of the word / Power of love, The / Shattered glass / Whatever I do (wherever I go) / Spirit of love / Name game / Touch / Cry wolf.
LP: . . . . **WX 119**
MC: . . . . **WX 119 C**

Brannigan, Owen

BRANNIGAN'S NORTHUMBRIA.
Tracks: / Blaydon races / Where ivver ye gan / Weshin' day, The / Come you not from Newcastle / Neighbours doon bela, The / Canny Tyneside / When this old hat was new / Lark in the clear air / Billy boy / Ma bonny lad / Bobby.
LP: . . . . **MWM 1007**
MC: . . . . **MWM C107**

EVERGREEN.
2LP: . . . . **MFP 1014**

Branscombe, Alan

SWINGIN' ON THE SOUND STAGE (Branscombe, Alan and Friends).
Tracks: / On Green Dolphin Street / Rose room / Blues for Alan, The / Out of nowhere / For Pete's sake / On the Alamo / Tangerine / Close your eyes.
LP: . . . . **ESQ 332**

SWINGING ON THE SOUND STAGE, VOL2.
LP: . . . . **ESQ 342**

Brasil

ULTIMATE COLLECTION, THE (Various artists).
MC: **8453004**

Brasil, Vera

BRAZIL - JUNE 1964.
LP: . . . . **REV 24**

Brass Band

TIJUANA (Various artists).
MC: . . . . **AIM 117**

Brass Bands

22 BRASS BAND FAVOURITES (Various artists).
LP: . . . . **MFP 50430**

40 BRASS BAND FAVOURITES (Various artists).
2LP: . . . . **PLD 8008**
MCSET: . . . . **PLDC 8008**

100 MINUTES OF BRASS BANDS (Various artists).
MC: . . . . **ZCTON 8171**

BEST OF BRASS (Various artists).
Tracks: / Colonel Bogey on parade: *Various artists* / Thunder and lightning polka: *Various artists* / Praise to the holiest: *Various artists* / Grand march from Aida: *Various artists* / Onward Christian soldiers: *Various* artists / Trumpet voluntary: *Various artists* / Thoughts: *Various artists* / Cornet polka brilliante: *Various* artists / Nights of gladness: *Various artists* / Marching with Sousa: *Various artists* / Overture: *Various artists* / Mini - variation on Welsh theme: *Various artists.*
MCSET: . . . . **DTO 10235**
MC: **TC2MOM 1546539**

BEST OF BRASS 1982 (Highlights from BBC TV brass band contest 1982) (Various artists).
Tracks: / Devil's gallop: *Various artists* / Pastorale: *Various artists* / Scherzo from 'Fantasy for brass': *Various* artists / Mal Sims from 'Giles Farnaby suite': *Various artists* / Trailblaze: *Various artists* / Le Cid: *Various* artists / Galop from 'Little suite no. 2': *Various artists* / Star wars: *Various artists* / Stage centre: *Various artists* / Entry of the huntresses: *Various artists* / Oranges and lemons: *Various artists* / Galop from 'Jeux d'Enfants': *Various artists* / High on a hill: *Various artists* / Frere Jacques: *Various artists* / Heroic march from 'Epic symphony': *Various artists.*
LP: . . . . **PRL 018**
MC: . . . . **CPRL 018**

BEST OF BRASS 1983 (Highlights from BBC TV Brass Band Contest 1983) (Various artists).
Tracks: / Billboard march: *Various artists* / Promenade: *Various artists* / March from 6th Symphony: *Various* artists / Greensleeves: *Various artists* / Blaydon races: *Various artists* / Fantastic fanfare: *Various* artists / March from 'Things to come': *Various artists* / Jubilate: *Various artists* / Bandstand boogie: *Various* artists / Finale from 'Faust': *Various artists* / March from 'Epic Symphony': *Various artists* / All through the night: *Various artists* / Shepherds' hey: *Various artists* / Finale from 'Checkmate': *Various artists* / Sweet nightingale: *Various artists* / Fantasia on 'Tico tico': *Various artists.*
LP: . . . . **PRL 022**
MC: . . . . **CPRL 022**

BEST OF BRASS 1984 (Highlights from BBC TV Brass Band Contest 1984) (Various artists).
Tracks: / Folk festival: *Various artists* / Malaguena: *Various artists* / Nessun dorma: *Various artists* / Doyen: *Various artists* / Lezghinka: *Various artists* / Dansa Brasiliera: *Various artists* / Introduction to Act3 of Lohengrin: *Various artists* / Rhythm & blues: *Various artists* / Toccata in D minor: *Various artists* / Tea for two: *Various artists* / Lark in the clear air: *Various artists* / Capriccio Espagnol: *Various artists* / Entry of the emperor: *Various artists* / Flight of the bumble bee: *Various artists* / West side story: *Various artists.*
LP: . . . . **PRL 024D**
MC: . . . . **CPRL 024D**

BEST OF BRASS 1986 (Highlights from BBC TV Brass Band Contest 1986) (Various artists).
Tracks: / Night flight to Madrid: *Various artists* / Presto from 'Norwegian Rhapsody': *Various artists* / Air from suite No. 3: *Various artists* / Jubilee overture: *Various artists* / Ceremony of the red bishops from 'Checkmate': *Various artists* / March from 'Coq d'Or': *Various artists* / Amazing Grace: *Various artists* / Daphnis and Chloe: *Various artists* / Fanfare: *Various artists* / Postcard from Mexico: *Various artists* / Swan, The: *Various artists* / Belford's carnival march: *Various artists* / Dance of the tumblers: *Various artists* / One voice: *Various artists* / French military march: *Various artists* / Indiana Jones and the Temple of Doom: *Various artists.*
LP: . . . . **PRL 026D**
MC: . . . . **CPRL 026D**

BRASS BAND FAVOURITES (Various artists).
Tracks: / Guns of Navarone: *Cory Band* / Magnificent seven, The: *Cory Band* / Over the rainbow: *Williams-Fairey* Engineering Band / Trouble with the tuba is, The: *Williams-Fairey Engineering Band* / Headless horseman: *Parc* & Dare Band / Men of Harlech: *Parc & Dare Band* / Marche militaire: *Mortimer, Harry & His All Stars* / Death or glass: *Mortimer, Harry & His All Stars* / Tea for two: *Britannia Building Society Foden Band* / Puttin' on the Ritz: *Britannia Building Society Foden Band* / Coronation Street: *G.U.S. Footwear Band* / March of the cobblers: *G.U.S. Footwear Band* / My way: *Hammonds Sauce Works Band* / Ein schnapps: *Hammonds Sauce Works Band*/ Swan, The: *Desford Colliery Band* / Sailing by: *Desford Colliery Band* / Tango taquin: *Harry Mortimer* & His All Star Brass / Can can, The: *Harry Mortimer & His All Star Brass* / Semper sousa: *Harry Mortimer & His All Star Brass* / Colonel Bogey: *Morris Concert Band.*
MC: . . . . **HR 8189**

BRASS BAND FAVOURITES (Various artists).
LP: . . . . **OCN 2041WL**
MC: . . . . **OCN 2041WK**

BRASS BAND FESTIVAL 1982 (HIGHLIGHTS) (Various Brass Bands) (Various artists).
2LP: . . . . **BBRD 1017/18**
MCSET: . . . . **BBTD 1017/18**

BRASS BAND MAGIC (Various artists).
MC: . . . . **CAR 002**

BRASS BANDS OF FODENS, FAREY AVIATION & MORRIS M (Various brass bands) (Various artists).
MC: . . . . **KCSP 306**
LP: . . . . **SPA 306**

BRASS BRITANNIA (Best of British brass) (Various artists).
Tracks: / Rule Britannia: *Various bands* / Jerusalem: *Various bands* / Dambusters march: *Various bands*/ Largo: *Various bands* / Trumpet voluntary: *Various bands* / Jesu, joy of man's desiring: *Various bands*/ Liberty bell: *Various bands* / Berceuse: *Various bands* / Superman suite: *Various bands* / Floral dance, The: *Various bands* / Greensleeves: *Various bands* / Ordinary people: *Various bands* / John Barleycorn: *Various bands* / Take a pair of sparkling eyes: *Various bands* / Onward Christian soldiers: *Various bands*/ Radetzky march: *Various bands* / Ash grove, The: *Various bands* / Pomp and circumstance march no.1: *Various bands.*
LP: . . . . **RTL 2089**
MC: **4CRTL 2089**

BRASS IN BLUE (Devon & Cornwall Constabulary).
LP: . . . . **BM 18**

BRITISH BRASS BANDS (Various artists).
LP: . . . . **JVLP 305**

CHANDOS SOUND OF BRASS (Various artists).
LP: . . . . **BBRD 1009**

COLCHESTER SEARCHLIGHT TATTOO 1980 (Various artists).
Tracks: / Colchester castle: *Fantasia Band* / Delilah: *Various bands* / Money, money, money: *Various bands*/ Children of the regiment: *Various bands* /

Toreadors' march: *Queen's Division* / Speed your journey: *Queen's* Division / Judges of the secret court: *Queen's Division* / Nun's chorus: *Queen's Division* / Goodbye: *Queen's* Division / Men of the hills: *Queen's Division* / Bir nepali: *Queen's Division* / Drummer boy: *Queen's* Division / Music from the Royal Fireworks: *Fantasia Band* / Abide with me: *Fantasia Band* / Last post: *Fantasia Band* / Kindly leave the stage: *Fantasia Band* / Hanoverian, The: *Fantasia Band.*
LP: . . . . **LR 20**

EUROPEAN BRASS BAND CHAMPIONSHIP 1984 (Various Brass Bands) (Various artists).
Tracks: / Radetzky march: *Various bands* / Russlan and Ludmilla overture: *Various bands* / Le cor vole': *Various* bands / Bohemian rhapsody: *Various bands* / Variations on laudate dominum: *Various bands* / Skirl-a Scottish carnival: *Various bands* / Poor wandering one: *Various bands* / Jamie's patrol: *Various bands* / Blight of the fumble bee: *Various bands* / Coronation scene: *Various bands* (From 'Boris Gudunov'.) / Born free: *Various* bands / Jesu, joy of man's desiring: *Various bands* / Battle hymn of the republic: *Various bands* / Auld lang syne: *Various bands* / Refrains and cadenzas: *Various bands* / Plantagenets, The: *Various bands.*
2LP: . . . . **BBRD 1025/6**
MCSET: . . . . **BBTD 1025/6**

EUROPEAN BRASS BAND CHAMPIONSHIP 1981 (featuring the winning bands) (Various artists).
Tracks: / Caliban: *Various artists* / Fantasy for brass band: *Various artists* / Journey into freedom: *Various artists* / Triumphant rhapsody: *Various artists* / Connotations: *Various artists.*
LP: . . . . **PRL 013**
MC: . . . . **CPRL 013**

FAVOURITE BRASS (Various artists).
Tracks: / March of the pacemakers: *Various artists* / First of the 'Three dale dances': *Various artists* / Send in the clowns: *Various artists* / Windmills: *Various artists* / (Overture) HMS Pinafore: *Various artists*/ Entry of the gladiators: *Various artists* / Sunset: *Various artists* / Manhattan Beach (March): *Various* artists / Jeanie with the light brown hair: *Various artists* / Stars and stripes forever: *Various artists*/ In a monastery garden: *Various artists* / March of the toys: *Various artists* / Overture to Nabucco: *Various* artists / March Wellington: *Various artists* / Redhead (Rock of ages): *Various artists* / Chorale and rock out: *Various artists* / Way out west: *Various artists* / If: *Various artists* / Hymn tune: St. Clements: *Various artists* / Dashing away with a smoothing iron: *Various artists* / Hora staccato: *Various artists*/ Divertimento: *Various artists* / Overture to the yeoman of the guard: *Various artists* / Acrobat: *Various artists* / Melodies from 'The Merry Widow': *Various artists* / Grand march from Tannhauser Act II: *Various artists.*
2LP: **41 1044 3**
MCSET: **41 1044 9**

FEAST OF BRASS AND VOICES (Various artists).
Tracks: / March of the peers: *Various artists* / Barber of Seville: *Various artists* / Sound an alarm: *Various* artists / Spin spin: *Various artists* / Speed your journey: *Various artists* / La Reine de Saba: *Various* artists / Love could I only tell thee: *Various artists* / Two roses: *Various artists* / Song of the jolly roger: *Various artists* / New world fantasy: *Various artists* / Soldiers Chorus: *Various artists* / Radetzky march: *Various artists* / By Babylon's wave: *Various artists* / Belmont: *Various artists* / Feasting I watch: *Various artists* / Standard of St. George, The: *Various artists* / Farandole: *Various artists*/ All through the night: *Various artists* / Morte Criste: *Various artists* / Laudamus: *Various artists*/ Pomp and circumstance march no.1: *Various artists.*
2LP: . . . . **LKLP 6403**

FESTIVAL OF FAMOUS BRASS BANDS (Various artists).
Tracks: / Semiramide: *Various artists* / Slavonic dance No. 8: *Various artists* / Simoraine: *Various artists*/ Edelweiss: *Various artists* / River of pearls: *Various artists* / Sounds of Sousa: *Various artists*/ Skye boat song: *Various artists* / Square dance: *Various artists* / Polka piquante: *Various artists*/ Trombola: *Various artists* / Marching trumpets: *Various artists* / Mellow wood: *Various artists.*
LP: . . . . **BD 3007**

GERMAN BRASS (ZUNFTIGE BLASMUSIK) (Various artists).
Tracks: / Ja, in der Birkenau...(...da ist der himmel blau): *Various artists* / Haxenschmeisser Polka: *Various artists*/ Ochsentrieiber glaopp: *Various artists* / Posaunisten vor: *Various artists* / Waldgeist: *Various artists*/ Der ratata hat apfel g'stohln: *Various artists* / Amboss polka: *Various artists* / Schimmel-galopp: *Various* artists / Der wamper gust: *Various artists* / Tiroler holzhacker buam: *Various artists* / Stockergassi: *Various artists.*
LP: **825 942-1**
MC: **825 942-4**

GOLDEN HOUR OF BRASS BANDS (Various artists).
MC: . . . . **ZCGH 521**
MC: . . . . **KGHMC 154**

GOLDEN HOUR OF TOP BRASS (Various artists).
MC: . . . . **ZCGH 641**

GOLDEN HOUR PRESENTS BRASS SPECTACULAR (Various artists).
Tracks: / Champions, The: *March Black Dyke Mills Band* / Watermill, The: *Scottish C.W.S. Band* / Hungarian dance: *Markham Main Colliery Band* / Sandon (lead kindly light): *Besses o' Th' Barn Band* / Cornet carillon: *Black* Dyke Mills Band / La belle Americaine: *Grimethorpe Colliery Band* / Pop goes the weasel: *Crossley's Carpet Works* Band / Marche militaire: *Carlton Main Colliery Band* / Russian and Ludmilla overture: *Various artists* / Paragon, The: *Black Dyke Mills Band* / Non pui andrai: *Hammonds Sauce Works Band* / Bold Gendarmes: *Carlton Main Colliery* Band / Padstow lifeboat: *March Black Dyke Mills Band* / Cock o' the north: *Besses o' Th' Barn Band* / Moon river: *Markham Main Colliery Band* / Gand march from Tannhauser: *Crossley's Carpet Works Band.*
LP: . . . . **GH 608**

GOLDEN HOUR PRESENTS THEMES IN BRASS (Various artists).
Tracks: / Colditz march: *Various artists* / Eye level: *Various artists* / Devil's gallop: *Various artists*/ New world: *Various artists* / Entertainer, The: *Various artists* / Clayhanger: *Various artists* / Moon river: *Various artists* / Jaws: *Various artists* / Swedish rhapsody: *Various artists* / Star wars: *Various artists* / Zorba's dance: *Various artists* / Duchess of Duke Street, The: *Various artists* / Entry of the gladiators: *Various artists* / Summertime: *Various artists* / Who pays the Ferryman: *Various artists* / Air from suite in D: *Various artists* / Godspell: *Various artists* / Prepare ye the way of the Lord (medley): *Various artists*/ Day by day: *Various artists* / I don't know how to love him: *Various artists* / Jesus Christ superstar: *Various artists.*
LP: . . . . **GH 662**

GREAT BRASS BANDS (Various artists).
Tracks: / 633 squadron: *Grand Massed Bands (Men O'Brass)* / Tricky trombones (Trombone trio): *Grand Massed Bands (Men O'Brass)* / Colditz march: *Grand Massed Bands (Men O'Brass)* / Three trumpeters, The: *Grand Massed Bands (Men O'Brass)*/ H.M.S. Pinafore overture: *Grand Massed Bands (Men O'Brass)* / Thunderbirds march: *Grand Massed Bands (Men O'Brass)*/ Can-can: *Grand Massed Bands (Men O'Brass)* (From 'Orpheus In The Underworld') / Rover's return, The: *Grand Massed* Bands (Men O'Brass) / New world fantasy: *Grand Massed Bands (Men O'Brass)* / Beau ideal: *Grand Massed Bands (Men* O'Brass) / Fireman's gallop: *Grand Massed Bands (Men O'Brass)* / Out of the blue: *G.U.S. Footwear Band* / Samum: *G.U.S. Footwear Band* / Espana: *G.U.S. Footwear Band* / R.A.F. march past: *G.U.S. Footwear Band*/ Spanish gypsy dance: *G.U.S. Footwear Band* / New Colonial dance, The: *G.U.S. Footwear Band* / Estudiantina: *G.U.S.* Footwear Band / Sons of the brave: *G.U.S. Footwear Band* / Bells across the meadow: *G.U.S. Footwear Band*/ Seventy-six trombones: *G.U.S. Footwear Band* / Tango taquin: *G.U.S. Footwear Band* / Lisbon carnival: *G.U.S. Footwear Band* / London Bridge march: *G.U.S. Footwear Band.*
MC: . . . . **TCEMS 1394**

LISTEN TO THE BANDS (Various artists).
Tracks: / Cross of honour: *Cory Band* / Arabella: *Cory Band* / Early one morning: *G.U.S. Footwear Band*/ Napoleon Galop: *G.U.S. Footwear Band* / Flying Scot, The: *Scottish C.W.S. Band* / Faithful hussar, The: *Harry Mortimer &* His All Star Brass (Novelty) / Farewell Waltz: *Harry Mortimer & His All Star Brass* / Black knight: *Wingates* Temperance Band / Skye boat song: *Wingates Temperance Band* / Overture le carnaval Romain: *G.U.S. Footwear Band*(Not on CD.) / Samum: *G.U.S. Footwear Band* (Symphonic foxtrot.) / Semper Sousa: *Men O' Brass* / Webers last waltz: *Wingates Temperance Band* / Bold Gendarmes: *Scottish C.W.S. Band* / Men of Harlech: *Cory Workmen's Band*/ Slaidburn: *Wingates Temperance Band* / Tantalus quelen: *Wingates Temperance Band* / Stardust: *Harry Mortimer* & His All Star Brass / Trombone galop: *Brighouse & Rastrick Band* / Battle of Britain: *Brighouse & Rastrick Band*/ Beau ideal: *Men O' Brass.*
MC: . . . . **TCDL 1108**
2LP: . . . . **DL 1108**

MAGICAL BRASS (Various artists).
MC: . . . . **AMP 009**

MOODS IN BRASS (Various artists).
MCSET: . . . . **DTO 10052**

MUSIC OF NEW ORLEANS (The brass bands) (Various artists).
Tracks: / Music of New Orleans: *Various artists.*
LP: . . . . **JCE 35**

NATIONAL BRASS BAND CHAMPIONSHIP GALA FESTIVAL C (Various artists).
Tracks: / Fanfare celebration: *Various artists* / Suite: Le Cid: *Various artists* / Shepherd's song: *Various* artists / Overture: Russian and Ludmilla: *Various artists* / Rhapsody: Espana: *Various artists* / Triumphal march from 'Caractacus': *Various artists* / Flying fingers: *Various artists* / Pictures at an exhibition: *Various artists.*
LP: . . . . **PRL 007**
MC: . . . . **CPRL 007**

NATIONAL BRASS BAND CHAMPIONSHIP GALA FESTIVAL, (Various artists).
Tracks: / Fanfare for a festival: *Various artists* / Submerged cathedral: *Various artists* / Duet for two cats: *Various artists* / Diversions: *Various artists* / Hungarian march: *Various artists* / Symphonic rhapsody for euphonium & band: *Various artists* / Occasion: *Various artists* / March from 6th symphony: *Various artists*/ Minstrels: *Various artists* / Napoli: *Various artists* / James Cook, circumnavigator: *Various artists*/ Clock and the dresden china figures, The: *Various artists* / Lost chord, The: *Various artists* / Daphnis and Chloe (2nd suite): *Various artists.*
2LP: . . . . **DPRL 001D**
MCSET: . . . . **CDPRL 001D**

NATIONAL BRASS BAND CHAMPIONSHIP GALA FESTIVAL C (Various artists).
Tracks: / Spirit of pageantry: *Various artists* / Prelude to a festival: *Various artists* / Carnival of Venice: *Various artists* / Spectrum: *Various artists* / European, The: *Various artists* / Resurgam: *Various artists* / Misty: *Various artists* / Finlandia: *Various artists.*
LP: . . . . **PRL 011**
MC: . . . . **CPRL 011**

NATIONAL BRASS BAND CHAMPIONSHIPS GALA FESTIVAL, (Various artists).
LP: . . . . **BBR 1003**
MC: . . . . **BBT 1003**

NATIONAL BRASS BAND CHAMPIONSHIP GALA FESTIVAL, (Various artists).
Tracks: / Flourish for a birthday: *Various artists* / Pastorale: *Various artists* / Trumpet concerto: *Various* artists / Procession to the minster: *Various artists* / Prelude to Act III-Lohengrin: *Various artists* / Mountain song: *Various artists* / Spinning song: *Various artists* / Harmony music: *Various artists.*
LP: . . . . **PRL 036D**
MC: . . . . **CPRL 036D**

NATIONAL BRASS BAND FESTIVAL 1976 (Various artists).
Tracks: / Coronation march: *Various artists* / Rhapsody on American gospel songs: *Various artists* / Carnival of Venice: *Various artists* / Salute to the six: *Various artists* / Forza del destino - overture: *Various* artists / I only have eyes for you: *Various artists* / Danza alegre: *Various artists* / La bamba: *Various artists* / Sinfonietta for brass band: *Various artists.*
LP: . . . . **LSA 3285**

NATIONAL BRASS BAND FESTIVAL 1977 (Various artists).
Tracks: / Coronation march: *Various artists* / Berne march: *Various artists* / Finale, from Concerto No. 2: *Various* artists / Introduction to Act 3 of Lohengrin: *Various artists* / Life divine: *Various artists* / Trumpet voluntary: *Various artists* / Concerto for trumpet: *Various artists* / Russlan and Ludmilla - overture: *Various artists.*
LP: . . . . **PL 25118**

POP BRASS (Various artists).
Tracks: / Spanish eyes: *Various artists* / I don't know how to love Him: *Various artists* / Shadow of your smile: *Various artists* / Plaisir d'amour: *Various artists* / Close to you: *Various artists* / Goodbye to love: *Various artists* / We've only just begun: *Various artists* / By the time I get to Phoenix: *Various artists*/ Black magic: *Various artists* / Streets of London: *Various artists* / Bye bye blues: *Various artists*/ Feelings: *Various artists* / Solitaire: *Various artists* / Scarboro' Fair: *Various artists* / I wish you love: *Various artists* / Sweet gingerbread man: *Various artists.*
LP: . . . . **TAB 7**

PRUSSIA'S GLORY: MILITARY BRASS BAND MUSIC (Various artists).
Tracks: / Alte kamaraden: *Various artists* / Fehrbelliner reitermarsch: *Various artists* / Der Hohenfriedberger: *Various artists* / Steinmetz-marsch: *Various artists* / Parademarsch nr. 1: *Various artists* / Preussens gloria: *Various artists* / Parademarsch der 18er Husaren (of the 18th Hussars): *Various artists* / Hoch Heidecksburg: *Various artists* / etc: *Various artists.*
LP: **6.21363**
MC: **421363**

REFLECTIONS IN BRASS VOL 1 (Various artists).
Tracks: / Bramwyn: *Various artists* / Rococo variations: *Various artists* / Over the sticks: *Various artists*/ Force of destiny, The: *Various artists* / Punchinello: *Various artists* / Shaggy dog: *Various artists*/ Triumphant rhapsody: *Various artists* / Dancing clown: *Various artists* / County Palatine: *Various artists.*
LP: . . . . **FB 101**
MC: . . . . **CFB 101**

REFLECTIONS IN BRASS VOL 2 (Various artists).
Tracks: / Bandology: *Various artists* / Blackfriars: *Various artists* / Roll away, Bet: *Various artists*/ Glastonbury: *Various artists* / B.B. & C.F.: *Various artists* / Little suite no. 2: *Various artists*/ Student days: *Various artists* / Lorenzo: *Various artists.*
LP: . . . . **FB 102**
MC: . . . . **CFB 102**

REFLECTIONS IN BRASS VOL 3 (Various artists).
Tracks: / Suite from 'The Mastersingers': *Various artists* / Early one morning: *Various artists* / March of the heralds: *Various artists* / Saga of the north: *Various artists* / Galopede: *Various artists* / Astronaut, The: *Various artists* / Wuthering heights: *Various artists* / Marche militaire: *Various artists.*
LP: . . . . **FB 103**
MC: . . . . **CFB 103**

SIMPLY BRASS (Various artists).
Tracks: / Radetzky march: *Brighouse & Rastrick Band* / Cornet carillon: *Black Dyke Mills Band* / Bold gendarmes: *Carlton Main* / Falcons, The: *Royal Doulton Band* / March medley: famous fragments: *Desford Colliery Band*/ Entertainer, The: *Hendon Band* / Quality plus: *Hammonds Sauce Works Band* / Thunder and lightning polka: *C.W.S.* (Manchester) Band / Colditz march: *Massed Bands Of..* (Yorkshire Imperial Metals, Cory Band, Fairey Band, Brighouse & Rastrick) / Holiday for trombones: *Band of Yorkshire Imperial Mints* / October festival: *G.U.S. Band* / Wingates: *Wingates Temperance Band* / Cock o' the north: *Besses O' The Barn* / Jerusalem: *Grimethorpe Colliery Band*/ Rule Britannia: *Crossley Carpet Works Band.*
LP: . . . . **PYL 6034**
MC: . . . . **PYM 6034**

SOUND OF BRASS (Various artists).
MC: **TC2MOM 129**

THEMES IN BRASS (Various artists).
Tracks: / Colditz march: *Various artists* / Godspell: *Various artists* / Jesus Christ superstar: *Various artists* / Duchess of Duke street: *Various artists* / Eye level: *Various artists* / Entry of the gladiators: *Various artists* / Entertainer, The: *Various artists* / Clayhanger: *Various artists* / Devil's gallop: *Various artists* / Summertime: *Various artists* / Air from suite in D: *Various artists* / Swedish rhapsody: *Various artists.*
MCSET: . . . . **DTO 10020**

TOUCH MORE BRASS (Various artists).
Tracks: / Crusader: *Various artists* / Thunderer, The: *Various artists* / Manhattan beach: *Various artists*/ Semper fidelis: *Various artists* / Picador: *Various artists* / Beau ideal: *Various artists* / Yesterday: *Various artists* / Help: *Various artists* / Daytripper: *Various artists* / Penny Lane: *Various*

artists/ Farnham town: *Various artists* / Liberty bell: *Various artists*.
2LP: **CR 5143**
MCSET: **CRT 5143**

TOUCH OF BRASS, A Brass band spectacular (Various artists).
MCSET: **DTO 10297**

WORLD OF BRASS BANDS VOL 2 (Various artists).
LP: **SPA 68**
MC: **KCSP 68**

WORLD OF BRASS BANDS VOL 4 (Various artists).
LP: **SPA 413**
MC: **KCSP 413**

WORLD OF BRASS BANDS VOL 5 (Various artists).
LP: **SPA 533**
MC: **KCSP 533**

Brass Connection

BRASS CONNECTION.
LP: **JC 0003**

NEW LOOK, THE.
LP: **JC 0005**

Brass Construction

ATTITUDES.
Tracks: / Can you see the light / Funtimes / Attitudes / Do that thang / Forever love / E.T.C. / Hotdog.
LP: **LBG 30348**

BRASS CONSTRUCTION.
LP: **UAS 29923**

BRASS CONSTRUCTION 4.
Tracks: / Get up / one to one / Perceptions / Pick yourself yp / Help yourself / Night chaser / Starting tomorrow / Sweet as sugar.
LP: **UAG 30210**

BRASS CONSTRUCTION 5.
Tracks: / Music makes you feel like dancing / Shake it / Get up to get down.
LP: **UAG 30285**

BRASS CONSTRUCTION 6.
Tracks: / Do ya / We can do it / I'm not gonna stop / How do you do / Working harder every day / We are brass / Don't try to change me.
LP: **UAG 30315**

CONQUEST.
Tracks: / Goodnews / Modern touch / Give and take / Startin' all over again / Comeback / Zig zag / Secret lover / My place / Conquest.
LP: **BRASS 1**
MC: **TCBRASS 1**

CONVERSATIONS.
Tracks: / We can work it out / Walk the line / Physical atraction / Easy / Breakdown / I do love you / It's a shame / No communication.
LP: **EST 4001701**

MOVIN' 1988 (Best of).
Tracks: / Movin' / Changing / Ha cha cha / Shakit / Music makes you feel like dancin' / Walkin' the line / Partyline / Give and take / Movin' 1988 / Can't you see the light / International (Only on CD and cassette.) / Get up and get down (Extra tracks on cassette only.).
MC: **TCSYLP 6002**
LP: **SYLP 6002**
LP: **SYLPX 6002**
MC: **SYTC 6002**

RENEGADES.
Tracks: / International / Never had a girl / We can bring it back / Fascinating you / Partyline / Renegades / Dangerous / Closer to you / What is the law.
LP: **EJ 2401601**

Brass Impact

BRASS IMPACT.
LP: **CODA 12**
MC: **COCA 12**

Brass Monkey

BRASS MONKEY.
Tracks: / Watermans hornpipe / Fable of the wings / Millers three sons / Maid and the palmer / Bad news / Sovay / Tip top hornpipe-Primrose polka / Jolly bold robber / Old grenadier.
LP: **12TS 431**

SEE HOW IT RUNS.
Tracks: / Wailing on the wire / Count on angels / Warmest kiss, The.
LP: **12TS 442**

Brass Target (film)

BRASS TARGET (Film Soundtrack) (Various artists).
LP: **VC 81082**

Brassens, Georges

GEORGES BRASSENS.
Tracks: / Les compains d'abord / La demande en mariage / Le petit joueur de flateau / La route aux 4 chansons / Les 4 z'arts / Le pornographe / Le temps ne fait rien a l'affaire / Supplique pour etre enterre a la plaga de sete / Le trompettes de la renommee / Jeanne / Dans l'eau de la Claire Fontaine / Lew quarte bacheliers / Au bois de mon coeur / Le grand chene / Aupres de mon arbre / Chanson pour l'auvergnat.
MC: **818 735 4**

Brat Pack

BRAT PACK, THE.
LP: **3952961**
MC: **3952964**

Bratton, James

SOUND OF A NEW ERA (Bratton, James Project).
LP: **CHAMP 1015**
MC: **CHAMPK 1015**

Brave Combo

BRAVE COMBO.
LP: **ROUNDER 9019**
MC: **ROUNDER 9019C**

MUSICAL VARIETIES.
LP: **ROUNDER 9013**
MC: **ROUNDER 9013C**

PEOPLE ARE STRANGE.
LP: **FMSL 4007**

POLKATHARSIS.
Tracks: / Happy wanderer, The / Crazy Serbian butchers dance / Old country polka / Anniversary song / Who stole the kishka / La Rufalina / Lovesick / Atotonilco / New mind polka / Jeusita en chihuahua / Westphalia waltz / Pretty dancing girl / Hey ba ba re bop.
LP: **REU 1018**
MC: **ROUNDER 9009C**
LP: **ROUNDER 9009**

Brave Little Tailor

BRAVE LITTLE TAILOR (Pleasance, Donald (nar)).
MC: **BKK 401**

BRAVE LITTLE TAILOR, THE (Well Loved Tales Up to Age 9).
MC: **PLB 206**

Brave One (film)

BRAVE ONE, THE (1956 film soundtrack) (Various artists).
LP: **AEI 3107**

Bravestarr

BRAVESTARR: THE MOONSTONE CRISIS.
MC: **0 00 102155 9**

BRAVESTARR: WATER FEVER.
MC: **0 00 102156 7**

Bravo, Soledad

VOLANDO VOY.
LP: **15965**

Braxton, Anthony

3 COMPOSITIONS OF NEW JAZZ.
LP: **DS 415**

ANTHONY BRAXTON.
LP: **AFF 15**

ANTHONY BRAXTON - LONDON NOV. '86 (Braxton, Anthony Quartet).
2LP: **LR 414/15**

COMPOSITION 96 FOR ORCHESTRA.
LP: **LR 169**

COVENTRY CONCERT, THE.
LP: **WW 001**

CREATIVE CONSTRUCTION COMPANY.
LP: **MR 5071**

CREATIVE CONSTRUCTION COMPANY VOL 2.
LP: **MR 5097**

CREATIVE MUSIC ORCHESTRA.
LPS: **RING 01024/5/6**

DUETS 1976.
LP: **AL 4101**

FOUR COMPOSITIONS (1973).
LP: **YX 7506**

IN THE TRADITON VOL.2.
LP: **SCS 1045**

LIVE - MOERS FESTIVAL 74.
2LP: **RING 01010/11**

ROYAL VOL 1 (Braxton, Anthony & Derek Bailey).
LP: **INCUS 43**

SOLO - LIVE AT MOERS FESTIVAL, 74.
LP: **RING 01002**

THIS TIME.
LP: **AFF 25**

TIME ZONES (see Teitelbaum, Richard) (Braxton, Anthony/Richard Teitelbaum).

TOGETHER ALONE (Braxton, Anthony & J. Jarman).
LP: **DS 428**

TRIO & DUET.
LP: **3007**

Bray Brothers

PRAIRIE BLUEGRASS (Bray Brothers & Red Cravens).
LP: **ROUNDER 0053**

Brazil

30 ANOS DA NOSSA BOSSA (30 Years Of Our Bossa Nova).
Tracks: / Imagem / Barquinho / Garota de Ipanema / Se todos fossem iguais a voce / Tristeza de nos dois / Samba de verao / Wave / Inutil paisagem / Terco / Manha de carnaval / Triste / Amor en paz.
LP: **VIS 50171**
MC: **VIS 50174**

AFRO - BRAZILIAN RELIGIOUS MUSIC (Various artists).
LP: **LLST 7315**

AMAZONIA - CULT MUSIC OF NORTHERN BRAZIL (Various artists).
LP: **LLST 7300**

BEST OF BOSSA NOVA (See under Best Of..) (Various artists).

BLACK MUSIC OF BAHAI (Various artists).
LP: **VPA 8318**
MC: **VC 4818**

BOSSA NOVA (Various artists).
Tracks: / Chega de saudade: *Jobim, Tom* / Brigas nuncha mais: *Regina, Elis* / Coisa mais Linda: *Veloso, Caetano* / Este teu olhar: *Telles,Sylvia/Lucio Alves* / So em teus bracos: *Various artists* / Garota de Ipanema: *Caroocas*, Os / Ela e carioca: *Mendes, Sergio E Bossa Rio* / Flaso baiana: *Gilberto, Joao* / E eu: *Leao, Nara*/ Surf board: *Menescal,Roberto E Seu Conjunto* / Desafinado: *Costa, Gal* / O Barquinho: *Tamba Trio* / Voce: *Farney, Dick E & Norma Bengell*.
LP: **826 666-1**
MC: **826 666-4**

BOSSA NOVA (2) (Various artists).
Tracks: / Chega de saudade: *Creuza, Maria* / Variacao/Garota de Ipanema: *Powell, Baden* / Berimbau: *Zimbo* Trio / Agaua de beber: *Maysa* / O samba da minha terra: *Tamba Trio* / Insensatez: *Creuza, Maria*/ Consolacao: *Zimbo Trio* / Rosa flor: *Vandre, Geraldo* / Tem do of min: *Quarteto Em Cy* / Samba do aviao: *Powell, Baden* / A felicidade: *Dos Santos, Agostinho* / Deixa: *Toquinho* / Vivo sonhando: *Wanda*/ Antes e depois: *Castro-Neves, Oscar* / Terra de Ninguem: *Valle, Marcos & His Regina* / Mulher, sempre mulher: *De Moraes, Vinicius* / Reza: *Zimbo Trio* / So danco samba: *Tamba Trio* / Arrastao: *Zimbo Trio*/ Zelao: *Nogueira, Paulinho*.
MC: **BZLMC 101**

BOSSA NOVA (NASCENTE) (Various artists).
Tracks: / Embola a bola: *Djavan* / Samba de bencao: *De Moraes, Vinicius* / Chega de saudade: *Creuza, Maria*/ Mais um adeus: *Toquinho & Marilla Medalha* / A felicidade: *Dos Santos, Agostinho* / Para viver um grande amor: *De Moraes, Vinicius* / Para que digladiar: *Ben, Jorge* / Desencontro: *Buarque, Chico & Toquinho* / Samba de veloso: *Zimbo Trio* / Sao demals os perigos desta vida: *Vinicius & Toquinho* / Apelo: *Bethania, Maria &* Vinicius / Canto de ossanha: *Creuza, Maria & Vinicius & Toquinho* / Na boca de beco: *Djavan* / Voce abusu: *Creuza, Maria* / Carolina: *Buarque, Chico* / Garota de ipanema: *De Moraes, Vinicius* / Corcovado: *Creuza*, Maria / Morena de flor: *De Moraes, Vinicius* / Marina: *Creuza, Maria* / Paiol de polvora: *De Moraes, Vinicius* / Trocando em miudo: *Hime, Francis* / Katarina, Katarina: *Ben, Jorge*.
MC: **NSMC 003**

BRASIL STARS (Various artists).
Tracks: / Bom bom: *Costa, Gal* / Uma rosa em minha mao: *Toquinho* / Roda: *Gil, Gilberto* / Uma vez um caso: *Lobo, Edu/Joyce* / Asa branca: *Gonzaga, Luiz* / Abre alas: *Lins, Ivan* / Muito obrigado: *Djavan*/ Requebra que eu duo um doce/ Um vestido de bolero: *Hime, Olivia/Dory Caymmi* / Poligamo fiel: *Da Via, Martinho*/ Euridice: *Powell, Baden* / Salve simpatia: *Ben, Jorge* / O bedado e o equilibrista: *Bosca, Joao* / Gol anulado: *Regina, Elis* / Cavaleiro: *Veloso, Caetano* / Voce abusa: *Creuza, Maria* / Homen feito: *Nascimento*, Milton/Francis Hime / Abeco Baia: *De Moraes, Vinicius* / Feito de Oracao: *Bethania, Maria* / Samba do aviao: *Jobim, Antonio Carlos/Miucha* / Luiza: *De Hollanda, Chico Buarque/Francis Hime*.
MC: **BZLMC 105**

BRAZIL CLASSICS (See under Byrne, David) (Various artists).

BRAZIL CLASSICS 1 (Beleza tropical) (Various artists).
Tracks: / Ponta de lanca Africano: *Ben, Jorge* / Sonho meu: *Bethania, Maria e Gal Costa* / So quero um xodo: *Gil*, Gilberto / Um canto de afoxe para o bloco do ile: *Various artists* / Leaozinho: *Veloso, Caetano* / Cacada: *Buarque, Chico* / Calice: *Buarque, Chico/Milton Nascimento* (Not on cassette.) / Equatorial: *Borges Lo*(Not on cassette.) / San Vincent: *Various artists* / Quilombo, O el dorado negro: *Gil, Gilberto* / Caramba...galileu de galileia: *Ben, Jorge* (Not on cassette.) / Caixa de sol: *Pereira, Nazare* / Maculele: *Pereira, Nazare*(Not on cassette.) / Queixa: *Veloso, Caetano* / Andar com fe: *Gil, Gilberto* / Fio maravilha: *Ben, Jorge*/ Anima: *Nascimento, Milton* / Terra: *Veloso, Caetano*.
LP: **EMC 3551**
MC: **TCEMC 3551**

BRAZIL DANCE PARTY (Various artists).
Tracks: / Lambadas: *Various artists* / Mexa mexa: *Various artists* / Lambada da Americana: *Various artists*/ Te futaco: *Various artists* / Quero ser grande amor: *Various artists* / Amor de piranha: *Various artists*/ Batucadasi: *Various artists* / Gold banana: *Various artists* / Sambas: *Various artists* / Os sambabom nao deixa: *Various artists* / O samba morrer: *Various artists* / Na cadencia dosamba: *Various artists*/ Mas que nada: *Various artists* / Aquela abraco: *Various artists* / A saudade ficou (O lencinho): *Various artists* / Feitico da vila: *Various artists* / O sol nascera (a sorrir): *Various artists* / Mexe, mexe: *Various artists* / Tengo, tengo: *Various artists* / Ninguem tasca: *Various artists* / Bum bum baticumbum: *Various* artists / Os sambabom foi um Rio que: *Various artists* / pasou na minha vida: *Various artists* / O conde: *Various artists* / Porta aberta: *Various artists* / Portela na avenida: *Various artists* / Batucadas: *Various artists* / Sweet roots: *Various artists*.
MC: **BZLMC 102**

BRAZIL IS BACK (Various artists).
LP: **BR 4011**
MC: **BRC 4011**

BRAZIL ORIGINAL (Various artists).
LP: **NL 70089**

BRAZIL STARS VOLUME 2 (Various artists).
LP: **445009**
MC: **845009**

BRAZIL TODAY (Various artists).
LP: **812849 1**
MC: **812849 4**

BRAZILIAN NIGHTS (Various artists).
MC: **CCH 539**

BRESIL '90 (Various artists).
MC: **824884**

CANTA BRAZIL (Great Brazilian Songbook vol.1) (Various artists).
MC: **8431154**

CARNIVAL OF BRAZIL (Various artists).
Tracks: / Imperatriz leopoldinesse: *Various artists* / Primeira de Mangueira: *Various artists* / Em cima da hora: *Various artists* / Porteia: *Various artists* / Imperio serrano: *Various artists* / Traz os montes: *Various* artists / Samba de Roda: *Various artists* / Capeoira: *Various artists* / Makulele: *Various artists*/ Frevo: *Various artists* / Maracatu: *Various artists* / Caboclinhos: *Various artists* / Ursos: *Various artists*.
LP: **PSTZ 2007**

CARNIVAL OF CHICOUTIMI, QUEBEC (Various artists).
Tracks: / Le reel du diable: *Various artists* / Le reel des nocus d'or: *Various artists* / Carnival du bout du monde: *Various artists* / Samba Murielle: *Various artists* / Le reel des montagnes: *Various artists* / Le reel des rioux: *Various artists* / Le granda vaise: *Various artists* / Le reel des Toussex: *Various artists*/ Bastringue: *Various artists* / Le reel du chemin de fer: *Various artists* / Reel de ste-anne, The: *Various* artists / Chant de l'alouette: *Various artists* / Les mouchoirs: *Various artists* / Brandy: *Various artists*/ Le reel de l'oiseau moqueur: *Various artists* / Le reel de St. Isidor: *Various artists* / La plongeuse: *Various artists*.
LP: **PSTZ 2006**

DANCA (Various artists).
Tracks: / Roda: *Gil, Gilberto* / Besta e tu: *Baianos, Novos* / Fato consumado: *Djavan* / Te futaco: *Guerreiro*, Cid / Taj Mahal/Filhomaravilha/Pais Tropical: *Ben, Jorge* / A tongo da mironga do kabulete: *Toquinho & Vinicius*/ Rei no bagaco coisas do vida: *De Belem, Fafa* / Salve simpatia: *Ben, Jorge* / Tiro de misericordia: *Bosco*, Joao & Chico Batera / Adelita: *Ben, Jorge* / A banda do

ze pretinho: *Ben, Jorge* / Nem ouro nem prata: *Maurity, Ruy* / Ague negra da lagoa: *Toquinho* / Africaner brother bound: *Shock, Obina & Gilberto Gil* / Gabriel Guerreiro galactico: *Ben, Jorge* / Mambembe: *De Belem, Fafa* / Perfume de cebola: *Filo* / Da cor do pecado: *Creuza, Maria* / Em matogrosso fronteira com: *Ben, Jorge*.
MC: . . . . **NSMC 006**

LAMBADA DO BRASIL (Carlos, Antonio & Jocafi).
Tracks: / Gato angora / Lambadi lambadia / menina moca / Minha rainha / Repucho / Meu broto / Muzenza / Por cima de min / Gostosa / Do jeito que voce vier / Meloza.
MC: . . . . **BZLMC 103**

MIDNIGHT IN BRAZIL (Various artists).
LP: **9279 477**

MUSIC FOR MAIDS AND TAXI DRIVERS (Brazil Forro) (Various artists).
Tracks: / Balenco da canoa: *Toinho De Alagaos* / De pernambulco aomaranhao: *Duda Da Passira* / Eu tambem quero beijar: *Orlando, Jose* / Bicho da cara preta: *Toinho De Alagaos* / Comeco de verao: *Heleno Dos Oito Baixos*/ Peca licenca pra falar de alagoas: *Toinho De Alagaos* / Recorda cao da passira: *Duda Da Passira* / Agricultor p'ra frente: *Orlando, Jose* / Entra e sai: *Heleno Dos Oito Baixos* / Linda menina: *Orlando, Jose* / Casa de tauba: *Duda Da Passira* / Morena da palmeira: *Orlando, Jose* / Carater duro: *Toinho De Alagaos* / Minha zeze: *Orlando, Jose* / Sonho de amor: *Toinho De Alagaos* / Namoro no escuro: *Toinho De Alagaos* / Forro da minha terra: *Duda Da Passira*.
LP: . . . . **ORB 048**
MC: . . . . **ORBC 048**

RHYTHM OF BRAZIL, THE (Various artists).
Tracks: / Mother Brasilier: *Various artists* / Bizantina bizancia: *Ben, Jorge* / Moenda: *Machado, Elaine*/ Tatmiro: *Vincius De Moraes* / Banda da carmen mirandes: *Armandinho & Trio Electrico* / Jovelina perola negro: *O Dia Se Zanoou* / Cinco criancas: *Lobo, Edo* / Roberto corta essa: *Ben, Jorge* / Festejando: *Various* artists / A Voz doz morro: *Melodia, Luiz* / Mulato latino: *Melodia, Luiz* / A bencao bahia: *Toquinho &* Vincius Da Moraes / Salve simpatia: *Ben, Jorge* / Como diza o poeta: *Toquinho & Vincius Da Moraes* / Viva meu samba: *Various artists* / Casa de samba: *Various artists*.
MC: . . . . **MCTC 013**

SAMBA (Various artists).
Tracks: / Bizantina bizancia: *Ben, Jorge* / La vem o Brasil descendo a ladeira: *Moreira, Moraes* / Prata da noite: *De Sa, Estacio* / O bebado e o equilibrista: *Bosca, Joao* / Moenda: *Machado, Elaine* / Swing de campo grande: *Balonos, Novos* / Flor de lis: *Djavan* / Fruta mulher: *Moreira, Moraes* / Acorda que eu quero ver: *Caymmi, Nana* / O dia que o sol declarou o seu amor pela terra: *Ben, Jorge* / Quem te viu, quem te ve: *Buarque*, Chico / Brasil pandeiro: *Balonos, Novos* / A rita: *Buarque, Chico* / No reino encantado do amor: *Ben*, Jorge / Maria vai com as outras: *Creuza, Maria* / Tem que se tirar da cabeca: *Do Salgeuiro, Academicos* / Quilombo do dumba: *De Jesus, Clementina* / Roda viva: *Buarque, Chico* / O dia se zangou: *Negra, Jovelina Perola*/ Era umas ves 13 pontos: *Ben, Jorge* / Contraste: *Macale, Jards* / Que maravilha: *Ben, Jorge & Toquinho*.
MC: . . . . **NSMC 002**

SAMBA COM JAZZ (Various artists).
Tracks: / Milagre: *Quarteto Em Cy* / Agua de beber: *Zimbo Trio* / Tres pontas: *Nascimento, Milton* / Samba do aviao: *Jobim, Antonio Carlos/Miucha* / Reza: *Zimbo Trio* / Mas que nada: *Creuza, Maria* / Samba sem voce: *Passos, Rosa & Emilio Santiago* / Bon tempo: *Buarque, Chico* / Muito obrigado: *Djavan* / Como dizia o poeta: *Vinicius & Toquinho* / Noite dos mascarados: *Buarque, Chico* / Consolacao: *Zimbo Trio*/ O morro nao engana: *Melodia, Luiz* / Cancao de busios: *Sa, Sandra* / Samba de verao: *Valle, Marcos*/ Bem bem: *Costa, Gal* / Pra fazer o sol nascer: *Gil, Gilberto* / Madalena ful pro mar: *Buarque, Chico*/ Requebra que eu dou um doce: *Hime, Olivia/Dory Caymmi* / Um vestido de bolero: *Hime, Olivia/Dory Caymmi* / Onde e que voce esteva: *Buarque, Chico* / Gira giro: *Nascimento, Milton* / Arrastao: *Zimbo Trio* / Espelho christalino: *Valenca, Alceu*.
MC: . . . . **NSMC 004**

SAMBA TROPICAL (Various artists).
Tracks: / Hoje tem marmalada: *Various artists* / Macunaima: *Various artists* / Ill-aye (terra da vida): *Various* artists / Lapa em tres tepos: *Various artists* / No reino da mae de ouro: *Various artists* / O mundo ecantado de Monteiro: *Various artists* / Lobato: *Various artists* / Lendas do abaete: *Various artists* / Festa docirio de nazate: *Various artists* / Meninha do gantois: *Various artists* / A festa do divino: *Various artists*/ Sonhar com rei da leao: *Various artists* / O sertoes: *Various artists* / A festa dos deluses Afro-Brasileiro: *Various artists* / Martin Cerere: *Various artists* / O que sera?: *Various artists* / O amanha: *Various* artists / Domingo: *Various artists* / Sonho de um sonho: *Various artists* / laia do cais dourado: *Various* artists / Alo alo tai Carmen Miranda: *Various artists* / Nordeste, seu povo, seu conto sua gloria: *Various artists*/ Herois da liberdade: *Various artists* / Exaltacao a tiradentes: *Various artists* / A lenda das sereias rainhas do mar: *Various artists* / Festa para um rei negro: *Various artists* / Bahia de todos os deuses: *Various artists*/ Chica Da Silva: *Various artists* / Mangueira minha querida: *Various artists* / Madrinha: *Various artists*.
MC: . . . . **BZLMC 104**

SAUDADE (Various artists).
Tracks: / No dia em que eu vim embora: *Regina, Elis* / Boca da noite: *Toquinho* / Cavaleiro: *Veloso, Caetano*/ Primavera: *Joyce* / Uma vez um caso: *Lobo, Edu/ Joyce* / Corsario: *Regina, Elis* / Gongaba: *Hime*, Olivia & Edu Lobo / Dindi: *Creuza, Maria* / Vivo sonhando: *Wanda* / Sem fantasia: *Buarque, Chico*/ Ultimo desejo: *Bethania, Maria* / Umas e outras: *Buarque, Chico* / Eu sei que vou te amar: *Creuza, Maria* & Vinicius & Toquinho / Pra nao mais voltar: *De Belem, Fafa* / Irmao de fe: *Nascimento, Milton* / Insensatez: *Creuza, Maria* / Sabia: *Buarque, Chico* / Da cor do pecado: *Creuza, Maria* / Acabou chorare: *Baianos, Novos* / Rosa flor: *Vandre, Geraldo* / Apelo: *Toquinho & Vincius Da Moraes*.
MC: . . . . **NSMC 005**

VOZES (Various artists).
Tracks: / Para-raio: *Djavan* / Ole ola: *Buarque, Chico* / Cavalgada: *De Belem, Fafa* / Mariano: *Camargo*, Cesar / Bodas de prata: *Regina, Elis* / Outubro: *Nascimento, Milton* / Denise rei: *Ben, Jorge* / Viramundo: *Bethania, Maria* / Maravilha: *Hime, Francis & Chico Buarque* / Abre alas: *Lins, Ivan* / Ive brussel: *Ben, Jorge & Caetano Veloso* / Toada: *Lobo, Edo* / Doce maggia: *De Belem, Fafa* / Ate segunda feira: *Buarque, Chico* / Curumin chama cunhata que eu vou contar: *Ben, Jorge* / Travessia: *Nascimento, Milton*/ Preta pretinha: *Baianos, Novos* / Coisas cristalinas: *Wando* / Ventos do norte: *Djavan* / Faz parte do meu show: *Creuza, Maria*.
MC: . . . . **NSMC 001**

Brazil Classics

BRAZIL CLASSICS 2 (Various artists).
LP: **926019 1**

Brazil, Som

SIVUCA.
LP: . . . . **SNTF 942**

Brazil Today

BRAZIL TODAY VOLUME 2 (Various artists).
LP: **824 010-1**
MC: **824 010-4**

Bread

BABY I'M A WANT YOU.
Tracks: / Baby I'm a want you / Mother freedom / Down on my knees / Everything I own / Nobody like you / Diary / Dream lady / Daughter / Games of magic / This isn't what the government / Just like yesterday / I don't love you.
LP: . . . . **K 42100**

BEST OF BREAD VOL.1.
Tracks: / Make it with you / Too much love / If / Let your love go / Everything I own / Been too long on the road / Baby I'm a want you / Down on my knees / It don't matter to me / Mother freedom / Look what you've done / Truckin'.
LP: . . . . **K 42115**
MC: **K4 42115**

BEST OF BREAD VOL.2.
Tracks: / Sweet surrender / Fancy dancer / Guitar man / Been too long on the road / Friends and lovers / Aubrey / Daughter / Dream lady / Yours for life / Just like yesterday / He's a good lad / London Bridge.
LP: . . . . **K 42161**
MC: **K4 42161**

BEST OF BREAD VOL 1 & 2.
Tracks: / Make it with you / Everything I own / Diary / Baby I'm a want you / It don't matter to me / If / Mother freedom / Down on my knees / Too much love / Let your love go / Look what you've done / Truckin' sweet surrender / Fancy dancer / Guitar man / Been too long on the road / Friends and lovers / Aubrey / Daughter / Dream lady / Yours for life / Just like yesterday / He's a good lad / London bridge.
MC: **9602844**

COLLECTION: BREAD.
Tracks: / Make it with you / Baby I'm A Want You / Lost without your love / Diary / Let Your Love Go / Never let her go / Took the last train / Everything I Own / If / Sweet Surrender / Guitar Man / Goodbye girl / It Don't Matter To Me / Hooked on you / London Bridge / Lorilee.
MC: . . . . **STAC 2303**
LP: . . . . **STAR 2303**

GUITAR MAN.
Tracks: / Guitar man / Welcome to the music / Make it be yourself / Aubrey / Fancy dancer / Sweet surrender / Tecolete / Let me go / Yours for life / Picture in your mind / Don't tell me no / Didn't even know her name.
LP: . . . . **K 52004**

LOST WITHOUT YOUR LOVE.
Tracks: / Hooked on you / She's the only one / Lost without your love / Change of heart / Belonging / Fly away / Lay your money down / Chosen one, The / Today's the first day / Hold tight / Our lady of sorrow.
LP: . . . . **K 52044**
MC: . . . . **K 452044**

MANNA.
Tracks: / Let your love go / Take comfort / Too much love / If / Be kind to me / He's a good lad / She was my lady / Live in your love / What a change / I say again / Come again / Truckin'.
LP: . . . . **K 52001**

ON THE WATERS.
Tracks: / Why do you keep me waiting / Make it with you / Blue satin pillow / Look what you've done / I am that I am / Been too long on the road / I want you with me / Coming apart / Easy love / In the afterglow / Call on me / Other side of love, The.
LP: . . . . **K 42050**
LP: **2469 005**

SOUND OF BREAD.
Tracks: / Make it with you / Dismal day / London Bridge / Anyway you want me / Look what you've done / It don't matter to me / Last time, The / Let your love go / Truckin' / If / Baby I'm a want you / Everything I own / Down on my knees / Just like yesterday / Diary / Sweet surrender / Guitar man / Fancy dancer / I She's the only one / Lost without your love.
LP: . . . . **K 52062**
MC: **K4 52062**

VERY BEST OF BREAD.
Tracks: / Baby I'm a want you / Make it with you / Guitar man / Everything I own.
LP: . . . . **SHM 3244**
MC: . . . . **HSC 3244**

Bread & Roses

BREAD & ROSES.
LP: . . . . **DRGN 883**

Break Beats

BREAK BEATS 4 (Original Unknown DJ's) (Various artists).
LP: . . . . **WRRLP 015**

BREAK BEATS 5 (Original Unknown DJ's) (Various artists).
LP: . . . . **WRRLP 016**

Break Machine

BREAK MACHINE.
LP: . . . . **SOHOLP 3**
MC: . . . . **SOHOTC 3**

Breakdance

BREAKDANCE FEVER (Various artists).
LP: . . . . **OP 210**
MC: . . . . **HOPC 210**

BREAKDANCING (Various artists).
Tracks: / Buffalo gals: *McLaren, Malcolm* / Rockit: *Hancock, Herbie* / I want to be real: *Rocca, John*/ White lines: *Grandmaster Melle Mel & The Furious Five*.
LP: . . . . **CBS 26310**
MC: **40 26310**

Breakdance (film)

BREAKDANCE (1984 Film soundtrack) (Various artists).
Tracks: / Breakin' There's no stopping us: *Ollie & Jerry* / When I.C.U: *Ollie & Jerry* / Radiotron: *Firefox*/ Stylin',profilin': *Firefox* / Din daa daa: *Kranz, George* / Gotta have the money: *Donn, Steve* / Believe in the beat: *Townes, Carol Lynn* / Set it out: *Midway* / I don't wanna come down: *Scott, Mark* / Oye mamacita: *Rags & Ritches*.
LP: . . . . **POLD 5147**
MC: . . . . **POLDC 5147**

BREAKDANCE 2 - ELECTRIC BOOGALOO (Film soundtrack) (Various artists).
Tracks: / Electric boogaloo: *Ollie & Jerry* / Radiotron: *Firefox* / Din daa daa: *Kranz, George* / When I.C.U.: *Ollie & Jerry* / Gotta have the money: *Donn, Steve* / Believe in the beat: *Townes, Carol Lynn*/ Set it out: *Midway* / I don't wanna come down: *Scott, Mark* / Stylin' profilin': *Firefox* / Oye Mamacita: *Rags & Ritches*.
LP: . . . . **POLD 5168**
MC: . . . . **POLDC 5168**

Breakfast At Tiffany's

BREAKFAST AT TIFFANY'S (1961 film soundtrack) (Various artists).
Tracks: / Moon river: *Mancini, Henry* / Something for cat: *Mancini, Henry* / Sally's tomato: *Mancini, Henry*/ Mr. Yunioshi: *Mancini, Henry* / Big blow-out, The: *Mancini, Henry* / Hub caps and tail lights: *Mancini*, Henry / Breakfast at Tiffany's: *Mancini, Henry* / Latin Golightly: *Mancini, Henry* / Holly: *Mancini*, Henry / Loose caboose: *Mancini, Henry* / Big heist, The: *Mancini, Henry* / Moon river cha cha: *Mancini, Henry*.
LP: . . . . **NL 89905**
MC: . . . . **NK 89905**

BREAKFAST AT TIFFANY'S (Various artists).
MCSET: **0502**

Breakfast Band

DOLPHIN RIDE.
Tracks: / Tokyo shuffle / Jazzabel / Constant spring / Tuna / Trinidad / Hadeed / L.A. 14 / Prelude in steel / Broadside rhumba.
LP: . . . . **IOU 001**

WATER'S EDGE.
LP: . . . . **SPIN 501**

Breakfast Club (Film)

BREAKFAST CLUB (1985 film soundtrack) (Various artists).
Tracks: / Don't you (forget about me): *Simple Minds* / Fire in the twilight: *Wang Chung* / We are not alone: *De* Vito, Karla / Heart too hot to hold: *Johnson, Jesse* / Waiting: *Daly, Elizabeth* / Didn't I tell you?: *Kennedy*, Joyce / I'm the dude: *Forsey, Keith* / Dream montage: *Forsey, Keith* / Reggae, The: *Forsey, Keith* / Love theme: *Forsey, Keith*.
LP: . . . . **AMA 5045**
MC: . . . . **AMC 5045**
MC: . . . . **MCFC 3368**
LP: . . . . **MCF 3368**

Breakfast Special

BREAKFAST SPECIAL.
LP: . . . . **ROUNDER 3012**

Breakheart Pass (bk)

BREAKHEART PASS (Ed Bishop) (MacLean, Alistair (aut)).
MC: . . . . **CAB 325**

Breaking Circus

ICE MACHINE, THE.
Tracks: / Song of The South / Daylight / Ancient axes / Caskets and clocks / Deadly China Doll / Laid so low / Took a hammering / Waiter / Sweat Blood / Where / Gun shy / Evil last night.
LP: . . . . **HMS 075**

VERY LONG FUSE.
LP: . . . . **HMS 012**

Breaking Glass (film)

BREAKING GLASS (1980 Film Soundtrack) (O'Connor, Hazel).
Tracks: / Writing on the wall / Monsters in disguise / Come into the air / Big brother / Who needs it / Will you? / Eighth day / Top of the wheel / Calls the tune / Blackman / Give me an inch / If only.
LP: . . . . **AMLH 64820**
MC: . . . . **CAM 64820**

Breaking The Back Of

BREAKING THE BACK OF LOVE (Various artists).
LP: . . . . **SDLP 1**

Breakout

BREAKOUT (22 roaring great hits by various original artists) (Various artists).
LP: . . . . **RTL 2081**
MC: . . . . **4 CRTL 2081**

Bream, Julian

MUSIC OF SPAIN VOLS. 7 & 8.
LP: . . . . **RL 45548**
MC: . . . . **RK 45548**

Breant, Francois

SONS OPTIQUES.
LP: **900553**

Breathe

ALL THAT JAZZ.
Tracks: / Jonah / All that jazz / Monday morning blues / Hands to heaven / All this I should have known / Any trick / Liberties of love / Won't you come back / For love or money / How can I fall / Don't tell me lies (extra track on Cassette).
LP: .... SRNLP 12
MC: .... SRNMC 12
MC: .... OVEDC 379

PEACE OF MIND.
LP: .... SRNLP 30
MC: .... SRNMC 30

Breathless

CHASING PROMISES.
LP: .... BREATHLP 7

THREE TIMES AND WAVING.
Tracks: / Solid down the river / Is it good news today / Three times and waving / Into the fire / Working for space / Waiting on the wire / Pizzy life / Say September sings / Let's make a night of it.
LP: .... BREATHLP 6
MC: .... BREATHCAS 6

Breau, Lenny

FIVE O'CLOCK BELLS.
LP: .... ECJ 405

Breaux, Cleoma

CAJUN CLASSIC.
LP: .... CW 203

Brecht, Bertold

DIE DREIGROSCHENOPER (L'Opera da Soldidi).
Tracks: / Moritat / Ballata dell'agiatezza / Canzone d'amour / Canzoni dei canoni / Jenny dei pirati / Finale / Barbara song / Duetto della gelosia / Addio e 2 finale / Ballata del macro / Canzone dell'inadeguatezza degli sforzi umani / Coro finale.
LP: .... SM 3061

Brecker Brothers

COLLECTION: BRECKER BROTHERS.
Tracks: / Skunk funk / Sponge / Squids / Funky sea, funky dew / Bathsheba / Dream theme / Straphangin' / East river.
LP: .... NL 90442
MC: .... NK 90442

Brecker, Michael

CLAUS OGERMANN ORCHESTRA WITH MICHAEL BRECKER (See under Ogermann, Claus) (Ogermann, Claus Orchestra & Michael Brecker).

DON'T TRY THIS AT HOME.
LP: .... MCA 42229
MC: .... MCAC 42229

MICHAEL BRECKER Z.
Tracks: / Sea glass / Syzygy / Choices / Nothing personal / Cost of living / Original rays.
LP: .... IMCA 5980
MC: .... IMCAC 5980
LP: .... MCA 5980
MC: .... MCAC 5980

NOW YOU SEE IT (NOW YOU DON'T).
Tracks: / Escher sketch / Minsk / Ode to the doo da day / Never alone / Peep / Dogs in the wine shop / Quiet city / Meaning of the blues, The.
LP: .... GR 9622
MC: .... GRC 9622

Brecker, Randy

AMANDA (Brecker, Randy & Elaine Elias).
Tracks: / Splash / Para nada / Pandamandium / Samba de bamba / Amandamada / Guaruja.
LP: .... SNTF 958
LP: .... PJ 88013
MC: .... PJC 88013

IN THE IDIOM.
Tracks: / No scratch / Hit and miss / Forever young / Sang / You're in my heart / There's a Mingus a Monks us / Moontide / Little Miss P.
MC: .... CC 15

LIVE AT SWEET BASIL.
LP: .... SNTF 1011

TOE TO TOE.
Tracks: / Mr. Skinny / Trading secrets / It creeps up on you / Glider, The / Toe to toe / It's up to you / What is the answer / Lost 4 words.
LP: .... UNKNOWN
LP: .... SNTF 1029

Bree, Barley

ANTHEM FOR THE CHILDREN.
LP: .... SH 52020
MC: .... SH 52020 C

CASTLES IN THE AIR.
LP: .... SHAN 52010

NO MAN'S LAND.
LP: .... SHAN 52012

Breed

GRIN.
LP: .... NISH 1217

Breeders

POD.
Tracks: / Glorious / Happiness is a warm gun / Hellbound / Fortunately gone / Opened / Lime house / Doe / Oh / When I was a painter / Irish / Only in 3's / Metal man.
LP: .... CAD 0006
MC: .... CADC 0006

Breedlove, Jim

JIM BREEDLOVE SINGS ROCK 'N' ROLL HITS.
Tracks: / Rock and roll music / Swanee River rock / Whole lotta shakin' goin' on / C.C. rider / Hound dog / My prayer / Long tall Sally / Lonesome road / Killer diller / Great pretender, The / Jailhouse rock / Mother's love, A.
LP: .... OFF 6013
LP: .... BFX 15327

Breege Kelly Sound

LITTLE COUNTRY TOWN IN IRELAND.
Tracks: / These are my mountains / Dear old Donegal.
LP: .... HRL 129
MC: .... CHRL 129

Breen, Ann

AN EVENING WITH ANN BREEN.
MC: .... CPLAY 1025

BOY OF MINE.
Tracks: / Among my souvenirs / I'm guilty of loving you / Where no one stands alone / Three good reasons / Will you love me tomorrow / Blue violets & red roses / Boy of mine / Teddy bear / Careless hands / By the light of the silvery moon / Carolina moon / Souvenirs.
LP: .... PHL 447
MC: .... CPHL 447
MC: .... CDHL 447

COLLECTION: ANN BREEN.
MC: .... CPLAY 1019
LP: .... PLAY 1019

IF I HAD MY LIFE TO LIVE OVER.
Tracks: / If I had my life to live over / When you & I were young Maggie / Walk right back / I'll be your sweetheart / Will you love me tomorrow / Save the last dance for me / Have you ever been lonely / I just called to say I love you / Who's sorry now / It's a sin to tell a lie / Among my souvenirs / You always hurt the one you love.
LP: .... DHL 714
MC: .... CDHL 714

I'LL BE YOUR SWEETHEART.
Tracks: / I'll be your sweetheart / In your heart / Have you ever been lonely / Music, music, music, put another nickle in / Don't think love ought to be that way / Spinning wheel / We all have a song in our hearts / Cottage by the Lee / Da doo ron ron / Skye boat song / I just called to say I love you / Carnival is over, The.
LP: .... DHL 705
MC: .... CDHL 705

IRISH STYLE.
Tracks: / Gentle mother / Noreen Bawn / Two loves / Cottage by the lee / Moon behind the hill / I'll remember you love in my prayers / Spinning wheel / Bunch of violets blue / Too-ra-loo-ra-loo-ra / Old rustic bridge / When you and I were young Maggie / By the light of the silvery moon.
LP: .... PHL 493
MC: .... CPHL 493
MC: .... CDHL 493

MEDALS FOR MOTHERS.
Tracks: / Pal of my cradle days / Among my souvenirs / Gentle mother / It's a sin to tell a lie / What a friend we have in mother / Noreen Bawn / Medals for mothers / Two loves / When you & I were young Maggie / If I had my life to live over / Carolina moon / (Dear little) boy of mine.
LP: .... PHL 487
MC: .... CPHL 487
MC: .... CDHL 487

PAL OF MY CRADLE DAYS.
Tracks: / Those brown eyes / Who's sorry now / Blue Kentucky girl / You needed me / Two loves / What a friend we have in mother / Walk right back / Save the last dance for me / Love is teasin' / Pal of my cradle days / Hey good lookin' / Heart you break will be your own, The.
LP: .... PHL 437
MC: .... CPHL 437
MC: .... CDHL 437

THIS ALBUM IS JUST FOR YOU.
Tracks: / Noreen Bawn / Last thing on my mind / Star, The / Too ra loo ra loo ra / This song is just for you / It's a sin to tell a lie / Whatever will be will be / Only you / Love by love / When I fall in love / It keeps right on a-hurtin' / Medals for mothers.
LP: .... DHL 703
MC: .... CDHL 703

WHEN I GROW TOO OLD TO DREAM.
LP: .... PLAY 1023
MC: .... CPLAY 1023

YOU ALWAYS HURT THE ONE YOU LOVE.
Tracks: / You always hurt the one you love / Jambalaya / Moon behind the hill / Bunch of violets blue / Save the last dance for me / If I had my life to live over / Behind the footlights / Old rustic bridge / When you & I were young Maggie / Tennessee waltz / Everybody's somebody's fool / Gentle mother / Maggie.
LP: .... DHL 701
MC: .... CDHL 701

Breen, Paddy

RAMBLING IRISHMAN.
Tracks: / Killiecrankie / Red-haired boy / Fisher's frolic / Rolling home polka / Biddy Durkin / Britches we do wear, The / My love she's but a lassie yet / Mayo moonlight / Wild colonial boy / Stone outside Dan Murphy's door, The / Frieze breeches / Pipe on the hob / Off she goes / Cuckoo's nest, The / Cross jig / Morning star / Rodney's glory / Orange in bloom / Mrs. Casey / Basket of oysters / Paddy's polka / Jolly tinker / Pretty girls of Mayo / Some say the devil's dead / Orange and blue / Johnny when you die / George White's favourite / Saddle the pony / Blackthorn stick / Swallow's nest / Waltzes / Quarrelsome piper, The / Harvest home / Girl with the blue dress on, The / Green grow the rushes-o / Green hills of Ireland, The / Boys from Blue Hill / Friendly visit, The.
MC: 60-078

Breeze

FRIED POTATOES.
LP: .... SOS 1163

Breeze, Jean Binta

TRACKS.
LP: .... LKJ 007

Brel, Jacques

BREL ALIVE IN PARIS.
2LP: .... VS 2LP 2779

JACQUES BREL.
Tracks: / Les prenoms de Paris / Clara / On n'oublie rien / Les singes / Madeleine / Les biches / Les paumes du petit matin / Zangra / La statue / Les bourgeois / Marieke / Ne me quitte pas / Le prochain amour / Le moribond / Au Printemps / La colombe / Les flamandes / L'Ivrogne / La valse a mille temps / Mivre debout.
MC: 818 359 4

LA CHANSON FRANCAISE.
Tracks: / J'aimais / Vasoul / Ces gens la / Amsterdam / Chanson des vieux amants / Les flamandes / Le plat pays / Quand on n'a l'amour / Les paumes du petit matin / Jef.
LP: 920492

MASTER SERIES: JACQUES BREL.
Tracks: / Jaures / Ne me quitte pas / Les vieux / La quete / On n'oublie rien / Le plat pays / Mathilde / Les remparts de varsovie / Amsterdam / J'arrive / Ces gens la / Jef / Vesoul / Au suivant / Madeleine / Les Bourgeois.
MC: 816458 4

MUSIC FOR THE MILLIONS.
LP: 6395 216
MC: 7206 216

SES PLUS GRANDES CHANSONS.
Tracks: / Madeleine / L'Ivrogne / La valise a mille temps / Ne me quitte pas / Le moribond / Les bourgeois / Les flamandes / Marieke / Buxelles / Le plat pays / La dame patronesse / Les vieux / Rosa / Mathilde / I'l neige sur liege / J'aimais / Amsterdam.
LP: 818 438 1
MC: 818 438 4

Bremner, Billy

BASH.
LP: 206170

Brendel, Alfred

ART OF ALFRED BRENDEL, THE (Virtuoso pieces - vol.1).
MC: .... VMTC 6701

ART OF ALFRED BRENDEL, THE (Virtuoso pieces - vol.2).
MC: .... VMTC 6702

Brennan, Dave

AMAZING GRACE.
LP: .... LC 12

BOUNCING AROUND.
LP: .... LC 20S

Brennan, Pascal

ONLY YOU.
LP: .... FRC 003

Brenston, Jackie

ROCKET 88.
Tracks: / Rocket 88 / I want to see my baby / Jackie's chewing gum / Make my love come down / In my real gone rocket / Mule / My baby left town / Hi ho baby / Lovin' time / Fat meat is greasy / 88 boogie / You won't be coming back / True love / Blues got me again, The.
LP: .... GCH 8107

Brent, Michael

SWEET SENSATION.
Tracks: / From this moment on / Certain smile, A / Vienna, city of my dreams / Under Paris skies / Tulips from Amsterdam / Country gardens / Misty / Stairway to the stars / You made me love you / Time after time / I got rhythm / Liza / Someone to watch over me / Why did I choose you / Scotland the brave / Ash grove, The / Come to the food / Londonderry air / One note samba / Wish me luck as you wave me goodbye.
LP: .... GRS 1103
MC: .... KGRS 1103

Brer Rabbit

BRER RABBIT (Uncle Remus) (Glover, Danny & Taj Mahal).
MC: .... WT 0709

SONGS OF BRER RABBIT (Glass, Dudley).
MC: .... TLP 410

Breschi, Antonio

MEZULARI.
LP: .... ELKAR 101

Brett, Adrian

ECHOES OF GOLD.
LP: .... WW 5062

MELLOW MUSIC (Brett, Adrian & The Brian Rogers Orchestra).
Tracks: / Cavatina / Portsmouth / Scarborough Fair / New world theme / Don't cry for me Argentina / Danny boy / Shepherd song / Yesterday once more / Scarlet ribbons / Mull of Kintyre / Elizabethan serenade / Yesterday / Morning has broken / Sleepy shores / Greensleeves / Sailing / Dance to your daddy / Send in the clowns / Skye boat song / Annie's song.
LP: .... WW 2013
MC: .... WW 20134

Brett, Ann & Ray

SOMEBODY LOVES YOU.
LP: .... SFA 070

Brett, Paul

EARTH BIRTH.
Tracks: / Christened by fire / Infant journey / Alone in space / Faint stirrings - new beginnings / Dance of the dawn herald / Infinite possibilities.
LP: .... PL 25080

ECLIPSE.
Tracks: / Nineteen ninety nine / Calypso Street / Silent runner / This side of heaven / Mental music / Eclipse / Overture for decadance / Red alert / Chaos / Take 5.
LP: .... PL 25219

GUITAR TREK.
Tracks: / Forever autumn / Before tequila / Summertime / Bishop went down to Fulham / In search of Aztecs / Even when the sun shines / Jazz for late night wife swappers / Hand built by robots / Blood on the frets.
LP: .... RCALP 25283

INTERLIFE.
Tracks: / Interlife / Celebration / Segregation / Isolation / Into life.
LP: .... PL 25149
MC: .... PK 25149

ROMANTIC GUITAR.
LP: .... ONE 1079

Brett, Simon

AFTER HENRY (See under After Henry) (Various artists).

Brewer, Jack

ROCKIN' ETHEREAL (Brewer, Jack Band).
LP: .... NAR 039LP
MC: .... NAR 039MC

Brewer, Jim

JIM BREWER.
LP: .... PHILO 1003

Brewer, Michael

BEAUTY LIES.
Tracks: / Without love / Any day now / Love's endless war / Beauty lies / Empty headed, broken hearted / Love in time /

Sunset woman / Tied to the wings of an angel / Hearts overflowing.
LP: K 99253
LP: 9238151

Brewer, Teresa

BEST OF TERESA BREWER.
Tracks: / Till I waltz again with you / Let me go lover / You send me / Empty arms / Jilted / Mutal admiration society / Sweet old fashioned girl / Pledging my love / Tear fell, A / I gotta go get my baby / Bell bottom blues / Boll weevil / Hula hoop song / Richochet / Anymore / Music music music.
LP: MCL 1633
MC: MCLC 1633

GOLDEN GREATS: TERESA BREWER.
Tracks: / Music music music / Let me go lover / Till I waltz again with you / Tear fell, A / Sweet old fashioned girl / You send me / Empty arms / Jilted / Mutual admiration society / Pledging my love / I gotta go get my baby / Bell bottom blues / Bo weevil / Hula hoop song / Ricochet / Anymore.
LP: MCM 5012
MC: MCMC 5012

GOOD NEWS.
Tracks: / Good news / I want to be bad / Button up your overcoat / Sunny-side up / Lucky in love / Varsity drag / Just imagine / Together / You're the cream in my coffee / Best things in life are free, The.
LP: ASLP 804
MC: ZCAS 804

I DIG BIG BAND SINGERS.
Tracks: / Got a date with an angel / Goo-hoo / I'm looking over a four leaf clover / Glenn Miller medley, The / Chattanooga Choo Choo / Jukebox Saturday night / Pennsylvania 6-5000 / I've got a gal in Kalamazoo / Elmer's tune / Don't sit under the apple tree / Benny Goodman medley / And the angels sing / Why don't you do right / Goody goody / Goodnight my love / Gotta be this or that / Loch Lomond / Jimmy Dorsey medley / Tangerine / Amapola / Besame mucho / Green eyes / Classic medley / I've heard that song before / In a shanty in old Shantytown / Daddy / Ragtime cowboy Joe / T'aint what you do (it's the way that you do it) / I'm beginning to see the light / Tommy Dorsey (medley) / On the sunny side of the street / Oh look at me now / Chicago / Yes indeed / Let's get away from it all / Deed I do / Marie.
LP: ASLP 1003
MC: ZCAS 1003

LIVE AT CARNEGIE HALL & MONTREUX, SWITZERLAND.
Tracks: / It don't mean a thing / Breaking up is hard to do / St. Louis Blues / After you've gone / It had to be you / I've got a crush on you / Romance in the dark / Mood indigo / Some songs / That's when the music takes me / I ain't got nobody / Baby won't you please come home / We love you Fats / Ain't misbehavin' / Find out what they like / Joint is jumpin', The / Come on and drive me crazy / It don't mean a thing / St. Louis Blues / New Orleans.
LP: ASLD 852
MC: ZCASD 852

ON THE ROAD AGAIN (Brewer, Teresa & Stephane Grappelli).
Tracks: / On the road again / It had to be you / Come on and drive me crazy / Them there eyes / Smile / After you've gone / I love a violin / Don't take your love from me / As time goes by.
LP: ASLP 801
MC: ZCAS 801

TERESA BREWER.
MC: ZCGAS 738

TERESA BREWER IN LONDON.
Tracks: / Music music music / Pilgrim- chapter 23, The / Another useless day / Up on Cripple Creek / Music to the man / Come running / Saturday night / Hot damn home made wine / School days / Whupin' it.
LP: SIGLP 7400
MC: ZCSIG 7400

WHEN YOUR LOVER HAS GONE.
Tracks: / When your lover has gone / Maybe you'll be there / I had the craziest dream / Darn that dream / Baby don't be mad at me / Faded summer dream / Mixed emotions / You go to my head / More than you know / Music Maestro please / Time out for tears / Fools rush in.
LP: JASM 1510

Brewers Droop

BOOZE BROTHERS, THE.
Tracks: / Where are you tonight / Roller coaster / You make me feel so good / My old lady / Sugar baby / Rock steady woman / Louise / What's the time / Midnight special / Dreaming.
LP: RL 077

Brewster, Kitty

SLEEPIN' ALONE.
Tracks: / Technique / I still feel the same / Sleepin' alone / Work on it / Your love will pull me through / One step at a time / Goin' thru the motions / Love for sale / Fool in me, The / We used to be so close.
MC: KBS1 TC

Brian & Michael

MATCHSTALK MEN AND MATCHSTALK ... (OLD GOLD) (See under Martell, Lena - One Day At A Time).

WE CAN COUNT OUR FRIENDS ON ONE HAND.
Tracks: / Bottle of gin / Thre's a place back home if things don't go .. / Pinocchio / Island in the sea / L.O.V.E. / Belong to me / You don't call me darling / Me and 10 CC / Our song / I can count my friends on one hand.
LP: N 113

Briar

CROWN OF THORNS.
LP: UKPAL 002

TOO YOUNG.
LP: HMRLP 41

TOO YOUNG.
MC: HMRMC 41

Brickell, Edie

EDIE BRICKELL: INTERVIEW PICTURE DISC.
LPPD: BAK 2157

GHOST OF A DOG (Brickell, Edie & New Bohemians).
Tracks: / Ghost of a dog.
LP: WX 386
MC: WX 386C
MC: GEFC 24304

SHOOTING RUBBERBANDS AT THE STARS (Brickell, Edie & New Bohemians).
Tracks: / What I am / Little Miss S / Air of December / Wheel, The / Love like we do / Circle / Beat the time / She / Nothing / Now / Keep coming back.
LP: 9241924
LP: WX 215
MC: WX 215C
MC: GEFC 24192
LP: GEF 24192

Brickhill, Paul (aut)

GREAT ESCAPE, THE (see under Great Escape (bk)) (Todd, Richard (nar)).

REACH FOR THE SKY (see under Reach for the Sky) (Britton, Tony (nar)).

Bride

SILENCE IS MADNESS.
LP: CMGLP 002

Bride at Whangatapu

BRIDE AT WHANGATAPU (Robyn Donald) (Boyd, Carole (nar)).
MC: PMB 012

Bride (Film)

BRIDE, THE (1985 film soundtrack) (Various artists).
LP: CST 8007
LP: STV 81254
MC: CTV 81254

Brides Of Funkenstein

FUNK OR WALK.
Tracks: / Disco to go / Warship Touchante / Nappy / Birdie / Just like you / When you're gone / Amorous.
LP: K 50545

Brideshead Revisited

BRIDESHEAD REVISITED (Evelyn Waugh) (Gielgud, Sir John (nar)).
MCSET: SAY 1
MCSET: ARGO 1001

Brideshead Revisited

BRIDESHEAD REVISITED (Original Television Theme) (Various artists).
Tracks: / Brideshead revisited: *Various artists* / Going to Brideshead: *Various artists* / First visit, The: *Various* artists / Venice nocturne: *Various artists* / Sebastian's summer: *Various artists* / Hunt, The: *Various* artists / Sebastian against the world: *Various artists* / Julia in love: *Various artists* / Julia: *Various* artists / Rain in Venice: *Various artists* / General strike: *Various artists* / Fading light: *Various* artists / Julia's theme: *Various artists* / Sebastian alone: *Various artists* / Orphans of the storm: *Various artists* / Finale: *Various artists.*
LP: CDL 1367
MC: ZCDL 1367
LPS: CBOX 1

Bridewell Taxis

INVISIBLE TO YOU.
LP: BLAG 007
MC: BLAG 007C

Bridge

BRIDGE, THE (A tribute to Neil Young) (Various artists).
Tracks: / Barstool blues: *Soul Asylum* / After the goldrush: *Flaming Lips* / Cinnamon girl: *Loop* / Winterlong: *Pixies* / Only love can break your heart: *Psychic TV* / Needle: *Kaiser, Henry & David Lindley* / Mr. Soul: *Bongwater* / Don't let me bring ....: *Williams, Victoria* / Captain Kennedy: *Sudden, Nikki & French Rev.* / Helpless: *Cave, Nick* / Computer age: *Sonic Youth* / Lotta love: *Dinosaur Jnr* / Out of the blue: *Ball* / Words: *Kaiser, Henry.*
LP: CARLP 5
MC: CARC 5
LP: KAR 002

BURNING THE BRIDGE.
LP: LLP 116

Bridge Ceili Band

BRIDGE CEILI BAND.
MC: HACS 7052

Bridge On The River

BRIDGE ON THE RIVER KWAI (Hardy, Robert (nar)).
MC: LFP 41 7152 5

BRIDGE ON THE RIVER KWAI (Mills, Sir John (nar)).
MC: CAB 021

Bridges, Alicia

ALICIA BRIDGES.
Tracks: / Body heat / Breakaway / High altitudes / We are one / City rhythm / I love the nightlife / In the name of love / Self applause / Diamond in the rough / Broken woman.
LP: 239 1364

Bridgewater Brothers

GENERATIONS SUITE.
Tracks: / African sunrise / Bororo / Sade / Synapse / Your ballad / Something I saw thru my mind / Samba para ustedos dos.
LP: YX 7802

LIGHTNING AND THUNDER.
Tracks: / Silent rain / Dear trane / Lightning and thunder.
LP: YX 7526

Bridgewater, Dee Dee

DEE DEE BRIDGEWATER.
Tracks: / Lonely disco dancer / When love comes knockin' / One in a million guy / Gunshots in the night / When you're in love / That's the way love should feel / Give in to love / Jody.
LP: K 52263

LIVE IN PARIS.
Tracks: / All blues / Misty / On a clear day / Doctor Feelgood / There is no greater love / Here's that rainy day / Medley blues / Cherokee.
LP: AFF 172
MC: TCAFF 172

Brief Lives (bk)

BRIEF LIVES (John Aubrey) (Dotrice, Roy (nar)).
MCSET: SAY 49
2LP: ZSW 522/3

Brigades

YOURS NEGATIVELY.
LP: NLP 003

Brigadier Jerry

JAMAICA JAMAICA.
Tracks: / Jah Jah move / Jah love music / Give thanks and praise / Everyman a me brethren / Kushunpeng / Armagideon style / Three blind mice / Jamaica Jamaica.
LP: RAS 3012

LIVE AT THE CONTROLS.
LP: DHS 001

ON THE ROAD.
LP: RAS 3071
MC: RASC 3071

Brigadoon (musical)

BRIGADOON (Various artists).
Tracks: / Almost like being in love: *Various artists* / There but for you go I: *Various artists* / Brigadoon: *Various artists* / Prologue: *Various artists* / Down on MacConnachy Square: *Various artists* / Heather on the hill: *Various artists* / Waitin' for my dearie: *Various artists* / I'll go home with Bonnie Jean: *Various artists* / Come to me, bend to me: *Various artists* / Brigadoon: *Various artists.*
LP: 4502331
MC: 4502334

BRIGADOON (1988 London cast recording) (Various artists).
LP: CAST 16
MC: CASTC 16

BRIGADOON (Original London cast) (Various artists).
MC: 1001.4
MC: GK 81001

BRIGADOON (Film soundtrack) (Various artists).
LP: MCA 39062
MC: MCAC 39062
LP: COS 2540
MC: BT 2540

BRIGADOON/KISS ME KATE (See under Kiss me Kate) (Various artists).

KISS ME KATE/BRIGADOON (See under Kiss Me Kate) (Various artists).

Brigandage

BRIGANDAGE.
MC: FYM 1

PRETTY LITTLE THING.
LP: GHLP 001

Briggs, Anne

ANNE BRIGGS.
Tracks: / Blackwater side / Snow it melts the soonest, The / Willie o' Winsbury / Go your way / Thorneymoor woods / Cuckoo, The / Reynardine / Young tambling / Living by the water / Ma bonny lad.
LP: 12T 207

BIRD IN THE BUSH (Briggs, Anne & Frankie Armstrong).
Tracks: / Two magicians / Old man from over the sea, The / Wanton seed, The / Gathering rushes in the month of May / Bonnie black hare / Whirly whori / Pretty Polly / Old bachelor, The / Stonecutter boy / Mower, The / Bird in the bush, The / Pegging awl, The / Mortinmas time / Widow of the Westmorland's daughter.
LP: 12T 135

CLASSIC ANNE BRIGGS (Complete Topic Recordings).
Tracks: / Recruited collier, The / Doffing mistress, The / Lowlands away / My bonny boy / Polly Vaughan / Rosemary Lane / Gathering rushes in the month of May / Whirly whorl, The / Stonecutter boy, The / Martinmas time / Blackwater side / Snow it melts the soonest, The / Willie O'Winsbury / Go your way / Thorneymoor woods / Cuckoo, The / Reynardine / Young Tambling / Living by the water / My bonny lad.
MC: FE 078C

Briggs, Brian

BRIAN DAMAGE.
Tracks: / Lookin' out / Nervous breakdown / See you on the other side / AEO (parts 1 & 2) / Psyclone / Goin' out of my head / Spy vs spy / Let me hear me talkin' / Lifer.
LP: AALP 6996
MC: BKR 6996
LP: ILPS 9644

COMBAT ZONE.
LP: BRK 3627
MC: ZCBRK 3627

Briggs, John

LOVE CLASSICS.
Tracks: / Nocturne / Operatic medley / Morgan / Ah what love / O my beloved father / Softly awakes my heart / I love thee / Waltz medley / My hero / Desert song, The / Love will find a way / Falling in love with love / Polovtsian dances / Flower song from Carmen / Novello medley / Waltz of my heart / I can give you the starlight / My dearest dear / Agagio / My love / Romeo and Juliet.
LP: KEYLP 1
MC: KEYCAS 1

Briggs, Noel

MAKE IT A PARTY WITH NOEL BRIGGS.
Tracks: / Make it a party / Blaze away / Who's sorry now? / Somebody stole my gal / Dance of the comedians / West Side story selection / Voices of Spring / Tiger rag.
MC: AC 168

WURLITZER STARS VOL. 1 (Briggs, Noel/Watson Holmes).
Tracks: / If you're Irish / Fiddler on the roof / I'm confessin' / Memories / 27 organists' signature tunes / Blue sapphire / Cheek to cheek / Fine romance, A / Moon River / Let's fall in love / Change partners / Four leaf clover / If I ruled the world / Jolly good company.
MC: AC 170

Briggs, Raymond

WHEN THE WIND BLOWS.
MC: ZCF 499

Brighouse & Rastrick

BANDSTAND.
Tracks: / March: The battle of Britain / Tone poem: Sinfonietta / Trumpet solo: Trumpet tune and Ayre / Finale for band / March: Farnham town / Trombone trio: Trombone galop / Overture: Oliver Cromwell.

LP: PVM 5

BRASS MASTERPIECES.
LPS: ADLS 613
MCSET: ADKS 613

BRIGHOUSE & RASTRICK.
MC: VCA 038

BRIGHOUSE & RASTRICK BAND.
Tracks: / Fest musik der Stadt Wien / Slavonik dance / Gladiolus rag / Salute to youth / Toccata and fugue in D minor / Cappriccio / Tombstone, Arizona.
LP: MOGO 4003

BRIGHOUSE & RASTRICK BAND (20 hits from 20 years).
Tracks: / You've lost that lovin' feeling / Groovy kind of love / Penny Lane / Delilah / Gentle on my mind / Leaving on a jet plane / Pushbike song / American pie / Get down / You make me feel brand new / Feelings / Silly love songs / Chanson d'amour / Hopelessly devoted to you / In the Navy / Stop the cavalry / Chi Mai / Heartbreaker / Uptown girl / Pipes of peace.
LP: MFP 415 721-1
MC: MFP 415 721-4

BRIGHOUSE & RASTRICK BAND IN CONCERT.
Tracks: / Overture-carnival op. 92 / I'll be still in love with you / Phil the Fluter's ball / Hey Jude / Lenzburg / Varied mood / Pavanne / Danses Polovtsiennes.
LP: PRL 008
MC: CPRL 008

BRIGHOUSE & RASTRICK BRASS BAND.
MC: 1A 220 1583274

DIADEM OF GOLD.
Tracks: / Fanfare romance and finale / Gymnopedie no.1 / Tuba tapestry / Eric's theme / Ravenswood / Prelude to comedy / Canto popolare / Diadem of gold.
LP: PRL 017
MC: CPRL 017

FLORAL DANCE.
Tracks: / Floral dance / Linconshire poacher / Lara's theme / Tijuana tuba / Zambesi / Solitaire / Bachelor girl / Try to remember / African waltz / Scarbourhg fair / Shaft / Strawberry fair.
LP: LOGO 1001
LP: TRS 109

FLORAL DANCE, THE.
MC: 495941

LUSHER SIDE OF..., THE.
Tracks: / Concert variations / Cornets a go-go / Almost a lullaby / Harlem Nocturne / Battle hymn of the Republic / Makin' whoopee / In the wee small hours of the morning / Phil the Fluter's ball / Trombone men, The / Mood indigo / Typewriter, The.
LP: GRS 1050

MUSIC.
Tracks: / Take a chance on me / Figaro / You needed me / I'll go where your music takes me / Don't it make my brown eyes blue / Copacabana / Clog dance / It's a heartache / Y.M.C.A. / My life / Music.
LP: MOGO 4004

ON THE BANDSTAND.
Tracks: / British bandsman, The / Romance from the 'Gadfly' / Alpine samba / Napoli / Jubilee overture / Rhythm and blues / Carnival of Venice / March to the scaffold / Flower duet from Lakme, The / Overture-Waverley.
LP: PRL 031D
MC: CPRL 031D

PLAY 20 GOLDEN NUMBER ONES.
Tracks: / Begin the beguine / Ebony and ivory / Super trouper / We don't talk anymore / Crying / Silver lady / M.A.S.H., Theme from / It's my party / When I need you / Japanese boy / Woman in love / No-one quite like Grandma / Winner takes it all, The / Bright eyes / You're the one that I want / One day at a time / Summer nights / Imagine / Three times a lady / Rivers of Babylon.
LP: MFP 5597
MC: TCMFP 5597

PLAY 30 ALL TIME CLASSIC HITS.
Tracks: / You've lost that lovin' feelin' / Penny Lane / American pie / Bright eyes / Imagine / Feelings / Silly love songs / Chanson d'amour / Stop the cavalry / Chi mai / Up-town girl / Pipes of peace / Groovy kind of love / Delilah / Gentle on my mind / Rivers of Babylon / Pushbike song / Begin the beguine / Ebony and ivory / Super trouper / We don't talk anymore / Crying / M.A.S.H. theme / Winner takes it all / Leaving on a jet plane / woman in love / One day at a time / You make me feel brand new / Heartbreaker / Three times a lady.
2LP: DL 1176
MC: TCDL 1176

THOUSAND YORKSHIRE MALE VOICES, A.
Tracks: / Song of Yorkshire, A / White rose, The / Psalm 126 / Litolff's Scherzo / Speed your journey / Sound an alarm / On Ilkley Moor baht'at / Long day closes, The / Soldier's chorus / Evening's pastorale, An / Yorkshire mixture, A / Pomp and circumstance march no.1.
LP: PRZ 003D
MC: CPRZ 003D

TOUCH OF BRASS.
Tracks: / Twelfth of never / So very close to me / It's a heartache / You needed me / Tenderly / When I fall in love / Misty / Take a chance on me / Till there was you / Can't smile without you / How deep is the ocean? / She was beautiful / My life / Figaro / Missing you / I'll go where your music takes me / I'm in the mood for love / Love you a little bit more / Don't it make my brown eyes blue? / Don't take your love from me.
2LP: CR 081
MCSET: CRT 081

VINTAGE BRASS.
LP: MFP 50472

Bright, Bette

RHYTHM BREAKS THE ICE.
Tracks: / When you were mine / On a night like this / Hello I am your heart / All girls lie / Take what you find / Talking whispers / Thunder & lightning / Shoorah shoorah / Some girls have all the luck / Tender touch / Hold on.
LP: KODE 4
MC: CODE 4

Bright Chimezie

AFRICAN STYLE.
LP: RAPSLPS 112

Bright, Len

LEN BRIGHT COMBO PRESENTS THE LEN BRIGHT COMBO (Bright, Len Combo).
LP: NICE 1

Bright Lights...(film)

BRIGHT LIGHTS, BIG CITY (Film Soundtrack) (Various artists).
Tracks: / Good Love: *Prince* / True faith: *New Order* / Divine emotions: *Narada* / Kiss and tell: *Ferry, Bryan* / Pleasure little treasure: *Depeche Mode* / Century's end: *Fagen, Donald* / Obsessed: *Noise Club*/ Love Attack: *Konk* / Ice cream days: *Hall, Jennifer* / Pump up the volume: *M/A/R/R/S.*
MC: 9256884
LP: 9256881

Bright Morning Star

SWEET AND SOUR.
LP: FF 478

Brighten The Corner...

BRIGHTEN THE CORNER WHERE YOU ARE (Various artists).
Tracks: / God shall wipe all tears away: *Kings Of Harmony* / Canaan's land: *Famous Blue Jay Singers* / Walk around: *Soul Stirrers* / Tree of level: *Fairchild Four* / Yield not to temptation: *Martin, Roberta singers* / Daniel in the lions den (he locked the lion's jaw): *Tharpe,Rosetta/K.Bell Nubin/S.Price/B TaylorSnr./H.Cowans* / Give me wings: *Various artists* / They led my Lord away: *Williams, Marion* / We're marching to Zion: *Congregation of Ridgecrest(N.C.)Baptist Conference Center* / Jesus is all the world to me: *Congregation of Ridgecrest(N.C.)Baptist Conference Center* / Ninety & nine, The: *Shea, George Beverly/Ira Sankey* / To God be the glory: *Graham, Billy London Crusade Choir* / Brighten the corner where you are: *Rodeheaver Co. Home Brass Band (Rodeheaver)* / In the garden: *Rodeheaver Co. Home Brass Band (Rodeheaver)* / Nearer my God to Thee: *Seagle, Oscar* / Saved by grace: *Gypsy Smith* / Just as I am: *Graham, Billy Australian Crusade Choir.*
LP: NW 224

Brightman, Sarah

ALL I ASK OF YOU (See under Richard, Cliff) (Brightman, Sarah & Cliff Richard).

AS I CAME OF AGE.
Tracks: / River cried, The / As I came of age / Some girls / Love changes everything / Alone again or / Bowling green / Something to believe in / Take my life / Brown eyes / Good morning starshine / Yesterday / It must be tough to be that cool.
LP: 843 563-1
MC: 843 563-4

BRITTEN FOLK SONGS.
LP: EL 749 510 1
MC: EL 749 510 4

HOWARD BLAKE: GRANPA (Brightman, Sarah & Peter Ustinov).
LP: HB 1
MC: HBC 1

MUSIC OF THE NIGHT (See Crawford, Michael) (Brightman, Sarah & Michael Crawford).

SONGS THAT GOT AWAY, THE.
LP: 839 116 1
MC: 839 116 4

Brighton Beach Memoirs

BRIGHTON BEACH MEMOIRS (1987 Film Soundtrack) (Various artists).
Tracks: / Good morning glory: *Various artists* / Drop me off in Harlem: *Various artists* / You and the night: *Various artists* / Nora on Broadway: *Various artists* / My inspiration: *Various artists* / Whistling in the dark: *Various artists* / As grand as you are: *Various artists* / Stickball: *Various artists* / Funeral procession, The: *Various artists* / I hate my name: *Various artists* / Mrs. Murphy: *Various artists* / Blanche's theme: *Various artists* / Cemetery sequence (main title): *Various artists* / Finale: *Various artists.*
LP: IMCA 6193
MC: IMCAC 6193

Brighton Festival,

BRIGHTON FESTIVAL, 1985 (Aba Daba) (Various artists).
Tracks: / Put on your tata, little girlie: *Glynn, Paddy* / Fallen star, A: *Hunter, Robin* / Johnny Jones (I know now): *Butler, Katy* / I won't dance: *Green, Teddy* / WAAF, The: *Butler, Katy* / Call round any old time: *Green, Teddy* / She was poor but she was honest: *Glynn, Paddy* / Boiled beef and carrots: *McManus, Jim*/ Little of what you fancy, A: *Butler, Katy* / Give my regards to Leicester Square: *Williams, Bronwen* / Let's all go down The Strand: *Various artists* / Man on the flying trapeze, The: *McManus, Jim* / On the sunny side of the street: *McManus, Jim* / Leslie Stuart medley: *Green, Teddy* / It ain't gonna rain no more: *Green, Teddy*/ Gipsy's warning, The: *Glynn, Paddy* / Oh, dem golden slippers: *Various artists.*
MC: TT 004

Brighton, Ian

MARSH GAS.
LP: BEAD 3

Brighton Rock

BRIGHTON ROCK.
Tracks: / We came to rock / Game of love / Change of heart / Can't wait for the night / Assault attack / Jack is back / Save me / Nobody's hero / Barricade / Rock and roll.
LP: K 253 055 1
MC: K 253 055 4

TAKE A DEEP BREATH.
Tracks: / Can't stop the earth from shakin' / Outlaw / One more try / Rebels with a cause / Whose foolin' who / Unleash the rage / High and dry / Ride the rainbow / Power overload / Love slips away.
LP: WX 272
MC: WX 272 C

Brightwell, Jumbo

SONGS FROM THE EEL'S FOOT.
Tracks: / Flower of London, The / Derby miller, The / Loss of the ramillies, The / Green mossy banks of the Lea, The / Blow the candle out / Bold Princess Royal, The / Newry Town / Indian lass, The / Muddley barracks / False hearted knight / Lost heiress, The / Down in the fields where the butter cups grow / Rumbleaway / Life of a man, The.
LP: 12TS 261

Brigman, George

HUMAN SCRAWL VAGABOND (Brigman, George & Split).
Tracks: / Mistress of desire / Lazy eyes / Symphony in efficacy / Vacation / Truth, The / Animal dope / Pull your pants down / Blowin' smoke / Status people / Grunts / Clap trap / Spaced / Sweet bulbs.
LP: R 33/8602

Brignola, Nick

MORE BIRDS, LESS FEATHERS (See under Berk, Dic) (Brignola, Nick/Dic Berk).

NEW YORK BOUND.
LP: IP 7719

NORTHERN LIGHTS (Brignola, Nick Quartet).
Tracks: / Lush life / Star trick / Shaw 'nuff.
LP: DS 917

SIGNALS...IN FROM SOMEWHERE (Brignola, Nick Quartet).
Tracks: / In from somewhere / Brother John / Night song / Tadd's delight / Signals / Frame, The / Once upon a samba / Fun.
LP: DS 893
MC: DSC 893

Brigo

LOVE IN THE PARTY.
Tracks: / Love in the party / When ya coming down / Lemme go / After carnival / Limbo break.
LP: GS 2284

Brilliant

KISS THE LIPS OF LIFE.
Tracks: / It's a man's man's man's world / Somebody / Ruby fruit jungle / How high the sun / Kiss the lips of life / Love is war / Crash the car / I'll be your lover / End of the world.
LP: BRILL 1
MC: BRILL 1C

Brilliant Corners

CREAMY STUFF.
LP: MCQLP 006

EVERYTHING I EVER WANTED.
Tracks: / Rambling rose / Growing up absurd / One of these days / Meet me on Tuesdays / Funniest thing, The / Under the bridge / Girl called property, A / Southern mystery / Mary / Jim's room / Everything I ever wanted / Trudy is a squeal.
LP: MCQLP 3

GROWING UP ABSURD.
LP: SS 24

HOOKED.
LP: MCQLP 005
MC: MCQMC 005

JOYRIDE.
Tracks: / You don't know how lucky you are / This girl / Grow cold / I didn't see you / Emily / Nothing / Hemingway's back / Accused by the angels.
LP: MCQLP 004

SOMEBODY UP THERE LIKES ME.
LP: MCQLP 1

WHAT'S IN A WORD.
LP: MCQLP 2
LP: SS 026

Brim, John

CHICAGO BLUES SESSIONS 12 (Brim, John/Pinetop Perkins).
LP: WOLF 120 858

JAMES/BRIM/JONES (See under James, Elmore) (Brim, John/Floyd Jones/Elmore James).

JOHN BRIM & LITTLE HUDSON (Brim, John & Little Hudson).
LP: FLY 568

Brimmer, Charles

BRIMFUL OF SOUL.
Tracks: / I love her / Dedicating my love to you / With you in mind / My sweet thing / That's how strong my love is / I want to be your breadwinner / Play something sweet / Don't break my heart / We've only just begun / Your man's gonna be in trouble.
LP: CRB 1123

Brimstone, Derek

CHEAPO ALBUM.
LP: BRIM 051

SHUFFLEBOAT RIVER FAREWELL.
Tracks: / Fairytale lullaby / Shuffleboat farewell / To Althea from prison / Wheel, The / Oh Lord how happy I am / Make me a pallet on the floor / Blues run the game / Columbine / Won't you come along / Silver coin / Scarlet town.
LP: RUB 017

VERY GOOD TIME.
Tracks: / Very good time / March rain / Mrs. Fisher / Ain't it a shame / All those songs / Bimbles rags / Sing a song of Summer / When the music starts to play / Piss off / Gavotte in H / I live not where I love / River, The / Gnome, The.
LP: RUB 005

Brimstone & Treacle

BRIMSTONE & TREACLE (1982 Film Soundtrack) (Various artists).
Tracks: / When the roll is called up yonder: *Various artists* / Brimstone and treacle: *Sting* / Narration: *Sting*/ How stupid Mr. Bates: *Police* / Only you: *Sting* / I burn for you: *Police* / Spread a little happiness: *Sting* / We got the beat: *Go-Go's* / You know I had the strangest dreams: *Sting* / Up the junction: *Squeeze*/ Bless this house: *Brimstone chorale The* / Kind of loving, A: *Police.*
LP: AMLH 64915
MC: CAM 64915

Bring on the... (bk)

BRING ON THE EMPTY HORSES (Niven, David).
MC: TC LFP 7067

Bringing It All...

BRINGING IT ALL BACK HOME (Various artists).
LPS: REF 844

MCSET: . . . . ZCD 844

Brinsley Schwarz

BRINSLEY SCHWARTZ.
LP: . . . . UAS 29111

DESPITE IT ALL.
LP: . . . . LBG 82437

FIFTEEN THOUGHTS BY BRINSLEY SCHWARTZ.
LP: . . . . UAK 30177

IT'S ALL OVER NOW.
LP: . . . . LIK 22
MC: . . . . TCLIK 22

NERVOUS ON THE ROAD.
Tracks: / Nervous on the road / It's been so long / Happy doing what we're doing / Surrender to the rhythm / Surrender to the rhythm / Feel a little funky / I like it like that / Brand new you, brand new me / Home in my hand / Why why why.
LP: . . . . LBR 1040
LP: . . . . UAS 29374

NEW FAVOURITES OF BRINSLEY SCHWARZ.
Tracks: / Peace, love and understanding / Ever since you're gone / Ugly things / I got the real thing / Look that's in your eye tonight, The / Now's the time / Small town, big city / Trying to love my life without you / I like you, I don't love you / Down in the dive.
LP: . . . . LBR 1033
LP: . . . . UAS 29641

ORIGINAL GOLDEN GREATS.
LP: . . . . USP 101

PLEASE DON'T EVER CHANGE.
Tracks: / Hooked on love / I worry / Home in my hand / I won't make it without you / Speedoo / Why do we hurt the one we love / Don't ever change / Play that fast thing / Down in Mexico / Version, The.
LP: . . . . ED 237
LP: . . . . UAS 29489

SILVER PISTOL.
Tracks: / Dry land / Merry go round / One more day / Nightingales / Silver pistol / Last time I was fooled / Unknown number / Range war / Egypt / Niki Hoeke speedway / Ju ju man / Rockin' chair.
LP: . . . . ED 190
LP: . . . . UAS 29217

SURRENDER TO THE RHYTHM (Best of Brinsley Schwarz).
Tracks: / Country girl / Surrender to the rhythm / Ugly things / Happy doing what we're doing / Look that's in your eye tonight / Last time I was fooled, The / Silver pistol / Nightingale / Hypocrite / Trying to live my life without you / I like it like that / Nervous on the road (but can't stay at home) / Down in Mexico / I worry ('bout you baby) / Play that fast thing (one more time) / Don't loose your grip on love / Ju Ju man / Down in the dive / Home in my hand / (What's so funny 'bout) peace, love and understanding.
LP: . . . . EMS 1407
MC: . . . . TCEMS 1407

Brisker, Gordon

NEW BEGINNING (Brisker, Gordon Big Band).
Tracks: / Just one of those things / Be my love / Prince of darkness / No matter where you are / In the land of the snake people.
LP: . . . . DS 938
MC: . . . . DSC 938

Bristol Bach Choir

WELCOME YULE.
Tracks: / Welcome yule / Hymn to the Virgin, A / Virga Jesse (Motet) / Spotless rose, A / Rose, The / Lully, lulla, thou little tiny child / Come to Bethlehem / This have I done for my true love / What sweeter music / Carol of the bells / Long, long ago / He smiles within His cradle / Ding Dong merrily on high / Wexford carol / There is no rose of such virtue / Stille nacht (Silent night) / O magnum mysterium / Hodie Christus natus est.
MC: . . . . CSDL 375

Bristol Cathedral

CAROLS FROM BRISTOL CATHEDRAL (Bristol Cathedral Choir).
Tracks: / Come, Thou redeemer of the Earth (German traditional.) / Sussex carol (English traditional.) / New year carol, A / There is no rose / Child is born in Bethlehem, A / In dulci jubilo (Old German.) / Sir Christemas / O little town of Bethlehem (English traditional.) / Once in royal David's city / In the bleak mid winter / I sing of a maiden / Of the Father's heart begotten (Thirteenth-century melody.) / Away in a manger / Coventry carol (Original version of 1591.) / Three kings, The / Hark the herald angels sing.
LP: . . . . ACA 552

Bristol, Johnny

BEST OF JOHNNY BRISTOL, THE.
Tracks: / You and I / I sho like groovin' with ya / Love me for a reason / Love takes years / All goodbyes aren't gone / Leave my world / Do it to my mind / Hang on in there baby / Memories don't leave like people do / She came into my life / Feeling the magic.
LP: . . . . SPELP 110
MC: . . . . SPEMC 110

FREE TO BE ME.
Tracks: / Take me down / Love no longer has a hold on me / Hold onto love / Till I see you again / Loving and free / Sweet and deep / Love is on tonight / Share with me my dreams / If I can't stop you / Rosebud.
LP: . . . . HANLP 2

HANG ON IN THERE BABY.
LP: 2315 303

Bristol Rovers FC

I'D DO ANYTHING (See under Hull, Rod & Emu) (Bristol Rovers FC/Rod Hull & Emu).

Britain

MUSIC OF BRITAIN, THE (Various artists).
MCSET: . . . . WW 6030

Britain At War

BRITAIN AT WAR (Various artists).
Tracks: / Gracie with the Air Force: *Fields, Gracie* (Not on CD.) / Heil Hitler, Ja Ja Ja: *Frankau, Ronald* (Not on CD.) / Black out Bella: *Byng, Douglas* / Any old iron?: *Champion, Harry* / Tiggerty boo!: *Warner, Jack* / I fell in love with an airman: *O'Shea, Tessie* / You can't take the breed from the British: *Western Brothers* (Not on CD.) / Careless talk (pts 1 & 2): *Henson, Leslie & Stanley Holloway* (Not on CD.) / Get in your shelter: *Askey*, Arthur / Is 'e an Aussie, Lizzie, is 'e!: *Mr. Flotsam & Mr. Jetsam* / Fanny is evacuated now: *Frankau, Ronald* / Oh what a surprise for the duce: *Desmond, Florence* (Not on CD.) / Vic Oliver joins the arms/The army joins Vic Oliver: *Oliver, Vic* (Not on CD.) / Out in the Middle East: *Formby, George (Junior)* (Not on CD.) / They've blown all the feathers off the Nightingale...: *Askey, Arthur* (...off the Nightingale in Berkeley Square. Not on CD.) / When moaning Minnie moans no more: *Korris, Harry/ Robby Vincent/Cecil Frederick* (From Happidrome.) / No lika da war: *Holloway, Stanley* (nar) / Mr. Wu's an air raid warden now: *Formby, George (Junior)* / Lords of the air: *Loss, Joe/Monte Ray* / Badge from yur coat, The: *White, Jack/ Dorothy Carless* (Not on CD.) / Spitfire song, The: *Loss, Joe/Sam Browne* / Ev'ry day is one day nearer: *White, Jack/ Tony Morris* (Not on CD.) / Victory roll rag (Swing with a swing): *Roy*, Harry (Not on CD.) / Last time I saw Paris, The: *Gibbons, Carroll & Savoy Hotel Orpheans* / I've got sixpence: *Loss*, Joe (Not on CD.) / Pair of silver wings, A: *Gibbons, Carroll Show/Anne Lenner* / When they sound the last all clear: *Roy, Harry* / Mister Brown of London town: *Loss, Joe & His Band with Chick Henderson* (Not on CD.) / Hey little hen: *Gonella, Nat* / He wants to be a pilot: *Layton, Turner* (Not on CD.) / When that man is dead and gone: *Bowlly*, Al & Jim Mesene / Sargeant Sally is coming home on leave: *Leader, Harry/Alan Kane* (Not on CD.) / V stands for victory: *Loss, Joe/ George Baker* / Girl who broke the sergeant major's heart, The: *RAOC Blue Rockets* / My sister and I: *Loss, Joe/ Bette Roberts* / This is worth fighting for: *'Hutch'* / Nightingales and bombers (The night of the Mannheim raid): *Various artists* (Pt. 2. - Bombers receding.).
2LP: . . . . EM 1366
MCSET: . . . . TCEM 1366

Britain Is Rockin'

BRITAIN IS ROCKIN' (Various artists).
LP: . . . . LL 5025

Britannia...

BAND OF THE YEAR (Britannia Building Society Foden Band).
Tracks: / Spanish dance / Winter / You'll never walk alone / Tea for two / Solveig's song / Eighteenth variation on a theme of Paganini / American in Paris, An / Postcard from Mexico / Pretty girl is like a melody, A / Puttin' on the ritz / Sweet and low / In the woods / Bolero.
LP: . . . . GRALP 33
MC: . . . . GRTC 33

BRASS WITH CLASS (Britannia Building Society Foden Band).
Tracks: / Britannia / Love's old sweet song / Dansa Brasiliera / To a wild rose / Bank holiday / On with the Motley / Cossack dance / Appalachian folk-song suite / Freedom / Dance sequence / Procession to the minster.

LP: . . . . PRL 037D
MC: . . . . CPRL 037D

British Caledonian..

ALBA.
Tracks: / Alba / Hornpipes / Slow airs / Cradle song / 6/8 marches / America - the beautiful medley / Intercontinental gathering, An / Competition medley / Waltz and march / 4/4 marches / Amazing grace / Farewell medley / Reprise drum salute.
LP: . . . . LIDL 6017
MC: . . . . LIDC 6017

British Comedy

BRITISH COMEDY CLASSICS (see under EMI Comedy Classics) (Various artists).

British Electric

MUSIC FOR LISTENING TO.
Tracks: / Groove thang / Optimum chant / Uptown apocalypse / BEF ident / Baby called Billy, A / Rise of the east / Music to kill your parents by.
LP: . . . . BEF 1

MUSIC FOR STOWAWAYS.
Tracks: / Optimum chant, The / Uptown apocalypse / Wipe the board clean / Rise of the East / Groove thang / Music to kill your parents by / Old at rest, The / Rise of the East / Decline of the West.
MC: . . . . OVEDC 230

British Isles

MUSIC OF THE BRITISH ISLES (Various artists).
Tracks: / John Peel: *Various artists* / Cherry ripe: *Various artists* / Ash grove, The: *Various artists* / Charlie is my darling: *Various artists* / Loch Lomond: *Various artists* / Greensleeves: *Various artists* / Linden Lea: *Various artists* / Swansea town: *Various artists* / All through the night: *Various artists* / Myfanwy: *Various artists* / Blaydon races: *Various artists* / Cushie Butterfield: *Various artists* / Campbells are coming, The: *Various artists* / Wi' a 100 pipers: *Various artists* / Border ballad: *Various* artists / Here we come a wassailing: *Various artists* / Twelve days of Christmas, The: *Various artists* / Covent Garden tarantelle: *Various artists* / Seventeen come Sunday: *Various artists* / Fine old English gentlemen, A: *Various artists* / To be a farmer's boy: *Various artists* / Here's a health unto his Majesty: *Various artists* / British Grenadiers, The: *Various artists* / Minstrel boy: *Various artists* / Annie Laurie: *Various artists* / Men of Harlech: *Various artists* / Londonderry air: *Various artists* / Dick's maggot: *Various artists* / Tomlinson: *Various artists* / Shepherd's hey: *Various artists* / Eriskay love lilt: *Various artists* / Green hills o'Somerset: *Various artists* / Blow the wind Southerly: *Various artists* / Glorious Devon: *Various* artists / Barwick green: *Various artists* / Fantasia on the Dargason: *Various artists* / Holst: *Various artists* / Suo: *Various artists* / Jerusalem: *Various artists*.
MC: TC2MOM 1546529
MC: TC2MOM 128

British Legion Central

LEGIONNAIRES ON PARADE.
MC: . . . . ZC BND 1051

British Lions (group)

TROUBLE WITH WOMEN (British Lions).
Tracks: / Trouble with woman / Any port in a storm / Lady don't fall backwards / High noon / Lay down your love / Waves of love / Electric chair / Won't you give him.
LP: . . . . ARED 7

British Music (film)

BRITISH MUSIC FOR FILM AND TELEVISION (Various artists).
Tracks: / Bridge too far: *Various artists* / Yanks: *Various artists* / Battle of britain: *Various artists* / Ideal husband: *Various artists* / Christopher Columbus: *Various artists* / Colditz march: *Various artists* / Watership down: *Various artists* / Overlanders: *Various artists* / Lady Caroline Lamb: *Various artists* / Frenzy: *Various artists* / Malta G.C.: *Various artists*.
LP: . . . . ED 2901091
LP: . . . . ASD 3797
MC: . . . . ED 2901094

British Music (tv

BRITISH MUSIC FOR FILM AND TELEVISION (see under British Music (film)) (Various artists).

British North American

BRITISH NORTH AMERICAN ACT.
LP: . . . . ANTAR 7

British Piano

MECHANICAL MEMORIES.
MC: . . . . ZCGH 625

British Psychedelic

BRITISH PSYCHEDELIC TRIP 1 (Various artists).
MC: . . . . SEEK 66

BRITISH PSYCHEDELIC TRIP 2 1965-1970 (Various artists).
Tracks: / My white bicycle: *Tomorrow* / Skeleton and the roundabout: *Idle Race* / In the land of the few: *Love Sculpture* / Kites: *Dupree, Simon & The Big Sound* / Mr. Armageddan: *Locomotive* / You've got a habit of leaving: *Jones, Davy* / Excerpt from a teenage opera: *West, Keith* / Rumours: *Kippington Lodge* / It's so nice to come home: *Lemon Tree* / Real love guaranteed: *Gods* / We are the Moles part 1: *Moles* / Friendly man: *July* / Sorrow: *Pretty Things* / I see: *July* / Lady on a bicycle: *Kippington Lodge* / On a Saturday: *West, Keith* / Worn red carpet: *Idle Race* / Strawberry fields forever: *Tomorrow* / She says good morning: *Pretty Things* / Hey bulldog: *Gods*.
LP: . . . . SEE 76

BRITISH PSYCHEDELIC TRIP 3 (Various artists).
Tracks: / Renaissance Fair: *Human Instinct* / Miss Pinkerton: *Cuppa T* / Toffee apple Sunday: *Twirl, Toby* / Green plant: *Cherry Smash* / Follow me: *Californians* / Just one more chance: *Outer Limits* / Heavenly club: *Les Sauterelles* / 'Cos I'm lonely: *Elliots Sunshine* / Turquoise tandem cycle: *Crest, Jason* / Jenny Artichoke: *Kaleidoscope* / Magic potion: *Open Mind* / Cast a spell: *Open Mind* / Deep inside your mind: *Shields, Keith* / Elf, The: *Stewart, Al* / Happy castle: *Crocheted Doughnut Ring* / Death at the seaside: *Human Instinct* / Secret: *Virgin Sleep* / In my magic garden: *Tinkerbell's Fairydust* / Woodstock: *Turquoise* / Desdemona: *Johns Children*.
LP: . . . . SEE 86

British Summer Time

POP OUT EYES.
LP: . . . . NATO 707

Britny Fox

BOYS IN HEAT.
Tracks: / In motion / Standing in the shadows / Hair of the dog / Livin' on a dream / She's so lonely / Dream on / Long way from home / Plenty of love / Stevie / Shine on / Angel in my heart / Left me / Stray / Long road.
LP: 4659541
MC: 4659544

BRITNY FOX.
Tracks: / Girlschool / Long way to love / Kick'n'fight / Save the weak / Fun in Texas / Rocky revolution / Don't hide / Gudbuy t'Jane / In America / Hold on.
LP: 4611111
MC: 4611114

Brits Awards

B.P.I. BRITS AWARDS 91 (See under BPI Awards) (Various artists).

BRITS AWARDS 90 (See under B.P.I. Awards) (Various artists).

BRITS - THE AWARDS 1989, THE (VIDEO) (see under BPI Awards) (Various artists).

Britt, Elton

BEST OF BRITT.
Tracks: / There's a star spangled banner waving somewhere / Blue eyes crying in the rain / Mockin' Bird Hill / I almost lost my mind / Roving gambler / It is no secret / Someday you'll want me to want you / Detour / I get the blues when it rains / Candy kisses / I hung my head and cried / Beyond the sunset.
LP: . . . . NL 89995
MC: . . . . NK 89995

YODEL SONGS.
Tracks: / Give me a pinto pal / Chime bells / St. James Avenue / Yodel blues, The / Tennessee yodel polka / St. Louis blues yodel / Maybe I'll cry over you / That's how the yodel was born / Alpine milkman, The / Cannonball yodel / Patent leather boots / Skater's yodel, The.
LP: . . . . HAT 3067
MC: . . . . HATC 3067

Brittany

CHANTS PROFONDS VOLUME 2 (Jean-Francois Quemener).
MC: . . . . ARN 40 34476

DIR HA TAN-VOL.4 (Dances du Pays de Vannes).
LP: . . . . ARN 34472
MC: . . . . ARN 40 34472

Britten (Composer)

ALBERT HERRING (English Chamber Orchestra).
LP: SET274-6

CEREMONY OF CAROLS, A (Christ Church Cathedral, Oxford Choir/ Frances Kelly).
Tracks: / Te Deum / Hymn to St. Peter, A / Hymn to the Virgin, A / Hymn to St. Cecilia.
MC: . . . . ZC QS 6030

FOLK SONGS (see under Pears, Peter) (Britten, Benjamin & Peter Pears).

NOYE'S FLUDDE - THE GOLDEN VANITY (Various artists).
MC: 4251614

SPRING SYMPHONY & OTHERS (Various artists).
MC: 4251534

YOUNG PERSON'S GUIDE TO THE ORCHESTRA (see under Peter and the Wolf) (Connery, Sean/Royal Philharmonic Orchestra).

YOUNG PERSONS GUIDE TO THE ORCHESTRA (London Philharmonic Orchestra).
MC: . . . . EG 763 777 4

Britton, Harold

ORGAN SPECTACULAR.
Tracks: / Light cavalry overture / Andantino (Lemare) ((Moonlight and roses)) / Grand march from Aida / Adagio / Ride of the valkyries, The (Wagner) / Toccata and fugue in D minor (Bach) / Entertainer, The (Joplin) / None but the lonely heart (Tchaikovsky) / Pomp and circumstance march no.1 (Elgar) (Land of hope and glory) / Liberty bell / Toccata from symphony no.5 (Widor).
MC: . . . . ZC QS 6028

Britton, Maggie

MAGGIE BRITTON.
Tracks: / Bright water / Josephine / My town / Extra days of you / No secrets / Good ship earth / What am I gonna do / Boys from Brazil.
LP: . . . . MON LP 025

Britton, Tony (nar)

REACH FOR THE SKY (see under Reach for the Sky).

STUDY IN SCARLET, A (see under Sherlock Holmes).
MC: . . . . TCLFP 417130-

Broadbent, Alan

EVERYTHING I LOVE.
Tracks: / Speak low / Lover man / It could happen to you / Softly as in a morning sunrise / You and the night and the music.
LP: . . . . DS 929
MC: . . . . DSC 929

Broadbent, Ernest

RECOLLECTIONS OF THE TOWER, BLACKPOOL (see under Dixon, Reginald) (Broadbent, Ernest/Reginald Dixon/Eric Lord).

Broadbent, Tim

SONGS OF THIS THAT AND THE OTHER.
Tracks: / City Of New Orleans / Petit garcon / Adieu sweet lovely Nancy / I want to see the bright lights tonight / Lah di dah di dah / Andrew Ross / Dorset four hand reel / I'm on my own grandpa / Great fish finger disaster, The / Ball of yarn / I had to say I loved you in a song / Wildwood flower / Town loved so well / Lord of the dance.
LP: . . . . SFA 099

Broadbery, Jo

REGGAE TREASURE (Broadbery, Jo & The Standouts).
LP: . . . . BREV LP 1

Broadhurst, Phil

SUSTENANCE (Broadhurst, Phil Quartet).
LP: . . . . SLC 176
MC: . . . . TC SLC 176

Broadside

MOON SHONE BRIGHT, THE.
Tracks: / Seventeen come Sunday / Lincolnshire wedding song / Bold grenadier, The / Gardener and the ploughman, The / Free and easy / Outlandish knight, The / Caister fair / Dick Turpin / Lisbon / American stranger, The / Maria Marten / Poacher, The / Creeping Jane / Banks of the sweet Dundee.
LP: 12TS 228

Broadside Band

JOHN PLAYFORD'S POPULAR TUNES.
Tracks: / Greenwood / Heart's ease / Excuse me / Lady Catherine Ogle / Scotchman's dance / In the Northern lass / Never love thee more / Miller's jig / Granadees march, The / Saraband by Mr.Simon Ives / Lady Hatton's almaine / Prins Robbert Masco / Prince Rupert's march / Daphne / Lilliburlero / Parthenia / La chabott (Corant) / Jocobella / Paul's steeple / Lady Nevils delight, The / Whisk, The / New rigaudon, A / Italian rant, An / Bouzar castle / Childgrove / Mr. Lane's minuet / Up with aily / Cheshire rounds / Hunt the squirrel.
LP: . . . . SAR 28
MC: . . . . CSAR 28

Broadway

BROADWAY BLOCKBUSTERS (Various artists).
Tracks: / There's no business like show business: *Various artists* / There is nothin' like a dame: *Various artists*/ Carosel waltz: *Various artists* / 76 trombones: *Various artists* / Everything's coming up roses: *Various* artists / Bali Ha'i: *Various artists* / Hello Dolly: *Various artists* / Baubles, bangles and beads: *Various* artists / People: *Various artists* / I love Paris: *Various artists* / Give my regards to Broadway: *Various* artists / Ol' man river: *Various artists* / 'Till there was you: *Various artists* / Wunderbar: *Various* artists / Some enchanted evening: *Various artists* / I talk to the trees: *Various artists* / Stranger in Paradise: *Various artists* / C'est magnifique: *Various artists* / What kind of fool am I?: *Various artists* / If I were a rich man: *Various artists* / I could have danced all night: *Various artists* / Gigi: *Various artists*/ I feel pretty: *Various artists* / I've grown accustomed to her face: *Various artists.*
MCSET: . . . . DTO 10239

BROADWAY HITS (Various artists).
MC: . . . . BRC 2506

BROADWAY MAGIC (Various artists).
Tracks: / Willkommen: *Various artists* / Tonight: *Various artists* / I could have danced all night: *Various* artists / Tomorrow: *Various artists* / If my friends could see me now: *Various artists* / Everything's coming up roses: *Various artists* / Ladies who lunch, The: *Various artists* / If he walked into my life: *Various artists* / Send in the clowns: *Various artists* / What I did for love: *Various artists.*
LP: 31809

BROADWAY MELODIES (Various artists).
Tracks: / I love Paris: *Chacksfield, Frank & His Orchestra* / If I were a rich man: *Mantovani & His Orchestra*/ You'll never walk alone: *Chacksfield, Frank & His Orchestra* / Do re mi: *Mantovani & His Orchestra* / Ol' man river: *Black, Stanley & London Festival Orchestra* / I whistle a happy tune: *Chacksfield, Frank & His Orchestra*/ I've never been in love before: *Mantovani & His Orchestra* / Baubles, bangles and beads: *Heath, Ted & His Music*/ Younger than Springtime: *Chacksfield, Frank & His Orchestra* / Party's over, The: *Aldrich, Ronnie, His Piano & The* Festival Orchestra / Mr. Wonderful: *Mantovani & His Orchestra* / Oh what a beautiful mornin': *Chacksfield, Frank &* His Orchestra / Tomorrow: *Black, Stanley & London Festival Orchestra* / Wand'rin star: *Mantovani & His Orchestra*/ Tonight: *Chacksfield, Frank & His Orchestra* / Till there was you: *Mantovani & His Orchestra* / I get a kick out of you: *Heath, Ted & His Music* / Wouldn't it be loverly: *Chacksfield, Frank & His Orchestra* / How are things in Glocca Morra?: *Mantovani & His Orchestra* / Slaughter on Tenth Avenue: *Chacksfield, Frank & His Orchestra.*
MC: 8440614

Broadway Danny Rose

BROADWAY DANNY ROSE (1984 Film Soundtrack) (Various artists).
LP: . . . . A 236
MC: . . . . C 236

Broadway Melody (film)

BROADWAY MELODY OF 1938 (Film Soundtrack) (Various artists).
LP: . . . . MPT 3

BROADWAY MELODY OF 1940 (Film soundtrack) (Various artists).
LP: . . . . CIF 3002

Broadway (show)

BROADWAY (Original Broadway Cast) (Various artists).
LP: . . . . RL 60150
MC: . . . . RK 60150

Broadway Syncopaters

BROADWAY SYNCOPATERS AND FOSDICKS HOOSIERS.
LP: . . . . FG 406

Brock, Dave

AGENT OF CHAOS (Brock, Dave & The Agent Of Chaos).
LP: . . . . SHARP 042
MC: . . . . CSHARP 042

DAVE BROCK & THE AGENTS OF CHAOS (Brock, Dave/Agents Of Chaos).
LP: . . . . SHARP 1842

EARTHED TO THE GROUND.
Tracks: / Earthed to the ground / Assassination / Green finned demon / Spirits / Sweet obsession / Oscillations / Machine dream / Now is the winter of our discontent / On the case.
LP: . . . . SHARP 018

Brock, Jim

TROPIC AFFAIR.
LP: . . . . RR 31

Brodsky Quartet

END GAMES.
Tracks: / String quartet no.16 op.135 (Beethoven) / String quartet no.15 op.144 (Shostakovich).
MC: 246 017-4

STRING QUARTETS NO.7-9 (SHOSTAKOVICH) (see under Shostakovich (composer)).

Brodsky, Vadim

VIOLIN CONCERTI (Brodsky, Vadim/ Polish Radio National Symphony Orchestra).
Tracks: / Violin concerto op.47 (Sibelius) / Violin concerto op.36 (Tchaikovsky).
MC: . . . . ZC QS 6016

Brody, Saul

TRAVELS WITH BRODY.
LP: . . . . AD 2011

Broggs, Peter

CEASE THE WAR.
Tracks: / Don't let the children cry / Cease the war / Mr. Sherriff man / My baby she's gone / Let's go party / Just can't stop praising Jah / Suzanne / Freedom for the people / I a field marshall / Ethiopia we're coming home.
LP: . . . . RAS 3022

RASTAFARI LIVETH.
LP: . . . . RAS 3001

REASONING.
LP: . . . . RAS 3051
MC: . . . . RASC 3051

RISE AND SHINE.
Tracks: / You got to be wise / Rise and shine / I admire you / International farmer / Leggo mi hand / Bloodstain / Fuss and fight / I love to play reggae / Jah is the ruler / Rastaman chant Nyahbingi.
LP: . . . . RAS 3011

Brogue

BROGUE (Saki) (Burden, Hugh (nar)).
MC: . . . . SA 6

Broken Bones

DECAPITATED.
LP: . . . . FALL LP 043
LPPD: . . . . FALL LP 043P

DEM BONES.
LP: . . . . FALL LP 028
LPPD: . . . . FALL LP 028P

F.O.A.D..
Tracks: / FOAD / Kick down the doors / Teenage kamikaze / Programme control / SOTO / Missing link / Best of both worlds / Never say die / Decapitated (Part 1) / Problems / Secret agent / Liquidated brains / Gotta get out of here / I O U nothing / Seeing through my eyes / Anihilation No.3 / Decapitated (Part 2).
LP: . . . . FALL LP 041

LOSING CONTROL.
LP: . . . . HMRLP 133
MC: . . . . HMRMC 133

TRADER IN DEATH.
LP: . . . . HMRLP 141
MC: . . . . HMRMC 141

Broken Consort

JADE TIGER.
LP: . . . . TWI 220

Broken Dreams

BROKEN DREAMS (Various artists).
Tracks: / She's out of my life: *Jackson, Michael* / You needed me: *Murray, Anne* / Love so right: *Bee Gees*/ One of us: *Abba* / Almost over you: *Easton, Sheena* / Wedding bells: *Godley & Creme* / Rose, The: *Midler*, Bette / Love will tear us apart: *Young, Paul* / Love is a stranger: *Eurythmics* / Just another winter's tale: *Essex, David* / In a broken dream: *Python Lee Jackson* / So sad(to watch love go bad): *Paige, Elaine*/ Tell me it's all over: *Frida* / Sometimes when we touch: *Tyler, Bonnie* / I guess that's why they call it the blues: *John, Elton* / Time after time: *Lauper, Cyndi* / I'd really love to see you tonight: *Coley, John Ford/ England* Dan / Breaking up is hard to do: *Sedaka, Neil* / When I stop dreaming: *Harris, Emmylou* / Lately: *Mathis,* Johnny / Best thing we can do is say goodbye: *Knight, Gladys* / I'm not in love: *10 CC* / Your love is king: *Sade* / Superstar/Until you come back: *Vandross, Luther* / To me(that's what i'm gonna do): *Wonder, Stevie*/ Wonderful tonight: *Clapton, Eric* / Diary: *Jones, Jack* / Broken dreams: *Palmer, Barry* / I will always love you: *Parton, Dolly.*
2LP: . . . . SLTD 1
MCSET: . . . . SLTK 1

Broken Glass

FAST MEAN GAME, A.
Tracks: / Worst of you yet / Back for more / Long way home / I can't follow / Searching for you / Mexico / Better left unsaid / Out of sight / Sense of these days / Lost and found / Into the light.
LP: . . . . CHR 1743
MC: . . . . ZCHR 1743

Broken Hearted

BROKEN HEARTED MELODIES (Various artists).
Tracks: / Hurt: *Various artists* / With pen in hand: *Various artists* / Cry: *Various artists* / Softly as I leave you: *Various artists* / Stormy weather: *Various artists* / One for my baby: *Various artists*/ It must be him: *Various artists* / Who can I turn to: *Various artists* / Smile: *Various artists* / I'll be seeing you: *Various artists* / Where are you: *Various artists* / I apologise: *Various artists.*
LP: . . . . SLS 50422

Broken Home

BROKEN HOME.
Tracks: / Stop looking at me / Shooting all the lights out / No chance / Death of Gog / Mona Lisa / Shot over hill / Run away from home / Jerusalem / Bird has flown / China in your heart.
LP: . . . . K 58148
MC: K4 58148

Broken Homes

WING AND A PRAYER.
LP: . . . . MCG 6109
MC: . . . . MCGC 6109

Brolly, Anne

BALLADS OF IRELAND (Brolly, Anne & Francie).
Tracks: / Beautiful Ireland / Banks of the Lee.
MC: . . . . CHRL 116

BLACKBIRD OF AVONDALE (Brolly, Anne & Francie).
Tracks: / Mass rock in the glen.
MC: . . . . CHRL 196
LP: . . . . HRL 196

FAREWELL TO DERRY (Brolly, Anne & Francie).
Tracks: / Lovely Derry on the banks of The Foyle / Town is not their own, The.
LP: . . . . HRL 138
MC: . . . . CHRL 138

FOLK SONGS (Brolly, Anne & Francie).
Tracks: / Beautiful Ireland / Slievegallion braes / Faughan side.
LP: . . . . HRL 116

IRELAND FREE... AND THE SONG THEY SANG (Brolly, Anne & Francie).
LP: . . . . CSDBL 520
LP: . . . . SDBL 520

Bromberg, Brian

BRIAN BROMBERG.
LP: . . . . BKH 524

MAGIC RAIN.
LP: . . . . ENVLP 546

Bromberg, David

HOW LATE'LL YA PLAY 'TIL.
Tracks: / Danger man / Get up and go / Summer wages / Whoopee ti yi to / Young Westley / Dyin' crapshooters blues / Idol with the golden head / Kaatskill serenade / Sloppy drunk / Bullfrog blues / Sweet home Chicago / Come on in my kitchen / Will not be your fool / Such a night / Dallas rag / Maple leaf rag / Chubby thighs / Bluebird.
2LP: . . . . FTSP 53

SIDEMAN SERENADE.
LP: . . . . ZS 91

Broms, Staffan

DID I REMEMBER?.
Tracks: / Night and day / Confessin' / Till Tom special / Until the real thing comes along / Hollering at the Watkins / Time on my hands / Did I remember? / I thought about you / Getting sentimental over you / Silhouetted in the moonlight / Everything I have is yours / You're dangerous.
LP: . . . . PHONT 7504

EVERGREENS (See Under Lind, Ove) (Broms, Staffan/Bengt Hallburg/Ove Lind).

EVERGREENS 2 (See Under Lind, Ove) (Broms, Staffan/Bengt Hallburg/Ove Lind).

Bron Area

TREES AND THE VILLAGES, THE.
Tracks: / Trees and the villages, The.
LP: . . . . **GLALP 005**

Bron, Eleanor (nar)

MARCH HARE MURDERS, THE (see under March Hare Murders (bk)).

Bronco Billy (film)

BRONCO BILLY (Film Soundtrack) (Various artists).
LP: . . . . **K 52231**
MC: **K4 52231**

Brond

BROND (THEME FROM) (See under Nelson, Bill) (Nelson, Bill).

Bronhill, June

LILAC TIME (Bronhill, June/Thomas Round).
LP: . . . . **CLP 1248**

MAGIC OF THE MUSICAL.
LP: . . . . **OU 2239**
MC: . . . . **TCOU 2239**

Bronski Beat

AGE OF CONSENT, THE.
Tracks: / Why / It ain't necessarily so / Screaming / No more war / Love and money / Smalltown boy / Heatwave / Junk / Need a man blues / I feel love.
LP: . . . . **BITLP 1**
MC: . . . . **BITMC 1**

HUNDREDS AND THOUSANDS.
Tracks: / Cadillac car / Heatwave (remix) / Why (remix) / Run from love / Hard rain / Smalltown boy (remix) / Junk / Infatuation / Close to the edge / I feel love.
LP: . . . . **BITLP 2**
MC: . . . . **BITMC 2**

SMALLTOWN BOY (1991 REMIX) (See under Somerville, Jimmy) (Somerville, Jimmy & Bronski Beat).

TRUTHDARE DOUBLEDARE.
Tracks: / Hit that perfect beat / Truthdare doubledare / C'mon, c'mon / Punishment for love / We know how it feels / This heart / Do it / Doctor John / In my dreams / What are you going to do about it (Extra track on CD only).
LP: . . . . **BITLP 3**
MC: . . . . **BITMC 3**

Bronson, Charles

MUSIC FROM CHARLES BRONSON FILMS (See under Films) (Various artists).

Bronstein, Stan

LIVING ON THE AVENUE.
LP: . . . . **MR 5113**

Bronte, Emily (aut)

WUTHERING HEIGHTS (see under Wuthering Heights (bk)).

Bronx

MIDNIGHT QUEEN.
LP: . . . . **MELP 003**

Bronz

TAKEN BY STORM.
Tracks: / Send down an angel / Heat of the night / Cold truth / Night runner / Taken by storm / Don't ever wanna lose ya / Sweet lady / Harder than diamond / Tiger / Loneliness is mine.
LP: . . . . **BRON 547**

Bronzini, Marco

DON'T LOOK BACK (See under Schutz, Michael) (Bronzini, Marco & Michael Schutz).

Brood

IN SPITE OF IT ALL.
LP: . . . . **NAKED 21**
MC: . . . . **NAKED 21C**

Brood, Herman

GO NUTZ (Brood, Herman & Wild Romance).
Tracks: / Go nutz / Love you like I love myself / I don't need you / I'll be doggone / Right on the money / Hot shot / Born before my time / Beauty is only skin deep / Easy pick up / Laurie.
LP: . . . . **ARL 5044**

HERMAN BROOD & HIS WILD ROMANCE (Brood, Herman & Wild Romance).
Tracks: / Saturday night / Doin' it / Champagne / Back / Doreen / Hit / Rock'n'roll junkie / Dope sucks / Never enough / Pain / Get lost / Hot talk / Prisoners / Skid row.
LP: . . . . **ARL 5029**

WAIT A MINUTE.
Tracks: / Dynamite / Girl of my dreams / Time to split / Keep playin' that rock 'n' roll / Outside lookin' in / Propaganda / All the girls are crazy / Brickyard blues / Workin' girl / Voices / Blew my cool.
LP: . . . . **ARL 5063**

Brooes, Jacqui

SOB STORIES.
Tracks: / Lost without your love / One that got away, The / Cold light of day / Another place for a dreamer / Trains and boats and planes / Haunted cocktails / Just another / I'm not ashamed / Thin air, The / Departures.
LP: . . . . **MCF 3202**
MC: . . . . **MCFC 3202**

Brook, Michael

HYBRID.
Tracks: / Hybrid / Distant village / Mimosa / Pond life / Ocean motion / Midday / Earth floor / Vacant.
LP: . . . . **EGED 41**
MC: . . . . **EGEDC 41**

SLEEPS WITH THE FISHES (See under Nooten, Pieter) (Brook, Michael/Pieter Nooten).

Brooker, Gary

ECHOES IN THE NIGHT.
Tracks: / Count me out / Two fools in love / Echoes in the night / Ghost train / Mr blue man / Saw the fire / Long goodbye / Hear what you're saying / Missing person / Trick of the night.
LP: . . . . **MERL 68**

LEAD ME TO THE WATER.
Tracks: / Mineral man / Another way / Hang on rose / Home loving / Cycle / Lead me to the water / Angler, The / Low flying birds / Sympathy for the hard of hearing.
LP: **6359 098**
MC: **7150 098**

Brookes, Paul

STEPS FROM BEYOND.
Tracks: / Steps from beyond (part 1) / Steps from beyond (part 2).
LP: . . . . **ETAT 21**

Brookins, Robert

IN THE NIGHT.
Tracks: / Our lives / If you only knew / In the beginning / You got me running / I'm holding on to U / Sensuality / Be my weakness / Are you bad enough / Come to me / In the night.
LP: . . . . **MCF 3373**
MC: . . . . **MCFC 3373**

Brooklyn

YOU NEVER KNOW WHAT YOU'LL FIND.
Tracks: / Two wheels / Breaking up / You never know what you'll find / Can't we be lovers / Hollywood / I wanna be a detective / Born to win / No replay / Late again / Rainbows end.
LP: . . . . **ABOUT 3**

Brooklyn Dreams

BROOKLYN DREAMS.
Tracks: / Music, harmony and rhythm / Sad eyes / I never dreamed / Don't fight the feeling / Another night at the Tango / On the corner / Street dance (baby) / You're the one / Old fashioned girl / Hollywood girl.
LP: . . . . **XL 13047**
MC: . . . . **XK 13047**

SLEEPLESS NIGHTS.
Tracks: / Make it last / That's not the way your mama taught you to be / Sleepless nights / Send me a dream / Fashion for me / First love / Street man / Touching in the dark / Long distance / Coming up the hard way / Heaven knows.
LP: . . . . **XL 13071**

Brookmeyer, Bob

AT THE VILLAGE VANGUARD (Brookmeyer, Bob with Mel Lewis & The Jazz Orchestra).
Tracks: / Ding dong ding / First love song / Hello and goodbye / Skylark / El co / Fan club.
LP: . . . . **RHAP 11**

BACK AGAIN.
Tracks: / Sweet and lovely / Carib / Caravan / You'd be so nice to come home to / Willow weep for me / I love you / In a rotten mood.
LP: . . . . **SNTF 778**
MC: . . . . **ZCSN 778**

BLUES HOT AND COLD (Brookmeyer, Bob Quartet).
Tracks: / Languid blues / On the sunny side of the street / Stompin' at the Savoy / I got rhythm / Smoke gets in your eyes / Hot and cold blues.
LP: **8215501**

BOBBY BROOKMEYER AND HIS ORCHESTRA (Brookmeyer, Bobby & His Orchestra).
Tracks: / Oh Jane snavely / Nature boy / Just you, just me / I'm old fashioned / Gone latin / Zing went the strings of my heart / Big city life / Confussion blues / Open country.
LP: . . . . **PL 43550**

GINGERBREAD (See Under Terry, Clark) (Brookmeyer, Bob & Clark Terry).

KANSAS CITY REVISITED (Brookmeyer, Bob KC Seven).
LP: . . . . **FS 33**

OSLO (Brookmeyer, Bob Quartet).
Tracks: / With the wind and the rain in your hair / Oslo / Later blues / Detour ahead / Tootsie samba / Alone together / Who could care / Caravan.
LP: . . . . **CJ 312**

STAN GETZ & BOB BROOKMEYER (see Getz, Stan) (Brookmeyer, Bob & Stan Getz).

STREETSWINGERS (see under Pacific Jazz II collection).

STRETCHING OUT (See under Sims, Zoot) (Brookmeyer, Bob & Zoot Sims).

TONITE'S MUSIC TODAY (See under Sims, Zoot) (Sims, Zoot & Bob Brookmeyer).

TRADITIONALISM REVISITED.
Tracks: / Louisiana / Santa Claus blues / Truckin' / Some sweet day / Sweet like this / Jada / Don't be that way / Honeysuckle rose.
LP: . . . . **AFF 127**

ZOOT SIMS AND BOB BROOKMEYER (See under Sims, Zoot) (Sims, Zoot & Bob Brookmeyer).

ZOOT SIMS WITH THE BOB BROOKMEYER QUINTET (see Sims, Zoot) (Brookmeyer, Bob Quintet & Zoot Sims).

Brooks, Bernard

SWING AND SWAY (Bernard Brooks way No. 3).
Tracks: / Rose Marie / Only a rose / At the Balalaika / Blue tango / Don't get around much any more / Makin' whoopee / Sunny side of the street / It's magic / Maybe / Sierra Sue / Marie Elena / I'm in the mood for love / Just one more chance / Carolina in the morning / You're driving me crazy / So what's new / Twelfth Street rag / Charleston / Are you lonesome tonight / Wonderful one / When you and I were seventeen / I wonder who's kissing her now / Carolina moon / Alice blue gown / You are my sunshine / Baby face / My blue heaven / Yes Sir that's my baby / Sugartime / I'm looking over a four leaf clover / Oh what it seemed to be / Where are you / Please be kind / Music maestro please / Oh my papa / I wish you love / My special angel / Moving south.
LP: . . . . **DL 1008**

Brooks, Elkie

BOOKBINDER'S KID.
Tracks: / Sail on / Stairway to heaven / You ain't leavin' / Keep it a secret / When the hero walks alone / What's the matter baby / Can't wait all night / Kiss me for the last time / Love is love / Foolish games / Only love will set you free (Available on cassette and compact disc only.) / I can dream, can't I.
LP: . . . . **LMA 3**
MC: . . . . **LMT 3**

COLLECTION: ELKIE BROOKS.
Tracks: / Where do we go from here / Try a little love / Be positive / Do right woman, do right man / Pearls a singer / Heartache is on, The / Mojo Hannah / Rock and roll circus / Night bird / Putting my heart on the line / He's a rebel / Shooting star / If you leave me now / Too much between us / Viva la money / Night run / Stay with me / Don't cry out loud / Goin' back / Loving arms / Lilac wine / Crossfire / Fool if you think it's over.
2LP: . . . . **CCSLP 166**
MC: . . . . **CCSMC 166**

EARLY YEARS, 1964-66, THE.
Tracks: / Something's got a hold on me / Hello stranger / Nothing left to do but cry / Strange tho' it seems / Blue tonight / Way you do the things you do, The / He's gotta love me / When you appear / All of my life / Can't stop thinking of you / Stop the music / Baby, let me love you.
MC: **C5K-506**
LP: **C5-506**

INSPIRATION.
Tracks: / You're my inspiration / Shame / Broken wings / Hard habit to break / Every little bit hurts / Is this love / Maybe I'm amazed / In it for the same thing / Touch of paradise / Black smoke / Ki, The / Tear it down / Three wishes.
LP: . . . . **STAR 2354**
MC: . . . . **STAC 2354**

LIVE AND LEARN.
Tracks: / Viva la money / On the horizon / He could have been an army / Rising cost of love, The / Dream dealer / Who's making love? / If you can't beat me rocking / Heartache is on, The / Not enough lovin' yet / Falling star.
LP: . . . . **AMID 116**
MC: . . . . **CMID 116**
LP: . . . . **SHM 3141**
MC: . . . . **HSC 3141**
LP: . . . . **AMLH 68509**

MINUTES.
Tracks: / Minutes / Driftin' / Night run / Take your freedom / Growing tired / Born lucky / I've been in love before / Too heavy, too strong / Crossfire / Work pay.
LP: . . . . **AMLX 68565**
MC: . . . . **CXM 68565**

NO MORE THE FOOL.
MC: . . . . **LMT 1**
LP: . . . . **LMA 1**

PEARLS.
Tracks: / Superstar / Fool if you think it's over / Giving it up for your love / Sunshine after the rain / Warm and tender love / Lilac wine / Pearl's a singer / Don't cry out loud / Too busy thinking about my baby / If you leave me now / Paint your pretty picture / Dance away.
MC: . . . . **CLK 1981**
LP: . . . . **ELK 1981**

PEARLS II.
Tracks: / Goin' back / Our love / Gasoline Alley / I just can't go on / Too much between us / Giving us hope / Money / Nights in white satin / Loving arms / Will you write me a song?.
LP: . . . . **ELK 1982**
MC: . . . . **CLK 1982**

PEARLS/PEARLS II.
Tracks: / Superstar / Giving it up for your love / Warm and tender / Pearl's a singer / Too busy thinking about / Paint your pretty picture / Goin' back / Gasoline Alley / Too much between us / Giving you hope / Nights in white satin / Will you write me a song / Fool if you think it's over / Sunshine after the rain / Lilac wine / Don't cry out loud / If you leave me now / Dance away / Our love / I just can't go on / Don't stop / Money / Loving arms.
MC: . . . . **AMC 24106**

RICH MAN'S WOMAN.
Tracks: / Where do we go from here / Take cover / Jigsaw baby / Roll me over / He's a rebel / One step on the ladder / Rock and roll circus / Try a little love / Tomorrow.
LP: . . . . **AMLH 64554**
MC: . . . . **CAM 64554**
LP: . . . . **SHM 3171**
MC: . . . . **HSC 3171**

SCREEN GEMS.
Tracks: / Am I blue / Me and my shadow / Some of these days / You'll never know / My foolish heart / 3 o'clock in the morning / Once in a while / That old feeling / Blue moon / Ain't misbehavin' / What'll I do / Love me or leave me.
LP: . . . . **SCREEN 1**

SHOOTING STAR.
LP: . . . . **AMLH 64695**

TWO DAYS AWAY.
LP: . . . . **AMLH 68409**
MC: . . . . **CAM 68409**

VERY BEST OF ELKIE BROOKS, THE.
LP: . . . . **ELK 1986**
MC: . . . . **CLK 1986**
LP: . . . . **STAR 2284**
MC: . . . . **STAC 2284**

Brooks, Garth

GARTH BROOKS.
Tracks: / Not counting you / I've got a good thing going / If tomorrow never comes / Everytime that it rains / Alabama clay / Much too young (to feel this damn old) / Cowboy Bill / Nobody gets off in this town / I know one / Dance, The.
LP: **C1 90897**
LP: **7 908 971**
MC: **C4 90897**

NO FENCES.
Tracks: / If tomorrow never comes / Not counting you / Much too young (to feel this damn old) / Dance, The / Thunder rolls, The / New way to fly / Two of a kind, workin' on a full house / Victim of the game / Friends in low places / Wild horses / Unanswered prayers / Same old story / Mr. Blue / Wolves.
LP: . . . . **EST 2136**
LP: **795 503 1**
MC: . . . . **TCEST 2136**
MC: **795 503 4**

Brooks, Hadda

QUEEN OF THE BOOGIE.
LP: . . . . **OL 2826**

ROMANCE IN THE DARK.
LP: . . . . **JB 1107**

Brooks, John Benson

FOLK JAZZ USA.
Tracks: / New saints, The / Venezuela / Black is the colour / Betsy / Randall my son / Turtle dove / Shenandoah / Joe's old folks / Sara Jane / Scarlet Town / Wayfaring stranger / Darling Corey.
2LP: . . . . **PM 43767**

Brooks, Karen

I WILL DANCE WITH YOU.
Tracks: / Nobody's angel / I'll dance with you / Hard way, The / Have a heart / Last time, The / I do blues / Last one to know, The / Other night, The / Too bad for love / Great divide, The.
MC: **925277 4**

Brooks, Leonard

CHIAPPA FAIRGROUND ORGAN VOL 1.
LP: . . . . **RESM 014**

CHIAPPA FAIRGROUND ORGAN VOL 2.
LP: . . . . **RESM 017**

Brooks, Lonnie

BAYOU LIGHTNING.
Tracks: / Voodoo daddy / Figure head / Watch dog / Breakfast in bed / Worked up woman / Alimony / Watch what you got / I ain't superstitious / You know what my body needs / In the dark.
LP: . . . . **SNTF 798**

BROKE AN' HUNGRY.
Tracks: / Wee, wee hours / Things they used to do / Go to the Mardi Gras / Texas flood / Tom cat blues / Rooster blues / Train and the horse, The / Broke and hungry / When there's no way out / Don't touch me,baby / Red bug blues.
LP: . . . . **CCR 1006**

CRAWL, THE.
Tracks: / Crawl / Family rules / I got it made / Tell me baby / Love me love me Mary Ann / Now you know / Pick me up on your way down / Roll roll roll / Broken hearted rollin teats / Oo wee baby / Knocks me out fine fine fine.
LP: . . . . **CRB 1068**

HOT SHOT.
Tracks: / Don't take advantage of me / Wrong number / Messed up again / Family rules / Back trail / I want all my money back / Mr. hot shot / One more shot.
LP: . . . . **SNTF 903**

LIVE AT PEPPERS.
LP: . . . . **BM 9008**

LIVE FROM CHICAGO.
Tracks: / Two headed man / Trading post / In the dark / Got me by the tail / One more shot / Born with the blues / Eyeballin' / Cold lonely nights / Hideaway.
LP: . . . . **AL 4759**

SATISFACTION GUARANTEED.
Tracks: / Temporary insanity / Man's gotta do, A / Feast or famine / Lyin' time / Little RR and CB / Wife for tonight / Family curse / Horoscope / Like father like son / Holding on to the memories / Accident / Price is right.
MC: . . . . **AC 4799**

TURN ON THE NIGHT.
Tracks: / Eyeballin' / Inflation / Teenage boogie man / Heavy traffic / I'll take care of you / T.V. mama / Mother nature / Don't go to sleep on me / Something you got / Zydeco.
LP: . . . . **SNTF 858**

WOUND UP TIGHT.
Tracks: / Got lucky last night / Jealous man / Belly rubbin' music / Bewitched / End of the rope / Wound up tight / Boomerang / Musta' been dreaming / Skid Row / Hush mouth money.
LP: . . . . **SNTF 974**
LP: . . . . **AL 4751**
MC: . . . . **ZCSN 974**

Brooks, Mel

GREATEST HITS:MEL BROOKS.
Tracks: / Main title / High anxiety / Anxious theme / If you love me baby, tell me loud / End title / Springtime for Hitler / Prisoners of love / Hope for the best, expect the worst / Vorobyaninov's theme (The walk through Russia) / Blazing saddles / French mistake, The / I'm tired / Puttin' on the ritz / Burt Reynolds' house / Silent movie march.
LP: . . . . **K 53076**

Brooks, Mike

FRAGILE SHORELINE.
MC: . . . . **C 128**

ONE LOVE.
LP: . . . . **VSLP 4035**

RESPECT DUE.
LP: . . . . **GTLP 001**

Brooks, Nigel

20 ALL TIME EUROVISION FAVOURITES (Brooks, Nigel Singers).
LP: . . . . **NE 712**

EVERYTHING BEAUTIFUL (Brooks, Nigel Singers).
Tracks: / Let it be / I can see so clearly now / Amazing grace / You are the sunshine of my life / You make me feel brand new / Put your hand in my hand / What a wonderful world / Raindrops keep falling on my head / Knock knock who's there / Let's put it all together / Ave Maria / Welcome home / Morning has broken / My sweet lord / Let your love flow / All kinds of everything / Everything is beautiful / Save your kisses for me / Say wonderful things to me / Let the music begin / Slaughter in the rain / Oh happy day.
2LP: . . . . **VSOPLP 105**
MC: . . . . **VSOPMC 105**

HYMNS AT HOME (Brooks, Nigel Singers).
Tracks: / Through all the changing scenes of life / Dear Lord and Father of mankind / O love that wilt not let me go / O thou who camest from above / Nearer still nearer / How I praise thee, precious saviour / Old rugged cross, The / Pleasant are thy courts above / Just as I am / Lead kindly light / God be with you till we meet again / Glory to thee my God this night.
LP: . . . . **QPLS 36**

SONGS OF JOY (Brooks, Nigel Singers).
LP: . . . . **NE 706**

Brooks, Patti

20 GREATEST HITS
LP: . . . . **NSPL 18591**

OUR MS. BROOKS.
Tracks: / After dark / This is the house where love died / Heartbreak in disguise / Come fly with me / Let's do it again / Back up singer.
LP: . . . . **CAL 2042**

Brooks, Randy

1945-1947 (Brooks, Randy & His Orchestra).
LP: . . . . **CLP 35**

RADIO DISCS OF ....1945, THE.
LP: . . . . **JLP 2003**

Brooks, Ray

SONGS WITHIN (Brooks, Ray & Full Force).
LP: . . . . **TRPL 114**

Brooks, Terry

RAW POWER (Brooks, Terry & Strange).
LP: . . . . **PSYCHO 21**

TRANSLUCENT WORLD (Brooks, Terry & Strange).
LP: . . . . **PSYCHO 34**

Brooks, Walter R.

FREDDY THE DETECTIVE (see under Freddy the Detective) (Carroll, Pat (nar)).

Broomfield

BROOMFIELD.
Tracks: / Where do I go from here / She can't get serious / Read my letter / Good times / You better get ready / Is it so hard / Through all the years / Don't cover up your feelings / Light up the world.
LP: **4611641**
MC: **4611644**

Broonzy, Big Bill

1927-32.
LP: . . . . **MSE 1004**

BACKWATER BLUES.
LP: . . . . **SM 3608**

BIG BILL BROONZY (1935-39) (Broonzy, Big Bill/Blind John Davis).
LP: . . . . **BD 2012**

BIG BILL BROONZY (1935-41).
LP: . . . . **BOB 2**

BIG BILL BROONZY (1935-49) VOL.2.
LP: . . . . **DLP 539**

BIG BILL BROONZY VOL.3 (1928-39).
LP: . . . . **DLP 581**

BIG BILL BROONZY, VOL. 1 1934-47 (Broonzy, Big Bill/Memphis Slim).
LP: . . . . **DLP 510**

BIG BILL BROONZY & WASHBOARD SAM (Broonzy, Big Bill/Washboard Sam).
Tracks: / Little city woman / Lonesome / Jacqueline / Romance without finance / By Myself / Shirt tail / Diggin' my potatoes / Bright Eyes / Minding my own business / Never never / Horse shoe over my door / I'm a lonely man.
LP: . . . . **GCH 8025**
MC: . . . . **GCHK 78025**

BIG BILL'S BLUES.
LP: **21122**
MC: **40-21122**

BLACK, BROWN AND WHITE.
LP: . . . . **SLP 4052**

DO THAT GUITAR RAG 1928-35.
LP: . . . . **L 1035**

FEELIN' LOW DOWN.
LP: **512510**
LP: . . . . **GNPS 10004**

GOOD TIME TONIGHT.
MC: **4672474**

HOLLERIN' AND CRYIN' THE BLUES VOL.3.
LP: **512511**

LAST SESSION VOL 1.
LP: **2304 559**

LAST SESSION VOL 2.
Tracks: / This train / Hush hush / Backwater blues / Blues / It hurts me too / Kansas city blues / When the sun goes down / Worried life blues / Trouble in mind / Take this hammer / Glory of love / Louise blues.
LP: **813 367-1**

LONESOME ROAD BLUES.
LP: . . . . **GNPS 10009**

MIDNIGHT STEPPERS.
LP: . . . . **BT 2001**

MY GAL IS GONE.
LP: . . . . **MAN 502**

REMEMBERING BIG BILL BROONZY.
LP: . . . . **BGOLP 91**

STORY VOL. 3.
Tracks: / Willie Mae Blues / Alberta / Old folks at home / Crawdad song / John Henry / Just a dream / Frankie and Johnny / Bill Bailey won't you please come home / Slow blues.
LP: **8177 791**

TROUBLE IN MIND.
Tracks: / Trouble in mind / This train / Willie Mae blues / In the evenin' / Glory of love / Midnight special / Ananias / Keep your hands off her / Nobody's business / Labour man blues / I'm gonna sit down at the feastin' table / Swing low sweet chariot / Make me a pallet on the floor / House rent stomp / Bill Bailey won't you please come home / I've been waiting for you / Goodnight Irene.
LP: . . . . **SPJ 900**

YOUNG BIG BILL BROONZY 1928-35 (Broonzy, Bill).
LP: . . . . **L 1011**
MC: . . . . **YAZMC 1011**

Bros

BROS: INTERVIEW PICTURE DISC.
LPPD: . . . . **BAK 2099**

CHRISTMAS BOX SET, THE.
LP: **4604290**

IN THE BEGINNING (Interview LP).
LPPD: . . . . **BAK 6007**

PUSH.
Tracks: / When will I be famous / Drop the boy / Ten out of ten / Liar / Love to hate you / I owe you nothing / It's a jungle out there / Shocked / Cat among the pigeons.
LP: **4606291**
MC: **4606294**
LPPD: **4606299**
LP: **4606290**

TIME, THE.
Tracks: / Madly in love / Too much / Chocolate box / Money / Streetwise / Club fool / Black and white / Don't bite the hand / Space sister.
LP: **4659181**
MC: **4659184**

Brosch

GLORIAMUNDI.
LP: . . . . **EFA 4887**

Brother Beyond

GET EVEN.
Tracks: / Chain-gang smile / Somebody, somewhere / Restless / Shipwrecked / Sunset bars / I should have lied / How many times / Sometimes good, sometimes bad, (sometimes better) / Think of you / King of blue / Act for love (ext. version) / Be my twin / Can you keep a secret? / He ain't no competition / Harder I try, The.
LP: . . . . **PCS 7322**
MC: . . . . **TCPCS 7322**
LP: . . . . **PCS 7314**

GET EVEN (ALTERNATIVE VERSION).
Tracks: / He ain't no competition / Can you keep a secret? / Chain gang smile / Restless / How many times / Call me lonely (get the sun remix) (Cassette only.) / Be my twin / Harder I try, The / I should have lied / Shipwrecked / King of blue / Act for love (ext.) (Cassette & CD only.) / Sometimes good, sometimes bad, (sometimes better) (CD only.).
LP: . . . . **PCS 7327**
MC: . . . . **TCPCS 7327**

TRUST.
Tracks: / Trust / You never tell me / I believe in you / Now I'm alone with you / Let me decide / Drive on / Perfect love / When willl see you again / Universal / Outside our lives.
LP: . . . . **PCS 7337**
LP: **793 413 1**
MC: . . . . **TCPCS 7337**
MC: **793 413 4**

Brother Can You...

BROTHER,CAN YOU SPARE A DIME? (Various artists).
Tracks: / Brother can you spare a dime?: *Crosby, Bing* / Boulevard of broken dreams: *Janis, Deane* / Life is just a bowl of cherries: *Vallee, Rudy & His Connecticut Yankies* / In the still of the night: *Gray, Glen & The Casa Loma* Orchestra / Love walked in: *Baker, Kenny Orchestra* / On the good ship lollipop: *Temple, Shirley* / Unemployment stomp: *Broonzy, Big Bill* / We're in the money: *Powell, Dick* / All in down and out blues: *Macon, Uncle Dave*/ Fifteen miles from Birmingham: *Delmore Brothers* / Coal loading machine, The: *Evening Breezes Sextet* / NRA blues: *Cox, Bill* / I ain't got no home: *Guthrie, Woody* / Death of Mother Jones, The: *Autry, Gene* / All I want: *Almanac Singers & Pete Seeger* / White cliffs of Dover, The: *Miller, Glenn Orchestra.*
LP: . . . . **NW 270**

Brother D

UP AGAINST THE BEAST (Brother D and Silver Fox).
MC: . . . . **A 130**

Brother Resistance

RAPSO TAKE OVER.
LP: . . . . **MCLP 001**

Brother Sun...(film)

BROTHER SUN SISTER MOON (Film soundtrack) (Various artists).
LP: . . . . **ORL 8482**
MC: . . . . **ORK 78482**

Brotherhood Lizards

LIZARDS LANDS.
LP: . . . . **DELTLP 5**
MC: . . . . **DELTMC 5**

Brotherhood Of Man

20 LOVE SONGS AND 20 DISCO GREATS.
LP: . . . . **WW 5110**

100 MINUTES OF THE BROTHERHOOD OF MAN.
MC: . . . . **ZCTON 118**

B FOR BROTHERHOOD.
LP: . . . . **NSPL 18567**

BEST OF THE BROTHERHOOD OF MAN.
Tracks: / Save your kisses for me / How deep is your love / My sweet rosalie / Middle of the night / Beautiful lover / Angelo / Oh boy / Lady / Send in the clowns / Be my lovin' baby / When love catches up on you / Figaro.
LP: . . . . **SPR 8513**
MC: . . . . **SPC 8513**

BROTHERHOOD OF MAN.
Tracks: / Papa Louis / Sleeping beauty / Light from your window / Tell me how / Taxi / Middle of the night / Ole ole / Brotherhood of man / Part of my life / Lonely one / Gypsy / Goodbye goodbye.
LP: . . . . **BML 7980**
LP: . . . . **N 105**

GOLDEN HOUR OF BROTHERHOOD OF MAN.
Tracks: / Save your kisses for me / Cry thief / Nothing in the world / Sweet lady from Georgia / Kiss me kiss you baby / Shame on you baby / Be my lovin' baby / Dream on / Love me for what I am / I'm so much in love / Your are love / Oh boy / Join the party / Welcome Sunday morning / Lady lady lady lay / When love catches up on you / Spring of 1912 / Lady / Movin' with Susan / Everyday of my life / Have you been a good boy / He ain't heavy he's my brother.
LP: . . . . **GH 676**

GREATEST HITS: BROTHER HOOD OF MAN.
Tracks: / Save your kisses for me / Angelo / How deep is your love / Highwayman / Greatest love / Beautiful lover / Images / Oh boy / Be my lovin' baby / Tell me, tell me, tell me / Figaro / Shimmy shimmy shamay / Lady / Send in the clowns / People all over the world.
LP: . . . . **GH 681**

LIGHTNING FLASH.
Tracks: / Lightning flash / Cry baby cry / I don't need it / I love everybody / Run

like hell / Too late the hero / When the kissing stops / Is it love / What more can I say / Heartbreaker / Jukebox serenade / Hanging on.
LP: EMC 1651491

LOVE AND KISSES FROM THE BROTHERHOOD OF MAN.
LP: NSPL 18490

SAVE YOUR KISSES FOR ME.
Tracks: / How deep is your love / Save your kisses for me / My sweet Rosalee / Middle of the night / Beautiful lover / Oh boy / Mood I'm in / Lady / Send in the clowns / Be my lovin' baby / Figaro / When love catches up on you.
LP: FBLP 8081
MC: ZCFBL 8081

SING 20 NUMBER ONE HITS.
LP: WW 5087

SING 20 SMASH HITS.
MCSET: DTO 10065

SINGING A SONG.
Tracks: / Tomorrow / Night the circus came to town / Singing a song / Only love / I saw yesterday today / Gold / Willie / I'll take you higher than high / Got a funny feeling / Our caravan / Vanishing lady / Andy McDougal.
LP: N 122

SPOTLIGHT ON BROTHERHOOD OF MAN.
Tracks: / Save your kisses for me / Oh boy / Taxi / Figaro / Lady / Angelo / Highwayman / Ole ole / Send in the clowns / He ain't heavy, he's my brother / Goodbye goodbye / My sweet rosalie / How deep is your love.
LP: SPOT 1011
MC: ZCSPT 1011

Brothers

BROTHERS,THE.
LP: BW 002

LOUD, PROUD AND PUNK - LIVE.
LP: SYNLP 6

Brothers Boys

BROTHERS BOYS.
MC: NH 1101

Brothers Christ

ECHOES OF LOST SOULS.
LP: COLONYLP 1

Brothers Four

GREATEST HITS: BROTHERS FOUR.
LP: 32207
MC: 40 32207

SONGBOOK.
LP: CBS 88599

THIS LAND IS YOUR LAND.
Tracks: / This land is your land / Both sides now / Green green / Don't think twice it's alright / Where have all the flowers gone / Lady Greensleeves / Walk right in / Marianne / Green leaves of summer / Try to remember / Green fields / John B sails / Scarlet ribbons for her hair / Lemon tree / If I had a hammer / Michael row the boat ashore / Shenandoah / Blowin' in the wind / Tom Dooley.
LP: MFP 50534
MC: TCMFP 50534

Brothers Grimm (auts)

VARIOUS RECORDINGS (see under Title of Book).

Brothers In Rhythm

BROTHERS IN RHYTHM (32 Chart Beating Hits from the 60's, 70's & 80's) (Various artists).
Tracks: / Reach out I'll be there: *Four Tops* / Ain't no stoppin' us now: *McFadden & Whitehead* / Oops upside your head: *Gap Band* / Let's groove: *Earth, Wind & Fire* / Tears of a clown: *Robinson, Smokey* / Boogie nights: *Heatwave* ((This track replaced by Blackbyrds - 'Walkin' in rhythm' on CD)) / Don't leave me this way: *Melvin*, Harold & The Bluenotes / Easy: *Commodores* / Walk the dinosaur: *Was Not Was* / Living in a box: *Living* In A Box / Real thing, The: *Jellybean featuring Steven Dante* / Dance to the music: *Various artists* / Word up: *Cameo* / Let's go round again: *Average White Band* / How sweet it is to be loved by you: *Walker, Junior* / Just my imagination (running away with me): *Temptations, The* / I want you back: *Jackson Five* / This old heart of mine: *Isley Brothers* / Letter, The: *Box Tops* / Harlem shuffle: *Bob & Earl* / Backstabbers: *O'Jays* / Working my way back to you: *Detroit Spinners* / Let's hang on: *Valli, Frankie & Four Seasons* / Maneater: *Hall* & Oates / I need you: *B.V.S.M.P.* / You to me are everything: *Real Thing* / Can't give you anything but my love: *Stylistics* / Ms. Grace: *Tymes* / Have you seen her: *Chi-lites* / Love machine: *Miracles* / Kissin' in the back row of the movies: *Drifters* / Under the boardwalk: *Willis, Bruce*.
2LP: 303.374
MCSET: 503.374

Brothers Johnson

BLAM!.
LP: AMLH 64714

BLAST.
Tracks: / Funk it / Welcome to the club / Great awakening / I'm giving you all of my love / Real thing / Ain't we funkin' now / Strawberry letter 23 / Stomp / Get the funk out ma face / I'll be good to you.
LP: AMLH 64927

KICKIN'.
Tracks: / Kick it to / Kick it to the curb / Real love / I fresh / Still in love / PO Box 2000 / Ball of fire / We must be in love / I'll give it up / This is our love / Party avenue.
LP: AMA 5162
MC: AMC 5162

LIGHT UP THE NIGHT.
LP: AMLK 63716

LOOK OUT FOR NUMBER ONE.
LP: AMID 121
MC: CMID 121

OUT OF CONTROL.
Tracks: / You keep me coming back / Lovers forever / Do you / Let's try love again / I came here to party / Out of control / Save me / Toyko / Dazed / It's all over now.
LP: AMLX 649 65

STOMP (THE BROTHERS JOHNSON'S GREATEST HITS).
Tracks: / I'll be good for you / Blam / Running for your lovin' / Ain't we funkin' now / Ride 'o' rocket / Real thing, The / This had to be / Get the funk out ma face / Streetwave / Strawberry letter 23 / Lovers forever.
LP: BJL 1
MC: BJC 1

WINNERS.
Tracks: / Real thing / Dancin' free / Sunlight / Teaser / Caught up / In the way / I want you / Do it for love / Hot mama / Daydreamer dream.
LP: AMLK 63724

Brothers Jones

FOLLOW ME.
Tracks: / Follow me / I wanna dance again / You're a loser / I won't write you no love letters / Friday night / Little help / Take me back / Sexy / Till I'm in love / I really want to know you.
LP: OV 1750

Brothers & Other...

BROTHERS & OTHER MOTHERS 2 (Various artists).
LP: SJL 2236

Brothers & Sisters

DYLAN'S GOSPEL.
LP: NEXLP 135

Brotzmann, Caspar

BLACK AXIS (Brotzmann, Caspar Massacre).
LP: MARAT 14

LAST HOME (Brotzmann, Caspar & Peter).
LP: PATH 4
MC: PATH 4C

Brough, Paul

ENGLISH ANTHEM, (THE) (c. 1900-1930) (see under Magdalen College) (Brough, Paul/Magdalen College Oxford Choir/Geoffrey Webber).

Broughton, Edgar

BUNCH OF 45'S, A (The Singles) (Broughton, Edgar Band).
LP: SHSM 2001

INSIDE OUT (Broughton, Edgar Band).
LP: BGOLP 59

LEGENDARY, THE (Broughton, Edgar Band).
Tracks: / Little one / Waiting for you / Drivin' to nowhere / Meglamaster / Didecoi / April in England / Side by side / Love in the rain / One to seven / Hotel room / Revelations one / Anthem / Down in the jungle / Rent a song / All I want to be / Young boys / Evening over rooftops / Freedom / Poppy / Smokestock / Signal projector.
2LP: DB 80073

OUT DEMONS OUT (Best of the Edgar Broughton Band Vol.1) (Broughton, Edgar Band).
Tracks: / Out demons out / Love in the rain / Green lights / I got mad / Hotel room / Poppy / Evening over rooftops / Apache dropout / Moth, The / People* / Peter / Gone blue / Why can't somebody love me / Capers.
LP: EMS 1122
MC: TCEMS 1122

SING BROTHER SING (Broughton, Edgar Band).
LP: SHVL 791
LP: BGOLP 7

WASA WASA (Broughton, Edgar Band).
LP: IC 038 04083

Broughtons

SUPER CHIP.
LP: SHEET 2

Broussard, Alex

CAJUN AND COUNTRY SONGS (see Happy Fats & Alex Broussard) (Broussard, Alex & Happy Fats).

Broussard, Van

MORE BAYOU BOOGIE.
LP: JIN 9025
MC: JIN 9025 TC

VAN BROUSSARD.
LP: JIN 9024
MC: JIN 9024 TC

Brouta, Eric

TOU PARE.
LP: HDD 2478

Brown, A. J

LOVE PEOPLE.
LP: UNKNOWN

Brown, Al

HERE I AM BABY.
LP: TRLS 99

Brown, Andrew

BIG BROWN'S CHICAGO BLUES.
LP: BM 9001

ON THE CASE.
LP: DT 3010

Brown, Art

CHICAGO '81 (Brown, Art & Milton Suggs).
LP: RF 2004

Brown, Arthur

CHISHOLM IN MY BOSOM.
LP: GULP 1023

CRAZY WORLD OF ARTHUR BROWN, THE.
Tracks: / Nightmare / Fanfare - fire poem / Fire / Come and buy / Time / I put a spell on you / Spontaneous apple creation / Rest cure / I've got money / Child of my kingdom.
LP: 2459 357
LP: 2485 114
LP: 612005

DANCE.
Tracks: / We've gotta get out of this place / Helen with the sun / Take a chance / Crazy / Hearts and minds / Dance / Out of time / Quietly with tact / Soul garden / Lord will find a way, The / Is there nothing beyond God?.
LP: GULP 1008

LOST EARS, THE.
Tracks: / Internal messenger / Space plucks / Trouble / Brains / Night of the pigs / Creep, The / Creation / Gypsy escape / Love is a spirit / Experiment / Hymn / Traffic light song, The / Spirit of joy / Time captives / Conception / Come alive / Sunrise / Triangles / Metal monster / Space plucks (Including Dem Bones.) / So high up here / Through the planets.
2LP: GUD 2003/4

STRANGELANDS, THE.
LP: RECK 2
MC: TCRECK 2

Brown, Barry

BARRY.
LP: STLP 1025

BEST OF BARRY BROWN.
LP: VSLP 5006

COOL PON YOUR CORNER.
LP: TRLS 191

RIGHT NOW.
LP: TILP 001

ROOTS AND CULTURE (Brown, Barry & Willie Williams).
LP: UTLP 003

Brown, Bertha

BERTHA BROWN-VOLUME 2 (see under Brown, Tom) (Brown, Bertha/Tom Brown).

Brown, Bobby (1)

DANCE YA KNOW IT.
LP: MCG 6074
MC: MCGC 6074

DON'T BE CRUEL.
Tracks: / Don't be cruel / My prerogative / Roni / Rock wit' cha / Every little step / I'll be good to you / All day all night / Take it slow.
LP: MCF 3425
MC: MCFC 3425

KING OF STAGE.
Tracks: / Baby I wanna tell you something / King of stage / Spending time / You ain't been loved tonight / Love obsession / Seventeen.
LP: MCL 1886
MC: MCLC 1886

SHE AIN'T WORTH IT (See under Medeiros, Glenn) (Medeiros, Glenn and Bobby Brown).

Brown, Bobby (2)

CANADA ON TOUR (Brown, Bobby & The Scottish Accent).
LP: WGR 046
MC: CWGR 046

ISLAND FLING (Brown, Bobby & The Scottish Accent).
LP: WGR 033
MC: CWGR 033

MAID OF THE MILL, THE (See Scottish Accent) (Brown, Bobby & The Scottish Accent).
LP: WGR 034
MC: CWGR 034

SALUTE TO SCOTLAND, A (Brown, Bobby (1)).
LP: WGR 082
MC: CWGR 082

TARRY A WHILE WITH.... (Brown, Bobby & The Scottish Accent).
LP: WGR 035
MC: CWGR 035

Brown, Boots

ROCKIN''N' RAVIN' (See Little Richard) (Brown, Boots/Little Richard).

Brown, Brian

PLANETS, THE.
LP: LRF 151

Brown, Bus

PORTRAIT: BUS BROWN & DRIFTWOOD (Brown, Bus & Driftwood).
LP: BSS 200

Brown, Buster

GOOD NEWS.
Tracks: / Fannie Mae / Is you is or is you ain't my baby / Good news / Madison, The / Gonna love my baby / Slow drag Pt. 1 / Sugar babe / John Henry / Blueberry Hill / Raise a ruckus tonight / Slow drag Pt. 2 / I get the blues when it rains / Don't dog your woman / Doctor Brown.
LP: CRB 1209

Brown, Charles

ALL MY LIFE.
Tracks: / Early in the morning / Fool's paradise / Bad bad whiskey / When the sun comes out / Nobody knows the trouble I've seen / That's a pretty good love / Virus called the blues, A / Seven long days / Joyce boogie / Trouble blues / Tell me who / All my life / Too late.
LP: BB 9501

DRIFTIN' BLUES.
LP: PM 1546 611

GREAT RHYTHM AND BLUES VOL.2.
Tracks: / Driftin' blues / Trouble blues / Rockin' blues / Baby let me hold your hand / Big legged woman / Livin' in misery / Black night / Merry christmas baby / It's getting to be evening / Let the sunshine in my life / Counting my tears / I want a girl.
LP: BDL 1001

I'M GONNA PUSH ON (Live at Nosebacke) (Brown, Charles & Hjartslag).
Tracks: / Teardrops from my eyes / Black night / Please don't drive me away / Trouble blues / Please come home for Christmas / (I love you) just the way you are / Bad bad whiskey / I'm gonna push on / I wanna go back home to Gothenburg / I'll do my best.
LP: RJ 200

LET'S HAVE A BALL (1945-1961).
Tracks: / In the evening / I've got that old feeling / Huggin' bug / Again / Gee / Tonight I'm alone / Alley batting / It's nothing / Cryin' and driftin' blues / Tender heart.
LP: KIX 34

ONE MORE FOR THE ROAD.
Tracks: / I cried last night / Save your love for me / Who will the next fool be / Cottage for sale / Travellin' blues / I stepped in quicksand / Route 66 / One for my baby / My heart is mended / He's got you / I miss you so / Get yourself another fool.
LP: FIEND 88

RACE TRACK BLUES.
Tracks: / Jukebox lil / More than you know / Race track blues / Changeable woman blues / Snuff dippin' mama / Peek-a-boo / Homesick blues / Did you ever love a woman / Let's walk / My silent love / Free lancin' again / Jilted

blues / Tomorrow / Hard times / Without your love / It's a sin to tell a lie.
LP: KIX 17

SAIL ON BLUES (Brown, Charles & Johnny Moore's Three Blazers).
Tracks: / Sail on blues / Johnny's bogie / Money's getting cheaper / I'm so happy I could cry / Lonesome blues / What do you know about love / Friendless blues / Way over there by the cherry tree.
LP: JB 1106

SUNNY ROAD.
Tracks: / Sunny road / New Orleans blues / Soothe me / It ain't gonna be like that / My baby's gone / Texas blues / I'll always be in love with you / I want to go home / Groovy movie blues / So there / Merry Christmas baby / Travelling blues / Honey slipper / My heart is mended / Please believe me / Angel baby.
LP: KIX 5

Brown, Chuck

ANY OTHER WAY TO GO?.
LP: RTLP 501
MC: RTC 501

BUSTIN' LOOSE (Brown, Chuck & Soul Searchers).
Tracks: / I gotcha now / Could it be love / Game seven / Berro e sombaro / Bustin' loose / Never gonna give you up / If it ain't funky.
LP: EG 2605201
MC: EG 2605204

LIVE DC BUMPIN'Y'ALL.
Tracks: / Dedication / Downright Country Boy / Stormy Monday / Kickin' the jams / Jazzy Jam / We Need Some Money / Loveboat / Sho' yuh right / Boogie on gogo woman / Peach And Love / We need some jazz / I am somebody / Rumours / Go go swing / It Don't Mean A Thing / Midnight sun, A / Moody's Mood / Woody Woodpecker / Here We Go Again / Message, The.
LP: MELTLP 3
MC: MELTCASS 3

Brown, Clarence

ALRIGHT AGAIN (Brown, Clarence 'Gatemouth').
Tracks: / Frosty / Strollin' with bones / Give me time to explain / Baby take it easy / Sometimes I slip / I feel alright again / Alligator boogaloo / Dollar got the blues / Honey in the bobo / Gate walks to the board.
LP: FIEND 2
LP: ROUNDER 2028
MC: ROUNDER 2028C

ATOMIC ENERGY.
LP: BB 305

GATE'S ON HEAT VOL.3.
LP: 80603

MORE STUFF.
LP: 33561

NASHVILLE SESSION 1965 (Brown, Clarence 'Gatemouth').
Tracks: / Cross my heart / Don't start me talkin' / Gate's salty blues / My time is expensive / Ninety nine / Going down slow / Long way home / Tippin' in / For now so long / May the bird of paradise fly up your nose.
LP: LPM 7003

ONE MORE MILE (Brown, Clarence 'Gatemouth').
Tracks: / Information blues / Song for Renee / Stranded / Sunrise cajun style / Big yard / Ain't that dandy / One more mile / I wonder / Flippin' out / Neat baku.
LP: FIEND 6
LP: ROUNDER 2034
MC: ROUNDER 2034C

ORIGINAL PEACOCK RECORDINGS (Brown, Clarence 'Gatemouth').
LP: ROUNDER 2039
MC: ROUNDER 2039C

PRESSURE COOKER.
LP: AL 4745

REAL LIFE.
Tracks: / Real Life / Okie Dokie Stomp / Frankie And Johnny / Next time you see me / Take the 'A' train / Please Send Me Someone To Love / Catfish / St. Louis Blues / What a shame what a shame.
LP: REU 1015
LP: ROUNDER 2054
MC: ROUNDER 2054C

SAN ANTONIO BALLBUSTER.
Tracks: / Gate's salty blues / It never can be that way / I've been mistreated / She winked her eye / Win with me baby / She walked right in / Boogie uproar / Baby take it easy / Just got lucky / Didn't reach my goal / You got money / Okie dokie stomp / Just before dawn / Dirty work at the crossroads / Sad hours / Rock my blues away.
LP: RL 010
LP: CR 30169

STANDING MY GROUND.
LP: AL 4779

TEXAS GUITARMAN (Duke-Peacock Story Vol.1).
Tracks: / Boogie rambler / Justice blues / Atomic energy / Two o'clock in the morning / Mary is fine / Didn't reach my goal / I live the life / My time is expensive / She walked right in / I've been mistreated / Win with me baby / Just got lucky / Mercy on me / Too late baby / Taking my chances / It can never be that way.
LP: CHD 161

Brown, Cleo

BOOGIE WOOGIE.
Tracks: / When Hollywood goes black and tan / When / You're my fever / Breakin' in a pair of shoes / Latch on / Love in the first degree / My gal Mezzanine / Here comes cookie / Boogie woogie / You're a heavenly thing / I'll take the south / Stuff is here and it's mellow, The / Never too tired for love / Give a broken heart a break / Mama don't want no peas 'n' rice 'n' coconut oil / Me and my wonderful one.
LP: OFF 3010

LIVING IN THE AFTERGLOW (Brown, Cleo & Marian McPartland).
2LP: AP 216

Brown, Clifford

ALTERNATE TAKES.
Tracks: / Bellarosa / Carvin' the clock / Cookin' / Get happy / Wail bait / Brownie eyes / Cherokee / Hymn of the orient.
LP: BST 84428

AT BASIN STREET (Brown, Clifford & Max Roach).
Tracks: / What is this thing called love? / Love is a many splendoured thing / I'll remember April / Powell's prences / Time / Scene is clean, The / Gertrude's bounce.
LP: 6336707

BLACK AND WHITE SERIES 1 - TRUMPET GENIUSES (Brown, Clifford & Chet Baker).
LP: 214W 13

BLUE AND BROWN.
MC: 771505

CHEROKEE 1954-55.
LP: LPJT 74

CLIFFORD BROWN (JAZZ IMMORTAL).
Tracks: / Daahoud / Minders keepers / Joy spring / Gone with the wind / Bones for Jones / Blueberry Hill / Tiny capers / Tiny capers (alternate take).
LP: AFF 129

CLIFFORD BROWN MEMORIAL (Various artists).
LP: QJC 7055

CLIFFORD BROWN VOL.1.
Tracks: / Jordu / I can't get started / I get a kick out of you / Parisian thoroughfare / All God's chillun got rhythm / Tenderly / Sunset eyes / Clifford's axe.
LP: JR 118

CLIFFORD BROWN VOL.2.
Tracks: / Brown skins / Deltitnu / Keeping up with the Joneses / Conception / All the things you are / I cover the waterfront.
LP: JR 136

CLIFFORD BROWN VOL.3.
Tracks: / Goofin' with me / Minority / Salute to the Bandbox / Strictly romantic / Baby / Quick step / Bum's rush / No start no end / Venez donc chez moi.
LP: JR 140

CLIFFORD BROWN VOL.4.
Tracks: / Hello / All weird / Blue and brown / I can dream, can't I / Song is you / Come rain or come shine / It might as well be spring / You're a lucky guy.
LP: JR 142

COMPACT JAZZ: CLIFFORD BROWN.
MC: 8429334

COMPLETE PARIS COLLECTION VOL. 3.
LP: JL 102
LP: 500102

COMPLETE PARIS COLLECTION VOL 4.
LP: 500109

DEAUX GEANTS.
2LP: 416008

IN CONCERT (Brown, Clifford & Max Roach).
Tracks: / Jor-du (minor encamp) / Can't get started, I / Get a kick out of you, I / Parisian thoroughfare / All god's chillun got rythm / Tenderly / Sunset eyes / Clifford's Axe.
LP: 500 751
LP: GNPS 18
MC: GNP5 18

LIVE AT BASIN STREET-1956 (Brown, Clifford & Max Roach).
Tracks: / Valse hot / I feel a song coming on / Sweet Georgia Brown / What's new? / Daahoud.
LP: INGO 2

MEMORIAL ALBUM.
Tracks: / Hymn of the Orient / Easy living / Minor mood / Cherokee / Wail bait / Brownie speaks / De-dah / Cookin' / Carvin' the rock / You go to my head.
MC: 4BN 81526
LP: BST 81526
LP: BLP 1526
LP: OJC 017

PARIS COLLECTION VOL. 1.
LP: JLA 53

PARIS COLLECTION VOL. 2.
LP: JL 86

PURE GENIUS (Brown, Clifford & Max Roach).
LP: K 52388

STUDY IN BROWN (Brown, Clifford & Max Roach).
Tracks: / Cherokee / Jacqui / Land's end / George's dilemma / Sandu / Gherkin for Perkin / If I love again / Take the 'A' train.
LP: 6336708

TRUMPET MASTERS (Brown, Clifford & D.Gillispie).
Tracks: / Trumpet masters.
2LP: VJD 507

WITH STRINGS.
Tracks: / Yesterdays / Laura / What's new? / Blue moon / Can't help lovin' dat man / Embraceable you / Willow weep for me / Smoke gets in your eyes / Portrait of Jennie / Where or when / Stardust.
LP: 6336711

Brown, Danny Joe

DANNY JOE BROWN & BROWN BAND (Brown, Danny Joe & Brown Band).
Tracks: / Sundance / Nobody walks on me / Alamo, The / Two days home / Edge of sundown / Beggarman, The / Run for your life / Hear my song / Gambler's dream / Hit the road.
LP: EPC 85122

Brown, Dennis

20 CLASSIC REGGAE TRACKS.
Tracks: / Ain't that lovin' you / Equal rights / Slave driver / Should i / Milk & honey / Jah love / Concrete castle king / Man next door / Home sweet home / Whip them jah / Open your eyes / Oh what a day.
LP: MTB 002

BAALGAD (Brown, Dennis & Enos the Clown).
LP: UNKNOWN

BEST OF DENNIS BROWN.
Tracks: / Ain't that lovin' you / Cassandra / Repatriation / Equal rights / Should I / So jah say / Slave driver / Money in my pocket / Drifter / Jah can do it / Oh mother / Words of wisdom.
LP: BMLP 005
MC: BMC 005

BEST, THE.
LP: AMA 5146
MC: AMC 5146

BROWN SUGAR.
LP: TAXI LP 004
LP: RAS 3207

DENNIS.
LP: STLP 1024

DENNIS BROWN COLLECTION, THE.
LP: DBPLP 1

DENNIS BROWN IN CONCERT.
LP: AYLLP 003

EXIT, THE.
LP: TRLS 238
MC: ZCTRL 238

GOOD TONIGHT.
LP: GREL 152
MC: GREEN 152

GOOD VIBRATIONS.
LP: CSESLP 01
MC: CSESCT 01

GREATEST HITS: DENNIS BROWN.
LP: RRTG 7709
MC: RRTGC 7709

HISTORY.
LP: LALP 009

HOLD TIGHT.
Tracks: / Hold tight / Indiscioline woman / Footstool / Let him go / When spring is around / I've got your number / Worried man / Things in life.
LP: LLLP 21
MC: LLC 21

INSEPARABLE.
Tracks: / So nice to be with you / For you / Hot lady / Inseparable / Early in the morning / Ababa jan hoi / Rain / Appreciate nature / Make ends meet / Since I've been loving you / Senorita.
LP: WKLP 7
MC: WKLC 7

JOSEPH'S COAT OF MANY COLOURS.
Tracks: / Slave driver / Open your eyes / Creator, The / Cup of tea, A / Together brothers / Oh what a day / Well without water / Three meals a day / Home sweet home / Man next door.
LP: BMLP 010
MC: BMC 010
LP: LASL 6
MC: LASC 6

JUDGE NOT (Brown, Dennis/Gregory Isaacs).
Tracks: / Crazy list / Judge not / Deceiving girl / Live and love / Street walker / Inner city lady.
LP: GREL 72
MC: GREEN 72

JUST DENNIS.
Tracks: / Show us the way / Cassandra / Run too tuff / Westbound train / Africa / Love Jah / No more will I roam / Some like it hot / I am the conqueror / Only a smile / Silver words / Yagga yagga you'll suffer).
LP: TRLS 107

LET OFF SUPM (see under Isaacs, Gregory) (Isaacs, Gregory & Dennis Brown).

LIVE AT MONTREUX: DENNIS BROWN.
Tracks: / So jah say / Wolves and leopards / Ain't that lovin' you / Words of wisdom / Drifter, The / Milk and honey / Yabby you / I don't feel no way / Whip them jah / Money in my pocket.
LP: BMLP 1016
LP: LASL 5
MC: LASC 5

LOVE HAS FOUND ITS WAY.
Tracks: / Love has found it's way / Get high on your love / Handwriting on the wall / Weep and moan / Blood sweat and tears / Halfway up halfway down / Any day now / I couldn't stand losing you / Why baby why / Get up.
LP: AMLH 64886
MC: CAM 64886

MISCHIEF (See under Ranks, Shabba).

MONEY IN MY POCKET.
Tracks: / Money in my pocket / Ah so we stay / Changing times / Silhouettes / Africa / Yagga yagga (you'll suffer) / I am the conqueror / Show us the way / Cassandra / No more will I roam.
LP: TRLS 197
MC: ZCTRL 197

MORE.
LP: DSR 9764

MY TIME.
MC: RRTGC 7713
LP: RRTG 7713

NO CONTEST (Brown, Dennis/Gregory Isaacs).
LP: GREL 133
MC: GREEN 133

OVERPROOF.
MC: SHMC 43086

PROPHET RIDES AGAIN, THE.
Tracks: / Out of the funk / Jasmine my way to fame / Save a little love for me / Wonders of the world / Too hot / Prophet rides again, The / Historical places / This love of mine / Shashamane living (country living) / Storms are raging.
LP: AMLX 64964
MC: CXM 64964

REGGAE SUPERSTARS MEET (Brown, Dennis/Horace Andy).
LP: BLP 4

REVOLUTION.
LP: YSLP 4

SATISFACTORY FEELING.
Tracks: / Revolution / If this world were mind / Oh girl / Easy take it easy / Rub-a-dub / Unite brotherman / Praise without raise / Money in my pocket.
LP: TRDLP 122582

SHEPARD BE CAREFUL (See under Cocoa Tea) (Cocoa Tea & Dennis Brown).

SLOW DOWN.
Tracks: / Slow down / Woman / Joy in the morning / They fight / Let's build our dreams / Love by the score / Can't keep a good man down / Icy road / Now and forever / Come on over / Africa we want to go.
LP: GREL 80
MC: GREEN 80

SMILE LIKE AN ANGEL.
Tracks: / Let me live / Pretend you're happy / Westbound train / Don't expect me to be your friend / Play girl / Smile like

an angel / Poorer side of town / We will be free / Summertime / Silver words / My kind / Golden streets.
LP: ... BMLP 034
MC: ... BMLC 034

SPELLBOUND.
Tracks: / Spellbound / Don't know why / Coming home tonight / It's too late / Bubbiing fountain / Gimme your lovin' / Come on home woman / Someone special / Sitting & watching.
LP: ... BMLP 026
LP: ... LASL 8

SUPER HITS.
Tracks: / Concentration / Silhouettes / Witchita lineman / How he can't spell / Musical heatwave / I didn't know / How could I let you get away / Lips of wine / Let me down easy / Changing times.
LP: ... TRLS 57

TIME AND PLACE.
Tracks: / Time and place.
LP: ... CT 007

UNCHALLENGED.
LP: ... GREL 138
MC: ... GREEN 138

VICTORY IS MINE.
Tracks: / Victory is mine / Call me / We are in love / Don't give up / Everyday people / Sea of love / Just because / Should I / Jah can do it / Sad news.
MC: ... BMC 084
LP: ... BMLP 084

VISIONS.
Tracks: / Deliverence will come / Oh mother / Love me always / Concrete castle / Malcolm X / Repatriation / Jah can do it / Milk and honey / Stay at home / Say what you say.
LP: ... LIP 7
LP: ... BMLP 021
LP: ... SHAN 44002
MC: ... SHANC 44002

WAKE UP.
LP: ... NCLP 004

WALLS AND LETTERS.
LP: ... JGML 6046

WILD FIRE (see under Holt, John) (Brown, Dennis & John Holt).

WOLVES AND LEOPARDS.
Tracks: / Wolves and leopards / Emanuel / Here I come / Whip the jab jab / Created by the father / Party time / Rolling down / Boasting / Children of Israel / Lately girl.
LP: ... BMLP 046
MC: ... TCEMC 3300
MC: ... BMC 046
LP: ... JGMLP 22
LP: ... EMC 3300

WORDS OF WISDOM.
Tracks: / So Jah say / Don't feel no way / Words of wisdom / Should I / True / Ain't that lovin' you / Cassandra / Jah love / Black liberation / Rasta children / Drifter / Money in my pocket.
LP: ... BMLP 002
LP: ... LASL 1
MC: ... LASC 1

YESTERDAY, TODAY & TOMORROW.
Tracks: / Little bit more, A / Tribulation / Rocking times / Carress me girl / Love light / Hold on to what you've got / Little village / Have you ever been in love?.
LP: ... BMLP 031

YOUR LOVE'S GOTTA HOLD ON ME.
Tracks: / Souls keep burning / Let love in / Your love's got a hold on me / Right fight / Hooligan / I can't stand it.
LP: ... BMLP 033
LP: ... JGML 600 79

Brown, Dougie

PRESENCE.
Tracks: / Reigning in all splendour / All because of your love / Lord and Father of mankind, The / For Thou O Lord / Jesus we enthrone You / River, wash over me / Living under the shadow / We worship and adore you / We place you on the highest place / Father's love / You laid aside your majesty / Father, we love you / I love you lord / Lord, we want to thank you / When I look into your holiness.
LP: ... SOP R 2016
MC: ... SOP C 2016

Brown, Errol

THAT'S HOW LOVE IS.
Tracks: / Maya / Love goes up and down / That's how love is / Higher desire / Personal touch / From the balcony / Afternoon siesta / One wish / Can't let you go.
LP: ... WX 209
MC: ... WX 209C

Brown Family

FAMILIAR FACES, FAMILIAR PLACES.
Tracks: / No ones' gonna love me / Millpond / Love is a contact sport / Tag along Joe / Stay with me / Dear hearts and gentle people / Love was on our side / Heaven's just a sin away / Way I love you.
LP: ... PL 42948

Brown, Floyd

FLOYD BROWN.
LP: ... JIN 9023

Brown, Foxy

FOXY.
MC: ... MCT 1025
LP: ... MLPS 1025

MY KINDA GIRL.
LP: ... RAS 3070
MC: ... RASCS 3070

Brown, Gabriel

GABRIEL BROWN 1944-52.
LP: ... KK 785

GABRIEL BROWN AND HIS GUITAR.
LP: ... FLY 591

Brown, General D

TRIAD.
Tracks: / Reality / I don't care a ... / War maker / Left out the coke / Set up a plant / Piece of culture / Don't walk / All jah people / Have to mention / Poll tax / Say a prayer.
LP: ... NRLP 4

Brown & Geuter

FORTUNE MY FOE (Various artists).
Tracks: / Anonymous 13th century dance: *Various artists* / C l'entrada del ten clar, eya: *Various artists* / Dulce solum: *Various artists* / Winder, wie ist nu din kraft: *Various artists* / El mois de mai: *Various artists*/ De se debent bigami: *Various artists* / Kyrie: *Various artists* / Estampie: *Various artists* / Der kuninc Rudolph: *Various artists* / Chose tassin: *Various artists* / Chramer gip diu varwe mier: *Various artists*/ Vite perdite: *Various artists* / Rex immense: *Various artists* / Vinum bonum cum sapore: *Various artists*/ Estampie: *Various artists* / In taberna quando sumus: *Various artists* / Exul ego clericus: *Various artists*/ Solis ortu, A: *Various artists* / Danse Royale: *Various artists*.
LP: ... BRO 127
MC: ... KBRO 127

Brown, Glen

GLEN BROWN SINGS, MELODICA TALKS.
LP: ... RRLP 444

NUMBER ONE SOUND.
LP: ... PRLP 444

Brown, Honey

SUMMER NIGHTS (See under Blake, Chris) (Blake, Chris & Honey Brown).

Brown, Hylo

HYLO BROWN.
Tracks: / Flower blooming in the wildwood / When it's lamplighting time in the valley / Old home town / I'll be all smiles tonight / Love and wealth / Gathering flowers from the hillside / Blue eyes darling / Will the angels play their harps for me / Put my little shoes away / Darling Nellie across the sea / Why do you weep dear willow.
LP: ... HAT 3077
MC: ... HATC 3077

HYLO BROWN MEETS THE LONESOME PINE FIDDLERS (Brown, Hylo/Lonesome Pine Fiddlers).
LP: ... SLP 220
MC: ... GT 5220

Brown, Ian

VIRTUOSO VIOLIN (See under Hasson, Maurice) (Brown, Ian/Maurice Hasson/ St Johns Smith Sq. Orchestra).

Brown, Jackie

DAY AT BUCKINGHAM, A (Brown, Jackie/Robinson Cleaver/William Davies).
MC: ... AC 176

WURLITZER STARS VOL. 2 (see under Welling, George) (Brown, Jackie/George Welling).

Brown, James

BEST OF JAMES BROWN (Godfather of Soul).
Tracks: / Living in America / Body heat / Hey America / Please, please, please / Hot pants / Think / I got you (I feel good) / Say it loud, I'm black and I'm proud / Get up, I feel like a sex machine / Make it funky / Papa's got a brand new bag / Get on the good foot / Gonna have a funky good time / Cold sweat / Honky tonk / It's a man's man's man's world / Gravity.
LP: ... NE 1376
MC: ... CE 2376

BEST OF JAMES BROWN (POLYDOR).
Tracks: / Say it loud, I'm black and I'm proud / Please, please, please / Try me / Lost someone / Papa's got a brand new bag / It's a man's man's man's world / Cold sweat / There was a time / Popcorn / Hot pants / Sex machine.
LP: ... 239 152 9
MC: ... 317 752 9

BODY HEAT.
Tracks: / Body heat / Woman / Kiss in 77 / I'm satisfied / What the world needs now is love / Wake up and give yourself a chance / Don't tell it.
LP: ... PHX 1025
LP: ... PD 6093
LP: ... 2391 258

BRING IT ON.
Tracks: / Bring it on, bring it on / Today / You can't keep a good man down / Tennessee waltz / Night time is the right time / For your precious love.
LP: ... SNTF 906

COLD SWEAT.
Tracks: / Cold sweat / Nature boy / Come rain or come shine / I love you Porgy / Back stabbin' / Fever / Mona Lisa / I want to be around / Good rockin' tonight / Stagger Lee / Kansas city.
LP: ... 8134 921

COLD SWEAT (LIVE).
Tracks: / Papa's got a brand new bag / Sex machine / Please please please / This is a man's world / Cold sweat.
LP: ... PER 33 8605

DEAD ON THE HEAVY FUNK 74-76.
Tracks: / Superbad,superslick / Your love / Body heat / Hot (I need to be loved,loved,loved) / Get up offa that thing / Funky president / Don't tell it / Future shock of the world / Woman.
LP: ... 827 439 1
MC: ... 827 439 4

DUETS.
Tracks: / Think / You've got the power / You can make it if you try / Baby, baby, baby / Let it be me / You've got to change your mind / Summertime / It's alright / Funky side of town / Gimme your love / What my baby needs now is a little more lovin' / Never get enough / You got to have a job / Think / You've got the power.
LP: ... 841 516 1
MC: ... 841 516 4

EXCITEMENT.
Tracks: / Have mercy baby / Good good lovin' / I don't mind / Dancin' little thing / Begging, begging / Come over here / Shout and shimmy / It was you / Just won't do right / You don't have to go / Tell me what you're gonna do.
LP: ... 2489 199

FEDERAL YEARS VOL.1.
LP: ... SS 8023

FEDERAL YEARS VOL.2.
LP: ... SS 8024

FUNKIN' IN AMERICA.
Tracks: / Pop corn '80s / Hot / Givin' up food for funk (part 1) / Let the funk flow / I go crazy / Don't stop the funk / Super bull - super bad / Give it up or turn it loose / Unity - part 1 (The third coming).
LP: ... 831 440-1
MC: ... 831 440-4

GIMME YOUR LOVE (See under Franklin, Aretha) (Brown, James & Aretha Franklin).

GRAVITY.
Tracks: / How do you stop / Living in America / Goliath / Repeat the beat (faith) / Return to me / Gravity / Let's get personal / Turn me loose / I'm Dr. Feelgood.
LP: ... SCT 57108
MC: ... 40 57108
LP: ... FZ 40380

GREATEST HITS:JAMES BROWN.
Tracks: / Please, please, please / Try me / Think / Papa's got a brand new bag / I got you (I feel good) / It's a man's man's man's world / Bring it up / Cold sweat / There was a time / I got the feelin' / Say it loud, I'm black and I'm proud / Sex machine / Hot pants / My thang / Funky President / Get up offa that thing.
LP: ... 823 352-1
MC: ... 823 352-4

HELL.
2LP: ... PD 29001

HOT.
LP: ... PD 6059

I'M REAL.
Tracks: / Tribute / I'm real / Static / Time to get busy / She looks all types a good / Keep keepin' / Can't git enuf / It's your money / Godfather running the joint.
LP: ... POLD 5230
MC: ... POLDC 5230

IN THE JUNGLE GROOVE.
Tracks: / It's a new day / Funky drummer / Give it up or turn it loose(remix) / I got to move (Previously unreleased) / Talking loud and saying nothing(remix) / Get up, get into it, get involved / Soul power (re-edit) / Hot pants / Funky drummer.
2LP: ... 829 624-1
MC: ... 829 624-4
2LP: ... URBLP 11
MCSET: ... URBDC 11

IT'S A MAN'S MAN'S MAN'S WORLD.
Tracks: / It's a man's man's man's world / Is it yes or is it no / Ain't that a groove (parts 1 & 2) / Scratch, (The) / Bewildered / Bells in the wee wee hours, The / Come over here / I don't mind / Just you and me / I love you, yes I do.
LP: ... 2489 197

JAMES BROWN AND FRIENDS (Brown, James and friends).
Tracks: / Papa's got a brand new bag / How do you stop / When a man loves a woman / I'll go crazy / I got you (I feel good) / Out of sight / Living in America / Show interest / Cold sweat / Try me.
LP: ... 834 085 1
MC: ... 834 085 4

JAMES BROWN LIVE AND LOW-DOWN AT THE APOLLO VOL.1.
Tracks: / I'll go crazy / Try me / Think / I don't mind / Lost someone / Please,please,please / You've got the power / I found someone / Why do you do me like you do / I want you so bad / I love you, yes I do / Why does everything happen to me / Bewildered / Please don't go / Night train.
MC: ... SPEMC 46
LP: ... SPELP 46

JAMES BROWN & THE SOUL G'S (Live at Chastain Park) (Brown, James & The Soul G's).
Tracks: / It's a man's man's man's world / Get up offa that thing / Papa's got a brand new bag / I got you (I feel good) / Cold sweat / It's a man's man's man's world.
LP: ... JAM 1984
MC: ... TCJAM 1984

JAMES BROWN'S FUNKY PEOPLE.
Tracks: / Gimme some more / Pass the peas / Think (about it) / Givin' up food for funk / Mama feel good / Hot pants / Rock me again & again & again..... / Damn right, I am somebody (part.1) / Take me just as I am / If you don't get it the first time....... / Parrty (Part 1) / It's not the express it's the JBs monaurail (part 1).
LP: ... 829 417 1
MC: ... 829 417 4

LIVE AT CHASTAIN PARK.
Tracks: / Give it up or turn it loose / It's too funky in here / Try me / Get on the good foot / Get up offa that thing / Georgia on my mind / Hot pants / I got the feelin' / It's a man's, man's, man's world / Cold sweat / I can't stand myself (when you touch me) / Papa's got a brand new bag / I got you / Please, please, please / Jam.
LP: ... BDL 3005

LIVE AT THE APOLLO.
Tracks: / Opening fanfare / Try me / I don't mind / Lost someone (part 1) / Lost someone (part 2) / Night train / I'll go crazy / Think / Medley / Closing.
LP: ... 843 479 1
MC: ... 843 479 4

LIVE AT THE APOLLO (PART 1).
LP: ... RNLP 217

LIVE AT THE APOLLO (PART 2).
LP: ... RNLP 218

LIVE - HOT ON THE ONE.
Tracks: / It's too funky in here / Gonna have a funky good time / Get up offa that thing / Body heat / I got the feelin' / Try me / Sex machine / It's a mans mans mans world / Get on the good foot / Papa's got a brand new bag / Please please please / Jam.
2LP: ... 2683085

LIVE IN NEW YORK.
MC: ... UMK 99018

LIVE IN NEW YORK.
Tracks: / Funky good time / Get up off that thing / Body heat / Sex machine / Try me / Brown's inferno / Papa's got a brand new bag / Good foot / This is a man's world / Got that feeling / Cold sweat / Please, please, please / Jam / Bay ridge boogy / Payback mix / Too funky in here.
2LP: ... A 150155
LP: ... AFESD 1030
MC: ... AC 150155

LIVE & LOWDOWN AT THE APOLLO VOL. 1.

Tracks: / I'll go crazy / Try me / Think / I don't mind / Lost someone / Please please please / You've got the power / I found someone / Why do you do me like you do / I want you so bad / I love you yes I do / Why does everything happen to me / Bewildered / Please don't go / Night train.
LP: **248 253 0**

LOVE OVERDUE.
Tracks: / (So tired of standing still we got to) move / Show me - dance, dance, dance / To the funk / Teardrops on your letter / Standing on higher ground / Later for dancing / You are my everything / It's time to love (put a little love).
LP: **510079-1**
MC: **510079-4**

MEAN ON THE SCENE.
Tracks: / Too funky in here / Please please please / Good foot / Get up offa that thing / Cold sweat / Browns inferno (instrumental).
LP: . . . . **PHX 1016**

MUTHUS NATURE.
LP: . . . . **PD 16111**

NON STOP.
LP: . . . . **PD 6318**

ORIGINAL DISCO MAN.
Tracks: / It's too funky in here / Let the boogie do the rest / Still / Star generation / Women are something else / Original disco man.
LP: **2391412**

PAPA'S GOT A BRAND NEW BAG.
Tracks: / Mashed potatoes / Papa's got a brand new bag / U.S.A. / This old heart of mine / Cross firing / Doin' the limbo / Baby, you're right / Love don't love nobody / Have mercy baby / And I do just what I want / I stay in the Chapel every night / You don't have to go.
LP: **2489 195**

PEOPLE.
Tracks: / Regrets / Don't stop the funk / That's sweet music / Let the funk flow / Stone cold drag / Are we really dancing / Sometimes that's all there is.
LP: . . . . **PD 16258**
LP: **2391 446**

PLEASE, PLEASE, PLEASE.
Tracks: / Please please please / Try me / I feel that old feeling coming on / That's when I lost my heart / Chonnie on chon / Hold my baby's hand / Tell me what I did wrong / Baby cries over the ocean / Begging, begging / No, no, no, no / That dood it / I don't know / I walked alone / Love or a game / Let's make it / Just won't do right.
LP: **2489 194**
LP: . . . . **SING 610**
MC: . . . . **SING 4610**

PRISONER OF LOVE.
Tracks: / Wait in the rain / Again / Lost someone / Bewildered / So long / Signed, sealed, delivered, I'm yours / Try me, can you (feel it part 1) / How long darling / Thing in 'G', The.
LP: **8134 911**

ROOTS OF A REVOLUTION.
Tracks: / I feel that old feeling coming on again / Hold my baby's hand / Chonnie on chon / Just won't do right / Let's make it / Fine old foxy self / Why does everything happen to me / Begging, begging / That dood it / There must be a reason / I want you so bad / Bewildered / Doodle bug / This old heart of mine / You've got the power / Baby you're right / I don't mind / Come over here / And I do just what I want / Tell me what you're gonna do / Hold it / Dancin' little thing / You don't have to go / Lost someone / Shout and shimmy / I found you / I don't care / I've got money / Mashed potatoes USA / Prisoner of love / Oh baby don't you weep / Maybe the last time.
LP: . . . . **REVO 1**

SEX MACHINE.
Tracks: / Get up, I feel like a sex machine / Brother Rapp (parts 1&2) / Bewildered / I got the feelin' / Give it up or turn it loose / Don't want nobody to give me nothing / Lickin' stick / Lowdown popcorn / Spinning wheel / If I ruled the world / There was a time / It's a man's man's world / Please,please,please / I can't stand myself (when you touch me) / Mother Popcorn.
2LP: **833 277-1**
MC: **833 277-4**

SEX MACHINE & OTHER SOUL CLASSICS.
LP: . . . . **POLD 5192**
MC: . . . . **POLDC 5192**

SOLID GOLD.
Tracks: / Please, please, please / Try me / Good good lovin' / I'll go crazy / Think / Night train / Out of sight / Papa's got a brand new bag / I got you / It's a man's man's man's world / Cold sweat / There was a time / I got the feelin' / Say it loud, I'm black and I'm proud / Give it up or turn it loose / Mother popcorn / Get up, I feel like a sex machine / Call me superbad / Soul power / Hot pants / Make it funky / Talking loud and saying nothing / Honky tonk / Get on the good foot / Payback mix / My thang / Papa don't take no mess / Funky president / Hot / Get up offa that thing.
2LP: **267 904 4**

SOUL CLASSICS.
Tracks: / Get up, I feel like a sex machine / My part / Cold sweat / I got you (I feel good) / Night train / Papa's got a brand new bag / Soul power / It's a man's man's man's world / Hot pants / Make it funky, Part 3 / Call me superbad / Money won't change you / Make it funky, Part 1 / Give it up and turn it loose / Out of sight.
LP: **2486 233**

SOUL JUBILEE.
Tracks: / Turn it loose / It's too funky in here / Gonna have a funky good time / Try me / Get on a good foot, get up off that thing / Georgia / Hot pants / I got the feelin' / It's a man's world / Cold sweat / I can't stand it / Papas got a brand new bag / I feel good / Please, please, please / Jam.
LP: . . . . **BMLP 081**

SOUL SYNDROME.
Tracks: / Rapp payback / Mashed potatoes / Funky men / Smokin' and drinkin' / Stay with me / Honky tonk.
LP: . . . . **RCALP 3048**
MC: . . . . **RCAK 3048**
LP: . . . . **RCALP 5006**

SOUL SYNDROME PLUS (Brown, James With Bobby Byrd & The JB's).
Tracks: / Rapp payback (where iz Moses) (long version) / Mashed potatoes / Funky men / Smokin' and drinkin' / Stay with me / Honky tonk / Bessie (part 1) / Nature (part 1) / Rock groove machine (part 1) / Just wanna make you dance (part 1) / Back from the dead / Way to get down, The / Headquarters (Augusta, GA) / Rapp payback (where iz Moses) (part 1).
2LP: . . . . **ROUS 1043**
MC: . . . . **TCROUS 1043**

SPECIAL.
LP: **2417 351**
MC: **3195 270**

STAR TIME.
MCSET: **849 108 4**

STATIC.
LP: . . . . **JSB 2**
MC: . . . . **JSBC 2**

TAKE A LOOK AT THOSE CAKES.
Tracks: / For goodness sakes, look at those cakes / Man understands, A / Someone to talk to / Spring / As long as I love you.
LP: **2391 384**

THIRD COMING.
Tracks: / Popcorn 80's / Give that bass player some / You're my only love / World cycle / Superbull / Superbad 80's / Love 80's / I go crazy.
LP: . . . . **POLS 1029**

TRY ME (Brown, James & The Famous Flames).
Tracks: / There must be a reason / I want you so bad / Why do you do me / I've got to cry / Strange things happen / Fine old foxy self / Messing with the blues / Try me / It was you / I've got to change / Can't be the same / It hurts to tell you / I won't plead no more / You're mine, you're mine / Gonna try / Don't let it happen to me.
LP: . . . . **SING 635**
MC: . . . . **SING 4635**

UNBEATABLE 16 HITS.
Tracks: / Try me / I've got to change / Strange things happen / I've got to cry / There must be a reason / Why do you do me? / Don't let it happen to me / Can't be the same / It hurts to tell you / Gonna try / You're mine / Fine old foxy self / I won't please no more / Messing with the blues / It was you / I want you so bad.
LP: **2459 198**

UNITY (PART 1 - THE THIRD COMING) (See under Bambaataa, Afrika).

Brown, Jeff (aut)

FLAT STANLEY (see under Flat Stanley) (Healy, David (nar)).

Brown, Jim Ed

GREATEST HITS:JIM ED BROWN & HELEN CORNELIUS (Brown, Jim Ed & Helen Cornelius).
Tracks: / I don't want to have to marry you / If the world ran out of love tonight / Bedroom, The / Morning comes to early / Born believer / Lying in love with you / You don't bring me flowers / Saying hello, saying I love you, saying goodbye / Fools / Don't bother to knock.
LP: . . . . **INTS 5113**
MC: . . . . **INTK 5113**

JIM ED BROWN & HELEN CORNELIUS (Brown, Jim Ed & Helen Cornelius).
Tracks: / I don't want to have to marry you / Love was what we had / I've rode with the best / I'm leaving it all up to you / Saying hello, saying I love you, saying goodbye / My heart cries for you / One man woman, one woman man / Burning bridges / There's always goodbye / Have I told you lately that I love you.
LP: . . . . **PL 12024**

Brown, Jocelyn

ONE FROM THE HEART.
Tracks: / Ego maniac / Love's gonna get you / Livin' without your love / I cry real tears / Caught in the act / My time will come / True love / Whatever satisfies you.
LP: **925445 1**
MC: **925445 4**

Brown, Joe

GOLDEN HOUR OF JOE BROWN, A.
MC: . . . . **KGHMC 121**

HERE COMES JOE.
LP: . . . . **DLP 500**

HITS'N'PIECES.
LP: . . . . **PYL 4017**
MC: . . . . **PYM 4017**

JOE BROWN - LIVE.
LP: . . . . **NPL 38006**

PICTURE OF YOU, A.
LP: . . . . **GGL 0146**

WHAT A CRAZY WORLD (See Under Films) (Brown, Joe & The Bruvvers).

Brown, J.T

ROCKIN' WITH J.T..
Tracks: / This tavern boogie / Blackjack blues / Sax-ony boogie / Kilroy won't help it / St. Louis blues / Dumb woman blues / Jimmy's jump / Dog house blues / Date bait / Talking baby blues / Brown's boogie / Round house boogie.
LP: . . . . **KK 7420**

WINDY CITY BOOGIE.
LP: . . . . **PL 9**

Brown, Julie

GODDESS IN PROGRESS.
LP: . . . . **RNEP 610**

Brown, Junior

FLY ME AWAY HOME.
LP: . . . . **SHAKA 844**

Brown, Kevin

ROAD DREAMS.
LP: . . . . **HNBL 1340**
MC: . . . . **HNBC 1340**

RUST.
Tracks: / Don't quit / Hey Joe Louis / Write a bible of your own / Telephone tears / We'll be with you / If I had my way / You don't have to tell me / Southern Streets / Meltdown / Sunny side up.
LP: . . . . **HNBL 1344**
MC: . . . . **HNBC 1344**

Brown, Lattimore

EVERYDAY I HAVE TO CRY.
Tracks: / I've got everything (my baby needs) / I'm not through loving you / Boogaloo Sue / It hurts me so bad / It's gonna take a little time / Otis is gone (parts 1 & 2) / I know I'm gonna miss you / It's such a sad world / Everyday I have to cry / Please, please, please / Don't trust no one / Bless your heart (I love you) / So says my heart / Nobody has to tell me (you were meant for me) / Cruise on Fanny (cruise on) / Shake & vibrate / Little bag of tricks.
LP: . . . . **CRB 1157**

Brown, Lawrence

INSPIRED ABANDON (Brown, Lawrence All-Stars & Johnny Hodges).
Tracks: / Stompy Jones / Mood indigo / Good Queen Bess / Little brother / Jeep's blues / Do nothing till you hear from me / Ruint / Sassy cue.
LP: . . . . **JAS 66**

Brown, Lee

LEE BROWN 1937-40 (Piano blues rarities).
LP: . . . . **BD 2005**

Brown, Les

20 GOLDEN PIECES: LES BROWN (Brown, Les & His Band of Renown).
Tracks: / Strictly instrumental / You made me love you / Blue flame / So rare / Lazy river / How high the moon / Baby elephant walk / Gentle on my mind / Sentimental journey / Pink panther (theme from) / Let's dance / Jersey bounce / Moonglow / At the woodchopper's ball / On the sunny side of the street / Ballin' the jack / Pretty girl is like a melody, A / Softly as in a morning sunrise / I want to hold your hand / Walk on by.
LP: . . . . **BDL 2024**
MC: . . . . **BDC 2024**

1943 BAND, THE.
Tracks: / OK for baby / I heard you cried last night / Canteen bounce, The / Baby knock me a kiss / Taking a chance on love / Later tonight / What's the good word Mr. Bluebird / Things ain't what they used to be.
LP: . . . . **FANFARE 30-130**

1946 (Brown, Les & His Orchestra).
LP: . . . . **CLP 90**

ALL WEATHER MUSIC (Brown, Les & His Band of Renown).
Tracks: / Clouds / Ill wind / Rain / Lost in a fog / Let it snow, let it snow, let it snow / Stormy weather / Over the rainbow / Blue skies / Azure / Heatwave / Moon was yellow (and the night was young), The / You are my sunshine.
LP: . . . . **JASM 1019**

AT THE HOLLYWOOD PALLADIUM.
MC: . . . . **SLC 61015**

BEST OF BIG BANDS (See under Day, Doris) (Brown, Les & Doris Day).

COMPLETE LES BROWN-VOL.2, THE.
LP: . . . . **AJAZ 415**

CONCERT AT THE HOLLYWOOD PALLADIUM, VOL 2 (Brown, Les & His Band of Renown).
Tracks: / Midnight sun / Begin the beguine / Happy hooligan / I would do anything for you / Laura / Jersey bounce / From this moment on / Crazy legs / Flying home / One o'clock jump / Cherokee / Sentimental journey.
LP: . . . . **JASM 1002**

CONCERT AT THE HOLLYWOOD PALLADIUM, VOL 1 (Brown, Les & His Band of Renown).
Tracks: / Opening announcement (Leap frog) / Moontoona clipper / Caravan / Strange / Baby / Speak low (when you speak of love) / Rain / Street of dreams / Brown's little jug / I let a song go out of my heart / Back in your own back yard / Invitation / You're the cream in my coffee.
LP: . . . . **JASM 1001**

DANCE TO SOUTH PACIFIC (Brown, Les & His Band of Renown).
Tracks: / Honey bun / Happy talk / Some enchanted evening / Loneliness of evening / Wonderful guy / Bloody Mary / Bali Ha'i / Dites-moi / Younger than Springtime / This nearly was mine / There is nothin' like a dame / I'm gonna wash that man right out of my hair.
LP: . . . . **ED 2604131**
MC: . . . . **ED 2604134**

DOUBLE DATE (see under Donahue, Sam) (Brown, Les/Sam Donahue).

DUKE BLUE DEVILS, THE.
LP: . . . . **GELP 15045**

FROM THE CAFE ROUGE.
LP: . . . . **GOJ 1027**

JAZZ SONG BOOK, THE.
Tracks: / King Phillip stomp / Willow weep for me / Don't get around much anymore / Wonderful / Apple honey / I remember you / Claw, The / Let's get away from it all / Pizza boy & love is here to stay / I only have eyes for you / Chelsea bridge.
LP: . . . . **JASM 1506**

LES BROWN AND HIS ORCHESTRA 1944/46 (Brown, Les & His Orchestra).
Tracks: / Leap frog / Invitation to the blues / Just a gigolo / Man with a horn / I can't help it / Flip lid / Lou's blues / Lover's leap / Sentimental journey / Ready to go steady / 12.55 express / Kiss to remember / I can't believe that you're in love with me / I'm making believe / I've got my love to keep me warm / Paper moon.
LP: . . . . **HMP 5039**

LES BROWN AND HIS ORCHESTRA 1946-50 (Brown, Les & His Orchestra).
LP: . . . . **FH 18**

LES BROWN, VOL.4 1956-57 (Brown, Les & His Orchestra).
LP: . . . . **HSR 199**

LES BROWN, VOL. 1, 1944-45.
Tracks: / Leap frog / Invitation to the blues / Just a gigolo / Man with a horn / Flip your lid / Lou's blues / Lover's leap / Sentimental journey / Ready to go steady / 12:55 express / Kiss to remember, A / I can't believe that you're in love with me / I'm making believe / I've got my love to keep me warm / Paper moon.
LP: . . . . **HSR 103**

LES BROWN, VOL. 2, 1949.

Tracks: / Sometimes I'm happy / Three little words / On the Alamo / Something cool / Honeysuckle rose / Negra consentida / Where are you / April showers / Song is ended, The / Just squeeze me / Pell mell / Stardust / Them there eyes / Lips / Black coffee / Bopple sauce.
LP: HSR 131
LP: HMP 5054

LES BROWN, VOL. 3, 1949.
Tracks: / Squawkin' 'bout my walkin' / All the things you are / Thank you, Count / September song / Baby, I need you / Tenderly / Don't do something to someone else / Moten stomp / Teasey toe / Shadow time / Ah-boo ah-boo / Pretty baby / Boptized / Dreamers holiday / Just a gigolo / Leap frog.
LP: HSR 132
LP: HMP 5059

LES BROWN'S IN TOWN.
Tracks: / Just you, just me / Harlem nocturne / Checkin' in / Moonlight in Vermont / Continental, The / Spanich monster / Meanwhile back on the bus / Ridin' high / Nina never knew / On a little street in Singapore / Piccolino, The.
LP: 2C 068 86543

ONE AND ONLY, THE.
Tracks: / On a sunny day / One more blues / Holiday in big band land / Say what? / Turn around / Perky / Bruised bones / Summer talk / LB special / Boogie train blues / Goldfish / Swing flow.
LP: ISST 170

ONE NIGHT STAND (Brown, Les/ Krupa/Osborne).
LP: JOYCE 1119

RHAPSODY IN BLUE (Brown, Les/Day, Doris).
Tracks: / Dig it / While the music played on / Celery stalks at midnight / Easy as pie / Keep cool fool / Come to baby do / We'll be together again / My dreams are getting better / Let's be buddies / Boogie wooglie piggy, The / Hotch kiss corner / I'd rather be with you / Last time I saw you / Till the end of time / Rhapsody in blue.
LP: F 20134
MC: 40134

SENTIMENTAL THING.
MC: CFH 31
LP: FH 31

SWEETEST SOUNDS (Brown, Les & Rosemary Clooney).
Tracks: / Sweetest sounds, The / How am I to know / My funny valentine / Why shouldn't I? / My romance / I get along without you very well / Angry / Some people / Man with a horn / Show me / Have you met Miss Jones? / Little Brown jug / Sleepy time girl / I didn't know what time it was.
LP: ART 003
MC: CART 003

SWING GOES ON VOL 5.
Tracks: / Ridin' high / Just you, just me / Swingin' down the lane / Checkin' in / Stardust / My melancholy baby / Piccolino, The / I've got my love to keep me warm / Sentimental journey / Happy talk / Continental, The / Sophisticated swing / Josephine / Leap frog.
LP: IC 054 52714

SWING SONG BOOK (Brown, Les & His Band of Renown).
Tracks: / Swing book blues / How high the moon / Early Autumn / King Porter stomp / Lullaby of Birdland / Moten swing / Just in time / I want to be happy / Take the 'A' train / I'm beginning to see the light / Pick yourself up / Lean baby.
LP: JASM 1503

THAT SOUND OF RENOWN.
Tracks: / I've got your love to keep me warm / New Mexican hat dance / I'm forever blowing bubbles / Bernie's tune / American in Paris, An (Highlights) / It's alright with me / Something's gotta give / Gal from Joe's, The / Lullaby in rhythm / Nutcracker suite op 71.
LP: JASM 1012

TODAY (Brown, Les & His Band of Renown).
Tracks: / On a clear day you can see forever / My kind of girl / Song sung blue / Sentimental journey / Thands for the memory / Airport 1975 / Bad bad Leroy Brown / Good man is hard to find, A / Sing / Juicy fruit / Everybody loves somebody.
LP: MPS 68 118

TRIO (See under Alexander, Monty) (Brown, Les/Monty Alexander).

Brown, Marion

LA PLACITA (LIVE IN WILLISAU) (Brown, Marion Quartet).
LP: SJP 108

MARION BROWN QUARTET (Brown, Marion Quartet).
LP: ESP 1022

Brown, Mark

GOOD FEELING.
Tracks: / Bang bang / Shall we dance / Through a friend of mine / Good feeling / My heart misses / It's not the way it used to be / Luv touch / Cruisin' / Betwee you and me / Let's go all the way / Distress signal (Only on CD.).
LP: MOT 6275
LP: ZL 72686
MC: ZK 72686

JUST LIKE THAT.
Tracks: / Next time / I can't get enough of you're love / Want you back / I used to be in love / She don't care / Contagious / What do you want from me? / Put a smile on your face / Why can't we be alone? / Stakeout.
LP: ZL 72623
MC: ZK 72623

Brown, Maxine

LIKE NEVER BEFORE.
Tracks: / It's torture / I want a guarantee / Baby cakes / Slipping through my fingers / He's the only guy I'll ever love / I've got a lot of love left in me / Do it now / When I fall in love / Gotta find a way / Ask me / Never had it so good / Losing my touch / Misty morning eyes / Do it in the name of love / Everybody needs love / O Lord what are you doing to me.
LP: KENT 047

ONE IN A MILLION.
Tracks: / One in a million / Since I found you / Let me give you my lovin' / Little girl lost / I wonder what my baby's doing tonight / Yesterday's kisses / One step at a time / It's gonna be alright / Oh no not my baby / Anything for a laugh / Put yourself in my place / I cry alone / You're in love / I don't need anything / Funny / All in my mind.
LP: KENT 028

Brown, Milton

DANCE-O-RAMA (Brown, Milton & The Brownies).
Tracks: / St. Louis blues / Sweet Jenny Lee / Texas hambone blues / Brownie special / Right or wrong / Washington and Lee swing / Beautiful Texas / Little Betty Brown.
LP: WS 1001

EASY RIDIN' PAPA (Brown, Milton & The Brownies).
Tracks: / Down by the O-H-I-O / Easy ridin' papa / Sweet Jenny Lee / Ida sweet as apple cider / Little Betty Brown (Traditional.) / Black and white rag / Brownie special / Wabash blues / Hesitation blues / St. Louis Blues / I've got the blues for my mamy / Texas hambone blues / Beautiful Texas / Right or wrong.
LP: CR 30264

TAKING OFF (Brown, Milton & The Brownies).
Tracks: / Chinatown, my Chinatown / St. Louis blues / In El Rancho Grande / Taking off / If you can't get five take two / Fan it / Little Betty Brown / Some of these days / Sweet Georgia Brown / Texas hambone blues / Washington and Lee swing / My Mary / Goofus / Honky tonk blues / Sweet Jenny Lee / There'll be some changes made.
LP: STR 804

Brown, Miquel

CLOSE TO PERFECTION.
Tracks: / Close to reflection / Number one love / Come any hearts.
LP: SOHO LP 8
MC: SOHO TC 8

MANPOWER.
LP: SOHOLP 1

SYMPHONY OF LOVE.
Tracks: / Symphony of love / Dancin' with the lights down low / This is something new to me / Day that they got disco in Brazil / Do it / Something made of love.
LP: 238 352 5

Brown, Nappy

APPLES AND LEMONS.
Tracks: / Fishin' blues / Ain't no way / Get along / Lemon squeezin' daddy / Daddy / You showed me love / Lonely and blue / Don't be angry / Small red apples / Somebody's gonna jump outta the bushes.
LP: ICH 1056
MC: ICH 1056 MC

AW, SHUCKS.
Tracks: / You know it ain't right / Let love take care (of the rest) / Aw, shucks, baby / Still holding on / It's not what you do / Mind your own business / True love / Chickadee / Night time (live jam version).
LP: ICH 9006
MC: ICH 9006MC

BLACK TOP BLUES-A-RAMA, LIVE AT TIPITINA'S (Vol. 2).
MC: BT 1045C
LP: BT 1045

DON'T BE ANGRY.
LP: SJL 1149

I NONE GOT OVER (Brown, Nappy/The Roosters).
LP: RJ 205

SOMETHING'S GONNA JUMP OUT THE BUSHES.
LP: BT 1039
MC: BT 1039C

THAT MAN.
Tracks: / That man / Is it true is it true / Open up that door / Bye bye baby / Right time, the / Down in the alley / Baby cry cry cry baby / Coal miner / Didn't you know / I wonder / Two faced woman / Little by little / My baby / Long time / Baby I got news for you / What's come over you baby / I've had my fun.
LP: RB 100

TORE UP (Brown, Nappy with The Heartfixers).
LP: NTFL 2002
MC: AC 4792

Brown, Neville

SCIENTIST PRESENTS.
Tracks: / Right one, The / Where did she go / Friend indeed, A.
LP: VSLP 4014

Brown, O'Chi

O'CHI.
Tracks: / Whenever you need somebody / Fantasy / 100% pure pain / Caught in a life / Lady / Two hearts beating as one / Learning to live (without your love) / Call me up / Another broken heart.
LP: MAGL 5070
MC: ZCMAG 5070

Brown, Pete (Lyricist)

BEFORE SINGING LESSONS.
Tracks: / Week looked good on paper, The / Station song / High flying electric bird / Things may come and things may go (Full title: Things may come & things may go (but the Art School dance go) / High sorrow / Raining pins and needles / Station song platform two / Thousands on a raft / Broken magic / My last band / Aeroplane head woman / Lost tribe / Mass debate / Spend my nights in armour / Night at Joan & Ray's / She used to come and see me when I slept on the floor / Late Fiona / Change of heart / Old rocksinger, The / Barbed wire nightdress / Big city cowboy.
2LP: LIKD 7

PARTY IN THE RAIN (Brown, Peter & Ian Lynn).
Tracks: / Broken windscreen dance / White room / Big city cowboy / Walk into the sun / Comeback / Still have the love / I read the funky times / Party in the rain.
LP: INT LP 01

Brown, Pete (Sax

HARLEM JUMP AND SWING (see Jones, Jonah) (Brown, Pete Sextet & Jonah Jones Sextet).

Brown, Peter

STARGAZER.
Tracks: / Crank it up / It's alright / Stargazer / Got to get the show on the road / Leadmeon / West of the North Star / Love in our hearts / Penguin.
LP: KTR 83354

Brown, Randy

CHECK IT OUT.
Tracks: / Sweet to the bone / Heaven knows / If it's love that you want / Two fools / If I had to do it all over / Thank you for the happiness / Without you / Smoking room.
LP: MPS 8512

INTIMATELY.
Tracks: / You say it's all / I'm here / I was blessed / Day I found you, The / I thought of you today / You make me happy / It scares me so / Use it / I wanna baby you / Crazy about you baby.
LP: RRL 2007

MIDNIGHT DESIRE.
Tracks: / Love formula 69 / We ought to be doin' it / Things that I could do to you / You're so good / With your love / Without you I can't make it through the night / Next best thing to being there / Do you love me / Love be with you.
LP: CCL 2010

WELCOME TO MY ROOM.
LP: RRL 2005
LP: WAY LP 1

Brown, Ray

AFTER YOU'VE GONE (See under Ellis, Herb) (Brown, Ray & Herb Ellis).

AIN'T BUT A FEW OF US LEFT (see Jackson, Milt) (Brown, Ray/ Milt Jackson/ Oscar Peterson/ Grady Tate).

BAM BAM BAM (Brown, Ray Trio).
LP: CJ 375
MC: CJ 375 C

BIG THREE, THE (see Jackson, Milt) (Brown, Ray/ Milt Jackson/ Joe Pass).

BYE BYE BLACKBIRD.
Tracks: / Everything happens to me / Mean to me / Things ain't what they used to be / The rev. / I remember / I should care.
LP: K 28P 6303

DON'T FORGET THE BLUES (Brown, Ray All Stars).
Tracks: / Blues'd out / Jim / Night Train / If I Could Be With You (One Hour Tonight) / Rocks in my bed / You Don't Know Me / Jumpin' the blues / Don't forget the blues.
LP: CJ 293
MC: CJC 293

ELLA & RAY (see Fitzgerald, Ella) (Brown, Ray & Ella Fitzgerald).

GIANTS, THE (see Peterson, Oscar) (Brown, Ray/Oscar Peterson/Joe Pass).

HOT TRACKS (See under Ellis, Herb) (Brown, Ray Sextet & Herb Ellis).

I FEEL THAT YOUNG MAN'S RHYTHM.
Tracks: / Deep sea diver / Bye bye bye / Lollipop mama / Woman's a wonderful thing / Miss Fanny Brown / Rockin' at midnight / Please don't go / Riding high / I feel that young man's rhythm / Gamblin' man / Crazy crazy women / Don't let it rain / Big town / Cryin' and singin' the blues / Rockabye baby / It's a crying shame.
LP: KIX 26

IT DON'T MEAN A THING (See Jackson, Milt) (Brown, Ray & Milt Jackson).

MILT JACKSON AND RAY BROWN JAM (see Jackson, Milt) (Brown, Ray & Milt Jackson).

ONE O'CLOCK JUMP 1953 (Brown, Ray, Ben Webster & Oscar Peterson).
LP: LP VRV 1
MC: MC VRVC 1

POLL WINNERS, THE (See Kessel, Barney) (Brown, Ray/Barney Kessel).

RAY BROWN THREE, A (Brown, Ray, Monty Alexander & Sam Most).
Tracks: / I wish you love / I can't stop loving you / Jamento / Blue monk / Candy man / Too late now / You're my everything / There is no greater love.
LP: CJ 213
MC: CJC 213

RED HOT RAY BROWN TRIO, THE.
Tracks: / Have you met Miss Jones? / Meditation / Street of dreams / Lady be good / That's all / Love me tender / How could you do a thing like this to me? / Captain Bill.
LP: CJ 315
MC: CJC 315

SOFT SHOE (See under Ellis, Herb) (Brown, Ray & Herb Ellis).

SOLAR ENERGY.
Tracks: / Exactly like you / Cry me a river / Teach me tonight / Take the 'A' train / Mistreated but undefeated blues / That's all / Easy does it / Sweet Georgia Brown.
LP: CJ 268
MC: CJC 268

SUMMER WIND - LIVE AT THE LOA.
Tracks: / Summer wind / Real blues, The / Li'l darlin' / It don't mean a thing (Only on CD) / Mona Lisa (Only on CD) / Buhaina buhaina / Can't help lovin' dat man / Bluesology.
MC: CJ 426 C

THIS ONE'S FOR BLANTON (See under Ellington, Duke) (Brown, Ray & Duke Ellington).

TRIPLE TREAT (See under Alexander, Monty) (Brown, Ray/ Monty Alexander/ Herb Ellis).

TRIPLE TREAT II (See under Alexander, Monty) (Brown, Ray/ Monty Alexander/ Herb Ellis).

TRIPLE TREAT III (See under Alexander, Monty) (Brown, Ray/ Monty Alexander/ Herb Ellis).

Brown, Reuben

STARBUST.
LP: AD 5001

Brown, Reverend Pearly

IT'S A MEAN OLD WORLD TO TRY TO LIVE IN.
LP: . . . . ROUNDER 2011

Brown, Robert

PIBROCH PIPE-MAJOR ROBERT BROWN.
MC: . . . . TGMMC 502

Brown, Roy

BATTLE OF THE BLUES (See Harris, Wynonie) (Brown, Roy & Wynonie Harris).

BATTLE OF THE BLUES VOL. 4 (See under Vinson, Eddie) (Brown, Roy, Eddie Vinson, Wynonie Harris).

BLUESWAY SESSIONS, THE.
Tracks: / Hard times / Higher and higher / New Orleans woman / Driving me mad / Till the end of never / Soul lover / Man in trouble blues / Standing on broadway (watching the girls) / Woman trouble blues / Cryin' with the blues / Deep down in my soul.
LP: . . . . CRB 1199

BOOGIE AT MIDNIGHT.
Tracks: / Mighty mighty man / Boogie at midnight / Cadillac baby / Hard luck blues / Love don't love nobody / Too much lovin' ain't no good / Big town / Rockabye baby / Answer to big town / Ain't no rockin' no more / My gal from kokomo / Fannie Brown got married / Black diamond / Shake em up baby / Adorable one / Good looking and foxy too.
LP: . . . . CRB 1093
MC: . . . . TCCRB 1093

CHEAPEST PRICE IN TOWN.
LP: 91020

GOOD ROCKIN' TONIGHT.
Tracks: / Travellin blues / Let the four winds blow / Love for sale / Boogie woogie blues / Good rockin' tonight / Boogie at midnight / Love don't love nobody / Losing hand / Tin pan alley.
LP: . . . . MFLP 1025

GOOD ROCKING TONIGHT.
Tracks: / Good rockin' tonight / Long about midnight / Whose what is that / Fore day in the morning / Dreaming blues / Butcher Pete part 2 / Good man blues / Miss Fanny Brown returns / Brown angel / Grandpa stole my baby / Teenage jamboree / Black diamond / This is my last goodbye / Mighty, mighty man.
LP: . . . . KIX 6

HARD LUCK BLUES.
MCSET: . . . . GD 5036
LP: . . . . BID 8025

LAUGHING BUT CRYING.
Tracks: / Roy Brown boogie / Special lesson No.1 / Rainy weather blues / End of my journey / Fool in love, A / Butcher Pete part 1 / New Rebecca / Double crossing woman / Letter from home / Hurry hurry baby / Up jumped the devil / School bell rock / Money can't buy love / Lonesome lover / Laughing but crying.
LP: . . . . KIX 2

SATURDAY NITE.
Tracks: / Mr. Hound dog's in town / Caldonia's wedding day / Everyday / Saturday nite / I'm sticking with you / I love you I need you / I'm ready to play / Good looking and foxy too / Midnight lover man / Bootleggin' baby / Tick of the clock, The / We're goin' rockin' tonight / Ain't gonna do it / Slow down little Eva / Rinky dinky doo / Let the four winds blow.
LP: . . . . RB 104

Brown, Roy 'Chubby'

BEST OF ROY CHUBBY BROWN.
MC: . . . . RDC 1202

FOUR FACES OF CHUBBY BROWN, THE.
LP: . . . . RDLP 1205
MC: . . . . RDC 1205

FROM INSIDE THE HELMET.
MC: 849 094 4
LP: 849 094 1

Brown, Rula

LOVE HAS NO COLOUR.
Tracks: / Stop giving away your life / Extra special / Love has no colour / Hard day's night, A / Gimme some time / Bide up / Two occasions / Breakaway / Your loving / Let's start over / We don't make love anymore.
LP: . . . . BCR 10LP

MANY A TIME.
LP: . . . . BCR 001

Brown, Ruth

BLACK IS BROWN AND BROWN IS BEAUTIFUL.
Tracks: / Yesterday / Please send me someone to love / Looking back / Try me and see / Miss Browns blues / My prayer / Since I fell for you / This bitter earth.
LP: . . . . RHAP 10

BROWN, BLACK AND BEAUTIFUL.
Tracks: / I want to sleep with you / What color is blue? / Brown sugar / Lot's more of me leaving (less of me coming) / Ain't no piece of cake / Stop knocking / Old fashioned good time loving you / Sugar babe / My ol' bed / I love my man.
LP: . . . . SDE 4023
MC: . . . . SDEMC 4023

BROWN SUGAR.
Tracks: / Sugar baby / Stop knocking / Old fashioned good time / I love my man / My old bed / Brown sugar / I want to sleep with you / What colour is blue / Lot more of me leaving / Life ain't no piece of cake.
LP: . . . . TOP 136
MC: . . . . KTOP 136

HITS, THE.
Tracks: / 5-10-15 hours / Teardrops from my eyes / (Mama) he treats your daughter mean / Oh what a dream / Mambo baby / I'll wait for you / Daddy daddy / Wild wild young men / I wanna do more / So long / As long as I'm moving / It's love baby / I don't know / Lucky lips / I know / Mend your ways.
LP: . . . . OFF 6053

I'LL WAIT FOR YOU.
Tracks: / I'll wait for you / Standing on the corner / I gotta have you / Love has joined us together / I still love you / Mam oh mam / I want to be loved / New love, A / Look me up / I'll step aside / Mama, he treats your daughter mean / What I wouldn't give / I burned your letter / Honey boy / Sure 'nuff / Here he comes.
LP: . . . . OFF 6004

ROCKIN' WITH RUTH.
Tracks: / Teardrops from my eyes / Five, ten, fifteen hours / Daddy, daddy / Mama, he treats your daughter mean / Wild, wild young men / Love contest / Hello, little boy / Oh what a dream / Somebody touched me / Bye bye young men / I can see everybody's baby / As long as I'm moving / This little girl's gone rockin' / I can't hear a word you say / Papa daddy / Don't deceive me.
LP: . . . . CRB 1069
MC: . . . . TCCRB 1069

SUGAR BABE.
Tracks: / Sugar babe / Stock knocking / Old fashioned good time / I love my man / Old bed / Brown sugar / I want to sleep with you / What colour is blue / You're gonna see a lot more of me / Leaving / Life ain't no piece of cake.
LP: . . . . PTLS 1067

SWEET BABY OF MINE.
Tracks: / Love my baby / I'll come someday / It's all in the mind / Mend your ways / Ever since my baby's been gone / I want to do more / Am I making the same mistakes / Tears keep tumbling down, the / It's raining / R.B. blues / Without love / Rain is a bringdown / Sweet baby of mine / My heart is breaking for you / I would if I could.
LP: . . . . KIX 16

TAKIN' CARE OF BUSINESS.
Tracks: / Takin' care of business / 5-10-15 hours / I can see everybody's baby / On my way / God holds the power / Oh what a dream / Teardrops from my eyes / So long / Seven days.
LP: . . . . RJ 202

Brown, Sam

APRIL MOON.
Tracks: / April moon / With a little love / Mindworks / Kissing gate / Where you are / Contradictions / Once in your life / Hypnotised / As one / Eye for an eye / Trouble soul / S'envoler / Henry (Only on cassette and CD.) / Pride and joy (Only on CD.) / Now and forever (Only on CD.) / Way I love you, The (Only on CD.).
LP: . . . . AMA 9014
MC: . . . . AMC 9014

STOP.
Tracks: / Walking back to me / Your love is all / It makes me wonder / This feeling / Tea / Piece of my luck / Ball and chain / Wrap me up / I'll be in love / Merry go round / Sometimes / Can I get a witness / High as a kite / Nutbush city limits (Available on CD only).
MC: . . . . AMC 5195
LP: . . . . AMA 5195

Brown, Sandy

CLARINET OPENING.
LP: . . . . CLPS 1009

IN THE EVENING (Brown, Sandy/Brian Lemon Trio).
Tracks: / Ole Miss / Oxford Brown / In the evening / Ebun / Eight / Legal Pete / Badger, The / True love's heart / Lucky Schiz and the big dealer / Minstrel song / Louis.
LP: . . . . HEP 2017

MCJAZZ (Brown, Sandy Jazz Band).
LP: . . . . DM 6

SPLANKY.
Tracks: / Splanky / In the evening / Roll em Pete / I got it bad and that ain't good / Royal Garden blues.
LP: . . . . SPJ 901

THREE B'S, THE (See under Bilk, Acker for details) (Brown, Sandy & Acker Bilk).

Brown, Sawyer

SHAKIN'.
Tracks: / When your heart goes (woo, woo, woo) / Secretary's song, The / Heart don't fall now / Shakin' / Sharin' the moonshine / Betty's being bad / I believe / Lonely girl / That's a no no / Billy does your bulldog bite.
LP: . . . . EST 2001
MC: . . . . TCEST 2001

Brown, Scott-Wesley

KINGDOM OF LOVE.
LP: . . . . BIRD 172
MC: . . . . TC BIRD 172

LANGUAGE OF JESUS IS LOVE, THE.
LP: . . . . BIRD R 189
MC: . . . . BIRD C 189

SOMEBODY'S BROTHER.
LP: . . . . BIRD R 181

Brown, Sheree

STRAIGHT AHEAD.
Tracks: / You'll be dancing all night / Happiness flows / You are beautiful / Get down / I'm so bad / Passing thing / Never do you wrong / Everything you do / I wanna be by your side / It's a pleasure / Straight ahead.
LP: . . . . EST 12153

Brown, Shirley

FIRE AND ICE.
LP: . . . . MALP 7451
MC: . . . . MALC 7451

FOR THE REAL FEELING.
Tracks: / When, where, what time / Crowding in on my mind / After a night like this / Dirty feelin' / Hang on Louie / Eyes can't see / Move me, move me / Love starved.
LP: . . . . STX 3014

INTIMATE STORM.
Tracks: / Boyfriend / I don't play that / Looking for the real thing / This love / I'm up to no good / Love fever / This used to be your house / Leave the bridges standing.
LP: . . . . BRLP 507
MC: . . . . BRCA 507

WOMAN TO WOMAN.
Tracks: / Woman to woman / Yes sir brother / It ain't no fun / Long as you love me / Stay with me baby / I've got to go on without you / It's worth a whipping / So glad to have you / Passion / I can't give you up / I need you tonight / Between you and me.
LP: . . . . STAXL 5001
MC: . . . . STAXK 5001
LP: . . . . SXE 002
LP: . . . . SX 002

Brown, Sidney

BEST OF TWO CAJUN GREATS (see Leblanc, Shorty) (Brown, Sidney & Shorty Leblanc).
LP: 6067
MC: . . . . 6067 TC

Brown, Simon

AULD BROON FAE FOGGIE TOON.
MC: . . . . CJR 005

Brown, Steven

COMPOSES POUR LE THEATRE ET LE CINEMA.
LP: . . . . TWI 872

DAY IS GONE, THE.
LP: . . . . SUB 33016 21

DOUZIEME JOURNEE: LE VERBE, LA PARURE, L'AMOUR (See Law, Benjamin) (Brown, Steven & Benjamin Lew).

LA GRACE DU TOMBEUR.
LP: . . . . LTM 2304

MUSIC FOR SOLO PIANO.
Tracks: / Piano No 1 / Waltz / Ball, The / Hold me while I'm naked / Close little sixes / Fanfare / Egypt / Fall / Fantasie for clarinet and violin / RWF.
LP: . . . . TWI 110

NEBKA (see Lew, Benjamin) (Brown, Steven & Benjamin Lew).

SEARCHING FOR CONTACT.
LP: . . . . BIAS 055

ZOO STORY.
LP: . . . . MASO 33044
MC: . . . . MASO 33044C

Brown, T. Graham

BRILLIANT CONVERSATIONALIST.
Tracks: / R.F.D 30529 / Save that dress / Talkin' to it / Anything to lose / Power of love, The / Brilliant conversationalist / She couldn't love me anymore / Walk on water / Last resort, The / (Sittin' on) the dock of the bay.
LP: . . . . EST 2037
MC: . . . . TCEST 2037

BUMPER TO BUMPER.
Tracks: / Moonshadow road / You can't make her love you / I'm expecting miracles / If you could only see me now / I'm sending one up for you / I've been loving you too long / Eyes wide open / Bring a change / Blues of the month club / We tote the note / For real (CD only.).
MC: C4 91780

I TELL IT LIKE IT USED TO BE.
Tracks: / Say when / Don't go to strangers / Rock it, Billy / I tell it like it used to be / I wish that I could hurt that way again / Later train / You're trying to hard / Hell and high water / Don't make a liar out of me / Is there anything that I can do.
LP: . . . . EST 2026
MC: . . . . TCEST 2026

Brown, Ted

IN GOOD COMPANY (Brown, Ted Quintet).
LP: . . . . CRISS 1020

TED BROWN & JIMMY RAINEY (Brown, Ted/ Jimmy Rainey).
LP: . . . . XX 1020

Brown, Tom

NO LONGER.
LP: . . . . MJ 1500
MC: . . . . MJC 1500

NORFOLK DRIFTERMAN VOL.1.
MC: 60-133

TOM BROWN-VOLUME 2 (Brown, Tom/Bertha Brown).
MC: 60-134

Brown, U

JAM IT TONIGHT.
Tracks: / Jam it tonight / Take your time / Get it in the line / Tu-sheng-peng / Walk with Jah love / Me have to get you / Stop your bouncing / Get ready shank steady / Gimme the music / Jah is my father still.
LP: . . . . CSLP 8

RAVERS PARTY.
Tracks: / Raver's party / Me chat you rock / Out of hand / Archibella / Reggae non-stop / It's me / Love life / Party in full swing / Hugging & kissing / Dangerous machine.
LP: . . . . TRLS 211

TU SHENG PENG.
LP: . . . . VSLP 2002

Brown, Vicki

LADY OF TIME.
Tracks: / Just for you / To me you are so beautiful / Sunflower / Can't let go / Seasons of our love / Parlez moi d'amour / If I thought / Lady of time / Nearness of you / Lady dance / Warm and tender love / Is it mine (lullaby).
LP: . . . . PL 74522
MC: . . . . PK 74522

Brown, Walter

CONFESSIN' THE BLUES.
LP: . . . . AFF 66

Brown, Wini

MISS BROWN TO YOU (Brown, Wini with Milt Jackson).
LP: . . . . SJL 1163

Browne, Allan

ALLAN BROWNE BAND.
LP: . . . . S 1416

Browne, Duncan

MUSIC FROM THE TRAVELLING MAN (Browne, Duncan & Sebastian Graham Jones).
Tracks: / Max's theme / Steve's theme / Lament for Billie / Andrea's theme / Berceuse / Family, The / Winter / Chase, The / Day for night / Morag / Zoot / Travelling man / Old flames / End of the line.
LP: . . . . TOWLP 12
MC: . . . . ZCTOW 12

PLANET EARTH.
Tracks: / American heartbeat / Things to come / Wild places, The / Planet earth / Fauvette / Streets of fire / Child of change (restless) / She's just a fallen angel / Crash, The / Cancion De Cuna.
LP: . . . . CFRC 540
MC: . . . . MCFRC 540

STREETS OF FIRE.
Tracks: / Fauvette / American heartbeat / She's just a fallen angel / Streets of fire / Nina Morena / Things to come / Cancion de Cuna.

LP: . . . . LOGO 1016

Browne, George MacKay

ORCADIAN POET, THE.
MC: 4CC 46
LP: . . . . CCA 6

Browne, Jackson

FOR EVERYMAN.
Tracks: / Take it easy / Our Lady of the Well / Colours of the sun / I thought I was a child / These days / Redneck friend / Times you come, The / Ready or not / Sing my songs to me / For everyman.
LP: . . . . K 43003
MC: K4 43003

HOLD OUT.
Tracks: / Disco apocalypse / Hold on, hold out / Of missing persons / Call it a loan / That girl could sing / Hold out / Boulevard.
LP: . . . . K 52226
MC: K4 52226

JACKSON BROWNE.
Tracks: / Jamaica say you will / Child in these hills, A / Song for Adam / Doctor my eyes / From silver lake / Something fine / Under the falling sky / Looking into you / Rock me on the water / My opening farewell.
LP: . . . . K 53022
MC: K4 53022

JACKSON BROWNE/RUNNING ON EMPTY.
Tracks: / Jamaica say you will / Child in these hills, A / Song for Adam / Doctor my eyes / From Silver Lake / Something fine / Under the falling sky / Looking into you / Rock me on the water / My opening farewell / Running on empty / Road, The / Rosie / You love the thunder / Cocaine / Shaky town / Love needs a heart / Nothing but time / Load-out, The / Stay.
MCSET: 960 277-4

LATE FOR THE SKY.
Tracks: / Late for the sky / Fountain of sorrow / Farther on / Late show, The / Road and the sky, The / For a dancer / Walking slow / Before the deluge.
LP: . . . . K 43007
MC: K4 43007

LAWYERS IN LOVE.
Tracks: / For a rocker / Lawyers in love / On the day / Cut it away / Downtown / Tender is the night / Knock on any door / Say it isn't true.
LP: K960 268 1
MC: 960 268-4

LIVES IN THE BALANCE.
Tracks: / For America / Soldier of plenty / In the shape of a heart / Candy / Lawless Avenue / Lives in the balance / Till I go down / Black and white.
LP: . . . . EKT 31
MC: . . . . EKT 31C

PRETENDER, THE.
Tracks: / Fuse, The / Your bright baby blues / Linda Paloma / Here come those tears again / Only child / Daddy's time / Sleep's dark and silent gate / Pretender.
LP: . . . . K 53048
MC: K4 53048

PRETENDER/LATE FOR THE SKY.
MC: K4 62041

RUNNING ON EMPTY.
Tracks: / Running on empty / Road, The / Rosie / You love the thunder / Cocaine / Shaky town / Love needs a heart / Nothing but time / Load-out, The / Stay.
LP: . . . . K 53070
MC: K4 53070

WORLD IN MOTION.
Tracks: / World in motion / Enough of the night / Chasing you into the night / How long / Anything can happen / When the stone begins to turn / Word justice, The / My personal revenge / I am a patriot / Lights and virtues.
LP: . . . . EKT 50
MC: . . . . EKT 50C

YOU'RE A FRIEND OF MINE (see Clemons, Clarence).

Browne, Sam

I TRAVEL ALONE.
LP: . . . . JOYD 291

Browne, Tom

BEST OF TOM BROWNE, THE.
Tracks: / Funkin' for Jamaica / Fungi mama / Mr. Business / Bye gones / Charisma / Thighs high (grip your hips and move) / Rockin' radio / Come for a ride / Brighter tomorrow / Secret fantasy.
MC: 410962

LOVE APPROACH.
Tracks: / Funkin' for Jamaica / Her silent smile / Forever more / Dreams of lovin' you / Nocturne / Martha / Moon rise / Weak in the knees.
LP: . . . . GRP 5008

MAGIC.
Tracks: / Let's dance / Magic / I know / Midnight interlude / God bless the child / Night wind / Thighs high (grip your hips and move) / Making plans.
LP: . . . . GRP 5503

ROCKIN' RADIO.
Tracks: / Rockin' radio / Never my love / Feel like makin' love / Cruisin' / Turn it up (come on y'all) / Angeline / Brighter tomorrow / Mr. Business.
LP: 205151
MC: 405151

TOMMY GUN.
LP: 206495
MC: 406495

YOURS TRULY.
Tracks: / Fungii mama / Bygonnes / Charisma / Can't give it away / Lazy bird / Naima / Come for a ride / My latin sky / Message, A: pride and pity.
LP: . . . . GRP 5507

Browning, Bill

BILL BROWNING.
LP: . . . . RR 2019

Browning, Elizabeth

SONNETS FROM THE PORTUGUESE (see under Sonnets from the...) (Various artists).

Browning, Robert

MY LAST DUCHESS & OTHER POEMS (see under My Last Duchess...) (Mason, James (nar)).

POETRY OF BROWNING, THE (Mason, James (nar)).
MC: 1048

Brownlee, Archie

YOU DONE WHAT THE DOCTOR COULDN'T DO.
Tracks: / Jesus gave me water / Amazing grace / Must be a god somewhere / You done what the doctor couldn't do / Take your burdens to Jesus / Have you talked to the man upstairs.
LP: . . . . RF 1402

Brown/Orpheus

CHAOCHAMBER, THE.
MC: . . . . CXC 002

Browns

20 OF THE BEST: BROWNS.
Tracks: / I take the chance / I heard the bluebirds sing / Would you care / Beyond the shadow of a doubt / Three bells, The / Scarlet ribbons / Teen ex / Old lamplighter / Ground hog / Blue Christmas / Send me the pillow that you dream on / Oh no / Then I'll stop loving you / Every body's darlin' plus mine / Meadow green / I'd just be fool enough / Coming back to you / I hear it now / Big daddy / I will bring you water.
LP: . . . . NL 89524
MC: . . . . NK 89524

LOOKING BACK TO SEE.
Tracks: / Lookin' back to see / Rio De Janeiro / Draggin' main street / You thought, I thought / Itsy witsy bitsy me / Your love is as wild as the west wind / Grass is green, The / Lookin' on / Jungle magic / Set the dawgs on 'em' ((Previously unissued track)) / I'm your man, I'm your gal (previously unissued track.) / Why am I falling / Do memories haunt me / It's love, I guess (Previously un-issued track) / Here today and gone tomorrow / Cool green.
LP: . . . . BFX 15190

ROCKIN' ROLLIN' BROWNS.
Tracks: / Three bells, The / Teen-ex / Blue bells ring / This time I would know / Heaven fell last night / Beyond a shadow / Margo (The ninth of May) (Previously unissued.) / You're so much apart of me / Bye bye love (Previously unissued.) / Only one way to love you / Buttons and bows / Brighten the corner where you are / Dream on (she'll break your heart) / Oh no / Tobacco road (Previously unissued.).
LP: . . . . BFX 15104

Brown's Ferry Four

16 GREATEST HITS: BROWN'S FERRY FOUR.
LP: . . . . SLP 3017
MC: . . . . GT 53017

Brownsville

AIR SPECIAL.
Tracks: / Taste of your love / Waitin' for the weekend / Who do you love / Tears of a fool / Cooda crawlin' / Airmail special / Never say die / Fever / Love stealer / Let it roll / Down the road apiece.
LP: . . . . EPC 83161

Brownsville Banned

IN ANY CASE.
Tracks: / Bad again / Come back, Corinna / I'm in the mood for love / Banjoreno / Emeline / Hot patella swing / Juggae, juggae / Dust / Longing blues / Cabaret time / Norman Mills live at the Conogo-Hogolo / Kick out your can.
LP: . . . . SFA 049

THAT'S SHOEBIZ.
Tracks: / Charles Lennon / Doc Roberts / Van blues / Mrs. Tas Pronk musical sink / Hang fire / Pick up / Julie the schooly / Getting older / Norman Mills at the Halltappers and Shouters / Six feet tall / Gordon.
LP: . . . . SFA 079

Brozman, Bob

DEVIL'S SLIDE.
MC: . . . . ROUNDER 3112C
LP: . . . . ROUNDER 3112

HELLO CENTRAL-GIVE ME DR. JAZZ (Brozman, Bob with George Winston).
LP: . . . . ROUNDER 3086
MC: . . . . ROUNDER 3086C

Brubeck, Dave

25TH ANNIVERSARY REUNION CONCERT.
Tracks: / St. Louis blues / Three to get ready / African times suite / 1st movement (African theme) / 2nd movement (African breeze) / 3rd movement (African dance) / Salute to Stephen Foster / Take five / Don't worry 'bout me.
LP: . . . . AMLJ 714

1975 THE DUETS (Brubeck, Dave/Paul Desmond).
LP: . . . . AMLJ 703

1954-1972.
LP: . . . . CBS 54490

BLUE RONDO (Brubeck, Dave Quartet).
Tracks: / How does your garden grow? / Festival hall / Easy as you go / Blue rondo a la turk / Dizzy's dream / I see, Satie / Swing bells / Strange meadowlark / Elana Joy.
LP: . . . . CJ 317
MC: . . . . CJC 317

COLLECTION: DAVE BRUBECK.
Tracks: / Take five / It's a raggy waltz / Castillian drums / St. Louis blues / Blue rondo a la turk / Tea for two / Blue moon / Let's fall in love / Some day my prince will come / Forty days / Summer song / For all we know.
MC: . . . . DVMC 2036

DAVE BRUBECK IN CONCERT.
Tracks: / Take five / Blue rondo a la turk / Mr. Broadway / Three to get ready / Unsquare dance / Its a raggy waltz / Rotterdam blues.
LP: . . . . K 20092
MC: K4 20092

DAVE BRUBECK OCTET, THE (Brubeck, Dave Octet).
LP: . . . . OJC 101

DAVE BRUBECK & PAUL DESMOND (Brubeck, Dave/Paul Desmond).
LP: . . . . LPJT 3

DAVE BRUBECK QUARTET With Paul Desmond (Brubeck, Dave Quartet).
Tracks: / Maria / I feel pretty / Somewhere / Tonight / Quiet girl / Dialogues for jazz combo and orchestra.
LP: 61995

DAVE BRUBECK/PAUL DESMOND.
Tracks: / Jeepers creepers / On a little street in Singapore / Trolley song (rehearsal) / Trolley song / I may be wrong / Blue moon / My heart stood still / Let's fall in love / You go to my head / Crazy girl / Give a little whistle / Over the rainbow / Crazy Chris / Lady be good / Tea for two / This can't be love.
2LP: . . . . OJCD 501

DAVE DIGS DISNEY (Brubeck, Dave Quartet).
Tracks: / Alice in Wonderland / Give a little whistle / Heigh-ho / When you wish upon a star / Some day my prince will come / One song.
LP: . . . . CBS 21060

ESSENTIAL, THE.
MC: 4671484

FOR IOLA (Brubeck, Dave Quartet).
Tracks: / Polly / I hear a rhapsody / Thank you / Big bad Basie / For Iola / Summer song / Pange lingua march.
LP: . . . . CJ 259
MC: . . . . CJC 259

GONE WITH THE WIND.
Tracks: / Swanee river / Lonesome road / Georgia on my mind / Camptown races / Sort'nin' bread / Basin Street blues / Ol' man river / Gone with the wind.
LP: 4509841
MC: 4509844

GREAT CONCERTS, THE.
Tracks: / Pennies from Heaven / Blue rondo a la turk / Take the 'A' train / Wonderful Copenhagen / Tangerine / For all we know / Take five / Real ambassador, The / Like someone in love.
LP: 4624031
MC: 4624034

GREATEST HITS: DAVE BRUBECK.
Tracks: / Take five / I'm in a dancing mood / In your own sweet way / Camptown races / Duke, The / It's a raggy waltz / Bossa nova USA / Trolley song, The / Unsquare dance / Blue rondo a la turk / Mr. Broadway, Theme from.
LP: . . . . CBS 32046
MC: 40 32046

JAZZ SUMMET (See under Getz, Stan) (Brubeck, Dave/Stan Getz).

LA FIESTA DE LA POSADA.
LP: . . . . CBS 73903

LIVE AT MONTREUX: DAVE BRUBECK.
Tracks: / It's a raggy waltz / Brandenburg gate / In your own sweet way / It could happen to you / God's love (made invisible) / Summer love.
LP: . . . . AFF 201

LIVE FROM BASIN STREET (Brubeck, Dave Quartet).
LP: . . . . EB 402

MOSCOW NIGHT.
MC: . . . . CJ 353 C
LP: . . . . CJ 353

MUSIC FROM WEST SIDE STORY..... (Brubeck, Dave with New York Philharmonic).
Tracks: / Maria / I feel pretty / Somewhere / Quiet girl, A / Tonight / Allegro I / Andante-ballad II / Adagio-ballad III / Allegro-blues IV.
LP: . . . . CBS 32734
MC: 40 32734

NEAR-MYTH.
LP: . . . . OJC 236

NEWPORT '58 Brubeck plays Ellington.
Tracks: / Things ain't what they used to be / Jump for joy / Perdido / Liberian suite dance No. 3 / Duke, The / Flamingo / C Jam blues.
LP: 4503171
MC: 4503174

PAPER MOON.
Tracks: / Music maestro please / I hear a rhapsody / Symphony / I thought about you / It's only a paper moon / Long ago and far away / St. Louis blues.
LP: . . . . CJ 178
MC: . . . . CJC 178

PHONOGRAPHIC MEMORIES.
MC: . . . . DVREMC 58

PLACE IN TIME, A (Brubeck, Dave Quartet).
Tracks: / Audrey / Jeepers creepers / Pennies from Heaven / Why do I love you / Stompin' for Milli / Keepin' out of mischief now / Fine romance, A / Brother can you spare a dime.
LP: . . . . BVL 012
LP: . . . . CBS 61900

PLAYS WEST SIDE STORY/PLAYS MY FAIR LADY (Brubeck, Dave/ Andre Previn).
Tracks: / Maria / I feel pretty / Somewhere / Tonight / On the street where you live / With a little bit of luck / Wouldn't it be lovely / Get me to the church on time.
LP: . . . . CBS 21065
MC: 40 21065

QUARTET, THE.
Tracks: / Castillian drums / Three to get ready / St. Louis Blues / Forty days / Summer song / Some day my prince will come / Brandenburg Gate / In your own sweet way.
MC: . . . . MC 7681

REFLECTIONS (Brubeck, Dave Quartet).
Tracks: / Reflections of you / Misty morning, A / I'd walk a country mile / My one bad habit / Blues for Newport / We will remember Paul / Michael,my second son / Blue Lake Tahoe.
LP: . . . . CJ 299
MC: . . . . CJC 299

SEE HOW IT FEELS (Brubeck, Dave Quartet).
LP: . . . . BKH 51401

SHISH KEBAB.
Tracks: / Shish kebab / Fairy day / Don't worry 'bout me / Lover come back to me / Royal Garden blues / Love walked in / How high the moon.
LP: . . . . SM 3804

SOUTHERN SCENE (Brubeck, Dave with Quartet/Trio/Duo).
LP: . . . . 20 AP 1433

'SUPERB' CANADIAN CONCERT OF.., THE (Brubeck, Dave/Paul Desmond).
LP: . . . . CA 1500

TAKE FIVE.
Tracks: / Take five / Bossa nova USA / Unsquare dance / Some day my prince will come / I'm in a dancing mood / It's a raggy waltz / Blue rondo a la turk / Kathy's waltz / My favourite things / Castillian drums / Duke, The / Trolley song, The.
LP: . . . . CBS 32084
MC: 40 32084
LP: . . . . CBS 31769

TAKE FIVE (DOUBLE CASSETTE).
MCSET: . . . . DTO 10205

TAKE ... THE GREATEST HITS.
Tracks: / Take five / Camptown races / Trolley song / Unsquare dance / Blue rondo a la turk / Pennies from heaven / For all we know / Like someone in love / Strange meadow lark / Maria / Somewhere / What is this thing called love / Most beautiful girl in the world, The / Night and day.
MC: . . . . ELITE 009 MC

TIME FURTHER OUT (Brubeck, Dave Quartet).
Tracks: / It's a raggy waltz / Bluesette / Charles Matthew hallelujah / Far more blues / Far more drums / Maori blues / Unsquare dance / Bru's boogie woogie / Blue shadows in the street.
LP: . . . . TFL 5161

TIME OUT.
Tracks: / Blue rondo a la turk / Strange meadowlark / Take five / Three to get ready / Kathy's waltz / Everybody's jumpin' / Pick up sticks.
LP: 4606111
MC: 4606114
LP: . . . . TFL 5085

TIME OUT / TIME FURTHER OUT.
Tracks: / Blue rondo a la turk / Strange meadowlark / Take five / Three to get ready / Kathy's waltz / Everybody's jumpin' / Pick up sticks / It's a raggy waltz / Bluesette / Charles Matthew hallelujah / Far more blues / Far more drums / Maori blues / Unsquare dance / Bru's boogie woogie / Blue shadows in the street.
2LP: . . . . CBS 22120
MCSET: 40 22120

WE'RE ALL TOGETHER AGAIN FOR THE FIRST TIME (Brubeck, Dave & Friends).
Tracks: / Truth / Unfinished woman / Koto song / Take five / Rotterdam blues / Sweet Georgia Brown.
LP: . . . . K 40489

WEST SIDE STORY.
LP: 4504101
MC: 4504104

Bruce, Ed

BEST OF ED BRUCE.
LP: . . . . MCF 3142

ED BRUCE.
Tracks: / Last thing she said, The / Last cowboy song, The / Red doggin' again / Love ain't something I can do alone / Girls, women and ladies / Neon fool / Blue umbrella / I still wish / Outlaw & the stranger, The.
LP: . . . . IMCA 27068

GREATEST HITS: ED BRUCE.
Tracks: / Last cowboy song, The / Girls, women, and ladies / Everything's a waltz (When you fall in love) / You're the best break this old heart ever had / Love's found you and me / Ever, never lovin' you / My first taste of Texas / You're not leavin' here tonight / If it was easy / After all.
LP: . . . . IMCA 5577

I WRITE IT DOWN.
Tracks: / My first taste of Texas / Ever, never lovin' you / Somebody's crying / One more shot of "Old back home again" / Songwriter, The (I write it down) / Brett Maverick / Memories can't stand to be alone / Your jukebox could use a few more sad songs / Babe in arms / Mamas don't let your babies grow up to be cowboys.
LP: . . . . IMCA 893
LP: . . . . MCF 3169
MC: . . . . MCFC 3169

LAST TRAIN TO CLARKESVILLE.
Tracks: / I know better / Why can't I come home / Walker's woods / Ninety seven more to go / I could just go home / By route of New Orleans / Shadows of her mind / Lonesome is me / I'm getting better / Her sweet love and the baby / I'll take you away / Last train to Clarksville / I'd best be leaving you / Tiny golden locket / Ballad of the drummer boy, The / Something else to mess your mind / Puzzles / Memphis morning / Painted girls and wine / Blue bayou.
LP: . . . . INTS 5199
MC: . . . . INTK 5199

NIGHT THINGS.
Tracks: / Nights / You are a rose / Fools for each other / Down the hall / Quietly / 15 to 43 / Fishin' in the dark / Somebody's somebody new / Memphis roots.
LP: . . . . PL 85808

ONE TO ONE.
Tracks: / When you fall in love / Evil angel / You're the best break this old heart ever had / It just makes me want you more / Hundred dollar lady / Love's found you and me / I take the chance / No regrets / Thirty nine and holding / Easy temptations.
LP: . . . . IMCA 27063

ROCK BOPPIN' BABY.
Tracks: / Rock boppin' baby / More than yesterday / Eight wheel (Previously unissued track) / Ballad of Ringo ((Previously un-issued track)) / King of fools (Previously un-issued track) / Just being with you (Previously un-issued track) / Alone with a broken heart (Previously un-issued track) / You come to me (Previously un-issued track) / Sweet woman / Doll baby (previously un-issued track) / Flight 303 / Sun gold.
LP: . . . . BFX 15194

TELL 'EM I'VE GONE CRAZY.
Tracks: / If I just knew what she said / She never could dance / It's all in your mind / Straight shooter / Devil inside, The / Tell 'em I've gone crazy / Old time's sake / Birds of paradise / Someone who would care / If she just helps me get over you.
LP: . . . . IMCA 5511

YOU'RE NOT LEAVIN' HERE TONIGHT.
Tracks: / You're not leavin' here tonight / It would take a fool / In Mexico / If it was easy / It's the lovers (who give love a bad name) / After all / Lucky arms / You've got her eyes / I think I'm in love / I'll be there to catch you.
LP: . . . . IMCA 5416
LP: . . . . MCF 3172
MC: . . . . MCFC 3172

Bruce, Fraser

FAREWELL TAE TARWATHIE.
LP: . . . . NEVLP 105

MRS. BRUCE'S BOYS VOL.1 (Bruce, Fraser & Ian).
Tracks: / Ryebuck shearers / Leaving the Dales / King's shilling, The / Rise up Jack / Ring a rosie / Cape Ann / Walking song, The / New railroad, The / Isle of Haut / Down where the drunkards roll / Gadie rins, The.
LP: . . . . LOCLP 1007
MC: . . . . ZCLOC 1007

MRS. BRUCE'S BOYS VOL.2 (Bruce, Fraser & Ian).
Tracks: / Idiot, The / Western boat / Man you don't meet every day, A / Catch me if you can / Tatties and herring / Edinburgh / Mrs. MacDonald's lament / Waiting for the lark / Deportees / Bonnie Susie Clelland / Wedding, The / Tak' a dram.
LP: . . . . LOCLP 1028
MC: . . . . ZCLOC 1028

SHAMROCK AND HEATHER.
LP: . . . . NEVLP 008

VEIL OF THE AGES (Bruce, Fraser & Ian).
Tracks: / Nostradamus / John O'Dreams / I don't belong to Glasgow / Can ye saw cushions / Crey funnel line / Hagged man, The / Sally Wheatley / Roll on the day / Roseville fair / Stumpy / Farewell to gold / Aye's the boy.
LP: . . . . LOCLP 1018
MC: . . . . ZCLOC 1018

Bruce, Ian

BLODWEN'S DREAM.
Tracks: / John / Factory life / Eldorado / Classical music / Ghost of the chair / Farewell deep blue / No noise / This peaceful evening / I can play you anything / Black fog / Blodwen's dream.
MC: . . . . FE 076 C

GOSPEL ACCORDION (Bruce, Ian/ May).
Tracks: / Amazing grace / Since Jesus came into my heart / Sweet by and by / This is the day / Wide, wide as the ocean / Running over / Whosoever will / Still sweeter everyday / Bringing in the sheaves / For God so loved the world / Somewhere beyond the blues / Jesus loves even me / Isn't he wonderful / What a friend we have in Jesus / Give me oil in my lamp / Thou art worthy / Hallelujah / There's something about that name / Old rugged cross, The / It is no secret / Whispering hope / This world is not my home / Thank you, Lord / All that thrills my soul / Sing when the day is bright / Christ is the answer / Windows of heaven are open, The.
LP: . . . . SHARON 316

TOO FAR FROM SHE.
LP: . . . . LUMS 0101

Bruce, Jack

AUTOMATIC.
Tracks: / Make love (Part II) / Uptown breakdown / Travelling child / New World / E. Boogie / Green and blue / Swarm / Encore / Automatic pilot.
LP: . . . . PTLS 1082
MC: . . . . PTLC 1082

GREATEST HITS: JACK BRUCE.
2LP: 2658 137
MCSET: 3524 218

HOW'S TRICKS (Bruce, Jack Band).
LP: 2394 180

I'VE ALWAYS WANTED TO DO THIS.
Tracks: / Hit and run / Running back / Facelift 318 / In this way / Mickey the fiddler / Dancing on air / Wind and the sea / Living without you / Out to lunch / Bird alone.
MC: 40 84672
LP: . . . . EPC 84672

QUESTION OF TIME, A.
Tracks: / Life on earth / Make love / No surrender / Flying / Hey now princess / Blues you can't lose / Obsession / Kwela / Let me be / Only playing games / Question of time, A.
LP: 4656921
MC: 4656924

SONGS FOR A TAILOR.
Tracks: / Never tell your mother / She's out of tune / Theme of an imaginary western / Tickets to water falls / Weird of Hermiston / Rope ladder to the moon / Ministry of bag, The / He the Richmond / Boston ball game, 1967 / To Isengard / Clearout, The.
LP: 2459 360
LP: 583-058

TRUCE (Bruce, Jack & Robin Trower).
Tracks: / Gonna shut you down / Gone too far / Thin ice / Last train to the stars / Take good care of yourself / Falling in love / Fat gut / Shadows touching / Little boy lost.
LP: . . . . CHR 1352
MC: . . . . ZCHR 1352

WILLPOWER.
LP: 837 806-1
MC: 837 806-4

Bruce, Lenny

CARNEGIE HALL.
Tracks: / Introduction- Don Friedman / Miracle on 57th street / Arlines, The / Sound / Kidnap, The / Point of view / Ku Klux Klan / What's it mean, A / Kennedy acceptance speech / On humour / Nightclubs / Dykes and faggots / Homosexuality / Girl ringing / Flag and communism, The / Dear Abbey / Las Vegas tits and ass / Clap, The / Christ and Moses / Equality / Interval revenue / Pills / Burlesque house / Judge Saperstein decision / On contemporaries / Shelley Berman / Operation, The / Joke, The / End, The.
LPS: . . . . UAT 9800

LENNY BRUCE IN CONCERT.
Tracks: / Introduction / Miracle on 57th street / Sound / Trip, The / Kidnap, The / Homosexuality / Flag, The / Communism / Christ and Moses.
LP: . . . . VERB 5

SICK HUMOUR OF LENNY BRUCE.
Tracks: / Non skeddo flies again / Kid in the well / Adolph Hitler and MCA / Ike, Sherm and Nick / Psychopathia sexualis / Religions Inc..
LP: . . . . VERB 2

UNEXPURGATED..THE VERY BEST OF...
Tracks: / Airplane glue / How to relax your coloured friends at parties / Father Flotski's triumph / Commercials / Religions inc. / Psychopathia sexualis / White collar drunks / Three message movies (Naracotics, truth, tolerence) / Esther Costello story / Marriage, divorce and motels / Non skeddo flies again.
LP: . . . . FASLP 5001
MC: . . . . FASK 5001

Bruce, Marjorie

ORGAN WORKS OF JEAN LANGLAIS.
Tracks: / Te Deum / La nativite / Chant de joie / Cantique / Canzona / Deux Noels / Evocation / Offering / Salve Regina.
LP: . . . . ACA 548

Bruce, Tommy

GREATEST HITS: TOMMY BRUCE.
MC: . . . . ASK 787

Bruce, Vin

CAJUN COUNTRY.
LP: 6015

GREATEST HITS: VIN BRUCE.
LP: 6006
MC: . . . . 6006 TC

VIN BRUCE SINGS COUNTRY.
LP: 6016

VIN BRUCE SINGS JOLE BLON.
LP: 6002
MC: . . . . 6002 TC

Bruch (Composer)

KOL NIDREI, OP 47 (See under Dvorak (composer) - cello concerto) (Various artists).

Brucken, Claudia

LOVE AND A MILLION OTHER THINGS.
LP: . . . . ILPS 9971
LP: 846 933 1
MC: . . . . ICT 9971
MC: 846 933 4

Bruckner, Anita (aut)

FRIEND FROM ENGLAND, A (see under Friend from England) (Lunghi, Cherie (nar)).

Bruckner (Composer)

SYMPHONY NO.8 (BRUCKNER) (see under Vienna Philharmonic) (Unknown).

Bruford, Bill

BRUFORD TAPES, THE.
LP: . . . . BRUBOOT 28
LP: . . . . EGED 6

DIG (Bruford's, Bill Earthworks).
Tracks: / Stromboli kicks / Gentle persuasion / Downtown / Pilgrims' way / Dancing on Fifth Street / Stone's throw, A / Libreville / Corroboree.
LP: . . . . EGED 60
MC: . . . . EGEDC 60

EARTHWORKS.
Tracks: / Thud / Making a song and dance / Up North / Pressure / My heart declares a holiday / Emotional shirt / It needn't end in tears / Shepherd is eternal, The / Bridge Of Inhibition.
LP: . . . . EGED 48
MC: . . . . EGEDC 48

FEELS GOOD TO ME.
Tracks: / Beelzebub / Back to the beginning / Seems like a lifetime ago / Sample and hold / Feels good to me / Either end of August / If you can't stand the heat / Springtime in Siberia / Adios la pasade.
LP: 2302 075
LP: . . . . EGLP 33

FLAGS (see under Moraz, Patrick) (Bruford, Bill & Patrick Moraz).

GRADUALLY GOING TORNADO.
LP: . . . . EGLP 44

MASTER STROKES 1978-85.
Tracks: / Hell's bells / Gothic 17 / Travels with myself / And someone else / Fainting in coils / Beelzebub / One of a kind-part one / One of a kind-part two / Drum also waltzes, The / Joe Frazier / Sahara of snow, The (part two) / Palewell park (CD & cassette only) / If you can't stand the heat... (CD & cassette only) / Five G (CD & cassette only) / Living space (CD & cassette) / Split seconds (CD & cassette only).
LP: . . . . EGLP 67
MC: . . . . EGMC 67

MUSIC FOR DRUMS AND PIANO (see under Moraz, Patrick) (Bruford, Bill & Patrick Moraz).

ONE OF A KIND.
Tracks: / Hell's bells / One of a kind / Travels with myself and someone else / Painting in coils / Five G / Abingdon Chasp / Forever until Sunday / Sahara of snow.
LP: . . . . POLD 5020
LP: . . . . EGLP 40

Bruh, Emil

VIRTUOSO KLEZMER VIOLINIST.
MC: . . . . GVMMC 102

Bruna, Dick (nar)

MIFFY AND OTHER STORIES (see under Miffy & Other... (bk).

Brunes, Cliff

WATCH OUT FOR CLIFF.
LP: . . . . LP 5002

Brunies, Albert

NEW ORLEANS SHUFFLE 1925-28 (Brunies, Albert & Halfway House Orchestra).
LP: . . . . VLP 62

Bruninghaus, Ranier

CONTINUUM.
LP: . . . . ECM 1266

FREIGEWEHT (BLOWN FREE).
LP: . . . . ECM 1187

Brunious, Wendell

IN THE TRADITION.
LP: . . . . GHB 194

Brunis, George

FRIARS INN REVISITED.
LP: . . . . DS 215

GEORGE BRUNIS AND THE RHYTHM KINGS (Brunis, George and Rhythm Kings).
LP: J 12

KING OF TAILGATE TROMBONE.
LP: 6.25896

TIN ROOF BLUES (Commodore Classics) (Brunis, George & Wild Bill Davison).
Tracks: / Royal Garden blues / Royal Garden blues (part 2) (Alternate choice-previously un-issued) / Ugly child (Based on 'You're some pretty doll'.) / Ugly child (2) (Based on 'You're some pretty doll'.) / Tin roof blues / Tin roof blues(2) (Alternate choice previously un-issued) / That da da strain / That da da strain (2) (Alternate choice previously un-issued) / High society / High society (2) (Alternate choice previously un-issued) / Wrap your troubles in dreams / Wrap your troubles in dreams (2) (Alternate choice previously un-issued) / I'm coming Virginia / I'm coming Virginia(2) (Alternate choice previously un-issued) / Wabash blues / Wabash blues(2) (Alternate choice previously un-issued).
LP: AG6 24094

Brunis, Merritt

MERRITT BRUNIS & HIS ORCH. 1924-26 (Brunis, Merritt & His Friars Inn Orchestra).
LP: FJ 124

Brunning Sunflower

BULLEN STREET BLUES.
LP: AP 039

I WISH YOU WOULD.
LP: AP 035

TRACKSIDE BLUES.
LP: AP 031

Bruno, Frank

URPNEY SONG, THE (See under Connolly, Billy) (Connolly, Billy/Bruno, Frank/Osbourne, Ozzy/Batt, Mike).

Brunskill, Bill

30 YEARS ON (Brunskill, Bill Jazzmen).
Tracks: / Marie / Kitchen man / Ampola / Coney Island / Washboard / Down in Honky Tonk Town / If you're a viper / Mama's gone goodbye.
LP: LC 34

Brunson, Tyrone

FRESH.
Tracks: / Fresh / At the show / Head games / In love with you / Serve go go / Jet City / Don't wanna stop the lovin'.
LP: EPC 25907

LOVE TRIANGLE.
Tracks: / Love triangle / Tell me why / Free bee / Method, The / Lot of pop, A / Tender touch / Knucklehead syndrome / Space boy.
LP: MCF 3378
MC: MCFC 3378

STICKY SITUATION.
Tracks: / Sticky situation / I need love / Go for it / Don't you want it / Smurf, The / Hot line / New wave disco punk funk rock.
LP: EPC 25291
MC: 40 25291

Brush Arbor

HERO.
Tracks: / Only for the love of the Lord / Come back home / Witness / All I want to be / Hero / Hey there stranger / Running / Trust in the Lord / God is good / St. Peter / Rescue me.
LP: MYR 1116
MC: MC 1116

Brutal Obscenity

DREAM OUTLOUD.
LP: CMFT 8

IT'S BECAUSE OF THE BIRDS AND THE FLOWERS.
Tracks: / Death is a damn good solution / Straight and stoned / Mom or dad? / 1,2,3 / God is just a fairy tale / No more feelings left / Overtaking, The / It's because of the birds and the flowers / Emotion suicide / It's cruel (part 2) / Useless immortality / Defensor minor / Hangover D.D.D..
LP: CMFT 2

SORRY BOYS AND GIRLS..
LP: CCG 001

Brute Force

BRUTE FORCE.
Tracks: / Diamond heat / Sledgehammer / Fist / White spirit / Quartz.
LP: MCF 3074

Bryan, Ashley

DANCING GRANNY & OTHER AFRICAN STORIES, THE (see under Dancing Granny...).

Bryan, Carlton

NUCLEAR YARD.
LP: CR 1391

Bryan, Dora

SINGS FIVEPENNY PIECE.
Tracks: / There's a great deal of difference / Down our street / Gradely prayer / Stalybridge market / Wish you were here / Brown photographs / Watercolour morning / Supposin' / Cum to your tea / Ee by gum / Gotta get away / They tell us owt.
LP: EMC 3170

Bryan, James

FIRST OF MAY, THE.
LP: ROUNDER 0215
MC: ROUNDER 0215C

LOOKOUT BLUES.
LP: ROUNDER 0175
MC: ROUNDER 0175C

Bryan, Mike

IN CONCERT (Bryan, Mike Sextet).
LP: SLP 825

MIKE BRYAN SEXTET (Bryan, Mike Sextet).
LP: SLP 4015

Bryant, Don

DOING THE MUSTANG.
LP: HIUKLP 420

Bryant, Felice

ALL I HAVE TO DO IS DREAM (Bryant, Felice & Boudleaux).
Tracks: / All I have to do is dream / Love hurts / Raining in my heart / Yeh bye love / Wake up little Susie.
LP: DBLP 3

Bryant, Jimmy

BRYANT'S BACK IN TOWN.
LP: HAT 3137
MC: HATC 3137

COUNTRY CABIN JAZZ.
LP: HAT 3078
MC: HATC 3078

GUITAR TAKE OFF.
Tracks: / Bryant's boogie / Leetle Juan Pedro / T-bone rag / Liberty bell polka / Okie boogie / Pickin' the chicken / Comin' on / Jammin' with Jimmy / Deep water / Stratosphere boogie / Arkansas traveller / Low man on a totem pole / Catfish boogie / Country capers / Old Joe Clark / Gotta give me whatcha got / Whistle stop / Chatterbox / Cotton pickin' / Sleepwalker's lullaby.
LP: SEE 267

TWO GUITARS COUNTRY STYLE (Bryant, Jimmy & Speedy West).
LP: PM 155 083-1

Bryant, Leon

FINDERS KEEPERS.
Tracks: / Finders keepers / Your kind of lovin' / I'm gonna put a spell on you / Are you ready / You're my everything / Honey / I can see me loving you / Never.
LP: DSR 5

LEON BRYANT.
Tracks: / Mighty body / Come and get it / Just the way you like it / Something more / You can depend on / Can I / I like that rock and roll / I promise.
LP: 6337174

Bryant, Lynn

YOU ARE (see under Cairo).

Bryant, Marie

DON'T TOUCH MY NYLONS.
Tracks: / Mary had a little lamb / Chi chi boom / Too much / Noisy spring / Watermelon / Don't touch my nylons / 60 minute man / Suede shoes calypso / Tomato.
LP: SPMP 5000
MC: SPMC 5000

Bryant, Ray

ALL BLUES (Bryant, Ray Trio).
Tracks: / All blues / C-jam blues / Please send me someone to love / Jumpin' with symphony Sid / Blues changes / Billie's bounce / Stick with it.
LP: 231 0820
MC: K10 820

ALONE WITH THE BLUES.
Tracks: / Blues No 3 / Joy / Lover man / Me and the blues / Rocking chair / Stocking feet.
LP: OJC 249

BEST OF RAY BRYANT.
Tracks: / Stick with it / Girl talk / In de back room / Please send me someone to love / Li'l darlin' / All blues / Moanin' / Good morning heartache.
LP: 231 0846
MC: K10 846

CON ALMA.
Tracks: / Con alma / Milestones / 'Round midnight / Django / Nuts and bolts / Cubano chant / Ill wind / Autumn leaves / C jam blues.
LP: 4610971
MC: 4610974

HERE'S RAY BRYANT.
Tracks: / Girl talk / Good morning heartache / Manteca / When sunny gets blue / Hold back mon / Li'l darlin' / Cold turkey / Prayer song.
LP: 231 0764
MC: K10 764

POTPOURRI (Bryant, Ray Trio).
Tracks: / D.B. blues / One o'clock jump / Milestones / Undecided / In walked Bud / In a mellow tone / My one and only love / Night in Tunisia.
LP: 231 0860
MC: K10 860

RAY BRYANT.
Tracks: / Take the 'A' train / Georgia on my mind / Jungletown jubilee / If I could just make it to heaven / Django / Blues No. 6 / Satin doll / Sometimes I feel like a motherless child / St. Louis blues / Things ain't what they used to be.
LP: 2308 201
MC: K 08 201

RAY BRYANT PLAYS (Bryant, Ray Trio).
LP: FS 183

SOLO FLIGHT.
Tracks: / In de back room / What are you doing the rest of your life / Monkey business / Blues in de big brass bed / Moanin' / St. Louis blues / Take the 'A' train / Lullaby.
LP: 231 0798
MC: K10 798

Bryant, Rusty

RUSTY BRYANT WITH THE BOSS 4.
Tracks: / Getting in the groove / Soft winds / St. Thomas / Rusty rides again / Entertainer, The / I'm old fashioned.
LP: LP 1001

RUSTY RIDES AGAIN (Bryant, Rusty & Boss 4).
LP: PHOENIX 1001

Bryant, Sharon

HERE I AM.
Tracks: / Here I am / Body talk / Let go / Old friend / Falling / Foolish heart / In the night time / No more lonely nights.
LP: 837 313-1
MC: 837 313-4

Bryars, Gavin

AFTER THE REQUIEM.
Tracks: / After the requiem / Alaric I or II / Allegrasco / Old tower of Lobenicht, The.
LP: ECM 1424

SINKING OF THE TITANIC.
LP: EGED 21
LP: OBS 1

THREE VIENNESE DANCERS.
LP: ECM 1323

Bryden, Beryl

BASIN STREET BLUES.
LP: LSP 14508

BIG DADDY.
LP: DB 010

CHICAGO.
LP: 25897

CONEY ISLAND WASHBOARD.
LP: EPH 21594

KANSAS CITY BLUES.
LP: D 18450

ROCK ISLAND LINE.
LP: D 18230

WEST END BLUES.
LP: 400/9003

YOUNG WOMAN'S BLUES.
LP: LK 4100

Brygada Kryzys

BRYGADA KRYZYS.
LP: FRESH LP 13

CRISIS BRIGADE.
LP: FRESH LP 3

Bryn Jones, Delme

I'LL SING THEE SONGS OF ARABY.
Tracks: / I'll sing thee songs of Araby / Waterboy / Sea fever / Drink to me only / Fishermen of England / Boatmen's dance / Simple gifts / Had a horse / Mourning in the village / Because I were shy / Road to Mandalay / Song of the flea / I am a roamer / Hiawatha's vision / When the Sergeant major's on parade / Go lovely rose.
LP: A 66029

Bryner, Yul

GYPSY AND I.
Tracks: / Line of fate / End of the road / Don't be angry / Sokolov's guitar / Hundred miles / Two guitars / Pacer / For the last time / Why get married / Shawl / Travelling gypsies / I am lost.
LP: VSD 79256

Bryony

LAST OF THE GREAT WHALES.
LP: DRGN 862

Bryson, Peabo

ALL MY LOVE.
Tracks: / Show and tell / All my love / Palm of your hand / When you're in love / One time for the lonely / Life goes on / True love / Meant to be / Like I need you.
LP: EST 2097
LP: 790 641 1
MC: TCEST 2097
MC: 790 641 4

BORN TO LOVE (See under Flack, Roberta) (Bryson, Peabo & Roberta Flack).

CAN YOU STOP THE RAIN.
Tracks: / Lost in the night / Can you stop the rain / Closer than close / Shower you with love / I can't imagine / I wish you love / You don't have to beg / I wanna be with you / I just had to fall / Soul provider / If it's really love.
LP: 4678571
MC: 4678574

CROSSWINDS.
Tracks: / Crosswinds / I'm so into you / Smile / She's a woman / Point of view / Spread your wings / Don't touch me / Love is watching you.
LP: EST 11875

LIVE - AND MORE (see Flack, Roberta) (Bryson, Peabo & Roberta Flack).

POSITIVE.
Tracks: / Come on over tonight / Without you / Hurt / I want to know / Tonight / Positive / When we need it bad / This time around / Still water.
LP: EKT 46
MC: EKT 46C

QUIET STORM.
Tracks: / Since I've been in love / Somebody in your life / Good combination / If you love me (let me know) / Higher you climb, The / Catch 22 / Only at night / After you.
LP: 9604841
MC: 9604844

STRAIGHT FROM THE HEART.
Tracks: / Slow dancin' / If ever you're in my arms again / Straight from the heart / There's no getting over you / I get nervous / Learning the ways of love / Real deal / Love means forever.
MC: 9603624
LP: 9603621

TAKE NO PRISONERS.
Tracks: / Take no prisoners / There ain't nothing out there / Let's apologise / Irresistible / Love always finds a way / Falling for you / I'm in love / Talk to me / She's over me.
LP: EKT 7
MC: EKT 7C

TONIGHT I CELEBRATE MY LOVE FOR YOU (See Flack, Roberta) (Bryson, Peabo & Roberta Flack).

TURN THE HANDS OF TIME.
Tracks: / I've been down / My life / Fool such as I / Man on a string / Turn the hands of time / Fiction / Why don't you make up your mind / Another love song / Piece of my heart / Dwellers of the city.
LP: EST 12138

B.T.Express

1980.
Tracks: / Takin' off / Heart of fire / Does it feel good / Give up the funk / Closer / Have some fun / Better late than never / Funk theory.
LP: CABLP 5002

OLD GOLD FUTURE GOLD.
Tracks: / Stretch / Peace pipe (remix) / Shout it out (remix) / Let me be the one / Express (remix) / Do it (till you're satisfied) / I wanna hold you / Midnight beat.
LP: EXCLP 5001

Buarque, Chico

OPERA DO MALANDRO (Film Soundtrack).
Tracks: / A volta do Malandro / Las muchachas de Copacabana / Tema da repressao / Aquela mulher / Viver do amor / Sentimental / Desafio do Malandro / O ultimo blues / Palavra de mulher / O meu amor / Tango do covil / Uma cancao desnaturada / Rio / Pedaco de mim.
LP: 830 120-1
MC: 830 120-4

Bubble Gum

BUBBLEGUM 68-70 (Various artists).
LP: NEXLP 113
MC: NEXMC 113

IT'S BUBBLE GUM MUSIC (Various artists).
Tracks: / Train: *1910 Fruitgum Co* / Go away: *1910 Fruitgum Co* / Special delivery: *1910 Fruitgum Co*/ No good Annie: *1910 Fruitgum Co* / Indian giver: *1910 Fruitgum Co* / Liza: *1910 Fruitgum Co* / When we get married: *1910 Fruitgum Co* / Goody goody gum drops: *1910 Fruitgum Co* / Mr. Cupid: *1910 Fruitgum Co*/ Simon says: *1910 Fruitgum Co* / Yummy yummy yummy: *Ohio Express* / Mercy, The: *Ohio Express* / Chewy chewy: *Ohio Express* / Polly wally doo da day: *1910 Fruitgum Co* / ABC I love you: *1910 Fruitgum Co* / On a summer night: *Rock 'n' Roll Double Bubble Trading Co. Of Philadelphia* / Quick Joey small: *Kasnetz Katz Singing Orchestral Circus.*
LP: SEE 237

Bubble Puppy

GATHERING OF PROMISES, A.
Tracks: / Hot smoke and sasafrass / Todds tune / I've got to reach you / Lonely / Gathering of promises, A / Hurry sundown / Elizabeth / It's safe to say / Road to St Stephens / Beginning.
LP: LIK 33

WHEELS GO ROUND.
Tracks: / Tell it to me straight / Love Loves to rock & roll / Hurry Sundown / For my love / Only a loner / Hot smoke and sasafrass / Wheels Go Round / Because I want to / No more tenderness / My Life.
LP: OBGLP 9004

Bubbles, John W.

BACK ON BROADWAY.
Tracks: / It ain't necessarily so / Belittling me / Somebody's gonna make you fall / Why was I born / Sweet mama / On the sunny side of the street / Bubbles blue / Wrap your troubles in dreams / Lady be good / Nobody knows / My mother's eyes / Somebody loves me.
LP: UP 27 03

Bubblies

BUBBLIES, THE.
MC: ZCBUB 1

Bubbling Brown Sugar

BUBBLING BROWN SUGAR (Original London cast) (Various artists).
2LP: NSPD 504

Bucca

HOLE IN THE HARPER'S HEAD, THE.
LP: PLR 039

Buchan, John (aut)

SELECTED STORIES OF JOHN BUCHAN (Cuthbertson, Iain).
MCSET: TTDMC 405

Buchanan, Isobel

WHITE CLIFFS OF DOVER, THE (Songs and Music of the 40's) (Buchanan, Isobel/English Chamber Orchestra).
Tracks: / Calling all workers / Dambusters march / Knightsbridge (London suite) / Spitfire prelude and fugue, The / There'll always be an England / We'll meet again / White cliffs of Dover, The / Nightingale sang in Berkeley square, A / When I grow too old to dream / Would you please oblige us with a Bren Gun / It's a lovely day tomorrow / I'll be seeing you / Love is the sweetest thing / All the things you are / Long ago and far away / So in love / Every time we say goodbye / I only have eyes for you / Always.
LP: DCA 598
MC: ZC DCA 598

Buchanan, Jack

ELEGANCE.
Tracks: / Night time / Living in clover / Fancy our meeting / Oceans of time / Like Monday follows Sunday / When we get our divorce / Not bad / Dancing honeymoon / And her mother came too / Who / Now that I've found you / You forgot your gloves / One I'm looking for, The / Sweet so an so / I think I can / Dapper Dan / Alone with my dreams / Two little bluebirds / Goodnight Vienna / It's not you / There's always tomorrow.
LP: AJA 5033
MC: ZC AJA 5033

GOLDEN AGE OF JACK BUCHANAN, THE.
Tracks: / Two little birds / It's not you / There's always tomorrow / Dancing honeymoon / And her mother came too / Who take a step / Alone with my dreams / You forgot your gloves / Leave a little for me / Yes Mr. Brown / Now that I've found you / In clover / Goodnight Vienna / Fancy our meeting / Weep no more / One good tune deserves another / I think I can / So green / Ooh la la / Adapted from the French.
LP: GX 41 2520-1
MC: GX 41 2520-4

SELECTIONS FROM LONDON STAGE SHOWS (Buchanan, Jack & Elsie Randolph).
Tracks: / Garden of flies / This year next year / Take a step / Do it for me / For my friend / Don't love you / Blotto / Selection / Fancy our meeting / Chirp chirp / Marching song / One I'm looking for / Sweet so and so / Parting time.
LP: SH 329

THAT'S A GOOD GIRL.
MC: TC SH 329

Buchanan, Roy

DANCING ON THE EDGE.
Tracks: / Peter Gunn / Chokin' kind, The / Jungle gym / Drowning on dry land / Petal to the metal / You can't judge a book by the cover / Cream of the crop / Beer drinking woman / Whiplash / Baby, baby, baby / Mathew.
LP: SNTF 961

EARLY ROY BUCHANAN.
Tracks: / Mule train stomp / Pretty please / Mary Lou / Shuffle, The / Jam, The / Braggin' / Ruby baby / Am I the one.
LP: KK 7450

HOT WIRE.
LP: SNTF 993

RESCUE ME.
Tracks: / Rescue me / I'm a ram / In the beginning / C.C. rider / Country preacher / You're killing my love / She can't say no / Wayfairing pilgrim.
LP: 2391 152

ROY BUCHANAN.
Tracks: / Sweet dreams / Tribute to Elmore James / Roy's bluz / Cajun / Country preacher / After hours / Messiah will come again The / Filthy teddy / Wayfairing pilgrim / Please don't turn me away / She once lived here / In the beginning.
LP: 2482 275

WHEN A GUITAR PLAYS THE BLUES.
Tracks: / When a guitar plays the blues / Mrs. Pressure / Nickel and a nail, A / Short fuse / Why don't you want me? / Country boy / Sneaking Godzilla through the alley / Hawaiian punch.
LP: SNTF 940

Buchman, Rachel

HELLO RACHEL, HELLO CHILDREN.
LP: ROUNDER 8006
MC: ROUNDER 8006C

Buck, John

CHI CHI.
Tracks: / Jalisco / Egal O.K. / Black is the colour of my true love's hair / La Bamba / Vaquero / Copenhagen carousel / Kibaba / Chi chi / Lola / Last dance / Forbidden city / Spanish farewell / Nan je di.
LP: BFX 15274

Buck Pets

BUCK PETS.
MC: ICT 9930
LP: ILPS 9930

Buck Rogers (tv theme)

BUCK ROGERS (TV soundtrack) (Various artists).
LP: MCF 3013

Buckeridge, Anthony

JENNINGS GOES TO SCHOOL.
MC: P 90004

Buckeye

BUCKEYE.
Tracks: / Wonder where / Mke it happen / Where you want to go / Forever in love / Sinkin' low / Just the way / Rainy day / Poor cheater / Nobody / That kind of man.
LP: 2391416

Buckingham, Lindsey

GO INSANE.
Tracks: / I want you / Go insane / Slow dancing / I must go / Play in the rain(parts 1& 2) / Loving cup / Bang the drum / D.W. suite.
LP: MERL 46
MC: MERLC 46

LAW AND ORDER.
Tracks: / Bwana / Trouble / Mary Lee Jones / I'll tell you now / It was I / September song / Shadow of the West / That's how we do it in LA / Johnny stew / Love from here love from there / Satisfied mind A.
MC: 7144 167
LP: 6302 167

Buckley, Lord

BLOWING HIS MIND AND YOURS TOO.
Tracks: / Subconcious mind / Fire chief / Let it down / Murder / Gasser, The / Maharaja / Scrooge.
LP: VERB 3

Buckley, Paul

SHINING BRIGHT.
LP: FUN 001

Buckley, Tim

DREAM LETTER (Live in London).
Tracks: / Introduction / Buzzin' fly / Phantasmagoria in two / Morning glory / Dolphins / I've been out walking / Earth is broken, The / Who do you love? / Pleasant Street - You keep me hanging on / Love from room 109 - Strange feelin' / Carnival song - Hi Lily, hi Lo (medley) / Hallucinations / Troubadour / Dream letter / Happy time / Wayfaring stranger / You got me runnin' / Once I was.
2LP: DFIEND 200

GOODBYE AND HELLO.
Tracks: / No man can find the war / Carnival song / Pleasant street / Hallucinations / I never asked to be your mountain / Once I was / Plantasmagoria in two / Knighterrant / Morning glory.
LP: K 42070

GREETINGS FROM L.A..
Tracks: / Move with me / Get on top / Sweet surrender / Night hawkin' / Devil eyes / Hong Kong bar / Make it right.
LP: K 46176

HAPPY SAD.
Tracks: / Strange feeling / Buzzin' fly / Love from room 109 at the islander / Dream letter / Gypsy woman / Sing a song for you.
LP: K 42072

LOOK AT THE FOOL.
Tracks: / Look at the fool / Bring it on up / Helpless / Freeway blues / Tijuana moon / Ain't it peculiar / Who could deny you / Mexicali voodoo / Down the street / Wanda Lu.
LP: K 59204
LP: ED 294

SEFRONIA.
Tracks: / Dolphins / Honey man / Because of you / Peanut man / Martha / Quicksand / Stone in love / Sefron-after asklepiades after Kafka / Sefronia- The kings chain / Sally go round the roses / I know I'd recognise your face.
LP: K 49201
LP: ED 277

Buckner, Milt

ALIVE AND JUMPING (see Hampton, Lionel).

EARLY YEARS, THE 1947-53.
Tracks: / Fatstuff boogie / Buck's bop / Milt's boogie / Oo-be-doop / M.B. blues / Who shot John / Buck-a-boo / Yesterdays / By the river Sainte Marie / Russian lullaby / Trapped / Boo it / Taking a chance on love / Flying home / There'll never be another you / Hawk talk, The.
LP: OFF 3033

PLAY MILT, PLAY.
Tracks: / Perdido / I don't stand a ghost of a chance / Swinging in Toulouse / Hey ba ba re bop / Play, fiddle, play / Cute / Caravan / Buckner's boogie woogie / Mighty low / Flying home / Stardust.
LP: FC 103

ROCKIN HAMMOND.
Tracks: / Count's basement / Mighty low / We'll be together again / Jumpin' at the woodside / One o'clock jump / Wild scene / Blue and sentimental / Deep purple / Jumpin' at the Zanzibar / When you wish upon a star / Late late show, The.
LP: 2C 068 85194

UNFORGETTABLE.
Tracks: / Hamp's boogie woogie / Honeysuckle rose / Pick yourself up / I de Clare / Willie's blues / Glady's dance / If I could be with you one hour tonight / Jitterbug waltz / God knows / Robbins nest.
LP: 5C 064 61178

Buckner, Teddy

JAZZ FESTIVAL.
LP: 500052

JAZZ TIME VOL.11.
LP: 502711

LA GRAND PARADE DE LA NOUVELLE ORLEANS.
2LP: 400022

PARISIAN ENCOUNTER (See under Bechet, Sidney) (Buckner, Teddy & Sidney Bechet).

TEDDY BUCKNER 1955: VOLUME 1.
Tracks: / Mahogany hall stomp / I want to linger / Dippermouth blues / Bluin' the blues / Tiger rag / Dear old southland / Big butter and egg man / Twelfth St. rag / Ain't misbehavin' / Memphis blues / Royal Garden blues.
LP: AIRCHECK 10

TEDDY BUCKNER AT THE CRESCENDO.
LP: DJA 516

TEDDY BUCKNER & HIS DIXIELAND BAND (Buckner, Teddy & His Dixieland Band).
LP: DJA 504

TEDDY BUCKNER IN CONCERT.
LP: DJA 503

TEDDY BUCKNER & THE ALL STARS (Buckner, Teddy & The All Stars).
LP: DJA 507

Bucks Fizz

ARE YOU READY.
Tracks: / Land of make believe / My camera never lies / Now those day's are gone / Easy love / Love dies hard / One way love / Are you ready / Breaking and entering / 20th century hero / Another night.
LP: RCALP 8000
MC: RCAK 8000

BUCKS FIZZ.
Tracks: / Making your mind up / Piece of the action / My camera never lies / Land of make believe / Midnight reservation / It's got to be love / Took it to the limit / One of those nights / Lady of the night / Getting kinda lonely / Shine on / Right situation The (Two tracks already in tracks file but on seperate records (piece of the).
LP: PL 70127
MC: PK 70127
LP: NL 70875
MC: NK 70875
LP: RCALP 5050

BUCKS FIZZ LIVE AT THE FAIRFIELD HALL, CROYDON.
LP: JETLP 1001
MC: JETCA 1001

GREATEST HITS: BUCKS FIZZ.
Tracks: / My camera never lies / London town / Piece of the action / Now those day's are gone / Making your mind up / When we were young / Land of make believe / Of one of nights / Oh Susannah / If you can't stand the heat / Run for your life / Rules of the game.
LP: PL 70022
MC: PK 70022

HAND CUT.
Tracks: / Run for your life / 10,9,8,7,6,5,4 / I do it all for you / Where the ending starts / Surrender your heart / If you can't stand the heat / I'd like to say I love you / You love love / Shot me through the heart / Running out of time.
LP: RCALP 6100
MC: RCAK 6100

I HEAR TALK.
Tracks: / I hear the talk / Indebted to you / Tears on the ballroom floor / Cold war / Golden days / Talking in your sleep / Breaking me up / January's gone / She cries / Thief in the night.
LP: PL 70397
MC: PK 70397

LAND OF MAKE BELIEVE, THE.
Tracks: / Land of make believe / My camera never lies / Run for your life / I do it all for you / When we were young / Thief in the night / Running out of time / Indebted to you / Januarys gone / Breaking me up.
LP: MFP 5762
MC: TCMFP 5762

MAKING YOUR MIND UP.
Tracks: / Making your mind up / I'd like to say I love you / Love dies hard / Shine on / Surrender your heart / Piece of the action / Are you ready / Easy love / Another night / Took it to the limit.
LP: CDS 1214
MC: CAM 1214

STORY SO FAR, THE (The Very Best of Bucks Fizz).
LP: SMR 870
MC: SMC 870

WRITING ON THE WALL, THE.
Tracks: / New beginning / You and your heart of blue / Soul motion / Magical / Keep each other warm / Love the one you're with / Love in a world gone mad / Don't turn back / Company you keep, The / I hear talk.
LP: POLH 30
MC: POLHC 30

Bucks, George

JAZZOLOGY ALLSTARS.
LP: J 48

Buckwheat Zydeco

100% FORTIFIED ZYDECO.
LP: BT 1024
MC: BT 1024C

BUCKWHEAT ZYDECO.
LP: REU 1005

ON A NIGHT LIKE THIS.

Tracks: / On a night like this / Time is tight / Space Zydeco / Hot Tamale baby / People's choice / Ma 'tit fille / Buckwheat's special / Zydeco honky tonk / Marie, Marie.
LP: . . . . ILPS 9877
MC: . . . . ICT 9877
MC: . . . . ICM 2016
MC: 842 739 4

TAKING IT HOME.
Tracks: / Creole country / These things you do / Make a change / Ooh wow / Taking it home / Down Dallas alley / Drivin' old grey / Why does love got to be so sad / In and out of my life / Creole country part 2.
MC: . . . . ICT 9917
LP: . . . . ILPS 9917
MC: . . . . ICM 2015
MC: 842 603 4

TURNING POINT.
LP: . . . . ROUNDER 2045
MC: . . . . ROUNDER 2045C

WAITIN' FOR MY YA-YA.
LP: . . . . ROUNDER 2051
MC: . . . . ROUNDER 2051C
LP: . . . . REU 1055

WHERE THERE'S SMOKE, THERE'S FIRE.
LP: 846215-1
LP: . . . . ILPS 9962
MC: 846215-4
MC: . . . . ICT 9962

Budd, Harold

LOVELY THUNDER.
Tracks: / Gunfighter, The / Sandtreader / Ice floes in Eden / Olancha farewell / Flowered knife shadows (for Simon Raymonde) / Gypsy violin.
LP: . . . . EGED 46
MC: . . . . EGEDC 46

MOON AND THE MELODIES, THE (Budd/Fraser/Guthrie/Raymonde).
Tracks: / Sea, swallow me / Memory gongs / Why do you love me / Eyes are mosaics / She will destroy you / Ghost has no home, The / Bloody and blunt / Ooze out and away, one how.
LP: . . . . CAD 611
MC: . . . . CADC 611

PAVILION OF DREAMS/ PLATEAUX OF MIRRORS.
Tracks: / Bismallahi'rrahmani'rrahim / Let us go into the house of the Lord / Butterfly Sunday / Mandrigals of the rose angel / Juno / First light / Steal away / Plateaux of mirrors, The / Above chiangmai / Arc of doves, An / Not yet remembered / Chill air, The / Among fields of crystal / Wind in lonely fences / Failing light.
MCSET: . . . . EGDC 5

PAVILION OF DREAMS, THE.
Tracks: / Bismallahi'rrahmani'rrahim / Let Us Go Into The House Of The Lord / Butterfly Sunday / Madrigals of the rose angel-rosetti noise,crystal garden,cod / Juno.
LP: . . . . EGED 30
MC: . . . . EGEDC 30
LP: . . . . OBS 10

PEARL, THE (Budd, Harold & Brian Eno).
Tracks: / Late October / Stream with bright fish A / Silver ball, The / Against the sky / Lost in the humming air / Dark-eyed sister / Their memories / Pearl, The / Foreshadowed / Echo of night, An / Still return / Against the sky.
MC: . . . . EGEDC 37
LP: . . . . EGED 37

PLATEAUX OF MIRRORS (Budd, Harold & Brian Eno).
Tracks: / First light / Steal away / Plateaux of mirror, The / Above Chiangmai / Arc of doves, An / Not yet remembered / Chill air, The / Among fields of crystal / Wind in lonely fences / Failing light.
LP: . . . . EGED 18
LP: . . . . EGAMB 2

SERPENT (IN QUICKSILVER)/ ABANDONED CITIES.
2LP: . . . . LAND 008

WHITE ARCADES, THE.
LP: . . . . LAND 003

Budd, Roy

HAVE A JAZZY CHRISTMAS (Budd, Roy Trio).
Tracks: / We three kings / Winter wonderland / When you wish upon a star / Ding dong merrily on high / Lieutenant Kije / Jingle bells.
LP: . . . . CHELP 9
MC: . . . . CHEMC 9

SEA WOLVES (See under Sea Wolves).

SPACE MOVIE THEMES (See under London Symphony Orchestra) (Budd, Roy & London Symphony Orchestra).

Buddah

BUDDAH ALL STARS (Various artists).
Tracks: / Hold back the night: *Various artists* / More more more: *Various artists* / Baby don't change your mind: *Various artists* / Captain Connors: *Various artists* / East 6th Street: *Various artists* / Mainline: *Various* artists / This is it: *Various artists* / Just in case: *Various artists* / Betcha by golly wow: *Various* artists / You are my starship: *Various artists* / Way we were: *Various artists* / Loving you losing you: *Various* artists / Zing went the strings of my heart: *Various artists* / What's your name, what's your number: *Various* artists / Phoenix: *Various artists* / Soul improvisations: *Various artists* / Free: *Various artists*/ Oh happy day: *Various artists* / Wait until the rain: *Various artists.*
LP: . . . . BDLP 4067

Buddhist...

BUDDHIST DRUMS, BELLS AND CHANTS (Various artists).
LP: . . . . LLST 7200

TOLLING OF BUDDHIST TEMPLE (Various artists).
MC: . . . . HRP 7294

Buddy Holly Sound

BUDDY HOLLY SOUND (Various artists).
LP: . . . . R&C 1020

Buddy's Song (film)

BUDDY'S SONG (Original Soundtrack featuring Chesney Hawkes) (Various artists).
Tracks: / One and only, The: *Various artists* / Nothing serious: *Various artists* / Feel so alive: *Various* artists / I'm a man not a boy: *Various artists* / It's gonna be tough: *Various artists* / Torn in half: *Various* artists / I'm young: *Various artists* / Secrets of the heart: *Various artists* / This is me: *Various* artists / Ordinary girl: *Various artists* / Crazy world like this, A: *Various artists* (Not included in Film Soundtrack.).
LP: . . . . CHR 1812
MC: . . . . ZCHR 1812

Budgie

BANDOLIER.
LP: . . . . MCF 2723
LP: . . . . MCL 1795

BEST OF BUDGIE.
Tracks: / Breadfan / I ain't no mountain / I can't see my feelings / Baby please don't go / Zoom club / Breaking all the house rules / Parents / In for the kill / In the grip of a tyre-fitter's hand.
LP: . . . . MCL 1637
MC: . . . . MCLC 1637

DELIVER US FROM EVIL.
Tracks: / Bored with Russia / Don't cry / Truth drug / Young girl / Flowers in the attic / N.O.R.A.D.(domesday city) / Give me the truth / Alison / Finger on the button / Hold on to love.
LP: . . . . RCALP 6054
MC: . . . . RCAK 6054

IN FOR THE KILL.
LP: . . . . MCF 2546

NEVER TURN BACK.
Tracks: / Breadfan / Baby please don't go / You're the biggest thing since powdered milk / You know I'll always love you / In the grip of a tyre-fitter's hand / Riding my nightmare / Parents / Apparatus / Superstar / Change your ways / Untitled lullaby.
LP: . . . . MCL 1855
MC: . . . . MCLC 1855

NIGHT FLIGHT.
Tracks: / I turned to stone / Keeping a rendezvous / Reaper of glory / She used me up / Don't lay down and die / Apparatus / Superstar / Change your ways / Untitled lullaby.
LP: . . . . RCALP 6003
MC: . . . . RCAK 6003

POWER SUPPLY.
Tracks: / Forearm smash / Hellbender / Heavy revolution / Gunslinger / Power supply / Secrets in my head / Time to remember / Crimes against the world.
LP: . . . . RCALP 3046
MC: . . . . RCAK 3046
LP: . . . . ACTLP 1

Budgie (Show)

BUDGIE (1988 show recording) (Various artists).
LP: . . . . MCG 6035
MC: . . . . MCGC 6035

Budimir, Dennis

ALONE TOGETHER.
Tracks: / Blues for Ray / Embraceable you / East of the sun / No cover, no minimum / I can't get started / All the things you are.
LP: . . . . REV 1

SECOND COMING, A.
Tracks: / Some day my prince will come / For every man there's a woman / Woodyn you / All the things you are / There is no greater love.
LP: . . . . REV 4

SESSION WITH ALBERT.
Tracks: / Warm up / Warm up blues / Au privave / There is no greater love.
LP: . . . . REV 14

SPRUNG FREE.
Tracks: / Blues sprung free, The / East of the sun / Sultry serenade / Blues by the bags.
LP: . . . . REV 8

Budwig, Monty

DIG.
LP: . . . . CJ 79

Bue, Papa

ALL THAT MEAT AND NO POTATOES (Bue, Papa Viking Jazz Band/Wild Bill Davison).
LP: . . . . SLP 280

ANNIVERSARY ALBUM 1956-1966 (Bue, Papa & His Viking Jazzband).
LP: . . . . SLP 191

BARBER/BUE BESTSELLERS (See under Barber, Chris).

DANISH JAZZ VOL.8 1957-77.
LP: . . . . SLP 417

DANSK (Liller & Papa Bue's Viking Jazzband).
LP: . . . . SLP 848

DE GO'E GAMIE MED LILLER (Liller & Papa Bue's Viking Jazzband).
LP: . . . . SLP 847

DIXIELAND (Bue, Papa Viking Jazz Band).
LP: . . . . SLP 833

GREATEST HITS: PAPA BUE'S VIKING JAZZ BAND (Bue, Papa Viking Jazz Band).
LP: . . . . SLP 836

IN THE MOOD (Bue, Papa & His Viking Jazzband).
Tracks: / In the mood / Just a little while / Stardust / Burgundy Street blues / Song is ended, The / Coffee grinder / Li'l Liza Jane / 1919 march / Walking with the king / You'll never walk alone / Beautiful dreamer.
LP: . . . . MLP 101
LP: . . . . TTD 539

JAZZ PARTY (Bue, Papa Viking Jazz Band).
LP: . . . . SLP 420

LIVE IN TIVOLI (Bue, Papa Viking Jazz Band).
LP: . . . . SLP 418

NEW ORLEANS (Bue, Papa Viking Jazz Band).
LP: . . . . SLP 832

ON STAGE (Bue, Papa Viking Jazz Band).
LP: . . . . TTD 511

PAPA BUE CLASSICS (Bue, Papa & His Viking Jazzband).
LP: . . . . SLP 197

PAPA BUE VIKING JAZZ BAND/WILD BILL DAVISON (See Davison, Wild Bill).

PAPA BUE'S VIKING JAZZ BAND (Bue, Papa Viking Jazz Band).
LP: . . . . SLP 405

PAPA BUE'S VIKING JAZZ BAND WITH WINGY MANONE (Bue, Papa Viking Jazz Band & Wingy Manone).
LP: . . . . SLP 210

TRIBUTE TO LOUIS (Liller & Papa Bue's Viking Jazzband).
LP: . . . . SLP 845

WINGY MALONE & PAPA BUE'S VIKING JAZZ BAND (see under Malone, Wingy).

WITH FRIENDS (Bue, Papa Viking Jazz Band).
LP: . . . . SLP 425

Buen, Hauk

RINGING STRINGS (FIDDLE MUSIC OF NORWAY) (Buen, Hauk/Knut Buen/ Tom Anderson/Vidar Lande).
Tracks: / Haugelatten / Seljord bridal march / Gravbakken / Fille-vern / Sordalen / Maggie O'Ham / Prestegangaren / Fykeruden / Markensmandagen / Knut lurasen / Margit hjukse / Siri rukaren / Bokkoen / Unst bride's march / Da bride is a boanie ting / Homslien / Skrubben / Norafjells.
LP: 12TS 429

Buen, Knut

RINGING STRINGS (FIDDLE MUSIC OF NORWAY) (see under Buen, Hauk) (Buen, Knut & Friends).

Buffalo Bop

BUFFALO BOP 35 (Various artists).
LP: . . . . BBLP 2045

BUFFALO BOP 37 (Various artists).
LP: . . . . BBLP 2047

BUFFALO BOP 38 (Various artists).
LP: . . . . BBLP 2048

BUFFALO BOP 39 (Various artists).
LP: . . . . BBLP 2051

BUFFALO BOP 40 (Various artists).
LP: . . . . BBLP 2052

BUFFALO BOP 41 (Various artists).
LP: . . . . BBLP 2053

Buffalo Springfield

AGAIN.
Tracks: / Mr. Soul / Child's claim to fame, A / Everydays / Expecting to fly / Bluebird / Hung upside down / Sad memory / Good time boy / Rock 'n' roll woman / Broken arrow.
LP: . . . . K 40014
MC: . . . . K 440 014

BEGINNING, THE.
Tracks: / For what it's worth / Go and say goodbye / Goodbye / Sit down I think I love you / Nowadays Clancy can't even sing / Hot dusty roads / Everybody's wrong / Flying on the ground / Burned / Do I have to come right out and say it / Leave / Out of my mind / Pay the price.
LP: . . . . K 30028

BUFFALO SPRINGFIELD.
Tracks: / For what its worth / Sit down I think I love you / Nowadays Clancy can't even sing / Go and say goodbye / Pay the price / Burned / Out of my mind / Mr. Soul / Bluebird / Broken arrow / Rock 'n' roll woman / Expecting to fly / Hung upside down / Child's claim to fame, A / Kind woman / On the way home / I am a child / Pretty girl why / Special care / Uno mundo / In the hour of not quite rain / Four days gone / Questions.
LP: . . . . K 70001

RETROSPECTIVE (The Best of Buffalo Springfield).
Tracks: / For what it's worth / Hello Mr. Soul / Sit down I think I love you / Kind woman / Bluebird / On the way home / Nowadays Clancy can't even sing / Broken arrow / Rock and roll woman / I am a child / Go and say goodbye / Expecting to fly.
LP: . . . . K 40071
MC: K4 40071

Buffalo Tom

BIRD BRAIN (ALBUM).
Tracks: / Birdbrain / Caress / Enemy / Fortune teller / Directive / Skeleton key / Guy who is me / Crawl / Baby / Bleeding heart.
LP: . . . . SITU 31
MC: . . . . SITC 31

BUFFALO TOM.
LP: . . . . SST 250
MC: . . . . SSTC 250

Buffett, Jimmy

CHANGES IN LATITUDES, CHANGES IN ATTITUDES.
Tracks: / Wonder why we ever go home / Banana republic / Tampico trauma / Lovely cruise / Margaritaville / In the shelter / Miss you so badly / Biloxi / Landfall.
LP: . . . . IMCA 1652
MC: . . . . IMCAC 1652

COCONUT TELEGRAPH.
LP: . . . . MCF 3097

FLORIDAYS.
Tracks: / Creola / I love the now / First look / Meet me in Memphis / Nobody speaks to the captain no more / Floridays / If it all falls down / No plane on Sunday / When the coast is clear / You'll never work in dis bisness again.
LP: . . . . IMCA 5730
MC: . . . . IMCAC 5730

LIVING AND DYING IN 3/4 TIME.
Tracks: / Pencil thin moustache / Come Monday / Ringling, Ringling / Brahma fear / Livinston's gone to Texas / Wino and I know, The / West Nashville grand ballroom gown / Ballad of Spider John / God's own drunk.
LP: . . . . IMCA 1588
MC: . . . . IMCAC 1588

OFF TO SEE THE LIZARD.
LP: . . . . MCA 6314
MC: . . . . MCAC 6314

VOLCANO (ALBUM).
LP: . . . . MCG 4006

Bufford, Mojo

EXCITING HARMONICA SOUND OF....
LPS: . . . . BRS 3241

MOJO BUFFORD'S CHICAGO BLUES SUMMIT.
LP: . . . . R 7603

Bugaloos

BUGALOOS.
LP: . . . . ROCK 8912

Bugatti & Musker

DUKES.
Tracks: / Mystery girl / I'm a survivor / Thank you for the party / Memories / Excitement of the new / Love dance / Soul mates / So much in love / Fate / Nite music.
LP: . . . . K 58497

Buggles

ADVENTURES IN MODERN RECORDING.
Tracks: / Adventures in modern recording / Beatnik / Vermillion sands / I'm a camera / On TV / Inner city / Lenny rainbow warrior.
LP: . . . . CAL 131
MC: . . . . CAC 131

AGE OF PLASTIC, THE.
Tracks: / Plastic age, The / Video killed the radio star / Kid dynamo / I love you / Clean, clean / Elstree / Astro boy / Johnny on the mono rail.
MC: . . . . ICM 9585
LP: . . . . ILPM 9585
LP: . . . . ILPS 9585

Bugnon, Alex

LOVE SEASON.
LP: D1 756 02

Bugs

DARKSIDE.
Tracks: / Just a bad dream / Bad News / End it all / Six string goddess / In retrospect / Hate / Dark side / Have you been there / It's About Time / Took a long time / Sarsaparilla sideway / One of These Days.
LP: . . . . WIKM 62

Bugs On The Wire

BUGS ON THE WIRE (Various artists).
LP: . . . . SAW 399

Bugsy Malone (film)

BUGSY MALONE (1976 film soundtrack) (Various artists).
Tracks: / Bad guys: *Various artists* / Bugsy Malone: *Various artists* / Down had out: *Various artists*/ Fat Sam's grand slam: *Various artists* / I'm feeling fine: *Various artists* / My name is Tallalah: *Various artists* / Ordinary fool: *Various artists* / So you wanna be a boxer: *Various artists* / Tomorrow: *Various artists* / You give a little love: *Various artists*.
LP: 2442 142
MC: 3170 285

Buhrman, Bert

CINEMA ORGAN ENCORES.
LP: . . . . DEROY 1027

Buirski, Felicity

REPAIRS AND ALTERATIONS.
Tracks: / Dream on / Heartless Hotel / Aha Song (I am the lord), The / Executioner's song / Come to me darling / Marilyn / Travelling home / Rumpelstiltskin / Let there be light.
LP: . . . . RRA 004

Buitlear, Eamon De

CROOKER ROAD, THE.
LP: . . . . CEF 035

Bulgarian Broadcasting

GERSHWIN: PORGY AND BESS HIGHLIGHTS (Bulgarian Broadcasting Symphony Orchestra).
LP: . . . . AVM 1027
MC: . . . . AVMC 1027

Bulgarian Folk Music

FOLK HEROES AND RUCHENITSAS.
LP: . . . . BHA 10216

Bulgarian Male ...

LITURGICAL CHANTS (Bulgarian Male Chamber Choir).
LP: . . . . BXA 1104

Bulgarian National...

PRIN FOLK (Bulgarian National Folk Ensemble).
MC: . . . . ZPRST 827

Bull City Red

BULL CITY RED 1935-39.
LP: . . . . BD 2030

Bull Durham

BULL DURHAM (1988 film soundtrack) (Various artists).
LP: C1 90586
MC: C4 90586

Bull, Geoff

IN NEW ORLEANS.
LP: . . . . GHB 203

Bull, Les

LIVE AT THE OUTGATE (Bull, Les Festival Jazz Band).
Tracks: / Hiawatha rag / Higher ground / Ponchartrain blues / Copenhagen / St.James Infirmary blues / Barefoot days / Everything stops for tea / Skeleton in the closet / Buddy's habits / Saturday night function / Take my hand prcious Lord / Fish seller, The / Someone's rocking my dreamboat.
LP: . . . . LA 5015
MC: . . . . LA 5015/C

Bullard, Marie

YOGA FOR ALL (see under Yoga For All).

Bulldog Drummond (bk)

BULLDOG DRUMMOND (McNeile, H.C.) (Todd, Richard (nar)).
MCSET: 418 186-4
MCSET: . . . . ARGO 1088

Bulldozer

DAY OF WRATH.
LP: . . . . RR 9779

FINAL SEPARATION, THE.
Tracks: / Final separation, The / Ride hard,die fast / Cave, The / Sex symbol's bullshit / Don Andras / Never relax / Don't trust the saint / Death of the gods, The.
LP: . . . . RR 9711

IX.
LP: . . . . SHARK 10

Bullenbush Band

WALTHAMSTOW MARKET.
LP: . . . . BB 001

Bullet Boys

BULLET BOYS.
LP: . . . . WX 213
MC: . . . . WX 213 C

FREAKSHOW.
LP: 7599261681
MC: 7599261684

Bullet For The General

BULLET FOR THE GENERAL (QUIEN SABE?), A (Original soundtrack) (Various artists).
LP: . . . . IMGM 011

Bullet La Volta

DEAD WRONG.
LP: . . . . FH 12012

GIFT, THE.
LP: . . . . EM 9449 1

Bullett

NO MERCY.
LP: . . . . HMILP 15

Bullock, Chick

CHICK BULLOCK & HIS LEVEE LOUNGERS (Bullock, Chick & His Levee Loungers).
LP: . . . . E 1001

Bullock, Hiram

FROM ALL SIDES.
Tracks: / Window shopping / Until I do / Hark the herald angels sing / Really wish I could love you / Say goodnight, Gracie / Funky Broadway / Mad dog days / Cactus / When the passion is played.
LP: . . . . K 781 685-1
MC: . . . . K 781 685-4

GIVE IT WHAT U GOT.
Tracks: / Down the pipe / Too hip 2 B needy / You send me / Half life / Give it what U got / Gotta get your jollys / Pretzel logic / Angelina.
LP: . . . . K 781 790 1
MC: . . . . K 781 790 4

Bullshit Detector

BULLSHIT DETECTOR VOLUME II.
LP: 1984/3

Bulluck, Janice

DON'T START A FIRE.
Tracks: / Don't start a fire / Do you really love me / Excited (about your love) / Turn on your radio / I'm ridin' high on your love / Right love - wrong man / We've got it right / If it turns you on.
LP: . . . . WIL 3003
MC: . . . . ZCWIL 3003

Bully Wee Band

MADMAN OF GOTHAM, THE.
Tracks: / Madman of Gotham, The / Girl that broke my heart, The / Tibbie Dunbar / Cheapside / Margaret's waltz / Patrick the fabulous magician / Way below the tide / Wedding at Stanton Drew / Geiranger/Gallaghers.
LP: . . . . SAW 1

Bulpitt, Chris

GAMES OF CHANCE.
MC: . . . . COCKPIT 6

SURFACE TENSION.
MC: . . . . COCKPIT 5

SURFACE TENSION/GAMES OF CHANCE.
MC: . . . . COCKPIT 5/6

Bumper 2 Bumper

BUMPER 2 BUMPER (Various artists).
Tracks: / Flashback: *Various artists* / Breakin' up (The best part of): *Various artists* / Nice & slow (US Remix): *Various artists* / Every way but loose: *Various artists* / Ease your mind: *Various artists* / Why can't we live together: *Various artists* / Thanks to you: *Various artists* / Puerto Rico (US remix): *Various artists*/ Like the way you funk with me: *Various artists* / Over like a fat rat: *Various artists* / Never let you go: *Various artists* / You don't like my music: *Various artists*.
LP: . . . . CBD 2001
MC: . . . . ZCCBD 2001

BUMPER 2 BUMPER VOL.2 (Various artists).
Tracks: / Just an illusion: *Imagination* / Touch: *Various artists* / Work me over: *Various artists* / Do it anyway you wanna: *Various artists* / Let's do it: *Various artists* / I'd like to: *Various artists*/ That's when (we'll be free): *Various artists* / He's gonna take you home (to his houser): *Various artists* / Mirda Rock: *Various artists* / Rock your baby: *Various artists* / Pull our love together: *Various artists*/ Tell tale heart: *Various artists*.
2LP: . . . . CBD 2002
MC: . . . . ZCCBD 2002

Bunch

ROCK ON.
LP: . . . . CGLP 4424
MC: . . . . CGC 4424

Bunch, John

BEST THING FOR YOU, THE (Bunch, John Trio).
Tracks: / Best thing for you would be me, The / I loves you Porgy / Deed I do / Emily / Star eyes / Lucky to be me / Wave / Au privave / I can't get started / Jitterbug waltz.
LP: . . . . CJ 328
MC: . . . . CJC 328

JUBILEE (Bunch, John Trio).
LP: . . . . AP 184

Bunkley, Jim

JIM BUNKLEY AND GEORGE HENRY BUSSEY (Bunkley, Jim/George Henry Bussey).
LP: . . . . ROUNDER 2001

Bunn, Teddy

TEDDY BUNN 1930-39.
LP: . . . . BD 2069

Bunny Drums

HOLY MOLY.
LP: . . . . SAVE 002

Bunny Lake Is...(film)

BUNNY LAKE IS MISSING (Original soundtrack) (Various artists).
LP: . . . . LSO 1115

Bunyan, John (aut)

PILGRIM'S PROGRESS, THE (see under Pilgrim's Progress (bk).

Burbage Band

CHATSWORTH HOUSE.
LP: . . . . GRS 1198

Burbank, Albert

CREOLE CLARINET.
LP: . . . . SMOKEY MARY 1969

Burch, Nigel

FACISTS IN THE SNUG BAR.
Tracks: / Hello young lovers / Sick of England / Blood red carpet / Mummy's kisses / Squabble and fight / Figures of fun / Happy sin / Colour of your blood, The / Purple wallpaper / Bachelor breakfast / Mad money / One big heartache no 1 / One big heartache no 2 / Barmaid's nightmare / World without sleep / Mr. Entertainment.
LP: . . . . CSCV 2

Burden, Ernest (nar)

NODDY STORIES (see under Blyton, Enid).

Burden, Hugh (nar)

BROGUE (see under Brogue).

COLONEL'S LADY, THE/LORD MOUNTDRAGO (see under Colonel's Lady).

HOUND OF THE BASKERVILLES, THE (see under Sherlock Holmes).

SHE WOLF & OTHERS (see under She Wolf (bk).

Burden Of Population

BURDEN OF POPULATION (See under UNESCO reports).

Burdett, Phil

RED BRICK SPLEEN.
Tracks: / Not everyone finds their rut... / Undertown / Better smile / Susquehannah babies / Haven't they grown / Revelation / They watered my whisky down / Patriots / Crane / Nature love / Laughter / Elm Park postcard / Sheet metal cubicle 3 / Epilogue.
LP: . . . . PEARL 1

Burdon, Eric

ANIMALS GREATEST HITS.
Tracks: / Don't let me be misunderstood / We gotta get out of this place / When I was young / Man / Funky fever / All I do / Rainbow / Tobacco Road / Real me, The / House of the rising sun / Spill the wine / Paint it black / Mother earth / It's my life / City boy / Gotta get it on / I'm lookin' up / Way it should be, The / Magic mountain / Nights in white satin.
LP: . . . . PLAT 06
MC: . . . . PLAC 06

ERIC BURDON DECLARES WAR.
LP: 2310-041

ERIC BURDON & THE ANIMALS.
Tracks: / Let it rock / Gotta find my baby / Bo Diddley / I'm almost grown / Dimples / Boom boom / C jam blues.
LP: . . . . CR 30016

ERIC BURDON & THE ANIMALS (Burdon, Eric & The Animals).
Tracks: / Don't bring me down / One monkey don't stop no show / Maudie / Sweet little sixteen / You're on my mind / Clapping / Inside looking out / Outcast / I put a spell on you / Cheating / Gin House blues / C.C. rider / Boom boom / I just want to make love to you / That's all I am to you / She'll return it / Help me girl / Mama told me not to come / Squeeze her, tease her / What a living for / Big boss man / Pretty thing / Let it rock / Gotta find my baby / Bo Diddley / I'm almost grown / Dimples / C jam blues.
LP: . . . . CR 30197
LP: . . . . SPELP 40
MC: . . . . SPEMC 40
LP: DP6 28621

ERIC BURDON & THE ANIMALS (POLYDOR) (Burdon, Eric & The Animals).
MC: 847046 4

GREATEST HITS: ERIC BURDON.
2LP: 2664 439
MC: 3578 486

GREATEST HITS: ERIC BURDON & THE ANIMALS (Burdon, Eric & The Animals).
LP: . . . . PLATB 06
MC: . . . . PLACB 06

GREATEST HITS: ERIC BURDON & THE ANIMALS (Burdon, Eric & The Animals).
LP: 20139
MC: 40139

HOUSE OF THE RISING SUN (Burdon, Eric & The Animals).
LP: . . . . PLP 26
MC: . . . . PMC 26

POWER COMPANY.
Tracks: / Power company / Devil's daughter / You can't kill my spirit / Do you feel it (today) / Wicked man / Heart attack / Who gives a f*** / Sweet blood call / House of the Rising Sun / Comeback.
LP: . . . . BDL 4006

PROFILE: ERIC BURDON (Burdon, Eric & The Animals).
Tracks: / I put a spell on you / Help me girl / Don't bring me down.
LP: 6.24784
MC: CL4 24784

ROAD, THE.
Tracks: / Wall of silence / Streetwalker / It hurts me too / Lights out / Bird on the beach / No more Elmore / Road, The / Crawling king snake / Take it easy / Dey don't.
LP: . . . . THBL 1.017

SAN FRANCISCAN NIGHTS (Burdon, Eric & The Animals).
Tracks: / Sky pilot / Winds of change / Monterey / Good times / San Franciscan nights / Ring of fire / Paint it black / Anything / River deep, mountain high.
LP: 825 800-1
MC: 825 800-4

WICKED MAN.
LP: . . . . GNPS 2194
MC: GNP5 2194

Burge, Jon

FAIR WAS THE CITY (see under Ryan, Mick) (Burge, Jon/Mick Ryan).

Burgess, Alan (aut)

SMALL WOMAN, THE (see under Small Woman) (Bergman, Ingrid (nar)).

Burgess, Anthony (aut)

CLOCKWORK ORANGE, A (see under Clockwork Orange (bk)).

EVE OF ST. VENUS/NOTHING LIKE THE SUN (see under Eve of St. Venus).

Burgess, John

ART OF THE HIGHLAND BAGPIPE VOL 3.
Tracks: / Alexandria place / Banks of the Farrar / Struan Robertson / Broadford Bay / Pipers bonnet / Grey Bob, The / Mrs William Ross / Corriechoillie blend / Pap of Glencoe / Campbell of Southall / Braes of Castle Grant, The / Irish slow air / Little house under the hill / Pibroch / Too long in this condition / Lament for Sir James / MacDonald of the Isles / Slow air / Malcolm MacPherson lullaby / Retreat marches / Heroes of St Valerie / Pipe major / Donald McCloud.
LP: **12TS 393**

ART OF THE HIGHLAND BAGPIPE VOL 1.
LP: **12TS 291**

ART OF THE HIGHLAND BAGPIPE VOL 2.
LP: **12TS 326**

KING OF HIGHLAND PIPERS,THE.
LP: **12T 199**

PLAYS THE GREAT HIGHLAND BAGPIPE (Burgess, Pipe Major John D).
Tracks: / Isle of Man highland gathering, The / Wade's welcome to Inverness / Lonely Loch Nan eun / Lewis soldier, The / Traditional / Hio hirum / Lewis wedding / 74th farewell to Edinburgh, The / Margaret Duncan / Pipe Major Angus MacDonald Scots Guards / Geese in the bog, The / Shieling, The / Caledonian Society of London, The / Flight of the eaglets, The / John MacColl's march to Kilbowie cottage / Edinburgh City Police pipe band / Old woman's lullaby, The.
LP: . . . . **LILP 5125**
MC: . . . . **LICS 5125**

Burgess, Sally

SALLY BURGESS SINGS JAZZ.
MC: . . . . **ZCVIR 8308**
LP: . . . . **VIR 8308**

Burgess, Sonny

FLOOD TAPES 1959-62, THE.
Tracks: / Flip flop and fly / Dizzy Miss Lizzy / Stones in love with you / K.K.'s boogie / Mellow soul / What ever happened to the girls I knew / City lights / We wanna boogie / Ain't got a thing / Crazy arms / Drinkin' wine spo / Dee o dee / Meet me anywhere / Sea cruise / Little town baby.
LP: . . . . **SJLP 561**

I NEED A MAN (Burgess, Sonny/ Barbara Pittman/Warren Smith/ M.Yelvington).
LP: . . . . **CFM 502**

LEGENDARY SUN PERFORMERS.
Tracks: / Red headed woman / Restless / Going home / Ain't got a thing / Find my baby for me / Tomorrow night / You're not the one for me / Thunderbird / We wanna boogie / Feel so good / Y.O.U / My bucket's got a hole in it / All my sins are taken away / Sally Brown / I love you so / Sadie's back in town.
LP: . . . . **CR 30136**

OLD GANG,THE.
LP: . . . . **CRM 2025**

RAW DEAL.
LP: . . . . **LPL 8601**

ROCK-A-BILLY (Burgess, Sonny & Larry Donn).
Tracks: / Honey bun / Milkcow boogie blues / Blue moon of Kentucky / I forgot to remember to forget / I'm left you're right she's gone / She's gone / Baby, let's play house / Mystery train / That's what I call a baby / She's mine / Brown eyed handsome man / Kentucky home rock / All night stomp / Sunshine rock / Girl next door.
LP: . . . . **WLP 8817**

SONNY BURGESS & THE PACERS (Burgess, Sonny & The Pacers).
Tracks: / Don't be that way / Oh Mama / Truckin' down the avenue / All my sins are taken away / My babe / My bucket's got a hole in it / Sweet misery / So glad you're mine / Mr. Blues / Tomorrow night / Feel so good / Find my baby for me / One night.
LP: . . . . **SUN 1027**

SONNY BURGESS VOLUME 3.
Tracks: / Itchy (Instrumental) / Always will / Little town baby / Changed my mind / Kiss goodnight, A / Sadie's back in town / Thunderbird (Instrumental) / So soon / Smootchin' Jill / Sweet Jenny / Tomorrow never comes / Oochie coochie / You're not the one for me.
LP: . . . . **SUN 1039**

SPELLBOUND.
Tracks: / Move it on over / Spellbound / I'll be there (if you ever want me) / I'm counting on you / Everybody's movin' again / Rock 'n' roll daddy / Raw deal / Get on the right track baby / Hot mama / Blue highway / Sunrock / Louisiana lady.
LP: . . . . **WIK 50**

WE WANNA BOOGIE (Burgess, Sonny & The Pacers).
Tracks: / We wanna boogie / Red headed woman / Feeling good / Ain't got a thing / Restless / Truckin' down the avenue / Fannie Brown / Going home / Sadie Brown / My bucket's got a hole in it / Sweet misery / All my sins are taken away / My babe / Tomorrow night / Daddy blues / So glad you're mine / Hoochie coochie man / Find my baby for me / One night / Itchy / Thunderbird / Little town baby / Kiss goodnight, A / Sadie's back in town.
LP: . . . . **SUN 1022**

Burgin, David

WILD CHILD.
LP: . . . . **FF 338**

Burglar Bill (bk)

BURGLAR BILL (Janet & Allan Alhlberg).
MC: **0 00 102199 0**

Burglar (film)

BURGLAR (1988 film soundtrack) (Various artists).
LP: . . . . **MCF 3340**
MC: . . . . **MCFC 3340**

Burial

DAY ON THE TOWN.
LP: . . . . **SKANLP 107**

Burke, Chris

CHRIS BURKE & HIS NEW ORLEANS MUSIC (Burke, Chris & His New Orleans Music).
LP: . . . . **GHB 175**

Burke, Joe

FUNNY REEL, THE (Burke, Joe & Friends).
LP: . . . . **SHAN 29012**

GALWAY'S OWN.
MC: . . . . **COX 1015**

HAPPY TO MEET, SORRY TO PART.
LP: . . . . **SIF 1069**
MC: . . . . **CSIF 1069**

IRISH TRADITIONAL MUSIC.
LP: . . . . **OLP 1015**

TAILOR'S CHOICE, THE.
LP: . . . . **SIF 1045**
MC: . . . . **CSIF 1045**

TRADITIONAL MUSIC OF IRELAND.
LP: . . . . **SIF 1048**

TRIBUTE TO MICHAEL COLEMAN, A (Burke, Joe/Andy McCann/F.Dolan).
MC: . . . . **GTDC 048**

Burke, Keni

ARTISTS SHOWCASE: KENI BURKE.
LP: . . . . **MUSIC 9**
MC: . . . . **ZCMUS 9**

CHANGES.
Tracks: / Shakin' / Hang tight / Can't get enough (do it all night) / Who do you love / Let somebody love you (On re-release only) / Changes / One minute more / Risin' to the top / All night / You're the best (On re-release only).
LP: . . . . **PL 89551**
LP: . . . . **NL 90555**
MC: . . . . **NK 90555**

YOU'RE THE BEST.
Tracks: / Let somebody love you / Gotta find my way back in your heart / Love is the answer / You're the best / Paintings of love / Night rides / Never stop loving me.
LP: . . . . **RCALP 5059**
MC: . . . . **RCAK 5059**

Burke, Kevin

AN FHIDIL: STRAITH 2 (Burke, Kevin/ Seamus Creagh/Sean Keane).
LP: . . . . **CEF 069**

EAVESDROPPER,THE (Burke, Kevin/ Jackie Daly).
LP: . . . . **LUN 039**
MC: . . . . **CLUN 039**

IF THE CAPS FITS.
LP: . . . . **LUN 021**
MC: . . . . **CLUN 21**

PORTLAND (Burke, Kevin & Michael O'Dohmnhaill).
LP: . . . . **SIF 1041**
MC: . . . . **CSIF 1041**

PROMENADE.
LP: . . . . **LUN 028**

UP CLOSE.
LP: . . . . **SIF 1052**
MC: . . . . **CSIF 1052**

Burke, Ray

RAY BURKE SPEAKEASY BOYS (Burke, Ray Speakeasy Boys).
LP: . . . . **NOR 7202**

Burke, Solomon

BISHOP RIDES SOUTH, THE.
Tracks: / Proud mary / These arms of mine / I'll be doggone / How big a fool (can a fool be) / Don't wait too long / Uptight good woman / That lucky old sun / I can't stop / Please send me someone to love / What am I living for / Generation of revelations, The / I'm gonna stay right here / God knows I love you / In the ghetto.
LP: . . . . **CRB 1187**
MC: . . . . **TCCRB 1187**

CHANGE IS GONNA COME, A.
Tracks: / Love buys love / Got to get myself some money / Let it be you and me / Love is all that matters / Don't tell me what a man won't do for a woman / Change is gonna come, A / Here we go again / It don't get no better than this / When a man loves a woman.
LP: . . . . **REU 1004**
LP: . . . . **ROUNDER 2053**
MC: . . . . **ROUNDERC 2053**

CRY TO ME.
Tracks: / Be bop grandma / Just out of reach / Cry to me / Down in the valley / I'm hanging up my heart for you / Stupidity / Can't nobody love you / If you need me / Won't you give him one more chance) / You're good for me / Goodbye baby (baby goodbye) / Everybody needs somebody to love / Yes I do / Price, The / Got to get you off my mind / Maggie's farm.
LP: . . . . **CRB 1075**
MC: . . . . **TCCRB 1075**

INTO MY LIFE YOU CAME.
LP: . . . . **SL 14679**

KING OF ROCK 'N' SOUL FROM THE HEART.
Tracks: / Boo hoo boo / Hold on I'm coming / Sweeter than sweetness / Sidewalks / Fences and walls / Let the love flow / More, The / Lucky / Please come back home to me.
LP: . . . . **CRB 1024**

LORD I NEED A MIRACLE RIGHT NOW.
LP: . . . . **SL 14660**

LOVE TRAP.
Tracks: / Love trap / Do you believe in the hereafter / Every breath you take / Daddy love bear / Isis / Nothing but the truth / Only God knows / Drive / Sweet spirit.
LP: . . . . **IV 21336**
MC: . . . . **IVMC 21336**

MUSIC TO MAKE LOVE BY.
Tracks: / Music to make love by (part 1) / Let me wrap my arms around you / Come rain or come shine / You and your baby blues / All the way / Thanks,I needed that / Everlasting love / Midnight and you / Music to make love by (part 2).
LP: . . . . **GCH 8098**

REST OF SOLOMON BURKE,THE.
LP: . . . . **SD 8109**

SILENT NIGHT: A CHRISTMAS PRAYER.
LP: . . . . **SCS 0002**

SOUL ALIVE.
Tracks: / Everybody needs somebody to love / I almost lost my mind / Just out of reach / If you need me / Tonight's the night / You're good for me / What am I living for / Monologue / Take me (just as I am) / Down in the valley / Proud Mary / Tonight's the night (reprise) / Beautiful brown eyes / Just a matter of time / Monologue / Hold what you've got / He'll have to go / Cry to me / Gotta get you off my mind / Meet me in the church / Price, The / Words / Monologue / You're good for me / Send me some lovin' / Gotta get you off my mind / Having a party / Amen.
2LP: . . . . **DFIEND 38**
2LP: . . . . **ROUNDER 2042/3**
MC: . . . . **ROUNDER 2042/3**

TAKE ME SHAKE ME.
LP: . . . . **SL 14717**

THIS IS HIS SONG.
LP: . . . . **SL 14738**

YOU CAN RUN BUT YOU CAN'T HIDE.
Tracks: / To thee / Why do that to me / This is it / My heart is a chapel / Picture of you / You can run but you can't hide / Friendship ring / I'm not afraid / Don't cry / Christmas presents / I'm in love / Leave my kitten alone / No man walks alone / I'm all alone / I need you tonight / Walking in a dream / You are my one love / For you and you alone.
LP: . . . . **RB 108**

Burke, Sonny

SONNY BURKE, 1951.
Tracks: / Stompin' at the Savoy / El choclo / I want to be happy / Fugue for tinhorns / Mulholland Drive / Samba Americano / Just one of those things / What where and when / Grabber, The / Dubonnet blonde / Balboa / Mambo jambo.
LP: . . . . **HSR 174**

Burke, Vinnie

VINNIE BURKE ALL STARS (Burke, Vinnie All Stars).
LP: . . . . **FS 264**

Burland, Dave

DALESMAN'S LITANY, A.
LP: . . . . **LER 2029**

DAVE BURLAND.
LP: . . . . **LER 2082**

DAVE BURLAND DOUBLE ALBUM.
Tracks: / Cruel mother / Banks of the Bann / King George hunt, The / Lakes of Shillin / Bitter withy / Brave wolfe / Old changing way, The / I'm a rover / Great silkie, The / His name is Andrew / Bright phoebus / Shooting of his dear, The / Farmer is the man / Collier laddie / Shaky nancy / Haul away for Rosie / Grey funnel line / Edward Hollander / Willie O'Winebury / You can't fool the fat man.
LP: . . . . **RUB 012/036**

SONGS AND BUTTERED HAYCOCKS.
MC: . . . . **RUBC 012**

SONGS OF EWAN MACCOLL (see under Gaughan, Dick) (Burland, Dave, Dick Gaughan & Tony Capstick).

YOU CAN'T FOOL THE FAT MAN.
Tracks: / Lamkin / Shooting of his dear, The / Farmer is the man / Collier laddie / Shaky Nancy / Haul away for Rosie / Grey funnel line / Edward Hollander / Willie o' Winsbury / You can't fool the fat man.
LP: . . . . **RUB 036**
MC: . . . . **RUBC 036**

Burmer, Richard

BHAKTI POINT.
LP: . . . . **LPFOR 047**
MC: . . . . **MCFOR 047**

MOSAIC.
LP: . . . . **LPFOR 025**
MC: . . . . **MCFOR 025**

Burnel, Jean-Jacques

EUROMAN COMETH.
Tracks: / Euroman / Jellyfish / Freddie Laker (Concorde and Eurobus) / Euromess / Do the European / Tout comprendre / Triumph (of the good city) / Pretty face / Crabs / Eurospeed (your own speed) / Deutschland Nicht Uber Alles.
LP: . . . . **UAG 30214**
MC: . . . . **TCK 30214**
LPPD: . . . . **PMAU 601**
LP: . . . . **MAU 601**

FIRE AND WATER (see under Greenfield, Dave) (Burnel, Jean-Jacques & Dave Greenfield).

RAIN, DOLE & TEA (see under Greenfield, Dave) (Burnel, Jean-Jacques & Dave Greenfield).

UN JOUR PARFAIT.
Tracks: / Un jour parfait (theme) / Week-end / Un jour parfait / Le whiskey / Garden of Eden / Waltz / Siyetais / Tristeville ce soir / Via dolorosa / She drives me crazy / Reves.
LP: **4624241**
MC: **4624244**

Burnett

RAMBLIN' WRECKLESS HOBO (Burnett & Rutherford).
LP: . . . . **ROUNDER 1004**

Burnett, Carl

PLAYS THE MUSIC OF RICHARD RODGERS (Burnett, Carl Quintet).
Tracks: / It never entered my mind / Spring is here / It's easy to remember / Bewitched / Sweetest sounds, The / I have dreamed / You are too beautiful.
LP: . . . . **DS 819**

Burnett, Frances

LITTLE PRINCESS, A (see under Little Princess (bk)) (Lipman, Maureen).

SECRET GARDEN, THE (see under Secret Garden).

Burnett, Richard

BRAHMS CLARINET TRIO AND SONATAS (see under Brahms (Composer)) (Burnett, Richard/Alan Hacker/Jennifer Ward Clarke).

CLARINET COLLECTION (see under Hacker, Alan) (Burnett, Richard/Alan Hacker).

FINCHCOCKS COLLECTION, THE.
LP: . . . . **SAR 6**
MC: . . . . **CSAR 6**

GOTTSCHALK PIANO MUSIC.
Tracks: / Le bananier / La savane / Le mancenellier / Souvenir de Porte Rico / Romance / Chanson du Gitano / Polkas

in Bb & Ab / Suis moi / Manchego / La Gallina / Minuit a Seville / Suveniers d'Andalouise / Mazurk / Because / Ballade no. 6 / Dying poet, The.
LP: .... SAR 32

ROMANTIC FORTEPIANO, THE.
LP: .... SAR 7
MC: .... CSAR 7

Burnett, T-Bone

BEHIND THE TRAP DOOR.
Tracks: / Strange combination / Amnesia and jealousy (oh Lana) / Having a wonderful time wish you were here / Law of average / My life and the women who lived it / Welcome home, Mr.Lewis.
LP: .... VEX 3

INTERVIEWS (see under Alpha Band) (Burnett, T-Bone/Alpha Band).

PROOF THROUGH THE NIGHT.
Tracks: / Murder weapon / Fatally beautiful / After all these years / Baby fall down / Sixties, The / Stunned / Pressure / Hula hoop / When the night falls / Hefner and Disney / Shut it tight.
LP: .... FIEND 14

TALKING ANIMALS, THE.
Tracks: / Wild truth, The / Monkey dance / Image / Dance, dance, dance / Killer moon, The / Relentless / Euromad / Purple heart / You could look it up / Strange case of Frank Cash and the morning paper, The.
LP: 4601621
MC: 4601624

T-BONE BURNETT.
LP: .... MCF 3347
MC: .... MCFC 3347

TRAP DOOR.
Tracks: / Hold on tight / Diamonds are a girl's best friend / I wish you could have seen her dance / Ridiculous man, A / Poetry / Trap door.
LP: .... VEX 2

TRUTH DECAY.
Tracks: / Quicksand / Talk talk talk talk talk / Boomerang / Love at first sight / Madison Avenue / Driving wheel / Come home / Power of love, The / House of mirrors / Tears tears tears / Pretty girls / I'm coming home.
LP: .... FIEND 71
MC: .... FIENDCASS 71
LP: .... CHR 1317

Burnette, Billy

BILLY BURNETTE.
Tracks: / In just a heartbeat / Oh Susan / Danger zone / Don't say no / Rockin' L.A. / Honey hush / Rockin' with somebody new / One night / Sittin' on ready / Angeline / Tear it up.
LP: 84642

Burnette, Dorsey

DORSEY BURNETTE.
LP: .... SKYLINE 1990

DORSEY BURNETTE VOL. 1 (Great shakin' fever).
LP: 501

DORSEY BURNETTE VOL. 2 (Keep a knockin').
LP: 502

TALL OAK TREE.
LP: .... EL 102

Burnette, Hank C.

DON'T MESS WITH MY DUCKTAIL.
Tracks: / Spinning rock boogie / Your driving licence please / Riders in the sky / Blue moon / Hank's 97 / Come on little mama / Don't mess with my ducktail / Fools like me / Gold in the morning sun / Rockin' daddy / Peggy Sue / Rockola jive.
LP: .... SNTF 693

HOT LICKS AND FANCY TRICKS.
Tracks: / Well...alright / I'm a king bee, baby / B.D.'s back in town / Bonnie Lee / That's alright / Sugaree / Clawdy / Beach slide / Hot rock Sally / J.T. starry eyed / Boppin' the blues / Maybe baby / King of rock 'n' roll.
LP: .... SNTF 792

MULTISIDED.
LP: 33.8014

NO.1 ROCKABILLY.
LP: 33.8006

ORIGINAL ONE MAN ROCKABILLY BAND, THE.
LP: .... R&C 1003

ROCKABILLY GASSEROONIE.
Tracks: / Dirty boogie / Pony tail girl / Guitar Nellie / Red cadillac and a black moustache / Sweet skinny Jenny / Patsy / Good good lovin' / Connie Lou / Too much / Rakin' and scrapin' / Over the rainbow / Sneaky Pete / Rocky road blues / Miss froggie.
LP: .... SNTF 750
MC: .... ZCSN 750

SPINNIN' ROCK BOOGIE.
LP: 33.8013

UNITED ALBUM, THE.
LP: .... R&C 1013

Burnette, Johnny

10TH ANNIVERSARY ALBUM.
LP: 2C 068 83099

14 DEMO RECORDINGS (Burnette, Johnny & Dorsey).
LP: .... ROCK 8112

20 ROCK'N'ROLL HITS: JOHNNY BURNETTE.
Tracks: / You're 16 / Little boy sad / You're the reason / Settin' the woods on fire / Walk on by / Fool, The / Why don't you haul off and love me / Me & the bear / Clown shoes / Cincinnati fireball / Lovesick blues / Finders keepers / Mona Lisa / Fool of the year, The / Just out of reach / Poorest boy in town, The / Moody river / Girl of my best friend / In the chapel in the moonlight / Dreamin'.
LP: .... IC 064 82751

JOHNNY BURNETTE ROCK 'N' ROLL TRIO, THE (Burnette, Johnny & R & R Trio).
LP: .... SS 8001

JOHNNY & DORSEY BURNETTE (Burnette, Johnny & R & R Trio).
LP: .... LPL 8112

LEGENDARY JOHNNY BURNETTE ROCK 'N' ROLL TRIO (Burnette, Johnny & R & R Trio).
Tracks: / Tear it up / You're undecided / Oh baby babe / Midnight train / Shattered dreams / Train kept a rollin' / Blues stay away from me / All by myself / Drinkin' wine spo-dee-o-dee / Chains of love / Honey hush / Lonesome tears in my eyes / I just found out / Please don't leave me / Rock therapy / Rockabilly boogie / Lonesome train (on a lonesome track) / Sweet love on my mind / My love you're a stranger / I love you so / Your baby blue eyes / Touch me / If you want it enough / Butterfingers / Eager beaver baby / On baby babe.
2LP: .... CDX 3
MC: .... TCCDX 3

ROCK 'N' ROLL (Burnette, Johnny & R & R Trio).
LP: .... SKYLINE 1254

ROCK 'N' ROLL MASTERS (Best of Johnny Burnette).
Tracks: / Dreamin' / Let me be with you / That's the way I feel / You'll learn to cry / It's my way / Walk on by / It's the after / Little boy sad / You're sixteen / Lover's question, A / Fools like me / Second chance / Girls / Standing on the outside of her door / Gimme gimme lovin' / Clown shoes / Dream lover (CD only.) / Some enchanted evening (CD only.) / Lonesome waters (CD only.) / Kentucky waltz (CD only.).
LP: .... EMS 1324
MC: .... TCEMS 1324

ROCK 'N' ROLL TRIO - TEAR IT UP.
Tracks: / Train kept a-rollin' / Lonesome train / Oh baby babe / All by myself / Blues stay away from me / Sweet love on my mind / Rock therapy / Please don't leave me / Rockbilly boogie / Drinkin' wine spo-dee-o-dee / Tear it up / You're undecided / If you want it enough / Eager beaver baby / Your baby blue eyes / Butterfingers / Honey hush.
LP: .... ROLI 306

SINGS COLLECTIBLE HITS (Burnette, Johnny & R & R Trio).
LP: .... LSP 1062

TOGETHER AGAIN (Burnette, Johnny & Dorsey).
Tracks: / Little ole you / I wanna love my baby / I'm happy / That's the way I feel / Just keep on a-goin' / Baby doll blue eyes / Cincinnati fireball / You're sixteen / Hey stranger / Address unknown / Lovesick blues / Finders keepers / Interview with Johnny Burnette / One-sided love affair.
LP: .... ROLI 308

WE'RE HAVING A PARTY (Burnette, Johnny & R & R Trio).
LP: .... RSRLP 1017

Burnette, Rocky

ROCKY BURNETTE.
Tracks: / Heartstopper / Making love / Crosswinds / Blue Haven Cafe / Tennessee / Hey little one / Tired of toein' the line / Fingerprints / Let me know / When you were mine / In the middle of the night / Alberta / It's all in your eyes.
LP: .... EMC 3421

SON OF ROCK 'N' ROLL, THE.
MC: .... TCEMC 332382

Burning (film)

BURNING, THE (See Wakeman, Rick) (Various artists).

Burning Flames

DIG.
MC: .... MCT 1088
LP: .... MLPS 1088

Burning Rain

VISIONS.
LP: .... RES 339031

Burning Skies Of

LAST REVOLVING DOOR.
Tracks: / Alone / For my eyes / Carousel / Death of the clowns / Far from the crowds / Beggarman thief / Domino / Out on the paperchase / Too late for tears / Fragments.
LP: .... EL 3

Burning Spear

BURNING SPEAR.
Tracks: / Far over / Burning spear / Greetings / Image / Rock / Education / She's mine / Message / Oh jah / Jah is my driver.
LP: .... RDC 2004

DRY AND HEAVY.
Tracks: / Any river / Sun, The / It's a long way around / I.W.I.N. / Throw down your arms / Dry and heavy / Wailing / Disciples / Shout it out.
LP: .... ILPS 9431

FAR OVER.
LP: .... HB 11
MC: .... HBC 11

FITTEST OF THE FITTEST, THE.
Tracks: / Fittest of the fittest / Fireman / Bad to worst / Repatriation / Old Boy Garvey / 2,000 years / For you / In Africa / Vision.
LP: .... RDC 1077681
MC: .... TC-RDC 1077684
LP: .... HB 22
MC: .... HBC 22

GARVEY'S GHOST.
Tracks: / Ghost, The / I and I survive / Black wa-da-da(Invasion) / John Burns shank (live good) / Brain food(give me) / Father east of Jack / 2000 years / Dread river (Jordan river) / Workshop (red, green and gold) / Reggaelation(Resting place).
LP: .... IPS 9382

HAIL H.I.M.
Tracks: / African teacher / African postman / Cry blood Africa / Hail H.I.M. / Jah a go raid / Columbus / Road foggy / Follow Marcus Garvey / Jah see and know.
LP: .... RDC 2003
LP: 2C 070 63753
MC: 2C 266 63753
LP: .... DSR 4422

HARDER THAN THE BEAT.
Tracks: / Marcus Garvey / Dry and heavy / Throw down your arms / Social living / Invasion / Black wa-da-da(Invasion) / Slavery days / Old Marcus Garvey / Man in the hills / Sun, The / Civilised reggae.
LP: .... ILPS 9567

JAH KINGDOM.
MC: .... MCT 1089
LP: .... MLPS 1089

LIVE: BURNING SPEAR.
LP: .... ILPS 9513

LIVE IN PARIS ZENITH '88'.
Tracks: / Spear of burning / Youth, The / African postman / Woman I love you / Creation rebel / Built this city / Driver / We are going / New experience / Happy day / Queen of the mountain / Mistress music / Wilderness / Door peep.
2LP: .... GREL 120
MC: .... GREEN 120

LIVING DUB VOL. 1.
LP: .... TG 5184
LP: .... RMM 1189

LIVING DUB VOL. 2.
LP: .... RMM 1209

MAN IN THE HILLS.
Tracks: / Man in the hills / It's good / No more way / Black soul / Lion / People get ready / Children / Mother / Door peep / Groovy.
LP: .... ILPS 9412
MC: .... RRCT 15

MARCUS' CHILDREN.
LP: .... WRLP 102

MARCUS GARVEY.
Tracks: / Marcus Garvey / Slavery days / Invasion / Live good / Give me / Old Marcus Garvey / Tradition / Jordan river / Red, gold and green / Resting place.
LP: .... ILPS 9377
LP: .... RMM 1654

MARCUS GARVEY / GARVEY'S GHOST.
MC: .... RRCT 20

MEK WI DWEET.
Tracks: / Mek wi dweet / Garvey / Civilization / Elephants / My roots / Great man / African woman / Take a look / One people / Mek we dweet in dub.
LP: .... MLPS 1045
MC: .... MCT 1045
LP: 846 273 1
MC: 846 273 4

MISTRESS MUSIC.
MC: .... GREEN 116
LP: .... GREL 116

PEOPLE OF THE WORLD.
Tracks: / People of the world / I'm not the worst / Seville land / Who's the winner / Distant drums / We are going / This experience / Built this city / No worry you'self / Little love song.
LP: .... GREL 100
MC: .... GREEN 100

REGGAE GREATS.
Tracks: / Door peep / Scavery days / Lion / Black disciples / Man in the hills / Tradition / Throw down your arms / Social living / Marcus Garvey / Dry and heavy / Black wa-da-da(Invasion) / Sun, The.
LP: .... IRG 5
MC: .... IRGC 5
MC: .... ICM 2017
MC: 842 870 4

RESISTANCE.
LP: .... HB 33
MC: .... HBC 33

ROCKING TIME.
LP: .... SOL 1123

SOCIAL LIVING.
Tracks: / Marcus children suffer / Social living / Nayah Keith / Institution / Marcus senior / Civilised reggae / Mister Garvey / Come / Marcus say Jah no dead.
LP: .... ILPS 9556

Burning The Midnight

BURNING THE MIDNIGHT SUN (Various artists).
LP: .... U 020
MC: .... U 020 MC

Burning Tree

BURNING TREE.
Tracks: / Burning tree / Wigs, blues and high heeled shoes / Fly on / Bakers song / Playing in the wind / Masquerade / Crush / Last laugh / Mistreated lover / Turtle.
LP: 4666331
MC: 4666334

Burning up

BURNING UP VOL 1 (Various artists).
LP: .... BS 1058
MC: .... BSC 1058

BURNING UP VOL 2 (Various artists).
LP: .... BS 1059
MC: .... BSC 1059

BURNING UP VOL 3 (Various artists).
LP: .... BS 1062

BURNING UP VOLS 1 & 2 (Various artists).
2LP: .... BSDLP 100

Burningham, John

BORKA AND OTHER STORIES (see under Borka & Other Stories).

Burnley Blues Festival

BURNLEY BLUES FESTIVAL (See under Blues) (Various artists).

Burns, Eddie

DETROIT BLACK BOTTOM (Burns, Eddie 'guitar').
LP: .... BEAR 7

DETROIT BLUES 1950-1951 (See under John Lee Hooker).

TREAT ME LIKE I TREAT YOU.
LP: .... BLP 106

Burns, Eddy

BY THE WAY.
LP: .... EB 23

Burns, George

I WISH I WAS EIGHTEEN AGAIN.
Tracks: / Arizona whiz, The / Old bones / Baby song / Only way to go / Forgive here a little / I wish I was eighteen again / Old dogs, children and watermelon wine / Real good cigar / One of the mysteries of life / Nickels and dimes.
LP: 9100074

ON THE RADIO (Burns, George & Gracie Allen).
LP: .... MR 1028

Burns, Gill

ALOAN AT LAST.
LP: .... GEB 8751

SIGHT MORE CURIOUS, A.
LP: .... GEB 8753

Burns, Jethro

BACK TO BACK (Burns, Jethro & Tiny Moore).
LP: . . . . **F 9**

JETHRO BURNS.
LP: . . . . **FF 042**

JETHRO LIVE.
LP: . . . . **FF 072**

TEA FOR ONE.
LP: . . . . **F 14**

Burns, Laura

LIGHT THIS NIGHT.
LP: . . . . **FF 376**

Burns, Ralph

BIJOU (Burns, Ralph Quartet).
LP: . . . . **FS 250**

RALPH BURNS CONDUCTS 1951-4.
LP: . . . . **RARETONE 5017**

Burns, Robert (aut)

JOHN CAIRNEY TELLS THE STORY OF ROBERT BURNS.
2LP: . . . . **REL 448**

POETRY OF ROBERT BURNS, THE (and Border ballads) (Various artists).
MC: **1103**

ROBERT BURNS SONGBOOK (Various artists).
Tracks: / Happy are we all together: *Various artists* / Ca'the ewes: *Various artists* / De'ils awa' with the exciseman, The: *Various artists* / My heart's in the highlands: *Various artists* / Of a' the airts: *Various artists*/ Oh, whistle and I'll come to you, my lad: *Various artists* / Ae fond kiss: *Various artists* / Highland lad, A: *Various artists* / Rosebud by my early walk, A: *Various artists* / John Anderson, my Jo: *Various artists*/ I'll ay ca' in by yon toun: *Various artists* / Ye banks and braes: *Various artists*.
LP: . . . . **LILP 5092**
MC: . . . . **LICS 5092**

Burns, Steve

WHISPERING WINDS.
LP: . . . . **BGC 159**

Burns, Tito

BUBBLES (Burns, Tito Orchestra).
Tracks: / I'm forever blowing bubbles / Salute to Bacharach, David and Distel / Hucklebuck / And the angels sing / Salute to Paul Simon / Yoga / Marie / Salute to Neil Diamond / Nina never knew / Salute to Cliff Richard / Team.
LP: . . . . **SCX 6618**

Burnside, R.L

MISSISSIPPI BLUES (Le Blues Dans Sa Tradition La Plus Pure).
Tracks: / Jumper hanging out on the line / Sweet little angel / Long-haired Doney / Nightmare blues / Poor black Mattie / Catfish blues / Death bells / Dust my broom / Bad luck and trouble / Rollin' and tumblin' / When my first wife quit me.
LP: . . . . **ARN 33765**
MC: . . . . **ARN 433765**

PLAYS AND SINGS THE MISSISSIPPI DELTA BLUES.
LP: **2101**

Buro

BURO.
Tracks: / Better than the rest / I can't take the runnings in a Babylon / If me a chat / Out of hand / Jolly bus / Tenament / Tell me what you want / Stumbling block / Rose Marie / Modulla.
LP: . . . . **CSLP 4**

Burrage, Harold

SHE KNOCKS ME OUT 1956-58.
LP: . . . . **FLY 579**

Burrell

BURRELL.
Tracks: / Trust in the music / I'll wait for you (take your time) (On 7" only) / I really like / Gonna make you dance / Dominate me / Sunshine / Let me love you tonight / No greater love / Calling / One and only lady.
LP: . . . . **DIX 76**
MC: . . . . **CDIX 76**

Burrell, Dave

ECHO.
LP: . . . . **AFF 36**

LUSH LIFE.
Tracks: / In a sentimental mood / Lush life / Come Sunday / Flower is a lovesome thing, A / Mexico city / Trade winds / Crucificade / Budapest conclusion.
LP: . . . . **YX 7533**

ROUND MIDNIGHT.
Tracks: / Straight no chaser / Round midnight / Blue monk / Black Roberts / No games / New York.
LP: . . . . **YX 7541**

Burrell, Kenny

A LA CARTE.
Tracks: / I've been in love before / Dreamy / Our love / St. Thomas / Tenderly / I thought about you / A la carte.
LP: . . . . **MR 5317**

AT THE FIVE SPOT CAFE VOL 1.
Tracks: / Birk's works / Lady be good / Lover man / Swingin' / Hallelujah / Beef stew blues / If you could see me now / 36-23-36.
LP: . . . . **BST 84021**

BLUESIN' AROUND.
LP: **25514**

CATS, THE (See under Flanagan, Tommy).

CHICAGO GOLDEN YEARS.
LP: **515001**

GENERATIONS.
Tracks: / Mark 1 / Fungii mama / Generation / Hi-fly / Jumpin' the blues / Lover man / Dolphin dance / Naima / Star crossed / Just friends / So little time.
LP: . . . . **BT 85137**

GROOVIN' HIGH.
Tracks: / Peace / Someone to light up my life / Lament / If I Love Again / Spring can really hang you up the most / Secret love / Groovin' high.
LP: . . . . **MR 5281**

GUITAR FORMS (Burrell, Kenny & Gil Evans).
Tracks: / Greensleeves / Last night when we were young / Breadwinner / Downstairs / Lotus land / Prelude No.2 / Moon and sand / Loie / Terrace theme.
LP: **2304 158**

HANDCRAFTED.
Tracks: / You and the night and the music / So little time / I'm glad there is you / All blues / It could happen to you.
LP: . . . . **MR 5144**

KENNY BURRELL.
LP: . . . . **JR 152**

KENNY BURRELL IN NEW YORK.
Tracks: / Pent up house / But beautiful / Begs groove / Makin' whoopee / Come rain or come shine / Love your magic spell is everywhere.
LP: . . . . **MR 5241**

LISTEN TO THE DAWN.
Tracks: / Yours is my heart / Alone / My one and only love / You're my everything / Listen to the dawn / Isabella / It amazes me / Never let me go / Papa Joe.
LP: . . . . **MR 5264**

LIVE AT THE VILLAGE VANGUARD (Burrell, Kenny Trio).
Tracks: / All night long / Will you still be in my mind / I'm a fool to want you / Trio / Broadway / Soft winds / Just a sittin' and a rockin' / Well you needn't / Second balcony jump / Willow weep for me / Work song / Woodyn' you / In the still of the night / Don't you know I care / Love you madly / It's getting dark.
LP: . . . . **ARC 500**
LP: . . . . **MR 5216**

MIDNIGHT BLUE.
Tracks: / Chitlins con carne / Mule / Soul lament / Midnight blue / Wavy gravy / Gee baby ain't I good to you / Saturday night blues.
LP: . . . . **BST 84123**
MC: **4BN 84123**

NIGHT SONG.
Tracks: / Night song / Blues for lues / Namely you / Love you madly / Just a sittin' and a rockin' / Shadow of your smile / Brother where are you / Night hawk / Teach me tonight.
LP: **2304 539**

PIECES OF BLUE AND THE BLUES (Burrell, Kenny & The Jazz Guitar Band).
Tracks: / Confessin' the blues / Raincheck / Blue days, blue dreams / Salty papa (A.K.A. blues chantez) / Jedannine / Round midnight / No hype blues.
LP: **B1 90260**

RECAPITULATION.
Tracks: / Mother in law / Hot bossa / Isabella / People / Tender gender,The / I'm a fool to want you / Broadway / Afternoon in Paris / Tricotism / Just a settin' and a rockin' / Well you need'nt / Suite for guitar and orchestra / So little time / Growing / Round and round we go / Recapitulation / I want my baby back / Blues fuse / Wild man / My state, my Kansas, my home / Pine cones and holly berries / My favourite things / Suzy / Wild is the wind.
2LP: . . . . **GCH 2-6034**

TOGETHERING (Burrell, Kenny & Grover Washington Jr.).
Tracks: / Soulero / Sails of your soul / Daydream / Beautiful friendship, A / Togethering / Romance dance / Asphalt canyon blues / What am I here for.
LP: . . . . **BT 85106**

TWO GUITARS (Burrell, Kenny & Jimmy Rainey).
LP: . . . . **OJC 216**

Burrell, Roland

BEST OF ROLAND BURRELL.
LP: . . . . **CSLP 009**

FLING REGGAE MUSIC.
LP: . . . . **PH 0011**

Burris, J.C.

ONE OF THESE MORNINGS.
LP: . . . . **ARHOOLIE 1075**

Burris, Warren

WARREN BURRIS.
Tracks: / Get up off your love / I want your love / Slow down / Dance / Secret lover / I've got it / Darling stay with me / Change my mind / You got the love / Don't let you know.
LP: . . . . **TRPL 121**

Burrito Brothers

BACK TO THE SWEETHEART OF THE RODEO.
2LP: . . . . **AP 054/55**
MCSET: . . . . **AP 054/55C**

WHEELS: TRIBUTE TO CLARENCE WHITE & GRAM PARSONS (Burrito Brothers & CO).
Tracks: / Six white horses / Emmy / Bugler / Promised land, The / Freeborn man / Games people play / Detroit City / 500 miles / Four strong winds / Shame on me / Streets of Baltimore / Millers cave / Christine's tune / Wheels.
LP: . . . . **AP 049**

Burrough, Roslyn

LOVE IS HERE.
Tracks: / Devil may care / Love is here(lonely tears) / Song for Jean-Gene / If I were a bell / Never let me go / Did he ever love me / All the things you are / So much in love / I want to make you smile / Young folks.
LP: . . . . **SSC 1009**

Burroughs, Chris

WEST OF TEXAS.
LP: . . . . **ROSE 203**

Burroughs, William

BREAKTHROUGH IN GREY ROOM.
Tracks: / Canine was in combat with the alien / Origin and theory of the tape cutup / Recalling all active agents / Silver Smoke of Dreams / Junkie relations / Joujouka (x 4) / Curse go back / Present time excersises / Working with the popular forces / Interview with Mr Martin / Soundpiece / Burroughs called the law.
LP: . . . . **SUB 33005-8**

DOCTOR IS ON THE MARKET, THE.
LP: . . . . **LTMV.XX**

Burrows, Stuart

GREAT WELSH SONGS (See under Wales) (Burrows, Stuart/John Constable).

GREAT WELSH SONGS (Yr hen Ffefrynnau) (Burrows, Stuart/John Constable).
Tracks: / Arafa don / Bugail Aberdyfi / Yr hen gerddor / Elen fwyn / Bugeilio'r gwenth gwyn / Y dieithryn / Gweddi y pechadur / Galwad u Tywysog / Sul y Blodau / O' na byddai 'n haf o hyd / O Blodwen F'anwylyd / Hiraeth / Paradwys y Bardd.
LP: . . . . **ACM 2007**
MC: . . . . **ZC ACM 2007**

LIFE'S SWEET MELODY.
Tracks: / Somewhere a voice is calling / Linden lea / Down in the forest / Stuttering lovers / Little road to Bethlehem, The / Gentle maiden, The / Lark in the clear air / I know of two bright eyes / God keep you is my prayer / Garden where the praties grow / Pleading / I love thee / Old house / Dream / For your dear sake / I'll take you home again, Kathleen / Kathleen.
LP: . . . . **DSLO 44**

OPERETTA FAVOURITES.
Tracks: / You are my heart's delight / O maiden maiden, my maiden / Farewell my love, farewell / Girls were made to love and kiss / Alone, always alone / Comrades this is the life for me / Vienna, city of my dreams / Serenade / My heart and I / Don't ask me why / Shine through my dreams / I'm only a strolling vagabond.
LP: . . . . **DSLO 16**

SONGS FOR YOU.
2LP: . . . . **DPA 607/8**
MCSET: . . . . **KDPC 607/8**

TO THE LAND OF DREAMS.
Tracks: / Marie my girl / Passing by / Oh, promise me / Trees / Gortnamona / I heard you singing / Kerry dance, The / Dry those tears / Smilin' thro / Parted / Dearest of all / Sitting by the windows / Gloaming, The.
LP: . . . . **DSLO 43**

WORLD OF FAVOURITE BALLADS.
Tracks: / Mother o' mine / Sunshine of your smile, The / I dream of Jeannie with the light brown hair / Roses of Picardy / I hear you calling me / Come into the garden, Maud / Star of Bethlehem, The / As I sit here / When you and I were young, Maggie / Silver threads among the gold / I give thanks for you / Danny boy / Silent worship / Thora / Maire my girl / Passing by / Oh, promise me / Cortnamona / I heard you singing / Kerry dance, The / O dry those tears.
MC: **4300904**

WORLD OF THE SACRED SONGS.
LP: . . . . **SPA 219**
MC: . . . . **KCSP 219**

Burrows, Terry

WATCHING THE BURNING BRIDE (see Tietchens, Asmus).

WHISPERING SCALE, THE.
LP: . . . . **HAM 26**

Bursen, Howie

BUILDING ROOM.
LP: . . . . **FF 441**

Burston, Clara

FRANKIE & CLARA 1929-30 (See Wallace, Frankie) (Burston, Clara & Frankie Wallace).

Burtnick, Glenn

HEROES AND ZEROS.
Tracks: / Follow you / Spinning my wheel / Walls came down / Stupid boys (suckers for love) / Love goes on / Heard it on the radio / Abalene / Here comes Sally / Scattered / Day your ship gets thru, The.
LP: . . . . **AMA 5166**
MC: . . . . **AMC 5166**

Burton, Gary

COOL LIGHTS.
Tracks: / Going home / Cool nights / With mallets of forethought / Take another look / I never left / Gorgeous / Huba Huba / Hopscotch / Artifacts / Last to know, The / Farmer's trust (Only on CD.).
LP: . . . . **GRP 96431**
MC: . . . . **GRP 96434**

COUNTRY ROADS AND OTHER PLACES (Burton, Gary Quartet).
Tracks: / Country roads / Green mountains, The / True or false / Gone, but forgotten / Ravel prelude / And on the third day / Singing song, The / Whichita breakdown / My foolish heart / Family joy, A.
LP: . . . . **PL 45139**

DREAMS SO REAL (Music of Carla Bley).
LP: . . . . **ECM 1072**

DUET: GARY BURTON & CHICK COREA (Burton, Gary & Chick Corea).
LP: . . . . **ECM 1140**

EASY AS PIE (Burton, Gary Quartet).
LP: . . . . **ECM 1184**

GARY BURTON IN CONCERT (see Corea, Chick).

GARY BURTON & THE BERKLEE ALL STARS (Burton, Gary & The Berklee All Stars).
MC: . . . . **JC 3301**
LP: . . . . **JLP 3301**

IN CONCERT, MIDEM 81 (See under Jamal, Ahmad).

LYRIC SUITE FOR SEXTET (see Corea, Chick) (Burton, Gary & Chick Corea).

MATCHBOOK (see Towner, Ralph).

PARIS ENCOUNTER (see Graphelli, Stephen) (Burton, Gary/Stephen Graphelli).

PASSENGERS (Burton, Gary & Eberhard Weber).
LP: . . . . **EMC 1092**

PICTURE THIS (Burton, Gary Quartet).
LP: . . . . **ECM 1226**

REUNION (Burton, Gary & Pat Metheny).
Tracks: / Autumn / Reunion / Origin / Will you say you will / House on the hill / Panama / Chairs and children / Wasn't always easy / Chief, The / Tiempos felice / Quick and running (CD only.).
LP: . . . . **GRP 95981**
MC: . . . . **GRP 95984**

RIGHT TIME RIGHT PLACE (Burton, Gary & Paul Bley).
Tracks: / Ida Lupino / Isn't it romantic / Laura's dream / Carla / Olhos de gato / Alcazar / Rightly so / Nothing to declare /

You don't know what love is / Eiderdown / Turn out the stars.
LP: SNTF 1038

SLIDE SHOW (see Towner, Ralph & Gary Burton) (Burton, Gary & Ralph Towner).

SOMETHING'S COMING.
LP: NL 89377

THAT'S JAZZ (Burton, Gary & Keith Jarrett).
Tracks: / Grow your own / Moonchild / In your quiet place / Como en Vietnam / Fortune smiles / Raven speaks, The.
LP: K 50242

TIMES LIKE THESE.
LP: GR 9569
MC: GRC 9569

WHIZ KIDS (Burton, Gary Quartet).
Tracks: / Last clown, The / Yellow fever / Soulful Bill / La divetta / Cool train / Loop, The.
LP: ECM 1329

WORKS: GARY BURTON.
Tracks: / Olhos de gato / Desert air / Tunnel of love / Vox humana / Three / Brotherhood / Chelsea bells / Coral / Domino biscuit.
LP: 8232671

ZURICH CONCERT (see Corea, Chick) (Burton, Gary & Chick Corea).

Burton, James

CORN PICKIN' & SLICK SLIDIN' (see Mooney, Ralph) (Burton, James/ Ralph Mooney).

Burton, Jay Arthur

MIDNIGHT DANCE.
Tracks: / Nothin' like your lovin' in the mornin' / Just a love song / Sweet Amy / Fooling around / Good love / I want a woman / For the nights / Lovin' you, baby (but it just don't feel the same) / Once-in-a-lifetime love / Midnight dance.
LP: PTLS 1071

Burton, Jenny

JENNY BURTON.
Tracks: / Bad habits / Dancing for my life / Let's get back to love / Love runs deeper than pride / Why can't I touch you / Load it up / Nobody can tell me (He don't love me) / Once in a lifetime love.
MC: 781 238-4

SOUVENIRS.
Tracks: / Do you want it bad enuff / Anticipation / Love me mechanically / Don't it feel good / Souvenirs / Can't forget the love / Until you come back to me / River, The.
LP: K 781 690-1
MC: K 781 690-4

Burton, John (nar)

BRITISH WILD BIRDS IN STEREO (see under British Wild Birds...) (Burton, John & David Tombs).

Burton, Pat

WE'VE BEEN WAITING FOR THIS (Burton, Pat & Bray Brothers).
LP: FF 005

Burton, Richard

ANTHOLOGY - POETRY READINGS.
MCSET: SAY 47
MCSET: ARGO 1046

LOVE POEMS OF JOHN DONNE, THE (See under Donne, John).

Burton, Robert

ROBERT BURTON.
LP: EM 9532 1

Burton, Tommy

IT AIN'T EXACTLY BACKGROUND MUSIC.
LP: TRALP 2002

TOMMY BURTON'S SPORTINGHOUSE QUARTET PLUS ONE (Burton, Tommy Quartet).
LP: TRAC 2002

TONIGHT'S MY... (Burton's, Tommy Sporting House Quartet).
LP: LRCLP 2003

Burton, W.E. 'Buddy'

SOUTHSIDE CHICAGO JAZZ & BLUES PIANO.
LP: WJS 1006

Burwell, Carter

DOC HOLLYWOOD.
LP: VS 5332
MC: VSC 5332

Bus Boys

AMERICAN WORKER.
Tracks: / American workers / New shoes / Last forever / Opportunity / Heart and soul / I get lost / Soul surfing USA / Yellow lights / Falling in love / I believe.
LP: 204833

Busby, Colin

BIG SWING BAND FAVOURITE (Busby, Colin Big Swing Band).
Tracks: / Woodchoppers ball / Sing sing sing / April in Paris / Take the 'A' train / String of pearls / Begin the beguine / One o'clock jump / Skyliner / In the mood / St. Louis blues march / Satin doll / Little brown jug.
LP: YU 100
MC: CYU 100
MC: CSIV 1117

TEN GREAT TV THEMES (Busby, Colin Swinging Brass).
Tracks: / Rocky / Charlie's Angels, Theme from / Hotel / Cagney and Lacey / Rockford files / Hill Street blues / Quincy / Dynasty / Soap / Dallas.
LP: YU 107
MC: CYU 107

Busby, Sid

PORTRAITS (Busby, Sid and the Berkeley Orchestra).
Tracks: / Portrait of my love / With a song in my heart / Days of wine and roses, The / I can't get started / My son, my son / Serenade in blue / Java / Stardust / As time goes by / Serenata / And this is my beloved / Love changes everything / Violino tzigano / When a love affair has ended.
MC: PTLC 1105

Bush, Blake

COUNTRY BLUE GRASS (Bush, Blake & Taylor).
LP: SNTF 704

Bush, Bobby

FUNKY WAY TO TREAT SOMEBODY (see under Party People) (Bush, Bobby/ Party People).

Bush, Charlie

LOCAL LIVING LEGEND.
LP: REV 33

Bush, Kate

DREAMING, THE.
Tracks: / Sat in your lap / There goes a tenner / Pull out the pin / Suspended in Gaffa / Leave it open / Dreaming, The / Night of the swallow / All the love / Houdini / Get out of my house.
LP: ATAK 45
LP: EMC 3419
MC: TCATAK 45
MC: TCEMC 3419

HOUNDS OF LOVE.
Tracks: / Running up that hill / Hounds of love / Big sky, The / Jig of life / Mother stands for comfort / Cloudbusting / And dream of sleep / Under ice / Waking the witch / Watching you without me / Hello earth / Morning fog.
LP: EJ 2403841
LP: KAB 1
MC: EJ 2403840
MC: EJ 2403844
MC: TCKAB 1
LP: ATAK 157
MC: TCATAK 157

KATE BUSH: INTERVIEW PICTURE DISC.
LPPD: BAK 2006

KATE BUSH: INTERVIEW PICTURE DISC.
LPPD: BAK 2073

KICK INSIDE, THE.
Tracks: / Moving / Saxophone song / Strange phenomena / Kite / Man with the child in his eyes, The / Wuthering heights / James and the cold gun / Feel it / Oh to be in love / L'amour looks something like you / Them heavy people / Room for the life / Kick inside, The.
LP: EMC 3223
MC: TCEMC 3223
LP: FA 3207
MC: TCFA 3207
LPPD: EMPC 3223

LIONHEART.
Tracks: / Symphony in blue / In search of Peter Pan / Wow / Don't push your foot on the heartbrake / Oh England my lionheart / Fullhouse / In the warm room / Kashka from Baghdad / Coffee homeground / Hammer horror.
LP: FA 4130941
MC: FA 4130944
LP: FA 3094
MC: TCFA 3094
LP: EMA 787

MUSIC AND MEDIA INTERVIEW PICTURE DISC.
LPPD: KB 1011

NEVER FOR EVER.
Tracks: / Babooshka / Delius / Blow away / All we ever look for / Egypt / Wedding list, The / Violin / Infant kiss, The / Night scented stock / Army dreamers / Breathing.
LP: EMA 794
MC: TCEMA 794
LP: ATAK 91
MC: TCATAK 91

ON STAGE.
LP: 1A 052Z 07133

SENSUAL WORLD, THE.
Tracks: / Sensual world, The / Love and anger / Fog, The / Reaching out / Heads we're dancing / Deeper understanding / Between a man and a woman / Never be mine / Rocket's tail / This woman's work / Walk straight down the middle (CD only.).
LP: EMD 1010
MC: TCEMD 1010

THIS WOMAN'S WORK (Anthology 1979-1990).
Tracks: / Empty bullring, The (Rarities vol. I.) / Ran tan waltz (Rarities vol. I.) / Pasing through air (Rarities vol. I.) / December will be magic again (Rarities vol. I.) / Warm and soothing (Rarities vol. I.) / Lord of the reedy river (Rarities vol. I.) / Ne t'en fui pas (Rarities vol. I.) / Un baiser d'enfant (Rarities vol. I.) / Under the ivy (Rarities vol. I.) / Burning bridge (Rarities vol. I.) / My lagan love (Rarities vol. II.) / Handsome cabin boy, The (Rarities vol. II.) / Not this time (Rarities vol. II.) / Walk straight down the middle (Rarities vol. II.) / Be kind to my mistakes (Rarities vol. II.) / I'm still waiting (Rarities vol. II.) / Ken (Rarities vol. II. From the comic strip film, "GLC".) / One last look around the house before we go... (Rarities vol. II.) / Wuthering heights (new vocal) (Rarities vol. II.) / Experiment IV (Rarities vol. II.) / Them heavy people (Rarities vol. III. Album box set only.) / Don't push your foot on the heartbrake (Rarities vol. III. Album box set only.) / James and the cold gun (Rarities vol. III. Album box set only.) / L'amour looks something like you (Rarities vol. III. Album box set only.) / Running up that hill (12" mix) (Rarities vol. III. Album box set only.) / Cloudbusting (The organon mix) (Rarities vol. III. Album box set only.) / Hounds of love (alternative) (Rarities vol. III. Album box set only.) / Big sky (The meteorological mix) (Rarities vol. III. Album box set only.) / Experiment IV (12" mix) (Rarities vol. III. Album box set only.).
LPS: KBBX 1
MCSET: TCKBBX 1

WHOLE STORY, THE.
Tracks: / Wuthering Heights / Cloudbusting / Man with the child in his eyes, The / Breathing / Wow / Hounds of love / Running up that hill / Army dreamers / Sat in your lap / Experiment IV / Dreaming, the / Babooshka / Big sky, the (On video only.).
LP: KBTV 1
MC: TCKBTV 1

Bush, Sam

LATE AS USUAL.
LP: ROUNDER 0195
MC: ROUNDER 0195C

TOGETHER AGAIN - FOR THE FIRST TIME (Bush, Sam & Alan Munde).
Tracks: / Stymied / Banjalin / Forked deer / Small change / Clear skies / Old widder woman / Cattle in the cane / Counterblast rag / Town and country / Foster's reel / Panhandle country / Howdy in Hickman County / Eleanor Rigby.
LP: RRR 0007

Bush, Stan

STAN BUSH AND BARRAGE (Bush, Stan & Barrage).
Tracks: / Temptation / Primitive lover / Crank that radio / Do you remember / Touch, The / Love don't lie / Heart vs head / Gates of paradise / Take it like a man / What is love.
LP: INT 147318
LP: 832 787-1
MC: 832 787-4

Bush Tetras

WILD THINGS.
MC: A 119

Bush Twangers

HERE WE GO AGAIN.
LP: AMLP 2008

Bushido

DELIVERANCE.
Tracks: / Question of identity, A / Lament / Intrigue / Imperial affair, An / High rise / Question of time, A.
LP: TMLP 12

SANDS OF NAKAJIMA, THE.
LP: TMLP 10

Bushmen Don't Surf

ALIVE.
LP: MRL 001

Bushwackers

BAND PLAYED WALTZING MATILDA.
MC: SMAC 9020

BENEATH THE SOUTHERN CROSS.
Tracks: / St. Annes real / WAltzing matilda / Band played waltzing Matilda, The / Catalpa / Lazy Harry's / South Australia / Beneath the Southern cross / Plate glass window / Battlers ballad / Spider by the Gwydir / Lachlan tigers / Fishing reels.
LP: CBS 85718

BUSHWACKERS DANCE ALBUM.
MC: SMAC 9019

SHEARER'S DREAM (Bushwackers & Bullockies Band).
LP: LRF 019

Busia, Kofi

OH AFRICA.
Tracks: / Oh Africa / Child of a survivor / Scramble / One day (the mountains) / There can be no blues / Deathless one, The / Missionary, The / Thirty men / Traveller, The / Green green green / N.M.Q. (Nelson Mandela Quintet) / Hold somebody.
LP: ANM 1228 L
MC: ANM 1228 C

Business

1980-81 THE OFFICIAL BOOTLEG.
LP: SYNLP 2

OFFICIAL BOOTLEG BACKED WITH LOUD, THE.
LP: WOW DLP 4

SATURDAY'S HEROES.
LP: SE 13
LP: LINKLP 115

SINGALONG A BUSINESS (The Best of the Business).
Tracks: / Suburban rebels / Blind justice / Loud, proud and punk / Real enemy, The / Spanish jails / Product / National insurance blacklist (employers blacklist) / Get out of my house / Saturday's heroes / Out in the cold / Smash the discos / Harry May / Drinking and driving / Hurry up Harry.
LP: DOJOLP 35

WELCOME TO THE REAL WORLD.
LP: LINK LP 035

Business Studies

BUSINESS STUDIES (COURSE) (See under G.S.C.E. Packs) (Longman/ Pickwick Pass Packs).

Business Trading

BUSINESS TRADING ETHICS (See under UNESCO reports).

Buskers

LIFE OF A MAN.
Tracks: / Drowsy / Maggie / Life of a man, The / Pretty Susan the pride of Kildare / Piper on the hob / Job of journeywork / Spancil hill / New York girls / Jack in the fog / Yellow tinker, The / Mary McMahon / Bill hearts / Beggarman, The / Off to sea once more / Fahey's no.1 / Humours of Tulla / Lord of the dance / Night visiting song / Banish misfortune.
LP: RUB 007

Buskers of London

BUSKERS OF LONDON (Various artists).
LP: PRIME 001

Buskin, Joe

WORLD IS WAITING 1942-46 (Buskin, Joe & Mel Powell).
Tracks: / When did you leave heaven / World is waiting for the sunrise / Blue skies / Mood at twilight / Lover man / Avalon / Pickin' at the pic / Fade out / Oh lady be good / Georgia.
LP: AG6 24063

Busse, Henry

1935 (Busse, Henry & His Orchestra).
Tracks: / Hot lips / Rose room / Clouds / Continental / Honeysuckle rose / Haunting blues / Here comes Cookie / idewalks of Cuba / When day is done / Ja da / Solitude / What's the reason / Haunting me / Darktown strutters ball / Love is just around the corner.
LP: HMP 5051

1949 (Busse, Henry & His Orchestra).
LP: CLP 76

1941/44 VOL 2 (Busse, Henry & His Shuttle Rhythm Orchestra).
LP: HSR 193

HENRY BUSSE, 1935.
Tracks: / Rose room / Clouds / Continental, The / Honeysuckle rose / Haunting clues / Here comes cookie / Sidewalks of Cuba / When day is done / Ja da / Solitude / What's the reason (I'm not pleasing you) / Hot lips / Haunting

me / Darktown strutters' ball / Love is just around the corner.
LP: . . . . HSR 122

Buster

BUSTER.
Tracks: / We love girls / Saturday night / I was born to sing your song / Pretty legs / Daybreak / Born to be wild / Love rules / She my girl / I'm a fool / Listen to what the man said / Sunday / We love girls (reprise).
LP: . . . . PL 25026

Buster (Film)

BUSTER (1988 film soundtrack) (Various artists).
Tracks: / Two hearts: *Collins, Phil* / Just one look: *Hollies* / Big noise: *Collins, Phil* / Robbery: *Dudley, Anne* / I got you babe: *Sonny & Cher* / Keep on running: *Davis, Spencer Group* (On LP & cassette only) / Loco in Acapulco: *Four Tops* / How do you do it: *Gerry & the Pacemakers* / I just don't know what to do with myself: *Springfield, Dusty* / Sweets for my sweet: *Searchers* / Will you still be waiting?: *Dudley, Anne*/ Groovy kind of love: *Collins, Phil.*
LP: . . . . V 2544
MC: . . . . TCV 2544

Busters

NO DOUBT.
LP: . . . . RUDELP 011

RUDER THAN RUDE.
LP: . . . . PHZA 27

Busters All Stars

SKINHEAD LOVE AFFAIR.
LP: . . . . BBSLP 005
MC: . . . . BBSMC 005

Butch & Bucky

LADY BE GOOD.
LP: . . . . DR 102

Butch Cassidy (film)

BUTCH CASSIDY AND THE SUNDANCE KID (Original soundtrack) (Various artists).
LP: . . . . SP 3159
MC: . . . . CS 3159

Butcher, Eddie

I ONCE WAS A DAYSMAN.
LP: . . . . FRR 003

SHAMROCK ROSE AND THISTLE.
LP: . . . . LED 2070

Butera, Sam

JUMP, JIVE AND WAIL (Butera, Sam & The Witnesses).
LP: . . . . PREP 100

Buthelezi, Mzikayifani

FASHION MASWEDI.
Tracks: / Amadyisi / Usizi / Umkhwewami / Mkami / Isighaza / Uze ungikhumbile / Inkunzi emmyama / Come back / Inyanga / Kuyesinda / Bangifuma ngandlela / Kungeneni laye khaya.
LP: . . . . GREL 2007

FASHION MASWEDI (IMPORT).
Tracks: / Amadyisi / Usizi / Umkhwewami / Mkami / Isighaza / Uzeungikhumbile / Inkunzi emmyama / Come back / Inyanga / Kuyesinda / Bangifuma ngandlela / Kungeneni laye khaya.
LP: . . . . ROUNDER 5032
MC: . . . . ROUNDER 5032C

Butler, Billy

RIGHT TRACK, THE (Butler, Billy & The Enchanters).
LP: . . . . ED 147

Butler, Frank

NIGHT FLIGHT TO DAKAR (see Cohn, Al/Billy Mitchell etc.).

STEPPER,THE.
LP: . . . . X 152

Butler, George

OPEN UP BABY.
Tracks: / Open up baby / Big Momma, little Momma / Axe and the wind / Jelly jam / Hold me baby / Do something baby / She walks like my Mary Ann / Put it all in there / My forty year old woman / Harmonica prayer / Gravy child / Best of wild child / Keep on (doin' what you're doin') / Hippy playground.
LP: . . . . CRB 1104

Butler, Henry

FIVIN' AROUND.
Tracks: / Fivin' around / L.A. samba / Eastern connection / Improvisation on an Afghanistan Theme / Giant steps / Swing it / My colouring book / Butler's blues, The / Old folks / I want Jesus to walk with me.
LP: . . . . IMCA 5707
MC: . . . . IMCAC 5707

Butler, Jerry

IT'S A LIFETIME THING (see under Houston, Thelma) (Butler, Jerry/Thelma Houston).

JERRY & BETTY (see Everett, Betty) (Butler, Jerry & Betty Everett).

LEGENDARY PHILADELPHIA HITS, THE.
LP: 822212 1
MC: 822212 4

NOTHING SAYS I LOVE YOU LIKE I LOVE YOU.
Tracks: / Cooling out / Let's make love / Sad eyes / Mighty good people / I'm glad to be back / Nothing says I love you like I love you / Dream world / Are you lonely tonight.
LP: . . . . PIR 83180

ONLY THE STRONG SURVIVE.
Tracks: / Send a telegram (western union man) / Only the strong survive / Lost / Don't let love hang you up / Got to see if I can get mommy (to come back home) / Just because I really love you / I could write a book / Whats the use of breaking up / Since I lost you baby / Been a long time / Moody woman / Brand new me / Can't forget about you baby / Are you happy / Go away (find yourself) / Never give you up.
LP: . . . . JABB 6
MC: . . . . JABBC 6

WHATEVER YOU WANT.
Tracks: / Rainbow Valley / Lonely soldier / Thanks to you / When trouble calls / Aware of love / Isle of sirens / It's too late / Moon River / Woman with soul / Let it be whatever it is / I almost lost my mind / Good times / Give it up / Believe in me / Just for you / For your precious love.
LP: . . . . CRB 1118

Butler, Jonathan

HEAL OUR LAND.
LP: . . . . HIP 102
MC: . . . . HIPC 102

INTRODUCING JONATHAN BUTLER.
LP: . . . . HIP 31
MC: . . . . HIPC 31

JONATHAN BUTLER.
LP: . . . . HIP 46
MC: . . . . HIPC 46

LIES (OLD GOLD) (See under Turner, Ruby).

MORE THAN FRIENDS.
Tracks: / There's one born every minute / Breaking away / More than friends / Take me home / True love never fails / She's a teaser / Sarah Sarah / She's hot / It's so hard to let you go / Sekona.
LP: . . . . HIP 70
MC: . . . . HIPC 70

Butler, Richard

PERFECT TRIANGLE, THE.
Tracks: / Derwentwater's farewell / Rowan tree hill, The / Wild hills of Wannies / Brackenrigg / Happy hours / Blow the wind southerly / Johnny Armstrong / Crooked bawbee / Rowan tree / Whittingham Green lane / Proudlock's hornpipe / Carrick hornpipe / Chevy Chase / Come you not from Newcastle / Bonnie woodside / Bonnie North Tyne / Lads of Alnwick, The / Rothbury hills / Bill Charlton's fancy.
LP: . . . . SDL 345
MC: . . . . CSDL 345

Butler, Steve

WAVING AND DROWNING.
LP: . . . . GUM 007

Butt, John

ORLANDO GIBBONS (see under Kings College) (Butt, John & Kings College Cambridge Choir).

Butterbeans & Susie

PAPA'S GOT THE MOJO.
LP: . . . . BT 2009

Butterfield 8

BLOW.
LP: . . . . AGOLP 12
MC: . . . . ZGOLP 12

Butterfield, Billy

BILLY BUTTERFIELD, 1946.
Tracks: / Moten stomp / Sophisticated lady / What is there to say / I only have eyes for you / I wonder who's kissing her now / Don't blame me / All the things you are / Blue moon / You've got me crying now / Night and day / All the cats join in / Stormy weather / Bidin' my time / Embraceable you.
LP: . . . . HSR 173

BILLY BUTTERFIELD & BENNY SIMKINS' BAND (Butterfield, Billy & Benny Simkin's Band).
LP: . . . . J 93

JUST FRIENDS.
LP: . . . . J 117

RAPPORT (Butterfield, Billy & Dick Wellstood).
LP: . . . . 77 S 54

TRIBUTE TO BENNY GOODMAN (See under Hucko, Peanuts).

WATCH WHAT HAPPENS.
LP: . . . . FLY 205

Butterfield, Erskine

1944 & 1956, PIANO SOLOS.
LP: . . . . HQ 2050

TUESDAY AT TEN.
LP: . . . . CLP 62

Butterfield, Paul

BETTER DAYS.
LP: . . . . NEXLP 127

EAST WEST (Butterfield Blues Band).
Tracks: / Walkin' blues / Get out of my life woman / I got a mind to give up living / All these blues / Work song / Mary mary / Two trains running / Never say no / East West.
LP: . . . . ED 212

IT ALL COMES BACK.
LP: . . . . NEXLP 128

OFFER YOU CAN'T REFUSE, AN (Butterfield, Paul & Walter Horton).
Tracks: / Easy / Have a good time / Mean mistreater / In the mood / West side blues / Louise / Tin pan alley / Walters boogie / Everything's gonna be alright / Poor boy / Got my mojo working / Last night / Loaded / One room country shack.
LP: . . . . RL 008

PAUL BUTTERFIELD BLUES BAND (Butterfield Blues Band).
Tracks: / Born in Chicago / Shake your moneymaker / Blues with a feeling / Thank you Mr. Poobah / I got my mojo working / Mellow down easy / Screamin' / Our love is drifting / Mystery train / Last night / Look over yonders wall.
LP: . . . . ED 150

RESURRECTION OF THE PIGBOY CRABSHAW (Butterfield Blues Band).
Tracks: / One more heartache / Driftin' and driftin' / Pity the fool / Born under a bad sign / Run out of time / Double trouble / Drivin' wheel / Droppin' out / Tollin' bells.
LP: . . . . ED 301
LP: . . . . K 42017

Butterfly Ball

BUTTERFLY BALL, THE/WIZARD'S CONVENTION (See under Glover, Roger) (Glover, Roger/Deep Purple).

Buttermountain Boys

BUTTERMOUNTAIN BOYS.
MC: . . . . BMB 001

FAT TUESDAY.
LP: . . . . FESTIVAL 5
MC: . . . . FESTIVAL 5C

Butthole Surfers

BUTTHOLE SURFERS.
LP: . . . . VIRUS 32

HAIRWAY TO STEVEN.
LP: . . . . BFFP 29
MC: . . . . BFFP 29C

LOCUST ABORTION TECHNICIAN.
Tracks: / Sweat loaf / Graveyard (1) / Graveyard (2) / Pittsburgh to Lebanon / Weber / Hay / Human cannonball / USSA / O-men, The / Kuntz / 22 going on 23.
LP: . . . . BFFP 15

PSYCHIC POWERLESS ANOTHER MANS SAC.
LP: . . . . SAVE 005

REMBRANDT PUSSYHORSE.
Tracks: / Creep in the cellar / Sea ferring / American woman / Waiting for Jimmy to kick / Stransgersdie / Perry / Whirling hall of knives / Mark says alright / In the cellar.
LP: . . . . RRELP 2

Button Down Brass

GOLDEN HOUR OF BUTTON DOWN BRASS.
LP: . . . . GH 588

Buttons And Bows

BUTTONS AND BOWS 1.
LP: . . . . DAM 003

BUTTONS AND BOWS 2.
LP: . . . . DAM 006

FIRST MONTH OF SUMMER, THE.
Tracks: / John D McGurk's / I les de la Madeleine / First month of summer, The / Fitmaurice's polka / Sir Sidney Smith / Man from Bundoran, The / Humours of Kinvara, The / Green garters / Inisheer / Gypsy hornpipe, The / Margaret's waltz / Four courts, The / Joyous waltz, The / Piper's despair, The.
LP: . . . . SIF 1079
MC: . . . . CSIF 1079

Butzman, Frieder

DAS MADCHEN AUF DER SCHAUKER.
2LP: . . . . ZSO 8/9

WAR PUR WAR (Butzman, Frieder & Thoma Kapir).
LP: . . . . ZSO 99LP

Buy Off The Bar

LEAVE IT BILLY.
Tracks: / It's up to you / Peanut butter bay / Numbers music / To shy to die / Commie comeback / Amuse yourself / Guitar mafia / I belong / Wishes.
LP: . . . . CALCLP 018

PAR-BOILED.
LP: . . . . BIJOOP 023

Buzz

BUZZ (Various artists).
LP: . . . . ABB 03

Buzz And The Flyers

BUZZ AND THE FLYERS.
LP: . . . . NERD 006

Buzzcocks

ANOTHER MUSIC IN A DIFFERENT KITCHEN.
Tracks: / Fast cars / No reply / You tear me up / Get on our own / Love battery / 16 / I don't mind / Fiction romance / Autonomy / I need / Moving away from the pulsebeat.
LP: . . . . ATAK 51
MC: . . . . TCATAK 51
LP: . . . . FC 021
LP: . . . . FA 3199
MC: . . . . TCFA 3199
LP: . . . . UAG 30159
MC: . . . . FC 021C

DIFFERENT KIND OF TENSION, A.
Tracks: / Paradise / Sitting 'round at home / You say you don't love me / You know you can't help it / Mad, mad Judy / Raison d'etre / I don't know what to do with my life / Money / Hollow inside / Different kind of tension / I believe / Radio nine.
LP: . . . . FC 023
LP: . . . . UAG 30260
MC: . . . . FC 023C

LEST WE FORGET.
MC: . . . . A 158

LIVE AT THE ROXY 2ND APRIL 1977.
Tracks: / Orgasm addict / Get on your own / What do I get? / Oh shit / No reply / Fast cars / Friends of mine / Time's up / Boredom.
LP: . . . . RRLP 131
MC: . . . . RRLC 131
LP: . . . . FREELP 002

LOVE BITES.
Tracks: / Real world / Ever fallen in love (with someone you shouldn't've) / Operator's manual / Nostalgia / Just lust / Sixteen again / Walking distance / Love is lies / Nothing left / E.S.P. / Late for the train.
LP: . . . . FA 3174
MC: . . . . TCFA 3174
LP: . . . . FC 022
LP: . . . . UAG 30197
MC: . . . . FC 022C

OPERATORS MANUAL (Buzzcocks Best).
Tracks: / Orgasm addict / What do I get? / I don't mind / Autonomy / Fast cars / Get on our owns / 16 / Fiction romance / Love you more / Noise annoys / Ever fallen in love (with someone you shouldn' / Operators manual / Nostalgia / Walking distance / Nothing left / ESP / Promises / Lipstick / Everybody's happy nowadays / Harmony in my head / You say you don't love me / I don't know what to do with my life / I believe / Are everything / Radio nine.
2LP: . . . . EM 1421
MC: . . . . TCEM 1421

PEEL SESSIONS: BUZZCOCKS (2).
LP: . . . . SFRLP 104
MC: . . . . SFRMC 104

PRODUCT.
Tracks: / Fast cars / No reply / You tear me up / Get on your own / Love battery / Sixteen / I don't mind / Fiction romance / Autonomy / I need / Moving away from the pulsebeat / Real world / Ever fallen in love (with someone you shouldn't've) / Operator's manual / Nostalgia / Just lust / Walking distance / Love is lies / Nothing left / E.S.P. / Late for the train / Paradise / Sitting 'round at home / You say you don't love me / You know you can't help it / Mad, mad Judy / Raison D'etre / I don't know what to do with my life / Money / Hollow inside / Different kind of tension, A / I believe / Radio nine / Orgasm addict / What do I get? / Love you more / Promises / Everybody's happy nowadays / Harmony in my head /

Whatever happened to? / Oh shit / Noise annoys / Lipstick / Why can't I touch it? / Something's gone wrong again / Breakdown / What do I get / Times up / Are everything / Strange thing / What do you know? / Why she's a girl from the chainstore / Airwaves dream / Running free / I look alone.
LPS: . . . . LPPRDT 1

SINGLES GOING STEADY.
Tracks: / Orgasm addict / What do I get / I don't mind / Love you more / Ever fallen in love (with someone you shouldn't've) / Promises / Everybody's happy nowadays / Harmony in my head / Whatever happened to / Oh shit! / Autonomy / Noise annoys / Just lust / Lipstick / Why can't I touch it / Somethings gone wrong again / Love you more / Ever fallen in love (with someone you shouldn't've) / What do I get / Promises.
LP: . . . . ATAK 52
MC: . . . . TCATAK 52
LP: . . . . LBR 1043
MC: . . . . TCLBR 1043
LP: . . . . FA 3241
MC: . . . . TCFA 3241

TOTAL POP.
Tracks: / Walking distance / E.S.P. / Strange thing / Harmony in my head / Why she's a girl from the chainstore / I believe / Breakdown / Love battery / Real world / I don't know what to do with my life / Airwaves dream / Ever fallen in love (with someone you shouldn't've).
LP: . . . . WS 021
MC: . . . . WS 021X1

B.V.S.M.P.

BEST BELONG TOGETHER, THE.
Tracks: / Anytime / Can we go on / Rock bottom / Grad dat botre / I need you / Gentle memory.
MC: . . . . ZCDB 503
LP: . . . . DBLP 503

Bwchadanas

CARIAD CYWIR.
LP: . . . . 1306 M

By All Means

BEYOND THE DREAM.
MC: . . . . BRCA 542
LP: . . . . BRLP 542

BY ALL MEANS.
Tracks: / I surrender to your love / I'm the one who loves you / You decided to go / I believe in you / I want to thank you / Let's get started now / Slow jam (can I have this dance with you) / Somebody save me / Does it feel good to you / We're into this groove.
MC: . . . . BRCA 520
LP: . . . . BRLP 520
MC: . . . . ICM 2018
MC: 842 573 4

By Invitation Only

BY INVITATION ONLY (See under Freeman, Alan) (Various artists).

By The Light

BY THE LIGHT OF THE SILVERY MOON/LULLABY OF BROA (Original soundtracks) (Various artists).
LP: . . . . P 18421
MC: . . . . BT 18421

Byard, Jaki

BLUES FOR SMOKE.
LP: . . . . CS 9018

FAMILY MAN.
Tracks: / Just rolling along / Mood indigo / Chelsea bridge / L.H. gatewalk rag / Ballad to Louise / Family suite.
LP: . . . . MR 5173

IMPROVISATIONS (Byard, Jaki & Ran Blake).
LP: . . . . SN 1022

LIVE AT THE ROYAL FESTIVAL HALL (Byard, Jaki/Riley, Howard).
LP: . . . . LR 133

THERE'LL BE SOME CHANGES MADE.
Tracks: / There'll be some changes made / Lonely town / Blues au gratin / Excerpts from songs of proverbs / Besame mucho / Spanish tinge / Journey night of departure / To Bob Vatel of Paris-Blues for Jennie / Some other spring-Every year / Tribute to Jimmy Slide.
LP: . . . . MR 5007

Byars, Betsy (aut)

EIGHTEENTH EMERGENCY, THE (See under Eighteenth Emergency) (Aubery, James (nar)).

NOT-JUST-ANYBODY FAMILY, THE (see under Not Just Anybody... (bk) (Fairman, Blain (nar)).

Byas, Don

ALL THE THINGS YOU ARE.
LP: 2673731
MC: 2673734

AMBIENCES ET SLOWS.
LP: 80970/1

ANTHROPOLOGY.
Tracks: / Anthropology / Moonlight in Vermont / Billie's bounce / Night in Tunisia / Don't blame me.
LP: . . . . BLP 30126

BEN WEBSTER MEETS DON BYAS (see Webster, Ben) (Byas, Don & Ben Webster).

DANISH BREW (See under Moore, Brew) (Byas, Don & Brew Moore).

DON BYAS.
LP: . . . . GNPS 9027

DON BYAS AND FRIENDS.
LP: . . . . AA 500

DON BYAS MEETS BEN WEBSTER (see Webster, Ben).

DON BYAS MEETS THE GIRLS.
LP: . . . . JL 95

JAZZ TIME VOL.1.
LP: 502701

JUMPIN' STUFF (see under Jordan, Louis) (Byas, Don/Louis Jordan/Hot Lips Page).

SAVOY JAM PARTY.
Tracks: / Riffin' and jivin' / Free and easy / Free and easy (2) / Worried and blue / Don's idea (1) / Don's idea (2) / Savoy jam party (2) / Savoy jam party (1) / 1944 stomp / What do you want with my heart / Bass C jam / Sweet and lovely / White rose kick / My deep blue dream / Byas'd opinion / Candy / How high the moon / Donby / Byas a drink / I don't know why / Danny boy / Old folks / Cherokee / September in the rain / Living my life / To each his own / They say it's wonderful / Cynthia's in love / September song / St. Louis blues / I've found a new baby / Marie.
2LP: . . . . SJL 2213
2LP: . . . . WL 70512

THOSE BARCELONA DAYS.
LP: . . . . FS 135

TWO KINGS OF THE TENOR SAX 44-45 (Byas, Don & Ben Webster).
LP: 6.24058
LP: AG6 24058

Bye Bye Birdie (film)

BYE BYE BIRDIE (Film Soundtrack) (Various artists).
LP: . . . . AYL 1 3947
MC: . . . . AYK 1 3947

BYE BYE BIRDIE (1960 Original Broadway Cast) (Various artists).
LP: . . . . COS 2025
MC: . . . . BT 2025
MC: . . . . JST 2025

BYE BYE BIRDIE (ORIGINAL ISSUE) (London cast) (Various artists).
LP: . . . . ABL 3385

Byers, Billy

JAZZ WORKSHOP.
LP: . . . . FS 301

Byfield, Trevor

YESTERDAY'S DREAMS.
Tracks: / Yesterdays dreams / Wondrous place / Lovin' you / Maybe tomorrow / Don't / I remember / Love me tender / Raining in my heart / Love hurts / Let it be me / My wish came true / Love me / Only the lonely / Love letters / True love ways.
LP: . . . . RRPLP 1
MC: . . . . RRPMC 1

Byfield, Ziggy

RUNNING (Byfield, Ziggy & Blackheart Band).
Tracks: / Running / Waiting for you / Will you stay / Sleazy dreamer / Move up close / Trixie / If I see you in the morning / Get off my back / Gonna ring your bell / Soldier boy.
LP: . . . . PVK 1

Bygraves, Max

6 TRACK HITS: MAX BYGRAVES.
Tracks: / You're my everything / Gentle on my mind / Deck of cards / Walk right back / For the good times / Rolling round the world.
MC: 7SC 5009

100 GOLDEN GREATS.
LP: . . . . RTDX 2065
MC: . . . . 4 C RTDX 2065

100 MINUTES OF MAX BYGRAVES.
MC: . . . . ZCTON 104

BEST OF MAX.
LP: . . . . SPR 8547
MC: . . . . SPC 8547

CLASSICS.
Tracks: / Cowpuncher's cantata / True loves and false lovers / Little Sir Echo / Big head / You're a pink toothbrush / I wish I could sing like Al Jolson / Gang that sang heart of my heart / Friends and neighbours / Gilly gilly ossenfeffer katzenellenbogen by the sea / Mister sandman / Pendulum song, The / Gretna Green / Meet me on the corner / Little Laplander, The / Out of town / Ballad of Davy Crockett, The / Dummy song, The / Nothin' to do / Try another cherry tree / By the light of the silvery moon / Peggy O'Neal / When you wore a tulip (and I wore a red, red rose) / If you were the only girl in the world / For me and my gal / Good idea son, A / Seventeen sons / Lovely dolla lolly / Chip chopper Charlie / Tomorrow / Say si si / She's a lassie from Lancashire (part of medley) / When Irish eyes are smiling / I belong to Glasgow / Any old iron.
2LP: . . . . DL 41 1054-1
MC: . . . . TCDL 41 1054-4

COLLECTION: MAX BYGRAVES.
Tracks: / Wish me luck as you wave me goodbye / We'll all go riding on a Rainbow, A / Sunny side up / When the guards are on parade / Good morning / Jingle jangle / I've got sixpence / Bless em all / Maizy doats and dozy doats / Far away places / You don't have to tell me (I know) / Let bygones be bygones / Boogie woogie bugle boy / You always hurt the one you love / Tangerine / That old black magic / There I've said it again / That lovely weekend / I don't know why.
MC: . . . . ZCMBY 1
LP: . . . . MAXBY 1
2LP: . . . . CCSLP 232
MC: . . . . CCSMC 232

DECK OF CARDS.
Tracks: / Tie a yellow ribbon / Little green apples / Heartbreaker / What a wonderful world / Kite, The (new version from single) / Mack the knife / Deck of cards / Whose sorry now / Singing the blues / Ramblin' Rose / Messing around on the river / You say something nice about everybody.
LP: . . . . FBLP 8073
MC: . . . . ZCFBL 8073

DISCOLONGAMAX.
Tracks: / Get me to the church on time / How ya gonna keep em down on the farm / You need hands / Autumn leaves / Moonlight serenade / Won't you come home Bill Bailey / Ma (he's making eyes at me) / My mammy / Tulips from Amsterdam / Love is a song / Somebody stole my gal / Feelings.
LP: . . . . N 110
MC: . . . . ZCN 110

EMI YEARS, THE: MAX BYGRAVES.
Tracks: / You're a pink toothbrush / Friends and neighbours / Little Sir Echo / Gang that sang heart of my heart, The / Mister Sandman / Big head / Ballad of Davy Crockett, The / Good idea son, A / Chip chopper Charlie / I wish I could sing like Jolson / Cowpuncher's cantata / Out of town / Nothin' to do / Dummy song, The / Gilly gilly ossenfeffer Katzenellenbogen by th / Meet me on the corner / Little Laplander, The / Pendulum song, The / Seventeen tons / True loves and false lovers.
MC: . . . . TCEMS 1396

FAMILY FAVOURITES.
LP: . . . . LR 003
MC: . . . . LR 003 C

FOCUS ON MAX BYGRAVES.
Tracks: / Heart / Whiffenpoof song, The / Over the rainbow / Oh mein papa / Don't bring Lulu / Get me to the church on time (medley) / Tonight / June is bustin' out all over / There is nothin' like a dame / You need hands / Riders in the sky / Lazybones / I whistle a happy tune / Whatever will be will be / It's alright with me (medley) / People will say we're in love / So in love / Shall we dance / Peg O my heart / My ukelele / Gilly gilly ossenfeffer katzenellenbogen by the sea / Did you ever see a dream walking / Down the lane / Oh what a beautiful morning / On the street where you live / I love Paris / Sit down you're rockin' the boat / Swinging on a star / Paddlin' Madelin' home / Who made the morning / Consider yourself / I'd do anything / What noise annoys an oyster / Standing on the corner (medley) / Hey look me over (medley) / Oklahoma / Seventy-six trombones.
2LP: . . . . FOS 55/56
MC: . . . . KFOC 28093

GOLDEN GREATS OF THE 30'S.
Tracks: / We'll all go riding on a rainbow / Sunnyside up / When the guards are on parade / I don't know why / Dancing in the dark / Way you look tonight / Life is nothing without music / Red sails in the sunset / You brought a new kind of love to me / Dream a little dream of me / Love is the sweetest thing / Play gypsy / Shoe shine boy / We just couldn't say goodbye / Glory of love / Once in a while / Song of the Islands / Blue Hawaii / Harbour lights / I only have eyes for you / Three little words / Exactly like you / I may be wrong / Wish me luck as you wave me goodbye.
LP: . . . . NSPL 18526
MC: . . . . ZCP 18526

GOLDEN GREATS OF THE 40'S.
Tracks: / Good morning / Jingle jangle / I've got sixpence / Bless em all / Maizy doats and dozy doats / You always hurt the one you love / Tangerine / Old black magic, The / You'll never know / Boogie woogie bugle boy / Little on the lonely side, A / I can't love you anymore / Only forever / Don't sit under the apple tree / Five minutes more / That's the moon my son / There, I've said it again / That lovely weekend / I'll never smile again / Heartbreaker / Far away places / You don't have to tell me I know / Let bygones be bygones / A-you're adorable.
LP: . . . . NSPL 18527
MC: . . . . ZCP 18527

GOLDEN GREATS OF THE 50'S.
Tracks: / Mack the knife / Tennessee waltz / Hi lili hi lo / My heart cries for you / Three coins in the fountain / Mister sandman / Who wants to be a millionaire / It's a lovely day today / Singing the blues / Dear hearts and gentle people / Young and foolish / Sugar hush / Music music music / She wears red feathers / Too young / Ungforgettable / That doggie in the window / Moments to remember / Blueberry Hill / Chanson d'amour / Because of you / My foolish heart / When I fall in love / Memories are made of this.
LP: . . . . NSPL 18532
MC: . . . . ZCP 18532

GOLDEN HOUR OF, A (Singalongamax).
MC: . . . . KGHMC 159

GOLDEN HOUR OF MAX BYGRAVES, A.
Tracks: / Out of town / Ramblin' rose / I can't stop loving you / Mame / Rolling around the world / I love to play my ukelele / Once a star of Music Hall / Day dream / Strollin' / Show me the way to go home / Remember when (we made those memories) / Second hand rose / You're my everything / I want a girl just like the girl / When I'm 64 / Little green apples / Hello Dolly / What's new / Those were the days / One of those songs / Messing about on the river / I don't want to set the world on fire / Charlie girl / That old straw hat.
MC: . . . . KGHMC 102

GOLDEN HOUR OF MAX BYGRAVES & VICTOR SILVESTER (Bygraves, Max & Victor Silvester).
Tracks: / Tie a yellow ribbon / Dancing in the dark / Let the rest of the world go by / Edelweiss / Is it true what they say about Dixie? / Deep in the heart of Texas / What now my love / How wonderful to know / You always hurt the one you love / Tangerine / That old black magic / Red roses for a blue lady / Old fashioned way, The / After you've gone / Everybody loves my baby / I could have danced all night / Tea for two / Oh, you beautiful doll / What'll I do / Last waltz, The / Three little words / Exactly like you / I may be wrong / Moonlight serenade / At last / Serenade in blue.
MC: . . . . KGHMC 140

GOLDEN HOUR OF MAX BYGRAVES VOLUME 2.
MC: . . . . DLCMC 122

HAPPY HITS.
Tracks: / Back in my childhood days / Let me call you sweetheart / Girl of my dreams / Where the blue of the night / Me and my shadow / Moonlight and roses / You were meant for me / You are my sunshine / Let the rest of the world go by / Say, has anybody seen my sweet Gypsy Rose? / Tie a yellow ribbon / Back in my young man's days / Happy days are here again / Powder your face with sunshine / I'm looking over a four leaf clover / When you're smiling / Put your arms around me, honey / It had to be you / I'll get by / I'll string along with you / I'll be seeing you / Bye bye blues / I'll see you in my dreams / It's time to say goodnight / Goodnight sweetheart / I love to play my ukelele / I can't stop loving you / Those were the days / Old straw hat, An / Little green apples / Ramblin' rose.
LP: . . . . SPR 8501
MC: . . . . SPC 8501

HOUR OF MAX BYGRAVES, AN.
Tracks: / Cowpunchers cantata / Cry of the wild goose / Riders in the sky / Mule train / Jezebel / True loves and false lovers / Little Sir Echo / Big head / You're a pink toothbrush / I wish I could sing like Al Jolson / Heart of my heart /

Out of town / Ballad of Davy Crockett, The / Try another cherry tree / By the light of the silvery moon / Peggy O'Neal / When you wore a tulip (and I wore a big red rose) / If you were the only girl in the world / For me and my gal / Friends and neighbours / Gilly gilly ossenfeffer katzenellenbogen by the sea / Mister Sandman / Pendulum song, The / Gretna Green / Meet me on the corner / Little laplander, The / Good idea son, A / Seventeen sons / Tomorrow / Say si si / She's a lassie from Lancashire / When Irish eyes are smiling / I belong to Glasgow / Any old iron.
MC: .... HR 8165

LINGALONGAMAX.
LP: .... RPL 2033

LINGALONGAMAX Vol 2.
Tracks: / Roll roll roll / Broadway melody / Chicago / 42nd Street / Lullaby of Broadway / Kite, The / Picking up pebbles / Dance in the old-fashioned way / You won't find another fool like me / Last farewell, The / Please do it again / Second hand Rose / Somebody loves me / Hard day's night, A / Shoeshine boy / We just couldn't say goodbye / Glory of love / Every now and then / What a rainy day / Sound of music, The / Climb every mountain / You'll never walk alone.
LP: .... N 126
MC: .... ZCN 126

MAX A MILLION.
Tracks: / Walk right back / Somethin' stupid / Delilah / Gentle on my mind / Strangers in the night / Hard day's night, A / Starry eyed / Congratulations / For the good times / Remember when / Little green apples / Snow bird / Yesterday / Both sides / My way.
LP: .... NSPL 18576

MAX BYGRAVES AT HIS VERY BEST.
Tracks: / My childhood days / You were meant for me / Tie a yellow ribbon / I'm looking over a four leaf clover / Ramblin' rose / When you wore a tulip / I'll string along with you / One of those songs / Swanee / Girl of my dreams / Everywhere you go / What a wonderful world / Bye bye blues / It's time to say goodnight.
LP: .... GH 671

MAX BYGRAVES NO.1.
Tracks: / You're my everything / Gentle on my mind / Deck of cards / Walk right back / For the good times / Rolling 'round the world / You're my everything / Charlie girl / One of those songs / Rolling around the world / Out of town / Hello Dolly.
MCSET: .... DTO 10017

MAX BYGRAVES NO.2.
MCSET: .... DTO 10215
MC: .... DTO 10051

MAX SINGS WHILE TED SWINGS (Bygraves, Max & Ted Heath).
Tracks: / It is true what they say about Dixie / Underneath the arches / Did you ever see a dream walking / Ten pretty girls / It's a sin to tell a lie / Oh ma-ma (the butcher boy) / Back to those happy days / Lazybones / You're driving me crazy / What did I do / All I do is dream of you / Scatterbrain / When my dreamboat comes home.
LP: .... PLE 506
MC: .... TC-PLE 506

MAXIMEMORIES.
LP: .... MAXLP 1

REMEMBERING (MAX BYGRAVES).
LP: .... CBR 1019
MC: .... KCBR 1019

SING IT AGAIN MAX.
Tracks: / Somebody stole my gal / Put on your old grey bonnet / Goodbye-ee / Bye bye blackbird / Bill bailey won't you please come home / Ma (he's making eyes at me) / Oh you beautiful doll / Alexanders ragtime band / Rolling around the world / Dance in the old-fashioned way / You won't find another fool like me / Is it true what they say about Dixie / Home in Pasedena / Deep in the heart of Texas / Sweet gypsy rose / Tie a yellow ribbon / If you were the only girl in the world / Marie / Mary's a grand old name / Daisy daisy / For me and my gal / I'll be with you in apple blossom time / If I have my way / Edelweiss / Whiffenpoof song, The / Pack up your troubles in your old kit bag / Tavern in the town / It's a long way to Tipperary / Goodbye Dolly Gray / Roll out the barrel.
LP: .... MAX 1
MC: .... ZC MAX 1

SINGALONG A CHRISTMAS.
Tracks: / Come Landlord fill the flowing bowl / Little brown jug / Just a wee deoch an' doris / Here's to the good old beer / Let's have another one / Rolling home / Little drummer boy / Winter wonderland / White Christmas / Merry Christmas everbody / I wish it could be Christmas everyday / Silver bells / Mary's boy child / Auld lang syne.
LP: .... HMA 265
MC: .... HSC 373

SINGALONG COLLECTION, THE.
LPS: .... PYL 1001
MCSET: .... PYM 1001

SINGALONG WITH MAX.
LP: .... NSPL 18361

SINGALONG WITH MAX VOL.2.
LP: 12/72

SINGALONG YEARS 1920-1990.
Tracks: / Don't bring Lulu / Ma (he's making eyes at me) / Yes sir, that's my baby / I wonder where my baby is tonight / Who's sorry now / Amy, wonderful Amy / Underneath the arches / Home town / South of the border / Is it true what they say about Dixie? / Baby face / California here I come / I've got a lovely bunch of coconuts / You're a pink toothbrush / Who wants to be a millionaire / Beatles medley / What a wonderful world / Tie a yellow ribbon round the ole oak tree / Dance in the old-fashioned way / Neighbours / It's bad / Repeats.
LP: 211221
MC: 411221

SINGALONGAMAX.
Tracks: / Cockney medley (Knees up mother brown/Waiting for the Robert E.Lee/How ya gonna keep dow) / Al Jolson medley (My mammy/Sonny boy/ Rock a bye your baby with a Dixie melody) / Sentimental medley (Mistakes/ Dancing with tears in my eyes/Are you lonsome tonight/When I gr) / Marching medley (It's a long way to tipperary/Pack up your troubles/Kiss me goonight sgt.) / Max's medley (May be it's because I'm a Londener/Shaddap you face/Australia) / Beatles medley (She loves you/All my loving/A hard day's night/Can't buy me love) / One for the road medley (Who's sorry now/You made me love you/For me and my gal/We'll meet again).
LP: .... MFP 5581
MC: .... TCMFP 5581

SINGALONGAMAX VOL.2.
Tracks: / Medley(1) (One of those songs/Baby face/Toot toot tootsie/One of those songs) / Medley(2) (I don't know why/You made me love you/Ramblin rose/Tiptoe through the tu) / Medley(3) (You'd be so nice to come home to/I love you because/True love) / Medley(4) (Let me call you sweetheart/Girl of my dreams/Where the blue of the night) / Medley(5) (Everybody loves somebody/ Just one more chance) / Medley(6) (Au revoir/Auf wiedersehen/Arrivederci/ Goodbye blues).
LP: .... NSPL 18383
MC: .... ZCP 18383

SINGALONGAMAX VOL.3.
LP: .... NSPL 18401

SINGALONGAMAX VOL.4.
LP: .... NSPL 18410

SINGALONGAMAX-MAS.
Tracks: / We wish you a merry Christmas / O come all ye faithful / Once in royal David's city / While shepherds watched their flocks by night / First Noel, The / Good King Wenceslas / Hark the herald angels sing / Christmas island / I saw mommy kissing Santa Claus / Rudolph the red nosed reindeer / Have yourself a merry little Christmas / Christmas alphabet / Just a wee deoch and doris / Here's to the good old beer / Mop it down / Let's have another one / Rollin' home / Little drummer boy / Winter wonderland / White Christmas / Merry Christmas everybody / I wish it could be Christmas everyday / Silver bells / Mary's boy child / Auld lang syne.
LP: .... NSPL 18439
MC: .... ZCP 18439

SINGALONGAPARTYSONG.
LP: .... NSPL 18419
MC: .... ZCP 18419

SINGALONGAWARYEARS.
LP: .... PMLP 5001
MC: .... PMMC 5001

SINGALONGAWARYEARS VOL.2.
Tracks: / This is the army Mr. Jones / Army, the Navy and the Air-force, The / I'm gonna get lit up / You don't have to tell me I know / Gal in Kalamazoo / Three little fishes / You'd be so nice to come home to / Hokey cokey / Under the spreading chestnut tree / Don't sit under the apple tree / Put your arms around me honey / It's been a long long time / Blueberry Hill / Pennies from Heaven / White Christmas / Fleets in Port again, The / Roll out the barrel / If I should fall in love again / Chattanooga choo choo / Jeepers creepers / One day when we were young / I remember you / Horsey horsey / Lambeth walk / Yes my darling daughter / You must have been a beautiful baby / Woodpecker song, The / Sentimental journey / That lovely weekend.
LP: .... PMLP 5006
MC: .... PMMC 5010

SINGALONGWITHMAX.
LP: .... NSPL 18361
MC: .... ZCP 18361

SONG AND DANCE MEN (Bygraves, Max & Victor Silvester).
Tracks: / Tie a yellow ribbon / Dancing in the dark / Let the rest of the world go by / Edelweiss / Is it true what they say about Dixie? / Deep in the heart of Texas / What now my love / How wonderful to know / Old fashioned way, The / After you've gone / Everybody loves my baby / I could have danced all night / Tea for two / Oh you beautiful doll / What'll I do? / Last waltz, The.
LP: .... NSPL 18574

SPOTLIGHT ON MAX BYGRAVES.
Tracks: / Tie a yellow ribbon / Ramblin rose / Whispering grass / Cabaret / Snowbird / What a wonderful world / Mack the knife / I only have eyes for you / When I'm sixty four / Remember when / Feelings / Deck of cards / Gentle on my mind / Singing the blues / Any dream will do / You say something nice about everybody / Little green apples / Memories are made of this / Hello dolly / Messing around on the river / Heart breaker / I don't know why / Who's sorry now / Kite, The.
2LP: .... SPOT 1021
MCSET: .... ZCSPT 1021

SPOTLIGHT ON MAX BYGRAVES VOL 2.
LP: .... SPOT 1030
MC: .... ZCSPT 1030

TWOGETHER (See under Bilk, Acker) (Bygraves, Max & Acker Bilk).

YOU MAKE ME FEEL LIKE SINGING A SONG.
LP: .... NSPL 18436

YOU'RE MY EVERYTHING.
Tracks: / Blue eyes don't make an angel / Ain't no pleasing you / Just one more chance / Ebony and ivory / Please / Long long singalong / It's hard to be humble / Bring me sunshine / You're my everything / Day I won the pools / Calypso medley / Everytime we say goodbye.
LP: .... MONLP 030

Byles, Junior

BEAT DOWN BABYLON (The Upsetter Years).
Tracks: / Beat down Babylon / Da-da / I've got a feeling / Don't know why / Demonstration / Coming home / Joshua's desire / Place called Africa / Poor chubby / Matter of time, A / Fun and games (motion dub) / Pretty fe true (pretty dub) / King of Babylon / Pharaoh hiding.
LP: .... TRLS 253
MC: .... ZCTR 253

JORDAN.
LP: .... HB 45
MC: .... CHB 45

RASTA NO PICKPOCKET.
LP: .... NHM 7493
MC: .... NHC 7493

WHEN WILL BETTER COME.
LP: .... TRLS 269
MC: .... ZCTRL 269

Byrd, Bobby

FINALLY GETTING PAID.
LP: .... RAP LP 3

WHAT GOES AROUND COMES AROUND (Byrd, Bobby/Maceo Parker/ Fred Wesley).
LP: .... RAPS 3

Byrd, Charlie

BOSSA NOVA YEARS, THE (Byrd, Charlie Trio).
Tracks: / Meditation / One note samba / Corcovado / Triste / Dindi / O pato / Girl from Ipanema / Samba d'orpheo / How insensitive / Wave / P'ra dizer adeus / O nosso amor.
MC: .... CJ 468C

BRAZILIAN SOUL (see Almeida, Laurindo).

BRAZILVILLE (Byrd, Charlie & Bud Shank).
Tracks: / Zingaro / Brazilville / Saquarema / Speak low / Yesterdays / Charlotte's fancy / What are you doing the rest of your life?.
LP: .... CJP 173
MC: .... CJPC 173

BYRD AT THE GATE.
Tracks: / Shiny stockings / More / Blues for night people / Big butter and egg man / Ela me Deixou / Broadway / I left my heart in san fransisco / Some other spring / Where are the hebrew children.
LP: .... OJC 262

BYRD & BRASS (Byrd, Charlie Trio/ Annapolis Brass Quintet).
Tracks: / Strike up the band / Byrd and brass / Thou swell / En memoria de chano pozo / Solitude / Franz und Johann / I'm getting sentimental over you / It don't mean a thing.
LP: .... CJ 304
MC: .... CJC 304

DESAFINADO (Byrd, Charlie & Stan Getz).
Tracks: / Samba deese day's / O pata / Samba triste / Samba de una nota so / E luxo so / Baia / Desafinado.
LP: 2615 054

GREAT GUITARS AT THE WINERY (See Kessel, Barney) (Byrd, Charlie/ Herb Ellis/ Barney Kessel).

HOLLYWOOD BIRD.
Tracks: / Time for love, A / Georgy girl / Alfie / Wishing doll, The / Wish me a rainbow / Born free / In the arms of love / Any Wednesday / Moment to moment / I'll be back.
MC: 40 32507
LP: .... CBS 32507

IN GREENWICH VILLAGE.
Tracks: / Just squeeze me / Why was I born? / You stepped out of a dream / Fantasia on / Which side are you on? / Shiny stockings / More / Blues for night people / Butter and egg man / Ela me Deixou / Broadway / I left my heart in San Francisco / Some other Spring / Where are the Hebrew children?.
2LP: .... M 47049

ISN'T IT ROMANTIC (Byrd, Charlie Trio).
Tracks: / Isn't it romantic / I could write a book / Cheek to cheek / Very thought of you, The / Thou swell / One morning in May / I didn't know what time it was / There's a small hotel / Someone to watch over me / Thought about me.
LP: .... CJ 252

IT'S A WONDERFUL WORLD (Featuring Scott Hamilton) (Byrd, Charlie Trio).
LP: .... CJ 374
MC: .... CJ 374 C

LATIN BYRD.
Tracks: / Mediticao / Samba de una nota so / Yvone voce e eu / Coisa mais Linda / O barquinho / Desafinado / Sambra triste / Carnaval / Ho ba la / Ela me deixou / O passaro / Otra vez / Presente de natal / Insensatez / Three note samba / Samba da minha terra / Limehouse blues / Saudade de Bahia / Anna / Socegadamente / Chega de saudade / Cancao de nimar par Carol.
2LP: .... M 47005

LATIN ODYSSEY (see under Almeida, Laurindo) (Byrd, Charlie & Laurindo Almeida).

MEDITATION.
LP: .... OJC 107

MUSIC OF THE BRAZILIAN MASTERS (see under Almeida, Laurindo).

TANGO (See Almeida, Laurindo) (Byrd, Charlie & Laurindo Almeida).

Byrd, Donald

AND 125TH STREET N Y C.
Tracks: / Pretty baby / Gold the moon, white the sun / Giving it up / Marilyn / People supposed to be free / Veronica / Morning, I love you.
LP: .... K 52199

AT THE HALF NOTE CAFE VOL. 1.
Tracks: / My girl Shirl / Soulful kiddy / Portrait of Jennie / Cecile / Pure D funk (theme) / Child's play / Chant.
LP: .... BST 84060

AT THE HALF NOTE CAFE VOL. 2.
Tracks: / Jeannine / Pure D funk / Between the devil and the deep blue sea / Mr. Lucky / Kimyas / When sunny gets blue.
LP: .... BLJ 84061

BLUE NOTE COLLECTION.
Tracks: / Lansana's priestess / Sister love / Flight time / Stepping into tomorrow / Where are we going / Think twice / Wild life / Love's so far away / Design a nation / Change / Places and spaces / Onward 'til morning / Wind parade / Just my imagination / Dominos.
LP: .... LCSP 1867013

BYRD IN HAND.
Tracks: / Witchcraft / Here I am / Devil whip / Bronze dance / Clarion calls / Injuns, The.
LP: .... BST 84019

BYRD IN PARIS VOL.1.
Tracks: / Dear old Stockholm / Paul's pals / Flute blues / Ray's idea / Blues walk.

LP: 833 394-1

BYRD IN PARIS VOL.2.
LP: 833 395-1

CAT WALK, THE.
Tracks: / Say you're mine / Duke's mixture / Each time I think of you / Cat walk, The / Cute / Hello bright sunflower.
LP: .... BST 84075

FREE FORM.
Tracks: / Pentecostal feelin' (Take 23) / Night flower (Take 15.) / Nai nai (Take 2) / French spice (Take 9) / Free form (Take 24) / Three wishes (CD only.).
LP: .... BST 84118

GETTING DOWN TO BUSINESS (Byrd, Donald Sextet).
Tracks: / Theme for Malcolm / That's all there is to love / Pomponio / I got it bad and that ain't good (Available on CD only) / Certain attitude, A / Loneliest, The / Around the corner.
LP: .... LLP 1523

GROOVIN' FOR NAT.
Tracks: / Hush / Child's play / Angel eyes / Smoothie / Suede / Friday's child / Out of this world / Groovin' for Nat.
LP: .... BLP 60134

HARLEM BLUES.
Tracks: / Harlem blues / Fly, little Byrd / Voyage a deux / Blue Monk / Alter ego / Sir Master Kool Guy.
LP: .... LLP 1516

HOUSE OF BYRD.
Tracks: / Round midnight / Dig / Third, The / Contour / When your lover has gone / Dewey Square / Dupeltook / Once more / House of Chan / In walked George / Lover man (oh where can you be).
2LP: .... PR 24066

I'M TRYIN' TO GET HOME.
Tracks: / Brother Isaac / Noah / I'm tryin' to get home / I've longed and searched for my mother / March children / Pearly gates.
LP: .... BST 84188

LOVE BYRD.
Tracks: / Love has come around / Butterfly / I feel like loving you today / I love your love / I'll always love you / Love for sale / Falling.
LP: .... K 52301
MC: K4 52301

NEW FORMULAS FROM THE JAZZ LAB (Byrd, Donald & Gigi Gryce).
LP: .... PL 43698

NEW PERSPECTIVE , A.
Tracks: / Elijah / Beast of burden / Cristo redentor / Black discipline, The / Chant.
LP: .... BST 84124

SEPTEMBER AFTERNOON (Byrd, Donald & Clare Fischer & Strings).
Tracks: / Stardust / Indian Summer / I'm a fool to want you / Some day my prince will come / Moon mist / I get along without you very well / Touch of your lips, The / Lazy afternoon / Varmeland / Love is the sweetest thing / September afternoon / Dearly beloved.
LP: .... DS 869

THANK YOU...FOR F.U.M.L..
Tracks: / Thank you...for F.M.U.L. / Sunning in your loveshine / Your life is ecstasy / Loving you / Have you heard the news / In love with love / Cristo Redentor / Close your eyes and look within.
LP: .... K 52097

TWO TRUMPETS (see under Farmer, Art & Donald Byrd).

WORDS, SOUNDS, COLOURS & SHAPES.
Tracks: / Sexy dancer / Midnight / So much in love / High energy / Star trippin' / I'm coming home / Forbidden love / Everyday.
LP: .... K 52427

Byrd Family

GOD DID WHAT NO OTHER COULD DO.
Tracks: / He did what no other could do / Let him in today / Thank you Lord / God's word / Memories / Heart like thine / Be real for Christ / Turn it over to Jesus.
LP: .... MIR 5024
MC: .... MIR 5024 MC

Byrd, John

COMPLETE RECORDINGS 1929-31 (Byrd, John & Walter Taylor).
LP: .... BD 2008

Byrd, William

MASS OF ST SYLVESTER (Byrd, William Choir).
LP: .... REGL 572

Byrds

5D.
LP: .... BGOLP 106

6 TRACK HITS.
Tracks: / Lay lady lay / Turn turn turn / Gon' back / So you want to be a rock'n'roll star / Chestnut mare / All I really want to do.
MC: 7SC 5016

BALLAD OF EASY RIDER.
LP: 63795
LP: 4670441
MC: 4670444

BYRDS PLAY DYLAN, THE.
Tracks: / Mr. Tambourine man / All I really want to do / Chimes of freedom / Spanish Harlem incident / Time they are a changin', The / Lay down your weary tune / My back pages / You ain't goin' nowhere / Nothing was delivered / This wheel's on fire / It's all over now / Baby blue / Lay lady lay / Positively 4th street.
LP: .... CBS 31795
MC: 40 31795
LP: .... CBS 31503

BYRDS, THE.
Tracks: / Full circle / Sweet Mary / Changing heart / For free / Born to rock 'n' roll / Things will be better / Cowgirl in the sand / Long live the King / Borrowing time / Laughing / See the sky about to rain.
LP: .... K 42006
LP: .... SYLA 8754

COLLECTION: BYRDS.
Tracks: / Lady friend / Chestnut mare / Bells of Rhymney / He was a friend of mine / Why / Everybody's been burned / Eight miles high / Girl with no name / Goin' back / So you want to be a rock 'n' roll star / 5D (fifth dimension) / Old John Robertson / Here without you / Wasn't born to follow / Draft morning / It won't be wrong / John Riley / My back pages / Mr. Tambourine man / Turn,turn,turn / Feel a whole lot better / Have you seen her face / All I really want to do / You ain't goin' nowhere.
2LP: .... CCSLP 151
MC: .... CCSMC 151

DOCTOR BYRDS & MR.HYDE.
LP: 63545

DR BYRDS & MR HYDE.
LP: .... BGOLP 107

FIFTH DIMENSION.
Tracks: / 5D (fifth dimension) / Wild mountain thyme / Mr. Space-man / I see you / What's happening?! / I come and stand at every door / Eight miles high / Hey Joe / Captain soul / John Riley / 2-4-2 foxtrot (the lear jet song).
LP: .... CBS 32284
MC: 40 32284
LP: .... BPG 62783

GOLDEN HIGHLIGHTS.
LP: 54737
MC: 40 54737

GREATEST HITS: BYRDS.
Tracks: / Mr. Tambourine man / I'll feel a whole lot better / Bells of Rhymney / Turn turn turn / All I really want to do / Chimes of freedom / Eight miles high / Mr. Spaceman / 5D (fifth dimension) / So you want to be a rock 'n' roll star / My back pages.
LP: .... CBS 32068
MC: 40 32068
LP: 4678431
MC: 4678434

HISTORY OF THE BYRDS.
Tracks: / Mr. Tambourine man / Turn turn turn / She don't care about time / Wild mountain thyme / Eight miles high / Mr. Spaceman / 5D (fifth dimension) / So you want to be a rock'n'roll star / Time between / My back pages / Lady friend / Goin back / Old John Robertson / Wasn't born to follow / You ain't goin nowhere / Hickory wind / Nashville West / Drug store truck driving man / Gunga din / Jesus is just alright / Ballad of easy rider / Chestnut mare / Yesterday's train / Just the season / Citizen Kane / America's great national pastime / Jamaica (say you will) / Tiffany queen.
LP: 4601151
MC: 4601154
LP: 68242

MR.TAMBOURINE MAN.
MC: 40 31503
LP: .... BPG 62571

NEVER BEFORE.
LP: .... MH 70318

NOTORIOUS BYRD BROTHERS, THE.
Tracks: / Artificial energy / Goin' back / Natural harmony / Draft morning / Wasn't born to follow / Get to you / Change is now / Old John Robertson / Tribal gathering / Dolphins smile / 2001.
LP: .... ED 262
LP: 63169

ORIGINAL SINGLES-VOL 1, THE.
Tracks: / Mr. Tambourine man / I knew I'd want you / All I really want to do / I'll feel a whole lot better / Turn, turn, turn / She don't care about time / Set you free this time / It won't be wrong / Eight miles high / Why / 5D (fifth dimension) / Captain Soul / Mr. Spaceman / What's happening? / So you want to be a rock 'n' roll star / Everybody's been burned.
LP: .... CBS 32069
MC: 40 32069
LP: .... CBS 31851

ORIGINAL SINGLES-VOL 2, THE.
Tracks: / My back pages / Renaissance fair / Have you seen her face / Don't make waves / Lady friend / Old John Robertson / Goin' back / Change is now / You ain't goin' nowhere / Artificial energy / I am a pilgrim / Pretty boy Floyd / Bad night at the whiskey / Drug store truck driving man / Lay lady lay / Old blue.
LP: .... CBS 32103
MC: 40 32103

SWEETHEART OF THE RODEO.
Tracks: / You ain't goin' nowhere / I am a pilgrim / Christian eye, The / You don't miss your water / You're still on my mind / Pretty boy Floyd / Hickory wind / One hundred years from now / Blue Canadian Rockies / Life in prison / Nothing was delivered.
MC: .... CED 234
LP: .... ED 234
LP: 4670471
MC: 4670474

TIME BETWEEN - A TRIBUTE TO THE BYRDS (See under Time Between ...) (Various artists).

TURN, TURN, TURN.
LP: .... BPG 62783
LP: 4670461
MC: 4670464

ULTIMATE BYRDS, THE.
MCSET: 4676114

UNTITLED.
LP: 66253

YOUNGER THAN YESTERDAY.
Tracks: / So you want to be a rock 'n' roll star / Have you seen her face / C.T.A. / Renaissance fair / Time between / Everybody's been burned / Thoughts and words / Mind gardens / My back pages / Girl with no name / Why.
LP: .... ED 227
MC: .... CED 227
LP: .... SBPG 62988
LP: 4670451
MC: 4670454

Byrne, Anne

FROM BUNCLODY TO AVONDALE.
LP: .... HPE 651
MC: .... HPC 651

Byrne, Bryan

SWEET CARNLOCH BAY.
LP: .... HPE 652
MC: .... HPC 652

Byrne, David

BRAZIL CLASSICS.
LP: .... K 9260191
MC: .... K 9260194

CATHERINE WHEEL, THE.
Tracks: / His wife refused / Two soldiers / Red house, The / My big hands(fall through the cracks) / Big business / Eggs in a briar patch / Poison / Cloud chamber / What a day that was / Big blue Plymouth / Light bath.
LP: .... SRK 3645
MC: .... SRC 3645

FOREST, THE.
LP: 7599265841
MC: 7599265844

FORRO.
LP: .... WX 385
MC: .... WX 385 C

JEZEBEL SPIRIT (see under Eno, Brian) (Byrne, David & Brian Eno).

MUSIC FOR THE KNEE PLAYS.
Tracks: / In the upper room / Tree (today is an important occasion) / Sound of business, The / Social studies / (Gift of sound) where the sun never goes down / Theadora is dozing / Admiral Perry / I bid you goodnight / I've tried / Winter / Jungle book / In the future.
LP: .... EJ 2403811
MC: .... EJ 2403814

MY LIFE IN THE BUSH OF GHOSTS (See under Eno, Brian) (Eno, Brian & David Byrne).

REI MOMO.
LP: .... WX 319
MC: .... WX 391C

Byrne, James

ROAD TO GLENLOUGH.
LP: .... CC 52
MC: 4CC 52

Byrne, Julie

COUNTRY.
MC: .... AIM 47
MC: .... AM 47

RAMBLIN' ROUND.
Tracks: / Route 65 to Nashville / Legend in my time, A / King of country music / I'm easy / I can't stop loving you / It don't worry me / Talk talk / Crazy arms / I'd like to go to Memphis / Ramblin' round / Honey / My babe.
LP: .... FHR 079

Byrne, Packie

HALF DOOR, THE (Byrne, Packie & Bonnie Shaljean).
Tracks: / Captain Taylor's air and march / I will lay ye doon / Min an Erin / Drummer boy at Waterloo / German barn dance / Recruited collier / I've got a bonnet / Munster buttermilk / Ghost's welcome / Our ship lays in harbour / Half door / Miss Hamilton and all alive / Lark in the clear air / Red haired man's wife / Hannigan's hooley.
LP: .... DIN 302

ROUNDTOWER (Byrne, Packie & Bonnie Shaljean).
LP: .... DIN 311

SONGS OF A DONEGAL MAN.
Tracks: / John and the farmer / Rich man's daughter / Holland handkerchief / Molly bawn / Jolly ploughboys, The / Young Alvin / Johnny O' Hazelgreen / Lament to the moon / Creel, The.
LP: 12TS 257

Byrne, Philip

SONGS OF THOMAS MOORE (Byrne, Philip & Percy French).
LP: .... EI 802

Byrnes, Martin

MARTIN BYRNES.
Tracks: / Duke of Leinster, The / Duke of Leinster's wife, The / Paddy Fahey's / Cliffs of Moher, The / Tarbolton / Longford collector, The / Sailor's bonnet, The / Bantry bay / Shack of barley, The / Farewell to Ireland / Irish Molly / Ashplant, The / Liffey banks, The / Shaskeen, The / Hitler's downfall / Battle of Aughrium, The / Humours of Lissadel, The / Blackbird, The / Rodney's glory / Colliers', The / Bucks of Oranmore, The.
LP: .... LEA 2004

Byron

BYRON.
LP: .... WKFMLP 173
MC: .... WKFMMC 173

NEW DAWNING (Plays Wersi Spectra).
MC: .... KGRS 1203

Byron Band

ON THE ROCKS.
Tracks: / Rebecca / Bad girl / How do you sleep? / Little by little / Start believing / Never say die / King / Piece of my love.
LP: .... CRX 2
MC: .... CRXC 2

Bystanders

BIRTH OF MAN.
Tracks: / That's the end / (You're gonna) hurt yourself / My love - come home / 98.6 / Royal blue summer sunshine day / Make up your mind / Green grass / Cave of clear light / Painting the time / This time / Have I offended the girl / If you walk away / Stubborn kind of fellow / Pattern people / When jezamine goes / This world is my world.
LP: .... SEE 301

Byzantine Omelette

BYZANTINE OMELETTE.
MC: .... SA 4

BZN

BEST OF BZN.
LP: 022 58018
MC: 222 58018

C

C & C Music Factory

GONNA MAKE YOU SWEAT (ALBUM).
Tracks: / Gonna make you sweat (everybody dance now) / Here we go let's rock and roll / Things that make you go hmmmm / Just a touch of love (everyday) / Groove of love (what's this world called love) / Live happy / Ooh baby / Let's get funkee / Givin' it to you / Bang that beat.
LP: **4678141**
MC: **4678144**

C.A. Quintet

TRIP THRU HELL.
LP: . . . . **PSYCHO 12**

Caballe, Montserrat

BARCELONA (see Mercury, Freddie) (Caballe, Montserrat & Freddie Mercury).

BARCELONA (ALBUM) (See under Mercury, Freddie) (Caballe, Montserrat & Freddie Mercury).

FREDDIE MERCURY & MONTSERRAT CABALLE (See under Mercury, Freddie).

GOLDEN BOY, THE (See under Mercury, Freddie) (Caballe, Montserrat & Freddie Mercury).

Cabaret (musical)

CABARET (1972 FILM) (Various artists).
Tracks: / Willkommen: *Various artists* / Mein herr: *Various artists* / Two ladies: *Various artists* / Maybe this time: *Various artists* / Sitting pretty: *Various artists* / Tiller girls: *Various artists*/ Money, money: *Various artists* / Heiraten: *Various artists* / If you could see her: *Various artists*/ Tomorrow belongs to me: *Various artists* / Cabaret: *Various artists* / Finale: *Various artists.*
LP: . . . . **MCL 1664**
MC: . . . . **MCLC 1664**
LP: . . . . **CBS 70273**
MC: **40 70273**

CABARET (BROADWAY CAST 1966) (Various artists).
MC: . . . . **PST 3040**

CABARET (LONDON CAST) (Various artists).
MC: **40 31490**

CABARET (ORIGINAL ISSUE) (Film Soundtrack) (Various artists).
Tracks: / Wilkommen: *Various artists* / Mein herr: *Various artists* / Two ladies: *Various artists* / Maybe this time: *Various artists* / Sitting pretty: *Various artists* / Tiller girls: *Various artists*/ Money, money,: *Various artists* / Heiraten: *Various artists* / If you could see her: *Various artists*/ Tomorrow belongs to me: *Various artists* / Cabaret: *Various artists* / Finale: *Various artists.*
LP: . . . . **SPB 1052**

CABARET (STAGE SHOW) (1986 London revival cast) (Various artists).
Tracks: / Wilkommen: *Various artists* / So what?: *Various artists* / Don't tell mama: *Various artists*/ Perfectly marvellous: *Various artists* / Two ladies: *Various artists* / It couldn't please me more: *Various* artists / Why should I wake up?: *Various artists* / Money, money, money: *Various artists* / Married: *Various* artists / Meeskite: *Various artists* / Tomorrow belongs to me: *Various artists* / If you could see her: *Various* artists / Maybe this time: *Various artists* / What would you do?: *Various artists* / Cabaret: *Various artists* / Auf wiedersehen (finale): *Various artists.*
LP: . . . . **CAST 5**
MC: . . . . **CASTC 5**

Cabaret Voltaire

2 X 45.
LP: . . . . **ROUGH 42**
LP: . . . . **CABS 9**
MC: . . . . **CABS 9 C**

8 CREPESCULE TRACKS.
Tracks: / Sluggin for Jesus (part 1) / Sluggin for Jesus (part 2) / Fools game-sluggin for Jesus (part 3) / Yashar / Your agent man / Gut level / Invocation / Shaft, Theme from.
LP: . . . . **IM 006**

CODE.
Tracks: / Don't argue / Sex money freaks / Thank you America / Here to go / Trouble (won't stop) / White car / No one here / Life slips by / Code (version) / Hey hey / Here to go (little dub) / Code.
LP: . . . . **PCS 7312**
MC: . . . . **TCPCS 7312**

COVENANT, THE SWORD AND THE ARM OF THE LORD, THE.
Tracks: / L 21st / I want you / Hell's home / Kick back / Arm of the Lord, The / Warm / Golden halos / Motion rotation / Whip blow / Web, The.
LP: . . . . **CV 3**
MC: . . . . **TCV 3**

CRACKDOWN, THE.
Tracks: / 24-24 / In the shadows / Talking time / Animation / Over and over / Just fascination / Why kill time (when you can kill yourself) / Haiti / Crackdown / Diskono (Cassette only) / Double vision (Cassette only) / Badge of evil (Cassette only) / Moscow (Cassette only).
LP: . . . . **OVED 156**
MC: . . . . **OVEDC 156**
LP: . . . . **CV 1**
MC: . . . . **TCV 1**

DRINKING GASOLINE.
Tracks: / Kino / Sleepwalking / Big funk / Ghost talk.
MC: . . . . **TCVM 1**
LP: . . . . **CVM 1**

GROOVY LAIDBACK AND NASTY.
Tracks: / Searchin' / Hypnotised / Minute by minute / Runaway / Keep on (I got this feeling) / Magic / Time beats / Easy life / Rescue me (city lights) (CD only.) / Runaway (Special only.) / Magic (Special only.) / Searchin' (Special only.) / Rescue me (City lights) (Special only.) / Easy life (Special only.).
LP: . . . . **PCS 7338**
MC: . . . . **TCPCS 7338**
LP: . . . . **PCSX 7338**

HAI.
LP: . . . . **RTD 1**

JOHNNY YES NO.
LP: . . . . **DVR 1**
LP: . . . . **CABS 10**

LISTEN UP WITH CABARET VOLTAIRE.
LP: . . . . **CABS 5**
MC: . . . . **CABS 5 C**

LIVE AT THE YMCA.
LP: . . . . **ROUGH 7**
LP: . . . . **CABS 4**

LIVING LEGENDS.
LP: . . . . **CABS 6**
MC: . . . . **CABS 6 C**

MICROPHONIES.
Tracks: / Do right / Operative, The / Digital rasta / Spies in the wires / Earthshaker, Theme from / James Brown / Slammer / Blue heat / Sensoria.
LP: . . . . **CV 2**
MC: . . . . **TCV 2**

MIX UP.
LP: . . . . **ROUGH 4**
LP: . . . . **CABS 8**
MC: . . . . **CABS 8 C**

PERCUSSION FORCE.
LP: . . . . **TWI 9511**

RED MECCA.
LP: . . . . **ROUGH 27**
LP: . . . . **CABS 3**

THREE MANTRAS.
LP: . . . . **CABS 7**
MC: . . . . **CABS 7 C**

VOICE OF AMERICA.
LP: . . . . **CABS 2**
MC: . . . . **CABS 2 C**

VOICE OF AMERICA, THE.
LP: . . . . **ROUGH 11**

Cabazz

CHINESE GARDEN.
LP: . . . . **DRLP 150**

Cabin In... (musical)

CABIN IN THE SKY (1943 film musical) (Various artists).
LP: . . . . **HS 5003**

CABIN IN THE SKY/PORGY & BESS (Original Broadway cast) (Various artists).
LP: . . . . **AEI 1107**

Cables, George

NO LIMIT (see Pepper, Art) (Cables, George/Art Pepper).

TRIP, THE (see Pepper, Art) (Cables, George/Art Pepper).

Cabo Frio

JUST HAVING FUN.
Tracks: / Prism / Just having fun / Find it (hold that note) / Only time / Fast lane / San Juan sunrise / Find a way / Rachel.
LP: . . . . **IZEB 5710**
MC: . . . . **IZEBC 5710**

Cabo Verde Show

DESTINO.
LP: . . . . **SYLL 8304**

Cabrel, Francis

77/78.
Tracks: / Petite Marie / Les murs de Poussiere / Je te suivrai / C'etait l'hiver / La dame de Haute-Savoie / Je pense a toi / Il faudra leur dire / Question d'equilibre / La fille qui m'accompagne / Respondez-moi / L'encre de tes yeux / Encore et encore / Je l'aime a mourir.
LP: **4605811**
MC: **4605814**

LES CHEMINS DE TRAVERSE.
Tracks: / Souviena toi de nous / Je l'aime a mourir / Les pantins de naphtaline / Je reve les volsins / Les chimins de traverse / Une star, a la facon / C'etait l'hiver / Mais le matin monnaie blues.
LP: **4601001**
MC: **4601004**

LES MURS DE POUSSIERE.
Tracks: / Ma ville / Petite Marie / Les murs de poussiere / Je reviens blentot / Imagine-toi / Je m'etais perdu / Madeleine / L'instant d'amour / Change de docteur / Ami / Automne.
LP: **4600971**
MC: **4600974**

SARBACANE.
Tracks: / Animal / Sarbacane / Le monde y pense / J'ai peur de l'avion / Petite sirene / C'est ecrit / Rosie / Je sais que tu danses / Dormir debout / Le pas des ballerines.
LP: **4624621**
MC: **462 462 4**

Cabrera, Jorge

CHARANGA VALLENATA.
Tracks: / Te seguire queriendo / Te quiero / Pimpinelas / Sin te / A fuego lento / Cuidate / Bonita / Cobijas.
LP: . . . . **ORB 019**

Cacavas, Chris

CHRIS CACAVAS AND JUNKYARD LOVE (Cacavas, Chris & Junkyard Love).
Tracks: / Driving misery / Wrecking yard / Angel on a mattress spring / Blue river / Jukebox lullabye / Truth / I didn't mean that / Load off me / Honeymoon.
LP: . . . . **SERV 006**

JUNK YARD LOVE.
LP: . . . . **HEY 006 1**
MC: . . . . **HEY 006 4**

Caceres, Emilio

ERNIE AND EMILIO CACERES (Caceres, Emilio & Ernie).
LP: . . . . **AP 101**

Cache Valley Drifters

CACHE VALLEY DRIFTERS.
Tracks: / Deep river / Sweet Mary / Masters / Dixieland lady / Sorrow of saying goodbye, The / Columbus stockade blues / Joanne / Roly poly / Russian river song / Angel from Montgomery / I shot the sheriff.
LP: . . . . **FF 081**

STEP UP TO BIG PAY.
LP: . . . . **FF 220**

TOOLS OF THE TRADE.
LP: . . . . **FF 290**

Cachet De Vois

PERSONAL.
Tracks: / Wrong / Nothing to lose / Personal / Simon says / I call on you, only you / Try me (what you see) / If only / To the limit / Can't give up.
LP: **925716 1**
MC: **925716 4**

Cacia, Paul

QUANTUM LEAP (Cacia, Paul & His Jazz Orchestra).
Tracks: / Eye of the tiger / Don't stop believing / Who's crying now / Open arms / Rock that / Flashpoint / Quantum leap / Shockwave / Cipher in silhouette, A / From Mars to Zarathustra / I have dreamed / All or nothing at all / No one ever tells you / Nightingale / 007, Theme from / Goldfinger / Diamonds are forever / Live and let die / For your eyes only.
2LP: . . . . **OUTSTANDING 56**

Cacophony

GO OFF.
Tracks: / X-ray eyes / Stranger / Black cat / Floating world, The / E.S.P. / Go off / Sword of the warrior / Images.
LP: . . . . **RR 94991**
MC: . . . . **RR 94994**

SPEED METAL SYMPHONY.
LP: . . . . **RR 95771**
MC: . . . . **RR 95774**

Cactus World News

BEARSVILLE.
LP: . . . . **MCG 6049**
MC: . . . . **MDGC 6049**

PLANET HOME TOWN.
LP: . . . . **UNKNOWN**
MC: . . . . **UNKNOWN**

URBAN BEACHES.
Tracks: / Worlds apart / In a whirlpool / Promise, The / Bridge, The / State of emergency / Years later / Church of the cold / Pilots of Beka / Jigsaw street / Maybe this time / Cashen bay stand (Only on CD.).
LP: . . . . **MCG 6005**
MC: . . . . **MCGC 6005**

Cadaver

HALLUCINATING ANXIETY.
LP: . . . . **NECRO 4**
MC: . . . . **NECRO 4 MC**

Caddick, Bill

REASONS BRIEFLY SET DOWN.
LP: . . . . **SHY 7006**

ROUGH MUSIC.
LP: . . . . **SHP 102**

SUNNY MEMORIES.
Tracks: / Sunny memories / Father's little black box / Military man / Ptarmigan and groaty Dick / Gibson girl / Sitting all alone / Cinderella / Tango Bleriot / Diabolo rag / All the king's ladies / Writing of Tipperary / It's a long way to Tipperary.
LP: . . . . **LER 2097**

WILD WEST SHOW, THE.
LP: **12TS 441**

Caddy, Alan

PIANO SERENADE.
MC: . . . . **AM 4**

Caddyshack (film)

CADDYSHACK (film soundtrack) (Various artists).
LP: . . . . **CBS 70192**

CADDYSHACK 2 (1983 Film Soundtrack) (Various artists).
LP: . . . . **SC 44317**
MC: **SCT44317**

Cadell, Elizabeth

OUT OF THE RAIN (See under Out of the Rain (bk)).

Cadets

CADETS MEET THE JACKS, THE.
Tracks: / Stranded in the jungle / Let's rock 'n' roll / I got loaded / Fools rush in / Hands across the table / Rollin' stone / Dancin' dan / Heartbreak hotel / Love bandit / I want you / Memories of you / Annie met Henry / My darling / I cried.
LP: . . . . **CH 196**

Cadillac

MARCH OF THE ROCKERS.
LP: . . . . **NEVLP 125**

Cadillac, Flash

FLASH CADILLAC AND THE CONTINENTAL KIDS (Cadillac, Flash & the Continental Kids).
LP: . . . . **LPM 8704**

Cadillac, Vince

MODERN BOY.
Tracks: / Loving you / Sneaking out the back door / Hello / Voodoo woman / She's a model / Memory lane / Moonshine man / Stowaway to India / Monday morning.
LP: . . . . **SATL 4010**

Cadillacs

PLEASE MR JOHNSON.
Tracks: / Speedoo / I want to know about love / That's all I need / Still you left me baby / Please Mr. Johnson / Oh oh Lolita / Rudolph the red nosed reindeer / Gloria / Wishing well / Cool it fool / Holy smoke baby / Tell me today / I want to know / About that girl named Lou.
LP: . . . . **H 801**

SOLID GOLD CADILLACS.
LP: **33.8030**

Cadman, John

EL CAD.
LP: . . . . **PLR 050**

Cadogan, Susan

SUSAN CADOGAN.
Tracks: / In the ghetto / Nice'n'easy / Hurt so good / Congratulations / If you need me / Lay down / I keep on loving you / Don't you burn your bridges / Feeling is right / Fever / Shame.
LP: . . . . **TRLS 122**

YOU MAKE ME FEEL SO GOOD (See under Thomas, Rudy).

Caedmon Players

PEOPLE IN THE WIND.
MC: **1772**

Caesar, Shirley

BEST OF SHIRLEY CAESAR & THE CARAVANS (Caesar, Shirley & The Caravans).
LP: . . . . **MG 14202**

LIVE IN CHICAGO.
LP: . . . . **REJR 5021**
MC: . . . . **REJC 5021**

REJOICE.
Tracks: / Whisper a prayer / He's got it all in control / He's coming to take me away / Satan, you're a liar / Come and go with me / Gotta serve somebody / I wanna be ready / It's in the book / I love you, mama.
LP: . . . . **MYR 1104**
MC: . . . . **MC 1104**

Caesarian Section

HEAL AMERICA.
LP: . . . . **INCIS 2**

Cafe Creme

CAFE CREME.
LP: . . . . **RSD 5002**

Cafe Jacques

INTERNATIONAL.
Tracks: / Boulevard of broken dreams / How easy / Waiting / Station of dreams / Chanting and raving / Can't stand still / Man in the meadow / Knife edge / This way up.
LP: . . . . **EPC 83042**

'ROUND THE BACK.
Tracks: / Meaningless / Ain't no love in the heart of the city / Sands of Singapore / Farewell my lovely / Eberehtel / Dark eyed Johnny / Sandra's a phonie / None of your business / Crime passionelle / Lifeline.
LP: . . . . **EPC 82315**

Cafferty, John

ON THE DARK SIDE (Cafferty, John & The Beaver Brown Band).
LP: . . . . **SCT 26450**
MC: **40 26450**

TOUGH ALL OVER (Cafferty, John & The Beaver Brown Band).
Tracks: / Voice of America's son / Tough all over / C-I-T-Y / Where the action is / Dixieland / Strangers in paradise / Small town girl / More than just one of the boys / Tex-Mex (crystal blue).
LP: . . . . **SCT 26450**

Cage, Butch

RAISE A RUCKUS TONIGHT.
Tracks: / Mean old Frisco / Black cat bone / Awful blue / If I had my way / She was a woman didn't mean no harm no good / Come on baby / Tomorrow gonna be my trying day / Raise a ruckus tonight / Corina, Corina.
LP: . . . . **FLY 545**

Cage, John

JOHN CAGE.
LP: . . . . **TOM 7016**

VOICES AND INSTRUMENTS.
LP: . . . . **OBS 5**

LP: . . . . **OBS 5**

Cagney, James

SUSPENSE (Cagney, James and Herbert Marshall).
Tracks: / No escape / Thirty nine steps.
LP: . . . . **LP 103**

Cagney & Lacey (tv)

CAGNEY AND LACEY (Original Soundtrack) (Various artists).
MC: . . . . **FILMC 704**

Cahill, Eddie

AH-SURELY.
LP: . . . . **SHAN 29014**

Cahn, Sammy

I'VE HEARD THAT SONG BEFORE.
LP: . . . . **WRS 1002**

Cain, Chris

LATE NIGHT CITY BLUES (Cain, Chris Band).
LP: . . . . **BR 105**

Cain, David

DAVID CAIN'S MUSIC.
LP: . . . . **REC 91**

Cain, Jackie

WE'VE GOT IT - THE MUSIC OF CY COLEMAN (Cain, Jackie & Roy Kral).
Tracks: / We've got it / Best is yet to come, The / When in Rome / Why try to change me now / I've got your number / You're a loveable lunatic / My city / Our private world / Doop do de oop / I love my wife / Witchcraft / It's a nice face / Riviera, The.
LP: . . . . **DS 907**
MC: . . . . **DSC 907**

Cain, Tane

TANE CAIN.
Tracks: / Temptation / Danger zone / My time to fly / Crazy eyes / Holdin' on / Almost any night / Vertigo / Hurtin' kind / Suspicious eyes.
LP: . . . . **PL 14381**
MC: . . . . **PK 14831**

Caine, Andrew

ONE.
Tracks: / What kind of world / What do we say to each other / New blood (this time tomorrow) / Talkin' / Watchin' the world go by / Move it / Wilderness years / Cathy come home / Physical contact / Still the night.
LP: . . . . **EPC 26837**
MC: **40 26837**

Caine, Daniel

A-TEAM, THE.
LP: . . . . **A-TP 4444**
MC: . . . . **A-TC 4444**

CAGNEY AND LACEY.
Tracks: / Cagney and Lacey / Mike Hammer / Lou Grant / St. Elsewhere / Magnum / Taxi / Simon & Simon / Hill street blues.
LP: . . . . **CALT 3333**
MC: . . . . **CALP 3333**

Caine, General

IN FULL CHILL.
Tracks: / Hairdooz / Wrassle / Buffaloes / Can't let go / All the way up / Crack killed Applejack / Ticket, The / Cuttin' it up / General speaks, The.
LP: . . . . **ZL 72538**
MC: . . . . **ZK 72538**

Caine, Marti

BEHIND THE SMILE.
LP: . . . . **NSPL 18564**

LADY'S GONNA SING, THE.
Tracks: / Quiet please, the lady's gonna sing / At seventeen / That's the way I always heard it should be / Ebony eyes / I'd rather leave while I'm in love / Fire and rain / I'm getting ready for love / With one more look at you / Love song / Joy inside my tears / If there were only time for love / One more night out.
LP: . . . . **N 114**

NOBODY DOES IT LIKE MARTI.
LP: . . . . **NSPL 18489**

POINT OF VIEW.
Tracks: / Can I speak to the world please / I'll never see you again / Bitch is love / Love is running through me / Who / Love the way you love me / You pick me up / Snowbird city / Tin heart and the rebel / Too much between us.
LP: . . . . **REB 408**

Cairney, John

ROBERT BURNS STORY, THE.
MC: . . . . **REC 448**

ROBERT SERVICE STORY, THE.
LP: . . . . **REL 467**
MC: . . . . **REC 467**

WILLIAM MCGONAGALL STORY, THE.
MC: . . . . **REC 471**

Cairns, Forrie

GOLDEN CLARINET, THE.
Tracks: / Wooden heart / May of Argyle / Petite fleur / Aloha / Paper roses / Precious Lord / Mona Lisa / Amazing Grace / Beautiful dreamer / Clarinet lullaby / Rowan tree / Poor butterfly / Brahms' lullaby / Lonesome / Enjoy yourself / Auf wiedersehen.
LP: . . . . **BGC 353**

Cajun

14 CAJUN HITS (Various artists).
LP: **6066**
MC: . . . . **6066 TC**

BEST OF THE CAJUN HITS (Various artists).
LP: **6001**
MC: **6001TC**

BON TEMPS ROULER (Various artists).
LP: **6040**
MC: . . . . **6040 TC**

CAJUN BLUES (Various artists).
Tracks: / Les blues du voyager: *Various artists* / Jonie Bassette: *Various artists* / Quo' Faire: *Various* artists / Le chicot a bois-sec: *Various* artists / Bon Soir, Moreau: *Various artists* / La Robe Barree: *Various* artists / 'Tit Monde: *Various artists* / Valse a canray: *Various artists* / La valse de la prison: *Various* artists / La dase de la misere: *Various artists* / La valse d'oberlin: *Various artists* / Les Haricots: *Various* artists / Fais Pas Ca: *Various artists* / Duralde Ramble: *Various artists* / 'Tit Galope: *Various artists*/ Allez-Vous-En: *Various artists.*
LP: . . . . **BMLP 1045**

CAJUN COUNTRY FRENCH CLASSICS-VOL. 3 (Various artists).
LP: **145**
MC: . . . . **145 TC**

CAJUN COUNTRY MUSIC (Various artists).
Tracks: / La branche de mon murier: *Stutes, Jay* / Mariez-vous donc jamais: *Stutes, Jay* / Bayou pom pom: *Bonsall, Joe* / Pauvre hobo: *Bonsall, Joe* / Mariez-vous donc jamais: *Bonsall, Joe* / Petite ou la grosse: *Bonsall, Joe* / Pardon pour ca qu j'aifait: *Bonsall, Joe* / J'ai fait mon idee: *Bergeron, Shirley & Alphee* / Attrape ma corde et mes eperons: *Bergeron, Shirley & Alphee* / Quel etoile: *Bergeron, Shirley & Alphee* / Perrodin two step (instrumental): *Bergeron, Shirley & Alphee* / Allons a lake Charles: *Bertrand, Roberrt* / S'en aller dedans lake Charles: *Bertrand, Roberrt* / Demain, moi je va m'marier: *Stutes, Jay.*
LP: . . . . **GCL 125**

CAJUN CRUISIN' VOL 1 (Various artists).
LP: . . . . **SNTF 816**

CAJUN CRUISIN' VOL 2 (Various artists).
LP: . . . . **SNTF 817**

CAJUN DANCE TUNES (Various artists).
Tracks: / Talking in the street: *Fusilier, J.B./Jimmy Stewart* / Viens a ma maison: *Fusilier, J.B./Jimmy Stewart*/ Fau pas qu tu m'dublies: *Fusilier, J.B.* / T'es trop jeune pour toi t'marier: *Fusilier, J.B.* / Sha ba ba (chere babe): *Brown, Sidney* / La valse de love lane: *Brown, Sidney* / Durald waltz: *Le June, Iry* / Cafe chaud: *Broussard, Leroy* / La valse de pauvre garconnet: *Broussard, Leroy* / New love bridge waltz: *Touchet, Linus*/ Clover club special: *Touchet, Linus* / Short two step (instrumental): *Stewart, Jimmy.*
LP: . . . . **GCL 109**

CAJUN DANCE TUNES, VOL.2 (Various artists).
Tracks: / B.O. sparkle waltz: *Broussard, Leroy* / Lemonade song: *Broussard, Leroy* / La valse de meche (the marsh waltz): *Brown, Sidney* / Traveler playboy special: *Brown, Sidney* / La valse demeche (alt take): *Brown, Sidney*/ Noir chaussette's two step: *Brown, Sidney* / Pestauche ah Tante Nana: *Brown, Sidney* / River two step: *Cormier, Licnel* / Mermentau breakdown: *Cormier, Lionel* / Big boy bounce: *Cormier, Lionel* / Diga ding ding dong: *Roger, Aldus* / Duson waltz: *Roger, Aldus.*
LP: . . . . **GCL 110**

CAJUN FAIS DO DO FROM MAMOU LOUISIANA (Nathan Abshire, Breaux Brothers, etc.) (Various artists).
LP: . . . . **ARHOOLIE 5004**

CAJUN HITS VOL 2 (Various artists).
LP: **6003**
MC: . . . . **6003 TC**

CAJUN HITS VOL 3 (Various artists).
LP: **6033**
MC: . . . . **6033 TC**

CAJUN HITS VOL 4 (Various artists).
LP: **6045**

CAJUN MUSIC: FIRST RECORDINGS (Various artists).
MC: . . . . **C 213**

CAJUN RENDEZVOUS (Various artists).
LP: **6007**

CAJUN ROCK'N'ROLL (Various artists).
Tracks: / Good morning blues: *Stutes, Jay* / Sugar bee: *Stutes, Jay* / Drunkard's dreams: *Stutes, Jay*/ Sweet thing: *Stutes, Jay* / Midnight blues (come back little girl): *Stutes, Jay* / Telephone Port Arthur: *Stutes,* Jay / Hound dog baby: *Leblanc, Shorty* / Linda Lee: *Bonsall, Joe* / Poor ole Kawliga: *Stutes, Jay*/ Belle promesse que t'as cassee: *Bonsall, Joe* / Sha catin: *Bonsall, Joe* / I'm leavin' you: *Bonsall, Joe*/ Playmates: *Stutes, Jay* / Comin' home: *Stutes, Jay.*
LP: . . . . **GCL 124**

CAJUN SWAMP POP SUPER HITS (Various artists).
LP: . . . . **JIN 9028**
MC: . . . . **JIN 9028 TC**

CAJUN TREAT (Various artists).
LP: **6053**
MC: . . . . **6053 TC**

CAJUN TWO STEP (Various artists).
LP: . . . . **SNTF 805**

CAJUN VOL.1 - ABBEVILLE BREAKDOWN 1929-1939 (Various artists).
MC: **4672504**

CONVERSATIONAL CAJUN FRENCH (Various artists).
2LP: **8002**

CROWLEY TWO-STEP (1960's cajun at it's best) (Various artists).
LP: . . . . **FLY 604**

FLOYD'S CAJUN FAIS DO DO (Various artists).
LP: . . . . **CH 304**
MC: . . . . **CHC 304**

FOLKSONGS OF THE CAJUNS (Various artists).
MC: . . . . **C 212**

FOLKSONGS OF THE LOUISIANA ARCADIANS vol. 2 (Various artists).
LP: . . . . **ARHOOLIE 5015**

FOLKSONGS OF THE LOUISIANA ARCADIANS Vol.1 (Various artists).
LP: . . . . **ARHOOLIE 5009**

FRENCH MUSIC FROM THE SOUTHWEST PRAIRIES VOL 1 (Various artists).
LP: . . . . **ROUNDER 6001**

FRENCH MUSIC FROM THE SOUTHWEST PRAIRIES VOL 2 (Various artists).
LP: . . . . **ROUNDER 6002**

GOLDEN DOZEN HITS (Various artists).
LP: . . . . **JIN 9001**
MC: . . . . **JIN 9001 TC**

GOLDEN DOZEN - VOLUME 2 (Various artists).
LP: . . . . **JIN 9004**
MC: . . . . **JIN 9004 TC**

GOLDEN DOZEN - VOLUME 3 (Various artists).
LP: . . . . **JIN 9013**

GOLDEN DOZEN - VOLUME 4 (Various artists).
LP: . . . . **JIN 9020**
MC: . . . . **JIN 9020 TC**

IT'S CAJUN COUNTRY (Various artists).
LP: . . . . **GRLP 7762**

JIN RECORDS - LOUISIANA BLUES (Various artists).
LP: . . . . **CHD 211**

JIN STORY VOL.1 - BAYOU BOOGIE (Various artists).
Tracks: / I lost again: *Martin, Lee & The Velvetones* / There goes that train: *Martin, Lee & The Velvetones* / She wears my ring: *Bo, Phil* / Tough: *Bo, Phil* / Double trouble: *McCoy, Mary & The Cyclones* / Take a ride: *Smiley, Red & The Valtones* / Breaking up is hard to do: *Jiving Gene* / Gone too far: *Rob & The Rhythm* Aces / Opelousas sostain: *Jagneaux, Rufus* / Boogie chillun: *West, Clint/Boogie Kings* / Please don't mess with my man: *White, Margo* / Whole lotta shakin' goin' on: *Thomas, Prentice* / Growing old: *Lewis, Billy* & The Rockin' Hearts / I'm a fool to care: *Barry, Joe* / I ran around: *Bersin, Johnny & The Dialtones* / I've had it: *Randall, Jay & The Dialtones.*
LP: . . . . **CH 144**

LOUISIANA BLUES (Various artists).
LP: . . . . **ARHOOLIE 1054**

LOUISIANA CAJUN AND CREOLE MUSIC 1934 (Lomax recordings, The) (Various artists).
2LP: 8003

LOUISIANA CAJUN MUSIC (1935-48) (Hackberry Ramblers).
LP: .... OT 127

LOUISIANA CAJUN MUSIC-1 (First recordings) (Various artists).
LP: .... OT 108

LOUISIANA CAJUN MUSIC-2 (Early thirties) (Various artists).
LP: .... OT 109

LOUISIANA CAJUN MUSIC-3 (Strings bands of the 30s) (Various artists).
LP: .... OT 110

LOUISIANA CAJUN MUSIC-4 (From the 30s to the 50s) (Various artists).
LP: .... OT 111

LOUISIANA CAJUN MUSIC-5 (1928-1938) (Various artists).
LP: .... OT 114

LOUISIANA CAJUN MUSIC VOL.6 (Ardoin, Amade).
LP: .... OT 124

LOUISIANA CAJUN MUSIC VOL.7 (Soileau, Leo).
LP: .... OT 125

LOUISIANA CAJUN SPECIAL (Various artists).
Tracks: / Hee haw breakdown: *Cormier, N* / Pine grove blues: *Abshire, Nathan* / Triangle club special: *Prejean*, Leeman / Louisiana acres special: *Badeaux* / Lacassine special: *Balfa Brothers* / Cypress inn special: *Cormier*, N / Zydeci Cha Cha: *Mouton* / Cankton two step: *Prejan* / Cajun ramblers special: *Derouen, Wallace*/ Eunice two step: *Barzas, Maurice* / Hippy ti yo: *Bonsall, Joe* / I am so lonely: *Herbert, Adam* / Choupique two step: *Abshire, Nathan* / Waltz of regret: *Mate, Doris* / Two steps de vieux temps: *Rambling Aces*.
MC: .... CHC 914

LOUISIANA CAJUN SPECIAL VOL.1 (Swallow Records) (Various artists).
Tracks: / Hee haw breakdown: *Cormier, Nolan & the LA Aces* / Saturday night special: *Cormier, Lesa & The Sundown Playboys*/ Pine grove blues: *Abshire, Nathan* / Cajun ramblers special: *Derouen, Wallace & The Cajun Ramblers* / Oh Lucille: *Richard, Belton* / Cajun stripper: *Richard, Belton* / Opelousas two step: *Walker, Lawrence* / Back door: *Badeaux & The Louisiana Aces* / Louisiana Aces special: *Badeaux & The Louisiana Aces* / Eunice two step: *Barzas*, Maurice & The Mamau Playboys / Hippy ti yo: *Bonsall, Joe* / Triangle club special: *Prejean, Leeman* / I am so lonely: *Hebert, Adam* / Lacassine special: *Balfa Brothers* / Don't shake my tree: *Pitre, Austin*.
LP: .... CH 141

LOUISIANA CHANKY-CHANK (Various artists).
LP: .... ZN 1002

LOUISIANA EXPLOSIVE BLUES (Various artists).
LP: 1006

LOUISIANA'S CAJUN-FRENCH VERSIONS OF POPULAR HITS (Various artists).
LP: 6047
MC: .... 6047 TC

MERRY CAJUN CHRISTMAS (Various artists).
Tracks: / La vielle de Christmas sur Le Grand Bayou: *Various artists* / Christmas on the bayou: *Various artists*/ Please come home for Christmas: *Various artists* / What Christmas means to me: *Various artists* / Silent night: *Various artists* / Jingle bells: *Various artists* / Blue Christmas: *Various artists* / You're all I want for Christmas: *Various artists* / Here comes Santa Claus: *Various artists* / Christmas Eve on the big bayou: *Various artists*.
LP: 6036
MC: .... 6036 TC

MERRY CAJUN CHRISTMAS -VOL. 2 (Various artists).
Tracks: / Cajun night before Christmas: *Various artists* / Twelve days of Christmas, The: *Various artists* / Cajun Christmas: *Various artists* / It came upon a midnight clear: *Various artists* / Christmas in Cajun land: *Various* artists / It's Christmas time in Louisiana: *Various artists* / La veille de Noel: *Various artists* / Santa Claus is coming to town: *Various artists* / White Christmas: *Various artists* / Rockin' around the Christmas tree: *Various artists* / Randolph the rouge nosed reindeer: *Various artists*.
LP: 6070
MC: .... 6070 TC

MORE SOUTH LOUISIANA JUKE BOX FAVORITES (Various artists).
LP: .... JIN 4010

MUSIC OF FRENCH AMERICA (Various artists).
LP: .... ROUNDER 6010

PIONEERS OF CAJUN MUSIC (Various artists).
LP: .... OT 128

ROCKIN' DATE WITH SOUTH LOUISIANA STARS (Various artists).
LP: .... JIN 4002
MC: .... JIN 4002 TC

SOUTH LOUISIANA JUKE BOX HITS
Various artists (Various artists).
LP: .... JIN 4006
MC: .... JIN 4006 TC

SWALLOW RECORDS LOUISIANA CAJUN NO. 2 (Various artists).
Tracks: / Choupique two step: *Abshire, Nathan* / Cypress inn special: *Cormier, Lionel* / Chinaball blues: *Pitre, Austin* / Cameron two step: *Barro* / Calcasieu rambler's special: *Broussard, August* / Waltz of regret: *Matte, Doris* / Little cajun boy: *Leger, Bobby* / Zydeco cha cha: *Mouzas & Lignos* / Mamou hot step: *Mamou Playboys* / Every night when it's dark: *Hebert, Adam* / La valse de grand bois: *Balfa Brothers* / Cankton two step: *Prejean, Leeman* / She didn't know I was married: *Menard, D.L.* / Family waltz: *Menard, Phil & Don Guillory* / Two steps de vieux temps: *Rambling Aces* / One step de duson: *Cormier, Louis*.
LP: .... CH 166

SWAMP BLUES, VOL 1 (Various artists).
LP: .... SNTF 773

SWAMP MUSIC VOL 1 (Various artists).
LP: .... EFA 0156

SWAMP MUSIC VOL 2 (Various artists).
LP: .... EFA 0157

SWAMP MUSIC VOL 3 (Various artists).
LP: .... EFA 0158

THIS IS MAMOU CAJUN RADIO (Various artists).
Tracks: / Layfayette two step: *Various artists* / Tous les soirs: *Various artists* / Cajun strip, The: *Various* artists / La valse de famille: *Various artists* / Pine grove blues: *Various artists* / La valse de gran mamou: *Various artists* / Cajun hour two step, The: *Various artists*.
LP: .... SNTF 802

Cajun Aces

DEAF HEIGHTS.
Tracks: / Les flames d'enfer / Madame Edourarde / New pinegrove blues / Grand Mamou / Moi et mon cousin / La danse de la limonade / Bosco strip / Bayou pom pom / Colinda / La robe barree / Allons a lafayette / 'Tit galot / Hackberry zydeco.
LP: .... TP 025
MC: .... CTP 025

Cajun Country

JIMMY C. NEWMAN AND CAJUN COUNTRY (See under Newman, Jimmy C) (Cajun Country/Jimmy C. Newman).

Cajun Gold

LA LUMIERE DANS TON CHASSIS (see Daigle, Paul) (Cajun Gold/ Paul Daigle/ Robert Elkins).

Cajun, R

BAYOU RHYTHMS.
Tracks: / Jambalaya / Cajun two step / Back door (La porte d'en arriere) / Trouble in mind / Madame Edward / Deportess / Lemonade dance (Le danse de limonade) / Mardi gras / Bayou pom pom / Criminal waltz, The (La valse criminelle) / It's hard to believe / I made a big mistake (J'ai fait un gros erreur).
LP: .... MOO 4
MC: .... MOOC 4

PIG STICKING IN ARCADIA (Cajun, R. & The Zedeco Brothers).
LP: .... EFNILP 001
MC: .... LPO 1

Cajun Tradition

A LA VEILLE FACON.
LP: 6076
MC: .... 6076 TC

Cal (film)

CAL (1984 Film Soundtrack) (Knopfler, Mark).
Tracks: / Irish boy, The / Road, The / Waiting for her / Irish love / Secret place, A/ Where will you go / Father and son / Meeting at the trees / Potato picking / In a secret place / Fear and hatred / Love and guilt / Long road, The.
LP: .... VERH 17
MC: .... VERHC 17

Calamity Jane

CALAMITY JANE/I'LL SEE YOU IN MY DREAMS (Original soundtrack) (Various artists).
LP: .... P 19661
MC: .... BT 19661

CALAMITY JANE/PYJAMA GAME (Various artists).
Tracks: / Deadwood stage: *Various artists* / I can do without you: *Various artists* / Black hills of Dakota, The: *Various artists* / Just blew in from the Windy City: *Various artists* / Woman's touch, A: *Various artists*/ Higher than a hawk (deeper than a well): *Various artists* / 'Tis Harry I'm plannin' to marry: *Various artists*/ Secret love: *Various artists* / Pajama game, The: *Various artists* / And racing with the clock: *Various* artists / I'm not at all in love: *Various artists* / I'll never be jealous again: *Various artists* / Once a year day: *Various artists* / Small talk: *Various artists* / There once was a man: *Various artists* / Hernando's hideaway: *Various artists* / Finale: *Various artists*.
LP: .... CBS 32196
MC: 40 32196
LP: 4676101
MC: 4676104

SONGS FROM PAJAMA GAME & CALAMITY JANE (See under Day, Doris) (Day, Doris).

Calder, Adrian

STORY BOOK OF CHILDRENS' SONGS (see under Children's Songs...).

Caldera

CALDERA.
Tracks: / Guanacastle / Coastin' / Exaltation / Synesthesia / Out of the blue / El Juguete.
LP: .... EST 11571

DREAMER.
Tracks: / To capture the moon / Rain forest / Dream child / Celebration / Reflections on Don Quioxote / Brujerias / Himalaya.
LP: .... EST 11952

Caldwell, Bobby

BOBBY CALDWELL.
Tracks: / Special to me / My flame / Love won't wait / Can't say goodbye / Come to me / What you won't do for love / Kalimba song / Take me back to then / Down for the third time.
LP: .... TKR 83362

CAT IN THE HAT.
Tracks: / Coming down from love / Wrong or right / To know what you've got / You promised me / It's over / Open your eyes / Mother of creation / I don't want to lose your love.
LP: .... TKR 83386

Cale, Bruce

CENTURY OF STEPS, A (Cale, Bruce Orchestra).
LP: .... LRF 071

Cale, Grace

HITTIES AND KASSITES (Cale's Dubset, Grace).
LP: .... POPEL 1

Cale, J.J.

EIGHT.
Tracks: / Money talks / Losers / Hard times / Reality / Takin' care of business / People lie / Unemployment / Trouble in the city / Teardrops in my tequila / Livin' here too.
LP: .... MERL 22
MC: .... MERLC 22

FIVE.
Tracks: / Thirteen days / Boilin' pot / I'll make love to you anytime / Don't cry sister / Too much for me / Sensitive kind / Friday / Lou easy Ann / Let's go to Tahiti / Katy Kool lady / Fate of a fool / Mona.
LP: .... PRICE 44
MC: .... PRIMC 44
LP: .... ISA 5018

GRASSHOPPER.
Tracks: / City girls / Devil in disguise / One step ahead of the blues / You keep me hangin' on / Downtown L.A. / Can't live here / Grasshopper / Drifter's wife / Thing going on, A / Nobody but you / Mississippi river / Does your mama like to reggae / Doctor Jive.
LP: .... PRICE 74
MC: .... PRIMC 74
LP: .... ISA 5022

LA FEMME DE MON POTE.
Tracks: / Bringing it back / City girls / Mons (5) / Right down here / Woman that got away, The / Ride me high / Starbound (okie) / You keep me hangin' on / Super blue / Magnolia.
LP: 814 401 1
MC: 814 401 4

NATURALLY.
Tracks: / Call me the breeze / Call the doctor / Don't go to strangers / Woman I love, The / Magnolia / Clyde / Crazy mama / Nowhere to run / After midnight / River runs deep / Bringing it back / Crying eyes.
LP: .... PRICE 25
MC: .... PRIMC 25

NATURALLY/OKIE.
Tracks: / Call me the breeze / Call the doctor / Don't go to strangers / Woman I love, The / Magnolia / Clyde / Crazy mama / Nowhere to run / After midnight / River runs deep / Bringing it back / Crying eyes / Crying / I'll be there if you ever want me / Starbound / Rock and roll records / Old man and me, The / Ever lovin' woman / Cajun moon / I'd like to love you, baby / Anyway the wind blows / Precious memories / Okie / I got the same old blues.
LP: 8301791

NIGHTRIDING: J.J. CALE.
Tracks: / Hey baby / Travellin' light / You got something / Ride me high / Hold on / Cocaine / You keep me hangin' on / Grasshopper / I'm a gypsy man / Woman that got away, The / Super blue / Let me do it to you / Cherry / You got me on so bad / City girls / Mississippi river.
MC: .... KNMC 10006
LP: .... KNLP 10006

OKIE.
Tracks: / Crying / I'll be there if you ever want me / Starbound / Rock and roll records / Old man and me, The / Ever lovin' woman / Cajun moon / I'd like to love you baby / Anyway the wind blows / Precious memories / Okie / I got the same old blues.
LP: .... PRICE 34
MC: .... PRIMC 34

REALLY.
Tracks: / Lies / Everything will be alright / I'll kiss the world goodbye / Changes / Right down here / If you're ever in Oklahoma / Ridin' home / Going down / Soulin' / Playin' in the streets / Mo Jo / Louisiana woman.
LP: .... PRICE 26
MC: .... PRIMC 26

SHADES.
Tracks: / Carry on / Deep dark dungeon / Wish I had not said that / Pack my jack / If you leave her / Mama don't / What do you expect? / Cloudy day / Love has been and gone.
LP: .... PRICE 65
MC: .... PRIMC 65
LP: .... ISA 5021

SPECIAL EDITION.
Tracks: / Cocaine / Don't wait / Magnolia / Devil in disguise / Sensitive kind / Carry on after midnight / Money talks / Call me the breeze / Lies / City girls / Cajun moon / Don't cry sister / Crazy mama.
LP: .... MERL 42
MC: .... MERLC 42
MC: 818 633 4
LP: 818 633 1

TRAVEL-LOG.
Tracks: / Lean on me / Who's talking / Humdinger / End of the line / Tijuana / Shanghaid / New Orleans.
LP: .... ORELP 507
MC: .... OREC 507

TROUBADOUR.
Tracks: / Hey baby / I'm a gypsy man / You got me on so bad / Trackin' light / Woman that got away, The / Cherry / You got something / Hold on / Let me do it to you / Ride me high / Cocaine / Super blue.
LP: .... PRICE 35
MC: .... PRIMC 35
LP: .... ISA 5011

Cale, John

ACADEMY IN PERIL.
Tracks: / Philosopher, The / Brahms / Legs Larry at television centre / Academy in peril, The / Intro: Days of steam / Faust / Balance, The / Captain Morgan's lament / King Harry John Milton.
LP: .... ED 182

ARTIFICIAL INTELLIGENCE.
Tracks: / Every time the dogs bark / Dying on the vine / Sleeper, The / Vigilante lover / Chinese takeaway / Song of the valley / Fade away tomorrow / Black rose / Satellite walk.
LP: .... BEGA 68
MC: .... BEGC 68
LP: .... BBL 68
MC: .... BBLC 68

CARIBBEAN SUNSET.
Tracks: / Hungry for love / Experiment number one / Where there's a will / Model Beirut recital / Caribbean sunset / Praetorian underground / Magazines / Hunt, The / Villa albani / Ides of March /

Protege, The / Fear is a man's best friend / Buffalo ballet / Barracuda / Emily / Ship of fools / Gun / Man who couldn't afford to orgy, The / You know more than I know / Momamma scuba.
LP: ILPS 7024
MC: ICT 7024

CHURCH OF ANTHRAX (Cale, John & Terry Riley).
Tracks: / Church of Anthrax / Hall of mirrors / Soul of Patrick Lee, The.
LP: 64 259

FEAR.
LP: ILPS 9301
MC: ICM 9301

GUTS.
Tracks: / Guts / Mary Lou / Helen of Troy / Pablo Picasso / Leaving it up to you / Fear is a man's best friend / Gun / Dirty-ass rock and roll / Rock and roll / Heartbreak hotel.
LP: ILPS 9459

HONI SOIT.
Tracks: / Honi soit / Dead or alive / Strange times in Casablanca / Fighter pilot / Wilson Joliet / Streets of Laredo / Riverbank / Russian roulette / Magic and lies.
LP: AMLH 64849

JOHN CALE COMES ALIVE.
LP: ILPS 7026
MC: ICT 7026

MUSIC FOR A NEW SOCIETY.
LP: ILPS 7019
MC: ICT 7019

ONE WORD (See under Eno, Brian) (Cale, John/Brian Eno).

PARIS 1919.
Tracks: / Child's Christmas in Wales / Hanky panky nohow / Endless plain of furtune, The / Andalucia / MacBeth / Paris 1919 / Graham Greene / Half past France / Antarctica starts here.
LP: K 44239

SLOW DAZZLE.
Tracks: / Mr. Wilson / Taking it all away / Dirty-ass rock and roll / Darling I need you / Rollaroll / Heartbreak Hotel / Ski patrol / I'm not the loving kind / Guts / Jeweller, The.
LP: ILPS 9317

SONGS FOR DRELLA (Cale, John & Lou Reed).
LP: WX 345
MC: WX 345 C

SONGS FOR DRELLA (VIDEO) (See Under Reed, Lou) (Cale, John & Lou Reed).

VINTAGE VIOLENCE.
Tracks: / Hello there / Gideon's bible / Adelaide / Big white cloud / Cleo / Please / Charlemagne / Bring it on up / Amsterdam / Ghost story / Fairweather friends.
LP: ED 230

WORDS FOR THE DYING.
LP: LAND 009
MC: LANDC 009

WRONG WAY UP (See under Eno, Brian) (Cale, John/Brian Eno).

Caledonian Fiddle ....

IN CONCERT (Caledonian Fiddle Orchestra).
MC: ZCLOC 1057

Caledonian Heritage

AMAZING GRACE.
MC: KITV 515

Calennig

CALENNIG.
LP: GVR 224

SNOWY DAYS OF JANUARY.
LP: SAIN 1325 M

SONGS AND TUNES FROM WALES.
LP: GVR 214

Calhoun, Andrew

GATES OF LOVE, THE.
LP: FF 341

WALK ME TO THE WAR.
LP: FF 398

Caliban

DEBUT ALBUM.
LP: STFC 0001

Caliche

DEEP FROM THE EARTH.
Tracks: / A mi tierra / Clavelito / N'guillatun / Camanchaca nortina / Charangeada ayacuchana / El condor pasa / Velando a un campesino / Oasis / Pajaro campana / Fiesta aymara.
LP: FSLP 10
MC: FSMC 10

WINDS FROM THE SOUTH.
Tracks: / Festival de la Flores / Volver a un tiempo nuevo / Recuerdos del lago / Camino de la chinchilla / Tierro del fuego / Vientos del sur / Amanecer un puno / P'al norte se van / Chucuito / El pillan.
LP: FSLP 11
MC: FSMC 11

California...

CALIFORNIA CONNECTION, THE (Various artists).
LP: 3970641
MC: 3970644

California Executives

DANCING AND ROMANCING, THE.
Tracks: / I can't forget you / You know what I like / How long (do I have to wait for you) / Same for me, The / Let me love you tonight / Baby I love you / What are you afraid of? / I can't let you go / I don't know why.
LP: GMIMP 1
LP: TRPL 126

California Jubilee

CALIFORNIA JUBILEE SINGERS.
LP: 850 045

California Raisins

CALIFORNIA RAISINS SING THE HIT SONGS.
LP: GRALP 1
MC: GRAMC 1

MEET THE RAISINS.
LP: K 781917 1
MC: K 781917 4

California Ramblers

1920'S FLAPPER PARTY.
Tracks: / Ev'rything is hotsy totsy now / Sweet Georgia Brown / I'm gonna charleston back to Charleston / Show me the way to go home / No foolin' / Girlfriend / Ya gotta know how to love / Stockholm stomp / We love the college girls / Yes she do - no she don't / Vo-do-do-de-o blues / Nothin' does-does like it used to do-do-do / Make my cot where the cot-cot-cotton grows / Mine - all mine / Singapore sorrows / Pay-off, The.
MC: CHAL 8
LP: HAL 8

CALIFORNIA RAMBLERS (California Ramblers, Rollini, Red Nichols, T.& J.Dorsey).
LP: JS 101

California, Randy

EURO AMERICAN.
Tracks: / Easy love / Fearless leader / Five in the morning / Skull and crossbones / Breakout / Toy guns / This is the end / Mon ami / Rude creation / Calling you / Wild thing.
LP: BEGA 36
MC: BEGC 36

KAPTAIN KOPTER AND HIS TWIRLY BIRDS.
Tracks: / Downer / Devil I don't want nobody / Day tripper / Mother and child reunion / Things yet to come / Rain / Rainbow.
MC: CED 164
LP: ED 164
LP: CBS 31829

RESTLESS.
Tracks: / Run to your lover / Restless nights / Second child / Shane / Jack rabbit / One man's heaven / Murphy's law / Camelot / Mattlemarch of the overlords / Childhood's end.
LP: VERL 19

WATCHTOWER.
LP: 6.25318

California Strings...

ROUND MIDNIGHT (California Strings & Singers).
MC: VCA 081

California Suite

CALIFORNIA SUITE (1978 film soundtrack) (Various artists).
Tracks: / California main title: *Various artists* / California suite (love theme): *Various artists* / Black battle: *Various artists* / Hannah's daughter: *Various artists* / Black folks: *Various artists* / Academy awards, The: *Various artists* / Beverly Hills: *Various artists* / California end credits: *Various artists.*
LP: CBS 70168
MC: 40 70168
LP: CBS 73991

Call

INTO THE WOODS.
Tracks: / I don't wanna / In the river / It could have been me / Woods, The / Day or night / Memory / Too many tears / Expecting / Walk walk.
LP: 9607391
MC: 9607394

LET THE DAY BEGIN.
Tracks: / Let the day begin / You run / Surrender / When / Jealousy / Same ol' story / For love / Closer / Communication / Watch / Uncovered.
LP: MCG 6065
MC: MCGC 6065

MODERN ROMANS.
Tracks: / Walls came down / Turn a blind eye / Time of your life / Modern Romans / Back from the front / Destination / Violent times / Face to face / All about you.
LP: 6337 263

RECONCILED.
Tracks: / Everywhere I go / I still believe (great design) / Blood red (America) / Morning / Tore the old place down / Oklahoma / With or without reason / Sanctuary / Even now.
LP: 9604401
MC: 9604404

SCENE BEYOND DREAMS.
Tracks: / Scene beyond dreams / Burden, The / Tremble / Delivered / Heavy hand / Promise and threat / One life leads to another / Apocalypse / Notified.
LP: 818 793 1
MC: 818 793 4

Call In The Night (bk)

CALL IN THE NIGHT (Susan Howatch (auth)).
MCSET: CAB 305

Call It Love (show)

CALL IT LOVE (Original London cast) (Various artists).
LP: TER 1083

Call Me Madam (show)

CALL ME MADAM (1952 Original London cast) (Various artists).
Tracks: / Washington square: *Various artists* / Lichtenburg: *Various artists* / Can you use any money today: *Various* artists / Marrying for love: *Various artists* / Ocarina, The: *Various artists* / It's a lovely day today: *Various artists* / Best thing for you, The: *Various artists* / Something to dance about: *Various artists*/ Once upon a time today: *Various artists* / They like Ike: *Various artists* / You're just in love: *Various artists* / Hostess with the mostes' on the ball, The: *Various artists.*
LP: TER 1062
MC: ZCTER 1062

CALL ME MADAM (1950 Original Broadway cast) (Various artists).
Tracks: / Hostess with the mostes' on the ball, The: *Various artists* / Can you use any money today?: *Various artists*/ Washington square dance: *Various artists* / Lichtenburg: *Various artists* / Marrying for love: *Various artists*/ Ocarina, The: *Various artists* / It's a lovely day: *Various artists* / Best thing for you, The: *Various* artists / Something to dance about: *Various artists* / Once upon a time today: *Various artists* / They like Ike: *Various artists.*
MC: MCLC 1726
LP: MCL 1726

Call Of The Valley

CALL OF THE VALLEY (Various artists).
LP: ECSD 2362
MC: TC 1109

Callas, Maria

GUISEPPE VERDI RECITAL.
LP: SMR 1281

MARIA CALLAS COLLECTION,THE.
Tracks: / One fine day / O my beloved daddy / Little voice within my heart / Ebben? ne andro lontana / Signore, asolta! / Love and music / Bolero / They call me Mimi / Shadow song / Come per me soreno / Mimi's farewell / Printemps qui commence / Waltz song / Je ne suis que faiblesse / Softly awakes my heart / Chanson boheme / J'ai perdu mon Eurydice / Porgi amor / Casta diva / Prendi, per me sei libero / Ave Maria / Mad scene.
2LP: SMR 732
MCSET: SMC 732

Calle, Oscar

OSCAR CALLE AND HIS CUBAN ORCHESTRA 1933-1939 (Calle, Oscar & His Cuban Orchestra).
Tracks: / La conga de la senora / Ali Baba / Canto de Cuba / Suena conga suene / Chango / Loca rhumba / Negro-bembon / Calabaza / Quiero una conga / Tonia.
LP: HQ 2079

Callier, Terry

FIRE ON ICE.
Tracks: / Be a believer / Holdin' on (to your love) / Street fever / Butterfly / I been doin' alright part II (Everything's gonna be alright) / Disco in the sky / American violet / Love two tone / Martin St Martin.
LP: K 52096

TURN YOU TO LOVE.
Tracks: / Sign of the times / Pyramids of love / Turn you to love / Do it again / Ordinary Joe / Occasional rain / Still water / You and me (will always be in love) / Mother's love, A.
LP: K 52140

Callies

ON YOUR SIDE.
Tracks: / Rockin' chair / January man / Monty's song / Make me happy / Reason to believe / Home town / Peggy Gordon / Is it surprising / Change of mind / Turning into winter / Top 40.
LP: RUB 002

Calloway

ALL THE WAY.
Tracks: / Sir Lancelot / I wanna be rich / Love circles / Freaks compete / You are my everything / All the way / I want you / Sugar free / You can count on me / Holiday.
LP: 4662271
MC: 4662274

Calloway, Blanche

BLANCHE CALLOWAY 1931.
LP: HQ 2057

Calloway, Cab

BOOG-IT.
LP: JJ 607

CAB AND CO..
Tracks: / Evenin' / Harlem hospitality / Lady with the fan, The / Harlem camp meeting / Zaz zuh zaz / Father's got his glasses on / Minnie the moocher (takes 1 & 2) / Scat song, The (takes 1 & 20 / Kicking the gong around / There's a cabin in the cotton / I learned about love from her (takes 3 & 4) / Little town gal / Long about midnight / Moon glow / Jitterbug / Hotcha razz ma tazz / Margie / Emaline / Ol' Joe Louis / Your voice / Rooming house boogie / I beeped when I shoulda bopped / I need lovin' / Just a crazy song / It looks like Susie / Growlin' Dan / Concentratin' on you / Last dollar / Oh you sweet thing.
2LP: NL 89560
MCSET: NK 89560

CAB CALLOWAY.
LP: GLS 9007

CAB CALLOWAY 1937-8.
LP: VA 7998

CAB CALLOWAY 1938-47.
LP: SM 4047
MC: MC 4047

CAB CALLOWAY COLLECTION (20 golden greats).
Tracks: / Minnie the moocher / Jumpin' jive / Honeydripper / Duck trot / That old black magic / Hoy hoy / Jungle king / We the cats shall help you / Oh grandpa / Everybody eats when they come to my house / Hi de ho / Calloway boogie / How big can you get? / St. James' Infirmary / Hey now, hey now / Nagasaki / Foo a little bally hoo / I can't give you anything but love / I want to rock / Birth of the blues.
MC: DVMC 2056
LP: DVLP 2056

CAB CALLOWAY STORY, THE.
Tracks: / Nagasaki / Hoy hoy / Jumpin' jive / Give baby give / I want to rock / Minnie the moocher / Honeydripper / Hi de ho / Jungle king / Calloway boogie / Two blocks down town to the left / Chicken ain't nothin' but a bird, A / I can't give you anything but love / Stormy weather / You got it / Everybody eats when they come to my house / Afternoon moon / This is always / Duck trot / That old black magic / How big can you get / Hey now hey now / Birth of the blues / We the cats shall help you / Foo a little bally hoo.
MCSET: DVREMC 22

CAB, ELLA & CHICK 1936 - 40 (Calloway, Cab/ Ella Fitzgerald/ Chick Webb).
LP: BS 7125

CLUB ZANZIBAR BROADCASTS.
Tracks: / For a little rally / Russian lullaby / I was here when you left me / St. Louis blues / Frantic in the Atlantic / 9/20 special / Great lie, The / I can't give you anything but love / Rose Marie / I'm not ashamed of my tears / One o'clock jump.
LP: UJ 06

CONJURE.
Tracks: / Author reflects on his 35th birthday / Sputin / General science / My brothers / St. Louis women / Beware - don't listen to this song / Loup garrou means change into / Nobody was there / Running for the office of love / Petit Kid Everett / Bitter chocolate / Minnie the moocher.
LP: AM 1015
MC: AMC 1015

COTTON CLUB REVUE 1958.

Tracks: / Born to be happy / Tzotskele / Sinful / Beginnin' of sinnin' / Sweeter than sweet / Never had it so good / Minnie the moocher / Copper coloured gal / Got the world on a string / She's tall, she's tan, she's terrific / Don't worry 'bout me / St James Infirmary.
LP: OFF 3000
LP: AFA 5031

FRANTIC IN THE ATLANTIC.
LP: DBD 10
MC: DBDC 10

GET WITH IT.
LP: SWH 38
MC: CSWH 38

HI DE HO.
LP: PAR 2008

HI-DE-HO MAN, THE.
Tracks: / Jumping jive, The / Minnie the moocher / It ain't necessarily so / St. James Infirmary / I see a million people / Hi de ho man, The / Summertime / Kicking the gong around / Stormy weather / You rascal you.
LP: PL 45163

JAZZ OF THE AIR (VOL 4).
Tracks: / We the cats shall help you / Dawn time / Minnie the moocher / Rhythm cocktail / Very thought of you, The / Foo a little bally hoo / Is you is or is you ain't my baby / Frantic in the Atlantic / Blue skies / Cruisin' with Cab / Body and soul / Minnie the moocher / Kabla / Lammar's boogie / Coastin' with JC.
LP: SPJ 148

JUMPIN' STUFF.
LP: GELP 15013

JUMPING AND JIVING 1930-37.
LP: ST 1001

JUMPING JIVE.
LP: SWH 15
MC: CSWH 15
LP: CBS 21115
MC: 40 21115

KICKING THE GONG AROUND.
Tracks: / Minnie the moocher / Without rhythm / Aw, you dog / Bugle call rag / Downhearted blues / Nightmare, The / Black rhythm / Yaller / Between the Devil and the deep blue sea / Nobody's sweetheart / Trickeration / St. Louis blues / Mood indigo / Farewell blues / You rascal you / My honey's lovin' arms / Some of these days / Six or seven times / Somebody stole my gal / Kicking the gong around.
LP: AJA 5013
MC: ZC AJA 5013

L'ART VOCAL VOLUME 6: LA SELECTION 1930 - 1939 (See Under L'Art Vocal).

LEGENDARY CAB CALLOWAY 1933/34, THE.
Tracks: / Harlem camp meeting / Father got his glasses on / Kicking the gong around / Scat song, The / Moonglow / Jitterbug / Harlem hospitality / Margie / Long about midnight / Minnie the moocher.
MC: MRT 40054

MAN FROM HARLEM, THE (1930-32).
LP: ET 5

MAN FROM HARLEM, THE.
LP: ET 4

MINNIE THE MOOCHER (RCA) (Calloway, Cab & His Orchestra).
Tracks: / Minnie the moocher / Evenin' / Lady with the fan, The / Harlem camp meeting / Zah zuh zaz / Father's got his glasses on / Little town gal / There's a cabin in the cotton / Harlem hospitality / Kicking the gong around / Long about midnight / Margie / Moon glow / Jitterbug / Hotcha razz ma tazz.
LP: NL 89338
MC: NK 89338

MINNIE THE MOOCHER 1930 - 34 (Calloway, Cab & His Orchestra).
LP: BS 7124
MC: BS 7124C

MINNIE THE MOOCHER (Big Band Era) (Calloway, Cab & His Orchestra).
LP: 20185
MC: 40185

MINNIE THE MOOCHER (Calloway, Cab & His Orchestra).
Tracks: / Scat song, The / You rascal you / Nobody's sweetheart / Between the devil and the deep blue sea / Kicking the gong around / Hotcha razz ma tazz / Jitterbug / Harlem hospitality / Lady with the fan, The / Zaz zuh zaz / Fathers got his glasses on / Little town girl / There's a cabin in the cotton / Harlem camp meeting / Minnie the moocher / Long about midnight / Moonglow / Margie.
LP: PLE 524

MINNIE THE MOOCHER (RCA) (Calloway, Cab & His Orchestra).
Tracks: / Harlem hospitality / Lady with the fan, The / Harlem camp meeting / Zah zu sah / Father's got his glasses on / Little town gal / There's a cabin in the cotton / Scat song / Minnie the moocher / Kicking the gong around / Long about midnight / Moonglow / Margie / Jitterbug / Hotcha razz ma tazz.
LP: INTS 5121

MISSOURIANS.
Tracks: / Market street stomp / Ozark mountain blues / You'll cry for me but I'll be gone / Missouri moan / I've got someone / 400 hop / Vine street drag / Scotty blues / Two hundred squabble / Swingin' dem cats / Stoppin' the traffic / Prohibition blues / Gotta darn good reason now / St. Louis blues / Sweet Jenny Lee / Happy feet / Yaller / Viper's drag / Is that religion? / Some of these days.
LP: VLP 58

MOST IMPORTANT RECORDINGS OF CAB CALLOWAY, THE.
Tracks: / Some of these days / Saint James Infirmary / Minnie the moocher / Six or seven times / Sweet Georgia Brown / Bugle call rag / Somebody stole my gal / Corina, Corina / Scat song, The / Minnie the moocher's wedding day / How come you do me like you do / Reefer man / Man from Harlem, The / Doin' the new low down / Lady with the fan, The / Zaz, zuh, zaz / Margie / Keep that hi-de-hi in your soul / Nagasaki / Wedding of Mr and Mrs Swing / Swing, swing, swing / Savage rhythm / At the clam-bake carnival / Jive / Ratamacue / Jumpin' jive / Ghost of a chance / Calling all bars / Jonah joins the cab / Hey, Doc / Hi de ho man, The / I beeped when I should'a bopped.
LPS: OFF 3041-2

ON FILM.
Tracks: / Minnie the moocher / Rail rhythm / Zaz zuh zaz / Lady with the fan, The / I got a right to sing the blues / Hi de ho man, The / Frisco Flo / Some of these days / Skunk song / Virginia, Georgia and Caroline / Blues in the night / Jumpin' jive / Sunday in Savannah / Geechie Joe / Calloway boogie.
LP: HQ 2005

SINGIN' AND SWINGIN'.
LP: GOJ 1012
MC: GOJC 1012

THAT OLD BLACK MAGIC.
LP: CL 004184

Calvert, Eddie

20 GOLDEN TRUMPET GREATS.
Tracks: / Laura / Forgotten dreams / Jealousy / Around the world / Midnight in Moscow / Hora staccato / You'll never walk alone / Malaguena / Little pixie / Quando, quando, quando / Manhattan / Besame mucho / Indian Summer / Man I love, The / Sidewalks of Cuba / Blue tango / Il silenzio / Volare / La vie en rose / Trumpet tango.
MC: TC NTS 178
LP: NTS 178

EDDIE CALVERT SALUTES THE GREATS.
MC: 1A 220 1583214

GOLDEN TRUMPET GREATS.
LP: 2384 105

MAN WITH THE GOLDEN TRUMPET, THE.
Tracks: / Oh mein papa / Mandy / Midnight / Getting sentimental over you / Tenderly / Roses of Picardy / Poor people of Paris, The / Stranger in Paradise / Spellbound / Oh my beloved daddy / April in Portugal / Little serenade / Summertime / My son, my son / Cherry pink and apple blossom white / John and Julia / Zambesi / Softly as in a morning sunrise / Serenata / Memories of you / Spanish flea / Around the world / London by night / Sucu sucu / I love Paris / Wonderful Copenhagen / On a slow boat to China / Vilia.
LP: OU 2199
2LP: DL 41 1064 3
MC: DL 41 1064 9

Calvert, Robert

CAPTAIN LOCKHEAD AND THE STARFIGHTERS.
LP: BGOLP 5

FREQ.
LP: SHARP 021

HYPE.
Tracks: / Over my head / Ambitious / It's the same / Hanging out on the seafront / Sensitive / Evil rock / We like to be frightened / Teen ballad of Deano / Flight 105 / Luminous green glow of the dashboard, The / Greenfly and the rose / Lord of the hornets.
LP: SEE 278

LUCKY LEIF AND THE LONGSHIPS.
Tracks: / Ship of fools / Lay of the surfers, The / Voyaging to vinland / Making of Midgard, The / Brave new world / Magical potion / Moonshine in the mountains / Storm chant of the skraelings / Volstead o vodeo do / Phase locked loop / Ragna rock.
LP: UNKNOWN

TEST TUBE CONCEIVED.
Tracks: / Telekinesis / I hear voices / Fanfare for the perfect race / On line / Save them from the scientists / Fly on the wall / Thanks to the scientists / Test tube conceived / In vitro breed / Rah rah man, The.
LP: DMLP 1010

Calypso

CALYPSO SEASON (Various artists).
Tracks: / Somebody: *Baron* / Maxi dub: *Bally* / Free up: *Tambu* / Shaking it: *McIntosh, Ronnie* / Jail them: *Roaring Lion* / Innocent Jimmy: *All Rounder* / Congo man: *Sparrow* / Yah: *Duke* / One more officer: *Rudder, David* / Somebody: *Desperadoes*.
LP: 828 172 1
MC: 828 172 4

Calypso Rose

LEH WE PUNTA.
Tracks: / Mama coming down / Leh we punta / In the party / Beat anything / Other woman, The / I don't know.
LP: GS 2271

ON TOP OF THE WORLD.
LP: GS 2281

SOCA EXPLOSION.
LP: GS 2299
MC: GSK 2299
LP: ICE 18

SOUL ON FIRE.
LP: ELP 008

Calzado, Rudy

RICA CHARANGA.
Tracks: / Dale al pilon / Mi clampina / Tumbao pa'gozar / La reina del cafe / Deja eso / Que me quiten lo bailao / Roses ni claveles / Prende la vela.
LP: ORB 025

Camara, Ladsi

AFRICA, NEW YORK (Master Drummer).
LP: LLST 7345

Camarata Symphony Orc.

VIENNA OF J STRAUSS (Camarata & Kungsway Symphony Orc.).
LP: PFS 4240 82

Camberwell Now

GHOST TRAIN, THE.
LP: INK 19

Cambourne Town Band

CELEBRATION.
MC: SENC 1075

Cambridge Band

CAMBRIDGE BAND.
Tracks: / Entry of the gladiators / Where e'er you walk / Professional march / In the cloisters / Holiday overture / El matador / Waltz memories of Schubert / Prelude (La Traviata) / Trumpet piece / Coppelia.
LP: TB 3020

Cambridge Buskers

ANOTHER SERIOUS ALBUM.
Tracks: / Stars and stripes forever / Tango ballade / Canon / Belfast reel / La vie en rose / Recorder concerto finale / Cod piece / Polovtsian dances / Here, there and everywhere / Sheep may safely graze / Carmen entr'acte / Good beer jig / Two Rumanian folk tunes / Lambeth walk / Gymnopedie No.1 / Bolero.
LP: 2372 057

CAMBRIDGE BUSKERS.
Tracks: / Hungarian dance no. 1 / Silken ladder overture / Largo / Sabre dance / Jig / Farandole / Ding dong merrily on high / Sweet William theme / Dance of the blessed spirits.
LP: 237 198 4

LITTLE STREET MUSIC, A.
Tracks: / Eine kleine nachtmusik / Rondo alla Turca / Mozart no.40 / Hora Staccato / William Tell / Theiving magpie / Hungarian dance no.5 / Two part invention / Entertainer, The / Badinerie / In dulci jubilo / Drunken sailor.
LP: 2535471

SOAP OPERA.
LP: 2532072
MC: 3303202

Cambridge City

BUD FREEMAN TAPES, THE (see Freeman, Bud) (Cambridge City Jassband & Bud Freeman).

CAMBRIDGE BLUES.
LP: PLJ 004

Cambridge Youth Choir

O DIVINE REDEEMER (Cambridge Silver Jubilee Youth Choir).
LP: BURL 026

SONG FOR ALL SEASONS, A (Cambridge Silver Jubilee Youth Choir).
LP: PLR 031

Camel

BREATHLESS.
LP: XSR 132R
MC: KTXCR 132
LP: TXS 132

CAMEL.
Tracks: / Slow yourself down / Mystic queen / Six ate / Separation / Never let go / Curiosity / Arubaluba.
LP: MCL 1601
MC: MCLC 1601
LP: FA 3054

CHAMELEON.
Tracks: / Echoes / Rhayader / Rhayader goes to town / Song within a song / Remote romance / Nude / Drafted / Lies / Supertwister / Unevensong / Rainbow's end.
LP: SKL 5325
MC: KSKC 5325

COLLECTION: CAMEL.
Tracks: / Aristillus / Freefall / Supertwister / Spirit of the water / Lunar sea / White rider, The / Earthrise / Song within a song / Rhayader goes to town / Migration / Rhayader alone / La princesse perdue / Great marsh, The / Drafted / Captured / Sasquatch / Rain dances / Highways of the sun / First light.
2LP: CCSLP 116
MC: CCSMC 116

I CAN SEE YOUR HOUSE FROM HERE.
Tracks: / Wait / Your love is stranger than mine / Eye of the storm / Who are we / Survival / Hymn to her / Neon magic / Remote romance.
MC: KTXCR 137
LP: TXS 137

LANDSCAPES.
Tracks: / City lights / Landscapes / Reflections / Freefall / Echoes / Refugee / Missing / Spirit of the water / Air born / First light / Skylines / Raindances / Sanctuary / Fritha / Last farewell, The / Beached / Stationary traveller / Cloak and dagger / Your love is stranger than mine.
MC: ELITE 003 PMC

LIVE RECORD, A.
Tracks: / Never let go / Song within a song / Lunar sea / Skylines / Ligging at Louis' / Lady fantasy / Great marsh, The / Rhayader / Rhayader goes to town / Sanctuary / Fritha / Snow goose, The / Friendship / Migration / Rhayader alone / Plight of the snow goose / Preparation / Dunkirk / Epitaph / Fritha alone / La princesse perdue / Great marsh, The.
2LP: DBC 7/8
MCSET: KDBC 7/8

MIRAGE.
Tracks: / Freefall / Supertwister / Nimrodel / Procession / White rider, The / Earthrise / Lady Fantasy / Encounter / Smiles for you.
LP: SML 1107

MOON MADNESS.
Tracks: / Aristillus / Song within a song / Chord change / Spirit of the water / Another night / Air born / Lunar sea.
LP: TXSR 115
MC: KTXCR 115

NUDE.
Tracks: / City life / Nude / Drafted / Dock's / Beached / Landscape / Changing places / Pomp and circumstance / Please come home / Reflections / Captured / Homecoming / Last farewell, The / Birthday cake, The / Nude's return / Lies.
LP: SKL 5323
MC: KSKC 5323

PRESSURE POINTS (Camel live).
Tracks: / Drafted / Captured / Lies / Sasquatch / West Berlin / Fingertips / Wait / Rhayader / Rhayader goes to town / Stationary traveller.
LP: SKL 5338
MC: KSKC 5338

RAIN DANCES.
Tracks: / First light / Metrognome / Tell me / Highways of the sun / Unevensong / One of these days I'll get an early night / Skylines / Elke / Rain dances.
LP: TXSR 124
MC: KTXCR 124

SINGLE FACTOR.
Tracks: / No easy answer / You are the one / Heroes / Selva / Lullaby / Sasquatch / Manic / Camelogue /

Today's goodbye / Heart's goodbye / Heart's desire / End piece.
LP: SKL 5328
MC: KSKS 5328

SNOW GOOSE.
Tracks: / Great marsh, The / Rhayader / Rhayader goes to town / Sanctuary / Fritha / Snow goose, The / Friendship / Rhayader alone / Flight of the snow goose / Preparation / Dunkirk / Epitaph / Fritha alone / La princesse perdue / Pressure points / Refugee / Stationary traveller.
LP: SKL 5207
MC: KSKC 5207

STATIONARY TRAVELLER.
Tracks: / Pressure points / Refugee / Vopos / Cloak and dagger man / Stationary traveller / West Berlin / Fingertips / Missing / Long goodbye / After words / Copos.
LP: SKL 5334
MC: KSKC 5334

Camelfoot, Humphrey

MARY ROSE (see Gutbucket, Arnold) (Camelfoot, Humphrey & Arnold Gutbucket).

Camelot (musical)

CAMELOT (1982 London revival cast) (Various artists).
Tracks: / Camelot overture (prologue): *Various artists* / Camelot: *Various artists* / Simple joys of maidenhood: *Various artists* / I wonder what the king is doing tonight: *Various artists* / C'est moi: *Various artists*/ Follow me: *Various artists* / Joust: *Various artists* / Lusty month of May, The: *Various artists* / Resolution: *Various artists* / Then you may take me to the fair: *Various artists* / How to handle a woman: *Various artists* / Entracle madrigal: *Various artists* / Before I gaze at you again: *Various artists* / Fie on goodness: *Various artists* / If ever I would leave you: *Various artists* / I loved you once in silence: *Various artists*/ Seven deadly virtues, The: *Various artists* / What do the simple folks do?: *Various artists* / Guenevere: *Various artists* / Finale: *Various artists.*
LP: TER 1030
MC: ZCTER 1030

CAMELOT (1967 film soundtrack) (Various artists).
Tracks: / Overture: *Various artists* / I wonder what the king is doing tonight: *Various artists* / Simple joys of maidenhood: *Various artists* / Camelot and the wedding ceremony: *Various artists* / C'est moi: *Various* artists / Lusty month of May, The: *Various artists* / Follow me: *Various artists* / How to handle a woman: *Various artists* / Take me to the fair: *Various artists* / If ever I would leave you: *Various artists*/ What do the simple folk do?: *Various artists* / I loved you once in silence: *Various artists* / Guenevere: *Various artists* / Finale: *Various artists.*
LP: K 56001
MC: K4 56001
LP: WS 1712

CAMELOT (1961 Original Broadway Cast) (Various artists).
Tracks: / Camelot: overture: *Various artists* / I wonder what the king is doing tonight?: *Various artists* / Simple joys of maidenhood, The: *Various artists* / Camelot: *Various artists* / Follow me: *Various artists* / Lusty month of may, The: *Various artists* / C'est moi: *Various artists* / Then you may take me to the fair: *Various* artists / How to handle a woman: *Various artists* / If ever I would leave you: *Various artists* / Parade: *Various artists* / Before I gaze at you again: *Various artists* / Seven deadly virtues, The: *Various artists*/ What do the simple folk do?: *Various artists* / Fie on goodness: *Various artists* / I loved you once in silence: *Various artists* / Guenevere: *Various artists* / Camelot: finale: *Various artists.*
MC: PST 32602
LP: CBS 7009
MC: 40 7009

CAMELOT (1964 Original London cast) (Various artists).
LP: OCR 4
MC: OCRC 4

CAMELOT (ORIGINAL ISSUE) (Broadway cast) (Various artists).
LP: APG 60001

CAMELOT (ORIGINAL ISSUE) (London cast) (Various artists).
LP: CLP 1756

Cameo

ALLIGATOR WOMAN.
LP: 6480 079

FEEL ME.
Tracks: / Throw it down / Your love takes me out / Keep it hot / Feel me / Is this the way / Roller skates / Better days.
LP: CCL 2016

KNIGHTS OF THE SOUND TABLE.
Tracks: / Knights by nights / Freaky dancin' / I never knew it / Use it or lose it / Sound table / Don't be so cool / I'll always stay / I like it.
LP: 6480041

MACHISMO.
Tracks: / You make me work / Skin I'm in / I like the world / Pretty girls / Promiscuous / Soul tightened / In the night / Money / DKWIG.
LP: 836 002-1
MC: 836 002-4

REAL MEN WEAR BLACK.
Tracks: / Close quarters / Me / Get paid / Time, fire and space / Just a broken heart / I want it now / Attitude / Am I bad enough / Nan yea.
LP: 846 297 1
MC: 846 297 4

SECRET OMEN.
Tracks: / Energy / I just want to be / Find my way / Macho / Rock / Sparkle / New York.
LP: CAL 2058

SHE'S STRANGE.
Tracks: / She's strange / Love you anyway / Talkin' out the side of your neck / Tribute to Bob Marley / Groove with you / Hangin' downtown / Leve toi.
LP: 8149 841
LP: PRICE 109
MC: PRIMC 109

SINGLE LIFE.
Tracks: / Attack me with your love / Single life / I'll never look for love / Little boys - dangerous toys / I've got your image / Goodbye.
LP: JABH 11
MC: JABHC 11
LP: 824 546-1

STYLE.
Tracks: / Aphrodisiac / This life is not for me / You're a winner / Can't help falling in love / Interlude / Serenity / Cameo's dance / Let's not talk shop / Slow movin' / Heaven only knows.
LP: 811 072 1

UGLY EGO.
Tracks: / I'll be with you / Insane / Give love a chance / Ugly ego / I want you / Anything you wanna do / Friend to me / Two of us.
LP: CAL 2038

WORD UP.
Tracks: / Word up / Urban warrior / Candy / Back and forth / Don't be lonely / She's mine / Fast, fierce and funny / You can have the world.
LP: JABH 19
MC: JABHC 19

Cameo (folk)

CHOICES.
Tracks: / Cocky, The / Down the Braes / Centenary march / Scarborough fair / Rare old times / Bunch thyme / Boolavogue / Plaisir d'amour / Atholl highlanders / Gentleman solider / Off to California / Chief O'Neil's favourite / Three score and ten / Swipesey cakewalk / Portsmouth.
MC: HB 9106

Camerata Bern

LODRON SERENADES, THE (MOZART) (see under Mozart(composer)).

Cameron

CAMERON.
Tracks: / Magic of you / Funkdown / Together / Let's get it off / Feelings / Can't live without ya.
LP: SALP 2

Cameron, Andy

ANDY'S TARTAN ALBUM.
LP: KLP 05

Cameron, Argo

TOAST TO THE HIGHLANDS.
LP: WGR 010
MC: CWGR 010

Cameron, Bruce

WITH ALL MY LOVE.
Tracks: / Sunrise / With all my love / Molino De Vento / Love is on the way / Night and morning low clouds / Azul / Kathleen's theme.
LP: DS 793

Cameron, G.C.

GIVE ME YOUR LOVE.
LP: MAL 7413

Cameron, Jim

COME SCOTTISH DANCING (Cameron, Jim Scottish Dance Band).
LP: WGR 066
MC: CWGR 066

Cameron, Mary

PRIDE OF BONNIE SCOTLAND, A.
Tracks: / Dumbarton's drums / Loch Lomond / Durisdeer / My ain folk / Silver darlings / Dark island / Pride of Bonnie Scotland, The / Way old friends do, The / Sky boat song / Wee laddie / Rothesay bay / I'm born again.
LP: ITV 450
MC: KITV 450

Cameron, Rafael

CAMERONS IN LOVE.
Tracks: / Number one / All that's good to me / Let's get married / Boogie's gonna get ya' / Funtown USA / I'd go crazy.
LP: SALP 7

Cameron, Steve

TITANIC SUITE, THE.
CD: VTRCD 1
MC: VTRMC 1

Cameroons

MUSIC FROM THE CAMEROONS (From The Fulani of the north) (Various artists).
LP: LLST 7334

Camille Claudel (film)

CAMILLE CLAUDEL (1989 Film Soundtrack) (Yared, Gabriel).
LP: 70673

Camilo, Michel

IN TRIO.
Tracks: / We three / Tombo in 7 / 4 / Las Olas / Cha-cha (used to be a) / Suntan.
LP: K 28P 6445

MICHEL CAMILO.
Tracks: / Suite sandrine part 1 / Nostalgia / Dreamlight / Crossroads / Sunset (Interlude/Suite sandrine) / Yarey / Pra voce / Blue brossa / Caribe.
LP: 463 330 1
MC: 463 330 4

MICHEL CAMILO TRIO.
LP: K 28P 6452

ON THE OTHER HAND.
Tracks: / On the other hand / City of angels / Journey / Impressions / Silent talk 1 / Forbidden fruit / Suite sandrine part 3 / Birk's works / Silent talk 2.
LP: 4669371
MC: 4669374

WHY NOT?.
Tracks: / Just kiddin' / Hello and goodbye / Thinking of you / Why not? / Not yet / Suite sandrine part V.
LP: K 28P 6371

Camla, Stan

SO VERY FIN DE SIECLE.
MC: SLOB 002

Camones, Ctutmay

PATRIA CHIQUITA MIA.
LP: FF 469

Camorra (film)

CAMORRA (THE NAPLES CONNECTION) (Film Soundtrack) (Various artists).
LP: A 291

Camouflage

METHODS OF SILENCE.
LP: K 7820021
MC: K 7820024

VOICES AND IMAGES.
LP: K 781 886 1
MC: K 781 886 4

Camp Creek Boys

KYLE CREED WITH BOBBY PATTERSON & THE CAMP CREEK (See Creed, Kyle) (Camp Creek Boys/ Bobby Patterson/Kyle Creed).

Camp, Steve

AFTER GOD'S OWN HEART.
LP: BIRD R 192
MC: BIRD C 192

FOR EVERY MAN.
Tracks: / Gimme what it takes / Jesus on our side / Farther and higher / Jesus drawing me / Net of Peter, The / Thank you / Only story, The / You just talk to me / Run to the battle / Back in the furnace / For every man.
LP: MYR 1106
MC: MC 1106

ONE ON ONE.
LP: BIRD R 180
MC: BIRD C 180

SAYIN' IT WITH LOVE.
Tracks: / Sayin' it with love / Me / If I were a singer / Gather in His name / Let not your heart be troubled / God loves you / Good news / Song for mom / Lord make me humble / Strong love, strange peace / Diamonds / Tell everybody.
LP: YR 1069
MC: MC 1069

SHAKE ME TO WAKE ME.
LP: BIRD R 169
MC: BIRD C 169

Campbell, Al

AIN'T THAT LOVING YOU.
LP: VSLP 4033

BAD BOY.
Tracks: / Me nah give up / Chant rub-a-dub / Time has changed / She loves me / Let your love shine / Leaving to Zion / No time to lose / I like your style / Bad boy / Watch your step.
LP: CSLP 14

FENCE TOO TALL.
Tracks: / Fence too tall / Spread your love / Every man has a right / Easy rocker / No leave Jamaica / Take it easy / Crazy crazy nigger / She likes it like that / Get physical (new wave) / I cry.
LP: LLLP 25

FORWARD NATTY (Campbell, Al/ Triston Palmer).
LP: MVLP 1

FREEDOM STREET.
LP: LDR LP 007

OTHER SIDE OF LOVE, THE.
Tracks: / Old-time loving / Land of the living / If you want my love / Keep moving / Come let me hold your hand / Being with you / Other side of love, The / Don't tell me / You've changed / Hello stranger.
LP: GREL 30

REGGAE '85 (Campbell, Al/Triston Palmer).
LP: BM 001

SHAGGY RAGGY.
LP: SPLP 01

Campbell, Alex

CRM (Campbell, Alex/Alan Roberts/ Dougie Maclean).
Tracks: / Trooper and the maid, The / I lo'ed nae a lassie but ane / Jute mill song / Her fa la la lo / Wha widna fecht for Charlie / Leis an lurgainn / Bonnie Mary of Argyle / Rattlin' roarin' Willie / John Anderson my Jo / Miss Elspeth Campbell / Alick C. MacGregor / Jock Stewart / Little song.
LP: BURL 002

LIVE IN BELGIUM.
LP: CCC 811

NO REGRETS.
LP: LKLP 6043

TRADITIONAL BALLADS OF SCOTLAND.
Tracks: / Battle of Otterbourne, The / Twa corbies / Bonnie James Campbell / Wae's me for Charlie / King fareweel / I will go / Bonnie Bessie Logan / Gypsy laddie, The / Bonnie Glenshee / Lord Gregory / Farewell farewell / Scottish settlers lament.
LP: SFA 095

WITH THE GREATEST RESPECT.
Tracks: / Soldiers joy / Richmond cotillion / Mrs. McLeods reel / Cherry tree carol, The / One summers evening / Chicago fire tragedy / Dreadful memories / Farewell to Tarwathie / Drinkin's o'er risky / Naomi wise / Jimmy Brown the newsboy / Pretty boy Floyd / Wars o' High Gairmany / My love is like a red red rose / San Francisco Bay blues / Gloryland / Railroad song / Stranger blues / Roll on buddy / Pretty Polly / Pay me my money down / Long gone from home / Pig song, The / East Virginia blues / Pretty Saro / I'll fly away.
2LP: SDLP 2.048

Campbell, Bill

ROMANCE.
Tracks: / Sugar sugar / Your love / Just say love is forever / Valley of love / Without your love / Missing you / I'm so blue / Come into my arms.
LP: BBLP 009

Campbell, Colin

COLIN CAMPBELL'S LOCAL RADIO I.
MC: CJR 004

COLIN CAMPBELL'S LOCAL RADIO II.
MC: CJR 007

COLIN CAMPBELL'S LOCAL RADIO III.
Tracks: / Radio Caithness / North of the Ord / Radio Bettyhill / Blach Isle radio / Eilean Dubh / Radio Morningside / Perthshire autumn, A / Radio back / Loch Duich once more / Radio Auchnagatt / Radio Papa Westray / Peedie boy.
MC: CWGRTV 4

COLIN CAMPBELL'S LOCAL RADIO IV.
Tracks: / Radio Caithness intro / Radio Bettyhill / Radio Auchnagatt / Kilbaddie's bonnie quine / Radio

Caithness / Caithness and you / Radio Caithness quiz / Deserted Highland discs / Song of the Spey / Radio back / Radio Morningside / Let me show you the Highlands / Radio Auchnagatt - Campbells of Slacktacktit / Lass of Suie Hill / Radio back - News / Radio Caithness - book at bedtime / Time is but a sigh.
MC: CWGRTV 10

COLIN CAMPBELL'S LOCAL RADIO VOL 5.
Tracks: / Radio Caithness - intro / Radio Bettyhill - news / Radio Back - weather forecast and letter spot / Celtic Queen / Radio Caithness - Nirex phone in / Radio Papa Westray - news / Radio Bettyhill - mastermind / Banffshire braes / Radio Caithness - It's your line phone in / Black Isle radio - news / Radio Auchnagatt - Campbells of Slacktackit / Radio Ballinluig - news / Menzies tree / Radio Back - Evening service / Radio Caithness - Nuclear fishin'? / Radio Scallowag - news / Slipway at Sandsayre / Findhorn challenge, The.
MC: CWGR TV 14

COLLECTION OF SONGS, A.
MC: CJR 006

HIGHLAND STYLE (Campbell, Colin & His Highland Band).
Tracks: / Highland Donald / Balmoral Highlanders, The / Haughs o' Cromdale / Braes of Lochiel / Doctor Bob Smith / Argyllshire cathering / Whistling Rufus / MacKenzie Hay / Cradh chaillean / Lady MacKenzie of Coull / Tocherless lass, The / Colonel Robertson.
LP: LILP 5003

LET'S ALL DANCE AND SING (Campbell, Colin & His Highland Band).
Tracks: / Gay Gordons / King George V's army / Braemar gathering, The / Alasdair an Duin / Muile na'm Fuar Bhann Mor / Ghoraidh / Chrobbhain / Failte rudha bhatairnis / Sine Bhan / Eight men of Moidart / Peat fire flame / Come let us dance and sing / Dark island / Blackthorn stick / Cherish the ladies / Rory O'Moore's jig / Pet o'the pipers / Coire cheathaich / Doctor Dorothy Main / Man from Skye, The / Green hills of Islay, The / J.F. Mackenzie / Alick C. Macgregor / 'S'Ann an ile / Bodaich na h odha / Caberfeidh / Sean Thruibhas / These are my mountains / Wade's welcome to Inverness / Maids of Kintail.
LP: SBE 129

Campbell, Cornell

CORNELL CAMPBELL COLLECTION, THE.
LP: TSL 111

CORNELL CAMPBELL MEETS THE GAYLADS.
LP: VSLP 5007

FIGHT AGAINST CORRUPTION.
LP: VSLP 4020

JOHNNIE CLARK MEETS CORNELL CAMPBELL IN NEW STYLE (see Clark, Johnnie) (Campbell, Cornell & Johnnie Clark).

SWEET BABY.
LP: BS 1034

TURN BACK THE HANDS OF TIME.
LP: TWS 913

Campbell, Del

POWER.
LP: BBLP 007

Campbell, Eamon

ROMANTIC RHAPSODY.
LP: HM 033

Campbell, Eddie

BADDEST CAT ON THE BLOCK, THE.
Tracks: / Hye baby / 19 years old / I'm in love with you baby / Tears are for losers / Early in the morning / Same thing / Cha cha blues / Cheaper to keep her.
LP: JSP 1087

KING OF THE JUNGLE.
LP: R 7602

LET'S PICK IT.
LP: BM 9007

MIND TROUBLE.
2LP: DT 3014/15

Campbell, Ethna

FOR THE GOOD TIMES.
Tracks: / All my trials / Early morning rain / For the good times / From Clare to here / Hallelujah I love him so / I'll be your baby tonight / I'm so lonesome I could cry / Isn't it funny / Love is strange / Loving you / Song of evening / Til tomorrow.
LP: 6381 138

OLD RUGGED CROSS, THE.
Tracks: / Airport song / Boulder to Birmingham / By the time I get to Phoenix / Going my way / House of gold / How great Thou art / It is no secret / Jeannie's afraid of the dark / Old rugged cross, The / Try to remember / Wedding song, The / Wichita lineman.
LP: 6382 115

PEACE IN THE VALLEY.
LP: ITV 439
MC: KITV 439

Campbell Family

CHAMPION FIDDLERS.
LP: FR 101

SINGING CAMPBELLS, THE.
Tracks: / Fur does bonnie lorna lie / Sleep till yer mammy / Nicky tams / Road and the miles to Dundee, The / Drumdelgie / I ken faur I'm gaun / My wee man's a miner / Fa, fa, fa wid be a bobby / Foul Friday / Me an' mi mither / We three kings of Orient are / Bogie's bonnie belle / Cruel mother / Lang a-growing / Lady Eliza / Will ye gang love / I wish I wish / McGinty's meal and ale.
LP: 12T 120

Campbell, Gene

TEXAS BLUES PIONEER.
LP: WSE 112

Campbell, Glen

20 CLASSIC TRACKS: GLEN CAMPBELL.
Tracks: / Southern nights / God only knows / If not for you / Amazing grace / Your cheatin' heart / Bonapartes retreat / Both sides now / All the way / Dreams of the everyday housewife / Rhinestone cowboy / Rose garden / Help me make it through the night / Dream baby / MacArthur park / Take these chains from my heart / Bridge over troubled water / You'll never walk alone / Yesterday when I was young / Galveston.
LP: MFP 50532
MC: TCMFP 50532

20 GOLDEN PIECES: GLEN CAMPBELL.
Tracks: / Dreams of the everyday housewife / If you go away / Twelfth of never / True grit / Homeward bound / Take my hand for a while / Straight life / Elusive butterfly / Where's the playground / Until it's time for you to go / Crying / Words / By the time I get to Phoenix / It's over / Turn around and look at me / Mary in the morning / Gentle on my mind / You're my world / (Sittin' on) the dock of the bay / Impossible dream, The.
LP: BDL 2031
MC: BDC 2031

ALL I HAVE TO DO IS DREAM (See under 'Gentry, Bobbie' for details) (Campbell, Glen & Bobbie Gentry).

ALL I HAVE TO DO IS DREAM (Campbell, Glen & Bobbie Gentry).
Tracks: / All I have to do is dream / Less of me / Gentle on my mind / Heart to heart talk / My elusive dreams / Let it be me / Little green apples / Mornin' glory / Terrible tangled web / Sunday morning / (It's only your) imagination / Scarborough fair / Canticle.
LP: MFP 5600
MC: TCMFP 5600

BASIC.
Tracks: / Sing it nice and loud for me Sonny / Stranger in the mirror / Can you fool / I see love / I got no love in me / Love takes you higher / Never tell you no lies / I'm gonna love you / California / Let's all sing a song about it / Grafhaidh me thu.
LP: EST 11722

BOBBIE GENTRY & GLEN CAMPBELL (See under Gentry, Bobbie) (Campbell, Glen & Bobbie Gentry).

COLLECTION: GLEN CAMPBELL (EMBER LABEL).
MCSET: ZCPP 601

COLLECTION: GLEN CAMPBELL (EMI GERMANY).
LP: IC 038 81964

COLLECTION: GLEN CAMPBELL (KNIGHT LABEL).
MC: KNMC 13050

COMPLETE GLEN CAMPBELL, THE (His 20 Greatest Hits).
Tracks: / Southern nights / All I have to do is dream / It's only make believe / Can't help it / Help me make it through the night / Little kindness, A / Bridge over troubled water / Dream baby / Rhinestone cowboy / Gentle on my mind / Wichita lineman / Honey come baby / Everything a man could ever need / Both sides now / Reason to believe / Galveston.
LP: SMR 979
MC: SMC 979

COUNTRY BOY.
Tracks: / Country boy (you got your feet in L.A.) / Back in the race / This land is your land / Galveston / Your cheatin' heart / Tennessee home / 12-string special / California / Rhinestone cowboy / Country girl / 500 miles / Gentle on my mind / Arkansas / I'm so lonesome I could cry / True grit / Oklahoma Sunday morning.
MC: 4XL 8352
LP: MFP 41 5692 1
MC: MFP 41 5692 4
MC: TCMFP 5692

COUNTRY COLLECTION.
MC: KNMC 13054

COUNTRY FAVOURITES.
Tracks: / Together again / Truck driving man / My elusive dreams / Your cheatin' heart / She thinks I still care / Manhattan Kansas / I want to be with you always / Help me make it through the night / Gentle on my mind / Burning bridges / Long black limousine / Heart-to-heart talk / I can't help it (if I'm still in love with you) / Rose garden / Bonaparte's retreat / Rhinestone cowboy.
LP: EG 2600521
MC: EG 2600524

FAVOURITE HYMNS.
MC: CAAC 9977
LP: CAAR 9977

GENTLE ON MY MIND.
Tracks: / Gentle on my mind / It's over / Rose garden / She thinks I still care / Homeward bound / Honey, come back / Last thing on my mind / Cold, cold heart / Southern nights.
MC: 4XL-9051

GLEN CAMPBELL ALBUM, THE.
LP: ST 22493

GLEN CAMPBELL SINGS WITH ANNE MURRAY & BOBBIE GEE.
LP: 1A 022 1582701
MC: 1A 222 1582704

GREATEST HITS: GLEN CAMPBELL.
Tracks: / Honey come back / Gentle on my mind / Everything a man could ever need / Galveston / Try a little kindness / Dreams of the everyday housewife / By the time I get to Phoenix / Where's the playground / It's only make believe / Wichita lineman / All I have to do is dream / Dream baby.
LP: ATAK 4
MC: TCATAK 4
LP: ST 21885
MC: TCST 21885

HIGHWAY MAN.
Tracks: / Highwayman / Hound dog man / I was just thinking about you / Love song / My prayer / Tennessee home / Don't lose me in the confusion / Cajun caper / Darlin' Darlinka / Fool ya.
LP: EST 12008

IT'S JUST A MATTER OF TIME.
Tracks: / It's just a matter of time / Wild winds / Cowboy hall of fame / Rag doll / Call home / Do what you gotta do / Cowpoke / Shattered / Sweet sixteen / Gene Autry, my hero.
LP: 790 483-1
MC: 790 483-4

IT'S THE WORLD GONE CRAZY.
Tracks: / Why don't we just sleep on it tonight / I don't want to know your name / In cars / It's the world gone crazy / Rollin' / Nothing quite like love / Daisy a day / Any which way you want / It's your world.
LP: EST 12124
MC: TC E-ST 12124

LETTER TO HOME.
Tracks: / I'll be faithful to you / Letter to home / Faithless love / Leavin' eyes / Goodnight lady / After the glitter fades / Tennessee / Lady like you / Scene of the crime / American trilogy.
LP: 790 164-1

LIVE: GLEN CAMPBELL.
Tracks: / Rhinestone cowboy / Gentle on my mind / Wichita lineman / Galveston / Country boy / By the time I get to Phoenix / Dreams of the everyday housewife / Heartache no.3 / Boston / Trials and tribulations / It's only make-believe / Crying / Blue grass medley / Milk cow blues / Rollin' in my sweet baby's arms / I'm so lonesome I could cry / Southern nights / Amazing grace / Try a little kindness / In your loving arms again / It's your world / Mull of Kintyre.
2LP: RCALP 9002
MC: RCAK 9002
LP: ENL 3619
MC: ENC 3619
LP: SB 21444

LOVE SONGS: GLEN CAMPBELL.
Tracks: / Gentle on my mind / Reason to believe / By the time I get to Phoenix / It's only make believe / Honey come back / Country girl / One last time / I'm getting used to the crying / Last thing on my mind / Everything a man could ever need / Dream baby (how long must I dream) / Hey little one / Your cheatin' heart / This is Sarah's song / Let go / God only knows / How high did we go (CD only.) / If this is love (CD only.) / Love is not a game (CD only.) / For my woman's love (CD only.).
MC: TCMFP 5881

NO MORE NIGHT.
LP: WST R 9653
MC: WST C 9653
LP: WST 9653

OLD HOME TOWN.
Tracks: / Old home town / I love how you love me / Hang on baby / Blue (my naughty sweetie gives to me / Few good men, A / On the wings of my victory / I was too busy loving you / Ruth / Womans touch, A / Mull of Kintyre.
LP: 9900161
MC: 790 016-4

RHINESTONE COWBOY.
Tracks: / Country boy (You got your feet in L.A.) / Comeback / Count on me / I miss you tonight / My girl / Rhinestone cowboy / I'd build a bridge / Pencils for sale / Marie / We're over.
LP: GO 2020
MC: TC 2020
LP: ESW 11430

SOMETHIN' 'BOUT YOU BABY I LIKE.
Tracks: / Somethin' 'bout you baby I like / Through my eyes / That kind / Part time love / Hollywood smiles / If this is love / Hooked on love / Show me you love me / Late night confession / It goes like it goes.
LP: EST 12075

SOUTHERN NIGHTS.
Tracks: / Southern nights / This is Sarah's song / For cryin' out loud / God only knows / Sunflower / Guide me / Early morning sun / I'm getting used to the crying / Let go / How high did we go.
LP: GO 2008
MC: TC GO 2008
LP: EST 11601

STILL WITHIN THE SOUND OF MY VOICE.
Tracks: / I'm a one woman man / Still within the sound of my voice / Hand that rocks the cradle, The / For sure, for certain, forever, for always / I have you / You are / Arkansas / In my life / Leavin's not the only way to go / I remember you.
LP: MCF 3394
MC: MCFC 3394

THAT CHRISTMAS FEELING.
Tracks: / Christmas is for children / Old toy trains / Little altar boy / It must be getting close to Christmas / Have yourself a merry little Christmas / Blue Christmas / Christmas song, The / Pretty paper / There's no place like home / I'll be home for Christmas / Christmas day.
LP: MFP 5589
MC: TCMFP 5589

TOGETHER (Campbell, Glen & Anne Murray).
Tracks: / You're easy to love / United we stand / Love story / Ease your pain / Let me be the one / My ecstasy / I say a little prayer / By the time I get to Phoenix / We all pull the load / Canadian sunset / Bring back the love.
LP: MFP 41 5689 1
MC: MFP 41 5689 4

TRY A LITTLE KINDNESS.
LP: ESW 389

TWENTY GOLDEN GREATS.
Tracks: / Rhinestone cowboy / Both sides now / By the time I get to Phoenix / Too many mornings / Wichita lineman / One last time / Don't pull your love, then tell me goodbye / Reason to believe / It's only make believe / Honey come back / Give me back that old familiar feeling / Galveston / Dreams of the everyday housewife / Last thing on my mind / Where's the playground / Try a little kindness / Country boy (you got your feet in L.A.) / All I have to do is dream / Amazing Grace.
LP: EMTV 2
MC: TCEMTV 2
MC: TCATAK 159
LP: ATAK 159

UNCONDITIONAL LOVE.
Tracks: / Unconditional love / We will / Right down to the memories / Livin' in a house full of love / Healing hands of time / Next to you / Somebody's doin' me right / I'm gone this time / Once a day / Light of a clear blue morning.
MC: C4 90992
LP: C2 90992

WALKIN' IN THE SUN.
Tracks: / She's gone, gone, gone / You will not lose / On a good night / If I could only get my hands on you now / Even a blind man can tell when walkin' in the sun / William Tell overture / Woodcarver /

Cheatin' is / Tied to the tracks / Somebody's leaving / Jesus on your mind.
LP: C1 93884
MC: C4 93884

WICHITA LINEMAN.
Tracks: / Wichita lineman / True grit / Hound dog man / By the time I get to Phoenix / Country girl / God only knows / Galveston / Let it be me / Your cheatin' heart / Kentucky means paradise / Early morning song / If you could read my mind / Rhinestone cowboy / Gentle on my mind / Until it's time for you to go / Heart to heart / Highwayman / Words / Southern nights / Take these chains from my heart / Part time love / Any which way you can / Too late to worry, too blue to cry.
2LP: . . . . VSOPLP 120
MC: . . . . VSOPMC 120

Campbell, Gloria

TONIGHT IS MY NIGHT OUT (See under Ginger, William) (Campbell, Gloria & William Ginger).

Campbell, Gordon

YOU ARE MY WOMAN.
Tracks: / You are my woman.
LP: . . . . HOLLY 007

Campbell, Ian

LIVE: IAN CAMPBELL (Campbell, Ian Folk Group).
LP: . . . . SLP 900

Campbell, James

NASHVILLE STREET BAND (Campbell, Blind James).
LP: . . . . ARHOOLIE 1015

Campbell, Jo Ann

BLONDE BOMBSHELL.
LP: 33.8008

FOR TWISTIN' AND LISTENIN'.
LP: . . . . ABCS 393

MISS REET PETITE.
Tracks: / Crazy Daisy / Motorcycle Michael / I changed my mind Jack / Mr. Lee / Dance with me Henry / Willie and the hand jive / Duane / Mama don't want no twistin' / Kookie little paradise, A / I wish it would rain all summer / You made me love you / Eddie my love / Bobby Bobby Bobby / Amateur night / Goodbye Jimmy goodbye / Puka puka pants.
LP: . . . . CR 30248

Campbell, John

CAPE BRETON VIOLIN MUSIC.
LP: . . . . ROUNDER 7003

MAN AND HIS BLUES, A.
LP: . . . . CCR 1019

WISPS OF BALLADS.
Tracks: / Boys of Mullabawn / Visions of Art Bennett / Old age pension / Fair vale of Creggan / Up the mountain / Land where the shamrock grows / Dalin' men from Crossmaglenn / Bard of Armagh, The / Lament for Paddy Quigley / Larry Morgan / New dole office / Urker Hill.
LP: . . . . OAS 3021
MC: . . . . COAS 3021

Campbell, Ken

GOING SOLO.
Tracks: / Bonnie lassie's answer / Kilbowie hill / Skye song / Drumakill / Waterson crook / Time and trouble / Whisky / Lassie of the morning / Baron of Buchlyvie / Lynsey gray / Boddam Annie / Rainbow.
LP: . . . . FE 063
MC: . . . . FE 063C

Campbell, Mike

SECRET FANTASY.
LP: . . . . PA 8020

Campbell, Pat

JUST A QUIET CONVERSATION.
LP: . . . . DRL 2017

Campbell, Patrick

WAVING ALL EXCUSES (see under Waving All Excuses) (Villiers, James (nar)).

Campbell, Pete

SOCA CALYPSO.
LP: . . . . BBLP 0015

Campbell & Reid

SWEET VIBRATIONS.
LP: . . . . SFA 080

Campbell, Rev. E.D.

REV. E.D. CAMPBELL 1927.
LP: . . . . ELE 8-220

Campbell, Robert

LIVING IN THE SHADOW OF A DOWNTOWN MOVIE SHOW.
LP: . . . . SKL 5285

Campbell, Rocky

BEDROOM EYES GIRL.
LP: . . . . KPLP 04

RHYTHM AND ROCK.
LP: . . . . OLP 015

VALLEY OF TEARS.
LP: . . . . ANG 001LP

YOU AND I.
LP: . . . . CSLP 001

Campbell, Sammy

STRANGER OF GALILEE (see McClelland, Harry/Sammy Campbell (Campbell, Sammy & Harry McClelland).

Campbell, Sarah

LITTLE TENDERNESS, A.
Tracks: / Mexico / I never meant to fall / Part of a story / Waltz with you / Geraldine and Ruthie Mae / Heartache / Tell me baby / To remember / My heart can't seem to forget / I could use a little tenderness.
MC: . . . . C 42

Campbell, Shona

SCOTLAND MY HOME.
Tracks: / Scotland my home / My native land / Bluebell polka / Smile in your sleep / Many a day / Count your blessings / Isle of my dreams / Rhymes and reasons / Farewell my love / When I was but a child / Lord's prayer, The / Soft lowland tongue o' the borders.
LP: . . . . LILP 5119
MC: . . . . LICS 5119

Campbell, Stan

STAN CAMPBELL.
Tracks: / Years go by / Crawfish / Seven more days / Save the world / Dancing troupe / Little more faith / You'll never know / Don't let me be misunderstood / Can't get enough / Strange fruit.
LP: . . . . WX 87
MC: . . . . W 787 C

Campbeltown Pipe...

MULL OF KINTYRE (Campbeltown Pipe Band).
Tracks: / Mull of Kintyre / Lara's theme / Legion's last patrol / Drummer's call / My land / Battle's o'er, The / Green hills of Tyrol / Liberton pipe band polka / Floral dance, The / Kilberry ball / Highland Mary / Wee highland laddie / Soldier's return / Malcolm Lang / Kyle sku / Flower of Scotland / Serenade of Heyken / Murray's welcome / Men of Argyle / Haughs o' Cromdale / Rhodesian regiment, The / Colin's cattle / Sheiling, The / Braes of Tullymet / Munlochy Bridge / Bogallan / Raven's rock / Banks of the Avon / Connaught man's rambles, The.
LP: . . . . MFP 41 5702 1
MC: . . . . MFP 41 5702 4
MC: . . . . TC MFP 5702
LP: . . . . SHM 3039

Camper Van Beethoven

CAMPER VAN CHADBOURNE (see under Chadbourne, Eugene).

II AND III AND PLUS.
2LP: . . . . FBLP 400320

KEY LIME PIE.
Tracks: / Opening theme / Jack Ruby / Sweethearts / When I win the lottery / (I was born in a) Landromat / Borderline / Light from a cake, The / June / All her favourite fruit / Interlude / Flowers / Humid press of days, The / Pictures of matchstick men / Come on darkness.
LP: . . . . VUSLP 8
MC: . . . . VUSMC 8
MC: . . . . OVEDC 383

OUR BELOVED REVOLUTIONARY SWEETHEART.
Tracks: / Eye of Fatima Pt. 1 / Turquoise jewelry / O death / She divines water / Devil song / One of these days / Waka waka / Change your mind / My path belated / Never go back / Eye of Fatima Pt. 2 / Tania / Life is grand / Fool, The.
LP: . . . . V 2516
MC: . . . . TCV 2516

TELEPHONE FREE LANDSLIDE VICTORY.
LP: . . . . ROUGH 95

THIRD LP, THE.
LP: . . . . ROUGH 109

VAMPIRE CAN MATING OVEN.
LP: . . . . PITCH 05

Campi, Ray

EAGER BEAVER BOY.
Tracks: / Hot dog / All the time / Boogie boogie boo / Rock it / Thought of losing, The / Waffle stompin' mama / Blue ranger / Ballin' keen / Let 'er roll / Dobro daddio from Del Rio / Born to be wild / How low can you feel / Where my sweet baby goes / Tribute to 'You know who' / Eager beaver boy / Pretty mama / One part stops where the other begins / Pinball millionaire / When two ends meet / Good time woman / It ain't me (piano version) / Chug-a-lug / Parts unknown / Wicked wicked woman / Shelby county penal farm / Don't give your heart to a rambler / Play anything / Major label blues.
LP: . . . . LP 008

GIVE THAT LOVE TO RAY CAMPI.
LP: . . . . DLP 1001

GONE, GONE, GONE.
LP: . . . . BRP 2008
LP: . . . . ROUNDER 3047
MC: . . . . ROUNDER 3047C

NEWEST WAVE, THE (Campi, Ray & His Rockabilly Rebels).
Tracks: / Newest wave, The / Lucky to be in love / Rockabilly music / Boo hoo / Cruisin / Once is enough / Will of love, The / I've been around / Sweet woman blues / You nearly lose your mind / Sweet mama baby / Do what you did / She don't belong to me / My heart's on fire / Right back where we started from.
LP: . . . . ABOUT 1000

ORIGINAL ROCKABILLY ALBUM, THE.
Tracks: / Caterpillar / It ain't me / Let go of Louie / Livin' on love / My screamin' screamin' mimi / Long tall Sally / Johnny's jive / Play it cool / Give that love to me.
LP: . . . . MFLP 063

RAY CAMPI ROLLIN' ROCK SINGLES COLLECTION 1971-1978, THE.
Tracks: / Eager beaver boy / Tore up / If it's all the same to you / Pan American boogie / Sixteen chicks / Baby left me / Li'l bit of heartache, A / Booze it / Wrong wrong wrong / Rockin' at the Ritz / Quit your triflin' / Rattlin' daddy / Wild one.
LP: . . . . ABOUT 1004

RAY CAMPI WITH FRIENDS IN TEXAS.
Tracks: / Guitar rag / Austin waltz / Quit your triflin' / Wee mouse / Blue ranger / Bobbro daddio from Del Rio / Merle's boogie woogie / Drifting Texas sands / Caterpillar / Sweet temptation / How low can you feel / Spanish two step.
LP: . . . . BFX 15258

ROCKABILLY LIVES.
LP: . . . . LP 004

ROCKABILLY MAN (Campi, Ray & His Rockabilly Rebels).
Tracks: / Rockabilly man / Love and lots more love / No way out / Don't come knockin' / Don't let the bad times let you down / Give me a taste / Can't you yodel blues / Hollywood cats / Recipe for love / Soul sisters / Little love lies / Hold that train / It's blowing away.
LP: . . . . ABOUT 1006

ROCKABILLY REBELLION.
LP: . . . . BRP 2001
LP: 6902

ROCKABILLY ROCKET.
Tracks: / Second story man / Don't get pushy / Cravin' / Separate ways / Gonna bid my blues goodbye / How can I get on top / Little young girl / Chew tobacco rag / You don't rock and roll at all / Ruby Ann / I don't know why you still come around / Runnin' after fools / Jimmie skins the blues.
LP: . . . . LP 013
LP: . . . . MFLP 046

WILDCAT SHAKEOUT (Campi, Ray & His Rockabilly Rebels).
Tracks: / Rockabilly rebel / Gone, gone, gone / Wildcat shakeout / Don't turn me down / Honey bop / Sack of love / She will come back to me / Teenage boogie / When a guitar gets the blues / Don't blame it on me / Mister Whizz / Mind your own business / Cat clothes shop / It ain't me.
LP: . . . . RAD 9

Campion (tv)

CAMPION (Flowers For the Judge) (Margery Allingham).
MCSET: . . . . LFP 7484

Campo, Antonio

FLYING DREAMS (Campo, Antonio & Orchestra).
LP: . . . . ISST 103

Camus

THEN AND NOW.
Tracks: / Lowlands of Holland, The / Bachelor / Felton lonnin / Deserter from Kent, The / My bonny light horseman / Chief O'Neills's favourite/The poppy leaf / O'Carolan's draught/The dancing tailor / Swindon/Proudlocks / Charlotte Dymond.
MC: . . . . BHC 9035

Can

CAN.
Tracks: / All gates open / Safe / Sunday jam / Sodom / Spectacle, A / E.F.S. Nr. 99 / Ping pong / Can be.
LP: . . . . LASL 2

CANNIBALISM 1.
Tracks: / Father cannot yell / Soup / Mother Sky / She brings the rain / Mushroom / One more night / Outside my door / Spoon / Hallelujah / Aumgn / Dizzy dizzy / Yoo doo right.
MCSET: . . . . SPOONCD 001/2

EGE BAMYASI.
Tracks: / Pinch / Sing swan song / One more night / Vitamin C / Soup / I'm so green / Spoon.
LP: . . . . UAS 29414

FLOW MOTION.
Tracks: / I want more / Cascade waltz / Laugh till you cry... live till you die / And more / Babylonian pearl / Smoke (E.F.S. No.59) / Flow motion.
LP: . . . . V 2071
LP: . . . . IC 064 31837
LP: . . . . OVED 88

INCANDESCENCE.
Tracks: / I want more / Full moon on the highway / Gomorrah / Hunters and collectors / Empress and the Ukraine king, The / Mother Upduff / Call me / Half past one / Laugh till you cry... live till you die / E.F.S. No. 38.
LP: . . . . OVED 3

INNER SPACE.
Tracks: / All gates open / Safe / Sunday jam / Sodom / Spectacle, A / Can can / Ping pong / Can be.
LP: . . . . THBL 020

LANDED.
Tracks: / Full moon on the highway / Half past one / Hunters and collectors / Vernal equinox / Red hot Indians / Unfinished.
LP: . . . . OVED 194

LIMITED EDITION.
LP: . . . . USP 103

OUT OF REACH.
Tracks: / Serpentine / Pauper's daughter and I / November / Seven days awake / Give me no 'roses' / Like inobe God / One more day.
LP: . . . . THBL 025

PREHISTORIC FUTURE.
MC: . . . . UNKNOWN

RITE TIME.
LP: 838 883 1
MC: 838 883 4

SAW DELIGHT.
Tracks: / Don't say no / Sunshine day and night / Call me / Animal waves / Fly by night.
LP: . . . . OVED 195

SOON OVER BABALUMA.
Tracks: / Dizzy dizzy / Come sta, la luna / Splash / Chain reaction / Quantom physics.
LP: . . . . UAG 29673

SOUNDTRACKS.
Tracks: / Deadlock / Tango whiskeyman / Don't turn the light on, leave me alone / Soul desert / Mother sky / She brings the rain.
LP: . . . . UAS 29283

TAGO MAGO.
Tracks: / Paperhouse / Mushroom / Oh yeah / Hallelujah / Aumgn / Peking O / Bring me coffee or tea.
MCSET: . . . . SPOONCD 006/7

Cana, Flor De

MUEVETE (MOVE IT).
LP: . . . . FF 463

Canada

BAGPIPES IN CANADA, THE (Various artists).
LP: . . . . LLST 7344

Canadian Brass

MOSTLY FATS (Fats Waller's greatest hits).
Tracks: / Grandpa's spells / Honeysuckle rose / Spreadin' rhythm around / Mean to me / Lounging at the Waldorf / I've got a feeling I'm falling / Ain't misbehavin' / Shreveport stomp / Alligator crawl / Carolina shout / Black and blue / Jitterbug waltz / Lookin' good but feelin' bad / Handful of keys / Just a closer walk with thee.
LP: . . . . RL 13212

UNEXPLORED TERRITORY.
Tracks: / Joust / En sueno / First gymnopedie / Amazing grace / Bourbon Street melody / Cathedral / Royal firework.
LP: . . . . MMG 1119

Canal (film)

CANAL/ASHES AND DIAMONDS/ GENERATION, A (Various artists).
LP: TER 1053

Canal Street Jazz Band

NEW ORLEANS STOMP.
LP: SOS 1005

Can-Can (film)

CAN-CAN (1960 film soundtrack) (Various artists).
Tracks: / Entr'acte: *Orchestra* / It's alright with me: *Sinatra, Frank* / Come along with me: *MacLaine, Shirley*/ Live and let live: *Chevalier, Maurice & Louis Jordan* / You do something to me: *Jordan, Louis* / Let's do it: *Sinatra, Frank & Shirley MacLaine* / Can-can: *Orchestra* / I love Paris: *Chorus* / Montmartre: *Sinatra*, Frank, Maurice Chevalier & Chorus / C'est magnifique: *Sinatra, Frank* / Maidens typical of France: *Chorus & Orchestra*/ Just one of those things: *Chevalier, Maurice* / I love Paris: *Sinatra, Frank & Maurice Chevalier*.
MC: ED 2605704
MC: TCV 2570
LP: ED 2605701
LP: V 2570

CAN-CAN (Film soundtrack) (Various artists).
LP: IC 038 80566
MC: 91248.4

Cancerous Growth

HMMLMMLUM.
Tracks: / Something's here / One side / Cohata can you do / Diabolica fx / Youth of when / Prey for the weak / Black doomy theme / Satan's stupid / Von scenemaster.
LP: NB 005

LATE FOR THE GRAVE.
Tracks: / No chance / Stupid people / Decide / Be yourself / Something I don't need / Sick of it / Revolution / Keep my peace.
LP: NB 004

Candi

CANDI.
Tracks: / Under your spell / Missing you / Shine on / Independent / Love makes no promises / Dancing under a Latin moon / Dance with me / Lucky night / Pleasure island / Closer than ever.
LP: EIRSA 1007
MC: EIRSAC 1007

Candice

MY HEART (see under Davis,Teddy " No,no sin").

Candide

CANDIDE (1) (1988 musical opera) (Various artists).
LP: TER 1156
MC: ZCTER 1156
LP: PS 2350
MC: PST 2350

CANDIDE (2) (Original Broadway cast) (Various artists).
Tracks: / (Candide) Overture: *Various artists* / Best of all possible worlds, The: *Various artists* / What's the use?: *Various artists* / It must be so: *Various artists* / Glitter and be gay: *Various artists* / Oh, happy me: *Various artists* / Mazurka: *Various artists* / You were dead you know: *Various artists* / My love: *Various artists* / I am easily assimilated: *Various artists* / Eldorado: *Various artists* / Quiet: *Various artists* / Bon Voyage: *Various artists* / Gavotte: *Various artists* / Make our garden grow: *Various artists*.
LP: CBS 60337
MC: 40 60337

CANDIDE (3) (New York city opera version) (Various artists).
Tracks: / Fanfare/ life is happiness indeed: *Various artists* / Best of all possible worlds, The: *Various artists*/ Happy instrumental/Oh happy we: *Various artists* / Candide begins his travels: *Various artists* / It must be so (Candide's meditation): *Various artists* / Westphalian fanfare/Chorale/Battle music: *Various artists* / Entrance of the Jew: *Various artists* / Glitter and be gay: *Various artists* / Earthquake music/Dear boy: *Various artists*/ Auto da fe: *Various artists* / Candide's lament: *Various artists* / You were dead you know: *Various artists*/ Travel(to the stables)/I am easily assimilated: *Various artists* / Quartet finale: *Various artists* / Entr'acte: *Various artists* / Ballad of the new world: *Various artists* / My love: *Various artists* / Barcarolle: *Various artists* / Alleluia: *Various artists* / Eldorado: *Various artists* / Sheep song: *Various* artists / Governor's waltz: *Various artists* / Bon voyage: *Various artists* / Quiet: *Various artists*/ Constantinople/What's the use?: *Various artists* / Finale: Make our garden grow: *Various artists*.
MC: NWMC 340/1
LP: NW 340/1

Candido

DANCIN' AND PRANCIN'.
Tracks: / Dancin' and prancin' / Jingo / Thousand finger man / Rock and shuffle.
LP: SSLP 1517

Candle

ANIMALS AND OTHER THINGS (Candle & The Agapeland Singers).
Tracks: / Animals and other things / Cock-a-doodle-doo / It's so great to be a beaver / Penguins / Gorilla walk / Waggin' of a tail, The / Itty-bitty flea / I love animals / I'm a galapagos / Livin' that givin' way / King of the jungle / Howdy-doo kangaroo.
LP: BW R 2031
MC: TC BWR 2031

BIRTHDAY PARTY, THE.
Tracks: / Hurry hurry / There's a party / What can we give to the King? / Snowflake / Hallelujah peace on earth / Gift of love / I will shine, I will sing / Can't help peekin' / Hear the chimes / It's a great day / Ballerina / Sparkle / Rejoice.
LP: BW R 2024
MC: TC BWR 2024

BULLFROGS AND BUTTERFLIES (Candle & The Agape Force Prep. School).
Tracks: / Welcome to Agapeland / Good morning / This is the day / Rainy day song / Kid talk / I like knowing God best / My hands belong to you / Friends / Practice makes perfect / Bullfrogs and butterflies / Noah / You're so good to me.
LP: BW R 2010
MC: TC BWR 2010

MUSIC MACHINE, THE (A Children's Musical).
Tracks: / Land called love / Music machine, The / Whistle song / Smile / String song, The / Patience / Gentleness / Faith / Joy / Peace / Goodness / Love / Self-control / Kindness / Reprise.
LP: WING 506
MC: TC WING 506

MUSIC MACHINE VOL. 2, THE.
MC: AC 547

SIR OLIVER'S SONG (Candle & The Agape Force Prep. School).
Tracks: / Sir Oliver's song / Only Elohim / Just one God is he / Love his name / Yodel song / Honour your parents / Handle with care / Danke schon / Always be true / Kalepo / Tell the truth / No dig mentiras / Be thankful / His love.
LP: BW R 2017
MC: TC BWR 2017

TO THE CHIEF MUSICIAN CHAPTER II.
Tracks: / Come on rejoice / Simple song / Surely goodness and mercy / Alpha and Omega / Love from the father / Lord, show me what it means / Whom have I in Heaven / Talk with me / Not to us / I trust you / In love / Holy is the Lord / I will praise thee / Freely sing / All I want to do / Voice of thankfulness / Greatest thing, The / Press on.
LP: WING 503
MC: TC WING 503

WITHIN THE GATE.
Tracks: / Soldiers of the army / Stay on the battlefield / I will sing / Fill me now / Lord of hosts / Glory to God in the highest / Glory, Jesus glory / I want to be in service for Jesus / Lord is my strength, The / Lay hold / Steadfast love of the Lord, The / Living fire / Hallelujah song / Scripture reading / Worthy / Greatest thing, The / Higher and higher.
LP: WING 507
MC: TC WING 507

Candlelight Dancing

CANDLELIGHT DANCING (Various artists).
Tracks: / Raindrops keep falling on my head: *Kaempfert, Bert* / Love story: *Marek & Vacek* / Poem: *Butterflies*/ Serenade: *Hause, Alfred* / Mondschein-melodie: *Hausser, Michel* / Dancing queen: *Delgado, Roberto* / Candlelight romance: *Forster, Fred* / This guy's in love with you: *Mauriat, Paul* / Danny boy: *Greger, Max*/ Wenn ich dich seh' - dann fange ich zu traumen an: *Schultz-Reichell, Fritz* / La Bonita: *Sanders, Bela* / One way wind: *Warner, Kai*.
LP: 2872 181
MC: 3472 181

Candlemass

ANCIENT DREAMS.
LP: ACTLP 7

CANDLEMASS LIVE IN STOCKHOLM 9TH JUNE 1990.
Tracks: / Well of souls / Bewitched / Dark reflections / Demons gate / Through the infinitive halls of death / Mirror, mirror / Sorceror's pledge / Dark are the veils / Solitude / Under the oak / Bells of Acheron / Samaritan / Gallow's end.
LP: MFN 109
MC: TMFN 109

NIGHTFALL.
LP: UNKNOWN
LP: ATV 3

TALES OF CREATION.
LP: MFN 95
MC: MFNT 95

Candler, Norman

BY CANDLELIGHT (Candler, Norman Strings).
Tracks: / Candlelight waltz / Fool / Petite fleur / Candy / Notturno / Spanish Harlem / With a song in my heart / Days of no return / Love's theme / Help me make it through the night / Theme of a summernight / Way we were / Like old times / Killing me softly with her song.
LP: DGS 14

DREAMING IN THE SUN (See under Bilk, Acker) (Candler, Norman/Acker Bilk).

NEW MAGIC, THE (Candler, Norman & The Magic Strings).
LP: ISST 188

SUPER DOUBLE DISC OF NORMAN CHANDLER.
2LP: GXC 9009/10

TRIBUTE TO JOHN LENNON, A.
Tracks: / Mind games / (Just like) Starting over / Woman / Whatever gets you through the night / Mother / Oh my love / Tribute to John, A / Oh Yoko / Happy Xmas (war is over) / Imagine / Power to the people.
LP: 6.24820
MC: CT4 24820
LP: AS 624820

Candles for the...

CANDLES FOR THE SURGEON (Helen Upshall) (Boyd, Carole (nar)).
MC: PMB 018

Candlestick Park

RE-INVENT THE WHEEL.
LP: CHIME 011

Candoli, Conte

FINE AND DANDY.
Tracks: / Fine and dandy / I'm getting sentimental over you / Night flight / I can't get started / On the Alamo / Groovin' higher / Tune for Tex / My funny Valentine / They can't take that away from me / Everything happens to me / Toot suite / I'll remember April.
LP: AFF 173

GETTIN' TOGETHER (See under Pepper, Art) (Candoli, Conte & Art Pepper).

GROOVIN' HIGHER (Candoli, Conte Quintet).
Tracks: / Toot suite / Jazz city blues / My old flame / Full count / I'm getting sentimental over you / Four / Groovin higher.
LP: AFF 92

WEST COASTING (Candoli, Conte & Stan Levy).
LP: FS 152

Candy Flip

MADSTOCK...THE ADVENTURES OF BUBBLEFISH CAR.
LP: DBLP 507
MC: ZCDB 507

Candy Man

AIN'T NO SHAME IN MY GAME.
Tracks: / Rap trivia / Ain't no shame in my game (show) / Candy Man theme / Don't leave home without it / Knockin' boots / Melt in your mouth / Playin' on me / Today's topic / Mack is back, The / Nightgown / Who shakes the best - skit / Keep on watcha doin' / 5 verses of def.
LP: 4674721
MC: 4674724

Candyskins

SPACE I'M IN, THE.
LP: BEACH 6
LP: DGC 24370
MC: DGCC 24370

Cane, Jackin

ONE MORE ROSE.
LP: AP 230

Canedy Feinstein

HOLLYWOOD (Canedy Feinstein, Bordonaro & Caudle).
LP: ZEB 8

Canevony Y Sireodd

CANEVONY Y SIREODD (Various artists).
LP: 1291 D

Cang, Jo

NAVIGATOR.
Tracks: / Navigator / Who knows / London / Girl / Islands / One love / Radio (Only on CD and cassette.) / Break all the mirrors / Hope / Morning comes / Cross the bridge (Only on CD and cassette.).
LP: 211377
MC: 411377

Canino, Bruno

HAYDN 'LONDON' TRIOS 1-3/PIANO TRIOS 15 & 16 (see under Haydn (composer)) (Nicolet, Aurele & Christiane /Rocco Filippini/Bruno Canino).

Canitz, William J.

SUSPECTS (see under Suspects (bk)).

Cankton Express

LIVE AT MULATE'S.
LP: 6073
MC: 6073 TC

Cann, Bob

WEST COUNTRY MELODEON.
Tracks: / Uncle George's hornpipe / Tommy Roberts' hornpipe / Hot punch / Uncle George's waltz / Uncle Jim's waltz / Primrose polka, The / Dorsetshire hornpipe / Kester rocky waltz, The / Family jig / Woodland flowers / Ford farm reel / Harry Gidley's waltz / When it's night time in Italy / Climbin' up de golden stairs / Lyrinka / Schottische hornpipe / Cokey hornpipe.
LP: 12TS 275

Cannanes

HAPPY SWING.
MC: KC 013

Canned Heat

BEST OF CANNED HEAT.
Tracks: / On the road again / Time was / Going up the country / Rollin' and tumblin' / That's alright mama / Let's work together / Owl song, An / Help me / My crime.
2LP: 5D128 60024/5
MC: 4XLL 9163

BEST OF HOOKER 'N' HEAT, THE (See under Hooker, John Lee) (Hooker 'N' Heat).

BOOGIE WITH CANNED HEAT.
Tracks: / My crime / On the road again / World in a jug / Turpentine moan / Whisky headed woman / Amphetamine Annie / Owl song, An / Marie / Laveau / Fried hookie boogie.
LP: SEE 62
MC: 3C 254 83083
LP: IC 064 90973
LP: LBL 83103

CANNED HEAT.
Tracks: / Rollin' and tumblin' / Bullfrog blues / Evil is going on / Going down slow / Catfish blues / Dust my brooms / Help me / Big road blues / Story of my life / Road song, The / Rich woman.
LP: SEE 268

CANNED HEAT '70 CONCERT.
LP: LBS 83333

CANNED HEAT COOKBOOK.
LP: LBS 83303

CANNED HEAT LIVE.
MC: MAMC 912185

FUTURE BLUES.
LP: LBS 83364
MC: BGOMC 49
LP: BGOLP 49

GREATEST HITS: CANNED HEAT.
LP: MA 1131683
MC: MAMC 11931683

HALLELUJAH.
Tracks: / Same all over / Change my ways / Canned Heat / Sic'em pigs / I'm her man / Time was / Do not enter / Big fat / Huautla / Get off my back / Down in the gutter, but free.
LP: SEE 248

HISTORICAL FIGURES AND ANCIENT HEADS.
Tracks: / Sneakin' around / Rockin' with the king / Long way from L.A. / That's all right / Hill's stomp / I don't care what you tell me / Cherokee dance / Utah.
LP: BGOLP 83

HISTORY (IMPORT).
LP: 062 261 2221

HOOKER 'N' HEAT.
2LP: LSP 103/4

HOOKER 'N' HEAT - LIVE (Hooker, John Lee & Canned Heat).
LP: RNLP 801

HUMAN CONDITION, THE.
LP: SNTF 783

INFINITE BOOGIE (See Hooker, John Lee) (Canned Heat & John Lee Hooker).

KINGS OF THE BOOGIE.

LP: . . . . PLP 20
MC: . . . . PMC 20

LET'S WORK TOGETHER (Best of Canned Heat).
Tracks: / On the road again / Bullfrog blues / Rollin' and tumblin' / Amphetamine Annie / Fried hockey boogie / Sic 'em pigs / Poor moon / Let's work together / Going up the country / Boogie music / Same all over / Time was / Sugar bee / Rockin' with the king / That's alright mama / My time ain't long / Future blues (CD only.) / Pony blues (CD only.) / So sad (the world's in a tangle) (CD only.) / Chipmunk song (CD only.).
LP: . . . . GO 2026
MC: . . . . TCGO 2026

LIVE AT THE TURKU ROCK FESTIVAL, 1971.
Tracks: / She don't want me no more / Let's work together / On the road again / That's all right / Hill stomp / Long way from L.A. / Watch yourself / Canned Heat boogie / Late night blues.
2LP: . . . . BTS 964410

LIVE IN AUSTRALIA (BOOGIE ASSAULT).
LP: . . . . BEDLP 5

LIVE IN EUROPE-'70.
LP: . . . . BGOLP 12
MC: . . . . BGOMC 12

LIVING THE BLUES.
Tracks: / Pony blues / My mistake / Sandy's blues / Going up the country / Walking by myself / Boogie music / One kind of favour / Parthenogenesis / Nebulosity / Rollin' and tumblin' / Five owls / Bear wires / Snooky flowers / Sunflower power / Ragi kafi / Icebag / Childhood's.
LP: . . . . SEE 97

MASTER OF ROCK.
LP: 5C 054 92656

NEW AGE.
LP: . . . . BGOLP 85

ON THE ROAD AGAIN.
Tracks: / On the road again / Amphetamine Annie / My crime / Time was / Going up the country / Sugar bee / Whiskey headed woman / Bullfrog blues / Let's work together / World in a jug / Fried hockey boogie / Rollin' and tumblin' / I'm her man / Dust by broom / Parthenogenesis (CD only.).
LP: . . . . FA 3222
MC: . . . . TCFA 3222

RE-HEATED.
LP: 088803

SUPER PACK.
LP: 5C 128 60024/25

Canned Rock

CANNED ROCK LIVE.
LP: . . . . CAN 003

KINETIC ENERGY.
LP: . . . . CAN 002

Cannibal Corpse

EATEN BACK TO LIFE.
Tracks: / Shredded humans / Put them to death / Scattered remains, splattered brains / Rotting head / Bloody chunks / Buried in the backyard / Edible autopsy / Mangled / Born in a casket / Undead will feast, The / Skull full of maggots.
MC: . . . . TZORRO 12

Cannibals

CRASH FOR TRASH.
LP: . . . . F-UK 3

PLEASE DO NOT FEED.
LP: . . . . FACE 017

REST OF THE CANNIBALS, THE.
LP: . . . . GMG 75004

RUN CHICKEN RUN VOLUME 1 (Cannibals/Surfadelics).
LP: . . . . CHICKEN 1

Cannon, Ace

AT HIS BEST.
LP: . . . . GT 0074

GOLDEN CLASSICS.
LP: . . . . GT 0061

GOLDEN SAX OF ACE.
LP: . . . . WC 153

SAXY SOUNDS OF ACE.
MC: . . . . WCW 17

TUFF.
Tracks: / Tuff / Sittin' tight / Deep elem blues / St. Louis blues / Cannonball / Wabash blues / Blues in my heart / Heartbreak hotel / Lonesome road / Kansas city / Careless love / Searchin' / Trouble in mind.
LP: . . . . HIUKLP 412

Cannon & Ball

GREATEST LOVE, THE.
Tracks: / Doing it all for my baby / Drive / Some guys have all the luck / Melody / Do you believe in love / Stand by me / Higher and higher / To all the girls I've loved before / Lost in the fifties tonight / Sometimes when we touch / Wind beneath my wings / Stranger in my house / Greatest love of all, The.
LP: . . . . SCENE 12
MC: . . . . SCENEC 12

ROCK ON TOMMY.
LP: . . . . SRT 8042
MC: . . . . SRT 80428

TOGETHER.
Tracks: / Together we'll be ok / Crying / Hold me in your arms / Everybody's making it big but me / Let me rock you / Bandido / Sun ain't gonna shine anymore, The / Dreamin' / Dream baby / Dream lover / Nellie the elephant / Remember the stars / Better love next time / This time.
LP: . . . . MFP 50561
MC: . . . . TCMFP 50561

Cannon, Freddy

EXPLOSIVE FREDDY CANNON,THE.
Tracks: / Abigail Beechet / Action / Buzz buzz a diddle it / California here I come / Chattanooga shoeshine boy / Dedication song, The / For me and my gal / Happy shades of blue / If you were a rock and roll record / Muskrat ramble / Okeefenokee / Palisades park / Tallahassee lassie / Teen queen of the week / Transistor sister / Way down yonder in New Orleans.
LP: . . . . SON 007
LP: 25 108

Cannon, Gus

GUS CANNON 1963.
LP: . . . . C 5523

Cannon, Noel

YOUR CAROLINA BUDDY.
LP: . . . . WGR 099
MC: . . . . CWGR 099

Cannon, Sean

ERIN THE GREEN (Irish Traditional Songs).
LP: . . . . BLB 5004

ROVING JOURNEY MAN.
Tracks: / Roving journey man, The / Wild rover / My Lagan love / Green fields of Canada / Banks of Bann, The / When a man's in love / Sally gardens / Merrily kiss the quakers wife / Lambs on the green hills / Song for Ireland, A.
LP: . . . . FSLP 1

Cannonball Fever

CANNONBALL FEVER (1989 Film Soundtrack) (Various artists).
LP: . . . . CST 8042
MC: . . . . CST 8042MC

Cannon's Jug Stompers

CANNON'S JUG STOMPERS.
LP: . . . . RL 336

Canny Cummerland

CANNY CUMMERLAND (Songs and Tales in Cumbrian Dialect).
Tracks: / Canny Cummerland / To t'milken / Shades o' John Peel / Dinah Grayson / Oyster girl, The / Willie whoar's ta bin? / Straw rope / Hoo happy we lived then / Branthet neuk boggle / Tarry woo' / Sally Gray / Cumberland reel / It's Winter.
LP: . . . . FE 013

Canny Fettle

VARRY CANNY.
LP: . . . . TSR 023
MC: . . . . TSR 023/CS

Canny Newcassel

BALLADS & SONGS (From Newcastle & Therabouts) (Various artists).
Tracks: / Canny Newcassel: *Various artists* / Sandgate girl's lament, The: *Various artists* / Miller's wife of Blaydon, The: *Various artists* / Ee aye, as cud hew: *Various artists* / Three crows: *Various artists*/ Billy boy: *Various artists* / Bonnie Gateshead lass, The: *Various artists* / My lad's a canny lad: *Various* artists / Till the tide comes in: *Various artists* / Silly galoot: *Various artists* / Fire on the quay: *Various* artists / Billy Oliver's ramble: *Various artists* / Jowl and listen: *Various artists* / Weary cutters: *Various* artists / Graveyard shift, The: *Various artists* / Wylam away: *Various artists* / Footy against the wall: *Various artists* / My old man's a dustman: *Various artists* / Four and twenty bob: *Various artists* / Blaydon races: *Various artists* / Keep your feet still, Geordie Hinny: *Various artists.*
LP: 12TS 219

Canny, Paddy

PADDY CANNY & P.J. HAYES.
LP: . . . . SHAN 33007

Canoldir Choir

HOW SWEET THE SOUND (Canoldir Male Voice Choir).
Tracks: / Arwelfa / Holy City, The / Nant y mynydd / Thanks be to God / Prayer / King of glory / Jack was every inch a sailor / O Isis and Osiris / Amazing grace / Eia Eia / Bridge over troubled water / Pilgrims' chorus.
LP: . . . . GRS 1115

LET ME SING AGAIN (Canoldir Male Voice Choir).
Tracks: / Soldier's chorus / Angel and the stranger, The / Gwahoddiad / Flight of ages, The / Vive l'amour / Virgin of the angel host, The / Battle hymn of the Republic / Llanfair / Impossible dream, The / De animals a-comin' / Lost chord, The / Sospan Fach / Take me home / There is nothin' like a dame / Hallelujah Amen.
LP: . . . . GRS 1066

WE RAISE OUR VOICES HIGH (Canoldir Male Voice Choir).
Tracks: / Roman war song from Rienzi / What shall we do with the drunken sailor? / Memory / We'll keep a welcome / Finnish forest, The / Shepherd, shepherd / Lord's prayer, The / How great thou art / Calm is the sea / Little innocent lamb / Eli Jenkin's prayer (From Under Milk Wood) / Speed your journey / My love is like a red red rose / Maja moja / Bryn myrddin.
LP: . . . . GRALP 3
MC: . . . . GRTC 3

Can't Stop The Music

CAN'T STOP THE MUSIC (Original Soundtrack) (Various artists).
MC: 7199 051
LP: 6399 051

Can't Stop The Party

CAN'T STOP THE PARTY 1 & 2 (Various artists).
LP: . . . . SOHOLP 11
MC: . . . . SOHOTC 11

Canta Brasil

CANTA BRASIL (See under Brasil for details) (Various artists).

Cantabile

HEAR NO EVIL.
Tracks: / Crepe suzette / Creole love call / Scarborough fair / Orpheus in the underground.
LP: . . . . PLR 069

MUSIC OF THE NIGHT.
Tracks: / Starlight Express (From Starlight Express) / Song on the sand (From La Cage aux Folles.) / Love makes the world go round (From Me & My Girl.) / Music of the night (From The Phantom of the Opera.) / Little shop of horrors (From the Film) / Oh what a circus (From Evita) / Losing my mind (From Follies) / Rum tum tugger, The (From Cats.) / Bring him home (From Les Miserables.) / Tell me it's not true (From Blood Brothers) / Anthem (From Chess.) / She's so beautiful (From Time).
LP: . . . . SCX 6712
MC: . . . . TC SCX 6712

OVERTURE.
LP: . . . . PLR 027

TOWN AND GOWN.
LP: . . . . PLR 047

Cantate Con Noi

ALPS CHORAL MUSIC & SONGS.
LP: . . . . GVM 678

Canteloube (Composer)

SONGS OF THE AUVERGNE (Various artists).
MC: . . . . VETC 6522

Canterbury Cathedral

BRIDGE THROUGH TIME (Canterbury Cathedral Choir).
LP: . . . . GRS 1030

IN QUIRES AND PLACES (Canterbury Cathedral Choir).
LP: . . . . LPB 818

ORGAN OF CANTERBURY CATHEDRAL (Flood, David).
Tracks: / Carillon de Westminster (Vierne) / Chorale prelude on Wacher auf (Bach) / Chorale prelude on Schmucke dich (Bach) / Trumpet tune and air (Purcell) / Piece Heroique (Franck) / Canon in D / Moto ostinato (Eben) / Fantaisie in E flat (Saint-Saens) / Chant de May (Jongen) / Tues es Petra (Mulet).
MC: . . . . YORKMC 108

SOUNDS OF CANTERBURY (Canterbury Cathedral Choir).
Tracks: / Zadok the priest / Jesus walking / Wonder / Spirit of the Lord, The / Miserere / Ecce vicit Leo / O clap your hands / Five mystical songs / Lord, thou hast been our refuge.
MC: . . . . YORKMC 107

VARIOUS CHRISTMAS RECORDINGS (see under Christmas) (Canterbury Cathedral Choir).

Canterbury Clerkes

FILL YOUR GLASSES (Canterbury Clerkes/London Serpent Trio).
Tracks: / Fill your glasses / Push about the bottle boys / When Bibo thought fit / Foresters sound the cheerful horn / When gen'rous wine expands my soul / We be three poor mariners / Hark the hollow woods resounding / There behold the mighty bowl / Life's a bumper / Music's the language of the blest above / Fear no danger to ensue / Peace to the souls of my heroes / Sportive little trifler / How merrily we live / Fair Aurora / Fear no more the heat o' the sun / O how sweetly Delia sings / Breathe soft ye winds / Of all the brave birds / Time has not thinned / Sleep while the soft evening.
LP: . . . . SDL 361
MC: . . . . CSDL 361

Canterbury Tales (bk)

CANTERBURY TALES (2) (see under Chaucer, Geoffrey (aut)) (Chaucer, Geoffrey (Author)).

CANTERBURY TALES, THE (see under Chaucer, Geoffrey (aut)) (Ashcroft, Dame Peggy (nar)).

CANTERBURY TALES, THE (see under Chaucer, Geoffrey (aut)) (Scales, Prunella (nar) & Martin Starkie (nar)).

CANTERBURY TALES, THE (see under Chaucer, Geoffrey (aut)) (Bessinger, J.B (nar)).

Canterbury Tales

CANTERBURY TALES (1968 Original London cast) (Various artists).
Tracks: / Canterbury tales: Overture: *Various artists* / Chaucer's prologue: *Various artists* / Song of welcome: *Various artists* / Goodnight hymn: *Various artists* / Canterbury day: *Various artists* / I have a noble cock: *Various artists* / Darling, let me teach you how to kiss: *Various artists* / Nicholas' and Alisons' love duet: *Various artists* / Some call it love: *Various artists* / Chanticleer and Pertelote duet: *Various artists*/ Chanticleer, Pertelote, Fox trio: *Various artists* / Fill your glass: *Various artists* / Pilgrims' riding music: *Various artists* / Come on and marry me, honey: *Various artists* / When I was a boy: *Various artists*/ Where are the girls of yesterday?: *Various artists* / If she has never loved before: *Various artists* / I'll give my love a ring: *Various artists* / Chaucer speech: *Various artists* / I am forever dated: *Various artists*/ Opening of the Wife of Bath's tale: *Various artists* / What do women most desire?: *Various artists* / April song: *Various artists* / Arrival at Canterbury, The: *Various artists* / Love will conquer all: *Various artists*/ Chaucer's epilogue: *Various artists* / Canterbury tales: Finale: *Various artists.*
LP: . . . . TER 1076
MC: . . . . ZCTER 1076

CANTERBURY TALES (Various artists).
MCSET: . . . . ARGO 1091

Canterville Ghost (bk)

CANTERVILLE GHOST, THE (Oscar Wilde).
MC: TTC/OWO2
MC: . . . . TS 350
MC: 2051

Cantico Del Sole

CANTICO DEL SOLE, CANTO 99... (And Other Poems) (Pound, Ezra (nar)).
MC: 2088

Cantor, Eddie

BEST OF EDDIE CANTOR.
Tracks: / If you knew Susie / Josephine please no lean on my bell / Makin' whoopee / Margie / Baby face / Ida sweet as apple cider / Yes sir that's my baby / How ya gonna keep em down on the farm / Ma she's making eyes at me / Waiting for the Robert E. Lee / Ballin' the jack / Ain't she sweet.
LP: . . . . INTS 5084
MC: . . . . INTK 5084

KID MILLIONS/ROMAN SCANDALS (Film soundtracks).
LP: . . . . CIF 3007

MAKIN' WHOOPEE.
Tracks: / That's the kind of a baby for me / Mandy / My wife is on a diet / Girl friend of a boy friend of mine, A / Okay, toots / When my ship comes in / There's nothing too good for my baby / Over somebody else's shoulder / Hello, sunshine, hello / Makin' whoopee / Earful of music, An / Put a tax on love / Making the best of each day / What a perfect combination / Man on the flying trapeze, The / Yes, yes my baby says

yes, yes / If I give up the saxophone / Look what you've done / Hungry women / Build a little home.
LP: . . . . CMS 006
MC: . . . . CMSC 006

Cantorial & Choral

CANTORIAL & CHORAL MUSIC (Hampstead Synagogue).
MC: . . . . L 007 161C

Cantorion Creigiau

CANTORION CREIGIAU.
LP: . . . . BM 59

Canvey Island Allstars

ESCAPE FROM OIL CITY.
MC: . . . . FOAMC 4

Cap, Etienne

FLIGHT OF FANCY (Cap, Etienne and orchestra).
LP: . . . . ISST 136

Capaldi, Jim

CONTENDER, THE.
Tracks: / Dirty business / Sealed with a kiss / Daughter of the night / You burn me / Game of love / Contender, The / Elixir of life / Short ends / Hunger and greed.
LP: 2383 490

ELECTRIC NIGHTS.
Tracks: / Shoe shine / Electric nights / Hotel blues / White jungle lady / Tabitha / Time / Wild dogs / 1890 / Wild geese.
LP: 2383 534

FIERCE HEART.
Tracks: / Tonight you're mine / Living on the edge / Bad breaks / Runaway / Back at my place / That's love / I'll always be your fool / Don't let them control you / Gifts of unknown things.
LP: . . . . U 0057

LET THE THUNDER CRY.
Tracks: / Let the thunder cry / Favella music / Child in the storm / Only love / Louie louie / Warm / Dreams do come true / Old photographs / We don't need / Anxiety.
LP: . . . . CAL 123
MC: . . . . CAC 123

OH HOW WE DANCED.
LP: . . . . ILPS 9187

ONE MAN MISSION.
Tracks: / One man mission of love / Tonight / Lost inside your love / I'll keep holding on / Nobody loves you / Young savages / Tales of power / Warriors of love / Ancient highway / Let the thunder cry / Favella music / Child in the storm / Only love / Louie louie / Warm / Dreams do come true / Old photographs / We don't need / Anxiety.
MC: 251350 4
LP: 251350 1

SHORT CUT DRAW BLOOD.
Tracks: / Goodbye love / It's all up to you / Love hurts / Johnny too bad / Short cut draw blood / Living on a marble / Boy with a problem / Keep on trying / Seagull.
LP: . . . . ILPS 9336

SOME COME RUNNING.
Tracks: / Something so strong / Love used to be a friend of mine / Dancing on the highway / Some come running / Voices in the night / You are the one / Take me home / Oh Lord why Lord.
MC: . . . . ICT 9921
LP: . . . . ILPS 9921
MC: . . . . ICM 2019
MC: 842 606 4

SWEET SMELL OF SUCCESS, THE.
Tracks: / Hold on to your love / Take me how you find me girl / Sweet smell of sucess, The / Every man must march to the beat of his own drum / Tonight / Low spark of high heeled boys, The / Fortune and fame / Man with no country / Going home.
LP: . . . . CAL 116
MC: . . . . CAC 116

Cape Breton...

CAPE BRETON SYMPHONY FIDDLE VOL.2 (Cape Breton Symphony Fiddle).
Tracks: / Sow's tail, The / Londonderry hornpipe / Duncan on the plainstone / Warlock's strathspeys and Athole commers / Nine pint coggie / Calum fhionnlaidh / Prince Charlie / Tarboton lodge / Donald MacLean's farewell to Oban / Christy Campbell / Port ic artair / Miss Drummond of Perth / Niel Gow's lamentation for Abercairney / Johnnie Pringle / Munlochy bridge / Duke of Gordon's birthday / Perrie werrie / Peggie Menzies / West mabou reel / Black sporran, The / Walking the floor / Glengarry's march / Donald Mac Masters strathspey.
LP: 12TS 354
LP: . . . . WGR 032
MC: . . . . CWGR 032

Capella

HELYCOM HALIB.
LP: . . . . SYDLP 1
MC: . . . . SYDMC 1

Capella Nova

CAPELLA NOVA.
LP: . . . . AKH 004

Capelli, Rachele

RACHELE CAPELLI.
Tracks: / I feel good / I'd put angels around you / I'm sorry / Truth'll set you free, The / Follow your heart / Mockingbird / No end in sight / Out of control / Emotions.
LP: . . . . K 781 856 1
MC: . . . . K 781 856 4

Capercaillie

BLOOD IS STRONG, THE.
Tracks: / Aignish / Arrival (theme from) / Iona / Calum's road / Fear / Dean Cadalan samhach / Grandfather mountain / An atairreachd ard / S fhada leam an oidhche gheamhraidh / Hebrides, The / Lordship of the isles / Arrival reprise / Colum cille / Downtown Toronto.
LP: . . . . GPN 1001
MC: . . . . GPNC 1001

CASCADE.
LP: . . . . SRT 4KL 178
LP: . . . . 4 KL 178

CROSSWINDS.
LP: . . . . SIF 1077
MC: . . . . CSIF 1077

SIDEWALK.
LP: . . . . SIF 1094
MC: . . . . SIF 1094 C

Capital Letters

HEADLINE NEWS.
Tracks: / Fire / Daddy was no murderer / President Amin / Smoking my ganja / Unemployed / Rejoice / Buzzrock / Run run run / Out of Africa.
LP: . . . . GREL 7

Capital Scum

TSJEMO KILLS.
LP: . . . . HH 005

Capitol Country

CAPITOL COUNTRY VOL.1 (Too hot to handle) (Various artists).
Tracks: / I believe in lovin' em: Various artists / Merle's boogie woogie: Various artists / Butane blues: Various artists / Automatic mama: Various artists / Too hot to handle: Various artists / Okeefenokee: Various artists / If you ain't lovin' (you ain't livin'): Various artists / Playin' dominoes & shootin' dice: Various artists / Smokey mountain boogie: Various artists / Lost John boogie: Various artists / I get the blues when it rains: Various artists / Double up & catch up: Various artists / My Tennessee talkin' doll: Various artists / Done gone crazy: Various artists / I'm a poor boy: Various artists / Humpty dumpty boogie: Various artists.
LP: . . . . CR 30255

CAPITOL COUNTRY VOL.2 (Oakie Boogie) (Various artists).
Tracks: / Freight train boogie: Various artists / My gal Gertie: Various artists / I'm gettin' rid of you: Various artists / Alone with you: Various artists / Wait a little younger: Various artists / I've got five dollars and its Saturday night: Various artists / Red hen boogie: Various artists / Stand up sit down shut your mouth: Various artists / You're there: Various artists / When I found you: Various artists / I've had enough: Various artists / Go ahead on: Various artists / Country junction: Various artists / Hambone: Various artists / Fatback Louisiana USA: Various artists.
LP: . . . . CR 30256
MC: . . . . TCCR 30256

Capitol (label)

CAPITOL BLACK MUSIC 82 (Various artists).
LP: 2C 068 86555

CAPITOL CLASSICS (1942-1958) (Various artists).
Tracks: / Cow cow boogie: Slack, Freddie & His Orch. / On the Atchison, Topeka and Santa Fe: Mercer, Johnny & The Pied Pipers / Hurry on down: Lutcher, Nellie and her rhythm / Twelfth St. rag: Hunt, Pee Wee and his orchestra/ No other love: Stafford, Jo / With a song in my heart: Froman, Jane / Here in my heart: Martino, Al/ High Noon: Ritter, Tex / Blacksmith blues: Morse, Ella Mae / Zambesi: Busch, Lou & His Orchestra/ Memories are made of this: Martin, Dean / You'll never know: Haymes, Dick / Zing went the strings of my heart: Garland, Judy / Tom Dooley: Kingston Trio.
LP: . . . . MFP 5610
MC: . . . . TCMFP 5610

CAPITOL COLLECTABLES (Various artists).
Tracks: / I'm in love: Thomas, Lillo / Why should I cry: Hendryx, Nona / All because of you: Williams, Beau / If you want me: Hyman, Phyllis / Take it to the limit: Ray, Goodman & Brown / Betcha don't know: Najee / If you were mine: Lynn, Cheryl / Working up a sweat: Full Circle / Tender moments: Blu, Peggi / Little bit more, A: Jackson, Freddie & Melba Moore / Don't take my love away: O'Jays.
LP: . . . . EST 2038
MC: . . . . TCEST 2038

CAPITOL COUNTRY CLASSICS - THE 1940'S (Various artists).
Tracks: / Jingle jangle: Ritter, Tex / Texas blues: Willing, Foy / I'm wastin' my tears on you: Ritter, Tex / Oklahoma hills: Guthrie, Jack / With tears in my eyes: Tuttle, Wesley / Divorce me C.O.D.: Travis, Merle / So round, so firm: Travis, Merle / Oakie boogie: Guthrie, Jack / Silver stars, purple sage, eyes of blue: Stone, Cliffie / Smoke smoke smoke (that cigarette): Williams, Tex / Humpty dumpty heart: Thompson, Hank / Peepin' through the keyhole: Stone, Cliffie / Rye whiskey: Ritter, Tex / Cigareets, whusky and wild, wild women: Ingle, Red & The Natural Seven / Cocaine blues: Hogsed, Roy / One has my name (the other has my heart): Wakely, Jimmy / Dear Oakie: Rivers, Jack / Life gits tee-jus, don't it: Williams, Tex / Candy kisses: Kirk, Eddie & The String Band / Tennessee border: Ford, Tennessee Ernie / Gamblin' polka dot blues: Duncan, Tommy / Slippin' around: Whiting, Margaret/Jimmy Wakely / Whoa sailor: Thompson, Hank / Give me a hundred reasons: Jones, Ann / I love you because: Payne, Leon / Mule train: Ford, Tennessee Ernie.
MC: . . . . TCEMS 1412

CAPITOL COUNTRY CLASSICS - THE 1950'S (Various artists).
Tracks: / Broken down merry-go-round: Whiting, Margaret/Jimmy Wakely / I'll never be free: Ford, Tennessee Ernie/ Kay Starr / Shot gun boogie, The: Ford, Tennessee Ernie / Hot rod race: Dolan, Jimmy / Mockin' Bird Hill: Paul, Les & Mary Ford / Wild side of life, The: Thompson, Hank & His Brazos Valley Boys / High noon: Ritter, Tex/ Don't let the stars get in your eyes: McDonald, Skeets / Goin' steady: Young, Faron / That's me without you: James, Sonny / Dear John letter, A: Shepard, Jean & Ferlin Husky / Forgive me, John: Shepard, Jean & Ferlin Husky / Wake up, Irene: Thompson, Hank / Release me: Heap, Jimmy & The Melody Mastg / You better not do that: Collins, Tommy / Watcha gonna do now: Collins, Tommy / Satisfied mind, A: Shepard, Jean / When I stop dreamin': Louvin Brothers / Sixteen tons: Ford, Tennessee Ernie / Waltz of the angels: Stewart, Wynn/ I gotta know: Jackson, Wanda / I don't believe you've met my baby: Louvin Brothers / Young love: James, Sonny / Gone: Husky, Ferlin / Alone with you: Young, Faron / Country music is here to stay: Husky, Ferlin.
MC: . . . . TCEMS 1413

CAPITOL COUNTRY CRUISIN' (Various artists).
LP: . . . . EST 24451

CAPITOL COUNTRY GEMS (Various artists).
Tracks: / Long black limousine: Various artists / Loving him was easier: Various artists / San Antonio rose: Various artists / Radiator man from Wasco: Various artists / Good hearted woman: Various artists / I got a new field to plough: Various artists / Jambalaya: Various artists / Take me home country roads: Various artists / Stand by your man: Various artists / Just a strand from a yellow curl: Various artists / Sad situation: Various artists / Wabash cannonball: Various artists / Lay some happiness on me: Various artists / To hear the family sing: Various artists.
LP: . . . . MFP 50550
MC: . . . . TCMFP 50550

CAPITOL COUNTRY KICKS (Various artists).
LP: . . . . CAPS 1005

CAPITOL ROCKABILLY ORIGINALS (Various artists).
LP: . . . . CAPS 1009

CAPITOL SOUL CASINO (Various artists).
Tracks: / Heartbeat: Jones, Gloria / I walked away: Paris, Bobby / They'll be coming: Ambrose, Sammy/ Ten miles high: David & The Giants / Lonely man: Outsiders / By yourself: Martin, Jay D / Love slipped through my fingers: Williams, Sam / End of our love, The: Wilson, Nancy / Nobody but me: Human Beinz/ Right on: Delory, Al / So is the sun: World Column / Police Story: Williams, Pat Orchestra / Baby mine: Houston, Thelma / Coloured Man, Theme from: Vann, Teddy.
LP: 1025

JAZZMEN (1943-47) (Various artists).
LP: . . . . S 1406

Capitol Punishment

SLUM WITH A VIEW.
LP: . . . . WEBITE 16

WHEN PUTSCH COMES TO SHOVE.
LP: . . . . DESTINY 6

Capitol Regiment Band

JOHN PHILIP SOUSA.
MC: . . . . OAK C 135

Capitols

COOL JERK.
LP: . . . . SS 8019

Capleton

CAPLETONGOLD.
LP: . . . . CRLP 5

Capon, Galliano

GALLIANO CAPON AND PERRIN (Capon, Galliano & Perrin).
Tracks: / Musique / Blue rondo a la turk / Sing me so softly of the blues / Spain / Violette / Point d'interrogation / Funky accordion / Blues ah bill.
LP: . . . . CARA 003

Cappella Istropolitana

BEATLES SEASONS.
Tracks: / She loves you / Goodnight / We can work it out / Lady Madonna / Fool on the hill / Hard day's night, A / Michelle / Penny Lane / Long and winding road, The / Girl / Here comes the sun / Hey Jude / Carry that weight / And I love her / Help / Paperback writer / She's leaving home / Honey pie / Eight days a week / Yellow submarine.
LP: . . . . SCX 6708
MC: . . . . TC-SCX 6708

Cappello, Tim

CRY LITTLE SISTER (See under McMann, Gerard) (Cappello, Tim & Gerard McMann).

Capp-Pierce Juggernaut

CAPP-PIERCE JUGGERNAUT.
Tracks: / Avenue 'C' / All heart / Moten swing / Basie / Mr. Softie / It's sandman / Dickie's dream / Take the 'A' train / Wee baby blues / Roll 'em Pete.
LP: . . . . CJ 72

JUGGERNAUT STRIKES AGAIN.
Tracks: / One for Marshall / I remember Clifford / New York shuffle / Chops, fingers and sticks / You are so beautiful / Parker's mood / Word from Bird / Charade / Things ain't what they used to be / Little Pony.
LP: . . . . CJ 183

LIVE AT THE ALLEY CAT.
LP: . . . . CJ 336
MC: . . . . CJC 336

Capstick, Tony

CAPSTICK COMES HOME.
Tracks: / Radio wassock news / Rocky's intro / Flat shep no.1 / Capstick comes home / Capstick comes home (German version) / Mathew / Capstick comes home (Chinese version) / Flat shep no.2 / Rocky's outro / England 1, Germany 0 / It's good to see you / Taffy Christmas / Capstick rocks home / They don't write 'em like that any more / One for my baby.
LP: . . . . CHR 1349
MC: . . . . ZCHR 1349

HIS ROUND.
Tracks: / I drew my ship / Foggy dew, The / Rambling royal, The / Arthur McBride / To Ramona / Lloyd George / Sir Thomas of Winesberry / Hello Hans / Captain Grant / Goodnight Irene.
LP: . . . . RUB 004

SONGS OF EWAN MACCOLL (See Gaughan, Dick) (Capstick, Tony, Dick Gaughan & Dave Burland).

TONY CAPSTICK DOES A TURN.
Tracks: / Dolphin, The / Donkey, The / Seeds of love / Moving-on song, The / Twins / Coat she wore, The / If I had a boat / Flock of lobsters, A / Casey's last ride / Scarecrow / Red wine and promises / Twelsh joke / They don't write 'em like that any more.
LP: . . . . RUB 023

Captain Beaky Stories

CAPTAIN BEAKY STORIES (Lloyd, Jeremy).
MC: . . . . PTB 617

CAPTAIN BEAKY VOLS 1 & 2 (Various artists).
2LP: 2664483

LP: 2383 588

Captain Beefheart

2 ORIGINALS OF CAPTAIN BEEFHEART.
Tracks: / I'm gonna booglarize you baby / Whit jam / Blabber 'n' smoke / When it blows its stacks / Spotlight kid, The / Click clack / Grow fins / There ain't no Santa Claus on the evenin stage / Gilder / Lick my decals off baby / Doctor Dark / I love you, you big dummy / Peon / Bellerin' plain / Woe is uh me bop / Japan in a dishpan / I wanna find a woman that'll hold my big toe / Petrified forest / One rose that I mean / Buggy boogie woogie, The / Smithsonian institute blues (or the big dig) / Space age couple / Clouds are full of wine not whiskey or rye / Flash Gordon's ape.
LP: . . . . K 84006

ABBA-ZABBA.
LP: . . . . MA 15784
MC: . . . . MAMC 915784

BLUE JEANS AND MOONBEAMS.
Tracks: / Captain's holiday / Pompadour swamp / Party of special things to do / Blue jeans and moonbeams / Twist ah luck / Further than we've gone / Rock 'n' roll's evil doll / Observatory quest / Same old blues.
LP: . . . . OVED 19

CAPTAIN BEEFHEART FILE, THE (Captain Beefheart & His Magic Band).
Tracks: / Sure 'nuff 'n yes I do / Zig-zag wanderer / Call on me / Dropout boogie / I'm glad / Electricity / Yellow brick road / Abba zaba / Plastic factory / Where there's woman / Grown so ugly / Autumn's child / Tarotplane / Kandy korn / 25th century quaker / Mirror man.
LP: . . . . FOLD 008

CLEAR SPOT (Captain Beefheart & His Magic Band).
Tracks: / Low yo yo stuff / Nowadays a woman's gotta hit a man / Too much time / Circumstances / My head is my only house unless it rains / Sun zoom spark / Clear spot / Crazy little thing / Long-neck bottles / Her eyes are a blue million miles / Big-eyed beans from Venus / Golden birdies.
LP: . . . . K 54007

DOC AT THE RADAR STATION.
Tracks: / Hothead / Ashtray heart / Carrot is as close a rabbit gets to a diamond, A / Run paint run run / Sue Egypt / Brickbats / Dirty blue gene / Best batch yet / Telephone / Flavour bud living / Sheriff of Hong Kong / Making love to a vampire with a monkey on my knee.
LP: . . . . OVED 68
LP: . . . . V 2172

ICE CREAM FOR CROW.
Tracks: / Ice cream for crow / Host the ghost the most holy-o, The / Semi-multicoloured caucasian / Hey Garland, I dig your tweed coat / Evening bells / Cardboard cut-out sundown / Past sure is tense, The / Ink mathematics / Witch doctor love, The / "81" poop hatch / Thousandth and tenth day of the human totem pole, The / Skeleton makes good.
LP: . . . . OVED 121
LP: . . . . V 2337

LEGENDARY A & M SESSIONS.
LP: . . . . BLIMP 902

LICK MY DECALS OFF BABY.
Tracks: / Lick my decals off baby / Doctor dark / I love you, you big dummy / Peon / Bellerin' plain / Woe-is-uh-me-bop / Japan in a dishpan / I wanna find a woman that'll hold my big toe / Petrified forest / One rose that I mean / Buddy, The / Boogie woogie / Smithsonian institute blues, The / Space age couple / Clouds are full of wine (not whisky or rye) / Flash Gordon's ape.
LP: . . . . K 44244

MIRROR MAN (Captain Beefheart & His Magic Band).
Tracks: / Tarotplane / Kandy korn / 25th century quaker / Mirror man.
LP: . . . . NCP 1006
LP: 2365 002
LP: . . . . ED 184

MUSIC IN SEA MINOR.
Tracks: / Electricity / Yellow brick road / Zig-zag wanderer / Kandy korn / Abba zaba / Dropout boogie / I'm glad / 25th century quaker.
LP: . . . . DOW 15
MC: . . . . ZCDOW 15

SAFE AS MILK (Captain Beefheart & His Magic Band).
Tracks: / Sure 'nuff 'n yes I do / Zig-zag wanderer / Call on me / Dropout boogie / I'm glad / Electricity / Yellow brick road / Abba zaba / Plastic factory / Where there's woman / Grown so ugly / Autumn's child.
LP: . . . . NCP 1004
LP: 2522601
MC: 2522604

SAFE AS MILK/MIRROR MAN.
2LP: . . . . TFOLP 11
MC: . . . . TFOMC 11

SHINY BEAST (BAT CHAIN PULLER).
Tracks: / Floppy boot stomp, The / Tropical hot dog night / Ice rose / Harru Irene / You know you're a man / Bat chain puller / When I see mummy I feel like a mummy / Owed I Alex / Candle mambo / Love lies / Suction prints / Apes-ma.
LP: . . . . OVED 67
LP: . . . . V 2149

SPOTLIGHT KID.
Tracks: / I'm gonna booglarize you baby / White jam / Blabber 'n' smoke / When it blows its stacks / Alice in Blunderland / Spotlight kid, The / Click clack / Grow fins / There ain't no Santa Claus on the evenin stage / Gilder.
LP: . . . . K 44162

STRICTLY PERSONAL.
LP: . . . . LBR 1006

TOP SECRET.
LP: . . . . PIXLP 4

TROUT MASK REPLICA.
Tracks: / Hair pie: Bake II / Pena / Well / When Big Joan sets up / Fallin' ditch / Sugar 'n' spikes / Ant man bee / Orange claw hammer / Wild life / She's too much for my mirror / Hobo chang ba / Blimp (mousetrapreplica), The / Steal softly thru snow / Old fart at play / Veteran's day poppy.
LP: . . . . K 64026
LP: . . . . STS 1053

UNCONDITIONALLY GUARANTEED.
Tracks: / Upon the my-o-my / Sugar bowl / New electric ride / Magic be / Happy love song / Full moon hot sun / I got love on my mind / This is the day / Lazy music / Peaches.
LP: . . . . OVED 66

Captain Horatio...

CAPTAIN HORATIO HORNBLOWER (Film Soundtrack) (Farnon, Robert).
Tracks: / Captain Horatio Hornblower / Rhapsody for violin and orchestra.
LP: . . . . CT 7009

Captain Rock

LOT OF FIST, A.
Tracks: / Return of Captain Rock, The / Captain Rock to the future shock / You stink / Space / Bongo beat / Cosmic blast.
LP: . . . . CAPT 1

Captain Sensible

POWER OF LOVE,THE.
Tracks: / I'm a spider / I love her / Stop the world / Sir Donald's song / It's hard to believe I'm not / Thanks for the night / Glad it's all over / Royal rave up / Secrets / It would be so nice / Power of love, The / I love you.
LP: . . . . AMLX 68561
MC: . . . . CXM 68561

REVOLUTION NOW.
LP: . . . . DELTLP 4
MC: . . . . DELTMC 4

SENSIBLE SINGLES.
Tracks: / Happy talk / Wot / It would be so nice / Martha the mouth / Stop the world / Relax / I love her / Glad it's all over / It's hard to believe I'm not / There are more snakes than ladders / I'm a spider / One Christmas catalogue / I love you.
LP: . . . . AMA 5026
MC: . . . . AMC 5026

WOMEN AND CAPTAIN FIRST.
Tracks: / Wot / Nice cup of tea, A / Brenda (Part 1) / Brenda (part 2) / Yanks with guns / Happy talk / Martha the mouth / Nobody's sweetheart / What d'ya give a man who's got everything / Who is melody Lee, Sid? / Gimme a uniform / Croydon.
LP: . . . . AMLH 68548
MC: . . . . CAM 68548

Captain Sinbad

SEVEN VOYAGES OF CAPTAIN SINBAD,THE.
Tracks: / Bam salute / All over me / Wa-dat / Girls, girls, girls / Sugar Ray / Sinbad and the eye of the tiger / Construction plan / Fisherman / Morning teacher / Mary Moore.
LP: . . . . GREL 34

SINBAD & METRIC SYSTEM (Captain Sinbad & Peter Metro).
Tracks: / Get on down / Metric system / This old man / Water jelly / 3 big sound / Ina this / Sammy dead / Rub-a-sound / Saturday night at the movies.
LP: . . . . CSLP 6

Captain & Tennille

6 TRACK HITS: CAPTAIN & TENNILLE.
Tracks: / Love will keep us together.
MC: 7SC 5040

20 GREATEST HITS: CAPTAIN & TENNILLE.
Tracks: / Love will keep us together / You never done it like that / Shop around / You need a woman tonight / Lonely nights / Love is spreading over the world / Good enough / Dixie hummingbird / Sweet love / Can't stop dancing / I write the songs / Wedding song, The / Way I want to touch you, The / Muskrat love / Circles / Come in from the rain / Disney girls / Sing a song of joy / Dream / We never really say goodbye.
LP: . . . . MFP 50492

CAPTAIN & TENNILLE.
MCSET: . . . . DTO 10094
LP: . . . . AMID 124
MC: . . . . CMID 124

KEEPING OUR LOVE WARM.
Tracks: / Keeping our love warm / Until you come back to me / Gentle stranger / But I think it's a dream / Since I fell for you / Don't forget me / Song for my Father / This is not the first time / Your good thing.
LP: . . . . NBLP 7250

MAKE YOUR MOVE.
Tracks: / Love on a shoestring / No love in the morning / Deep in the dark / How can you be so cold? / Do that to me one more time / Happy together / Baby you still got it / Never make your move too soon.
LP: 9128 029
LP: . . . . CAL 2060

Captains Of Industry

ROOMFUL OF MONKEYS,A.
Tracks: / Land of the faint at heart / Our neck of the woods / Julie / Home and away / Lucky ones / Reputation (a serious case of ...) / Food factory / Lifeline / Lady of the manor / Playtime is over.
LP: . . . . AGOLP 5
LP: . . . . BSS 210

Captive (film)

CAPTIVE (See under Edge (U2 guitarist)) (Edge & Sinead O'Connor).

Car Trouble (film)

CAR TROUBLE (1986 Film Soundtrack) (Various artists).
Tracks: / Car trouble...Hearts on fire!: *Meatloaf* / Unchained melody: *Sayer, Leo* / Mated: *Grant, David* & Jaki Graham / Second choice: *Flesh* / Send my heart: *Adventures* / Mony mony: *Idol, Billy* / Break these chains: *Icehouse* / Only ones, The: *UFO* / Stay away: *Woyehyeh* / True love ways: *Adventures*.
LP: . . . . CHR 1523
MC: . . . . ZCHR 1523

Car Wash (film)

BEST OF CAR WASH (See under Rose Royce) (Rose Royce).

Cara, Irene

ANYONE CAN SEE.
Tracks: / Reach out I'll be there / My baby (he's something else) / Anyone can see / Don't throw your love away / Slow down / Fame / Wha dya want? / You hurt me once / Thunder in my heart / Why? / True love.
LP: . . . . EPC 25250
MC: 40 25250

CARASMATIC.
Tracks: / Get a grip / Give me love / We're gonna get up / Now that it's over / Say goodnight Irene / Don't wanna let go / Girlfriends / Be your number one / Falling in love.
LP: 9607241
MC: 9607244

WHAT A FEELIN'.
Tracks: / Why me / Breakdance / You took my life away / Receiving / Keep on / Dream / Flashdance...what a feeling / Romance '83 / Cue me up / Talk too much / You were made for me.
LP: . . . . EPC 25730

Carabali

CARABALI.
MC: . . . . MCT 1069
LP: . . . . MLPS 1069

CARABALI II.
LP: . . . . MLPS 1083
MC: . . . . MCT 1083

Caram, Ana

RIO AFTER DARK.
Tracks: / Rio after dark / Alagoas / Meditation / Viola fora de moda / Summer days / La cumbia / Looks like December / Renovacao / Rainbow / O que vier eu traco / Sem legenda / Forever / O tempo e o lugar / Serrado / You've got a friend.
LP: . . . . JR 28

Caratini, Patrice

LA BORDONA (See under Beytelman) (Caratini, Patrice/Beytelman).

TROIS TEMPS BIEN FAIRE (Caratini; Azzola; Fosset).
Tracks: / Azzola 2,000 / Monsieur Astor / Majeur / Lise & Fatty / Quartier saint-merri / Beguine des lavandieres / Index / Double scotch / Pouce / Canal Saint-Martin / Valse des crayons / Trois temps bien faire.
LP: . . . . CARA 002

Caravaggio 1610

CARAVAGGIO 1610 (See under Turner, Simon Fisher) (Turner, Simon Fisher).

Caravan

ALBUM, THE.
Tracks: / Heartbreaker / Corner of me eye / Watcha gonna tell me / Piano player / Make yourself at home / Golden mile / Bright shiny day / Clear blue sky / Keepin' up de fences.
LP: . . . . KVL 9003
MC: . . . . CKVL 9003

AND I WISH I WERE STONED DON'T WORRY.
Tracks: / And I wish I were stoned again / No backstage pass / Dog, the dog, he's at it again, The.
LP: . . . . SEE 46

BACK TO FRONT.
Tracks: / Back to Herne Bay front / Bet you wanna take it all / Hold on hold on / A.A man / Videos of Hollywood / Sally don't change it / Take my breath away / Proper job / Back to front / All aboard.
LP: . . . . KVS 5011

BEST OF CARAVAN.
Tracks: / And I wish I were stoned again / Can't be long now (Medley.) / Warlock / No backstage pass / Dog, the dog, he's at it again, The / To catch me a brother / In the land of grey and pink / Memory lain, Hugh.
LP: C5-505
MC: C5K-505

BLIND DOG AT ST.DUNSTAN'S.
Tracks: / Here I am / Chiefs and indians / Very smelly, grubby little oik, A / Bobbing wide / Come on back / Very smelly, grubby little oik, A (reprise) / Jack and Jill / Can you hear me / All the way.
LP: . . . . BTM 1007

CARAVAN IN CONCERT.
MC: . . . . WINMC 003

COLLECTION: CARAVAN.
Tracks: / It's never too late / Watcha gonna tell me / All aboard / Piano player / Clear blue sky / Bet you wanna take it all / Hold on hold on / Corner of me eye / Taken my breath away.
LP: . . . . KVC 6003

CUNNING STUNTS.
LP: . . . . SKL 5210

IF I COULD DO IT ALL OVER AGAIN.
Tracks: / If I could do it all over again / And I wish I were stoned again / Don't worry / As I feel I die / With an ear to the ground I can make it / Martinian / Only cox / Reprise / Hello, hello / Asforteri / Can't be long now / Francoise / For Richard / Warlock / Limits.
LP: . . . . SKL 5052

IN THE LAND OF GREY AND PINK.
Tracks: / Golf girl / Winter wine / Love to love you / In the land of grey and pink / Nine feet underground: Nigel blows a tune / Love's a friend / Make it 76 / Dance of the seven paper hankies- hold grandad by the nose / Honest I did-disassociation / 100% proof.
LP: . . . . SDL 1

SHOW OF OUR LIVES,THE.
Tracks: / If I could do it all over again / Golf girl / Waterloo Lily / Lover / Hello hello / Show of our lives, The / Stuck in a hole / World is yours, The / Love to love you / Virgin on the ridiculous.
LP: . . . . TAB 23

SONGS AND SIGNS.
Tracks: / Songs and signs / Love in your eye, The / World is yours, The / Mirror the day / Show of our lives, The / Welcome the day / Surprise surprise / Hello hello / Winter wine / For Richard.
MC: . . . . ELITE 002 PMC

WATERLOO LILY.
Tracks: / Waterloo Lily / It's coming soon / Nothing at all / Song and signs / Aristocracy / Love in your eye, The / To catch me a brother / Subsultus / Debouchement / Tilbury kecks / World is yours, The.
LP: . . . . SDL 8

Caravans

BEST OF....
LP: . . . . DBL 7012

EASY MONEY.

Tracks: / Rough diamonds / Sneakin' out / I've lost, you win / Crying / Easy money / Better place, A / Stranded / Blues train / Goodbye goodbye / In the heat of the day.
LP: .... NERD 036

Caravans (Film)

CARAVANS (Various artists).
LP: .... CBS 70164

Carawan, Guy

HAMMER DULCIMER (Carawan, Guy & Evan).
LP: .... FF 329

LAND KNOWS YOU'RE THERE, THE.
LP: .... FF 391

SONGS OF STRUGGLE AND CELEBRATION.
LP: .... FF 272

Carbia Ole

CARBIA OLE (Happy South America for dancing) (Various Orchestras).
Tracks: / A banda / La bostella / El cumbanchero / Matilda, Matilda / Cielito lindo / Copacabana / El condor pasa / Jambalaya / Guantanamera / Fernando / Rum and coca colsa / La cucaracha / Jamaica farewell / Banana boat song / Caribia.
LP: 2872 169
MC: 3472 169

Carbo, Chuck

WITH ED FRANK'S NEW ORLEANS BAND (Carbo, Chuck and Ed Frank's New Orleans Band).
LP: .... LPS 22

Carcamo, Pablo

FLY AWAY HOME.
LP: .... EULP 1128
MC: .... EUMC 1128

Carcass

REEK OF PUTRIFICATION.
Tracks: / Genital grinder / Regurgitation of giblets / Pyosisified / Carbonized eye-sockets / Frenzied detruncation / Vomited anal tract / Festerday / Fermenting innards / Excreted alive / Suppuration / Foeticide / Microwaved uterogestation / Splattered cavities / Psychopathologist / Burnt to a crisp / Pungent excruciation / Manifestation of verrucose urethra / Oxidised razor masticator / Malignant defecation.
LP: .... MOSH 6
MC: .... MOSH 6 MC

SYMPHONIES OF SICKNESS.
LP: .... MOSH 18
MC: .... MOSH 18 MC
LPPD: .... MOSH 18 P

Card, Michael

KNOWN BY THE SCARS.
LP: .... BIRD 167
MC: .... TC BIRD 167

SCANDALON.
LP: .... BIRD R 174
MC: .... BIRD C 174

WAY OF WISDOM, THE.
LP: .... SPR 1223
MC: .... SPC 1223

Cardell, Vince

LIBERANCE PRESENTS....
LP: .... NSPL 28246

Cardenas, Louis

ANIMAL INSTINCT.
LP: .... TOONLP 1

Cardiacs

BIG SHIP.
Tracks: / Big ship / Two / Tarred and feathered / Burn your house brown / Stone age dinosaurs / Planning against the grain.
LP: .... ALPH 004

CARDIACS LIVE.
Tracks: / Icing on the world / In a city lining / Tarred and feathered / Loosefish scapegrace / Is this the life / To go off and things / Gina Lollibrigida / Goosegash / Cameras / Big ship.
LP: .... ALPHLP 010

LITTLE MAN AND A HOUSE AND THE WHOLE WORLD WINDOW, A.
Tracks: / Back to the cave / Little man and a house / In a city lining / Is this the life? / Interlude / Dive / Icing on the world, The / Breakfast line, The / Victory / R E S / Whole world window, The.
LP: .... ALFLP 007

LIVE AT THE PARADISO.
LP: .... ALPH 010

LIVE FROM READING.
LP: .... ALPH 005

ON LAND AND IN THE SEA.
LP: .... ALP 012
MC: .... ALPHMC 012

SEASIDE.
LP: .... ALPHLP 013
MC: .... ALPHMC 013

Cardiff...

CARDIFF SEARCHLIGHT TATTOO 1983 (Various military bands).
Tracks: / Artillery salvo and opening fanfare / Quick silver, light division display / Georgia on my mind / Alexander's ragtime band / Mounted regiment of the Household Cavalry / Ich dien / Sospan fach / March of the men of Harlech / Triple crown / St.Louis blues march / Hallelujah chorus / Cwm rhondda / All through the night / Sunset / O Canada / Land of my fathers / God save the Queen / Day trip to Bangor.
LP: .... BND 1015
MC: .... ZC BND 1015

COME ALIVE (Cardiff City Temple Youth Choir).
Tracks: / Come alive / Our God is marching on / I'm gonna keep on singing / Blood will never lose it's power, The / Walk with Him in white / Come Holy Spirit / Never in a million years / Let me touch Him / That's the way to find happiness / Why should I worry or fret / It's God who watches / King of kings / I cannot fail the Lord.
LP: .... PC 815

Cardiff Polyphonic

CARDIFF POLYPHONIC CHOIR (Cardiff Polyphonic Choir).
LP: .... BM 64

CHRISTMAS CANTATA, A (Cardiff Polyphonic Choir).
Tracks: / Lullay, Jesu, lullay / First good joy that Mary had, The / When Jesus Christ was four years old / Little Jesus, sweetly sleep / Rejoice, O make we merry / I sing of a Maiden / By by lullay / I saw three ships / Shiao bao-bao / Angel Gabriel, The / Ar gyfer heddiw'r bore / Silent night / Tua Bethlem dref / This endless night / Good King Wenceslas.
LP: .... SDL 352
MC: .... CSDL 352

Cardinal (film)

CARDINAL, THE (1963 film soundtrack) (Various artists).
Tracks: / Stonebury: *Various artists* / Dixieland: *Various artists* / Tango: *Various artists* / Cardinal's faith, The: *Various artists* / They haven't got the girls in the USA: *Various artists* / Cardinal in Vienna, The: *Various artists* / Anne-Marie: *Various artists* / Cardinal's decision, The: *Various artists* / Way down South: *Various artists* / Cardinal themes, The: *Various artists.*
LP: .... ERS 6518
MC: .... NK 43754
LP: .... NL 43754

Cardona, Milton

BEMBE.
LP: .... AMCL 1004

Care Bears (film)

CARE BEARS MOVIE (1985 film soundtrack) (Various artists).
Tracks: / Care-a-lot: *King, Carole* / Home is in your heart: *King, Carole* / Nobody cares like a bear: *Sebastian, John* / When you care you are not afraid to try: *Sebastian, John* / In a Care Bear family: *Sebastian, John* / Look out, he's after you: *Woodward, Walt & David Bird.*
LP: .... PIPLP 717
MC: .... ZCPIP 717

CARE BEARS TO THE RESCUE (Edelman, Randy).
LP: .... ELF 23802
MC: .... ZCELF 23802
MC: 00 104 127-4

Careful He Might...

CAREFUL HE MIGHT HEAR YOU (1983 film soundtrack) (Various artists).
LP: .... STV 81221

Careless Talk (film)

NANOU/CARELESS TALK (Film soundtrack) (See under Nanou) (Various artists).

Caretaker Race

HANGOVER SQUARE.
LP: .... FOUND 2
MC: .... FOUND MC 2

Carey, Mariah

LOVE TAKES TIME.
Tracks: / Love takes time / Vanishing / You need me / Vision of love.
MC: 6563644

MARIAH CAREY.
Tracks: / Vision of love / There's got to be a way / I don't wanna cry / Someday / Vanishing / All in your mind / Alone in love / You need me / Send from up above / Prisoner / Love takes time.
LP: 4668151
MC: 4668154

Carey, Tony

SOME TOUGH CITY.
Tracks: / Fine fine day, A / Lonely life, A / Eddie goes underground / First day of summer, The / Reach out / Tinsel Town / Hungry / I can't stop the world / Some tough city / She can bring me love.
LP: .... MCF 3212
MC: .... MCFC 3212

Cargo Sect

INDEPENDENCE.
LP: .... RS 1044

Caribbean...

CARIBBEAN COCKTAIL (Various artists).
Tracks: / Caribbean surfer: *Various artists* / Island in the sun: *Various artists* / Rivers of Babylon: *Various artists* / America: *Various artists* / Sloop John B: *Various artists* / Montego bay: *Various artists*/ Yellow bird: *Various artists* / Coconut woman: *Various artists* / Soul limbo: *Various artists* / Under the mango tree: *Various artists* / Brown girl in the ring: *Various artists* / Jamaican coffee: *Various artists*/ Don't stop the carnival: *Various artists* / Banana boat song: *Various artists* / Jamaica farewell: *Various artists* / La bamba: *Various artists* / Guantanamera: *Various artists.*
LP: .... REC 559
MC: .... ZCM 559

CARIBBEAN SONGS AND DANCES (Various artists).
LP: .... H 72047

DANCE CADENCE (Style dance music from the Caribbean) (Various artists).
Tracks: / L'essential: *Group guad'm* / Les dorlanes: *Come Back* / Mise en nou: *Batako* / Rangatabac: *Godzom Son Traditionnel* / Nous pas bisouin: *Plonquitte, Georges* / Nwel: *Decimus, Georges* / Konesans: *Makandjia* / Mi lago: *Mona, Eugene.*
LP: .... ORB 002
MC: .... ORBC 002

STEEL BAND DES CARAIBES (Various artists).
Tracks: / Hot soca: *Various artists* / Rent a bungalow: *Various artists* / Help me make it through the night: *Various artists* / Etel: *Various artists* / Cupid: *Various artists* / Negril: *Various artists*/ I shot the sheriff: *Various artists* / Bang bang woman: *Various artists* / Island in the sun: *Various artists*/ Ras mas: *Various artists* / Feeling: *Various artists.*
LP: .... ARN 33612
MC: .... ARN 433612

TOP HITS CARAIBES (Various artists).
Tracks: / Oh Madiana: *Various artists* / Faut aller au charbon: *Various artists* / Karambole: *Various artists*/ Guidonner: *Various artists* / Baissez bas: *Various artists* / Hot music (la fiesta): *Various artists*/ Reminiscence: *Various artists* / Debar debar: *Various artists* / News and politik's: *Various artists*/ Mwin ka devine: *Various artists* / Who's that lady: *Various artists* / Nocturne West Indies: *Various artists*/ La baie des flamants: *Various artists.*
LP: 829 516-1
MC: 829 516-4

Carignan, Jean

HOMMAGE A JOSEPH ALLARD.
LP: .... PH 2012

JEAN CARIGNAN.
LP: .... PH 2001

Carillon Bells

SOUND OF THE CARILLON, THE (Various).
Tracks: / Cuckoo rondo / Last rose of Summer / Cockles and mussels / Crimond / Schubert serenade.
LP: .... SDL 291
MC: .... CSDL 291

Carillyon

MARY, MARY.
MC: .... BM 101

Carini, Baronessa De

CARINI, BARONESSA DE, VOL. 2.
MC: .... GVMMC 677

SICILIAN TRADITIONAL SONGS AND MUSIC, VOL.1.
MC: .... GVMMC 676

Carisse, Terry

NONE OF THE FEELING IS GONE.
MC: .... SVMC 9404

Carl & Carol

STREET DANCING.
LP: .... UNKNOWN

Carl, Joe

DUKES OF RHYTHM 1960 (See under Dukes of rhythm).

Carle, Frankie

1944-1946 (Carle, Frankie & His Orchestra).
LP: .... CLP 43

GOLDEN TOUCH, THE.
LP: .... CLP 138

Carless, Dorothy

WHISPERING GRASS (Carless, Dorothy/Benny Lee/Adelaide Hall/Issy Bonn).
Tracks: / I hear a rhapsody / Lonely serenade / As if you didn't know / We both told a lie / Why don't we do this more often / When they sound the last 'all clear' / What more can I say / I don't want anybody at all (if I can't have you) / Who told you I cared? / Careless / I'm getting sentimental over you / Don't make me laugh / I heard you cried last night / Ain't it a shame about mame / Serenade in blue / Sophisticated lady / There, I've said it again / It's a wonderful world (after all) / Across the bridge of gold / Someday you'll want me to want you / Somewhere beyond the stars / Goodnight till tomorrow / Waiting / Till then / My little sailor man / Whispering grass / Autumn nocturne / Jim / How about you / Do you care? / I'll always remember / We three / Beat me daddy, eight to the bar / Five o'clock whistle / Number ten lullaby lane / I guess I'll have to dream the rest.
2LP: .... RECDL 19
MCSET: .... RECDC 19

Carley, Raymond

BEAUTIFUL WEEKEND.
LP: .... NORLP 1003

Carlin, Bob

BANGING AND SAWING.
LP: .... ROUNDER 0197
MC: .... ROUNDER 0197C

OLD TIME BANJO.
LP: .... ROUNDER 0132

WHERE DID YOU GET THAT HAT?.
LP: .... ROUNDER 0172
MC: .... ROUNDER 0172C

Carlin, George

EVENING WITH WALLY LONDO, AN.
Tracks: / New news / Teenage masturbation / Mental hot foots / High on the plane / Bodily functions / Wurds / For name's sake / Baseball - football / Good sports / Flesh colored band aids / Religious life / Radio dial / Y'ever unrelated things.
LP: .... K 59655

TOLEDO WINDOW BOX.
Tracks: / Goofy shit / Toledo window box / Nursery rhymes / Some werds / Water sex / Metric system, The / God gay lib / Snot the original rubber cement / Urinals are 50% universal / Few more farts, A.
LP: .... K 59652

Carlin, Joanna

FANCY THAT.
Tracks: / Dancing in the dark / Valentino / Laziest girl in town / Anyway my guru says no / Hearse, The / Sugar in my bowl / So close / Fancy / I wanna roo you / Honesty / There's something in the way he moves / First time.
LP: .... DJF 20508
MC: .... DJH 40508

Carling Family

CARLING FAMILY HOT SIX (Carling Family Hot Six).
LP: .... PHONT 7577

I LOST MY HEART IN DIXIELAND.
LP: .... PHONT 7558

Carlisle, Belinda

BELINDA.
Tracks: / Mad about you / I need a disguise / Since you're gone / I feel the magic / I never wanted a rich man / Band of gold / Gotta get to you / From the heart / Shot in the dark / Stuff and nonsense.
LP: .... MIRF 1012
MC: .... MIRFC 1012

HEAVEN ON EARTH.
Tracks: / Heaven is a place on Earth / Circle in the sand / I feel free / Should I let you in? / World without you / I get weak / We can change / Fool for love / Nobody owns me / Love never dies.
LP: .... V 2496
MC: .... TCV 2496
LP: .... OVED 330
MC: .... OVEDC 330

RUNAWAY HORSES.
Tracks: / Leave a light on / Runaway horses / Vision of you / Summer rain / La luna / (We want) the same thing / Deep deep ocean / Valentine / Whatever it takes / Shades of Michaelangelo.
LP: .... V 2599
MC: .... TCV 2599

Carlisle, Cliff

CLIFF CARLISLE VOL.1.
LP: . . . . OT 103

CLIFF CARLISLE VOL.2.
LP: . . . . OT 104

Carlisle, Elsie

SHE'S THE TALK OF THE TOWN.
Tracks: / It's the talk of the town / One little kiss / When a woman loves a man / Home James and don't spare the horses / Snowball / Porter's love song, The / I cover the waterfront / I'm gonna wash my hands of you (Duet with Sam Browne.) / We just could't say goodbye / Smoke gets in your eyes / Place in your heart, A / Girl next door, The / No, no, a thousand times no (Duet with Sam Browne.) / Clouds will soon roll by, The / You're my everything / No more love / There's no more you can say / Show is over, The.
MC: . . . . MCHD 126
LP: . . . . CHD 126

STAR GAZING (1932-1936).
Tracks: / Star gazing / Solitude / Mama I long for a sweetheart / Dancing with my shadow / Place in your heart, A / Conversation for two / Poor butterfly / You try somebody else / When a man loves a woman / Whisper sweet / Making conversation / Up The Wooden Hill To Bedfordshire / To be worthy of you / Deep water / Come up and see me sometime / My shadow's where my sweetheart used to be / He wooed her and wooed her and wooed her / My darling.
LP: . . . . OLD 10
MC: . . . . COLD 10

THAT'S LOVE.
Tracks: / Pardon me pretty baby / Ladies and gentlemen that's love / My cutie's due at two to two today / My handy man / Body and soul / So this is your old lady / Ten cents a dance / Nobody's business / Exactly like you / I love my baby / My handy man ain't handy no more / I like to do things for you / Ya gotta know how to love / My man o' war / Crying myself to sleep / Why can't you / Poor kid / I wonder what is really on his mind / He's my secret passion / You're driving me crazy.
LP: . . . . AJA 5019
MC: . . . . ZC AJA 5019

Carlisle, Una Mae

UNA MAE CARLISLE (Savannah Churchill 1944) (Carlisle, Una Mae & Savannah Churchill 1944).
Tracks: / 'Tain't yours / Without you baby / I'm a good good woman / Ain't nothin' much / I like it 'cause I love it / You gotta take your time / He's the best little Yankee to me / I speak so much about you / Teasin' me / You and your heart of stone / You're gonna change your mind / Rest of my life / He's commander in chief of my heart / Two faced man / Tell me your blues / Fat meat is good meat.
LP: . . . . HQ 2002

UNA MAE CARLISLE & LIL ARMSTRONG (See under Armstrong, Lil) (Carlisle, Una Mae & Lil Armstrong).

Carlisles

BUSY BODY BOOGIE.
Tracks: / New Liza Jane / Busy body boogie / Money tree / Pickin' peas / Goo goo da da (baby latin meaning daddy) / Female Hercules / Honey love / That little difference / No help wanted / I need a little help / Leave that liar alone / Is that you, Myrtle / I'm rough stuff / Knot hole / Old fashioned love / Too old to cut the mustard.
LP: . . . . BFX 15172

Carlo & The Belmonts

CARLO AND THE BELMONTS.
Tracks: / We belong together / Such a long way / Santa Margherita / My foolish heart / Teenage Clementine / Little orphan girl / Five minutes more / Write me a letter / Brenda the great pretender / Ring-a-ling / Baby doll / Maizy doats and dozy doats / Story of love, The / Kansas City.
LP: . . . . CHD 251

Carlos, Don

DAY TO DAY LIVING.
Tracks: / Hog and goat / I like it / Dice cups / Roots man party / Hey Mr. Babylon / Street life / English woman / I'm not crazy / At the bus stop.
LP: . . . . GREL 45
MC: . . . . GREEN 45

DEEPLY CONCERNED.
Tracks: / Deeply concerned / Cool Johnny cool / Ruff we ruff / Jah people unite / Black station white station / Satan control them / Money lover / Night rider / Crazy girl.
LP: . . . . RAS 3029
MC: . . . . RASC 3029

FIREHOUSE CLASH (Carlos, Don/ Junior Reid).
Tracks: / Chanting / Respect due / Mirror / Children playing / Living in the city / No trouble this / No follow Babylon / Never gonna give up.
LP: . . . . LLLP 20

GHETTO LIVING (Carlos, Don & Gold).
LP: . . . . TWLP 1010

HARVEST TIME.
Tracks: / Fuss fuss / I Love Jah / Harvest time / In Picese / White Squall / Magic Man / Young girl / Music crave / Hail the roots.
LP: . . . . BMLP 066

JUST A PASSING GLANCE.
Tracks: / Just a passing glance / Just a passing glance (dj version) / Knock knock / I just can't stop / You are my sunshine / Front line / Springheel skanking / Heartbreaker / I'm leaving / Zion train.
LP: . . . . RAS 3008

NEVER RUN AWAY (Carlos, Don & Gold).
Tracks: / Every time I see you / It was love / Go find yourself a fool / Angel-face woman / Come over / Them say / Ghetto living / Never run away / Judgement day / Right now.
LP: . . . . KVL 9017

PLANTATION (Carlos, Don & Gold).
Tracks: / Plantation / Promise to be true / Tear drops / Declaration of rights / Aint too proud to beg / Pretty baby.
LP: . . . . CSLP 15
MC: . . . . ZCSLC 15

PROPHECY.
Tracks: / Gimme gimme your lovin' / Crucial situation / Version / Working everyday / Live in harmony / Prophecy / Jah hear my plea.
LP: . . . . BMLP 054

PURE GOLD: DON CARLOS.
LP: . . . . VSLP 4029

RASTA BROTHERS.
LP: . . . . DFLP 3004

RAVING TONIGHT (Carlos, Don & Gold).
LP: . . . . RAS 3005

SHOWDOWN VOL.II.
LP: . . . . JJ 164

SPREAD OUT.
LP: . . . . BS 1053

Carlos, Roberto

ROBERTO CARLOS.
Tracks: / Honestly / At peace in your smile / Loneliness / Sail away / Niagra / Buttons on your blouse / Breakfast / Come to me tonight / You will remember me / It's me again.
LP: . . . . S 25798
MC: 40 25798
LP: . . . . CBS 85267

Carlos, Walter

WALTER CARLOS-BY REQUEST.
MC: 40 73163
LP: 73163

Carlos, Wendy

BEAUTY IN THE BEAST.
LP: . . . . SYN 200
MC: . . . . SYNC 200

BEST OF CARLOS.
Tracks: / Clockwork orange, A / What's new pussycat / Eleanor Rigby / La gazza ladra / Water music / Jesu, joy of man's desiring / Air on a G string / Brandenberg
LP: . . . . CBS 74110

Carlson, Pete

YOU WERE THERE.
Tracks: / In this quiet hour / He promise / Evermore / Tell me all your troubles / Hope of my salvation / You were there / Jesus is all the world to me / Simple story / You ask me why / I don't wanna go home.
LP: . . . . PC 108

Carlson, Ralph

THANKS FOR THE DANCE.
Tracks: / Thanks for the dance / Ain't got time / John's / Out of the snow / Southern bells / Somebody's woman / Silence on the line / Lights of Denver / General store of Silas McVie / Looking for someone
LP: . . . . WRS 160

Carlton

CALL IS STRONG, THE.
LP: 828 194 1
MC: 828 194 4

Carlton, Carl

CARL CARLTON.
Tracks: / Sexy lady / Let me love you 'til the morning comes / Don't you wanna make love? / This feeling's X-rated / She's a bad mama jama (she's built, she's stacked) / I've got that boogie fever / I think it's gonna be alright / Fighting in the name of love.
LP: . . . . T 628
MC: . . . . C 628

DROP BY MY PLACE.
Tracks: / Competition ain't nothing / Three way love / Look at Mary wonder (how I got over) / Don't walk away / Drop by my place / I can feel it / I won't let that chump break your heart / You can't stop a man in love / Everlasting love / Smokin' room / Morning noon and nighttime / Ain't gonna tell anybody ('bout you) / Two timer / Sure miss loving you / You've got so much to learn about / Wild child.
LP: . . . . CRB 1198

Carlton, Larry

ALONE BUT NEVER ALONE.
Tracks: / Smiles and smiles to go / Perfect peace / Carrying you / Lord's prayer, The / High steppin' / Whatever happens / Pure delight / Alone but never alone.
LP: . . . . IMCA 5689
MC: . . . . IMCAC 5689

COLLECTION: LARRY CARLTON.
Tracks: / Small town girl / Smiles and smiles to go / Minute by minute / For heaven's sake / Nite crawler / Blues for TJ / 10 p.m. / Sleepwalk / Tequila / Bubble shuffle / Hello tomorrow / High steppin'.
LP: . . . . GR 9611
MC: . . . . GRC 9611

DISCOVERY.
Tracks: / Hello tomorrow / Those eyes / Knock on wood / Discovery / My home away from home / March of the jazz angels / Minute by minute / Place for skipper, A / Her favourite song.
LP: . . . . IMCA 42003
MC: . . . . IMCAC 42003

FRIENDS.
Tracks: / Breaking ground / South town / Tequila / Blues for TJ / Song in the 5th grade / Cruisin' / L A N Y / Friends.
LP: 923834 1
MC: 923834 4

LARRY CARLTON.
Tracks: / Room 335 / Where did you come from / Nite crawler / Point it up / Rio samba / I apologise / Don't give it up / (It was) only yesterday.
LP: . . . . K 56548

LAST NITE.
Tracks: / So what / Don't give it up / B.P. blues / All blues / Last nite / Emotions wound us so.
LP: . . . . MCF 3353
MC: . . . . MCFC 3353

LIVE IN JAPAN.
LP: . . . . P 10643

ON SOLID GROUND.
LP: . . . . MCA 6237
MC: . . . . MCAC 6237

SLEEPWALK.
Tracks: / Last nite / Blues bird / Song for Katie / Frenchman's flat / Upper kern / 10.00 p.m. / You gotta get it while you can / Sleepwalk.
LP: . . . . K 56974
MC: K4 56974

Carlton Main...

BANDING WITH BALL (Carlton Main Frickley Colliery Band).
LP: . . . . ABL 401

CARLTON MAIN FRICKLEY COLLIERY BAND (Best of) (Carlton Main Frickley Colliery Band).
Tracks: / F.C.B. / Fingals cave / Serenade for trombone / Masquerade / Hunting polka / Caractacus / Gay gnu / Streets of London / Epic theme.
LP: . . . . SB 339

CONCERT PROGRAMME (Carlton Main Frickley Colliery Band).
Tracks: / Mephistopheles / Finale from Faust / Love story / Carnival de Venice / Troublemaker / Procession of the nobles / Hava nagila / Concerto for French horn and brass band / Slavonic dance no.8.
LP: . . . . TB 3022

Carlton Sisters

JUMP.
MC: . . . . CHV 320

Carluke Primrose...

CARLUKE PRIMROSE FLUTE BAND IN CONCERT (Carluke Primrose Flute Band).
LP: . . . . BGC 316

Carman

CHAMPION, THE.
LP: . . . . MYR R 6827
MC: . . . . MYR C 6827

COMIN' ON STRONG.
LP: . . . . MYRR 1190
MC: . . . . MYRC 1190

LIVE... RADICALLY SAVED.
LP: . . . . R 02463
MC: . . . . C 02463

Carman, Pauli

DIAL MY NUMBER.
Tracks: / Dial my number / Flashback / You impress me / Big on pleasure / Lose control / High and low / Close to the bone / Dangerous.
LP: . . . . CBS 26960
MC: 40 26960

Carmel

CARMEL.
Tracks: / Tracks of my tears / Sugar daddy / Guilty / Thunder / Love affair / Storm.
LP: . . . . RFM 9

COLLECTED (A Collection of Work 1983-1990).
Tracks: / And I take it for granted / Sally / It's all in the game / I'm not afraid of you / Every little bit / I have fallen in love (Je suis tombee' amoureuse) / More, more, more / You can have him / Bad day / J'oublierai ton nom / I'm over you.
LP: 828 219 1
MC: 828 219 4

DRUM IS EVERYTHING, THE.
Tracks: / More, more, more / Stormy weather / Drum is everything, The / I thought I was going mad / Prayer / Rockin' on suicide / Rue St Denis / Willow weep for me / Tracks of my tears / Bad day.
LP: . . . . SH 8555
MC: . . . . KSAC 8555

EVERYBODY'S GOT A LITTLE...SOUL.
Tracks: / Hey hey (everybody's got a little...soul) / It's all in the game / Every little bit / Nothing good / Azure / Sweet and lovely / Jazz robin / Lay down / I do and do / Hey hey (reprise).
MC: . . . . LONC 40
LP: . . . . LONLP 40

FALLING, THE.
Tracks: / I'm not afraid of you / Let me know / Tok / Falling, The / Mama told me not to come / Mercy / Easy for you / Sticks and stones / Sally.
LP: . . . . LONLP 17
MC: . . . . LONC 17

SET ME FREE.
Tracks: / Napoli / You can have him / I have fallen in love (je suis tombee amoureuse) / I'm over you / God, put your hand on me / Take it for granted / Circles / If birds can fly / One fine day / Onward / Waterfall, The (On MC and CD only) / Life is hard (On CD only).
LP: 828 148 1
MC: 828 148 4

Carmen, Eric

ERIC CARMEN.
Tracks: / I wanna hear it from your lips / I'm through with love / American as apple pie / Livin' without your love / Come back to my love / She remembered / Maybe my baby / Spotlight / Way we used to be, The.
LP: . . . . GEF 26056
MC: 4026056
LP: . . . . ARTY 120

ERIC CARMEN.
Tracks: / Sunrise / That's rock'n'roll / Never gonna fall in love / Last night / All by myself / My girl.
LP: . . . . FA 3049
MC: . . . . TCFA 3049

GREATEST HITS: ERIC CARMEN.
Tracks: / All by myself / Never gonna fall in love again / That's rock'n'roll / Hey Deanie / Hungry eyes / Make me lose control / Change of heart / She did it / It hurts too much / No hard feelings / Boats against the current.
LP: 208999
MC: 408999

Carmen (film)

CARMEN (1) (Film soundtrack 1983) (Various artists).
Tracks: / Introduction/The search for Carmen: *Various artists* / Stop crying: *Various artists* / Bulerias: *Various* artists / Adagio: *Various artists* / Women's knife fight, The: *Various artists* / Soldiers arrest Carmen, The: *Various artists* / Guitar strumming: *Various artists* / Intermezzo: *Various artists* / Company rehearses, The: *Various artists* / Last scene and premonition: *Various artists* / Fight with sticks: *Various artists*/ Carmen's infidelity: *Various artists* / El Gato Montes: *Various artists* / Showdown between Escamilo and Don Jose: *Various artists* / Carmen:Finale: *Various artists.*
MC: . . . . POLDC 5134

LP: .... POLD 5134

CARMEN (2) (Film soundtrack 1984) (Various artists).
LPS: .... NUM 75113
MC: .... MCE 75113

CARMEN (HIGHLIGHTS) (Film soundtrack 1984:Highlights) (Various artists).
MC: .... MCE 75120
LP: .... NUM 75120

Carmen, Pauli

IT'S TIME.
LP: .... BFC 40801

Carmichael, Hoagy

16 CLASSIC TRACKS: HOAGY CARMICHAEL.
Tracks: / I may be wrong, but, I think you're wonderful / Talking is a woman / Shh the old man's sleepin' / Don't forget to say no baby / Casanova cricket / Man could be such a wonderful thing, A / Put yourself in my place baby / Tune for humming, A / That's a plenty / Gonnna get a girl / For every man there's a woman / Ten to one it's Tennessee / Coney Island washboard / Some days there just ain't no fish / Monkey song, The / Rogue river valley.
LP: .... MCL 1692
MC: .... MCLC 1692

BALLADS FOR DANCING.
Tracks: / I walked with music / Sky lark / I get along without you very well / Two sleepy people / Lamplighter's serenade, The / Heart and soul / Nearness of you, The / Ivy / One morning in May / How little we know / Blue orchids / Star dust.
LP: .... MCL 1819

CLASSIC HOAGY CARMICHAEL (Various artists).
Tracks: / Stardust: *Various artists* / Georgia on my mind: *Various artists* / Lazy river: *Various artists*/ Nearness of you, The: *Various artists* / Skylark: *Various artists* / Lazybones: *Various artists* / Rockin' chair: *Various artists.*
LPS: .... BBC 4000
MCSET: .... ZCJ 4000

CURTIS HITCH & HOAGY CARMICHAEL 1923-28 (See under Hitch, Curtis) (Carmichael, Hoagy & Curtis Hitch).

HOAGY.
Tracks: / Rockin' chair / Georgia on my mind / Sing it way down low / Lazybones / March of the hoodlums / Snowball / Walking the dog / Pap's gone goodbye / Bessie couldn't help it / One morning in May / Washboard blues / Moon country / Cosmics / Sittin' and whittlin' / Stardust / Lazy river / Judy / Barnacle Bill the sailor.
LP: .... NL 89096
MC: .... NK 89096
LP: .... INTS 5181
MC: .... INTK 5181

HOAGY CARMICHAEL 1951.
LP: .... HQ 2000

HOAGY CARMICHAEL, 1944-45 (V-discs).
Tracks: / Baltimore oriole / Hong Kong blues / Stardust / No more toujours l'amour / Billy-A-dick / Memphis in June / Sleepy time gal / Ginger and spice / Am I blue? / Everybody's seen him but his daddy / Rogue river valley / Riverboat shuffle / Two sleepy people / Doctor, lawyer, indian chief / Old spinning wheel / Huggin' and chalkin'.
LP: .... TOTEM 1039

HOAGY CARMICHAEL SINGS HOAGY CARMICHAEL.
Tracks: / Old music master, The / Hong Kong blues / Memphis in June / Ode buttermilk sky / My resistance is low / Rockin' chair / Riverboat shuffle / Georgia on my mind / Lazy river / Judy / Stardust / In the cool cool cool of the evening (From the film "Here comes the groom".) / Moon country / Baltimore oriole / Little old lady / Washboard blues.
LP: .... MCL 1620
MC: .... MCLC 1620

HOAGY SINGS CARMICHAEL.
Tracks: / Georgia on my mind / Winter moon / New Orleans / Memphis in June / Skylark / Two sleepy people / Baltimore oriole / Rockin' chair / Ballad in blue / Lazy river / Georgia on my mind (instrumental).
LP: .... EG 2602951
MC: .... EG 2602954

INDIANA SUMMER, 1923-28 (Carmichael, Hoagy & Curtis Hitch).
MC: .... CFJ 109

SELECTION OF STANDARDS... (See under Fame, Georgie) (Fame, Georgie, Hoagy Carmichael & Annie Ross).

SONG IS...HOAGY CARMICHAEL (Various artists).
Tracks: / Lazybones: *Various artists* / Georgia on my mind: *Various artists* / Heart and soul: *Various artists*/ Rockin' chair: *Various artists* / Two sleepy people: *Various artists* / Stardust: *Various artists* / Lazy river: *Various artists.*
MC: .... ZC AJA 5074
LP: .... AJA 5074

STARDUST.
Tracks: / In the cool cool cool of the evening / Heart and soul / Honky Kong blues / Old music master / Who killed 'er / Stardust / Ole buttermilk sky / Doctor, lawyer, indian chief.
LP: .... MFP 50558
LP: .... NL 88333
MC: .... NK 88333

Carmichael, John

DANCE AWAY (Carmichael, John & His Band).
MC: .... ZCLOC 1055

HOP SCOTCH (Carmichael, John/ Accordion Bonanza Band).
LP: .... C 1008

JOHN CARMICHAEL'S CEILIDH BAND.
Tracks: / Swinging westward / Sicilian dance / Looking lively / Jigtime / Continental waltz / Toast to Nova Scotia, A.
LP: .... LILP 5083

TUNES OF THE GAELN (Carmichael, John & His Band).
Tracks: / My mother / On the space / Come over with me / White banner / Good health and joy / My tiree / I sailed last night / Isle of my love / Helen.
MC: .... ZCLB 2007

YOURS ACCORDIONLY.
Tracks: / Pipers delight / Norman's waltz / Jan's dance / Fiona Carmichael / La russe reel / Highland Schottische / Jole blon / Gaelic waltz.
LP: .... BGC 251
MC: .... KBGC 251

Carmichael, Judy

JAZZ PIANO.
LP: .... SLP 8074

PEARLS.
LP: .... SLP 8078

TWO HANDED STRIDE.
Tracks: / Christopher Columbus / Viper's drag / Ja da / Honeysuckle Rose / Ain't misbehavin' / Handful of keys / I ain't got nobody / (I would do) anything for you.
LP: .... PRO 7065
LP: .... SLP 8072

Carmichael, Ralph

CHRISTMAS JOYS (Carmichael, Ralph Orchestra & Chorus).
Tracks: / Wonderful world of Christmas, The / Caroling, caroling / Silent night / Birthday of a king / O holy night / Messiah medley / Inspirational world of Christmas, The / Ove in Bethlehem / Little drummer boy / Some children see him / Christmas joys medley.
LP: .... LS 7041
MC: .... LC 7041

I'M HERE, GOD'S HERE, NOW WE CAN START (Carmichael, Ralph & Kurt Kaiser).
Tracks: / Let it ring / God is here right now / Lookin' for the man called Jesus / Now we can start to hear music / Are you in control Lord? / Now we can start to be thankful / Nothing but amazing / Now we can start to have peace / Symbols and tokens / Now we can start to be free / I will lift up my eyes / Now we can start to love / God loved so much / Rough old roads / Road to glory, The / Come as you are / He'll go with you now.
LP: .... LS 7056
MC: .... LC 7056

Carmilla (bk)

CARMILLA (See under Guest Of Honour) (Dramatised by Graham Pomeroy & John Douglas).

Carmody, Simon

LAST BANDITS, THE (Carmody, Simon, Nikki Sudden, Johnny Fean).
LP: .... HWLP 8504

YOU CAN'T ALWAYS GET WHAT YOU WANT (see Friday, Gavin) (Carmody, Simon & Gavin Friday).

Carnaby, Cas Five

MR MORRIS' FUNERAL.
LP: .... NCHLP 15

Carnage

DARK RECOLLECTIONS.
LP: .... NECRO 3
MC: .... NECRO 3 MC

FACE THE FACTS.
LP: .... REAL 7

MAY THE FARCE BE WITH YOU.
LP: .... REAL 12

Carnahan, Danny

CONTINENTAL DRIFT (See under Petrie, Robin) (Carnahan, Danny/Robin Petrie).

TWO FOR THE ROAD (See under Petrie, Robin) (Carnahan, Danny/Robin Petrie).

Carnaval Alegria

CARNAVAL ALEGRIA (Various artists).
LP: .... CEL 6736

Carne, Jean

ARTISTS SHOWCASE: JEAN CARNE.
Tracks: / We got some catching up to do / Lonely girl in a cold cold world / My love don't come easy / Trust me / I'm in love once again / No no you can't come back now / Bet your lucky star / Start the fire / When I find you love / Love don't love nobody / Free love / If you wanna go back / Sweet and wonderful / Was that all it was / You got a problem / Dindi / If you don't know me by now / Don't let it go to your head / Mystic stranger / Let's stay together / Happy to be with you.
LP: .... MUSIC 7
MC: .... ZCMUS 7

CLOSER THAN CLOSE.
LP: .... OMN LP 2

TRUST ME.
Tracks: / Steady on my mind / Don't let me slip away / Trust me / Super explosion / My baby loves me / If you don't know me by now / Completeness / Better to me.
LP: .... STML 12172

YOU'RE A PART OF ME.
Tracks: / You're a part of me / Heartache / Ain't no way / Givin' up on love / Let me be the one / Closer to you / Walkin' the line / Don't want to love any more / Early morning love / Closer than close (Extra track on CD only.) / Break up to make up (Extra track on CD only.) / Flame of love (Extra track on CD only.) / Lucky charm (Extra track on CD only.).
LP: .... PL 71624
MC: .... PK 71624

Carnes, Kim

CAFE RACERS.
Tracks: / You make my heart beat faster / Young love / Met you at the wrong time of my life / Hurricane / Universal song / Invisible hands / I pretend / Hangin' on by a thread / Kick in the heart / I'll be here where the heart is.
LP: AML7171061

DON'T FALL IN LOVE WITH A DREAMER (See under Rogers, Kenny) (Carnes, Kim with Kenny Rogers).

LIGHTHOUSE.
Tracks: / Divided hearts / I'd lie to you for your love / Black and white / Piece of the sky / You say you love me (but I know better) / Dancin' at the lighthouse / Love me like you never did before / Along with the radio / Only lonely lore / That's where the trouble lies.
LP: .... AML 3106
MC: .... TCAML 3106

MAKE NO MISTAKE, HE'S MINE (see Streisand, Barbra) (Carnes, Kim & Barbra Streisand).

MISTAKEN IDENTITY.
Tracks: / Bette Davis eyes / Hit and run / Mistaken identity / When I'm away from you / Draw of the cards / Break the rules tonite / Still hold on / Don't call it love / Miss you tonite / My old pals.
LP: .... FA 41 3146 1
MC: .... FA 41 3146 4
MC: .... TCFA 3146
LP: .... AML 3018

ROMANCE DANCE.
Tracks: / Swept me off my feet / Cry like a baby / Will you remember me / Tear me apart / Changing / More love / In the chill of the night / Where is your heart / Still be loving you.
LP: .... AML 3012

ST. VINCENT'S COURT.
Tracks: / What am I gonna do until you come home / Jamaica Sunday morning / Stay away / Lookin' for a big night / Paris without you / Hurt so bad / Lose in love / Skeptical shuffle / Take me home to where my heart is / Blinded by love / Goodnite moon.
LP: .... FA 3038
LP: .... AML 3001

VIEW FROM THE HOUSE.
Tracks: / Brass and batons / Heartbreak radio / If you don't want my love / Speed of the sound of loneliness / Fantastic fire of love / Just to spend the night with you / Crazy in love / Willie and the hand jive / Blood from the bandit / Crimes of the heart.
LP: .... MCAF 3428
MC: .... MCFC 3428

VOYEUR.
Tracks: / Voyeur / Looker / Say you don't know me / Does it make you remember / Breakin' away from sanity / Undertow / Merc man / Arrangement / Thrill of the grill / Take it on the chin.
LP: .... AML 3026

Carney/Hild/Kramer

HAPPINESS FINALLY CAME TO THEM.
Tracks: / Hands / Telephone / Clown / Nothing / Bank / Slowly / Wanda / Larry / Name / Barometer / Treefrog / Turkeyfaced / Javalena / Disguise / Lotto / End / 3-D.
LP: .... SHIMMY 007

Carnival Art

THRUMDRONE.
LP: .... SITU 32
MC: .... SITUC 32

Carnival (show)

CARNIVAL (Various artists).
MC: .... BOPMARP 001

Carnivore

CARNIVORE.
Tracks: / Predator / Male supremacy / Legion of doom / Thermonuclear warrior / Carnivore / Armageddon / God is dead / World wars III & IV.
LP: .... RR 9754
MC: .... GWC 90534

RETALIATION.
LP: .... RR 9597

Carny (film)

CARNY (1980 film soundtrack) (Various artists).
LP: .... HS 3455

Carnyx

SOUNDS OF THE ROMAN WORLD.
Tracks: / Lacrimosa / In the forum / Lutatia's dance / Outpost / Reflections / Gladiators, The.
MC: .... APX 862

SOUNDS OF THE VIKING AGE.
Tracks: / Watchman / Lamentation / Utre-mi / Pilgrim song / Nightingale, The / Come sweet love.
MC: .... APX 851

Carolan, Lucy

FLUTE COLLECTION (see under Preston, Stephen) (Carolan, Lucy/ Stephen Preston).

Carolan, Mary-Ann

SONGS FROM THE IRISH TRADITION.
Tracks: / Bold Doherty / Maid of Ballymore, The / Bob Riddley / Old oak tree, The / Tinker's old budget, The / Bonnie light horseman, The / In London so fair / My father's a hedger and a ditcher / Highland Mary / Wedding at Baltray, The.
LP: 12TS 362

Carolina Slim

CAROLINA BLUES AND BOOGIE (1950-1952).
Tracks: / Money blues / Mama's boogie / Black chariot / Worrying blues / One more drink / Carolina boogie / I'll get by somehow / Rag mama / Sugarfree / Blues go away from me / Blues knockin' at my door / Worry you off my mind / Wine head baby / Slo freight blues.
LP: .... TM 805

Caroline K.

NOW WAIT FOR LAST YEAR.
LP: .... EARTH 001

Caroline Miniscule

CAROLINE MINISCULE (Jarvis, Martin (nar)).
MCSET: .... ZBBC 1158

Carousel (musical)

CAROUSEL (1945) (1945 Broadway cast) (Various artists).
Tracks: / Carousel waltz: *Various artists* / You're a queer one, Julie Jordan: *Various artists* / Mister snow: *Various artists* / If I loved you: *Various artists* / Soliloquy: *Various artists* / June is bustin' out all over: *Various artists* / When the children are asleep: *Various artists* / Blow high, blow low: *Various* artists / Real nice clambake: *Various artists* / There's nothin' so bad for a woman: *Various artists* / What's the use of wondering?: *Various artists* / Highest judge of all: *Various artists* / You'll never walk alone: *Various artists.*
LP: .... MCL 1661
MC: .... MCLC 1661

CAROUSEL (1956) (1956 Film soundtrack) (Various artists).
Tracks: / Carousel waltz: *Various artists* / You're a queer one, Julie Jordan: *Various artists* / Mister snow: *Various artists* / If I loved you: *Various artists* / When the children are asleep: *Various*

artists / June is bustin' out all over: Various artists / Soliloquy: Various artists / Blow high, blow low: Various artists / Real nice clambake: Various artists / Stonecutters cut it on stone: Various artists / What's the use of wondering?: Various artists / You'll never walk alone: Various artists.
LP: . . . . SLCT 6105
MC: . . . . TCSW 694

Carousel Van Der Beek

MARCHING AND WALTZING.
LP: . . . . ECS 2085

SOUNDS FAIRGROUND.
Tracks: / Wonderful Copenhagen / Thank heaven for little girls / Second hand rose / Que sera sera / Many a new day / Carousel waltz / My fair lady medley / Mary Poppins medley / Sound of music medley.
LP: . . . . MOR 27

Carpenter, John

HALLOWEEN (Film soundtrack) (See under Films) (Various artists).

Carpenter, Mary Chapin

STATE OF THE HEART.
Tracks: / How do / Something of a dreamer / Never had it so good / Read my lips / This shirt / Quittin' time / Down in Mary's land / Goodbye again / Too tired / Slow country dance / It don't bring you.
LP: 4666911
MC: 4666914

Carpenter, Richard

SOMETHING IN YOUR EYES (see under Springfield, Dusty).

TIME.
Tracks: / Say yeah! / Who do you love? / When time was all we had / Time / Calling your name again / In love alone / Remind me to tell you / That's what I believe / I'm still not over you.
LP: . . . . AMA 5117
MC: . . . . AMC 5117

Carpenters

BEST OF THE CARPENTERS.
LPS: . . . . ALBUM 92

CARPENTERS.
MC: 393502-4

CARPENTERS CASSETTE COLLECTION (1990).
MCSET: . . . . CARMC 12

CARPENTERS, THE.
LP: . . . . AMLS 63502

CHRISTMAS PORTRAIT.
Tracks: / O come, o come Emmanuel / Overture / Christmas waltz / Sleigh ride / It's Christmas time / Sleep well little children / Have yourself a merry little Christmas / Santa Claus is coming to town / Christmas song, The / Silent night / Jingle bells / First snowfall / Merry Christmas darling / I'll be home for Christmas.
MC: . . . . CAM 64726
LP: . . . . AMLH 64726

CLOSE TO YOU.
Tracks: / We've only just begun / Love is surrender / Maybe it's you / Reason to believe / Help / Close to you / Baby it's you / I'll never fall in love again / Crescent moon / Mr. Guder / I kept on loving you / Another song.
LP: . . . . AMLS 998
MC: . . . . CAM 998

COLLECTION: CARPENTERS.
Tracks: / Close to you / Jambalaya / Saturday / Help / For all we know / Song for you, A / Sing / Let me be the one / Mr. Guder / I'll never fall in love again / Goodbye to love / Rainy days and Mondays / Love is surrender / Heather / Maybe it's you / Druscilla Penny / This masquerade / Superstar / Flat baroque / I won't last a day without you / I keep on loving you / Crystal lullaby / I can't make music / Yesterday once more / Bacharach / Knowing when to leave / Make it easy on yourself / Always something there to remind me / Walk on by / Do you know the way to San Jose? / Baby it's hurting you / Hurting each other / Reason to believe / Sometimes / We've only just begun / Top of the world / One love / It's going to take some time / Hideaway / Another song.
LPS: . . . . CARP 1000

HIT COLLECTION, THE.
MC: 10114
LP: 10111

HORIZON.
Tracks: / Aurora / Only yesterday / Desperado / Please Mr. Postman / I can dream can't I / Solitaire / Happy / Goodbye and I love you (I'm caught between) / Love me for what I am / Eventide.
LP: . . . . AMLK 64530
MC: 394530-4

MC: . . . . CS 4530

KIND OF HUSH, A.
Tracks: / There's a kind of hush / You / Sandy / Goofus / Can't smile without you / I need to be in love / One more time / Boat to sail / I have you / Breaking up is hard to do.
LP: . . . . AMID 117
MC: . . . . CMID 117
LP: . . . . AMLK 64581

LIVE AT THE PALLADIUM.
Tracks: / Flat baroque / There's a kind of hush / Jambalaya / Piano picker / Strike up the band / 'S wonderful / Fascinating rhythm / Warsaw concerto / From this moment on / Carpenters' medley / We've only just begun.
LP: . . . . SHM 3142
MC: . . . . HSC 3142
LP: . . . . AMLS 68403

LOVELINES.
Tracks: / Lovelines / Where do I go from here / Uninvited guest / If we try / When I fall in love / Kiss me the way you did last night / Remember when lovin' took all night / You're the one / Honolulu City lights / Slow dance / If I had you / Little girl blue.
LP: . . . . AMA 3931
MC: . . . . AMC 3931

MADE IN AMERICA.
Tracks: / Those good old dreams / Strength of a woman / Back in my life again / When you've got what it takes / Somebody's been lyin' / I believe you / Touch me when we're dancing / When it's gone / Beechwood 4-5789 / Because we are in love.
LP: . . . . AMLK 63723
MC: 393723-4

NOW AND THEN.
Tracks: / Sing / This masquerade / Heather / Jambalaya / I can't make music / Yesterday once more / Fun, fun, fun / End of the world / Da doo ron ron / Deadman's curve / Johnny angel / Night has a thousand eyes, The / Our day will come / One fine day.
LP: . . . . AMLH 63519
MC: . . . . CAM 63519

OLD-FASHIONED CHRISTMAS, AN.
Tracks: / It came upon a midnight clear / Overture / Old fashioned Christmas, An / O holy night / Home for the holidays / Medley / Little altar boy / Do you hear what I hear? / My favourite things / He came here for me / Santa Claus is coming to town / What are you doing New Year's Eve? / I heard the bells on Christmas Day.
LP: . . . . AMA 3270
MC: . . . . AMC 3270

ONLY YESTERDAY (Richard & Karen Carpenter's Greatest Hits).
LP: . . . . AMA 1990
MC: . . . . AMC 1990

PASSAGE.
LP: . . . . AMLK 64703
MC: 393199-4

SINGLES 1969-73, THE.
Tracks: / We've only just begun / Top of the world / Ticket to ride / Superstar / Rainy days and Mondays / Goodbye to love / Yesterday once more / It's going to take some time / Sing / For all we know / Hurting each other / Close to you.
LP: . . . . AMLH 63601
MC: . . . . CAM 63601

SINGLES 1969-73/SINGLES 1974-78, THE.
MC: . . . . AMC 24105

SINGLES 1974-1978, THE.
Tracks: / Sweet sweet smile / Jambalaya / Can't smile without you / I won't last a day without you / All you get from love is a love song / Only yesterday / Solitaire / Please Mr. Postman / I need to be in love / Happy / There's a kind of hush / Calling occupants of interplanetary craft.
MC: . . . . CTM 19748
LP: . . . . AMLT 19748

SONG FOR YOU, A.
Tracks: / Song for you, A / Top of the world / Hurting each other / It's going to take some time / Goodbye to love / Intermission / Bless the beasts and children / Flat baroque / Piano picker / I won't last a day without you / Crystal lullaby / Road ode / Song for you, A.
LP: . . . . AMLS 63511
MC: 393511-4

TICKET TO RIDE.
MC: . . . . TC MFP 50431
LP: . . . . AMLS 64342
LP: . . . . AMLP 8001
LP: . . . . MFP 50431
MC: 394205-4

VOICE OF THE HEART.
Tracks: / Now / Sailing on the tide / Make believe it's your first time / Two lives / At the end of a song / Ordinary fool / Your baby doesn't love you anymore / Look to your dreams.
LP: . . . . AMLX 64954

YESTERDAY ONCE MORE.
Tracks: / Yesterday once more / I need to be in love / Sing / Only yesterday / Ticket to ride / Sweet sweet smile / I won't last a day without you / Now / For all we know / Top of the world / Solitaire / Those good old dreams / Jambalaya / Close to you / Superstar / Rainy days and Mondays / Goodbye to love.
LP: . . . . SING 1

Carpettes

FIGHT AMONGST YOURSELVES.
Tracks: / Nothing ever changes / Since you went away / False foundations / Fight amongst yourselves / Dead or alive / If your heart stopped now / Friday night, saturday morning / Last lone ranger, The / Youth rebellion / Reason I'm lonely, The / Total insecurity / Silly games.
LP: . . . . BEGA 21

FRUSTRATION PARADISE.
Tracks: / Frustration paradise / Reach the bottom / I don't mean it / 3 a.m. / Away from it all / Johnny won't hurt you / Lost love / It don't make sense / ABC / Cruel honesty / How to handle a woman / Indo-china.
LP: . . . . BEGA 14

Carr, Allan

ATLANTIC BRIDGE (see under Rotherfield, Jane) (Carr, Allan/Jane Rotherfield).

THERE AND BACK (See under Rotherfield, Jane) (Carr, Allan/Jane Rotherfield).

Carr, Dave

CARR FOR SALE.
LP: . . . . SRTZ CUS 060

Carr, Georgia

SOFTLY BABY.
Tracks: / Softly / Is that bad / Sun forgot to shine, The / I don't know any better / I'm not gonna letcha in / Whispering serenade / You made me love you / I dream of you / From man to man / Wasted tears / Lonely / Make me a present of you / Laugh / Why darling why / All of me / Gimme the simple life.
LP: . . . . EMS 1143
MC: . . . . TCEMS 1143

Carr, Ian

DIRECT HIT (Carr, Ian Nucleus).
LP: 9286 019

IN FLAGRANTE DELICTO (Carr, Ian Nucleus).
Tracks: / Gestalt / Mysteries / Heyday / In flagrante delicto.
LP: . . . . EST 11771

OLD HEARTLAND.
Tracks: / Open country / Interiors / Disjunctive boogie / Spirit of place / Full fathom five / Old heartland / Things past.
LP: . . . . MMC 1016
MC: . . . . TCMMC 1016

OUT OF THE LONG DARK (Carr, Ian Nucleus).
Tracks: / Gone with the weed / Lady bountiful / Solar wind / Selina / Out of the long dark / Sassy (American girl) / Simply this (The human condition) / Black ballad / For Liam.
LP: . . . . EST 11916

Carr, James

TAKE ME TO THE LIMIT.
Tracks: / Take me to the limit / Sugar shock / Love attack / You gotta love your woman / High on your love / She's already gone / Our garden of Eden / I can't leave your love alone / What's a little love between friends / Lack of attention.
LP: . . . . CH 310

Carr, Joe 'Fingers'

BEST PIANO OF JOE CARR, THE.
MC: 4XL 9293

Carr, Joyce

JOYCE CARR.
LP: . . . . AP 148

Carr, Larry

FIT AS A FIDDLE.
LP: . . . . AP 223

LARRY CARR SINGS VERSE AND CHORUS.
LP: . . . . AP 13

Carr, Leroy

BLUES BEFORE SUNRISE.
Tracks: / Barrelhouse woman / I believe I'll make a change / Midnight hour blues / Talk a walk around the corner / Southbound blues / Mean mistreater mama / Big four blues / Blues before sunrise / It's too short / My woman's gone wrong / Hustler's blues / Bobo stomp / Shining pistol / Shady lane blues / Corn Likker blues / Hurry down sunshine.
LP: . . . . OFF 6023

GREAT PIANO, GUITAR DUETS, 1929-35 (Carr, Leroy & Scrapper Blackwell).
LP: . . . . OT 1204

LEROY CARR (1928).
Tracks: / My own lonesome blues / How long how long blues / Broken spoke blues / Tennessee blues / Truthful blues / Mean old train blues / You got to reap what you sow / Low down dirty blues / How long how long blues no.2 and part 3 / Baby don't you love me no more / Tired of your low down ways / I'm going away and leave my baby / Prison bound blues / You don't mean me no good.
LP: . . . . MSE 210

LEROY CARR: 1929-34 (Carr, Leroy & Scrapper Blackwell).
LP: . . . . DLP 543

LEROY CARR & SCRAPPER BLACKWELL, 1930-58 (Carr, Leroy & Scrapper Blackwell).
LP: . . . . BD 2074

LEROY CARR & SCRAPPER BLACKWELL, 1929-35 (Carr, Leroy & Scrapper Blackwell).
LP: . . . . BOB 13

LEROY CARR, VOL. 2.
LP: . . . . CC 50

NAPTOWN BLUES (Carr, Leroy & Scrapper Blackwell).
LP: . . . . L 1036

Carr, Melinda

ENDLESS LOVE.
MC: . . . . CHV 334

Carr, Mike

LADY FROM SAVANNAH, THE (See also Reid, Irene) (Carr, Mike Quartet & Irene Reid).

LIVE AT RONNIE SCOTT'S (Carr, Mike Trio).
Tracks: / Claremont Avenue / Teach me tonight / Shaw 'nuff / It's impossible / Footloose.
LP: . . . . SPJ 517

Carr, Richard

AFTERNOON IN NEW YORK.
LP: . . . . AP 194

Carr, Vikki

IT MUST BE HIM.
LP: . . . . LBS 83037

LIBERTY YEARS, THE (Best of Vikki Carr).
Tracks: / It must be him / Goin' out of my head / Surrey with the fringe on top / Meditation / You don't have to say you love me / Can't take my eyes off you / With pen in hand / Cuando calienta el sol / I will wait for you / Until it's time for you to go / Glory of love / Carnival (A day in the life of a fool) / Lesson, The / When in Rome / There I go / For once in my life.
LP: . . . . EMS 1323
MC: . . . . TCEMS 1323

LOVE STORY.
Tracks: / I've never been a woman before / If you could read my mind / If I were your woman / I'll be home / I keep it hid / Six weeks every summer / Hurt / Ain't no mountain high enough / One less bell to answer / Where do I begin / For all we know.
LP: . . . . CBS 32494

WAY OF TODAY.
LP: . . . . SLBY 1331

Carr, Wynona

HIT THAT JIVE, JACK.
Tracks: / Jump Jack jump / Till the well runs dry / Boppity bop / Should I ever love again / I'm mad at you / Old fashioned love / Hurt me / It's raining outside / Nursery rhyme rock / Ding dong daddy / Somebody, somewhere, somehow / Act right / What do you know about love / Now that i'm free / Heartbreak melody / Please Mr. Jailer.
LP: . . . . CH 130

Carra, Raffaella

RAFFAELLA.
Tracks: / Do it,do it again / Black cat / Sono nera / Dancin' in the sun / Tango / California / Rumore / Tanti Auguri / Luca / Amoa, ci vidiamo domani / Million dollars, A.
LP: . . . . EPC 82832

Carrack, Paul

ACE MECHANIC.
Tracks: / Silent running (On dangerous ground) / Little unkind / Why did you leave me? / Always better with you / C'est la vie / I need you / How long / Tempted / From now on / Sniffin' about / Lesson in love / I think it's gonna last / Do me lover / I found love.

LP: . . . . FIEND 83

CARRACKTER REFERENCE.
MC: . . . . FIENCASS 700

GROOVE APPROVED.
LP: . . . . CHR 1709
MC: . . . . ZCHR 1709

NIGHTBIRD.
Tracks: / Beauty is only skin deep / There's a good chance / In love with me / Love is all it takes / Where you going babe / Foregone conclusion / Bet you never been in love / Nightbird.
LP: 6359 016

ONE GOOD REASON.
Tracks: / One good reason / When you walk in the room / Button off my shirt / Give me a chance / Double it up / Don't shed a tear / Fire with fire / Here I am / Collraine / Do I figure in your life?.
LP: . . . . CDL 1578
MC: . . . . ZCDL 1578

SUBURBAN VOODOO.
Tracks: / Lesson in love / Always better with you / I need you / I'm in love / Don't give my heart a break / Little unkind / Out of touch / What a way to go / So right so wrong / From now on / Call me tonight / I found love.
LP: . . . . EPC 85992

Carradine, John

TALES FOR A WINTER NIGHT.
LP: . . . . PELICAN 2002

Carrageen

FROM CLARE TO HERE.
Tracks: / From Clare to here / Johnny I hardly knew you / Travelling people / Wind in the willows / Highland Paddy / Jug of punch / Will you go lassie go / I'm a rover / Carrickfergus / Many young men of twenty / McAlpine's men / Band played waltzing Matilda, The.
MC: . . . . CHRL 173
LP: . . . . HRL 173

Carrasco, Joe 'King'

BANDIDO ROCK (Carrasco, Joe 'King' Y Las Coronas).
MC: . . . . ROUNDER 9012C
LP: . . . . ROUNDER 9012

BORDER TOWN (Carrasco, Joe 'King' & The Crowns).
Tracks: / Escondido / Hola coca cola / Who bought the guns / Are you Amigo / Put me in jail / Mr. Bogota / Walk it like you talk it / Current events (are making me tense) / Cucaracha taco / Baby let's go to Mexico / Vamos a bailar / Tamale baby.
LP: . . . . WIK 26
MC: . . . . WIKC 26
LP: . . . . ROSE 40

EL MOLINO.
Tracks: / Jalapeno con big red / Mexcal Road / Black cloud / Tell me / I'm a fool to care / Rock esta noche / Funky butt / Every woman / Please Mr. Sandman / Just a mile away.
LP: . . . . WIK 11

JOE 'KING' CARRASCO (Carrasco, Joe 'King' & The Crowns).
Tracks: / Buena / Betty's world / I get my kicks on you / One more time / Don't bug me baby / Nervoused out / Caca de vaca / Susan friendly / Party doll / Federals / Wild 14 / Let's get pretty.
LP: . . . . SEEZ 28

JOE KING CARRASCO & THE CROWNS (Carrasco, Joe 'King' & The Crowns).
LP: . . . . HNBL 1308

LAS CORONAS BANDIDO ROCK.
LP: . . . . ROSE 116

PARTY SAFARI.
LP: . . . . HNBL 3301

SYNAPSE GAP (Mundo total) (Carrasco, Joe 'King' & The Crowns).
Tracks: / Imitation class / Person-person / Don't let a woman make a fool out of you / Where we at? / Senor Lover / I wanna get that feel again / Bad rap / Front me some love / Rip it up, shake it up, go go / That's the love / Man overboard.
LP: . . . . MCF 3143
MC: . . . . MCFC 3143

TALES FROM THE CRYPT.
MC: . . . . A 128

Carreras, Jose

COLLECTION: JOSE CARRERAS.
MC: . . . . CCSMC 289

ESSENTIAL JOSE CARRERAS, THE.
Tracks: / Che gelida manina / Vesti la giubba / Donna non vidi mai / Una furtiva lagrima / Di quella pira / E Lucevan le stelle / Nessun dorma / O paese d'o sole / Gloria / Granada / Tonight / O sole mio / Core 'ngrato / A vucchella / Mattinata / Oh fede negar potessi / Panis angelicus / Tu che a dio spiegastil'ali.
MC: 432 692 4
LP: 432 692 1

IN CONCERT (With Pavarotti, Domingo and Mehta) (Carreras, Jose with Domingo, Pavarotti and Mehta).
Tracks: / Lamento di Federico (From L'Arlesiana) / Beau paradis (From L'Africane) / Recondita armonia (From Tosca) / Dein ist mein ganzes herz (From Das Land de Lachelns) / Rondine al nido / Core 'ngrato / Torna a surriento / Granada / No puede ser (From La Tabernera) / Improviso (From Andrea Chesnier) / E Lucevan le stelle (From Tosca) / Nessun dorma (From Turandot) / Maria / Tonight / Mattinata / Memory / O sole mio!.
MC: 4304334
LP: 4304331

JOSE CARRERAS COLLECTION.
Tracks: / Torna a surriento / Fenesta che lucive / E lucevan le stelle / My own true love / Nessun dorma / Non tiscorda di me / Una furtiva lagrima / Granada / Core'n grato / Che gelida manina / Love is a many splendoured thing / Pourquoi me reveiller / Memory / Mattinata / Ave Maria / Tonight / Tue che a dio spegasti l'ali / Because you're mine / A vucchella / Di rigori armato / Forse la soglia attinse / Parlami d'amore mariu / Vesti la giubba / As time goes by / Oh fede negar potessi...quando le sere al Placido / Panis angelicus / O sole mio / E la solita storia / Be my love / Dein ist mein ganzes herz / Because / Donna mon vidi mai / You belong to my heart / Di quella pira.
2LP: . . . . SMR 860
MCSET: . . . . SMC 860

JOSE CARRERAS & FRIENDS.
MC: . . . . CANMC 001

JOSE CARRERAS SINGS ANDREW LLOYD WEBBER.
Tracks: / Memory / Phantom of the opera / Music of the night, The / You / Pie Jesu / Tell me on a Sunday / Half a moment / There's me / Starlight express / Unexpected song / Love changes everything.
LP: . . . . WX 325
MC: . . . . WX 325C

YOU BELONG TO MY HEART.
Tracks: / You belong to my heart / Mattinata / El dia que me quieras / Fenesta che lucive / Concerto d'autojno / Siboney / Te quiero dijiste / Because / Quiereme mucho / Anema e core / La danza / Aquellos ojos verdes.
LP: 411 422-1
MC: 411 422-4

Carrere (label)

CARRERE B.P.M. (Various artists).
LP: . . . . CAL 211

Carrie (film)

CARRIE/DRESSED TO KILL/BODY DOUBLE (Brian De Palma film soundtracks) (Various artists).
LP: . . . . A 384
MC: . . . . C 384

Carriere Brothers

LA LA - LOUISIANA BLACK FRENCH MUSIC (Carriere Bros./Lawtell Playboys).
LP: 1004

Carrie's War

CARRIE'S WAR (Nina Bawden) (Clarke, Zela (nar)).
MC: 881999

Carrig

CARRIG.
LP: . . . . CAR 001

Carrington, Nigel

VANISHMENT OF THOMAS TULL, THE (See under Vanishment of Thomas...(bk).

Carrington, Terri Lyne

REAL LIFE STORY.
LP: 837 679-1
MC: 837 679-4

Carroll, Barbara

AT THE PIANO.
Tracks: / Emily / Soon it's gonna rain / Child is born, A / Dream dancing / Gal in calico, A.
LP: . . . . DS 847

JULY 24TH, 1959 (Carroll, Barbara Trio).
LP: . . . . JV 114

Carroll, Cath

ENGLAND MADE ME.
LP: . . . . FACT 210
MC: . . . . FACT 210C

Carroll, Diahann

DIAHANN CARROLL.
Tracks: / Perfect love / I can't give back the love I feel for you / I mean to shine / Somewhere between love and tomorrow / Sweet sweet candy / I've never been a fool like this before / Easy to love / Anybody else / After being your lover / I've been there before.
LP: . . . . WL 72382
MC: . . . . WK 72382

Carroll, Jeanne

BLIND JOHN DAVIS WITH JEANNE CARROLL (see under Davis,Blind John) (Carroll, Jeanne & Blind John Davis).

Carroll, Jim

CATHOLIC BOY (Carroll, Jim Band).
Tracks: / Wicked gravity / Three sisters / Day and night / Nothing is true / People who die / City drops in the night / Crow / It's too late / I want the angel / Catholic boy.
LP: . . . . CBS 84901

DRY DREAMS.
Tracks: / Work not play / Dry dreams / Them / Jealous twin / Lorraine / Jody / Barricades / Evengeline / Rooms / Still life.
LP: . . . . CBS 85614

Carroll, John

GOLDEN MOMENTS.
LP: . . . . HM 046

TOUCH OF CLASS, A.
MC: . . . . HMC 020

Carroll, Johnny

CRAZY HOT ROCK.
Tracks: / You two timed me two times too often / Crazy crazy lovin' / Trying to get to you / Rock 'n' roll Ruby / Hot rock.
LP: . . . . CR 30241

JOHNNY CARROLL.
LP: . . . . SKYLINE 1515

ROCK (see Curtis, Mac) (Carroll, Johnny/Mac Curtis).

ROCK 'N' ROLL RARITIES.
Tracks: / Rockin' Maybelle / Sugar baby / Crazy crazy lovin' / Wild wild women / Lonesome / Love me baby / Cut out / Trudy / Run come see / Hearts of stone / Why cry / Love is a merry go round / Stingy thing / Crazy little mama / Sexy ways / Cry.
LP: . . . . SJLP 581

SCREAMIN' DEMON HEATWAVE.
Tracks: / Screamin' demon heatwave / Ooby dooby / Sarah Lee / Rockabilly daddy / Don't that road look rough and rocky / Feel so bad / Hang up my rock 'n' roll shoes / Rattle my bones / Fujiyama mama / Don't tear me up / Maybe / Blue Levi jeans / Shove it on home / Baby let's play house.
LP: . . . . SEL 7

SHADES OF VINCENT (Carroll, Johnny & Judy Lindsey).
Tracks: / Rock road blues / I gotta baby / Git it / Dance to the bop / Wear my ring / Lotta lovin' / Maybe / Swing, The / Dance at Billy Bob's / Honey don't / Baby let's play house / I've had it / Savin' my love / I want you to be my baby / What I'd say / Hurt so good / Love me up.
LP: . . . . CR 30249

TEXABILLY.
Tracks: / Li'l bit of your time, A / Is it easy to be easy / Judy Judy Judy / Does your mama know / My bucket's got a hole in it / Sixteen tons rockabilly / Who's to say / People in Texas like to dance / Two timin' / Whatcha gonna do / Why don't cha quit that teasin' / Lonesome boy.
LP: . . . . MFLP 054
LP: . . . . LP 014

Carroll, Lewis (aut)

ALICE IN WONDERLAND.
MLP: . . . . D 306
MC: . . . . D 23DC

ALICE IN WONDERLAND.
MC: . . . . STC 014

ALICE IN WONDERLAND.
MC: . . . . DIS 006

ALICE IN WONDERLAND (Scott, Margaretta & Jane Asher).
MCSET: . . . . SAY 7

ALICE IN WONDERLAND (Rushton, Willie (nar)).
MCSET: . . . . LFP 7391

ALICE IN WONDERLAND.
LP: . . . . REC 563
MC: . . . . ZCM 563
MC: . . . . SBC 127

ALICE IN WONDERLAND (Children's Classics).
MC: . . . . PLBC 194

ALICE IN WONDERLAND (Greenwood, Joan/Stanley Holloway).
MC: 1097

ALICE IN WONDERLAND.
MC: . . . . STK 026

ALICE IN WONDERLAND (Routledge, Patricia (nar)).
MCSET: CC/020

ALICE IN WONDERLAND AND ALICE THROUGH THE LOOKING GLASS (Bennett, Alan (nar)).
MCSET: . . . . ZBBC 1013

ALICE THROUGH THE LOOKING GLASS (Unknown narrator(s)).
MCSET: . . . . DTO 10575

ALICE THROUGH THE LOOKING GLASS (Asher, Jane & Margaretta Scott).
MCSET: . . . . SAY 43

ALICE'S ADVENTURES IN WONDERLAND (Various artists).
MC: . . . . UNKNOWN

ALICE'S ADVENTURES IN WONDERLAND (Hawthorne, Nigel (nar)).
MC: 0600560600

ALICE'S ADVENTURES IN WONDERLAND (Unknown narrator(s)).
MCSET: . . . . DTO 10573

COMPLETE ALICE IN WONDERLAND, THE (Plummer, Christopher).
MC: 0001042696

NONSENSE POETRY (see under Lear, Edward) (Various artists).

NONSENSE VERSE (Holloway, Stanley (nar)).
MC: 1078

THROUGH THE LOOKING GLASS (Greenwood, Joan/Stanley Holloway).
MC: 1098

THROUGH THE LOOKING GLASS (Rushton, Willie (nar)).
MCSET: . . . . TCLFP 417 116-5

THROUGH THE LOOKING GLASS & WHAT ALICE SAW THERE (Plummer, Christopher).
MCSET: 129

Carroll, Liz

FRIEND INDEED, A.
LP: . . . . SHAN 92013

KISS ME KATE (Carroll, Liz & Tommy McGuire).
LP: . . . . SHAN 29010

LIZ CARROLL.
LP: . . . . SHAN 29013

Carroll, Pat (nar)

FREDDY THE DETECTIVE (see under Freddy the Detective).

Carrott, Jasper

BEAT THE CARROTT.
Tracks: / Introduction / Television / Scunthorpe baths / Acne / Australian sticky tape / Car insurance (Australian style) / Driving lesson / Pets / Truck driving / Biffer / Day trip to Blackpool.
LP: . . . . DJF 20575
MC: . . . . DJH 40575

BEST OF JASPER CARROTT.
Tracks: / Bastity Chelt / Jersey / Football match, The / America / Zits / Number plates / Bus trip, The / Car insurance / Magic roundabout.
LP: . . . . DJF 20549
MC: . . . . DJH 40549

BEST OF JASPER CARROTT/ CARROTT IN NOTTS.
MCSET: . . . . TWO 414

CARROTTS IN NOTTS.
Tracks: / Give me an 'F' / Top of the pops / My cottage / New faces / Now all join in / Bastity chelt / Mal's shirt / Wor Malcolm / Radio adverts / My mate Jake / Bantam cock / Football news / European cup / Cup final 76 / I'm a goalie / You know / What sa teem / Complete C & W, The / Dem blues / Blue goldfish / French O level / Hava nagila.
LP: . . . . DJF 20482
MC: . . . . DJH 40482

CARROTT'S LIB.
LP: . . . . DJF 20580
MC: . . . . DJH 40580

COSMIC CARROT.
Tracks: / 60's, The / Cowards / Alternatives / Plumbers / Mechanics / Boy scouts / Store detectives / Cruise missiles / More cars / Fear / Animals / Xmas time / Cosmic carrott.
LP: . . . . LAUGH 1
MC: . . . . LAUGH 401

LIVE IN AMERICA.
LP: . . . . RNLP 817

PAIN IN THE ARM, A.
Tracks: / Introduction / Hangman / Getting here / Football match, The / Local radio promotion / Hare Krishna / America / Zits / Number plates / Bus trip,

The / Car insurance / Twelve days of Christmas, The.
LP: . . . . DJF 20518
MC: . . . . DJH 40518

RABBITTS ON AND ON AND ON....
Tracks: / Introduction / Spaghetti junction / Boggery, The / Sex supermarket / In concert / Local radio / BBC medical / Magic roundabout / Jersey / Waggy's testimonial / Learner driver / Tribute to Eric Idle my idol.
LP: . . . . DJF 20462
MC: . . . . DJH 40462
LP: . . . . DJLPS 462

RABBITTS ON & ON/PAIN IN THE ARM.
MCSET: . . . . TWO 415

STUN-CARROTT TELLS ALL, THE.
LP: . . . . DJF 20582
MC: . . . . DJH 40582

UNRECORDED JASPER CARROTT, THE.
Tracks: / Introduction / Muppets / Gleemodemt / Zits / Mole, The / Microphones / Punk rock / Local radio / Nutter on the bus, The / Mug job / Explosive gasses.
LP: . . . . DJF 20560
MC: . . . . DJH 40560

Carry Nation

CARRY NATION.
LP: . . . . HEY 020 1
MC: . . . . HEY 020 4

Cars

CANDY O.
Tracks: / Let's go / Since I held you / It's all I can do / Double life / Shoo-be-doo / Candy O / Nightspots / You can't hold on too long / Lust for kicks / Got a lot on my head / Dangerous type.
LP: . . . . K 52148
MC: . . . . K 452148

CARS, THE.
Tracks: / Good times roll / My best friend's girl / Just what I needed / I'm in touch with your world / Don't cha stop / You're all I've got tonight / Bye bye love / Moving in stereo / All mixed up.
LP: . . . . K 52088
MC: K4 52088

DOOR TO DOOR.
Tracks: / Leave or stay / You are the girl / Double trouble / Fine line / Everything you say / Ta ta wayo wayo / Strap me in / Coming up you / Wound up on you / Go away / Door to door.
LP: . . . . EKT 42
MC: . . . . EKT 42C

GREATEST HITS: CARS.
Tracks: / Just what I needed / Since you're gone / You might think / Good time roll / Touch and go / Drive / Tonight she comes / My best friend's girl / Heartbeat city / Let's go / Magic / Shake it up.
LP: . . . . EKT 25
MC: . . . . EKT 25 C

HEARTBEAT CITY.
Tracks: / Looking for love / Jackie / Not the night / Drive / Shooting for you / Why can't I / Magic / You might think / I do refuse / Stranger eyes / Hello again.
LP: 9602961
MC: 9602964

PANORAMA.
Tracks: / Panorama / Touch and go / Gimme some slack / Don't tell me no / Getting through / Misfit kid / Down boys / You wear those eyes / Running to you / Up and down.
LP: . . . . K 52240
MC: K4 52240

SHAKE IT UP.
Tracks: / Since you're gone / Shake it up / I'm not the one / Victim of love / Cruiser / Dream away / Think it over / This could be love / May be baby.
LP: . . . . K 52330
MC: K4 52330

Carson, Ernie

ERNIE CARSON AND HIS CAPITOL CITY JAZZ BAND (Carson, Ernie & His Capitol City Jazz Band).
LP: . . . . J 54

ERNIE CARSON AND RHYTHM.
LP: . . . . J 89

JAZZ GOES COUNTRY (with Marilyn Stafford) (Carson, Ernie and the Wrecking Crew).
LP: . . . . CLP 66

SOUTHERN COMFORT (Carson, Ernie & His Capitol City Jazz Band).
LP: . . . . GHB 162

WITH CHARLIE BORNEMAN ALLSTARS (Carson, Ernie and Charlie Borneman Allstars).
LP: . . . . J 45

Carson, Fiddlin' John

OLD HEN CACKLED.., THE.
LP: . . . . ROUNDER 1003

Carson, Joe

IN MEMORIAM.
LP: . . . . PM 1550761

Carson, Lori

SHELTER.
LP: 7599 24256 1
MC: 7599 24256 4

Carson, Martha

EXPLODES.
Tracks: / Music drives me crazy, especially rock'n'roll / Dixieland roll / Let the light shine down on me / OK amen / Now stop / Git on board, li'l chilun / Saints and chariot / Let's talk about that old time religion / Just whistle or call / Rocka my soul / This ole house / I'm gonna walk and talk with the Lord / All these things / Satisfied / Be not disencouraged / Get that golden key.
LP: . . . . BFX 15215

SATISFIED.
LP: . . . . HAT 3109
MC: . . . . HATC 3109

Carson, Mike

MIDEM - LIVE,'80 (see Getz, Stan) (Carson, Mike/Stan Getz/Paul Horn).

Carson, Tee

BASICALLY COUNT (Carson, Tee & The Basie Bandsmen).
LP: . . . . PA 8005

Carsten, Per

ANDROMEDA.
LP: . . . . MLP 15678

Carter, Anita

FOLK SONGS OLD AND NEW.
Tracks: / Love's ring of fire / All my trials / Sour grapes / Fair and tender ladies / My love / Voice of the Bayous / Fly pretty swallow / Johnny I hardly knew you / Satan's child / Few short years ago, A ((Previously unissued)) / Kentuckian song, The ((Previously unissued)) / Brian running back / As the sparrow goes.
LP: . . . . BFX 15004

Carter, Benny

ADDITIONS TO FURTHER DEFINITIONS.
Tracks: / Fantastic that's you / Come on back / We were in love / If dreams come true / Prohibido / Doozy / Rock bottom / Titmouse.
LP: . . . . JAS 57
MC: . . . . JAS C57

ALL OF ME.
LP: . . . . NL 83000
MC: . . . . NK 83000

ALONE TOGETHER (Carter, Benny & Oscar Peterson).
Tracks: / Isn't it romantic? / Long ago and far away / Alone together / Bewitched.
LP: 2304 512

BENNY CARTER 1945: METRONOME ALL STARS.
Tracks: / Who's sorry now? / Co-ed / Prelude to a kiss / Back bay boogie / I got it bad and that ain't good / Patience and fortitude / I surrender, dear / Stompin' at The Savoy / King Porter stomp / Royal flush / Dear old Southland / I got rhythm / Sweet Lorraine / Nat meets June, takes 1 & 2.
LP: . . . . QU 009

BENNY CARTER, 1928-1952.
Tracks: / Charleston is the best dance, after all / Old fashioned love / Apologies / Sendin' the vipers / Thirty fifth and Calumet / I'm in the mood for swing / Push out / I just got a letter / When lights are low / Walkin' by the river / All of me / Very thought of you, The / Cocktails for two / Takin' my time / Cuddle up, huddle up / Babalu / There, I've said it again / Midnight / My favourite blues / Lullaby to a dream / What a difference a day made / Sunday / Ill wind / Back bay boogie / Tree of hope / Lullaby in blue / Cruisin' / I wanna go home / You belong to me / Love is Cynthia / Sunday afternoon / Georgia on my mind.
2LP: . . . . PM 42406

BENNY CARTER ALL STARS (Featuring Nat Adderley and Red Norvo).
Tracks: / Easy money / Memories of you / Here's that rainy day / Blues for lucky lovers / Work song / When lights are low.
LP: . . . . SNTF 947

BENNY CARTER AND ORCHESTRA 1944 (Carter, Benny & His Orchestra).
LP: . . . . HSR 218

BENNY CARTER COLLECTION (16 Golden Greats).
Tracks: / Charleston is the best dance, after all / Once upon a time / Lonesome nights / Waltzing the blues / Out of nowhere / My buddy / Sunday / Rockin' chair / Stardust / Riffamarole / Jump call / Off dah / Cruisin' / 9:20 special / Blue Lou / Rose room.
LP: . . . . DVLP 2112
MC: . . . . DVMC 2112

BENNY CARTER FOUR.
Tracks: / Three little words / In a mellow tone / Wave / Undecided / Body and soul / On Green Dolphin Street / Here's that rainy day.
LP: 2308 204
MC: . . . . K 08 204

BENNY CARTER IN HOLLYWOOD.
LP: . . . . AA 502

BEST OF BENNY CARTER.
Tracks: / Three little words / In a mellow tone / Wave / Squattyroo / It don't mean a thing.
LP: 231 0853
MC: K10 853

CARTER, GILLESPIE INC (Carter, Benny & Dizzy Gillespie).
Tracks: / Sweet and lovely / Broadway / Courtship, The / Constantinople / Nobody knows the trouble I've seen / Night in Tunisia, A / Three little words / In a mellow tone / Waves / Undecided / Body and soul / On Green Dolphin Street / Here's that rainy day.
LP: 2310 781
MC: K10 781

CENTRAL CITY SKETCHES (Carter, Benny & The American Jazz Orchestra).
Tracks: / Lonesome nights / Easy money / Doozy / When lights are low / Kiss from you, A / Sleep / Central City blues / Hello / People / Promenade / Remember / Sky dance / Lonesome nights / Doozy (2nd version) / Symphony in riffs / Souvenir / Blues in my heart.
LPS: CIJD20126Z/27X
MCSET: CIJD40126Y/27W

DELUXE RECORDINGS VOL 1.
LP: . . . . ST 1013

EARLY FORTIES.
Tracks: / By the watermelon vine / Lindy Lou / Last kiss you gave me, The / Boogie woogie sugar blues / I've been in love before / Poinciana / Just a baby's prayer at twilight / Hurry, hurry / Love for sale / I can't escape from you / I'm lost / I can't get started / I surrender dear / Malibu / Forever blues / Prelude to a kiss / Just you, just me.
LP: . . . . OFF 3019

FURTHER DEFINITIONS.
Tracks: / Honeysuckle rose / Midnight sun will never set, The / Crazy rhythm / Blue star / Cottontail / Body and soul / Cherry / Doozy.
LP: . . . . JAS 14
MC: . . . . JAS C14

GENTLEMAN AND HIS MUSIC, A.
Tracks: / Sometimes I'm happy / Blues for George / Things ain't what they used to be / Lover man / Idaho / Kiss from you, A.
LP: . . . . CJ 285

GENTLEMAN OF JAZZ.
LP: . . . . MERITT 17

IN PARIS 1935-1946 (Carter, Benny & Coleman Hawkins).
LP: . . . . SW 8403
MC: . . . . SWC 8403

IN THE MOOD FOR SWING.
Tracks: / I'm in the mood for swing / Another time, another place / Courtship, The / Rock me to sleep / Janel / Romp, The / Summer serenade / Not so blue / You, only you / Blue moonlight / South side samba.
MC: . . . . CIJD 20144 X
LP: . . . . CIJD 40144 W

JAZZ GIANT.
Tracks: / Old fashioned love / I'm coming Virginia / Walkin' thing / Blue Lou / Ain't she sweet / How can you lose / Blues my naughty sweetie gives to me.
LP: . . . . COP 015

JAZZ OFF THE AIR, VOL 3 (Carter, Benny & His Orchestra).
Tracks: / Rose room / Boy meets horn / Stardust / Tea for two / Roll 'em / Jump call / My gal Sal / Just you, just me / Untitled.
LP: . . . . SPJ 147

KING, THE.
Tracks: / Walkin' thing, A / My kind of trouble is you / Easy money / Blue star / I still love him so / Green wine / Malibu / Blues in D flat.
LP: 231 0768
MC: K10 768

LATE FORTIES, THE.
Tracks: / Melodrama in a v-disc record room / Prelude to a kiss / Sweet Georgia Brown / Out of my way / What'll be / Cadillac Slim / Baby you're mine for keeps / You'll never break my heart again / Chilpancingo / Old love story, An / Reina / Let us drink a toast together / Cottontail / Time out for blues / Surf board / You are too beautiful.
LP: . . . . OFF 3006

LIVE AND WELL IN JAPAN.
Tracks: / Squattyroo / Tribute to Louis Armstrong / When it's sleepy time down South / I'm confessin' / When you're smiling / Them there eyes / It don't mean a thing.
LP: 2308 216
MC: . . . . K 08 216

MELANCHOLY BENNY.
LP: . . . . M 8004

OVER THE RAINBOW (Carter, Benny All Star Sax Ensemble).
Tracks: / Blues for lucky lovers / Straight talk / Over the rainbow / Out of nowhere / Gal from Atlanta / Pawnbroker, The / Easy money / Ain't misbehavin / Blues for lucky lovers.
LP: . . . . CIJD 40196Z

SOMEBODY LOVES ME (Carter, Benny & His Orchestra).
LP: . . . . AWE 28
MC: . . . . CAWE 28

SUMMER SERENADE (Carter, Benny Quartet).
LP: . . . . SLP 4047

SWINGIN' AT MAIDA VALE (Carter, Benny & His Orchestra).
Tracks: / Swingin' at Maida Vale / Nightfall / I've got two lips / There'll be some changes made / If only I could read your mind / Gin and jive / Accent on swing / Just a mood / Royal Garden blues / When lights are low / Waltzing the blues / When day is done.
LP: . . . . JASM 2010

SWINGIN' THE 20'S.
LP: 1007 561

WHEN LIGHTS ARE LOW (Carter, Benny & His Orchestra).
Tracks: / When lights are low / Nightfall / Big Ben blues / These foolish things / When day is done / I've got two lips / Just a mood / Swingin' the blues / Gin and jive / If I could only read your mind / I gotta go / When lights are low / Poor butterfly / Drop in next time you're passing / Man I love, The / That's how the first song was born / Swingin' at Maida Vale.
LP: . . . . CHD 131
MC: . . . . MCHD 131

Carter, Betty

AUDIENCE WITH BETTY CARTER.
Tracks: / Sounds (movin' on) / I think I got it now / Caribbean sun / Trolley song, The / Everything I have is yours / I'll buy you a star / I could write a book / Can't we talk it over? / Either it's love or it isn't / Deep night / Spring can really hang you up the most / Tight / Fake / So / My favourite things / Open the door.
2LP: . . . . MK 1003

BEBOP GIRL, THE.
Tracks: / Moonlight in Vermont / Thou swell / I could write a book / Gone with the wind / Way you look tonight, The / Can't we be friends / Tell him I said hello / Social call / Runaway / Frenesi / Let's fall in love.
LP: . . . . OFF 3023

BETTY CARTER VOL 1.
Tracks: / By the bend of the river / Ego / Body and soul / Heart and soul / Surrey with the fringe on top / Girl talk / I didn't know what time it was / All the things you are / I could write a book / Sun dies, The / Please do something.
LP: . . . . MK 1001

BETTY CARTER VOL 2.
Tracks: / You're a sweetheart / I can't help it / What is it? / On our way up / We tried / Happy / Sunday, Monday or always / Tight / Children learn what they live / Sounds.
LP: . . . . MK 1002

COMPACT JAZZ: BETTY CARTER.
MC: 843 274 4

DROPPIN' THINGS.
MC: 8439914

FINALLY.
Tracks: / Blue moon / Sun died, The / I only have eyes for you / Girl talk / You're a sweetheart / Ego / All through the day.
LP: . . . . ROU 1024

INSIDE BETTY CARTER.
Tracks: / This is always / Look no further / Beware my heart - this time / Something big (from Kwamina) / My favourite things / Some other time / Open the door / Spring can really hang you up the most.
LP: . . . . MK 1000

LOOK WHAT I GOT.
LP: 835 661 1
MC: 835 661 4

OUT THERE.
LP: .... FS 172

WHATEVER HAPPENED TO LOVE?.
Tracks: / What a little moonlight can do / New blues / I cry alone / Abre la Puerta / Every time we say goodbye / Cocktails for two / Social call / Goodbye / With no words.
LP: .... MK 1004

Carter, Bill

STOMPIN' SOUNDS.
LP: .... CCR 1023

Carter, Bo

BANANA IN YOUR FRUIT BASKET, A
LP: .... L 1064

BO CARTER 1928-38.
LP: .... DLP 524

BO CARTER VOL. 1 1928-40.
LP: .... BD 610

BO CARTER'S GREATEST HITS 1930-40.
LP: .... L 1014

MISSISSIPPI BLUES SINGER 1931-40.
LP: .... OT 1203

RAREST, THE - VOL.2 1930-38.
LP: .... BD 618

TWIST IT BABE 1931-40.
LP: .... L 1034

Carter, Carlene

BLUE NUN.
Tracks: / Love is a 4 letter verb / That boy / 300 pounds of hongry / Tougher stuff / I need a hit / Rockababy / Me and my .38 / Do me lover / Home run hitter / Billy / Born to move / Think dirty.
LP: .... XXLP 12
MC: .... XXC 12

CARLENE CARTER.
LP: .... K 56502

C'EST C BON.
Tracks: / Meant it for a minute / Heart to heart / Third time charm / Heart's in traction / I'm the kinda sugar daddy likes / Love like a glove / Cool reaction / Don't give my heart a break / That boy / One way ticket / Patient love.
LP: .... EPC 25523
MC: 40 25523

I FELL IN LOVE.
LP: 7599261391
MC: 7599261394

MUSICAL SHAPES.
Tracks: / Cry / Madness / Baby ride easy / Bandit of love / I'm so cool / Appalachian eyes / Ring of fire / Too bad about Sandy / Foggy mountain top / That very first kiss / To drunk (to remember) / Too proud.
LP: .... XXLP 3

Carter, Chris

MONDO BEAT.
LP: .... CTILP 3

Carter, Clarence

BETWEEN A ROCK AND A HARD PLACE.
Tracks: / Things ain't like they used to be / Straw that broke the camel's back, The / I ain't leaving, girl / Too weak to fight / Pickin' 'em down layin' 'em down / I'm between a rock and a hard place / I've got a thing for you baby / If you see my lady / Love building.
LP: .... ICH 1068
MC: .... ICH 1068 MC

DOCTOR CC.
Tracks: / Doctor CC / I stayed away too long / If you let me take you home / Left over love / You been cheatin' on me / Try me / Let's funk / Strokin'.
LP: .... ICH 1003
MC: .... ZCICH 1003
LP: .... LPLUTE 2

DOCTOR'S GREATEST PRESCRIPTIONS, THE (Best of Clarence Carter).
Tracks: / Strokin' / Trying to sleep tonight / Messin' with my mind / I was in the neighbourhood / Dr C.C. / Love me with a feeling / I'm not just good / I'm the best / Slip away / Grandpa can't fly his kite / Kiss you all over / I've got a thing for you baby / I'm between a rock and a hard place.
LP: .... ICH 1116
MC: .... ICH 1116MC

HOOKED ON LOVE.
LP: .... ICH 1016
MC: .... ZCICH 1016

MESSIN' WITH MY MIND.
LP: .... ICH 001
MC: .... ZCICH 001

SOUL DEEP.
Tracks: / She ain't gonna do right / Road of love / Slip away / That old time feeling / Let me comfort you / Too weak to fight / I'd rather go blind / Snatching it back / Making love (at the dark end of the street) / Soul deep / I can't leave your love alone / Patches / It's all in your mind / Thread the needle / Getting the bills / I'm the one.
LP: .... ED 125

TOUCH OF BLUES.
Tracks: / I'm not just good, I'm the best / Rock me baby / Why do I stay here / It's a man down there / All night, all day / Kiss you all over / Stormy Monday blues / Dance to the blues.
LP: .... ICH 1032
MC: .... ZCICH 1032

Carter, Dean

AVERAGE MAN (Carter, Dean & The High Commission).
LP: .... DMLP 1028

Carter Family

20 OF THE BEST: CARTER FAMILY.
Tracks: / Keep on the sunny side / Little darling pal of mine / John Hardy / Wildwood flower / Sweet fern / My Clinch Mountain home / I'm thinking of my blue eyes / Lula wall / Foggy mountain top / Jimmy Brown the newsboy / Carters' blues / Wabash cannonball / Diamonds in the rough / Kitty waltz / Cannonball / Worried man blues / Lonesome valley / Lonesome pine special / Church in the wildwood, The / I never will marry.
LP: .... NL 89369
MC: .... NK 89369

CARTER FAMILY ALBUM.
LP: .... HAT 3103
MC: .... HATC 3103

CARTER FAMILY ON BORDER RADIO.
LP: .... JEMF 101

COLLECTION OF FAVOURITES BY..., A.
LP: .... HAT 3022
MC: .... HATC 3022

LAND OF MANY CHURCHES, THE (See Under Haggard, Merle) (Carter Family/ Merle Haggard).

WILDWOOD FLOWER.
MC: .... MERHC 128
LP: .... MERH 128

Carter, Gaylord

MIGHTY WURLITZER, THE (See under Leaf, Ann) (Carter, Gaylord & Ann Leaf).

Carter, Goree

ROCK A WHILE (Carter, Goree & His Hepcats).
Tracks: / Rock awhile / I'll send you / My love is coming down / I just thought of you / Serenade / Is it true / Come on let's boogie / I've got news for you / Bullcorn blues / Back home blues / How can you love me / Hoy hoy / Working with my baby / She's old fashioned / What a friend will do / Tell me is there still a chance / I'm just another fool.
LP: .... BB 306

Carter, Joe

CHESTNUT (Carter, Joe & Lee Konitz).
LP: .... E 1002

ORIGINAL CHICAGO BLUES (Carter, Joe & Kansas City Red).
Tracks: / Mama talk to your daughter / You're the one / Rock me / Open your heart / Crawling king snake / Sweet black angel / Rollin' and tumblin' / Standing around cryin' / Moon is rising, The.
LP: .... JSP 1038

TOO MARVELLOUS FOR WORDS (Carter, Joe & Rufus Reid).
LP: .... E 1001

Carter, John

FIELDS.
LP: 188809 1
MC: 188809 4

SECRETS (Carter, John & Bobby Bradford).
Tracks: / Rosevita's dance / Ballad circle / Pretty place.
LP: .... REV 18

SHADOWS ON THE WALL.
Tracks: / Sippi strut / Spats / City streets / And I saw them / 52nd Street stomp / Hymn to freedom.
LP: 794 221
MC: 794 224

Carter, June & Anita

JOHNNY AND JUNE (see Cash, Johnny) (Carter, June & Anita & Johnny Cash).

Carter, Lynda

LYNDA CARTER.
Tracks: / All night song / She's always a woman / Tumbledown love / Just one look / Fantasy man / Lines / Want to get beside you / You're the only one who understands / Put on a show / Toto.
LP: .... EPC 83052

Carter, Mother

MOTHER MAYBELLE CARTER.
Tracks: / Dialogue / Good old mountain dew / Still / Arkansas traveller / Waterloo / Black mountain rag / Jimmy Rogers and train / Wabash Cannonball / Rocky top / Release me / Hey liberty / Chinese breakdown / Bells of St. Mary's / World need a melody, The / Never on Sunday / Tennessee waltz / Red wing.
2LP: .... KG 32436

Carter, Mrs Mabel

NEAR THE CROSS.
LP: .... NOLA LP 11

Carter, Ralph

YOUNG AND IN LOVE.
LP: .... SRM 11080

Carter, Ron

ALL BLUES.
LP: .... CTI 9017

ALONE TOGETHER (See Hall, Jim) (Carter, Ron & Jim Hall).

CEDAR WALTON PLAYS (See Under Walton, Cedar) (Carter, Ron/Cedar Walton/Billy Higgins).

ETUDES.
Tracks: / Last resort, The / Bottoms up / Arboretum / Rufus / Echoes / Doctors' row.
LP: .... E 0214

HEART AND SOUL (Carter, Ron & Cedar Walton).
LP: .... SJP 158

LIVE AT VILLAGE WEST (Carter, Ron & Jim Hall).
Tracks: / Bag's groove / All the things you are / Blue Monk / New waltz / St. Thomas / Embraceable you / Laverne walk / Baubles, bangles and beads.
LP: .... CJ 245

NEW YORK SLICK.
Tracks: / Slight smile / Tierra Espanola / Aromatic / Alternate route.
LP: .... M 9096

PARADE.
Tracks: / Parade / Theme in 3/4 / Sometimes I feel like a motherless child / Tinderbox / Gipsy / G.J.T..
LP: .... M 9088

PATRAO.
Tracks: / Ah, Rio / Nearly / Tail feathers / Yours truly / Third plane.
LP: .... M 9099

PICK 'EM.
LP: .... M 9092

SOMETHING IN COMMON (See Under Person, Houston) (Carter, Ron & Houston Person).

SONG FOR YOU.
Tracks: / Song for you / El ojo de dios / Quiet place / Good time / Someday my prince will come / N.O. blues.
LP: .... M 9086

TELEPHONE (Carter, Ron & Jim Hall).
Tracks: / Telephone / Indian Summer / Candlelight / Chorale and dance / Alone together / Stardust / Two's blues.
LP: .... CJ 270
MC: .... CJC 270

VOYAGE (See under Sardaby, Michel) (Carter, Ron/ Michel Sardaby).

Carter Sisters

MAYBELLE, ANITA, JUNE & HELEN.
Tracks: / I like my lovin' overtime / Like all get out / Unfit mother / You're right but I wish you were wrong / You flopped when you got me alone / Jukebox blues / We've got things to do / Don Juan / Heartless romance / Faithless Johnny Lee / There'll be no teardrops tonight / Keep it a secret / Cool, cold, colder / Love, oh, crazy love / Time's a wastin' / He went slippin' around.
LP: .... BFX 15080

Carter, Sydney

LOVELY IN THE DANCES (Carter, Sydney & Maddy Prior).
Tracks: / George Fox / Julian of Norwich / Carol of the creatures / Holy horses / Like the snow / Friday morning / Lord of the dance / Cocks are crowing, The / John Ball / First of my lovers, The / Bitter was the night / Come love / Caroling / I used to dance / I come like a beggar.
LP: .... PLR 032

Carter T.U.S.M.

30 SOMETHING (Carter The Unstoppable Sex Machine).
Tracks: / My second to last will and testament / Anytime anyplace anywhere / Prince in a pauper's grave, A / Shoppers' paradise / Billy's smart circus / Bloodsport for all / Sealed with a Glasgow kiss / Say it with flowers / Falling on a bruise / Final comedown, The.
LP: .... R 20112701

101 DAMNATIONS.
Tracks: / Road to domestos, The / Every time a church bell rings / Twenty-four minutes from Tulse Hill / All-American national sport, An / Sheriff Fatman / Taking of Peckham 123 / Crimestoppers A go-go / Good grief Charlie Brown / Midnight on the murder mile / Perfect day to drop the bomb, A / G.I. blues.
LP: .... ABB 101
MC: .... ABB 101C

Carter, Valerie

JUST A STONE'S THROW AWAY.
Tracks: / Ooh, child / Ringing doorbells in the rain / Heartache / Face of Appalachia / So, so happy / Stone's throw away, A / Cowboy angel / City lights / Back to blue some more.
LP: .... CBS 81958

WILD CHILD.
Tracks: / Crazy / Da doo rendezvous / What's become of us / Taking the long way home / Lady in the dark / Story of love / Blue side / Change in luck / Trying to get to you / Wild child.
LP: .... CBS 82556

Carter, Wilf

MONTANA SLIM (Carter, Wilf (Montana Slim)).
LP: .... SLP 300
MC: .... GT 5300

REMINISCIN' WITH.
LP: .... HAT 3085
MC: .... HATC 3085

Carthage In Flames

CARTHAGE IN FLAMES (Film soundtrack) (Various artists).
LP: .... IM 010

Carthy, Martin

BECAUSE IT'S THERE.
Tracks: / Nothing rhymed / May song / Swaggering Boney / Lord Randal / Long John, old John and Jackie North / Jolly tinker / Lovely Joan / Three cripples / Siege of Delhi / Death of young Andrew.
LP: 12TS 389
LP: .... ROUNDER 3031

BUT TWO CAME BY (Carthy, Martin & Dave Swarbrick).
Tracks: / Ship in distress / Banks of the sweet primroses / Long lankin / Brass band music.
LP: 12TS 343

BYKER HILL.
Tracks: / Man of Burnham Town, The (Dave Swarbrick plays fiddle and mandolin) / Fowler Jack, The (Dave Swarbrick plays fiddle and mandolin) / Gentleman soldier (Dave Swarbrick plays fiddle and mandolin) / Brigg fair (Dave Swarbrick plays fiddle and mandolin) / Bloody gardener (Dave Swarbrick plays fiddle and mandolin) / Barley straw (Dave Swarbrick plays fiddle and mandolin) / Byker Hill (Dave Swarbrick plays fiddle and mandolin) / Davy Lowston (Dave Swarbrick plays fiddle and mandolin) / Our captain cried all hands / Domeama (Dave Swarbrick plays fiddle and mandolin) / Wife of the soldier, The (Dave Swarbrick plays fiddle and mandolin) / John Barleycorn (Dave Swarbrick plays fiddle and mandolin) / Lucy Wan (Dave Swarbrick plays fiddle and mandolin) / Bonnie black hare (Dave Swarbrick plays fiddle and mandolin).
LP: 12TS 342

CROWN OF HORN.
Tracks: / Bedmaking, The / Locks and bolts / King Knapperty / Geordie / Willie's lady / Virginny / Worcestershire wedding, The / Bonnie lass o' Anglesey, The / William Taylor the poacher / Old Tom of Oxford / Palaces of gold.
LP: 12TS 300
LP: .... ROUNDER 3019
MC: .... ROUNDER 3019C

LANDFALL.
Tracks: / Here's adieu to all judges and juries / Brown Adam / O'er the hills / Cruel mother / Cold haily windy night / His name is Andrew / Bold poachers, The / Dust to dust / Broomfield hill / January man.
LP: 12TS 345

LIFE AND LIMB (Carthy, Martin & Dave Swarbrick).
LP: .... SPD 1030
MC: .... SPDC 1030

MARTIN CARTHY.
Tracks: / High Germany / Trees they do grow high, The / Sovay / Ye mariners all /

Queen of hearts / Broomfield hill / Springhill mine disaster / Scarborough fair / Lovely Joan / Barley and the rye, The / Wind that shakes the barley, The / Two magicians / Handsome cabin boy, The / And a begging I will go.
LP: 12TS 340

OUT OF THE CUT.
Tracks: / Devil and the feathery wife, The / Reynard the fox / Song of the lower classes, The / Rufford Park poachers / Molly Oxford / Rigs of the time / I sowed some seeds / Frair in the well, The / Jack Rowland / Old horse.
LP: 12TS 426
LP: . . . . ROUNDER 3075

PRINCE HEATHEN (Carthy, Martin & Dave Swarbrick).
Tracks: / Arthur McBride / Salisbury Plain / Polly on the shore / Rainbow, The / Died for love / Staines Morris / Reynardine / Seven yellow gypsies / Little Musgrave / Wren, The.
LP: 12TS 344

RIGHT OF PASSAGE.
LP: 12TS 452
MC: . . . . KTSC 452

SECOND ALBUM.
Tracks: / Two butchers / Ball 'o' yarn / Farewell Nancy / Lord Franklin / Ramblin' sailor / Lowlands of Holland, The / Fair maid on the shore / Bruton town / Box on her head / Newlyn town / Brave Wolfe / Peggy and the soldier / Sailor's life.
LP: 12TS 341

SHEERWATER.
LP: . . . . CREST 008
MC: . . . . CRESTMC 008
LP: . . . . CREST 25

SWEET WIVELSFIELD.
LP: 12TS 418
LP: . . . . ROUNDER 3020

THIS IS MARTIN CARTHY.
Tracks: / Barley straw / Bonnie black hare / Brigg fair / Byker hill / Fowler Jack, The / Orion / John Barleycorn / Lord of the dance / Poor murdered woman / Ship in distress / Streets of Forbes / White hare, The.
LP: 6382 022

Cartland, Barbara

ALBUM OF LOVE SONGS (Cartland, Barbara with the LPO).
LP: . . . . MON MT 103
MC: . . . . MON TC 103

LOVE SONGS.
Tracks: / I'll follow my secret heart / Desert song, The / Nightingale sang in Berkeley Square, A / How deep in the ocean / If you were the only girl in the world / Ill see you again / Mr. Wonderful / Dream lover / Love is my reason / Always / If you are but a dream / Goodnight sweetheart.
LP: . . . . ETAT 22

VARIOUS RECORDINGS (see under Title of Book).

Cartridge Brothers

GOLD 'N' BEANS.
LP: . . . . DRLP 172

Cartwright, Dave

DON'T LET YOUR FAMILY DOWN.
LP: . . . . TRA 284

Cartwright, Lionel

LIONEL CARTWRIGHT.
LP: . . . . MCA 42276
MC: . . . . MCAC 42276

Carty, J.J.

ACCORDION ESPECIALLY RECORDED FOR IRISH DANCERS Vol.2.
Tracks: / Introduction (O'Neills march) / Fairy reel, The / High cauled cap, The / Planxty drury / Three sea captains / Double jig / Hornpipe / Kilkenny races / Blackthorn stick / Downfall of Paris, The / Orange rouge, The.
LP: . . . . LPCL 502
MC: . . . . CL 502

ACCORDION ESPECIALLY RECORDED FOR IRISH DANCERS.
Tracks: / Beginners reel / Introduction (O'Neill's march) / Advanced reel / Slip jig / Light jig / Single jig / Three tunes, The / Trip to the cottage / Blackbird, The / Garden of daisies, The / Job of journeywork / Jocky to the fair / St. Patrick's day.
LP: . . . . LPCL 501
MC: . . . . CL 501

Carty, Paddy

PADDY CARTY & MICK O'CONNER (Carty, Paddy & Mick O'Conner).
LP: . . . . SHAN 29001

Carus, Zena

SECRET OF KELLY'S MILL, THE (see under Secret of Kelly's... (bk) (Greaves, Nigel (nar)).

Caruso, Enrico

ENRICO CARUSO-VOL.1.
Tracks: / Marta (Act III) m'appari / Mamma mia che vo'sape? / Rigoletto / L'Africana / La forza del destino (act III) solenne in quest'ora / Adorables tourments - valse lente / Il trovatore (Act IV) ai nostri monti / Il trovatore (Act III) miserere / Lucia di Lammermoor / La favorita (Act IV) spirito gentil / Pagliacci / Madame butterfly (Act I).
LP: . . . . GVC 503

ENRICO CARUSO-VOL.2.
Tracks: / Tosca (Act I) recondita armonia / Un ballo in maschera / Il trovatore (Act III) di quella pira / Otello (Act II) si, pel ciel / Il trovatore (Act IV) ai nostri monti / Cavalleria rusticana (brindisi) / Aida (Act IV) gia i sacerdoti adunansi / Aida (Act IV) la fatal Pietra and O Terra Addio / Don sebastiano - in terra solo / La boheme (act I) che gelida manina.
LP: . . . . GVC 504

Cary, Dick

DICK CARY WITH TED EASTON'S JAZZBAND (Cary, Dick & Ted Easton's Jazzband).
LP: . . . . SLP 18

Casa Loma Orchestra

CASA LOMA STOMP.
LP: . . . . HEP 1010

ONE NIGHT STAND WITH GLEN GRAY & CASA LOMA ORCHE (See under Gray, Glen for details) (Casa Loma Orchestra & Glen Gray).

WHITE JAZZ 1931-34.
LP: . . . . OLD 5

Casablanca (film)

CASABLANCA & OTHER CLASSIC THEMES FROM HUMPHREY BOGART FILMS (Film Soundtracks) (National Philharmonic Orchestra).
LP: . . . . AGL 13782
MC: . . . . AGK 18782

Casablanca (label)

CASABLANCA DANCE HITS (Various artists).
LP: 8840531
MC: 8840534

Casanovas

CASANOVAS.
LP: . . . . RELIC 5073

Cascade

LET IT BE ME.
LP: . . . . OKLP 3007
MC: . . . . ZCOK 3007

Cascading Strings

GOLDEN MELODIES.
MC: 846 052 4

Case Book Of

CASE BOOK OF SHERLOCK HOLMES, THE (see under Sherlock Holmes (bk)) (Hardy, Robert (nar)).

Case, Harry

IN A MOOD.
Tracks: / Ride 'em off / Native drums / Chasing the goon / Quick wire / Jam (at your party) / Carry me home / Midnight samba / In a mood / Air dancer / Mother-san.
LP: . . . . ICH 1037
MC: . . . . ZCICH 1037

MAGIC CAT.
Tracks: / Niagra / Easy vamp / Never say goodbye / Shake it / Wendy's song / Storm, The / Can't find you.
LP: . . . . ICH 1020
MC: . . . . ZCICH 1020

Case, Peter

MAN WITH THE BLUE POST, THE.
Tracks: / Charlie James / Travellin' light / Old part of town / Rise and shine / Hidden love / Put down the gun / Poor old town / Two angels / This town's a riot.
LP: . . . . K 924 238 1
MC: . . . . K 924 238 4

PETER CASE.
Tracks: / Echo wars / Steel strings / Three days straight / More than curious / I shook his hand / Small town spree / Old blue car / Walk in the woods / Horse and crow / Ice water / Satellite beach / Brown eyes.
LP: 9241051
MC: 9241054

Case, Russ

RUSS CASE AND ORCHESTRA 1950 (Case, Russ & Orchestra).
LP: . . . . CLP 119

Casey, Al

AL CASEY REMEMBERS KING CURTIS.
LP: . . . . JSP 1095

BEST OF FRIENDS (Casey, Al/Jay McShann).
Tracks: / Deed I do / One o clock jump / Going to Kansas City / One sweet blues / How deep is the ocean / Anything hallo / Little girl / Honky tonk train blues.
LP: . . . . JSP 1051

FESSOR'S SESSION BOYS.
LP: . . . . SLP 429

GENIUS OF THE JAZZ GUITAR.
Tracks: / Tenderly / Wash your troubles away / Was it a lie / Buck jumping / Rosetta / Lady be good / Just a closer walk with thee.
LP: . . . . JSP 1062

SIX SWINGING STRINGS.
LP: . . . . JSP 1026

SURFIN' HOOTENANNY.
LP: . . . . STM 100

Casey, Nollaig

LEAD THE KNAVE (See under McGlynn, Arty for details) (Casey, Nollaig/Arty McGlynn).

Casey, Terence

LITTLE BIT OF HEAVEN, A.
LP: . . . . DEROY 1234

Cash, Andrew

BOOMTOWN.
Tracks: / 100 years / Boomtown / What am I gonna do with these hands / Sleepwalking / These days / Nothing at all / We have heard / Wishing / Times talkin' trouble now / Any kind of love / When the rain falls down.
MC: . . . . ICT 9936
LP: . . . . ILPS 9936
MC: . . . . ICM 2021
MC: 842 597 4

TIME AND PLACE.
Tracks: / Smile me down / Midnight gone / Time and place / Flower / Places / Do not adjust your set / Trail of tears / It's not forever / When is it gonna come / Morning train / When the wind blows.
MC: . . . . ICT 9905
LP: . . . . ILPS 9905
MC: . . . . ICM 2022
MC: 842 851 4

Cash, Bernie

CONTRA BACH.
LP: . . . . WAVE LP 20

Cash, Johnny

6 TRACK HITS.
Tracks: / Boy named Sue, A / I walk the line / Ring of fire / If I were a carpenter / Folsom Prison blues / What is truth?.
MC: 7SC 5015

18 GOLDEN HITS.
LP: . . . . MA 91183
MC: . . . . MAMC 91191183

20 FOOT TAPPIN' GREATS (Itchy Feet).
Tracks: / Folsom Prison blues / I walk the line / Ring of fire / Forty shades of green / I still miss someone / There ain't no good chain gang / Busted / 25 minutes to go / Orange blossom special / It ain't me babe / Boy named Sue, A / San Quentin / Don't take your guns to town / One on the right is on the left, The / Jackson / Hey porter / Daddy sang bass / I got stripes / Thing called love, A / One piece at a time.
LP: . . . . CBS 10009
MC: 40 10009

1958-1986 THE CBS YEARS.
Tracks: / Oh, what a dream / I still miss someone / Pickin' time / Don't take your guns to town / Five feet high and rising / Seasons of my heart / Legend of John Henty's hammer / Ring of fire / Ballad of Ira Hayes, The / Orange Blossom special / Folsom Prison blues / San Quentin / Boy named Sue, A / Sunday morning coming down / Man in black / One piece at a time / Riders in the sky / Without love / Baron, The / Highway patrolman.
LP: 4504661
MC: 4504664

ADVENTURES OF JOHNNY CASH.
Tracks: / I've been to Georgia on a fast train / John's / Fair weather friends / Paradise / We must believe in magic / Only love / Good old American guest / I'll cross over Jordan / Sing a song / Ain't gonna hobo no more.
LP: . . . . CBS 85881

AT FOLSOM PRISON.
Tracks: / Folsom Prison blues / Dark as a dungeon / I still miss someone / Cocaine blues / Twenty five minutes to go / Orange blossom special / Long black veil / Send a picture of mother / Wall, The / Dirty old egg-sucking dog / Flushed from the bathroom of your heart / Jackson / Give my love to Rose / I got stripes / Green green grass of home / Greystone Chapel.
LP: . . . . CBS 63308
MC: 40 63308

BALLAD OF A TEENAGE QUEEN.
LP: . . . . XELLP 111
MC: . . . . XELMC 111

BARON.
Tracks: / Baron / Mobile Bay / Magnolia blossoms / Hard way, The / Ceiling, four walls and a floor / Hey train / Reverend Mr. Black / Blues keep gettin' bluer / Chattanooga city limit sign / Thanks to you / Greatest love affair.
LP: . . . . CBS 84990

BELIEVE IN HIM.
Tracks: / Believe in Him / Another wide river to cross / God ain't no stained glass window / Over there / Old rugged cross, The / My children walk in truth / You're drifting away / Belshazar / Half a mile a day / One of these days I'm gonna sit down and talk to Paul.
LP: . . . . WST R 9678
MC: . . . . WST C 9678
LP: . . . . MFP 5840
MC: . . . . TC MFP 5840

BELIEVER SINGS THE TRUTH.
Tracks: / Wings in the morning / Gospel boogie / Over the next hill / He's alive / I've got Jesus in my soul / When He comes / I was there when it happened / I'm a newborn man / There are strange things happening everyday / Children go where I send thee / I'm just an old chunk of coal / Lay me down in Dixie / Don't take everybody for your friend / You'll get yours, I'll get mine / Oh come, angel band / This train is bound for glory / I'm gonna try to be that way / What on earth / That's enough / Greatest cowboy of them all, The.
LP: . . . . CBS 84123

BEST OF JOHNNY CASH.
MC: 16-23
LP: . . . . CBS 10000

BIGGEST HITS.
Tracks: / Don't take your guns to town / Ring of fire / Understand your man / One on the right is on the left, The / Rosanna's going wild / Folsom Prison blues / Baddy sand bass / Boy named Sue, A / Sunday morning coming down / Flesh and blood / Thing called love, A / One piece at a time / There ain't no good chain gang / Riders in the sky / Baron, The.
LP: . . . . CBS 32304
MC: 40 32304

BITTER TEARS (Ballads of The American Indian).
Tracks: / As along as the grass shall grow / Apache tears / Custer / Talking leaves, The / Ballad of Ira Hayes, The / Drums / White girl / Vanishing race, The.
LP: . . . . BPG 62463

BITTER TEARS.
Tracks: / Big foot / As long as the grass shall grow / Apache tears / Custer / Talking leaves, The / Ballad of Ira Hayes, The / Drums / White girl / Old Apache squaw / Vanishing race, The / Intro.
LP: . . . . BFX 15127

BOOM CHICKA BOOM.
Tracks: / Backstage pass / Farmer's almanac / Family bible / I love you, I love you / Monteagle Mountain / Cat's in the cradle / Don't go near the water / Harley / Hidden shame / That's one you owe me.
LP: 8421551
MC: 8421554

BORN TO LOSE.
Tracks: / I walk the line / Ballad of a teenage queen / Big river / Wreck of the old 97 / Guess things happen that way / Born to lose / Give my love to Rose / Folsom prison blues / Rock Island line / Luther played the boogie / Straight A's in love / Get rhythm / Next in line / You're the nearest thing to heaven.
MC: . . . . TCINS 5007
LP: . . . . INS 5007

BOY NAMED SUE.
Tracks: / Boy named Sue, A / Green green grass of home / Still in town / Peace in the valley / When papa played the dobro / Tall men / After taxes / Pick the wild wood flowers / Praise the Lord and pass the soup / Old Shep / Keep on the sunny side / Time changes everything / Second honeymoon / Diamonds in the rough / Whirl and the suck, The / San Quentin.
LP: 31827
MC: 40 31827

CHRISTMAS SPIRIT, THE.
Tracks: / Christmas spirit, The / I heard the bells on Christmas day / Blue Christmas / Gifts they gave, The / Here

was a man / Christmas as I knew it / Silent night / Little drummer boy / Ringing the bells for Jim / We are the shepherds / Who kept the sheep / Ballad of the harp weaver, The.
LP: **4604611**
MC: **4604614**

CLASSIC CASH.
Tracks: / Get rhythm / Long black veil / I still miss someone / Blue train / Five feet high and rising / Don't take your guns to town / Guess things happen that way / I walk the line / Ballad of Ira Hayes, The / Folsom Prison blues / Tennessee flat top box / Thing called love, A / Cry cry cry / Sunday morning coming down / Peace in the valley / Home of the blues / I got stripes / Ring of fire / Ways of a woman in love, The / Supper time.
LP: **834 526-1**
MC: **834 526-4**

COLLECTION: JOHNNY CASH.
Tracks: / Wide open road / Cry cry cry / Folsom Prison blues / So doggone lonesome / Mean eyed cat / New Mexico / I walk the line / I love you because / Straight A's in love / Home of the blues / Rock Island line / Country boy / Doin' my time / Big river / Ballad of a teenage queen / Oh lonesome me / You're the nearest thing to heaven / Always alone / You win again / Hey good lookin' / Blue train / Katy too / Fools hall of fame / Ways of a woman in love, The / Down the street to 301.
2LP: . . . . **CCSLP 146**
MC: . . . . **CCSMC 146**

COLLECTION: JOHNNY CASH VOL 3.
Tracks: / Seasons of my heart / I feel better all over / I couldn't keep from crying / Time changes everything / I'd just be fool enough / Transfusion blues / Why do you punish me / I'm so lonesome I could cry / Just one more / Honky tonk gal / Drink to me / Man on the hill / Hank and Joe and me / Clementine / Great speckled bird, The / Austin prison / I want to go home / Caretaker / Old Apache squaw / Don't step on mother's roses / My grandfather's clock / It could be you.
2LP: . . . . **PDA 062**

COUNTRY BOOGIE.
Tracks: / Wreck of the old 97 / Get rhythm / Luther played the boogie / Two timin' woman / Next in line / Belshazar / Hey porter / I heard that lonesome whistle blow / Train of love / Sugartime / Don't make me go / There you go / Boy named Sue, A / Jackson / Daughter of the railroad man / Go on blues / Mamas baby / So do I / Folsom prison blues (live) / In a young girls mind / One piece at a time / How did you get away from me / Rodeo hand / Walkin' the blues.
2LP: . . . . **VSOPLP 121**
MC: . . . . **VSOPMC 121**

COUNTRY STORE: JOHNNY CASH.
Tracks: / Thing called love, A / Long black veil / Jackson / Ring of fire / Don't take your guns to town / One piece at a time / Boy named Sue, A / Folsom Prison blues / Busted / Daddy sang bass / Let there be country / What is truth / Johnny 99 / Greatest love affair / Ghost riders in the sky (Only on CD.) / Song of the patriot (Only on CD.) / Gambler, The (Only on CD.) / It'll be her (Only on CD.).
LP: . . . . **CST 11**
MC: . . . . **CSTK 11**

COWBOYS, THE (Cash, Johnny & Marty Robbins).
Tracks: / Dont' take your guns to town / Big iron / Twenty five minutes to go / Hangin' tree, The / Cottonwood tree, The / Long black veil / Bury me not on the lone prairie / Cool water / Riders in the sky / Red river valley / Old Doc Brown / Meet me tonight in Laredo / Bonanza / Take me back to the prairie / Ira Hayes / Running gun / Ballad of Boot Hill / Mr. Garfield / El Paso / Billy the Kid / Streets of Laredo / Five brothers / Last gunfighter ballad, The / Shifting, whispering sands / Saddle tramp / Remember the Alamo / Sweet Betsy from Pike / Little Joe the wrangler / Give my love to Rose / Stampede.
2LP: . . . . **RTL 2070A/B**
MCSET: **4CRTL 2070A/B**

DESTINATION VICTORIA STATION.
LP: . . . . **BFX 15021**

DIAMOND IN THE ROUGH, A.
Tracks: / Jesus / Preacher said "Jesus said" (With Billy Graham) / That's enough / Miracle man, The / I never met a man like you before / Look for me / I talk to Jesus every day / Peace in the valley / Pie in the sky / Supper time / Far banks of Jordan / Matthew 24 (is knocking at the door) / Diamonds in the rough / I'm just an old chunk of coal.
LP: . . . . **WST 9629**
MC: . . . . **WC 9629**

EVERYBODY LOVES A NUT.
LP: . . . . **BPG 62717**

FIRST YEARS, THE.
Tracks: / Folsom Prison blues / I can't help it / You win again / Mean eyed cat / My treasure / Hey porter / Straight A's in love / Two timin' woman / Oh lonesome me / Sugartime.
LP: . . . . **ALEB 2303**
MC: . . . . **ZCALB 2303**

FOLSOM PRISON BLUES.
Tracks: / If the good Lord's willing / I was there when it happened / Down the street to 301 / Blue train / Don't make me go / I could never be ashamed of you / There you go / Thanks a lot / I couldn't keep from crying / Just about time / Straight A's in love / I just thought you'd like to know / You're the nearest thing to heaven / Rock Island line / Cold cold heart / Folsom Prison blues / Hey good lookin' / Ways of a woman in love, The.
LP: . . . . **SHLP 126**
MC: . . . . **SHTC 126**
MC: **511444.6**

FROM SEA TO SHINING SEA.
LP: . . . . **CBS 62972**

GET RHYTHM (Cash, Johnny & The Tennessee Two).
Tracks: / Get rhythm / Mean eyed cat / You win again / Country boy / Two timin' woman / Oh lonesome me / Luther's boogie / Doin' my time / New Mexico / Belshazah / Sugartime.
LP: **6467014**

GONE GIRL.
Tracks: / Gone girl / I will rock'n'roll with you / Diplomat / No expectations / It comes and goes / It'll be her / Gambler, The / Cajun born / You and me / Song for the life.
LP: . . . . **CBS 83323**

GOSPEL ROAD, THE (see under Gospel Road).

GOSPEL ROAD, THE (FILM SOUNDTRACK) (See under Gospel Road).

GRAFFITI COLLECTION.
MC: . . . . **GRMC 02**

GREAT JOHNNY CASH, THE (BRAVO LABEL).
MC: . . . . **BRC 2501**

GREAT JOHNNY CASH, THE (DITTO).
MCSET: . . . . **DTO 10249**

GREAT SONGS OF JOHNNY CASH.
Tracks: / I walk the line / Rock Island line / Folsom Prison line / Born to lose / Remember me / Wreck of the old '97 / Ballad of a teenage queen / I heard that lonesome whistle blow / Home of the blues.
LP: . . . . **F 50004**
MC: . . . . **MF 950004**
LP: **20086**
MC: **40086**

GREAT SONGS OF JOHNNY CASH.
Tracks: / I walk the line / Rock Island line / Sugartime / Folsom Prison blues / Born to lose / Remember me / Wreck of the old '97 / Ballad of a teenage queen / I heard that lonesome whistle / Home of the blues.
LPPD: . . . . **PD 50004**

GREATEST HITS: JOHNNY CASH VOL.2 A Johnny Cash portrait.
Tracks: / Boy named Sue, A / Hey porter / Guess things happen that way / Blistered / Big river / Long legged guitar pickin' man / Folsom Prison blues / Sunday morning coming down / If I were a carpenter / Frankie's man Johnny / Daddy sang bass.
LP: . . . . **CBS 32766**
MC: **40 32766**

GREATEST HITS: JOHNNY CASH VOL. 2.
MC: **40 64506**

GREATEST HITS: JOHNNY CASH VOL. 1.
Tracks: / Jackson / I walk the line / Ballad of Ira Hayes, The / Orange blossom special / One on the right is on the left, The / Ring of fire / It ain't me babe / Understand your man / Rebel - Johnny Yuma, The / Five feet high and rising / Don't take your guns to town.
LP: . . . . **CBS 32565**
LP: . . . . **CBS 63062**

HELLO I'M JOHNNY CASH.
LP: . . . . **CBS 63796**

HEROES (Cash, Johnny & Waylon Jennings).
Tracks: / Folks out on the road / I'm never gonna roam again / American by birth / Field of diamonds / Heroes / Even cowgirls get the blues / Love is the way / Ballad of forty dollars / I'll always love you - in my own crazy way / One too many mornings.
LP: . . . . **CBS 26922**
MC: **40 26922**

I LOVE COUNTRY.
Tracks: / Ghost riders in the sky / Highway patrolman / Who's Gene Autry / Baron / Boy named Sue, A / Diplomat / No charge / To beat the devil / Gambler, The / Rev.Mr. Black / Ballad of Ira Hayes, The.
LP: . . . . **CBS 54938**
MC: **40 54938**
LP: . . . . **SHM 739**

I WALK THE LINE.
Tracks: / I walk the line / Ballad of a teenage queen / Big river / Wreck of the old 97 / Guess things happen that way / Born to lose / Give my love to Rose / Rock Island line / Luther played the boogie / Straight A's in love / Get rhythm / I walk the line / You win again / Hey good lookin' / Cold cold heart / Sugartime / I heard that lonesome whistle blow / Goodnight Irene / Folsom Prison blues / I forgot to remember to forget / Oh lonesome me.
LP: . . . . **TOP 129**
MC: . . . . **KTOP 129**
LP: . . . . **SM 3988**
MC: . . . . **MC 3988**
LP: . . . . **BGP 62371**

I WALK THE LINE (OCEAN LABEL).
MC: . . . . **OCN 2032WK**
LP: . . . . **OCN 2032WL**

I WILL DANCE WITH YOU (See under Brooks, Karen) (Cash, Johnny & Karen Brooks).

I'M SO LONESOME I COULD CRY.
Tracks: / I'm so lonesome I could cry / Cottonfields / My shoes keep walking back to you / I feel better all over / I still miss someone / I want to go home / One more ride / Delia's gone / Pickin' time / Suppertime.
MC: . . . . **HSC 3027**
LP: . . . . **SHM 3027**

INSIDE A SWEDISH PRISON.
Tracks: / Orleans parish prison / Jacob green / Me and Bobby McGee / Prisoner's song / Invertebrate, The / That silver haired daddy of mine / City jail of a prisoner / Looking back in anger / Nobody cared / Help me make it through the night / I saw a man.
LP: . . . . **BFX 15092**

IS COMING TO TOWN.
Tracks: / Big light, The / Ballad of Barbara, The / I'd rather have you / Let him roll / Night Hank Williams came to town, The / Sixteen tons / Letters from home / W.Lee O'Daniel and the Light Crust Dough Boys / Heavy metal (don't mean rock and roll to me) / My ship will sail.
LP: . . . . **MERH 108**
MC: . . . . **MERHC 108**

ITCHY FEET - 20 FOOT-TAPPIN' GREATS.
MC: **4681164**

JOHNNY 99.
Tracks: / Highway patrolman / That's the truth / God bless Robert E.Lee / New cut road / Johnny 99 / Ballad of the ark / Joshua gone Barbados / Girl from the canyon / Brand new dance / I'm ragged but I'm right.
LP: . . . . **CBS 25471**

JOHNNY AND JUNE (Cash, Johnny, June Carter & Anita Carter).
Tracks: / (I'm proud) the baby is mine / Cotton pickin' hands / Thunderball ((Previously unissued)) / One too many mornings ((Previously unissued)) / Wer kennt wer weg (I walk the line) / Smiling Bill McCall / In Virginia / Close the door lightly ((Previously unissued)) / Adios aloha ((Previously unissued)) / Ain't you ashamed ((Previously unissued)) / That's what it's like to be lonesome ((Previously unissued)) / How did you get away from me ((Previously unissued)).
LP: . . . . **BFX 15030**

JOHNNY CASH AT SAN QUENTIN.
Tracks: / Wanted man / Wreck of old 97 / I walk the line / Darling companion / Starkville city jail / San Quentin / Boy named Sue, A / Peace in the valley / Folsom prison blues.
LP: . . . . **CBS 63629**
MC: **40 63629**
LP: **63629**
LP: . . . . **CBS 32209**
MC: **40 32209**

JOHNNY CASH COLLECTION (DEJA VU LABEL) (20 Country Greats).
Tracks: / Wreck of the old '97 / Ballad of a teenage queen / I heard that lonesome whistle blow / Rock island line / Goodbye little darling / Train of love / Down the street to 301 / Give my love to Rose / Come in, stranger / Get rhythm / Folsom Prison blues / I walk the line / Hey porter / Guess things happen that way / Ways of a woman in love, The / There you go / Big river / Sugartime / Blue train / Doin' my time.
LP: . . . . **DVLP 2103**
MC: . . . . **DVMC 2103**

JOHNNY CASH COLLECTION (PICKWICK).
Tracks: / Folsom Prison blues / Country boy / Doin' my time / Cold cold heart / Sugar time / Wide open road / I walk the line / There you go / Rock Island line / Wreck of the old '97 / Cry cry cry / Big river / I can't help it / Don't make me go / Hey porter / New Mexico / Mean eyed cat / You win again / Life goes on / I could never be ashamed of you.
MCSET: . . . . **DTOL 10001**
MCSET: . . . . **PDC 005**
MCSET: . . . . **PDC 033**

JOHNNY CASH (EMBASSY LABEL).
Tracks: / I walk the line / Streets of Laredo / Don't take your guns to town / Five feet high and rising / I promise you / I'm gonna try to be that way / Don't think twice / It's alright / Hey porter / Give my love to Rose / Big river / I still miss someone / All God's children ain't free.
LP: . . . . **CBS 31495**
MC: **40 31495**

JOHNNY CASH (HAMMER LABEL).
LP: . . . . **HMB 7001**

JOHNNY CASH SHOW.
LP: . . . . **CBS 64089**

JOHNNY CASH'S TOP HITS (Cash, Johnny & The Tennessee Two).
Tracks: / Cry cry cry / Luther played the boogie / Folsom Prison blues / So doggone lonesome / Mean eyed cat / Wide open road / Two timin' woman / There you go / I walk the line / Country boy / Train of love / Get rhythm / Hey, porter!.
LP: . . . . **SUN 1015**

LADY.
Tracks: / Kate / Oney / Any ole wind that blows / Lady came from Baltimore, The / Ragged old flag / My old Kentucky home / Sold out of flag poles / Last gunfighter ballad, The / Lady / After the ball / I would like to see you again / Gone girl / I will rock and roll with you / Ghost riders in the sky.
LP: . . . . **PMP 1004**
MC: . . . . **PMPK 1004**

LAST GUNFIGHTER BALLAD, THE.
MC: **40 81566**

MAN IN BLACK.
LP: . . . . **CBS 64331**

MORE OF OLD GOLDEN THROAT.
Tracks: / Bottom of a mountain / You beat all I ever saw / Put the sugar to bed / Girl from Saskatoon / Time and time again / Honky tonk gal / Locomotive man / Second honeymoon / I'll remember you / Lorena / Roll call / Blues for two / Jerry and Nina's melody / Bandana / Wabash blues.
LP: . . . . **BFX 15073**

MYSTERY OF LIFE, THE.
Tracks: / Greatest cowboy of them all, The / I'm an easy rider / Mystery of life,The / Hey porter / Beans for breakfast / Goin' by the book / Wanted man / I'll go somewhere and sing my songs again / Hobo song, The / Angel and the badman.
LP: **8480511**
MC: **8480514**

OLD GOLDEN THROAT (BEAR FAMILY).
Tracks: / I got stripes / Certain kinda hurtin', A / Little at a time, A / All over again / Still in town / Smiling Bill McCall / Wind changes, The / Sons of Katie Elder, The / Dark as a dungeon / Tennessee flat top box / Matador, The / Send a picture of mother / You dreamer you / Red Velvet.
LP: . . . . **BFX 15072**

OLD GOLDEN THROAT (CHARLY & CBS).
Tracks: / Big river / Luther's boogie / You are my baby / Folsom Prison blues / Hey porter / Next in line / Oh lonesome me / Belshazar / Get rhythm / Rock Island line / Country boy / Train of love / I walk the line / Katy too / Ballad of a teenage queen / Mean eyed cat.
LP: . . . . **CR 30005**
LP: . . . . **CBS 63316**

ONE PIECE AT A TIME.
Tracks: / Let there be country / One piece at a time / In a young girl's mind / Mountain lady / Michigan city howdy do / Sold out of flagpoles / Committed to Parkview / Daughter of the railroad man / Love has lost again / Go on blues.
LP: . . . . **SHM 3179**
MC: . . . . **HSC 3179**
LP: . . . . **CBS 81416**

ORIGINAL GOLDEN HITS, VOL. 1 (Cash, Johnny & The Tennessee Two).
Tracks: / Folosom Prison blues / Hey porter / So doggone lonesome / There you go / Next in line / Cry cry cry / I walk

the line / Don't make me go / Train of love / Home of the blues / Get rhythm.
LP: **6467001**

ORIGINAL GOLDEN HITS, VOL. 2 (Cash, Johnny & The Tennessee Two).
Tracks: / Ballard of a teen-age queen / Come in stranger / Ways of a woman in love / You're the nearest thing to heaven / I just thought you'd like to know / Give my love to Rose / Guess things happen that way / Just about time / Luther's boogie / Thanks a lot / Big river.
LP: **6467007**

ORIGINAL HITS.
LP: **2230712**
MC: **2130712**

ORIGINAL JOHNNY CASH, THE.
Tracks: / Don't make me go / Next in line / Home of the blues / Give my love to Rose / Guess things happen that way / Come in stranger / Ways of a woman in love, The / You're the nearest thing to heaven / I just thought you'd like to know / It's just about time / You tell me / Goodbye little darling / Story of a broken heart, The / Down the street to 301 / Blue train / Born to lose.
MC: . . . . **TCCR 30113**
LP: . . . . **CR 30113**

PORTRAIT IN MUSIC, A.
Tracks: / Just about time / Straight A's in love / I just thought you'd like to know / You're the nearest thing to heaven / Rock Island line / Cold cold heart / Folsom Prison blues / Hey good lookin' / I love you because / Big river / Ballad of a teenage queen / Goodbye little darling / I could never be ashamed of you / Next in line / Port of lonely hearts / Sugar-time / There you go / Two timin' woman.
LP: . . . . **CBR 1015**
MC: . . . . **KCBR 1015**

RAINBOW.
Tracks: / I'm leaving now / Here comes that rainbow again / They're all the same to me / Easy street / Have you ever seen the rain / You beat all I ever saw / Unwed fathers / Love me like you used to / Casey's last ride / Borderline.
LP: . . . . **CBS 26689**
MC: **40 26689**

RAMBLER, THE.
MC: **40 82156**

REPLAY ON JOHNNY CASH.
LP: . . . . **FEDB 5015**
MC: . . . . **FEDC 5015**

RIDING THE RAILS.
MCSET: **40 88153**

RING OF FIRE.
Tracks: / Ring of fire / I'd still be there / What do I care / I still miss someone / Forty shades of green / Were you there / Rebel / Johnny Yuma / Bonanza / Big battle, The / Remember the Alamo / Tennessee flat top box / Peace in the valley.
MC: . . . . **HSC 367**
LP: . . . . **SHM 988**

ROCK ISLAND LINE.
Tracks: / Belshazar / If the good Lord's willing / Wreck of the old '97 / You tell me / Oh lonesome me / Big river / Doin' my time / Rock Island line / Home of the blues / Straight A's in love / Come in stranger / Blue train / Next in line / Hey good lookin' / Life goes on / Katy too.
LP: . . . . **SUN 1047**

ROCKABILLY BLUES.
Tracks: / Cold lonesome morning / Without love / W.O.M.A.N. / Cowboy who started the fight, The / Twentieth century is almost over, The / Rockabilly blues (Texas 1955) / Last time, The / She's a go-er / It ain't nothing new babe / One way rider.
LP: . . . . **CBS 84607**
MC: **40 84607**

SILVER.
Tracks: / L and N don't stop here anymore, The / Lonesome to the bone / Bull rider / I'll say it's true / Riders in the sky / Cocaine blues / Muddy Waters / West Canterbury subdivision blues / Lately I been leanin' toward the blues / I'm gonna sit on the porch & pick on my old ...
LP: . . . . **CBS 83757**
MC: **40 83757**

SINGS THE BALLADS OF THE TRUE WEST.
Tracks: / Hiawatha's vision / Road to Kaintuck, the / Shifting whispering sands, The / Ballad of Boot Hill, The / I ride an old paint / Hardin' wouldn't run / Mr. Garfield / Streets of Laredo, The / Johnny Reb / Letter from home, A.
LP: . . . . **BPG 62538**

SINGS THE BALLADS OF THE TRUE WEST, VOL. 2.
Tracks: / Bury me not on the Lone Prairie / Mean as hell / Sam Hall / 25 minutes to go / Blizzard, The / Sweet Betsy from Pike / Green grow the lilacs / Stampede / Shifting whispering sands, The / Reflections.
LP: . . . . **BPG 62591**

STAR PORTRAIT: JOHNNY CASH.
2LP: . . . . **CBS 67201**

STORY SONGS OF THE TRAINS AND RIVERS (Cash, Johnny & The Tennessee Two).
Tracks: / Hey porter / Train of love / Blue train / I heard that lonesome whistle blow / Port of lonely hearts / Wreck of the old 97 / Rock island line / Big river / Wide open road / Down the street to 301 / Life goes on.
LP: **6467012**

SUN SOUNDS SPECIAL.
Tracks: / Cry cry cry / I'm so doggone lonesome / There you go / I heard that lonesome whistle blow / Doin' my time / If the good Lord's willing / Wide open road / Two timin' woman / Cold cold heart / Hey good lookin' / I could never be ashamed of you / Always alone / Thanks a lot / I forgot to remember to forget / New Mexico / I couldn't keep from crying.
LP: . . . . **CR 30153**

SUN YEARS, THE.
Tracks: / Wide open road / You're my baby / Folsom Prison blues / Two timin' woman / Goodnight Irene / Port of lonely hearts / My treasure / Cry cry cry / Hey porter / Luther played the boogie / So doggone lonesome / Mean-eyed cat / I couldn't keep from crying / New Mexico / Rock 'n' roll Ruby / Get rhythm / I walk the line / Train of love / There you go / One more ride / Goodbye little darling / I love you because / Straight A's in love / Don't make me go / Next in line / Give my love to Rose / Home of the blues / Wreck of the old '97 / Rock Island line / Belshazar / Leave that junk alone / Country boy / Doin' my time / If the good Lord's willing / I heard that lonesome whistle blow / Remember me / I was there when it happened / Come in stranger / Big river / Ballad of a teenage queen / Oh lonesome me / Guess things happen that way / You're the nearest thing to Heaven / Sugartime / Born to lose / Always alone / Story of a broken heart, The / You tell me / Life goes on / You win again / I could never be ashamed of you / Cold cold heart / Hey good lookin' / I can't help it / Blue train / Katy too / Ways of a woman in love, The / Thanks a lot / It's just about time / I just thought you'd like to know / I forgot to remember to forget / Down the street to 301.
LPS: . . . . **SUN BOX 103**

SURVIVORS, THE (Cash, Johnny/Jerry Lee Lewis/Carl Perkins).
Tracks: / Get rhythm / I forgot to remember to forget / Goin' down the road feeling bad / That silver-haired daddy of mine / Matchbox / I'll fly away / Whole lotta shakin' goin' on / Rockin' my life away / Blue suede shoes / There will be peace in the valley for me / Will the circle be unbroken? / I saw the light.
LP: . . . . **CBS 85609**
MC: **40 85609**
LP: . . . . **SHM 3180**
MC: . . . . **HSC 3180**

TALL MAN.
Tracks: / Tall man / Foolish questions ((Previously unissued)) / Pick a bale of cotton / I tremble for you ((Previously unissued)) / Besser so, Jenny Joe / My old faded rose ((Previously unissued)) / Kleine Rosmarie / Rodeo hand ((Previously unissued)) / Sound of laughter, The ((Previously unissued)) / Hammer and nails / Engine 143 / On the line.
LP: . . . . **BFX 15033**

THE MAN, THE WORLD, HIS MUSIC.
Tracks: / Born to lose / Story of a broken heart / Two timin' woman / Goodbye little darling / Port of lonely hearts / I forgot to remember to forget / Goodnight Irene / My treasure / I heard that lonesome whistle blow / Mean eyed cat / New Mexico / Sugartime / Life goes on / Wreck of the old 97 / Belshazah / You're my baby / Fools hall of fame / Blue train / Country boy / Wide open road / I just thought you'd like to know / Down the street to 301.
LP: **6641008**

THING CALLED LOVE, A.
Tracks: / Kate / Melva's wine / Thing called love / I promise you / Papa was a good man / Tear stained letter / Mississippi sand / Daddy / Arkansas lovin' man / Miracle man.
LP: . . . . **CBS 64898**
LP: . . . . **CBS 32698**

UNISSUED JOHNNY CASH, THE.
Tracks: / Mama's baby / Fool's hall of fame / Walking the blues / Cold shoulder / Viel zu spat / Wo ist zu hause, mama / Fable of Willie Brown, The / Losing kind of love / So do I / Shamrock doesn't grow in California / Danger zone / I'll be all smiles tonight.
LP: . . . . **BFX 15016**

VERY BEST OF JOHNNY CASH.
Tracks: / What is truth / All over again / I'm so lonesome I could cry / Understand your man / Daddy sang bass / Busted / Let there be country / Ghost riders in the sky / Thing called love, A / It ain't me babe / Don't take your guns to town / Wreck of the old '97 / Ring of fire / If I were a carpenter / Green green grass of home / Folsom Prison blues.
LP: . . . . **SHM 3146**
MC: . . . . **HSC 3146**

WATER FROM THE WELLS OF HOME.
Tracks: / As long as I live / Ballad of a teenage queen / Last of the drifters / Where did we go right / Call me the breeze / That ole wheel / Sweeter than the flowers / Ballad of Robb MacDunn / New moon over Jamaica.
LP: **834778-1**
MC: **834778-4**

WELCOME FRIEND.
Tracks: / Man in black / No earthly good / Papa was a good man / Song to Mamma, A / That silver haired Daddy of mine / Daddy / Daddy sang bass / Good earth, The / Good morning friend / Best friend / Thing called love, A / Jesus was a carpenter / Were you there? / God shine / Welcome back Jesus / Great speckled bird, The.
LP: . . . . **WRD 3008**
MC: . . . . **TCWR 3008**

...WITH HIS HOT AND BLUE GUITAR.
Tracks: / Rock Island line / I heard that lonesome whistle blow / Country boy / If the good Lord's willing and the creeks don't rise / Cry cry cry / Remember me / I'm so doggone lonesome / I was there when it happened / I walk the line / Wreck of the old '97 / Folsom Prison blues / Doin my time.
LP: . . . . **CRM 2013**

WORLD OF..., THE.
MC: **40 66237**
LP: . . . . **CBS 66237**

Cash Money

WHERE'S THE PARTY AT (Cash Money & Marvellous).
LP: . . . . **SBUKLP 4**
MC: . . . . **SBUKC 4**

Cash, Rosanne

I LOVE COUNTRY.
LP: **4510041**
MC: **4510044**

INTERIORS.
Tracks: / On the inside / Dance with the tiger / On the surface / Real woman / This world / What we really want / Mirror image / Land of nightmares / I want a cure / Paralyzed.
LP: **4673311**
MC: **4673314**

KING'S RECORD SHOP.
Tracks: / Rosie strikes back / Way we make a broken heart, The / If you change your mind / Real me, The / Somewhere sometime / Runaway train / Tennessee flat top box / I don't have to crawl / Green, yellow and red / Why don't you quit leaving me alone.
LP: **4509161**
MC: **4509164**

RETROSPECTIVE 1979-1989.
Tracks: / Seven year ache / Hold on / My baby think's he's a train / Tennessee flat top box / I don't wanna spoil the party / Blue moon with heartache / No memories hangin' around / Black and white.
LP: **4633281**
MC: **4633284**

RHYTHM AND ROMANCE.
Tracks: / Hold on / I don't know why you don't want me / Never be you / Second to no one / Halfway house / Pink bedroom / Never alone / My old man / Never gonna hurt / Closing time.
LP: . . . . **CBS 26366**
MC: **40 26366**

SOMEWHERE IN THE STARS.
Tracks: / Ain't no money / Down on love / I wonder / Oh yes I can / Looking for a corner / It hasn't happened yet / That's how I got to Memphis / Third rate romance / I look for love / Somewhere in the stars.
LP: **204 848**

Cashflow

BIG MONEY.
Tracks: / That's the ticket / Come closer / Devastation / Love education / All systems go / You know that / Big money / Love's funky.
LP: **832 187-1**
MC: **832 187-4**

CASHFLOW.
Tracks: / Party freak / Mine all mine / Can't let love pass us by / Spending money / Reach out / I need your love / Just a dream.
LP: . . . . **JABH 17**
MC: . . . . **JABHC 17**

Cashmere

CASHMERE.
LP: . . . . **BRLP 503**

LET THE MUSIC TURN YOU ON.
Tracks: / Try your lovin' / Inner feelings / Contemplation / Light of love / Let the music turn you on / Tracks of my tears / Do it any way you wanna.
LP: . . . . **PWLP 1005**

Casino Lights

CASINO LIGHTS (Various artists).
Tracks: / Your precious love: *Various artists* / Who's right, who's wrong: *Various artists* / Sure enough: *Various* artists / Imagine: *Various artists* / Monmouth College fight song: *Various artists* / Theme from 'Love is not enough': *Various artists* / Hideaway: *Various artists* / Casino lights: *Various artists*.
LP: **9237181**

Casino Music

JUNGLE LOVE.
Tracks: / Do the proton / Jungle love / Vite et bien / C'est extraordinaire / St. Tropez / Burger city / Higher / Jingle gangster / Do you feel blue / Do the troton.
LP: . . . . **ILPS 7000**

Casino Royale (film)

CASINO ROYALE (Film soundtrack) (Various artists).
Tracks: / Casino Royale theme: *Alpert, Herb* / Money penny goes for broke: *Bacharach, Burt* / Home James, don't spare ...: *Bacharach, Burt* / Look of love, The: *Bacharach, Burt* / Little French boy: *Bacharach, Burt*/ Venerable Sir James Bond: *Bacharach, Burt* / Big cowboys and indians: *Bacharach, Burt* / Look of love, The: *Springfield, Dusty* / Le chiffre's torture of ...: *Bacharach, Burt* / Sir James' trip to find ...: *Bacharach, Burt* / Hi there Miss Good Thighs: *Bacharach, Burt* / Flying saucer: *Bacharach, Burt* / Dream on James: *Bacharach, Burt*.
LP: . . . . **SF 7874**
MC: . . . . **VSC 5265**

SOMEONE SAYS.
LP: . . . . **PHZA 32**

Casino Steel

RUBY (DON'T TAKE YOUR LOVE TO TOWN) (See under Holton, Gary) (Casino Steel & Gary Holton).

Casiopea

DOWN UPBEAT (Cassiopea).
LP: . . . . **SNTF 926**

MINT JAMS.
Tracks: / Take me / Asayaka / Midnight rendezvous / Time limit / Domino line / Tears of the star / Swear.
LP: . . . . **SNTF 924**

SOUNDOGRAPHY, THE.
Tracks: / Asayaka / Mid-Manhattan / Looking up / Misty lady / What can't speak a lie / Fabbydabby / Soundography, The / Gypsy wind / Eyes of the mind / Sunnyside feeling.
LP: . . . . **SNTF 919**

Casket & Crush

YOUNG GUYS WILL DO ANYTHING.
LP: . . . . **M 3**

Cass Cass

CASS CASS.
LP: . . . . **STERNS 1018**

Cassady, Linda

INTRODUCING LINDA CASSADY.
LP: . . . . **AMOLP 002**

Cassandra

DON'T READ THE LETTERS.
LP: . . . . **RRLP 3**

Cassandra Complex

CYBERPUNX.
LP: . . . . **BIAS 148**

FEEL THE WIDTH.
LP: . . . . **BIAS 068**

GRENADE.
LP: . . . . **CXRA 1**
MC: . . . . **CXRAC 1**

HELLO AMERICA.
Tracks: / Moscow Idaho / Beyond belief / Datakill / Clouds / Fragile / Wintry weather song / David Venus / Three cities.
LP: . . . . **CXRA 002**

LIVE IN LEATHER.
MC: . . . . **CXC 004**

SATAN, BUGS BUNNY AND ME.
LP: . . . . SPV 08 8158
LP: . . . . BIAS 118

THEOMANIA.
Tracks: / God John / Oz / Too stupid to sin / Honeytrap / One millionth happy customer / Ground / Second shot / Defcon 1.
LP: . . . . BIAS 088

Cassandra Crossing

CASSANDRA CROSSING (Film soundtrack) (Various artists).
LP: . . . . CT 6020

Cassiber

PERFECT WORLD.
LP: . . . . RE 0000

Cassidy, David

BILLY AND BLAZE (See under Billy & Blaze - Spoken Word).

CHERISH.
LP: . . . . BELLS 210

DAVID CASSIDY.
Tracks: / Labour of love / You remember me / Lyin' to myself / Boulevard of broken dreams / Hi-heel sneakers / Message to the world / Livin' without you / Stranger in your heart / Prisoner / All because of you.
LP: . . . . ENVLP 1011
MC: . . . . TCENV 1011

DREAMS ARE NOTHIN' MORE THAN WISHES.
LP: . . . . BELLS 231

GREATEST HITS: DAVID CASSIDY.
LP: . . . . MFP 50324

HIGHER THEY CLIMB, THE.
LP: . . . . RS 1012

HIS GREATEST HITS LIVE.
Tracks: / Tenderly / Darlin' / Thin ice / Someone / Daydreamer / Romance / Cherish / Rock me baby / Last kiss, The / Please please me / I'm a clown / I think I love you / How can I be sure.
LP: . . . . TRACK 3
LP: . . . . SLTD 21
MC: . . . . SLTK 21

LIVE: DAVID CASSIDY.
LP: . . . . BELLS 243

ROCK ME BABY.
LP: . . . . BELLS 218

ROMANCE (LET YOUR HEART GO).
Tracks: / Letter, The / Heart of emotion / Tenderly / She knows all about boys / Remember me / Romance (let your heart go) / Touched by the lightning / Last kiss, The / Thin ice / Someone.
LP: 206983
MC: 406983

Cassidy, Jane

EMPTY ROAD, THE.
LP: . . . . CCF 14
MC: 4CCF 14

WAVES OF TIME.
LP: . . . . CCF 6

Cassidy, Shaun

UNDER WRAPS.
Tracks: / Hard love / Taxi dancer / Lie to me / Right before / Skies, The / It's like Heaven / She's right / Midnight sun / One more night of your love / Our night.
LP: . . . . K 56535

Cassle

CASSLE.
LP: . . . . A 67

Cast

GALLERY.
Tracks: / Multi storey car park / Out of my mind / Trains / Sharp bends / Lullaby / Juliet / Willow / Procession.
MC: . . . . HOP 1

Cast A Giant Shadow

CAST A GIANT SHADOW (1966 film soundtrack) (Various artists).
LP: . . . . MCA 25093
MC: . . . . MCAC 25093

EXODUS/CAST A GIANT SHADOW (see under Exodus) (Various artists).

Cast of Thousands

PASSION.
Tracks: / This is love / Passion / September / Tear me down / Girl / Immaculate deception / Colour fields / This experience / Thin line / Nothing is forever.
LP: . . . . AFTER 6
MC: . . . . TFTER 6

Castanarc

JOURNEY TO THE EAST.
Tracks: / Peyote / Travelling song / Ami / Goodbye to all that / Fool, The / Rhyme / Soon / Journey to the east.
LP: . . . . CR 002
LP: . . . . PENCIL 010

RUDE POLITICS.
LP: . . . . CUE 003

Castaway (film)

CASTAWAY (Film soundtrack) (Various artists).
Tracks: / Be kind to my mistakes: *Various artists* / Catamaran: *Various artists* / Chemistry: *Various artists* / Clair de lune: *Various artists* / Fata Morgana: *Various artists* / End title: *Various artists* / Island, The: *Various artists* / Memories of tango: *Various artists* / Healing: *Various artists* / Castaway: *Various artists.*
LP: . . . . EMC 3529
MC: . . . . TCEMC 3529

Castille, Hadley J.

GOING BACK TO LOUISIANA (Castille, Hadley J. and the Cajun Grass Band).
LP: 6057
MC: . . . . 6057 TC

Castle Blak

BABES IN TOYLAND.
LP: . . . . HMUSA 60

Castle, David

CASTLE IN THE SKY.
Tracks: / Loneliest man on the moon, The / You're too far away / Make believe you're near me / Lady on the other side of town / Ten to eight / With love and with care / All I ever wanna be is yours / Pretending / Finally.
LP: . . . . RRL 2001

LOVE YOU FOREVER.
Tracks: / Love you forever / No matter what / Hold me just a little bit longer / Status consiousness / Everything I love / Musette / Pure love / Baby the rain won't last forever / I will always be here when you need me / At one with the universe and you.
LP: . . . . RRL 2009

Castle, Lee

DIXIELAND HEAVEN.
Tracks: / Stars and stripes forever / Alabama blues / Save it pretty Mama / Birmingham special / Trombone jitters / Feeling sentimental / My wild Irish rose / Fair Jennie's lament / Dixieland mambo / On the banks of the Wabash / Mood in blue / When the saints go marching in.
LP: . . . . HQ 2003

Castle of the Mist

CASTLE OF THE MIST (Valentina Luellen (aut)) (Boyd, Carole (nar)).
MC: . . . . PMB 022

Castle of Yew

CASTLE OF YEW, THE (Lucy M. Boston (auth).
MC: 88162X

Castle of...(bk)

CASTLE OF ADVENTURE, THE (see under Blyton, Enid (aut)) (Cribbins, Bernard (nar)).

Castle, Pete

RAMBLING ROBIN.
LP: . . . . BURL 013

TRADITIONAL ENGLISH FOLK SONGS VOLUME 1.
MC: . . . . VCA 023

Castle, Roy

RECORD BREAKERS.
LP: . . . . GLR 626

Castlereagh Choir

LET'S BE SINGING (Castlereagh Male Testimony Choir).
Tracks: / Let's be singing / Jesus, rose of Sharon / My redeemer liveth / Hallelujah chorus / 'Twas Jesu's blood / Rock of ages / Prepare to meet thy God / Grand old highway, A / O Lord remember me / At even, when the sun was set / Who is that knocking? / Wonderful grace of Jesus / Nothing but Thy blood / I am his and he is mine.
LP: . . . . PC 862

LIGHT OF THE WORLD, THE (Castlereagh Male Testimony Choir).
Tracks: / Where the roses never fade / God is our refuge / Angels from the realms of glory / Shall I crucify him? / Roll, billows, roll / Oh, be saved / Shepherd, hear my prayer / How much more? / Behold, the mountain of the Lord / I'm living in Canaan now / Holy spirit, love divine / Take up thy cross / With what resplendant beauty shone / Light of the world.
LP: . . . . PC 327

Castor, Jimmy

SUPER SOUND (Castor, Jimmy Bunch).
Tracks: / Supersound / King Kong / Bom bom / Groove will make you move, A / Drifting / Magic in the music / What's best.
LP: . . . . K 50190

Castro-Neves, Oscar

BRAZILIAN SCANDALS.
MC: . . . . JC 3302
LP: . . . . JLP 3302

Casualites Of War

CASUALITES OF WAR (1989 Film Soundtrack) (Various artists).
Tracks: / Casulties of war: *Various artists* / Trapped in a tunnel: *Various artists* / No escape: *Various artists* / Abduction: *Various artists* / No hope: *Various artists* / Rape, The: *Various artists* / Death of Oahn, The: *Various artists* / Healing, The: *Various artists* / Fragging, The: *Various artists*/ Waste her: *Various artists* / Elegy for a dead cherry: *Various artists* / Elegy for Brown: *Various artists.*
LP: 4660161
MC: 4660164
LP: . . . . CB 45359
MC: CBT45359

Casuals

JESAMINE (OLD GOLD) (see Honeybus'I can't let Maggie go' (Old Gold)).

Cat & Mouse Band

FROM THE CAVES OF THE WHISTLING FISH MONKS.
LP: . . . . LMLP 675

Cat People (film)

CAT PEOPLE (1982 film soundtrack) (Various artists).
Tracks: / Cat people (putting out fire): *Bowie, David & Giorgio Moroder* / Autopsy: *Moroder, Giorgio* / Irena's theme: *Moroder, Giorgio* / Night rabbit: *Moroder, Giorgio* / Leopard tree dream: *Moroder, Giorgio* / Paul's theme: *Moroder, Giorgio* / Myth, The: *Moroder, Giorgio* / To the bridge: *Moroder, Giorgio* / Transformation seduction: *Moroder, Giorgio* / Bring the prod: *Moroder, Giorgio.*
LP: . . . . MCF 3138
MC: . . . . MCFC 3138

Cat Rapes Dog

GOD, GUNS AND GASOLINE.
LP: . . . . KK 034

MAXIMUM OVERDRIVE.
LP: . . . . KKUK 9

Catchings, John

JOY IN THE JOURNEY.
Tracks: / Sweet hour of prayer / Holy, holy, holy / O sacred head, now wounded / And can it be? / Going home / Blessed assurance (in 12/8 time!) / Take my life, and let it be... / Come, Thou long-expected Jesus / It is well with my soul / Joy in the journey / Finlandia.
LP: . . . . SP R 1199
MC: . . . . SP C 1199

Cate Bros.

CATE BROS..
Tracks: / Time for us, A / Union man / Standin' on a mountain top / Always waiting / When love comes / I just wanna sing / Can't change my heart / Easy way out / Lady luck / Livin' on dreams.
LP: . . . . K 53019

RENDEZVOUS.
Tracks: / Woman I'm tryin' / Stranger at the door / Out on a limb / Let it slide / I'm no pretender / I can't give it up / Yield not to temptation / Give me a reason.
LP: . . . . K 53064

Cateran

ACHE.
LP: . . . . GOESON 30

BITE DEEPER.
Tracks: / Don't like what I do / She doesn't say much / Bit put out, A / Small dark hand / Surplus to need / Mirror / Love scars / This is what becomes of the broken... / Knowing what I am / Strung along.
LP: . . . . SOL 9

LITTLE CIRCLES.
LP: . . . . DISPLP 5

Caterwaul

PIN AND WEB.
Tracks: / Sheep's a wolf, The / Humming bird whir / What I hear you can't, how come / Dizzy delirium / Catervowels / Throw like thunder / Pin and web / Not today / Barnacle / Lay down to rest / Nevertheless / Behold the night / On the front porch.
LP: . . . . EIRSA 1015
MC: . . . . EIRSAC 1015

PORTENT HUE.
LP: . . . . EIRSA 1027

Cates, Demo

CHARIOTS OF FIRE.
LP: . . . . AALP 41

IN FLIGHT.
LP: . . . . AALP 55

SEEMS A MILLION SAX VOL. 1.
Tracks: / All strung out on you / Girl I love you / Right here is where we stay / Sometimes / How could I let you get away / Right place right time / My adorable one / Seems a million years.
LP: . . . . DK 0003

SEEMS A MILLION SAX VOL. 2.
LP: . . . . DK 7775

Catfish Hodge Band

EYE WITNESS BLUES.
LP: . . . . AD 4113

Catheads

HUBBA.
LP: . . . . ENIG 21951

Cathedral Choir

SOUNDS OF ST NICHOLAS.
LP: . . . . MWM 1025

Catherine, Philippe

GUITARS.
Tracks: / We'll find a way / Five thousand policemen / Sneezing bull / Rene Thomas / Moss and weeds / Homecoming / Charlotte / Noburl / Isabelle.
LP: . . . . K 50193

SPLENDID (Catherine, Philippe & Larry Coryell).
Tracks: / One plus two blues / Snowshadows / Transvested express / Deus Xango / My serenade / No more booze / Father Christmas / Quiet day in Spring, A / Train and the river, The.
LP: . . . . K 52086

TWIN HOUSE (Catherine, Philippe & Larry Coryell).
Tracks: / Ms. Julie / Homecoming / Airpower / Twin house / Mortgage on your soul / Gloryell / Nuages / Twice a week.
LP: . . . . K 50342

Catingub, Matt

HI TECH BIG BAND.
LP: . . . . SB 2025

LAND OF LONG WHITE CLOUD (Catingub, Matt New Zealand Youth Jazz Orchestra).
LP: . . . . SB 3006

MATT CATINGUB BIG BAND WITH MAVIS RIVERS (Catingub, Matt big band with Mavis Rivers).
LP: SB2013

Catley, Marc

IN DIFFERENCE (Catley, Marc & Geoff Mann).
Tracks: / Calling, The / Love is the only way / This time / Freedom / Closer to you / True riches / War is won, The / All along the way / Growth.
MC: . . . . PCN 123

THIS IS THE BIRTH OF CLASSICAL ACOUSTIC ROCK.
Tracks: / Love / Write your will on my heart / Help me peace the answer / New life / Hosea.
MC: . . . . PCN 115

Catmen

CATMEN.
Tracks: / Tell me / Who was she / Glad to see you baby / Running man, The / She's driving me mad / Tonight / There's a girl in my heart / Be good to me / Will you stay / Lost without you / My little girl / Trivialities.
LP: . . . . NERD 044

Cats (Blues)

CATS, THE (Various artists).
LP: . . . . QJC 8217

SUPERGOLD (Cats (show)).
LP: . . . . IC 134 26327/8

Cats Eye (film)

CATS EYE (1985 Original soundtrack) (Various artists).
LP: . . . . STV 81241
MC: . . . . CTV 81241

C.A.T.S. Eyes

C.A.T.S. EYES (THEME FROM) (See under Kongos, John) (Kongos, John).

Cats In Boots

KICKED AND KLAWED.
Tracks: / Shotgun Sally / 9 lives (save me) / Her monkey / Whip it out / Long, long way from home / Coast to coast / Every sunrise / Evil angel / Bad boys are back / Judas kiss / Heaven on a heartbeat.
LP: . . . . MTL 1049
MC: . . . . TCMTL 1049

Cats (show)

CATS (Original Broadway cast) (Various artists).
2LP: . . . . GEF 88615

CATS (1981 Original London cast) (Various artists).

Tracks: / Jellicle songs for jellicle cats: *Various artists* / Old gumbie cat: *Various artists* / Naming of cats: *Various artists* / Rum rum tugger, The: *Various artists* / Grizabella: *Various artists* / Bustopher Jones: *Various artists* / Memory: *Various artists* / Mungojerrie and Rumpleteazer: *Various artists* / Old Deuteronomy: *Various artists* / Moments of happiness: *Various artists* / Gus, Theatre cat: *Various artists* / Cats:Overture/ Prologue: *Various artists* / Invitation to the Jellicle ball: *Various artists* / Jellicle ball, The: *Various artists*/ Journey to the heavy side, The: *Various artists* / Addressing of cats, The: *Various artists* / Growltiger's last stand: *Various artists* / Ballad of Billy McCaw's Skimbleshanks, The: *Various artists* / Macavity: *Various artists* / Mr. Mistoffolees: *Various artists*.
MCSET: . . . . **CATXC 001**
2LP: . . . . **CATX 001**

HIGHLIGHTS FROM CATS (Various artists).
LP: **839 415-1**
MC: **839 415-4**

Catullus (poet)

POETRY OF CATULLUS (see under Poetry of Catullus) (Mason, James (nar)).

Caudel, Stephen

BOW OF BURNING GOLD.
MC: . . . . **NAGEC 17**
LP: . . . . **NAGE 17**

WINE DARK SEA.
Tracks: / Wine dark sea (the outward journey) / Wine dark sea (the return journey).
LP: . . . . **NAGE 6**
MC: . . . . **NAGEC 6**

Caught On The Hop

FROZEN FLAMES.
LP: . . . . **DRGN 863**

Cause Of Death

OBITUARY.
Tracks: / Obituary.
LP: **RO93708**

Caution

SHOULD I PUT MY TRUST IN YOU (See under Priest, Maxi) (Caution & Maxi Priest).

THROW MY CORN (see Priest, Maxi) (Caution & Maxi Priest).

Cautionary Verses

CAUTIONARY VERSES (Various artists).
MC: . . . . **ANV 628**

Cava Sessions

CAVA SESSIONS (Various artists).
LP: . . . . **TLV 003**
MC: . . . . **TLV 003 MC**

Cavalcade (show)

CAVALCADE (Original London cast) (Various artists).
LP: . . . . **AEI 1149**

Cavaliere, Felix

CASTLES IN THE AIR.
Tracks: / Good to have love back / Only a lonely heart sees all or nothing / Castles in the air / People got to be free / Dancin' the night away / Love is the first day of spring / Outside your window / Don't hold back your love / You turned me around.
LP: . . . . **EPC 83817**

DESTINY.
Tracks: / Destiny / Flip flop / Never felt love before / I can remember / Light of my life / Can't stop loving you / Try to believe / You came and set me free / Love came / Hit and run.
LP: . . . . **K 55505**

YOUNG RASCAL, A.
Tracks: / High price to pay / I'm a gambler / Summer in El Bario / Long times, gone / Funky Friday / It's been a long time / I'm free / Destiny / Flip flop / Never felt love before / I can remember / Light of my life / Can't stop loving you / Hit and run.
LP: . . . . **SEE 232**

Cavallaro, Carmen

CARMEN CAVALLARO, 1946.
Tracks: / My sentimental heart (opening theme) / Zing went the strings of my heart / I didn't know what time it was / I'll follow my secret heart / It's delovely / On the waterfall / I've got you under my skin / Souvenir / Rose room / Lover / I want to be happy / By the waters of Minnetonka / Carefree / Sweet Lorraine / To a wild rose / Kiss me again / Just one of those things / My sentimental heart (closing theme).
LP: . . . . **HSR 112**

DANCING IN A DREAM.
Tracks: / I had the craziest dream / There goes my heart / Desafinado / Everything I have is yours / If I give my heart to you / In the still of the night / Dancing on the ceiling / I can dream, can't I / But beautiful / I've got a pocketful of dreams / It's magic / Let's face the music and dance.
LP: . . . . **JASM 1508**

Cavatina

MUSIC OF CHRISTMAS, THE.
Tracks: / Sleigh ride / Ding dong merrily on high / Good King Wenceslas / First Nowell, The / Ave Maria / What child is this? / God rest ye merry gentlemen / Little drummer boy / Holly and the ivy, The / Golden bells / Past three o clock / O Little town of Bethlehem / Christmas song, The / Walking in the air / Little shepherd boy / In the bleak mid winter / Trio from l'enfance du Christ, Opus 25 / Coventry carol / We three kings of Orient are / Holy boys, The / Interlude from 'ceremony of carols', Opus 28 / Amid the roses Mary sits / Rudolph the red nosed reindeer / White Christmas / Silent night.
MC: . . . . **HSC 3291**

Cave, Nick

BURNING THE ICE (See Die Haut) (Cave, Nick/Die Haut).

FIRST BORN IS DEAD, THE (Cave, Nick & The Bad Seeds).
LP: . . . . **STUMM 21**
MC: . . . . **CSTUMM 21**

FROM HERE TO ETERNITY (Cave, Nick & The Bad Seeds).
Tracks: / Avalanche / Cabin fever / Well of misery / From here to eternity / In the ghetto / Moon in the ghetto / Saint Huck / Wings off flies / Box for black Paul, A / From her to eternity (1987).
LP: . . . . **STUMM 17**

GOOD SON, THE (Cave, Nick & The Bad Seeds).
LP: . . . . **STUMM 76**
MC: . . . . **CSTUMM 76**

KICKING AGAINST THE PRICKS (Cave, Nick & The Bad Seeds).
LP: . . . . **STUMM 28**
MC: . . . . **C STUMM 28**

TENDER PREY (Cave, Nick & The Bad Seeds).
LP: . . . . **STUMM 52**
MC: . . . . **CSTUMM 52**

YOUR FUNERAL, MY TRIAL (Cave, Nick & The Bad Seeds).
LP: . . . . **STUMM 34**
MC: . . . . **CSTUMM 34**

Cavello, Jimmy

JIMMY CAVELLO AND THE HOUSE ROCKERS (Cavello, Jimmy & the House Rockers).
LP: **93 209**

Caveman

POSITIVE REACTION.
LP: . . . . **FILER 406**
MC: . . . . **FILERCT 406**

Cavendish Dance Band

DANCING REELS.
Tracks: / Dashing white sergeant / Hamilton House / Duke of Perth / Reel of the 51st division / Eightsome reel / Foursome reel / Duke and Duchess of Edinburgh / Inverness country dance.
LP: . . . . **TRS 100**

ENCORE.
Tracks: / Eightsome reel / Foursome reel / Hamilton House / Duke and Duchess of Edinburgh / Duke of Perth / Scottish reform / Reel of the 51st division / Inverness country dance.
LP: . . . . **TRS 102**

Cawood, Garth

GARTH CAWOOD'S FUNHOUSE.
LP: . . . . **SRTZ 76377**

Cayenne

EVENING IN JAFFA.
LP: . . . . **CODA 11**
MC: . . . . **COCA 11**

HOT NIGHTS.
LP: . . . . **CODA 22**
MC: . . . . **COCA 22**
LP: **834165-1**

ROBERTO WHO?.
LP: . . . . **GPLP 30**

CB Radio

OFFICIAL GUIDE TO CB RADIO (Various artists).
MC: . . . . **SP 101**

CBS (label)

CBS ARTISTS VOL 1 (Various artists).
MC: **40 2622**

CBS ARTISTS VOL 2 (Various artists).
MC: **40 2630**

CBS ROCKABILLY (See under Rockabilly) (Various artists).

C-Cat Trance

KHAMU.
LP: . . . . **INK 6**

PLAY MASEKO COMBUTBA.
LP: . . . . **INK 33**

ZOUAVE.
LP: . . . . **INK 20**

CCCP

1964-1984.
LP: . . . . **APR 10**

CCM

INTO THE VOID.
LP: . . . . **BEL 007**

CCS

BEST OF CCS.
Tracks: / Whole lotta love / Boom boom / Walkin' / Hurricane evening / I want you back / Band played the boogie / Brother / (I can't get no) satisfaction / Wade in the water / Living in the past / Primitive love / Tap turns on the water.
LP: . . . . **SRAK 527**

CCS.
LP: . . . . **SRAK 503**

WHOLE LOTTA LOVE.
Tracks: / Whole lotta love / Boom boom / Sunrise / Wade in the water / Walking / Salome / Tap turns on water / Save the world / Brother / Black dog / I want you back / Whole lotta rock 'n' roll / School day / Lucille / Long tall Sally / Chaos / Can't we ever get it back / Sixteen tons / Band played the boogie, The / Lola / Our man in London / Cannibal sheep / Primitive love / Hurricane coming.
MC: . . . . **TCEMS 1426**

Ceannt, Eamonn

CEILI TIME IN IRELAND (Ceannt, Eamonn Ceili Band).
MC: . . . . **COX 1025**

RECALL AND STEP ABOUT (Ceannt, Eamonn Ceili Band).
MC: . . . . **CT 129**

Celebrated Ratliffe

BEHIND THE MASK.
Tracks: / Have you got a penny / Circus comes to town, The / Highland plaid and tink a trink / Rothwell market / Song and dance man / Old George Dawson / Season's talke - jubilee jump, A / England / Tickeli and Marjoret / Summer will be with us by and by / Goodbye dear friends.
LP: . . . . **PLR 020**

VANLAG.
Tracks: / Greenwood tree / All in a garden green / Wolsey's wild / Goddesses / Morris room / Old spies never die / Vanlag / Dug deveam's dream / Bright lit pier, The.
LP: . . . . **PLR 030**

Celebrity Selection

CELEBRITY SELECTION RHYMES (Various artists).
LP: . . . . **STMP 30**

Celebrity Skin

GOOD CLEAN.
LP: . . . . **TX 93111**
MC: . . . . **TX 93114**

Celestial Sounds

ETERNITY.
MC: . . . . **C 162**

SANCTUARY.
MC: . . . . **C 161**

Celestin, Papa

CELESTIN'S ORIGINAL TUXEDO JAZZ ORCHESTRA (1926-28) (Celestin's Original Tuxedo Orchestra).
LP: . . . . **VLP 33**

DOWN ON THE DELTA (see under Johnson, Bunk Band) (Celestin, Papa/ Bunk Johnson Band).

PAPA CELESTIN AND HIS NEW ORLEANS JAZZ BAND (Celestin, Papa, & His New Orleans Jazz Band).
LP: . . . . **FL 9030**

PAPA CELESTIN & HIS NEW ORLEANS RAGTIME BAND (Celestin, Papa, & His New Orleans Ragtime Band).
LP: . . . . **JCE 28**

Celi Bee

ALTERNATING CURRENTS (Celi Bee & The Buzzy Bunch).
MC: . . . . **TKR 82531**

Celibate Rifles

BLIND EAR.
LP: . . . . **RAT 503**

KISS KISS BANG BANG.
Tracks: / Back in the red / Temper temper / JNS / Pretty colours / Nether world / Some kinda feeling / New mistakes / Carmine vattelly (N.Y.N.Y.C.) / City of fun / Conflict of instinct / Sometimes / Burn my eye / S.O.S..
LP: . . . . **GOES ON 08**

MINA, MINA, MINA,.
LP: . . . . **GOES ON 05**

PLATTERS DU JOUR.
LP: . . . . **RAT 504**

QUINTESSENTIALLY YOURS.
LP: . . . . **RIFLE 1**

TURGID MIASMA OF EXISTENCE, THE.
LP: . . . . **HOT 1024**

Cellmates

ON PAROLE.
LP: . . . . **RAGELP 103**

Cellos

CELLOS.
LP: . . . . **RELIC 5074**

Celtic Frost

CELTIC FROST STORY, THE (Chris Tetley presents).
LPPD: . . . . **ROHALP 1**
MC: . . . . **ROHAMC 1**

COLD LAKE.
LP: . . . . **N 0125**
LP: . . . . **NUK 125**
MC: . . . . **ZCNUK 125**
MC: . . . . **N 0125 2**

EMPEROR'S RETURN.
LPPD: . . . . **NUKPD 024**
MLP: . . . . **NUK 024**
MLP: . . . . **N 0024**

INTO THE PANDEMONIUM.
Tracks: / Mexican radio / Mesmerized / Inner sanctum / Sorrows of the moon / Babylon sell / Caress into oblivion / One in their pride / I won't dance / Rexirae (requiem) / Oriental masquerade.
LP: . . . . **NUK 065**
LP: . . . . **N 0065**
MC: . . . . **N 0066**

MORBID TALES.
MLP: . . . . **N 0017**
MLP: . . . . **NUK 017**

TO MEGA THERION.
LP: . . . . **N 0031**
LP: . . . . **NUK 031**

VANITY/NEMESIS.
Tracks: / Heart beneath, The / Wine in my hand (third from the sun) / Wings of solitude / Name of my bride, The / This island earth / Restless seas / Phallic tantrum / Kiss or a whisper, A / Vanity / Nemesis / Heroes (CD only.).
LP: . . . . **EMC 3576**
MC: . . . . **TCEMC 3576**

Celtic Thunder

CELTIC THUNDER.
LP: . . . . **SIF 1029**
MC: . . . . **CSIF 1029**

Censorship Sucks

CENSORSHIP SUCKS (Various artists).
Tracks: / Fateful: *Pastels* / No filthy nuclear power: *Oi Polloi* / Don't like what I do: *Cateran* / Shitting on Britain: *Shamen* / Helicopters: *Bayonet Babies* / J't'accuse: *Househunters* / All fours: *Fini* Tribe / Shat on by angels: *Dog Faced Hermans* / Penal landscape gardener: *Membranes* / Coko-kola U.S.A.: *Rodney* Relax With... / Hey sister: *Primevals* / Rosemary Ledingham: *BMX Bandits* / Jack Ruby: *Beat Poets*/ Jackman II: *Jackhammer 5* / Virginia's wolf: *Poolkas* / Losing your grip: *Meat Whiplash*.
LP: . . . . **DISPLP 13**

Census Taker (film)

CENSUS TAKER, THE (Film Soundtrack) (Residents).
Tracks: / Creeping dread / Census taker, The / Talk / End of home / Emotional music / Secret seed / Easter woman/Simple song / Hellno / Where is she / Innocence decayed / Romanian/ Nice old man / Margaret Freeman / Lights out/Where is she / Passing the bottle / Census taker returns, The.
LP: . . . . **ED 21**

Centennial Summer

CENTENNIAL SUMMER/STATE FAIR (Film soundtrack) (Various artists).
LP: . . . . **CIF 3009**

Central Band of...

SALUTE TO HEROES (VIDEO) (See under Royal Air Force) (Central Band of the RAF).

Central Council

BELLS-THE RHYTHM OF THE BELLS (Central Council Of Church Bell Ringers).
LP: . . . . **SDL 211**

Central Hall Choir

20 FAVOURITE HYMNS OF CHARLES WESLEY.
LP: . . . . **MVP 828**

Central Line

BREAKING POINT.
Tracks: / Walking into sunshine / I need your love / Breaking point / Goodbye / That's no way to treat my love / Don't tell me (you know) / You can do it / Shake it up.
LP: . . . . MERA 001
MC: . . . . MERC 001

CHOICE.
Tracks: / Time for some fun / Betcha gonna / How about you / Lost in love / Bad floyd / Nature boy / Man at the top / Surprise surprise / You've said enough.
LP: . . . . MERL 33

Central Park Sheiks

HONEYSUCKLE ROSE.
LP: . . . . FF 026

Century Of Sound

CENTURY OF SOUND 1877-1977 (Various artists).
2LP: . . . . PL 42146

Ceol Tradisiunta

ROULEDOM.
MC: . . . . GTDC 019

Cephas, Bowling Green

DOG DAYS OF AUGUST.
LP: . . . . FF 394

SWEET BITTER BLUES (Bowling Green John Cephas & Phil Hea Wiggins).
LP: . . . . LR 42.054

Cerebral Fix

LIFE SUCKS AND THEN YOU DIE.
LP: . . . . SOL 15

TOWER OF SPITE.
LP: . . . . RO 93561
MC: . . . . RO 93564

Cerebus

TOO LATE TO PRAY.
LP: . . . . GWD 90542
MC: . . . . GWC 90542

Cerletti, Marco

RANDOM AND PROVIDENCE.
Tracks: / Setting the sales / Glasshouse in the desert / La ville blanche / Sundown / Random and providence / Light over darkness / Encore toi / Web, The / Birds of paradise / Art of weathering November, The.
LP: . . . . VBR 20391

Cerrone

CERRONE'S PARADISE.
Tracks: / Take me / Time for love, A / Cerrone's paradise.
LP: . . . . K 50377

GOLDEN TOUCH.
Tracks: / Je suis music / Rocket in the pocket / Look for love / Music of life.
LP: . . . . CBS 83282

IN CONCERT.
Tracks: / Gimme some lovin' / Africanism / Love in C minor / Living it up / Cerrone's paradise / Je suis music / Supernature / Sweet drums / Rocket in my pocket / Give me love.
LP: . . . . CBS 88459

LOVE IN 'C' MINOR.
Tracks: / Love in 'C' minor / Black is black / Midnite lady.
LP: . . . . K 50334

SUPERNATURE.
Tracks: / Supernature / Sweet drums / In the smoke / Give me love / Love is the answer.
LP: . . . . K 50431

Certain Fury (film)

CERTAIN FURY (1985 Original soundtrack) (Various artists).
LP: . . . . STV 81239

Certain General

SEXTET.
LP: . . . . FACT 55
MC: . . . . FACT 55 C

THESE ARE THE DAYS.
LP: . . . . ID 024

Certain Smile (film)

CERTAIN SMILE, A (Original soundtrack) (Various artists).
LP: . . . . LAALP 004

Cervenka, Exene

TWIN SISTERS (Cervenka, Exene & Wanda Coleman).
LP: . . . . FRWY 1057

Cesare

MOVE IT (See under Stereo MC's) (Cesare & Stereo MC's).

C'Est What

BALANCE.
LP: . . . . PJ 88036
MC: . . . . PJC 88035

Cetera, Peter

AFTER ALL (See under Cher).

IF I WASN'T THE ONE (WHO SAID GOODBYE) (see under Faltskog, Agnetha) (Cetera, Peter/Agnetha Faltskog).

ONE MORE STORY.
Tracks: / Best of times, The / One good woman / Peace of mind / Heaven help this lonely man / Save me / Holding out / Body language (there in the dark) / You never listen to me / Scheherazade / One more story.
LP: . . . . WX 161
MC: . . . . WX 161 C

PETER CETERA.
Tracks: / Livin' in the limelight / I can feel it / How many times / Holy Moly / Mona Mona / On the line / Not afraid to cry / Evil eye / Ivy covered walls / Practical man.
LP: . . . . K 99193

SOLITUDE/SOLITAIRE.
Tracks: / Big mistake / They don't make 'em like they used to / Glory of love / Queen of the masquerade ball / Daddy's girl / Next time I fall, The / Wake up love / Solitude/Solitaire / Only love knows why.
LP: 925474 1
MC: 925474 4

Cha Cha (film)

CHA CHA (Film soundtrack) (Various artists).
Tracks: / Love you like I love myself: *Brood, Herman* / Doin' it: *Brood, Herman* / You can't beat me: *Brood*, Herman / Jilted: *Brood, Herman* / Elvis: *Brood, Herman* / Never be clever: *Brood, Herman* / Home: *Lovich, Lene* / Pick up: *Phoney & The Hardcore* / Foolin': *Phoney & The Hardcore* / Sweet memories: *Floor* Van Zutphen / Take it all in: *Meteors* / It's you, only you: *Meteors* / Herman's door: *Hagen, Nina* / Herman's first high: *Hagen, Nina* / You don't fit: *Inside Nipples* / 2-2-get-her: *Monika Tuen A Kkwoei* / Sonny blues: *Sonny & The Dulfer Gang* / No more conversations: *Street Beats* / Bop: *Dulfer Gang* / I don't wanna lose you: *White Honey*.
LP: . . . . ARL 5039

Chacksfield, Frank

BEAUTIFUL MUSIC, VOLUME 1 (Chacksfield, Frank Orchestra).
Tracks: / Limelight / Ebb tide / All the things you are / In the still of the night / Stardust / Man and a woman, A / Just one of those things / Fool on the hill / Close to you / Where do I begin / Bewitched / This is my song.
LP: . . . . CN 2039
MC: CN4 2039

CHARIOTS OF FIRE (Chacksfield, Frank Orchestra).
Tracks: / Chariots of fire / Rose, The / Dolannes melodie / That look in your eyes / Seduction, The / Inishannon / We just couldn't say goodbye / Ballade pour Adeleine / I've heard that song before / Time after time / Midnight in Malibu / Mister Sandman / I can't begin to tell you / Soft lights / Aren't you glad you're you / Near you.
LP: . . . . CBR 1042
MC: . . . . KCBR 1042

COULD I HAVE THIS DANCE (Chacksfield, Frank Orchestra).
LP: . . . . DS 042

FOCUS ON FRANK CHACKSFIELD (Chacksfield, Frank Orchestra).
2LP: . . . . FOS 25/26

HAWAII (Chacksfield, Frank & His Orchestra).
Tracks: / Hawaiian war chant / Maori farewell song / Red sails in the sunset / On the beach at Waikiki / Sweet Leilani / Bali Ha'i / Hawaiian wedding song / Coco-nut / Blue Hawaii / My little grass shack / Moon of Manakoora / Aloha, oe.
LP: . . . . DGS 1

LIMELIGHT AND OTHER FAVOURITES (Chacksfield, Frank Orchestra).
Tracks: / Limelight / Why do you pass me by / Speak to me of love / Zigeuner / Smile / Anema e core / Barcarolle / Love walked in / Intermezzo / Where are you / I'll see you again / Mean to me / My own / Lady of Spain.
LP: . . . . PLE 521

LITTLE MORE LOVE, A (Chacksfield, Frank Orchestra).
Tracks: / Dancing queen / With a little luck / Took the last train / Grease / London Town / Sam / Sir Duke / Don't cry out loud / Raining in my heart / Silly love songs / Even now / (Our love) don't throw it all away / I'm dreaming / Too much heaven / Little more love, A / Higher and higher / Shadow dancing / Come in from the rain / I just wanna be your everything / It's a miracle / Almost like a song / Early morning rain / I need to be in love / Sunflower / Here you come again / Lucille / Bluer than blue / Wasted nights and wasted days / Heartbreaker / Forever in blue jeans / Blue bayou / Southern nights / Closer I get to you, The / Before the next teardrop falls / I guess it doesn't matter anymore / Carefree highway / How can I leave you again? / Luckenbach, Texas / Walk right back / Last thing on my mind.
2LP: . . . . PPD 2002
MC: . . . . PPK 2002

LOVE IS IN THE AIR (Chacksfield, Frank Orchestra).
Tracks: / After the lovin' / I can't smile without you / When I need you / Nobody does it better / I just want to be your everything / We're all alone / Don't it make my brown eyes blue / You don't bring me flowers / You light up my life / Looks like we made it / How deep is your love / Sometimes when we touch / Just the way you are / Three times a lady / Hopelessly devoted to you / Love is in the air / Talking in your sleep / Ready to take a chance again / You needed me / Too much too little too late.
LP: . . . . CBR 1002
MC: . . . . KCBR 1002

NICE 'N' EASY (Chacksfield, Frank Orchestra).
Tracks: / There, I've said it again / I couldn't live without your love / Just my imagination / Things we do for love, The / Nice 'n' easy / Love, or something like it / Fifty ways to leave your lover / Lover come back to me / You are my destiny / Just walking in the rain / Chances are / Rise / Little things mean a lot / Kiss an angel good morning / Love song / Walking in rhythm / Right time of the night / Early morning rain / Air that I breathe, The / Tonight you belong to me.
LP: . . . . CBR 1034
MC: . . . . KCBR 1034

NOBODY DOES IT BETTER (Chacksfield, Frank Orchestra).
LP: . . . . SPR 8565
MC: . . . . SPC 8565

THANKS FOR THE MEMORIES (The Academy Award Winners 1934-1955) (Chacksfield, Frank & His Orchestra).
Tracks: / Continental, The / Lullaby of Broadway / Way you look tonight, The / Sweet Leilani / Thanks for the memory / Over the rainbow / When you wish upon a star / Last time I saw Paris, The / White Christmas / You'll never know / Swinging on a star / It might as well be Spring / On the Atchison, Topeka and the Santa Fe / Zip-a-dee-doo-dah / Buttons and bows / Baby it's cold outside / Mona Lisa / In the cool cool cool of the evening / High noon / Secret love / Three coins in the fountain / Love is a many splendoured thing.
MC: 8440634

WORLD OF....
Tracks: / Ebb tide / Moulin rouge waltz / My prayer / Fascination / Jealousy / Born free / Limelight / Temptation / Blue Danube / Love letters in the sand / Cuban boy / Lawrence of Arabia.
LP: . . . . SPA 5

WORLD OF IMMORTAL SERENADES (Chacksfield, Frank Orchestra).
LP: . . . . SPA 298

Chadborne, Eugene

CAMPER VAN CHADBORNE (Chadborne, Eugene/Camper Van Beethoven).
Tracks: / Reason to believe / I talk to the wind / Fayettenam / Evil filthy preacher / Games people play / Zappa medley / Ba-lue bolivar ba-lues are / Boy with the coins / Psychedelic basement / Hum-allah hum-allah / Careful with that axe Eugene / They can make it rain bombs.
LP: . . . . SAVE 046

CORPSES OF FOREIGN WARS.
MC: . . . . CAVE 010
LP: . . . . SAVE 010

COUNTRY MUSIC OF EUGENE CHADBORNE.
LP: . . . . RRR 001

COUNTRY PROTEST.
LP: . . . . SAVE 007

EDDIE CHATTERBOX DOUBLE TRIO LOVE ALBUM, THE.
LP: . . . . SAVE 069
MC: . . . . SAVE 069MC

I'VE BEEN EVERYWHERE.
LP: . . . . SAVE 068
MC: . . . . SAVE 068MC

KULTURAL TERRORISTS (Chadborne, Eugene/John Rose).
LP: . . . . ST 7551

LSD C AND W, THE.
2LP: . . . . SAVE 019/020

THERE WILL BE NO TEARS.
LP: . . . . SAVE 006

VERMIN OF THE BLUES (Chadborne, Eugene, Evans Johns & The Ha Bombs).
LP: . . . . SAVE 018

Chadwick, Doreen

DOREEN CHADWICK IN MANCHESTER.
LP: . . . . CF 280

OH, LADY BE GOOD.
Tracks: / Waltzing through the years / Jolly juggler / Tenement symphony / Onedin line theme / Meditation / Tiger rag.
MC: . . . . AC 185

PRINCESS OF THE THEATRE ORGAN.
LP: . . . . DO 1415

Chafe, Winnie

HIGHLAND AIRS OF CAPE BRETON.
LP: . . . . ROUNDER 7012
MC: . . . . ROUNDER 7012C

Chaheb, Lem

SAHARA ELEKTRIK (see under Dissidenten) (Chaheb, Lem & Dissidenten).

Chain Men

FOOL'S GOLD.
LP: . . . . COL 269511

Chain Reaction

CHANGE OF ACTION.
LP: . . . . CPLPS 1

CHASE A MIRACLE.
LP: . . . . CPLPS 2

INDEBTED TO YOU.
Tracks: / Never lose, never win / Why can't we be lovers / Quicksand / Think I'll keep this song just like it is / Cold steel / Miss Lovely, Miss Beautiful / Hogtied / Indebted to you / Chase a miracle.
LP: . . . . GULP 1021

X RATED DREAM.
LP: . . . . LAT 1135

Chain, Ruby

SHARON'S SMILE.
LP: . . . . RUBY 01

Chainsaw

HELL'S BURNIN' UP.
Tracks: / Hell's burnin' up / Dungeon, The / Last fortress / Cut loose / Rage and revenge / Midnight hunter / Born to kill / He knows you are alone / Ageless force.
LP: . . . . BONE 2

Chainsaws

PART TIME HEROES.
LP: . . . . BIAS 123

Chairmen Of The Board

AGM.
LP: . . . . HDH LP 006

SALUTE THE GENERAL.
LP: . . . . HDH LP 001

SKIN I'M IN.
LP: . . . . INV 65868

SOUL AGENDA.
Tracks: / Chairman Of The Board / Working on a building of love / Bravo, hooray / (You've got me) dangling on a string / Everything's Tuesday / I'll come crawling / Elmo James / Give me just a little more time / All we need is understanding / Men are getting scarce / Let me down easy / Pay to the piper / Patches / Tricked and trapped (by a tricky trapper) / Bless you (Available on CD only) / When will she tell me she needs me (Available on CD only) / Try on my love for size (Available on CD only) / Bittersweet (Available on CD only) / Everybody's got a song to sing (Available on CD only) / Finders keepers (Available on CD only).
LP: . . . . HDH LP 007

Chakk

TEN DAYS IN AN ELEVATOR.
Tracks: / Stare me out / Imagination / Big hot blues / Over the edge / Lovetrip / She conceives destruction / Falling / Years I worked / Murder (Available on bonus EP only.) / Big hot mix (Available on bonus EP only.) / Stare me out - crash mix (Available on bonus EP only.) / Cut the dust (Available on bonus EP only.).
LP: . . . . MCG 6006
MC: . . . . MCGC 6006

Chaliapin, Feodor

FEODOR CHALIAPIN.
LP: . . . . GVC 507

Chalice

CROSSFIRE.
LP: . . . . DSR 8141

Chalice (Reggae)

CATCH IT.
LP: RRTG 7737

LIVE AT REGGAE SUNSPLASH.
LP: VSLP 8902

STAND UP.
Tracks: / Hit you like a bomb / Dangerous disturbances / Wicked intention / Back way evil forces / Stand up / Go slow / Point dem finger / Easy street / Shine on / I never knew love.
LP: CSLP 19

UP TILL NOW.
LP: RAS 3026

Chalkdust

MASTER, THE.
Tracks: / Two chords and Heston Paul / Dey lucky an have children / Coke talk / Eric Williams dead / Calypso cricket / Two chords and Heston Paul.
LP: GS 2283

TOTAL KAISO.
LP: GS 2298
MC: GSC 2298

Chalker, Bryan

CROSS TRACKIN'.
LP: GES 5013

EARLY DAYS.
LP: SFA 020

SONGS AND BALLADS.
Tracks: / Going from cotton fields / Molly darling / Great Titanic, The / Give me your love / When I swim the Golden river / Rosewood casket / Wreck on the highway / Long black veil / Mary on the wild moore / Legend of the Irish rebel / Ballad of the blue tail fly / Blue Ridge Mountain blues.
LP: SFA 025

Chalker, Curly

NASHVILLE SUNDOWN.
LP: GNPS 2099

SONGS OF GORDON LIGHTFOOT.
LP: SNTF 694

Challengers

25 GREATEST INSTRUMENTAL HITS.
2LP: GNPS 2609

SIDEWALK SURFING.
LP: GNPS 2093

SURF BEAT.
LP: ED 143

VANILLA FUNK.
LP: GNPS 2056

WIPE OUT.
LP: GNPS 2031
MC: GNP5 2031

Challis, Bill

BILL CHALLIS AND HIS ORCHESTRA 1936 (Challis, Bill and His Orchestra).
LP: CLP 71

GOLDKETTLE PROJECT, THE.
LP: CLP 118
MC: CLMC 118

MORE 1936 (Challis, Bill and His Orchestra).
LP: CLP 72

Chaloff, Serge

BLUE SERGE.
Tracks: / Handful of stars, A / Goof and I, The / Thanks for the memory / All the things you are / I've got the world on a string / Susie's blues / Stairway to the stars.
LP: AFF 146

BOSTON BLOW UP (Chaloff, Serge Sextet).
Tracks: / Bob, the robin / Yesterday's gardenias / Sergical / What's new / J.R. / Body and soul / Kip / Diana's melody / Unison.
LP: AFF 63

Cham, Gustave

LE SQUIRRE (Cham, Gustave & Stevy).
LP: SC 100

Chamber Jazz Sextet

PLAYS PAL JOEY.
Tracks: / I could write a book / My funny valentine / I didn't know what time it was / Zip / Lady is a tramp, The.
LP: CS 9030

Chamberlain, Richard

RICHARD CHAMBERLAIN SINGS.
LP: MGM C 923

Chamberland, Linc

PLACE WITHIN, A.
LP: MR 5064

YET TO COME.
Tracks: / I hear a rhapsody / Virgo / Have you met Miss Jones / Footprints / Yet to come / Autumn leaves.
LP: MR 5263

Chambers, James C

23RD PSALM - LIVE IN CHICAGO.
Tracks: / Good news / Lamb of God / I will praise Him / Soul'd out / 23rd psalm / Heaven belongs to you / Great is thy faithfulness / Victory through Jesus Christ / No matter.
LP: GCR 4034
MC: GCR 4034MC

Chambers, Joe

SUPER JAZZ TRIO, THE (see under Flanagan, Tommy) (Chambers, Joe and Tommy Flanagan and Reggie Workman).

Chambers, Paul

EASE IT (Chambers, Paul & Cannonball Adderly).
Tracks: / Ease it / Just friends / I got rhythm / Julie Ann / Awful mean / There is no greater love.
LP: AFF 115

WE THREE (see under Haynes, Roy) (Haynes, Roy Trio).

WEST COAST CONFERENCE (see Perkins,Bill) (Chambers, Paul/Bill Perkins/Philly Joe Jones).

Chamblee, Eddie

ROCKIN' AND WALKIN' RHYTHM OF EDDIE CHAMBLEE.
Tracks: / Backstreet / Last call / Song of India / Dureop / Cradle rock / Lazy mood / Blue steel / All out / Wooden soldiers swing / Six string boogie / Walkin' home / Lonesome road / Come on in / Lal lal lal lady / Goin' long / Back up.
LP: OFF 6031

Chambre Jaune

BETTER DEAD THAN ALIEN.
LP: SCHEMER 8906

BLESSINGS OF A HATCHMAN.
Tracks: / Deathpoint valley / Hatch agaony / Frits / Tommy gun / Ignorance / Your black eyes / Collective / Guilts / Pogo reprise.
LP: JIGPROD 003

HUGGING THE HEAD.
LP: JIGPROD 004

Chameleon

CHAMELEON.
LP: FLYLP 100
MC: FLYMC 100

Chameleons

FAN AND THE BELLOWS, THE.
LP: CHAMLP 1
MC: CHAMC 1

PEEL SESSIONS: THE CHAMELEONS.
LP: SFRLP 114
MC: SFRMC 114

SCRIPT OF THE BRIDGE.
Tracks: / Don't fall / Here today / Monkeyland / Seal skin / Up the down escalator / Less than human / Pleasure and pain / Thursday's child / As high as you can go / Person isn't safe anywhere these days, A / Paper tiger / View from a hill / Nostalgia / In shreds.
LP: STAT LP 17
MC: STAT C 17

STRANGE TIMES.
Tracks: / Mad Jack / Caution / Soul in isolation / Swamp thing / Time / End of time, The / Seriocity / In answer / Childhood / I'll remember / Tears.
LP: 9241191
MC: 9241194

WHAT DOES ANYTHING MEAN BASICALLY ?.
LP: STAT LP 22
MC: STAT C 22

Champ (film)

CHAMP, THE (Film soundtrack) (Various artists).
Tracks: / If you remember me: *Various artists* / Main title: *Various artists* / Cha cha do Brazil, A: *Various artists* / Serenade in G, K 525 eine kleine nachtmusik: *Various artists* / Nothing but a groove: *Various artists*/ Find out way: *Various artists* / Gym montage: *Various artists* / T.J.'s theme: *Various artists* / Champ, The (theme from): *Various artists* / Salon du Miami: *Various artists* / Visiting hours: *Various artists*/ Gone: *Various artists*.
LP: K 52152

Champagne, Connie

LA STRADA.
MC: HEY 022CS

Champagne Country

CHAMPAGNE COUNTRY (See under Country...).

Champagne & Roses

CHAMPAGNE AND ROSES (Various artists).
LP: ROSTV 1

Champaign

HOW 'BOUT US.
Tracks: / Can you find the time / Party people / Whiplash / I'm on fire / How 'bout us / Spinnin' / Dancin' together again / Lighten up / If one more morning.
LP: CBS 84927

MODERN HEART.
Tracks: / Let your body rock / Try again / Party line / Cool running / Walkin' / Keep it up / Love games / Get it again / International feel.
LP: CBS 25038
MC: 40 25038

WOMAN IN FLAMES.
Tracks: / Off and on love / This time / Prisoner / Intimate strangers / Woman in flames / Mardi gras / Be mine tonight / Capture the moon.
LP: CBS 26018

Champion (label)

CHAMPION CLASSICS (Various artists).
LP: CHAMP 1019
MC: CHAMPK 1019

CHAMPION TRAX (Various artists).
LP: CHAMP 1018
MC: CHAMPK 1018

Champion String Band

CHAMPION STRING BAND.
Tracks: / Man of the house / Humours of old Knockaree, The / Ivy leaf, The / Farewell lovely Nancy / Hunter, The / Ruby, The / Laurell hill hunt / Midnight on the water / Julia Delaney / Moving cloud, The / Kerry huntsman, The / Lady Rothes / General Garibaldi / Champion hornpipe, The / Song of temptation, The / Dean Brig / Banks hornpipe / Gardener, The / James Hill's no.8 / Pear tree, The / Eighteen-sixties, The / South shore, The.
LP: CRO 201
MC: CROC 201

Champions

MEET THE CHAMPIONS.
LP: SOLP 1026

Champs

TEQUILA.
Tracks: / Tequila / Train to nowhere / Sombrero / Experiment in terror / La cucaracha / Too much tequila / Turn pike / Beatnik / El rancho rock / Midnighter / Chariot rock / Subway / Limbo rock / Red eye / Gone train / Caramba.
LP: CH 227

Chance, Bob

IT'S BROKEN.
Tracks: / Brown skinned girl / Honey lips / It's broken / Van man, The / I see her / Colors / Jungle talk.
LP: MORRHYTHM 40

ROCK COUNTRY.
Tracks: / Oh pretty woman / Mr. Doormat / Dixieland / Another Twentieth Centry Fox / Headin' down to New Orleans / If you want a woman's love / Goodbye chicago / My heart has been sentenced to jail / If I were a carpenter / Anaheim.
LP: MORRHYTHM 41

Chance, James

LIVE IN NEW YORK (Chance, James & the Contortions).
MC: A 100

Chance, Trevor

EVERYTHING MUST CHANGE.
Tracks: / This masquerade / Everything must change / It seems like yesterday / I think it's going to rain today / Why don't you see the show again / All in love is fair / Fifty ways to leave your lover / One day I'll fly away / In your eyes / Trying to get the feeling again / Lady / Between the lines.
LP: LAM 701

LOVE IS....
Tracks: / Love is / We're all alone / I'd love you to want me / Cowboys and daddies / Yesterday's heroes / Living in world of make believe / Air that I breathe, The / Thank you baby / You and me against the world / When love was all we had.
LP: SIMON LP 1

Chancler, Ndugu

OLD FRIENDS, NEW FRIENDS.
LP: MCA 6302

Chandell, Tim

BREAKING UP.
Tracks: / Breaking up / Talk to me / It's raining / Think it over / Believe in love / Dream of love / Keep coming round / Go on with your wedding.
LP: ANG LP 00

LITTLE LOVE, A.
LP: SKLP 55

LOVE MUSIC.
LP: SKYLP 50

LOVING MOODS OF TIM CHANDELL.
LP: OLP 011
MC: COLP 011

SEND ME SOME LOVING.
LP: UNKNOWN

TOGETHER AGAIN (Chandell, Tim & Ornell Hinds).
Tracks: / There will come love / Baby come back / Since you're gone / You don't want me / Don't take away your love / Hurting me badly / O what a smile / Together again.
LP: OLP 020

YOU'RE GONNA HURT ME SO.
LP: OLP 014
MC: COLP 014

Chandler, Gene

60'S SOUL BROTHER.
Tracks: / If you can't be true (find a part time love) / Bet you never thought / Gonna be good times / Nothing can stop me / There goes the lover / I'm just a fool for you / What now / Girl don't care, The / There was a time / From the teacher to the preacher / Those were the good old days / Little like lovin', A / Pretty little girl / My baby's gone / Tell me what I can do / Here comes the tears.
LP: KENT 049

80.
Tracks: / Does she have a friend / Lay me gently / All about the paper / Rainbow '80 / Do it baby / You've been so sweet to me / I'll be there / Let me make love to you.
LP: T 605

DUKE OF EARL.
LP: 2636494

DUKE OF SOUL, THE.
Tracks: / Duke of Earl / You threw a lucky punch / Night owl / Check yourself / Tear for tear / Think nothing about it / Rainbow / Rainbow '65 / What now / God bless our love / Just be true / Man's temptation.
LP: CXMB 7201

GET DOWN.
Tracks: / Get down / Please sunrise / Tomorrow I may not feel the same / I'm the travelling kind / Greatest love ever known / Give me the cue / What now / Lovequake.
LP: BT 578

LIVE AT THE REGAL.
Tracks: / Rainbow / If you can't be true (find a part time love) / Soul hootenanny / Monkey time / What now / Just be true / Ain't no use / Bless our love / Song called soul, A.
LP: CRB 1117

WHEN YOU'RE NUMBER 1.
Tracks: / That funky disco rhythm / When you're number one / I'll remember you / Do what comes so natural / Stay here in my heart / Dance fever.
LP: T 598

Chandler, Omar

OMAR CHANDLER.
LP: MCA 10057
MC: MCAC 10057

Chandler, Raymond

BIG SLEEP, THE (see under Big Sleep (bk)) (Massey, Daniel (nar)).

Chandos, Fay (aut)

SWEET ROSEMARY (see under Sweet Rosemary (bk)) (Andrews, June (nar)).

Chandra, Sheila

NADA BRAHMA.
Tracks: / Nada brahma / Awakening, The / Question the answer / Raqs / In essence.
LP: SCH 4

OUT ON MY OWN.
Tracks: / All you want is more / Out on my own / Village girl / Storm trance / From a whisper to a scream / Prema, Shanti, Dharma, Satya / Unchanged malady / Missing the voice / Fly to me / Songbird / Awakening, The (On CD only) / Question the answer (On CD only) / Raqs (On CD only) / In essence (On CD only).
LP: SCH 1

QUIET.
Tracks: / Quiet 1 / Quiet 2 / Quiet 3 / Quiet 4 / Quiet 5 / Quiet 6 / Quiet 7 / Quiet 8 / Quiet 9 / Quiet 10 / Nada brahma 1 (On CD only) / Nada brahma 2 (On CD only) / Nada brahma 3 (On CD only) / Nada brahma 4 (On CD only) / Mecca.
LP: SCH 2

ROOTS AND WINGS.
Tracks: / One / Shanti, shanti, shanti / Roots and wings / Struggle, The

(Slagverk's mix) / Roots and wings (Madras mix) / Mecca / Konnokol al dente / Escher's triangle / Struggle, The - The dream / Shanti, shanti, shanti (version).
LP: . . . . **SCH 5**
MC: . . . . **SCHMC 5**

SILK 1983-1990.
Tracks: / Village girl / Quiet 2 / Lament / Strange minaret / Quiet 9 / Satyam shisam sundaram / All you want is more / Rags / Out on my own / Lament of McCrimmon / Song of the banshee.
LP: . . . . **SILKLP 1**
MC: . . . . **SILKMC 1**

STRUGGLE, THE.
Tracks: / Strange minaret / Puppet tears / Struggle, The / Satyam, Shisam, Sundaram / Mukta gaana / Yon / Lament / Om shanti om / Struggle, The - The dream (On CD only) / Struggle, The (Slagverk's mix) (On CD only) / Strange minaret (Ximerre mix) (On CD only).
LP: . . . . **SCH 3**

Change

CHANGE OF HEART.
Tracks: / Say you love me again / Change of heart / Warm / True love / You are my melody / Lovely lady / Got my eyes on you / It burns me up.
LP: . . . . **WX 5**
MC: . . . . **WX 5C**

GLOW OF LOVE, THE.
Tracks: / Lover's holiday / It's a girl's affair / Angel in my pocket / Glow of love, The / Searching / End, The.
LP: . . . . **K 99107**
MC: **K4 99107**

MIRACLES.
Tracks: / Paradise / Hold tight / Your move / Stop for love / On top / Heaven of my life / Miracles.
LP: . . . . **K 99140**
MC: **K4 99140**

SHARING YOUR LOVE.
LP: . . . . **SH 8550**
MC: . . . . **KSAC 8550**

TURN ON YOUR RADIO.
Tracks: / Turn on the radio / Let's go together / Examination / You'll always be part of me / Oh what a feeling / Mutual attraction / Love the way you love me / If you want my love.
LP: . . . . **CHR 1504**
MC: . . . . **ZCHR 1504**

Channel 3

I'VE GOT A GUN.
LP: . . . . **PUNK 2**

WHEN THE LIGHTS GO OUT.
LP: . . . . **PUNK 7**

Channing, Carol

KIDDING AROUND WITH CAROL CHANNING.
LP: . . . . **TC 1494**

PETER AND THE WOLF AND TUBBY THE TUBA.
LP: . . . . **TC 1623**

Chanson

CHANSON.
Tracks: / Don't hold back / I can tell / I love you more / Why / Did you ever / All the time you need.
LP: . . . . **ARL 5018**

Chant Village Stories

CHANT VILLAGE STORIES (St. Clair, Isla (nar)).
MC: . . . . **TBC 9503**

MORE CHANT VILLAGE STORIES (St. Clair, Isla (nar)).
MC: . . . . **TBC 9506**

Chantalls

CHANTALLS COLLECTION.
LP: . . . . **UNKNOWN**

Chantels

CHANTELS, THE.
LP: . . . . **END LP 301**

WAITING IN THE PARK.
LP: . . . . **PRFLP 002**
MC: . . . . **PRFC 002**

Chanter Sisters

READY FOR LOVE.
Tracks: / You've lost that lovin' feeling / Never thought fall in love (could be so wild) / Dance, dance, dance / Talking too much about my baby / When the lights go out / Na na hey hey (kiss him goodbye) / It's too late now / Just your fool / Sunshiny day / Nashville.
LP: . . . . **LONG 3**

SHOULDER TO SHOULDER.
Tracks: / Shoulder to shoulder / Oh what a shame / I wanna get closer / I love you / Born to lose / Can't stop dancing / Carrie Blue / I'll be there / I've got your number / Thanks to you.
LP: . . . . **LONG 4**

Chaos (label)

CHAOS IN EUROPE (Various artists).
LP: . . . . **KS 19872**

Chaos UK

CHIPPING SODBURY BONFIRE TAPES.
LP: . . . . **SLAPLP 1**

EAR SLAUGHTER (Chaos UK & Extreme Noise Terror).
LP: . . . . **ACHE 001**

SHORT SHARP SHOCK (Lawless Britain).
LP: . . . . **GURT 1**

Chaotic Dischord

CHAOTIC DISCORD LIVE.
LP: . . . . **CITY 008**

F*CK OFF YOU C*NT WHAT A LOAD OF BOLLOCKS.
LP: . . . . **SYNLP 12**

FUCK RELIGION, FUCK POLITICS AND FUCK THE LOT OF.
LP: . . . . **CITY 004**

GOAT FUCKING VIRGIN KILLERZ FROM HELL.
LP: . . . . **GRR 2**

NOW THAT'S WHAT I CALL A FUCKING RACKET VOL.1.
LP: . . . . **GRR 1**

VERY FUCKIN' BAD.
Tracks: / Where have all the glueheads gone / Aussie song / Mrs. Meat curtains / Anarchy in Harvey Proctor's y-fronts / Fuck off ripcord / Ricks arsehole / Some shit about cricket / Mega metal death and thunder god grandad / Hey goth fuck off / Fergie's baby is a dischord baby / Chip on my shoulder / Berkshire cowboy / Sill fuckin' dying / We're fuckin' glad.
LP: . . . . **GRR 3RV**

Chapel Choir...

CHAPEL CHOIR OF BLUECOAT SCHOOL (Chapel Choir of Bluecoat School).
LP: . . . . **LPB 645**

Chaperals

ANOTHER SHOW.
Tracks: / Hello everybody / Lucky guy / Falling leaves / Lover's question, A / Sh boom / White cliffs of Dover / Motorbiene / Angels listened / Jitterburg Mary / Sitting in my room / Zoom, zoom, zoom / So Allein / In gee-home is where the heart is.
LP: . . . . **BFX 15320**

COME OUT TONIGHT.
Tracks: / Come out tonight / I'm yours (zippitydoo) / Only you / Shouldn't I / Stuck on you / Bells, The / Story of love, A / Come go with me / Doo wop memories / I hear bells / Voodoo man, The / That's my desire / Come along with me / Rum and coca cola.
LP: . . . . **BFX 15318**

Chapin, Harry

ANTHOLOGY - HARRY CHAPIN.
Tracks: / W.O.L.D / Any old kind of day / Cats in the cradle / 30,000 pounds of bananas / Taxi / She is always seventeen / Sunday morning sunshine / I wanna learn a love song / Better place to be / Song man.
LP: . . . . **EKT 16**
MC: . . . . **EKT 16 C**

DANCE BAND ON THE TITANIC.
Tracks: / Dance band on the Titanic / Why should people stay the same / My old lady / We grew up a little bit / Bluesman / Country dreams / I do it for you, Jane / I wonder what happened to him / Paint a picture of yourself / Mismatch / Mercenaries / Manhood / One light in a dark valley (an imitation spiritual) / There was only one choice.
LP: . . . . **K 62021**
MC: **K4 62021**

GREATEST STORIES-LIVE.
Tracks: / Dreams go by / W.O.L.D. / Saturday morning / I wanna learn a love song / Mr. Tanner / Better place to be / Let time go lightly / Cats in the cradle / Taxi / Circle / 30,000 pounds of bananas / She is always seventeen / Love is just another world / Shortest story, The.
LP: . . . . **K 62017**

HEADS AND TALES.
Tracks: / Could you put your light on, please / Greyhound / Everybody's lonely / Sometime, somewhere wife / Empty taxi / Any old kind of day / Dogtown / Same sad singer.
LP: . . . . **K 42107**

LAST PROTEST SINGER, THE.
Tracks: / Last of the protest singers / November rains / Basic protest song / Last stand / Sounds like America to me / Word wizard / Anthem / Quiet little love affair, A / I don't want to be president / Silly little girl / You own the only light.
LP: . . . . **NEXLP 101**
MC: . . . . **NEXMC 101**

LEGEND OF THE LOST AND FOUND - NEW GREATEST STORY.
Tracks: / Stranger with the melodies / Copper / Day they closed the factory down, The / Pretzel man / Old folkie / Get on with it / We were three / Odd job man / Legends of the lost and found / You are the only song / Mail order Annie / Tangled up puppet / Poor damned fool / Corey's coming / If my Mary were here / Flowers are red.
LP: . . . . **K 62026**

LIVING ROOM SUITE.
Tracks: / Dancin' boy / If you want to feel / Poor damned fool / I wonder what would happen to this world / Jenny / It seems you only love me when it rains / Why do little girls / Flowers are red / Somebody said.
LP: . . . . **K 52089**
MC: **K4 52089**

ON THE ROAD TO KINGDOM COME.
Tracks: / On the road to kingdom come / Parade's still passing by, The / Mayor of Candor lied, The / Laugh man / Corey's coming / If my Mary were here / Fall in love with him / Caroline / Roll down the river.
MC: . . . . **K 452040**
LP: . . . . **K 52040**

PORTRAIT GALLERY.
Tracks: / Dreams go by / Tangled up puppet / Star tripper / Babysitter / Someone keeps calling my name / Rock, The / Sandy / Dirt gets under the fingernails / Summer / Stop singing those sad songs / Dancin' boy / If you want to feel / Poor damned fool / I wonder what happened to this world / Jenny / It seems you only love me when it rains / Why do little girls / Flowers are red / Somebody said.
LP: . . . . **K 52023**

SEQUEL.
Tracks: / Sequel / I miss America / Story of a life / Remember when the music / Up on the shelf / Salt & pepper / God babe, you've been good for me / Northwest 222 / I finally found it Sandy.
MC: **40 84996**
LP: . . . . **FW 36872**
LP: . . . . **EPC 84996**

SHORT STORIES.
Tracks: / Short stories / W O L D / Song for myself / Song man / Changes / They call her easy / Mr. Tanner / Mail order Annie / There's a lot of lonely people tonight / Old college avenue.
LP: . . . . **K 42155**

SNIPER AND OTHER LOVE SONGS.
Tracks: / Sunday morning sunshine / Sniper / And the baby never cries / Burning herself / Barefoot boy / Better place to be / Circle / Woman child / Winter song.
LP: . . . . **K 42125**

VERITIES AND BALDERDASH.
Tracks: / Cat's in the cradle / I wanna learn a love song / Shooting star / 30,000 pounds of bananas / She sings songs without words / What made America famous / Vacancy / Halfway to heaven / Six string orchestra.
LP: . . . . **K 52007**

Chapin, Tom

LET ME BACK INTO YOUR LIFE.
LP: . . . . **FF 401**

Chaplain, Paul

MR NICOTINE (Chaplain, Paul & The Emeralds).
Tracks: / Mr. Nicotine / Time time / Caldonia / Shortnin' bread / Baby please don't leave / I did it all night long / I'll be waiting on Heartbreak Avenue / Swingtime in the rockers / I saw her standing on the corner / I get the bug / Movin' / Bye bye baby / My lovey dovey.
LP: . . . . **WLP 8915**

Chaplin, Blondie

BLONDIE CHAPLIN.
Tracks: / Bye bye babe / Can you hear me / Crazy love / Woman don't cry / Loose lady / Be my love / Lonely traveller / Riverboat queen / Say you need me for your love / Gimme more rock'n'roll.
LP: . . . . **K 53062**

Chaplin, Charlie

CHAPLIN CHANT.
LP: . . . . **TWLP 1020**

DANCE HALL ROCKERS.
LP: . . . . **Unknown**

KNEE AFRICA.
LP: . . . . **DSR 8367**

NEGRIL CHILL (See under Yellowman) (Yellowman & Charlie Chaplin).

ONE OF A KIND.
Tracks: / One of a kind / Foreign man skank / Trouble in a earth / Walk with Jah / Skanky producer / Sturgav special / Tribute to super Don / Quenchie.
LP: . . . . **TRLS 216**

PRESENTING CHARLIE CHAPLIN.
Tracks: / Mother-in-law / Naw leave me chalwa / Air is polluted / Chaplin's chant / Ann Marie / Youthman / Fussing and fighting / Jamaican calley / Electric skank.
LP: . . . . **KVL 9012**

QUE DEM.
LP: . . . . **DSR 4753**

RED POND.
LP: . . . . **TWLP 1014**

ROOTS OF CULTURE.
LP: . . . . **VSLP 4063**

SOUND SYSTEM.
LP: . . . . **RLP 012**

TAKE TWO.
LP: . . . . **RAS 3060**
MC: . . . . **RASC 3060**

TWO SIDES OF CHARLIE CHAPLIN.
LP: . . . . **RAS 3043**
MC: . . . . **RASC 3043**

YELLOWMAN MEETS CHARLIE CHAPLIN (See under Yellowman) (Chaplin, Charlie & Yellowman).

Chaplin, Sid

DAY OF THE SARDINE.
MC: . . . . **SOUND 23**

Chapman, Ben

BEN CHAPMAN.
LP: . . . . **PL 74931**
MC: . . . . **PK 74931**

Chapman, Marshall

TAKE IT ON HOME.
LP: . . . . **ROUNDER 3069**
MC: . . . . **ROUNDER 3069C**

Chapman, Michael

ALMOST ALONE.
Tracks: / Dogs got more sense / Fireside hound / I'm sober now / Movie of the same name, Theme from / Nuages / Deal gone down / SHC / Kodak ghosts / Waiting for Miguel (Northern lights) / Fahey's flag / No thanks to me / Falling apart / Among the trees / In the trees.
LP: . . . . **CRO 202**
MC: . . . . **CROC 202**

BEST OF MICHAEL CHAPMAN, THE (1969-1971).
Tracks: / Naked ladies and electric ragtime / Rainmaker / You say / In the valley / Kodak ghosts / Postcards of Scarborough / It didn't work out / Last lady song / Wrecked again / First leaf of autumn, The / Soulful lady / Polar bear fandango (Available on CD only) / All in all (Available on CD only) / Fennario (Available on CD only) / Shuffle boat river farewell (Available on CD only) / Small stones (Available on CD only).
LP: . . . . **SEE 230**

FULLY QUALIFIED SURVIVOR.
Tracks: / Fishbeard sunset / Soulful lady / Rabbit hills / March rain / Kodak ghosts / Andru's easy rider / Trinkets and rings / Aviator / Naked ladies and electric ragtime / Stranger in the room / Postcards of Scarborough.
LP: . . . . **HIFLY 38**
LP: **C5-527**
LP: . . . . **SHVL 764**

HEARTBEAT.
Tracks: / Heartbeat / All is forgiven / Chuckie, The / Africa / Minute you leave, The / Tristesse / Redskin bridge / Tendresse / Heartbeat reprise.
LP: . . . . **NAGE 12**
MC: . . . . **NAGEC 12**

LIFE ON THE CEILING.
LP: . . . . **STEAL 5**

MAN WHO HATED MORNINGS.
LP: . . . . **STEAL 3**

MICHAEL CHAPMAN LIVED HERE FROM 1968-72.
Tracks: / Naked ladies and electric ragtime / Rainmaker / You say / In the valley / Kodak ghosts / Postcards of Scarborough / It didn't work out / Last lady song / Wrecked again / First leaf of autumn, The / Soulful lady.
LP: . . . . **GNAT 1**

ORIGINAL OWNERS (Chapman, Michael & Rick Kemp).
LP: . . . . **KOMA 788003**

PLAY THE GUITAR THE EASY WAY.
LP: . . . . **STEAL 2**

PLEASURES OF THE STREET.
LP: **6.22321**

Chapman, Morris

VOICE OF PRAISE (Chapman, Morris & Friends).
LP: . . . . MM R 0133
MC: . . . . MM C 0133

Chapman, Philip

KEEPER OF DREAMS.
MC: . . . . C 164

KINGDOM, THE.
MC: . . . . C 163

SOUL MATES - MUSIC OF LOVE.
MC: . . . . C 169

Chapman, Roger

CHAPPO.
Tracks: / Midnite child / Hang on to a dream / Face of stone / Pills / Always gotta pay in the end / Moth to a flame / Shapes of things.
LP: . . . . SPART 1083
LP: 604629

HE WAS SHE WAS YOU WAS WE WAS.
LP: 2646 106
LP: 084624

HYENAS ONLY LAUGH FOR FUN.
LP: 6.24850
MC: . . . . HCT 4 24850
LP: 604625

LIVE IN BERLIN.
Tracks: / Shadow on the wall / How how how / Let me down / Mango crazy.
LP: 604639

LIVE IN HAMBURG.
Tracks: / Moth to a flame / Keep forgettin' / Midnight child / Who pulled the nite down / Talking about you / Going down / Short list / Can't get in / Keep a knockin' / I'm your hoochie coochie man / Let's spend the night together.
LP: 6.24720
LP: 604628
LP: . . . . ACTC 7

MAIL ORDER MAGIC.
LP: . . . . KAM 001
LP: 604627

MANGO CRAZY.
LP: 604623

SHADOW KNOWS, THE.
LP: . . . . ZL 70482
MC: . . . . ZK 70482

Chapman, Tracy

CROSSROADS.
Tracks: / Crossroads / Freedom now / Be careful of my heart / Born to fight / This time / Bridges / Material world / Subcity / Hundred years, A / All that you have is your soul.
LP: . . . . EKT 61
MC: . . . . EKT 61C

TRACY CHAPMAN.
Tracks: / Talkin' bout a revolution / Fast car / Across the lines / Behind the wall / Baby can I hold you / Mountains O' things / She's got her ticket / Why? / For my lover / If not now... / For you.
LP: . . . . EKT 44
MC: . . . . EKT 44C

Chapman & Whitney

STREETWALKERS.
Tracks: / Parisienne high heels / Roxiana / Systematic stealth / Call ya / Creature feature / Sue and Betty Jean / Showbiz Joe / Just four men / Tokyo Rose / Hangman.
LP: . . . . K 54017

Chappelat, Jean-Robert

PRINCE DE L'ACCORDEON.
Tracks: / Polka satellite / Belle et sentimentale / Toboggan rag / Shocking valse / Senhor sivuca / Matins qui chantent / Accordeon Bresilien / Cornaline / Drole de rigolade / System A / L'oiseau mouche / Slalom tres special.
LP: . . . . UNKNOWN
MC: . . . . Unknown

Chapter 8

FOREVER.
Tracks: / Stronger love / Give me a chance / So in love / Understanding / I can't wait / One and only / Real love / Forever / Last time, The / Long time to love.
LP: . . . . EST 2073
MC: . . . . TCEST 2073

Chapter House Choir

TEDDY BEAR'S PICNIC.
Tracks: / Teddy bears' picnic / Christopher Robin is saying his prayers / Lullaby of Birdland / Moon river / Bluebell polka / Sweet and low / Over the rainbow / Night and day / Shenandoah / I got shoes / Summertime / Radetzky march / Every time we say goodbye / Autumn leaves / Deep purple / Feller from fortune.
LP: . . . . HAR 812
MC: . . . . HAC 812

Chapterhouse

WHIRLPOOL.
LP: . . . . DEDLP 001
MC: . . . . DEDMC 001

Chaquito

THIS CHAQUITO (Chaquito & Quedo Brass).
LP: . . . . SFXL 50

THRILLER THEMES.
LP: 6308 087

Charge

PERFECTION.
LP: . . . . KAM 013

Charig, Marc

PIPEDREAM.
LP: . . . . OG 710

Chariot

BURNING AMBITION.
LP: . . . . SHADE 4

WARRIOR, THE.
LP: . . . . SKULL 8392
LP: . . . . SHADES 1

Chariots of Fire

CHARIOTS OF FIRE (See under Vangelis) (Vangelis).

Charisma

ONE FOR THE ROAD.
LP: . . . . SRTZ 76367

Charisma (label)

CHARISMA REPEAT PERFORMANCE (Various artists).
Tracks: / Theme one: *Van Der Graaf Generator* / Lady Eleanor: *Lindisfarne* / Gaye: *Ward, Clifford T.* / Sympathy: *Rare Bird* / It's a game: *Various artists* / Liar: *Various artists* / America: *Various* artists / I know what I like: *Genesis* / I get a kick out of you: *Shearston, Gary* / Spanish wine: *Various* artists / Solsbury Hill: *Gabriel, Peter* / It's all over now: *Various artists* / Everyday: *Various artists*/ Reggae for it now: *Lovelady, Bill.*
LP: . . . . BG 1
MC: . . . . BGC 1

Charity Churchmouse

ON THE FRONTLINE.
MC: . . . . MMC 0191

Charlatans

SOME FRIENDLY.
LP: . . . . SITU 30
MC: . . . . SITC 30

Charlebois, Jeanne

HOMMAGE A MADAME BOLDUC.
LP: . . . . PH 2014

Charlemagne Palestine

STRUMMING MUSIC.
LP: . . . . SHAN 83517

Charlene

HIT AND RUN LOVER.
LP: . . . . ZL 72176
MC: . . . . ZK 72176

I'VE NEVER BEEN TO ME.
Tracks: / I've never been to me / It ain't easy comin' down / Can't we try / Hungry / Hey mama / I won't remember ever loving you / Johnny doesn't live here anymore / After the ball / I need a man / If I could see myself.
LP: . . . . STML 12171
MC: . . . . CSTML 12171

SKY IS THE LIMIT.
Tracks: / Sky is the limit / Living still goes on / Rise up / I want the world to know he's mine / There was nothing to believe in / Jesus is love / Prayer / You knew just what I needed / Cover me.
LP: . . . . CLS 8011
MC: . . . . TC CLS 8011

USED TO BE.
Tracks: / If you take away the pain until the morning / Used to be / Heaven help us all / I want to go back there again / Rainbows / Last song, The / Some things never change / Richie's song / You're home.
LP: . . . . STML 12179
MC: . . . . CSTML 12179

USED TO BE (SINGLE) (See under Wonder, Steve) (Charlene & Stevie Wonder).

Charles Augustus...

CHARLES AUGUSTUS MILVERTON (Various artists).
Tracks: / Charles Augustus Milverton: *Various artists* / Black Peter: *Various artists.*
MC: . . . . ANV 642

Charles, Bobby

BOBBY CHARLES.
Tracks: / Watch it sprocket / Yeah yeah / You know I love you / Good lovin' / I'd like to know / Ain't got no home / Time will tell / Take it easy greasy / You can suit yourself / See you later alligator / On bended knee / I'll turn square for you / Put your arms around me, honey / I ain't gonna do it no more / Lonely street / Mr. Moon / One eyed Jack / Hey good lookin'.
LP: . . . . CXMP 2009

CHESS MASTERS: BOBBY CHARLES.
LP: . . . . GCH 8094
MC: . . . . GCHK 78094

CLEAN WATER.
LP: . . . . ZS 35

SMALL TOWN TALK.
Tracks: / Street people / Long face / I must be in a good place now / Save me Jesus / He's got all the whisky / Let yourself go / Grow too old / I'm that way / Tennessee blues.
LP: . . . . SEE 218

Charles, Cathy (aut)

SECRET OF THE GLEN (see under Secret Of The Glen (bk)) (Craig, Karen (nar)).

Charles, Ray

14 ORIGINAL GREATEST HITS:RAY CHARLES.
LP: . . . . K 5011

16 GREATEST HITS.
Tracks: / What'd I say / Busted / Here we go again / I can't stop loving you / That lucky old sun / Let's go get stoned / Hide nor hair / Georgia on my mind / Unchain my heart / I got a woman / Hit the road Jack / Eleanor Rigby / Don't set me free / America the beautiful.
MC: 264823 4

16 ORIGINAL HITS: RAY CHARLES.
MC: . . . . MC 1631

20 GOLDEN PIECES: RAY CHARLES.
Tracks: / Alone in the city / Can anyone ask for more? / Rockin' chair blues / Let's have a ball / How long how long blues / Sentimental blues, A / You always miss the water (when the well runs dry) / I've had my fun / Sitting on top of the world / Ain't that fine? / Don't put all your dreams in one basket / Ray Charles blues / Honey honey / She's on the ball / Baby won't you please come home? / If I give you my love / This love of mine / Can't you see me, darling? / Someday / I'm going down to the river.
LP: . . . . BDL 2012

20 GREATEST HITS: RAY CHARLES.
LP: . . . . B 90108
MC: . . . . MB 990108

25TH ANNIVERSARY IN SHOW BUSINESS.
LP: . . . . K 60014

1950.
LP: 522 011

AIN'T IT SO.
Tracks: / Some enchanted evening / Blues in the night / Just because / What'll I do / One of these days / Love me or set me free / Drift away / Love me tonight.
LP: . . . . SHL 8537

BROTHER RAY.
Tracks: / Compared to what / Anyway you want to / Don't you love me anymore / Poor man's song / Now that we've found each other / Ophelia / I can't change it / Questions.
LP: . . . . SH 8546

CAN'T STOP LOVING YOU.
LP: . . . . PLP 22
MC: . . . . PMC 22

C.C. RIDER.
Tracks: / C.C. Rider / I wonder who's kissing her now / Going down slow / Lovin' the girls / Kiss me baby / All alone again / Sitting on top of the world / Tell me baby / Baby let me hold your hand / Hey now / All to myself alone / Walkin' and talkin'.
LP: . . . . CBR 1018
MC: . . . . KCBR 1018

CLASSIC DUO (See under Como, Perry) (Charles, Ray/Perry Como).

COLLECTION: RAY CHARLES (2).
Tracks: / Yesterday / Your cheatin' heart / Georgia on my mind / I can't stop loving you / Busted / Together again / Take these chains from my heart / Crying time / Half as much / Here we go again / Born to lose / Eleanor Rigby / You don't know me / Hit the road Jack / I gotta woman (live) / What'd I say (live).
LP: . . . . RCLP 101
MC: . . . . RCLC 101

COLLECTION: RAY CHARLES (20 GOLDEN GREATS).
Tracks: / Georgia on my mind / What'd I say / Sitting on top of the world / Ain't that fine / Can't you see darling / Sentimental blues, A / If I give you my love / She's on the ball / Ray Charles blues / How long / Come rain or come shine / Alone in the city / Someday / This love of mine / I'm going down to the river / You always miss the water (when the well runs dry) / Baby won't you please come home / Don't put all your dreams in one basket / I've had my fun / Let's have a ball.
LP: . . . . DVLP 2005
MC: . . . . DVMC 2005

COLLECTION: RAY CHARLES (CASTLE COLLECTOR).
2LP: . . . . CCSLP 241
MC: . . . . CCSMC 241

COLLECTION: RAY CHARLES (STAR JAZZ USA).
LP: . . . . SJAZZ 1
MC: . . . . SJAZZC 1

COLLECTION: RAY CHARLES (THE LOVE SONGS).
Tracks: / I wonder who's kissing her now / Here am I / Oh baby / I used to be so happy / Honey honey / Ego song, The / Hey now / Late in the evening blues / I live only for you / St. Pete's blues / I'm glad for your sake / I'm just a lonely boy / All night long / See see rider / All to myself alone / Blues is my middle name.
LP: . . . . DVLP 2123
MC: . . . . DVMC 2123

COME LIVE WITH ME.
LP: . . . . SHU 8467

COUNTRY SIDE OF RAY CHARLES.
LP: . . . . ADAH 447
MC: . . . . ADAHC 447

DO I EVER CROSS YOUR MIND?.
Tracks: / I had it all / Do I ever cross your mind / Woman sensuous woman / Then I'll be over you / Lay around and love on you / Love of my life / They call it love / If I were you / Workin' man's woman / I was on Georgia time.
LP: . . . . CBS 25764
MC: 40 25764

EARLY YEARS.
LP: . . . . ZET 707

EVERYTHING.
Tracks: / Kiss me baby / Sitting on top of the world / I'm gonna drown myself / All alone again / Lovin' the girls / I will not let you go / I'm glad for your sake / Walkin' and talkin'.
LP: . . . . MAN 5029

FANTASTIC RAY CHARLES, THE.
Tracks: / Going down slow / Blues is my middle name / If I give you my love / Can't you see, darling? / Goin' away blues / Sitting on top of the world / Late in the evening blues / Here am I / Ray's blues / I'm just a lonely boy / St. Pete blues / Easy ridin' gal / See see rider / I wonder who's kissing her now / I'm going down to the river / I'm glad for your sake / Ego song, The / I used to be so happy / Hey now / What have I done? / All night long / All to myself alone / Oh baby / I live only for you.
2LP: . . . . ALB 103

FRIENDSHIP.
Tracks: / Two old cats like us / This old heart of mine / We didn't see a thing / Who cares / Rock and roll shoes / Friendship / It ain't gonna worry my mind / Little hotel room / Crazy old soldier / Seven Spanish angels.
LP: . . . . CBS 26060
MC: 40 26060

GENIUS + SOUL = JAZZ.
LP: . . . . ESSLP 009
MC: . . . . ESSMC 009

GENIUS, THE.
Tracks: / Sitting on top of the world / Kiss my baby / I'm gonna drown myself / All alone again / I had my fun / Snow is falling / Blues is my middle name / Oh baby / C.C. rider / Hey now / Tell me baby / Going down slowly / Walkin' and talkin' / I'm glad for your sake / Baby let me hold your hand / All to myself alone.
LP: . . . . XELLP 106
MC: . . . . XELMC 106

GEORGIA ON MY MIND.
LP: . . . . SM 3926

GOIN' DOWN SLOW.
Tracks: / Going down slow / Alone in the city / Now she's gone / Rockin' chair blues / Can anyone ask for more / Let's have a ball / This love of mine / Can't see you darling? / If I give you my love.
LP: . . . . MTM 002

GREAT HITS.
Tracks: / Going down slow / All night long / I'm givin' up / Guitar blues / Talkin' 'bout you / I found my baby there / I'm wonderin' and wonderin' / By myself / Snowfall.
LP: . . . . PHX 1013

GREATEST COUNTRY AND WESTERN HITS.
Tracks: / Your cheating heart / Hey good lookin' / Take these chains from my heart / Don't tell me your troubles / I

can't stop loving you / Just a little lovin' / It makes no difference now / You don't know me / You are my sunshine / Someday (you'll want me to want you) / I love you so much it hurts / Careless love / Oh, lonesome me / Midnight / No letter today / Crying time / Together again / Don't let her know / I'll never stand in your way (Only on CD.) / Hang your head in shame (Only on CD.).
LP: . . . . NEXLP 100
MC: . . . . NEXMC 100

GREATEST HITS: RAY CHARLES.
LP: . . . . CLP 1626

GREATEST HITS: RAY CHARLES, VOL. 2.
LP: . . . . SSL 10241

HEART TO HEART - 20 HOT HITS.
LP: . . . . RAY TV 1

HERE AM I.
Tracks: / Easy riding gal / Tapeworld / Ray's blues / Here am I / Blow my baby back home / Blues is my middle name.
LP: . . . . B 10106
MC: MB9 10106

HIT THE ROAD JACK.
LP: . . . . PLP 21
MC: . . . . PMC 21

HITS OF A GENIUS.
LP: 39009
MC: 69009

I CAN'T STOP LOVING YOU.
Tracks: / Hit the road Jack / Hallelujah I love her so / Mess around / Let's go get stoned / Don't let the sun catch you cryin' / What'd I say / Georgia on my mind / I got a woman / Drown in my own tears / Night time is the right time / Eleanor Rigby / I can't stop loving you.
LP: . . . . SSP 3075
LP: 24004

I WISH YOU WERE HERE TONIGHT.
Tracks: / 3/4 time / I wish you were here tonight / Ain't your memory got no pride at all? / Born to love me / I don't want no stranger sleepin' in my bed / Let your love flow / You feel good all over / String bean / You've got the longest leaving act in town / Shakin' your head.
LP: . . . . CBS 25065
MC: 40 25065

IF I GIVE YOU MY LOVE.
Tracks: / Alone in the city / Can anyone ask for more / Rockin' chair blues / Let's have a ball / If I give you my love / Can't see you darling? / This love of mine / Sentimental blues, A / Now she's gone / Going down slow.
LP: . . . . F 50014
MC: . . . . MF 950014

JAMMIN' THE BLUES.
LP: 20078
MC: 40078

JUST BETWEEN US.
Tracks: / Nothing like a hundred miles / I wish I'd never loved you at all / Too hard to love you / Now I don't believe that anymore / Let's call the whole thing off / Stranger in my own hometown / Over the top / I'd walk a little more for you / If that's what'cha want / Save the bones for Henry Jones.
LP: 4611831
MC: 4611834

KING OF THE BLUES.
MC: . . . . AMP 011

LIVE : RAY CHARLES.
2LP: 2-503

MODERN SOUNDS IN COUNTRY AND WESTERN MUSIC VOL.2.
LP: . . . . CLP 1613

MODERN SOUNDS IN COUNTRY AND WESTERN MUSIC VOL.1.
LP: . . . . CLP 1580

PAGES OF MY MIND, THE.
Tracks: / Pages of my mind, The / Slip away / Anybody with the blues / Class reunion / Caught a touch of your love / Little bit of heaven, A / Dixie moon / Over and over (again) / Beaucoup love / Love is worth the pain.
LP: . . . . CBS 26856
MC: 40 26856

PERRY COMO/RAY CHARLES (see under Como, Perry) (Charles, Ray/Perry Como).

RAY CHARLES.
MC: . . . . SSC 3075
MC: . . . . ZCGAS 729
LP: . . . . ENT 13005
LP: . . . . BID 8011
LP: . . . . ENT LP 13005
MC: . . . . ENT MC 13005

RAY CHARLES AND BETTY CARTER (Charles, Ray & Betty Carter).
Tracks: / Every time we say goodbye / You and I / Goodbye, we'll be together again / People will say we're in love / Cocktails for two / Side by side / Baby it's cold outside / Together / For all we know / It takes two to tango / Alone together / Just you and me / But on the other hand baby / I never see Maggie alone / I like to hear it sometimes.
LP: . . . . ESSLP 012
MC: . . . . ESSMC 012

RAY CHARLES BLUES.
LP: 20079
MC: 40079

RAY CHARLES (DOUBLE CASSETTE).
MCSET: . . . . DTO 10202

RAY CHARLES (JOKER (USA)).
LP: . . . . SM 3712

RAY CHARLES STORY, THE.
Tracks: / Baby won't you please come home / Ego song, The / You always miss the water (when the well runs dry) / St. Pete's blues / I live only for you / What have I done / C.C. rider / I've had my fun / Honey honey / Here am I / I wonder who's kissing her now / Ray Charles blues / She's on the ball / If I give you my love / I'm going down to the river / Let's have a ball / Hey now / Sitting on top of the world / Sentimental blues, A / I used to be so happy / Ain't that fine / All to myself alone / Georgia on my mind / What'd I say / Come rain or come shine.
MCSET: . . . . DVREMC 02

RAY CHARLES VOL.2.
Tracks: / Alone in the city / Can anyone ask for more / Rockin' chair blues / Let's have a ball / If I give you my love / Can't see you darling? / This love of mine / Sentimental blues, A / Now she's gone / Going down slow.
LP: . . . . SM 3729

RAY OF HOPE.
Tracks: / See see rider / I wonder who's kissing her now / Hey now / Tell me baby / Kiss me baby / I'm gonna drown myself / Winter scene / Lovin' the girls.
LP: . . . . MAN 5020

RIGHT TIME, THE.
Tracks: / Leave my woman alone / My Bonnie / That's enough / Drown in my own tears / Fool for you, A / Hallelujah I love her so / This little girl of mine / Mary Ann / I got a woman / Yes indeed / Swanee River rock / Lonely avenue / I had a dream / Early in the morning / Right time, The / I'm movin' on / What kind of man are you (Extra track on CD only) / I want to know (Extra track on CD only) / What'd I say (part 1) (Extra track on the CD only) / What'd I say (part 2) (Extra track on the CD only) / Jumpin' in the mornin'.
LP: 241 119-1
MC: 241 119-4

ROCKIN' WITH RAY.
LP: . . . . SM 3871

SIMPLY RAY.
Tracks: / All to myself alone / Going down slow / Baby let me hold your hand / I won't let you go / Sitting on top of the world / By myself / Winter scene / Lovin' the girls.
LP: . . . . MAN 5019

SOUL MEETING (Charles, Ray & Milt Jackson).
Tracks: / Hallelujah I love her so / Blue genius / X-ray blues / Soul meeting / Love on my mind / Bags of blues.
LP: . . . . K 50234

SPIRIT OF CHRISTMAS, THE.
Tracks: / What child is this / Little drummer boy / Santa Claus is coming to town / This time of the year / Rudolph the red nosed reindeer / That spirit of Christmas / All I want for Christmas / Christmas in my heart / Winter wonderland / Christmas time.
MC: 40 26562
LP: . . . . CBS 26562

STAR COLLECTION.
Tracks: / I got a woman / Let the good times roll / Ray, The / Loosing hand / Mess around / Mary Ann / This little girl of mine / Talkin' bout you / Undecided / Alexanders ragtime band / Don't let the sun catch you crying.
LP: . . . . K 20015
MC: K4 20015

TELL THE TRUTH.
Tracks: / Mess around / It should've been me / Losing hand / Greenbacks / I got a woman / This little girl of mine / Hallelujah I love her so / Drown in my own tears / Leave my woman alone / Lonely Avenue / That's enough / Talkin' 'bout you / You be my baby / Right time, The / Tell the truth / What'd I say?.
LP: . . . . CRB 1071
MC: . . . . TCCRB 1071

THIS LOVE OF MINE.
Tracks: / Kiss me baby / Baby let me hold your hand / C.C. rider / I wonder who's kissing her now / I'm going down to the river / They're crazy about me / Going down slow / Sentimental blues, A / Can anyone ask for more / Rockin' chair blues / If I give you my love / This love of mine.
LP: . . . . TOP 126
MC: . . . . KTOP 126

TRUE TO LIFE.
LP: . . . . SHU 8509

WHAT IS LIFE?.
Tracks: / Going to the river / Steppin' out baby / Dear heart / Glow worm / Take some and leave some / All alone / I'll do anything but work / My mama told me / I'm yours for the asking / Blow my baby back home / Too late to change / What is life?.
LP: . . . . B 90112
MC: MB9 90112

Charles, Ronnie

HANDS OFF.
LP: . . . . TELP 001

Charles, Teddy

ON CAMPUS (Charles, Teddy & Zoot Sims).
LP: . . . . FS 237

SALUTE TO HAMP.
LP: . . . . FS 151

Charles, Tina

DANCE LITTLE LADY.
MC: . . . . HSC 3047
LP: . . . . SHM 3047
LP: . . . . CBS 81617

HEART'N'SOUL.
LP: . . . . CBS 82180

I LOVE TO LOVE.
Tracks: / I love to love (teenage mix) / I love to love.
LP: . . . . CBS 81290

JUST ONE SMILE.
Tracks: / Just one smile / I'm just as bad as you / Lover boy / Dance with me / Makin' all the right moves / Somewhere / Love is a many splendoured thing / Secret love / Fire down below / Boogie round the clock.
LP: . . . . CBS 84240

TINA SINGS.
LP: . . . . MAME 3001

Charleston Chasers

CHARLESTON CHASERS 1925/28.
LP: . . . . VLP 26

CHARLESTON CHASERS 1929/31.
LP: . . . . VLP 44

Charley's War

TIME TO SURVIVE.
Tracks: / Intro / Promises / Ignorant attitudes (the war begins) / Wise up / Your path / Time to survive / We're young / Open your eyes / Be yourself / Think about your life / See a chance.
LP: . . . . AGR 056-1
MC: . . . . AGR 056-4

Charlie

CHARLIE AND HIS ORCHESTRA VOL.3 (1939-44) (Charlie & His Orchestra).
Tracks: / British soldiers song / Lili Marlene / Man with the big cigar, The / I'm sending you to the Siegfried line / Bye bye blackbird.
LP: . . . . HQ 2067

CHARLIE AND HIS ORCHESTRA VOL. 2 (1934-1937) (Charlie & His Orchestra).
Tracks: / I'm putting all my eggs in one basket / King's horses, The / I've got a pocketful of dreams / When day is done / Lambeth walk / I, I, I love you very much / Three little fishes / J'en ai marre / It's a lovely day tomorrow / You stepped out of a dream / Miss Annabelle Lee / Why'd ya make me fall in love / South of the border / Hold tight / Cachita / Germany calling broadcasts.
LP: . . . . HQ 2059

GERMAN PROPAGANDA SWING VOL.1 (1940-1941) (Charlie & His Orchestra).
Tracks: / Stormy weather / It's a long way to Tipperary / You're driving me crazy / You can't stop me from dreaming / With a smile and a song / St. Louis blues / Slumming on Park Avenue / Adieu mon pere / Dinah / Daisy / I'm playing with fire / Goody goody / F.D.R. Jones / After you've gone / Who'll buy my bublitchki / Sketch uber das abhorverbot auslandischer sender.
LP: . . . . HQ 2058

Charlie Brown

BOY NAMED CHARLIE BROWN (Film Soundtrack) (Various artists).
Tracks: / Boy named Charlie Brown: *Various artists* / Cloud dreams: *Various artists* / Charlie Brown and his allstars: *Various artists* / We lost again: *Various artists* / Blue Charlie Brown: *Various artists* / Time to go to school: *Various artists* / I only dread one day at a time: *Various artists* / Failure face: *Various artists*/ By golly I'll show 'em: *Various artists* / Class champion: *Various artists* / I before E: *Various artists*/ School spelling bee: *Various artists* / Champion Charlie Brown: *Various artists* / Start boning up on your spelling: *Various artists* / Charlie Brown: *Various artists* / You'll either be a hero or a goat: *Various artists*/ Bus station: *Various artists* / Bus wheel blues: *Various artists* / Do piano players make a lot of money: *Various* artists / I've got to get my blanket back: *Various artists* / Big city: *Various artists* / Snoopy on ice: *Various artists* / Found blanket: *Various artists* / National spelling bee: *Various artists* / B E A G E L: *Various artists* / Bus wheel blues: *Various artists* / Homecoming: *Various artists* / I'm never going to school again: *Various artists* / Welcome home Charlie Brown: *Various artists* / Boy named Charlie Brown: *Various artists.*
LP: 70078

CHARLIE BROWN'S ALL STARS (Various artists).
MC: 82DC 82

HE'S YOUR DOG, CHARLIE BROWN (Various artists).
MC: 83DC 83

IT'S THE GREAT PUMPKIN, CHARLIE BROWN (Various artists).
MC: 84DC 84

YOU'RE IN LOVE, CHARLIE BROWN (Various artists).
MC: 85DC 85

Charlie Chalk (T.V.)

CHARLIE CHALK (TV Soundtrack) (Various artists).
LP: . . . . CHARLP 1
MC: . . . . ZCHARL 1

Charlie Girl (show)

CHARLIE GIRL (1986 London revival cast) (Various artists).
Tracks: / Charlie Girl (overture): *Various artists* / Most ancestral home of all, The: *Various artists* / Bells will ring: *Various artists* / I love him, I love him: *Various artists* / What would I get from being married?: *Various artists* / Let's do a deal: *Various artists* / My favourite occupation: *Various artists* / What's the magic?: *Various artists* / When I hear music I dance: *Various artists* / I 'ates money: *Various artists*/ Charlie Girl waltz: *Various artists* / Party of a lifetime: *Various artists* / Like love: *Various artists*/ That's it: *Various artists* / Washington: *Various artists* / Fish and chips: *Various artists* / Society twist: *Various artists* / You never know what you can do: *Various artists* / Finale: *Various artists.*
LP: . . . . CAST 3
MC: . . . . CASTC 3

Charlie (Group)

FANTASY GIRLS.
Tracks: / Fantasy girls / Miss Deluxe / TV dreams / Prisoners / First class traveller / Greatcoat guru / Please let me know / Don't let me down / It's your life / Summer romances.
LP: 2383 373

FIGHT DIRTY.
Tracks: / California / Fight dirty / Don't count me out / Heartless / Runaway / Killer out / So alone / Just one more smiling face / End of it all / Too late.
LP: . . . . POLD 5017
LP: . . . . PPD 001

GOOD MORNING AMERICA.
Tracks: / Good morning America / I can't get over you / Roll the dice / Heading for home / Saturday night / My perfect lover / All my life / Fool for your love / I'm angry with you / Just one more chance / Girl won't dance with me, The.
LP: . . . . RCALP 5040
MC: . . . . RCAK 5040

HERE COMES TROUBLE.
Tracks: / Jealous / There you go again / Five years / Writing on the wall / Literary love / Take the money / Don't stand in my way / Only dreaming / Mind your own business / Zero.
LP: . . . . POLS 1053

LINES.
Tracks: / She loves to be in love / No more heartache / Life so cruel / Watching TV / Out of control / L.A. dreamer / No stranger in paradise / Keep me in mind / I like to rock'n'roll.
LP: 2383 487

NO SECOND CHANCE.
Tracks: / No second chance / Don't look back / Pressure point / Turning to you / Thirteen / Lovers / Johnny hold back / Love is alright / Guitar hero.
LP: 2383 422

Charlie & Sgt.Pepper

GIRL IS MINE (see under Sane Inmates).

Charlie's Oldtimers

CRAZY DAYS ARE BACK AGAIN.
LP: ISST 196

Charlottes

LOVE HAPPY.
LP: SUBORG 12

THINGS COME APART.
Tracks: / Liar / Prayer song / See me, feel me / By my side / Mad girls love song / Beautify / Love in the emptiness / We're going wrong / Blue / Venus.
LP: BRED 92

Charlotte's Web (film)

CHARLOTTE'S WEB (Film Soundtrack) (Various artists).
Tracks: / Charlotte's web (main theme): *Various artists* / There must be something more: *Various artists* / I can talk: *Various artists* / Chin up: *Various artists* / Mother Earth and Father Time: *Various artists*/ We've got lots in common: *Various artists* / Vertiable smorgasbord: *Various artists* / Deep in the dark: *Various* artists / Chin up march: *Various artists* / Zuckerman's famous pig: *Various artists* / Charlotte's farewell: *Various artists* / End title: *Various artists*.
LP: SPFL 285

Charlton, George

STRICTLY FOR DANCING (Charlton, George & Peter Scatter).
Tracks: / Heykens serenade / Dear old Donegal / Garden where the praties grow / With me shillelagh / Parnells march / Horo my nut brown maiden / Lovely Stornoway / Wee tod / Morag of Dunvegen / Uist my love / Dancing in Kyle / Moonlight and roses / Someday / Me and my shadow / Who's sorry now? / Bonawe Highlanders, The / Muckin' o' Geordie's byre / Farewell to the Tay / Bugle horn, The / 51st Highland division / Teribus / Pulling bracken / Mrs. MacPherson of Drumochter / Gentle maiden, The / Come back home to Erin / Teddy O'Neale / I'll remember you love in my prayers / You're the cream in my coffee / Best things in life are free, The / I may be wrong / Ma toot-tootsie goodbye / Baby face / California, here I come / If you knew Susie / Anchors aweigh / Ramona / Marcheta / Girl that I marry, The / Anniversary waltz / When I grow too old to dream / Some day I'll find you / Tangerine / Easter parade / Rockabye your baby with a Dixie melody / Let's face the music and dance / I've got my love / Cheek to cheek / Who were you with last night? / Don't dilly dally / Sweet Georgia Brown.
LP: MWM 1014

Charly (label)

CHARLY BLACK MUSIC SAMPLER (Various artists).
LP: CRM 2018

CHARLY DANCE PARTY (Various artists).
Tracks: / Let's go, let's go, let's go: *Various artists* / Shake your moneymaker: *Various artists* / I'm gonna love you: *Various artists* / Stormy weather: *Various artists* / Rebound: *Various artists* / Surely I love you: *Various artists* / Feeling good: *Various artists* / Look out Mabel: *Various artists* / Convention, The: *Various artists* / She's the most: *Various artists* / Sapphire: *Various artists* / I wanna know: *Various artists* / Wildcat tamer: *Various artists* / Black diamond: *Various artists* / Breaking up the house: *Various artists*.
LP: CR 30261

CHARLY R & B PARTY (Various artists).
Tracks: / Barefootin': *Parker, Robert* / Ride your pony: *Harris, Betty* / Picking wild mountain berries: *Scott*, Peggy & Jo Jo Benson / Neighbour neighbour: *Hughes, Jimmy* / I stand accused: *Butler, Jerry* / Shame shame shame: *Reed, Jimmy* / If you gotta make a fool of somebody: *Ray, James* / Let's stick together: *Harrison*, Wilbert / It's alright: *Impressions (group)* / Hey girl don't bother me: *Tams* / Tell it like it is: *Neville*, Aaron / Get out of my life woman: *Dorsey, Lee* / Boom boom: *Hooker, John Lee* / Dust my broom: *James, Elmore* / Nothing can stop me: *Chandler, Gene* / It's in his kiss: *Everett, Betty*.
LP: CRB 1088
MC: TCCRB 1088

CHARLY'S ANGELS (Various artists).
Tracks: / Leader of the pack: *Shangri-Las* / Give him a great big kiss: *Shangri-Las* / I wanna love him so bad: *Jelly Beans* / Baby, be mine: *Jelly Beans* / So long: *Jelly Beans* / Boy from New York City: *Ad Libs* / I'm just a down home girl: *Ad Libs* / Butterflies: *Ad Libs* / Goodnight baby: *Ad Libs* / I can't let go: *Sands, Evie* / Chapel of love: *Dixie Cups* / People say: *Dixie Cups* / Gee baby gee: *Dixie Cups* / All grown up: *Dixie Cups* / Iko iko: *Dixie Cups* / Ain't that nice?: *Dixie Cups*.
LP: CR 30143

CHICAGO BLUESMASTERS (See under Blues) (Various artists).

CHICAGO SOUL UPRISING (See under Soul) (Various artists).

THIS IS CHARLY RHYTHM AND BLUES (Various artists).
Tracks: / Look at little sister (live): *Ballard, Hank & The Midnighters* / Lovin' machine: *Harris, Wynonie* / It's in his kiss: *Everett, Betty* / Need your love so bad: *Little Willie John* / All these things: *Neville*, Aaron / That's what you're doing to me: *Dominoes* / Hide away: *King, Freddie* / Howlin' for my baby: *Howlin' Wolf* / Dimples: *Hooker, John Lee* / It hurts me too: *James, Elmore* / Shame shame shame: *Reed, Jimmy* / Think: *Five Royales* / Look ka py py: *Meters* / Holy cow: *Dorsey, Lee* / Your friends: *Clark, Dee* / I'm gonna forget about you: *Cray Band, Robert* / Cuttin' in: *Watson, Johnny 'Guitar'* / Make it easy on yourself: *Butler, Jerry* / Sad shade of blue: *Davis, Geator* / Rainbow: *Chandler, Gene* / Aged and mellow blues: *Little Esther*.
LP: SAM 2
MC: TCSAM 2

THIS IS CHARLY SOUL (Charly R & B sampler) (Various artists).
Tracks: / Coming to bring you some soul: *Baker, Sam* / Nothing can stop me: *Chandler, Gene* / Working in a coalmine: *Dorsey, Lee* / Tippi toes: *Meters* / He called me baby: *Washington, Ella* / Lover's holiday: *Scott*, Peggy & Jo Jo Benson / He will break your heart: *Butler, Jerry with Curtis Mayfield* / Somebody shot my eagle: *Blast*, C.L. / Land of a thousand dances: *Kenner, Chris* / All these things: *Neville, Aaron* / United: *Holman*, Eddie / Sidewalks, fences and walls: *Burke, Solomon* / When something is wrong with my baby: *Williams, Charles* with Johnny Otis Band / I'm his wife, you're just a friend: *Sexton, Ann* / I'm useless: *Smith, Charles* / Turn on your lovelight: *Gaines, Earl*.
LP: SAM 1
MC: TCSAM 1

Charm School

BREAKING DOWN THE WALLS (see under Marshall, John).

KARMA CHAMELEON.
MC: CHV 311

Charmers, Lloyd

BEST OF LLOYD CHARMERS, THE.
LP: TRLS 86

SO SOON WE CHANGE.
LP: SPA 15

SWEET MEMORIES - VOL I.
LP: TRLS 235

SWEET MEMORIES - VOL II.
LP: TRLS 236

SWEET MEMORIES - VOL III.
LP: TRLS 237

SWEET MEMORIES VOL III. (REMIX).
LP: SRL 1007

Charon

CHARON.
LP: HMILP 20

Charquet & Co

CHARQUET & CO.-VOLUME 3.
LP: SOS 1053

CHARQUET & CO.-VOLUME 4.
LP: SOS 1076

DANS LES JUNGLES DU POITOU.
LP: PRG LP 16

LIVE AT THE JOSEPH LAM JAZZ CLUB.
LP: SOS 1039

YOU'LL LONG FOR ME.
LP: SOS 1195

Chart

60'S CHART CLASSICS (Various artists).
MCSET: WW 6046

CHART ACTION 1 (Various artists).
LPS: IMP 91
MCSET: IMPC 91

CHART ACTION 2 (Various artists).
Tracks: / Fame: *Cara, Irene* / Use it up wear it out: *Odyssey* / Funky town: *Lipps Inc.* / Good thing going: *Various artists* / Hi fidelity: *Kids From Fame* / Shirley: *Stevens, Shakin'* / Instant replay: *Hartman, Dan* / Rabbit: *Chas & Dave* / I don't like Mondays: *Boomtown Rats* / Einstein a go go: *Landscape* / Never knew love like this before: *Mills, Stephanie* / Going back to my roots: *Odyssey* / Love come down: *King*, Evelyn "Champagne" / Thunder in the mountains: *Toyah* / Oh Julie: *Stevens, Shakin'* / Wedding bells: *Godley & Creme* / I only want to be with you: *Tourists* / Danger games: *Pinkees* / I want to be free: *Toyah* / Waiting for an alibi: *Thin Lizzy* / This ole house: *Stevens, Shakin'* / Don't leave me this way: *Melvin*, Harold & The Bluenotes / Inside out: *Odyssey* / Everyday hurts: *Sad Cafe* / Land of make believe: *Bucks* Fizz / Don't stop the music: *Yarbrough & Peoples* / Night birds: *Shakatak* / Everlasting love: *Gibb*, Andy / Hold on to my love: *Ruffin, Jimmy* / You're looking for a way out: *Odyssey* / Ain't no pleasing you: *Chas & Dave* / Shuffle, The: *McCoy, Van*.
LPS: IMP 95
MCSET: IMPC 95

CHART ACTION 3 (Various artists).
LPS: IMP 99
MCSET: IMPC 99

CHART ATTACK (Various artists).
Tracks: / Romeo and Juliet: *Dire Straits* / Something about you: *Level 42* / Rockin' all over the world: *Status Quo* / Rough justice: *Bananarama* / Wishing I was lucky: *Wet Wet Wet* / Change: *Tears For Fears* / Johnny come home: *Fine Young Cannibals* / Don't go: *Hothouse Flowers* / Tunnel of love: *Dire Straits*/ Lessons in love: *Level 42* / This is the world calling: *Geldof, Bob* / Brand new friend: *Cole, Lloyd & The* Commotions / I'll sail this ship alone: *Beautiful South* / It ain't necessarily so: *Bronski Beat* / I say nothing: *Voice Of The Beehive*.
LP: PWKLP 4023 P
MC: PWKMC 4023 P

CHART BEAT, CHART HEAT (Various artists).
2LP: NE 1180 AB
MCSET: CE 2180 AB

CHART ENCOUNTERS OF THE HIT KIND (Various artists).
2LP: RTL 2091 AB
MCSET: 4CRTL 2091AB

CHART EXPLOSION (Various artists).
LP: NE 1103

CHART HITS 81 VOL.1 & 2 (Various artists).
2LP: NE 1142
MCSET: CE 2142 AB

CHART HITS 82 (Various artists).
2LP: NE 1195 AB

CHART HITS 83 (Various artists).
2LP: NE 1256
MC: CE 2256

CHART RUNNERS (Various artists).
LP: RTL 2090
MC: 4CRTL 2090

CHART STARS (Various artists).
LP: NE 1225
MC: CE 2225

CHART STRINGS (Various artists).
MCSET: WW 6045

CHART, THE (Various artists).
2LP: STAR 2278
MCSET: STAC 2278

CHART TRACKING-THE HIT SQUAD (Various artists).
2LP: RONLP 1
MCSET: CRON 1

CHART WARS (Various artists).
LP: RTL 2086
MC: 4CRTL 2086

Chart Show

CHART SHOW: DANCE ALBUM (Various artists).
Tracks: / I found lovin': *Fatback (Band)* / Real thing, The: *Jellybean featuring Steven Dante* / Lies: *Butler, Jonathan* / C'est la vie: *Nevil, Robbie* / Rock steady: *Whispers* / Living in a box: *Living In A Box* / Looking for a new love: *Watley, Jody* / Boops (here to go): *Sly & Robbie* / You sexy thing: *Hot Chocolate* / Once bitten twice shy: *Williams, Vesta* / Pump up the volume: *M/A/R/R/S* / House nation: *Housemaster Boyz & The Rude Boy Of House* / Don't stop (jammin'): *L.A. Mix* / This brutal house: *Nitro Deluxe* / Put the needle to the record: *Criminal Element Orchestra* / F.L.M.: *Mel & Kim* / Crush on you: *Jets (American)* / Another step (closer to you): *Wilde, Kim & Junior* / Step right up: *Graham, Jaki* / I found lovin': *Walsh, Steve*.
2LP: ADD 1
MCSET: ZDD 1

CHART SHOW: DANCE ALBUM VOL. 2 (Various artists).
2LP: ADD 7
MC: ZDD 7

CHART SHOW: ROCK THE NATION (Various artists).
LP: CHR 1629
MC: ZCHR 1629

CHART SHOW: ROCK THE NATION VOL.2 (Various artists).
LP: ADD 4
MC: ZDD 4

Charta 77

INSTITUTION, JUSTICE AND POVERTY.
LP: SKIT 010

Charters, Ann

GENIUS OF SCOTT JOPLIN.
LP: GNPS 9032

JOPLIN BANQUET, A.
LP: GNPS 9021
MC: GNP5 9021

SCOTT JOPLIN AND HIS FRIENDS.
Tracks: / Sugar cane / Lily Queen / Felicity rag / Country club / Swipsy / Kismet rag / Magnetic rag / Searchlight rag / Sensation.
LP: SNTF 682

Chartists

CAUSE FOR COMPLAINT.
LP: SPR 1004

CHARTISTS, THE.
LP: SPR 1001

Chas & Dave

ALL THE BEST FROM CHAS AND DAVE.
Tracks: / Rabbit / In sickness and in health / Strummin' / Wish I could write a love song / Sideboard song, The / Gertcha / Diddle um song / When the leaves come tumbling down / Someday / Black hills of Dakota, The / Clouds will soon roll by, The / Every little while / Silvery moon / Ain't no pleasing you / Bye bye blues / Whispering / My melancholy baby.
LP: NE 1427
MC: CE 2427

BUDDY (Chas & Dave/Mike Berry).
MC: ASK 794

CHAS AND DAVE.
Tracks: / Ponders End allotments club / Better get your shoes on / Dry party (Track not on CD.) / Ballad of the rich / Deceived / One fing'n'anuvver / It's so very hard / Woortcha / I'm a rocker / Old time song / Old dog and me / Gertcha / Rabbit / Banging in your head / Got my beer in the sideboard here / What a miserable Saturday night / Pay up and look big / Lunatic asylum / Who d'ya think you're talking to? / I'm a rocker (live version) / Scruffy old !*?!!*?.
2LP: DL 1094
MC: TCDL 1094

CHAS AND DAVE'S CHRISTMAS CAROL ALBUM.
LP: STAR 2293
MC: STAC 2293

CHAS AND DAVE'S KNEES UP.
LP: ROC 911
MC: ZCROC 911

CHRISTMAS JAMBOREE BAG.
Tracks: / Stars over 45 / Rabbit / Laughing policeman, The / Somebody stole my gal / Fall in and follow me / Are you from Dixie? / Margie / Where did you get that hat / Who were you with last night? / Swanee / Sideboard song, The / Baby face.
LP: WW 5116
MC: WW 45116
LP: ROCM 1
MC: ACROCM 1

DON'T GIVE A MONKEY'S.
Tracks: / Gertcha / Rabbit / Banging in your head / Got my beer in the sideboard here / What a miserable Saturday night / Pay up and look big / Lunatic asylum / Who d'ya think you're talking to / Scruffy old / I'm a rocker.
LP: EMC 3303

FLYING.
Tracks: / Flying / Exhibition rag.
LP: BUNLP 1
MC: ZCBUN 1

GERTCHA.
LP: MFP 5632
MC: TCMFP 5632

GREATEST HITS: CHAS & DAVE.
LP: ROC 913
MC: ZCROC 913

JAMBOREE BAG NUMBER 3.
LP: ROC 914
MC: ZCROC 914

JOB LOT.
LP: ROC 910
MC: ZCROC 910

LIVE AT ABBEY ROAD.

Tracks: / I'm a rocker / Gertcha / So surprising / Scruffy old cow / Send me some lovin' / Better get your shoes on / Big fat rat / Breathless / Rufus Rastus Johnson Brown / Shotgun boogie / Sea cruise.
LP: EMC 3367

MUSN'T GRUMBLE.
LP: ROC 909

OILY RAGS.
Tracks: / Come up and see me anytime / Boiled beef and carrots / Time to kill / Baby doll / Holy cow / Silver dollar / Mailman bring me no more blues / Barefoot days / Jody and the kid / Country boy picker.
LP: NL 89708
MC: NK 89708

ON THE ROAD (LIVE).
LP: ROC 915
MC: ZCROC 915

ONE FING 'N' ANUVVER.
Tracks: / Ponders End allotments club / Better get your shoes on / Dry party / Ballad of the rich / Deceived / One fing 'n' anuvver / It's so very hard / Woortcha / I'm a rocker / Old time song / Old dog and me.
LP: NUT 17

ROCKNEY.
Tracks: / That's what it's all about / Big fat rat / Strummin' / Love and days gone by / Punchy and the willer warbler / Massage parlour / Billy Tyler / I'm in trouble / Edmonton Green / Sling your hook.
MC: TCEMC 3288
LP: EMC 3288

WELL PLEASED.
LP: ROC 912
MC: ZCROC 912

Chasar

CHASAR.
LP: APK 11

Chase, Tommy

DRIVE.
Tracks: / Drive / Close your eyes / Love for sale / Sunset eyes / Bogata George / Honest John / Whisper not / Straight edge / Tin tin red / Ray's idea.
LP: PAL 5

GROOVE MERCHANT.
LP: SEEZ 66
MC: ZSEEZ 66
LP: MRILD 009

HARD (Chase, Tommy Quartet).
Tracks: / Minority / Blue sunset / Message, The / Del Sasser / No problem / Ladybirds.
LP: BOP 5

ONE WAY (Chase, Tommy & Ray Warleigh).
Tracks: / I remember you / Stars fell on Alabama / Speak low / Like someone in love / Chasin' the Bimpt / What's new?.
LP: SPJ 510

REBEL FIRE.
Tracks: / Sneakin' in / I have a dream / Trouble in the Casbah / Predator, The / Calypso blues / Rebel fire / Cry freedom / My groove, your move.
LP: MRIL 002

Chastain

FOR THOSE WHO DARE.
Tracks: / Mountain whispers, The / Please set us free / Night of anger / Light in the dark / Not much breathing / For those who dare / I am the rain / Barracuda / Secrets of the damned / Once before.
LP: RR 93984

MYSTERY OF ILLUSION.
Tracks: / Black knight / Mystery of illusion / Endlessly / Fear on evil / We shall overcome / Winds of change / When the battle's over / I've seen tomorrow / Requiem / Night at the coods / March out.
LP: RR 9742

RULER OF THE WASTELAND.
LP: RR 9689

VOICE OF THE CULT, THE.
Tracks: / Voice of the cult, The / Live hard / Chains of love / Share yourself with me / Child of evermore / Soldiers of the flame / Evil for evil / Take me home / Fortune teller / Share yourself with me.
LP: RR 9548 1

WITHIN THE HEAT.
Tracks: / Excursions into reality / Visionary, The / Nightmares / Zfunknc / In your face / Desert nights / Dangerzone F107 / Return of the 6, The / Within the heat / It's still in your eyes / Pantheon.
LP: RR 9484 1
MC: RR 9484 4

Chastain, David T.

7TH OF NEVER, THE.
LP: BD 025

INSTRUMENTAL VARIATIONS.
LP: LA 872

WORLD GONE MAD.
LP: BD 007

Chateau Vallon (T.V.)

CHATEAU VALLON (TV Soundtrack) (Various artists).
Tracks: / La commanderie: *Various artists* / Puissance et loire: *Various artists* / Les kovalic: *Various artists* / Le commissaire nicolo: *Various artists* / La mort d'antonin: *Various artists* / La depeche: *Various artists* / Suspence aux sablions: *Various artists* / Les rues de' chateavallon: *Various artists* / Berg, Theme des: *Various artists* / When fortune reigns: *Sanderson, Richard* / Chateau Vallon: *Various artists* / Paul et Catherine: *Various artists* / Florence, Theme de: *Various artists* / Magouille: *Various artists*/ Bernard et Albertas: *Various artists* / La chantage: *Various artists.*
LP: CAL 225
MC: CAC 225

Chateaux

CHAINED AND DESPERATE.
LP: EBON 13

FIRE POWER.
LP: EBON 18

HIGHLY STRUNG.
LP: EBON 31

Chatham, Rhys

DIE DONNERGOTTER.
LP: ST 7538
LP: HMS 120 1
MC: HMS 120 4

Chathasaigh, Maire Ni

LIVING WOOD, THE (Chathasaigh/ Chris Newman).
LP: SIF 1090
MC: CSIF 1090

Chatmon, Sam

LIVING COUNTRY BLUES - INTRODUCTION (Chatmon, Sam & Hammie Nixon).
2LP: LR 42.030

SAM CHATMON & HIS BARBECUE BOYS (Chatmon, Sam & His Barbecue Boys).
LP: FF 202

SAM CHATMON'S ADVICE.
LP: ROUNDER 2018

Chatton

PLAYING FOR TIME.
Tracks: / Take my love and run / Everybody's somebody's fool / Comin' on stronger / Thru' the window / I'll give you what you want / Enough for you, enough for me / While I'm with you now / You got it comin' / Milly Molly Mandy / Rock on.
LP: RCALP 5058
MC: RCAK 5058

Chatton, Brian

SPELLBOUND.
Tracks: / Illumination / Baroque / Opal / Celestine / Pulse / A to Z (Whooway, who, ha, ha) / Outcry / Moroccan roll / Dawn sequence / Out of nowhere / Spellbound.
LP: MMC 1017
MC: TCMMC 1017

Chatwell, J.R.

JAMMIN' WITH JR.
Tracks: / Never slept a wink last night / Little coquette / Jammin' with JR / Ragged but right / Right or wrong / Pipedreams / Corina Corina / Pipeliner's blues / John the baptist / You can count on me / Worried over you.
LP: SDLP 063

Chaucer, Geoffrey

CANTERBURY TALES (2).
Tracks: / Nun's priests tale / Knight's tale.
MCSET: SAY 91

CANTERBURY TALES, THE (Scales, Prunella (nar) & Martin Starkie (nar)).
MCSET: LFP 7320

CANTERBURY TALES, THE (Parson's tale) (Bessinger, J.B (nar)).
MC: 1151

CANTERBURY TALES, THE.
MCSET: SAY 24

CANTERBURY TALES, THE (Wife of Bath) (Ashcroft, Dame Peggy (nar)).
MC: 1102

FRANKINS, THE - PROLOGUE AND TALE.
MC: THE 616

GENERAL PROLOGUE, THE / PARDONER'S TALE, THE.
MC: THE 607

GENERAL PROLOGUE, THE / REEVE'S TALE, THE.
MC: THE 606

GLORY OF THE GARDEN, THE.
MC: GEMM 7352

MILLER'S TALE, THE.
MC: THE 595

TROILUS & CRISEYDE (Various artists).
MCSET: SAY 74

WIFE OF BATH, THE - PROLOGUE AND TALE.
MC: THE 612

WIFE OF BATH'S TALE (Scales, Prunella (nar) & Richard Bebb (nar)).
MCSET: SAY 23

Chauke, Thomas

SHIMATSATSA NO.8.
Tracks: / Ma-jumble sale / Vafana vanharhu / Valungu / Malume No. 2 / Swilo a swi ringani / Nuna wa makoya / Vunghamula / U ta ndzi ehleketa / Swivilelo swo hlomula mbilu / Mukwana emakatleni.
LP: TUS 8005
MC: TUS 8005MC

Chaurasia, Hariprasad

ETERNITY.
LP: ECSD 2988

MUSIC OF INDIA.
LP: ECSD 2388

MUSICAL HOUR GLASS.
LP: ECSD 2952

Chavis, Boozoo

BOOZOO ZYDECO.
LP: 1021
MC: 1021 TC

LA ZYDECO MUSIC.
LP: 1017
MC: 1017 TC

LIVE AT RICHARD'S ZYDECO DANCE HALL VOL.1 (Chavis, Boozoo & The Magic Sounds).
LP: ROUNDER 2069
MC: ROUNDER 2069C

PAPER IN MY SHOE.
Tracks: / Paper in my shoe / Motor dude special / Blues all round my bed / Leona had a party / Dance all night / Deacon Jones / Dog hill / Oh yes I want my baby / Boogie woogie all nite long / Worried life blues / My toot toot / LA women love uncle Bud.
LP: CHD 214

Che

GUERRILLA WARFARE AND SOAPOWDER.
LP: EXPAL 9
MC: EXPALMC 9

NARCOTIC.
Tracks: / Scream like a swift / Fireflies in summer / I wish he didn't trust me so much / Moving the silence / Imperfections / Be my powerstation / Jerusalem / View from a new perspective / Celebrating life.
LP: SRNLP 16
MC: SRNMC 16

Che & Ray

CALIFORNIA.
Tracks: / Sunset / Midnight / Goin' down / Juicu Lucy / Blue melody, blue memory / Lilian / Sunrise / Boogie machine / Disco breakdown / So what / Big band boogie woogie / California.
LP: EMC 3335

CHE & RAY & THE BOOGIE BAND (Che & Ray & The Boogie Band).
LP: SCX 6597

Cheap In August

CHEAP IN AUGUST Greene,Graham (Burden, Hugh (nar)).
MC: TTC/GG 04

Cheap 'n' Nasty

BEAUTIFUL DISASTER.
LP: WOL 1002
MC: WOLMC 1002

Cheap Trick

ALL SHOOK UP.
Tracks: / Stop this game / Just got back / Baby loves to rock / Can't stop it but I'm gonna try / World's greatest lover / High priest of rhythmic noise / Love comes a-tumblin' down / I love you honey but I hate your friends / Go for the throat / Who'd king.
LP: EPC 86124

AT THE BUDOKAN.
Tracks: / Hello there / Come on, come on / Lookout / Big eyes / Need your love / Ain't that a shame / I want you to want me / Surrender / Goodnight now / Clock strikes ten.
LP: EPC 86083
LP: EPC 32595
MC: 40 32595

BUSTED.
Tracks: / Black 'n' blue / I can't understand it / Wherever would I be / If you need me / Can't stop fallin' into love / Busted / Walk away / You drive, I'll steer / When you need someone / Had to make you mine / Rock 'n' roll tonight.
LP: 4668761
MC: 4668764

CHEAP TRICK.
Tracks: / Hot love / Speak now or forever hold your peace / He's a whore / Mandocello / Ballad of T.V. violence / Ello kiddies / Daddy should have stayed in High School / Taxman / Mr. Thief / Cry, cry / Oh Candy.
LP: EPC 81917
LP: EPC 32070
MC: 40 32070

DOCTOR, THE.
Tracks: / It's up to you / Rearview mirror romance / Doctor, The / Are you lonely tonight / Name of the game / Kiss me red / Good girls go to heaven (bad girls go everywhere) / Man-u-lip-u-lator / It's only love.
MC: 40 57087
LP: EPC 57087

DREAM POLICE.
Tracks: / Dream police / Way of the world / House is rockin', The / Gonna raise hell / I'll be with you tonight / Voices / Writing on the wall / I know what I want / Need your love.
LP: EPC 83522

IN COLOR.
MC: 40 82214

LAP OF LUXURY.
Tracks: / Let go / No mercy / Flame / Space / Never had a lot to lose / Don't be cruel / Wrong side of love / All we need is a dream / Ghost town / All wound up.
LP: 4607821
MC: 4607824

NEXT POSITION PLEASE.
Tracks: / I can't take it / Borderline / I don't love her anymore / Next position please / Younger girls / Dancing the night away / 3-D / You say jump / Y.O.Y.O.Y / Won't take no for an answer / Heaven's falling / Invaders of the heart.
LP: EPC 25490
MC: 40 25490

ONE ON ONE.
Tracks: / I want you / One on one / If you want my love / Oh la la la / Lookin' out for number one / She's tight / Time is runnin' / Saturday at midnight / Love's got a hold on me / I want to be a man / Four letter word.
LP: EPC 85740
LP: EPC 32654

STANDING ON THE EDGE.
Tracks: / Little sister / Tonight it's you / She's got motion / Love comes / How about this / Standing on the edge / This time around / Rock all night / Cover girl / Wild wild women.
LP: EPC 26374
MC: 40 26374

Cheaters

HIT ME I'M HAPPY.
LP: HOLP 001
MC: HOLC 001

Cheatham, Doc

BLACK BEAUTY.
Tracks: / Travellin' all alone / Some of these days / Love will find a way / After you've gone / Someday you'll be sorry / Old fashioned love / I'm coming Virginia / Squeeze me / Memphis blues / I've got a feeling I'm falling / Louisiana.
LP: 3029

DOC AND SAMMY (Cheatham, Doc & Sammy Price).
Tracks: / Honeysuckle rose / Sam and Doc's blues / Summertime / Tishomingo blues / Sheik of Araby, The / I can't give you anything but love / You can depend on me / Ain't misbehavin' / Dear old Southland.
LP: 3013

ECHOES OF HARLEM (Cheatham, Doc & George Kelly).
LP: ST 265

FABULOUS DOC CHEATHAM, THE.
LP: PARKWOOD 104

FESSOR'S NIGHTHAWKS (Cheatham, Doc/John Williams/Herb Hall).
LP: SLP 430
LP: MELP 627

IT'S A GOOD LIFE (Cheatham, Doc & His New York Quartet).
LP: PARKWOOD 101

I'VE GOT A CRUSH ON YOU, VOL.2.
Tracks: / I've got a crush on you / I'd do most anything for you / It's been a long time / Squeeze me / Upstairs with the judge / It's that great Basie band.
LP: . . . . J 003

TOO MARVELLOUS FOR WORDS, VOL.1.
Tracks: / It's been so long / East St. Louis toodle-oo / Let's do it / Procurement, Smith here / Too marvellous for words / Blues in the night / It's that great Basie Band.
LP: . . . . J 002

TRIBUTE TO BILLIE HOLIDAY (Cheatham, Doc & Swedish All Stars).
LP: . . . . KS 2061

TRIBUTE TO LOUIS ARMSTRONG see also under Carey, Dick (Cheatham, Doc & Dick Carey).
LP: . . . . KS 2062

Cheatham, Jeannie

BACK TO THE NEIGHBORHOOD (Cheatham, Jeannie & Jimmy).
LP: . . . . CJ 373
MC: . . . . CJ 373C

HOMEWARD BOUND (Cheatham, Jeannie & Jimmy).
Tracks: / Permanent solution / Going down slow / Daddy o / Trouble in mind / You don't have to go / Hello, little boy / Detour ahead / Sometimes it be that way.
LP: . . . . CJ 321
MC: . . . . CJC 321

LUV IN THE AFTERNOON (Cheatham, Jeannie & Jimmy).
Tracks: / Messin' round with the boogie / Luv in the afternoon / Mama's blues / Comin' back to South Chicago / Trav'lin light (Only on CD.) / Don't you feel my leg (Only on CD) / You won't let me go / Wee baby blues / Baby please don't go / Raunchy Rita.
MC: . . . . CJ 429 C

MIDNIGHT MAMA (Cheatham, Jeannie & Jimmy).
Tracks: / Wrong direction blues / C.C. rider / Worried life blues / Big fat daddy blues / Midnight mama / Piney Brown / Finance company / How long blues / Reel ya' deel ya dee dee dee..
LP: . . . . CJ 297
MC: . . . . CJC 297

SWEET BABY BLUES (Cheatham, Jeannie & Jimmy).
Tracks: / Brand new blues blues / Roll 'em Pete / Sweet baby blues / I got a mind to ramble / Ain't nobody's business / Muddy water blues / Cherry red / Meet me with your black drawers on.
LP: . . . . CJ 258

Cheatham, Oliver

GO FOR IT.
Tracks: / Go for it / Wish on a star / Celebrate / S.O.S. / Show me / Can't wait for Saturday night / All for me / Good times.
LP: . . . . CHAMP 1006
MC: . . . . CHAMPK 1006

SATURDAY NIGHT.
Tracks: / Get down Saturday night / Make your mind up / Something about you / Bless the ladies / Do me right / Never gonna give you up / Through it all / Just to be with you.
LP: . . . . MCF 3179

Checker, Chubby

20 GREATEST HITS: CHUBBY CHECKER.
Tracks: / Let's twist again / Twist, The / Hucklebuck, The / Hooka tooka / Twist it up / Pony time.
LP: . . . . FUN 9038
MC: . . . . FUNC 9038

20 TWISTIN' HITS.
MC: 2636034

BEST OF CHUBBY CHECKER.
MC: 16-7
MC: . . . . GM 0201

FOR TWISTERS ONLY.
LP: 33SX 1341

GARY US BONDS MEETS CHUBBY CHECKER (See Bonds, Gary US) (Checker, Chubby & Gary US Bonds).

GREATEST HITS: CHUBBY CHECKER.
Tracks: / Twist, The / Limbo rock / Dancin' party / Hey bobba needle / Loddy lo / Slow twistin' / Fly, The / Pony time / Let's twist again / Let's limbo some more / Birdland / Dance the mess around / Popeye (the hitchiker) / Twenty miles / Twist it up / Hucklebuck, The.
LP: . . . . NE 1361

LET'S TWIST AGAIN.
LP: . . . . NE 1209
MC: . . . . CE 2209

STILL TWISTIN'.
Tracks: / Let's twist again / Twist, The / Slow twistin / Pony time / Fly, The / Birdland / Limbo rock / Let's limbo some more / Dancin' party / Hucklebuck, The / Dance the mess around / Twist it up.
LP: . . . . TOP 155
MC: . . . . KTOP 155

TWIST DOCH MAL MIT MIR.
Tracks: / Baby kiss kiss kiss / Twist doch mal mit mir / Holla hi, holla ho / Der twist beginnt / Troola trolla trolla / Autobahn baby / Twist mit mir.
LP: . . . . BF 15339

TWIST WITH CHUBBY CHECKER.
LP: 33SX 1315

TWIST (YO TWIST), THE (See under Fat Boys) (Checker, Chubby/Fat Boys).

Cheech & Chong

BIG BAMBU.
Tracks: / Sister Mary Elephant / Ralph and Herbie / Streets of New York or Los Angeles or San Francisco or... / Continuing adventures of Pedro de Pacas and man, The / Bust, The / Television medley: Tortured old man / Empire hancock / Let's make a new dope deal / Unamerican bandstand.
LP: . . . . BSK 3251
MC: M5 3251

CHEECH AND CHONG.
Tracks: / Blind melon chitlin' / Wink dinkerson / Acapulco gold filters / Vietnam / Trippin' in court / Dave / Emergency ward / Welcome to Mexico / Pope: live at the Vatican, The / Cruisin' with Pedro De Pacas / Waiting for Dave.
LP: . . . . BSK 3250
MC: M5 3250

LET'S MAKE A NEW DOPE DEAL.
Tracks: / Queer wars / Disco disco / Chinatown / Rainbow bar and grill / Bloat on / Dork radio / Let's make a new dope deal / Acupuncture / More money / 17th American tour.
LP: . . . . HS 3391
MC: . . . . W 53391

LOS COCHINOS.
Tracks: / Sargeant Stadanko / Peter rooter / Up his nose / Pedro and man at the drive-inn / Strawberry revival festival, The / Don't bug me / Evelyn Woodhead speed reading course / Les morpions / Cheborneck / White world of sports / Basketball Jones featuring Tyrone Shoelaces.
LP: . . . . BSK 3252
MC: M5 3252

SLEEPING BEAUTY.
Tracks: / Big sniff, The / Adventures of red and roy, The / T W A T (Tactical women's alert team) / Pedro's request / Framed / Jimmy / Uncle Pervy / Sleeping Beauty.
LP: . . . . BSK 3254
MC: M5 3254

UP IN SMOKE.
Tracks: / Finkelstein shit kid, The / Up in smoke / Low rider / 1st gear, 2nd gear / Framed / Searchin' / Ajax lady, The / Strawberry's / Here come the Mounties to the rescue / Sometimes when you gotta go you can't / Lost due to incompetence / Lard ass / Rock fight / I didn't know your name was Alex / Earache my eye / Up in smoke (reprise).
LP: . . . . BSK 3249
MC: M5 3249

WEDDING ALBUM.
Tracks: / Championship wrestling / Other tapes, The / Testimonial by R. Eimmerman / Hey Margaret / Earache my eye / Wake up America / Black lassie (A great American dog) / Wake up America (conclusion) / Baby Sitters, The / Three little pigs, The / Coming attractions.
LP: . . . . BSK 3253
MC: M5 3253

Cheek To Cheek...

CHEEK TO CHEEK (Various artists).
LP: . . . . NOST 7657

CHEEK TO CHEEK (2) (Various artists).
Tracks: / I want to know what love is: *Foreigner* / Anything for you: *Estefan, Gloria* / I don't want to talk about it: *Everything But The Girl* / Is this love: *Moyet, Alison* / Hold me now: *Logan, Johnny* / Every time you go away: *Young, Paul* / Through the barricades: *Spandau Ballet* / Take my breath away: *Berlin*/ Sign your name: *D'arby, Terence Trent* / Just the way you are: *Joel, Billy* / Baby I love your way/Freebird: *Will to Power* / Different corner, A: *Michael, George* / Miracle of love: *Eurythmics* / Lady in red: *De Burgh, Chris.*
LP: . . . . MOOD 6
MC: . . . . MOODC 6

Cheeks, Judy

NO OUTSIDERS.
Tracks: / Gonna wait on love / No outsiders / Just another lie / Step too far, A / I still love you / I'm in love with you baby / Other woman, The / Tell him / Love me like you used to / Believe / One way.
LP: . . . . POLD 5231
MC: . . . . POLDC 5231

Cheeky Bee

SWEET DREAMS.
Tracks: / I'm nearly famous now / I'll get over you / Everything old is new again / How great thou art / Operator / Walking talking dolly / I could be so good for you / Could I have this dance / Miss Glasgow 1952 / Ain't no pleasing you / Your good girl's gonna go bad / Sweet dreams.
LP: . . . . GES 1222

Cheeky Chaps

GET YOUR LAUGHING GEAR ROUND THIS.
Tracks: / Things she wouldn't do / Bent bobby / Vegan's revenge / Wouldn't it be nice / Angel delight / My oh my / Knees up mother Brown / Swiss maid.
MC: . . . . DHC 23

Cheepskates

CONFESSIONAL.
LP: . . . . MMLP 031

IT WINGS ABOVE.
LP: . . . . MMLP 018

REMEMBER.
LP: . . . . MMLP 010

RUN BETTER RUN.
LP: . . . . MIR 104

WAITING FOR ONTA.
LP: . . . . MMLP 024

Cheers...

CHEERS...THE ESSENTIAL PARTY ALBUM (Various artists).
LP: . . . . HOP 215
MC: . . . . HOPC 215

Cheetah Chrome Mother

PERMANENT SCAR.
LP: . . . . GURT 3

Cheetahs

ROCK AND ROLL WOMAN.
Tracks: / Bang bang / Suffering love / Spend the night / Rock & roll woman / Scars of love / My man / N.I.T.E / Come and get it / Let the love begin / I'm yours.
LP: . . . . EPC 85522

Cheever, John

SWIMMER, THE/DEATH OF JUSTINA.
MC: . . . . CDL 51668

Chekasin, Vladimir

1 + 1 = 3 (Live Lemans 1987).
LP: . . . . LR 160

EXERCISES (Chekasin, Vladimir, Big Band).
LP: . . . . LR 115

NEW VITALITY (Chekasin, Vladimir, Big Band).
LP: . . . . LR 142

NOSTALGIA (Chekasin, Vladimir Quartet).
LP: . . . . LR 119

Chekhov, Anton

THREE SISTERS (Various artists).
MCSET: 0325

Chelsea

BACKTRAX.
LP: . . . . ILP 024

CHELSEA.
Tracks: / I'm on fire / Decide / Free the fighters / Your toy / Fools and soldiers / All the downs / Government / Twelve men / Many rivers / Trouble is the day.
LP: . . . . SFLP 2

EVACUATE.
Tracks: / Evacuate / War across the nation / 40 people / Running free / Last drink / Only thinking / Tribal song / How do you know / Cover up / Bodies.
LP: . . . . SFLP 7

JUST FOR THE RECORD.
LP: . . . . SFLP 10

ROCKS OFF.
LP: . . . . FREUD 14

UNDERWRAPS.
Tracks: / Somebody got murdered / Cheat / Give me mercy / Nice girls / No respect / Life of crime / Switchblade / Fool / Time after time / Come on.
LP: . . . . EIRSA 1011
MC: . . . . EIRSAC 1011

UNRELEASED STUFF.
Tracks: / I'm on fire / Come on / No flowers / Urban kids / 12 men / Trouble is the day / Young toy / Decide / Curfew / Look at the outside / Don't get me wrong / Fools and soldiers.
LP: . . . . CLAYLP 101

Cheltenham Ladies...

CANTIQUE (Cheltenham Ladies College Choir).
Tracks: / All my trials / Donna Donna / Jamaica farewell / Lady Mary / Annie's song / Windmills of your mind / Lord's prayer, The / Give ear unto me / All people that on Earth do dwell / Cantique de Jean Racine / Come my way / Star carol / Away in a manger / In dulci jubilo / When Jesus Christ was born / Sussex carol / White blue and gold / Shepherd's cradle song, The / Christmas bell song.
LP: . . . . APS 321
MC: . . . . CAPS 321

Chemical People

GET AWAY (See under Big Drill Car 'Surrender').

RIGHT THING, THE.
LP: . . . . CRZ 013
MC: . . . . CRZ MC 013

SO SEXIST.
LP: . . . . CRZ 002
MC: . . . . CRZ 002 CA

TEN-FOLD HATE.
LP: . . . . CRZ 007
MC: . . . . CRZ 007 CA

Chemist

DUB MIXTURE.
Tracks: / Dub mixture / Mellow dub / Crazy lady dub / Spirit dub / Suzanne dub / Damnation dub / Mean woman dub / Judgement dub / Leaving home dub / Milk and honey dub.
LP: . . . . KVL 9020

DUB PRESCRIPTION.
Tracks: / Ital juice dub / Jah dub / Spliff dub / Rice and peas dub / Level vibes dub / Red stripe dub / Ackee and saltfish dub / Rum and clay dub / Good woman dub / Roots dub.
LP: . . . . KVL 9018

Chemist, Peter

CHEMIST FORMULA VOL. 1.
LP: . . . . BMLP 029

PETER CHEMIST MEETS THE MAD PROFESSOR (Chemist, Peter/Mad Professor).
LP: . . . . TEMPLP 001

Chenier, Clifton

BAYOU BLUES.
Tracks: / Boppin' the rock / Things I did for you, The / Yesterday / Clifton's squeeze box / I'm on my way (part 1) / Eh, petite fille / All night long / Opelousas hop / I'm on my way (part 2) / Think it over / Zydeco stomp / Cat's dreaming, The.
LP: . . . . SNTF 5012

BAYOU SOUL.
LP: 1002

BLACK SNAKE BLUES (October 10, 1967).
MC: . . . . C 1038
LP: . . . . ARHOOLIE 1038

BOGALUSA BOOGIE (Zydeco accordion dance music).
LP: . . . . F 1076
MC: . . . . C 1076

BON TON ROULET.
LP: . . . . ARHOOLIE 1031
MC: . . . . C 1031

BOOGIE IN BLACK AND WHITE (See under Bernard, Rod) (Chenier, Clifton & Rod Bernard).

BOOGIE'N'ZYDECO.
Tracks: / Shake it don't break it / Oh my Lucille / Choo choo ch' boogie / Nonc helaire / You can't sit down / Road runner / You used to call me / Je me fu pas mal.
LP: . . . . SNTF 801
LP: 1003
MC: 1003TC

CAJUN SWAMP.
LP: . . . . TOM 2-7002

CLASSIC CLIFTON.
LP: . . . . ARHOOLIE 1082
MC: . . . . C 1082

CLIFTON CHENIER & HIS RED HOT LOUISIANA BAND.
LP: . . . . ARHOOLIE 1078

CLIFTON CHENIER IN NEW ORLEANS.
LP: . . . . GNPS 2119
MC: GNP5 2119

CLIFTON CHENIER SINGS THE BLUES (Home Cookin' & Prophesy sides from 1969).
LP: . . . . ARHOOLIE 1097

COUNTRY BOY NOW (Grammy award winner 1984).

LP: 1012
MC: 1012 TC

FRENCHIN' THE BOOGIE.
Tracks: / Caldonia / Laissez le bon temps roulez / Tu peux cogner mais tu peux pas rentrer (Keep-a-knockin'...) (Full Translation: Keep-a-knockin' but you can't come in.) / Blues de la vache a lait, Le (Milkcow blues) / Moi, j'ai une petite femme (I got a woman) / Tous les jours mon coeur est blue / Je veux faire l'amour a toi (I just wanna make love to you) / Choo choo ch' boogie / La valse de Paris / Shake, rattle and roll / Going down slow (in Paris) / Aye, aye mama / Don't you lie to me.
LP: 80608

HOT ROD (Chenier, Clifton & His Red Hot Louisiana Band).
Tracks: / I feel all right / Got my eyes on you / It's a shame / Zydeco express / You're still the king to me / Before it's too late / Harmonica zydeco / Your time to cry / Hot rod / Old fashioned party / Jole blon / Just the beginning.
LP: 8282401
MC: 8282404

I'M HERE (Chenier, Clifton & His Red Hot Louisiana Band).
LP: SNTF 882

KING OF THE BAYOUS.
LP: ARHOOLIE 1052
MC: C 1052

KING OF ZYDECO.
Tracks: / My baby she's gone to stay / Driftin' blues / Tutti frutti / Love me or leave me / Old time waltz / Zydeco boogie / What'd I Say / Moon is rising blues / Zydeco jazz / Zydeco is back again / Mama told papa / Tired of being alone.
LP: CHD 234
MC: C 1086
LP: ARHOOLIE 1086

LET ME IN YOUR HEART (Chenier, Clifton & His Red Hot Louisiana Band).
LP: F 1098

LIVE AT A FRENCH DANCE.
LP: ARHOOLIE 1059
MC: C 1059

LIVE AT MONTREUX: CLIFTON CHENIER.
Tracks: / Tu est si jolie / No salt in your snap beans / You're just fussing too much / Pinetop's boogie woogie / Marcher plancher / Here little girl / Release me / Jambalaya / I'm a hog for you / Louisiana two step / When you going to sing for me / Who who who / You promised me love / Black girl / Money / Hush hush / Calinda / Duo (encore).
2LP: CDX 2

LIVE AT THE SAN FRANCISCO BLUES FESTIVAL.
LP: ARHOOLIE 1093
MC: C 1093

LOUISIANA BLUES AND ZYDECO.
LP: ARHOOLIE 1024
MC: C 1024

OUT WEST.
LP: ARHOOLIE 1072
MC: C 1072

RED HOT LOUISIANA BAND.
LP: ARHOOLIE 1098
MC: C 1098

Chequered Past

CHEQUERED PAST.
LP: HMUSA 53
MC: HMAMC 53

Chequered Silence (bk)

CHEQUERED SILENCE, A (Jacqueline Gilbert) (Boyd, Carole (nar)).
MC: PMB 021

Chequers

CHECK US OUT.
LP: CRLP 504

Cher

ALL I REALLY WANT TO DO.
LP: LBY 3058

BEST OF CHER (EMI).
Tracks: / Dream baby / All I really want to do / I go to sleep / Come and stay with me / Where do you go / See see blues (C.C. rider) / Bang bang (my baby shot me down) / Needles and pins / Come to your window / Alfie / She's no better than me / Behind the door / Magic in the air / Mama (when my dollies have babies) / You better sit down, kids / Click song number one, The / But I can't love you more / It all adds up now / I wasn't ready / Take me for a little while / Song called children / Reason to believe.
MC: TCEMS 1382
MC: 792 773 4

BEST OF CHER (LIBERTY).
Tracks: / Bang bang (my baby shot me down) / All I really want to do / Where do you go / Hey Joe / Mama (when my dollies have babies) / I feel like something in the air (magic in the air) / Like a rolling stone / Come to your window / Gypsies, tramps and thieves / You'd better sit down kids / Pied piper / I want you / Young girl, A / Come and stay with me / Dark lady / Half breed.
LP: EG 2607231
MC: EG 2607234

CHER.
Tracks: / I found someone / We all sleep alone / Bang bang (my baby shot me down) / Main man / Give our love a fightin' chance / Perfection / Dangerous times / Skin deep / Working girl / Hard enough getting over you.
LP: WX 132
MC: WX 132C
MC: GEFC 24164
LP: GEF 24164

GOLDEN GREATS: CHER.
Tracks: / Dark lady / Way of love, The / Don't hide your love / Half breed / Train of thought / Fire and rain / He ain't heavy, he's my brother / Never been to Spain / Gypsies, tramps and thieves / I saw a man and he danced with his wife / Carousel man / Living in a house divided / Melody / Rescue me / I hate to sleep alone / Long and winding road, The.
LP: MCM 5019
MC: MCMC 5019
MC: MCLC 1717

GREATEST HITS: CHER.
LP: MCL 1674

GYPSIES, TRAMPS AND THIEVES.
Tracks: / Gypsies, tramps and thieves / Fire and rain / Dark lady / Long and winding road / He ain't heavy, he's my brother / Half breed / All I really want to do / Sunny / Alfie / Hey Joe / Bells of Rhymney / Bang bang (my baby shot me down).
LP: MFP 50521
MC: TCMFP 50521

HEART OF STONE.
Tracks: / If I could turn back time / Just like Jesse James / You wouldn't know love / Heart of stone / Still in love with you / Love on a rooftop / Emotional fire / All because of you / Does anybody really fall in love anymore / Starting over / Kiss to kiss / After all (love theme from Chances Are).
LP: WX 262
MC: WX 262C
MC: GEFC 24239
LP: GEF 24239

I PARALISE.
Tracks: / Rudy / Games / I paralyse / When the love is gone / Say what's on your mind / Back on the street again / Walk with me / Book of love / Do I ever cross your mind.
LP: 85850

LOVE HURTS.
LP: GEF 24427
MC: GEFC 24427

PRISONER.
Tracks: / Prisoner / Holdin' out for love / Shoppin' / Boys and girls / Mirror image / Hell on wheels / Holy smoke / Outrageous.
LP: NBLP 7184

SONNY SIDE OF CHER.
LP: LBY 3072

TAKE ME HOME.
Tracks: / Take me home / Wasn't it good / Say the word / Happy was the day we met / Get down / Pain in my heart / Let this be a lesson to you / I'ts too late to love me now / My song.
LP: CAL 2047

TWO THE HARD WAY (Cher & Gregg Allman).
LP: K 56436

Cherish

CHERISH (Various artists).
LP: NE 1212
MC: CE 2212

Cherish the Ladies

IRISH WOMEN MUSICIANS IN AMERICA.
LP: SHAN 79053

Chernobai, S

RUSSIA:KUBAN COSSAKS CHORUS.
LP: CM 04447-8

Cherrelle

AFFAIR (ALBUM).
Tracks: / Looks aren't everything / Pick me up / Discreet / Affair / What more can I do for you / Everything I miss at home / Keep it inside / My friend / Crazy / Lucky / Home / Happy that you're with me / Saturday love.
LP: OZ 441 48
MC: 460734 4
LP: 460734 1
LP: 466790 1
MC: 466790 4

FRAGILE - HANDLE WITH CARE.
Tracks: / Fragile handle with care / I didn't mean to turn you on / Like I will / I will wait for you / Who's it gonna be / Stay with me / When you look in my eyes / I need you now.
LP: TBU 26064
MC: 40 26064

HIGH PRIORITY.
Tracks: / Opening, The / You look so good to me / Artifical heart / New love / Oh no it's u again / Saturday love / Will you satisfy / Where do I run to / High priority / New love (reprise).
LP: TBU 26699
MC: 40 26699

WOMAN I AM, THE.
LP: 364005 1
MC: 364005 4

Cherrington & Ward

HAND OF FATE.
Tracks: / Yarmouth town / Sandgate dandling song / I live not where I love / Grinders' hardships / Victory rag / There but for fortune / Freight train / Sportin' life blues / Delia / Fairytale lullaby / Greenwood laddie / Dargai.
LP: BH 8804
MC: BHC 8804

Cherry, Ava

STREET CAR NAMED DESIRE.
Tracks: / Having been near / Street car named Desire / Fast lover / Love to be touched / Protection / Awkward situation / This time around / Street victim / Techno love / Having been far.
LP: EST 12175

Cherry Blades

IN-DEPENDANCE.
LP: ILLUSION 028

Cherry Bombz

COMING DOWN SLOW.
LP: HD 021
MC: HDT 021

Cherry, Don

ART DECO.
Tracks: / Art deco / Body and soul / Maffy / Blessing, The / I've grown accustomed to her face / When will the blues leave / Bemsha swing / Folk medley / Passing / Compute.
LP: 395 258-1
MC: 395 258-4

AVANTE-GARDE (Cherry, Don & John Coltrane).
Tracks: / Cherryco / Focus on sanity / Blessing, The / Invisible, The / Bemsha swing.
LP: K 50523

COMPLETE COMMUNION.
Tracks: / Complete communion / And now / Golden heart / Remeberance / Elephantasy / Our feelings / Bishmallah / Wind sand and stars.
LP: BST 84226

DON CHERRY.
LP: AMLJ 717

EL CORAZON (Cherry, Don & Ed Blackwell).
LP: ECM 1230

ETERNAL NOW, THE.
Tracks: / Gamla Stan / Old town by night, The / Love train / Piano piece for two pianos and three piano players / Moving pictures for the ear.
LP: SNTF 653

ETERNAL RHYTHM.
LP: 21-20680

HOME BOY, SISTER OUT.
Tracks: / Butterfly friend / I walk / Rappin' recipe / Reggae to the high tower / Art deco / Call me / Treat your lady right / Alphabet city / Bamako love.
LP: 827 488 1
MC: 827 488 4

IN ANKARA.
Tracks: / Gandalf's travels / Ornette's concert / Ornette's tune / St. John and the dragon / Efeler / Anadolu havasi / Discovery of Bhupala / Water boy / Yaz geldi / Tamzara / Kara Deniz / Kocekce / Man on the moon / Creator has a master plan, The / Two flutes.
LP: SNTF 669

MU-FIRST PART.
Tracks: / Brilliant action / Amejelo / Total vibration (part 1) / Total vibration (part 2) / Sun of the East / Terrestrial beings.
LP: AFF 8

MULTIKULTI.
MC: 3953234

MU-SECOND PART.
LP: AFF 17

ORIENT.
Tracks: / Eagle eyes / Si ta ra ma / Togetherness.
2LP: AFFD 82

VIBRATIONS (See under Ayler, Albert) (Cherry, Don & Albert Ayler).

Cherry, Neneh

NENEH CHERRY: INTERVIEW PICTURE DISC.
LPPD: BAK 2140

RAW LIKE SUSHI.
Tracks: / Buffalo stance / Manchild / Kisses on the wind / Inna city mamma / Next generation, The / Love ghetto / Heart / Phoney ladies / Outre risque / Locomotive / So here I come / My bitch / Heart (it's a demo) / Buffalo stance (sukka mix) / Manchild (the old school mix) / Executive producer / Booga bear.
LP: CIRCA 8
MC: CIRC 8

Cherry Orchard

HEALING FAITH LIKE FIRE.
LP: ORCHARD 2

Cherry Vanilla

VENUS D'VINYL.
Tracks: / Amanda / Young boys / Lover like you / Wayni's sweet / Mr. Spider / You belong to me / California / Tear myself away / Round dance / Moonlight.
LP: PL 25217

Chesapeake Minstrels

CREOLE BELLES.
Tracks: / Plantation medley / Jeanie with the light brown hair / Some folks / Creole medley / Pasquinade / Gentle Annie / Dixie's land / Hiawatha / Bethena / Creole belles / Maple leaf rag / My old Kentucky home / Waiting for the Robert E. Lee.
LP: A 66069
MC: KH 88009

Chescoe, Laurie

LAURIE CHESCOE'S GOOD TIME JAZZ.
Tracks: / I wanna girl / Dans les rues D'Antibes / Is you is or is you ain't my baby / My blue heaven / Limehouse blues / I want a little girl / Bloodshot eyes.
LP: JLP 002
MC: JC 002

Cheshire Regiment

CHESHIRE REGIMENT.
Tracks: / Children of the regiment / Tantlusqualen / Bouree / Pop looks Bach / Canadian sunset / Irish tune from County Derry / Irish washerwoman, The / Rakes of mallow / Jamaican folk suite / Marche militaire.
LP: MM 0601

Chess (Label)

CHICAGO BLUES ANTHOLOGY (See under Blues) (Various artists).

Chess (show)

CHESS (1984 London cast) (Various artists).
Tracks: / Merano: *Various artists* / Russian and Molokov: *Various artists* / Where I want to be: *Various artists* / Opening ceremony: *Various artists* / Quartet: *Various artists* / American and Florence: *Various artists* / Nobody's side: *Various artists* / Chess: *Various artists* / Mountain duet: *Various artists*/ Florence quits: *Various artists* / Embassy lament: *Various artists* / One night in Bangkok: *Various artists*/ Heaven help my heart: *Various artists* / Argument: *Various artists* / I know him so well: *Various artists*/ Deal (no deal): *Various artists* / Pity the child: *Various artists* / Endgame: *Various artists* / You and I: *Various artists.*
2LP: PL 70500
MC: PK 70500
LP: BL 87700

CHESS PIECES (Studio cast recordings) (Various artists).
Tracks: / Merano: *London Symphony Orchestra / Ambrosian Singers* / Arbiter, The: *Skifs, Bjorn* / Nobody's side: *Paige, Elaine* / Chess: *London Symphony Orchestra* / Mountain duet: *Paige, Elaine and Tommy Korberg* / Embassy lament: *Bamber, Peter, Alan Byers, Leslie Fyson & Vernon Midgley* / Anthem: *Korberg, Tommy* / One night in Bangkok: *Head, Murray* / I know him so well: *Paige, Elaine & Barbara Dickson* / You and I - the story of Chess: *Paige, Elaine, Tommy Korberg & The Ambrosian Singers.*
LP: STAR 2274
MC: STAC 2274

Chester, Bob

1940: BOB CHESTER (Chester, Bob & His Orchestra).
LP: CLP 44

EASY DOES IT. (Chester, Bob & His Orchestra).
LP: .... **GELP 15003**

MORE 1940-1941 (Chester, Bob & His Orchestra).
LP: .... **CLP 74**

OCTAVE JUMP 1939 - 42 (Chester, Bob & His Orchestra).
LP: .... **BS 7103**

Chester Recorders

CHESTER RECORDERS, THE (Chester Recordings).
LP: .... **PLR 019**

Chesterfield Choir

IN QUIRES AND PLACES, NO.23.
LP: .... **LPB 788**

Chesterfield Kings

DON'T OPEN TIL DOOMSDAY.
LP: .... **ROSE 128**
MC: .... **ROSE 128C**

HERE ARE THE CHESTERFIELD KINGS.
LP: .... **MIRROR 9**

STOP.
LP: .... **MIRROR 10**

Chesterfields

CROCODILE TEARS.
LP: .... **HOLD 4 LP**

KETTLE.
Tracks: / Nose out of joint / Ask Johnny Dee / Two girls and a treehouse / Shame about the rain / Everything a boy could ever need / Kiss me stupid / Thumb, The / Storm Nelson / Holiday hymn / Oh Mr. Wilson / Boy who sold his suitcase, The / Completely and utterly.
LP: .... **SUBORG 003**

WESTWARD HO.
Tracks: / Sweet revenge / What's your perversion? / Love mountain / Best of friends / Completely and utterly / Girl on a boat / Ask Johnny Dee / Pop anarchy!.
LP: .... **SUBORG 005**

Chesters Peace

EVERY FACE TELLS A STORY.
MC: .... **KITV 507**

SONGS OF FRIENDSHIP.
Tracks: / Snow white dove / You've got a friend / Rose, The / Let me be there / Boulder to Birmingham / Where peaceful waters flow / Try a little kindness / Like a clown / Wind beneath my wings / Streets of London / Gospel changes / Rhymes and reasons.
MC: .... **KITV 475**

Chesterton, G.K. (aut)

INNOCENCE OF FATHER BROWN, THE (see under Innocence of...(bk) (Hawthorne, Nigel (nar)).

MORE FATHER BROWN STORIES (See under Father Brown) (Hawthorne, Nigel (nar)).

NAPOLEON OF NOTTINGHILL, THE (see under Napoleon of...(bk) (Scofield, Paul (nar)).

SCANDAL OF FATHER BROWN, THE (see under Scandal Of Father (bk).

THREE FATHER BROWN STORIES (see under Three Father Brown (bk)) (Hawthorne, Nigel (nar)).

Chesworth, David

NO PARTICULAR PLACE.
LP: .... **MLRR 011**

Chevalier Brothers

CHEVALIER BROTHERS.
LP: .... **GG 2**

CLOSETS IN THE CUPBOARD.
LP: .... **GG 003**

LIVE AND JUMPING.
LP: .... **GG 1**

Chevalier, Christian

FORMIDABLE.
LP: .... **FS 186**

SIX PLUS SIX.
LP: .... **FS 185**

Chevalier, Maurice

BING CROSBY WITH MAURICE CHEVALIER & FRANKIE LAINE (see Crosby, Bing) (Crosby, Bing/Maurice Chevalier/Frankie Laine).

BONJOUR D'AMOUR (Chevalier, Maurice & Juliet Greco).
Tracks: / Momes de mon quartier / Louise / Dites moi ma mere / Mimi / Moi avec une chanson / Un clochard m'a dit / La lelluia / Le monde est beau / Au jardin d'amour / Mons fills chante / Valentine / Mes theatres.
LP: **2872 225**
MC: **3472 225**

BRAVO MAURICE.
Tracks: / Quand on R'vient / Moonlight saving time / Oh, that Mitzi / You took the words right out of my mouth / Balance la / Poor Apache, The / Mon p'tit Tom / Louise / Prosper / My love parade / La romance de la pluie (rhythm of the rain) / I was lucky / Je ne dis pas non / My ideal / Mimi / Oh, Maurice.
LP: .... **AJA 5034**
MC: .... **ZC AJA 5034**

COLLECTION: MAURICE CHEVALIER (20 golden greats).
Tracks: / Balance-la / Quand on r'vient / Wait till you see ma cherie / Louise / My love parade / Paris stay the same / Up on top of a rainbow (sweepin' the clouds away) / All I want is just one girl / Livin' in the sunlight, lovin' in the moonlight / You brought a new kind of love to me / My ideal / Moonlight saving time / Qu'auriez-vous fait? / Oh that Mitzi / Mimi / Poor Apache, The / Romance de la pluie / I was lucky / You took the words right out of my mouth / Prosper.
LP: .... **DVLP 2100**
MC: .... **DVMC 2100**

ENCORE MAURICE.
Tracks: / Hello beautiful / Up on top of a rainbow (sweepin' the clouds away) / Ca m'est egal / On top of the world alone / Mais ou est ma Zou-Zou? / It's a great life / Mama Inez / Toi et moi / Savez-vous? / Bon soir / Goodnight Cherie / Paris, je t'aime d'amour / Walkin' my baby back home / Mon coeur / Nobody's using it now / Vous etes mon nouveau bonheur / Right now / Les ananas / O come on be sociable / Lovin' in the moonlight / Paris stay the same / You brought a new kind of love to me / Mon cocktail d'amour / Dites-moi ma mere.
LP: .... **AJA 5016**
MC: .... **ZC AJA 5016**

GOLDEN AGE OF MAURICE CHEVALIER, THE.
Tracks: / Louise / Wait till you see ma cherie / Mimi / All I want is just one girl / Livin' in the sunlight / You brought a new kind of love to me / Personne ne s'en sert maintenant / Mon coktail d'amour / Paris, stay the same / Mon ideal / Quand on tient le coup / Qu'auriez-vous fait / Oh, gette mitzi.
LP: .... **GX 41 2522-1**
MC: .... **GX 41 2522-4**

MA POMME.
LP: **2C 178 15402/3**

...SINGS.
Tracks: / Marche de Menilmontant / Appelez ca comme vous voulez / Ah, si vous connaissiez ma poule / Femmes de France / Place pigalle / Prosper / Pour les amants / Quai de Bercy / C'est en flamant dans les rules de Paris / Ca sent si bon la France / S'il vous plait Mlle / Jardinier de Paname / Louise / Wait till you see ma cherie / Mimi / All I want is just one girl / Sweepin' the clouds away / Livin' in the sunlight, lovin' in the moonlight / You brought a new kind of love to me / Personne ne s'en sert maintenant / Mon cocktail d'amour / Paris stay the same / Mon ideal / Quand on tient le coup / Qu'auriez-vous fait / Oh, cette Mitzi.
LP: .... **SH 120**
LP: .... **SH 156**

STAR PORTRAIT: MAURICE CHEVALIER.
LP: .... **AEI 2124**

YOU BROUGHT A NEW KIND OF LOVE TO ME.
LP: .... **MES 7028**

Cheviot Ranters

CHEVIOT BARN DANCE.
Tracks: / Dashing white sergeant / Rakes of mallow / Catherine's reel / Call of the pipes / Sweet maid of Glendaruch / Earl of Mansfield / Nottingham swing: Marquis O' Lorne / Showman's fancy / Beggar boy / Military two step: I do like to be beside the seaside / Here we are again / Mademoiselle from Armentiers / Hello hello, who's your lady friend / Swedish masquerade / Lucky seven / Toland dance / Aiken drum / La russe / Good humour / Come let us dance and sing / Keel row, The / There's nae much luck about the house / Castles in the air / Bridge of Athlone / Pet of the pipers / Smash the windows / Circle waltz / I belong to Glasgow / Oh oh Antonio / Peggie O'Beill / Cheviot rant / Cloudy crags / Traditional air / Polka: the brownieside polka.
LP: **12TS 245**

CHEVIOT HILLS.
Tracks: / My love she's but a lassie yet / Caddam Woods / Rose tree, The / Sylph, The / Hermitage / Bryce Anderson / Roxburgh castle (Original:) / Sheffield hornpipe / Mallorca (Northumbrian Waltz.) / Cheviot hills, The / I have seen the roses blow / Winster galop / Teribus / Jimmy Allen / Jack Thompson's fancy / Newcastle / Nancy / Molly's fancy / Perfect cure, The / Stool of repentance / Linton ploughman / Road to the Isles / Roamin' in the gloamin' / Show me the way to go home / Danish double quadrille / Blaydon races / Keep your feet still Geordie Hinny / Wherever ye can yer sure tae find a geordie.
LP: **12TS 222**

SOUND OF THE CHEVIOTS.
Tracks: / Circassian circle - part 1 / Rugley Ford / Hesleyside reel / Redesdale hornpipe / King of the fairies, The / Lads of Whickham, The / Bugle horn, The / Farewell / Jackson's morning brush / Northumbrian waltz / Berwick fair / Ma bonny lad / Keach in the creel, The / Morpeth rant / Banks of coquet, The / Rob Roy's cave / Kirk's hornpipe / Cumberland reel / Quayside shaver, The / Geordie's jig / Corn rigs / Dunstanburgh castle / Goodnight and joy / Bonnie Tyneside / Whittingham green lane / Drops of brandy / Goswick kirn / Old drove road, The / Circassian circle - part 2 / Lannigan's ball / Ellingham hall.
LP: **12TS 214**
MC: .... **KTSC 214**

Chevis, Wilfred

FOOT STOMPIN' ZYDECO (Chevis, Wilfred & the Texas Zydeco Band).
LP: **1013**
MC: .... **1013 TC**

Chevvy

OUT ON THE STREET.
LP: .... **KO 1003**

TAKER.
LP: .... **AALP 5001**

Chiasson, Warren

GOOD VIBES FOR KURT WEILL.
LP: .... **MES 7083**

Chibadura, John

ESSENTIAL JOHN CHIBADURA, THE.
Tracks: / Nhamo yatakawona / Hupenyu hwangu / Chisingapere / Kurera / Diya wangu / 5000 dollars (kuroora) / Mukadzi wangu / Shirah / Linda / Mharadzi.
LP: .... **CSLP 5002**
MC: .... **ZCSLP 5002**

MORE OF THE ESSENTIAL JOHN CHIBADURA.
LP: .... **CSLP 5004**
MC: **C2CSLC 5004**

Chic

BELIEVER.
Tracks: / Believer / You are beautiful / Party everybody / Give me the lovin' / In love with music / You got some love for me / Take a closer look / Show me your light.
LP: **780 107-1**
MC: **780 107-4**

C'EST CHIC.
Tracks: / Le freak / Chic cheer / I want your love / Happy man / Dance, dance, dance / Savoir faire / At last I am free / Sometimes you win / Funny bone / Everybody dance.
LP: .... **K 50565**
MC: **K4 50565**

CHIC.
Tracks: / Dance, dance, dance / Sao Paulo / You can get by / Everybody dance / Est-ce que c'est chic / Falling in love with you / Strike up the band.
LP: .... **K 50441**

CHIC'S GREATEST HITS.
Tracks: / Le freak / I want your love / Dance, dance, dance / Everybody dance / My forbidden lover / Good times / My feet keep dancing.
LP: .... **K 50686**
MC: **K4 50686**

FREAK OUT (Chic & Sister Sledge).
Tracks: / Le freak / I want your love / He's the greatest dancer / Everybody dance / We are family (Remix) / Thinking of you / My forbidden lover / All American girls / Lost in music (remix) / Frankie / Good times / Mama never told me / Dance, dance, dance / My feet keep dancing / Got to love somebody / Jack le freak (edit).
LP: .... **STAR 2319**
MC: .... **STAC 2319**

MEGACHIC (ALBUM) (The Best of Chic).
LP: **2292417501**
MC: **2292417504**

REAL PEOPLE.
Tracks: / Real people / Rebels are we / You can't do it alone / Chip off the old block / I got protection / Open up / I loved you more / 26.
LP: .... **K 50711**
MC: **K4 50711**

RISQUE.
Tracks: / Good times / Warm summer night, A / My feet keep dancing / My forbidden lover / Can't stand to love you / Will you cry (when you hear this song) / What about me.
LP: .... **K 50634**
MC: **K4 50634**

TAKE IT OFF.
Tracks: / Flash back / Take it off / Just out of reach / Telling lies / Stage fright / So fine / Baby doll / Your love is cancelled / Play Ray / Would you be my baby.
LP: .... **K 50845**

THEIR GREATEST HITS (See under Rose Royce) (Chic & Rose Royce).

TONGUE IN CHIC.
Tracks: / Hangin' / I feel your love comin' on / When you love someone / Chic / Hey fool / Sharing love / City lights.
LP: **780 031-1**

Chicago

BEGINNINGS (CHARLY).
Tracks: / 25 or 6 to 4 / Beginnings / Does anybody know what time it is / I'm a man / Liberation / Purple song / Questions 67/68.
LP: .... **TOP 116**
MC: .... **KTOP 116**
LP: .... **MTLP 1003**

BEST OF CHICAGO, THE.
LP: .... **RMB 5649**

CHICAGO.
LP: .... **WX 174 925 714-1**
MC: **7599263914**

CHICAGO 3.
LP: .... **CBS 66260**

CHICAGO 5.
LP: .... **CBS 69018**

CHICAGO 6.
LP: .... **CBS 89041**

CHICAGO 7.
LP: .... **CBS 32610**

CHICAGO 10.
LP: .... **CBS 86010**

CHICAGO 11.
LP: .... **CBS 86010**

CHICAGO 13.
Tracks: / Street player / Mama take / Must have been crazy / Window dreamin' / Run away / Paradise Alley / Aloha mama / Reruns / Loser with a broken heart / Life is what it is.
LP: .... **CBS 86093**

CHICAGO 15.
Tracks: / Manipulation / Upon arrival / Song for you / Where did the lovin' go / Birthday boy / Hold on / Overnight cafe / Thunder and lightning / I'd rather be rich / American dream.
LP: .... **CBS 86118**

CHICAGO 16.
Tracks: / What you're missing / Waiting for you to decide / Bad advice / Chains / Hard to say I'm sorry / Get away / Follow me / Sonny think twice / Rescue you / What can I say? / Love me tomorrow.
LP: .... **K 99235**
MC: **K4 99235**

CHICAGO 17.
Tracks: / Stay the night / We can stop the hurtin' / Hard habit to break / Only you / Remember the feeling / Along comes a woman / You're the inspiration / Please hold on / Prima donna / Once in a lifetime.
LP: **925060 1**
MC: **925060 4**
CD: **925060 2**

CHICAGO 18.
Tracks: / Niagra falls / Forever / If she would have been faithful.... / 25 or 6 to 4 / Will you still love me? / Over and over / It's alright / Nothin's gonna stop us now / I believe / One more day.
LP: .... **WX 61**
MC: .... **WX 61 C**

CHICAGO 19.
Tracks: / Heart in pieces / Don't want to live without your love / Stand up / We can last forever / Come in from the night / Look away / What kind of man would I be / Runaround / You're not alone / Victorious.
MC: .... **WX 174 C**
LP: .... **WX 174**

CHICAGO TRANSIT AUTHORITY, THE (Chicago Transit Authority).
Tracks: / Does anybody really know what time it is / Beginnings / Questions 67 and 68 / Listen / Poem 58 / Free form guitar / South California purples / I'm a man / Proloque, August 29 / Someday / Liberation / Introduction.
LP: **4601111**
MC: **4601114**
LP: .... **CBS 66221**

GREATEST HITS: CHICAGO.
Tracks: / 25 or 6 to 4 / Does anybody really know what time it is? / Colour my world / Just you 'n' me / Saturday in the park / Never been in love before / Feeling stronger every day / I'm a man / Make me smile / Wishing you were here / Call on me / I've been searchin' so long / Beginnings.
LP: . . . . CBS 32535
MC: 40 32535

GREATEST HITS: CHICAGO VOL.2.
Tracks: / Baby what a big surprise / Dialogue, parts 1 & 2 / No tell lover / Alive again / Old days / If you leave me now / Questions 67 and 68 / Happy man / Gone long gone / Take me back to Chicago.
LP: . . . . CBS 85444
MC: 40 85444

GREATEST ORIGINAL HITS.
Tracks: / If you leave me now / 25 or 6 to 4 / Baby what a big surprise / Wishing you were here.
MC: 40 3064

HEART OF CHICAGO, THE.
LP: . . . . WX 328
MC: . . . . WX 328C

IF YOU LEAVE ME NOW.
Tracks: / If you leave me now / Saturday in the park / Feeling stronger every day / (I've been) searchin' so long / 25 or 6 to 4 / Baby what a big surprise / Wishing you were here / No tell lover / Another rainy day in New York City / Does anybody really know what time it is? / Song for you, A.
LP: . . . . CBS 32391
MC: 40 32391
LP: . . . . CBS 25133

LIVE: CHICAGO.
Tracks: / Beginnings / Purples / I'm a man / 25 or 6 to 4 / Questions 67 and 68 / Liberation / Does anybody really know what time it is?.
LP: . . . . SHLP 121
MC: . . . . SHTC 121
LP: . . . . B 90105
MC: . . . . MB 90105

LOVE SONGS: CHICAGO.
LP: . . . . TVA 6
MC: . . . . TVC 6

STREET PLAYER.
LP: . . . . CBS 86095

THAT'S ORIGINAL.
Tracks: / Anyway you want / Brand new love affair / Never been in love before / Hideaway / Till me meet again / Harry Truman / Oh thank you / Great spirit / Long time no see / Ain't it blue / Old days / Street player / Mama take / Must have been crazy / Window dreamin' / Paradise alley / Aloha mama / Reruns / Loser with a broken heart / Life is what it is / Run away.
2LP: . . . . TFOLP 18
MC: . . . . TFOMC 18

TORONTO ROCK 'N' ROLL REVIVAL 1969.
LP: . . . . PIXLP 2

V.
Tracks: / Hit by Varese / All is well / Now that you've gone / Dialogue / While the city sleeps / Saturday in the park / State of the union / Goodbye / Alma mater.
LP: . . . . SHM 3134
MC: . . . . HSC 3134

Chicago Blues

CHICAGO BLUES (See under Blues) (Various artists).

Chicago Blues Band

FLAT FOOT BOOGIE (See under Red, Piano 'C').

Chicago Blues Meeting

SNAKE IN MY BEDROOM.
Tracks: / For my love / I can't stop / When the cat is gone / Take a walk with me / You can't lose what you ain't never had / Snake in my bedroom / 'Bout the break of day / Doing the dishes / Blues for an unhappy girl / You got to notify your lover / Fine body / Tribute to Walter Horton / Bad boy / Going down slow.
LP: . . . . RL 0073

Chicago Hot Six

STOMPING AT THE GOOD TIME.
LP: . . . . GHB 176

Chicago Rhythm

CAUTION BLUES.
LP: . . . . J 157

REMEMBERS HERITAGE OF '20S & '30S.
LP: . . . . SOS 1026

ROUND EVENING.
LP: . . . . J 127

Chicago Rock Band

MOUNTAIN MOVING DAY (Chicago Rock Band/New Haven Women's Liberation).
LP: . . . . ROUNDER 4001

Chicago String Band

CHICAGO STRING BAND.
LP: . . . . T 2220

Chicaynes

PHARAOH'S LAND/SECOND THOUGHTS (see Patriots/Chicaynes).

Chichester Cathedral

CAROLS FROM CHICHESTER.
LP: . . . . ACA 504
MC: . . . . CACA 504

Chickasaw Mudd Puppies

8 TRACK STOMP.
MC: 843 935-4
LP: 843 935-1

WHITE DIRT.
LP: 8432171
MC: 8432174

Chicken Chokers

SHOOT YOUR RADIO.
LP: . . . . ROUNDER 0241
MC: . . . . ROUNDER 0241C

Chicken Licken

CHICKEN LICKEN (Well Loved Tales up to Age 9).
MC: . . . . PLB 94

Chicken Rhythms

NORTHSIDE.
Tracks: / Northside.
LP: . . . . FACT 310
MC: . . . . FACT 310C

Chicken Scratch

IMPORTANT PEOPLE LOSE THEIR PANTS.
Tracks: / Habit camp / Possum / Undertoe / Fertilizer / Finding the guilty pig / No birds in this circus / Trail of thread / My boss is a thimble / What's in the courtyard / Flying chair / Cardboard box / Delivery service.
LP: . . . . COMM 39031

Chicken Shack

40 BLUE FINGERS FRESHLY PACKED.
LP: 7 63203

CHICKEN SHACK.
LP: . . . . GULP 1034

COLLECTION: CHICKEN SHACK.
Tracks: / Letter, The / When the train comes back / Lonesome whistle blues / You ain't no good / Baby's got me crying / Right way is my way / Get like you used to be / Woman is blues, A / I wanna see my baby / Remmington ride / Mean old world / San-ho-zay / Way it is, The / Tears in the wind / Maudie / Some other time / Andalucian blues / Crazy 'bout you baby / Close to me / I'd rather go blind.
2LP: . . . . CCSLP 179
MC: . . . . CCSMC 179

CREEPER, THE.
LP: 9132031

IN THE CAN (Featuring Christine Perfect).
Tracks: / See see baby / When the train comes back / Webbed feet / You ain't no good / Letter, The / Woman is the blues, A / Way it is, The / Tears in the wind / I'd rather go blind / San-ho-zay / Get like you used to be / Fishing in your river / Pocket / I wanna see my baby / Andalucian blues / Sad clown.
LP: 31811
MC: 40 31811

OK KEN.
LP: 7 63209

Chicot, Mario

KE AN MWEN.
LP: . . . . AKA 008

Chief John

BYE & BYE (Chief John & His Mahogany Hall Stompers).
LP: . . . . LPS 13
MC: . . . . 504 TC 13

Chiefs of Relief

CHIEFS OF RELIEF.
LP: . . . . RRLP 122

Chieftains

BALLAD OF THE IRISH HORSE (Film Soundtrack Recording).
LP: . . . . SHAN 79051
LP: . . . . CCF 15
MC: 4CCF 15

BOIL THE BREAKFAST EARLY.
LP: . . . . CBS 84081
MC: 40 84081

BONAPARTES RETREAT.
LP: . . . . CBS 82990
MC: 40 82990

CELTIC WEDDING.
LP: . . . . RL 86358
MC: . . . . RK 86358

CHIEFTAINS CELEBRATION, A.
Tracks: / O'Mahoney's frolics / Galicia / Coolin medley / Here's a health to the company / Planxty Brown/The William Davis's/Lady Wrixon / Boffyflow and Spike / Strayaway child, The / Iron man / Wexford carol, The / Gaftai baile bui / Millennium celtic suite.
LP: . . . . RL 87858
MC: . . . . RK 87858

CHIEFTAINS LIVE.
LP: . . . . CBS 82995
LP: . . . . CC 21
MC: 4CC 21
MC: 40 82995

CHIEFTAINS VOL.4.
Tracks: / Drowsy Maggie / Morgan Magan / Tip of the whistle / Bucks of Oranmore, The / Battle of Aughrium, The / Morning dew / Carrickfergus / Hewlett / Cherish the ladies / Lord Mayo / Mna ban / Star above the garter, The / Weavers, The.
LP: . . . . CBS 82989
LP: . . . . CC 14
MC: 4CC 14

CHIEFTAINS VOL.9.
LP: . . . . CC 30
MC: 4CC 30

CHIEFTAINS, VOL 1.
LP: . . . . CC 2
MC: 4CC 2

CHIEFTAINS, VOL 2.
LP: . . . . CC 7
MC: 4CC 7

CHIEFTAINS, VOL 3.
Tracks: / Strike the gay harp / Lord Mayo / Lady on the island, The / Sailor on the rock, The / Sonny's mazurka / Tommy Hunt's jig / Eibi gheal chiuin ni chearbhaill / Defahunty's hornpipe / Hunter's purse, The / March of the King of Laois / Carolan's concerto / Tom Billy's / Road to Lisdoonvarna, The / Merry sister's, The / An ghaoth aneas / Lord Inchiquinn / Trip to Sligo, The / An raibh tu ag an Gcarraig / John Kelly's / Merrily kiss the Quaker / Denis Murphy's.
LP: . . . . CBS 82987
LP: . . . . CC 10
MC: 4CC 10
LP: . . . . SHAN 79023

CHIEFTAINS VOL 5.
Tracks: / Timpan reel, The / Tabhair dom do lamh / Three Kerry polkas / Ceol Bhriotanach / Chieftains' knock on the door, The / Robbers glen, The / An ghe agus an gra geal (The goose and bright love) / Humours of Carolan, The / Sambradh Sambradh (Summertime Summertime) / Kerry slides.
LP: . . . . CBS 82991
LP: . . . . CC 16
MC: 4CC 16

CHIEFTAINS, VOL 6.
LP: . . . . CC 20
MC: 4CC 20

CHIEFTAINS, VOL 7.
LP: . . . . CC 24
MC: 4CC 24

CHIEFTAINS, VOL 8.
Tracks: / Session / Doctor John Hart / Sean sa cheo / Fairies' hornpipe / Sea image / If I had Maggie in the wood / An speic seogheach / Dogs among the bushes / Miss Hamilton the job of journeywork / Wind that shakes the barley / Reel with the Beryle.
LP: . . . . CBS 83262
LP: . . . . CC 29
MC: 4CC 29

CHIEFTAINS, VOL 10.
LP: . . . . CC 33
MC: 4CC 33
LP: . . . . SHAN 79019

COLLECTION: CHIEFTAINS.
Tracks: / Carolan's welcome / Robbers glen, The / Boys of Ballisodare, The / If I had Maggie in the wood / Boil the breakfast early / Brian Boru's march / Round the house and mind the dresser / Tabhair dom lo lamh / Morgan Magan / Chieftains knock on the door, The / Carrickfergus / Bucks of Oranmore, The / When a man's in love / Lord Inchiquin / Foxhunt, The / Cherish the ladies / Doctor John Hart / For the sakes of old decency / Boy in the gap, The / Bonaparte's retreat / Session, The.
2LP: . . . . CCSLP 220
MC: . . . . CCSMC 220

I'LL TELL ME MA (See under Morrison, Van) (Morrison, Van & the Chieftains).

IRISH HEARTBEAT (See under Morrison, Van) (Morrison, Van & the Chieftains).

LIVE IN CHINA.
LP: . . . . CC 42
MC: 4CC 42
LP: . . . . SHAN 79050

REEL MUSIC (Filmscore Music by Paddy Moloney).
Tracks: / Treasure Island (opening theme) / Loyals march / Island theme / Setting sail / French leave / Blind pew / Treasure cave / Hispanola, The (Silver and Loyal's march) / Three wishes for Jamie (love theme) / Matchmaking, The / Mountain fall (main theme) / Tristan and Isolde (love theme) / March of the King of Cornwall / Falcon, The / Escape and chase / Departure, The / Grey fox, The (main theme) / Year of the French, The (The french march) / Cooper's tune (the bolero) / Closing theme and march.
MC: . . . . RK 60412

WOMEN OF IRELAND.
Tracks: / Women of Ireland / Morning dew.
LP: . . . . ILPS 9380

YEAR OF THE FRENCH, THE (Original Soundtrack).
LP: . . . . CC 36
MC: 4CC 36
LP: . . . . CCLP 36

Chiffons

20 GREATEST HITS: CHIFFONS.
LP: . . . . BRLP 18
MC: . . . . BRMC 18

DOO-LANG DOO-LANG DOO-LANG.
Tracks: / He's so fine / My boyfriend's back / Stop look and listen / Tonight I met an angel / Oh my lover / Love so fine / Why am I so shy / I have a boyfriend / Nobody knows what's going on / One fine day / When the boy's happy (the girl's happy too) / Sweet talking guy / My block / I'm gonna dry my eyes / Did you ever go steady / Out of this world.
LP: . . . . ACT 002

EVERYTHING YOU EVER WANTED TO HEAR ... BUT COULDN'T.
Tracks: / One fine day / Tonight I'm gonna dream / Out of this world / He's so fine / I have a boyfriend / Nobody knows what's going on / When the boy's happy (the girl's happy too) / Tonight I met an angel / Sweet talking guy / Love so fine / Open your eyes / Sailor boy / Stop look and listen / My block / Oh my lover / Just for tonight.
LP: . . . . NL 89022
MC: . . . . NK 89022
LP: . . . . LRSLP 1001

FLIPS, FLOPS AND RARITIES.
Tracks: / He's a bad one / Lucky me / What am I gonna do with you / Dream dream dream / Heavenly place / March / Tonight I'm gonna dream / Just for tonight / Up on the bridge / Real thing, The / Love me like you're gonna lose me / Easy to love / Teach me how / When I go to sleep at night / Open your eyes / If I knew then.
LP: . . . . ACT 007

GREATEST RECORDINGS.
Tracks: / He's so fine / My boyfriend's back / Stop, look and listen / Oh my lover / One fine day / Love so fine, A / Nobody knows what's going on (in my mind but me) / Out of this world / Mystic voice / Up on the bridge / Dream, dream, dream / My block / Did you ever go steady / March / Keep the boy happy / When the boy's happy (the girl's happy too) / Real thing, The / Sweet talking guy / I have a boyfriend / Sailor boy / I'm gonna dry my eyes (Available on CD format only.) / Open your eyes (I will be there) (Available on CD format only.) / Heavenly place, The (Available on CD format only.) / Teach me how (Available on CD format only.) / He's a bad one (Available on CD format only.) / If I knew then (what I know now) (Available on CD format only.) / Lucky me (Available on CD format only.) / Why am I so shy (Available on CD format only.) / Tonight I met an angel (Available on CD format only.) / When I go to sleep at night (Available on CD format only.) / Tonight I'm gonna dream (Available on CD format only.) / Down down down (Available on CD format only.) / My sweet lord (Available on CD format only.).
LP: . . . . CH 293
MC: . . . . CHC 293

PICK HITS OF THE RADIO GOOD GUYS.
Tracks: / Easy to love / He's so fine / I have a boyfriend / It's my party / Just for tonight / Locomotion, The / Love so fine / Nobody knows what's going on / Oh my lover / One fine day / Out of this world / Sailor boy / Stop, look and listen / Sweet talking guy / Tonight I met an angel / Tonight I'm gonna dream.

LP: . . . . SON 005

Chiktay

DOUCEUR DES ILES.
LP: . . . . AKA 009

Child

TOTAL RECALL.
Tracks: / You are my destiny / I don't want our lovin' to die / Only you / Yummy yummy yummy / Take good care of my baby / Don't turn your back on me / Shape I'm in / It might as well rain until September / Dream lover / Here comes summer / It's only make believe / Wild one.
LP: . . . . AHALB 8010

Child, Desmond

DESMOND CHILD AND ROUGE (Child, Desmond & Rouge).
Tracks: / Westside pow wow / Our love is insane / Lovin' your love / Fight / Main man / City in heat / Lazy love / Otti / Givin' in to my love.
LP: . . . . EST 11908

RUNNERS IN THE NIGHT (Child, Desmond & Rouge).
Tracks: / Truth comes out / My heart's on fire / Night was not / Goodbye baby / Runners in the night / Tumble in the night / Scared to live / Feeling like this / Imitation of love / Rosa.
LP: . . . . EST 11999

Child In The Forest

CHILD IN THE FOREST Foley, W (Phillips, Sian).
MC: . . . . CAB 003

Child, Jane

JANE CHILD.
LP: . . . . K 92585 1
MC: . . . . K 92585 4

Childers, Buddy

JUST BUDDY'S (Childers, Buddy Big Band).
Tracks: / Nica's dream / Try a little tenderness / Arriving soon / Underdog has arizen / Looking up old friends / Crimp cut / Just Buddy's / What the hell / Pretty / Off Broadway.
LP: . . . . TR 539

SAM SONGS (Childers, Buddy & Erskine).
LP: . . . . FS 141

Childers, Erskine

RIDDLE OF THE SANDS, THE (Jarvis, Martin (nar)).
MCSET: . . . . ZC SWD 358

RIDDLE OF THE SANDS, THE (2) (see under Riddle Of The...(bk) (Jarvis, Martin (nar)).

Childish, Wild Billy

50 ALBUMS GREAT.
LP: . . . . HANG 37UP

1982 CASSETTES.
Tracks: / Oh Maudie / Col' Col' Chillen / When I got no one / I hate my little baby / Dog end of a dog end / Tennesee blues / Ammonia '81 / Monkey Bissness / Lets make it / Guillotine device / Todays menu / Matter of timing, A / Evil snake catcher / I'm home grown / Little Queenie.
LP: . . . . HANG 9 UP

COMPANIONS IN A DEATH BOAT (see under Companions in a..(bk).

CONVERSATIONS WITH DOCTOR X (See under Conversations...(bk)).

I REMEMBER....
LP: . . . . HANG 13 UP

I'VE GOT EVERYTHING I NEED.
LP: . . . . HANG 2 UP

LAUGHING GRAVY (Childish, Wild Billy/Big Russ Wilkins).
Tracks: / Baby what you want to do / We are what we own / 2 x 7 / Black girl / Little Bettina / Laughing gravy / I need lovin' / Quartet after nine / Gotta get you out of my head / Bring it on home.
LP: . . . . LPO 195

LONG LEGGED BABY.
LP: . . . . HANG 30 UP

PLAY CAPT'N CALYPSO'S HOODOO PARTY.
Tracks: / Rum and coca cola / Under the mango tree / I love Paris / Long tall shorty / Capt'n Jack is boss / Sen' me to the 'lectric chair / Anarchy in the UK / Three blind mice / Tequila / Yella skinned babies / Dread luck.
LP: . . . . HANG 21 UP

PLUMP PRIZES AND LITTLE GEMS (Childish, Wild Billy & Sexton Ming).
LP: . . . . HANG 10 UP

POEMS FROM THE BARRIER BLOCK (see under Poems From The...(bk).

POEMS OF LAUGHTER AND VIOLENCE (see under Poems Of Laughter (bk)).

POEMS WITHOUT RHYME (see under Poems Without Rhyme (bk)).

TO THE QUICK.
LP: . . . . WORDUP 007

TO THE QUICK (see under To The Quick (bk)).

WHICH DEAD DONKEY DADDY? (Childish, Wild Billy & Sexton Ming).
Tracks: / Muscle horse / Smousgiss / I ain't gonna see Kansas no more / Mi Mi and Mi / Cable sausage girls, The / Major dog be kind to cats / O'Riley / Woods are dangerous, The / Here on my knee / Sweat and grit with Arnie / Yummy yellow girls / Sons of the desert / Fry-up / Firework man, The / Caribou of intelligence, The / Bizzer oxen / Wild breed is here, The / Dearist.
LP: . . . . HANG 5 UP

YPRES 1917 OVERTURE (Childish, Wild Billy & Sexton Ming).
LP: . . . . HANG 12 UP

Childre, Lew

OLD TIME GET TOGETHER.
LP: . . . . SLP 153
MC: . . . . GT 5153

Children of Eden

CHILDREN OF EDEN (Original Cast) (Various artists).
Tracks: / Let there be: *Page, Ken & Company* / Naming, The: *Smith, Martin & Shezwae Powell* / Spark of creation, The: *Powell, Shezwae* / In pursuit of excellence: *Lloyd King, Richard & Snake* / World without you: *Smith*, Martin / Wasteland: *Various artists* / Lost in the wilderness: *Various artists* / Close to home: *Various* artists / Children of Eden: *Powell, Shezwae & Company* / Generations: *Shell, Ray & Company* / Civilised society: *Colson, Kevin & Company* / Shipshape: *Various artists* / Return of the animals, The: *Various artists*/ Stranger to the rain: *Ruffelle, Frances* / In whatever time we have: *Barclay, Anthony & Frances Ruffelle* / Degenerations: *Page, Ken* / Dove song, The: *Ruffelle, Frances* / Hardest part of love, The: *Colson, Kevin* / Ain't it good: *Dubois, Jacqui & Company* / In the beginning: *Various artists.*
2LP: 8282341
MC: 8282344

Children Of Selma

WHO WILL SPEAK FOR THE CHILDREN?.
MC: . . . . ROUNDER 8008C
LP: . . . . ROUNDER 8008

Children Of Tane

NEW ZEALAND BIRDS OF THE FOREST.
LP: . . . . VP 429

Children Of The Corn

CHILDREN OF THE CORN (Original soundtrack) (Various artists).
LP: . . . . STV 81203

Children Of...(film)

CHILDREN OF A LESSER GOD (1986 Film Soundtrack) (Various artists).
Tracks: / Silence and sound: *Various artists* / Sarah sleeping: *Various artists* / Rain pool: *Various artists*/ Underwater love: *Various artists* / On the ferry: *Various artists* / James and Sarah: *Various artists*/ Goodnight: *Various artists* / Boomerang: *Various artists.*
LP: . . . . GNPS 8007
MC: GNP5 8007

Children's...

3 HOURS OF FAVOURITE CHILDREN'S STORIES (Various artists).
MCSET: . . . . TR 4115425
MCSET: . . . . TR 1542
MCSET: . . . . MFP 411 542 5

3 LITTLE PIGS & OTHER FAVOURITE STORIES (for children aged 3-7) (Various artists).
MC: . . . . VCA 605

40 FAVOURITE NURSERY RHYMES (Various artists).
MC: . . . . HACS 7601

40 FAVOURITE NURSERY RHYMES (Various artists).
LP: 2384 084
LP: . . . . HALP 161
LP: . . . . KIDS 6401
MC: . . . . KIDS 6421

50 CHILDRENS FAVOURITES (Various artists).
MCSET: . . . . TR 1506
MCSET: . . . . MFP 411 506 5

70 GOLDEN NURSERY RHYMES (Various artists).
LP: . . . . STMP 9031
MC: STMP4 9031

ADD ON ... TAKE AWAY (Various artists).
Tracks: / Introduction: *Various artists* / Add on: *Various artists* / 1 to 9: *Various artists* / Add on 10: *Various artists* / Take away: *Various artists* / 1 to 10: *Various artists.*
MC: . . . . CC 007

ALL ABOARD (All Time Children's Favourites) (Various artists).
Tracks: / Laughing policeman, The: *Penrose, Charles* / Ugly duckling, The: *Kaye, Danny* / Robin Hood: *James*, Dick / Right, said Fred: *Cribbins, Bernard (nar)* / Hippopotamus song, The: *Wallace, Ian* / Banana boat song: *Freberg, Stan* / Goodness gracious me: *Sellers, Peter/Sophia Loren* / Bee song: *Askey, Arthur* / Who's afraid of the big bad wolf?: *Pinky & Perky* / I know an old lady: *Ives, Burl* / My boomerang won't come back: *Drake*, Charlie / Teddy bears' picnic: *Hall, Henry* / Nellie the elephant: *Miller, Mandy* / Sparky's magic piano: *Blair, Henry/Ray Turner* / Owl and the pussycat, The: *Hayes, Elton* / Ernie (the fastest milkman in the west): *Hill, Benny* / Buckingham Palace: *Stephens, Anne* / Windmill in old Amsterdam, A: *Hilton, Ronnie* / Grandad: *Dunn, Clive* / My brother: *Scott, Terry* / Morningtown ride: *Seekers* / Gnu song, The: *Flanders, Michael/Donald Swann* / Two little boys: *Harris, Rolf* / Runaway train: *Holliday, Michael.*
LP: . . . . EMTX 101
MCSET: . . . . TCEMTX 101

ALPHABET, THE (Various artists).
Tracks: / World of ABC song, The: *Various artists* / Introduction: *Various artists* / Alphabet, The A-Z: *Various* artists / Test singalong: *Various artists* / My friends from A to Z: *Various artists* / Happy birthday party singalong: *Various artists* / Alphabet countdown, The: *Various artists* / General test: *Various artists.*
MC: . . . . CC 005

ANIMAL MAGIC (Various artists).
Tracks: / Introduction: *Various artists* / Hello to the world of animals: *Various artists* / Magic: *Various* artists / Lazy cat, The: *Various artists* / Tips on pet care: *Various artists* / Trip to the zoo, A: *Various* artists / Meet some wild animals: *Various artists* / Duggy the dog: *Various artists* / Sing a theme: *Various* artists / More tips of pet care: *Various artists* / Magic frog: *Various artists* / Animal sounds: *Various* artists / Yellow canary, The: *Various artists* / Mr & Mrs Mouse: *Various artists* / Test time: *Various artists.*
MC: . . . . CC 011

BUMPER FUN ALBUM FOR CHILDREN (Various artists).
Tracks: / Play time: *Various artists* / Laughing policeman, The: *Various artists* / Mr. Men: *Various artists*/ Party time: *Various artists* / Chestnut tree, The: *Various artists* / London burning: *Various artists*/ Simon says: *Various artists* / Flumps mon shot song: *Various artists.*
LP: . . . . REC 376

CALENDAR, THE (Various artists).
Tracks: / Introduction: *Various artists* / Calendar song, The: *Various artists* / 7 days of the week, The: *Various* artists / Test - The week: *Various artists* / How many days in each month ?: *Various artists* / Test - The months: *Various artists* / Four seasons, the: *Various artists* / Test - The seasons: *Various artists*/ Special days in the calendar: *Various artists* / Test - The calendar: *Various artists.*
MC: . . . . CC 004

CHILDREN'S ANIMAL FARMYARD (Various artists).
MC: . . . . BBM 149

CHILDREN'S CHRISTMAS COLLECTION (Various artists).
MC: . . . . PT 232D

CHILDRENS' CHRISTMAS SONGS (Various artists).
MC: . . . . VCA 624

CHILDRENS' CHRISTMAS SONGS VOL. 2 (Various artists).
MC: . . . . VCA 625

CHILDREN'S CLASSIC (Various artists).
LP: . . . . STMP 9013
MC: STMP4 9013

CHILDREN'S FAVOURITES (Various artists).
MC: . . . . TCIDL 24

CHILDREN'S FAVOURITES (Various artists).
Tracks: / Carnival of the animals: *Various artists* / Flight of the bumble bee, The: *Various artists.*
MC: 4255054

CHILDREN'S FAVOURITES 2 (Various artists).
MC: . . . . TCEXE 77

CHILDREN'S HOUR (Introduced by David Davis) (Various artists).
MCSET: . . . . ZBBC 1028

CHILDREN'S LAND OF MAKE BELIEVE (Various artists).
MC: . . . . BBM 151

CHILDREN,S NUMBER SONGS AND STORIES (19 favourite songs and stories) (Various artists).
MC: . . . . BBM 150

CHILDRENS' NURSERY RHYMES (Various artists).
LP: . . . . CFRC 548
MC: . . . . MCFRC 548

CHILDREN'S PARTY SONG'S AND GAMES (Various artists).
LP: . . . . KIDS 6400
MC: . . . . KIDS 6420

CHILDREN'S PARTY TIME (24 favourite party games, songs and stories) (Various artists).
MC: . . . . BBM 152

CHILDRENS PLAY ALBUM, THE (Various artists).
LP: . . . . PIPLP 716
MC: . . . . ZCPIP 716

CHILDREN'S SING-A-LONG BOOK.
MC: . . . . STK 018

CHILDREN'S SINGING GAMES (Various artists).
Tracks: / Rosy apple: *Various artists* / Lemon and a pear: *Various artists* / King William was King David's son: *Various artists* / Cock Robin is dead: *Various artists* / There came a gypsy riding: *Various artists*/ Rushing bluebells, The: *Various artists* / Down by the meadow: *Various artists* / Rise, Sally Walker: *Various* artists / Here we go gathering nuts in May: *Various artists* / I've come to see you Janie Jones: *Various artists*/ We are the Roman soldiers: *Various artists* / Queen Mary has lost her gold ring: *Various artists* / Here comes Mrs. Macaroni: *Various artists.*
LP: . . . . SDL 338
MC: . . . . CSDL 338

CHILDREN'S TALES FROM AROUND THE WORLD (James, Sally).
LP: . . . . STMP 9011
MC: STMP4 9011

CHILDREN'S TV FAVOURITES.
MCSET: . . . . DTO 10526

CHILDRENS WORLD T.V. THEMES (Various artists).
Tracks: / Going live: *Various artists* / Flintstones: *Various artists* / Batman: *Various artists* / Mickey Mouse: *Various artists* / Monkeys, The: *Various artists* / Neighbours: *Various artists* / Postman Pat: *Various artists* / Gordon the Gopher: *Various artists* / Jetsons, The: *Various artists* / Pink Panther: *Various artists* / Stingray: *Various artists* / Grange Hill: *Various artists* / Wide awake club: *Various* artists / Thunderbirds: *Various artists* / Top of the pops: *Various artists* / Dr. Who: *Various artists*/ Top Cat: *Various artists* / Dangermouse: *Various artists* / Yogi Bear: *Various artists* / Jim'll fix it: *Various artists* / Eastenders: *Various artists* / Home and away: *Various artists* / Count Duckular: *Various artists* / Turtle power: *Various artists.*
LP: . . . . ADD 22
MC: . . . . ZDD 22

CHILD'S PLAY (Various artists).
Tracks: / Getting dressed: *Various artists* / Heigh ho: *Various artists* / House at Pooh Corner: *Various* artists / Orville's song: *Various artists* / Willo the wisp: *Various artists* / Doctor Who: *Various artists*/ Clapping song, The: *Various artists* / Henry's cat: *Various artists*/ Mr. Greedy's song: *Various artists*/ If your happy and you know it: *Various artists* / Mr. Happy: *Lowe, Arthur* / Train song: *Various artists*/ Winkle the zoo cat is lost and found: *Morris, Johnny (nar)* / Polly put the kettle on: *Various artists.*
LP: . . . . REB 498
MC: . . . . ZCF 498

CLOCK, THE (Various artists).
Tracks: / Introduction to the clock: *Various artists* / Minutes, The - Long hand: *Various artists* / Hours and minutes, The (up to 5-30): *Various artists* / Up to twelve o'clock: *Various artists* / Hours and minutes continued, The: *Various artists* / Test - What's the time?: *Various artists.*
MC: . . . . CC 002

COLOURS (Various artists).
Tracks: / Introduction: *Various artists* / Rainbow song, The: *Various artists* / Talking colours: *Various* artists / Red song, The: *Various artists* / Primary colours: *Various artists* / Green song, The: *Various* artists / Test time: *Various artists* / Mixing colours: *Various artists* / Yellow song, The: *Various* artists / Black and white world: *Various artists* / Blue song, The: *Various artists* / Test time: *Various artists.*
MC: . . . . **CC 009**

COUNTDOWN (Various artists).
Tracks: / Song - simple as 1 2 3: *Various artists* / From 1 to 10: *Various artists* / Fruit bowl, The: *Various* artists / 1 to 10 singalong: *Various artists* / Shopping with Mum: *Various artists* / Eleven plus - 11-20: *Various artists* / Test - 11-20: *Various artists* / Counting: *Various artists.*
MC: . . . . **CC 006**

COUNTING SONGS (Various artists).
LP: . . . . **PLB 262**

DREAM STONE, THE (Various artists).
MC: . . . . **ADVTC 1001**
LP: . . . . **ADVTLP 1001**

FAIRY TALES (Various artists).
Tracks: / Corn dolly, The: *Various artists* / Silly king, The: *Various artists* / Wonderful cake horse, The: *Various* artists / Fly-by-night, The: *Various artists* / Three raindrops: *Various artists* / Butterfly who sang, The: *Various artists* / Jack one-step: *Various artists* / Glass cupboard, The: *Various artists* / Katy-make-sure: *Various artists* / Wooden city, The: *Various artists* / Ship of bones, The: *Various artists* / Simple Peter's mirror: *Various artists* / Brave Molly: *Various artists* / Sea tiger, The: *Various artists* / Wind ghosts, The: *Various artists* / Big noses, The: *Various artists* / Fish of the world, A: *Various artists*/ Tim O'Leary: *Various artists* / Witch and the rainbow cat, The: *Various artists* / Monster tree, The: *Various* artists / Snuff-box, The: *Various artists* / Man who owned the earth, The: *Various artists* / Why birds sing in the morning: *Various artists* / Key, The: *Various artists* / Wine of Li-Po, The: *Various artists* / Island of purple fruits: *Various artists* / Beast with a thousand teeth, The: *Various artists* / Faraway castle: *Various artists* / Doctor Bonocolus's devil: *Various artists* / Boat that went nowhere: *Various artists.*
MCSET: **414 760-4**

FAVOURITE EUROPEAN TALES (Katherine Hepburn (nar)) (Various artists).
Tracks: / Jack & The Beanstalk: *Various artists* / Nightingale, The: *Various artists* / Musicians of Bremen, The: *Various artists* / Tattercoats: *Various artists* / Emperor's new clothes, The: *Various artists* / Beauty and the beast: *Various artists.*
MC: . . . . **LFP 41 7180 5**

FAVOURITE FAIRY STORIES (Sally James (nar)) (Various artists).
LP: . . . . **STMP 9019**
MC: **STMP4 9019**
MC: . . . . **TBC 9304**

FROG HE WOULD A WOO'ING GO, A (Various artists).
Tracks: / Frog he would a woo'ing go, A: *Various artists* / Dame get up and bake your pies: *Various artists* / Hush-a-bye baby: *Various artists* / I have four sisters: *Various artists* / I love little pussy: *Various artists*/ Jack and Jill: *Various artists* / John Cook had a little grey mare: *Various artists* / Lavender blue: *Various* artists / Little Bo Peep: *Various artists* / Mary had a little lamb: *Various artists* / Polly put the kettle on: *Various artists* / Simple Simon: *Various artists* / Sing a song of sixpence: *Various artists* / Derby ram, The: *Various artists* / Lion and the unicorn, The: *Various artists* / There was a lady loved a swine: *Various artists* / There was a little man and he woo'd a little m: *Various artists* / Where was a monkey: *Various artists*/ Three blind mice: *Various artists* / Three little kittens: *Various artists* / Where are you going to my pretty maid: *Various artists* / Who killed cock Robin: *Various artists.*
LP: . . . . **REC 224**
MC: . . . . **MRMC 039**

GERALD MCBOING BOING AND OTHER STORIES (Various artists).
MC: **13491 6001 4**

GOLDEN HOUR OF CHILDREN'S TV FAVOURITES (Various artists).
Tracks: / Sesame street: *Various artists* / Tra la la song, The: *Various artists* / Medley - Play school, Magic roundabout: *Various artists* / Rupert the bear: *Various artists* / Cuckoo clock, (The): *Various artists*/ Joe: *Various artists* / Hatty town: *Various artists* / Felix the cat: *Various artists* / Lollipop loves Mrs. Mole: *Various artists* / Sir Prancealot: *Various artists* / Old McDonald: *Various artists* / Parsley: *Various artists* / Jackanory: *Various artists* / Oh Susannah: *Various artists* / Shaun the leprechaun: *Various artists* / Andy Pandy: *Various artists* / Doctor Who: *Various artists* / Scooby Doo: *Various* artists / Thunderbird: *Various artists* / Bonanza: *Various artists* / Aqua Marina: *Various artists*/ Captain Scarlet: *Various artists* / Virginian, The: *Various artists* / Lidsville: *Various artists* / Pink panther: *Various artists* / Song of the diddymen: *Various artists* / Maverick: *Various artists.*
LP: . . . . **GH 547**

HANDFUL OF SONGS, A.
MCSET: . . . . **DTO 10531**

HELLO (Various artists).
Tracks: / How do you feel today: *Various artists* / Trumpet song: *Various artists* / Fool: *Various artists*/ Here's juice in your eye: *Various artists* / Eggs and bacon: *Various artists* / English pud: *Various artists*/ Frying tonight: *Various artists* / Getting dressed: *Various artists* / Hands feet cars and horses: *Various* artists / One day a hand went walking: *Various artists* / Jogging song: *Various artists* / Talking about my automobile: *Various artists* / Give me the old fashioned horse: *Various artists* / Talk about my automobile (reprise): *Various artists* / Talking tick tock talk: *Various artists* / How high does a fly fly: *Various artists*/ I'd rather be me: *Various artists* / Million pound song, The: *Various artists* / Never song, The: *Various* artists / Summertime is over: *Various artists* / Aunty Nellie: *Various artists* / Catch it if you can: *Various artists* / Stand up sit down: *Various artists* / Footnotes: *Various artists.*
LP: . . . . **REC 425**
MC: . . . . **ZCM 425**

HOW MUCH IS THAT DOGGIE (Various artists).
MC: . . . . **BBM 119**

I CAN COUNT (Various artists).
MC: . . . . **ST 3634**

IT'S NURSERY RHYME TIME (Various artists).
LP: . . . . **SIT 60068**

JUNIOR CHOICE (Ed Stewarts Junior Choice) (Various artists).
LP: . . . . **BEMP 002**

JUNIOR CHOICE (FAVOURITE REQUESTS) (Various artists).
Tracks: / Under the moon of love: *Various artists* / Day trip to Bangor: *Various artists* / My brother: *Various* artists / Captain Beaky: *Various artists* / Matchstalk men and matchstalk cats and dogs: *Various artists*/ Jonathan's zoo: *Various artists* / King's breakfast, The: *Various artists* / Let's go to Misterland: *Various* artists / Thank you for the music: *Various artists* / Sparrow: *Various artists* / Taste of aggro: *Various* artists / Morning has broken: *Various artists* / Me and the elephant: *Various artists* / Orinoco kid: *Various artists.*
MC: . . . . **ZCR 396**

JUNIOR CHOICE VOL.1 (Various artists).
Tracks: / Nellie the elephant: *Miller, Mandy* / Runaway train, The: *Dalhart, Vernon* / Gilly gilly ossenfeffer katzenellenbogen by the sea: *Bygraves, Max* / You're a pink toothbrush: *Bygraves, Max* / Robin Hood: *James,* Dick / I taut I taw a puddy-tat: *Blanc, Mel* / Woody Woodpecker: *Blanc, Mel* / Ernie (the fastest milkman in the West): *Hill, Benny* / I've lost my mummy: *Harris, Rolf* / Jake the peg: *Harris, Rolf* / My boomerang won't come back: *Drake, Charlie* / Mr. Custer: *Drake, Charlie* / Little boy fishin': *Abicair, Shirley*/ Laughing policeman, The: *Penrose, Charles* / Ragtime Cowboy Joe: *Chipmunks* / Buckingham Palace: *Stephens,* Anne / Hippopotamus song, The: *Flanders & Swann* / Ballad of Davy Crockett, The: *Ford, Tennessee Ernie* / Grandad: *Dunn, Clive.*
MC: . . . . **TCMFP 5890**

JUNIOR CHOICE VOL.2 (Various artists).
Tracks: / Ugly ducking, The: *Kaye, Danny* / King's new clothes, The: *Kaye, Danny* / Little white duck: *Kaye,* Danny / Tubby the tuba: *Kaye, Danny* / Little red monkey: *Nicols/ Edwards/ Bentley* / Grandfather's clock: *Radio Revellers* / Kitty in the basket: *Dekker, Diana* / I know an old lady: *Ives, Burl* / Big Rock Candy Mountain: *Ives, Burl* / There's a friend for little children: *Uncle Mac* / All things bright and beautiful: *Uncle* Mac / Three billy goat gruff, The: *Luther, Frank* / Owl and the pussycat, The: *Hayes, Elton* / Puffin' Billy: *Melodi Light Orchestra* / How much is that doggy in the window: *Roza, Lita* / Mister Cuckoo (sing your song): *Ross,* Edmundo / Typewriter, The: *Anderson, Leroy* / Little shoemaker, The: *Michael Twins* / Bimbo: *Miller, Suzi* / Swedish rhapsody: *Mantovani.*
MC: . . . . **TCMFP 5891**

LEARNING TREE, THE (12 Songs About the Conservation of the Environment) (Various artists).
Tracks: / Story of learning tree, The: *Learning Tree* / Rubbish bin song, The: *Learning Tree* / Counting song: *Learning Tree* / It's not much fun when you're a caterpillar: *Learning Tree* / At otter oughter know: *Learning* Tree / Learning tree, The: *Learning Tree* / I'm glad I'm me: *Learning Tree* / Fish have feelings: *Learning* Tree / Don't bother birds: *Learning Tree* / Just in the nick of time: *Learning Tree* / Dormouse lullaby, The: *Learning Tree* / Best possible house, The: *Learning Tree.*
LP: . . . . **EME 6506**

LISTEN WITH MOTHER (Various artists).
LP: . . . . **REC 525**
MC: . . . . **ZCM 525**

LITTLE BO PEEP (Various artists).
MC: . . . . **STC 308A**

LITTLE RED RIDING HOOD (Various artists).
MC: . . . . **STC 006**

LITTLE TIN SOLDIER, THE (Various artists).
MC: . . . . **STC 308C**

MIFFY & OTHER STORIES (Various artists).
MC: . . . . **TS 321**

MOTHER GOOSE (Various artists).
MC: **1091**

MULTIPLICATION (Various artists).
Tracks: / Introduction to the tables: *Various artists* / Tables 2 to 7: *Various artists* / Test: *Various artists* / Tables 8 to 12: *Various artists* / Test: *Various artists.*
MC: . . . . **CC 001**

MUSIC MACHINE, THE (see under Music Machine) (Various artists).

MUSICAL FUN AND GAMES (Various artists).
Tracks: / Childrens games: *Various artists* (MCPO/Batiz) / Sorcerer's apprentice, The: *Various artists* (MSSO/ Batiz) / Dolly Suite (Faure): *Academy Of St.Martin In The Field & Neville Marriner* / Musical box, The (Liadov): *Various artists*(MCPO/Batiz) / Nutcracker suite: *Royal Philharmonic Orchestra* (cond. Batiz) / Pied piper, The (Mourant): *MacDonald,* George/Northern Sinfonia of England (cond. Steuart Bedford) / Themes for Narnia: *Robles, Marisa Ensemble/Christopher Hyde-Smith*/ Scaramouche-Braziliera: *Johnson, Emma/Gordon Back.*
LP: . . . . **DCA 673**
MC: . . . . **ZC DCA 673**

MUSICAL SOUNDS (Various artists).
Tracks: / Introduction: *Various artists* / Beat on the bass drum: *Various artists* / I love a snare drum: *Various* artists / Explaining the rhythm: *Various artists* / Instruments: *Various artists* / Tambourine, The: *Various* artists / Let's play: *Various artists* / String bass, The: *Various artists* / Trumpet on parade: *Various* artists / Explaining the melody: *Various artists* / Instruments: *Various artists* / Toot on your flute: *Various* artists / I am a keyboard: *Various artists* / Meet the guitar: *Various artists* / Altogether: *Various artists.*
MC: . . . . **CC 012**

MY 40 FAVOURITE NURSERY RHYMES (Various artists).
Tracks: / Oranges and lemons: *Various artists* / Polly put the kettle on: *Various artists* / Twinkle twinkle little star: *Various artists* / Little Bo Peep: *Various artists.*
LP: **41 5726 1**
MC: **41 5726 4**
LP: . . . . **MFP 5726**
MC: . . . . **TC MFP 5726**

MY BOOK OF PETS (Various artists).
MC: . . . . **ST 3635**

MY BOOK OF WORDS (Various artists).
MC: . . . . **ST 3634**

NON STOP NURSERY RHYMES Featuring John Edmonds (Various artists).
LP: . . . . **PIPLP 702**
MC: . . . . **ZCPIP 702**

NON STOP NURSERY RHYMES (2) (Various artists).
LP: . . . . **PIPLP (B) 715**
MC: . . . . **ZCPIP (B) 715**

NUMBER & NATURE SONGS & RHYMES sung by children (Various artists).
LP: . . . . **KIDS 6 403**

NUMBERS (BLUEY LEARNS TO COUNT).
MC: . . . . **STK 022**

NURSERY RHYMES (Various artists).
LP: . . . . **MMT LP 106**
MC: . . . . **MMT TC 106**

NURSERY RHYMES (Various artists).
MC: . . . . **AC 109**

OLD MACDONALD (Various artists).
MC: . . . . **STC 016**
MC: . . . . **STC 309C**

ONCE UPON A TIME VOL.1 (Various artists).
Tracks: / Cinderella: *Various artists* / When the boat comes in: *Various artists* / Aladdin and his lamp: *Various artists* / Ding dong bell: *Various artists* / Little gingerbread boy, The: *Various artists* / John Peel: *Various* artists (end s1) / Beauty and the beast: *Various artists* / Cockles and mussels: *Various artists* / Pied piper: *Various artists* / Who killed Cock Robin?: *Various artists* / Tom Thumb: *Various artists* / Polly wolly doodle: *Various artists.*
LP: . . . . **CBR 1032**
MC: . . . . **KCBR 1032**

ONCE UPON A TIME VOL.2 (Various artists).
Tracks: / Dick Whittington and his cat: *Various artists* / Lavender blue: *Various artists* / Sleeping beauty: *Various artists* / This old man: *Various artists* / Three billy goats gruff, The: *Various artists* / Oh dear, what can the matter be?: *Various artists* / Pease pudding hot: *Various artists* (end s1) / Emperor's new clothes, The: *Various artists* / Spider and the fly, (The): *Various artists* / Goldilocks and the three bears: *Various artists* / Girls and boys come out to play: *Various artists* / Snow White and the seven dwarfs: *Various artists* / Nursery rhymes medley: *Various artists* / Times tables: *Various artists.*
LP: . . . . **CBR 1044**
MC: . . . . **KCBR 1044**

ONCE UPON A TIME VOL.3 (Various artists).
Tracks: / Three little pigs, (The): *Various artists* / Little tin soldier: *Various artists* / Ugly duckling, (The): *Various artists* / Little Red Riding Hood (story): *Various artists* / Rumpelstiltskin: *Various artists*/ Hansel and Gretel: *Various artists* / Thumbelina: *Various artists.*
LP: . . . . **CBR 1045**
MC: . . . . **KCBR 1045**

PADDINGTON BEAR'S MAGICAL MUSICAL (Various artists).
LP: . . . . **TV 18**
MC: . . . . **TVC 18**

PLAY AWAY (Various artists).
Tracks: / Party is about to begin (ding dong), The: *Various artists* / All change: *Various artists* / Superstition: *Various artists* / Say when: *Various artists* / Umbarbarumba: *Various artists* / Captain Kipper's clipper: *Various artists* / If I had a hammer: *Various artists* / Stops and starts: *Various artists* / Rabbit and pork: *Various artists* / Rain makes all things beautiful, The: *Various artists* / Words, words, words: *Various* artists / Sitting by the river: *Various artists* / Hokey cokey: *Various artists* / Hippo song, The: *Various* artists / Train to Glasgow, The: *Various artists* / First things: *Various artists* / Singalong: *Various artists.*
LP: . . . . **REC 244**
MC: . . . . **MRMC 003**

PLAY LISTEN AND LEARN WITH RONALD MCDONALD (Various artists).
LP: . . . . **SPR 8549**
MC: . . . . **SPC 8549**

PLAY ON (Songs from Playschool) (Various artists).
Tracks: / Play on: *Various artists* / I'm the man with the wellington boots: *Various artists* / Paddle your own canoe: *Various artists* / Tick tock, song of the clock: *Various artists* / Squash and a squeeze: *Various artists*/ What's it like in the place where you live: *Various artists* / Elephants on a piece of string: *Various artists*/ Funny face: *Various artists* / Insect songs: *Various artists* / Fling on a thing: *Various artists* / Two by two: *Various artists* / Little ted bear: *Various artists* / Sing a song of seashores: *Various artists*/ Wiggle my ears: *Various artists* / Tortoise: *Various artists* / King of the kingdom of song: *Various artists*/ Well Jemima, let's go shopping: *Various artists* / Tea time treats: *Various artists* / Follow the Bangalorey man: *Various artists* / Song a sing of Mrs Twisty: *Various artists.*

LP: . . . . REC 332
MC: . . . . ZCM 332

PLAY SCHOOL AND PLAY AWAY, SONGS FROM (Various artists).
Tracks: / Early in the morning: *Scott, P.R./Peter Gosling* / Brush, brush, brush: *Gosling, Peter* / Sunbeams play: *Beebee, Graham* / I am here: *Gosling, Peter* / Caterpillars only crawl: *Charlton, Sue & Peter* / Wheels keep turning: *Beebee, Graham* / I like peace, I like quiet: *Cole, Michael/Gosling, Peter* / Building up my house: *Charlton, Peter* / I think I've caught a cold: *Horrox, Alan/ Peter Gosling* / Israeli boat song, The: *Morton,* Lionel / One potato, two potato: *Charlton, Peter, Paul Reade* / Bang on a drum: *Jones, Rick* / Jump: *Morton,* Lionel / Paper song, The: *Whitfield, Judy/Paul Reade* / Down on the farm: *Beebee, Graham* / Come to the shops: *Carrick, Malcolm* / What do we do with this and that?: *Blezard, William* / Circus is coming, The: *Charlton,* Peter, Paul Reade / Build it up: *Charlton, Peter* / Fidget: *Whitfield, Judy/Paul Reade* / You can stamp your feet: *Whitfield, Judy/ Paul Reade* / Play away: *Morton, Lionel* / How do you feel today?: *Diamond* / Trumpet song: *Carrick, Malcolm* / Here's juice in your eye: *Wilson* / Eggs and bacon: *Reade/Charlton* / English pud: *Cole/Gosling* / Frying tonight: *Charlton, Peter* / Getting dressed: *Sullivan/Adams* / One day a hand went walking: *Charlton, Peter, Paul Reade* / Jogging song: *Sullivan/Adams* / Talk about my automobile: *Wilson*/ Give me the old fashioned horse: *Harris/Moses* / Talk about my automobile (reprise): *Wilson* / Talking tick tock talk: *Rowe* / How high does a fly fly?: *Sarony/Holmes* / I'd rather be me: *Cole/Gosling* / Million pound song: *Atkin* / Never song, The: *Lipton* / Summertime is over: *Haldane/ Omer* / Aunty Nellie: *Various artists* / Catch it if you can: *Atkin* / Stand up, sit down: *Gosling* / Footnotes: *Charlton/Le Sage.*
2LP: . . . . DL 1114
MC: . . . . TC-DL 1114

PLAY SONGS (Various artists).
MC: . . . . PLB 269

PLAYGROUP FAVOURITES (Various artists).
Tracks: / Grand old Duke of York, The: *Various artists* / Oranges and lemons: *Various artists* / John Brown's baby: *Various artists* / Head and shoulders, knees and toes: *Various artists* / Music man: *Various artists*/ Pop goes the weasel: *Various artists* / All creatures: *Various artists* / London bridge is falling down: *Various* artists / One two three four five once I caught a fish a: *Various artists* / Wheels on the bus, The: *Various artists*/ Cat went fiddle I fee, The: *Various artists* / Have you ever noticed your nose: *Various artists* / One finger, one thumb: *Various artists* / Millie millipede: *Various artists* / Teddy bear: *Various artists* / Ostrich, The: *Various artists* / Little rabbit, A: *Various artists* / Elephant: *Various artists* / Smile please!: *Various artists* / Ring a ring a roses: *Various artists* / I jump out of bed: *Various artists* / Someone's in the kitchen with Dinah: *Various artists* / Peter hammers with one hammer: *Various artists* / This old man: *Various* artists / If you're happy and you know it: *Various artists* / Here we go gathering nuts in May: *Various artists*/ Grandma and grandpa: *Various artists* (Tune: Happy Birthday to you) / Billy Bumble: *Various artists* / Cherry stone, The: *Various artists* / All creatures: *Various artists* / Before you cross the road: *Various artists.*
MC: . . . . TCMFP 5772
LP: . . . . MFP 5772

PLAYGROUP SONGTIME (Various artists).
Tracks: / Farmers in his den: *Various artists* / Two little dicky birds: *Various artists* / Ring a ring of roses: *Various artists* / Oranges & lemons: *Various artists.*
LP: . . . . MFP 50350
MC: . . . . TCMFP 50350

PRIMARY FRENCH (Various artists).
Tracks: / Introduction: *Various artists* / Frere Jacques: *Various artists* / Simple words: *Various artists*/ Counting un, deux, trois: *Various artists* / Colours: *Various artists* / Test time: *Various artists*/ Sur le pont d'avignon: *Various artists* / Simple phrases: *Various artists* / Je suis un petit garcon: *Various* artists / Alouette: *Various artists* / Questions and answers: *Various artists* / Au clair de la lune: *Various* artists / Wolf story, The: *Various artists* / Premenons nous dans le bois: *Various artists* / Shopping: *Various artists* / Test time: *Various artists* / Il court il court le furet: *Various artists.*

MC: . . . . CC 008

RHYMES TO REMEMBER (Various artists).
Tracks: / Clock which struck 13, The: *Various artists* / ABC: *Various artists* / Monday's child: *Various* artists / Thirty days hath September: *Various artists* / Calendar rhymes: *Various artists* / Winds: *Various* artists / Who killed Cock Robin?: *Various artists* / One two three four five once I caught a fish alive: *Various artists.*
LP: . . . . KIDS 6405
MC: . . . . KIDS 6425

RHYMING WORDS (Various artists).
Tracks: / Introduction: *Various artists* / Explanation of phonetical vowels: *Various artists* / A sound test, The: *Various artists* / E sound test, The: *Various artists* / I sound test, The: *Various artists* / O sound test, The: *Various artists* / U sound test, The: *Various artists.*
MC: . . . . CC 010

SIMON SAYS (Various artists).
LP: . . . . GH 862

SING A SONG OF PLAYSCHOOL (Various artists).
Tracks: / Sing a song of play school: *Various artists* / Standing on one leg: *Various artists* / Seagull: *Various* artists / Train song: *Various artists* / Ground: *Various artists* / Underneath the spreading chestnut tree: *Various artists* / Flying: *Various artists* / Elephant wobbles: *Various artists* / Wiper flop: *Various* artists / Simple song: *Various artists* / Whether the weather: *Various artists* / Seeds: *Various artists*/ Heads and shoulders, knees and toes: *Various artists* / Time for a bath: *Various artists* / Little ticks of time: *Various artists* / Spiders: *Various artists* / Wouldn't it be funny?: *Various artists* / Play school theme: *Various artists.*
LP: . . . . REC 212
MC: . . . . MRMC 031

SINGING & DANCING GAMES (Various artists).
LP: . . . . KIDS 6402
MC: . . . . KIDS 6422

SINGING IN THE BAND (Songs From Play School & Play Away) (Various artists).
Tracks: / When you're in my band: *Various artists* / Reggae Rita: *Various artists* / Fish disco: *Various* artists / On the ning nang nong: *Various artists* / Magnificent sanctuary band, The: *Various artists* / Do your ears hang low?: *Various artists* / Simple Simon says: *Various artists* / Clapping song, The: *Various* artists / All delicious: *Various artists* / Stop start medley: *Various artists* / Three little fishes: *Various* artists / My hat it has three corners: *Various artists* / Blue blues: *Various artists* / Ugly duckling market day, The: *Various artists* / If you're happy and you know it: *Various artists.*
LP: . . . . REC 495
MC: . . . . ZCM 495

SPARKY'S MAGIC PIANO (Film soundtrack) (Various artists).
Tracks: / Sparky's magic piano: *Various artists* / Sparky and the talking train: *Various artists.*
LP: . . . . EMS 1188
MC: . . . . TCEMS 1188

STREETWISE (Various artists).
Tracks: / Streetwise theme: *Various artists* / Green cross code: *Various artists* / Road safety song: *Various* artists / Road is not a playground, A: *Various artists* / Do not play with danger: *Various artists* / Never talk to strangers: *Various artists* / Police are your friends, The: *Various artists* / What to do in an emergency: *Various artists.*
MC: . . . . CC 003

SUPERMAN & NIGHTMARE.
MC: . . . . MFP 415 712 4
MC: . . . . TCMFP 5712

TALE OF A DONKEY'S TAIL (And other Playschool stories) (Various artists).
LP: . . . . REC 232
MC: . . . . MRMC 045

THEMES FROM CHILDREN'S BBC (Various artists).
Tracks: / Postman Pat: *Various artists* / Fireman Sam: *Various artists* / Doctor Who: *Various artists*/ Muppet babies, The: *Various artists* / Jim'll fix it: *Various artists* / Grange Hill: *Various artists*/ Mop 'n' Smiff: *Various artists* / Trumpton: *Various artists* / Heads and tails: *Various artists* / Family Ness, The: *Various artists* / Paddington Bear: *Various artists* / Willy Fog: *Various artists* / Camberwick Green: *Various artists* / Hokey cokey: *Various artists* / Magic roundabout: *Various artists* / Bertha: *Various artists* / Henry's cat: *Various artists* / Willo the wisp: *Various artists* / Playschool: *Various artists* / Dogtanian and The Three Muskethounds: *Various artists.*
MC: . . . . HSC 650

THREE BEARS, THE Children's story (Various artists).
MC: . . . . TS 302

TOBERMORY & OTHER STORIES (see under Munro, H.H.) (Various artists).

TODAYS POPS FOR TODAYS TOTS (Various artists).
MC: . . . . BRC 2524

TONY THE TURTLE (Various artists).
MC: . . . . ANV 610

TWENTY-FIVE ALL-TIME FAVOURITE NURSERY RHYMES (Various artists).
Tracks: / Boys and girls come out to play: *Various artists* / Hickory dickory dock: *Various artists* / Old King Cole: *Various artists* / Hot cross buns: *Various artists* / Three blind mice: *Various artists* / Pop goes the weasel: *Various artists* / London Bridge: *Various artists* / Baa, baa, black sheep: *Various artists*/ Little Polly Flinders: *Various artists* / Bobby Shaftoe: *Various artists* / Little Miss Muffet: *Various* artists / Old Mother Hubbard: *Various artists* (end s1) / Oranges and lemons: *Various artists* (instrumental) / Sing a song of sixpence: *Various artists* / Polly put the kettle on: *Various artists* / Ride a cock horse: *Various* artists / Here we go round the mulberry bush: *Various artists* / Humpty Dumpty: *Various artists* / Pussy cat, pussy cat: *Various artists* / Jack and Jill: *Various artists* / Hey diddle diddle: *Various artists* / My little nut tree: *Various artists* / What are little boys made of?: *Various artists* / Horsey, horsey: *Various artists* / Hush-a-bye, baby: *Various artists.*
LP: . . . . CBR 1037
MC: . . . . KCBR 1037

VERY BEST OF PLAYSCHOOL, THE (Various artists).
Tracks: / How do you feel today?: *Various artists* / Trumpet song: *Various artists* / Hands, feet, cars and horses: *Various artists* / Million pound song, The: *Various artists* / Never song, The: *Various artists* / Simple Simon says: *Various artists* / Clapping song, The: *Various artists* / Jump up time with Floella's Carribbean medley: *Various artists* / How high does a fly fly: *Various artists* / I'd rather be me: *Various artists* / On the ning nang nong: *Various artists* / Three little fishes: *Various artists* / Ugly duckling, The: *Various artists* / Blue blues: *Various artists* / Stop start medley: *Various artists.*
MC: . . . . HSC 653

WONDERFUL WORLD OF CHILDREN'S CHRISTMAS (Various artists).
LP: . . . . HDY 1932
MC: . . . . ZCHDY 1932

WONDERFUL WORLD OF CHILDREN'S CHRISTMAS - VOL.2 (Various artists).
LP: . . . . HDY 1933
MC: . . . . ZCHDY 1933

WONDERFUL WORLD OF CHRISTMAS (Various artists).
LP: . . . . HDY 1929
MC: . . . . ZCHDY 1929

WONDERFUL WORLD OF COUNTRY (Various artists).
LP: . . . . SPR 8562
MC: . . . . SPC 8562

WONDERFUL WORLD OF COUNTRY MUSIC (Various artists).
LP: . . . . CDS 1180
MC: . . . . CAM 1180

WONDERFUL WORLD OF GLASS (Various artists).
LP: . . . . GLASS 101

WONDERFUL WORLD OF GLASS, VOL.2 (see under Shadow & Substance) (Various artists).

WONDERFUL WORLD OF NURSERY RHYMES (Vocals - Vera Lynn & Kenneth McKellar) (Various artists).
LP: . . . . SPA 485

YOUR ABC OF SONGS AND MUSIC (Chilcren's...).
MCSET: . . . . DTO 10568

Children's Bible Choir

BIBLE STORIES IN SONG (Children's Bible Hour Choir).
Tracks: / I'm acquainted with the author / Only a boy named David / Gideon had the Lord / Jonah and the whale / Keep walking with the Lord / Wise man and the foolish man, The / Hornets / Count your blessings / Something more than gold / In the same wonderful way / Bible chorus medley / Fourth man / Battle belongs to God, The / Daniel prayed / Daniel was a man of prayer / I believe what the bible says / Standing on the promises / I see Jesus / Jesus gave me water / Then Jesus came / Ten thousand angels / I thank the Lord I am saved.
LP: . . . . PC 841

SING ALONG SONGS FOR CHILDREN VOL 1 (Children's Bible Hour Choir).
Tracks: / Boys and girls for Jesus / Mile after mile / Behold, behold / Jesus loves me / That's the way to find happiness / Boys and girls assurance march / He owns the cattles on a thousand hills / Happy all the time / All through the week / Grumblers / Heaven came down and glory filled the soul / Christian cowboy, A / Only a boy named David / How did Moses cross the Red Sea / Ot's new heart that you need / I'm a soldier / I'm not growing old / Mansion over the hilltop / Saved every day of the week / Onward Christian soldiers / If I were only bigger / In the same wonderful way / B.I.B.L.E., The / Sunday go to meetin' Christian / I have the joy / I'm on the rock / I am the door / One door / This little light of mine / Isn't he wonderful / My sins are gone / Why worry when you can pray / I'm in the Lord's army / Clap your hands / Do you know that you've been born again / Lord is watching over me, The / Why should I care if the sun doesn't shine / Happiness is the Lord.
LP: . . . . PC 747

SINGALONG SONGS FOR CHILDREN VOL 2 (Children's Bible Hour Choir).
Tracks: / Jesus loves even me / Jewels / Oh how I love Jesus / Do you wonder why / I'll be a sunbeam / Jesus bids us shine / Birds upon the treetop, The / Gospel train / Do Lord / Trust in the Lord / Jesus is coming / Mighty army of the young / Give me oil in my lamp / I just keep trusting my Lord / Amen, brother, amen / Windows of Heaven, The / Labourers together with God / He's able / I'll do it all for Jesus / I love him better every day / Like a melody / I am determined / Jesus, the wonderful friend / Which way are you travelling / Along the road / Jesus said that whosoever will / Brighten up your pathway / Let's talk about Jesus / It's all different now / O say, but I'm glad.
LP: . . . . PC 827

Children's Day

MESSAGE TO PRETTY, A.
Tracks: / Bad train ride / Medicine / Hanging tree, The / I told you / Lilith / Message to pretty, A / Bad train ride (reprise).
LP: . . . . VDK 5003

Children's Musical

I WANT YOU (Children's Musical F&T Adair).
LP: . . . . S 7030 79

Children's Songs

STORY BOOK OF CHILDRENS' SONGS (Calder, Adrian).
Tracks: / Lavender blue / I had a little nut tree / Twinkle little star / This old man.
MC: . . . . ERON 021

Childs, Billy

HIS APRIL TOUCH.
Tracks: / Where it's at / His April touch / Four by five / Miles to go before I sleep / New world disorder, A / Memory and desire / Rapid transit / Hand picked rose of fading a dream.
MC: . . . . WT 0131

Child's Play

RAT RACE.
Tracks: / Good ol' rock and roll / Day after night / My bottle / Rat race / Wind / Evicted / Knock me out / Girl like you, A / Capricorn/Band bang / Pay your dues / Damned if I do / When hell freezes over.
LP: . . . . CHR 1758
MC: . . . . ZCHR 1758

Childs, Toni

HOUSE OF HOPE.
LP: 3971491
MC: 3971494

UNION.
Tracks: / Don't walk away / Walk and talk like angels / Stop you're fussin' / Dreamer / Let the rain come down / Zimbabwe / Hush / Tin drum / Where's the ocean.
LP: . . . . AMA 5175
MC: . . . . AMC 5175

Chile

CHILE VENCERA (Anthology of Chilian new song 1962-73) (Various artists).
2LP: ROUNDER4009/10

TRADITIONAL CHILEAN MUSIC (Various artists).
MC: . . . . D 58001

VIVA CHILE (Various artists).
Tracks: / La fiesta de San Benito: *Various artists* / Longuita: *Various artists* / Cancion del poder popular: *Various*

artists / Alturas: *Various artists* / La segunda: *Various artists* / Independancia: *Various* artists / Cuenca de la C.U.T.: *Various artists* / Tatai: *Various artists* / Venceremos: *Various artists*/ Ramis: *Various artists* / Rin del angelito: *Various artists* / Subida: *Various artists* / Simon Bolivar: *Various artists*.
MC: 3C 254 95765

Chilingirian

LAST THREE QUARTETS (SCHUBERT) (see also under Schubert) (Chilingirian String Quartet).

STRING QUARTETS NO.1 & 2 (BARTOK) (see under Bartok (composer)) (Chilingirian String Quartet).

Chi-lites

20 GOLDEN PIECES: CHI-LITES.
Tracks: / I'm ready (if I don't get to go) / Love uprising / Coldest day of my life / Oh girl / I wanna pay you back / I like your loving / Have you seen her? / For God's sake give more power to the people / Are you my woman (tell me so) / We are neighbours / Letter to myself, A / Homely girl / Too good to be forgotten / I found sunshine / Stoned out of my mind / Toby / Give it away / Lonely man / Living in the footsteps of another man / Devil's doing his work, The.
LP: . . . . BDL 2040

CHANGING FOR YOU.
Tracks: / Bad motor scooter / Changing for you / Touch me / Making love / Bottoms up / I just wanna hold you / You take the cake / I love.
LP: . . . . RBLP 1003
MC: . . . . ZCRB 1003

CHI-LITES CLASSICS.
Tracks: / Have you seen her? / Give it away / I want to pay you back / Love uprising / I never had it so good / Too good to be forgotten / Toby / Coldest day of my life / Homely girl / Lonely man / I found sunshine / Stoned out of my mind / Oh girl / For God's sake give more power to the people.
LP: . . . . LIT 101
MC: . . . . ZC LIT 101

GREATEST HITS: CHILITES.
LP: 226 2535
MC: 216 2535

HEART AND SOUL OF THE CHI-LITES.
Tracks: / Have you seen her? / Vanishing love / My first mistake / If I had a girl / Heavenly body / Me and you / All I wanna do is make love to you / Oh girl / Happy being lonely / Hot on a thing called love / Whole lotta good loving / Never speak to a stranger / Tell me where it hurts / Love shock.
MC: . . . . KNMC 12059

HEAVENLY BODY.
Tracks: / Heavenly body / Strung out / Round and round / Love shock / Have you seen her? / All I wanna do is make love to you / Give me a dream / Super mad (about you, baby).
LP: . . . . T 619

JUST SAY YOU LOVE ME.
Tracks: / Happy music / Solid love affair / Just you and I tonite / Just say you love me / Inner city blues / There's a change / Eternity / Only you.
LP: . . . . ICH 1057
MC: . . . . ICH 1057 MC

LOVE SONGS.
LP: 211855
MC: 411855

ME AND YOU.
Tracks: / Me and you / Tell me where it hurts / Whole lot of good good lovin' / Oh girl / Get down with me / Try my side (of love) / Hot on a thing (called love) / Never speak to a stranger.
LP: . . . . T 635

VERY BEST OF: CHI-LITES.
LP: . . . . BRLP 47
MC: . . . . BRMC 47

Chill Fac-torr

CHILL FAC-TORR.
Tracks: / Shout / Fox hunting / Twist (round 'n' round) / I'll satisfy your desire / Burning desires / It's been a long time / Let's get closer.
LP: . . . . PWLP 1006
MC: . . . . ZCPW 1006

Chilli Willi

BONGOS OVER BALHAM (Chilli Willi & Red Hot Peppers).
LP: . . . . CREST 007
MC: . . . . CRESTMC 007

Chilliwack

WANNA BE A STAR.
Tracks: / Sign here / So you wanna be a star? / Tell it to the telephone / Too many enemies / Living in stereo / Mr. Rock / My girl / Don't wanna live for a living / Walk on / I believe.
LP: . . . . XL 17759

Chillout, Chuck

MASTERS OF THE RHYTHM.
Tracks: / Rhythm is the master / No D.J. like Chuck / Gimme minze / Roll call: Bronxwood Productions / Mic I grip, The / I'm large / That's life / No holding back / Time to rhyme / Son of a gun / Chuck is chillin'.
LP: 838 406 1
MC: 838 406 4

Chills

KALEIDOSCOPE WORLD.
LP: . . . . CRELP 008
LP: . . . . FNE 13

SUBMARINE BELLS.
Tracks: / Heavenly pop hit / Tied up in chain / Oncoming day, The / Part past part fiction / Singing in my sleep / I soar / Dead wee / Familiarity breeds contempt / Don't be a memory / Efforesce and deliquesce / Sweet times / Submarine bells.
LP: 828 191 1
MC: 828 191 4

Chilton, Alex

BLACK LIST.
LP: . . . . ROSE 194

DOCUMENT.
Tracks: / Kizza me / Downs / Holocaust / Kangaroo / Big black car / Dream lover / Hey little child / My rival / Hook or crook / Like flies on sherbert / Bangkok / September gurls / In the street.
LP: . . . . AUL 732
MC: . . . . AUC 732

FEUDALIST TARTS.
LP: . . . . ROSE 68

HIGH PRIEST.
LP: . . . . ROSE 130
MC: . . . . ROSE 130C

LIKE FLIES ON SHERBERT.
LP: . . . . AUL 710

LOST DECADE.
LP: . . . . FC 015
MC: . . . . FC 015C

Chilton, John

LET'S DO IT (see under Melly, George).

RUNNING WILD (See under Melly, George) (Chilton, John Feetwarmers & George Melly).

Chimes

CHIMES.
Tracks: / Love so tender / Heaven / True love / 1-2-3 / Underestimate / Love comes to mind / I still haven't found what I'm looking for (street mix) / Don't make me wait / Stronger together / Stay / Heaven (physical mix) / I still haven't found what I'm looking for.
LP: . . . . C 46008
LP: 4664811
MC: 4664814
MC: . . . . CK 46008

ONCE IN A WHILE.
LP: . . . . LP 1001

Chimps At Work

CHIMPS AT WORK (See under Bangers & Mash (tv)).

Chimurenga

AFRICAN DAWN.
LP: . . . . AD 300

Chin Chin

STOP YOUR CRYING.
Tracks: / Stop your crying / Never surrender / Revolution / My guy / Dark days / Cry in van / Stay with me / Jungle of fear.
LP: . . . . AGAS 001

China

ANCIENT CHINESE MELODIES (Various artists).
LP: . . . . LLST 7352
MC: . . . . LLCT 7352

CHINA'S INSTRUMENTAL HERITAGE (Various artists).
Tracks: / Wild geese alighting on the sandy shore: *Various artists* / Old monk sweeping the Buddhist temple: *Various* artists / Ascending to the top of a tower: *Various artists* / Hundred birds courting the phoenix, The: *Various* artists / Farewell, The: *Various artists* / Freedom march: *Various artists* / Flowers on brocade: *Various* artists / Remembering an old old friend: *Various artists* / Relieving my heart: *Various artists* / Winter ravens sporting over the water: *Various artists* / Spring river in the flowery moonlight, The: *China*.
LP: . . . . LLST 792
MC: . . . . LLCT 792

CHINA'S TREASURES (Various artists).
LP: . . . . LLST 7227

CHINESE BUDDHIST MUSIC (Various artists).
LP: . . . . LLST 7222

CHINESE CLASSICAL MASTERPIECES FOR THE PI-PA & CH'IN (Various artists).
LP: . . . . LLST 7182

CHINESE CLASSICAL MUSIC (Various artists).
LP: . . . . LLST 772

CHINESE MASTERPIECES FOR THE CH'IN-ANCIENT & MODERN (Ming-Yeuh Ling, David).
LP: . . . . LLST 7342

CHINESE MASTERPIECES FOR THE CHUNG (Various artists).
LP: . . . . LLST 7142

CHINESE MASTERPIECES FOR THE ERH-HU (Various artists).
LP: . . . . LLST 7132

CHINESE OPERA (Various artists).
LP: . . . . LLST 7212

CHINESE OPERA (Various artists).
LP: . . . . LLST 7232

CHINESE OPERA AND FOLK MELODIES (Various artists).
LP: . . . . LLST 7362
MC: . . . . LLCT 7362

CHINESE TAOIST MUSIC (Various artists).
LP: . . . . LLST 7223

CHINESE ZITHER MUSIC (Various artists).
LP: . . . . H 72089

EXOTIC MUSIC OF ANCIENT CHINA (Various artists).
Tracks: / Four tokens of happiness: *Various artists* / Spring thoughts at Han Palace: *Various artists* / Bird's song, The: *Various artists* / Sound of the temple: *Various artists* / Great ambuscade, The: *Various artists*/ Yearning on River Shiang: *Various artists* / Flowering streams, The: *Various artists* / In remembrance of an old friend: *Various artists* / Elegant orchid, The: *China*.
LP: . . . . LLST 7122

LOTUS LANTERN (Chinese classical orchestra) (Various artists).
LP: . . . . LLST 7202
MC: . . . . LLCT 7202

MUSIC FROM THE PEOPLE'S REPUBLIC OF CHINA (Various artists).
LP: . . . . ROUNDER 4008

PHASES OF THE MOON (TRADITIONAL CHINESE MUSIC).
LP: . . . . CBS 74038
MC: 40 74038

SHANTUNG FOLK MUSIC & TRADITIONAL INSTRUMENTAL PIECES.
LP: . . . . H 72051

TWO MASTERS PLAY THE CHINESE ZITHER The Cheng (Chen, Louis/ Professor Tsai-Ping).
LP: . . . . LLST 7262

China Crisis

CHINA CRISIS COLLECTION.
Tracks: / African and white / No more blue horizons / Christian / Tragedy and mystery / Working with fire and steel / Wishful thinking / Hanna Hanna / Black man ray / King in a catholic style / You did cut me / Arizona sky / Best kept secret / It's everything / St. Saviour square.
LP: . . . . V 2613
MC: . . . . TCV 2613

DIARY OF A HOLLOW HORSE.
Tracks: / St. Saviour Square / Stranger by nature / Sweet charity and adoration / Day after day / Diary of a hollow horse / Red letter day / In Northern skies / Singing the praises of finer things / All my prayers / Age old need / Back home (Only on CD.).
LP: . . . . V 2567
MC: . . . . TCV 2567

DIFFICULT SHAPES AND PASSIVE RHYTHMS (Some People Think It's Fun To Entertain).
Tracks: / Seven sports for all / No more blues horizons / Feel to be driven away / Some people I know to lead fantastic lives / Christian / African and white / Are we a worker / Red sails / You never see it / Temptations big blue eyes / Jean walks in fresh fields.
LP: . . . . V 2243
MC: . . . . TCV 2243
LP: . . . . OVED 173
MC: . . . . OVEDC 173

FLAUNT THE IMPERFECTION.
Tracks: / Highest high / Strength of character / You did cut me / Black man Ray / Wall of God / Gift of freedom / King in a catholic style / Bigger the punch I'm feeling / World spins, The, I'm part of it / Blue sea.
LP: . . . . V 2342
MC: . . . . TCV 2342
LP: . . . . OVED 272
MC: . . . . OVEDC 272

WHAT PRICE PARADISE.
Tracks: / It's everything / Arizona sky / Safe as houses / World's apart / Hampton beach / Understudy, The / Best kept secret / We do the same / June bride / Day's work for the day's done, A / Trading in gold (CD only).
MC: . . . . TCV 2410
LP: . . . . V 2410
LP: . . . . OVED 214
MC: . . . . OVEDC 214

WORKING WITH FIRE AND STEEL-POSSIBLE POP SONGS VOL.2.
Tracks: / Working with fire and steel / When the piper calls / Hanna Hanna / Animals in the jungle / Here comes a raincloud / Wishful thinking / Tragedy and mystery / Papua / Gates of door to door, The / Soulful awakening.
LP: . . . . V 2286

China (group)

CHINA.
Tracks: / Intro / Shout it out / Back to you / Fight is on, The / Wild jealousy / Rock city / Hot lovin' night / Living on the stage / I need your love / One shot to the heart / Staying alive.
LP: . . . . VERH 57
MC: . . . . VERHC 57

SIGN IN THE SKY.
Tracks: / Great wall, The / Dead lights / Animal victim / In the middle of the night / Won't give it up / Sign in the sky / Don't ever say goodbye / Broken dream / Second chance / Bitter cold / Take your time / Harder than hell / So long.
LP: 847 247 1
MC: 847 247 4

Chinatown (film)

CHINATOWN (Original soundtrack) (Various artists).
LP: 255 092.1

Chinese Orchestra

CHINESE FOLK SONGS.
Tracks: / Picnic in Spring / Choice of a lover, The / Sorrow of Lady Wang Chao-Sun, The / Sweet memory of repose / West lake under Autumn moonlight / Heavenly song / Swallows return when willows are green / Warning of Autumn / Love in three stages / Agony in Autumn, The.
LP: . . . . LLST 7152

Chinese Sheng

SONG OF THE PHOENIX.
Tracks: / North East: Chinese folk melody / Thinking about the world / Red flower of Tachai blooms everywhere, The / Beautiful Spring / Bai Yuan kills his wife / Golden phoenix / Spring morning on Hainan Island / Mother of clouds / Love song of the Hmong / Spring on South Mountain.
LP: . . . . LLST 7369

Chiodini, John

WEIGHTLESS.
Tracks: / Ginger / Tahitian dude / Spacescape / Weightless / Famous amos / Joe's place / Gardens, The / Memory of a tree / Smiles.
LP: . . . . MCF 3369
MC: . . . . MCFC 3369

Chipmunks

20 ALL TIME GOLDEN GREATS.
Tracks: / Ragtime cowboy Joe / Alvin's harmonica / Chitty chitty bang bang / I'm Henery the eighth I am / Swanee river / Coming round the mountain / Alvin's orchestra / Pop goes the weasel / Talk to the animals / America the beautiful / Yankee doodle / Supercalifragilisticexpialidocious / Home on the range / Alvin's all star Chipmunk band / Witch doctor / On top of old Smokey / Alvin twist / Polly wolly doodle / And the band played on / She loves you.
LP: . . . . A 48226

CHIPMUNK PUNK.
Tracks: / Let's go / Good girls don't / How do I make you? / Refugee / Frustrated / Call me / You may be right / Crazy little thing called love / My Sharona.
LP: 6302 064

CHIPMUNKS SING THE BEATLES.
Tracks: / All my loving / Do you want to know a secret / She loves you / From me to you / Love me do / Twist and shout / Hard day's night, A / P.S. I love you / I saw her standing there / Can't buy me love / Please please me / I want to hold your hand.
LP: . . . . NUTM 31

MERRY CHRISTMAS FROM THE HAPPY CHIPMUNKS.
LP: . . . . **HDY 1950**
MC: . . . . **ZCHDY 1950**

URBAN CHIPMUNK.
Tracks: / Gambler, The / I love a rainy night / Mamas don't let your babies grow up to be cowboys / Chipmunks / Luckenbach, Texas / Lunchbox / On the road again / Coward of the county / Another somebody done somebody wrong song / Made for each other / Thank God I'm a country boy.
LP: . . . . **INTS 5122**
MC: . . . . **INTK 5122**

Chipperfield, Norma

NORMA CHIPPERFIELD.
LP: . . . . **SRTZ CUS 089**

Chippington, Ted

MAN IN A SUITCASE.
LP: . . . . **YUS 6**

REAL TRUTH ABOUT TRUCKING, THE.
LP: . . . . **SINCERE 001**

Chirag Penchan

DEKHO DEKHO.
LP: . . . . **MUT 1073**
MC: . . . . **CMUT 1073**

RAIL GADDI.
LP: . . . . **MUT 1039**
MC: . . . . **CMUT 1039**

Chisel

HONEST WORK.
LP: . . . . **CHIL 2**
MC: . . . . **CHIC 2**

Chish & Fips (tv)

CHISH AND FIPS SONGBOOK (Television Soundtrack) (Various artists).
LP: . . . . **SCENE 11**
MC: . . . . **SCENEC 11**

Chisholm, Angus

EARLY RECORDINGS OF.....,THE.
LP: . . . . **SHAN 14001**

Chisholm, George

CHISHOLM TRAIL (Chisholm, George All Stars).
LP: . . . . **77 SEU 12/43**

GATEWAY JAZZ BAND WITH GEORGE CHISHOLM (see Gateway Jazz Band & George Chisholm) (Chisholm, George & The Gateway Jazz Band).

GEORGE CHISHOLM/KEITH SMITH/ HEFTY JAZZ (Chisholm, George/Keith Smith/Hefty Jazz).
LP: . . . . **HJ 107**

KENNY BAKER HALF DOZEN (See under Baker, Kenny) (Baker, Kenny featuring George Chisolm).

SALUTE TO SATCHMO (see Welsh, Alex) (Chisholm, George/Alex Welsh/ Humphrey Lyttleton/Bruce Turner).

SWINGING MR.C.
Tracks: / Swinging Mr.C / Tin roof blues / Sophisticated lady / One for monk / Flip flop / You've changed / Don't worry 'bout me / Old feeling, The / Dear Bix / I'm beginning to see the light.
LP: . . . . **ZR 1026**

THAT'S A PLENTY (Chisholm, George Jazz Giants).
LP: . . . . **ZR 1025**

WITH MAXINE DANIELS & JOHN PETTERS BAND (Chisholm, George/ Maxine Daniels & John Petters).
Tracks: / Swinging down memory lane / Riverboat shuffle / Happiness is a thing called Joe / Do nothing till you hear from me / I've got my love to keep me warm / Zing went the strings of my heart.
MC: . . . . **CMJMC 011**

Chisholm & Spence

CHISHOLM AND SPENCE.
Tracks: / You can't get near enough to be the one you / One kiss / I wouldn't leave you crying alone / Dirty work / Dearest John / Your last letter / I didn't know / Stay with me tonight / Down, down nights / Come to bed.
LP: . . . . **CBS 84198**

Chiswick (label)

CHISWICK CHARTBUSTERS VOL.1 (Various artists).
LP: . . . . **CH 2**

CHISWICK CHARTBUSTERS VOL.2 (Various artists).
LP: . . . . **CH 5**

Chittison, Herman

AT THE PIANO.
MC: . . . . **HM 05**

COCKTAIL PIANO FAVOURITES (Chittison, Herman Trio).
Tracks: / Memories of you / Dancing in the ceiling / September in the rain / Can't we be friends / My blue heaven / I've had my moments / Continental, The / Should I / Let's fall in love / Isn't it romantic / They can't take that away from me / On the sunny side of the street / Just a memory / On the Alamo / Ain't misbehavin'.
MC: **4610784**

ELEGANT PIANO STYLING OF....
LP: **88-UR 006**

MASTER OF STRIDE PIANO.
LP: . . . . **MERITT 20**

PIANO GENIUS.
Tracks: / Song has ended, The / How high the moon / Poor butterfly / I should care / These foolish things / I had the craziest dream / Where or when.
LP: . . . . **MVS 506**

Chitty Chitty

CHITTY CHITTY BANG BANG (Film soundtrack) (Various artists).
LP: . . . . **SULP 1200**

Chiweshe, Stella

AMBUYA/NDIZVOZVO (Chiweshe, Stella & The Earthquake).
Tracks: / Chachimurenga / Nehondo / Njuzu / Mugomba / Chamakuwende / Kasahwa / Chipindura / Ndinogarochema / Sarura Wako.
LP: . . . . **ORB 029**

NDIZVOZVO.
LP: . . . . **FEZ 003**

Choates, Harry

FIDDLE KING OF CAJUN SWING.
LP: . . . . **ARHOOLIE 5027**
MC: . . . . **C 5027**

FIVE TIMES LOSER.
Tracks: / Louisiana boogie / She's sweet sweet / Old cow blues / My pretty brunette / Big mamou / What's the use / Five time loser / Je passa durvan ta port / Cat'n around / Big woods.
LP: . . . . **KK 7453**

JOLE BLON.
LP: **7000**

TRIBUTE TO....
LP: . . . . **FLY 572**

Choc Stars

AWA ET BEN.
Tracks: / Nocha / Lascar pa kapi / Miyo motema / Awa et Ben.
LP: . . . . **ORB 010**

CHOC=SHOCK=CHOC.
Tracks: / D.V. / Lieven / Gina / Santa.
LP: . . . . **ORB 009**

Chocolate

AFROCUBAN MAGIC.
LP: . . . . **CLP 166**

Chocolate Dandies

CHOCOLATE DANDIES (1928-1933).
LP: . . . . **S 1249**

JAZZ BANDS 1926/30.
LP: . . . . **HLP 16**

Chocolate Dream

DISCO SUNSET.
MC: . . . . **ORC 013**

Chocolate Factory

45 MINUTES OUT OF 3 YEARS.
LP: . . . . **FABL 006**

LET IT ROLL.
LP: . . . . **FABME 08**

Chocolate Milk

BLUE JEANS.
Tracks: / Blue jeans / Like my lady's love / Running on empty / Honey bun / Let's go all the way / I've been loving you too long / Video queen.
LP: . . . . **RCALP 3070**

COMIN'.
Tracks: / Comin' / Something new / Do unto others / Feel the need / With all our love / Starbright / I refuse / Island love.
LP: . . . . **PL 11830**

HIPNOTISM.
Tracks: / I'm your radio / Forever and a day / Hey lover / Body rhythm / I can't believe you said it's over / Hipnotism / Would it be alright / Dawn / Showdown.
LP: . . . . **PL 13569**

Chocolate Soldier

CHOCOLATE SOLDIER/NAUGHTY MARIETTA (Original Stage Cast) (Various artists).
LP: . . . . **P 13707**
MC: . . . . **BT 13707**

Chocolate Watch Band

44.
Tracks: / Don't need your lovin' / No way out / It's all over now, baby blue / I'm not like everybody else / Misty lane / Loose lip sync ship / Are you gonna be there (at the love-in)? / Gone and passes by / Sitting there standing / She weaves a tender trap / Sweet young thing / I ain't no miracle worker / Blues theme.
LP: . . . . **WIKA 25**

BEST OF CHOCOLATE WATCH BAND.
LP: . . . . **RNLP 108**

Chocolateland Singers

SQUEAKALONG CHRISTMAS.
Tracks: / Jingle bells / Rudolph the red nosed reindeer / Joy to the world / Santa Claus is coming to town / White Christmas / Winter wonderland / God rest ye merry gentlemen / Have yourself a merry little Christmas / Jingle bells (reprise) / In the bleak mid winter / Christmas song, The / Good King Wenceslas / One Christmas tree / Deck the hall / We wish you a merry Christmas / First Noel, The / Silent night / Hark the herald angels sing.
MCSET: . . . . **KIDM 8001**

SQUEAKING IN THE RAIN.
MC: . . . . **KIDM 8002**

Choice Of Arms (film)

CHOICE OF ARMS (Original Soundtrack Recording) (Various artists).
LP: . . . . **SL 9510**

Choices Of The Heart

CHOICES OF THE HEART (Various artists).
2LP: . . . . **SMR 8511**
MCSET: . . . . **SMC 8511**

Choir

CHASE THE KANGAROO.
LP: . . . . **MYR R 6869**
MC: . . . . **MYR C 6869**

DIAMONDS AND RAIN.
LP: . . . . **MYR R 6855**
MC: . . . . **MYR C 6855**

OVERTURES.
LP: . . . . **AMLH 68553**

Choirboys (film)

CHOIRBOYS (Film soundtrack) (Various artists).
LP: . . . . **MCA 2326**

Choirs

850 VOICES (Various artists).
Tracks: / Bandit's chorus: *Fourth Festival Masses Male Choirs* (From 'Ernani') / Linden lea: *Fourth Festival Masses* Male Choirs / Bobby shaftoe: *Fourth Festival Masses Male Choirs* / Jerusalem: *Fourth Festival Masses Male Choirs*/ Grandfathers clock: *Fourth Festival Masses Male Choirs* / Jacobs ladder: *Fourth Festival Masses Male Choirs*/ 23rd psalm: *Fourth Festival Masses Male Choirs* / Early one morning: *Fourth Festival Masses Male Choirs* / When the saints go marching in: *Fourth Festival Masses Male Choirs* / Lily of the valley: *Fourth Festival Masses Male Choirs*/ Calm is the sea: *Fourth Festival Masses Male Choirs* / Huntsman chorus: *Fourth Festival Masses Male Choirs* / Toccata in D minor: *Fourth Festival Masses Male Choirs* / Three Hungarian folk songs: *Fourth Festival Masses Male Choirs*/ Dear Lord and father of mankind: *Fourth Festival Masses Male Choirs* / 23rd psalm: *Fourth Festival Masses Male Choirs*/ Land of hope and glory: *Fourth Festival Masses Male Choirs* / Jerusalem: *Fourth Festival Masses Male Choirs.*
LP: . . . . **BNB 2008**
MC: . . . . **ZC BNB 2008**

1000 STRONG (Various artists).
Tracks: / National anthem: *Third Festival Of Massed English Male Choirs, The* / Three English folk songs: *Third Festival Of* Massed English Male Choirs, The / Crown imperial: *Third Festival Of Massed English Male Choirs, The* / Two traditional love songs: *Third Festival Of Massed English Male Choirs, The* / Entrance and march of the peers: *Third Festival Of* Massed English Male Choirs, The / Battle hymn of the Republic: *Third Festival Of Massed English Male Choirs, The* / For the good times: *Third Festival Of Massed English Male Choirs, The* / Roman war song: *Third Festival Of Massed English* Male Choirs, The / What shall we do with the drunken sailor: *Third Festival Of Massed English Male Choirs, The* / Land of hope and glory: *Third Festival Of Massed English Male Choirs, The* / Lord prayer, The: *Third Festival Of Massed English Male Choirs, The* / Jerusalem: *Third Festival Of Massed English Male Choirs, The.*
LP: . . . . **BNB 2003**

CHORAL WORKS (See under Williams, Vaughan) (Christ Church Cathedral, Oxford Choir).

FESTIVAL OF MASSED ENGLISH MALE CHOIRS (Various artists).
Tracks: / National anthem: *Various artists* / Cavalry of the Steppes: *Various artists* / Pilgrims' chorus: *Various* artists / Comrades in arms: *Various artists* / Deus salutis: *Various artists* / Two roses: *Various artists*/ Gwahoddiad: *Various artists* / Speed your journey: *Various artists* / Long day closes, The: *Various artists*/ Soldiers' chorus: *Various artists.*
LP: . . . . **GRS 1071**

GOLDEN HOUR OF CHORAL CLASSICS (Various artists).
LP: . . . . **GH 660**

GREAT CHORAL CLASSICS (Various artists).
MC: **TC2MOM 116**
LP: . . . . **CFP 4548**
MC: . . . . **TCCFP 4548**

GREAT WELSH MALE VOICE CHOIR TRADITION (Various artists).
Tracks: / God bless the Prince of Wales: *Various artists* / Kalinka: *Various artists* / Just out of reach: *Various* artists / Song of the Jolly Roger: *Various artists* / Gipsy chorus: *Various artists* / 23rd Psalm: *Various* artists / Llef: *Various artists* / Blue tail fly: *Various artists* / Steal away: *Various artists*/ Ash Grove, The: *Various artists* / Llanfair: *Various artists* / Abide with me: *Various artists.*
2LP: . . . . **DPA 3071/2**

MAKE WE JOY (See under Christ Church Cathedral Choir for details) (Christ Church Cathedral, Oxford Choir).

MASSED ENGLISH MALE CHOIRS (Various artists).
Tracks: / God bless the Prince Of Wales: *Various artists* / Lass of Richmond Hill: *Various artists* / John Peel: *Various artists* / Drink to me only: *Various artists* / Cavalry of the Steppes: *Various artists* / Soldiers chorus (Faust): *Various artists* / Thunder and lightning polka: *Various artists* / Jerusalem: *Various artists*/ National anthem: *Various artists.*
LP: . . . . **ABRD 1030**

PALESTRINA (See under Christ Church Cathedral Choir for details) (Christ Church Cathedral, Oxford Choir).

RIDE THE CHARIOT (Various artists).
Tracks: / Sanctus from Requiem: *Various artists* / Passing by: *Various artists* / Mor fawr wyt ti: *Various* artists / Gypsy chorus from "Il travatore": *Various artists* / Dies irae: *Various artists* / Y dref wen: *Various* artists / Impossible dream, The: *Various artists* / Finlandia: *Various artists* / Ride the chariot: *Various* artists / Crusader: *Various artists* / Cavalry of the Steppes: *Various artists* / Ti a dy ddoniau: *Various* artists / Diolch I'r Ior: *Various artists* / Evening's pastorale, An: *Various artists* / Christus redemptor (hyfrydol): *Various artists* / Welsh national anthem, The: *Various artists.*
LP: . . . . **REH 551**
MC: . . . . **ZCR 551**

SIXTH FESTIVAL OF EVANGELICAL CHOIRS (Various artists).
Tracks: / Come ye thankful people come: *Various artists* / Rejoice, the Lord is King: *Various artists* / Sweet, sweet spirit: *Various artists* / If with all your hearts: *Various artists* / Hiding place: *Various artists*/ Then the Lord stood by me: *Various artists* / Far out on the desolate billow: *Various artists* / Boundless ocean: *Various artists* / Jesu, lover of my soul: *Various artists* / Walk with me: *Various artists* / Family of God, The: *Various artists* / Llan Baglan: *Various artists* / Love was when: *Various artists* / Hold the fort, for I am coming: *Various artists* / Let trumpets sound: *Various artists* / Jesus is coming: *Various* artists / Lord's prayer, The: *Various artists* / Praise the Lord, for He is glorious: *Various artists* / I believe in miracles: *Various artists* / Ye shall be witnesses: *Various artists* / Worthy is the lamb: *Various artists* / King is coming: *Various artists* / May the mind of Christ my saviour: *Various artists.*
LP: . . . . **PC 856**

Chokers & Flies

OLD TIME MUSIC.
LP: . . . . **ROUNDER 0213**
MC: . . . . **ROUNDER 0213C**

Chopin (composer)

CHOPIN (Various artists).
MC: . . . . **DLCMC 211**

CHOPIN/SCHUMANN PIANO CONCERTI (see under Vasary, Tamas) (Vasary, Tamas/Northern Sinfonia of England).

FANTASIE IN F (Barenboim, Daniel).
Tracks: / Fantasie in F minor / Berceuse in D flat. Op. 57 / Barcarolle / Polonaise fantaisie Op. 61 / Souvenir de Paganini / Variations brillantes, Op. 12.
MC: . . . . **TCEMX 2117**

NINETEEN WALTZES (Magaloff).
MC: 426 069-4

PIANO CONCERTOS NOS. 1 & 2 (Israel Philharmonic Orchestra).
MC: 4044922
LP: 40922

PIANO FORTE SONATA 14/ SONATAS (See under Beethoven (Horowitz).

PIANO WORKS - BACH, DEBUSSY, CHOPIN (See under Perlemuter, Vlado) (Perlemuter, Vlado).

PRELUDES; BERCEUSE; FANTASIE (Rev, Livia).
MC: . . . . KA 66324

RACHMANINOV AND CHOPIN CELLO SONATAS (see under Gregor-Smith, Bernard) (Gregor-Smith, Bernard/ Yolande Wrigley).

Chopin, Djanga

BEST AFRICAN SOUND, THE.
LP: . . . . PG 87103

Chopin, Henri

AUDIOPOEMS.
LP: . . . . TGS 106

Choral Guild Of...

CHRISTMAS MUSIC (Choral Guild Of America).
LP: P5002
MC: P5402

Choral Music

REGENT CHAMBER CHOIR, THE (Choral Music Of Zoltan Kodlay).
LP: . . . . REG 103

Chorale

CHORALE.
Tracks: / Warrior / Come the night time / Riu riu / Child of space / Heavy load.
LP: . . . . ARTY 163

NATIONWIDE CAROL COMPETITION.
LP: . . . . MOR 506

Choralerna

BORNE ON WINGS.
LP: . . . . MYR 1095
MC: . . . . MC 1095

LET THERE BE LIGHT.
LP: . . . . MYR 1047
MC: . . . . MC 1047

Chorchazade

MADE TO BE DEVOURED.
LP: . . . . GET 1

Chord Of Love

CHORD OF LOVE.
LP: . . . . PC 843

OUR GOD REIGNS.
LP: . . . . PC 429

Chordettes

CHORDETTES, THE.
Tracks: / No wheels / Eddie my love / Girls work is never done, A / Photographs / Mr. Sandman / Lollipop / Charlie Brown / Zorro / Baby come-a-back-a / Hummingbird / Love is a two way street / Wedding, The / Lonely lips / Lay down your arms.
LP: . . . . CH 82

FABULOUS CHORDETTES, THE.
Tracks: / Lollipop / Born to be with you / Eddie my love / Wedding, The / Mister Sandman / Teenage goodnight / Just between you and me / Soft sands / Zorro / No other arms, no other lips / Lay down your arms / Never on Sunday.
MC: . . . . FABC 005

Chords

SO FAR AWAY.
Tracks: / Maybe tomorrow / Happy families / Breaks my heart / Tumbling down / Hold on I'm coming / I'm not sure / Something's missing / It's no use / What are we gonna do now? / She said, she said / Dreamdolls / So far away.
LP: . . . . POLS 1019

Chorus Line (musical)

CHORUS LINE (Original Broadway cast) (Various artists).
Tracks: / I hope I get it: *Various artists* / I can do that: *Various artists* / At the ballet: *Various artists*/ Sing: *Various artists* / Hello twelve, hello thirteen, hello love: *Various artists* / Nothing: *Various artists*/ Music and the mirror, The: *Various artists* / Dance:Ten looks three: *Various artists* / One: *Various artists*/ What I did for love: *Various artists* / One, reprise: *Various artists* / Chorus line:finale: *Various artists*.
LP: 70149
MC: 40 70149

Chosen Brothers

SING AND SHOUT.
LP: . . . . W 2457

Chosen (film)

CHOSEN (HOLOCAUST 2000), THE (Film soundtrack) (Various artists).
LP: . . . . C'BUS 103

Chou Pahrot

CHOU PAHROT LIVE.
Tracks: / Pantomine shrub / Syphlonic diplivits / Wee thing / Random shoggy / Itchy face / Lemons / May submarine / Day o' the mug / Yaw yaw song.
LP: . . . . KLP 19
MC: . . . . ZCKLP 19

Chouans (film)

CHOUANS (1988 film soundtrack) (Various artists).
LP: 66.538
MC: 76.538

Chow-Chow

HIDE.
Tracks: / Hide.
MLP: . . . . ANT 027

Chris & Cosey

ACTION.
Tracks: / Akshun / Talk to me / Relay / Send the magic down / Do or die / Love cuts / Shilvers / Delivium.
LP: . . . . LD 875

CHRIS & COSEY.
LP: . . . . BIAS 108
MC: . . . . BIASC 108

EUROPEAN RENDEZVOUS.
LP: . . . . DVR 8

EXOTICA.
LP: . . . . NTL 30016
LP: . . . . BIAS 069

HEARTBEAT.
LP: . . . . ROUGH 34
LP: . . . . CTILP 004

SONGS OF LOVE AND LUST.
LP: . . . . CTILP 006
LP: . . . . ROUGH 64

TECHNO PRIMITIV.
LP: . . . . ROUGH 84

TRANCE.
LP: . . . . ROUGH 44
LP: . . . . CTILP 005

TRUST.
LP: . . . . BIAS 124

Chris, D

TIME STAND STILL (Chris, D/Divine Horseman).
LP: . . . . ROSE 46

Christ Church

CAROLS FROM CHRIST CHURCH (Christ Church Cathedral, Oxford Choir).
Tracks: / Tomorrow shall be my dancing day / Remember thou, oh man / I sing of a maiden / Sing lullaby / Bethlehem down / Here is the little door / Sir Christemas / In dulci jubilo / Jesu, Thou art our Saviour / O sweet little one / Crown of roses, The / Spotless rose, A / Allelujah, a new work is come on hand.
LP: . . . . ALH 938
MC: . . . . ZC ALH 938

CEREMONY OF CAROLS, A (see under Britten) (Christ Church Cathedral, Oxford Choir/Frances Kelly).

CHORAL WORKS (See under Williams, Vaughan) (Christ Church Cathedral, Oxford Choir).

MISSA CORONA SPINEA (see under Taverner) (Christ Church Cathedral, Oxford Choir).

O FOR THE WINGS OF A DOVE (Christ Church Cathedral, Oxford Choir).
Tracks: / O for the wings of a dove / Ave verum corpus (Mozart) / Jesu, joy of man's desiring.
MC: . . . . ZC QS 6019

Christ On Parade

MIND IS A TERRIBLE THING, A.
LP: . . . . THOUGHT 9

SOUNDS OF NATURE.
LP: . . . . PUS 0012-08

Christabel (tv)

CHRISTABEL (TV soundtrack) (Various artists).
Tracks: / Christabel: *Various artists*.
MLP: . . . . 12 RXL 229

Christensen

MIROSLAV VITOUS GROUP (see under Vitous) (Christensen/Vitous/ Surman/Kirkland).

Christensens

TIME TO FLY (Christensen, Chris/ Laura).
LP: . . . . WST R 9695
MC: . . . . WST C 9695

Christian, Bobby

BIG BAND IN ACTION.
LP: . . . . GELP 15057

Christian, Charlie

1941 LIVE SESSIONS.
LP: 500114

CHARLIE CHRISTIAN.
LP: . . . . LPJT 13

CHARLIE CHRISTIAN & BENNY GOODMAN SEXTET (Christian, Charlie/Benny Goodman Sextet & Orch.).
LP: . . . . JA 23

CHARLIE CHRISTIAN WITH BENNY GOODMAN SEXTET & ORCHESTRA (Christian, Charlie/Benny Goodman Sextet & Orch.).
LP: 525 38

GENIUS OF THE ELECTRIC GUITAR.
Tracks: / Rose room / Seven come eleven / Till Tom special / Gone with "what" wind / Grand slam / Six appeal / Wholly cats / Royal Garden blues / As long as I live / Benny's bugle / Breakfast feud / I found a new baby / Solo flight / Blue in B / Waiting for Benny / Airmail special.
LP: 4606121
MC: 4606124

HARLEM JAZZ SCENE 1941.
LP: . . . . FS 278

Christian, Colin

COLIN CHRISTIAN.
LP: . . . . BSS 368

Christian Death

ALIVE.
LP: . . . . FREUD 29
MC: . . . . FREUDC 29

ANTHOLOGY OF BOOTLEGS.
LP: . . . . NOS 1006

ASHES.
LP: . . . . NORMAL 15

ATROCITIES.
LP: . . . . NORMAL 18

CATASTROPHE BALLET.
LP: . . . . SD 5
LP: . . . . CONTE 105

DEATHWISH.
LP: . . . . SD 4

DECOMPOSITION OF VIOLETS, THE (Live in Hollywood).
MC: . . . . A 138

ONLY THEATRE OF PAIN.
LP: . . . . SD 1

PART 1: ALL THE LOVE (All the Love, All the Hate).
LP: . . . . FREUD 33
MC: . . . . FREUDC 33

PART 2: ALL THE HATE (All the Love, All the Hate).
LP: . . . . FREUD 34
MC: . . . . FREUDC 34

SCRIPTURES.
LP: . . . . FREUD 18

SEX, DRUGS AND JESUS CHRIST.
LP: . . . . FREUD 25
MC: . . . . FREUDC 25

THEATRE OF PAIN.
LP: . . . . FL 2

WIND KISSED PICTURES.
LP: . . . . SF 003

Christian, Emile

EMILE CHRISTIAN & HIS NEW ORLEANS JAZZ BAND (Christian, Emile & His New Orleans jazz band).
LP: . . . . SLP 223

Christian, Herman

MELODY LINGERS ON, THE (Christian, Herman Trio).
LP: . . . . AP 39

Christian, Michael

BOY FROM NEW YORK CITY.
Tracks: / Leader of the band / Ya gotta believe / See my baby / Jamaica sun / Surprise / Spirit / Rock together / Lainee / Little Ms Rite / Rock'n'roll baby.
LP: . . . . N 5002

Christian, Roger

CHECKMATE.
Tracks: / Take it from me / Checkmate / Stop start / Stop yourself from falling / Stay with me tonight / Loving you is so easy / Chains / Worlds apart / Mwanzia / Love will find a way.
MC: . . . . ICT 9941
LP: . . . . ILPS 9941

Christiane F (film)

CHRISTIANE F.WIR KINDER VOM BAHNOF ZOO (See under Bowie, David) (Bowie, David).

Christianhound

BUDGERIGAR.
LP: . . . . DMC 006

CYNICOY.
Tracks: / Gravitation / Antidote / Dizzy bullets / Easy scandals / Where is / Shuffle off / Feelings / Sexgod / Kiss me like / My hero.
LP: . . . . CON 00017

Christians

CHRISTIANS, THE.
Tracks: / Forgotten town (Theme for BBC TV series It's My City) / When the fingers point / Born again / Ideal world / Save a soul in every town / And that's why / Hooverville / One in a million / Sad songs.
LP: . . . . ILPS 9876
MC: . . . . ICT 9876

COLOUR.
Tracks: / Man don't cry / I found out / Greenbank Drive / All talk / Words / Community of spirit / There you go again / One more baby in black / In my hour of need.
MC: . . . . ICT 9948
LP: . . . . ILPS 9948

WORDS.
Tracks: / Words / Long gone.
LPPD: 12ISP 450

Christie, Agatha (aut)

BLUE GERANIUM AND MORE STORIES (see under Blue Geranium (bk) (Hickson, Joan (nar)).

HERB OF DEATH (see under Herb Of Death (bk)) (Hickson, Joan (nar)).

MURDER IN THE MEWS (see under Murder In The...(bk) (Hawthorne, Nigel (nar)).

MURDER IS ANNOUNCED, A (see under Murder is... (bk)) (Leach, Rosemary (nar)).

MURDER OF ROGER ACKROYD/ MURDER ON THE LINKS (Various artists).
MCSET: . . . . ZBBC 1057

POIROT INVESTIGATES VOL. 1 (see under Poirot ...(bk)) (Suchet, David (nar)).

POIROT INVESTIGATES VOL. 2 (see under Poirot ...(bk)) (Suchet, David (nar)).

SITTAFORD MYSTERY, THE (see under Sittaford Mystery (bk)).

THIRTEEN PROBLEMS, THE (see under Thirteen Problems (bk)) (Hickson, Joan (nar)).

UNEXPECTED GUEST (see under Unexpected Guest (bk)).

VEILED LADY AND THE THIRD FLOOR FLAT, THE (Rees, Roger).
MC: 1769

Christie, Keith

HOMAGE TO THE DUKE (Christie, Keith/Dankworth/Hodges/Nance).
LP: . . . . ESQ 336

Christie, Lou

LIGHTNIN' STRIKES (OLD GOLD) (see under Sam The Sham).

Christie, P.T

IF YOU'RE NOT THERE.
Tracks: / Once a day / Carry me back / Four walls / Gambler, The / Little folks, The / Running bear / If you're not there / Geisha girl / Amanda / Here I am in Dallas / Crossroads / Take good care of her.
LP: . . . . NA 120
MC: . . . . NC 120

Christie, Tony

AT HIS BEST.
LP: . . . . MFP 5622
MC: . . . . TCMFP 5622

BABY I'M A WANT YOU.
Tracks: / Solitaire / Way we were, The / Happy birthday baby / Bewitched / Here's that rainy day / House is not a home, A / Feelings / (Sittin' on) the dock of a bay / Didn't we? / Drive safely darlin' / Easy to love / Daddy don't you walk so fast / My sweet lord / I'm gonna make you love me / Baby I'm a want you / You and I / Part time love / Drift away / Have you ever been to Georgia / Like sister and brother / On this night of a thousand stars / I did what I did for Maria / Las Vegas / Is this the way to Amarillo / Avenues and alleyways / Love hurts / Most beautiful girl in the world, The / On Broadway.
2LP: . . . . CR 5158
MCSET: . . . . CRT 5158

BEST OF TONY CHRISTIE.
LP: . . . . MCF 2769
LP: . . . . MCL 1602

GOLDEN GREATS: TONY CHRISTIE.

Tracks: / Is this the way to Amarillo / Avenues and alleyways / Solitaire / I did what I did for Maria / Don't go down to Reno / So deep is the night / Feelings / Like sister and brother / Las Vegas / Happy birthday baby / Most beautiful girl in the world, The / Words are impossible / Drive safely darlin' / I'm not in love / Way we were, The / Queen of the mardis gras.
LP: . . . . MCM 5020
MC: . . . . MCMC 5020

I DID WHAT I DID FOR MARIA.
LP: . . . . MKPS 2016

LADIES MAN.
LP: . . . . PL 28382
MC: . . . . TC-PL 28382

TONY CHRISTIE LIVE.
Tracks: / You've lost that lovin' feeling / Ol' man river / If it feels good do it / Las Vegas / Don't go down to Reno / I did what I did for Maria / MacArthur Park / Didn't we / Is this the way to Amarillo / West side story / Something's coming / Maria / Somewhere / Tonight / Your love keeps lifting me higher and higher / Help me make it through the night / So deep is the night / Hey Jude / Solitaire.
LP: . . . . MFP 50489
LP: . . . . MCF 2703

WITH LOVING FEELING.
LP: . . . . MUPS 468

Christine (film)

CHRISTINE (1984 Film Soundtrack) (Various artists).
Tracks: / Bad to the bone: *Thorogood, George & The Destroyers* / Not fade away: *Holly, Buddy & The Crickets* / Pledging my love: *Ace, Johnny* / We belong together: *Robert & Johnny* / Keep a knockin': *Little Richard*/ I wonder why: *Dion & The Belmonts* / Harlem nocturne: *Viscounts* / Little bitty pretty one: *Harris, Thurston*/ Rock 'n' roll is here to stay: *Danny & The Juniors* / Christine attacks: *Carpenter, John & Alan Howarth* / Bony Moronie: *Williams, Larry*.
LP: . . . . STMR 9022
MC: . . . . CSTMA 9022
LP: . . . . ZL 72139
MC: . . . . ZK 72139

CHRISTINE (2) (1984 film soundtrack) (Carpenter, John).
LP: . . . . VS 5240
MC: . . . . VSC 5240

Christmann, Gunter

SOLOMUSIKEN FUR POSAUNE ETC.
LP: . . . . RING 01032

Christmann

LIVE - MOERS FESTIVAL 76 (Christmann Schoenenberg Duo).
LP: . . . . RING 01012

TOPIC (Christmann Schoenenberg Duo).
LP: . . . . RING 01020

Christmas

20 TRADITIONAL CHRISTMAS CAROLS (Girl Guides).
Tracks: / Deck the hall / We wish you a merry Christmas / O little town of Bethlehem / Silent night / Away in a manger / Still, still, still / Once in Royal David's City / Go tell it on the mountain / Hydom / Good King Wenceslas / Shepherds shake off your drowsy sleep / I saw three ships / Child in a manger / Rocking carol, The / Rise up shepherd / See, amid the winter's snow / What child is this / Torches / On Christmas night.
MC: . . . . ZCM 288
LP: . . . . REC 288

ADVENT AND CHRISTMAS AT PORTSMOUTH CATHEDRAL (Various artists).
Tracks: / O come, O come, Emmanuel: *Portsmouth Cathedral Choir* / Hymn to the virgin, A: *Portsmouth Cathedral Choir*/ Jesus Christ, the apple tree: *Portsmouth Cathedral Choir* / Of the father's heart begotten: *Portsmouth Cathedral* Choir / Tender shoot, A: *Portsmouth Cathedral Choir* / Come, Thou long-expected Jesus: *Portsmouth Cathedral Choir*/ Advent collect, The: *Portsmouth Cathedral Choir* / Lo He comes with clouds descending: *Portsmouth Cathedral Choir*/ Wachet auf ruft uns die Stimme: *Portsmouth Cathedral Choir* / Once in royal David's city: *Portsmouth Cathedral Choir*/ Maiden most gentle, A: *Portsmouth Cathedral Choir* / Hark the herald angels sing: *Portsmouth Cathedral Choir*/ O leave your sheep: *Portsmouth Cathedral Choir* / Come, thou Redeemer of the earth: *Portsmouth Cathedral Choir*/ Christmas collect, The: *Portsmouth Cathedral Choir* / Unto us a boy is born: *Portsmouth Cathedral Choir* / In dulci jubilo: *Portsmouth Cathedral Choir*.
MC: . . . . HAC 835

BEST OF CHRISTMAS (Various artists).
MC: . . . . ZCHDY 1935
LP: . . . . HDY 1935

BING CROSBY CHRISTMAS COLLECTION (see under Crosby, Bing) (Crosby, Bing).

CANTERBURY CAROLS (Canterbury Cathedral Choir).
Tracks: / O come, all ye faithful / Sussex carol / Stille nacht (Silent night) / Once in royal David's city / Ding dong merrily on high / Candlelight carol / God rest ye merry, gentlemen / Three kings, The / O little town of Bethlehem / Gaudete, Christus est natus / In the bleak mid winter / While shepherds watched / Away in a manger / Hark the herald angels sing / Tocatta for organ (Dubois).
MC: . . . . YORKMC 109

CAROLS BY CANDLELIGHT (Various artists).
Tracks: / O come all ye faithful: *Various artists* / Silent night: *Various artists* / In dulce decorum: *Various artists* / In the bleak mid Winter: *Various artists* / While shepherds watched their flocks by night: *Various artists*/ O little town of Bethlehem: *Various artists* / Ding dong merrily on high: *Various artists* / Once in Royal David's city: *Various artists* / Sussex carol: *Various artists* / I saw three ships: *Various artists* / Shepherd's type carol: *Various artists* / Coventry carol: *Various artists* / Away in a manger: *Various artists*.
LP: . . . . TRX 703
MC: . . . . TRXC 703

CAROLS FROM CLARE (Clare College Singers & Orchesta).
Tracks: / Shepherd's pipe carol / Infant holy / Angel tidings / Quelle est cette odeur / Once in Royal David's city / Il est ne le divin enfant / I saw three ships / In dulci jubilo / Nativity carol / Quem pastores / Rockin' / Twelve days of Christmas, The / Here we come a wassailing / Coming of our King, The / O come, o come Emmanuel / Infant King, The / Shepherd's noel / Noel nouvelet / O little town of Bethlehem / Gabriel's message / Sans day carol / Stille nacht / Flemish carol / Past three o'clock.
LP: . . . . EG 7699501
MC: . . . . EG 7699504

CHILDREN'S CHRISTMAS COLLECTIOHN (See under Children's) (Various artists).

CHILDREN'S CHRISTMAS SONGS (See under Children's) (Various artists).

CHRISTMAS (1) (Various artists).
LP: . . . . SP R 1176
MC: . . . . SP C 1176

CHRISTMAS ALBUM (see under Crosby, Bing) (Crosby, Bing & Rosemary Clooney).

CHRISTMAS ALBUM, THE (Various artists).
Tracks: / O come all ye faithful: *Secombe, Harry* / Ding dong merrily on high: *Bach Choir* / Away in a manger: *Lynn, Vera* / In dulci jubilo: *Clare College Singers & Orchesta* / While shepherds watched: *King's Singers*/ In the bleak mid winter: *Anderson, Moira* / First noel, The: *Canterbury Cathedral Choir* / Good King Wenceslas: *Whittaker, Roger* / Twelve days of Christmas, The: *Epworth Choir* / Holly and the ivy, The: *Laine, Cleo*/ Cowboy carol, A: *Epworth Choir* / O little town of Bethlehem: *King's Singers* / Silent night: *Lynn, Vera*/ Once in Royal David's City: *Laine, Cleo* / Infant king, The: *Canterbury Cathedral Choir* / God rest ye, merry gentlemen: *Whittaker, Roger* / Carol of the drum: *Epworth Choir* / See amid the winter's snow: *Anderson, Moira*/ Hark the herald angels sing: *Secombe, Harry*.
MC: . . . . TCIDL 108
MC: 795 463 4

CHRISTMAS AT HOME (Various artists).
Tracks: / God rest ye merry gentlemen: *Various artists* / Sussex carol: *Various artists* / Ding dong merrily on high: *Various artists* / Angels from the realms of glory: *Various artists* / First Noel, The: *Various artists*/ Away in a manger: *Various artists* / We wish you a merry Christmas: *Various artists*.
MCSET: . . . . DTO 10038

CHRISTMAS BONANZA (Various artists).
LP: . . . . XLPC 1

CHRISTMAS CAROLS (Various artists).
Tracks: / God rest ye merry gentlemen: *Various artists* / While shepherds watched their flocks by night: *Various artists*/ See, amid the winter's snow: *Various artists* / Silent night: *Various artists* / Good King Wenceslas: *Various* artists / O little town of Bethlehem: *Cathedral Choir Guildford, The* / Unto us is born a son: *Various artists*/ Away in a manger: *Various artists* / Rockin': *Various artists* / In dulci jubilo: *Choir Of Westminster Abbey*/ Ding dong merrily on high: *Various artists* / Coventry carol: *Various artists* / I saw three ships: *St. Paul's Cathedral* / Holly and the ivy, The: *Various artists* / Angels from the realms of glory: *St. Paul's Cathedral*/ First Noel, The: *Various artists* / O come all ye faithful: *Various artists* / Once in Royal David's City: *Cathedral Choir Exeter* / Hark the herald angels sing: *Cathedral Choir Exeter*.
MC: . . . . HR 8168

CHRISTMAS CAROLS AND FESTIVE SONGS (Save The Children) (Various artists).
LP: . . . . SCFLP 1
MC: . . . . SCFMC 1

CHRISTMAS CAROLS AT CANTERBURY CATHEDRAL (Canterbury Cathedral Choir).
LP: . . . . XMS 670
MC: . . . . XMSC 670

CHRISTMAS CAROLS FROM CANTERBURY (Various artists).
Tracks: / O come all ye faithful: *Various artists* / Gabriel's message: *Various artists* / How far is it to Bethlehem: *Various artists* / O come, o come Emmanuel: *Various artists* / Silent night: *Various artists* / Unto us a boy is born: *Various artists* / Infant king, The: *Various artists* / In dulci jubilo: *Various artists*/ Personent hodie: *Various artists* / Ding dong merrily on high: *Various artists* / Angels from the realms of glory: *Various artists* / Tomorrow shall be my dancing day: *Various artists* / Holly and the ivy, The: *Various artists*/ Masters in this hall: *Various artists* / Kings of Orient: *Various artists* / God rest ye merry gentlemen: *Various* artists / Seven joys of Mary, The: *Various artists* / Hark the herald angels sing: *Various artists* / Chorale prelude "In dulci jubilo: *Various artists* / Bells of Canterbury Cathedral: *Various artists*.
LP: . . . . REC 429
MC: . . . . ZCM 429

CHRISTMAS CAROLS FROM SALISBURY CATHEDRAL (Various artists).
LP: . . . . BD 3002

CHRISTMAS CHANT (Prinknash Abbey Monks/Stanbrook Abbey Nuns).
Tracks: / Laetundebus (Sequence) / Christus factus est (Invitatory (from Matins as are all tracks to Alma Redemptoris Mater)) / Christe Redemptor (Hymn (Melody from Ely manuscript)) / Dominus dixit (Ps 2) (Antiphon) / Isiah ch. 9, vv. 1-6 (Lesson) / Verbum Caro (Responsory) / Alma Redemptoris Mater (Marian anthem. end s1) / Dominus dixit (Introit - Midnight Mass (all tracks to In splendoribus are Mass chants)) / Kyrie eleison (Missa IV: Cunctipotens) / Gloria in excelsis / Omnes de Saba (Gradual for Epiphany) / Alleluia (Dawn Mass) / Laetentur (Offortory - Midnight Mass) / Sanctus (and Benedictus) / Agnus Dei / In splendoribus (Communion - Midnight Mass) / Angelus ad Virginem (Hymn) / Ecce Nomen (Anthem) / Quem Vidistis (Antiphon) / Angelus ad pastores (Antiphon) / Hodie Christus natus est (Antiphon (II vespers of Christmas)) / Puer natus (Recessional).
MC: . . . . CSDL 369

CHRISTMAS COLLECTION, A (Various artists).
Tracks: / Christmas song, The: *Cole, Nat King* / Adeste fideles: *Cole, Nat King* / Walking in the air: *Jones, Aled* / Santa Claus is coming to town: *Lee, Peggy* / Christmas waltz: *Lee, Peggy* / Rudolf the red-nosed reindeer: *Martin, Dean* / White Christmas: *Martin, Dean* / Jingle bells: *Paul, Les & Mary Ford* / Silent night: *Paul, Les & Mary Ford* / When a child is born: *Rogers, Kenny* / Christmas is my favourite time of year: *Rogers, Kenny* / Little drummer boy: *Lynn, Vera* / Mary's boy child: *Lynn, Vera* / Have yourself a merry little Christmas: *Campbell, Glen* / Christmas is for children: *Campbell, Glen* / O' holy night: *Rodgers, Jimmie (2)* / I'll be home for Christmas: *Beach Boys* / Winter wonderland: *Mercer, Johnny* / What child is this (Green Sleeves): *Rodgers, Jimmie (2)* (CD only.) / We three kings of Orient are: *Beach Boys* (CD only.).
MC: . . . . TCMFP 5903

CHRISTMAS COLLECTION, THE (Various artists).
Tracks: / White Christmas: *Crosby, Bing* / Jingle bells: *Cole, Nat King* / Have yourself a merry little Christmas: *Sinatra, Frank* / Adeste fideles: *Crosby, Bing* / Christmas song, The: *Torme, Mel* / Santa Claus is coming to town: *Cole, Nat King* / It came upon a midnight clear: *Sinatra, Frank* / Rudolph the red nosed reindeer: *Crosby, Bing* / Mr. Santa Claus: *Cole, Nat King* / Baby, it's cold outside: *Stewart, James* / Silent night: *Crosby*, Bing / Take me back to Toyland: *Cole, Nat King* / O little town of Bethlehem: *Sinatra, Frank* / Silver bells: *Crosby, Bing* / Mele kalikimaka: *Cole, Nat King* / Deck the halls with boughs of holly: *Crosby, Bing*/ Away in a manger: *Crosby, Bing* / First Noel, The: *Crosby, Bing* / Christmas dreaming: *Sinatra, Frank*/ God rest ye merry gentlemen: *Crosby, Bing*.
LP: . . . . DVLP 2080
MC: . . . . DVMC 2080

CHRISTMAS COUNTRY (Various artists).
Tracks: / Please come home for Christmas: *Lee, Johnny* / Little drummer boy: *Williams, Hank* / Silver bells: *Tompall* & The Glaser Brothers / Blue Christmas: *Raven, Eddy* / Christmas song, The: *Curtis, Fonny* / Silent night: *Sun, Joe* / Rudolph the red nosed reindeer: *Tillis, Mel & Nancy Sinatra* / O holy night: *Cornelius, Helen*/ White Christmas: *Tillis, Mel*.
LP: . . . . K 52326

CHRISTMAS CRACKERS (A selection of the most famous Christmas tunes) (Various artists).
LP: . . . . RIM 3005

CHRISTMAS FANTASY (Huddersfield C.S./Black Dyke...).
Tracks: / We wish you a merry Christmas / O come all ye faithful / Sussex carol / Ding dong merrily on high / First Noel, The / In dulci jubilo / Silent night.
LP: . . . . LBRD 021
MC: . . . . LBTD 021

CHRISTMAS GIFT FOR YOU FROM PHIL SPECTOR, A (Various artists).
Tracks: / White Christmas: *Love, Darlene* / Frosty the snowman: *Ronettes* / Bells of St. Mary's: *Soxx, Bob* B. & The Blue Jeans / Santa Claus is coming to town: *Crystals* / Sleigh ride: *Ronettes* / Marshmallow world: *Love, Darlene* / I saw mommy kissing Santa Claus: *Ronettes* / Rudolph the red-nosed reindeer: *Crystals*/ Winter wonderland: *Love, Darlene* / Parade of the wooden soldiers: *Crystals* / Christmas (baby please come home): *Love, Darlene* / Here comes Santa Claus: *Soxx, Bob B. & The Blue Jeans* / Silent night: *Spector, Phil & Artists*.
LP: . . . . PSL 1005
MC: . . . . TCPSL 1005

CHRISTMAS IN THE FOREST (Various artists).
MC: . . . . C 02

CHRISTMAS JOYS (See under Carmichael, Ralph) (Various artists).

CHRISTMAS MESSAGE, A (Various artists).
LP: 847 310-1
MC: 847 310-4

CHRISTMAS MUSIC BOX (Original music box medley of Christmas songs) (Various artists).
Tracks: / Silent night: *Various artists* / O Sanctissima: *Various artists* / Ave maria: *Various artists*/ Adeste fideles: *Various artists* / Rosary, The: *Various artists* / Hark the herald angels sing: *Various* artists / Monastery bells: *Various artists* / Jingle bells: *Various artists* / Come all ye children: *Various artists* / First Noel, The: *Various artists* / O Tannenbaum: *Various artists* / Cloister bells: *Various* artists / Song of the bells: *Various artists* / Auld lang syne: *Various artists* / Chimes of trinity: *Various artists*.
LP: . . . . AB 3
MC: . . . . AB-C 3

CHRISTMAS NEW ORLEANS STYLE (Various artists).
LP: . . . . DC 12020

CHRISTMAS NIGHT IN BETHLEHEM (Various artists).
LP: . . . . XMAS 1

CHRISTMAS PARTY SINGALONG (Various artists).
Tracks: / First Noel: *Various artists* / Have yourself a merry little Christmas: *Various artists* / Silent night: *Various artists* / Santa Claus is coming to town: *Various artists* / Away in a manger: *Various artists*/ Winter wonderland: *Various artists* / Mary's boy child: *Various artists* / God rest ye merry gentlemen: *Various* artists / Little drummer boy: *Various artists* / O come all ye faithful: *Various artists* / Jingle bells: *Various artists* / Little donkey: *Various artists* / White Christmas: *Various artists* / Christmas song, The: *Various artists* / Good king Wenceslas: *Various artists* / While shepherds watched: *Various artists*/ Hark the herald angels sing: *Various artists* / Let it

snow, let it snow, let it snow: *Various artists* / Rudolf the red nosed reindeer: *Various artists.*
LP: . . . . **SHM 811**
MC: . . . . **HSC 811**

CHRISTMAS RAP (Various artists).
Tracks: / Christmas in Hollis: *Run D.M.C.* / Let the jingle bells rock: *Sweet Tee* / Dana Dane is coming to town: *Dane, Dana* / Ghetto santa: *Spyder D* / Christmas in the city: *King Sun-D Moet* / Chillin' with Santa: *Derek B* / He's Santa Claus: *Disco 4* / That's what I want for Christmas: *Showboys* / Surf M.C. New Year, A: *Surf M.C.'s.*
LP: . . . . **LONLP 52**
MC: . . . . **LONLC 52**

CHRISTMAS RAP (IMPORT) (Various artists).
LP: . . . . **PRO 1247**

CHRISTMAS RECORD (Various artists).
LP: . . . . **ILPS 7022**

CHRISTMAS SINGALONG BOOK (Unknown narrator(s)).
MC: . . . . **STK 024**

CHRISTMAS SONGS (Various artists).
MC: . . . . **PLB 263**

CHRISTMAS SOUL SPECIAL (Various artists).
Tracks: / Jingle bells: *Various artists* / Silent night: *Various artists* / Drummer boy: *Various artists*/ Oh holy night: *Various artists* / Jingle bell rock: *Various artists* / Christmas song, The: *Various artists*/ Santa Claus is coming to town: *Various artists* / Noel: *Various artists* / Winter wonderland: *Various artists*/ Oh come all ye faithful: *Various artists* / Frosty the snowman: *Various artists* / Silver bells: *Various artists.*
LP: . . . . **BMLP 056**
LP: . . . . **V 015**
MC: . . . . **V 015 C**

CHRISTMAS STING (Various artists).
LP: . . . . **DSR 6778**

CHRISTMAS TEEN (Various artists).
LP: . . . . **NE 1189**
MC: . . . . **CE 2189**

CHRISTMAS WITH BING CROSBY (see under Bing Crosby) (Crosby, Bing).

CHRISTMAS WITH THE STARS (Various artists).
LP: . . . . **MFP 50484**
MC: . . . . **TCMFP 50484**

CHRISTMAS WITH THE STARS (Various artists).
LP: . . . . **SHM 3020**
MC: . . . . **HSC 3020**

COUNTRY CHRISTMAS (see under Country...) (Various artists).

ENCHANTED CAROLS (Various artists).
Tracks: / Church bells: *Townsend, Dave/Nick Hooper* / Hark the herald angels sing: *Various* (Barrel organ, musical boxes, roller barrel organ, Orpheus disc piano.) / Virgin most pure, A: *Dartington Handbell Choir* / Jingle bells: *Penny* piano / Star of Bethlehem: *Musical Boxes* / Angels from the realms of glory: *Grosmont Handbell Ringers* (Medley, 4 items) / Away in a manger: *Grosmont Handbell Ringers* / O little town of Bethlehem: *Grosmont Handbell Ringers*/ First Noel, The: *Grosmont Handbell Ringers* (end of medley) / As, with gladness, men of old: *Sun Life Stanshawe Band*/ Glory to God in the highest: *Sun Life Stanshawe Band* / See, amid the winter's snow: *Sun Life Stanshawe Band*/ O come all ye faithful: *Various artists* (Barrel organ, musical box, disc piano. End s1) / Silent Night: *Musical* Boxes / Down in yon forest: *Dartington Handbell Choir* / Good King Wenceslas: *Various* (Musical boxes, barrel organ) / Little Jesus, sweetly sleep: *Launton Handbell Ringers* / Little drummer boy: *Launton Handbell Ringers*/ Deck the halls: *Launton Handbell Ringers* / Little donkey: *Launton Handbell Ringers* / While shepherds watched their flocks by night: *Barrel Organ...* / Auld lang syne: *Musical Boxes* / Church bells: *Townsend, Dave/ Nick Hooper.*
LP: . . . . **SDL 327**
MC: . . . . **CSDL 327**

FAMILY CHRISTMAS (Various artists).
LP: . . . . **MM R 0168**

FAVOURITE CHRISTMAS CAROLS (Various artists).
LP: . . . . **FA 4130001**
MC: . . . . **FA 4130004**
LP: . . . . **WHS 4130001**
MC: . . . . **TCWHS 4130004**
MC: . . . . **WHS 4130004**

FESTIVAL OF CAROLS (Various artists).
Tracks: / Once in royal David's city: *Guildford Cathedral Choir* / While shepherds watched their flocks by night: *Sunbury* Junior Singers of the Salvation Army / Holly and the ivy, The: *St. Paul's Cathedral Choir* / God rest ye merry gentlemen: *Guildford Cathedral Choir* / Unto us is born a son: *Westminster Abbey Choir* / As with gladness men of old: *Guildford* Cathedral Choir / O little town of Bethlehem: *St. Paul's Cathedral Choir* / Hark the herald angels sing: *Guildford* Cathedral Choir / I saw three ships: *St. Paul's Cathedral Choir* / Silent night: *Sunbury Junior Singers of the Salvation Army* / In dulci jubilo: *Westminster Abbey Choir* / First Noel, The: *Guildford Cathedral Choir* / In the bleak mid winter: *St. Paul's Cathedral Choir* / Good King Wenceslas: *Guildford Cathedral Choir* / Rocking carol, The: *Sunbury Junior Singers of the Salvation Army* / Coventry carol: *St. Paul's Cathedral Choir* / It came upon a midnight clear: *Guildford Cathedral Choir* / Away in a manger: *Westminster Abbey Choir* / Ding dong merrily on high: *Sunbury Junior Singers of the Salvation Army* / O come all ye faithful: *Guildford Cathedral Choir.*
LP: . . . . **MFP 50487**
MC: . . . . **TCMFP 50487**

FESTIVAL OF CHRISTMAS, A (Royal Liverpool Philharmonic Orchestra).
Tracks: / Ding dong merrily on high / Silent night / O come all ye faithful / In the bleak mid winter / Infant king, The / Deck the halls with boughs of holly / Cradle song.
LP: . . . . **LBRD 006**
MC: . . . . **LBTD 006**

GHOSTS OF CHRISTMAS PAST (Various artists).
LP: . . . . **TWI 058**

GLORY OF XMAS, THE (Various artists).
LP: . . . . **SENS 1080**
MC: . . . . **SENC 1080**

GOSPEL AT CHRISTMAS (See under Gospel..) (Various artists).

IT'S CHRISTMAS (Various artists).
Tracks: / Happy Xmas (war is over): *Lennon, John & Yoko Ono* (With The Plastic Ono Band.) / Do they know it's Christmas?: *Band Aid* / I wish it could be Christmas everyday: *Wood, Roy & Wizzard* / Merry Xmas everybody: *Slade*/ Step into Christmas: *John, Elton* / Merry Christmas everybody: *Stevens, Shakin'* / Wonderful Christmastime: *McCartney*, Paul / I believe in Father Christmas: *Lake, Greg* / December will be magic again: *Bush, Kate* / Mistletoe and wine: *Richard, Cliff* / Walking in the air: *Jones, Aled* / Spaceman came travelling, A: *De Burgh, Chris*/ Stop the cavalry: *Lewie, Jona* / Little Saint Nick: *Beach Boys* / Rockin' around the Christmas tree: *Lee*, Brenda / Lonely this Christmas: *Mud* / Christmas song, The: *Cole, Nat King* / White Christmas: *Crosby, Bing.*
LP: . . . . **EMTV 49**
MC: . . . . **TCEMTV 49**

IT'S CHRISTMAS TIME AGAIN (Various artists).
Tracks: / It's Christmas time again: *Lee, Peggy* / It's beginning to look like Christmas: *Crosby, Bing* / Winter wonderland: *Andrews Sisters* / Sleigh ride: *Andrews Sisters* / White Christmas: *Crosby, Bing.*
LP: . . . . **SHM 3254**
MC: . . . . **HSC 3254**

JOY OF CHRISTMAS (Various artists).
2LP: . . . . **DPA 3047/8**

LA BORDONA (see under Cardiff Polyphonic) (Cardiff Polyphonic Choir).

LITTLE CHRISTMAS MUSIC, A (King's Singers/Kiri Te Kanawa/City of London Sinfonia).
Tracks: / Here we come a-wassailing / It came upon a midnight clear / Little drummer boy / White Christmas / I wonder as I wander / We wish you a merry Christmas / Es ist ein ros' entsprungen / Ding dong merrily on high / Stille nacht / O little town of Bethlehem / Little Christmas music, A / Coventry carol / Boar's Head carol / Gaudete / Joy to the world / Riu, riu, chiu / Il nino querido / Villancico catalan / Deck the hall / Wexford carol, The / Gift, The / Patapan and farandole.
LP: . . . . **KINGS 3**
LP: . . . . **EL 749 909 1**
MC: . . . . **TCKINGS 3**
MC: . . . . **EL 749 909 4**

MAGIC OF CHRISTMAS (Various artists).
LP: . . . . **HDY 1937**
MC: . . . . **ZCHDY 1937**

MERRY CHRISTMAS (Various artists).
Tracks: / Silent night: *Fitzgerald, Ella* / Adeste fideles: *Cole, Nat King* / Let it snow, let it snow, let it snow: *Martin, Dean* / Have yourself a merry little Christmas: *Gleason, Jackie* / I like a sleighride (jingle bells): *Lee, Peggy* / I'll be home for Christmas: *Beach Boys* / Christmas dinner country syle: *Crosby, Bing* / O holy night: *Cole, Nat King* / Little drummer boy: *Stafford, Jo* / White Christmas: *Martin, Dean* / O little town of Bethlehem: *Fitzgerald, Ella* / Do you hear what I hear?: *Crosby, Bing* / Santa Claus is coming to town: *Beach Boys* / First Noel, The: *Fitzgerald, Ella* / Christmas song, The: *Cole, Nat King* / Christmas waltz: *Lee, Peggy.*
LP: **3C 054 86009**
MC: **3C 254 86009**

MERRY CHRISTMAS (Various artists).
Tracks: / Twelve days of Christmas: *Simone, Harry Chorale* / Sleigh ride: *Simone, Harry Chorale* / Good King Wenceslas: *Secombe, Harry* / White Christmas: *Secombe, Harry* / Silent night: *Secombe, Harry* / O come all ye faithful: *Secombe, Harry* / God rest ye merry gentlemen: *Secombe, Harry* / Holly and the ivy, The: *Gregory Strings & Voices* / While shepherds watched: *Gregory Strings & Voices* / I saw three ships: *Gregory Strings & Voices*/ First noel: *Gregory Strings & Voices* / Away in a manger: *Gregory Strings & Voices.*
LP: **6498073**

MERRY CHRISTMAS (Various artists).
LP: . . . . **LELP 501**
MC: . . . . **LEMC 501**

MERRY CHRISTMAS (2) (Various artists).
LP: . . . . **ENT LP 13033**
MC: . . . . **ENT MC 13033**

MERRY CHRISTMAS FROM BLACK ROOTS (Various artists).
LP: . . . . **BRLP 008**

MERRY CHRISTMAS TO YOU (Various artists).
LP: . . . . **WW 5141**
MC: . . . . **WW 4 5141**

MIDNIGHT CHRISTMAS MESS (Various artists).
LP: . . . . **MIRLP 106**

MUSIC OF CHRISTMAS, THE (see under Cavatina) (Cavatina).

NIGHT BEFORE CHRISTMAS, THE (Various artists).
MC: . . . . **STC 310C**

NOEL (Various artists).
Tracks: / White Christmas: *Williams, Andy* / It's beginning to look like Christmas: *Como, Perry* / Let it snow, let it snow, let it snow: *Day, Doris* / What child is this: *Previn, Andre* / Christmas in Dixie: *Como, Perry*/ Twelve days of Christmas, The: *Whittaker, Roger* / Feliz Navidad: *Feliciano, Jose* / Have yourself a merry little Christmas: *Fiedler, Arthur* / Joy to the world: *Shaw, Robert.*
2LP: . . . . **TRX 701**
MC: . . . . **TRXC 701**

NON STOP CHRISTMAS DISCO (Various artists).
Tracks: / We wish you a merry Christmas: *Roller Disco Orchestra* / Good King Wenceslas: *Roller Disco Orchestra*/ I saw mommy kissing Santa Claus: *Roller Disco Orchestra* / Deck the halls: *Roller Disco Orchestra* / Jingle bell rock: *Roller Disco Orchestra* / White Christmas: *Roller Disco Orchestra* / Little drummer boy: *Roller Disco* Orchestra / Joy to the world: *Roller Disco Orchestra* / Sleigh ride: *Roller Disco Orchestra* / We three kings of Orient are: *Roller Disco Orchestra* / Santa Claus is coming to town: *Roller Disco Orchestra* / O Tannenbaum: *Roller Disco Orchestra* / Rockin' around the Christmas tree: *Roller Disco Orchestra* / Silver bells: *Roller* Disco Orchestra / Rudolf the red nosed reindeer: *Roller Disco Orchestra* / Twelve days of Christmas: *Roller Disco* Orchestra / Winter wonderland: *Roller Disco Orchestra* / Hark the herald angels sing: *Roller Disco Orchestra*/ Jingle bells: *Roller Disco Orchestra* / Auld lang syne: *Roller Disco Orchestra.*
2LP: . . . . **PDA 070**

NONSTOP XMAS 20 (Various artists).
Tracks: / Sleigh ride: *Various artists* / Lily the pink: *Various artists* / Have yourself a merry little Christmas: *Various artists* / Jingle bells: *Various artists* / White Christmas: *Various artists* / Little drummer boy: *Various artists* / Rudolph the red nosed reindeer: *Various artists* / We wish you the merriest: *Various* artists / Winter wonderland: *Various artists* / I saw mommy kissing Santa Claus: *Various artists* / Do you hear what I hear: *Various artists* / Scarlet ribbons: *Various artists* / My two front teeth: *Various artists*/ Mary's boy child: *Various artists* / First Noel: *Various artists* / Hark the herald angels sing: *Various artists* / Cokey cokey: *Various artists* / Christmas song, The: *Various artists.*
LP: . . . . **SPG 8000**

NOW - THE CHRISTMAS ALBUM (18 Original Christmas Hits) (Various artists).
Tracks: / Do they know it's Christmas: *Band Aid* / I wish it could be Christmas everyday: *Wood, Roy & Wizzard*/ Merry Xmas everybody: *Slade* / Last Christmas: *Wham* / Step into Christmas: *John, Elton* / In dulci jubilo: *Oldfield, Mike* / Another rock'n'roll Christmas: *Glitter, Gary* / Wonderful Christmas time: *McCartney*, Paul / Blue Christmas: *Stevens, Shakin'* / Happy Xmas (war is over): *Lennon, John/Plastic Ono Band* / I believe in Father Christmas: *Lake, Greg* / Spaceman came travelling, A: *De Burgh, Chris* / Stop the cavalry: *Lewie*, Jona / Little Saint Nick: *Beach Boys* / Thank God it's Christmas: *Queen* / Lonely this Christmas: *Mud*/ When a child is born: *Mathis, Johnny* / White Christmas: *Crosby, Bing.*
LP: . . . . **NOX 1**
MC: . . . . **TCNOX 1**

NOWELL (Various artists).
Tracks: / God rest ye merry gentlemen: *Various artists* / Deck the hall: *Various artists* / Away in a manger: *Various artists.*
MC: **4255154**

SANTA'S GREATEST HITS (Various artists).
Tracks: / White Christmas: *Crosby, Bing* / First Noel, The: *Williams, Andy* / God rest ye merry gentlemen: *Humperdinck,* Engelbert / Santa Claus is coming to town: *Bennett, Tony* / Silent night: *Domingo, Placido* / O come all ye faithful: *Mormon Tabernacle Choir* / Peace on earth: *Crosby, Bing & David Bowie* / Rudolph the red nosed reindeer: *Autry, Gene* / I saw mommy kissing Santa Claus: *Boyd, Jimmy* / Christmas story: *Ives, Burl* / Mary's boy child: *Belafonte, Harry* / Sleigh ride: *Anderson, Leroy* / Rockin' around the Christmas tree: *Lee, Brenda*/ Jingle bells: *Knight, Gladys* / Christmas song, The: *Como, Perry* / I'll be home for Christmas: *Day, Doris*/ Blue Christmas: *Cash, Johnny* / Santa baby: *Kitt, Eartha* / Have yourself a merry little Christmas: *Streisand*, Barbra / Silver bells: *Denver, John* / O little town of Bethlehem: *Nelson, Willie* / It came upon a midnight clear: *Lanza, Mario* / When a child is born: *Mathis, Johnny* / Happy new year: *Abba.*
2LP: . . . . **SGH 1**
MCSET: . . . . **SGHC 1**

SING WE NOEL Christmas music from England and early America (Various artists).
LP: . . . . **H 71354**

SONGS OF CHRISTMAS PAST (Various artists).
Tracks: / Christmas alphabet: *Various artists* / Rudolph the red nosed reindeer: *Various artists* / Christmas and you: *Various artists* / Away in a manger: *Various artists* / Christmas island: *Various artists* / I'm sending a letter to Santa Claus: *Various artists* / Silent night, holy night: *Various artists* / St. Nicholas waltz: *Various artists* / Santo Natale (Merry christmas): *Various artists* / Little boy that Santa Claus forgot, The: *Various artists* / Jingle bells: *Various artists* / White Christmas: *Various artists* / Christmas song, The: *Various artists* / I saw mommy kissing Santa Claus: *Various artists* / Little donkey: *Various artists*/ Christmas in Killarney: *Various artists* / Merry Christmas: *Various artists* / Adeste fideles: *Various artists.*
2LP: . . . . **RECDL 7**
MC: . . . . **RECMC 7**

SOUL CHRISTMAS Various artists (Various artists).
LP: . . . . **SD 33269**

SOUNDS FOR CHRISTMAS (Various artists).
MC: . . . . **KMORC 18**

SPIRIT OF CHRISTMAS (Various artists).
LP: . . . . **HDY 1941**
MC: . . . . **ZCHDY 1941**

STARS SING AT CHRISTMAS (Various artists).
LP: . . . . **SHM 3205**
MC: . . . . **HSC 3205**

STARS SING FOR CHRISTMAS (Various artists).
Tracks: / Silent night: *Various artists* / Christmas song, The: *Various artists* / I saw mommy kissing Santa Claus: *Various artists* / Christmas Island: *Various artists* / Spirit of Christmas: *Various artists* / Christmas dreaming: *Various artists* / Rudolph the red nosed reindeer: *Various artists* / I believe in Santa Claus: *Various* artists / Have yourself a merry little Christmas: *Various artists* / Do you hear what I hear: *Various*

artists/ Snow: *Various artists* / Twelve days of Christmas, The: *Various artists* / Little drummer boy: *Various artists*/ First Noel, The: *Various artists* / Christmas alphabet: *Various artists* / Santa baby: *Various artists*/ We wish you a merry Christmas: *Various artists* / White Christmas: *Various artists*.
LP: MCL 1813
MC: MCLC 1813

STASH CHRISTMAS ALBUM (16 Blues & Jazz Classics) (Various artists).
LP: ST 125

SWEDISH CHRISTMAS SONGS (Various artists).
LP: PHONT 7405

TENNESSEE CHRISTMAS (Various artists).
Tracks: / Away in a manger: *Various artists* / Tennessee Christmas: *Various artists* / Please come home for Christmas: *Various artists* / One bright star: *Various artists* / First Noel, The: *Various artists* / Greatest little Christmas ever was: *Various artists* / Christmas song, The: *Various artists* / Christmas in the Caribbean: *Various artists* / Christmas is paintin' the town: *Various artists* / Winter wonderland: *Various artists*.
LP: IMCA 5620

TWENTY CHRISTMAS CLASSICS (Various artists).
Tracks: / Rudolph the red nosed reindeer: *Temptations* / Frosty the snowman: *Jackson Five* / What Christmas means to me: *Wonder, Stevie* / Twinkle twinkle little me: *Ross, Diana & The Supremes* / Jingle bells: *Robinson, Smokey & The Miracles* / Little Christmas tree: *Jackson, Michael* / Some day at Christmas: *Wonder, Stevie*/ Let it snow, let it snow, let it snow: *Temptations* / I saw mommy kissing Santa Claus: *Jackson Five* / Christmas lullaby: *Robinson, Smokey & The Miracles* / My Christmas tree: *Ross, Diana & The Supremes* / Up on the house top: *Jackson Five* / Christmas song, The: *Wonder, Stevie* / Little bright star: *Ross, Diana & The Supremes*/ Silent night: *Temptations* / God rest ye merry gentlemen: *Robinson, Smokey & The Miracles* / Christmas won't be the same this year: *Jackson Five* / Silver bells: *Ross, Diana & The Supremes* / White Christmas: *Ross, Diana & The Supremes*.
LP: WL 72546
MC: WK 72546
LP: STMR 9013

VERY SPECIAL CHRISTMAS, A (Various artists).
Tracks: / Santa Claus is coming to town: *Pointer Sisters* / Winter Wonderland: *Eurythmics* / Do you hear what I say?: *Houston, Whitney* / Merry Christmas baby: *Springsteen, Bruce & The E Street Band* / Have yourself a merry little Christmas: *Pretenders* / I saw mommy kissing Santa Claus: *Mellencamp, John Cougar* / Gabriel's message: *Sting* / Christmas in Hollis: *Run D.M.C.* / Christmas (baby please come home): *U2* / Santa baby: *Madonna*/ Little drummer boy: *Seger, Bob & The Silver Bullet Band* / Run Rudolph run: *Adams, Bryan* / Back door Santa: *Bon Jovi* / Coventry carol: *Moyet, Alison* / Silent night: *Nicks, Stevie*.
LP: AMA 3911
MC: AMC 3911

WARNER BROTHERS RECORDS PRESENTS A CHRISTMAS TRA (Various artists).
Tracks: / White Christmas makes me blue: *Travis, Randy* / Carpenter, a mother and a King, A: *Forrester Sisters*/ Colorado Christmas: *Various artists* / Silent night: *Everly Brothers* / Have yourself a merry little Christmas: *Gayle, Crystal* / It came upon a midnight clear: *Highway 101* / Cowboy's Christmas ball, The: *Murphy, Michael* Martin / Light of the stable: *Harris, Emmylou* / Blue Christmas: *Raven, Eddy* / Sleigh ride: *O'Connor, Mark*.
LP: 925630 1
MC: 925630 4

WHITE CHRISTMAS (Various artists).
Tracks: / Jingle bells: *Various artists* / Silent night: *Various artists* / Sleigh ride: *Various artists*/ White Christmas: *Various artists*.
MC: 4255144

WORLD OF CHRISTMAS MUSIC (Kent College Choir).
LP: SPA 501

Christmas Bunch

GET OUT OF MY FACE.
Tracks: / Private property / Hit number one / Dreamtime / Elephant bar, The / Last chance / Fridge, The.
LP: BUNCH 1

Christmas Carol

CHRISTMAS CAROL, A (see Dickens, Charles).

Christmas Carols

CHRISTMAS CAROLS (Winchester Cathedral Choir).
Tracks: / God rest ye merry gentlemen / Good King Wenceslas / Angels from the realms of glory / First Noel / Away in a manger / Hark the herald angels sing / Sussex carol / Ding dong merrily on high / I saw three ships / O come all ye faithful / Once in Royal David's City.
LP: SHM 778/R
MC: HSC 183/R

CHRISTMAS NOW IS DRAWING NEAR (Sneaks Noyse).
Tracks: / Good people all this Christmastide / Sweet was the song the virgin sang / Down in yon forest / Holly and the ivy, The / Joseph was an old man / Angelus ad Virginem / Hail Mary full of grace / Tomorrow shall be my dancing day / Furry day carol / Deck the hall with boughs of holly / God bless you merry gentlemen.
LP: SDL 371
MC: CSDL 371

FESTIVAL OF LESSONS AND CAROLS (King's College).
LP: SPA 528

WELL LOVED CAROLS (Unknown artist(s)).
MC: PLB 191

Christmas (Group)

ULTRA PROPHETS OF THE PSYKICK REVOLUTION.
Tracks: / Stupid kids / This is not a test / Richard Nixon / Hot dog / Punch and Judy / Great wall of China / Human chain / Warhog / He loves them all too much / Royal klutch tattoo / My operator / Hymn.
LP: EIRSA 1012
MC: EIRSAC 1012

Christmas, Keith

BRIGHTER DAY.
Tracks: / Brighter day / Foothills / Country farm / Bargees / Lover's cabaret / Robin head / Gettin' religion / Could do better / Song of a drifter.
LP: K 53503

STORIES FROM THE HUMAN ZOO.
Tracks: / Dancer / Nature of the man, The / Golden rules / Souvenir affair / Last of the dinosaurs, The / Astronaut, The / High times / Tomorrow never ends / Life in Babylon.
LP: K 53509

Christmas Rose

CHRISTMAS ROSE (Various artists).
LP: SHE 82

Christopher Columbus

CHRISTOPHER COLUMBUS (Film soundtrack) (Various artists).
LP: CST 8006

CHRISTOPHER COLUMBUS (History for ages 8+) (Various artists).
MC: PLBH 104

CHRISTOPHER COLUMBUS (TV soundtrack) (Various artists).
LP: STV 81245

Christopher, Gavin

GAVIN CHRISTOPHER.
Tracks: / Feeling the love / Talkin' your love away / What can I do / Dancin' up a storm / We're in love / This side of heaven / Lady mysterious / We'll always be together / Be your own best friend.
LP: RSS 8

ONE STEP CLOSER TO YOU.
Tracks: / Once you get started / Love is knocking at your door / Sparks turn into fire / Could this be the night / That's the kind of guy I am / One step closer to you / Are we running from love / In the heat of passion / Back in your arms.
LP: MTL 1002
MC: TCMTL 1002

Christy, June

BEST OF JUNE CHRISTY.
Tracks: / Just a-sittin' and a-rockin' / Midnight sun / They can't take that away from me / Bewitched / How high the moon / My heart belongs to only you / Willow weep for me / Across the alley from the Alamo / Nobody's heart / Sing something simple / Something cool.
LP: CAPS 2600091

BEST THING FOR YOU.
Tracks: / When lights are low / My one and only love / How high the moon / Easy street / Kissin' bug / My heart belongs to only you / Something cool / Midnight sun / I'll take romance / This time the dream's on me / Dearly beloved / Until the real thing comes along / This year's kisses / When sunny gets blue / Best thing for you, The / Give me the simple life.
LP: AFF 145

CAPITOL YEARS: THE: JUNE CHRISTY (The Best of).
Tracks: / Give me the simple life / Imagination / It's a most unusual day / When sunny gets blue / I want to be happy / I'm thrilled / They can't take that away from me / Something cool / It don't mean a thing / I should care / When lights are low / My ship / Give a little whistle / Do nothing till you hear from me / Just a sittin' and a rockin' / How high the moon.
LP: EMS 1336
LP: 792 588 1
MC: TCEMS 1336
MC: 792 588 4

CHRISTY YEARS, THE (1945-47) (See under Kenton, Stan) (Christy, June & Stan Kenton).

HOLLYWOOD BOWL PART 1 (See under Kenton, Stan) (Christy, June & Stan Kenton).

IMPROMPTU (Christy, June & Lou Levy Sextet).
Tracks: / Everything must change / I'll remember April / Angel eyes / Willow weep for me / My shining hour.
LP: IP 7710
LP: DS 836

INTERLUDE.
Tracks: / It's so peaceful in the country / When the sun comes out / It's a most unusual day / Interlude / Love turns winter to spring / When you awake / Lazy after-noon / When the world was young / Gone for the day / Lost in a summer night / Give me the simple life / Love's got me in a lazy mood.
LP: DS 911
MC: DSC 911

JUNE CHRISTY AND THE KEYTONES 1946.
LP: HSR 219

JUNE TIME (Christy, June & Friends).
Tracks: / How high the moon / What's new / Wrap your troubles in dreams / Can't help lovin' dat man / I'm thrilled / Stompin' at the Savoy.
LP: SWH 20
MC: CSWH 20

JUNE'S GOT RHYTHM.
LP: FS 12

LOVELY WAY TO SPEND AN EVENING, A.
LP: SG 5009

LOVELY WAY TO SPEND AN EVENING, A (JASMINE).
Tracks: / Lovely way to spend an evening / From this moment on / Let there be love / I'll take romance / Midnight sun / How high the moon / Rock me to sleep / It's a most unusual day / Willow weep for me / It don't mean a thing / Lullaby in rhythm / That's all.
LP: JASM 2528
MC: JASMC 2528

MISTY MISS CHRISTY.
Tracks: / That's all / I didn't know about you / Daydream / Sing something simple / Maybe you'll be there / Dearly beloved / Round midnight / Lovely way to spend an evening, A / Wind, The / This years' kisses / For all we know / There's no you.
LP: EMS 1132
MC: TCEMS 1132

MISTY MISS CHRISTY (IMPORT).
Tracks: / That's all / I didn't know what time it was / Daydream / Sing something simple / For all we know / There's no you / Maybe you'll be there / Dearly beloved / Round midnight / Lovely way to spend an evening, A / This year's kisses.
LP: DS 919
MC: DSC 919

RECALL THOSE KENTON DAYS.
Tracks: / Just a sittin' and a rockin' / Hundred years from today / Lonesome road / He's funny that way / It's a pity to say goodnight / Willow weep for me / Easy street / Across the valley from the Alamo / Come rain or come shine / How high the moon.
LP: EMS 1286
MC: TCEMS 1286

SOMETHING COOL.
Tracks: / Not I / Whee baby / Why do you have to go home / You're making me crazy / Something cool / Magazines / Midnight sun / Lonely house / I should care / It could happen to you / First thing you know you're in love, The / Stranger called the blues, A / I'll take romance / Look out up there / Softly as in the morning sunrise / Out of somewhere / Love doesn't live here anymore / I'm thrilled / This time the dream's on me / Night we called it a day, The / Kicks / Pete Kelly's blues / Until the real thing comes along / I never want to look into those eyes again.
MC: B4 96329

THIS IS JUNE CHRISTY.
Tracks: / My heart belongs to only you / Whee baby / You took advantage of me / Get happy / Look out up there / Great Scot / Kicks / Why do you have to go home / Bei mir bist du schon / Until the real thing comes along / I'll remember April / I never wanna look in those eyes again.
LP: CAPS 2600511
MC: TC CAPS 2600514

TOGETHER AGAIN (see Kenton, Stan) (Christy, June & Stan Kenton).

WAY TO THE WEST (Christy, June/ Parker, Johnny/Ferguson, Maynard).
LP: FS 28

Chromatics

CHROMATICS, THE.
Tracks: / 99 / Do it again / I'm a rep / Doctor please / Drinkin' beer and playin' pool / You're late / Do you love me / Eat 'em up / Who's that man / Noise annoys / Woman like a limousine / Ain't gonna be your dog / Summertime romance / De-vo-t.
LP: RTLP 001

FIRST.
Tracks: / Summertime romance / I'm a rep / Drinking beer and playing pool.
LP: TLP 001

LIVE MUSIC.
Tracks: / Correction / I love to ride on the choo choo / Live music / Right legs but the wrong dress, The / Miss teacher / T'tongue tied on the telephone line / Mean trucker / I wanna be a spaceman / Working at the bar / You never know / Playin' in the band / They'd never believe me.
LP: CROM 1

Chrome

3RD FROM THE SUN.
Tracks: / Third from the Sun / Firebomb / Future ghosts / Armageddon / Heart beat / Off the line / Shadows of 1,000 years.
LP: X 18

ALIEN SOUNDTRACKS II.
LP: EFA 5853

ANOTHER WORLD.
LP: ST 7503

BLOOD ON THE MOON.
Tracks: / Need / Inner vacuum / Perfumed metal / Planet strike / Strangers / Insect human / Out of reach / Brain scan / Blood on the moon.
LP: DOSSIER 001
LP: X6

CHRONICLES 2, THE.
Tracks: / Chronicles of the beacons / Chronicles of Gehenna, The / Chronicles of Canaan.
LP: ST 003

CHRONICLES, THE.
Tracks: / Chronicles of sacrifice, The / Chronicles of the tribes / Chronicles of the open door / Chronicles of born in the night, The.
LP: DOSSIER 002

DREAMING IN SEQUENCE.
Tracks: / Everyone's the same / Seeing everything / Touching you / Windows in the wind / Venusian dance, The / White magic / Love to my rock (cause of me) / She is here.
LP: ST 7527

HALF MACHINE LIP MOVES.
Tracks: / T.V. as eyes / Zombie warfare (can't let you down) / March of the chrome police (a cold clamey bombing) / You've been duplicated / Mondo anthem / Half machine lip moves / Abstract nympho / Turned around / Zero time / Creature eternal / Critical mass.
LP: BEGA 18
MC: BEGC 18

INTO THE EYES OF THE ZOMBIE KINGS (Chrome/Damon Edge).
LP: ST 7513

LIVE IN GERMANY.
LP: EFA 5859

LYON CONCERT, THE.
LP: ST 3004

RED EXPOSURE.
Tracks: / New age / RM 101 / Eyes on Mars / Jonestown / Animal / Static gravity / Eyes in the center / Electric chair, The / Night of the earth / Isolation.
LP: BEGA 15
MC: BEGC 15

Chrome Molly

ANGST.
Tracks: / Thanx for the angst / Take me I'm yours / Don't let go / Come back / I want to find out / Take it or leave it / Living a lie / Cut loose / Too far gone / Set me free.
LP: MIRF 1033
MC: MIRFC 1033

SLAP HEAD.
Tracks: / Out of our minds / Gimme that line again / Red hot red rock / Shotgun / Loosen up / Caught with the bottle again / Sitter the children / Assinine nation / Pray with me / Now / Little voodoo magic, A.
LP: MFN 98
MC: TMFN 98

STICK IT OUT.
Tracks: / C.M.A. / Breakdown / Something special / That's the way it is / Steel against the sky / Bob Geldof / Stand proud / Before you go / Look out for number one / Let go (Cassette only).
LP: AMP 12
MC: AMP 12C

Chron Gen

APOCALYPSE LIVE TOUR JUNE'81.
LP: APOCA 1

CHRON GEN.
LP: RAZS 20
LP: SEC 3

NOWHERE TO RUN.
LP: PIK 002

Chronical Diarrhoea

SALOMO SAYS.
LP: NB 001R

Chronicle Of

CHRONICLE OF A DEATH FORETOLD (1987 Film Soundtrack) (Piccioni, Piero).
Tracks: / Bolero lento / Seis cuerdas de amor / El manicero / Pavana para una meurte anunciada / Una cancion / Flora / Canoa / Presagio nocturno / Amar y vivir / Suite final.
LP: V 2441
MC: TCV 2441
LP: OVED 266
MC: OVEDC 266

Chronicles Of Narnia

CHRONICLES OF NARNIA, THE (See under Lewis, C.S. (aut)) (Chronicles Of Narnia).

Chrysanthemum ...

BRINGIN' EM BACK (Chrysanthemum Ragtime Band).
LP: SOS 1047

CHRYSANTHEMUM RAGTIME BAND (Chrysanthemum Ragtime Band).
LP: SOS 1079

DANCING ON THE EDGE (Chrysanthemum Ragtime Band).
LP: SOS 1168

JOY RAG (Chrysanthemum Ragtime Band).
LP: SOS 1196

PRESERVES (Chrysanthemum Ragtime Band).
LP: SOS 1123

Chrysanthemum (show)

CHRYSANTHEMUM (Original London cast) (Various artists).
LP: AEI 1108

Chrysanthemums

IS THAT A FISH ON YOUR SHOULDER OR ARE YOU JUST PLEASED....
LP: TWO EGGS

LITTLE FLECKS OF FOAM AROUND BARKING EGG PLANT.
2LP: FOUR EGGS

Chrystijo

FEY A VOLONTE.
Tracks: / La pergre / Feu a volonte / Rue des Polyanthas / Accordeon de nuit / Waltz and boogie / Indifference / Vivre sans toi / Nouba / Ce que tu m'avais dit / Maldonne / Mon ami le boulanger / Regine / Les chevaux de bois.
LP: 742059
MC: UNKNOWN

Chu Chin Chow

CHU CHIN CHOW (Various artists).
Tracks: / Prelude: *Various artists* / Here be oysters: *Various artists* / I am Chu Chin Chow: *Various artists*/ Cleopatra's nile: *Various artists* / When a pullet is plump: *Various artists* / Serenade: *Various artists*/ Mambubah: *Various artists* / I'll sing and dance: *Various artists* / I long for the sun: *Various artists*/ Robber's march: *Various artists* / I love thee so: *Various artists* / Behold: *Various artists* / Any time's kissing time: *Various artists* / Cobbler's song, The: *Various artists* / I built a fairy palace in the sky: *Various artists* / We bring ye fruits: *Various artists* / Finale: *Various artists.*
LP: WRS 1007

Chubb Rock

CHUBB ROCK (Chubb Rock featuring Hitman Howie Tee).
Tracks: / D J Innovator / Daddy's home / I feel good / Joker / Momma was a rolling stone / Caught up / Do it again / Girl I love you / Punk / Rock 'n' roll dude / It's so hot / This is so hard.
LP: CHAMP 1013
MC: CHAMPK 1013

Chuck D

BRING THE NOISE (See under Anthrax) (Chuck D & Anthrax).

Chuck, Raymond

BEST OF BOTH WORLDS.
MC: ABRC 103

Chud Convention

CHUD CONVENTION,A.
LP: CIRCLE 3

Chulas Fronteras

CHULAS FRONTERAS (Film soundtrack) (Various artists).
LP: ARHOOLIE 3005
MC: C 3005

Chumba Wamba

100 SONGS ABOUT SPORT.
2LP: PROP 004

NEVER MIND THE BALLOT: HERE'S THE REST OF YOUR LIFE.
LP: PROP 002

PICTURES OF STARVING CHILDREN.
LP: PROP 001

Chung, Myung-Whun

WIND AND STRING SERENADES (see under Dvorak).

Church

BLURRED CRUSADE, THE.
Tracks: / Almost with you / When you were mine / Field of Mars / Interlude / Secret corners / Just for you / Fire burns / To be in your eyes / You took / Don't look back.
LP: CAL 140

CHURCH, THE.
Tracks: / For a moment we're strangers / Chrome injury / Unguarded moment / Memories in future tense / Bel-Air / Is this where you live / She never said / Tear it all away / Don't open the door to strangers.
LP: CAL 130

CONCEPTION.
Tracks: / When you were mine / Chrome injury / Different man, A / To be in your eyes / Is this where you live / Unguarded moment / Just for you / Memories and future times / Almost with you / You took.
LP: CAL 229
MC: CAC 229

GOLD AFTERNOON FIX.
Tracks: / Pharoah / Metropolis / Terra nova Cain / City / Monday morning (Only on cassette and CD.) / Russian Autumn heart / Essence / You're still beautiful / Disappointment / Transient / Laughing / Fading away / Grind.
LP: 210541
MC: 410541

HEYDAY.
Tracks: / Myrrh / Tristesse / Already yesterday / Columbus / Happy hunting ground / Tantalized / Disenchanted / Night of light / Youth worshipper / Roman / As you will / View, The.
LP: EMC 3508
MC: TCEMC 3508

OF SKINS AND HEART.
LP: PCS 07583

ORTHODOX CHURCH MUSIC (Ecumenical Quartet).
LP: IKO 15

REMOTE LUXURY.
Tracks: / Constant in opal / Violet town / No explanation / 10,000 miles / Maybe these boys / Into my hands / Month of Sundays / Volumes / Shadow cabinet / Remote luxury.
LP: CAL 213
LP: BUG 5
LP: 209649
MC: 409649

SEANCE, THE.
LP: CAL 201
LP: MID 166097

STARFISH.
Tracks: / Destination / Under the Milky Way / Blood money / Lost / North, South, East and West / Spark / Antenna / New season / Hotel womb.
LP: 208895
MC: 408895

Church Bells

BELL PEALS FOR CAMPANOLOGISTS/CHURCHES (Bells of Frome).
LP: GRS 1046

BELLS OF LONDON, THE (Various).
Tracks: / St. Vedast / St. Lawrence Jewry / St. Giles Cripplegate / St. Clement Danes / St. Sepulchre / St. Mary-le-bow / St. Olave / St. Michael Cornhill / St. Bartholomew / Westminster Abbey / St. Martin-in-the-fields.
LP: SDL 337
MC: CSDL 337

BELLS OF THE COTSWOLDS (Bells of eight Cotswold churches).
LP: SDL 290
MC: CSDL 290

CHANGE RINGING FROM ST. MARY REDCLIFFE, BRISTOL (St. Mary Redcliffe, Bristol).
LP: SDL 243
MC: CSDL 243

CHURCH BELLS OF KENT (Various).
LP: SDL 302
MC: CSDL 302

Church In The City

I JUST WANT TO PRAISE YOU.
MC: SSC 8070

WORSHIP 2.
MC: SSC 0046
LP: SSR 0046

Church Of Raism

CHURCH OF RAISM.
LP: CRELP 057

Churchill, Savannah

TIME OUT FOR TEARS.
LP: JB 1101

Churchill, Sir Winston

25 YEARS OF HIS SPEECHES 1918 - 1943 VOL.2.
MCSET: ARGO 1232

SELECTION OF HIS WARTIME SPEECHES 1939-1945.
MCSET: SAY 79
MCSET: ARGO 1118

VOICE OF CHURCHILL, THE.
LP: LXT 6200

Churchman, Ysanne

ANDY PANDY AND TEDDY AT THE ZOO (See under Andy Pandy...).

ANDY PANDY AND THE BADGER (See under Andy Pandy...).

C.I.A.

IN THE RED.
Tracks: / Extinction / In the red / N.A.S.A. / Flight 103 / Turn to stone / Natas / Buried alive / Mind over matter / Moby Dick (part 2) / Samantha.
LP: FLAG 40
MC: TFLAG 40

Ciani, Suzanne

HISTORY OF MY HEART.
Tracks: / Inverness / Sumukee / Drifting / Anthem / Driving / Eagle / Mozart / Jacques / Italian movie / Terra mesa / Anthem (piano version) (Only on CD.).
LP: 210.359
MC: 410.359

NEVERLAND.
Tracks: / Neverland / Tuscany / Mosaic / Aegean wave / Summer's day / Life in the moonlight / When love dies / Adagio / Mother's song / Lumiere.
LP: 209758
MC: 409758

PIANISSIMO.
Tracks: / Anthem / Tuscany / Neverland / Adagio / Aegan wave / Rain / Inverness / Simple song / She said yes / Drifting / Summers day / Mozart / When love dies / Berceuse.
LP: 210946
MC: 410946

SEVEN WAVES.
Tracks: / First wave, The / Birth of Venus / Second wave, The / Sirens / Third wave, The / Love in the waves / Fourth wave, The / Wind in the sea / Fifth wave, The / Water lullaby / Sixth wave, The / Deep in the sea / Seventh wave, The / Sailing away.
LP: 209.968
MC: 409.968

Ciccone Youth

WHITEY ALBUM, THE.
Tracks: / Needle gun / G force / Platform 11 / Me and Jill / Hi everybody / Children of Satan / Moby Dick / Into the groovy / March of the Ciccone robots / Macbeth / Burning up / Two cool rock chicks listening to Neu / Addicted to love / Making the nature scene / Tuff titty rap / Into the groovy.
LP: BFFP 28
MC: BFFP 28C

Ciccu, Bianca

GUSCH, THE (Ciccu, Bianca & Randy Brecker).
LP: ITM 0040

Cicero, Eugene

SPRING SONG (Cicero, Eugene Trio).
Tracks: / Prelude No.2 (Taken from "The well tempered calvier") / Caprice No.24 / Spinning son / Moldau, The / Spring song / Largo from preludes / Air from suite No. 3 / Paraphrase in G flat.
MC: SJP 1198
LP: SJP 198

Cider With Rosie (bk)

CIDER WITH ROSIE (Lee, Laurie (aut)).
MCSET: SAY 55
MCSET: ARGO 1094

Cilmeri

CILMERI.
LP: SAIN 1168 M

HANFFYNCH WELL.
LP: SAIN 1236 M

Cima, Alex

SOLID STATE (Cima, Alex/On-Line).
LP: GNPS 2186
MC: GNP5 2186

Cimarons

IN TIME.
Tracks: / Ship ahoy / Over the rainbow / I wanna please you / Utopian feeling / You can get it if you really want / Time passage / Moving on up / Didn't I fool you / Reggae time / My blue Heaven / Kush maroons.
LP: TRLS 87

REGGAEBILITY.
Tracks: / With a little luck / Big girls don't cry / Poor people of Paris, The / Pickin' a chicken / Mull of Kintyre / Love me do / Walk like a man / C moon / Meet me on the corner / That'll be the day / Arrivederci Roma.
LP: SHM 3106
MC: HSC 3106

Cincinnati Kid (film)

CINCINNATI KID, THE (1965 film soundtrack) (Various artists).
LP: MCA 25012
MC: MCAC 25012

Cincinnati Pops

STAR TRACKS (Cincinnati Pops Orchestra).
Tracks: / Star wars / Empire strikes back, The / Return of the Jedi / Close Encounters of the Third Kind / Superman / E.T., Theme from / Raiders of the lost ark.
LP: DG 10094

Cinderella (bk)

CINDERELLA (Well Loved Tales age up to 9).
MC: TS 301
MC: D 6DC
MC: PLB 61

CINDERELLA (Well loved tales age up to 9).
MLP: D 308
LP: D 3908

CINDERELLA.
Tracks: / Cinderella / Four clever brothers, The / Bright brownie / Fire on the mountain / Brave tailor, The / Fibbers, The.
MC: ANV 661

CINDERELLA (Various artists).
MC: STC 304A

CINDERELLA.
MC: DIS 027

CINDERELLA.
MC: STK 003

CINDERELLA (1957 TV MUSICAL) (Rogers & Hammerstein's Show Time).
MC: PST 2005

CINDERELLA/BABES IN THE WOOD (Crowther, Leslie (nar)).
MC: LPMC 300

CINDERELLA-STORY (Hampshire, Susan).
MC: 3601

Cinderella (film)

CINDERELLA (Film soundtrack) (Various artists).
LP: WD 012
MC: WDC 012

CINDERELLA (Film Soundtrack) (Various artists).
Tracks: / Cinderella: *Various artists* / Dream is a wish your heart makes: *Various artists* / Oh sing sweet nightingale: *Various artists* / Work song: *Various artists* / Dream a wish your heart makes, A: *Various artists* / Bibbidi

bobbidi boo: *Various artists* / Cinderella arrives at the ball: *Various artists* / So this is love: *Various artists* / Finale: *Various artists*.
LP: . . . . **DQ 1207**

PETER PAN/CINDERELLA (Film soundtracks) (See under Peter Pan) (Various artists).

Cinderella (Group)

CINDERELLA: INTERVIEW PICTURE DISC (Cinderella (bk)).
LPPD: . . . . **BAK 2084**

HEARTBREAK STATION.
Tracks: / More things change, The / Love's got me doin' time / Shelter me / Heartbreak station / Sick for the cure / One for rock and roll / Dead man's road / Make your own way / Electric love / Love gone bad / Winds of change.
LP: **8480181**
MC: **8480184**

LONG COLD WINTER.
Tracks: / Falling apart at the seams / Gypsy road / Last mile, The / Long cold winter / If you don't like it / Coming home / Fire and ice / Take me back / Bad seamstress blues / Don't know what you got (til it's gone) / Second wind.
LP: . . . . **VERH 59**
MC: . . . . **VERHC 59**

NIGHT SONGS.
Tracks: / Night songs / Shake me / Nobody's fool / Nothin' for nothin' / Once around the ride / Hell on wheels / Somebody save me / In from the outside / Push push / Back home again.
LP: . . . . **VERH 37**
MC: . . . . **VERHC 37**

Cinderella (musical)

CINDERELLA (1959 Original London cast) (Various artists).
Tracks: / Cinderella:Overture: *Various artists* / In my own little corner: *Various artists* / Very special day, A: *Various artists* / Do I love you because you're beautiful?: *Various artists* / Prince is giving a ball, The: *Various artists* / Marriage type love: *Various artists* / Stepsisters' lament: *Various artists* / Your magesties, a list of bare necessities: *Various artists* / When you're driving through the moon light: *Various artists*/ Lovely night, A: *Various artists* / Impossible: *Various artists* / No other love: *Various artists* / Ten minutes ago: *Various artists* / You and me: *Various artists* / Cinderella (finale): *Various artists*.
LP: . . . . **TER 1045**
MC: . . . . **ZCTER 1045**

Cinderella (tv)

CINDERELLA (TV soundtrack) (Various artists).
MC: . . . . **JST 02005**
LP: . . . . **AOS 2005**
MC: . . . . **BT 2005**

Cinderford Band

FOREST FESTIVAL BRASS.
LP: . . . . **GRS 1070**

Cindy & Roy

FEEL IT.
Tracks: / Can you feel it? / Changing jobs / I wanna testify / While we still have time / Gotta love somebody else.
LP: . . . . **K 58053**

Cindy-ella (musical)

CINDY-ELLA (Original London cast) (Various artists).
Tracks: / High summer day: *Various artists* / Like a peach: *Various artists* / Let me hold your hand: *Various artists* / Hush-a-bye: *Various artists* / Cindy-Ella: *Various artists* / Motherless child: *Various artists*/ Li'l Ella, play on yo'harp: *Various artists* / You gotta look distainful: *Various artists* / Go 'way f'om mah window: *Various artists* / Look on me with a loving eye: *Various artists* / Oh the first time: *Various artists*/ Plenty good room: *Various artists* / Shoe shine shoe: *Various artists* / You're worried now: *Various artists*/ Stranger: *Various artists* / Bring a little bit pumpkin: *Various artists* / Cindy: *Various artists*/ Nobody's business: *Various artists* / Raise a ruckus: *Various artists* / You ain't a-gonna sit and take yo' ease: *Various artists* / There's a man goin' roun' givin' cards: *Various artists* / De midnight special: *Various artists* / Git along home: *Various artists* / Cindy, cindy: *Various artists* / I gotta shoe: *Various artists*/ Man no good for nothin': *Various artists* / Nobody knows the trouble I've seen: *Various artists* / Swing low sweet chariot: *Various artists* / Troubles of the world: *Various artists*.
LP: . . . . **DS 15023**

Cindytalk

CAMOUFLAGE HEART.
LP: . . . . **CHIME 0006 S**

IN THE WORLD.
LP: . . . . **CHIME 027**

WIND IS STRONG, THE.
LP: . . . . **CHIME 0103**

Cinema

CINEMA FAVOURITES (Various artists).
LP: . . . . **BUR 023**
MC: . . . . **4 BUR 023**

Cinema Organ

BBC PRESENTS AT THE CINEMA ORGAN, THE.
LP: . . . . **REC 137**

Cinnamond, Robert

YOU RAMBLING BOYS OF PLEASURE.
Tracks: / You rambling boys of pleasure / Van Diemans land / You ribbonmen of Ireland / Rich shipowner's daughter, The / Napoleon Bonaparte / Weaver / Youghal harbour / Beggarman, The / Fly up, my cock / I'm a rambling youth / Aughalee heroes / Early early in the spring / Young Willie Reilly / Drowsy Maggie / Old man rocking the cradle, The.
LP: **12TS 269**

Cinquetti, Gigliola

SUPER DISC OF GIGIOLA CINQUETTI.
LP: . . . . **GXM 9008**

Ciosi, Antoine

LA CORSE (Ciosi, Antoine/Gregale/ Martino Dicelli).
Tracks: / Tristeza / Li Re / Sirinata a luna / Ritornu in Corti / Pescado dell'onda / La vieille guitare / L'estrade / Niolo / Dimmi perche / Nanna di cusciono / Campagnola / Singhiozzi / Terre brulee.
LP: . . . . **ARN 33377**
MC: . . . . **ARN 433377**

Cipolina, John

MONKEY BUSINESS (See under Gravenites, Nick) (Cipolina, John & Nick Gravenites).

MONKEY MEDICINE (Cipolina, John & Nick Gravenites).
Tracks: / Blues in the bottle / Six weeks in Reno / I'll pull the trigger / Trust me / Buried alive / Bad luck baby / Signs of life / Pride of man / Hot rods and cool women.
LP: . . . . **NED 5**

Cipolla, Rudy

WORLD OF RUDY CIPOLLA.
LP: . . . . **ROUNDER 0189**
MC: . . . . **ROUNDER 0189C**

Circle Confusion

MEAT DEPT.
LP: . . . . **ARTY 4**

Circle Dance

CIRCLE DANCE (Hokey Pokey Charity Compilation) (Various artists).
LP: . . . . **UKNOWN**

Circle Jerks

GROUP SEX.
LP: . . . . **WS 031**

VI.
Tracks: / Beat me senseless / Casulty vampire / Protection / American way / All wound up / Fortunate son / Patty's killing me / Tell me why / I'm alive / Status clinger / I don't / Living.
LP: . . . . **RR 9584**

WILD IN THE STREETS.
LP: . . . . **SFLP 8**
LP: **46171**
MC: **46174**

WONDERFUL.
LP: . . . . **JUST 1**

Circuit II

CAN'T TEMPT FATE.
Tracks: / Fool for you, A / Can't run away / One for the money / Can't tempt fate / Looking down / Horizon / Rock this (take me out) / Can't live without you.
LP: . . . . **EKT 18**

Circus Circus Circus

LESLIE HOPE TOWN.
LP: . . . . **SAX 031**

Circus Comes To Town

CIRCUS COMES TO TOWN (Various artists).
LP: . . . . **TENT 001**

Circus Of Power

CIRCUS OF POWER.
Tracks: / Call of the wild / Motor / Heart attack / In the wind / Machine / White trash mama / Needles / Crazy / Letters home / Backseat mama / Turn up the jams (Only on cassette and CD.).
LP: . . . . **84641 R**
LP: . . . . **PL 88464**
MC: . . . . **PK 88464**

STILL ALIVE.
Tracks: / Still alive and well / Motor (live) / Letters home (live) / White trash queen (live) / Heart attack (live) / Turn up the jams (live).
LP: . . . . **PL 90377**
MC: . . . . **PK 90377**

VICES.
Tracks: / Gates of love / Two river highway / Don't drag me down / Doctor potion / Got hard / Junkie girl / Desire / Fire in the night / Vices / Last call Rosie / Los Angeles / Temptation / Simple man / Simple woman.
LP: . . . . **PL 90461**
MC: . . . . **PK 90461**

Cirith Ungol

KING OF THE DEAD.
LP: . . . . **RR 9832**

ONE FOOT IN HELL.
LP: . . . . **RR 9681**

Cirkus

ONE.
Tracks: / You are / Seasons / April '73 / Song for Tavish / Prayer / Brotherly love / Those were the days.
LP: . . . . **TOCK 1**

CIS

SUMMER OF '85 AND OTHER SEASONS.
LP: . . . . **ISST 167**

Cisco

CISCO SINGS WOODY GUTHRIE.
LP: . . . . **VNP 6403**

Cithares Malgache

CITHARES MALGACHE (Various artists).
MC: . . . . **G 4057**

City

FOUNDATION.
Tracks: / Seasons of the heart / Invisible man, The / Aim for the heart / Parallel / Planets in motion / Walkaway / From this day on / Fatal attraction / When the smoke clears.
LP: . . . . **CHR 1559**

City Boy

BOOK EARLY.
Tracks: / 5-7-0-5 / Summer in the school yard / Goodbye Laurelie / Raise your glass (to foolish me) / Cigarettes / What a night / Do what you do, do well / World loves a dancer, The / Beth / Moving in circles / Dangerous ground.
LP: **9102 028**

CITY BOY.
Tracks: / (Moonlight) shake my head and leave / Deadly delicious / Surgery hours (doctor doctor) / Sunset boulevard / Oddball dance / 5000 years / Don't know, can't tell / Hap-ki-do kid, The / Greatest story ever told / Haymaking time.
LP: **6360 126**

DAY THE EARTH CAUGHT FIRE.
Tracks: / Day the earth caught fire, The / It's only the end of the world / Interrupted melody / Modern love affair / New York times / Up in the eighties / Machines / Ambition.
LP: **9102036**

DINNER AT THE RITZ.
Tracks: / Mommas boy / Walk on the water / Narcissus / Dinner at the Ritz / Goodbye blue Monday / Violin, The / State secrets -a thriller.
LP: **6360 136**

HEADS ARE ROLLING.
Tracks: / Mr. Shoes / Heads are rolling / Need a little loving / Change in the weather / Domino / Speechless / Bloody Sunday / Sound of the bell, The / You're leaving me / Heaven for the holidays / Life on the balcony.
LP: **6359 024**

YOUNG MEN GONE WEST.
Tracks: / Dear Jean (I'm nervous) / Bordello night / Honeymooners / She's got style / Bad for business / Young men gone West / I've been spun / One after tub / Runaround, The / Man who ate his car, The / Millionaire.
LP: **6360 151**

City Heat (Film)

CITY HEAT (Film soundtrack) (Various artists).
LP: . . . . **WEA 9252191**

City Lights (film)

CITY LIGHTS (Film Soundtrack) (Davis, Carl).
MC: . . . . **FILMC 078**

City Of Birmingham...

ERIC COATES, FAVOURITE MUSIC (City Of Birmingham Symphony Orchestra).
LP: . . . . **ESD 7005**

City of Coventry Band

40TH ANNIVERSARY CELEBRATION.
Tracks: / Fest musik der stadt wien / Watermill / Mexican march / Lark in the clear air / Gopak / Line of life / Blaze of light / Swan / March of the toys / Concierto de Aranjuez / Solveig's song / Anitra's dance / Toccata marziale.
LP: . . . . **TB 3019**

CITY CRUISER.
Tracks: / City cruiser / Pastorale / Keel row, The / Turkish delight / Lisbon carnival / Espana / Traffic tangle / For your eyes only / Oranges & lemons / Carambina / Corsair, The.
LP: . . . . **PRL 014**
MC: . . . . **CPRL 014**

City Of Glasgow...

CITY OF GLASGOW POLICE PIPE BAND (City Of Glasgow Police Pipe Band).
Tracks: / Scotland the brave / Nut Brown maiden / Jenny's bawbee / 6/8 marches / Midlothian pipe beaton / MacDonald's awa' tae the war / Muckin' o' Geordie's byre / Heilan' whisky / Hot punch / Raven's rock / Inverinate house / Dark island / Caberfeidh / 5 (Quicksteps) / Man's a man for a' that, A / My love she's but a lassie yet / Corn rigs / Gaelic airs, hornpipe and jig / Waters of Kylesku / Mull of the bens / Mary with the witching eyes / Boys from Blue Hill / Paddy's leather breeches / 1-(2/4 marches) / Highland Laddie / Corriechoillie / Teribus / Bonnie Galloway / Rowan tree / Kenmore's up and awa' / March of the Cameron men / Because he was a bonny lad / Louden's bonnie woods / Tail toddle / Fairy dance, The / 5 (Slow march, Retreat Air & Quicksteps) / Road to the isles / Battle is o'er, The / Earl of Mansfield / Drum fanfare / 7-Pubroch variation 1: / Hail to my country / 8 (Scottish Air & Quickstep) / We're no awa' tae bide awa' / Happy we've been a'thegither / Campbells are coming, The.
LP: . . . . **BER 007**
MC: . . . . **KBER 007**

City of London...

LITTLE CHRISTMAS MUSIC, A (See under King's Singers).

City Of York

CITY OF YORK, THE (Various artists).
MC: . . . . **AC 112**

City Waites

SOCIAL MUSIC FOR A 17TH CENTURY ENGLISHMAN.
Tracks: / Jamaica or the jovial broom man / Winchester wedding, The / Ayre and Sarabande / Almain / Galliard / Hunt is up, The / Who liveth so merry / Jolly barber, The / Miller Dee, The / Sonata in G / Saint turned sinner, The / Seldom cleanly / Martin said to his man / As I walked forth / Pox on you for a fop / Tomorrow the fox will come to town / Gather your rosebuds / Packington's pound / Bellman's song, A.
LP: . . . . **A 66008**

Civil, Alan

SALUTE TO AMERICA, A (Civil, Alan Band).
LP: . . . . **PFS 4363**

Civil War (tv)

CIVIL WAR, THE (Music From the BBC TV Series) (Various artists).
MC: **7559792564**

Civilised Society

SCRAP METAL.
LP: . . . . **ACHE 02**

VIOLENCE SUCKS.
LP: . . . . **ACHE 07**

YOU WERE WARNED.
LP: . . . . **ACHE 021**
MC: . . . . **ACHEMC 021**

CJ & Co

DEADEYE DICK.
Tracks: / Burning drums of fire / Deadeye Dick / Beware the stranger / Big city sidewalk / Hear say / You're still the sweetest thing in my life.
LP: . . . . **K 50491**

DEVIL'S GUN.
Tracks: / Devil's gun / We got our own thang / Free to be me / Get a groove in order to move / Sure can't go to the Moon.
LP: . . . . **K 50380**

Clae, John

SWINGING 40'S (Clae, John & Nat Gonella).
Tracks: / Stompin' at the Savoy / How am I to know / I heard / Chattanooga choo choo / Watch the birdie / Nobody knows de trouble I've seen / Fascinating rhythm / My Bonnie lies over the ocean /

Whistler's mother in law, The / Playhouse party / Oh Buddy I'm in love / Boogie wooglie piggy, The / Man who comes around, The / I got rhythm / It's a pair of wings for me / Yes, my darling daughter / Vox poppin' / Hot dogs / Hut-Sut song, The / Do I worry.
LP: C5-544
MC: C5K-544

Clail, Gary

EMOTIONAL HOOLIGAN (Clail, Gary & On U Sound System).
Tracks: / Food, clothes and shelter / Food, clothes and shelter (part 2) / Monk track / Escape / Emotional hooligan, The / Magic penny / Human nature / Crocodile eyes / Rumours / Beef (extended version) / Temptation / False leader (Only on CD and Cassette.).
LP: .... PL 74965
MC: .... PK 74965

Claim

ARMSTRONGS REVENGE.
LP: .... TBR 001
LP: .... CUO 387

BOOM TELLA.
Tracks: / Not so simple Sharon says / Love letters / Beneath the reach / All about hope / Las Regas El Resoto / Down the chimney / Mrs. Shepherd / Sanity starts at home / On my way / Christopher.
LP: .... PACE 3

Clair Obscur

PILGRIM'S PROGRESS.
LP: .... MAD 10

Clampets

LAST HOEDOWN.
LP: .... L 38818

Clan

ROKE, THE.
MC: .... CTP 038

Clan Campbell

CAMPBELLS ARE COMING (Clan Campbell Scotch Whisky Pipes & Drums Band).
Tracks: / Campbells are coming, The / Themes from dreams / Wooden heart / Road to the isles / Westering home / McPherson's rant / Cameron men, The / Jingle bells / Dark island / Seven tears.
LP: .... LOCLP 1016
MC: .... ZCLOC 1016

SCOTS BY TRADITION (Clan Campbell Pipes & Drums).
Tracks: / Ob la di ob la da / Green hills of Tyrol / Lochanside / Nearer my God to thee / Clydeside hornpipe / Loch Ness monster / Crooked bawbee / How great Thou art / Way old friends do, The / Bright eyes / Bonnie Galloway / Balmoral / When the saints go marching in.
LP: .... LOCLP 1023
MC: .... ZCLOC 1023

Clan Of The... (film)

CLAN OF THE CAVE BEAR (1986 Film Soundtrack) (Various artists).
LP: .... CST 8013
LP: .... STV 81274
MC: .... CTV 81274

Clancy Brothers

28 SONGS OF IRELAND (Clancy Brothers & Tommy Makem).
MC: .... IHMC 10

BEST OF THE CLANCY BROTHERS, VOL 1 (Clancy Brothers & Tommy Makem).
LP: .... HPE 620
MC: .... HPC 620

BEST OF THE CLANCY BROTHERS, VOL 2 (Clancy Brothers & Tommy Makem).
LP: .... HPE 625
MC: .... HPC 625

BOYS WON'T LEAVE THE GIRLS ALONE, THE (Clancy Brothers & Tommy Makem).
LP: .... SHAN 52015
MC: .... SH 52015 C

CHRISTMAS WITH THE CLANCY BROTHERS.
LP: .... SHAN 52017
MC: .... SHAN 52017 C

EVERY DAY.
Tracks: / Working together / Timetaker / Seconds out / You have made my life so sweet / Jeka Jose / You don't understand / Good judgement / Jealousy.
LP: .... K 56206

GOLDEN HOUR PRESENTS.
Tracks: / Jug of punch / Whistling gypsy / Mountain dew / Mermaid / Holy ground / Maid of Fife / Leaving of Liverpool / Irish rover, The / Haul away Joe / Nightingale / Bonnie Charlie / Jolly tinker / Shoals of herring / Gallant forty twa / Old woman from Waxford / MacPherson's lament / Whiskey you're the devil / Young Roddy McCorley / Rosin the bow / Father's grave / Kelly the boy from Killane / Johnny McAdoo / Castle of Dromore.
LP: .... GH 880

GREATEST HITS: CLANCY BROTHERS.
LP: .... VMLP 5307
MC: .... VMTC 6307

HEARTY AND HELLISH (A night club performance) (Clancy Brothers & Tommy Makem).
LP: .... SHAN 52014

ISN'T IT GRAND BOYS (Clancy Brothers & Tommy Makem).
LP: .... BPG 62674

REUNION (Clancy Brothers & Tommy Makem).
LP: .... BLB 5009

RISING OF THE MOON.
LP: .... TLP 1006

SERIOUSLY SPEAKING.
Tracks: / Back on love / Lose me / Body to body / Steal away / Sign of the times / Southern boogie / Money / Long time coming / Move on / Eat gook.
LP: .... K 56103

Clancy, John

MEMORIES OF SCOTLAND.
MC: .... CM 3551

Clancy, Liam

TOMMY MAKEM & LIAM CLANCY (see Makem, Tommy) (Clancy, Liam & Tommy Makem).

Clancy, Robert

SO EARLY IN THE MORNING.
LP: .... TLP 1034

Clancy, Willie

MINSTREL FROM CLARE, THE.
Tracks: / Langstern pony uilleann pipes / Templehouse, The / Over the moor to Maggie whistle / Bruachna carraige baine pipes / Erin's lovely lea vocal / Killavel fancy, The / Dogs among the bushes whistle / Family ointment vocal, The / Dear Irish boy pipes, The / Caoindeadh an spailpin whistle / Pipe on the hob / Gander vocal, The / Legacy jig whistle, The / Flogging reel pipes / Song of the riddles vocal, The / Spailpin a ruin pipes.
LP: 12T 175

PIPERING OF WILLIE CLANCY, VOL 1.
LP: .... CC 32
MC: 4CC 32

PIPERING OF WILLIE CLANCY, VOL 2.
LP: .... CC 39
MC: 4CC 39

WEST WIND.
MC: 30 173

Clannad

AN AM.
Tracks: / Ri na cruinne / An am (soul) / In fortune's hand / Poison glen / Wilderness / Why worry? / Uirchill an chreagain / Love and affection / You're the one / Dobhar.
MC: .... PK 74762
LP: .... PL 74762

ANGEL AND THE SOLDIER BOY, THE (See under Angel and the ...) (Clannad & Tom Conti).

ATLANTIC REALM.
Tracks: / Atlantic realm / Predator / Moving thru / Berbers, The / Signs of life / In flight / Ocean of light / Drifting / Under Neptune's cape / Voyager / Primeval sun / Child of the sea / Kirk pride, The.
LP: .... REB 727
MC: .... ZCF 727

CLANNAD IN CONCERT.
LP: .... BLB 5001
LP: .... SHAN 79030

CLANNAD: VOLUME 2.
LP: .... CEF 041
LP: .... SHAN 79007

COLLECTION: CLANNAD.
Tracks: ' / Dulaman / Down by the Sally gardens / Nil sen la / Harry's game (theme from) / Robin (the hooded man).
LP: .... KLP 215
MC: .... KMC 215

CRANNULL.
LP: 6373 016
MC: 7233 016
LP: .... TA 3007
MC: 4TA 3007

DULAMAN.
LP: .... CEF 058
LP: .... SHAN 79008
LP: .... INT 160065

FUAIN.
Tracks: / Na Buachailli Alainn / Mheall Si Lena Glorthai Me / Bruachna carraige baine pipes / La Brea Fan Dtuath / An tull / Strayed away / Ni La Na Gaoithe La Na Scoib / Lish young buy a broom / Mhorag's Na Horo Ghealladh / Green fields of Gaothdobhair, The / Buaireadh / An Phosta.
LP: .... TA 3008
MC: 4TA 3008
LP: .... COOK 035
MC: .... COOKC 035

LEGEND.
Tracks: / Robin (the hooded man) / Now is here / Herne / Together we / Darkmere / Strange land / Scarlet inside / Lady Marian / Battles / Ancient forest.
LP: .... PL 70188
MC: .... PK 70188
LP: .... NL 71703
MC: .... NK 71703
LP: .... TA 3012

MACALLA.
Tracks: / Caislean oir / Wild cry, The / Closer to your heart / Almost seems too late to turn / In a lifetime / Buchaill on Eirne / Blackstairs / Journey's end / Northern skyline.
LP: .... PL 70894
MC: .... PK 70894
LP: .... TA 3016

MAGICAL RING.
Tracks: / Harry's game (theme from) / Tower hill / Searchran charn tsail / I see red / Passing time / Coinleach glas an fhomair / Ta 'me mo shui / New grange / Fairy queen, The / Thios fa'n chosta.
LP: .... NL 71473
MC: .... NK 71473
LP: .... PL 70003
LP: .... RCALP 6072
LP: .... TA 3010

PAST PRESENT.
Tracks: / Harry's game, Theme from / Closer to your heart / Almost seems (too late to turn) / Hunter, The / Lady Marian / Sirius / Coinleach glas an fhomair / Second nature / World of difference / In a lifetime / Robin (the hooded man) / Something to believe in / Newgrange / Buachaill an eirne / White fool / Stepping stone.
LP: .... PL 74074
MC: .... PK 74074

PRETTY MAID, THE.
LP: 6392 013

ROBIN OF SHERWOOD.
LP: .... ERLC 1
MC: .... ERLK 1

SIRIUS.
Tracks: / In search of a heart / Second nature / Turning tide / Skellig / Stepping stone / White fool / Something to believe in / Live and learn / Many roads / Sirius.
LP: .... PL 71513
MC: .... PK 71513
LP: .... TA 3021

Clansmen

FLYING SCOTSMEN.
MC: .... KITV 489

Clanton, Jimmy

JUST A DREAM.
Tracks: / Just a dream / Wayward love / You aim to please / Don't look at me / Go, Jimmy, go / You better settle down / Another sleepless night / I'm gonna try / It takes a long time / Nothing left for me / Ship on a stormy sea / Somebody please help me / I feel those tears coming on / I wanna go home.
LP: .... CH 93

Clapton, Eric

461 OCEAN BOULEVARD.
Tracks: / Get ready / Give me strength / I can't hold out much longer / I shot the sheriff / Let it grow / Mainline Florida / Motherless children / Please be with me / Steady rollin' man / Willie and the hand jive.
LP: .... SPELP 24
MC: .... SPEMC 24
LP: 2479 118

461 OCEAN BOULEVARD/ANOTHER TICKET.
MC: .... TWOMC 6

AFTER MIDNIGHT.
Tracks: / After midnight / I shot the sheriff / Let it grow / Swing low, sweet chariot / Motherless children / Knockin' on Heaven's door / Layla / Cocaine / Carnival / Hello, old friend / Lay down Sally / Wonderful tonight / Black rose / Another ticket / I can't stand it.
LP: 815 994-1
MC: 815 994-4

ANOTHER TICKET.
Tracks: / Something special / Black rose / Another ticket / I can't stand it / Hold me Lord / Floating bridge / Catch me if you can / Rita Mae / Blow wind blow.
LP: .... SPELP 67
MC: .... SPEMC 67
LP: .... RSD 5008

AUGUST.
Tracks: / It's in the way that you use it / Run / Tearing us apart / Bad Influence / Hung up on your love / I take a chance / Hold on / Miss you / Holy Mother / Behind the mask.
LP: .... WX 71
MC: .... WX 71 C

BACKLESS.
Tracks: / Early in the morning / Golden ring / If I don't be there by morning / I'll make love to you anytime / Promises / Roll it / Tell me that you love me / Tulsa time / Walk out in the rain / Watch out for Lucy.
LP: .... SPELP 1
MC: .... SPEMC 1
LP: .... RSD 5001

BACKLESS/461 OCEAN BOULEVARD/SLOWHAND.
Tracks: / Early in the morning / Golden ring / If I don't be there by morning / I'll make love to you anytime / Promises / Roll it / Tell me that you love me / Tulsa time / Walk out in the rain / Watch out for Lucy / Get ready / Give me strength / I can't hold out much longer / I shot the sheriff / Let it grow / Mainline Florida / Motherless children / Please be with me / Steady rollin' man / Willie and the hand jive / Cocaine / Core / Lay down Sally / May you never / Mean old 'Frisco blues / Next time you see her / Peaches and diesel / We're all the way / Wonderful tonight.
LPS: .... BOX 3

BACKTRACKIN'.
Tracks: / Cocaine / Strange brew / Spoonful / Let it rain / Have you ever loved a woman? / Presence of the Lord / Crossroads / Roll it over / Can't find my way home / Blues power / Further on up the road / I shot the Sheriff / Knockin' on heaven's door / Lay down Sally / Promises / Swing low sweet chariot / Wonderful tonight / Sunshine of your love / Tales of brave Ulysses / Badge / Little wing / Layla.
2LP: .... ERIC 1
MCSET: .... ERIK 1
MCSET: 8219374
2LP: 8219371

BEHIND THE SUN.
Tracks: / She's waiting / See what love can do / Same old blues / Knock on wood / Something's happening / Forever man / It all depends / Tangles in love / Never make you cry / Just like a prisoner / Behind the sun.
LP: 925166 1
MC: 925166 4

BIG BOSS MAN.
LP: .... MA 12784
MC: .... MAMC 912784

BLUES WORLD OF ERIC CLAPTON, THE.
Tracks: / Steppin' out / They call it stormy Monday / Ramblin' on my mind / Hideaway / Key to love / Have you heard? / Calcutta blues / Third degree / Lonely years / Bernard Jenkins / Shim-sham-shimmy / Pretty girls everywhere.
LP: .... SPA 387
MC: .... KCSP 387

BLUESBREAKERS (Clapton, Eric & John Mayall).
Tracks: / All your love / Hideaway / Little girl / Another man / Double crossing time / What'd I say / Key to love / Parchman farm / Have you heard? / Ramblin' on my mind / Steppin' out / It ain't right.
LP: .... SKL 4804

CREAM OF ERIC CLAPTON.
Tracks: / Layla / Badge / I feel free / Sunshine of your love / Strange brew / White room / Cocaine / I shot the sheriff / Behind the mask / Forever man / Lay down Sally / Knockin' on heaven's door / Wonderful tonight / Let it grow / Promises / I've got a rock 'n' roll heart / Heart / Crossroads.
LP: .... ECTV 1
MC: .... ECTVC 1

CROSSROADS.
LPS: .... ROAD 1
MCSET: .... ROADC 1

DON'T CARE NO MORE.
LP: .... PLP 23
MC: .... PMC 23

EARLY COLLECTION: ERIC CLAPTON.
Tracks: / Got to hurry / I ain't got you / Good morning little schoolgirl / Let it rock (live) / Certain girl, A / Take it easy baby (live) / Too much monkey business (live) / Draggin' my tail / Tribute to Elmore / Snake drive / West Coast idea / Coker / Freight loader / Miles road / Maudie (live) / It hurts to be in love (live) / Steppin' out / Have you heard / Lonely

years / Bernard Jenkins / I'm your witch doctor / Telephone blues / They call it stormy Monday / On top of the world.
2LP: . . . . **CCSLP 162**
MC: . . . . **CCSMC 162**

E.C. WAS HERE.
Tracks: / Have you ever loved a woman / Presence of the Lord / Drifting blues / Can't find my way home / Rambling on my mind / Further on up the road.
LP: . . . . **SPELP 21**
MC: . . . . **SPEMC 21**
LP: **2394 160**

ERIC CLAPTON.
Tracks: / Slunky / Bad boy / Lonesome and a long way from home / After midnight / Easy now / Blues power / Bottle of red wine / Lovin' you loving me / I've told you for the last time / I don't know why / Let it rain.
LP: . . . . **SPELP 54**
LP: **2383 021**

ERIC CLAPTON AND THE YARDBIRDS (Clapton, Eric & The Yardbirds).
LP: . . . . **CR 30012**

ERIC CLAPTON AND THE YARDBIRDS (2) (Clapton, Eric & The Yardbirds).
LP: . . . . **XELLP 110**
MC: . . . . **XELMC 110**

ERIC CLAPTON (CASSETTE).
Tracks: / Bell bottom blues / Slunky / Have you ever loved a woman / Let it rain / Anyday / Key to the highway / Peaches and diesel / Watch out for Lucy / I shot the sheriff / Promises / Knockin' on heaven's door / Wonderful tonight / Cocaine / Lay down Sally / Willie and the hand jive / After midnight / Swing low sweet chariot / Let it grow / Blues power.
MCSET: **3272 117**

ERIC CLAPTON LIVE.
LP: . . . . **WX 373**
MC: . . . . **WX 373 C**

FIVE LONG YEARS.
Tracks: / Smokestack lightnin' / Good morning little schoolgirl / I don't care no more / Five long years / Here 'tis / Bye bye bird / Mister Downchild / Too much monkey business / Got love if you want it.
LP: **2215515**
MC: **2115515**

GOT LOVE IF YOU WANT IT (Clapton, Eric & The Yardbirds).
Tracks: / Too much monkey business / Got love if you want it / Smokestack lightning / Good morning little schoolgirl / I don't care anymore / Five long years / Here 'tis / Bye bye bird / Mister Downchild / I wish you would / For your love / Certain girl, A / Twenty / Three hours too long / Got to hurry.
LP: . . . . **SHLP 108**
MC: . . . . **SHTC 108**

GREATEST HITS: ERIC CLAPTON.
LP: . . . . **ADAH 428**
MC: . . . . **ADAHC 428**
LP: **6.22282**

HISTORY OF ERIC CLAPTON.
Tracks: / I ain't got you / Hideaway / Tales of brave Ulysses / I want to discuss it / Teasin' / Blues power / Spoonful / Badge / Tell the truth / Jam / Layla.
LP: **2671 107**
MC: . . . . **TWOMC 10**

JOURNEYMAN.
LP: . . . . **WX 322**
MC: **926 074-4**

JUST ONE NIGHT.
Tracks: / Tulsa time / Early in the morning / Lay down Sally / Wonderful tonight / If I don't be there by morning / All our past times / Worried life blues / Blues power / Knockin' on heaven's door / Double trouble / Setting me up / After midnight / Rambling on my mind / Cocaine / Further on up the road.
2LP: . . . . **RSDX 2**
2LP: **265 813 5**

LAYLA.
Tracks: / Let it rain / Anyday / Key to the highway / Layla / Little wing / After midnight / Bell bottom blues.
LP: **2479 194**
MC: **3215 056**

MAGIC OF ERIC CLAPTON, THE.
MC: . . . . **VENUMC 4**

MONEY AND CIGARETTES.
Tracks: / Everybody oughta make a change / Shape you're in, The / Ain't going down / I've got a rock 'n' roll heart / Man overboard / Pretty girl / Man in love, A / Crosscut saw / Slow down Linda / Crazy country hop.
LP: . . . . **W 3773**
MC: . . . . **W 3773 4**

MUSIC FOR THE MILLIONS.
Tracks: / Let it rain / Anyday / Key to the highway / Layla / Little wing / After midnight / Bell bottom blues.
LP: **811987 1**
MC: **811987 4**

NO REASON TO CRY.
Tracks: / Beautiful things / County jail / Carnival / Sign language / Country jail blues / All our past times / Hello, old friend / Double trouble / Innocent times / Hungry / Black summer rain.
LP: . . . . **SPELP 2**
MC: . . . . **SPEMC 2**
LP: **2479 179**

RAINBOW CONCERT.
Tracks: / Badge / Roll it over / Presence of the Lord / Pearly queen / After midnight / Little wing.
LP: . . . . **SPELP 23**
MC: . . . . **SPEMC 23**

SLOWHAND.
Tracks: / Cocaine / Core, The / Lay down Sally / May you never / Mean old 'Frisco blues / Next time you see her / Peaches and diesel / We're all the way / Wonderful tonight.
LP: . . . . **SPELP 25**
MC: . . . . **SPEMC 25**
MC: **3524 229**
LP: **2479 201**

STEPPIN' OUT.
Tracks: / Ramblin' on my mind / Little girl / All your love / Key to love / Double crossin' time / Have you heard? / Hideaway / Third degree / Lonely years / Pretty girls everywhere / Calcutta blues / Steppin' out.
LP: . . . . **TAB 21**
MC: . . . . **KTBC 21**

SURVIVOR.
Tracks: / I wish you would / For your love / Certain girl, A / Got to hurry / Too much monkey business / I don't care no more / Bye bye bird / Twenty three hours too long / Baby don't worry / Take it easy baby.
LP: . . . . **THBL 013**
MC: . . . . **THBC 013**

THERE'S ONE IN EVERY CROWD.
Tracks: / We've been told (Jesus coming soon) / Swing low sweet chariot / Little Rachel / Don't blame me / Sky is crying, The / Singing the blues / Better make it through the day / Pretty blue eyes / High / Opposite.
LP: **2479 132**
LP: . . . . **SPELP 92**
MC: . . . . **SPEMC 92**

TIME PIECES.
Tracks: / I shot the sheriff / After midnight / Wonderful tonight / Layla / Willie and the hand jive / Knockin' on heaven's door / Let it grow / Swing low sweet chariot / Cocaine / Lay down Sally / Promises.
LP: . . . . **RSD 5010**
MC: . . . . **TRSD 5010**

TIME PIECES VOL.II ('Live' In The Seventies).
Tracks: / Tulsa time / Knockin' on heaven's door / If I don't be there by morning / Rambling on my mind / Presence of the Lord / Can't find my way home / Smile / Blues power.
LP: . . . . **SPELP 87**
MC: . . . . **SPEMC 87**
LP: . . . . **RSD 5022**

TIME PIECES VOLS. 1 AND 2.
Tracks: / I shot the sheriff / Badge / After midnight / Wonderful tonight / Layla / Willie and the hand jive / Knockin' on heaven's door / Let it grow / Swing low sweet chariot / All our past times / Blues power / Hideaway / Have you heard? / Sunshine of your love / Presence of the Lord / Bell bottom blues / Cocaine / Lay down Sally / Hello old friend / Promises / I can't stand it / Tulsa time.
2LP: . . . . **RSDX 3**

TOO MUCH MONKEY BUSINESS.
LP: **20118**

Clare, Alan

MIDNIGHT MOODS.
MCSET: . . . . **DTO 10269**

THOU SWELL (see Deucher, Jimmy) (Clare, Alan/Jimmy Deucher/Victor Feldman/Tony Kinsey).

Clare College..

CAROLS FROM CLARE (See under Christmas Carols) (Clare College Singers & Orchestra).

Clare's New Baby

CLARE'S NEW BABY BROTHER (Snell, Nigel).
MC: . . . . **LL 41 8040 4**

Claret, Cathy

SOLEIL Y LOCURA.
LP: . . . . **TWI 932**

Clark, Anne

CHANGING PLACES.
LP: . . . . **RF 22**

HOPELESS CASES.
Tracks: / Poem without words 1 - The 3rd meeting / Homecoming / Cane Hill / This must be the verse / Now / Hope road / Armchair theatre / Leaving / Poem without words 2 / Up / Journey by night.
LP: . . . . **DIX 48**
MC: . . . . **CDIX 48**
MC: . . . . **CXID 26**
LP: . . . . **XID 26**

JOINED UP WRITING.
LP: . . . . **MINK 5**

ORDINARY LIFE, AN.
LP: . . . . **PIPLP 017**
MC: . . . . **PIPMC 017**

R.S.V.P..
Tracks: / Up / Homecoming / Red sands / Power game, The / Cane Hill / Leaving / Heaven / Last emotion, The / Killing time / Wallies / Our darkness / Now / This is the verse / Sleeper in Metropolis.
LP: . . . . **DIX 72**
MC: . . . . **CDIX 72**

Clark, Benny

WORLD HITS PLAYED ON THE MOUTH ORGAN (see Toots, Thielmans) (Clark, Benny/Thielemans Toots).

Clark, Buddy

BUDDY CLARK.
Tracks: / Come rain or come shine / I get a kick out of you / Way down yonder in New Orleans / Let's face the music and dance / If I had my life to live over / But not for me / One more time / There's a great day coming, Manana / So in love / You'll never walk alone / It ain't necessarily so / Five foot two, eyes of blue / Just look at me / Baby, it's cold outside.
LP: . . . . **AJAZ 516**

COLLECTION: BUDDY CLARK (The Columbia years 1942-49).
Tracks: / It's a big wide, wonderful world / Here I'll stay / I'll get by / Just one more chance / Linda / I'll dance at your wedding / You're too dangerous, cherie / Dreamer's holiday, A / I'll see you in my dreams / Apple blossom wedding, An / How are things in Glocca Morra? / That old gang of mine / My darling, my darling (with Doris Day) / Peg o' my heart / South America, take it away / Ballerina / Girl of my dreams / If this isn't love / You'd be so nice to come home to / When day is done.
2LP: **P2-18848**

Clark, Dave

25 THUMPING GREAT HITS (Clark, Dave Five).
Tracks: / Glad all over / Do you love me? / Bits and pieces / Can't you see? / Catch us if you can / Because / Over and over / Reelin' and rockin' / You got what it takes / Everybody knows / Good old rock 'n' roll / Sweet little sixteen / Long tall Sally / Chantilly lace / Whole lotta shakin' goin' on / Blue suede shoes / Wild weekend / Here comes summer / Live in the sky / Red balloon / Come home / Sweet city woman / Sha-na-na / Put a little love in your heart / Everybody get together.
LP: . . . . **POLTV 7**

CATCH US IF YOU CAN (Clark, Dave Five).
LP: **33SX 1756**

SESSION WITH THE DAVE CLARK FIVE, A (Clark, Dave Five).
LP: **33SX 1598**

Clark, Dee

DELECTABLE SOUND OF DEE CLARK.
Tracks: / Seven nights / Just like a fool / 24 boyfriends / Why don't you come home / Blues get off my shoulder / Just can't help myself / Because I love you / Money (that's what I want) / Dance on little girl / Drums in my heart / You are like the wind / Fever / Ol' man river / Little boy blue / How is he treating you / I'm going back to school.
LP: . . . . **CRB 1113**

KEEP IT UP.
LP: . . . . **CRB 1010**

RIDE A WILD HORSE (OLD GOLD) (See under Carr, Linda/High wire).

Clark, Gene

GENE CLARK & THE GOSDIN BROTHERS (Clark, Gene & The Gosdin Brothers).
Tracks: / Echoes / Think I'm gonna feel better / Tried so hard / Is yours is mine / Keep on pushing / I found you / So you say you lost your baby / Elevator operator / Same one, The / Couldn't believe her / Needing someone.
LP: . . . . **ED 263**

NO OTHER.
Tracks: / Life's greatest fool / Silver raven / No other / Strength of strings / From a silver phial / Some misunderstanding / True one, The / Lady of the North.
LP: **K53 005**
LP: . . . . **ED 299**

ROADMASTER.
Tracks: / She's the kind of girl / One in a hundred / Here tonight / Full circle song / In a misty morning / Rough and rocky / Roadmaster / I really don't want to know / I remember the railroad / She don't care about the time / Shooting star.
LP: . . . . **ED 198**

SO REBELLIOUS A LOVER (Clark, Gene & Carla Olsen).
Tracks: / Drifter, The / Gypsy rider / Every angel in heaven / Del gato / Deportees / Fair and tender ladies / Almost Saturday night / I'm your toy / Why did you leave me / Don't it make you wanna go home / Are we still making love.
LP: . . . . **FIEND 89**

TWO SIDES TO EVERY STORY.
Tracks: / Home run king / Lonely Saturday / In the pines / Kansas City Southern / Give my love to Marie / Sister moon / Marylou / Hear the wind / Past address / Silent crusade.
LP: **2394 176**

Clark, Guy

BEST OF GUY CLARK.
Tracks: / Rita Ballou / L.A. freeway / She ain't going nowhere / That old feeling / Texas, 1947 / Desperados waiting for the train / Instant coffee blues / Nickel for the fiddler, A / Texas cookin' / Anyhow I love you / Virginia's real / Broken hearted people / Black haired boy / Last gunfighter ballad, The / Let him roll / Like a coat from the cold.
LP: . . . . **INTS 5196**
MC: . . . . **INTK 5196**

BETTER DAYS.
LP: **238801**

GUY CLARK.
Tracks: / Fool on the roof / Roots for each other / Shade of all greens / Voila, an American dream / One paper kid / In the jailhouse now / Comfort and crazy / Don't you take it too bad / Houston kid / Fool on the roof blues.
LP: . . . . **K 56565**

OLD FRIENDS (MOTHER LABEL).
Tracks: / Old friends / Hands / I'm all through throwin' good love / Immigrant eyes / Heavy metal (don't mean rock & roll to me) / Come from the heart / Indian cowboy, The / To live is to fly / Watermelon days / Doctor Good Doctor.
MC: . . . . **MUMC 893**
LP: . . . . **MUM 893**

OLD FRIENDS (SUGARHILL USA).
LP: . . . . **SH 1025**

OLD NUMBER ONE.
Tracks: / Rita Ballou / L.A. freeway / She ain't goin' nowhere / Nickel for the fiddler, A / That old time feeling / Texas - 1947 / Desperados waiting for the train / Like a coat from the cold / Instant coffee blues / Let him roll.
LP: **APL1 1303**
LP: . . . . **ED 285**

SOUTH EAST OF TEXAS, THE.
LP: . . . . **BSK 3381**

TEXAS COOKIN'.
Tracks: / Texas cookin' / Anyhow, I love you / Virginia's real / It's about time / Good to love you lady / Broken hearted people / Black haired boy / Me I'm feelin' the same / Ballad of Laverne and Captain Flint / Last gunfighter ballad, The.
LP: . . . . **ED 287**

Clark, Ian

IAN CLARK PLAYS THE MELODIES OF SCOTLAND.
MC: . . . . **ZCSLP 615**

Clark, John

FACES.
LP: . . . . **ECM 1176**

Clark, Johnnie

JOHNNIE CLARK MEETS CORNELL CAMPBELL IN NEW STYLE (see Campbell, Cornell) (Clark, Johnnie & Cornell Campbell).

Clark, Johnny

MAGIC ORGAN VOL. 1 (20 All Time Favourites).
Tracks: / Agadoo / Birdie song, The / Entertainer, The / Pennsylvania polka / Alabama jubilee / Beer barrel polka / Anniversary waltz / Take a chance on me / Brown girl in the ring / Hands up / Your cheatin' heart / Don't stay away too

long / In the mood / Under the double eagle / When the saints go marching in / Zip-a-dee-doo-dah / Leichtenstein polka / Bluebell polka / Little brown jug / Abanda.
LP: . . . . PLATB 08
MC: . . . . PLACB 08

MAGIC ORGAN VOL. 2 (20 More All Time Favourites).
Tracks: / Do the conga / Blaze away / Hokey cokey / Tico tico / Y Viva Espana / Zorba the Greek / Simon says / Tulips from Amsterdam / Floral dance, The / Camptown races / Never on Sunday / Spanish eyes / Liberty bell / Music box dancer / Last waltz, The / Cherry pink and apple blossom white / Let's twist again / When your old wedding ring was new / April showers / If I had a talking picture of you.
LP: . . . . PLATB 09
MC: . . . . PLACB 09

Clark, LaRena

CAMADOAM GARLAND, A.
Tracks: / Kettle on the stovepipe / Lord Gregory / Thyme 'tis a pretty flower / Rifle boys, The / House carpenter / Gallant hussar, The / Banks of the Nile / I once loved a lass / Dapple grey, The / Old county fair, The / There was a Lord in Edinburgh / Faggot cutter, The.
LP: 12T 140

Clark, Louis

LEGENDS.
Tracks: / Oh pretty woman / Dancing queen / She's not there / You can't hurry love / Macarthur Park / You've lost that loving feeling / Will you love me tomorrow / When will I see you again / River deep mountain high / Dancing in the dark.
LP: . . . . UNIONLP 1
MC: . . . . UNIONMC 1

PER-SPEK-TIV.
LP: . . . . JETLP 218

Clark, O' Neil

FRESH AGONY.
LP: . . . . VPRL 001

Clark, Octa

ENSEMBLE ENCORE (Clark, Octa & Hector Duhon).
LP: . . . . ROUNDER 6011

OCTA CLARK/HECTOR DUHON (Clark, Octa & Hector Duhon).
LP: . . . . ARHOOLIE 5026

Clark, Paul

NEW HORIZON, A.
Tracks: / Tell them all / Breakaway / Broken fool / One you love, The / He'll use me / Every breath / Here to stay / Hold on / Distant shore / More than survivors.
LP: . . . . MYR 1122
MC: . . . . MC 1122

Clark, Petula

20 ALL TIME GREATEST.
LP: . . . . NE 945

100 MINUTES OF PETULA CLARK.
MC: . . . . ZCTON 108

C'EST MA CHANSON.
Tracks: / Chariot / La nuit ne'en finit plus / Cover blesse / Ceux qui ont un coeur / Marin / Romeo / C'est le refrain de ma vie / Elle est finit / La derniere valse / Petite fleur / Hello Dolly / Tout le monde / O O sheriff / Les colimacons / La gadoule / Dans le temps / Je me sans bien / C'est ma chanson.
MC: 771 042

COLOUR MY WORLD.
LP: . . . . NSPL 18171

DOUBLE GOLD DISC.
LP: . . . . VG 416013

DOWNTOWN.
Tracks: / Downtown / Sign of the times, A / This is my song / I couldn't live without your love / You're the one / I know a place / Kiss me goodbye / Colour my world / Mad about you / Don't sleep in the subway / Good life / Other man's grass, The / My love / Give it a try / Strangers in the night.
LP: . . . . PYL 17
MC: . . . . PYM 17

EARLY YEARS.
Tracks: / Teasin' / Card, The / Boy in love, A / Who-is-it song, The / Million stars above, A / Pendulum song, The / Tuna puna Trinidad / Fascinating rhythm / Majorca / Suddenly there's a valley / Another door opens / Fortune teller / Fibbin' / Band of gold / Alone / Long before I knew you / Gonna find me a bluebird / Memories are made of this / With all my heart / Who needs you? / Love me again / In a little moment / Baby lover / Ever been in love / Devotion / I've grown accustomed to his face / My favourite things / Little blue man / To you my love / Lucky day / Suddenly / Watch your heart / Long way to go / Made in heaven / Little shoemaker, The / Christmas cards / Little Johnny Rainbow / Romance in Rome / Chee chee oo chee.
MC: . . . . ZCPCL 101
2LP: . . . . PCL 101

EP COLLECTION, THE: PETULA CLARK.
LP: . . . . SEE 306
MC: . . . . SEEK 306

GOLDEN HOUR OF.
MC: . . . . KGHMC 151

GOLDEN HOUR OF PETULA CLARK, A.
MC: . . . . DLCMC 130

GREATEST HITS: PETULA CLARK.
LP: . . . . GNPS 2170

GREATEST HITS: PETULA CLARK (IMPORT).
LP: . . . . BRLP 55
MC: . . . . BRMC 55

GREATEST HITS:PETULA CLARK.
Tracks: / Little shoemaker, The / Thank you / I love a violin / Little blue man / I don't know how to love him / Sailor / Memories are made of this / Majorca / Christopher Robin at Buckingham Palace / Suddenly there's a valley / Other man's grass, The / Romeo / Downtown / Sign of the times / Baby lover / Band of love / With all my heart / I know a place / Alone / Fascinating rhythm / My friend the sea / Where did my snowman go? / Devotion / Don't sleep in the subway.
MCSET: . . . . DTO 10021

HIT PARADE.
LP: . . . . NPL 18159

HIT SINGLES COLLECTION, THE.
Tracks: / Majorca / Little shoemaker, The / Suddenly there's a valley / With all my heart / Alone / Baby lover / Sailor / Something's missing / Romeo / My friend the sea / I'm counting on you / Ya ya twist / Casanova / Chariot / Downtown / I know a place / You'd better come home / Round every corner / You're the one / My love / Sign of the times / I couldn't live without your love / Who am I? / Colour my world / This is my song / Don't sleep in the subway / Cat in the window, The / Other man's grass, The / Kiss me goodbye / Don't give up / Song of my life, The / I don't know how to love him.
2LP: . . . . PYL 7002
MCSET: . . . . PYM 7002

HOUR IN CONCERT, AN.
Tracks: / Don't sleep in the subway / Sorry seems to be the hardest word / This is my song / Out here on my own / Colour my world / I wish / You are the sunshine of my life / Isn't she lovely / Music people / Life is a song / Could it be magic / My love / On with the show / Every little thing you do is magic / Downtown.
LP: . . . . MFP 5636
MC: . . . . TCMFP 5636
LP: . . . . MFP 4156361

I COULDN'T LIVE WITHOUT YOUR LOVE.
LP: . . . . NPL 18148

MY GREATEST.
Tracks: / Down town / If you ever go away / I couldn't live without your love / This is my song / Got it / Turn to me / Song of my life, The / Send away the clowns / We'll still be friends / Don't sleep in the subway / My love / All my life / Other man's grass, The / Colours of love / Kiss me goodbye / Show is over, The.
LP: . . . . MFP 5853
MC: . . . . TCMFP 5853

MY LOVE.
MCSET: . . . . DTO 10281

OTHER MAN'S GRASS IS ALWAYS GREENER, THE.
LP: . . . . NSPL 18211

PETULA CLARK.
Tracks: / Sign of the times, A / This is my song / Downtown / I couldn't live without your love / You're the one / I know a place / Kiss me goodbye / Colour my world / Mad about you / Don't sleep in the subway / Other man's grass, The / My love / Give it a try.
LP: . . . . OR 0056

PETULA CLARK.
Tracks: / This is my song / Cherish / Life and soul of the party, The / What would I be without your love / Other man's grass, The / You'd better come home / Don't give up / Call me / Fool on the hill, The / Song of my life, The / Don't sleep in the subway / My love / Good life / Goin out of my head / Winchester cathedral / I couldn't live without your love / Sailor / Happy together / I don't know how to love him / We can work it out / You're the one / No one better than you / I know a place.
MCSET: . . . . CRT 006

PETULA CLARK AT ROYAL ALBERT HALL.
LP: . . . . GNPS 2069
MC: GNP5 2069

PORTRAIT OF A SONG STYLIST.
MC: . . . . HARMC 119

SPECIAL COLLECTION.
Tracks: / Sailor / I know a place / After the hill / Spring in September / City lights / Today / Don't give up / Down town / Beautiful in the rain / Sun shines out of your shoes, The / Why can't I cry / We're falling in love again / Don't sleep in the subway / I couldn't live without your love / He made me a woman / For all we know / One step behind / Man in a million / Other man's grass, The / My funny valentine / That's what life is all about / Neon rainbow / It don't matter to me / If.
MC: . . . . CCSMC 236

SPOTLIGHT ON PETULA CLARK.
Tracks: / Downtown / I know a place / Round every corner / Other man's grass, The / Sign of the times / You're the one / Colour my world / Who am I? / Just say goodbye / Happy heart / Kiss me goodbye / Heart / Sailor / This girl's in love with you / Where did we go wrong / Let it be me / Last waltz, The / Imagine / This is my song / You'd better come home / My love / Don't sleep in the subway / Strangers in the night / I couldn't live without your love.
2LP: . . . . SPOT 1012
MCSET: . . . . ZCSPT 1012

THESE ARE MY SONGS.
LP: . . . . NSPL 18197

THIS IS MY SONG.
Tracks: / Downtown / My love / Don't sleep in the subway / Round every corner / Colour my world / Other man's grass, The / Sailor / This is my song / Romeo / I know a place / My friend the sea / I couldn't live without your love.
LP: . . . . FBLP 8072
MC: . . . . ZCFBL 8072

UN BOUQUET DE SUCCESS.
LPS: 000304

YOU ARE MY LUCKY STAR.
Tracks: / It's foolish but it's fun / Sonny boy / Zing went the strings of my heart / Alone / I, yi, yi, yi / Goodnight my love / I wish I knew / Slumming on Park Avenue / As time goes by / It's the natural thing to do / Afraid to dream / You are my lucky star.
LP: C5-551

Clark, Roy

20 GOLDEN PIECES: ROY CLARK.
Tracks: / Then she's a lover / Unchained melody / Me and Bobby Magee / For once in my life / All the way / I still miss someone / Make the world go away / Days of sand and shovels, The / Simple thing as love, A / September song / You don't have very far to go / Come live with me / Daddy don't you walk so fast / Somewhere between love and tomorrow / Most beautiful girl, The / Why me / I really don't want to know / I'll paint you a song / Kiss an angel good morning / Onward christian soldiers (good old time religion).
LP: . . . . BDL 2038
MC: . . . . BDC 2038

BEST OF ROY CLARK.
Tracks: / Simple thing as love, A / Then she's a lover / Do you believe this town / September song / I never picked cotton / Tips of my fingers, The / Yesterday when I was in love / Right or left at Oak street / Love is just a state of mind / Thank God and greyhounds / Malaguena.
LP: . . . . IMCA 27015

LIVE IN CONCERT.
Tracks: / Rocky top / Riders in the sky / If I had to do it all over again / Somewhere my love / Duellin' banjos / Back up and push / Think summer / Malaguena.
LP: . . . . MCL 1657

ROY CLARK IN CONCERT.
LP: . . . . ABCL 5268

Clark, Sanford

FOOL, THE.
Tracks: / Fool, The / Man who made an angel cry, The / Love charms / Cheat / Lonesome for a letter / Ooh baby / Darling dear / Modern romance / Travellin' man / Swanee river rock / Lou be doo / Usta be my baby / Nine pound hammer / Glory of love.
LP: . . . . CH 83

ROCKIN' ROLLIN' VOL.1.
Tracks: / Modern romance / That's the way I feel / Man who made an angel cry, The / Ooo baby / Cross-eyed alley cat, A / Till my baby comes back / Lou be doo / Travellin' man / Lonesome for a letter / Fool, The / Love charms / Every minute of the day / Ain't nobody here but us chickens / Don't care / Cheat / Usta be my baby / Nine pound hammer / Swanee river rock.
LP: . . . . BFX 15198

ROCKIN' ROLLIN' VOL.2.
Tracks: / Darling dear / Don't cry / Why did I choose you / Come what may / Fool's blues, A / Juice / Guitar man / Run boy run / I can't help it / Son of a gun / New kind of fool / Sing 'em some blues / Bad luck / Go on home / Pledging my love / Still as the night / My jealousy / Promise me baby / Glory of love.
LP: . . . . BFX 15199

Clark Sisters

CHANNEL FOLK.
Tracks: / Devoted to you / You've got a friend / Pack up your sorrows / Be bye love / This will be our last song together / Streets of London / Jet plane.
MC: . . . . ERON 010 CA

HEART AND SOUL.
LP: . . . . REJ R 5010
MC: . . . . REJ C 5010

MORE THAN CONQUERORS.
LP: . . . . REJ R 5022
MC: . . . . REJ C 5022

SALUTE TO THE GREAT SINGING GROUPS, A.
Tracks: / My blue Heaven / Until the real thing comes along / Bei mir bist du schon / Paper doll / I'll get by / I've got a gal in Kalamazoo / Dream / Sugartime / Getting sentimental over you / Undecided / I'm forever blowing bubbles / When I take my sugar to tea.
LP: . . . . JASM 1501

SING SING SING.
LP: . . . . JASM 1038

SWING AGAIN.
LP: . . . . JASM 1518

Clark, Sonny

COOL STRUTTIN'.
Tracks: / Cool struttin' / Blue minor / Sippin' at bells / Deep night / Royal flush / Lover.
LP: . . . . BLJ 81588

LEAPIN' AND LOPIN'.
Tracks: / Something special / Deep in a dream / Melody for C / Melody for C (alternate take) / Eric walks / Voodoo / Midnight mambo / Zellmar's delight.
LP: . . . . BST 84091

Clark, Spencer

PLAY SWEET AND HOT (Clark, Spencer & His Bass Sax).
LP: . . . . AP 131

Clark, Willie

BROSE FOR WILLIE.
MC: . . . . CWGR 111

Clarke, Allan

BEST OF ALLAN CLARKE.
Tracks: / Born to run / Blinded by the light / If I were the priest.
LP: . . . . AUL 718

I WASN'T BORN YESTERDAY.
Tracks: / I wasn't born yesterday / Hope / New blood / I'm betting my life on you / Man who manufactures daydreams / No prisoner taken / Shadow in the street / Light of my smiles / Who's goin' out the back door? / Off the record.
LP: . . . . AUL 704

ONLY ONE, THE.
LP: . . . . AUL 711

Clarke, Ann

UNSTILL LIFE.
LP: 0888361
MC: 0888364

Clarke, Arthur C (aut)

2001: A SPACE ODYSSEY (see under 2001...(bk)).

CHILDHOOD'S END.
MC: . . . . CDL 51614

FOUNTAINS OF PARADISE (see under Fountains Of... (bk)).

TRANSIT OF EARTH AND OTHER STORIES (see under Transit Of Earth (bk)).

Clarke, Austin (aut)

BEYOND THE PALE (see under Beyond The Pale (bk)).

Clarke, Christopher

ONE MAN.
LP: . . . . VIR 83006

Clarke, Grainnie

SONGS OF ROGUES AND HONEST MEN.

Tracks: / Lakes of Coolfin / Uir chill a chreagain / Granemore hare / Seamous Mac Murphaidh / Dobbin's flowery vale / Willie Archer / Ard ti cuain / Red is the rose / Green linnet / Donal og / Mary of the moorlands / Blacksmith / Ur chnoc chein mhic cainte / Bunch of thyme.
LP: .... OAS 3028
MC: .... CPAS 3028

Clarke, Johnny

20 MASSIVE HITS.
LP: .... TSL 110

DON'T TROUBLE TROUBLE.
LP: .... ATLP 107

ENTER INTO HIS GATES WITH PRAISE.
LP: .... ATLP 105

GIVE THANKS.
LP: .... ARILP 022

JOHNNY CLARKE MEETS CORNELL CAMPBELL IN NEW STYLE.
LP: .... VSLP 4016

REGGAE PARTY.
LP: .... STLP 1020

REGGAE PARTY (SINGLE) (see under Deneb, Lenny).

ROCKERS' TIME NOW.
LP: .... V 2058

SLY AND ROBBIE PRESENT.
LP: .... STLP 1033

Clarke, Kenny

ALL BLUES.
LP: .... MPS 68 227

AT HER MAJESTY'S PLEASURE (BLACK LION) (Clarke, Kenny & Francy Boland Big Band).
Tracks: / Pentonville / Wormwood Scrubs: dawn / Doing time / Broadmoor / Holloway / Reprieve / Going straight.
LP: .... BLP 30109

AT HER MAJESTY'S PLEASURE (CODE O) (Clarke, Kenny & Francy Boland Big Band).
LP: 2460 131

KENNY CLARKE MEETS THE DETROIT JAZZMEN.
LP: .... WL 70515

LIVE IN PARIS.
LP: 2M 056 64848
MC: 2M 256 64848

PARIS/COLOGNE 1957 AND 1960.
LP: .... SW 8411

PLAYS ANDRE HODEIR (Clarke, Kenny Sextet).
LP: 834 542-1

Clarke, Marie

FLOWERS FROM THE DOCTOR (See under Flowers From the...).

Clarke, Mick

LOOKING FOR TROUBLE (Mick Clarke Band).
LP: .... AP 038

ROCK ME (Mick Clarke Band).
LP: .... AP 050

Clarke, Phil

THAT'S LIFE.
LP: .... LILP 5065

Clarke, Rhonda

BETWEEN FRIENDS (IMPORT).
LP: .... FZ 40882

Clarke, Rick

TIME KEEPS MOVING ON.
LP: .... WALP 1
MC: .... WALMC 1

Clarke, Roy (aut)

SUMMER WINE CHRONICLES - GALA WEEK (see under Summer Wine... (bk).

Clarke Soundbook

CLARKE SOUNDBOOK Clarke, A.C. (Various artists).
LPS: .... SBC 121

Clarke, Stanley

3 (Clarke, Stanley & George Duke).
Tracks: / Pit bulls (An endangered species) / Oh Oh / No place to hide / Somebody else / Mothership connection / Right by my side / From the deepest corner of my heart / Lady / Find out who you are / Quiet time / Fingerprints / Always.
LP: 4670111
MC: 4670114

CLARKE/DUKE PROJECT II (Clarke, Stanley & George Duke).
Tracks: / Put it on the line / Heroes / Try me, baby / Every reason to smile / Great danes / Good times / You're gonna love it / Trip you in love / Atlanta.
LP: .... EPC 25685
MC: 40 25685

COLLECTION: STANLEY CLARKE.
2LP: .... CCSLP 242
MC: .... CCSMC 242

FIND OUT (Clarke, Stanley Band).
Tracks: / Find out / What if I should fall in love? / Born in the USA / Sky's the limit, The / Don't turn the lights out / Campo Americano / Stero typica / Psychedelic / My life.
LP: .... EPC 26521
MC: 40 26521

FUSE ONE (Clarke, Stanley/Larry Coryell/John McLaughlin).
LP: 1063

HEAVEN SENT YOU (OLD GOLD) (See under Brazilian Love Affair (Old Gold)).

HIDEAWAY.
Tracks: / Overjoyed / My love, her inspiration / Where do we go / Boys of Johnson street / Old friends / When it's cold outside / Listen to the beat of your heart / Basketball / I'm here to stay.
MC: 40 26964

I WANNA PLAY FOR YOU.
Tracks: / Rock'n'roll jelly / All about / Jamaican boy / Christopher Ivanhoe / My greatest hits / Strange weather / I wanna play for you / Just a feeling / Streets of Philadelphia / School days / Quiet afternoon / Together again / Blues for Mingus / Off the planet / Hot fun.
MCSET: 40 88331
2LP: .... EPC 22133

IF THIS BASS COULD ONLY TALK.
Tracks: / If this bass could talk / I wanna play for you / Funny how time flies / Bassically taps / Working man / Come take my hand / Stories to tell / Tradition.
LP: 4608831
MC: 4608834

JOURNEY TO LOVE.
Tracks: / Silly putty / Journey to love / Hello, Jeff / Song to John / Concerto for jazz-rock orchestra.
LP: .... EPC 32093
MC: 40 32093
LP: .... K 50187

LET ME KNOW YOU.
Tracks: / Straight to the top / Let me know you / You are the one for me / I just want to be your brother / Force of love / Play the bass / Secret to my heart / New York City.
LP: .... EPC 85846

MODERN MAN.
Tracks: / Opening (statement) / He lives on / More hot fun / Slow dance / Interlude / Serious occasion / Got to find my own place / Dayride / It's what she didn't say / Modern man / Relaxed occasion / Rock 'n' roll jelly / Closing (statement).
LP: .... CBS 32108
MC: 40 32108

PROJECT (Clarke, Stanley & George Duke).
Tracks: / Wild dog / Louie Louie / Sweet baby / I just want to love you / Never judge a cover by it's book / Let's get started / Winners / Touch and go / Finding my way.
LP: .... EPC 84848

ROCKS, PEBBLES AND SAND.
Tracks: / Danger street / All hell broke loose / Rocks, pebbles & sand / You / Me together / Underestimation / We supply / Story of a man and a woman / She thought I was Stanley Clarke / Fool again, A / I nearly went crazy (until I realised what had occurred).
LP: .... EPC 32300
MC: 40 32300
LP: .... EPC 84342

SCHOOL DAYS.
Tracks: / School days / Quiet afternoon / Danger / Desert song, The / Hot fun / Life is just a game / Dancer.
LP: .... EPC 32094
MC: 40 32094
LP: .... K 50296

SHIELDSTONE (Clarke, Stanley & Bill Shields).
LP: .... RSVP 9001

STANLEY CLARKE.
Tracks: / Vulcan princess / Yesterday Princess / Lopsy lu / Power / Spanish phases for strings and bass / Life suite (part 1) / Life suite (part 2) / Life suite (part 3) / Life suite (part 4).
LP: .... K 50101
LP: .... EPC 32042

TIME EXPOSURE.
Tracks: / Play the bass 103 / Are you ready / Speedball / heaven sent you / Time exposure / Future shock / Future / Spacerunner / I know just how you feel.
LP: .... EPC 25486
MC: 40 25486

Clarke, Terry

CALL UP A HURRICANE.
Tracks: / Rock the baby / New Camelot, The / Stars of Austin, The / Blow wind blow / Wish you were here / Tennessee wind / Why don't you take me / Blue hills / Arizona girls / Valley of the blue eyes / Buddy's waitin; on the Flatland road / Warbirds.
LP: .... MILP 001
MC: .... MILC 001

Clarke, William

BLOWIN' LIKE HELL.
LP: .... AC 4788

CAN'T YOU HERE ME CALLING?.
LP: .... RR 502

ROCKIN' THE BOAT.
LP: .... RR 503

TIP OF THE TOP.
LP: .... DT 3016

Clarke, Zela (nar)

CARRIE'S WAR (See under Carrie's War).

Clark-Hutchison

GESTALT.
Tracks: / Man's best friend / Love is the light / Light burns on, The / Come up here / Disorientated, Part 1 / Boat in the mist, A / Orientated / First reminder / Mix elixir / Poison / Disorientated, Part 2.
LP: .... SML 1090

Clash

12" TAPE: CLASH.
Tracks: / London calling / Magnificent dance, The / This is radio clash / Rock the Casbah / This is England / Last chance.
MC: 4501234

BLACK MARKET CLASH.
Tracks: / Capitol Radio One / Prisoner, The / Pressure drop / Cheat / City of the dead / Time is tight / Bankrobber (robber dub) / Armagideon time / Justice tonight / Kick it over.
MC: 4687634

CLASH: INTERVIEW PICTURE DISC.
LPPD: .... BAK 2029

COMBAT ROCK.
Tracks: / Inoculated city / Know your rights / Car jamming / Should I stay or should I go? / Rock the Casbah / Red angel dragnet / Straight to hell / Overpowered by funk / Atom tan / Sean Flynn / Ghetto defendant / Death is a star.
LP: .... CBS 32787
MC: 40 32787
LP: .... FMLN 2

CUT THE CRAP.
Tracks: / Dictator / Dirty punk / We are The Clash / Are you red? / Cool under heat / Movers and shakers / This is England / Three card trick / Play to win / Finger poppin' / North and South / Life is wild.
LP: .... CBS 26601
MC: 40 26601

ESCAPADES OF FUTURA 2000 (see Futura 2000 featuring The Clash) (Clash/ Futura 2000).

FIRST ALBUM.
Tracks: / Janie Jones / Remote control / I'm so bored with the USA / White riot / Hate and war / What's my name? / Deny / London's burning / Career opportunities / Cheat / Protex blue / Police and thieves / 48 hours / Garage lane / Clash city rockers.
LP: .... CBS 32232
MC: 40 32232
LP: .... CBS 82000

GIVE 'EM ENOUGH ROPE.
Tracks: / Safe European home / English civil war / Tommy gun / Julie's been working for the drug squad / Last gang in town / Guns on the roof / Drug-stabbing time / Stay free / Cheapstakes / All the young punks (new boots and contracts).
LP: .... CBS 32444
MC: 40 32444
LP: .... CBS 82431

LONDON CALLING.
Tracks: / London calling / Brand new cadillac / Jimmy Jazz / Hateful / Rudie can't fail / Spanish bombs / Right profile / Lost in the supermarket / Clampdown / Guns of Brixton / Wrong 'em / Boyo / Death or glory / Koka cola / Card cheat / Lover's rock / I'm not down / Revolution rock / Four horsemen.
LP: 4601141
MC: 4601144
LP: .... CLASH 3

SANDINISTA.
Tracks: / Hitsville UK / Junco partner / Leader / Rebel waltz / Look here / One more time / Corner soul / Equaliser / Call up, The / Broadway / Junkie slip / Version city / Crooked beat / Up in heaven / Midnight log / Lose this skin / Kingston advice / Let's go crazy.
LP: .... CBS FSLN 1
MC: .... FSLN 491

STORY OF THE CLASH VOL 1.
Tracks: / Magnificent seven, The / This is radio clash / Straight to hell / Train in vain / I fought the law / Somebody got murdered / Bank robber / Rock the Casbah / Should I stay or should I go / Armagideon time / Guns of Brixton / Clampdown / Lost in the supermarket / (White man) in Hammersmith Palais / London's burning / Janie Jones / Tommy gun / Complete control / Capital radio / White riot / Career opportunities / Clash City rockers / Safe European home / Stay free / London calling / Spanish bombs / English civil war / Police and thieves.
2LP: 4602441
MCSET: 4602444

Clash Of The... (film)

CLASH OF THE TITANS (Film Soundtrack) (Various artists).
LP: .... CBS 73588

Classic...

CLASSIC COMMERCIALS (Various artists).
Tracks: / Carl Orff-Carmina Burana: *Various artists* / Dvorak new world symphony: *Various artists* / Nimrod variation: *Various artists* / Kanon: *Various artists* / Pastoral symphony: *Various artists* / Pizzicato from Sylvia: *Various artists* / Gymnopedie no.1: *Various artists* / Dance des mirlitons: *Various artists* / Morning: *Various artists* / Pavane: *Various artists* / Air on a G string: *Various artists* / Can-can: *Various artists*.
LP: .... SPA 555
MC: .... KCSP 555

CLASSICS GO SOLAR (Various artists).
2LP: .... CR 085
MCSET: .... CRT 085

Classic Experience

CLASSIC EXPERIENCE, THE (Music used in TV commercials) (Various artists).
Tracks: / Arrival of the Queen of Sheba, The: *Various artists* / Intermezzo: *Various artists* (This Week) / Bolero: *Various artists* / Air: *Various artists* / Adagio: *Various artists* (From Spartacus) / Rhapsody in blue: *Various artists* / Dance of the reed flutes: *Various artists* / Sugar plum fairy: *Various artists* / 1812 overture: *Various artists* / Sleeping beauty waltz: *Various artists* / Dance of the little swans: *Various* artists / Morning - Peer Gynt suite No. 1: *Various artists* / Spring (The Four Seasons): *Various artists*/ Rhapsody on a theme by Paganini: *Various artists* / Largo 'From The New World' symphony: *Various artists* / Nimrod from enigma variations: *Various artists* / Pomp and circumstance march no.1: *Various artists* / Meditation from 'Thais': *Various artists* / Fantasia on 'Greensleeves': *Various artists* / Canon and gigue: *Various artists*/ Fanfare for the common man: *Various artists* / William Tell: *Various artists* (The Lone Ranger) / Ride of the Valkyries: *Various artists* (Apocalypse now.) / Montagues and Capulets: *Various artists* / Troika: *Various* artists / Night on a bare mountain: *Various artists* (Maxell tape) / Mars from 'The Planets': *Various artists*/ Radetzky march: *Various artists* / Blue Danube: *Various artists* / Minuet: *Various artists* / Turkish rondo: *Various artists* / Barcarolle: *Various artists* / Intermezzo from 'Cavalleria Rusticana': *Various artists*.
2LP: .... EMTVD 45
MCSET: .... TCEMTVD 45

CLASSIC EXPERIENCE, THE VOL. II (Various artists).
Tracks: / O fortuna (Carmina Burana): *Philharmonia Chorus & Orchestra* (Orff.) / Scene - Act II (Swan Lake): *Royal* Philharmonic Orchestra (Tchaikovsky) / Flower duet (Lakme): *Mesple Mady & Danielle Millet* (Delibes, arr. Bates. With Chorus et Orchestre du Theatre Nationale.) / In the hall of the mountain king (Peer Gynt): *Halle Orchestra* (Greig.) / Overture (Carmen): *Orchestre du Theatre Nationale de L'Opera de Paris* (Bizet) / Chanson Boheme (Carmen): *Callas, Maria/Nadine* Sautereau (Bizet) / Rondo (Eine Kleine Nachtmusik): *Academy Of St.Martin In The Field* (Mozart.) / Largo al factotum (Barber Of Seville): *Gobbi, Tito/Philharmonia Orchestra* (Rossini.) / Rondo (Horn Concerto No. 4): *Tuckwell, Barry/ Academy* Of St. Martin In The Field (Mozart) / Albinoni's adagio: *Brown, Iona/Academy Of St.Martin In The Field* (Giazotto) / Waltz of the flowers (Nutcracker): *Royal Philharmonic Orchestra* (Tchaikovsky) / Fur Elise:

Lymphany. Moura(Beethoven) / Cello concerto: *Du Pre, Jacqueline/London Symphony Orchestra* (Elgar) / Pavanne: *French National Radio* Orchestra (Faure) / Pizzicati (Sylvia): *New Philharmonia Orchestra* (Delibes) / Gymnopedie no. 1: *City Of Birmingham* Symphony Orchestra (Debussy) / Nessun dorma (Turandot): *Carreras, Jose/Orchestre Philharmonique de Strasbourg* (Puccini) / Adagio for strings: *Philadelphia Orchestra* (Barber) / O mio babbino caro (Gianni Schicchi): *Caballe, Montserrat/ London* Symphony Orchestra (Puccini) / Alla hornpipe: *Royal Philharmonic Orchestra* (From Handel's Water Music) / Summer (Four Seasons): *Kennedy, Nigel & English Chamber Orchestra* (Vivaldi) / Sleepers 'wake: *South German Madrigal Choir & Consortium* Musicum (Bach, arr. Bates) / Pastoral - Shepherds hymn (Symphony No. 6): *Philadelphia Orchestra* (Beethoven, arr. Bates) / Skater's waltz, The: *Orchestre de L'Opera de Monte Carlo* (Waldteufel, arr. Bates) / Badinerie (Orchestral suite No. 2): *Academy Of St.Martin In The Field* (Bach) / La donna e mobile (Rigoletto): *Gedda, Nicolai/Orchestra Of Rome Opera House*(Verdi) / Rondo (A Musical Joke): *Philharmonia Orchestra* (Mozart) / Daybreak (Daphnis et Chloe): *London Symphony Orchestra*(Ravel) / Excerpt from Symphony No. 6: *New Philharmonia Orchestra* (Vaughan Williams) / Sunrise (Also Sprach Zarathustra): *London Philharmonic Orchestra* (Richard Strauss) / Prelude Act III (Lohengrin): *New Philharmonia Orchestra* (Wagner) / Jupiter, from the Planets: *New Philharmonia Orchestra* (Holst) / Romeo and Juliet: *London Symphony Orchestra*(Tchaikovsky, arr. Bates) / Thieving magpie overture, The: *Philharmonia Orchestra* (Rossini, arr. Bates) / Symphony No. 6 and Manfred symphony: *Philharmonia Orchestra* (Tchaikovsky, arr. Bates) / Symphonic poem (Finlandia): *Halle Orchestra*(Sibelius).
2LP: . . . . **EMTVD 50**
MCSET: . . . . **TCEMTVD 50**

CLASSIC EXPERIENCE VOL. III (Various artists).
Tracks: / Symphony No. 9 (New World) (Dvorak): *Various artists* / Vitava from 'My country' (Smetana): *Various artists/* Barber of Seville overture: *Various artists* / Brindisi from 'La Traviata' (Verdi): *Various artists* / Va pensiero (Chrous of the slaves) from 'Nabucco' (Verdi): *Various artists* / Die Fledermaus (overture) (Straus II): *Various artists/* Symphony No. 4 'Italian' (Mendelssohn): *Various artists* / Hebrides, The: *Various artists* / Tea (Chinese Dance) from 'The Nutcracker' (Tchaikovsky): *Various artists* / Trepak (Russian dance) from 'The Nutcracker' (Tchaikovsky): *Various* artists / Italian caprice: *Various artists* / Waltz in D flat (Minute waltz) (Chopin): *Various artists* / Symphony No. 40 (Mozart): *Various artists* / Chanson de matin: *Various artists* / Symphony No. 1 (Elgar): *Various* artists / Concierto de Aranjuez: *Various artists* / Aria: *Various artists* ((Cantilena)from 'Bachianas Brasileiras No.5 (Lobos)) / In the depths of the temple: *Various artists* (From Pearl Fishers. Bizet.) / Farandole: *Various artists/* Clair de Lune: *Various artists* / Vesti la giubba from 'I Pagliacci' (Leoncavallo): *Various artists* / Sheep may safely graze (J.S. Bach): *Various artists* / Piano concerto No. 5 'Emperor' (Beethoven): *Various artists/* Symphony No. 9 (Choral) (Beethoven): *Various artists* / Scheherazade (Rimsky-Korsakov): *Various artists* / Flight of the bumble bee, The (Rimsky-Korsakov): *Various artists* / Peter and the wolf (Prokofiev): *Various artists* / Ballet Egyptian: *Various artists* / Dance of the hours (Ponchielli): *Various artists* / Sabre dance from 'Gayaneh' (Khachaturian): *Various artists* / Sorcerer's apprentice, The (Dukas): *Various artists* / Rite of spring, The (Stravinsky): *Various artists* / Espana (Chabrier): *Various artists.*
LP: . . . . **EMTVD 59**
MC: . . . . **TCEMTVD 59**

Classic Film Scores...

CLASSIC FILM SCORES (see under Films) (Various artists).

Classic Ghost... (bk)

CLASSIC GHOST STORIES (Pasco, Richard (nar)).
MCSET: . . . . **TTDMC 403**

Classic Jazz Ensemble

CLASSIC BLUES.
LP: . . . . **DS 221**

Classic Jazz Piano

CLASSIC JAZZ PIANO (1927-1957) (See under Jazz...) (Various artists).

Classic Jazz Quartet

CLASSIC JAZZ QUARTET.
LP: . . . . **J 139**
LP: . . . . **SOS 1125**

Classic Love Stories

CLASSIC LOVE STORIES (Various artists).
MCSET: . . . . **TTDMC 402**

Classic Movie

CLASSIC MOVIE MUSIC VOL 1 (See under Film Music) (Various artists).

CLASSIC MOVIE MUSIC VOL 2 (See under Film Music) (Various artists).

CLASSIC MOVIE MUSIC VOL 3 (See under Film Music) (Various artists).

Classic New York

CLASSIC NEW YORK MEMORIES (Various artists).
LP: . . . . **OCN 2040WL**
MC: . . . . **OCN 2040WK**

Classic On Parade

CLASSICS ON PARADE (Classics On Parade Orchestra).
Tracks: / Nutcracker suite / Warsaw concerto.
LP: . . . . **MAN 5043**

Classic Overtures

CLASSIC OVERTURES (Various artists).
LP: . . . . **ADL 509**
MC: . . . . **ADK 509**

Classic Rock

CLASSIC ROCK (See under Rock...) (Various artists).

CLASSIC ROCK (ATLANTIC) (See under Rock) (Various artists).

Classic Rockabilly

CLASSIC ROCKABILLY (See under Rockabilly) (Various artists).

Classic Rock'n'Roll

CLASSIC ROCK'N'ROLL (See under Rock'n'Roll) (Various artists).

Classic Ruins

RUINS CAFE.
LP: . . . . **ROSE 174**

Classic Songwriters

CLASSIC SONGWRITERS, THE (Various artists).
MCSET: . . . . **WW 6035**

Classic Soul

CLASSIC SOUL MIX (See under Soul) (Various artists).

Classic Soul Years

CLASSIC SOUL YEARS SERIES 1964 (See Under Soul) (Various artists).

CLASSIC SOUL YEARS SERIES 1965 (See under Soul) (Various artists).

CLASSIC SOUL YEARS SERIES 1966 (See under Soul) (Various artists).

CLASSIC SOUL YEARS SERIES 1967 (See under Soul) (Various artists).

CLASSIC SOUL YEARS SERIES 1968 (See under Soul) (Various artists).

Classic Tales... (bk)

CLASSIC TALES OF MYSTERY AND THE SUPERNATURAL (Bailey, Robin (nar)).
MCSET: . . . . **TTDMC 404**

Classic Veji

VANCOUVER ENSEMBLE OF JAZZ IMPROVISION.
LP: . . . . **BBN 1003**

Classic Years...

CLASSIC YEARS IN DIGITAL STEREO (see under Crosby, Bing).

CLASSIC YEARS IN DIGITAL STEREO (see under Astaire, Fred).

CLASSIC YEARS IN DIGITAL STEREO (see under Bowlly, Al) (Bowlly, Al with Ray Noble & His Orchestra).

CLASSIC YEARS IN DIGITAL STEREO (see under Fields, Gracie).

CLASSIC YEARS IN DIGITAL STEREO (see under Waller, Fats).

SACRED SONGS (Classic years in digital stereo) (Various artists).
Tracks: / Sacred hour: *Dawson, Peter* / Bless this house: *McCormack, John* / Nun's chorus: *Frind, Annie/* Lord's prayer, The: *Thomas, John Charles* / Lost chord, The: *Butt, Dame Clara* / Star of Bethlehem: *Crooks*, Richard / Rosary, The: *Novis, Donald* / Ave Maria: *Fields, Gracie* / All through the night: *Crooks, Richard/* In a monastery garden: *Dawson, Peter* / Hear my prayer: *Lough, Master Ernest* / O for the wings of a dove: *Robeson,* Paul / Still night holy night: *Robeson, Paul* / Jesus Christ is risen today: *Crooks, Richard* / Abide with me: *Thomas, John Charles* / Ave Maria: *Schumann, Elisabeth.*
LP: . . . . **REB 689**
MC: . . . . **ZCF 689**

Classical...

3 HOURS OF CLASSICAL FAVOURITES (Various artists).
MCSET: . . . . **TR 1527**
MCSET: . . . . **MFP 411 527 5**

CLASSICAL CLASSICS (Various artists).
2LP: . . . . **STAR 2007**
MC: . . . . **STAC 2007**

CLASSICAL FAVOURITES (Various artists).
MCSET: . . . . **DTO 10031**

CLASSICAL FAVOURITES WITH ANDRE PREVIN (Previn, Andre and the London Symphony Orchestra).
Tracks: / (Candide): Overture / Adagio for strings / Orb and sceptre-Coronation march (Walton) / Sorceror's apprentice, The (Dukas) / Hansel and Gretel overture / Adagio in G minor / Slavonic dance No. 9 in B Op.72 No. 1 (Dvorak) / Rumanian rhapsody, No. 1 (Enuscu).
MC: . . . . **TCEMX 2127**

CLASSICAL ROMANTIC CLASSICS (Various artists).
2LP: . . . . **STAR 2008**
MCSET: . . . . **STAC 2008**

PIANO MAGIC Over 80 rhapsodies of piano masterpieces (Various artists).
LPS: . . . . **RML 106**
MC: . . . . **RML 4C 106**

POP INVITATION TO THE CLASSICAL MUSIC (Various artists).
LP: . . . . **SX 7004**

POP INVITATION TO THE CLASSICAL MUSIC VOL.2 (Various artists).
Tracks: / Symphony No. 9 (Dvork): *Various artists* / Serenade: *Various artists* / Die fledermaus: *Various* artists / Suite no.2 II aire: *Various artists* / Der freischutz: *Various artists* / Hungarian rhapsody no. 2: *Various artists* / Il barbiere di siviglia overture: *Various artists* / Violin concerto Op 64: *Various* artists / Peer Gynt suite: *Various artists* / Traumerei: *Various artists* / Bolero: *Various artists/* Pictures at an exhibition: *Various artists.*
LP: . . . . **SX 7005**

SYMPHONY NO.8 (SCHUBERT) (Various artists).
MC: **4236554**

SYMPHONY NO.8 (SCHUBERT) Unfinished (Various artists).
MC: . . . . **MC 4236554 GH**

SYMPHONY NO.9 (SCHUBERT) (Various artists).
MC: **4236564**

SYMPHONY NO.9 (SCHUBERT) (Various artists).
MC: . . . . **MC 4236564 GH**

WAGNER HIGHLIGHTS V1 (Various artists).
LP: . . . . **DCA 595**
MC: . . . . **ZC DCA 595**

WAGNER HIGHLIGHTS V2 (Various artists).
LP: . . . . **DCA 611**
MC: . . . . **ZC DCA 611**

WINTERREISE (Various artists).
MC: . . . . **CSAR 41**

Classics

CLASSICS UP TO DATE (Various artists).
LP: . . . . **ADL 514**
MC: . . . . **ADK 514**

Classics By

CLASSICS BY CANDLELIGHT (Various artists).
2LP: . . . . **SMR 620**
MCSET: . . . . **SMC 620**

Classix Nouveaux

LA VERITE.
Tracks: / Foreward / Is it a dream / To believe / Because you're young / Six to eight / La verite / Never again / It's all over / 1999 / I will return / Finale.
LP: . . . . **LBG 30346**

NIGHT PEOPLE.
Tracks: / Guilty / Run away / No sympathy no violins / Inside outside / 623 degrees / Every home should have one / Tokyo / Or a movie / Soldier / Protector of the night.
LP: . . . . **LBG 30325**

SECRET.
Tracks: / All around the world / Manitou / Heart from the start / Fire inside, The / Forever and a day / Never never comes / Unloved / When they all have gone / No other way.
LP: **LBG1834241**

Claudius The God (bk)

CLAUDIUS THE GOD (Robert Graves) (Jacobi, Derek (nar)).
MCSET: . . . . **SAY 45**
MC: . . . . **K 180K 22**
MCSET: . . . . **ARGO 1163**

Clausen, Thomas

RAIN Vol. 3.
LP: . . . . **MTX 29202**

THOMAS CLAUSEN 3.
Tracks: / Julie / Rain / Home suite / Blueberry Hill / Green grass / Thojala / Love spring.
LP: . . . . **MTX 1003**

Clawson, Cynthia

HYMN SINGER.
LP: . . . . **DAY R 4162**
MC: . . . . **DAY C 4162**

Clay Idols

EVERY DAY STARTS LIKE THIS.
Tracks: / Nothing lasts forever / I told the world / It's raining voices / Blind go quietly, The / New history book, The.
LP: . . . . **MGLALP 032**

Clay, James

I LET A SONG GO OUT OF MY HEART.
LP: . . . . **ANLP 8761**
MC: . . . . **ANC 8761**

WIDE OPEN SPACES (see under Newman, David 'Fathead') (Clay, James & David 'Fathead' Newman).

Clay, Joe

DUCKTAIL.
Tracks: / Ducktail / Did you mean jelly bean (what you said cabbage head) / Crackerjack / Goodbye goodbye / Sixteen chicks / Slipping out and sneaking in / Doggone it / Get on the right track baby / You look good to me.
LP: . . . . **BFX 15224**

Clay, Judy

PRIVATE NUMBER (OLD GOLD) (See under Johnnie Taylor - Who's Making Love) (Clay, Judy & William Bell).

Clay, Otis

CALL ME.
LP: . . . . **WAY 269510-1**
MC: . . . . **WAY 269510-4**

LIVE IN JAPAN.
2LP: . . . . **STING 004/5**

LIVE IN TOKYO.
MC: . . . . **WAY 269503-4**

ONLY WAY IS UP, THE.
MC: . . . . **WAY 269504-4**

SOUL MAN LIVE IN JAPAN.
2LP: . . . . **R 7609**

TRYING TO LIVE MY LIFE WITHOUT YOU.
Tracks: / Trying to live my life without you / I die a little each day / Holding on to a dying love / I can't make it alone / You can't keep running from my love / Let me be the one / Brand new thing / Precious, precious / I don't know the meaning of pain / That's how it is / Too many hands / I love you, I need you / Home is where the heart is.
LP: . . . . **HIUKLP 406**

Clay, Sonny

SONNY CLAY 1922-1960.
Tracks: / Mama likes to do it / What a wonderful time / Lou / Yama yama man / Weary blues / Front room blues / I found a new baby / Chimes blues / Tack head blues / Gang o'blues / Punishing the piano / Sister Kate / If I could be with you / Honeysuckle rose / After you've gone / Ain't misbehavin'.
LP: . . . . **HQ 2007**

Clay, Tiggi

TIGGI CLAY.
Tracks: / Flashes / Top of the world / Winner gets the heart, The / Ali Baba / Billy was a good time / Spooks in the house / That's the way to go / Roses for Lydia / Who shot Zorro.
LP: . . . . **ZL 72150**

Clayborn, Rev. Edward

GUITAR EVANGELIST - 1926-1929, THE.
LP: . . . . **BD 614**

Clayderman, Richard

A COMME AMOUR (Clayderman, Richard & Nicholas De Angelis).
Tracks: / A comme amour / A l'ombre des glycines / Le fragile parfum des roses / Les petits animaux de la foret / Bianconi melody / Promenade dans les Bois / Les fleurs sauvages / Au bord de la riviere.
LP: **1700 025**
MC: **C700 025**

A PLEYEL.

Tracks: / Reve d'amour / A comme amour / Concerto pour une jeune fille nommee je t'aime / Bach gammon / Lettre a ma mere / West side story / Nostalgie / Quelques notes pour Anna / Amours interdits / Asturias / Amour mon amour / Minor swing / Souvenir d'enfance / Melodie des souvenirs / Marriage d'amour / Lady Di / Coup de coueur / Rhapsody in blue / Couleur tendresse / Blue rondo a la Turk / Give a little time to your love / Ballade pour Adeline / Root beer rag / Cavatina.
2LP: 1700 065
MC: C700 065

BALLADE POUR ADELINE (2).
Tracks: / Secret of my life / L'enfant et la mer / Black deal / Lyphard melody / La milliere / Old fashion / Romantique serenade / Histoire d'un reve / Nostalgy / Tendresses / Moon river / La mer / Melodie des souvenirs / Barcarolle / A comme amour / Les fleurs sauvages / Secret of my life / Lys river / Ballade pour Adeline.
LP: 1700 016
MC: C700 016

BALLADE POUR ADELINE (IMPORT).
Tracks: / Secret of my love / L'enfant et la mer / Lys river / Black deal / Lyphard melody / La milliere / Secret of my love / Romantique serenade / Old fashion.
LP: BRLP 32
MC: BRMC 32

BALLADE POUR ADELINE (LIMITED EDITION).
LP: CNR 447 030
MC: CAS 885 074

BALLADE POUR ADELINE (THE LOVE SONG).
Tracks: / In the purple shadows / Reflections in the river Lys / Lyphard melody / Walk in the woods, A / Les fleurs sauvages / Romantique serenade / Waters edge, The / Bianconi melody / Fragile rose, The / Love song, The.
LP: SNTF 847
MC: ZCSN 847

CHRISTMAS (RICHARD CLAYDERMAN).
Tracks: / White Christmas / Handel's largo / Jesu, joy of man's desiring / On Christmas night the lights are burning / Silver bells / Christmas concerto / He was born the holy child / Moonlight sonata / Leise rieselt der schnee / Romance / Candles twinkle, The / On the Christmas tree.
LP: SKL 5337
MC: KSKC 5337

CLASSIC TOUCH.
Tracks: / Dream of Olwen / Variation of a theme of Paganini / Pathetique (Beethoven) / Liebestraum (Liszt) / Warsaw concerto / Piano concerto in A minor (Grieg) / Cornish rhapsody / Piano concerto No. 2 (Rachmaninov) / Rhapsody in blue / Clair de lune (Debussy) / Concerto No.1 in B flat minor Op. 23 / Piano concerto No.21 in C major.
LP: SKL 5343
MC: KSKC 5343

COEUR FRAGILE.
Tracks: / Quand les enfants s'aiment / Les nuages / Solitude / L'Italienne / Vivre sans toi / L'amour-tendresse / Tes yeux dans mes yeux / Une si jolie petite valse / Souviens toi de moi / Comme un rayon de lune / Dis dame / L'Asiatique / Coeur fragile.
LP: 822 517-1
MC: 822 517-4

DREAMING.
LP: 6.23872

DREAMING 2.
LP: 6.24500
MC: CU4 24500

DREAMING 3 (See under Traumereien 3).

ELEANA.
Tracks: / Eleana / La sorellina / Blue concerto / Boulevard des Solitudes / Colin Maillard / Les poissons lune / Les Colombes du Tenere / Dernier printemps / Revivre sa vie / Roses pastel / Eleana / L'heure des adieux.
LP: 174 060 1
MC: 174 060 4

FRANCE - MON AMOUR.
LP: 17406-1
MC: 17406-4

FROM THE HEART.
Tracks: / Clouds / Tender love / Your eyes in my eyes / Remember me / Moonlighting / Italian girl / Loneliness / Living without you / Such a beautiful waltz / Broken heart / First love / Lady said, The / Girl from Asia, The.
LP: CN 2093
MC: CN4 2093

HOLLYWOOD AND BROADWAY.
Tracks: / Night and day / Bewitched / Embraceable you / Long ago and far away / Way you look tonight / Smoke gets in your eyes / People / All the things you are / I've grown accustomed to her face / On the street where you live / If I loved you / You'll never walk alone.
LP: SKL 5344
MC: KSKL 5344

ICH LIEBE DICH.
Tracks: / Rondo / Liebeslied / Vanessa / Die hoffnung / Zetlos / Einsames herz / Concerto / Liebeslied / Der ozean / Die blaue stunde / Wiegenlied / Rondo (piano solo).
LP: 6 24633
MC: 4 24633

LES SONATES (Clayderman, Richard & Nicholas De Angelis).
Tracks: / Diva / Mon pere / Les jours heureux / Pastorale / Les premiers pas / La fete / Angelica devina / L'amour heureux / La petite etoile / La mort d'un oiseau / L'offrandee / Les adieux.
LP: 826 088-1
MC: 826 088-4
LP: ADAH 434

LETTRE A MA MERE.
Tracks: / Souvenir d'enfance / Nostalgia / Histoire d'un reve / Melodie des souvenirs / Tendresses / Les elans de coeur / Marriage d'amour / Premiers chagrins / Souvenir d'enfance (instrumental) / Nostalgia (instrumental) / Lettre a ma mere.
LP: 7 00040
MC: C700 040

LITTLE NIGHT MUSIC, A (12 Classic Love Songs).
Tracks: / I just called to say I love you / I'm not in love / Sailing / For all we know / We've only just begun without you / Nights in white satin / Careless whisper / Power of love, The / Whiter shade of pale, A / Nothing's gonna change my love for you / Just the way you are / Princess of the night.
LP: 828 125-1
MC: 828 125-4

MARIAGE D'AMOUR.
Tracks: / La vraie musique de l'amour / My way / Lara's theme / Strangers in the night / Ave Maria / Aline / Dolannes melodie / Plaisir d'amour / Bridge over troubled water / Barcarolle / Voyage a Venise / When a man loves a woman / Medley (West Side story) / Rondon pour un tout petit enfant / Concerto pour une jeune fille nommee je t'aime / Nommee je t'aime / Love is a many splendoured thing / Marriage d'amour / Serenade / Les chagrins oublies / Couleur tendresse / Les armes de joie / Les premiers sourires de vanessa / Ne dis rien je t'aime / Romance / Les feuilles mortes.
2LP: 814 918-1
MC: 814 918-4

MARIAGE D'AMOUR.
Tracks: / La vraie musique de l'amour / My way / Lara's theme / Strangers in the night / Ave maria / Aline / Dolannes melodie / Plasir d'amour / Bridge over troubled water / Barcarolle / Voyage a venise / When a man loves a woman / West side story medley / Rondon pour un tout petit enfant / Concerto pour une jeune fille nommee je t'aime / Love is a many splendoured thing / Mariage d'amour / Serenade / Les chagrins oublies / Couleur tendresse / Les armes de joie / Les premiers sourires de vanessa / Ne dis rien je t'aime / Romance / Les feuilles mortes.
2LP: IMS 8149

MELODY CONCERTO.
Tracks: / Rhapsody in blue / Bye bye Tristesse / Bee flies at midnight, The / Bach gammon / Sentimental melody / Rhapsody in blue (long version) / Give a little time to your love.
LP: 7 00034
MC: C700 034

MUSIC OF LOVE, THE.
Tracks: / Till / How deep is your love / Begin the beguine / Hello / Only you / Way we were, The / Thorn birds / Memory / Strangers in paradise / And I love you so / As time goes by / Le vrai musique d'amour / Chariots of fire / Shadow of your smile / Dolannes melodie / Blue eyes / Yesterday / Flashdance... what a feeling.
LP: SKL 5340
MC: KSKC 5340

MUSIC OF RICHARD CLAYDERMAN, THE.
Tracks: / Feelings / Roses de sable / Cavatina / Reveries / L'amour exile / Greensleeves / Fiancee imaginaire / Le cygne / Maria / Tonight / America / Lady Di / Couleur tendresse / Valse des adieux / Serenade / Les derniers jours D'Anastasia Kensky / Les feuilles mortes / Blue rondo a la Turk / Root beer rag.
LP: SKL 5333
MC: KSKC 5333

MUSIQUES DE L'AMOUR.
Tracks: / Man and a woman, A / My way / Lara's theme / Parlez-moi d'amour / When a man loves a woman / Strangers in the night / Voyage a Venise / Ave Maria / Aline / La vraie musique de l'amour / Feelings / Tristesse / Un homme et une femme / Love me tender / Plaisir d'amour / Michelle / Jardin Street.
LP: 1700 045
MC: C700 045
LP: SKL 5330
MC: KSKC 5330

MY CLASSIC COLLECTION.
Tracks: / Four seasons: spring / Swan, The / Italian symphony no.1 - A sharp/ opus 90 / Aria / Waltz in A flat / Cavalleria rusticana / Barcarolle / Nocturne - D flat major/ opus 27 / Forever green / Hill Street blues / Mahogany, Theme from / Sleepy shores / Evergreen / Tara's theme / Over the rainbow / Medley of the Four Seasons.
MC: 828 228 4
LP: 828 228 1

PLAYS THE LOVE SONGS OF ANDREW LLOYD WEBBER.
Tracks: / Phantom of the opera / Music of the night / Love changes everything / High flying adored / Seeing is believing / All I ask of you / Don't cry for me Argentina / Another suitcase in another hall / Tell me on a Sunday / I don't know how to love him / Memory / Take that look off your face.
MC: 828 175 4
LP: 828 175 1

PLAYS THE ROMANTIC MELODIES OF ROBERT STOLZ.
Tracks: / Salome / Frag Nicht, warum ich gehe / Ungekubt sollst du nicht schlafen gehn / Wird bei nacht erst schon / Behalt mich lieb cheri / Tattoo for lovers / Komm in den park von Sanssouci / Walzertraume.
LP: 1700 080
MC: C1700 080

PROFILE: RICHARD CLAYDERMAN.
2LP: DO6 28506
MCSET: CR4 28506

PROFILE: RICHARD CLAYDERMAN VOL.2.
LP: 6.24382
MC: CL4 24382

PROFILE: RICHARD CLAYDERMAN VOL.1.
LP: 6.24381
MC: CL4 24381

REVERIES.
Tracks: / Dolannes melodie / Yesterday / Liebestraum / Don't cry for me Argentina / La vie en rose / Hymne a la joie / Pour elise / Exodus / Ballade pour Adeline / Romeo and Juliet / Elizabethan serenade / Bridge over troubled water / Love story / Moon river / Sonate au Clair du Lune (Debussy) / La mer / Barcarolle.
LP: 1700 036
MC: C700 036
MC: KSKC 5332

REVERIES/LETTRE A MA MERE/LES MUSIQUES DE L'AMOUR.
LPS: 1700 603

RICHARD CLAYDERMAN.
Tracks: / L for love (A comme armour) / La mer / My way / Lyphard melody / Tristesse / Fur Elise / Ballade pour Adeleine / Rhapsody in blue / Bach gammon / Sentimental melody / Liebestraum / Moonlight sonata / Romeo and Juliet / Murmers / I have a dream / Woman in love / Thorn birds / Feelings / Up where we belong / Bright eyes / Ebony and ivory / Bridge over troubled water / Chariots of fire / Memory / Only you / How deep is your love / Don't cry for me Argentina.
MC: ADAHC 434
LP: 1700 081
MC: C700 081
LP: SKL 5329
MC: KSKC 5329

RICHARD CLAYDERMAN COLLECTION.
LPS: CLBXL 1
MCSET: CLBXLC 1

RICHARD CLAYDERMAN (DECCA).
Tracks: / Ballad for Adeline / Secret of my love / L'enfant et la mer / Lys river / Black deal / Lyphard melodie / La milliere / Romantique serenade / Old fashioned.
LP: SKLR 5310

RICHARD CLAYDERMAN IN CONCERT.
Tracks: / Rhapsody in blue / Vanessa / Love me tender / Moon river / Love story / La vie en rose / Rondo / Don't cry for me Argentina / Tristesse / Help / La mer / Yesterday / Brief an meine / Mutter.
2LP: DP6 28577
MCSET: CT4 28577

ROMANTIC.
Tracks: / Broken hearts / Heartbeat / Love in vain / Because / Dancing alone / Moonlit shores / Listen oh my love / Longing / Piano solo / Lonely sea, The.
LP: 830 272-1
MC: 830 272-4
LP: CN 2090
MC: CN4 2090

RONDO POUR UN TOUT PETIT ENFANT.
Tracks: / L'heure bleue / Berceuse / Murmures / Les Premiers sourires de Vanessa / L'espoire / La fuite du temp / Triste coeur / Concerto pour une Jeune fille nommee / Je t'aime / Les chagrins oublies / L'ocean / Rondo pour un tout petit enfant (piano solo).
LP: SKL 5331
MC: KSKC 5331
LP: 1700 049
MC: C700 049

SONGS OF LOVE.
Tracks: / Bretts, Theme from / Howards Way / Eastenders / Nikita / Do you know where you're going to / Lady in red / Take my breath away / You are my world / We are the world / I know him so well / Eleana / Colin Maillard / Eroica / La sorellina / All by myself / I dreamed a dream / All I ask of you.
LP: SKL 5345
MC: KSKC 5345

SOUVENIRS.
Tracks: / Lettre a ma mere / Don't cry for me Argentina / Bridge over troubled water / Voyage a venise / Lettre a Elise / Souvenir d'enfance / Feelings / Ballade pour adeline / Dolannes melodie / When a man loves a woman / Hymne a la joie / Love me tender / Man and a woman, A / Barcarole.
LP: SNTF 877
MC: ZCSN 877

SOUVENIRS.
Tracks: / Love at first sight / Letter to my mother / Ocean, The / Wedding of love / Sagittarius / Diva / So sad / Secret garden / Journey to Venice / Dream story, A / Pastoral / Rondo for a little child / Doves from the Tenere / Regrets / Childhood memories / Time passing.
MC: PWKMCS 4030P

SWEET MEMORIES.
LP: BRLP 31
MC: BRMC 31

TRAUMEREIEN 3.
Tracks: / Liebeslied / Zarte rose / Rondo / Die hoffnung / Vanessa / Zeitlos / Einsames herz / Schattenspiele / Die blaue stunde / Concerto / Am ufer des flusses / Hochzeitsglocken / Erste tranen / Der ozean / Wiegenlied / Bilder aus der kindheit / Sommertraum.
LP: 6 24900
MC: 4 24900

WITH LOVE.
2LP: BRLP 31/32
MCSET: BRMC 31/32

Clayson, Alan

WHAT A DIFFERENCE A DECADE MADE (Clayson, Alan & The Argonauts).
Tracks: / Eleanor on bondage / Only for a moment / Sol nova / Edwy the fair / Landwaster / Crusader / Pagan Mercia / Do the scot bop / On the waterfront / Lost in the wilderness / Days in old Rotterdam / Searchlight / Rue Morgue / Steer straight.
LP: BUTT 005

Clayton, Buck

1966: BUCK CLAYTON & HUMPHREY LYTTELTON (Clayton, Buck & Humphrey Lyttleton).
LP: HQ 3002

A LA BUCK.
LP: 500106

ALL THE CATS JOIN IN.
LP: FS 272

ART FORD'S JAZZ PARTY (July 1958).
Tracks: / Foolin' myself / Perdido / It don't mean a thing / I surrender dear / I found a new baby / Easy to remember.
LP: AFJP 1

BUCK CLAYTON JAM SESSION, A.
LP: 4633361
MC: 4633364

BUCK CLAYTON WITH HUMPHREY LYTTLETON VOL.2 (Clayton, Buck & Humphrey Lyttleton).
LP: HQ 3005

CAT MEETS CHICK (Clayton, Buck/Ada Moore/Jimmy Rushing).
LP: FS 269

FEEL SO FINE (Clayton, Buck & Joe Turner).
Tracks: / Honeysuckle rose / I'm in a world of trouble / I can't get started / Feel so fine / Perdido / I want a little girl / Too late too late.
LP: . . . . BLP 30145

HUCKLE-BUCK AND ROBIN'S NEST 1953, THE.
LP: . . . . 20 AP 1427

JAM SESSION FEATURING WOODY HERMAN.
LP: . . . . FS 268

JAZZ FESTIVAL JAZZ (Clayton, Buck & Duke Ellington).
Tracks: / Perdido / Finger-bustin' / Squeeze me / Tea for two / Diminuendo and crescendo in blue (Featuring tenor saxist Paul Gonsalves' famous 37 choruses) / Blues jam / Mood indigo.
LP: . . . . QU 044

LIVE IN PARIS (Clayton, Buck & Jimmy Witherspoon).
Tracks: / Swingin' at the Camarillo / Polka dots and moonbeams / Outerdrive / Robin's nest / Moonglow / Swingin' the blues / I'll always be in love with you / Gee baby ain't I good to you / See see rider / I make a lot of money / Blowin' the blues away / T'aint nobody's business if I do / Roll 'em Pete / Everything you do is wrong.
2LP: . . . . VJD 527

OLYMPIA CONCERT 1961.
LP: 500054

RARITIES VOL 1.
LP: . . . . ST 1024

SWINGIN' DREAM, A (Clayton, Buck & Swing Band).
LP: . . . . ST 281

TRUMPET SUMMIT (Clayton, Buck & Roy Eldridge).
LP: . . . . PUMPKIN 101

VERY SPECIAL BUCK CLAYTON, THE.
LP: . . . . JJ 608

Clayton, Jay

AS TEARS GO BY (Clayton, Jay & John Lindberg).
LP: . . . . ITM 1429

STRING TRIO OF NEW YORK & JAY CLAYTON (See under String Trio of New York) (Clayton, Jay & String Trio of New York).

Clayton, John

SUPER BASS (Clayton, John & Ray Brown).
MC: 740184

TRIBUTE TO JOHN CLAYTON BIG BAND (Clayton, John Big Band).
LP: . . . . JC 11005

Clayton, John & Jeff

GROOVE SHOP (Featuring Hamilton Jazz Orchestra).
MC: 740214

Clayton, Kid

EXIT STARES, THE (Clayton's, Kid Happy Pals).
LP: . . . . JCE 22

FIRST SESSION 1952, THE.
LP: . . . . FJ 2859

Clayton, Lee

ANOTHER NIGHT.
LP: . . . . PRL 70081
MC: . . . . PRLC 70084

BORDER AFFAIR.
Tracks: / Silver stallion / If you can touch her at all / Back home in Tennessee / Border affair / Old number nine / Like a diamond / My woman my love / Tequila is addictive / My true love / Rainbow in the sky.
LP: . . . . EST 11751

DREAM GOES ON.
Tracks: / What's a mother gonna do / Industry / Won't you give me one more chance / Draggin' them chains / Where is the justice / Whatcha gonna do / Oh how lucky I am / Dream goes on, The.
LP: . . . . EST 12139

NAKED CHILD.
Tracks: / Saturday night special / I ride alone / 10,000 years / Sexual moon / Wind and rain / I love you / Jaded virgin / Little cocaine / If I can do it.
LP: . . . . EST 11942

Clayton, Michael

MICHAEL CLAYTON.
Tracks: / Friends and lovers / All of my heart / Driftin' on a dream / Call my name / You're the one for me / Serious / Friends and lover theme (instrumental).
LP: . . . . GEM 4027
MC: . . . . GEM 4027MC

Clayton, Paul

BLUEGRASS SESSION, 1952, A (see Clifton, Bill) (Clayton, Paul & Bill Clifton).

DAYS OF MOBY DICK.
LP: . . . . TLP 1005

Clayton, Vikki

HONOR TOKENED.
MC: . . . . VIKKI 1

MIDSUMMER CUSHION.
MC: . . . . CASSGP 008

Clayton, Willie

FOREVER.
LP: . . . . TRPL 127

TELL ME.
LP: 889 659 1

Claytown Troupe

THROUGH THE VEIL.
MC: . . . . ICT 9933
LP: . . . . ILPS 9933

Clea & McLeod

BEYOND OUR MEANS.
LP: . . . . UTIL 009

Clean

CLEAN COMPILATION.
Tracks: / Billy two / At the bottom / Tally ho / Anything could happen / Point that thing somewhere else / Flowers / Fish / Beatnik / Getting older / Slug song / Oddity / Whatever I do (wherever I go).
LP: . . . . FNUK 3

ODDITIES.
MC: . . . . ODD 001

VEHICLE.
LP: . . . . ROUGH 143
MC: . . . . ROUGHC 143

Clean Tape

CLEAN TAPE (Various artists).
Tracks: / My fathers house: *Various artists* / Perfect love: *Various artists* / Rise up: *Various artists*/ Hold on: *Various artists* / Royal rendezvous: *Various artists* / Susanne: *Various artists* / Your love: *Various artists* / Gap, The: *Various artists* / Listen: *Various artists* / How do I get to you?: *Various artists.*
LP: . . . . CLS 8014

Cleaners From Venus

GOING TO ENGLAND.
Tracks: / Julie profumo / Living with Victoria Grey / Clara Bow / Follow the plough / Armistice day / What's going on (in your heart) / Girl on a string / Mercury girl / Illya Kuryakin looked at me / You must be out of my mind.
LP: . . . . CLEANLP 1

TOWN AND COUNTRY.
LP: . . . . DELTLP 1
MC: . . . . DELTMC 1

UNDER WARTIME CONDITIONS.
MC: . . . . TAO 008

Cleanse The Bacteria

CLEANSE THE BACTERIA (Various artists).
LP: 0012-02

Clear Light

BLACK ROSES.
Tracks: / Black roses / Sand / Child's smile, A / Street singer / Ballad of Freddie and Larry, The / With all in mind / She's ready to be free / Mr. Blue / Think again / They who have nothing / How many days have passed? / Night sound loud.
LP: . . . . ED 245

Clearey, Michael Fr.

IN CONCERT.
MC: . . . . MB LP 1028

Clearwater, Eddy

CHIEF, THE.
LP: . . . . R 2615

FLIM DOOZIE.
LP: . . . . R 2622

TWO TIMES NINE.
LP: . . . . CRB 1025

Cleary, Jon (aut)

HIGH COMMISSIONER, THE (see under High Commissioner (bk)) (Wheeler, Peter (nar)).

Cleary, Paul

IMPOSSIBLE (Cleary, Paul & The Partisans).
LP: . . . . HWLP 8507

Cleaver, Emrys

AMBELL I GAN (Folksongs in Welsh).
Tracks: / Ambell i gan / Ar ben waun Tredegar / Ar lan y mor / Bachgen ifanc ydwyf / Y bachgen main / Bwmba / Y ceffyl du / Y deryn du / Dywetse'r hen ddyn wrth ei ferch / Y farn a fydd / Ffarweliwch, rhy 'n madal a'm gwlad / Seirhpmuh nhojdranoel / Fy morwyn ffein I / Y gwgw / Gwenith Gwyn / Hen ladi fowr benfelen / Yr hen wr mwym / Lisa lan / Lodes lan / Mae 'nghariad i'n fenws / Y march glas / Y feri lwyd / Rown i'n rhodio mynwent eglwys / Tafran y rhos / Tren o bala i ffestiniog.
MC: 60-005

Cleaver, Robinson

DAY AT BUCKINGHAM, A (see under Brown, Jackie) (Cleaver, Robinson/ Jackie Brown/William Davies).

ROBINSON CLEAVER IN CONCERT.
Tracks: / Autumn concerto / MacNamara's band / Spanish eyes / Lady of Spain / Spartacus, Theme from / Patricia / Wheels / Slippery samba / Tico tico / Cumbanchero / Radetzky march / Finlandia / Dambusters march.
MC: . . . . AC 198
LP: . . . . AML 309

THREE SCORE YEARS AND TWENTY.
Tracks: / Paint your wagon selection / House of the rising sun / Jack in the box / Rhapsody in blue / Fiddler on the roof / Good, the bad and the ugly, The / Whiter shade of pale, A / Rustle of spring / Lover / Lady is a tramp, The.
MC: . . . . AC 172

Clegg, Johnny

CRUEL, CRAZY BEAUTIFUL WORLD (Clegg, Johnny & Savuka).
Tracks: / One man one vote / Cruel, crazy beautiful world / Jericho / Dela / Moliva / It's an illusion / Bombs away / Woman be my country / Rolling ocean / Warsaw 1941 / Vezandlebe (CD only.).
MC: 793 446 4
LP: . . . . EMC 3569

THIRD WORLD CHILD (Clegg, Johnny & Savuka).
Tracks: / Are you ready / Asimbonanga / Giyana / Scatterlings of Africa / Great heart / Missing / Ring on her finger / Third world child / Berlin wall / Don't walk away.
LP: . . . . EMC 3526
MC: . . . . TCEMC 3526

WAITING (Clegg, Johnny & Savuka).
Tracks: / Human rainbow / Siyayilanda / Joey don't do it / Dance across the centuries / Talk to the people / African shadow man / Waiting, The / Take my heart away / I call your name / Too early for the sky.
LP: . . . . EMC 3547
MC: . . . . TCEMC 3547

Clement, Jack

ALL I WANT TO DO IN LIFE.
Tracks: / Gone girl / Roving gambler / We must believe in magic / Good hearted woman / When I dream / All I want to do in life / It'll be her / There she goes / Queen Bee / You ask me to.
LP: . . . . K 52126

Clements, Boots

GHOST RIDERS IN THE SKY.
LPS: . . . . WLP 1004

WALKIN' PROUD.
Tracks: / You can have her / Sukiyaki (my first lonely night) / Other side of love, The / So long lady / Never gonna fall in love again / I can't find me / Walkin' proud / (Ghost) riders in the sky / Night has a thousand eyes, The / I keep thinking about you every day.
LP: . . . . WLP 1005

Clements, Roberta

CHANNEL OF PEACE.
Tracks: / Help me / Adopted / I'm sorry Lord / Jesus, the shepherd / Prayer of St. Francis / Prodigal son / My Jesus I love thee / In this old troubled world / Take up your cross / He filled a longing / Why me Lord? / When you hear the saviour call.
LP: . . . . PC 333

Clements, Rod

LEATHER LAUNDERETTE (see under Jansch, Bert) (Clements, Rod/Bert Jansch).

Clements, Vassar

BLUEGRASS SESSION, THE.
Tracks: / Reno shuffle / Vasillee II / It's mighty dark / Nine pound hammer / Stompin' grazz / Six more miles / Scuffin' / White house blues / Swingin' low / Rocky top / Silly Millie.
LP: . . . . FF 038
LP: . . . . SNTF 748

CLEMENTS, HARTFORD & HOLLAND (Clements, Vassar/John Hartford/Dave Holland).
LP: . . . . ROUNDER 0207
MC: . . . . ROUNDER 0207C

CROSSING THE CATSKILLS.
LP: . . . . ROUNDER 0016
MC: . . . . ROUNDER 0016C

HILLBILLY JAZZ RIDES AGAIN.
Tracks: / Hillbilly jazz / Don't hop don't skip / Airmail special / Say goodbye to the blues / Swing street / Woodsheddin' / Be a little discreet / Your mind is on vacation / Caravan / How can I go on without you / Triple stop boogie / Take a break.
LP: . . . . FF 385
MC: . . . . FF 385C

NASHVILLE JAM (Clements, Vassar/ Doug Jernigan/J. McReynolds).
LP: . . . . FF 073

TOGETHER AT LAST (See under Grapelli, Stephane) (Clements, Vassar/ Stephane Grapelli).

VASSAR (Clements, Vassar Band).
LP: . . . . FF 232

Clemmens, Ginni

LOPIN' ALONG THRU THE COSMOS.
LP: . . . . FF 320

Clemmons, Angela

ANGELA CLEMMONS.
MC: 4508894

THIS IS LOVE.
Tracks: / B.Y.O.B. (Bring your own baby) / Love life / Miracles / This is love / Just have a heart / One night baby / Rock and a hard place, A / I could love you better / Nothing can stop my love.
LP: 450889 1
MC: 450889 4

Clemons, Clarence

HERO (Clemons, Clarence & The Red Bank Rockers).
Tracks: / You're a friend of mine / Temptation / It's alright with me girl / Liberation fire / Sun ain't gonna shine anymore, The / I wanna be your hero / Cross the line / Kissin' on U / Christina.
LP: . . . . CBS 26743
MC: 40 26743

RESCUE (Clemons, Clarence & The Red Bank Rockers).
Tracks: / Jump start my heart / Rock 'n' roll DJ / Money to the rescue / Woman's got the power, A / Man in love, A / Heartache 99 / Savin' up / Resurrection shuffle.
LP: . . . . CBS 25699
MC: 40 25699

Clennell, Claire

ENCHANTED ISLE - MELODIES FOR A MILLENIUM, THE.
Tracks: / Enchanted Isle, The / Roish my row flaunys / Kiree-Kate / Ushag vag ruy / Deemster's daughter, The / Sheep under the snow, The / Silver and gold / Ushtey millish 'sy gharee / Song for the children / O inneen zion / Heritage / Baase Illiam Dhone / Hush little darling / Man from Ballasella, The / Ellan Vannin / Dalby song, The.
LP: . . . . GES 1202

Cleobury, Stephen

MUSIC IN ROYAL WESTMINSTER.
LP: . . . . CLP 251

WEDDING FAVOURITES.
LP: . . . . SPA 554
MC: . . . . KCSP 554
MC: 4216384

Clerc, Julien

DISQUE D'OR VOLUME 2.
Tracks: / Travailler c'est trop dur.
LP: 2C 070 72014

JULIEN CLERC.
LP: . . . . V 2327
MC: . . . . TCV 2327

THERE IS NO DISTANCE.
Tracks: / No bad thing / Wine of words / Hard as love / Lovers and dancers / There is no distance / Ring around the moon / Helene / Robots / Project eros / Singian san.
LP: . . . . DIX 62
MC: . . . . CDIX 62

Clermont, Rene

BONJOUR CHRISTIANE.
LP: 6435 128
MC: 7106 128

Cleveland, Barry

MYTHOS.
LP: . . . . SYN 101
MC: . . . . SYNC 101

Cleveland Crochet

CLEVELAND CROCHET AND ALL THE SUGAR BEES.
LP: . . . . GRLP 7749

Cleveland, James

PRESENTS GOSPEL MUSIC WORKSHOP.
LP: . . . . DBL 7096
MC: . . . . DBLC 7096

REUNION (Cleveland, James & Albertina Walker).
LP: . . . . SL 14502

SING WITH THE WORLD'S GREATEST GOSPEL STARS VOL2.
LP: . . . . SL 14732

SING'S WITH THE WORLD'S GREATEST CHOIRS.
LP: . . . . SC 7059

Cleveland, Jimmy

TROMBONE SCENE (Cleveland, Jimmy/Green, Urbie/Rehack, Frank).
LP: . . . . FS 30

Cleveland Orchestra

PICTURES AT AN EXHIBITION (See under Mussorgsky for details).

Cleveland, Sara

SARA CLEVELAND.
LP: . . . . PH 1020

Clew, Simon

LIVING ON A PROMISE (See under Greenaway, Gavin) (Greenaway, Gavin and Simon Clew).

Cliburn, Van

ROMANTIC COLLECTION, A.
MC: . . . . GK 60414

Click Click

PARTY HATE.
LP: . . . . ROR 5

RORSCHACH TESTING.
Tracks: / Awake and watching / Perfect stranger / 15 minutes / Playground / Head fuck / Whirlpool / Vacuum shop, The / What a word.
LP: . . . . BIAS 90

Cliff, Dave

RIGHT TIME, THE (Cliff, Dave Quintet).
Tracks: / Right time, The / For minors only / Nicole / Birds blues / Signal / Four on six / Valse hot / Peace / So do it.
LP: . . . . MM 074

Cliff, Jimmy

ANOTHER CYCLE.
Tracks: / Take a look at yourself / Please tell me why / Rap, The / Opportunity only knocks once / My friend's wife / Another cycle / Sitting in limbo / Oh, how I miss you / Inside out, upside down / Our thing is over.
LP: . . . . ILPS 9159

BEST OF JIMMY CLIFF.
Tracks: / Hard road to travel / Sooner or later / Sufferin' in the land / Keep your eye on the sparrow / Struggling man / Wild world / Vietnam / Another cycle / Wonderful world, beautiful people / Harder they come, The / Let your yeah be yeah / Synthetic world / I'm no immigrant / Give and take / Many rivers to cross / Going back west / Sitting in limbo / Come into my life / You can get it if you really want / Goodbye yesterday.
LP: . . . . ICD 6

BEST OF JIMMY CLIFF IN CONCERT.
Tracks: / You can get it if you really want / Vietnam / Fountain of life / Many rivers to cross / Wonderful world / Beautiful people / Under the sun, moon and stars / Wild world / Sitting in limbo / Struggling man / Harder they come, The.
LP: . . . . K 54086

CLIFF HANGER.
Tracks: / Hitting with music / American sweet / Arrival / Brown eyes / Reggae Street / Hot shot / Sunrise / Dead and awake / Now and forever / Nuclear war.
LP: . . . . CBS 26528
MC: 40 26528

COLLECTION: JIMMY CLIFF.
LP: . . . . IC 028 07536

FOLLOW MY MIND.
Tracks: / Look at the mountains / News, The / I'm gonna live, I'm gonna love / Going mad / Dear mother / Who feels it, knows it / Remake the world / No woman no cry / Wahjahka man / Hypocrite / If I follow my mind / You're the only one.
LP: . . . . K 54061

FUNDAMENTAL REGGAE.
Tracks: / Fundamental reggae / Under the sun, moon and stars / Rip off / On my life / Commercialization / You can't be wrong and get right / Oh Jamaica / No. 1 rip off man / Brother / House of exile / Long time no see / My love is as solid as rock / My people / Actions speak louder than words / Brave warrior.
LP: . . . . SEE 83

GIVE THANKX.
Tracks: / Bongo man / Stand up and fight back / She is a woman / You left me standing by the door / Footprints / Meeting in Afrika / Wanted man / Lonely street / Love I need / Universal love (beyond the boundaries).
LP: . . . . K 56558

GIVE THE PEOPLE WHAT THEY WANT.
Tracks: / Son of man / Give the people what they want / Experience / Shelter of your love / Majority rule / Let's turn the tables / Material world / World in trap / What are you doing with your life / My philosophy.
LP: . . . . K 99160

HANGING FIRE.
Tracks: / Love me love me / Hanging fire / Girls and cars / She was so right for me / It's time / Reggae down Babylon / Hold tight (eye for an eye) / Soar like an eagle.
LP: 4601391
MC: 4601394
LP: . . . . FC 40845

HARDER THEY COME (Film soundtrack) (See under Harder They Come).

I AM THE LIVING.
Tracks: / I am the living / All the strength we got / It's the beginning of the end / Gone clear / Love again / Morning train / Satan's kingdom / Another summer.
MC: . . . . K 4 99089
LP: . . . . K 99089

JIMMY CLIFF.
Tracks: / Many rivers to cross / Vietnam / My ancestors / Hard road to travel / Wonderful world, beautiful people / Sufferin' in the land / Hello sunshine / Use what I got / That's the way life goes / Come into my life.
LP: . . . . TRLS 16
MC: . . . . ZCTRLS 16

OH JAMAICA.
Tracks: / Born to win / On my life / My love is as solid as a rock / Fundamental reggae / Don't let it die / Music makers / I've been dead 400 years / Oh Jamaica / My people / I want to know / Actions speak louder than words / Under the sun, moon and stars / House of exile / Every tub.
LP: . . . . NUT 3

POWER AND THE GLORY, THE.
Tracks: / We all are one / Sunshine in the music / Reggae nights / Piece of the pie / American dream / Roots woman / Love solution / Power and the glory / Journey.
MC: 40 25761
LP: 25761

REGGAE GREATS.
Tracks: / Vietnam / Sitting in limbo / Struggling man / Let your yeah be yeah / Bongo man / Harder they come, The / Sufferin' in the land / Many rivers to cross / Hard road to travel / You can get it if you really want / Sooner or later.
LP: . . . . IRG 14
MC: . . . . IRGC 14
MC: . . . . RRCT 22

SAVE OUR PLANET EARTH.
LP: 106 551
MC: 106 554

SPECIAL.
Tracks: / Special / Love is all / Peace officer / Treat the youths right / Keep on dancing / Rub-a-dub partner / Roots radical / Love heights / Originator / Rock children / Where there is love.
LP: . . . . CBS 85878
MC: 40 85878

UNLIMITED.
Tracks: / Under the sun, moon and stars / Fundamental reggae / World of peace / Black Queen / Be true / Oh Jamaica / Commercialization / Price of peace, The / On my life / I see the light / Rip off / Poor slave / Born to win.
LP: . . . . EMA 757

UNLIMITED (REISSUE).
LP: . . . . TRJC 100
MC: . . . . ZCTRJ 100

Clifford, Billy

TRADITIONAL FLUTE SOLOS & BAND MUSIC....
Tracks: / Fermoy lassies / Honeymoon, The / Upperchurch polkas, The / Jigs / Polkas / Padraig O'Keefe's / Munster, The / Reel / No name / Polkas / Danny Green's reels / Hollyford jigs, The / Flowing tide, The / Bracken brae, The / Napoleon's grand march / Top of Maol, The / Hetty O'Hady / Milliner's daughter, The / Durang's / Bill the waiver's / Home brew, The / Druid's field, The / Willie Doherty's / Up on the waggon / Lilting banshee, The / Moycarkey, The / Byrne's / Charlie Mulvihill's / Muckross abbey.
LP: 12TS 312

Clifford, Bob

HOT ROCK (Clifford, Bob & The Hep Cats).
LP: . . . . BOB 501

Clifford, Buzz

BABY SITTIN' WITH BUZZ CLIFFORD.
LP: . . . . BOW 8420

Clifford, John

HUMOURS OF LISHEEN, THE (Music from Sliabh Luachra vol. 3) (Clifford, John & Julia).
Tracks: / Humours of Lisheen, The / Art O'Keefe's / Tap the barrel / Jenny tie the bonnet / Frisco, The / Biddy Crowley's ball / Bold trainor o, The / Blue riband, The / Up and away / Cailin an ti' Mhoir / Untitled track / Freddy Kimmel's / Home brew, The / Padraig O'Keefe's / Pol ha'penny / John Mahinney's no. 2 / Ducks and the oats, The / I looked east and I looked west / Worn torn petticoat, The / Taimse I'm Chodladh / Julia Clifford's / Bill the waiver's / Johnny Cope / John Clifford's / Behind the bush in the garden / Going for water.
LP: 12TS 311

Clifford, Linda

GREATEST HITS: LINDA CLIFFORD.
Tracks: / If my friends could see me now / Don't give it up / Runaway love / Red light / Shoot your best shot / From now on.
LP: . . . . CUR 2007
MC: . . . . CUR 2007MC

IF MY FRIENDS COULD SEE ME NOW (ALBUM).
Tracks: / If my friends could see me now / You are you are / Runaway love / Broadway gypsy lady / I feel like falling in love / Please darling, don't say goodbye / Gypsy lady.
LP: . . . . K 56498

I'M YOURS.
Tracks: / Shoot your best shot / I had a talk with my man / It don't hurt no more / Red light / I want to get away with you / If you let me / I'm yours.
MC: 3216 281
LP: 239 428 1

LET ME BE YOUR WOMAN.
Tracks: / Let me be your woman / Bridge over troubled water / Don't give it up / Hold me close / One of those songs / Don't let me have another bad dream / I can't let this good thing get away / Sweet melodies.
LP: . . . . RSD 5005

RIGHT COMBINATION (Clifford, Linda/ Curtis Mayfield).
Tracks: / Rock you to your socks / Right combination / I'm so proud / Ain't no love lost / It's lovin' time / Love's sweet sensation / Between you baby and me.
LP: 2394269

RIGHT COMBINATION (IMPORT) (Clifford, Linda/Curtis Mayfield).
MC: . . . . RSC 13084

Cliffords

STAR OF MUNSTER TRIO (Music from Sliabh Luachra, Vol 2).
Tracks: / Dublin porter / Mountain lark, The / Lark in the bog, The / Mountain road, The / Paddy Cronin's / Ballydesmond / Knocknabowl / Boil the breakfast early / Bunker Hill / Red-haired boy / Lucy's reel / Clare reel, The / Bill Black's / O'Donovan's / John Mahinney's no.1 / No name / Grandfather's thought / Madam, if you please / Napoleon's retreat / Connie the soldier / Humours of Glen / Palatine's daughter, The / Jim Mac's jig / Cherish the ladies / Harlequin, The / Old bush, The / Within a mile of Dublin.
LP: 12TS 310

Clifton, Bill

ARE YOU FROM DIXIE? (see Rector, Red) (Clifton, Bill & Red Rector).

BEATLE CRAZY.
Tracks: / Beatle crazy / Little girl dressed in blue (Original Decca recording) / Keep that wheel a turning (Original Decca recording.) / Jug of punch / Baby lie easy / Green to grey.
LPPD: . . . . BFP 15121

BLUE RIDGE MOUNTAIN BLUEGRASS (Clifton, Bill & The Dixie Mountain Boys).
Tracks: / Little whitewashed chimney / Mary dear / Pal of yesterday / Cedar grove / Livin' the right life now / Another broken heart / Girl I left in sunny Tennessee, The / Corey / Are you alone? / Lonely heart blues / You go to your church / Dixie Mountain express / Dixie darling / Blue Ridge Mountain blues.
LP: . . . . WRS 047

BLUEGRASS SESSION, 1952 (A) (Clifton, Bill & Paul Clayton).
Tracks: / John Henry / Watermelon on the vine / Roll on the ground (1) / Pleasant and delightful / Fox, The / John Hardy / East Virginia blues / Jealous lover / Beautiful Mabel Clare / Bury me beneath the willow / Poor boy / Roll on the ground (2).
LP: . . . . BF 15001

GETTING FOLK OUT OF THE COUNTRY (see West, Hedy) (Clifton, Bill/Hedy West).

GOING BACK TO DIXIE.
Tracks: / Going back to Dixie / Your mother still prays for you, Jack / Moonshiner / Just a smile / Lonely little cabin / Dream of the miner's child / Ground hog hunt / Engine 23 / Jim Hartfield's son / Saturday night / Lonesome for you / Lazy courtship / Across the shining river / Roll the cotton down / Take me back / Lonesome field / Little green valley / When I lay my burden down / At my window / Gonna lay down my old guitar / Where the willow gently sways / When I'm with you / My nights are lonely / I'm gonna blow out the lamp in the window / Louis Collins / I'll be satisfied / Old Reuben / My Cindy girl / Dixie ramble / Big Bill / Bringing Mary home / Mother, where is your daughter tonight? / Prisoner's dream / Sweet fern / Forsaken love / Sales tax to the woman.
2LP: . . . . BFD 15000

MOUNTAIN FOLK SONGS.
LP: . . . . SLP 111
MC: . . . . GT 5111

Clifton, Chris

MEMORIES OF A FRIEND (Clifton, Chris & His New Orleans All Stars).
LP: . . . . GHB 190

Climax Blues Band

BEST OF CLIMAX BLUES BAND.
LP: . . . . CL 25201

CLIMAX BLUES BAND PLAYS ON, THE.
Tracks: / Flight / Cubano chant / Mum's the word / So many roads / Crazy 'bout my baby / Hey baby everything / Little girl / Twenty past two / City ways.
LP: C5-556

CLIMAX, THE.
LP: C5-555

COULDN'T GET IT RIGHT.
Tracks: / Couldn't get it right / Berlin blues / Chasing change / Losin' the humbles / Shopping bag people / Sense of direction / Before you reach the grave / Sky high / Loosen up / Running out of time / Mr. Goodtime / I am constant / Mighty fire.
LP: C5-508
MC: C5K-508

DRASTIC STEPS.
LP: . . . . CLAYLP 26
MC: . . . . CLAYMC 26
LP: . . . . SONICLP 7
LP: C5 573

FLYING THE FLAG.
Tracks: / Gotta have more love / So good after midnight / Horizontalised / I love you / Hold on to your heart / Dance the night away / Money talking / Black Jack and me / Nothing but starlight / One for me and you.
LP: . . . . K 56871
MC: K4 56871

FM ALIVE.
Tracks: / All the time in the world / Flight / Seventh son, The / Let's work together / Standing by a river / So many roads, so many trains / You make me sick / Shake your love / Going to New York / I am constant / Mesopopmania / Country hat.
LP: . . . . SEE 279

GOLD PLATED.
Tracks: / Together and free / Mighty fire / Chasing change / Berlin blues / Couldn't get it right / Rollin' home / Sav'ry gravy / Extra.
LP: . . . . BTM 1009

LOOSEN UP (1974-76).
Tracks: / Couldn't get it right / Berlin blues / Chasing change / Losin' the humbles / Shopping bag people / Sense of direction / Before you reach the grave / Sky high / Loosen up / Running out of time / Mr. Goodtime / I am constant / Mighty fire.
LP: . . . . CM 128

LOT OF BOTTLE, A.
Tracks: / Country hat / Everyday / Reap what I've sowed / Brief case / Alright blues? / Seventh son / Please don't help me / Morning noon and night / Long lovin' man / Louisiana blues / Cut you loose.
LP: C5-548

LUCKY FOR SOME.
Tracks: / Victim / Cuttin' up rough / Shake it Lucy baby / Oceans apart / Breakdown / Darlin' / This time you're the singer / Last chance saloon / They'd never believe us.
LP: . . . . K 56962
MC: K4 56962

REAL TO REEL.
Tracks: / Summer rain / Money in your pocket / Children of the nightmare /

Long distance love / Lovin' wheel / Fallen in love (for the very last time) / Fat city / Crazy world.
LP: . . . . K 56642

RICH MAN.
LP: C5-553

SAMPLE AND HOLD.
Tracks: / Listen to the night / Church.
LP: . . . . V 2258

SHINE ON.
Tracks: / Making love / Mistress Moonshine / When talking is too much / Gospel singer, The / Watcha feel? / Teardrops / Like a movie / Champagne and rock 'n' roll.
LP: . . . . K 56461
MC: K4 56461

STAMP ALBUM.
Tracks: / Power, The / Mr. Goodtime / I am constant / Running out of time / Sky high / Rusty nail / Devil knows, The / Loosen up / Spirit returning / Cobra.
LP: . . . . BTM 1004

TIGHTLY KNIT.
LP: C5-557

Climax Male Voice

BORN IN SONG.
MC: . . . . SENC 1019

REASON WHY, THE.
MC: . . . . SENC 1020

Climie Fisher

COMING IN FOR THE KILL.
Tracks: / Facts of love / Fire on the ocean / It's not supposed to be that way / Hold on through the night / Buried treasure / Power of the dreamworld / Best part of living is loving you, The / Coming in for the kill / Don't mess around / You keep me coming back for more / Memories (If I could relive your love) (CD only.).
LP: . . . . EMC 3565
MC: . . . . TCEMC 3565

EVERYTHING.
Tracks: / Love changes everything / Rise to the occasion / I won't bleed for you / Room to move / Precious moments / Rise to the occasion (hip-hop mix) / This is me / Never let a chance go by / Bite the hand that feeds / Break the silence / Keeping the mystery alive.
LP: . . . . EMC 3538
MC: . . . . TCEMC 3538
LP: . . . . ATAK 144
MC: . . . . TCATAK 144

Cline, Alex

LAMP AND THE STAR, THE.
Tracks: / Blue robe in the distance, A / Eminence / Emerald light / Altar stone / Accepting the chalice.
LP: . . . . ECM 1372

Cline, Charlie

COUNTRY DOBRO.
LP: . . . . AD 2001

MORE DOBRO (Cline, Charlie with the Marakesh Express).
LP: . . . . AD 2008

Cline, Patsy

20 CLASSIC TRACKS.
Tracks: / If I could stay asleep / Heart you break may be your own, The / Try again / Three cigarettes in an ashtray / If I could see the world / Cry not for me / Yes I understand / Dear God / I'm blue again / Love me, love me honey do / Stop look and listen / Don't ever leave me / You'll know, The / Come on in (and make yourself at home) / Pick me up on your way down / Turn the cards slowly / I cried all the way to the altar / Honky tonk merry go round / I'm moving along / Gotta lot of rhythm in my soul.
LP: . . . . SMT 005
MC: . . . . SMTC 005

20 GOLDEN GREATS: PATSY CLINE.
LP: 20066
MC: 40066

20 GOLDEN HITS: PATSY CLINE.
LP: . . . . MA 41285
MC: . . . . MAMC 941285

20 GOLDEN PIECES: PATSY CLINE.
Tracks: / I don't wanta / Let the teardrops fall / I've loved and lost again / Fingertips / I can't forget / Just out of reach / Hungry for love / If I could only stay asleep / Today, tomorrow and forever / I love you honey / Never no more / Walking after midnight / Pick me up on your way down / Honky tonk merry go round / I cried all the way to the altar / Too many secrets / Three cigarettes in an ashtray / In care of the blues / Stop the world / I can see an angel.
LP: . . . . BDL 2003
MC: . . . . BDC 2003

20 GREATEST HITS: PATSY CLINE.
Tracks: / Stop the world / Walking after midnight / I can see an angel / Three cigarettes in an ashtray.
LP: . . . . FUN 9019
MC: . . . . FUNC 9019

ALWAYS.
Tracks: / Always / Love letters in the sand / Crazy arms / Bill Bailey won't you please come home / Have you ever been lonely / You made me love you / I can see an angel / That's my desire / Your cheatin' heart / That's how a heartache begins / I love you so much it hurts / Half as much / You belong to me.
LP: . . . . SHM 3219
MC: . . . . HSC 3219

BEST OF PATSY CLINE.
Tracks: / Walking after midnight / I fall to pieces / Crazy / Who can I count on / She's got you / Strange / When I get thru with you / Imagine that / Someone / Heartaches / Sweet dreams / Faded love / When you need a laugh / He called me baby / Anytime.
LP: . . . . SHM 3192
MC: . . . . HSC 3192

COUNTRY MUSIC HALL OF FAME, THE.
Tracks: / Walking after midnight / I fall to pieces / Crazy / Who can I count on / She's got you / Strange / When I get thru with you / Imagine that / So wrong / Heartaches / Leavin' on your mind / Sweet dreams / Faded love / When you need a laugh / He called me baby / Anytime.
LP: . . . . MCL 1739
MC: . . . . MCLC 1739
LP: . . . . CDLM 8077

CRAZY DREAMS.
Tracks: / Hidin' out / Turn the cards slowly / Church, a courtroom and then goodbye, A / Honky tonk merry go round / I love you honey / Come on in (and make yourself at home) / I cried all the way to the altar / Stop, look and listen / I've loved and lost again / Dear God / He will do for you (what he's done for me) / Walkin' after midnight / Heart you break may be your own, The / Pick me up on your way down / Poor man's (or a rich man's gold), A / Today, tomorrow and forever / Fingertips / Stranger in my arms, A / Don't ever leave me again / Try again / Too many secrets / Then you'll know / Three cigarettes (in an ashtray) / That wonderful someone / (Write me) in care of the blues / Hungry for love / I can't forget / I don't wanta / Ain't no wheels on this ship / Stop the world (and let me off) / Walking dream / Cry not for me / If I could see the world / Just out of reach / I can see an angel / Come on in (and make yourself at home) / Let the teardrops fall / Never no more / I I could only stay asleep / I'm moving along / I'm blue again / Love love, love me honey do / Yes I understand / Gotta lot of rhythm in my soul / Life's railway to heaven / Just a closer walk with thee / Lovesick blues / How can I face tomorrow / There he goes / Crazy dreams.
LPS: . . . . SDBS 001
MC: . . . . CDC 3.001

DREAMING.
Tracks: / Sweet dreams / I fall to pieces / Crazy / Heartaches / Tra le la le la triangle / Have you ever been lonely? / Faded love / Your cheatin' heart / She's got you / Walking after midnight / San Antonio rose / Three cigarettes in an ashtray / When I need a laugh / Always.
LP: . . . . PLAT 303
MC: . . . . PLAC 303

GOLDEN GREATS: PATSY CLINE.
Tracks: / I fall to pieces / She's got you / Crazy / Walkin' after midnight / Sweet dreams / Who can I count on / Strange / When I get thru with you / Imagine that / So wrong / Heartaches / Leavin' on your mind / Faded love / When you need a laugh / He called me baby / Anything.
LP: . . . . MCM 5008
MC: . . . . MCMC 5008

GREATEST HITS: PATSY CLINE & JIM REEVES (Cline, Patsy & Jim Reeves).
Tracks: / Have you ever been lonely? / Welcome to my world / He'll have to go / Crazy / Sweet dreams / Four walls / Am I losing you? / Golden memories and silver tears / I fall to pieces / She's got you.
LP: . . . . RCALP 3057
MC: . . . . RCAK 3057
LP: . . . . NL 85152
MC: . . . . NK 85152

HAVE YOU EVER BEEN LONELY?.
LP: . . . . MCF 2725

LEGENDARY PATSY CLINE, THE.
Tracks: / Walking after midnight / Just out of reach / I've loved and lost again / Fingerprints / I can't forget / Hungry for love / If I could only stay asleep / I love you honey / Never no more / Pick me up on your way down / Honky tonk merry go round / I cried all the way to the altar / Three cigarettes in an ashtray / Stop the world and let me off.
LP: . . . . MFP 50460

OFF THE RECORD WITH....
Tracks: / I love you honey / Never no more / Walking after midnight / I don't wanna / Let the teardrops fall / I've loved and lost again / Fingerprints / I can't forget / Just out of reach / Hungry for love / Don't ever leave me / Then you'll know / If I could see the world / I'm moving along / Gotta lot of rhythm in my soul / Stop, look and listen / Love me, love me, honey do / I'm blue again / Dear god / Yes, I understand.
2LP: . . . . FEDD 1007
MCSET: . . . . CFEDD 1007

ORIGINAL HITS.
LP: 35006
MC: 65006

PATSY CLINE.
Tracks: / Just a closer walk with thee / Never no more / Ain't no wheels on this ship / He'll do for now / Honky tonk merry go round / Poor man's roses, A / Pick me up / Turn the cards slowly / Dear God / I love you honey / I can't forget you / Crazy dreams.
MC: . . . . ZCGAS 711

PATSY CLINE SHOWCASE.
Tracks: / I fall to pieces / Foolin' round / Wavering wind, The / South of the border / I love you so much it hurts / Seven lonely days / Crazy / San Antonio rose / True love / Walking after midnight / Poor mans roses, A.
LP: . . . . HAT 3036
MC: . . . . HATC 3036

PATSY CLINE STORY.
Tracks: / Heartaches / She's got you / Walking after midnight / Strange / Leavin' on your mind / South of the border / Foolin' round / I fall to pieces / Poor man's roses, A / Tra le la le la triangle / True love / Imagine that / Back in baby's arms / Crazy / You're stronger than me / Seven lonely days / Sweet dreams / Your cheatin' heart / San Antonio rose / Why can't he be you / Wayward way, The / So wrong / I love you so much it hurts / You belong to me.
2LP: . . . . IMCA 24038

PORTRAIT OF PATSY CLINE, A.
Tracks: / Who can I count on / You took him off my hands / Your kinda love / Does your heart beat for me / Faded love / I'll sail my ship alone / When you need a laugh / Crazy arms / Always / When I'm through with you (you'll love me too) / Blue moon of Kentucky / Someday you'll want me to want you.
LP: . . . . IMCA 224

QUEEN OF COUNTRY.
Tracks: / Just a closer walk with thee / Never no more / Ain't no wheels on this ship / He'll do for now / Honky tonk merry go round / Poor man's roses, A / Gotta lot of rhythm in my soul / I've loved and lost again / Lovesick blues / Cry not for me / Stranger in my arms, A / In care of the blues / Just out of reach / Three cigarettes in an ashtray / Heart you break may be your own, The / That wonderful someone / I cried all the way to the altar / Church, a courtroom, then goodbye, A / Pick me up (on your way down) / Turn the cards slowly / Dear God / I love you honey / I can't forget you / Crazy dreams.
MCSET: . . . . DTOL 10006
MCSET: . . . . DTO 10006

REMEMBERING (Cline, Patsy & Jim Reeves).
Tracks: / Fall to pieces / So wrong / Misty moonlight / Back in baby's arms / Missing you / Walking after midnight / Blizzard / Why can't he be you / Distant drums / Leavin' on your mind (Patsy).
LP: . . . . IMCA 1467
MC: . . . . IMCAC 1467

REPLAY ON PATSY CLINE.
LP: . . . . FEDB 5033
MC: . . . . CFEDB 5033

SONGWRITER'S TRIBUTE.
Tracks: / Lovin' in vain / Crazy / I love you so much it hurts / You're stronger than me / Imagine that / So wrong / When you need a laugh / Your kinda love / That's how a heartache begins / He called me baby / You took him off my hands.
LP: . . . . IMCA 25019
MC: . . . . IMCAC 25019

SWEET DREAMS WITH....
LP: . . . . ENT LP 13018
MC: . . . . ENT MC 13018

TOO MANY SECRETS.
Tracks: / Walking after midnight / I've loved and lost again / I love you honey / Fingerprints / Never no more / Hiding out / Walking dream / Let the teardrops fall / Just out of reach / Ain't no wheels on this ship / I can't forget / Too many secrets / In care of the blues / Hungry for love / I don't wanna / If I could see the world / Stop the world / I can see an angel / Today tomorrow and forever / Life's railway to heaven.
LP: . . . . SMT 013
MC: . . . . SMTC 013

TRIBUTE TO PATSY CLINE, A.
Tracks: / Leavin' on your mind / Tra le la le la triangle / Imagine that / Back in baby's arms / You're stronger than me / Sweet dreams / Why can't he be you / So wrong / When I get thru with you / Lovin' in vain / Who can I count on / Crazy.
LP: . . . . HAT 3008
MC: . . . . HATC 3008

WALKIN AFTER MIDNIGHT (28 Country Classics).
MC: . . . . PLAC 27

Cline, Tammy

SINGS THE COUNTRY GREATS WITH THE SOUTHERN COMFORT BAND.
Tracks: / Here you come again / Help me make it through the night / Rose garden / Hurt / Harper Valley PTA / Carolina Moon / Stand by your man / Don't it make my brown eyes blue / Coalminers daughter / Love letters / Sweet dreams / I fell in love again last night.
LP: . . . . MFP 5787
MC: . . . . TC-MFP 5787

TAMMY CLINE & THE SOUTHERN COMFORT BAND (Cline, Tammy & The Southern Comfort Band).
Tracks: / He's a rounder / Crazy / Street talk / Yesterday just passed my way again / Take good care of my baby / Last cheater's waltz, The / My baby thinks he's a train / You've got a friend / Single girl / Miss the Mississippi / Way we make a broken heart, The / I wish I'd wrote that song.
LP: . . . . PRCV 114

TAMMY CLINE'S COUNTRY GOSPEL ALBUM.
Tracks: / Our God reigns / One day at a time / It is no secret / I saw the light / I believe / Old rugged cross, The / It's good to be home / This little light of mine / He is my everything / Heaven's gonna be a blast / Softly and tenderly / How great Thou art.
LP: . . . . WRD R 3032
MC: . . . . WRD C 3032

Clinkscale, Jimmy

ACCORDION BONANZA NO.1.
LP: . . . . C 1001

ACCORDION BONANZA NO.2.
LP: . . . . C 1003

ACCORDION BONANZA NO.3.
LP: . . . . C 1007

Clinton, George

CINDERELLA THEORY.
LP: . . . . K 925 994 1
MC: . . . . K 925 994 4

COMPUTER GAMES.
Tracks: / Get dressed / Man's best friend / Loopzilla / Pot sharing totts / Computer games / Atomic dog / Free alterations / One fun at a time.
LP: . . . . EST 12246
MC: . . . . TCEST 12246

SOME OF MY BEST JOKES ARE FRIENDS.
Tracks: / Some of my best jokes are friends / Double oh oh / Bullet proof / Pleasures of exhaustion (do it till I drop) / Bodyguard / Bangla Desh / Thrashin'.
LP: . . . . CLINT 1
MC: . . . . TC CLINT 1

YOU SHOULDN'T NUF BIT FISH.
Tracks: / Nusbian nut / Quickie / Last dance / Silly millameter / Stingy / You shouldn't nuf bit fish.
LP: . . . . EST 712308-1
MC: . . . . TCEST 712308-

Clinton, Larry

1941 AND 1949 (Clinton, Larry & His Orchestra).
LP: . . . . CLP 58

DIPSY DOODLE 1938 - 39 (Clinton, Larry & His Orchestra).
Tracks: / Dipsy doodle theme / East of the sun / Chopsticks / Sunday / Wishing / In a mist / Lonesome road / One rose, The / S'good enough for me / There's that faraway look in your eye / Midnight in the madhouse / Chant of the jungle / Chew, chew, chew, chew (your bubble gum) / Study in blue / Limehouse blues.
LP: . . . . BS 7133

FROM THE GLEN ISLAND CASINO 1938/9 (Clinton, Larry & His Orchestra).
LP: . . . . KAYDEE 3

IN A PERSIAN MARKET 1939 - 41 (Clinton, Larry & His Orchestra).
LP: . . . . BS 7102

LARRY CLINTON & HIS ORCHESTRA 1937-38 (Clinton, Larry & His Orchestra).
Tracks: / Dipsy doodle / Glen Island hop / Whistle while you work / Let her go / Hollywood pastime / Where in the world (Vocal by Bea Wain) / Chris and his gang / Zig zag / Feeling like a dream / Saving myself for you / Remember / I double dare you / Martha / Sugarfoot stomp / You go to my head / I want to rock.
LP: . . . . HSR 109
LP: . . . . HMP 5045

MY REVERIE 1937-38 (Clinton, Larry & His Orchestra).
LP: . . . . BS 7109
MC: . . . . BS 7109C

Clitheroe, Jimmy

CLITHEROE KID, THE (see under Clitheroe Kid (bk).

Clitheroe Kid

CLITHEROE KID, THE (Jimmy Clitheroe).
MCSET: . . . . ZBBC 1104

Clitheroe, Ricky

COCKNEY CORNMAN.
MC: . . . . SENC 1082

Clive's Jive Five

CLIVE'S JIVE FIVE.
LP: . . . . ROCK 8906

Clock DVA

ADVANTAGE.
Tracks: / Tortured heroine / Beautiful losers / Resistance / Eternity in Paris / Secret life of the big black suit / Breakdown / Dark encounter / Poem.
LP: . . . . POLS 1082
MC: . . . . POLSC 1082
LP: . . . . EFA 1706

THIRST.
LP: . . . . FR 2002
LP: . . . . DVR 19

TRANSITIONAL VOICES.
LP: . . . . EFA 01718

Clock Tower Ghost (bk)

CLOCK TOWER GHOST, THE (Gene Kemp).
MCSET: 086 222 0458

Clockwork Orange (bk)

CLOCKWORK ORANGE, A (Anthony Burgess).
MC: 1417

Clockwork Orange

CLOCKWORK ORANGE, A (Film Soundtrack) (Various artists).
Tracks: / Clockwork orange, A: *Carlos, Walter* / Thieving magpie, The: *Various artists* / Ninth Symphony (Second Movement-Abridged): *Various artists* / March From A Clockwork Orange: *Carlos, Walter* / William Tell: *Carlos,* Walter / Pomp and circumstance march no.1: *Various artists* / Pomp and circumstance march no.4: *Various artists*/ Timesteps (excerpt): *Carlos, Walter* / Overture to the sun: *Carlos, Walter* / I want to marry a lighthouse keeper: *Various artists* / Suicide Scherzo: *Carlos, Walter* / Singin' In The Rain: *Astaire, Fred.*
LP: . . . . K 46127
MC: K4 46127

Clooney, Rosemary

BEST OF ROSEMARY CLOONEY.
MC: 16-20

BLUE ROSE (Clooney, Rosemary & Duke Ellington).
LP: 84402

CHRISTMAS ALBUM (See under Crosby, Bing) (Clooney, Rosemary & Bing Crosby).

CLAP HANDS.
Tracks: / Clap hands, here comes Rosie / Everything's coming up roses / Give me the simple life / Bye bye blackbird / Aren't you glad you're you / You got / Too marvellous for words / Something's gotta give / Hooray for love / Mean to me / Oh what a beautiful morning / It could happen to you / Makin' whoopee.
LP: . . . . NL 89461
MC: . . . . NK 89461

FANCY MEETING YOU HERE (Clooney, Rosemary and Bing Crosby).
Tracks: / Fancy meeting you here / On a slow boat to China / I can't get started / Hindustan / It happened in Monterey / You came a long way / From St. Louis / You can take the boy out of the country / Love won't let you get away / How about you / Brazil / Here we are (face to face again) / Isle of Capri / Say si si / Calcutta.
LP: . . . . INTS 5217
MC: . . . . INTK 5217
LP: . . . . NL 89315
MC: . . . . NK 89315

FOR THE DURATION.
Tracks: / No love, no nothin' / Don't fence me in / I don't want to walk without you baby / Every time we say goodbye (CD only.) / You'd be so nice to come home to / Sentimental journey / For all we know / September song / These foolish things (remind me of you) / They're either too young or too old / More I see you, The / (There'll be blue birds over) the White cliffs of Dover / Saturday night is the loneliest night of the year (CD only.) / I'll be seeing you.
MC: . . . . CJ 444C

GREATEST HITS: ROSEMARY CLOONEY.
Tracks: / This old house / Hey there / Tenderly / Half as much / Mambo Italiano / You're just in love / Come on-a my house / Botch-a-me / Mangos / Blues in the night / Too old to cut the mustard / Beautiful brown eyes / Where will the baby's dimple be? / Be my life's companion / If teardrops were pennies / I could have danced all night.
LP: . . . . CBS 32263
MC: 40-32263

HERE'S TO MY LADY.
2LP: . . . . CJ 81

MIXED EMOTIONS.
Tracks: / Bless this house / Beautiful brown eyes / Lady is a tramp, The / Be my life's companion / Why don't you haul off and love me / Too young / While we're young / I laughed until I cried / Close your eyes (Brahms' Lullaby) / Mixed emotions.
LP: . . . . CBS 32708

MY BUDDY (Clooney, Rosemary & Woody Herman Big Band).
Tracks: / I believe in love / Summer knows, The / Glory of love / You're gonna hear from me / Don't let me be lonely / Tonight / I'm beginning to see the light / My buddy / You've made me so very happy.
LP: . . . . CJ 226

OUR FAVOURITE THINGS (Clooney, Rosemary with Les Brown and His Band).
Tracks: / Sweetest sounds, The / How am I to know / My funny valentine / Why shouldn't I? / My romance / I get along without you very well / Angry / Some people / Man with a horn / Show me / Have you met Miss Jones / Little brown jug / Sleepy time gal / I didn't know what time it was / One o'clock jump.
LP: . . . . DBD 06
MC: . . . . DBDC 06

RING AROUND ROSIE (Clooney, Rosemary and Bing Crosby).
Tracks: / Doncha go 'way mad / Moonlight becomes you / Love letters / I could write a book / I'm in the mood for love / Coquette / Together / Everything happens to me / What is there to say / I'm glad there is you / How about you.
LP: . . . . MOIR 114
MC: . . . . CMOIR 114

ROSEMARY CLOONEY.
LP: . . . . HSR 234

ROSEMARY CLOONEY SING BALLADS.
LP: . . . . CJ 282
MC: . . . . CJC 282

ROSEMARY CLOONEY SINGS COLE PORTER.
LP: . . . . CJ 185
MC: . . . . CJC 185

ROSEMARY CLOONEY SINGS HAROLD ARLEN.
Tracks: / Hooray for love / Happiness is a thing called love / One for my baby / Get happy / Ding dong the witch is dead / Out of this world / My shining hour / Let's take the long way home / Stormy weather.
LP: . . . . CJ 210
MC: . . . . CJC 210

ROSEMARY CLOONEY SONGBOOK, THE.
2LP: 88598
MCSET: 4088598

ROSIE SOLVES THE SWINGIN' RIDDLE.
Tracks: / Get me to the church on time / Angry / I get along without you very well / How am I to know / You took advantage of me / April in Paris / I ain't got nobody / Some of these days / By myself / Shine on harvest moon / Cabin in the sky / Limehouse blues.
LP: . . . . INTS 5057
MC: . . . . INTK 5057

SHOW TUNES.
Tracks: / I wish I were in love again / I stayed too long at the fair / How are things in Glocca Morra / When do you start / I'll see you again / Guys and dolls / Manhattan / Everything I've got / Come back to me / Taking a chance on love / All the things you are.
LP: . . . . CJ 346
MC: . . . . CJ 346C

SINGS BING.
LP: . . . . CJ 60

SINGS RODGERS, HART & HAMMERSTEIN.
Tracks: / Oh, what a beautiful morning / People will say we're in love / Love, look away / Gentleman is a dope, The / It might as well be Spring / Sweetest sounds, The / I could write a book / You took advantage of me / Lady is a tramp, The / Little girl blue / My romance / Yours sincerely (CD only.).
MC: . . . . CJ 405 C

SINGS SHOW TUNES.
LP: . . . . CJ 364

SINGS THE LYRICS OF IRA GERSHWIN.
Tracks: / But not for me / Nice work if you can get it / How long has this been going on / Fascinating rhythm / Love is here to stay / Strike up the band / Long ago and far away / They all laughed / Man that got away, The / They can't that away from me.
LP: . . . . CJ 112

SINGS THE LYRICS OF JOHNNY MERCER.
LP: . . . . CJ 333
MC: . . . . CJC 333

SINGS THE MUSIC OF IRVING BERLIN.
Tracks: / It's a lovely day today / Be careful, it's my heart / Cheek to cheek / How about me / Best thing for you would be me, The / I got lost in his arms / There's no business like show business / Better luck next time / What'll I do / Let's face the music and dance.
LP: . . . . CJ 255
MC: . . . . CJC 255

SINGS THE MUSIC OF JIMMY VAN HEUSEN.
Tracks: / Love won't let you get away / I thought about you / My heart is a hobo / Second time around / It could happen to you / Imagination / Like someone in love / Call me irresponsible / Walking happy / Last dance.
LP: . . . . CJ 308
MC: . . . . CJC 308

SWING AROUND ROSIE (Clooney, Rosemary with The Buddy Cole Trio).
Tracks: / Deed I do / You took advantage of me / Blue moon / Sing you sinners / Touch of the blues, A / Goody, goody / Too close for comfort / Do nothing till you hear from me / Moonlight Mississippi / I wish I were in love again / Sunday in Savannah / This can't be love.
LP: . . . . JASM 1502

THAT TRAVELIN' TWO-BEAT (See under Crosby, Bing) (Clooney, Rosemary & Bing Crosby).

WITH LOVE.
Tracks: / Just the way you are / Way we were, The / Alone at last / Come in from the rain / Meditation / Hello young lovers / Just in time / Tenderly / Will you still be mine?.
LP: . . . . CJ 144

Close, A.E.

TRUMPET CALLS FOR THE ARMY.
MC: . . . . CDR 44

Close Encounters...

CLOSE ENCOUNTERS OF THE 3RD KIND (See under National Philharmonic Orchestra) (National Philharmonic Orchestra).

CLOSE ENCOUNTERS OF THE THIRD KIND (Film soundtrack) (Various artists).
Tracks: / Close Encounters of the Third Kind (mountain visions): *Various artists* / Nocturnal pursuit: *Various artists*/ Abduction of Barry, The: *Various artists* / I can't believe it's real: *Various artists* / Climbing devil's tower: *Various artists* / Arrival of sky harbour, The: *Various artists.*
LP: . . . . DLART 2001
MC: . . . . TLART 2001

CLOSE ENCOUNTERS/STAR WARS (Los Angeles Philharmonic Orchestra).
Tracks: / Star wars(main title) / Princess Leia's theme / Little people work, The / Cantina band / Battle, The / Throne room and end title, The / Close Encounters of the Third Kind.
MC: . . . . KSXC 6885
MC: 4178464

Close Lobsters

FOXHEADS STALK THIS LAND.
LP: . . . . FIRELP 9

HEADACHE RHETORIC.
LP: . . . . FIRELP 17
MC: . . . . FIREMC 17

Cloud

RESTING PLACE, THE.
LP: . . . . DOVE 62

WATERED GARDEN.
LP: . . . . DOVE 44

Cloud, Michael

LOVE BROUGHT ME BACK.
Tracks: / Dear Jesus, I love you / You been good to me / You gotta be patient / What's going on / Precious Lord / Moving on up / He hears your every prayer / What's going on (reprise).
LP: . . . . MIR 5019
MC: . . . . MIR 5019MC

Cloud, Pat

HIGHER POWER.
LP: . . . . FF 284

Clout

CLOUT.
Tracks: / Substitute / Without love / Let it grow / You've got all of me / Ms. America / Since you've been gone / Feel my need / You make my world so colourful / Don't stop / Save me.
LP: . . . . EMC 3279
MC: . . . . TCEMC 3279

SIX OF THE BEST.
Tracks: / Oowatanite / Under fire / Love talk / Oh how I long to be with you again / Hard to get over a heartbreak / Don't hold back / To make love / Tom-morrow / Gimme some lovin'.
LP: . . . . EMA 792

THREAT AND A PROMISE, A.
Tracks: / Threat and a promise, A / Best of me, The / Wish I were loving you / Dead telephone / You / Portable radio / Hot shot / Lovers on the sidewalk / Gonna get it to you / Can't we talk it over.
LP: . . . . EMC 3363

Cloven Hoof

CLOVEN HOOF.
Tracks: / Nightstalker / March of the damned / Gates of Gehenna / Crack the whip / Laying down the law / Return of the passover.
LP: . . . . NEAT 1013
MC: . . . . NEATC 1013

DOMINATOR.
Tracks: / Rising up / Nova battlestar / Reach for the sky / Warrior of the wasteland / Invaders, The / Fugitive, The / Dominator / Road of eagles.
LP: . . . . HMRLP 113
MC: . . . . HMRMC 113

FIGHTING BACK.
LP: . . . . CH 002

SULTAN'S RANSOM, A.
LP: . . . . HMRLP 129
MC: . . . . HMRMC 129

Clover

BEST OF CLOVER.
Tracks: / Love love love / Oh senorita / Streets of London / Chicken funk / Travellin' man / Keep on rolling / Southern belles / Chain gang / California kid / I lie awake (and dream of you) / Still alive / Route '66.
LP: . . . . MERB 98

Clover Chronicle

BEST OF THE FANTASY YEARS.
Tracks: / Lizard rock 'n' roll band / Could you call it love / Monopoly / Southbound train / Stealin' / Shot gun / Mr. Moon / Mitch's tune / Chicken butt / Sunny Mexico / Old man blues / Keep on trying.
LP: . . . . FT 550

Clovers

ALL RIGHTY OH SWEETIE.
Tracks: / Wonder where my baby's gone / I confess / Needless / Hey doll baby / Comin' on good / Good golly Miss Molly.
LP: . . . . H 807

FIVE COOL CATS.
Tracks: / One mint julep / Good lovin' / Lovey dovey / I got my eyes on you / Down in the alley / Your cash ain't nothin' but trash / In the morning time / Don't you know I love you / Blue velvet / Love bug / If I could be loved by you / Nip sip / Devil or angel / Your tender lips / So young / All about you.
LP: . . . . ED 126
MC: . . . . CED 126

Clovis Sessions

CLOVIS SESSIONS VOLUME 1 (Various artists).
Tracks: / Believe me: *Huddle, Jack* / Starlight: *Huddle, Jack* / Cast iron arm: *Wilson, Peanuts* / Little ditty baby: *Webb, Don* / Leave them cats alone: *Don & The Roses* / Lookie, lookie, lookie: *Smith, Ronnie*/ That'll be alright: *Ivan* / School is out: *Wayne, Terry* / No minors allowed: *Locke, Ramona* / Fireball: *Fireballs* / Because I love you: *Montgomery, Bob* / My Suzanne: *Henry, R.* / You've got love:

Wilson, Peanuts / Tiny kiss, A: *Smith, Ronnie* / I don't know: *Fireballs* / Since you went away to school: *Don & The Roses* / Jitterbuggin': *Five Bops* / Right now: *Don & The Roses*.
LP: . . . . **CR 30236**

Clower, Jerry

JERRY CLOWER'S GREATEST HITS.
LP: . . . . **IMCA 37247**

RUNAWAY TRACK.
Tracks: / Trucker and the lady, The / Marcell, The truck driver / Feudin's stars / Pulpit committee, The / Peanuts / John Dunn / Preacher's water, The / Mean brothers, The / Grassers, The / How to tell time / Runaway truck / Baptizing, The / Negativism / Procto / Sonny and rambo / Temerance meeting / Positive attitude, A / Clowerisms / Coon huntin' on TV / Shake it off.
LP: . . . . **IMCA 5773**
MC: . . . . **IMCAC 5773**

Clown Alley

CIRCUS OF CHAOS.
LP: . . . . **VM 101**

Club Class

CLUB CLASS COMPILATION (Various artists).
LP: . . . . **FILER 400**

Club de Rome

CLUB DE ROME.
Tracks: / Viva la vita / A l'est and a l'quest du crepscule / TV dells Rodeo / Grinehita / Sex, fun, CDR / Painting on your skin / Brisure de syuetrie.
LP: . . . . **ARTY 10**

Club It 90

CLUB IT 90 VOL.2 (See under Dance...) (Various artists).

Club Nouveau

LIFE LOVE AND PAIN.
Tracks: / Jealousy / Why you treat me so bad / Lean on me / Promises promises / Situation number / Heavy on my mind / Let me go / Lean on me.
LP: . . . . **WX 100**
MC: . . . . **WX 100 C**
LP: **9255311**

LISTEN TO THE MESSAGE.
Tracks: / It's a cold cold world / Listen to the message / Dancin' to be free / Why is it that / For the love of Francis / Envious / What's going 'round / Only the strong survive / Better way.
LP: . . . . **WX 159**
MC: . . . . **WX 159C**

UNDER A NEW NOUVEAU GROOVE.
LP: **7599259911**
MC: **7599259914**

Club Paradise (film)

CLUB PARADISE (1986 film soundtrack) (Various artists).
LP: . . . . **CBS 70298**
MC: **40 70298**

Club UK

CLUB UK (See under Dance...) (Various artists).

CLUB UK VOL.2 (See under Dance...) (Various artists).

Clubsound

CLUBSOUND CAPERS.
Tracks: / Y viva Espana / Tonga lol / Belfast, Belfast / Andy McFadden / Professionals, The / That's my desire.
MC: . . . . **KBER 020**

Cluster

CLUSTER 11.
LP: **0001 006**

STIMMUNGEN.
LP: . . . . **SKY 93**

ZUCKERZEIT.
Tracks: / Hollywood / Caramel / Rote Riki / Rosa / Caramba / Fotschi tong / James / Marzipan / Rotor / Heisse Lippen.
LP: **0040.116**

Cluster & Eno

OLD LAND.
LP: . . . . **SKY 105**

Cluster Of Nuts Band

FRIDGE IN THE FAST LAND.
LP: . . . . **PROD 001**

Clutha

BONNIE MILLE DAMS.
Tracks: / My apron / Bonnie Susie / Fareweel tae kemper / Kilworth hills / High Jeanie, high / Braes o'Lochie, The / Terrible twins, The / Banks of Allan / Ochitree walls / Binnorie-o / Logan water / Neil Gow / Captain MacDuff's reel / Among the blue flowers and the yellow / False bride, The / Maids o' the black glen / Back o' the moon / Donald Willie and his dog / I laid a herrin' in saut / Mossie and his mare.
LP: **12TS 330**

CLUTHA, THE.
Tracks: / Soor milk cairt / Donald blue / Dell in the lum / Jigs / Andro and his cutty gun / Rigs O' Rye / Johnny Sangster / Wha's fu / Andrew Ross / Gaberlunzie man, The.
LP: **12TS 242**

Clyde Valley Stompers

FIDGETY FEET.
Tracks: / At the jazz band ball / Isle of Capri / When my dreamboat comes home / Fidgety feet / Salty dog / Creole love call / Tiger rag / My mother's eyes / Hiawatha rag / Goodnight, my sweet prince / When the saints go marching in / I can't stop loving you.
LP: . . . . **BGC 351**
MC: . . . . **KBGC 351**

REUNION '81.
Tracks: / Hindustan / Old rugged cross / Sister Kate / High Society / Bourbon Street parade / Old tyme religion / Savoy blues / Bill Bailey won't you please come home.
LP: . . . . **BGC 300**
MC: . . . . **KBGC 300**

Clydesiders

CLYDESIDERS ALBUM.
Tracks: / Waverly polka, The / All the good times / Kelty clippie / Mormond braes / Wee room, The / Annie's song / Johnny's fancy / Spanish ladies / Pack up your sorrows / Sludge boat song, The / Rollin' in my sweet baby's arms / Rigs o' Rye / Fitba referee / Closing time.
LP: . . . . **LILP 5095**
MC: . . . . **LICS 5095**

IT'S GOOD TO SEE YOU.
Tracks: / Maybe someday / Morning glory / Skye boat song / Dill pickle rag / Come by the hills / Till you return to me / It's good to see you / Sloop John B / Mountains of Mourne / Primrose, The / You took advantage of me / With friends like you.
LP: . . . . **KLP 54**
MC: . . . . **ZCKLP 54**

LEGENDS OF SCOTLAND, THE.
Tracks: / Wild mountain thyme / Lowland low / Athole highlanders, The / Soldiers joy / Fairie dance / Killiecrankie / Corn rigs / Will ye no come back again / Banks and braes / Thinking of home / Tenpenny piece / Blackthorn stick / Rakes of Kildare, The / Island of Arran / With friends like you.
MC: . . . . **ZCCLS 712**

SAILING HOME.
Tracks: / Killiecrankie / Can't help but wonder where I'm bound / Dashing white sergeant / Breakdown / Leaving Nancy / All God's creatures / Goodbye America / Sailing home / Switch out the sun / Land I have left, The / Athole highlanders, The / Soldiers joy / Fairie dance / Hills of Connemara / Will ye no come back again.
LP: . . . . **LOCLP 1010**
MC: . . . . **ZCLOC 1010**

THINKING OF HOME.
Tracks: / We've lived in a dream / Turn a deaf ear / Take the high road / Banks and braes / Tenpenny piece / Rakes of Kildare, The / Blackthorn stick / Just my old lady / Island of Arran / Ukelele lady / Thinking of home / Bogman's pig / Goodnight Irene / Catfish / When you were sweet sixteen / Wild mountain thyme / Glasgow lullaby.
LP: . . . . **KLP 47**
MC: . . . . **ZCKLP 47**

TOUCH OF THE CLYDESIDERS.
Tracks: / McPhersons rant / Land I love so well, The / Fiddlers choice / Loch Lomond / Wee china pig / Paddy Kelly's brew / Home boys home / Wee kirkcudbright centipede, The / I hae seen the heilans / Ramblin' boy / Ballad of Jesse James / Always Argyll / Mirsheen durkin / Scotland's jim Watt.
LP: . . . . **LOCLP 1001**
MC: . . . . **ZCLOC 1001**

WILD MOUNTAIN THYME.
Tracks: / River / Corn rigs / There was a lad / Silver darlings / Little suite, A / Parahandy polka / Sponge / Trumpet hornpipe / Welcome home to Glasgow / My love is like a red red rose / Home to the Kyles / Lowlands low / Burnie boozie / If wishes were fishes / Barren rocks of Aden / La russe / Cadder Woods.
LP: . . . . **KLP 41**
MC: . . . . **ZCKLP 41**

Clyne, Jeff

TWICE UPON A TIME (See Lee, Phil) (Clyne, Jeff & Phil Lee).

Coal Miner's Daughter

COAL MINER'S DAUGHTER (1980 film soundtrack) (Various artists).
Tracks: / Titanic, The: *Various artists* / Blue moon of Kentucky: *Various artists* / There he goes: *Various artists* / I'm a honky tonk girl: *Various artists* / Amazing grace: *Various artists* / Walking after midnight: *Various artists* / Crazy: *Various artists* / I fall to pieces: *Various artists* / Sweet dreams: *Various* artists / Back in my baby's arms: *Various artists* / One's on the way: *Various artists* / You ain't woman enough: *Various artists* / You're lookin' at country: *Various artists* / Coal miner's daughter: *Various artists*.
LP: . . . . **MCL 1847**
MC: . . . . **MCLC 1847**
LP: . . . . **MCF 3068**
MC: . . . . **MCFC 3068**

Coast To...

COAST TO COAST (See under Rock...) (Various artists).

Coast To Coast

COASTING.
Tracks: / Do the hucklebuck / I'm hooked on you baby / Jamie's theme / Baby why let go / Surfin' time / Coasting / Let's jump the broomstick / Born to rock 'n' roll / Leave me baby / Some kind of fool / Mama don't you hit that boy / Woolly bully.
LP: . . . . **POLS 1040**
MC: . . . . **POLSC 1040**

DO THE HUCKLEBUCK/OLDEST SWINGER IN TOWN (See under Wedlock, Fred).

Coasters

20 GREAT ORIGINALS.
Tracks: / Riot in cell block 9 / Smokey Joe's cafe / Framed / Turtle dovin' / Down in Mexico / Young blood / Searchin' / Idol with the golden head / Yakety yak / Zing went the strings of my heart / Shadow knows Charlie Brown, The / Along came Jones / Poison ivy / What about us / I'm a hog for you baby / Run red run / Shoppin' for clothes / Little Egypt / Bad blood.
LP: . . . . **K 30057**

JUKE BOX GIANTS.
Tracks: / Run red run / Yakety yak / As quiet as it's kept / Young blood / Whip it on me, baby / Poison ivy / It don't take much / Along came Jones / Down in Mexico / It ain't sanitary / Little Egypt / Searchin' / Deodorant song / Charlie Brown / T.V. fanatic / Love potion No.9.
LP: . . . . **AFEMP 1019**

LET'S GO TO THE DANCE (Rare Early Rock 'n' Roll Sides).
LP: . . . . **LS 13**

THUMBIN' A RIDE.
Tracks: / That is rock'n'roll / Three cool cats / (Ain't that) just like me / Keep on rolling / Wait a minute / Stewball / Snake and the bookworm, The / Wake me, shake me / Girls, girls, girls (part 1) / Gee golly / Sorry but I'm gonna have to pass / What is the secret of your success / Lady like / Besame mucho (part 2) / Thumbin' a ride / Ridin' hood.
LP: . . . . **ED 156**
MC: . . . . **CED 156**

WHAT'S THE SECRET OF YOUR SUCCESS.
LP: . . . . **RB 102**

Coatbridge...

CELTIC - THAT'S THE TEAM FOR ME (Coatbridge Accordion Band).
LP: . . . . **CZLP 1700**

Coates, Ann

PLEASE DON'T CUT THE ROSES.
LP: . . . . **WRS 129**

Coates, Eric

BY THE SLEEPY LAGOON (And other Eric Coates favourites) (Royal London Philharmonic...).
Tracks: / By the sleepy lagoon / From meadow to Mayfair / Springtime in Angus / Dambusters / Saxo-Rhapsody / Three bears, The / London suite / London again suite / Cinderella (Phantasy).
MC: **TC2-MOM 1546519**

GOLDEN AGE OF ERIC COATES, THE (Various artists).
Tracks: / Knightsbridge: *Various artists* (Eric Coates conducting London Philharmonic Orchestra (on labels as 'Symp) / Rustic dance: *Various artists* (From 'Meadow to Mayfair' suite. Eric Coates conducting London Symphony O) / Calling all workers: *Various artists* (Eric Coates conducting Symphony Orchestra.) / By the sleepy lagoon: *Various artists*(Eric Coates conducting Light Symphony Orchestra.) / Merrymakers, The: *Various artists* (Eric Coates conducting London Symphony Orchestra.) / Three bears, The: *Various artists* (Eric Coates conducting London Symphony Orchestra.) / Television march: *Various artists* (Eric Coates conducting London Symphony Orchestra.) / At the dance: *Various artists* (Eric Coates conducting Light Symphony Orchestra.) / London calling: *Various artists* (Eric Coates conducting London Symphony Orchestra.) / Saxo-rhapsody: *Various artists* (Eric Coates conducting Symphony Orchestra & Sigurd Rascher (alto saxopho) / Wood nymphs: *Various artists* (Eric Coates conducting London Philharmonic Orchestra.) / Oxford Street: *Various artists*.
LP: . . . . **GX 41 25431**
MC: . . . . **GX 41 25434**

MUSIC OF ERIC COATES (Royal Liverpool Philharmonic Orchestra).
2LP: . . . . **CFPD 4456**
2LP: . . . . **CFPD 4144563**
MCSET: . . . . **CFPD 4144565**
MCSET: . . . . **TCCFPD 4456**
MCSET: **TC2MOM 127**

Coati Mundi

FORMER 12 YEAR OLD GENIUS.
Tracks: / Sey hey! / Oh that love decision / Beat back the bullies / Como esta usted? / Everybody's on an ego trip / Prisoner of my principles / Pharaoh / I'm corrupt / Hold on to that lovely lady / Tropical hot dog night.
LP: . . . . **OVED 89**
MC: . . . . **OVEDC 89**

Cobb, Arnett

AND HIS MOB (Cobb, Arnett & Dinah Washington).
Tracks: / Jumpin' the blues / Cocktails for two / Smooth sailing / Someone to watch over me / Shy one, The / Go red go / When I grow too old to dream / Make believe dreams / Journey's end / It's magic / I got it bad and that ain't good.
LP: . . . . **LP 18**

ARNETT COBB IS BACK.
Tracks: / Flying home / Big red's groove / Cherry / Sweet Georgia Brown / Blues for Shirley / Take the 'A' train / I don't stand a ghost of a chance / Funky butt.
LP: . . . . **PRO 7037**

BLOW ARNETT, BLOW.
Tracks: / When I grow too old to dream / Go power / Dutch kitchen bounce / Go red go / Eely one, The / Fluke, The.
LP: . . . . **PR 7151**
MC: . . . . **PRC 7151**

COMPLETE APOLLO SESSIONS.
LP: **500116**

FUNKY BUTT.
Tracks: / Radium springs swings / Jumpin' at the woodside / Satin doll / Georgia on my mind / I got rhythm / September in the rain / Isfahan.
LP: . . . . **PRO 7054**

LIVE AT SANDY'S (Cobb, Arnett & The Muse All Stars).
Tracks: / Just a closer walk with thee / Blue and sentimental / On the sunny side of the street / September song / Broadway / Blues for Lester / Go red go / Smooth sailing / Flying home.
LP: . . . . **MR 5191**
LP: . . . . **MR 5236**

LIVE IN PARIS, 1974 (Cobb, Arnett & Tiny Grimes).
LP: . . . . **FC 133**

PARTY TIME.
LP: . . . . **OJC 219**

TENOR TRIBUTE (Cobb, Arnett, Jimmy Heath & Joe Henderson).
LP: **121 184 1**

Cobb, Jimmy

THIS HERE IS BOBBY TIMMONS (see Timmons, Bobby) (Cobb, Jimmy & Bobby Timmons & Sam Jones).

Cobb, Junie C.

JUNIE C.COBB 1926-9 (South side Chicago jazz).
LP: . . . . **S 852**

Cobham, Billy

B.C..
Tracks: / Mendocino / Dana / What is your fantasy / Little travelin' music / Lonely bull / I don't want to be without you / Bring up the house lights / Vlastar an encounter.
LP: . . . . **CBS 83641**

BEST OF BILLY COBHAM (CBS).
Tracks: / On a magic carpet ride / Bolinas / Pocket change / Puffinstuff / What is your fantasy / Anteres the star / Indigo / Mendocino.
LP: . . . . **CBS 84235**

BEST OF BILLY COBHAM, THE.
Tracks: / Quadrant 4 / Snoopy's search / Red baron / Spanish moss - A sound portrait / Moon germs / Stratus / Pleasant pheasant, The / Solo panhandler / Do what cha wanna.
LP: . . . . **K 50620**
MC: **K4 50620**

BILLY'S BEST HITS.

LP: GRPA 9575-1

MC: GRPM 9575-4

CROSSWINDS.

Tracks: / Spanish moss - "A sound portrait" / Spanish moss / Savannah the serene / Storm / Flash flood / Pleasant pheasant, The / Heather / Crosswinds.

LP: K 50037

FLIGHT TIME.

LP: SMP 2112

FUNKY THIDE OF SINGS, A.

Tracks: / Panhandler / Sorcery / Funky thide of sings, A / Thinking of you / Some skunk funk / Light at the end of the tunnel / Funky kind of thing, A / Moody modes.

LP: K 50189

LIFE AND TIMES.

LP: K 50253

LIVE ON TOUR IN EUROPE (Cobham, Billy, George Duke Band).

Tracks: / Hip pockets / Ivory tattoo / Space lady / Almustafa the beloved / Do what cha wanna / Frankenstein goes to the disco / Sweet wine / Juicy.

LP: K 50316

MC: K4 50316

PICTURE THIS.

Tracks: / Two for Juan / Same ole love / Taurian matador / You within me within you / This one's for Armando / Sign of the times / Juggler, The / Danse for noh masque.

LP: GRP 91040

MC: GRPM 91040

POWER PLAY.

Tracks: / Times of my life / Zanzibar breeze / Radioactive / Light shines in your eyes, A / Summit Afrique / Foundation, The - Isisekelo Zulu / Dance of the blue men / Nomads, The / Debate, The (Indaba) / Little one / Dessicated coconuts / Tinsel Town.

LP: GRP 91027

MC: GRPM 91027

SHABAZZ.

Tracks: / Shabazz / Taurian matador / Red baron / Tenth pinn.

LP: K 50147

SMOKIN'.

Tracks: / Some other kind / Chiquita Linda / Looks bad, feel good / Red Baron / Situation comedy.

LP: 9602331

SPECTRUM.

Tracks: / Quadrant 4 / Searching for the right door / Spectrum / Anxiety / Taurian matador / Stratus / To the women in my life / Le lis / Snoopy's search / Red Baron.

LP: K 40506

TOTAL ECLIPSE.

Tracks: / Solarization / Second phase / Crescent sun / Voyage / Solarization - recapitulation / Lunarputians / Total eclipse / Bandits / Moon germs / Moon ain't made of green cheese, The / Sea of Tranquility / Last frontier, The.

LP: K 50098

WARNING.

Tracks: / Moziak / Red and yellow cabriolet / Slow body poppin' / Unknown Jeromes / Dancer / Stratus / Come join me / Go for it.

LP: GRP 91020

MC: GRPM 91020

Cobla Perpinya

LES PLUS BELLES SARDANES.

Tracks: / Roca ventosa / Ballem - La Tots / Aplec de germanor / Sardana de tardor / Cantemb-cant / Dolces caricies / Rosabella / Reus sardanista / Bella Pilar / Els degotalls / Floretes del llac / Record de tarrara.

LP: ARN 33664

MC: ARN 433664

Cobos, Luis

MEXICANO.

Tracks: / Mexicano / Mexico / Jorge Negrete, A / Auga del pozo / Jesusita en chihuahia / Ay jalisco no te rajes / Adios mariquita Linda / Carta a ufemia / La adelita / Mexica lindo y qurido / Tu, Maria Bonita / Ella.. La que se fue / Carzon carazon / La cama de piedra / Cielito lindo / La malaguena / Serenata Mexicana / Huapango / Estrellita / Guadalajara / Alla en el rancho grande / Las bicicletas / Jarabe tapatio / Intermezzo / La bamba / Los machetes / El rascapetate / Las altenitas / La negra / La zandunga / La llonora / Las chiapanecas (while there's music there's romance) / La cucaracha / La raspa / Las mananitas / Solamente una vez / Verde tropical / Som bras nada mas / El reloj / Cuando vuelve a tu lado / Noche de ronda / Besame mucho.

LP: S 26053

MC: 40 26053

SOL Y SOMBRA.

Tracks: / Marchas u pasacalles de zaruela / Espanolerias / Pasodobles / Habaneras y canciones.

LP: S 25559

MC: 40 25559

SUITE 1700.

Tracks: / Suite 1700 / Summer / Aria / Autumn / Queen of Sheba, The / Suite 1702 / Winter / Winter II / Adagio / Spring / Canon / Badinerie.

LP: 4676031

MC: 4676034

Cobra (film)

COBRA (1986 Film Soundtrack) (Various artists).

Tracks: / Voice of America's son: *Cafferty, John & The Beaver Brown Band* / Feel the heat: *Beauvoir, Jean* / Loving on borrowed time: *Knight, Gladys & Bill Medley* / Skyline: *Levay, Sylvester* / Hold on to your vision: *Wright,* Gary / Suave: *Miami Sound Machine* / Cobra: *Levay, Sylvester* / Angel of the city: *Tepper, Robert*/ Chase, The: *Levay, Sylvester* / Two into one: *Medley, Bill and Carmen Twillie.*

LP: SCT 70297

MC: 40 70297

Cocarelli, Jose Carlos

EIGHTH VAN CLIBURN INTERNATIONAL PIANO COMPETITION. (see under Sultanov, Aleksei) (Cocarelli, Jose Carlos/Aleksei Sultanov/Benedetto Lupo).

Cocciante, Richard

SINCERITY.

LP: V 2293

Cochereau, Pierre

60 MINUTES OF MUSIC.

Tracks: / Toccata et fugue / En re mineur / Toccata / Andante en fa majeur / Choral prelude op.122 no.10 / Toccata de la 5 symphonie / Chorale no.2 / Toccata pour l'elevation / Berceuse / Toccata / Toccata - marche des rois.

MC: 4169114

Cochran, Charles

HAUNTED HEART.

LP: AP 177

Cochran, Eddie

20TH ANNIVERSARY ALBUM.

LPS: ESCP 20

20TH ANNIVERSARY SPECIAL.

LP: RSREP 2007

25TH ANNIVERSARY ALBUM: EDDIE COCHRAN.

Tracks: / Summertime blues / Teresa / Weekend / Teenage cutie / Never / Completely sweet / Sittin' in the balcony / Think of me / Hallelujah I love her so / Am I blue / My love to remember / Three steps to heaven / Eddie's blues / Little Lou / Cut across shorty / Long tall Sally / C'mon everybody / Mean when I'm mad / Pretty girl / Rock and roll blues / Milk cow blues / Boll weevil / Something else / Teenage heaven / Twenty flight rock / Love again / Jeannie, Jeannie, Jeannie / Cherished memories / Little angel / Sweetie pie / My way / I remember.

LP: EN 2605323

MC: EN 2605325

BEST OF EDDIE COCHRAN.

Tracks: / Summertime blues / C'mon everybody / Twenty flight rock / Jeannie, Jeannie, Jeannie / Something else / Weekend / Cut across shorty / Sweetie pie / Three steps to heaven / Teenage heaven / Drive in show / My way / Teresa / Sittin' in the balcony / Lonely / Hallelujah I love her so.

LP: EG 2607571

MC: EG 2607574

CHERISHED MEMORIES.

Tracks: / Cherished memories / I've waited so long / Never / Skinny Jim / Half loved / Weekend / Nervous breakdown / Let's go together / Rock and roll blues / Dark lonely street / Pink pegged slacks / That's my desire / Sweetie pie / Think of me.

LP: LBR 1827011

MC: TC-LBR 1827104

LP: LBY 1109

LP: 2 C 068 82701

C'MON EVERYBODY.

Tracks: / C'mon everybody / Sweetie pie / I almost lost my mind / Proud of you / Guybo / I remember / Stockings and shoes / Rock and roll blues / Undying love / My love to remember / Never / Little angel / Nervous breakdown / Teenage heaven / Weekend / Sittin' in the balcony / Twenty flight rock / Milk cow blues / Blue suede shoes / Hallelujah I love her so / Something else / Summertime blues / Jeannie Jeannie Jeannie / My way / Cherished memories / Teenage cutie / Long tall Sally / Eddie's blues / Cut across shorty / Pretty girl / Three steps to heaven.

LP: SLS 50155

LP: ECR 1

MC: TCECR 1

C'MON EVERYBODY (IMPORT).

Tracks: / C'mon everybody / Stockings and shoes / I remember / Rock and roll blues.

LP: FUN 9044

MC: FUNC 9044

COUNTRY STYLE.

LP: RSREP 2006

EARLY YEARS, THE.

Tracks: / Skinny Jim / Half loved / Tired and sleepy / That's what it takes to make a man / Pink pegged slacks / Open the door / Country jam / Don't bye bye baby me / My love to remember / Guybo / Dark lonely street / If I were dying / Jelly bean / Latch on / Slow down / Fool's paradise / Bad baby doll (Available on CD and cassette only) / Itty bitty Betty (Available on CD and cassette only) / Heart of a fool (Available on CD and cassette only) / Instrumental blues (Available on CD and cassette only).

LP: CHA 237

MC: CHC 237

EDDIE.

LP: PM 1551743

EDDIE COCHRAN.

Tracks: / Summertime blues / My way / I remember / Three steps to heaven / Skinny Jim / Completely sweet / Lonely / Long tall Sally / C'mon everybody / Teenage heaven / Boll Weevil / Pretty girl / Cherished memories / I'm ready / Sweetie pie / Eddie's blues.

LP: LBYF 1174

LP: MFP 5748

MC: TC MFP 5748

EDDIE COCHRAN BOX SET, THE.

Tracks: / Tired and sleepy / Fool's paradise / Open the door / Slow down / Pink peg slacks / Latch on / My love to remember / Yesterday's heartbreak / I'm ready / Blue suede shoes / Long tall Sally / Half loved / Skinny Jim / I almost lost my mind / Twenty flight rock / That's my desire / Completely sweet / Cotton picker / Sittin' in the balcony / Dark lonely street / One kiss / Mean when I'm mad / Drive-in show / Cradle baby / Undying love / Am I blue / Tell me why / Sweetie pie / I'm alone because I love you / Stockings 'n' shoes / Proud of you / Lovin' time / Teenage cutie / Never / Jeannie, Jeannie, Jeannie / Pocketful of hearts / Little Lou / Pretty girl / Teresa / Nervous breakdown / Summertime blues / Love again / Let's get together / Lonely / C'mon everybody / Don't ever let me go / Teenage heaven / I've waited so long / My way / I remember / Three stars / Rock and roll blues / Weekend / Think of me / Boll weevil / Three steps to heaven / Cut across shorty / Cherished memories / Guybo / Strollin' guitar / Eddie's blues / Jam sandwich / Hammy blues / Fourth man theme / Country jam / Hallelujah I love her so / Something else / Money honey / Have I told you lately that I love you / Milk cow blues / I don't like you no more / Sweet little sixteen / White lightning / Jelly bean / Little angel / Don't bye, bye baby me / You oughta see grandma rock / Heart-breakin' mama / Slowly but surely / Keeper of the key / Let's coast awhile / I want Elvis for Christmas / How'd ja do / Don't wake up the kids / Willa Mae / It happened to me / Chicken shot blues.

LPS: ECB 1

MCSET: TCECB 1

EDDIE COCHRAN & GENE VINCENT (See under Vincent, Gene).

EDDIE COCHRAN SINGLES ALBUM.

Tracks: / C'mon everybody / Three steps to heaven / Cut across shorty / Jeannie, Jeannie, Jeannie / Twenty flight rock / Weekend / Sittin' in the balcony / Hallelujah I love her so / Lonely / Sweetie pie / Summertime blues / Something else / My way / Three stars / Drive in show / Nervous breakdown / Skinny Jim / Completely sweet / Rock and roll blues / Cherished memories.

LP: UAK 30244

MC: TCK 30244

EP COLLECTION, THE: EDDIE COCHRAN.

Tracks: / Skinny Jim / Twenty flight rock / Sittin' in the balcony / Blue suede shoes / Pink peg slacks / Mean when I'm mad / Stockin's 'n' shoes / Jeannie Jeannie Jeannie / Pretty girl / Teresa / Sweetie pie / C'mon everybody / Summertime blues / I remember / Rock 'n' roll blues / Milk cow blues / Little angel / Cherished memories / Three steps to heaven.

LP: SEE 271

MC: SEEK 271

HOLLYWOOD ROCKER.

LP: SJLP 571

HOLLYWOOD SESSIONS, THE.

LP: RSRLP 1009

INEDITS.

LP: LBYF 1209

LEGEND IN OUR TIME.

LP: CR 30168

LEGENDARY MASTERS.

Tracks: / Skinny Jim / Let's get together / Eddie's blues / Little Lou / Pink pegged slacks / Jeannie, Jeannie, Jeannie / Something else / Pretty little devil / Who can I count on / Thinkin' about you / Opportunity / Latch on / I'm ready / Three stars / Cotton picker / Summertime blues / Cut across shorty / Milk cow blues / My way / Blue suede shoes / Nervous breakdown / C'mon everybody / Sittin' in the balcony / Twenty flight rock / Teenage cutie / Hallelujah, I love her so / Fourth man theme / Weekend / Boll weevil / Long tall Sally.

LP: UAD 60017

LET'S COAST AWHILE.

LP: RSREP 2003

MANY SIDES OF EDDIE COCHRAN.

LP: RSRLP 1001

MANY STYLES OF..., THE.

Tracks: / Pink pegged slacks / Fool's paradise / Skinny Jim / Instrumental blues / Half loved / Slow down / If I were dying / Country jam / Don't bye, bye baby me / Heart of a fool / My love to remember / Latch on / Chicken shot blues / Mr. Fiddle / Dark lonely street.

LP: CFRC 505

MC: MCFRC 505

MEMORIAL ALBUM.

Tracks: / C'mon everybody / Three steps to heaven / Cut across shorty / Jeannie, Jeannie, Jeannie / Pocketful of hearts / Hallelujah, I love her so / Don't ever let me go / Summertime blues / Teresa / Something else / Pretty girl / Teenage heaven / Boll weevil / I remember.

LP: LBS 83009

LP: HAG 2267

LP: LBY 1127

MY WAY.

Tracks: / My way / Little angel / Love again / I almost lost my mind / Little Lou / Gwybo.

LP: LBYF 1205

ON THE AIR.

LP: 2C 068 93841

PORTRAIT OF A LEGEND.

LP: RSRLP 1008

RECORD DATE.

LP: BLK 7706

REMEMBER ME.

LP: LBYF 1133

ROCK 'N' ROLL HEROES (Cochran, Eddie & Gene Vincent).

Tracks: / Say mama / Summertime / Something else / Hallelujah I love her so / Wildcat / My heart / What'd I say / Milk cow blues / Rock road blues / Be bop a lula / Twenty flight rock.

LP: 2610221

MC: 2610224

LP: RSRLP 1004

SINGIN' TO MY BABY.

LP: LBYF 1158

LP: HAU 2093

SOMETHIN' ELSE.

LP: 5003

SUMMERTIME BLUES AND OTHER HITS.

Tracks: / Summertime blues / Drive-in show / Sittin' in the balcony / Jeannie, Jeannie, Jeannie / Blue suede shoes / Nervous breakdown / Three steps to heaven / Cut across shorty / Teenage heaven.

MC: 4XLL 9086

THEIR FINEST YEARS 1956 & 1958 (Cochran, Eddie & Gene Vincent).

Tracks: / Be bop a lula / Woman love / Race with the devil / Gonna back up baby / Blue jean bop / Who slapped John / Important words / Crazy legs / Summertime blues / Jeannie, Jeannie, Jeannie / Love again / C'mon everybody / Don't ever let me go / Pretty girl / Teenage heaven / I remember.

LP: CGB 1007

MC: TC GB 1007

LP: IC 046 78036

THINKIN' ABOUT YOU.

Tracks: / Thinkin' about you / Song of New Orleans / My love to remember / I hates rabbits / Pushin' / I.O.U. / My lovin' baby / Borrowed love / Don't bye, bye baby me / Tood a loo / Annie has a party / Quick like / Fast jivin' / Half loved / Pretty little devil / Love charms / Jelly

bean / Scratchin' / Dark lonely street / So fine be mine / Walkin' stick boogie / Rollin' / Broken hearted fellow / Cryin' in one eye.
LP: RSRLP 1019

VERY BEST OF EDDIE COCHRAN (15th anniversary album).
Tracks: / C'mon everybody / Three steps to heaven / Weekend / Skinny Jim / Completely sweet / Milk cow blues / Cut across shorty / Hallelujah, I love her so / Something else / Blue suede shoes / Eddie's blues (instrumental) / Sittin' in the balcony / Summertime blues / Twenty flight rock / Three stars / Cherished memories.
LP: FA 3019
MC: TCFA 3019
LP: LBS 83337

WALKIN'.
LP: RSREP 2004

WORDS AND MUSIC.
LP: RSRLP 1005

YOUNG EDDIE COCHRAN.
LP: RSRLP 1006

Cochran, Jack Waukeen

LONESOME DRIFTER.
Tracks: / Swamp Billy / Hell to pay / Mama don't you think I know? / After midnite blues / My mama laid the law down / It's alright with me / Lonesome drifter / Rock on / Don't wanna be lonely, I / Tender loving care / Lonesome town / Live it up / I musta drove my mules too hard / Bullhead city.
LP: ABOUT 1005

Cochran, Jackie Lee

FIDDLE FIT MAN.
Tracks: / Fiddle fit man / Out across the tracks / Trouble is her name / Why don't I leave you alone / Rock and roll blues / Wasting love / Bayou Joe / She's mine all mine / Peace of mind / Greasy dollar bill / Rock'n'roll refrain / Billy is a rocker.
LP: WIK 44

JACK THE CAT.
LP: BLK 7701

ROCKABILLY LEGEND.
Tracks: / Rockabilly legend / Gal's wicked, The / They oughta call you Miss Heartbreak / Lovin' I crave, The / Walkin', cryin' blues / Lulu / Dance doll / Ain't gonna let it happen / Boogie woogie man gonna getcha / Memories / I love you a thousand ways / She rocks me.
LP: MFLP 045
LP: LP 010

SWAMP FOX.
LP: LP 005

Cochrane, Brenda

FRANKIE (see under D,agostino, Frankie) (Cochrane, Brenda/D,agostino, Frankie).

IN DREAMS.
Tracks: / Homeland / Crazy / My foolish heart / In dreams / Love has no pride / Sacrifice / Bridge over troubled water / Always on my mind / I can't let go / Desperado / Unchained melody / Flame.
MC: 8490344
LP: 8490331

SINGER, THE.
LP: DAZLP 1
MC: ZCDAZ 1

VOICE, THE.
Tracks: / You're the voice / Pearl's a singer / Right here waiting for you / New York, New York / You've lost that lovin' feeling / You make lovin' fun / I want to know what love is / Wind beneath my wings / Easy to love / Put the weight on my shoulders / All night long.
LP: 843 141 1
MC: 843 141 4

Cock 'n' Bull Band

CONCRETE ROUTES, SACRED COWS.
LP: FMSL 2015
MC: FMSL 2015C

EYES CLOSED AND ROCKING.
LP: 12TS 440

Cock Robin

AFTER HERE THROUGH MIDLAND.
Tracks: / Just around the corner / Biggest fool of all, The / El norte / I'll send them your way / Another story / Coward's courage / Every moment / Precious dreams / After here through midland.
LP: 4508901
MC: 4508904

COCK ROBIN.
Tracks: / Thought you were on my side / Just when you're having fun / Promise you made, The / Because it keeps on working / Born with teeth / Once we might have known / More than willing / Little innocence, A / When your heart is weak.
LP: 26448
MC: 40 26448

FIRST LOVE/LAST RITES.
Tracks: / Stumble and fall / Straighter line / Win or lose / One joy bang / For experiencing sake / Hunting down a killer / Any more than I could understand / My first confession / Manzanar / Worlds apart.
LP: 4659431
MC: 4659434

Cock Sparrer

LIVE AND LOUD.
LP: LINK LP 05

RUNNING RIOT IN '84.
LP: SYNLP 7

SHOCK TROOPS.
Tracks: / Working / Out on an island / Take 'em all / We're coming back.
LP: RAZ 9

TRUE GRIT.
Tracks: / We love you / Sister Suzie / Platinum blonde / Taken for a ride / Again again / Runnin' riot / Chip on my shoulder / Watcha gonna do about it / Teenage heart / I need a witness.
LP: RAZ 26

Cockburn, Bruce

BIG CIRCUMSTANCE.
Tracks: / If a tree falls / Shipwrecked at the stable door / Gospel of bondage / Don't feel your touch / Tibetan side of town / Understanding nothing / Where the death squad lives / Radium rain / Pangs of love / Gift, The / Anything can happen.
LP: REVLP 122
MC: REVMC 122

BRUCE COCKBURN.
LP: WTN 1
MC: WTNT 1

CIRCLES IN THE STREAM.
LP: GTN 30

DANCING IN THE DRAGON'S JAWS.
Tracks: / Creation dream / Hills of the morning / Badlands flashback / Northern lights / After the rain / Wondering where the lions are / Incandescent blue / No footprints.
LP: TN 37
LP: MYR R 6840
MC: MYR C 6840
LP: FL 17747
MC: REVMC 127
LP: REVLP 127

FURTHER ADVENTURES OF....
LP: TN 30

HIGH WINDS, WHITE SKY.
LP: WTN 3

HUMANS.
Tracks: / Grim travellers / Rumours of glory / More not more / You get bigger as you go / What about the bond? / How I spent my fall vacation / Guerilla betrayed / Tokyo / Fascist architecture / Rose above the sky, The.
LP: FL 17752
LP: TN 42
MC: TNT 42
LP: REVLP 124
MC: REVMC 124

IN THE FALLING DARK.
Tracks: / Lord of the starfields / Vagabondage / In the falling dark / Little seahorse / Water into wine / Silver wheels / Giftbearer / Gavin's woodpile / I'm gonna fly someday / Festival of friends.
LP: WTN 26

INNER CITY FRONT.
LP: P 88479
LP: TN 47
MC: TNT 47

JOY WILL FIND A WAY.
LP: WTN 23
MC: WTNT 23

LIVE.
Tracks: / Silver wheels / World of wonders / Rumours of glory / See how I miss you / After the rain / Call it democracy / Wondering where the lions are / Nicaragua / Broken wheel / Stolen land / Always look on the bright side of life / Tibetan side of town (CD and cassette only.) / To raise the morning star (CD and cassette only.) / Maybe the poet (CD and cassette only.).
LP: COOK 034
MC: COOKC 034

NIGHT VISION.
LP: TN 11
MC: TNT 11

SALT, SUN AND TIME.
MC: WTNT 16
LP: WTN 16

STEALING FIRE.
LP: SPIN 112
MC: REVMC 125
LP: REVLP 125

SUNWHEEL DANCE.
LP: STN 7
MC: WTNT 7
LP: WTNX 7

TROUBLE WITH NORMAL.
LP: TN 53
MC: TNT 53
LP: REVLP 126
MC: REVMC 126

WAITING FOR A MIRACLE (Singles 1970-1987).
Tracks: / Mama just wants to barrelhouse all night long / All the diamonds in the world / Burn / Silver wheels / Laughter / Wondering where the lions are / Tokyo / Fascist architecture / Trouble with normal, The / Rumours of glory / Coldest night of the year / You pay your money and take your chance / Lovers in a dangerous time / If I had a rocket launcher / Peggy's kitchen wall / People see through you / Call it democracy / Stolen land / Waiting for a miracle / One day I walk / It's going down slow.
2LP: REV LP 90
MC: REV MC 90

WORLD OF WONDERS.
Tracks: / They call it democracy / Lily of the midnight sky / World of wonder / Berlin tonight / People see through you / See how I miss you / Santiago dawn / Dancing in paradise / Down here tonight.
LP: REV LP 73
MC: REV MC 73

Cocker, Joe

16 GREATEST HITS: JOE COCKER.
LP: FUN 9015

CIVILIZED MAN.
Tracks: / Civilized man / There goes my baby / Come on in / Tempted / Long drag off a cigarette / I love the night / Crazy in love / Girl like you, A / Hold on (I feel our love is changing) / Even a fool would let go.
LP: EJ 2401391
MC: EJ 2401394
LP: ATAK 115
MC: TCATAK 115

COCKER.
Tracks: / You can leave your hat on / Heart of the matter / Inner city blues / Love is on a fade / Heaven / Shelter me / A to Z / Don't you love me anymore / Livin' without your love / Don't drink the water.
LP: EST 2009
MC: TCEST 2009
LP: ATAK 114
MC: TCATAK 114
LP: FA 3227
MC: TCFA 3227

COCKER HAPPY.
LP: FEDB 5011
MC: CFEDB 5011
MC: CLAMC 238

COLLECTION: JOE COCKER.
Tracks: / I can stand a little rain / It's a sin when you love somebody / Jamaica say you will / High time we went / Just like a woman / Do I still figure in your life / With a little help from my friends / Lawdy Miss Clawdy / Darling be home soon / Hello little friend / Pardon me sir / Marjorine / Midnight rider - live in L.A. / Love the one you're with (live) (In L.A.) / Bird on the wire / Feeling alright / Let's go get stoned / Girl from the north country / Give peace a chance / She came in through the bathroom window / Space captain / Letter, The / Delta lady / Honky tonk women / Cry me a river.
MC: CCSMC 126
2LP: CCSLP 126

GREATEST HITS: JOE COCKER VOL.1.
LP: SHM 954

GREATEST HITS:JOE COCKER.
LP: PLP 32
MC: PMC 32

I CAN STAND A LITTLE RAIN.
Tracks: / Put out the light / I can stand a little rain / I get mad / Sing me a song / Moon is a harsh mistress, The / Don't forget me / You are so beautiful / It's a sin when you love somebody / Performance / Guilty.
LP: HIFLY 18
MC: ZCFLY 18
LP: CLALP 144
MC: CLAMC 144

JAMAICA SAY YOU WILL.
MC: CLAMC 237

JAMAICA SAY YOU WILL/COCKER HAPPY.
Tracks: / (That's what I like) in my woman / Where am I now / I think it's going to rain today / Forgive me now / Oh Mama / Lucinda / If I love you / Jamaica say you will / It's all over but the shouting / Jack o' diamonds / Hitchcock railway / She came in through the bathroom window / Marjorine / She's so good to me / Hello little friend / With a little help from my friends / Delta lady / Darling be home soon / Do I still figure in your life / Feeling alright / Something's coming on / Letter, The.
2LP: TFOLP 4
MC: TFOMC 4

JOE COCKER.
Tracks: / With a little help from my friends / Just like a woman / I shall be released / I can stand a little rain / Something / Midnight rider / Feeling alright / Cry me a river / High time we went / Marjorine / Letter, The / Something to say.
LP: COUNT 12
MC: ZC CNT 12
MC: CLAMC 236

JOE COCKER LIVE.
Tracks: / Feeling alright / Shelter me / Hitchcock railway / Up where we belong / Guilty / You can leave your hat on / When the night comes / Unchain my heart / With a little help from my friends / You are so beautiful / Letter, The / She came in through the bathroom window / High time we went / What are you doing with a fool like me / Living in the promise land.
2LP: ESTSP 25
2LP: 793 417 1
MC: TCESTSP 25
MC: 793 416 4

JOE COCKER/WITH A LITTLE HELP FROM MY FRIENDS.
2LP: TOOFA 1/2

LIVE IN L.A..
Tracks: / Dear landlord / Early in the mornin' / Didn't you know you've got to cry sometimes / St. James infirmary / What kind of man are you / Hitchcock railway / Midnight rider / High times we went / Love the one you're with.
LP: FEDB 5037
MC: CFEDB 5037
LP: CLALP 189
MC: CLAMC 189

LUXURY YOU CAN AFFORD.
Tracks: / Fun time / Watching the river flow / Boogie baby / Whiter shade of pale, A / I can't say no / Southern lady / I know (you don't want me no more) / What you did to me last night / Lady put the light out / Wasted years / I heard it through the grapevine.
LP: K 53087

MAD DOGS AND ENGLISHMEN.
Tracks: / Honky tonk women / Sticks and stones / Cry me a river / Bird on the wire / Feeling alright / Superstar / Let's go get stoned / I'll drown in my own tears / When something is wrong with my baby / I've been loving you too long / Girl from the North Country / Give peace a chance / She came in through the bathroom window / Space captain / Letter, The / Delta lady.
2LP: AMLD 6002
2LP: AMLS 6002
MCSET: CDM 6002

NIGHT CALLS.
Tracks: / Love is alive / Little bit of love, A / Please no more / There's a storm coming / You've got to hide your love away / I can hear the river / Don't let the sun go down on me / Night calls / Five women / Can't find my way home / Not too young to die of a broken heart / Out of the rain.
LP: ESTU 2156
MC: TCESTU 2156

NIGHTRIDING: JOE COCKER.
Tracks: / With a little help from my friends / Marjorine / Delta lady / Letter, The / Dear landlord / Hitchcock railway / That's your business now / Something's coming on / Just like a woman / Don't let me be misunderstood / Sandpaper cadillac / I shall be released.
MC: KNMC 10001
LP: KNLP 10001

OFF THE RECORD WITH JOE COCKER.
2LP: FEDD 1002
MCSET: CFEDD 1002

ONE NIGHT OF SIN.
Tracks: / When the night comes / I will live for you / I've got to use (my imagination) / Letting go / Just to keep from drowning / Unforgiven, The (Not on album.) / Another mind gone / Fever / You know it's gonna hurt / Bad bad sign / I'm your man / One night.
MC: TCEST 2098
LP: EST 2098

PLATINUM COLLECTION.
Tracks: / With a little help from my friends / Don't let me be misunderstood /

Bird on the wire / I shall be released / Just like a woman / Do right woman, do right man / Let it be / Something / Where am I now? / Darling be home soon / Do I still figure in your life? / I can stand a little rain / Letter, The / Marjorine / She came in through the bathroom window / Dear landlord / High time we went / St. James' Infirmary / Delta lady / Feeling alright / Cry me a river / Midnight rider / Hitchcock railway / Sandpaper cadillac.
LP: . . . . . **PLAT 1004**
MC: . . . . . **ZCPLT 1004**

SHEFFIELD STEEL.
Tracks: / Look what you've done / Shocked / Seven days / Marie / Ruby Lee / Many rivers to cross / Talking back to the night / Just like always / Sweet little woman / So good, so right.
LP: . . . . . **ILPS 9700**
MC: . . . . . **ICT 9700**

SOMETHING TO SAY.
Tracks: / Pardon me sir / High time we went / She don't mind / Black eye blues / Something to say / Night rider / Do right woman / Woman to woman / St. James infirmary.
LP: . . . . . **CLALP 207**
MC: . . . . . **CLAMC 207**

SPACE CAPTAIN.
Tracks: / Honky tonk women / Love the one you're with / Letter, The / She came in through the bathroom window / Cry me a river / Delta lady.
LP: . . . . . **ICS 1002**
MC: . . . . . **ZCICS 1002**

UNCHAIN MY HEART.
Tracks: / Unchain my heart / One, The / Two wrongs (don't make a right) / I stand in wonder / River's rising, The / Isolation / All our tomorrows / Woman loves a man, A / Trust in me / Satisfied / You can leave your hat on.
LP: . . . . . **EST 2045**
MC: . . . . . **TC EST 2045**
LP: . . . . . **FA 3240**
MC: . . . . . **TCFA 3240**

UP WHERE WE BELONG (See under Warnes, Jennifer) (Cocker, Joe & Jennifer Warnes).

VERY BEST OF JOE COCKER, THE (The Voice).
Tracks: / With a little help from my friends / Honky tonk women / Delta lady / Marjorine / Don't let me be misunderstood / Something / Pardon me sir / Talking back to the night / Up where we belong (With Jennifer Warnes.) / She came in through the bathroom window / Letter, The / Just like a woman / Jamaica say you will / Cry me a river / Midnight rider / Let it be.
LP: . . . . . **STAR 2258**
MC: . . . . . **STAC 2258**

WITH A LITTLE HELP FROM MY FRIENDS.
Tracks: / Feeling alright / Bye Bye blackbird / Change in Louise / Marjorie / Just like a woman / Do I still figure in your life / Sandpaper Cadillac / Don't let me be misunderstood / With a little help from my friends / I shall be released.
LP: . . . . . **CLALP 172**
MC: . . . . . **CLAMC 172**

WITH A LITTLE HELP FROM MY FRIENDS.
Tracks: / With a little help from my friends / Marjorine / Letter, The / Dear landlord / Bird on the wire / Lawdy Miss Clawdy / She came in through the bathroom window / Hitchcock railway / That's your business now / Something / Delta lady / Hello little friend / Darling be home soon / Feeling alright / Bye bye blackbird / Change in Louise / Just like a woman / Do I still figure in your life? / Sandpaper cadillac / Don't let me be misunderstood / I shall be released.
LP: . . . . . **TOOFA 1**
MC: . . . . . **ZCTOF 1**

Cockerel Boys

MBUBE JIVE & SOUL.
LP: . . . . . **LR 44.009**

Cockers Dale

DOIN' THE MANCH'.
Tracks: / Doin' the manch / Black and bitter night / Jack Ashton / Coal town road / Normandy orchards / Knocking at the door / Weary cutters / When all the world / Morley main / Home lads home.
LP: . . . . . **FE 072**
MC: . . . . . **FE 072C**

PROSPECT, PROVIDENCE.
LP: . . . . . **ESLP 001**

Cockney Rebel

HUMAN MENAGERIE, THE.
Tracks: / Hideaway / What Ruthy said / Loretta's tale / Crazy raver / Sebastian / Mirror freak / My only vice / Muriel the actor / Chameleon / Death trip / Judy Teen (CD only.) / Rock and roll parade (CD only.).
LP: . . . . . **IC 072 05438**

HUMAN MENAGERIE/ PSYCHOMODO.
Tracks: / Sweet dreams / Psychomodo / Mr. Soft / Singular band / Ritz / Cavaliers / Bed in the corner / Sling it / Tumbling down / Hideaway / What Ruthy said / Loretta's tale / Crazy raver / Sebastian / Mirror freak / My only vice / Muriel the actor / Chameleon / Death trip.
2LP: . . . . . **EDP 154 677 3**

MR SOFT (SINGLE) (see under Harley, Steve).

PSYCHOMODO, THE.
Tracks: / Sweet dreams / Psychomodo / Mr. Soft / Singular band / Ritz / Cavaliers / Bed in the corner / Sling it / Tumbling down / Big big deal (CD only.) / Such a dream (CD only.).
LP: . . . . . **FA 41 3135 1**
MC: . . . . . **FA 41 3135 4**
LP: . . . . . **EMC 3033**

Cockney Rejects

GREATEST HITS: COCKNEY REJECTS VOL.2.
Tracks: / War on the terraces / In the underworld / Oi oi oi / Hate of the city / With the boys / Urban guerilla / Rocker, The / Greatest cockney rip off / Sitting in a cell / On the waterfront / We can do anything / It's alright / Subculture / Blockbuster.
LP: . . . . . **ZONO 102**

GREATEST HITS: COCKNEY REJECTS VOL 1.
Tracks: / Rocker, The / Bad man / I'm not a fool / On the waterfront / On the run / Hate of the city / Easy life / War on the terraces / Fighting in the streets / Greatest cockney rip off / Join the Rejects / Police car / East end / Motorhead.
LP: . . . . . **ZONO 101**
MC: . . . . . **TC ZONO 101**

LETHAL.
LP: . . . . . **NEAT 1049**

LIVE AND LOUD.
LP: . . . . . **LINK LP 09**

POWER AND THE GLORY.
Tracks: / Power and the glory / Because I'm in love / On the run / Lemon / Friends / Van Bollocks / Teenage fantasy / It's over / On the streets again / BYC / Greatest story ever told.
LP: . . . . . **ZONO 105**

UNHEARD REJECTS.
LP: . . . . . **WOW LP 2**

WE ARE THE FIRM.
Tracks: / I'm forever blowing bubbles / War on the terraces / On the water front / East end / Where the hell is Babylon / Headbanger / Oi, oi, oi / Greatest cockney rip off / Bad man / Power and the glory / Join the Rejects / I'm not a fool / Police car / Motorhead / We are the firm.
LP: . . . . . **DOJOLP 32**

Cocktail (film)

COCKTAIL (1988 Film Soundtrack) (Various artists).
Tracks: / Wild again: *Starship* / Powerful stuff: *Fabulous Thunderbirds* / Since when: *Nevil, Robbie*/ Don't worry, be happy: *McFerrin, Bobby* / Hippy hippy shake: *Georgia Satellites* / Kokomo: *Beach Boys*/ Rave on: *Mellencamp, John Cougar* / All shook up: *Cooder, Ry* / Oh, I love you so: *Smith, Preston* / Tutti frutti: *Little Richard.*
LP: . . . . . **EKT 54**
MC: . . . . . **EKT 54C**

Coco Tea

COCO TEA.
LP: . . . . . **JWH 871**

COME AGAIN.
LP: . . . . . **SPLP 2**

HOLDING ON (See under Home, T) (Coco Tea & Home T & Shabba Ranks).

RIKERS ISLAND (ALBUM).
LP: . . . . . **GREL 156**
MC: . . . . . **GREEN 156**

SETTLE DOWN.
LP: . . . . . **DSR 6160**

Cocoanuts (film)

COCOANUTS (Film soundtrack) (Marx Brothers).
LP: . . . . . **SH 2059**
MC: . . . . . **CSH 2059**

Coconuts (film)

COCONUTS (1929 film soundtrack) (Various artists).
LP: . . . . . **STK 109**

Cocoon (film)

COCOON (1985 Film Soundtrack) (Various artists).
Tracks: / Ascension, The: *Various artists* / Cocoon, Theme from: *Various artists* / Thru' the window: *Various artists* / Lovemaking, The: *Various artists* / Chase, The: *Various artists* / Rose's death: *Various artists*/ Boys are out, The: *Various artists* / Returning to the sea: *Various artists* / Gravity: *Various artists*/ Discovered in the poolhouse: *Various artists* / First tears: *Various artists* / Sad goodbyes: *Various artists.*
LP: **827 041-1**
MC: **827 041-4**

COCOON: THE RETURN (1989 Film Soundtrack) (Various artists).
LP: . . . . . **VS 5211**
MC: . . . . . **VSC 5211**

Cocteau, Jean (aut)

HUMAN VOICE, THE (see under Human Voice (bk) (Bergman, Ingrid (nar)).

Cocteau Twins

BLUE BELL KNOLL.
Tracks: / Blue bell knoll / Athol brose / Carolyn's fingers / For Phoebe still a baby / Itchy Glowbo / Cico buff / Suckling The Mender / Spooning good singing gum / Kissed out red floatboat, A / Ella megalast burls forever.
LP: . . . . . **CAD 807**
MC: . . . . . **CADC 807**
DAT: . . . . . **CAD T 807**

COCTEAU TWINS: INTERVIEW PICTURE DISC.
LPPD: . . . . . **BAK 2016**

GARLANDS.
Tracks: / Blood bitch / Wax and wane / But I'm not / Blind dumb deaf / Gail overfloweth / Shallow than hallow / Hollow men, The / Garlands.
LP: . . . . . **CAD 211**
MC: . . . . . **CADC 211**

HEAD OVER HEELS.
Tracks: / When mama was moth / Sugar hiccup / In our angelhood / Glass candle grenades / Multifoiled / In the gold dust rush / Tinderbox, The (of a heart) / My love paramour / Musette and drums / Five ten fiftyfold.
MC: . . . . . **CADC 313**
LP: . . . . . **CAD 313**
LP: . . . . . **ROSE 25**

HEAVEN OR LAS VEGAS.
Tracks: / Cherry coloured funk / Pitch the baby / Iceblink luck / Fifty-fifty clown / Heaven or Las Vegas / I wear your ring / Fotzepolitic / Wolf in the breast / River, road and rail / Frou-frou foxes in the midsummer fires.
LP: . . . . . **CAD 0012**
MC: . . . . . **CADC 0012**

PINK OPAQUE.
LP: . . . . . **ENC 8040**

TREASURE.
Tracks: / Ivo / Lorelei / Beatrix / Persephone / Pandora - for Cindy / Amelia / Aloysius / Cicely / Otterley / Donimo.
LP: . . . . . **CAD 412**
MC: . . . . . **CADC 412**

VICTORIA LAND.
Tracks: / Lazy calm / Fluffy tufts / Throughout the dark months of April and May / Whales tales / Oomingmac / Little spacey / Feet-like fins / How to bring a blush to the snow / Thinner the air, The.
LP: . . . . . **CAD 602**
MC: . . . . . **CADC 602**

Code Blue

CODE BLUE.
Tracks: / Whisper / Touch / Modern times / Hurt / Face to face / Burning bridges / Somebody knows / Other end of town / Where I am / Settle for less / Need, The / Paint by numbers.
LP: . . . . . **K 56868**

Code Industry

METHOD ASSEMBLY.
LP: . . . . . **AS 5020**

Codley

CODLEY.
LP: . . . . . **CEF 044**

Codona

CODONA 2.
LP: . . . . . **ECM 1177**

CODONA 3.
Tracks: / Goshakabuch / Hey da ba doom / Travel by night (Lullaby.) / Trayra boia / Clicky clacky / Inner organs.
LP: . . . . . **ECM 1243**

Coe, David Allan

CASTLE IN THE SAND.
Tracks: / Cheap thrills / Son of a rebel son / Fool inside of me / Castle in the sand / Gotta serve somebody / Ride / I can't let you be a memory / Missin' the kid / Don't be a stranger / For lovers only.
LP: . . . . . **CBS 25346**

D.A.C.
Tracks: / Looking in the mirror / Lyin' comes so easy to your lips / Last time she'll leave me this time, The / I gave up (on trying to get over you) / Voices / She loved the leavin' out of me / I'll never regret loving you / It's a sad situation / Those low down blues / Whisky, whisky (take my mind).
LP: . . . . . **CBS 85880**
MC: **40 85880**

DAVID ALLAN COE (I love country).
Tracks: / Would you lay with me (in a field of stone) / This bottle / Please come to Boston / Divers do it deeper / Stand by your man / Take it easy rider / Ride / Willie, Waylon and me.
LP: . . . . . **CBS 54945**
MC: **40 54945**

FOR THE RECORD - THE FIRST 10 YEARS.
Tracks: / You never even called me by my name / Please come to Boston / Jody like a melody / Longhaired redneck / If that ain't country / Tennessee whisky / Now I lay me down to cheat / What made you change your mind / Ride, The / Mona Lisa's lost her smile.
LP: . . . . . **CBS 88655**
MC: **40 88655**

HELLO IN THERE.
Tracks: / Crazy old soldier / Out of your mind / Mister, don't speak bad about my music / Drinkin' to forget / Gotta travel on / He will break your heart / For lovers only / Hello in there / Someone special / I ain't gonna let you go again.
LP: . . . . . **CBS 25722**

JUST DIVORCED.
Tracks: / Mona Lisa's lost her smile / Sweet Angeline / He's taking it hard / For lovers only / Thief in my bedroom / Just divorced / It's great to be single again / Blue grass morning / I wanna know I'm goin' home / For your precious love.
LP: . . . . . **CBS 26012**

MATTER OF LIFE AND DEATH, A.
Tracks: / Ten commandments of love / Jody like a melody / Tanya Montana / If only your eyes could lie / Need a little time off for bad behaviour / Southern star / Actions speak louder than words / Child of God / Wild Irish rose / It's a matter of life and death.
LP: **4504791**
MC: **4504794**

TEXAS MOON.
Tracks: / Got you on my mind / These days / Satisfied mind, A / Why you been gone so long / Why me, Mary Magdeline / Fuzzy was an outlaw / That old time feeling / Ride me down easy / Give my love to Rose.
LP: . . . . . **CRL 5006**

UNCHAINED.
LP: . . . . . **CBS 26742**
MC: **40 26742**

Coe, Jimmy

AFTER HOUR JOINT.
LP: . . . . . **DL 443**

Coe, Pete

GAME OF ALL FOURS (Coe, Pete & Chris).
LP: . . . . . **SHY 7007**

GREATEST PUB BAND IN THE LAND (Coe, Pete Big Band).
LP: . . . . . **JAM 647**

IT'S A MEAN OLD SCENE.
LP: . . . . . **BASH 39**

LIVE AT LEATHER BOTTLE (Coe, Pete Big Band).
LP: . . . . . **JAM 650**

OPEN THE DOOR AND LET US IN (Coe, Pete & Chris).
Tracks: / Acting song / Banks of red roses, The / Cheshire May day carol / Lady diamond / False knight / Joseph Baker / Wizard of Alderley Edge, The / Wife of ushers well, The / Egloshayle ringers / Plains of Waterloo, The / High of Lincoln / Gay fusiliers, The.
LP: . . . . . **LER 2077**

OUT OF SEASON OUT OF RHYME (Coe, Pete & Chris).
LP: . . . . . **LER 2098**

RIGHT SONG AND DANCE, A.
LP: . . . . . **BASH 43**

Coe, Tony

CANTERBURY SONG.
Tracks: / Canterbury song / How beautiful is the night / Light blue / Sometime ago / Re: person I knew / I guess I'll hang my tears out to dry / Lagos / Blue in green.
LP: . . . . . **HH 1005**
MC: . . . . . **HHMC 1005**

COE-EXISTENCE.
LP: . . . . . **LAM 100**

LE CHAT SE RETOURNE.

Tracks: / Marche funebre d'une marionnette - gounod / Paul / Petite suite en Avion I / Three for thee / Petite suite en Avion II / Les yeux prasins (I) / Les yeux prasins (II) / An-og mhadainn.
LP: NATO 257

MAINLY MANCINI.
Tracks: / Pink panther / Crazy world / Hank neuf / Mister lucky / Mancinissimo / Days of wine and roses / Charade.
LP: CHABADA 08

MER DE CHINE (See under Films).

TONY COE.
LP: HEP 2038

TOURNEE DU CHAT.
Tracks: / Jolly corner, The / Makoko / Vive la chantenay / Iberiana / Debussy.
LP: NATO 19

Coen, Charlie

IRISH MUSIC FESTIVAL - FOURTH ANNIVERSARY.
MC: GVMMC 501

Coen, Jack

BRANCH LINE, THE (Irish Traditional Music From Galway to New York) (Coen, Jack & Charlie).
Tracks: / Scatter the mud / Larry Redigan's jig / Sailor's cravat, The / Repeal of the union / John Conroy's jig / Peach blossom, The / Fiddler's contest / Jim Conroy's reel / Pullet, The / Redican's mother / Humours of Kilkenny, The / Mike Coen's polka / Branch line, The / Have a drink with me / Blarney pilgrim / Two woodford flings / Waddling gander, The / O'Connell's jig on top of Mount Everest / Lads of Laois / Green groves of Erin, The / Tongs by the fire, The / Spinning wheel / Whelan's reel / Jenny dang the weaver / Jack Coen's jig / Paddy O'Brien's jig.
LP: 12TS 337

Coetzee, Basil

SABENZA.
LP: BIG 001

Coffee

SLIPPIN' AND DIPPIN'.
Tracks: / Slip and dip / Mom and Dad 1980 / I wanna be with you / Casanova / Promise / Can you get to this.
LP: 6359 028

Coffey, Dennis

BACK HOME.
Tracks: / Funk connection / Back home / Free spirit / Our love goes on / Forever / High on love / Boogie magic / Wings of fire.
LP: K 50371

INSTANT COFFEY.
LP: LPSX 9

Coffin Break

RUPTURE.
LP: TUPLP 20

Coffin Nails

EIN BIER BITTE.
LP: NERD 031

LIVE 'N' ROCKIN'.
LP: LINKLP 118

Cogan, Alma

ALMA COGAN.
LP: IM 048 05512

ALMANAC, THE.
Tracks: / I love to sing / Cheek to cheek / Life is just a bowl of cherries / They can't take that away from me / Taking a chance on love / Ain't we got fun / You do something to me / I wish you love / Love is a word / Today I love ev'rybody / If this isn't love / As time goes by / Comes love / Blue skies / Love you I will / Que bueno, que beuno / Let her go / Trains and boats and planes / Ticket to ride / I get a kick out of you / There's a time and place / Eight days a week / Yesterday / I feel fine / Jolly good company / More / Don't you know / Yokomo? / Now that I've found you / Help.
2LP: DL 1191
MC: TCDL 1191

CELEBRATION, A.
Tracks: / Why do fools fall in love / Tennessee waltz / I can't tell a waltz from a tango / We got love / Dreamboat / Somebody loves me / Lizzie Borden / Never do a tango with an eskimo / Bell bottom blues / Banjo's back in town / To be worthy of you / Stairway of love / Where will the baby's dimple be / Sycamore tree, The / Sitting in the sun / That's happiness / If I had a golden umbrella / Do do do do it again (with Frankie Vaughan) / Love and marriage / Willie can / Eight days a week / Baubles, bangles and beads / There is a time and place / I love to sing / Love is just around the corner / My one and only love / Naughty lady of Shady Lane / He just couldn't resist her with her pocket transistor / Tell him / Hava nagila / Cheek to cheek / Love is / I get a kick out of you / Come love / Blue skies / Wouldn't it be loverly / I want to whisper something / You were meant for me / Give a fool a chance / Jolly good company.
2LP: EM 1280
MCSET: TCEM 1280

EMI YEARS, THE: ALMA COGAN (Best Of).
Tracks: / You me and us / Bell bottom blues / Mambo Italiano / Got 'n idea / Last night on the back porch / It's all been done before / Lucky lips / Fly away lovers / Little shoemaker, The / Chiqu chaqui / I can't tell a waltz from a tango / Ricochet / I love you bit, The / Never do a tango with an eskimo / Little things mean a lot / Gettin' ready for Freddy / Mama says / Dreamboat / Said the little moment / In the middle of the house.
LP: EMS 1378
MC: TCEMS 1378

SECOND COLLECTION.
LP: OU 2213

VERY BEST OF ALMA COGAN (16 Favourites of the 50's).
Tracks: / Last night on the back porch / Willie can / Birds and the bees, The / Dreamboat / Hernando's hideaway / Little things mean a lot / In the middle of the house / Never do a tango with an eskimo / Twenty tiny fingers / You me and us / I can't tell a waltz from a tango / Go on by / Why do fools fall in love / Bell bottom blues / Whatever Lola wants (Lola gets) / Sugartime.
LP: MFP 415 643 1
MC: TCMFP 4156434

WITH LOVE IN MIND.
Tracks: / Somebody loves me / Can't help falling in love / Hello young lovers / Our love affair / Love me as though there were no tomorrow / Love is just around the corner / Let me love you / If love were all / With you in mind / I dream of you more than you dream I do / Let's fall in love / In other words / My heart stood still / But beautiful / You'll never know / All I do is dream of you / What is there to say / Don't blame me / Falling in love with love / More I see you, The / Can't give you anything but love / I've never been in love before / Lady's in love with you, The / I'm in the mood for love.
2LP: DL 41 1084 3
MC: DL 41 1084 9
2LP: DL 1084
MC: TC DL 1084

YOU BELONG TO ME.
MC: CMOIR 401

Coghill, Bobby

FAR FAE HAME.
LP: WGR 005
MC: CWGR 005

FROM SCOTLAND TO CANADA WITH BOBBY COGHILL'S BAND SHOW (Coghill, Bobby Band Show).
MC: CWGR 100

HIGHLAND DANCE ALBUM.
LP: WGR 041
MC: CWGR 041

HIGHLAND GATHERING (Coghill, Bobby Scottish Dance Band).
LP: WGR 083
MC: CWGR 083

PIPING HOT ACCORDION.
MC: CWGR 036

SCOTTISH BAND SHOW.
LP: WGR 009
MC: CWGR 009

Coghill, Bryan

BY NORTHERN SHORES.
MC: CWGR 039

CHEORDAG SITHERLAND AT'E LETHERAN SHOW.
MC: CJR 001

Coghill, Sandy

JUST FOR THE CRACK.
Tracks: / Seamus McNeil / Piper Major Sam Scott / Apple tree, The / CTS Empress / Agnes Ritchie / Inverness gathering, The / Agnes waltz, The / Jig of slurs, The / Lochhaber gathering, The / Madame Bonaparte / MacNeils of Ugadale / Glens of Angus, The / Teetotaller, The / Arthur Bignold of Loch Rosque / Livingstone accordion club, The / Duke of Fife's welcome to Deeside.
LP: REL 457
MC: REC 457

OUT THE BOX (Coghill, Sandy & Neil McMillan).
LP: LAP 103
MC: LAP 103 C

Cogic Choir

FORGIVEN.
LP: MYR 1178
MC: MC 1178

HE'S GOT THE WHOLE WORLD IN HIS HANDS.
LP: MYR R 1225
MC: MYR C 1225

Cohan, George M.

YANKEE DOODLE DANDY.
LP: OL 7111

Cohen, David

HOW TO PLAY FOLK GUITAR.
Tracks: / Blues for my honey / Butcher boy / When you and I were young Maggie / Bank of the Ohio / Tisket a tasket, A / God rest ye merry gentlemen / This land is your land / Freight train / Wilson rag / Deck the halls / Fair and tender ladies / Bolden's farethewell blues / Hop high ladies / Greenland whale fisheries / Wildwood flower / Ragtime cowgirl / Chromatic octaves / My creole belle.
LP: SNKF 118

ROCK 'N' ROLL GUITAR (Cohen, David Bennett).
Tracks: / Chains / Trucking rockabilly blues / Easy rider / Get down Lulu / C.B. rocket / Home fries / Patchwork / Corina, Corina / Humboldt county / House of the rising sun.
LP: SNKF 141
LP: KM 153

Cohen, Izhar

MAKE A LITTLE LOVE (Cohen, Izhar & Alphabeta).
Tracks: / Make a little love / We go dancing / Life's a long way to run / Gingette / Blue / A-ba-ni-bi / Phoenix / Fly with the samba / What exactly do you want / Is that you / Deep inside.
LP: 231 063 1

Cohen, Leonard

6 TRACK HITS: LEONARD COHEN.
Tracks: / Paper thin hotel / Bird on the wire / Lady Midnight / Joan of Arc / Suzanne / Hey, that's no way to say goodbye.
MC: 7SC 5022

DEATH OF A LADIES MAN.
Tracks: / True love leaves no traces / Iodine / Paper thin hotel / Memories / I left a woman waiting / Don't go home with your hard-on / Fingerprints / Death of a ladies man.
LP: 32661
MC: 40 32661
LP: CBS 86042

GREATEST HITS: LEONARD COHEN.
Tracks: / Suzanne / Sisters of mercy / So long, Marianne / Bird on the wire / Lady Midnight / Partisan, The / Hey, that's no way to say goodbye / Famous blue raincoat / Last year's man / Chelsea Hotel no.2 / Who by fire / Take this longing.
LP: CBS 32644
MC: 40 32644

I'M YOUR MAN.
Tracks: / First we take Manhattan / Ain't no cure for love / Everybody knows / I'm your man / Take this waltz / Jazz police / I can't forget / Tower of song.
LP: 4606421
MC: 4606424

NEW SKIN FOR THE OLD CEREMONY.
Tracks: / Is this what you wanted / Chelsea Hotel no.2 / Lover lover lover / Field Commander Cohen / Why don't you try / There is a war / Singer must die, A / I tried to leave you / Leaving green sleeves / Who by fire / Take this longing.
MC: 40 32660
LP: CBS 69087

RECENT SONGS.
Tracks: / Guests, The / Humbled in love / Window / Came so far for beauty / Lost Canadian, The (Un Canadien errant) / Traitor / Our lady of solitude / Gypsy's wife, The / Smokey life, The / Ballad of the absent mare.
LP: CBS 86097

SONGS FROM A ROOM.
Tracks: / Bird on the wire / Story of Isaac / Bunch of lonesome heroes, A / Seems so long ago / Nancy / Old revolution, The / Butcher, The / You know who I am / Lady Midnight / Tonight will be fine.
LP: CBS 32074
MC: 40 32074
LP: CBS 63587
LP: 32071
MC: 32074

SONGS OF LEONARD COHEN, THE.
Tracks: / Suzanne / Master song / Winter lady / Stranger song, The / Sisters of mercy / So long, Marianne / Hey, that's no way to say goodbye / Stories of the street teachers / One of us cannot be wrong.
LP: CBS 63241
MC: 40 63241

SONGS OF LOVE AND HATE.
Tracks: / Avalanche / Last year's man / Dress rehearsal rag / Diamonds in the mine field / Love calls you by your name / Famous blue raincoat / Sing another song, boys / Joan of Arc.
LP: CBS 32219
LP: CBS 69004
MC: 40 32219

VARIOUS POSITIONS.
Tracks: / Dance me to the end of love / Coming back to you / Law, The / Night comes on / Hallelujah / Captain, The / Hunter's lullaby / Heart with no companion / If it be your will.
LP: CBS 26222
LP: 4655691
MC: 4655694

Cohn, Al

AL AND ZOOT (Cohn, Al Quintet feat. Zoot Sims).
Tracks: / It's a wonderful world / Brandy and beer / Two funky people / Chasing the blues / Halley's comet / You're a lucky guy / Wailing boat, The / Just you, just me.
LP: JASM 1014

AMERICA.
LP: XAN 138

BODY AND SOUL (Cohn, Al & Zoot Sims).
LP: MR 5016

BROTHERS, THE (Cohn, Al/Bill Perkins/ Richie Kamuca).
Tracks: / Blixed / Kim's kaper / Rolling stone / Sioux zan / Walrus, The / Blue skies / Gay blade / Three of a kind / Hags / Pro-ex / Strange again / Cap snapper.
LP: PL 43240

DATE IN NEW YORK VOL 2 (Cohn, Al & Jay Jay Johnson).
LP: 500096
LP: JL 96

EITHER WAY (Cohn, Al & Zoot Sims).
Tracks: / P-Town / I like it like that / Sweet Lorraine / Autumn leaves / Thing, The / I'm tellin' ya / Nagasaki / Morning fun.
LP: ZMS 2002

FOUR BRASS, ONE TENOR.
Tracks: / Rosetta / Song is ended, The / Linger awhile / Every time / Haroosh / Just plain Sam / I'm coming, Virginia / Cohn, not Cohen / Little song / Foggy water / Sugar Cohn / Alone together.
2LP: PM 45164

FROM A TO Z (Cohn, Al & Zoot Sims Sextet).
Tracks: / Mediolistic / Crimea river / New moan, A / Moment's notice, A / My blues / Sandy's swing / Somebody loves me.
LP: PM 42303
LP: NL 89644

HAPPY OVER HOAGY (See under Sims, Zoot) (Sims, Zoot & Al Cohn Septet).

KEEPER OF THE FLAME (Cohn, Al Metts Jazz Seven).
Tracks: / Bilbo Baggins / Mood indigo / Casa 50 comp / Keeper of the flame / High on you / Feel more like I do now.
LP: FRG 717

MOTORING ALONG (Cohn, Al & Zoot Sims).
Tracks: / Stockholm - LA / My funny Valentine / Yardbird suite / Motoring along / Falling / What the world needs now is love.
LP: SNTF 684
MC: ZCSN 684

MPS JAZZ TIME,VOLUME 10 (Cohn, Al & James Moody).
LP: 5C 064 61173

NATURAL RHYTHM (see under Greene, Freddie) (Green, Freddie/Al Cohn).

NATURAL SEVEN, THE.
LP: NL 89278

NIGHT FLIGHT TO DAKAR (Cohn,Al/ Billy Mitchell/D. Coker/Leroy Vinnegar/ Frank Butler).
Tracks: / Night flight to Dakar / Don't let the sun catch you cryin' / Blues up and down / Sweet Senegelese Brown / King, The.
LP: XAN 185

NON PAREIL.
LP: CJ 155

OVERTONES.
Tracks: / P-Town / Woody's lament / High on you / I love you / Vignette / Pensive / I don't want anybody at all / Let's be buddies.

LP: . . . . CJ 194

PROGRESSIVE AL COHN, THE.
LP: . . . . WL 70508

RIFFTIDE.
Tracks: / Speak low / Hot house / Blue monk / Thing, The / We'll be together again / Rifftide.
LP: . . . . SJP 259

STANDARDS OF EXCELLENCE.
Tracks: / Russian lullaby / When your lover has gone / O grande amor / You say you care / I want to be happy / Embraceable you / Remember you / When day is done.
LP: . . . . CJ 241
MC: . . . . CJC 241

TENOR CONTRASTS VOLUME 2 (See under Sims, Zoot) (Cohn, Al & Zoot Sims).

TOUR DE FORCE (Cohn, Al/Scott Hamilton/Buddy Tate).
Tracks: / Blues up and down / Tickle toe / Let's get away from it all / Soft winds / Stella by starlight / Broadway / Do nothing till you hear from me / Jumpin' at the woodside / Bernie's tune / Rifftide / If.
2LP: . . . . CJ 172

UNDERDOG, THE (See under Mauro, Turk) (Cohn, Al/Mauro Turk).

Cohn, Marc

MARC COHN.
Tracks: / Walking in Memphis / Ghost train / Silver Thunderbird / Dig down deep / Walk on water / Miles away / Saving the best for last / Strangers in a car / 29 ways / Perfect love / True companion.
MC: 7567821784
LP: 7567821781

Coil

CONSEQUENCES OF RAISING HELL, THE.
LP: . . . . OIL 001

GOLD IS THE METAL.
LP: . . . . THRESHOLD 1

HELLRAISER.
MC: . . . . COILC 001

HORSE ROTAVATOR.
Tracks: / Anal staircase / Slur / Baby Lero / Austoi (The death of Passolini) / Herald / Pentralia / Circles of mania / Who by fire / Blood from the air / Golden section / First five minutes after death, The.
LP: . . . . ROTA 1

SCATOLOGY.
LP: . . . . FKK 1

Coker, Dolo

ALL ALONE.
LP: . . . . XAN 178

NIGHT FLIGHT TO DAKAR (see Cohn,Al/Billy Mitchell/etc.).

Coker, Jerry

MODERN MUSIC FROM INDIANA UNIVERSITY.
LP: 1902116

Cola, Kid Sheik

IN ENGLAND.
LP: . . . . GHB 187

KID SHEIK COLA (Cola, Kid Sheik/ Sadie Goodson Cola/Frank Fields/M. Dolliole).
LP: . . . . LPS 12

KID SHEIK & JOHN HANDY.
MC: . . . . TC 001

N.O. - THE LEGENDS LIVE (Cola, Kid Sheik - Sheik's Swingers).
LP: . . . . JCE 31

SHEIK OF ARABY, THE (Sheik, Kid Storyville Ramblers).
LP: . . . . LPS 1
MC: . . . . TCS 1

WENDELL EUGENE AND FRIENDS (See Under Eugene, Wendell (Cola, Kid Sheik, Wendell Eugene, Teddy Riley, Michael White).

Colby

COLBY'S MISSING MEMORY.
LP: . . . . MAC R 5105
MC: . . . . MAC C 5105

GOD USES KIDS.
MC: . . . . MMC 0192

MAKE A JOYFUL NOISE.
LP: . . . . MAC 5103
MC: . . . . TC MAC 5103

SAVE COLBY'S CLUBHOUSE.
MC: . . . . MMC 0182

Colchester...

INTERNATIONAL COLLECTION (Colchester Accordion Orchestra).
Tracks: / Drie rhapsodische miniaturen / Springtime symphony / Sinfonische suite / Intermezzo in blue.
LP: . . . . CAS LP 002

Cold Chisel

CIRCUS ANIMALS.
Tracks: / You got nothing I want / Bow river / Forever now / Taipan / Hound dog / Wild colonial boy / No good for you / Numbers fall / When the war is over / Letter to Allan.
LP: . . . . POLS 1065

COLD CHISEL.
LP: . . . . LILP 400155

EAST.
Tracks: / Standing on the outside / Never before / Choir girl / Rising sun / My baby / Tomorrow / Cheap wine / Best kept lies / ITA / Star hotel / Four walls / My turn to cry.
LP: . . . . K 90003

RADIO SONGS - A BEST OF.
LP: 252362 1

SWINGSHIFT.
Tracks: / Conversations / Shipping steel / Khe Sanh / Knockin' on Heaven's door / Goodbye.
2LP: . . . . LIDLP 500010

TWENTIETH CENTURY.
LP: 250390 1

Cold Comfort Farm (bk)

COLD COMFORT FARM (Stella Gibbons) (Scales, Prunella (nar)).
MCSET: . . . . SAY 15
MCSET: . . . . ARGO 1148

COLD COMFORT FARM (Stella Gibbons) (Margolyes, Miriam (nar)).
MCSET: . . . . ZBBC 1076

Cold Crush Brothers

TROOPERS.
Tracks: / Feel the horns / She's no good / We can do this / Troopers / Pump it up / Cold crush / Bronx / My guitar.
LP: . . . . BBOY 6
MC: . . . . ZCBBY 6

Cold Cut

OUT TO LUNCH WITH AHEAD OF OUR TIME (Various artists).
LP: . . . . A HOT 1 4 U

SOME LIKE IT COLD.
LP: . . . . CCUT LP 2
MC: . . . . CCUT MC 2

WHAT'S THAT NOISE.
LP: . . . . CCUTLP 1
MC: . . . . CCUTMC 1

Cold Cuts

MEAT THE COLD CUTS.
LP: . . . . BT 1021

Cold Feet (film)

COLD FEET (Film Soundtrack) (Various artists).
Tracks: / Afternoon roundup: *Various artists* / Shoot the doc: *Various artists* / Just remember: *Various* artists / Watch my lips: *Various artists* / Cowboy reggae: *Various artists* / Monty shows off infidel: *Various* artists / Maureen and Kenny on the road: *Various artists* / Survival camp: *Various artists* / Infidel's and inspiration: *Various artists* / Isometrics: *Various artists* / Monty stole the horse: *Various artists*/ It's a sham/ Workin' man: *Various artists* / Sheriff's a preacher, The: *Various artists* / Lizard boots, size 100: *Various artists* / Good morning: *Various artists* / Maureen's monologue: *Various artists* / Sceered fitless: *Various artists* / Monty hides infidel: *Various artists* / Have a Turkish fig: *Various artists*/ Chasin' Monty: *Various artists* / Kenny's in the vat: *Various artists* / Happy now and forever: *Various artists.*
LP: . . . . VS 5231
MC: VSC5231

Cold Steel

DEAD BY DAWN.
LP: . . . . CCG 004

Cold Sweat

BREAKOUT.
Tracks: / Four on the floor / Cryin' shame / Love struck / Waiting in vain / Take this heart of mine / Killing floor / Riviera / Long way down / Let's make love / Fistful of money / Jump the gun / I just wanna make love to you.
LP: . . . . MCG 6100
MC: . . . . MCGC 6100

PLAYS JB.
LP: 8344261

Cold Tap

EVIL PRINCE, THE.
MC: . . . . TUX 11

Colder, Ben

GOLDEN HITS: BEN COLDER.
LP: . . . . GT 0051

Colditz Story (bk)

COLDITZ STORY, THE (Allen, Patrick (nar)).
MC: . . . . P 90018

Coldman, Richard

HOME COOKING (Coldman, Richard & John Russell).
LP: . . . . INCUS 31

Coldstream Guards Band

CHANGING THE GUARDS AT BUCKINGHAM PALACE (Coldstream Guards Regimental Band).
Tracks: / Blaydon races / Shirley Bassey showcase / Corcoran cadets / Espana / Trafalgar / Figaro / Mikado overture / Galop / Dance of the hours / Duke of York / Europe united / Le reve passe.
LP: . . . . DR 105

CROWN IMPERIAL (Coldstream Guards Regimental Band).
Tracks: / Crown imperial / Orb and sceptre / Pioneer spirit / Grand march 'Spirit of Pageantry' / Milanollo / Coldstream march / Figaro / Pomp & Circumstance marches Nos. 1 & 2.
LP: . . . . BND 1004
MC: . . . . ZC BND 1004

FOCUS ON JOHN PHILIP SOUSA.
MC: . . . . ZCFPA 1015

GOLDEN HOUR PRESENTS COLDSTREAM GUARDS BAND.
Tracks: / Milanollo / Coldstream march, The / Age of kings, An / Cherokee / Old comrades / Three blades of Toledo / Strike up the band (medley) / Northumbrian airs / Winds on the run / State occasion: A festive overture / Clarinet candy / Royal Windsor / Jeanie with the light brown hair / Bandolero / Deep river / March: Soldier's medley.
LP: . . . . GH 603

HOUR OF SOUSA MARCHES, AN (Coldstream Guards/Royal Marines).
Tracks: / Stars and stripes forever / King Cotton / National fencibles / High school cadets / Manhattan beach / Semper fidelis / Invincible eagle, The / Gladiators, The / Washington post / Hands across the sea / Royal Welsh Fusiliers, The / Legionaires, The / Daughters of Texas / Gallant seventh, The / Golden jubilee / Pride of the wolverines / Hail to the spirit of liberty / Kansas wildcats / Sound off / Thunderer, The.
MC: . . . . HR 8142

MASTERPIECES FOR BAND (Coldstream Guards Regimental Band).
Tracks: / Two Irish tone sketches / Folk song suite / Toccata marziale / Gaelic fantasy / Suites for military band / Three humouresques / Theme & variations.
2LP: . . . . BNC 3002
MCSET: . . . . ZC BNC 3002

QUEEN'S SILVER JUBILEE (Coldstream Guards/Welsh Guards).
2LP: . . . . AJP 1003/4

Cole, Ann

GOT MY MOJO WORKING.
Tracks: / Got my mojo working / Easy easy baby / Each day / Are you satisfied / You're mine / My tearful heart / I'm waiting for you / Got nothing working now / Darling don't hurt me / I've got a little boy / In the chaple / Brand new house / Nobody but me / That's enough.
LP: . . . . KK 782

Cole, B.J

TRANSPARENT MUSIC.
LP: . . . . HNBL 1325
MC: . . . . HNBC 1325

Cole, Bobby

CHANGE PARTNERS.
Tracks: / Viyos con dios - waltz / I live for you / Stranger on the shore / Aria (Saunter) / Let this great big world keep turning / My buddy / What a swell party this is - swing / I'll never smile again / So what's new - quickstep / For once in my life / Change partners - rumba / Dream is a wish your heart makes, A / Again - cha-cha-cha / Watch what happens / Caravan / It must be him (Tango) / Eye level / Rendezvous.
LP: . . . . SUS 517

DANCE AND BE HAPPY.
Tracks: / When your hair has turned to silver / Love's last word is spoken / Underneath the arches / Strollin' / Dancing on the ceiling / Among my souvenirs / If I had my way / Let me call you sweetheart / When I grow too old to dream / Best things in life are free, The / Beyond the blue horizon / Rolling round the world / Let's have another one / One of those songs / Feelings / Roses of Picardy / You made me love you / Love walked in / Little brown jug / I want to be happy / Tango for Tanya / Something stupid / How about you?.
LP: . . . . SUS 502

DANCE MY WAY.
Tracks: / I wonder who's kissing her now / Cara Mia / When your old wedding ring was new / My way / She loves you / I wanna be like you / Back in your own back yard / I've got my love to keep me warm / All of you / To all the girls I've loved before / Love me tender / I love you (for sentimental reasons) / Bewitched / Consuelo's love theme / Sunny side of the street / Mame.
LP: . . . . SUS 507

DANCE TO THE ORCHESTRAL MAGIC OF JIMMY SMITH - V (Jimmy Smith-known to all as...Bobby Cole).
Tracks: / You're nobody's sweetheart now / I could have danced all night / My baby just cares for me / Funny(medley) / This can't be love / If I had my way(medley) / You always hurt the one you love / Forgotten dreams / Way down upon the Swanee River / Somewhere over the rainbow / I'll see you in my dreams / Violin concerto / What are you doing the rest of your life / This guy's in love with you / Never the same / Czardas / You do something to me.
LP: . . . . SUS 527

DANCE-DANCE-DANCE.
Tracks: / Diana / Thorn birds / Look for the silver lining / Music maestro please / Whispering / On Mother Kelly's doorstep / Rockabye your baby with a Dixie melody / Don't bring Lulu / Put your arms around me, honey / My blue Heaven / Bring me sunshine / Sheik of Araby, The / Powder your face with sunshine / Memories / For ever and ever / I'm always chasing rainbows / Something tells me / All my loving / Hey Jude / I love Paris / Serenata / Melancholy baby / Sleepy time gal.
LP: . . . . SUS 500

DANCING BY NIGHT.
Tracks: / London by night / One day when we were young / Thanks for the memory / In a shady nook / If you were the only girl in the world / I'm a dreamer, aren't we all? / Who stole my heart away? / Great day / Eastenders / Moon over Naples / Senorita de Islas / Super trouper / Always true to you in my fashion / Midnight in Moscow / Sailing / Tango verdes / Anniversary waltz.
LP: . . . . SUS 510

DANCING IS MAGIC.
Tracks: / True love / Last farewell, The / I love you because / Welcome home / One I love belongs to somebody else, The (Foxtrot.) / Can't smile without you / Alexander's ragtime band / Put on your Sunday clothes / I can't give you anything but love / And I love you so / Could it be magic / Can't help falling in love / Let's do it / Is it true what they say about dixie / Who were you with last night / Yes sir, that's my baby / You were meant for me / Sunshine of your smile, The / Chattanooga choo choo / World is waiting for the sunrise, The / It's time to say goodnight.
LP: . . . . SUS 504

I BELIEVE IN DANCING.
Tracks: / I believe in music / Happy days are here again / Lover come back to me / Days of wine and roses / Things we did last summer, The / Sway / Sometimes when we touch / Green cockatoo, The / Fools rush in / My own true love - Tara's theme / Juliet bravo, Theme from / Vienna, city of my dreams / Charade / Autumn leaves / Nevertheless.
LP: . . . . SUS 519

JUST LOVE DANCING.
Tracks: / My blue Heaven / Amazing grace / I can dream, can't I / When Mabel comes in the room / Who's sorry now? / Ma (he's making eyes at me) / There in your eyes / Honeysuckle rose / Who wants to be a millionaire? / Song of the brass key / Make believe / Warsaw concerto / Blue moon / My heart belongs to daddy / Ballin' the jack / Give my regards to Broadway / Loveliest night of the year, The / Sitting on top of the world / Save your kisses for me / Two sleepy people.
LP: . . . . SUS 503

JUST ONE MORE DANCE.
Tracks: / Just one more chance / I don't know why / Love sends a little gift of roses / Sunshine of your smile, The / Look what happened to Mabel / You won't find another fool like me / Time after time / With a song in my heart / My favourite things / You're just in love / Will you remember? / Melody of love / It's almost tomorrow / Lovely lady / Bobby's girl / I've got you under my skin / Yesterday when I was young / Gigi / It happened in Monterey / Silly note song /

I could be so good for you / Tell me I'm forgiven.
LP: . . . . **SUS 512**
MC: . . . . **CSUS 512**

WHILE YOU'RE DANCING.
Tracks: / On the air / Musetta's waltz / You my love / Moonglow (Best things happen while you're dancing) / Love me tonight / Silver wings in the moonlight / I love a piano.
LP: . . . . **SUS 530**

WITH YOU IN MY ARMS.
Tracks: / Tennessee waltz / Are you lonesome tonight / Do, do, do-I'm bidin' my time / Time on my hands / Falling in love again / One / Dance little lady / This ole house / Somewhere (From the musical 'West Side Story'.) / Just the way you are / It's a heartache / Isn't this a lovely day / Phantom of the opera (From the musical by Andrew Lloyd Webber.) / Allure tango, The / Easter parade.
LP: . . . . **SUS 515**

Cole, Buddy

BUDDY COLE REMEMBERED.
LP: . . . . **DO 1421**

CINEMA ORGAN ENCORES.
LP: . . . . **DEROY 1031**

NEW TRICKS (See under Crosby, Bing) (Cole, Buddy/Bing Crosby).

Cole, Cozy

ALL STAR SWING GROUPS (Cole, Cozy/Pete Johnson).
Tracks: / Jericho / Talk to me / Concerto for Cozy / Body and soul / Nice and cozy / Ol' man river / Wrap your troubles in dreams / Ridin' the riff / Flat rock / Jersey jump off / Stompin' at the Savoy / On the sunny side of the street / Jump a while / Pete's lonesome blues / Mr. Drum meets Mr. Piano / Mutiny in the doghouse / Mr. Clarinet knocks twice / Ben rides out / Ben rides out (master) / Page Mr. Trumpet / Page Mr. Trumpet (master) / J.C. from K.C. / Pete's house warming blues / Atomic boogie / Backroom blues / Twelve eighty (1280) stomp / I may be wonderful / Man wanted.
2LP: . . . . **SJL 2218**

EARL'S BACKROOM AND COZY'S CARAVAN (see under Hines, Earl) (Cole, Cozy Septet/Hines, Earl Quartet).

Cole, Eddie

THAT'S ALRIGHT (Cole, Eddie/Three Peppers).
LP: . . . . **KK 831**

Cole, Freddy

COLE NOBODY KNOWS, THE.
LP: . . . . **AP 123**

RIGHT FROM THE HEART.
Tracks: / Right from the start / She believes in me / Girl from the piano bar / I loved you for a minute / Summer love / Somewhere down the line / Teach me tonight / This song's for you / To be with you / Day that my heart caught fire.
LP: . . . . **SKL 5321**

Cole, Gardner

TRIANGLES.
LP: **925739 1**
MC: **925739 4**

Cole, George (nar)

ADVENTURES OF HEGGARTY HAGGERTY (See under Adventures of...).

Cole, Gordon

DRIVING TEST, THE.
LP: . . . . **SGR 101**

Cole, Jude

JUDE COLE.
Tracks: / Like lovers do / Walls that bend / You were in my heart / Something that you want / Life of luxury / Hurt, The / Everyone's in love / Better days / Walk on water / Crying Mary.
LP: **925553 1**
MC: **925553 4**

VIEW FROM 3RD STREET.
Tracks: / Hallowed ground / House full of reasons / Time for letting go / This time it's us / Compared to nothing / Baby, it's tonight / Get me through the night / Stranger to myself / Heart of blues / Prove me wrong.
LP: **7599261641**
MC: **7599261644**

Cole, Lloyd

1984 - 1989 (Cole, Lloyd & The Commotions).
LP: **837 736-1**
MC: **837 736-4**

DON'T GET WEIRD ON ME BABE.
LP: **51109321**
MC: **51109324**

EASY PIECES (Cole, Lloyd & The Commotions).
Tracks: / Rich / Why I love country music / Pretty gone / Grace / Cut me down / Brand new friend / Lost weekend / James / Minor character / Perfect blue.
LP: . . . . **LCLP 2**
MC: . . . . **LCMC 2**

LLOYD COLE.
Tracks: / Don't look back / What do you know about love? / No blue skies / Loveless / Sweetheart / To the church / Downtown / Long way down, A / Ice cream girl / Undressed / I hate to see you baby doing that stuff / Waterline / Mercy killing.
MC: **841 907 4**
LP: **841 907 1**

MAINSTREAM (Cole, Lloyd & The Commotions).
Tracks: / My bag / 29 / Mainstream / Jennifer she said / Mister malcontent / Sean Penn blues / Big snake / Hey rusty / These days.
LP: . . . . **LCLP 3**
MC: . . . . **LCMC 3**

RATTLESNAKES (Cole, Lloyd & The Commotions).
Tracks: / Perfect skin / Speedboat / Rattlesnakes / Down on Mission Street / Forest fire / Charlotte Street / 2 CV / Four flights up / Patience / Are you ready to be heartbroken?.
LP: . . . . **LCLP 1**
MC: . . . . **LCMC 1**

RATTLESNAKES/ EASY PIECES (Cole, Lloyd & The Commotions).
MC: **8477334**

Cole, Maggie

GUITAR COLLECTION (see under North, Nigel) (Cole, Maggie/Nigel North).

Cole, Nat King

16 ORIGINAL HITS: NAT KING COLE.
MC: . . . . **MC 1628**

20 GOLDEN GREATS: NAT KING COLE.
Tracks: / Sweet Lorraine / Straighten up and fly right / Nature boy / Dance ballerina dance / Mona Lisa / Too young / Love letters / Smile / Around the world / For all we know / When I fall in love / Very thought of you, The / On the street where you live / Unforgettable / It's all in the game / Ramblin' rose / Portrait of Jennie / Let there be love / Somewhere along the way / Those lazy, hazy, crazy days of summer.
LP: . . . . **EMTV 9**
MC: . . . . **TC EMTV 9**

20 GREATEST LOVE SONGS.
Tracks: / Stardust / Answer me / Autumn leaves / Walkin' my baby back home / These foolish things / There goes my heart / Nightingale sang in Berkeley Square, A / You made me love you / Blossom fell, A / More / Love letters / Oh, how I miss you tonight / Brazilian love song / You're my everything / Love is a many splendoured thing / You'll never know / He'll have to go / Stay as sweet as you are / More I see you, The / Party's over, The.
LP: . . . . **EMTV 35**
MC: . . . . **TC EMTV 35**

AFTER MIDNIGHT.
Tracks: / Just you, just me / Sweet Lorraine / Sometimes I'm happy / Caravan / It's only a paper moon / You're lookin' at me / What is there to say / I was a little too lonely / Two loves have I / Lonely one, The / Don't let it go to your head / I know that you know / Blame it on my youth / When I grow too old to dream / Route 66 / You can depend on me / Candy.
LP: . . . . **EMS 1103**
MC: . . . . **TCEMS 1103**

ANATOMY OF A JAM SESSION.
Tracks: / Black market stuff / Laguna leap / I'll never be the same / Swingin' on central / Kicks.
LP: . . . . **BLP 30104**

ANY OLD TIME (Cole, Nat King Trio).
Tracks: / Little joy from Chicago / Sunny side of the street / Candy / Any old time / Indiana / Man I love, The / Trio grooves in Brooklyn, A / That'll just about knock me out / Too marvelous for words / Besame mucho / Wouldn't you like to know / Any old time.
LP: . . . . **GOJ 1031**
MC: . . . . **GOJC 1031**

AT HIS RAREST OF ALL RARE PERFORMANCES VOL.1.
LP: . . . . **KLJ 20029**

BALLADS OF THE DAY.
Tracks: / Blossom fell, A / Unbelievable / Blue gardenia / Angel eyes / It happens to be me / Smile / Darling, je vous aime beaucoup / Alone too long / My one sin (in life) / Return to paradise / If love is good to me / Sand and the sea, The.
LP: . . . . **EMS 1102**
MC: . . . . **TCEMS 1102**

BEST OF NAT KING COLE VOL. 1.
Tracks: / Unforgettable / Nature boy / When I fall in love / Ramblin' Rose / Let there be love / Too young / Mona Lisa.
LP: **1A 022 58069**
MC: **1A 222 58069**
LP: . . . . **ST 21139**

BEST OF NAT KING COLE VOL. 2.
LP: . . . . **ST 21687**

BEST OF NAT KING COLE VOL. 3.
LP: . . . . **ST 21874**

BIG BAND COLE.
Tracks: / She's funny that way / Anytime, anyday, anywhere / I want a little girl / Modd indigo / Blues don't care, The / Avalon / Baby, won't you please come home / Late, late show, The / Welcome to the club / Look out for love / Wee baby blues / Madrid / Orange coloured sky / Jam-bo / Steady / My love.
MC: **B4 96259**

BODY AND SOUL.
Tracks: / It's only a paper moon / Don't cry, cry baby / Cole's bop blues / Frim fram sauce / If you can't smile and say yes / On the sunny side of the street / Miss thing / Sweet Lorraine / Satchel mouth baby / Body and soul / Trouble with me is you / Sweet Georgia Brown / Yes sir, that's my baby / Last but not least.
LP: . . . . **TOP 112**

CAPITOL COLLECTORS SERIES: NAT KING COLE.
Tracks: / Straighten up and fly right / Route 66 / I love you for sentimental reasons / Christmas song, The / Nature boy / Too young / Walkin' my baby back home / Pretend / Answer me / Darling, je vous aime beaucoup / Blossom fell, A / Send for me / Non dimenticar (Don't forget) / Ramblin' rose / Dear lonely hearts / All over the world / Those lazy-hazy-crazy days of summer / L-O-V-E / Mona Lisa / Unforgettable.
MC: **C4 93590**
MC: **793 590 4**

CAPITOL YEARS: NAT KING COLE (The best of Nat King Cole).
Tracks: / Unforgettable / Sings for two in love / Ballads of the day / After midnight / Love is the thing / Just one of those things / Very thought of you, The / Welcome to the club / To whom it may concern / Tell me all about yourself / At the sands / Touch of your lips, The / Let's face the music / Nat King Cole sings / George Shearing plays / Where did everyone go? / Ramblin' rose / Those lazy hazy crazy days of summer / L.O.V.E. / Piano style of Nat King Cole, The.
LPS: . . . . **NKC 20**

CHRISTMAS SONG, THE.
Tracks: / Christmas song, The / Deck the hall / Adeste fideles / Tannenbaum / O little town of Bethlehem / I saw three ships / O holy night / Hark the herald angels sing / Cradle in Bethlehem, A / Away in a manger / Joy to the world / First Noel, The / Caroling, caroling / Silent night.
LP: . . . . **EG 2603221**
MC: . . . . **EG 2603224**
LP: . . . . **MFP 50313**

CHRISTMAS WITH NAT & DEAN (Cole, Nat King & Dean Martin).
Tracks: / Christmas song, The / Let it snow, let it snow, let it snow / White Christmas / Frosty the snowman / Winter wonderland / Happiest Christmas tree, The / Deck the hall / O tannenbaum / Silent night / Brahms lullaby / Buon natale / Adeste fideles / Rudolf the red-nosed reindeer / Little boy that Santa Claus forgot, The / Cradle in Bethlehem, A / Christmas blues / Mrs Santa Claus / Caroling, caroling / O little town of Bethlehem / O holy night / Joy to the world (CD only.) / God rest ye merry gentlemen.
MC: . . . . **TCMFP 5902**

CHRISTMAS WITH NAT KING COLE.
Tracks: / Little boy that Santa Claus forgot, The / I saw three ships / Deck the hall / O come all ye faithful / Nature boy / Joy to the world / Cradle in Bethlehem, A / Away in a manger / Hark the herald angels sing / Caroling caroling / First Noel, The.
LP: . . . . **SMR 868**
MC: . . . . **SMC 868**

CLASSICS.
2LP: . . . . **PM 155 1863**

COLE, CHRISTMAS AND KIDS.
Tracks: / All I want for Christmas (is my two front teeth) / Frosty the snowman (With the Singing Pussycats.) / Little Christmas tree / Little boy that Santa Claus forgot, The / Mrs Santa Claus / Christmas song, The / Take me back to Toyland / Buon natale / Happiest Christmas tree, The / O come all ye faithful / God rest ye merry gentlemen / Brahm's lullaby / Toys for tots (Pub. service spot for Marine Reserve 'Toys For Tots' campaign.).
MC: **C4-94685**
MC: **794 685 4**

COLE ESPANOL AND MORE VOL.1.
Tracks: / Cachita / Maria Elena / Quizas quizas quizas / Las mananitas / Acercate Mas (come close to me) / El Bodeguero / Noche de Ronda / Te quiero dijiste / Adelita / Ay, Cosita Linda / Aguellos ojus verdes / Saus Maos / Capullito de aleli / Fantastico / Nadie me ama.
LP: . . . . **1 A 038 80402**

COLLECTION: NAT 'KING' COLE.
Tracks: / Don't cry, cry baby / Last but not least / On the sunny side of the street / Sweet Georgia Brown / Yes sir that's my baby / Body and soul / Cole's bop blues / Frim fram Sauce / If you can't smile and say yes / Miss thing / Satchel mouth baby / Sweet Lorraine / Trouble with me is you / Old piano plays the blues / It's only a paper moon / Greatest invention, The / Bugle call rag / Blues / I'm lost / Nat meets June / Rosetta / Tea for two / Man on the little white keys, The.
2LP: . . . . **CCSLP 144**
MC: . . . . **CCSMC 144**

COOL COLE, THE.
LP: . . . . **SR 5003**

DISQUE D'OR (COLLECTION).
Tracks: / Love / Those lazy, hazy, crazy days of summer / Stardust / St. Louis blues / Blue gardenia / Girl from Ipanema / Unforgettable / Brazilian love song / Ramblin' rose / Three little words / Darling, je vous aime beaucoup / All over the world / Miss you / Les feuilles mortes.
LP: **2C 070 81267**

EMBRACEABLE YOU.
LP: . . . . **VS 3408**
MC: . . . . **VSK 3408**

FASCINATION.
MC: . . . . **ENT MC 13042**
LP: . . . . **ENT LP 13042**

FAVOURITE BALLADS BY NAT KING COLE.
MC: **4XL 8318**

FOR THOSE IN LOVE.
Tracks: / When I fall in love / Love is here to stay / Almost like being in love / This can't be love / Love is the thing / L-O-V-E / Love letters.
MC: **4XL 8316**

FOREVER NAT.
MC: **U3013-2**

FORGOTTEN YEARS (Cole, Nat King Trio).
Tracks: / On the sunny side of the street / Man on the little white keys, The / Frim fram sauce / If you can't smile and say yes / Trouble with me is you / Sweet Georgia Brown / Satchel mouth baby / Miss thing / Sweet Lorraine / Paper moon.
LP: . . . . **GOJ 1013**

FROM THE VERY BEGINNING.
Tracks: / Honeysuckle rose / Sweet Lorraine / This side up / Gone with the draft / Stompin' at the Panama / Early morning blues / Babs / Slow down / Honey hush / I like to riff / This will make you laugh / Hit the ramp / Stop, the red light's on / (Bedtime) sleep, baby, sleep / Call the police / That ain't right / Are you fer it? / Hit that jive Jack / Thunder.
LP: . . . . **MCL 1671**
MC: . . . . **MCLC 1671**

GREAT CAPITOL MASTERS.
Tracks: / I'm an errand boy for rhythm / Kee mo ky mo / I used to love you / These foolish things / Dream a little dream of me / Love nest, The / But all I've got is me / I've got a way with women / When I take my sugar to tea / I miss you so / You're the cream in my coffee / But she's my buddy's chick / Naughty Angeline / Best man, The / I think you get what I mean / That's what.
LP: . . . . **EMS 1142**
MC: . . . . **TCEMS 1142**

GREAT FILMS AND SHOWS, THE.
Tracks: / Around the world / Smile / When I fall in love / Love letters / Ain't misbehavin' / At last / Stay as sweet as you are / More I see you, The / You're my everything / More / Am I blue / Spring is here / It's all in the game / But beautiful / Paradise / Very thought of you, The / Because you're mine / Again / Affair to remember, An / Mood indigo / Only forever / I remember you / Don't get around much anymore / I should care / Just one of those things / Party's over, The / Song is ended (but the melody

lingers on), The / Bidin' my time / Ebony rhapsody / Let's face the music and dance / Cold cold heart / Lover come back to me / Who's sorry now / Almost like being in love / This can't be love / You stepped out of a dream / Best thing for you, The / For you / How little we know / Like someone in love / Beale Street blues / St. Louis blues / Ballad of Cat Ballou / In the good old summertime / With a little bit of luck / I could have danced all night / Rain in Spain, The / On the street where you live / I'm an ordinary man / Get me to the church on time / Show me / I've grown accustomed to her face / You did it / Wouldn't it be luverly / Hymn to him / I got it bad and that ain't good / Pick yourself up / September song / All by myself / They can't make her cry / Three little words / You'll never know / I am in love / Your cheatin' heart / Mona Lisa / Love is here to stay / Let's fall in love / There will never be another you / Blue gardenia / China gate / Hajji baba / Never let me go / Return to paradise / Night of the quarter moon / To whom it may concern / Nightingale sang in Berkeley Square, A / Magic moments / People / Love is a many splendoured thing / Sometimes I'm happy / Caravan / Just you, just me / It's only a paper moon / When I grow too old to dream / Route 66 / September song / It's only a paper moon.
LPS: . . . . NKC 1
LPS: 793 207 1

GREATEST HITS: NAT 'KING' COLE.
Tracks: / Nature boy / Mona Lisa / Too young / When I fall in love / Quizas quizas quizas / Unforgettable / Fly me to the moon / Let there be love / Love / Darling, je vous aime beaucoup / Ramblin' rose / Those lazy hazy crazy days of summer / Lost April / Answer me / Sweet Lorraine / I don't want to hurt anymore / Route 66 / Dear lonely hearts / Ay cosita Linda / Perfidia / Blue gardenia / It's only a paper moon / Acerta te mast / Smile / Blossom fell, A / Stardust / Love is the thing.
LPS: 5C 180 82269/7

HAVIN' FUN WITH NAT KING COLE.
Tracks: / Open up the doghouse / Long, long ago / If I may / My personal possession / That's all there is to that / My baby just cares for me / For you my love / Can I come in for a second / Get out and get under the moon / Hey, not now / Save the bones for Henry Jones / Harmony.
LP: . . . . OFF 12003
MC: . . . . OFF 412003

HIS GREATEST SUCCESS.
Tracks: / Darling, je vous aime beaucoup / Crazy but I'm in love / Sand and the sea, The / Stompin' down Broadway / Somebody loves me / I've grown accustomed to her face / Tea for two / Unforgettable / This can't be love / Beautiful friendship, A / Mona Lisa / Thou swell / Two different worlds / It's only a paper moon / Early American / Till the end of the years / Sweet Sue / I'm shooting high / Autumn leaves / Just one of those things / Little girl / When you're smiling / Night lights / Take me back to Toyland / Just in time / House with love in it, A / Mr. Santa Claus / You stepped out of a dream / Pick yourself up / Jingle bells / Christmas song, The / Cuba.
2LP: . . . . ALB 223

IF I GIVE MY HEART TO YOU.
Tracks: / If I give my heart to you / Walkin' my baby back home / Somewhere along the way / Funny (not much) / More I see you, The / Ballerina / It's all in the game / Laughing on the outside (crying on the inside) / Teach me tonight.
MC: 4XL 9050

IN THE COOL OF THE EVENING (Cole, Nat King Trio).
Tracks: / Jumpin' at Capitol / Is it better to be yourself / Everyone is sayin' hello again / To a wild rose / Oh, but I do / You should have told me / In the cool, cool, cool of the evening / That's the beginning of the end / I want to thank you folks / Come in out of the rain / You don't learn that in school / Can you look me in the eyes / Meet me at no special place / I can't be bothered now / There I've sold it again / Trouble with me is you, The.
LP: . . . . OFF 3026

INCOMPARABLE.
Tracks: / You're the cream in my coffee / Embraceable you / Prelude in 'C' sharp / Nature boy / For all we know / Gee baby ain't I good to you / Love is a many splendoured thing / Route 66 / You stepped out of a dream / Stardust / Don't get around much anymore / Coquette.
LP: . . . . MTM 008

IT'S ALMOST LIKE BEING IN LOVE (Cole, Nat King Trio).
LP: . . . . DBD 15
MC: . . . . DBDC 15

JUST ONE OF THOSE THINGS.
Tracks: / When your lover has gone / Cottage for sale / Who's sorry now / Once in a while / These foolish things / Just for the fun of it / Don't get around much anymore / I understand / Just one of those things / Song is ended, The / I should care / Party's over, The / Day in, day out / I'm gonna sit right down (and write myself a letter) / Something makes me want to dance with you.
LP: . . . . EMS 1105
MC: . . . . TCEMS 1105

KING COLE TRIO, THE.
LP: . . . . LPJT 14

LEGENDARY NAT KING COLE, THE.
Tracks: / Just can't see for looking / Hit the jive Jack / Swinging the blues / I'm in the mood for love / On the sunny side of the street / Sweet Georgia Brown / Baby won't you please come home / Too marvellous for words.
MC: . . . . MRT 40052

LET THERE BE LOVE (Cole, Nat King & George Shearing).
Tracks: / September song / Pick yourself up / I got it bad and that ain't good / Let there be love / Azure te / Lost April / Beautiful friendship, A / Fly me to the moon / Serenata / I'm lost / There's a lull in my life / Don't go.
LP: . . . . MFP 5612
MC: . . . . TCMFP 5612

LET'S FACE THE MUSIC.
Tracks: / Ebony Rhapsody / Too little, too late / Let's face the music and dance / Day in, day out / Bidin' my time / When my sugar walks down the street / Warm and willing / I'm gonna sit right down and write myself a letter / Cold, cold heart / Something makes me want to dance with you / Moon love / Rules of the road, The.
LP: . . . . EMS 1112
MC: . . . . TCEMS 1112

LET'S FALL IN LOVE.
Tracks: / When I fall in love / Stardust / Around the world / Too young / Very thought of you, The / On the street where you live / Ramblin' rose / Just one of those things / Let's fall in love / Almost like being in love / Don't get around much anymore / Once in a while / These foolish things remind me of you / I'm gonna sit right down and write myself a letter / This can't be love / For all we know / Somewhere along the way (Available on CD only.) / Cottage for sale (Available on CD only.) / There goes my heart (Available on CD only.) / Ain't misbehavin' (Available on CD only.).
LP: . . . . MFP 5895
MC: . . . . TCMFP 5895

LIVE - KONGRESSHAUS, ZURICH (Oct. 19th 1950) (Cole, Nat King Trio).
LP: . . . . D 1014

L.O.V.E..
Tracks: / L.O.V.E. / Girl from Ipanema / Three little words / There's love / My kind of girl / Thanks to you / Your love / More / Coquette / How I'd love to love you / Swiss retreat.
LP: . . . . EMS 1117
MC: . . . . TCEMS 1117

LOVE IS THE THING.
Tracks: / When I fall in love / End of a love affair, The / Stardust / Stay as sweet as you are / Where can I go without you / Maybe it's because I love you too much / Love letters / Ain't misbehavin' / I thought about Marie / At last / It's all in the game / When Sunny gets blue / Love is the thing.
LP: . . . . EMS 1104
MC: . . . . TCEMS 1104

LOVE SONGS: NAT KING COLE.
MC: 4XL 8355

MEETS THE MASTER SAXES.
Tracks: / Heads / Pro-sky / It had to be you / I can't give you anything but love / Indiana / I can't get started / Tea for two / Body and soul / I found a new baby / Rosetta / Sweet Lorraine / I blowed and gone.
LP: . . . . SPJ 136

MORE COLE ESPANOL.
LP: 5C 038 80483

MY KIND OF GIRL.
Tracks: / Ramblin' rose / Goodnight Irene / My kind of girl / Portrait of Jennie / Ballerina / Miss Otis regrets / Here's to my lady / Adelita / Sweet Lorraine / On a bicycle built for two / Girl from Ipanema / I thought about Marie / Marnie / Mona Lisa / Maria Elena / Annabelle.
LP: . . . . ST 21873

NAT KING COLE (Cole, Nat King/ Dorsey Brothers/Nelson Riddle).
MC: . . . . CATOM 5

NAT KING COLE.
Tracks: / Non dimenticar / Too young / Smile, A / When I fall in love / Quizas quizas quizas / Tenderly / Darling, je vous aime beaucoup / Love is a many splendoured thing / Blue gardenia / Tres palabras / Unforgettable / It's only a paper moon / Mona Lisa / Acerate Mas (come close to me) / Autumn leaves / Stardust / Unforgettable / Those lazy hazy crazy days of summer / Ramblin' rose / Because you're mine.
LP: 1868201
LP: 1868201
MC: 1868204

NAT KING COLE (2).
LP: . . . . LPJT 62
LP: . . . . ENT LP 13003
MC: . . . . ENT MC 13003

NAT KING COLE 1947-48.
MC: . . . . CCH 335

NAT KING COLE AT THE SANDS.
Tracks: / Ballerina / Funny - not much / Continental, The / I wish you love / You leave me breathless / Thou swell / My kind of love / Surrey with the fringe on top / Where or when / Miss Otis regrets (she's unable to lunch today) / Joe Turner blues.
LP: . . . . EMS 1110
MC: . . . . TCEMS 1110

NAT KING COLE COLLECTION (20 Golden Greats).
Tracks: / Too young / Mother Nature and Father Time / This can't be love / Autumn leaves / Somebody loves me / Lush life / Just in time / Route 66 / Because you're mine / Unforgettable / Mona Lisa / Crazy but I'm in love / Sand and the sea, The / I've grown accustomed to her face / Tea for two / It's only a paper moon / Till the end of the years / Sweet Sue / Summertime (medley) / Sweet Lorraine.
LP: . . . . DVLP 2012
MC: . . . . DVMC 2012

NAT KING COLE LIVE (Cole, Nat King/ Nelson Riddle Orchestra).
Tracks: / Two different worlds / Thou swell / Mona Lisa / Night lights / Too young / That's my girl / But not for me / Repeat after me / True love / Little girl / Love letters / Just in time, A / Unforgettable / Love me tender / My foolish heart / Sweet Sue / Somewhere along the way / This can't be love / I'm sitting on top of the world / You are my first love / It's just a little street / Toyland.
LP: . . . . ATOM 1
MC: . . . . CATOM 1

NAT KING COLE (SET).
2LP: . . . . ALBUM 46
MCSET: . . . . CASSETTE 46

NAT KING COLE SINGS, THE GEORGE SHEARING QUINTET PLAYS.
Tracks: / September song / Pick yourself up / I got it bad and that ain't good / Let there be love / Azure te / Lost April / Everything happens to me / Beautiful friendship, A / Fly me to the moon / Serenata / I'm lost / There's a lull in my life / Don't go / Guess I'll go back home.
LP: . . . . EMS 1113
MC: . . . . TCEMS 1113
LP: . . . . W 1675

NAT KING COLE TRIO (Cole, Nat King Trio).
LP: . . . . EJLP 08
MC: . . . . EJMC 08

NAT KING COLE TRIO 1943/49 (The Vocal Sides) (Cole, Nat King Trio).
LP: 20808

NAT KING COLE TRIO COLLECTION (20 Golden Greats) (Cole, Nat King Trio).
Tracks: / Man I love, The / This way out / Sweet Georgia Brown / Embraceable you / Is you is or is you ain't my baby / Route 66 / What is this thing called love? / Boogie a la king / I'm in the mood for love / For sentimental reasons / Honeysuckle rose / Baby won't you please come home? / Sweet Lorraine / It's only a paper moon / Somebody loves you / Swingin' the blues / Easy-listening blues / Straighten up and fly right / Rhumba Azul / Just can't see for looking.
LP: . . . . DVLP 2048
MC: . . . . DVMC 2048

NAT KING COLE WITH GEORGE SHEARING (Cole, Nat King & George Shearing).
MC: . . . . TC CAPS 1020

NATURE BOY.
LP: 20108

NATURE BOY VOL. 4.
LP: . . . . SM 4053

ONE AND ONLY NAT KING COLE, THE.
Tracks: / Sweet Lorraine / Love is here to stay / Autumn leaves / Dance ballerina dance / September song / Beautiful friendship, A / Fly me to the moon / Let there be love / Mona Lisa / Pick yourself up / More I see you, The / Just one of those things / Let's fall in love / Love is the thing / Stay as sweet as you are / Love letters / Azure te (CD only.) / Serenata (CD only.) / Party's over, The (CD only.).
LP: . . . . MFP 5850
MC: . . . . TCMFP 5850

PIANO STYLE OF NAT KING COLE, THE.
Tracks: / Love walked in / My heart stood still / Imagination / I never knew / Stella by starlight / What can I say after I say I'm sorry / I didn't know what time it was / Taking a chance on love / April in Paris / I want to be happy / I see your face before me / Just one of those things / I get a kick out of you / If I could be with you one hour tonight / I hear music / Tea for two.
LP: . . . . EMS 1271
MC: . . . . TCEMS 1271

PIECES OF COLE.
Tracks: / It's almost like being in love / It's only a paper moon / Bop kick / Yes sir tha's my baby / Flo and Joe / I'm through with love / Gee baby ain't I good to you / Love me sooner / Sentimental blues.
LP: . . . . SWH 12
MC: . . . . CSWH 12

RAMBLIN' ROSE.
Tracks: / Ramblin' Rose / Wolverton mountain / Twilight on the trail / I don't want it that way / He'll have to go / When you're smiling / Dear lonely hearts (Extra track on CD only.) / All over the world (Extra track on CD only.) / All by myself (Extra track on CD only.) / Goodnight, Irene / Your cheatin' heart / One has my name the other has my heart / Skip to my Lou / Good times / Sing another song (and we'll all go home).
LP: . . . . EMS 1115
MC: . . . . TCEMS 1115

REPLAY ON NAT KING COLE.
LP: . . . . FEDB 5002
MC: . . . . CFEDB 5002

SHOOTING HIGH (Songs from the TV Shows).
Tracks: / I'm shooting high / Tenderly / Makin' whoopee / Fascination / There's a goldmine in the sky / Little girl / There will never be another you / Song of Raintree country / Breezin' along with the breeze / My personal possession / When rock 'n' roll comes to Trinidad / I thought about Marie / Love is the thing / It's only a paper moon / Christmas song, The / Pretend / I'm gonna sit right down and write myself a letter / I've grown accustomed to her face / Send for me / St. Louis blues.
LP: . . . . EMS 1370
LP: 793 252 1
MC: . . . . TCEMS 1370
MC: 793 252 4

SINGS AND PLAYS.
Tracks: / Sweet Lorraine / Honeysuckle rose / Gone with the draft / This side up / Babs / Scotchin' with soda / Early morning blues / This will make you laugh / I like to riff / Call the police / Are you fer it? / That ain't right.
LP: . . . . SM 3611
MC: . . . . MC 3611

SINGS FOR TWO IN LOVE.
Tracks: / Love is here to stay / Handful of stars, A / This can't be love / Little street where old friends meet, A / Autumn leaves / Let's fall in love / There goes my heart / Dinner for one please James / Almost like being in love / Tenderly / You stepped out of a dream / Too much / Thousand thoughts of you, A / If you said no.
LP: . . . . EMS 1101
MC: . . . . TCEMS 1101

SOMETIMES.
LPPD: . . . . PD 30033

SOMEWHERE ALONG THE WAY.
Tracks: / Darling je vous aime beaucoup / It's crazy but I'm in love / Sand and the sea, The / Unforgettable / Love letters / Mona Lisa / Too young / My foolish heart.
MC: . . . . CONE 3

SONGS FOR LOVERS VOL 2.
LP: 22013
MC: 42013

SPECIAL YEARS.
Tracks: / Sweet Georgia Brown / Body and soul / Sweet lorraine / Miss thing / Cole's bop blues / It's only a paper moon / On the sunny side of the street / Bugle call rag / I'm lost, I'm lost / Let's spring one / My lips remember your kisses / Got a penny / Let's pretend / Satchel mouth baby / Pitchin up a boogie / Fine, sweet and tasty / It ain't necessarily so /

Let's pretend again / This is my night to dream / Smooth sailing.
LP: ARA 1005
MC: ARAC 1005

STRING ALONG WITH NAT KING COLE.
LP: ENC 102

SWEET HOUR OF PRAYER.
MC: 4XL 9375

SWEET LORRAINE VOL. 2.
LP: SM 4051

TELL ME ALL ABOUT YOURSELF.
Tracks: / Tell me all about yourself / Until the real thing comes along / Best thing for you, The / When you walked by / Crazy she calls me / You've got the Indian sign on me / For you / Dedicated to you / You are my love / This is always / My life / I would do - anything for you.
LP: EMS 1109
MC: TCEMS 1109

THIS IS NAT 'KING' COLE.
Tracks: / Dreams can tell a lie / I just found out about love / Too young to go steady / Forgive my heart / Annabelle / Nothing ever changes my love for you / To the ends of the earth / I'm gonna laugh you out of my life / Someone you love / Love me as though there were no tomorrow / That's all / Never let me go.
LP: EG 2606041
MC: EG 2606044
LP: PM 1552931
MC: PM 1552934

THOSE LAZY-HAZY-CRAZY DAYS OF SUMMER.
Tracks: / Get out and get under the moon / There is a tavern in the town / On a bicycle built for two / That Sunday, that summer / On the sidewalks of New York / Our old home team / After the ball / You tell me your dream (Adapted by Nat King Cole.) / That's what they meant by the good old summertime / Don't forget / In the good old summertime / Those lazy hazy crazy days of summer.
LP: EMS 1116
MC: TCEMS 1116

TO WHOM IT MAY CONCERN.
Tracks: / Thousand thoughts of you, A / You're bringing out the dreamer in me / My heart's treasure / If you said no / Can't help it / Lovesville / Unfair / This morning it was summer / To whom it may concern / Love-wise / Too much / In the heart of Jane Doe.
LP: EMS 1108
MC: TCEMS 1108

TOO YOUNG VOL. 5.
LP: SM 4054

TOP POPS.
Tracks: / Somewhere along the way / If I give my heart to you / Faith can move mountains.
LP: T 9110

TOUCH OF YOUR LIPS, THE.
Tracks: / Touch of your lips, The / I remember you / Illusion / You're mine you / Funny / Poinciana / Sunday, Monday or always / Not so long ago / Nightingale sang in Berkeley Square, A / Only forever / My need for you / Lights out.
LP: EMS 1111
MC: TCEMS 1111
MC: 4XL 9166

TRIO DAYS (Big Band Bounce & Boogie) (Cole, Nat Trio).
Tracks: / Honeysuckle rose / Sweet Lorraine / This side up / Gone with the draft / Call the Police / That ain't right / Are you fer it? / Hit that jive Jack / Early morning blues / Babs / Scotchin' with soda / Slow Down / I like to Riff / This will make you laugh / Hit the Ramp / Stop, the red light's on.
MC: TCAFS 1001
LP: AFS 1001

UNFORGETTABLE.
Tracks: / Unforgettable / Too young / Mona Lisa / I love you - for sentimental reasons / Pretend / Answer me / Portrait of Jennie / What'll I do / Lost April / Red sails in the sunset / Make her mine / Hajji baba.
LP: EMS 1100
MC: TCEMS 1100
LP: 2C 068 54579
MC: TCSW 20664
MC: 4XL 9110
LP: SPR 8587
MC: SPC 8587
LP: W 20664
LP: 2C 068 54571

UNFORGETTABLE (IMPORT).
Tracks: / Too young / Party's over, The / More I see you, The / Love is here to stay / Quizas, quizas, quizas / Angel eyes / Portrait of Jennie / Teach me tonight / Ballerina / Very thought of you, The / She's funny that way / I wish I knew the way to your heart / You made me love you / Ramblin' rose / Love letters / Fascination / Unforgettable / Piel Canela / These foolish things / Around the world.
LP: 186826 3
MC: 186826 5

UNFORGETTABLE: NAT KING COLE (16 Golden Classics).
Tracks: / Don't cry, cry baby / Last but not least / On the sunny side of the street / Yes sir that's my baby / Frim fram sauce / If you can't smile and say yes / Satchel mouth baby / Sweet Lorraine / Trouble with me is you / Old piano plays the blues / It's only a paper moon / Greatest invention, The / Bugle call rag / I'm lost / Nat meets June / Tea for two.
LP: UNLP 002
MC: UNMC 002

UNRELEASED, THE.
Tracks: / How little we know / When I'm alone / Who's who / For a moment of your love / Should I / I'm shooting high / How did I change / Like someone in love / I heard you cried last night / Come to the Mardi Gras.
LP: EMS 1279
MC: TCEMS 1279

VERY BEST OF NAT 'KING' COLE.
Tracks: / Those lazy, hazy, crazy days of summer / When my sugar walks down the street / You're my everything / Unforgettable / Love letters / Ramblin' rose / Route 66 / Autumn leaves / Affair to remember, An / I found a million dollar baby / Your cheatin' heart / Dance, ballerina, dance / On the street where you live / There's a goldmine in the sky / Nightingale sang in Berkeley Square, A / Stardust.
MC: TCEST 23165
LP: EST 23165

VERY THOUGHT OF YOU, THE.
Tracks: / Very thought of you, The / But beautiful / Impossible / I wish I knew the way to your heart / I found a million dollar baby / Magnificent obsession / My heart tells me - should I believe my heart / Paradise / This is all I ask / Cherie, I love you / Making believe you're here / Cherchez la femme / For all we know / More I see you, The / I wish I knew.
LP: EMS 1106
MC: TCEMS 1106

WELCOME TO THE CLUB.
Tracks: / Welcome to the club / Anytime, anyday, anywhere / Blues don't care, The / Mood indigo / Baby won't you please come home? / Late late show, The / Avalon / She's funny that way / I want a little girl / Wee baby blues / Look out for love.
LP: EMS 1107
MC: TCEMS 1107
LP: PM 154 769 1
MC: PM 154 769 4

WHERE DID EVERYONE GO?.
Tracks: / Where did everyone go? / Say it isn't so / If love ain't there / Ah, the apple trees - when the world was young / Am I blue / Someone to tell it to / End of a love affair, The / I keep going back to Joe's / Laughing on the outside - crying on the inside / No, I don't want her / Spring is here / That's all there is there isn't any more.
MC: TCEMS 1114
LP: EMS 1114

WHITE CHRISTMAS (Cole, Nat King & Dean Martin).
LP: MFP 5224

Cole, Natalie

EVERLASTING.
Tracks: / Everlasting / Jump start / Urge to merge, The / Split decision / When I fall in love / Pink cadillac / I live for your love / In my reality / I'm the one / More than the stars / What I must do (Track on cassette only.).
LP: MTL 1012
MC: TCMTL 1012
LP: ATAK 161
MC: TCATAK 161
MC: 7559611144

EVERLASTING (REISSUE).
LP: MTLX 1012
MC: TC-MTLX 1012

GOOD TO BE BACK.
Tracks: / Safe / As a matter of fact / Rest of the night / Miss you like crazy / I do / Good to be back / Gonna make you mine / Starting over again / Don't mention my heartache / I can't cry / Someone's rocking my dreamboat / Wild women do (power mix with rap) (Reissue only.).
LP: MTL 1042
MC: TCMTL 1042
LP: MTLX 1042
LP: 792 933 1
MC: TCMTLX 1042
MC: 7559611154

HAPPY LOVE.
Tracks: / You were right girl / Only love / Nothin' but a fool / Joke is on you / These eyes / When a man loves a woman / I can't let go / Love and kisses / Across the nation.
LP: EST 12165

HEART AND SOUL OF NATALIE COLE.
Tracks: / This will be / Inseparable / Mr Melody / Gimme some time / Sophisticated lady / Lucy in the sky with diamonds (live).
MC: KNMC 12055

I LOVE YOU SO.
Tracks: / I love you so / You're so good / It's been you / Your lonely heart / Winner / Oh, daddy / Sorry / Stand by / Who will carry on.
LP: EST 11928

I'M READY.
Tracks: / Too much mister / I won't deny you / I'm ready / Keep it on the outside / Time / Straight from the heart / Where's your angel? / I'm your mirror.
LP: EPC 25039
MC: 40 25039

NATALIE COLE COLLECTION.
LP: SN 16310

NATALIE LIVE.
Tracks: / Sophisticated lady / Que sera sera / Lovers / I'm catching hell living here alone / Mr. Melody / This will be / Party lights / I've got love on my mind / Lucy in the sky with diamonds / Inseparable / Cry baby / Can we get together again? / I can't say no if you ask me / Something's got a hold on me / Be thankful / Our love.
2LP: E-STSP 18

SOUL OF NATALIE COLE, THE (1975-1980).
Tracks: / This will be / Lovers / Mr. Melody / Annie Mae / I can't break away / La costa / Peaceful living / (I've seen) Paradise / Stairway to the stars / Inseperable / I love him so much / Be mine tonight / What you won't do for love / Still i love / Love will find you / Party lights / This will be (remix).
MC: TCEST 2157

THANKFUL.
Tracks: / Lovers / Our love / La costa / Nothing stronger than love / Be thankful / I can't stay away / Annie Mae / Keeping a light.
LP: EST 11708

UNFORGETTABLE.
LP: EKT 91
MC: EKT 91C

UNFORGETTABLE (SINGLE) (See under Cole, Nat "King") (Cole, Natalie & Nat King Cole).

WE'RE THE BEST OF FRIENDS (Cole, Natalie & Peabo Bryson).
Tracks: / Gimme sometime / This love affair / I want to be where you are / Your lonely heart / What you won't do for love / We're the best of friends / Let's fall in love / You send me / Love will find you.
LP: EST 12019

Cole, Richie

3 R'S, THE (see Rodney,Red/Richie Cole/Ricky Ford) (Cole, Richie/Red Rodney/Ricky Ford).

ALTO ANNIE'S THEME.
LP: PA 8036

ALTO MADNESS.
Tracks: / Price is right, The / Common touch, The / Last tango in Paris / Island breeze / Big Bo's paradise / Remember your day off... / Moody's mood.
LP: MR 5155

HOLLYWOOD MADNESS.
Tracks: / Hooray for Hollywood / Hi-fly / Tokyo rose sing the Hollywood blues / Relaxin' at Camarillo / Malibu breeze / I love Lucy / Waiting for Waits / Hooray for Hollywood (reprise).
LP: MR 5207

KEEPER OF THE FLAME.
Tracks: / Harold's house of jazz / New York afternoon / As time goes by / I can't get started / Keeper of the flame / Holiday for strings / Strange groove.
LP: MR 5192

LIVE AT THE VILLAGE VANGUARD.
LP: MR 5270

NEW YORK AFTERNOON.
Tracks: / Dorothy's den / Waltz for a rainy be-bop evening / Alto madness / New York afternoon / It's the same thing everywhere / Stormy weather (Trenton style.) / You'll always be my friend.
LP: MR 5119

POP BOP.
Tracks: / Overjoyed / Eddie Jefferson / On a misty night / L dorado kaddy / La Bamba / When you wish upon a star / Spanish Harlem / Star Trek 1 / Sonomascope / Saxophobia.
LP: MX 9152

PURE IMAGINATION.
Tracks: / White cliffs of Dover, The / Dreamy / Come fly with me / Concord blues / Tin Palace shuffle / Flying down to Rio / Pure imagination / Blue room / Starburst.
LP: CJ 314
MC: CJC 314

RETURN TO ALTO ACRES.
MC: PAC 8023
LP: PA 8023

SIDE BY SIDE.
Tracks: / Save your love for me / Naughayde reality (Live spiral.) / Scrapple from the apple / Donna Lee / Polka dots and moonbeams (Richie Cole alto sax solo.) / Eddie's mood / Side by side.
LP: MR 5237

STILL ON THE PLANET (Cole, Richie & E. Jefferson).
LP: MR 5063

YAKETY MADNESS! (Cole, Richie & Boots Randolph).
LP: PA 8041
MC: PAC 8041

Colegrove, Jim

PANTHER CITY BLUES.
LP: CR 30209

Coleman, B.B.

ROMANCE WITHOUT FINANCE IS A NUISANCE.
Tracks: / She ain't ugly / Don't give away that recipe / If you see my one eyed woman / Dealin' from the bottom of the deck / Romance without finance is a nuisance / Food stamp Annie / Mr. Chicken Stew / Mr. B's frosting.
LP: ICH 1107
MC: ICH 1107 MC

Coleman, Bill

1935-37.
LP: PM 1552571

...IN PARIS (Vol 2 (1936-38)).
LP: S 1308

...IN PARIS Vol 1 (1935-38).
LP: S 1307

IN PARIS 1936-1938.
LP: SW 8402
MC: SWC 8402

MAINSTREAM AT MONTREUX (Coleman, Bill & George Lafitte).
Tracks: / Blue Lou / Idaho / Sur les quais du vieux Paris / L and L blues / Tour de force / Montreux jump.
LP: BLP 30150

SWINGIN' IN LONDON (Coleman, Bill & Ben Webster).
Tracks: / Bill Coleman / But not for me / Pound horn / Sunday / For all we know / Satin doll / For Max.
LP: BLP 30127

TALE OF TWO CITIES, A.
LP: TFD 5.010

TOWN HALL CONCERT 1945 (VOL.2) (Coleman, Bill, G Krupa, C Ventura, T Wilson, S Smith,R Norvo).
LP: 6.26168
LP: 6.26169

Coleman Country...

MUSIC FROM THE COLEMAN COUNTRY (Coleman Country Trad Music Society).
LP: LEA 2044

Coleman, Cy

BARNUM (Coleman, Cy Trio).
Tracks: / One brick at a time / Black and white / Love makes such fools of us all / Bigger isn't better / Colours of my life / Join the circus / I like your style / There is a sucker born ev'ry minute / At least I tried / Thank God I'm old / Come follow the band.
LP: RHAP 12

COMIN' HOME.
Tracks: / But not for me / Time after time / Fly me to the moon.
LP: SL 5205

WE'VE GOT IT - THE MUSIC OF CY COLEMAN (see under Cain, Jackie).

Coleman, Earl

STARDUST.
LP: ST 243

THERE'S SOMETHING ABOUT AN OLD LOVE.
LP: XAN 175

Colemah, Gary B. B.

BEST OF GARY BB COLEMAN.
Tracks: / One eyed woman / Baby scratch my back / Cloud nine / Word of warning, A / I fell in love on a one night stand / Merry Christmas baby / Watch

where you stroke / Think before you act / If you can beat me rockin' (you can have my) / St. James infirmary / I won't be your fool; / Christmas blues (instrumental).
LP: . . . . ICH 1065
MC: . . . . ICH 1065 MC

DANCIN' MY BLUES AWAY.
Tracks: / Word of warning, A / Think before you act / What's the name of that thing / I gotta play the blues for you / Dancin' my blues away / Maybe love wasn't meant for me / Can't spend my money / Blues at sunrise.
LP: . . . . ICH 1049
MC: . . . . ZCICH 1049

IF YOU CAN'T BEAT ME ROCKIN'.
Tracks: / Watch where you stroke / Cloud nine / Please don't dog me / If the washing don't get you / If you can beat me rockin' / It just ain't right / Rub my back / St. James Infirmary / Hide away / Tell me what to do / Los conquestadores chocolates / Lost on 23rd street / Fantasy / Shifting gears / Can't we smile.
LP: . . . . ICH 1018
MC: . . . . ZCICH 1018

NOTHIN' BUT THE BLUES.
LP: . . . . KK 7443
LP: . . . . ICH 1005

ONE NIGHT STAND.
Tracks: / Baby scratch my back / Sitting and waiting / I just can't lose this blues / I'll take care of you / I wrote this song for you / As the years go passing by / I fell in love on a one night stand / Going down.
LP: . . . . ICH 1034
MC: . . . . ZCICH 1034

Coleman, George

AMSTERDAM AFTER DARK.
Tracks: / Amsterdam after dark / New arrival / Lo-Joe / Autumn in New York / Apache dance / Blondie's waltz.
LP: . . . . SJP 129

AT YOSHI'S.
Tracks: / They say it's wonderful / Good morning heartache / Laig gobblin' blues / Ten / Up jumped Spring / Father / Soul eyes.
LP: . . . . TR 126

BIG GEORGE (Coleman, George Octet).
Tracks: / On Green Dolphin Street / Frank's tune / Big George / Jogging / Body and soul / Revival.
LP: . . . . AFF 178

BONGO JOE.
LP: . . . . ARHOOLIE 1040

EASTER REBELLION (see Walton,Cedar) (Coleman, George/Cedar Walton/Sam Jones/Billy Higgins).

GEORGE COLEMAN LIVE.
Tracks: / Blues inside out / Walking / Stella by starlight.
LP: . . . . N 121

GEORGE COLEMAN OCTET.
LP: . . . . AFF 52

MAMA ROOTS (Coleman, George & Charlie Earland).
Tracks: / Undecided / Dozens, The / Red, green and black blues / Mama roots / Old folks / Bluesette.
LP: . . . . MR 5156

MEDITATION (Coleman, George & Tete Montoliu).
Tracks: / Lisa / Dynamic duo / First time down / Waltzing at Rosa's place / Meditation / Sophisticated lady.
LP: . . . . SJP 110

PLAYING CHANGES.
Tracks: / Laura / Siorra / Moment's notice.
LP: . . . . JHR 002
MC: . . . . JHC 002

STABLEMATES (See under Cook, Junior) (Coleman, George/Junior Cook).

Coleman, Jacoby (nar)

MATHILDE MOUSE AND THE STORY OF SILENT NIGHT (see under Mathilde Mouse... (bk).

Coleman, Jaz

MINARETS AND MEMORIES (See under 'Dudley, Anne') (Dudley, Anne & Jaz Coleman).

SONGS FROM THE VICTORIOUS CITY (See under Dudley, Anne) (Dudley, Anne & Jaz Coleman).

Coleman, Michael

CLASSIC RECORDINGS OF MICHAEL COLEMAN, THE.
LP: . . . . SHAN 33006

LEGACY OF MICHAEL COLEMAN, THE.
LP: . . . . SHAN 33002

Coleman, Mick

MATCHSTALK MAN, THE (Billy the snake).
Tracks: / My name is Billy / Clarence the zebra / Harry the hedgehog / High in the sky / Princess rainbow / B.I.L.L.Y..
LP: . . . . MSLPH 501

Coleman, Ornette

AT THE GOLDEN CIRCLE VOL 1.
Tracks: / Announcement / Faces and places / European echoes / Dee Dee / Dawn.
LP: . . . . BST 84224

AT THE GOLDEN CIRCLE VOL 2.
Tracks: / Snowflakes and sunshine, The / Morning song / Riddle, The / Antiques.
LP: . . . . BST 84225

BEAUTY PORTRAIT.
LP: . . . . PRT 461 1193 1

BODY META.
LP: . . . . AH 1

DANCING IN YOUR HEAD.
Tracks: / Theme from a symphony (variation one) / Theme from a symphony (variation two) / Midnight sunrise.
LP: . . . . AMLJ 722

EUROPEAN CONCERT (Coleman, Ornette Quartet).
Tracks: / Street woman / Song for Che / Whom do you work for? / Rock the clock / Written word.
LP: . . . . UJ 13

EVENING WITH ORNETTE COLEMAN. VOL 2.
Tracks: / Falling stars / Silence / Happy fool / Ballad / Doughnuts.
LP: . . . . BLM 51504

EVENING WITH ORNETTE COLEMAN, VOL 1.
Tracks: / Sounds and forms for wind quintet / Sadness / Clergyman's dream.
LP: . . . . BLM 51503

FREE JAZZ - THAT'S JAZZ.
Tracks: / Free jazz (part 1) / Free jazz (part 2).
LP: . . . . K 50240

IN ALL LANGUAGES.
Tracks: / Peace warriors / Feet music / Africa is the mirror of all colors / Word for bird / Space church / Latin genetics / In all mercury / Sound manual / Mothers of the veil / Cloning / Music news / Art of love is happiness, The / Today, yesterday and tomorrow / Listen up / Feet up / Biosphere / Story tellers.
LP: . . . . CDP 85008
MC: . . . . CDPT 85008

OF HUMAN FEELINGS.
LP: . . . . AN 2001

OPENING THE CARAVAN OF DREAMS (Coleman, Ornette & Prime Time).
LP: . . . . CDP 85001

ORNETTE LIVE AT PRINCE STREET.
Tracks: / Friends and neighbours / Long time no see / Let's play / Forgotten songs / Tomorrow.
LP: . . . . PL 43548

SOAPSUDS SOAPSUDS (Coleman, Ornette & Charlie Haden).
LP: . . . . AH 6

SOMETHING ELSE.
LP: . . . . COP 024

SONG X (Coleman, Ornette/Pat Metheny).
Tracks: / Song X / Mob job / Endangered species / Video games / Kathelin Gray / Trigonometry / Song X duo / Long time no see.
LP: 9240961
MC: 9240964

THAT'S JAZZ SERIES.
LP: . . . . ATL 50240

TOMORROW IS THE QUESTION.
Tracks: / Tomorrow is the question / Tears inside / Mind and time / Compassion / Giggin' / Rejoicing / Lorraine / Turnaround / Endless.
LP: . . . . COP 002

UNPRECEDENTED MUSIC OF ORNETTE COLEMAN, THE.
Tracks: / Lonely woman / Monsieur Le Prince / Forgotten children / Buddah blues.
LP: . . . . LPPS 111 16

VIRGIN BEAUTY.
Tracks: / Three wishes / Bourgeois boogie / Happy hour / Virgin beauty / Healing the feeling / Singing in the shower / Desert players / Honeymooners / Chanting / Spelling the alphabet.
LP: 4611931
MC: 461193 4

WHO'S CRAZY?.
Tracks: / January / Sortie le coquard / Dans la neige / Changes / Better get yourself another self / Duel, The / Two psychic lovers and eating time / Misused blues, The / Poet, The / Wedding day and fuzz / Fuzz / Feast / Breakout / European echoes / Alone and the arrest.
2LP: . . . . AFFD 102
2LP: . . . . IRI 5006/1

Coleman, Steve

RHYTHM PEOPLE.
Tracks: / Rhythm people / Blues shifting / No conscience / Neutral zone / Ain't goin' out like that / Step'n / Dangerous / Ice moves / Posse, The / Armageddon (Cold blooded).
LP: . . . . PL 83092
MC: . . . . PK 83092

SINE DIE (Coleman, Steve & Five Elements).
Tracks: / Destination / Cinema saga / Soul melange / Circle C / Proteus / Passage / First sunrise / UR-beat / Dark to light / Profile man / Proteus revamp.
LP: 461159 1
MC: 461159 4

WORLD EXPANSION (Coleman, Steve & Five Elements).
Tracks: / Desperate move / Stone bone Jr / Mad monkey / Dream state / Tang lung / Yo ho / And they parted ... / In the park / Just a funky old song / Urilai Thrane / To perpetuate the funk / Koshine Koji / Tlydor's bane.
LP: . . . . JMT 780010

Colenso Parade

GLENTORAN.
LP: . . . . FIRELP 6

Coleridge, Samuel

POETRY OF COLERIDGE, THE (Richardson, Sir Ralph (nar)).
MC: 1092

Coles, Maury

MAURY COLES.
LP: . . . . SERIES 003

SOLO SAXOPHONE RECORD.
Tracks: / Yonge Street traveller / Hats off / Goats Hill Road / Tip top pop / Prepared plastic number one.
LP: . . . . ONARI 003

Colette (show)

COLETTE (Original Stage Cast) (Various artists).
Tracks: / You can be sure of spring: *Various artists* / He's a captain: *Various artists* / I'm special: *Various* artists / Ambitious: *Various artists* / I never make the same mistake: *Various artists* / Paree: *Various* artists / Our relationship: *Various artists* / Attention will wander: *Various artists* / Alone with myself: *Various artists* / You've got to do what you will do: *Various artists* / We'll stick together: *Various artists*/ Little girl: *Various artists* / Nothing special: *Various artists* / Little touch of powder: *Various artists*/ Love with someone younger: *Various artists* / Will he ever be back: *Various artists* / Little red room: *Various artists*.
LP: . . . . RSR 1006
MC: . . . . RSC 1006

Coley, John Ford

DOCTOR HECKLE AND MR. JIVE (see England Dan) (Coley, John Ford/ England Dan).

DOWDY FERRY ROAD (see England Dan) (Coley, John Ford/England Dan).

I HEAR THE MUSIC (see England Dan) (Coley, John Ford/England Dan).

LESLIE, KELLY & JOHN FORD COLEY.
Tracks: / Without you / Is it any wonder / American boy / Go for the heart / Somebody to love / There's a love / Long distance telephone / Come back to me / Let's go to the movies / Love has got to start with us / Don't wake me now / Children's prayer.
LP: . . . . AMLH 64841

NIGHTS ARE FOREVER (see England Dan) (Coley, John Ford/England Dan).

SOME THINGS DON'T COME EASY (see England Dan) (Coley, John Ford/ England Dan).

Colianni, John

BLUES O MATIC (Colianni, John Trio).
LP: . . . . CJ 367
MC: . . . . CJ 367 C

JOHN COLIANNI.
Tracks: / Raincheck / Soft shoe / Pick yourself up / Homegrown / Slow blues / I am in love / Get happy / All of you / Jitterbug waltz / Long ago and far away.
LP: . . . . CJ 309
MC: . . . . CJC 309

Colina, Michael

RITUALS.
Tracks: / Rituals / Shambhala / Lolita's room / Cherry high / I shot the sheriff / Magic / Black panther / Drala.
LP: 210554
MC: 410554

SHADOW OF URBANO.
Tracks: / Joy dancing / Shades / Shadow of Urbano, The / Hong Kong flu / Doctor of desire / Fast break / Lady and the tramp / Drifter.
LP: 209.967
MC: 409.967

Coll, Brian

BEST OF BRIAN COLL.
Tracks: / Sweet Mary & the miles between / Picture on the wall / Hello darlin / I'll be glad / These are my mountains / Your old love letters / China doll / When my blue moon turns to gold again / Second fiddle / Silver haired Daddy of mine / They'll never take her love from me / Farmer, The.
MC: . . . . CPHL 477
LP: . . . . PHL 477

COUNTRY CALLING.
Tracks: / Home town on the Foyle / Picture on the wall / She's mine / Tonight I'll throw a party / China doll / These are my mountains / Farmer, The / Time changes everything / Little bit slow to catch on / Fool's castle / Mail call / Second fiddle.
LP: . . . . PHL 412
MC: . . . . CPHL 412

COVER MAMAS FLOWERS.
LP: . . . . HPE 603

OLD LOVES NEVER DIE.
LP: . . . . HM 031

SILVER HAIRED DADDY OF MINE.
Tracks: / That silver haired daddy of mine / Remember me / Lonesome heart, A / From heart to heart / Not once but 100 times / Hello darlin / Your old love letters / They'll never take her love from me / Tell me / Doors of love / Sweet Mary and the miles between.
LP: . . . . PHL 420
MC: . . . . CPHL 420

THESE ARE MY MOUNTAINS.
LP: . . . . HPE 636

Collage

SHINE THE LIGHT.
LP: . . . . CF 3297

Collection D'Arnell

UN AUTOMNE A LOROY.
LP: . . . . ARTY 19

Collective Nox

COLLECTIVE NOX.
Tracks: / Sizabo / Jetai / Kecekece / Final / Sadbassad / Megusta / Chantguerrier / Assault.
LP: . . . . ST 7524

Collectors

SEVENTH SUMMER.
Tracks: / Make it easy / Fat bird / Fisherwoman / Listen to the words / Old man / Looking at a baby / What is love? / Lydia purple / She (will-o-the-wind) / Seventeenth summer / Teletype click / Things I remember / Don't turn away / Long rain, The / Dream of desolation / Rainbow of fire / Early morning.
LP: . . . . ED 214

Collector's Items

COLLECTOR'S ITEMS (Various artists).
Tracks: / I feel like I'm fixin' to die rag: *Unknown* / Super bird: *Unknown* / Thing called love, A: *Unknown*/ Bass strings: *Unknown* / Section 43: *Unknown* / Fire in the city: *Unknown* / Johnny's gone to war: *Unknown*/ Kiss my ass: *Unknown* / Tricky dicky: *Unknown* / Free some day: *Unknown*.
LP: . . . . LIK 7

Collegiate Church

18 POPULAR HYMNS (Collegiate Church, St. Mary, Warwick, Choir).
LP: . . . . XMAS 687

Collett, Dave

BACK TO BOOGIE WOOGIE (see Williams, G.O.) (Collett, Dave & G.O. Williams).

Collie, Max

20 YEARS JUBILEE (Collie, Max & his Rhythm Aces).
LP: . . . . TTD 519

AT THE BEIDERBECKE FESTIVAL 1975.
LP: . . . . BBMS 5

BACK-LINE VOLUME 2 (Collie, Max & his Rhythm Aces).
LP: . . . . TTD 508

BATTLE OF TRAFALGAR (Collie, Max & his Rhythm Aces).
2LP: . . . . R 106

BY POPULAR DEMAND (Collie, Max & His Rhythm Aces).
Tracks: / When you're smiling / Passport to Paradise / Doctor Jazz / Summertime / Begin the beguine / Just a

gigolo / Onions / Willie the weeper / As time goes by / Maryland / Margie / Tres moutarde.
LP: . . . . **BLP 12181**

FRONT-LINE VOLUME 1 (Collie, Max & his Rhythm Aces).
LP: . . . . **TTD 504**

GOSPEL TRAIN.
Tracks: / Gospel train / Over the rainbow / Nobody knows you (when you're down and out) / Woodworm stomp / My blue Heaven / Lullaby / After you've gone / Clarinet marmalade.
LP: . . . . **BLP 12147**

JAZZ ROOLS OK.
LP: . . . . **BLP 12168**

LIVE IN SWEDEN (Collie, Max & His Rhythm Aces).
Tracks: / Light from the lighthouse / Original Dixieland one-step / Summertime / Black cat on a fence / World is waiting for the sunrise, The / Travelling blues / Mad dog / East Coast trot / Wabash blues / Pretty baby / Cheek to cheek / Snag it / Martinique, The / Ostrich walk / Short-dress gal / Entertainer, The.
2LP: . . . . **SFAX 108**

LIVE: MAX COLLIE (Collie, Max & His Rhythm Aces).
Tracks: / Runnin' wild / At a Georgia camp meeting / Shimme-sha-wabble / Blue bells goodbye / Tiger rag / Yellow dog blues / Ice cream.
LP: . . . . **B 90029**
MC: . . . . **MB 90029**

MAX COLLIE'S RHYTHM ACES VOL 1 (Collie, Max & his Rhythm Aces).
LP: . . . . **WAM/O No.1**

MAX COLLIE'S RHYTHM ACES VOL 2 (Collie, Max & his Rhythm Aces).
LP: . . . . **WAM/O No.2**

TEN YEARS TOGETHER (Collie, Max & His Rhythm Aces).
Tracks: / Georgia grind / Give me your telephone number / I guess I'll have to change my plans / Dippermouth blues / Everybody loves my baby / I'm gonna sit right down and write myself a letter / Girl in clover / Beautiful dreamer / Hindustan / Ace in the hole / Dallas blues / Buddy's habits / Kneedrops / Jumping Jack sax / Rainbow round my shoulder / Cielito Lindo / Wolverine blues / Hi lili hi lo.
2LP: . . . . **SFAX 118**

THRILL OF JAZZ, THE (Collie, Max & His Rhythm Aces).
MC: . . . . **R 111C**

WORLD CHAMPIONS OF JAZZ (Collie, Max & His Rhythm Aces).
Tracks: / Too bad / Sweet like this / Salutation march / 'S wonderful / I'm crazy 'bout my baby / Didn't he ramble / Ragtime dance / Dans les rues D'Antibes / Fidgety fingers.
2LP: . . . . **BLPX 12137/8**

Collier, Graham

DARIUS (Collier, Graham & Various artists).
LP: . . . . **GCM 741**

DAY OF THE DEAD.
2LP: . . . . **GCMD 783/4**

MIDNIGHT BLUE.
LP: . . . . **GCM 751**

NEW CONDITIONS.
LP: . . . . **GCM 761**

SYMPHONY OF SCORPIONS.
LP: . . . . **GCM 773**

Collier, Mitty

SHADES OF GENIUS.
Tracks: / Come back baby / I had a talk with my man / Would you have listened / I gotta get away from it all / My babe / Hallelujah (I love him so) / Drown in my own tears / No faith,no love / Together / Let them talk / Little Miss Loneliness / Ain't that love.
LP: . . . . **GCH 8049**
MC: . . . . **GCHK 78049**

Collier, Sheila

CHANGE IS GONNA COME, A.
Tracks: / Change is gonna come, A / On my way / I've had it / Why don't you do right? / What a day for a daydream / Blues, get off my shoulder / Do your duty / Harmony alone / Sweet man / On revival day / Am I blue?.
LP: . . . . **PLJ 005**

TRIBUTE TO BESSIE SMITH.
LP: . . . . **SR 3785**

Collingwood, Charles

ALL FAMOUS FIVE RECORDINGS (see under Blyton, Enid (aut)) (Bennett, Judy (nar) & Charles Collingwood (nar)).

FIVE ON A HIKE TOGETHER (see under Blyton, Enid (aut)) (Bennett, Judy (nar) & Charles Collingwood (nar)).

Collins, Albert

ALBERT COLLINS & BARRELHOUSE LIVE (Collins, Albert & Barrelhouse).
LP: . . . . **BM 150225**

ALIVE AND COOL.
Tracks: / How blue can you get / Thaw out / So tired / Funky / Deep freeze / Baby what you want me to do / Mustang Sally / Backstroke.
LP: . . . . **RL 004**

COLD SNAP.
Tracks: / Cash talkin' / Bending like a willow tree / Good fool is hard to find, A / Lights are on but nobody's home / I ain't drunk / Hooked on you / Too many dirty dishes / Snatchin' it back / Fake ID.
LP: . . . . **SNTF 969**
MC: . . . . **ZCSN 969**

COOL SOUND OF ALBERT COLLINS, THE.
Tracks: / Frosty / Hot and cold / Frost bite / Tremble / Thaw out / Dyin' flu / Don't lose your cool / Backstroke / Kool aide / Shiver and shake / Icy blue / Sno-cone (part 2).
LP: . . . . **CCR 1011**

DON'T LOSE YOUR COOL.
Tracks: / Got togettin' / My mind is trying to leave me / I'm broke / Don't loose your cool / When a guitar plays the blues / But I was cool / Melt down / Ego trip / Quicksand.
LP: . . . . **SNTF 896**

FROSTBITE.
Tracks: / If you love me like you say / Blue Monday hangover / I got a problem / Highway is like a woman / Brick / Don't go reaching across my plate / Give me my blues / Snowed in.
LP: . . . . **SNTF 837**

FROZEN ALIVE.
Tracks: / Frosty / Angel of mercy / I got that feeling / Caledonia / Things I used to do, The / Got a mind to travel / Cold cuts.
LP: . . . . **SNTF 874**

ICE COLD BLUES.
Tracks: / Harris county line / Conversation with Collins / Jawing / Grapeland gossip / Chatterbox / Trash talkin' / Leftovers / Got a good thing goin' / Lip service / Talking slim blues / Backyard backtalk / Tongue lashing / And it started raining / Stump poker.
LP: . . . . **CRB 1119**
MC: . . . . **TCCRB 1119**

ICE PICKIN'.
Tracks: / Talking woman blues / When the welfare turns its back on you / Ice pick / Cold, cold feeling / Too tired / Master charge / Conversation with Collins / Avalanche.
LP: . . . . **SNTF 707**

ICEMAN.
LP: . . . . **VPBLP 3**
MC: . . . . **VPBTC 3**

LIVE IN JAPAN (Collins, Albert & The Icebreakers).
Tracks: / Listen here / Tired man / If trouble was money / Jealous man / Stormy Monday / Skatin' / All about my girl.
LP: . . . . **SNTF 911**

SHOWDOWN (Collins, Albert/Johnny Copeland/Robert Cray).
Tracks: / T-Bone shuffle / Moon is full, The / Lion's den / She's into something / Bring your fine self home / Black cat bone / Dream, The / Albert's alley / Black Jack.
LP: . . . . **SNTF 954**

Collins, Ansell

ANSELL COLLINS.
LP: . . . . **HB 40**

RIDING HIGH.
Tracks: / It's raining / Double -000 / Spiderman / Zambia river / Skully bone / Sniff your coke / Riding high / I don't want to be hurt / Kahunda / Night of love.
LP: . . . . **DSR 2501**

SO LONG.
LP: . . . . **HB 48**

Collins, Bootsy

PLAYER OF THE YEAR.
Tracks: / As in 'I love you' / Bootsy / Bootzilla / Hollywood squares / Funk attack / May the force be with you / Roto Tooter / Very yes 'player of the year'.
LP: . . . . **K 56424**

WHAT'S BOOTSY DOIN'.
Tracks: / Party on plastic / Subliminal seduction (funk me dirty) / Leakin' / Electro-cutie (shock it to me) / First one to the egg wins (the human race) / Love song / (I wannabee) kissin' the luv gun / Yo moma loves ya / Save what's mine for me.
LP: . . . . **FC 44107**
LP: **4629181**
MC: **4629184**

Collins, Cal

CAL COLLINS.
LP: . . . . **CJ 71**

CROSS COUNTRY.
Tracks: / Corina Corina / My gal Sal / On the Atchison, Topeka and Santa Fe.
LP: . . . . **CJ 166**

OHIO BOSS GUITAR.
LP: . . . . **HL 123**

Collins, Dave

DOUBLE BARREL (Collins, Dave & Ansel).
LP: . . . . **TBL 162**

Collins, Earl

BLUEGRASS CARDINALS.
LP: . . . . **SBR 4205**

THAT'S EARL.
LP: . . . . **SBR 4204**

Collins, Edwyn

HELLBENT ON COMPROMISE.
LP: . . . . **FIEND 195**
MC: . . . . **FIENDCASS 195**

HOPE AND DESPAIR.
Tracks: / Coffee table song / 50 shades of blue / You're better than you know / Pushing it to the back of my mind / Darling, they want it all / Wheels of love, The / Beginning of the end / Measure of the man, The / Testing time / Let me put your arms around you / Wide eyes child in me, The / Ghost of a chance.
LP: . . . . **FIEND 144**
MC: . . . . **FIENDCASS 144**

PALE BLUE EYES (See under Quinn, Paul) (Collins, Edwyn & Paul Quinn).

Collins, Glenda

BEEN INVITED TO A PARTY (1963-1966).
Tracks: / I lost my heart at the fairground / I feel so good / If you gotta pick a baby / Baby it hurts / Nice wasn't it / Lollipop / Everybody got to fall in love / Johnny loves me / Paradise for two / Thou shalt not steal / Been invited to a party / Something I got to tell you / My heart didn't lie / It's hard to believe it / Don't let it rain on Sunday / In the first place.
LP: . . . . **CSAP 108**

Collins, Henrietta

DRIVE BY SHOOTING.
LP: . . . . **TH 03**
LP: . . . . **HOLY 005**

Collins, Jacqui

LOVE UNITE (See under Collins, Dave) (Collins, Jacqui & Dave Collins).

Collins, Johnny

FREE AND EASY.
LP: . . . . **TSR 041**

JOHNNY'S PRIVATE ARMY (Collins, Johnny & Co.).
LP: . . . . **TSR 020**

TRAVELLER'S REST (Collins, Johnny & Friends).
LP: . . . . **TSR 014**

Collins, Joyce

MOMENT TO MOMENT (Collins, Joyce Quartet).
Tracks: / Don't ever leave me / Sunshowers / I get along without you very well / Alone together / Some other time.
LP: . . . . **DS 828**

Collins, Judy

AMAZING GRACE.
Tracks: / Somebody soon / Since you asked / Both sides now / Sons of / Suzanne / Farewell to Tarwathie / Father / Albatross / In my life / Amazing Grace.
LP: . . . . **K 42110**
MC: **K4 42110**

AMAZING GRACE (RE-ISSUE).
LP: . . . . **STAR 2265**
MC: . . . . **STAC 2265**

BOTH SIDES NOW.
Tracks: / Both sides now / Michael from the mountains / Story of Isaac / Pirate Jenny / Since you asked / Just like Tom Thumb's blues / I pity the poor immigrant / In my life / I think its going to rain today / Who knows where the time goes.
LP: . . . . **SHM 3061**
MC: . . . . **HSC 3061**

BREAD AND ROSES.
Tracks: / Bread and roses / Everything must change / Special delivery / Out of control / Plegaria del labrador / Come down in time / Spanish is the loving tongue / I didn't know about you / Take this longing / Love hurts / Marjorie / King David.
LP: . . . . **K 52039**

FIRES OF EDEN.
Tracks: / Blizzard / Fortune of soldiers / Test of time / Fires of Eden / Home before dark / Air that I breathe, The / City of cities / Dreaming / Queen of the night / From a distance / Blizzard reprise, The.
LP: **4673731**
MC: **4673734**

HARD TIMES FOR LOVERS.
Tracks: / Hard times for lovers / Marie / Happy end / Desperado / I remember sky / Starmaker / Dorothy / I'll never say goodbye / Through the eyes of love / Where or when.
LP: . . . . **K 52121**

HOME AGAIN.
Tracks: / Only you / Sweetheart on parade / Everybody works in China / Yellow kimono / From where I stand / Home again / Shoot first / Don't say love / Dream on / Best is yet to come, The.
LP: **9603041**

JUDITH.
Tracks: / Moon is a harsh mistress, The / Angel spread your wings / Houses / Loving of the game, The / Song for Duke / Send in the clowns / Salt of the earth / Brother can you spare a dime / City of New Orleans / I'll be seeing you / Pirate ships / Born to the breed.
LP: . . . . **K 52019**
MC: . . . . **K 452019**

RUNNING FOR MY LIFE.
Tracks: / Running for my life / Bright morning star / Greenfinch and Linnet bird / Marieke / Pretty woman / Almost free / I could really show you around / I've done enough dying for today / Anyone would love you / Rainbow connection, The / This is the day / Wedding song, The.
LP: . . . . **K 52205**
MC: **K4 52205**

SANITY AND GRACE.
Tracks: / History / Wind beneath my wings / Lovin' and learning / From a distance / Sanity and grace / Daughters of time / Cats in the cradle / Pretty Polly / Born to the breed.
LP: . . . . **VGC 11**
MC: . . . . **TCVGC 11**
MC: . . . . **OVEDC 373**

SO EARLY IN THE SPRING, THE FIRST 15 YEARS.
Tracks: / Pretty Polly / So early, early in the spring / Pretty Saro / Golden apples of the sun / Bonnie ship the diamond, The / Farewell to Tarwathie / Hostage, The / La Colombe / Coal tattoo / Carry it on / Bread and roses / Marat / Sade / Special delivery / Lovin' of the game, The / Both sides now / Marieke / Send in the clowns / Bird on the wire / Since you've asked / Born to the breed / My father / Holly Ann / Houses / Secret gardens.
LP: . . . . **K 62019**

TIME OF OUR LIVES.
Tracks: / Great expectations / Rest of your life / Grandaddy / It's gonna be one of those nights / Memory / Sun son / Mama mama / Drink a round to Ireland / Angel on my side / Don't say goodbye love.
LP: . . . . **K 52347**

TRUE STORIES AND OTHER DREAMS.
Tracks: / Cook with honey / So begins the task / Fishermen song / Dealer (down and losin'), The / Secret gardens / Holly Ann / Hostage, The / For Martin / Che.
LP: . . . . **K 42132**

TRUST YOUR HEART.
Tracks: / Trust your heart / Amazing grace / Jerusalem / Day by day / Life you dream, The / Rose, the / Moonfall / Morning has broken / When a child is born / When you wish upon a star.
LP: . . . . **VGC 7**
MC: . . . . **TCVGC 7**
MC: . . . . **OVEDC 372**

WHALES AND NIGHTINGALES.
Tracks: \/ Song for David / Sons of / Patriot game, The / Prothalamium / Oh had I a golden thread / Gene's song / Farewell to Tarwathie / Time passes slowly / Marieke / Nightingale I / Nightingale II / Simple gifts / Amazing grace.
LP: . . . . **K 42059**
LP: . . . . **EKS 75010**

WHO KNOWS WHERE THE TIME GOES.
Tracks: / Hello, hooray / Story of Isaac / My father / Someday soon / Who knows where the time goes / Poor immigrant / First boy I loved, The / Bird on the wire / Pretty Polly.
LP: . . . . **K 42044**

WILD FLOWERS.
Tracks: / Michael from the mountains / Since you asked sisters of mercy / Priests / Ballata of Francesco Landini, A / Lasso di Donna / Both sides now / La chanson des vieux amants (the song of

old lovers) / Sky fell / Albatross / Hey that's no way to say goodbye.
LP: . . . . K 42014

Collins, Kathleen

TRADITIONAL MUSIC OF IRELAND.
LP: . . . . SHAN 29002

Collins Kids

COLLINS KIDS 1959-60.
LP: . . . . RFD 9002

INTRODUCING LARRY AND LORRIE.
Tracks: / Hoy hoy / Rock boppin' baby / Just because / Hop skip and jump / Hurricane / Shortnin' bread rock / Whistle bait / Mercy / Soda poppin' around / Walking the floor over you / Hot rod / Party.
LP: . . . . EPC 25334

ROCKIN' ROLLIN'.
Tracks: / Hurricane / Early American / Rockin' gypsy / Bye bye Joe Maphis / Flying fingers / Rock and roll / Tennessee two step / Fire on the strings / You've been gone too long (Previously unissued.) / One step down / Hey mama boom a lacka / Wild and wicked love / What about tomorrow / Pied piper poodle (Previously unissued.) / T-Bone / Rebel - Johnny Yuma, The.
LP: . . . . BFX 15106

ROCKIN' ROLLIN' COLLINS KIDS.
Tracks: / Cuckoo rock, The (Previously unissued.) / Beetle bug hop / Rockaway rock, The / They're still in love / Make him behave / Go away, don't bother me / Hush money / I wish (Previously unissued.) / Rock & roll polka / Shortnin' bread rock (Previously unissued.) / Just because / Hoy hoy / Hot rod (Previously unissued.) / Soda poppin' rock (2nd recording) (Previously unissued.) / Mercy / Sweet talk.
LP: . . . . BFX 15074

ROCKIN' ROLLIN' COLLINS KIDS VOL.2.
Tracks: / Whistle bait / Party / In my teens / Rock boppin' baby / Mama worries / Heartbeat / My first love / Young heart / Hop skip and jump / Soda Poppin around (1st recording) (Previously unissued.) / Walking the floor over you / Missouri Waltz / You are my sunshine / There'll be some changes made (Previously unissued.) / Lonesome road (Previously unissued.) / Cuckoo rock, The / Beetle bug hop / Rockaway road, The / They're still in love / Make him behave / Go away don't bother me / I wish / Rock and roll polka / Shortnin' bread rock / Just because / Hoy hoy / Jones progress / Hot rod / Soda poppin' around / Mercy / Sweet talk.
LP: . . . . BFX 15108

TELEVISION PARTY.
LP: . . . . TV 5758

Collins, Lee

IN THE 30'S.
LP: . . . . CI 009

NIGHT AT THE VICTORY CLUB, A.
LP: . . . . NOR 7203

RALPH SUTTON'S JAZZOLA SIX-VOL.1.
Tracks: / Do you know what it means / Down in jungle town / Panama / After you've gone / Little Rock getaway / West End blues / Indiana / St. James infirmary / Honeysuckle rose / Johnson rag / Sunny side of the street / Hindustan.
LP: . . . . RARITIES 31

RALPH SUTTON'S JAZZOLA SIX-VOL.2.
Tracks: / Do you know what it means / I've found a new baby / Buddy Bolden's blues / Muskrat ramble / Our Monday date / Clarinet marmalade / Do you know what it means (2) / Fidgety feet / Chinatown, my Chinatown / Viper's drag / Basin Street blues / Big butter and egg man.
LP: . . . . RARITIES 32

Collins, Lyn

LYN COLLINS (THE FEMALE PREACHER).
LP: . . . . URBLP 7
MC: . . . . URBMC 7

Collins, Paul

PAUL COLLINS' BEAT.
Tracks: / Rock'n'roll girl / I don't fit in / Different kind of girl / Don't wait up for me / You won't be happy / Walking out on love / Work a day world / USA / Let me into your life / Working too hard / You and I / Look but don't touch.
LP: 83895

Collins, Phil

...BUT SERIOUSLY.
Tracks: / Hang in long enough / That's just the way it is / Do you remember / Something happened on the way to Heaven / Colours / I wish it would rain down / Another day in paradise / Heat on the street / All of my life / Saturday night and Sunday morning / Father to son / Find a way to my heart.
LP: . . . . V 2620
MC: . . . . TCV 2620

EASY LOVER (see also Phillip Bailey) (Collins, Phil & Phillip Bailey).

FACE VALUE.
Tracks: / In the air tonight / This must be love / Behind the lines / Roof is leaking / Droned / Hand in hand / I missed again / You know what I mean / I'm not moving / If leaving me is easy / Tomorrow never knows / Thunder and lightning.
LP: . . . . V 2185
MC: . . . . TCV 2185

HELLO I MUST BE GOING.
Tracks: / I don't care anymore / I cannot believe it's true / Like China / Do you know, do you care? / You can't hurry love / It don't matter to me / Thru' these walls / Don't let him steal your heart away / West side, The / Why can't it wait till morning.
LP: . . . . OVED 212
MC: . . . . OVEDC 212
LP: . . . . V 2252

NO JACKET REQUIRED.
Tracks: / Sussudio / Only you know and I know / Long long way to go / Don't want to know / One more night / Don't lose my number / Who said I would / Doesn't anybody stay together anymore / Inside out / Take me home / We said hello goodbye (CD only).
MC: . . . . TCV 2345
LP: . . . . V 2345

PHIL COLLINS: INTERVIEW PICTURE DISC.
LPPD: . . . . BAK 2020

SERIOUS HITS LIVE.
Tracks: / Something happened on the way to heaven / Against all odds / Who said I would / One more night / Don't lose my number / Do you remember / Another day in paradise / Separate lives / In the air tonight / You can't hurry love / Two hearts / Sussudio / Groovy kind of love / Easy lover / Take me home.
LP: . . . . PCLP 1
MC: . . . . PCMCX 1

Collins, Ronan

GAMES PEOPLE PLAY.
Tracks: / Games people play / Cavan girl / Rare ould times / Maybe / Garden party / Feeling single seeing double / Pretty woman / Margaritaville / Miss you nights / Wind beneath my winds / Somebody's baby / I remember you.
MC: . . . . MCLP 1004

Collins, Shirley

ADIEU TO OLD ENGLAND.
Tracks: / Mistress's health / Lumps of plum pudding / Down by the seaside / Chiner's song, The / Adieu to old England / Ashen faggot wassail / I sing to a maiden that is makeless / Banks of the Mossom, The / Ram of Berbish town / Portsmouth / Horkstow grange / Come all you little streamers / Spaniards cry / Sherborne jig / One night as I lay on my bed / Death of Nelson / Coronation jig.
LP: 12TS 238

ANTHEMS IN EDEN SUITE (Collins, Shirley & Dolly).
Tracks: / Meeting, A - searching for lambs / Courtship, A - the wedding song / Denying, A - the blacksmith / Foresaking, A - our captain cried / Dream, A - lowlands / Leavetaking, A (pleasant and delightful) / Awakening, An (whitsun dance) / New beginning, A - the staines morris / Rembleaway / C'the yowes / God dog / Bonnie cuckoo / Nellie / Gathering rushes in the month of May / Gower wassail / Beginning, A.
LP: . . . . SEE 57
LP: . . . . SHSM 2008

FOLK ROOTS NEW ROUTES (Collins, Shirley & Davey Graham).
LP: . . . . GDC 001

FOR AS MANY AS WILL (Collins, Shirley & Dolly).
Tracks: / Lancashire lass / Never again / Lord Allenwater / Beggar's opera medley / O Polly you might have toy'd and kist / Oh what pain it is to part / Miser thus a shilling sees, The / Youth's the season made for joys / Hither dear husband, turn your eyes / Lumps of plum pudding / Gilderoy / Rockley firs / Sweet Jenny Jones / German tune / Moon shines bright, The / Harvest home medley (Peas, beans, oats and the barley) / Mistress's health / Poor Tom.
LP: 12TS 380
MC: . . . . KTSC 380

LOVE, DEATH AND THE LADY (Collins, Shirley & Dolly).
Tracks: / Death of the lady / Glenlogie / Oxford girl / Are you going to leave me? / Outlandish knight, The / Go from my window / Young girl cut down in her prime / Geordie / Salisbury / Fair maid of Islington / Six dukes / Polly on the shore / Plains of Waterloo.
LP: . . . . BGOLP 1

NO ROSES (Collins, Shirley & The Albion Country Band).
Tracks: / Claudy banks / Little gypsy girl, The / Banks of the bann / Van dieman's land / Just as the tide was flowing / White hare, The / Hal-an-tow / Poor murdered woman / Claudy banks.
MC: . . . . ZCEST 11
LP: . . . . CREST 11
MC: . . . . CRESTMC 11

POWER OF THE TRUE LOVE KNOT.
Tracks: / Bonnie boy / Richie story / Lovely Joan / Just as the tide was flowing / Unquiet grave, The / Black eyed Susan Brown / Seven yellow gipsies / Over the hills and far away / Greenwood laddie / Lady Margaret and sweet William / Maydens came, The / Polly Vaughan / Barley straw / Barbara Allen.
LP: . . . . HNBL 1327

SWEET ENGLAND.
Tracks: / Sweet England / Hares on the mountain / Hori-horo / Bonnie Irish boy / Tailor and the mouse, The / Lady and the swine, The / Turpin hero / Cuckoo, The / Bonnie labouring boy, The / Cherry tree carol, The / Sweet William / Omie wise / Blackbirds and thrushes / Keeper went a hunting, A / Polly Vaughan / Pretty Saro / Barbara Allen / Charlie.
LP: . . . . SEE 212

SWEET PRIMROSES, THE.
Tracks: / All things are quite silent / Cambridgeshire May carol / Spencer the rover / Rigs of time, The / Cruel mother / Bird in the bush, The / Streets of Derry / Brigg fair / Higher Germanie / St. George Collins / Babes in the wood / Down in yon forest / Magpie's nest, The / False true love / Sweet primroses.
LP: 12T 170

Collins, Tom

FIDGETY FEET (Collins, Tom Jazz Band).
Tracks: / Fidgety feet / Saratoga swing / Charleston / Bugle boy march / King of the road / Summertime / Bei mir bist du schon / Savoy blues / Big butter and egg man / Gotta travel on.
LP: . . . . SFA 067

SATURDAY NIGHT FUNCTION (Collins, Tom Jazz Band).
Tracks: / Give me sunshine / Saturday night function / Milo's other samba / Cottonfields / Tuxedo Junction / Lou-easy-an-i-a / Wabash blues / Fish seller / Wolverine blues / Struttin' with some barbeque / If I had you / Hindustan.
LP: . . . . SFA 107

WHERE ARE YOU NOW ? (Collins, Tom & Joe).
LP: . . . . PLAY 1024

Collins, Tommy

THIS IS TOMMY COLLINS.
Tracks: / You better not do that / I always get a souvenir / United / How do I say goodbye / I'll be gone / It tickles / You gotta have a licence / High on a hilltop / Boob-i-lak / Smooth sailing / Love a me s'il vous plait / What'cha gonna do now.
LP: . . . . HAT 3071
MC: . . . . HATC 3071
LP: . . . . PM 1550771

WORDS AND MUSIC COUNTRY STYLE.
Tracks: / All of the monkeys ain't in the zoo / How do I say goodbye / Love a me s'il vous plait / Those old love letters from you / Man we all ought to know, A / Feet of the traveller, The / Smooth sailing / I'll always speak well of you / Think it over boys / I think of you yet / Are you ready to go / Upon this rock.
LP: . . . . HAT 3050
MC: . . . . HATC 3050

Collins, William (aut)

MOONSTONE, THE (see under Moonstone (bk)) (Jeffrey, Peter (nar)).

WOMAN IN WHITE, THE (see under Woman In White (bk)) (Holm, Ian (nar)).

Collins, William

ONE GIVETH, THE COUNT TAKETH AWAY, THE.
Tracks: / Shine o'Myte (rap popping) / Landshark / Count Dracula / Funkateer, I / Lexicon (of love) / So nice you name him twice / What's wrong radio / Music to smile by / Play on playboy / Take a lickin' and keep on kickin' / Funky funkateer, The.
LP: . . . . K 56998

Collins, Willie

WHERE YOU GONNA BE TONIGHT.
Tracks: / Ain't no woman / Determination (Featuring McFadden & Whitehead.) / First time making love / Let's get started / Girl in the corner / Where you gonna be tonight / Restless / Sticky situation.
LP: . . . . EST 2012
MC: . . . . TCEST 2012

Collins/Ellis

INTERPLAY.
LP: . . . . CJ 137

Collinson, Lee

LIMBO.
LP: . . . . SPIV 102
MC: . . . . SPIV 102C

Collister, Christine

CHANGE IN THE WEATHER, A (See Gregson & Collister (Collister, Christine & Clive Gregson).

I WOULDN'T TREAT A DOG (see Gregson, Clive) (Collister, Christine & Clive Gregson).

MISCHIEF (Collister, Christine & Clive Gregson).
LP: . . . . SPD 1010
MC: . . . . SPDC 1010

Collodi, Carlo (aut)

PINOCCHIO.
MCSET: 41 7030 5

PINOCCHIO (see under Pinocchio (bk) (Cribbins, Bernard (nar)).

PINOCCHIO (see under Pinocchio (bk)) (Ritchard, Cyril (nar)).

Colloseum

COLLOSEUM GOLDEN DECADE.
MC: . . . . KNMC 10016

Colm & Sundowners

COUNTRY IS MY STYLE.
Tracks: / It's time to pay the fiddler / Hello darlin / Stop the world / If we don't make it home before the sunrise / Hell blues and down the road I go / You're still the only one I'll ever love / Everybody's reaching out for someone / Ghost of Jim Bob Wilson / Some broken hearts never mend / I wouldn't want to live if you didn't love me / I wouldn't want to live if you didn't love me / Cowboy / You're the only good thing that's happened to me / Southern comfort / You're my best friend.
LP: . . . . PHL 403
MC: . . . . CPHL 403

DEAR LITTLE IRELAND.
Tracks: / Wild Irish rose / Galway Bay / Irish eyes.
LP: . . . . HRL 131
MC: . . . . CHRL 131

Colombia

TROPICAL SOUNDS OF COLOMBIA (Various artists).
LP: . . . . MLPS 1058
MC: . . . . MCT 1058

Colombier, Michael

ABEL GANCE'S NAPOLEON (see under Davis, Carl).

MICHAEL COLOMBIER.
Tracks: / Sunday / Take me down / Dreamland / Queen's road / Overture / Bird song / Layas / Do it / Spring / Dancing bull / Autumn land.
LP: . . . . CHR 1212
MC: . . . . ZCHR 1212

Colon, Willie

AMERICAN COLOR (Colon, Willie/ Legal Alien).
Tracks: / Aerolinea desamor / Color Americano / Me voy / Estoy por ti rezando / Carmelina / Vida nocturna / Colgaditos / Hasta que te conoci.
LP: 158031
MC: 158034

CONTRABANDO.
Tracks: / Bailando asi / Manana amor / Contrabando / Che che cole / Barrunto / Te conozco / Calle luna calle sol / Lo que es de juan / Pregunta por ahi / Especial no.5 / Soltera / Quien eres.
LP: 1015958

CORAZON GUERRERO.
LP: . . . . SLP 619

HONRA Y CULTURA.
Tracks: / No / Quinientos anos (five hundred years) / Cuando vuelva a verte (if you were mine) / Fragilidad (fragility) / Honra y cultura (honour and culture) / Scandal / Mi gran amor (my great love) / Divino maestro (divine teacher) / Si fuera mia (when I return).
MC: 158094

METIENDO MANO (See under Blades, Reuben) (Colon, Willie/Reuben Blades).

SIEMBRA (Colon, Willie/Reuben Blades).
LP: . . . . SLP 537

TIEMPO PA'MATAR.
Tracks: / El diablo / Tiempo pa'matar / Noche de lose enmascarados / Callejon sin salido / Volo / Falta de consideracion / Gitana / Serenata.
LP: 1115927
LP: . . . . SLP 631

TOP SECRETS (Colon, Willie/Legal Alien).
LP: 15979
MC: 15978

WINNERS, THE (see Cruz, Celia) (Cruz, Celia/Willie Colon).

Colonel Kilgore's...

COLONEL KILGORE'S VIETNAMESE FORMATION SURF TEAM (Colonel Kilgore's Vietnamese Formation Surf Team).
LP: . . . . HANG 10

Colonel Lloydie

TENDER TOUCH.
LP: . . . . IKLP 001

Colonel Mite

LIFE (See under 'Frighty') (Frighty & Colonel Mite).

Colonel Redl (film)

COLONEL REDL-ZDENKO TAMASSI (1985 Film Soundtrack) (Colonel Kilgore's Vietnamese Formation Surf Team).
LP: . . . . ACH 018
MC: . . . . CCH 018

Colonel's Lady (bk)

COLONEL'S LADY, THE / LORD MOUNTDRAGO (Somerset W. Maugham (aut)) (Burden, Hugh (nar)).
MC: TTC/M10

Color Disc (label)

COLOR SUPPLEMENT (Various artists).
Tracks: / Golden legend: *Modern Art* / Forbidden universe: *Various artists* / Cutting water: *Various artists* / Snakebite: *Various artists* / Burning desire: *Various artists* / Crazy bombs: *Various artists* / Look out kid: *Various artists* / Red suit: *Lives of Angels* / After dark: *Lives of Angels* / Bread: *WeR7* / Caped Crusader, The: *WeR7* / Now wash your hands: *WeR7*.
LP: . . . . COLOR 4

Color Me Badd

COLOR ME BADD.
LP: . . . . WX 425
MC: . . . . WX 425C

Color Of Money (film)

COLOR OF MONEY, THE (1986 film soundtrack) (Various artists).
Tracks: / Who owns this place?: *Henley, Don* / It's in the way that you use it: *Clapton, Eric* / Let yourself in for it: *Palmer, Robert* / Don't tell me nothin': *Dixon, Willie* / Two brothers and a stranger: *Knopfler*, Mark / Standing on the edge of love: *King, B.B.* / Modern blues: *Robertson, Robbie* / Werewolves of London: *Zevon, Warren* / My baby's in love with another guy: *Palmer, Robert* / Color of money (main title): *Robertson, Robbie*.
LP: . . . . MCG 6023
MC: . . . . MCGC 6023

Color Purple (film)

COLOR PURPLE, THE (Film soundtrack) (Various artists).
Tracks: / Overture: *Various artists* / Main title: *Various artists* / Celie leaves with Mr Corrine and Olivia: *Various artists* / Nettie teaches Celie: *Various artists* / Separation: *Various artists* / Celie and Harpo grow up: *Various artists* / Mr. dresses to see Shug: *Various artists* / Sophia leaves Harpo: *Various artists*/ Celie cooks Shug breakfast: *Various artists* / Three on the road: *Various artists* / Bus pulls out: *Various* artists / First letter: *Various artists* / Letter search: *Various artists* / Nellie's letters: *Various* artists / High life: *Various artists* / Heaven belongs to you: *Various artists* / Katutoka Corrine: *Various* artists / Celie shaves Mr: *Various artists* / Scarification ceremony: *Various artists* / I'm here: *Various* artists / Champagne train: *Various artists* / Reunion: *Various artists* / Finale: *Various artists*/ Careless love: *Vega, Tata* / Dirty dozens: *Vega, Tata* / Miss Celie's blues: *Vega, Tata* / Junk bucket blues: *Get Happy Band* / Don't make me, no never mind: *Hooker, John Lee* / My heart will always lead me back to you: *Various artists* / Body and soul: *Hawkins, Coleman* / Maybe God is tryin' to tell you somethin': *Vega, Tata & Jacquelyn Farris*.
2LP: 925389 1
MCSET: 925389 4

Colorado (1)

BERWICK SPEEDWAY PRESENT.
MC: . . . . CTT 105

EXCLUSIVE.
Tracks: / Crazy celtic music / You two timed me one time too many / Will the circle be unbroken / Making friends / Little bit crazy / Leavin' eyes / Dary Farrow / Free to be / I won't take less than your love / Dark Island.
LP: . . . . TT 107
MC: . . . . CTT 107

STILL BURNING.
Tracks: / Something to say / Stories we could tell / After the night has gone / I've tried to write a love song / Savin' the best for last / We're still burnin' / He'll never be a superstar / Back to the country / Good for nothin' guitar pickin' man / Whisky man.
LP: . . . . TT 104
MC: . . . . CTT 104

Colorado (2)

SINGS COUNTRY MUSIC.
LP: . . . . BRA 1008
MC: . . . . BRC 1008

TENNESSEE INSPIRATION.
LP: . . . . BRA 1014
MC: . . . . BRC 1014

Colorblind James...

COLORBLIND JAMES EXPERIENCE (Colorblind James Experience).
Tracks: / German girls, The / Different Bob, A / First day of Spring / Walking my camel home / Gravel Road / Considering a move to Memphis / Fledgling circus / Dance critters / Great Northwest / Why'd the boy throw the clock out....
LP: . . . . SAVE 050
MC: . . . . CAVE 050

STRANGE SOUNDS FROM THE BASEMENT (Colorblind James Experience).
LP: . . . . COOK 042
MC: . . . . COOKC 042

WHY SHOULD I STAND UP (Colorblind James Experience).
Tracks: / Why should I stand up / She'll break yours too / Buster Cornelius / Polka girl / Ride aboard / I'm a sailor / That's entertainment / He must've been quite a guy / Wedding at Cana / Rocking as fast as I can / Hi-fi alphabet / If nobody loves you in heaven.
LP: . . . . COOK 028
MC: . . . . COOKC 028

Colors (film)

COLORS (1988 film soundtrack) (Various artists).
Tracks: / Colors: *Ice-T* / Six gun: *Decadent Dub Team* / Let the rhythm run: *Salt 'N' Pepa* / Butcher shop: *Kool G Rap* / Paid in full: *Eric B & Rakim* / Raw: *Big Daddy Kane* / Mad mad world: *Seven A 3* / Go on girl: *Shante, Roxanne* / Mind is a terrible thing to waste, A: *M.C. Shan* / Everywhere I go: *James, Rick*.
LP: . . . . K 925713 1
MC: . . . . K 925713 4

Colosseum

COLLECTORS COLOSSEUM, THE.
Tracks: / Jumping off the sun / Those about to die / I can't live without you / Beware the Ides of March / Walking in the park / Bolero / Rope ladder to the moon / Grass is greener, The.
LP: . . . . ILPS 9173
LP: . . . . BRON 173

COLOSSEUM.
LP: . . . . S 5510

COLOSSEUM (LIVE).
Tracks: / Rope ladder to the moon / Walking in the park / Skelington / Tanglewood '63 / Encore... / Stormy Monday blues / Lost angeles.
LP: . . . . CLALP 122
MC: . . . . CLAMC 122
LP: . . . . ICD 1

DAUGHTER OF TIME.
LP: 6360 017

EPITAPH.
Tracks: / Walking in the park / Bring out your dead / Those about to die / Beware the Ides of March / Daughter of time / Valentine suite.
LP: . . . . RAWLP 014
MC: . . . . RAWTC 014

VALENTYNE SUITE.
LP: . . . . VO 1

Colosseum II

ELECTRIC SAVAGE.
Tracks: / Put it this way / All skin and bone / Rivers / Am I / Scorch, The / Lament / Desperado / Intergalactic strut.
LP: . . . . MCL 1696

STRANGE NEW FLESH.
Tracks: / Dark side of the moon / Down to you / Gemini and Leo / Secret places / On second thoughts / Winds.
LP: . . . . CLALP 104
MC: . . . . CLAMC 104

WARDANCE.
Tracks: / Wardance / Major keys / Put it that way / Castles / Fighting talk / Inquisition, The / Star maiden / Mysterious / Quasar / Last exit.
LP: . . . . MCL 1603
LP: . . . . MCF 2817

Colourbox

COLOURBOX.
Tracks: / Suspicion / Arena / Say you / Just give 'em whiskey / You keep me hangin' on / Moon is blue, The / Manic / Sleepwalker / Inside informer / Punch.
LP: . . . . CAD 508
MC: . . . . CADC 508

COLOURBOX MINI LP.
MLP: . . . . MAD 315

Coloured Stone

BLACK ROCK FROM THE RED CENTRE.
LP: . . . . HOT 1026
LP: . . . . ROUNDER 5022
MC: . . . . ROUNDER 5022C

Colourfield

DECEPTION.
Tracks: / Badlands / Running away / From dawn to distraction / Confession / Miss Texas 1967 / She / Heart of America / Digging it deep / Monkey in Winter / Goodbye Sun Valley.
LP: . . . . CDL 1546
MC: . . . . ZCDL 1546

VIRGINS AND PHILISTINES.
Tracks: / Thinking of you / Faint hearts / Castles in the air / Take / Cruel circus / Hammond song / Virgins and Philistines / Yours sincerely / Armchair theatre / Sorry.
LP: . . . . CHR 1480
MC: . . . . ZCHR 1480

Colourman

KICK UP RUMPUS.
LP: . . . . CRELP 001

Colours

COLOURS (Various artists).
MC: . . . . PLB 275

HARVEST, THE.
Tracks: / Humble yourself in the sight of the Lord / Seek ye first the kingdom of God / Shield about us, A.
LP: . . . . MM R 0143
MC: . . . . MM C 0143

PALETTE.
LP: . . . . MM R 0165
MC: . . . . MM C 0165

REFLECTIONS.
LP: . . . . MM R 0196
MC: . . . . MM C 0196

RULES OF ATTRACTION.
LP: . . . . WX 341
MC: . . . . WX 341 C

SPECTRUM (The Colours Sampler).
Tracks: / Humble thyself in the sight of the Lord / Sweet hour of prayer / Joy to the world / I love you Lord.
LP: . . . . MM R 0144
MC: . . . . MM C 0144

TIME FOR JOY, A (Reflections in Guitar).
Tracks: / Jesu, Joy of man's desiring (Bach) / Rejoice in the Lord always / Joy of the Lord is my strength, The.
LP: . . . . MM R 0142
MC: . . . . MM C 0142

TIME FOR PEACE, A (Ivory Sessions).
Tracks: / Abraham's Theme / Lord's prayer, The / Hiding place / Amazing grace.
LP: . . . . MM R 0141
MC: . . . . MM C 0141

Colours (bk)

COLOURS (THE RAINBOW SHIP).
MC: . . . . STK 016

Colours Series (label)

COLLECTION, THE (Various artists).
Tracks: / Curtain: *Haines, Denis* / Homeland: *Haines, Denis* / Harbinger: *Hall, G.P.* / Manifestations: *Hall, G.P.* / Dream pilot: *Sarstedt, Peter & Clive* / India: *Sarstedt, Peter & Clive* / River, The: *Sarstedt*, Peter & Clive / Dreams of gold: *Parsons, Steve* / Helios, Parts 1 & 2 excerpts: *Parsons, Steve* / Solid air: *Thornton, Phil* / As above so below: *Thornton, Phil*.
LP: . . . . KNEWL 06
MC: . . . . KNEWMC 06

Colter, Jessi

COUNTRY STAR IS BORN, A.
Tracks: / Too many rivers / Cry softly / I ain't the one / It's not easy / He called me baby / Why you been gone so long / If she's where you like livin' / Healing hands of time / That's the chance I'll have to take / Don't let him go / It's all over now.
MC: . . . . INTK 5072
LP: . . . . INTS 5072

Coltrane, Alice

ETERNITY.
Tracks: / Spiritual eternal / Wisdom eye / Los caballos / Om supreme / Morning worship / Spring rounds / From rite of spring.
LP: . . . . K 56198

Coltrane, John

1951-65.
LP: . . . . RARE 11

AFRICA AND INDIA.
LP: . . . . CJZ LP 3

AFRICA BRASS (Coltrane,John Quartet).
Tracks: / Greensleeves / Africa / Blues minor.
LP: . . . . JAS 8
MC: . . . . JAS C8

AFRICA BRASS SESSIONS 1 & 2.
Tracks: / Africa / Blues minor / Greensleeves (version) / Greensleeves / Song of the underground railroad / Africa (version).
LP: . . . . MCA 42232

AFRICA BRASS VOL.2.
Tracks: / Song of underground railroad / Africa.
LP: . . . . JAS 59
MC: . . . . JAS C59

AFRO BLUE IMPRESSIONS.
Tracks: / Lonnie's lament / Naima / Chasin' the trane / My favourite things / Afro blue / Cousin Mary / I want to talk about you / Spiritual / Impressions.
2LP: 262 0101
MCSET: . . . . K 20 101

ART OF JOHN COLTRANE.
Tracks: / Sveeda's song flute / Aisha / Countdown / Mr. Knight / My shining hour / Blues to Bechet / Invisible, The / My favourite things / Giant steps / Central Park West / Like Sonny / Body and soul.
LP: . . . . K 60052

ASCENSION (Coltrane, John Orchestra).
Tracks: / Ascension, parts 1 & 2.
LP: . . . . JAS 45
MC: . . . . JAS C45

AVANTE-GARDE (See under Don Cherry) (Coltrane, John & Don Cherry).

BAGS AND TRANE (Coltrane, John & Milt Jackson).
Tracks: / Bags and trane / Three little words / Night we called it a day, The / Be-bop / Late late blues, The.
LP: . . . . K 30016

BALLADS (Coltrane,John Quartet).
Tracks: / Say it (over and over again) / You don't know what love is / Too young to go steady / All or nothing at all.
LP: . . . . JAS 37
MC: . . . . JAS C37

BLACK PEARLS.
Tracks: / Black pearls / Lover come back to me / Sweet sapphire blues / Believer / Nakatini serenade / Do I love you because your beautiful.
2LP: . . . . PR 24037

BLUE TRAIN.
Tracks: / Blue train / Moments notice / Locomotion, The / I'm old fashioned / Lazy bird.
LP: . . . . BST 81577
MC: . . . . TCBST 81577

BLUES FOR COLTRANE (See under Blues) (Various artists).

BRAZILIA (Coltrane,John Quartet).
LP: . . . . AR 705

BYE BYE BLACKBIRD.
Tracks: / Bye bye blackbird / Traneing in.
LP: . . . . CJZ LP 4
LP: 230 8227

CATS, THE (See under Flanagan, Tommy) (Coltrane, John/Tommy Flanagan).

COLETRANE QUARTET AND QUINTET.
LP: . . . . JC 112

COLLECTION: JOHN COLTRANE.
Tracks: / Love supreme, A (part 1) (Acknowledgement) / Love supreme, A (part 2) (Resolution) / Love supreme, A (part 3) (Pursuance) / Love supreme, A

(part 4) (Psalm) / Traneing in / Bye bye blackbird.
MC: . . . . DVMC 2037

COLTRANE (Coltrane,John Quartet).
Tracks: / Out of this world / Soul eyes / Inch woman / Tunji / Miles made.
LP: . . . . JAS 10
MC: . . . . JAS C10

COLTRANE LEGACY, THE.
Tracks: / 26 - 2 / To her Ladyship / Untitled original / Centerpiece / Stairway to the stars / Blues legacy.
LP: . . . . K 40120

COLTRANE TIME.
LP: . . . . BOP 001

COLTRANOLOGY VOLUME 1.
LP: . . . . AFF 14

COLTRANOLOGY VOLUME 2 (McCoy Tyner, Jimmy Garrison, Elvin Jones.).
LP: . . . . AFF 16

COPENHAGEN 1960 (See under Davis, Miles) (Coltrane, John & Miles Davis).

COPENHAGEN CONCERTS, THE (Coltrane,John Quartet).
Tracks: / Chasin' the trane / Every time we say goodbye / I want to talk about you / Mr. P.C..
LP: . . . . INGO 4

COUNTDOWN (Coltrane, John & Wilbur Harden).
Tracks: / Wells Fargo - take 1 / Wells Fargo - take 2 / E.F.F.P.H. / Countdown (Take 1) / Countdown (Take 2) / Rhodomagnetics 1 / Rhodomagnetics 2 / Snuffy / West 42nd street.
2LP: . . . . WL 70529
MCSET: . . . . WK 70529

CREATION (Coltrane,John Quartet).
LP: . . . . AR 700

CRESCENT (Coltrane,John Quartet).
Tracks: / Crescent / Wise one / Bessie's blues / Lonnie's lament / Drum thing, The.
LP: . . . . JAS 41
MC: . . . . JAS C41

DAKAR.
Tracks: / Dakar / Mary's blues / Route 4 / Velvet scene / Witches' pet / Cat walk / C.T.A. / Interplay / Anatomy / Light blue / Soul eyes.
2LP: . . . . P 24104

DIAL AFRICA (Coltrane, John & Wilbur Harden).
LP: . . . . SJL 1110

DREAMWEAVERS, THE/ SUITE BEAT (see Adderley, Cannonball) (Coltrane, John/ Cannonball Adderley).

DUKE ELLINGTON AND JOHN COLTRANE (see under Ellington, Duke) (Coltrane, John/Duke Ellington).

EUROPEAN TOUR, THE.
Tracks: / Promise, The / I want to talk about you / Naima / Mr. P.C..
LP: 2308 222
MC: . . . . K 08 222

EXOTICA - ONE AND FOUR (Coltrane, John & Lee Morgan).
LP: 500 889

EXPRESSIONS.
Tracks: / Ogunde / To be / Offering / Expression.
LP: . . . . JAS 73

FIRST STEPS 1951/1954/1956.
Tracks: / Birk's works / Good bait / Night in Tunisia / Sideways / Don't blame me / In a mellow tone / Tune up / Walkin'.
LP: . . . . BLJ 8039

GIANT STEPS.
Tracks: / Giant steps / Cousin Mary / Countdown / Spiral / Syeeda's song flute / Naima / Mr. P.C..
LP: . . . . K 50239

GOLD COAST.
Tracks: / Tanganyika strut / Dial Africa / Gold coast / B.J..
LP: . . . . WL 70518
MC: . . . . WK 70518

IMPRESSIONS.
Tracks: / India / Up against the wall / Impressions / After the rain.
LP: . . . . CJZ LP 2
LP: . . . . JAS 39
MC: . . . . JAS C39
MC: . . . . ASC 42

IMPRESSIONS OF EUROPE.
Tracks: / Impressions / I want to talk about you / Inch worm, The.
LP: . . . . INGO 7

JOHN COLTRANE.
Tracks: / Slow dance / Bass blues / You leave me breathless / Soft lights and sweet music / Good bait / I want to talk about you / You say you care / Theme for Ernie / Russian lullaby.
2LP: . . . . PR 24003

JOHN COLTRANE LIVE AT THE VILLAGE VANGUARD.
Tracks: / Spiritual / Softly as in a morning sunrise / Chasin' the 'Trane.
LP: . . . . JAS 9
MC: . . . . JAS C9

JOHN COLTRANE QUARTET (Coltrane,John Quartet).
LP: . . . . UJ 32

JOHN COLTRANE WITH RAY DRAYPER (Coltrane, John & Ray Draper).
Tracks: / Essie's dance / Doxy / I talk to the trees / Yesterdays / Oleo / Angel eyes.
LP: . . . . JR 147

KENNY BURRELL & JOHN COLTRANE (See under Burrell, Kenny) (Coltrane, John/Kenny Burrell).

KONSERTHUSET, STOCKHOLM (see Davis, Miles) (Coltrane, John & Miles Davis).

KULU SE' MAMA.
Tracks: / Kulu Se' Mama / Visil / Welcome.
LP: . . . . JAS 51
MC: . . . . JAS C51

LEGENDARY MASTERS, THE (Unissued or rare 1951-65).
LPS: . . . . RARELP 11/15

LEGENDARY MASTERS, THE (1951-58) (Unissued or rare).
Tracks: / Good bait / Birk's works / Thru for the night / Castle rock / Don't blame me / I've got a mind to ramble blues / Don't cry baby blues / In a mellow tone / Globetrotter / Tune up / Walkin' / Four.
LP: . . . . RARELP 11

LEGENDARY MASTERS, THE (1961-62) (Unissued or rare).
Tracks: / Chim chim cheree / Naima / Bye bye blackbird / I want to talk about you.
LP: . . . . RARELP 13

LEGENDARY MASTERS, THE (1961-65) (Unissued or rare).
Tracks: / Love supreme, A (part 1) / Resolution - part III / Pursuance - part IV / Psalm / Good bait / Thru for the night / Don't blame me / Don't cry baby blues / Globetrotter / Walkin' / Chim chim cheree / Bye bye blackbird / Roy / Impressions / Mr. P.C. / Cousin Mary / Lonnie's lament / Birk's works / Castle rock / I've got a mind to ramble blues / In a mellow tone / Tune up / Four / Acknowledgement - part I / Pursuance - Part IV / Spiritual / Naima / I want to talk about you / Chasin' the trane / Afro blue / My favourite things / Miles mode / Body and soul.
LP: . . . . RARELP 12

LEGENDARY MASTERS, THE (1962-63) (Unissued or rare).
Tracks: / Roy / Chasin' the trane / Impressions / Afro blue / Mr. P.C..
LP: . . . . RARELP 14

LEGENDARY MASTERS, THE (1962-63) (Unissued or rare).
Tracks: / My favourite things / Cousin Mary / Miles mode / Lonnie's lament / Body and soul.
LP: . . . . RARELP 15

LIKE SONNY.
Tracks: / One and four (aka Mr. Day) / Exotica (alternate take) / Exotica / Like Sonny / Essie's dance / Doxy / Oleo / I talk to the trees (CD only.) / Yesterdays (CD only.) / Angel eyes (CD only.).
LP: . . . . ROU 1012
LP: 793 901 1

LIVE 1962.
Tracks: / My favourite things / Improvisation / Miles' mode / Inch worm, The / Every time we say goodbye / Impressions.
2LP: . . . . ALB 378

LIVE AT BIRDLAND (Coltrane,John Quartet).
Tracks: / Afro blue / I want to talk about you / Promise, The / Alabama / Your lady.
LP: . . . . JAS 11
MC: . . . . JAS C11

LIVE AT BIRDLAND (2).
Tracks: / Mr. P.C. / Miles mode / My favourite things / Body and soul.
LP: . . . . AFF 79

LIVE AT THE VILLAGE VANGUARD AGAIN.
Tracks: / Naima / My favourite things.
LP: . . . . JAS 16
MC: . . . . JAS C16

LIVE IN ANTIBES 1965 / LIVE IN PARIS 1965.
LP: . . . . FC 119

LIVE IN PARIS.
Tracks: / Naima / Impressions / Blue valse / Afro blue / Impressions (2nd version).
2LP: . . . . AFFD 24

LIVE: JOHN COLTRANE & MILES DAVIS (see Davis, Miles) (Coltrane, John & Miles Davis).

LOVE SUPREME, A (CRUSADER).
LP: . . . . CJZLP 1

LOVE SUPREME, A (ESOLDUN).
LP: . . . . FC 106

LOVE SUPREME, A (IMPULSE).
Tracks: / Acknowledgement (part 1) / Resolution (part 2) / Pursuance (part 3) / Psalm (part 4).
LP: . . . . MCL 1648
MC: . . . . MCLC 1648
LP: . . . . AS 42
MC: . . . . ASC 54

LOVE SUPREME, A (INGO).
LP: . . . . INGO 11

LOVE SUPREME, A (MCA).
MC: . . . . MCLC 1648

LUSH LIFE.
Tracks: / Like someone in love / I love you / Tranes's slow blues / Lush life / I hear a rhapsody.
LP: . . . . PR 7188
MC: . . . . PRC 7188

MEDITATIONS.
Tracks: / Love / Consequences / Serenity / Father, Son and Holy Ghost.
LP: . . . . JAS 80

MILES AND COLTRANE see under Davis, Miles (Coltrane, John & Miles Davis).

MONK WITH COLTRANE (See under Monk, Thelonious) (Monk, Thelonious & John Coltrane).

MORE LASTING THAN BRONZE.
Tracks: / Lush life / I hear a rhapsody / Like someone in love / I love you / 'Tranes's slow blues / Bakai / Violets for your furs / Time was / Straight Street / While my lady sleeps / Chronic blues.
2LP: . . . . PR 24014
LP: . . . . OJCD 502

MY FAVOURITE THINGS.
LP: . . . . CJZ LP 5

NEW THING AT NEWPORT (Coltrane, John & Archie Shepp).
Tracks: / Le matin des noire / Scag / Call me by my rightful name / Introduction / One down, one up / Rufus.
LP: . . . . JAS 22
MC: . . . . JAS C22

NEWPORT FESTIVAL 1961.
LP: 2MJP 1051

OM.
LP: . . . . MCA 39118

ON A MISTY NIGHT.
Tracks: / How deep is the ocean / Just you, just me / Bob's boys / Tenor conclave / On a misty night / Romas / Super jet / Mating call / Gnid / Soultrain.
2LP: . . . . PR 24084

ONE, TWO AND FOUR (See Morgan, Lee) (Coltrane, John & Lee Morgan).

PARIS CONCERT, THE.
Tracks: / Mr. P.C. / Inch worm, The / Every time we say goodbye.
LP: 2308 217
MC: . . . . K 08 217

RARE JOHN COLTRANE QUARTET (Coltrane,John Quartet).
Tracks: / Impressions / Inch worm, The / My favourite things.
LP: . . . . D 1016

REFLECTIONS.
Tracks: / Untitled original / Impressions / Chim chim cheree.
LP: . . . . AFEMP 1041

SETTIN' THE PACE.
Tracks: / I see your face before me / If there's someone lovelier than you / Little Melonae / Rise and shine.
LP: . . . . OJC 078

SOUL JUNCTION (see under Garland, Red) (Coltrane, John & Red Garland Quintet).

STANDARD COLTRANE.
LP: . . . . OJC 246

STARDUST SESSION, THE.
Tracks: / Spring is here / Invitation / I'm a dreamer aren't we all / Love thy neighbour / Don't take your love from me / My ideal / Stardust / I'll get by.
2LP: . . . . PR 24056

THELONIUS MONK AND JOHN COLTRANE (See under Monk, Thelonius) (Coltrane, John & Thelonious Monk).

TRANE'S BLUES.
LP: . . . . LPJT 72

UNISSUED CONCERT IN GERMANY 1963 PART 1 (Coltrane,John Quartet).
MC: 1001

WHEELIN'.
Tracks: / Wheelin' (take 1) / Wheelin' (take 2) / Dealin' (take 1) / Dealin' (take 2) / Things ain't what they used to be / Robbin's nest cha cha / Blue calypso / Falling in love with love.
2LP: . . . . PR 24069

Colum, Padraic

TWELVE LABOURS OF HERACLES, THE (see under Twelve Labours (bk)) (Quayle, Anthony (nar)).

Colum Sands

MARCH DITCH, THE.
LP: . . . . SLP 1014
MC: . . . . CSP 1014

UNAPPROVED ROAD.
LP: . . . . SLP 1001

Columbia Orchestra

BEST OF SCREEN MUSIC.
Tracks: / Love story / Godfather love theme / Some enchanted evening / Melodie en sous sol / Lara's theme / Treize jours en France / Around the world / Pein soleil / La lacon particuliere, Theme de / Ticuliere / Il ferroviere / From Russia with love.
LP: . . . . SX 7001

Columbo, Russ

ON THE AIR 1933-4.
Tracks: / More than you know / Time on my hands / Easy come, easy go / With my eyes wide open, I'm dreaming / Stardust / True / Rolling in love / I've had my moments / I'm dreaming.
LP: . . . . TOTEM 1031
LP: . . . . SH 2038

RARE RADIO PERFOMANCES.
LP: . . . . SH 2006
MC: . . . . CSH 2006

RUSS COLUMBO 1931 AND 1934.
LP: . . . . SH 1006

Columbus, Christopher

CHRISTOPHER COLUMBUS(TV SERIES SOUNDTRACK) (see under Christopher Columbus) (Various artists).

Colvin, Shawn

STEADY ON.
Tracks: / Steady on / Diamond in the rough / Shotgun down the avalanche / Stranded another long one / Cry like an angel / Something to believe in / Story, The / Ricochet in time / Dead of the night, The.
LP: 4661421
MC: 4661424

Colyer, Ken

1957 - A VERY GOOD YEAR (Colyer, Ken Jazzmen & George Lewis).
Tracks: / Happy wanderer, The / Gatemouth / Workingman blues / One sweet letter from you / Dusty rag / Joplins sensation / Over the waves / Walking with the king / Corina Corina / Ice cream / Running wild.
LP: . . . . KC 1

CONCERT VOL.1.
LP: . . . . WAM/O No.3

CRANE RIVER JAZZ BAND, 1950-53 (see Crane River Jazz Band) (Colyer, Ken & The Crane River Jazz Band).

DARKNESS ON THE DELTA.
Tracks: / Lord, Lord you've sure been good to me / Darkness on the delta / Yaaka hula hickey dula / Gettysburg march / Deep Bayou blues / Shine / Auf wiedersehen.
LP: . . . . BLP 12136

DECCA SKIFFLE SESSION 1954-57.
Tracks: / Midnight special / Casey Jones / K.C. Moan / Take this hammer / Down by the riverside / Go down, old Hannah / Streamline train / Old Riley / Down bound tain / Stack o lee blues / Muleskinner blues / Grey goose / Sporting life / House rent stomp / I can't sleep / This train / Midnight hour blues / Go down sunshine / Ella Speed.
LP: . . . . LA 5007
MC: . . . . LA 5007C

DECCA YEARS VOL.3, THE (Club session with Colyer) (Colyer, Ken Jazzmen).
Tracks: / Uptown rumps / Blame it on the blues / Creole song / Chysanthemum rag / Snag it / Thriller rag / Black cat / Old rugged cross, The / Walking with the King / Home sweet home / Auf wiedersehen.
LP: . . . . LA 5006
MC: . . . . LA 5006C

GREAT REVIVAL, THE.
Tracks: / South / Yama yama blues / Shimme-sha-wabble / Big chief battle axe / Won't you come over to my house baby / Come back sweet papa / I'll walk

through the streets of the city / Nobody knows you when you're ai / Bucket got a hole in it / Cielito Lindo.
LP: . . . . **ESQ 312**

HISTORIC RECORDINGS VOL 2 (The Guvnor) (Colyer, Ken Skiffle Group & Jazzmen).
Tracks: / How long blues / Streamline train / Poor Howard / Highway blues / This train / Sporting life / House rent stomp / Heebie jeebies / Tin roof blues / Red wing / Aunt Hagar's blues / Maryland.
LP: . . . . **KC 2**

IN NEW ORLEANS 1953.
LP: . . . . **DC 12025**

IN THE BEGINNING - DECCA YEARS, VOL.6 (Colyer, Ken Jazzmen).
Tracks: / Isle of Capri / Harlem rag / Too busy / Going home / La harpe street blues / Cataract rag / Stockyard strut / Early hours / Saturday night function / Shimme sha wabble / Sing on / Lord, Lord, Lord / Far away blues / Moose march.
LP: . . . . **LA 5014**
MC: . . . . **LA 5014 C**

IT LOOKS (See under Bilk, Acker for details) (Colyer, Ken/Acker Bilk).

KEN COLYER AND WHITE EAGLE NEW ORLEANS BAND (Colyer, Ken & White Eagle New Orleans Band).
LP: . . . . **WAM/O No.9**

KEN COLYER & HIS HAND PICKED JAZZMEN 25/01/72 (Colyer, Ken & His Hand Picked Jazzmen).
Tracks: / Some of these days / Gatemouth / Blame it on the blues / Lord lord lord / Over in gloryland / Michigan water / Bugle boy march / Panama.
LP: . . . . **KCT 2R**

KEN COYLER AT THE THAMES HOTEL (Colyer, Ken Jazzmen).
Tracks: / Milneburg joys / Lowlands blues / Trombonium / Short dress gal / Blue skies / Glory of love / Hindustan / Hiawatha rag.
LP: . . . . **JOYS 170**

LIVE 1953/54 (Dixie Gold) (Colyer, Ken Jazzmen).
LP: **8208791**

LIVE AT THE 100 CLUB (Colyer, Ken Jazzmen).
LP: . . . . **GHB 161**
MC: . . . . **CC 17**

LIVE AT THE DANCING SLIPPER 1969 (Colyer, Ken Jazzmen).
Tracks: / Drop me off in Harlem / Teasin' rag / Sweet fields / High society / Barefoot boy / Get out of here / Harlem rag / Salutation march / Shoe shine boy / Peanut vendor / Birth of the blues / Home sweet home / Auf wiedersehen.
LP: . . . . **LC 35**

LONESOME ROAD (Decca Years Vol 5) (Colyer, Ken Jazzmen).
Tracks: / Beautiful doll / Over the rainbow / All of me / Pretty baby / Swanee river / Underneath the bamboo tree / Lonesome road / Bluebells / Goodbye Dinah / Curse of an aching heart, The.
LP: . . . . **LA 5010**
MC: . . . . **LA 5010 C**

ONE FOR MY BABY (Colyer, Ken Jazzmen).
Tracks: / Royal Garden blues / High society / Drop me off in Harlem / Bogalousa strut / One for my baby / Stardust / Tiger rag.
LP: . . . . **JOYS 140**

OUT OF NOWHERE (Colyer, Ken Jazzmen).
Tracks: / Melancholy blues / Lady is a tramp, The / Indiana / Eccentric rag / There's yes yes in your eyes / Lily of the valley / Out of nowhere / Ole' miss rag / Darktown strutters ball.
LP: . . . . **GNP 101**

RAGTIME REVISITED (Colyer, Ken Jazzmen).
Tracks: / Cataract rag / Grace and beauty / Minstrel man / Pineapple rag / Chrysanthemum / Tuxedo rag / Joplin's sensation / Harlem rag / Heliotrope bouquet / Ragtime oriole / Fig leaf rag / Kinklets / Thriller rag.
LP: . . . . **JOYS 194**

RAREST KEN COYLER, THE.
LP: . . . . **NOLA LP 15**

SENSATION (Colyer, Ken Jazzmen).
Tracks: / Dippermouth blues / Heliotrope bouquet / Beale Street blues / Fig leaf rag / Gravier Street blues / Canal St. Blues / World is waiting for the sunrise, The / Girls go crazy, The / Entertainer, The / If ever I cease to love / Sensation / Perdido street blues / Kinklets / Maryland my Maryland.
LP: . . . . **LA 5001**
MC: . . . . **LA 5001C**

SPIRITUALS VOL.1 (Colyer, Ken Jazzmen).
Tracks: / We shall walk through the streets of the city / Darkness on the Delta / It's nobody's fault but mine / My life will be sweeter someday / Were you there when they satisfied my soul / Sometimes my burden is so hard to bear / Old rugged cross, The.
LP: . . . . **JOYS 235**

SPIRITUALS VOL.2 (Colyer, Ken Jazzmen).
Tracks: / Ghost soldier / Precious Lord / In the sweet bye and bye / Ain't you glad / Sing on / Just a closer walk with thee / Lead me saviour.
LP: . . . . **JOYS 236**

SWINGING AND SINGING.
Tracks: / Darktown strutters' ball / Tishomingo blues / Shine / Going home to New Orleans / Celito lindo / Louisana I.A. / K.C. moon / Doctor Jazz / St. James infirmary.
LP: . . . . **B 90016**
MC: . . . . **MB 90016**

TOO BUSY (1985 at Harlow).
Tracks: / Tunes too busy / My old Kentucky home / Tishamingo blues / Down home rag / Old rugged cross, The / One sweet letter from you / Bogalusa strut / Snag it / Nobody's fault but mine / Home sweet home.
MC: . . . . **CMJMC 008**

TUXEDO RAG (Colyer, Ken Jazzmen).
Tracks: / Perdido Street blues / Dippermouth blues / Heliotrope bouquet / Beale Street blues / Fig leaf rag / Gravier Street blues / Canal Street blues / World is waiting for the sunrise, The / Girls go crazy, The / Entertainer, The / If I ever cease to love / Sensation / Kinklets / Maryland, my Maryland.
LP: . . . . **LA 5004**
MC: . . . . **LA 5004C**

WATCH THAT DIRTY TONE OF YOURS (There are ladies present) (Colyer, Ken Jazzmen).
Tracks: / Till then / One sweet letter from you / Arkansas blues / Poor butterfly / Bugle boy march / If you're a viper / Runnin' wild / My gal Sal / Black and blue / Swipsey cake walk.
LP: . . . . **JOYS 164**

Comateens

DEAL WITH IT.
LP: . . . . **V 2321**
MC: . . . . **TCV 2321**

Combat 84

DEATH OR GLORY.
LP: . . . . **LINK LP 017**

SEND IN THE MARINES.
LP: . . . . **VIC 3**

Combelle, Alix

1937-40.
LP: . . . . **PM 155 2591**

Comber Quintette

COMING HOME.
Tracks: / Stories of Jesus, The / Lord I'm coming home / Pure in heart / Redeemed / Shall I crucify / That beautiful land / Goin' to shoot all over God's heaven / When you know Jesus too / Where he leads me / Cross was his own, The / Let the lower lights be burning / My Jesus, I love thee / Jesus we took to thee.
LP: . . . . **PC 846**

Combined Calvary

OLD COMRADES.
Tracks: / Sons of the brave / With sword and lance / Old comrades / Nimrod / O valiant hearts verse 1 / Last post / O valiant hearts verse 2 / Reveille / O valiant hearts verse 3 / Trumpet tune and air / Golden spurs / Glorious victory / Queensmen, The / Under freedom's flag / On the square / Imperial echoes / Calvary brigade.
LP: . . . . **PRD 2009**

Combos, Ove Lind

SUMMER NIGHT.
LP: . . . . **PHON 3**

Come Imparai (film)

COME IMPARAI AD AMARE LE DONNE (Film soundtrack) (Various artists).
LP: . . . . **SP 8020**

Come In Spinner (tv)

COME IN SPINNER (TV Soundtrack) (Jones, Vince & Grace Knight).
Tracks: / I've got you under my skin / Man I love, The / Mood indigo / (Don't know) how much I love you / Li'l darlin' / Don't get around much anymore / I get along without you very well / Sophisticated lady / You go to my head / Loose lips / Body and soul / Joy juice / In a sentimental mood / Lover come back to me.
MC: . . . . **INT 30524**

Come Josephine...

COME JOSEPHINE IN MY FLYING MACHINE (Various artists).
Tracks: / Oceana roll: *Morton, Eddie* / Girl on the magazine cover, The: *MacDonough, Harry* / Hello, Frisco: *Morris,* Elida & Sam Ash / On the 5.15: *American Quartet* / He'd have to get under, get out and get under...: *Haley, Will/* Come, Josephine, in my flying machine: *Ring, Blanche* / Take your girlie to the movies: *Murray, Billy* / Everybody wants a key to my cellar: *Williams, Bert* / Argentines, the Portugese and the Greeks, The: *Bayes, Nora* / Mr. Radio man (tell my mammy to come back home): *Jolson, Al, Isham Jones & His Orchestra* / Alabamy bound: *Seeley, Blossom/* All alone: *James, Lewis* / Little white house (at the end of Honeymoon Lane), The: *Harris, Frank, Howard Lannin & His Orchestra* / Lindbergh (the eagle of the USA): *Dalhart, Vernon* / Henry's made a lady out of Lizzie: *Happiness Boys* / If I had a talking picture of you: *Baker, Belle.*
LP: . . . . **NW 233**

Come Together Again

COME TOGETHER AGAIN (See under Owens, Jimmy) (Owens, Jimmy & Carol).

Comebuckley

COMEBUCKLEY (Homage to Tim Buckley 1947-75) (Various artists).
LP: . . . . **BOY 001**

Comedians (Film)

COMEDIANS, THE (film '67 soundtrack) (Various artists).
LP: . . . . **MCA 25002**
MC: . . . . **MCAC 25002**

Comedy...

20 GOLDEN GOBS (Spitting Image Cast) (Various artists).
Tracks: / Commons of house: *Various artists* / Blues at ten: *Various artists* / M 25: *Various artists/* Kylie Minogue: *Various artists* / Keepin' on rockin': *Various artists* / Our God: *Various artists* / Let's go drinking and driving: *Various artists* / Jails are packed, The: *Various artists* / Perry Como: *Various* artists / Christmas singles, The: *Various artists* / Sick as a moon: *Various artists* / Dawn of a new age: *Various artists* / Apart aid: *Various artists* / I'm sure living since I died: *Various artists* / Estate agent song: *Various artists* / Ayatollah song: *Various artists* / Mad song, The: *Various artists* / Safe viewing: *Various artists* / We're the has beens: *Various artists* / Chicken song, The: *Various artists.*
LP: . . . . **EMC 3585**
MC: . . . . **TCEMC 3585**

24 JAZZ COMEDY CLASSICS (see under Jazz) (Various artists).

BEYOND THE FRINGE (At the Fortune Theatre/On Broadway) (Various artists).
Tracks: / Royal box, The: *Cook, Peter & Dudley Moore* / Heat, The-Death of the universe: *Miller, Jonathan* / Bollard: *Company* / Deutscher chansons: *Moore, Dudley* (Dudley Moore at the piano.) / T.V.P.M.: *Cook, Peter* / Aftermyth of war: *Company* / Real class: *Company* / Little Miss Britten: *Moore, Dudley* / Black equals white: *Cook, Peter & Jonathan Miller* / Take a pew: *Bennett, Alan (nar)* / End of the world: *Company/* Sadder and the wiser beaver, The: *Cook, Peter & Alan Bennett* / Sitting on the bench: *Cook, Peter* / And the same to you/ Colonel Bogey: *Moore, Dudley* (Dudley Moore at the piano.) / Portrait from memory: *Miller, Jonathan/* So that's the way you like it: *Company* / English way of death, The: *Bennett, Alan (nar)* / Song: *Whitehead,* Paxton/Dudley Moore / Home thoughts from abroad: *Various artists* / One leg too few: *Cook, Peter & Dudley Moore/* Two English songs: *Whitehead, Paxton/Dudley Moore* / Lord Cobbold/The Duke: *Cook, Peter/Paxton Whitehead/Dudley Moore/* Piece of my mind, A: *Whitehead, Paxton* / Great train robbery: *Cook, Peter & Alan Bennett.*
MCSET: . . . . **ECC 1**

BRITISH COMEDY CLASSICS (Various artists).
Tracks: / Song of the Australian outlaw: *Williams, Kenneth (nar)* / Society wedding stakes, The: *Hudd, Roy* / Football results: *Bentine, Michael* / Stop press: *Cope, Kenneth/David Frost* / You need feet: *Bresslaw, Bernard/* Ton up boy: *Morecambe & Wise/* Gossip calypso: *Cribbins, Bernard (nar)* / Letter from Bill, A: *Various* artists (The Rag Trade) / Lovely lunch: *Bird, John/John Fortune* / Goodness gracious me: *Sellers, Peter/Sophia* Loren / Impressions: *Morecambe & Wise* / Holiday commercial: *Bentine, Michael* / Right said Fred: *Cribbins,* Bernard (nar) / Drats: *Bentine, Michael* / My boomerang won't come back: *Drake, Charlie* / Green grow my nadgers oh: *Williams, Kenneth (nar)* / Phoney folk-lore: *Ustinov, Peter* / Ad nauseum (That was the week that was): *Various* artists / Gnu song, The: *Flanders & Swann* / Mad passionate love: *Bresslaw, Bernard* / Royal box, The: *Cook,* Peter & Dudley Moore / Get it right corporal: *Morecambe & Wise* / Lolly commercial: *Bentine, Michael* / Boom oo yatta ta ta: *Morecambe & Wise* / Notice to quit: *Hudd, Roy* / Old girls school reunion: *Grenfell, Joyce/* Funny game politics: *Various artists* / Moscow radio commercial: *Bentine, Michael* / Ballad of the woggler's moulie: *Williams, Kenneth (nar)* / Take a pew: *Bennett, Alan (nar)* / You gotto go oww: *Milligan, Spike/* Indians: *Morecambe & Wise* / Ice cream commercial: *Bentine, Michael* / Q5 piano tune, The: *Milligan, Spike/* Fly buttons: *Martin, Millicent/Roy Kinnear/* / Hole in the ground: *Cribbins, Bernard (nar)* / Hippopotamus song, The: *Flanders & Swann* / Sitting on the bench: *Cook, Peter* / Narcissus: *Grenfell, Joyce & Norman Wisdom/* Horse show, The: *Bentine, Michael* / Madeira m'dear: *Flanders & Swann* / Drop of the hard stuff, A: *Sellers, Peter* / And the same to you/Colonel Bogey: *Moore, Dudley.*
MCSET: . . . . **ECC 7**

BRITISH COMEDY CLASSICS VOL. 2 (Various artists).
Tracks: / Judge not: *Cleese, John, Tim Brooke Taylor, Bill Oddie* / Mock Mozart: *Ustinov, Peter* / Grieg's piano concerto: *Morecambe & Wise* / French for beginners: *Bentine, Michael* / Bus driver: *Hudd, Roy* / Transport of delight, A: *Flanders & Swann* / Car commercial: *Bentine, Michael* / Couple: *Bron, Eleanor & John Fortune/* Shame and scandal in the family: *Percival, Lance (nar)* / Wormwood Scrubs tango: *Various artists* / My dear Prime Minister: *Percival, Lance & William Rushton* / Runcorn splod cobbler's song: *Williams, Kenneth (nar)* / Charlie Brown: *Bresslaw, Bernard* / Real class: *Various artists* (Beyond the Fringe Company) / Singing the blues: *Morecambe* & Wise / Finale: *Milligan, Spike* / Astronauts, The: *Bentine, Michael* / Nursery school: *Grenfell, Joyce/* Balham - Gateway to the South: *Sellers, Peter* / How green was my button hole: *Various artists* / Gas man cometh, The: *Flanders & Swann* / Terrible tale of the Somerset nog, The: *Williams, Kenneth (nar)* / Underneath it all: *Milligan, Spike* / Train commercial: *Bentine, Michael* / Stroll down Memory Lane, A: *Hudd, Roy* (Interpolating 'Together' - Munro/Smith/ Percival.) / BBC B.C.: *Hatch, David & John Cleese* / My September love: *Milligan, Spike/* Scotland Yard: *Bentine, Michael* / Ambassador of Khasiland: *Morecambe & Wise* / Song of the bogle clencher: *Williams, Kenneth (nar)* / Fuller's earth: *Sellers, Peter/Graham Stark* / End of the world: *Various artists* (The Company).
MCSET: . . . . **ECC 17**

CLASSIC YEARS IN DIGITAL STEREO (See under Classic years...) (Various artists).

CLASSICS OF MUSICAL COMEDY (Various artists).
Tracks: / Geisha medley: *Various artists* / Soldiers in the park: *Various artists* / She is the belle of New York: *Various artists* / Tell me pretty maiden: *Various artists* / Walking home with Angeline: *Various artists/* Under the deodar: *Various artists* / Yo-ho, little girl, Yo-ho: *Various artists* / Half past two: *Various* artists / Moonstruck: *Various artists* / Come to the ball: *Various artists* / Chu chin chow medley: *Various artists* / Love will find a way: *Various artists* / Lilac domino waltz: *Various artists.*
MC: . . . . **MSCB 25**
MC: **MSCC25**

COMEDIAN HARMONISTS (Various artists).
2LP: . . . . **IC 148 32255/5**

COMEDIAN HARMONISTS VOL.2 (Various artists).
2LP: . . . . **IC 148 46078/7**

COMEDIANS SING, THE (Various artists).
LP: . . . . **REB 251**

COMEDY SPECTACULAR (Various artists).
LP: . . . . **REB 249**

COMIC AND CURIOUS VERSE (Various artists).
MCSET: . . . . **ARGO 1208**

COMIC CUTS (Various artists).
Tracks: / Ernie (The fastest milkman in the west): *Hill, Benny* / Right said Fred: *Cribbins, Bernard (nar)* / My boomerang won't come back: *Drake, Charlie* / Bloodnock's rock 'n' roll: *Goons* / Hole in

the ground: *Cribbins*, Bernard (nar) / I'm walking backwards for Christmas: *Goons* / Funky moped: *Carrott, Jasper* / You've got to show it to mother(before you can show it to me: *Whitcomb, Ian* / Sheik of Araby, The: *Cooper, Tommy* / Life's not all that bad: *Whitcomb, Ian* / You are awful (but I like you): *Emery, Dick* / My old man's a dustman: *Donegan*, Lonnie / Convoy G.B.: *Lingo, Laurie and The Dipsticks* / Purple people eater meets the space invaders: *Various* artists / Does your chewing gum lose its flavour?: *Donegan, Lonnie* (Full title: Does your chewing gum lose it's flavour (on the bedpost over) / We'll meet again: *Cooper, Tommy*.
LP: . . . . **LSMLP 1**
MC: . . . . **ZCLSM 1**

COMIC CUTS (2) (Lots of Fun for Everyone) (Various artists).
Tracks: / Laughing policeman, The: *Penrose, Charles* / I'm going back to Himazas: *Somers, Debroy & His Band* / Don't do that to the poor puss cat: *Sarony, Leslie* / Because I love you: *Fields, Gracie* / I lift up my finger and I say tweet tweet: *Lupino, Stanley* / I faw down an' go boom: *Payne, Jack Orchestra* / Is izzy azzy wozz?: *Hylton, Jack & His Orchestra* / Airman airman don't put the wind up me: *Payne, Jack Orchestra* / Fall in and follow the band: *Fields, Gracie* / Chinese laundry blues: *Formby, George* / Let's all sing like the birdies sing: *Payne*, Jack Orchestra / Wheezy Anna: *Noble, Ray Orchestra & Al Bowlly* / Sing Holly, go whistle, hey hey: *Payne, Jack* & The BBC Dance Orchestra / Sun has got his hat on, The: *Ambrose & His Orchestra* / Who's afraid of the big bad wolf?: *Hall, Henry & BBC Dance Orchestra* / All over Italy (they sing so prettily): *Noble, Ray Orchestra & Al Bowlly*/ What can you give a nudist for her birthday: *Holmes, Leslie* / Blaze away: *New Mayfair Dance Orchestra*.
LP: . . . . **OLD 2**
MC: . . . . **COLD 2**

COMIC CUTS (2) VOL 2 (Various artists).
Tracks: / Oi song, The: *Various artists* / Give yourself a pat on the back: *Various artists* / Pig got up and slowly walked away, The: *Various artists* / You can't do that 'ere: *Various artists* / You ought to know better a girl like you: *Various artists*.
LP: . . . . **OLD 13**
MC: . . . . **COLD 13**

COMICAL CUTS (THE 1930'S & 40'S) (Various artists).
Tracks: / Laurel & Hardy: *Laurel & Hardy* / Dance of the cuckoos: *Laurel & Hardy* / Mr Potter wanders on: *Potter*, Gillie / Laughing gas: *Courtneidge, Cicely & Company* / Trip to Brighton, A: *Constandurous, Mabel/Michael Hogan* & Company (Recorded on the Southern Railway.) / Digging holes parts 1 & 2: *Flanegan & Allen* (Whatever happened tothe breakdown man.) / Old school tie, The: *Western Brothers* / Joe Ramsbottam sells pills: *Evans, Norman* / Spot of fishing, A: *Clapham & Dwyer* / Cycling: *Tilley, John* / Kids and the char (part 2) out shopping, The: *Hemsley*, Harry/Suzette Tarri / Kids and the char (part 2) doin' a bit of busking, The: *Hemsley, Harry/Suzette Tarri* / It wouldn't have done for the Duke, sir: *Long, Norman* / Cyril Fletcher tells a couple: *Fletcher, Cyril* / Little Red Hooding Ride: *Bacon, Max* / Common sense: *King, Nosmo* (Introductory dialogue with Hubert.) / Dizzy: *Burns, George* & Gracie Allen / With her head tucked underneath her arm: *Holloway, Stanley (nar)* / Beefeater, The: *Holloway*, Stanley (nar) / Crazy Gang at sea, The: *Crazy Gang* / On behalf of the working classes: *Russell, Billy* (Recorded live in the Theatre.) / Tommy introduces McChumley & sings 'You lucky people': *Trinder, Tommy* / Tommy lets you into a few pilgrim family secrets: *Trinder, Tommy* / Tommy picks one out from 'The Classics' and recites: *Trinder, Tommy*/ Tommy sings S'artnoon: *Trinder, Tommy* / Gardening: what to do with your aspidistra: *Wakefield, Oliver* (The voice of inexperience.) / Rags, bottles and bones: *Walker, Syd* / Old mother Riley's budget: *Lucan & McShane* / Old mother Riley takes her medicine: *Lucan & McShane* / Sid Field plays golf: *Field, Sid*.
MCSET: . . . . **ECC 12**

COMICAL CUTS VOL. 2 (Various artists).
Tracks: / Goodnight, everybody goodnight: *Wilton, Robb* (Comedian with orchestra.) / I should say so: *Wilton, Robb*(Comedian with orchestra.) / Fire station, The (part 1): *Wilton, Robb* (Comedy sketch.) / Fire station, The (part 2): *Wilton*, Robb (Comedy sketch by Robb Wilton with Florence Palmer.) / Police station, The: *Wilton, Robb* (Comedy sketch by Robb Wilton with Florence Palmer.) / Home guard, The: *Wilton, Robb* (Comedy sketch by Robb Wilton.) / Munitions worker, The: *Wilton, Robb* (Comedy sketch by Robb Wilton.) / Fourth form at St Michael's (part 1): *Hay, Will* / Fourth form at St Michael's (part 2): *Hay, Will* / Fourth form at St Michael's (part 3): *Hay, Will* / Fourth form at St Michael's (part 4): *Hay, Will* / Fourth form at St Michael's (part 5): *Hay, Will* / Fourth form at St Michael's (part 6): *Hay, Will* / Convict 99 (part 1): *Hay, Will*(With Moore Marriott & Graham Moffatt) / Convict 99 (part 2): *Hay*, Will (With Moore Marriott & Graham Moffatt) / Nell: *Bennett, Billy* / Green tie on the little yellow dog, The: *Bennett*, Billy / No power on earth: *Bennett, Billy* / Charge of the tight brigade: *Bennett, Billy* / Ogul mogul (A kanakanese love lyric): *Bennett, Billy* / Tightest man I know, The: *Bennett, Billy* / Mandalay: *Bennett, Billy* & Orchestra / Coffee stall keeper, The: *Bennett, Billy & Orchestra* / Foreign legion, The: *Bennett, Billy*(With piano.) / Bookmaker's daughter, The: *Bennett, Billy* (With piano.) / Funny face - a few drinks: *Howard, Sydney/Leslie* Henson / Our village concert (part 1): *Howard, Sydney* (With Vera Pearce, Leonard Henry & Co. with orchestra .) / Our village concert (part 2): *Howard, Sydney* (With Vera Pearce, Leonard Henry & Co. with orchestra .) / Swanker's 'You don't say so', The: *Howard, Sydney* (With Vera Pearce and the Four Bright Sparks.) / Happiest couple in Lancashire, The: *Howard*, Sydney & Orchestra / Sex, sobs and slaughter (part 1): *Howard, Sydney* (With Company.) / Sex, sobs and slaughter (part 2): *Howard, Sydney* (With Company.).
MCSET: . . . . **ECC 14**

COMICAL CUTS VOL. 3 (Various artists).
Tracks: / Interviewed: *Oliver, Vic* (With Jeradyne Jarvis) / Vic Oliver calling: *Oliver, Vic* / Knock knock, who's there?: *Oliver, Vic* (With Sarah Churchill) / Vic Oliver ambles on: *Oliver, Vic* / Vic Oliver versus Gloria Day - butting in: *Oliver, Vic* / Vic Oliver goes naughty: *Oliver, Vic* / Vic Oliver's twists: *Oliver, Vic*/ Tickling your fancy/Tickling the ivories: *Oliver, Vic* / O dear dear: *Frankau, Ronald* / Good morning Mr. Barlow: *Frankau, Ronald* / They have a much better time when they're naughty: *Frankau, Ronald* / I'd like to have a honeymoon with her: *Frankau, Ronald* / Uncle Bill has much improved: *Frankau, Ronald* / I'd rather be a woman than a man: *Frankau, Ronald* / Through a momentary loss of self-control: *Frankau, Ronald* / Upper class love: *Frankau*, Ronald / Chinese nights: *Frankau, Ronald* / He's a twirp: *Frankau, Ronald* / Headmistress, The: *Marshall*, Arthur / School girls story, A: *Marshall, Arthur* / Showing the school: *Marshall, Arthur* / Games mistress: *Marshall, Arthur* / Hostess, The: *Marshall, Arthur* / Nature walk, A: *Marshall, Arthur* / Botany class, The: *Marshall, Arthur* / Reading with children: *Marshall, Arthur* / Out with the guides: *Marshall, Arthur*/ Miss Pritchard's tricycle: *Marshall, Arthur* / Cabaret boys, The: *Byng, Douglas* (With Lance Lister) / Sunday school has done a lot for me: *Byng, Douglas* / Oriental Emma of the 'arem: *Byng, Douglas* / Sex appeal Sarah: *Byng*, Douglas / Mexican Minnie: *Byng, Douglas* / I'm one of the Queens of England: *Byng, Douglas* / I'm the pest of Budapest: *Byng, Douglas* / I must have everything Hungarian: *Byng, Douglas* / I'm a bird: *Byng, Douglas*/ Mayoress of Mould On The Puddle, The: *Byng, Douglas*.
MCSET: . . . . **ECC 19**

COMPLEAT RUGBY SONGS (Various artists).
LP: . . . . **SPD 1085**

COUNTRY COMEDY TIME - LONZO AND OSCAR (see under Country...) (Various artists).

GOLDEN HOUR OF COMEDY,A (Various artists).
MC: . . . . **KGHMC 157**

HEDGEHOG SANDWICH (TV soundtrack) (Various artists).
Tracks: / Loyal apology: *Various artists* / News summary: *Various artists* / Constable Savage: *Various artists*/ Baronet Ernold Oswald Mosley: *Various artists* / University challenge: *Various artists* / (I like) trucking: *Various artists* / Sir Robert Mark: *Various artists* / Hi-fi shop: *Various artists* / England my leotard: *Various artists* / Divorce: *Various artists* / Main points again, The: *Various artists* / Bad language: *Various artists* / Gift shop: *Various artists* / Hedgehog apology: *Various artists* / Supa dupa: *Various* artists / Soccer violence: *Various artists* / (Because I'm) wet and lonely: *Various artists* / That's lies: *Various artists* / Creed (The new revised version): *Various artists* / I believe: *Various artists* / Aide, The: *Various artists* / Main points again, The: *Various artists* / Not the parrot sketch: *Various artists*/ Open marriage: *Various artists* / Lager: *Various artists* / And finally: *Various artists*.
LP: . . . . **REB 421**
MC: . . . . **ZCF 421**

I'M SORRY I'LL READ THAT AGAIN (Various artists).
MCSET: . . . . **ZBBC 1100**

IT AIN'T HALF HOT MUM (Various artists).
LP: . . . . **EMC 3074**

I.T.M.A. (It's that man again) (Various artists).
MCSET: . . . . **ZBBC 1011**

LAUGH IN (Various artists).
LP: . . . . **REH 493**
MC: . . . . **ZCR 493**

LAUGHING STOCK OF THE BBC (Various artists).
LP: . . . . **LAF 1**
MC: . . . . **ZCLAF 1**

LIVE AT JONGLEURS (Various artists).
LP: . . . . **JONG 1**
MC: . . . . **JONGC 1**

MEDICAL STUDENTS SING RUGBY SONGS (Various artists).
LP: . . . . **ILP 1084**

MEMORIES OF GREAT WIRELESS COMEDY SHOWS (1939-41) (Various artists).
LP: . . . . **SH 388**

MEMORY KINDA LINGERS, THE/NOT IN FRONT OF THE AUDIENCE (TV soundtrack & Live at Drury Lane) (Various artists).
Tracks: / Spy who came in from the cold, The: *Various artists* / News, The: *Various artists* / Budget: *Various* artists / Question: *Various artists* / Headbangers: *Various artists* / Rock interview: *Various artists*/ Game for a laugh: *Various artists* / Typical bloody typical: *Various artists* / Well, Mr. Glossop: *Various* artists / Financial times: *Various artists* / Hey Bob: *Various artists* / New glea: *Various artists*/ Holiday habits: *Various artists* / Pizza moment: *Various artists* / Failed in Wales: *Various artists*/ Rinbley's pies: *Various artists* / Made from whales: *Various artists* / Brain death: *Various artists*/ Swedish chemists: *Various artists* / Hey wow: *Various artists* / Nice video, shame about the song: *Various* artists / Jackanory: *Various artists* / Golf trousers: *Various artists* / News, The: *Various artists*/ Two ninnies song: *Various artists* / Aussie pilot: *Various artists* / Does God exist: *Various artists*/ Re-altered images: *Various artists* / McEnroe's breakfast: *Various artists* / Ah come in Rawlinson: *Various* artists / Ask the family: *Various artists* / Polish show: *Various artists* / Aleebee: *Various artists*/ Main points again, The: *Various artists* / What a load of willies: *Various artists* / Kinda lingers, (The memory): *Various artists* / Grow up you bastards: *Various artists* / Confrontation song: *Various artists* / American improv: *Various artists* / Duke of Kent: *Various artists* / Alien: *Various artists* / Oh oh oh means I respect you: *Various artists* / Simon and Garfunkel: *Various artists* / Awards: *Various artists* / S.A.S.: *Various artists* / Prompt: *Various artists* / Barry Manilow: *Various artists* / Return of Constable Savage, The: *Various artists* / Gob on you: *Various artists* / The pope's visit: *Various artists*.
2LP: . . . . **REF 453**
MC: . . . . **ZCD 453**

NOT THE DOUBLE ALBUM (TV soundtrack) (Various artists).
LP: . . . . **REH 516**
MC: . . . . **ZCR 516**

NOT THE NINE O'CLOCK NEWS (TV soundtrack) (Various artists).
Tracks: / Death of a princess (apology to the Saudis): *Rhys Jones, Griff* (With: "The News" - Pamela Stephenson and Mel Smith.) / Gorilla interview, The: *Atkinson, Rowan/Mel Smith/Pamela Stephenson* / Confrontation (song): *Smith, Mel*(Brewis) / Airline safety: *Stephenson, Pamela* (One word from Billy Connolly.) / National wealth beds: *Smith, Mel*/ Simultaneous translation: *Atkinson, Rowan/Pamela Stephenson* (With "The News" (main points again)- Pamela Stephenson and Mel Smith.) / General synod's, The "Life of Monty Python": *Atkinson, Rowan/Mel Smith/ Pamela Stephenson* / There's a man (in Iran)...: *Stephenson, Pamela* / Closedown: *Rhys Jones, Griff/Rowan Atkinson/Mel Smith/Pamela Stephenson* / Point of view: *Rhys Jones, Griff/Rowan Atkinson/Mel Smith/ Pamela Stephenson* / Rowan's rant: *Rhys Jones, Griff/Rowan* Atkinson/Mel Smith/Pamela Stephenson / Stout life: *Rhys Jones, Griff/Rowan Atkinson/Mel Smith/Pamela Stephenson* / Gob on you: *Smith, Mel* (With: "The News" - Pamela Stephenson and Mel Smith (Chris Judge Smith)) / Gay Christian: *Smith*, Mel / Bouncin' (song): *Atkinson, Rowan & Sox* (With: "The main points of the news again" - Mel Smith & Pamela Stephenso) / Oh Bosanquet (song): *Stephenson, Pamela* / I believe: *Rhys Jones, Griff/Rowan Atkinson/Mel Smith/ Pamela Stephenson*.
LP: . . . . **MFP 5810**
MC: . . . . **TCMFP 5810**

NOT THE NINE O'CLOCK NEWS Original cast (Various artists).
LP: . . . . **REB 400**
MC: . . . . **ZCF 400**

NOT THE NINE O'CLOCK NEWS (Various artists).
MCSET: . . . . **ZBBC 1009**

ONE HUNDRED COMEDY INSERTS VOL 3 (Various artists).
LP: . . . . **EAP 1007 SLP**
MC: . . . . **EAP 1007 CAS**

ONE HUNDRED COMEDY INSERTS VOL 2 (Various artists).
LP: . . . . **EAP 1006 SLP**
MC: . . . . **EAP 1006 CAS**

PRIVATE EYE GOLDEN SATIRICALS (Various artists).
LP: . . . . **HAHA 6002**
MC: . . . . **CHACHA 6002**

RUGBY SONGS (Various artists).
MC: **C5LK 571**

SECRET POLICEMAN'S BALL (Original Soundtrack) (Various artists).
Tracks: / Interesting facts: *Various artists* / Country and western supersong: *Various artists* / How do you do it?: *Various artists* / School master: *Various artists* / Pregnancy test: *Various artists* / Name's the game: *Various artists* / Stake your claim: *Various artists* / Entirely a matter for you: *Various artists*/ Cheese shop: *Various artists* / Please: *Various artists* / Four Yorkshiremen: *Various artists* / Two little boys in blue: *Various artists* / End of the world: *Various artists*.
LP: . . . . **ILPS 9601**
MC: . . . . **ICT 9601**
MC: . . . . **LAFFC 3**

SECRET POLICEMAN'S OTHER BALL (Various artists).
LP: . . . . **HAHA 6003**

SECRET POLICEMAN'S OTHER BALL - THE MUSIC (Various artists).
LP: . . . . **HAHA 6004**

SECRET POLICEMAN'S THIRD BALL (The music) (Various artists).
Tracks: / Running up that hill: *Bush, Kate* (With Dave Gilmour) / Save a prayer: *Duran Duran* / Voices of freedom: *Reed, Lou* (With Browne, Gabriel & N'Dour) / This is the world calling: *Geldof, Bob* / For everyman: *Browne*, Jackson / Victim of love: *Erasure* / Wouldn't it be good: *Kershaw, Nik* / Call me names: *Armatrading*, Joan / Imagine: *Knopfler, Mark/Chet Atkins* / Biko: *Gabriel, Peter* (With Reed, N'Dour, Faye, Bell & N'Gom) / Ship of fools: *World Party* (CD only).
LP: . . . . **V 2458**
MC: . . . . **TCV 2458**
LP: . . . . **OVED 271**
MC: . . . . **OVEDC 271**

SECRET POLICEMAN'S THIRD BALL (The comedy) (Various artists).
LP: . . . . **V 2459**
MC: . . . . **TCV 2459**

THREE OF A KIND (Various artists).
LP: . . . . **REB 480**
MC: . . . . **ZCF 480**

WORLD OF THE GOONS (Various artists).
Tracks: / Ying tong song: *Goons* / I love you: *Goons* / Ehh ah oh ooh: *Goons* / Bloodnocks rock 'n' roll: *Goons* / Whistle your cares away: *Goons* / Raspberry song, The: *Goons* / Blue bottle blues: *Goons*/ Russian love song, A: *Goons* / Rhymes: *Goons* / I'm walking backwards for Christmas: *Goons* / Teddy bears' picnic (boogie): *Ellington, Ray Quartet* / Slow coach: *Ellington, Ray Quartet* / Blues: *Ellington*, Ray Quartet / Sally: *Ellington, Ray Quartet* / My melancholy baby: *Ellington, Ray Quartet* / Little red riding hood: *Ellington, Ray Quartet*.
LP: . . . . **SPA 569**
MC: . . . . **KCSP 569**
MC: **8206464**

Comedy Of Errors

COMEDY OF ERRORS, THE (see under Shakespeare, William) (Various artists).

Comfort & Joy (film)

COMFORT & JOY (See under Knopfler, Mark) (Knopfler, Mark).

Comhaltas (label)

COMHALTAS CHAMPIONS ON TOUR (Various artists).
LP: . . . . CL 11

Comic Relief

UTTERLY UTTERLY LIVE.
LP: . . . . WX 51
MC: . . . . WX 51C

Comic Strip (tv)

BAD NEWS TOUR/FISTFUL OF TRAVELLERS CHEQUES (See under Bad News) (Bad News).

COMIC STRIP (Various artists).
LP: . . . . HAHA 6001
MC: . . . . CHACHA 6001

MORE BAD NEWS (VIDEO) (See under Bad News) (Bad News).

Comical Cuts

COMICAL CUTS (THE 1930'S & 40'S) (see under EMI Comedy Classics) (Various artists).

Comin' Home to ...

COMIN' HOME TO THE BLUES (see under Blues) (Various artists).

Coming of Arthur

COMING OF ARTHUR, THE (Various artists).
Tracks: / Coming of Arthur, The: *Various artists* / Balin and Balan: *Various artists.*
MC: . . . . ANV 605

Coming to America

COMING TO AMERICA (1988 film soundtrack) (Various artists).
Tracks: / Coming to America: *System* / Better late than never: *Cover Girls* / All dressed up: *DeBarge, Chico* / I like it like that: *Rodgers, Michael* / That's the way it is (acid house remix): *Mel & Kim* / Addicted to you: *Levert* / Comin' correct: *Fad, J.J.* / Living the good life: *Sister Sledge* / Transparent: *Hendryx, Nona* / Come into my life: *Branigan, Laura/Joe Esposito.*
LP: 790 958-1
MC: 790 958-4

Coming Up Roses

I SAID BALLROOM.
LP: . . . . UTIL 005

Commancheros (film)

COMMANCHEROS/TRUE GRIT (Film soundtracks) (Various artists).
LP: 704.280
MC: . . . . C 704.280

Command Performance

COMMAND PERFORMANCE (Various artists).
LP: . . . . SHM 912
MC: . . . . HSC 284
2LP: . . . . DARC 11106

COMMAND PERFORMANCE VOL. 2 (Night on the Town) (Various artists).
Tracks: / Moonlight serenade: *Lawrence, Syd* / Granada: *Secombe, Harry* / Welcome home: *Peters & Lee* / Fad-eyed fal: *Hill, Benny* / My happiness: *Francis, Connie* / Snowbird: *Kaempfert, Bert* / Strangers in the night: *Kaempfert, Bert* / With a song in my heart: *Secombe, Harry* / Don't stay away too long: *Peters & Lee* / Ting a ling a loo: *Hill, Benny* / Among my souvenirs: *Francis, Connie* / Nightingale sang, A: *Lawrence, Syd.*
LP: . . . . SHM 3033
MC: . . . . HSC 3033

Commander

HIGH 'N' MIGHTY.
LP: . . . . IW 1028

Commander Cody

CODY RETURNS FROM OUTER SPACE (Commander Cody & His Lost Planet Airmen).
Tracks: / Minnie the moocher / It's gonna be one of those nights / I been to Georgia on a fast train / Lightning bar blues / Tina Louise / Shadow knows, The / Roll your own / Southbound / Don't let go / Boogie man boogie, The / Hawaii blues / House of blue lights / Four or five times / That's what I like about the South / Gypsy fiddle.
LP: . . . . ED 202

COMMANDER CODY.
Tracks: / Southbound / California okie / Willing / Boogie man boogie, The / Hawaii blues / House of blue lights / Keep on lovin' her / Devil and me / Four or five times / That's what I like about the South.
LP: . . . . K 56108

LET'S ROCK.
Tracks: / Let's rock / Rockin' over China / Midnight on the strand / Do you mind? / Angel got married / Truckstop at the end of the world / One more ride / Your cash ain't nothin' but trash / Rockabilly funeral / Transfusion / Home of rock 'n' roll.
MC: . . . . SPDC 1001
LP: . . . . SPD 1001
LP: BP-2086

TALES FROM THE OZONE.
Tracks: / Minnie the moocher / It's gonna be one of those nights / Connie / I been to Georgia on a fast train / Honky tonk music / Lightning bar blues / Paid in advance / Cajun baby / Tina Louise / Shadow knows, The / Roll your own / Gypsy fiddle.
LP: . . . . K 56158

VERY BEST OF COMMANDER CODY AND HIS LOST PLANET (Commander Cody & His Lost Planet Airmen).
Tracks: / Back to Tennessee / Wine do yer stuff / Seeds and stems (again) / Daddy's gonna treat you right / Family Bible / Lost in the ozone / Hot rod Lincoln / Beat me daddy, eight to the bar / Truckstop rock / Truck drivin' man / It should've been me / Watch my .38 / Everybody's doing it now / Rock that boogie / Smoke, smoke, smoke / Honeysuckle honey / Sunset on the sage (live) / Cryin' time (live).
LP: . . . . SEE 64

WE'VE GOT A LIVE ONE HERE (Commander Cody & His Lost Planet Airmen).
Tracks: / One of those nights / Semi truck / Smoke, smoke, smoke / Big mamou / San Antonio rose / 18 wheels / Mama hated diesels / Lookin' at the world through a windshield / My window faces the south / Milkcow blues / It should've been me / Back to Tennessee / Seeds and stems / Rock that boogie / Riot in cell block 9 / Don't let go / Too much fun / Hot rod Lincoln / Lost in the ozone.
2LP: . . . . K 66043

Commando

BATTLE OF THIS WEEK.
MC: . . . . MNWK 190
LP: . . . . MNWLP 190
LPPD: . . . . MNWP 190

VELVET TONGUES.
MC: . . . . TALKTC 2
LP: . . . . TALKLP 2

VI.
LP: . . . . MNWP 150

Commercials

COMMERCIAL BREAK VOL.2 (Various artists).
LP: . . . . CBS 60302
MC: 40 60302

COMMERCIAL BREAKS (The Top 30) (Various artists).
Tracks: / Old Spice: *Various artists* / Hovis: *Various artists* / British Airways: *Various artists* / Nescafe: *Various artists* / Hamlet: *Various artists* / Lou Lou: *Various artists* / Royal Bank of Scotland: *Various artists* / Electricity: *Various artists* / Heinz: *Various artists* / Ryvita: *Various artists* / Fiat Mirafiori: *Various artists* / Coalite firelighters: *Various artists.*
LP: . . . . AVM 5001
MC: . . . . AVMC 5001

COMMERCIAL BREAK-TV ADVERTS (Various artists).
MC: 40 61836

COMMERCIAL CLASSICS (Various artists).
LP: . . . . SPA 581
MC: . . . . KCSP 581

Commissioned

GO TELL SOMEBODY.
MC: . . . . LS C 5711
LP: . . . . LS R 5711

Commodores

13.
Tracks: / I'm in love / Turn off the lights / Nothing like a woman / Captured / Touchdown / Welcome home / Do woman you / Only you.
LP: . . . . STMA 8039
MC: . . . . CSTMA 8039

ALL THE GREAT HITS.
Tracks: / Still / Easy / Flying high / Three times a lady / Lady (you bring me up) / Brick house / Lucy / Painted picture / Sail on / Reach high / Wonderland / Oh no / Why you wanna try me / Machine gun / Zoo, The (the human zoo) / Heroes.
LP: . . . . ZL 72051
MC: . . . . ZK 72051

BEST OF THE COMMODORES, THE.
Tracks: / Three times a lady / Still / Sail on / Lady (you bring me up) / Wonderland / Oh no / Too hot ta trot / Zoom / Nightshift / Easy / Janet / Flying high / Lucy / Just to be close to you / Machine gun / Brick house.
LP: . . . . STAR 2249
MC: . . . . STAC 2249

CAUGHT IN THE ACT.
Tracks: / Wide open / Slippery when wet / Bump, The / I'm ready / This is your life / Let's do it right / Better never than forever / Look what you've done to me / You don't know that I know.
LP: . . . . STMS 5032
MC: . . . . CSTMS 5032

GREAT LOVE SONGS BY LIONEL RICHIE.
Tracks: / Just to be close to you / Sweet love / Easy / Three times a lady / Still / Endless love / Sail on / Oh no / Lucy / Girl I think the world about you.
LP: . . . . WL 72437
MC: . . . . WK 72437

GREATEST HITS: COMMODORES.
Tracks: / Three times a lady / Zoom / Brick house / Sweet love / Too hot ta trot / I feel sanctified / Easy / Flying high / Just to be close to you / Slippery when wet / Machine gun / Zoo, The.
LP: . . . . STML 12100
MC: . . . . CSTML 12100
LP: . . . . ZL 72030
MC: . . . . ZK 72030

HEROES.
Tracks: / Got to be together / Celebrate / Old fashioned love / Heroes / All the way down / Sorry to say / Wake up children / Mighty spirit / Jesus is love.
LP: . . . . STMA 8034
MC: . . . . CSTMA 8034

HOT ON THE TRACKS.
Tracks: / Lets get started / Girl I think the world about you / High on sunshine / Just to be close to you / Fancy dancer / Come inside / Thumpin music / Quick draw / Can't let you tease me.
LP: . . . . STMS 5076
MC: . . . . CSTMS 5076

IN THE POCKET.
Tracks: / Lady (you bring me up) / Saturday night / Keep on taking me higher / Oh no / Why you wanna try me / This love / Been lovin' you / Lucy.
LP: . . . . STML 12156
MC: . . . . CSTML 12156

LIVE: COMMODORES.
Tracks: / Won't you come dance with me / Slippery when wet / Come inside / Just to be close to you / Zoom / Easy / Funny feelings / Fancy dancer / Sweet love / I feel sanctified / Brick house / Too hot ta trot.
2LP: . . . . WL 72439
MC: . . . . WK 72439
2LP: . . . . TMSP 6007
MCSET: . . . . CTMSP 6007

LOVE SONGS: COMMODORES.
Tracks: / Three times a lady / Old-fashioned love / This love / Sail on / Wonderland / Zoom / Still / Sweet love / Saturday night / Lucy / Just to be close to you / Heaven knows / Oh no.
LP: . . . . NE 1171
MC: . . . . CE 2171

MACHINE GUN.
Tracks: / Machine gun / Young girls are my weakness / I feel sanctified / Bump rapid fire, The / Assembly line, The / Zoo (human zoo), The / Gonna blow your mind / There's a song in my heart / Superman.
LP: . . . . STMS 5002
MC: . . . . CSTMS 5002

MIDNIGHT MAGIC.
Tracks: / Midnight magic / Gettin' it / You're special / Still / Wonderland / Loving you / Sexy lady / Sail on / 12.01 am.
LP: . . . . STMA 8032
MC: . . . . CSTMA 8032
LP: . . . . WL 72249
MC: . . . . WK 72249

MOVIN' ON.
Tracks: / Hold on / Free / Mary, Mary / Sweet love / Can't get a witness / Gimme my mule / Time / Cebu.
LP: . . . . STMS 5003
MC: . . . . CSTMS 5003

NIGHTSHIFT.
Tracks: / Nightshift / Animal instinct / I keep running / Lay back / Slip up the tongue / Play this record twice / Janet / Woman in my life / Lightin' up the night.
LP: . . . . ZL 72343
MC: . . . . ZK 72343
LP: . . . . WL 72652
MC: . . . . WK 72652

RISE UP.
Tracks: / Cowboys to girls / Rise up / Losing you / Who's making love / Sing a simple song / Baby this is forever / Love canoe / Come by here / Keep on dancing.
LP: . . . . BMLP 035
MC: . . . . BMLC 035
LP: . . . . PER 33 8602
MC: . . . . PER 733 8602
MC: . . . . BMC 035

ROCK SOLID.
Tracks: / Grrip / Bump the la la / Solitaire / Miracle man / Strechhh / So nice / Thank you / I'm gonna need your loving / Homeless / Right here 'n now / Ain't givin' up.
LP: 835369-1
MC: 835369-4

THERE'S A SONG IN MY HEART.
LP: . . . . PLP 47
MC: . . . . PMC 47

UNITED.
Tracks: / Going to the bank / Take it from me / United in love / Can't dance all night / You're the only woman I need / Land of the dreamer / Talk to me / I wanna rock you / Let's apologise / Serious love.
LP: . . . . POLH 31
MC: . . . . POLHC 31

ZOOM.
Tracks: / Squeeze the fruit / Funny feelings / Heaven knows / Zoom / Won't you come dance with me? / Brick house / Funky situation / Patch it up / Easy.
LP: . . . . WL 72101
MC: . . . . WK 72101
LP: . . . . STMS 5061

Communards

COMMUNARDS.
Tracks: / Don't leave me this way / La dolarosa / Disenchanted / Reprise / So cold the night / You are my world / Lover man / Don't slip away / Heaven's above / Forbidden love / Breadline Britain (CD and cassette only.) / Disenchanted (dance mix) (CD and cassette only.).
LP: . . . . LONLP 18
MC: . . . . LONC 18

COMMUNARDS: INTERVIEW PICTURE DISC.
LPPD: . . . . BAK 2077

RED.
Tracks: / Tomorrow / T.M.T. loves T.B.M.G. / Matter of opinion / Victims / For a friend / Never can say goodbye / Lovers and friends / Hold on tight / If I could tell you / C minor.
LP: . . . . LONLP 39
MC: . . . . LONC 39

Como, Perry

16 MILLION HITS.
Tracks: / And i love you so / It's impossible / Catch a falling star.
LP: . . . . CL 42839
MC: . . . . CL 42839

20 GREATEST HITS: PERRY COMO (VOL.1).
Tracks: / Magic moments / Caterina / Catch a falling star / I know / When you were sweet sixteen / I believe / Try to remember / Love makes the world go round / Prisoner of love / Don't let the stars get in your eyes / Hot diggity / Round and round / If I loved you / Hello, young lovers / Delaware / Moonglow / Killing me softly with her song / More / Dear hearts and gentle people / I love you and don't you forget it.
LP: . . . . NL 89019
MC: . . . . NK 89019
LP: . . . . INTS 5043

20 GREATEST HITS: PERRY COMO (VOL.2).
Tracks: / And I love you so / For the good times / Close to you / Seattle / Tie a yellow ribbon / Walk right back / What kind of fool am I? / Days of wine and roses / Where do I begin? / Without a song / It's impossible / I think of you / If / We've only just begun / I want to give / Raindrops keep falling on my head / You make me feel so young / Temptation / Way we were, The / Sing.
LP: . . . . NL 89020
MC: . . . . NK 89020
LP: . . . . INTS 5118

AND I LOVE YOU SO.
Tracks: / And I love you so / Killing me softly with her song / For the good times / Aubrey / Sing / I want to give / Tie a yellow ribbon / I thought about you / It all seems to fall into line / I believe in music.
LP: . . . . CDS 1219
MC: . . . . CMS 1219
LP: . . . . NL 83672
MC: . . . . NK 83672
MC: . . . . CAM 1219
LP: . . . . SF 8360
MC: . . . . PK 11666

BEST OF BRITISH, THE.
Tracks: / My kind of girl / Greensleeves / Michelle / Nightingale sang in Berkeley Square, A / Someday I'll find you / Kind of a hush, A / Where is love / Other

man's grass is always greener / Smile / Very thought of you, The / We'll meet again.
LP: PL 12373
MC: PK 12373

BEST OF PERRY COMO.
Tracks: / You are the sunshine of my life / It's impossible / Prisoner of love / Hands of time, The / We've only just begun / More / Something / Tie a yellow ribbon / And I love you so / Raindrops keep falling on my head / I believe in music / El condor pasa / Sing / Close to you.
LP: 107 4064
MC: 770 4064

BEST OF TIMES, THE.
Tracks: / All I do is dream of you (from Singin' in the Rain') / Gigi / Way you look tonight (from 'Swing Time') / What kind of fool am I? (from 'Stop the world, I want to get off') / They can't take that away from me (from 'The Berkleys of Broadway') / Red sails in the sunset (from 'Provincetown Follies') / Hello, young lovers (from 'The King and I') / I had the craziest dream (from 'Springtime in the Rockies') / Try to remember (from'The Fantasticks') / Father of girls, The / Moon river / Begin the beguine (from 'Jubilee') / Song on the sand (La da da da) (from 'La Cage aux Folles') / It's easy to remember (from 'Mississippi') / Best of times, The / How to handle a woman (from 'Camelot') / Days of wine and roses / It had to be you (from 'Show Business').
LP: PL 89970
MC: PK 89970

CHRISTMAS GREETINGS FROM PERRY COMO.
LP: CDS 1113
MC: CAM 440

COLLECTION: PERRY COMO.
Tracks: / Catch a falling star / Magic moments / Delaware / Wanted / For the good times / I think of you / Don't let the stars get in your eyes / Hot diggity / Love makes the world go round / Caterina / Kewpie doll / Papa loves mambo / Lollipops and roses / What kind of fool am I? / Tie a yellow ribbon / Sunrise, sunset / Way we were, The / Yesterday / Moon river / Young at heart / Michelle / You'll never walk alone / Most beautiful girl in the world / Close to you.
2LP: CCSLP 202
MC: CCSMC 202

COMO PERRY WITH TED WEEMS & HIS ORCHESTRA.
MC: MRT 40043

COMO'S GOLDEN HITS.
Tracks: / Catch a falling star / No other love / Delaware / Till the end of time / Don't let the stars get in your eyes / Arrivederci Roma.
LP: CDS 1148
MC: CAM 450

COMO'S GOLDEN RECORDS.
LP: RD 27100

DEAR PERRY.
LP: RD 27078

ESPECIALLY FOR YOU.
Tracks: / Maria / Once upon a time / I left my heart in San Francisco / Lollipops and roses / Slightly out of tune (Desafinado) / Moon river / Days of wine and roses / Carnival / Tina Marie / What kind of fool am I? / What's new? / More than likely.
LP: INTS 5019
MC: INTK 5019

FIRST THIRTY YEARS, THE.
Tracks: / And I love you so / Hello young lovers / Delaware / Father of girls, The / Caterina / Catch a falling star / Ave Maria / I know / No other love / Mandolins in the moonlight / Love makes the world go round / Hot diggity / More / You'll never walk alone / It's impossible / 'Round and round / Some enchanted evening / I'm always chasing rainbows / Temptation / Kewpie doll / Don't let the stars get in your eyes / I think of you / Seattle / Dream on, little dreamer / Walk right back / When you were sweet sixteen / Papa loves mambo / I left my heart in San Francisco / For the good times / Till the end of time / Arrivederci Roma / Sunrise, sunset / Shadow of your smile, The / Because / If I loved you / I love you and don't you forget it / It all seems to fall into line / Vaya con dios / Tomboy / Mi casa, su casa / Gonna love that girl / You make me feel so young / Magic moments / Glendora / If wishes were kisses / Prisoner of love / Moon talk / Scarlet ribbons / Dear hearts and gentle people / Hawaiian wedding song / Wanted / It had to be you / Accentuate the positive / You came a long way from St. Louis / I may never pass this way again / Dream along with me.
LPS: LFL4 7522

FLY ME TO THE MOON.
Tracks: / Sweetest sounds, The / Fly me to the moon / Hawaiian wedding song / In the still of the night / Sunrise, sunset / Shadow of your smile.
LP: CDS 1137

FOR THE GOOD TIMES.
Tracks: / For the good times / Close to you / Most beautiful girl in the world, The / You are my world / Catch a falling star / Try to remember / I think of you / Days of wine and roses / When you were sweet sixteen / And I love you so / It's impossible / Killing me softly with her song / Send in the clowns / Magic moments / I know / Mandolins in the moonlight / Don't let the stars get in your eyes / Love makes the world go round / Way we were, The / We've only just begun.
LP: STAR 2235
MC: STAC 2235

HERE IS...VOL.1.
Tracks: / Magic moments / Catch a falling star / I'll remember April / Some enchanted evening / Hello young lovers / Without a song / Scarlet ribbons / Father of girls, The / He's got the whole world in his hands / I believe / Ave Maria / When you come to the end of the day / Moon river / Moonglow / Picnic, Theme from / We kiss in a shadow / I wanna be around / Till the end of time / Yesterday / (I left my heart) in San Francisco / Shadow of your smile, The / Fly me to the moon (in other words) / Days of wine and roses / My colouring book / What kind of fool am I?.
2LP: DPS 2018
MC: DPMK 1004

HERE IS...VOL.2.
Tracks: / It's impossible / Dear hearts and gentle people / Try to remember / Deep in your heart / Hawaiian wedding song / Anema e core / You came a long way from St. Louis / I think of you / Happiness comes, happiness goes / Manha de carnaval / Sunrise, sunset / Moon river / Dream on little dreamer / Young at heart / In these crazy times / My days of loving you / Raindrops keep fallin' on my head / My colouring book / You make me feel so young / Lollipops and roses.
2LP: DPS 2036
MC: DPMK 1023

I WISH IT COULD BE CHRISTMAS FOREVER.
Tracks: / I wish it could be Christmas forever / Toyland / Christ is born / Christmas song, The / Ave Maria / Here we come a-carolling / We wish you a merry Christmas / Silver bells / Christmas dreams / White Christmas / Bless this house.
LP: NL 84526
MC: NK 84526

IT'S IMPOSSIBLE.
Tracks: / El condor pasa / Close to you / I think I love you / We've only just begun / It's impossible / It's impossible / And I love you so / Raindrops keep falling on my head (From the film 'Butch Cassidy & The Sundance Kid'.) / Something / Snowbird / House is not a home, A / Everybody is looking for an answer.
LP: MFP 5767
MC: TCMFP 5767
LP: SF 8175
MC: PK 1667

JUKEBOX BABY.
Tracks: / Kewpie doll / Jukebox baby / Love makes the world go round / Tina Marie / Ko ko mo (I love you so) / You're following me / Glendora / Hubba hubba hubba / Dancin' / Moon talk / Just born to be your baby / Angry / Bella Bella Sue / Swinging down the lane / Birth of the blues / Marching along to the blues.
LP: BFX 15306

LEGENDARY PERFORMER, A.
Tracks: / It's impossible / And I love you so / Father of girls, The / This is all I ask / Souvenir d'Italie / Dream along with me / Temptation / My favourite things / Anema e core / Manha de carnaval / Hot diggity (dog ziggity boom) / Surnise, sunset.
LP: RS 1092
MC: PK 11750

LIGHTLY LATIN.
Tracks: / How insensitive / Stay with me / Shadow of your smile / Meditation / And roses and roses / Yesterday / Coo coo roo coo coo Paloma / Dindi / Baia / Once I loved / Manha de carnaval / Quiet nights of quiet stars.
LP: NL 89053

LIVE ON TOUR.
Tracks: / Catch a falling star / Temptation / It's impossible / Swingin' on a star / White Christmas / Till the end of time / Don't let the stars get in your eyes / You'll never walk alone / Send in the clowns.
LP: RCALP 5009

LOVE SONGS: PERRY COMO.
Tracks: / And I love you so / It's impossible / Way we were, The.
LP: CDS 1226
MC: CAM 1226

MAGIC MOMENTS.
Tracks: / Magic moments / Round and round / More / Don't let the stars get in your eyes / In the still of the night / Papa loves mambo / Me and my shadow / I've got a feeling I'm falling / Catch a falling star / Hot diggity / Wanted / It happened in Monterey / You do something to me / For me and my gal / One for my baby / It's a good day.
LP: LP 13028
MC: MC 13028

MAGIC MOMENTS WITH PERRY COMO.
Tracks: / Magic moments / Catch a falling star / Caterina / I know / When you were sweet sixteen / I believe / Try to remember / Love makes the world go round / Prisoner of love / Don't let the stars get in your eyes / Hot diggity / Round and round / If I loved you / Hello, young lovers / Killing me softly with her song / Moonglow / Delaware / More / Dear hearts and gentle people / I love you and don't you forget it / And I love you so / For the good times / Walk right back / It's impossible / If / We've only just begun / Raindrops keep falling on my head / You make me feel so young / Temptation / Way we were, The.
MC: NK 89401

MEMORIES ARE MADE OF HITS.
Tracks: / And I love you so / Way we were, The / Seattle / Close to you / Father of girls, The / For the good times / Hands of time, The / I think of you / Most beautiful girl in the world, The / Yesterday / It's impossible / Love makes the world go round / Don't let the stars get in your eyes.
LP: INTS 5151
MC: INTK 5151
LP: RS 1005
MC: PK 11676

PERRY COMO.
Tracks: / Not while I'm around / Regrets / When / There'll never be another night like this / Love / When she smiles / Colours of my life / Save me the dance / Someone is waiting / You are my world.
LP: PL 13629

PERRY COMO CHRISTMAS ALBUM, THE.
Tracks: / Christmas Eve / Do you hear what I hear? / Christ is born / Little drummer boy / There is no Christmas like a home Christmas / O Holy night / Caroling caroling / First Noel, The / Hark the herald angels sing / Silent night / Silver bells / Toyland / Have yourself a merry little Christmas / Ave Maria.
MC: NK 81929

PERRY COMO CHRISTMAS COLLECTION, THE.
Tracks: / Have yourself a merry little Christmas / That Christmas feeling / Joy to the world / Jingle bells / Santa Claus is coming to town / White Christmas / O holy night / O little town of Bethlehem / Silent night.
2LP: PDA 027

PERRY COMO COLLECTION (20 Golden Greats).
Tracks: / I wonder who's kissing her now / Rose of the Rockies / In my little red book / Rainbow on the river / Lazy weather / Simple and sweet / Out where the blue begins / Angeline / Picture me without you / Goodnight, sweet dreams, goodnight / Temptation / When day is done / I'm sorry I didn't say I'm sorry / Dance, ballerina, dance / Some enchanted evening / I walked in / Love is the sweetest thing / I concentrate on you / I walk alone / To know you, to love you.
LP: DVLP 2109
MC: DVMC 2109

PERRY COMO COLLECTION.
Tracks: / Carolina moon / Somebody loves me / Jukebox baby / Fly me to the moon / In the still of the night / Shadow of your smile.
2LP: PDA 011
MCSET: PDC 011

PERRY COMO SINGS.
Tracks: / I had the craziest dream / If I had to be with you / I found a million dollar baby / Say it isn't so / If I could be with you / Dream is a wish your heart makes, A.
LP: CDS 1091

PERRY COMO SINGS JUST FOR YOU.
Tracks: / You're adorable / I'm confessin' / Long ago and far away / It's only a paper moon / My one and only heart / I love you.
LP: CDS 1130

PERRY COMO SINGS LOVE SONGS.
Tracks: / Look to your heart / My cup runneth over / Love in a home / In these crazy times / Try to remember / Sunrise, sunset / How to handle a woman / When you're in love / You're nearer / Father of girls, The.
LP: NL 42076

PERRY COMO TODAY.
Tracks: / Making love to you / Sing along with me / Tonight I celebrate my love / Butterfly (I'll set you free) / Bless the beasts and children / That's what friends are for / Wind beneath my wings / I'm dreaming of Hawaii / You're nearer / My heart stood still / Do you remember me / Best of times, The.
LP: PL 86368
MC: PK 86368

PERRY COMO/RAY CHARLES (Como, Perry & Ray Charles).
MCSET: WW 6051

POP SINGERS ON THE AIR (See under Pop Singers On The Air) (Various artists).

RELAX WITH PERRY COMO.
Tracks: / Dream on, little dreamer / Days of wine and roses / What kind of fool am I? / I left my heart in San Francisco.
MC: CAM 465

SO IT GOES.
Tracks: / What's one more time? / So it goes / Here comes that song again / Goodbye for now / Second time, The / Jason / As my love for you / Fancy dancer / Is she the only girl in the world? / You are so beautiful.
LP: RCALP 6081
MC: RCAK 6081

SOMEBODY LOVES ME.
Tracks: / Miss me and kiss me and kiss me / Carolina moon / Somebody loves me / Jukebox baby / Mandolins in the moonlight / Island of forgotten lovers / That ol' gang of mine.
LP: CDS 1101

SOMETHIN' SPECIAL.
Tracks: / You light up my life / For all we know / You are the sunshine of my life / Feelings / When I need you / Where you're concerned / Girl, you make it happen / Behind closed doors / Then you can tell me goodbye / Just out of reach / Dream baby (how long must I dream) / Bridge over troubled water.
LP: PL 42679
MC: PK 42679

TAKE IT EASY.
Tracks: / Bridge over troubled water / El condor pasa / Way we were, The / When I need you / Feelings / Wind beneath my wings, The / Michelle / Yesterday / For the good times (Only on CD) / You are so beautiful / Killing me softly with her song / Most beautiful girl, The / You are the sunshine of my life / Sunrise sunset / Sing / (They long to be) Close to you / We've only just begun / And I love you so (Only on CD).
MC: NK 90490

THIS IS PERRY COMO.
2LP: 26 28028

WARM AND MELLOW.
2LP: NL 43047

YOUNG PERRY COMO (1936-41) (Como, Perry/Ted Weems & His Orchestra).
Tracks: / Lazy weather / Until today / Picture me without you / Trouble ends out where the blue begins / Rainbow on the river / Goodnight, sweet dreams, goodnight / Gypsy told me, A / In my little red book / Simple and sweet / Goody goodbye / Two blind loves / That old gang of mine / I wonder who's kissing her now / Rose of the Rockies / It all comes back to me now / Angeline.
LP: MCL 1805
MC: MCLC 1805

Comolli, Phil

CITY LIGHTS.
MC: TC 003

Companion

ON THE LINE.
LP: SRLP 109

Companions in a..(bk)

COMPANIONS IN A DEATH BOAT (Wild Billy Childish).
LP: WORDUP 001

Company

FICTIONS.
LP: INCUS 38

Company B

COMPANY B.
Tracks: / Fascinated / Spin me around / Signed in your book of love / I'm satisfied / Perfect lover / Jam on me / Full circle / Infatuate me.
LP: LPBR 2

MC: . . . . MCBR 2

Company Of State

DROWNING IN FIRE.
Tracks: / Hound / Ghostkin / Slow side of the night / Good friends / Get lost / Paint my boots / Somebody else / Harem / Stained forever.
LP: . . . . ANT 073

Company Of Wolves

COMPANY OF WOLVES.
Tracks: / Call of the wild / Hangin' by a thread / Jilted / Distance, The / Romance on the rocks / Can't love ya, can't leave ya / Hell's kitchen / St James Infirmary / My ship / I don't wanna be loved / Girl / Everybody's baby.
LP: 842 184 1
MC: 842 184 4

Company She Keeps

AMANDA.
LP: . . . . COLD 8

Company (Show)

COMPANY (Broadway cast) (Various artists).
LP: . . . . PS 3550
MC: . . . . PST 3550

Compass Flow

BUSH TELEGRAPH.
LP: . . . . GLALP 033

Competition (Film)

COMPETITION, THE (Original soundtrack) (Various artists).
LP: . . . . MCA 1520
MC: . . . . MCAC 1520

Complete Control

BRICKS, BLOOD AND GUTS (IN 1985).
LP: . . . . OIR 001

Compton Swing

SWITCH IN TIME.
Tracks: / Li'l darlin' / Cute / Moon river / Girl talk / Taurian matador / String of pearls / Intermission riff / Switch in time / Flirty flutes / Montuna cha-cha / This guy's in love with you / Love story / St. Louis blues / Woodchoppers ball.
LP: . . . . AL 4502

Compton, Tony

CAFE' CONTINENTAL (Compton, Tony and Brian Dexter).
LP: . . . . SAV 156

TONY COMPTON.
Tracks: / One note samba / Girl from Ipanema / Windmills of your mind (Medley includes: Sweet gingerbread man and Summer knows.) / Jealousy / Walk in the Black Forest, A / Sid goes west / When sunny gets blue / Elephant walk / Brazil.
LP: . . . . Unknown

Comsat Angels

7 DAY WEEKEND.
Tracks: / Forever young / Day one / You move me / I'm falling / Believe it / New heart and hand / Close your eyes / You're the heroine / High tide / Still it's not enough.
LP: . . . . HIP 29
MC: . . . . HIPC 29

CHASING SHADOWS.
Tracks: / Thought that counts, The / Cutting edge, The / Under the influence / Carried away / You'll never know / Lost continent / Flying dream / Pray for rain.
LP: . . . . ILPS 9855

ENZ.
Tracks: / Independence day / Do the empty house / Total war / It's history / Another world / Eye of a lens / At sea / Mass / Home is the range / After the rain.
LP: 810735 1

FICTION.
Tracks: / After the rain / Zinger / Now I know / Not a word / Ju nu money / More / Pictures / Birdman / Don't look now / What else ?.
LP: . . . . POLS 1075

LAND.
Tracks: / Will you stay tonight / Alicia / World away, A / Independence day / Nature trails / Mister memory / Island heart / I know that feeling / As above, so below.
LP: . . . . HIP 8
MC: . . . . HIPC 8

SLEEP NO MORE.
Tracks: / Eye dance / Sleep no more / Be brave / Gone / Dark parade / Diagram / Restless / Goat of the West / Light years / Our secret.
LP: . . . . POLS 1038

WAITING FOR A MIRACLE.
Tracks: / Baby / Independence day / Waiting for a miracle / Total war / On the beach / Monkey pilot / Real story / Map of the world / Postcard.
LP: 2383 578

Comstock, Bobby

TENNESSEE WALTZ.
LP: . . . . MOHAWK 124

Con Funk Shun

BURNIN' LOVE.
Tracks: / Do ya / Burnin' love / How long / Jo Jo / She's sweet / She's a star / It's time girl / You make me wanna love again / Burnin' love (single) / Burnin' love (dub edit).
LP: 826 963-1
MC: 826 963-4

ELECTRIC LADY.
Tracks: / Turn the music up / Rock it all night / I'm leaving baby / Tell me what you're gonna do / Electric lady / Don't go / Circle of love / Pretty lady.
LP: 824 345-1

FEVER.
Tracks: / Can you feel the groove tonight / Indiscreet sweet / Baby, I'm hooked (right into your love) / Thinking about you, baby / Don't let your love grow cold / Lovin' fever / Hard lovin' / If I'm your lover.
LP: 814 447 1

SPIRIT OF LOVE.
Tracks: / Got to be enough / By your side / Curtain call / Early morning sunshine / Spirit of love / Happy face / All up to you / Juicy / Honey wild / Lovestruck.
LP: 6337 102

TO THE MAX.
Tracks: / Got the body / Lets ride and slide / Ever love / Hide and freak / You are the one / Take it to the Max / Love's train / Ain't nobody baby / Freak, The.
LP: 6337 258

TOUCH.
Tracks: / Too tight / Lady's wild / Give your love to me / Play wid it / Pride and glory / Kidnapped / Welcome back to love / Touch / Can't say goodbye.
LP: 6337 154

Conan the... (film)

CONAN THE BARBARIAN (film soundtrack) (Various artists).
Tracks: / Anvil of crom: *Various artists* / Riddle of steel - riders of doom: *Various artists* / Gif of fury: *Various artists* / Wheel of pain: *Various artists* / Atlantean sword: *Various artists* / Theology civilization wifeing: *Various artists* / Seach, The: *Various artists* / Orgy: *Various artists* / Funeral pyre: *Various artists* / Battle of the mounds: *Various artists* / Orphans of doom: *Various artists* / Awakening, The: *Various artists.*
LP: . . . . MCF 3146
LP: . . . . MCA 1566
MC: . . . . MCAC 1566
LP: . . . . PL 37666
MC: . . . . PK 37666

CONAN: THE DESTROYER (1983 film soundtrack) (Various artists).
LP: . . . . MCA 6135
MC: . . . . MCAC 6135

Concert A La Carte

CONCERT A LA CARTE.
MC: 4042175

Concert Arban

RAGTIME FROM SCOTT JOPLIN TO CLAUDE BOLLING.
LP: . . . . ARN 33786
MC: . . . . ARN 40.33786

Concert Royal

MUSIC AT BOWES.
Tracks: / Silent worship / Arne / Sonata in G for harpsichord / Rule Britannia / Marriage of Figaro, The / Serenade from string quartet opus 3 no. 5 / Violet, The / Sonata in C / Trout, The / Wild rose, The.
LP: . . . . PLR 029

Concord Jazz All Stars

AT THE NORTHSEA FESTIVAL VOL. 2.
Tracks: / Vignette / Emily / That's your red wagon / Sweet Lorraine / Can't we be friends? / Out of nowhere / Once in a while / In a mellow tone.
LP: . . . . CJ 182
LP: . . . . CJ 205
MC: . . . . CJC 205

OW!.
Tracks: / Ow! / Fungi mama / My shining hour / I'll close my eyes / Why did I choose you / Blue hodge / I love being here with you / All blues / Down home blues.
LP: . . . . CJ 348
MC: . . . . CJ 348 C

TAKE EIGHT.
LP: . . . . CJ 347
MC: . . . . CJ 347 C

Concord Super Band

CONCORD SUPER BAND IN TOKYO.
LP: . . . . CJ 80

IN TOKYO.
LP: . . . . CJ 89

Concrete Blonde

BLOODLETTING.
LP: . . . . EIRSA 1028
MC: . . . . EIRSAC 1028

CONCRETE BLONDE.
Tracks: / True / Your haunted head / Dance along the edge / Still in Hollywood / Song for Kim (she said) / Beware of darkness / Over your shoulder / Little sister / (You're the only one) can make me cry / Cold (part of town) / True (instrumental).
LP: . . . . MIRF 1018
MC: . . . . MIRFC 1018

FREE.
Tracks: / God is a bullet / Run, run, run / It's only money / Help me / Sun / Roses grow / Scene of a perfect crime / Happy birthday / Little conversations / Carry me away / Free.
LP: . . . . EIRSA 1004
MC: . . . . EIRSAC 1004

Concrete Box

SEWERSIDE.
LP: . . . . KISS 1

Concrete Sox

HERESY/CONCRETE SOX (See under Heresy) (Concrete Sox & Heresy).

WHOOPS SORRY VICAR!.
Tracks: / Prophecy / No trust no faith / Scientific slaughter / Comparison / Rumour well out of hand / Think now / False insight / Dream, The / Salt of the earth / Facts / Moustache cacting / Like a maniac.
LP: . . . . ACHE 11

YOUR TURN NEXT.
LP: . . . . GURT 10

Concrete Temple

MAMMON (See under Sixth Comm) (Concrete Temple/Sixth Comm).

Condemned 84

BATTLE SCARRED.
Tracks: / Survive / Teenage slag / Unite / Skinheads / Youngblood / Gang warfare / Riot squad / Under her thumb.
LP: . . . . OIR 003
LP: . . . . MLP 1

Condo, Ray

HOT 'N' COLD.
LP: . . . . CRA 001

Condon, Eddie

1938 (His Windy City Seven jam session) (Condon, Eddie & His Windy City Seven).
Tracks: / Love is just around the corner / Beat to the shocks / Carnegie drag / Carnegie jump / Ja da / Embraceable you / Meet me tonight in dreamland / Diana / Serenade to a Shylock.
LP: AG6 24054

1944 JAM SESSIONS.
2LP: . . . . J 101/102

AT THE JAZZ BAND BALL.
Tracks: / At the jazz band ball / Aunt Hagar's blues / There'll be some changes made / Somebody loves me / Improvisation for march of time / We called it music / She's funny that way / Impromptu ensemble / Nobody's sweetheart / Farewell blues / Down among the sheltering palms / Stars fell on Alabama / Nobody knows / Grace and beauty / Sheik of Araby, The / Friars point shuffle.
LP: . . . . AFS 1021

CHICAGO STYLE.
Tracks: / Sugar / China boy / Nobody's sweetheart / Liza / There'll be some changes made / I've found a new baby / My baby came home / From Monday on / One step to heaven / Shimme-sha-wabble / Oh baby / Indiana / I'm sorry I made you cry / Making friends / I'm gonna stomp, Mr. Henry Lee / That's a serious thing / Tennessee twilight / Madame Dynamite / Eel, The / Home cookin'.
LP: . . . . VLP 55

CHICAGO STYLE RHYTHMAKERS.
LP: . . . . JA 1

CHICAGO STYLED.
LP: . . . . S 1358

CHICAGOANS (see McKenzie, Red) (Condon, Eddie & Red McKenzie).

COMMODORE CLASSICS (Condon, Eddie & Fats Waller).
LP: AG6 24095

CONDON CONCERT (Condon, Eddie & His All Stars).
LP: . . . . J 10

EDDIE CONDON.
Tracks: / I must have that man / Time on my hands / Ballin' the Jack / Sheik of Araby, The / Zaza / I've found a new baby / Jazz me blues.
LP: . . . . KLJ 20018

EDDIE CONDON AND HIS JAZZ CONCERT ORCHESTRA (Condon, Eddie & His Orchestra).
LP: . . . . JAZ 2012
MC: . . . . ZCJAZ 2012

EDDIE CONDON BAND 1945 (Condon, Eddie Band).
Tracks: / Sunday / How come you do me like you do / Every night / Keep smiling at trouble / That's a plenty / Sugar / Carnegie leap / September in the rain / Body and soul / Rose room / Monday date / How long has this been going on / Jazz band ball.
LP: . . . . RARITIES 37

EDDIE CONDON - VOL 1 (1938).
LP: 6.24054

FLOORSHOW, VOL. 1.
Tracks: / Blues / Riverboat shuffle / Ja da / In a little Spanish town / Everything happens to me / Hotter than that / Look at me now / Fascinating rhythm / I've got a crush on you / 'S wonderful / They can't take that away from me / Man I love, The / Embraceable you / I got rhythm / At the Jazz Band Ball / As time goes by / Running wild / I'm gonna sit right down and write myself a letter / My funny valentine.
LP: . . . . QU 030
LP: . . . . QUEEN 030

FLOORSHOW, VOL. 2.
Tracks: / Sheik of Araby, The / I've got a feeling I'm falling / Keepin' out of mischief now / Handful of keys / Squeeze me / Joint is jumpin', The / Stars fell on Alabama / Limehouse blues / Ain't misbehavin' / Seems like an old time / Ballin' the jack / Relaxin' at the Touro / But not for me / Muskrat ramble / Birth of the blues / Louisiana / New Orleans / High society / My old flame / Dixieland band.
LP: . . . . QU 031
LP: . . . . QUEEN 031

GOOD BAND IS HARD TO FIND, A.
LP: 6.25526

INTOXICATING DIXIELAND (1944/45) (Condon, Eddie & The Dorsey Brothers).
Tracks: / My blue heaven / Through a veil of indifference / After you've gone / Pee Wee original / Riverside blues / Wherever there's love / Impromptu ensemble / Honeysuckle rose / Baby won't you please come home? / China boy / Body and soul / I can't believe that you're in love with me / Royal Garden blues / Any old time.
LP: . . . . RARITIES 44

JAM SESSION (Condon, Eddie & Bobby Hackett).
Tracks: / Oh baby / Wrap your troubles in dreams / Struttin' with some barbecue / On the sunny side of the street / My honey's loving arms / Fidgety feet.
LP: . . . . AIRCHECK 28

LIEDERKRANZ SESSIONS, THE (Condon, Eddie & His Band).
LP: 6.24295

SPIRIT OF CONDON,THE.
LP: . . . . J 73

TOWN HALL BROADCASTS VOL 2 (1944-45).
Tracks: / Strut Miss Lizzie / Indiana / Relaxing at the Tuoro / Some day sweetheart / I found a new baby / None of my Jellyroll / Clarinet marmalade / Ballin' the Jack / Peg o' my heart / Jada / Dinah / That's a plenty / Impromptu ensemble.
LP: . . . . RHA 6029

TOWN HALL CONCERTS (Condon, Eddie & Various artists).
2LP: . . . . JCE 1005/6

TOWN HALL CONCERTS VOL 1 (Condon, Eddie & His All Stars).
Tracks: / Jazz me blues / Cherry / I'm coming Virginia / Love nest, The / Big butter and egg man / Oh Katharina / Impromptu ensemble / Sugar / It's been so long / Mandy make up your mind / September in the rain / Song of the wanderer / Walking the dog.
LP: . . . . RHA 6028

TOWNHALL CONCERTS VOL 2.
2LP: . . . . JCE 1003/4

Condon Gang

JACK TEAGARDEN AND THE CONDON GANG 1944 (see Teagarden, Jack) (Condon Gang/Jack Teagarden).

Conexion Latina

CALORCITO.
LP: . . . . ENJA 4072

Coney Hatch

CONEY HATCH.
Tracks: / Devil's deck / You ain't got me / Stand up / No sleep tonight / Love poison / We've got the night / Hey operator / I'll do the talking / Victim of rock / Monkey bars.
LP: . . . . MERS 15
MC: . . . . MERSC 15

FRICTION.
Tracks: / This ain't love / She's gone / Wrong side of town / Girls from last night's dream / Coming to get you / Fantasy / He's a champion / State love / Burning love.
LP: . . . . VERL 23

OUTA HAND.
LP: . . . . VERL 7

Conflict

AGAINST ALL ODDS.
LP: . . . . MORT 60
MC: . . . . MORTC 60

FINAL CONFLICT, THE.
LP: . . . . MORT 50

FROM PROTEST TO RESISTANCE.
LP: . . . . FUND 1

HOUSE NATION.
LP: . . . . CHRIST 16

INCREASE THE PRESSURE.
LP: . . . . MORT 6

IT'S TIME TO SEE WHO'S WHO.
LP: . . . . CHRIST 3

ONLY STUPID BASTARDS USE EMI.
LP: . . . . THIS NOT 599

STANDARD ISSUE (Singles Comp).
LP: . . . . MORT 40
MC: . . . . MORTC 40

TURNING REBELLION INTO MONEY.
Tracks: / Banned in the UK / Piss in the ocean, The / Increased pressure / Serenade is dead / They said that / From protest to resistance / Big hand / G song / I ain't thick, it's a trick / So what / Punk is dead / Rival tribal / Statement.
2LP: . . . . MORT 30
MCSET: . . . . MORT 30C

UNGOVERNABLE FORCE, THE.
LP: . . . . MORT 20

Congo

CONGO.
Tracks: / Days chasing days / Jackpot / Hail the world of Jah / Education of brainwashing / Youth man / Yoyo / Nana / Thief is in the vineyard.
LP: . . . . CBS 83796

Congo Ashanti Roy

BREAKING DOWN THE PRESSURE (see Dread, Mikey) (Congo Ashanti Roy/ Mikey Dread).

LEVEL VIBES.
LP: . . . . SBLP 2001

SIGN OF THE STAR.
Tracks: / Stay red / Time is running out / Big shot / Running from reality / Chant Niabinghi / Cloudy day / Two shall be together / Righteous man / Man of word / Weeping and wailing.
LP: . . . . PREX 8

Congos

HEART OF THE CONGOS.
Tracks: / Fisherman / Congo man / Open up the gate / Children crying / La la bam bam / Can't come in / Sodom and Gomorrah / Wrong thing, The / Ark of covenant / Solid foundation.
LP: . . . . BEAT 2

Conjunto

CONJUNTO: TEXAS-MEXICAN BORDER MUSIC (vol. 1) (Various artists).
LP: . . . . ROUNDER 6023
MC: . . . . ROUNDER 6023C

CONJUNTO VOL.2 (Various artists).
LP: . . . . ROUNDER 6024
MC: . . . . ROUNDER 6024C

Conjure

MUSIC FOR THE TEXTS OF ISHMAEL REED.
Tracks: / Jes' grew / Wardrobe master of paradise, The / Dualism (1) / Oakland blues / Skydiving / Judas / Betty Ball's blues / Untitled II / Fool-ology (the song) / From the files of agent 22 / Dualism (2) / Rhythm in philosophy.
LP: 461155 1
MC: 461155 4
LP: . . . . AMCL 10061

Conlee, John

BUSTED.
Tracks: / Busted / Shame / Guilty / Two hearts / Little of you, A / Nothing behind you, nothing in sight / Common man / I don't remember loving you / Ain't no way to make a bad love grow / Woman's touch, A.
LP: . . . . IMCA 887

JOHN CONLEE GREATEST HITS.
Tracks: / Baby, you're something / Backside of thirty / Miss Emily's picture / Busted / Common man / I don't remember loving you / Rose coloured glasses / Friday night blues / Lady lay down / She can't say that anymore.
LP: . . . . IMCA 5405

JOHN CONLEE GREATEST HITS VOLUME 2.
Tracks: / Lifetime guarantee / Years after you / In my eyes / As long as I'm rockin' with you / I'm only in it for love / Old school / Way back / Before my time / Working man / Blue highway.
LP: . . . . IMCA 5642

ROSE-COLOURED GLASSES.
LP: . . . . MCF 3040

SONGS FOR THE WORKING MAN.
Tracks: / Common man / Busted / Arthur and Alice / Nothing behind you, nothing in sight / She loves my troubles away / Friday night blues / Working man / But she loves me / In crowd, The / American trilogy.
LP: . . . . IMCA 5699

Conley, Arthur

ARTHUR CONLEY.
Tracks: / Funky Street / Aunt Dora's love soul shack / Burning fire / Ha ha ha / I've been loving you too long / Sweet soul music / Shake, rattle and roll / Baby what you want me to do / Let nothing separate us / People sure act funny / Wholesale love / Ob la di ob la da.
LP: . . . . K 20062
MC: K4 20062

SWEET SOUL MUSIC.
LP: . . . . SD 33215

Conley, Earl Thomas

GREATEST HITS: EARL THOMAS CONLEY.
Tracks: / Nobody falls like a fool / Holding her and loving you / Somewhere between right and wrong / Angel in disguise / Fire and smoke / Once in a blue moon / I have loved you girl-but not like this before / Don't make it easy for me / Your love's on the line / Silent treatment / Heavenly bodies / Too many times (Duet with Anita Pointer.) / That was a close one / I need a good woman bad / Love don't care (whose heart it breaks) / Too hot to handle.
LP: . . . . NL 90314
MC: . . . . NK 90314

HEART OF IT ALL, THE.
Tracks: / What she is (is a woman in love) / Love out loud / What I'd say / You must not be drinking enough / Carol / No chance, no dance / I love the way he left you / Finally Friday / We believe in happy endings / Too far from the heart of it all.
LP: . . . . PL 86824
MC: . . . . PK 86824

Conlon, Bill

WITH YOU IN MIND.
Tracks: / Lucille / I know one / Cowboys don't get lucky all the time / I don't have far to fall / Please please (tell me that you...) / Chair, The / Carmen / Not counting you / She's holding her own now / That ain't like your memory / Let's start forever / Streets of Bakersfield.
MC: . . . . ETCAS 189
MC: . . . . ETMC 189

WOMAN YOUR LOVE.
Tracks: / Got no reason now for going home / Woman your love / Bunch of thyme / Living on these back streets / Rose of Clare / Mother's love's a blessing, A / Old loves never die / You took off my hands / Gentle mother / Old rustic bridge / Angeline.
LP: . . . . ETLP 188
MC: . . . . ETCAS 188

Conn, Tony

TOTAL INSANITY.
LP: . . . . ROLL 18

Connection

THIRD EYE.
LP: . . . . RING 01030

Connection (film)

CONNECTION (1961 film soundtrack) (Various artists).
LP: . . . . UNKNOWN

Conneff, Kevin

WEEK BEFORE EASTER, THE.
LP: . . . . CCF 23
MC: 4CCF 23

Connells

DARKER DAYS.
Tracks: / Darker days / Much easier / 1934 / Brighter worlds / In my head / Hats off / Holding pattern / Seven / Unspoken words.
LP: . . . . VEX 1

FUN AND GAMES.
Tracks: / Something to say / Fun and games / Sal / Upside down / Motel / Hey wow / Ten pins / Inside my head / Uninspired / Sat nite (USA) / Lay me down / Fine tuning (Available on CD only).
LP: . . . . FIEND 153

Connelly, Peggy

WITH RUSS GARCIA BAND.
LP: . . . . FS 206

Conners, Gene

COPENHAGEN STEW (Conners, Gene 'Mighty Flea" (with Fessors session boys)).
LP: . . . . SLP 436

Connick, Harry Jr

20.
Tracks: / Avalon / Blue skies / Imagination / Do you know what it means to miss New Orleans / Basin Street blues / Lazy river / Please don't talk about me when I'm gone / Stars fell on Alabama / 'S wonderful / If I only had a brain / Do nothing till you hear from me.
LP: 4629961
MC: 4629964

LOFTY'S ROACH SOUFFLE.
Tracks: / One last pitch / Hudson bommer / Lonely side / Mr. Spill / Lofty's roach souffle / Mary Ruth / Harronymous / One last pitch (take two) / Colomby Day / Little dancing girl / Bayou maharajah.
LP: 4669491
MC: 4669494

WE ARE IN LOVE.
Tracks: / We are in love / Only 'cause I don't have you / Recipe for love / Drifting / Forever for now / Nightingale sang in Berkley Square, A / Heavenly / Just a boy / I've got a great idea / I'll dream of you again / It's alright with me / Buried in blue.
LP: 4667361
MC: 4667364

WHEN HARRY MET SALLY (Original soundtrack).
LP: 4657531
MC: 4657534

Connie & Babe

BACKWOODS BLUEGRASS (Connie & Babe & The Backwoods Boys).
LP: . . . . ROUNDER 0043

BASIC BLUEGRASS (Connie & Babe & The Backwoods Boys).
LP: . . . . ROUNDER 0042

Conniff, Ray

ALWAYS IN MY HEART.
Tracks: / Maria Elena / Ramona / Don't cry for me Argentina / La violetera / La vie en rose / Fernando / Summer place, A (theme from) / Valencia / Blowin' in the wind / Adios muchachos.
LP: 4605451
MC: 4605454

AMOR, AMOR (Conniff, Ray & His Orchestra).
Tracks: / Amor / Ven con el alma desnuda / Don diablo / Eternas ondas / Apariencias hablame del marinero / My cha chorina / Esa triste guitarra / Paraiso / Emociones / Cama y mesa / Dueno de nada.
LP: . . . . S 25219
MC: 40 25219

BRIDGE OVER TROUBLED WATER.
LP: . . . . CBS 64020

EXCLUSIVAMENTE LATINO (Conniff, Ray & His Orchestra).
Tracks: / Amigo / Chiquitita / Recuerdos / Hey / Pajaro chogui boogie / Vereda tropical / Exclusivamente latino / El dia que me quieras / Mi querido, mi viejo, mi amigo / La bikina / Ansiedad.
LP: . . . . S 84780
MC: 40 84780

FANTASTICO (Conniff, Ray & His Orchestra).
Tracks: / Caballo viejo / Amiga / Gloria / Y como es el / Ese no / Fantastico / No me vuelvo a enamorar / Como tu / La paloma / Ave Maria / Muito estranho.
LP: . . . . S 25744
MC: 40 25744

HELLO YOUNG LOVERS (Conniff, Ray & His Orchestra & Chorus).
Tracks: / Hello young lovers / As time goes by / You do something to me / People will say we're in love / Moonlight serenade / It might as well be Spring / I'll see you again / Where or when / Cheek to cheek / Easy to love / Laura / Way you look tonight / I could have danced all night / Smoke gets in your eyes / They can't take that away from me.
LP: . . . . SHM 3181
MC: . . . . HSC 3181

HI-FI COMPANION ALBUM.
LP: . . . . BET 101
LP: . . . . DP 66011

HIS ORCHESTRA HIS CHORUS HIS SINGERS HIS SOUND.
LP: . . . . SPR 27

I WILL SURVIVE (Conniff, Ray & Singers).
Tracks: / I will survive / Reunited / I want your love / She believes in me / Practice makes perfect / If not for you / Hallelujah / Twenty third psalm / Little music box dancer / Love you inside out.
LP: . . . . CBS 83934

I'D LIKE TO TEACH THE WORLD TO SING.
LP: . . . . CBS 64449

IMAGES: RAY CONNIFF (Conniff, Ray & His Orchestra).
Tracks: / Where is the love / Close to you / For the good times / Cherish / Song sung blue / Clair / Shaft, Theme from / We've only just begun / It's too late / Baby I'm a want you / If you don't know me by now / You are the sunshine of my life / Killing me softly / Run to me.
MC: . . . . KNMC 16012

IT'S THE TALK OF THE TOWN.
LP: . . . . BBL 7354

LOVE STORY.
LP: . . . . CBS 64294

MEMORIES ARE MADE OF THIS.
LP: . . . . BBL 7439

NASHVILLE CONNECTION (Conniff, Ray & Singers).
Tracks: / I love you so much it hurts / Oh, lonesome me / Badly broken heart / Too far gone / We had it all / Most beautiful girl / Very special love song / Touch my heart / Smoke gets in your eyes / As time goes by.
LP: . . . . CBS 85867

PERFECT 10 CLASSICS (Conniff, Ray & His Orchestra).
Tracks: / Melody from Mozart / Mini minuet in G / Improvisation on Carmen / Lullaby for Tamara / Improvisation on Pagliacci / Bit of Beethoven / Theme for Elise / Boogie woogie humoresque / Moonlight sonata / Mozart in Latin.
LP: . . . . CBS 84533

RAY CONNIFF SONGBOOK, THE.
2LP: 88596
MC: 40 88596

S'AWFUL NICE.
LP: . . . . BBL 7281

SMOKE GETS IN YOUR EYES (Conniff, Ray & Singers).
Tracks: / I only have eyes for you / Little green apples / Scarborough fair / Canticle / People / Can't take my eyes off you / Moon river / You'll never walk alone / Smoke gets in your eyes / It was a very good year / I love how you love me / Love is a many splendoured thing / Goodnight sweetheart.
LP: . . . . CBS 32492
MC: 40 32492

SOMEWHERE MY LOVE.
LP: . . . . SBPG 62740

S'WONDERFUL, S'MARVELLOUS.
LP: . . . . DPG 66001

WE WISH YOU A MERRY CHRISTMAS (Conniff, Ray & Singers).
Tracks: / Jolly old St. Nicholas / Little drummer boy / Holy night / We three kings of Orient are / Deck the halls with boughs of holly / Ring Christmas bells / Let it snow, let it snow, let it snow / Count your blessings (instead of sheep) / We wish you a merry christmas / Twelve days of Christmas, The / First noel, The / Hark the herald angels sing / O come all ye faithful.
LP: 4605791
MC: 4605794
LP: . . . . BPG 62092

Connolly, Billy

ATLANTIC BRIDGE.
LP: 2383 419

BIG YIN DOUBLE HELPING, A.
Tracks: / Donkey / Crucifixion / Travel away / Telling lies / Nobody's child / Joe Dempsey / Near you / 9 and a half guitars / Oh dear / Good love / Jobbie weecha / Leo McGuire's song / Little blue lady.
2LP: . . . . CR 133
MCSET: . . . . CRT 133

BILLY AND ALBERT.
Tracks: / President of America / Pope, The / Australian talent show / Edinburgh festival / Learning the banjo / Dachshund / Nuclear / Jet lag / Box of chocolates / Hotel room in Perth / Condoms / Variety theatre / Childhood songs / Visiting Scotland / Wee brown dogs / Neck lumps / Casual vomit, The / Driving the porcelain truck / Something has to give.

LP: . . . . DIX 65
MC: . . . . CDIX 65

BILLY CONNOLLY IN CONCERT.
Tracks: / Glasgow accents / Everybody knows that / Harry Campbell and the heavies / Silk pyjamas / Jobbie wheecha, The / Why don't they come back to Dunoon / Short haired police cadet.
LP: . . . . SPR 8530
MC: . . . . SPC 8530

BILLY CONNOLLY LIVE.
Tracks: / Stainless steel wellies / Song for a small man / Donkey, The / Telling lies / Glasgow central / Good love / Little of your time, A / Near you / Winchburgh junction / Oh dear / McGinty.
LP: . . . . TRS 103
MC: . . . . KTRS 103

CHANGE IS AS GOOD AS A REST, A.
Tracks: / Jesus Christ I'm nearly 40 / Bram Stoker sucks / Hey Dolores / Jack's rap / You take my photograph (I break your face) / Day in the country, A / Oz moz / Goodbye Wranglers, hello Calvin Klein / Half bottle, The / I wish I was in Glasgow.
LP: . . . . POLD 5077
MC: . . . . POLDC 5077
LP: . . . . SPELP 89
MC: . . . . SPEMC 89

COP YER WHACK OF THIS.
LP: 2383 310

GET RIGHT INTAE HIM.
LP: 2383 368

HUMBLEBUMS, THE (Connolly, Billy & Gerry Rafferty).
Tracks: / Oh no / Cruisin' / Patrick / Rick rack / My apartment / Silk pyjamas / Harry / My singing bird / Coconut tree / Cripple creek / Joe Dempsey / Open up the door / Song for Simon.
2LP: . . . . CR 134

ON TOUR WITH THE BIG YIN.
Tracks: / Glasgow accents / Nine and a half guitars / Marie's wedding / Jobbie wheecha, The / Short haired police cadet, The / Harry Campbell and the heavies / Life in the day of, A / Stainless steel wellies / Crucifixion, The.
2LP: . . . . CCSLP 218
MC: . . . . CCSMC 218

PICK OF BILLY CONNOLLY, THE.
Tracks: / D.I.V.O.R.C.E. / Tell Laura I love her / Football violence / Welly boot song / When in Rome / Scottish highland national dress / Sexy Sadie and lovely Raquel / C & W super song, The / Marvo and the lovely Doreen / In appreciation.
LP: . . . . SPELP 57
MC: . . . . SPEMC 57
LP: . . . . POLTV 15

PORTRAIT, THE.
Tracks: / Glasgow accents / Nine and a half guitars / Maries wedding / Harry Campbell and the Heavies / Nobody's child / Life in the day of, A / Short haired police cadet / Jobbie wheecha, The / Leo McGuires song / Crucifixion.
LP: . . . . ITV 451
MC: . . . . KITV 451

RAW MEAT FOR THE BALCONY.
LP: 2383 463

RIOTOUS ASSEMBLY.
Tracks: / In the brownies / When in Rome / Teenage parties / Marvo and the lovely Doreen / Old fashioned Tennessee waltz / Welly blues / Doctor / Optician / Glasgow high court / Sexie Sadie and lovely Rachel / In appreciation.
LP: 2383 543
MC: 3170 543

SOLO CONCERT.
Tracks: / Glasgow accents / Marie's wedding (musical arrangement) / Harry Campbell and the Heavies / Nobody's child / Life in the day of, A / Jobbie wheecha, The / Short haired police cadet / Leo McGuire's song / Crucifixion.
LP: . . . . TRA 279

WORDS AND MUSIC.
LP: . . . . TRA SAM 32

WRECK ON TOUR.
LP: . . . . PHH 2
MC: . . . . PHHC 2

Connolly, Martin

FORT OF KINCORA, THE (Connolly, Martin & Maureen Glynn).
MC: . . . . MCMG 1

Connor, Bob

BOB CONNOR'S NEW YANKEE RHYTHM.
LP: . . . . SOS 1050

BOB CONNOR'S NEW YANKEE RHYTHM KINGS (Connor, Bob New Yankee Rhythm Kings).
LP: . . . . SOS 1015

BOB CONNORS NEW YANKEE RHYTHM KINGS & JIMMY MAZZY (Connor, Bob & Jimmy Mazzy).
LP: . . . . SOS 1067

Connor, Chris

AMERICAN JAZZ FESTIVAL IN LATIN AMERICA (see also: Eldridge, Roy & Hawkins, Coleman) (Connor, Chris/Roy Eldridge/Coleman Hawkins).
LP: . . . . WW 0025

DOUBLE DATE WITH HELEN FORREST & CHRIS CONNOR (See under Forrest, Helen for details) (Connor, Chris/Helen Forrest).

I HEAR MUSIC (Connor, Chris & Carmen McRae).
Tracks: / You made me care / Last time for love / Too much in love to care / Misery / Easy to love / If I'm lucky / Old devil moon / Tip toe gently / What is there to say? / Try a little tenderness / Lullaby of Birdland / Spring is here / Stella by starlight / Gone with the wind / Blame it on my youth / It's alright with me / Thrill is gone, The / I concentrate on you.
LP: . . . . AFF 97

LOVE BEING HERE WITH YOU.
LP: . . . . ST 232

OUT OF THIS WORLD.
Tracks: / I hear music / All about Ronnie / Why shouldn't I / Come back to Sorrento / Out of this world / Cottage for sale / How long has this been going on / Goodbye / Lush life / He's coming home / Riding high / All dressed up with a broken heart / Trouble is a man / All this and heaven too / Someone to watch over me / In other words (fly me to the moon) / From this moment on.
LP: . . . . AFF 122

SWEET AND SWINGING.
Tracks: / Things are swinging / Any place I hang my hat is home / Just in time / Here's that rainy day / Out of this world / Sweetest sounds, The / Where flamingos fly / I've got you under my skin / I wish you love / I feel a song coming on / When Sunny gets blue.
LP: . . . . PRO 7028
LP: . . . . AP 208

Connors, Gene

SANCTIFIED.
Tracks: / Marco's tune / Sanctified / Disconnected / Maha's tune / Good rockin' tonight / Goobers / Blueberry hill / Tunk for monk / It was a dream / Biscuits.
LP: . . . . JSP 1031

Connors, Norman

BEST OF NORMAN CONNORS (The Buddah Collection).
Tracks: / Once I've been there / You are my starship / Mother of the future / Captain Connors / Be there in the morning / Kwasi / This is your life / Betcha by golly wow / Valentine love / Stella / Butterfly / Kingston / We both need each other / Romantic journey.
LP: . . . . NEXLP 118
MC: . . . . NEXMC 118

BEST OF NORMAN CONNORS AND FRIENDS, THE.
Tracks: / You are my starship / We both need each other / Betcha by golly wow / Dindi / Romantic journey / Once I've been there / This is your life / Wouldn't you like to see / Valentine love.
LP: . . . . BDLP 4057

INVITATION.
Tracks: / Your love / Handle me gently / Be there in the morning / Invitation / Together / Disco land / I have a dream / Beijo partido / Kingston.
LP: . . . . DISC 06
MC: . . . . ZCDX 06

PASSION.
Tracks: / ! am your melody / You're my one and only love / Heaven in your eyes / Private stock / Loving you / Shabba / That's the way of the world / Welcome to my life / Samba for Maria / Passion.
LP: . . . . EST 2056
MC: . . . . TCEST 2056

ROMANTIC JOURNEY.
Tracks: / You are everything / Once I've been there / Destination moon / Romantic journey / Last tango in Paris / For you are everything / Thembi.
LP: . . . . BDLP 4045

TAKE IT TO THE LIMIT.
Tracks: / Take it to the limit / Melancholy fire / You've been on my mind / I don't need nobody else / Justify / Black cow / You bring me joy / Everywhere inside of me.
LP: . . . . AL 9534

THIS IS YOUR LIFE.
LP: . . . . BDLP 4053

YOU ARE MY STARSHIP.
Tracks: / We both need each other / Betcha by golly wow / Bubbles / Just imagine / You are my starship / So much love / Creater has a master plan (peace), The.
LP: . . . . BDLP 4043

Connors, Shag

COUNTRY CAPERS (Connors, Shag & The Carrot Crunchers).
Tracks: / On the boghorn / I can't read the thought / Bristol city streaker, The / Girl with the big blue eyes, The / Poking the fire / I never told you / Irish washerwoman, The / Gypsy Joe / Rich man's daughter / Nellie from Poole / Missing kissing blues / Skinniest legs, The / I ain't got no money for my wedding / Chicken reel.
LP: . . . . SFA 064

SING COUNTRY STYLE (Connors, Shag & The Carrot Crunchers).
Tracks: / Trip to Heaven / Snowbird / There'll be no teardrops tonight / Oh Susannah jig / Five hundred miles / Everybody's talking to me / Abilene / What made Milwaukee famous / Little green apples / So lonesome I could cry / Ruby / Time is right / Help me make it through the night / Okie from Muskogee.
LP: . . . . SFA 084

Conover, Willis

WILLIS CONOVER'S HOUSE OF SOUND.
Tracks: / I've got you under my skin / One for Kenny / Song is you, The / Pill box, The / Light green / Flamingo / Something to remember you by / Taking a chance on love / Blue room / Sheriff Crane (of Jack Pott County) / Playground / Tiger, The / Moonlight in Vermont / Willis.
LP: . . . . JASM 1016

Conqueroo

FROM THE VULCAN GAS CO.
LP: . . . . TOCK 8

Conrad, Joseph (auth)

END OF THE TETHER, THE (see under End Of The... (bk) (Andrews, Harry (nar)).

HEART OF DARKNESS (see under Heart Of Darkness (bk)) (Scofield, Paul (nar)).

HEART OF DARKNESS (Quayle, Anthony (nar)).
MCSET: 2043

SECRET AGENT, THE (Pigott-Smith, Tim (nar)).
MCSET: 418 192-4

Conseill De... (film)

CONSEILL DE FAMILLE (Original soundtrack) (Various artists).
LP: . . . . A 264
MC: . . . . C 264

Consolidated

CONSOLIDATED.
MLP: . . . . ANT 118

FRIENDLY FASCISM.
LP: . . . . NET 033

Consort Of Musicke

MADRIGALS AND WEDDING SONGS FOR DIANA.
Tracks: / All creatures now are merry minded / Hence stars too dim of light / Songs from a wedding maske / 1607 / Now hath Flora robb'd her bowers / Move now with measur'd sound / Shows and nightly revels / Triumph now with joy / Time that leads the fatal round / Lady Oriana, The / Welcome back night / Hark all ye lovely saints / Come gentle swains / As Vesta was from Latmos hill descending / 1614 / Bring away this sacred tree / Go happy man / While dancing rests / Come ashore merry mates / Woo her and win her / You meaner beauties of the night / Mark how the blushful morn / Long live fair Oriana.
LP: . . . . A 66019

Conspiracy

CONSPIRACY.
LP: 8282161
MC: 8282164

Conspiracy Of Hope

CONSPIRACY OF HOPE (Amnesty International) (Various artists).
Tracks: / Higher love: *Winwood, Steve* / Biko: *Gabriel, Peter* / Passengers: *John, Elton* / I believe: *Tears For Fears* / No one is to blame: *Jones, Howard* / Pipes of peace: *McCartney, Paul* / Strange fruit: *Sting* / Brothers in arms: *Dire Straits* / Pink houses: *Mellencamp, John Cougar* / Ghostdancing: *Simple Minds* / Tonight: *Adams, Bryan.*
LP: . . . . MERH 99
MC: . . . . MERHC 99

Constanduros, Denis

MY GRANDFATHER (Whitrow, Benjamin).
Tracks: / My grandfather / Father dear father.
MCSET: . . . . ZBBC 1095

Constantin

CONSTANTIN.
LP: . . . . JUNGLE 70060

Contardo, Johnny

CHANGEOVER.
Tracks: / Until the night / You'll never get over heartbreak / Quit holdin' back / Long distance love affair / I want to walk you home / Are you happy baby / It's always been you / Let it out / Twelfth of never / Ain't that peculiar.
LP: . . . . BKLP 1001

Contella, Sandy

BETWEEN TWO HEARTS.
Tracks: / Between two hearts / Slowdown / Don't ever say goodbye / Strangers / Life song / You bring out the best in me / You know how to hurt a guy / Together again / Someone to love / Country lullaby / When it's just you and me / Seasons.
LP: . . . . EMC 3299

Contemporaries

HE IS LORD.
Tracks: / He is Lord / He holds the world together / Nothing is impossible / God and his children / Trust in the Lord / Bond of love, The / Alleluiah / Jesus is coming / Jesus, Son of the Father / That the world may know / Day of liberation, The / He died for us / Happy is the man / God loves you / Come, Holy Spirit / Your invitation / Take me, Lord / Thank you Lord / Faith is so simple / Chariots of clouds / Is it any wonder / All of me / Love theme / Reach out and touch (somebody's hand) / In the arms of sweet deliverance / Discovery / I'm so glad / He turned the water into wine / My hope of glory / It's a happy day / Love was when / His grace is sufficient for me / One solitary life / Love is a man / Come along with me / This is the hope / Oh, happy day / Do you want peace / Holy spirit, be my guide.
LP: . . . . PC 788

Contemporary Jazz...

CONTEMPORARY JAZZ MASTERPIECES (See under Jazz...) (Various artists).

Conti, Robert

JAZZ QUINTET.
LP: . . . . DS 834

LATIN LOVE AFFAIR (Conti, Robert Jazz Quintet).
Tracks: / Latin love affair / Midnight in Monte Carlo / Last time, The / Sunrise in Rio / Acapulco strut / Evening in Portugal.
LP: . . . . VDS 100

LAURA.
Tracks: / Softly as I leave you / You are the sunshine of my life / People / My favourite things / Like someone in love / Laura / His eyes, her eyes / Tenderly / When we met again / Hello young lovers / Stella by starlight / Little girl blue / Nuages / My romance / I love you/ Easy to love.
LP: . . . . TR 540
MC: . . . . TRC 540

SOLO GUITAR.
Tracks: / Time for love, A / My funny Valentine / Yesterday / Man and a woman, A / Feelings / I've grown accustomed to your world.
LP: . . . . TR 519

Conti, Tom

ANGEL AND THE SOLDIER BOY, THE (See under Angel and the ...) (Clannad & Tom Conti).

Continental Singers

AND THERE WAS LIGHT.
Tracks: / And there was light / No darkness / Shine like the day / What would it be like / It's a lamp / Light of the world / Light of life, The / I'm just too young / I think so / Let me see what you're hiding / No time left / I'm gonna finish the song this time / They tried to kill the light / He is the light / Light finale.
LP: . . . . WST 9601

Continentals

ALL OVER THE WORLD.
LP: . . . . WST R 9674
MC: . . . . WST C 9674

COME TRUST THE LORD.
Tracks: / Something beautiful / Take my life / Lord, be glorified / I surrender all / To be like Jesus / Make me more like you / From glory to glory / He's all I need / Light of life, The / I must have Jesus / All my life / Fill me Jesus / Sing, oh sing unto the Lord / There's something about that name / It's a lovely name / Jesus is the name / Glory to his name / Take the name of Jesus with you / Lift him up / His

name is wonderful / Holy is the Lord / All hail the power of Jesus name / There is a fountain / Nothing but the blood / I know of a fount / At the cross / Redeemed / There is a fountain (reprise) / When we all get to Heaven / Victory in Jesus / I will praise him / My tribute / Get all excited / He's alive / Following Jesus / God leads us along / Singing I go / Jacob's ladder / Lead me on, lead me up / Keep me true / I have decided to follow Jesus / Our God reigns / Get all excited (reprise).
LP: . . . . WST 9607
MC: . . . . WC 9607

CONTINENTAL COUNTRY.
Tracks: / God loves the country people / Lead me on, lead me up / Touch of the master's hand, The / I'll never let go of your hand / Traveller, The / Smack dab in the middle / Sing me a good ol' gospel song / Grandpa's song / Ol' branch / Can't stop the music.
LP: . . . . WST 9620
MC: . . . . WC 9620

ELIJAH.
LP: . . . . WST R 9687
MC: . . . . WST C 9687

ENCORES.
MC: . . . . WST C 9677

FOR YOU BABY.
LP: . . . . LP 8605

REASON WE SING, THE.
LP: . . . . WST R 9696
MC: . . . . WST C 9696

TOGETHER WE WILL STAND.
LP: . . . . WST 9660
MC: . . . . WC 9660

Continuum

MAD ABOUT TADD.
LP: . . . . PA 8029

Contortions

BUY.
LP: . . . . ILPS 7002

Contours

DO YOU LOVE ME? (NOW THAT I CAN DANCE).
Tracks: / Do you love me / Just a little misunderstanding / Shake Sherrie / Can you do it? / Don't let her be your baby / First I look at the purse / Whole lotta woman / Can you jerk like me? / It's so hard being a loser / You get ugly.
MC: . . . . WK 72731

Contraband

BOTH SIDES OF THE COIN.
MC: . . . . FTC 6019

CONTRABAND.
Tracks: / All the way from Memphis / Kiss by kiss / Intimate outrage / Bad for each other / Loud guitars, fast cars & wild, wild livin' / Good rockin' tonight / If this is love / Stand / Tonight you're mine / Hang onto yourself.
LP: . . . . EMC 3594
MC: . . . . TCEMC 3594

Controlled Bleeding

CURD.
LP: . . . . ST 7516

HEADCRACK.
LP: . . . . SR 12

LES NOUVELLES MISTIQUES DE CHAMBRE.
LP: . . . . SUB 33015-20

MUSIC FROM THE SCOURGING GROUND.
LP: . . . . SUB 33008-11

SONGS FROM THE DRAIN.
LP: . . . . ST 7550

TRUDGE.
LP: . . . . WAX LP 090

Controllers

CONTROLLERS, THE.
Tracks: / Love's in need / I'll miss you always / Hello / If somebody cares / You ain't fooling me / Somebody's gotta win / Reaper, The / Sho nuff a blessin' / Listen to the children.
LP: . . . . MCF 3241
MC: . . . . MCFC 3241
LP: . . . . TRLP 106

FOR THE LOVE OF MY WOMAN.
Tracks: / Sleeping alone / Play time / Knocking at your door / For the love of my woman / Keep in touch / Love is on our side / My secret fantasy.
LP: . . . . MCF 3404
MC: . . . . MCFC 3404

JUST IN TIME.
LP: . . . . C 191100

MY LOVE IS REAL.
Tracks: / People want music / Heaven I only one step away / This train / My love is real / Fill your life with love (love's in) / Just for love / Gettin' over you / Castles in the sky / If tomorrow never comes.
LP: . . . . TRPL 112

NEXT IN LINE.
Tracks: / I can't turn the boogie loose / If tears were pennies / Let me entertain you / We don't / Gunning for your love / Ankle chain / I just don't know / Hurt again by love.
LP: . . . . TRPL 102

STAY.
Tracks: / Distant lover / Stay / So glad / Bad bad jama / My secret fantasy / Breakout the love / Deep in love / Got a thang.
MC: . . . . MCFC 3324
LP: . . . . MCF 3324

Controls

DON'T ADJUST THE CONTROLS.
MC: . . . . SRT 002

GOOD THING, THE.
MC: . . . . SRT 009

I DIDN'T KNOW YOU WERE LEAVING.
MC: . . . . SRT 008

KEEP ME HERE.
MC: . . . . SRT 010

LATE NIGHT LOVE SONGS.
MC: . . . . SRT 003

SEARCHING FOR THE PERFECT PARTNER.
MC: . . . . SRT 006

SOCK IT TO 'EM DAVE.
MC: . . . . SRT 001

Conveniens

CLEAR.
Tracks: / Death by poetry / Route 66 / Night caution / Ball park song / Efiltsitra / Mazman / Da da ack / Electroflux / Cadmium red / Rollin'.
LP: . . . . LP 004

CONVENIENS.
Tracks: / Know it ain't / Rain kite / Morning lobotomy / Afrishanki / Regular grind / Barney Klark / Druhm rum / Procession of bone / Blink.
LP: 973110 (LP001)

VICTIMS OF CONVENIENCE.
Tracks: / Commercial dance song / Pidgeion memory / Onn (Ond) / Piano piece / Salmineo / Industrial mylasia / Geomoshadowdive / Cigarette / Victims of convenience.
LP: 293130 (LP003)

Conversations...(bk)

CONVERSATIONS WITH DOCTOR X (Wild Billy Childish).
LP: . . . . WORDUP 006

Convict

GO AHEAD...MAKE MY DAY.
LP: . . . . RR 9746

Convoy, Billy

ROTHBURY HILLS.
MC: 30 122

Convoy (film)

CONVOY (film soundtrack) (Various artists).
Tracks: / Convoy: *McCall, C.W.* / Lucille: *Rogers, Kenny* / Don't it make my brown eyes blue?: *Gayle, Crystal* / Cowboys don't get lucky all the time: *Watson, Gene* / I cheated on a good woman's love: *Craddock, Billy Crash* / Okie from Muskogee: *Haggard, Merle* / Southern nights: *Campbell, Glen* / Keep on the sunny side: *Watson, Doc* / Blanket on the ground: *Spears, Billie Jo* / Walk right back: *Murray, Anne.*
LP: . . . . ICK 064 85597
LP: . . . . EST 24590

Convoy Truk

CONVOY TRUK 1.
MC: . . . . VCA 619

Conway Brothers

LADY IN RED.
Tracks: / Por-sha / Why you wanna do me like you do / What love will do / B.O.C / I can't fight it / Lady in red / If you love me / Oio jamova me / Medley fire / Skin tight / O-H-I-O.
LP: . . . . ICH 1006
MC: . . . . ZCICH 1006

TURN IT UP.
Tracks: / Raise the roof / Set it out / Over and over / Get live / Gonna refuse your love / Turn it up / Call me / Together.
MC: . . . . CXID 9
LP: . . . . XID 9

Conway, Francie

WAKE UP.
Tracks: / Wake up (introduction) / New York skyline / It's a bedsit / Sweet Carronlaoe / Not even the president / Wake up / Striking it rich / Your drug is Hollywood / Somebody stole my girl / Walking on seashells / Spanish nights / She haunts me / Somewhere in heaven / To the edge of time / One night in Amsterdam.
MC: . . . . RTMMC 22
LP: . . . . RTMLP 22

Conway, Lee

LOVE STILL MAKES THE WORLD GO ROUND.
LP: . . . . GES 5005

Conway, Mario

CONWAY.
Tracks: / Elergy and dance / Dance of the comedians / Pastorale / Trieste overture / Duo concertante / Prelude english suite / Vivo / Don rhapsody.
LP: . . . . AFA 833

Conway, Russ

24 PIANO GREATS: RUSS CONWAY.
LP: . . . . RTL 2022

ALWAYS YOU AND ME.
Tracks: / Concerto for memories theme, The / It could happen to you / Song is you, The / As time goes by / I'm old fashioned / More / My concerto for you / Way to the stars, The / Dream of Olwen / Dusk / Lonely melody / Warsaw concerto / Always / Time after time / More I see you, The / But beautiful / Among my souvenirs / Long ago (and far away) / High and mighty / Autumn concerto / Forgotten dreams / Cornish rhapsody / Jeannie / Till / La mer / Always you and me.
2LP: . . . . MFP 1023
MCSET: . . . . TCMFP 1023

EMI YEARS, THE : BEST OF RUSS CONWAY.
Tracks: / Side saddle / Forgotten dreams / China tea / Mack the knife / Snow coach / Warsaw concerto / Toy balloons / Always / Roulette / Royal event / Pepe / Lesson one / Always you and me / La mer / Passing breeze.
LP: . . . . EMS 1337
MC: . . . . TCEMS 1337

EP COLLECTION, THE.
LP: . . . . SEE 310
MC: . . . . SEEK 310

FAMILY FAVOURITES.
LP: 33SX 1169

GREATEST HITS: RUSS CONWAY.
Tracks: / Side saddle / Mack the knife / Westminster waltz / Pixillated penguin / Snow coach / Sam's song / Always / Wedding of the painted doll, The / World outside, The / China tea / Lesson one / When you're smiling / I'm looking over a four leaf clover / When you wore a tulip (and I wore a red, red rose) / Row, row, row / For me and my gal / Shine on, harvest moon / By the light of the silvery moon / Side by side / Roulette / Toy balloons / Pepe / Royal event / Lucky five / Passing breeze / Got a match? / Always you and me / Pablo / Fings ain't wot they used t'be / Polka dots / Where do little birds go? / Forgotten dreams / Music, music, music / If you were the only girl in the world / I'm nobody's sweetheart now / Yes sir, that's my baby / Some of these days / Honeysuckle and the bee, The / Hello, hello, who's your lady friend? / In a shanty in old Shantytown.
MC: . . . . HR 8108
MC: . . . . HR 4181084

LONG TIME AGO, A.
LP: . . . . RCLP 1
MC: . . . . RCLC 1

MAGIC PIANO OF RUSS CONWAY.
Tracks: / Walk in the Black Forest, A / Ain't misbehavin' / Cast your fate to the wind.
MCSET: . . . . DTO 10207

MY CONCERTO FOR YOU.
LP: 33SX 1214

ONE AND ONLY, THE.
Tracks: / Side saddle / China tea / Snow coach / Roulette / Pepe / Trampolina / Mack the knife / Birthday cakewalk, The / Pixillated penguin.
LP: . . . . MFP 50426

PACK UP YOUR TROUBLES.
LP: 33SX 1120

PARTY TIME.
LP: 33SX 1279

PARTY TIME.
Tracks: / Darktown strutters ball / Oh Johnny, oh Johnny, oh / You were meant for me / Toot toot tootsie / When the red red robin comes bob bob bobbin' / Give my regards to Broadway / Miss Annabelle Lee / Rock a bye your baby with a dixie melody / Put your arms around me honey / Rolling round the world / Painting the clouds with sunshine / Down yonder / Gal in calico, A / I'm sitting on top of the world / Carolina in the morning / Swanee.
LP: . . . . MOIR 136
MC: . . . . CMOIR 136

RUSS CONWAY AND HIS HAPPY PIANO.
LP: . . . . SAV 130

SONGS FROM STAGE AND SCREEN.
Tracks: / Cabaret / Man and a woman, A / Love story / I want to be happy / Born free / Everything's coming up roses / Days of wine and roses / Hello Dolly / Good old bad old days / I will wait for you / Charly girl / Charade / Raindrops keep falling on my head / Moon river / Put on a happy face / Thoroughly modern Millie.
LP: . . . . FBLP 8097
MC: . . . . ZCFBL 8097

SONGS TO SING IN YOUR BATH.
LP: 33SX 1149

TIME TO CELEBRATE.
LP: 33SX 1197

TWO SIDES OF RUSS CONWAY, THE.
Tracks: / Lesson one / Side saddle / Underneath the arches / Ma, he's making eyes at me / Me and my girl / Tiptoe through the tulips / Third man, Theme from / Westminster waltz / Roulette / China tea / April showers / As time goes by / La mer / Strangers in the night / Dream of Olwen / World outside, The / Warsaw concerto.
LP: . . . . PLAT 13
MC: . . . . PLAC 13

VERY BEST OF RUSS CONWAY, THE.
Tracks: / Side saddle / Roulette / Snow coach / Toy balloons / Pepe / Roll the carpet up / Pixillated penguin / Royal event / Lucky five / Matador from Trinidad / China tea / Time to celebrate / Lesson one / Soho Fair / Trampolina / Westminster waltz / Wee boy of Brussels, The / Passing breeze / Birthday cakewalk, The / Forgotten dreams.
LP: . . . . EMC 3126

Conway, Steve

EMI YEARS, THE: STEVE CONWAY (Best of).
Tracks: / Gypsy, The / Moment I saw you / Promises / Stars will remember, The / Isn't it romantic? / I wish I didn't love you so / I'll make up for everything / How little we know / Brother can you spare a dime / Daddy's little girl / My foolish heart / My thanks to you / Autumn leaves / Good luck, good health, God bless you / Bless this house / At the end of the day.
LP: . . . . EMS 1353
MC: . . . . TCEMS 1353

MEMORIES OF STEVEN CONWAY.
Tracks: / Good luck, good health, God bless you / My foolish heart / Mona Lisa / Our anniversary day / Ashes of roses / White wedding / Mary Rose / At the end of the day / Autumn leaves / Look for the silver lining / Daddy's little girl / Love like ours, A / Dream is a wish your heart makes, A / Too young / Bless this house / My thanks to you.
LP: . . . . MWM 1027
MC: . . . . MWMC 1027

UNFORGETTABLE, THE.
LP: . . . . ENC 143

Conwell, Tommy

RUMBLE (Conwell, Tommy & The Young Rumblers).
Tracks: / I'm not your man / Half a heart / If we never meet again / Love's on fire / Workout / I wanna make you happy / Everything they say is true / Gonna breakdown / Tell me what you want me to be / Walking on the water.
LP: 4624311
MC: 4624314

Cooder, Ry

BLUE CITY (Film soundtrack).
Tracks: / Blue city down / Elevation 13 foot / True believers/Marianne / Nice bike / Greenhouse / Billy and Annie / Pops and timer /Tell me something slick / Blue city / Don't take your guns to town / Leader of men, A / Not even key west.
LP: 925386 1
MC: 925386 4

BOOMER'S STORY.
Tracks: / Boomer's story / Cherry ball blues / Crow black chicken / Ax sweet Mama / Maria Elena / Dark end of the street / Rally 'round the flag / Coming in on a wing and a prayer / President Kennedy / Good morning Mr. Railroad man.
LP: . . . . K 44224

BOP TILL YOU DROP.
Tracks: / Little sister / Go home girl / Very thing that makes you rich makes me poor / I think it's going to work out fine / Down in Hollywood / Look at granny run run / Trouble / Don't mess up a good thing / I can't win.
LP: . . . . K 56691
MC: K4 56691

BORDERLINE.
Tracks: / 634-5789 / Speedo is back / Why don't you try me / Down in the boon-docks / Johnny Porter / Way we make a broken heart, The / Crazy 'bout an automobile / Girls from Texas, The / Borderline / Never make a move too soon.
LP: . . . . **K 56864**
MC: **K4 56864**

CHICKEN SKIN MUSIC.
Tracks: / Bourgeois blues / I got mine / Always lift him up / He'll have to go / Smack dab in the middle / Stand by me / Yellow roses / Chloe / Goodnight Irene.
LP: . . . . **K 54083**

CROSSROADS (1986 film soundtrack).
Tracks: / See you in hell, blind boy / Nitty gritty Mississippi / He made a woman out of me / Feeling bad blues / Somebody's calling my name / Willie Brown blues / Walkin' away blues / Crossroads / Down in Mississippi / Cotton needs pickin' / Viola lee blues.
LP: **925399 1**
MC: **925399 4**

GET RHYTHM.
Tracks: / Get rhythm / Low commotion / Going back to Okinawa / 13 question method / Women will rule the world / All shook up / I can tell by the way you smell / Across the borderline / Let's have a ball.
LP: . . . . **WX 121**
MC: . . . . **WX 121 C**

INTO THE PURPLE VALLEY.
Tracks: / How can you keep on moving / Billy the kid / Money honey / F.D.R. in Trinidad / Teardrops will fall / Denomination blues / On a Monday / Hey porter / Great dreams of heaven / Taxes on the farmer feeds us all / Vigilante man.
LP: . . . . **K 44142**
MC: **444142**

JAZZ.
Tracks: / Big bad Bill is sweet William now / Face to face that I shall meet him / Pearls, The / Tia Juana / Dream, The / Happy meeting in glory / In a mist / Flashes / Davenport blues / Shine / Nobody / We shall be happy.
LP: . . . . **K 56488**

JOHNNY HANDSOME (Film soundtrack).
LP: . . . . **WX 307**
MC: . . . . **WX 307C**
LP: **925996 1**
MC: **925996 4**

LONG RIDERS, THE (Film soundtrack).
Tracks: / Long riders, The / I'm a good old rebel / Seneca square dance / Archie's funeral (hold to God's unchanging hand) / I always knew that you were the one / Rally round the flag / Wildwood boys / Better things to think about / My grandfather / Cole Younger / Escape from Northfield / Leaving Missouri / Jesse James.
LP: . . . . **K 56826**
MC: **K4 56826**

MUSIC FROM THE MOTION PICTURE ALAMO BAY (see Alamo Bay).

PARADISE AND LUNCH.
Tracks: / Tamp 'em up solid / Tattler / Married man's a fool / Jesus on the mainline / It's all over now / Fool about a cigarette / Feeling good / If walls could talk / Mexican divorce / Ditty wa ditty.
LP: . . . . **K 44260**
MC: **K4 44260**

PARIS, TEXAS (Film soundtrack) (See under Paris, Texas).

PECOS BILL (See under Pecos Bill) (Williams, Robin & Ry Cooder).

RY COODER.
Tracks: / Alimony / France chance / One meat ball / Do-re-mi / Old Kentucky home / How can a poor man stand such times / And live / Available space / Pig meat / Police dog blues / Goin' to Brownsville / Dark is the night.
LP: . . . . **K 44093**
MC: **K4 44093**

RY COODER LIVE.
Tracks: / Crazy 'bout an automobile (live) / If walls could talk (live) / Jesus on the mainline (live).
LP: **923810 1**

SHOW TIME.
Tracks: / School is out / Alimony / Jesus on the mainline / Dark end of the street / Viva sequin / Do-re-mi / Volver, volver / How can a poor man stand such times and live / Smack dab in the middle.
LP: . . . . **K 56386**

SLIDE AREA,THE.
Tracks: / UFO has landed in the ghetto / I need a woman / Gypsy woman / Blue suede shoes / Mama, don't treat your daughter mean / I'm drinking again / Which came first / That's the way love turned out for me.
LP: . . . . **K 56976**
MC: **K4 56976**

WHY DON'T YOU TRY ME TONIGHT.
Tracks: / How can a poor man stand such times and live / Available space / Money honey / Tattler / He'll have to go / Smack dab in the middle / Dark end of the street / Down in Hollywood / Little sister / I think it's gonna work out fine / Crazy 'bout an automobile / 634-5789 / Why don't you try me.
LP: . . . . **WX 37**
MC: . . . . **WX 37 C**

Cook, Barbara

AS OF TODAY.
LP: . . . . **APC 34493**
MC: . . . . **BT 34493**

BARBARA COOK SINGS THE WALT DISNEY SONG BOOK.
Tracks: / When you wish upon a star / Give a little whistle / Pink elephants on parade / When I see an elephant fly / With a smile and a song / Lavender blue / Zip-a-dee-doo-dah / Dream is a wish your heart makes, A / Second star to the right / Baby mine / Someone's waiting for you / Sooner or later / I'm late / Some day my prince will come.
LP: . . . . **SHM 3248**
MC: . . . . **HSC 3248**

IT'S BETTER WITH A BAND.
Tracks: / Come in from the rain / Sing a song with me / I never knew that men cried / It's better with a band / Remember / I love a piano / Chant la vie / Marianne / Them there eyes / Bernstein medley / I never meant to hurt you / Inside / Lullaby in ragtime / Ingenue, The / If love were all / Another Mr. Right left / Sweet Georgia Brown.
LP: . . . . **DMMG 104**
MC: . . . . **CMG 104**

LIVE AT CARNEGIE HALL.
LP: . . . . **M 33438**

Cook, Doc

1924: DOC COOK (see Armstrong, Louis) (Cook, Doc's Dreamland Orchestra/Louis Armstrong/Freddie Kepp).

BROWN SUGAR (Cook, Doc & His Dreamland Orchestra).
Tracks: / Here comes the old Tamale man / Brown sugar / High fever / Sidewalk blues / Cutie blues / Chinaman blues / Alligator crawl / Brainstorm / Willie the weeper / Slue foot / I got worries / Hum and strum.
LP: . . . . **SM 3102**

DOC COOK DREAMLAND ORCHESTRA (Cook, Doc & His Dreamland Orchestra).
LP: . . . . **VLP 27**

Cook, Drummond

TAE GA YER LOUP (Cook,Drummond Scottish Country Dance Band).
LP: . . . . **JW 001**
MC: . . . . **CJW 001**

Cook Island

COOK ISLAND SPECTACULAR (Various artists).
LP: . . . . **VP 361**

Cook, Junior

GOOD COOKIN'.
Tracks: / I'm getting sentimental over you / Play together again / Waltz for Junior / I waited for you / Mood.
LP: . . . . **MR 5159**

ICHI-BAN (See under Hayes, Louis) (Cook/Mathews/James/Shaw/Guilherme).

PRESSURE COOKER.
LP: . . . . **AFF 53**

SOMETHIN'S COOKIN'.
LP: . . . . **MR 5218**

STABLEMATES (Cook, Junior/George Coleman).
Tracks: / Sweet lotus lips / Crucifier, The / Not quite that / Yardbird suite / Moment to moment / Green Dolphin street / Frank's tune / Big George / Jogging / Body and soul / Revival.
LP: . . . . **AFF 766**

Cook, Peter

AD NAUSEAM (See under Derek & Clive).

CLEAN TAPES (Cook, Peter & Dudley Moore).
Tracks: / Newsreel overture, The / Music teacher, The / Tramponuns / Lovely lady of the roses / Dud and Pete on sex / Isn't she a sweetie / Real stuff, The / Aversion therapy / Father and son / Lengths / Goodbye-ee.
LP: . . . . **HIFLY 26**
MC: . . . . **ZCFLY 26**
MC: . . . . **RDC 1206**

DEREK & CLIVE COME AGAIN (Cook, Peter & Dudley Moore).
LP: . . . . **V 2094**
MC: . . . . **TCV 2094**

DEREK & CLIVE LIVE (Cook, Peter & Dudley Moore).
LP: . . . . **ILPS 9434**
MC: . . . . **ICT 9434**
MC: . . . . **ZCI 9434**
MC: . . . . **ICM 2020**
MC: **842 740 4**

HERE COMES THE JUDGE (Live in concert).
LP: . . . . **VR 4**

ONCE MORE WITH COOK (Cook, Peter & Dudley Moore).
LP: . . . . **LK 4785**

WORLD OF PETE AND DUD (Cook, Peter & Dudley Moore).
Tracks: / Art gallery / Bit of a chat including all things bright and / Lengths / Psychiatrist, The / Dud dreams / Ravens, The / Father and son / Six of the best.
LP: . . . . **SPA 311**

Cook, The Thief...

COOK, THE THIEF, HIS WIFE AND HER LOVER, THE (1989 film soundtrack) (Various artists).
Tracks: / Memorial: *Nyman, Michael Band* / Miserre paraphase: *Nyman, Michael Band* / Miserere: *London Voices/ Coupling: Nyman, Michael Band* / Book depository: *Nyman, Michael Band.*
MC: . . . . **TCVE 53**
LP: . . . . **VE 53**

Cooke, Alistair (auth)

LETTERS FROM AMERICA.
MC: . . . . **TC LFP 7055**
MCSET: . . . . **ZBBC 1039**

Cooke, Derek

INSIDE INFORMATION.
Tracks: / Love was when / Down from his glory / If that isn't love / Victory in Jesus / Shepherd of love / Saviour is waiting, The / Give him your heart / Stranger of Galilee / When I survey / Amazing grace / Battle hymn of the republic / Take my life.
LP: . . . . **PC 37**

Cooke, Sam

3 GREAT GUYS (Paul Anka/Sam Cooke/Neil Sedaka).
Tracks: / Laugh laugh laugh / I remember / I ain't gonna cheat on you no more / Talkin' trash / Without your love / Another day, another heartache / I can't say a word / No, no / I'm gonna forget about you / Tenderness / This endless night / Too late.
LP: . . . . **NL 89456**
MC: . . . . **NK 89456**

BEST OF SAM COOKE.
Tracks: / You send me / Only sixteen / Everybody loves to cha cha / For sentimental reasons / Wonderful world / Summertime / Chain gang / Cupid / Twistin' the night away / Sad mood / Having a party / Bring it on home to me.
LP: . . . . **PMP 1010**
MC: . . . . **PMPK 1010**

BEST OF SAM COOKE (RCA).
LP: **26. 21355**

FABULOUS SAM COOKE, THE.
Tracks: / Having a party / Sad mood / Twistin' the night away / Try a little tenderness / Good times / For sentimental reasons / Another Saturday night / Summertime / Shake / Only sixteen / Everybody loves to cha cha / Send me some lovin' / Wonderful world / Nothing can change this love / Ain't that good news? / Little red rooster / Cupid / Chain gang / Frankie and Johnny / Bring it on home to me / Tennessee waltz / Win your love for me / You send me.
2LP: . . . . **CR 050**
MCSET: . . . . **CRT 050**

FEEL IT.
Tracks: / Feel it / Chain gang / Cupid / It's all right / I love you for sentimental reasons / Twistin' the night away / Somebody have mercy / Bring it on home to me / Nothing can change this love / Having a party.
LP: . . . . **PL 85181**
MC: . . . . **PK 85181**

GOLDEN AGE OF SAM COOKE.
Tracks: / You send me / Win your love / Love you most of all / Only sixteen / Wonderful world / Chain gang / Sad mood / Cupid / Frankie and Johnny / Twistin' the night away / Having a party / Bring it on home to me / Nothing can change this love / Another Saturday night / Little red rooster / Ain't that good news / Good times / Tennessee waltz / Shake / Change is gonna come, A.
LP: . . . . **RS 1054**
LP: . . . . **PL 89021**

GRAFFITI COLLECTION.
MC: . . . . **GRMC 04**

HEAVEN IS MY HOME (Cooke, Sam & The Soul Stirrers).
Tracks: / That's heaven to me / Deep river / I thank God / Heaven is my home / God is standing by / Pass me not / Steal away / Must Jesus bear his cross alone / Lead me Jesus / Trouble in mind / Sometimes / Somebody.
LP: **C5-523**

HIS GREATEST HITS.
LP: **CL.42065**

IN THE BEGINNING (Cooke, Sam & The Soul Stirrers).
Tracks: / He's my friend 'til the end / I'm gonna build on that shore / Jesus, wash away my troubles / Must Jesus bear the cross alone / Jesus, I'll never forget / Nearer to thee / Any day now / Touch the hem of his garment / I don't want to cry / Lovable / Forever (alternative take) (Available on CD only) / I'll come running back to you / Happy in love / I need you now / That's all I need to know / Happy in love / One more river (Available on CD only) / He's so wonderful (Available on CD only) / Jesus gave me water (Available on CD only) / That's all I need to know (alternative take) (Available on CD only) / I don't want to cry (alternative take) (Available on CD only) / Forever / Lovable (alternative take) (Available on CD only).
LP: . . . . **CHD 280**

MAN AND HIS MUSIC, THE.
Tracks: / Meet me at Mary's place / Good times / Shake / Sad mood / Bring it on home to me / That's where it's at / That's heaven to me / Touch the hem of his garment / You send me / I'll come running back to you / Win your love for me / Wonderful world / Cupid / Just for you / Chain gang / Only sixteen / When a boy falls in love / Rome wasn't built in a day / Everybody loves to cha cha / Nothing can change this love / Love will find a way / Another Saturday night / Having a party / Twistin' the night away / Somebody have mercy / Ain't that good news / Soothe me / Change is gonna come, A.
2LP: . . . . **PL 87127**
MCSET: . . . . **PK 87127**

MR. SOUL.
Tracks: / I wish you love / Willow weep for me / Smoke rings / All the way / Send me some lovin' / Cry me a river / Driftin' blues / I love you for sentimental reasons / Nothing can change this love / Little girl / These foolish things.
LP: . . . . **INTS 5024**
MC: . . . . **INTK 5024**

SAM COOKE.
Tracks: / Only sixteen / Let's go steady again / When I fall in love / Crazy in love with you / Desire me / Little things you do, The / You send me / Steal away / Tammy / Darling, I need you now / You were made for me / What a wonderful world.
LP: . . . . **DVLP 2095**
MC: . . . . **DVMC 2095**
LP: . . . . **COUNT 2**
MC: . . . . **ZC CNT 2**
MC: . . . . **ZCGAS 721**

SAM COOKE LIVE AT HARLEM SQUARE 1963.
Tracks: / Feel it / Chain gang / Cupid / It's alright / For sentimental reasons / Twistin' the night away / Somebody have mercy / Bring it home to me / Nothing can change this love / Having a party.
MC: . . . . **NK 90454**

SOLITUDE.
Tracks: / All of my life / You send me / Danny boy / Ol' man river / Ain't misbehavin' / When I fall in love / God bless the child / That lucky old sun / Only sixteen / Solitude / Summertime / Tammy / Almost in your arms.
2LP: . . . . **CR 117**
MCSET: . . . . **CRT 117**

SWING OUT BROTHER.
Tracks: / Solitude / Talk of the town / Crazy in love with you / I've got a right to sing the blues / Good morning heartache / Ain't nobody's business / Lover come back to me / That lucky old sun / They can't take that away from me / Moonlight in Vermont / When I fall in love.
LP: . . . . **TOP 171**
MC: . . . . **KTOP 171**

THIS IS SAM COOKE.
Tracks: / Frankie and Johnny / You send me / Sad mood / Summertime / Chain gang / Feel it / For sentimental reasons / Another Saturday night / Wonderful world / Having a party / Baby, baby, baby / Only sixteen / Love will find a way / Bring it on home to me / Twistin' the night away / Little red rooster / Cupid /

Sugar dumpling / Send me some lovin' / Everybody loves to cha cha.
2LP: . . . . DPS 2007

TWISTIN' THE NIGHT AWAY.
Tracks: / You send me / Only sixteen / Everybody loves to cha cha / For sentimental reasons / Wonderful world / Summertime (end s1) / Chain gang / Cupid / Twistin' the night away / Sad mood / Having a party / Bring it on home to me.
LP: . . . . CBR 1012
MC: . . . . KCBR 1012

WHEN I FALL IN LOVE.
Tracks: / There, I've said it again / Let's go steady again / When I fall in love / Little things you do, The / You send me / Ol' man river / Moonlight in Vermont / Around the world / Everybody loves to cha cha / Along the Navajo trail / Someday / I cover the waterfront / Mary Mary-Lou / Love most of all / Only sixteen / Win your love for me.
LP: . . . . ARA 1007
MC: . . . . ARAC 1007
LP: . . . . NUTM 23
MC: . . . . TC NUTM 23

WONDERFUL WORLD (2).
Tracks: / There, I've said it again / Let's go steady again / When I fall in love / Little things you do, The / You send me / Ol' man river / Moonlight in Vermont / Around the world / Danny boy / Ain't misbehavin' / Summertime / Wonderful world / Everybody loves to cha cha / Along the Navajo trail / Someday you'll want me to want you / I cover the waterfront / Mary, Mary Lou / Love you most of all / Only sixteen / Win your love for me.
LP: . . . . FA 3195
MC: . . . . TCFA 3195
LP: . . . . PFP 1008
MC: . . . . PFC 1008

WORLD OF SAM COOKE, THE.
Tracks: / Only sixteen / Everybody loves to cha cha / There, I've said it again / Steal away / Lover come back to me / Moonlight in Vermont / Comes love / You send me / Win your love for me / I love you most of all / Good morning heartache / Talk of the town / Little things you do, The / Stealing kisses.
MC: . . . . TCINS 5001
LP: . . . . INS 5001

YOU SEND ME.
Tracks: / You send me / Stealing kisses / There, I've said it again / Ol' man river / All of my life / Steal away / Little things you do, The / Everybody loves to cha cha / Only sixteen / Win your love for me / I love you most of all / God bless the child / When I fall in love / Good morning heartache / Almost in your arms / Bells of St. Mary's / Danny boy / I cover the waterfront / Solitude / That lucky old sun / Ain't misbehavin' / When I fall in love / Stealing kisses / Only sixteen.
LP: . . . . TOP 125
MC: . . . . KTOP 125

YOU SEND ME (2).
LP: . . . . RMB 5615

Cookie Crew

BORN THIS WAY.
Tracks: / Yo what's up / From the South / Come on and get some / Pick up on this / Feeling proud / Bad girls (rock the spot) / Got to keep on / Born this way / Black is the word / Places and spaces for your mind / Rhymes and careers / Dazzle's theme.
LP: 828 134 1
MC: 828 134 4

Cookie & The Cupcakes

COOKIE AND THE CUPCAKES - VOL. 2.
LP: . . . . JIN 9018

FEATURING SHELTON DUNAWAY AND LITTLE ALFRED.
Tracks: / I cried / Got you on my mind / All my loving baby / Close up the back door / Franko Chinese cha-cha / Trouble in my life / Just one kiss / Mary Lou doing the Popeye / Mathilda / Walking down the aisle / Even though / Feel so good / Until then / Breaking up is hard to do / I heard that story before / I'm twisted.
LP: . . . . CH 142

LEGENDARY COOKIE & THE CUPCAKES.
LP: . . . . GRLP 7757

THREE GREAT ROCKERS.
LP: . . . . JIN 9003
MC: . . . . JIN 9003 TC

Cookman, Brian

GRINNIN'.
LP: . . . . DAM 010
LP: . . . . MUMR 001

JACK'S RETURN HOME.
LP: . . . . MUMRV 002
MC: . . . . MUMR 002

Cookson, Catherine

CULTURED HANDMAIDEN, THE (Jameson, Susan (nar)).
MC: . . . . CAB 336

DEVIL AND MARY ANN (Jameson, Susan (nar)).
MC: . . . . CAB 013

Cool JC

WE JUST CAME TO PRAISE (Cool JC International Mass Choir).
Tracks: / Praise thy name / We come to worship / Saviour like a shepherd / We just came to praise / Last days.
LP: . . . . MIR 5027
MC: . . . . MIR 5027MC

Cool Notes

DOWN TO EARTH.
LP: . . . . MMM 1001

HAVE A GOOD FOREVER.
Tracks: / Look what you've done to me / My love is hot / Why not / Come on back to me / Have a good forever / Spend the night / You're never too young / I don't wanna stop / All I wanna do / I love you / In your car.
LP: . . . . ADLP 1
MC: . . . . ADCAS 1

Cool, Phil

NOT JUST A PRETTY FACE.
Tracks: / Trouble with being an impressionist, The / Practising in the bathroom / Academy awards, The / Whicker's world / Hellraisers / Caviar to pigs / Billy Connolly / Mike Harding / Depression / Adverts / Wogan - the space creature / Day after / Reagan / Australians / Pope, The / Rolf Harris.
LP: . . . . OVED 228
MC: . . . . OVEDC 228

Cool Runners

CHECKING OUT (see under Kool, Nat King) (Cool Runners, The/Nat King Kool).

Cool-Down Zone

NEW DIRECTION, THE.
Tracks: / Heaven knows / Waiting for love / New direction / Till the weekend / When you call / What I feel like / So amazing / Prisoner of love / Never counted on loving you / Don't be shy.
LP: . . . . DIX 84
MC: . . . . CDIX 84

Cooley High (film)

COOLEY HIGH (Various artists).
LP: . . . . STML 12045

Cooley, Pat

DOUBLE TALK.
Tracks: / Double talk / I never loved a man (the way I love you) / I ain't goin' where you go / When something is wrong with my baby / Take it easy (don't do something) / Borrow me / Main thing / I'm gonna trade you in / I let you get over.
LP: . . . . ICH 1010
MC: . . . . ZCICH 1010

Cooley, Spade

ROMPIN', STOMPIN', SINGIN', SWINGIN' (Cooley, Spade & Tex Williams).
Tracks: / Bronco buster's ball / Shame on you / Sinful / Shrimp boats / Miracle waltz / What did ya mean (when you said I love you) / Don't call me, I'll call you / Sweet little boogalie / Only polickin' / All aboard for Oklahoma / Big chief boogie / Hillbilly fever / You can't get Texas out of me / Wagon wheels / Last round-up, The / Like someone in love / Isn't it romantic / Something wonderful / I'm comin' Virginia / Cheek to cheek.
LP: . . . . BFX 15110

SWINGING THE DEVIL'S DREAM.
Tracks: / Chew tobacco rag / Horse hair boogie / Down yonder / Hitsitty hotsitty / Rhumba boogie, The / Crazy cause I love you / Carmen's boogie / Nashville special / Y'hear / You clobbered me / Break up down / Swinging the devil's dream / Anita / One sweet letter from you / Cowboy waltz / Down by the pecos / Y'ready.
LP: . . . . CR 30239

Coolidge, Rita

ANYTIME...ANYWHERE.
Tracks: / Your love keeps lifting me higher and higher / Way you do the things you do, The / We're all alone / I feel the burden (being lifted off my shoulders) / I don't want to talk about it / Words / Good times / Who's to bless and who's to blame / Southern lady / Hungry years.
LP: . . . . AMLH 64616
MC: . . . . CAM 64616

BREAKAWAY (Coolidge, Rita & Kris Kristofferson).
MC: 40 32775
LP: . . . . CBS 32775

FULL MOON (Coolidge, Rita & Kris Kristofferson).
Tracks: / Hard to be friends / It's all over / I never had it so good / From the bottle to the good / Take time to love / Tennessee blues / Part of your life / I'm down (but I keep falling) / I heard the bluebirds sing / After the fact / Loving arms / Song I'd like to sing.
LP: . . . . AMLH 64403

HEARTBREAK RADIO.
Tracks: / Walk on in / One more heartache / Closer you get / Wishin' and hopin' / Heartbreak radio / Man and woman / I did my part / Hold on / Basic lady / Stranger to me now / Take it home.
LP: . . . . AMLK 63727

INSIDE THE FIRE.
Tracks: / Hit me on the loveside / Do you believe in love / I can't afford that feeling anymore / Games / Wishing star / I'm comin' home / Love from Tokyo / Something said love / Survivor / Love is muddy water.
LP: . . . . AMA 5003

LADY'S NOT FOR SALE, THE.
Tracks: / Donut man / Inside of me / Fever / Bird on the wire / My crew / I'll be your baby tonight / Woman left lonely, A / Shiskey whiskey / Everybody loves a winner / Lady's not for sale, The.
LP: . . . . SPR 8568
MC: . . . . SPC 8568
LP: . . . . MFP 50500

LOVE ME AGAIN.
LP: . . . . AMLH 64699

NATURAL ACT (see Kristofferson, Kris) (Coolidge, Rita & Kris Kristofferson).

NEVER LET YOU GO.
Tracks: / You do it / Fools in love / Do you really want to hurt me / You ought to be with me / We've got tonite / I'll never let you go / Stop wasting your time / Tempted / Only you / All time high.
LP: . . . . AMLX 64914

SATISFIED.
Tracks: / One fine day / Fool in me / Trust it all to somebody / Let's go dancing / Pain of love / I'd rather leave while I'm in love / Sweet emotion / Crime of passion / Can she keep you satisfied.
LP: . . . . AMLH 64781

VERY BEST OF RITA COOLIDGE, THE (Greatest hits).
Tracks: / We're all alone / I'd rather leave while I'm in love / Higher and higher / One fine day / Only you know and I know / Bye, bye love / Fever / Am I blue? / Slow dancer / Way you do the things you do, The / Let's go dancing / Keep the candle burning / I don't want to talk about it / Fool that I am / Mean to me.
LP: . . . . AMLH 68520
MC: . . . . CAM 68520

WE'RE ALL ALONE.
Tracks: / Higher and higher / Way you do the things you do, The / We're all alone / I feel the burden (being lifted off my shoulders) / I don't want to talk about it / Words / Good times / Who's to bless and who's to blame / Southern lady / Hungry years.
LP: . . . . SHM 3140
MC: . . . . HSC 3140

Coolidge, Susan M.

WHAT KATY DID (Watford, Gwen (nar)).
MCSET: . . . . LFP 7322

Coolies

DIG.
Tracks: / Scarborough Fair / Bridge over troubled water / 59th Street Bridge song / I am a rock / Having my baby / El Condor Pasa / Cecilia / Homeward Bound / Mrs. Robinson / Only living boy in New York, The.
LP: . . . . SAVE 026

DOUG.
Tracks: / Talkin' bout Doug / Ice cold soul / Pussy cook / Shirts and skins / Coke light ice / Doug / Forty foot strength / Last supper, The / Ain't gonna eat no more / Crack pipe / Talkin' bout Doug (reprise) / Poverty.
LP: . . . . SAVE 063

Coolin Band

MORNING STAR, THE.
MC: . . . . GTDC 038

Cooling Waters

WE SHALL BE CHANGED.
Tracks: / We shall be changed / This friend of mine / Deliver you / No not one / Down by the river / Take it to Jesus / Look what you've done for me / When we all get to heaven.
LP: . . . . MIR 5017
MC: . . . . MIR 5017MC

Coon, Jackie

JAZZIN' AROUND.
LP: . . . . SB 1009

Cooney, Chris

CHRIS COONEY'S BREW (Cooney, Chris Brew).
LP: . . . . LRF 137

Cooper, Al

JUMP STEADY (Big band bounce & boogie) (Cooper, Al & His Savoy Sultans).
Tracks: / Jump steady / Thing, The / Looney / Rhythm doctor man / Getting in the groove / Jeep's blues / Stitches / Jumpin' at the Savoy / We'd rather jump than swing / Draggin' my heart around / Little Sally Water / Jumpin' the blues / Frenzy / Sophisticated jump / Norfolk ferry / Second balcony jump.
LP: . . . . AFS 1009

LIVE ADVENTURES OF MIKE BLOOMFIELD AND AL COOPER (See Bloomfield, Mike) (Cooper, Al/Mike Bloomfield).

Cooper, Alice

ALICE COOPER: INTERVIEW PICTURE DISC.
LPPD: . . . . CT 1015
LPPD: . . . . BAK 2059

ALICE COOPER SHOW, THE.
Tracks: / Under my wheels / Eighteen / Only women bleed / Sick things / Is it my body / I never cry / Billion dollar babies / Devil's food / Black widow / You and me / I love the dead / Go to hell / Wish you were here / School's out.
LP: . . . . K 56439
MC: K4 56439

BEAST OF ALICE COOPER, THE.
Tracks: / School's out / Under my wheels / Billion dollar babies / Be my lover / Desperado / Is it my body? / Only women bleed / Elected / I'm eighteen / Hello hooray / No more Mr. Nice Guy / Teenage lament '74 / Muscle of love / Department of youth.
LP: . . . . WX 331
MC: . . . . WX 331C

BILLION DOLLAR BABIES.
Tracks: / Hello hooray / Raped and freezin' / Elected / Unfinished sweet / No more Mister Nice Guy / Generation landslide / Sick things / Mary Ann / I love the dead / Billion dollar babies.
LP: . . . . K 56013

CONSTRICTOR.
LP: . . . . MCF 3341
MC: . . . . MCFC 3341

DA DA.
Tracks: / Da da / Enough's enough / Former Lee Warner / No man's land / Dyslexia / Scarlet and Sheba / I love America / Fresh blood / Pass the gun around.
LP: . . . . K 923969 1

FLUSH THE FASHION.
Tracks: / Talk talk / We're all clones / Pain / Leather boots / Aspirin damage / Nuclear infected / Grim facts / Model citizen / Dance yourself to death / Headlines.
LP: . . . . K 56805
MC: K4 56805

FREAK OUT SONG.
Tracks: / Freak out song / Ain't that just like a woman / Painting a picture / I've written home to mother / Science fiction / Going to the river / A.C. Instrumental / Nobody likes me.
LP: . . . . SHLP 115
MC: . . . . SHTC 115

FROM THE INSIDE.
Tracks: / From the inside / Wish I were born in Beverley Hills / Quiet room, The / Nurse Rozetta / Millie and Billie / Serious / How you gonna see me now / For Veronica's sake / Jack-knife Johnny / Inmates (we're all crazy).
LP: . . . . K 56577

GOES TO HELL.
Tracks: / Go to hell / You gotta dance / I'm the coolest / Didn't we meet / I never cry / Give the kid a break / Guilty / Wake me gently / Wish you were here / I'm always chasing rainbows / Going home.
LP: . . . . K 56171

GREATEST HITS: ALICE COOPER.
Tracks: / I'm eighteen / Is it my body / Desperado / Under my wheels / Be my lover / School's out / Hello hooray / Elected / No more Mister Nice Guy / Billion dollar babies / Teenage lament '74 / Muscle of love.
MC: K4 56043
LP: . . . . K 56043

HEY STOOPID.
Tracks: / Hey stoopid / Love's a loaded gun / Snakebite / Burning our bed / Dangerous tonight / Might as well be on Mars / Feed my Frankenstein /

Hurricane years / Little by little / Die for you / Dirty dreams / Wind up toys.
LP: 4684161
MC: 4684164

KILLER.
Tracks: / Under my wheels / Be my lover / Halo of flies / Desperado / You drive me nervous / Yeah yeah yeah / Dead babies / Killer.
LP: . . . . K 56005

LACE AND WHISKEY.
Tracks: / Damned if you do / My God / It's hot tonight / Lace and whiskey / Road rats / No more love at your convenience / Ubangi stomp / You and me / I never wrote those songs.
LP: . . . . K 56365

LADIES MAN.
Tracks: / Freak out / Painting a picture / I've written home to mother / Science fiction / For Alice / Nobody likes me / Going to the river / Ain't that just like a woman.
LP: . . . . THBM 005
MC: . . . . THBMC 005
MC: . . . . THBC 090

LOVE IT TO DEATH.
Tracks: / Caught in a dream / I'm eighteen / Long way to go / Black Juju / Is it my body / Hallowed be my name / Second coming / Ballad of Dwight Fry / Sun arise.
LP: . . . . K 46177

MUSCLE OF LOVE.
LP: . . . . K 56018

RAISE YOUR FIST AND YELL.
Tracks: / Lock me up / Give the radio back / Freedom / Step on you / Not that kind of love / Prince of darkness / Time to kill / Chop, chop, chop / Gail / Roses on white lace.
LP: . . . . MCF 3392
MC: . . . . MCFC 3392
LPPD: . . . . MCFP 3392

SCHOOL'S OUT.
Tracks: / Luney tune / Gutter cat vs the jets / Blue turk / My stars / Public animal no. 9 / Alma master / Grand finale / Schools out.
LP: . . . . K 56007

SPECIAL FORCES.
Tracks: / Who do you think we are / Seven and seven is / Skeletons in the closet / You're a movie / You want it, you got it / Vicious rumours / Prettiest cop on the block / Generation landslide '81 (Live) / You look good in rags / Don't talk old to me / Look at you over there, ripping the dust from my teddybear.
LP: . . . . K 56927
MC: K4 56927

TORONTO ROCK 'N' ROLL REVIVAL.
LP: . . . . PIXLP 3

TRASH.
Tracks: / Poison / Spark in the dark / House of fire / Why trust you / Only my heart talkin' / Bed of nails / This maniac's in love with you / Trash / Hell is living without you / I'm your gun.
LP: 4651301
MC: 4651304

WELCOME TO MY NIGHTMARE.
LP: . . . . ANCL 2011
LP: . . . . SD 19157

ZIPPER CATCHES THE SKIN.
Tracks: / Zorro's ascent / Make that money / I am the future / No baloney homosapiens / Adaptable (Anything for you) / I like girls / Remarkably insincere / Tag, you're it / I better be good / I'm alive (that was the day my dead pet return.
LP: . . . . K 57021

Cooper, Amanda

WHEN YOU WALK IN THE ROOM.
Tracks: / When you walk in the room / Life and love / Next time / Moon over Malaya.
MC: . . . . AMCO 1

Cooper, Bob

GROUP ACTIVITY (Cooper, Bob Sextet & Bill Holman Octet).
LP: . . . . AFF 65

PLAYS THE MUSIC OF MICHEL LEGRAND (Cooper, Bob & The Mike Wofford Trio).
Tracks: / Watch what happens / What are you doing the rest of my life / His eyes / Discovery me / Where's the love.
LP: . . . . DS 822

SHIFTING WINDS.
LP: . . . . AFF 59

TENOR SAX JAZZ IMPRESSIONS.
Tracks: / We'll be together again / I've got the world on a string.
LP: . . . . TR 518

Cooper Brothers

DREAM NEVER DIES, THE.
Tracks: / Rock 'n' roll cowboys / Dream never dies, The / Melody's in my mind / Old angel midnight / Life names the tune / We dance / Away from you / Portrait / Crazy Sunday.
LP: 2429 171

Cooper Clarke, John

ME AND MY BIG MOUTH.
Tracks: / I married a monster from outer space / I don't want to be nice / Valley of the lost women / Thirty six hours / I.T. man / Kung fu international / Twat / Majorca / Bronze adonis / Gimmix / Beasley Street.
LP: . . . . EPC 84979

OU EST LA MAISON DE FROMAGE?.
Tracks: / Gimmix / Nothing / Pyscle sluts / Action man / Cycle accident, The / Reader's wives / Ten years in an open neck shirt / Serial, The / Split beans / Sperm test.
LP: . . . . NOZE 1
LP: . . . . RRLP 110

SNAP CRACKLE AND BOP.
Tracks: / Evidently chickentown / Conditional discharge / Sleepwalk / 23rd / Beasley street / Thirty six hours / Belladonna / The it man / Limbo / Distant relation.
LP: . . . . EPC 84083

WALKING BACK TO HAPPINESS.
Tracks: / Gaberdine Angus / Majorca / Bronze adonis / Split beans / Twat / Pest / Nothing / Limbo / Who stole the marble index / Gimmix play loud.
LP: . . . . JCC 1

ZIP STYLE METHOD.
Tracks: / Midnight shift / New assasin / Face behind the scream / I travel in biscuits / Day the world stood still, The / Heart disease called love / Ghost of Al Capone / Ninety degrees in my shades / Day my pad went mad, The / I wanna be yours / Drive she said / Night people.
LP: . . . . EPC 85667

Cooper, Craig.T.

COOPER PROJECT (IMPORT).
LP: . . . . D 172947

GET THAT THANG.
LP: . . . . D 172992

Cooper, Dolly

AY LA BAH.
Tracks: / My man / Ay la bah / Teenage prayer / Down so long / Teenage wedding bells / Every day and every night / Is it true? / Believe in me / I wanna know / I'd climb the highest mountain / Me and my baby / Alley cat / I need romance / You gotta be good to yourself / Love can't be blind / Time brings about a change.
LP: . . . . OFF 6019

Cooper, Gary

BING CROSBY WITH PEGGY LEE, JACK BENNY, GARY COOPER (See under Crosby, Bing) (Cooper, Gary/ Bing Crosby/ Peggy Lee/ Jack Benny).

Cooper, Giles

UNDER THE LOOFAH TREE.
MC: . . . . ZCF 507

Cooper, Harry

HARRY COOPER, R.Q. DICKERSON AND THE COTTON CLUB ORCHESTRA.
LP: . . . . CI 006

Cooper, James Fenimore

LAST OF THE MOHICANS, THE (Mason, James (nar)).
MC: 1239

LAST OF THE MOHICANS, THE (children's classics) (Unknown narrator(s)).
MC: . . . . PLBC 125

Cooper, Jilly

CLASS (Keith, Penelope).
MCSET: . . . . LFP 7406

Cooper, Jimmy

IN CONCERT - HAMMERED DULCIMER.
MC: . . . . FTC 6023

Cooper, Lindsay

GOLD DIGGERS (Film Soundtrack) (See under Gold Diggers).

GOLD DIGGERS (see under Gold Diggers (film).

MUSIC FOR OTHER OCCASIONS.
LP: . . . . SP 3

Cooper, Michael

JUST WHAT I LIKE.
Tracks: / Just what I like / Turn the lights out / Girl's got it goin' on / Best, The / Should have been you / Do you love me baby / My baby's house / Over and over / Wild side.
LP: . . . . K 9259231
MC: . . . . K 9259234

LOVE IS SUCH A FUNNY GAME.
Tracks: / To prove my love / You've got a friend / Dinner for two / Just thinkin' 'bout cha / No other lover / Oceans wide / Love is such a funny game / Quickness / Look before you leave.
LP: 925653 1
MC: 925653 4

Cooper, Mike

CONTINUOUS PREACHING BLUES, THE (Cooper, Mike & Ian Anderson).
LP: . . . . AP 037

JOHNNY RONDO DUO PLUS... (see under Coxhill, Lol) (Cooper, Mike/Lol Coxhill/David G. Holland).

Cooper, Ogbe Jerry

EVERYTHING FOR A WHILE.
LP: . . . . JECO 002
MC: . . . . JECO 002C

Cooper, Pete

FROSTY MORNING (see under Tannen, Holly) (Cooper, Pete & Holly Tannen).

PETA WEBB AND PETE COOPER (See under Webb, Pete) (Cooper, Pete & Peta Webb).

Cooper, Rowena

QUEST OF NURSE MAYHEW (Cooper, Rowenta).
MCSET: . . . . MRC 1032

Cooper, Thelma

THELMA COOPER/DAISY MAE & HER HEP CATS (Cooper, Thelma/Daisy Mae & Her Hep Cats).
Tracks: / I need a man / Let's try again / Ooh daddy / Cute poppa / Talk to my baby / Down by the woodshed / Fanny Duncan (2 takes) / Lonesome playgirl / Want me a man / Stuff you got to watch / Woman trouble / Hop scotch / Frosty's groove.
LP: . . . . KK 822

Cooper, Tom

TOM COOPER SINGS GREAT SONGS FROM MOVE MUSICALS.
Tracks: / Lullaby of Broadway / I'm old fashioned / I got out of bed on the right side / This is the moment / Spring will be a little late this year / Strictly USA / I've got my love to keep me warm / Long ago and far away / Pick yourself up / My heart tells me / Change partners / Maybe this time.
LP: . . . . IN 218

Cooper, Wilma Lee

CARTER FAMILY'S GREATEST HITS (Lee, Wilma & Stoney Cooper).
LP: . . . . SLP 980
MC: . . . . GT 5980

DAISY A DAY.
Tracks: / Daisy a day / Tomorrow I'll be gone / Pretty Polly / Uncle pen / Shackles and chains / I'm tying the leaves / Peggy Lou / I closed my hearts / Ain't gonna work tomorrow / I couldn't believe it was true / No one now / As long as I live.
LP: . . . . REBEL 1625

WHITE ROSE.
LP: . . . . REBEL 2623
MC: . . . . REBELMC 1623

WILMA LEE COOPER.
Tracks: / You tried to ruin my name / Forsaken love / Curly headed baby / Far beyond the starry sky / Sinful to flirt / What'll do with baby - o / Still there's a spark of love / Nobody's darling but mine / Bury me beneath the willow / Who's gonna shoe your pretty little feet / Cowards over Pearl Harbour.
LP: . . . . ROUNDER 0143

WILMA LEE & STONEY COOPER (Lee, Wilma & Stoney Cooper).
LP: . . . . ROUNDER 0066

Co-optimists (show)

CO-OPTIMISTS, THE (Highlights by original artists) (Various artists).
Tracks: / If winter comes: *Gideon, Melville* / Ghost of a chance: *Gideon, Melville* / Amagu: *Gideon, Melville*/ When the sun goes down: *Gideon, Melville* / I'm tickled to death I'm single: *Gideon, Melville* / Golfing love: *Gideon, Melville* / Crinoline gown: *Gideon, Melville* / I've fallen in love with a voice: *Gideon, Melville*/ You forgot to remember: *Co-optimists (show)* / Love them all a little bit: *Gideon, Melville* / Tale of a guinea pig, The: *Gideon, Melville* / I wonder where my baby is tonight: *Gideon, Melville* / Why couldn't it be poor little me: *Gideon, Melville* / I used to sing: *Gideon, Melville* / Thank the moon: *Gideon, Melville* / Little lacquer lady: *Gideon, Melville* / Amsterdam: *Gideon, Melville* / Always: *Gideon, Melville* / Don't let 'em scrap the British Navy: *Child, Gilbert* / While the rich man drives by: *Child, Gilbert* / We'll go to church on sunday: *Monkman, Phylis & Laddie Cliff* / Conversation: *Monkman, Phylis & Laddie Cliff* / You're the sort of girl: *Monkman, Phylis & Laddie Cliff* / Down love lane: *MacFarlane, Elsa & Stanley Holloway* / Memory street: *MacFarlane, Elsa & Stanley Holloway* / Pierrot moon: *Chester, Betty* / Tommy the whistler: *Holloway, Stanley (nar)* / London town (you haunt me): *Holloway, Stanley (nar)* / Wheel tapper, The: *Holloway, Stanley (nar)* / Miss Lemon: *Burnaby, Davy* / Alouette: *Holloway, Stanley & Gilbert Childs* / You've such a lot: *Monkman, Phyllis & Austin Melford.*
LP: . . . . SHB 25

Cope, Julian

FRIED.
Tracks: / Reynard the fox / Bill Drummond said / Laughing boy / Me singing / Sunspots / Bloody assizes, The / Search party / O king of chaos / Holy love / Torpedo.
LP: . . . . MERL 48

JULIAN COPE: INTERVIEW PICTURE DISC.
LPPD: . . . . BAK 2058

MY NATION UNDERGROUND.
Tracks: / 5 o'clock world / Charlotte Anne / China doll / I'm not losing sleep / Vegetation / My nation underground / Someone like me / Great white hoax, The.
MC: . . . . ICT 9918
LP: . . . . ILPS 9918
MC: . . . . ICM 9918

PEGGY SUICIDE.
2LP: . . . . ILPSD 9977
MC: . . . . ICT 9977

SKELLINGTON.
LP: . . . . JULP 088

ST. JULIAN.
Tracks: / Crack in the clouds, A / Trampoline / Shot down / Eve's volcano (covered in sin) / Space hopper / Planet ride / World shut your mouth / St. Julian / Pulsar / Screaming secrets.
LP: . . . . ILPS 9861
MC: . . . . ICT 9861
MC: 842 686 4
MC: . . . . ICM 2023

WORLD SHUT YOUR MOUTH.
Tracks: / Umpteenth unnatural blues (Included in box set only.) / World shut your mouth / Bandy's first jump / Greatness and perfection of love / Elegant chaos, An / Kolly Kibber's birthday / Head hang low / Metranil vavin / Sunshine playroom / Lunatic and fire pistol.
LP: . . . . MERL 37
MC: . . . . MERLC 37

Copeland, Greg

REVENGE WILL COME.
Tracks: / Used / Starting place / Full Cleveland / Eagleston / That'll never be the same / Richard Hill / At the warfield / Wrong highway / El Salvador / Revenge will come.
LP: . . . . GEF 85579

Copeland, James (nar)

WEE MACGREEGOR (see under Wee MacGreegor).

Copeland, Johnny

AIN'T NOTHIN' BUT A PARTY (Live in Houston, Texas).
LP: . . . . ROUNDER 2055
MC: . . . . ROUNDER 2055C

BRINGIN' IT ALL BACK HOME.
Tracks: / Kasavubu / Jungle / Ngote / Djeli, djeli blues / Abidjan / Bozalimalamu / Same thing / Conakry.
LP: . . . . FIEND 47
LP: . . . . ROUNDER 2050
MC: . . . . ROUNDER 2050C

COPELAND COLLECTION, VOL 1.
LP: . . . . HCS 107
MC: . . . . HCS 107 TC

COPELAND SPECIAL.
Tracks: / Claim jumper / I wish I was single / Everybody wants a piece of me / Copeland special / It's my own tears that's being wasted / Third party / Big time / Down on bended knee / Done got over it / St. Louis blues.
LP: . . . . FIEND 3
LP: . . . . ROUNDER 2025
MC: . . . . ROUNDER 2025C

DEDICATED TO THE GREATEST.
Tracks: / It's me / Love attack / I waited too long / Stealing / Mother Nature / Invitation / Wizard of art / Old man blues / Dear mother / Johnny Ace medley / No puppy love / Oh how I miss you.
LP: . . . . KENT 067

DOWN ON BENDED KNEES.

Tracks: / Down on bended knees / There's a blessing / May the best man win / I got to go home / Coming to see about you / It's my own tears that's being wasted / I wish I was single / It's me / I'm going to make my home where........ / If love is your friend / You're gonna reap what you sow / Suffering city / Hurt hurt hurt / Old man blues / Love prayer.
LP: . . . . RB 1002

HOUSTON ROOTS.
Tracks: / Rock me baby take 1 / Late hours / I wish I was single / Hear what I said / Please let me know / Baby please don't go / I don't want nobody / Night time is the right time (part 1) / Night time is the right time (part 2) / I need you now / Heebie jeebies / All these things / Rock me baby take 2.
LP: . . . . CHD 238

I'LL BE AROUND.
Tracks: / Rock and roll Lilly / Year round blues / It don't bother you / Mama told me / Heebie jeebies / Just one more time / Working man's blues / Funny feeling / I'll be around / Ain't nobody's business / That's alright mama / Trying to reach my goal / Hear what I said / Ghetto child / Do better somewhere else / You must believe in yourself.
LP: . . . . RB 1001

MAKE MY HOME WHERE I HANG MY HAT.
Tracks: / Natural born believer / Make my home where I hang my hat / Devil's hand / Cold outside / Love Utopia / Boogie woogie nighthawk / Honky tonkin' / Well well baby-la / Old man blues / Rock 'n' roll Lilly.
LP: . . . . ROUNDER 2030
LP: . . . . FIEND 4
MC: . . . . ROUNDER 2030C

SHOWDOWN (see Collins, Albert) (Copeland, Johnny/Robert Cray/Albert Collins).

TEXAS TWISTER.
Tracks: / Midnight fantasy / North Caroline / Don't stop by the creek son / Excuses / Jessanne / Houston / When the rain starts fallin' / I de go now / Early in the morning / Twister / Idiom / Easy to love / Media / Morning coffee / Jelly roll / Where or when.
LP: . . . . FIEND 15
LP: . . . . ROUNDER 2040
MC: . . . . ROUNDER 2040C

Copeland, Martha

MARTHA COPELAND VOL. 1 1923-27.
LP: . . . . BD 2071

MARTHA COPELAND VOL. 2 1927-28.
LP: . . . . BD 2072

Copeland, Stewart

EQUALIZER, THE.
Tracks: / Love lessons / Green fingers / Archie David in dark ships / Flowership quintet / Flag pole dance / Archie David in overtime / Lurking solo / Music box / Equalizer busy equalizing, The.
LP: . . . . MIRF 1029
MC: . . . . MIRFC 1029

RHYTHMATIST, THE.
Tracks: / Koteja / Brazzaville / Liberte / Coco / Kemba / Samburu sunset / Gong rock / Franco / Serengeti / Long walk / African dream.
LP: . . . . AMA 5084
MC: . . . . AMC 5084

RUMBLE FISH (Film soundtrack).
Tracks: / Don't box me in / Tulsa tango / Our mother is alive / Part at someone else's place / Biff gets stomped by Rust James / Brothers on wheels / West Tulsa rags / Father on the stairs.
LP: . . . . AMLX 64983
MC: . . . . CXM 64983

Copernicus

FROM BACTERIA.
Tracks: / I won't hurt you / Nagasaki / Atomic nevermore / Blood / In terms of money / From bacteria / Lies! / Victim of the sky / White from black.
LP: . . . . DMC 017

Copkiller (film)

COPKILLER (1983 film soundtrack) (Various artists).
LP: 803 074
MC: 804 074

Copland (composer)

BILLY THE KID (Slatkin, Leonard).
LP: . . . . EL 2703981
MC: . . . . EL 2703984

COPLAND CONDUCTS COPLAND.
MC: 40 72872

COPLAND'S GREATEST HITS (Various artists).
Tracks: / Appalachian spring: *Various artists* / Billy the Kid: *Various artists* / Rodeo: *Various artists*/ El Salon Mexico: *Various artists*.
MC: 40 79020

FANFARE (Mexico City Philharmonic Orchestra).
Tracks: / Fanfare (Copland, Aaron) / Saloon Mexico (Copland, Aaron) / Rodeo (Copland, Aaron).
MC: . . . . TCEMX 2147

THIRD SYMPHONY.
LP: 61869

Copley, Al

HANDFUL OF KEYS, A.
Tracks: / Sentimental journey / Sheik of araby / Yancey that / Stormy weather / When my dreamboat comes home / Stormy monday blues / Yin yang / Mr Jellyroll Baker / Tell me how do you feel / Sit on it baby / Saints.
LP: . . . . WIK 52

Copper, Bob

BOB COPPER (Countryside songs from the south).
Tracks: / Trooper, The / Bold Princess Royal, The / Farmer from Chester, The / Mistletoe bough, The / Bold dragoon, The / Young Johnnie / Parson and the sucking pig, The / Lord Thomas / Squire's lost lady / Bold General Wolfe / Dick Turpin / Fox, The / Dogs and ferrets / Fisherman / Rose in June.
LP: 12TS 328

TWANKYDILLO (Copper, Bob, Ron & Jim).
Tracks: / Threshing machiner's song, The / Jones's ale / Innocent hare, The / Sweep, chimney sweep / Hard times of Old England / Merry haymakers / Spencer the rover / Good ale / Time passes over / Shepherds arise / Irish girl, The / Bold General Wolfe / Ship in distress / Bold fisherman / Spotted cow, The / Hampshire farmer, The / Lemonay / Christmas presents.
MC: 60-082

TWO BRETHREN (Copper, Bob & Ron).
Tracks: / Claudy banks / When the old Duncow caught fire / Lark in the morning, The / Hungry fox, The / Babes in the wood / Cupid's garden / Warlike seamen / Spring glee / Ploughshare, The / Shepherd of the downs / Week before Easter, A / By the green grove / Honest labourer / Dame Durden / Acre of land / No, John, no / Banks of the sweet primroses.
MC: 60-081

Copper Family

COPPERSONG, A LIVING TRADITION.
LP: . . . . VWML 004

SONG FOR EVERY SEASON, A.
Tracks: / Dame Durden / By the green grove / Spencer the rover / Charming Molly / Sweep chimney sweep / Rose of Allandale / Pleasant month of May / When spring comes on / Spotted cow / Wop she 'ad it-io / Week before Easter, A / Brisk and lively lad / Sheep shearing song / Adieu sweet lovely Nancy / Claudy banks / Sweet lemeny / Corduroy / Come all bold Britons / No John no / Shepherd's song / Thousands or more / Shepherd of the downs / As I walked out / Seamen bold / When Adam was first created / Lawyer bold, A / Gentlemen of high renown / My love has gone / Battle of Alma / Warlike seamen / Brisk and bonny lad / Sportsmen arouse / Admiral Benbow / Wind across the moor / Oh good ale / Shepherds arise / Softly the night / Christmas song, The / Babes in the wood / Dying soldier, The / Brisk young ploughboy / Heigh ho sing Ivy / Jolly good song / Two young brethren / Ploughshare, The / Come write me down.
LP: . . . . LED 2067
2LP: . . . . LEAB 404

Copperhead

COPPERHEAD.
LP: . . . . ED 136

Coppieters, Francis

COLOURS IN JAZZ.
LP: . . . . ISST 184

Coppin, Johnny

EDGE OF DAY (See under Lee, Laurie for information).

ENGLISH MORNING (Songs of Gloucestershire and beyond).
Tracks: / English morning / Everlasting mercy / Dover's hill / Hill, The / Tom Long's post / High hill, The / Holy brook, The / East wind / Nailsworth hill / Hill and vale / Cotswold tiles / Christmas Eve / Winter / Forest carol / Under Robinswood.
LP: . . . . RSK 107
MC: . . . . RSKC 107

FOREST AND VALE AND HIGH BLUE HILL.
Tracks: / In Flanders / Song of Gloucestershire, A / Piper's wood / Fisherman of Newnham / Cotswold love / Briar roses / Legacy / Warning / High road, The / Field of autumn / Cotswold lad / Song of Minsterworth Perry / Have wandered / Cotswold farmers, The / This night the stars.
LP: . . . . R 015
MC: . . . . RSKC 015

GET LUCKY.
Tracks: / New day / Get lucky / First time love / Contrary / Celebrate my life / Heaven knows / Never fly you way / Catherine / For you / Everybody knows.
LP: . . . . SWL 2003

GLORIOUS GLOSTERS, THE (See under First Battalion Glos).

LINE OF BLUE.
Tracks: / It's your life / Hurricane of '15, The / Everything to me / Keep a little light / Lost in love with you / Changing life / Rydal / Every roll of thunder / Hallelujah / Pride of all the ocean / Shine silently.
LP: . . . . RSK 106
MC: . . . . RSKC 106

NO GOING BACK.
Tracks: / No going back / Can you feel it / Young girl town / Falling for you / Run to her / Part in my heart / Believe in you / Birmingham / He will let you know / We shall not pass.
LP: . . . . R 002LP

ROLL ON DREAMER.
Tracks: / Liberty / Never lost for love / Angelus / If that's the way you feel / Roll on dreamer / Worm forgives the plough / Archangel / Roads go down,The / Midwinter / Warm love.
LP: . . . . AVA 102

WEST COUNTRY CHRISTMAS.
Tracks: / Intro: Lord of all this Revelling / Gloucestershire Wassail / Song for loders / My dancing day / Sans day carol / Come all you worth Christian friends / Sailor's carol / Glastonbury thorn (theme), The / Oxen, The / Innocent's song / O little town of Bethlehem / Wiltshire carol / Virgin most pure, A / Birth, The / Campden carol, The / Flowering of the thorn, The / Glastonbury thorn (theme), The.
MC: . . . . RSKC 111

Cops & Robbers (bk)

COPS AND ROBBERS (Janet and Allan Ahlberg).
MC: 0 00 102198 2

Coral Island (bk)

CORAL ISLAND (R.M. Ballantyne) (Heller, Martin (nar)).
MCSET: . . . . COL 3001

Corbett, Harry H.

MORE JUNK (Corbett, Harry H./Wilfred Brambell).
LP: . . . . NPL 18090

STEPTOE & SON (Corbett, Harry H./ Wilfred Brambell).
LP: . . . . HMA 238
LP: . . . . NPL 18081
LP: . . . . MAL 1160

STEPTOE & SON VOL.2 (Corbett, Harry H./Wilfred Brambell).
LP: . . . . GGL 0217

Corbett, Ronnie

TWO RONNIES (see Barker, Ronnie) (Corbett, Ronnie & Ronnie Barker).

TWO RONNIES VOL 2 (see Barker, Ronnie) (Corbett, Ronnie & Ronnie Barker).

Corbies

CORBIES, THE.
LP: . . . . FLC 5022

Corboz, Michel

SCHUMANN MASS REQIUE.
MC: . . . . MCE 75542

Corchia, Louis

TEMPO GRANDE VITESSE.
Tracks: / Rancho grande / El matinos / Roses de picardie / Tempo grande vitesse / Bal de la marine / Lettre a Evelyn / Tango des jours heureux / J'attendrai / Nationale / Rue de charenton / Ave Maria / La banboula.
LP: . . . . ILD 42046

Cordell, Frank

BRITISH FILM MUSIC (Cordell, Frank & The Phoenix Orchestra).
Tracks: / Ring of bright water / Demon (God told me to).
LP: . . . . DGS 1004

Cordells

IN A MELLOW MOOD.
LP: . . . . HPL 01

Cordner, Rodney

DON'T LOOK AWAY.
Tracks: / Brainwashed / I fade away / Passing thru' / Trial, The / World said "no" / Key, The / Only just begun / This land / Naked tree / Thank you letter.
LP: . . . . PC 861

Corea, Chick

AGAIN AND AGAIN (The Jo'burg session).
Tracks: / No.3 / Waltz / Again and again / 1 - 2 - 1234 / Diddle diddle / Twang.
LP: . . . . E 0167

AKOUSTIC BAND, THE.
Tracks: / Autumn leaves / So in love / Morning sprite / Circles / Spain.
LP: . . . . GRP 95821
MC: . . . . GRP 95824

ALIVE (Corea, Chick Akoustic Band).
Tracks: / On Green Dolphin Street / Round midnight / Hackensack / Sophisticated lady / U.M.M.G / Humpty dumpty / How deep is the ocean / Morning sprite.
LP: . . . . GRP 96271
MC: . . . . GRP 96274

A.R.C. (Corea, Chick & Holland & Altschul).
Tracks: / Nefertiti / Ballad for Tillie / A.R.C. / Vedana / Thanatos / Games.
LP: . . . . ECM 1009

BENEATH THE MASK (Corea, Chick Elektric Band).
Tracks: / Beneath the mask / Little things that count / One of us is over 40 / Wave goodbye, A / Lifescape / Jammin' E. Cricket / Charged particles / Free step / 99 Flavours / Illusions.
LP: . . . . GRP 96491
MC: . . . . GRP 96494

BLISS.
Tracks: / Turkish woman at the baths / Dancing girls / Love planet / Marjoun / Bliss / Sin street / And so.
LP: . . . . MR 5011
LP: . . . . MA 99058

CHICK COREA (Compact/Walkman jazz).
Tracks: / Captain Marvel / Captain Senor Mouse / Armando's Rhumba / 500 miles high / Love Castle / Vulcan worlds / No mystery / Spain.
MC: 831 365 4

CHILDREN'S SONGS.
LP: . . . . ECM 1267

DELPHI, VOL 1.
Tracks: / Delphi 1-8 / Children's song No. 20 / Stride time 1-7.
LP: 2490150

DREAM (see under Honda, Toshiyuki) (Corea, Chick/Toshiyuki Honda).

DUET: GARY BURTON & CHICK COREA (see under Burton, Gary) (Corea, Chick & Gary Burton).

EARLY DAYS.
Tracks: / Brain, The / Converge / Waltz for Bill Evans / Sundance / Dave / Vamp, The / Jamala.
MC: . . . . MC 7969

ELEKTRIC BAND,THE.
Tracks: / Rumble / Side walk / Cool weasel boogie / Got a match / Elektrik city / No zone / King cockroach / India Town.
LP: . . . . GRP 91026
MC: . . . . GRPM 91026

EVENING WITH HERBIE HANCOCK AND CHICK COREA, AN (See under Hancock, Herbie) (Corea, Chick/Herbie Hancock/Keith Jarret).

EYE OF THE BEHOLDER (Corea, Chick Elektric Band).
Tracks: / Home Universe / Eternal child / Passage / Beauty / Cascade (part 1) / Trance dance / Eye of the beholder / Cascade (part 2).
LP: . . . . GRP 91053
MC: . . . . GRPM 91053

FEMME FATALE (Corea, Chick & Garbor Szabo).
Tracks: / Femme fatale / Xingaro / Sarena / Thousand times / Out of the night.
LP: . . . . SLPR 707

FIESTA.
Tracks: / Sea journey / Moment's notice / Fiesta / I ain't mad at you / Come rain or come shine.
LP: . . . . B 90061

GOMEZ (see under Gomez, Eddie) (Corea, Chick & Eddie Gomez).

INNER SPACE.
Tracks: / Straight up and down / This is new / Tones for Joan's bones / Litha / Inner space / Windows / Guijira / Trio for flute, bassoon and piano.
LP: . . . . K 60081

INSIDE OUT (Corea, Chick Elektric Band).
Tracks: / Inside out / Make a wish (part 1) / Make a wish (part 2) / Stretch it (part 1) / Stretch it (part 2) / Kicker / Child's play / Tale of daring (chapter 1) / Tale of

daring (chapter 2) / Tale of daring (chapter 3) / Tale of daring (chapter 4).
LP: . . . . **GRP 96011**
MC: . . . . **GRP 96014**

LIGHT AS A FEATHER.
Tracks: / You're everything / Light as a feather / Captain Marvel / 500 miles high / Children's song / Spain.
LP: . . . . **MID 1006**
LP: **2482497**

LIGHT YEARS.
LP: . . . . **GRP 91036**
MC: . . . . **GRPM 91036**
DAT: . . . . **GRT 9546**

LIVE AT MIDEM, 1978 (Corea, Chick & Lionel Hampton).
Tracks: / Sea breeze / Moment's notice / Come rain or come shine / Fiesta piano solo / I ain't mad at you.
LP: . . . . **GATE 7005**
MC: . . . . **CGATE 7005**

LYRIC SUITE FOR SEXTET (Corea, Chick & Gary Burton).
Tracks: / Overture / Waltz / Sketch / Rollercoaster / Brasilia / Dream / Finale.
LP: . . . . **ECM 1260**

MEETING, THE (see Gulda, Friedrich) (Corea, Chick & Friedrich Gulda).

MIRROR MIRROR (see under Henderson, Joe) (Corea, Chick/Joe Henderson).

MY SPANISH HEART.
Tracks: / Love castle / Gardens, The / Day danse / My Spanish heart / Night streets / Hilltop, The / Sky, The - parts 1 & 2 / Wind danse / Armando's rhumba / Prelude to El Bozo - parts 1-3 / Spanish fantasy (parts 1-4).
2LP: **2672 031**

NOW HE SINGS, NOW HE SOBS.
Tracks: / Matrix / My one and only love (CD only.) / Now he beats the drum now he stops / Bossa (CD only.) / Now he sings, now he sobs / Steps - what was / Fragments (CD only.) / Windows (CD only.) / Pannonica (CD only.) / Samba yantra (CD only.) / I don't know (CD only.) / Law of falling and catching up, The / Gemini (CD only.).
LP: **B1 90055**

RETURN TO FOREVER.
Tracks: / Return to forever / Crystal silence / What game shall we play today / Sometime ago - la fiesta.
MC: **3101022**

SEA JOURNEY.
LP: . . . . **PLP 31**
MC: . . . . **PMC 31**

SECRET AGENT.
Tracks: / Golden dawn / Slinky / Mirage / Drifting / Glebe Street blues / Fickle funk / Bagatelle No.4 / Hot news blues / Central Park.
LP: **2391 381**

SEPTET.
Tracks: / 1st movement / 2nd movement / 3rd movement / 4th movement / 5th Movement / Temple of Isfahan, The.
LP: . . . . **ECM 1297**

SONG OF SINGING.
Tracks: / Toy room / Ballad I. / Rhymes / Flesh / Ballad III / Nefertiti.
LP: . . . . **BST 84353**

SUPER LIVE 2 (See under Grusin, Dave) (Corea, Chick/Dave Grusin/Lee Ritenour).

TAP STEP.
Tracks: / Samba L.A. / Embrace, The / Tap step / Magic carpet / Slide, The / Grandpa blues / Flamenco.
LP: . . . . **K 56801**

THREE QUARTETS.
Tracks: / Quartet No.1 / Quartet No.2 / Quartet No.3.
LP: . . . . **K 56908**

TONES FOR JOAN'S BONES.
Tracks: / Litha / This is new / Tones for Joan's Bones / Straight up and down.
LP: . . . . **K 50302**

TRIO MUSIC.
Tracks: / Trio improvisations 1,2,3 / Duet improvisation 1,2,3,4,5 / Slippery when wet / Rhythm-a-ning / Round midnight / Eronel / Think of one / Little Rootie Tootie. / Reflections / Hackensack / Music of Thelonious Monk.
2LP: . . . . **ECM 1232/33**

TRIO MUSIC LIVE IN EUROPE.
Tracks: / Loop / I hear a rhapsody / Night and day / Summer night / Prelude no 2 / Mock up / Hittin it / Microvisions.
LP: . . . . **ECM 1310**

VOYAGE.
Tracks: / Mallorca / Diversions / Star Island / Free fall / Hong Kong.
LP: . . . . **ECM 1282**

WHERE HAVE I KNOWN YOU BEFORE?.
Tracks: / Beyond the seventh galaxy / Earth juice / Shadow of Lo, The / Song to the pharoah kings / Vulcan worlds / Where have I danced with you before / Where have I known you before / Where have I loved you before.
LP: **2482 502**
LP: . . . . **MID 1005**

WORKS: CHICK COREA.
Tracks: / Where are you now / Noon song / Children's song / Brasilia / Slippery when wet / Duet improvisation / New place, A / La Fiesta / Return to forever / Song of the wind / Round midnight / Rhythm-a-ning / Senor Mouse / Sometime ago / Addendum.
MC: **3100 392**
LP: **8254261**

ZURICH CONCERT (Corea, Chick & Gary Burton).
2LP: . . . . **ECM 1182**

Corelli, Capella

FOR YE LOVERS & MASTERS OF MUSIQUE.
LP: . . . . **LRF 069**

Corelli (Composer)

JESU, JOY OF MANS DESIRING (see under Bach, J.S.) (Various artists).

Coren, Alan

ARTHUR AND THE BELLY BUTTON DIAMOND (Barker, Tom).
MC: . . . . **TTC/K 05**

Corey, Brioid

GUNS AND SONGS OF THE IRA.
MC: . . . . **CT 107**

Coriolanus

CORIOLANUS (see under Shakespeare, William) (Various artists).

Corkscrew

FOR OPENERS.
LP: . . . . **SHY 7005**

Corley, Al

SQUARE ROOMS.
LP: **822 316-1**
MC: **822 316-4**

Cormack, Arthur

NUAIR BHA MI OG.
LP: . . . . **TP 006**

RUITH NA GAOITH.
MC: . . . . **CTP 032**

Cormier, Joseph

DANCES DOWN HOME, THE.
LP: . . . . **ROUNDER 7004**

SCOTTISH VIOLIN MUSIC FROM CAPE BRETON ISLAND.
LP: . . . . **ROUNDER 7001**

Corn Bread

IT'S HOT.
LP: . . . . **SBR 4208**

LEROY MAC.
LP: . . . . **SBR 4209**

Corn Dollies

CORN DOLLIES.
LP: . . . . **CHIME 0044 S**

EVERYTHING BAG.
LP: . . . . **MC 015 LP**

Cornelius, Helen

HELEN CORNELIUS.
Tracks: / Don't bother to knock / Mama he's crazy / Love is too close to be too far away / Time of my life, The / He thinks hearts were made to break / Give me one more chance / You don't bring me flowers / I don't want to have to marry you / Old friends / God bless the U.S.A..
LP: . . . . **IMCA 39034**
MC: . . . . **IMCAC 39034**

I DON'T WANNA HAVE TO MARRY YOU (see under Brown, Jim Ed) (Cornelius, Helen/Jim Ed Brown).

Cornelius, Kay

AEROBIC WORKOUT EXERCISE PROGRAMME FOR MEN & WOMEN.
LP: . . . . **NE 1242**
MC: . . . . **CE 2242**

Cornfield

DESIGNER STUBBLE.
MC: . . . . **PR 1**

Cornwell, Charlotte

NO EXCUSES.
LP: . . . . **CBS 70234**
MC: **40 70234**

Cornwell, Hugh

NOSFERATU (Cornwell, Hugh & Robert Williams).
Tracks: / White room / Losers in a lost land.
LP: . . . . **UAG 30251**

WOLF.
Tracks: / Another kind of love / Cherry rare / Never never / Real slow / Clubland / Dreaming again / Decadence / All the tea in China / Getting involved / Break of dawn.
LP: . . . . **V 2420**
MC: . . . . **TCV 2420**
LP: . . . . **OVED 298**
MC: . . . . **OVEDC 298**

Coronation Street (tv)

CORONATION STREET (Original cast) (Various artists).
LP: . . . . **ONE 1378**
MC: . . . . **OCE 2378**

Coroner

MENTAL VORTEX.
LP: . . . . **NO 1771**
MC: . . . . **NO 1774**

NO MORE COLOUR.
LP: . . . . **NUK 138**
MC: . . . . **ZCNUK 138**
LP: . . . . **N 0138 1**

PUNISHMENT FOR DECADE.
LP: . . . . **NUK 119**
MC: . . . . **ZCNUK 119**
LP: . . . . **N 0119 1**
MC: . . . . **N 0119 2**

R.I.P..
LP: . . . . **N 0075**
LP: . . . . **NUK 075**
MC: . . . . **ZCNUK 075**
MC: . . . . **N 0076**

Corporation Of One

BLACK LIKE ME.
LP: . . . . **LUVLP 3**
MC: . . . . **LUVMC 3**

Corpse Grinders

LEGEND OF CORPSE GRINDERS, THE.
LP: . . . . **FC 004**

VALLEY OF FEAR.
LP: . . . . **ROSE 39**

Corpses As Bedmates

VENUS HANDCUFFS.
Tracks: / Venus handcuffs / Haebsibah / Thought through the shadows, A / Fur man / Birds fly out / Dear dear / Gus black box / Phantom / For the rest of the day / Best home.
LP: . . . . **DMC 016**

Correll, Denny

STANDIN' IN THE LIGHT.
Tracks: / Wings of the wind / Lead me home / Paradise / Witness, The / Glory road / Living water / Faith / Standin' in the light / Noah / Redeemer / He's comin' again.
LP: . . . . **MM 0058**
MC: . . . . **TC MM 0058**

Corrib Folk

BEST OF CORRIB FOLK.
LP: . . . . **HRL 170**
MC: . . . . **CHRL 170**

CAREFREE.
LP: . . . . **DIN 329**

CORRIB FOLK.
MC: . . . . **CHRL 107**

IRISH FOLK.
Tracks: / Town I loved so well, The / Whiskey on a Sunday / Claddagh ring.
LP: . . . . **HRL 107**

SING IRISHMEN SING.
Tracks: / Galway Races / Where 3 counties meet / Only our rivers run free.
LP: . . . . **HRL 117**
MC: . . . . **CHRL 117**

Corrie Folk Trio

IN RETROSPECT (see Bell, Paddie) (Corrie Folk Trio/Paddie Bell).

Corries

16 SCOTTISH FAVOURITES.
Tracks: / Collier laddie / Where two hawks fly / Castle of Dromore, The / Jock O'Hazeldean / Man's a man, A / Helen of Kirkconnel / Sheriffmuir / Scots wha' hae / News from Moidart, The / Kate Dalrymple / Petronella / Heidless cross, The / I know my love / Lark in the morning, The / Heiland Harry / Bluebells of Scotland.
LP: . . . . **GLN 1005**
MC: . . . . **TCGLN 1005**

BARRETT'S PRIVATEERS.
Tracks: / North Sea shoals / Jock O'Braidislee / Tortoise, The / Rise rise / Loch Lomond / Dashing arts / Twa racruiting sergeants / Water o' Tyne, The / Folker, The / Barrett's privateers / Strangest dream / Rosin the beau.
LP: . . . . **PA 083**
MC: . . . . **CPA 083**

BEST OF THE CORRIES.
Tracks: / Flower of Scotland / Road to Dundee, The / Skye boat song, The / Will ye lassie go / Annie Laurie / Parcel o'rogues / Lord of the dance / Ae fond kiss / Wild rover / October song / Highland lament / Tiree love song / Blow ye winds / Kismuil's galley / Lowlands of Holland, The / I'm a rover.
MC: . . . . **PWKMC 4054P**

BONNET, BELT AND SWORD.
Tracks: / Hot asphalt / Cam ye o'er frae France / Joy of my heart / Jolly beggar, The / Bring back my granny to me / Glenlyon lament / Johnny Cope / Gaberlunzie king / Haughs o' Cromdale / Banks of Newfoundland / Parcel o' rogues / North sea holes / Katie Bairdie / Oor wee school / I once loved a lass / Blow ye winds in the morning / My brother Bill's a fireman.
LP: . . . . **PRICE 67**
MC: . . . . **PRIMC 67**

COMPACT COLLECTION, THE.
Tracks: / Flower of Scotland / Dumbarton's drums / Portree kid / Glencoe / Bricklayers song / Come o'er the stream / MacPherson's rant / Roses of Prince, The / Lammas tide, The / Massacre of Glencoe / Ettrick lady / Turn ye tae me / Sherramuir fight, The / Dark Lochnagar / King fareweel / Man's a man, A.
LP: . . . . **LILP 6032**
MC: . . . . **LIMC 6032**

CORRIES.
Tracks: / Sheriffmuir / Sound the pibroch / Kate Dalrymple / Petronella / Where two hawks fly / Bluebells of Scotland / Heidless cross, The / Rattlin' roarin' wullie / Jock O'Hazeldean / Black Douglas / Wha wadna fecht for Charlie / Helen of Kirkconnel / Scots wha hae / Isle of Skye / I know my love / Lark in the morning, The / Hen's march / Peeire hoose ahint the burn / Norwick wedding / Man's a man, A / Westgering home / Dowie dens o' Yarrow, The (CD only.) / News from Moidart, The (CD only.) / Gartan mothers lullaby (CD only.).
MC: . . . . **TCIDL 101**

CORRIES, THE.
LP: . . . . **PA 070**
MC: . . . . **CPA 070**

FLOWER OF SCOTLAND.
Tracks: / Stirling brig / Kelvingrove / Vicar and the frog, The / Bona line, The / Loo song, The / Black Douglas / Bonnie ship the Diamond, The / Mothers, daughters, wives / Tibbie dunbar / Shenandoah / Castle of Drumore, The / Food blues, The / Flower of Scotland.
LP: . . . . **REB 820**
MC: . . . . **ZCF 820**

LEGENDS OF SCOTLAND.
Tracks: / Black Douglas / Wha widna fecht for Charlie / Isle of Skye / I will go / Sound the Pibroch / Derwentwater's farewell / Flood Garry / Bonnie Dundee / Peggy Gordon / Boys from Blue Hill / Abigail / Gartan mothers lullaby / Maids when you're young, never wed an old man / Rose of Allandale / Kiss the children for me, Mary / Westering home.
MC: . . . . **ZCLLS 707**

LIVE AT THE ROYAL LYCEUM THEATRE EDINBURGH.
Tracks: / Wha widna fecht for Charlie / Liberty / Side by side / Tramps and hawkers / Great silkie, The / Lyceum blues / Ye Jacobites by name / Lowlands away / Abigail / Old triangle, The / Dream Angus / Maids, when you're young, never wed an old man / Bonnie Dundee.
LP: . . . . **NTS 109**

MAN'S A MAN, A.
MC: . . . . **TCIDL 8**

SCOTTISH LOVE SONGS.
LP: **6309004**

SOUND OF PIBROCH.
LP: . . . . **SCX 6511**

SPOTLIGHT ON....
Tracks: / Fond kiss, A / Bring back my granny to me / Ca' the ewes / Cruel brother / Flower of Scotland / Gallus bloke / Haughs o' Cromdale / Highland lament / Hills of Ardmorn / Johnny lad / Katie Bairdie / Kismuil's galley / Lewis bridal song / Oor wee school / Road to Dundee, The / Sally free and easy / Bonnie lass o' Fyvie / Gallus bloke / Glenlyon lament / Haughs o' Cromdale / Lowlands of Holland, The / My brother Bill's a fireman / Parcel o' rogues / Roving journey man, The / Toon o' Kelso / Twa corbies / Wild rover / Will ye go lassie go.
LP: **6625035**

VERY BEST OF THE CORRIES.
Tracks: / Black Douglas / Wha wadna fecht for Charlie / Isle of Skye / I will go / Sound the pibroch / Derwentwater's farewell / Flood Garry / Bonnie Dundee / Peggy Gordon / Boys of Barehill and Derry hornpipe / Abigail / Tartan mother's lullaby / Maids when you're

young, never wed an old man / Rose of Allendale / Kiss the children for me Mary / Westering home.
LP: . . . . MFP 50478
MC: . . . . HR 8181
MC: . . . . TCMFP 50478

Corrigan, Ian

IRISH COUNTRY.
Tracks: / Gallant John Joe / You can't judge a book by the cover / Irish eyes / Blue hills of Breffni / She's leavin' / Marjie's at the Lincoln Park Inn / Steppin' stone / Little Pedro / Orchid and the rose / You're the only one / Shores of Lake Macnean / In spring the roses always turn red / County Cavan / Clap your hands / Hang my picture in your heart / Sweet Charlotte Ann.
MC: . . . . CPHL 417
LP: . . . . PHL 417

Corrin, Stephen (nar)

SELECTED STORIES FOR UNDER 5'S (see under Selected Stories...) (Corrin, Stephen & Sara).

Corrosion Of

ANIMOSITY.
LP: . . . . RR 9764

EYE FOR AN EYE.
Tracks: / Tell me / Indifferent / Rabid dogs / Redneckkk / Minds are controlled / Broken will / L.S. / Co-exist / Dark thoughts / What? / Positive outlook / College town / Eye for an eye / Poison planet / Negative outlook / No drunk / Not safe / Nothing's gonna change.
LP: . . . . TXLP 04
LP: . . . . CAROL 1356
MC: . . . . CAROLMC 1356
LP: . . . . INCLP 2

SIX SONGS WITH MIKE SINGING.
Tracks: / Eye for an eye / Citizen / What? / Center of the world / Not for me / Negative outlook.
LP: . . . . CAROL 1365
MC: . . . . CAROLMC 1365
LP: . . . . INCLP 3

Cortex

YOU CAN'T KILL THE BOOGEY MAN.
LP: . . . . CALCLP 006

Cortez, John

JOHN CORTEZ SINGS 20 LOVE SONGS.
LP: . . . . SIRELP 1114

Corvini, Alberti

FIREWORKS (Corvini, Alberti Jazz Big Band).
LP: . . . . IJC 004

Cory Band

AMERICAN EXPRESS.
Tracks: / Liberty bell / Overture 'Iolanthe' / El cumbanchero / All through the night / Glory, glory / Music from the Elizabethan court / Trumpets wild / Magic flute overtures.
LP: . . . . XTRA 1169

CORY BAND.
Tracks: / Aces high / Myfanwy / Rule Britannia / Symphony of marches / March, Opus 99 / Y deryn pur / Blue and the gray, The / Tuxedo junction / Londonderry air / Pennsylvania 65000 / Anvil chorus.
LP: . . . . SB 340

CORY BAND IN CONCERT.
Tracks: / Skyrider / Hungarian dance / Country scene / Nocturne and interlude / Girl I left behind me, The / Blue rondo a la Turk / Lullaby for Lisa / Lucky for some / Scarborough Fair / First shoot / Castleway / Fanfare for Rocky / Procession of the sirdar / Land of the long white cloud / Blow the wind southerly / Variations on a ninth / Cory Band.
LP: . . . . PRL 027D
MC: . . . . CPRL 027D

CORY BAND, THE (1884 - 1984).
Tracks: / Fanfare for Rocky / Procession for the Sirdar / Serenata / Land of the long white cloud / Castleway / Blow the wind southerly / Variations on a ninth.
LP: . . . . PRL 021
MC: . . . . CPRL 021
LP: . . . . TB 3023

DANCES AND ARIAS.
Tracks: / Continental caprice / Dances and arias / Doyen / March paraphrase: Men of Harlech / Siegfried's funeral march / Year of the dragon.
LP: . . . . PRL 025 D
MC: . . . . CPRL 025 D

PRIDE OF THE RHONDA.
Tracks: / Maple leaf rag / Land of the mountain and the flood, The / Concert overture / Albertie / Les girls / Sweet gingerbread man / Magnificent seven, The (Theme from 'The Guns Of Naverine') / La domino noir / Overture / Il silenzio / Prince of Denmark's march, The / Virginian, Theme from / Miller magic / Guns of Navarone.
LP: . . . . OU 2165

SALUTE TO THE NEW WORLD.
Tracks: / Salute to the New World overture / Rule Britannia / Chorale and rock out / Elegy from an epic symphony / Dashing away with a smoothing iron / March / Manhattan beach / Jeannie / Marche des Bouffons / Largo from the new world symphony / Fantasia on the dargason / Fanfare for Rocky / Procession of the sirdar / Land of the long white cloud / Castleway / Blow the wind southerly / Variations on a ninth.
LP: . . . . GRS 1052

Coryell, Larry

ASPECTS.
Tracks: / Kowloon jag / Titus / Pyramids / Rodrigo reflections / Yin-yang / Woman of truth and future.
LP: . . . . ARTY 133

AT VILLAGE GATE.
LP: . . . . VSD 6573

BACK TOGETHER (Coryell, Larry & Alphonse Mouzon).
Tracks: / Beneath the earth / Express / Back together again / Phonse, The / Transvested express / Crystallization / Rock 'n' roll lovers / Get on up / Reconciliation / Mr. C / High love.
LP: . . . . K 50382

BAREFOOT BOY.
LP: . . . . CL 13961

COMING HOME.
Tracks: / Good citizen swallow / Glorielle / Twelve and twelve / Confirmation / It never entered my mind.
LP: . . . . MR 5303

DRAGON GATE.
LP: . . . . SHAN 97005

EQUIPOISE.
Tracks: / Unemployed Floyd / Tender tears / Equipoise / Christina / Joy Spring / First things first.
LP: . . . . MR 5319

FUSE ONE (see under Clarke, Stanley) (Coryell, Larry & Philip Catherine).

INTRODUCING 11TH HOUSE.
LP: . . . . VSD 79342

JUST LIKE BEING BORN (Coryell, Larry & Brian Keane).
LP: . . . . FF 337

LEVEL ONE.
Tracks: / Other side, The / Level one / Diedra / Some greasy stuff / Nyctaphobia / Suite.
LP: . . . . ARTY 113

L'OISEAU DE FEU (THE FIREBIRD)/ PETROUCHKA.
LP: 8128 641

PLANET END.
LP: . . . . VSD 79367

RESTFUL MIND, THE.
Tracks: / Improvisation on Robert De Visee's Minuet II / Ann Arbor / Pavane for a dead princess / Improvisation on Robert De Visee's Sarabande / Song for Jim Webb / Julie La Belle / Restful mind, The.
LP: . . . . VSD 79353

RETURN.
Tracks: / Cisco at the disco / Rue Gregoire du Tour / Three mile island / Return / Sweet shuffle / Mediterranean sundance / Entre dos Aguas.
LP: . . . . VSD 79426

SHINING HOUR.
LP: . . . . VG 651600632

SPACES.
Tracks: / Spaces / Rene's theme / Gloria's step / Wrong is right / Chris / New year's day in Los Angeles-1968.
LP: . . . . VSD 79345
LP: . . . . VMLP 5305
MC: . . . . VMTC 6305

SPLENDID (See under Catherine, Philippe) (Catherine, Philippe & Larry Coryell).

STANDING OVATION.
LP: . . . . AN 3024

TRIBUTARIES.
Tracks: / File, The / Mother's day / Little B's poem / Zimbabwe / Solo on Wednesday / Thurman Munson / Equinox / Alster fields.
LP: . . . . NL 83072
MC: . . . . NK 83072

TWIN HOUSE (See under Catherine, Phillip) (Coryell, Larry & Philip Catherine).

Cosby, Bill

BEST OF BILL COSBY.
Tracks: / Medic / Go carts / $75 / Noah right / Noah, and the neighbour / Noah / Me and you Lord / Tonsils / Kindergarten / Playground, The.
LP: . . . . K 46002

BILL'S BEST FRIEND.
Tracks: / Roland and the rollercoaster / Puberty / People who drink / Frisbies / Chinese mustard / Famous people / Let's make a deal / Cars / Illegal drugs / Parents and grandparents.
MCSET: . . . . ECC 211

FOR ADULTS ONLY.
MC: . . . . LAFFC 2

MUSIC FROM THE BILL COSBY SHOW (Various artists).
Tracks: / Resthatherian: *Various artists* / Camille: *Various artists* / Love in its proper place: *Various* artists / Poppin': *Various artists* / Kitchen jazz: *Various artists* / Clair: *Various artists* / Huxtable kids, The: *Various artists* / Outstretched hands (Gloria): *Various artists* / Look at this: *Various artists* / House full of love,A: *Various artists.*
LP: . . . . CBS 26824
MC: 40 26824

MY FATHER CONFUSED ME... WHAT DO I DO?.
Tracks: / English language, The / Henry Kissinger / UFO / My father confused me / Glazed donut monster, The / Mothers enunciate / FCC and mothers, The / Mothers will hit you for nothing / Fathers are the funniest people / Marriage and duties / New husbands kill things / Lizard and the mouse, The / Dudes on dope / Dentist, The.
MCSET: . . . . ECC 212

THOSE OF YOU WITH OR WITHOUT CHILDREN.
Tracks: / Genesis / Great quote, The / Window of life, The.
LP: 9241041

WHERE YOU LAY YOUR HANDS.
MC: 8419304

Cosey Fanni Tutti

TIME TO TELL.
LP: . . . . CRL 22
LP: . . . . CRL 24

Cosma, Vladimir

DIVA SOUNDTRACK.
LP: . . . . A 120061
MC: . . . . C 120061

KIDNAPPED (TV soundtrack) (Cosma, Vladimir Orchestra).
LP: . . . . MORR 525
MC: . . . . KMORCR 525

Cosmetic

SO TRANQUILIZIN.
Tracks: / All things must change / Be my girl / Take it to the top / All my love / N-er-gize me / About the money / So tranquilizin / Jet set, The.
LP: 1883101
MC: 1883104

Cosmic Psychos

COSMIC PSYCHOS.
LP: . . . . GOES ON 23

SLAVE TO THE GRAVE.
LP: . . . . RAT 505

Cosmos (tv)

COSMOS (TV Soundtrack) (Various artists).
Tracks: / Heaven and hell: *Vangelis* / Symphony No. 11 (Shostakovich): *Shostakovich (composer)* / Alpha: *Vangelis*/ Depicting the cranes in their nest: *Japanese Trad* / Canon A 3 in D on ground: *Various artists* / Four seasons (spring), The: *Vivaldi (composer)* / Sea named Solaris: *Bach(composer)* / Partita no. 3: *Bach(composer)*/ Symphony No. 19 (Hovhaness): *Hovhaness* / Legacy: *Synergy* / Russian easter festival overture: *Rimsky-Korsakov* (composer) / Inside the heart of the universe: *Takemitsu* / Fly night bird: *Buchanan* / Beauborg (part 2): *Vangelis* / Rite of spring, The / Entends tu les chiens aboyer: *Various artists* / Sky: *Vangelis* / Bulgarian shepherdess song: *Trad* / Heaven and hell (part 1): *Vangelis.*
LP: . . . . BL 89334
MC: . . . . BK 89334
LP: . . . . RCALP 5032

Cosmotheka

COSMOTHEKA.
LP: . . . . DAM 008

GOOD TURN OUT, A.
LP: . . . . SHY 7015

KEEP SMILING THROUGH (Hit songs of World War II).
Tracks: / Smiling through / Wish me luck as you wave me goodbye / I love to sit with Sophie in the shelter / I did what I could with my gas mask / Whitehall warriors / Lili Marlene / D Day dodgers / Roll me over / We'll meet again (instrumental) / Follow the white line / I get along without you very well / Hey little hen / Dig dig dig to victory / They're all under the counter / I'm gonna get lit up when the lights go out in London / Knees up Mother Brown / Medley.
LP: . . . . REH 746
MC: . . . . ZCR 746

LITTLE BIT OFF THE TOP,A.
LP: . . . . SHY 7002

WINES AND SPIRITS.
LP: . . . . SHY 7001

Cossu, Scott

ISLANDS.
Tracks: / Ohana / Gypsy dance / St. Croix / Islands / Harlequin messenger / Vashon poem / Oristano sojourn / Fawn.
LP: 371033-1
MC: 371033-4
LP: . . . . WHA 1033

SWITCHBACK.
Tracks: / Desert lightning / Country fair / Switchback / Serpentine wall / Infinite circles / Manhattan underground / Child's eye / Stehekin / Last snow / Beyond the looking glass.
LP: 371 081-1
MC: 371 081-4

WIND DANCE.
LP: C-1016

Costa, Eddie

EDDIE COSTA-VINNIE BURKE TRIO (Costa, Eddie & Vinnie Burke).
LP: . . . . FS 129

PHOENIX JAZZ FIFTH ANNIVERSARY ALBUM (see Harris, Bill) (Costa, Eddie/ Bill Harris/Dizzy Gillespie/Coleman Hawkins).

Costa, Gal

FANTASIA.
LP: 6328 365

Costa, Nikka

NIKKA COSTA.
Tracks: / Someone to watch over me / I believe in love / Out here on my own / Grown up world / Ice castles (through the eyes of love), Theme from / Go away, little boy / Maybe / It's your dream / Bubble full of rainbows / Chained to the blues / You / So glad I have you.
LP: . . . . RCALP 3091

Costello, Cecilia

GREENWOOD SIDE-I-O (Two Midlands singers) (Costello, Cecilia & Sam Bennett).
Tracks: / My Barney (lies over the ocean) / Ghost of Willie-o, The / Love, it is a killing thing / Fare you well cold winter / Betsy of Ballantown Brae / I'm a maid that's deep in love / Shule aveel agra / Female cabin boy, The / Green bushes / Green wedding / I wish, I wish / Jew's garden, The / Frog and the mouse, the / Wedding song, The / Wexford murder / American stranger, The / Foggy dew, The / Bailiff's daughter of Islington / Gipsies glee, The / Spring glee / Blow away the morning dew / Brave Admiral Benbow.
MC: 60-098

Costello, Elvis

ALMOST BLUE (Costello, Elvis & The Attractions).
Tracks: / Why don't you love me / Sweet dreams / I'm your toy / Tonight the bottle let me down / Brown to blue / Good year for the roses, A / Sittin' and thinkin' / Colour of the blues / Too far gone / Honey hush / How much I've lied.
LP: . . . . FIEND 33
MC: . . . . FIENDCASS 33
LP: . . . . XXLP 13
MC: . . . . XXC 13

ARMED FORCES.
Tracks: / Senior service / Oliver's army / Big boys / Green shirt / Party girl / Goon squad / Busy bodies / Sunday's best / Chemistry class / Two little Hitlers / Accidents will happen.
LP: . . . . FIEND 21
MC: . . . . FIENDCASS 21
LP: . . . . XXLP 5
MC: . . . . XXC 5
LP: . . . . RAD 14

BEST OF ELVIS COSTELLO - THE MAN.
Tracks: / Watching the detectives / Olivers army / Alison / Accidents will happen / Pump it up / High fidelity / Pills and soap / (I don't want to go to) Chelsea / New lace sleeves / Good year for the roses, A / I can't stand up for falling down / Clubland / Beyond belief / New Amsterdam / Green shirt / Everyday I write the book / I wanna be loved / Shipbuilding.
LP: . . . . FIEND 52
MC: . . . . FIENDCASS 52
LP: . . . . STAR 2247
MC: . . . . STAC 2247

BLOOD AND CHOCOLATE.

Tracks: / Uncomplicated / I hope you're happy now / Tokyo storm warning / Home is anywhere you hang your head / I want you / Honey are you straight or are you blind / Blue chair / Battered old bird / Crimes of Paris / Poor Napoleon / Next time round.
LP: . . . . XFIEND 80
MC: . . . . FIENDCASS 80

ELVIS COSTELLO: INTERVIEW PICTURE DISC.
LPPD: . . . . BAK 2001

G.B.H. (TV Soundtrack).
LP: . . . . DSLP 4
MC: . . . . DSCASS 4

GET HAPPY (Costello, Elvis & The Attractions).
Tracks: / Love for tender / Opportunity / Imposter / Secondary modern / King horse / Possession / Man called uncle / Clowntime is over / New Amsterdam / High fidelity / I can't stand up for falling down / Black and white world / Five gears in reverse / B movie / Motel matches / Human touch / Beaten to the punch / Temptation / I stand accused / Riot act.
LP: . . . . FIEND 24
MC: . . . . FIENDCASS 24
LP: . . . . XXLP 1
MC: . . . . XXC 1

GIRLS, GIRLS, GIRLS.
Tracks: / Watching the detectives / (I don't want to go to) Chelsea / Alison / Shipbuilding / I want you / American without tears / Oliver's army.
LP: . . . . DFIEND 160
MC: . . . . FIENDCASS 160
DAT: . . . . FIENDDAT 160

GIRLS, GIRLS, GIRLS VOL.2.
Tracks: / Alison / Almost blue / I want you / Oliver's army / Pills and soap / American without tears.
MC: . . . . FIENDCASS 161

GOODBYE CRUEL WORLD (Costello, Elvis & The Attractions).
Tracks: / Only flame in town, The / Home truth / Room with no number / Inch by inch / Worthless thing / Love field / I wanna be loved / Comedians, The / Joe Porterhouse / Sour milk cow blues / Great unknown, The / Deportees club, The / Peace in our time.
LP: . . . . FIEND 75
LP: . . . . ZL 70317
MC: . . . . ZK 70317

IMPERIAL BEDROOM.
Tracks: / Beyond belief / Tears before bedtime / Shabby doll / Long honeymoon, The / Man out of time / Almost blue / And in every home / Loved ones, The / Human hands / Kid about it / Little savage / Boy with a problem / Pidgin English / You little fool / Town crier / Only flame in town, The / Room with no number / Inch by inch / Worthless thing / Love field / I wanna be loved / Comedians, The / Joe Porterhouse / Sour milk cow blues / Great unknown, The / Deporteess club, The / Peace in our time.
LP: . . . . FIEND 36
MC: . . . . FIENDCASS 36
LP: . . . . XXLP 17

KING OF AMERICA (See Costello Show).

LIVE AT RONNIE SCOTT'S (See under Baker, Chet) (Baker, Chet & Elvis Costello).

MIGHTY LIKE A ROSE.
LP: . . . . WX 419
MC: . . . . WX 419 C

MY AIM IS TRUE.
Tracks: / Welcome to the working week / Miracle man / No dancing / Blame it on Cain / Alison / Sneaky feelings / (Angels wanna wear my) red shoes / Less than zero / Mystery dance / Pay it back / I'm not angry / Waiting for the end of the world.
LP: . . . . FIEND 13
MC: . . . . FIENDCASS 13
LP: . . . . SEEZ 3
MC: . . . . ZSEEZ 3

OUT OF OUR IDIOT.
Tracks: / Blue chair / Seven day weekend / Turning the town red / Heathrow Town / People's limousine / So young / American without tears (No. 2 Twilight version) / Get yourself another fool / Walking on thin ice / Baby its you / From head to toe / Shoes without heels / Baby's got a brand new hairdo / Flirting kind, The / Black sails in the sunset / Imperial bedroom / Stampling grams, The.
LP: . . . . XFIEND 67
MC: . . . . FIENDCASS 67

PUNCH THE CLOCK.
Tracks: / Everyday I write the book / Pills and soap / Shipbuilding / Let them all talk / Boxing day / Love went mad / Greatest thing, The / Element within, The / Charm school / Invisible man, The / Mouth almighty / King of thieves / World and his wife, The.
LP: . . . . FIEND 72
LP: . . . . ZL 70026
MC: . . . . ZK 70026
LP: . . . . XXLP 19
MC: . . . . FIENDCASS 72

SPIKE.
Tracks: / This town / Let him dangle / Deep dark truthful mirror / Veronica / God's comic / Chewing gum / Tramp the dirt down / Stalin Malone / Satellite / Pads, paws and claws / Baby plays around / Miss Macbeth / Any king's shilling / Coal train robberies / Last boat leaving.
LP: . . . . WX 238
MC: . . . . WX 238 C

STRANGER IN THE HOUSE (See under Jones, George) (Jones, George/Elvis Costello).

TEN BLOODY MARYS AND TEN HOW'S YOUR FATHERS (Costello, Elvis & The Attractions).
Tracks: / Clean money / Girls talk / Talking in the dark / Radio sweetheart / Big tears / Crawling to the USA / Just a memory / Watching the detectives / Stranger in the house / Clowntime is over (no.2) / Getting mighty crowded / Hoover factory / Tiny steps / (What's so funny 'bout) peace love and understanding / Doctor Luther's assistant / Radio radio / Black and white world / Wednesday week / My funny valentine / Ghost train.
LP: . . . . FIEND 27
MC: . . . . FIENDCASS 27
MC: . . . . XXC 6

THIS YEAR'S MODEL.
Tracks: / Beyond belief / Tears before bedtime / Shabby doll / Long honeymoon, The / Man out of time / Almost blue / And in every home / Loved ones, The / Human hands / Kid about it / Little savage / Beat, The / Pump it up / Hand in hand / Lip service / Living in Paradise / Lipstick vogue / Night rally / No action / This years girl / Little triggers / You belong to me / (I don't want to go to) Chelsea.
LP: . . . . FIEND 18
MC: . . . . FIENDCASS 18
LP: . . . . XXLP 4
MC: . . . . XXC 4
LP: . . . . RAD 3

TRUST.
Tracks: / Clubland / Lover's walk / You'll never be a man / Pretty words / Strict time / Luxembourg / Watch your step / New lace sleeves / From a whisper to a scream / Different finger / White knuckles / Shot with his own gun / Fish'n'chip paper / Big sisters clothes.
LP: . . . . XXLP 11
MC: . . . . XXC 11
LP: . . . . FIEND 30
MC: . . . . FIENDCASS 30

Costello Show

KING OF AMERICA.
Tracks: / Brilliant mistake / Lovable / Our little angel / Don't let me be misunderstood / Glitter gulch / Indoor fireworks / Little palaces / I'll wear it proudly / American without tears / Eisenhower blues / Poisoned rose / Big light, The / Jack of all parades / Suit of lights / Sleep of the just.
LP: . . . . FIEND 78
MC: . . . . FIENDCASS 78
LP: . . . . ZL 70946

Cotswolds

COTSWOLD CHARACTERS.
Tracks: / Shepherd Tidmarsh / Life as a roadsweeper.
LP: . . . . SDL 222
MC: . . . . CSDL 222

COTSWOLD CRAFTSMEN.
MC: . . . . CSDL 247

COTSWOLD VOICES.
MC: . . . . CSDL 267

WHILE I WORK I WHISTLE.
Tracks: / Granny's old armchair / Nettle tea.
LP: . . . . SDL 300
MC: . . . . CSDL 300

Cottam, Geoff

JUBILEE STREET (Contemporary blues & love songs).
MC: 60-093

Cotten, Beverly

CLOGGING LESSONS.
LP: . . . . FF 237

Cotten, Elizabeth

ELIZABETH COTTEN LIVE.
LP: . . . . ARHOOLIE 1089

Cotton, Billy

BILLY COTTON (Cotton, Billy & His Band).
Tracks: / New tiger rag / Why did she fall for the leader of the band? / Dancing with my shadow / Bessie couldn't help it / Tattooed lady, The / St. Louis blues / What a difference a day made / Avalon / Nobody loves a fairy when she's forty / Hyde Park Corner / Truckin' / They all start whistling Mary / After you've gone / She was only somebody's daughter / I'll never say "never again" again.
LP: . . . . SH 141

CRAZY WEATHER (Cotton, Billy & His Band).
Tracks: / Crazy weather / Isle of Capri / Why am I blue? / Margie / Lazybones / Annie doesn't live here any more / St. Louis blues / Two cigarettes in the dark / Judy / Hold me / I was in the mood / Man from Harlem, The / Ole faithful / Oh mother, mother (please speak to Willie) / Third tiger, The (tiger rag no.3) / Hand in hand (we go together) / Down a long, long road / Who made little boy blue?.
LP: . . . . CHD 125
MC: . . . . MCHD 125

GOLDEN AGE OF BILLY COTTON, THE.
Tracks: / New tiger rag / Why did she fall for the leader of the band / Dancing with my shadow / Bessie couldn't help it / Tattooed lady, The / St. Louis blues / What a difference a day made / Avalon / Nobody loves a fairy when shes forty / Hyde Park Corner / Truckin' / Shine / They all start whistling Mary / She was only somebody's daughter / I'll never say "never again" again.
LP: . . . . GX 412521-1
MC: . . . . GX 412521-4

LET'S ALL JOIN IN (Cotton, Billy & His Orchestra).
Tracks: / When you're smiling / Put your arms around me honey / Side by side / Tea for two / I can't give you anything but love / Ain't she sweet? / Dream / Are you lonesome tonight? / Oh what a beautiful morning / Daisy Bell / Ma (he's making eyes at me) / Woody Woodpecker / Jeepers creepers / Beer barrel polka / Alexander's ragtime band / Me and my shadow / My blue Heaven / Who's sorry now? / Just one more chance / You were meant for me / Black bottom / Deep in the heart of Texas / Around the world in 80 days / True love / Ballin' the jack / After the ball / Goodnight sweetheart / Last mile home.
LP: . . . . BDL 1050

MELODY MAKER (Cotton, Billy & His Band).
Tracks: / Melody maker / You and i / Bring out the little brown jug / You'll be happy little sweetheart in the spring / Turn your money in your pocket / Yeah man / Don't worry 'bout me / Over and done with / Somebody stole my gal / Ten little men with feathers / When you know you're not forgotten / Hold tight / Do I love you / Hut sut song / Wishing / Somebody cares about you / I know why / Something to remember you by.
LP: . . . . RFL 27

NOBODY'S SWEETHEART (Cotton, Billy & His Orchestra).
2LP: . . . . SVLD 006
MCSET: . . . . CSVLD 006

ROCK YOUR CARES AWAY (Cotton, Billy & His Band).
Tracks: / Somebody loves you / Clouds will soon roll by, The / Thompson's old grey mule / Say it isn't so / We just couldn't say goodbye / There's another trumpet playing in the sky / Georgia on my mind / Just another dream of you / Rock your cares away / Nightfall / Wrap your arms around me / Now that you're gone / Listen to the German band / Leave the pretty girls alone / Goodnight Vienna / Let's all sing like the birdies sing.
LP: . . . . JOY 279

SING A NEW SONG (Cotton, Billy & His Band).
Tracks: / Sing a new song / Day by day / I'm crazy 'bout my baby / Give me your affection honey / Nina Rosa / They all start whistling Mary / Let's get friendly / Smile darn ya smile / Sunshine and roses / Whistle and blow your blues away / Ooh that kiss / I heard / What'd ja do to me / Bungalow, a piccolo and you / Too many tears / We're a couple of soliders / How'm I doin' / That's where the South begins / Roll on, Mississippi, roll on / I'm just wild about Harry.
LP: . . . . SVL 160

SOMEBODY STOLE MY GAL (Cotton, Billy & His Band).
Tracks: / Diggin' my potatoes / Ying yang / 23 hours too long / No more doggin' / No cuttin' loose / Ain't doing too bad / Sunny road / Superharp / Easy loving / High compression.
LP: . . . . OLD 7

THAT RHYTHM MAN (Cotton, Billy & His Band).
Tracks: / Sing a new song / We just couldn't say goodbye / Leave the pretty girls alone / Look what I've got / Margie / Georgia on my mind / Somebody loves you / You rascal you / Day by day / Bessie couldn't help it / I wanna be loved by you / That rhythm man / Auf wiedersehen my dear / Goodnight Vienna / Just another dream of you / Clouds will soon roll by, The / In the park in Paree / Now that you're gone.
LP: . . . . BUR 007
MC: . . . . 4 BUR 007

THAT RHYTHM MAN VOL 2 (1928-1931) (Cotton, Billy & His Orchestra).
Tracks: / From Monday on / My Southern home / Puttin' on the Ritz / That rhythm man / You brought a new kind of love to me / New tiger rag, The / Bessie couldn't help it / You're lucky to me / Memories of you / That Lindy hop / It looks like love / Were you sincere? / Why shouldn't I? / You wouldn't / Parkin' in the moonlight / It's the girl / You call it madness (but I call it love) / Yes-yes (my baby said Yes-yes) / Nobody's sweetheart / Sleepy time down south.
LP: . . . . SVL 149
MC: . . . . CSVL 149

WAKEE WAKEE! (Cotton, Billy & His Band).
Tracks: / Somebody stole my girl / Bugle call rag / I'm just wild about Harry / Third tiger, The / Mood indigo / Fancy our meeting / So green / Ooo-la-la / It's only a paper moon / Rhapsody in blue / Skirts / Best wishes / Sweep / Mrs Bartholomew / You don't understand / Why has a cow got four legs? / St. Louis blues / She was only somebody's daughter / Night owl / Young and healthy / You're getting to be a habit with me / Shuffle off to Buffalo / Forty second steet / Smile darn ya, smile.
LP: . . . . AJA 5037
MC: . . . . ZC AJA 5037
LP: C5-513
MC: C5K-513

Cotton Chopper.....

COTTON CHOPPER COUNTRY (Various artists).
LP: . . . . REDITA 126

Cotton Club

COTTON CLUB RECORDINGS (see under Jazz) (Various artists).

Cotton Club (film)

COTTON CLUB (Film soundtrack) (Barry, John).
LP: . . . . GHS 24062
MC: M5G 24062

COTTON CLUB (Film soundtrack) (Various artists).
Tracks: / Mooche, The: *Various artists* / Cotton Club stomp No 2: *Various artists* / Drop me off in Harlem: *Various artists* / Creole love call: *Various artists* / Ring dem bells: *Various artists* / East St. Louis toodle-oo: *Various artists* / Truckin': *Various artists* / Ill wind: *Various artists* / Cotton Club stomp No 1: *Various artists* / Mood indigo: *Various artists* / Minnie the moocher: *Various artists* / Copper coloured gal: *Various artists* / Dixie kidnaps Vera: *Various artists* / Depression hits, The: *Various artists* / Best beats sandman: *Various artists* / Daybreak Express medley: *Various artists.*
LP: . . . . GEF 70260
MC: 4070260
LP: . . . . LOP 14 105

Cotton Comes to...

COTTON COMES TO HARLEM (Film soundtrack) (Various artists).
Tracks: / Cotton comes to Harlem: *Various artists* / Coffin Ed and Grave Digger: *Various artists* / Going home: *Various artists* / Sunlight shining: *Various artists* / Man in distress: *Various artists* / Harlem medley: *Various artists* / Black enough: *Various artists* / Stockyard: *Various artists* / Loving ballad: *Various* artists / Deke: *Various artists* / Down in my soul: *Various artists* / Harlem by day: *Various artists*/ My salvation: *Various artists* / Ed and Digger: *Various artists.*
LP: . . . . MCA 25133
MC: . . . . MCAC 25133
LP: . . . . UAS 29119

Cotton, J

COTTON STYLE (Cotton, J & the Lord Son).
LP: . . . . SEMLP 01

Cotton, James

CUT YOU LOOSE.
MC: . . . . MCCV 79283

FROM COTTON WITH VERVE.
LP: . . . . **BM 9009**

HIGH COMPRESSION.
Tracks: / Diggin' my potatoes / Ying yang / 23 hours too long / No more doggin' / No cuttin' loose / Ain't doing too bad / Sunny road / Superharp / Easy loving / High compression.
LP: . . . . **SNTF 928**

LIVE AND ON THE MOVE VOL.I (Cotton, James Band).
LP: . . . . **BRP 2028**

LIVE AND ON THE MOVE VOL.II (Cotton, James Band).
LP: . . . . **BRP 2029**

LIVE AT ANTONES.
LP: . . . . **AN 007**

LIVE FROM CHICAGO (Mr Superharp himself).
Tracks: / Here I am / Part time love / Just to be with you / Hard headed / When it rains it really pours / Cross your heart / Come back baby / Born in Chicago / Creeper, The.
LP: . . . . **SNTF 959**

MIGHTY LONG TIME.
Tracks: / Straighten up baby / Everything gonna be alright / Black nights / Blow wind blow / Sugar sweet / Moanin' at midnight / Baby please / Hold me in your arms / Call it stormy Monday / Three hundred pounds of joy / Northside cadillac / Mighty long time.
MC: . . . . **ANTMC 15**

MY FOUNDATION.
LP: . . . . **WOW 720**

TAKE ME BACK.
LP: **BP-2587**

Cotton, Joseph

COTTON STYLE.
LP: . . . . **SEMLP 117**

TAKE OF THE TOWN.
LP: . . . . **DSR 3242**

Cotton, Josie

FROM THE HIP.
Tracks: / Jimmy loves Maryann / Licence to dance / Life after love / Stop me / No use crying / Straight talk / Gina / Come with me / School is in / Way out west.
LP: **9603091**

Cotton Mill Boys

AS IS.
LP: . . . . **Unknown**

BEST OF THE COTTON MILL BOYS VOL.1.
LP: . . . . **HPE 627**
MC: . . . . **HPC 627**

ORANGE BLOSSOM SPECIAL.
MC: . . . . **HACS 7058**

Cotton, Sylvester

DETROIT BLUES VOL.1.
Tracks: / Wife lovin' blues / Stranger in your town / I tried / Waterlee blues / Single man blues / Thanksgiving blues / Big chested mama blues / Stormy weather blues / When i'm gone / Pay day blues / Christmas blues / Brown skinned woman / Cottonfield blues / 3 cent stamp blues.
LP: . . . . **KK 7422**

Cotton/Lloyd/Christian

COTTON, LLOYD & CHRISTIAN.
Tracks: / Good things don't last forever / Crying in the rain / Childhood dreams / One more river / Lover who was born to wander / I go to pieces / After the fall / Day by day / Workin' my way back to you / I don't know why you love me / Buffalo.
LP: . . . . **BT 519**

Cottrell, Louis

CLARINET LEGENDS (Cottrell, Louis & Herb).
LP: . . . . **GHB 156**

Couchon, Wolf

MAJOR HANDY.
LP: . . . . **GNPS 2177**
MC: **GNP5 2177**

Cougar, Johnny

BIOGRAPHY, A.
Tracks: / Born reckless / Factory / Night slumming / Taxi dancer / I need a lover / Alley of the angels / High C Cherrie / Where the sidewalk ends / Let them run your lives / Goodnight.
LP: . . . . **RVLP 6**
MC: . . . . **RV 46**

Coughlan, Mary

ANCIENT RAIN.
LP: . . . . **MRLP 004**

TIRED AND EMOTIONAL.
Tracks: / Double cross / Beach, The / Meet me where they play the blues / Delaney's gone back on the wind / Sense of silence (S.O.S) / Nobody's business - the tango / Mamma just wants to barrelhouse all night long / Country fair dance (The cowboy song) / Lady in green / Seduced.
LP: . . . . **WX 103**
MC: . . . . **WX 103C**
LP: . . . . **MRLP 001**

UNCERTAIN PLEASURES.
LP: . . . . **WX 333**
MC: . . . . **WX 333C**

UNDER THE INFLUENCE.
Tracks: / Laziest girl / Ice cream van / Parade of clowns / My land is too green / Ride on / Good morning heartache / Fifteen only / Awol / Dice, The / Don't smoke in bed / Blue surrender / Sunday morning / Copa.
LP: . . . . **WX 116**
MC: . . . . **WX 116 C**
LP: . . . . **MRLP 006**

Coulter, Phil

CLASSIC TRANQUILLITY.
MC: . . . . **KMC 160**
LP: . . . . **KLP 160**

FORGOTTEN DREAMS.
LP: . . . . **HM 040**

PEACE AND TRANQUILITY.
LP: . . . . **HM 001**
MC: . . . . **HMC 001**

PHIL COULTER'S CHRISTMAS.
LP: . . . . **HM 035**

PHIL COULTER'S IRELAND.
LP: . . . . **ONE 1296**
MC: . . . . **OCE 2296**

SCOTTISH TRANQUILITY.
LP: . . . . **DINTV 15**

SEA OF TRANQUILITY.
LP: . . . . **KLP 185**
MC: . . . . **KMC 185**

SERENITY.
LP: . . . . **HM 016**
MC: . . . . **HMC 016**

Counce, Curtis

CARL'S BLUES.
Tracks: / Pink lady / I can't get started / Nica's dream / Love walked in / Larue / Butler did it, The / Carl's blues.
LP: . . . . **COP 040**

COUNCELTATION.
LP: **1007 539**

CURTIS BLUES.
Tracks: / Pink lady / I can't get started / Nica's dream / Love walked in / Larue / Butler did it, The / Carl's blues.
LP: **1007 574**

EXPLORING THE FUTURE (Counce, Curtis Quintet).
Tracks: / So nice / Angel eyes / Into the orbit / Move / Race for space / Someone to watch over me / Countdown, The.
LP: . . . . **BOP 007**

Count

INTUITION ELEMENT.
LP: . . . . **ROSE 28**

LOVE AND FLAME.
LP: . . . . **ROSE 10**

NEW CHANGES.
LP: . . . . **ROSE 87**

Count Bishops

GOOD GEAR.
LP: . . . . **LOLITA 5014**

Count Duckula.

COUNT DUCKULA: NO SAX PLEASE WE'RE EGYPTIAN.
MC: **0 00 109021 6**

COUNT DUCKULA: RESTORATION COMEDY.
MC: **0 00 109020 8**

COUNT DUCKULA: THE GHOST OF CASTLE DUCKULA.
MC: **0 00 109018 6**

COUNT DUCKULA: VAMPIRE VACATION.
MC: **0 00 109019 4**

Count Five

PSYCHOTIC REACTION.
Tracks: / Double-decker bus / Pretty big mouth / World, The / Psychotic reaction / Peace of mind / They're gonna get you / Morning after, The / Can't get your lovin' / You must believe me / Teeny bopper, teeny bopper / Merry-go-round / Contrast / Revelation in slow motion / Declaration of independence.
LP: . . . . **ED 225**
LP: . . . . **OLLP 5215**

Count Of Luxembourg

COUNT OF LUXEMBOURG (Sadler's Wells Cast) (Various artists).
LP: . . . . **TER 1050**
MC: . . . . **ZCTER 1050**

Count Offie

MAN FROM HIGHER HEIGHTS.
LP: . . . . **VSLP 4060**

Count Raven

STORM WARNING.
LP: . . . . **ATV 16**

Countess Maritza

COUNTESS MARITZA (Sadler's Wells cast) (Various artists).
LP: . . . . **TER 1051**
MC: . . . . **ZCTER 1051**

Counting Is Fun

COUNTING IS FUN (Unknown narrator(s)).
MC: . . . . **DIS 013**

Country...

6 TRACK HITS: COUNTRY (Various artists).
MC: **7SC 5041**

14 COUNTRY FAVOURITES (Various artists).
LP: . . . . **GES 5012**
MC: . . . . **KGEC 5012**

16 NUMBER ONE COUNTRY HITS (Various artists).
Tracks: / Boy named Sue, A: *Cash, Johnny* / Most beautiful girl, The: *Rich, Charlie* / Rose garden: *Anderson,* Lynn / When it's Springtime in Alaska: *Horton, Johnny* / Grand tour, The: *Jones, George* / I can help: *Swann,* Billy / Teddy bear song: *Fairchild, Barbara* / Big bad John: *Dean, Jimmy* / Stand by your man: *Wynette,* Tammy / Ballad of Jed Clampett: *Flat, Lester, Earl Scruggs & The Foggy Mountain Boys* / El Paso: *Robbins, Marty*/ Baby, baby (I know you're a lady): *Houston, David* / For the good times: *Price, Ray* / Golden ring: *Jones,* George & Tammy Wynette / Thinkin' of a rendezvous: *Duncan, Johnny (1)* / Blue eyes crying in the rain: *Nelson, Willie.*
LP: **31456**

20 COUNTRY GREATS (Various artists).
LP: . . . . **WW 2010**
MC: . . . . **WW 20104**

20 COUNTRY LOVE SONGS (Various artists).
Tracks: / It's only make believe: *Campbell, Glen* / When I dream: *Gayle, Crystal* / There'll be no teardrops tonight: *Nelson, Willie* / July, you're a woman: *Stewart, John* / Come to me: *Newton, Juice* / Summer wind: *Newton,* Wayne / Will you love me tomorrow?: *Ronstadt, Linda* / You're the reason I'm living: *Darin, Bobby* / Misty blue: *Spears, Billie Jo* / For the good times: *Ford, Tennessee Ernie* / Sharing the night together: *Dr. Hook*/ Let it be me: *Campbell, Glen & Bobbie Gentry* / I'll take you home again, Kathleen: *Whitman, Slim* / Stand by your man: *Jackson, Wanda* / It doesn't matter anymore: *Anka, Paul* / Give me your word: *Ford, Tennessee Ernie*/ Everything a man could ever need: *Campbell, Glen* / Think I'll go somewhere and cry myself to sleep: *Shepard, Jean*/ Minute you're gone, The: *James, Sonny* / We must believe in magic: *Gayle, Crystal* / Don't it make my brown eyes blue: *Gayle, Crystal.*
LP: . . . . **MFP 41 5722 1**
MC: . . . . **MFP 41 5722 4**
LP: . . . . **MFP 5722**
MC: . . . . **TCMFP 5722**

20 GOLDEN PIECES: COUNTRY CHARTS (Various artists).
Tracks: / I walk the line: *Cash, Johnny* / Poor man's riches: *Barnes, Benny* / Girl most likely, The: *Riley,* Jeannie C. / Am I that easy to forget: *Belew, Carl* / King of the road: *Miller, Roger* / A-11: *Paycheck,* Johnny / Roll truck roll: *Simpson, Red* / Give my love to Rose: *Cash, Johnny* / Deck of cards: *Tyler,* T Texas / Auctioneer, The: *Van Dyke, Leroy* / Six days on the road: *Dudley, Dave* / Slippin' around: *Tillman,* Floyd / Window up above: *Jones, George* / Blue suede shoes: *Perkins, Carl* / All for the love of a girl: *Horton,* Johnny / Fancy pants: *Cramer, Floyd* / Big river: *Cash, Johnny* / Little green apples: *Miller, Roger*/ Sally let your bangs hang down: *Maddox Bros.* / Don't let the stars get in your eyes: *Willet, Slim.*
LP: . . . . **BDL 2015**

20 GOLDEN PIECES: COUNTRY HITS (Various artists).
Tracks: / Heartaches by the number: *Jones, George* / I love you so much it hurts: *Lewis, Jerry Lee* / Thanks a lot: *Cash, Johnny* / Born to ramble: *Locklin, Hank* / Dang me: *Miller, Roger* / In a cotton candy world: *Wallace, Jerry* / Remember me: *Tyler, T Texas* / I can't help it (if I'm still in love with you): *Tillman,* Frank singers / Pickin' sweethearts: *Dean, Jimmy* / Folsom Prison blues: *Cash, Johnny* / Wishful thinking: *Stewart, Wynn* / No help wanted: *Carlisles* / Domino: *Orbison, Roy* / 42 in Chicago: *Kilgore, Merle*/ Cotton patch, The: *Riley, Jeannie C.* / Born to sing the blues: *Twitty, Conway* / Release me: *Wallace, Jerry*/ Down the street to 301: *Cash, Johnny* / With pen in hand: *Miller, Roger* / C.C. rider: *Various artists.*
LP: . . . . **BDL 2014**

20 GOLDEN PIECES: COUNTRY MUSIC (Various artists).
Tracks: / Stop the world: *Cline, Patsy* / I heard the jukebox playing: *Young, Faron* / Rock Island line: *Cash,* Johnny / Doin' my time: *Flatt, Lester & Earl Scruggs* / Honey: *Miller, Roger* / Heartbreak, Tennessee: *Paycheck,* Johnny / Your cheatin' heart: *Tillman, Frank singers* / Misty blue: *Smith, Jerry* / Letter you promised to write, The: *Husky, Ferlin* / You're the nearest thing to Heaven: *Cash, Johnny* / Shutters and boards: *Wallace,* Jerry / Crazy dreams: *Twitty, Conway* / Walk right in: *Campbell, Glen* / Box of memories: *Riley, Jeannie* C. / My heart cries for you: *Rich, Charlie* / Train of love: *Cash, Johnny* / I love you because: *Jones,* George / Miss Brown: *Houston, David* / I wish I could fall in love again: *Howard, Jan* / Oh lonesome me: *Dudley, Dave.*
LP: . . . . **BDL 2017**

20 GOLDEN PIECES: COUNTRY NOSTALGIA (Various artists).
Tracks: / Do wacka do: *Miller, Roger* / He made a woman out of me: *Riley, Jeannie C.* / Careless love: *Tyler,* T Texas / There she goes: *Wallace, Jerry* / Everybody's trying to be my baby: *Perkins, Carl* / I heard that lonesome whistle blow: *Cash, Johnny* / High geared daddy: *Pierce, Webb* / Bouquet in Heaven: *Flatt, Lester* & Earl Scruggs / Little Miss Heartache: *Belew, Carl* / I'm a free man now: *Young, Faron* / Will the circle be unbroken?: *Lewis, Jerry Lee* / Cold, cold heart: *Jones, George* / Get rhythm: *Cash, Johnny* / Crazy over you: *Locklin, Hank* / Done rovin': *Horton, Johnny* / Man with the golden gun, The: *Campbell, Glen*/ In case of the blues: *Cline, Patsy* / Dear heart: *Miller, Roger* / Seven lonely days: *Dudley, Dave*/ There you go: *Cash, Johnny.*
LP: . . . . **BDL 2016**

20 GREAT COUNTRY RECORDINGS OF THE 50'S VOL.2 (Various artists).
Tracks: / Texas honky tonk: *Baker, Clay* / Diesel smoke: *Barnes, Benny* / Time lock: *Barnes, Benny* / Tender age: *Dee & Patty* / Would you be waiting (for my ship to come in): *Davis, Link* / Pappy Daily's breakdown: *Allen, Ward* / Shackled: *Sadie & Bobby* / Must I leave it there: *Burns, Sonny* / Guy you used to be, The: *Cornish, Joyce* / Big town baby: *Adams, Don* / Night life: *Nelson, Willie* / Thunder and lightning: *Nelson,* Willie / Cotton: *Bowman, Cecil* / Go home letter: *Barber, Glen* / Love's gonna live here: *Jones, George*/ There goes my heart: *Drake, Charles* / Storm has just begun, The: *Nelson, Willie* / Wanderin' Oakie: *Noack, Eddie* / No memories: *Dollar, Johnny* / Race is on, The: *Jones, George.*
MC: . . . . **CROP 1011**
LP: . . . . **DROP 1011**

20 GREAT COUNTRY RECORDINGS OF THE 50'S AND 60'S (Various artists).
Tracks: / Man with the blues: *Nelson, Willie* / I shot Sam: *Ward, Margie* / If you see my baby: *Burns, Sonny*/ Much to much: *Various artists* / Family bible: *Gray, Claude* / Never been so weary: *Jones, George* / Cup of loneliness: *Jones, George* / Crawling back to you: *Dollar, Johnny* / Lights are on, The: *Busby, Jim*/ Me and my baby: *Noack, Eddie* / Living high and wide: *Barber, Glen* / I'm a real gone Jesse (I'm hot to trot): *Tabor, Gene* / Poor man's riches: *Various artists* / Poor little heart: *Morris, Fitz* / Dead lost: *Jones,* Neal / What a way to live: *Nelson, Willie* / When I came thru town: *Mathis, Johnny* / Careless words: *Carson, Joe* / I dare you to love me: *Faulkner, Dessie* / Stranger shake hands with a fool: *Carter, Bill.*
LP: . . . . **DROP 1004**
MC: . . . . **CROP 1004**

20 OF THE BEST COUNTRY DUETS (Various artists).
LP: . . . . **NL 89521**
MC: . . . . **NK 89521**

20 ORIGINALS FROM THE COUNTRY & WESTERN HALL OF (Various artists).
LP: . . . . **PLE 7006**
MC: . . . . **PLC 7006**

20 STAR STUDDED COUNTRY HITS (Various artists).
LP: . . . . **PLE 7003**
MC: . . . . **PLC 7003**

24 ORIGINAL NUMBER ONE COUNTRY HITS (Various artists).
Tracks: / Jolene: *Various artists* / 9,999,999 tears: *Various artists* / (I'd be a) legend in my own time: *Various artists* / Lord, Mr Ford: *Various artists* / She's acting single (I'm drinking doubles): *Various artists* / I'm a ramblin' man: *Various artists* / Door is always open, The: *Various artists* / Out of hand: *Various artists* / Marie Laveau: *Various artists* / Are you sure Hank done it this way: *Various artists* / She called me baby: *Various artists*.
LP: . . . . **NL 89175**
MC: . . . . **NK 89175**

25 COUNTRY BALLADS (Various artists).
MC: . . . . **ZCWW 17072**

25 COUNTRY BALLADS - VOL.2 (Various artists).
MC: . . . . **ZCWW 17075**

25 COUNTRY STORIES (Various artists).
MC: . . . . **ZCWW 17071**

30 FIDDLERS GREATEST HITS (Various artists).
2LP: . . . . **GTV 104**

32 GOLDEN COUNTRY HITS - VOL.1 (Various artists).
2LP: . . . . **NL 43886(2)**
MCSET: . . . . **NK 43886(2)**

32 GOLDEN COUNTRY HITS - VOL.2 (Various artists).
2LP: . . . . **NL 43887(2)**
MCSET: . . . . **NK 43887(2)**

40 COUNTRY CLASSICS (Various artists).
2LP: . . . . **PLD 8011**
MCSET: . . . . **PLDC 8011**

40 COUNTRY MASTERPIECES (Various artists).
2LP: . . . . **PLD 8002**
MCSET: . . . . **PLDC 8002**

40 SMASH HITS COUNTRY STYLE (Various artists).
2LP: . . . . **MFP 1006**
MCSET: . . . . **TCMFP 1006**
MC: . . . . **TC DL 1006**

50 ALL TIME COUNTRY HITS (Various artists).
2LP: **50DA 300**
MCSET: **50DA 4300**

50 COUNTRY CLASSICS (Various artists).
MCSET: . . . . **DBXC 001**

50 COUNTRY FAVOURITES (Various artists).
MCSET: . . . . **TR 1509**
MCSET: . . . . **MFP 411 509 5**

50 MORE COUNTRY FAVOURITES (Various artists).
Tracks: / Folsom Prison blues: *Cash, Johnny* / Treat me mean, treat me cruel: *Twitty, Conway* / I'm building heartaches: *Nelson, Willie* / I'm blue again: *Cline, Patsy* / Time has made a change in me: *Oak Ridge Boys* / Love's gonna live here: *Jennings, Waylon* / Daddy sang bass: *Perkins, Carl* / Promises and hearts: *Jackson, Stonewall* / I fall to pieces: *Young, Faron* / Lost and I'll never find the way: *Skaggs, Ricky* / Where do we go from here?: *Williams, Don* / Little jewels: *Parsons, Gene* / All that's keeping me alive: *Fargo, Donna* / Livin' in the sunshine of your love: *Pillow, Ray* / Baby I want to love you: *Fender, Freddy* / That's all it took: *Parsons, Gram/Emmylou Harris* / Blue is the way I feel: *Twitty, Conway* / Will you remember mine?: *Nelson, Willie* / Girl I used to know, A: *Jones, George* / Just out of reach: *Cline, Patsy* / Take my hand for a while: *Williams, Don* / Sticks and stones: *Fargo, Donna* / Home is where you're happy: *Nelson, Willie* / Wild and windy night: *Little Sister* / You made me what I am: *Twitty, Conway* / Say, won't you be mine?: *Skaggs, Ricky* / Hey porter: *Cash, Johnny* / Release me: *Parton, Dolly* / World's worst loser: *Jones, George* / Your cheatin' heart: *Young, Faron* / I've loved and lost again: *Cline, Patsy* / What am I living for?: *Perkins, Carl* / Forgive and forget: *Cunningham, Tom* / We're together again: *Pillow, Ray* / I don't need to know that right now: *Paycheck, Johnny* / Two different worlds: *Skaggs, Ricky* / I can't help it: *Cash, Johnny* / And so will you, my love: *Nelson, Willie* / Where I stand: *Twitty, Conway* / It wasn't God who made honky tonk angels: *Parton, Dolly* / Lighthouse bar: *Blackwater Band* / Silver wings: *Fender, Freddy* / Love hurts: *Parsons, Gram/Emmylou Harris* / Tonight, ain't gonna fight again: *Little Sister* / It's so easy: *Jennings, Waylon* / Is there something on your mind?: *Nelson, Willie* / Sugartime: *Cash, Johnny* / I can't change overnight: *Jones, George* / You still want to go: *Henderson, Kelvin* / You'll never walk alone: *Oak Ridge Boys*.
MC: . . . . **T 1569**

50 YEARS OF COUNTRY MUSIC - VOL.1 (Various artists).
LP: . . . . **CDS 1179**
MC: . . . . **CAM 491**

70'S COUNTRY (Various artists).
Tracks: / Country boy (you got your feet in L.A.): *Campbell, Glen* / Country Willie: *Nelson, Willie* / Today I sarted loving you again: *Haggard, Merle* / Everytime two fools collide: *Rogers, Kenny & Dottie West* / Have a dream on me: *McDaniel, Mel* / He thinks I still care: *Murray, Anne* / She believes in me: *Rogers, Kenny* / Misty blue: *Spears, Billie Jo* / Mama's don't let your babies grow up to be cowboys: *Bruce, Ed* / I cheated on a good woman's love: *Craddock, Billy Crash* / Just a matter of time: *James, Sonny* / I'm not Lisa: *Colter, Jessi* / Lover's question, A: *Reeves, Del* / I could almost say goodbye: *Harden, Arlene* / I'm leaving it up to you: *Mosby, Johnny & Jonie* / Hank and Lefty raised my country soul: *Edwards, Stoney* / Lay back in the arms of someone: *Newton, Juice* (CD only.) / Angel of the morning: *Montgomery, Melba* (CD only.) / Another lonely night: *Shepard, Jean* (CD only.) / Mr Bojangles: *Nitty Gritty Dirt Band* (CD only.).
LP: . . . . **MFP 5876**
MC: . . . . **TCMFP 5876**

ALL STAR COUNTRY DUETS (Various artists).
MCSET: . . . . **DTO 10223**

ALL STAR COUNTRY ROUND UP (Various artists).
Tracks: / Oh lonesome me: *Various artists* / Geisha girl: *Various artists* / Six days on the road: *Various artists* / What am I worth: *Various artists* / Things go better with love: *Various artists* / Mississippi woman: *Various artists* / Jambalaya: *Various artists* / Pick me up on your way down: *Various artists* / DJ for a day: *Various artists* / Night life: *Various artists* / Flyin' south: *Various artists* / Yes Mr. Peters: *Various artists* / Sixteen tons: *Various artists* / Folsom Prison blues: *Various artists*.
LP: . . . . **SPR 8515**
MC: . . . . **SPC 8515**

ALL TIME COUNTRY AND WESTERN (Various artists).
Tracks: / Kentucky waltz: *Cowboy Copas* / I'll sail my ship alone: *Mullican, Moon* / Tennessee tango: *York Brothers* / Signed, sealed and delivered: *Cowboy Copas* / Tennessee wig-walk: *Lou, Bonnie* / Old rattler: *Grandpa Jones* / Tennessee waltz: *Cowboy Copas* / Blues stay away from me: *Delmore Brothers* / New Jole Blon: *Mullican, Moon* / Filipino baby: *Cowboy Copas* / I'm the talk of the town: *Smiley, Red* / Why don't you haul off and love me: *Raney, Wayne*.
LP: . . . . **SING 537**

ALL TIME COUNTRY HITS (Various artists).
2LP: **80010**
MCSET: **850101/2**

BEER PARLOR JIVE (Western Swing 1935-1941) (Various artists).
Tracks: / Yes sir: *Various artists* / Draggin' the bow: *Various artists* / Chicken reel: *Various artists* / Settle down blues: *Various artists* / Train song: *Various artists* / Joe Turner blues: *Various artists* / When you're smiling: *Various artists* / Somebody's been using that thing: *Various artists* / Hi-flyer stomp: *Various artists* / Sally's got a wooden leg: *Various artists* / Sundown blues: *Various artists* / Black and white rag: *Various artists* / Holding the sack: *Various artists* / Beer parlor jive: *Various artists*.
LP: . . . . **STR 801**

BEST OF 80'S COUNTRY (Various artists).
Tracks: / Stranger in my house: *Milsap, Ronnie* / John Deere tractor: *Judds* / From where I stand: *Collins, Judy* / Read all about it: *Sylvia* / Stand on it: *McDaniel, Mel* / Out goin' cattin': *Brown, Sawyer* / Jagged edge of a broken heart: *Davies, Gail* / Out on the front line: *Seals, Dan* / Feels so right: *Alabama* (Group) / Then it's love: *Williams, Don* / Memphis roots: *Bruce, Ed* / You're still new to me: *Osmond*, Marie / I tell it like it used to be: *Brown, T. Graham* / Letter from home: *Rabbitt, Eddie* / Turn me loose: *Gill, Vince* / Just another love: *Tucker, Tanya*.
LP: . . . . **MFP 5788**
MC: . . . . **TC-MFP 5788**

BEST OF 90'S COUNTRY (Various artists).
Tracks: / If tomorrow never comes: *Brooks, Garth* / Shotgun: *Tucker, Tanya* / Never ending song of love: *Gayle*, Crystal / On a good night: *Campbell, Glen* / I'm a survivor: *Dalton, Lacy J* / My side of the story: *Bogguss*, Suzy / Race is on, The: *Brown, Sawyer* / On the bayou: *Wild Rose* / Moonshadow Road: *Brown, T. Graham* / Other side of love, The: *Davies, Gail* / Do you know where your man is: *Mandrell, Barbara* / Good times: *Seals*, Dan / Everything: *Chapman, Cee Cee* / What would you do about you (if you were me): *Osmond, Marie* / Country girl heart: *Gatlin, Larry & The Gatlin Brothers* / Tear it up: *Harms, Jonie*.
MC: . . . . **TCMFP 5912**

BEST OF BRITISH COUNTRY (Various artists).
LP: . . . . **SDLA 4001**

BEST OF COUNTRY 1 (Various artists).
LP: . . . . **NL 89176**
MC: . . . . **NK 89176**

BEST OF COUNTRY 2 (Various artists).
LP: **26.21182**
MC: **24.21182**

BEST OF COUNTRY 3 (Various artists).
LP: **26.21187**
MC: **24.21187**

BEST OF COUNTRY AND WESTERN 4 (Various artists).
Tracks: / Distant drums: *Various artists* / Rose garden: *Various artists* / All I ever need is you: *Various artists* / Taker, The: *Various artists* / Just for what I am: *Various artists* / Never ending song of love: *Various artists* / Four strong winds: *Various artists* / Morning: *Various artists* / Snowbird: *Various artists* / One tin soldier: *Various artists* / Thing called love, A: *Various artists* / I'm movin' on: *Various artists*.
LP: **26.21189**
MC: **24.21589**

BEST OF COUNTRY GOSPEL (Various artists).
LP: . . . . **HRL 179**
MC: . . . . **CHRL 179**

BEST OF COUNTRY (MFP LABEL) (Various artists).
Tracks: / Dukes of Hazzard: *Jennings, Waylon* / Jolene: *Parton, Dolly* / Forty hour week (for a livin'): *Alabama* (Group) / Why not me: *Judds* / Here come's my baby: *West, Dottie* / Kiss an angel good morning: *Pride*, Charley / Gonna get along without you now: *Davis, Skeeter* / Canadian Pacific: *Hamilton, George IV* / I've always been crazy: *Jennings, Waylon* / Here you come again: *Parton, Dolly* / Love in the first degree: *Alabama* (Group) / Would you hold it against me: *West, Dottie* / Just between you and me: *Pride, Charley* / Night life: *Nelson, Willie* / I'm a lover (not a fighter): *Davis, Skeeter* / Rose and a baby Ruth, A: *Hamilton, George* IV / Always on my mind: *Presley, Elvis* / Most beautiful girl, The: *Rich, Charlie* / Rose garden: *Anderson*, Lynn / Lay down beside me: *Williams, Don* / Stand by your man: *Wynette, Tammy* / I can help: *Swann, Billy* / Wind beneath my wings: *Greenwood, Lee* / Let your love flow: *Bellamy Brothers* / Two doors down: *Parton*, Dolly / There's no getting over me: *Milsap, Ronnie* / It's only make believe: *Twitty, Conway* / Thing called love, A: *Cash, Johnny* / Luckenbach, Texas: *Jennings, Waylon* / Funny face: *Fargo, Donna* / Georgia on my mind: *Nelson, Willie*.
LP: . . . . **MFP 5843**
MC: . . . . **TCMFP 5843**

BEST OF COUNTRY MUSIC (Various artists).
LP: . . . . **FUN 9020**
MC: . . . . **FUNC 9020**

BEST OF COUNTRY (TRAX LABEL) (Various artists).
LP: . . . . **TRX 501**
MC: . . . . **TRXMC 501**

BEST OF THE TRUCK DRIVER SONGS (Various artists).
LP: . . . . **SLP 454**
MC: . . . . **GT 5454**

BIG COUNTRY 50'S VOL.1 (Various artists).
LP: . . . . **TRX 507**
MC: . . . . **TRXC 507**

BIG COUNTRY 50'S VOL.2 (Various artists).
Tracks: / I forgot to remember to forget: *Presley, Elvis* / Sixteen tons: *Ford, Tennessee Ernie* / There stands the glass: *Pierce, Webb* / I want to be with you: *Frizzell, Lefty* / My special angel: *Helms, Bobby* / Story of my life: *Robbins, Marty* / It wasn't God who made honky tonk angels: *Wells, Kitty* / I'm movin' on: *Snow*, Hank / Young love: *James, Sonny* / Billy Bayou: *Reeves, Jim* / Blue blue day: *Gibson, Don* / Cattle call: *Arnold, Eddy* / In the jailhouse now: *Pierce, Webb* / Loose talk: *Smith, Carl* / Slow poke: *King*, Pee Wee / Singing the blues: *Robbins, Marty* / Whole lotta shakin' goin' on: *Lewis, Jerry Lee* / Guess things happen that way: *Cash, Johnny* / Wake up little Susie: *Everly Brothers* / Bird dog: *Everly Brothers*.
LP: . . . . **TRX 508**
MC: . . . . **TRXC 508**

BIG COUNTRY 60'S VOL.1 (Various artists).
Tracks: / Distant drums: *Reeves, Jim* / I love you more today: *Twitty, Conway* / Please help me: *Locklin*, Hank / Ode to Billy Joe: *Gentry, Bobbie* / Act naturally: *Owens, Buck* / Once a day: *Various artists* / Mama sang a song: *Anderson, Bill* / Crazy arms: *Price, Ray* / Ballad of Jed Clampett: *Flatt & Scruggs* / Harper Valley PTA: *Riley, Jeannie C.* / Love's gonna live here: *Owens, Buck* / Ribbons of darkness: *Robbins*, Marty / Wings of love: *Husky, Ferlin* / Misery loves company: *Wagoner, Porter* / Wichita lineman: *Campbell*, Glen / Ring of fire: *Cash, Johnny* / Once a day: *Smith, Connie* / I don't wanna play house: *Wynette*, Tammy / Baby baby: *Houston, David* / Make the world go away: *Arnold, Eddy* / There goes my everything: *Greene, Jack*.
LP: . . . . **TRX 509**
MC: . . . . **TRXC 509**

BIG COUNTRY 60'S VOL.2 (Various artists).
Tracks: / Folsom prison blues: *Cash, Johnny* / She's got you: *Cline, Patsy* / Big bad John: *Dean, Jimmy* / Running bear: *Jones, Sonny* / I don't care: *Owens, Buck* / All I have to offer you is me: *Pride, Charley* / With one exception: *Houston, David* / Walk on by: *Van Dyke, Leroy* / Next in line: *Twitty, Conway* / Galveston: *Campbell, Glen* / I guess I'm crazy: *Reeves, Jim* / What's he doin'...: *Arnold, Eddy* / All the time: *Greene, Jack* / Honey: *Goldsboro, Bobby* / Devil woman: *Robbins, Marty* / Stand by your man: *Wynette, Tammy* / City lights: *Price, Ray* / Still: *Anderson, Bill* / I've been everywhere: *Snow, Hank* / I've a tiger by the tail: *Owens, Buck*.
LP: . . . . **TRX 510**
MC: . . . . **TRXC 510**

BIG COUNTRY 60'S VOL. 3 (Various artists).
Tracks: / You're the one: *James, Sammy* / Almost persuaded: *Houston, David* / Girl on the billboard: *Reeves*, Del / Saginaw Michigan: *Frizzell, Lefty* / Together again: *Owens, Buck* / Throw it away: *Anderson, Bill* / It's such a pretty world today: *Stewart, Wynn* / Heartbreak USA: *Wells, Kitty* / This is it: *Reeves, Jim* / Daddy sang bass: *Cash, Johnny* / Turn the world around: *Arnold, Eddy* / Abliene: *Hamilton, George IV* / BJ the DJ: *Jackson, Stonewall* / Begging to you: *Robbins, Marty* / Laura: *Ashley, Leo* / Woman of the world: *Lynn, Loretta* / North to Alaska: *Horton, Johnny* / D.I.V.O.R.C.E.: *Wynette, Tammy* / I fall to pieces: *Jackson, Wanda* / Tall dark stranger: *Owens, Buck*.
LP: . . . . **TRX 511**
MC: . . . . **TRXC 511**

BIG COUNTRY CLASSICS VOL.1 (Various artists).
LP: . . . . **TRX 502**
MC: . . . . **TRXMC 502**

BIG COUNTRY CLASSICS VOL.2 (Various artists).
LP: . . . . **TRX 503**
MC: . . . . **TRXMC 503**

BIG COUNTRY CLASSICS VOL.3 (Various artists).
Tracks: / Moody blue: *Presley, Elvis* / Till I can make it on my own: *Wynette, Tammy* / Chantilly lace: *Lewis*, Jerry Lee / Jolene: *Parton, Dolly* / Year that Clayton Delaney died, The: *Hall, Tom T.* / You're my best friend: *Williams, Don* / Georgia on my mind: *Nelson, Willie* / Let your love flow: *Bellamy Brothers* / You've never been this far: *Lynn, Loretta* / Near you: *Bare, Bobby* / It couldn't: *Duncan, Johnny (1)* / Shoulder to cry on: *Pride, Charley* / Luckenbach, Texas: *Jennings, Waylon*.
LP: . . . . **TRX 504**
MC: . . . . **TRXMC 504**

BIG COUNTRY CLASSICS VOL.4 (Various artists).
Tracks: / Two doors down: *Parton, Dolly* / Amanda: *Jennings, Waylon* / Way down: *Presley, Elvis* / Somebody, somewhere: *Lynn, Loretta* / Faster horses: *Milsap, Ronnie* / All for the love of sunshine: *Williams, Don* / Convoy: *McCall, C.W.* / If I said you had a beautiful body: *Bellamy Brothers* / Say it again: *Rich, Charlie* / Mamas don't let your babies grow up to be cowboys:

Jennings, Waylon & Willie Nelson / Amazing love: *Pride, Charley*/ Among my souvenirs: *Robbins, Marty* / Touch the hand: *Twitty, Conway*.
LP: . . . . **TRX 505**
MC: . . . . **TRXMC 505**

BIG COUNTRY CLASSICS VOL.5 (Various artists).
Tracks: / I'm just a country boy: *Williams, Don* / Old dogs, children and watermelon wine: *Hall, Tom T.* / Lady lay down: *Conlee, John* / Do you know you: *Statler Brothers* / You and me: *Wynette, Tammy* / Don't all the girls get prettier: *Gilley, Mickey* / Heaven's just a sin away: *Kendalls* / Funny face: *Fargo, Donna*/ Out of my head and back in my bed: *Lynn, Loretta* / Only one love in my life: *Milsap, Ronnie* / Would you lay with me (in a field of stone): *Rich, Charlie* / There must be more to love than this: *Lewis, Jerry Lee* / I can help: *Swann, Billy* / All the gold in California: *Gatlin, Larry*.
LP: . . . . **TRX 506**
MC: . . . . **TRXMC 506**

BIG COUNTRY COLLECTION (Various artists).
2LP: . . . . **CR 068**
MCSET: . . . . **CRT 068**

CALIFORNIA COUNTRY CLASSIX (Various artists).
Tracks: / Hands: *Various artists* / There goes that song again: *Various artists* / Friend of a friend of mine: *Various artists* / Whispering grass: *Various artists* / Whoa mule whoa: *Various artists* / Pancho: *Various* artists / Tears: *Various artists* / Jamestown Ferry: *Various artists* / You mean all the world to me: *Various* artists / Fallen star: *Various artists* / Jambalaya: *Various artists* / Gimme that Western swing: *Various artists*.
LP: . . . . **ITW 2**

CAPITOL COUNTRY CLASSICS (see under Capitol (label) (Various artists).

CAPITOL COUNTRY CRUISIN' (see under Capitol (label)) (Various artists).

CAPITOL COUNTRY GEMS (see under Capitol (label)) (Various artists).

CAPITOL COUNTRY KICKS (see under Capitol (label)) (Various artists).

CAPITOL COUNTRY MUSIC CLASSICS - 1980'S (Various artists).
Tracks: / Nothing sure looked good on you: *Watson, Gene* / Something 'bout you baby I like: *Campbell, Glen & Rita* Coolidge / Could I have this dance: *Murray, Anne* / (You say you're) a real cowboy: *Craddock, Billy Crash*/ Louisiana Saturday night: *McDaniel, Mel* / Sweetest thing (I've ever know): *Newton, Juice* / Step that step: *Brown, Sawyer* / Meet me in Montana: *Osmond, Marie & Dan Seals* / I tell it like it used to be: *Brown, T.* Graham / Darlene: *Brown, T. Graham* / Heartbeat in the darkness: *Williams, Don* / Old coyote town: *Williams,* Don / Just another love: *Tucker, Tanya* / I don't want to set the world on fire: *Bogguss, Suzy* / Unconditional love: *New Grass Revival* / I won't take less than your love: *Tucker, Tanya/Paul Davis & Paul Overstreet* / I didn't (every chance I had): *Rodriguez, Johnny* / New never wore off my sweet baby, The: *Dilon, Dean* / Addicted: *Seals,* Dan / I wish I could fall in love today: *Mandrell, Barbara* / Much too young (to feel this damn old): *Brooks, Garth* / If tomorrow never comes: *Brooks, Garth*.
MC: . . . . **TCEMS 1424**

CAPITOL COUNTRY MUSIC CLASSICS - 1970'S (Various artists).
Tracks: / Fightin' side of me, The: *Haggard, Merle & the Strangers* / Cherokee maiden: *Haggard, Merle & the Strangers*/ All I have to do is dream: *Campbell, Glen & Bobbie Gentry* / Big wheel cannonball: *Curless, Dick* / Snowbird: *Murray, Anne* / Something to brag about: *Louvin, Charlie & Melba Montgomery* / Empty arms: *James, Sonny*/ I'm a truck: *Simpson, Red* / She's my rock: *Edwards, Stoney* / Comin' after Jinny: *Ritter, Tex* / Fiddle man, The: *Stegall, Red* / Bonparte's retreat: *Campbell, Glen* / Rhinestone cowboy: *Campbell, Glen* / Get on my love train: *La Costa* / I'm not Lisa: *Colter, Jessi* / What's happened to blue eyes: *Colter, Jessi*/ Hurt: *Connie Cato* / Letter that Johnny Walker read, The: *Asleep At The Wheel* / Miles and miles of Texas: *Asleep* At The Wheel / Couple more years, A: *Dr. Hook* / Bluest heartache of the year: *Dale, Kenny* / Paper Rosie: *Watson, Gene* / Gambling polka dot blues: *Texas Playboys* / I cheated on a good woman's love: *Craddock, Billy Crash* / Gambler, The: *Schitz, Don* / Ain't life hell: *Cochran, Hank & Willie Nelson*.
MC: . . . . **TCEMS 1423**

CAPITOL COUNTRY MUSIC CLASSICS - 1960'S (Various artists).
Tracks: / Six pack to go, A: *Thompson, Hank* / He'll have to stay: *Black, Jeanne* / Wings of a dove: *Husky*, Ferlin / Hello walls: *Young, Faron* / Right or wrong: *Jackson, Wanda* / In the middle of a heartache: *Jackson*, Wanda / I dreamed of a hillbilly heaven: *Ritter, Tex* / Sing a little song of heartache: *Maddox, Rose* / Must you throw dirt in my face: *Louvin Brothers* / Tips of my fingers, The: *Clark, Roy* / Second fiddle (to an old guitar): *Shepard, Jean* / I don't love you anymore: *Louvin, Charlie* / Just between the two of us: *Owens, Bonnie &* Merle Haggard / You're the only world I know: *James, Sonny & the Southern Gentleman* / Born to be with you: *James,* Sonny & the Southern Gentleman / (My friends are gonna be) Strangers: *Haggard, Merle* / Tombstone every mile, A: *Curless*, Dick / Queen of the house: *Miller, Jody* / Hicktown: *Tennessee Ernie Ford* / Yodel, sweet Molly: *Louvin,* Ira / I'll take the dog: *Shepard, Jean & Ray Pillow* / Burning bridges: *Campbell, Glen* / Gentle on my mind: *Campbell, Glen* / It's such a pretty world today: *Stewart, Wynn* / Just hold my hand: *Mosby, Johnny & Jonie*/ Mr Walker, it's all over: *Spears, Billie Jo* / Okie from Muskogee: *Haggard, Merle & the Strangers*.
MC: . . . . **TCEMS 1422**

CHAMPAGNE COUNTRY (Various artists).
Tracks: / Stardust: *Nelson, Willie* / Miss the Mississippi and you: *Gayle, Crystal* / For the good times: *Kristofferson*, Kris / Sweet music man: *Wynette, Tammy* / Always: *Nelson, Willie & Leon Russell* / Most beautiful girl, The: *Rich, Charlie* / Here we are: *Jones, George & Emmylou Harris* / Thing called love, A: *Cash, Johnny* / Things I might have been, The: *Kristofferson, Kris/Rita Coolidge* / Best of my love: *Tucker, Tanya* / Faded love: *Nelson, Willie & Ray Price* / Very special love song, A: *Rich, Charlie* / Near you: *Jones, George & Tammy* Wynette / Me and the elephant: *Goldsboro, Bobby* / Please help me I'm falling (in love with you) / I don't know why: *Robbins, Marty*.
LP: . . . . **SHM 3187**
MC: . . . . **HSC 3187**

CHRISTMAS COUNTRY (See under Christmas...) (Various artists).

CLASSIC COUNTRY DUETS (Various artists).
LP: . . . . **IMCA 5599**

CLASSIC COUNTRY ROCK (Various artists).
Tracks: / Last gunfighter ballad, The: *Various artists* / Montgomery in the rain: *Various artists* / Such a waste of love: *Various artists* / Dreamer: *Various artists* / If you could touch her at all: *Various artists*/ I ain't living long like this: *Various artists* / Broken hearted people: *Various artists* / Renegade picker: *Various artists* / L.A. freeway: *Various artists* / Desperados waiting for the train: *Various artists*/ Luckenbach, Texas: *Various artists* / Your place or mine: *Various artists*.
LP: . . . . **INTS 5027**
MC: . . . . **INTK 5027**

CLASSIC SONGS (I love country) (Various artists).
Tracks: / Please help me, I'm falling: *Fricke, Janie* / Jambalaya: *Bandy, Moe* / Goodnight Irene: *Bare, Bobby*/ Tumbling tumbleweeds: *Robbins, Marty* / I'm just here to get my baby out of jail: *Robbins, Marty* / Sweet temptation: *Skaggs, Ricky* / Mom and Dad's waltz: *Nelson, Willie* / Roll in my sweet baby's arms: *Paycheck, Johnny*/ Tennessee waltz: *Dalton, Lacy J.*
LP: **4504301**
MC: **4504304**

CLASSIC SONGS II (I love country) (Various artists).
Tracks: / To all the girls I've loved before: *Haggard, Merle* / He'll have to go: *Goldsboro, Bobby* / Crying in the rain: *Gayle, Crystal* / Blue bayou: *Whitman, Slim* / Wound time can't erase, A: *Bandy, Moe* / Some days are diamonds: *Bare, Bobby* / Snowbird: *Anderson, Lynn* / If I said you had a beautiful body would you hold it ...: *Duncan, Johnny (1)* / Gambler, The: *Cash, Johnny* / Funny face: *Wynette, Tammy* / Window up above: *Gilley, Mickey* / Almost persuaded: *Jones, George* / Stand by your man: *Coe, David Allan* / Mr. Bojangles: *Paycheck, Johnny* / Big river: *Cash, Rosanne with Bobby Bare*.
LP: **4510031**
MC: **4510034**

"COUNTRY" 50 GREAT NASHVILLE HITS (Various artists).
2LP: . . . . **RML 103**
MCSET: . . . . **RML 4 C 103**

COUNTRY ALL STARS (Various artists).
Tracks: / Face of a fighter: *Various artists* / Rueben's train: *Various artists* / Wings of a dove: *Various* artists / I've gotta be somebody: *Various artists* / Those other boys: *Various artists* / Gambler's guitar: *Various artists* / Have I stayed away too long: *Various artists* / Ramblin' man: *Various artists* / We belong together: *Various artists* / Snowbird: *Various artists* / Hurt (a chil): *Various artists* / I'm afraid the masquerade is over: *Various artists* / All I need is you: *Various artists* / Love my man: *Various* artists / I didn't know what time it was: *Various artists* / I got it bad (and that ain't good): *Various artists*/ If: *Various artists* / Maybe you'll be there: *Various artists* / I can dream, can't I: *Various artists*/ Johnny: *Various artists* / There must be a way: *Various artists* / My foolish heart: *Various artists*/ I'm still around: *Various artists* / Cuttin' in: *Various artists*.
LP: . . . . **SDM 001**

COUNTRY AND WESTERN (Various artists).
LP: . . . . **SM 3856**
MC: . . . . **MC 3856**
LP: **668061**

COUNTRY AND WESTERN GOSPEL HYMNAL VOL. 4 (Various artists).
MC: . . . . **ZL C 03599**

COUNTRY BOYS (Various artists).
Tracks: / Country boy: *Campbell, Glen* / Amazing grace: *Campbell, Glen* / Reuben James: *Rogers, Kenny*/ Son on Hickory Hollers tramp, The: *Rogers, Kenny* / Crazy: *Nelson, Willie* / Night life: *Nelson, Willie*/ Rose Marie: *Whitman, Slim* / Red River valley: *Whitman, Slim* / Folsom Prison blues: *Haggard, Merle*/ San Antonio rose: *Haggard, Merle* / Desperately: *Williams, Don* / Another place another time: *Williams,* Don / I heard you crying in your sleep: *Jones, George* / I get lonely in a hurry: *Jones, George* / Jambalaya: *Nitty Gritty Dirt Band* / Sweet dreams: *Young, Faron* / Baby's got her blues jeans on: *McDaniel, Mel*(CD only) / I just had you on my mind: *Craddock, Billy Crash* (CD only) / I've got a tiger by the tail: *Owens, Buck*(CD only) / Wings of a dove: *Husky, Ferlin* (CD only).
MC: . . . . **TCMFP 5910**

COUNTRY CAVALCADE (Various artists).
MC: . . . . **VCA 111**

COUNTRY CHART BUSTERS (Various artists).
LP: . . . . **SHM 3189**
MC: . . . . **HSC 3189**

COUNTRY CHRISTMAS (Various artists).
Tracks: / White Christmas: *Wynette, Tammy* / Little drummer boy: *Cash, Johnny* / Angels we have heard on high: *McCoy, Charlie* / Cowboy's prayer: *Dean, Jimmy* / Rockin' around the Christmas tree: *Various artists*/ Happy birthday, Jesus (a child's prayer): *Ives, Burl* / Jingle bells: *Price, Ray* / Merry Christmas to you from me: *Robbins, Marty* / Rudolph the red nosed reindeer: *Autry, Gene* / Away in a manger: *Smith, Connie*/ Silent night: *Smith, Connie* / When you're 21: *Perkins, Carl* / Christmas is for kids: *Robbins, Marty*/ Jingle bell rock: *Anderson, Lynn* / Christmas as I knew it: *Cash, Johnny* / First Noel, The: *McCoy, Charlie*.
LP: . . . . **CBS 31605**

COUNTRY CHRISTMAS (Various artists).
Tracks: / It's Christmas time again: *Various artists* / Silent night: *Various artists* / Adeste fideles: *Various* artists / Away in a manger: *Various artists* / Silver bells: *Various artists* / Christmas time's a coming: *Various artists* / Christmas at home: *Various artists* / White Christmas: *Various artists* / Jingle bell rock: *Various artists* / Rudolph the red nosed reindeer: *Various artists* / Pretty paper: *Various artists*/ Little drummer boy: *Various artists* / Winter wonderland: *Various artists* / Blue Christmas: *Various artists*/ Here comes Santa Claus: *Various artists* / Christmas is just another day: *Various artists*.
LP: . . . . **MCL 1812**
MC: . . . . **MCLC 1812**

COUNTRY CHRISTMAS (Various artists).
LP: . . . . **PL 84809**
MC: . . . . **PK 84809**

COUNTRY CLASSICS (Various artists).
LP: . . . . **NE 1214**
MC: . . . . **CE 2214**
LP: . . . . **NE 1369**
MC: . . . . **CE 2369**

COUNTRY CLASSICS (Various artists).
Tracks: / Diggy liggy lo: *Newman, Jimmy C.* / Harper Valley PTA: *Riley, Jeannie C.* / Please help me, I'm falling: *Locklin, Hank* / Auctioneer, The: *Van Dyke, Leroy* / Me and ole CB: *Dudley, Dave* / Honky tonk song: *Pierce*, Webb / What a way to live: *Nelson, Willie* / Angel of the morning: *Remington, Rita* / Rockin' cajun: *Thibodeaux*, Rufus / Big river: *Cash, Johnny* / Why you been gone so long: *Coe, David Allan* / Big boss man: *La Beef, Sleepy* / Just...: *Various artists*.
LP: . . . . **TOP 134**
MC: . . . . **KTOP 134**

COUNTRY CLASSICS (Various artists).
Tracks: / Just...: *Wagoner, Porter/Dolly Parton* / 500 miles away from home: *Bare, Bobby* / When you're hot you're hot: *Reed, Jerry* / Would you hold it...: *Various artists* / Angels don't lie: *Reeves, Jim* / Then you can tell me goodbye: *Arnold, Eddy* / Please help me, I'm falling: *Locklin, Hank* / Cold hard facts of love, The: *Wagoner, Porter* / I never once stopped loving you: *Smith, Connie* / Brown eyed handsome man: *Jennings, Waylon*/ Country hall of fame: *Locklin, Hank* / Lonesome number one: *Gibson, Don* / Coat of many colours: *Parton*, Dolly / Amos Moses: *Reed, Jerry* / Big wing: *Wagoner, Porter* / End of the world: *Davis, Skeeter*/ Taker, The: *Jennings, Waylon* / Mule skinner blues: *Parton, Dolly* / I won't come in while he's there: *Reeves, Jim* / Better...: *Wagoner, Porter/Dolly Parton*.
LP: . . . . **PMP 1014**
MC: . . . . **PMPK 1014**

COUNTRY CLASSICS (3 LP SET) (Various artists).
LPS: . . . . **STAR 2001**
MCSET: . . . . **STAC 2001**

COUNTRY CLASSICS VOL.1 (Various artists).
Tracks: / Heartbreaker: *Parton, Dolly* / Dukes Of Hazzard: *Jennings, Waylon* / Bargain store: *Parton, Dolly*/ Shadows of my mind: *Everette, Leon* / Delta dawn: *West, Dottie* / You made a believer out of me: *Bare, Bobby*/ Foggy mountain breakdown: *Hall, Tom T.* / Touch your woman: *Parton, Dolly* / We had it all: *Jennings, Waylon*/ Shelter of your eyes, The: *Bare, Bobby & Jeanne* / I know one: *Reeves, Jim* / If you can touch her at all: *Nelson, Willie* / Devil went down to Georgia: *Reed, Jimmy* / Tennessee river: *Alabama (Group)*.
LP: . . . . **PLS LP 501**
MC: . . . . **PLS MC 501**

COUNTRY CLASSICS VOL.2 (Various artists).
Tracks: / Old flames (can't hold a candle to you): *Parton, Dolly* / You win again: *Pride, Charley* / Cowboys and daddies: *Bare, Bobby* / Put it off until tomorrow: *Davis, Skeeter* / Giving up easy: *Everette, Leon* / It was love while it lasted: *West, Dottie* / Mr. Bojangles: *Hall, Tom T.* / Cowgirl and the dandy: *Parton*, Dolly / Lord, Mr. Ford: *Reed, Jerry* / Back on my mind again: *Milsap, Ronnie* / Sweet memories: *Nelson, Willie* / Night games: *Stevens, Ray* / Hollywood: *Alabama (Group)* / Singing the blues: *Gibson, Don*.
LP: . . . . **PLS LP 502**
MC: . . . . **PLS MC 502**

COUNTRY CLASSICS VOL.3 (Various artists).
Tracks: / But you know I love you: *Parton, Dolly* / When you're hot you're hot: *Reed, Jerry* / It's not supposed to be that way: *Everette, Leon* / Bigger they are, harder they fall: *West, Dottie* / True life country music: *Bailey*, Razzy / Cowboys and clowns: *Milsap, Ronnie* / Honky tonk blues: *Pride, Charley* / You're the one that taught me to swing: *Parton, Dolly* / Legend in my own time, A: *Milsap, Ronnie* / You ought to hear me cry: *Nelson*, Willie / Why lady why: *Alabama (Group)* / Mama's don't let your babies grow up to be cowboys: *Jennings, Waylon*/ Burgers and fries: *Pride, Charley* / She's a little bit country: *Hamilton, George IV*.
LP: . . . . **PLS LP 503**
MC: . . . . **PLS MC 503**

COUNTRY CLASSICS VOL.4 (Various artists).
Tracks: / Two doors down: *Parton, Dolly* / Detroit City: *Pride, Charley* / Tonight she's gonna love me: *Bailey*, Razzy / Queen of the silver dollar: *Dave & Sugar* / Only one love in my life: *Milsap, Ronnie* / Guitar man: *Reed, Jerry* / Sweet music man: *Jennings, Waylon* / Life's like poetry: *Parton, Dolly* / Early morning rain: *Hamilton, George IV* / Take your love: *Stevens, Ray* / Good-hearted woman: *Nelson, Willie* / I'm your country girl: *West, Dottie* / From a jack to a king: *Reeves, Jim* / Ride the train: *Alabama (Group)*.
LP: . . . . **PLS LP 504**
MC: . . . . **PLS MC 504**

COUNTRY CLASSICS VOL.5 (Various artists).
Tracks: / He'll have to go: *Reeves, Jim* / End of the world: *Davis, Skeeter* / Rhiannon: *Jennings, Waylon*/ Oh lonesome me: *Gibson, Don* / Canadian Pacific: *Hamilton, George IV* / Crystal chandeliers: *Pride, Charley*/ Jolene: *Parton, Dolly* / Ruby don't take your love to town: *Jennings, Waylon* / Make the world go away: *Arnold, Eddy* / I'm movin' on: *Snow, Hank* / 500 miles away from home: *Bare, Bobby* / Last date: *Cramer, Floyd*/ Ringo: *Greene, Lorne* / Spanish eyes: *Snow, Hank*.
LP: . . . . **PLS LP 505**
MC: . . . . **PLS MC 505**

COUNTRY CLASSICS VOL.6 (Various artists).
Tracks: / Green green grass of home: *Waggoner, Porter* / Once a day: *Smith, Connie* / Pure love: *Milsap*, Ronnie / Fire and rain: *Nelson, Willie* / You don't bring me flowers: *Brown, Jim Ed & Helen Cornelius* / Would you hold it against me: *West, Dottie* / My Tennessee mountain home: *Parton, Dolly* / Gentle on my mind: *Hartford*, John / I fall to pieces: *Nesmith, Michael* / Let's go all the way: *Norma Jean* / Funny, familiar, forgotten feelings: *Newbury, Mickey* / Tennessee waltz: *Pee Wee King* / Wabash cannonball: *Davis, Danny* / Orange blossom special: *Monroe, Bill*.
LP: . . . . **PLS LP 506**
MC: . . . . **PLS MC 506**

COUNTRY CLASSICS VOL.7 (Various artists).
Tracks: / Do I ever cross your mind: *Atkins, Chet & Dolly Parton* / Invisible tears: *Bare, Bobby & Skeeter Davis*/ Am I that easy to forget: *Davis, Skeeter* / Lonesome number one: *Gibson, Don* / Send me the pillow (that you dream on): *Locklin, Hank* / One in a row: *Nelson, Willie* / Hurtin's all over, The: *Smith, Connie* / Just the two of us: *Waggoner, Porter/Dolly Parton* / Healing hands of time: *Colter, Jessi* / Your cheating heart: *Davis*, Skeeter / Make up your mind: *Wells, Kitty* / Don't throw it all away: *Dave & Sugar* / Together again: *Bare, Bobby & Skeeter Davis* / Young love: *James, Sonny*.
LP: . . . . **PLS LP 507**
MC: . . . . **PLS MC 507**

COUNTRY CLASSICS VOL.8 (Various artists).
Tracks: / I can't stop loving you: *Reeves, Jim* / Take me home country roads: *Davis, Skeeter* / From here to there to you: *Locklin, Hank* / Take these chains from my heart: *Gibson, Don* / Abilene: *Hamilton, George IV*/ Me and Bobby McGee: *Pride, Charley* / Coat of many colours: *Parton, Dolly* / Amanda: *Jennings, Waylon*/ Witchita lineman: *Arnold, Eddy* / I don't hurt anymore: *Snow, Hank* / Son of Hickory Holler's tramp, The: *Bare*, Bobby / San Antonio rose: *Cramer, Floyd* / My elusive dreams: *Davis, Skeeter* / Have I told you lately that I love you: *Nelson, Willie*.
LP: . . . . **PLS LP 508**
MC: . . . . **PLS MC 508**

COUNTRY CLASSICS VOL 1 (Various artists).
MC: . . . . **CIN 1**

COUNTRY CLASSICS VOL 2 (Various artists).
MC: . . . . **CIN 2**

COUNTRY CLASSICS VOL 3 (Various artists).
MC: . . . . **CIN 3**

COUNTRY CLASSICS VOL 4 (Various artists).
MC: . . . . **CIN 4**

COUNTRY CLASSICS VOL 5 (Various artists).
MC: . . . . **CIN 5**

COUNTRY CLASSICS VOL 6 (Various artists).
MC: . . . . **CIN 6**

COUNTRY CLASSICS VOL 7 (Various artists).
MC: . . . . **CIN 7**

COUNTRY CLASSICS VOL 8 (Various artists).
MC: . . . . **CIN 8**

COUNTRY CLASSICS VOL 9 (Various artists).
MC: . . . . **CIN 9**

COUNTRY CLASSICS VOL 10 (Various artists).
Tracks: / One day at a time: *Various artists* / Married by the Bible: *Various artists* / When God comes and gathers his jewels: *Various artists* / Why me Lord?: *Various artists* / Dear God: *Various artists* / Little country church: *Various artists* / Farmer and the Lord: *Various artists* / Picture from life's other side: *Various artists* / Old rugged cross: *Various artists* / On the wings of a dove: *Various artists*.
MC: . . . . **CIN 10**

COUNTRY CLASSICS VOL 11 (Various artists).
MC: . . . . **CIN 11**

COUNTRY CLASSICS VOL 12 (Various artists).
MC: . . . . **CIN 12**

COUNTRY CLASSICS VOL 13 (Various artists).
MC: . . . . **CIN 13**

COUNTRY CLASSICS VOL 14 (Various artists).
MC: . . . . **CIN 14**

COUNTRY CLASSICS VOL 15 (Various artists).
MC: . . . . **CIN 15**

COUNTRY CLASSICS VOL 16 (Various artists).
MC: . . . . **CIN 16**

COUNTRY CLASSICS VOL 17 (Various artists).
MC: . . . . **CIN 17**

COUNTRY CLASSICS VOL 18 (Various artists).
MC: . . . . **CIN 18**

COUNTRY CLASSICS VOL 19 (Various artists).
MC: . . . . **CIN 19**

COUNTRY CLASSICS VOL 25 (Various artists).
MC: . . . . **CWIN 106**

COUNTRY COLLECTION (3) (Various artists).
LP: . . . . **MA 11587**
MC: . . . . **MAMC 911587**

COUNTRY COLLECTION (5) (Various artists).
MCSET: . . . . **BOXC 5**

COUNTRY COLLECTION VOL.1 (Various artists).
Tracks: / Help me make it through the night: *Various artists* / Singing the blues: *Robbins, Marty* / There goes my everything: *Wynette, Tammy* / Outlaws prayer, The: *Paycheck, Johnny* / I just started living today: *Wynette, Tammy* and George Jones / Love is worth it all: *Fricke, Janie* / Still doin' time: *Jones, George* / I've been to Georgia on a fast train: *Cash, Johnny* / Blues eyes crying in: *Nelson, Willie* / All around cowboy: *Robbins*, Marty / Cowboys don't shoot straight: *Wynette, Tammy* / Very special love song, A: *Rich, Charlie* / Easy on the eye: *Gatlin, Larry* / To all the girls: *Haggard, Merle* / Miss the Mississippi: *Gayle, Crystal* / Jackson: *Cash/Carter*.
LP: . . . . **SHM 3211**
MC: . . . . **HSC 3211**

COUNTRY COLLECTION VOL.2 (Various artists).
Tracks: / It's four in the morning: *Young, Faron* / Harper Valley PTA: *Riley, Jeannie C.* / Luckenbach, Texas: *Russell, Johnny* / Blue eyes crying in the rain: *Russell, Johnny* / Take this job and shove it: *Paycheck*, Johnny / No charge: *Montgomery, Melba* / From a jack to a king: *Miller, Ned* / Please help me, I'm falling: *Locklin, Hank* / Wolverton mountain: *King, Claude* / I love you because: *Jackson, Stonewall* / Big bad John: *Dean, Jimmy* / Rose garden: *Anderson, Lynn* / Everything is beautiful: *Felts, Narvel* / Good hearted woman: *Russell, Johnny*.
LP: . . . . **SHM 3227**
MC: . . . . **HSC 3227**

COUNTRY COLLECTION VOL.3 (Various artists).
Tracks: / Blue eyes crying in the rain: *Various artists* / Country girl: *Anderson, Lynn* / I forgot more than you'll ever know: *Various artists* / Mississippi: *Various artists* / Barstool Mountain: *Various artists*/ Come a little bit closer: *Various artists* / Kiss it all goodbye: *Various artists* / Almost persuaded: *Various artists* / Man in black: *Cash, Johnny*.
MC: . . . . **HSC 3231**
LP: . . . . **SHM 3231**

COUNTRY COLLECTION VOL 4 (Various artists).
Tracks: / Stand by your man: *Wynette, Tammy* / She thinks I still care: *Jones, George* / I still sing the old songs: *Tucker, Tanya* / From cotton to satin: *Paycheck, Johnny* / Everyday I have to cry some: *Stampley, Joe*/ February snow: *Bare, Bobby* / Love is just a game: *Gatlin, Larry* / Tall handsome stranger: *Robbins, Marty*/ What're you doing tonight: *Fricke, Janie* / I don't know why (I just do): *Robbins, Marty* / In the jailhouse now: *Cash, Johnny* / Red red wine: *Duncan, Johnny (1)*.
LP: . . . . **SHM 3260**
MC: . . . . **HSC 3260**

COUNTRY COLLECTIONS (Various artists).
MC: . . . . **NC 118**
LP: . . . . **NB 118**

COUNTRY COMEDY TIME - LONZO AND OSCAR (Various artists).
LP: . . . . **HAT 3123**

COUNTRY COMMENT (Various artists).
Tracks: / Hello, I'm Johnny Credit (ain't never had no cash): *Credit, Johnny* / If I could sing a country song (exactly like George Jones): *O'Gwynne, James* / Good Lord giveth and Uncle Sam taketh away: *Pierce, Webb* / Before the next teardrop falls: *Martell, Linda* / Baby, you're habit forming: *Adams, Rusty* / Blue moon of Kentucky: *Ellis, Jimmy* / I'm ragged but right: *La Beef, Sleepy* / Stormy Monday blues: *La Beef, Sleepy* / Harper Valley PTA: *Riley, Jeannie C.* / School bus: *Cutrer, Tommy* / Hippy from Mississippi: *Adams, Rusty* / She hates to be alone: *Russell, Ryan* / Uncle Boogie Red and Byrdie Nelle: *Allen, Rex Jnr.* / Cajun interstate: *Bernard, Rod* / Night they drove old Dixie down, The: *Bluegrass Alliance*.
LP: . . . . **CR 30118**

COUNTRY COMPILATION NO. 1 (Various artists).
LP: . . . . **SM 4002**

COUNTRY COMPILATION NO. 2 (Various artists).
LP: . . . . **SM 4003**

COUNTRY COOKING (Various artists).
LP: . . . . **ROUNDER 0006**

COUNTRY CROSSOVER (Various artists).
Tracks: / It's only make believe: *Twitty, Conway* / As usual: *Young, Faron* / Pretend: *Smith, Margo*/ Little things mean a lot: *Kendalls* / Love me tender: *Haggard, Merle* / You don't have to say you love me: *Tucker*, Tanya / Crying: *Thomas, B.J.* / Crazy: *Lynn, Loretta* / Everlasting love: *Hamilton, George IV* / Tear fell, A: *Craddock, Billy Crash* / True love: *Cline, Patsy*.
MC: . . . . **HSC 3298**

COUNTRY CRYIN' (Various artists).
Tracks: / It's a crying shame: *Mandrell, Barbara* / As usual: *Young, Faron* / Think I'll go somewhere and cry myself to sleep: *Craddock, Billy Crash* / We had it all: *Twitty, Conway* / Too far: *Gayle, Crystal* / Who broke your heart?: *Thomas, B.J.* / Tears of the lonely: *Williams, Don* / I've cried the blue right out of my eyes: *Gayle, Crystal* / Last thing she said, The: *Bruce, Ed* / You only broke my heart: *Lee, Brenda* / Morning after baby let me down: *Tillis, Mel* / If only I'd known it was the last time: *Young, Faron* / Tear fell, A: *Craddock, Billy Crash* / Sometime, somewhere, somehow: *Mandrell, Barbara* / I'm getting good at missing you: *Williams, Don* / I'll be seeing you: *Tillis, Mel* / Broken trust: *Lee, Brenda* / Burning memories: *Jennings*, Waylon / Just out of reach: *Thomas, B.J.* / Broken down in tiny pieces: *Craddock, Billy Crash* / Some broken hearts never mend: *Williams, Don* / Years: *Mandrell, Barbara*.
MCSET: . . . . **CRT 038**

COUNTRY DOUBLE (Various artists).
MCSET: . . . . **WW 6052**

COUNTRY DUETS (Various artists).
LP: . . . . **SPR 8559**
MC: . . . . **SPC 8559**

COUNTRY DUETS (Various artists).
Tracks: / Vision of mother, A: *Skaggs, Ricky/Dolly Parton* / Candy man: *Gilley, Mickey & Charly McClain* / Sometimes when we touch: *Wynette, Tammy/Mark Gray* / Rock and roll shoes: *Charles, Ray/B.J. Thomas* / It's a dirty job: *Bare*, Bobby/Lacy J. Dalton / Golden ring: *Wynette, Tammy and George Jones* / Get a little dirt on your hands: *Coe, David* Allan/Bill Anderson / No memories hangin' around: *Cash, Rosanne/Bobby Bare* / All the soft places to fall: *Haggard*, Merle & Willie Nelson / On my knees: *Rich, Charlie/Janie Frickie* / It's only make believe: *Twitty, Conway/Ronnie* McDowell / Where's the dress: *Bandy, Moe & Joe Stampley* / There ain't no country music on this juke box: *Scruggs, Earl & Tom T Hall* / Making believe: *Haggard, Merle & George Jones*.
LP: . . . . **CBS 54947**
MC: **40 54947**

COUNTRY DUETS CLASSICS 1935-1955 (Various artists).
LP: . . . . **OT 126**

COUNTRY FARE (Various artists).
MCSET: . . . . **WW 6028**

COUNTRY FAVOURITES (I can't stop loving you) (Various artists).
Tracks: / I fall to pieces: *Jackson, Wanda* / Big bad John: *Dean, Jimmy* / Rose garden: *Anderson, Lynn*/ Green green grass of home: *Wagoner, Porter* / Top of the world: *Anderson, Lynn* / Please help me, I'm falling: *Locklin, Hank* / Crazy: *Jackson, Wanda* / It's four in the morning: *Young, Faron*.
LP: . . . . **OCN 2018WL**
MC: . . . . **OCN 2018WK**

COUNTRY FESTIVAL (Various artists).
LP: **1A 022 58070**
MC: **1A 222 58070**

COUNTRY FIDDLERS (Various artists).
LP: . . . . **RL 316**

COUNTRY FRIENDS (I love country) (Various artists).
Tracks: / Yesterday's wine: *Haggard, Merle & George Jones* / Slow movin' outlaw: *Nelson, Willie/Lacy J Dalton*/ Chet's country: *Atkins, Chet & Albert Coleman's Atlanta Pops* / I still hold her body (but I think I've lost her mind): *Jones, George/Dennis & Ray (Dr. Hook)* / You can lead a heart to love (but you can't make it fall): *Wynette, Tammy/ Oakridge* Boys / Country side: *Bandy, Moe/Becky Hobbs* / Big river: *Jennings, Waylon, Willie Nelson,Johnny Cash,K. Kristofferson*/ Ridin' high: *Fricke, Janie & Merle Haggard* / This bottle (in my hand): *Coe, David Allan/George Jones* / Beer drinkin' christian: *Dalton, Lacy J/ Bobby Bare* / Don't sing me no songs about Texas: *Bandy, Moe/Merle Haggard*/ Mamas don't let your babies grow up to be cowboys: *Gilley, Mickey & Johnny Lee* / Indian Summer: *Gatlin, Larry/Gatlin Bros. Band/Roy Orbison/ Barry Gibb* / Friendship: *Charles, Ray & Ricky Skaggs*.
LP: **4504261**
MC: **4504264**

COUNTRY FRIENDS OF PAT & ROGER JOHNS VOL.3 (Various artists).
LP: . . . . **FER 013**

COUNTRY GALA (Various artists).
LP: **01436022**
MC: **01436041**

COUNTRY GEMS (Various artists).
Tracks: / Honey come back: *Campbell, Glen* / Cry me a river: *Gayle, Crystal* / Daytime friends: *Rogers, Kenny*/ Wayward wind: *Ritter, Tex* / Raindrops keep falling on my head: *Gentry, Bobbie* / Deulin banjos: *Jackson*, Carl / Race is on, The: *Jones, George* / Angel of the morning: *Newton, Juice* / Life gits tee-jus don't it: *Wiliams, Tex* / Tumbling tumbleweeds: *Husky, Ferlin* / Lesson in leavin', A: *West, Dottie* / Sing me an old fashioned song: *Spears, Billie Jo* / Hello walls: *Nelson, Willie* / Country girl: *Young, Faron* / Home on the range: *Whitman, Slim* / Destiny: *Murray, Anne* / I got a new field to plough: *McDonald, Skeets*/ Take me home country roads: *Newton-John, Olivia* / Loving him was easier: *Carter, Anita* / Jambalaya: *Axton*, Hoyt / Stand by your man: *Jackson, Wanda* / Mercy: *Shepard, Jean* / Mule train (CD only): *Ford, Tennessee Ernie* / Young love (CD only): *James, Sonny*.
MC: . . . . **HR 8172**

COUNTRY GENTLEMEN (Various artists).
MC: . . . . **GM 0210**

COUNTRY GIANTS (Various artists).
Tracks: / So close I can taste it: *Various artists* / Smoke, smoke, smoke: *Various artists* / Darktown poker club: *Various artists* / Decks of cards: *Various artists* / Wild card: *Various artists* / Night Miss Nancy Ann's hotel ..., The: *Various artists* / How long will she keep loving me: *Various artists* / Just like the night before: *Various artists* / You know how to keep me satisfied: *Various artists* / Honey please change your mind: *Various artists* / You don't love me yet: *Various artists* / Only for me: *Various artists*.
LP: . . . . **MAN 5032**

COUNTRY GIANTS (Various artists).
MCSET: . . . . **DTO 10313**

COUNTRY GIANTS COLLECTION VOL.2 (Various artists).
2LP: . . . . **PDA 041**

COUNTRY GIANTS USA (Various artists).
LP: . . . . **SHM 3028**

COUNTRY GIANTS VOL.3 (Various artists).
2LP: . . . . **PDA 059**

COUNTRY GIANTS, VOL. 1 (Various artists).
2LP: . . . . **PDA 019**
MCSET: . . . . **PDC 019**

COUNTRY GIANTS VOL 8 (Various artists).
LP: . . . . **CDS 1169**
MC: . . . . **CAM 480**

COUNTRY GIRLS (Various artists).

MC: . . . . **TCB 1030**
LP: . . . . **LBR 1030**

COUNTRY GIRLS (2) (Various artists).
Tracks: / Wrong road again: Gayle, Crystal / Somebody loves you: Gayle, Crystal / What I've got in mind: Spears, Billie Jo / '57 Chevrolet: Spears, Billie Jo / Daddy and home: Tucker, Tanya / Strong enough to bend: Tucker, Tanya / All I have to do is dream: Newton, Juice / Sweetest thing (I've ever known), The: Newton, Juice/ I wish that I could fall in love today: Mandrell, Barbara / It all came true: Mandrell, Barbara / Pinkertons flowers, The: Montgomery, Melba / Hey Mr. Dream Maker: West, Dottie / Still crazy after all these years: Dalton, Lacy J / Reuben James: Jackson, Wanda / Mississippi delta: Gentry, Bobbie / Under the sun: Bogguss, Suzy / Slippin' away: Shepard, Jean (CD only) / Coat of many colours: Peppers, Nancy (CD only) / It's morning (and I still love you): Colter, Jessi (CD only) / Simple little words: Lane, Cristy (CD only).
MC: . . . . **TCMFP 5911**

COUNTRY GIRLS 1926-29 (Various artists).
Tracks: / Kitchen blues: Miller, Lillian / Harbour blues: Miller, Lillian / You just can't keep a good woman down: Miller, Lillian / Butcher shop blues: Miller, Lillian / Dead drunk blues: Miller, Lillian / Doggone my good luck soul: Hudson, Hattie / Black hand blues: Hudson, Hattie / No easy rider blues: Perkins, Gertrude/ Gold daddy blues: Perkins, Gertrude / 12 pound daddy: Dickson, Pearl / Little Rock blues: Dickson, Pearl/ He's coming soon: Henton, Laura / Heavenly sunshine: Henton, Laura / Lord you've sure been good to me: Henton, Laura / I can tell the world about this: Henton, Laura / Pretty good room in my Father's kingdom: Henton, Laura/ Lord I just can't keep from crying: Henton, Laura / Sometimes: Henton, Laura / Carbolic acid blues: Cadillac, Bobbie.
LP: . . . . **MSE 216**

COUNTRY GIRLS AND BOYS (Various artists).
Tracks: / One piece at a time: Cash, Johnny / Take this job and shove it: Paycheck, Johnny / I'll leave the bottle on the bar: Paycheck, Johnny / If drinkin' don't kill me (her memory will): Jones, George / Honky tonk merry go round: Bandy, Moe / Loving arms: Duncan, Johnny/Janie Fricke / Other side of me, The: Gayle, Crystal/ True love ways: Gilley, Mickey / Roland the rodeo and Gertrude: Dr. Hook / Tumbling tumbleweeds: Robbins, Marty / Baby it's you: Fricke, Janie / Gambler, The: Bare, Bobby / Right in the wrong direction: Jones, George & Tammy Wynette / Would you lay with me (in a field of stone)?: Tucker, Tanya / You needed me: Wynette, Tammy / Silence of the mornin': Gatlin, Larry / San Antonio rose: Nelson, Willie & Ray Price / Hard times: Dalton, Lacy J / Lonely heart cafe: Anderson, Lynn / Just one look: Carter, Lynda.
MCSET: . . . . **DTO 10136**

COUNTRY GIRLS, COUNTRY HITS (Various artists).
Tracks: / Mississippi: Various artists / Lonely hearts club: Various artists / River road: Various artists.
LP: . . . . **HRL 167**
MC: . . . . **CHRL 167**

COUNTRY GOLD (Various artists).
LP: . . . . **EGS 4 5001**
MC: . . . . **EC EGS 4 5001**

COUNTRY GOLD (Various artists).
Tracks: / Harper Valley PTA: Riley, Jeannie C. / Oh lonesome me: Cash, Johnny / Night life: Nelson, Willie/ Please help me, I'm falling: Locklin, Hank / Sixteen tons: La Beef, Sleepy / Jambalaya: Newman, Jimmy C..
MC: **7SC 5029**

COUNTRY GOLD (Various artists).
Tracks: / Tie a yellow ribbon: Carver, Johnny / Turn your radio on: Davis, Skeeter / Tennessee birdwalk: Jack & Misty / Let's think about living: Luman, Bob / From a jack to a king: Miller, Ned / Gonna find me a bluebird: Rainwater, Marvin / Wild side of life: Thompson, Hank / Heartbreak USA: Wells, Kitty / Tears: Williams, Don / Harper Valley PTA: Riley, Jeannie C. / Old rugged cross, The: Philips, Bill / Please help me, I'm falling: Locklin, Hank / Nashville: Huston, David / Three hearts in a tangle: Drusky, Roy / Amazing grace: Warner, Mack / Help me make it through the night: Smith, Sammi / Four in the morning: Young, Faron/ Put your hand in the hand: Posey, Sandy / Girl on the billboard: Reeves, Del / Wings of a dove: Husky, Ferlin / Send me the pillow that you dream on: Locklin, Hank / Peace in the valley: Price, Kenny / Where do I go from here?: Williams, Don & Susan Taylor / Ruby, don't take your love to town: Darrell, Johnny / My elusive dreams: Huston, David / In the middle of a heartache: Jackson, Wanda / Wolverton mountain: King, Claude/ Ruby Tuesday: Williams, Don.
MCSET: . . . . **CRT 021**

COUNTRY GOLD - 30 ALL TIME COUNTRY & WESTERN HIT (Various artists).
Tracks: / I'm so lonesome I could cry: Various artists / So fine: Various artists / I need a thing called love: Various artists / Back home again: Various artists / Can't you see: Various artists / Blue train: Various artists / I'm gonna feed them now: Various artists / Who's been here since I've been gone: Various artists/ When I stop leaving: Various artists / Look who I'm cheating on tonight: Various artists / I can't believe that's it all over: Various artists / Loving arms: Various artists / Shadows of my mind: Various artists/ It don't hurt to dream: Various artists / If I keep on going crazy: Various artists / Fair and tender ladies: Various artists / Let's take the long way round the world: Various artists / If you gotta make a fool of somebody: Various artists / Hurtin's all over, The: Various artists / Then you can tell me goodbye: Various artists/ Whisky trip: Various artists / On the road again: Various artists / That's the way love should be: Various artists / Far far away: Various artists / Light of a clear blue morning: Various artists / I'm a trucker: Various artists / Shine on: Various artists / It should have been easy: Various artists / True life country music: Various artists / Loving you: Various artists / Soldier of fortune: Various artists.
LP: . . . . **NL 89500**
MC: . . . . **NK 89500**

COUNTRY GOLD (HALLMARK) (Various artists).
Tracks: / Jambalaya: Lewis, Jerry Lee / Everybody's trying to be my baby: Perkins, Carl / I love you because: Cash, Johnny / Cold cold heart: Pittman, Barbara / Honeycomb: Van Dyke, Leroy / Wayward wind: Dudley, Dave / I hope I don't talk in my sleep: Pillow, Ray / Before the next teardrop falls: Riley, Jeannie C./ Crazy arms: Lewis, Jerry Lee / Unchained melody: Rich, Charlie / Blue eyes crying in the rain: Walker, Charlie / Oh lonesome me: Drusky, Roy / Matchbox: Perkins, Carl / Ride me down easy: Coe, David Allan/ Help me make it through the night: Riley, Jeannie C. / Jeanie with the light brown hair: Rich, Charlie / Rainy day blues: Nelson, Willie.
MC: . . . . **HSC 3276**

COUNTRY GOLD VOL.III (Various artists).
LP: . . . . **CDS 1119**
MC: . . . . **CAM 1119**

COUNTRY GOLD VOL.IV (Various artists).
LP: . . . . **CDS 1127**
MC: . . . . **CAM 1127**

COUNTRY GOSPEL (Various artists).
Tracks: / Family bible: Wells, Tracy / Farther along: Wells, Tracy / Life's railway to Heaven: Wells, Tracy/ I love you Jesus: Wells, Tracy / Wait a little longer, Dear Jesus: Greer, John / Dust on the bible: Greer, John / Kneel down and pray: Greer, John / One day at a time: Leon / Pastors on vacation: McFarland, Billy / When God comes and gathers his jewels: Countrymen / Old rugged cross: Goodacre, Tony.
LP: . . . . **HRL 163**
MC: . . . . **CHRL 163**

COUNTRY GOSPEL GUITAR CLASSICS (Various artists).
LP: . . . . **WSE 115**

COUNTRY GREATS (Various artists).
Tracks: / Harper Valley P.T.A.: Riley, Jeannie C. / I walk the line: Cash, Johnny / Before the next teardrop falls: Martell, Linda / In the jailhouse now: Pierce, Webb / Nightlife: Nelson, Willie / Send me the pillow you dream on: Locklin, Hank / Jambalaya: Newman, Jimmy C. / We're gonna go fishin': Locklin, Hank/ C.B. savage: Hart, Rod / Got you on my mind: Coe, David Allan / You are my sunshine: Davis, Jimmie/ From a jack to a king: Miller, Ned / Dreaming: Travis, Randy / Six days on the road: Dudley, Dave.
MC: . . . . **TCINS 5015**
LP: . . . . **INS 5015**

COUNTRY GREATS 76 (Various artists).
MC: . . . . **VCA 014**

COUNTRY GREATS USA (Various artists).
MC: . . . . **HSC 3028**

COUNTRY HARVEST (Various artists).
Tracks: / Fools rush in: Nelson, Rick(y) / Little bitty tear, A: Ives, Burl / Easy: Oak Ridge Boys/ Love me tender: Haggard, Merle / San Antonio rose: Cline, Patsy / Satin sheets: Pruett, Jeannie / Sleeping single in a double bed: Mandrell, Barbara / One step at a time: Lee, Brenda / Your cheatin' heart: Lynn, Loretta / Oh lonesome me: Anderson, Bill / Ruby, don't take your love to town: Tillis, Mel / Games that daddies play, The: Twitty, Conway.
LP: . . . . **SSP 3082**
MC: . . . . **SSC 3082**

COUNTRY HARVEST 16 GOLDEN COUNTRY HITS (Various artists).
Tracks: / Behind closed doors: Rich, Charlie / Big City: Haggard, Merle / Gambler, The: Bare, Bobby/ Just started livin' today: Jones, George & Tammy Wynette / Take this job and shove it: Paycheck, Johnny / Till I gain control again: Nelson, Willie & Waylon Jennings / Key Largo: Higgins, Bertie / Stand by your man: Wynette, Tammy / Thing called love, A: Cash, Johnny / Very special love song, A: Mandrell, Barbara / Rose garden: Anderson, Lynn / He stopped loving her today: Jones, George / Sleeping with your memory: Fricke, Janie/ Delta dawn: Tucker, Tanya / If you ever change your mind: Gayle, Crystal / El Paso: Robbins, Marty.
LP: . . . . **WW 2008**
MC: . . . . **WW 20084**

COUNTRY HEARTBREAK (Various artists).
LP: . . . . **NE 1215**
MC: . . . . **CE 2215**

COUNTRY HITS (Various artists).
MC: . . . . **NK 89625**

COUNTRY HITS, VOL. 1 (Various artists).
Tracks: / Heartbreaker: Parton, Dolly / Dukes of Hazzard: Jennings, Waylon / Bargain store: Parton, Dolly/ Shadows of my mind: Everette, Leon / Delta dawn: West, Dottie / You made a believer out of me: Bare, Bobby/ Crystal chandeliers: Pride, Charley / Touch your woman: Parton, Dolly / We had it all: Jennings, Waylon/ Shelter of your eyes, The: Bare, Bobby & Jeanne / I know one: Reeves, Jim / If you can touch her at all: Nelson, Willie / Pure love: Milsap, Ronnie / Pretend: Stevens, Ray / Seeker, The: Parton, Dolly / Tennessee River: Alabama (Group) / My heroes have always been cowboys: Jennings, Waylon / Making believe: Davis, Skeeter/ Devil went down to Georgia, The: Reed, Jerry / Is anybody going to San Antone?: Pride, Charley / Dreaming my dreams with you: Jennings, Waylon / My eyes can only see you: Parton, Dolly / Door is always open, The: Dave & Sugar / You don't bring me flowers: Brown, Jim Ed & Helen Cornelius.
2LP: . . . . **CR 030**
MCSET: . . . . **CRT 030**

COUNTRY HITS, VOL. 2 (Various artists).
Tracks: / Dreaming my dreams with you: Jennings, Waylon / I know one: Reeves, Jim / Bargain store: Parton, Dolly / Shadows of my mind: Everette, Leon / Delta dawn: West, Dottie / You make a believer out of me: Bare, Bobby / Pretend: Stevens, Ray / Seeker, The: Parton, Dolly / Tennessee River: Alabama (Group)/ Making believe: Davis, Skeeter / My eyes can only see you: Parton, Dolly / Crystal chandeliers: Pride, Charley / Touch your woman: Parton, Dolly / We had it all: Jennings, Waylon / Shelter of your eyes, The: Bare, Bobby & Jeanne / If you can touch her at all: Nelson, Willie / Pure love: Milsap, Ronnie / Dukes of Hazzard: Jennings, Waylon / Devil went down to Georgia, The: Reed, Jerry / Is anybody going to San Antone?: Various artists / Heartbreaker: Parton, Dolly / My heroes have always been cowboys: Jennings, Waylon/ Door is always open, The: Dave & Sugar / You don't bring me flowers: Brown, Jim Ed & Helen Cornelius.
2LP: . . . . **CR 045**
MCSET: . . . . **CRT 045**

COUNTRY IN CONCERT (Various artists).
Tracks: / Kaw-liga: Various artists / Mississippi cotton picking delta town: Various artists / Louisiana man: Various artists / Jolene: Various artists / Love is like a butterfly: Various artists / That girl who waits tables: Various artists / Slippin' and slidin' (medley): Various artists / I'm in love again: Various artists / Johnny B. Goode: Various artists / Whole lotta shakin' goin' on: Various artists / Kiss an angel good morning: Various artists / Chaplin in new shoes: Various artists / Entertainer, The: Various artists.
LP: . . . . **CL 43350**
MC: . . . . **CK 43350**

COUNTRY JUKEBOX HITS (Various artists).
2LP: **DLP2061**
MCSET: **DMC4061**

COUNTRY LADIES (I love country) (Various artists).
Tracks: / Little bit of rain, A: Prentice, Suzanne / Tell me a lie: Fricke, Janie / If you ever change your mind: Gayle, Crystal / Livin' in these troubled times: Gayle, Crystal / Sea of heartbreak: Anderson, Lynn/ Hillbilly girl with the blues: Dalton, Lacy J / Everybody makes mistakes: Dalton, Lacy J / I'm not losin' any sleep: Blanch, Jewel / Laying it on the line: Riggir, Patsy / Radio heart: McLain, Charly / I don't know why you don't want me: Cash, Rosanne / Mississippi: Fairchild, Barbara / Would you lay with me (in a field of stone): Tucker, Tanya.
MC: **40 54942**
LP: . . . . **CBS 54942**

COUNTRY LEGENDS (Various artists).
Tracks: / Your cheatin' heart: Lewis, Jerry Lee / Gentle on my mind: Page, Patti / Trying to get to you: Orbison, Roy / Help me make it through the night: Riley, Jeannie C. / Truck drivin' son of a gun: Dudley, Dave / Turn around: Perkins, Carl / Please help me I'm falling: Locklin, Hank / Night life: Nelson, Willie/ Blue eyes crying in the rain: Walker, Charlie / My heart cries for you: Rich, Charlie / Woman's world, A: Brewer, Teresa / Night time is crying time: Newman, Jimmy C. / Folsom Prison blues: Cash, Johnny / Am I that easy to forget: Belew, Carl / Why me Lord?: Coe, David Allan / Blackland farmer: La Beef, Sleepy / Walk on by: Van Dyke, Leroy.
LP: . . . . **SHM 3183**
MC: . . . . **HSC 3183**

COUNTRY LEGENDS (Various artists).
LP: . . . . **RTL 2050**

COUNTRY LIFE (Various artists).
LP: . . . . **EMTC 16**

COUNTRY LINE SPECIAL (Various artists).
LP: . . . . **MFP 50427**

COUNTRY LIVING (Various artists).
Tracks: / It's only make believe: Various artists / It's four in the morning: Various artists / Teddy bear song: Various artists / Heartbreak USA: Various artists / Carroll County accident, The: Various artists / My last date with you: Various artists / Wild side of life: Various artists / Once a day: Various artists/ Don't break the heart that loves you: Various artists / Mr. Walker it's all over: Various artists / Harper Valley PTA: Various artists / Girl on the billboard: Various artists / DJ for a day: Various artists/ Oh lonesome me: Various artists / No charge: Various artists / From a jack to a king: Various artists/ Deck of cards: Various artists / Bridge washed out, The: Various artists / Please help me, I'm falling: Various artists / Rose garden: Various artists.
LP: . . . . **CRX 15**
MC: . . . . **CRXC 15**

COUNTRY LOVE (Various artists).
LP: . . . . **NE 1068**
LP: . . . . **TRX 512**
MC: . . . . **TRXC 512**

COUNTRY LOVE (2) (Various artists).
2LP: . . . . **MCMD 7005**
MCSET: . . . . **MCMDC 7005**

COUNTRY LOVE AND COUNTRY HEARTACHE (Various artists).
MCSET: . . . . **DTO 10237**

COUNTRY LOVE SONGS (Various artists).
Tracks: / Just to satisfy you: Jennings, Waylon / Can't forget about you: Alabama (Group) / I'll hold you: Arnold, Eddy / From here to there to you: Locklin, Hank / You are: Bare, Bobby / Help me make it through the night: Nelson, Willie.
MC: . . . . **CAM 1227**

COUNTRY LOVIN', VOL. 1 (Various artists).
Tracks: / If loving you is wrong I don't want to be right: Mandrell, Barbara / It's not love (but it's not bad): Robbins, Marty / You don't have to say you love me: Tucker, Tanya / Easy to love: Kendalls / Never loved a woman like you: Hamilton, George IV / Love me over again: Williams, Don / I can't stop loving you: Twitty, Conway/ Rest your love on me: Twitty, Conway / I'm still loving you: Stampley, Joe / Tell me that you love me: Gibbs, Terri / When you fall in love: Bruce, Ed / Sea of love: Thomas, B.J. / Loving you so long now: Williams, Don / Everybody loves a rain song: Thomas, B.J. / Love me tender: Haggard, Merle / Goodbye love: Lee, Brenda / True love: Cline, Patsy / Wasted love: Gibbs, Terri.

MCSET: . . . . **CRT 039**

COUNTRY LOVIN', VOL. 2 (Various artists).
Tracks: / Hurtin's all over, The: *Various artists* / Just the two of us: *Wagoner, Porter/Dolly Parton* / Fire and rain: *Davis, Skeeter* / Healing hands of time: *Coulter, Jessie* / Make up your mind: *Wells, Kitty*/ San Antonio rose: *King, Pee Wee* / Do I ever cross your mind?: *Atkins, Chet & Dolly Parton* / Invisible tears: *Bare, Bobby & Skeeter Davis* / Together again: *Bare, Bobby & Skeeter Davis* / Queen of the silver dollar: *Dave & Sugar* / Don't throw it all away: *Dave & Sugar* / Am I that easy to forget?: *Davis, Skeeter* / Lonesome number one: *Gibson, Don* / There's a story going round: *Gibson, Don & Dottie West* / Shelter of your eyes, The: *Bare*, Bobby / Send me the pillow that you dream on: *Locklin, Hank* / Sweet memories: *Nelson, Willie* / In the ghetto: *Parton, Dolly* / Four strong winds: *Bare, Bobby* / Young love: *James, Sonny* / Early morning rain: *Hamilton*, George IV / End of the world: *Davis, Skeeter* / Careless hands: *West, Dottie* / Green green grass of home: *Hamilton, George IV*.
2LP: . . . . **CR 043**
MCSET: . . . . **CRT 043**

COUNTRY MUSIC (South & West) (Various artists).
Tracks: / There'll come a time: *Blue Sky Boys* / Wanna be a cowboy's sweetheart: *Montana, Patsy & The Prairie Ramblers*/ Rescue from moose river gold mine, The: *Carter, Wilf* / Railroad boomer: *Acuff, Roy & His Smokey Mountain Boys*/ Born to lose: *Daffan, Ted & The Texans* / It won't be long: *Choates, Harry* / Chant of the wanderer, The: *Sons* of Pioneers / Dark as a dungeon: *Travis, Merle* / Cotton-eyed Joe: *Various artists* / Georgia wildcat breakdown: *McMichen, Clayton & His Georgia Wildcats* / Blue yodel no. 11: *Rodgers, Jimmie & Billy Burke* / Sweet fern: *Carter* Family / Dreaming with tears in my eyes / Gospel ship: *Carter Family* / Fais pas ca: *Hackberry Ramblers* / Last round-up, The: *Autry, Gene* / Forgotten soldier boy: *Monroe Brothers* / Ida, sweet as apple cider: *Brown, Milton & The Brownies*.
LP: . . . . **NW 287**

COUNTRY MUSIC COUNTRY STYLE (Various artists).
MC: . . . . **AIM 13**

COUNTRY MUSIC EMBERS (Various artists).
Tracks: / I saw your face in the moon: *Various artists* / Making believe: *Various artists* / Excuse me: *Various* artists / Keep on the sunny side: *Various artists* / I'll make it all up to you: *Various artists* / Crying heart blues: *Various artists* / Blue bonnets o'er the border: *Various artists* / Forever yours: *Various artists*/ I'll take the chance: *Various artists* / You are my sunshine: *Various artists* / Hidin' out: *Various artists*/ Are you from Dixie?: *Various artists* / Korea's mountain Northland: *Various artists* / Beyond the sunset: *Various* artists / Corina, Corina: *Various artists* / Prison grey: *Various artists* / Heartbreak USA: *Various* artists / I'll sail my ship alone: *Various artists* / Last date: *Various artists* / I saw the light: *Various* artists / Mental cruelty: *Various artists* / Tattooed lady: *Various artists* / It's your world: *Various* artists / We need a lot more of Jesus: *Various artists* / Window up above: *Various artists* / Medley: *Various* artists / Au revoir: *Various artists* / Charlie's shoes: *Various artists* / Wound time can't erase: *Various* artists / Your old love letters: *Various artists* / Red River Valley: *Various artists* / Setting my tears to music: *Various artists* / Big big day tomorrow: *Various artists* / Back in the race: *Various artists*/ People: *Various artists* / Mama's hungry eyes: *Various artists* / Comin' after Jenny: *Various artists*/ Country girl: *Various artists* / I took a memory to lunch: *Various artists* / It's a little more like Heaven: *Various artists*.
2LP: . . . . **EMBD 2004**

COUNTRY MUSIC EXPRESS VOL.1 (Various artists).
2LP: . . . . **SUCCESS 2038X**
MCSET: . . . . **SUCCESS 2038**

COUNTRY MUSIC FESTIVAL - VOL 2 (Various artists).
Tracks: / Distant drums: *Reeves, Jim* / (Never promised you) A rose garden: *West, Dottie* / All I ever need is you: *Reed, Jerry & Chet Atkins* / Taker, The: *Jennings, Waylon* / Just for what I am: *Smith, Connie* / Never ending song of love: *Lee, Dickey* / Four strong winds: *Bare, Bobby* / Morning: *Brown, Jim Ed* / Snowbird: *Davis, Danny* / One tin soldier: *Davis, Skeeter* / Thing called love, A: *Reed, Jerry* / I'm movin' on: *Snow, Hank*.
LP: . . . . **MPK 173**

COUNTRY MUSIC FESTIVALS (Wembley Highlights) (Various artists).
MCSET: . . . . **DTO 10080**

COUNTRY MUSIC HITS, VOL.1 (Various artists).
Tracks: / Green green grass of home: *Various artists* / King of the road: *Miller, Roger* / Together again: *Drusky*, Roy / Anymore: *Brewer, Teresa* / Mule train: *Laine, Frankie* / Please help me, I'm falling: *Draper, Rusty*/ Gentle on my mind: *Young, Faron* / We know it's over: *Dudley, Dave & O'Donnal, Karen* / Take me home country roads: *Statler Brothers* / Pass me by: *Rodriguez, Johnny* / Singing the blues: *Jones, George* / Easier: *Miller, Roger* / Year that Clayton Delaney died, The: *Hall, Tom T.* / Yes Mr. Peters: *Drusky, Roy & Priscilla Mitchell*.
LP: **6463 179**
MC: **7145 179**

COUNTRY MUSIC HOOTENANNY (Various artists).
Tracks: / Opening and introduction: *Various artists* / Y'all come: *Henson, Cousin Herb* / Down to the river: *Maddox*, Rose / Your Mother's prayer: *Cagle, Buddy* / Green corn: *Kentucky Colonels* / Blue Ridge Mountain blues: *Bond*, Johnny / Paper of pins: *Lee Maphis, Joe & Rose* / I got mine: *Collins, Tommy* / You took her off my hands: *Campbell, Glen* / Foggy mountain top: *Shepard, Jean* / Silver bells: *Nichols, Roy* / Midnight special: *Travis, Merle* / Comedy routine, A: *Clark, Roy* / Alabama jubilee: *Clark, Roy* / God be with you: *Henson, Cousin Herb* / Hurry back: *Henson, Cousin Herb*.
LP: . . . . **SEE 254**

COUNTRY MUSIC IN THE MODERN ERA (Various artists).
Tracks: / Bouquet of roses: *Arnold, Eddy* / Never no more blues: *Frizzell, Lefty* / Much too young to die: *Price*, Ray / Squid jiggin' ground: *Snow, Hank* / There's poison in your heart: *Wells, Kitty* / Try me one more time: *Tubb, Ernest* / Love letters in the sand: *Cline, Patsy* / Jean's song: *Atkins, Chet* / Mystery train / Little ole you: *Reeves, Jim* / Jimmy Martinez: *Robbins, Marty* / I'm a honky tonk girl: *Lynn, Loretta*/ Lorena: *Cash, Johnny* / Don't let her know: *Owens, Buck* / All I love is you: *Miller, Roger* / Sing a sad song: *Haggard, Merle* / Coat of many colours: *Parton, Dolly* / Help me make it through the night: *Kristofferson, Kris*.
LP: . . . . **NW 207**

COUNTRY MUSIC LEGENDS (Various artists).
MC: . . . . **ORC 020**

COUNTRY MUSIC PEOPLE, VOL. 2 (Various artists).
Tracks: / Sunny side of the mountain: *Various artists* / Montgomery in the rain: *Various artists* / Little rock getaway: *Various artists* / Jolie blonde: *Various artists* / Old cane press: *Various artists* / Waiting for a train: *Various artists* / Somewhere my love: *Various artists* / Cocaine blues: *Various artists*/ San Antonio blues: *Various artists* / Lost in a world: *Various artists* / Some old day: *Various artists*/ Milwaukee blues: *Various artists* / It's over: *Various artists* / Bottle baby boogie: *Various artists*/ McKinley's blues: *Various artists* / Rocky top: *Various artists*.
LP: . . . . **SNTF 797**

COUNTRY MUSIC SAMPLER (Various artists).
Tracks: / Never been to Spain: *Various artists* / Country roads: *Various artists* / Dream a little dream: *Various* artists / Sunday morning: *Various artists* / Hobo Bill: *Various artists* / North to Alaska: *Various artists*/ Sidewalks of Chicago: *Various artists* / Hawaiian wedding song: *Various artists* / Battle of New Orleans: *Various artists* / Orange blossom special: *Various artists* / Me and Bobby McGee: *Various artists*.
LP: . . . . **SFA 050**

COUNTRY MUSIC STANDARDS, VOL.2 (Various artists).
MC: . . . . **BBM 114**

COUNTRY MUSIC STORY (Various artists).
MC: . . . . **VCA 087**

COUNTRY MUSIC, VOL.2 (Various artists).
MC: . . . . **VCA 003**

COUNTRY MUSIC,VOL.4 (Take Me Home Country Roads) (Various artists).
MC: . . . . **VCA 007**

COUNTRY 'N' IRISH (Various artists).
Tracks: / Forty shades of green: *Various artists* / Gentle mother: *Various artists* / My wild Irish Rose: *Various* artists / Two little orphans: *Various artists* / I'll take you home again Kathleen: *Various artists* / Rose is a rose, A: *Various artists* / I'll get over you: *Various artists* / Wonderin' what to do: *Various artists*/ Mother's love's a blessing, A: *Various artists* / How are things in Gloccamorra?: *Various artists* / Rose of Tralee, The: *Various artists* / She's got you: *Various artists* / That silver haired daddy of mine: *Various* artists / Sunset years of life, The: *Various artists* / Nobody's child: *Various artists* / Irish way to love, The: *Various artists*.
MC: . . . . **4 HOM 006**

COUNTRY NO.1'S VOL 1 (Various artists).
Tracks: / Jambalaya: *Williams, Hank* / Fraulein: *Helms, Bobby* / He'll have to go: *Reeves, Jim* / El paso: *Robbins, Marty* / Three bells, The: *Browns* / Please help me, I'm falling: *Locklin, Hank* / Make the world go away: *Arnold, Eddy* / She called me baby: *Rich, Charlie* / Walk on by: *Van Dyke, Leroy* / I fall to pieces: *Cline, Patsy* / Big bad John: *Dean, Jimmy* / My elusive dreams: *Houston, D./Tammy Wynette*/ Still: *Anderson, Bill* / Ring of fire: *Cash, Johnny* / King of the road: *Miller, Roger* / Stand by your man: *Wynette, Tammy*.
LP: . . . . **OG 1508**
MC: . . . . **OG 2508**

COUNTRY NO.1'S VOL 1 (Various artists).
MCSET: . . . . **CK 74334**

COUNTRY NO.1'S VOL 1 (Various artists).
2LP: . . . . **CL 74334**

COUNTRY NO.1'S VOL 2 (Various artists).
Tracks: / Is it really over: *Reeves, Jim* / There goes my everything: *Greene, Jack* / Almost persuaded: *Houston*, David / Harper Valley PTA: *Riley, Jeannie C.* / D.I.V.O.R.C.E.: *Wynette, Tammy* / Bridge washed out, The: *Warner, Mack* / Oh lonesome me: *Gibson, Don* / North to Alaska: *Horton, Johnny* / Boy named Sue, A: *Cash*, Johnny / All I have to offer you is me: *Pride, Charley* / Next in line: *Twitty, Conway* / Coal miner's daughter: *Lynn, Loretta* / Rose garden: *Anderson, Lynn* / When you're hot you're hot: *Reed, Jerry* / It's four in the morning: *Young, Faron* / Year that Clayton Delaney died, The: *Hall, Tom T.*.
LP: . . . . **OG 1509**
MC: . . . . **OG 2509**

COUNTRY NO.1'S VOL 2 (Various artists).
MCSET: . . . . **CK 74335**
2LP: . . . . **CL 74335**

COUNTRY NO.1'S VOL 3 (Various artists).
Tracks: / Then you can tell me goodbye: *Arnold, Eddy* / Distant drums: *Reeves, Jim* / Folsom Prison blues: *Cash*, Johnny / Hello darlin': *Twitty, Conway* / Happiest girl in the whole USA: *Fargo, Donna* / Chantilly Lace: *Lewis, Jerry Lee* / Is anybody going to San Antone: *Pride, Charley* / Good hearted woman: *Waylon & Willie*/ Behind closed doors: *Rich, Charlie* / Satin sheets: *Pruett, Jeannie* / Teddy bear song: *Fairchild, Barbara*/ Eleven roses: *Williams, Hank Jr.* / Keep me in mind: *Anderson, Lynn* / I will always love you: *Parton, Dolly*/ Convoy: *McCall, C.W.* / Before the next teardrop falls: *Fender, Freddy*.
LP: . . . . **OG 1510**
MC: . . . . **OG 2510**

COUNTRY NO.1'S VOL 4 (Various artists).
Tracks: / Jolene: *Parton, Dolly* / I can help: *Swan, Billy* / (I'd be a) legend in my own time: *Milsap, Ronnie*/ Would you lay with me (in a field of stone)?: *Tucker, Tanya* / Hello love: *Snow, Hank* / Wasted days and wasted nights: *Fender, Freddy* / Are you sure Hank done it this way: *Jennings, Waylon* / One piece at a time: *Cash*, Johnny / You're my best friend: *Williams, Don* / Blue eyes crying in the rain: *Nelson, Willie* / She's got you: *Lynn, Loretta* / You've never been this far before: *Twitty, Conway* / We're gonna hold on: *Jones, George* & Tammy Wynette / Abilene: *Hamilton, George IV* / For the good times: *Price, Ray* / I'll be leaving alone: *Pride, Charley*.
LP: . . . . **OG 1511**
MC: . . . . **OG 2511**

COUNTRY OVATIONS (Various artists).
MC: . . . . **C 390**

COUNTRY PEOPLE, VOL.2 (Live at the British Country Music Festival) (Various artists).
MC: . . . . **BBM 138**

COUNTRY PIE (Session Artists) (Various artists).
MC: . . . . **AM 11**

COUNTRY PORTRAITS (Various artists).
LP: . . . . **WW 5057**
MC: **1A 220 1583374**

COUNTRY RAINBOW (Various artists).
LPS: . . . . **WW 1001**
MC: . . . . **WW 10014**

COUNTRY ROUND-UP (Various artists).
MCSET: . . . . **M 10144**

COUNTRY ROUNDUP (Various artists).
MCSET: . . . . **DTO 10025**
MC: . . . . **AM 64**

COUNTRY ROUNDUP, VOL.2 (Various artists).
MC: . . . . **AIM 20**

COUNTRY SCENE (Various artists).
Tracks: / Galveston: *Campbell, Glen* / Don't it make my brown eyes blue: *Gayle, Crystal* / Little bit more, A: *Dr. Hook* / It doesn't matter anymore: *Ronstadt, Linda* / Hey won't you play another somebody done somebody wrong song: *Shepard, Jean* / I don't want to put a hold on you: *Flint, Berni(e)* / Snowbird: *Murray, Anne* / Gambler, The: *Schlitz, Don* / Ode to Billy Joe: *Gentry, Bobbie* / Blanket on the ground: *Spears, Billie Jo*/ You needed me: *Murray, Anne* / If not you: *Dr. Hook* / When will I be loved: *Ronstadt, Linda* / I love you because: *Spears, Billie Jo* / Talking in your sleep: *Gayle, Crystal* / Me and my guitar: *Jennings, Frank* Syndicate / I'll never fall in love again: *Gentry, Bobbie* / Games people play: *South, Joe* / I'm a believer (in a whole lot of lovin'): *Shepard, Jean* / Rhinestone cowboy: *Campbell, Glen*.
LP: . . . . **MFP 5571**
MC: . . . . **TCMFP 5571**

COUNTRY SHOWCASE (Various artists).
MCSET: . . . . **DTO 10138**
MCSET: . . . . **DTO 10314**

COUNTRY SPECIAL (Various artists).
Tracks: / Queen of hearts: *Locklin, Hank* / Big big day tomorrow: *Clark, Sanford* / People: *Conway, Lee*/ Let the teardrops fall: *Cline, Patsy* / Country girl: *Young, Faron* / When love is gone: *Bare, Bobby*/ Red haired boy: *Country Deputies* / Fingerprints: *Cline, Patsy* / There goes my love: *Owens, Buck* / I took a memory to lunch: *Bare, Bobby* / You're wasting your time girl: *Jordinaires* / That's the way I feel: *Jones, George*.
LP: . . . . **BDL 1006**

COUNTRY SPECIAL, VOL.1 (Various artists).
Tracks: / Blanket on the ground: *Quinn, Brendan* / Me and Bobby McGee: *Morris, Mick* / I fall to pieces: *Little* Lynda / When my blue moon turns to gold again: *Coll, Brian* / Family Bible: *Lynam, Ray* / River road: *Leon*/ Blue eyes crying in the rain: *Ely, Pat* / Devil woman: *Hamilton, Joe E.* / 500 miles from home: *Dunphy, Tom* / Drunken driver: *McFarland, Billy*.
MC: . . . . **CWIN 101**

COUNTRY SPECIAL, VOL.2 (Various artists).
Tracks: / Four in the morning: *Quinn, Brendan* / Little ole wine drinker me: *Mitchell, Mark* / Red necks, white socks and blue ribbon beer: *Ely, Pat* / Don't read the letter I wrote you: *Chucknees, Margo* / Mother went a walkin: *McFarland, Billy* / Lucille: *Morris, Mike* / Heaven's just a sin away: *Leon* / Happy anniversary: *Tony & Ventures* / She's mine: *Coll, Brian* / Ghost of Jim Bob Wilson: *Colm & Sundowners*.
MC: . . . . **CWIN 102**

COUNTRY SPECIAL, VOL.3 (Various artists).
Tracks: / Turn out the light (love me tonight): *Glenn, John* / Lonely hearts club: *Margo* / That's what makes the jukebox play: *Kid Wayne* / Blackboard of my heart: *Williams, Texas T.* / Behind closed doors: *Brendan* Quinn / Wild side of life: *Williams, Texas T.* / San Antonio rose: *Margo* / Some broken hearts never mend: *Colm & Sundowners* / Little country town in Ireland: *Devlin, Sheila* / Deck of cards: *McFarland, Billy*.
MC: . . . . **CWIN 103**

COUNTRY SPIRITUALS (Various artists).
LP: . . . . **SLP 135**

COUNTRY STARDUST (Various artists).
2LP: **6686 038**
MCSET: **7523 038**

COUNTRY STARS (Various artists).
Tracks: / Rhinestone cowboy: *Campbell, Glen* / Talking in your sleep: *Gayle, Crystal* / Riders in the sky: *Whitman*, Slim / If you ain't lovin' (you ain't livin'): *Young, Faron* / Wabash

cannonball: Jackson, Wanda / Country Willie: Nelson, Willie / United we stand: Murray, Anne & Glen Campbell / I still miss someone: Ronstadt, Linda / Orange blossom special: Jackson, Carl / Gambler's guitar: Travis, Merle / One woman man: Colter, Jessi / Every time two fools collide: Rodgers,Kenny & Dottie West / Sing me an old fashioned song: Shepard, Jean/ Wild side of life: Thompson, Hank / Tip of my fingers, The: Clark, Roy / Harper Valley PTA: Spears, Billie Jo / High noon: Ritter, Tex / Angel of the morning: Newton, Juice / King of the road: Ford, Tennessee Ernie / Act naturally: Miller, Jody / Ode to Billy Joe: Gentry, Bobbie.
MC: HR 8120
MC: HR 4181204

COUNTRY STARS (CAMBRA) (Various artists).
2LP: CR 040
MCSET: CRT 040

COUNTRY STARS LIVE AT CHURCH ST. STATION (Various artists).
MC: PLAC 360

COUNTRY STARS LIVE AT CHURCH ST. STATION (See under Church St. Station for details) (Various artists).

COUNTRY STARS (PICKWICK) (Various artists).
Tracks: / I recall a gypsy woman: Williams, Don / Always: Cline, Patsy / I'm knee deep in loving you: Tucker, Tanya / Most beautiful girl, The: Stampley, Joe / Sweet dreams: Lynn, Loretta / Burning memories: Jennings, Waylon / Remember me - I'm the one who loves you: Haggard, Merle / Forever young: Hamilton, George IV / I believe you: Mandrell, Barbara / I'm wanting you: Robbins, Marty / Too far: Gayle, Crystal / Dream on: Oak Ridge Boys / We had it all: Twitty, Conway.
LP: SHM 3262
MC: HSC 3262

COUNTRY STARTIME, VOLUMES 1 AND 2 (Various artists).
2LP: CMCSB 003

COUNTRY STORYTELLERS (I Love Country) (Various artists).
Tracks: / Poncho and lefty: Haggard, Merle & Willie Nelson / Let him roll: Bare, Bobby / He stopped loving her today: Jones, George / 16th Avenue: Dalton, Lacy J / Weevils in the flour: Bushwackers / Engineers don't wave from trains anymore, The: Scruggs, Earl & Tom T Hall / Baron, The: Cash, Johnny / Seven Spanish Angels: Charles, Ray/ Willie Nelson / She used to sing on Sunday: Gatlin, Larry & The Gatlin Brothers / Country Comfort: Scruggs, Earl / Music man: Blanch, Arthur / Ride, The: Coe, David Allan / El Paso City: Robbins, Marty / Red headed stranger: Nelson, Willie.
LP: CBS 54951
MC: 40 54951

COUNTRY SUNRISE (Various artists).
MCSET: DTO 10137

COUNTRY SUNRISE (Various artists).
Tracks: / I saw the light: Price, Ray / One day at a time: Bryant, Anita / Using things and loving people: Thomas, B.J. / Since Jesus came into my heart: Ives, Burl / What a friend we have in Jesus: Various artists / Walk with me the rest of the way: Payne, Jimmy / Breaker breaker a sweet Jesus: Thrasher Brothers / This little light of mine: Davies, Jimmie / Sweetest song, The: Boone, Pat / Last Sunday, The: Cathedrals / You got the power: Mills, Walt / Heavens gonna be a blast: Jackson, Wanda / Our little old home town: Florida Boys/ He is everything: Clark, Roy / Jesus is coming very soon: Bagwell, Wendy & The Sunliters / I like the old time way: Ford, Tennessee Ernie / I didn't stop dancing: Wilkin, Marijohn / I heard my mother call my name in prayer: Wiseman, Mac / I'll fly away: Rogers,Roy/Dale Evans / This old house: Hambin, Stuart.
LP: TWE 6007
MC: TC TWE 6007

COUNTRY SUNRISE & COUNTRY SUNSET (Various artists).
Tracks: / I love a rainy night: Rabbitt, Eddie / Blue bayou: Ronstadt, Linda / There ain't no good chain gang: Jennings, Waylon & Johnny Cash / Applejack: Parton, Dolly / I'm so lonesome I could cry: Boxcar Willie/ Girls, women, and ladies: Bruce, Ed / Enough of each other: Fricke, Janie / Kaw-liga: Williams, Hank Jr./ Dear John: Shepard, Jean / Something's burning: Rogers, Kenny / Boxer, The: Harris, Emmylou / Somewhere over the rainbow: Lewis, Jerry Lee / Any which way you can: Campbell, Glen / What the world needs now is love: Spears, Billie Jo / You light up my life: Drusky, Roy / Sometimes when we touch: Robbins, Marty / True love ways: Gilley, Mickey / He's out of my life: Mandrell, Barbara / Good old boys: Prophet, Ronnie/ Help yourself to me: Gatlin, Larry / Mamas don't let your babies grow up to be cowboys: Nelson, Willie / She never knew me: Williams, Don / Miss the Mississippi: Gayle, Crystal / Mr. Bojangles / He'll have to go: Reeves, Jim / Sweet dreams: Cline, Patsy / Lay lady lay: Drake, Pete / I wouldn't want to live: Powers, Earl/ Dallas: Ely, Joe / Do I have to draw a picture?: Various artists / Last time, The: Bare, Bobby / Maybellene: Jones, George & Johnny Paycheck / Drivin' my life away: Rabbitt, Eddie / Coal miner's daughter: Lynn, Loretta / Abilene: Hamilton, George IV / Teddy bear: Kilgore, Merle / I washed my hands in muddy waters: Jackson, S. / Your cheatin' heart: Williams, Hank / Faded love: Kennedy, Blair / Blue blue day: Gibson, Don.
2LP: RTL 2059 A/B
MCSET: 4CRTL 2059 A/B

COUNTRY SUNSET (Various artists).
Tracks: / Jolene: Parton, Dolly / Are you sure Hank done it this way: Jennings, Waylon / Lonesome number one: Gibson, Don / Once a day: Smith, Connie / Where do I put her memory: Pride, Charley / Have mercy: Judds/ Jagged edge of a broken heart: Davies, Gail / I need a good woman bad: Conley, Earl Thomas / Baby I lied: Allen, Deborah / It was almost like a song: Milsap, Ronnie / Eighties ladies: Oslin, K.T. / Am I that easy to forget: Davis, Skeeter / Birmingham turnaround: Whitley, Keith / So long baby goodbye: Sonnier, Jo El / Louisiana saturday night: Boxcar Willie / My home's in Alabama: Alabama (Group).
LP: NL 90375
MC: NK 90375

COUNTRY SUPERSESSION, THE (Various artists).
Tracks: / With the one who loves you: Various artists / Scarlet revisted: Various artists / Face from the past: Various artists / All I can do is sing: Various artists / Big city: Various artists / In my time: Various artists / New York city: Various artists / Time will make it right: Various artists / Place in the country, A: Various artists / Maybe Monday: Various artists / Country boy: Various artists / Man: Various artists / Demolition zone: Various artists.
LP: SDLP 059

COUNTRY SUPERSTARS (Various artists).
MCSET: DTO 10247

COUNTRY SUPERSTARS (Various artists).
LP: WH 5014

COUNTRY SUPERSTARS (20 Golden hits) (Various artists).
LP: MA 261285
MC: MAMC 9261285

COUNTRY SUPERSTARS, VOLS. 1 & 2 (Various artists).
Tracks: / Gentle on my mind: Snow, Hank / Taker, The: Jennings, Waylon / Special: Flatt, Lester & Mac Wiseman/ Misery loves company: Prophet, Ronnie / I never promised you a rose garden: West, Dottie / Early morning rain: Hamilton, George IV / Am I that easy to forget?: Gibson, Don / Paper roses: Smith, Connie / Oh what a woman: Reed, Jerry / Release me: Locklin, Hank / Cold hard facts of life: Wagoner, Porter / I'm getting better: Reeves, Jim / Need in me, The: Baker, Carroll / It's four in the morning: Arnold, Eddy / Four walls: Gibson, Don / Scarlet ribbons: Brown, Jim Ed / West Texas highway: Hamilton, George IV / Ruby, don't take your love to town: Jennings, Waylon / I'm a lover not a fighter: Davis, Skeeter / Honey: Snow, Hank / Send me the pillow that you dream on: Locklin, Hank / Four strong winds: Bare, Bobby / Guilty: Reeves, Jim / I'm so lonesome I could cry: Davis, Skeeter.
2LP: SSD 8034 A/B
MCSET: SSC 8034 A/B

COUNTRY TRAIL (Various artists).
MCSET: DTO 10056

COUNTRY WAY, THE (Various artists).
Tracks: / Too hard to say I'm sorry: Various artists / Little folks, The: Various artists / Crystal chandeliers: Various artists / Act naturally: Various artists / Does my ring hurt your finger: Various artists / Mama don't cry for me: Various artists / Day the world stood still, The: Various artists / Gone, on the other hand: Various artists / You can tell the world: Various artists / I'll wander back to you: Various artists/ Life turned her that way: Various artists / I threw away the rose: Various artists.
LP: NL 89997
MC: NK 89997

COUNTRY & WESTERN CARAVAN, 1954 (Various artists).
Tracks: / Anything can happen: Arthur, Charline / I'm having a party all by myself: Arthur, Charline / Downhill drag: Atkins, Chet / Yankee doodle dixie: Atkins, Chet / I'd like to sit with the babysitter: Lone Pine, Hal / I want to be a cowboy's sweetheart: Cody, Betty / On treasure island: Cody, Betty / Sugar booger: Hill, Eddie / Heap of lovin', A: Hawkins, Hawkshaw / Rebound: Hawkins, Hawkshaw / Rockabye Basie: Davis Sisters / I forgot more than you'll ever know: Davis Sisters / Gotta git a goin': Davis Sisters / How to catch a man: Pearl, Minnie / I'm movin' on: Snow, Hank / Rhumba boogie: Snow, Hank / Honeymoon on a rocketship: Snow, Hank / Golden rocket: Snow, Hank.
LP: BFX 15276

COUNTRY & WESTERN FESTIVAL VOL. 3 (Various artists).
MC: SUCCESS 2029

COUNTRY & WESTERN FESTIVAL VOL. 1 (Various artists).
MC: SUCCESS 2027

COUNTRY & WESTERN FESTIVAL VOL. 2 (Various artists).
MC: SUCCESS 2028

COUNTRY & WESTERN HITS (Various artists).
Tracks: / Ring of fire: Various artists / High noon: Various artists / Fugitive: Various artists / Oh lonesome me: Various artists / Take good care of her: Various artists / King of the road: Various artists/ Ruby: Various artists / 16 tons: Various artists / Jackson: Various artists / My cabin in Carolina: Various artists / I can't stop loving you: Various artists / Kansas City: Various artists.
LP: 818 284 1

COUNTRY & WESTERN HYMNAL, NO.2 (Various artists).
Tracks: / Cleanse me: Various artists / Amazing grace: Various artists / Surely goodness and mercy: Various artists / I'll fly away: Various artists / In the valley: Various artists / He restoreth my soul: Various artists / Oh how I love Jesus: Various artists / Whispering hope: Various artists / Old rugged cross, The: Various artists / Love lifted me: Various artists / Beyond the sunset: Various artists / Now I belong to Jesus: Various artists / Heaven came down and glory filled my soul: Various artists / No one understands like Jesus: Various artists / Pass me not: Various artists / Brighten the corner where you are: Various artists/ Somebody bigger than you and I: Various artists / Whisper a prayer: Various artists / Higher ground: Various artists / No, never alone: Various artists / Where could I go: Various artists.
LP: PC 849

COUNTRY'S GREATEST HITS (Various artists).
Tracks: / Lucille: Rogers, Kenny / Stand by your man: Wynette, Tammy / By the time I get to Phoenix: Campbell, Glen / Ode to Billy Joe: Gentry, Bobbie / Always on my mind: Nelson, Willie / Honey: Goldsboro, Bobby/ Rose garden: Anderson, Lynn / Boy named Sue, A: Cash, Johnny / Don't it make my brown eyes blue: Various artists / Funny how time slips away: Nelson, Willie / Games people play: Various artists / Jolene: Parton, Dolly / Take me home country roads: Denver, John / Bobby McGee: Kristofferson, Kris / Oh lonesome me: Gibson, Don / Long long time: Rondstadt, Linda / Dukes of Hazzard (theme from): Jennings, Waylon / He'll have to go: Reeves, Jim / Snowbird: Murray, Anne / Behind closed doors: Rich, Charlie / I believe in you: Williams, Don / Blanket on the ground: Spears, Billie Jo.
LP: CGH 1
MC: CGHC 1

COUNTRY'S GREATEST HITS (Various artists).
Tracks: / Lucille: Rogers, Kenny / By the time I get to Phoenix: Campbell, Glen / Always on my mind: Nelson, Willie / Rose garden: Anderson, Lynn / Don't it make my brown eyes blue: Gayle, Crystal / Games people play: South, Joe / Behind closed doors: Rich, Charlie / Coat of many colours: Parton, Dolly / I ain't living long like this: Jennings, Waylon / Rose Marie: Whitman, Slim / Devil woman: Robbins, Marty / Stand by your man: Wynette, Tammy / Ode to Billy Joe: Gentry, Bobbie / Honey: Goldsboro, Bobby / Boy named Sue, A: Cash, Johnny / Funny how time slips by: Nelson, Willie / He'll have to go: Reeves, Jim / Blanket on the ground: Spears, Billie Jo / Oh lonesome me: Gibson, Don / Rhinestone cowboy: Campbell, Glen/ We love each other: Rich, Charlie / Mason Dixon line: Jennings, Waylon.
LP: STAR 2433
MC: STAC 2433

COZY LABEL, THE (Various artists).
Tracks: / Hot guitars: Anderson, Keith / I need a hit: Anderson, Keith / She's gone: Vandergift Bros./ Sittin' here a' cryin': Vandergift Bros. / Ambridge boogie: Brooks, Dale / I can read between the lines: Lambert, Bruce / Let's rock: Watson, Johnny / I'm not crazy: Watson, Johnny / Mexican rock: Lewis, Dorse/ Hot rod boogie: Lewis, Dorse / Baby I don't mind: Jones, E/V. Dickerson / Rosie: Lester, Butch / One little teardrop too late: Plain Slim / Popcorn boogie: Hank The Cowhand / She's a humdinger: Hank The Cowhand / Fan it and cool it: Hank The Cowhand.
LP: WLP 8823

CREAM OF COUNTRY (Various artists).
LP: BRA 1015

CROSS COUNTRY (Various artists).
LP: 2403871

DEDICATED TO YOU (18 More Songs From The Heart) (Various artists).
Tracks: / Coward of the county: Rogers, Kenny / I will always love you: Parton, Dolly / Have I told you lately that I love you: Reeves, Jim / Roses are red: O'Donnell, Daniel / Who's sorry now: Francis, Connie/ Years from now: Various artists / I don't know why I love you: Rose Marie / Blanket on the ground: Spears, Billie Jo / Honey: Goldsboro, Bobby / Crystal chandeliers: Pride, Charley / Sunshine of your smile, The: Berry, Mike / You are my sunshine: Boxcar Willie / Love is like a butterfly: Parton, Dolly / I need you: O'Donnell, Daniel / Anniversary waltz: Rose Marie / Little green apples: Miller, Roger / Single girl: Posey, Sandy / Last farewell, The: Whittaker, Roger.
LP: PLAT 3901
MC: PLAC 3901

DIESEL SMOKE AND DANGEROUS CURVES (Various artists).
LP: SLP 250
MC: GT 5250

DISCOVER NEW COUNTRY (Various artists).
2LP: DNC 1
MC: DNCK 1

DON'T CALL IT DIXIE (Various artists).
2LP: BAJC 513/14

DUELLING BANJOS (20 Country and Western Bluegrass Hits) (Various artists).
Tracks: / Duelling banjos: Various artists / Eighth of January: Various artists / Farewell blues: Various artists / Pony Express: Various artists / Mountain dew: Various artists / Old Joe Clark: Various artists/ Little Maggie: Various artists / Buffalo girls: Various artists / Rawhide: Various artists / Earl's breakdown: Various artists / Reuben's train: Various artists / Fire on the mountain: Various artists/ Hard ain't it hard: Various artists / Movin' on: Various artists / Foot tappin': Various artists/ Riding the waves: Various artists / End of a dream: Various artists / Eight more miles to Louisville: Various artists / Shuckin' the corn: Various artists / You're looking at country: Various artists.
MC: AIM 120
MC: AM 120
LP: PLAT 02
MC: PLAC 02

EASYRIDING: COUNTRY & WESTERN (Various artists).
Tracks: / Jambalaya: Lewis, Jerry Lee / Detroit City: Drusky, Roy / King of the road: Miller, Roger/ Six days on the road: Dudley, Dave / Battle of New Orleans: Drusky, Roy / You can have her: Rich, Charlie/ Ring of fire: Drusky, Roy / Rawhide: Young, Faron / Jackson: Lewis, Jerry Lee/Linda Gail Lewis / Green, green grass of home: Miller, Roger / Mule-skinner blues: Draper, Rusty / Shutters and boards: Wallace, Jerry / More and more: Draper, Rusty / Save the last dance for me: Young, Faron / North to Alaska: Lewis, Jerry Lee / Don't let the stars get in your eyes: Dudley, Dave / I washed my face in the morning dew: Various artists / Let's do what's right even if it's wrong: Drusky, Roy & Priscilla Mitchell / Chug a lug: Miller, Roger/ Sweet thang: Lewis, Jerry Lee/Linda Gail Lewis / Truck drivin' son of a gun: Dudley, Dave / Foggy mountain breakdown: Flatt, Lester & Earl Scruggs.
MC: KNMC 11004
LP: KNLP 11004

ENCHANTING WORLD OF COUNTRY MUSIC (Various artists).
MC: AIM 73

ESSENTIAL COUNTRY (Various artists).
LP: . . . . KNLP 15004
MC: . . . . KNMC 15004

FEELIN' COUNTRY: VOL 1 (Various artists).
Tracks: / Daddy sang bass: *Various artists* / Just out of reach: *Various artists* / Some other time: *Various* artists / You made me a fool: *Various artists* / Where love used to live: *Various artists* / Help me make it through the night: *Various artists* / White lightning: *Various artists* / Double dare: *Various artists*/ He really must have loved you: *Various artists* / Let the teardrops fall: *Various artists* / Sunday morning coming down: *Various artists* / Moment isn't very long, A: *Various artists* / You win again: *Various artists*/ Tennessee waltz: *Various artists* / It's four in the morning: *Various artists* / Living in a house full of love: *Various artists*.
LP: . . . . CBR 1026
MC: . . . . KCBR 1026

FEELIN' COUNTRY: VOL 2 (Various artists).
Tracks: / Walk through this world with me: *Various artists* / Ease the want in me: *Various artists* / Cold, cold heart: *Various artists* / There goes my everything: *Various artists* / Last thing on my mind: *Various artists*/ Enough to make a grown man cry: *Various artists* / Have I been coming too long?: *Various artists* / Hey good lookin': *Various artists* / All the time: *Various artists* / You make me what I am today: *Various artists*/ I can't help it (if I'm still in love with you): *Various artists* / It could have been: *Various artists* / Moment isn't very long, A: *Various artists* / Good year for the roses, A: *Various artists*.
LP: . . . . CBR 1043
MC: . . . . KCBR 1043

FIRST LADIES OF COUNTRY (Various artists).
Tracks: / Don't it make my brown eyes blue: *Gayle, Crystal* / Snowbird: *Anderson, Lynn* / Ode to Billy Joe: *Wynette*, Tammy / Dumb blonde: *Parton, Dolly* / Delta dawn: *Tucker, Tanya* / 57 chevrolet: *Spears, Billie Jo*/ No charge: *Wynette, Tammy* / It's only make believe: *Anderson, Lynn* / Fuel to the flame: *Parton, Dolly*/ Stand by your man: *Wynette, Tammy* / Blanket on the ground: *Spears, Billie Jo* / Divorce: *Wynette, Tammy*/ Wrong road again: *Gayle, Crystal* / Honey come back: *Anderson, Lynn* / You are so beautiful: *Tucker, Tanya*/ Your ole handy man: *Parton, Dolly* / Little bit more, A: *Anderson, Lynn* / Let me be there: *Tucker, Tanya*/ Rose garden: *Anderson, Lynn*.
LP: 32235
MC: 40 32235
LP: 10018

GOD LOVES COUNTRY MUSIC (Various artists).
Tracks: / God loves country music: *Various artists* / O Lord I thank you: *Various artists* / Servant of all: *Various* artists / If we walk in the light: *Various artists* / Draw me nearer: *Various artists* / Freely, freely: *Various* artists / Psalm 5: *Various artists* / From the rising of the sun: *Various artists* / Come let us worship and bow down: *Various artists* / Create in me a clean heart: *Various artists* / Christian life, The: *Various artists*.
LP: . . . . MM 0080
MC: . . . . TC MM 0080

GOING WEST (Various artists).
Tracks: / Folsom Prison blues: *Cash, Johnny* / Just another rhinestone: *Drum, Don* / Country comes west: *Henderson,* Kelvin / Hey little cowboy: *Meister, Gary* / Run boy run: *Country Cats* / Yours and mine: *Turner, Mary* Lou / Get the bird flyin': *Campbell, Glen* / Takin' it easy: *Henderson, Kelvin* / Rock Island line: *Cash*, Johnny / Boy from Indiana, The: *Kahlenberg Company* / Don't turn around: *Dickey, Bob* / It's alright: *Sinatra, Frank*.
LP: . . . . Q 90033
MC: . . . . MQ 990033

GOLDEN COUNTRY (Various artists).
Tracks: / Stand by your man: *Wynette, Tammy* / Daddy won't be home anymore: *Parton, Dolly* / Love is just a game: *Gatlin, Larry* / Blue skies: *Nelson, Willie* / Cowboys ain't supposed to cry: *Bandy, Moe* / Me and Bobby McGhee: *Various artists* / Delta dawn: *Tucker, Tanya* / Very special love song, A: *Rich, Charlie* / Colorado cool aid: *Paycheck, Johnny* / Little bit more, A: *Anderson, Lynn* / Maria Elena: *Robbins, Mary* / It ain't me babe: *Cash, Johnny*.
LP: . . . . SHM 3058
MC: . . . . HSC 3058

GOLDEN COUNTRY HITS (Various artists).
MCSET: 850121/2

GOOD OLE MEMPHIS COUNTRY (Various artists).
Tracks: / Feeling low: *Chaffin, Ernie* / Laughin' and jokin': *Chaffin, Ernie* / Destiny: *King, Cast*/ Baby doll: *King, Cast* / Round and round: *King, Cast* / Please believe me: *King, Cast* / When you stop lovin' me: *King, Cast* / Easy to love: *Self, Mack* / Down on the border: *Simmons, Gene* / Goin' crazy: *Self, Mack* / Poor boy: *Holt, O.C.* / This train: *Holt, O.C.* / Pink wedding gown: *Holt, O.C.*/ Satisfied with me: *King, Cast*.
LP: . . . . SUN 1016

GRAND COUNTRY TOUR (Various artists).
Tracks: / Grand country tour: *Various artists* / City of New Orleans: *Various artists* / Detroit City: *Various* artists / Mississippi: *Various artists* / Canadian sunset: *Various artists* / Colorado cool aid: *Various* artists / Dixie on my mind: *Various artists* / El Paso: *Various artists* / Dallas: *Various artists*/ Georgia on my mind: *Various artists* / Cincinnati: *Various artists* / Abilene: *Various artists* / Banks of the Ohio: *Various artists* / Nashville: *Various artists* / Wolverton Mountain: *Various artists* / America the beautiful: *Various artists*.
LP: . . . . CBS 31764

GREAT AMERICAN COUNTRY HITS (Various artists).
MC: . . . . AM 31

GREAT COUNTRY FESTIVAL (Various artists).
LP: 6600 003

GREAT COUNTRY HITS (Various artists).
2LP: 80019
MCSET: 850191/2

GREAT COUNTRY HITS OF THE 70'S (Various artists).
MC: . . . . VCA 018

GREAT COUNTRY MUSIC SHOW (Various artists).
2LP: . . . . RTD 2083
MCSET: 4CRTD 2083

GREATEST COUNTRY DUETS (Various artists).
Tracks: / Reasons to quit: *Various artists* / Thinkin' of a rendezvous: *Various artists* / It's only make believe: *Various artists* / It's a dirty job: *Various artists* / C.C. Waterback: *Various artists* / Whiter shade of pale: *Various artists*.
LP: . . . . EPC 25933
MC: 40 25933

HOOKED ON COUNTRY (Various artists).
LP: . . . . NE 1459
MC: . . . . CE 2459

I LOVE COUNTRY (Golden oldies) (Various artists).
LP: 4510011

I LOVE COUNTRY (Cowboy songs) (Various artists).
LP: 4510091

I'M A HILLBILLY YANKEE DOODLE BOY (Various artists).
Tracks: / I'm a hillbilly yankee doodle boy: *Lewis, Texas Jim* / Smoke on the water: *Tuttle, Wesley* / Mother's prayer: *Tuttle, Wesley/Travis Merle* / Cannon song, The: *Rodgers, Slim* / Soldiers last letter: *Colorado Hillbillies*/ I'm comin' home to you: *Rodgers, Slim* / I'd like to give my dog to Uncle Sam: *Waters, Ozzie* / Gold star in her window: *Colorado Hillbillies* / Rodeo down in Tokyo: *Waters, Ozzie* / Tommy gun boogie: *Rodgers, Slim*/ Hillbilly soldier Joe: *Johnson Sisters* / If it's gonna help win the way: *Hoosier Hot Shots*.
MC: . . . . K 1004

IMPRESSIONS OF DON WILLIAMS (Various Session Musicians) (Various artists).
MC: . . . . AIM 65

IN CONCERT WITH HOST CHARLEY PRIDE (Various artists).
Tracks: / Kaw-liga: *Pride, Charley* / Mississippi cotton picking delta town: *Pride, Charley* / Louisiana man: *Pride, Charley* / Jolene: *Parton, Dolly* / Love is like a butterfly: *Parton, Dolly* / Girl who waits on tables: *Milsap, Ronnie* / Slippin' and slidin' (medley): *Milsap, Ronnie* / Kiss an angel good morning: *Pride*, Charley / Chaplin in new shoes: *Atkins, Chet* / Entertainer, The: *Atkins, Chet* / Rollin' in my sweet baby's arms: *Milsap, Ronnie & Dolly Parton* / Let's sing our song: *Reed, Jerry* / Thing called love: *Reed, Jerry*/ Lord, Mr Ford: *Reed, Jerry* / Coat of many colours: *Parton, Dolly* / Bargain store: *Parton, Dolly* / Out of hand: *Stewart, Gary* / Colonel Bogey: *Reed, Jerry & Chet Atkins* / For the good times: *Pride, Charley*/ John Henry: *Atkins, Chet & Jerry Reed*.
2LP: . . . . DPS 2064

INTERNATIONAL FESTIVAL OF COUNTRY MUSIC, AN (Various artists).
Tracks: / Keep on the sunny side: *Hamilton, George IV* / Healing hands of time: *Colter, Jessi* / Leaning on your love: *Ryles, John Wesley* / Honky tonk heart: *Walker, Charlie* / Blue is my lonely room: *Hillsiders* / Blue, blue day: *Gibson, Don* / Permanent kind of lovin': *Glaser, Jim* / Best guitar picker: *Atonemans*/ Nobody's child: *Snow, Hank* / Mouth to mouth resuscitation: *Hartford, John* / I can't get enough of you, baby: *Baker, Carroll* / Night coach out of Dallas: *Withers, Tex* / Mowing the lawn: *Brown, Jim Ed & Vernon Oxford*/ At least part of the way: *Gems* / Make up your mind: *Wells, Kitty* / Travelling minstrel man: *Payne, Jimmy*/ Last letter, The: *Smith, Connie* / Someone else's arms: *Houston, David* / Little Rosa: *Red Sovine* / Rocky top: *West, Dottie* / Dreaming country: *Young Johnny Four* / Morning after baby let me down: *Mercey Brothers*/ You can't go in the red playing bluegrass: *Wiseman, Mac* / I'm the mail she's waiting for: *Owens, George* / Organized noise: *Newbury, Mickey* / In the good old days: *Parton, Dolly* / Where you been so long: *Hall, David*/ It's my time: *Loudermilk, John D.* / As a matter of fact: *Pruett, Jeanne* / Gardenia waltz, The: *Waylors & Johnny Gimble* / Colour of the blues: *Davis, Skeeter* / Orange blossom: *Monroe, Bill & His Blue Grass Boys*.
2LP: . . . . PL 42407

JOLIE BLONDE"ROCKS AND ROLLS (Various artists).
Tracks: / Castro rock: *Chevalier, Jay* / Puppy love: *Parton, Dolly* / Honey baby oh: *Earl, Little Billy*/ Rock and roll jolie blonde: *Lee, Charlie* / Oh well well well: *Lee, Charlie* / My glass is empty: *Various* artists / Twitterpated: *Various artists* / Jelly Nelly: *Buck Wheat* / Couple in the car: *Earl, Little Billy* / High voltage: *Jano, Johnny* / Mable's gone: *Jano, Johnny* / Coffins have no pockets: *Hart, Larry*.
LP: . . . . GCL 114

JUKE BOX COLLECTION - KING OF THE ROAD (60's country music hits) (Various artists).
Tracks: / It's four in the morning: *Young, Faron* / Make the world go away: *Arnold, Eddy* / Send me the pillow that you dream on: *Tillotson, Johnny* / Sea of heartbreak: *Gibson, Don* / I fall to pieces: *Cline, Patsy*/ I won't forget you: *Reeves, Jim* / King of the road: *Miller, Roger* / Walk on by: *Van Dyke, Leroy* / There goes my everything: *Greene, Jack* / Next in line, The: *Twitty, Conway* / What made Milwaukee famous: *Lewis*, Jerry Lee / Detroit City: *Bare, Bobby* / Satin sheets: *Pruett, Jeannie* / Coal miner's daughter: *Lynn, Loretta*.
LP: . . . . OG 1718
MC: . . . . OG 2718

KENTUCKY FIDDLE BAND MUSIC (Various artists).
LP: . . . . MS 45003

KINDA COUNTRY VOL. 1 (Various artists).
2LP: . . . . CR 064
MCSET: . . . . CRT 064

KINGS OF THE ROAD (Various artists).
Tracks: / King of the road: *Miller, Roger* / Most beautiful girl, The: *Rich, Charlie* / Devil woman: *Robbins*, Marty / I can help: *Swan, Billy* / Gambler, The: *Bare, Bobby* / Don't take your guns to town: *Cash, Johnny*/ Heroes: *Cash, Johnny & Waylon Jennings* / Whiter shade of pale, A: *Nelson, Willie* / Help me make it through the night: *Kristofferson, Kris* / Oh pretty woman: *Orbison, Roy* / I'll see you in my dreams: *Atkins, Chet* & Mark Knopfler / Good year for the roses, A: *Jones, George* / Highwayman: *Jennings, Waylon, Willie Nelson,Johnny* Cash,K. Kristofferson / Eagle, The: *Jennings, Waylon* / Devil went down to Georgia, The: *Daniels, Charlie Band*/ Under the gun: *Nelson, Willie/Kris Kristofferson/ Dolly Parton*.
MC: 4680844

LEGENDARY COUNTRY & WESTERN HITS (Various artists).
Tracks: / Gentle on my mind: *Young, Faron* / Me and Bobby McGee: *Statler Brothers* / Sweet dreams: *McEntire, Reba* / Mama don't let your babies grow up to be cowboys: *White, Tony Joe* / Touble in mind: *Lewis, Jerry Lee*/ Rock Island line: *Donegan, Lonnie* / Week in a country jail, A: *Various artists* / Green green grass of home: *Miller, Roger* / Early morning rain: *Lewis, Jerry Lee* / Street of Laredo, The: *Young, Faron* / Country boy: *Wolf, Micky* / That's the way a cowboy rocks and rolls: *Ward, Jacky* / Cold cold heart: *Jones, George*/ Sixteen tons: *Dudley, Dave* / Sunday morning coming down: *Kennedy, Jerry* / Country roads: *Donegan, Lonnie*.
MC: 818 229 4

LOVE COUNTRY (Various artists).
Tracks: / Almost persuaded: *Rich, Charlie* / There goes my everything: *Wynette, Tammy* / Woman in my...: *Robbins*, Marty / Right time of the night: *Anderson, Lynn* / Thing called love, A: *Cash, Johnny* / Love's a hurting thing: *Robbins, Marty* / Loving arms: *Tucker, Tanya* / Satisfied man, A: *Rich, Charlie* / We loved it away: *Jones, George & Tammy Wynette* / Very special love song, The: *Mandrell, Barbara* / Let it be me: *Tucker*, Tanya / Your sweet lies: *Wynette, Tammy* / I'd run a mile to you: *Anderson, Lynn* / I lost her to a Dallas cowboy: *Bandy, Moe* / My elusive dreams: *Rich, Charlie* / Honey come back: *Anderson, Lynn* / Another lonely song: *Wynette, Tammy* / If I were a carpenter: *Cash, Johnny* / Satisfied: *Mandrell, Barbara* / Near you: *Various artists*.
MCSET: . . . . DTO 10264
MCSET: . . . . DTOL 10264

MASTER OF COUNTRY (Various artists).
LP: . . . . MFP 41 5690 1
MC: . . . . MFP 41 5690 4

MUSIC FOR THE MILLIONS (Various artists).
LP: 8125 841
MC: 8125 844

MUSIC ON THE MOVE (20 COUNTRY GREATS) (Various artists).
MC: . . . . INTK 9001

MUSIC THAT MATTERS (Various artists).
Tracks: / I'll go steppin' too: *Sutton,Glenn* / Amazing Grace: *Statlers* / Waitin' for the sun to shine: *McEntire*, Reba / Old violin, An: *Paycheck, Johnny* / Do you mind if I step into your dreams: *Cannons* / She's the trip that I've been on: *Boone, Larry* / These shoes: *Unknown* / Hard baby to rock: *Hensley, Tari* / Walk the way the wind blows: *Mattea, Kathy* / Down at the Mall: *Various artists* / Everybody needs love on a Saturday night: *Maines Brothers Band* / That's what her memory is for: *Baker, Butch* / Winners: *Fargo, Donna* / Love is the way: *Kristofferson, Kris*.
LP: . . . . PRICE 102
MC: . . . . PRIMC 102

NASHVILLE COUNTRY ROCK, VOL 3: STEPPIN' OUT TONI (Various artists).
LP: . . . . REDITA 121

NASHVILLE COUNTRY ROCK, VOL 4: CRAZY ABOUT THE B (Various artists).
LP: . . . . REDITA 122

NASHVILLE STARS IN DEUTSCHLAND (Various artists).
LP: . . . . BFX 15040

NASHVILLE TODAY VOL.2 (Various artists).
LP: . . . . PL 43284

NASHVILLE TODAY VOL. 1 (Various artists).
LP: . . . . PL 43475

NASHVILLE WEST (Various artists).
Tracks: / Nashville west: *Various artists* / Mental revenge: *Various artists* / I wanna live: *Various artists*/ Sweet Suzanna: *Various artists* / Green green grass of home: *Various artists* / Love of the common people: *Various* artists / Tuff and stringy: *Various artists* / Washed my hands in muddy water: *Various artists* / Ode to Billy Joe: *Various artists* / Louisiana rain: *Various artists* / Send me back home: *Various artists* / Memphis: *Various artists* / By the time I get to Phoenix: *Various artists*.
LP: . . . . SRS 8701
LP: . . . . SDLP 1011

NASHVILLE'S FINEST HOUR (Various artists).
LP: . . . . PL 43207

NEW NASHVILLE COUNTRY MUSIC (Various artists).
MCSET: . . . . DFG 8410

NO.1 COUNTRY - 80'S COUNTRY (Various artists).
Tracks: / Rockin' with the rhythm of the rain: *Judds* / Do ya': *Oslin, K.T.* / Strong heart: *Sheppard, T.G.*/ Crying my heart out over you: *Skaggs, Ricky* / Houston means I'm one day closer to you: *Gatlin, Larry* / Can't stop my heart from loving you: *O'Kanes* / Love in the first degree: *Alabama (Group)* / Seven year ache: *Cash*, Rosanne / Once in a blue moon: *Conley, Earl Thomas* / Somebody lied: *Van Shelton, Ricky* / It'll be me: *Exile*/ Got my heart set on you: *Conlee, John* / My only love: *Statler Brothers* / True love ways: *Gilley, Mickey*.
LP: . . . . KNLP 13005

MC: KNMC 13005

NO.1 COUNTRY - COUNTRY BALLADEERS (14 country no.1's) (Various artists).
Tracks: / Coward of the county: Rogers, Kenny / El Paso: Robbins, Marty / Don't take your guns: Cash, Johnny/ Wichita lineman: Campbell, Glen / Golden ring: Jones, George & Tammy Wynette / When it's Springtime in Alaska: Horton, J. / Tennessee flat top box: Cash, Rosanne / Ballad of Jed Clampett: Flatt & Scruggs / BJ the DJ: Jackson, Stonewall / What's your mama's name: Tucker, Tanya / She thinks I still care: Jones, George/ Girl on the billboard: Reeves, Del / Running bear: James, Sonny / Saginaw, Michigan: Frizzell, Lefty.
LP: KNLP 13010
MC: KNMC 13010

NO.1 COUNTRY - COUNTRY BOYS (Various artists).
Tracks: / One piece at a time: Cash, Johnny / Me and Bobby McGee: Lewis, Jerry Lee / Living in the promised land: Nelson, Willie / I cheated me right out of you: Bandy, Moe / Country boy: Skaggs, Ricky / Faster horses: Hall, Tom T. / Lucille (you won't do your Daddie's will): Jennings, Waylon / Why baby why: Pride, Charley / Natural high: Haggard, Merle / I always get lucky with you: Jones, George / Lost in the fifties tonight: Milsap, Ronnie / Love don't care (whose heart it breaks): Conley, Earl Thomas / Lonely nights: Gilley, Mickey / My woman my woman my wife: Robbins, Marty.
LP: KNLP 13003
MC: KNMC 13003

NO.1 COUNTRY - COUNTRY CLASSICS (Various artists).
Tracks: / Walk on by: Van Dyke, Leroy / Stand by your man: Wynette, Tammy / Tender years: Jones, George/ For the good times: Price, Ray / Eleven roses: Williams, Hank Jr. / Year that Clayton Delaney died, The: Hall, Tom T. / I ain't never: Tillis, Mel / Big bad John: Dean, Jimmy / King of the road: Miller, Roger/ North to Alaska: Horton, Johnny / Rose garden: Anderson, Lynn / Sunday morning coming down: Cash, Johnny/ It's four in the morning: Young, Faron / There must be more to love than this: Lewis, Jerry Lee / Almost persuaded: Houston, David / Devil woman: Robbins, Marty.
LP: KNLP 13006
MC: KNMC 13006

NO.1 COUNTRY - COUNTRY DUETS (Various artists).
Tracks: / Near you: Jones, George & Tammy Wynette / Poncho and Lefty: Nelson, Willie & Merle Haggard / Why not me?: Judds / Both to each other (friends and lovers): Rabbitt, Eddie/Juice Newton / On my knees: Rich, Charlie/ Janie Frickie / I don't want to have to marry you: Brown, Jim Ed & Helen Cornelius / Just good ol' boys: Bandy, Moe & Joe Stampley / Mamas don't let your babies grow up to be cowboys: Jennings, Waylon & Willie Nelson / Please don't stop loving me: Waggoner, Porter/Dolly Parton / My elusive dreams: Houston, D./Tammy Wynette / Paradise tonight: McLain, C./M.Gilley / Tear time: Dave & Sugar / Yes Mr. Peters: Drusky, Roy & Priscilla Mitchell / Yesterdays wine: Haggard, Merle & George Jones.
LP: KNLP 13004
MC: KNMC 13004

NO.1 COUNTRY - COUNTRY GIANTS (14 country no.1's) (Various artists).
Tracks: / Guess I'm crazy: Reeves, Jim / Lucille: Rogers, Kenny / Flesh and blood: Cash, Johnny / Ruby Ann: Robbins, Marty / Sixteen tons: Ford, Tennessee Ernie / This time: Jennings, Waylon / Southern nights: Campbell, Glen / Blue eyes crying in the rain: Nelson, Willie / I've been everywhere: Snow, Hank/ She's just an old love...: Pride, Charley / She's actin' single: Stewart, Gary / You've got the touch: Alabama (Group) / Am I losing you: Milsap, Ronnie / Grand tour, The: Jones, George.
LP: KNLP 13008
MC: KNMC 13008

NO.1 COUNTRY - COUNTRY GIRLS (Various artists).
Tracks: / Think about love: Parton, Dolly / It's like we never said goodbye: Gayle, Crystal / Never be you: Cash, Rosanne / What a man my man is: Fairchild, Barbara / Drifter: Sylvia / You and me: Wynette, Tammy / Have mercy: Judds / Hurt: Newton, Juice / Always have, always will: Fricke, Janie / Who's cheating who: McLain, Charly / Would you lay with me (in a field of stone): Tucker, Tanya / Once a day: Smith, Connie / You're the first time I've thought about: McIntyre, Reba.
LP: KNLP 13002
MC: KNMC 13002

NO.1 COUNTRY - COUNTRY GOLD (14 country no.1's) (Various artists).
Tracks: / Most beautiful girl in the town: Rich, Charlie / Boy named Sue, A: Cash, Johnny / I can help: Swan, Billy / Battle of New Orleans: Horton, Johnny / When you're hot, you're hot: Reed, Jerry / Wild side of life, The: Thompson, Hank / Cattle call: Arnold, Eddy / Crazy arms: Price, Ray / Great balls of fire: Lewis, Jerry Lee / Waterloo: Jackson, Stonewall / White sports coat, A: Robbins, Marty / Mexican Joe: Reeves, Jim / Shotgun boogie: Ford, Tennessee Ernie / Harper valley PTA: Riley, Jeannie C..
LP: KNLP 13012
MC: KNMC 13012

NO.1 COUNTRY - COUNTRY LADIES (Various artists).
Tracks: / Old flames: Parton, Dolly / Talking in your sleep: Gayle, Crystal / Keep me in mind: Anderson, Lynn / My baby thinks he's a train: Cash, Rosanne / Nobody: Sylvia / Blood red and going down: Tucker, Tanya / Maybe your baby's got the blues: Judds / Ways to love a man: Wynette, Tammy / Radio heart: McClain, Charly / You make me want to make: Newton, Juice / He's a heartache: Fricke, Janie / I'm not Lisa: Colter, Jessi / If you ever change your mind: Gayle, Crystal / One day at a time: Lane, Cristy.
LP: KNLP 13009
MC: KNMC 13009

NO.1 COUNTRY - COUNTRY LEGENDS (14 country no.1's) (Various artists).
Tracks: / Ring of fire: Cash, Johnny / Blue side of lonesome: Reeves, Jim / Door, The: Jones, George/ Hello walls: Young, Faron / (I'm a) ramblin' man: Jennings, Waylon / Hello love: Snow, Hank / Ribbon of darkness: Robbins, Marty / Blanket on the ground: Spears, Billie Jo / Too many lovers: Gayle, Crystal/ You're my man: Anderson, Lynn / Take me to your world: Wynette, Tammy / It ain't easy bein' easy: Fricke, Janie / Every time two hearts collide: Rogers, Kenny & Dottie West / You're the only one: Parton, Dolly.
LP: KNLP 13011
MC: KNMC 13011

NO.1 COUNTRY - COUNTRY LOVE (Various artists).
Tracks: / Always on my mind: Nelson, Willie / Cry myself to sleep: Judds / When we make love: Alabama (Group)/ I'm a stand by my woman man: Milsap, Ronnie / Till I make it on my own: Wynette, Tammy / I love: Hall, Tom T. / Very special love song, A: Rich, Charlie / Luckenbach, Texas: Jennings, Waylon / Would you like to take another chance on me: Lewis, Jerry Lee / That's the way love goes: Haggard, Merle / Way we make a broken heart, The: Cash, Rosanne / Love put a song in my heart: Rodriguez, Johnny / I don't want to be a memory: Exile/ I will always love you: Parton, Dolly.
LP: KNLP 13001
MC: KNMC 13001

NO.1 COUNTRY - COUNTRY NIGHTS (14 country no.1's) (Various artists).
Tracks: / Tonight, Carmen: Robbins, Marty / Night games: Pride, Charley / What goes on when the sun goes down: Milsap, Ronnie / City lights: Price, Ray / She can put her shoes under my bed: Duncan, J / First thing ev'ry morning: Dean, Jimmy / Georgia on my mind: Nelson, Willie / (There's a) fire in the night: Alabama (Group) / Stand by me: Gilley, Mickey / She called me baby: Rich, Charlie / Moon is still over me: Johnson, M / Woke up in love: Exile / Twinkle twinkle lucky star: Haggard, M. / Bedtime story: Wynette, Tammy.
LP: KNLP 13007
MC: KNMC 13007

OFF THE RECORD...COUNTRY CLASSICS (Various artists).
2LP: FEDD 1009
MCSET: CFEDD 1009

OKEH WESTERN SWING (Various artists).
Tracks: / Hesitation blues: Bernard, Al/ Goofus Five / Lovesick blues: Miller, Emmett/Georgia Crackers / Sadie Green: Newman, Roy/his boys / Give me my money: Blue Ridge Playboys / Range riders stomp: Range riders/ There'll be some changes made: O'Daniel, W. Lee/ His Hillbilly boys / Fort Worth stomp: Crystal Springs Ramblers/ Get with it: Willia, Bob/his Texas boys / Who walks in when I walk out?: Various artists / Too busy: Various artists / Play boy stomp: Various artists / Ozzlin' daddy blues: Various artists / Pray for the lights to go out: Various artists / Girl I left behind me, The: Various artists / Hot as I am: Sadie tramps / One more river to cross: Sons Of The Pioneers / Knocky knocky: Light Crust Doughboys / Zeke Terney's stomp: Hi-Neighbour boys / Chill tonic: Penny, Hank & His Radio Cowboys / When I put on my long white robe: Swift / I love your fruit: Sweet Violet Boys / Bass man jive: Stockard, Ocie/his Wanderers / Reno Street blues: Hi-Flyers/ Panhandle shuffle: Sons of the West / Gulf Coast special: Hofner, Adolf/ his orchestra / Brown bottle blues: Harbert, Slim/His boys / Three way boogie: Cooley, Spade & Tex Williams / Take it away, Leon: McAuliffe, Leon/his Western swing band.
2LP: EPC 22124
MC: 40 22124

OLE TENNESSEE COUNTRY (Various artists).
Tracks: / Feeling low: Various artists / Laughin' and jokin': Various artists / Round and round: Various artists / My destiny: Various artists / Baby doll: Various artists / Believe me: Various artists/ When you stop lovin' me: Various artists / Easy to love: Various artists / Down on the border: Various artists / Goin' crazy: Various artists / Poor boy: Various artists / This train: Various artists/ Pink wedding gown: Various artists / Satisfied with me: Various artists.
LP: SUN 1032

ON STAGE AT THE GRAND OLE OPRY (Various artists).
Tracks: / Little Ida Red: Various artists / South of the border (down Mexico way): Various artists / Well maybe: Various artists / Bye bye love: Various artists / Rest of the way: Various artists / Last heartbreak: Various artists / Old rugged cross, The: Various artists / Lovesick blues: Various artists / Our paths crossed again: Various artists / On and on and on: Various artists / Where were you: Various artists/ Blue grass part one (twist): Various artists / Please keep me in mind: Various artists / Acorn Hill breakdown: Various artists.
LP: HAT 3010
MC: HATC 3010

OPEN COUNTRY (Various artists).
Tracks: / Drag 'em off the interstate, sock it to 'em J.P.blues: Curless, Dick / I'll always be waiting for you: Jim & Jesse / Hank and Lefty raised my country soul: Edwards, Stoney / Bump bounce boogie: Asleep At The Wheel/ Man likes things like that, A: Louvin, Charlie & Melba Montgomery / Lovesick blues: Curtis, Sonny / Bucket to the south: Peterson, Colleen / Man of the hour: Ballard, Larry / Runaway heart: Rose, Pam / Eighteen wheels: Buffalo, Norton / Woman, don't you try to sing my song: Curless, Dick / Just wondering why: Jim & Jesse / Even cowgirls get the blues: La Costa / Ladies love outlaws: Rabbit, Jimmy & Renegade / Where's Patricia now: Curtis, Sonny / Dynamite rock & roll band: Peterson, Colleen / Hangin' tree, The: Buffalo, Norton / I'm so glad: Rose, Pam / Take a ride on a riverboat: Louisianna's Leroux / Let's get down to the truth: Ballard, Larry & Tracey Nelson.
LP: SEE 211

OPRY TIME IN TENNESSEE (Various artists).
LP: SLP 177
MC: GT 5177

QUEENS OF COUNTRY MUSIC (Various artists).
Tracks: / Just out of reach: Cline, Patsy / You belong to me: Page, Patti / Am I that easy to forget: Riley, Jeannie C. / Walking after midnight: Cline, Patsy / Stop the world: Cline, Patsy / I can see an angel: Cline, Patsy / Why don't you believe me: Page, Patti / Mockin' Bird Hill: Page, Patti / Tennessee waltz: Page, Patti / Gentle on my mind: Page, Patti / Things go better with love: Riley, Jeannie C. / Help me make it through the night: Riley, Jeannie C. / Before the next teardrop falls: Riley, Jeannie C. / Roses and thorns: Riley, Jeannie C. / Harper Valley PTA: Riley, Jeannie C..
MC: HSC 3274

REAL SOUND OF COUNTRY, THE (Various artists).
MC: CONE 2

RED HOT VICTOR (20 American country chart hits) (Various artists).
Tracks: / If you can touch her at all: Nelson, Willie / Here in love: Dottsy / May the force be with you always: Hall, Tom T. / You know what: Reed, Jerry & Seidina / Quits: Stewart, Gary / Love is a word: Lee, Dickey / Leona: Russell, Johnny / It should have been easy: Dottsy / It ain't easy lovin' me: Prophet, Ronnie / Born believer: Brown, Jim Ed & Helen Cornelius / Eastbound and down: Reed, Jerry / Baby me, baby: Miller, Roger / If it ain't love by now: Brown, Jim Ed & Helen Cornelius / Lean on Jesus: Craft, Paul/ (After sweet memories) play born to lose again: Dottsy / Ten years of this: Stewart, Gary / I'm a memory: Nelson, Willie / Two doors down: Lehr, Zella / Virginia, how far will you go?: Lee, Dickey / I wished I loved somebody else: Hall, Tom T..
LP: PL 42528
MC: PK 42528

RICH IN LOVE (Various artists).
LP: GRQ 104
MC: GRC 104

RITZ RADIO FAVOURITES (VOLUME 1 - COUNTRY) (Various artists).
LP: RITZSP 411
MC: RITZSC 411

SANCTIFIED COUNTRY GIRLS 1927-31 (Various artists).
LP: WSE 119

SATURDAY NIGHT AT THE GRAND OLE OPRY (Various artists).
Tracks: / Bitter creek: Various artists / Must it be me: Various artists / Words come easy: Various artists/ Thinking about you: Various artists / Livin' on love: Various artists / I like mountain music: Various artists / How can I believe: Various artists / Flowing water and shifting sands: Various artists / Lovin' in vain: Various artists / Love problem: Various artists / Which one will it be: Various artists / Fiddlers dream: Various artists.
LP: HAT 3059
MC: HATC 3059

SHELBY COUNTRY COUNTRY (Various artists).
LP: REDITA 110

SILVER HEART COUNTRY, VOL 1 (Various artists).
LP: DEAGLE 1
MC: DEAGLE 1C

SINGALONG (Country & Western Hymnal) (Various artists).
Tracks: / Put your hand in the hand: Various artists / Reach out to Jesus: Various artists / Something good is going to happen to you: Various artists / Happiness is the Lord: Various artists / Fill my cup, Lord: Various artists / I've a home beyond the river: Various artists / Turn your radio on: Various artists / Jesus and me: Various artists / God can do anything: Various artists / Follow me: Various artists / His name is wonderful: Various artists / Burdens are lifted at Calvary: Various artists / We'll talk it over: Various artists / Shepherd of love: Various artists / I know who holds tomorrow: Various artists / Springs of living water: Various artists / Jesus is coming: Various artists / I will serve Thee: Various artists / Old fashioned meeting, The: Various artists / I feel like travelling on: Various artists / I'll never be lonely: Various artists / Mansion over the hilltop: Various artists / Along the road: Various artists / He lovingly guards every footstep: Various artists.
LP: PC 745

SIZZLING COUNTRY INSTRUMENTALS (Various artists).
LP: SPR 8560
MC: SPC 8560

SOLID GOLD COUNTRY (Various artists).
Tracks: / Your cheatin heart: Arnold, Eddy / Green green grass of home: Bare, Bobby / Wayward wind: Browns, The / Ruby don't take your love to town: Jennings, Waylon / I love you because: Snow, Hank / Roses are red: Reeves, Jim / Take these chains from my heart: Gibson, Don / I walk the line: Davis, Skeeter / Release me: Hamilton, George IV / Everything is beautiful: Hamilton, George IV / Rose garden: West, Dottie/ Silver threads and golden needles: Davis, Skeeter / Behind closed doors: Milsap, Ronnie / Paper roses: Smith, Connie / It wasn't God who made honky tonk angels: Norma Jean / Gonna find me a bluebird: Davis, Skeeter & Porter Wagoner / Love sick blues: Milsap, Ronnie / I can't stop loving you: Locklin, Hank / Banks of the Ohio: Wagoner, Porter / Act naturally: Pride, Charley.
MC: INTK 9011

SON OF REDNECK (Various artists).
MC: MCAC 10367

SONGBIRDS (Various artists).
Tracks: / I've never been to me: Charlene / Hurtin's all over, The: Smith, Connie / There goes my everything: Wynette, Tammy / I've cried the blue right out of my eyes: Gayle, Crystal / Songbirds: Brown, Polly/ Delta dawn: Tucker, Tanya / Other side of me, The: Gayle, Crystal/ Rose garden: Anderson, Lynn / Help me make it through the night: Smith, Sammi / Diamonds and rust:

Baez, Joan / Single girl: *Posey, Sandy*/ Just the way I am: *Parton, Dolly* / Misty blue: *Burgess, Wilma* / We're all alone: *Coolidge, Rita* / Will you love me tomorrow?: *Ronstadt, Linda* / Blanket on the ground: *Spears, Billie Jo* / Harper Valley PTA: *Riley*, Jeannie C. / True love: *Cline, Patsy* / End of the world: *Davis, Skeeter* / There's a party going on: *Miller*, Jody / I love how you love me: *Various artists* / Don't it make my brown eyes blue?: *Gayle, Crystal* / Take me to your world: *Wynette, Tammy* / Put your hand in the hand: *Posey, Sandy* / For all the right reasons: *Fairchild*, Barbara / What're you doing tonight?: *Fricke, Janie* / Careless hands: *West, Dottie* / Lonely comin' down: *Parton, Dolly*.
2LP: . . . . **STD 3**
MCSET: . . . . **STDK 3**

SONGS OF FAITH (I love country) (Various artists).
Tracks: / Jesus was a carpenter: *Cash, Johnny* / Amazing grace: *Various artists* / Steps: *Gatlin, Larry* & The Gatlin Brothers Band / Far side of Jordan: *Carter Family* / Silent night holy night: *Thomas, B.J.* / Just a closer walk with thee: *James, Sonny* / Preacher said "Jesus said": *Cash, Johnny with Billy Graham* / Where the soul never dies: *Oak Ridge Boys* / Why me Lord: *Jones, George* / What a friend we have in Jesus: *Jackson*, Stonewall / Leaning on the everlasting arms: *Dean, Jimmy* / Children go where I send thee: *Skaggs, Ricky*/ Lonesome valley: *Scruggs, Earl with Tom T.Hall* / When the roll is called up yonder: *Robbins, Marty* / How great thou art: *Statler Brothers* / Trouble maker: *Various artists*.
LP: **4510051**
MC: **4510054**

SONGS OF LOVE,COUNTRY STYLE (Various artists).
LP: . . . . **MCTV 7**
MC: . . . . **MCTVC 7**

SOUTHERN NIGHTS (Various artists).
Tracks: / Southern nights: *Campbell, Glen* / Let your love flow: *Bellamy Brothers* / Blue bayou: *Rondstadt*, Linda / Coward of the county: *Rogers, Kenny* / Wind beneath my wings, The: *Greenwood, Lee* / I will always love you: *Parton, Dolly* / Feels so right: *Alabama (Group)* / Help me make it through the night: *Kristofferson*, Kris / I love a rainy night: *Rabbitt, Eddie* / I just fall in love again: *Murray, Anne* / I'd be a legend in my time: *Milsap, Ronnie* / All my ex's live in Texas: *Strait, George* / Together again: *Harris, Emmylou*/ Hey won't you play another: *Thomas, B.J.* / You're my best friend: *Williams, Don* / Hurt: *Newton, Juice*/ Ain't misbehavin': *Williams, Hank Jr.* / Streets of Bakersfield: *Yoakam, Dwight* / Talking in your sleep: *Gayle*, Crystal / Country boy: *Skaggs, Ricky* / Dukes of Hazzard, Theme from: *Jennings, Waylon* / Way we make a broken heart, The: *Cash, Rosanne* / Yesterday's wine: *Jones, George & Merle Haggard* / Hold me: *Oslin, K.T.* / Cry myself to sleep: *Judds* / Delta Dawn: *Reddy, Helen* / Forever and ever, Amen: *Travis, Randy* / Always on my mind: *Nelson, Willie*.
2LP: . . . . **KTVLP 1**
MC: . . . . **KTVMC 1**

SOUTHERN NIGHTS (The very best of country) (Various artists).
Tracks: / Southern nights: *Campbell, Glen* / Somebody loves you: *Gayle, Crystal* / When you're in love with a beautiful woman: *Dr. Hook* / It keeps right on a-hurtin': *Shepard, Jean* / Angel of the morning: *Newton, Juice*/ Six days on the road: *Dudley, Dave* / Sing me an old fashioned song: *Spears, Billie Jo* / Daydream believer: *Murray, Anne* / Hello walls: *Nelson, Willie* / I fall to pieces: *Ronstadt, Linda* / Raindrops keep falling on my head: *Gentry, Bobbie* / Better love next time: *Dr. Hook* / Break my mind: *Murray, Anne* / I'll be your baby tonight: *Ronstadt, Linda* / Route 66: *Asleep At The Wheel* / All I have to do is dream: *Gentry*, Bobbie & Glen Campbell / Why have you left the one you left me for: *Gayle, Crystal* / Honey come back: *Campbell, Glen* / He loves everything he gets his hands on: *Shepard, Jean* / What I've got in mind: *Spears, Billie Jo*.
LP: . . . . **MFP 41 5671 1**
MC: . . . . **MFP 41 5671 4**
LP: . . . . **MFP 5671**
MC: . . . . **TCMFP 5671**

STAR SPANGLED COUNTRY: THE HITS OF '84 (Various artists).
Tracks: / Don't cheat in your home town: *Skaggs, Ricky* / Candy man: *Gilley, Mickey & Charly McClain* / Double shot: *Stampley, Joe* / You made a wanted man of me: *McDowell, Ronnie* / Someday when things are good: *Haggard*, Merle / Left side of the bed: *Gray, Mark* / Let's stop talkin' about it: *Fricke, Janie* / Woke up in love: *Exile* / You've really got a hold on me: *Gilley, Mickey* / Sentimental ol' you: *McClain, Charly* / Two car garage: *Thomas, B.J.* / That's the way love goes: *Haggard, Merle* / We didn't see a thing: *Charles, Ray* & George Jones / Honey: *Skaggs, Ricky* / I dream of women like you: *McDowell, Ronnie* / Without a song: *Nelson, Willie*.
LP: . . . . **EPC 26090**
MC: **40 26090**

STARS OF THE COUNTRY (Various artists).
Tracks: / If you could read my mind: *Riley, Jeannie C.* / Crazy dreams: *Twitty, Conway* / Tumbling tumbleweeds: *Newman, Jimmy C.* / It's too late: *Orbison, Roy* / I forgot to remember to forget: *Lewis, Jerry Lee* / Hey good lookin': *Cash, Johnny* / Tennessee waltz: *Page, Patti* / You love me, don't you?: *Locklin, Hank*/ King of the road: *Dudley, Dave* / Yellow rose of Texas: *Newman, Jimmy C.* / Sail away: *Lewis, Jerry Lee/Charlie* Rich / Goodnight, Irene: *Cash, Johnny* / Gentle on my mind: *Page, Patti* / Say you'll stay until tomorrow: *Drusky, Roy* / Truck drivin' son of a gun: *Dudley, Dave* / Sweethearts or strangers?: *Perkins, Carl* / Devil doll: *Orbison, Roy* / Little ole wine drinker me: *Walker, Charlie* / Welcome home: *Drusky, Roy*/ Games people play: *Riley, Jeannie C.* / I heard that lonesome whistle blow: *Cash, Johnny* / Give me some love: *Twitty, Conway* / Walk on by: *Van Dyke, Leroy* / Together again: *O'Gwynn, James*.
MCSET: . . . . **DTO 10060**

STARS OF THE GRAND OLE OPRY (Various artists).
Tracks: / Railroadin' and gamblin': *Macon, Uncle Dave* / San Antonio rose: *King, Pee Wee* / Orange blossom special: *Monroe, Bill* / Jealous hearted me: *Pearl, Minnie* / Anytime: *Arnold, Eddy* / Father's table grace: *Flatt*, Lester / I'm my own grandpa: *Lonzo & Oscar* / Yakety axe: *Atkins, Chet* / I don't hurt anymore: *Snow*, Hank / I'm thinking tonight of my blue eyes: *Carter Family* / Down yonder: *Wood, Del* / Satisfied: *Carson*, Martha / Ashes of love: *Johnnie & Jack* / Old blue: *Grandpa Jones* / How far is heaven: *Wells, Kitty*/ Four walls: *Reeves, Jim* / Carroll country accident, The: *Wagoner, Porter* / I can't stop loving you: *Gibson*, Don / Trouble in the Amen corner: *Campbell, Archie* / End of the world: *Davis, Skeeter* / Early morning rain: *Hamilton, George IV* / Send me the pillow you dream on: *Locklin, Hank* / Young love: *James, Sonny* / Morning: *Brown, Jim Ed* / Three bells, The: *Browns* / Country girl: *West, Dottie* / Four strong winds: *Bare*, Bobby / Ribbon of darkness: *Smith, Connie* / Mule skinner blues (blue yodel No. 8): *Parton, Dolly* / Just a little after heartaches: *Pruett, Jeanne*.
2LP: **CPL2 0466**

STARS OF THE GRAND OLE OPRY (Various artists).
LP: . . . . **SPR 8561**
MC: . . . . **SPC 8561**

STARS OF THE PEDAL STEEL GUITAR (Various artists).
LP: . . . . **SLP 350**
MC: . . . . **GT 5350**

STOMPIN' AT THE HONKY TONK (Western swing in Houston 1936-1941) (Various artists).
LP: . . . . **STR 805**

SUPER COUNTRY VOL.1 (Various artists).
Tracks: / You're my best friend: *Various artists* / Just out of reach: *Various artists* / Picture of your mother: *Various artists* / Coat of many colours: *Various artists* / Waiting for a train: *Various artists* / Don't let me cross over: *Various artists* / Stand by me Jesus: *Various artists* / Hello blues and down the road I go: *Various artists* / Philadelphia lawyer: *Various artists* / Hello darlin': *Various artists*.
MC: . . . . **CWIN 104**

SUPER COUNTRY VOL.2 (Various artists).
Tracks: / Hard to be humble: *Various artists* / Harper Valley PTA: *Various artists* / Four strong winds: *Various* artists / Tennessee waltz: *Various artists* / Help me make it through the night: *Various artists* / Gypsy Joe and me: *Various artists* / What things money can't buy: *Various artists* / Church, a courtroom and then goodbye, A: *Various artists* / Pinto the wonder horse is dead: *Various artists* / Mama say a prayer: *Various artists*.
MC: . . . . **CWIN 105**

SUPER COUNTRY VOL.3 (Various artists).
Tracks: / Spanish eyes: *Various artists* / Streets of Baltimore: *Various artists* / I'm gonna be a country girl again: *Various artists* / Mama sang a song: *Various artists* / Shenandoah: *Various artists* / China doll: *Various artists* / My son calls another man Daddy: *Various artists* / North to Alaska: *Various artists*/ They're all going home but one: *Various artists* / 57 chevrolet: *Various artists*.
MC: . . . . **CWIN 106**

SWEET DREAMS (20 country ballads) (Various artists).
Tracks: / Cry myself to sleep: *Judds* / Thing called love, A: *Cash, Johnny* / Stand by your man: *Wynette*, Tammy / I won't forget you: *Reeves, Jim* / Lay lady lay: *Byrds* / Rose garden: *Anderson, Lynn* / It's four in the morning: *Young, Faron* / Kiss an angel good morning: *Pride, Charley* / End of the world: *Davis*, Skeeter / Always on my mind: *Nelson, Willie* / Help me make it through the night: *Kristofferson, Kris* / In dreams: *Orbison, Roy* / You and I: *Rabbitt, Eddie & Crystal Gayle* / Amanda: *Jennings, Waylon* / Delta dawn: *Tucker, Tanya* / Crystal chandeliers: *Hamilton, George IV* / I've been loving you: *Mandrell, Barbara*/ Little green apples: *Miller, Roger* / Coat of many colours: *Parton, Dolly* / Lonesome number one: *Gibson, Don*.
MC: . . . . **STDMC 29**

SWEET SOUNDS OF SUMMER (Various artists).
LP: **646 303 3**

TENNESSEE COUNTRY (Various artists).
Tracks: / Boogie blues: *Peterson, Earl* / In the dark: *Peterson, Earl* / Now she cares no more for me: *Poindexter*, Doug / I must be saved: *Serrat, Howard* / It's me baby: *Yelvington, Malcolm* / I've got the blues (Way down blues): *Yelvington, Malcolm* / Goodbye Marie: *Yelvington, Malcolm* / Rockin' with my baby: *Yelvington, Malcolm*/ I'm lonesome: *Chaffin, Ernie* / Please don't ever leave me: *Chaffin, Ernie* / Jump right out of this jukebox: *Wheeler, Onie* / Me and my blues: *Reidel, Teddy* / Born to lose: *McVoy, Carl* / I guess I'd better go: *Strength, Texas Bill* / Call of the wild: *Strength, Texas Bill* / Ghost of Mary Lou, The: *Stinit, Dane*.
LP: . . . . **CR 30150**

TENNESSEE LEGENDS (Various artists).
LP: . . . . **SLP 14**

TEX ARKANA LOUISIANA COUNTRY 1927-32 (Various artists).
LP: . . . . **L 1004**

TEXAS COUNTRY BLUES 1948-52 (Various artists).
LP: . . . . **KK 7434**

TEXAS COUNTRY MUSIC VOL.1 (Various artists).
LP: . . . . **RL 312**

TEXAS COUNTRY MUSIC VOL.2 (Various artists).
LP: . . . . **RL 315**

TEXAS COUNTRY MUSIC VOL.3 (Various artists).
LP: . . . . **RL 327**

TEXAS COUNTRY ROAD SHOW (Various artists).
LP: . . . . **BFX 15035**

TEXAS & LOUISIANNA COUNTRY (Various artists).
LP: . . . . **RL 335**

TEXAS SAND (Various artists).
Tracks: / Tune wranglers: *Various artists* / Everybody's trying to be my baby: *Various artists* / Ida sweet as apple cider: *Newman, Roy* / That's what I like about the south: *Brown, Milton* / Deep elem blues: *Brunes*, Cliff / Let me live and love you: *Prairie Ramblers* / I never see my baby alone: *Revard, Jimmie* / Southern belle from southern Tennessee: *Tyler, Johnny* / Lonesome blues: *Williams, Curly* / Old waterfall: *Tune Wranglers*/ Texas stomp: *Revard, Jimmie* / No good for nothin' blues: *Newman, Roy* / Betty Ann: *Various artists*/ Tex Tyler ride: *Ashlock, Jesse*.
LP: . . . . **RAMBLER 101**

THAT DOBRO SOUND'S GOIN' ROUND (Various artists).
LP: . . . . **SLP 340**
MC: . . . . **GT 5340**

THIS IS COUNTRY MUSIC (Various artists).
Tracks: / End of the world: *Davis, Skeeter* / Fantasy: *Alabama (Group)* / Abilene: *Hamilton, George IV*/ Too many rivers: *Colter, Jessi* / 500 miles away from home: *Bare, Bobby*/ Dukes of Hazzard: *Jennings, Waylon*/ She called me baby: *Rich, Charlie* / Nobody's child: *Snow, Hank* / Sea of heartbreak: *Gibson, Don* / (I'd be a) legend in my own time: *Milsap, Ronnie* / Guitar man: *Reed, Jerry* / Once a day: *Smith, Connie*/ He'll have to go: *Reeves, Jim* / Send me the pillow that you dream on: *Locklin, Hank* / Here you come again: *Parton, Dolly* / Kiss an angel good morning: *Pride, Charley*.
LP: . . . . **MFP 5786**
MC: . . . . **TCMFP 5786**

THIS IS COUNTRY MUSIC (2) (Various artists).
Tracks: / Eyes big as Dallas: *Stewart, Wynn* / Down on the farm: *Stewart, Wynn* / Could I talk you into lovin' me again: *Various artists* / Wild one: *Reno, Jack* / Blue roses: *Reno, Jack* / Divorce suit: *Phillips*, Bill / Goldie is an oldie: *Carlisle, Bill* / Too old to cut the mustard: *Carlisle, Bill* / Country music lovin' cowboy: *Pillow, Ray* / Justin Tubb: *Pillow, Ray* / Red necks, white socks and blue ribbon beer: *Pillow, Ray*/ Warm, warm love: *Louvin, Charlie* / Store up love: *Louvin, Charlie* / Pull the covers over me: *Collins, Tommy* / Hello hag: *Collins, Tommy* / Hogtown: *Curless, Dick* / Iceman, The: *Curless, Dick*.
LP: . . . . **BFX 15020**

TODAY'S COUNTRY CLASSICS (Various artists).
Tracks: / Cowboy rides away, The: *Strait, George* / How blue: *McEntire, Reba* / Make my life with you: *Oak Ridge* Boys / Knock on wood: *Baily, Razzy* / Mississippi squirrel revival: *Stevens, Ray* / Country girls: *Schneider*, John / Sweet country music: *Atlanta* / What I didn't do: *Wariner, Steve* / Happy birthday dear heartache: *Mandrell, Barbara* / God bless the U.S.A: *Greenwood, Lee*.
LP: . . . . **IMCA 390 29**

TOGETHER AGAIN (14 country duets) (Various artists).
Tracks: / Something to brag about: *Louvin, Charlie & Melba Montgomery* / Together again: *Rogers, Kenny & Dottie West*/ What's in your heart: *Jones, George/Melba Montgomery* / Heart to heart talk: *Campbell, Glen & Bobbie Gentry*/ Let your love flow: *Reeves, Del & Billie Jo Spears* / Something 'bout you baby I like: *Campbell, Glen & Rita Coolidge*/ We've got tonight: *Rogers, Kenny & Sheena Easton* / Love story (you and me): *Campbell, Glen & Anne Murray* / Don't fall in love with a dreamer: *Rogers, Kenny & Kim Carnes* / Willingly: *Nelson, Willie & Shirley Collie* / Forgive me John: *Shepard, Jean & Ferlin Husky* / Why don't we just sleep on it tonight: *Campbell, Glen & Tanya Tucker*/ Vaya con dios: *Paul, Les & Mary Ford* / I'll take the dog: *Shepard, Jean & Ray Pillow*.
LP: . . . . **MFP 5771**
MC: . . . . **TCMFP 5771**

TOP COUNTRY HITS (Various artists).
MC: . . . . **AM 36**

TOP COUNTRY SOUND IN CONCERT (Various artists).
Tracks: / Rollin' in my sweet baby's arms: *Various artists* / Crystal chandeliers: *Various artists* / If I said you had a beautiful body: *Various artists* / From here to there to you: *Various artists* / Blue eyed girl of Berlin: *Various artists* / American trilogy: *Various artists* / Scarlet ribbons: *Various artists* / Fishing for fish: *Various artists* / This song is just for you: *Various artists* / Do what you do do well: *Various artists*/ Folsom Prison blues: *Various artists* / Ghost riders in the sky: *Various artists*.
LP: . . . . **FHR 115**

TRADITIONAL COUNTRY FAVOURITES (Various artists).
MC: . . . . **AM 114**

TRAILBLAZERS (Various artists).
Tracks: / We're gonna go fishin': *Various artists* / Ride me down easy: *Various artists* / I walk the line: *Various* artists / Help me make it through the night: *Various artists* / Pool shark: *Various artists* / Cry cry darlin': *Various artists* / Blue moon of Kentucky: *Various artists* / New Jole Blon: *Various artists* / Sittin' and thinkin': *Various artists* / Swinging doors: *Various artists* / Hey good lookin': *Various artists*/ If the whole world stopped loving: *Various artists* / My shoes keep walking back to you: *Various artists* / Send me the pillow that you dream on: *Various artists*.
LP: . . . . **SPR 8525**
MC: . . . . **SPC 8525**

TRIBUTE TO HANK WILLIAMS, A (Various artists).
Tracks: / Lonesome whistle: *Snow, Hank* / Hey, good lookin': *Brown, Jim Ed* / Lovesick blues: *Milsap, Ronnie*/ Wedding bells: *Oxford, Vernon* / Take these chains from my heart: *West, Dottie* / Why don't you love me: *Davis*, Danny / May you never be alone: *Locklin, Hank* / Jambalaya: *Family Brown* / House of gold: *Wagoner, Porter*/ Alone and forsaken: *Atkins, Chet* / Half as much: *Arnold, Eddy* / Pan American: *Rivers,*

Hank / Mansion on the hill: *Browns* / I'm so lonesome I could cry: *Lee, Dickey* / Kaw-liga: *Living Strings* / Your cheatin' heart: *Davis, Skeeter* / There'll be no teardrops tonight: *Locklin, Hank* / I'm gonna sing: *Monroe, Charlie* / I can't help it (if I'm still in love with you: *Pridesmen* / Tramp on the street, The: *Jean, Norma* / I saw the light: *Buck, Gary* / They'll never take her love from me: *Gibson, Don* / I've been down that road before: *Wagoner, Porter* / Honky tonkin': *Brown, Jim Ed* / Picture from life's other side: *Wagoner, Porter* / Cold, cold heart: *Nashville string band* / Settin' the woods on fire: *Gibson, Don* / You win again: *Cramer, Floyd* / Crazy heart: *Sons Of The Pioneers* / Hank Williams will live forever: *Johnnie & Jack*.
2LP: . . . . **PL 42281**

TWENTY TRACKS OF COUNTRY HITS VOL 4 (Various artists).
Tracks: / 1460 Elder Street: *Grant, Manson* / Rose garden: *Karen* / Walk tall: *Rhodes, Roy* / Green rolling hills: *Rendall, Ruby* / Some broken hearts never mend: *Wilson, Tug* / Teddy Bear's last ride: *Wells, Tracy* / I wish I was 18 again: *Cannon, Noel* / Rocky top: *Devine, Mike* / Sweet little miss blue eyes: *Mackie* / Don't let me cross over: *Grant, Manson* / Always on my mind: *Rendall, Ruby* / Fiddler Joe: *Mackie* / Snowbird: *Karen* / Banks of the Ohio: *Rhodes, Roy* / Ashes of love: *Mackie* / Part of me, A: *Devine*, Mike / Never look back: *Rendall, Ruby* / Acadian rose: *Mackie* / Keeping up appearances: *Karen* / Never ending song of love: *Rhodes, Roy*.
MC: . . . . **CWGR 125**

TWENTY TRACKS OF COUNTRY HITS VOL 6 (Various artists).
Tracks: / Bring back the waltzes: *Grant, Manson* / Bright lights and country music: *Karen* / Try a little kindness: *Rhodes, Roy* / Honey: *Mackie* / Time goes by: *Rendall, Ruby* / Wedding bells: *Devine, Mike* / From here to there to you: *Rhodes, Roy* / Slow healing heart: *Mackie* / Heartaches by the number: *Karen* / Phantom 309: *Cannon, Noel* / Mansion on the hill: *Grant, Manson* / Ring around the rosie: *Karen* / I'm gonna be a country boy again: *Rhodes, Roy* / Amanda: *Mackie* / Let me be there: *Rendall, Ruby* / Tonight the bottle let me down: *Wilson, Tug* / Never been this far before: *Wells, Tracy* / Born for loving you: *Devine, Mike* / Stone cold heart: *Mackie* / Home town gossip: *Rendall, Ruby*.
MC: . . . . **CWGR 127**

TWENTY TRACKS OF COUNTRY HITS VOL 5 (Various artists).
Tracks: / Ruby red wine: *Rendall, Ruby* / Waltz across Texas: *Grant, Manson* / Blanket on the ground: *Karen* / Little ole wine drinker me: *Rhodes, Roy* / He stopped loving her today: *Mackie* / Down River Road: *Wilson*, Tug / Fool number one: *Wells, Tracy* / Colorado cool aid: *Cannon, Noel* / In the middle of nowhere: *Devine*, Mike / Blue blue day: *Rhodes, Roy* / Silver threads and golden needles: *Rendall, Ruby* / Union mare and confederate grey: *Grant, Manson & James Smith* / Apartment No.9: *Karen* / Wedding bells: *Rhodes, Roy* / Ruby don't take your love to town: *Mackie* / Me and Bobby McGee: *Wilson, Tug* / Bright city lights: *Rendall, Ruby* / Arizona whiz, The: *Cannon, Noel* / Pick me up (on your way down): *Grant, Manson* / Good hearted woman: *Karen*.
MC: . . . . **CWGR 126**

UK NEW COUNTRY VOL.1 (Various artists).
LP: . . . . **BGE LP 1002**
MC: . . . . **BGE C 1002**

UP COUNTRY (Various artists).
MC: . . . . **DY 05**

US COUNTRY CHARTS 1950-1959 (Various artists).
LP: **812793 1**

US COUNTRY CHARTS 1960-1969 (Various artists).
LP: **812794 1**

VINTAGE COUNTRY (I love country) (Various artists).
Tracks: / Back in the saddle again: *Autry, Gene* / I love you a thousand years: *Frizzell, Lefty* / Strawberry roan, The: *Robbins, Marty* / Foggy mountain breakdown: *Flatt, Lester & Earl Scruggs* / When it's Springtime in Alaska: *Horton, Johnny* / Deep water: *Smith, Carl* / Rawhide: *Laine, Frankie* / Folsom Prison blues: *Cash*, Johnny / Big iron: *Robbins, Marty* / All for the love of a girl: *Horton, Johnny* / Wabash cannonball: *Carter*, Mother Maybelle / Big river: *Cash, Johnny* / High noon: *Laine, Frankie* / Mom and dad's waltz: *Frizzell, Lefty* / Goodnight Irene: *Autry, Gene* / Pride: *Price, Ray*.
LP: . . . . **CBS 54949**
MC: **40 54949**

WESTERN SWING (Various artists).
MC: . . . . **C 214**

WESTERN SWING VOL.1 (Various artists).
LP: . . . . **OT 105**

WESTERN SWING VOL.3 (Various artists).
LP: . . . . **OT 117**

WESTERN SWING VOL.6 (From the 40s to the 50s) (Various artists).
LP: . . . . **OT 121**

WESTERN SWING VOL.7 1950's (Various artists).
LP: . . . . **OT 122**

WESTERN SWING VOL.8 1940s & 50s (Various artists).
LP: . . . . **OT 123**

WESTERN SWING VOL 2 (Various artists).
LP: . . . . **OT 116**

WESTERN SWING VOL 5 (From the 1930s) (Various artists).
LP: . . . . **OT 120**

WILL THE CIRCLE BE UNBROKEN (Various artists).
Tracks: / Grand Ole Opry song: *Various artists* / Keep on the sunny side: *Various artists* / Nashville blues: *Various artists* / You are my flower: *Various artists* / Precious jewel, The: *Various artists* / Dark as a dungeon: *Various artists* / Tennessee stud: *Various artists* / Black mountain rag: *Various artists* / Wreck on the highway, The: *Various artists* / End of the world: *Various artists* / I saw the light: *Various* artists / Sunny side of the mountain: *Various artists* / Nine pound hammer: *Various artists* / Losin' you (might be the best thing yet): *Various artists* / Honky tonkin': *Various artists* / You don't know my mind: *Various* artists / My walkin' shoes: *Various artists* / Lonesome fiddle blues: *Various artists* / Cannonball rag: *Various* artists / Avalanche: *Various artists* / Flint Hill special: *Various artists* / Togary mountain: *Various* artists / Earl's breakdown: *Various artists* / Orange blossom special: *Various artists* / Wabash cannonball: *Various artists* / Lost highway: *Various artists* / Doc Watson & Merle Travis: First meeting: *Various artists* / Way downtown: *Various artists* / Down yonder: *Various artists* / Pins and needles (in my heart): *Various* artists / Honky tonk blues: *Various artists* / Sailin' on to Hawaii: *Various artists* / I'm thinking tonight of my blue eyes: *Various artists* / I am a pilgrim: *Various artists* / Wildwood flower: *Various artists* / Soldier's joy: *Various artists* / Will the circle be unbroken: *Various artists* / Both sides now: *Various artists*.
LPS: **1867063**
MC: **1867099**
MC: **1867109**

WILL THE CIRCLE BE UNBROKEN VOL.II (Various artists).
Tracks: / Life's railway to heaven: *Various artists* / Grandpa was a carpenter: *Various artists* / When t' get my rewards: *Various artists* / Don't you hear Jerusalem moan: *Various artists* / Little mountain church house: *Various artists* / And so it goes: *Various artists* / Mary danced with soldiers: *Various artists* / Riding alone: *Various artists* / I'm sitting on top of the world: *Various artists* / Lovin' on the side: *Various* artists / Lost river: *Various artists* / Bayou jubilee: *Various artists* / Blueberry Hill: *Various artists* / Turn of the century: *Various artists* / One step over the line: *Various artists* / You ain't going nowhere: *Various* artists / Valley road, The: *Various artists* / Will the circle be unbroken: *Various artists* / Amazing grace: *Various artists*.
2LP: . . . . **MCFD 9001**
MCSET: . . . . **MCFDC 9001**

Country All Stars

JAZZ FROM THE HILLS.
Tracks: / Stompin' at the Savoy / Tennessee rag / Do something / Indiana march / Sweet Georgia Brown / Midnight train / In a little spanish town / My little girl / Lady in red, The / Marie / It goes like this / What's the reason (I'm not pleasing you) / When it's darkness on the delta / Vacation train, The / Fiddle patch / Fiddle sticks.
LP: . . . . **BFX 15350**

Country Blues...

COUNTRY BLUES BOTTLENECK GUITAR CLASSICS (Various artists).
LP: . . . . **L 1026**

COUNTRY BLUES COLLECTOR ITEMS (Various artists).
LP: . . . . **BD 2042**

COUNTRY BLUES COLLECTOR ITEMS, VOL.2 (Various artists).
LP: . . . . **BD 2057**

COUNTRY BLUES, LIVE (Various artists).
LP: . . . . **DLP 525**

COUNTRY BLUES OBSCURITIES VOL. 2 (Various artists).
LP: . . . . **RL 340**

COUNTRY BLUES OBSCURITIES VOL. 1 (Various artists).
LP: . . . . **RL 334**

COUNTRY BLUES VOL.1 (Various artists).
LP: . . . . **BC 5**

COUNTRY BLUES VOL.2 (Various artists).
LP: . . . . **BC 6**

COUNTRY BLUES VOL.3 (Various artists).
LP: . . . . **BC 7**

COUNTRY BLUES VOL.4 (Various artists).
LP: . . . . **BC 14**

COUNTRY BLUES-THE FIRST GENERATION 1927 (Various artists).
Tracks: / Gang of brown skin women: *Papa Harvey Hull & Long Cleve Reed* / France blues: *Various artists* / Two little tommie blues: *Papa Harvey Hull & Long Cleve Reed* / Don't you leave me here: *Papa Harvey Hull & Long Cleve Reed* / Mama you don't know how: *Long Cleve Reed & The Down Home Boys* / Original stack o' lee blues: *Long Cleve Reed & The* Down Home Boys / James Alley blues: *Richard 'Rabbit' Brown* / Never let the same bee sting you twice: *Richard* 'Rabbit' Brown / I'm not jealous: *Richard 'Rabbit' Brown* / Mystery of the Dunbar's child: *Richard 'Rabbit' Brown* / Sinking of the Titanic: *Richard 'Rabbit' Brown*.
LP: . . . . **MSE 201**

FAVOURITE COUNTRY BLUES (Piano guitar duets 1929-35) (Various artists).
LP: . . . . **L 1015**

FEMALE COUNTRY BLUES (Vol.1-1924/28) (Various artists).
LP: . . . . **BD 2040**

GIANTS OF COUNTRY BLUES GUITAR 1966-82 (Various artists).
LP: . . . . **WOLF 120 911**

GIANTS OF COUNTRY BLUES GUITAR 2 (Various artists).
LP: . . . . **WOLF 120 917**

GIANTS OF COUNTRY BLUES PIANO (Various artists).
LP: . . . . **WOLF 120 910**

GIANTS OF COUNTRY BLUES VOL. 1 1927-32 (Various artists).
LP: . . . . **WSE 116**

KINGS OF COUNTRY BLUES (Various artists).
LP: . . . . **ARHOOLIE 1084**

KINGS OF COUNTRY BLUES VOL.2 (Various artists).
LP: . . . . **ARHOOLIE 1085**

LIVING COUNTRY BLUES U.S.A., VOL.6 (The road is rough & rocky) (Various artists).
LP: . . . . **LR 42.036**

LIVING COUNTRY BLUES U.S.A., VOL.8 (Lonesome home blues) (Various artists).
LP: . . . . **LR 42.038**

LIVING COUNTRY BLUES U.S.A., VOL.9 (Mississippi moan) (Various artists).
LP: . . . . **LR 42.039**

LIVING COUNTRY BLUES U.S.A., VOL.10 (Country boogie) (Various artists).
LP: . . . . **LR 42.040**

LIVING COUNTRY BLUES U.S.A., VOL.11 (Country gospel rock) (Various artists).
LP: . . . . **LR 42.041**

LIVING COUNTRY BLUES U.S.A., VOL.12 (East Coast blues) (Various artists).
LP: . . . . **LR 42.042**

LIVING COUNTRY BLUES U.S.A., VOL.13 (More country gospel rock) (Various artists).
LP: . . . . **LR 42.043**

LIVING COUNTRY BLUES U.S.A., VOL.14 (Bottle up and go) (Various artists).
LP: . . . . **LR 42.044**

LIVING COUNTRY BLUES U.S.A.,VOL.1 (Various artists).
LP: . . . . **LR 42.031**

LIVING COUNTRY BLUES U.S.A.,VOL.2 (Various artists).
LP: . . . . **LR 42.032**

LIVING COUNTRY BLUES U.S.A.,VOL.3 (Various artists).
LP: . . . . **LR 42.033**

LIVING COUNTRY BLUES U.S.A.,VOL.4 (Various artists).
LP: . . . . **LR 42.034**

LIVING COUNTRY BLUES U.S.A.,VOL.5 (Various artists).
LP: . . . . **LR 42.035**

LIVING COUNTRY BLUES U.S.A.,VOL.7 (Various artists).
LP: . . . . **LR 42.037**

OLD COUNTRY BLUES (Various artists).
LP: . . . . **FLY 537**

RARE PARAMOUNT COUNTRY BLUES 1926-29 (Various artists).
LP: . . . . **BD 2041**

Country Breeze

ALWAYS.
Tracks: / When God comes and gathers his jewels / When my blue moon turns to gold again / Together again / Always / Let the rest of the world go by / Tennessee waltz / Country roads / Love me tender / If you need a friend / Making plans / Could I have this dance / Rockin' alone in an old rocking chair / Say it again / Through the eyes of a child.
LP: . . . . **KMLP 308**

BEAUTIFUL THINGS.
Tracks: / One day at a time / You and me / Boil them cabbage down / White rose of Athens, The / Run to the door / Old Scotia's drum / Beautiful things / Wrong road again / Glad to be back home again / Sweetest gift, The / I wanna see Nashville / Spinning wheel.
LP: . . . . **NA 119**
MC: . . . . **NC 119**

CENTRE SOUND OF COUNTRY BREEZE, THE.
LP: . . . . **NEVLP 141**

COUNTRY BREEZE.
Tracks: / Do what you do do well / Dear John / Crying time / Ain't love good.
LP: . . . . **LILP 5071**
MC: . . . . **LICS 5071**

Country Code

SHELLEY'S WINTER LOVE.
Tracks: / Just out of reach / Someday you'll call my name / No one will ever know (how much I love you).
LP: . . . . **HRL 122**

Country Diary Of...

COUNTRY DIARY OF AN EDWARDIAN LADY (Read by Francesca Annis) (Annis, Francesca).
LPS: . . . . **WW 5077**
MC: . . . . **WW 4 5077**

COUNTRY DIARY OF AN EDWARDIAN LADY (TV SERIES) (See under Lord, Jon) (Lord, Jon).

Country (film)

COUNTRY (1985 film soundtrack) (Various artists).
LP: . . . . **WH 1039**
MC: . . . . **WHC 1039**

Country Gazette

AMERICAN AND CLEAN.
LP: . . . . **FF 253**

AMERICA'S BLUEGRASS BAND.
LP: . . . . **FF 295**

BLUEGRASS TONIGHT.
LP: . . . . **FF 383**
MC: . . . . **FF 383C**

BLUEGRASS TONIGHT VOL.2.
LP: . . . . **FF 384**

FROM THE BEGINNING.
Tracks: / Keep on pushing / Sounds of goodbye / Huckleberry hornpipe / My Oklahoma / Hot burrito breakdown / Aggravation / Forget me not / Fallen eagle, The / Lonesome blues / Deputy Dalton / Down the road / Tried so hard / Snowball / Lost indian.
LP: . . . . **SLS 50414**

OUT TO LUNCH.
Tracks: / Still feeling blue / Sure didn't take him long / Out to lunch / Melody for baby / Sing a sad song / Sunny side of the mountain / Down down down / Why you been gone so long / Forked deer / Time left to wander / Last thing on my mind / Uncle Cloony played the banjo / Blue light.
LP: . . . . **FF 027**

STRICTLY INSTRUMENTAL.
LP: . . . . **FF 446**

Country Gentlemen

25 YEARS (25 SONGS).
2LP: . . . . **REBEL 2202**

MC: REBELMC 2202

AWARD WINNING, THE.
LP: REBEL 1506

BLUEGRASS AT CARNEGIE HALL.
LP: GT 0102

BRINGING MARY HOME.
LP: REBEL 1478

CALLING MY CHILDREN HOME.
LP: REBEL 1574

COUNTRY GENTLEMEN FEAT. RICKY SKAGGS ON FIDDLE.
Tracks: / Travelling kind / Souvenirs / Leaves that are green, The / Irish Spring / Home in Louisiana / City of New Orleans / House of the rising sun / Catfish John / Heartaches / One morning in May / Bringing Mary home / Welcome to New York.
LP: VMLP 73123
MC: VMMC 73123

COUNTRY SONGS OLD AND NEW.
LP: SF 40004
MC: SFC 40004

GOOD AS GOLD.
LP: SH 3734
MC: ZCSH 3734

JOE'S LAST TRAIN.
LP: REBEL 1559

ONE WIDE RIVER.
LP: REBEL 1497

RETURN ENGAGEMENT.
LP: REBEL 1663

RIVER BOTTOM.
LP: SH 3723
MC: ZCSH 3723

SIT DOWN YOUNG STRANGER.
Tracks: / Come sit down by the river / Meet me on the other side / Love and wealth / Likes of you, The / You're always the one / Darby's Castle / Sit down young stranger / It's just like Heaven / For the first time / South Elm Street / Blue Ridge Mountains turning green / Lonely dancer.
LP: SH 3712
MC: ZCSH 3712

SOUND OFF.
LP: REBEL 1501

YESTERDAY AND TODAY VOL.1.
LP: SAVE 030

YESTERDAY AND TODAY VOL.2.
LP: SAVE 031

Country Jays

SILVER MEDALS AND SWEET MEMORIES.
Tracks: / What goes on when the sun goes down / When the roses bloom again / Green grass / Triangle song, The / Mama I'm not the boy I used to be / Running bear / Big wheel cannonball / Lord made a hobo out of me, The / I saw the light / Silver medals and sweet memories / Cover mama's flowers / Apache / If your lonesome at your table / Take me back to yesterday once more.
LP: BGC 325
MC: KBGC 325

Country Rock

COUNTRY ROCK (Various artists).
Tracks: / Long train runnin': *Doobie Brothers* / Let your love flow: *Bellamy Brothers* / That'll be the day: *Ronstadt, Linda* / Tulsa time: *Williams, Don* / You're only lonely: *Souther, J.D.* / Cover of the Rolling Stone: *Various artists* / Weight, The: *Band* / More than a feeling: *Boston* / Bad moon rising: *Creedence Clearwater Revival* / Rocky mountain way: *Walsh, Joe* / Going up the country: *Canned Heat* / Feeling single seeing double: *Harris, Emmylou* / American girl: *McGuinn, Roger* / Hotel ritz: *Axton, Hoyt* / Rose of Cimarron: *Poco* / Sweet home Alabama: *Skynard, Lynard* / Dixie chicken: *Little Feat.*
LP: WW 5120
MC: WW 4 5120

COUNTRY ROCK SIDES (Various artists).
Tracks: / Your lovin' man: *Taylor, Vernon* / This kind of love: *Taylor, Vernon* / Please be mine (come to me): *Pendarvis, Tracy* / Tonight will be the last night: *Smith, Warren* / So young: *Smith, Ray* / Forever yours: *Smith, Ray* / Me and my rhythm guitar: *Powers, Johnny* / Waiting for you: *Powers, Johnny* / Huh huh oh yeah: *Pendarvis, Tracy* / Love love memory: *Self, Mack* / Dear John: *Smith, Warren* / I'm movin on - golden rocket: *Smith, Warren* / Mystery train: *Taylor, Vernon* / Eight wheel: *Bruce, Edwin.*
LP: SUN 1031

DON'T SHOOT (Various artists).
Tracks: / Bend in the road: *Danny & Dusty* / Hello walls: *Jimmy & The Rhythm Pigs* / I'll get out somehow: *McCarthy, Steve* / Wreckin' ball: *Doe, John* / Almost persuaded: *Christensen, Julie* / Tears fall away: *Divine Horsemen* / Tear it down: *Gilkyson, Terry* / Never get out of this world alive: *Waterson, Jack* / Blind justice: *Band Of Blacky Ranchette* / Freight train: *Allison, Clay* / Tear it all to pieces: *Romans.*
LP: ZONG 009

FESTIVAL TAPES, THE (Various artists).
LP: FF 068

GREAT MOMENTS IN VINYL HISTORY (Various artists).
Tracks: / Walkin' with Barrence: *Whitfield, Barrence & The Savages* / Twist with the Morningstars: *Rogie, S.E.* / Jean's reel: *Cunningham, Phil & Gary Peterson* / Moving cloud, The: *Cunningham, Phil & Gary Peterson* / Cold and bitter tears: *Hawkins, Ted & Billy Bragg* / A.B. hornpipe: *Tickell, Kathryn* / Mrs. Bolowski's: *Tickell, Kathryn* / Ultru horas: *Orchestre Baobab* / Harlan County: *Ford, Jim* / Duba duba: *Tshohle, Makgona Band* / Masane siise: *Jobarteh, P.A.* / Mystery train: *Yoakam, Dwight* / Solo na mutsa: *Moyo, Johah & Devera Ngwena* / Broke down and hungry: *Phillips, Steve.*
LP: SPD 1009

Country Rockers

COUNTRY ROCKERS, VOL.1 (Various artists).
LP: TH 275

COUNTRY ROCKERS, VOL.2 (Various artists).
LP: TH 376

COUNTRY ROCKERS, VOL.3 (Various artists).
LP: TH 576

COUNTRY ROCKERS, VOL.4 (Various artists).
LP: TH 676

COUNTRY ROCKERS, VOL.5 (Various artists).
LP: TH 583

Country Rockers

FREE RANGE.
Tracks: / Rockin' daddy / Finally / See you later alligator / Fan it and cool it / Rancho Grande / Guitar polka / My bucket's got a hole in it / Pistol packin' mama / Drivin' nails in my coffin / There stands the glass / My happiness / Barrooms to bedrooms.
LP: ROSE 165

Country Sailor

HEARTACHES ARE KNOCKING.
LP: SRTZ 78/105

Country Shack

PORTRAIT, A.
Tracks: / How can I / Lonely street / All I want is you / Just out of reach / Sunset on the sage / Shall we meet / Good-hearted woman / Milwaukee here I come / What I've got in mind / Back home again / Fill my cup, Lord / Ain't that a shame / Sweet folk and country.
LP: SFA 056

WHICH WAY IS GONE?.
Tracks: / If you want me / I'll do anything / Special kind of man, A / Help me make it through the night / Wine in the cellar / Your good girl's gonna go bad / I'll be there / Come on home / Namedropper / Never miss a real good thing / Silver threads and golden needles / Which way is gone.
LP: SFA 076

Country Startracks

COUNTRY STARTRACKS (Various artists).
Tracks: / Love is a rose: *Ronstadt, Linda* / Mockingbird hill: *Fargo, Donna* / Coat of many colours: *Harris, Emmylou* / Diggy uggy lo: *Kershaw, Doug* / Chokin' king, The: *Gosdin, Vern* / Sweet dreams: *Robbins, Hargus 'Pig'* / Why me: *Montgomery, Melba* / Heartaches by the number: *Smith, Margo* / Sure thing: *Rabbitt, Eddie* / Streets of Laredo: *Allen, Rex Jnr.* / Danger of a stranger, The: *Parton, Stella* / Ruby, don't take your love to town: *Rogers, Kenny & The First Edition* / I can't stop loving you: *Smith, Sammi* / Black mountain rag: *Dillards & Byron Berline* / Here, there and everywhere: *Harris, Emmylou* / My Tennesse mountain home: *Muldaur, Maria* / I really had a ball last night: *Taylor, Carmol* / Our old mansion: *Owens, Buck* / Brand new Tennessee waltz: *Winchester, Jesse* / Texas tornado: *Owens, Buck.*
LP: K4 58040

Countryman (film)

COUNTRYMAN (1980 film soundtrack) (Various artists).
2LP: ISTDA 1
MCSET: ZISTDA 1

Countrymen

19 GREAT SONGS.
LP: HRL 127
MC: CHRL 127

County, Jayne

AMERIKAN CLEOPATRA.
LP: KOMA 788016

BETTY GRABLE'S LEGS.
MLP: FREUD 27

PRIVATE OYSTER.
Tracks: / Private oyster / Man enough to be a woman / Fun in America / I fell in love with a Russian soldier / Bad in bed / Are you a boy or are you a girl / When queens collide (part 1) / Double shot / Xerox that man / That lady dye twist / Love lives on lies.
LP: REV LP 86

ROCK 'N' ROLL.
LP: LIVE 1

County Singers

FAVOURITE SONGS OF IRELAND.
Tracks: / Boys from County Armagh / MacNamara's band / Spinning wheel / I'll tell me ma / Danny boy / Sweets of May / St. Patrick's day / Holy ground / Minstrel boy / Harp that once through Tara's Hall, The / Jug of punch / Galway bay / Irish rover, The / Slattery's mounted fut / Molly Malone / Wearing of the green, The / Let Erin remember.
MC: 823 419-4

County, Wayne

STORM GATES OF HEAVEN (County, Wayne & The Electric Chairs).
Tracks: / Storm gates of heaven / Cry of angels / Speed demon / Mr. Norman / Man enough to be a woman / Trying to get on the radio / I had too much to dream last night / Tomorrow is another day.
LP: GOOD 1

WHAT YOUR MOTHER NEVER TOLD YOU.
Tracks: / Wonder woman / Wall city girl / Boy with the stolen face / Berlin / C3 / Midnight pal / Waiting for the marines / Think straight.
LP: GOOD 2

Courage (Guard Dog)

COURAGE THE GUARD DOG (Sound effect).
MC: WIV 4-001

Courage Of Lassie

SING OR DIE.
LP: TMLP 041
LP: A 528
MC: C 528
LP: TMLP 055

Courbois, Pierre

INDEPENDENCE.
LP: SJP 100

Courier (film)

COURIER (1988 film soundtrack) (Various artists).
Tracks: / Burn clear: *Something Happens* / Wild white house: *Hothouse Flowers* / Kill the one I love: *Lord* John White / Courier (it's a dangerous game): *Aslan* / Silly dreams: *Cry Before Dawn* / Walk to the water: *U2* / Painted villain: *McManus, Declan* / Stalkin': *McManus, Declan* / Funeral music: *McManus, Declan* / Rat poison: *McManus, Declan* / Unpainted villain: *McManus, Declan* / Last boat leaving: *McManus, Declan.*
LP: V 2517
MC: TCV 2517

Courtenay, Tom (nar)

LUCKY JIM (See under Lucky Jim).

Courtneidge, Cicely

CICELY COURTNEIDGE & JACK HULBERT (Courtneidge, Cicely & Jack Hulbert).
LP: SH 113

GOLDEN AGE OF..., THE (Courtneidge, Cicely & Jack Hulbert).
LP: GX 41 2523-1
MC: GX 41 2523-4

Courtney, Terry

COURT IN THE ACT.
LP: BSS 366

Courville, Sady

LA VIEILLE MUSIQUE ACADIENNE (Courville, Sady/Dennis McGhee).
LP: 6030

Cousin Joe

GOSPEL WAILING, JAZZ PLAYING.
Tracks: / When a woman loves a man / Checking out / Touch me / I got news for you / Too late to turn back now / Lipstick trails / Railroad avenue / You talk too much / Barefoot boy / How come my dog don't bark / Night life.
LP: BEAR 3

IN HIS PRIME (Cousin Joe from New Orleans).
LP: OL 8008

RELAXING IN NEW ORLEANS.
LP: 11011
MC: 11011 TC

Cousin Phyllis

COUSIN PHYLLIS (see Gaskell, Elizabeth) (Branagh, Kenneth).

Cousins, Dave

OLD SCHOOL SONGS.
LP: SLURP 1

Cousins, Roy

PICK UP THE PIECES (Cousins, Roy & The Royals).
LP: TWLP 1004

TEN YEARS AFTER (Cousins, Roy & The Royals).
LP: TWLP 1005

Cousteau's Amazon

COUSTEAU'S AMAZON (Film soundtrack) (Various artists).
LP: STV 81220

Couture,Charlelie

CHARLELIE COUTURE.
LP: IMA 12
MC: IMC 12

Couza, Jim

ENCHANTED VALLEY, THE (see under Monger, Eileen) (Couza, Jim/Eileen Monger).

FRIENDS AND NEIGHBOURS.
LP: GVR 221

JUBILEE.
Tracks: / Mississippi jubilee (year of jubilo) / You've joined our hearts / My old man / Invention No. 13 / Gallow de cielo / Cranes over Hiroshima / Puncheon floor (Oklahoma rooster) / St. Paul's song / Poor wayfaring stranger / There were roses / If you don't love your neighbour / Jubilee (reprise).
LP: FSLP 6
MC: FSMC 6

Covay, Don

HOUSE OF... (Covay, Don/Lemon Jefferson Blues Band).
LP: K 550255

MERCY (Covay, Don & The Goodtimers).
Tracks: / See-saw / I never get enough of your love / Iron out the rough spots / Sookie sookie / Woman's love / Watching the late late show / Somebody's got to love you / Temptation was too strong / Mercy, mercy / Boomerang / Can't stay away / Come see about me / Take this hurt off me / You're good for me / Precious you / Daddy loves baby.
LP: ED 127

SWEET THANG.
Tracks: / Sweet thang / Daddy please don't go tonight / Why did you put your shoes under my bed / Stop by / Bad luck / Hitchin' a ride / Standing in the grits line / In the sweet bye and bye / Ain't nothing a young girl can do / If there's a will there's a way / What's in the headlines.
LP: TOP 137
MC: KTOP 137

Coven, Randy

SAMMY SAYS OUCH.
MC: 107274

Coventry City...

COVENTRY CITY BAND IN CONCERT (Coventry City Band).
LP: GRS 1053

SOUNDS OF BRASS SERIES VOL.7 (Coventry City Band).
Tracks: / President's march, The / Carmen - suite / Romanza - The Mikado / Prince Igor - overture / Men of Harlech - March / Bobby Shaftoe / Two songs / Love songs - Creation's hymn.
LP: SB 307

Cover Girl (Film)

COVER GIRL/YOU WERE NEVER LOVELIER (1944 film soundtracks) (Various artists).
LP: CC 100.24

Cover Me

COVER ME (Various artists).
LP: RNIN 70700

Coverdale, David

NORTHWINDS.
Tracks: / Keep on giving me love / Give me kindness / Time and again / Queen of Hearts / Only my soul / Say you love me / Breakdown / Northwinds.
LP: FA 413 097 1
MC: FA 413 097 4
LP: IC 064 604 14
LP: TTS 3513

WHITESNAKE.
Tracks: / Lady / Blindman / Goldies place / Whitesnake / Time on my side / Peace lovin' man / Sunny days / Hole in the sky / Celebration.
LP: . . . . TPS 3509

WHITESNAKE/NORTHWINDS.
Tracks: / Lady / Time on my side / Blindman / Goldies place / Whitesnake / Peace lovin' man / Sunny days / Hole in the sky / Celebration / Keep on giving me love / Northwinds / Give me kindness / Time and time again / Queen of hearts / Only my soul / Say you love me / Breakdown.
2LP: . . . . VSOPLP 118
MC: . . . . VSOPMC 118

Covington, Julie

JULIE COVINGTON.
Tracks: / I want to see the bright lights / By the time it gets dark / Sip the wine / How / Barbara's song / Little bit more, A / Let me make something in your life / I can't dance / Kick inside, The / Dead weight / Dancing in the dark.
LP: . . . . FA 3041

Coward, Noel

1928-38 CLASSIC RECORDINGS.
LP: . . . . CHD 168
MC: . . . . MCHD 168

AT LAS VEGAS.
Tracks: / I'll see you again / Dance little lady / Poor little rich girl / Room with a view / Some day I'll find you / I'll follow my secret heart / If love were all / Play, orchestra, play / Uncle Harry / Loch Lomond / Bar on the Piccola Marina / World weary / Nina / Mad dogs and Englishmen / Matelot / Alice is at it again / Let's do it / Party's over, The.
LP: . . . . CBS 32667
MC: 40 32667

COMPACT COWARD, THE.
Tracks: / I'll see you again / Dance little lady / Poor little rich girl / Room with a view / Mad dogs and Englishmen / Mary make believe / Mrs. Worthington / Parisian pierrot / Love scene (act 1 private lives) / Some day I'll find you / Let's say goodbye / Twentieth century blues / I'll follow my secret heart / Has anybody seen our ship? / Men about town / Most of ev'ry day (CD only.) / I travel alone / Any little fish / Could you please oblige me with a Bren gun? / London pride / I wonder what happened to him / There are bad times just around the corner / I like America / You were there / Some day I'll find you / If love were all / Play orchestra play / Party's over, The.
LP: . . . . EMS 1331
MC: . . . . TCEMS 1331

GOLDEN AGE OF NOEL COWARD, THE.
Tracks: / Mad dogs and Englishmen / London pride / We were dancing / There are bad times just around the corner / I'll see you again / Half caste woman / Matelot / Mrs. Worthington / Stately homes of England, The / Ziguener / Poor little rich girl / Dance little lady / Family album, The.
LP: . . . . GX 2502
MC: . . . . TCGX 2502

GREAT BRITISH DANCE BANDS PLAY THE MUSIC OF NOEL COWARD (See under Dance Bands...) (Various artists).

GREAT SHOWS.
Tracks: / I'll see you again / If love were all / Dear little cafe' / Zigeuner / Lover of my dreams / Twentieth century blues / Toast to England / I'll follow my secret heart / Regency rakes / Charming, charming / Dear little soldiers / There's always something fishy about the French / English lessons / Melanie's aria / Nevermore / Countess Mitzi / Dearest love / Gipsy melody / Stately homes of England, The / Where are the songs we sung? / Nothing can last forever / I'd never know / Something about a sailor / My kind of man / This could be true / Josephine / Sail away / Why does love get in the way / In a boat on a lake with my darling / Chase me Charlie / Evening in summer / I like America / Three juvenile delinquents / Josephine (2) / Why does love get in the way (2) / I like America (2).
2LP: . . . . SHB 179
MCSET: . . . . TC SHB 179

MASTER, THE (Coward, Noel & Gertrude Lawrence).
Tracks: / Some day I'll find you / I never realised / If you were the only girl in the world / Soldiers of the Queen / Goodbye Dolly Gray / Lover of my dreams / I do like to be beside the seaside / Goodbye my bluebell / Alexander's ragtime band / Everybody's doing it now / Let's all go down The Strand / Take me back to dear old Blighty / There's a long long trail / Keep the home fires burning / Twentieth Century blues / Bright was the day / This is a changing world / His excellency regrets / Uncle Harry / Then / Play, orchestra, play / You were there / Has anybody seen our ship? / Men about town / Here's a toast / Hearts and flowers / Sail away / I travel alone / Most of ev'ry day / Love in bloom / Fare thee well / We were so young / Just let me look at you / Last time I saw Paris, The / Could you please oblige me with a Bren gun? / There have been songs in England / Imagine the Duchess's feelings / It's only you / Don't let's be beastly to the Germans / Welcoming land, The / I'm old fashioned / You'd be so nice to come home to / I'll see you again / Dance little lady / Poor little rich girl / Room with a view / Any little fish / You were there / I'll follow my secret heart / If love were all / Peter Pan.
2LP: . . . . EN 2600653
MCSET: . . . . EN 2600655
2LP: . . . . SHB 50

MORE COMPACT COWARD.
Tracks: / Room with a view / Shadow play / We were dancing / Something to do with spring / I'll see you again / Poor little rich girl / Zigeuner / Stately homes of England, The / Dearest love / World weary / Uncle Harry / Half caste woman / Family album / Dance little lady / Don't let's be beastly to the Germans / Nina / Matelot / Don't make fun of the festival / Wait a bit Joe / Sail away.
MC: . . . . TCEMS 1417

NOEL COWARD DOUBLE BILL (Private lives & Hayfever) (Scofield, Paul/Peggy Ashcroft).
MCSET: . . . . ZBBC 1042

NOEL COWARD & GERTRUDE LAWRENCE.
LP: . . . . MES 7042

NOEL COWARD READING.
MC: 1094

NOEL COWARD SINGS HIS SCORE (The girl who came to supper).
LP: . . . . SL 5178

PRIVATE LIVES (see Private Lives) (Various artists).

REVUES, THE.
Tracks: / Parisian pierrot (From London Calling.) / There's life in the old girl yet (From London Calling.) / What love means to girls like me (From London Calling.) / Poor little rich girl (From On With The Dance.) / Room with a view (From This Year of Grace.) / Dance little lady (From This Year of Grace.) / Try to learn to love (From This Year of Grace.) / Lorelei (From This Year of Grace.) / Dream of youth, A (From This Year of Grace.) / Half caste woman (From Cochran's 1931 Revue.) / Any little fish (From Cochran's 1931 Revue.) / Let's say goodbye (From Words and Music.) / Something to do with spring (From Words and Music.) / Party's over, The (From Words and Music.) / Mad dogs and Englishmen (From Words and Music.) / Three white feathers (From Words and Music.) / World weary (From Words and Music.) / Mrs. Worthington (From Words and Music.) / London Pride (From Words and Music.) / I wonder what happened to him (From Sigh No More.) / Sigh no more (From Sigh No More.) / Matelot (From Sigh No More.) / Nina (From Sigh No More.) / Never again (From Sigh No More.) / Wait a bit, Joe (From Sigh No More.) / Don't make fun of the festival (From The Lyric Revue.) / There are bad times just around the corner (From The Globe Revue.) / Time and again (From The Globe Revue.).
LP: . . . . SHB 44
MC: . . . . TC SHB 44

TALENT TO AMUSE, A.
Tracks: / Any little fish / You were there / Some day I'll find you / Let's say goodbye / I'll follow my secret heart / If love were all / Play orchestra play / Poor little rich girl / Mad dogs and Englishmen / Party's over, The / Dearest love / Stately homes of England, The / I travel alone / Matelot / Time and again / London Pride / Sail away / Room with a view / Mrs. Worthington / There are bad times just around the corner / Dance little lady / I'll see you again.
LP: . . . . PMC 7158

TOGETHER WITH MUSIC (Coward, Noel & Mary Martin).
2LP: . . . . DARC 21103

Cowardy Custard (show)

COWARDY CUSTARD (Original London cast) (Various artists).
Tracks: / If love were all: *Gale, Peter* / I'll see you again: *Routledge, Patricia (nar)* / Time and again: *Waring,* Derek / Has anybody seen our ship?: *Sharkey, Anna* / Try to learn to love: *Stubbs,Una* / Kiss me: *Cecil,* Jonathon / Go slow, Johnny: *Davies, Tudor* / Tokay: *Gale, Peter* / Dearest love: *Sharkey, Anna* / Could you please oblige me with a Bren gun: *Various artists* / Come the wild, wild weather: *Delmar, Elaine* / Spinning song: *Routledge, Patricia (nar)* / Parisian pierrot: *Company* / Boy actor, The: *Moffatt, John* / Play orchestra play: *Company* / Shadow play ... you were there: *Routledge, Patricia (nar)* / Any little fish: *Sharkey,* Anna / Room with a view, A: *Ford, Laurel* / New York poverty: *Davies, Tudor* / When you want me: *Delmar,* Elaine / Specially for you: *Routledge, Patricia (nar)* / Beatnik love affair: *Stubbs,Una* / Success: *Waring,* Derek / I'm mad about you: *Company* / Poor little rich girl: *Waring, Derek* / Louisa: *Breeze, Olivia*/ Mad about the boy: *Routledge, Patricia (nar)* / Stately homes of England, The: *Cecil, Jonathon* / Twentieth century blues: *Delmar, Elaine* / I went to a marvellous party: *Routledge, Patricia (nar)* / Magic of an empty theatre, The: *Moffatt, John* / Auditions: *Waring, Derek* / Mrs. Worthington: *Moffatt, John* / Excerpts from Noel Coward's views on theatre: *Company* / Why must the show on?: *Company* / London pride: *Waring, Derek* / London is a little bit of all right: *Sharkey, Anna* / What ho Mrs. Brisket: *Routledge, Patricia (nar)* / Don't take our Charlie for the army: *Stubbs,Una* / Saturday night at the Rose and Crown: *Delmar, Elaine* / London at night: *Moffatt, John* / London finale: *Company* / Return to London, 1941: *Waring, Derek* / There are bad times just around the corner: *Gale, Peter* / Alice is at it again: *Davies, Tudor* / I love travelling: *Moffatt,* John / Passenger's always right, The: *Waring, Derek* / Useful phrases: *Routledge, Patricia (nar)* / Why do the wrong people travel?: *Davies, Tudor* / St. Peter's: *Routledge, Patricia (nar)* / Mad dogs and Englishmen: *Delmar,* Elaine / Nina: *Moffatt, John* / I like America: *Gale, Peter* / Bronxville Darby and Joan: *Routledge,* Patricia (nar) / Darjeeling: *Cecil, Jonathon* / I wonder what happened to him: *Cecil, Jonathon* / Miss Mouse: *Stubbs,Una* / Let's do it: *Burridge, Geoffrey* / Last worlds: *Stubbs,Una* / Boy actor, The (reprise): *Moffatt, John* / Touring days: *Routledge, Patricia (nar)* / Nothing can last for ever: *Gale, Peter* / Would you like to stick a pin in my balloon: *Stubbs,Una* / Mary make-believe: *Delmar, Elaine* / Dance little lady: *Waring, Derek* / Men about town: *Burridge, Geoffrey* / Forbidden fruit: *Delmar, Elaine* / Sigh no more: *Sharkey, Anna* / Younger generation: *Company* / I'll follow my secret heart: *Routledge, Patricia (nar)*/ If love were all: *Davies, Tudor.*
2LP: . . . . SER 5656/7

Cowboy Copas

16 GREATEST HITS: COWBOY COPAS.
MC: . . . . GT 53012
LP: . . . . SD 3012

BEST OF THE COWBOY COPAS.
LP: . . . . SLP 958

MISTER COUNTRY MUSIC.
Tracks: / Sal / Thousand miles of ocean, A / Soft rain / Penny for your thoughts, A / You are the one / How do you talk to a baby / Black eyed Susan Brown / Seven seas from you / Louision / There'll come a time someday / First things first / I dreamed of a Hillbilly heaven.
LP: . . . . OFF 9001

NOT FORGOTTEN (Cowboy Copas, Patsy Cline, Hawkshaw Hawkins).
LP: . . . . SLP 346
MC: . . . . GT 5346

OPRY STAR SPOTLIGHT ON COWBOY COPAS.
Tracks: / Sixteen fathoms / Now that you're gone / Sweet lips / Mental cruelty / Wings of a dove / Flat top pickin' / Rebel, The / Johnny Yuma / That's all I can remember / Loose talk / Sleepy eyed John / Twenty fourth hour, The / Satisfied mind, A.
LP: . . . . OFF 9003

Cowboy (Film)

COWBOY (Film soundtrack) (Various artists).
LP: . . . . DL 8684

Cowboy Jazz

SWING BOOGIE.
LP: . . . . ROUNDER 0173
MC: . . . . ROUNDER 0173C

THAT'S WHAT WE ALL LIKE ABOUT THE WEST.
LP: . . . . ROUNDER 0149
MC: . . . . ROUNDER 0149C

Cowboy Junkies

CAUTIOUS HORSES, THE.
Tracks: / Sun comes up, it's Tuesday morning / 'Cause cheap is how I feel / Thirty summers / Mariner's song / Powderfinger / Where are you tonight / Witches / Rock and bird / Escape is so easy / You will be loved again.
LP: . . . . PL 90450
MC: . . . . PK 90450

COWBOY JUNKIES: INTERVIEW PICTURE DISC.
LPPD: . . . . BAK 2155

TRINITY SESSION, THE.
Tracks: / Mining for gold / I don't get it / To love is to bury / Dreaming my dreams with you / Postcard blues / Misguided angel / I'm so lonesome I could cry / 200 more miles / Sweet Jane / Walking after midnight / Blue moon revisited (song for Elvis) (CD only.) / Working on a building (CD only.).
LP: . . . . COOK 011
MC: . . . . COOKC 011

WHITES OFF EARTH NOW!!.
Tracks: / Shining moon / State trooper / Me and the devil / Decoration day / Baby please don't go / I'll never get out of these blues alive / Take me / Forgive me / Crossroads.
LP: . . . . PL 82380
MC: . . . . PK 82380

Cowboy Killers

KOYAANISQATSI.
Tracks: / Blinded by colour / Surfy / Money cancer / Civilised / Russian roulette / Carrot / Just one more / Hoopla stand / Sargeant Bastard / Roger Ramjet / Smoking is very sophisticated / Looking good / Jesus hotel.
LP: . . . . WOWLP 7

Cowboy & Spingirl

COWBOY AND SPINGIRL.
LP: . . . . SUBORG 10

Cowboys...

COWBOY SONGS (Various artists).
MC: 4510094

COWBOYS (Various artists).
Tracks: / Mama's don't let your babies grow up to be cowboy: *Various artists* / All around cowboy: *Various artists*/ Jo and the cowboy: *Various artists* / Bull rider: *Various artists* / Cosmic cowboy: *Various artists*/ Sweetwater Texas: *Various artists*/ Don't take your guns to town: *Various artists* / Texas lullaby: *Various artists* / Cowboys ain't supposed to cry: *Various artists* / Gambler, The: *Various artists.*
LP: . . . . CBS 84693

COWBOYS & TRUCKS RIDING HARD (Various artists).
LP: . . . . GT 0082

Cowboys International

ORIGINAL SIN, THE.
Tracks: / Pointy shoes / Thrash / Part of steel / Here comes a Saturday / Original sin / Aftermath / Hands / Memorie 62 / Lonely boy / No tune / Wish.
LP: . . . . V 2136

Cowell, Stanley

BACK TO THE BEAUTIFUL.
Tracks: / Theme for Ernie / Wall / It don't mean a thing / But beautiful / Sylvia's place / Come Sunday (on CD only) / Carnegie six / St. Croix / Prayer for peach (on CD only) / Nightingale sang in Berkeley Square, A.
MC: . . . . CJ 398C

BLUES FOR THE VIET CONG.
LP: . . . . FLP 41032

LIVE AT CAFE DES COPAINS.
LP: . . . . DDA 1004

LIVE AT MAYBECK RECITAL HALL, VOL 5.
Tracks: / Softly, as a morning sunrise / Stompin' at the Savoy / I am waiting (Only on CD) / Nefertiti / Jitterbug waltz / Stella by starlight / I'll remember April (Only on CD) / Lament / Out of this world / Django / Big Foot (Only on CD) / Little sunny / Autumn leaves / Cal Massey.
MC: . . . . CJ 431 C

NEW WORLD.
Tracks: / Come Sunday / Ask him / Island of Haitoo / I'm tryin' to find a way / El space-o / Sienna / Welcome to this new world.
LP: . . . . GXY 5131

TALKIN' 'BOUT LOVE.
LP: . . . . GXY 5111

WAITING FOR THE MOMENT.
LP: . . . . GXY 5104

Cowie, Charlie

FIDDLE FROLIC.
Tracks: / Caledonia march, The / Strathspey and reel / Canadian reels / Irish jig / Mississippi cajun / Hangman's reel, The / Irish slip jig and reel / Slow air / Hornpipe and reel.
LP: . . . . LILP 5091

Cowles, Barry

SHADOW OF YOUR SMILE, THE (Cowles, Barry & the Riha Orchestra).
MC: . . . . **VCA 078**

Cox, Derek

20 PIANO FAVOURITES (Cox, Derek & His Music).
Tracks: / As time goes by / One day I'll fly away / Canadian sunset / With one more look at you / Impossible dreams / Can't smile without you / Three times a lady / Eleanor Rigby / Michele / With a little help from my friends / Memory / I know him so well / Serenata / Hello / Moonlight serenade / She's out of my life / Greensleeves / How deep is your love / I just called to say I love you / My way.
LP: . . . . **YU 111**
MC: . . . . **CYU 111**

MAGIC OF ANDREW LLOYD WEBBER.
Tracks: / Phantom of the opera, The / All I ask of you / Music of the night, The / Memory / King Herod's song / Any dream will do / Jesus Christ superstar / I don't know how to love him / Don't cry for me Argentina / Mr. Mistoffelees / Starlight express / Close every door / Unexpected song.
MC: . . . . **CSIV 1113**

Cox, Harry

BARLEY STRAW.
Tracks: / A-going to the fair / Pretty ploughboy, The / Talk about his life / What will become of England / Father / Waltz (melodeon) / Talking about music / Pub singing / Foggy dew, The / Nancy and Johnny / Firelock style / Crabfish / Barley straw / Barton Broad / Babbing ballad / Prentice boy, The / Windy old weather / Newlyn town / Bonnie bunch of roses, The / Adieu to old England / Blackberry fold / Week of matrimony, the.
MC: **60-034**

JACK ON THE ROCKS.
Tracks: / Yarmouth fishermen, The / Captain's apprentice, The / Smuggler's boy, The / Bold fisherman / Sweet William / Soldier and sailor / Greenland whale catchers / Turkish lady, the / Cruisin' round Yarmouth / Jack Tarr on the shore / John Reilly / Dolphin, the / Death of Nelson / Scarborough's banks / Good luck ship / Sailor cut down / Young Edmund / Pretty ploughboy, The.
MC: **60-033**

SEVENTEEN COME SUNDAY.
Tracks: / Spotted cow, The / Next monday morning / Greasy cook / Colin and Phoebe / Birmingham boys / Betsy the serving maid / Long peggin' awl / Old miser of London / Bonnie labouring boy, The / Female drummer / Squire and the gipsy / Marrowbones / Groggy old tailor / Rigs of London / Old German musician / Maid of Australia / Farmer's servant man, the.
MC: **60-032**

Cox, Ida

IDA COX AND BERTHA CHIPPIE HILL (Cox, Ida & Bertha Chippie Hill).
Tracks: / Off my mind / Last mile blues / I can't quit that man / How long blues / Careless love / Darktown strutters' ball / Lonesome road / Don't leave me daddy / Baby won't you please come home / Some of these days / Blues, The.
LP: . . . . **QU 048**

IDA COX VOL.1 (1923).
LP: . . . . **FB 301**

IDA COX VOL.2 (1923-1924).
LP: . . . . **FB 304**

Cox, Jess

THIRD STEP (Cox, Jess Band).
Tracks: / One in a million / Fallen hero / Two time loser / Ghosts / Danger signs / Bridges / Living your love (off the wall) / Tunnel.
LP: . . . . **NEAT 1010**

Cox, Marie

WATER IS WIDE, THE.
MC: . . . . **MB LP 1029**

Coxhill, Lol

10:02 (Coxhill, Lol & Daniel Deshays).
Tracks: / On golden flaque / Fromage a varese incl. Regardez Edgar / Solitudinette / Ceux qu ils aiment / Cleito (Including Tape Dancing.) / Un homme au plafond / Amies Americaines / Choral a tchang / Sgt. De Ville tres occupe / Tea for two.
LP: . . . . **NATO 439**

CHANTENAY 80 (see Horsthuis, Maurice) (Coxhill, Lol/Raymond Boni/ Maurice Horsthuis).

C/M/M/C (Coxhill, Lol & Steve Miller).
LP: . . . . **C 1503**

COUSCOUS.
Tracks: / West lawn dirge / Hotlavaband extensions / Variations pour violoncelle, Contrebasse, Sopranino et piano / And lo, the chapel walls trembled at the voice of the M.C.
LP: . . . . **NATO 157**

DIVERSE.
LP: . . . . **OG 510**

DUNOIS SOLOS, THE.
Tracks: / Dunois solos, The / Distorted reminiscences / Further developments.
LP: . . . . **NATO 95**

FLEAS IN CUSTARD.
LP: . . . . **C 1515**

FRENCH GIGS (Coxhill, Lol/Fred Frith).
Tracks: / French gigs.
LP: . . . . **AAA AO2**

INIMITABLE, THE.
Tracks: / Moon was yellow, The / Spring is here / Folks who live on the hill, The / It never entered my mind / Little froggies / Certain smile, A / Time after time / Change partners / Requiem major / Cocktails for two / Two sleepy people.
LP: . . . . **CHABADA 09**

INSTANT REPLAY.
Tracks: / Le bagad de kemperle / La Chantenay / Sienne / Embraceable you / Potpourri / Caravan.
LP: . . . . **NATO 25/32**

JOHNNY RONDO DUO PLUS MIKE COOPER (Coxhill, Lol/ David G.Holland/ Mike Cooper).
Tracks: / Johnny Rondo duo plus.
LP: . . . . **SAJ 29**

JOY OF PARANOIA, THE.
LP: . . . . **OG 525**

LOL COXHILL WITH TOTSUZEN DANBALL (See under Danball, Totsuzen) (Coxhill, Lol with Totsuzen Danball).

STORY SO FAR-OH REALLY (Coxhill, Lol & Steve Miller).
LP: . . . . **C 1507**

Coyle, Peter

I'D SACRIFICE EIGHT ORGASMS WITH SHIRLEY MACLAINE (Just to be there).
LP: . . . . **BMMLP 001**

SLAP IN THE FACE FOR PUBLIC TASTE, A.
Tracks: / Down / Young conservatives / Stallion / Black dogs / Dead house / Let the world fall / Heaven and hell / Plant life / Best of a dark world / Those Russian hills / Scrub me.
LP: . . . . **CALCLP 037**

Coyne, Kevin

BABBLE (Coyne, Kevin & Dagmar Krouse).
LP: . . . . **V 2128**

BEAUTIFUL EXTREMES ET CETERA.
Tracks: / Something gone wrong / Looking for the river / Red roses in your room / Face in the mirror / Love in your heart / Poor little actress / Right in hand / Hello friends, hello everybody / Mona, where's my trousers? / So strange / Rainbow curve.
LP: . . . . **BRED 43**

BLAME IT ON THE NIGHT.
Tracks: / River of sin / Sign of the times / I believe (in love) / Don't delude me / Wanting you / Take a train / Blame it on the night / Poor swine / Light up your little light / Choose / Witch / Right on her side.
LP: . . . . **V 2012**

BURSTING BUBBLES.
LP: . . . . **V 2152**

COMPLETE PEEL SESSIONS: KEVIN COYNE.
LP: . . . . **SFRLP 112**
MC: . . . . **SFRMC 112**

DANDELION YEARS.
LP: . . . . **BUTBOX 1**

EVERYBODY'S NAKED.
MC: . . . . **IMC 57218022**

HEARTBURN.
Tracks: / Strange locomotion / Don't make waves / Happy band / I love my mother / Shangri-la / America / Big white bird / Games, games, games / My mother's eyes / Daddy.
LP: . . . . **V 2047**

IN LIVING BLACK AND WHITE.
Tracks: / Case history No 2 / Fat girl / Talking to no one / My mother's eyes / Ol' nan river / Eastbourne ladies / Sunday morning sunrise / One fine day / Marjory Razorblade / Coconut Island / Turpentine / House on the hill / Knockin' on Heaven's door / Saviour / Mummy / Big white bird / America.
LP: . . . . **VD 2505**

LEGLESS IN MANILA.
LP: . . . . **RTD 22**

MARJORY RAZORBLADE.
Tracks: / Marjory Razorblade / Marlene / Talking to no one / Eastbourne ladies / Old soldier / I want my crown / Nasty, lonesome valley / House on the hill / Cheat me / Jack and Edna / Everybody says / Mummy / Heaven in my view / Karate king / Dog Latin / This is Spain / Chairman's ball / Good boy / Chicken wing.
LP: . . . . **VLD 2501**

MATCHING HEAD AND FEET.
Tracks: / Saviour / Lucy / Lonely lovers / Sunday morning sunrise / Rock 'n' roll hymn / Mrs. Hooley go home / It's not me / Turpentine / Tulip / One fine day.
LP: . . . . **V 2033**

POINTING THE FINGER.
Tracks: / There she goes / As I recall / Children of the deaf / One little moment / Let love reside / Sleeping, waking / Pointing the finger / You can't do that / Song of the womb / Old lady.
LP: . . . . **BRED 23**

POLITICZ.
Tracks: / Your Holiness / Liberation / Fun flesh / Flashing back / Tell the truth / Banzai / Poisoning you / Magnolia Street / I've got the photographs.
LP: . . . . **BRED 30**

Coyote Sisters

COYOTE SISTERS.
LP: . . . . **ZL 72173**
MC: . . . . **ZK 72173**

C.P.O.

TO HELL AND BLACK.
Tracks: / Ballad of menace / C.P.Osis / Ren's rhythm / Flow to the rhythm / Wall, The / Homicide / Somethin' like dis / Movement, The / This beat is funky / Gangsta melody.
LP: **C1 94522**
LP: **794 522 1**
MC: **C4 94522**
MC: **794 522 4**

CPO Disco Strings

DISCO ROUND THE MOON.
LP: . . . . **DLP 901**

Craaft

CRAAFT.
Tracks: / I wanna look in your eyes / Breakin' walls ain't easy / Hold me / You're the best thing in my life / I guess you are the number one / Stranger / Don't wanna wait no more / Now that you're gone / Wasted years / Cool town lovers.
LP: . . . . **EPC 26880**
MC: **40 26880**

SECOND HONEYMOON.
Tracks: / Run away / Chance of your life / Gimme what you got / Hey babe / Don't you know what love can be / Right to your heart / Twisted up all inside / Jane / Running on love / Illusions / Are you ready to rock.
LP: . . . . **PL 71826**
MC: . . . . **PK 71826**

Crab That Played

CRAB THAT PLAYED/HOW THE RHINO (Ogilvy, Ian).
Tracks: / Crab that played with the sea / How the rhinoceros got his skin.
MC: . . . . **LP 207**

Crack The Sky

ANIMAL NOTES.
Tracks: / We want mine / Animal skins / Wet teenager / Maybe I can fool everybody (tonight) / Rangers at midnight / Virgin / Invaders from Mars / Play on / No.
LP: . . . . **LSLP 6005**

SAFETY IN NUMBERS.
Tracks: / Safety in numbers / Nuclear apathy / Long nights / Flashlight / Relude to safety in numbers / Lighten up McGraw / Give myself to you / Night on the town, A.
LP: . . . . **LSLP 6015**

Cracked Mirror

CRACKED MIRROR.
Tracks: / On fire / I think you're crazy / Waiting for the man / We shall not forget / Changing your mind / Bomb blast / Follow the leader / Won't get away with that / Old Rose.
LP: . . . . **CMLP 001**

Crackle Rattle Bash

CRACKLE RATTLE BRASH.
LP: . . . . **ROCK 2**

Craddock, Billy Crash

BEST OF BILLY CRASH CRADDOCK.
Tracks: / Rub it in / Broken down in tiny pieces / You better move on / First time / Sweet magnolia blossom / Easy as pie / Still thinkin' bout you / Ain't nothing shakin' / Don't be angry / Slippin' and slidin' / Knock three times / Dream lover / I'm gonna knock on your wall / Walk softly / I love the blues / Ruby baby / Tear fell, A / Till the water stops runnin' / Afraid i'll want to love her one more time / You rubbed it in all wrong.
2LP: **IMCA2 4165**

BILLY 'CRASH' CRADDOCK.
Tracks: / I cheated on a good woman's love / Jailhouse rock / Roll in my sweet baby's arms / Rock and roll madness / You're the girl / I've been too long lonely baby / Not a day gone by / Blue eyes crying in the rain / Say you'll stay until tomorrow / We never made it to Chicago.
LP: . . . . **EST 11758**

CRASH CRADDOCK.
LP: . . . . **IMCA 39054**

GREATEST HITS: BILLY CRASH CRADDOCK.
MC: . . . . **CORONET 1707**
LP: . . . . **CR 721**

Cradle Will Rock

CRADLE WILL ROCK, THE (1985 Original London cast) (Various artists).
Tracks: / Moll's song: *Various artists* / I'll show you guys: *Various artists* / Solicitin': *Various artists*/ Hard times/ The sermon: *Various artists* / Croon spoon: *Various artists* / Freedom of the press, The: *Various artists* / Let's do something: *Various artists* / Honolulu: *Various artists* / Summer weather: *Various artists* / Love duet (Gus and Sadie): *Various artists* / Don't let me keep you: *Various artists* / Ask us again: *Various artists* / Art for arts sake: *Various artists* / Nickel under your foot, The: *Various artists*/ Cradle will rock, The: *Various artists* / Joe worker: *Various artists* / Cradle will rock, The (Final scene): *Various artists.*
LP: . . . . **TER 1105**
MC: . . . . **ZCTER 1105**

Craft

CRAFT.
Tracks: / Cancer / Aires / Taurus / Gemini / Leo / Virgo.
LP: . . . . **HAI 106**

Crafton, Harry

HARRY CRAFTON.
Tracks: / Get off mama / Let me tell you baby / Roly poly mama / I don't want your money, honey / Guitar boogie / Bring my cadillac back / It's been a long time baby / Rust dusty / In the middle of the night / She got a mule kick / Big fat hot dog / So long baby / Saturday night boogie.
LP: . . . . **KK 818**

Craftsmen

YOUR COUNTRY AND IRISH REQUESTS.
Tracks: / Gypsy woman / Hannigan's hooley / Old bog road.
LP: . . . . **HRL 135**
MC: . . . . **CHRL 135**

Craig, Gary

BLUE RIDGE MOUNTAIN.
LP: . . . . **LEA 4012**

NORTH CAROLINA BOYS.
LP: . . . . **LEA 4040**

Craig, Gerry

ELVIS PRESLEY'S LOVE SONGS.
MC: . . . . **ZCFPA 1014**

Craig, Karen (nar)

SECRET OF THE GLEN (see under Secret Of The Glen (bk)).

Craig, Lorraine

SHADES OF BLUE AND GREEN (Craig, Lorraine & National Jazz Youth Orchestra).
Tracks: / Another always / Deflated bounce, The / As if I cared / Insignificant song / I thought I was through with love / Where is the music / With you in mind / Shades of blue and green / I have been here before / But me no buts.
LP: . . . . **REN 702**
MC: . . . . **ZCN 702**

Craig, Wendy (nar)

CHILDREN'S HOUR.
LP: . . . . **MMT LP 105**

HANS CHRISTIAN ANDERSEN FAIRY TALES (See under Andersen, Hans).

PETER PAN (See under Peter Pan (bk)).

SHOW ME THE WAY.
LP: . . . . **MMR 002**
MC: . . . . **MMC 002**

TREASURY OF FAIRY TALES CHAPTER ONE (Craig, Wendy/Lesley Judd).
Tracks: / Snow White and the seven dwarfs / Hansel and Gretel / Babes in the wood / Frog prince, The / Pied piper / Puss 'n' boots / Tom Thumb / Wild swan, The.
2LP: **2668 017**

YOUR FAVOURITE FAIRY STORIES.
Tracks: / Babes in the wood / Frog prince, The / Snow White and the seven dwarfs / Hansel and Gretel.
LP: SPR 8541
MC: SPC 8541

Crain, Jimmy

ROCKIN' WITH JIMMY CRAIN.
Tracks: / Guitar playin' son of a gun / Why worry / I'm gonna get ya' / London fog / C'mon baby / Maybe someday / Rockin' / Shig a shag / Spooky village / Baby what's wrong with you / Rock a sock a hop / I keep hearing rumours / J.C.'s boogie.
LP: WLP 8809

ROCKS ON.
Tracks: / Learning how to rock and roll / Mixin' it up / Suzie Q is the one for me / We're goin' rockin' / Jimmy's nothin' like it rock / She loves rock 'n' roll / Why worry (part 2) / Rockin' all night long / Cruisin' / Hey hey / We're gonna rock / Messin' around / Just let me know / You name it rock.
LP: WLP 8845

Cram, Paul

BLUE TALES IN TIME.
LP: ONARI 006

Cramer, Floyd

20 OF THE BEST: FLOYD CRAMER.
Tracks: / On the rebound / Java / Flip flop and bop / Lovesick blues / Corn crib symphony / Dream baby / Honky tonk (part 2) / Maple leaf rag / Sugarfoot rag / Boogie, boogie, boogie / What'd i say / Boogie woogie / Proud Mary / In crowd, The / Work song / Himmo a la Alegria / My melody of love / Games people play / Smile / Last date.
LP: NL 89850
MC: NK 89850

BEST OF FLOYD CRAMER.
Tracks: / Let's go / Impossible dream, The / Yesterday / Look of love, The / Java / You are the sunshine of my life / Do you know the way to San Jose / Proud Mary / Sunny / Valley of the dolls, Theme from / Strangers in the night / This guy's in love with you / Man and a woman, A / Goin' out of my head / Can't take my eyes off you.
LP: 107 4066
MC: 770 4066

BEST OF FLOYD CRAMER (1980).
Tracks: / Last date / Tricky / Lovesick blues / Unchained melody / Satan's doll / San Antonio rose / On the rebound / Your last goodbye / Java / Swing low / Young years, The / Flip flop and bop.
LP: INTS 5008
MC: INTK 5008

DALLAS.
Tracks: / Dallas (Dallas dreams), Theme from / Incredible Hulk, Theme from / Taxi, Theme from / All in the Family / Waltons - theme / Little house on the prairie / Young and the restless, Theme from / M.A.S.H., Theme from / Laverne and Shirley (Theme) / Knots Landing.
LP: INTS 5155
MC: INTK 5155
LP: PL 13618

Crammed Discs (label)

CRAMMED CRAMMED WORLD II (Various artists).
LP: CRAM 063

Cramps

DATE WITH ELVIS, A.
Tracks: / How far can too far go / Hot pearl snatch / People ain't no good / What's inside a girl? / Kizmiaz / Cornfed dames / Chicken / Womanneed / Aloha from hell / It's just that song.
LP: WIKA 46
MC: WIKC 46
LP: ROSE 81
MC: ROSE 81C

GRAVEST HITS.
Tracks: / Human fly / Way I walk, The / Domino / Surfin' bird / Lonesome town.
LP: ILS 12013

LOOK MOM NO HEAD!.
LP: WIKAD 101
MC: WIKDC 101

OFF THE BONE.
Tracks: / Human fly / Way I walk, The / Domino / Surfin' bird / Lonesome town / Garbage man / Fever / Drug train / Love me / I can't hardly stand it / Goo goo muck / She said / Crusher, The / Save it / New kind of kick.
LP: ILP 12

PSYCHEDELIC JUNGLE.
Tracks: / Greenfuz / Goo goo muck / Rockin bones / Voodoo idol / Primitive / Caveman / Crusher, The / Don't eat stuff off the sidewalk / Can't find my mind / Jungle hop / Natives are restless, The / Under the wires / Beautiful gardens / Green door.
LP: SP 70016
LP: SP70016

SMELL OF FEMALE.
Tracks: / Most exalted potentate of love, The / You got good taste / Call of the wig hat / Faster pussycat / I ain't nothin' but a gorehound / Psychotic reaction.
LP: NED 6
LPPD: NEDP 6
MC: WIKMC 95

SONGS THE LORD TAUGHT US.
LP: ILP 005

STAY SICK.
Tracks: / Bop pills / God damn rock 'n' roll / Bikini girls with machine guns / All women are bad / Creature from the black leather lagoon, The / Shortnin' bread / Daisys up your butterfly / Everything goes / Journey to the center of a girl / Mamma oo pow pow / Saddle up a buzz buzz / Muleskinner blues / Her love rubbed off (CD only.).
LP: ENVLP 1001
LP: 773 543 1
MC: TCENV 1001
LPPD: ENVLPPD 1001

WHAT'S INSIDE A GHOUL.
LP: POW 002

Crane River Jazz Band

CRANE RIVER JAZZ BAND, 1950-53.
LP: DM 18

LEGENDARY CRANE RIVER JAZZ BAND.
LP: DC 12026

Crane, Stephen

RED BADGE OF COURAGE, THE (O'Brien, Edmund).
MC: 1040

Cranes

SELF NON SELF.
LP: BB 017

WINGS OF JOY.
LP: DEDLP 003
MC: DEDMC 003

Cranford

CRANFORD (see under Gaskell, Elizabeth) (Scales, Prunella (nar)).

Cranitch, Matt

EISTIGH SEAL.
LP: CEF 104
MC: CEFC 104

Cranshaw, Bob

UNDERDOG, THE (See under Mauro, Turk) (Cranshaw, Bob/Mauro Turk).

Crary, Dan

B-C-H (See under Berline, Byron) (Berline, Byron & Dan Crary & John Hickman).

GUITAR.
Tracks: / Cotton patch rag / Stanley Brothers medley / Sweet laree / Memories of Mozart / Green in the blue medley, The / Tom and Jerry / Bill Monroe medley.
LP: SH 3730

LADY'S FANCY.
Tracks: / Huckleberry hornpipe / Lime rock / If the devil dreamed about playing flamenco / With a flatpick / Jenny's waltz / Sally goon'n / Julie's reel / Dill pickle rag / Pretty little indian / Grey eagle / Lady's fancy.
LP: ROUNDER 0099
MC: ROUNDER 0099C

NIGHT RUN (See under Berline, Byron) (Berline, Byron & Dan Crary & John Hickman).

NOW THERE ARE FOUR (See under Berline, Byron) (Berline, Byron & Dan Crary & John Hickman).

SWEET SOUTHERN GIRL.
Tracks: / Sweet southern girl / Blackbird, The / Devil played the fiddle, The / Jesse James was an outlaw / Stories we could tell / Butcher boy / Foggy mountain special / Big river / Lovin' her was easier / Don't mess around with Jim / Sally Ann / Mama said yeah / Cajun train.
LP: SH 3707
MC: ZCSH 3707

Crash

I FEEL FINE.
Tracks: / Almost / Craig egg / International velvet / I go round / Superfly / Everything under the sun / I feel fine / My machine / On and on / Rings, chains and groups / Get set / John stood by / What I found.
LP: REMLP 2

Crash, Johnny

NEIGHBOURHOOD THREAT.
Tracks: / Hey kid / No bones about it / All the way in love / Thrill of the kill / Axe to the wax / Sink or swim / Crack of dawn / Freedom road / Halfway to heaven / Trigger happy / Baby's like a piano.
LP: 4662241
MC: 4662244

Crash 'N' Burn

FEVER.
LP: PL 74899
MC: PK 74899

Crass

BEST BEFORE 1984.
2LP: CATNO 5

CHRIST THE ALBUM.
2LP: BOLLOX2U2

FEEDING OF THE 5,000.
2LP: CRASS 621984

PENIS ENVY.
LP: CRASS 321984
MC: CRASS 321981

STATIONS OF THE CRASS.
2LP: CRASS 521984

YES SIR I WILL.
LP: 121984/2
MC: 121981

Cravats

CRAVATS IN TOYTOWN.
Tracks: / Still / In your eyes / Welcome / Pressure sellers / One in a thousand / X.M.P / All around the corner / Ceasing to be / Gordon / Live for now / Tears on my machine / Hole, The / All on standby / Triplex zone.
LP: CRAVAT 1

Craven, Beverley

BEVERLEY CRAVEN.
Tracks: / Promise me / Holding on / Woman to woman / Memories / Castle in the clouds / You're not the first / Joey / Two of a kind / I listen to the rain / Missing you.
LP: 4670531
MC: 4670534

Craven, John (nar)

ADVENTURES OF DOCTOR SNUGGLES (See under Adventures of ...).

Craven, Sara

FLAME OF DIABOLO (See also Lesley Seaward).
MC: PMB 011

Cravens, Red

419 WEST MAIN (Cravens, Red & Bray Brothers).
LP: ROUNDER 0015

Craver, Mike

FISHING FOR AMOUR.
LP: FF 330

Crawdaddys

CRAWDADDY EXPRESS.
Tracks: / I'm a lover not a fighter / You can't judge a book / Down the road apiece / Let's make it / Raining in my heart / I'm movin' on / Mystic eyes / Oh baby doll / Bald headed woman / Come see me / Got you in my soul / Times are getting tougher than tough / Down in the bottom / Crawdaddy Express / I wanna put a tiger in your tank.
LP: HA-Z 8571

Crawford, Carolyn

HEARTACHE.
LP: MOTCLP 42

Crawford, Hank

CAJUN SUNRISE.
Tracks: / What a difference you've made in my life / I don't want no happy songs / New York's one soulful city / Take this job and shove it / Just the way you are / Daytime friends / Evergreen / Cajun sunrise.
LP: KU 39

HANK CRAWFORD'S BACK.
Tracks: / Funky pigeon / I can't stop loving you / You'll never find another love like mine / Canadian sunset / Midnight over Memphis.
LP: KU 33

ROADHOUSE SYMPHONY (Crawford, Hank & Doctor John).
Tracks: / Roadhouse symphony / Track magick / Jubilee / Say it isn't so / Time is on our side / Precious Lord / Sugar ditch.
LP: M 9140

SOUL BROTHERS (Crawford, Hank & Jimmy McGriff).
LP: MX 9171

SOUL SURVIVORS (see McGriff, Jimmy) (Crawford, Hank & Jimmy McGriff).

TICO RICO.
Tracks: / Tico Rico / Teach me tonight / Lady Soul / Lullaby of love / I've just seen a face / Lament / Funky rooster.
LP: KU 35

Crawford, Jesse

CINEMA ORGAN ENCORES.
LP: DEROY 1200

Crawford, Joan

SELECTIONS FROM HER FILMS.
LP: CC 100-23

Crawford, Johnny

BEST OF JOHNNY CRAWFORD.
LP: RNDF 202

Crawford, Michael

BILLY.
MC: 40 70133

MICHAEL CRAWFORD - STAGE AND SCREEN.
Tracks: / West Side story / What'll I do / Unexpected song / If loved you / Before the parade passes by / When you wish upon a star / In the still of the night / Memory / Not a day goes by / Bring him home / You'll never walk alone.
LP: STAR 2308
MC: STAC 2308

WITH LOVE.
LP: STAR 2340
MC: STAC 2340

Crawford, Randy

ABSTRACT EMOTIONS.
Tracks: / Can't stand the pain / Actual emotional love / World of fools / Betcha / Higher than anyone can count / Desire / Getting away with murder / Overnight / Almaz / Don't wanna be normal.
LP: WX 46
MC: WX 46C

EVERYTHING MUST CHANGE.
Tracks: / Everything must change / I let you walk away / I'm easy / I had to see you one more time / I've never been to me / Don't let me down / Something so right / Soon as I touched him / Only your love song lasts / Gonna give lovin a try.
LP: K 56328
MC: K4 56328

GREATEST HITS: RANDY CRAWFORD.
Tracks: / Streetlife / Secret combination / One hello / Rainy night in Georgia / You bring the Sun out / Imagine / Tender falls the rain / Windsong / One day I'll fly away / He reminds me / You might need somebody / Endlessly / Take it away from her (put it on me) / Happy feet / Nightline / Last night at danceland.
LP: NE 1281
MC: CE 2281

LOVE SONGS: RANDY CRAWFORD.
Tracks: / One day I'll fly away / You might need somebody / Rainy night in Georgia / Trade winds / He reminds me / Nightline / Windsong / Secret combination / Almaz / Imagine / In real life / Everything must change / I don't want to lose him / Someone to believe in / One Hello.
LP: STAR 2299
MC: STAC 2299

MISS RANDY CRAWFORD.
Tracks: / Hallelujah glory hallelujah / I can't get you off my mind / I'm under the influence of you / Over my head / Desperado / Take it away from her (put it on me) / Single woman, married man / Half steppin' / This man / At last.
LP: K 56882
MC: K4 56882

NIGHTLINE.
Tracks: / Happy feet / This old heart of mine / Lift me up / Ain't no foolin' / Go on and live it up / Nightline / Living on the outside / Why / Bottom line / In real life.
LP: 923976 1
MC: 923976 4

NOW WE MAY BEGIN.
Tracks: / Now we may begin / Blue flame / When your life was low / My heart is not as young as it used to be / Last night at danceland / Tender falls the rain / One day I'll fly away / Same old story, same old song.
LP: K 56791
MC: K4 56791

RAW SILK.
Tracks: / I stand accused / Declaration of love / Someone to believe in / Endlessly / Love is like a newborn child / Where there was darkness / Nobody / I hope you'll be very unhappy without me / I got myself a happy song / Just to keep you satisfied / Blue mood.
MC: K4 66114
LP: K 56592
MC: K4 56592

RICH AND THE POOR, THE.
LP: WX 308
MC: WX 308 C

SECRET COMBINATION.
Tracks: / You might need somebody / Rainy night in Georgia / That's how heartaches are made / Two lives / You

bring the Sun out / Rio De Janeiro blue / Secret combination / When I lose my way / Time for love, A / Trade winds.
LP: . . . . K 56904
MC: K4 56904

WINDSONG.
Tracks: / Look who's lonely now / I have ev'rything but you / He reminds me / Letter full of tears / This night won't last forever / One hello / Windsong / When I'm gone / Don't come knockin' / I don't want to lose him / We had a love so strong.
LP: . . . . K 5701 1
MC: K4 57011

Crawford, Ray

SMOOTH GROOVE.
LP: . . . . CS 9028

Crawford, Sugar Boy

CHICAGO YEARS.
2LP: 427017

SUGAR BOY CRAWFORD.
LP: . . . . PM 156 1351

Crawley, Wilton

CRAWLEY CLARINET MOAN 1927-28.
LP: . . . . HQ 2035

Crawling Chaos

C.
LP: . . . . FOETUS 3

WAQQUZZ.
LP: . . . . WAQQUZZ 001

Crawling Walls

INNER SECRETS.
LP: . . . . LOLITA 5043

Crawlspace (film)

CRAWLSPACE (1985 film soundtrack) (Various artists).
LP: . . . . STV 81279

Craxton, Janet

ART OF JANET CRAXTON.
LP: . . . . REN 635
MC: . . . . ZCN 635

Cray, Robert

BABY LEE (See under Hooker, John Lee) (Hooker, John Lee & Robert Cray).

BAD INFLUENCE (Cray, Robert Band).
Tracks: / Phone booth / Grinder / Got to make a comeback / So many women, so little time / Where do I go from here? / Waiting for a train / March on / Don't touch me / No big deal / Bad influence.
LP: . . . . FIEND 23
MC: . . . . FIENDCASS 23

DON'T BE AFRAID OF THE DARK (Cray, Robert Band).
Tracks: / Don't be afraid of the dark / Your secret's safe with me / Acting this way / Don't you even come / I can't go home / Across the line.
LP: . . . . MERH 129
MC: . . . . MERHC 129

FALSE ACCUSATIONS (Cray, Robert Band).
Tracks: / Porch light / Change of heart, change of mind / She's gone / Playin' in the dirt / I've slipped her mind / False accusations / Last time, The / Payin' for it now / Sonny.
LP: . . . . FIEND 43
MC: . . . . FIENDCASS 43
LP: CCR1012

MIDNIGHT STROLL (Cray, Robert Band feat. Memphis Horns).
LP: 8466521
MC: 8466524

SHOWDOWN (see Collins, Albert) (Cray, Robert/Albert Collins/Johnny Copeland).

STRONG PERSUADER (Cray, Robert Band).
Tracks: / Smoking gun / I guessed I showed her / Right next door (because of me) / Nothin' but a woman / Still around / More than I can stand / Foul play / I wonder / Fantasized / New blood.
LP: . . . . MERH 97
MC: . . . . MERHC 97

WHO'S BEEN TALKIN' (Cray, Robert Band).
Tracks: / Too many cooks / Score, The / Welfare, The (turns its back on you) / That's what I'll do / I'd rather be a wino / Who's been talkin' / Sleeping in the ground / I'm gonna forget about you / Nice as a fool can be / If you're thinkin' what I'm thinkin'.
LP: . . . . CRB 1140
MC: . . . . TCCRB 1140
LP: 269 601 1
MC: 269 601 4
LP: . . . . CLM 101
MC: . . . . TCCLM 101

Crayton, Pee Wee

AFTER HOURS BOOGIE.
LP: . . . . BB 307

BLUES AFTER DARK.
Tracks: / I got news for you / Baby, won't you please come home / Piney Brown blues / Call it stormy Monday / Good rockin' tonight / Blues after dark / How long how long blues / Tie it down / Fiddle de dee / Frosty night, A / Telephone is ringing, The / Blues after hours / I found my peace of mind / I love her still.
LP: . . . . CRB 1186

BLUES AFTER HOURS.
Tracks: / Blues after hours / My baby's on the line / Lucille / Need your love so bad / In the evening / Texas hop / Don't forget to close the door / If I ever get lucky / Blues in the ghetto / Louella Brown.
LP: . . . . BMLP 1060

BLUES GUITAR GENIUS.
Tracks: / Poppa stoppa / Good little woman / Guitar boogie / Cool evening / Dedicating the blues / Brand new woman / Telephone call from my baby / Bop hop / Huckle boogie / Rosa Lee.
LP: . . . . 10 CH 23

EARLY HOURS.
LP: . . . . MB 1007

EVERY DAY I HAVE THE BLUES (Crayton, Pee Wee/Sonny Stitt/Joe Turner).
Tracks: / Stormy Monday / Piney Brown blues / Martin Luther King southside / Everyday / Shake rattle and roll / Lucille.
LP: 231 0818
MC: K10 818
LP: . . . . CL 918983

GREAT RHYTHM AND BLUES VOL.5.
Tracks: / Texas hop / Don't forget to close the door / If I ever get lucky / Blues in the ghetto / Louella Brown / Blues after hours / My baby / On the line / Lucille / Need your love so bad / In the evening.
LP: . . . . BDL 1004

MAKE ROOM FOR PEE WEE.
LP: . . . . MB 1005

MEMORIAL ALBUM.
Tracks: / Texas hop / Miserable old feeling / Blues for my baby / Californian women / Walkin' with Crayton / Old fashioned baby / Bop hop / Money is all we need / Mistreated so bad / All or nothing at all / Twinky / Blue night / Mojo blues / Need your love so bad.
LP: . . . . CHD 177

PEACE OF MIND.
Tracks: / Tie it down / Fiddle de dee / Frosty night, A / Telephone is ringing, The / Blues after hours / I don't care / Is this the price I pay / Second hand love / I love her still.
LP: . . . . CFM 601

ROCKING DOWN ON CENTRAL AVENUE.
Tracks: / Austin boogie / Tired of travellin' / Crayton's blues / Change your way of loving / Answer to blues after hour / T for Texas (mistreated blues) / Rockin the blues / Huckle boogie / Central Avenue blues / Long after hours / Louella Brown / When a man has the blues / Please come back / Pee Wee's wild.
LP: . . . . CHA 61

Craze

SPARTANS.
Tracks: / Spartans / Lucy / Time / Circle / Good from the bad / Unhappy girl / Motions / Heart attack / Stop living in the past / Another interview / From time to time.
LP: . . . . SHSP 4114

Crazy

NANI WINE.
LP: . . . . TR 001

Crazy Backward...

CRAZY BACKWARD ALPHABET (Crazy Backward Alphabet).
Tracks: / Blood and the ink, The / Det Enda Raka? / Get it you / Welfare elite, The / Ghosts / Lobster on the rocks / Sarayushka (La Grange) / Dropped D / Book of Joel, The / Bottoms Up! / We are in control / Maran II.
LP: . . . . SST 110

Crazy Cats

SWISS KISS.
Tracks: / Miss Betty / Rockin' daddy / I wanna rock / For one night with you / One hand loose / I can't lose / Milkcow blues / Feed up / Cat's rhythm / Rock around with Ollie Vee / I've got a good woman / Ghost in a white Cadillac.
LP: . . . . MFLP 012

Crazy Cavan

COOL & CRAZY ROCK-A-BILLY (Crazy Cavan & The Rhythm Rockers).
Tracks: / Big black Cadillac / Lonesome baby blues / Standing in your window / Are you still crazy child / Train of love / I forgot to tell my baby / Crazy stomp, The / Johnny's gone walking / Teenage heart / Betty Lou's got a new pair of shoes / Boogie woogie country girl.
LP: . . . . MFLP 010
LP: . . . . BBR 1007

CRAZY RHYTHM (Crazy Cavan & The Rhythm Rockers).
Tracks: / She's the one to blame / Teddy boy rock 'n' roll / Sadie / Bob little baby / Cross my heart / Caroline / Wildest cat in town / Got a date with Sally / Fancy Nancy / Rockabilly star / Why can't we be / Rita / Hard rock / Cafe / Crazy boogie / Marilyn / Goin' down the road / Teddy boy boogie / Crazy rhythm.
LP: . . . . CR 30156
LP: . . . . LP 7510

CRAZY TIMES (Crazy Cavan & The Rhythm Rockers).
Tracks: / Stompin' shoes / Wildest cat in town / Boppin' and shakin' / Rockabilly rules / Teddy boy boogie / Teddy jive / Gonna rock gonna roll gonna boogie / Ole black Joe / Saturday night / Trouble trouble / Alabama shake / Knock knock / Bonnie / Sweet little pretty baby / Sweet baby Jean / Hey pretty baby / Delores / Sadie / Waitin' for my baby / Rock around with Ollie Vee / Bop pretty baby / My little sister's got a motorbike / She's the one to blame / Okie boogie / Get yourself a band / Rockabilly star / Gonna leave this town / Real gone lover.
2LP: . . . . INSD 5029
MCSET: . . . . TCINSD 5029

LIVE AT PICKETTS LOCK VOL.1 (Crazy Cavan & The Rhythm Rockers).
Tracks: / Wildest cat in town / Teddy boy rock and roll / Saturday nite / Sadie / Long tall Sally / Blue suede shoes / My little teddy girl / Nobody else like you / Tongue tied Jill / Old black Joe / Teddy boy blues / Bop pretty baby.
LP: . . . . CFM 103

LIVE AT PICKETTS LOCK VOL.2 (Crazy Cavan & The Rhythm Rockers).
Tracks: / Caroline / Monkey and the baboon / One hand loose / Big blon' baby / Watcha gonna do when the creek runs dry / Alabama shake / Rockabilly star / Rockin' at hard rock cafe / Put on your stompin' shoes / She's the one to blame / Saturday nite / Nervous fella.
LP: . . . . CFM 105

LIVE AT THE RAINBOW (Teddy boy gear) (Crazy Cavan & The Rhythm Rockers).
Tracks: / She's the one to blame / Okie boogie / Teddy boy rock 'n' roll / Stompin' shoes / Rock around with Ollie Vee / Bop little baby / Tongue tied Jill / Teddy boy boogie / Ol' black Joe / My little sister's gotta motorbike / Real gone lover.
LP: . . . . CR 30139
MC: . . . . CFK 1016

MR COOL (Crazy Cavan & The Rhythm Rockers).
LP: . . . . CR 30203

OUR OWN WAY OF ROCKIN' (Crazy Cavan & The Rhythm Rockers).
Tracks: / Boppin' 'n' shakin' / Watcha gonna do when the creek runs dry / Ol' black Joe / My own way of rockin' / Drinkin' wine / That's my house / My little sister's gotta motorbike / Why don't somebody / Tennessee border / Teddy jive / Gotta be my baby / Monkey and the baboon / Gonna rock, gonna roll, gonna boogie / Saturday nite.
LP: . . . . CRL 5004

RED HOT N' ROCKABILLY (Crazy Cavan & The Rhythm Rockers).
Tracks: / Wildest cat in town / Sweet baby Jean / Teddy boy boogie / Sweet little pretty thing / Boppin 'n' shakin' / Rockabilly star / Ol' black Joe / Saturday night / Teddy jive / Sadie / My little sister's gotta motorbike / Drinkin' wine spo-dee-o-dee / Gonna rock, gonna roll, gonna boogie / Knock knock / Stompin' shoes / Alabama shake.
LP: . . . . CR 30174
MC: . . . . CFK 1013

ROCKABILITY (Crazy Cavan & The Rhythm Rockers).
Tracks: / Get yourself a band / Stompin' shoes / Sweet baby Jean / Knock, knock / Waitin' for my baby.
LP: . . . . CRL 5001

ROCKABILLY IN PARIS (Crazy Cavan & The Rhythm Rockers).
Tracks: / I'll be there / Betty Lou / My bonnie / I hear you knocking / Pins and needles.
LP: . . . . MFM 003

STILL CRAZY (Crazy Cavan & The Rhythm Rockers).
LP: . . . . CRAZY 09

TEDDY JIVE (Crazy Cavan & The Rhythm Rockers).
LP: . . . . CFM 101

Crazy Horse

CRAZY MOON (See under Young, Neil).

LEFT FOR DEAD.
LP: . . . . SERV 009

RUST NEVER SLEEPS (see Young, Neil) (Crazy Horse/Neil Young).

Crazy House

STILL LOOKING FOR HEAVEN ON EARTH.
Tracks: / Burning rain / This means everything to me / Feel the fire / Heaven said my name / Only belief, The / Whole creation, The / Shake (sell your soul) / Find the words (to change your mind) / Edge of the night.
LP: . . . . CHR 1576
MC: . . . . ZCHR 1576

THEY DANCED LIKE THIS FROM AS FAR OFF AS THE CRAZY HOUSE.
LP: . . . . PROP 2

WE EMPHATICALLY DENY THAT PIGS CAN FLY.
Tracks: / Sun Beat my face / Talk about the way we live / Second to none / Maybe someday / Sun will shine, The / We can't talk louder / Jealous in love / Elephant eyes / Poison / Mother Superior.
LP: . . . . PROP 3

Crazy Pink Revolvers

AT THE RIVERS EDGE.
LP: . . . . ABCLP 17

FIRST DOWN.
Tracks: / First down and go / This day forever / Behind the wire / Machine smile / Psychedelic cowboy / Day of dreams / Seven, The / Suddenly / Slow down.
LP: . . . . SEX 013

Crazy Rhythm

HALVFRANSKT.
LP: . . . . KS 2057

Crazyhead

DESERT ORCHID.
Tracks: / In the sun / Jack the scissorman / Time has taken its toll on you / Have love will travel / What gives you the idea you're so amazing baby? / I don't want that kind of love / Dragon City / Buy a gun / Rags / Tower of fire / Cardinal Phink / Bang bang (CD & Cassette only.) / Out on a limb (CD only.) / Down (CD only.) / Time has taken its toll on you (ext. mix) (CD only.).
LP: . . . . FOODLP 1
MC: . . . . FOODTC 1

SOME KIND OF FEVER.
LP: . . . . REVLP 162
MC: . . . . REVMC 162

Creagh, Seamus

JACKIE DALY & SEAMUS CREAGH (see Daly,Jackie & Seamus Creagh) (Creagh, Seamus & Jackie Daly).

Cream

BEST OF CREAM.
LP: . . . . ADAH 429
LP: 583 060
MC: 3216 031
MC: 811 639 4

CREAM.
Tracks: / N.S.U. / Sleepy time time / Dreaming / Sweet wine / Spoonful / Wrapping paper / Cat's squirrel / Four until late / Coffee song, The / Rollin' and tumblin' / I'm so glad / Toad.
LP: 2384 067

CREAM 2.
MC: 3228 005

CREAM BOX SET.
LPS: 2658 142

DISRAELI GEARS.
Tracks: / Strange brew / Sunshine of your love / World of pain / Dance the night away / Blue condition / Tales of brave Ulysses / We're going wrong / Outside woman blues / Take it back / Mother's lament.
LP: 239 412 9
LP: 594 003
MC: 823 636 4

FRESH CREAM.
LP: . . . . SPELP 42
LP: 593 001
LP: 594 001
MC: 827 576-4

GOODBYE CREAM.
Tracks: / I'm so glad / Politician / Sitting on top of the world / Badge / Doing that scrapyard thing / What a bringdown.
LP: . . . . SPELP 75
MC: . . . . SPEMC 75
LP: 583 053
MC: 823 660-4

GREATEST HITS: CREAM.
2LP: 2658 139
MC: 3524 220

HEAVY CREAM.
2LP: **2659 022**
LP: **2472 244**
MC: **3472 244**

I FEEL FREE.
Tracks: / White room / I feel free / Badge / Anyone for tennis / Spoonful / Wrapping paper / N.S.U. / Strange brew / Sunshine of your love / I'm so glad / Politician / Take it back.
LP: **2872 244**

LIVE CREAM.
Tracks: / N.S.U. / Sleepy time time / Lawdy mama / Sweet wine / Rollin' and tumblin'.
LP: . . . . **SPELP 93**
MC: . . . . **SPEMC 93**
MC: **827577 4**

LIVE VOL 1.
LP: **2383 016**

LIVE VOL 2.
LP: **2383 119**

STORY OF CREAM VOL.1.
Tracks: / Traintime / Toad / White room / Sitting on top of the world / Strange brew / Tales of brave Ulysses / Sunshine of your love / Take it back.
LP: **2479 212**
MC: **3215 038**

STORY OF CREAM VOL.2.
Tracks: / I'm so glad / Politician / Spoonful / Born under a bad sign / Badge / Crossroads / N.S.U. / Passing the time / I feel free / Mothers Lament.
LP: **2479 213**
MC: **3215 039**

STRANGE BREW - THE VERY BEST OF CREAM.
Tracks: / Badge / Sunshine of your love / Crossroads / White room / Born under a bad sign / Swlabr / Strange brew / Anyone for tennis / I feel free / Tales of brave ulysses / Politician / Spoonful.
LP: . . . . **RSD 5021**
MC: . . . . **TRSD 5021**

VERY BEST OF CREAM, THE.
Tracks: / White room / I feel free / Tales of brave Ulysses / I'm so glad / Toad / Sunshine of your love / Strange brew / NSU / Born under a bad sign / Badge / Crossroads.
LP: **817 172-1**
MC: **817 172-4**

WHEELS OF FIRE.
Tracks: / White room / Sitting on top of the world / Passing the time / As you said / Pressed rat and warthog / Politician / Those were the days / Born under a bad sign / Deserted cities of the heart / Crossroads / Spoonful / Train time / Toad.
LP: **583 033**
LP: **2394 136**
MC: **3216 036**

WHEELS OF FIRE (In the Studio - Live at the Fillmore).
2LP: . . . . **SPDLP 2**
MCSET: **3216 037**
2LP: **583 031/2**
MCSET: **827 578 4**

WHEELS OF FIRE (LIVE AT FILLMORE).
LP: **2394 137**

Creaming Jesus

TOO FAT TO RUN, TO STUPID TO HIDE.
LP: . . . . **FREUD 36**

Creasey, John

THREE DAY'S TERROR.
MC: . . . . **CAT 4032**

Creation

HOW DOES IT FEEL TO FEEL.
Tracks: / How does it feel to feel / Life is just beginning / Through my eyes / Ostrich man / I am the walker / Tom Tom / Girls are naked, The / Painter man / Try and stop me / Biff bang pow / Making time / Cool jerk / For all that I am / Nightmares / Midway down / Can I join your band?.
LP: . . . . **ED 106**

RECREATION.
LP: . . . . **OLLP 5242**

WE ARE PAINTERMEN.
LP: . . . . **OLLP 5234**

Creation (Label)

CREATION SOUP VOL 1 (Various artists).
LP: . . . . **CRELP 101**

CREATION SOUP VOL 2 (Various artists).
LP: . . . . **CRELP 102**

CREATION SOUP VOL 3 (Various artists).
LP: . . . . **CRELP 103**

CREATION SOUP VOL 4 (Various artists).
LP: . . . . **CRELP 104**

CREATION SOUP VOL 5 (Various artists).
LP: . . . . **CRELP 105**

DOING GOD'S WORK (A Creation compilation) (Various artists).
Tracks: / Ten miles: *Wilson, Phil* / In a mourning town: *Biff Bang Pow* / Murderers, the hope of women: *Momus*/ Shine on: *House Of Love* / Cut me deep: *Jasmine Minks* / Word around town, The: *Westlake* / Kiss at dawn: *Sudden, Nikki* / Catch me: *Blow Up*.
LP: . . . . **CRELP 024**

DOING IT FOR THE KIDS (Various artists).
LP: . . . . **CRELP 037**

KEEPING THE FAITH (Various artists).
LP: . . . . **CRELP 081**
MC: . . . . **CREC 081**

WILD SUMMER, WOW (Various artists).
LP: . . . . **CRELP 002**

Creation Of Death

PURIFY YOUR SOUL.
LP: . . . . **FLAG 62**

Creation Rebel

LOWS AND HIGHS.
Tracks: / Independent man / Rebel party / Reasoning, A / No peace / Love I can feel / Rubber skirt / Creation rebel / Creative involvements.
LP: . . . . **BRED 33**

STARSHIP AFRICA.
LP: . . . . **ONULP 8**

THREAT TO CREATION (Creation Rebel/New Age Steppers).
Tracks: / Chemical specialists / Threat to creation / Eugenic device / Last sane dream / Pain staker / Earthwire line / Ethos / Design / Final frontier.
LP: . . . . **BRED 21**

Creator, Carlos

PURE GUITAR.
MC: . . . . **PTLC 1113**

Creatures

BOOMERANG.
Tracks: / Standing there / You / Killing time / Pluto drive / Fruitman / Venus sands / Manchild / Pity / Willow / Fury eyes / Strolling wolf / Morrina.
LP: **841 463 1**
MC: **841 463 4**

FEAST.
Tracks: / Morning dawning / Inoa'ole / Ice house / Dancing on glass / Gecko / Sky train / Festival of colours / Miss the girl / Strutting rooster, A / Flesh.
LP: . . . . **SHELP 1**
MC: . . . . **SHEMC 1**

Creatures the World...

CREATURES THE WORLD FORGOT/ WHEN DINOSAURS RULED (Film soundtracks) (Various artists).
LP: . . . . **LD 3**

Cree, Wounded John

WIVABANDON ONEZONE.
Tracks: / Side by side / Sensous man, The / His greatest hits / Bar wars / Incident at Hammersmith Palais.
LP: . . . . **NSPL 18598**
MC: . . . . **ZCP 18598**

Creed, Kyle

KYLE CREED WITH BOBBY PATTERSON & THE CAMP CREEK (Creed, Kyle/Bobby Patterson/Camp Creek Boys).
Tracks: / Dance all night / Roustabout / Red wing / Old country church / John Hardy / Weeping willow / Pig in the pen / Cacklin' hen, The / Lost indian / Sunny side of the mountain / Sweet sunny South / Coleman ridge / Backstep / Soldier's joy / I don't love nobody.
LP: . . . . **LED 2053**

Creedence Clearwater

BAYOU COUNTRY.
Tracks: / Born on the bayou / Bootleg / Graveyard train / Good golly Miss Molly / Penthouse pauper / Proud Mary / Keep on chooglin'.
LP: . . . . **FASLP 5003**
MC: . . . . **FASK 5003**
MC: . . . . **FACC 502**
LP: . . . . **FACE 502**
LP: . . . . **LBS 83261**

BEST OF CREEDENCE CLEARWATER REVIVAL VOL.2.
Tracks: / Hey tonight / Run through the jungle / Fortunate son / Bootleg / Lookin' out my back door / Molina / Who'll stop the rain / Sweet hitchhiker / Good golly Miss Molly / Don't look now / I put a spell on you / Porterville / Up around the bend / Lodi.
LP: . . . . **FACE 510**
MC: . . . . **FACC 510**

BEST OF CREEDENCE CLEARWATER REVIVAL VOL.1.
Tracks: / Proud Mary / Down on the corner / Bad moon rising / Green river / Long as I can see the light / Travellin' band / Midnight special, The / Have you ever seen the rain / Born on the Bayou / Susie Q.
LP: . . . . **FACE 509**
MC: . . . . **FACC 509**
LP: . . . . **FAX 509**

CHRONICLE (20 Greatest hits).
Tracks: / Susie Q / I put a spell on you / Proud Mary / Bad moon rising / Lodi / Green river / Commotion / Down on the corner / Fortunate son / Travellin' band / Who'll stop the rain / Up around the bend / Run through the jungle / Lookin' out my back door / Long as I can see the light / I heard it through the grapevine / Have you ever seen the rain / Hey tonight / Sweet hitchhiker / Some day never comes.
2LP: **1081115**
MCSET: **1681115**

CONCERT, THE.
Tracks: / Born on the bayou / Green river / Tombstone shadow / Don't look now / Travellin' band / Who'll stop the rain / Bad moon rising / Proud Mary / Fortunate son / Commotion / Midnight special, The / Night time (is the right time) / Down on the corner / Keep on chooglin'.
LP: . . . . **FACE 511**
MC: . . . . **FACC 511**
LP: . . . . **MPF 4501**
MC: . . . . **MPF 54501**

COSMO'S FACTORY.
Tracks: / Ramble tamble / Before you accuse me / Lookin' out my back door / Run through the jungle / Up around the bend / My baby left me / Who'll stop the rain / I heard it through the grapevine / Long as I can see the light / Travellin' band / Ooby dooby.
LP: . . . . **FASLP 5006**
MC: . . . . **FASK 5006**
LP: **5C 062 91666**
LP: . . . . **FACE 505**
MC: . . . . **FACC 505**
LP: . . . . **LBS 83388**

CREEDENCE CLEARWATER REVIVAL.
Tracks: / I put a spell on you / Working man / Suzie Q / Ninety-nine-and-a-half (won't do) / Get down, woman / Porterville / Gloomy / Walk on the water.
LP: . . . . **FASLP 5002**
MC: . . . . **FASK 5002**
MC: . . . . **FACC 501**
LP: . . . . **FACE 501**

CREEDENCE CLEARWATER REVIVAL HITS ALBUM.
Tracks: / Bad moon rising / Travellin' band / Up around the bend / Long as I can see the light / Who'll stop the rain? / Lodi / Commotion / Fortunate son / Born on the corner / Green river / Have you ever seen the rain? / Sweet hitchhiker / Lookin' out my back door / Hey tonight / I heard it through the grapevine / Good golly Miss Molly / Suzie Q.
LP: . . . . **MPF 4500**
MC: . . . . **MPF 54500**

CREEDENCE COLLECTION, THE.
Tracks: / Suzie Q / I put a spell on you / Proud Mary / Born on the bayou / Bootleg / Good golly Miss Molly / Keep on chooglin' / Bad moon rising / Lady / Green river / Commotion / Cottonfields / Down on the corner / Fortunate son / Travellin' band / Who'll stop the rain? / Up around the bend / Run through the jungle / Lookin' out my back door / Long as I can see the light / I heard it through the grapevine / Have you ever seen the rain? / Hey tonight / Sweet hitchhiker.
2LP: . . . . **IMDP 3**
MC: . . . . **IMDK 3**

GOLD.
LP: **1A 022 58089**

GREATEST HITS: CREEDENCE CLEARWATER REVIVAL.
Tracks: / Bad moon rising / Travelin' band / Up around the bend / Long as I can see the light / Who'll stop the rain / Lodi / Commotion / Fortunate son / Run through the jungle / I put a spell on you / Proud Mary / Down on the corner / Green river / Have you ever seen the rain / Sweet hitch-hiker / Lookin' out my back door / Hey tonight / I heard it through the grapevine / Someday never comes / Susie Q.
LP: . . . . **FT 558**

GREEN RIVER.
Tracks: / Bad moon rising / Cross-tie walker / Sinister purpose / Night time is the right time / Green River / Commotion / Tombstone Shadow / Wrote a song for everyone / Lodi.
LP: . . . . **FASLP 5004**
MC: . . . . **FASK 5004**
LP: . . . . **LBS 83273**
MC: . . . . **FACC 503**
LP: . . . . **FACE 503**

LIVE IN EUROPE.
Tracks: / Born on the bayou / It came out of the sky / Fortunate son / Lodi / Proud Mary / Hey tonight / Green River / Suzie Q / Travelin' band / Commotion / Bad moon rising / Up around the bend / Keep on chooglin'.
LP: . . . . **FACE 514**
MC: . . . . **FACC 514**

MARDI GRAS.
Tracks: / Looking for a reason / Take it like a friend / Need someone to hold / Tearin' up the country / Some day never comes / What are you gonna do? / Sail away / Hello Mary Lou / Door to door / Sweet hitchhiker.
LP: . . . . **FASLP 5008**
MC: . . . . **FASK 5008**
LP: . . . . **FACE 513**
MC: . . . . **FACC 513**

MUSIC FOR THE MILLIONS.
Tracks: / Proud Mary / Down on the corner / Bad moon rising / I heard it through the grapevine / Midnight special / Have you ever seen the rain? / Born on the bayou / Suzie Q.
LP: **817870 1**
MC: **817870 4**

PENDULUM.
Tracks: / Pagan baby / I wish I could hide away / It's just a thought / Rude awakening number two / Sailor's lament / Chameleon / Born to move / Hey tonight / Molina / Have you ever seen the rain?.
LP: . . . . **FASLP 5007**
MC: . . . . **FASK 5007**
LP: . . . . **LBG 83400**
LP: . . . . **FACE 512**
MC: . . . . **FACC 512**

ROYAL ALBERT HALL CONCERT, THE (See under Concert, The).

SINGLES 1968-72.
Tracks: / Suzie Q / I put a spell on you / Proud Mary / Bad moon rising / Green river / Down on the corner / Who'll stop the rain? / Up around the bend / Long as I can see the light / Have you ever seen the rain? / Sweet hitchhiker / Some day never comes.
LP: **5C 038 62427**

WILLY AND THE POORBOYS.
Tracks: / Down on the corner / It came out of the sky / Cottonfields / Poor boy shuffle / Feeling blue / Fortunate son / Don't look now / Midnight special, The / Side of the road / Effigy.
LP: . . . . **FACE 504**
MC: . . . . **FACC 504**
LP: . . . . **FASLP 5005**
MC: . . . . **FASK 5005**
LP: . . . . **LBS 83338**

Creek

CREEK.
Tracks: / Love found me / Reach and touch / Arthur Whiteside / You don't owe me / Institute of rock 'n' roll / Six days to Sunday / Dialling numbers / Love will stay / Just another fool / Lead me down that road.
LP: . . . . **MFN 67**

STORM THE GATE.
Tracks: / Storm the gate / Foxy / I love / Passion / Fountain of youth / On my way / Rock me tonight / Girl is crying / Hanky panky / Climb, The / Bad light.
MC: . . . . **UNKNOWN**
LP: . . . . **MFN 102**

Creekmore, Tom

SHE IS IT.
LP: . . . . **DS 791**

Creepers (film)

CREEPERS (1985 film soundtrack) (Various artists).
Tracks: / Phenomena: *Simonetti, Claudio* / Flash of the blade: *Iron Maiden* / Jennifer: *Goblin* / Wind, The: *Goblin* / Transmute: *Goblin* / Sleepwalking: *Goblin* / Jennifer's friend: *Goblin* / Quick and the dead, The: *Various artists* / Valley: *Various artists* / Locomotive: *Motorhead* / Maggots, The: *Boswell, Simon*.
LP: . . . . **HMILP 47**

MISERABLE SINNERS.
LP: . . . . **IT 039**
MC: . . . . **IT 039C**

ROCK 'N' ROLL LICORICE FLAVOUR.
LP: . . . . **REDLP 082**
MC: . . . . **REDC 082**

Creeping Disaster

COUNTDOWN.
LP: **086122**

Creeps

BLUE TOMATO.
LP: 2292462461
MC: 2292462464

ENJOY THE CREEPS.
LP: . . . . NIXON 2

NOW DIG THIS.
LP: . . . . KENNEDY 3

Creepshow

13 BAD VIBRATIONS.
LP: . . . . PUT 1

Creepshow (Film)

CREEPSHOW (1982 film soundtrack) (Various artists).
LP: . . . . STV 81160

Cregagh Presbyterian

WORLD'S 100 BEST LOVED HYMNS VOL.1.
Tracks: / Praise my soul the King of Heaven / Lord's my shepherd, The / In Heavenly love abiding / Rock of ages cleft for me / Be thou my vision / How great thou art / Jesu, lover of my soul / Guide me o thou great Jehovah / O for a closer walk with God / I need thee every hour / What a friend we have in Jesus / When I survey the wondrous cross / O love that wilt not let me go / Abide with me.
LP: . . . . GES 1088
MC: . . . . KGEC 1088

Creganna

RAMBLING OF SPRING.
MC: . . . . GTDC 57

Crelier, Louis

33 DETOURS.
LP: . . . . JUNGLE 70061

Crenshaw, Marshall

DOWNTOWN.
Tracks: / Little wild one / Yvonne / Blues is king / Terrifying love / Like a vague memory / Distance between / We're gonna shake up their minds / I'm sorry / Lesson number one.
LP: 925319 1
MC: 925319 4

FIELD DAY.
Tracks: / Whenever you're on my mind / Our town / One more reason / Try / One day with you / For her love / Monday morning rock / All I know right now / What time is it? / Hold it.
LP: 923873 1
MC: 923873 4

LIFE'S TOO SHORT.
LP: . . . . MCA 10223
MC: . . . . MCAC 10223

MARSHALL CRENSHAW.
Tracks: / There she goes again / Someday, someway / Girls / I'll do anything / Rockin' round in New York City / Usual thing, The / She can't dance / Cynical girl / Mary Anne / Soldier of love / Not for me / Brand new lover.
LP: . . . . K 57010

MARY JEAN AND 9 OTHERS.
Tracks: / This is easy / Hundred dollars, A / Calling out for love (at crying time) / Wild abandon / This street / Somebody crying / Mary Jean / Steel strings / Till that moment / They never will know.
LP: 925583 1
MC: 925583 4

Crentsil, A.B.

HIGH LIFE IN CANADA.
LP: . . . . RAP 002

TANTE ALABA.
LP: . . . . ERT 1005

TORONTO BY NIGHT.
LP: . . . . WAZ 101

Creole Jazzband

DELVING BACK TO HUMPH.
LP: . . . . SOS 1051

Creque, Neal

BLACK VELVET ROSE.
Tracks: / Rafiki / Years of regret / Sis daisy / Nina / Whatcha call it / Black velvet rose / Cease the bombing / Before the rain came.
LP: . . . . MR 5226

Cresick, Paul

ADVENTURES OF ROBIN HOOD, THE (Quayle, Anthony (nar)).
MC: 109

HOW ROBIN BECAME AN OUTLAW (Quayle, Anthony (nar)).
MC: 1369

OUTLAW BAND OF SHERWOOD FOREST, THE (Quayle, Anthony (nar)).
MC: 1370

ROBIN AND HIS MERRY MEN (Quayle, Anthony (nar)).
MC: 1372

ROBIN'S ADVENTURES WITH LITTLE JOHN (Quayle, Anthony (nar)).
MC: 1371

Cresswell, Helen

ELLIE AND THE HAGWITCH.
MCSET: 086 222 043-1

LIZZIE DRIPPING (Heath, Tina).
MCSET: CC/044

Crest Of The Wave

CREST OF THE WAVE (see under Novello, Ivor) (Various artists).

Crests

16 FABULOUS HITS.
LP: . . . . COED 904

BEST OF THE CRESTS, THE (Crests featuring Johnny Maestro).
Tracks: / Sixteen candles / Step by step / Trouble in Paradise / Angels listened in, The / Pretty little angel / Model girl / Six nights a week / I thank the moon / Journey of love / It must be love / Mr. Happiness / What a surprise / Gee (but I'd give the world) / Flower of love / Isn't it amazing / Year ago tonight, A / Young love / I'll remember in the still of the night.
LP: . . . . CHD 297

CRESTS SING ALL BIGGIES.
LP: . . . . COED 901

Cretu, Michael

INVISIBLE MAN, THE.
LP: . . . . V 2354
MC: . . . . TCV 2354

Crew

DOIN' OVERTIME.
LP: . . . . STING 006

NO PEACE OF MIND.
LP: . . . . STING 010

Crew Cuts

CREW CUTS (Various artists).
LP: . . . . IMA 11
MC: . . . . IMC 11

CREW CUTS- LESSON 2 (Various artists).
LP: . . . . IMA 14
MC: . . . . IMC 14

Crew Cuts (Group)

ROCK 'N' ROLL BASH.
Tracks: / Party night / Music drives me crazy / Crazy 'bout you baby / Don't be angry / Honey hair, sugar lips, eyes of blue / Ring a rosie rock / Two hearts, two kisses / Gum drop / Suzie Q / Slam bam / Sh'boom / Kokomo / Story untold, A / Oop shoop / Tell me why / Earth angel.
LP: . . . . BFX 15206

THEIR TOP HITS.
LP: . . . . UNKNOWN

Crews, Harry

NAKED IN GARDEN HILLS.
Tracks: / About the author / Distopia / Gospel singer, The / (She's in a) bad mood / Bring me down / S.O.S. / Man hates a man / You're it / Knockout artist / Way out, The / Car / Orphans.
LP: . . . . ABB 21

Cribbins, Bernard

ARABEL'S RAVEN.
LP: . . . . REC 292

CASTLE OF ADVENTURE, THE (see under Blyton, Enid (aut)).

DANGEROUS DAVIES THE LAST DETECTIVE (See also Leslie Thomas (auth)).

GIGGLING GERTIE.
MC: . . . . TC OU 2234

MANY PADDINGTON RECORDINGS (see under Paddington Bear).

MR. SHIFTER & THE REMOVAL MEN (Cribbins, Bernard/John Junkin).
LP: . . . . CES 1012

PINOCCHIO (see under Pinocchio (bk)).

SNOWMAN, THE (see under Film Soundtrack & Story).

WOMBLE STORIES.
LP: . . . . REC 253

Cricket

ANOTHER BLOODY TOUR (See under Another Bloody Tour).

BRADMAN - THE DON DECLARES (see under Bradman, Don) (Bradman, Donald).

CRICKET - THE GOLDEN AGE (Various artists).
MCSET: . . . . ZBBC 1027

GREAT CRICKET MATCHES (Commentaries and Interviews) (Various artists).
Tracks: / England V Australia 1948: *Various artists* / England V West Indies 1950: *Various artists* / England V Australia 1953: *Various artists* / England V Australia 1956: *Various artists* / England V West Indies 1957: *Various artists* / England V West Indies 1963: *Various artists* / England V Australia 1968: *Various artists* / Australia V West Indies 1975: *Various artists.*
MCSET: . . . . ZBBC 1181

VOICE OF CRICKET, THE (See under Voice of Cricket) (Arlott, John (nar)).

Cricket, Jimminy

WHEN YOU WISH UPON A STAR (See under Jimminy Cricket).

Crickets

COMPLETE CRICKETS.
Tracks: / After it's over / Smooth guy / More than I can say / Baby my heart / So you're in love / Someone, someone / Great balls of fire / Sweet love / Time will tell / Just this once / I fought the law / When you ask about love / Doncha know / Peggy Sue got married / Rockin' pneumonia / Deborah / Ting a ling / Love's made a fool of you / Why did you leave me?.
LP: . . . . CR 30226

CRICKETS FILE 1961 - 1965.
Tracks: / He's old enough to know better / I'm feeling better / I'm not a bad guy / Parisian girl / My little girl / Don't try to change me / Lost and alone / April Avenue / Don't say you love me / You can't be in between / Right or wrong / Money / Fool never learns, A / From me to you / California sun / All over you / I pledge my love to you / Now hear this / We gotta get together / Everybody's got a little problem.
LP: . . . . SEE 79

IN STYLE WITH THE CRICKETS.
LP: . . . . LVA 9142

ROCK 'N' ROLL MASTERS (Best of The Crickets).
Tracks: / My little girl / Teardrops fall like rain / Lost and alone / Little Hollywood girl / What'd I say / Right or wrong / Blue Monday / La bamba / Lonely Avenue / Don't ever change / Willie and the hand jive / I think I've caught the blues / Summertime blues / Love is strange / I'm not a bad guy / Now hear this / Thoughtless (CD only.) / Slippin' and slidin' (CD only.) / Someday (CD only.) / I believe in you (CD only.).
LP: . . . . EMS 1318
LP: 791 757 1
MC: . . . . TCEMS 1318
MC: 791 757 4

SOMETHING OLD, SOMETHING NEW.
LP: . . . . PM 1550781

THREE PIECE.
LP: . . . . ROLL 2014

T-SHIRT (ALBUM).
Tracks: / Your m-m-memory is t-t-torturing me / Rockin' socks / Weekend, The / Holly would / T-Shirt / Forever in mind / Cruise in it / Tree piece / Don't tell me that you can't come out tonight / That's all she wrote.
LP: 4628761
MC: 4628764

Crikey Its The

SNOTTY NOSED PIG.
LP: . . . . CROMP 001

Crime & the City

BRIDE SHIP, THE.
Tracks: / Shadow of no man / Stone / Keepsake / Free world / Greater head, The / Dangling man, The / Bride ship, The / New world.
LP: . . . . STUMM 65
MC: . . . . CSTUMM 65

JUST SOUTH OF HEAVEN.
LP: . . . . STUMM 22

PARADISE DISCOTHEQUE.
LP: . . . . STUMM 78
MC: . . . . CSTUMM 78

ROOM OF LIGHTS.
LP: . . . . STUMM 36

SHINE.
Tracks: / All must be love / Fray so slow / Angel / On every train (grain will bear grain) / Hunter / Steal to the sea / Home is far from here / On every train (grain will bear grain)(12") / All must be love (early version).
LP: . . . . STUMM 59

Crimeless Criminals

SOUL INSPIRING.
MC: . . . . PCN 114

Crimes of Passion

CRIMES OF PASSION (See under Wakeman, Rick) (Wakeman, Rick).

Crimes of the...

CRIMES OF THE HEART (1987 film soundtrack) (Various artists).
Tracks: / Crimes of the heart: Introduction: *Various artists* / Crimes of the heart: *Various artists* / Meg: *Various artists* / Ice cream: *Various artists* / Doc Porter: *Various artists* / Babe: *Various artists* / Night to day: *Various artists* / Broom chase: *Various artists* / Lonely hearts club: *Various artists* / Meg and Babe: *Various artists* / Study: *Various artists* / Flirtation: *Various artists* / Wily Jay: *Various* artists / Toes: *Various artists* / Bus ride: *Various artists* / Old Grandaddy: *Various artists* / Sunset: *Various artists* / Crimes of the heart:main theme: *Various artists* / Wily Jay away: *Various artists*/ Dusk for night: *Various artists* / Crimes: *Various artists* / Crimes of the heart:End title: *Various artists.*
MC: . . . . CTV 81298
LP: . . . . TER 1130

Criminal Element

LOCKED UP.
Tracks: / When the funk hits the fan / Here we go again / Feels so good / How low can you go? / Do you like it? / House time, anytime / Hit me with the beat / Put the needle to the record / Get funky / Give me the music / Got something to tell ya.
LP: 4569191
MC: 4569194

Criminal Law (film)

CRIMINAL LAW (1988 film soundtrack) (Various artists).
LP: . . . . VS 5210
MC: . . . . VSC 5210

Criminals

CRIMINALS.
LP: . . . . FC 008

Crimson Glory

CRIMSON GLORY.
LP: . . . . RR 9655
MC: . . . . RR 96554

STRANGE AND BEAUTIFUL.
LP: . . . . RR 93011
MC: . . . . RR 93014

TRANSCENDENCE.
LP: . . . . RR 9508 1
MC: . . . . RR 9508 4

Crimson Tide

CRIMSON TIDE.
Tracks: / Long goodbye / Love stop / You're the answer / Funky side of town / Music / Set myself free / Burned and branded / Southern boogie / Turning back / Blue reeds.
LP: . . . . EST 11806

RECKLESS LOVE.
Tracks: / Reckless love / Trick rider / Wayward lover / I want you to see / Piece of the rock / Taxi girls / Jessie / One from the heartland.
LP: . . . . EST 11939

Criner, Clyde

BEHIND THE SUN.
Tracks: / Song to tell a tale to sing, A / Just might be that way / Arco iris / Spider / Black Manhattan / Morning until night / Kinesis / Behind the sun.
LP: . . . . PL 83029
MC: . . . . PK 83029

COLOUR OF DARK, THE.
Tracks: / Celebration / Divine providence / Colors / Man from two planets, The / Anima de novo / Tarot / Llaquic llaguic (sad sad) / Blue rose / Zenith cycle, The / Coincidence / Llaquic, llaquic (sad sad) part 2 / Colour of dark, The.
LP: . . . . PL 83066
MC: . . . . PK 83066

Crippled Pilgrims

UNDERWATER.
LP: . . . . FOY 014

Cripps, Geoff

ICARUS (Cripps, Geoff/Louisa Rugg).
LP: . . . . SPR 1003

Crishan, Horea

PAN FLUTE MAGIC VOLUME 2.
Tracks: / Eurydike / Cent mille chansons / Le tango du pan / Calgary / Jenseits von Eden / Palermo / El bandalero / Teresa / Syrinx / Indian Summer / Erinnerung / Memory / Air on a heart string.
LP: 8216981
MC: 8216984

Crisis

ARMED TO THE TEETH.
LP: . . . . BULP 4

Crisis Party

RUDE AWAKENING.
LP: . . . . EM 94421

Crisp, John

WEEKEND IN EAST ANGLIA, THE.
LP: . . . . **FARML 103**

Crisp, Quentin

AN EVENING WITH QUENTIN CRISP.
2LP: **S2L 5188**
MC: **S2LC 5188**
2LP: . . . . **DRED 2**

Crispell, Marilyn

AND YOUR IVORY VOICE SINGS (Crispell, Marilyn and Doug James).
LP: . . . . **LR 126**

GAIA (Crispell, Marilyn/Reggie Workman/Doug James).
LP: . . . . **LR 152**

QUARTET IMPROVISATIONS.
LP: . . . . **LR 144**

RHYTHMS HUNG IN UNDRAWN SKY.
LP: . . . . **LR 118**

Crispy Ambulance

BLUE AND YELLOW OF THE YACHT CLUB.
MC: . . . . **CSBT 7**

LIVE: CRISPY AMBULANCE.
LP: . . . . **LTMVX**

OPEN GATES OF FIRE.
MC: . . . . **CSBT 8**

Crispy & Co.

CRISPY & CO..
LP: . . . . **CRLP 505**

Criss, Peter

KISS.
LP: . . . . **NBLP 7122**

OUT OF CONTROL.
Tracks: / Out of control / Time after time / I'm without you / Standin' on the edge / Hittin' below the belt / I've got a secret / All I wanna do / I hate you / I should have known better.
LP: . . . . **NBLP 7231**

PETER CRISS SOLO ALBUM.
LP: **6399086**

Criss, Sonny

AT THE CROSSROADS.
LP: . . . . **FS 173**

CINCH, THE (Criss, Sonny & Buddy Rich Quintet).
LP: . . . . **SPJ 125**

CRISSCRAFT.
Tracks: / Isle of Celia, The / Blues in my heart / This is for Ben / All night long / Crisscraft.
LP: . . . . **MR 5068**

I'LL CATCH THE SUN.
Tracks: / Don't rain on my parade / I thought about you / Cry me a river / Blue sunset / California screamin' / I'll catch the sun.
LP: . . . . **PR 7628**
MC: . . . . **PRC 7628**

LIVE IN ITALY.
LP: . . . . **FS 310**

OUT OF NOWHERE.
Tracks: / All the things you are / Dreamer, The / El tiante / My ideal / Out of nowhere / Brother can you spare a dime / First one, The.
LP: . . . . **MR 5089**

SONNY CRISS IN PARIS (Mr Blues pour flirter).
LPS: . . . . **FSBOX 2**

Cristina

CRISTINA.
Tracks: / Jungle love / Don't be greedy / Mama mia / La poupee qui fait non / Temporarily yours / Blame it on disco.
LP: . . . . **ILPS 7004**

SLEEP IT OFF.
Tracks: / Don't mutilate my mink / Ticket to the tropics / She can't say that anymore / Quicksand lovers / Rage and fascination / Ballad of immoral earnings / What's a girl to do? / Lie of love, The / Blue money / He dines out on death.
LP: **814 980 1**
LP: . . . . **CODA 9**
MC: . . . . **COCA 9**

Critchinson, John

SUMMER AFTERNOON.
Tracks: / Summer afternoon / 5 for 3 / Doing it right / Another fine mess / Yet another yesterday / Love lies bleeding / Eype down / La pigalle.
LP: . . . . **CODA 1**

Critchlow, Slim

COWBOY SONGS.
LP: . . . . **ARHOOLIE 5007**

Critical Rhythm

IT COULD NOT HAPPEN.
LP: . . . . **NG 044**

Critics Choice

CRITICS CHOICE (Various artists).
LP: . . . . **YL 0108**

Critters

NEW YORK BOUND (Best of the Critters).
Tracks: / Younger girl / It just won't be that way / Gone for a while / Bad misunderstanding / Walk like a man again / Forever or no more / He'll make you cry / Children and flowers / Mr. Dieingly sad / New York bound / Don't let the rain fall down on me / Marrying kind of love / Dancing in the street / Little girl / Heart of love (head of stone) / Everything but time.
LP: . . . . **WIK 70**

Critton Hollow

BY AND BY.
LP: . . . . **FF 355**

Cro Mags

AGE OF QUARREL.
LP: . . . . **GWLP 9**
MC: . . . . **GWTC 9**
LP: . . . . **RR 9613**

BEST WISHES.
Tracks: / Death camps / Only one, The / Crush the demoniac / Then and now / Days of confusion / Down but not out / Fugitive / Age of quarrel.
LP: . . . . **FILER 274**
MC: . . . . **FILECT 274**

Croad, Terry Orchestra

JOHN WILLIAMS WORKS (Croad, Terry Grand Orchestra).
Tracks: / Superman / Close Encounters of the Third Kind suite / Jaws 2, Theme from / Star wars / Black Sunday, Theme from / Midway march / Fury, The (main title) / I want to spend my life with you / Earthquake - Main title / Eiger Sanction, Theme from / Cinderella Liberty, love theme.
LP: . . . . **SX 7006**

SCREEN REPORT (Croad, Terry Grand Orchestra).
Tracks: / Death on the Nile love theme / Don't ask to stay until tomorrow / Heaven can wait / Convoy / Love song / Superman / Nobody does it better / Goodbye girl / Olivers story love theme / How deep is your love / You light up my life.
LP: . . . . **SX 7011**

Croatia

MEMORIES OF CROATIA (Croatia : Croatian Folkel Re Group Koleda).
LP: . . . . **VP 453**

Croce, Jim

COLLECTION: JIM CROCE.
Tracks: / Time in a bottle / Operator (that's not the way it feels) / Salon Saloon / Alabama rain / Dreamin' again / It doesn't have to be this way / I'll have to say I love you in a song / Lover's cross / Thursday / These dreams / Long time ago, A / Photographs and memories.
2LP: . . . . **CCSLP 154**
MC: . . . . **CCSMC 154**

DOWN THE HIGHWAY.
Tracks: / I got a name / Mississippi lady / New York's not my home / Chain gang medley / Chain gang / He don't love you / Searchin' / You don't mess around with Jim / Ol' man river / Which way are you going / Bad, bad Leroy Brown / Walkin' back to Georgia / Box no.10 / Speedball Tucker / Alabama rain.
LP: . . . . **CLALP 118**
MC: . . . . **CLAMC 118**

FACES I'VE BEEN, THE.
Tracks: / This is your land / Greenback dollar / Pig's song / Gunga din / Sun come up / Big fat woman / Charlie Green play that slide trombone / Railroads and riverboats / Railroad song / Way we used to, The / Maybe tommorow / Stone walls / I remember Mary / Country girl / Which way are you going / King's song / Mississippi lady / Chain gang medley / Ol' man river / Carmella / South Philly / Cars and dates / Chrome and clubs / Chinese, The / Trucks and ups / Army, The / Give me moonlight / It's my mother's birthday today.
2LP: . . . . **LSDP 900**

FINAL TOUR, THE.
Tracks: / Operator (that's not the way it feels) / Roller derby queen dialogue / Roller derby queen / Next time,this time / Trucker dialogue / Speedball trucker / New York's not my home / Hard time losin' man / Ball of Kerrymuir dialogue / Ball of Kerrymuir / You don't mess around with Jim / It doesn't have to be that way / Careful man dialogue / Careful man / Shopping for clothes / These dreams.
LP: . . . . **ESSLP 020**
MC: . . . . **ESSMC 020**

FIRST ALBUM (Croce, Jim & Ingrid).
LP: **5C 038 82022**

GREATEST HITS: JIM CROCE.
LP: **39010**
MC: **69010**

GREATEST HITS: JIM CROCE (PLATINUM).
LP: . . . . **PLP 42**
MC: . . . . **PMC 42**

HIS GREATEST HITS.
LP: . . . . **LSLP 5000**

PHOTOGRAPHS AND MEMORIES (His greatest hits).
Tracks: / Bad bad Leroy Brown / Operator (that's not the way it feels) / Photographs and memories / Rapid Roy (The stock car boy) / Time in a bottle / New York's not my home / Workin' at the car wash blues / I got a name / I'll have to say I love you in a song / You don't mess around with Jim / Lover's cross / One less set of footsteps / These dreams / Roller Derby Queen.
LP: . . . . **CLALP 119**
MC: . . . . **CLAMC 119**

SONGBOOK.
2LP: **80044**
MCSET: **85044**

TIME IN A BOTTLE.
Tracks: / Time in a bottle / Operator (that's not the way it feels) / Salon and saloon / Alabama rain / Dreamin' again / It doesn't have to be this way / I'll have to say I love you in a song / Lovers cross / Thursday / These dreams / Long time ago, A / Photographs and memories.
LP: . . . . **CLALP 117**
MC: . . . . **CLAMC 117**

Crocker, Barry

NEIGHBOURS THEME (See under Neighbours (TV)).

Crocker, John

EASY LIVING (Crocker, John Quartet).
Tracks: / Avalon / I can't get started / Lady be good / Shine / Fine time / I hadn't anyone till you / Have you met Miss Jones / Easy living / Rose room / After you've gone.
LP: . . . . **JCJ 001**

FINE AND DANDY (Crocker, John Quartet).
LP: . . . . **JJ 1**

Crockett, David

STOVEPIPE NO. 1 1924-30.
LP: . . . . **BD 2019**

Crocodile Dundee

CROCODILE DUNDEE (1986 film soundtrack) (Various artists).
Tracks: / Mick and his mate: *Various artists* / Cyril: *Various artists* / Walkabout bounce, The: *Various* artists / Goodnight Walter: *Various artists* / In the truck: *Various artists* / Buffalo, The: *Various* artists / In the boat: *Various artists* / Never never land: *Various artists* / Death roll, The: *Various* artists / Sunset: *Various artists* / Nice one Skippy: *Various artists* / Walk in the bush: *Various artists*/ Would you mind?: *Various artists* / Mick meets New York: *Various artists* / G'day: *Various artists*/ Yessir: *Various artists* / Mad, bad and dangerous: *Various artists* / Pimp, The: *Various artists* / Stone the crows: *Various artists* / That's not a knife: *Various artists* / Oh Richard: *Various artists*/ Pimp returns, The: *Various artists* / Crocodile Dundee, Theme from: *Various artists.*
LP: . . . . **FILM 009**
MC: . . . . **FILMC 009**

Crocodile Tears

CROCODILE TEARS.
LP: . . . . **DOD G1**

Crocodiles

NEW WAVE GOODBYE.
LP: . . . . **AUL 716**

Croker, Brendan

BOAT TRIPS IN THE BAY (Croker, Brendan & The 5 O'Clock Shadows).
LP: . . . . **REDLP 077**
MC: . . . . **REDC 077**
LP: . . . . **ORELP 510**
MC: . . . . **OREC 510**

BRENDAN CROKER & THE 5 O'CLOCK SHADOWS (Croker, Brendan & The 5 O'Clock Shadows).
Tracks: / No money at all / Shine on / Wrong decision / All mixed up / My government / Just an old waltz / You don't need me here / This man / That's why I'm leaving here / This kind of life / Ain't gonna smile / Mister.
LP: . . . . **ORELP 505**
MC: . . . . **OREC 505**

CLOSE SHAVE, A (Croker, Brendan & The 5 O'Clock Shadows).
LP: . . . . **BRAVE 1**
MC: . . . . **BRAVE 1C**

GREAT INDOORS.
LP: . . . . **ORELP 517**
MC: . . . . **OREC 517**

Crombie, Tony

ATMOSPHERE (Crombie, Tony and his Rockets).
Tracks: / Beryl's bounce / Ninth man / St James Infirmary / Invitation / Stompin' at the Savoy / Duke's joke / Panic stations / I'll close my eyes / Small talk / Perpetual lover / Shapes / Copy cats.
LP: . . . . **REN 002**
MC: . . . . **ZCREN 002**

RELAUNCH (Crombie, Tony and his Rockets).
Tracks: / We're gonna rock tonight / Big beat, The / Rock, rock, rock / Let's you and I rock / Sham rock / Brighton rock / London rocker / Teach you to rock / Short'nin' bread rock / Rock shuffle boogie / Forgive me, baby / Dumplin's / Town special / Ungang / Pickukauugong / Rock cha cha / Lonesome train (on a lonesome track) / Red for danger / Sticks and stones / Stop it (I like it) / Rock 'n' roller coaster / Rex rocks.
LP: . . . . **CM 115**

SWEET, WILD AND BLUE.
Tracks: / Cocktails for two / Wrap your troubles in dreams / So near, so far / I've got the world on a string / Embraceable you / Tulip or turnip / To each his own / Love is the tender trap / Hold my hand / All the way / It's magic / High and mighty / So rare / Percussion staccato / I should care / For you alone / Summertime / You are my lucky star.
LP: . . . . **REN 003**

TONY CROMBIE AND FRIENDS.
Tracks: / Tango '89 / Sophisticated lady / Moonglow / 12 note samba / Raising the temperature / Fallen bird / I don't stand a ghost of a chance with you / Serenade in blue / Allson adamant / Autumn rustle / Prelude to a kiss / So near, so far / Rabbit pie / Child of fancy / Raising the temperature / Viva Rodriguez.
LP: . . . . **REN 001**
MC: . . . . **ZCREN 001**

Cromlech

GWILTH Y BORE.
LP: . . . . **SAIN 1169**

IGAM OGAM.
LP: . . . . **SAIN 1243**

Crompton, Barry

HARBINGER.
LP: . . . . **DOVE 57**

Crompton, Richmal

JUST WILLIAM STORIES (Williams, Kenneth (nar)).
MCSET: **0600560880**
MCSET: . . . . **SAY 4**
MCSET: . . . . **ARGO 1010**

MORE WILLIAM STORIES (Williams, Kenneth (nar)).
MCSET: . . . . **SAY 84**
MCSET: . . . . **ARGO 1259**

Cromwell (film)

CROMWELL (Dialogue And Music From Soundtrack) (Various artists).
Tracks: / Main title - Why are you leaving England ?: *Various artists* / This is the common land: *Various artists*/ Declare war on my own people: *Various artists* / Parliament...is not a gathering of lackeys...: *Various artists*/ My Lord Strafford, you will rid us of ...: *Various artists* / Warrant upon a charge of high treason: *Various artists*/ Institution known as democracy, An: *Various artists* / This nation is now in a state of civil war: *Various artists*/ Battle at Edgehill: *Various artists* / New army: *Various artists* / Of God, we have him: *Various artists*/ Battle at Naseby: *Various artists* / King Charles is arrested: *Various artists* / Army will not stand down: *Various* artists / England without a king is unthinkable, An: *Various artists* / I will have this king's head, aye...: *Various* artists / I am no ordinary prisoner, sir: *Various artists* / Warrant for the death of a king: *Various artists*/ From a corruptible to an incorruptible crown: *Various artists* / I will see this nation properly governed: *Various artists* / Epilogue: *Various artists.*
LP: . . . . **EST 640**

Cronaca Familiare

CRONACA FAMILIARE/BANDITI A ORGOSOLO (Film soundtracks) (Various artists).
LP: . . . . **IM 015**

Cronin, A.J

SPANISH GARDENER, THE.
MC: . . . . **SOUND 32**

Cronshaw, Andrew

'A' IS FOR ANDREW - 'Z' IS FOR ZITHER.
LP: XTRA 1139

EARTHED IN CLOUD VALLEY.
Tracks: / Murdo Mackenzie of Torridon / Eleanor Plunkett / Prince William / Fanny Power / A stor, a stor, a ghra / Bell ringing, The / Elsie Marley / Go from my window / Green mossy bank, The / Christmas in the morning / Glen cottage / Dhu cottage / Midnight on the water / Pandeirada de entrimo / Somewhere to stay / Cutty Wren, The.
LP: LER 2104

GREAT DARK WATER, THE.
LP: WF 009

TILL THE BEASTS RETURNING.
LP: 12TS 447

WADE IN THE FLOOR.
LP: LTRA 508

Crook Brothers

OPRY OLD TIMERS (Crook Brothers with Sam & Kirk McGee).
LP: SLP 182
MC: GT 5182

Crooked Mile (show)

CROOKED MILE, THE (Original London cast) (Various artists).
LP: AEI 1115

Crooked Oak

FOOT O'WOR STAIRS, THE.
Tracks: / Bonnie Woodall / Band o'shearers / Lowlands of Holland, The / A U (me) / Hinny bird / Will Jobling.
LP: ERON 019 LP
MC: ERON 019 MC

Crookfinger Jack

BEGGAR BOY OF THE NORTH (see Stephens, Jack) (Crookfinger Jack/Jack Stephens).

Crooks

JUST RELEASED.
Tracks: / All the time in the world / Waiting for you / Let's get together / Sound of today / Hold me / 1,000 faces / Beat goes on / You don't have to tell me / I'm in love / Me & my friends / I don't love you / Understanding.
LP: BLUP 5002

Crooks, Richard

ALL OF MY HEART.
Tracks: / All of my heart / My song goes round the world / Ah' fuyez / Douce image / Mother o' mine / Thora / E Lucevan le stelle / Ah / Moon of my delight / Neapolitan love song (t'amo) / Il mio tesoro / Until una furtive lagrima / Little love, A / Little kiss, A (Un peu d'amour) / Preislied / Songs my mother taught me / Nirvana / O song divine.
LP: CHD 167
MC: MCHD 167

Cropdusters

60 MPH IN REVERSE (Live).
LP: DDTEP 003

IF THE SOBER GO TO HEAVEN.
LP: LINK LP 110

Cropper, Steve

JAMMED TOGETHER (Cropper, Steve/ Pop Staples / Albert King).
Tracks: / What'd I say? / Opus de soul / Big bird / Trashy dog / Water / Tupelo / Baby what you want me to do / Homer's theme / Don't turn your heater down / Knock on wood.
LP: SXE 028

WITH A LITTLE HELP FROM MY FRIENDS.
Tracks: / Drop dustin' / Land of a thousand dances / 99 1/2 (won't do) / Boogaloo down Broadway / Funky Broadway / With a little help from my friends / Oh pretty woman / I'd rather drink muddy water / Way I feel tonight, The / In the midnight hour / Rattlesnake.
LP: SXE 008
LP: SX 008

Crops

CROPS, THE.
LP: ATR 1103

Crosby, Bing

10TH ANNIVERSARY COLLECTION, THE.
LP: WW 1005
MC: WW 4 1005

16 GOLDEN CLASSICS.
Tracks: / As time goes by / Way we were, The / Hey Jude / Little green apples / Both sides now / It's all in the game / Those were the days / Carolina in the morning / Way down yonder in New Orleans / Georgia on my mind / Besame mucho / Spanish eyes / If you should ever need me / Swanee / Night is young and you're so beautiful, The / Breeze and I.
LP: UNLP 016
MC: UNMC 016

20 GOLDEN GREATS: BING CROSBY.
Tracks: / Swinging on a star / Gone fishin' / White Christmas / You are my sunshine / Moonlight bay / Pennies from Heaven / MacNamara's band.
LP: MCTV 3

20 GOLDEN GREATS: BING CROSBY (VOL.2).
MC: 42015

ADVENTURES OF TOM SAWYER (See under Adventures of... (Spoken Word)).

AL & BING (See under Jolson, Al).

ALL THE CLOUDS WILL ROLL AWAY (Crosby, Bing/Judy Garland/Andrews Sisters).
MC: JSP 702

ALL THE WAY.
Tracks: / What is there to say? / Ford gives more convertable value / Now if you want a wagon / All the way / Everybody's eyeing a Ford / You're ahead in a Ford / Forever and ever / Witchcraft / Catch a falling star / Gigi / Chances are.
LP: B&G 1

BEST OF BING.
Tracks: / Where the blue of the night / Swinging on a star / You are my sunshine / It's been a long long time / MacNamara's band / Sweet Leilani / I'm an old cowhand / Pennies from Heaven / White Christmas / Mexicali rose / Whiffenpoof song, The / I can't begin to tell you / Play a simple melody / Sam's song / Now is the hour / Dear hearts and gentle people / Galway Bay / In the cool cool cool of the evening / Too-ra-loo-ra-loo-ra.
LP: MCL 1607
MC: MCLC 1607
LP: MCF 2540

BEST OF BING CROSBY.
Tracks: / Where the blue of the night / Pennies from Heaven / Swinging on a star / MacNarmara's band / Don't fence me in / Whiffenpoof song, The / Sam's song / Dear hearts and gentle people / In the cool cool cool of the evening / Mr. Gallagher and Mr. Shean / Waiter, the porter and the upstairs maid, The / Accentuate the positive / In the good old summertime / When Irish eyes are smiling / Chattanooga shoeshine boy / Danny boy.
MC: TC MFP 5814
LP: MFP 5814

BING AND AL VOL.1 (Crosby, Bing & Al Jolson).
Tracks: / Running around in circles / What am I gonna do about you? / Let me sing and I'm happy / Rockabye your baby with a Dixie melody / Who paid the rent for Mrs Rip Van Winkle? / Back in your own back yard / You made me love you / Waiting for the Robert E. Lee / Anniversary song / There'll be a hot time in the old town tonight / Nobody / Oh Susannah / Goin' to heaven on a mule / Hear dem bells / In the evening by the moonlight / Beautiful dreamer / On the banks of the Wabash / My mammy / Alabamy bound.
LP: TOTEM 1003

BING AND AL VOL.2 (Crosby, Bing & Al Jolson).
Tracks: / I've got a lovely bunch of coconuts / Sorry / Swanee / When the red, red robin comes bob, bob, bobbin' along / I only have eyes for you / Waiting for the Robert E. Lee / I can dream, can't I / Dear hearts and gentle people / Bye bye baby / Is it true what they say about Dixie? / Carolina in the morning / My blue Heaven / Alabamy bound / One I love belongs to somebody else, The / All by myself.
LP: TOTEM 1007

BING AND AL VOL.3 (Crosby, Bing & Al Jolson).
Tracks: / New Ashmolean, The / Happy times / California, here I come / Yaaka hula hickey dula / Whispering / Bye, bye baby / Waiting for the Robert E. Lee / You're wonderful / I've got a lovely bunch of coconuts / Toot, toot, tootsie / Back in your own back yard / Baby face / That lucky old sun.
LP: TOTEM 1013

BING AND AL VOL.4 (Crosby, Bing & Al Jolson).
Tracks: / Pass that peace pipe / Kate / Ma blushin' Rosie / Sunbonnet Sue / Pretty girl is like a melody, A / Best things in life are free, The / Country style / Linda / Oh how I hate to get up in the morning / Lazy / All by myself / Alexander's ragtime band / Easter parade.
LP: TOTEM 1015

BING AND AL VOL.5 (Crosby, Bing & Al Jolson).
Tracks: / Horse told me, The / I hadn't anyone till you / Stay with the happy people / Give my regards to Broadway / Ma blushin' Rosie / Avalon / Lullaby of Broadway / My old Kentucky home / Rainy night in Rio, A / Anniversary song / April showers / Ma blushin' Rosie / Swanee / Philco singing commercial, The / One I love belongs to somebody else, The.
LP: TOTEM 1016

BING AND AL VOL.6 (Crosby, Bing & Al Jolson).
Tracks: / April showers / For me and my gal / Whiffenpoof song, The / George Gershwin medley / Toot, toot, tootsie / Malaguena / Waiting for the Robert E. Lee / Sleepy time gal / Carolina in the morning / But beautiful / Beautiful dreamer.
LP: TOTEM 1017

BING AND BOB HOPE (Crosby, Bing & Bob Hope).
Tracks: / Swinging on a star / Take it easy / One I love belongs to somebody else, The / Speak to me of love / It's love, love, love / Amor / Bless 'em all / Milkman, keep those bottles quiet / Day after forever, The / Together / Put it there, pal / I'll be seeing you.
LP: SPOKANE 22

BING AND CONNIE BOSWELL (Crosby, Bing & Connie Boswell).
Tracks: / Manhattan / You ain't kidding / Hut sut song, The / Everything happens to me / Number ten lullaby lane / Rose O'Day / Basin street blues / Look at me now / Yes, indeed! / East Street / Between 18th and 19th on Chestnut Street.
LP: SPOKANE 18

BING AND DINAH SHORE (Crosby, Bing & Dinah Shore).
Tracks: / My old Kentucky home / Bing and Dinah medley 1 / Tipperary / It ain't necessarily so / Bing and Dinah medley 2 / Easter parade / Summertime / Over there / Mr. Crosby and Mr. Carpenter / Basin street blues / Mr. C and Miss Dinah / How deep is the ocean / San Antonio rose / Bing, Dinah and Ukie medley / Bing and Dinah medley 3 / Oh what a beautiful morning.
LP: SPOKANE 31

BING AND THE MUSIC MAIDS.
Tracks: / I've got a lot of dreaming to do / Honolulu / In a bungalow where the red roses grow / You're the only star in my blue heaven / Stop It's wonderful / El Rancho Grande / Scatterbrain / You're a lucky guy / Looking at the world through rose coloured glasses / Holy smoke can't you take a joke / Little red fox, The / Confucius say / Sunday / Sweet potato piper / I've got my eyes on you / Woodpecker song, The / Ma, he's making eyes at me / Down by the O-H-I-O / If I had my way / Friendly tavern, The.
LP: SPOKANE 21

BING AND TRUDY ON THE AIR (Crosby, Bing & Trudy Erwin).
Tracks: / Constantly / Hit the road to dreamland / My heart stood still / You'll never know / You took advantage of me / Wait for me Mary / People will say we're in love / Right kind of love, The / One alone / Stormy weather / My ideal / My shining hour / Oh what a beautiful morning / Way you look tonight.
LP: SPOKANE 23

BING, BOB AND JUDY (Crosby, Bing, Bob Hope & Judy Garland).
Tracks: / Sam's song / Get happy / I cross my fingers / Mona Lisa / Goodnight Irene / Tzena, Tzena, Tzena / All my love / Friendly star / Third man, Theme from / High on the list.
LP: TOTEM 1009

BING CROSBY.
LP: ENT LP 13021
MC: ENT MC 13021
LP: SM 4011
MC: 495040

BING CROSBY AND FRIENDS VOL.1.
Tracks: / Dearie / Lazybones / Wedding samba, The / Lonesome in the saddle / Just the way you are / Yes sir that's my baby / Yakka hula hicky dula / Enjoy yourself / Have I told you lately that I love you / Play a simple melody / Let's take an old fashioned walk / Blueberry Hill / To prove that I'm in love.
LP: AWE 3
MC: CAWE 3

BING CROSBY AND FRIENDS VOL.2.
LP: AWE 10
MC: CAWE 10

BING CROSBY CHRISTMAS COLLECTION (Bing's Christmas Greats).
Tracks: / White Christmas / Silent night / Adeste fideles / Christmas song, The / Too-ra-loo-ra-loo-ra / Silver bells / God rest ye merry gentlemen / Rudolph the red nosed reindeer / MacNamara's band / Baby, it's cold outside / Hark the herald angels sing.
LP: DVLP 2078
MC: DVMC 2078

BING CROSBY COLLECTION (20 Golden Greats).
Tracks: / White Christmas / Silent night / Adeste fideles / Christmas song, The / Rudolph the red nosed reindeer / Silver bells / MacNamara's band / Sweet Leilani / Don't fence me in / Swinging on a star / Thousand violins, A / You are my sunshine / Mexicali rose / I'm an old cowhand / Pennies from Heaven / Too-ra-loo-ra-loo-ra / Galway Bay / Now is the hour / You must have been a beautiful baby.
LP: DVLP 2027
MC: DVMC 2027

BING CROSBY COLLECTION VOL.1 (14 sides never released on LPs).
LP: 31618
MC: 40 31618

BING CROSBY COLLECTION VOL.2 (14 sides never released on LPs).
Tracks: / I'll follow you / Try a little tenderness / You're getting to be a habit with me / Young and healthy / You're beautiful tonight my dear / What do I care its home / You're crying again / I've got to pass your house to get my house / Shadow waltz / I've got to sing a torch song / Little Dutch mill / Shadows of love / Ridin' around in the rain / Give me a heart to sing to.
LP: 31656
MC: 40 31656

BING CROSBY COLLECTION VOL.3 (14 sides never released on LPs).
Tracks: / My Angeline / Orange blossom time / I'm sorry dear / Can't we talk it over / Waltzing in a dream / Let's try again / Someday we'll meet again / It's within your power / I'm playing with fire / Here is my heart / My love / I would if I could but I can't / Home on the range / Lets spend an evening at home.
LP: 31751
MC: 40 31751

BING CROSBY, JUDY GARLAND AND THE ANDREWS SISTERS (Crosby, Bing/Judy Garland/Andrews Sisters).
Tracks: / Ol buttermilk sky / I've got to get me somebody to love / I've got you under my skin / Liza / Wait till the sun shines Nellie / All by myself / You gotta get me somebody to love / Very thought of you, The / South America take it away / You don't have to know the language / So would I.
LP: BLM 52003

BING CROSBY ON THE AIR.
LP: SH 2002

BING CROSBY ON THE AIR VOL 1.
Tracks: / I'm hummin', I'm singin' / Heebie jeebies / I kiss your hand madame / Just a-wearyin' for you / Why don't you practise what you preach? / Love in bloom / On the sentimental side / I simply adore you / Smiles / Remember me / Guilty / Kissable baby / I cried for you / As time goes by.
LP: SPOKANE 1

BING CROSBY SINGS MORE GREAT SONGS.
Tracks: / There's no business like show business / Secret love / Stranger in paradise / Accentuate the positive / I'll be seeing you / I love Paris / People will say we're in love / They can't take that away from me / You must have been a beautiful baby / Nightingale sang in Berkeley Square, A / You made me love you / Red sails in the sunset / Wrap your troubles in dreams / Georgia on my mind / Autumn leaves.
LP: SHM 3259
MC: HSC 3259

BING CROSBY STORY, THE.
Tracks: / Where blue of the night meets gold of the day / Someday, sweetheart / I'm an old cowhand / Pennies from Heaven / Marie / Folks who live on the hill, The / When you wore a tulip / I still love to kiss you goodnight / I don't want to get well / Once in a while / Mexicali rose / Thousand violins, A / Christmas song, The / Silent night / White Christmas / Silver bells / Adeste fideles / Down yonder / Glow worm / Mr. Moon / Maybe it's because / Pittsburgh Pennsylvania / Please Mr. Sun / Blues my naughty sweetie gives to me / Whispering.
MCSET: DVREMC 16

BING CROSBY WITH AL JOLSON (Crosby, Bing & Al Jolson).
Tracks: / There'll be a hot time in the old town tonight / Nobody / Oh Susannah / Going to the Heavens / Mammy / Alabamy bound / Getting nowhere /

What am I gonna do about you? / Let me sing and I'm happy / Rockabye your baby with a Dixie melody.
LP: . . . . **BLM 52023**

BING CROSBY WITH MAURICE CHEVALIER AND FRANKIE LAINE (Crosby, Bing/Maurice Chevalier/ Frankie Laine).
Tracks: / Smile right back at the sun / I want to thank your folks / You brought a new kind of love to me / My love parade / Hello beautiful / My ideal / Learn to croon / Louise / Mimi / I'll close my eyes / Old chaperon, The / That's my desire / Two loves have I.
LP: . . . . **BLM 52043**

BING CROSBY WITH PEGGY LEE, JACK BENNY, GARY COOPER (Crosby, Bing/ Peggy Lee/ Jack Benny/ Gary Cooper).
Tracks: / I do do like you / I love you for sentimental reasons / What am I gonna do about you? / Lover / Love in bloom / Margie / Anniversary song / My heart is a hobo / It takes a long, long train / Mam'selle (medley) / Home on the range / El Rancho Grande / You do.
LP: . . . . **BLM 52033**

BING CROSBY WITH SPIKE JONES AND JIMMY DURANTE (Crosby, Bing/ Spike Jones/Jimmy Durante).
Tracks: / My heart goes crazy / Hawaiian war chant / Love in bloom / Fascinating rhythm / Little surplus me / All by myself / Blue skies.
LP: . . . . **BLM 52013**

BING CROSBY'S CHRISTMAS CLASSICS.
Tracks: / Winter wonderland / Have yourself a merry little Christmas / What a child is this? / Holly and the ivy, The / Little drummer boy / O holy night / Littlest angel, The / Let it snow, let it snow, let it snow / Hark the herald angels sing / It came upon a midnight clear / Frosty the snowman / I wish you a merry Christmas.
LP: . . . . **ED 2607211**
MC: . . . . **ED 2607214**

BING IN THE THIRTIES VOL.1.
Tracks: / Someone else may be there while I'm gone / At long last love / I'm just wild about Harry / Have you forgotten? / I'm building a sailboat of dreams / That sly old gentleman / Ciribiribin / After all / Blame it on my youth / Japanese sandman / Things might have been different / Easy to remember / Alexander's ragtime band / Old faithful / Lullaby of Broadway.
LP: . . . . **SPOKANE 12**
LP: . . . . **JSP 1076**

BING IN THE THIRTIES VOL.2.
LP: . . . . **JSP 1084**

BING IN THE THIRTIES VOL.3 (On the air from Kraft Music Hall).
Tracks: / Where or when / Can I forget you / Smarty / Remember me / Smile / On the beach at Waikiki / Let's call a heart a heart / So do I / 1,2, button your shoe / With all my heart / Here lies love / Please.
LP: . . . . **SPOKANE 24**
LP: . . . . **JSP 1104**

BING IN THE THIRTIES VOL.4 (On the air from Kraft Music Hall).
Tracks: / Dipsy doodle, The / On the sentimental side / On moonlight bay / I see your face before me / Moon of Manakoora / Gypsy love song / Thanks for the memory / Gypsy in my soul / You're a sweetheart / My heart stood still / Side by side / Old flame never dies, An / Sympathy / My heart is taking lessons / Down where the trade wind blows / Whistle while you work / Let's waltz for old times sake / I'd love to live in loveland / I simply adore you.
LP: . . . . **SPOKANE 25**

BING IN THE THIRTIES VOL.5 (On the air from Kraft Music Hall).
Tracks: / Ti-pi-ti-pi-tin / On the sentimental side / Mexicali rose/Sweet as a song / Where the blue of the night / My heart is taking lessons / I can dream, can't I / Don't be that way / Home town / Call me up some rainy afternoon / Love walked right in / One song / Cuddle up a little closer / Little lady make believe / You're an education / Hello Hawaii, how are you? / Flat foot floogie / Lovelight in the starlight / Silver on the Sage / Someone else may be there while I'm gone / Naturally.
LP: . . . . **SPOKANE 26**

BING IN THE THIRTIES VOL.6.
Tracks: / Small fry / Now it can be told / Ride, Tenderfoot, ride / Sleep Kentucky baby / Garden of the moon / You must have been a beautiful baby / Ya got me / Red wing / My reverie / Dipsy doodle / Who blew out the flame / Don't be that way / Lullaby in rhythm / Hurry home / When you're a long, long way from home / Funny old hills, The / I cried for you / I have eyes / Old folks / Lonesome road.
LP: . . . . **SPOKANE 27**

BING IN THE THIRTIES VOL.7.
Tracks: / Between a kiss and a sigh / Thanks for everything / Deep in a dream / Together / Missouri waltz / Could be / Teacher teacher / Umbrella man / Penny serenade / Yaaka hula hickey dula / I dream of Jeannie with the light brown hair / S'posin' / Little Sir Echo / Sing a song of sunbeams / East side of heaven / Honolulu / I get along without you very well / Sweet Genevieve / You're the only star in my blue heaven.
LP: . . . . **SPOKANE 28**

BING IN THE THIRTIES VOL.8.
Tracks: / Hang your heart on a hickory limb / I want a girl / Little Sir Echo / I'm building a sailboat of dreams / Class will tell / We've come a long way together / Mickey / Our love / Tuck me to sleep in my old Kentucky home / Delightful delirium / Wishing will make it so / Snug as a bug in a rug / Oh by jingo, oh by gee / Go fly a kite / Apple for teacher, An / Are you having any fun? / If I knew then / Scatterbrain / I can't believe that you're in love with me.
LP: . . . . **SPOKANE 29**

BING IN THE THIRTIES VOL. 2.
Tracks: / Some of these days / With all my heart / One, two, button your shoe / So do I / Let's call a heart a heart / Stop and reconsider / Lost and found / Thanks / I wonder what's become of Sally / Gypsy in my soul / Get out and get under the moon / Says my heart / I let a song go out of my heart / Honeysuckle rose / Blues my naughty sweetie gives to me / It must be true / I promise you / Pessimistic character.
LP: . . . . **SPOKANE 14**

BING IS BACK (Philco Radio Time Programme).
Tracks: / I got the sun in the morning / Moonlight bay / Put it there, pal / Love on a greyhound bus / Cynthia / Connecticut / A-huggin' and a-chalkin' / I've got you under my skin / Tearbucket Jim / And so to sleep.
LP: . . . . **TOTEM 1002**

BING SINGS BROADWAY.
LP: . . . . **MCL 1730**
MC: . . . . **MCLC 1730**

BING SINGS THE GREAT SONGS.
Tracks: / Begin the beguine / Fine romance, A / Ol' man river.
MC: . . . . **HSC 3235**
LP: . . . . **SHM 3235**

BING - THE FINAL CHAPTER.
Tracks: / Introduction / Feels good feels right / Bing and Alan Dell / Nevertheless / Only way to go, The / Summer wind / Variety bandbox / Night is young, The / Final chapter / There's nothing that I haven't sung about / As time goes by / Once in a while.
LP: . . . . **REB 398**
MC: . . . . **ZCF 398**

BING'S BUDDIES (1951 Crosby and guests).
Tracks: / Bright eyes / Painting the clouds / Sweet violets / Wang wang blues / Domino / I only have eyes for you / Buttermilk sky.
MC: . . . . **CAWE 41**

BINGS MAGIC.
LP: . . . . **AWE 1**
MC: . . . . **CAWE 1**

BING'S MUSIC HALL HIGHLIGHTS.
Tracks: / It's only a paper moon / You brought a new kind of love to me / Candlelight and wine / Easter parade / Nevada / Put your arms around me honey / As time goes by / My ideal / After you've gone / After a while / I'm making believe / Cuddle up a little closer / Moonlight bay / Side by side.
LP: . . . . **SPOKANE 16**

BING'S PARTY.
Tracks: / Love is so terrific / But beautiful / Ballerino / Lady be good / Someone to watch over me / Gershwin medley / I got rhythm / Third piano prelude / Saturday date / Some sunny day / Civilization / Wonderful / To see you is to love you / When the blue of the night / Down by the river.
LP: . . . . **ART 001**
MC: . . . . **CART 001**

BIRTH OF THE BLUES JANUARY 23, 1951.
Tracks: / Birth of the blues / Cake walk, The / Basin Street blues / Thats what I like about the south / Ida, sweet as apple cider / That's a plenty / Cuddle up a little closer / Memphis blues / Wait till the sun shines Nellie / Dixieland band / My melancholy baby / Way down yonder in New Orleans / Waiter, the porter & the upstairs maid, The / St Louis blues / Ballin' the Jack.
LP: . . . . **SPOKANE 9**

BIX 'N' BING (see under Beiderbecke, Bix) (Crosby, Bing/Bix Beiderbecke/ Paul Whiteman orchestra).

BLACK MOONLIGHT.
Tracks: / Once in a blue moon / Snuggled on your shoulder / If you should ever need me / Home on the range / Where the blue of the night / Black moonlight / Just one more chance / How deep is the ocean / Song of the islands / Our big love scene / May I / Out of nowhere / Brother can you spare a dime / Lazy day / Goodnight sweetheart / Star dust / Try a little tenderness / Sweet Georgia Brown.
LP: . . . . **JOY'D 290**
MC: . . . . **TC-JOYD 290**

BOTH SIDES OF....
LP: . . . . **CC 100/2**

CHRISTMAS ALBUM (Crosby, Bing & Rosemary Clooney).
Tracks: / White Christmas / Adeste fideles / Rudolph the red nosed reindeer / Away in a manger / O little town of Bethlehem / Silent night / Christmas song, The / It came upon a midnight clear / Have yourself a merry little Christmas / Little drummer boy / Jingle bells.
LP: . . . . **MTM 024**
MC: . . . . **MTC 024**
MC: . . . . **MTMC 004**

CHRISTMAS WITH BING CROSBY.
Tracks: / Christmas is a comin' / Rudolph the red nosed reindeer / Sleigh ride / Deck the halls / That Christmas feeling / Looks like a cold cold winter / I heard the bells on Christmas day / Silent night, holy night / First snowfall / Marshmallow world, A / Snow / Sleigh bell serenade / Is Christmas only a tree / Little Jack Frost get lost / Snowman, The / Happy holiday.
LP: . . . . **SHM 3292**
MC: . . . . **HSC 3292**

CHRONOLOGICAL BING CROSBY 1.
LP: . . . . **JZ 1**

CHRONOLOGICAL BING CROSBY 2.
LP: . . . . **JZ 2**

CHRONOLOGICAL BING CROSBY 3 (1928).
LP: . . . . **JZ 3**

CHRONOLOGICAL BING CROSBY 4 (1928).
LP: . . . . **JZ 4**

CHRONOLOGICAL BING CROSBY 5 (1928).
LP: . . . . **JZ 5**

CHRONOLOGICAL BING CROSBY 6.
LP: . . . . **JZ 6**

CHRONOLOGICAL BING CROSBY 7 (1928-29).
LP: . . . . **JZ 7**

CHRONOLOGICAL BING CROSBY 8.
LP: . . . . **JZ 8**

CHRONOLOGICAL BING CROSBY VOL.12 (1931-1932).
LP: . . . . **JZ 12**

CHRONOLOGICAL BING CROSBY VOL. 9 (1929-1930).
Tracks: / I'm a dreamer / If I had a talking picture of you / Song of the dawn / Bench in the park, A / Three little words.
LP: . . . . **JZ 9**

CHRONOLOGICAL BING CROSBY-VOL.10.
LP: . . . . **JZ 10**

CLASSIC YEARS IN DIGITAL STEREO (Classic Crosby 1931-1938).
Tracks: / Sweet Georgia Brown / Dinah / Once in a blue moon / May / Home on the range / After sundown / Basin Street blues / How deep is the ocean / Love thy neighbour / Goodnight lovely little lady / My honey's lovin' arms / You've got me crying again / Some of these days / I'm falling in love ... / Blues serenade.
LP: . . . . **REB 766**
MC: . . . . **ZCF 766**

CLASSIC YEARS IN DIGITAL STEREO (Bing Crosby 1927-1934).
Tracks: / Someday, sweetheart / Mary / So the bluebirds and the blackbirds got together / I surrender, dear / Where the blue of the night / Please / Thanks / Last round-up, The / St. Louis blues / Black moonlight / Beautiful girl / We'll make hay while the sun shines / Temptation / Did you ever see a dream walking? / She reminds me of you / Love in bloom.
LP: . . . . **REB 648**
MC: . . . . **ZCF 648**

COLLECTION: BING CROSBY.
MC: . . . . **CCSMC 275**
2LP: . . . . **CCSLP 275**

COME RAIN OR COME SHINE.
LP: **6359.013**

COME SHARE THE WINE.
LP: . . . . **UAG 30294**

CROSBYANA VOL. 6 (From Bings' Personal Collection).
LP: . . . . **BR 136**

DANCING IN THE DARK.
LP: . . . . **DBD 14**
MC: . . . . **DBDC 14**

DARK MOON.
Tracks: / Maybe it's because / Blacksmith blues / Come what pay / Pittsburgh Pennsylvania / Please Mr. Sun / Everything I have is yours / Thousand violins, A / Dark moon / Blues my naughty sweetie gives to me / Down yonder / Feet up / Glow worm / Cock-eyed optimist / Now that I need you / Chi chi o chi / Blame it on my youth / Lady play your mandolin.
LP: . . . . **AWE 7**
MC: . . . . **CAWE 7**

DER BINGLE: VOLUME 1.
Tracks: / White cliffs of Dover, The / Army Air Corps song, The / Yankee doodle dandy / I don't want to walk without you / Song of freedom / You'd be so nice to come home to / What do you do in the infantary / Coming in on a wing and a prayer / Wait for me Mary / Brother Bill / Stardust / It's always you / Basin Street blues.
LP: . . . . **SPOKANE 5**

DER BINGLE: VOLUME 2.
Tracks: / Riding herd on a cloud tonight / Get on the road to victory / What do you do in the infantary / Sunday, Monday or always / Victory polka / It's all over now / As time goes by / I'll be seeing you / Shoo shoo baby / There'll be a hot time in the town of Berlin / Song of the bombadiers / Long ago and far away / I'll get by / Is you is or is you ain't my baby / Saturday night.
LP: . . . . **SPOKANE 10**

DER BINGLE: VOLUME 3.
Tracks: / Swinging on a star / You belong to my heart / Too-ra-loo-ra-loo-ra / Ida, sweet as apple cider / Bless 'em all / Is you is or is you ain't my baby / Fifth marines, The / Amphibians battle hymn, The / Sunday, Monday or always / Riding herd on a cloud tonight / Bombadiers song, The / Coming in on a wing and a prayer / Shoo shoo baby.
LP: . . . . **SPOKANE 20**

DER BINGLE: VOLUME 4.
Tracks: / Where the blue of the night / White Christmas / Easter parade / Shoo shoo baby / You are my sunshine / San Fernando valley / If I had my way / There's no place like home / You're a grand old flag / Darling Nellie Gray / De Camptown races / Home on the range / Friend of ours, A / When you were sweet sixteen / And the band played on / God bless America.
LP: . . . . **SPOKANE 30**

DER BINGLE: VOLUME 5.
Tracks: / My darling Clementine / Stardust / You are my sunshine / Abraham / Miss you / Great day / As time goes by / It can't be wrong / I never mention your name / Sunday, Monday or always / On moonlight bay / Swinging on a star / Long ago and far away / You must have been a beautiful baby.
LP: . . . . **SPOKANE 32**

EARLY YEARS, THE (Volume 5, 1934).
MC: . . . . **NEO 922**

EASY TO REMEMBER 1931-36.
Tracks: / Out of nowhere / Now that you're gone / Love you funny thing / You're still in my heart / Let's try again / I'm playing with fire / What do I care it's home / I've got to pass your house to get to my house / I would if I could but I can't / Let's spend an evening at home / I'm hummin'-I'm whistlin'-I'm singin' / Someday, sweetheart / Two cigarettes in the dark / It's easy to remember / My heart and I / Moonburn / Lovely lady / Let's call a heart a heart / South sea island magic / I never realised.
LP: . . . . **SVL 190**
MC: . . . . **CSVL 190**

FANCY MEETING YOU HERE (see Clooney, Rosemary) (Crosby, Bing & Rosemary Clooney).

FOREVER (30 evergreens).
Tracks: / Whispering / Some sunny day / Exactly like you / Mack the knife / Them there eyes / It's a good day / Mary / Muddy water / Loveable / Brazil / Ol' man river / How about you / Isle of Capri / High water / Just a gigolo / I'm through with love / Just one more chance / Mama loves papa.
2LP: . . . . **NL 89535**
MCSET: . . . . **NK 89535**
2LP: . . . . **NL 43860**
MCSET: . . . . **TC-NL 43860**

FRANK SINATRA & BING CROSBY (see Sinatra, Frank) (Crosby, Bing & Frank Sinatra).

GIVE ME THE SIMPLE LIFE.
Tracks: / Give me the simple life / Any town in Paris when you're young / Dance ballerina dance / Kiss in your eyes, The / Pretty baby / Marrying for love / Watermelon weather / Love thy neighbour / Sunshine cake / When the world was young / But beautiful / I love Paris / It's more fun than a picnic / Some enchanted evening / When you're in love / Laroo, laroo Lilli Bolero.
LP: . . . . **MCL 1848**
MC: . . . . **MCLC 1848**

GOING HOLLYWOOD.
Tracks: / Stein song, The / Out of nowhere / Ya got love / You're getting to be a habit with me / Ghost of a chance / Please / Here lies love / Down the old ox road / One, two, button your shoe / House that Jack built for Jill / Where the turf meets the surf / After all / Incurably romantic / It came upon a midnight clear / You tell me your dream / Second time around / Mister booze / Style / Don't be a do-badder.
LP: . . . . **UNKNOWN**

GOLDEN AGE OF AMERICAN RADIO.
Tracks: / Where the blue of the night / Lady of Spain / Hello, hello / For me and my gal / Young at heart / Lazy river / Paper doll / Where is your heart / It might as well be Spring / It's only a paper moon / That's a plenty / You go to my head / Zip-a-dee-doo-dah / Tell me why / I can dream, can't I / Takes two to Tango / Mona Lisa / I'd have baked a cake (If I knew you were comin') / On a slow boat to China / You brought a new kind of love to me / My love parade / Louise / Mimi / You gotta start off each day / You belong to me / Wish you were here / May the Good Lord bless and keep you / Lullaby of Broadway.
LP: . . . . **UAK 30115**

GOLDEN GREATS 1: BING CROSBY.
LP: **22014**
MC: **42014**

GOLDEN GREATS 2: BING CROSBY.
LP: **22015**
MC: **42015**

HAPPY HOLIDAY.
Tracks: / Adeste fideles / Jingle bells / I dream of you / I'm making believe / Slip of the lip / What a difference a day made / Beautiful saviour / God is beside me / Silent night / Happy holiday / Let's start the New Year right / God rest ye merry gentlemen / Let it snow, let it snow, let it snow / I'll be home for Christmas / White Christmas.
LP: . . . . **SPOKANE 6**

HAVIN' FUN (Live Broadcasts 1949-50) (Crosby, Bing & Louis Armstrong).
LP: . . . . **JASM 2508**
MC: . . . . **JASMC 2508**
LP: . . . . **SR 5009**

HERE LIES LOVE (A Selection of Love Songs).
Tracks: / Very thought of you, The / Love thy neighbour / June in January / You've got me crying again / May I? / With every breath I take / Temptation / Let me call you sweetheart / Sweet and lovely / Love in bloom / You're getting to be a habit with me / I love you truly / Someday, sweetheart / You're beautiful tonight, my dear / Love is just around the corner / Just a-wearyin' for you / It must be true / Here lies love.
LP: . . . . **AJA 5043**
MC: . . . . **ZC AJA 5043**

HOLIDAY INN AND THE BELLS OF ST. MARY (Radio Adaptations).
Tracks: / White Christmas / Happy holiday / Abraham / Be careful, it's my heart / Easter parade / Aren't you glad you're you / Bells of St. Mary's.
LP: . . . . **SPOKANE 15**

IN DEMAND.
Tracks: / Getting to know you / Love walked in / Isle of Innisfree / Waltz you saved for me, The / Dearly beloved / Golden earrings / Out of this world / Rosalie / Vaya con dios / La vie en rose / Beautiful love / Indian Summer / It had to be you / Rose of Tralee, The / Story of Sorrento, The / I'll remember April / One rose (that's left in my heart) / Yours in my heart alone / Granada.
LP: . . . . **MCG 6004**

JAZZIN' BING CROSBY, THE.
Tracks: / I'm comin', Virginia / Dinah / Shine / Some of these days / My honey's loving arms / Somebody stole Gabriel's horn / Stay on the right side of the road / Someday, sweetheart / Moonburn / I'm an old cowhand / Basin Street blues / You must have been a beautiful baby.
LP: . . . . **SM 3053**

JOIN BING AND SING ALONG.
LP: . . . . **WM 4021**

JUST BREEZIN' ALONG.
Tracks: / Breezin' along with the breeze / How are things in Glocca Morra / Heatwave / Best things in life are free, The / My heart stood still / I got rhythm / Good old times, The / Cabaret / Send in the clowns / Only way to go, The / Have a nice day / Some sunny day / At my time of life / With a song in my heart / Razzle dazzle / That's what life is all about.
LP: . . . . **EMS 1274**
MC: . . . . **TCEMS 1274**

KRAFT MUSIC HALL APRIL 16, 1942.
Tracks: / K-K-K-Katy / Arthur Murray taught me dancing in a hurry / Miss you / He comes from timbuckthree / Make believe / I'll be with you in apple blossom time / Little Bo Peep has lost her Jeep / Pass the bisquits Mirandy / It's Mary / Way you look tonight / Song of the islands.
LP: . . . . **SPOKANE 4**

KRAFT MUSIC HALL APRIL 30, 1942.
Tracks: / Hey Mable, Wait for me / He's wonderful / Friendship / It's Mary / It's somebody else's Moon not mine / I'll be with you in apple blossom time / Malaguena / Blues in the night / Oh how I miss you tonight / Embraceable you / I remember you.
LP: . . . . **SPOKANE 3**

KRAFT MUSIC HALL DECEMBER 24, 1942.
Tracks: / Adeste fideles / Steam is on the beam, The / Why don't you fall in love with me? / Red river valley / God rest ye merry gentlemen / You'd be so nice to come home to / Silent night.
LP: . . . . **SPOKANE 13**

KRAFT MUSIC HALL JANUARY 29, 1942.
Tracks: / Caisson's go rolling along, The / Chattanooga choo choo / You made me love you / Deep in the heart of Texas / Blue Danube / Blues in the night / Rose O'Day / Gypsy airs / Home on the range / Who calls?.
LP: . . . . **SPOKANE 11**

KRAFT MUSIC HALL MARCH 12, 1942.
Tracks: / I like it, how about you? / MacNamara's band / I don't want to walk without you / Story of Jenny, The / My darling Nellie Gray / That's a plenty / Three young fillies / We're the gang that feeds the army / Anvil chorus / Miss you.
LP: . . . . **SPOKANE 2**

KRAFT MUSIC HALL MAY 27, 1937.
Tracks: / How could you? / My melancholy baby / You're here, you're there / Land of the sky blue water / Time on my hands / My little buckaroo / Forgotten waltz / Lullaby for a bazooka / Flight of the bumble bee / Where are you?.
LP: . . . . **SPOKANE 7**

KRAFT MUSIC HALL MAY 29, 1941.
Tracks: / Can't you tell? / Kerry dance, The / You're a double lovely / It was wonderful then / Stomp Caprice / Frankie and Johnny / All through the night / Hut sut song, The / Maria Elena / Things I love, The / Because of you.
LP: . . . . **SPOKANE 17**

LEGENDARY BING CROSBY AND FRIENDS, THE.
Tracks: / That old gang of mine / On top of old Smokey / I can dream, can't I / Rosie / Lazy river / Paper doll.
MC: . . . . **MRT 40051**

LEGENDARY PERFORMER, A.
Tracks: / Ol' man river / Three little words / It must be true / Wrap your troubles in dreams / Just a gigolo / I'm thru with love / Just one more chance / Some sunny day / I'm gonna sit right down and write myself / Mack the knife / Dream a little dream of me / Whispering / Down among the sheltering palms.
LP: . . . . **PL 12086**
MC: . . . . **PK 12086**

LEGENDARY, THE.
MC: . . . . **MRT 40045**

LIVE AT THE LONDON PALLADIUM.
LP: . . . . **NE 951**

MANY HAPPY RETURNS.
Tracks: / Where the blue of the night / Out of nowhere / If you should ever need me / Were you sincere / Just one more chance / I'm through with love / Many happy returns / I found a million dollar baby / At your command / I apologise / Dancing in the dark / Stardust / Sweet and lovely / Too late / I'm sorry dear / Goodnight sweetheart.
LP: . . . . **VLP 1**

MR. CROSBY AND MR. MERCER.
Tracks: / Mr. Gallagher & Mr. Shean / Too marvellous for words / Blues in the night / Bob White / You must have been a beautiful baby / On behalf of the visiting fireman / In the cool cool cool of the evening / I'm an old cowhand / Autumn leaves / Accentuate the positive / When the world was young / Waiter, the porter and the upstairs maid.
LP: . . . . **MFP 50554**
MC: . . . . **TCMFP 50554**

MUSIC HALL HIGHLIGHTS (Crosby, Bing & John Scott Trotter Orchestra).
Tracks: / My minds on you / Moonlight on the Ganges / Moon won't talk, The / Maria Elena / Last night's gardenias / Yours / Play fiddle, play / Goodbye now / It was wonderful then / You walked by / Say si si / Fool's rush in / May I never love again / Loch Lomond / My heart tells me / It makes no difference now.
LP: . . . . **SPOKANE 19**

MUSIC, MUSIC, MUSIC.
Tracks: / Music music music / Marta / Copper canyon / Wedding samba, The / Yes sir that's my baby / Whispering hope / I'll walk alone / Hoop and holler / Heart and soul / Dipsey doodle / Till I waltz again with you / Why don't you believe me / Enjoy yourself / Candy and cake / Everybody loves my baby / From the vine.
LP: . . . . **GRAP 1001**
LP: . . . . **MTLP 1.016**

NEW TRICKS (Crosby, Bing & Buddy Cole Trio).
Tracks: / When I take my sugar to tea / On the Alamo / I'm confessin' / Between the devil and the deep blue sea / Georgia on my mind / Chicago / You're driving me crazy / Avalon / Chinatown, my Chinatown / If I could be with you / Softly as in a morning sunrise / Alabamy bound.
LP: . . . . **MOIR 202**
MC: . . . . **CMOIR 202**

ON THE SENTIMENTAL SIDE (20 Classic Tracks of the 30's).
Tracks: / Black moonlight / How deep is the ocean? / Stardust / Dancing in the dark / I'm through with love / Sweet is the word for you.
LP: . . . . **AJA 5072**
MC: . . . . **ZC AJA 5072**

PORTRAIT OF A SONG STYLIST.
MC: . . . . **HARMC 120**

RADIO MEMORIES.
Tracks: / When the blue of the night / Little lady make believe / My heart is taking lessons / Gypsy in my soul / Whistle when you work.
MC: . . . . **TRM 20029**

RADIO YEARS, VOL 1.
LP: . . . . **NCP 704**
MC: . . . . **ZCN 704**
LP: . . . . **PYL 6036**
MC: . . . . **PYM 6036**
LP: . . . . **GNPS 9044**
MC: **GNP5 9044**

RADIO YEARS, VOL 2.
LP: . . . . **NCP 707**
MC: . . . . **ZCNCP 707**
LP: . . . . **PYL 6037**
MC: . . . . **PYM 6037**
LP: . . . . **GNPS 9046**
MC: **GNP5 9046**

RADIO YEARS, VOL 3.
Tracks: / Zip a dee doo dah / Takes two to tango / Valencia / How are things in Glocca Morra / On top of Old Smokey / Great day / If this is love / Luck old sun / Louise / Mimi / Don't let the stars get in your eyes.
LP: . . . . **NCP 710**
MC: . . . . **ZCNCP 710**
LP: . . . . **PYL 6038**
MC: . . . . **PYM 6038**
LP: . . . . **GNPS 9047**
MC: **GNP5 9047**

RADIO YEARS, VOL 4.
Tracks: / Hello Hello / Moonlight Bay / Cuanto Lagusta / Lullaby of Broadway / I can dream, can't I / Hand holdin' music / Surrey with the fringe on top / May the good Lord bless and keep you / If I knew you were coming I'd've baked a cake / You've gotta start each day with a song / I don't know why, I just do.
LP: . . . . **NCP 711**
MC: . . . . **ZCNCP 711**
LP: . . . . **PYL 6039**
MC: . . . . **PYM 6039**
LP: . . . . **GNPS 9048**
MC: **GNP5 9048**

REMEMBERING.
Tracks: / Please / Did you ever see a dream walking / I've got the world on a string / Sweet Georgia Brown / I don't stand a ghost of a chance / My honey's loving arms / Down the old ox road / How deep is the ocean / Temptation / St. Louis blues / Dinah / Somebody stole Gabriel's horn / Stay on the right side of the road / Someday, sweetheart / Some of these days / Shine / I'm coming Virginia / There's a cabin in the pines.
LP: . . . . **CHD 123**
MC: . . . . **MCHD 123**

REPLAY ON BING CROSBY.
LP: . . . . **FEDB 5034**
MC: . . . . **CFEDB 5034**

SEASONS.
Tracks: / Seasons / On the very first day of the year / June in January / Spring will be a little late this year / April showers / June is bustin' out all over / In the good old summertime / Summer wind / Autumn in New York / September song / Sleigh ride / Yesterday when I was young.
LP: **2442 151**
LP: **2384 125**

SENTIMENTAL BING.
Tracks: / There's nothing that I haven't sung about / I'm getting sentimental over you / Nevertheless / What's new / As time goes by / Old fashioned love / Time on my hands / That of black magic / Way we were / Once in a while / Rose in her hair / Night is young and you're so beautiful / At last / When I leave the world behind.
LP: . . . . **TAB 31**

SHE LOVES ME NOT (NOVEMBER 8, 1937) (Crosby, Bing/Joan Blondell).
Tracks: / I'm whistlin', I'm singin' / Straight from the shoulder / Love in bloom.
LP: . . . . **TOTEM 1004**

SHHH VOL.4.
Tracks: / Love thy neighbour / May I? / Straight from the shoulder / Hang your heart on a hickory limb / Skylark / All you want to do is dance / Door will open, A / Hello mom / Road to Morocco, The / Who threw the overalls in Mrs Murphy's Chowder / You belong to my heart / Three caballeros / I only want a buddy not a sweetheart / Jingle bells / Christmas greeting to New York employees / Duke the spook.
LP: . . . . **LLM 023**

SING YOU SINNERS (January 15, 1940).
Tracks: / I've got a pocketful of dreams / Don't let that moon get away.
LP: . . . . **SPOKANE 8**

SONGS OF A LIFETIME.
Tracks: / Ain't misbehavin' / At sundown / Don't blame me / I can't get started / I wish you love / I've grown accustomed to her face / Keepin' out of mischief now / Little man you've had a busy day / Love's old sweet song / Misty / Nice work if you can get it / She's funny that way / Straight down the middle / They didn't believe me / Try a little tenderness / Way down yonder in New Orleans / You'll never know / You're the top.
2LP: **6641 923**

SPECIAL MAGIC OF BING AND SATCHMO, THE (Crosby, Bing & Louis Armstrong).
Tracks: / Way down yonder in New Orleans / Brother Bill / Little ol' tune / At the Jazz Band Ball / Rocky Mountain moon / Bye bye blues / Muskrat ramble / Sugar / Preacher, The / Dardanella / Let's sing like a Dixieland band.
LP: **2353 084**

SPECIAL MAGIC OF BING CROSBY, THE.
LP: **2353 101**

THAT OLD FEELING (Crosby, Bing & Louis Armstrong).
LP: **2872 217**
MC: **3472 217**

THAT TRAVELLIN' TWO-BEAT (Crosby, Bing & Rosemary Clooney).
Tracks: / Vienna Woods / Mother Brown / Roamin' in the gloamin' / Come to the Mardi Gras / Hear that band / Daughter of Molly Malone, The / Poor people of Paris, The / I get ideas / Ciao, ciao bambina / That travelin' two beat.
LP: . . . . **CAPS 1017**

THAT'S WHAT LIFE IS ALL ABOUT.
LP: . . . . **UAG 29730**

THIS IS....
Tracks: / Some sunny day / Down among the sheltering palms / I can't get started / Whispering / Slow boat to China / Along the way to Waikiki / Let a smile be your umbrella / Fancy meeting you here / Brazil / Dream a little dream of me / How about you? / Love won't let you get away / It happened in Monterey / Calcutta / Last night on the back porch / Say si si / Mama loves papa / Hindustan / Tell me / You came a long way from St Louis / I'm gonna sit right down and write myself a letter / Exactly like you.
2LP: . . . . **DPS 2066**

TRIBUTE TO....
Tracks: / Sweet Sue / I surrender, dear / Gonna love you / Brother, can you spare a dime? / Somebody stole Gabriel's horn / Moonburn / Please / St. Louis blues /

Lazybones / Just a gigolo / She reminds me of you / Sweet Georgia Brown.
LP: **SRTX 79/CUS 565**

TRUE LOVE.
Tracks: / Yes sir, that's my baby / Moonglow / Love is the sweetest thing / True love / It's alright with me / You're sensational / Manhattan / Unchained melody / Way down yonder in New Orleans / You'll never know / Lady is a tramp, The / I've got a crush on you / She's funny that way / At sundown / Picnic, Theme from.
LP: **8126 601**
MC: **8126 604**

WHERE THE BLUE OF THE NIGHT.
Tracks: / Where the blue of the night / I found a million dollar baby / Sweet and lovely / I apologise / Stardust / Just one more chance / Too late / Dancing in the dark / Faded summer love, A / I'm sorry dear / If you should ever need me / Can't we talk it over? / Many happy returns / I found you / I'm through with love / Goodnight, sweetheart.
LP: **MTLP 1007**

WHERE THE BLUE OF THE NIGHT (DITTO).
Tracks: / Where the blue of the night / Mexicali rose / Just one more chance / Sweet and lovely / Bob White / Don't let that moon get away / Way you look tonight / When you dream about Hawaii / Sweet Leilani / I have eyes / Let me whisper I love you / Stardust / In a little hula Heaven / Funny old hills, The / Can I forget you / Basin street blues / Songs of the Islands / Dancing under the stars / Folks who live on the hill, The / Let me call you sweetheart / Just a wearyin' for you / Sail along silv'ry moon / Dancing in the dark / Goodnight sweetheart.
MCSET: **DTO 10299**

WHITE CHRISTMAS.
Tracks: / God rest ye merry gentlemen / Silent night / Adeste fideles / White Christmas / Faith of our fathers / I'll be home for Christmas / Jingle bells / Santa Claus is coming to town / Silver bells / It's beginning to look like Christmas / Christmas in Killarney / Mele kalikimaka.
LP: **MFP 5590**
MC: **TCMFP 5590**

WHITE CHRISTMAS.
LP: **SM 4048**
LP: **MCF 2568**

WHITE CHRISTMAS (Crosby, Bing/Nat King Cole).
LP: **SM 3930**

WHITE CHRISTMAS (RADIO SHOW).
LP: **BLM 52099**

WHITE CHRISTMAS (VIDEO) (See under White Christmas) (Various artists).

WITH THE RHYTHM BOYS (1930) (Crosby, Bing and the Rhythm Boys).
LP: **ARCADIA 5001**

WRAP YOUR TROUBLES IN DREAMS.
Tracks: / Mary (what are you waiting for?) / Ol' man river / Make believe / Loveable / I'm afraid of you / It must be true / Fool me some more / Little things in life, The / I surrender, dear / Wrap your troubles in dreams / Just a gigolo / One more time / Thanks to you / I'm gonna get you / I'm through with love / Just one more chance.
LP: **LSA 3094**

Crosby, Bob

20 GOLDEN PIECES: BOB CROSBY (Crosby, Bob & His Orchestra).
Tracks: / Washington and Lee swing / When the saints go marching in / Ja da / Love's got me in a lazy mood / Tiger rag / Gin mill blues / High society / Pennies from Heaven / Tin roof blues / Georgy girl / Thoroughly modern Millie / Big noise from Winnetka / Winchester Cathedral / Ballin' the jack / Java / Summertime / Little Rock getaway / March of the bob cats / Mame / Patricia.
LP: **BDL 2026**
MC: **AJKL 2026**

ACCENT ON SWING (Crosby, Bob & His Ochestra).
LP: **GOJ 1021**

AT THE RAINBOW GRILL (Crosby, Bob & The Bop Cats).
LP: **MES 6815**

BAND AND SMALL (Crosby, Bob & Bing Crosby).
LP: **T 5004**

BIG APPLE, THE 1936 - 40 (Crosby, Bob & His Orchestra).
LP: **BS 7111**

BOB CROSBY.
LP: **KLJ 20015**

BOB CROSBY 1941-42.
Tracks: / Mexicali rose / I'm gonna move to the outskirts of town / Barrelhouse Bessie from Basin Street / Mirage / Zoot suit, A / Just a dream / Catalina jump / Marchetta / Yank's lament / Swingin' on nothin' / Soft jive / This love of mine / Don't get around much anymore / Where do we go from here.
LP: **HSR 192**

BOB CROSBY AND HIS ORCHESTRA (1935-36) (Crosby, Bob & His Orchestra).
Tracks: / Roll, roll, rolling along / Oh my goodness / Dixieland shuffle / I'd rather lead a band / Farewell blues / It's you I'm talking about, baby / I'm just beginning to care / It ain't right / Glory of love / Here comes your pappy / There'll be some changes made / Let's make up again / I'll never say "never again" again / Tin roof blues / Fidgety feet / Muscrat ramble / But definitely / Eeny meeny miney mo / Rockin' chair / When Icky Morgan plays his organ.
LP: **RARITIES 41**

BOB CROSBY AND HIS ORCHESTRA (Crosby, Bob & His Orchestra).
Tracks: / Theme - Introduction / Over the waves / Sister Kate / We're in the money / Big noise from Winnetka / Yancey special / It's a long way to Tipperary / Diga diga doo / Smokey Mary / Theme - close / Swing concert / In a minor mood / Dogtown blues / Between the devil and the deep blue sea / South Rampart Street Parade / Gin Mill Blues.
LP: **JASM 2512**
MC: **JASMC 2512**

BOB CROSBY AND ORCHESTRA (1937-42) (Crosby, Bob Orchestra).
LP: **SWINGFAN 1016**

BOB CROSBY ON THE AIR 1940 (Crosby, Bob & His Orchestra).
Tracks: / Summertime / Skaters Waltz / Shake down the stars / Vous tout de vey, a vous, A / Complainin' / In the mood / Where the blue of the night / It's you, you darlin' / It's a small world / Wolverine blues / Boogie woogie Maxine / Fools rush in / Cecilia / Old county down, The / Jazz me blues / Reminiscing time / Ooh what you said / Starlight hour, The / Sugarfoot stomp.
LP: **AIRCHECK 17**

BOB CROSBY VOL.1 (1935).
LP: **AJAX 144**

BOB CROSBY VOL.2 (1935).
LP: **AJAX 151**

BOB CROSBY VOL.3 (1936/7).
LP: **AJAX 159**

BOB CROSBY VOL. 2 (1952-53).
LP: **HUK 209**

BOB CROSBY'S BOB CATS VOL.1.
Tracks: / Stumbling / Who's sorry now / Coquette / Fidgety feet / You're driving me crazy / Can't we be friends / Loopin' the loop / Mama's gone, goodbye / March of the bob cats / Palesteena / Slow mood / Big foot jump / Big crash from China / Five point blues / Way down yonder in New Orleans / Do you ever think of me.
LP: **S 1245**

BOB CROSBY'S BOB CATS VOL.2 (1938-1942).
Tracks: / Hindustan / Mournin' blues / Till we meet again / Love nest, The / All by myself / Jazz me blues / Speak to me of love / Big bass viol / I hear you talking / Call me a taxi / Big noise from Winnetka / Peruna / Spain / That da da strain / Tin roof blues.
LP: **S 1288**

CAMEL CARAVANS THE SUMMER OF 39.
LP: **GOJ 1037**

DIXIELAND BAND, THE.
LP: **HDL 110**
MC: **CHDL 110**

DIXIELAND SHUFFLE, VOL.2 (1935/6) (Crosby, Bob & His Orchestra).
Tracks: / Little bit independent, A / No other one / Goody goody / I don't want to make history / Christopher Columbus / You're Toots to me / You start me dreaming / Mommy / Muscrat ramble / Dixieland shuffle.
LP: **HDL 120**
MC: **CHDL 120**

JAZZ CLASSICS IN DIGITAL STEREO (Bob Crosby 1937-1938).
Tracks: / South Rampart Street parade / Gin Mill blues / Squeeze me / Stumbling / Who's sorry now / Coquette / Fidgety feet / You're driving me crazy / Can't we be friends / Dogtown blues / March of the bob cats / Slow mood / Big foot jump / Big crash from China / Five point blues / Big noise from Winnetka / Swingin' at the sugar bowl / Honky tonk train blues.
LP: **REB 688**
MC: **ZCF 688**

MARDI GRAS PARADE (Crosby, Bob & The Bop Cats).
LP: **MES 7026**

MORE 1938 (Crosby, Bob & His Ochestra).
LP: **CLP 34**

MOURNIN' BLUES (Crosby, Bob & The Bop Cats).
Tracks: / Mournin' blues / South Rampart Street parade / Washington and Lee swing / Love nest, The / Squeeze me / Spain / Call me a taxi / Yancey special / Gin mill blues / Who's sorry now / I hear you talking / All by myself / Jazz me blues / Till we meet again / Tin roof blues / I'm praying humble.
LP: **AFS 1014**
MC: **TCAFS 1014**

PLAYS (Crosby, Bob & His Ochestra).
LP: **CLP 1**

SUDDENLY IT'S 1939 (Crosby Caravans) (Crosby, Bob & His Orchestra).
Tracks: / Lady's in love with you, The / I've got the world on a string / Little Rock getaway / If I didn't care / Hindustan / Newsy blues / Pagan love song / South Rampart Street parade / Get on board and ride / Sunrise serenade / Stumbling / Memphis blues / Big noise from Winnetka / Then I'll be happy.
MC: **GOJC 1032**
LP: **GOJ 1032**

SUGARFOOT STRUT 1936 - 42 (Crosby, Bob & His Orchestra).
LP: **BS 7121**

THAT DA DA STRAIN (Crosby, Bob & His Orchestra).
Tracks: / That da da strain / Royal Garden blues / Squeeze me / Panama / Who's sorry now? / Big crash from China / High society / Milenberg joys / March of the bob cats / Russian sailor's dance / Vultee special / Jimtown blues.
LP: **SM 3243**

Crosby, David

CROSBY & NASH.
Tracks: / Southbound train / Whole cloth / Blacknotes / Strangers room / Where will I be / Page forty three / Frozen smiles / Games / Girl to be on my mind / Wall song, The / Immigration man.
LP: **K 50011**

IF I COULD ONLY REMEMBER MY NAME.
Tracks: / Music is love / Cowboy movie / Tamalpais high at about 3 / Laughing / What are their names / Traction in the rain / Song with no words / Tree with no leaves / Orleans / I'd swear there was somebody here.
LP: **K 40320**
LP: **2401 005**

OH YES I CAN.
Tracks: / Drive my car / Melody / Monkey and the underdog / In the wide ruin / Tracks in the dust / Drop down mama / Lady of the harbor / Distances / Flying man / Oh yes I can / My country 'tis of thee.
LP: **AMA 5232**
MC: **AMC 5232**

WIND ON THE WATER.
LP: **2310 428**

Crosby & Nash

BEST OF CROSBY & NASH.
Tracks: / Love work out / Wall song, The / Wild tales / Carry me / Out of the darkness / Southbound train / Laughing / Chicago / Bittersweet / To the last whale / Critical mass.
LP: **2482 490**
MC: **3192 616**
LP: **231 0626**

Crosby, Stills, ...

4 WAY STREET (Crosby, Stills, Nash & Young).
Tracks: / On the way home / Cowgirl in the sand / Southern man / Teach your children / Don't let it bring you down / Ohio / Triad / 49 bye byes / Carry on / Lee shore / Love the one you're with / Find the cost of freedom / Chicago / Pre road downs / Right between the eyes / Long time gone.
LP: **K 60003**
MC: **K4 60003**
LP: **2956004**

AMERICAN DREAM (Crosby, Stills, Nash & Young).
Tracks: / American dream / Got it made / Name of love / Don't say goodbye / This old house / Nighttime for the generals / Shadowland / Drivin' thunder / Clear blue skies / That girl / Compass / Soldiers of peace / Feel your love / Night song.
LP: **WX 233**
MC: **WX 233 C**

DEJA VU (Crosby, Stills, Nash & Young).
Tracks: / Carry on / Teach your children / Almost cut my hair / Helpless / Woodstock / Deja vu / Our house / 4 + 20 / Country girl / Everybody I love you.
LP: **K 50001**
MC: **K4 50001**
LP: **2401 001**

SO FAR (Crosby, Stills, Nash & Young).
Tracks: / Deja vu / Helplessly hoping / Wooden ships / Teach your children / Ohio / Find the cost of freedom / Woodstock / Our house / Helpless / Guenevere / Judy blue eyes.
LP: **K 50023**
MC: **K4 50023**

Crosby, Stills & Nash

ALLIES.
Tracks: / War games / Raise a voice / Turn your back on love / He played real good for free / Barrel of pain / Shadow captain / Dark star / Blackbird / For what it's worth / Wasted on the way.
LP: **780 075-1**

CROSBY, STILLS AND NASH.
Tracks: / Judy blue eyes / Marrakesh express / Guinevere / You don't have to cry / Pre-paid downs / Wooden ships / Lady of the island / Helplessly hoping / Long time gone / 49 by pass.
LP: **K 40033**
LP: **588 189**

CSN.
Tracks: / Shadow captain / See the changes / Carried away / Fair game / Anything at all / Cathedral / Dark star / Just a song before I go / Run from tears / Cold rain / In my dreams / I give you give blind.
LP: **K 50369**
MC: **K4 50369**

DAYLIGHT AGAIN.
Tracks: / Turn your back on love / Wasted on the way / Southern cross / Into the darkness / Delta / Since I met you / Too much love to hide / Song for Susan / You are alive / Might as well have a good time / Daylight again.
LP: **K 50896**

LIVE IT UP.
LP: **7567 82101-1**
MC: **7567 82101-4**

REPLAY.
Tracks: / Carry on / Marrakesh express / Just a song before I go / First things first / Shadow captain / To the last whale / Love the one you're with / Pre-road downs / Change partners / I give you give blind / Cathedral.
MC: **K4 50766**
LP: **K 50766**

Cross

MAD, BAD AND DANGEROUS TO KNOW.
Tracks: / Top of the world ma / Liar / Closer to you / Breakdown / Penetration guru / Power to love / Sister blue / Foxy lady (Available on CD only) / Better things / Passion for trash / Old men (lay down) / Final destination.
LP: **PCS 7342**
MC: **TCPCS 7342**

SHOVE IT.
Tracks: / Shove it / Heaven for everyone / Love on a tightrope (like an animal) / Cowboys and indians / Stand up for love / Love lies bleeding (she was a wicked, wily waitress) / Rough justice / 2nd shelf mix, The (CD only) / Contact.
LP: **V 2477**
MC: **TCV 2477**
LP: **OVED 302**
MC: **OVEDC 302**

Cross, Christopher

ANOTHER PAGE.
Tracks: / No time for talk / Baby says no / What am I supposed to believe / Deal 'em again / Think of Laura / Talking in my sleep / Nature of the game / Long world / Words of wisdom.
LP: **W 3757**
MC: **W 3757 4**

BACK OF MY MIND.
Tracks: / Someday / Never stop believing / Swept away / Any old time / I will / Sue told me so / Back of my mind / I'll be alright / Alibi / Just one look.
LP: **WX 158**
MC: **WX 158 C**

CHRISTOPHER CROSS.
Tracks: / Say you'll be mine / I really don't know anymore / Spinning / Never be the same / Poor Shirley / Ride like the wind / Light is on / Sailing / Minstrel gigolo.
LP: **K 56789**
MC: **K4 56789**

EVERY TURN OF THE WORLD.
Tracks: / Every turn of the world / Charm the snake / I hear you call / Don't say goodbye / It's you that really matters

/ Love is love / Swing street / Love found a home / That girl / Open your heart.
LP: **925341 1**
MC: **925341 4**

Cross, David

MEMOS FROM PURGATORY.
Tracks: / Poppies / Meantime / First policeman, The / Animal / New dawn / Postcript / Bizarre bazaar / Basking in the blue.
LP: . . . . **R 103**

Cross, Mike

BORN IN THE COUNTRY.
LP: . . . . **SH 1002**

BOUNTY HUNTER, THE.
LP: . . . . **SH 1003**

CAROLINA SKY.
LP: . . . . **SH 1006**

CHILD PRODIGY.
LP: . . . . **SH 1001**

LIVE AND KICKIN'.
LP: . . . . **SH 1005**

ROCK 'N RYE.
LP: . . . . **SH 1004**

SOLO AT MIDNIGHT.
LP: . . . . **SH 1007**

Cross of Iron (film)

CROSS OF IRON (Film soundtrack) (Various artists).
Tracks: / Steiner's theme: *Various artists* / Main title: *Various artists* / Mikael: *Various artists*/ Steiner's report: *Various artists* / Captain Stransky: *Various artists* / Mikael's death: *Various artists*/ Terrace, The: *Various artists* / Memories and hallucinations: *Various artists* / Eva: *Various artists*/ Return to the front: *Various artists* / I hate all officers: *Various artists* / Bridge house, The: *Various artists* / Massacre, The: *Various artists* / Last confrontation: *Various artists* / Finale: *Various artists.*
LP: . . . . **EMA 782**

Cross, Sandra

COMET IN THE SKY.
Tracks: / Who's finally won / Comet in the sky / Blinded by love / White wash / I need a man / My only desire / Styler boy / Why oh why / Free South Africa / I want you so badly.
LP: . . . . **ARILP 034**
MC: . . . . **ARIC 034**

COUNTRY LIFE.
LP: . . . . **ARILP 026**
MC: . . . . **CLP 026**

CROSSING OVER.
LP: . . . . **FIRM 222**

Cross, Tim

CLASSIC LANDSCAPE.
LP: . . . . **NAGE 3**
MC: . . . . **NAGEC 3**

Crossen, Howard

CROSSEN LIVELY.
Tracks: / Deep purple / Brother Jim / Honky tonk / Sweet Georgia Brown / La vie en rose / Tippin' in / Newport beach to ensenada run / Breakfast at the beachcomber / Harlem nocturne / Night train / Poor butterfly / Sleep.
MC: . . . . **MORRHYTHM 28**

Crossfire

HYSTERICAL ROCHORDS.
Tracks: / No hands jive / Hysterical rochords / Youth in Asia / Miles away / Trinity / Let it slide down easy.
LP: . . . . **K 90032**

SECOND ATTACK.
LP: . . . . **SKULL 8356**
MC: . . . . **TAPE 78356**

SEE YOU IN HELL.
LP: . . . . **SKULL 8314**
MC: . . . . **TAPE 78314**

Crossfire Choir

CROSSFIRE CHOIR.
LP: . . . . **PB 6056**
MC: . . . . **PBCC 6056**

Crossing Delancey

CROSSING DELANCEY (1988 film soundtrack) (Various artists).
LP: . . . . **VS 5201**
MC: . . . . **VSC 5201**

Crossing (film)

CROSSING, THE (Original Soundtrack) (Various artists).
LP: . . . . **CHR 1826**
MC: . . . . **ZCHR 1826**

Crossover Dreams

CROSSOVER DREAMS (1986 film soundtrack) (Various artists).
Tracks: / Elegua soyu: *Various artists* / Good for baby: *Various artists* / Rudy's theme: *Various artists*/ Todos vuelven: *Various artists* / Liz's theme: *Various artists* / Goodbye el barrio: *Various artists*/ Llora timbero: *Various artists* / Sin te: *Various artists* / Ecue-yambo-o: *Various artists* / Ban-con-tim: *Various artists* / Otra dia, otra amore: *Various artists* / El down: *Various artists* / Todos vuelven reprise: *Various artists* / Rudy's theme (reprise): *Various artists.*
LP: . . . . **EKT 36**
MC: . . . . **EKT 36 C**

Crossroads (film)

CROSSROADS (See under Cooder, Ry) (Cooder, Ry).

Crothers, Scat Man

ROCK 'N' ROLL.
LP: . . . . **L 1511**

Crouch, Andrae

AUTOGRAPH.
LP: . . . . **LS R 5710**
MC: . . . . **LS C 5710**

BEST OF ANDRAE CROUCH AND THE DISCIPLES, THE (Crouch, Andrae & Disciples).
Tracks: / Take a little time / Everything changed / Tell them / Keep on singing / My tribute / Jesus is the answer / Through it all / Satisfied / Jesus (every hour) / I come that you might have life / Bless His holy name / I'm coming home / Just like He said He would / If heaven never was promised to me / Take me back / I don't know why / I didn't think it could be / Oh I need Him / I've got confidence / It won't be long.
2LP: . . . . **LS D 7034**
MCSET: . . . . **LCD 7034**

I'LL BE THINKING OF YOU (See under Wonder, Stevie) (Crouch, Andrae & Stevie Wonder).

LIVE AT CARNEGIE HALL (Crouch, Andrae & Disciples).
Tracks: / Opening / You don't know what you're missing / He looked beyond my fault / I didn't think it could be / Hallelujah, Hallelujah Jesus is the answer / Andrae preachin' / Can't nobody do me like Jesus / Invitation / It won't be long.
LP: . . . . **LS 7018**
MC: . . . . **LC 7018**

LIVE IN LONDON: ANDRAE CROUCH (Crouch, Andrae & Disciples).
Tracks: / Introduction / Perfect peace / I surrender all / Greetings by Andrae / You don't have to jump no pews (I've been born again) / Take a little time / Tell them / If I was a tree (the highest praise) / Hallelujah / Revive us again / Power in the blood / Reprise / I just want to know you / Andrae talking / Just like he said he would / I'll keep on loving you Lord / You gave to me / Oh taste and see / Praise God, praise God / This is another day / Praise God reprise / Well done / My tribute.
2LP: . . . . **LSD 7048**
MCSET: . . . . **LCD 7048**

MORE OF THE BEST....
Tracks: / Soon and very soon / I'll be thinking of you / They shall be mine / Please come back / Quiet times / It's gonna rain / Sweet love of Jesus, The / Jesus is Lord / Praises / I just wanna know you.
LP: . . . . **LS 7061**
MC: . . . . **LC 7061**

NO TIME TO LOSE.
LP: . . . . **MYR 1188**
MC: . . . . **MC 1188**

TAKE ME BACK (Crouch, Andrae & Disciples).
Tracks: / I'll still love you / Praises / Just like he said he would / All I can say (I really love you) / You can depend on me / Take me back / Sweet love of Jesus, The / It ain't no new thing / They shall be mine / Oh saviour / Tell them.
LP: . . . . **LSX 7025**
MC: . . . . **LC 7025**

THIS IS ANOTHER DAY (Crouch, Andrae & Disciples).
Tracks: / Perfect peace / My peace I leave with you / This is another day / Quiet times / Soon and very soon / We expect you / You gave to me / All that I have / Choice, The / Polynesian praise song (I love you).
LP: . . . . **LSX 7042**
MC: . . . . **LC 7042**
LP: . . . . **DJF 20496**

VOLUME 1 - THE CLASSICS.
MC: . . . . **RMC 046**

VOLUME 2 - WE SING THE PRAISES.
MC: . . . . **RMC 047**

VOLUME 3 - CONTEMPORARY MAN.
MC: . . . . **RMC 048**

Crouch End All Stars

CROUCH END ALL STARS.
LP: . . . . **J 148**

Crouch, Sandra

WE'RE WAITING.
LP: . . . . **LSR 7079**
MC: . . . . **LSC 7079**

Croudson, Henry

PARAMOUNT PERFORMANCE, A.
LP: . . . . **CF 270**

Crow, Alvin

WELCOME TO TEXAS.
LP: . . . . **TRP 851**

Crow, Dan

OOPS.
MC: . . . . **ROUNDER 8007C**
LP: . . . . **ROUNDER 8007**

Crow, Noel

SOMETHING TO CROW ABOUT.
LP: . . . . **LRF 081**

Crow & Wodwo

CROW & WODWO (Read by Ted Hughes).
MC: . . . . **CDL 51628**

Crowded House

CROWDED HOUSE.
Tracks: / World where you live / Now we're getting somewhere / Don't dream it's over (live) / Mean to me / Love you 'til the day I die / Something so strong / Hole in the river / I walk away / Tombstone / That's what I call love.
LP: . . . . **EST 2016**
MC: . . . . **TCEST 2016**

TEMPLE OF LOW MEN.
Tracks: / I feel possessed / Kill eye / Into temptation / Mansion in the slums / When you come / Never be the same / Love this life / Sister madly / In the lowlands / Better be home soon.
LP: . . . . **EST 2064**
MC: . . . . **TCEST 2064**

WOODFACE.
Tracks: / Chocolate cake / It's only natural / Fall at your feet / Tall trees / Weather with you / Whispers and moans / Four seasons in one day / There goes God / Fame is / All I ask / As sure as I am / Italian plastic / She goes on / How will you go.
LP: . . . . **EST 2144**
MC: . . . . **TCEST 2144**

Crowe, Bobby

THIS LASTING PRIDE (Crowe, Bobby & His S.C. Band).
Tracks: / Memories of Lindsay Ross / St. Bernard's waltz / Wild geese, The / Slow air / Fourth Road Bridge silver jubilee, The / Glasgow / Fiddle feature (pigeon pie) / Opening of the Forth Railway Bridge / Air / Call of the pipes / Gaelic waltz / Northlands, The / Strip the willow / Queen Victoria's visit quadrilles / Gay gordons / Polka / Gaelic medley, A / Fourth Railway Bridge centenary reel.
LP: . . . . **LILP 5187**
MC: . . . . **LICS 5187**

Crowe, J.D.

BLACKJACK.
Tracks: / Born to be with you / Sin City / Somehow tonight / Ramblin' boy / Black Jack / Bouquet in heaven / I'll stay around / Please search your heart / Portrait of the blues / There'll be no blind ones there / So afraid of losing you again.
LP: . . . . **SDLP 046**
LP: . . . . **REB 1583**
MC: . . . . **REBMC 1583**

BLUEGRASS HOLIDAY.
Tracks: / Little girl in Tennessee / Down where the river bends / Philadelphia lawyer / Will you be satisfied that way / Train 45 / You go to your church / Helen / Before I met you / Orange blossom special / Dark hollow / She's just a cute little thing / Little Bessie.
LP: . . . . **REB 1598**

J.D. CROWE AND THE NEW SOUTH (Crowe, J.D. & The New South).
Tracks: / Old home place / Some old day / Rock salt and nails / Sally Goodin / Ten degrees / Nashville blues / You are what I am / Summer wages / I'm walkin' / Home sweet home revisited / Cryin' Holly.
LP: . . . . **ROUNDER 0044**
MC: . . . . **ROUNDER 0044C**

LIVE IN JAPAN (Crowe, J.D. & The New South).
LP: . . . . **ROUNDER 0159**
MC: . . . . **ROUNDER 0159C**

MODEL CHURCH, THE.
Tracks: / I'll talk it all over with him / It's me again Lord / I shall be at home with Jesus / Journeys End / Model Church, The / Going up / Let the spirit descend / Look For Me / Are you lost in sin / No Mother or Dad / Oh heaven.
LP: . . . . **SDLP 038**
LP: . . . . **REB 1585**

MY HOME AIN'T IN THE HALL OF FAME (Crowe, J.D. & The New South).
LP: . . . . **ROUNDER 0103**
MC: . . . . **ROUNDER 0103C**

SOMEWHERE BETWEEN (Crowe, J.D. & The New South).
Tracks: / I never go around mirrors / I would have loved you all night long / Another town / Dance with me Molly / Long black limosine / To be loved by a woman / Girl from the canyon / Where are all the girls I used to chat with / Somewhere between / Family tree.
LP: . . . . **ROUNDER 0153**
MC: . . . . **ROUNDER 0153C**

STRAIGHT AHEAD.
LP: . . . . **ROUNDER 0202**
MC: . . . . **ROUNDER 0202C**

YOU CAN SHARE (Crowe, J.D. & The New South).
Tracks: / You can share my blanket / As tears go by / Hesitating / Too long / Hurtin' when you go, The / Ten miles from Natchex / Did she mention my name / Are you sad tonight / I don't know you / Hickory wind / Gypsy woman.
LP: . . . . **ROUNDER 0096**
MC: . . . . **ROUNDER 0096C**

Crowell, Rodney

AIN'T LIVING LONG LIKE THIS.
Tracks: / Elvira / Fool such as I, A / Leaving Louisiana in the broad daylight / Voila, An American dream / I ain't living long like this / Baby, better start turning 'em down / Song for the life / I thought I heard you calling my name/California Earthquake.
LP: . . . . **K 56564**

BEST OF RODNEY CROWELL.
LP: . . . . **K 9259651**
MC: . . . . **K 9259654**

DIAMONDS AND DIRT.
Tracks: / Crazy baby / I couldn't leave you if I tried / She's crazy for leaving / After all this time / I know you're married / Above and beyond / It's such a small world / I didn't know I could lose you / Brand new rag / Last waltz, The.
LP: **4608731**
MC: **4608734**

KEYS TO THE HIGHWAY, THE.
Tracks: / My past is present / If looks could kill / Soul searchin' / Many a long and lonesome highway / We gotta go on meeting like this / Faith is mine, The / Tell me the truth / Don't let your feet slow you down / Now that we're alone / Things I wish I'd said / I guess we've been together for too long / You've been on my mind.
LP: **4660021**
MC: **4660024**

RODNEY CROWELL.
Tracks: / Stars on the water / Just wanta dance / She ain't going nowhere / Don't need no other now / Shame on the moon / Only two hearts / Victim or a fool / All you've got to do / Till I gain control again / Old pipeliner.
LP: . . . . **K 56934**
MC: **K4 56934**

Crowley, Jimmy

BEST OF JIMMY CROWLEY AND STOKER'S LODGE.
LP: . . . . **RGLP 14**

BOYS OF FAIR HILL, THE.
LP: . . . . **LUN 014**

CAMP HOUSE BALLADS (Crowley, Jimmy & Stokers Lodge).
LP: . . . . **LUN 031**

JIMMY MO MHILE STOR.
LP: . . . . **CEF 113**

Crowley, Patrick

DO YA WANNA FUNK? (see Sylvester) (Crowley, Patrick/Sylvester).

Crown

ALL THAT ROCK AND ROLL.
Tracks: / Harder way to live / Music is freedom / Love me my way / Magic time / Right thru / Feeling easy / Two sides of the life / All that rock 'n' roll music / I believe in tomorrow's love / Dance the night away.
LP: . . . . **THBL 019**

RED ZONE.
Tracks: / Song for you, A / It's rock 'n' roll to me / Life in a minutes / You, oh you / Hollywood / Rising star / Lonely man / Ain't no coming back / Love is light in the night / Heaven or hell.
LP: . . . . **THBL 021**

Crown Heights Affair

DANCE LADY DANCE.
Tracks: / Come fly with me / Dance lady dance / Empty soul of mine / Number

one woman / Rock is hit / You don't have to say you love me.
LP: **637 276 2**

DREAM WORLD.
Tracks: / Galaxy of love / I love you / Say a prayer for two / Dream world / Things are going to get better / I'm gonna love you forever / Cherry.
LP: **6372 754**

SURE SHOT.
Tracks: / You gave me love / I don't want to change you / Sure shot / You've been gone / I see the light / Use your body and soul / Tell me you love me.
LP: **637 276 7**

THINK POSITIVE.
Tracks: / Somebody tell me what to do / Love rip off / Heart upside down / Think positive / I got somethin' for ya / Wine and dine you / Your love makes me hot / Let me ride on the wave of your love.
LP: . . . . **DSR 2**

Crown House

CROWN HOUSE (Various artists).
MCSET: . . . . **ZBBC 1045**

Crows

CROWS.
LP: . . . . **DIN 317**

NO BONES OR GREASE.
LP: . . . . **DRGN 861**

Crowther, Leslie (nar)

CINDERELLA/BABES IN THE WOOD
(see under Cinderella (bk)).

Crozier, Trevor

TROUBLE OVER BRIDGWATER.
Tracks: / Lamorna / Dead dog scrumpy / If the piddlethenride Jug Band hits the charts / Tavistock Goosey fayre / First medley of Breton tunes / I like bananas / Humours of Earl's Court, The / Mendip Mazurka, The / Trouble over Bridgwater / Pub with no beards, A / Don't tell I, tell'ee / Jambalaya / Teeth.
LP: . . . . **OU 2185**

Crucial Robbie

CRUCIAL VIEW.
LP: . . . . **ARILP 056**
MC: . . . . **ARIMC 056**

Crucial Youth

POWER OF POSITIVE THINKING, THE.
LP: . . . . **REM 002**

Crucif...

CRUCIF....
LP: . . . . **VIRUS 38**

Crucifix

DEHUMANIZATION.
LP: . . . . **CHRIST 11**

Crudup, Arthur 'Big

BIG BOY CRUDUP AND LIGHTNIN' HOPKINS (Crudup, Arthur Big Boy & Lightnin' Hopkins).
Tracks: / Shake that thing / I'm leaving with you now / Walk a long time / Bring me my shotgun / Just picking / If I get lucky / Death valley blues / Angel child / My mama don't allow me / I'm in the mood / I love her just the same / Looka there, she's got no hair / Last night.
LP: . . . . **KK 7410**

CRUDUP'S MOOD.
LP: . . . . **DS 621**
LP: . . . . **DL 621**

CRUDUP'S ROCKIN'.
Tracks: / My baby left me / If I get lucky / Mean old Frisco blues / Who's been fooling you / So glad you're mine / Shout sister shout / Cool disposition / I don't know it / That's alright / She's just like Caledonia / Rock me mama / Hand me down my walking cane / I love you / Gonna dig myself a hole / She's got no hair / Never no more / Too much competition.
LP: . . . . **NL 89385**
MC: . . . . **NK 89385**

GIVE ME A 32-20.
Tracks: / Give me a 32-20 / Kind lover blues / I don't know it / Raised to my hand / That's your red wagon / Boyfriend blues / Hoodoo lady blues / Black pony blues / That's why I'm lonesome / Roberta blues / Just like a spider / Someday / She's just like Caledonia / Behind closed doors / Tired of worry / Nelvina.
LP: . . . . **IG 403**

I'M IN THE MOOD.
Tracks: / Second man blues / Standing at my window / Come back, baby / Katie Mae / Crudup's Vicksburg blues / Gonna follow my baby / Hey, mama, everything's alright / Mercy blues / Mama don't allow / Nobody wants me / Pearly Lee / Hand me down my walking cane / Looking for my baby / Do it if you want to / You know that I love you / I'm in the mood.
LP: . . . . **KK 7416**

LOOK ON YONDERS WALL.
LP: . . . . **DS 614**
LP: . . . . **DL 614**

MEAN OL' FRISCO.
Tracks: / Mean ol' Frisco / I'm in the mood / That's alright / Standing at my window / Angel child / Katie Mae / Look on yonder wall / Dig myself a hole / If I get lucky / Death valley / I love her just the same / Angel child (take 2) / Rock me mama / Ethel Mae / My Mama don't allow me.
LP: . . . . **CRB 1206**

SHOUT, SISTER, SHOUT.
LP: . . . . **BWLP 1001**

STAR BOOTLEGGER.
LP: . . . . **KK 7402**

THAT'S ALL RIGHT MAMA.
LP: . . . . **MB 901**

Cruel Count (bk)

CRUEL COUNT, THE (Barbara Cartland) (Sinden, Jeremy (nar)).
MC: . . . . **IAB 88113**

Cruella

VENGEANCE IS MINE.
LP: . . . . **US 013**

Cruickshank, Andrew

STORIES GRANDAD TELLS.
MC: . . . . **VCA 099**

Cruickshank, Ian

HIGHLAND SPIRIT.
Tracks: / Reels / Hayfield twostep / Road To The Isles / Topsy / Whisky set / Bonnie lass O'Ballochmyle / Irish jars / Jigs / Gaelic Waltz / Spinning wheel / Spick And Span / Slow Air / MacPherson's Rant.
MC: . . . . **DACS 8602**

Cruise, Julee

FLOATING INTO THE NIGHT.
LP: **7599258591**
MC: **7599258594**

Cruisers

SWINGIN' ROCKIN' & ROLLIN'.
LP: . . . . **CR 30191**
LP: . . . . **LP 8810**

Cruisin'

CRUISIN' (Various artists).
Tracks: / Donna: *Valens, Ritchie* / La Bamba: *Valens, Ritchie* / Let's dance: *Montez, Chris* / Rhythm of the rain: *Cascades* / Sea cruise: *Ford, Frankie* / Surfer girl: *Beach Boys* / Venus in blue jeans: *Clanton, Jimmy* / He's a rebel: *Crystals* / Love potion No.9: *Various artists* / Come softly to me: *Fleetwoods*/ Little Honda: *Hondels* / Surf City: *Jan & Dean* / Louie Louie: *Kingsmen* / Runaway: *Shannon, Del*/ Wipe out: *Surfaris* / Night has a thousand eyes, The: *Vee, Bobby* / Cherish: *Association*.
LP: . . . . **SHM 3068**
MC: . . . . **HSC 3068**

CRUISIN' (1955) (A history of rock'n'roll radio) (Various artists).
Tracks: / Rock and roll: *Morrow, Buddy* / I got a woman: *Charles, Ray* / Sincerely: *Moonglows* / My babe: *Little Walter* / Earth angel: *Penguins* / Maybellene: *Berry, Chuck* / Only you: *Platters* / Ain't that a shame: *Domino, Fats* / Story untold, A: *Nutmegs* / Bo Diddley: *Diddley, Bo* / Pledging my love: *Ace, Johnny*.
LP: . . . . **INCM 1955**
MC: **INCR5 1955**

CRUISIN' (1956) (A history of rock'n'roll radio) (Various artists).
Tracks: / Robin Seymour theme: *Four Lads* / Roll over Beethoven: *Berry, Chuck* / Eddie my love: *Teen Queens*/ Ooby dooby: *Orbison, Roy* / Tonite tonite: *Mello Kings* / Great pretender, The: *Platters* / Tutti frutti: *Little Richard* / Stranded in the jungle: *Cadets* / Oh what a night: *Dells* / In the still of the night: *Five Satins* / Blue suede shoes: *Perkins, Carl*.
LP: . . . . **INCM 1956**
MC: **INCR5 1956**

CRUISIN' (1957) (A history or rock'n'roll radio) (Various artists).
Tracks: / Suzie Q: *Hawkins, Dale* / Happy happy birthday baby: *Tune Weavers* / School days: *Berry, Chuck*/ Goodnight sweetheart: *Spaniels* / Little darlin': *Diamonds* / Over the mountain across the sea: *Johnny & Joe* / Bony Moronie: *Williams, Larry* / To the aisle: *Five Satins* / Whole lotta shakin' goin' on: *Lewis, Jerry Lee* / Long lonely nights: *Andrews, Lee & The Hearts*.
LP: . . . . **INCM 1957**
MC: **INCR5 1957**

CRUISIN' (1958) (A history of rock'n'roll radio) (Various artists).
Tracks: / At the hop: *Danny & The Juniors* / Tequila: *Champs* / Book of love: *Monotones* / Rock and roll music: *Berry, Chuck* / Short shorts: *Royal Teens* / Chantilly lace: *Big Bopper* / Rockin' Robin: *Day, Bobby* / Get a job: *Silhouettes* / Ten commandments of love: *Harvey & The Moonglows* / Rebel rouser: *Eddy, Duane*.
LP: . . . . **INCM 1958**
MC: **INCR5 1958**

CRUISIN' (1959) (A history of rock'n'roll radio) (Various artists).
Tracks: / Baby hully gully: *Olympics* / There is something on your mind: *Big Jay McNeely* / Almost grown: *Berry, Chuck* / What a difference a day made: *Washington, Dinah* / Say man: *Diddley, Bo* / Sixteen candles: *Crests*/ Personality: *Price, Lloyd* / It's just a matter of time: *Benton, Brook* / Sea of love: *Phillips, Phil*/ Kansas city: *Harrison, Wilbert*.
LP: . . . . **INCM 1959**
MC: **INCR5 1959**

CRUISIN' (1960) (A history of rock'n'roll radio) (Various artists).
Tracks: / Big boy Pete: *Olympics* / Baby (you've got what it takes): *Benton, Brook & Dinah Washington* / What in the world's come over you: *Scott, Jack* / Angel baby: *Rosie & The Originals* / Alley oop: *Hollywood Argyles*/ Stay: *Williams, Maurice & The Zodiacs* / Running bear: *Preston, Johnny* / Big hurt, The: *Fisher, Toni*/ Because they're young: *Eddy, Duane* / Fannie Mae: *Brown, Buster*.
LP: . . . . **INCM 1960**
MC: **INCR5 1960**

CRUISIN' (1961) (A history of rock'n'roll radio) (Various artists).
Tracks: / Arnie Ginsburg theme: *3D's* / My true story: *Jive Five* / Nadine: *Berry, Chuck* / But I do: *Henry, Clarence 'Frogman'* / Those oldies but goodies: *Little Caesar & The Romans* / Tossin' & Turnin': *Lewis, Bobby* / Daddy's home: *Shep and the limelites* / Runaway: *Shannon, Del* / Ya Ya: *Dorsey, Lee* / Peanut butter: *Marathons* / Wooden heart: *Dowell, Joe*.
LP: . . . . **INCM 1961**
MC: **INCR5 1961**

CRUISIN' (1962) (A history of rock'n'roll radio) (Various artists).
Tracks: / Soldier boy: *Shirelles* / I need your lovin': *Gardner, Don & Dee Dee Ford* / Hey baby: *Channel, Bruce* / Duke of earl: *Chandler, Gene* / You'll lose a good thing: *Lynn, Barbara* / Let me in: *Sensations*/ What's your name: *Don & Juan* / Wanderer, The: *Dion* / Sealed with a kiss: *Hyland, Brian* / I know you don't love me no more: *George, Barbara*.
LP: . . . . **INCM 1962**
MC: **INCR5 1962**

CRUISIN' (1963) A history of rock'n'roll radio (Various artists).
Tracks: / Hand clappin': *Prysock, Red* / Sally go round the roses: *Jaynettes* / He's so fine: *Chiffons*/ Twist and shout: *Isley Brothers* / Baby it's you: *Shirelles* / It's my party: *Gore, Lesley* / Walk right in: *Rooftop Singers* / Denise: *Randy & The Rainbows* / Mama didn't lie: *Bradley, Jan* / Hey Paula: *Paul & Paula* / Louie Louie: *Kingsmen*.
LP: . . . . **INCM 1963**
MC: **INCR5 1963**

CRUISIN' (1964) A history of rock'n'roll radio (Various artists).
Tracks: / Harlem shuffle: *Bob & Earl* / Nitty gritty: *Ellis, Shirley* / Dang me: *Miller, Roger* / Chapel of love: *Dixie Cups* / Since I fell for you: *Welch, Lenny* / Girl from Ipanema: *Getz, Stan & Astrud Gilberto*/ Shoop shoop song: *Everett, Betty* / Talk back tremblin' lips: *Tillotson, Johnny* / It's alright: *Impressions (group)* / Funny: *Hinton, Joe* / Remember (walking in the sand): *Shangri-Las* / Suspicion: *Stafford, Terry*.
LP: . . . . **INCM 1964**
MC: **INCR5 1964**

CRUISIN' (1965) (A history of rock'n'roll radio) (Various artists).
Tracks: / Wooly bully: *Sam The Sham & The Pharaohs* / You've lost that lovin' feeling: *Righteous Brothers* / Birds and the bees, The: *Akens, Jewel* / King of the road: *Miller, Roger* / Sweet little sixteen: *Berry, Chuck*/ Name game: *Ellis, Shirley* / In crowd, The: *Lewis, Ramsey* / It ain't me babe: *Turtles* / Yes I'm ready: *Mason, Barbara* / Eve of destruction: *McGuire, Barry*.
LP: . . . . **INCM 1965**
MC: **INCR5 1965**

CRUISIN' (1966) (A history of rock'n'roll radio) (Various artists).
Tracks: / Sunny: *Hebb, Bobby* / Wipe out: *Surfaris* / Soul and inspiration: *Righteous Brothers* / Psychotic reaction: *Count Five* / Born a woman: *Posey, Sandy* / Pushin' too hard: *Seeds* / Walk away Renee: *Left Banke* / Li'l Red Riding Hood: *Sam The Sham & The Pharaohs* / California dreamin': *Mamas & Papas* / Sweet pea: *Roe, Tommy*.
LP: . . . . **INCM 1966**
MC: **INCR5 1966**

CRUISIN' (1967) (A history of rock'n'roll radio) (Various artists).
Tracks: / Judy in disguise: *John Fred & Playboy Band* / Apples peaches and pumpkin pie: *Jay & The Techniques*/ Happy together: *Turtles* / Gimme little sign: *Wood, Brenton* / We ain't got nothin' yet: *Blue Magoos*/ Snoopy v the Red Baron: *Royal Guardsmen* / 98.6: *Keith* / Little bit o' soul: *Music Explosion* / Rain the park and other things: *Cowsills* / Incense and peppermints: *Strawberry Alarm Clock*.
LP: . . . . **INCM 1967**
MC: **INCR5 1967**

CRUISIN (1969) (Various artists).
LP: . . . . **INCM 1969**
MC: **INCR5 1969**

CRUISIN' USA (Various artists).
LP: . . . . **OCN 2043WL**
MC: . . . . **OCN 2043WK**

CRUISIN' YEARS, THE (Various artists).
Tracks: / I got a woman: *Charles, Ray* / Roll over Beethoven: *Berry, Chuck* / Suzie Q: *Hawkins, Dale*/ At the hop: *Danny & The Juniors* / Hully gully: *Olympics* / Teen angel: *Dinning, Mark* / Blue moon: *Marcels* / My true story: *Jive Five* / Sally go round the roses: *Jaynettes*.
MC: **INCR5 1000**
LP: . . . . **INCM 1000**

CRUISING COLLECTION, THE (Various artists).
Tracks: / Rumble: *Wray, Link & His Raymen* / Batman: *Wray, Link & His Raymen* / Sea cruise: *Ford, Frankie*/ Go Jimmy go: *Clanton, Jimmy* / Goodnight my love: *Belvin, Jesse* / Great shakin' fever: *Burnette, Dorsey*/ High blood pressure: *Smith, Huey "Piano"* / Good rockin' daddy: *James, Etta* / Dance with me Henry: *James, Etta* / Snake eyes: *Tyler, Alvin 'Red'* / Leave my woman alone: *Everly Brothers* / When will I be loved: *Everly Brothers* / Eddie my love: *Teen Queens* / Tossin' and turnin': *Lewis, Bobby* / Mr. Sandman: *Chordettes*/ Tramp: *Fulson, Lowell* / Poetry in motion: *Tillotsen, Johnny* / Teenager in love: *Dion & The Belmonts*/ Mary Lou: *Young Jessie* / Stranded in the jungle: *Cadets* / White lightning: *Jones, George* / Wanderer: *Dion* / Runaround Sue: *Dion*.
2LP: . . . . **CCSLP 140**
MC: . . . . **CCSMC 140**

SUMMER CRUISIN' (Various artists).
Tracks: / Surf city: *Jan & Dean* / Little GTO: *Ronny & Daytonas* / Pipeline: *Chantays* / Palisades Park: *Cannon, Freddy* / I live for the sun: *Vanity Fair* / Summer love sensation: *Bay City Rollers* / Daydream believer: *Monkees* / Summer in the city: *Lovin' Spoonful* / Remember (walking in the sand): *Shangri-Las*/ Little old lady from Pasadena: *Jan & Dean* / In the Summertime: *Mungo Jerry* / What are you doing Sunday: *Dawn*/ New girl in school: *Magnificent Mercury Brothers* / It's the same old song: *Weathermen* / Wipe out: *Surfaris*/ California sun: *Jones, Joe* / Sea cruise: *Ford, Frankie* / California GL903: *Lee, Curtis* / New Orleans: *Bonds, Gary U.S.* / Let's twist again: *Checker, Chubby*.
LP: . . . . **NE 918**

Cruising (Film)

CRUISING (Film Soundtrack) (Various artists).
Tracks: / Heat of the moment: *Various artists* / Loneliness: *Various artists* / Spy boy: *Various artists*/ When I close my eyes I see blood: *Various artists* / Lump: *Various artists* / Shakedown: *Various artists*/ Pullin' my string: *Various artists* / Lion's share: *Various artists* / It's so easy: *Various artists*/ Hypnotize: *Various artists*.
LP: **70182**

Crumb, R

ELEPHANT SONGS AND COW COW CLUBS (Crumb, R & the Cheap Suit Serenaders).
LP: . . . . **BG 2025**

R. CRUMB & HIS CHEAPSUIT SERENADERS (Crumb, R & the Cheap Suit Serenaders).
LP: . . . . **BG 2019**

Crumbsuckers

BEAST ON MY BACK (B.O.M.B.).
Tracks: / Breakout / Jimmie's dream / Charge / Initial shock / I am he /

Connection, The / Rejuvenate / Remembering tomorrow / Beast on my back.
LP: . . . . JUST 9

LIFE OF DREAMS.
LP: . . . . JUST 4

Crumit, Frank

EVERYBODY'S BEST FRIEND.
Tracks: / Riding down from Bangor / There's no one with endurance like a man who sells insurance / Wrap me up in my tarpaulin jacket / Pig got up and slowly walked away, The / Frankie and Johnny / My girl ran away / Prune song, The / Antonio Pasquale Ramonio / Donald the dub / I'm in love with Susan / Nagasaki / Three trees, The / King of Zulu, The / Who, Josephine / I don't work for a living / Tale of a ticker, The / What kind of noise annoys an oyster? / High silk hat and a gold top walking cane, A / Grandson of Abdul Abulbul Amir, The / Dashing marine, The.
LP: . . . . CHD 139
MC: . . . . MCHD 139

MOUNTAIN GREENERY.
Tracks: / Bride's lament, The / Mountain greenery / Abdul Abulbul Amir / Thanks for the buggy ride / Kingdom coming and the year of Jubilo / Ukelele lady / Jack is every inch a sailor / Oh by jingo, oh by gee / Prune song, The / Girlfriend / Billy boy / King of Borneo, The / Get away old man get away / Down in the cane break / Crazy words, crazy tune / Gay caballero, A / Insurance man, The (CD only).
LP: . . . . AJA 5001
MC: . . . . ZC AJA 5001

RETURN OF THE GAY CABELLERO.
Tracks: / I'm bettin' the roll on roamer / Donald the dub / Lady of my dreams taught me how to play second fiddle, The / I learned about women from her-around the corner / Pretty little dear / O'Hooligans ball / Return of the Gay Cabellero / My grandfather's clock / My little bimbo down on the bamboo isle / Granny's old armchair / I'm a specialist / Would you like to take a walk? / And then he took up golf / Wake Nicodemus / Oh, baby (don't say no say maybe) / Dolan's poker party / I married the Bootlegger's daughter / Little brown jug / Return of Abdul Abulbul Amir.
LP: . . . . AJA 5012
MC: . . . . ZC AJA 5012

Crumly, Peter

THIRD WORLD SKETCHES (Crumly, Peter Sextet).
Tracks: / Urban urchins / Minds and memories / Bhoodan-ce / Senufo chant / Ethiopia / Better tomorrow.
LP: . . . . SPJ 531

Crusaders

BEST OF THE CRUSADERS.
Tracks: / Put it where you want it / Stomp and buck dance / Greasy spoon / Scratch / So far away / Hard times / So far away (live) / Don't let it get you down / Keep that same old feeling / That's how I feel / Soul caravan / Chain reaction / Ballad for Joe / Do you remember when / Way back home.
2LP: . . . . ABCD 612
MCSET: . . . . CABD 612

CHAIN REACTION.
LP: . . . . CAB 5144
LP: . . . . MFSL 1-010

CRUSADERS, THE.
MC: . . . . GTDC 083

FREE AS THE WIND.
Tracks: / Free as the wind / I felt the love / Way we was, The / Nite crawler / Feel it / Sweet n sour / River rat / It happens every day.
LP: . . . . MCL 1764
MC: . . . . MCLC 1764

GHETTO BLASTER.
LP: . . . . MCF 3176

GOOD AND BAD TIMES, THE.
Tracks: / Good times / Way it goes, The / Sweet dreams / Mischievious ways / Sometimes you can take it or leave it / Three wishes.
LP: . . . . MCF 6022
MC: . . . . MCFC 6022

HEALING THE WOUNDS.
Tracks: / Pessimisticism / Mercy, mercy, mercy / Little things mean a lot / Cause we've ended as lovers / Shake dance / Maputo / Running man / Healing the wounds.
LP: . . . . GR 9638
MC: . . . . GRC 9638

IMAGES.
Tracks: / Fair tales / Marcella's dream / Bayou bottoms / Merry go round / Cosmic reign / Covert action / Snow flake.
LP: . . . . MCL 1625
MC: . . . . MCLC 1625

LIFE IN THE MODERN WORLD.
Tracks: / Passion fruit / A C / Life in the modern world / Samplin' / Mulholland nights / Let me prove myself tonight / Destiny / D C / Some people just never learn / Coulda', woulda, shoulda'.
LP: . . . . MCF 3420
MC: . . . . MCFC 3420

ONGAKU DAI-LIVE IN JAPAN.
Tracks: / Introduction / Rainbow seeker / Hustler, The / Sweet gentle love / Drum introduction / Spiral / Carmel / In all my wildest dreams / Put it where you want it.
LP: . . . . CRP 16002

RHAPSODY AND BLUES.
Tracks: / Soul shadows / Honky tonk struttin' / Elegant evening / Rhapsody and blues / Last call / Sweet gentle love.
LP: . . . . MCL 1771
MC: . . . . MCLC 1771
LP: . . . . MCG 4010

RHAPSODY AND BLUES/STREET LIFE.
Tracks: / Street life / My lady / Rodeo drive (high steppin') / Carnival of the night / Hustler, The / Night faces / Soul shadows / Honky tonk struttin' / Elegant evening / Rhapsody and blue / Last call / Sweet gentle love.
MCSET: . . . . MCA 2 102

ROYAL JAM.
Tracks: / I'm so glad I'm standing here today / One day I'll fly away / Fly with wings of love / Burnin' up the carnival / Last call / Thrill is gone, The / Better not look down / Hold on (I feel our love is changing) / Street life / I just can't leave your love alone / Never make a move too soon.
LP: . . . . MCDW 455
MC: . . . . MCDC 455

SAMPLE A DECADE (1).
Tracks: / So far away / Bayou bottoms / Soul shadows / Don't let it get you down / My mama told me so / I'm so glad I'm standing here today / Soul caravan / Nite crawler / Fairytales / Honky tonk struttin' / Chain reaction / And then there was the blues / Street life / Hold on / Snow flake / Rhapsody and blues / Sweet'n'sour / Night ladies / Rodeo drive (high steppin') / Free as the wind.
2LP: . . . . VSOPLP 131
MC: . . . . VSOPMC 131

SCRATCH.
Tracks: / Scratch / Eleanor Rigby / Hard times / So far away / Way back home.
LP: . . . . MCL 1709
MC: . . . . MCLC 1709

STANDING TALL.
LP: . . . . MCF 3122

STREET LIFE.
Tracks: / Street life / My lady / Rodeo drive (high steppin') / Carnival of the night / Hustler, The / Night faces / Inherit the wind.
LP: . . . . MCL 1815
MC: . . . . MCLC 1815
LP: . . . . MCF 3008

THOSE SOUTHERN NIGHTS.
Tracks: / Spiral / Keep that same old feeling / My Mama told me so / Till the sun shines / And then there was the blues / Serenity / Feeling funky.
LP: . . . . MCL 1645
MC: . . . . MCLC 1645

VOCAL ALBUM, THE.
Tracks: / Street life / This old world's too funky for me / Better not look down / Inherit the wind / Hold on (I feel our love is changing) / Help / Soul shadows / Way it goes, The / I'm so glad I'm standing here today / I'll still be lookin' up to you, (no matter how high I get) / Burnin' up the carnival.
LP: . . . . MCF 3395
MC: . . . . MCFC 3395

VOCAL TAPE, THE.
LP: . . . . MCF 3171
MC: . . . . MCFC 3171

Crush, Bobby

BOBBY CRUSH.
LP: 6308 135

BOBBY CRUSH PLAYS ELTON JOHN.
Tracks: / Goodbye yellow brick road / Candle in the wind / Part time love / Rocket man / Someone saved my life tonight / Crocodile rock / Island girl / Song for Guy / Bitter fingers / Daniel / Don't go breaking my heart / Little Jeannie / Your song.
LP: . . . . ACLP 008

BOBBY CRUSH SINGALONG ALBUM, THE.
LP: . . . . WW 5138
MC: . . . . WW 45138

FIRST LOVE.
Tracks: / Lonely ballerina / Pepe / Brendan's theme / Orville's song / Memory / Dreamers / First love / Up where we belong / Angelique / Father to son / Slightly latin / On golden pond.
LP: . . . . PRCV 115
MC: . . . . TC PRCV 115

INCREDIBLE DOUBLE DECKER PARTY, THE.
2LP: . . . . WW 5126/7
MCSET: . . . . WW 4 5126/7

Crust

SACRED HEART OF CRUST.
LP: . . . . TR 01

Crutchfield, James

ORIGINAL BARREL-HOUSE BLUES.
Tracks: / Piggly wiggly blues / Pearly mae / I believe you need a shot / Forty four blues / Bogalusa blues / My baby cooks my breakfast / Black woman / US-russian blues / Barrelhouse blues / My little Lucille.
LP: 2109

Cruz, Celia

BRILIANTE, THE.
LP: . . . . VS 77

CELIA, RAY & ADALBERTO.
LP: . . . . SLP 623

CELIA & WILLIE.
LP: . . . . JMVS 93

DE NUEV (Cruz, Celia & Pacheco).
LP: . . . . JMVS 106

INTRODUCING CELIA CRUZ.
Tracks: / Quimbara / Soy antillana / A Santa Barbara / Yerbero moderno / Ritmo tambor y flores / Sabroso son cubano / Bemba colora / Me voy contigo / Cuca la / Cuando tu me quieras / Besitos de coco / Berimbau / El tumbao y Celia / Historia de una rumba / Bombora quina / Aye mi Cuba.
LP: . . . . HOT 112
MC: . . . . TCHOT 112

RITMO EN EL CORAZON (Cruz, Celia & Ray Barretto).
Tracks: / El chisme / No me cambie camino / Para decir adios / Mala suerte / En que quedamos / Tu musica popular / Bambaraka tunga / Ritmo en el corazon.
LP: . . . . HOT 124
MC: . . . . TCHOT 124

WINNERS, THE (Cruz, Celia/Willie Colon).
Tracks: / Un bembe pa' yemaya / Son matamoros / Vendedores / El paraiso / Dice anto / Yo si soy veneno / Se tambalea / Ache para todos.
LP: . . . . HOT 113
MC: . . . . TCHOT 113

Cruzados

AFTER DARK.
Tracks: / Small town love / Bed of lies / Road of truth / Last ride, The / Time for waiting / Young and on fire / Summer's come, summer's gone / I want your world to turn / Chains of freedom / Blue sofa (still a fool).
LP: 208212
MC: 408212

CRUZADOS.
LP: 207106
MC: 407106

Cry

QUICK, QUICK, SLOW.
LP: 206338
MC: 406338

Cry Before Dawn

CRIMES OF CONSCIENCE.
Tracks: / Seed that's been sown, The / Girl in the ghetto / Tender years / Flags / Second sight / Gone forever / White strand / Nobody knows / Stateside Europe.
LP: 4509971
MC: 4509974

WITNESS FOR THE WORLD.
Tracks: / Witness for the world / Yesterday's girl / Only want you for your soul / Your little world / Big wheels / No livin' without you / Always to win / Last of the sun / Best you can find, The / Victorians.
LP: 4633201
MC: 4633204

Cry No More

CRY NO MORE.
Tracks: / Cry no more / You don't hurt / Tears on the ballroom floor / Recipe for romance / Oh Bessie / Real love / Every single time / Marion Jones / Hit the big drum / Don't leave me here.
LP: . . . . PCS 7315
MC: . . . . TCPCS 7315

SMILE.
LP: . . . . COLDLP 003

Cryan Shames

SUGAR AND SPICE.
Tracks: / Sugar and spice / We could be happy / Heatwave / We'll meet again / Ben Franklin's almanac / Mr. Unreliable / Up on the roof / Hey Joe / If I needed someone / July / I wanna meet you / We gotta get out of this place / Young birds fly / Greenberg, Glickstein, Charles, David, Smith & Jones / It could be we're in love.
LP: . . . . LIK 37

Cryar, Morgan

FUEL ON THE FIRE.
LP: . . . . SR R 2066
MC: . . . . SR C 2066

Crybabys

CRYBABYS, THE.
LP: . . . . RRLP 142
MC: . . . . RRLC 142

Cryptadia

CRYPTADIA (Various artists).
LP: . . . . ERON 005 LP
MC: . . . . ERON 005 CA

Cryptic Slaughter

CONVICTED.
LP: . . . . RR 9680

MONEY TALKS.
LP: . . . . RR 9607

SPEAK YOUR PEACE.
Tracks: / Born too soon / Insanity by the numbers / Deathstyles of the poor and lonely / Divided minds / Killing time / Still born, again / Co-exist / One thing or another / Speak your piece.
LP: . . . . ZORRO 6

STREAM OF CONSCIOUSNESS.
Tracks: / Circus of fools / Aggravated / Last laugh / Overcome / Deteriorate / See through you / Just went back / Drift / Altered visions / One last thought / Whisker biscuit / Addicted.
LP: RR9 521 1

Crystal

CLEAR.
LP: . . . . BKH 51501

Crystal, Conrad

TRUE LOVE.
LP: . . . . LLQLP 3

Crystal Remedy

CRYSTAL REMEDY.
LP: . . . . SRTZ CUS 072

Crystallized Movements

MIND DISASTER.
LP: . . . . PSYCHO 28

WIDENESS COMES.
LP: . . . . KAR 003

Crystals

CRYSTALS MEET THE SHANGRI-LAS, THE (Crystals and the Shangri-las).
MC: U3015-2

PHIL SPECTOR WALL OF SOUND, VOL.3.
Tracks: / He's a rebel / Uptown / There's no other / Oh yeah / Maybe baby / Please hurt me / No one ever tells you / Da doo ron ron / Mashed potato time / Another country / Another world / He's sure the boy I love / Then he kissed me / On Broadway / What a nice way to turn seventeen / He hit me (and it felt like a kiss) / I love you, Eddie / Look in my eyes.
LP: 2307 006

Crywolf

FIRST 12 INCHES, THE.
Tracks: / Twelve o clock / Stay with me / Light up my life / Nothing to lose / Girls like you.
LP: . . . . OSGW 101

C.S.A

STOCKADE.
LP: . . . . GOAT 001

CTI

ELEMENTAL 7 (CTI(Creative Technology Institute)).
LP: . . . . DVR 3

Cua, Rick

CAN'T STAND TOO TALL.
LP: . . . . RRA R 0030
MC: . . . . RRA C 0030

WEAR YOUR COLOURS.
LP: . . . . BIRD R 182
MC: . . . . BIRD C 182

Cub Coda Crazy

CUB CODA CRAZY SHOW (Various artists).
LP: . . . . CH 108

Cub Koda

LET'S GET FUNKY.
MLP: . . . . NEW 23

Cuba (country)

CUBANS IN PARIS, 1930-38 (Various artists).
Tracks: / Bruno Zayas: *Various artists* / Cuba en Paris: *Various artists* / Mi

Tumbao: *Various artists*/ Marta: *Various artists* / Quatro Palomas: *Various artists* / Melody's bar: *Various artists* / Rumba Guajira: *Various artists* / Songoro cosongo: *Various artists* / Invitation a la rumba: *Various artists*/ Les trois coups: *Various artists* / Chivo que rompe tambo: *Various artists* / Ven Guaricha: *Various artists*/ Son de la loma: *Various artists* / Trinitaria: *Various artists* / Rico son: *Various artists* / Son retozon: *Various artists*.
LP: . . . . **HQ 2063**

Cuba, Joe

BREAKING OUT.
LP: . . . . **SCLP 9292**

HANGING OUT.
Tracks: / My man speedy / Quinto sabroso / La malanga brava / Ritmo de Joe Cuba / Hey Joe, hey Joe / Talk about luv / Alafia / No coman cuento / Joe Cuba's madness / Psychedelic baby.
LP: . . . . **HOT 126**
MC: . . . . **TCHOT 126**

Cuban Heels

WORK OUR WAY TO HEAVEN.
LP: . . . . **V 2210**

Cubeiro, Emilio

DEATH OF AN ASSHOLE, THE.
LP: . . . . **WSP 022**

Cuber, Ronnie

CUBER LIBRE.
LP: . . . . **XAN 135**

ELEVENTH DAY OF AQUARIUS, THE (Cuber, Ronnie/Tom Harrell/Rein deGraff/Sam Jones/Louis Hayes).
LP: . . . . **XAN 156**

NEW YORK JAZZ (Cuber, Ronnie/Tom Harrell/Rein deGraff/Sam Jones/Louis Hayes).
Tracks: / Fifty six / Monk's dream, A / Wail / Solar / 81st and 1st / Au privave.
LP: . . . . **SJP 130**

PASSION FRUIT.
Tracks: / Passion fruit / You promised to be true / What it is / Love notes / Come dance with me / It's only in your mind.
LP: . . . . **K 28P 6347**

PIN POINT.
LP: . . . . **K 28P 6415**

Cuca Records Story

CUCA RECORDS STORY, VOL 1 (Various artists).
Tracks: / I'm movin' on: *Hiorns, Dick* / Frankie's rock: *Tremain, Willie Thunderbirds* / Midnight express: *Tremain*, Willie Thunderbirds / You didn't listen: *Kennedy, Dave* / Rotation: *Six Shooters* / Don't you just know it?: *Six Shooters* / Weary blues: *Don & The Dominoes* / Just let me be: *Don & The Dominoes* / Rockin' Abe: *Tranes, Nigh* / Miami road: *Phillipson, Larry Lee* / If you are a coward: *Phillipson, Larry Lee* / Say mama: *Rock-a-Fellas* / Reaction: *Rock-a-Fellas* / Peenin' and hidin': *Kennedy, Dave* / Rocker: *Montereys*/ Rockin' fool: *Montereys*.
LP: . . . . **WLP 8847**

CUCA RECORDS STORY, VOL 2 (Various artists).
Tracks: / Like now: *Squires, Bud* / Spin out: *Squires, Bud* / Orbit rock: *Orbits* / Molly and ten brooks: *Sun, Jimmy* / Wasted: *Zakins* / Trackin': *Zakins* / Jitterbug Joe: *Nighthawks* / Hawk, The: *Nighthawks*/ That ain't so: *Sperry, Steve* / What's all this?: *Mattice, Bob* / Safari: *Mattice, Bob* / Kaw-liga: *Mattice, Bob* / I'm wondering now: *Phillipson, Larry Lee* / Muleskinner: *Kannon, Ray* / This way out: *Furys* / St. Louis blues: *Furys*.
LP: . . . . **WLP 8848**

CUCA RECORDS STORY, VOL 3 (Various artists).
Tracks: / Little Boy Blue: *Blihovde, Marv* / Bye bye baby: *Blihovde, Marv* / White lightning: *Blihovde, Marv*/ Nobody's darlin' but mine: *Blihovde, Marv* / Sweet little wife: *Blihovde, Marv* / Sensation: *Blihovde, Marv*/ Ramblin' on: *Vigilantes* / Badger, The: *Vigilantes* / Cherokee song: *Miller, Dick* / I might have known: *Teen Kings* / Told ya, little baby: *Teen Tones* / Borderline: *Teen Tones* / St. Louis: *Smith, Bobby*/ Sitting on top of the world: *Hodge, Bobby* / Sidewinder, The: *Vibratones* / White lightnin' effect: *Lavenders*/ War party: *Catalinas* / Rocky road blues: *Muleskinners* / Sands of Arabia: *Teen Tones*.
LP: . . . . **WLP 8849**

Cuchulainn the Hero

CUCHULAINN THE HERO (Various artists).
MC: . . . . **ANV 604**

Cuckoo Sister (bk)

CUCKOO SISTER, THE (Vivien Alcock) (Hayman, Carole (nar)).
MC: **3CCA 3057**

Cud

ELVIS' BELT.
LP: . . . . **ILLUSION 013**
MC: . . . . **ILLC 013**

LEGGY MAMBO.
LP: . . . . **ILLUSION 021**
MC: . . . . **ILLC 021**

WHEN IN ROME, KILL ME.
LP: . . . . **ILLUSION 005**

Cuddly Toys

GUILLOTINE THEATRE.
LP: . . . . **FRESH LP 1**

TRIALS AND CROSSES.
Tracks: / It's a shame / One close step / Fall down / Trials and crosses / Normandy nightfall.
LP: . . . . **FRESH LP 6**

Cuddy, Joe

JOE CUDDY FAVOURITES.
LP: **829 991 4**

Cudu

DELIVERY.
LP: . . . . **MASO 33039**

Cues

CRAZY, CRAZY PARTY.
Tracks: / Burn that candle / Charlie Brown / You're on my mind / Much obliged / Oh my darling / Don't make believe / Crazy crazy party / Rock 'n' roll Mr Oriole / Destination 2100 and 65 / Why / Be my wife / Crackerjack / Girl I love, The / Killer diller / Prince or pauper / I pretend.
LP: . . . . **BFX 15309**

Cuevas, Sergio

LA HARPE INDIENNE DU PARAGUAY.
Tracks: / Camino de San Juan / Maquinita / Feliz Navidad / Harpa serenata / Pajaro campana / A mi dos amores / Nuevo baile / Poncho cuatro colores / Golpe llanero / Danza indiana / Barrio rincon / Magnolia / Balada de mi sueno / Pa i Zacaria.
LP: . . . . **ARN 30131**

Cuffe, Tony

WHEN FIRST I WENT TO CALEDONIA.
Tracks: / When first I went to Caledonia / Miss Wharton Duff/The mare / Iron horse / Caledonia / Doctor MacInnes' fancy / Buchan turnpike, The / Lass o' paties mill / Weary pund o' tow, The / Paddy Kelly's brew / Otterburn / Scalloway lassies / Humours of Tulla / Miss Forester.
LP: . . . . **IR 011**
MC: . . . . **IRC 011**

Cugat, Xavier

1944/5 (Cugat, Xavier & His Orchestra).
LP: . . . . **CLP 59**

TO ALL MY FRIENDS.
Tracks: / New Cucaracha / Golden sunset / La bamba / Que lindas in Mexicanas / Despedida / Cielito lindo / Banana boat song / Cuban holiday / Adius marquita Linda / Barbados baila / Diamante negro / Braziliana.
LP: . . . . **ISST 106**

Cugny, Laurent

BIG BAND LUMIERE (See under Evans, Gil).

Culbert, Hugh

UNTIL THEN.
Tracks: / Found the answer / For all my sins / Sweetest song I know, The / My yielded heart / Jesus is all you need / Follow me / Until then / That one lost sheep / My bondage was ended / Loveliness of Christ, The / It's in my heart / Song of the soul set free, The.
MC: . . . . **CGSOL 113**

Culbertson, Clive

BELFAST ROCK.
LP: . . . . **R11 (E) 101**

Cull, Bob

WELCOME TO THE FAMILY.
LP: . . . . **HS 20**

Cullen, Gerry

MANY'S THE FOOLISH YOUTH (Cullen, Gerry/Phil Callery/Fran McPhail).
LP: . . . . **SPIN 996**
MC: **4SPIN 996**

Culley, Frank

INSTRUMENTAL FOR DANCING (see under Tate, Buddy) (Culley, Frank Orchestra).

ROCK AND ROLL.
Tracks: / Snap, The / Floorshow / Cole slow / Central Avenue breakdown / Waxie maxie boogie / After hour session / Rumboogie jive / Hop'n twist / My silent love / Mona Lisa / Gone after hours / Little Miss Blues / I've got you under my skin / Culley-flower.
LP: . . . . **OFF 6057**

Cullum, Jim

SUPER SATCH (Cullum, Jim Big Band).
LP: . . . . **SOS 1148**

Culpepper County

AT HOME: CULPEPPER COUNTY.
LP: . . . . **SFA 051**

YOUR REQUEST OUR PLEASURE.
LP: . . . . **BUFFL 2003**

Cult

CULT: INTERVIEW PICTURE DISC.
LPPD: . . . . **BAK 2050**

DREAMTIME.
Tracks: / Horse nation / Butterflies / Flower in the desert / Bad medicine waltz / Spiritwalker / 83rd dream / Go West / Gimmick / Dreamtime / Rider in the snow.
LP: . . . . **BEGA 57**
LPPD: . . . . **BEGA 57 P**
MC: . . . . **BEGC 57**
LP: . . . . **BBL 57**
MC: . . . . **BBLC 57**

ELECTRIC.
Tracks: / Wild flower / Peace dog / Li'l devil / Aphrodisiac jacket / Electric ocean / Bad fun / King country man / Born to be wild / Love removal machine / Outlaw / Memphis hip shake.
LP: . . . . **BEGA 80**
MC: . . . . **BEGC 80**

LOVE.
Tracks: / Nirvana / Big neon glitter / Love / Brother wolf, sister moon / Rain / Phoenix / Hollow man / Revolution / She sells sanctuary / Black angel.
LP: . . . . **BEGA 65**
MC: . . . . **BEGC 65**

MUSIC AND MEDIA INTERVIEW PICTURE DISC.
LPPD: . . . . **MM 1223**

SONIC TEMPLE.
Tracks: / Fire woman / Sun king / Sweet soul sister / Soul asylum / Soldier blue / Edie (ciao baby) / American horse / Automatic blues / Wake up time for freedom / New York City.
MC: . . . . **BEGC 98**
LP: . . . . **BEGA 98**

Cult Jam

LOST IN EMOTION (see under Lisa Lisa) (Cult Jam/Lisa Lisa).

Cultural Roots

HELL A GO POP.
Tracks: / Hell a go pop / Every man has a right / Execute / Thief, liars, criminals / Where have you been / Reggae music / Tell it to her / Won't co-operate / Loving feelings / Lump sum.
LP: . . . . **GREL 62**

REGGAE RULE.
LP: . . . . **CRLP 001**

ROUGHER YET.
LP: . . . . **GREL 128**

RUNNING BACK TO ME.
Tracks: / Big finger / Running back to me / Get up / Warnes a me yard / His majesty reign / Sweet lady / Passion love / Distant lover / This woman / Runaround girl.
LP: . . . . **ILPS 9887**
MC: . . . . **ICT 9887**

Culture

BALD HEAD BRIDGE.
Tracks: / Them a payaka / How can I leave jah / Bald head bridge / Behold I come / Love shine bright / Jah love / Zion gate / So long babylon / Fool I (and I), A.
LP: . . . . **BMLP 012**
LP: . . . . **LASL 7**

CULTURE AT WORK.
LP: . . . . **BMLP 014**
MC: . . . . **BMC 014**
LP: . . . . **SHAN 43047**
MC: . . . . **SHANC 43047**

CUMBOLO.
Tracks: / They never love in this time / Innocent blood / Cumbolo / Poor Jah people / Natty never get weary / Natty dread naw run / Down in Jamaica / This train / Pay day / Mind who you beg for help.
LP: . . . . **FL 1040**
LP: . . . . **SHAN 44005**

GOOD THINGS.
Tracks: / Hand 'a' bowl / Good things / Love music (extended) / Psalm of Bob Marley / Cousin rude boy / Youthman move (extended) / Righteous loving / Chanting on.
LP: . . . . **RAS 3048**
MC: . . . . **RASC 3048**

HARDER THAN THE REST.
Tracks: / Behold / Holy Mount Zion / Stop the fussing and fighting / Iron sharpening iron / Vacancy / Tell me where you get it / Free again / Work on natty / Love shine bright / Play skillfully.
LP: . . . . **FL 1016**

INTERNATIONAL HERB.
Tracks: / International herb / Jah rastafari / If a guh dread / Rally around Jahoviah's Throne / Land we belong, The / Ethiopians waan guh home / Chiney man / I tried / Shepherd, The / Too long in slavery.
LP: . . . . **FL 1047**

LION ROCK.
LP: . . . . **HB 12**
MC: . . . . **HBC 12**

NUFF CRISIS.
Tracks: / Peace love and harmony / Want go see / Crack in a New York / How did I stray / Revolution time / Jah rastafari / Jump out of frying pan / Never gonna get away.
LP: . . . . **BMLP 022**
MC: . . . . **BMC 122**
MC: . . . . **BMTC 122**

STAND ALONE.
LP: . . . . **ADI 735**

TOO LONG IN SLAVERY.
Tracks: / Behold / Poor jah people / Stop the fussing and fighting / Cumbolo / Work on Natty / Tell me where you get it / Iron sharpening iron / International herb / Too long in slavery / Shepherd, The / Holy mount zion / Never get weary / Citizen as a peaceful dub.
MC: . . . . **FLC 9011**

TOO LONG IN SLAVERY (THREE FROM THE ...) (See under Three From The ...).

TWO SEVENS CLASH.
Tracks: / Calling Rasta Far I / I'm alone in the wilderness / Pirate days / Two sevens clash / I'm not ashamed / Get ready to ride the lion to Zion / Black star liner / Jah pretty face / See them a-come / Natty dread taking over.
LP: . . . . **BMC 004**
LP: . . . . **BMLP 004**
LP: . . . . **LIP 1**
LP: . . . . **SHAN 44001**
MC: . . . . **JGMC 3200**
MC: . . . . **SHANC 44001**
LP: . . . . **JGMLP 003**

VITAL SELECTION.
Tracks: / Behold / Poor Jah people / Stop the fussing and fighting / Work on natty / Never get weary / Citizen as a peaceful dub / Iron sharpening iron / International herb / Too long in slavery / Shepherd, The / Holy Mount Zion.
LP: . . . . **VX 1001**

Culture Beat

HORIZON.
Tracks: / Horizon / It's too late / Hyped affect, The / Tell me that you wait / Black flowers / I like you / No deeper meaning / Serious / Der erdbeermund.
LP: **4679621**
MC: **4679624**

Culture Club

BEST OF CULTURE CLUB, THE.
Tracks: / Do you really want to hurt me? / White boy / Church of the poison mind / Changing everyday / War song, The / I'm afraid of me / Dream, The / Time (clock of the heart) / Dive, The / Victims / I'll tumble 4 ya / Miss me blind / Mistake No. 3 / Medal song, The / Karma Chameleon.
LP: . . . . **VVIP 102**
MC: . . . . **VVIPC 102**

COLOUR BY NUMBERS.
Tracks: / Karma chameleon / It's a miracle / Black money / Changing everyday / That's the way / Church of the poison mind / Miss me blind / Mister man / Storm keeper (CD and cassette only) / Victims.
LP: . . . . **V 2285**
MC: . . . . **TCV 2285**
LP: . . . . **OVED 238**
MC: . . . . **OVEDC 238**

FROM LUXURY TO HEARTACHE.
Tracks: / I pray / Work on me baby / Gusto blusto / Heaven's children / God thank you woman / Reasons / Too bad / Come clean / Sexuality / Move away (extended version) (CD only) / God thank you woman (extended version) (CD only).
LP: . . . . **V 2380**
MC: . . . . **TCV 2380**
LP: . . . . **OVED 251**
MC: . . . . **OVEDC 251**

KISSING TO BE CLEVER.
Tracks: / White boy (dance mix) / You know I'm not crazy / I'll tumble 4 ya / Take control / Love twist / Boy boy (I'm the boy) / I'm afraid of me (remix) / White boys can't control it / Do you really want to hurt me?.
LP: . . . . **OVED 209**
MC: . . . . **OVEDC 209**

LP: . . . . V 2232

THIS TIME.
Tracks: / Do you really want to hurt me / Move away / I'll tumble 4 ya / Love is love / Victims / Karma chameleon / Church of the poison mind / Miss me blind / Time (Clock of the heart) / It's a miracle / Black money / War song / I'll tumble 4 ya (US 12" remix) (CD only) / Miss me blind (US 12" remix) (CD only).
LP: . . . . VTV 1
MC: . . . . VTVC 1

WAKING UP WITH THE HOUSE ON FIRE.
Tracks: / Dangerous man / War song / Unfortunate thing, The / Crime time / Mistake no.3 / Dive, The / Medal song, The / Don't talk about it / Mannequin / Hello goodbye.
LP: . . . . V 2330
MC: . . . . TCV 2330
LPPD: . . . . VP 2330
LP: . . . . OVED 184
MC: . . . . OVEDC 184

Culture, Peter

FACING THE FIGHT.
LP: . . . . ARILP 018

PRESSURE MAN.
Tracks: / Put a stop / Everywhere that I go / Dance hall music / I love you baby / Behold / Must take me home with you / Tonight / Pressure man / Hold me tight / Never gonna let you go / African girl.
LP: . . . . KVL 9026

Culture Shock

GO WILD.
LP: . . . . FISH 18

ONWARDS AND UPWARDS.
LP: . . . . FISH 20
MC: . . . . FISH 20C

Culture, Smiley

ORIGINAL SMILEY CULTURE, THE.
LP: . . . . TOPLP 003

TONGUE IN CHEEK.
Tracks: / School time chronicle / Mr. Kidnapper / Customs officer / Here comes the style / Sling ting / Police officer / Cockney translation / Westland helicopter / Nuclear weapon / I've got the time / Nuff personality (Extra track on cassette.).
LP: . . . . POLD 5200
MC: . . . . POLDC 5200

Cultured Handmaiden

CULTURED HANDMAIDEN, THE (See also Catherine Cookson) (Jameson, Susan (nar)).

Culverwell, Andrew

TAKE ANOTHER LOOK.
Tracks: / Love is what you have / I have nothing (without your love) / We owe it all to you / You taught me how to fly / Song about freedom / Home again / May this be the place / Take another little look / Got it all together / Miracles happen all the time.
LP: . . . . DAY 4002

Cummings, E.E.

E.E. CUMMINGS READING.
MC: 1017

E.E. CUMMINGS READS HIS POETRY 1920-1940.
MCSET: 2080

E.E. CUMMINGS READS HIS POETRY 1943-1958.
MCSET: 2081

Cunliffe, John (auth)

POSTMAN PAT (Barrie, Ken (nar)).
MCSET: 00 104 125 8

POSTMAN PAT GOES ON SAFARI (Barrie, Ken (nar)).
MC: 0 00 102175 3

POSTMAN PAT MAKES A SPLASH (Barrie, Ken (nar)).
MC: 0 00 109022 4

POSTMAN PAT PLAYS FOR GREENDALE (Barrie, Ken (nar)).
MC: . . . . 0 00 102177 X

POSTMAN PAT STORIES, THE (Barrie, Ken (nar)).
MC: . . . . TS 336

POSTMAN PAT & THE CHRISTMAS PUDDING (Barrie, Ken (nar)).
MC: 0 00 109026 7

POSTMAN PAT & THE DINOSAUR BONES (Barrie, Ken (nar)).
MC: 0 00 109025 9

POSTMAN PAT & THE GREENDALE GHOST (Barrie, Ken (nar)).
MC: 0 00 109024 0

POSTMAN PAT'S 123 STORY (Barrie, Ken (nar)).
MCSET: 00 103 208 9

POSTMAN PAT'S ABC STORY (Barrie, Ken (nar)).
MCSET: 00 103 207 0

POSTMAN PAT'S DAY IN BED (Barrie, Ken (nar)).
MC: 0 00 109023 2

POSTMAN PAT'S MESSY DAY (Barrie, Ken (nar)).
MC: 0 00 102176 1

POSTMAN PAT'S PARCEL OF FUN (Barrie, Ken (nar)).
MC: 00 1034502

POSTMAN PAT'S WET DAY (Barrie, Ken (nar)).
MC: 0 00 102178 8

Cunningham, Andrew

20 GOLDEN GREATS: ANDREW CUNNINGHAM.
LP: . . . . DV 1201

Cunningham, David

COME AND SEE SCOTLAND.
Tracks: / Come and see with me / Dream Angus / I know where I'm going / Trotting to the fair / I tell you, you'll be sorry lad / Battle is o'er, The / Drivin' doon tae Glasca / Jean / Morag's fairy glen / My highland home / Down in the glen / Bonnie Scots lassie o' mine.
LP: . . . . SBE 125

Cunningham, Earl

JOHN TOM.
LP: . . . . TRLP 002

SHOW CASE.
LP: . . . . VSLP 4021

Cunningham, John

AGAINST THE STORM (Cunningham, John & Phil).
LP: . . . . SHY 7011
LP: . . . . SHAN 79017

FAIR WARNING.
LP: . . . . SIF 1047
MC: . . . . CSIF 1047

JOHN CUNNINGHAM.
LP: . . . . SHAN 79029

THOUGHTS FROM ANOTHER WORLD.
LP: . . . . SHY 7013

Cunningham, Larry

20 BEST SONGS.
LP: . . . . PHL 446
MC: . . . . CPHL 446

BEST OF COUNTRY AND IRISH.
LP: . . . . HPE 601

COME BACK TO ERIN.
LP: . . . . HPE 629
MC: . . . . HPC 629

SHARE OUR WORLD (Cunningham, Larry & Margo).
LP: . . . . SOLP 1011
MC: . . . . SOCAS 1011

THIS IS LARRY CUNNINGHAM.
Tracks: / Don't let me cross over / 90 years old / Bracer o / Shoe goes on the other foot, The / Church, a courtroom and then goodbye, A / Ramblin' Irishman / Cottage by the Lee / Too many chiefs and not enough indians / Lovely Derry on the banks of the Foyle / That's a sad affair / Sweet youghal bay.
LP: . . . . PHL 406
MC: . . . . CPHL 406

WHERE THE GRASS GROWS THE GREENEST.
LP: . . . . RITZLP 0017
MC: . . . . RITZLC 0017
MC: . . . . BTC 306

Cunningham, Matt

CEOL CEILI.
MC: . . . . GTDC 071

DANCE MUSIC OF IRELAND, VOL.1.
MC: . . . . GTDC 053

DANCE MUSIC OF IRELAND, VOL.2.
MC: . . . . GTDC 054

GREEN HILLS OF ERIN, THE.
LP: . . . . GTD 027
MC: . . . . GTDC 027

MEMORIES OF IRELAND.
MC: . . . . GTDC 070

Cunningham, Phil

AIRS AND GRACES.
LP: . . . . REL 474
MC: . . . . REC 474
LP: . . . . SIF 3032

FIRE IN THE GLEN (see Stewart, Andy M) (Cunningham, Phil, Andy M.Stewart, Manus Lunny).

RELATIVITY (Cunningham, Phil & Johnny/O Domhnaill,M/Ni Dhomhnail,T).
LP: . . . . SIF 1059
MC: . . . . CSIF 1059

Cunts

REMEMBER HAVE FUN.
Tracks: / Apocalyptic breakfast / C*nt theme / Way out west / There are electric filaments on my... / There's a demon in my hair / Musician in a bathtub / Fires of spring, The / I don't want food, I don't want sex / Children swept out to sea by a tidal wave / Jukebox in heaven / Every crease in Donna's brain / Cracked cat.
LP: . . . . R 338710

Cupar & District...

CUPAR & DISTRICT PIPE BAND (Cupar & District Pipe Band).
MC: . . . . SPRC 502

Cupp, Pat

MODERN ROCKABILITY (Cupp, Pat & His Flying Saucers).
Tracks: / Long gone daddy / Do me no wrong / Baby come back / That girl of mine / I guess it's meant that way / Pink Cadillac / Snake eyed mama / Don't go pretty baby / Red hot rockin' blues / South's gonna rise again.
LP: . . . . 10 CH 32

Curb In The Sky

CURB IN THE SKY AND OTHER THURBER STORIES (Ustinov, Peter).
LP: . . . . TC 1641
MC: . . . . CP 1641

Cure

ALL THE HITS/UNAVAILABLE 'B' SIDES.
Tracks: / Killing an arab / Boys don't cry / Jumping someone elses train / Forest, A / Primary / Charlotte sometimes / Hanging gardens, The / Let's go to bed / Walk, The / Love cats, The / Caterpillar, The / In between days / Close to me / I'm cold / Another journey by train / Descent / Splintered in her head / Mr. Pink eyes / Happy the man / Throw your foot / Exploding boy / Few hours after this, A / Man inside my mouth, A / Stop dead / New day.
MC: . . . . FIXHC 12
LP: . . . . FIXH 12

BETWEEN THE FOREST AND THE SEA (Interview picture disc).
LPPD: . . . . BAK 6006
MC: . . . . MBAK 6006

BOYS DON'T CRY.
Tracks: / Boys don't cry / Plastic passion / 10.15 Saturday night / Accuracy / Object / Jumping someone else's train / Subway song / Killing an arab / Fire in Cairo / Another day / Grinding halt / World war / Three imaginary boys.
LP: . . . . SPELP 26
MC: . . . . SPEMC 26

CONCERT - THE CURE LIVE.
Tracks: / Shake dog shake / Primary / Charlotte sometimes / Hanging gardens, The / Give me it / Walk, The / One hundred years / Forest, A / 10.15 Saturday night / Killing an arab / Curiosity - Cure anomalies 1977-84 (On double cassette only) / Heroin face / Boys don't cry / Subway song / At night / In your house / Drowning man, The / Other voices / Funeral party / All mine / Forever.
LP: . . . . FIXH 10
MC: . . . . FIXHC 10

CURE: INTERVIEW PICTURE DISC.
LPPD: . . . . BAK 2011

CURE: INTERVIEW PICTURE DISC, VOL 2.
LPPD: . . . . BAK 2105

DISINTEGRATION.
Tracks: / Plainsong / Closedown / Last dance / Fascination street / Same deep water as you / Homesick / Pictures of you / Love song / Lullaby / Prayers for rain / Disintegration / Untitled.
LP: 839 353 1
MC: 839 353 4
LP: . . . . FIXH 14
MC: . . . . FIXHC 14
LPPD: 841 946 1

FAITH.
Tracks: / All cats are grey / Carnage visors / Doubt / Drowning man, The / Faith / Funeral party / Holy hour, The / Other voices / Primary.
LP: . . . . FIX 6

FAITH/CARNAGE VISORS.
MCSET: . . . . FIXC 6

HEAD ON THE DOOR, THE.
Tracks: / In between days / Kyoto song / Blood, The / Six different ways / Push / Baby screams, The / Close to me / Night like this, A / Screw / Sinking.
LP: . . . . FIXH 11
MC: . . . . FIXHC 11

JAPANESE WHISPERS.
Tracks: / Lets go to bed / Walk, The / Lovecats, The / Dream, The / Just one kiss / Upstairs room, The / Lament / Speak my language.
MLP: . . . . FIXM 8
MC: . . . . FIXMC 8

KISS ME, KISS ME, KISS ME.
Tracks: / Kiss, The / Catch / Torture / If only tonight we could sleep / Why can't I be you? / How beautiful you are... / Snakepit / Just like heaven / Hot hot hot / All I want / One more time / Like cockatoos / Icing sugar smooth / Perfect girl / Thousand hours, A / Shiver and shake / Fight.
2LP: . . . . FIXH 13
MCSET: . . . . FIXHC 13
2LP: . . . . FIXHA 13

MIXED UP.
Tracks: / Lullaby (1989 extended mix) / Close to me (1990 Paul Oakenfold mix) / Fascination Street (USA 1989 mix) / Walk, The (1990 re-recording) / Lovesong (1989 remix) / Forest, A (1990 remix) / Pictures of you (Bryan Chuck new 1990 mix) / Hot, hot, hot (1988 extended mix) / Why can't I be you ? (extended mix) / Caterpillar, The (1990 Bryan Chuck mix) / In between days (1990 William Orbit shiver mix) / Never enough (Big mix 1990 recording).
2LP: 847 099 1
MC: 846 099 4

PORNOGRAPHY.
Tracks: / Pornography / Hanging gardens, The / One hundred years / Siamese twins / Figurehead / Strange day, A / Cold / Short term effect, A.
LP: . . . . FIX 7
MC: . . . . FIXC 7

SEVENTEEN SECONDS.
Tracks: / At night / Final sound, The / Forest, A / In your house / M / Play for today / Reflection, A / Secrets / Seventeen seconds / Three.
LP: . . . . FIX 4

THREE IMAGINARY BOYS.
Tracks: / Accuracy / Another day / Fire in Cairo / Foxy lady / Grinding halt / It's not you / Meat hook / Object / So what / Subway / 10.15 Saturday night / Three imaginary boys.
LP: . . . . FIX 1
MC: . . . . FIXC 1

TOP, THE.
Tracks: / Caterpillar, The / Piggy in the mirror / Empty world / Bananafish bones / Top, The / Shake dog shake / Bird mad girl / Wailing wall / Give me it / Dressing up.
LP: . . . . FIXS 9
MC: . . . . FIXSC 9

WALK, THE.
Tracks: / Upstairs room, The / Dream, The / Lament / Let's go to bed / Just one kiss.
MLP: 810752 1

Curing Depression

CURING DEPRESSION (Kline, Nathan S.).
MC: . . . . PT 42

Curiosity Killed...

GETAHEAD (Curiosity Killed The Cat).
LP: 842 010 1
MC: 842 010 4

KEEP YOUR DISTANCE (Curiosity Killed The Cat).
Tracks: / Misfit / Down to earth / Free / Know what you know / Curiosity killed the cat / Ordinary day / Mile high / Red lights / Shallow memory.
LP: . . . . CATLP 2
MC: . . . . CATMC 2
LP: . . . . CATLP 1
LP: 832 025 1
MC: 832 025 4

Curious Collection

CURIOUS COLLECTION (Various artists).
LP: . . . . STLP 007

Curless, Dick

20 GREAT TRUCK HITS: DICK CURLESS.
Tracks: / Big wheel cannonball / Drag 'em off the interstate, sock it to 'em J.P.blues / Hard, hard travelling man / Goin' down the road feeling bad / Truck stop / Jukebox man / Drop some silver in the juke box / Leaving it all behind / Coastline Charlie / 6 days on the road / Tombstone every mile / Golden girl / Old ramblin Alabama me / Woman, don't try to sing my song / Hot springs / Carter boys / Born on country music / Homing pigeon / Chick inspector / Pinch o' powder, A.
LP: 7C 062 85894

IT'S JUST A MATTER OF TIME.
LP: . . . . HAT 3139
MC: . . . . HATC 3139

LONG, LONESOME ROAD.
LP: . . . . HAT 3102

MC: . . . . HATC 3102

Curlew

CURLEW.
Tracks: / Panther burn / Bear, The / Bitter thumbs / Victim, The / Hardwood, The / Sports / Bruno / But get it / Rudders / Binoculars / Ole miss exercise song, The.
LP: . . . . LD 1004

FIDDLE MUSIC FROM SHETLAND AND BEYOND.
LP: 12TS 435

Curley, Carlo

CONCERT CURIOS.
Tracks: / Entertainer, The / Watchet auf, ruft uns die stimme / Christmas / Sketch in F minor / Hallelujah chorus / Pomp and circumstance / Washington post march / Melody in A / Turkish march / Solemn melody / Banjo.
LP: . . . . RL 25314

Curran, Eamonn

FAREWELL TO EIREANN (Curran, Eamonn & Dolores Keane & John Faulkner).
LP: . . . . FF 4004

Curran, James

JAMES CURRAN.
MC: . . . . JD 101

Currency

FIRST EXCHANGE.
LP: . . . . LRF 093

Current 93

CHRIST AND THE PALE QUEENS.
LP: . . . . MAL 666

CROWLEY MASS (Current 93/H.O.H.).
LP: . . . . MAL 108

DOGS BLOOD RISING.
LP: . . . . LAY 008

EARTH COVERS.
LP: . . . . UD 029

FAITH'S FAVOURITES (See Nurse With Wound) (Current 93/Nurse with wound).

IMPERIUM.
LP: . . . . MAL 777

IN MENSTRUAL NIGHT.
LPPD: . . . . UDO 22M
LP: . . . . UDO 022

NATURE UNVEILED.
LP: . . . . LAY 004

NIGHTMARE CULTURE (Current 93/ Sickness of snake).
2LP: . . . . LAY 014

RED FACE OF GOD.
LP: . . . . MAL 088

SWASTIKAS FOR NODDY.
Tracks: / Benediction / Blessing / North / One eye / Black sun bloody moon / Oh coal black Smith / Panzer rune / Black flowers please / Final church / Summer of love, The / Hey ho the Noddy (oh) / Beau soleil / Scarlet woman / Stair song, The / Angel / Since yesterday / Valediction / Malediction.
LP: . . . . LAY 020

TANTRIC NYING MA CHANT OF TIBET (Current 93 present C.R. Lama).
LP: . . . . MAL 111

Currie, Alastaire

CHOICE BLEND FROM THE SALEN HOTEL.
MC: . . . . MR 1004

Currie, Billy

STAND UP AND WALK.
LP: . . . . HFMLP 001
MC: . . . . HFMTC 001

TRANSPORTATION.
Tracks: / Airlift / Traveller / Transportation / Rakaia river / India / Perfect flight / Over soul / English home.
LP: . . . . ILP 030

Currie Brothers

BY SPECIAL REQUEST.
Tracks: / Tico tico / Pipe selection / Orpheus in the underworld / Jig and reel / Boum mussette / South Rampart street parade / Orange blossom special.
LP: . . . . ASLP 001

HOT STUFF.
LP: . . . . LILP 5077
MC: . . . . LICS 5077

TAKE THREE.
Tracks: / Shetland two-step / Style musette / Jig and reel / March / Curries of Milngavie / Riders in the sky / Nola / Cumbanchero.
LP: . . . . LILP 5102
MC: . . . . LICS 5102

TAKE TWO.
Tracks: / Accordions on parade / March, strathespey and reel / Cuckoo waltz / Scottish reels / Scotch polka / Irish reels / Scottish waltzes / Pipe march and reel / Musette pour tous / Slow air jig and reel.
LP: . . . . LILP 5094

Currie, Cherie

MESSIN' WITH THE BOYS (Currie, Cherie & Marie).
Tracks: / Messin' with the boys / Since you've been gone / I just love the feeling / All I want / Overnight sensation / Elaine / This time / Wishing well / Secrets / We're through.
LP: . . . . EST 12022

Curry Memorial Choir

LIFT JESUS UP.
LP: . . . . MAL 04376

Curry, Mini

100 PER CENT.
Tracks: / 100 per cent / If they only knew / I think I'm over you / I like it / Have we lost / Serious / Doll in the window / First time.
LP: . . . . TRPL 118

Curry, Tim

FEARLESS.
Tracks: / Right on the money / Hide this face / I do the rock / S.O.S. / Cold blue steel and sweet fire / Paradise garage / No love on the street / Something short of paradise / Charge it.
LP: . . . . AMLH 64773

SIMPLICITY.
Tracks: / Working on my tan / She's not there / Simplicity / On a roll / Take me I'm yours / Dancing in the streets / Betty Jean / Out of pawn / Summer in the city / I put a spell on you.
LP: . . . . AMLH 64830

Curry, Tyrone

TYRONE CURRY.
Tracks: / I'm so in love / Take this love / Overload / Joy ride / Have we lost / Let's have some fun tonight / Play it cool / Need your lovin' / Give it up.
LP: . . . . TRLP 120

Curson, Ted

CANADIAN CONCERT OF TED CURSON, THE (Live at La' Tete de L'art).
LP: . . . . CA 1700

I HEARD MINGUS.
LP: . . . . IP 7729

TED CURSON & CO.
LP: . . . . IN 1054

TRIO, THE.
LP: . . . . IP 7722

Curtin, D.J.

ALMOST PERSUADED.
LP: . . . . HPE 644

Curtin, Glen

IRISH IN ME, THE.
MC: . . . . SMAC 9012

MY FAVOURITE IRISH SONGS.
MC: . . . . CARC 6

Curtis, Chantal

GET ANOTHER LOVE (ALBUM).
Tracks: / Get another love / Hey taxi driver / I'm burnin' / Hit man / Bet your bottom dollar / I gotta know.
LP: . . . . DISC 02

Curtis, Dave

BROKEN HILL.
LP: . . . . BSS 132

TAKIN' THE ROUGH WITH THE SMOOTH.
LP: . . . . BSS 306

Curtis, King

20 GOLDEN PIECES: KING CURTIS (Curtis, King & The Noble Knights).
Tracks: / Tequila / Night train / Java / Harlem nocturne / Honky tonk / Soul twist / Memphis / Watermelon man / Soul serenade / Swingin' shepherd blues / My last date (with you) / Wiggle wobble / Tanya / Tennessee waltz / Bill Bailey won't you please come home? / Misty / Sister Sadie / Ain't that good news? / Peter Gunn / One mint julep.
LP: . . . . BDL 2009

BLUES AT MONTREUX (Curtis, King & Champion Jack Dupree).
LP: . . . . SD 1637
MC: . . . . CS 1673

DIDN'T HE PLAY.
Tracks: / Home cookin' / Soul groove part 1 / Soul groove part 2 / Pickin' chicken / Clementine / Blowin' off steam / Didn't he play / Blue nocturne / Hello sunshine / Count your blessings / Write me a love letter / Jealous fool / Don't put me down like this.
LP: . . . . RL 074

INSTANT GROOVE.
Tracks: / Castle rock / Chili / Restless guitar / Honey dripper / Birth of the blues / Peter Gunn / Boss / Rocky roll / This is soul / Quicksand / Memphissoul stew / Cookout / There is something on your mind / Instant groove / Patty cake / Pop corn Willy.
LP: . . . . ED 315

IT'S PARTY TIME WITH KING CURTIS.
Tracks: / Free for all / Easy like / Hot saxes / I'll wait for you / Party time twist, The / Low down / Keep movin' / (Let's do) the hully gully twist / Slow motion / Firefly / Something frantic.
LP: . . . . CH 262

JAZZ GROOVE.
Tracks: / Da duh dah / Have you heard / Willow weep for me / Little brother soul / In a funky groove / Soul meeting / Lazy soul / All the way / Jeep's blues / What is this thing called love / Do you have soul now.
2LP: . . . . PR 24033

KING CURTIS LIVE AT FILLMORE WEST.
LP: . . . . SD 33359

LIVE IN NEW YORK.
Tracks: / Jaywalk / Trouble in mind / African waltz / What'd I say / I have to worry / Twist / Canadian sunset / How high the moon / K.C. special.
LP: . . . . JSP 1091

SINGS THE BLUES / TROUBLE IN MIND.
LP: . . . . OBC 512

SOUL BATTLE (See under Nelson, Oliver) (Nelson, Oliver/Jimmy Forrest/ King Curtis).

SOUL GROOVE.
Tracks: / Blowin' off steam / Dark eyes / Who's sorry now / Sweet Georgia Brown / Sometimes I'm happy / Pickin' chicken / Soul groove part 1 / Soul groove part 2 / Clementine / Take me out to the ball game.
LP: . . . . BMLP 1036

SOUL TWIST (Curtis, King & Others).
LP: . . . . COL 5119

THAT'S ALRIGHT.
LP: . . . . RL 042

Curtis, Mac

GOOD ROCKIN' TOMORROW.
LP: . . . . LP 007

GRANDADDY'S ROCKIN'.
LP: . . . . KAY 5046

ROCK ME.
Tracks: / Side thang / That's how much I love you / Turn away from me / Making it right / Real good itch / She knows all the good ways to be bad / Suntan girl / You can't take the boogie woogie outta me / Good love sweet love / Don't you love me / Rock me.
LP: . . . . LP 016
LP: . . . . MFLP 047

ROCKIN' MOTHER.
Tracks: / Ducktail / Grandaddy's rockin' you / You've oughta see Gramma rock / How long will it take / If I had me a woman / Good rockin' tomorrow / Rockin' mother / How come it / Slip slip slippin' in / Johnny Carroll rock / Turn away from me / That ain't nothin' but time / Crazy crazy lovin' / Hungry Hill.
LP: . . . . RAD 22

RUFFABILLY.
LP: . . . . LP 002

Curtis, Ronald

BYE BYE BLUES.
Tracks: / Whispering / Lullaby of the leaves / Alone / Five foot two, eyes of blue / Autumn concerto / Lover / Only make believe / Caribbean honeymoon / Nightingale sang in Berkeley Square, (A) / Tango bolero / Only a rose / Top hat, white tie and tails / Why do I love you?.
LP: . . . . SDL 323
MC: . . . . CSDL 323

PLAYS THE MIGHTY COMPTON ORGAN....
Tracks: / I got rhythm / Heartaches / I cover the waterfront / Begin the beguine / Jolly gilette / Yesterday / Summer holiday / Limelight / Jeepers creepers / Ain't she sweet / Perfidia / La Cumparsita / Five foot two eyes of blue / When you wish upon a star / My wonderful one / Autumn concerto / One day when we were young / That lucky old sun.
LP: . . . . AML 313

RON CURTIS AT HAMMERSMITH.
Tracks: / I got rhythm / Heartaches / Begin the beguine / Summer holiday / Limelight / Five foot two / When you wish upon a star / Jeepers Creepers / Wonderful one / That lucky old sun.
MC: . . . . AC 184

YES I REMEMBER IT WELL.
Tracks: / When I take my sugar to tea / Amor, amor / Yesterday / Syncopated clock / Mer, La / Walk right back / True love / Sway / Dream / Begin the beguine / Smile / Caravan / I'll be seeing you / Bei mir bist du schon.
LP: . . . . SDL 324
MC: . . . . CSDL 324

Curtis, Sonny

NO STRANGER TO THE RAIN.
Tracks: / I'm no stranger to the rain / Hello Mary Lou / You are the lesson I never learned / When Amarillo blows / Back when has been lover / I saved my last name for you / Bad case of love / Think it over / That'll be the day / More than I can say / Well alright / Rock around with Ollie Vee / Midnight shift.
LP: . . . . RITZLP 0055
MC: . . . . RITZLC 0055

SPECTRUM.
LP: . . . . COLT 2003

Curtis, T.C

STEP BY STEP.
LP: . . . . CURTIS 1
MC: . . . . CURTIS 14

Curtis, Tony

CIRCUMSPECT.
LP: . . . . WRMS 003

Curved Air

AIR CONDITIONING.
Tracks: / It happened today / Stretch / Screw / Blind man / Vivaldi / Hide and seek / Propositions / Rob one / Situation / Vivaldi.
LP: . . . . K 56004
LP: . . . . WSX 3012

AIR CUT.
Tracks: / Purple speed queen, The / Fifth boy / U.H.F. / Two three two / Easy / Metamorphosis / World / Arrlin.
LP: . . . . K 46224

AIRBORNE.
Tracks: / Desiree / Kids to blame / Broken lady / Juno / Touch of tequila / Moonshine / Heaven (never seemed so far away) / Hot and bothered / Dazed.
LP: . . . . BTM 1008

BEST OF CURVED AIR.
Tracks: / It happened today / Vivaldi / You know / Backstreet luv / Melinda (more or less) / Cheetah / Metamorphosis / Purple speed queen, The.
LP: . . . . K 36015

LOVE CHILD.
LP: . . . . ESSLP 024
MC: . . . . ESSMC 024

MIDNIGHT WIRE.
Tracks: / Woman on a one night stand / Day breaks my heart / Pipe of dreams / Orange Street blues / Dance of love / Midnight wire / It happened today.
LP: . . . . BTM 1005

PHANTASMAGORIA.
Tracks: / Marie Antoinette / Melinda (more or less) / Not quite the same / Cheetah / Ultra Vivaldi / Phantasmagoria / Whose shoulder are you looking over anyway / Over and above / Once a ghost always a ghost.
MC: K4 46158
LP: . . . . K 46158

SECOND ALBUM.
Tracks: / Young mother / Backstreet luv / Jumbo / You know / Puppets / Everdance / Bright summer's day / Piece of mind.
LP: . . . . K 46092

Cusack, Cyril (nar)

SAMUEL BECKETT (see under Beckett, Samuel).

Cusack, Michael

PIPERS OF DISTINCTION.
MC: . . . . ZCMON 807

Cusack, Peter

AFTER BEING IN HOLLAND.
LP: . . . . BEAD 5

Cussick, Ian

DANGER IN THE AIR.
Tracks: / Supernatural, The / Aerial combat / I read your letter / Gone in your eyes / Send my love through / Don't turn your back on the man / American women / Meaning rock on, The / Nucleus, The.
LP: . . . . AMLX 68562

Cut & Dry Band

CUT AND DRY NO. 2.
Tracks: / Barrington hornpipe, The / Glen Aln / Wild hills of Wannies / Swallow's tail / Jim Hall's fancy / Breamish / Random jig / Archie's fancy / Little Hennie / Lea rig, The / Sir Sidney Smith's march / Mrs. Elder / Doctor Whittaker's hornpipe / Nancy / Nae guid luck aboot the hoose / Oh dear, what can the matter be? / East neuk of Fife / Locomotive / South shore, The / Bonnie Woodside / Coffee bridge.

LP: 12 TS 413

Cut Tunes

STRANGE DRUM.
LP: SLATE 10

Cuthbertson, Iain

ROBERT BURNS.
Tracks: / Such a parcel of rogues in a nation / Fig for those by law protected, A / Holly Willie's prayer / Gie the lass her fairin' / To a love-begotten daughter / To a mouse / Epitaphs - dove, wag / O my luve's like a red, red rose / Scots prologue, A / For a' that and a' that / Address to the Unico Guid... / Book worms, The / Mary Morrison / Henpeck'd husband, The / Grace (before dinner), A / To a haggis / Grace (after dinner), A / Scotch drink / On Maxwell of Cardoness - extempore / To a painter / Ae fond kiss.
MC: CWGR 120

SELECTED STORIES OF JOHN BUCHAN (see under Buchan, John).

Cutler, Adge

ADGE CUTLER & THE WURZELS (Cutler, Adge & The Wurzels).
Tracks: / I am a cider drinker / Tractor song, The (The pushbike song) / Our village band / I got my beady little eye on thee / Blackbird, The / Speedy Gonzales (CD only.) / Give me England / Farmer Bill's cowman / Funky Farmyard (CD only.) / I'll never get a scrumpy here / My Somerset crumpet horn / Drunk on a Saturday night / Combine harvester / Easton in Gordano (CD only.) / Twice daily / Wurple-diddle-I-doo-song / Don't tell I, tell 'ee / Saturday night at the crown / Ferry to Glastonbury (CD only.) / Shepton Mallett matador, The / When the Common Market comes to Stanton Drew / Champion dung spreader / All over Mendip / I wish I was back on the farm / Drink up thy zider.
MC: TCIDL 114

ADGE CUTLER & THE WURZELS (Cutler, Adge & The Wurzels).
LP: SCX 6126
LP: SX 6126

CIDER DRINKING FAVOURITES (Best of Adge Cutler & The Wurzels) (Cutler, Adge & The Wurzels).
Tracks: / Easton in Gordano / Poor poor farmer / Twice daily / Wurple diddle I doo song / Don't tell I, tell ee / Saturday night at the Crown / Riley's cowshed / Ferry to Glastonbury / Up the clump / Thee's got'n where thee cassn't back'n' hassnt / Moonlight on the Malago / Shepton Mallet matador / When the common market comes to Stanton Drew / Champion dung spreader / Aloha Severn beach / All over Mendip / I wish I was back on the farm / Drink up thy zider.
LP: NTS 199

DON'T TELL I, TELL 'EE (Cutler, Adge & The Wurzels).
Tracks: / Drink up thy zider / Don't tell I, tell'ee / Oom pah pah / Poor poor farmer / Chitterling / My threshing machine / I wish I was back on the farm / Dorset is beautiful / Up the clump / Wild west show, The / I'd love to swim in the Zuider Zee / Faggots is the stuff / Virtute et industrial / Wurple diddle I doo song, The / Chandler's wife, The.
LP: ONCR 502

VINTAGE ZIDER (Cutler, Adge & The Wurzels).
Tracks: / Pub with no beer / Oh Sir Jasper / Bristol song / Marrow song / Charlton Mackrell jug band / In the haymaking time / Five foot flirt / Dorset is beautiful / Up the clump / Chandler's wife, The / Wurple diddle I doo song.
LP: MFP 50476

Cutler, Ivor

DANDRUFF.
Tracks: / Solo on mbira / Dad's lapse / I worn my elbows / Hair grips / I believe in bugs / Fremsley / Goozeberries and bilberries / Time / I'm walking to a farm / Railway sleepers, The / Life in a Scotch sittingroom vol 2 ep 1 / Three sisters / Baby sits / Not big enough / Men / Trouble trouble / Vein girl / Five wise saws / Painful league / Piano tuner song A.D.2000 / Self knowledge / Old oak tree, The / Aimless dawnrunner, The / Face like a lemon / Bird, A / Hole in my toe, A / My mother has two red lips / I like sitting / Forgetful fowl, The / If everybody / For sixpence / I used to lie in bed / If all the cornflakes / My sock / When I entered / Two balls / Miss Velvetlips / Lean / Fur coats / Darkness / Beautiful woman / Making tidy.
MC: OVEDC 33
LP: OVED 33

GRUTS.
LP: ROUGH 98

JAMMY SMEARS.
Tracks: / Bicarbonate of chicken / Filcombe cottage, Dorset / Squeeze bees / Turn, The / Life in a Scotch sittingroom vol 2 ep 11 / Linnett, A / Jumping and pecking / Other half, The / Beautiful cosmos / Path, The / Barabadabada / Big Jim / In the chestnut tree / Dust / Rubber toy / Unexpected join / Wooden tree / When I stand in an open cart / High is the wind / Surly buddy, The / Pearly-winged fly / Garden path at Filcombe / Paddington Town / Cage of small birds / Irk / Lemon flower / Red admiral / Everybody got / Wasted call, The.
LP: OVED 12
MC: OVEDC 12

LIFE IN A SCOTCH SITTING ROOM VOL.2.
LP: SPOUT 2001
MC: SPOUT 2001C

PRIVILEGE (Cutler, Ivor & Linda Hirst).
LP: ROUGH 59

VELVET DONKEY.
Tracks: / If your breasts / I got no commonsense / Useful cat / Oho my eyes / Dirty dinner, The / Yellow fly / Mother's love / Meadow's go, The / Phonic poem / Life in a Scotch sittingroom vol 2 ep 2 / Birdswing / Nobody knows / Uneventful day / Little black buzzer / Bread and butter / Nuance, A / Go and sit upon the grass / Even keel, The / Pearly gleam / Best thing / Life in a Scotch sittingroom vol 2 ep 7 / Once upon a time / There's got to be something / Purposeful culinary instruments, The / Gee, ain't I lucky / Curse, The / I think very deeply / I slowly / Sleepy old snake / Titchy digits / Stranger, The.
LP: OVED 34
MC: OVEDC 34

Cutting Crew

BROADCAST.
Tracks: / Any colour / One for the mockingbird / I've been in love before / Life in a dangerous time / Fear of falling / (I just) died in your arms tonight / Don't look back / Sahara / It shouldn't take too long / Broadcast, The.
MC: SRNMC 7
LP: SRNLP 7
MC: OVEDC 352
LP: OVED 353

SCATTERING, THE.
Tracks: / Year in the wilderness / Scattering, The / Big noise / Everything but my pride / Handcuffs for Houdini / (Between a) rock and a hard place / Tip of your tongue / Reach for the sky / Last thing, The / Feel the wedge / Binkies return (Only on CD and MC.) / Brag (Only on CD and MC.).
LP: SRNLP 25
MC: SRNMC 25
MC: OVEDC 379

Cutting Edge (group)

CUTTING EDGE.
LP: ODINLP 04
MC: MC 04

OUR MAN IN PARADISE.
LP: ODINLP 10
MC: MC 10

Cutty, Gordon

GRAND OLD FASHIONED DANCE, A.
LP: FRR 006

Cutty Sark

DIE TONIGHT.
LP: SKULL 8339
MC: TAPE 78339

HEROES.
LP: SKULL 8375

Cuzacq, Gilles

FUNK DANS MON ACCORDEON.
Tracks: / Femmes ne changez pas / Fleur de caves ou de paves / Winner, The / Y du funk dans mon accordeon / One two three / Accordeon disco march / Ivie l'auvergne et les auvernats / Sensibility inspiration / Genius twist / Toros el paso / Marche armoricaine.
LP: ILD 42061

Cwmbran...

CWMBRAN MALE CHOIR, THE (Conducted by Huw Davis).
Tracks: / Fantasia on Welsh hymn tunes / Silent night / Christmas medley / Christmas fantasy / Laudamus / Alleluia / When a child is born / O praise the Lord with one consent / Christmas swing along / Christmas overture.
LP: TB 3018

CWR Singers

COME ALIVE.
LP: WST 9637
MC: WC 9637

COME ALIVE II.
LP: WST R 9662
MC: WST C 9662

O MAGNIFY THE LORD WITH US.
LP: WST R 9675
MC: WST C 9675

Cwrt-Y-Gollen

STAND AND FIGHT (Cwrt-Y-Gollen Junior Band & Choir).
LP: MM 0570

C.W.S. (Manchester)

FESTIVAL OF MARCHES FOR BRASS BAND, A.
Tracks: / March from A Moorside suite / Berne patrol / Symphony of marches / Airline / Brunebal raid / American salute / Arnhem.
LP: BNB 2002
MC: ZC BNB 2002

Cybertron

C.Y.B..
LP: CYBLP 1

Cycle Of The West

CYCLE OF THE WEST (Read by John Neilhardt).
MC: CDL 51665

Cyclic Amp

GIFT OF TEARS.
LP: PROBE 14

Cymbal, Johnny

MR BASSMAN.
LP: KS 3324

Cymbeline

CYMBELINE (see under Shakespeare, William) (Various artists).

Cymone, Andre

A.C..
Tracks: / Dance electric / Lipstick lover / Pretty wild girl / Book of love / Satisfaction / Sweet sensuality / Vacation / Neon pussycat.
LP: CBS 26597
MC: 40 26597

SURVIVIN' IN THE 80'S.
Tracks: / M.O.T.F / Survivin' in the 80's / Make me wanna dance / Lovedog / Body thanu / Filay / What are we doing here / Don't let the furniture (come down on you).
LP: CBS 25767
MC: 40 25767

Cynics

TWELVE FLIGHTS UP.
LP: R 3388-13

Cypress City

SWAMP POP HITS.
LP: JIN 9029
MC: JIN 9029 TC

Cyprus

CHANTS EPIQUES ET POPULAIRES DE CHYPRE (Various artists).
Tracks: / Sarakinos: *Various artists* / Le dit du sarrasin: *Various artists* / Tessera tsie tessera: *Various* artists / Roulla-Mou, Maroulla-Mou: *Various artists* / T'ayi Giorki: *Various artists* / Myrologue: *Various artists* / Kavouras: *Various artists* / Le dit du crabe: *Various artists.*
LP: ARN 33640
MC: ARN 433640

FOLK MUSIC OF CYPRUS (Various artists).
LP: LLST 7329

Cyrano De Bergerac

CYRANO DE BERGERAC (Film Soundtrack) (Petit, Jean Claude).
MC: ETKY 310C

Cyrille, Andrew

CELEBRATION.
LP: ST 002

JUNCTION.
LP: ST 003

NUBA.
LP: BSR 0030

PAINTINGS (See under Zepf, Manfred) (Cyrille, Andrew & Manfred Zepf).

WHAT ABOUT.
Tracks: / What about / From whence I came / Rhythmical space / Rims and things / Pioneering.
LP: AFF 75

Czechoslovak Brass

MILITARY MASTERPIECES (Czechoslovak Brass Orchestra).
LPS: ADLS 620
MCSET: ADKS 620

Czukay, Holger

DER OSTEN IST ROT.
Tracks: / Photo song, The / Bankel rap '82 / Michy / Rhonrad / Collage / Esperanto socialiste / Der osten ist rot / Das massenmedium / Schaue vertrauensvoll in die zukunft / Traum mal wieder!.
LP: OVED 161
MC: OVEDC 161

FLUX AND MUTABILITY (See under Sylvian, David) (Czukay, Holger & David Sylvian).

MOVIES.
Tracks: / Cool in the pool / Oh Lord give us more money / Persian love / Hollywood symphony.
LP: EMC 3319

ON THE WAY TO THE PEAK OF NORMAL.
Tracks: / Ode to perfume / On the way to the peak of normal / Witches multiplication table / Two bass shuffle / Hiss'n'listen.
LP: EMC 3394

PLIGHT & PREMONITION (see under Sylvian, David) (Czukay, Holger & David Sylvian).

RADIO WAVE SURFER.
LP: V 2651
MC: TCV 2651

ROME REMAINS ROME.
Tracks: / Hey ba ba re bop / Blessed Easter / Sudetenland / Hit hit flop flop / Perfect world / Music in the air / Der osten ist rot (the east is red) (CD only) / Das massenmedium (CD only) / Photo song, The (CD only) / Ronrad (CD only) / Michy (CD only) / Esperanto socialiste (CD only) / Traum mal wieder (CD only).
LP: V 2408
MC: TCV 2408

SNAKE CHARMER (See under Jah Wobble) (Czukay, Holger/Jah Wobble/ Edge).

D

D Mob

LITTLE BIT OF THIS, A.
Tracks: / C'mon and get my love / All I do / It really don't matter / That's the way of the world / It really don't matter / It is time to get funky / Put your hands together / Rhythm from within, A / Trance dance / We call it acieed.
LP: **828 159 1**
MC: **828 159 4**

D & V

D & V.
LP: . . . . **CAT 1**

Da

DA/MY LEFT FOOT (FILM SOUNDTRACK) (Bernstein, Elmer).
Tracks: / Mother / Therapy / Study for Christy / For mother / Love spoken / Temptress / Secrets / Goodbye / Unspoken fear / Church and witches / Happy moment / Struggle and frustration / Da and memories / Drown the dog / Old matters / Resolution.
LP: . . . . **VS 5244**
MC: . . . . **VSC 5244**

Da Costa, Glen

SERENADE OF LOVE (Da Costa, Glen & The Wailers).
LP: . . . . **VSLP 4065**

Da Costa, Paulino

AGORA.
Tracks: / Simbora / Terra / Toledo bagel / Berimbau variations / Belisco / Ritmo number one.
LP: **2310 785**
MC: **K10 785**
LP: **2335 747**

HAPPY PEOPLE.
Tracks: / Deja vu / Put your mind on vacation / Take it on up / Love till the end of time / Seeing is believing / Dreamflow / Carnival of colours / Let's get together / Happy people.
LP: **231 2102**
MC: . . . . **K 12 102**

SUNRISE.
Tracks: / Taj Mahal / I'm going to Rio / African sunrise / Walkman / O mar e meu chao / You came into my life / My love / You've got a special kind of love / Carioca / Groove.
LP: **2312 143**
MC: . . . . **K 12 143**

TUDO BEM (Da Costa, Paulino & Joe Pass).
Tracks: / Corcovado / Tears / Wave / Voice / If you went away / Que que ha / Gentle rain, The / Barquinho / Luciana / I live to love.
LP: **231 0824**
MC: **K10 824**

D'a Dev

DON'T PUSH.
LP: . . . . **EXACT 029**

Da Posse

DA POSSE IS LARGE.
LP: . . . . **LICLP 45**

Da Willys

SATUHDAY NITE PALSY.
LP: . . . . **OUTLP 105**

Dab Hand

HIGH ROCK AND LOW GLEN.
LP: . . . . **CM 025**

D'Abo, Mike

INDESTRUCTIBLE.
Tracks: / Loving on a shoestring / Love indestructible / Horns of Memphis / Nobody else but you / Easy Street / Time warp / Thank you / Wonder of a woman / Slow-burning love / Whose heart? / Ships / Revival / There's a lovely lake in London / Isle of Capri / South American Joe / Mockingbird went cuckoo / Keeping up with the Joneses / Cherie / In my little bottom drawer / I'm ninety nine today / Sally / Sing as we go / Roll along prairie moon / One of the little orphans of the storm / Just one more chance / Winter draws on / Red sails in the sunset / What can you give a nudist on his birthday / Love, life and laughter / I took my harp to a party.
2LP: . . . . **PTLS 1084**
MC: . . . . **PTLC 1084**

TOMORROW'S TROUBADOR (LP) (D'Abo, Mike & His Mighty Quintet).
Tracks: / Tomorrow's troubador / Twinkle in the eye / Velvet glove / Hurricane / Isle of debris / Jump boogie and jive / Build me up buttercup / Just like a woman / Mighty Quinn, The / Handbags and gladrags / Fox on the run / Rock 'n' roll crusade.
LP: . . . . **PTLS 1090**
MC: . . . . **PTLC 1090**

D.A.D.

DRAWS A CIRCLE.
LP: . . . . **MRLP 3057**

NO FUEL LEFT FOR THE PILGRIMS.
LP: . . . . **WX 288**
MC: . . . . **WX 288C**

Dad (Film)

DAD (1989 Film Soundtrack) (Various artists).
Tracks: / Dad prologue and main title: *Various artists* / Saying goodnight/ Mopping the floor: *Various artists*/ Playing catch: *Various artists* / Vigil, The/Taking dad home: *Various artists* / Dad/Recovery: *Various artists* / Greenhouse, The: *Various artists* / Goodbyes: *Various artists* / Farm, The: *Various artists.*
LP: . . . . **MCA 6359**
MC: . . . . **MCAC 6359**

Dad & The Kids

DAD & THE KIDS PLAY FOR DANCING.
LP: . . . . **GNPS 2145**

Daddy Freddie

CATER FE SHE.
Tracks: / All night passion / Birthright / Daddy Freddie come again / No pressure me / Bad boy patrol / Have faith / Cater fe she / She bran new.
LP: . . . . **OSLP 1002**

DANCEHALL CLASH (See under Tenor Fly for details) (Daddy Freddie/Tenor Fly).

HYPOCRITES (See under Prophet, Michael) (Daddy Freddie & Michael Prophet).

STRESS.
LP: . . . . **FREDDY 1**
MC: . . . . **FREDDYC 1**

Daddy Lilly

HEARD ABOUT MY LOVE (See Meeks, Carl) (Daddy Lilly & Carl Meeks).

Dad's Army (tv theme)

DAD'S ARMY.
Tracks: / Dad's Army overture / Put that light out / Carry on on the home front / Command post / When can I have a banana again / King is still in London, The / Lords of the air / Siefgried line - We'll meet again / Floral dance, The / Nightingale sang in Berkeley Square, A / Radio personalities of 1940.
LP: . . . . **K 56186**

DAD'S ARMY (Original TV cast) (Various artists).
Tracks: / When did you last see your money: *Various artists* / Time on my hands: *Various artists* / Jumbo sized problem, A: *Various artists* / Ten seconds from now: *Various artists.*
MCSET: . . . . **ZBBC 1140**

DAF

ALLES IST GUT.
Tracks: / Sato-sato / Der Mussolini / Rote lippen / Mein herz macht bum / Der rauber und der prinz / Ich und die wirklichkeit / Als wars das letze mal / Verlier nicht den kopf / Alle gegen alle / Alles ist gut.
LP: . . . . **OVED 59**
LP: . . . . **V 2202**

DAF ('Best of' compilation).
Tracks: / Verschwende deine jugend / Der Mussolini / Mein herz macht bum (my heart goes boom) / El que / Ich und die wirklichkeit (Me and reality.) / Die gotter sins weib / Der rauber und der prinz / Liebe auf den ersten blick / Im dschungel der liebe / Prinzessin / Greif nach den sternen / Kebab traume / Die lippe / Als wars das lezte mal.
LP: . . . . **V 2533**
MC: . . . . **TCV 2533**

DIE KLEINEN UN DIE BOSEN (Deutsch Amerikanische Freundschaft).
LP: . . . . **STUMM 1**

FUR IMMER.
Tracks: / Im dschungel der liebe / Win bisschen krieg / Die gotter sind weiss / Verlieb dich in mich / Geheimnis / Kebab traume / Prizessin / Die lippe / Verehert euren haarschnitt / Wer schon will mussleiden.
LP: . . . . **OVED 82**
MC: . . . . **OVEDC 82**
LP: . . . . **V 2239**

GOLD UND LIEBE.
Tracks: / Liebe auf den ersten blick / El que / Sex unter wasser / Was ziehst du an heute nacht / Goldenes spielzeug / Ich will / Muskel / Absolute korperkontrolle / Verschwende deine jugend / Greif nach den sternen.
LP: . . . . **OVED 81**
LP: . . . . **V 2218**

LIVE IN BERLIN 1980.
MC: . . . . **MFM 40**

Dagar, Nasir A

RG MIAN MALHAR.
LP: . . . . **EASD 1420**

Daggermen

DAGGERS IN MY MIND.
LP: . . . . **DAG 001**

Dagnasty

CAN I SAY?.
LP: . . . . **DISCHORD 19**
MC: . . . . **DISCHORD 19C**

FIELD DAY.
LP: **081274**

WIG OUT AT DENKO'S.
Tracks: / Godfather, The / Trying / Space / Fall / When I love / Simple minds / Wig out at denko's / Exercise / Dagnasty / Crucial three.
LP: . . . . **DISCHORD 26**
MC: . . . . **DISCHORD 26C**

Dagradi, Tony

DREAMS OF LOVE.
LP: . . . . **ROUNDER 2071**
MC: . . . . **ROUNDER 2071C**

LUNAR ECLIPSE.
Tracks: / Les deux couleurs / Heart to heart / Duplicity / Lunar eclipse / Whirl.
LP: . . . . **GR 8103**

OASIS.
LP: . . . . **GR 8001**

D'Aguilar, Faith

I WANT YOU AND MY SWEETHEART TO BE FRIENDS (See under Jones, John) (D'Aguilar, Faith & John Jones).

Dahill, Tom

IRISH MUSIC FROM ST PAUL TO DONEGAL.
LP: . . . . **FF 397**

Dahl, Jeff

SCRATCH UP SOME ACTION (Dahl, Jeff Group).
LP: . . . . **YEAH HUP 007**

ULTRA UNDER.
LP: . . . . **TX 93171**

Dahl, Roald (aut)

CHARLIE & THE CHOCOLATE FACTORY.
MCSET: . . . . **LFP 7104**
MC: **1476**
MCSET: . . . . **LFP 4171045**
MCSET: . . . . **TCLFP 7104**

ENORMOUS CROCODILE, THE (see under Enormous Crocodile (bk)) (Blake, Roger (nar)).

ENORMOUS CROCODILE & THE MAGIC FINGER, THE.
LP: . . . . **TC 1633**
MC: **1633**

FANTASTIC MR. FOX (Jeffries, Lionel).
MCSET: **CC/016**

FANTASTIC MR. FOX.
MC: **1576**

GIRAFFE, THE PELLEY AND ME, THE (Read by Roald Dahl).
MC: **00 102210 5**

GREAT SWITCHEROO, THE (Neal, Patricia).
MC: **1545**

JAMES & THE GIANT PEACH.
MC: **1543**

ROALD DAHL COLLECTION, THE.
MC: **0001042718**

ROALD DAHL COLLECTION, VOL 2 (Blake, Roger/Richard Griffiths/Ann Clement).
MCSET: **00 104 130-4**

ROALD DAHL SOUNDBOOK.
LPS: . . . . **SBR 122**
MCSET: **122**

Daho, Etienne

POUR NOS VIES MARTIENNES.
Tracks: / Quatre hivers / Bleu comme toi / Caribbean sea / Where's my monkey? / Affair classee / Des ir / Stay with me / Le plaisir de Perdre / Musc et ambre / Winter blue / Des heures Indoues.
LP: . . . . **V 2566**
MC: . . . . **TCV 2566**

Daigle, Paul

CAJUN EXPERIENCE (Daigle, Paul with Robert Elkins/Michael Doucet).
LP: **6058**
MC: . . . . **6058 TC**

CAJUN GOLD (Daigle, Paul/ Robert Elkins/ Cajun Gold).
LP: **6060**
MC: . . . . **6060 TC**

COEUR FAROUCHE (Daigle, Paul/ Robert Elkins/ Cajun Gold).
LP: **6077**

LA LUMIERE DANS TON CHASSIS (Daigle, Paul/ Robert Elkins/ Cajun Gold).
LP: **6068**

Daigrepont, Bruce

STIR UP THE ROUX.
Tracks: / Laissez-faire / La valse de la riviere rouge / Disco et fais do-do / Les traces be mon bogue / Le two step de marksville / Les filles cajines / Un autre soir ennuyant / Frisco zydeco / Stir up the roux.
LP: . . . . **REU 1026**
LP: . . . . **ROUNDER 6016**
MC: . . . . **ROUNDER 6016C**

Daiko, O Suwa

JAPANESE DRUMS.
LP: . . . . **G 1029**
MC: . . . . **G 4029**

Dailey, Albert

POETRY (See Getz, Stan) (Dailey, Albert & Stan Getz).

TEXTURES.
LP: . . . . **MR 5256**

Dailey, Dusky

DUSKY DAILEY 1937-39.
LP: . . . . **DLP 537**

Daily Flash

I FLASH DAILY.
LP: . . . . **PSYCHO 32**

Daim, Lushus

MORE THAN YOU CAN HANDLE (Daim, Lushus & The Pretty Vain).
Tracks: / Pretty poison / For you / Attention addict / Payback / More than you can handle / One you love / Be there for me / Rhythm of love.
LP: . . . . **ZL 72392**

Dairo, I.K.

MO YEGE.
LP: . . . . **MOLPS 110**

Daisy, Miss

PIZZA CONNECTION (See under Miss Daisy).

Dalbello, Lisa

SHE.
Tracks: / Black on black / Baby doll / Talk to me / Danger danger / Intimate secrets / Tango / Body and soul / Imagination / Why stand alone? / Immaculate eyes.
LP: . . . . **EST 2047**
MC: . . . . **TCEST 2047**

Dalby, Graham

LET'S DO IT AGAIN (ALBUM) (Dalby, Graham/Grahamophones).
Tracks: / Let's do it again / Charleston / Hair of the dog / Crazy weather / Thinking of you / Jealousy / Breakaway / Sheik of Araby / Minnie the moocher / I wasn't there / Dance little lady / Steppin' out with my baby / I wonder if you know what it means / Love's melody / Is you is or is you ain't my baby.
MC: . . . . **PTLC 1108**

Dale, Archie

THANK YOU LORD (Dale, Archie & The Tones Of Joy).
LP: MIR 5010
MC: ZCMIR 5010

Dale, Dick

GREATEST HITS: DICK DALE & HIS DEL-TONES (Dale, Dick & His Del-Tones).
LP: GNPS 2095
MC: GNP5 2095

KING OF THE SURF GUITAR.
LP: RNLP 70074

Dale & Grace

I'M LEAVING IT UP TO YOU.
LP: MICHELLE 100
MC: MICHELLE 100TC

Dale, Jackie

SWEET AND MELLOW (Dale, Jackie & Friends).
LP: VG LP 004

Dale, Ronnie

GREAT SCOT, IT'S RONNIE DALE.
Tracks: / For the good times / Petite fleur / Bagpipe rock / Red yo yo, The / Concertina cantrip / Let me try again / Bye bye blackbird / I don't know why I love you like I do / I can't give you anything but love / Stranger on the shore / Coulter's candy / Kenmore's up and awa' / My way / Going home.
LP: LILP 5024

Dale, Syd

ONCE UPON A SUMMERTIME (Syd Dale Orchestra).
Tracks: / I don't know why / April love / Mistique / But beautiful / Can I forget you / I can dream, can't I / No flowers for my lady / Sunday kind of love / I should care / Never saw a girl so pretty / Once upon a summertime / Can't help loving her / Second time around.
LP: GALP 107

SENTIMENTAL JOURNEY (Syd Dale Orchestra).
Tracks: / For sentimental reasons / Love is here to stay / I love paris / Truly / Together again / Sentimental journey / Something to remember you by / I get along without you very well / Until love song ends / Hey / Misty moments / All the love in the world.
LP: GALP 109

SYD DALE & HIS ORCHESTRA (Dale, Syd & His Orchestra).
LP: RES 806

WHEN I FALL IN LOVE (Syd Dale Orchestra).
Tracks: / When I fall in love / Paradise / Warm & willing / Pretend / Stay as sweet as you are / I'll never smile again / Affair to remember, An / Love me as though there was no tommorow / Dinner for one, please James / There goes my heart / You're mine you / Party's over.
LP: GALP 108

Dalek I Love You

COMPASS KUMPAS.
Tracks: / World, The / Destiny / Suicide, A / We're all actors / You really got me / Missing fifteen minutes / Eight truck / Kiss, The / Two chameleons / Freedom fighters / Heat.
LP: OPEN 1
LP: 8368941
MC: 8368944

DALEK I LOVE YOU.
Tracks: / Holiday in Disneyland / Horror-scope / Health and happiness / Mouse that roared / Dad on fire / Ambition / Lust / 12 hours of blues / Sons of Sahara / Africa Express.
LP: KODE 7
MC: CODE 7

Dales & Wales 1984

ENTER HIS GATES.
LP: SGLP 35
MC: SG 35

Daley, J

TUBA TRIO VOL 1 (see under Rivers, Sam) (Daley, J & W Smith & Sam Rivers).

TUBA TRIO VOL 2 (See under Rivers, Sam) (Daley, J & W Smith & Sam Rivers).

TUBA TRIO VOL 3 (See under Rivers, Sam) (Daley, J & W Smith & Sam Rivers).

Daley, Larry

CHICKEN ON A RAFT (Plymouth folk sounds).
MC: 60-091

Daley, Martin

ARCHITECTS OF TIME (Daley, Martin & Duncan Lorien).
Tracks: / Structure / Bermuda / Architects of time / Into the oasis / 11 days / Thank you / Waiting for Karl / Spirit warrior.
LP: LPLTD 004
MC: MCLTD 004
LP: EULP 1154
MC: EUMC 1154

Dalglish, Malcolm

THUNDERHEAD (Dalglish, Malcolm & Grey Larsen).
LP: FF 266

Dali, Miranda

MIRANDA DALI.
LP: TWI 938
MC: TWIMC 938

Dalida

BORN TO SING.
LP: VIR 83003
MC: ZCVIR 83003

DALIDA VOL.1.
LP: 96031

DALIDA VOL.2.
LP: 96032

GREATEST HITS: DALIDA.
2LP: 96039/40

Dali's Car

WAKING HOUR.
Tracks: / Dali's car / His box / Cornwall stone / Artemis / Create and melt / Moonlife / Judgement is the mirror, The.
LP: DOXLP 1
MC: DOXC 1
LP: BBL 52
MC: BBLC 52

Dallas, Rex

REX DALLAS SINGS.
Tracks: / Fireside yodel / Roaming yodeller, The / Dutch girl yodel / My Swiss miss yodel / Yodel and smile / Happy free yodel / Yodelling Erich / Mexican yodel / Hear the yodeller / My Lancashire yodelling lass / Yodeller's dream girl / Cuckoo yodel / My yodelling lady / Australian yodel / Prairie yodel / Mississippi yodel / Gypsy yodel.
LP: WRS 123

Dallas, T.R.

HARD TO BE HUMBLE.
LP: CMRLP 1004

IN CONCERT.
LP: FRC 001

SOLID GOLD.
MC: CMCS 1015
LP: CMRLP 1015

T.R. DALLAS.
2LP: CMCSB 001

Dallas (tv theme)

DALLAS (THEME FROM) (See under Lee, Johnny) (Lee, Johnny).

DALLAS-THE MUSIC STORY (T.V. soundtrack) (Various artists).
Tracks: / I wanna reach out and touch: *Brooks, Karen* / Makin' up for lost time (the Dallas lovers' song): *Gayle,* Crystal & Gary Morris / Few good men, A: *Forester Singers* / J.R., who do you think you are?: *Keel, Howard*/ Working man's song (the Ewing/Barnes legacy): *Cook, Bob* / Loneliness in Lucy's eyes (the life Sue Ellen is living): *Lee,* Johnny / I'm a survivor: *Harrison, Jenilee as Jamie Ewing* / If I knew then what I know now: *Morris, Gary*/ Dallas, Theme from (Dallas dreams): *Ripp, Artie & Black Gold* / Who killed Jock Ewing?: *Various artists.*
LP: 925325 1
MC: 925325 4

Dalli, Toni

BEST OF TONI DALLI, THE.
MC: C5K 570

Dalls, Leroy

BLUES ALL AROUND MY BED (See under Blues Roots vol.2).

Dallwitz, Dave

CINDERELLA GIRL.
LP: S 1413

CINDERELLA GIRL (Dallwitz, Dave Jazz Band).
LP: S 1407

DAVE DALLWITZ EUPHONIC RAGTIME ENSEMBLE (Dallwitz, Dave Euphonic Ragtime Ensemble).
LP: SOS 1098

ELEPHANT STOMP (Dallwitz, Dave Jazz Band).
LP: SOS 1112

ERN MALLY JAZZ SUITE (Dallwitz, Dave Jazz Band).
LP: S1360

FLOATING PALAIS (Dallwitz, Dave Jazz Band).
LP: S 1409

GOLD FEVER (1977) (Dallwitz, Dave Jazz Band).
LP: S 1377

GULGONG SHUFFLE (1977) (Dallwitz, Dave Jazz Band).
LP: S 1378

ILLAWARRA FLAME(1974) (Dallwitz, Dave Jazz Band).
LP: S 1354

MELBOURNE SUITE(1973) (Dallwitz, Dave Jazz Band).
LP: S 1342

RAGTIME (Dallwitz, Dave Euphonic Ragtime Ensemble).
LP: S 1393

SUNDAY MORNING RAG (Dallwitz, Dave & The Schampus All Stars).
LP: DC 33002
LP: DCS 33002

Dalmellington Band

DOON VALLEY BRASS.
Tracks: / President, The / Frolic for trombones / Poem / Triumphant rhapsody / Moray firth, The / Tantalus quelen / Caledonian, The / March of the clowns / West side story.
LP: NA 103

Dalpin

DYNAMITE.
LP: GS 2309

IT'S REAL HARD.
LP: GS 2292

Dalto, Jorge

URBAN OASIS.
Tracks: / Samba all day / Love of my life / Killer Joe / Ease my pain / Skydive / La costa / Sentido de sete.
LP: CJP 275
MC: CJPC 275

Dalton & Dubarri

CHOICE.
Tracks: / There is love in everybody / Caught in the act / How I hate the nightime / I can dance all by myself / Flyin' free / Keepin' it up / Sweet sweet sweet thang / 'Til the day I started lovin' you.
LP: DJF 20565

Dalton, Lacy J

BLUE EYED BLUES.
Tracks: / That's good, that's bad / Gotta serve somebody / I'll love them whatever they are / Hillbilly girl with the blues / 16th Avenue / My old yellow car / Love gone cold / Have I got a heart for you / It's a dirty job / Blue eyed blues.
LP: 4508711
MC: 4508714

CAN'T RUN AWAY FROM YOUR HEART.
Tracks: / You can't run away from your heart / Too late to stop lovin' you now / Don't fall in love with me / Over you / Perfectly crazy / If that ain't love / Night has a heart of its own, The / Silver eagle / Adios and run / Slow movin' outlaw.
LP: CBS 26452
MC: 40 26452

HARD TIMES.
Tracks: / Hard times / Hillbilly girl with the blues / China doll / Old soldier / Ain't nobody who could do it like my daddy could / You can't fool love / Wide eyed and willing / Girls from Santa Cruz, The / Whisper / Me 'n' you.
LP: CBS 32769
MC: 40 32769

HIGHWAY DINER.
Tracks: / Working class man / 12:05 / Changing all the time / Taking it all in stride / Can't see me without you / This ol' town / Up with the wind / Boomtown / Gone again / Closing time.
LP: CBS 57042
MC: 40 57042

I LOVE COUNTRY.
Tracks: / Dream baby / That's good, that's bad (with George Jones) / Slow down / Crazy blue eyes / Takin' it easy / Whisper / Wild turkey / 16th Avenue / Tennessee waltz / My old yellow car.
LP: 4504241
MC: 4504244

TAKIN' IT EASY.
Tracks: / Takin' it easy / Everybody makes mistakes / Where were you when I needed you / Come to me / Comes a time / Wild turkey / Golden memories / Let me in the fast lane / Feedin' the fire / Somebody killed Dewey Jones' daughter.
LP: CBS 85048

Dalton, Mike

COUNTRY SIDE OF MIKE DALTON.
LP: BSS 216

Daltons

THIS HEAT.
LP: PUT 4

WATCHING THE BLOOD FLOW.
LP: SC 881

Daltrey, Roger

BEST OF ROGER DALTREY.
Tracks: / Martyrs and madmen / Say it isn't so Joe / Oceans away / Treasury / Free me / Without your love / It's a hard life / Giving it all away / Avenging Annie / Proud / You put something better inside me.
LP: 2480641

CAN'T WAIT TO SEE THE MOVIE.
Tracks: / Hearts of fire / When the thunder comes / Ready for love / Balance on wires / Price of love, The / Heart has it's reasons / Alone in the night / Lover's storm / Miracle of love / Take me home.
LP: DIX 54
MC: CDIX 54

DALTREY.
Tracks: / Giving it all away / One man band / Way of the world / You are yourself / Thinking / You and me / It's a hard life / Story so far, The / When the music stops / Reasons.
LP: 2485 219
MC: 3201 219

MCVICAR (Film soundtrack).
Tracks: / Bitter and twisted / Escape / Free me / Just a dream away / McVicar / My time is gonna come / Waiting for a friend / White City lights / Without your love.
LP: POLD 5034
MC: POLDC 5034

ONE OF THE BOYS.
Tracks: / Parade / Single man's dilemma / Avenging Annie / Prisoner, The / Leon / One of the boys / Giddy / Written on the wind / Satin and lace / Doing it all again.
LP: 2442 146

PARTING WOULD BE PAINLESS.
Tracks: / Walking in my sleep / Parting would be painless / Is anybody out there / Would a stranger do / Going strong / Looking for you / Somebody told me / One day / How does the cold wind cry / Don't wait on the stairs.
LP: 250298 1

RIDE A ROCK HORSE.
Tracks: / Get your love / Hearts right / Oceans away / Proud / Near to surrender / Feeling / Walking the dog / Milk train / I was.
LP: 2442 135
LP: 2660 111

UNDER A RAGING MOON.
Tracks: / Under a raging moon / After the fire / Don't talk to strangers / Breaking down Paradise / Pride you hide, The / Move better in the night / Let me down easy / It don't satisfy me / Rebel / Fallen angel / Love me like you do (CD & cassette only).
LP: DIX 17
MC: CDIX 17
MC: CXID 22
LP: XID 22

Daly, Bryan

VELVET GUITAR OF BRYAN DALY.
Tracks: / It's impossible / Romeo and Juliet / Till love touches your life / Wave / Cavatina / Amazing grace / Carnival / Love story / Souvenir d'Espagne / Once upon a summertime / Two for the road / Bridge over troubled water.
LP: DGS 19

Daly, Glen

CABARET TIME.
Tracks: / Cabaret time at the Ashfield / Rolling round the world / All go riding on a rainbow / I wonder who's kissing her now / All by yourself in the moonlight / Shine on harvest moon / Lily of Laguna / Bonnie Mary of Argyle / Bye bye blackbird / Isle of Innisfree / Little bit of Glasgow / O my Jock McKay / Pretty baby / Green hills of Antrim, The / Comin' thro' the rye / Bonnie banks of Loch Lomond, The / Westering home / Star o' Rabbie Burns, The.
LP: PKL 5566
MC: ZCPKB 5566

GLASGOW NIGHT OUT, A.
LP: ZCMA 1563
LP: GGL 0479

GLEN'S BIRTHDAY PARTY.
Tracks: / Happy birthday to you / G.L.A.S.G.O.W. / McDougal, McNab and McKay / Let the rest of the world go by / O'er the hills to Ardentinny / Flower o' the heather / Hame of mine / Peggy O'Neill / Little Annie Rooney / Black velvet band / Stone outside Dan Murphy's door, The / Old Scots pal o' mine / We're all Scotch / When the bloom is on the heather / Swanee / Waiting for the Robert E. Lee / My mammy / Flower of Scotland / And they call it Barrer Land / Toorie on his bonnet / Will ye no come back again.
LP: PKL 5536

MC: . . . . ZCP 5536

HUNDRED THOUSAND WELCOMES, A.
Tracks: / Hundred thousand welcomes, A / Scotland medley / Tipperary medley / Misty islands of the highlands / For me and my gal / Show me the way to go home / Suvla bay / Green oak tree / Auld lang syne.
MC: . . . . ZCSMPS 8922

LEGENDS OF SCOTLAND.
Tracks: / Scotland the brave / Dacent Irish boy, The / Northern lights of old Aberdeen / Road and the miles to Dundee, The / China doll / Wild colonial boy / Auld Scots mither o' mine / You need hands / Gordon for me, A / When I leave this world behind / When I leave old Glasgow behind / Come in, come in / Bonnie Scotland I adore thee / MacNamara's band / Granny's heilan' hame / In dear old Glasgow toon / Little grey home in the West / On mother Kelly's doorstep / Lovely Stornoway / Why did you make me care / I'm glad that I was born in Glasgow / I belong to Glasgow.
MC: . . . . ZCLLS 704

LIVE AT THE ASHFIELD,GLASGOW.
LP: . . . . GGL 0434
MC: . . . . ZCMA 1426

LIVE AT THE PAVILION THEATRE, GLASGOW.
Tracks: / Wedding of Sandy Mac, The / Pal of my cradle days / I love a lassie / Bonnie wells o' Wearie / Paddy McGinty's goat / Amazing grace / Oh boy what joy we had in barefoot days / Dear little boy of mine / Just a wee deoch and doris / Now is the hour.
MC: . . . . ZCSMPS 8924

MEMORIES.
Tracks: / Keep your sunny side up / Great day / In the good old summertime / Memories / Friends and neighbours / Heart of my heart / If I had my way / That's Glasgow / That lucky old sun / Happy days are here again / Roll out the barrel / Little street where old friends meet / April showers / When I lost you / Who were you with last night? / Hello, hello, who's your lady friend? / Christmas time in Scotland.
LP: . . . . PKL 5551
MC: . . . . ZCPKB 5551

MERRY PLOUGHBOY.
LP: . . . . ZMAL 1233

Daly, Jackie

BUTTONS AND BOWS (Daly, Jackie & McGuire, Seamus & Manus).
LP: . . . . SIF 1051
MC: . . . . CSIF 1051

JACKIE DALY & SEAMUS CREAGH (Daly, Jackie & Seamus Creagh).
LP: . . . . CEF 057

MUSIC FROM SLIABH LUACHRA VOL.6.
Tracks: / Tom Sullivan's / Johnny Leary's / Jim Keefe's / Keefe's / Clog, The / Tir na nog / Callaghan's hornpipe / Rising sun, The / Pope's toe, The / Glin cottage polkas, The / Paddy scully's / Gallant tipperay, The / Walsh's / Ballyvourine polka / Johnny Mickey's / Trip to the Jacks / Where is the cat / Banks of Sullane, The / Biddy Martin's / Ger the rigger / Glenside cottage, The / Tdim gan airgead / Willy Reilly / Murphy's / Going to the well for water.
LP: 12TS 358

D.A.M.

HUMAN WRECKAGE.
Tracks: / M.A.D / Death warmed up / Killing time / Left to rot / Prophets of doom / Terror squad / Total destruction / Infernal torment / Vendetta / Human wreckage / Aliens (CD only.) / F.O.D (CD only.).
LP: . . . . NUK 149
MC: . . . . ZCNUK 149

INSIDE OUT.
Tracks: / Man of violence / House of cards / Appointment with fear / Winter's tears / Innocent one, The / My twisted mind / No escape / Beneath closed eyes / Thought for the day circles (Bonus track on CD only.).
LP: . . . . NO 1641
MC: . . . . NO 1644

KICKING ASS AT TJ'S.
Tracks: / Army of fools / Christian fantasy land / Four more years / Shake your foundations / Kicking thought, A / Into the field / Madmen and the foul / Pressure point / Poster paint / Go with the brain / Blind ignorance / Attitude hits, An / Dream come true / Vicious circle / Cull, The / Et amour / Happy 1970.
LP: . . . . COX 013

WHERE HAVE ALL THE CHILDREN GONE.
Tracks: / Ploppy's revenge / Deliverer / Into the field / Conversation / Cut the cord / Possession / Pressure point / Cull, The / Lust is greed / Office boys and cats / I think I should / Wall of fear.
LP: . . . . COX 002

Dambert No Bacon

UNFAIRYTALE, THE.
LP: . . . . FM 008

D'Ambrosia, Meredith

IT'S YOUR DANCE.
Tracks: / Giant steps / Once upon a tempo / Listen little girl / Devil may care / August moon / Nobody else but me / Humpty dumpty heart / It's your dance / Underdog / It isn't so good it couldn't be better / Off again on again / No one remembers but me / Miss Harper goes bizarre / Strange meadowlark.
LP: . . . . SSC 1011

LITTLE JAZZ BIRD.
LP: . . . . PA 8019

MEREDITH....ANOTHER TIME.
Tracks: / All of us in it together / Aren't you glad you're you / It's so peaceful in the country / Rain rain (don't go away) / Dear Bix / Lazy afternoon / Where's the child I used to hold / Love is a simple thing / You are there / While we're young / Small day tomorrow / Child is born, A / Piano player / Some day my prince will come / Such a lonely girl am I / Wheelers and dealers / I was doin' all right / Skylark.
LP: . . . . SSC 1017

Dame Margot Fonteyn

DAME MARGOT FONTEYN (see under Fonteyn, Margot) (Fonteyn, Margot).

Dameron, Tadd

BIG 10/ROYAL ROOST JAM.
LP: . . . . BEP 503

CROSS CURRENTS (See under Tristano, Lennie) (Dameron, Tadd & Lennie Tristano).

KEYBOP (Dameron, Tadd & Dodo Marmarosa).
Tracks: / 52nd Street theme / Good bait / Focus / Webb's delight.
LP: . . . . BLJ 8032

MATING CALL.
LP: . . . . OJC 212

Dameronia

LOOK STOP LISTEN (See under Jones, Philly Joe) (Dameronia & Philly Joe Jones).

Dames At Sea (show)

DAMES AT SEA (Original Broadway cast) (Various artists).
LP: . . . . AOS 3330
MC: . . . . BT 3330

DAMES AT SEA (1989 touring cast) (Various artists).
Tracks: / Wall Street: *Various artists* / It's you: *Various artists* / Broadway baby: *Various artists* / That mister man of mine: *Various artists* / Choo choo honeymoon: *Various artists* / Sailor of my dreams, The: *Various artists* / Singapore Sue: *Various artists* / Broadway baby (reprise): *Various artists* / Good times are here to stay: *Various artists* / Entracte: *Various artists* / Dames at sea: *Various artists* / Beguine, The: *Various artists* / Raining in my heart: *Various artists* / There's something about you: *Various artists* / Echo waltz, The: *Various artists* / Star tar: *Various artists* / Let's have a simple wedding: *Various artists* / Dames at sea (overture): *Various artists*.
LP: . . . . TER 1169
MC: . . . . ZCTER 1169

Damhnaigh, Oro

ORO DAMHNAIGH.
LP: . . . . CEF 056

Damien Thorne

SIGN OF THE JACKAL, THE.
LP: . . . . RR 9691

Dammaj

MUTINY.
Tracks: / Smuggler / Devils and angels / March of the gladiators / Without you / Mutiny / Leather master / Clashes of steel / To the bitter end.
LP: . . . . RR 9636

D.A.M.N.

DON'T ACCEPT MASS NOTION.
LP: . . . . PRL 70111

Damn Yankees (Group)

DAMN YANKEES.
LP: 7599261591
MC: 7599261594

Damn Yankees (Show)

DAMN YANKEES (1958 film musical) (Various artists).
LP: . . . . LOC 1047

DAMN YANKEES (1955 Original Broadway cast) (Various artists).
LP: . . . . AYL 1 3848
MC: . . . . AYK 1 3848
MC: . . . . GK 83948

Damned

ANYTHING.
Tracks: / Alone again or / Portrait / Restless / In dulce decorum / Girl goes down / Gigolo / Anything / Tightrope walk / Psychomania.
LP: . . . . MCG 6015
MC: . . . . MCGC 6015

BEST OF THE DAMNED.
Tracks: / New rose / Neat neat neat / I just can't be happy today / Jet boy jet girl / Hit and miss / There ain't no sanity clause / Smash it up (parts 1 & 2) / Plan 9 channel 7 / Ra bid (over you) / Wait for the blackout / History of the world (part 1).
LP: . . . . DAM 1
MC: . . . . DAMC 1

BLACK ALBUM, THE.
Tracks: / Wait for the blackout / Lively arts / Silly kids games / Drinking about my baby / Hit and miss / Doctor Jekyll and Mr. Hyde / 13th floor vendetta / Curtain call (Available on CD only) / Twisted nerve / Sick of this and that / History of the world (part 1) / Therapy.
2LP: . . . . DAM 3
MCSET: . . . . TC CWK 3015
MCSET: . . . . DAMC 3
2LP: . . . . ACWKL 23015
LP: . . . . CWK 3015
2LP: WIKM2 91

CAPTAIN'S BIRTHDAY PARTY, THE.
LP: . . . . GET 4

COLLECTION: THE DAMNED.
Tracks: / Ignite / Generals / Dozen girls / Bad time for Bonzo / Gun fury / Thanks for the night / History of the world (part 1) / Lively arts / There ain't no sanity clause / White rabbit / Melody Lee / Lovely money / Disco man / I think I'm wonderful / Help (live) / I just can't be happy today (live) / Love song (live) / Neat neat neat (live) / New rose (live) / Noise noise noise (live) / Smash it up (live) / Wait for the blackout (live).
2LP: . . . . CCSLP 278
MC: . . . . CCSMC 278

DAMNED BUT NOT FORGOTTEN.
Tracks: / Dozen girls / Lovely money / I think I'm wonderful / Disguise / Take that / Torture me / Disco man / Thanks for the night / Take me away / Some girls are ugly / Nice cup of tea, A / Billy bad breaks.
LP: . . . . DOJOLP 21
MC: . . . . DOJOTC 21

DAMNED, DAMNED, DAMNED.
Tracks: / Neat neat neat / Fan club / I fall / Born to kill / Stab your back / Feel the pain / New rose / Fish / See her tonite / 1 of the 2 / So messed up / I feel alright.
LP: . . . . FIEND 91
MC: . . . . FIENDCASS 91
LP: . . . . SEEZ 1
LPPD: . . . . PFIEND 91

DAMNED: INTERVIEW PICTURE DISC.
LPPD: . . . . BAK 2012

FINAL DAMNATION.
Tracks: / See her tonite / Neat neat neat / Born to kill / I fall / Fan club / Fish / Help / New rose / I feel alright / I just can't be happy today / Wait for the blackout / Melody Lee / Noise noise noise / Love song / Smash it up / Looking at you / Last time, The.
LP: . . . . ESSLP 008
MC: . . . . ESSMC 008

INTERVIEW (ALBUM).
LP: . . . . SOC 886

LIGHT AT THE END OF THE TUNNEL.
2LP: . . . . MCSPC 312

LIVE AT SHEPPERTON.
Tracks: / Love song / Second time around / I just can't be happy today / Melody Lee / Help / Neat neat neat / Looking at you M.C. / Smash it up (parts 1 & 2) / New rose / Plan 9 channel 7.
LP: . . . . WIKM 27
MC: . . . . WIKC 27

LIVE IN NEWCASTLE.
LP: . . . . DAMU 2

LONG LOST WEEKEND (Best of Vol One-and-a-half).
Tracks: / Over the top / Ballroom blitz / White rabbit / I believe the impossible / Sugar and spice / Limit club, The / Nasty / Disco man / Billy bad breaks / Generals / Ignite / Bad time for Bonzo / Stranger on the town / Thanks for the night.
LP: . . . . WIK 80
MC: . . . . WIKC 80

MACHINE GUN ETIQUETTE.
Tracks: / Love song / Machine gun etiquette / I can't be happy today / Melody Lee / Anti-Pope / These hands / Plan 9, channel 7 / Noise, noise, noise / Looking at you / Liar / Smash it up (Part 1) / Smash it up (Part 2) / Ballroom blitz (Available on CD only) / Suicide (Available on CD only) / Rabid (over you) (Available on CD only) / White rabbit (extended version) (Available on CD only).
LP: . . . . DAM 2
MC: . . . . TC CWK 3011
MC: . . . . DAMMC 2
LP: . . . . CWK 3011

MINDLESS, DIRECTIONLESS ENERGY.
Tracks: / Fail / I just can't be happy today / Plan 9 channel 7 / Smash it up / Drinking about my baby / Looking at you / I feel alright / Love song / Ballroom blitz.
LP: . . . . NOSE 18
LP: . . . . NOSE 18X
MC: . . . . KOSE 18X

MUSIC AND MEDIA INTERVIEW PICTURE DISC.
LPPD: . . . . MM 1216

MUSIC FOR PLEASURE.
Tracks: / Problem child / Don't cry wolf / One way love / Politics / Stretcher case / Idiot box / You take my money / Alone / Your eyes / Creep (you can't fool me) / You know.
LP: . . . . FIEND 108
MC: . . . . FIENDCASS 108
LP: . . . . SEEZ 5

NOT THE CAPTAIN'S BIRTHDAY PARTY.
Tracks: / You take my money / Creep (you can't fool me) / Fan club / Problem child / I fall / So messed up / New rose / Feel alright / Born to kill.
LP: . . . . VEX 7

PHANTASMAGORIA.
Tracks: / Street of dreams / Shadow of love / There'll come a day / Sanctum sanctorum / Is it a dream? / Grimly fiendish / Edward the bear / Eighth day / Trojans / I just can't be happy today.
LP: . . . . MCF 3275
MC: . . . . MCFC 3275
LPPD: . . . . MCFP 3275

STRAWBERRIES.
Tracks: / Ignite / Generals / Stranger on the town / Dozen girls / Dog, The / Gun fury / Pleasure and pain / Life goes on / Bad time for Bonzo / Under the floor again / Don't bother me.
LP: . . . . LLM 3000
MC: . . . . LLMK 3000
LP: . . . . DOJOLP 46
LP: . . . . BRON 542

Damon Edge

SURREAL ROCK, THE.
LP: . . . . ST 7537

Damone, Vic

20 GOLDEN PIECES: VIC DAMONE.
Tracks: / Song is you, The / All I need is just a girl like you / By the time I get to Phoenix / Little green apples / Moment of truth, The / Didn't we / Look of love, The / Can't take my eyes off you / When you laughed all your laughter (and cried your tears) / La vita / MacArthur park / Time after time / Don't let me go / They call the wind Maria / Where / Come back to me / For once in my life / Here's that rainy day / Almost close to you / We have all the time in the world / Why can't I walk away / Watch what happens / If you are but a dream / Stardust.
LP: . . . . BDL 2001
MC: . . . . BDC 2001

CAPITOL YEARS, THE:VIC DAMONE (The Best of).
Tracks: / On the street where you live / Younger than Springtime / I am in love / Shangri-la / Laura / Marie / Tonight / Poinciana / Sound of music, The / Ruby / I could write a book / Till there was you / Moon of Manakoora / Something's coming / Lost in the stars / She loves me.
LP: . . . . EMS 1334
LP: 792 449 1
MC: . . . . TCEMS 1334
MC: 792 449 4

CHRISTMAS WITH VIC DAMONE.
LP: . . . . HDY 1936
MC: . . . . ZCHDY 1936

CLOSER THAN A KISS.
Tracks: / Closer than a kiss / I kiss your hand / Madam / We kiss in a shadow / Cuddle up a little closer / A toujours / You and the night and the music / Prelude to a kiss / How deep is the ocean? / Day by day / As time goes by / Close as pages in a book / Out of nowhere / Night has a thousand eyes, The / Oh my love / You stepped out of a dream / I cried for you / Spring is here / Deep purple / Toot toot tootsie /

Swingin' down the lane / I got it bad and that ain't good.
LP: . . . . CBS 22183
MC: 40 22183

DAMONE TYPE OF THING, THE.
Tracks: / Time after time / I got it bad and that ain't good / Guess I'll hang my tears out to dry / Gone with the wind / I never go there any more / Two for the road / Make me rainbows / It never entered my mind / More I see you, The / I'll find you a rainbow / Arriverderci, my love.
LP: . . . . NL 89261
MC: . . . . NK 89261

DAMONE'S FEELINGS 1978.
LP: . . . . REBECCA 1212

DIDN'T WE?.
Tracks: / Song is you, The / All I need is a girl / By the time I get to Phoenix / Little green apples / Moment of truth, The / Didn't we? / Look of love, The / Can't take my eyes off you / Feelings / If / Ghost riders in the sky / Windmills of your mind / People / Top of the world / Over the rainbow.
LP: . . . . SHLP 112
MC: . . . . SHTC 112

FEELINGS.
Tracks: / Feelings / Lazy afternoon / Ghost riders in the sky / Softly / Windmills of your mind / People / Top of the world / Farewell to paradise / Over the rainbow.
LP: . . . . PRCV 118
MC: . . . . TC PRCV 118

LINGER AWHILE.
Tracks: / Linger awhile / Soft lights and sweet music / Close your eyes / Deep night / Stella by starlight / One love / Let's face the music and dance / After the lights go down low / Change partners / There, I've said it again / In the still of the night / When lights are low.
LP: . . . . CAPS 1867471

LIVELY ONES, THE.
Tracks: / Charmaine / Cherokee / Laura / Diane / Nina never knew / Lively ones, The / Marie / Most beautiful girl in the world, The / Ruby / Dearly beloved / I want a little girl.
LP: . . . . ED 2604141
MC: . . . . ED 2604144

LOVE LETTERS.
Tracks: / Breaking up is hard to do / How deep is your love? / Love letters / Are you lonesome tonight? / My foolish heart / Solitaire / Call me irresponsible / I'll be seeing you / Misty / Just the way you are / I can see clearly now / If I loved you / You don't bring me flowers / Evergreen / What are you doing the rest of your life? / Come in from the rain / When I dream / Loving you / She believes in me / Still.
LP: . . . . BDL 3002
MC: . . . . BDC 3002

MAGIC MOMENTS WITH VIC DAMONE.
Tracks: / Meditation / Once I loved / How insensitive / Girl from Ipanema, The / Stay with me / Someone to light up my life / Shadow of your smile, The / Time for love, A / Ciao compare / On the south side of Chicago / Stay / You don't have to say you love me / Time after time / Two for the road / It never entered my mind / More I see you, the / Arrivederci my love / Why can't I walk away / Watch what happens / If you are but a dream / Stardust / Like someone in love / I should care / Goin' out of my head.
MC: . . . . NK 89622

MAGIC OF VIC DAMONE.
Tracks: / Song is you, The / All I need is a girl / Little green apples / Moment of truth, The / Didn't we / Look of love, The / Can't take my eyes off you / La vita / MacArthur Park / Time after time / They call the wind Maria / Where / Come back to me / For once in my life / Here's that rainy day feeling / Almost close to you / We have all the time in the world.
LP: . . . . ARA 1003
MC: . . . . ARAC 1003

MAKE SOMEONE HAPPY.
Tracks: / Make someone happy / Call me irresponsible / Stella by starlight / Where is the love? / Misty / Everytime I look at you / Deja vu / Here's that rainy day / This masquerade / Just the way you are / I can see clearly now / For all we know.
LP: . . . . INTS 5125
MC: . . . . INTK 5125

MY BABY LOVES TO SWING.
Tracks: / I'm nobody's baby / Everybody loves my baby / You must have been a beautiful baby / Alright, okay, you win / My melancholy baby / Let's sit this one out / My baby loves to swing / My baby just cares for me / Is you is or is you ain't my baby / Baby, baby all the time / Baby won't you please come home? / Make this a slow goodbye.
LP: . . . . EMS 1151
MC: . . . . TCEMS 1151

NOW.
Tracks: / If I loved you / You needed me / When I dream / You don't bring me flowers / My foolish heart / She believes in me / Love is blue / Should've never let you go / Still / Love letters / Loving you / I'll be seeing you.
LP: . . . . NL 70134
MC: . . . . NK 70134
LP: . . . . INTS 5080

NOW AND FOREVER.
Tracks: / Solitaire / Red roses / Are you lonesome tonight? / Come in from the rain / Make it with you / Melancholy baby / Evergreen / Singin' in the rain / Bewitched / Don't worry 'bout me / What are you doing the rest of your life?.
LP: . . . . INTS 5234
MC: . . . . INTK 5234

ON THE SOUTH SIDE OF CHICAGO.
Tracks: / It makes no difference / Quiet tear, A / Ciao compare / I'll sleep tonight / You've never kissed her / On the south side of Chicago / What is a woman? / Love me longer / Stay / You don't have to say you love me.
LP: . . . . NL 89263
MC: . . . . NK 89263

POP SINGERS ON THE AIR (See under Pop Singers On The Air) (Various artists).

PORTRAIT OF A SONG STYLIST.
MC: . . . . HARMC 110

PORTRAIT OF A SONG STYLIST (2).
MC: . . . . HARMC 121

SINGS THE GREAT SONGS.
Tracks: / On the street where you live / Pleasure of her company / Affair to remember, An / Second time around / Almost like being in love / If ever I should lose you / Gigi / Maria / Arrivederci Roma / You're breaking my heart / You and the night and the music / How deep is the ocean? / As time goes by / It had to be you / Very thought of you, The / Every time we say goodbye.
LP: . . . . CBS 32261
MC: 40-32261

STAY WITH ME.
Tracks: / Pretty butterfly / Meditation / Once I loved / How insensitive / Girl from Ipanema / You are / Stay with me / Someone to light up my life / Quiet nights of quiet stars / Shadow of your smile / Sinning sea, The / Time for love, A.
LP: . . . . NL 89262
MC: . . . . NK 89262

STRANGE ENCHANTMENT.
Tracks: / Strange enchantment / Hawaiian wedding song / Shangri-la / Humming waters / Poinciana / Flamingo / Beyond the reef / You're loveable / Moon of manakoora / Bali Ha'i / Forevermore / Ebb tide.
LP: . . . . CAPS 2600031

TIME FOR LOVE,A.
Tracks: / More I see you / Girl from Ipanema / Stardust / Shadow of your smile / Quiet nights / Stay / It never entered my mind / Two for the road / Once I loved / Time after time / What is a woman / Stay with me.
2LP: . . . . CR 073
MCSET: . . . . CRT 073

UNFORGETTABLE: VIC DAMONE (16 Golden Classics).
Tracks: / Feelings / If / Ghost riders in the sky / Softly / Windmills of your mind / People / Top of the world / Over the rainbow / Song is you, The / All I need is a girl / By the time I get to Phoenix / Little green apples / Moment of truth, The / Didn't we? / Look of love, The / Can't take my eyes off you.
LP: . . . . UNLP 006
MC: . . . . UNMC 006

VIC DAMONE & DICK HAYMES (see Haymes, Dick & Vic Damone) (Damone, Vic & Dick Haymes).

VIC DAMONE'S BEST.
Tracks: / On the south side of Chicago / Shadow of your smile / Pretty butterfly / If you are but a dream / It never entered my mind / You don't have to say you love me / It makes no difference / Star dust / Meditation / Gone with the wind / More I see you, The / Two for the road.
LP: . . . . NL 89170
MC: . . . . NK 89170

WHY CAN'T I WALK AWAY.
Tracks: / Like someone in love / When you've laughed all your laughter / I should care / Glory of love / Guess who's coming to dinner / Take it from me girl / Nothing to lose / Goin' out of my head.
LP: . . . . NL 89264
MC: . . . . NK 89264

Damron, Dick

LOST IN THE MUSIC.
Tracks: / Minstrel, The / Whiskey Jack / My good woman (that ain't right) / It ain't easy goin' home / When Satan spins the bottle / Lost in the music / California friends / Only way to say goodbye, The / Woman / Sweet lady.
LP: . . . . PL 42490
MC: . . . . PK 42490

NORTHWEST REBELLION (Damron, Dick/ Roy Warhurst).
LP: . . . . WRS 102

SOLDIER OF FORTUNE.
LP: . . . . WRS 099

THOUSAND SONGS OF GLORY, A.
LP: . . . . WRS 119

Damsel In Distress

DAMSEL IN DISTRESS/THE SKY'S THE LIMIT (Film soundtracks) (Various artists).
LP: . . . . CC 100.19

Dan

ATTITUDE HITS, AN.
LP: . . . . MADLP 009

MOTHER WITH CHILD AND BUNNY.
LP: . . . . PLAY LP 4

Dan Ar Bras

MUSIC FOR THE SILENCES TO COME.
LP: . . . . SHAN 96001

Dan Band

LITTLE BLACK MAGIC.
Tracks: / Can't resist it / Touch too much / Trying to get to you / Wild about you baby / Crossed / Driving too hard in the rain / China cup / Money / D'fer.
LP: . . . . LLP 134
MC: . . . . LLK 134

Dan Dare

DAN DARE (Various artists).
MCSET: . . . . ZBBC 1129

Dan & Farmers

COUNTRY BOY.
Tracks: / Combine harvester / My lovely Irish rose.
LP: . . . . HRL 120

DOWN ON THE FARM.
Tracks: / Spencil Hill / Poor poor farmer / Any dream will do.
LP: . . . . HRL 101

Dan The...

AMONG MY SOUVENIRS (Dan The Street Singer).
LP: . . . . RBA 120

THROUGH THE YEARS (Dan The Street Singer).
LP: . . . . RBA 110

Dana

ALL KINDS OF EVERYTHING (OLD GOLD) (See under Neil Reid - Mother Of Mine).

IF I GIVE MY HEART TO YOU.
LP: . . . . RITZLP TV 2
MC: . . . . RITZLC TV 2

LET THERE BE LOVE.
Tracks: / Let there be love / I saw my Lord this morning / O Lord / Christ is my light / Ag croist an fiol / Run that race / Hosanna / Diamond in the rough / Portait of Jesus / Hallelujah.
LP: . . . . WST 9635
MC: . . . . WC 9635

MAGIC.
Tracks: / Dream lover / You never gave me your love / I feel love comin' on.
LP: . . . . CRLP 515

MORNING STAR (See under Dave & Dana) (Dana & Dave).

NO GREATER LOVE.
Tracks: / Totus totus / Let there be love / Mary's song / Portrait of Jesus / Little baby / I saw my Lord this morning / Hosanna / Hallelujah / Simple song of love / Praise the Lord / Soft rain / Oh Lord.
LP: . . . . KMR 482
MC: . . . . KMC 482
MC: . . . . HMC 038

PLEASE TELL HIM THAT I SAID HELLO.
Tracks: / Please tell him that I said hello / There's a kind of hush / I get a little sentimental over you / Country pie / Fairytale / Totus totus / I love how you love me / All my loving / Never gonna fall in love again / Crying game, The / Over the rainbow / I'm not in love.
LP: . . . . SPR 8542
MC: . . . . SPC 8542

TOTALLY YOURS.
Tracks: / Praise the Lord / Mary's song / I rocked him as a baby / Sing for me / O so wonderful / Soft rain, The / Totus totus / Home where I belong / Little baby / He cares for you / Simple song.
LP: . . . . WST 9608
MC: . . . . WC 9608

WORLD OF DANA, THE.
Tracks: / Crossword puzzle / Silent movies / Say I love you / Trying to say goodbye / I'll string along with you / All kinds of everything / Day by day / Who put the lights out / New days...new ways / Do I still figure in your life / Love's a friend of mine / Skyline person.
LP: . . . . SPA 415
MC: . . . . KCSP 415

Dana, Bill

BEST OF JOSE JIMENEZ.
LP: . . . . GNPS 7001
MC: GNP5 7001

Danball, Totsuzen

LOL COXHILL WITH TOTSUZEN DANBALL (Danball, Totsuzen & Lol Coxhill).
LP: . . . . FLOOR 2

Dance

20 CRUCIAL DANCE TRACKS (Various artists).
LP: . . . . BIGAD 2
MC: . . . . BIGAC 2

25 WEST 38TH (Nu Groove compilation) (Various artists).
Tracks: / Feel it: *Various artists* / Legends: *Various artists* / Quad 1: *Various artists* / Secret code: *Various artists* / Kenny's jazz: *Various artists* / Virgin eyes: *Various artists* / When can I call you: *Various artists* / I've just begun to love you: *Various artists* / File no.2: *Various artists* / Searchin': *Various artists* / Annihilate: *Various artists* / Illusion, An: *Various artists*.
LP: . . . . NGV 91

100 ALL TIME CLASSIC DANCE HITS OF THE 1970'S (See Under 70's) (Various artists).

100 DANCE HITS OF THE 80'S (Various artists).
Tracks: / Ride on time: *Black Box* / Pump up the jam: *Technotronic featuring Felly* / Only way is up, The: *Yazz* & The Plastic Population / Doctorin' the house: *Cold Cut featuring Yazz & The Plastic Population* / People hold on: *Coldcut & Lisa Stansfield* / Numero uno (radio edit): *Starlight* / Lambada: *Kaoma* / Don't make me over: *Sybil* / Fake '88: *O'Neal, Alexander* / Who found who: *Jellybean & Elisa Fiorillo* / Lovely day (sunshine mix): *Withers, Bill* / I really didn't mean it: *Vandross, Luther* / Tribute (right on): *Pasadenas* / Hustle (to the music) (radio 1): *Funky Worm* / Roadblock: *Stock/ Aitken/Waterman* / Respectable: *Mel & Kim* / Loco in Acapulco: *Four Tops* / Shake you down: *Abbott, Gregory* / Real thing, The: *Jellybean featuring Steven* Dante / Automatic: *Pointer Sisters* / Midas touch: *Midnight Star* / In the name of love '88: *Thompson* Twins / Let's hear it for the boy: *Williams, Deniece* / Now that we've found love: *Third World* / Lost in music: *Sister Sledge* / Ghostbusters: *Parker, Ray Jnr.* / System addict: *Five Star* / Wap bam boogie: *Matt Bianco* / Dance sucker: *Set The Tone* / Dr. Beat: *Estefan, Gloria/Miami Sound Machine* / Takes a little time: *Total Contrast* / Let the music play: *Shannon* / Gotta get you home tonight: *Wilde, Eugene* / I wonder if I take you home: *Lisa Lisa/Cult Jam* / She's strange: *Cameo* / Money's too tight to mention: *Simply* Red / I found lovin': *Fatback (Band)* / Finest, The: *S.O.S. Band* / I can't wait: *Nu Shooz* / Going to the bank: *Commodores* / Jump (for my love): *Pointer Sisters* / Dancin' in the key of life (remix): *Arrington,* Steve / Showing out (get fresh at the weekend): *Mel & Kim* / Rappers delight: *Sugarhill Gang* / Breaks, The: *Blow, Kurtis* / Message, The: *Grandmaster Flash* / Get on the dancefloor: *Base, Rob & D.J. E-Z Rock* / I know you got soul: *Eric B & Rakim* / White lines (don't do it): *Grandmaster Flash & Melle Mel* / (Nothin' serious) just buggin': *Whistle* / Break 4 love: *Raze* / Alice I want you just for me: *Full Force* / (Bang Zoom) let's go go: *Real Roxanne* / Let's get brutal: *Nitro Deluxe* / Jack the groove: *Raze* / Jack le freak: *Chic* / Jack to the sound of the underground: *Hithouse* / Don't stop the music: *Yarbrough & Peoples* / Jump to the beat: *Lattisaw, Stacy* / Get down on it: *Kool & The Gang* / Jump to it: *Franklin, Aretha* / Stomp: *Brothers Johnson* / Love come down: *King, Evelyn "Champagne"* / Funkin' for Jamaica: *Browne, Tom* / Searching: *Change* / I'll be good: *Rene & Angela* / Razzamatazz: *Jones, Quincy* / She's a bad mama jama: *Carlton, Carl* / Once bitten twice shy: *Williams, Vesta* / Back and forth: *Cameo* / Groove, The: *Franklin,* Rodney / Who's zoomin' who?: *Franklin, Aretha* / I'm in love: *King, Evelyn "Champagne"* / Walking on

sunshine: *Rockers Revenge* / Juicy fruit: *Mtume* / Silver shadow: *Atlantic Starr* / Keepin' love new: *Johnson, Howard* / Save your love (for number one): *Rene & Angela* / Night to remember, A: *Shalamar* / Love town: *Newberry, Booker III* / We got the funk: *Positive Force* / Let's groove: *Earth, Wind & Fire* / Inside out: *Odyssey*/ Going back to my roots: *Odyssey* / Rockit: *Hancock, Herbie* / Celebration: *Kool & The Gang* / Mama used to say: *Junior* / (Sexual) healing: *Gaye, Marvin* / Make that move: *Shalamar* / There it is: *Shalamar*/ Candy girl: *New Edition* / I.O.U.: *Freeez* / 19: *Hardcastle, Paul* / Funky town: *Lipps Inc.*/ Walking into sunshine: *Central Line* / Southern Freeez: *Freeez* / Ai no corrida: *Jones, Quincy* / Everybody salsa: *Modern Romance* / Flashback: *Imagination* / And the beat goes on: *Whispers*.
LPS: . . . . **DBOXLP 101**
MCSET: . . . . **DBOXMC 101**

B.BOY BOOGIE DOWN SAMPLER (Various artists).
Tracks: / Bronx is back, The: *Tall Dark & Handsome* / Feel: *Cold Crush Brothers* / Nothing like Hip-Hop: *Cold City Crew* / Stars are: *Money Earning Crew* / Cold kickin': *Frozen Explosion* / Bassman: *Michael G.*/ Force is the boss: *J.V.C.F.O.R.C.E.* / Classical: *Busy Boy* / Something different: *Levi 167* / In full effect: *5 Star Motet*.
LP: . . . . **BBOY 1**
MC: . . . . **ZCBBY 1**

B.BOY BOOGIE DOWN SAMPLER VOL.2 (Various artists).
LP: . . . . **BBOY 4**
MC: . . . . **ZCBBY 4**

BEAT THIS: THE BEST OF RHYTHM KING (Various artists).
Tracks: / Burn it up: *Beatmasters* / Don't make me wait: *Bomb The Bass* / Born free: *Merlin* / These things happen: *Wills, Viola* / I say a little prayer: *Bomb The Bass* / Rok da house: *Beatmasters, featuring* The Cookie Crew / Cruising for a bruising: *Wize Men* / Funky sensation: *McCrae, Gwen* / Rock this house: *Hotline*/ Superfly guy: *S. Express* / I love my radio: *Taffy* / We need some money: *Brown, Chuck* / Chikki chikki ahh ahh: *Baby Ford* / Theme from S.Express: *S. Express* / Hey love: *King Sun-D Moet* / East West: *Strongman, Jay* / Beat dis: *Bomb The Bass*.
LP: . . . . **SMR 973**
MC: . . . . **SMC 973**

BEST OF BELGIAN NEW BEAT, THE (Various artists).
Tracks: / Rock the beat '89': *Lisa M* / Doughnut dollies: *HNO3* / Fatal error: *Fatal Error* / Public relations: *Public Relations* / Cheebala: *Ghention* / Eighty eight: *Public Relations* / Mandate my ass: *Space Opera* / Baby wants to ride: *Bart* / Total recall: *Spectrum* / New beat mind: *Public Relations*.
LP: . . . . **HOP 230**
MC: . . . . **HOPC 230**

BEST OF BRITISH FUNK (Various artists).
Tracks: / Love games: *Various artists* / Starchild: *Various artists* / Feels like the right time: *Various artists* / Easier said than done: *Various artists* / Can't keep holding on: *Various artists* / Fall in love: *Various artists* / Walking into sunshine: *Various artists* / Mama used to say: *Various artists*.
LP: **2480 659**
MC: **3194 659**

BEST OF EASYSTREET (Various artists).
LP: . . . . **EEZY 1**
MC: . . . . **ZCEEZY 1**

BEST OF GARAGE VOL. 1 (Various artists).
LP: . . . . **GARA 1**
MC: . . . . **ZCRA 1**

BEST OF HIGH ENERGY (Various artists).
LP: . . . . **LELEP 1001**
MC: . . . . **CELEP 1001**

BEST OF HOUSE '88 (Various artists).
LP: . . . . **STAR 2347**
MC: . . . . **STAC 2347**

BEST OF HOUSE MEGAMIX VOL.1 (Various artists).
LP: . . . . **BOIT 1**
LP: . . . . **ZCIT 1**

BEST OF HOUSE MEGAMIX VOL.3 (Various artists).
LP: . . . . **BOIT 3**
MC: . . . . **ZCIT 3**

BEST OF HOUSE MEGAMIX VOL 2 (Various artists).
Tracks: / Theme from S. Express: *S. Express* / Release your body: *Bang The Party* / Zone: *Ingram, Kurtis*/ And the break goes on: *Break Boys* / Delta house: *Housemaster Baldwin* / Get busy: *M D Emm* / Let's dance: *Keynotes* / Totally serious: *Motto, Denise* / Can you party: *Royal House* / Grooving without a doubt: *Reese & Mayday*.
MC: . . . . **ZCIT 2**
LP: . . . . **BOIT 2**

BEST OF HOUSE (SERIOUS LABEL) (Various artists).
LP: . . . . **BEHO 6**
MC: . . . . **ZCHO 6**

BEST OF HOUSE VOL.1 (Various artists).
LP: . . . . **BEHO 1**
MC: . . . . **ZCHO 1**

BEST OF HOUSE VOL.2 (Various artists).
LP: . . . . **BEHO 2**
MC: . . . . **ZCHO 2**

BEST OF HOUSE VOL.3 (Various artists).
LP: . . . . **BEHO 3**
MC: . . . . **ZCHO 3**

BEST OF HOUSE VOL.5 (Various artists).
LP: . . . . **BEHO 5**
MC: . . . . **ZCHO 5**

BIO RHYTHM (Various artists).
Tracks: / Take me back (bass head mix): *Rhythmatic* / Mood (optimystic mix): *Symbols & Instruments* / Free: *Kate B* / Emanon: *Rhythim Is Rhythim* / Fall into a trance: *Critical Rhythm* / Self hypnosis: *Nexus 21*/ Somebody new: *MK* / Bio rhythms: *C & M Connection* / Indulge: *Howard, Neal* / Don't lead me (2001 mix): *Paris Grey*.
LP: . . . . **BIOLP 1**
MC: . . . . **BIOMC 1**

BLACK HAVANA (Various artists).
Tracks: / Can't take it: *Thompson, Keith* / Always there: *Char-Voni* / Like this like that: *Madagascar*/ Time is now for action, The: *Three Big Men* / Happy: *Three Big Men* / Do it steady: *Vice Versa* / Cuban gigolo: *Sound Factory* / Throw 'em the chicken: *Crowd Control* / Somebody to love me: *Toby, Glenn 'Sweety G'* / Twilight: *Trio Zero*.
LP: . . . . **SYLP 6003**
MC: . . . . **TCSYLP 6003**

BODY JAMS VOL. 1 (Various artists).
Tracks: / Feel it for you: *Alterations* / Raindrops: *Rhythm Club* / Indifferent faces: *Wyman, James*/ Standing in the cold: *House Of 'O'* / Give me the reason: *Wyman, James* / Don't try to change me: *Rhythm Club* / Snow white: *Alternations* / Play house: *House Of 'O'*.
LP: . . . . **PL 90438**
MC: . . . . **PK 90438**

BREAK BEATS 3 (Original Unknown DJ's) (Various artists).
Tracks: / Bass beats II: *Various artists* / Funky drummer 1: *Various artists* / Funky drummer III: *Various artists* / Pumpin' 1: *Various artists* / Pumpin' II: *Various artists* / Boyee: *Various artists* / Dizzy: *Various artists* / Stoned: *Various artists* / Catch a groove: *Various artists* / Funky drummer II: *Various artists* / Power: *Various artists* / Little love, A: *Various artists* / Jazz 1: *Various artists* / Man: *Various artists* / No sympathy: *Various artists* / Samples and effects: *Various artists*.
LP: . . . . **WRRLP 013**

BREAKS, BASS AND BLEEPS (Various artists).
LP: . . . . **RAID 502**
MC: . . . . **ZCRAID 502**

BREAKS, BASS AND BLEEPS 2 (Various artists).
LP: . . . . **RAID 504**
MC: . . . . **ZCRAID 504**

BUILT FOR THE 90'S (Dedicated to your audio) (Various artists).
Tracks: / Psyko funk: *Nomad Soul* / Happy: *Owens, Robert* / Wash your face in my sink: *Dream Warriors*/ Now's the B turn: *Laquan* / Wicked in Mombassa: *Summers, Mark* / Grand verbaliser, what time is it: *X-Clan*/ Phunky as phuck: *Def Jef*.
LP: . . . . **BRLM 553**
MC: . . . . **BRCM 553**

BUMPER ISSUE (The Rhythm King compilation) (Various artists).
LP: . . . . **LEFTLP 7**
MC: . . . . **LEFTC 7**

CAN U FEEL IT - THE CHAMPION LEGEND (Various artists).
Tracks: / Reachin': *Charles, Kelly* / Don't make me over: *Sybil* / Falling in love (remix): *Sybil* / Share my joy (club mix): *Jones, Jo Ann* / As always: *Farley "Jackmaster" Funk & Dillard* / My love is guaranteed: *Sybil* / My love is right: *Douglas, Shana* / Free at last: *Farley "Jackmaster" Funk* / Push it: *Salt 'N' Pepa* / Break 4 love: *Raze* / Ready 4 love: *Razzette* / Ya bad chubbs: *Chubb Rock featuring Hitman* Howie Tee / 2 hot 2 stop: *L.U.S.T.* / Women beat their men: *Voodoo Doll* / Sex 4 daze: *Lake Eerie*/ Jungle fever: *Kinkina*.
LP: . . . . **NE 1452**
MC: . . . . **CE 2452**

CAPITOL CLASSICS VOL. 1 (Various artists).
Tracks: / Key to the world: *Reynolds, L.J.* / Boogie oogie oogie: *Taste Of Honey* / On the beat: *B B & Q* Band / Prance on: *Henderson, Eddie* / Love on a summer night: *McCrarys* / It's a pleasure: *Brown, Sheree* / Sound of music, The: *Dayton* / Doin' alright: *O'Bryan* / Just can't give you up: *Mystic Merlin* / Music is my sanctuary: *Bartz, Gary*.
LP: . . . . **EMS 1316**
MC: . . . . **TCEMS 1316**

CAPITOL CLASSICS VOL. 3 (Various artists).
Tracks: / I ain't with it (heart to heart mix): *Laurence, Paul* / Magic spell (hocus pocus mix): *Lynch* / I promise: *Bleu, Mikki* / Gitchi U (ext. dance mix): *Z'Looke* / Have you had your love today: *O'Jays* / Rising to the top: *Pieces Of A Dream* / Wanna make love: *Sun* / Tender moments: *Blu, Peggi* / Feeling lucky lately: *High Fashion* / I am down: *Bryson, Peabo* / Call on me: *Maze* (CD only.) / Annie Mae: *Cole, Natalie*(CD only.) / Just can't give you up: *Mystic Merlin* (CD only.) / Boogie oogie oogie: *Taste Of Honey* (CD only.).
LP: . . . . **EMS 1344**
LP: **793 846 1**
MC: . . . . **TCEMS 1344**

CAPITOL COLLECTABLES II (Various artists).
Tracks: / Hold on to what you've got: *King, Evelyn "Champagne"* / Da'butt: *E.U.* / Wishing you were here: *Gyrlz*/ You're my one and only love: *Connors, Norman* / Personality: *Najee* / Irresistible: *Wheeler, Audrey*/ Rising to the top: *Pieces Of A Dream* / Off the hook: *RJ's Latest Arrival* / Wasn't I good to ya?: *Dakrash*/ Keeps me runnin' back: *Moore, Melba* / Flirt: *King, Evelyn "Champagne"*.
MC: . . . . **TCCMP 1001**
LP: . . . . **CMP 1001**

CARRY ON BREAKBEATS (Various artists).
LP: . . . . **BOOLP 1**

CATCH THIS BEAT - THE ROCKSTEADY YEARS (Various artists).
LP: . . . . **IRSP 7**

CHARLY DANCE PARTY (See under Charly (label)) (Various artists).

CHART SHOW - DANCE ALBUM (See under Chart Show (T.V.)) (Various artists).

CHECK IT OUT VOL.1 (Various artists).
LP: . . . . **GRYLP 1**
MC: . . . . **GRYMC 1**

CHECK OUT THE GROOVE (Various artists).
Tracks: / Can you handle it: *Various artists* / I like what you're doing to me: *Various artists* / Love rescue: *Various artists* / Do it (till you're satisfied): *Various artists* / Check out the groove: *Various artists*/ Body talk: *Various artists* / Love is gonna be on your side: *Various artists* / I wanna do it: *Various artists*/ Breakaway: *Various artists* / Hit and run lover: *Various artists*.
LP: . . . . **CRX 6**
MC: . . . . **CRCX 6**

CHICAGO LP (Various artists).
LP: . . . . **HIP 93**
MC: . . . . **HIPC 93**

CHICAGO TRAX VOL.1 (Various artists).
LP: . . . . **TRAXLP 701**
MC: . . . . **ZCTRAX 701**

CHUNKS OF FUNK (Various artists).
LP: . . . . **CHUNK 1**

CITYBEAT BEATS IN TIME (Various artists).
LP: . . . . **CBLP 8**
MC: . . . . **CBMC 8**

CLASSIC DANCE HITS (Various artists).
LP: . . . . **TVDLP 17**
MCSET: . . . . **ZCTVD 17**

CLASSIC DANCE TRACKS (Various artists).
LP: . . . . **BRLP 84**
MC: . . . . **BRMC 84**

CLASSIC MIX MASTERCUTS VOL.1 (Various artists).
2LP: . . . . **CUTSLP 1**
MC: . . . . **CUTSMC 1**

CLASSIC PRELUDES (Various artists).
Tracks: / Check out the groove: *Thurston, Bobby* / In the bush (remix): *Musique* / Body music: *Strikers*/ Stretchin' out (remix): *Adams, Gayle* / Never give you up: *Redd, Sharon* / You're the one for me: *D-Train*/ You'll never know: *Hi-Gloss* / Come on dance dance: *Saturday Night Band* / What I got is what you need: *Unique*/ Can U handle it (remix): *Redd, Sharon*.
LP: **210.376**
MC: **410.376**

CLUB IT 90 VOL.1 (Various artists).
Tracks: / Wanted: *Princess Ivori* / Boogie down: *Catch 22* / Ariel state: *Technofusion* / Total science: *Audio One* / Thoughts of you: *Alliance* / Play it again...: *Out Of The Ordinary* / Afrodizziact...: *Cry Sisco* / I'll be a freak...: *Royal Delite* / Open up baby: *Logg*.
LP: . . . . **CLUB LP 1**
MC: . . . . **CLUB ZC 1**

CLUB IT 90 VOL.2 (Various artists).
LP: . . . . **CLUBLP 2**
MC: . . . . **CLUBZC 2**

CLUB SOUNDS (Various artists).
LP: . . . . **LELEP 1002**
MC: . . . . **CELEP 1002**

CLUB TRACKS VOLUME 3 (Various artists).
Tracks: / She's strange: *Cameo* / Let me run it: *Omni* / Don't give me up: *Melvin, Harold & The Bluenotes*/ I wanna make you feel good: *System* / Give me tonight: *Shannon* / Weigh all the facts: *Reynolds, L.J.*/ Baby doll: *Malemen* / Someday: *Gap Band* / Live wire (I want a girl that sweats): *Bootee, Duke*.
LP: . . . . **JABB 2**
MC: . . . . **JABBC 2**

CLUB UK (Ten extended UK club hits) (Various artists).
Tracks: / Down on the street: *Shakatak* / Magic touch: *Loose Ends* / Minefield: *I-Level* / Hi-Tension: *Hi Tension* / Southern freeez: *Freeez* / You're lying: *Linx* / Spend the night: *Cool Notes* / London town: *Light Of The World* / Love games: *Level 42* / You can't hide your face: *Joseph, David*.
LP: . . . . **OG 1801**
MC: . . . . **OG 2801**

CLUB UK VOL.2 (Various artists).
Tracks: / Somebody help me out: *Beggar & Co* / As time goes by: *Funkapolitan* / Tears are not enough: *ABC*/ Flashback: *Imagination* / Time like this, A: *Haywoode* / All fall down: *Five Star* / Riding on a train: *Pasadenas* / Chant no.1 (I don't need this pressure): *Spandau Ballet* / Half the day's gone and we haven't earned a penny: *Lynch, Kenny* / Guilty: *Hardcastle, Paul*.
LP: . . . . **OG 1804**
MC: . . . . **OG 2804**

COME WITH CLUB - 2 (Various artists).
Tracks: / Ladies night: *Kool & The Gang* / I'm out to catch: *Haywood, Leon* / Something special: *Harvey, Steve* / Surprise surprise: *Central Line* / Love town: *Newbury, Booker* / Come with me: *Maria, Tania*/ You're a winner: *Cameo* / Mi sabrina tequana: *Ingram*.
LP: . . . . **CLUBL 002**
MC: . . . . **CLUBC 002**

CORE (Various artists).
LP: . . . . **BIAS 095**

COVER UP (Various artists).
Tracks: / Don't make me over: *Sybil* / Walk on by: *Carroll, Dina* / Sexual healing rap: *Young Love* / Why can't we live together: *Illusion* / Sunshine 89: *Fax Yourself* / Tainted love: *Impedance* / Going back to my roots: *F.P.I. Project present Rich In Paradise* / Let's get horny: *Mister B* / Think: *Farley "Jackmaster" Funk* / Spring rain: *Rico*.
LP: . . . . **CUPWL 5002**
MC: . . . . **CUPWK 5002**

CREAM OF SUPREME (Various artists).
LP: . . . . **LPSU 3**
MC: . . . . **ZCSU 3**

CRUCIAL ELECTRO (Various artists).
Tracks: / Smurf, The: *Brunson, Tyrone* / Light years away: *Warp 9* / Hip hop be bop: *Various artists*/ Rockit: *Hancock, Herbie* / Electric kingdom: *Twilight 22* / Clear: *Cybotron* / Al naafiysh: *Hashim*/ Return of Captain Rock, The: *Various artists* / Wild style: *Time Zone*.
LP: . . . . **ELCST 999**
MC: . . . . **ZCELC 999**

CRUCIAL ELECTRO 2 (Various artists).
LP: . . . . **ELCST 1000**
MC: . . . . **ZCELC 1000**

CRUCIAL ELECTRO 3 (Various artists).
LP: . . . . **ELCST 1002**
MC: . . . . **ZCELC 1002**

CUT LOUD VOLUME 1 (Various artists).
Tracks: / Let's get busy: *Clubland featuring Quartz* / Every kinda people:

Various artists / Winter days: Gage, Yvonne featuring Me / Chaka vaedo: Black, Peter / (Who'd) I'd be loving you: Jones, Hannah / (Another one) War: First Impact / Love so strong: Mind Power / People of the world: Johnson, Sorrell / Force of habit: Over 2 U / Colours: Mason & Hamlin.
LP: . . . . **WDRLP 001**
MC: . . . . **ZCWDR 001**

CUTTIN' A GROOVE (Various artists).
LP: . . . . **HQLP 1**

DANCE BOX (Various artists).
LP: . . . . **IMP 0102**
MC: . . . . **IMPC 0102**

DANCE CAN'T LAST NICE WITHOUT WE (Various artists).
LP: . . . . **OPLP 11**

DANCE CHART (Various artists).
Tracks: / Reet petite: Wilson, Jackie / Showing out (Get fresh...): Mel & Kim / Jack the groove: Raze/ Gap band: Gap Band / Private life: Jones, Grace / Rumours: Timex Social Club / You keep me hangin' on: Wilde, Kim / I love my radio: Taffy / Male stripper: Man 2 Man meets Man Parrish / I.O.U.: Freeez/ Can't wait another minute: Five Star / Midas touch: Midnight Star / I wonder: Lisa Lisa/Cult Jam with Full Force / Mr. D.J.: Concept / (Nothing serious) Just buggin': Whistle / Wham rap (enjoy what you do?): Wham.
LP: . . . . **STAR 2285**
MC: . . . . **STAC 2285**

DANCE COMPILATION (Various artists).
LP: **088 417**

DANCE CRASHER (Ska to Rock Steady) (Various artists).
Tracks: / Big bamboo: Lord Creator / Latin goes ska: Skatalites / Garden of love: Drummond, Don / Rough and tough: Cole, Stranger / Beardman ska: Skatalites / Shame and scandal: Tosh, Peter & The Wailers/ Street corner: Skatalites / Bonanza ska: Malcolm, Carlos & Afro Caribs / Dance crasher: Ellis, Alton & The Flames / Let George do it: Drummond, Don / Rudie bam bam: Clarendonians / Doctor Dick: Perry, Lee & The Soulettes / Ball o' fire: Skatalites / Independence ska: Brooks, Baba & Band / Don't be a rude boy: Rulers / Ska jam: McCook, Tommy & The Soulettes / Hallelujah: Maytals / Owe me no pay me: Ethiopians.
LP: . . . . **TRLS 260**
MC: . . . . **ZCTRL 260**

DANCE DANCE DANCE (Various artists).
LP: . . . . **INCH 2**
MC: . . . . **ZCINCH 2**
LP: . . . . **NE 1143**
MC: . . . . **CE 2143**

DANCE DANCE DANCE (2) (Non-Stop Classic Soul Mix) (Various artists).
Tracks: / Check out the groove: Thurston, Bobby / You got the power: War / Funkin' for Jamaica: Browne, Tom / Heart's desire: Blackman, Donald / Unlock the funk: Locksmith / Expansions: Smith, Lonnie Liston/ All I need is you: Starship / You're the one for me: D-Train / I just gotta have you (lover turn me on): Kashif/ Meet me halfway there: Jones, Glenn / (Do you really love me) Tell me love: Wycoff, Michael / Never give you up: Redd, Sharon / What I got is what you need: Unique / Shame: King, Evelyn "Champagne" / In the bush: Musique / Body music: Strikers / Everybody up: Ohio Players.
MC: **411398**

DANCE DECADE (Dance hits of the 80's) (Various artists).
Tracks: / Don't leave me this way: Communards / Relax: Frankie Goes To Hollywood / Good thing: Fine Young Cannibals / Tainted love: Soft Cell / Breakout: Swing Out Sister / Love in the first degree: Bananarama/ Oh l'amour: Dollar / Kiss: Art Of Noise & Tom Jones / Only way is up, The: Yazz / Push it: Salt 'N' Pepa / Got to keep on: Cookie Crew / People hold on: Coldcut & Lisa Stansfield / House arrest: Krush/ Jack your body: Hurley, Steve 'Silk' / Wipe out: Fat Boys / Walk this way: Run D.M.C. / She works hard for the money: Summer, Donna / Living in America: Brown, James / Word up: Cameo / Get down on it: Kool & The Gang / Oops up side your head: Gap Band / Ain't nothin' goin' on but the rent: Guthrie, Gwen/ Walk the dinosaur: Was Not Was / Mama used to say: Junior / Smalltown boy: Bronski Beat / Poison arrow: ABC / Let the music play: Shannon / Funky town: Lipps Inc. / Obsession: Animotion/ Night train: Visage / Maniac: Sembello, Michael / Fame: Cara, Irene.
2LP: . . . . **DDTV 1**
MCSET: . . . . **DDTVC 1**

DANCE DECADE 1973-1983 (Various artists).
LPS: . . . . **DEC 7383**
MCSET: . . . . **ZCDEC 7383**

DANCE ENERGY (Various artists).
Tracks: / Elevation: Xpansions / Everybody (rap): Criminal Element Orchestra / Killer: Adamski / Fascinating rhythm (Lisa loud mix): Bass-O-Matic / Cult of snap (world power radio mix): Snap / Get yourself together: Young Disciples / Contribution (transistor mix): Paris, Mica Featuring Rakim / Tell me why: Sindecut / It's a shame (my sister): True Image / Solid gold: Ashley & Jackson / What time is love: K.L.F. / Wash your face in my sink: Dream Warriors / Now is tomorrow: Definition of Sound / Mama said knock you out: L.L. Cool J / La raza (cantina mix): Kid Frost / Jazz thing (movie mix): Gang Starr (2) / People (US remix): Soul II Soul / Let's push it: Innocence / Livin' in the light: Wheeler, Caron / Don't be a fool: Loose Ends/ Can't stop: After 7 / Masterplan, The: Brown, Diana & Barrie K Sharpe / Hold on: En Vogue / Barefoot in the head: Man Called Adam / Make it mine: Shamen / I'm free: Soup Dragons / Daydreaming: Massive Attack / Mustt mustt (duckpond dub): Nusrat Fateh Ali Khan / Rhythm takes control (12" version): Unique 3/ Aftermath (LFO remix): Nightmares On Wax / Cubik: 808 State / Floatation: Grid / Theme two burn: Sense 8 / Dance energy theme: Various artists.
2LP: . . . . **VTDLP 3**
MCSET: . . . . **VTDMC 3**

DANCE ENERGY 2 (Various artists).
MC: . . . . **VTMC 4**
LP: . . . . **VTLP 4**

DANCE FLOOR AUTHORITY (Various artists).
Tracks: / Another lover: Lydell & The People / I need a beat: Oliver, Mickey / Way to go home: Starr, Bart/ Alibi: Me & Mr B / Who'd have thought: Jones, Hannah / Je t'aime: Harman, Claire / Very well: Bazz/ Generation: Mr. Di Angelo / Running away: Ska Ta (Ralphi Rosario) / Don't hold back: Blade Boy.
LP: . . . . **DFA 001**
MC: . . . . **ZCDFA 001**

DANCE FLOOR HITS (Various artists).
LP: . . . . **COP 214**
MC: . . . . **HOPC 214**

DANCE FOREVER (Various artists).
LPS: . . . . **2 C 17078254/6**
LPS: . . . . **2 C 15678252/3**
2LP: . . . . **2 C 15064644/45**

DANCE HITS '86 (Various artists).
LP: . . . . **NE 1344**
MC: . . . . **CE 2344**

DANCE HITS ALBUM (Various artists).
Tracks: / Say I'm your number one: Princess / Caribbean queen: Ocean, Billy / Frankie: Sister Sledge/ All fall down: Five Star / Treat her like a lady: Temptations / Rhythm of the night: DeBarge / Body and soul: Mai Tai / Knock on wood: Stewart, Amii / Automatic: Pointer Sisters / Nightshift: Commodores/ Yah mo b there: Ingram, James / Your personal touch: King, Evelyn "Champagne" / Turn it up: Conway Brothers/ Let it all blow: Dazz Band / Mated: Grant, David & Jaki Graham.
LP: . . . . **TVLP 8**

DANCE HITS - DANCE MIX VOLUME 4 (Various artists).
Tracks: / You can't have my love: Jones Girls / Fresh: Brunson, Tyrone / Thriller: Jackson, Michael/ Magic: Anderson, Carl / I wanted your love: Vandross, Luther / Smooth operator: Slade / They only come out at night: Brown, Pete (Lyricist) / Stay on in the groove: Franklin, Rodney / West End girls: Pet Shop Boys / Night moves: Patrick, Rikki / It's raining men: Weather Girls.
LP: . . . . **DM 4**
MC: **404**

DANCE I.D NO.1 (Various artists).
Tracks: / Love bizarre, A: Sheila E / Let my people go: Winans (group) / Heat of heat, The: Austin, Patti/ Love's gonna get you: Brown, Jocelyn / Color of success: Shirley Murdock / It doesn't really matter: Zapp/ My magic man: Rochelle / Funky sensation: McCrae, Gwen / Don't cha go nowhere: Dee, Donald.
LP: . . . . **WX 48**
MC: . . . . **WX 48 C**

DANCE I.D NO. 2 (Various artists).
Tracks: / Sex machine: Fat Boys / Stop and think: Fire On Blonde / Doo wa ditty: Zapp / Shante: Mass Production / Bambaataa's theme: Various artists / Two of hearts: Stacey Q / Cool: Time, The / You're a star: Aquarian Dream.
LP: . . . . **WX 66**
MC: . . . . **WX 66C**

DANCE LOGIC (Various artists).
Tracks: / Ooops up (AMV remix): Snap / Push it harder (Dub Hard club mix): Cross That Line / Relax your soul: Fun 4 Fun / Love can do (Ambiente mix): Blue Tattoo / There ain't no stoppin' this: Moses, P / Lite side mix: Co Dependents Of... / Is it serious?: Caelum Aspics Mix / Hi score (Level 02 mix): 16 Bit.
LP: **211033**
MC: **411033**

DANCE MACHINE (Various artists).
LP: . . . . **TMS 3512**
MC: . . . . **TMC 3512**

DANCE MANIA VOL.1 (Various artists).
Tracks: / Let no man put asunder: Various artists / Across the tracks: Various artists / Corina, Corina: Various artists / House nation: Various artists / Dancing in the night: Various artists / Jazz it up: Various artists / Rocky steady: Various artists / Fantasize me: Various artists / Funky nassau: Various artists/ Ill return: Various artists.
LP: . . . . **DAMA 1**
MC: . . . . **ZCMA 1**

DANCE MIX '87 (Various artists).
Tracks: / I wanna dance with somebody: Houston, Whitney / Jimmy Lee: Franklin, Aretha / Must be missing an angel: Tavares / It only takes a minute: Tavares / Loverboy: Chairmen Of The Board / Digging your scene: Blow Monkeys / It doesn't have to be this way: Blow Monkeys / Set me free: Graham, Jaki / Mated: Various artists / Learning to live (without your love): Brown, O'Chi / La bamba: Valens, Ritchie / Walking on sunshine: Katrina & The Waves / Roadblock: Stock/Aitken/Waterman / Serious mix: Mirage / Jack mix II: Mirage/ Respectable: Mel & Kim / Showing out: Various artists / Jack the groove: Raze / House nation: Housemaster Boyz / My love is guaranteed: Sybil / Victim of love: Erasure / Jive talkin': Boogie Box High/ Once bitten twice shy: Williams, Vesta / Rumours: Timex Social Club / Lies: Butler, Jonathan / Just don't want to be lonely: McGregor, Freddie / One dance won't do: Hall, Audrey / I'll keep on loving you: Princess/ Have a nice day: Shante, Roxanne / (Nothing serious) Just buggin': Whistle / Let's dance: Rea, Chris/ Caribbean queen: Ocean, Billy / When the going gets tough (the tough get going): Ocean, Billy / Touch me (I want your body): Fox, Samantha / Nothing's gonna stop me now: Fox, Samantha / Let yourself go: Sybil/ I can prove it: Fearon, Phil / Easier said than done: Booth, Patrick / Spirit in the sky / French kissin' in the USA: Harry, Debbie / Let's go all the way: Sly Fox / You keep me hangin' on: Wilde, Kim / Who's that mix: This Years Blonde / Looking for a new love: Watley, Jody / And the beat goes on: Whispers/ Rock steady: Whispers / Midas touch: Midnight Star / Curiosity: Jets (American) / Crush on you: Jets (American) / I found lovin': Walsh, Steve / Smile: Hall, Audrey / Girlie girlie: George, Sophia/ This brutal house: Nitro Deluxe / Jack the opera: Makossa, Jack E / Male stripper: Man 2 Man meets Man Parrish / I.O.U.: Freeez / Another step closer your heart: Wilde, Kim & Junior.
LP: . . . . **STAR 2314**
MC: . . . . **STAC 2314**

DANCE MIX - DANCE HITS (Various artists).
Tracks: / Keep giving me love: D-Train / Feel the need in me: Forrest / Don't you give your love away: Shelto, Steve / Wanna be startin' something: Jackson, Michael / Juicy fruit: Mtume / Jam hot: Dynell, Johnny & New York 88 / Save the overtime for me: Knight, Gladys & The Pips / Reach out: Duke, George / Men of the music: Band AKA.
LP: . . . . **EPC 25564**
MC: **40 25564**
LP: . . . . **DM 84**

DANCE MIX - DANCE HITS VOLUME 2 (Various artists).
Tracks: / Rock it: Hancock, Herbie / Put our heads together: O'Jays / Crazy: Manhattans / What I got is what you need: Unique / Show me the way: NY Skyy / Just be good to me: S.O.S. Band / When you're far away: Various artists / Time like this, A: Haywoode.
LP: . . . . **DM 2**
MC: . . . . **40 DM 2**

DANCE MIX - DANCE HITS VOLUME 3 (Various artists).
Tracks: / Serious: Griffin, Billy / Somebody save the night: Redd, Sharon / Just can't get enough: Kirton, Lew / I'll let you slide: Vandross, Luther / Just let me wait: Holliday, Jennifer / Something's on your mind: D-Train / Heaven only knows: Pendergrass, Teddy / This love is for real: Banks, Ron / She's so good to me: Banks, Ron / Share the night: World Premiere.
LP: . . . . **DM 3**
MC: . . . . **DM 403**

DANCE PARTY (Various artists).
Tracks: / Birdie song, The: Tweets / Barbados: Typically Tropical / Honey polie (all over the world): Russell, Big John / Una paloma blanca: King, Jonathan / Feels like I'm in love: Marie, Kelly / Zing went the strings of my heart: Trammps / Save your kisses for me: Brotherhood Of Man / Simon says: 1910 Fruitgum Company/ Mony mony: James, Tommy & The Shondells / Blue moon: Marcels / Puppet on a string: Shaw, Sandie / My old man's a dustman: Donegan, Lonnie / Johnny reggae: Piglets / My ding a ling: Berry, Chuck.
LP: . . . . **NCP 1008**
MC: . . . . **ZCNCP 1008**

DANCE POWER VOL. 1 (Club Classics) (Various artists).
Tracks: / Car wash: Jiani, Carol / I'm not in love: Payne, Scherrie / Starman: Free Style / One night only: Payne, Scherrie / Up the ladder to the roof: Kydd, John & The Supreme Event / My guy: Angie / Knowing me, knowing you: Springate, John / Born to be alive: Meantime / Guilty: Alexander, Ross / Can't help falling in love: Absolutely / Pick up the pieces: Enterprise 7 / Can you feel the force: Prime DC/ Queen of clubs: Springate, John / Shame, shame, shame: Linda & The Funky Boys / Love machine: Sidewalk/ Come together: Free Style / Magic fly: Raw Recruits / Uptown top ranking: Tight N Up / Future brain: Huntington, Eddie / Mickey: XYZ.
MC: . . . . **PWKMC 4073**

DANCE SOUND OF DETROIT VOL.1 (Former artists of Motown re-unite) (Various artists).
Tracks: / Step into my shoes: Reeves, Martha / Don't burn your bridges: Wells, Mary / Needle in a haystack: Velvelettes / Emotion: Weston, Kim / Heaven must have sent you: Elgins / What goes around: Gaye, Frankie / All over the world: Jackson, Chuck / Run like a rabbit: Johnson, Marv / Wake me up when it's over: Ruffin, Jimmy / If the shoe fits: Syreeta / Holding on with both hands: Marvelettes / After dark: Campbell, Choker.
MC: . . . . **DSDMC 01**

DANCE SOUND OF DETROIT VOL.2 (Former artists of Motown re-unite) (Various artists).
Tracks: / What's going on: Gaye, Frankie / You're the answer to my dreams: Wells, Mary / Angel in disguise: Reeves, Martha / Stop dead in my tracks: Elgins / Relight my fire: Jackson, Chuck / On the rebound: Ruffin, Jimmy/ Brenda Holloway / By hook or by crook: Johnson, Marv / Let's fall in love tonight: Starr, Edwin / Do unto others: Taylor, Bobby & The Vancouvers / Restless feet: Weston, Kim / Love is my middle name: Wylie, Richard 'Popcorn' / If at first you don't succeed: Ward, Sammy.
MC: . . . . **DSDMC 02**

DANCE SOUND OF DETROIT VOL.3 (Former artists of Motown re-unite) (Various artists).
Tracks: / It takes two: Gaye, Frankie & Kim Weston / Don't get mad get even: Wilson, Mary / Ain't nothing like the real thing: Johnson, Marv/Carolyn Gill / You made a believer out of me: Starr, Edwin / Helpless: Weston, Kim / Lightning never strikes twice: Andantes / Heading away from heartaches: Elgins / Give me a little inspiration: Holloway, Brenda / Down to love town: Taylor, Bobby & The Vancouvers / Running out of luck: Velvelettes/ Honey from a bee: Three Ounces Of Love / Signal your intention: Weston, Kim.
MC: . . . . **DSDMC 03**

DANCE SOUND OF DETROIT VOL.4 (Various artists).
Tracks: / Just a little misunderstanding: Stubbs, Joe / Who's gonna have the last laugh: Weston, Kim / Major investment: Moy, Sylvia / Extraordinary girl: Gaye, Frankie / Pure energy: Payne, Scherrie / Timeless: Crawford, Carolyn / Pull my heartstrings: Velvelettes / Detroit City: Van Dyke, Earl / Destination unknown: Stubbs, Joe / Joke's on you, The: Randolph, Barbara / Hurry up: Robinson, Claudette / Cross that bridge: Gaye, Frankie.
MC: . . . . **DSDMC 04**

DANCE TIME (Various artists).
MCSET: . . . . **WW 6029**

DANCE TIME (Various artists).
MC: . . . . **AM 32**

DANCE TO IT (Various artists).
LP: . . . . **LM LP 002**

DANCE YOURSELF TO DEATH (Various artists).
LP: **100 762**

DANCEMASTER - VOLUME 1 (Various artists).
Tracks: / Walking on sunshine: *Rockers Revenge* / Go deh yaka (Go to the top): *Monyaka* / Candy girl: *New Edition* / Love town: *Newbury, Booker* / Sun goes down (living it up), The: *Various artists* / I think I want to dance with you: *Various artists* / Body work: *Hot Streak* / Dressing up: *Street Angels* / Tonight: *Harvey, Steve* / All my life: *Major Harris*.
LP: . . . . **DX 1**
MC: . . . . **DXC 1**

DANCEMASTERS - VOLUME 1 (Various artists).
Tracks: / Move to the bigband (extended club mix): *Liebrand, Ben* / Heaven (physical mix): *Chimes* / Boomin' system, The (The underground mix): *L.L. Cool J* / My kinda girl (LP version): *Babyface* / Right here right now (extended mix): *Western Block* / Can't do nuttin' for ya man (bass in your face: *Public Enemy* / I'll be around (after dark mix): *Nayobe* / Steppin' to the A.M. (soiree mix): *3rd Bass* / Good lovin' (Frankie Foncett mix): *Belle, Regina*/ Tubular bells (extended version): *Plutonic* / Double Dutch on the sidewalk (extended mix): *Newkirk* / Flowers (wizdum mix): *Emotions* / Emotions electric (Frankie Foncett mix): *Guy Called Gerald* / Get free (Eden upstairs remix): *Mwale, Anna* / Money can't buy you love: *Midnight Star* / Pianonegro (Honky Tonk remix): *Pianonegro*/ Since day one (Jazzie B mix): *Marie, Teena* / Family affair (echo vox mix): *Sly & the Family Stone* / Jazz thing (video mix): *Gangstarr* / Feel it (long version): *Afros*.
LP: . . . . **DD 1**
MC: . . . . **DDC 1**

DANCIN' (Various artists).
Tracks: / Dancing in the street: *Reeves, Martha* / Cloud nine: *Temptations* / This old heart of mine: *Isley* Brothers / Tears of a clown: *Robinson, Smokey* / There's a ghost in my house: *Taylor, Dean* / For once in my life: *Wonder, Stevie* / I'm a roadrunner: *Walker, Junior* / War: *Starr, Edwin* / Ball of confusion: *Temptations* / Reach out and touch (somebody's hand): *Four Tops* / Upside down: *Ross, Diana* / Signed, sealed, delivered (I'm yours): *Wonder, Stevie* / River deep, mountain high: *Supremes & Four Tops* / Love machine (part 1): *Various artists* / Machine gun: *Commodores* / Let's get serious: *Jackson, Jermaine* / Behind the groove: *Marie, Teena* / Papa was a rollin' stone: *Temptations* / Long hangover: *Ross, Diana* / I want you back: *Jackson Five*.
LP: . . . . **STAR 2225**
MC: . . . . **STAC 2225**

DANCIN' (Various artists).
LP: . . . . **INRLP 2**
MC: . . . . **INRC 2**

DANCING THRU THE DARK (Various artists).
Tracks: / Paradise: *Various artists* / Power and the glory, The: *Various artists* / Jam it jam: *Various artists*/ Dancin' thru the dark: *Various artists* / Shoe shine: *Various artists* / I'm livin' a life of love: *Various artists* / Caribbean queen: *Various artists* / Get busy: *Various artists* / People all around the world: *Various artists* / So many people: *Various artists* / Once in a lifetime: *Various artists*.
LP: . . . . **HIP 92**
MC: . . . . **HIPC 92**

DECODED AND DANCED UP (Rhythms of DeConstruction) (Various artists).
Tracks: / Fantasy remixed: *Black Box* / Everybody (Capital mix): *Williams, Wendell* / Give it up: *Creation*/ Anthem: *N. Joi* / Dance (revisited): *Edens Paradise* / Amor!: *Chapman, Ben* / Talk to me: *Coloursound* featuring Siobahn / Freaky dreamer: *Freaky Dreamer* / Sly one (Melbourne mix): *Van-Rooy, Marina* / Amazing grace: *Vandal* / Future FJP: *Liaison D* / Warehouse requiem: *Guru Josh*.
LP: . . . . **PL 74855**
MC: . . . . **PK 74855**

DEEP HEAT (Various artists).
2LP: . . . . **STAR 2345**
MCSET: . . . . **STAC 2345**

DEEP HEAT 2 - THE SECOND BURN HOUSE (Various artists).
2LP: . . . . **STAR 2356**
MCSET: . . . . **STAC 2356**

DEEP HEAT 3 - THE THIRD DEGREE SINGLE (Various artists).
2LP: . . . . **STAR 2364**
MCSET: . . . . **STAC 2364**

DEEP HEAT 4 - PLAY WITH FIRE (Various artists).
Tracks: / Numero uno: *Starlight* / Don't make me over: *Sybil* / Never give up: *Slique* / I'll be there: *Smooth, Joe* / Forever together: *Raven Maize* / I feel good all over: *Bang The Party* / Hello, I love you: *T-C* / Hey boy: *Lucas, Tammy* / Pump up the jam: *Technotronic featuring Felly* / Mastermix: *D.J.* Fast Eddie / Cool chillin': *Melody* / Dream, The: *Out Of The Ordinary* / Ain't nobody better: *Inner City*/ Just rock: *Smokin' Gang* / Grandpa's party: *Love, Monie* / Illusion: *R-Tyme* / Definition of love: *Kaos*/ Do you know who you are: *Virgo* / Your love: *Aphrodisiac* / Let me love you for tonight: *Karia* / Get funky: *Royal House* / Get into the dance: *Maurice* / Chase, The: *Model 500* / Hey DJ: *Beatmasters*/ Ya bad chubb: *Chubb Rock* / Your love: *Knuckles, Frankie* / It's you: *ESP* / Say no go: *De La Soul*/ Think: *Farley "Jackmaster" Funk* / House the Japanese: *Samurai* / Don't think about it: *Total Eclipse*/ Sinister: *Mayday (dance)*.
2LP: . . . . **STAR 2388**
MCSET: . . . . **STAC 2388**

DEEP HEAT 5 - FEED THE FEVER (Various artists).
Tracks: / 20 seconds to comply: *Silver Bullet* / Somebody in the house...: *2 In A Room* / Going back to my roots: *Rich In Paradise* / Warm love: *Beatmasters* / Planet E: *K.C. Flightt* / Move your body: *Knuckles*, Frankie / All through the night: *Sybil* / Deep heat '89: *Latino Rave* / Grand piano: *Mixmaster* / Good vibrations: *J.D.* / Pain: *Marrow, Lee* / Goodbye kiss: *Fowlkes, Eddie "Flashin"* / Time to party: *Jones, Shay* / Sunshine and brick: *Homeboy* / Love system: *Pavesi, Maurizio* / Heavens, The: *Rees*/ Got to get: *Rob 'N' Raz* / Your wish is my command: *Santos* / Seduzieteu: *Attillas* / Lambada: *Lips-Kiss*/ This way, that way: *Pandella* / Security: *Beat Club* / What u r: *Tot* / Paradise megamix: *Inner* City / I thank you: *Adeva* / Eye know: *De La Soul* / Dog a baseline: *Intense* / What's done is done: *92nd & 5th* / Deep: *Helmer, John* / Believe: *Julie X* / Don't break the rules: *Invision* / Burn the house down: *Menz Club*.
2LP: . . . . **STAR 2411**
MCSET: . . . . **STAC 2411**

DEEP HEAT 6 - THE SIXTH SENSE (Various artists).
Tracks: / Get up (before the night is over) (wing command mix): *Technotronic featuring Felly* / G'ding g'ding: *Anna G* / Beautiful Love: *Adeva* / Show'm the bass: *M.C. Miker G* / This time: *Liaz* / Hold me back: *West* Bam / Power, The: *Snap* / N.R.G: *Adamski* / Infinity: *Guru Josh* / Blackout: *Lil Louis*/ Tearing down the walls: *Streetlife* / Survival: *Dawning with Lamya Al Mugheiry* / Dirty cash: *Stevie V*/ Right before my eyes: *Patte Day* / Wigan: *Baby Ford* / Feeling good: *Pressure Drop* / Stories (I've a novella edit): *Izit* / Magic number, The: *De La Soul* / Turn it out (go base) (Full control meltdown): *Base*, Rob / Atomic house: *D.J. Atomico 'Herbie'* / Self respect: *Rush, Donell* / Just another dream: *Dennis*, Cathy / Turn up those party lights: *Exclusive T* / Your lies: *Dionne* / Brits 1990 (dance medley). The: *Various artists* / Down on love: *One World* / Wishing on a star (Wing command remix): *Dickey, Gwen* / Amoeba: *Man Called Adam* / Time to say peace: *Poor Righteous Teachers* / Don't hold back the feeling (Don't hold back t: *2 Mad* / Space shuttle: *Scott-Heron, Gil* / Motherland a-fri-ca: *Tribal House*.
2LP: . . . . **STAR 2412**
MCSET: . . . . **STAC 2412**

DEEP HEAT 7 - SEVENTH HEAVEN (Various artists).
2LP: . . . . **STAR 2422**
MCSET: . . . . **STAC 2422**

DEEP HEAT 8 - THE HAND OF FATE (Various artists).
Tracks: / Cult of snap: *Snap* / Rainforest serenade: *It* / Tricky disco: *Tricky Disco* / Love is gonna get'cha: *Boogie Down Productions* / I can't stand it: *Twenty 4 Seven* / Bonita Applebum: *Tribe Called Quest*/ Come together: *Primal Scream* / Groovy train: *Farm* / Flowers: *Titiyo* / Hands across the ocean: *She* Rockers / Super freak: *James, Rick* / Madness: *Sons Of Soul* / Prisoner, The: *F.A.B. Featuring MC No. 6* / Movin': *Marrow, Lee* / LFO: *LFO* / Self hypnosis: *Nexus 21* / Livin' in the light: *Wheeler*, Caron / Silly games: *Layton, Lindy* / I don't even know if I should call you baby: *Soul Family Sensation*/ What time is love: *K.L.F.* / Nothing to lose: *S. Express* / Coolin': *2 Live Crew* / Make it mine: *Shamen*/ Spin that wheel: *Hi-Tek 3* / Another sleepless night: *Wilson, Mike* / Rub you the right way: *Gill, Johnny*/ Bump, The: *Wee Papa Girl Rappers* / La Serenissima: *DNA* / Dance: *Earth People* / Hell or Heaven: *L.U.P.O*/ Frequency: *Rhythmatic* / In sync: *Fade II Black*.
2LP: . . . . **STAR 2447**
MCSET: . . . . **STAC 2447**

DEEP HEAT 9 - NINTH LIFE (Various artists).
2LP: . . . . **STAC 2470**
MCSET: . . . . **STAR 2470**

DEEP HEAT 10 - THE AWAKENING (Various artists).
MC: . . . . **STAC 2515**
LP: . . . . **STAC 2490**

DEEP HEAT '89 (Various artists).
2LP: . . . . **STAR 2380**
MCSET: . . . . **STAC 2380**

DEEP HEAT 1990 (Various artists).
MCSET: . . . . **STAC 2438**
2LP: . . . . **STAR 2438**

DESIGNED FOR DANCING (Various artists).
LP: . . . . **DESLP 1**
MC: . . . . **DSK 1**
LP: . . . . **GCLP 002**
MC: . . . . **GCMC 002**

DISC DRIVE (Various artists).
LP: . . . . **HOP 212**
MC: . . . . **HOPC 212**

DO IT FLUID: 6 RARE GROOVES (Various artists).
LP: . . . . **BGP 1002**
MC: . . . . **BGPC 1002**

DON'T STOP (Various artists).
Tracks: / Be thankful for what you've got: *Scratch Band* / Your place or mine: *Scratch Band* / What it is: *Parker*, Cecil / Really, really love you: *Parker, Cecil* / You never had it so good: *Young, Roy* / Venus: *Young, Roy* / It's up to you / Maria Verano: *Various artists* / Manana amor: *Kid* / Don't stop: *Kid*.
MC: . . . . **TCEMS 1002**

DON'T STOP THE MUSIC (Various artists).
LP: . . . . **SMR 977**
MC: . . . . **SMC 977**

DREAMS AND FREQUENCIES VOL 2 (Various artists).
LP: . . . . **DBLP 509**

EIGHTIES ACCESS (Various artists).
LP: . . . . **DINTV 4**
MC: . . . . **DINMC 4**

ELECRO 5 (Various artists).
LP: . . . . **ELCST 005**

ELECTRIC BODY MUSIC (Various artists).
LP: . . . . **ANT 111**
MC: . . . . **ANT 111MC**

ELECTRONIC BODY MUSIC (Various artists).
LP: . . . . **CALCLP 071**

ENCORE (Various artists).
Tracks: / Loving you: *Massivo* / Venus (the piano mix): *Don Pablo's Animals* / Going back to my roots: *F.P.I.* Project / Another day in paradise (the Sidney mix): *Jamtronik* / I'm not in love: *Ij & The Soundwave* / Strawberry fields forever: *Candy Flip* / Don't you forget about me: *Impedance* / Shine on you crazy diamond: *Dream In Goa* / Guilty: *Clarke, Sharon Dee* / Free: *Pasha*.
LP: . . . . **KUVALP 1**
MC: . . . . **KUVAMC 1**

ENERGY (DJ's in the house) (Various artists).
LP: . . . . **NGYLP 001**
MC: . . . . **NGYMC 001**

EUROBEAT (Various artists).
LP: . . . . **EBEAT 1**
MC: . . . . **ZCBET 1**

EURODANCE VOLUME 1 (Various artists).
LP: . . . . **BOLP 1001**

EURO-HITS (Various artists).
LP: . . . . **CAL 219**
MC: . . . . **CAC 219**

EURORAVE (Various artists).
Tracks: / Another day in paradise: *Jamtronik* / Whip: *Secci, Chicco* / You make me funky: *Magic Max*/ Unstoppable: *Magic Concept* / Soul mix: *Soul To Love* / Jam to the beat: *Alix* / Let there be house: *Dee, Daisy* / Going back to my roots: *F.P.I. Project* / Soul in paradise: *Doctor Woos* / You make me funky: *Magic Box*.
LP: . . . . **DINLP 8**
MC: . . . . **DINMC 8**

EVERYBODY DANCE NOW (Various artists).
Tracks: / Gonna make you sweat (everybody dance now): *C & C Music Factory* / Found love (Mozart remix): *Double Dee* featuring Dany / I can't take the power (riva 12" mix): *Offshore* / Must Bee the music (club mix): *King Bee featuring* Michele / This beat is hot (club mix): *B.G. The Prince Of Rap* / I say yeah (curiosity mix): *Secchi Featuring* Orlando / Daddy's little girl (main mix): *Nikki D* / All true man (classic club mix): *O'Neal, Alexander* / Through (the Jazzie B mix): *Wilson-James, Victoria* / Around the way girl (crypt 12" remix): *L.L. Cool J*.
LP: **4680501**
MC: **4680504**

EVERYBODY DANCE NOW II (Various artists).
LP: **4685971**
MC: **4685974**

EVERYBODY GET UP...AND DO YOUR STUFF (Various artists).
LP: . . . . **MFP 5583**
MC: . . . . **TCMFP 5583**

FIERCE (Dance cuts number one) (Various artists).
Tracks: / Do it properly: *2 Puerto Ricans* / Let's get brutal: *Nitro Deluxe* / Living in a box: *Living In* A Box / Show you how to jack: *House Hustlers* / I know you got soul: *Eric B & Rakim* / I ain't into that: *Rappin' Reverend* / Put the needle to the record: *Criminal Element Orchestra* / Heartbeat: *Octavia* / Last night: *Kid 'N Play*.
LP: . . . . **CTLP 4**
MC: . . . . **ZCTLP 4**

FIERCE 2 (Various artists).
Tracks: / I know you've got so: *Eric B & Rakim* / I got da feelin': *Sweet Tee* / Do this my way: *Kid 'N Play*/ Wham bam: *N.T.Gang* / Real thing, The: *Jellybean* / Let's get brutal: *Nitro Deluxe* / Faith hope and charity: *Fun Boy Three* / You are the one: *Taurous Boyz*.
LP: . . . . **CTLP 5**
MC: . . . . **ZCTLP 5**

FIRST RODGER NEW BEAT COMPILATION (Various artists).
LP: . . . . **RODGER 012**

FLY GUYS ROCK THE UNDERGROUND (Dance album) (Various artists).
Tracks: / People need people: *Stewart, Richard* / Dance: *Logical Choice* / I'll do anything: *Crown Heights* Affair / Get on up: *Kool, D.L.* / Love joy and happiness: *Foster, Vernell* / Give me good love: *Logical* Choice / Heart set on loving you: *Stockley, Eddie* / I still believe: *Stockley, Eddie* / Misused: *Foster, Vernell* / This is hip house: *Kool, D.L.*.
LP: . . . . **SBKLP 1001**
MC: . . . . **SBKTC 1001**

FREEDOM 2 (The Ultimate Rave) (Various artists).
LP: . . . . **BWTX 4**
MC: . . . . **BWTXC 4**

FROM OUR MINDS TO YOURS VOL. 1 (Various artists).
LP: . . . . **CHAMP 1026**
MC: . . . . **CHAMPC 1026**

GARAGE CLASSIQUE (Various artists).
Tracks: / Don't make me wait: *Peech Boys* / This time: *Private Possession* / Somebody save me (garage mix): *By All Means* / Release the tension: *Circuit* / Your life: *Konk* / Are you wid it (club mix): *Private Possession*/ I will always love you: *Stockley, Eddie* / Love's got 2 be strong: *Edwards, Keyman*.
MC: . . . . **BRCA 528**
LP: . . . . **BRLP 528**
MC: . . . . **ICM 2060**
MC: **846 604 4**

GARAGE SOUND OF DEEPEST NEW YORK (Various artists).
Tracks: / Reachin': *Phase 2* / I'm a lover: *Mazelle, Kym* / You're gonna miss me: *Turntable Orchestra*/ Can't win for losin': *Blaze* / I can't wait too long: *Church, Joe* / Houselights / Take some time out: *Jarvis, Arnold* / Let's work it out: *Exit* / Feel the music: *Ruff Neck*.
2LP: . . . . **LICLP 010**
MC: . . . . **LICC 010**

GARAGE SOUNDS OF NEW YORK VOL.III (Various artists).
LP: . . . . **UNKNOWN**
MC: . . . . **UNKNOWN**

GARAGE TRAX (Various artists).
LP: . . . . **BONY 1**
MC: . . . . **CBONY 1**

GARY BYRD'S SWEET INSPIRATIONS (Various artists).
LP: . . . . **REH 548**
MC: . . . . **ZCR 548**

GEE STREET- THE ALBUM (RE-ISSUE) (Various artists).
MC: . . . . **GEEMC 4**
LP: . . . . **GEEA 4**

GET ON THIS (Various artists).
Tracks: / Rockin' over the beat: *Technotronic* / Freestyle megamix: *Brown, Bobby (1)* / Affection: *Liaz &* Lisa Stansfield / Loving you: *Massivo featuring Tracey* / Naked in the rain: *Blue Pearl* / Thunderbirds are go: *F.A.B. featuring MC Parker* / Dub be good to me: *Beats International* / Don't stop the

music: *Harris, Simon* / Poison: *Bell Biv Devoe* / Free: *Payne, Tammy* / I'm not in love: *Ij & The Soundwave* / Rebel music: *Rebel MC* / Opposites atttract: *Abdul, Paula* / Art of love: *Art Of Noise* / Dance dance dance: *Deskee* / Last night a DJ saved my life: *Olimax* / Treat me good: *Yazz* / Come into my house: *Queen Latifah* / Monie in the middle: *Love, Monie* / I'm free: *Soup Dragons* / Hear the drummer (get wicked): *Jackson, Chad* / It is jazz: *Tingo Tango* / I love music: *Pandy, Darryl* / World in motion: *England New Order*/ This can be real: *Candy Flip* / Love don't live here anymore: *Fresh Connection* / Hippychick: *Soho*/ Drive my car: *Da Yeene* / Good love: *Klymaxx* / Venus: *Don Pablo's Animals* / It could not happen: *Critical Rhythm* / Yaaah: *D-Shake*.
MC: . . . . **STAC 2424**
LP: . . . . **STAR 2424**

GET ON UP (Various artists).
Tracks: / Such a feeling: *Aurra* / I am somebody: *Jones, Glenn* / Ooh I love it (love break): *Salsoul Orchestra*/ Get on up: *Dee, Jazzy* / Beverley: *Thornton, Fonzi* / Be mine tonight: *Jammers* / Girl I'm watching you: *Platinum Hook* / No stoppin' that rockin': *Instant Funk*.
LP: . . . . **BSLP 5001**
MC: . . . . **BSK 5001**

GOLD ON BLACK (Various artists).
Tracks: / Masterplan, The: *Brown, Diana & Barrie K Sharpe* / Hold you back (slammin' edit): *Blacksmith* / Chime (the helium mix): *Orbital* / I won't dance (the x mix): *Planet X* / And I loved you (classic club mix): *Tomiie, Satoshi & Arnold Jarvis* / C'mon + get my love (romance mix): *D Mob* / Down on love (mo bass remix): *I World*/ Do you dream (mo bass mix): *Carlton* / Dirty mind (e-zee remix): *Shakespear's Sister* (Only on CD and MC.) / Stories (the mellow mix): *Izit*(Only on CD and MC.).
LP: **828 2071**
MC: **828 2074**

GOTTA GO GO (Various artists).
LP: . . . . **SSG 01**
MC: . . . . **ZCG 01**

GREATEST HI-NRG HITS (Various artists).
LP: . . . . **ERCLP 1002**
MC: . . . . **ZCERC 1002**

GROOVE ZONE SECTOR 1 (Various artists).
Tracks: / Fake: *O'Neal, Alexander* / In the heat: *Princess* / All night long: *Mary Jane Girls* / Showing out: *Mel & Kim* / Love fever: *Culture Clash Dance Party* / Let's go together: *Change* / All that I can be: *Mitchell, Lauren* / It's raining men: *Weather Girls* / Automatic: *Pointer Sisters* / I am what I am: *Gaynor, Gloria* / Love hangover: *Ross, Diana* / Runaway: *Sterling Void* / Caribbean queen: *Ocean, Billy* / Let's groove: *Earth, Wind & Fire* / Never too much: *Vandross, Luther* / My love is guaranteed: *Sybil*/ Thinking about your love: *Skipworth & Turner* / Inside out: *Odyssey* / Promised land: *Smooth, Joe* / Love come down: *King, Evelyn "Champagne"*.
LP: . . . . **DRXLP 703**
MC: . . . . **DRXC 703**

GROOVE ZONE SECTOR 2 (Various artists).
Tracks: / It's a disco night (rock don't stop): *Isley Brothers* / Gone gone gone: *Mathis, Johnny* / Another man: *Mason, Barbara* / Love or money: *Hood, Mutha* / You're the one for me: *D-Train* / Flashback: *Imagination*/ Stomp: *Brothers Johnson* / Shame: *King, Evelyn "Champagne"* / I just gotta have: *Kashif* / Ain't no stoppin' us now: *McFadden & Whitehead* / Rumours: *Timex Social Club* / Razzmatazz: *Jones, Quincy* / I.O.U.: *Freeez*.
LP: . . . . **DRXLP 704**
MC: . . . . **DRXC 704**

GROOVE ZONE SECTOR 3 (Various artists).
Tracks: / Boogie wonderland: *Earth, Wind & Fire* / Native New Yorker: *Odyssey* / Grace: *Band AKA* / Funkin' for Jamaica: *Browne, Tom* / Hi tension: *Hi Tension* / Play that funky music: *Wild Cherry* / Ain't gonna bump no more: *Tex, Joe* / That lady: *Isley Brothers* / In the bush: *Musique* / Disco nights: *G.Q.*/ Bama boogie woogie: *Eaton, Cleveland* / Al no corrida: *Jones, Quincy* / Backstabbers: *O'Jays* / Jump to it: *Franklin, Aretha*.
LP: . . . . **DRXLP 705**
MC: . . . . **DRXC 705**

GROOVY GHETTO (Various artists).
MC: . . . . **ARC 925604**
LP: . . . . **ARC 925601**

GUERILLA GROOVES VOLUME 1 (Various artists).
LP: . . . . **GRLP 1**
MC: . . . . **GRMC 1**

GYRATIONS ACROSS THE NATIONS (Various artists).
LP: . . . . **HYBRID 1**

GYRATIONS ACROSS THE NATIONS VOL.2 (Various artists).
LP: . . . . **HYBRID 2**

HARDCORE DANCEFLOOR (Various artists).
LP: . . . . **DINTV 24**

HARDCORE UPROAR (Various artists).
MC: . . . . **DIMNC 20**
LP: . . . . **DINTV 20**

IBIZA MIX, VOLUME 3 (Various artists).
LP: **20090**

IN HOUSE (Various artists).
Tracks: / I wanna have some fun: *Fox, Samantha* / Get up on this: *She Rockers* / It's a trip: *Children Of The Night* / Love fever: *Culture Clash Dance Party* / We know it: *Wee Papa Girl Rappers* / House will never die: *Adonis*.
LP: . . . . **HOP 231**
MC: . . . . **HOPC 231**

INSPIRATION DANCE (Various artists).
LP: . . . . **GOSPL 1**

ITALIA - DANCE MUSIC FROM ITALY (Various artists).
Tracks: / Ride on time: *Black Box* / No sorry: *Latino, Gino* / Numero uno: *Starlight* / Gimme the funk: *Kekkotronics & LTJ* / Everyday: *Jam Machine* / I.C. love affair: *D.F.C. Team* / Teacher of the house music, The: *Latino, Gino* / First job: *Kekkotronics & LTJ* / Interplanetary adventures: *Doctor Zarkhov* / Pyscho: *Pyscho Team*.
LP: . . . . **PL 74289**
MC: . . . . **PK 74289**

ITALO DANCE CLASSICS (Various artists).
LP: **01435022**
MC: **01435131**

IT'S FRESH VOLUME 1 (Various artists).
LP: . . . . **TRDLP 1187**

IT'S IN THE MIX (Various artists).
Tracks: / Voice of Q: *Q* / Don't touch that dial: *Captain Sky* / Last night a dj saved my life: *Indeep*/ You can't have your cake and eat it too: *Taylor, Brenda* / Creme de creme: *Devaughan, William* / Changes: *Imagination*.
LP: . . . . **CAMIX 1**

IT'S IN THE MIX 1 (Various artists).
Tracks: / Last night a DJ saved my life: *Various artists* / You can't have your cake and eat it too: *Taylor, Brenda*/ Creme de creme: *Various artists* / Changes: *Imagination*.
LP: . . . . **STH 5001**

IT'S IN THE MIX (VOL 2) (Various artists).
Tracks: / Twist (round 'n' round): *Chill Fac-torr* / Watching you: *Venna* / I'd like to squeeze you hold you: *Deville* / When boys talk: *Indeep* / Under my thumb: *Fast Radio* / Midnight: *Push*.
LP: . . . . **CAMIX 2**
MC: . . . . **ZCAMIX 2**
LP: . . . . **ITH 1001**

IT'S IN THE MIX (VOL 3) (Various artists).
Tracks: / You make it heaven: *Wells, Terri* / Changing for you: *Chi-lites* / All night long: *La Famille*/ That's when (we'll be free): *State Of Grace* / Looking at midnight: *Imagination* / Let's start the dance III: *Bohannon (Hamilton)* / Never too late: *Smith, Lonnie Liston* / On the dance floor: *New Guys On The Block*.
LP: . . . . **CAMIX 3**
MC: . . . . **ZCAMIX 3**

IT'S IN THE MIX (VOL 4) (Various artists).
Tracks: / White lines (don't don't do it): *Grandmaster Flash & Melle Mel* / Jam on revenge: *Newcleus* / All night long (waterbed): *Kevie Kev* / New dimension: *Imagination* / Breakdancin' electric boogie: *West Street Mob*/ I wanna be with you: *Armenta* / Jingo: *Candido* / So different: *Kinky Foxx*.
LP: . . . . **CAMIX 251**
MC: . . . . **ZCAMIX 251**

JACK TRAX 3 (Various artists).
LP: . . . . **JTRAX 3**
MC: . . . . **CJTRAX 3**

JACKBEAT (Various artists).
MC: . . . . **LEFTC 3**
LP: . . . . **LEFTLP 3**

JACKMASTER 3 (Various artists).
Tracks: / How far I go: *House of Peter Black* / I want you back: *Reyes, Kario & Joe Nell* / Acid thunder: *Fast Eddie* / Pump it up homeboy: *Mix Masters*.
LP: . . . . **JACKLP 503**

JAMES BROWN'S FUNKY PEOPLE PART 2 (Various artists).
Tracks: / I know you got soul: *Byrd, Bobby* / From the love side: *Ballard, Hank & The Midnighters* / What do I have to do to prove my love to you: *Whitney, Marva* / Soul power '74: *Maceo & The Macks* / Put it on the line: *Collins, Lyn* / You can have Watergate, but gimme some bucks: *Wesley, Fred & The J.B.'s* / Message from the soul sisters (parts 1 & 2): *Barnes, Myra* / Hot pants...I'm coming, coming I'm coming: *Byrd, Bobby* / Do you your thing: *Collins, Lyn* / I'm paying taxes, what am I buying: *Wesley, Fred & The J.B.'s* / Super good (parts 1 & 2): *Barnes*, Myra / Cross the track (we better go back): *Maceo & The Macks* (On CD only) / Blow your head: *Wesley, Fred & The J.B.'s*.
LP: . . . . **URBLP 14**
MC: . . . . **URBMC 14**

JAZZ JUICE (Various artists).
LP: . . . . **SOUND 1**
MC: . . . . **ZCSND 1**

JAZZ JUICE (Various artists).
LP: . . . . **MUSIC 1**

JAZZ JUICE 2 (Various artists).
LP: . . . . **SOUND 4**
MC: . . . . **ZCSND 4**

JAZZ JUICE 3 (Various artists).
LP: . . . . **SOUND 5**
MC: . . . . **ZCSND 5**

JAZZ JUICE 4 (Various artists).
LP: . . . . **SOUND 6**
MC: . . . . **ZCSND 6**

JAZZ JUICE 5 (Various artists).
LP: . . . . **SOUND 8**
MC: . . . . **ZCSND 8**

JAZZ JUICE 6 (Various artists).
LP: . . . . **SOUND 9**
MC: . . . . **ZCSND 9**

JAZZ JUICE 8 (Various artists).
Tracks: / My favourite things: *Coltrane, John* / Sugar / Samba de Orfeu: *Mann, Herbie* / Dance with me: *McFerrin*, Bobby / Gators groove: *Jackson, Willis* / New York afternoon: *Cole, Richie* / Last nite: *Mar Keys*/ Braun blek blu: *dom um romao*.
LP: . . . . **SOUND 11**
MC: . . . . **ZCSND 11**

JUMPIN AND PUMPIN VOL. 1 (Various artists).
LP: . . . . **LPTOT 1**
MC: . . . . **MCTOT 1**

JUST 17- GET KICKIN' (Various artists).
Tracks: / What time is love?: *K.L.F.* / Naked in the rain: *Blue Pearl* / Thunderbirds are go: *F.A.B. featuring* MC Parker / Rockin' over the beat: *Technotronic featuring Ya Kid K* / Put your hands together: *D Mob* / I'm free: *Soup Dragons* / La serenissima: *DNA* / Bonita applebum (Why? version): *Tribe Called Quest* / I called U (over the edge mix): *Lil Louis* / Love don't live here anymore: *Fresh Connection* / You've got to look up: *Derek* B. / Dub be good to me: *Beats International* / Opposite attract (street mix): *Abdul, Paula* / Freestyle megamix: *Brown, Bobby (1)* / Band of gold (England mix): *N.R.G. UK featuring Ellie* / Treat me good: *Yazz* / Beyond your wildest dreams: *Gordon, Lonnie* / Silent voice: *Innocence* / Tricky disco: *Tricky Disco* / Pure (pure energy): *G.T.O.* / Gotta turn the music up: *M.C. Show Bizz & Lap One Crew* / Monie in the middle: *Love, Monie*/ Lamborghini: *Shut Up & Dance* / Nobody (blue mix): *Tongue 'N' Cheek*.
2LP: . . . . **ADD 16**
MCSET: . . . . **ZDD 16**

KAOS ACID NEW BEAT COMPILATION (2) (Various artists).
LP: . . . . **KAOS 024**

KOOLKAT COMPILATION (Various artists).
LP: . . . . **UNKNOWN**
MC: . . . . **UNKNOWN**

LET'S DANCE SERIES (DENON CD) (See under: Columbia Orchestra) (Columbia Orchestra).

LONDON DREAD COLLECTIVE (Various artists).
LP: . . . . **RAGGA 1**
MC: . . . . **RAGGA 1 C**

LOVE HOUSE (Various artists).
LP: . . . . **NE 1446**
MC: . . . . **CE 2446**

MAKE YOU SWEAT (Various artists).
MC: . . . . **STAC 2542**
LP: . . . . **STAR 2542**

MARKED FOR DEATH (Various artists).
LP: . . . . **BRLP 561**
MC: . . . . **BRMC 561**

MASTERS OF THE BEAT (Various artists).
Tracks: / Lisa's coming: *Latin Rascals* / Sweet beat: *Whiz Kid* / It's nasty (genius of love): *Hashim*/ Manoeuvres: *Leblanc, Keith* / Just do what you want: *Latin Rascals* / Yeah right: *Whiz Kid* / Uh: *Leblanc, Keith* / Dust cloud: *Rubin, Rick*.
LP: . . . . **ILPS 9834**
MC: . . . . **ICT 9834**

MEGABASS (Ultimate Megamix of the Hottest Club Hits) (Various artists).
MC: . . . . **STAC 2425**
LP: . . . . **STAR 2425**

MEGABASS 2 (The Hottest Dance Hits of the Decade) (Various artists).
MC: . . . . **STAC 2448**
LP: . . . . **STAR 2448**

MEGABASS 3 (Various artists).
MC: . . . . **STAC 2483**
LP: . . . . **STAR 2483**

MIGHTY DANCE (Various artists).
LP: . . . . **SATLP 401**

MOTOR CITY (Various artists).
LP: . . . . **VYKLF 11**

MOTOR CITY ROOTS - THE ROOTS OF DETROIT SOUL (Various artists).
Tracks: / You've got what it takes: *Johnson, Marv & The Falcons* / You've got to move two mountains: *Johnson, Marv* & The Falcons / Happy days: *Johnson, Marv & The Falcons* / Come to me: *Johnson, Marv & The Falcons* / He gave me you: *Johnson, Marv & The Falcons* / Easier said (than done): *Johnson, Marv & The Falcons* / I need you: *Johnson, Marv* & The Falcons / All the love I've got: *Johnson, Marv & The Falcons* / You're so fine: *Johnson, Marv & The* Falcons / Pow you're in love: *Johnson, Marv & The Falcons* / You're mine: *Johnson, Marv & The Falcons* / Teacher, The: *Johnson, Marv & The Falcons* / Waiting for you: *Johnson, Marv & The Falcons* / Goddess of angels: *Johnson, Marv & The Falcons* / I plus love plus you: *Johnson, Marv & The Falcons* / Country shack: *Johnson, Marv & The Falcons*.
LP: . . . . **SSL 6009**
MC: . . . . **TCSSL 6009**

MOTORCITY SOUL SAMPLER VOL.1 (Various artists).
LP: . . . . **MOTCLP 11**

MOTORCITY SOUL SAMPLER VOL.2 (Various artists).
LP: . . . . **MOTCLP 12**

MOTORCITY SOUL SAMPLER VOL.4 (Various artists).
LP: . . . . **MOTCLP 14**

MOTOR-TOWN SOUND OF DETROIT VOL.3 (Various artists).
LP: . . . . **MOTCLP 3**

MOTOR-TOWN SOUND OF DETROIT VOL.2 (Various artists).
LP: . . . . **MOTCLP 2**

MOTOR-TOWN SOUND OF DETROIT VOL.1 (Various artists).
LP: . . . . **MOTCLP 1**

NEUE BEAT COLLECTIONE (Various artists).
LP: . . . . **VW 1003**

NEW ACID HOUSE TECHNO BEAT (Various artists).
LP: . . . . **SUB 046**

NEW BEAT - EDIT 1 (Various artists).
Tracks: / Move your ass and feel the beat: *Erotic Dissidents* / Hmm hmm: *Taste Of Sugar* / Don't talk about sex: *Electric Shock* / Secrets of China: *Chinese Ways* / Agreppo: *Kings Of Agreppo* / Beat in the street: *Beat* Beat Beat / Euroshima-Wardance: *Snowy Red* / Virgin In-D skies: *In-D* / 'D' bop: *Dirty Harry* / 'S.M.': *SM* / Rainbows: *Jade 4 U* / Flesh: *Split Second* / Awakening, The: *Shakti* (extra track on MC & CD only) / Blow up the DJ: *TNT Clan* (Extra track on MC & CD only).
LP: **828 136-1**
MC: **828 136-4**
LP: . . . . **ZYX 20127**

NEW BEAT - EDIT 2 (Various artists).
LP: . . . . **ZYX 20136**

NEW BEAT MEGAMIX (Various artists).
LP: **36181**

NEW BEAT SAMPLER VOL.1 (Various artists).
LP: . . . . **LP 66001**
MC: . . . . **MC 66001**
LP: . . . . **SOB 0001**
MC: . . . . **SOBC 0001**

NEW BEAT - TAKE 1 (Various artists).
LP: . . . . **SUB 034**
MC: . . . . **SUB 034 MC**

NIGHTMARE VOL.3 (Various artists).
LP: . . . . **MARELP 3**
MC: . . . . **MAREC 3**

NIGHTMARE VOL 1 (Various artists).
Tracks: / Don't stop the war: *Pennington, Barbara* / Animal

magnetism: Pandy, Darryl / On the house: Midnight Sunrise / Act of war: Powell, S / Footprints in the sand: Brown, M. / Tightrope: Thomas, E / Who knows what evil: Man 2 man / Take one step: Wells, V/McCalla, N / Don't delay: Beautley, E / In at the deep end: Midnight Surprise / Love's the cure for me: Wells, James & Susan / Every waking hour: Taylor, Linda.
LP: . . . . **MARELP 1**
MC: . . . . **MAREC 1**

NON STOP ELECTRICTIY (Various artists).
LP: . . . . **NOSTO 2**

NORTH - THE SOUND OF THE DANCE UNDERGROUND (Various artists).
Tracks: / Dream 17: Annette / I ain't nightclubbing: T-Coy / House fantaz-ee: D.C.B / Acid to ecstasy: ED 209 / Voodoo ray: Guy Called Gerald / Megagrip: Masters Of Acid / Carino: T-Coy / Get on one: Frequency 9.
LP: . . . . **PL 71939**
MC: . . . . **PK 71939**

NOW DANCE 901 12" mixes (Various artists).
Tracks: / Get up (before the night is over): Technotronic featuring Ya Kid K / Going back to my roots: FPI Project featuring Sharon Dee Clarke / Put your hands together: D Mob featuring Nuff Juice / Got to have your love: Mantronix featuring Wondress / Dub be good to me: Beats International, featuring Lindy Layton / Get a life: Soul II Soul/ Touch me: 49ers / You make me feel (mighty real): Somerville, Jimmy / In private: Springfield, Dusty/ Sit and wait: Youngblood, Sydney / Magic number, The: De La Soul / Welcome: Latino, Gino / I called U: Lil Louis / Destiny: Electra / Love on love: Ezee Possee featuring Dr Mouthquake / Whatcha gonna do with my lovin': Inner City / Inna city mamma: Cherry, Neneh / Encore: Tongue 'N' Cheek / Higher than heaven: Age Of Chance.
2LP: . . . . **NOD 4**
MCSET: . . . . **TCNOD 4**

NOW DANCE 902 (12" mixes) (Various artists).
Tracks: / Dirty cash: Adventures Of Stevie V / Hear the drummer (get wicked): Jackson, Chad / Freestyle mega mix, The: Brown, Bobby (1) / U can't touch this: M.C. Hammer / Won't talk about it: Beats International/ First time ever I saw your face, The: Law, Joanna / Dreams a dream, A: Soul II Soul / Love don't live here anymore: Double Trouble / Thinking of you: Walsh, Maureen / Close to you: Priest, Maxi / World in motion: England New Order / Doin' the do: Boo, Betty / Venus: Don Pablo's Animals / Wild women do: Cole, Natalie / Take your time: Mantronix featuring Wondress / N-R-G: Adamski / Treat me good: Yazz/ Masterplan, The: Brown, Diana & Barrie K Sharpe / Joy and heartbreak: Movement .98 feat Carroll Thompson / Snappiness: BBG.
2LP: . . . . **NOD 5**
MCSET: . . . . **TCNOD 5**

NOW DANCE 903 (Various artists).
Tracks: / Megamix: Technotronic / Where are you baby?: Boo, Betty / I can't stand it: Twenty 4 Seven/ That man (he's all mine): Inner City / She ain't worth it: Medeiros, Glenn and Bobby Brown / Naked in the rain: Blue Pearl / LFO: LFO / Mother Universe: Soup Dragons / Groovy train: Farm / You're walking: Electribe 101 / Fascinating rhythm: Bass-O-Matic / What time is love ?: K.L.F. / Body language: Adventures Of Stevie V / It's a shame (my sister): Love, Monie / I've got you under my skin: Cherry, Neneh / Don't be a fool: Loose Ends / Let's push it: Innocence / Get yourself together: Young Disciples / Burundi blues: Beats International / Hardcore uproar: Together.
2LP: . . . . **NOD 6**
MCSET: . . . . **TCNOD 6**

NOW DANCE VOL.1 (Various artists).
Tracks: / Easy lover (extended remix): Bailey, Philip & Phil Collins / Some like it hot: Power Station / Would I lie to you: Eurythmics / Kiss me: Duffy, Stephen "Tin Tin" / Imagination: Some, Belouis / Hangin' on a string (extended dance mix): Loose Ends / Clouds across the moon: Rah Band / Solid (special club mix): Ashford & Simpson / Spend the night (remix): Cool Notes / Do what you do (remix): Jackson, Jermaine / Rhythm of the night: DeBarge / I want your lovin' (just a little bit): Hairston, Curtis / You should have known better: Curtis, T.C / Groovin': War / Move closer (new mix): Nelson, Phyllis / Shaft, Theme from (hot pursuit mix): Eddie & The Soulband / Who comes to boogie: Little Benny & The Masters / Bustin' loose: Brown, Chuck & His Soul Searchers / Like I like it: Aurra / Settle down (extended remix): Thomas, Lillo.
2LP: . . . . **NOD 1**
MCSET: . . . . **TCNOD 1**

NOW DANCE VOL.2 (Various artists).
Tracks: / Pull up to the bumper: Jones, Grace / So macho: Sinitta / Hit that perfect beat: Bronski Beat/ I can prove it (full version): Fearon, Phil / I wanna wake up with you: Gardiner, Boris / Chain reaction: Ross, Diana / We don't have to take our clothes off: Stewart, Jermaine / Don't leave me this way: Communards / Can't wait another minute: Five Star / Midas touch (extended remix): Midnight Star / Ain't nothin' goin' on but the rent (club mix): Guthrie, Gwen / Love can't turn around: Farley "Jackmaster" Funk / Rumours (long version): Timex Social Club / All and all: Sims, Joyce / Mine all mine: Cashflow / Who's zoomin' who?: Franklin, Aretha / Heaven must be missing an angel (angel mix): Tavares / Don't waste my time (new extended version): Hardcastle, Paul / Breaking away (extended version): Graham, Jaki / Holiday rap: M.C. Miker G & Deejay Sven.
2LP: . . . . **NOD 2**
MCSET: . . . . **TCNOD 2**

NOW DANCE VOL.3 (Various artists).
Tracks: / My prerogative (ext. remix): Brown, Bobby (1) / Buffalo stance: Cherry, Neneh / Ain't nobody better (groove corporation remix): Inner City / Keep on movin': Soul II Soul/Caron Wheeler / Joy and pain: Maze/ Funky cold medina: Tone Loc / Got to keep on: Cookie Crew / Who's in the house (the hip house anthem): Beatmasters & Merlin / It is time to get funky: D Mob featuring LRS / Turn up the bass (super duper mix parts 1 & 2): Tyree/Kool Rock Steady / She drives me crazy: Fine Young Cannibals / Straight up (12" remix): Abdul, Paula / Where has all the love gone (US ext. remix): Yazz / Workin' overtime: Ross, Diana / Helyom halib (part one): Cappella/ People hold on: Coldcut & Lisa Stansfield / Musical freedom (free at last) (ext. freedom mix): Simpson, Paul & Adeva/ One man (one mix): Chanelle / Just keep rockin' (sk'ouse mix): Double Trouble Feat. Rebel MC / Got to get you back (groovy piano mix): Mazelle, Kym.
2LP: . . . . **NOD 3**
MCSET: . . . . **TCNOD 3**

PARADISE A GO GO (Various artists).
Tracks: / Paradise a go go: Various artists / Body moves: Various artists / Virginia gone go go: Various artists / DC drug free: Various artists / Mary: Various artists / Chillin' out: Various artists.
LP: . . . . **LEFT LP 4**
MC: . . . . **LEFT C4**

PASSION TRACKING VOL 1 (Various artists).
Tracks: / Catch me, I'm falling in love: Raven, Marsha / Got to get to you: Charade / They call me the Queen of fools: Williams, Jessica / Spring rain: Cascade Orchestra / I'm the one: Charade / Save yourself for me: Martin, Dee Dee.
LP: . . . . **PADLP 101**

PASSION TRACKING VOL 2 (Various artists).
LP: . . . . **PADLP 102**
MC: . . . . **ZCPAD 102**

PASSION TRACKING VOL 3 (Various artists).
LP: . . . . **PADLP 103**

PASSION TRACKING VOL 4 (Various artists).
Tracks: / Eat you up: Gold, Angie / Don't let the flame die out: Marie, Kelly / Reincarnation (coming back for love)(US Mix): People Like Us / Fighter, The: Arpeggio (Featuring Quartario.) / Midnight lover (US Mix): People Like Us / Are you ready for love: Marie, Kelly / Time bomb: Gold, Angie / Feels like love: Thomas, Louise / Fire me up: Astaire.
LP: . . . . **PADLP 104**

PASSION TRACKING VOL 5 (Various artists).
LP: . . . . **PADLP 105**

PASSION TRACKING VOLUME 6 (Various artists).
LP: . . . . **PADLP 106**

PERFECT BEAT (Various artists).
LP: . . . . **POLD 5095**
MC: . . . . **POLDC 5095**

PHILADELPHIA STORY, THE (Various artists).
LP: . . . . **PHST 1986**
MC: . . . . **ZCPHS 1986**

POWER JAM 85 various artists (Various artists).
LP: . . . . **ILPS 9833**

PRESENTING THE POSSE (Various artists).
LP: . . . . **UTLP 001**

PRESENTING THE POSSE VOLUME II (Various artists).
LP: . . . . **UTLP 002**

PRESENTING THE POSSE VOLUME III (Various artists).
LP: . . . . **TEMPLP 005**

PRIME KUTS VOL 1 (Various artists).
Tracks: / Better bring a gun: King Tee / Underwater rimes: Digital Underground / This beat be smooth: Tee, Toddy / N.Y. Rapper: Jimmy, Bobby / My posse: Ice Cube / 6 in the morning: Ice-T / Do you wanna go to the liquor store: Tee, Toddy / Payback's a mutha: King Tee / What I like: 2 Live Crew / All about money: Kool Rock Jay.
LP: . . . . **INS 5026**
MC: . . . . **TCINS 5026**

PRIME KUTS VOL 1 (See under Prime Kuts) (Various artists).

PRIME KUTS VOL 2 (Various artists).
Tracks: / Gangster boogie: Tee, Toddy / Dog 'n the wax: Ice-T / Coolest, The: King Tee / It's about time: Kool Rock Jay / Rhyme Crew / Let it go: Mistress & DJ Madame E / It's my turn: Dezo Daz / Ya don't quit: Ice-T / 7 A 3 will rock you: Seven A 3 / Ill legal: Ice Cube.
LP: . . . . **INS 5027**
MC: . . . . **TCINS 5027**

PULSATING RYHTHMS (Various artists).
LP: . . . . **PULSELP 1**
MC: . . . . **PULSEMC 1**

PUMP UP EUROPE (Various artists).
LP: . . . . **LD 8823**

PUMP UP THE DANCE (Various artists).
Tracks: / I don't want to be a hero: Johnny Hates Jazz / Touched by the hand of God: New Order / Pump up the volume (remix): M/A/R/R/S.
LP: **30132**

QUIET STORM 1 (Various artists).
Tracks: / I wanna be that woman: Cole, Natalie / Heart of gold: Robinson, Bert / Day by day: Najee/ Love changes: Morgan, Meli'sa / I wanna be that woman*: Cole, Natalie (*12" version) / Heart of gold: Robinson, Bert / Day by day: Najee / I am your melody: Connors, Norman / Loving you: O'Jays / When your heart says yes: King, Evelyn "Champagne" / Love on the inside: Wheeler, Audrey / Love and kisses: Moore, Melba / Miracles: RJ's Latest Arrival / You are who you love: Christopher, Gavin / I.O.U.: Winans, Bebe & Cece.
MC: . . . . **TCCMP 1002**
LP: . . . . **CMP 1002**

RAGE COMPILATION (Various artists).
LP: . . . . **AMTV 1**
MC: . . . . **AMTC 1**

RAGGA HIP HOP (Various artists).
Tracks: / We are the champions: Asher D / Welfare recipients: Just Ice / Money mad: London Posse / Why do fools fall in love: Leo, Phillip & C.J. Lewis / Vibes: Demon Boyz / Kuff: Thunder, Shelley / We're really ragga: Papa T / Redders posse: Masters Of Ceremony / Money mad (instrumental): London Posse/ We're really ragga (instrumental): Papa T.
MC: . . . . **ICT 9951**
LP: . . . . **ILPS 9951**

RAGGA HIP HOP VOL.2 (Various artists).
LP: . . . . **MLPS 1063**
MC: . . . . **MCT 1063**

RAVE (Various artists).
LP: . . . . **REMULP 01**
MC: . . . . **REMUMC 01**

RAVE ALBUM, THE (Various artists).
MC: . . . . **STAC 2453**
LP: . . . . **STAR 2453**

RAW BEATS (Various artists).
Tracks: / For love: Kiss The Beat / Descendants of the funk: Afro Boys / Eternity: Alpha B / For the idle: Congress / Descendants of the funk (remix): Afro Boys / Experiment: Kulture Skool / Streets of gold: Congress / Relas: Kiss The Beat / Experiment (instrumental): Kulture Skool / Eternity (ambient mix): Alpha B.
LP: . . . . **WRR 12 009**

REACHIN' 1 (Various artists).
Tracks: / Take me higher: Pisces / Everything I do: Dexmaniax / We've only just begun: Ingram Inc/ Don't go away: Boneshakers / We've only just begun (trance mix): Ingram Inc / Everything I do (hardcore): Dexmaniax/ Givin' you: Marie, Lincoln Jean / Why couldn't I see: Original Sin / Ragga house: Harris, Simon / Ladies (let's go): T.D.P. / Givin' you (instrumental): Marie, Lincoln Jean.
LP: . . . . **RERE 1**
MC: . . . . **REREC 1**

REBIRTH OF COOL (Various artists).
LP: . . . . **BRLP 563**
MC: . . . . **BRCA 563**

RECORD SHACK PRESENTS VOLUME THREE MIXES (Various artists).
Tracks: / High energy: Various artists / Second best: Various artists / He's a saint, he's a sinner: Various artists / Manpower: Various artists / So many men,so little time: Various artists / Caught in the act: Various artists / I'm caught living on my own: Various artists / Boys come to town, The: Various artists / Fan the flame: Various artists / On a crowded street: Various artists / Out of the darkest night: Various artists.
LP: . . . . **RSPV 3**
MC: . . . . **RSPVK 3**

RECORD SHACK PRESENTS...VOL.2 (Various artists).
LP: . . . . **RSPV 2**
MC: . . . . **RSVPK 2**

REMIX LP (Various artists).
LP: . . . . **EASYLP 1**
MC: . . . . **EASYMC 1**

RE-MIXTURE (Various artists).
Tracks: / Mr. Mack: Various artists / Love money: Various artists / Slide: Various artists / Double journey: Various artists / Friends again: Various artists.
MC: . . . . **CHAMP C1**
LP: . . . . **CHAMP 1**

RETRO TECHNO (Various artists).
LP: . . . . **RETROLP 1**
MC: . . . . **RETROMC 1**

RHYTHM KINGDOM (Various artists).
LP: . . . . **LEFTLP 5**

RHYTHM ZONE (Various artists).
LP: . . . . **KOOLLP 001**
MC: . . . . **KOOLMC 001**

RIGHT STUFF 2 - NOTHIN' BUT A HOUSE PARTY (Various artists).
2LP: . . . . **SMR 098**
MC: . . . . **SMC 098**

RIGHT STUFF, THE (REMIX 89) (Various artists).
LP: . . . . **SMR 990**
MC: . . . . **SMC 990**

ROOFTOPS (Various artists).
Tracks: / Avenue D: James, Etta/David A Stewart / Freedom: Seymour, Pat / Drop: London Beat / Loving number one: Kisses From The Kremlin / Meltdown: Jamison, Joniece / Rooftops (title song): Osborne, Jeffrey/ Revenge (part II): Eurythmics / Stretch: Wilson, Chris / Bullet proof heart: Jones, Grace / Keep runnin': Trouble Funk.
LP: . . . . **EST 2101**
LP: **791 736 1**
MC: . . . . **TCEST 2101**
MC: **791 736 4**

SERIOUS BEATS (Various artists).
2LP: . . . . **SASB 1**

SERIOUS BOX SET (Various artists).
LPS: . . . . **SSBX 15**
LPS: . . . . **ZCSS 15**

SHARP MIXES (Various artists).
LP: **240418**

SILVER ON BLACK (Various artists).
Tracks: / It is time to get funky: D Mob featuring LRS / I need your love: Montana, June / Shelter: Circuit/ Salsa house (remix): Rich, Richie / Get back to love: Blacksmith / Tears: Knuckles, Frankie Presents Satoshi Tomie / Walking on sunshine '89: Rockers Revenge & Donnie Calvi / London's finest: Harris, Simon & Asher D/ Turn up the bass (super duper mix): Tyree / Rock to the beat (new mix): Reese & Santonio / Jibaro: Electra/ We call it acieed (matey mix): D Mob / Shake your thang (it's your thing): Salt 'N' Pepa / Born this way: Cookie Crew / Open our eyes (the world mix): Jefferson, Marshall / Baby wants to ride (x-rated): Principle, Jamie.
2LP: **828155-1**
MC: **828155-4**

SLAMMIN' (Various artists).
Tracks: / Tom's diner: DNA and Suzanne Vega / English man in New York: Sting / Hard up: Awesome 3/ Wash your face in my sink: Dream Warriors / Touch me: 49ers / Feel the rhythm: Jazzi P / Naked in the rain: Blue Pearl / I'm free: Soup Dragons / What time is love (live): K.L.F. / Rockin' over the beat: Technotronic / Silent voice: Innocence / Thinking of you: Maureen / I come off: Young MC/ La serenissima: DNA / Come together: Primal Scream / Treat me good: Yazz / Bonita applebum: Tribe Called Quest / Warp outa rhythm: Tricky Disco.
LP: . . . . **SLAMM 1**
MC: . . . . **SLACC 1**

SLEEPING BAG MIXDOWN VOL.1 (Various artists).

LP: . . . . SBUKLP 6
MC: . . . . SBUKMC 6

SLOW JAM 1 (Various artists).
LP: . . . . SLJAM 1
MC: . . . . ZCJAM 1

SLOW JAM 2 (Various artists).
LP: . . . . SLJAM 2
MC: . . . . ZCJAM 2

SLOW JAM 3 (Various artists).
LP: . . . . SLJAM 3
MC: . . . . ZCJAM 3

SMASH HIT MIXES (Various artists).
LP: . . . . SMIX 1
MC: . . . . ZCMIX 1

SMASH HITS MASSIVE (Various artists).
Tracks: / One and only: *Hawkes, Chesney* / Whole of the moon, The: *Waterboys* / Games: *New Kids on the Block*/ Strike it up: *Black Box* / Ring ring ring: *De La Soul* / Gonna make you sweat: *C & C Music Factory*/ Move your body: *Xpansions* / You got the love: *Staton, Candi* / Hippychick: *Soho* / Megamix: *Snap*/ All together now: *Farm* / Caravan: *Inspiral Carpets* / International bright young thing: *Jesus Jones*/ What do I have to do: *Minogue, Kylie* / Can't take the power: *Offshore* / Hyperreal: *Shamen* / Think about: *D.J.H. Featuring Stefy* / Footsteps following me: *Nero, Frances* / Ice ice baby: *Vanilla Ice* / Outstanding: *Thomas, Kenny*.
LP: . . . . ADD 24
MC: . . . . ZDD 24

SMASH HITS - RAVE (Various artists).
Tracks: / Venus (piano mix): *Don Pablo's Animals* / Hear the drummer (get wicked): *Jackson, Chad* / Doin' the do: *Boo, Betty* / Mama gave birth to the soul children: *Queen Latifah & De La Soul* / Yaaah: *D-Shake*/ This beat is technotronic: *Technotronic featuring MC Eric* / Strawberry fields forever: *Candy Flip* / C'mon and get my love: *D Mob featuring Cathy Dennis* / Touch me (sexual version): *49ers* / Blame it on the bassline: *Beats International* / N-R-G: *Adamski* / Don't miss the partyline: *Bizz Nizz* / Find a way: *Coldcut featuring* Queen Latifah / Inna city mamma: *Cherry, Neneh* / We got the love: *Touch Of Soul* / Loving you: *Massivo* featuring Tracey / Walk on by: *Sybil* / Sit and wait: *Youngblood, Sydney* / What is life (life time edit): *P.S.P. featuring Due Respect* / I thank you: *Adeva*.
2LP: . . . . ADD 14
MC: . . . . ZDD 14

SMURF AND BREAKDANCE various artists (Various artists).
LP: . . . . PG 70301
MC: . . . . PH 70301

SOLAR BOX SET (Various artists).
LPS: . . . . SOLBX 1

SOLID SOUNDS - HARDCORE HYPNOTIC DANCE (Various artists).
LP: . . . . CHAMP 1024
MC: . . . . CHAMPK 1024

SOUL ALL DAYER (Various artists).
LP: . . . . RMLP 005

SOUL IN DARKNESS (Various artists).
MC: . . . . BRCA 536
LP: . . . . BRLP 536
MC: . . . . ICM 2056
MC: 846 603 4

SOUND OF BELGIUM SAMPLER (2) (Various artists).
LP: . . . . SOBLP 0002
MC: . . . . SOBMC 0002

SOUND OF COOLTEMPO (Various artists).
Tracks: / Beautiful love: *Adeva* / Natural thing (sunset mix): *Innocence* / Don't funk wid the Mo: *Love, Monie* / Stomp: *K-Y-ZE* / Motherland: *Tribal House* / We got the love: *Touch Of Soul* / Techno trance: *D-Shake* / Don't miss the partyline: *Bizz Nizz* / 2 hype: *Kid 'N Play* / K-Jee: *Cooltempo Unlimited Orchestra* / Savannah: *Savannah* (Cassette & CD only.).
LP: . . . . CTLP 19
MC: . . . . ZCCTLP 19

SOUND OF COOLTEMPO, VOL. 11 (Various artists).
LP: . . . . CTLP 23
MC: . . . . ZCT 23

SOUNDWAVE NO.7 (Various artists).
MC: . . . . SW 07

STREET SOUNDS (Various artists).
LP: . . . . STSND 001

STREET SOUNDS 20 (Various artists).
LP: . . . . STSND 020
MC: . . . . ZCSTS 20

STREET SOUNDS 87 (Various artists).
LP: . . . . STSND 871
MC: . . . . ZCSTS 871

STREET SOUNDS '87 VOL. 3 (Various artists).
LP: . . . . STSND 873
MC: . . . . ZCSTS 873

STREET SOUNDS 19/20 (Various artists).
MC: . . . . ZCSTS 1920
LP: . . . . LPSTSND 1920

STREET SOUNDS ANTHEMS (Various artists).
Tracks: / I found lovin': *Fatback* / What's missing: *O'Neal, Alexander* / Bring the family back: *Paul, Billy*/ Ain't no stoppin' us now: *McFadden & Whitehead* / Dominoes (Live): *Byrd, Donald* / Movin: *Brass Construction*/ Encore: *Lynn, Cheryl* / Hard work: *Various artists* / Groove: *Franklin, Rodney* / Prance on: *Henderson, Eddie*.
MC: . . . . ZCMUS 5
LP: . . . . MUSIC 5

STREET SOUNDS ANTHEMS 2 (Various artists).
LP: . . . . MUSIC 10
MC: . . . . ZCMUS 10

STREET SOUNDS ANTHEMS 3 (Various artists).
LP: . . . . MUSIC 11
MC: . . . . ZCMUS 11

STREET SOUNDS ARTISTS VOL.3 (Various artists).
LP: . . . . ARTIS 3
MC: . . . . ZCART 3

STREET SOUNDS BREAKBEATS (Various artists).
LP: . . . . BRBLP 501

STREET SOUNDS EDITION 3 (Various artists).
LP: . . . . STSND 003
MC: . . . . ZCSTS 003

STREET SOUNDS EDITION 4 (Various artists).
LP: . . . . STSND 004

STREET SOUNDS EDITION 5 (Various artists).
LP: . . . . STSND 005
MC: . . . . ZCSTS 005

STREET SOUNDS EDITION 6 (Various artists).
LP: . . . . STSND 006
MC: . . . . ZCSTS 006

STREET SOUNDS EDITION 7 (Various artists).
LP: . . . . STSND 007
MC: . . . . ZCSTS 007

STREET SOUNDS EDITION 8 (Various artists).
LP: . . . . STSND 008
MC: . . . . ZCSTS 008

STREET SOUNDS EDITION 9 (Various artists).
LP: . . . . STSND 009
MC: . . . . ZCSTS 009

STREET SOUNDS EDITION 10 (Various artists).
LP: . . . . STSND 010
MC: . . . . ZCSTS 010

STREET SOUNDS EDITION 11 (Various artists).
LP: . . . . STSND 011
MC: . . . . ZCSTS 11

STREET SOUNDS EDITION 12 (Various artists).
LP: . . . . STSND 012
MC: . . . . ZCSTS 012

STREET SOUNDS EDITION 14 (Various artists).
LP: . . . . STSND 014

STREET SOUNDS EDITION 15 (Various artists).
LP: . . . . STSND 015
MC: . . . . ZCSTS 15

STREET SOUNDS EDITION 16 (Various artists).
LP: . . . . STND 16
MC: . . . . ZCSTS 16

STREET SOUNDS EDITION 17 (Various artists).
LP: . . . . STSND 017
MC: . . . . ZCSTS 17

STREET SOUNDS EDITION 18 (Various artists).
Tracks: / Rumours (long version): *Social Club* / Dreamer (long version - vocal): *B B & Q Band* / Falling: *Moore, Melba* / Breaking away (Extended Version): *Graham, Jaki* / Holiday rap: *M.C. Miker G & Deejay Sven* / Midas touch (Vocal/Ext. Version): *Midnight Star* / What does it take (to win your love) (Rerapped mix): *Kenny G.* / Give me your love (extended version): *Active Force* / Excite me: *Smith, Carlton* / Fool's paradise (Paradise mix): *Morgan, Meli'sa*.
LP: . . . . STNSD 18
MC: . . . . ZCSTS 18

STREET SOUNDS HI-ENERGY NO.1 (Various artists).
LP: . . . . HINRG 16
MC: . . . . ZCNRG 16

STREET SOUNDS HI-ENERGY NO.2 (Various artists).
LP: . . . . HINRG 17
MC: . . . . ZCNRG 17

STREET SOUNDS HIP HOUSE (Various artists).
Tracks: / Slam: *Humanoid* / Hardcore hip house: *Tyree* / Yoyo get funky: *D.J. Fast Eddie* / Hip house: *D.J. Fast Eddie* / Respect rap: *K.G.B.* / Oh yeah: *Tyree* / Get off your butt: *Kook Rock Steady*/ Get off your butt: *M & M*.
LP: . . . . HIHO 1
MC: . . . . ZCHIHO 1

STREET SOUNDS NO. 1S OF 1983 (Various artists).
2LP: . . . . STNO 1
MCSET: . . . . ZCSNO 1

STREET SOUNDS PREVIEW (Various artists).
LP: . . . . PRELP 101
MC: . . . . ZCPRE 101

STREET SOUNDS (UK ELECTRO 1) (Various artists).
LP: . . . . ELCST 1984
MC: . . . . ZCELC 1984

STREET SUITE (Various artists).
Tracks: / Groovin' (that's what we're doin'): *S.O.S. Band* / Enuff is enuff: *Franklin, Rodney* / Spunky: *James*, Bob / Phone home: *Chingas, Johnny* / Chou chow: *Square, The* / Ride on: *Watanabe, Sadao* / Positive energy: *Duke, George* / What's going on: *Various artists* / Hannibal: *Tyner, McCoy* / Give it all your heart: *Hancock, Herbie* / I'll never see you smile again: *James, Bob & Earl Klugh* / Portuguese love: *Ferguson, Maynard* / Patamar: *Montarroyos, Marcio* / Steppin' out: *Mangione, Chuck* / Only one, The: *Earland, Charles*.
LP: . . . . CBS 22226
MC: 40 22226

STREETNOISE (Various artists).
Tracks: / Go with the flow: *Various artists* / Seconds: *Various artists* / Chance for hope: *Various artists* / Let's get horny: *Various artists* / You're gonna loose my love: *Various artists*.
LP: . . . . EPC 32234
MC: 40 32234
LP: . . . . STR 32234

STREETSOUNDS 13 (Various artists).
LP: . . . . STSND 013

STREETSOUNDS VOL 2 (Various artists).
Tracks: / Keep the fire burning: *Various artists* / Magic's wand: *Various artists* / 3 a.m.: *Various artists*/ Step in the light: *Various artists* / Heavy vibes: *Various artists* / Message II: *Various artists* / I wanna know: *Various artists* / Soul makossa: *Various artists*.
LP: . . . . STSND 002

STREETWAVE - THE FIRST 3 YEARS VOL. 1 (Various artists).
MC: . . . . ZCMKLD 7
LP: . . . . MKLD 7

SURVIVAL DANCE REPORT (See under Survival) (Various artists).

SURVIVAL DANCE REPORT (1) (Various artists).
LPS: . . . . REPORT 3

SURVIVAL DANCE REPORT (2) (Various artists).
LPS: . . . . REPORT 5

SWAY (Various artists).
LP: . . . . SWAY 1

TABU'S FINEST (Various artists).
LP: 4673511
MC: 4673512

TECHNO 2 - THE NEXT GENERATION (Various artists).
Tracks: / Love takes me over: *Area 10* / Aftermath: *Reel By Real* / Stark: *K.G.B.* / Mirror mirror: *MK*/ I believe: *Octave One* / Techno por favor: *Infinity* / Elements: *Psyche* / Ritual: *Vice*.
LP: . . . . DIX 89
MC: . . . . CDIX 89
MC: . . . . OVEDC 358
LP: . . . . OVED 358

TECHNO - THE DANCE SOUND OF DETROIT (Various artists).
Tracks: / It is what it is: *Rhythm is Rhythm* / Forever and a day: *Baxter, Blake* / Time to express: *Fowkes*, Eddie 'Flashin' / Electronic dance: *K.S. Experience* / Share this house (radio mix): *Members Of The House*/ Feel surreal: *A Tongue & D Groove* / Spark: *Hesterley, Mia* / Techno music: *Juan* / Big Fun: *Inner* City / Ride 'em boy: *Baxter, Blake* / Sequence 10: *Shakir* / Un, deux, trois: *Idol Making* / Detroit is jacking: *Various artists*.

2LP: . . . . DIXG 75
MC: . . . . CDIXG 75
MC: . . . . OVEDC 357

TECHNO UK VOL.1 (Various artists).
LP: . . . . WRRLP 005

TECHNOPOLIS (Various artists).
LP: . . . . AS 5004

TEKNO ACID BEATS (Various artists).
LP: . . . . TOPY 39

TEN REVOLUTIONARY RHYTHMS AND FIFTY SAMPLES (Various artists).
LP: . . . . TOVE 2

TEUTONIC BEATS: OPUS 2 (Various artists).
Tracks: / Love park: *Marathon* / Sato agrepo: *Future Perfect* / Money: *Fischerman's Friend* / Cool and complicated: *De Part Ment X* / Movin': *His Name Is Dime* / And party: *West Bam* / Catherine wheel: *Zaza* Lang / Crackerjack has appeared (crack attack): *Cracker Jack* / Trance: *Ready Made* / Brain drain: *Best* Boy / Radical, The (Latimo mix): *NSLA* (Only on CD and MC.) / I want you: *De Part Ment X* (Only on CD and MC.) / Celebrate: *Third Electric* (Only on CD and MC.).
LP: 260.261
MC: 210.261
LP: . . . . EGLP 74
MC: . . . . EGMC 74

THAT NIGHTMARE SOUND VOL. 4 (Various artists).
LP: . . . . MARELP 4
MC: . . . . MAREC 4

THIN ICE 2 (The Second Shiver) (Various artists).
MC: . . . . STAC 2535
LP: . . . . STAR 2535

THIS IS ELECTRONIC BODY MUSIC (Various artists).
LP: . . . . EBM 001

THIS IS GARAGE (Various artists).
LP: . . . . CTLP 12
MC: . . . . ZCT 12

THIS IS STRICTLY RHYTHM (Various artists).
LP: . . . . DIXG 110

THIS IS URBAN (Various artists).
Tracks: / Party rock: *T.A.G.G.* / Eso valle: *Pharmacy Of Soul* / Step to the rhythm: *Xtra Bass* / Jump to the rhythm: *2-Wize* / Wake up: *Nu-Civilisation* / Reachin': *White, M.J.* / Get up to my groove: *Martian*/ Body and soul: *Perkins, Cliff* / Hearing things: *Frequency X* / Nothing can stop us now: *B.A.D. Rep*/ Broken promises: *Red Follies* / Mastermind: *B.M.O.* / Don't stop your love: *Pandella* / Under your spell: *Inro* / Dance to the bass: *M.C. Ric* / Sync into: *Delta 12*.
LP: . . . . PATLP 101
MC: . . . . PATMC 101

TOMMY BOY - GREATEST HITS (Various artists).
2LP: . . . . ILPS 9825
MC: . . . . ICT 9825

TOTAL DANCE (Various artists).
LP: . . . . TOTLP 1
MC: . . . . TOTMC 1

TUNE IN, TURN ON UPFRONT (Various artists).
LP: . . . . LOWD 1
MC: . . . . ZCWD 1

TURN IT UP (A Dance compilation) (Various artists).
Tracks: / More they knock the more I love you, The: *Brown, Gloria D.* / Who comes to boogie: *Little Benny & The Masters*/ You never had a love like mine (sensual mix): *Naima* / Please don't break my heart: *Affair featuring Alyson*/ City life (special remix): *Sass* / Things are not the same: *First Love* / Turn it up (The full Monty mix): *Conway* Brothers / Like I like it (remix): *Aurra* / Groovin': *War* / Treat her sweeter (dance mix): *Simpson, Paul Connection* / Stand on the word: *Joubert Singers* / History: *Mai Tai*.
2LP: . . . . DIXD 1
MC: . . . . CDIXD 1

ULTIMATE BREAKS & BEATS, VOL 507 (Various artists).
LP: . . . . SBR 707

ULTIMATE BREAKS & BEATS VOL. 517 (Various artists).
LP: . . . . SBR 517

ULTIMATE HOUSE (Various artists).
LP: . . . . CHAMP 1016
MC: . . . . CHAMPK 1016

ULTIMATE TRAX VOL.1 (Battle of the D.J.'s vol.1) (Various artists).
LP: . . . . CHAMP 1003
MC: . . . . CHAMPK 1003

ULTIMATE TRAX VOL.2 (Various artists).

Tracks: / I like it: Libra Libra / Time (time to party): Gary L / It's my beat: Sweet Tee & Jazzy Joyce/ I've gotta be tough: M.C. Shy D. / Funk box party: Masterdon Committee / Magnificent: D.J. Jazzy Jeff & Fresh Prince / Whatcha gonna do: Blaze / My Mike sounds nice: Salt 'N' Pepa / Jackin' it: Home Wreckers/ Triple M bass: Worse 'Em / Battle of the deejays: D.J. Jazzy Jeff / Battle of the deejays: Whiz Kid.
LP: CHAMP 1005
MC: CHAMPK 1005

ULTIMATE TRAX VOL.3 Battle of the D.J.'s (Various artists).
Tracks: / Let yourself go: Sybil / Coolin' out: Private Joy / After...: True Maths/ Invisible empire/ Rhythm of the...: Fatback (Band) / Keep it warm: Voices In The Dark / Touch: D.J. Jazzy Jeff & Fresh Prince/ Can u dance: Jason, Kenny "Jammin" & "Fast" Eddie Smith / Take me to the top: Advance / This is the night (prog mix): Sweet Heat / Superappin': Grandmaster Flash.
LP: CHAMP 1008
MC: CHAMPK 1008

UNBELIEVABLE (The Indie Dance Album) (Various artists).
LP: UNB 101
MC: UNBC 101

UNITED HOUSE NATIONS (DJ Mark Kamin's United House Nations project) (Various artists).
Tracks: / Holle holle: Deepak & Khan / Mbuluna: Prince Mambasa / Just a moment please: Satoh, Akiko/ Chez Rai: Djhay, Cheb / Mohamed's house: Sheik Fawaz / Oi Jimmy: McGregor, Angus / Agua de coco: Lindao, Ze / Bella vista: Sevilla, Paco / Oi Jimmy: MacGregor, Jimmy (CD only) / Mbuluna (Zoomin' Zaire): Prince Mambasa (CD only).
LP: CIRCA 5
MC: CIRC 5

UP FRONT 1 (Various artists).
LP: UPFT 1

UP FRONT 1 (NEW SERIES) (Various artists).
LP: UPFT 901
MC: UPMC 901

UP FRONT 2 (Various artists).
2LP: UPFT 2
MCSET: ZCFT 2

UP FRONT 4 (Various artists).
LP: UPFT 4
MC: ZCFT 4

UP FRONT 5 (Various artists).
LP: UPFT 5

UP FRONT 6 (Various artists).
LP: UPFT 6
MC: ZCFT 6

UP FRONT 7 (Various artists).
LP: UPFT7
MC: ZCFT7

UP FRONT 8 (Various artists).
LP: UPFT 8
MC: ZCFT 8

UPBEAT 2 (Various artists).
Tracks: / Criticize: O'Neal, Alexander / System of survival: Earth, Wind & Fire / I need love: L.L. Cool J / You got the love (remix): Belle, Regina / Communicate: Full House / Dance little sister (part 1): D'Arby, Terence Trent / Lovey dovey: Terry, Tony / B.Y.O.B. (Bring your own baby): Clemmons, Angela / Lost in emotion: Lisa Lisa/Cult Jam / Nothing ventured nothing gained (silly dance remix): Singleton, Charlie / Show a little love: Mission USA.
LP: ONUP 2
MC: ONUPC 2

UPFRONT (Various artists).
LP: UPFT 12
MC: ZCFT 12

UPFRONT 9 (Various artists).
Tracks: / Say you'll be (US mix): Prister, Jerome / Kelly 16-33: Arrington, Steve / Don't you want me (remix): Whately, Jody / Mystery: Phase 2 / Bedroom scene, The: Triple XXX / Overweight lovers in..., The: Heavy D & The Boyz / Soul touch (import mix): St. Paul / Give it to me: Bam Bam / Off to Battle: Model 500/ Females: Cookie Crew / Run away: Holoway, Loeatta / Give me some: L.A. Boppers / You're just the...: Salsoul Orchestra / Wrap you up: L.A. Boppers.
LP: UPFT 9
MC: ZCFT 9

UPFRONT 10 (Various artists).
Tracks: / Beat Dis: Bomb The Bass / It takes two: Base, Rob / 100%: Mini Curry / I know you got soul: Various artists / Give It To Me: Bam Bam / Put that record back on: Cut To Shock / Party people: Royal House / This Brutal House: Nitro Deluxe / Magic: Khan, Bou / Cool and dry: Frost, Jack / Get The Hole: Townsell, Lidell / Mad on acid (mega mix): Double Trouble.
LP: UPFT 10
MC: ZCFT 10

UPFRONT 11 (Various artists).
Tracks: / Theme from S.Express (extended): S. Express / Slam: Phuture Fantasy Club / I surrender to your love: By All Means / Can you party: Royal House / You make me so hot: Lynn, Barbara / I'm too scared: Dante, Steven / Turntables do it: Cybertron T / Feels good: Mr. Lee / Back to the beat: Reese & San Antonio/ You are the one: Taurus Boyz / Do that right: Disco Twins & Starchild.
LP: UPFT 11
MC: ZCFT 11

UPFRONT 89 (Various artists).
Tracks: / Upfront 89: Various artists.
2LP: UPFT 89
MC: ZCFT 89

UPTOWN IS KICKING IT (Various artists).
LP: MCG 4001
MC: MCGC 4001

UPTOWN - 'THE FUTURE' (Various artists).
LP: MCA 10333
MC: MCAC 10333

URBAN 88 (Various artists).
Tracks: / Payback mix: Brown, James / Everybody (get loose): Phoenix / Why did you do it?: Groove Train/ I'm so happy: Beasley, Walter / It's a choice: Visions / Theme from P.O.P.: Perfectly Ordinary People/ It began in Africa: Cook, Norman / Starsky and Hutch, Theme from: JTQ (James Taylor Quartet) / It's your thing: Rockaway Three / Got to have a mother for me: Brown, James / Ace of clubs: Ace Of Clubs / Running away: Ayers, Roy.
LP: 837 664-1
MC: 837 664-4

VAULTAGE FROM ELECTRIC LIGHTING STATION (Various artists).
Tracks: / Im Nin' Alu: Haza, Ofra / Get a job: Commercial Music / Ella, elle l'a: Gall, France / Radio 1: Hustle / Tumbao: Matt Bianco / Heart of glass: Associates / Islamatron: Grid / Certain things are likely: Kissing The Pink / Acid love: Beloved / Houseplan: Terrajacks / Do it again Emilio: Pasquez, Emilio / House nation: Housemaster Boyz.
LP: WX 237
MC: WX 237C

VITAMIN E (Various artists).
Tracks: / 3 a.m. eternal: K.L.F. / Afro dizzi act: Cry Sisco / Droid: Hipnosis / Love park: Marathon/ Your love: Knuckles, Frankie / Melt your body: Summers, Mark / Guns of Boogie Town: Corporation Of One/ Somebody somewhere: Dean, Johnson / Dreams: Adonte / Shall we: Forgemasters.
LP: VITE WL5003
MC: VITE WD5003

WAR PARTY (Various artists).
LP: BRLP 554
MC: BRCA 554

WAREHOUSE RAVES (Various artists).
LP: RUMLD 101
MC: ZCRUMD 101

WAREHOUSE RAVES VOL.2 (Various artists).
LP: RUMLD 102

WAREHOUSE RAVES VOL.3 (Various artists).
LP: RUMLD 103
MC: ZCRUMD 103

WAREHOUSE RAVES VOL.4 (Various artists).
LP: RUMLD 104
MC: ZCRUMD 104

WAREHOUSE RAVES VOL.5 (Various artists).
MC: ZCRUMD 105
LP: RUMLD 105

WAREHOUSE WAX (Various artists).
LP: UNILP 001

WARE'S THE HOUSE (Various artists).
Tracks: / Going back to my roots: F.P.I. Project / Grand piano: Mixmaster / Magic attio II: D.J. Lelewell/ Tainted love: Impedance / Do you want me: Skeletor / Let the rain come down: Intense / Just as long as I got you: 101 / Ladies first: Queen Latifah & Monie Love / Dreams: Adonte / Superbad superslick: Redhead Kingpin & The FBI / Right before my eyes: Day, Patti / Rescue me: Malone, Debbie / Let yourself go: Sybil / Message is love, The: Baker, Arthur / I can't get over your love: Simphonia / Theme, The: Unique 3 / Security: Beat Club / Let there be house: Deskee / Good vibrations: J.D. / Somebody in the house say yeah: 2 In A Room.
LP: SMR 997
MC: SMC 997

WEST END STORY (Various artists).
Tracks: / Hot shot: Young, Karen / Do it to the music: Raw Silk / You can't have your cake and eat it too: Taylor, Brenda / Another man: Mason, Barbara / Don't make me wait: Peech Boys / Heartbeat rap, A: Sweet Georgia Brown / Hard times: McCall Allie / Ride on the rhythm: Mahogany / Rescue me: Thomas, Sybil / Heartbeat: Gardner, Taana / Time: Stone / Everybody get dancin': Bombers / Is it all over my face: Loose Joints.
LP: WTND 1
MC: WCTND 1

WORD, THE, VOL.1 (Various artists).
LP: HOP 217
MC: HOPC 217

WORD, THE VOL. 2 (Various artists).
Tracks: / How ya like me now: Kool Moe Dee / My philosophy: KRS One / New kids on the block: D.J. Jazzy Jeff / I'm def: Jump Back & Kiss Myself / Bring the beat back: Steady B / Coqui 900: Schoolly D/ Faith: Wee Papa Girl Rappers / It's fresh: Ms Melodie / I wanna be like: Various artists / London bridge is falling down: Various artists.
LP: HOP 220
MC: HOPC 220

WORD, THE VOL. 3 (Various artists).
Tracks: / Get pepped: Skinny Boys / Flaunt it: Wee Papa Girl Rappers / You brought it all on yourself: Whodini/ Another poem: Schooly / Brand new: D.J. Jazzy Jeff & Fresh Prince / Let's go: Kool Moe Dee / Rockin' music: Steady B / You know what I mean: Too Short / Classical 2 is back: Classical Two / People on the subway: D.J. Jazzy Jeff.
LP: HOP 229
MC: HOPC 229

WORD VOL 4 (Various artists).
LP: HIP 76
MC: HIPC 76

X + Y = 8 (Mixdown II) (Various artists).
LP: SBUKLP 10
MC: SBUKMC 10

XL RECORDINGS - THE SECOND CHAPTER (Various artists).
MC: XLMC 108
LP: XLLP 108

Dance A Little Closer

DANCE A LITTLE CLOSER (Broadway Cast) (Various artists).
MC: ZCTER 1035

Dance 'All Style

DANCE 'ALL STYLE.
Tracks: / I found love / Miserable woman / Jack slick / Man in a house / Legal / She loves me now / Paro them paro / No good girl / Rude boys / Icky all over / No sound like we / Fools fighting.
LP: BM 112

Dance Bands

BEST OF BRITISH DANCE BANDS (Various artists).
Tracks: / Happy days are here again: Ambrose & His Orchestra (Recorded: 29/1/30) / After the sun's kissed the world goodbye: Elizalde, Fred Rhythmicians (Recorded: 4/12/29) / It's the girl: Cotton, Billy & His Band (Recorded:10/10/31) / By the river Sainte Marie: Bowlly, Al (Recorded:16/6/31) / My baby just cares for me: Payne, Jack & His BBC Dance Orchestra (Recorded:15/10/31) / Crazy rhythm: Starita, Ray & His Ambassadors (Recorded:29/9/28) / How can you say no: Hall, Henry & His BBC Dance Orchestra (Recorded:4/11/32) / My silent love: Gibbons, Carroll & The Hotel Orpheans(Recorded:19/9/32) / I'm in the market for you: Ambrose & His Orchestra (Recorded:24/4/30) / Too many tears: Cotton, Billy & His Band (Recorded:3/6/32) / Good little, bad little you: New Mayfair Dance Orchestra (Recorded:19/2/29) / Any times the time to fall in love: New Mayfair Dance Orchestra (Recorded:20/6/30) / Honeymoon Hotel: Hylton, Jack & His Orchestra (Recorded:27/2/33) / Wind's in the west, The: Fox, Roy & His Band (Recorded:31/10/33) / Baby face: Savoy Orpheans (Recorded:13/10/26) / Like taking candy from a baby: Roy, Harry (Recorded: / 7/34) / Say it: Roy, Harry (Recorded: / 9/34) / Play to me gypsy: Costa, Sam (Recorded:16/1/34) / Kiss me dear: Jackson, Jack & His Orchestra (Recorded:1/9/34) / For all we know: Gibbons, Carroll & The Hotel Orpheans (Recorded:23/10/34).
LP: SVL 177
MC: CSVL 177

BIG BANDS ARE BACK VOL.1 (Various artists).
Tracks: / In the mood: Miller, Glenn / Cherolee: Barnet, Charlie / Seven come eleven: Goodman / Jumpin' at the woodside: Basie Big Band / Trumpet blues: James, Harry.
MC: CONE 6

BRITISH DANCE BANDS OF THE FORTIES (Various artists).
Tracks: / If I had my way / More & more / Cookhouse serenade: Various artists / Better not roll those blue blue eyes: Various artists / Hour never passes, An: Various artists / I threw a kiss in the ocean / Shrine of St Cecilia / My wubba dolly / Coming in on a wing and a prayer: Various artists / It's a blue world: Stone, Lew & His Band/ In a little rocky valley: Stone, Lew & His Band / There's nothing new to tell you: Stone, Lew & His Band / Sing a round up song: Stone, Lew & His Band / Too romantic: Stone, Lew & His Band / Hut sut song, The: Stone, Lew & His Band / Mother's prayer at twilight, A: Stone, Lew & His Band / And so do I: Stone, Lew & His Band/ We'll meet again: Stone, Lew & His Band / Keep an eye on your heart: Royal Airforce Dance Orchestra / Blue champagne: Royal Airforce Dance Orchestra / It's foolish but it's fun: Royal Airforce Dance Orchestra / Out of nowhere: Royal Airforce Dance Orchestra / There I go: Royal Airforce Dance Orchestra / Whistler's mother-in-law, The: Royal Airforce Dance Orchestra / Lover's lullaby: Royal Airforce Dance Orchestra / All our tomorrows: Royal Airforce Dance Orchestra / You started something: Royal Airforce Dance Orchestra / Apple for teacher, An: Rabin, Oscar & His Band / You're mine: Rabin, Oscar & His Band / When the night is thru': Rabin, Oscar & His Band/ Sometimes: Rabin, Oscar & His Band / Man and his dream, A: Rabin, Oscar & His Band / Moonlight avenue: Rabin, Oscar & His Band / When the rose of Tralee met Danny boy: Rabin, Oscar & His Band / Basin Street ball: Rabin, Oscar & His Band / Sing,everybody,sing: Rabin, Oscar & His Band.
2LP: RECDL 2
MCSET: RECDC 2

BUFFALO RHYTHM (Various dance bands of the 1920's) (Various artists).
Tracks: / Since my best gal turned me down: Various artists / Back in your own back yard: Various artists / I'm tickled pink: Various artists / Breakaway: Various artists / Charleston baby o' mine: Various artists/ Baby's blue: Various artists / Sitting on top of the world: Various artists / Voice of the Southland, The: Various artists / Nobody but you: Various artists / Waitin' for Katy: Various artists / Say it again: Various artists / Buffalo rhythm: Various artists / True blue Lou: Various artists / Tin ear: Various artists / Dusky stevedore: Various artists / When sweet Suzie goes steppin' by: Various artists / I'm riding to glory: Various artists / Say, who is that baby doll?: Various artists / Lazy weather: Various artists/ Suzie's feller: Various artists.
LP: VLP 56

CLASSIC YEARS IN DIGITAL STEREO (see under Classic Years...) (Various artists).

DANCE BAND HITS OF THE BLITZ (Various artists).
Tracks: / It can't be wrong: Geraldo & His Orchestra / Long ago and far away: Geraldo & His Orchestra / Humpty Dumpty heart: Geraldo & His Orchestra / Every night about this time: Geraldo & His Orchestra / I don't want to set the world on fire: Geraldo & His Orchestra / Anywhere on earth is heaven: Geraldo & His Orchestra / I'm nobody's baby: Gonella, Nat & His New Georgians / Aurora: Gonella, Nat & His New Georgians / I can't get Indiana off my mind: Gonella, Nat & His New Georgians / Be careful it's my heart: Roy, Harry & His Band / Daddy: Roy, Harry & His Band / Sand in my shoes: Roy, Harry & His Band / Pennsylvania polka, The: Roy, Harry & His Band / That lovely weekend: Roy, Harry & His Band / Five o'clock whistle, The: Roy, Harry & His Band / White Christmas: Roy, Harry & His Band / Down Forget-Me-Not Lane: Loss, Joe & His Orchestra / I'll never smile again: Loss, Joe & His Orchestra / You made me care: Loss, Joe & His Orchestra / How sweet you are: Benson, Ivy & Her Girl's Band / If I had my way: Benson, Ivy & Her Girl's Band / I'm sending my blessing: Benson, Ivy & Her Girl's Band/ Home coming waltz, The: Benson, Ivy & Her Girl's Band / Does she love me: Leader, Harry & His Band.
2LP: DL 1185
MC: TCDL 1185

DANCE BAND YEARS, THE (Various artists).
Tracks: / It's de-lovely: Geraldo & His Orchestra / Dipsy doodle, The: Fox, Roy & His Orchestra / Born to love: Lipton, Sydney & His Grosvenor House

Orchestra / I go for that: *Geraldo & His Orchestra* / Heavenly party, A: *Fox, Roy & His Orchestra* / La-de-de, la-de-da: *Lipton, Sydney & His Grosvenor House Orchestra* / Raindrops: *Geraldo* & His Gaucho Tango Orchestra / Little robin told me so, A: *Liter, Monia & His Orchestra* / Change partners: *Geraldo* & His Orchestra / Goodbye to summer: *Lipton, Sydney & His Grosvenor House Orchestra* / Piccolino, The: *Liter*, Monia & His Orchestra / And the angels sing: *Geraldo & His Orchestra* / Smarty: *Lipton, Sydney & His Grosvenor* House Orchestra / Two shadows: *Fox, Roy & His Orchestra* / Jam session: *Lipton, Sydney & His Grosvenor House Orchestra*/ I love you with all my heart: *Geraldo & His Orchestra* / Shoe shine boy: *Liter, Monia & His Orchestra* / Blue Caribbean sea: *Geraldo & His Orchestra* / Bob White: *Fox, Roy & His Orchestra* / Pennies from Heaven: *Liter*, Monia & His Orchestra / You can't stop me from dreaming: *Lipton, Sydney & His Grosvenor House Orchestra* / Harbour lights: *Geraldo & His Orchestra*.

LP: . . . . **SVL 168**
MC: . . . . **CSVL 168**

DANCE BAND YEARS, THE (1940's) (Various artists).
Tracks: / I've got a gal in Kalamazoo: *Geraldo & His Orchestra* / Indian Summer: *Geraldo & His Orchestra* / In the mood: *Geraldo & His Orchestra* / I hear a rhapsody: *Geraldo & His Orchestra* / South American way: *Geraldo* & His Orchestra / Do I worry: *Geraldo & His Orchestra* / You gorgeous dancing doll: *Geraldo & His Orchestra*/ Swingin on Lennox Avenue: *Skyrockets Dance Orchestra* / So dumb, but so beautiful: *Skyrockets Dance Orchestra*/ Is you is or is you ain't my baby?: *Skyrockets Dance Orchestra* / Shoo shoo baby: *Preager, Lou & His Band* / I heard you cried last night: *Preager, Lou & His Band* / Boy is jumping, The: *Skyrockets Dance Orchestra* / My prayer: *Skyrockets Dance Orchestra* / San Fernando valley: *Skyrockets Dance Orchestra* / It jumps like mad: *Skyrockets Dance Orchestra* / Do you believe in dreams?: *Skyrockets Dance Orchestra*.

LP: . . . . **SVL 145**
MC: . . . . **CSVL 145**

DANCE BAND YEARS, THE (1920's) (Various artists).
Tracks: / Charleston: *Savoy Orpheans* / Yes sir, that's my baby: *Hylton, Jack & His Orchestra* / I wonder where my baby is tonight: *Mackey, Percival & His Band* / Paddlin' Madelin' home: *Hylton, Jack & His Orchestra* / Five foot two eyes of blue: *Firman, Bert & His Dance Orchestra* / Fascinating rhythm: *Mackey, Percival & His Band* / Breezing along with the breeze: *Hylton, Jack Kit Cat Band* / Clap hands here comes Charlie: *Savoy Orpheans* / My cutie's due at two-to two today: *Firman, Bert & His Dance Orchestra* / When the red red robin comes bob bob bobbin along: *Hylton, Jack & His Orchestra* / Black bottom: *Firman, Bert & His Dance Orchestra* / Let's all go to Mary's house: *Whidden, Jay & His New Midnight Follies Band* / Baby face: *Savoy Orpheans* / I never see Maggie alone: *Ralton*, Bert & His Havana Band / Ain't she sweet: *Payne, Jack & His Hotel Cecil Orchestra* / Here am I broken-hearted: *Kit Kat* Band / Deed I do: *Payne, Jack & His Hotel Cecil Orchestra* / Ain't that a grand and glorious feeling?: *Firman*, Bert & His Dance Orchestra / Crazy words, crazy tune: *Payne, Jack & His Hotel Cecil Orchestra* / Varsity drag, The: *Hylton, Jack & His Orchestra*.

LP: . . . . **SVL 169**
MC: . . . . **CSVL 169**

DANCE BANDS ON THE AIR - VOLUME 2 (Various artists).
Tracks: / Stagecoach: *Winstone, Eric & His Band* / Tangerine: *Squadronaires* / Moonlight cocktail: *Geraldo* & His Orchestra / Cruising down the river: *Preager, Lou & His Orchestra* / Fanfare boogie: *Stapleton, Cyril* & His Show Band / Copacabana: *Ross, Edmundo & His Rumba Band* / Creep, The: *Mackintosh, Ken & His Orchestra*/ Why worry?: *Cotton, Billy & His Band* / Hot toddy: *Heath, Ted & His Music* / Midnight in Moscow: *Ball, Kenny* & His Jazzmen / Lady is a tramp, The: *Miller, Bob & The Millermen* / Pennsylvania 6 5000: *Various artists*/ Come dancing: *McVay, Ray & His Orchestra*.

LP: . . . . **REC 140**

DANCE BANDS ON THE AIR - VOLUME 1 (Various artists).
Tracks: / On the air: *Gibbons, Carroll & The Savoy Hotel Orpheans* / Happy feet: *Hylton, Jack & His Orchestra*/ I like a little girl like that: *Payne, Jack & The BBC Dance Orchestra* / If I didn't have you: *Fox, Roy & His Band*/ What a little moonlight can do: *Roy, Harry & His Orchestra* / Heart of gold: *Kunz, Charlie & The Casani Club Orchestra*/ Lazy rhythm: *Stone, Lew & The Monseigneur Band* / Hors d'ouvres: *Various artists* / Sweetest music this side of Heaven, The: *Winnick, Maurice and his Orchestra* / Glory of love: *Hall, Henry & The BBC Dance Orchestra* / Moon of Manakoora / I double dare you: *Harris, Jack & His Orchestra* / That lovely weekend: *Loss, Joe & His Orchestra*/ You're dancing on my heart: *Sylvester, Victor & His Ballroom Orchestra* / Don't say goodbye: *Sylvester, Victor & His Ballroom Orchestra*.

LP: . . . . **REC 139**

DANCE BANDS THROUGH THE YEARS (Various artists).
Tracks: / Too beautiful for words: *Various artists* / She wore a little jacket of blue: *Various artists* / Boo hoo: *Various artists* / It's the natural thing to do: *Various artists* / There's something in the air: *Various* artists / Rainbow on the river: *Various artists* / Little old lady: *Various artists* / So many memories: *Various* artists / Sweet someone: *Various artists* / Love walked in: *Various artists* / Says my heart: *Various* artists / Tears in my heart: *Various artists* / Whistle while you work: *Various artists* / Lambeth walk: *Various* artists / Tisket a tasket, A: *Various artists* / Heigh ho: *Various artists* / Doing the Blackpool walk: *Various* artists / Meet me down in the Sunset Valley: *Various artists* / Little lady make believe: *Various artists*/ Over Wyoming: *Various artists* / Shoo shoo baby: *Various artists* / Gal in Calico, A: *Various artists*/ Another spring is on the way: *Various artists* / You belong to me: *Various artists*.

MCSET: . . . . **DTO 10311**

DANCE BANDS UK (Classic years in digital stereo) (Various artists).
Tracks: / Choo choo: *Various artists* / Masculine women, feminine men: *Various artists* / Singapore sorrows: *Various* artists / Nobody's using it now: *Various artists* / Leven thirsty Saturday night: *Various artists* / Harmonica Harry: *Various artists* / I wanna be loved by you: *Various artists* / Sun has got his hat on, The: *Various* artists / Somebody stole my gal: *Various artists* / I always keep my girl out late: *Various artists* / Blue jazz: *Various artists* / Without that certain thing: *Various artists* / You ought to see Sally on Sunday: *Various* artists / Listen to that rhythm: *Various artists* / Troublesome trumpet: *Various artists* / Everything's in rhythm with my heart: *Various artists*.

LP: . . . . **REB 681**
MC: . . . . **ZCF 681**

DANCE BANDS USA 1925-1935) (Classic Years in Digital Stereo) (Various artists).

LP: . . . . **REB 650**
MC: . . . . **ZCF 650**

FANCY FOOTWORK.
Tracks: / Three strings / Beat of the street / Stacks of tracks / What you gonna do about it / Soul shake / Happy hour / Adultery / Run away / Little bit of soul.

LP: . . . . **DDLP 1**

GOLDEN AGE OF BRITISH DANCE BANDS (Various artists).
Tracks: / South American Joe: *Roy, Harry & His Band* / Avalon: *Roy, Harry & His Band* / Build a little home: *Roy*, Harry & His Band / Limehouse blues: *Roy, Harry & His Band* / Spanish shawl: *Roy, Harry & His Band* / Margie: *Roy, Harry & His Band* / Music, Maestro, please: *Roy, Harry & His Band* / Piano madness: *Roy, Harry* & His Band / I ain't got nobody: *Stone, Lew & His Band* / Red sails in the sunset: *Stone, Lew & His Band* / Dinner for one please, James: *Stone, Lew & His Band* / She's a Latin from Manhattan: *Stone, Lew & His Band* / She wore a little jacket of blue: *Stone, Lew & His Band* / Continental, The: *Stone, Lew & His Band* / Cheek to cheek: *Stone, Lew & His Band* / Afraid to dream: *Fox, Roy & His Band* / These foolish things: *Fox, Roy & His Band* / Let's call the whole thing off: *Fox, Roy & His Band* / This year's kisses: *Fox, Roy & His Band* / Too marvellous for words: *Fox, Roy & His Band* / That old feeling: *Fox, Roy & His Band* / Harbour lights: *Fox, Roy & His Band*/ I let a song go out of my heart: *Fox, Roy & His Band* / Maybe it's because I love you too much: *Noble, Ray* & His Band / Lazy day: *Noble, Ray & His Band* / You ought to see Sally on Sunday: *Noble, Ray & His Band* / How could we be wrong?: *Noble, Ray & His Band* / Close your eyes: *Noble, Ray & His Band* / Time on my hands: *Noble, Ray & His Band* / Mad about the boy: *Noble, Ray & His Band* / One morning in May: *Noble, Ray & His Band*.

LPS: . . . . **ALBUM 32**
MCSET: . . . . **CASSETTE 32**
2LP: . . . . **SH 118/9**

GOLDEN AGE OF THE DANCE BAND (Various artists).
Tracks: / You and the night and the music: *Somer's, Deboy Band* / Blue skies are round the corner: *Hylton, Jack* & His Orchestra / Yes yes (my baby says yes) / She had to go and lose it at the Astor: *Roy, Harry & His Orchestra* / Solitude: *Stone, Lew & His Orchestra* / You gorgeous dancing doll: *Geraldo & The Savoy Hotel Orchestra* / Hold my hand: *Noble, Ray & His Orchestra* / Pennies from Heaven: *Levy, Louis & His Gaumont British Symphony Orchestra*/ Dancing in the dark: *Gibbons, Carroll & The Savoy Hotel Orpheans* / Let's dance at the make believe ballroom: *Loss*, Joe & His Orchestra / Happy days are here again: *Payne, Jack & His BBC Dance Orchestra* / Half of it dearie blues, The: *Mackey's, Percival Band* / I've got my love to keep me warm: *Fox, Roy & His Orchestra* / Lambeth walk: *Munro*, Ronnie & His Orchestra / I took my harp to a party: *Cotton, Billy & His Band* / Here's to the next time: *Hall, Henry & The BBC Dance Orchestra*.

LP: . . . . **GX 2556**
MC: . . . . **TCGX 2556**

GREAT BRITISH DANCE BANDS (Play the Hits of Jimmy Kennedy & Michael Carr) (Various artists).

MC: . . . . **TC SH 340**
LP: . . . . **SH 340**

GREAT BRITISH DANCE BANDS PLAY COLE PORTER (Various artists).
Tracks: / Let's do it: *Various artists* / What is this thing called love: *Various artists* / Love for sale: *Various artists* / Night and day: *Various artists* / Experiment: *Various artists* / Miss Otis regrets (she's unable to lunch today: *Various artists* / Anything goes: *Various artists* / I get a kick out of you: *Various artists*/ You're the top: *Various artists* / Easy to love: *Various artists* / I'm in love again: *Various artists*/ Banjo, The: *Various artists* / What is this thing called love?: *Various artists* / Looking at you: *Various* artists / They all fall in love: *Various artists* / After you, who?: *Various artists* / How could we be wrong?: *Various artists* / It's bad for me: *Various artists* / All through the night: *Various artists* / Blow, Gabriel, blow: *Various artists* / Thank you so much, Mrs Lowsborough: *Various artists* / Goodbye, little dream, goodbye: *Various artists*.

2LP: . . . . **SHB 66**
2LP: . . . . **EG 2604431**
MC: . . . . **EG 2604434**

GREAT BRITISH DANCE BANDS PLAY GEORGE GERSHWIN (Various artists).
Tracks: / Swanee: *Savoy Quartet* / Drifting along with the tide: *Queens Dance Orchestra* / Please do it again: *Queens Dance Orchestra* / Yankee doodle blues: *Savoy Havana Band* / I'll build a stairway to Paradise: *Savoy* Havana Band / My fair lady: *Savoy Havana Band* / Nice baby: *Savoy Havana Band* / Sweetheart: *Hylton*, Jack & His Orchestra / Innocent, lonesome, blue baby: *Hylton, Jack & His Orchestra* / Someone: *Hylton, Jack* & His Orchestra / Lady be good: *Hylton, Jack & His Orchestra* / Clap yo' hands: *Hylton, Jack & His Orchestra*/ Do do do: *Hylton, Jack & His Orchestra* / 'S wonderful: *Hylton, Jack & His Orchestra* / My one and only: *Hylton*, Jack & His Orchestra / Virginia: *Midnight Follies Orchestra* / Wait a bit: *Various artists* / Susie: *Various* artists / Why do I love you?: *Various artists* / Tell me more: *Various artists* / Hang on to me: *Various* artists / So am I: *Various artists* / Someone to watch over me: *Various artists* / Somebody loves me: *Darewski*, Max & His Band / I'd rather Charleston: *Mackey, Percival & His Band* / Half of it dearie blues, The: *Mackey, Percival* & His Band / Looking for a boy: *Mackey, Percival & His Band* / When do we dance?: *Mackey, Percival & His Band*/ That certain feeling: *Cabaret Novelty Band* / Man I love, The: *Piccadilly Revels Band* / Funny face: *Piccadilly Players* / He loves and she loves: *Piccadilly Players*.

2LP: . . . . **SHB 45**

GREAT BRITISH DANCE BANDS PLAY LONDON PRIDE (1925-1949) (Various artists).
Tracks: / Home town: *Various artists* / Sing a song of London: *Various artists* / Lambeth walk: *Various artists*/ Did you go down Lambeth way: *Various artists* / King's horses, The: *Various artists* / Limehouse blues: *Various* artists / Foggy day, A: *Various artists* / Underneath the arches: *Various artists* / There's something about that town: *Various artists* / Follow the white line: *Various artists* / Leicester Square rag: *Various artists*/ Parade of the fire brigade, The: *Various artists* / Carry on London: *Various artists* / Life begins at Oxford Circus: *Various artists* / 'Ampstead way', The: *Various artists* / Round the Marble Arch: *Various artists*/ Nightingale sang in Berkeley square, A: *Various artists* / Piccadilly strut: *Various artists* / London pride: *Various artists* / Hyde Park corner: *Various artists* / London on a rainy night: *Various artists* / Big Ben is saying goodnight: *Various artists*.

MC: . . . . **EG 2601574**
LP: . . . . **EG 2601571**

GREAT BRITISH DANCE BANDS PLAY THE MUSIC OF IRVING BERLIN (Various artists).

LP: . . . . **SH 353**

GREAT BRITISH DANCE BANDS PLAY THE MUSIC OF NOEL COWARD (Various artists).
Tracks: / I'll see you again: *Hylton, Jack & His Orchestra* / Kiss me: *Hylton, Jack & His Orchestra* / Zigeuner: *Hylton, Jack & His Orchestra* / If love were all: *Hylton, Jack & His Orchestra* / Dear little cafe: *Hylton*, Jack & His Orchestra / Russian skies: *Hylton, Jack & His Orchestra* / Specially for you: *Various artists*/ Poor little rich girl: *Various artists* / Mad about the boy: *Various artists* / I'm mad about you: *Starita* & The Piccadilly Band / Teach me to dance like grandma: *Starita, Ray & His Ambassadors* / Half caste woman: *Various* artists / Try to learn to love / Dance little lady: *Various artists* / Lover of my dreams: *Payne, Jack & His BBC* Dance Orchestra / Mirabelle waltz: *Payne, Jack & His BBC Dance Orchestra* / Something to do with spring: *Noble*, Ray & His New Mayfair Orchestra / Let's live dangerously: *Noble, Ray & His New Mayfair Orchestra* / Let's say goodbye: *Noble, Ray & His New Mayfair Orchestra* / Children of the Ritz: *Noble, Ray & His New Mayfair Orchestra* / Party's over, The: *Noble, Ray & His New Mayfair Orchestra* / Younger generation, The: *Noble, Ray & His New Mayfair Orchestra*/ Most of ev'ry day: *Jackson, Jack & His Orchestra* / Room with a view: *Jackson, Jack & His Orchestra*.

LP: . . . . **SH 278**

GREAT BRITISH DANCE BANDS PLAY THE HITS OF THE 60'S (Various artists).
Tracks: / Singin' in the rain: *Various artists* / In the mood: *Various artists* / Continental, The: *Various* artists / Tuxedo Junction: *Various artists* / Lullaby of Broadway: *Various artists* / I only have eyes for you: *Various artists* / Whispering grass: *Various artists* / What a difference a day made: *Various artists*/ Smoke gets in your eyes: *Various artists* / If I didn't care: *Various artists* / I get a kick out of you: *Various* artists / Lazybones: *Various artists* / Maria Elena: *Various artists* / Love letters in the sand: *Various* artists / More I see you, The: *Various artists* / Bye bye blues: *Various artists* / Deep purple: *Various* artists / I'm confessin': *Various artists* / I remember you: *Various artists* / Diane (I'm in Heaven when I see you smile): *Various artists*.

LP: . . . . **SH 390**
MC: . . . . **TC SH 390**

GREAT BRITISH DANCE BANDS PLAY THE MUSIC OF HARRY WARREN (Various artists).
Tracks: / Rose of the Rio Grande: *Original Capitol Orchestra* / Pasadena: *Midnight Follies Orchestra* / Oh Eva: *Various artists* / Seminola: *Various artists* / I love my baby: *New Prince Toronto Band* / Ya gotta know how to love: *Cabaret Novelty Orchestra* / Where do you work?: *Firman, Bert & His Dance Orchestra* / Away down south in Heaven: *Firman, Bert & His Dance Orchestra* / Lily, my regular girl: *Kit Cat Band* / An' furthermore: *Starita*, Ray & His Ambassadors / Where the shy little violets grow: *Hylton, Jack & His Orchestra* / Cheerful little earful: *Hylton, Jack & His Orchestra* / When Eliza rolls her eyes: *Kunz, Charlie & His Chez Henri Club Band* / Have a little faith in me: *Various artists* / Crying for the Carolines: *Cotton, Billy & His Band*.

LP: . . . . **SHB 298**

GREAT BRITISH DANCE BANDS PLAY VIVIAN ELLIS (Various artists).

LP: . . . . **SH 260**

IRVING BERLIN - CENTENARY CELEBRATION (Various artists).

LP: . . . . **SH 512**
MC: . . . . **TC SH 512**

MUSIC OF IRVING BERLIN (Played by the great British dance bands) (Various artists).

2LP: . . . . **SHB 35**

THOSE DANCE BAND YEARS-VOL 1 (Various artists).
Tracks: / Paddlin' Madelin' home: *New Prince Toronto Band* / Everybody stomp: *Savoy Havana Band* / At sundown: *Savoy Havana Band* / Charleston Charley: *Carlton Hotel Dance Orchestra* / Valencia: *Various artists* / Vo-do-do-de-o blues: *Various artists* / You've got those wanna-go-back-again blues: *Whidden, Jay & His New Midnight* Follies Band / Up and at 'em: *Whidden, Jay & His New Midnight Follies Band* / Hello, aloha, how are you?: *Munro,* Ronnie & His Dance Orchestra / Crazy quilt: *Hylton, Jack Kit Cat Band* / Jig walk: *Devonshire restaurant Dance* Band / Brainstorm: *Somers, Debroy & His Band* / Ain't she sweet?: *Piccadilly Revels Band* / Just the same: *Piccadilly Revels Band* / I need lovin': *Sylvans* / Devil is afraid of music, The: *London Radio Dance Band*.
LP: . . . . **SH 361**

THOSE DANCE BAND YEARS-VOL 2 (Various artists).
Tracks: / Mississippi mud: *Sylvians* / Nebrasca: *Munro, Ronnie & His Dance Orchestra* / Kiss and make up: *Piccadilly* Players / You wouldn't fool me, would you?: *Piccadilly Players* / Blue butterfly: *Rhythm Band* / There's a blue ridge 'round my heart, Virginia: *Rosebery, Arthur & His Kit Kat Dance Band* / Broadway melody: *Rosebery, Arthur &* His Kit Kat Dance Band / You went away once too often: *Kunz, Charlie & His Chez Henri Club Band* / Wake up, chillun, wake up: *Starita, Ray & His Ambassadors' Club Band* / Do something: *Payne, Jack & His BBC Dance Orchestra* / Everyday away from you: *Four Bright Sparks* / Eleven-thirty, Saturday night: *Arcadian Dance Orchestra* / Tap your feet: *Hylton, Jack & His Orchestra* / If I could be with you one hour tonight: *Ambrose & His Orchestra* / Time on my hands: *Mackay, Percival & His Band* / Got the bench, got the park: *Noble, Ray & The New Mayfair Orchestra* / Would you like to take a walk?: *Noble, Ray & The New Mayfair Orchestra* / Reaching for the moon: *Noble, Ray & The New Mayfair Orchestra* / Hello beautiful: *Noble, Ray & The New Mayfair Orchestra*.
LP: . . . . **SH 362**

THOSE DANCE BAND YEARS-VOL 3 (Various artists).
Tracks: / Miss Elizabeth Brown: *Noble, Ray & The New Mayfair Orchestra* / Sil'vry Rio Grande: *Noble, Ray & The New* Mayfair Orchestra / River stay 'way from my door: *Noble, Ray & The New Mayfair Orchestra* / Oh Rosalita: *Noble,* Ray & The New Mayfair Orchestra / Down Sunnyside Lane: *Payne, Jack & His BBC Dance Orchestra* / That's my desire: *Kyte,* Sidney & his Piccadilly Hotel Band / All of me: *Blue Lyres* / You rascal you: *Blue Lyres* / Clouds will soon roll by, The: *Various artists* / Mean music: *Brown, Philip's Grosvenor Band* / Sadie the shaker: *Lipton, Sydney* & His Grosvenor House Orchestra / You're an old smoothie: *Somers, Debroy & His Band* / I like to go back in the evening: *Jackson, Jack & His Orchestra* / Japanese sandman: *Noble, Ray & His Orchestra* / April in Paris: *Hall, Henry &* The BBC Dance Orchestra / We'll make hay while the sun shines: *Merrin, Billy & His Commanders* / Annie doesn't live here any more: *Cotton, Billy & His Band* / Better think twice: *Gibbons, Carroll & Savoy Hotel Orpheans*.
LP: . . . . **SH 363**

THOSE DANCE BAND YEARS-VOL 4 (Various artists).
Tracks: / Carioca: *Geraldo's Gaucho Tango Orchestra* / Deep forest: *Foresythe, Reginald* / Tina: *Stone, Lew &* His Band / Pop, goes your heart: *Stone, Lew & His Band* / What a little moonlight can do: *Levy, Louis & The* Gaumont British Dance Band / June in January: *Joyce, Teddy & His Orchestra* / Holiday express: *Joyce, Teddy &* His Orchestra / Buchanan stomp: *Perritt, Harry & His Orchestra* / Medley: *Roy, Harry & His Orchestra* / Footloose and fancy free: *Hylton, Jack & His Orchestra* / St. Louis blues: *Daniels, Joe & His Hotshots* / Roll along, prairie moon: *Jackson, Jack & His Band* / From the top of your head: *Gibbons, Carroll & Savoy Hotel Orpheans* / Love is a dancing thing: *Winnick, Maurice* / My sweetie went away: *Leader, Harry & His Band*.
LP: . . . . **SH 364**

THOSE DANCE BAND YEARS-VOL 5 (Various artists).
Tracks: / Moon over Miami: *Winnick, Maurice* / Woe is me: *Rabin, Oscar & His Romany Band* / Oh by jingo, oh by gee: *Krakajax* / Pretty girl is like a melody, A: *Fox, Roy & His Orchestra* / Free: *Cotton, Billy & His Band*/ When my dreamboat comes home: *Martin, Bram & His Band* / West End blues: *Various artists* / Boo hoo: *Gonella,* Nat/his Georgians / Swing high, swing low: *Firman, Bert & His Dance Orchestra* / Never in a million years: *Bissett,* Billy & His Orchestra / Love is good for anything that ails you: *Orlando & His Orchestra* / Swing session in Siberia: *Elrick, George & His Swing Music Makers* / Getting some fun out of life: *Jacobs, Howard & His Golden Tone Sax & Orchestra*/ Chinese laundry blues: *Seymour, Syd & His Mad Hatters* / You started something: *Ternent, Billy & His Orchestra*/ She's the daughter of the old grey mare: *Donovan, Dan & His Music*.
LP: . . . . **SH 365**

THOSE DANCE BAND YEARS-VOL 6 (Various artists).
Tracks: / Someday, sweetheart: *Millward, Sid & His Band* / Sweet as a song: *White, Jack & His Collegians* / Mama, I wanna make rhythm: *Harris, Jack & His Orchestra* / Plain Jane: *Harris, Jack & His Orchestra* / How'd ja like to love me: *Fox, Roy & His Orchestra* / Love makes the world go round: *Hall, Henry & His Orchestra* / Penny serenade: *Geraldo & His Orchestra* / My own: *Carroll, Eddie & His Music* / There's a new apple tree: *Thorburn, Billy &* His Dance Band / You must have been a beautiful baby: *Rignold, Hugo & His Orchestra* / I'm madly in love with you: *Williams, Reginald & His Futurists* / Heaven can wait: *Thorburn, Billy & His Dance Band* / South of the border (down Mexico way): *Loss, Joe & his band* / Begin the beguine: *Loss, Joe & his band* / Lady's in love with you, The: *Stratton, Von & His Music* / Wishing (will make it so): *Darewski, Herman & His Band*.
LP: . . . . **SH 366**

THOSE DANCE BAND YEARS-VOL 7 (Various artists).
LP: . . . . **SH 367**

VINTAGE BANDS, THE (Various artists).
Tracks: / Music, Maestro, please: *Hylton, Jack & His Orchestra* / Alexander's ragtime band: *Roy, Harry & His Orchestra*/ Nagasaki: *Gonella, Nat/ his Georgians* / Nobody loves a fairy when she's forty: *Cotton, Billy & His Band* / My brother makes the noises for the talkies: *Payne, Jack & His BBC Dance Orchestra* / Stay as sweet as you are: *Stone,* Lew & His Orchestra / In the mood: *Loss, Joe & His Orchestra* / Let's face the music and dance: *Fox, Roy & His* Orchestra / Nightingale sang in Berkeley Square, A: *Gibbons, Carroll & The Savoy Hotel Orpheans* / Dancing in the dark: *Ambrose* / Here's to the next time: *Hall, Henry & The BBC Dance Orchestra* / Say it with music: *Payne, Jack* & His BBC Dance Orchestra / I'm going to get lit up when the lights go up in London: *Gibbons, Carroll & The Savoy Hotel* Orpheans / Change partners: *Loss, Joe & His Orchestra* / Did you ever see a dream walking?: *Hall, Henry & The* BBC Dance Orchestra / Shine: *Cotton, Billy & His Band* / She had to go and lose it at the Astoria: *Roy, Harry &* His Orchestra / Easy to remember: *Stone, Lew & His Orchestra* / Have you met Miss Jones?: *Hylton, Jack & His* Orchestra / I can't dance: *Gonella, Nat/ his Georgians* / Night is young and you're so beautiful, The: *Fox, Roy & His Orchestra* / Let's put out the lights: *Ambrose*.
MC: . . . . **HR 8114**
MC: . . . . **HR 4181144**

VOICES OF GREAT BRITISH DANCE BANDS (Various artists).
Tracks: / Let's call a heart a heart: *Stediford, Marjorie* / I've got you under my skin: *Stediford, Marjorie*/ Greatest mistake of my life: *Henderson, Chick* / Bottoms up: *Logan, Ella* / Bigger and better than ever: *Logan,* Ella / You go to my head: *Donovan, Don* / On the sentimental side: *Donovan, Don* / Mine alone: *Lynn,* Vera / Here comes the sandman: *Lynn, Vera* / Gee gee: *Mallin, Bob* / You must have been a beautiful baby: *Carless, Dorothy & Sam Costa* / I'll see you in my dreams: *Rosing, Val & His Swing Stars* / I can't give you anything but love: *Rosing, Val & His Swing Stars* / Broken record, The: *Costa, Sam* / Did your mother come from Ireland?: *Dell, Peggy* / With every breath I take: *Fitzgerald, Gerry*.
LP: . . . . **SH 336**

WE'LL MEET AGAIN (The music of Hugh Charles 1938-45) (Various artists).
Tracks: / I won't tell a soul: *Fox, Roy & His Orchestra* / Blue skies are round the corner: *Hylton, Jack & His Orchestra*/ I shall always remember you smiling: *Hylton, Jack & His Orchestra* / There'll always be an England: *Loss, Joe Concert* Orchestra / We'll meet again: *Hylton, Jack & His Orchestra* / I shall be waiting: *Lipton, Sydney & His Grosvenor* House Orchestra / I'm in love for the last time: *Johnson, Ken 'Snakehips' & his West Indian Orchestra* / Little king without a crown: *Loss, Joe & His Orchestra* / Moonlight And mimosa: *Loss, Joe & His Orchestra* / Where the waters are blue / Get into the spirit of Spring: *Lipton, Sydney & his Orchestra* / Memories live longer than dreams: *Lipton,* Sydney & his Orchestra / When your train has gone: *Loss, Joe & His Orchestra* / King is still in London, The: *Gibbons,* Carroll & Savoy Hotel Orpheans / There's a land of begin again: *Winstone, Eric Accordion Band* / Let the bands play: *Loss, Joe & His Orchestra* / Russian Rose: *Geraldo & His Orchestra* / Potato Pete: *Roy, Harry & His Band*/ Silver wings in the moonlight: *Gibbons, Carroll & Savoy Hotel Orpheans* / Till all our prayers are answered: *Payne, Jack Orchestra*.
LP: . . . . **RD 1**

Dance Busters

DANCE BUSTERS VOL.2 (Various artists).
LP: . . . . **WAMLP 002**

Dance Class

DANCE CLASS.
LP: . . . . **AMLH 68547**

Dance Craze (film)

DANCE CRAZE (1981 film soundtrack) (Various artists).
Tracks: / Concrete jungle: *Specials* / Mirror in the bathroom: *Beat* / Lip up Fatty: *Bad Manners* / Three minute hero: *Selector* / Easy life: *Bodysnatchers* / Big shot: *Beat* / One step beyond: *Madness*/ Ranking full stop: *Beat* / Man at C & A: *Specials* / Missing words: *Selector* / Inner London violence: *Bad Manners* / Night boat to Cairo: *Madness* / Too much pressure: *Selector* / Nite klub: *Specials*.
LP: . . . . **CHRTT 5004**
MC: . . . . **ZCHRT 5004**

Dance Hits

DANCE HITS ALBUM, VOL. 2 (Various artists).
LP: . . . . **TVLP 13**
MC: . . . . **ZCTV 13**

Dance On

DANCE ON (Youth club classics) (Various artists).
Tracks: / Some people: *Mountain,Valene* / Picture of you ,A: *Brown, Joe* / War Paint: *Brook Brothers* / Night train: *Checkmates* (Not on CD) / Venus in blue jeans: *Wynter, Mark* / Sailor: *Clark, Petula* / When my little girl is smiling: *Justice, Jimmy* / Bristol express: *Eagles* / Pick a bale of cotton: *Donegan,* Lonnie / Go away little girl: *Wynter, Mark* / Wipeout: *Saints* / It only took a minute: *Brown, Joe*/ Spanish harlem: *Justice, Jimmy* / Welcome home baby: *Brook Brothers* / Up on the roof: *Grant, Julie*/ Desperadoes: *Eagles* / Your tender look: *Brown, Joe* / Who put the bomp: *Viscounts* / Honest I do: *Storm,* Danny / Ya Ya twist: *Clark, Petula* / Johnny's tune: *Eagles* / Ain't gonna wash for a week: *Brook Brothers*/ Yes you did: *Mountain,Valerie* (Not on CD.) / Walk right in: *Kestrels* (Not on CD.) / Dance on: *Eagles*/ That's what love will do: *Brown, Joe* / It's almost tomorrow: *Wynter, Mark* / Too late: *Mountain,Valerie*/ Trouble is my middle name: *Brook Brothers* / Ain't that funny: *Justice, Jimmy* / Count on me: *Grant, Julie*/ Pipeline: *Eagles*.
2LP: . . . . **NEDLP 103**
MCSET: . . . . **NEDMC 103**

Dance People

FLY AWAY.
Tracks: / Flyaway / Funk attack / Dance people / Give your feet a treat / Snakes and ladders / Midnight breeze / Dance the night away.
LP: . . . . **SATL 4013**

Dance With A Stranger

FOOL'S PARADISE.
Tracks: / Do what you wanna do / Invisible man, The / Stop locking for love (through blue eyes) / African road / Fool's paradise / Explosion of time / Another day / Hey Joann / Show what you got / Little woman.
LP: . . . . **PL 74551**
MC: . . . . **PK 74551**

Dance With A Stranger (film)

DANCE WITH A STRANGER (1985 film soundtrack) (Various artists).
LP: . . . . **PACT 7**
MC: . . . . **CPACT 7**
LP: . . . . **STV 81251**

Danceable Weird Shit

HERE'S THE RECORD.
LP: . . . . **WD 6662**

Dancers (film)

DANCERS (1987 film soundtrack) (Various artists).
LP: . . . . **CBS 42565**
MC: **40 42565**

Dances With Wolves

DANCES WITH WOLVES (Film Soundtrack) (Barry, John).
Tracks: / Dances With Wolves / Looks like a suicide / John Dunbar theme, The / Journey to Fort Sedgewick / Ride to Fort Hays / Death of Timmons, The / Two Socks - the wolf theme / Pawnee Attack / Kicking Bird's gift / Journey to the buffalo killing ground / Buffalo hunt, The / Stands with a fist / Remembers / Love theme, The / John Dunbar theme, The (2) / Two Socks at play / Death of Cisco, The / Rescue of Dances With Wolves / Loss of the journal and the return to winter camp, The / Dances With Wolves: Farewell and end title.
LP: **4675911**
MC: **4675912**

Dancetime Orchestra

DANCETIME YEARS, THE.
LP: . . . . **DTL 3002**

DANCETIME YEARS VOL.2.
LP: . . . . **DTL 3005**

LANCERS AND QUADRILLES.
LP: . . . . **DTL 3004**

TIME FOR OLD TIME.
LP: . . . . **DTL 3003**

D'Ancey, Graham

ALLUMA.
LP: . . . . **SHLP 100**

Dancin' Machine

DOWN STREET (see Kutash, Jeff) (Dancin' Machine/Jeff Kutash).

Dancing At...

DANCING AT CONFECTIONERS HALL (Various artists).
LP: . . . . **GHB 205**

Dancing Did

AND DID THOSE FEET.
LP: . . . . **KAM 009**

Dancing Granny...

DANCING GRANNY & OTHER AFRICAN STORIES, THE (Ashley Bryan).
MC: **1765**

Dancing Hoods

12 JEALOUS ROSES.
Tracks: / Pleasure / Impossible years / Build a house / Blue letter / Girls problems / Surfing all over the world / Bye bye Jim / Watching you sleep / (Take my) chances / She may call you up tonight / Wild and the lonely.
LP: . . . . **AFTER 1**

Dancing Party

DANCING PARTY (Various artists).
LP: . . . . **MFP 50496**

Dancing Princesses

DANCING PRINCESSES (Various artists).
Tracks: / Dancing Princesses: *Various artists* / Snake leaves, The: *Various artists* / Prince Milan: *Various* artists / Prince Ring and Prince Ring: *Various artists* / Six sillies, The: *Various artists* / Black thief, The: *Various artists*.
MC: . . . . **ANV 649**

Dandelion Seed (bk)

DANDELION SEED, THE (Lena Kennedy) (Boyd, Carole (nar)).
MC: . . . . **CAB 323**

Dando Shaft

KINGDOM.
Tracks: / Follow you / If I could let you go / Barbara Allen / Stroller in the air / Kingdom / Feel like I wanna go home / Day star / Trees / Tenpenny bit, The / Oak tree, The / Lady and the man / Glow worm.
LP: . . . . **RUB 034**
MC: . . . . **RUBC 034**

REAPING THE HARVEST.
Tracks: / Coming home to me / Railway / Magnetic beggar / Pass it on / Kalyope driver / Prayer / Sometimes / Waves upon the ether / Dewet / Riverboat / Harp lady I bombed / Black prince of paradise / When I'm weary / Till the morning comes / Whispering Ned / Road song / Is it me? / It was good / Rain (Available on CD only) / Cold wind (Available on CD only) / In the country (Available on CD only) / End of the game, The (Available on CD only).
LP: . . . . **SEE 291**

Dando, Suzanne

AT CHRISTMAS TIME (see Hughes, Emlyn).

D'Andrea, Franco

MADE IN ITALY.
Tracks: / Rag and blues / Zitti Zitti non destatelo / Quiet children / Oasis / Luci sul fondo.
LP: .... **NS 200**

Dandridge, Putney

CHRONOLOGICAL STUDY 1.
Tracks: / You're a heavenly thing / My bluebird / Nagasaki / Chasing shadows / When I grow too old to dream / I'm in the mood for love / Isn't this a lovely day / Cheek to cheek / That's what you think / Shine / I'm on a seesaw / Eeny meeny miney mo / Double trouble / Santa Claus came in the Spring.
LP: .... **RARITIES 26**

CHRONOLOGICAL STUDY 2.
Tracks: / You hit the spot / No other one / Little bit independent, A / You took my breath away / Sweet violets / Dinner for one, please James / Honeysuckle Rose / It's a sin to tell a lie / All of my life / Ol' man river / Why was I born? / These foolish things / Cross patch / Shine / Eeny meeny miney mo / Santa Claus came in the Spring / Beautiful lady in blue, A.
LP: .... **RARITIES 27**

CHRONOLOGICAL STUDY 3.
Tracks: / Star fell out of heaven, A / Mary had a little lamb / Here comes your pappy / If we never meet again / Sing, baby sing / You turned the tables on me / It's the gypsy in me / When a lady meets a gentleman down South / High hat, a piccolo and a cane, A / Easy to love / You do the darndest things baby / Skeleton in the closet, The / I'm in a dancing mood / With plenty of money and you / That foolish feeling / Gee but you're swell.
LP: .... **RARITIES 34**

Dandy, Jim

BLACK ATTACK IS BACK (See Black Oak Arkansas) (Dandy, Jim/Black Oak Arkansas).

READY AS HELL.
LP: .... **HMUSA 5**
LPPD: .... **HMPD 5**

Dane, Barbara

DENVER CONCERT (See under Ewell, Don) (Dane, Barbara & Don Ewell).

GIPPER GATE BLUES.
LP: .... **ARHOOLIE 1600**

Dane, Clem

CLEM DANE'S GREATEST HITS.
LP: .... **KLP 01**

GREAT DANE, THE.
LP: .... **KMLP 306**
MC: .... **ZCKLP 306**

Dane, Dana

4 EVER.
LP: .... **FILER 298**
MC: .... **FILECT 298**

Daneman, Paul (nar)

NOT A PENNY MORE, NOT A PENNY LESS (See under Archer, Jeffrey (aut)).

Dang, Ken

KEN DANG.
LP: .... **SRM 101**

Danger

DANGER.
LP: .... **SKULL 8305**

Danger, Donna

CHEROKEE CHICK, THE.
LP: **33.8020**

Danger UXB (tv)

DANGER UXB (Performed by the Simon Park Orchestra).
Tracks: / Danger UXB (main title) / Waltz theme / We'll meet again / Honeysuckle and the bee, The / Nightingale sang in Berkeley Square / Till the lights of London shine again / Where or when / You are my sunshine / Moonlight becomes you / Who's taking you home tonight / Into each life some rain must fall.
LP: .... **SKL 5304**
MC: .... **KSKL 5304**

Dangermouse

DANGERMOUSE AND PUBLIC ENEMY NO.1 (Various artists).
MC: .... **TTS 9807**

DANGERMOUSE AND THE PLANET OF THE CATS (Various artists).
MC: .... **TTS 9804**

DANGERMOUSE - THE GREAT BONE IDOL (Various artists).
MC: .... **TTS 9809**

Dangermouse (Group)

DANGERMOUSE (Dangermouse).
MC: .... **KC 003**

Dangerous Friends

DANGEROUS FRIENDS.
LP: .... **MSQ 8701**

Dangerous Liaisons

DANGEROUS LIAISONS (1988 film soundtrack) (Various artists).
Tracks: / Dangerous Liasons (main title): *Various artists* / O Malheureuse iphigenie: *Various artists* / Beneath the surface: *Various artists* / Her eyes are closing: *Various artists* / Tourvel's flight: *Various artists*/ Concerto in A minor for 4 harpsichords: *Various artists* / Success: *Various artists* / Madame de Tourvel: *Various* artists / Valmont's first move: *Various artists* / Staircase, The: *Various artists* / Key, The: *Various* artists / Ombra mau fu: *Various artists* / Ombra mai fu reprise / the mirror: *Various artists* / Beyond my control: *Various artists*.
LP: .... **V 2583**
MC: .... **TCV 2583**
MC: .... **OVEDC 365**
LP: .... **OVED 365**

Dangerous Toys

DANGEROUS TOYS.
Tracks: / Teas'n pleas'n / Scared / Bones in the gutter / Take me drunk / Feels like a hammer / Sport'n a woody / Queen of the Nile / Outlaw / Here comes trouble / Ten boots (stompin') / That dog.
LP: **4654231**
MC: **4654234**

Dangerously Close

DANGEROUSLY CLOSE (Various artists).
LP: **3204 1**

Dangerously, Johnny

INTRODUCING JANE (See under Debuchias).

Danhill, Tom

RAGGED HANK OF YARN (Danhill, Tom & Glenn Walker Johnson).
LP: .... **FF 490**

Daniel, Goleman

MEDITATION.
MC: .... **PT 32**

Daniel, Louella

HOLD ON.
Tracks: / Hold on / It was your spirit / Glory to his name / Rescue, The / All glory be thine / Army of the Lord, The / Great creator.
LP: .... **MIR 5002**
MC: .... **ZCMIR 5002**

Daniels, Bebe

NOSTALGIA TRIP TO THE STARS 1920-50 (Daniels, Bebe & others).
LP: .... **MES 7030**

Daniels, Billy

AT THE CRESCENDO.
Tracks: / Them there eyes / Love is a many splendoured thing / Sway / Autumn leaves / My yiddishe momme / You were meant for me / Lady of the evening / If I should lose you / How deep is the ocean / I can dream, can't I / I live for you / Introduction and that old black magic.
LP: .... **PKL 5569**
LP: .... **T 1278**
LP: .... **GNPS 16**

Daniels, Charlie

DECADE OF HITS (Daniels, Charlie Band).
Tracks: / Devil went down to Georgia / South's gonna do it again / Stroker's theme / Uneasy rider / Let it roll / In America / Still in Saigon / Long haired country boy / Legend of Wooley swamp / Everytime I see him.
LP: .... **EPC 15587**

FIRE ON THE MOUNTAIN (Daniels, Charlie Band).
Tracks: / Cabello Diablo / Long haired country boy / Trudy / Georgia / Feeling free / South's gonna do it / New York City / Kingsize rosewood bed / No place to go / Orange blossom special.
LP: .... **CBS 31830**

FULL MOON (Daniels, Charlie Band).
Tracks: / Legend of Wooley swamp / Carolina / Lonesome boy from Dixie / No potion for the pain / El toreador / South Sea song / Dance gypsy dance / Money / In America.
LP: .... **EPC 84461**

ME AND THE BOYS (Daniels, Charlie Band).
Tracks: / Me and 4he boys / Still hurtin' me / Talking to the moon / Class of 63 / American farmer / M.I.A. / American rock 'n' roll / Ever changing lady / Louisiana fai dodo / Drinkin' my baby goodbye.
LP: .... **EPC 26700**
MC: **40 26700**

MILLION MILE REFLECTIONS (Daniels, Charlie Band).
Tracks: / Passing lane / Blue star / Jitterbug / Behind your eyes / Reflections / Devil went down to Georgia / Mississippi / Blind man / Rainbow ride.
LP: .... **EPC 83446**

NIGHT RIDER (Daniels, Charlie Band).
Tracks: / Texas / Willie Jones / Franklin Limestone / Evil / Everything is kinda alright / Funky funky / Birmingham blues / Damn good cowboy / Tomorrow's gonna be another day.
LP: .... **KSLP 7009**

POWDER KEG (Daniels, Charlie Band).
LP: **4600341**
MC: **4600344**

SIMPLE MAN (Daniels, Charlie Band).
Tracks: / What this world needs is a few more rednecks / Was it 26 / Oh Atlanta / Midnight wind / Saturday night down South / Play me some fiddle / Simple man / Old rock 'n' roller / Mister DJ / It's my life.
LP: **4664951**
MC: **4664954**

VOLUNTEER JAM VI (Daniels, Charlie Band).
Tracks: / Rich kids / New Orleans ladies / Night they drove old Dixie down / Same old story / Funky junky / Amazing grace / Will the circle be unbroken / Keep on smilin' / So long / Down home blues / Carol / Do the funky chicken / Lady luck.
2LP: .... **EPC 22107**

WINDOWS (Daniels, Charlie Band).
Tracks: / Still in action / Ain't no ramblers anymore / Lady in red / We had it all one time / Partyin' gal / Ragin' cajun / Makes you want to go home / Blowing along with the wind / Nashville moon / Universal hand.
LP: .... **EPC 85443**

Daniels, Chris

THAT'S WHAT I LIKE ABOUT THE SOUTH (Daniels, Chris & The Kings).
LP: .... **PRL 70171**

Daniels, Dee

LETS TALK BUSINESS.
MC: **740274**

Daniels, Dennis

SOMETHING BIG.
LP: .... **MBC JAZZ 300**

Daniels, Eddie

BLACKWOOD.
LP: .... **GRP 95841**
MC: .... **GRP 95844**

BREAKTHROUGH.
Tracks: / Solfeggietto / Metamorphosis / Circle dance / Aja's theme / Divertimento / Concerto for jazz concerto / Allegro / Adagio / Presto.
LP: .... **GRP 91024**
MC: .... **C 1024**

BRIEF ENCOUNTER.
Tracks: / Brief encounter / Child is born, A / Path, The / Sway / There is no greater love / Ligia.
LP: .... **MR 5154**

MEMO'S FROM PARADISE.
Tracks: / Spectralight / Dreaming / Heartline / Love of my life / Homecoming / Memo's from Paradise / Seventh Heaven / Capriccio twilight / Impressions from ancient dreams / Flight of the dove / Eight-pointed star (Bonus track on CD only.).
LP: .... **GRP 91050**
MC: .... **GRPM 91050**

NEPENTHE (NO SORROW).
Tracks: / Sun dance / Equinox / Nepenthe / Waltz of another colour / Suenos (dreams) / Chaser / Only one, The / Chant / Quiet space / Reverie for a rainy day (Available on CD only) / Soul eyes (Available on CD only).
LP: .... **GRP 96071**
MC: .... **GRP 96074**

SING SING SING (See under Pizzarelli, John Jr).

THIS IS NOW.
Tracks: / 34 skidoo / It was always you / How my heart sings / New thing, A / Soft shoe for Thad / Double image / Cry / 3 and 1 / All the stars are out / In a sentimental mood / That was then.... This is now / Body and soul.
LP: .... **GRP 96351**
MC: .... **GRP 96354**

TO BIRD WITH LOVE.
Tracks: / She rote / East of the sun / Just friends / Old folks / Little suede shoes / Passport / Repitition / This is the time.
LP: .... **GRP 91034**
MC: .... **GRPM 91034**

Daniels, Joe

STEPPIN' OUT TO SWING (Daniels, Joe & His Hotshots).
Tracks: / Good to me / Steppin' out to swing / Southern fried / Eep-ipe wanna piece of pie / Whirlwind / Abbey road hop / Red light / Red robin rag / Fats in the fire / When you're smiling / Lady be good / Time on my hands / Down beat / Canzonetta / Snug as a bug / Alike as two peas / Shandy / Don't be that way / It's the talk of the town / Nice going.
LP: .... **SVL 167**

SWING HIGH, SWING LOW 1935-37.
Tracks: / I got rhythm / It don't mean a thing / Chinatown my chinatown / Twelfth St. rag / Wabash blues / Swing high, swing low / After you've gone / Big boy blues / Sheik of Araby, The / In the shade of the old apple tree / Farewell blues / Who / I can't give you anything but love / Drummer goes to town.
LP: .... **HQ 3023**

Daniels, Julius

ATLANTA BLUES (1927-30) (Daniels, Julius & Lil McClintock).
Tracks: / My mama was a sailor / Ninety nine year blues / I'm gonna tell God how you doin' / Slippin' and slidin' up the golden street / Can't put the bridle on that mule this mornin' / Richmond blues / Crow Jane blues / Furniture man / Don't think I'm Santa Claus / Sow good seeds / Mother called her child to her dying bed.
LP: .... **MSE 219**

Daniels, Maxine

BEAUTIFUL FRIENDSHIP, A (Daniels, Maxine & Ted Taylor Trio).
Tracks: / I got it bad and that ain't good / I'm always chasing rainbows / Foggy day, A / I can't give you anything but love / Dancing on the ceiling.
MC: .... **MAXAM 001**

EVERY NIGHT ABOUT THIS TIME.
LP: .... **CLGLP 007**

MAXINE DANIELS.
LP: .... **MC 589**

MAXINE DANIELS.
Tracks: / Saturday night is the loneliest night of ... / All the things you are / How about me / But not for me / I'm gonna lock my heart / Love walked in / I got rhythm / Heather on the hill / Long ago and far away / You're driving me crazy / P.S. I love you / Way you look tonight, the / That's all.
MC: .... **ZCLG 023**
LP: .... **CLGLP 023**

POCKET FULL OF DREAMS.
Tracks: / I've got a pocketful of dreams / With you in mind / Deep purple / Seems like old times / Change partners / Sunshine of love / Something 'bout you baby / When you wish upon a star / Leaning on a lamp post / Into each life some rain must fall / Broken doll / For all we know / Over the rainbow / Talk to the animals.
LP: .... **CLGLP 016**
MC: .... **ZCLG 016**

Daniels, Mike

1957-1959 (Daniels, Mike Delta Jazzmen).
Tracks: / Milenberg joys / You're just my type / At a Georgia camp meeting / Riverboat shuffle / Weather bird rag / Baby doll / Aunt Hagar's blues / I'm confessin' / You made me love you / Blues are brewin' / When you and I were young, Maggie / That's my weakness now / Don't forget to mess around.
LP: .... **HQ 3007**

Daniels, Paul

PAUL DANIELS MAGIC SHOW (Paul Daniels explains some of his magic tricks).
LP: .... **REB 434**

Daniels, Phil

PHIL DANIELS & THE CROSS (Daniels, Phil & The Cross).
Tracks: / Penultimate person / Pond / Welcome to the party / Class enemy / Free you / Lost romance / Kill another night / Shout across the river / Stop watch / News at ten / Wet day in London / Cromer aroma.
MLP: .... **PL 25259**

Daniels, Philip

ALIBI OF GUILT.
MC: .... **SOUND 9**

GOLDMINE LONDON W1 (Chambers, Peter).
MCSET: .... **SOUND 3**

Daniels, Roly

BEST OF ROLY DANIELS.
LP: .... **HPE 646**

CLASSIC LOVE SONGS.
2LP: .... **HM 036D**

I CAN FLY HIGHER.
Tracks: / Wind beneath my wings / She's gonna win your heart / Part of me / Hey Lord it's me / More of you / Touch me / Only a lonely heart knows / If all the magic is gone / I'm the one who's breaking up / Seven Spanish angels / Let's leave the lights on tonight / Womans touch, A.
LP: MINT 14
MC: KMINT 14

I WISH YOU LOVE.
Tracks: / Sometimes when we touch / Someone I ain't / I will love you all my life / You've lost that lovin' feeling / Hello Darlin' / Rest your love on me / Stand by me / What's forever for? / I will always love you / Together again / He stopped loving her today / Happy the clown.
LP: MINT 12
MC: KMINT 12

LAST CHEATER'S WALTZ.
Tracks: / Do you wanna go to Heaven? / I feel like loving you again / Lying blue eyes / In memory of a memory / Foolish feelings / Girls, women, and ladies / Last cheater's waltz, The / She can't say that anymore / I don't wanna lose you / One in a million / Tennessee waltz / No one but you.
LP: JULEP 26
MC: KJULEP 26

LET'S FALL IN LOVE.
Tracks: / Ain't no California / If you've got ten minutes-lets fall in love / Friend, lover, wife / Almost someone / Your eyes / Normal crazy person / Do you ever fool around / Mr. Jones / Heart on fire / Devil went down to Georgia, The / I'm comin' home mama / Sweet love.
LP: BER 002
MC: KBER 002

ROLY DANIELS' GREATEST HITS.
Tracks: / Last cheater's waltz, The / Wind beneath my wings / I will love you all my life / Mr. Jones / She can't say that anymore / He stopped loving her today / Hello darlin' / Do you wanna go to heaven / Seven Spanish angels / Part of me / Hearts on fire / Sometimes when we touch / Love don't come any better than this / If all the magic is gone.
LP: ERTV 4
MC: ERTVC 4

Daniels, Trevor

TIME WAS....
Tracks: / Girl from Southend On Sea / Who can I turn to / What I did for love / Lisa / Nightingale sang in Berkeley Square, A / You only live twice / Watch what happens / Chi mai / Close to you / Memory / Rise / Time was... / Bluesette / Quiet nights of quiet stars / Arrival of the Queen of Sheba, The.
LP: GRS 1113

Danielson, Palle

TRILOGUE-LIVE (See under Mangelsdorff, Albert) (Danielson, Palle/ Mangelsdorff/Pastorius).

WIDE POINT, THE (See under Mangelsdorff) (Danielson/Mangelsdorff/ Jones).

Danish Accordion...

MARCHENFARBEN (Danish Accordion Ensemble).
Tracks: / Abendied and Marchenfarben / Introduction and tocatta(per norgard) / Dansk rapsodi / Anno and Mikko.
LP: SLP 1637

Danish Jazz

DANISH JAZZ VOL.1 (See under Ewans, Kai).

DANISH JAZZ VOL.2 (See under Mathisen, Leo).

DANISH JAZZ VOL.3 (See under Jensen, Theis).

DANISH JAZZ VOL.4 (See under Johansen, Henrik).

DANISH JAZZ VOL.5 (See under Rasmussen, Peter).

DANISH JAZZ VOL.6 (See under Asmussen, Svend).

DANISH JAZZ VOL.7 (See under Bentzon, Adrian).

DANISH JAZZ VOL.8 (See under Bue, Papa).

Danish Radio Big Band

BY JONES, I THINK WE'VE GOT IT.
LP: MLP 15629

CRACKDOWN (1st UK tour (1987)).
Tracks: / Mr CT / Vismanden / Ballad for Benny / Crackdown / From one to another / Say it / Malus scorpio ritus / Cherry juice / Big dipper.
LP: HEP 2041

GOOD TIME WAS HAD BY ALL, A (Danish Radio Big Band & Thad Jones).
LP: MLP 15644

Danko, Harold

INK AND WATER.
Tracks: / Snow blossoms / Sand storms / Dew and petals / High mountain pines / Children's walking song / Footbridge over the rushing stream / Animals on a four-screen landscape / Leaves in a rock garden / Play song / Across the cliffs / Sunrise watch / Walk at dawn / Willow, wind and water / Roots and vines / Icicles in the cave / Reflections in a pond.
LP: SSC 1008

MIRTH SONG (Danko, Harold & Rufus Reid).
LP: SSC 1001

Danko, Rick

RICK DANKO.
Tracks: / What a town / Brainwash / New Mexico / Tired of waiting / Sip the wine / Java blues / Sweet romance / Small town talk / Shake it / Once upon a time.
LP: ED 317

Dankworth, John

1953-58, FEATURING CLEO LAINE.
Tracks: / Experiments with mice / Somebody loves me / Honeysuckle rose / It's the talk of the town / I got rhythm / Idaho / I got it bad and that ain't good / Take the 'A' train / Big jazz story / Runnin' wild / Easy living / Get happy / You go to my head / Ain't misbehavin' / All Clare / I know you're mine / Adios.
LP: EG 2601871
MC: EG 2601874

ALL THAT JAZZ (Dankworth, John & Humphrey Lyttelton).
Tracks: / Just sittin' and a rockin' / Memories of you / Experiments with mice / Oo-be-doop / Runnin' wild / Hullabaloo / Big jazz story / Take the 'A' train / Adios / Jersey bounce / It's the talk of the town / Blues at dawn / Early call / Slippery horn / It's Mardi Gras / Creole serenade / Red beans and rice / That's my home / Looking for Turner / March hare.
2LP: DL 1200
MC: TCDL 1200

BOP AT CLUB 11 (Dankworth, John Quartet/Ronnie Scott Boptet).
LP: ESQ 315

FAIR OAK FUSIONS (Dankworth, John & Julian Lloyd Webber).
LP: RSR 1007
MC: ZCRRT 1007

GET HAPPY (Dankworth, John Seven & Cleo Laine).
LP: ESQ 317

GONE HITCHIN' (Dankworth, John Quintet).
Tracks: / First time, last time / Thigh boots / Gone hitchin' / Son of Sparky / Triple Tyne / Layoff / Silver ray / Key stone corner.
LP: RSR 2012
MC: ZC RRT 2012

HOMAGE TO THE DUKE (See under Christie, Keith) (Dankworth, John/Ray Nance/Johnny Hodges/Keith Christie).

IN RETROSPECT (see Laine, Cleo) (Dankworth, John & Cleo Laine).

LOVER AND HIS LASS, A (Dankworth, John & Cleo Laine).
LP: ESQ 301

METRO.
LP: RSR 2013

OCTAVIUS (Dankworth, John & Paul Hart Octet).
LP: RSR 1001

ROULETTE YEARS, THE.
Tracks: / Curtain up / Winter wail / Esso blues / International / Desperate Dan / Blue furs / Tribute to Chanucy / Slo twain / Dauphine blues / Honey dew melon / Joe and ol's blues / Caribe / Kool Kate / New Forest / When my sugar walks down the street / Avengers, The / Cannonball / Sack o'woe.
MC: TCROU 1034

STARBURST (see Midland Youth Jazz Orchestra) (Dankworth, John & The Midland Youth Jazz Orchestra).

SYMPHONIC FUSIONS (Dankworth, John & The London Symphony Orchestra).
Tracks: / Every time we say goodbye / Decline and fall of a bridge / Afterglow / Sing, sing, sing / Further experiments with mice / Shadow of your smile / African waltz / Fantasia enigma / Paganini in perpetuo.
LP: SHM 3191
MC: HSC 3191

VINTAGE YEARS, THE.
MC: RSK 2014

WHAT THE DICKENS? (Dankworth, John & His Orchestra).
Tracks: / Prologue / Weller never did / Little Nell / Infant phenomenon / Damdest little fascinator / Dotheboys hall / Ghosts / David and the bloaters / Please sir I want some more / Artful Dodger, The / Waiting for something to turn up / Dodson and Fogg / Pickwick Club / Sgt. Buzfuz.
LP: RSR 2010

ZODIAC VARIATIONS (Dankworth, John & His Orchestra).
Tracks: / Way with the stars / Aquarius / Pisces / Aries / Taurus / Gemini / Cancer / Leo / Virgo / Libra / Scorpio / Sagittarius / Capricorn and Coda.
LP: RSR 2011

Dann, Colin (aut)

ANIMALS OF FARTHING WOOD (See under Animals of Farthing...) (Gordon, Hannah (nar)).

Danniebelle

LET ME HAVE A DREAM.
Tracks: / Let me have a dream / Theme on the 31st (He can work it out) / Because I'm me, Jesus loves me / I'm a believer / Ordinary people / I'll be right there / We all need each other / God leads us along / It's freedom / You're the only one.
LP: BIRD 113
MC: TC BIRD 113

LIVE IN SWEDEN WITH CHORALERNA.
Tracks: / I got to the rock / That's what he's looking for / Day by day / Dialogue / Turn it over to Jesus / Instrumental praise / Sunshine and rain / Lord is my light, The / My tribute / He's the best thing that ever happened to me / You must open the door / His spirit is here.
LP: BIRD 116
MC: TC BIRD 116

Danny & Dusty

LOST WEEKEND, THE.
LP: ZONG 007

Danny & The Juniors

ROCK 'N' ROLL IS HERE TO STAY.
LP: 569

Danny Wilson

BEBOP MOPTOP.
Tracks: / Imaginary girl / Second summer of love, The / I can't wait / If you really love me (let me go) / If everything you said was true / Loneliness / I was wrong / Charlie boy / Never gonna be the same / Desert hearts / NYC Shanty / Goodbye Shanty Town / Ballad of me and Shirley Maclaine.
LP: V 2594
MC: TCV 2594
MC: OVEDC 387

MEET DANNY WILSON.
Tracks: / Davy / Mary's prayer / Lorraine parade / Aberdeen / Nothing ever goes to plan / Broken china / Steamtrains to the milkyway / Spencer Tracey / You remain an angel / Ruby's golden wedding / Girl I used to know, A / Five friendly aliens / I won't be here when you get home.
LP: V 2419
MC: TCV 2419
LP: OVED 297
MC: OVEDC 297

Dansan Orchestra

DREAM LOVER.
LP: DS 060

Danse Society

HEAVEN IS WAITING.
Tracks: / Wake up / 2000 light years from home / Heaven is waiting.
LP: 205972
MC: 405972
LP: PIPLP 024
MC: PIPMC 024

LOOKING THROUGH.
LP: SOC 886

SEDUCTION.
LP: SOC 882

Dante

DIVINE COMEDY, THE (Inferno cantos 1-6) (Richardson, Ian).
MC: CDL 51632

Dante, Steven

FIND OUT.
Tracks: / I'm too scared / Ready to love / Imagination / Candy / Real thing, The (With Jellybean.) / Love follows / Find out / Taking love to the limit / It's only love / Ghosts.
LP: CTLP 6
MC: ZCTLP 6

Dante & The ...

ALLEY OOP (Dante & The Evergreens).
LP: LP 1002

Danzig

DANZIG.
Tracks: / Twist of Cain / Not of this world / She rides / Soul on fire / Am I demon / Mother / Possession / End of time / Hunter, The / Evil thing.
LP: DEF 24208
LP: 828 124-1
LP: 838 487 1
MC: 838 487 4

LUCIFUGE.
Tracks: / Long way back from hell / Killer wolf / I'm the one / Devil's plaything / Blood and tears / Pain in the world / Snakes of Christ / Tired of being alone / Her black wings / 777 / Girl.
LP: 8463751
MC: 8463754

Danziger, Paula

CAT ATE MY GYMSUIT, THE.
MC: 1745

Daouda

LE SENTIMENTAL.
Tracks: / Mon coeur balance / Bouquet de fleurs / Maimouna / Je suis fatique / Yafa nema / Le sentimental.
LP: STERNS 1008

Dapogny, Jim

BACK HOME IN ILLINOIS (Dapogny, Jim Chicago Jazz Band).
LP: J 140

HOW COULD WE BE BLUE.
LP: SOS 1183

IF YOU DON'T I KNOW WHO (see under Leigh, Carol).

JIM DAPOGNY'S CHICAGO JAZZ BAND (Dapogny, Jim Chicago Jazz Band).
LP: J 120

VOLUME 2 (See under Leigh, Carol) (Dapogny, Jim & Carol Leigh).

Darby, Blind Terry

ST. LOUIS COUNTRY BLUES 1929-1937.
LP: BD 611

Darby, James

SOUTHERN REGION BREAKDOWN.
Tracks: / Snake dance / Sunday / Wanderer / Bombay shuffle / Amazing grace / Mountain laurel / I'm going nowhere / Overlander, The / 40 going North / Down yonder / Heartland / Southern region breakdown / Full house / Country ramble.
LP: PTLS 1093
MC: PTLC 1093

Darby & Tarlton

DARBY & TARLTON SING THE BLUES.
LP: OT 112

D'Arby, Terence Trent

INTRODUCING THE HARDLINE ACCORDING TO TERENCE TRENT D'ARBY.
Tracks: / If you all get to Heaven / If you let me stay / Wishing well / I'll never turn my back on you (fathers words) / Dance little sister / Seven more days / Let's go forward / Rain / Sign your name / As yet untitled / Who's loving you?.
LP: 4509111
MC: 4509114
LPPD: 4509110

NEITHER FISH NOR FLESH.
Tracks: / Declaration / Neither fish nor flesh / I have faith in these desolate times / It feels so good to love someone like you / I'll be alright / Billy don't fall / This side of love / Attracted to you / Roly poly / You will pay tomorrow / I don't want to bring your Gods down / And I need to be with someone tonight.
LP: 4658091
MC: 4658094

TERENCE TRENT D'ARBY: INTERVIEW PICTURE DISC.
LPPD: BAK 2145

TOUCH WITH TERENCE TRENT D'ARBY, THE.
LP: 839 308 1
MC: 839 308 4

Darc, Daniel

PARCE QUE (Darc, Daniel & Bill Pritchard).
LP: BIAS 100

SOUS INFLUENCE DIVINE.
LP: BIAS 111
MC: BIAS 111MC

Dardanelle

COLORS OF MY LIFE, THE.
LP: ST 217

DOWN HOME.
LP: AP 214

ECHOES SINGING LADIES.

LP: . . . . AP 145

GOLD BRAID.
LP: . . . . AP 32

TWO OF US, THE (Dardanelle/Vivian Lord).
LP: . . . . ST 231

WOMAN'S INTUITION, A (Dardanelle Quintet).
LP: . . . . AP 191

Dardis, Paul

BYE BYE LOVE (EVERLY BROTHERS HITS).
MC: . . . . VCA 110

Dare

BLOOD FROM STONE.
LP: 3953601
MC: 3953604

OUT OF THE SILENCE.
Tracks: / Abandon / Into the fire / Nothing is stronger than love / Runaway / Under the sun / Raindance, The / King of spades / Heartbreaker / Return the heart / Don't let go.
LP: . . . . AMA 5221
MC: . . . . AMC 5221

Darensbourg, Joe

BARRELHOUSIN' WITH JOE.
LP: . . . . GHB 90

PETITE FLEUR (Darensbourg, Joe & His Dixie Flyers).
LP: . . . . DJA 515

YELLOW DOG BLUES (Darensbourg, Joe & His Dixie Flyers).
LP: . . . . DJA 514

Dari, Luciano

BEN RACH AB SHALOSHTEM YECHAUD THAUBODO (See Hafler Trio) (Dari, Luciano/ Hafler Trio).

Darin, Bobby

AS LONG AS I'M SINGIN'.
LP: . . . . JASS 9

COLLECTION: BOBBY DARIN (16 golden greats).
Tracks: / I can't give you anything but love / Mack the knife / You'd be so nice to come home to / Love for sale / Bill Bailey won't you please come home / By myself / When your lover has gone / I have dreamed / Dream lover / Swing low, sweet chariot / Lonesome road / Alright, OK you win / Clementine / Some of these days / I got a woman / That's all.
LP: . . . . DVLP 2096
MC: . . . . DVMC 2096

DARIN 1936-1973.
Tracks: / I won't last a day without you / Wondrin' where it's gonna end / Sail away / Another song on my mind / Happy / Blue Monday / Don't think twice, it's alright / Letter / If I were a carpenter / Moritat.
LP: . . . . STMS 5062
MC: . . . . CSTMS 5062

FROM HELLO DOLLY TO GOODBYE CHARLIE.
Tracks: / Hello, Dolly / Call me irresponsible / Days of wine and roses / More / End of never / Charade / Once in a lifetime / Sunday in New York / Where love has gone / Look at me / Goodbye, Charlie.
LP: . . . . T 2194

GRAFFITI COLLECTION.
MC: . . . . GRMC 10

GREATEST MOMENTS.
Tracks: / Splish splash / Early in the morning / Queen of the hop / Plain Jane / Dream lover / Mack the knife / Beyond the sea / Clementine / Bill Bailey won't you please come home / Artificial flowers / Somebody to love / Lazy river.
LP: . . . . K 40547

HITS BY BOBBY DARIN.
Tracks: / 18 yellow roses / You're the reason I'm living / Hello, Dolly / If a man answers / Good life / Things in this house, The / Be mad little girl / Treat my baby good / I wonder who's kissing her now.
MC: 4XL 9087

LEGEND OF BOBBY DARIN, THE.
2LP: . . . . SMR 8504
MCSET: . . . . SMC 8504

OH LOOK AT ME NOW.
Tracks: / All by myself / My buddy / There's a rainbow round my shoulder / Roses of Picardy / You'll never know / Blue skies / Always / You made me love you / Nightingale sang in Berkeley Square, A / I'm beginning to see the light / Oh look at me now / Party's over, The.
LP: . . . . EMS 1150
MC: . . . . TCEMS 1150

THAT'S ALL.
LP: . . . . HAE 2172

THIS IS DARIN.
LP: . . . . HA 2235

TWO OF A KIND (Darin, Bobby & Johnny Mercer).
LP: 90484-1-Y

VERSATILE BOBBY DARIN, THE.
Tracks: / Days of wine and roses / Nightingale sang in berkely square / You'll never know / 18 yellow roses / I'm beginning to see the light / You're the reason why i'm leaving / Goodbye Charlie / Always / Sunday in New York / End of never / Softly as I leave you / There ain't no sweet girl / Look at me / World without you.
LP: . . . . ED 2606711
MC: . . . . ED 2606714

Dark

CHEMICAL WARFARE.
LP: . . . . FRESH LP 9

LIVING END,THE.
Tracks: / Living end, The.
MLP: . . . . FALL LP 005

Dark Angel

DARKNESS DESCENDS.
Tracks: / Darkness descends / Burning of Sodom, The / Hunger of the undead / Merciless death / Death is certain (life is not) / Black prophesies / Perish in flames.
LP: . . . . FLAG 6

LEAVE SCARS.
LP: . . . . FLAG 30
MC: . . . . TFLAG 30

MERCILESS DEATH.
LP: . . . . MS 8602

TIME DOES NOT HEAL.
2LP: . . . . FLAG 54
MCSET: . . . . TFLAG 54

WE HAVE ARRIVED.
LP: . . . . MS 8501

Dark City

DARK CITY.
Tracks: / Rescue me / Forever / Solid gone / Insecure / Come on over / Indecision / Untouchable / Rules of the game / Almost there.
LP: . . . . V 2388

Dark Crystal (film)

DARK CRYSTAL, THE (Film soundtrack) (Various artists).
LP: . . . . CBS 702 33

Dark Eyes (film)

DARK EYES (Film soundtrack) (Various artists).
LP: . . . . SBL 12592
MC: . . . . SBLC 12592

Dark Heart

SHADOWS OF THE NIGHT.
LP: . . . . RR 9849

Dark Of The Sun

DARK OF THE SUN, THE (see under Smith, Wilbur (aut)) (Smith, Wilbur).

Dark Shadows (tv

DARK SHADOWS II (TV soundtrack) (Various artists).
LP: . . . . DS 00001

Dark Star

ON TOUR.
LP: . . . . AALP 5003
MC: . . . . ZCAAA 5003

REAL TO REEL.
Tracks: / Voice of America / Rock 'n' roll heroes / Only time will tell / Spy zone / Homicide on first and last / Stadium of tears / Sad day in London town / One way love / Going nowhere / Two songs don't make a right.
LP: . . . . WKFMLP 97
MC: . . . . WKFMMC 97

Dark Star (Film)

DARK STAR (Film Soundtrack) (Various artists).
LP: . . . . CST 8043

Dark Throne

SOULSIDE JOURNEY.
LP: . . . . VILE 22

Dark Wizard

DEVIL'S VICTIM.
LP: . . . . FIST 8337

REIGN OF EVIL.
LP: . . . . SKULL 8386

Darkman (film)

DARKMAN (See Under Elfman, Danny) (Elfman, Danny).

Darkness

DARKNESS.
LP: 805253

DEFENDER OF JUSTICE.
LP: 805855

Darko, George

HIGH LIFE TIME.
Tracks: / High life time / Kaakyire mua / Children's song / Akoo te brofo / Medo menuanom.
LP: . . . . OVLP 509

MONI PALAVA.
Tracks: / Dance / Party freak / Obi abayewa / Ashewa / Adikanafo / Moni palava / Tell me.
LP: . . . . ABL 001

Darkside

ALL THAT NOISE.
LP: . . . . SITU 29
MC: . . . . SITC 29
LPPD: . . . . SITU 29P

Darktown Strutters

JAZZ THE WAY IT USED TO BE.
LP: . . . . TRL 026
MC: . . . . TC TRL 026

Darky, Tommy

FROM STORNOWAY TO BOTANY BAY.
Tracks: / Balmoral Highlanders, The / Dancing dustman, The / Dark Lochnagar / Bluebell polka.
LP: . . . . WGR 026
MC: . . . . CWGR 026

HAPPY WANDERER, THE.
Tracks: / Sailors delight / Australian ladies / Pride of Erin / Flowers of the forest / Snowbird / Silver threads among the gold / Finlays request / Morning has broken / Inverness gathering, The.
MC: . . . . CWGR 071
LP: . . . . WGR 071

HOMECOMING.
Tracks: / Braes of Mar / Rakes of Kildare / Caiora / Papa picolino / Maggie May / Heart of Scotland, The / Mari's wedding / Irish jaunting car / Miss drummond of perth / Road by the river / Red river valley / Balaich an lasgaich / Captain Carswell.
LP: . . . . LOCLP 1034
MC: . . . . ZC LOC 1034

UNIQUE ACCORDION SOUND OF...., THE.
Tracks: / Dark island / March hare, The / Accordion polka.
LP: . . . . WGR 008
MC: . . . . CWGR 008

Darlinda

DARLINDA REVEALS THE TAROT.
LP: . . . . KLP 38
MC: . . . . ZCKLP 38

Darling, Alvin

MOTHER CRIES, A (Darling, Alvin Celebration Choir).
Tracks: / I won't go back / You were there / You can't hurry God / I've been born again / Mother cries, A / I won't turn back never / See you better now / Twenty third psalm, The.
LP: . . . . MIR 5018
MC: . . . . MIR 5018MC

Darling Buds

CRAWDADDY.
Tracks: / It makes no difference / Tiny machine / Crystal clear / Do you have to break my heart / You won't make me die / Fall / Little bit of heaven, A / Honeysuckle / So close / End of the beginning, The.
LP: 4670121
MC: 4670124

POP SAID.
Tracks: / Hit the ground / Uptight / Big head / She's not crying / You've got to choose / When it feels good / Burst / Other night, The / Let's go round there / Shame on you / Spin / Things we do for love, The.
LP: 4628941
MC: 4628944

SHAME ON YOU (ALBUM) (Greatest hits).
LP: . . . . NTVLP 44
MC: . . . . NTVC 44

Darling, David

CYCLES.
LP: . . . . ECM 1219

EOS (see under Rypdal, Terje) (Darling, David/Terje Rypdal).

Darling, Gloria

GLORIA DARLING.
LP: . . . . BRL 4082

Darling Happy

DARLING HAPPY ANNIVERSARY (Various artists).
Tracks: / You're my best friend: *Various artists* / Hello, darling: *Various artists* / Stand by your man: *Various* artists / Wedding, The: *Various artists* / Turn out the lights (love me tonight): *Various artists* / I'd rather love and lose you (than never know your love): *Various artists* / She wears my ring: *Various artists* / Together again: *Various artists* / I can't stop loving you: *Various artists* / Happy anniversary: *Various artists*/ Could I have this dance?: *Various artists* / Save the last dance for me: *Various artists*.
LP: . . . . PHL 464
MC: . . . . CPHL 464

Darnell, Larry

I'LL GET ALONG SOMEHOW.
Tracks: / I'll get along somehow (parts 1 & 2) / For you my love / Pack your rags and go / My kind of baby / My baby don't love me / Sundown / Christmas blues / I love my baby / What more do you want me to do ? / Ramblin' man / Just tell me when.
LP: . . . . KIX 19

Daron, Mal

LADIES MAN.
LP: . . . . FHR 089

Darrell, Johnny

GREATEST HITS: JOHNNY DARRELL.
LP: . . . . GT 0048

Darren, Jenny

CITY LIGHTS.
Tracks: / City lights / All you got to do / Maybe I'm amazed / Hold on / If you loved me / Where did our love go / Sure sugar / You got the power / Loving you is sweeter than ever / Love potion no.9 / We had it all / Love you baby.
LP: . . . . DJF 20497

DEAR ANYONE.
Tracks: / I don't know the answer / I'll put you together again / You'd be amazed / Sleeping like a baby now / Shortcomings / What about us? / One sided love / Dear anyone / All rocked out / Don't stop him if you've heard it / Pandora / Why the panic? / Have you heard about Pandora? / I don't know the answer / Orange county / My turn.
LP: . . . . DJF 20541
MC: . . . . DJH 40541

JENNY DARREN.
Tracks: / Ladykiller / I got the feelin' / Too many lovers / Do it to me / I'm a woman / Good feeling inside / Wind talking to the pines, The / Boogie boots / Love and devotion / Hold on / Woman I'm supposed to be, The / Travelling down the road.
LP: . . . . DJF 20523
MC: . . . . DJH 40523
LP: . . . . DJF 20569

QUEEN OF FOOLS.
Tracks: / Heartbreaker / Use what you got / Burning love / I'm a woman (I'm a backbone) / So many people / Queen of fools / I keep it hid / Crying shame / Taking it for the love / Lay me like a lady.
LP: . . . . DJF 20547
MC: . . . . DJH 40547

D'Arrow, Philip

PHILIP D'ARROW.
Tracks: / Burn the disco down / I'm barely bruised / Same kind of woman / Hamburgers, cheeseburgers / Alias love / Moonlight bay / Fallen angel / Suburbian bliss / Wisdom, madness and folly / Rock and roll respectable.
LP: 2391406

Darts

6 TRACK HITS.
MC: 7SC 5056

AMAZING DARTS.
LP: . . . . DLP 7981

DART ATTACK.
Tracks: / Duke of Earl / Runaround / Don't say yes / Cuckoo / One off the wrists / Cool jerk / Don't hang up / Honey bee / Can't get enough of your love / Reet petite / Don't mess around with love / Don't look back / This is the night / Goodbye Brenda.
LP: . . . . MAGL 5030
MC: . . . . TCMAGL 5030

DARTS GREATEST HITS.
Tracks: / Daddy cool / Girl can't help it, The / Come back my love / It's raining / Can't get enough of your love / Peaches / Don't let it fade away / Boy from New York City / Let's hang on / Duke of Earl / Reet petite / Get it.
LP: . . . . MAGL 5037
MC: . . . . ZCMAG 5037
LP: . . . . SPR 8543
MC: . . . . SPC 8543

DOUBLE TOP.
Tracks: / Boy from New York City / Daddy Cool / Girl can't help it, The / Come back my love / It's raining / Make it / Too hot in the kitchen / Zing went the strings of my heart / Bones / Young blood / Late last night / Stay away / Sometime lately / Bells in my heart / Don't let it fade away / Get it / Shotgun.
LP: . . . . SHM 3087
MC: . . . . HSC 3087

EVERYONE PLAYS DARTS.
LP: . . . . . MAG 5020

Daruwala, Zarin

ORNATE STRINGS.
MC: . . . . . TCS 7448

Darwen Ladies Choir

DARWEN LADIES CHOIR.
LP: . . . . . CAS LP 006

Darxon

KILLED IN ACTION.
LP: . . . . . WBLP 2

Das Damen

ENTERTAINING FRIENDS.
LP: 04061 08

MARSHMELLOW CONSPIRACY.
MC: . . . . . SSTC 218
LP: . . . . . SST 218

TRISKAIDEKAPHOBE.
LP: . . . . . SST 190

Dash Rip Rock

ACE OF CLUBS.
LP: . . . . . MR 0014

Data

2 TIME.
LP: . . . . . JAMS 26

ELEGANT MACHINERY.
Tracks: / Stop / Richocheted love / Burning / Over 21 / Hooked up / Playing / In blue / Cubismo / D.J. / Blow.
LP: . . . . . DATA 1
MC: . . . . . DATA 1 C

OPERA ELECTRONICA.
LP: . . . . . JAMS 22

Data-Bank

CONTINENTAL DRIFT.
LP: . . . . . ARTY 2

SALAD DAYS.
LP: . . . . . ARTY 16

Datblygu

PYST.
LP: . . . . . OFN 12

WYAU.
LP: . . . . . ANHREFN 014

Datchler, Clark

RAINDANCE.
Tracks: / State of play, The / Drowning my sorrows / Crown of thorns / Close to the edge / It's better this way / Last emotion, The / Raindance / Heart of hearts / Tue confessions / Autumn years.
MC: . . . . . TCV 2622
LP: . . . . . V 2622

Daughter Of Darkness

DAUGHTER OF DARKNESS (Various artists).
MC: . . . . . VCA 020

Dave & Bobby

REGGAE SEGGAE, VOL 1.
LP: . . . . . STLP 1008

Dave & Dana

MORNING STAR.
Tracks: / Morning star / Mystery (born again) / I've left them all behind / Friend of mine, A / Seek him / Being myself / Picking up the pieces / He's not a rumour / Just a little while / Grand arrival.
LP: . . . . . PC 124

Dave Dee, Dozy...

BEND IT (Dave Dee, Dozy, Beaky, Mick & Tich).
Tracks: / Help me / I'm on the up / Hideaway / Shame / Hands off / Loos of England / Bang / Master Llewellyn / You make it move / All I want / Hair on my chinny chin chin / Bend it.
LP: 2872 117
MC: 43472 117

DEE, DAVE, DOZY, BEAKY, MICK & TICH (Dee, Dave, Dozy, Beaky, Mick & Tich).
LP: . . . . . STL 5350

DOUBLE HITS COLLECTION (See under Troggs) (Troggs/Dave Dee, Dozy, Beaky, Mick & Tich).

GREATEST HITS: DAVE DEE, DOZY, BEAKY, MICK & TITCH (Dave Dee, Dozy, Beaky, Mick & Tich).
Tracks: / You make it move / Hold tight / Hideaway / Bend it / Save me / Touch me, Touch me / Okay / Zabadak / Legend of Xanadu / Last night in Soho / Wreck of the Antoinette / Snake in the grass.
LP: 6438087
MC: 7251016
MC: . . . . . ASK 789
LP: . . . . . PRICE 61
MC: . . . . . PRIMC 61

IF MUSIC IS THE FOOD OF LOVE... (Prepare for indigestion) (Dee, Dave, Dozy, Beaky, Mick & Tich).
LP: . . . . . STL 5388

Dave & Sugar

DAVE AND SUGAR.
Tracks: / I'm gonna love you / Door is always open, The / Can't help but wonder / Whole lotta things to sing about, A / Queen of the silver dollar / I've been so wrong for so long / Fools / Late nite country lovin' music / I'm leavin' the leavin' to you / Queen of my heart.
LP: . . . . . RS 1079

DAVE AND SUGAR (2).
Tracks: / How 'bout us / Two broken hearts / Got my heart set on you / No secret anymore / My angel baby / Signal for help / Feel good with me / Take it from the heart / Don't walk away / Queen of the silver dollar.
LP: . . . . . IMCA 39050

GREATEST HITS: DAVE AND SUGAR.
Tracks: / It's a heartache / Queen of the silver dollar / Tear time / Golden tears / Door is always open, The / Don't throw it all away / Gotta quit lookin at you baby / Baby take your coat off / I'm knee deep in loving you / My world begins and ends with you / Can't help but wonder.
LP: . . . . . INTS 5112
MC: . . . . . INTK 5112

NEW YORK WINE & TENNESSEE SHINE.
Tracks: / New York wine and Tennesse shine / You / Make believe it's your first time / Things to do / Changing / Delta queen / It ain't easy lovin' me / Learning to feel love again / Just a whole lotta love / Love song.
LP: . . . . . PL 13623

STAY WITH ME/GOLDEN TEARS.
Tracks: / Stay with me / Golden tears / What I feel is you / Take a ride on a river boat / Why did you have to be so good / I thought you'd never ask / Don't stop now / That's how much I love you / My world begins and ends with you / Remember me.
LP: . . . . . PL 13360

TEAR TIME.
Tracks: / Tear time / It's a heartache / Gotta quit lookin' at you baby / We are the one / Tie me to your heart again / How can I stop my lovin' you / Somebody wake me / Nothing makes me feel as good as a love song / Baby take your coat off / Easy to love.
MLP: . . . . . PL 12861
MC: . . . . . PK 12861

THAT'S THE WAY LOVE SHOULD BE.
Tracks: / That's the way love should be / Don't throw it all away / Got leavin' on her mind / We've got everything / I'm knee deep in loving you / I love to be loved by you / Feel like a little love / It's a beautiful morning with you / I ain't leavin' Dallas 'til the fire goes out / Livin' at the end of the rainbow.
LP: . . . . . PL 12477
MC: . . . . . PK 12477

Davenport, Bob

BEES ON HORSEBACK (Davenport, Bob & June Tabor).
LP: . . . . . FRR 016

BOB DAVENPORT.
LP: . . . . . LER 3008

BOB DAVENPORT & THE RAKES 1977.
Tracks: / With my love on the road / Wild colonial boy / Ploughboy lad, The / Man in the moon, The / Patsy Geary's / Peeler and the goat, The / Princess Royal / Lakes of Coolfin / Jealous sailor, The / Jealous heart / Keep your feet still Geordie Hinnie / Three men went a hunting / Country dance / Three around three / Dowie dens of Yarrow, The / McCuskers no.1 (polka) / McCuskers no.2 (polka) / Jenny Lind / Slievegallion braes / Star of the County Down / Old green river.
LP: 12TS 350

DOWN THE LONG ROAD.
LP: 12TS 274

PAL OF MY CRADLE DAYS.
LP: . . . . . LER 2088

POSTCARDS HOME.
Tracks: / Byker hill / Blackleg miner / Durham goal selection / Gypsy poacher, The / Durham gaol / First time I saw Durham city, The / Ball of yarn / Breaking sticks / Wait till the work comes round / Winter time is coming in, The / Old changing way, The / When a man looks pale / There's nae much luck about the house / We plough and sow / Get up, stand up / Once I had as a true love / Lowlands / My bonnie lad / Great little army march / Unemployed men stand on the corner / McCafferty / I don't want to join the army / House is crammed / House is crammed / Good morning good morning / Our soldiers went to war / If I was fierce / If you want to find the colonel / They didn't believe me / Have you forgotten yet / When this bloody war is over.
LP: 12TS 318

Davenport, Cow Cow

ALABAMA STRUT.
LP: . . . . . PY 1814

COW COW BLUES.
LP: . . . . . OL 2811

COW COW DAVENPORT 1926-38.
LP: . . . . . BOB 7

COW COW DAVENPORT 1927-29.
LP: . . . . . DLP 557

Davenport, Nigel (nar)

ALL OUR TOMORROWS (See under All Our Tomorrows).

SNOW TIGER, THE (See under Snow Tiger).

Davenport, Wallace

DARKNESS ON THE DELTA.
LP: . . . . . SLP 512
LP: . . . . . GHB 146

Davern, Kenny

EL RADO SCHUFFLE (A tribute to Jimmy Noone).
LP: . . . . . KS 2050

IN A MELLO ROLL (see Wellstood, Dick) (Davern, Kenny Quartet/Dick Wellstood).

LIVE AND SWINGING (Davern, Kenny & John Peters).
Tracks: / That's a plenty / Man I love, The / Poor butterfly / Royal Garden blues / Blue monk / Love me or leave me.
MC: . . . . . CMJMC 001

LIVE HOT JAZZ (Davern, Kenny, Dick Wellstood, Chuck Riggs).
LP: . . . . . SLP 8077
MC: . . . . . SC 8077

ONE HOUR TONIGHT (Davern, Kenny Quartet/Dick Wellstood).
Tracks: / Elsa's dream / Pretty baby / Love is the thing / If I could be with you.
LP: . . . . . MMD 20148 A
MC: . . . . . CIJD 40148 Z

SOPRANO SUMMIT 2 (see under Wilber, Bob) (Davern, Kenny & Bob Wilder).

SOPRANO SUMMIT CONCERTO (see under Wilber, Bob) (Davern, Kenny & Bob Wilder).

SOPRANO SUMMIT - LIVE AT CONCORD '77 (See Under Wilber, Bob) (Wilber, Bob & Kenny Davern).

THIS OLD GANG OF OURS (Davern, Kenny & Humphrey Littleton).
Tracks: / Mood Hollywood / Porter's love song to a chamber maid, A / My mama socks me / Jackass blues / Undecided / Of all the wrongs you've done to me.
LP: . . . . . CLGLP 012

Davey, Shaun

GRANUAILE.
Tracks: / Dubhdarra / Ripples in the rockpools / Defence of Hens Castle, The / Free and easy / Rescue of Hugh de Lacy, The / Dismissal, The / Hen's march / Death of Richard-an-Irainn / Sir Richard Bingham / Spanish Armada, The / New age, The.
LP: . . . . . TA 3017
MC: 4TA 3017

PILGRIM.
LP: . . . . . TA 3011

David, Alan

ALAN DAVID.
Tracks: / Get your love right / Take it easy / Feel so good / Mainstreet / Life's a long way to run / Hold on to what'ya got / Dreaming / One and only love / Heartache / Angeline.
LP: . . . . . EMC 3365

David Copperfield

DAVID COPPERFIELD (see under Dickens, Charles) (Rodgers, Anton).

David & David

BOOMTOWN.
Tracks: / Boomtown / Rock for the forgotten, A / Welcome to the boomtown / Swallowed by the cracks / Ain't so easy / Being alone together / River's gonna rise / Swimming in the ocean / All alone in the big city / Heroes.
MC: . . . . . AMC 5134
LP: . . . . . AMA 5134

David Disco Dance

DON'T WALK GO (Go to a disco) (David Disco Dance Orchestra).
LP: . . . . . KM 12826

David, F.R.

LONG DISTANCE FLIGHT.
LP: . . . . . CAL 214

WORDS.
Tracks: / Words / Take me back / Someone to love / Porcelain eyes / Rocker blues / Givin' it up / Pick up the phone / Can't get enough.
LP: . . . . . CAL 145

David, Ian

I MUST JUST LEAVE A KISS.
Tracks: / I must just leave a kiss / Sail with you only / Our room / Let me at least stay in your heart / Power behind the throne / Latin calipso / Babe / My airline hostess (coffee or tea) / Chivalry and song / Now I find.
LP: . . . . . DVDA 1
MC: . . . . . DVDT 1
MCSET: . . . . . DVDCBS 1
2LP: . . . . . DVDDBA 1
MCSET: . . . . . DVDDBC 1

David & Jonathan

LOVERS OF THE WORLD UNITE (See under St Peters, Crispian/You were on my mind).

LOVERS OF THE WORLD UNITE (LP).
Tracks: / Michelle / Softly whispering I love you / You ought to meet my baby / This golden ring / Bye bye brown eyes / I know / Speak her name / Ten storeys high / I've got that girl on my mind / You've got your troubles / Lovers of the world unite / Laughing fit to cry / Be sure / Scarlet ribbons / Gilly gilly ossenfeffer katzenellenbogen by the sea / How bitter the taste of love / Every now and then / One born every minute / See me cry / She's leaving home.
LP: . . . . . CM 129

LOVERS OF THE WORLD UNITE (OLD GOLD) (See under Congregation - Softly whispering).

VERY BEST OF DAVID & JONATHAN.
Tracks: / Michelle / Softly whispering your name / You ought to meet my baby / This golden ring / Bye bye brown eyes / I know / Speak her name / Ten storeys high / I've got that girl on my mind / You've got your troubles / Lovers of the world unite / Laughing fit to cry / Be sure / Scarlet ribbons / Gilly gilly ossenfeffer katzenellenbogen by the sea / How bitter the taste of love / Every now and then / One born every minute / See me cry / She's leaving home.
LP: C5-507

David & Michael

CAMBRIDGE BUSKERS-ZWISCHEN PINTE UND PODIUM.
Tracks: / Die diebische elster overture / Turkischer marche / Drunken sailor / Hornpipe / Entertainer, The / Badienerie aus der suite / Bouree / Dance of the cuckoos / Minuett / Hora staccato.
LP: 2371 766

David & Sylvain

TOKYO DOLLS LIVE.
LP: . . . . . FC 018

David & The Giants

INHABITANTS OF THE ROCK.
LP: . . . . . MYR 1189
MC: . . . . . MC 1189

UNDER CONTROL.
LP: . . . . . MYRR 6825
MC: . . . . . MYRC 6825

Davidson, Billy

ON THE ROAD.
Tracks: / Out in the country / Bonnie Drummore / Song on the Anglo-Scots / O gie tae me a pint o' wine / Worn-out, flat top box / You're young my son / Let Ramensky go / Mountains of Mourne / Glasgow taxi-driver, The / Rolling hills of the borders / Land o' burns medley (instruments) / I'll keep going.
LP: . . . . . LILP 5039

STAR WARS OF DARKNESS AND LIGHT.
Tracks: / Star wars of darkness and light / Darkness and light / Fig tree, The / Good Friday / Just wanna tell you / Tribulation praise / If Jesus came today / Carousel / Sit still Christian / This is God / Greatest thing, The / It is finished.
LP: . . . . . PC 119

Davidson, Fiona

UAITHNE.
MC: . . . . . MR 1023

Davidson, Harry

OLD TIME DANCES, 1 (Davidson, Harry & His Orchestra).
LP: . . . . . DTL 3016

OLD TIME DANCES, 2 (Davidson, Harry & His Orchestra).
LP: . . . . . DTL 3017

THOSE WERE THE DAYS VOL.1 (Davidson, Harry Orchestra).
LP: DTL 3006

THOSE WERE THE DAYS VOL.2 (Davidson, Harry Orchestra).
LP: DTL 3007

Davidson, Howard

DISCOVERIES UNDERWATER.
Tracks: / B'Breath / Panarea / No one shall enter the ship / Aqua sub aqua / Isle Royal / Atocha / Truk lagoon.
LP: REB 677
MC: ZCF 677

Davidson, Jim

ANOTHER DIRTY WEEKEND.
LP: JDC 2

JIM DAVIDSON ALBUM, THE.
LP: WEF 1
MC: ZCWEF 1

JIM DAVIDSON LIVE...TOO RISKY.
LP: RCRL 1

TOO RISKY.
Tracks: / Eve of the war, The / Jim Davidson TV theme, The / Karn evil 9 / Fly me / Devil went down to Brixton / Alex / Too risky / Wand'rin' star / Windmill in old Amsterdam, A / 72.
LP: SCRL 5003
MC: SCRK 5003

YOU WON'T BE BLUE, WILL YOU?.
Tracks: / Close Encounters of the Third Kind / Once in a lifetime / Snooker game, The / Tonsilitis / At the airport / Gone with the wind / Happy birthday to you / Gertcha / London (part 1) / London (part 2) / Chalkie / Nick nick / M 6 way / Kung fu / Let the sun shine in / Pinball wizard.
LP: N 142
MC: ZCN 142

Davidson, Judith

GOING PLACES.
LP: LAP 107
MC: LAP 107 C

Davies, Allun

MUSIC FOR ALL (LIVE).
LP: GRS 1168

YOU'LL NEVER WALK ALONE.
Tracks: / You will return to Vienna / My dearest dear / So deep is the night / Serenata / When I grow too old to dream / You'll never walk alone / Serenade / If I only had time / Loveliest night of the year, The / Come back to Sorrento / Girls were made to love and kiss / I'll walk with God.
LP: GRS 1109

Davies, Anthony

HEMISPHERES.
Tracks: / Esu at the crossroads / Little Richard's new wave / Ifa: The Oracle / Esu the trickster / Walk through the shadow, A.
LP: GR 8303

Davies, Bobby

SING SONGS FROM THE TWO OF US (Davies, Bobby & Annette Hawes).
LP: SV 001

Davies, Carol

HEART OF GOLD.
Tracks: / It's in my genes / When my money's gone / Sexual favours / Sticky situation / Serious money / Dissin' Jerome / Thigh's the limit, The / Mirror mirror on the wall / Frown is just a smile upside down, A.
LP: K 9259031
MC: K 9259034

Davies, Craig

GROOVIN' ON A SHAFT CYCLE.
LP: ROUGH 132
MC: ROUGHYC 132

LIKE NARCISSUS.
LP: ROUGH 22

Davies, Dave

ALBUM THAT NEVER WAS, THE.
Tracks: / Death of a clown / Love me till the sun shines / Suzannah's still alive / Funny face / Lincoln County / There is no life without love / Hold my hand / Creepin' Jean / Mindless child of motherhood / This man he weeps tonight.
LP: PYL 6012
MC: PYM 6012

CHOSEN PEOPLE.
Tracks: / Tapas / Charity / Mean disposition / Love gets you / Danger zone / True story / Take one more / Freedom lies / Matter of decision / Is it any wonder / Fire burning / Chosen people / Cold winter.
LP: 923917 1
MC: 923917 4

DAVE DAVIES.
Tracks: / Where do you come from / Doing the best for you / Visionary dreamer / Nothin' more to lose / Imagination real / World is changing hands, The / Move over / See the beast / In you I believe / Run.
LP: PL 13603
MC: PK 13603

GLAMOUR.
Tracks: / Is this the only way? / Glamour / Reveal yourself / World of our own, A / Body / Too serious / Telepathy / 7th channel / Eastern eyes.
LP: RCALP 6005
MC: RCAK 6005

Davies, Dennis Russell

RITUAL.
LP: ECM 1112

Davies, Gail

GAIL DAVIES.
Tracks: / No love have I / What can I say? / Are you teasing me? / Bucket to the south / Soft spoken man / Someone's looking for someone like me / Need your lovin' / It's no wonder I'm still blue.
LP: KZ 35504
MC: KZ 35504C

GAME, THE.
Tracks: / Blue heartache / Game, The / Good lovin' man / Careless love / Love is living around us / Sorry that you're leavin' / Never seen a man like you / Drown in the flood / Like strangers / When I had you in my arms.
LP: BSK 3395

I'LL BE THERE.
Tracks: / I'll be there / It's a lovely world / Mama's gonna give you sweet things / Kentucky / Honky tonk waltz / Farewell song / Object of my affection / Get that feelin' inside / I'm hungry, I'm tired / Grandma's song / No one to welcome me home.
LP: BSK 3509
LP: K 56981

OTHER SIDE OF LOVE, THE.
Tracks: / I'm a little bit lonely / Happy ever after / Holdin' out for you / Someone like me / Love that could last, A / With a boy like you / Remember / I need my baby back / Other side of love / One more night with you.
LP: 94105

PRETTY WORDS.
Tracks: / Waiting here for you / I don't know why / Hearts in the wind / I've had enough / Somewhere tonight / Pretty words / It's just a matter of time / I'm ready to fall in love again / Meet me halfway / I will rise and shine again.
LP: MCA 42274
MC: MCAC 42274

WHAT CAN I SAY.
Tracks: / Boys like you / Following you around / On a real good night / Hallelujah / I love him so / What can I say / You're a hard dog (to keep under the porch) / It's you alone / If you can lie a little bit / Boy in you is showing, The / Setting me up.
LP: 23972-1
MC: 23972-4

WHERE IS A WOMAN TO GO?.
Tracks: / Lion in the winter / Diffferent train of thought / Where is a woman to go / Jagged edge of a broken heart / Not a day goes by / Trouble with love / Breakaway / Nothing can hurt me now / Lovin' me too / Unwed fathers.
LP: PL 81587
MC: PK 81587

Davies, H.G.

ALL IN THE GAME (See Miller, Paulette) (Davies, H.G. & Paulette Miller).

Davies, Jumpin' Jack

JUMPIN' JACK DAVIES.
Tracks: / Moonlight becomes you / Isn't it romantic / Darn that dream.
LP: T 974

Davies, Leslie

WHEN I FALL IN LOVE.
Tracks: / When I fall in love / She is gone / Can I have your number / I won't let you down / Say you wanna be my girl / Girl I never stop wanting you / In and out of love / Only you / Hooked on you girl / Dry your eyes.
LP: BBLP 0013

Davies, Oliver

VIRTUOSO CLARINETTIST, THE (see under Bradbury, Colin) (Davies, Oliver/ Colin Bradbury).

Davies, Ray

HOLLYWOOD HITS vol. 1 (Davies, Ray Orchestra).
LP: DS 072

I LOVE LATIN (Davies, Ray & Button Down Brass).
Tracks: / Adios mariquita Linda / La golondrina / Amor / Choo choo samba / La cumparsita / Pato loco / Punta prima / Pilar / Sweet and gentle / La bamba / Historia de un amor / Sway / Kiss kiss jive.
LP: DS 069

Davies, Ryan

CWMANFA GANU.
LP: BM 22

FO A FE.
LP: BM 28

RYAN AT THE RANK, VOL 1.
LP: BM 2
LP: BM 47

RYAN AT THE RANK, VOL 2.
LP: BM 48

Davies, William

AT THE ORGAN OF TATTON HALL, KNUTSFORD, CHESHIRE.
LP: LTOT 8420

DAY AT BUCKINGHAM, A (see under Brown, Jackie) (Davies, William/Jackie Brown/Robinson Cleaver).

EVERY NIGHT IS MUSIC NIGHT.
LP: CF 250

MUSIC FROM THE MOVIES.
Tracks: / Diane / Spitfire prelude / Charade / Wedding processional / Tara's theme / Exodus / Somebody loves me / I didn't know what time it was / I could write a book / Warsaw concerto / Thoroughly modern Millie / Summer place, A (theme from) / Summer of '42.
MC: AC 175

MUSIC FROM THE MOVIES, VOL 2.
Tracks: / Dream of Olwen / Harry Lime theme / Moonglow waltz from Murder on the Orient Express / As time goes by / Laura / Impossible dream, The / Apartment, The (Theme from) / Moonlight becomes you / Way to the stars, Theme from / 633 Squadron / Evergreen / March from things to come.
MC: AC 195

TROCADERO CINEMA ORGAN, THE.
LP: REC 349
MC: ZCM 349

Davies, Windsor

SING LOFTY (See under Estelle, Don) (Davies, Windsor & Don Estelle).

Davincis

EATING GIFTED CHILDREN.
LP: PMM 1

Davis, Andy

CLEVEDON PIER.
Tracks: / Women of Ireland / Jabe / 5 saxes / Hunger / Clevedon Pier / Basso symphonie / Over and over / Changes / Prelude / Clear dawns.
LP: LPMMC 1019
LP: 792 402 1
MC: TCMMC 1019
MC: 792 402 4

Davis, Anthony

EPISTEME.
LP: GR 8101
LP: GR 8102

HOMAGE TO CHARLES PARKER (See also Lewis, George) (Davis, Anthony & George Lewis).

I'VE KNOWN RIVERS (Davis, Anthony, James Newton & Abdul Wadud).
LP: GR 8201

MIDDLE PASSAGE.
Tracks: / Behind the rock / Middle passage / Particle W / Proposition for life.
LP: GR 8401
MC: GRC 8401

OF BLUES AND DREAMS.
Tracks: / Blues and dreams / Lethe / Graef / Madame Xola / Estraven.
LP: 3020

PAST LIVES.
LP: VPA 134

SONGS FOR A NEW WORLD.
LP: IN 1036

TRIO 2 (Davis, Anthony, James Newton & Abdul Wadud).
Tracks: / Who's life / Thursday's child / Eclipse / Kiano / Invisible island / 1st movement / 2nd movement / 3rd movement / Simultaneity / Flat out.
LP: 794 411
MC: 794 414

Davis, Art

REEMERGENCE.
LP: IP 7728

Davis, Ben

PARTY (Davis, Ben & The Past Hits).
MC: SENC 1082

Davis, Bette

MISS BETTE DAVIS.
Tracks: / They're either too young or too old / Life is a lonely thing / Until it's time for you to go / Growing older, feeling younger / It can't be wrong / I've written a letter to daddy / Loneliness / Mother of the bride / Hush hush sweet Charlotte / Speech from 'All About Eve' / I wish you love.
LP: PRS 1001

Davis, Billie

BEST OF BILLIE DAVIS, THE.
MC: CASSGP 004

TELL HIM (OLD GOLD) (See under Vernons Girls - Lover please).

Davis, Blind Joe

BLIND JOE DAVIS VOL 1 (The Incomparable).
LP: OL 2803

Davis, Blind John

BLIND JOHN DAVIS 1938.
LP: DLP 505

BLIND JOHN DAVIS WITH JEANNE CARROLL (Davis, Blind John & Jeanne Carroll).
LP: LR 42.056

IN MEMORIAM 1938.
LP: DOC 505

Davis, Carl

BEN HUR (See under Ben Hur) (Davis, Carl/Liverpool Philharmonic Orch).

CITY LIGHTS (See under City Lights).

COMMANDING SEA, THE (TV Soundtrack).
Tracks: / Golden Hind / Pipeline and underwater / Sailing from Plymouth and storm / Fair stood the wind for France / Prayer / Freedom ride / Finale ride / Oppenheimer / Investigations / Here comes the army / Glorious New Mexico / Old curiosity shop, The / Punch and Judy / Waxworks and the races / Respect the law / Malignant dwarf, The.
LP: EMC 3361
MC: TCEMC 3361

GLENLIVET FIREWORKS MUSIC (Davis, Carl/Scottish Chamber Orchestra).
MC: TCCFP 4542
LP: CFP 4542

MICHAEL COLOMBIER (See under Colombier, Michael) (Davis, Carl/ Michael Colombier).

NAPOLEON (Film soundtrack) (Davis, Carl/Michael Colombier).
Tracks: / Eagle of destiny / Teaching the Marseillaise / Reunion in Corsica / Pursued / Double storm / Drums of the 6th Regiment / Victor of Toulon / Bal des victimes / Tambourin / Acting lesson / Ghosts / Peroration / Strange conductor in the sky.
LP: CDL 1423
MC: ZCDL 1423

SILENTS, THE (Music to 10 silent movies) (Davis, Carl/London Philharmonic Orchestra).
Tracks: / Napoleon / Crowd, The / Flesh and the devil / Show people / Broken blossoms / Wind, The / Thief of Baghdad, The / Big parade / Greed / Old Heidelberg.
MC: VC 790 785 4
LP: VC 790 785 1

Davis, Carlene

CHRISTMAS REGGAE ROCK.
LP: PRL 1050

NO BIAS.
LP: FSJLP 003
MC: FSJMC 003

PARADISE.
Tracks: / Don't ever change / It must be love / Way old friends do, The / Stealing love / Making it through / His world, my world / Forever without you / Going down to paradise.
LP: OLP 1002
LP: DSR 3225

REGGAE SONGBIRD.
LP: RRTG 7703
MC: RRTGC 7703

TAKING CONTROL.
LP: PRL 1040

YESTERDAY, FOREVER, TODAY.
LP: VPRL 1030

Davis, David (nar)

BLACK BEAUTY (see under Black Beauty (bk)).

Davis, Eddie 'Lockjaw'

AFRO-JAWS.
Tracks: / Wild rice / Guanco lament / Tin tin deo / Jazz-A (samba) / Alma alegre / Star eyes / Afro-jaws.
LP: RSLP 373

BEST OF EDDIE 'LOCKJAW' DAVIS.
Tracks: / Wave / Lover / I'll never be the same / Chef, The / On a clear day / Angel

eyes / Telegraph / Land of dreams / Blue Lou.
LP: **2310 858**
MC: **K10 858**

CHEWIN' THE FAT.
Tracks: / Cherokee / Stompin' at the Savoy / Ghost of a chance / On Green Dolphin Street / Avalon / Wave / Tangerine / Oh gee.
LP: . . . . **SPJ LP 15**

COUNTIN' WITH BASIE.
LP: **500118**

EDDIE DAVIS AND HOT JAZZ ORCHESTRA (Davis, Eddy & The Hot Jazz Orchestra).
LP: . . . . **J 88**
LP: . . . . **J 67**

EDDIE DAVIS & STANLEY'S WASHBOARD KINGS - JAPAN (1983).
Tracks: / New Orleans shuffle / Was I to blame for falling in love with you / Sunset Cafe stomp / Hustlin' and bustlin' for baby / Doctor Heckle and Mr. Jibe / Sweet mama / Oriental man / Kiss me sweet / Dream man / Nuages / Sow a wild oat / Doin' ya good.
LP: . . . . **J 007**

EDDIE 'LOCKJAW' DAVIS FOUR.
Tracks: / This can't be love / I wished on the moon / Breeze and I / Telegraph / Land of dreams / Blue Lou.
LP: **2308 214**
MC: . . . . **K 08 214**

EDDIE'S FUNCTION.
Tracks: / People will say we're in love / You are too beautiful / All the things you are / Ladybird / Scotty boo / Tia juana / I wished on the moon / Ebb tide / Eddie's function / Out of nowhere.
LP: . . . . **AFF 153**

GRIFF AND LOCK (See under Griffin, Johnny) (Davis, Eddie 'Lockjaw' & Johnny Griffin).

HARRY 'SWEETS' EDISON & EDDIE 'LOCKJAW' DAVIS (See Under Edison, Harry 'Sweets') (Davis, Eddie 'Lockjaw' & Harry Sweets Edison).

HEAVY HITTER, THE.
Tracks: / When your lover has gone / Just one of those things / Old folks / Out of nowhere / Secret love / Comin' home baby / You stepped out of a dream / Jim dog.
LP: . . . . **MR 5202**

HEY LOCK!.
Tracks: / My blue Heaven / Bewitched, bothered and bewildered / Blues in my heart / Hey lock / I only have eyes for you / Chihuahua / Secret love / Nightingale / Metalmouth / Locked in / Hey Jim / Beano / Marchin' / I can't get started / S.O.S. / Jaws.
LP: . . . . **VJD 548**

JAWS.
LP: . . . . **OJC 218**

JAWS BLUES.
LP: . . . . **ENJA 3097**

MODERN JAZZ.
Tracks: / Dizzy atmosphere / It's the talk of the town / Leapin' on Lenox / This is always / Bean-o / I'll remember April / Moonlight in Vermont / Johnny come lately / You go to my head / Foggy day / Tenderly / Way you look tonight.
LP: . . . . **SING 506**

MPS JAZZ TIME VOL 8.
Tracks: / Again 'n' again / Tin tin deo / If I had you / Jim Dawg / When we were one / Gigi.
LP: **5C 064 61174**

OPUS FUNK VOL.2 (See under Edison, Harry Sweets) (Davis, Eddie 'Lockjaw' & Harry Sweets Edison).

RAREST SESSIONS OF THE '40'S, THE.
Tracks: / Surgery / Lockjaw / Foxy / Real gone guy / But beautiful / Black pepper.
LP: . . . . **FC 5009**

SAVE YOUR LOVE FOR ME.
Tracks: / On Green Dolphin Street / Oh gee / Speak low / Save your love for me / Good life / I wished on the moon / When your lover has gone / Bye bye blackbird / Call me / Day by day / Out of nowhere / Man with the horn, The / Weaver of dreams, A / We'll be together again.
LP: . . . . **NL 86463**
MC: . . . . **NK 86463**

STRAIGHT AHEAD.
Tracks: / Lover / Wave / On a clear day / Chef, The / Gigi / Last train from Overbrook / Good life / I'll never be the same / Watch what happens / Lucky so and so / I may be wrong but I think you're wonderful / Smoke gets in your eyes / Stompin' at the Savoy / Time after time / Secret love / It could happen to you / Slow drag.
LP: **2310 778**

MC: **K10 778**

SWEETS AND JAWS (Davis, Eddie "Lockjaw"/Harry Edison).
LP: **502601**

SWINGIN' TIL GIRLS.
LP: . . . . **SCS 1058**

TENOR BATTLES (See under Stitt, Sonny) (Davis, Eddie Lockjaw & Sonny Stitt).

THAT'S ALL.
Tracks: / Exactly like you / L'amour est une drole de chose / Pitch-tree thing, The / Out of nowhere / That's all / Chef, The / George / Satin doll.
LP: . . . . **GATE 7019**
MC: . . . . **CGATE 7019**
LP: **2400601**

UPTOWN.
LP: . . . . **ST 1021**
MC: . . . . **SC 1021**

Davis, Eddy

EDDY DAVIS & THE HOT JAZZ ORCHESTRA.
Tracks: / New Orleans shuffle / Because it's you that puts the music in my head / Minority blues / Rene's bar-b-que / Ragtime dance / Rocking chair / Blame it on the blues / China boy / My man / I can't believe that you're in love with me.
LP: . . . . **J 005**

Davis, Eunice

SINGS THE CLASSIC BLUES OF VICTORIA SPIVEY.
LP: . . . . **LR 42.016**

Davis, Geater

SAD SHADES OF BLUE.
Tracks: / I ain't worried about Jody / Your heart is so cold / I know my baby loves me / I'll meet you / Why does it hurt so bad / Whole lot of woman / Sad shade of blue / Will it be him or me / Long cold winter / I've got to pay the price / I'm gonna change / Two that sticks together / I'm so in love with you.
LP: . . . . **CRB 1132**

Davis, Hank

NEW YORK COUNTRY ROCK.
LP: . . . . **REDITA 115**

ROCK IN THE WOODS.
LP: . . . . **REDITA 120**

Davis, Jackie

JACKIE DAVIS.
LP: **1A 054 26474**

JUMPIN' JACKIE.
LP: **1A 038 85585**

Davis, James (2)

CHECK-OUT TIME (Davis, James "Thunderbird").
Tracks: / I'm ready now / You did me wrong / Hello sundown / Check our time / What else is there to do? / If I had my life to live over / Your turn to cry / Come by here / I should've known better / Case of love, A / Bloodshot eyes / Dark end of the street.
MC: . . . . **BT 1043C**
LP: . . . . **BT 1043**
LP: . . . . **FIEND 149**

Davis, Jimmie

BARNYARD STOMP.
Tracks: / Barnyard stomp / Doggone that train / Down at the old country church / Wampus Kitty Mama / Market house blues / Alimony blues / Midnight blues / Get on board, Aunt Susan / Shotgun wedding / Keyhole in the door / Bear cat mama from Horner's corners / She's a hum-dinger / She's a hum-dinger (part 2) / Out of town blues / Pea-picking papa / Woman's blues, A.
LP: . . . . **BFX 15285**

ROCKIN' BLUES.
Tracks: / There's evil in ye children, gather round / Red nightgown blues / Davis salty dog / Saturday night stroll / Sewing machine blues / Easy rider blues / Davis' last day blues (1982 blues) / High behind blues / Rockin' blues (Previously unissued.) / Home town blues / Tom cat and pussy blues / Organ grinder blues / Penitentiary blues / She left a runnin' like a sewing machine / Lonely hobo / Arabella blues.
LP: . . . . **BFX 15125**

YOU ARE MY SUNSHINE.
LP: . . . . **HAT 3121**

Davis, Joe

BIG BAND JAZZ 1940-1952.
LP: . . . . **HQ 2047**

R'N'B FROM JOE DAVIS 1952-53 (Vol 1) (Various artists).
LP: . . . . **KK 795**

R'N'B FROM JOE DAVIS 1955-56 (Vol 2) (Various artists).
LP: . . . . **KK 796**

Davis, John

AIN'T THAT ENOUGH FOR YOU? (Davis, John & The Monster Orchestra).
Tracks: / Ain't that enough for you? / Disco fever / I've got the hots for you / Bite of the apple, A / I'll be the music / Whatever happened to me and you?.
LP: . . . . **MLP 3002**

Davis Jr., Walter

URANUS.
Tracks: / Blackgammon / Night song / Cheryl / Just one of those things / Ronnie's a dynamite lady / Glass enclosure / Uranus / Bloosy (live).
LP: . . . . **PAL 15008**

Davis, Larry

FUNNY STUFF.
LP: . . . . **R 2616**

Davis, Link

BIG MAMOU.
Tracks: / Big mamou / Pretty little dedon / Mamou waltz / Hey, garcon / Lonely heart / Time will tell / Gumbo ya-ya (everybody talks at once) / Falling for you / Crawfish crawl, The / You're little but you're cute / Mama say no / Every time I pass your door / You show up missing / Cajun love / Kajalena / Va t'cacher (go hide yourself).
LP: . . . . **ED 279**

Davis, Louise 'Candy'

BETTER THAN BLESSED.
LP: . . . . **MAL 04405**

Davis, Mac

20 GOLDEN SONGS.
LP: **20112**
MC: **40112**

IT'S HARD TO BE HUMBLE.
Tracks: / It's hard to be humble / Greatest gift of all / Let's keep it that way / It was time / Gravel on the ground / Tequila Sheila / I will always love you / Why don't we sleep on it / I wanta make up with you / I know you're out there somewhere.
LP: . . . . **NBLP 7207**

MIDNIGHT CRAZY.
Tracks: / Midnight crazy / Dammit girl / I've got the hots for you / You're my bestest friend / Comfortable / Tell me your fantasies / You are so lovely / Kiss it and make it better / Something burning / Float away.
LP: **6480 057**
MC: **7190 057**

SOFT TALK.
Tracks: / Caroline's still in Georgia / Good news bad / Patch of blue / Most of all / Soft talk / Springtime in Dixie / Nickel dreams / Put a bar in my car / Deep down / I've got a dream.
LP: . . . . **CANL 9**
MC: . . . . **CANLC 9**

TEXAS IN MY REAR VIEW MIRROR.
Tracks: / Texas in my rear view mirror / Hooked on music / Remember when / Me 'n' fat boy / Hot Texas night / Sad songs / Hello Hollywood / Rodeo clown / Secrets / In the eyes of my people.
LP: . . . . **NBLP 7239**

TILL I MADE IT WITH YOU.
Tracks: / I never made love (till I made it with you) / Too big for words / Shake, Ruby, shake / Rainy day lovin' / Regrets / Special place in heaven, A / Save that dress / I think I'm gonna rain / I feel the country callin' me / Sexy young girl.
LP: . . . . **IMCA 5590**

Davis, Martha

YOU'RE ON THE RIGHT TRACK BABY (Davis, Martha & Her Torrid Trio).
Tracks: / I'm fer it too / Same old boogie / Lovin' blues / Be-bop bounce, The / You're on the right track baby / Bread and gravy / Sarah Sarah / When I say goodbye / Cincinnati / Kitchen blues / Experience / No deposit no return / Honey honey honey / Ooh wee / Player piano boogie / What's become of you / I ain't gettin' any younger.
LP: . . . . **JB 1104**

Davis, Mary

SEPARATE WAYS.
Tracks: / Don't wear it out / Baby, baby (you ain't treating me right) / Separate ways / I'm gonna love you better / I get nervous / I wanna be sure / Some kind of lover / Have you been loved / Sweet obsession.
LP: **465 877 1**
MC: **465 877 4**

Davis, Maxwell

FATHER OF WEST COAST R & B.
Tracks: / Boogie cocktails / Bristol drive / Resistor / Belmont special / Cool diggin' / Rocking With Maxie / Tempo rock / Gene jumps the blues / Boogie cocktails / Flying home / Royal boogie / Jumpin' with Lloyd / Thunderbird / Bluesville.
LP: . . . . **CHAD 239**

Davis, Meg

CLADDAGH WALK, THE.
Tracks: / For Ireland I'd not tell her name / Castle of Dromore, The / Burning West Indies, The / She moved through the fair / Broom o'the Cowdenknowes / Claddagh walk, The / Lake of Ponchartrain, The / If I were a blackbird / 'P' stands for Paddy / Eileen Aroon / My Lagan love / Loch Tay boat song, The / Queen of May, The / Last Leviathan, The.
LP: . . . . **LILP 3005**
MC: . . . . **LICS 3005**

Davis, Meyer

MEYER DAVIS PLAYS COLE PORTER.
LP: . . . . **MES 6813**

Davis, Miles

1954- THE MASTERPIECES.
LP: . . . . **LPJT 55**

1958 MILES.
LP: . . . . **20 AP 1401**

AGHARTA.
2LP: . . . . **CBS 88159**
MC: **4678974**

AMANDLA.
Tracks: / Catembe / Big time / Jo Jo / Jilli / Cobra / Hannibal / Amandla / Mr. Pastorius.
LP: . . . . **WX 250**
MC: . . . . **WX 250 C**

AT BIRDLAND, 1951.
LP: . . . . **BEP 501**

AT BIRDLAND: MILES DAVIS (Davis, Miles Sextet).
Tracks: / Hot house / Embraceable you / Ouverturia / 52nd Street theme / Wee Chubb's blues.
LP: . . . . **BLJ 8023**

AT HIS RAREST OF ALL RARE PERFORMANCES: VOL 1.
LP: . . . . **KLJ 20025**

AT LAST (Davis, Miles & The Lighthouse All Stars).
Tracks: / Infinity promenade / Round midnight / Night in tunisia / Drum conversation / At last.
LP: . . . . **COP 001**

AURA.
Tracks: / Intro / White / Yellow / Orange / Red / Green / Blue / Electric red / Indigo / Violet.
2LP: **4633511**
MC: **4633514**

BAGS' GROOVE.
Tracks: / Bag's groove / Airegin / Oleo / But not for me (take 2) / Doxy / But not for me (take 1).
LP: . . . . **OJC 245**
LP: . . . . **PR 7109**
MC: . . . . **PRC 7109**

BALLADS.
Tracks: / Baby won't you please come home / I fall in love too easily / Bye bye blackbird / Basin Street blues / Once upon a summertime / Song no.2 / Wait till you see her / Corcovado.
LP: **4610991**
MC: **4610994**

BIRTH OF THE COOL.
Tracks: / Move / Jeru / Moon dreams / Venus De Milo / Budo / Deception / Darn that dream (CD only.) / Godchild / Boplicity / Rocker / Israel / Rouge.
LP: . . . . **CAPS 1024**

BITCHES BREW.
Tracks: / Pharaoh's dance / Bitches brew / Spanish key / John McLaughlin / Miles runs down the voodoo down / Sanctuary.
LP: **4511261**
MC: **4511264**
2LP: . . . . **CBS 66236**

BLUE CHRISTMAS.
Tracks: / Little Melonae / Budo / Sweet Sue / On Green Dolphin Street / Fran dance / Stella by starlight / Blue Christmas.
LP: . . . . **CBS 21070**
MC: **40 21070**

BLUE HAZE.
LP: . . . . **OJC 093**

BOPPING THE BLUES.
Tracks: / Don't sing me the blues (Take 1) / Don't sing me the blues (Take 2) / I've always got the blues (Take 1, incomplete) / I've always got the blues (Take 2) / I've always got the blues (Take 3) / Don't explain to me, baby (Take 1) / Don't explain to me, baby (Take 2) / Don't explain to me, baby (Take 3) / Don't explain to me, baby (Take 4) / Baby, won't you make up your mind?

(Take 1) / Baby, won't you make up your mind? (Take 2) / Baby, won't you make up your mind? (Take 3).
LP: . . . . **BLP 60102**

CARNEGIE HALL 1961 (see also under Evans,Gil) (Davis, Miles & Gil Evans).

CBS YEARS 1955-85.
Tracks: / Generique / All blues / Eighty-one / Blues for Pablo / Summertime / Straight, no chaser / Footprints / Florence sur les Champs Elysees / I thought about you / Some day my prince will come / Bye bye blackbird / My funny valentine / Love for sale / Budo / Miles / Files de Kilimanjaro / Fran dance / Seven steps to heaven / Flamenco sketches / So what / Water babies / Saeta / Masqualero / Pinocchio / Summer night / Fall / It's about that time / Sivad / What it is / Ms. Morrisine / Shout / Honky Tonk / Star on Cicely / Thinkin' one thing and doin' another / Miles runs the voodoo down.
LP: **463 246 1**
MC: **463 246 4**

CHARLIE PARKER & MILES DAVIS (See under Parker, Charlie) (Davis, Miles & Charlie Parker).

CHARLIE PARKER, MILES DAVIS & DIZZY GILLESPIE, VOL 2 (see Parker, Charlie) (Davis, Miles/Charlie Parker/ Dizzy Gillespie).

CHRONICLE: THE COMPLETE PRESTIGE RECORDINGS.
Tracks: / Ahmad's blues / Airegin / Bag's groove / Bemsha swing / Bitty ditty / Blue haze / Blue 'n' boogie / Blue room / Blues by five / Bluing / But not for me / Changes / Compulsion / Conception / Denial / Diane / Dig / Doctor Jackle / Down / Doxy / Ezz-thetic / Floppy / For adults only / Four / Gal in Calico, A / Green haze / Half nelson / Hibeck / How am I to know? / I could write a book / I know / I didn't / I see your face before me / I'll remember April / If I were a bell / In your own sweet way / It could happen to you / It never entered my mind / It's only a paper moon / Just squeeze me / Love me or leave me / Man I love, The / Miles ahead / Minor march / Morpheus / My funny valentine / My old flame / Night in Tunisia / No line / Odjenar / Old devil moon / Oleo / Out of the blue / Round about midnight / Salt peanuts / Serpent's tooth / Smooch / Solar / Something I dreamed last night / S'posin' / Stablemates / Surrey with the fringe on top / Swing spring / Tasty pudding / Theme / There is no greater love / Trane's blues / Tune up / Vierd blues / Walkin' / Well you needn't / When I fall in love / When lights are low / Whispering / Will you still be mine? / Willie the wailer / Wouldn't you? / Yesterdays / You don't know what love is / You're my everything.
LPS: . . . . **P 012**

CIRCLE IN THE ROUND.
Tracks: / Circle in the round / Two bass hit / Love for sale / Blues No. 2 / Teo's bag / Side car / Splash sanctuary / Guinevere.
2LP: . . . . **CBS 22132**
2LP: . . . . **CBS 88471**
MC: **4678984**

CLASSICS.
2LP: **88138**

COLLECTION: MILES DAVIS.
2LP: . . . . **CCSLP 243**
MC: . . . . **CCSMC 243**

COLLECTION: MILES DAVIS.
Tracks: / My funny valentine / So what? / Straight, no chaser / Milestones / Some day my prince will come / Autumn leaves / Oleo / Fran dance / Oh-leu-cha / Walkin' / Theme.
MC: . . . . **DVMC 2039**

COLLECTOR'S ITEM.
Tracks: / Compulsion / Serpent's tooth / Round about midnight / In your own sweet way / Vierd blues / No line / My old flame / Nature boy / There's no you / Easy living / Alone together.
2LP: . . . . **OJC 071**
2LP: . . . . **PR 24022**

COMPLETE AMSTERDAM CONCERT, THE.
LP: . . . . **CEL 6745**
MC: . . . . **CEL 6746**

COOKIN' AT THE PLUGGED NICKEL.
Tracks: / If I were a bell / Stella by starlight / Walkin' / Miles.
LP: **4606071**

DECOY.
Tracks: / Decoy / Robot 415 / Code MD / Freaky deaky / What is it? / That's right / That's what happened.
LP: . . . . **CBS 25951**
MC: **40 25951**

DIRECTIONS.
Tracks: / Song of our country / Round midnight / So near so far / Limbo / Water on the pond / Fun / Directions / Ascent / Duran / Londa / Willie Nelson.
2LP: **88514**

E.S.P..
MC: **4678994**

ESSENTIAL, THE.
MC: **4671444**

EZZ-THETIC (Davis, Miles & Lee Konitz).
LP: **1902119**

FILLES DE KILIMANJARO.
MC: **4670884**

FOUR AND MORE.
LP: . . . . **CBS 85560**

FRIDAY NIGHT AT THE BLACK HAWK VOL.1.
LP: **4633341**
MC: **4633344**

GET UP WITH IT.
Tracks: / He loved him madly / Maiysha / Honky tonk / Rated X / Calypso frelimo / Red China blues / Mtume / Billy Preston.
LP: **88092**

GOLDEN HIGHLIGHTS OF MILES DAVIS.
LP: **54733**
MC: **40 54733**

GREATEST HITS: MILES DAVIS.
Tracks: / Seven steps to Heaven / All blues / Some day my prince will come / Walkin' / My funny valentine / E.S.P. / Round midnight / So what.
LP: . . . . **CBS 63620**

GREEN HAZE.
Tracks: / Will you still be mine / I see your face before me / I didn't / Gal in Calico, A / Night in Tunisia, A / Green haze / Just squeeze me (but don't tease me) / No greater love / How am I to know / S'posin' / Theme, The / Stablemates.
2LP: . . . . **PR 24064**

HEARD 'ROUND THE WORLD.
Tracks: / If I were a bell / My funny valentine / So what / Walkin' / All of you / Milestones / Autumn leaves.
LP: . . . . **CBS 88626**

IMMORTAL CONCERTS (Konserthuset, Stockholm, March 22, 1960) (Davis, Miles & John Coltrane).
Tracks: / So what? / Fran dance / All blues / Theme / On green Dolphin Street / Walkin' / Theme.
2LP: . . . . **DRLP 129/130**
2LP: . . . . **DRLP 90/91**

IN A SILENT WAY.
Tracks: / Ssh peaceful / In a silent way / It's about that time.
LP: . . . . **CBS 63630**
LP: **4509821**
MC: **4509824**

IN EUROPE Antibes 1964.
LP: . . . . **CBS 62390**
LP: . . . . **F 1028**

KIND OF BLUE.
Tracks: / So what / Freddie Freeloader / Blue in green / Al blues / Flamenco sketches.
LP: **4606031**
MC: **4606034**
LP: . . . . **CBS 62066**

LEGENDARY MASTERS, THE (1960).
Tracks: / Walkin' (theme) / Fran dance / On Green Dolphin Street / So what?.
LP: . . . . **RARELP 10**

LEGENDARY MASTERS, THE (1948-1952).
Tracks: / Why do I love you? / Godchild / Moon dreams / Hallucinations / Darn that dream / Move (mood) / Conceptions / Opmet (out of the blue) / Chase, The / Why do I love you / S'il vous plait / Move / Max is making wax / Tune up / Bye bye blackbird / Rollin' blowin' walkin' / But not for me / Night in Tunisia / Fran dance / Godchild / Walkin' / It never entered my mind / Round about midnight / What's new / Blues for pablo / On Green Dolphin Street.
LP: . . . . **RARELP 08**

LEGENDARY MASTERS, THE (1956-1959).
Tracks: / Tune up / Walkin' / Bye bye blackbird / It never entered my mind / Rollin' blowin' walkin' / Round about midnight / But not for me / What's new? / Night in Tunisia / Blues for Pablo.
LP: . . . . **RARELP 09**

LEGENDARY MASTERS, THE (BOX SET) (Unissued or rare 1948-60).
LPS: . . . . **RARELP 08/10**

LIVE AT CARNEGIE HALL:MILES DAVIS.
Tracks: / Concierto de Aranjuez / Concierto de Aranjuez (part 2) / Teo / Walkin' / I thought about you.
LP: **4600641**
MC: **4600644**

LIVE AT THE PLUGGED NICKEL.
Tracks: / Walkin' / Agitation / On Green Dolphin Street / So what / Theme / 'Round about midnight / Stella by starlight / All blues / Yesterdays.
2LP: **88606**

LIVE IN 1958.
LP: . . . . **EBC 418**

LIVE IN COPENHAGEN, 1960 (Davis, Miles Quintet).
LP: . . . . **RJ 501**

LIVE: MILES DAVIS & JOHN COLTRANE (Davis, Miles & John Coltrane).
Tracks: / Green Dolphin Street / Walkin' / Theme / So what / Round midnight.
LP: . . . . **UJ 19**

MAN WITH THE HORN (Davis, Miles & John Coltrane).
Tracks: / Fat time / Backseat Betty / Shout Aida / Man with the horn, the / Ursula.
MC: **40 84708**
LP: . . . . **CBS 84708**

MILES AHEAD (CBS).
Tracks: / Springsville / Maids of Cadiz, The / Duke, The / My ship / Miles ahead / Blues for Pablo / New rhumba / Meaning of the blues, The / Lament / I don't wanna be kissed.
LP: **62496**
LP: **4606061**

MILES AHEAD (PRESTIGE).
Tracks: / Compulsion / Maids of Cadiz, The / My ship / Meaning of the blues, the / I don't wanna be kissed / Round midnight / Duke, The / Miles ahead / New rhumba / Lament.
LP: . . . . **PR 7822**
MC: . . . . **PRC 7822**

MILES & COLTRANE (Davis, Miles & John Coltrane).
Tracks: / Ah leu cha / Straight, no chaser / Fran dance / Two bass hit / Bye bye blackbird / Little Melonae / Budo.
LP: **4608241**
MC: **4608244**

MILES DAVIS (Walkman/Compact jazz).
Tracks: / Jitterbug waltz / Django / Wild man blues / Round midnight / Generique / L'assassinat de Carala / Sur l'autoroute / Julien dans l'asceseur / Florence sur les Champs Elysees / Diner au motel / Evasion de Julien / Visite du vigile / Au bar du petit bac / Chez le photographe du motel / Au privave / She rote / K.C. blues / Star eyes.
MC: **838 254-4**

MILES DAVIS 1945-51 VOL 1 (Early days, The).
LP: . . . . **LPJT 24**
MC: . . . . **MCJT 24**

MILES DAVIS ALL STARS AND GIL EVANS (Davis, Miles & Gil Evans).
LP: . . . . **BEP 502**

MILES DAVIS ALLSTARS (Feat.John Coltrane/Cannonball Adderley).
LP: . . . . **EB 409**
MC: . . . . **EBC 409**

MILES DAVIS, DIZZY GILLESPIE & CHARLIE PARKER (Davis, Miles/Dizzy Gillespie/Charlie Parker).
2LP: . . . . **VJD 529**

MILES DAVIS IN L.A., 1946.
LP: . . . . **SM 3717**

MILES DAVIS STORY.
LP: **4679581**
MC: **4679584**

MILES DAVIS & THE HI-HAT ALL STARS.
LP: . . . . **FS 280**

MILES DAVIS, VOL 1.
Tracks: / Tempus fugit / Kelo / Enigma / Ray's idea / How deep is the ocean? / C.T.A. / Dear old Stockholm / Chance it / Yesterdays / Donna / Woody 'n you / Woody 'n you (alt. take).
LP: . . . . **BST 81501**
MC: . . . . **TCBST 81501**
LP: . . . . **BLP 1501**

MILES DAVIS, VOL 2.
Tracks: / Take off / Weirdo / Woodyn' you / I waited for you / Ray's idea / Donna / Well you needn't / Lazy Susan / Tempus fugit / It never entered my mind.
LP: . . . . **BST 81502**
MC: **4BN 81502**
LP: . . . . **BLP 1502**

MILES IN PARIS (Davis, Miles Orchestra).
LP: . . . . **JAZZDOOR 1201**

MILES IN ST LOUIS (Davis, Miles Quintet).
Tracks: / I thought about you / All blues / Seven steps to Heaven / Trio, The.
LP: . . . . **VGM 0003**

MILES OF FUN.
Tracks: / Moose the mooche / Yardbird suite / Ornithology / Night in Tunisia / Bird's nest / Bird of paradise.
LP: . . . . **MAN 5028**

MILES OF JAZZ (Davis, Miles & Charlie Parker).
LP: . . . . **SJAZZ 7**
MC: . . . . **SJAZZC 7**

MILESTONES.
Tracks: / Doctor Jekyll / Sid's ahead / Two bass hit / Miles / Billy boy / Straight, no chaser.
LP: **4608271**
MC: **4608274**

MUSINGS OF MILES, THE.
Tracks: / I didn't / Will you still be mine / Green haze / I see your face before me / Night in Tunisia / Gal in Calico, A.
LP: . . . . **OJC 004**

NEFERTITI.
MC: **4670894**

NIGHT IN TUNISIA, A.
Tracks: / Embraceable you / Bird of paradise / Out of nowhere / My old flame / Don't blame me / Scrapple from the apple.
LP: . . . . **SJAZZ 2**
MC: . . . . **SJAZZC 2**

ON THE CORNER.
LP: . . . . **CBS 85549**
LP: . . . . **BGOLP 30**

PANGAEA.
MC: **4670874**

PORGY & BESS (Davis, Miles & Gil Evans Orchestra).
Tracks: / Buzzard song / Bess, you is my woman now / Gone gone gone / Summertime / Bess, oh where's my Bess? / Prayer / O Doctor Jesus / Fisherman / Strawberry and devil crab / My man's gone now / It ain't necessarily so / Here comes de honey man / I loves you, Porgy / There's a boat that's leaving shortly for New York.
LP: . . . . **CBS 32188**
MC: **40 32188**
LP: **4509851**
MC: **4509854**

PORTRAIT OF MILES DAVIS, A.
Tracks: / Bye bye blackbird / On Green Dolphin Street / Oleo / Autumn leaves / Sanctuary / Spanish key / Konda / Come get it / Jean Pierre / Decoy / Time after time / Something's on your mind.
LP: **4505931**
MC: **4505934**

PRE-BIRTH OF THE COOL (Davis, Miles & His Tuba Band).
Tracks: / Why do I love you? / Godchild / S'il vous plait / Moon dreams / Hallucinations / Darn that dream / Move.
LP: . . . . **BLJ 8003**

QUINTET.
Tracks: / 'Round midnight / S'posin' / There is no greater love / Stablemates / Budo / Just squeeze me / Vierd blues / So what.
LP: . . . . **LPJT 57**

ROUND ABOUT MIDNIGHT.
Tracks: / Round about midnight / Ah leu cha / All of you / Bye bye blackbird / Tadd's delight' / Dear old Stockholm.
LP: **4606051**
MC: **4606054**

SATURDAY NIGHT AT THE BLACK HAWK.
LP: **4651911**
MC: **4651914**

SEVEN STEPS TO HEAVEN.
LP: . . . . **CBS 62170**

SIESTA (Film Soundtrack) (Davis, Miles/ Marcus Miller).
Tracks: / Lost in Madrid part 1 / Kitt's kiss / Theme for Augustine / Seduction, The / Submission / Conchita / Lost in Madrid part 4 / Clair / Afterglow / Siesta / Lost in Madrid part 2 / Wind / Kiss / Lost in Madrid Part 3 / Lament / Rat dance - the call / Lost in Madrid part 5 / Ls Felez.
LP: . . . . **K 925655 1**
MC: . . . . **K 925655 4**

SKETCHES OF SPAIN.
Tracks: / Concierto de Aranjuez / Amor brujo / Pan piper / Saeta / Solea.
LP: . . . . **CBS 32023**
MC: **40 32023**
MC: **40 22146**
LP: **4606041**
MC: **4606044**

SOME DAY MY PRINCE WILL COME.
LP: . . . . **CBS 62104**

SOMETHIN' ELSE (See under Adderley, Cannonball) (Davis, Miles & Cannonball Adderley).

SORCERER.
Tracks: / Prince of darkness / Vonetta / Limbo / Masqualero / Pee Wee / Sorcerer, The.

LP: . . . . CBS 21143
MC: 40 21143

STAR PEOPLE.
Tracks: / Come get it / It gets better / Speak / Star people / U'un I / Star on Cicely.
LP: 25395

TALLEST TREES.
Tracks: / Bag's groove / Smooch / Miles ahead / Airegin / Oleo / But not for me / Doxy / Man I love, The / Swing spring / Blue haze / Round midnight / Bemsha swing.
2LP: . . . . PR 24012

TROIS GEANTS DU JAZZ (See Parker, Charlie) (Davis, Miles/Charlie Parker/ Dizzy Gillespie).

TUNE UP.
Tracks: / When lights are low / Tune up / Four / That old devil moon / Solar / You don't know what love is / Love me or leave me / I'll remember April / Walkin' / Blue 'n' boogie / But not for me / Bags' groove / Man I love, The.
2LP: . . . . PR 24077

TUTU.
Tracks: / Tutu / Tomaas / Portia / Splatch / Backyard ritual / Perfect way / Don't lose your mind / Full nelson.
LP: 925490 1
MC: 925490 4

UNIQUE VOL 2, THE.
LP: . . . . LPJT 43

WALKIN'.
LP: . . . . OJC 213

WATER BABIES.
Tracks: / Water babies / Sweet pea / Duel Mr.Tillman Anthony / Two faced / Capricorn.
LP: . . . . CBS 21136
MC: 40 21136

WE WANT MILES.
Tracks: / Jean Pierre / Backseat Betty / Fast track / My man's gone now / Kix.
2LP: 88579

WORKIN' AND STEAMIN'.
Tracks: / It never entered my mind / Four / In your own sweet way / Theme, The (take 1) / Trane's blues / Ahmad's blues / Half Nelson / Theme, The (take 2) / Surrey with the fringe on top / Salt peanuts / Something I dreamed last night / Diane / Well you needn't / When I fall in love.
2LP: . . . . PR 24034

WORLD OF JAZZ.
Tracks: / Yardbird suite / Cool blues / Lover's theme / Hot lips / Mr. Lucky.
LP: . . . . MAN 5022

YOU'RE UNDER ARREST.
Tracks: / One phone call / Street scenes / Human nature / Ms. Morrisine / Katia (prelude) / Time after time / You're under arrest / Then there were none / Something's on your mind.
LP: . . . . CBS 26447
MC: 40 26447

Davis, Nathan

LONDON BY NIGHT.
LP: . . . . HH 1004

RULES OF FREEDOM (Davis, Nathan Quartet).
LP: . . . . HH 1002

Davis, Ossie

TSHINDAO (Aarsema, Verna) (Davis, Ossie & Ruby Dee).
LP: 1499

UP FROM SLAVERY.
2LP: . . . . TC 2072

Davis, Paul

COOL NIGHT.
Tracks: / Cool night / You came to me / One more time for the lonely / Nathan Jones / Oriental eyes / 65 love affair / Somebody's gettin to you / Love or let me be lonely / What you got to say about love? / We're still together.
LP: . . . . SPART 1187

SONG OF CHANTER (Davis, Paul & Brian Vallelly).
LP: . . . . SOLP 1028

Davis, Peter

COME OUT FIGHTING GHENGIS SMITH.
LP: . . . . CBS 31544

SOPHISTICATED BEGGAR.
MC: . . . . ASK 791
LP: . . . . BBX 502

WHATEVER HAPPENED TO 1214 A.D. (see under Page, Jimmy) (Harper, Roy with Jimmy Page).

Davis Pinckney Project

YOU CAN DANCE IF YOU WANT TO (OLD GOLD) (See under Ollie & Jerry (Breakin')).

Davis, Rev. Gary

BEST OF GARY DAVIS IN CONCERT.
Tracks: / I'm going to sit on the banks of the river / Twelve gates to the city / Angels singing / Twelve sticks / It's a long way to Tipperary / I'll meet you at the station / Come down and see me sometime / Buck dance / Soldier's drill.
LP: . . . . SNKF 152

BLIND GARY DAVIS (at Allegheny College, Meadville PA, 1964).
LP: . . . . DLP 527

BLIND GARY DAVIS.
LP: . . . . DLP 521

CHILDREN OF ZION (IN CONCERT).
Tracks: / I'm going to sit down on the banks / Twelve gates to the city / I heard the angels singing / Twelve sticks / Tipperary / When the train comes along / Come down and see me sometime / Buck dance / Soldier's drill.
LP: . . . . HT 308

GOSPEL BLUES & STREET SONGS (Davis, Rev. Gary/Pink Anderson).
LP: . . . . OBC 524

I AM A TRUE VINE (1962-63).
Tracks: / I am a true vine / Lord stand by me / Won't you hush? / Mean old world / Moon is goin' down / Sportin' life blues / Get right church / Blow Gabriel / Slippin' til my gal comes in partner / Wall hollow blues / Blues in E / Piece without words / Whoopin' blues / I want to be saved.
LP: . . . . HT 307

LET US GET TOGETHER.
Tracks: / Oh glory / How happy I am / Cocaine blues / Death don't have no mercy / Let us get together / There's destruction in that land / Tired my soul needs a'restin' / Georgia camp meeting / Blues in A / Fox chase, The / You're gonna' quit me baby.
LP: . . . . SNKF 103

LIVE: BLIND GARY DAVIS 1964.
LP: . . . . WOLF 120.915

LO, I BE WITH YOU ALWAYS.
LP: . . . . SNKD 1

NEW BLUES AND GOSPEL.
Tracks: / How happy I am / I heard the angels singing / Samson and Delilah / Children of Zion / Soon my work will be done / Talk on the corner / Sally where'd you get your whiskey / Hesitation blues / Whistling blues / Lost John.
LP: . . . . BMLP 1040

O GLORY.
LP: . . . . AD 1008

RAGTIME GUITAR.
LP: . . . . HT 309
LP: . . . . KM 106

REVEREND GARY DAVIS 1935-49.
LP: . . . . L 1023

SAY NO TO THE DEVIL.
LP: . . . . OBC 519

Davis, Richard

EPISTROPHY/NOW'S THE TIME.
Tracks: / Epistrophy / Now's the time.
LP: . . . . MR 5002

FANCY FREE.
LP: . . . . GXY 5102

HARVEST.
LP: . . . . MR 5115

WAY OUT WEST.
Tracks: / Peace for Richard / Elephant boy / Do a dog a favour / On the trail / I'm old fashioned / Sienna:Waiting for the moment / Warm canto / Song of gratitude / Don't worry 'bout a thing.
LP: . . . . MR 5180

WITH UNDERSTANDING (Davis, Richard & Chick Corea).
Tracks: / Dear old Stockholm / Monica / Oh, my God / Rabbi, The / Baby sweets / Juan Valdez.
LP: . . . . MR 5083

Davis, Richie

LOVE SONGS.
LP: . . . . PSPLP 001

SUGAR MY COFFEE (See also Demon Rocka) (Davis, Richie & Demon Rocka).

Davis, Ronnie

RONNIE DAVIS SINGS FOR YOU AND I.
LP: . . . . VSLP 4040

Davis, Russell

WORLD OF BUDDY BOLDEN, THE (See under Lyttelton, Humphrey).

Davis, Ruth

YOU'RE GONNA GET NEXT TO ME (see under Kirkland, Bo) (Davis, Ruth & Bo Kirkland).

Davis, Sammy Jnr.

AT THE COCONUT GROVE.
LP: . . . . R 6063/2

BEST OF SAMMY DAVIS JNR.
Tracks: / That old black magic / Hey there / Stand up and fight / New York's my home / Earthbound / Love me or leave me / I'll know / Something's gotta give / Song and dance man / Someone to watch over me / In a Persian market / Five / Because of you / Happy to make your acquaintance / All of you / Lady is a tramp, The.
LP: . . . . MCL 1701
MC: . . . . MCLC 1701

CAPITOL COLLECTORS SERIES: SAMMY DAVIS JNR..
Tracks: / I don't care who knows / Way you look tonight, The / Please don't talk about me when I'm gone / I'm sorry dear / I ain't got nobody / Be-bop the beguine / You are my lucky star / Can't you see I've got the blues? / Dreamy blues (Recorded under the name Charlie Green.) / What can I do (Recorded under the name Charlie Green.) / Got a great big shovel (Recorded under the name Shorty Muggins.) / We're gonna roll (Recorded under the name Shorty Muggins.) / Smile, darn ya, smile / Dedicated to you / Azure / Inka dinka doo / Yours is my heart alone / Wagon wheels / Laura / Here lies love.
MC: C4 94071
MC: 794 071 2

COLLECTION: SAMMY DAVIS JR.
Tracks: / After today / Candy man / Fabulous places / Where are the words / All that jazz / I'm always chasing rainbows / Lonely is the name / We'll be together again / Every time we say goodbye / Going's great, The / If my friends could see me now / I'm a brass band / All the good things in life / People tree, The / Good life / Please don't take your time / Come back to me / I've gotta be me / She believes in me / At the crossroads.
2LP: . . . . CCSLP 225
MC: . . . . CCSMC 225

GREAT, THE.
Tracks: / That old black magic / Hey there / Something's gotta give / Stan' up an' fight (until you hear de bell) / Someone to watch over me / I'll know / Frankie and Johnny / Sit down you're rockin' the boat / Because of you (parts 1 & 2) (CD only) / Back track (CD only) / Glad to be unhappy (CD only) / Lonesome road (CD only) / Lady is a tramp, The / Song and dance man / Circus / Adelaide / New York's my home / Love me or leave me / Easy to love / All of you.
LP: . . . . MFP 5858
MC: . . . . TCMFP 5858

ME AND MY SHADOW (see under "Sinatra, Frank") (Davis, Sammy Jnr. & Frank Sinatra).

MOST BEAUTIFUL SONGS OF, THE.
Tracks: / West side story / Jet song / Something's coming / Cool / Tonight / A-me-ri-ca / Gee officer Krupke / Paris / What kind of fool am I / Falling in love again / I've got you under my skin / I'm a brass band / Sit down you're rockin' the boat / Another Spring / If I ruled the world / Sweet November / If my friends could see me now / Come back to me / Guys and dolls / That's for me / Hey there / Speak low / Tracy / Talk to the animals / Shelter of your arms, The / What now my love / Ten out of ten / Here's that rainy day / Too close for comfort / Bee bom.
LP: . . . . K 64014

SAMMY DAVIS JNR. IN PERSON, 1977.
Tracks: / I've got you under my skin / Bye, bye blackbird / I write the songs.
LP: . . . . PL 40591
MC: . . . . PK 40591

SONG AND DANCE MAN, THE.
Tracks: / Baretta's theme / Love is all around / We'll make it this time / Mary Hartman / My love / You can count on me / Song and dance man / I heard a song / Legend in my time, A / Snap your fingers / Chico and the man.
LP: . . . . BT 426

ULTIMATE EVENT, THE (VIDEO) (see under Sinatra, Frank for full details) (Davis, Sammy Jnr/Liza Minnelli/Frank Sinatra).

WHAT I'VE GOT IN MIND.
Tracks: / What I've got in mind / Come sundown / Mention a mansion / You're gonna love yourself in the morning / Smoke, smoke, smoke / Oh lonesome me / We could have been the closest of friends / Another somebody done somebody wrong song / Please don't tell me how the story ends / River's too wide, The.

LP: . . . . PRCV 120
MC: . . . . TC PRCV 120

Davis, Skeeter

20 OF THE BEST: SKEETER DAVIS.
Tracks: / I forgot more than you'll ever know / Set me free / Homebreaker / Am I that easy to forget? / (I can't help you) I'm falling too / My last date (with you) / Hand you're holding now, The / Optimistic / Where I ought to be / End of the world / I can't stay mad at you / I'm saving my love / Gonna get along without you now / He says the same things to me / Dear John letter, A / Fuel to the flame / What does it take to keep a man like you / There's a fool born every minute / I'm a lover (not a fighter) / Bus fare to Kentucky.
LP: . . . . NL 89522
MC: . . . . NK 89522

BEST OF SKEETER DAVIS.
Tracks: / End of the world / I can't help you (I'm falling too) / I will / Something precious / Now I lay me down too sleep / Gonna get along without you now / He says the same things to me / I can't stay mad at you / I forgot more than you'll ever know / My last date (with you) / Am I that easy to forget.
LP: . . . . NL 89319
MC: . . . . NK 89319
LP: . . . . CDS 1218
MC: . . . . CAM 1218
LP: . . . . INTS 5011
LP: . . . . LSA 3153

END OF THE WORLD.
Tracks: / End of the world / Silver threads and golden needles / Mine is a lonely life / Once upon a time / Why I'm walkin' / Don't let me cross over / My colouring book / Where nobody wants me (I want to go) / Keep your hands off my baby / Something precious / Longing to hold you again / He called my baby.
LP: . . . . NL 90001
MC: . . . . NK 90001

HOMEBREAKER.
Tracks: / End of the world / Gonna get along without you now / What does it take (to win your love) / Goin' down the road feeling bad / I forgot more than you'll ever know / Set him free / Homebreaker / My last date with you / Am I that easy to forget / I can't help you (I'm falling too) / I can't believe it's over.
LP: . . . . TOP 152
MC: . . . . KTOP 152

MORE TUNES FOR TWO (see Bare, Bobby & Skeeter Davis) (Davis, Skeeter & Bobby Bare).

SHE SINGS THEY PLAY (Davis, Skeeter & NRBQ).
Tracks: / Things to you / Everybody wants a cowboy / I can't stop loving you now / Heart to heart / Ain't nice to talk like that / Everybody's clown / Some day my prince will come / How many tears / You don't know what you got till you lose it / Roses on my shoulder / Temporarily out of order / May you never be alone.
LP: . . . . ROUNDER 3092
LP: . . . . FIEND 81
MC: . . . . ROUNDER 3092C

SINGS BUDDY HOLLY.
Tracks: / Early in the morning / Well...alright / True love ways / It doesn't matter anymore / Heartbeat / Think it over / Maybe baby / That'll be the day / Its so easy / I'm looking for someone to love / Oh boy / Raining in my heart.
LP: . . . . DT 33002

TUNES FOR TWO (See under Bare, Bobby) (Davis, Skeeter & Bobby Bare).

YOU'VE GOT A FRIEND.
Tracks: / Hello darlin' / Daddy sang bass / Angel of the morning / My colouring book / Place in the country / Son of a preacher man / If you could read my mind / I'm so lonesome I could cry / I can't seem to say goodbye / Today I started loving you again / He wakes me with a kiss.
LP: . . . . CDS 1173
MC: . . . . CAM 485

Davis, Spencer

2ND LP, THE (Davis, Spencer Group).
LP: . . . . TL 5295

AUTUMN '66 (Davis, Spencer Group).
LP: . . . . TL 5359

BEST OF THE SPENCER DAVIS GROUP (Davis, Spencer Group).
Tracks: / Back into my life again / Waltz from Lumumba / Together til the end of time / Keep on running / Trampoline / When I come home / Strong love / Somebody help me / She put the hurt on me / Goodbye Stevie / I'm a man / Gimme some lovin' / Every little bit hurts / This hammer.
LP: . . . . ILPM 9070
MC: . . . . ICM 9070
MC: 846 135 4

CROSSFIRE.
Tracks: / Blood runs hot / Don't want you no more / Love is on a roll / Crossfire / Private number / Just a gigolo / Careless love / Pretty girl is like a melody, A / When day is done / Hush-a-bye.
LP: . . . . ALE 5603
MC: . . . . ZCALE 5603

GIMME SOME LOVIN' (Davis, Spencer Group).
Tracks: / Gimme some lovin' / Keep on running / I'm a man / Midnight special / Every little bit hurts / Georgia on my mind / Searchin' / Somebody help me / Back into my life again.
MC: 4XLL 9055

THEIR 1ST LP (Davis, Spencer Group).
LP: . . . . TL 5242

Davis, Tyrone

CAN I CHANGE MY MIND?.
Tracks: / If you wanna keep him / Where have you been? / I gotta tell somebody / After loving you / Happiness / Your love is doggone good / You've become a part of me / I'll take you all the way there / Home / Seems like I gotta do wrong.
LP: . . . . MAN 5034

FLASHIN' BACK.
LP: . . . . FR 1003

I'LL ALWAYS LOVE YOU.
Tracks: / I'll always love you / Prove my love / Talk to you / Let me love you / Do U still love me / Can I change your mind / Woman needs to be loved, A / Mom's apple pie.
LP: . . . . ICH 1103
MC: . . . . ICH 1103 MC

IN THE MOOD AGAIN.
Tracks: / Give it up (turn it loose) / Close to you / All you got / This I swear / I got carried away / In the mood / Ain't nothing I can do / How sweet it is.
LP: . . . . CRB 1214

MAN OF STONE.
Tracks: / I'm in love again / You are the one / You make me feel so good / All of me / You're everything (I want in a woman) / I wanna talk love / I've got you (you've got me) / Serious love.
LP: . . . . TRPL 116

PACIFIER.
Tracks: / Turning point / Are you serious / Overdue / You can win if you want / Be honest with me / Let me be your pacifier / You stay on my mind / Where did we lose / One in a million / Sexy thing / More and more.
LP: . . . . TRLP 104

TYRONE DAVIS STORY, THE.
Tracks: / Can I change my mind? / One way ticket / Turning point / I wish it was me / After all this time / So good to be home with you / I had it all the time / Woman needs to be loved / Turn back the hands of time / Is it something you've got / Without you in my life / Have you ever wondered why / There's got to be a answer / You keep me holding on / I keep coming back.
LP: . . . . KENT 037

Davis, Walter

ABIDE WITH ME.
Tracks: / Abide with me / Crowded elevator / La strada / Biribinya / Nos states / Just one of those things / Pranayama / I'll keep loving you.
LP: . . . . YX 7528

BULLET SIDES 1949-52, THE.
LP: . . . . KK 7441

CRIPPLE CLARENCE LOFTEN & WALTER DAVIS (see under Loften, Cripple Clarence) (Davis, Walter & Cripple Clarence Loften).

LET ME IN YOUR SADDLE.
Tracks: / M and O blues / That stuff you sell ain't no good / Howling wind blues / L and N blues / Travellin' this lonesome road / Sad and lonesome blues / Minute man blues parts 1 and 2 / Sweet sixteen / Root man blues / Moonlight is my spread / Ashes in my whiskey / Think you need a shot / Let me in your saddle / Only woman, The / New come back baby.
LP: . . . . BT 2004

NIGHT SONG.
LP: . . . . YX 7550

WALTER DAVIS 1937-41.
LP: . . . . BOB 5

WALTER DAVIS VOL.1 (1935-41).
LP: . . . . BD 2084

Davis, Wild Bill

ILLINOIS JACQUET (see Jacquet,Illinois) (Davis, Wild Bill & Illinois Jacquet).

JOHNNY HODGES AND WILD BILL DAVIS, 1965 - 1966 (see Hodges, Johnny) (Davis, Wild Bill & Johnny Hodges).

Davis, William

BEST OF BRITISH BRASS (Davis, William Construction Band).
Tracks: / March country Palatine / You'll never walk alone / Rondoletto / King's hunting jigg, The / Count down / High society / Teetoller, The / What a friend I have in Jesus / Tiger rag / Lass of Richmond Hill / Third movement from Sinfonietta for brass band / Swedish march, A.
LP: . . . . ALM 4007
MC: . . . . ZC ALM 4007

CONSTRUCTIVE BRASS (Davis, William Construction Band).
LP: . . . . GRS 1048

SPICE OF LIFE, THE (Davis, William Construction Band).
Tracks: / Blenheim flourishes / One voice / One fine day / Meridian / Norwegian dance no. 2 / Mack and Mabel / Pop looks Bach / Bacchanale / Deep inside the sacred temple / Tritsch tratsch polka / Greensleeves / Orient express.
LP: . . . . PRL 034D
MC: . . . . CPRL 034D

Davison, Peter (nar)

ISLAND OF ADVENTURE (see under Blyton, Enid (aut)).

STORY OF CHRISTMAS, THE.
Tracks: / Away in a manger / In the bleak mid winter / Silent night.
MC: . . . . TCWHS 3171

Davison, Wild Bill

ALL AMERICAN BAND.
Tracks: / I'll be a friend with pleasure / Who's sorry now / I may be wrong / Runnin' wild / Sleep / Sweet and lovely / Limehouse blues / On the Alamo / I surrender dear / Blues my naughty sweeties gives to me.
LP: . . . . SNTF 880
MC: . . . . ZCSN 880

ALL STARS.
Tracks: / I can't believe that you're in love with me / Old folks / Doctor Jazz / Sweet & lovely / I never knew / Sweet Georgia Brown / Lover man / Sweet Sue / Save it pretty mama / When you're smiling / I surrender dear.
LP: . . . . TTD 545

BEAUTIFULLY WILD.
LP: . . . . AP 149

BLOWIN' WILD (Davison, Wild Bill & Alex Welsh).
LP: . . . . J 18

BUT BEAUTIFUL.
LP: . . . . SLP 4048

CHICAGO JAZZ.
Tracks: / Hindustan / How can you do me like you do? / Just one of those things / Blue turning grey over you / I may be wrong / Runnin' wild.
LP: 9198 204
MC: 7298 024

CLASSIC JAZZ COLLEGIUM.
LP: . . . . J 70

INDIVIDUALISM OF WILD BILL DAVISON.
2LP: . . . . SJL 2229

JAZZ GIANTS.
Tracks: / Struttin' with some barbecue / Dardanella / Black and blue / I would do anything for you / I found a new baby / Blue again / I surrender, dear / Yesterdays / Them there eyes.
LP: . . . . GOJ 1002
LP: 3002

JAZZ ON A SATURDAY AFTERNOON.
LP: . . . . J 38

LADY OF THE EVENING.
LP: . . . . J 128

LIVE AT THE MEMPHIS FESTIVAL.
LP: . . . . J 133

RUNNING WILD.
Tracks: / Blue room / I surrender dear / Monday date / Am I blue / You took advantage of me / If I had you / I never knew / Indiana / Sleepy time down south / I want to be happy / Sunny side of the street / Running wild.
LP: . . . . JSP 1044

SURFSIDE JAZZ.
LP: . . . . J 25

SWEET AND LOVELY (Davison, Wild Bill With Strings).
LP: . . . . SLP 4060
LP: . . . . SLP 260

THAT'S A PLENTY - VOL.1 (1943) (Davison, Wild Bill & His Commodores).
LP: AG6 24059

THIS IS JAZZ (Volume 1).
LP: . . . . SLP 4067

TIN ROOF BLUES (See Brunis, George) (Davison, Wild Bill & George Brunis).

TOGETHER AGAIN (Davison, Wild Bill & Ralph Sutton).
Tracks: / Limehouse blues / Am I blue / Grandpa's spells / Three little words / Reunion blues / Back in your own back yard / I've got the world on a string / Rockin' chair.
LP: . . . . SLP 4027
MC: . . . . CMJMC 003

WILD BILL DAVISON.
Tracks: / Blues my naughty sweetie gives to me / Mandy make up your mind / St James infirmary / Way down yonder in New Orleans / I found a new baby / Sing the blues / Wildcat blues / Wildcat blues / If I had you / Wolverine blues.
LP: . . . . JC 003

WILD BILL DAVISON.
LP: . . . . SLP 4005

WILD BILL DAVISON AND PAPA BUE (Davison, Wild Bill & Papa Bue).
LP: . . . . SLP 4029
LP: . . . . SLP 250

WILD BILL DAVISON AND PAPA BUE'S VIKING JAZZBAND (Davison, Wild Bill & Papa Bue).
LP: . . . . SLP 264

WILD BILL DAVISON AND THE JAZZOLOGISTS.
LP: . . . . J 2

WILD BILL DAVISON GREATEST OF GREATS.
LP: . . . . DJA 508

WILD BILL DAVISON IN LONDON.
LP: . . . . J 121

WILD BILL DAVISON IN NEW ORLEANS.
LP: . . . . J 170

WILD BILL DAVISON ON THE AIR.
Tracks: / Blues, The / Ain't gonna give nobody none of my jelly roll / Honeysuckle rose / Don't take your love from me / Willow weep for me / I'm comin', Virginia / Oh by jingo, oh by gee.
LP: . . . . AIRCHECK 31

WILD BILL DAVISON WITH FREDDY RANDALL (Davison, Wild Bill/Freddy Randall & His Band).
Tracks: / Royal Garden blues / Memories of you / Hindustan / If I had you / All of me / Wolverine blues / I don't stand a ghost of a chance with you / Struttin' with some barbecue / Tin roof blues / Sunday.
LP: . . . . BLP 30187
LP: . . . . J 160

WILD BILL DAVISON'S 75TH ANNIVERSARY JAZZ BAND.
LP: . . . . J 151

WILD TRUMPETS (Davison, Wild Bill & Valdemars Orchestra).
LP: . . . . CLPS 1011

Davy D

DAVY'S RIDE.
Tracks: / Davy's ride / Get busy / Keep your distance / Feel for you / Bustin' loose / Your love is like money in the bank / Live on hollis day / Oh girl / Have you seen Davy / Do ya do / Bring it / Let's rock.
LP: 4504811
MC: 4504814

Dawa, Mwendo

FOUR VOICES.
LP: . . . . DRLP 47

NEW YORK LINES.
LP: . . . . DRLP 41

Dawai

DAWAI (Various artists).
LP: . . . . EFA 15353

ROCK 'N' ROLL.
LP: . . . . EFA 15853

Dawgs

ON THE ROAD TO YOU.
LP: . . . . ROSE 22

Dawkins, Jimmy

ALL BLUES.
LP: . . . . JSP 1102

ALL FOR BUSINESS.
LP: . . . . DS 634

BLISTERSTRING (Dawkins, Jimmy Band).
LP: . . . . DS 641

FAST FINGERS.
LP: . . . . DS 623

FEEL THE BLUES (1985 Chicago studio recording).
Tracks: / Feel the blues / Highway man blues / Last days / Love somebody / Christmas time blues / Have a little mercy.
LP: . . . . JSP 1093

TRANSATLANTIC 770.
Tracks: / Things I used to do, The / Made my way in this world / Think twice before you speak / 1011 Woodland / Mighty hawk, The / All for business / High cost of living / Stoned dead / Love and understanding / No more trouble.
LP: . . . . SNTF 758

Dawn

GOLDEN RIBBONS.
LP: . . . . BELLS 236

TIE A YELLOW RIBBON.
LP: . . . . SSP 3071
MC: . . . . SSC 3071

Dawn, Elizabeth

WORLD OF SMILES.
Tracks: / World of smiles.
LP: . . . . BOW 152

Dawn Of Love

DAWN OF LOVE, THE (Carson, John).
MC: . . . . PTB 609

Dawn Of The Dead

DAWN OF THE DEAD (Original soundtrack) (Various artists).
LP: . . . . VC 81106
LP: . . . . CIA 5035
MC: . . . . CIAK 75035

Dawson, Dan

N.O. TEA PARTY (Dawson, Dan & Teddy Johnson).
Tracks: / Four or five times / My gypsy dream girl / In the groove / Some of these days / Caldonia / Should I / Outskirts of town / Enjoy yourself / Indiana / Jambalaya / I can't stop loving you / Space stout boogie.
LP: . . . . NOLA LP 18

Dawson, Julian

AS REAL AS DISNEYLAND (Dawson, Julian & The Flood).
LP: 831 607-1
MC: 831 607-4

LUCKIEST MAN IN THE WESTERN WORLD.
LP: 837 422-1

Dawson, Les

LAUGH WITH LES DAWSON.
Tracks: / Appeal, An / Transport / Mission impossible / Cissie and Ada / Getting about / Dissertation / Barnsley Dracula, The / Leisure - the Allan evil / Time off / Strange experience, A / Money - the sin of mankind / Holiday, The.
LP: . . . . REB 346
MC: . . . . ZCF 346

Dawson, Peter

FLORAL DANCE, THE.
Tracks: / Floral dance, The / Glorious Devon / Cobbler's song, The / When the sergeant major's on parade / Friend of mine, A / Boots / Somewhere a voice is calling / Bachelor gay, A / Phil the fluter's ball / In a monastery garden / On the road to Mandalay / Fishermen of England / Drake's drum / Old Father Thames / Wandering the King's highway / I'll walk beside you / I travel the road / Rocked in the cradle of the deep / Shipmates o'mine / In a Persian market.
LP: . . . . ONCM 506

FULL SAIL: SONGS OF THE SEA.
Tracks: / We saw the sea / Full sail / Fishermen of England, The / Sea call, A / Cargoes / Admiral's broom / Rolling down to Rio / Little admiral, The / Captain Harry Morgan / Asleep in the deep / Songs of the sea, op. 91 / Drake's drum / Outward bound / Devon, O Devon / Homeward bound / Old superb, The / Smugglers, The / Drake goes west / Glory of the sea, The / Admiral's yarn, The / Hearts of oak / Lads in navy blue / Three cheers for the red white and blue / Rule Britannia.
LP: . . . . CHD 142
MC: . . . . MCHD 142

GOLDEN AGE OF PETER DAWSON, THE.
Tracks: / Jolly Roger, The / When the sergeant major's on parade / Roses of Picardy / Gay highway, The / Song of the flea / Fishermen of England / Erl king, The / Winding road, The / Rolling down to Rio / Bandolero / Boots / Some where a voice is calling / Old Father Thames / Song of the Volga boatmen / I travel the road / Song of the highway.
LP: . . . . GX 2515
MC: . . . . TCGX 2515

GOLDEN ALBUM, THE.
Tracks: / Roses of Picardy / Kashmiri love song / Bedouin love song / Mountains of Mourne, The / Holy City, The / Lost chord, The / Bless this house / Sacred hour / Waltzing Matilda / Joggin' along the highway / Trumpeter, The / Kerry dance, The / Wiata poi /

Song of the Volga boatmen / That lucky old sun / Simon the cellarer / Love, could I only tell thee.
LP: . . . . SH 107 823 1
MC: . . . . TCSH 107 823 4

PETER DAWSON.
Tracks: / Sergeant Major's on parade / Up from Somerset / Boys of the old Brigade / Admiral's broom / Deathless army / Heavy dragoon.
LP: . . . . GEMM 200

PETER DAWSON (PEARL LABEL).
Tracks: / Floral dance, The / Drake goes west / Glorious Devon / Up from Somerset / When the Sergeant Major's on parade / Vulcan's song / Non piu'andrai / Largo al factotum / Toreador's song (Bizet 'Carmen') / Bachelor gay, A / Smugglers song, The / Yeomen of England, The / Old father Thames / Phil the fluter's ball / Waltzing Matilda / Ol' man river / Waiata poi / Drum major, The / I am a roamer.
MC: . . . . GEMM 7336

SONGS OF THE SEA.
Tracks: / Drake's drum / Outward bound / Old superb, The / Devon O Devon / Homeward bound / Sons of the sea / Shipmates o'mine / Admiral Broom, The / At Santa Barbara / Cargoes / Rocked in the cradle of the deep / Tune the bosun played, The / Jolly Roger, The / Anchored / Rolling down to Rio / Little Admiral, The.
LP: . . . . SH 135
MC: . . . . GEMM 9381

Dawson, Ronnie

ROCKIN' BONES.
LP: . . . . NOHIT 001

Dawson, Sandy

GOING TO SANDY'S CEILIDH.
MC: . . . . CWGR 098

Dax, Danielle

BLAST THE HUMAN FLOWER.
LP: 7599261261
MC: 7599261264

DARK ADAPTED EYE.
LP: . . . . UNKNOWN
MC: . . . . UNKNOWN

INKY BLOATERS.
LP: . . . . AOR 13
MC: . . . . AOR 13CS

JESUS EGG THAT WEPT, THE.
LP: . . . . AOR 1

POP EYES.
Tracks: / Here come the harvest buns / Bed caves / Tower of lies / Numb companions / Everyone squeaks quietly.
LP: . . . . IRC 009
LP: . . . . AOR 2

Day At The Zoo (bk)

DAY AT THE ZOO, A.
MCSET: . . . . DTO 10524

Day, Bobby

ROCKIN' ROBIN.
Tracks: / Rockin' Robin / Bluebird, The buzzard & the oriole, The / Over and over / Come seven / Honeysuckle baby / My blue Heaven / I don't want to / When the swallows come back to Capistrane / Beep beep beep / Ain't gonna cry no more / Little bitty pretty one / Life can be beautiful / That's all I want / Mr. and Mrs. rock 'n' roll / Sweet little thing / Three young rebs from Georgia.
LP: . . . . CH 200
LP: . . . . CLASS 5002

Day, Doris

20 GOLDEN GREATS.
LP: . . . . PR 5053

BEST OF BIG BANDS (Day, Doris & Les Brown).
MC: 4669184

BEST OF DORIS DAY (CBS).
Tracks: / Secret love / Teacher's pet / Bewitched / Everybody loves a lover / It's magic / Bushel and a peck, A / Again / Sentimental journey / Whatever will be will be / Black hills of Dakota, The / Hernando's hideaway / If I give my heart to you / Deadwood stage / Tunnel of love / Move over, darling / Love me or leave me.
LP: 31825
MC: 40 31825

BEST OF DORIS DAY (SPOT).
Tracks: / Love me or leave me / Small talk / Guy is a guy, A / Tunnel of love / When I fall in love / Deadwood stage / Bewitched / Bushel and a peck, A / Move over, darling / Black Hills of Dakota, The / Whatever will be will be.
LP: . . . . SPR 8533
MC: . . . . SPC 8533

CALAMITY JANE/PAJAMA GAME (Film soundtracks) (See under Calamity Jane) (Various artists).

COLLECTION: DORIS DAY (20 Golden Greats).
Tracks: / Secret love / Que sera sera / My blue Heaven / Pillow talk / Sentimental journey / Blue skies / Move over, darling / Somebody loves me / At sundown / Fine and dandy / Please don't talk about me when I'm gone / You made me love you / Lullaby of Broadway / Just one of those things / It's magic / Mean to me / Please don't eat the daisies / Do not disturb / Everybody loves my baby / Love me or leave me.
LP: . . . . DVLP 2088
MC: . . . . DVMC 2088

DAY AT THE MOVIES, A.
MC: . . . . JST 44371

DORIS DAY.
Tracks: / Que sera sera / Fine and dandy / Love me or leave me / Everybody loves my baby / Sentimental journey / Somebody loves me / Please don't talk about me when I'm gone / Lullaby of Broadway / My blue Heaven / It's magic / Blue skies / You made me love you / Just one of those things / Mean to me / At sundown / Secret love.
LP: . . . . ENT LP 13010
MC: . . . . ENT MC 13010

DORIS DAY AND ANDRE PREVIN (Day, Doris & Andre Previn).
Tracks: / Falling in love again / Give me time / My one and only love / Remind me / Wait 'til I see him / Close your eyes / Fools rush in / Control yourself / Who are we to say (obey your heart) / Yes / Nobody's heart / Daydreaming.
MC: . . . . HSC 3306
LP: . . . . MRS 601

DORIS DAY AND PAGE CAVANAUGH TRIO, VOL. 2 1952-3 (Day, Doris/Page Cavanaugh Trio).
LP: . . . . HSR 226
MC: . . . . HSC 226

DORIS DAY CHRISTMAS ALBUM.
Tracks: / Silver bells / I'll be home for Christmas / Snowfall / Toyland / Let it snow, let it snow, let it snow / Be a child at Christmas time / Winter wonderland / Christmas song, The / Christmas present / Have yourself a merry little Christmas / Christmas waltz / White Christmas.
LP: 4604621
MC: 4604624
MC: . . . . PWKMC 4034

DORIS DAY SONGBOOK, THE.
LP: 88597
MC: 40 88597

DORIS DAY'S GREATEST HITS.
Tracks: / Everybody loves a lover / It's magic / Guy is a guy, A / Secret love / Teacher's pet / Bewitched / Whatever will be will be / If I give my heart to you / Why did I tell you I was going to Shanghai / When I fall in love / Lullaby of Broadway / Love me or leave me.
LP: . . . . CBS 32500
MC: 40 32500

GREAT MOVIE HITS.
Tracks: / Do not disturb / What every girl should know / Move over, darling / Canadian capers / Twinkle lullaby / Pillow talk / Please don't eat the daisies / Tunnel of love / Julie / Send me no flowers / More I see you, The / At last / Come to baby do / I had the craziest dream.... / I'll never smile again / I remember you / Serenade in blue / I'm beginning to see the light / It could happen to you / It's been a long long time / Sentimental journey.
LP: . . . . CBS 22181
MC: 40 22181

GREAT MOVIE STARS.
Tracks: / Que sera sera / It's magic / Secret love / Somebody loves me (From the movie 'Lullaby of Broadway'.) / Please don't talk about me when I'm gone / Lullaby of Broadway / Just one of those things / Everybody loves my baby / Love me or leave me / Never look back / I'll never stop loving you / At sundown / I want to be happy / Tea for two / Oh me, oh my / You my love / Hold me in your arms / Moonlight bay / By the light of the silvery moon / Julie.
LP: . . . . LOP 14 132
MC: . . . . LCS 14132

HEART FULL OF LOVE.
Tracks: / Lady's in love with you, The / I got lost in his arms / Dansero / you do something to me / Night we called it a day, The.
LP: . . . . MOIR 511
MC: . . . . CMOIR 511

HOORAY FOR HOLLYWOOD.
2LP: AC2 5
MC: . . . . XPT 5

LULLABY OF BROADWAY (VIDEO) (See under Lullaby Of Broadway) (Various artists).

ON THE AIR - WITH LES BROWN.
LP: . . . . SH 2011
MC: . . . . CSH 2011

ON THE AIR - WITH LES BROWN, VOL 2.
LP: . . . . SH 2078
MC: . . . . CSH 2078

PAJAMA GAME, THE (VIDEO) (See under Pajama Game, The) (Various artists).

PORTRAIT OF A SONG STYLIST.
Tracks: / More / Fly me to the moon / Some day I'll find you / Slightly out of tune (desafinado) / Autumn leaves / People will say we're in love / In the still of the night / You stepped out of a dream / Little girl blue / On the street where you live / Stepping out with my baby / Softly as I leave you / Oh but I do / Quiet nights of quiet stars / Hello my lover, goodbye / Night and day / Stars fell on Alabama / My ship.
LP: . . . . HARLP 101
MC: . . . . HARMC 101

PORTRAIT OF DORIS DAY.
LP: . . . . SMR 984
MC: . . . . SMC 984

REMEMBERING DORIS DAY.
Tracks: / I'll never smile again / It could happen to you / I remember you / Do not disturb / Time to say goodnight / Pillow talk / Moonglow / Lullaby of Broadway / Serenade in blue / Send me no flowers / More I see you, The / It's been a long, long time / Singin' in the rain / I'm beginning to see the light / It's easy to remember / That old feeling / I had the craziest dream / I don't want to walk without you / Please don't eat the daises / Come to baby do / Close your eyes.
MCSET: . . . . DTOL 10302

RHAPSODY IN BLUE (see Brown, Les) (Day, Doris & Les Brown).

SENTIMENTAL JOURNEY.
Tracks: / More I see you, The / At last / Come to baby do / I had the craziest dream / I don't want to walk without you / I'll never smile again / I remember you / Serenade in blue / I'm beginning to see the light / It could happen to you / It's been a long long time / Sentimental journey.
LP: . . . . CBS 32257
MC: 40 32257

SONGS FROM PAJAMA GAME & CALAMITY JANE (See under Calamity Jane for details).

TEA FOR TWO (VIDEO) (See under Tea For Two) (Various artists).

THROUGH THE EYES OF LOVE.
Tracks: / When you're smiling / Fool such as I, A / Three coins in the fountain / April in Paris / Close your eyes / Caprice / Through the eyes of love / Make someone happy / Ten cents a dance / If I were a bell / With a song in my heart / Let it ring / Sorry / I'll buy that dream.
LP: . . . . MOIR 123
MC: . . . . CMOIR 123

UNCOLLECTED DORIS DAY, THE.
Tracks: / I can't give you anything but love / Sentimental journey / You oughta be in pictures / Blue skies / Be anything / My blue Heaven / Love to be with you / Don't worry 'bout me / I'm a big girl now / Everything I have is yours / Hundred years from today / I've gotta sing away these blues / I got it bad (and that ain't good).
LP: . . . . HUK 200

VERY BEST OF DORIS DAY.
Tracks: / Secret love / Guy is a guy, A / Deadwood stage (whip crack away) / Tunnel of love / Everybody loves a lover / Black hills of Dakota, The / Sentimental journey / Bewitched / If I give my heart to you / Love me or leave me / Whatever will be will be (que sera sera) / Small talk / Hernando's hideaway / Just blew in from the windy city / Move over darling / It's magic / Woman's touch, A / Bushel and a peck, A / When I fall in love / Teacher's pet.
MCSET: . . . . DTOL 10276

WHAT EVERY GIRL SHOULD KNOW.
Tracks: / What every girl should know / Mood indigo / When you're smiling / Fellow needs a girl, A / My kinda love / What's the use of wond'rin' / Something wonderful / Hundred years from today, A / You can't have everything / Not only should you love him / What does a woman do / Everlasting arms, The / I enjoy being a girl.
MC: . . . . PWKMC 4042

WHATEVER WILL BE WILL BE.
Tracks: / Singin' in the rain / Close your eyes / It's easy to remember / If I give my heart to you / That old feeling / Whatever will be will be / Time to say goodnight / Moonglow / Lamp is low, The.
LP: . . . . CBS 32705
MC: 40 32705

Day, Edith

EDITH DAY.
Tracks: / Alice blue gown / Irene / Pretty thing / Door of my dreams / Indian love call / Desert song, The / French military marching song / Romance / Sabre song, The / You are love / Make believe / Why do I love you / Dance away the night / If you're in love you'll waltz / You're always in my arms / I'd rather have a memory of you.
LP: . . . . SH 138

EDITH DAY IN RIO RITA, ROSE MARIE & SHOWBOAT.
LP: . . . . MES 7058

Day In Hollywood

DAY IN HOLLYWOOD A NIGHT IN UKRAINE, A (Original Broadway cast) (Various artists).
LP: . . . . SBL 12580
MC: . . . . SBLC 12580

Day, Margie

I'LL GET A DEAL (Day, Margie & The Griffin Brothers Orchestra).
Tracks: / Little red rooster / I'll get a deal / Sadie Green / Mole in the hole / Stormy night / One steady baby / Do I (look like a fool to you) / Clock song (let your pendulum swing),The / I'm gonna raise a ruckus tonight / Pitty Pat band / Snatchin' it back / Something told me / Dumplin' dumplin' / Ho ho / Just couldn't keep it to myself / My story / Old time lovin'.
LP: . . . . RB 109

Day, Morris

COLOR OF SUCCESS.
Tracks: / Color of success / Character, The / Oak tree, The / Love sign / Don't wait for me / Love addiction.
LP: 925320 1
MC: 925320 4

DAY DREAMING.
Tracks: / Daydreaming / Yo luv / Fishnet / Man's pride,A / Are you ready / Love is a game / Moonlite / Sally.
LP: . . . . K 925651 1
MC: . . . . K 925651 4

Dayglow Abortions

FEED US FOETUS.
LP: 083602

Dayne, Taylor

CAN'T FIGHT FATE.
Tracks: / With every beat of my heart / I know the feeling / Heart of stone / Up all night / Wait for me / I'll be your shelter / You can't fight fate / Love will lead you back / You meant the world to me / Ain't no good.
LP: 210321
MC: 410321

TELL IT TO MY HEART.
Tracks: / Tell it to my heart / In the darkness / Don't rush me / I'll always love you / Prove your love / Do you want it right now? / Carry your heart / Want ads / Where does that boy hang out? / Upon the journey's end.
LP: 208898
MC: 408898

Days Of Thunder (film)

DAYS OF THUNDER (Film soundtrack) (Various artists).
Tracks: / Last note of freedom, The: *Coverdale, David* / Deal for life: *Waite, John* / Break through the barrier: *Turner, Tina* / Hearts in trouble: *Chicago* / Trail of broken hearts: *Cher* / Knockin' on heaven's door: *Guns 'n' Roses* / You gotta love someone: *John, Elton* / Show me heaven: *McKee, Maria* / Tinder box: *Appollo Smile* / Long live the night: *Jett, Joan & The Blackhearts* / Gimme some lovin': *Reid, Terry.*
LP: 4571591
MC: 4571594

Dayton

FEEL THE MUSIC.
Tracks: / Sound of music, The / It must be love / Out tonight / So what / Love you anyway / Caught in the middle / Eyes / Promise me / Looking up.
LP: . . . . EST 7122971
MC: . . . . TCEST 712297 4

Dazz Band

GREATEST HITS: DAZZ BAND.
Tracks: / Let it whip / Joystick / Invitation to love / Party right here / Swoop (I'm your's) / Keep it live / Cheek to cheek / Knock knock / On the one for fun / Let it all blow.
LP: . . . . WL 72433
MC: . . . . WK 72433

HOT SPOT.
Tracks: / If only you were in my shoes / Hot spot / Paranoid / All the way / S.C.L. & P. / She used to be my girl / When you needed roses / Slow rap.
LP: **ZL72391**

INVITATION TO LOVE.
Tracks: / Shake it up / Invitation to love / Magnetized / Hello girl / Skate lovers / Carry on / Do it again / Sooner or later / Beyond the horizon.
LP: . . . . **STML 12146**

JOYSTICK.
Tracks: / To the roof / Joystick / Swoop (I'm yours) / Until you / Rock with me / Straight out of school / Now that I have you / Laughing at you / T.Mata (instrumental).
LP: . . . . **STML 12201**
MC: . . . . **CSTML 12201**

JUKEBOX.
Tracks: / Let it all blow / Keep you comin' back for more / She's the one / Dream girl / Heartbeat / Undercover lover / I've been waiting / Main attractions / So much love.
LP: . . . . **ZL 72335**
MC: . . . . **ZK 72335**

KEEP IT LIVE.
Tracks: / Let it whip / Gamble with my love / I'll keep on lovin' you / Just can't wait till the night / Shake what you got / Keep it live / Just believe in love / Can we dance / Let me love you until.
LP: . . . . **STML 12173**

ON THE ONE.
Tracks: / Party right here / Cheek to cheek / On the one for fun / Don't get caught in the middle / Love song / Bad girl / Nice girls / Stay a while with me / We have more than love.
LP: . . . . **STML 12181**

ROCK THE ROOM.
Tracks: / Anticipation / Single girl / Open sesame / One time lover / Body drum / Huff and puff / All the way / Rock the room / Once in a lifetime love.
LP: . . . . **PL 86928**
MC: . . . . **PK 86928**

WILD AND FREE.
Tracks: / Wild and free / Body and mind / Time / Beat that's right, The / All I need / Love M.I.A. / Hooks in me / Sunglasses / It's alright / Something you said / Wild and free.
LP: **9241101**
MC: **9241104**

Dazzlers

DAZZLERS,THE.
LP: . . . . **LP 8310**

FEELING FREE.
Tracks: / Crying shame / Feeling free / Feeling in your heart / Heartdrop / I know all about you / Just a fantasy / Lovely crash / No-one ever knows / Oh last night / Phonies / Too much of everything / You're an island.
LP: . . . . **CLASS 7**

GET AWAY FROM MY BRAIN.
LP: . . . . **ROCK 3346**

D.B.F.

NOT BOUND BY THE RULES.
Tracks: / You deceive yourself / Election's just a farce / Suicide Billy / Make it a lie / Too wide apart / Narrow-minded / Not bound to rules / Nothing to prove / Rape your mind / Too much wasn't said / Am I too weak / Religion / Blank minds / No personality.
LP: **083880**

D'Bora

DREAM ABOUT YOU.
LP: **8672791**

DB's

AMPLIFIER.
Tracks: / Nothing is wrong / Neverland / In Spain / Happenstance / Living a lie / From a window to a scream / Ask for Jill / Amplifier / Bad reputation / Big brown eyes / Moving in your sleep / Black and white / I feel good today / Ups and downs.
LP: . . . . **DOJOLP 33**

LIKE THIS.
LP: . . . . **RNLP 70891**

REPERCUSSION.
LP: . . . . **ALB 109**
MC: . . . . **ALBC 109**
LP: . . . . **ALLP 400032**

SOUND OF MUSIC.
Tracks: / Never say when / Change with the changing times / I lie / Molly says / Bonneville / Any old thing / Think too hard / Working for somebody else / Never before and never again / Better place, A / Looked at the sun too long / Today could be the day.
LP: . . . . **MIRF 1031**
MC: . . . . **MIRFC 103**

STAND FOR DECIBELS.
LP: . . . . **ALLP 400009**

D.C.3

VIDA.
LP: . . . . **SST 156**
MC: . . . . **SSTC 156**

DC Lacroix

LIVING BY THE SECOND.
LP: **721991**

D.C.Nighthawks

D.C. NIGHTHAWKS.
Tracks: / Mainline / Upside your head / Everynight and everyday / Back to the city / One night stand / Pretty girls and cadillacs / Brand new man / Little sister / Don't go further / Teenage letter / I wouldn't treat a dog (the way you treated me).
LP: **6337 111**

D.C.S.

BHANGRA'S GONNA GET YOU.
LP: . . . . **MUT 1086**
MC: . . . . **CMUT 1086**

FROM EAST TO WEST (D.C.S.with Runa Laila).
LP: . . . . **ECSD 41526**

TERI SAUHN.
Tracks: / Aa kudiye / Patli Patang / Bale bale / London di mutyaar / Rang gora gora / Sun meri Jean / Rahe Mere Kolon / Video.
LP: . . . . **MUT 1013**
MC: . . . . **CMUT 1013**

D.D. Dance

IT'S GETTING ROUGH (See X, Rocky).

D.D. Sound

CAFE.
Tracks: / She's not a disco lady / Backstreet baby / Show me your love.
LP: . . . . **SKLR 5306**

DDAA

POEMS OF RONSARD.
Tracks: / Ronsard did celebrate / Planet of Helen, The / Me.
LP: . . . . **KK 011**

WHEN A CAP IS RAISING.
Tracks: / Chemin de Pierre / Little boy / Exploration / Kemboo / Geisha girl / Passage / Nihon bridge / Terror interdit / Dig it's dig / Pourquoi un homme et un chat et un chat.
LP: . . . . **BNIA TWO**

DDHE

DET DANSKE HARMONIKA ENSEMBLE.
Tracks: / Donna Diana / Bach goes to town / Champagne gallop / Florentiner march / Russian and Ludmilla overture / Concert suite for accordion / Sabeldans fra balletten gayaneh.
LP: . . . . **SLP 1586**

VIVA (DDHE, Jeanette Dyremose).
LP: . . . . **TM 10002**

DDK

SOMETHING FOR THE WEEKEND.
MC: . . . . **DHC 21**

De Angelis, Jim

GRIDLOCK (See under Tony Signa).

STRAIGHT FROM THE TOP (De Angelis, Jim/Tony Signa).
LP: . . . . **SLP 8084**

De Angelis, Nicolas

GOA.
Tracks: / Goa / El condor pasa / L'amour amour / Solamente una vez / Une lle au soleil (island in the sun) / Soleil rouge / Les jardins d'alcantara / Girl from Ipanema / Texanita / Santa angelica / La nina paloma / Cuando calienta el sol.
LP: **824 177-1**
MC: **824 177-4**

GUITAR GUITAR.
Tracks: / El condor pasa / Island in the sun / Girl from Ipanema / Cuando calienta el sol / L'espagnole / Guantanamera / Maria Helena / La paloma / Begin the beguine / Mas que nada / Brazil / Amor amor / Les jardins d'alcantara / Vaya con dios / Solamente una vez / La nina paloma / O'cangaceiro / Ave Maria.
LP: **8302714**

IMAGES: NICOLAS DE ANGELIS.
Tracks: / Concierto de Aranjuez / Island in the sun / Goa / El condor pasa / Sabre dance / Moonlight sonata / O sole mio / Cuando calienta el sol / Girl from Ipanema / Capricho arabe / Recuerdos de la Alhambra / Quelques notes pour Anna / Asturias / Eine kleine nachtmusik.
MC: . . . . **KNMC 16005**

NICOLAS DE ANGELIS.
Tracks: / Song for Anna / Goa / Only once / Guantanamera / Farewell to childhood / Amor amor / Importance of love / Evidence of the heart / La nina paloma / Voyage / Le coeur a contre choeurs / Ce lui qui reste / L'espagnole / Amour mon amour.
LP: . . . . **SKL 5342**
MC: . . . . **KSKC 5342**
LP: . . . . **SEX 010**

QUELQUES NOTES POUR ANNA.
Tracks: / Quelques notes pour Anna / Pres du coeur / Caprichio arabe / Adieu L'enfance / Recuerdos de la Alhambra / Rodolphe, ici, present / Le coeur a contre choeurs / Amour fou, amour loup / Asturias / Splendid melody / Amours interdits.
LP: **1700052**
MC: . . . . **C 700052**

SOLEIL.
Tracks: / Besame mucho / Perfidia / Orfeo negro / Solamante el amor / El cumbanchero / La esperanza / Volare / La Bamba / Venetian nights / Moliendo Cafe / Sunny / Amor mi amor / Arrivederci Roma / Mexican hat dance.
LP: **174167 1**
MC: **174167 4**

De Angelo, Nino

NINO DE ANGELO.
MC: . . . . **CAC 210**
LP: . . . . **CAL 210**

De Blaiso, Frank

NELSON MANDELA.
LP: . . . . **AT 089**

De Brest St-Marc,

BRETAGNE ETERNELLE.
Tracks: / Suite traditionnelle du Pays de Vannes / Plac'hig koad rouan / An enez c'hlaz / Suite traditionnelle de Haute-Cornouaille / Suite de marches de creation recente / Suite d'airs traditionnels / Melodie de Haute-Bretagne / Al logodenn / Suite traditionnelle du Morbihan / Suite de marches traditionnelles du Pays Rouzi / Cantique Leonard / An erminig / En tri cheminod yaouank.
LP: . . . . **ARN 33176**
MC: . . . . **ARN 433176**

De Brunhoff, Jean

BABAR AT HOME AND OTHER STORIES (Nettleton, John).
MC: . . . . **TS 343**

BABAR & FATHER CHRISTMAS / BABAR & HIS CHILDREN (Jourdan, Louis).
MC: **1488**

BABAR THE KING / BABAR & ZEPHIR (Jourdan, Louis).
MC: **1487**

BABAR'S MYSTERY / BABAR & THE WULLY-WULLY (De Brunhoff, Laurent).
MC: **1583**

STORY OF BABAR.
Tracks: / Babar's travels / Babar the king.
MC: . . . . **TS 342**

STORY OF BABAR / TRAVELS OF BABAR (Jourdan, Louis).
MC: **1486**

De Buitlear, Eamonn

STAR OF MUNSTER, THE.
LP: . . . . **CEF 047**

De Burgh, Chris

AT THE END OF A PERFECT DAY.
Tracks: / Broken wings / Round and around / I will / Summer rain / Discovery / Brazil / In a country churchyard / Rainy night in Paris, A / If you really love her let her go / Perfect day.
LP: . . . . **AMLH 64647**
MC: . . . . **CAM 64647**

BEST MOVES.
Tracks: / Every drop of rain / In a country churchyard / Patricia the stripper / Satin green shutters / Spanish train / Waiting for the hurricane / Broken wings (live version) / Lonely sky / Spaceman came travelling, A / Crusader / Traveller, The.
LP: . . . . **AMLH 68532**
MC: . . . . **CAM 68532**

CRUSADER.
Tracks: / Carry on / I had the love in my eyes / Something else again / Girl with April in her eyes, The / Just in time / Devil's eyes, The / It's such a long way home / Old fashioned people / Quiet moments / Crusader / You and me.
LP: . . . . **AMLH 64746**
MC: . . . . **CAM 64746**

EASTERN WIND.
Tracks: / Traveller, The / Record company bash, The / Tonight / Wall of silence / Flying home / Shadows and light / Some things never change / Tourist attraction / Eastern wind.
LP: . . . . **AMLH 64815**
MC: . . . . **CAM 64815**

FAR BEYOND THESE CASTLE WALLS.
Tracks: / Hold on / Key, The / Windy night / Sin city / New moon / Watching the world / Lonesome cowboy / Satin green shutters / Turning around / Goodnight.
MC: . . . . **AMC 3287**
LP: . . . . **AMA 3287**
LP: . . . . **AMID 119**
LP: . . . . **SHM 3151**

FLYING COLOURS.
Tracks: / Sailing away / Carry me (like a fire in your heart) / Tender hands / Night on the river, A / Leather on my shoes / Suddenly love / Missing you / I'm not scared anymore / Don't look back / Just a word away / Risen Lord, The / Last time I cried, The / Simple truth (a child is born), The (On CD only.).
LP: . . . . **AMA 5224**
MC: . . . . **AMC 5224**

GETAWAY, THE.
Tracks: / Don't pay the ferryman / Living on the island / Crying and laughing / I'm counting on you / Getaway / Ship to shore / Borderline / Where peaceful waters flow / Revolution, The / Light a fire / Liberty.
LP: . . . . **AML 68549**
MC: . . . . **CAM 68549**

HIGH ON EMOTION- LIVE FROM DUBLIN.
LP: **3970861**
MC: **3970864**

INTO THE LIGHT.
Tracks: / One word straight to the heart / For Rosanna / Leader / Vision, The / What about me / Last night / Fire on the water / Ballroom of romance / Lady in red / Say goodbye to it all / Spirit of man,The / Fatal hesitation.
LP: . . . . **AMA 5121**
MC: . . . . **AMC 5121**

INTO THE LIGHT/ FLYING COLOURS.
Tracks: / Last night / Ballroom of romance / Say goodbye to it all / Fata hesitation / For Rosanna / What about me / Carry me / Night on the river, A / Suddenly love / Fire on the water / Lady in red / Spirit of man, The / One word / Leader / Sailing away / Tender hands / Leather on my shoes.
MC: . . . . **AMC 24108**

MAN ON THE LINE.
Tracks: / Ecstasy of flight (I love the night) / Sight and touch / Taking it to the top / Head and the heart, The / Sound of a gun, The / High on emotion / Much more than this / Man on the line / Moonlight and vodka / Transmission ends.
LP: . . . . **AMLX 65002**
MC: . . . . **CXM 65002**

SIMPLE TRUTH (A CHILD IS BORN), THE.
LP: . . . . **SP 79804**

SPANISH TRAIN AND OTHER STORIES.
Tracks: / Spanish train / Lonely sky / This song for you / Patricia the stripper / Spaceman came travelling, A / I'm going home / Painter, The / Old friend / Tower, The / Just another poor boy.
LP: . . . . **AMLH 68343**
MC: . . . . **CAM 68343**

SPARK TO A FLAME.
Tracks: / This waiting heart / Don't pay the ferryman / Much more than this / Sailing away / Lady in red / Borderline / Say goodbye to it all / Ship to shore / Missing you / Diamond in the dark / Tender hands / Spaceman came travelling, A / Where peaceful waters flow / High on emotion / Spanish train / Fatal hesitation.
LP: . . . . **CDBLP 100**
MC: . . . . **CDBMC 100**

VERY BEST OF CHRIS DE BURGH.
Tracks: / Ecstasy of flight (I love the night) / Ship to shore / Don't pay the ferryman / Flying home / Satin green shutters / Spaceman came travelling, A / Spanish train / High on emotion / Borderline / Lonely sky / In a country churchyard / Waiting for the hurricane / Traveller, The / Patricia the stripper.
LP: . . . . **STAR 2248**
MC: . . . . **STAC 2248**

De Cap Organ

BEERSE.
Tracks: / Sophia Loren / Keep smiling / Dutch waltz / Sweet Georgia Brown / Whispering / Margie / Kitchen door, The / Pikkettanussie / Blue Danube / Vienna blood / What a talker that man is / Turnhout foxtrot / Last dance / Ding dong bama lama sing song / Lily the pink / Organ fun / Heren van sichen / Hinter den kulissen von Paris / Lantern / Oh lady Mary / Gina Lollibrigida.

LP: JOYS 213

ENGLAND'S PRIDE (121 KEY BAND ORGAN).
Tracks: / Music music music / Banana boat song / Harry Lime theme / Too young / Cuanto Lagusta / Sail along silv'ry moon / Sucu sucu / Whatever will be will be / Liechtensteiner polka / Save the last dance for me / Melodie d'amour / Ta ra ra boom de ay / Memories are made of this / Peppermint twist / Come prima / For ever and ever / Elephant's tango, The / Tequila / Baioue, The / Buona sera / Story of a starry night / Maria from Bahia / Carioca.
LP: JOY 237

De Cervantes, Miguel

EXPLOITS OF DON QUIXOTE (See Under Don Quixote) (Quayle, Anthony (nar)).

De Dakar, Etoile

ABSA GUEYE.
LP: PAM 02

De Danann

ANTHEM.
LP: DARA 013
MC: DARAC 013

BALLROOM.
LP: DDLP 1
MC: DDMC 1

BANKS OF THE NILE.
MC: KSKC 5318

BEST OF DE DANANN.
LP: SHAN 79047

DE DANANN.
Tracks: / Tripping up the stairs (a trip to Athlone) / Sunny banks, The (Farewell to Erin.) / Mountain streams, The / Cathleen Henir's / Eighteen years old / Green fields of Rossbeigh / Toss the feathers / Duke of Leinsterl, The / Blackbird, The - The jolly clamdiggers / Rambling Irishman / Gold ring, The / Shores of Lough Bran, The / Glenbeigh hornpipe / Mountain lark.
LP: 2904005
MC: 3163105

JACKET OF BATTERIES, A.
LP: HM 048
MC: HMC 048

MIST COVERED MOUNTAIN,THE.
LP: CEF 087

SELECTED JIGS, REELS & SONGS.
LP: SHAN 79001
LP: KSKC 5287

SONG FOR IRELAND.
LP: CARA 0001
LP: SH 1130
LP: DDLP 3

STAR SPANGLED MOLLY, THE.
LP: BLB 5006
LP: SHAN 79018
MC: 5 SH 79018

De Falla Trio

DE FALLA TRIO, THE.
Tracks: / Symphony No. 1 / Aragon / Fandango / Suite from El amor brujo / Spain.
LP: CC 2011

De Forest, Carmaig

I SHALL BE RELEASED.
LP: ROSE 121

SIX LIVE CUTS (De Forest, Carmaig & Band).
Tracks: / One more time / You can't always get what you want / Kathy McVay / Risks in spring / Kate said / Dan Olmsted.
LP: ROSE 143

De France, Jean Michel

FEELINGS (The music of the pan flute).
Tracks: / Woman in love / Man and a woman, A / La mer / My heart in my hands / About the clouds / Love serenade / Dolannes melodie / Guernica / We are the world / Feelings / Autumn leaves / Adagio / Song for Anna / Liebestraum / L for love / Ave Maria / Summer love affair / El condor pasa.
LP: SHM 3304
MC: HSC 3304

De Franco, Buddy

BLACK MAGIC (De Franco, Buddy & Helen Forest).
LP: LP 1801

BLUES BAG (See under Blakey, Art).

BORINQUIN.
Tracks: / Borinquin / Song is you, The / Three summers ago / Easy living / But not for me / Pendulums.
LP: SNTF 724
MC: ZCSN 724

BORN TO SWING.
LP: SS 711

GARDEN OF DREAMS (De Franco, Buddy & Martin Taylor).
LP: HEP 2039

GROOVING (De Franco, Buddy Quintet).
LP: HEP 2030

HARK (De Franco, Buddy & Oscar Peterson Quartet).
Tracks: / All too soon / Summer me, winter me / Llovisna (Light rain) / By myself / Joy spring / This is all I ask / Hark / Why am I?.
LP: 231 0915
MC: K10 915

JAZZ PARTY - FIRST TIME TOGETHER (see Gibbs, Terry) (De Franco, Buddy & Terry Gibbs).

LIKE SOMEONE IN LOVE (De Franco, Buddy Quintet).
Tracks: / Like someone in love / Melancholy Stockholm / Playa Del Sol / How long has this been going on? / Coasting at the Palisades / I love you, Porgy.
LP: PRO 7014

LIVELIEST, THE.
Tracks: / Billie's bounce / Triste / Ja da / Yesterdays.
LP: HEP 2014

MOOD INDIGO.
LP: HEP 2018

MR LUCKY.
Tracks: / Mr. Lucky / Bye, bye blackbird / Mar descancado / In a sentimental mood / Your smile / Close enough for love / Danielle / Lolita's theme.
LP: 231 0906
MC: K10 906

ON TOUR UK (De Franco, Buddy Quintet).
LP: HEP 2023

De Gaetani, Jan

CLASSIC COLE (De Gaetani, Jan & Leo Smit).
Tracks: / At long last love / I've got you under my skin / Just one of those things / Easy to love / It's bad for me / Night and day / I get a kick out of you / Goodbye, little dream, goodbye / Love for sale / In the still of the night / I concentrate on you / You're sensational / What is this thing called love? / Riding high / You don't remind me / Use your imagination / Find me a primitive man / Most gentlemen don't like love / Every time we say goodbye.
LP: CBS 61987

SONGS BY STEPHEN FOSTER (De Gaetani, Jan/Leslie Guinn/Gilbert Kalish).
Tracks: / Voice of bygone days / Better times are coming / Linger in blissful repose / There are plenty of fish in the sea / My old Kentucky home / Soiree polka / Larry's goodbye / Come where my love lies dreaming.
LP: H 71333

De Garmo

D & K (DeGarmo and Key).
MC: MYRC 1254
LP: MYRR 1254

ROCK SOLID (Absolutely live) (DeGarmo and Key).
LP: MYR R 1256
MC: MYR C 1256

De Goal, Charles

3.
LP: ROSE 48

ALGORYTHMICS.
LP: ROSE 2

DOUBLE FACE.
LP: ROSE 96

ICI L'OMBRE.
LP: ROSE 7

De Graaff, Rein

CHASIN' THE BIRD.
LP: SJP 159

DRIFTIN' ON A REED.
Tracks: / Drifting on a reed / I waited for you / For Lennie & Lee / Blue possa / Anthropology / Alone together / Lonely Friday blues / Sunrise.
LP: SJP 105

DUO (De Graaff, Rein & Koosserierse).
LP: SJP 213

MODAL SOUL (De Graaff, Rein & Dick Vennick Quartet).
Tracks: / Sweet Basil / Detour ahead / Short rainbow / Lonely hunter / Modal soul.
LP: SJP 117

NEW YORK JAZZ (see Cuber, Ronnie).

De Havilland, Peter

BOIS DE BOULOGNE.
Tracks: / Escher / Shaku (cause) / Myoho / Shaku / Shaku (effect) / Bois de Boulogne (Theme & improvisation) / Shaku (chant).
LP: VE 3
MC: TCVE 3

De Hora, Sean

SEAN DE HORA.
LP: CEF 063

De Hugard, Dave

FREEDOM ON THE WALLABY.
LP: LRF 112
MC: LRC 112

MAGPIE IN THE WATTLE.
LP: LRF 158

De Johnette, Jack

ALBUM ALBUM (Special edition).
Tracks: / Festival / New Orleans strut / Zoot suite / Ahmad the terrible / Monk's mood / Third world anthem.
LP: ECM 1280

AUDIO VISUALSCAPES (DeJohnette, Jack's Special Edition).
2LP: MCA 28029

IRRESISTIBLE FORCES (DeJohnette, Jack's Special Edition).
LP: MCA 5992

JACK DE JOHNETTE/ WENER PIRCHER / HARRY PEPL (DeJohnette, Jack/Wener Pircher/Harry Pepl).
Tracks: / African godchild / Air, love and vitamins / Goodbye, baby post / Better times in sight.
LP: ECM 1237

JACK DE JOHNETTE'S SPECIAL EDITION.
LP: ECM 1244

NEW DIRECTIONS.
LP: ECM 1128

NEW DIRECTIONS IN EUROPE.
Tracks: / Salsa for Eddie / Bayou fever / Where or Wayne / Multo spillagio.
LP: ECM 1157

PARALLEL REALITIES.
Tracks: / Jack in / Exotic isles / Dancing / Nine over reggae / John McKee / Indigo dreamscapes / Parallel realities.
LP: MCA 42313
MC: MCAC 42313

SPECIAL EDITION (DeJohnette, Jack's Special Edition).
Tracks: / One for Eric / Zoot suite / Central Park West / India / Journey to the twin planet.
LP: ECM 1152

TALES OF... (see Peacock, Gary) (DeJohnette, Jack/G. Peacock/K. Jarrett).

TIN CAN ALLEY (DeJohnette, Jack's Special Edition).
LP: ECM 1189

WORKS: JACK DEJOHNETTE.
Tracks: / Bayou fever / Gri gri man, The / To be continued / One for Eric / Unshielded desire / Blue.
LP: 8254271

ZEBRA.
LP: MCA 42160

De La Fe, Alfredo

CABAS GREATEST HITS.
LP: MLPS 1059
MC: MCT 1059

SALSA.
MC: MCT 1026
LP: MLPS 1026

De la Mare, Walter

CINDERELLA AND OTHER FAIRY TALES (Bloom, Claire (nar)).
MC: 1330

LITTLE RED RIDING HOOD (Bloom, Claire (nar)).
MC: 1331

De La Soul

3 FEET HIGH AND RISING.
Tracks: / Intro / Magic number, The / Change in speak / Cool breeze on the rocks / Can U keep a secret / Jenifa (taught me) / Ghetto thang / Transmitting live from Mars / Eye know / Take it off / Little bit of soap, A / Tread water / Say no go / Do as De La does / Plug tunin' / De La orgee / Buddy / Description / Me myself and I / This is a recording 4 living in a fulltime era / I can do anything / D.A.I.S.Y. age / Plug tunin' (12" mix) / Potholes in my lawn.
LP: DLSLP 1
MC: DLSMC 1
MC: TBC 1019

DE LA SOUL IS DEAD.
Tracks: / De la soul is dead.
LP: BRLP 8
MC: BRMC 8

MAMA GAVE BIRTH TO THE SOUL CHILDREN (See Under Queen Latifah) (Queen Latifah & De La Soul).

De Lampedusa, Giuseppe

LEOPARD, THE (Houseman, John).
MC: 1720

De Lay, Paul

YOU'RE FIRED.
Tracks: / Mine all mine / Harpoon man / Heartbreaker / Cry to me / Don't drink / Signed, sealed and delivered / Rode myself crazy / Everynight / This ol' life / Who will be next? / Something's got a hold on me / Havin' that fun / All my money gone / This old heart / I want to be loved / Take me back baby / Sad as a man can be / Your just the one.
LP: RL 0081

De Los Rios, Waldo

GREATEST HITS: WALDO DE LOS RIOS.
LP: 66101
MC: 76101

SINFONIAS.
LP: 66100
MC: 76100

SYMPHONIES FOR 70'S.
LP: K 56130

UPBEAT CLASSICS (De Los Rios, Waldo/Manuel De Falla Orchestra).
Tracks: / Symphony No. 40 in G minor (1st movement) (Mozart) / Eine kleine nachtmusik (Mozart.) / Le nozze di figaro (overture) (Mozart.) / Piano concerto No. 21 in D (2nd movement) (Mozart.) / Musikalischer spass (4th movement) (Mozart.) / Variations on 'o cara armonia' (Mozart. (From 'The Magic Flute').) / 9th symphony (4th movement - Ode to joy) (Beethoven.) / Unfinished symphony (1st movement) (Schubert.) / 3rd symphony in F (Brahms.) / New World symphony (2nd & 4th movements) (Dvorak.) / Symphony in C - 'Toy' (2nd movement-minuet) (Haydn.) / 5th symphony (2nd movement) (Tchaikovsky.).
MC: TCEMS 1319

De Lucia, Paco

FRIDAY NIGHT IN SAN FRANCISCO (See Under Di Meola, Al) (De Lucia, Paco & Al Di Meola & John McLaughlin).

GUITARRA FLAMENCA.
MC: 746501

ONE SUMMER NIGHT.
Tracks: / Altamar / Solo quero caminar / Chiquito / Gitanos andaluces / Palenque.
LP: MERL 52
MC: MERLC 52

SIROCCO.
LP: 830 913 1

ZYRYAB.
MC: 846 707 4
LP: 846 707 1

De Maupassant, Guy

STORIES OF GUY DE MAUPASSANT (Bloom, Claire (nar)).
MC: 1268

De Michel, Rey

FOR BLOOZERS ONLY (De Michel, Rey Orchestra).
LP: FS 57

De Monte Heraldo

CORDAS VIVAS.
Tracks: / Cabloca electrico / Mordida De Abelha / Valsa Pr'A Tutuca / Moreneide / Pingo a pingo / Coisa / Teia De Aranha / Um cantinho e dois violes / Fugidinha R'O D'Alma / Giselle / La grima nordesting / Dois na brincadeira.
LP: RRPL 006

De Moussy, Pierre

O-BOLANE MBA.
LP: MOU 15

De Oliveira, Coaty

LE FORRO BRESILIEN.
Tracks: / Transamazonia / Aboio / Terno de salao / Calumba da praia / Bambaleo / Caatinga / Processao / Bahianada no rio / Capoeira de santana / Carnaval no recife.
LP: ARN 33263

SAUDADES DO BRASIL.
Tracks: / Capoeira na vila / P'ra chatea / Queimada grande / Pernambucco no frevo / Roda maxixe / Escola de samba / A coroa do rei / Boa vida / Chorinho em alaude / Agua de poco / Que bom que e' / Sua historia / Cangaco novo.
LP: ARN 33198

De Paola, Tomie

STREGA NONA'S MAGIC LESSONS & OTHER STORIES (Grimes, Tammy (nar)).
MC: 1714

De Paris Brothers

JIMMY RYANS & THE UPTOWN CAFE SOCIETY... (See under Ryans, Jimmy).

De Paris, Wilbur

COMMODORE CLASSICS (see under Ryan, Jimmy) (De Paris, Wilbur/Jimmy Ryan/Edmond Hall).

De Paul, Lynsey

LYNSEY SINGS.
Tracks: / Sugar me / Ivory tower / Doctor, doctor / Crossword puzzle / Way it goes, The / Won't somebody dance with me / Getting a drag / So good to you / Storm in a teacup / Mama do / Sleeping blue nights / All night.
LP: MAME 3002

NO HONESTLY.
Tracks: / No honestly / Love bomb / Moonrise / Season to season / Let's boogie / When I'm alone with you.
LP: SHM 923

TIGERS AND FIREFLIES.
Tracks: / Hollywood romance / My man and me / Without you / Forever and a day / Tigers and fireflies / Melancholy melon / Losin' the blues for you / Before you go tonight / 'Twas / Beautiful.
LP: POLS 1007

De Plata, Manitas

ASI SE TOTA.
Tracks: / Mi tierra / La danse du feu / Bella gitana / Caminando / Camaguesita / Prieres / Manolette / Amor amor / Calhino / Discordances / Guitares en liberte / Mediterranee / Morocco.
LP: 4609131
MC: 4609134

BEST OF MANITAS DE PLATA.
LP: VSD 37-8

FERIA GITANE.
Tracks: / Galop de Camargue / Fantasia Arlatane / Rumba des Launes / Soleil des Saintes Maries / Africana / Saga gitane / Autour du feu / Fandangos de los cunados / Ma premiere guitare / O li li / Hermanitos del albaicin / Rumba de los cinco / Larmes gitanes / Hommage a Sabicas / Rumba de los tre companeros.
LP: 4606671

FLAMENCO GUITAR.
LP: SBL 7786

GUITARS EN FETE.
LP: 26912
MC: 40 26912

SAGA OF MANITAS, THE.
LP: 25834
MC: 40.25834

De Porao, Ratos

BRASIL.
LP: RO 94241

De Pra, Sylvio

SOUVENIRS FOR YOU.
Tracks: / Marina / Quando, quando, quando / Old fashioned way, The / I love you so / Melody of love / Turkish march / Can't help falling in love / Buon natale / Top of the world / Snowbird / Guantanamera / Marilena / Who pays the ferryman? / Beautiful song / Sole mio / Danza / Viva espana / Roma.
LP: SODE 155

De Saint-Exupery,

LITTLE PRINCE, THE (Jourdan, Louis).
MC: 1695
MCSET: MCFR 113/4

De Sario, Teri

CAUGHT.
Tracks: / Caught / By myself / In trouble again / Feel like letting go / Where will they run / I found love / There's nothing better / Words / You better run / My life.
LP: 6302065

VOICES IN THE WIND.
LP: DAY R 4036

De Sio, Teresa

AFRICANA.
Tracks: / Scura / UFO / Mano a mano / Africana / Ma che bella cosa / Tamburo / Camminando sull'orlo dei mari / L'anno del sole intero / Sotto 'o cielo / Veneno e vanno.
LP: 824 810-1
MC: 824 810-4

De Soto, Lucy

HELP ME RHONDA, MY BOYFRIEND'S BACK.
LP: CLP 6

De Souza, Edward

RENDEZVOUS AND OTHER STORIES, THE (See also Daphne Du Maurier (Authoress)).

De Souza, Paul

DON'T ASK MY NEIGHBOURS.
Tracks: / Don't ask my neighbours / La la song / Daisy Mae / Beauty and the beast / Fortune / Overture / At the concert / I believe you / Jump street.
LP: EST 11774

'TIL TOMORROW COMES.
Tracks: / 'Til tomorrow comes / Only when you can / Fe-no-me-nol / Pleasurize / Up and at it / Everybody's got to dance to the music / Self sealing / Boogie shoes.
LP: EST 11918

De Tocqueville, Alexis

DEMOCRACY IN AMERICA (Quayle, Anthony (nar)).
MC: 2039

De Tulle, Ecole

CHANTS ET DANSES DE CORREZE.
Tracks: / Polka piquee / La demi-valse / Bourree carree / L'ajasso / La varsovienne / La cati / Le panliran / Le brise pied / La bourree d'egletons / La bourree du salut / La chaine valsee / Le turlututu / La bourree de chanac / La polka de Madranges / Le cotillon vert / Le menuguet / Passant par la prairie / La bourree ronde / Le pelele / La chabrorure / Marche de Nicolas.
LP: ARN 33492

De Valois, Dame

PATH OF MORNING, THE (Shearer, Moira (nar)).
MCSET: ZC SWD 364

De Ville, Willy

MIRACLE.
Tracks: / Due to gun control / Could you would you / Heart and soul / Assassin of love / Spanish Jack / Storybook love / Southern politician / Angel eyes / Miracle.
LP: POLH 39
MC: POLHC 39

STORYBOOK LOVE (See under Knopfler, Mark) (Deville, Willy/Mark Knopfler).

De Vito, Karla

IS THIS A COOL WORLD OR WHAT?.
Tracks: / Cool world / I can't stand to reminisce / Heaven can wait / Midnight confession / Big idea / Almost Saturday night / Boy talk / Just one smile / I'm just using you / Work / Bloody Bess / Just like you.
LP: EPC 84841

De Winkel, Torsten

HUMANIMAL TALK (De Winkel, Torsten & Hellmut Hattler).
Tracks: / Sapiens / Gamelan / Humanimal chat / Humanimal talk / Dinner for three / Lieblingslied / Duv (...dijuvi) / Mooloo / Cafe d'art.
LP: VBR 20231

MASTERTOUCH.
Tracks: / Lilo and Max / Double blue / Pyromantic / Tao / Coconuts / Sara's touch / (What lies) beyond.
LP: VBR 20121

De Young, Dennis

DESERT MOON.
Tracks: / Don't wait for heroes / Please / Boys will be boys / Fire / Desert moon / Suspicious / Gravity / Dear darling, I'll be there.
LP: AMA 5006
MC: AMC 5006

Deacon Blue

DEACON BLUE: INTERVIEW PICTURE DISC.
LPPD: BAK 2138

FELLOW HOODLUMS.
Tracks: / James Joyce soles / Fellow hoodlums / Your swaying arms / Cover from the sky / Day that Jackie jumped the jail, The / Wildness, The / Brighter star than you will shine, A / Twist and shout / Closing time / Goodnight Jamsie / I will see you tomorrow / One day I'll go walking.
LP: 4685501
MC: 4685504

OOH LAS VEGAS.
Tracks: / Disneyworld / Ronnie Spector / My America / S.H.A.R.O.N. / Undeveloped heart / Souvenirs / Born again / Down in the flood / Back here in Beanoland / Love you say / Let your hearts be troubled / Gentle teardrops / Little Lincoln / That country (beneath your skin) / Is it cold beneath the hill / Circus lights / Trampolene / Las Vegas / Killing the blues / Long window to love / Christine / Take me to the place / Don't let the teardrops start.
2LP: 4672421
MC: 4672424

RAINTOWN.
Tracks: / Born in a storm / Raintown / Ragman / He looks like Spencer Tracy now / Loaded / When will you (make my telephone ring) / Chocolate girl / Dignity / Very thing, The (Theme from BBC TV series'Take Me Home') / Love's great fears / Town to be blamed / Riches / Kings of the Western world / Shifting sands / Suffering / Ribbons and bows / Angeliou / Just like boys.
LP: 4505491
MC: 4505494
2LP: 4505490
MCSET: 4505498

RAINTOWN/WHEN THE WORLD KNOWS YOUR NAME.
Tracks: / Born in a storm / Raintown / Ragman / He looks like Spencer Tracy now / Loaded / When will you (make my telephone ring) / Chocolate girl / Dignity / Very thing, The / Love's great fears / Town to be blamed / Riches / Kings of the Western world / Queen of the New Year / Wages day / Real gone kid / Love and regret / Circus lights / This changing light / Sad love girl / Fergus sings the blues / World is lit by lightning, The / Silhouette / One hundred things / Your constant heart / Orphans.
2LP: 466533

WHEN THE WORLD KNOWS YOUR NAME.
Tracks: / Queen of the New Year / Real gone kid / Circus lights / Sad loved girl / One hundred things / Silhouette / Wages day / Love and regret / This changing light / Fergus sings the blues / Orphans / World is lit by lightning, The.
LP: 4633211
MC: 4633214

Dead Allison

TOYS AND DREAMS.
LP: SCH 9011

Dead Beats

ON A TAR BEACH.
LP: ROSE 59

Dead Boys

NIGHT OF THE LIVING DEAD BOYS.
LP: LOLITA 5013
LP: LILP 400200

WE HAVE COME FOR YOUR CHILDREN.
Tracks: / 3rd generation nation / I won't look back / (I don't wanna be no) Catholic boy / Flame thrower love / Son of Sam / Tell me / Big city / Calling on you / Dead and alive / Ain't it fun.
LP: SRK 6054

YOUNG LOUD AND SNOTTY.
Tracks: / Sonic reducer / All this and more / What love is / Not anymore / Ain't nothin' to do / Caught with the meat in your mouth / Hey little girl / I need lunch / High tension wire / Down in flames.
LP: SR 6038

YOUNGER, LOUDER AND SNOTTIER.
LP: NECR 0001

Dead Brain Cells

DBC.
Tracks: / Deadlock / Monument / Lies / Power and corruption / Tempest / Public suicide / Negative reinforcement / Outburst / M.I.A. / Terrorist mind / Vice, The / Trauma X / Final act / Midnight special / Casey Jones / K.C. Moan / Take this hammer / Down by the riverside / Go down, old Hannah / Streamline train / Old Riley / Downbound train / Stack o lee blues / Muleskinner blues / Grey goose / Sporting life / House rent stomp / I can't sleep / This train / Midnight hour blues / Go down sunshine / Ella speed.
LP: JUST 10

DEAD BRAIN CELLS.
LP: 88561-8161-1

Dead Can Dance

AION.
Tracks: / Arrival and the reunion, The / Mephisto / Fortune presents gifts not according / End of words, The / Wilderness / Garden of Zephirus, The / Saltarello / Song of Sibyl, The / As the bell rings the Maypole sign / Black sun / Promised womb, The / Radharc.
LP: CAD 0007
MC: CADC 0007

DEAD CAN DANCE.
Tracks: / Fatal impact, The / Trial, The / Frontier / Fortune / Ocean / East of Eden / Threshold / Passage in time, A / Wild in the woods / Musica eternal.
LP: CAD 404

SERPENTS EGG, THE.
Tracks: / Host of Seraphim / Orbis de ignis / Severance / Writing on my father's hand, The / In the kingdom of the blind / Chant of the paladin / Song of Sophia / Echolalia / Mother tongue / Ulysses.
LP: CAD 808
MC: CADC 808

SPLEEN AND IDEAL.
Tracks: / This tide / De profundis / Ascension / Circumradiant dawn / Cardinal sin, The / Mesmerism / Enigma of the absolute / Advent / Abatar / Indoctrination / Out of the depth of sorrow / Design for living, A.
LP: CAD 512
MC: CADC 512

WITHIN THE REALM OF A DYING SUN.
Tracks: / Anywhere out of the world / Windfall / In the wake of adversity / Xavier / Dawn of the iconoclast / Cantara / Summoning up the muse / Persphone (the gathering of flowers).
LP: CAD 705
MC: CADC 705

Dead End

GHOST OF ROMANCE.
LP: 722381

Dead Facts

WHO NEEDS THE TRUTH?.
Tracks: / Chemical panic / Party's over / You can see what I see / No way / Suicide / Real man in a ... / Who needs the truth? / Miss you / Run away / Kill this city.
LP: 089026

Dead Famous People

ARRIVING LATE IN TORN AND FILTHY JEANS.
LP: UTIL 007

Dead (film)

DEAD, THE (1988 film soundtrack) (Various artists).
LP: STV 81341
MC: CTV 81341

Dead Fingers Talk

STORM THE REALITY STUDIOS.
Tracks: / Electric city / Nobody loves you when you're old and gay / New directions / Someone, everyone / Storm the reality studios / Fight our way out of here / We got the message / Everyday / Into the future / Hold on to rock 'n' roll / Can't think straight.
LP: NSPH 24

Dead Goldfish Ensemble

MUSIC FOR BOWLS.
Tracks: / Intro / Grey earls / All the hands / Dazzle one / Little bit of nonsense, A / Openings / Eric / Cool walls.
MC: PVO 28

STRUCTURES AND STRICTURES.
Tracks: / Dead goldfish / Don't fight back / Modes of thought / Important haircuts / No static at all.
MC: PVO 14

Dead Heat (film)

DEAD HEAT ('88 film soundtrack) (Various artists).
LP: 704.570

Dead Kennedys

BEDTIME FOR DEMOCRACY.
LP: VIRUS 50
MC: VIRUS 50C

DEAD KENNEDYS: INTERVIEW PICTURE DISC.
LPPD: BAK 2090

FRANKENCHRIST.
LP: VIRUS 45
LP: ROSE 75

FRESH FRUIT FOR ROTTING VEGETABLES.
Tracks: / Kill the poor / Forward to death / When ya get drafted / Let's lynch the landlord / Drug me / Your emotions / Chemical warfare / California uber alles / I kill children / Stealing people's mail / Funland at the beach / Ill in the head / Holiday in Cambodia / Viva Las Vegas.
LP: BRED 10

GIVE ME CONVENIENCE OR GIVE ME DEATH.
LP: VIRUS 57

MUSIC AND MEDIA INTERVIEW PICTURE DISC.
LPPD: DK 1001

PLASTIC SURGERY DISASTERS.
Tracks: / Government flu / Terminal preppie / Trust your mechanic / Well paid scientist / Buzzbomb / Forest fire / Halloween / Winnebago warrior / Riot / Bleed for me / I am the owl / Dead end / Moon over marin / In God we trust (Only on CD.).
LP: STAT LP 11
LP: ROSE 19

Dead Mans Shadow

TO MOHAMMED....A MOUNTAIN.
LP: CRIMP 110

Dead Milkmen

BEELZEBUBBA.
Tracks: / Brat in the frat / RC's mom / Stuart / I walk the thinnest line / Sri Lanka sex hotel / Bad party / Punk rock girl / Bleach boys / My many smells / Smokin' banana peels / Born to love volcanos / Everybody's got nice stuff but

me / I against Osbourne / Howare beware / Ringo buys a rifle / Life is shit / Guitar song, The.
LP: ENVLP 514
MC: TCENV 514

BUCKY FELLINI.
LP: 3260 1

EAT YOUR PAISLEY.
LP: 2131 1

METAPHYSICAL GRAFFITI.
LP: LS 93591

Dead Moon

13 OFF MY HOOK.
Tracks: / Kicked out - kicked in / War baby / Street of despair / Milk cow blues / Social contender / Unknown passage / Walking on my grave / Claim to fame / D.O.A. / I'm out nine / Too many people / Revenge / Running scared / We won't change / Not the only one.
LP: MMLP 032

DEAD MOON NIGHT.
Tracks: / Dead moon night / Time has come today / 54/40 or fight / Graveyard / I'm wise / I tried / Dead in the saddle / Echoes to you / I hate the blues / My escape / Black September / Hey Joe.
LP: MMLP 022

Dead Neighbors

HARMONY IN HELL.
LP: BITE 1

STRANGE DAYS, STRANGE WAYS.
LP: TUFT 1

WILD WOMAN VS RUBBER FISH.
LP: TUFT 003

Dead On

DEAD ON.
Tracks: / Salem girls / Beat a dead horse / Widower, The / Matador's nightmare, The / Full moon / Escape / Merry ship / Different breed / Dead on.
LP: K1 93249
LP: 793 249 1
MC: K4 93249

Dead or Alive

MAD, BAD AND DANGEROUS TO KNOW.
Tracks: / Brand new lover / I'll save you all my kisses / Son of a gun / Then there was you / Come inside / Something in my house / Hooked on love / I want you / Special star.
LP: 4502571
MC: 4502574
LP: 4655741
MC: 4655744

NUDE.
Tracks: / Turn around and count 2 ten / Give it back that love is mine / Baby don't say goodbye / Stop kicking my heart around / Come home with me baby / I don't wanna be your boyfriend / Get out of my house / I cannot carry on / My forbidden lover.
LP: 4650791
MC: 4650794

SOPHISTICATED BOOM BOOM.
Tracks: / I'd do anything / That's the way I like it / Absolutely nothing / What I want / Far too hard / You make me wanna / Sit on it / Wish you were here / Misty circles / Do.
LP: 4501641
MC: 4501644
MC: 40 25835
LP: EPC 25835

YOUTHQUAKE.
Tracks: / You spin me round (like a record) / I wanna be a toy / D.J. hit that button / In too deep / Big daddy of the rhythm / Cake and eat it / Lover come back to me / My heart goes bang / It's been a long time / You spin me round (like a record) / Lover come back to me (extended mix).
LP: EPC 26420
MC: 40 26420

Dead Poets... (film)

DEAD POETS SOCIETY (Film soundtrack) (Various artists).
LP: A 558
MC: C 558

Dead Sea Surfers

DON'T SING ALOHA.
LP: PLR 048

Deadly Friend (film)

DEADLY FRIEND (1986 film soundtrack) (Various artists).
LP: STV 81291

Deadly Spawn (film)

DEADLY SPAWN, THE (Various artists).
Tracks: / Son of a gun: *Broken Jug* / Rock party: *Velvet Monkeys* / She lied: *Monster Rock* / Writing on the wall: *Brood* / Better off without you: *Creeping Pumpkins* / Wrong side of your mind, The: *Thee Fourgiven* / I love you: *Liquid Generation* / Everytime: *Dusters* / Legend of the headless surfer: *Skeptics, The* / Hammer of love: *Subterraneans* / Bells are ringing: *Real Gone, The* / Harvest time: *Mutant Drone* / Walk without me: *Scattered Limbs* / Restless soul: *No Kings* / Egypto-tek: *Turnups, The.*
LP: R 33/8601

Deadspot

ADIOS DUDE.
LP: HMRLP 149
MC: HMRMC 149

Deaf Dealer

KEEPER OF THE FLAMES.
LP: NEAT 1035

Deaf School

2ND HONEYMOON.
Tracks: / What a way to end it all / Where's the weekend / Cocktails at 8 / Bigger splash / Knock knock knocking / 2nd honeymoon / Get set ready go / Nearly moonlight night motel / Room service / Hi Jo hi / Snapshots / Final act / Night cruiser / East side strut / Skatin' / Uncle Funk / Love magic / Groovitation.
LP: K 56280

DON'T STOP THE WORLD.
Tracks: / Don't stop the world / What a jerk / Darlin' / Everything for the dancer / Capaldi's cafe / Hypertension / It's a boy's world / Rock ferry / Taxi / Operator.
LP: K 56364

ENGLISH BOYS/WORKING GIRLS.
Tracks: / Working girls / Golden shower / Thunder and lightning / What a week / Refugee / Ronny Zamora / English boys with guns / All queued up / I wanna be your boy / Morning after / Fire / O blow.
LP: K 56450

SECOND COMING.
Tracks: / What a way to end it all / Shake some action / Hi Jo hi / Nearly moonlight night motel / Taxi! / Ronnie Zamora / Thunder and lightning / Blue velvet / Princess princess / I wanna be your boy / Lines / Capaldis cafe / 2nd honeymoon / Final act.
LP: FIEND 135

Deal, Bill

BILL DEAL & THE RHONDELLS (Deal, Bill & The Rhondells).
LP: RNLP 70129

DeAlberto

MOVING ON.
LP: LPL 005

Dealer

FIRST STRIKE.
Tracks: / When midnight comes / Victims of the night / Son of a bitch / Epitaph / Choose your weapons / Bring the walls down / Final conflict (parts 1, 2 and 3).
LP: EBON 42

Dean, Carl

CARL DEAN & HIS PIANO.
LP: WLP 8944

Dean, Chris

MY FIRST CHOICE.
Tracks: / Pieces of dreams / He's a tramp / Beautiful friendship, A / All the things you are / Wave / Mas que nada / Old devil moon / Shadow of your smile / Mr. Lucky / Misty / Catherine / Tristeza.
LP: DR 15

Dean, Elton

BOLOGNA TAPE, THE (Dean's, Elton Quintet).
LP: OG 530

CHEQUE IS IN THE MAIL.
LP: OG 610

HAPPY DAZE (Dean's, Elton Ninesense).
LP: OG 910

OH FOR THE EDGE (Dean's, Elton Ninesense).
LP: OG 900

Dean, Hazell

ALWAYS.
Tracks: / They say it's gonna rain (Zulu mix) / Who's leaving who (Bob's tambourine mix) / Turn it into love / You're my rainbow / Always doesn't mean forever / Maybe (we should call it a day) / Walk in my shoes / Nothing in my life / Danger / No fool (for love) (Cassette & CD only.) / Ain't nothing like the real thing (Cassette & CD only.).
LP: EMC 3546
MC: TCEMC 3546

HEART FIRST.
Tracks: / Searchin' / Whatever I do (wherever I go) / Back in my arms (once again).
LP: DEAN 1
MC: CDEAN 1

Dean, James

ON THE AIR (Radio Dramas from 1954/55).
MC: CSH 2103

Dean & Jean

HEY JEAN, HEY DEAN.
Tracks: / I can get him / Mack the knife / Lovingly yours / Sticks and stones / I cry / Seven day wonder / Thread your needle / In my way / Goddess of love / Tra la la la Suzy / I wanna be loved.
LP: ACT 009

Dean, Jimmy

HIS TOP HITS.
MC: 804

Dean, Joanna

MISBEHAVIN'.
Tracks: / Ready for Saturday night / Kiss this / Misbehavin' / I Miss the money / Once is enough / Dirty fingers / Burnin' rubber / She's been hearing about me / Gimme shelter.
LP: 835 272-1
MC: 835 272-4

Dean, Peter

WHERE DID THE MAGIC GO?.
LP: MES 7092

Dean, Roger

CYCLES (Dean, Roger/Lysis).
LP: GCM 774

LYSIS LIVE (Dean, Roger/Lysis).
LP: GCM 762

LYSIS PLUS KENNY WHEELER (see under Lysis, Roger Dean's) (Dean, Roger/Lysis).

SOMETHING BRITISH MADE IN HONG KONG.
LP: GCM 871

Dean, Terry

TERRY DEAN'S APACHE BAND.
Tracks: / Mama's don't let your babies grow up to be cowboys / Rainy day woman / Memories of you / Okie from Muskogie / Today I started loving you again / Self confess / Everybody's making it big / Sneaky / Dead dad / Wasted days and wasted nights / Me and Paul / 10% (everybody wants their 10%).
LP: 2204

Dean, Tommy

DEANIE BOY PLAYS HOT RHYTHM AND BLUES.
Tracks: / Cool-one, groove two / Lonely Monday / Hour past midnight / Scamon boogie / Just about right / Sweet and lovely / Deanie boy / Eventime / How can I let you go / Why don't chu / Gold coast / Straight and ready / Skid row / One more mile.
LP: OFF 6038

Deane, Uel

EVERGREEN.
Tracks: / Lark in the clear air / Over here / My Aunt Jane / Trottin' to the fair / Ould turf fire, The / Lovely armoy.
LP: VAL 8055
MC: VAL 68055

Dear Mr. President

DEAR MR. PRESIDENT.
Tracks: / Hey daddy have you / Fate / What's the world coming to / Love and violence / Queen of my parade? / Fatal desire / Get It Together / Who killed Santa Claus?.
LP: WX 217
MC: WX 217 C

Dear World (show)

DEAR WORLD (Original Broadway cast) (Various artists).
LP: ABOS 3260
MC: BT 3260

Dearie, Blossom

BLOSSOM DEARIE.
Tracks: / Lover man / Deed I do / I won't dance / It might as well be spring / Thou swell.
LP: 2304 357
LP: FS 213
MC: ZDAF 1

BLOSSOM DEARIE SINGS: 1973.
LP: DAFFODIL 101

BLOSSOM DEARIE SINGS: 1975.
LP: DAFFODIL 102

ET TU BRUCE, VOL. 8.
Tracks: / Bruce / Hey John / Someone's been sending me flowers / You have lived in autumn / Alice in Wonderland / Satin doll / Riviera, The / Inside a silent tear.
LP: CHELP 5
MC: ZCHE 5

FEATURING BOBBY JASPAR.
LP: FS 215

MAY I COME IN?.
LP: SM 2066

MY NEW CELEBRITY IS YOU.
2LP: DAFFODIL 103

NEEDLEPOINT MAGIC.
LP: CHELP 3
MC: CHEMC 3

SONGS OF CHELSEA.
LP: DAF 1
MC: ZCDAF 1

WINCHESTER IN APPLE BLOSSOM TIME (REISSUE).
Tracks: / Spring can really hang you up the most / Sunday afternoon / Wonderful guy, A / To touch the hand of love / Wheelers and dealers, The / Jazz musician / Surrey with a fringe on top / Love is an elusive celebration / Lucky to be me / You're for loving / Summer is gone / Sammy / It amazes me / If I were a bell.
MC: CHEMC 8

WINCHESTER IN APPLE BLOSSOM TIME.
2LP: DAFFODIL 104

Death

LEPROSY.
Tracks: / Leprosy / Forgotten past / Pull the plug / Primitive ways / Born dead / Left to die / Open casket / Choke on it.
LP: FLAG 24
MC: TFLAG 24
LPPD: FLAG 26P

SCREAM BLOODY GORE.
Tracks: / Infernal death / Zombie ritual / Denial of life / Sacrificial / Mutilation / Regurgitated guts / Baptized in blood / Torn to pieces / Evil dead, The / Scream bloody gore.
LP: FLAG 12

SPIRITUAL HEALING.
LP: FLAG 38
MC: TFFLAG 38

Death Angel

ACT III.
LP: 7599242801
MC: 7599242804

FALL FROM GRACE.
LP: RO 93331
MC: RO 93334

FROLIC THROUGH THE PARK.
Tracks: / 3rd floor / Road mutants / Why you do this / Bored / Confused / Guilty of innocence / Open up / Shores of sin / Cold gin / Mind rape.
LP: ENVLP 502
MC: TCENV 502

ULTRA-VIOLENCE.
Tracks: / Thrashers / Evil priest / Voracious souls / Kill as one / Ultra violence / Mistress of pain / Final death / IPFS.
LP: FLAG 14

Death Before... (film)

DEATH BEFORE DISHONOUR (Original soundtrack) (Various artists).
LP: STV 81310

Death, Glory &...

DEATH, GLORY AND RETRIBUTION (Various artists).
Tracks: / Endless sleep: *Reynolds, Jody* / Dead Man's Curve: *Jan & Dean* / D.O.A.: *Bloodrock* / Sam Stone: *Gibson, Bob* / Universal soldier: *Campbell, Glen* / Home of the brave: *Miller, Jody* / God, country and my baby: *Burnett, Johnny* / Then I kissed her: *Beach Boys* / Queen of the house: *Miller, Jody* / He'll have to stay: *Black, Jeanne* / My Bologna: *Jankovic, Weird Al* / You should know I'm still your baby: *Various artists* / Gary, please don't sell my diamond ring: *Hill, Wendy* / Billy, I've got to go to town: *Stevens, Geraldine* / Surf and shout: *Isley Brothers.*
LP: EG 2605741
MC: EG 2605744

Death In Action

TOXIC WASTE.
LP: WEBITE 032

Death in Andamans

DEATH IN ANDAMANS (See under Kaye, M.M.) (Kaye, M.M.).

Death In June

93 DEAD SUN WHEELS.
LP: BADVC 093

BROWN BOOK, THE.
LP: BADVC 11

MISANTHROPY.
LP: BADVC 726

NADA.
LP: BC 13

OH, HOW WE LAUGHED.
LP: EYAS 011

WORLD THAT SUMMER, THE.
LP: BADVC 9

Death in Venice (film)

DEATH IN VENICE (1971 film soundtrack) (Various artists).
LP: 26.21149
LP: CBS 70097

Death Mask

SPLIT THE ATOM.
Tracks: / Split the atom / I'm dangerous / Reign, The / Lust for fire / Tortured mind / Nightmare (a lesson for the innocent) / Hell rider / Walk alone / Death has no boundaries / Commando.
LP: KILP 4004

Death Of A Scoundrel

DEATH OF A SCOUNDREL (Film soundtrack) (Various artists).
LP: ERM 6004

Death Of A Soldier

DEATH OF A SOLDIER (1987 film soundtrack) (Various artists).
Tracks: / Boys from the USA: *Various artists* / Annie's jive: *Various artists* / In the mood: *Various artists*/ Dinah might: *Various artists* / Sentimental dreams: *Various artists* / Boogie woogie bugle boy: *Various* artists / Jersey Trott: *Various artists* / Sweetie pie: *Various artists* / When Johnny comes marching home: *Various artists* / Swanston Street parade: *Various artists* / Overture: *Various artists* / Mud murder: *Various artists* / Shoot-out: *Various artists* / Pauline's murder: *Various artists.*
LP: SBL 12001

Death of an Alderman

DEATH OF AN ALDERMAN (See under Hilton, John) (West, Timothy (nar)).

Death Of Samantha

LAUGHING IN THE FACE OF.
LP: HMS 071

WHERE THE WOMEN WEAR THE GLORY.
LP: HMS 121
MC: HMS 121C

Death Strike

FKIN' DEATH.**
LP: NB 044

Deathcore

SPONTANEOUS.
LP: 082976

Deathrage

SELF CONDITIONED SELF LIMITED.
LP: SHARK 011

Deathrow

DECEPTION IGNORED.
LP: NUK 128
MC: ZCNUK 128
LP: N 0128 1
MC: N 0128 4

RAGING STEEL.
LP: N 0081
LP: NUK 081
MC: ZCNUK 081
MC: N 0082

RIDERS OF DOOM.
LP: NUK 044
LP: N 0044

Deathtrash

10,000 RPM GROOVE ORGY.
LP: PIG 001

Deathwish

AT THE EDGE OF DAMNATION.
LP: VOV 667

DEMON PREACHER.
LP: GWLP 33
MC: GWTC 33
LP: RO 9478 1

Deathwish (film)

DEATHWISH II (Film soundtrack) (See under Page, Jimmy).

Debaba

KI NGODI NGODI.
LP: KBK 909

DeBarge

IN A SPECIAL WAY.
Tracks: / Be my lady / Stay with me / Time will reveal / Need somebody / Love me in a special way / Queen of my heart / Baby won'cha come quick / I give up on you / Dream, A.
LP: STML 12200
MC: CSTML 12200

RHYTHM OF THE NIGHT.
Tracks: / Prime time / Heart is not so smart / Who's holding Donna now? / Give it up / Single heart / You wear it well / Walls come tumbling down / Share my world / Rhythm of the night.
LP: ZL 72340
MC: ZK 72340

DeBarge, Bunny

IN LOVE.
LP: ZL 72570
MC: ZK 72570

DeBarge, Chico

CHICO DEBARGE.
Tracks: / Talk to me / Who are you kidding? / You can make it better / I'll love you for now / I like my body / Girl next door / Cross that line / You're much too fast / If it takes all night.
LP: ZL 72524
MC: ZK 72524

DeBarge, El

EL DEBARGE.
Tracks: / Who's Johnny? / Secrets of the night / I wanna hear it from my heart / Someone / When love has gone / Private line / Love always / Lost without her love / Thrill of the chase / Don't say it's over.
LP: ZL 72441
MC: ZK 72441

GEMINI.
Tracks: / Real love / Cross my heart / Somebody loves you / Broken dreams (think about it) / Broken dreams (think about it) (reprise) / Turn the page / After you / Love life / Broken dreams (think about it) / Make you mine.
LP: ZL 72621
MC: ZK 72621

Debussy (composer)

DEBUSSY (Various artists).
MC: DLCMC 223

DEBUSSY'S GREATEST HITS (Various artists).
Tracks: / Clair de lune: *Various artists* / Reverie: *Various artists* / Danse: *Various artists* / La mer: *Various artists* / Prelude to the afternoon of a faun: *Various artists.*
MC: 40 79023

FAVOURITE DEBUSSY (Adni, Daniel).
Tracks: / Golliwogg's cake-walk / Suite Bergamasque / Ballade / Mouvement / Arabesque No.1 / Arabesque No.2 / L'isle joyeuse / Poissons d'or / Reflets dans l'eau / La fill aux cheveux de lin / Feux d'artifice.
MC: TCEMX 2055

FRENCH IMPRESSIONS (Prometheus Ensemble).
LP: DCA 664
MC: ZC DCA 664

LA MER (Montreal Symphony Orchestra).
Tracks: / La mer / Jeux / Le matryre de saint Sebastien / Prelude a l'apres-midi d'un faune.
MC: 4302404

PIANO WORKS - BACH, DEBUSSY, CHOPIN (See under Perlemuter, Vlado) (Perlemuter, Vlado).

RAVEL (String quartets) (Galimir Quartet).
MC: VETC 6521

STRING QUARTET (See under Medici String Quartet for details) (Medici String Quartet).

STRING QUARTETS (Orlando Quartet).
MC: 422 837-4

VIOLIN, CELLO, FLUTE, VIOLA, HARP SONATAS (Various artists).
MC: 422 839-4

Debut

DEBUT 01 (Various artists).
LP: MAG 1

DEBUT 02 (Various artists).
LP: MAG 2

DEBUT 03 (Various artists).
LP: MAG 3

DEBUT 04 (Various artists).
LP: MAG 4

DEBUT 05 (Various artists).
LP: MAG 5

DEBUT 06 (Various artists).
Tracks: / Deeper and deeper: *Fixx* / Ball and chain: *Savage Progress* / Don't take it all away: *Roman Holliday*/ Mist: *Precious Few* / Flesh and steel: *Flying Lizards* / Sweet thing: *Torch Song* / Silly me you're killing me: *Kantata* / Can't cloud my view: *Sunset Gun* / You are on my side: *1'O Clock Gang* / Within these walls of without you: *Difford & Tilbrook* / Pretty girls make graves: *Smiths.*
LP: MAG 6

Decadence Within

SOULWOUND.
LP: VILE 21

THIS LUNACY.
LP: VILE 010

Decameron (bk)

DECAMERON (McCallum, D.).
MC: CDL 51650

Decameron (group)

MAMMONTH SPECIAL.
LP: CREST 19

Decca, Grace

BESOIN D'AMOUR.
LP: SNFL 1001

Decca (label)

DECCA ORIGINALS VOLUME 1 (1960-4) (Various artists).
Tracks: / Wimoweh: *Denver, Karl* / Memphis Tennessee: *Berry, Dave* / Just like Eddie: *Heinz* / Money: *Elliott, Bern & The Fenmen* / Crying game, The: *Berry, Dave* / Man with the Golden Arm, Theme from: *Harris,* Jet / Halfway to paradise: *Fury, Billy* / Hold me: *Proby, P.J.* / Do you love me?: *Poole, Brian & the* Tremeloes / Well I ask you: *Kane, Eden* / Tell him: *Davis, Billie* / Telstar: *Tornados, The* / Loco-motion, The: *Little Eva* / Tell me when: *Applejacks* / It might as well rain until September: *King, Carole* / Diamonds: *Harris, Jet & Tony Meehan.*
LP: TAB 46
MC: KTBC 46

DECCA ORIGINALS VOLUME 2 (1965-9) (Various artists).
LP: TAB 47

DECCA ORIGINALS VOLUME 3 (Various artists).
LP: TAB 61

DECCA ORIGINALS VOLUME 4 (Various artists).
LP: TAB 65

Deceivers (Film)

DECEIVERS, THE (1988 film soundtrack) (Various artists).
LP: BL 87722
MC: BK 87722

Decimator

CARNAGE CITY.
Tracks: / Raider / Mutoids / F H Blood Island / C.C.S.M.P. / Devil's bridge / Rogue decimator / Dustbowl / Stealer of souls.
LP: UNKNOWN

Decimus, Georges

LA VIE.
LP: GP 4001

YELELE (Decimus, Georges & Jacob Desvarieux).
LP: GREL 2006
MC: GREEN 2006

Deckchairs Overboard

DECKCHAIRS OVERBOARD.
Tracks: / Fight for love / Can't stop the motor / It's all in the game / I need you more / Love takes over / Every other day / Teach me to cry / I get hungry / Overboard / Walking in the dark.
LP: 252215 1

Decline Of... (film)

DECLINE OF THE AMERICAN EMPIRE (1986 film soundtrack) (Various artists).
LP: CAR 66390 1
LP: A 298

Declino

MUCCHIO MCLVAGGIO (See under Negazione) (Declino & Negazione).

Decorators

TABLETS.
Tracks: / Curious / Strange one / We know it / Red sky over Wembley / American ways.
LP: RF 1

Dede Saint Prix

DEDE SAINT PRIX & AVAN VAN (Dede Saint Prix & Avan Van).
LP: GD 007

Dedicated ...

DEDICATED TO THE ONES WE LOVE (Various artists).
Tracks: / Chapel of love: *Dixie Cups* / And then he kissed me: *Crystals* / End of the world: *Davis, Skeeter*/ Dedicated to the one I love: *Shirelles* / April love: *Boone, Pat* / Why: *Avalon, Frankie* / To know him is to love him: *Teddy Bears* / Hey Paula: *Paul & Paula* / Teen angel: *Dinning, Mark.*
LP: OCN 2010WL
MC: OCN 2010WK

Dedrick, Rusty

ISHAM JONES EVERGREENS (Dedrick, Rusty, Orchestra).
LP: MES 6603

SALUTE TO BUNNY.
LP: FS 196

Dedringer

DIRECT LINE.
LP: DID 7

SECOND ARISING.
Tracks: / Rock night / Going to the movies / Sold me lonely / I'm on the outside / Donna / Comin out fightin / Throw me the line / Never gonna lose it / Eagle never falls, The.
LP: NEAT 1009

Dee, Brian

HOMING IN (Dee, Brian Trio).
MC: SPJCS 539

SIDE BY SIDE WITH TWO BRYANS (sic) (Dee, Brian/Bryan Smith).
Tracks: / Mame / Charlie girl / Memories / Arm in arm / Desert song / Born free / Solitude / Blue moon / C'est magnifique / Fine romance, A / Bye bye Blues.
LP: DS 044

SWING DOODLE (Dee, Brian, quintet).
Tracks: / Shady lane / Nova bossa nova / Everyday affair / Takin my time / Swing doodle / Cos I'm in love / Toe tapper / Minor degrees / Brightly shining / Angelique / Anytime at all / Burt's back.
LP: RRS 104

Dee, David

GOIN' FISHIN'.
Tracks: / Heatin' me up / Rainy night in Georgia / If I knew then / Special way of making love / Part time love / Goin' fishin' / Workin' this dream overtime / Lead me on / Thought my lovin' was over.
LP: ICH 1114
MC: ICH 1114MC

Dee Dee

DEE DEE.
MC: JZC 36370

Dee, Jeannie

INTRODUCING JEANNIE.
Tracks: / Your good girl's gonna go bad / You and me / I fall to pieces / Peaceful easy feeling / Standing tall / What I've got in mind / Blue eyes crying in the rain / How many lovers / Crazy arms / Fight and scratch / Stand by your man.
LP: STON 8405
MC: CSTON 8405

SYLVANTONE SHOWCASE, THE (see Goodacre, Tony).

Dee, Joey

HEY, LET'S TWIST (Best of Joey Dee & The Starliters) (Dee, Joey & The Starlighters).
Tracks: / Peppermint twist - part I / Peppermint twist - part II / Hey, let's twist / Roly, poly / Joey's blues (Featuring Dave Brigati. CD only.) / Shout - part I / Irresistible you (CD only.) / Crazy love (CD only.) / Everytime (I think about you) - part I / What kind of love is this / I lost my baby / Keep your mind on what you're doing (CD only.) / Help me pick up the pieces / Baby, you're driving me crazy / Hot pastrami / Dance, dance, dance / Ya ya / Fannie Mae.
MC: TCROU 5010
MC: 794 896 4

Dee, Kiki

ANGEL EYES.
Tracks: / I fall in love too easily / Stay close to you / I'll build a tower over you / Pay / We cry on / Knowing you like I do / Another day comes (another day goes) / Keep it to yourself / Good times / Angel eyes.
LP: SCX 6701
MC: TCSCX 6701

BITE YOUR LIP (See under John, Elton) (Dee, Kiki & Elton John).

KIKI DEE.
LP: ROLA 3

LOVING AND FREE.
LP: ROLL 5

PERFECT TIMING.
Tracks: / Star / Loving you is sweeter than ever / Wild eyes / 24 Hours / Perfect timing / Midnight flyer / There's a need / Another break / Love is just a moment away / You are my hope in this world.
LP: 4157451
LP: ARL 5050
MC: ZCARL 5050

STAY WITH ME.
Tracks: / Dark side of your soul / Don't stop loving me / Holding me too tight / Love is a crazy feeling / One jump ahead of the storm / One step / Safe harbour / Stay with me baby / Talk to me.
LP: TRAIN 3

Dee, Lenny

LOONEY TUNES VOL.1 (See under Bones, Frankie) (Dee, Lenny & Frankie Bones).

Dee, Mercy

G I FEVER.
Tracks: / G.I. fever / Homely baby / Evil and hanky / Empty life / Get to gettin' / Bird brain baby / Crepe on your door / Please understand / Fall guy, The / Come back Maybeline / Bought love / Happy bachelor / Romp and stomp blues / Roamin' blues / Oh, oh, please / Anything in this world / True love.
LP: IG 406

Dee, Michael

PORTRAITS.
LP: CALCLP 005

Dee, Ruby

TSHINDAO (see Davis, Ossie).

Dee, Sammy

CHICAGO - THAT'S JAZZ (Dee, Sammy All Stars).
Tracks: / Please don't talk about me / Mama's gone goodbye / Everybody loves my baby / I cried for you / Blue and brokenhearted / I can't believe that you're in love with me / I want a little girl / Spain / Glad rag doll / Roses of Picardy / At sundown / If I could be with you / Ain't she sweet / Blues my naughty sweetie gives to me.
MC: LA 5017C

Deebank, Maurice

INNER THOUGHT ZONE.
LP: BRED 61

Deee-Lite

WORLD CLIQUE.
LP: EKT 77
MC: EKTC 77

Deems

LIVING.
LP: CHAMP 1010
MC: CHAMPK 1010

Deenie (bk)

DEENIE (Judy Blume) (Braden, Kim (nar)).
MCSET: LFP 7278

Deep Freeze Mice

GATES OF LUNCH, THE.
LP: MOLE 002

LIVE IN SWITZERLAND.
LP: LOGICAL FISH 1

MY GERANIUMS ARE BULLETPROOF.
LP: MOLE 001

SAW A RANCH HOUSE BURNING LAST NIGHT.
LP: MOLE 004

TEENAGE HEAD IN MY REFRIGERATOR.
LP: MOLE 003

TENDER YELLOW PONIES.
LP: ERICAT 027

Deep Lancashire

DEEP LANCASHIRE (Songs and ballads of the industrial northwest) (Various artists).
Tracks: / Hand loom weaver's lament, The: *Various artists* / Hop hop hop: *Various artists* / Beg your leave: *Various artists* / Ale is physic for me: *Various artists* / Gettin' wed: *Various artists* / Clogs: *Various artists* / Merry little doffer, The: *Various artists* / Rawtenstall annual fair: *Various artists* / Coqlouse medley: *Various artists* / Cob a coalin': *Various artists* / Seaur pies: *Various artists* / Bury new loom, The: *Various artists* / Ten per cent: *Various artists* / Man like thee, A: *Various artists* / Lancashire liar, The: *Various artists*.
LP: 12T 188

Deep Purple

24 CARAT PURPLE.
Tracks: / Woman from Tokyo / Fireball / Strange kind of woman / Never before / Black night / Speed king / Smoke on the water / Child in time.
LP: TPSM 2002
MC: TC EXE 139
LP: FA 41 3133 1
MC: FA 41 3132 4
LP: FA 3132
MC: TCFA 3132

ANTHOLOGY, THE.
Tracks: / Hush / Mandrake root / Shield / Wring that neck / Bird has flown / Bloodsucker / Speed king / Black night / Child in time / Fireball / Strange kind of woman (live) / Highway star / Smoke on the water (live) / Pictures of home / Woman from Tokyo / Smooth dancer / Sail away / Lay down stay down / Burn (live) / Stormbringer / Hold on / Gypsy / Mistreated (live) / Gettin' tighter / Love child / You keep on movin' / No one came.
LPS: EN 5013
MCSET: TCEN 5013

BEST OF DEEP PURPLE, THE.
Tracks: / Speed king / Strange kind of woman / Black night / Fireball / Smoke on the water / Hush / Emmaretta / Woman from Tokyo / Demon's eye / Stormbringer.
LP: STAR 2312
MC: STAC 2312

BOOK OF TALIESYN.
Tracks: / Listen, learn, read on / Wring that neck / Kentucky woman / Exposition / We can work it out / Shield / Anthem / River deep, mountain high.
LP: SHVL 751
MC: TCSHVL 751

BURN.
Tracks: / Burn / Might just take your life / Lay down, stay down / Sail away / You fool no-one / What's goin' on here? / Mistreated / 'A' Zoo.
LP: ATAK 11
MC: TCATAK 11
LP: TPS 3505
MC: TCTPS 3505

BUTTERFLY BALL, THE/WIZARD'S CONVENTION (See under Glover, Roger).

COME TASTE THE BAND.
Tracks: / Comin' home / Lady Luck / Gettin' tighter / Dealer / I need love / Drifter / Love child / This time around / Owed to 'G' / You keep on moving.
LP: TPSA 7515
MC: TC TPSA 7515

CONCERTO FOR GROUP AND ORCHESTRA.
Tracks: / Wring that neck / Child in time / Moderato - allegro: First movement / Andante: Second movement / Vivace - presto: Third movement.
LP: SHVL 767

DEEP PURPLE IN CONCERT.
Tracks: / Speed king / Wring that neck / Child in time / Mandrake root / Highway star / Strange kind of woman / Lazy / Never before / Space truckin' / Lucille.
2LP: SHDW 412
MC: TCSHDW 412

DEEP PURPLE IN ROCK.
Tracks: / Speed king / Blood sucker / Child in time / Flight of the rat / Into the fire / Living wreck / Hard lovin' man.
LPPD: EJ 2603430
LP: FA 3011
MC: TCFA 3011
LP: SHVL 777

DEEP PURPLE: INTERVIEW PICTURE DISC.
LPPD: BAK 2039

DEEPEST PURPLE.
Tracks: / Black night / Speed king / Fireball / Strange kind of woman / Child in time / Woman from Tokyo / Highway star / Space truckin' / Burn / Demon's eye / Stormbringer / Smoke on the water.
LP: EMTV 25
MC: TC EMTV 25
LP: ATAK 138
MC: TCATAK 138
LP: FA 3239
MC: TCFA 3239

FIREBALL.
Tracks: / Fireball / No, no, no / Demon's eye / Mule, The / Fools / No one came / Anyone's daughter.
LP: EMS 1255
MC: TCEMS 1255
LP: FA 413093-1
MC: TCFA 41 30934
LPPD: EJ 2403440
LP: ATAK 105
MC: TCATAK 105
LP: SHVL 793

HARD ROCK HEROES.
Tracks: / Highway star / Hush / Stormbringer / Lady double dealer / Strange kind of woman / Mandrake root / Woman from Tokyo / Black night / Demons eye / Lay down, stay down / Hold on / Burn / Why didn't Rosemary / Mistreated / Emeretta / Smoke on the water / Help / Hey Joe / Speed king / Into the fire / Child in time.
LPS: 1552413

HOUSE OF BLUE LIGHT.
Tracks: / Bad attitude / Unwritten law / Call of the wild / Mad dog / Black and white / Hard lovin' woman / Spanish archer / Strange-ways / Mitzi dupree / Dead or alive.
LP: POLH 32
MC: POLHC 32
LP: 831 318-1
MC: 831 318-4

KNEBWORTH LIVE 1985.
LP: DPVSOPLP 163
MC: DPVSOPMC 163

LAST CONCERT IN JAPAN.
LP: 2C 066 60900

LIVE IN LONDON: DEEP PURPLE.
Tracks: / Burn / Might just take your life / Lay down, stay down / Mistreated / Smoke on the water / You fool no-one / Mule, The.
LP: SHSP 4124
MC: TCSHSP 4124

MACHINE HEAD.
Tracks: / Highway star / Maybe I'm a Leo / Pictures of home / Never before / Smoke on the water / Lazy / Space truckin'.
LP: FA 3158
MC: TCFA 3158
LP: ATAK 39
MC: TC-ATAK 39
LP: TPSA 7504
LPPD: EJ 2603450

MADE IN EUROPE (LIVE).
Tracks: / Burn / Mistreated / Lady double dealer / You fool no-one / Stormbringer.
LP: TPSA 7517
MC: TCTPSA 7517

MADE IN JAPAN.
Tracks: / Highway star / Child in time / Smoke on the water / Mule, The / Strange kind of woman / Lazy / Space truckin'.
2LP: TPSP 351
MCSET: TC2 TPSP 351

MALICE IN WONDERLAND (See under Paice Ashton Lord).

MARK 1 AND MARK 2.
Tracks: / Hush / Mandrake root / Why didn't Rosemary? / Hey Joe / Wring that neck / Emmaretta / Help / Chasing shadows / Black night / Speed king / Strange kind of woman / Into the fire / When a blind man cries / Smoke on the water / Woman from Tokyo / Highway star.
2LP: IC 172 94865/6

MARK 2 SINGLES.
Tracks: / Black night / Smoke on the water / Child in time / Woman from Tokyo / Never before / When a blind man cries / Painted horse.
LP: 1C 064 61695
LP: TPS 3514
LP: 3C064 61695

NOBODY'S PERFECT.
Tracks: / Highway star / Strange kind of woman / Perfect strangers / Hard lovin' woman / Bad attitude / Knocking on your back door / Child in time / Lazy / Black night / Woman from Tokyo / Smoke on the water / Space truckin'.
2LP: PODV 10
MCSET: PODVC 10
MCSET: 835 897-4
LP: 835 897-1

PERFECT STRANGERS.
Tracks: / Knocking on your back door / Under the gun / Nobody's home / Mean streak / Perfect strangers / Gypsy's kiss, A / Wasted sunsets / Hungry daze / Not Responsible (Cassette only).
LP: POLH 16
MC: POLHC 16
LPPD: POLHP 16
MC: 823 777-4
LP: 823 777-A

POWERHOUSE.
Tracks: / Painted horse / Hush / Wring that neck / Child in time / Black night / Cry free.
LP: TPS 3510
MC: TCTPS 3510

SCANDANAVIAN NIGHTS.
Tracks: / Wring that neck / Speed king / Into the fire / Paint it black / Mandrake root / Child in time / Black night.
2LP: DPVSOPLP 125
MCSET: DPVSOPMC 125

SHADES OF DEEP PURPLE.
Tracks: / And the address / Hush / One more rainy day / Prelude: happiness / I'm so glad / Mandrake root / Help / Love help me / Hey Joe.
LP: SHSM 2016

SINGLES - A'S & B'S.
Tracks: / Hush / One more rainy day / Emmaretta / Wring that neck / Hallelujah / April, part 1 / Black night / Speed king / Strange kind of woman / I'm alone / Demon's eye / Fireball.
LP: FA 3212
MC: TCFA 3212

SLAVES AND MASTERS.
Tracks: / King of dreams / Cut runs deep, The / Fire in the basement / Truth hurts / Breakfast in bed / Love conquers all / Fortune teller / Too much is not enough / Wicked ways.
LP: PL 90535
MC: PK 90535

STORMBRINGER.
Tracks: / Stormbringer / Love don't mean a thing / Holy man / Hold on / Lady double dealer / You can't do it right / High ball shooter / Gypsy, The / Soldier of fortune.
LP: ATAK 70
MC: TCATAK 70
LP: TPS 3508
MC: TCTPS 3508

THIRD ALBUM.
Tracks: / Chasing shadows / Blind / Lalena / Painter, The / Why didn't Rosemary? / Bird has flown / April.
LP: SHVL 759
MC: TCSHVL 759

WHO DO WE THINK WE ARE.
Tracks: / Woman from Tokyo / Mary Long / Super trouper / Smooth dancer / Rat bat blue / Place in line / Our lady.
LP: TPSA 7508
MC: TC TPSA 7508
LP: ATAK 127
MC: TCATAK 127

Deep River Boys

ROCK A BEATIN BOOGIE.
Tracks: / Not too old to rock and roll / That's right / Shake, rattle and roll / Rock-a-beatin' boogie / Just a little bit more / Adam never had no mammy / Settle down / Itchy twitchy feeling / I shall not be moved / Slow train to nowhere / Ashes of roses / St. Louis blues / Honey Honey / Whole lotta shakin' goin' on / Smack dab in the middle / Rock around the clock.
LP: SEE 55

Deep Sea Jivers

RAPTURES OF THE DEEP.
LP: MMD 101

Deep Switch

NINE INCHES OF GOD.
LP: SWITCH 1

Deep Throat (film)

DEEP THROAT (1974 film soundtrack) (Various artists).
LP: SH 2036

Deep Voices

SOUNDS OF WHALES, THE.
Tracks: / Whales charging a boat / Left over sea running / Herd noises / Drifting off / Blues, deep voices (first section) / Blue whales in range / Rights right whales (second section) / Surrounded by snoring / Deep breathing.
LP: EST 11598

Deerhunter (film)

DEERHUNTER, THE (1978 film soundtrack) (Various artists).
LP: SOO 11940
MC: 4 XOO 11940
MC: 92058.4

Deering, Richard

BEATLES CONCERTO, THE.
LP: OX 7125

Deeside Ladies ...

WHITE BALMORALS, THE (Deeside Ladies Pipe Band).
Tracks: / Bonnie galloway / Rowan tree / Kirkhill / Nicky tams / Moonstar / Auld Adam / Deeside ladies farewell to grade 3 / Waterhole, The / Flett from flotta / Ichyt fingers / Rocking the baby / Lochanside / Bonnie lass o' Fyvie / White balmorals, The / Wings / Dornie ferry.
LP: LOCLP 1044
MC: ZCLOC 1044

Def America (label)

DEF AMERICAN SAMPLER - TIL DEF DO US PART (Various artists).
LP: 8485741
MC: 8485744

Def Beats

DEF BEATS 1 (Compilation Recordings) (Various artists).
LP: MODEF 1
MC: MODEF 1C

Def Con (film)

DEF CON 4: DEFENCE CONDITION NO. 4 (1985 film soundtrack) (Various artists).
LP: C'BUS 212
LP: 7599260491
MC: 7599260494

Def Jam (label)

DEF JAM CLASSICS VOL 1 (Various artists).
Tracks: / Rock the bells: *L.L. Cool J* / Can U feel it: *Original Concept* / Rhymin' and stealin': *Beastie Boys* / (You gotta) Fight for your right (to party): *Beastie Boys* / Cold chillin' in the spot: *Rush, Russell & Jazzy Jay* / Son of Public Enemy: *Public Enemy* / Are you my woman: *Black Flames* / Rebel without a pause: *Public Enemy* / Jack the ripper: *L.L. Cool J* / I'm bad: *L.L. Cool J* / I'm a girl watcher: *Love, Poppa Ron* / Have you seen Davy: *Davy D* / Ruler's back: *Slick Rick*.

LP: 4632891
MC: 4632894

DEF JAM CLASSICS VOL 2 (Various artists).
Tracks: / Fight the power: *Public Enemy* / Jingling baby: *L.L. Cool J* / Triple stage darkness: *3rd Bass* / This house is smokin': *3rd Bass* / Moment I feared, The: *Slick Rick* / Can't do nuttin' for ya man: *Flavor Flav* / Illegal search: *L.L. Cool J* / Childrens story: *Slick Rick* / Welcome to the terrordrome: *Public Enemy* / Steppin' to the AM: *3rd Bass* / Lettin' off steam: *Nikki D.*
LP: 4671581
MC: 4671584

DEF JAM SAMPLER (Various artists).
Tracks: / Rock hard: *Beastie Boys* / Def jam: *Jazzy Jay* / Word, The: *Junkyard Band* / Sardines: *Junkyard* Band / Pump that bass: *Original Concept* / Live: *Original Concept* / Finer things in life, The: *Various* artists / I'm bad: *L.L. Cool J* / Read my mind: *Tashan* / Can you feel it: *Original Concept* / You're gonna get yours: *Public Enemy* / Here I go again: *Jones, Oran "Juice"*.
LP: KIKIT 1
MC: KIKITC 1

Def Jef

JUST A POET WITH SOUL.
Tracks: / Droppin' rhymes on drums / Givin' 'em rhythm / On the real tip / Poet with a soul / Give it here / Do you wanna get housed / Black to the future / Do it baby / God made me funky / Downtown / Just a poet.
MC: BRCA 546
LP: BRLP 546
MC: ICM 2069
LP: ILPM 2069

SOUL FOOD.
LP: BRLP 578
MC: BRCA 578

Def Leppard

DEF LEPPARD: INTERVIEW PICTURE DISC.
LPPD: CT 1011

DEF LEPPARD: INTERVIEW PICTURE DISC.
LPPD: BAK 2067

HIGH 'N' DRY.
Tracks: / High 'n' dry (Saturday night) / You got me runnin' / Let it go / Another hit and run / Lady strange / On through the night / Mirror mirror (look into my eyes) / No, no, no / Bringin' on the heartbreak / Switch 625.
LP: 6359 045
MC: 7150 045
MC: 818 836 4
LP: 818 836 1

HYSTERIA.
Tracks: / Women / Rocket / Animal / Love bites / Pour some sugar on me / Armageddon it / Gods of war / Don't shoot shot gun / Run riot / Hysteria / Excitable / Love and affection / I can't let you be a memory.
LPPD: HYSPD 1
LP: HYSLP 1
MC: HYSMC 1

MUSIC AND MEDIA INTERVIEW PICTURE DISCS.
LPPD: DL 1021

ON THROUGH THE NIGHT.
Tracks: / Answer to the master / Hello America / It could be you / It don't matter / Overture / Rock brigade / Rocks off / Satellite / Sorrow is a woman / When the walls came tumblin down.
LP: 9102 040
MC: 7231 028
MC: 8225 334
LP: 8225 331

PYROMANIA.
Tracks: / Rock rock ('til you drop) / Photograph / Stagefright / Too late for love / Die hard the hunter / Foolin' / Rock of ages / Comin' under fire / Action not words / Billy's got a gun.
LP: VERS 2
MC: VERSC 2

Def Reggae

DEF REGGAE, THE BEST (Various artists).
LP: HOP 232

Def Squad

HARD HITTIN'.
Tracks: / Hard hittin' / Love is blind / I'm Def and I'm proud / We rock hard / Doggin' the axe / Microwave / Kingdom of rhymes / Drop that bass / Hard-core hip-hop / It's killer.
LP: MRH 4026
MC: MRH 4026 MC

Defecation

PURITY DILUTION.
LP: NB 018

Defects

DEFECTIVE BREAKDOWN.
LP: LMNOP 2

Defiance

PRODUCT OF SOCIETY.
Tracks: / Fault / Product of society / Lock jaw / Deadly intentions / Tribulation / Death machine / Forgotten / Insomnia / Aftermath / Hyperthermia.
LP: RO 95041

VOID, TERRA, FIRMA.
Tracks: / Void terra firma / Questions / Slayground / Steamroller / Buried or burned / Deception of faith / Skitz - illusions / Killers / Checkmate / Last resort (welcome to poverty).
LP: RO 93951
MC: RO 93954

Defilm

DEFILM.
Tracks: / I saw your dream / Bitter surprise / Yellow / Julia / Here we are / 747 / Telegram / Turkish delight / Love is over / Cuba libre.
LP: PRT 26849

Definition of Sound

LOVE AND LIFE.
LP: CIRC 14
MC: CIRCA 14

Defoe, Daniel (author)

MOLL FLANDERS (McKenna, Siobhan).
MC: 1090

MOLL FLANDERS (Leigh-Hunt, Barbara).
MCSET: ARGO 1244

Defries, David

SECRET CITY.
Tracks: / Secret city / Naledi's dreamsong / Le marche a la marche des peches / Bubbles / Charge of the water brigade, The / Reflections on the great invocation.
MC: TCMMC 1009
LP: MMC 009

Defunkt

AVOID THE FUNK (Defunkt Anthology).
LP: HNBL 1320
MC: HNBC 1320

DEFUNKT.
Tracks: / Make them dance / Strangling me with your love / In the good times / Blues / Defunkt / Thermonuclear sweat / Melvin's tune / We all dance together.
LP: HNBL 1301
MC: HNBC 1301

MADE IN AMERICA.
Tracks: / Smooth love / Eraserhead / Peace of mind / In America / Change / Love you from afar / Tell me / Spiritual sponsor / Self-disclosure.
MC: ANC 8730
LP: AN 8730

THERMONUCLEAR SWEAT.
LP: HNBL 1311

Degen, Bob

CHARTREUSE.
LP: ENJA 3015

CHILDREN OF THE NIGHT.
LP: ENJA 3027

SEQUOIA SONG.
LP: ENJA 2072

DeGrassi, Alex

ALTIPLANO.
Tracks: / Altiplano / First time / Doumbek / Digital interlude / Fat boy / Lila / McCormick / MTY.
LP: PL 83016

CLOCKWORK.
LP: C-1018

DEEP AT NIGHT.
Tracks: / Mirage / Deep at night / Charlotte / Short order / Indian Summer / Blue trout / Waltz (4) / Arcos / Mirror, The / Hidden voices.
MC: WT 1100

SOUTHERN EXPOSURE.
Tracks: / Overland / Blue and white / Thirty six / Cumulus / Southern exposure / Western / Street waltz / Heavy feet / Empty rooms / Subway.
LP: 371030-1
MC: 371030-4

Degville, Martin

WORLD WAR FOUR.
LP: RRLP 138
MC: RRLC 138

Dehumanizers

END OF TIME.
LP: NEGFX 006

Deicide

DEICIDE.
Tracks: / Lunatic of God's creation / Oblivious to evil / Blasphererein / Carnage in the temple of the damned / Day of darkness / Sacrificial suicide / Dead by dawn / Deicide / Mephistopheles / Crucifixion.
LP: RO 93811

Deighton Family

ACOUSTIC MUSIC TO SUIT MOST OCCASIONS.
Tracks: / Travelling light / Matchbox / Two little boys / Muddy roads / Boll weevil / Keep that candle burning / All shook up / Tennessee wig walk / Money / Handsome molly / Tin whistle / Blue suede shoes / Going down the road / Give the fiddler a dram.
LP: FMSL 2010
LP: PH 1120

Deivert, Bert

APRIL FOOLS (See under Bibb, Eric) (Deivert, Bert & Eric Bibb).

HANDCRAFTED SONGS.
LP: OP 7811

RIVER ROAD (See under Bibb, Eric) (Deivert, Bert & Eric Bibb).

WHEN I LOOK AT YOU.
LP: OP 8006

Deja

SERIOUS.
Tracks: / You and me tonight / Serious / Somethings turn around / That's where you'll find me / Heart beat / Premonition / Life / What to do now / Summer love / Straight to the point.
LP: DIX 58
MC: CDIX 58

Deja Vu

ROCKBUSTERS.
MCSET: CBK 301

Dejan, Joseph

DUO (Dejan, Joseph and Gerrard Maurais).
LP: OP 03

Dejan's Olympia Brass

DEJAN'S OLYMPIA BRASS BAND 1968.
LP: NOLA LP 4

JAZZY YOURS.
LP: 1011
MC: 1011 TC

Dekka Danse

WALTZ IN THE WILDERNESS.
Tracks: / Soul separation / I can't believe it / Waltz in the wilderness / Waiting game / I live in sound / Movement is tranquility / Immagnetized / Desire / Open secret / Great divide, The.
LP: CBS 25963

Dekker, Desmond

20 GOLDEN PIECES: DESMOND DEKKER.
Tracks: / You can get it if you really want / I believe / Perseverance / Get up little Suzie / Pickney gal / Rudy got soul / That's the way life goes / Peace of mind / Man / Ah it mek / Israelites / It's not easy / Intensified / Tips of my fingers, The / Too much too soon / Nincompoop / Problems / For once in my life / Rude boy train / My precious love.
LP: BDL 2054
MC: BDC 2054

BEST OF AND THE REST OF, THE (Dekker, Desmond & The Aces).
Tracks: / You can get it if you really want it / Archie wah wah / Mother nature / Where did it go / More you live, The / What will you gain / Look what they're doing to me / Israelites / Reggae recipe / Lickin' / Pickney gal / It mek / Life of opportunity / I believe / My reward / 007 (shanty town).
MC: ARLC 1002

BLACK AND DEKKER.
Tracks: / Israelites / Lickin' stick / It mek / Please don't bend / Many rivers to cross / Hippo / 007 / Workout / Problems / Rude boy train / Pickney girl / Why fight?.
LP: SEEZ 26

COMPASS POINT.
Tracks: / I'll get by / Moving on / We can and shall / Hurt so bad / Isabella / Come back to me / Cindy / I do believe / My destiny / Big headed / That's my woman / Allamanna.
LP: SEEZ 36

GREATEST HITS: DESMOND DEKKER.
LP: 226 2515
MC: 216 2515

ISRAELITES.
Tracks: / Israelites / Beware / Everybody join hands / It mek / Sing a little song / Busted lad / My world is blue / Mother nature / Money and friends / No place like home.
LP: CTLP 111

ISRAELITES (SCOOP EP).
Tracks: / Israelites / I believe / It mek / You can get it if you really want / When I'm cold / Please don't bend.
MC: 7SC 5043

OFFICIAL LIVE AND RARE (Dekker, Desmond & The Aces).
2LP: TRLD 404
MC: ZCTRD 404

ORIGINAL REGGAE HITSOUND, THE (Dekker, Desmond & The Aces).
Tracks: / 007 / Get up, Edina / Beautiful and dangerous / Shing a ling / Pretty Africa / Wise man / Sabotage / Unity / It pays / Israelites / It mek / Warlock / Archie wah wah / Pickney girl / Reggae recipe / You can get it if you really want / Hippopotamus song, The / Lickin' stick / More you live, The.
LP: TRLS 226
MC: ZCTRL 226

PROFILE: DESMOND DEKKER.
MC: CL4 24479
LP: 6.24479

SWEET 16 HITS.
Tracks: / Reggae recipe / Lickin' stick / Pickney girl / It mek / Life of opportunity / I believe / My reward / 007 / You can get it if you really want / Archie wah wah / Mother nature / Where did it go? / More you live, The / What will you gain? / Look what they're doing to me / Israelites.
LP: TRLS 154
MC: ZCTRL 154

THIS IS DESMOND DEKKER.
LP: TTL 4

Dekker, George

DON'T FORGET TO REMEMBER ME.
LP: KPLP 03

Del Amitri

DEL AMITRI.
Tracks: / Heard through a wall / Hammering heart / Former owner / Sticks and stones girl / Deceive yourself (in ignorant heaven) / I was here / Crows in a wheatfield / Keepers / Ceasefire / Breaking bread.
LP: CHR 1499
MC: ZCHR 1499

WAKING HOURS.
Tracks: / Kiss this thing goodbye / Opposite view / Move away Jimmy Blue / Stone cold sober / You're gone / When I want you / This side of the morning / Empty / Hatful of rain / Nothing ever happens.
LP: AMA 9006
MC: AMC 9006

Del Fuegos

BOSTON, MASSACHUSSETTS.
LP: SLAP 9
MC: SMAC 9

LONGEST DAY, THE.
Tracks: / Nervous and shakey / Backseat nothing / I should be the one / Missing you the one / Anything you want / When the news is on / Longest day, The / Out for a ride / Mary don't change / Have you forgotten / Call my name.
LP: SLMP 14
MC: SLMC 14
MC: SMMC 14
LP: ROUGH 79

SMOKING IN THE FIELDS.
Tracks: / Move with me sister / Down in Allen's mills / I'm inside you / Headlights / Breakaway / Dreams of you / Offer, The / Part of this earth / Stand by me / Lost weekend / No no never / Friends again.
LP: PL 90422
MC: PK 90422

STAND UP.
Tracks: / Wear it like a cape / New old world / Names names / Long slide (for an out) / He had a lot to drink today / Town called love, A / I can't take this place / News from nowhere / Scratching at your door / I'll sleep with you.
LP: SLAP 20
MC: SMAC 20

Del Lords

BASED ON A TRUE STORY.
Tracks: / Crawl in bed / Judas kiss / Ashes to ashes / I'm gonna be around / Poem of the river / Cool and the crazy / Cheyenne / Lover's prayer / Whole lotta nothin' goin' on / River of justice.
LP: ENVLP 508
MC: TCENV 508

FRONTIER DAYS.
Tracks: / How can a poor man stand such times and live / Get tough / Livin' on love / Double life / I play the drums / Burning in the flame of love / Pledge of love / Shame on you / Mercenary / Going home.
LP: FIEND 53

JOHNNY COMES MARCHING HOME.

Tracks: / Heaven (Scott Kempner.) / love lies dying (Scott kempner) / Drug deal (Scott Kempner, Eric Ambel, Manny Caiate, Frank Funaro.) / Soldier's home (Scott Kempner) / St. Jake (Scott Kempner) / Dream come true (Scott Kempner) / True love (Scott Kempner) / Everlovin (Scott Kempner) / Against my will (Scott Kempner) / No waitress no more (Scott Kempner).
LP: . . . . AML 3103
MC: . . . . TCAML 3103

Del Mero Corazon

DEL MERO CORAZON (Film Soundtrack).
LP: . . . . ARHOOLIE 3015

Del Monaco, Mario

DEL MONACO, MARIO.
Tracks: / Serenade / Musica prohibita / Loves last word is spoken / Tonight / To veglio tanto bene / Catari catari / Be my love / Girls were made to love and kiss / Cara mia / Lolita.
LP: 4116171

Del Rubio Triplets

THREE GALS, THREE GUITARS.
LP: . . . . BY 333

Del Sonto, Dan

IN SOUTH AFRICA/SUN CITY.
LP: 7005

Delafose, John

JOE PETE GOT TWO WOMEN.
MC: . . . . C 1083

LIVE AT RICHARD'S ZYDECO DANCE HALL vol. 2 (Delafose, John & The Eunice Playboys).
LP: . . . . ROUNDER 2070
MC: . . . . ROUNDER 2070C

UNCLE BUD ZYDECO.
LP: . . . . ARHOOLIE 1088
MC: . . . . C 1088

ZYDECO EXCITEMENT.
LP: 1015
MC: . . . . 1015 TC

ZYDECO LIVE.
LP: . . . . R 2070

ZYDECO MAN.
LP: . . . . ARHOOLIE 1083

Delaney & Bonnie

ACCEPT NO SUBSTITUTE.
Tracks: / Get ourselves together / Someday / Ghetto, The / When the battle is over / Dirty old man / Love me a little bit longer / I can't take it much longer / Do right woman, do right man / Soldiers of the cross / Gift of love.
LP: . . . . THBL 050

BEST OF DELANEY & BONNIE.
LP: . . . . K 40429

ON TOUR (Delaney & Bonnie & Eric Clapton).
LP: . . . . K 30030
LP: 2400 013

Delaney, Kate

BLACKWATERSIDE (Delaney, Kate & Gordon McIntyre).
LP: . . . . LRB 077

Delaware Water Gap

STRING BAND MUSIC.
LP: . . . . AD 2004

Del-Byzanteens

LIES TO LIVE BY.
Tracks: / Lies to live by / Draft riot / War / Sally go round the roses / Girl's imagination / Welcome machines / Apartment 13.
LP: . . . . X 14

Delegation

DELEGATION.
Tracks: / Feels so good / Dance prance boogie / In love's time / Singing / Twelfth house / In the night / Turn on to city life / Free to be me / I wantcha' back / Gonna keep my eyes on you.
LP: . . . . ARL 5062

DEUCES HIGH.
Tracks: / What took you so long / I figure I'm out of your life / If you were a song / Gonna bring the house down / Tell her / Dance like Fred Astaire / No words to say / Would you like to start a thang with me / Dance-time USA.
LP: . . . . ARL 5070

EAU DE VIE.
Tracks: / Heartache no.9 / Sho'nuff sold on you / One more step to take / Blue girl / Darlin' / You and I / Stand up / Welcome to my world / Put a little love on me.
MC: . . . . ZCARL 5035
LP: . . . . ARL 5035

PROMISE OF LOVE, THE.
Tracks: / Promise of love / You've been doing me wrong / We can make it / Heaven is by your side / Back door love / Where is the love / We used to know / Soul trippin' / You and your love / Someone oughta write a song (about you baby) / Steppin' out of line.
LP: . . . . ETAT 14

Delerium

FACES FORMS AND ILLUSIONS.
LP: . . . . EFA 5858

Delerium Tremolo

BANJOPHOBIA.
LP: . . . . SOS 1177

Delerue, Georges

BEST FILM MUSIC OF GEORGES DELERUE VOL 1 (See under Film Music) (Various artists).

BEST FILM MUSIC OF GEORGES DELERUE VOL 2 (See under Film Music) (Various artists).

GEORGES DELERUE CONDUCTS MAURICE JAUBERT.
LP: . . . . VND 1033

LONDON SESSION VOL 1, THE.
Tracks: / Rich and famous / Platoon / Beaches.
MC: . . . . VSC 5241

LONDON SESSIONS VOL 2, THE.
Tracks: / Hommage a Francois Truffaut.
MC: . . . . VSC 5245

LONDON SESSIONS VOL 3, THE.
MC: . . . . VSC 5256

SILKWOOD (See under Streep, Meryl).

SUMMER STORY, A (See under Summer Story).

Delfonics

ECHOES - THE BEST OF THE DELFONICS.
Tracks: / La la means I love you / When you get right down to it / Walk right up to the sun / Somebody loves you / Tell me this is a dream / I'm sorry / Face it girl it's over / Ready or not here I come / Didn't I (Blow your mind this time) / Trying to make a fool of me / Break your promise / I don't want to make you wait / Hey love / I told you so / Over and over / You got yours and I'll get mine.
MC: 410627
LP: 210627

SUPER HITS.
Tracks: / La la means I love you / Didn't I blow your mind / When you get right down to it / Ready or not here I come.
LP: . . . . BELLS 204

SYMPHONIC SOUL: GREATEST HITS.
Tracks: / La la means I love you / I'm sorry / Break your promise / Ready or not here I come / Somebody loves you / Funny feeling / You get yours and I'll get mine / Trying to make a fool of me / Didn't I blow your mind this time / When you get right down to it / Hey love / Over and over / Walk right up to the sun / With these hands / Loving him / Face it girl it's over.
LP: . . . . CRB 1184
MC: . . . . TCCRB 1184

Delgado, Gabi

MISTRESS.
Tracks: / Sex goddess / History of a kiss / Amor / Young lions / Victim / Mistress.
LP: . . . . OVED 93
LP: V2266

Delgado, Junior

BUSHMASTER.
LP: . . . . UNKNOWN

CLASSICS.
LP: . . . . MPC LP JD 1

IN GRIECHENLAND.
LP: . . . . ADAH 435
MC: . . . . ADAHC 435

IT TAKES TWO TO TANGO.
Tracks: / Gone is the love / My heart will follow you / It's love / Magic of love / It takes two to tango / Labba labba / Hot stuff / Rebel sold in captive / Rebels sold.
LP: . . . . FADLP 003
MC: . . . . FADC 003

MOVIN' DOWN THE ROAD.
LP: . . . . LALP 007

ONE STEP MORE.
Tracks: / What am I doing here? / Hanging tree, The / One day / Forward revolution / One step more / Love will bring a sunshine day / Riot in the juvenile prison / Night patrol / King James / Hey good lookin'.
LP: . . . . ILPS 9903
MC: . . . . ICT 9903

RAGAMUFFIN YEAH.
Tracks: / Chilly / I'm tipping / Love you tonight / Prisoner of love / King of kings / Hope that is for real / Promised land / Call me.
LP: . . . . ILPS 9856
MC: . . . . ICT 9856

SISTERS AND BROTHERS.
Tracks: / Row fisherman row / Caution / Warning / Effort / Hold me tighter / She's gonna marry me / Easy girl / Live like a hermit / My miss world / Sisters and brothers.
LP: . . . . BMLP 027

TASTE OF THE YOUNG HEART.
LP: . . . . DSR 7504

Delgado, Roberto

BLUE TROPICAL.
LP: 2372 095
MC: 3151 095

BOUZOUKI MAGIC.
Tracks: / Star of Mykonos, The / When bouzoukis played / Velvet mornings / Marie me ta Kitrina / Love in your eyes / Zorba's dance / Siko horepse sirtaki / Dirlada / Lovely lady of Arcadia / Train / My friend the wind / Lindia / Goodbye my love goodbye / White rose of Athens, The / Never on Sunday / Akropolis Adieu.
LP: 2371 468

ROBERTO DELGADO & HIS ORCHESTRA (Delgado, Roberto & His Orchestra).
Tracks: / Be in / Shadow of your smile / Spanish harlem / Maria Elena / Fly me to the moon / Tequila / Guantanamera / Corcovado / Man of La Mancha / Sabor a mi / Cast your fate to the wind / Maria / Mexico / Cielito Lindo / Vaya con dios / Pata pata / Latin romance / Memories are made of this / Island in the sun / Cindy, oh Cindy / Cu-cu-rru-cu-cu-paloma / Trip to Nicaragua / Cayenne pepper / Bonsoir dame.
2LP: 263 009 3

ROBERTO DELGADO MEETS KALINKA (Delgado, Roberto & His Orchestra).
Tracks: / Two guitars / Stenka Rasin / Volga boatman, The / Kat juschka / Nadja's theme / Lara's theme / Kalinka my love / Polovsian dance / Dark eyes / Cossack patrol / Midnight in Moscow / Evening bells.
LP: . . . . MOIR 108
MC: . . . . CMOIR 108

Y VIVA ROBERTO.
Tracks: / Y viva Espana / Dolores / A banda / Chequitta / Dancing queen / Guantanamera / Bei mir bist du schon / Tanze samba mit mir / Some enchanted evening / They say it's wonderful / Ich bin gewohnt an dein gesicht / Bahia blanca / Sentimental journey / La bamba / Farewell Jamaica farewell.
LP: 2872 148
MC: 3472 148

Delharmonics

DELHARMONICS,THE.
LP: . . . . SRTZ CUS 053

Delicious (label)

EAT TO THE BEAT - (THIS IS DELICIOUS VINYL) (Various artists).
LP: . . . . BRLP 524
MC: . . . . BRCA 524

Delight In Disorder

DELIGHT IN DISORDER (Various artists).
MC: . . . . DELIGHT 001

Delinquents (film)

DELINQUENTS (Film soundtrack) (Various artists).
LP: . . . . HF 11
MC: . . . . HFC 11

Delirious

DELIRIUM.
LP: . . . . BRT 52

Delius (Composer)

SEA DRIFT & APPALACHIA (Various artists).
MC: 4251564

Deliverance

DEVIL'S MEAT.
LP: . . . . VOV 666

EVIL FRIENDSHIP.
LP: . . . . VOV 673
MC: . . . . VOV 673C

Deliverance (Film)

DELIVERANCE (See under Weissberg, Eric) (Various artists).

Delixx

UPRISING IN DUB.
MC: . . . . KINCK 1
LP: . . . . KNICK 1

Dello, Pete

INTO YOUR EARS (Dello, Pete & Friends).
Tracks: / It's what you've got / There's nothing that I can do for you / I'm a gambler / Harry the earwig / Do I still figure in your life / Uptight Basil / Taking the heart out of love / Here me only / Taking the heart out of love / On a time said Sylvie / Good song, A / It's the way / Go away / Arise Sir Henry / Uptight Basil / Madam Chairman (of the committee).
LP: . . . . SEE 257

Dells

BREEZY BALLADS & TENDER TUNES.
LP: . . . . SS 8029

FROM STREETCORNER TO SOUL.
Tracks: / She's just an angel / Now I pray / Why do you have to go / You're still in my heart / Q-bop she bop / My best girl / I'm calling / Rain don't tell nobody / Hold on to what you've got / Wait until tomorrow / Stay in my corner / Let's do it over / Hey sugar (don't get serious) / Poor little boy / It looks like it's over.
LP: . . . . CRB 1055

I TOUCHED A DREAM.
Tracks: / So you are love / All about the paper / Passionate breezes / I touched a dream / Just a little love / Look at us now / Your song.
LP: . . . . T 618

OH WHAT A NIGHT.
MC: 2636504

ROCKIN' ON BANDSTAND.
Tracks: / Jo jo / Zing zing zing / I can't help myself / Dance, dance, dance / Baby do / Time makes you change / Wedding day / Oh what a night / Come on baby / At the bandstand / Cherry Bea / Swinging teens / Baby open up your heart / Restless days, sleepless nights / I can't dream / I wanna go home.
LP: . . . . CRB 1056

SECOND TIME.
Tracks: / Can we skip that part / You can depend on me / My lady, so perfect for me / No win situation / Hott / That's how heartaches are made / Thought of you just a little too much / Sweetness.
LP: . . . . URG 4108
MC: . . . . URG 4108MC

TOGETHER AGAIN (Greatest hits vol.1).
LP: . . . . CHESS 203

WHATEVER TURNS YOU ON.
Tracks: / Happy song / It took a woman like you to make a man out of me / Whatever turns you on / How can we find the love we lost / When we don't know how it got away / Ain't it a shame (every time I hold you) / Heavens just a step away / Is it it? / Stay in my corner.
LP: . . . . T 633

Delmar, Elaine

ELAINE DELMAR AND FRIENDS (Delmar, Elaine & Friends).
Tracks: / I've got the world on a string / My funny valentine / Honeysuckle rose / When the world was young / I got it bad and that ain't good / September song / Basin Street blues / Mountain greenery / More than you know / Don't get around much anymore / Stardust / I gotta right to sing the blues / Puttin' on the Ritz / Tea for two / Boy next door, The / I'm glad there is you / Just one of those things / It amazes me / Bewitched / He was too good to me / Looking for a boy / Little girl blue / Spring is here / Nobody else but me.
2LP: 268 101 0

IN TOWN.
LP: . . . . HEP 2035

I'VE GOT THE WORLD ON A STRING.
Tracks: / When the world was young / I've got the world on a string / My funny valentine / Honeysuckle rose / I got it bad and that ain't good / September song / Basin Street blues / Mountain greenery / More than you know / Don't get around much anymore / Stardust / I gotta right to sing the blues.
LP: . . . . WRS 1004

Delmonas

DANGEROUS CHARMS.
Tracks: / Peter Gunn locomotion / You did him wrong / Hello I love you / Comin' home baby / Lies / C.C. rider / He tells me he loves me / Hidden charms / Twist and shout / I'm the one for you / Fever / Chains / Please don't tell my baby / I want you / Take me home tonight / Woa now.
LP: . . . . WIK 35

DELMONAS.
LP: . . . . HANG 28 UP

DELMONAS FIVE.
Tracks: / Doctor Goldfoot / Heard about him / Why don't smile now / Black elm speaks / Hound Dog / Delmona / I feel like giving in / Keep your big mouth shut / When I Want You / Black Ludella / Your Love / Don't fall in love / Jealousy.
LP: . . . . UXF 228
LP: . . . . HANG 20 UP
LP: . . . . SYF 095

Delmondi

CAFE CONTINENTALE.
Tracks: / Norwegian polka / My Florence waltz / Temperamental tango / Rue de Bal / Havana by night / Zingarella / Leger papillon / Triolets / Valise des as / Bandoneon infranto / Geraldine / Gilou.
LP: CA 104

Delmore Brothers

BEST OF THE DELMORE BROTHERS.
LP: SLP 962
MC: GT 5962

WHEN THEY LET THE HAMMER DOWN (Delmore Brothers & Wayne Raney).
Tracks: / Red ball to nather / Jack and Jill boogie / Lost John boogie / Beale street boogie / Peach Tree Street boogie / Boogie woogie baby / When they let the hammer down / Barnyard boogie / Hillbilly boogie / Freight train boogie / Down home boogie / Stop that boogie / Del Rio boogie / Pan American boogie / Real hot boogie / Used car blues.
LP: BFX 15167

Delneil, Mike

OPUS 21.
Tracks: / Opus 21 theme mix.
MC: SBK 21

REFLECTIONS.
MC: DEL 1

Deloria, Vine

GREAT AMERICAN INDIAN SPEECHES.
2LP: TC 2082

Delta 5

SEE THE WHIRL....
LP: PREX 6
MC: PRICS 6

Delta Angel

SILHOUETTE.
LP: FILER 413
MC: FILERCT 413

Delta Blues Band

SUNNYLAND SLIM'S BLUES JAM.
LP: SLP 245

Delta Force (film)

DELTA FORCE/KING SOLOMON'S MINES (Original Sound Track) (Various artists).
LP: A 290
MC: C 290

Delta Heavy Hitters

DELTA HEAVY HITTERS.
LP: HER 214

Deltas

BOOGIE DISEASE.
LP: NERD 002

MAD FOR IT.
LP: NOSE 011

Deltones

NANA CHOC CHOC IN PARIS.
LP: PHZA 31

Deluxe

JUST A LITTLE MORE.
LP: UNQLP 1
MC: UNQC 1

Deluxe Blues Band

DELUXE BLUES BAND.
Tracks: / Avocado Eldorado / Something inside of me / Mary, Mary / Calling in the flag / Cold cold feeling / Steel truckin' man / I held my baby last night / Freight house blues / One way out / Sun went down, The.
LP: BLUH 004

STREET CAR NAMED DELUXE, A.
LP: AP 020

Del-Vikings

COME GO WITH ME.
Tracks: / Come go with me / I want to marry you / What made Maggie run / Billy boy / Don't be a fool / Willette / Whispering bells / Down by the stream / Down in Bermuda / How can I find true love / When I come home / Girl, girl.
LP: OFF 6005

COOL SHAKE.
Tracks: / Cool shake / What'cha gotta lose / Somewhere over the rainbow / How could you / No ha ha / Gates of Paradise / Can't wait / Jitterbug Mary / Flat tyre / You cheated / Snow bound / When I come home / I'm spinning / There I go.
LP: BB 2064

DEL-VIKINGS.
Tracks: / Big beat, The / Oh tonight / That's why / What you have done to me / Voodoo man, The / Oh I love you / Oh baby / Friendly moon / Meeting of the eyes, A / Falling in love again / Nobody's kisses but yours / String alone / Heaven on earth ((unissued)) / Bells, The ((2 recordings) (unissued)) / You are invited ((unissued)) / Pretty little things called girls ((unissued)).
LP: BB 2060

THEY SING...THEY SWING.
Tracks: / Sunday kind of love, A / Come along with me / Yours / Down in Bermuda / I'm sitting on top of the world / White cliffs of Dover, The / You cheated / Somewhere over the rainbow / Heart and soul / Your book of life / Summertime / Is it any wonder / My foolish heart / Now is the hour.
LP: DJXLP 2063
LP: BB 2063

DeLys, Helaine

DELOVELY DELYS.
LP: AP 42

Delysia, Alice

ALICE DELYSIA.
Tracks: / Cliquot / Habanera / Summer days (from 'Poll Moll') / Dardanella / You'd be surprised / Night was made for love, The / Garden of make believe, A (All from 'Agfar') / Helen of Troy / Poor little rich girl / That means nothing to me / Babying you / Every woman thinks she wants to wander / Alice Delysia memories / Ninon / I like a man / Please do it again / Sometimes when I am far away.
LP: SH 164

Demenga, Thomas

CELLORGANICA (Demenga, Thomas & Heinz Reber).
LP: ECM 1196

COMPOSITIONS BY J.S. BACH AND ELLIOTT CARTER.
LP: ECM 1391

COMPOSITIONS BY J.S. BACH AND HEUNZ HOLLIGER.
LP: ECM 1340

Demented Are Go

DAY THE EARTH SPAT BLOOD.
LP: LINK LP 084

IN SICKNESS AND IN HEALTH.
LP: NOSE 9

LIVE 'N' ROCKIN'.
LP: LINKLP 116

SICK, SICK, SICK.
Tracks: / Rubber love / Be bop a lula / PVC chair / Vibrate / Midnight blues / Do the slug / Cast iron arm / Rubber buccaneer / Pervy in the park / Pickled and preserved / Holy hack Jack.
LP: NOSE 15

SOD IT.
Tracks: / Satan's rejects / Human slug / Cripple in the woods / Decomposition / Cast iron arm / Call of the wired / Rubber plimsoles / Shadow crypt / Surf ride to oblivion / Old black Joe / Sick spasmoid / Vietnam / Jet tone boogie.
LP: NOSE 21

Dementia

DEMENTIA.
LP: SAW 001

DeMerle, Les

ON FIRE.
LP: PA 8008

Demian, Max

TAKE IT TO THE MAX.
Tracks: / Havin' such a good day / See me comin' down / Burnin' up inside / Still hosed / High school star / Through the eye of a storm / Paradise / Lizard song / Hear my song.
LP: PL 13273

Demolition Hammer

TORTURED EXISTENCE.
LP: 0897131
MC: 0897134

Demon

BREAKOUT.
LP: CLAYLP 23

BRITISH STANDARD APPROVED.
LP: CLAYLP 15
LP: SONICLP 4

HEART OF OUR TIME.
LP: CLAYLP 18
LP: CLAYCLP 18
LP: SONICLP 5

NIGHT OF THE DEMON.
Tracks: / Full moon (Instrumental) / Night of the demon / Into the nightmare / Father of time / Decisions / Liar / Big love / Ride the wind / Fool to play the hard / One helluva night.
LP: CLAYLP 25
LP: WEA 125
LP: SONICLP 1

ONE HELLUVA NIGHT (Live in West Germany).
2LP: DEMONLP 1

PLAGUE, THE.
LP: CLAYLP 6
LP: CLAYCLP 6
LPPD: CLAYLP 6P
LP: SONICLP 3

TAKING THE WORLD BY STORM.
LP: CLAYLP 27
LP: SONICLP 8
MC: SONICMC 8

UNEXPECTED GUEST, THE.
Tracks: / Introduction / Observation, An / Don't break the circle / Spell, The / Total possession / Sign of a madman / Victim of fortune / Have we been here before? / Strange institution / Grand illusion / Beyond the gates / Deliver us from evil.
LP: CLAYLP 22
LP: CAL 139
MC: CAC 139
LP: SONICLP 2

Demon Boyz

RECOGNITION.
Tracks: / Recognition / Vibes / Lyrical culture / Don't touch it / Gifted and we're going far / We call him DJ Devastate / Northside / With AZ / Rougher than an animal.
LP: DEMON 1
MC: DEMONC 1

Demon Eyes

RITES OF CHAOS.
LP: EBON 19

Demon (label)

DEMONS IN BRENTFORD Various artists (Various artists).
LP: BRENT 1

Dempsey, Little Jimmy

GOLDEN GUITAR.
MCSET: DTO 10243

Dempsey, Tommy

GREEN GROW THE LAURELS.
LP: LER 2096

Demus, Chaka

EVERYBODY LOVES THE CHAKA.
LP: BSCLP 06

ORIGINAL CHAKA, THE.
LP: MMLP 0017

Demus, Junior

CABIN STABIN (See under Super Cat) (Demus, Jnr., Nicodemus & Super Cat).

Demus, Shaka

RUFF AND TUFF (Demus, Shaka & Shabba).
LP: VPRL 1041

Dene, Terry

LONDON ROCK.
LP: 33.8024

TERRY DENE STORY.
Tracks: / White sports coat / Start movin' / C'mon and be loved / Bimbombey / Lover lover / Stairway of love / Pretty little pearly / Golden age, The / Boy without a girl / Now and always.
LP: CLP 001

Denke, Frank

FABULOUS FRANK AT THE PIANO.
LP: DO 1403

SALUTES GREAT JAZZ PIANISTS.
LP: DO 1408

Denning, Darryl

TWO WORLDS OF THE CLASSICAL GUITAR.
LP: GLS 8008

Dennis, Cathy

MOVE TO THIS.
LP: 8495031
MC: 8495034

Dennis, Denny

DENNY DENNIS AND LEE ALLEN (Dennis, Denny & Lee Allen).
Tracks: / Until the real thing comes along / I'll sing you a thousand love songs / To Mary - with love / Here's love in your eyes / Thru' the courtesy of love / Time on my hands / May I have the next romance with you? / Goodnight my love / Little man, you've had a busy day / I saw stars / Ole faithful / One, two, button your shoe / Where are you? / Once in a while / Afraid to dream / Let's break the good news.
LP: SH 319
MC: TC-SH 319

Dennis, Matt

WELCOME MATT.
LP: FS 120

Denny & Dunipace...

PLAY SCOTLANDS BEST (Denny & Dunipace Pipe Band).
Tracks: / Scotland the brave (Traditional.4/4 March.) / Rowan tree (Traditional.4/4 March.) / Bonnie Galloway (Traditional.4/4 March.) / Old rustic bridge (Traditional.4/4 March.) / Black Watch polka (Polka & Jias) / Mull of Kintyre (Polka & Jias) / Green hills (3/4 March) / When the battle is over / Lynn Shannon's wedding / Dunipace (Traditional) / Danish knife grinder's spring song, The (Traditional) / Crossing the Minch (Traditional) / A. Cameron's Strathspey (Traditional) / Miller of Drone, The (Traditional) / Donald's wedding (Traditional) / McFarlane's reel (Traditional) / John Wilson / Muckin' o' Geordie's byre / Glendurel Highlander / Bonnie Dundee / Amazing grace / Day thou gavest, Lord is ended, The / Flower of Scotland (Slow Air & 2/4 March) / MacKay's farewell to the 71st / Rose among the heather / Fiddlers' joy / De'il amang the tailors / Pigeon on the gate / Kate Dalrymple / Going home / Mist-covered mountains / Morag of Dunvegan / Skye boat song / Dark island / Highland wedding / Susan Macleod / Kate Robertson / Barren rocks of Aden, The / Highland laddie / Mhairi's wedding / Black bear, The / Flowers of the forest / Drum salute.
LP: ITV 385
MC: KITV 385

Denny, Sandy

BEST OF SANDY DENNY.
LP: SDC 100
MC: HNBC 1328

FOTHERINGAY (see under Fotheringay).

LIKE AN OLD FASHIONED WALTZ.
LP: CGLP 4425
MC: CGC 4425

NORTH STAR GRASSMAN AND THE RAVENS.
Tracks: / Late November / Blackwater side / Sea Captain / Down in the flood / John the gun / Next time around / Optimist / Let's jump the broomstick / Wretched Wilbur / North star grassman and the ravens / Crazy lady blues.
LP: ILPM 9165
LP: CGLP 4429
MC: CGC 4429
MC: ICM 9165

ORIGINAL SANDY DENNY, THE.
LP: CREST 28
MC: ZCEST 28
LP: CREST 002
MC: CRESTMC 002

RENDEZVOUS.
Tracks: / I wish I was a fool for you / Gold dust / Candle in the wind / Take me away / One way donkey ride / I'm a dreamer / All our days / Silver threads and golden needles / No more sad refrains.
LP: HNBL 4423
MC: HNBC 4423

SANDY.
MC: ICM 9207

SANDY AND THE STRAWBS (Denny Sandy & The Strawbs).
Tracks: / Nothing else will do / Who knows where the time goes / How everyone but Sam was a hypocrite / Sail away to the sea / And you need me / Poor Jimmy Wilson / All I need is you / Tell me what you see in me / I've been my own worst friend / Two weeks last summer / Always on my mind / Stay a while with me / On my way.
LP: HNBL 1361
MC: HNBC 1361

WHO KNOWS WHERE THE TIME GOES?.
Tracks: / Lady, The / Nothing more / Memphis Tennessee. / Solo / John the gun / Knockin' on Heaven's door / Who knows where the time goes? / Music weaver, The / Take away the load / Sweet Rosemary / Now and then / By the time it gets dark / What is true? / Sail away to the sea / Farewell, farewell / Quiet joys of brotherhood / Tamlin / You never wanted me / Autopsy / One more chance / Stranger to himself / Pond and the stream, The / Banks of the Nile / Two weeks last summer / Late November / Gypsy Davey / Winter winds / Sea, The / When will I be loved (Solo.) / Listen listen / Next time around / Tomorrow is a long time / One way donkey ride / Burton Town / Blackwater side / It'll take a long time / Walking the floor over you / Friends / For shame of doing wrong / I'm a dreamer / Full moon.
LPS: SDSP 1
LPS: HNBX 5301

Dent, Ian

IAN DENT.
MC: LDC 5006

Dentists

BEER BOTTLE & BANNISTER SYMPHONIE.

Tracks: / Writhing on the shagpile / You took me by suprise / Strange way to go about things / She dazzled me with Basil / Dawn overdone / I had an excellent dream / Strawberries are growing in my garden / Turquoise castle, The / Calm you down / Chainsaw the horses / Peppermint dreams / Just like Oliver Reed.
LP: . . . . ANT 072

SOME PEOPLE.
LP: . . . . SPR 001

YOU AND YOUR BLOODY ORANGES.
LP: . . . . SP 004

Denton, Richard

HONG KONG BEAT & OTHER BBC FAVOURITES (Denton, Richard & Martin Cook).
Tracks: / Hong Kong beat / Tomorrows world / Jet lag / Spangler / Quiller / Inside story, The / Great egg race / Diamonds in the sky / General direction / Circuit eleven Miami / Chasing the dragon / Scramble.
LP: . . . . REH 385

Denver, Jeannie

LIVE - SPUR AND SADDLE.
LP: . . . . WRS 105

QUEEN OF THE SILVER DOLLAR.
LP: . . . . WRS 094

WITH LOVE.
Tracks: / Cash on the barrelhead / I don't wanna cry / Dolly's drive / With love / Standing room only / Jacob and Marcie / That's what friends are for / Devoted to you / Some of Shelly's blues / Mississippi, you're on my mind / One more day away / Country baptizing.
LP: . . . . WRS 128

YORKSHIRE ROSE.
LP: . . . . WRS 056

Denver, John

AERIE.
Tracks: / Starwood in Aspen / Everyday / Casey's last ride / City of New Orleans / Friends with you / Sixty second song for a bank with the phrase / May we help you today? / Spanish pipe dream / All of my memories / She won't let me fly away / Readjustment blues / Eagle and the hawk, The / Tools.
LP: . . . . SF 8252

AUTOGRAPH.
Tracks: / Dancing with the mountains / Mountain song / How mountain girls can love / Song for the life / Ballad of St. Anne's reel / In my heart / Wrangell mountain song / Whale bones and crosses / American child / You say that the battle is over / Autograph.
LP: . . . . PL 13449

BACK HOME AGAIN.
Tracks: / Back home again / On the road / Grandma's feather bed / Matthew / Thank God I'm a country boy / Music is you, The / Annie's song / It's up to you / Cool and green and shady eclipse / Sweet surrender / This old guitar.
LP: . . . . NL 85193
MC: . . . . NK 85193
LP: APL1 0548
MC: APK1 0548

BEST OF JOHN DENVER.
Tracks: / Take me home, country roads / Follow me / Starwood in Aspen / For baby (for Bobbie) / Rhymes and reasons / Leaving on a jet plane / Eagle and the hawk, The / Sunshine on my shoulders / Goodbye again / Poems, prayers and promises / Rocky mountain high.
LP: APL1 0374
MC: APK1 0374

BEST OF JOHN DENVER VOL.2.
Tracks: / Annie's song / Welcome to my morning (farewell Andromeda) / Fly away / Like a sad song / Looking for space / Baby you look good to me tonight / Grandma's feather bed / I'd rather be a cowboy / I'm sorry / My sweet lady / Calypso / This old guitar.
LP: . . . . RCALP 3019
MC: . . . . RCAK 3019
LP: . . . . PL 42120
MC: . . . . PK 42120

COLLECTION: JOHN DENVER.
Tracks: / Annie's song / Take me home country roads / Rocky mountain high / Starwood in Aspen / Follow me / I'd rather be a cowboy / Rhymes and reasons / Perhaps love (With Placido Domingo.) / Calypso / Country love / Leaving on a jet plane / Thank God I'm a country boy / Dancing with the mountains / Baby you look good to me tonight / Wild Montana skies / Love again (With Sylvie Vartan.).
LP: . . . . STAR 2253
MC: . . . . STAC 2253

DREAMLAND EXPRESS.
Tracks: / Dreamland express / Claudette / Gimme your love / Got my heart set on you / Harder they fall / Don't close your eyes tonight / Wild heart looking for home / Desired / Trail of tears / African sunrise.
LP: . . . . PL 85458
MC: . . . . PK 85458

EARTH SONGS.
MC: . . . . MCTC 035

EVENING WITH JOHN DENVER, AN.
Tracks: / Music is you, The / Farewell Andromeda / Mother Nature's son / Summer / Today / Saturday night / Mathew / Rocky mountain suite / Sweet surrender / Grandma's feather bed / Annie's song / Eagle and the hawk, The / My sweet lady / Annie's other song / Boy from the country / Rhymes and reasons / Forest lawn / Pickin' the sun down / Thank God I'm country boy / Take me home, country roads / Poems, prayers and promises / Rocky mountain high / This old guitar.
2LP: . . . . LSA 3211-12
MC: . . . . DPTK 5014

FAREWELL ANDROMEDA.
Tracks: / I'd rather be a cowboy / Berkeley woman / Please daddy / Angel from Montgomery / River of love / Rocky mountain suite / Whisky basin blues / Sweet misery / Zachary and Jennifer / We don't live here no more / Farewell Andromeda.
LP: . . . . NL 85195
MC: . . . . NK 85195
LP: . . . . SF 8369

GREATEST HITS: JOHN DENVER.
Tracks: / Take me home country roads / Follow me / Starwood in Aspen / For baby (for Bobbie) / Rhymes and reasons / Leaving on a jet plane / Eagle and the hawk, The / Sunshine on my shoulders / Goodbye again / Poems, prayers and promises / Rocky mountain high.
LP: . . . . PL 80374
MC: . . . . PK 80374
MC: . . . . NK 90523

GREATEST HITS: JOHN DENVER VOL.3.
Tracks: / Dancing with the mountains / Wild Montana skies / I want to live / Gold and beyond / Autograph / How can I leave you again? / Some days are diamonds / Shanghai breezes / Seasons of the heart / Perhaps love / Love again.
LP: . . . . PL 85313
MC: . . . . PK 85313

GREATEST HITS: JOHN DENVER VOL.2.
Tracks: / Annie's song / Perhaps love (With Placido Domingo.) / Fly away (With Olivia Newton John.) / Like a sad song / Looking for space / Thank God I'm a country boy / Grandma's feather bed / Back home again / I'm sorry / My sweet lady / Calypso / This old guitar.
LP: . . . . PL 82195
MC: . . . . PK 82195
LP: . . . . RCALP 3106

HIGHER GROUND.
Tracks: / Alaska and me / Higher ground / Whispering Jesse / Never a doubt / Deal with the ladies / Sing Australia / Country girl in Paris, A / For you / All this joy / Falling leaves / Bread and roses / Homegrown tomatoes.
LP: . . . . PL 90240
MC: . . . . PK 90240

I WANT TO LIVE.
Tracks: / How can I leave you / Tradewinds / Bet on the blues / It amazes me / To the wild country / Ripplin' waters / Thirsty boots / Dearest Esmerelda / Singing skies and dancing waters / I want to live / Druthers.
LP: . . . . PL 12521
MC: . . . . PK 12521

IT'S ABOUT TIME.
Tracks: / Hold on tight / Thought of you, The / Somethin' about / On the wings of a dream / Fight (the higher we fly) / Falling out of love / I remember romance / Wild Montana skies / World game / It's about time.
LP: . . . . PL 84740
MC: . . . . PK 84740
LP: . . . . RCALP 6087

JOHN DENVER.
Tracks: / Downhill stuff / Sweet Melinda / What's on your mind / Joseph and Joe / Life is so good / Berkeley woman / Johnny B. Goode / You're so beautiful / Southwind / Garden song / Songs of....
LP: . . . . PL 13075

LIVE IN LONDON: JOHN DENVER.
Tracks: / Starwood in Aspen / Sunshine on my shoulders / Back home again / Grandma's feather bed / Pickin' the sun down / Thank God I'm a country boy / Eagle and the hawk, The / Spirit / Calypso / Amsterdam / Annie's song / Take me home country roads / Leaving on a jet plane.
LP: . . . . RS 1050
MC: . . . . PK 89225
LP: . . . . PL 89255
MC: . . . . PK 11725

ONE WORLD.
Tracks: / Along for the ride / I can't escape / One world / It's a possibilty / Love is the master / Love again / Let us begin / Flying for me / I remember you / Hey there lonely heart / True love takes time.
LP: . . . . PL 85811
MC: . . . . PK 85811

PERHAPS LOVE (see Domingo, Placido) (Denver, John & Placido Domingo).

POEMS, PRAYERS AND PROMISES.
Tracks: / Poems, prayers and promises / Let it be / My sweet lady / Wooden Indian / Junk / Gospel changes / Take me home, country roads / I guess he'd rather be in Colorado / Sunshine on my shoulders / Around and around / Fire and rain / Box, The.
LP: . . . . NL 85189
MC: . . . . NK 85189
LP: . . . . SF 8219
MC: . . . . PK 11647

RHYMES AND REASONS.
Tracks: / Love of the common people / Catch another butterfly / Daydream / Ballad of Spiro Agnew / Circus / When I'm sixty-four / Ballad of Richard Nixon, The / Rhymes and reasons / Yellow cat / Leaving on a jet plane / My heart / My old man / I wish I knew how it would feel to be free / Today is the first day of the rest of my life.
LP: . . . . SF 8348
MC: . . . . PK 11658

ROCKY MOUNTAIN CHRISTMAS.
Tracks: / Aspenglow / Christmas song, The / Rudolph the red nosed reindeer / Silver bells / Please, daddy don't get drunk this Christmas / Christmas for cowboys / Away in a manger / What child is this? / Coventry carol / Oh holy night / Silent night, holy night / Baby just like you, A.
LP: APL1 1201
MC: . . . . PK 11696

ROCKY MOUNTAIN HIGH.
Tracks: / Rocky mountain high / Mother nature's son / Paradise / For baby (for Bobbie) / Darcy Farrow / Prisoners / Goodbye again / Season suite.
LP: . . . . NL 85190
MC: . . . . NK 85190
LP: . . . . SF 8308
MC: . . . . PK 11649

SEASONS OF THE HEART.
Tracks: / Seasons of the heart / Opposite tables / Relatively speaking / Dreams / Nothing but a breeze / What one man can do / Shanghai breezes / Islands / Heart to heart / Perhaps love / Children of the Universe.
LP: . . . . PL 84256
MC: . . . . PK 84256
LP: . . . . RCALP 6032

SOME DAYS ARE DIAMONDS.
Tracks: / Some days are diamonds / Gravel on the ground / San Francisco Mabel Joy / Sleepin' alone / Easy on Easy Street / Cowboy and the lady, The / Country love / Till you opened my eyes / Wild flowers in a mason jar / Boy from the country.
LP: . . . . PL 84055
MC: . . . . PK 84055
LP: . . . . RCALP 5034

SPIRIT.
Tracks: / Come and let me look in your eyes / Eli's song / Wrangle mountain song / Hitchhiker / In the grand way / Polka dots and moonbeams / It makes me giggle / Baby you look good to me tonight / Like a sad song / San Antonio rose / Pegasus / Wings that fly us home.
LP: . . . . NL 85194
MC: . . . . NK 85194
LP: APL1 1694
MC: . . . . PK 11731

TAKE ME TO TOMORROW.
Tracks: / Take me to tomorrow / Isabel / Follow me / Forest lawn / Aspenglow / Amsterdam / Anthem - revelation / Sticky summer weather / Carolina on my mind / Jimmy Newman / Molly.
LP: . . . . SF 8354

WHOSE GARDEN WAS THIS?.
Tracks: / Tremble if you must / Sail away home / Night they drove old Dixie down, The / Mr. Bojangles / I wish I could have been there (Woodstock) / Whose garden was this / Game is over, The / Eleanor Rigby / Old folks / Jingle bells.
LP: . . . . SF 8355

WINDSONG.
Tracks: / Windsong / Cowboy's delight / Spirit / Looking for space / Shipmates and Cheyenne / Late nite radio / Love is everywhere / Two shots / I'm sorry / Fly away / Calypso / Song of Wyoming / Amor Jibaro / First of May / Windmills of your mind / By the time I get to Phoenix / Miss Otis regrets / Little red rooster / She's a woman / Lady Madonna / Rain / Hey Jude.
LP: . . . . NL 85191
MC: . . . . NK 85191
LP: APL1 1183
MC: . . . . PK 11693

Denver, Karl

GREATEST HITS: KARL DENVER.
MC: . . . . ASK 776

VERY BEST OF KARL DENVER.
LP: . . . . TAB 90

WIMOWEH.
LP: . . . . ACL 1098

Denver Mexicans

DENVER MEXICANS.
LP: . . . . SANE 1

Denver Spur

FIRST TIME OUT.
Tracks: / My funny story / Ode to formula two / Snowbird / Tequila sunrise / Lyin' eyes / Daydreams / What I've got in mind / Love me tonight / Canadian Pacific / What can you do / Rodeo man / More like the movies.
LP: . . . . SFA 043

Denyer, Frank

WHEAT.
Tracks: / On, on, it must be so / Quick, quick, the tamberan is coming / I await the sea's red hibiscus / Wheat / Quite white.
LP: . . . . OR 3

Deodato, Eumir

DEODATO.
LP: . . . . ENALP 1
MC: . . . . ZCENA 1

HAPPY HOUR.
Tracks: / Keep on moving / Happy hour / Just this one night / Tears of a clown / Sweet magic / Keep it in the family / I never get enough.
LP: . . . . K 56983

JOAO DONATO.
LP: . . . . MR 5017

LOVE ISLAND.
LP: . . . . K 56416

MOTION.
LP: 9251751

NIGHT CRUISER.
Tracks: / Night cruiser / East side strut / Skatin' / Uncle funk / Love magic / Groovitation.
LP: . . . . K 56848

PRELUDE.
Tracks: / Also sprach Zarathustra / Spirit of summer / Carly and Carole / Baubles, bangles and beads / Prelude to the afternoon of a faun / September 13 / Area code 808 / Pina Colada / Love Island / Whistle bump / San Juan sunset / Take the 'A' train / Tahiti hut (Ta Pa E) / Chariot of the Gods.
LP: . . . . CTI 6021

VERY TOGETHER.
Tracks: / Peter Gunn / Spanish boogie / Amani / Black widow / Juanita / I shot the sheriff / Star trek / Univac loves you.
LP: . . . . MCF 2774

WHIRLWINDS.
Tracks: / Moonlight serenade / Ave Maria / Do it again / West 42nd Street / Havana strut / Whirlwinds.
LP: . . . . MCG 3518

Depeche Mode

101.
Tracks: / Pimpf (intro) / Behind the wheel / Strange love / Sacred (not on LP version) / Something to do / Blasphemous rumours / Stripped / Somebody / Things you said / Black celebration / Shake the disease / Nothing (not on LP version) / Pleasure little treasure / People are people / Question of time, A / Never let me down again / Question of lust, A / Master and servant / Just can't get enough / Everything counts.
2LP: . . . . STUMM 101
MC: . . . . CSTUMM 101

BLACK CELEBRATION.
Tracks: / Black celebration / Fly on the windscreen (Final) / Question of lust, A / Sometimes / It doesn't matter / Question of time, A / Stripped / Here is the house / World full of nothing / Dressed in black / New dress / But not tonight (Only on CD.) / Breathing in fumes (Only on CD.) / Black day (Only on CD.).
LP: . . . . STUMM 26
MC: . . . . CSTUMM 26

BROKEN FRAME, A.
LP: . . . . STUMM 9

CONSTRUCTION TIME AGAIN.
LP: . . . . STUMM 13

MC: CSTUMM 13

DEPECHE MODE: INTERVIEW PICTURE DISC.
LPPD: BAK 2071

INTERVIEWS 83/85.
LPPD: BASILD ONE

MUSIC AND MEDIA INTERVIEW PICTURE DISC.
LPPD: DM 1022

MUSIC FOR THE MASSES.
MC: CSTUMM 47
LP: INT 146833
LP: STUMM 47

SINGLES '81-'85.
Tracks: / People are people / Master and servant / It's called a heart / Just can't get enough / See you / Shake the disease / Everything counts / New life / Blasphemous rumours / Leave in silence / Get the balance right / Love in itself / Dreaming of me.
LP: MUTEL 1
MC: CMUTEL 1

SOME GREAT REWARD.
Tracks: / If you want to / Master and servant / Lie to me / Something to do / Blasphemous rumours / Somebody / People are people / It don't matter / Stories of old / Pipeline / Everything counts / Two minute warning.
LP: STUMM 19
MC: CSTUMM 19

SPEAK AND SPELL.
Tracks: / New life / Just can't get enough / I sometimes wish I was dead / Puppets / Boys say go / No disco / What's your name / Photographic / Tora tora tora / Big muff / Any second now.
LP: STUMM 5
MC: CSTUMM 5

TOUR BUS TAPES, THE (Interview album).
LPPD: BAK 6004
MC: MBAK 6004

VIOLATOR.
LP: STUMM 64
MC: CSTUMM 64

Depraved

COME ON DOWN.
LP: GURT 6

STUPIDITY MAKETH THE MAN.
LP: GURT 14

Depress

ON THE OTHER SIDE.
LP: U 013
MC: U 013 MC

Depression

ULTRA HARD CORE MEGA HEAVY PUNK METAL THRASH.
LP: CLP 232

Der Plan

FETTE JAHRE.
LP: WR 34

Deram (label)

DREAM DAYS (Various artists).
Tracks: / Happy new year: *Beverly* / Breaking down: *Societe, The* / Renaissance fair: *Human Instinct* / She's not there: *McArthur,Neil* / Halo in my hair: *Bulldog Breed* / Portebello Road: *Stevens, Cat* / Nite is a comin': *Warm Sound* / Michael Angelo: *Twenty Third Turnoff* / Some good advice: *Say, Bill* / Catherines wheel: *Laine, Denny* / Mythological Sunday: *Friends* / Supermarket full of cans: *Eyes Of Blue* / Say you don't mind: *Laine, Denny* / Summer of last year: *Pyramid* / Bird has flown: *Societe, The* / Sycamore Sid: *Focus* / Summer evening: *Pyramid* / Doo dah: *Warm Sound.*
LP: LIK 9

Derek B.

BULLET FROM A GUN.
Tracks: / Bullet from a gun / Bad Young Brother / Power move / Human time bomb / Get Down / We've got the juice / All right now / Good groove / Success.
LP: DRKLP 1
MC: DRKMC 1

Derek & Clive

AD NAUSEAM.
Tracks: / Endangered species / Racing / T.V. / Bruce / Records / Soul time / Russia / Sir / Celebrity suicide / Politics / Labels / Street music / Horn / Mona / Critics.
LP: OVED 162
MC: OVEDC 162
LP: V 2112

COME AGAIN.
Tracks: / Coughing contest / Cancer / Non-stop dancer/My mum song / Joan Crawford / Norman the carpet / How's your mother / Back of the cab / Alfie Noakes / In the cubicles / Nurse / Ross Mc Pharter / Hello Colin / Having a wank / I saw this bloke / Parking offence / Members only.
LP: OVED 110
MC: OVEDC 110

Derek, Jon

WITH A LITTLE HELP FROM MY FRIENDS.
LP: WRS 098

Derek & The Dominoes

20TH ANNIVERSARY EDITION.
MCSET: 847 083 4

DEREK AND THE DOMINOES IN CONCERT.
Tracks: / Why does love got to be so sad? / Got to get better in a little while / Let it rain / Presence of the Lord / Tell the truth / Bottle of red wine / Roll it over / Blues power / Have you ever loved a woman?.
2LP: 265 902 0
MC: 831 416 4

LAYLA AND OTHER ASSORTED LOVE SONGS.
Tracks: / I looked away / Bell bottom blues / Keep on growing / Nobody knows you / I am yours / Anyday / Key to the highway / Tell the truth / Why does love got to be so sad / Have you ever loved a woman / Little sing / It's too late / Thorn tree in the garden / Layla.
2LP: SPDLP 1
MC: 8232774

LAYLA (OLD GOLD) (See under Allman Brothers/Jessica).

Derise, Joe

BLUES ARE OUT OF TOWN.
LP: AP 174

HOUSE OF FLOWERS.
LP: AP 153

JOE DERISE SINGS AND PLAYS JIMMY VAN HEUSEN (Vol 1).
LP: AP 231

TENTETTE IS MAD ABOUT YOU.
LP: AP 215

Derksen, Arnie

MY DANCIN' SHOES.
Tracks: / Crazy me / Blue streets / Let the whole world know / She wanna rock / I'd like to be alone / My dancin' shoes / K4WO / Party was over, The / There stands the glass / I'm with you.
LP: BF 15362

Derri Airs

IF YOU'RE IRISH COME INTO THE PARLOUR.
Tracks: / If you're Irish come into the parlour / Irish washerwoman, The / Planxty Drury / Dan Murphy's jig / Where are you going my bonnie wee lass / Pop goes the weasel / Brahms' lullaby / Trip to Sligo, The / Gillian's apples / Flowers of Edinburgh / Derry air (Danny boy) / Nora Lee / Piper through the meadow straying / Home boys home / Let him go, let him tarry / Coortin in the kitchen / Will you go lassie go.
LP: STOL 143
MC: CT 143

Derringer, Rick

GUITARS AND WOMEN.
Tracks: / Something warm / Guitars and women / Everything / Man in the middle / It must be love / Desires of the heart / Timeless / Hopeless romantic / Need a little girl / Don't ever say goodbye.
LP: SKY 83746

RICK DERRINGER.
Tracks: / Runaway / You'll get yours / Big city loneliness / Burn the midnight oil / Let the music play / Jump jump jump / I want a lover / My my hey hey.
LP: SKY 84462

Derry, Pat

FISTFUL OF COUNTRY.
Tracks: / Kentucky in the morning / Is anybody going to San Antone? / Crystal chandeliers / Kiss an angel good morning / Some broken hearts never mend / Hello blues and down the road I go / Turn out the lights (love me tonight) / Take these chains from my heart / You win again / Wedding bells / I still miss someone / I'm gonna be a country boy again / Blizzard / I dreamed about mama last night / Sing me back home / Today I started loving you again / Swinging doors / Welcome to my world / Have I told you lately that I love you / I won't forget you / This world is not my home / Beautiful life / Me & Jesus / There goes my everything / Wanted man / I got stripes / San Quentin.
LP: PHL 430
MC: CPHL 430

GHOST RIDERS IN THE SKY.
Tracks: / Frankie and Johnny / Little box of pine in the 7:29, The / Life to go / Sunday morning coming down / Alamo, The / Silver target / Old dogs, children and watermelon wine / Drunkards child / Country hall of fame / Precious memories / Ghost riders in the sky / Don't step on mother's roses.
LP: PHL 458
MC: CPHL 458

Derviches Tourneurs...

DERVICHES TOURNEURS DE TURQUIE (Musique soufi vol.2) (Various artists).
Tracks: / Ceremonie des Mevievi: *Various artists.*
LP: ARN 34603

Des Airs

LUNGA NOTTE.
LP: CRAM 018

Des Barres, Michael

I'M ONLY HUMAN.
Tracks: / Baited breath / I'm only human / Someone somewhere in the night / Nothing's too hard / Right or wrong / Dancin' on the brink of disaster / Boy meets car / Scandal papers / Five hour flight / Catch phrase / Bullfighter / I don't have a thing to wear / Outro.
LP: 2394279

Des Plantes, Ted

SHOUT, SISTER, SHOUT (Des Plantes', Ted Washboard Wizards).
LP: SOS 1174

SWEDISH AMERICAN HOT JAZZ COLLABORATION.
LP: SOS 1136

Desair

LOVELY LADY OF THE ROSES.
Tracks: / Lovely lady of the roses.
LP: CRAM 017

Desanto, Sugar Pie

DOWN IN THE BASEMENT (THE CHESS YEARS).
Tracks: / In the basement (part1) / I want to know / Mama didn't raise no fools / There's gonna be trouble / I don't feel sorry / Maybe you'll be there / Do I make myself clear / Use what you got / Can't let you go / Soulful dress / I don't wanna fuss / Going back to where I belong / It won't be long / She's got everything / Wish you were mine / Slip-in mules.
LP: LPM 7001
LP: CH 9275

LOVIN' TOUCH.
LP: DD 4310

SISTERS OF SOUL (See under Bass, Fontella).

Descendents

ALL.
LP: SST 112
MC: SSTC 112

ENJOY.
LP: SST 242
MC: SSTC 242

HALLRAKER.
LP: SST 205

I DON'T WANT TO GROW UP.
MC: SSTC 143

LIVEAGE.
Tracks: / All / I'm not a loser / Silly girl / I wanna be a bear / Coolidge / Weinerschnitel / I don't want to grow up / Kids / Wendy / Get the time / Descendents / All-o-gistics / Myage / My dad sucks / Van / Surburban home / Hope / Clean sheets.
LP: SST 163

Descloux, Lizzy

LIZZY MERCIER DESCLOUX.
Tracks: / It's all my imagination / Abyssinia / Gazelles / Dolby sisters / Saliva brothers / Eclipse / Les dents de l'amour / Wakwazulu kwezizulu rock / Mono on my mind / I'm liquor / Queen of overdub kisses / Sun's jive / All the same.
LP: CBS 25936

ONE FOR THE SOUL.
Tracks: / One for the soul / Simply beautiful / Fog horn blues / Women don't like me / My funny valentine / Sound of Leblon beach / Garden of Alas / God-spell me wrong / Off off pleasure / Long voodoo ago / Love streams.
LP: 827 910-1
MC: 827 910-4

PRESS COLOR.
Tracks: / Fire / Torso corso / Mission impossible / No golden throat / Jim on the move / Wawa / Tumour / Aya mood.
LP: ILPS 7001

Desert & Her ...

DESERT AND HER DAUGHTERS, THE (See under Gabriel, Peter) (Gabriel, Peter Passion Sources & John Hassell).

Desert Rose Band

DESERT ROSE BAND.
Tracks: / One step forward / Love reunited / He's back and I'm blue / Leave this town / Time between / Ashes of love / One that got away / Once more / Glass hearts / Hard times.
LP: ZL 90202
MC: ZK 90202

Desert Song (show)

DESERT SONG (Various artists).
Tracks: / Overture and opening chorus: *Various artists* / Riff song: *Various artists* / Why did we marry soldiers: *Various artists* / French military marching song: *Various artists* / Romance: *Various artists* / Then you will know: *Various artists* / Desert song: *Various artists* / Let love go: *Various artists* / One flower: *Various artists* / One alone: *Various artists* / Sabre song: *Various artists* / Finale: *Various artists.*
LP: SRS 5053

DESERT SONG (Various artists).
LP: ACL 831
MC: BT 831

DESERT SONG Romberg, Sigmund (composer) (Various artists).
Tracks: / Desert Song overture and opening chorus: *Various artists* / Riff song, The: *Various artists* / Why did we marry soldiers: *Various artists* / Romance: *Various artists* / French military marching song: *Various artists* / Then you'll know: *Various artists* / Desert song, The: *Various artists* / Let love go: *Various artists* / One flower: *Various artists* / One alone: *Various artists* / Sabre song, The: *Various artists.*
LP: MES 7054

DESERT SONG Original London cast (1920's) (Various artists).
Tracks: / Riff song, The: *Various artists* / French military marching song: *Various artists* / Romance: *Various* artists / It: *Various artists* / Desert song, The: *Various artists* / Eastern and western love: *Various artists* / One alone: *Various artists* / Sabre song, The: *Various artists.*
LP: SH 254

Desert String Band

DESERT STRING BAND, THE.
LP: SHAN 79041

Desford Colliery Band

CELEBRATION.
Tracks: / Overture-Henry V / Le Cid / Yesterday / Bolero / Celebration / Greensleeves / Liebesfreud / Watch your step / Adagio / March from 6th symphony.
LP: PRL 009
MC: CPRL 009

ENGLISH HERITAGE SERIES-ELGAR: VOL.1 (Desford Colliery Band/Foden O.T.S. Band).
Tracks: / Enigma variations / Two interludes from 'Falstaff' / Froissart overture.
LP: EHS 001D
MC: CEHS 001D

ENGLISH HERITAGE SERIES-ELGAR: VOL.2 (Desford Colliery Band/Foden O.T.S. Band).
Tracks: / Suite from the wand of youth / Chanson de matin / Cello concerto (excerpts) ((arr. for Euphonium and Brass Band)) / Prelude to 'The dream of Gerontius' / Imperial march / Canto popolare / Triumphal march from 'Caractacus'.
LP: EHS 002D
MC: CEHS 002D

SHOWCASE.
Tracks: / Perpetium mobile / Air on a G string / Folk festival / Swan, The / Golliwogg's cake-walk / Girl with the flaxen hair, The / Duet for two cats / Polovtsian dances / Czardas / Poeme / President, The / Sailing by / Clock and the dresden china figures, The / Apres un reve / Dances from West Side Story.
LP: MFP 5782
MC: TC MFP 5782

SOMETHING OLD, SOMETHING NEW.
Tracks: / Fanfare for the common man / Zampa / Requiem chorus / Feelings / Don Quoxote Quixote / Exhibition can can / Who pays the ferryman / Zelda / Finlandia.
LP: SB 335

DeShannon, Jackie

SKY HIGH (See Sky High (film)).

Deshotel, Ed & Bee

CAJUN TROUBADOURS.
LP: 6025

LA VIE DES CAJUNS.
LP: 6017

Design For Living

SLOWLY SHOUTING.
Tracks: / Onions and operas / Pictures of me / Stunned monkies / We bought a gun / Thrill of the chase / Pass that gun.
LP: . . . MFL 13

Desmond, Andy

ANDY DESMOND.
Tracks: / Canada / Captain of the crew / Schooldays are over.
LP: . . . ARL 5001

Desmond, Johnny

MEMORIAL ALBUM.
LP: . . . AWE 16
MC: . . . CAWE 16

Desmond, Paul

BLUES IN TIME (See under Mulligan Gerry) (Desmond, Paul & Gerry Mulligan).

EAST OF THE SUN.
Tracks: / I get a kick out of you / Time after time / For all we know / 2 degrees east / 3 degrees west.
LP: . . . DS 840
MC: . . . DSC 840

EASY LIVING.
Tracks: / When Joanna loved me / That old feeling / Polka dots and moonbeams / Here's that rainy day / Easy living / I've grown accustomed to her face / Bewitched / Blues for fun / All through the night / Rude old man.
LP: . . . NL 82306
MC: . . . NK 82306

GREATEST HITS: PAUL DESMOND.
Tracks: / Take ten / I've grown accustomed to her face / Black orpheus / Hi lili hi lo / Desmond blue / Embarcadero / All the things you are / El prince / Alone together / Taste of honey, A / O Gato.
LP: . . . CL 89809
MC: . . . CK 89809

LATE LAMENT.
Tracks: / My funny valentine / Like someone in love / I should care / Then I'll be tired of you / Ill wind / Desmond blue / Body and soul / I've got you under my skin / Imagination.
LP: . . . NL 85778
MC: . . . NK 85778

MASTER OF JAZZ.
LP: . . . CL 42790

ONLY RECORDED PERFORMANCE, THE (Desmond, Paul Quartet).
Tracks: / Greensleeves / You go to my head / Blue dove / Jesus Christ superstar / Here's that rainy day / East of the sun / Bags new groove.
LP: . . . FINLP 6050
MC: . . . ZCFIN 6050

PAUL DESMOND.
LP: . . . AH 2

PAUL DESMOND, JIM HALL, PERCY HEATH, CONNIE KAY (Desmond, Paul/ Jim Hall/Percy Heath/Connie Kay).
Tracks: / Greensleeves / You go to my head / East of the sun / Time after time / I get a kick out of you / For all we know / Two degrees east, three degrees west.
LP: . . . K 56294

PAUL DESMOND QUARTET LIVE (Desmond, Paul Quartet).
Tracks: / Wendy / Wave / Things ain't what they used to be / Nancy / Manha de carnaval / Here's that rainy day / My funny valentine / Take five.
2LP: . . . AMLJD 850

PURE DESMOND.
LP: . . . CTI 9007

TWO OF A MIND (Desmond, Paul & Gerry Mulligan).
Tracks: / All the things you are / Stardust / Two of a mind / Blight of the fumble bee / Way you look tonight / Out of nowhere.
LP: . . . NL 89654
MC: . . . NK 89654
MC: . . . NK 90364
LP: . . . NL 90364

Desolation Angels

DESOLATION ANGELS.
Tracks: / Rock and roll / Crazy circles / Gone gone gone / Evil wind / Early in the morning / Oh Atlanta / Take the time / Rhythm machine / She brings me love.
LP: . . . TRR 111

Desotos

CRUISIN' WITH THE DESOTOS.
LP: . . . W 9026

Despair

DECAY OF HUMANITY.
Tracks: / Decay of humanity / Delusion / Distant territory, A / Radiated / Cry for liberty / Victims of vanity / Silent screaming / Satantic verses.
LP: . . . 0897121
MC: . . . 0897124

HISTORY OF HATE.
LP: . . . MB 1002

Desperadoes

CABINET FULL OF CURIOSITIES, A (See Garon, Jesse) (Desperadoes & Jesse Garon).

DESPERADOES, THE.
Tracks: / Don't leave me this way / No pan / Don't make me wait too long / Symphony in G / Zampa overture, The / Flight of the bumble bee / El relicario / Brazil / Greatest love, The / Another town another Saturday night / On and on, round and round / Going down / Song in the moonlight / Each and every day.
LP: . . . CLASS 11
LP: . . . 7199 246

YOU'LL NEVER BE (See Garon, Jesse) (Desperadoes & Jesse Garon).

Desperate Danz Band

SEND 3 AND FOURPENCE.
LP: . . . HAPPAS 1

Desperate Hours

DESPERATE HOURS (See under Mansford, David) (Mansfield, David).

Dessau

EXERCISE IN TENSION.
LP: . . . CAR 269516

Dessau, Joanna

AMAZING GRACE.
MC: . . . SOUND 1

Destination Moon

DESTINATION MOON (Original soundtrack) (Various artists).
LP: . . . STV 81130

Destination Zero

SUICIETY.
LP: . . . EFA 1654

SURVIVE.
LP: . . . 081150

Destiny

ATOMIC WINTER.
LP: . . . US 014

NOTHING LEFT TO FEAR.
LP: . . . ATV 18

Destri, Jimmy

HEART ON A WALL.
Tracks: / Bad dreams / Don't look around / Livin' in your heart / My little world / Little metal drummer / Numbers don't count (on me) / King of steam, The / Under the ice / Heart on the wall.
LP: . . . CHR 1368
MC: . . . ZCHR 1368

Destroy All Monsters

DESTROY ALL MONSTERS (LIVE).
LP: . . . FC 050

Destroyers

NIGHT OF THE LUSTY DESTROYERS, A.
Tracks: / Introduction / Terrible anathema / Call of blood / Czarina's warm pubes / Wine and sex / Night of the lusty queen, The / Kingdom of evil, The / Temple of pleasure, The / Angry Bastard.
LP: . . . 080702

Destruction

CRACKED BRAIN.
LP: . . . NUK 136
MC: . . . ZCNUK 136

ETERNAL DEVASTATION.
LP: . . . SH 0046
LP: . . . 081885

INFERNAL OVERKILL.
LP: . . . 081 086

LIVE WITHOUT SENSE.
LP: . . . NUK 126
MC: . . . ZCNUK 126
LP: . . . 087578

MAD BUTCHER.
MLP: . . . 601 897

RELEASE FROM AGONY.
LP: . . . 087503
MC: . . . 087505

SENTENCE OF DEATH.
MLP: . . . 601 838

Destructors

BOMB HANOI, BOMB SAIGON, BOMB DISNEYLAND.
LP: . . . KILL 666

Destry

GLASSHOUSE.
Tracks: / Forever my love / Better day / Never be alone / Did you find a heart / Art of love / Only the lonely hearts / Matter of time, A / Glasshouse.
LP: . . . LUVLP 10
MC: . . . LUVMC 10

Destry Rides... (show)

DESTRY RIDES AGAIN (Original 1979 London cast) (Various artists).
Tracks: / Bottle neck: *Various artists* / Ladies: *Various artists* / Hoop-de-dingle: *Various artists*/ Tomorrow morning: *Various artists* / Ballad of gun: *Various artists* / I know your kind: *Various artists*/ I hate him: *Various artists* / Anyone would love you: *Various artists* / Ev'ry once in a while: *Various* artists / Destry rides again:Finale act I: *Various artists* / Are you ready Gyp Watson?: *Various artists*/ Not guilty: *Various artists* / Only time will tell: *Various artists* / That ring on the finger: *Various* artists / I say hello: *Various artists* / Destry rides again: Finale act II: *Various artists* / Curtain call: *Various artists*.
LP: . . . TER 1034
MC: . . . ZCTER 1034

Desvarieux, Jacob

BANZAWA.
LP: . . . GD 016
MC: . . . C 501

CHWAZI (Desvarieux, Jacob & Georges Decimus).
LP: . . . GD 022
MC: . . . C 503

GOREE.
LP: . . . GD 035

OH MADIANA.
LP: . . . GD 025
MC: . . . C 505

YELELE (See under Decimus, Georges) (Desvarieux, Jacob & Georges Decimus).

DeSylva, Brown & ...

SONGS BY DE SYLVA, BROWN AND HENDERSON (Various artists).
LP: . . . MES 7076

Detail

OKHELA (To make a fire).
LP: . . . AFF 125

Details At Eleven

DETAILS AT ELEVEN.
LP: . . . ST 7522

Detective

BAG BUSINESS.
Tracks: / Hong Kong calls me / Rampage / As young as you feel / Green dream / Reagan is a moron / Green eyes / Reluctant hero / Can I please you / As young as you feel (slurry mix) / Red / End bag.
MC: . . . PV 029

DETECTIVE.
Tracks: / Recognition / Got enough love / Grim reaper / Nightingale / Detective man / Ain't none of your business / Deep down / Wild hot summer / One more heartache.
LP: . . . SSK 59405

IT TAKES ONE TO KNOW ONE.
Tracks: / Help me up / Competition / Are you talkin' to me / Dynamite / Something beautiful / Warm love / Betcha won't dance / Fever / Tear jerker.
LP: . . . SSK 59406

Detente

RECOGNIZE NO AUTHORITY.
LP: . . . RR 9695

Determination

HOT HOT HOT.
LP: . . . D 102

SHOW CASE Volume 1.
LP: . . . D 103

Dethrone

LET THE DAY BEGIN.
LP: . . . FLAG 41

Detonators

GANGSTER.
LP: . . . BR 1008

Detritus

PERPETUAL DEFIANCE.
LP: . . . FLAG 55
MC: . . . TFLAG 55

Detroit Emeralds

FEEL THE NEED (ALBUM).
Tracks: / Set it out / Take it or leave me / Feel the need / Wednesday / Love for you / Look what's happened to our love / Sexy ways / Love has come to me.
LP: . . . K 50372

I'M IN LOVE WITH YOU.
Tracks: / Shake your head / You're getting a little too smart / Whatcha gonna wear tomorrow / My dreams have got the best of me / So long / I think of you (you control me) / Heaven couldn't.
LP: . . . SEW 006
MC: . . . SEWC 006

LET'S GET TOGETHER.
LP: . . . K 50452

YOU WANT IT, YOU GOT IT.
Tracks: / You want it, you got it / There's a love for me somewhere / I'll never sail the sea again / Take my love / Feel the need in me / I've got to move / Baby let me take you (in my arms) / I bet you get the one you love / Till you decide to come home.
LP: . . . SEW 011
MC: . . . SEWC 011

Detroit Gold

DETROIT GOLD (See under Soul) (Various artists).

Detroit Jazz Tradition

ALIVE AND WELL.
LP: . . . PARKWOOD 102

Detroit Spinners

8.
Tracks: / I'm gonna getcha / I'm tired of giving / Painted magic / You got the love that I need / Heaven on Earth / Back in the arms of love / Love is one step away / Easy come, easy go / Baby I need your love.
LP: . . . K 50418

20 GOLDEN CLASSICS: DETROIT SPINNERS.
Tracks: / It's a shame / Together we can make such sweet music / I'll always love you / Tomorrow may never come / We'll have it made / Where is that girl / Truly yours / At sundown / Sing a rainbow / Love is blue weather / That's what girls are made for / It hurts to be in love / For all my me know / O-o-oh child / I've got to find myself a brand new baby / My lady love / Message from a blackman / My whole world ended.
LP: . . . STMR 9011
MC: . . . CSTMR 9011

CAN'T SHAKE THIS FEELING.
Tracks: / Can't shake this feeling / Knack for me / You go your way and I'll go mine / Love connection (raise the window down) / Never thought I'd fall in love / Didn't I blow your mind / Send a little love / Love is such a crazy feeling.
LP: . . . K 50838

CROSSFIRE.
Tracks: / Two of a kind / Right or wrong / Our time for love / Crossfire / Keep on keepin' on / Not just another lover / Love is in season / All your love / Secrets.
LP: . . . 780 165-1

DANCIN' AND LOVIN'.
Tracks: / Disco ride / Body language / Let's boogie, let's dance / Medley: Working my way back to you / Forgive me girl / With my eyes / One one two two boogie woogie avenue (home of the boogie....
MC: . . . K4 50667
LP: . . . K 50667

FROM HERE TO ETERNALLY.
Tracks: / It's a natural affair / Don't let the man get you / Plain and simple love song / Are you ready for love / I love the music / One man wonderful band / If you wanna do a dance / Once you fall in love.
LP: . . . K 50544

GOLDEN GREATS: DETROIT SPINNERS.
Tracks: / Could it be I'm falling in love? / Ghetto child / We belong together / Rubber band man, The / Right or wrong / I'll be around / Mighty love / Just can't get you out of my mind / One of a kind (love affair) / Love is in season.
LP: . . . 781 627-1
MC: . . . 781 627-4

GRAND SLAM.
Tracks: / City full of memories / Magic in the moonlight / If I knew / I'm calling you now / So far away / Just let love in / Funny how time slips away / Loverboy / No other love.
LP: . . . 780 020-1
MC: . . . 790 020-4

LABOUR OF LOVE.
Tracks: / Long live soul music / Standing on the rock / Yesterday once more / Nothing remains the same / Almost all the way to love / Winter of our love / Be my love / Give your lady what she wants / Man just don't know what a woman goes through / Deacon.
LP: . . . K 50777

LOVE TRIPPIN'.
Tracks: / Love trippin' / Heavy on the sunshine / Medley - Cupid / I've loved you for a long time / I just want to be with you / Streetwise / Working my way back to you / I just want to fall in love / Now that you're mine again / Split decision / I'm takin' you back / Pipedream / Body language.
LP: . . . K 50731
MC: . . . K4 50731

LOVIN' FEELING.

Tracks: / Put us together again / I found an angel / You're number one / She does / That's what girls are made for / More today than yesterday / Witness / Two can be one / Show me your magic.
LP: 790 456-1
MC: 790 456-4

SMASH HITS.
Tracks: / Rubber band man, The / One of a kind (love affair) / Ghetto child / Games people play / Could it be I'm falling in love / Sadie / Mighty love / Then came you / I'll be around / Clown, The / Just can't get you out of my mind / How could I let you get away / Living a little, laughing a little / Wake up Susan.
LP: . . . . K 50363
MC: K4 50363

Deuces Wild

BRUTAL PURITY.
LP: . . . . F 3010

Deuchar, Jimmy

SCOTS CONNECTION, THE (Deuchar, Jimmy Quintet).
LP: . . . . HEP 2006

THOU SWELL (Deuchar, Jimmy/ Alan Clare/ Victor Feldman/ Tony Kinsey).
Tracks: / They can't take that away from me / Close as pages in a book / Folks who live on the hill, The / Thou swell / Why do I love you? / Things we did last summer, The / This can't be love / Just one of those things.
LP: . . . . ESQ 330

Deuringer, H.

SWING AND HAPPY (see Wunderlich, Klaus) (Deuringer, H. & Klaus Wunderlich).

Deuter-D

CALL OF THE UNKNOWN-SELECTED PIECES 1972-1986.
Tracks: / Starchild / Peru le Peru / Call of the unknown / Sky beyond clouds / Cathedral / From here to here / High road, The / Alchemy / Pacifica / Silence is the answer (Parts 4 & 5) / Haleakala mystery / Album / Solitary bird / Echo of the beast / Back to a planet / La Ilaha il allah.
2LP: . . . . LPKUCK 076/077
MCSET: . . . . MCKUCK 076/077

CICADA.
Tracks: / From here to here / Light / Cicada / Sun on my face / From here to here (reprise) / Sky beyond clouds / Haiku / Alchemy / Between two breaths.
LP: . . . . LPKUCK 056
MC: . . . . MCKUCK 056

DEUTER-D.
LP: . . . . LPKUCK 017

LAND OF ENCHANTMENT.
Tracks: / Pierrot / Maui morning / Silver air / Waves and dolphins / Santa Fe / Celestial harmony / Peru le Peru / Petite fleur / Wind of dawn.
LP: . . . . LPKUCK 081
MC: . . . . MCKUCK 081

NIRVANA ROAD.
LP: . . . . LPKUCK 068

Deutscher, Drafi

DIE DECCA JAHRE 1963-68.
Tracks: / Teeny / Shu-bi-do the slop / Grun, grun ist Tennessee / Kleine Peggy Lou / Shake hands / Come on, let's go / Cinderella baby / Es ist besser, wenn du gebst / Keep smiling / Es war einmal / Hast du alles vergessen / Heute male ich dein Bild, Cindy Lou / Mr. Tambourine man / Keiner weiss, wie es morgen sein wird / Nimm mich so wie ich bin / Ich geh' durch's Feuer fur dich / Marmor, Stein und Eisen bricht / Das sind die einsamen jahre / Honey bee / Hello little girl / Ich hab' den mond in meiner tasche / An deiner seite / Old, old Germany / Mit schirm, Frack und Melone / Mit schirm, charme und melone / Die goldene zeit / Take it easy / Was sind sie ohne Regen / Sweet dreams for you my love / Darlin' / Der hauptmann von Kopenick / Zwei fremde augen / Rock and roll lady / Alice im Wunderland / Marble breaks, iron bends / Wanna take you home / Summertime / Bachelor boy / Trouble / Amanda / Wake up / Crying in the morning / Bleib, oh bleib / Junge leute brauchen liebe / Shake your hands / Good golly Miss Molly / Memphis, Tennessee / Roll over Beethoven / What'd I say / What's the matter baby / Mit siebzehn fangt das Leben erst an / Komm zu mir / Zip a dee doo dah / Lion sleeps tonight, The / Teeny / Hippy hippy shake / Shakin' all over / Ready Teddy / Marnor, stein und eisen bricht / Wunder / I don't need that kind of lovin' / Language of love / Tranen der liebe / Ich will frei sein / Welche farbe had die welt / He's got the whole world in his hands / Noah's arche / Waterloo / Denn da waren wir beide noch kinder / Liebe, gluck und treue / Bring grusse zu Mary.

LPS: . . . . BFX 15287/4

TEENY.
Tracks: / Teeny / Grun, grun ist Tennessee / Zwei fremde Augen / Shu-bi-do the slop / Kleine Peggy Lou / Das sind die einsamen jahre / Es war einmal / Come on, let's go / Marble breaks, iron bends / Trouble (Alice im Wunderland) / I wanna take you home / Mister tambourine man / Keiner weiss, wie es Morgen sein wird / An deiner seite / Ich geh durch's Feuer fur dich / Hello little girl.
LP: . . . . BFX 15063

Deux Filles

DAY FOR NIGHT.
MC: . . . . T 5

DOUBLE HAPPINESS.
LP: . . . . PULP 32

SILENCE AND WISDOM.
LP: . . . . PULP 31

Deux Hommes... (film)

DEUX HOMMES DANS LA VILLE/LES SEINS DE GLACE (Original soundtrack) (Various artists).
LP: . . . . PHCAM 05

Devastation

SIGNS OF LIFE.
Tracks: / Eye for an eye / Manic depressive / Retribution / Contaminated / Escape to violence / Desolation / Signs of life / Tomorrow we die / Fear of the unknown.
LP: . . . . FLAG 44
MC: . . . . TFLAG 44

VIOLENT TERMINATION.
LP: . . . . ZR 0269

Devaughan, William

BE THANKFUL FOR WHAT YOU'VE GOT.
LP: . . . . CHELV 1002
MC: . . . . CHELC 1002

FIGURES CAN'T CALCULATE.
Tracks: / Figures can't calculate / Love comes so easy with you / Boogie Dan / You send me / Be thankful for what you've got / I've never found a girl / Hold on to love.
LP: . . . . EMC 3347

Deviants

DEVIANTS.
Tracks: / Billy the monster / Broken biscuits / First line / People's suite / Rambling / Death of a dream machine / Play time / Black George does it with his mouth / Junior Narco Rangers / People of the city / Metamorphosis exploration.
LP: . . . . TRANDO 8

HUMAN GARBAGE (Live at Dingwalls '84).
LP: . . . . PSYCHO 25

PTOOFF.
LP: . . . . PSYCHO 16

THIRD ALBUM.
LP: . . . . DEMON 8

Deviated Instinct

GUTTERAL BREATH.
LP: . . . . VILE 16
MC: . . . . VILE 16 MC

ROCK 'N' ROLL CONFORMITY.
Tracks: / Pearls before swine / Laugh in your face / Conquest for eternity / House of cards / Putrid scum / Through the looking glass / Time and tide / When the chapter closes / Return of frost / Mechanical extinction / Rock 'n' roll conformity.
LP: . . . . VILE 003

Device

22B3.
Tracks: / Hanging on a heart attack / Who says? / Pieces on the ground / Tough and tender / When love is good / Didn't I read you right? / Fall apart, golden heart / I've got no room for your love / Who's on the line? / Sand, stone, cobwebs and dust.
LP: . . . . CHR 1526
MC: . . . . ZCHR 1526

Devil At 4 (film)

DEVIL AT 4 O CLOCK, THE (Original soundtrack) (Various artists).
LP: . . . . STV 81136

Devil & Daniel... (bk)

DEVIL AND DANIEL WEBSTER, THE (Stephen Vincent Benet) (Hingle, Pat (nar)).
MC: 1591

Devil & Mary Ann

DEVIL AND MARY ANN (see under Cookson, Catherine) (Jameson, Susan (nar)).

Devil Rides Out

DEVIL RIDES OUT, THE (See under Wheatley, Dennis) (Rodgers, Anton).

Devil Wielding

SHE'S A HEMINGWAY.
LP: . . . . DRAM 0197
MC: . . . . DRAM 0197MC

WORRY DOLLS.
LP: 0892131

Devils In Disguise

REVEALED.
LP: . . . . GET 1
MC: . . . . GET 1C

Devil's Paradise

DEVIL'S PARADISE, THE (1987 film soundtrack) (Various artists).
LP: . . . . ACH 034

Devine, Eddie

STOP CHILDREN ADULTS ONLY.
LP: . . . . KMLP 309

Devine, Mike

AFTER ALL THESE YEARS.
Tracks: / Cramen / Maggie / Rose of ol' Pawnee / Country hall of fame / Funny face / Can I say it's new / Down river road / Massacre of Glencoe / Older than the violin, The / She taught me how to yodel.
MC: . . . . HHC 001

PART OF ME, A.
LP: . . . . WGR 012
MC: . . . . CWGR 012

Devine & Statton

CARDIFFIANS.
LP: . . . . TWI 906

PRINCE OF WALES, THE.
LP: . . . . TWI 873

Devine Styler

WORD POWER.
Tracks: / Free styler / Get up on it / Last black house on the left, The / It's a black thing / Play it for divine / Koxistin U4RIA / Ain't sayin' nothin' / Divinity stylistics / Tongue of labyrinth / In divine style / Rain / Word power.
LP: 4661451
MC: 4661454

Devine, Sydney

25TH ANNIVERSARY ALBUM: SYDNEY DEVINE.
Tracks: / Three steps to heaven / Love is just a game / Crazy / Let me be there / It's too soon to know / She's my woman / Crystal chandeliers / My friend / Blanket on the ground / I don't wanna cry / I'm afraid to go back home / I really don't want to know / There goes my everything / Don't forget to remember / I believe.
LP: 6382 152
MC: 7252 707

50 COUNTRY WINNERS.
Tracks: / Country roads / Early morning rain / Gentle on my mind / Hello Mary Lou / Oh lonesome me / Sea of heartbreak / Lonesome number one / Blue, blue day / Four walls / He'll have to go / You're free to go / Sweet dreams / Send me the pillow that you dream on / Satin sheets / Wild side of life / This song is just for you / Blackboard of my heart / Married by the Bible / Crying time / Together again / I can't stop loving you / Take these chains from my heart / Dear God / Where could I go but to the Lord / House of gold / You'll never walk alone / Blanket on the ground / Old flames / Blowing in the wind / Sing me / Tiny bubbles / Early shells / Stand beside me / Gypsy woman / You're my best friend / 'Till the rivers all run dry / Please help me, I'm falling / Fraulein / I fall to pieces / It keeps right on a-hurtin' / Eighteen yellow roses / Ramblin' rose / Red roses for a blue lady / Irene / Lucille / Amanda / Lovesick blues / Singing the blues / Knee deep in the blues / Long gone lonesome blues.
2LP: . . . . PLAT 18
MCSET: . . . . PLAC 18

ALWAYS AND FOREVER.
Tracks: / Molly darling / Distant drums / Daisy a day / Mockin' Bird Hill / When you were sweet sixteen / There stands the glass / Sweet bunch of daisies / Born to love me / More and more / Let the heartaches begin / Remember you're mine / Always on your mind words / What do you want to make those eyes... / Anytime (You're feeling lonely).
LP: . . . . ITV 430
MC: . . . . KITV 430

BY REQUEST.
Tracks: / Pearly shells / Mansion on the hill / Some days are diamonds / If I were a blackbird / We're gonna go fishin' / Hawaiian wedding song / Heartaches by the number / Release me / Bigger leirinmore / You win again / Flyin' South.
LP: . . . . BGC 352
MC: . . . . KBGC 352

COUNTRY.
Tracks: / Lovesick blues / I can't stop loving you / Fraulein / Blackboard of my heart / Bye bye, love / It keeps right on a-hurtin' / May the bird of paradise fly up your nose / Help me make it through the night / Donna / She wears my ring / You're sixteen / You'll never miss a woman.
LP: . . . . GES 1093
MC: . . . . KGEC 1093

CRYING TIME.
Tracks: / Crying time / Broken engagement / My son calls another man daddy / Long black limousine / Two little orphans / Eighteen yellow roses / Old Shep / Letter edged in black / Nobody's child / I ain't crying, mister / Gentle mother / Come home, rolling stone.
LP: . . . . GES 1111
MC: . . . . KGEC 1111
MC: . . . . 4 HOM 007

DEVINE TIME.
LP: 6308 283

DOUBLE DEVINE.
LP: 6625 019

ENCORES.
Tracks: / Nobody's child / Singing the blues / Down the trail of aching hearts / Tiny bubbles / Church, a courtroom and then goodbye, A / China doll / Have a drink on me / Mockin' Bird Hill / Am I that easy to forget / Forty shades of green / There's nothing there / Jealous heart / Things / When Mexico gave up the rumba.
LP: . . . . BER 014
MC: . . . . KBER 014

FAVOURITE MEMORIES OF MINE.
Tracks: / I'm back / Favourite memory of mine / Till the rivers all run dry / With one exception / Long black veil / Love me tender / Last kiss, The / Pretty woman / Merry-go-round world / Travelling light / Almost persuaded / She called.
LP: . . . . BGC 336
MC: . . . . KBGC 336

FROM SCOTLAND WITH LOVE.
Tracks: / Scotland we love you / Silver threads / Mother I love you / Careless love / Suvla bay / My ain folk / Maggie / Old rustic bridge / Scotty boy / Wild mountain thyme / Born again / Red red rose / From Scotland with love / Scotland for me.
LP: . . . . ITV 373
MC: . . . . KITV 373

GREATEST HITS: SYDNEY DEVINE.
Tracks: / Lovesick blues / Send me the pillow that you dream on / Rose Marie / Two little orphans / May the bird of paradise fly up your nose / Take these chains from my heart / Crying time / It keeps right on a-hurtin' / Corina Corina / Room full of roses / Ain't that a shame / Blueberry Hill / I ain't crying, mister.
LP: . . . . GES 1183
MC: . . . . KGEC 1183

GREEN GRASS OF HOME, THE.
MC: . . . . KITV 530

HEARTACHES.
Tracks: / Hurt / He'll have to go / Dear John / I can't help it / I'd rather die young / Teddy Bear / You're free to go / When I leave the world behind / Oh lonesome me / Party's over / She's not you / Guilty one / Free to be lonely again / Blue eyes crying in the rain / Nothing in the world's too good for you / I'm here to get my baby out of jail.
MC: 7150 051
LP: 6359 051

LIVE FROM THE CITY HALL, GLASGOW.
Tracks: / Wolverton Mountain / Send me the pillow that you dream on / My truly, truly fair / Song sung blue / Room full of roses / When you and I were young, Maggie.
LP: . . . . SHM 958

MY WORLD OF MUSIC.
Tracks: / Bed of roses / Bluest heartache of the year / Burning bridges / Dreaming / Can't help falling in love / That's all right / Wonder of you / Favourite memory of mine / Forget me not / Here in love / Hickory Holler's tramp / It's a sin to tell a lie / John B / Long black veil / Love letters / Lucy, ain't your loser looking good / Me and Bobby McGee / My world is filled with music / Other people's sad songs / Save the last dance for me / Spanish / Till you can make it on your own / Tips of my fingers / Valentine partner / What made Milwaukee famous / You needed me / You're my world.
2LP: 6641930

SYDNEY DEVINE COLLECTION, THE.
Tracks: / Love is a good thing / Tear fell / Ain't that a shame / Blueberry Hill / Corrine Corrina / Spread it around / No one will ever know / Laura / Take these chains from my heart / Kelly / Rose

Marie / From a jack to a king / Walk on by / Wolverton Mountain / Woman sensuous woman / Send me the pillow you dream on / Road to Dundee / My truly truly fair / Only you / Married man blues / Song sung blue / Railroad burn / Teddy bear / All shook up / Room full of roses / When you and I were young Maggie blues / One night / It's now or never / Everything is beautiful.
2LP: .... PDA 060
MCSET: .... PDC 060

SYDNEY DEVINE SINGS YOUR FAVOURITE COUNTRY SONGS.
Tracks: / This song is just for you / Ten guitars / Tennessee waltz / Only the heartaches / Married by the Bible, divorced by the law / Do what you do do well / Wild side of life / Act naturally / When you and I were young Maggie / Your cheatin' heart / I love you because / Little arrows.
MC: .... KBER 012
LP: .... BER 012

SYD'S SING-SONG COUNTRY ALBUM.
Tracks: / Country roads / Early morning rain / Gentle on my mind / Hello Mary Lou / Gypsy woman / You're my best friend / 'Till the rivers all run dry / Four walls / He'll have to go / You're free to go / Tiny bubbles / Pearly shells / Stand beside me / Sweet dreams / Send me the pillow that you dream on / Satin sheets / Eighteen yellow roses / Room full of roses / Ramblin' rose / Red roses for a blue lady / Dear God / Where could I go but to the Lord / House of gold / You'll never walk alone / Oh lonesome me / Sea of heartbreak / Lonesome / Blue blue day / Blanket on the ground / Old flames / Blowing in the wind / Sing me / Irene / Lucille / Amanda / Please help me, I'm falling / Fraulein / I fall to pieces / It keeps right on a-hurtin' / Lovesick blues / Singing the blues / Knee deep in the blues / Long gone lonesome blues / Wild side of life / This song is just for you / Blackboard of my heart / Married by the Bible / Crying time / Together again / I can't stop loving you / Take these chains from my heart.
LP: .... BGC 398
MC: .... KBGC 398

TAKE MY HAND, PRECIOUS LORD.
Tracks: / Old rugged cross, The / Peace in the valley / Midnight special (I'd like to see Jesus) / What a friend we have in Jesus / Only believe / Take my hand, precious Lord / Precious memories / We call on Him / Family Bible / It is no secret / Who am I? / Only if you praise the Lord.
LP: .... GES 1220
MC: .... KGEC 1220

VERY BEST OF SYDNEY DEVINE.
Tracks: / I can't stop loving you / Laura / Road to Dundee, The / Fraulein / My son calls another man daddy / From a jack to a king / Eighteen yellow roses / She wears my ring / Nobody's child / My truly, truly fair / Kelly / When you and I were young, Maggie.
LP: .... GES 1142
MC: .... KGEC 1142

Devlin, Johnny

AUSTRALIAN ROCKER.
LP: .... PLP 1201

REAL NERVOUS (Devlin, Johnny & The Devils).
LP: .... REBEL 1006

Devlin, Sheila

COUNTRY GIRL.
Tracks: / Philadelphia lawyer / Once a day / Island of dreams / Gathering flowers for the master's bouquet / L.A. international airport / Little country town in Ireland / '57 Chevrolet / Three ways to love you / Make the world go away / I never had a doubt in my mind about you / My mother pray again / Faithful sailor boy, The.
MC: .... CPHL 461

Devo

DEVO LIVE.
Tracks: / Gates of steel / Be stiff / Planet earth / Freedom of choice (Theme song.) / Whip it / Girl U want.
LP: .... OVED 1

DUTY NOW FOR THE FUTURE.
Tracks: / Devo corporate anthem / Clockout / Timing x / Wiggly world / Block head / Strange pursuits / S.I.B. (swelling itching brain) / Triumph of the will / Day my baby gave me a surprise, The / Pink pussycat / Secret agent man / Smart patrol / Redeye express / Mr. DNA.
LP: .... OVED 38
LP: .... V 2125

FREEDOM OF CHOICE.
Tracks: / Girluwant / It's not right / Snowball / Ton o' lov / Freedom of choice / Gates of steel / Cold war / Don't you know / That's pep / Mr. B's ballroom / Planet Earth.
LP: .... OVED 39
LP: .... V 2162

HARD CORE DEVO.
LP: .... FC 065
MC: .... FC 065C

HARDCORE VOLUME 1 1974-1977.
Tracks: / Mechanical man / Auto modown / Space girl blues / Social fools / Soo bawls / Satisfaction / Jocko homo / Golden energy / Buttered beauties / Midget / I'm a potato / Uglatto / Stop look and listen / Ono / Mongoloid.
LP: .... ESSLP 134
MC: .... ESSMC 134

HARDCORE VOLUME 2.
LP: .... RACS 0208

LIVE: DEVO.
LP: 203 866

NEW TRADITIONALISTS.
Tracks: / Through being cool / Jerkin' back 'n' forth / Pity you / Soft things / Race of doom / Going under / Love without anger / Super thing, The / Beautiful world / Enough said.
LP: .... OVED 73
MC: .... OVEDC 73
LP: .... V 2191

NOW IT CAN BE TOLD.
2LP: .... ENVLP 532

OH NO IT'S DEVO.
Tracks: / Time out for fun / Peek-a-boo / Out of sync / Explosions / That's good / Patterns / Big mess / Speed racer / What I must / I desire / Deep sleep.
LP: .... OVED 122
MC: .... OVEDC 122

Q:ARE WE NOT MEN?.A:WE ARE DEVO.
Tracks: / Uncontrollable urge / Satisfaction / Praying hands / Space junk / Monogoloid / Jocko homo / Too much paranoias / Gut feeling / Slap your mammy / Sloppy (I saw my baby gettin') / Shrivel up / Come back Jonee.
LP: .... OVED 37
MC: .... OVEDC 37
LP: .... V 2106

SHOUT.
Tracks: / Shout / Satisfied mind / Don't rescue me / 4th dimension / C'mon / Here to go / Jurisdiction of love / Puppet boy / Please please / Are you experienced.
LP: 9250971

SMOOTH NOODLE MAPS.
Tracks: / Stuck in a loop / Post post-modern man / When we do it / Spin the wheel / Morning dew / Chance is gonna cum, A / Big picture, The / Pink jazz trancers / Jimmy / Devo has feelings too / Dawghaus.
LP: .... ENVLP 1006
MC: .... TCENV 1006

TOTAL DEVO.
Tracks: / Baby doll / Disco dancer / Some things never change / Plain truth / Happy guy / Shadow, The / I'd cry if you died / Agitated / Man turned inside out / Blow up.
LP: 3303 1
MC: 3303 4
LP: .... ENVLP 503
MC: .... TCENV 503

Devon...

DEVON MUSEUM OF MECHANICAL MUSIC (See under Mechanical Music) (Various artists).

Devon Inn Folk

ALL ALONG DOWN ALONG.
Tracks: / Made of sand / Old 97 / Water is wide, The / Widecombe fair / Irish rover, The / Cuckoo's nest, The / Wake, lady wake / Nightingales sing / Roddy McCorley / Whistling gypsy.
MC: 30-095

Devonshire & Dorset...

DEVONSHIRE & DORSET BRASS BAND Military band series (Devonshire & Dorset Brass Band).
MC: .... VCA 042

JANNERS IN CONCERT (Devonshire & Dorset Regiment).
LP: .... MM 0571

Devonshire Haymakers

SONG AND DANCES.
MC: 45 407

Devonsquare

WALKING ON ICE.
Tracks: / Walking on ice / Black Africa / Caffe Lena / World without walls / Chinalight / Straightaway / Sandman / Las Vegas brides / Elevator man / Just like paradise.
LP: 781 843-1
MC: 781 843-4

Devore, Charlie

MILENBERG JOYS (see Thompson, Butch) (Thompson, Butch/Hal Smith/ Charlie Devore).

Devotion, Sheila B.

KING OF THE WORLD.
Tracks: / Spacer / Mayday / Charge plates and credit cards / Misery / King of the world / Cover girls / Your love is good / Don't go.
LP: .... CAL 112
MC: .... CAC 112

LITTLE DARLIN'.
Tracks: / Little darlin / It's only make believe / Stranded / I'm still believing / Put it in writing / Waiting for the night / Runner / Nothing less than love / Saturday night.
LP: 67 793
MC: 70 793

Devoto, Howard

JERKY VERSIONS OF THE DREAM.
Tracks: / Rainy season / Cold imagination / Topless / I admire you / Way out of shape / Out of shape with me / Some will pay (for what others pay to avoid) / Waiting for a train / Taking over heaven / Seeing is believing.
LP: .... V 2272
MC: .... TCV 2272
LP: .... OVED 129

Dewar, Colin

COLIN DEWAR & HIS SCOTTISH DANCE BAND (Dewar, Colin & His Scottish Dance Band).
Tracks: / Grand march / Circassian circle / Canadian barn dance / 4/4 marches / Trip to Aberdeen, A / Irish reels / Fiddle solo / Eva three step / Continental waltz / Duke of Perth / Gaelic waltzes / Octocentenary jig, The.
LP: .... LAP 116
MC: .... LAP 116 C

Dewhurst, Brian

FOLLOW THAT WITH YOUR SEA-LIONS.
Tracks: / Loyne barbershop quartet / British Grenadiers, The / Brighton camp / Garry Owen / Night visiting song / Golden rain, The / Peggy and the soldier / Turf duffing song / Silver coin / Vicar and the frog / Larnin pills / Honky tonk music / Lilliburlero / Roxburgh castle / Down where the drunkards roll / Dainty Davie / Back o' the bike shed / Broomfield hill / Don't write 'em like that anymore / Busk busk bonnie lassie / All the good times are past and gone.
LP: .... FE 009

HUNTER AND THE HUNTED, THE.
Tracks: / Bird in the bush, The / Silver spear / Brown Adam / Valentine's day hunt / White hare of Oldham / Hunt, The / Horn of the hunter / Bonnie black hare / Keepers and poachers / Innocent hare, The / Huntsman's chorus, The / Radcliffe otter hunt, The / Manchester cornstalk / Foxhunter's jig, The / Gallant poacher / Furness hunt, The / Noble Duke of Buckingham's hounds, The / Hills of Greenmore / Bugle, The.
LP: .... FHR 075

Dex

BACKS AGAINST THE WALL.
Tracks: / Backs against the wall / One love / Long live love / Silicon chip / Don't blame me / Losing you / Listen to me / She's an artist / I need you / Heartbreaker.
LP: .... AS 15874

Dexter, Al

SINGS AND PLAYS HIS GREATEST HITS.
LP: .... HAT 3101
MC: .... HATC 3101

Dexter, Brian

CAFE' CONTINENTAL (See under Compton, Tony) (Compton, Tony and Brian Dexter).

Dexter, Ray

SOUND SHOW.
LP: .... SFA 042

UP COUNTRY.
MC: .... AM 6

Dexy's Midnight

DON'T STAND ME DOWN.
Tracks: / Occasional flicker / This is what she's like / Knowledge of beauty / Reminisce part two / Listen to this / Waltz / One of those things.
LP: .... MERH 56

GENO (LP).
Tracks: / Geno / Plan B / Breakin'down the walls of heartache / Dance stance / Horse, The / There, there my dear / Keep it / One way love / I'm just looking / Soul finger.
LP: .... ATAK 72
MC: .... TCATAK 72
LP: .... FA 3189
MC: .... TCFA 3189
LP: .... EMS 1007

SEARCHING FOR THE YOUNG SOUL REBELS.
Tracks: / Burn it down / Tell me when my light turns to green / Teams that meet in the caffs / I'm just looking / Geno / Seven day's to long / I couldn't help it if I tried / Thankfully not living in Yorkshire, it doesn't / Keep it / Love part one / There, there my dear.
LP: .... PCS 7213
MC: .... TCPCS 7213

TOO-RYE-AY.
Tracks: / Celtic soul brothers / Let's make this precious / All in all / Old / Plan B / Jackie Wilson said / I'll show you / Liars to be / Until / Come on Eileen.
LP: .... PRICE 89
MC: .... PRIMC 89
LP: .... MERS 8
MC: .... MERSC 8
LP: .... MERS 5

VERY BEST OF DEXY'S MIDNIGHT RUNNERS, THE.
Tracks: / Come on Eileen / Jackie Wilson said (I'm in heaven when you smile) / Let's get this straight / Because of you / Show me / Celtic soul brothers / Liars A to E / One way love / Old / Geno / There, there my dear / Breaking down the walls of heartache / Dance stance / Plan B / Keep it / I'm just looking / Soon / This is what she's like / Soul finger.
MC: 846 460-4
LP: 846 460-1

Dey, Charley

TIME ON MY HANDS.
Tracks: / Bed of roses / Saginaw Michigan / Green fields of France.
MC: .... CWGR 090

Deyanova, Marta

RAKHMANINOV PRELUDES (See under Rakhmaninov for full details).

Dezerter

UNDERGROUND OUT OF POLAND.
LP: .... MRR 003

Dharma, Buck

FLAT OUT.
Tracks: / Born to rock / That summer night / Cold wind / Your loving heart / 5.35 / Wind weather and storm / All tied up / Anwar's theme.
LP: .... PRT 85997

Dharma Bums

HAYWIRE.
Tracks: / Timeyard / Boots of leather / Cruel acres / Over / Under / Walking stick / Mutiny / Hope of the hour / Jet pilot / Dropping out / Farmyard / Flowers / Haywire.
LP: .... SORC 5

Dhu, Duncan

DUNCAN DHU.
LP: .... CRELP 042

D.I.

ANCIENT ARTIFACTS.
LP: 51006 1

HORSE BITES DOG CRIES.
LP: 51007 1

TEAM GOON.
LP: XXX1002

TRAGEDY AGAIN.
Tracks: / Tragedy again / Chiva / Nick the whip / Manhole / Sashu / Diablo I / Blue velvet / Backseat driver / Love to me is a sin / On our way / Diablo II.
LP: .... EM 94261

WHAT GOOD IS GRIEF TO A GOD.
LP: .... EM 9547 1

Di Angelo, Mr

GENERATION (See under Mr. Di Angelo).

Di Di

DAS WAR EIN HARTER TAG (Beatles songs) (Di Di & His ABC Boys).
Tracks: / Nicht eine mark (Can't buy me love) / Das war ein harter tag (A hard days night) / Schliess die augen (All my lovin') / Jung wie du (Love me do) / Ja das hatt ich wissen mussen / Wie du (If I fell) / Hello Susann (It won't be long) / Alright / Das ist musik / Bye bye Barbara / Ich werde nie eine andere lieben / Hundertmal / Daraus mach ich kein geheimnis / Sei mir treu wie gold (Tell me why).
LP: .... BTS 943403

Di Franco, Linda

RISE OF THE HEART, THE.
Tracks: / T.V. Scene / Look of love, The / Yankee / Stay / Dance it up / My boss / Bless my soul / Fran / Blame it on Rio / Rise of the heart, The.
LP: .... WX 50
MC: .... WX 50C

Di Meola, Al

CASINO.
Tracks: / Egyptian danza / Chasin' the voodoo / Dark eye tango / Senor mouse / Fantasia suite for two guitars / Viva la danzarina / Guitars of the exotic isle / Rhapsody Italia / Bravoto fantasia / Casino.
LP: CBS 32071
MC: 40 32071

CIELO E TERRA.
Tracks: / Traces of a tear / Vertigo shadow / Cielo e Terra / Enigma of desire / Atavism of twilight / Coral / When your gone / Etude / Solace.
LP: EJ 2403321
MC: EJ 2403324

ELECTRIC RENDEZVOUS.
Tracks: / God bird / Change / Electric rendezvous / Passion, grace and fire / Cruisin' / Black cat shuffle / Ritmo de la noche / Somalia / Jewel inside a dream.
LP: CBS 85437
MC: 40 85437

ELEGANT GYPSY.
Tracks: / Flight over Rio / Midnight tango / Mediterranean sundance / Race with devil on Spanish highway / Lady of Rome / Sister of Brazil / Elegant gypsy suite.
LP: CBS 81845
MC: 40 81845

FRIDAY NIGHT IN SAN FRANCISCO (Di Meola, Al & John McLaughlin & Paco De Lucia).
Tracks: / Mediterranean sundance / Rio Ancho / Short tales of the Black Forest / Frevo resgado / Fantasia suite for two guitars / Guardian angel.
LP: CBS 84962
MC: 40 84962

GREATEST HITS: AL DI MEOLA.
LP: 4669951
MC: 4669954

LAND OF THE MIDNIGHT SUN.
Tracks: / Wizard / Sarabande from violin sonata in B minor / Pictures of the sea (love theme) / Land of the midnight sun / Golden dawn suite (morning fire) / Calmer of the tempests / From ocean to the clouds / Short tales of the Black Forest.
LP: CBS 32027

PASSION GRACE AND FIRE (See under McLaughlin, John) (McLaughlin, John/Al Di Meola/Paco De Lucia).

SOARING THROUGH A DREAM.
Tracks: / Capoeira / Traces (of a tear) / Ballad / July / Marina / Soaring through a dream.
LP: EJ 2403981
MC: EJ 2403984

SPLENDIDO HOTEL.
Tracks: / Alien chase on an Arabian desert / Silent story in her eyes / Roller jubilee / Two to tango / Al Di's dream.
LP: CBS 88468
MC: 4670904

TIRAMI SU.
Tracks: / Beijing demons / Arabella / Smile from a stranger / Rhapsody of fire / Song of the Pharoah kings / Andonea / Maraba / Song with a view.
LP: MTL 1019
MC: TCMTL 1019

TOUR DE FORCE (LIVE).
Tracks: / Elegant gypsy suite / Nena / Advantage / Egyptian danza / Race with the devil on Spanish highway / Cruisin'.
LP: CBS 25121

Diabate, Sekou

MONTAGNE.
LP: ESP 8419

Diabate, Sidiki

BA TOGOMA (Diabate, Sidiki & Ensemble).
LP: NSA 001
MC: NSC 001

SIDIKI DIABATE & ENSEMBLE BA TOGOMA (Diabate, Sidiki & Ensemble).
LP: FMS/NSA 001

Diabate, Sona

SAHEL (Diabate, Sona & M'Mah Sylla).
LP: TERRA 106
MC: TERRAC 106

Diabate, Toumani

KAIRA.
LP: HNBL 1338
MC: HNBC 1338

Diabelli (Composer)

TRUMPET CONCERTOS AND FANFARES (See under Trumpet Music - Classical) (Philharmonia Orchestra).

Dial Masters

DIAL MASTERS 1 (BOX SET) (See under Charlie Parker) (Various artists).

DIAL MASTERS 2 (BOX SET) (Modern jazz) (Various artists).
LPS: SPJ BOX 7

Diambrini, Alex

OUT OF THE DARK.
Tracks: / In a way / My loving is for free / Way you love me, The / Love so strong / You slow me down / Start, The / Shadow of my heart / Want you.
LP: MORRHYTHM 57

Diamond

DIAMOND MISTRESS.
LP: RR 9766

Diamond Accordion Band

25 GREAT COUNTRY HITS.
Tracks: / Stand by your man / Banks of the Ohio / Jealous heart / I walk the line / Love you because / He'll have to go / Crystal chandeliers / I'm fallin' / Yellow ribbons / Right on / China doll / Nobody's child / Cheating heart / Pillow you dream on / Fraulein / Folsom Prison blues / I still miss someone / Tennessee waltz / Mexicali rose / I really don't want to know / Blackboard of my heart / I can't help it / Does my ring hurt your finger? / It keeps right on a-hurtin' / Wild side of life / Blanket on the ground.
LP: GES 1145
MC: KGEC 1145

AT HOME IN IRELAND.
Tracks: / Wild colonial boy / Noreen bawn / Mother's love's a blessing, A / Black velvet band / Isle of Innisfree / Forty shades of green / Does your mother come from Ireland / I'll take you home again Kathleen / With my shillelagh under me arm / Eileen Oge / Ould Lammas fair / I met her in the garden where the praties grow / MacNamara's band / Green fields of France / Girl from Donegal / Homes of Donegal / Star of Donegal, The / Hills of Donegal / Green bushes / Lovely Derry on the banks of The Foyle / Mountains of Mourne / Bard of Armagh, The / Cockles and mussels / Come back to Erin / Boys from County Armagh / Old bog road / By the light of the silvery moon / Fields of Athenry / Town I loved so well, The / I'll tell me ma / Courtin' in the kitchen / Dacent Irish boy, The / Let him go let him tarry / Doonaree / Rose of Tralee, The / Little town in the ould County Down / My wild Irish rose / Too-ra-loo-ra-loo-ra / Biddy Mulligan the pride of Coombe / Come back Paddy Reilly to Ballyjamesduff / Stone outside Dan Murphy's door, The / Rose of Arranmore / Isle of Spey.
LP: GES 1238
MC: KGEC 1238

DIAMOND ACCORDION BAND PLAY COUNTRY GREATS.
Tracks: / Help me make it through the night / Rhinestone cowboy / One day at a time / Cold cold heart / My son calls another man daddy / Stand by your man / I love you because / Crystal chandeliers / Tie a yellow ribbon / Down river road / Letter edged in black / You're my best friend / Once around the dance floor / Where the blue and lonely go / You're cheating heart / Folsom Prison blues / He'll have to go / Blackboard of my heart / I'm nobody's child / Blanket on the ground.
MC: 4 HOM 001

DIAMOND ACCORDION BAND PLAYS JOLSON.
Tracks: / Waiting for the Robert E. Lee / California here I come / Baby face / I'm looking over a four leaf clover / Carolina in the morning / Pretty baby / Mammy / Toot toot tootsie / Chinatown, my Chinatown / Ma (he's making eyes at me) / April showers / Rockabye your baby with a Dixie melody / Swanee / Bye bye blackbird / I want a girl / Broadway melody / When the red, red robin comes bob, bob, bobbin' along / Sonny boy / Lullaby of Broadway / Give my regards to Broadway / Avalon / Melancholy baby / For me and my gal / My blue Heaven / I'm sitting on top of the world.
LP: GES 1168
MC: KGEC 1168

GO COUNTRY.
Tracks: / Make it through the night / Old Shep / Rhinestone cowboy / My best friend / One day at a time / Love was / Cold cold heart (Medley.) / Blue and the lonely, The / River road / Release me / Wrong road / Door is always open, The / Letter edged in black / When you and I were young, Maggie / You win again / Wedding bells / Take these chains from my heart / My son calls another man daddy / All I have to offer you is me / Take these chains from my heart (Medley.) / Year for Mexico.
LP: GES 1195
MC: KGEC 1195

JUST A CLOSER WALK WITH THEE.
Tracks: / When the saints go marching in / Marching on / Fight the good fight / Love lifted me / Praise my soul / Lord's my shepherd, The / How great thou art / Rivers of Babylon / Closer walk with thee, A / Take my hand, precious Lord / Plough the fields / Whispering hope / When the roll is called up yonder / Shall we gather at the river? / Our God is marching on / Safe in the arms of Jesus / Jesu, lover of my soul / Jesus loves me / Once in royal David's city / Work, for the night is coming / Brighten the corner where you are / Count your blessings.
LP: GES 1208
MC: KGEC 1208

MARCHING WITH JESUS.
Tracks: / Old old story, The / It is no secret / Nearer my God / Amazing grace / In ages past / Wondrous cross / Green hill / I need Thee every hour / Old rugged cross, The / Rock of ages / Tell me the old, old story / What a friend we have in Jesus / Onward Christian soldiers / Stand up, stand up for Jesus / Abide with me / It is no secret / Nearer my God to thee / Lead kindly light / O god our help in ages past / When I survey the wondrous cross / There is a green hill / Old rugged cross, The / Be Thou my vision.
LP: GES 1094
MC: KGEC 1094

WALTZING AROUND THE WORLD.
Tracks: / Four in the morning / Morning has broken / Oh what a beautiful morning / Three o'clock in the morning / Softly softly / Good luck, good health, God bless you / Old rockin' chair / There goes my everything / Annie's song / Tulips from Amsterdam / By the side of the Zuyder Zee / Reine de musette / Last waltz, The / Adios, amigo / Funny, familiar forgotten feelings / Moon river / Plaisir d'amour / Edelweiss / We will make love / Delilah / Lady of Spain / Twelfth of never / Are you lonesome tonight / Eternally / Gordon for me, A / Northern lights of old Aberdeen / These are my mountains / Bourrasque / Anna Marie / When the girl in your arms / You're the only good thing that's happened to me / I wonder who's kissing her now / Far away places / Ramona.
LP: GES 1234
MC: KGEC 1234

YOUR FAVOURITE SINGALONGS.
Tracks: / My guy's come back / Little brown jug / American patrol / In the mood / Lobby song, The / Snow waltz / Blacksmith / Old flames / Yellow submarine / Lily the pink / Match of the day / Bunch of thyme / Catch me if you can / Shine on harvest moon / Birdie song, The / I love a lassie / Roamin' in the gloamin' / Little peace, A / Portsmouth / Scotch on the rocks / When you were sweet sixteen / Le yenka / Hucklebuck, The / Pal of my cradle days / Could I have this dance.
LP: GES 1224
MC: KGEC 1224

YOUR FAVOURITE SINGALONGS VOLUME II.
Tracks: / Here we are again / Ship ahoy / If I had my way / Man on the flying trapeze, The / Bless 'em all / In the shade of the old apple tree / I'm forever blowing bubbles / I've got a lovely bunch of coconuts / I do like to be beside the seaside / Man who broke the bank at Monte Carlo, The / Blaydon races / Side by side / White cliffs of Dover, The / We'll meet again / She's a lassie from Lancashire / Down at the old Bull and Bush / Don't dilly dally on the way / Goodbye Dolly Gray / Run, rabbit, run / Wish me luck as you wave me goodbye / You made me love you / Maybe it's because I'm a Londoner / Underneath the arches / Whatever will be will be (medley) / Liverpool Lou / How much is that doggie in the window / After the ball / Happy wanderer, The / Roll out the barrel / It's a long way to Tipperary / Pack up your troubles in your old kit bag / By the light of the silvery moon / Lily of Laguna / Mockin' Bird Hill / Oh dear what can the matter be? / Two lovely black eyes / Two little girls in blue / I'll be your sweetheart / Oh, oh, Antonio / Take me back to dear old Blighty / Hello, hello, who's your lady friend? / Gang that sang heart of my heart / Shine on harvest moon / If you were the only girl in the world.
LP: GES 1229
MC: KGEC 1229

YOUR FAVOURITE WALTZES.
Tracks: / Carnival of Venice / Anniversary waltz/Beautiful dreamer / Somewhere my love / Springtime in the Rockies / Florence / Home on the range / Too old to dream / Cruising down the river / Blue of night / Goodnight, Irene / Blossom time / Liebestraum / Tipitina / Now is the hour / Beautiful dreamer / Loveliest night of the year, The / Who's taking you home tonight? / Let the rest of the world go by / Carolina moon / Under the bridges of Paris / Windmill song / Whiffenpoof song, The / It's a sin to tell a lie / My bonnie lies over the ocean / On top of Old Smokey / I'll be with you in apple blossom time / Always / Let me call you sweetheart / Loch Lomond / I belong to Glasgow / Flower of Scotland / Auld lang syne / Charmaine.
LP: GES 1216
MC: KGEC 1216

Diamond Brothers

SILVER MEDALS AND SWEET MEMORIES.
Tracks: / Some I wrote / Movies / Silver medals and sweet memories / Bed of roses / Do you remember these / Flowers on the wall / Class of '57, The / I'll go to my grave loving you / Susan when she tried / Whatever happened to Randolph Scott?.
LP: GES 5018

Diamond, Dyan

IN THE DARK.
Tracks: / Baby what you want me to do / Western Avenue / Hot / Teenage radio stars / Someone like me / Back on the strip / Mystery dance / Animal girl / Nervous / Your neighbourhood / In the dark / Gonna rock ourselves to death.
LP: MCF 2875

Diamond, Greg

STARCRUISER.
Tracks: / Fancy dancer / Island boogie / Starcruiser / Bring back your love / Holding back / This side of midnight / Too hot to reggae / Arista vista.
LP: TKR 82549

Diamond Head

AM I EVIL?.
Tracks: / Am I evil? / Heat of the night / Don't you ever leave me / Borrowed time / To Heaven from Hell / Dead reckoning / Lightning to the nations / Sucking my love.
LP: WKFMLP 92
MC: WKFMMC 92
LPPD: WKFMPD 92

BEHOLD THE BEGINNING.
LP: METALP 110
LP: HMRLP 165
MC: HMRMC 165

BORROWED TIME.
Tracks: / In the heat of the night / To Heaven from Hell / Call me / Lightning to the nations / Borrowed time / Don't you ever leave me / Am I evil?.
LP: MCL 1783
MC: MCLC 1783
LP: DH 1001

CANTERBURY.
LP: DH 1002

DIAMOND HEAD.
LP: HMRLP 92
MC: HMRMC 92

DIAMOND HEAD - IN THE BEGINNING.
LP: WKFMLP 165
MC: WKFMMC 165

Diamond, Jim

DESIRE FOR FREEDOM.
Tracks: / Desire / So strong / Young love (carry me away) / My weakness is you / I can't stop / Maybe one day / Hi ho silver / Judy's not that tough / You'll go crazy.
LP: AMA 5131
MC: AMC 5131

DOUBLE CROSSED.
Tracks: / Double crossed / I sleep alone at night / After the fire / I should have known better / Stumblin' over / Remember I love you / New generation / Co-operation / She is woman / I'm yours / Impossible dream, The / Caledonia.
LP: AMA 5029
MC: AMC 5029

TONY BANKS (EP) (see Banks, Tony).

Diamond, Neil

12 GREATEST HITS VOL.2.
Tracks: / Beautiful noise / Hello again / Forever in blue jeans / September morn / Desiree / You don't bring me flowers / America / Be / Longfellow serenade / If you know what I mean / Yesterday's songs / Love on the rocks.
LP: 85844

20 GOLDEN GREATS: NEIL DIAMOND.
LP: EMTV 14
MC: MCTV 2

AND THE SINGER SINGS HIS SONG.
Tracks: / Captain Sunshine / Free life / Hurtin' you don't come easy / Coldwater morning / Walk on water / Stones / And the grass won't pay no mind / If I never knew your name / Merry go round /

Juliet / Brooklyn roads / And the singer sings his song.
LP: . . . . **MCL 1629**
MC: . . . . **MCLC 1629**

BEAUTIFUL NOISE.
Tracks: / Beautiful noise / Stargazer / Lady oh / Don't think / Feel / Surviving the life / If you know what I mean / Street life / Home is a wonderful heart / Jungletime / Signs / Dry your eyes.
LP: **4504521**
MC: **4504524**
LP: **86004**

BEST OF NEIL DIAMOND.
Tracks: / Sweet Caroline / Play me / If you go away / High rolling man / Soolaimon / Glory road / Holly holy / I am ... I said / Cherry, Cherry / Canta Libre / Song sung blue / Girl, you'll be a woman soon.
LP: . . . . **SHM 3200**
MC: . . . . **HSC 3200**
LPS: . . . . **ALBUM 91**
LP: **1A022 58248**
MC: **1A222 58248**

BEST YEARS OF OUR LIVES.
Tracks: / Best years of our lives / Hard times for young lovers / This time / Everything's gonna be fine / Hooked on the memory of you / Take care of me / Baby can I hold you / Carmelita's eyes / Courtin' disaster / If I couldn't see you again / Long hard climb.
LP: **4632011**
MC: **4632014**

BROTHER LOVE'S TRAVELLING SALVATION SHOW.
Tracks: / Brother Love's travelling salvation Show / Dig in / River runs, newgrown plums / Juliet / Long gone / And the grass won't pay no mind / You're so sweet, horse-flies keep hangin' round your face / Hurting / You don't come easy.
LP: . . . . **MCF 2536**
MC: . . . . **MCFC 2536**

CLASSICS - THE EARLY YEARS.
Tracks: / Kentucky woman / Cherry Cherry / Solitary man / You got to me / I got the feelin' / Thank the Lord for the night time / I'm a believer / Girl you'll be a woman soon / Shilo / Do it / Red red wine / Boat that I row, The.
LP: **32349**
MC: **40 32349**

DIAMONDS.
Tracks: / Rosie / Free life / Coldwater morning / He ain't heavy he's my brother / Modern day version of love, A / Honeydrippin' times / Sunday sun / Practically newborn / Long gone / Glory Road / Deep in the morning / If I never knew your name / Sweet Caroline (good times never seemed so good) / Mr. Bojangles / Ain't no way holy holy / Cherry Cherry / Kentucky woman / Song sung blue / High rolling man / Play me / Gitchy goomy / Walk on water / Prelude in E major / Morningside.
2LP: . . . . **MCLD 603**
MCSET: . . . . **MCLDC 603**

GOLD.
Tracks: / Lordy / Both sides now / Solitary man / Holly holy / Cherry, cherry / Kentucky woman / Sweet Caroline / Thank the lord for the night time / Singer sings his songs / Brother love's travelling salvation show.
LP: . . . . **MCL 1767**

GREATEST HITS: NEIL DIAMOND.
LP: . . . . **BRLP 58**
MC: . . . . **BRMC 58**

GREATEST ORIGINAL HITS: NEIL DIAMOND.
Tracks: / You don't bring me flowers / If you know what I mean / September morn / Beautiful noise.
MC: **40 3065**

HEADED FOR THE FUTURE.
Tracks: / Headed for the future / Man you need, The / I'll see you on the radio (Laura) / Stand up for love / It should have been me / Lost in Hollywood / Story of my life / Angel / Me beside you / Love don't live here anymore.
LP: **26952**
MC: **40 26952**

HEARTLIGHT.
Tracks: / Heartlight / I'm alive / I'm guilty / Hurricane / Lost among the stars / In Ensenada / Fool for you, A / Star flight / Front page story / Comin' home / First you have to say you love me.
LP: **25073**

HOT AUGUST NIGHTS.
Tracks: / Prologue / Crunchy granola suite / Done too soon / Dialogue / Solitary man / Cherry cherry / Sweet Caroline / Porcupine pie / You're so sweet / Red red wine / Soggy pretzels / And the grass won't pay no mind / Shilo / Girl you'll be a woman soon / Play me / Canta libre / Morningside / Song sung blue / Cracklin' Rosie / Holly holy / I am ... I said / Walk off / Soolaimon / Brother Love's travelling salvation show / Encore.
2LP: . . . . **UND 1**
2LP: . . . . **MCSP 255**

HOT AUGUST NIGHTS II.
Tracks: / Song of the whales (fanfare) / Headed for the future / September morn / Thank the Lord for the night time / Cherry, Cherry / Sweet Caroline / Hello again / Love on the rocks / America / Forever in blue jeans / You don't bring me flowers / I dreamed a dream / Back in L.A. / Song sung blue / Cracklin' Rosie / I am ... I said / Holly holy / Soolaimon / Brother Love's travelling salvation show / Heartlight.
LP: **4604081**
MC: **4604084**

I'M GLAD YOU'RE HERE WITH ME TONIGHT.
Tracks: / God only knows / Let me take you in my arms again / Once in a while / Let the little boy sing / I'm glad you're here with me tonight / Lament in D minor / Dance of the sabres / Desiree / You don't bring me flowers / Free man in Paris.
LP: **86044**
LP: . . . . **CBS 32395**
MC: **40 32395**

JAZZ SINGER, THE (Film soundtrack).
Tracks: / America / Adorn o lume / You baby / Love on the rocks / Amazed and confused / Robert E. Lee, The / Summer love / Hello again / Acapulco / Hey Louise / Songs of life / Jerusalem / Kol nidre / My name is Yussel / America (reprise).
LP: . . . . **EAST 12120**
MC: . . . . **TCEAST 12120**

JONATHAN LIVINGSTONE SEAGULL (Film Soundtrack).
Tracks: / Jonathan Livingstone Seagull (prologue) / Flight of the gull / Dear father (part 1) / Skybird (part 1) / Lonely looking sky / Odyssey, The / Dear father (part 2) / Anthem / Be (part 1) / Skybird (part 2) / Dear father (part 3) / Be (part 3).
LP: **4676071**
MC: **4676074**

LIVE DIAMOND.
LP: . . . . **MCF 3137**

LIVE GOLD.
Tracks: / Lordy / Both sides now / Solitary man / Holly holy / Cherry, Cherry / Kentucky woman / Sweet Caroline / Thank the Lord for the night time / And the singer sings his song / Brother Love's travelling salvation show.
LP: . . . . **MFP 5815**
MC: . . . . **TCMFP 5815**
LP: . . . . **UNLS 116**

LOVE AT THE GREEK.
Tracks: / Kentucky woman / Sweet Caroline / Last Picasso / Longfellow serenade / Beautiful noise / Lady oh / Stargazer / If you know what I mean / Surviving the life / Glory road / Song sung blue / Holly Holy / Brother Love's travelling salvation show / Jonathan Livingstone Seagull / I've been this way before / Be / Dear father / Lonely looking sky / Sanctus / Skybird / Be (encore) / I've been this way before.
LP: **95001**

LOVE SONGS: NEIL DIAMOND.
Tracks: / Theme / If you go away / Last thing on my mind / Coldwater morning / Juliet / Both sides now / Play me / Hurtin' you don't come easy / Husbands and wives / Until it's time for you to go / And the grass won't pay no mind / Modern day version of love / Suzanne.
LP: . . . . **MCF 3092**
MC: . . . . **MCFC 3092**

LOVE SONGS/GOLD.
Tracks: / Theme / Stones / If you go away / Last thing on my mind / Coldwater morning / Juliet / Both sides now / Play me / Hurtin' you don't come easy / Husbands and wives / Until it's time for you to go / And the grass won't pay no mind / Modern day version of love / Suzanne / Lordy / Solitary man / Holly holy / Cherry, Cherry / Kentucky woman / Sweet Caroline / Thank the Lord for the night time / And the singer sings his song / Brother Love's travelling salvation show.
MCSET: . . . . **MCA 2 119**

MOODS.
Tracks: / Song sung blue / Porcupine pie / High rolling man / Canta Libre / Captain sunshine / Play me / Gitchy goomy / Walk on water / Theme / Prelude in E Major / Morningside.
LP: . . . . **UNLS 128**

NEIL DIAMOND.
Tracks: / Cracklin' Rosie / New York boy / Sunday sun / Grass won't pay no mind / Free life / Thank the Lord for the night time / Sweet Caroline / Mr. Bojangles / Merry go round / Chelsea morning / Honey drippin' times / Juliet.
LP: . . . . **MFP 50449**

NEIL DIAMOND.
Tracks: / Song sung blue / Morning side / Play me / Brother Louie / Salvation show / Cracklin' Rosie / Sweet Caroline / Mr. Bojangles.
LP: **022-58248**
MC: **222-58248**

ON THE WAY TO THE SKY.
Tracks: / Yesterdays songs / On the way to the sky / Right by you / Only you / Save me / Be mine tonight / Drifter / Fear of the market place / Rainy day song / Guitar heaven / Love burns.
LP: . . . . **CBS 85343**

PRIMITIVE.
Tracks: / Turn around / Primitive / Fire on the tracks / Brooklyn on a Saturday night / Sleep with me tonight / Crazy / My time with you / Love's own song / It's a trip / You make it feel like Christmas / One by one.
LP: **86306**

RAINBOW.
Tracks: / Everybody's talkin' / Both sides now / Husbands and wives / Chelsea morning / Until it's time for you to go / Last thing on my mind / Suzanne / Mr. Bojangles / If you go away / I think it's gonna rain today / He ain't heavy, he's my brother.
MC: . . . . **MCFC 2529**
LP: . . . . **MCF 2529**

RAINBOW/VELVET GLOVES & SPIT.
Tracks: / Two bit manchild / Modern day version of love / Honeydrippin' times / Pot smoker's song / Brooklyn roads / Shilo / Sunday sun / Holiday inn blues / Practically newborn / Knackelflerg / Merry-go-round / Everybody's talkin' / Both sides now / Husbands and wives / Chelsea morning / Until it's time for you to go / Last thing on my mind / Suzanne / Mr. Bojangles / If you go away / I think it's going to rain today / He ain't heavy, he's my brother.
MCSET: . . . . **MCA 2108**

RED RED WINE.
Tracks: / I am ... I said / Suzanne / New York boy / Red red wine / Everybody's talkin' / Husbands and wives / I never knew your name / Until it's time for you to go / Brooklyn roads / Cherry cherry / Chelsea morning / Mr. Bojangles / And the grass won't pay no mind / If you go away.
LP: . . . . **SHM 3230**
MC: . . . . **HSC 3230**

SEPTEMBER MORN.
Tracks: / September morn / Mama don't know / That kind / Jazz time / Good Lord loves you, The / Dancing in the street / Shelter of your arms, The / I'm a believer / Sun ain't gonna shine anymore, The / Stagger Lee.
LP: **86096**

SERENADE.
Tracks: / I've been this way before / Rosemary's wine / Lady Magdelene / Last Picasso / Longfellow serenade / Yes I will / Reggae strut / Gift of song, The.
LP: **69067**
LP: **32012**
LP: **902195 1**
MC: **902195 4**

SOLITARY MAN.
Tracks: / And the singer sings his song / Everybody's talkin' / He ain't heavy, he's my brother / I think it's gonna rain today / Holly holy / Walk on water / Last thing on my mind / Chelsea morning / Gitchy goomy / Red wine / Both sides now.
LP: . . . . **SHM 3093**
MC: . . . . **HSC 3093**

SONG SUNG BLUE.
Tracks: / Song sung blue / Until it's time for you to go / Stones / Brooklyn roads / Shilo / Solitary man / I am ... I said / Captain Sunshine / Porcupine pie / Coldwater morning / Knackelflerg / Holly holy.
LP: . . . . **MFP 5582**
MC: . . . . **TCMFP 5582**

STONES.
Tracks: / I am ... I said / Last thing on my mind / Husbands and wives / Chelsea morning / Crunchy Granola Suite / Stones / If you go away / Suzanne / I think it's gonna rain today.
MC: . . . . **MCFC 2530**
LP: . . . . **UNLS 121**

TAP ROOT MANUSCRIPT.
Tracks: / Cracklin' Rosie / Free life / Coldwater morning / Done too soon / He ain't heavy, he's my brother / African trilogy / I am the lion / Madrigal / Soolaimon / Missa / African suite / Child's song.
LP: . . . . **MCL 1707**
MC: . . . . **MCLC 1707**
LP: . . . . **UNLS 117**

TOUCHING YOU, TOUCHING ME / MOODS.
Tracks: / Everybody's talkin' / Mr. Bojangles / Smokey lady / Holly holy / Sweet Caroline (good times never seem so good) / And the singer sings his song / Ain't no way / New York boy / Until it's time for you to go / Song sung blue / Porcupine pie / High rolling man / Canta libre / Captain sunshine / Play me / Gitchy goomy / Walk on water / Theme / Prelude in E Major / Morningside.
MCSET: . . . . **MCA 2 106**

VELVET GLOVES AND SPIT.
Tracks: / Two bit manchild / Modern day version of love / Honeydrippin' times / Pot smoker's song / Brooklyn roads / Shilo / Sunday sun / Holiday Inn blues / Practically newborn / Knackelflerg / Merry go round.
LP: . . . . **MCL 1640**
MC: . . . . **MCLC 1640**

VERY BEST OF NEIL DIAMOND.
Tracks: / Sweet Caroline / Cracklin' rosie / Song sung blue / I am ... I said.
LP: . . . . **NE 1265**

WAY TO THE SKY, THE.
LP: **85343**

YOU DON'T BRING ME FLOWERS.
Tracks: / American popular song / Forever in blue jeans / Remember me / You've got your troubles / You don't bring me flowers / Dancing bumble bee bumble boogie / Mothers and daughters, fathers and sons / Memphis flyer / Say maybe / Diamond girl.
LP: **86077**
MC: **4687824**

YOU DON'T BRING ME FLOWERS (SINGLE) (See under Streisand, Barbra) (Diamond, Neil & Barbra Streisand).

Diamond Skulls

DIAMOND SKULLS (See under Zimmer, Hans) (Zimmer, Hans).

Diamonds

DIAMONDS (Various artists).
LP: . . . . **CHIMP 599P**

THEIR TOP HITS.
MC: **820**

Di'Anno, Paul

CHILDREN OF MADNESS (Di'Anno, Paul Battlezone).
LP: . . . . **AMP 13**

FIGHTING BACK (Di'Anno, Paul Battlezone).
Tracks: / Fighting back / Welcome to the battlezone / War child / In the darkness / Land God gave to Caine, The / Running blind / Too much to heart / Voice on the radio / Welfare warriors / Feel the rock.
LP: . . . . **RAWLP 020**
MC: . . . . **RAWTC 020**

HEARTUSER.
Tracks: / Heartuser / Tales of the unexpected / Antigue.
LP: . . . . **WKFMLP 1**

Diary Of A Nobody

DIARY OF A NOBODY, THE (see under Grossmith, G & W) (Various artists).

Dias, Sergio

MIND OVER MATTER.
LP: . . . . **EXPAL 8**
MC: . . . . **EXPALMC 8**

Diatta, Pascal

SIMNADE (Diatta, Pascal and Sona Mane).
LP: . . . . **FMSL 2017**
MC: . . . . **FMSC 2017**

Diaz, Diomedes

CANDTANDO (Diaz, Diomedes & Nicholas Colacho Mendoza).
Tracks: / Esperanza / Cantando / Te necesito / Myriam / Cardon guarjiro / El medallon / Por amor a dios / Paisana mia / Siempre contigo / Las cosas del amos.
LP: . . . . **ORB 055**

Diaz, Julio Benavente

CHARANGO CUZQUENO.
LP: . . . . **G 1504**
MC: . . . . **G 4504**

SONGS & CHARANGO.
LP: **455 903 7**

Dibango, Manu

AFRIJAZZY.
Tracks: / Masa lemba / Bushman promenade / Gombo sauce / Soir au village / Makossa '87 (Big blow) / Kango / Doula serenade / Abelley sphere.
LP: . . . . **URBLP 1**
MC: . . . . **URBMC 1**

AMBASSADOR.
Tracks: / Happy feeling / Cava chouia / Bona sango / Choci / Mumbele style / Night jet.

LP: .... ILPS 9658

DELIVERANCE.
LP: .... AF 1984

GONE CLEAR.
Tracks: / Full up / Goro city / Doctor Bird / Tek time / Reggae makossa / Frozen soul.
LP: .... ILPS 9539

HAPPY FEELING.
MC: .... C 1003

HOMEMADE.
LP: 362018

MANU DIBANGO.
Tracks: / Andy / Matumba / Motapo / Sun explosion.
LP: .... SKLR 5303
LP: .... ALB 364

POLYSONIK.
LP: .... CPLP 1
MC: .... CPMC 1
LP: .... EXPAL 7
MC: .... EXPALMC 7

RASTA SOUVENIR.
2LP: .... ESP 7512/3
MC: .... C 1002

SOUL MAKOSSA.
Tracks: / Soul makossa / Rencontre / Taoumba / Moni / New bell 'hard pulsation' / O Boso / Kata kata / Soukouss / Pepe soup / Essimo / Nights in Zeralda.
LP: 403651
MC: .... FC 065C

SUN EXPLOSION.
MC: .... C 1001

WAKA JUJU.
LP: .... ESP 7515
LP: 2933 130

Dibate, Zani

SUPER DJATA (Dibate, Zani & Super Djata).
Tracks: / Super Djata / Bina / Djegnogo djougou / Bandjila / Tindoro / Noumousso / Facia / Farima / Fadingna kouma.
LP: .... ILPS 9899
MC: .... ICT 9899

Diblo & Matchatcha

BOUM TONNERRE.
LP: .... LP 005

Dice Clay, Andrew

DICE.
LP: 8281621
MC: 8281624

Dicey, Bill

FOOL IN LOVE.
LP: .... JSP 1118

Dick Barton

DICK BARTON (Various artists).
MCSET: .... ZBBC 1063

Dick Tracy

BIG BOY TURNS UP THE HEAT (Unknown narrator(s)).
MC: .... DIS 023W

EVERYTHING COMES UP BLANK (Unknown narrator(s)).
MC: .... DIS 024W

Dick Turpin(tv)

DICK TURPIN (THEME FROM) (See under King, Denis) (King, Denis).

Dick Whittington

DICK WHITTINGTON (Brandreth, Gyles).
MC: .... LPMC 301

DICK WHITTINGTON (Unknown narrator(s)).
MC: .... STC 303C

DICK WHITTINGTON & HIS CAT (well loved tales up to age 9) (Unknown narrator(s)).
MC: .... PLB 56

Dickens, Charles

BLEAK HOUSE (Dickson, Hugh (nar)).
MCSET: CC/038

BLEAK HOUSE (Gielgud, Sir John (nar)).
MCSET: 414 751-4
MCSET: .... ARGO 1070

CHRISTMAS CAROL, A (Richardson, Sir Ralph (nar)).
MC: 1135

CHRISTMAS CAROL, A (Jarvis, Martin (nar)).
Tracks: / Christmas Eve / Marley's ghost / Christmas past / Christmas past, Christmas present / Cratchits' Christmas, The / Final visions, The / Scrooge perplexed / God bless us, every one.
MCSET: .... ZBBC 1033

CHRISTMAS CAROL, A (children's classics) (Unknown narrator(s)).
MC: .... PLBC 137

CHRISTMAS CAROL, A (Unknown narrator(s)).
MCSET: .... DTO 10583

CHRISTMAS CAROL, A.
MC: .... LFP 41 7176 5
MC: .... TS 318

CHRISTMAS CAROL, A (Massey, Daniel (nar)).
MCSET: 414 775-4
MCSET: .... ARGO 1142

CHRISTMAS CAROL, A (Dotrice, Roy (nar)).
2LP: .... ZSW 5845

DAVID COPPERFIELD (Rodgers, Anton).
MCSET: .... LFP 7346

DAVID COPPERFIELD (Rees, Roger).
MC: 1706

EXCERPTS FROM CHRISTMAS STORIES (Williams, Emlyn (nar)).
MCSET: .... SAY 71

GREAT EXPECTATIONS (Pasco, Richard (nar)).
MC: 0600560457

GREAT EXPECTATIONS (Jarvis, Martin (nar)).
MCSET: CC/010

GREAT EXPECTATIONS (Jeffrey, Peter (nar)).
MCSET: .... ARGO 1172
MCSET: 414 709-4

HARD TIMES (Thorne, Stephen).
MCSET: CC/019

HARD TIMES (Jeffrey, Peter (nar)).
MCSET: 418 042-4
MCSET: .... ARGO 1217

NICHOLAS NICKLEBY (Rees, Roger).
MC: .... CP 1702
MCSET: .... SAY 77
MCSET: .... ARGO 1049
MC: 1702

OLIVER TWIST (children's classics) (Unknown narrator(s)).
MC: .... PLBC 195

OLIVER TWIST (four chapters) (Quayle, Anthony (nar)).
MC: 1484

SIGNALMAN, THE/TO BE READ AT DUSK (Various artists).
MC: .... TS 355

TALE OF TWO CITIES (Mason, James (nar)).
MCSET: 2079

TALE OF TWO CITIES, A (Pasco, Richard (nar)).
MCSET: CC/037

TALE OF TWO CITIES, A (Carson, John).
MCSET: .... TCLFP 7059
MCSET: .... LFP 7412

TALE OF TWO CITIES, A (Gielgud, Sir John (nar)).
MCSET: 414 721-4

TALE OF TWO CITIES, A VOL. 2 (Dance, Charles).
MCSET: .... ZBBC 1075

TALE OF TWO CITIES VOL 1, A (Dance, Charles).
MCSET: .... ZBBC 1074

Dickens, Hazel

BY THE SWEAT OF MY BROW.
Tracks: / Beyond the river bend / Only the lonely / By the sweat of my brow / Scars from an old love / Old and in the way / Ballad of Ira Hayes, The / Go away with me / Mama's hands / Your greedy heart / Little Lenaldo / Here today and gone tomorrow.
LP: .... ROUNDER 0200
MC: .... ROUNDER 0200C

HARD HITTING SONGS FOR HARD HITTING PEOPLE.
Tracks: / Busted / Aragon mill / Old calloused hands / Scraps from your table / Out among the stars / Tomorrow's already lost / Lonesome pine special / Lost patterns / Beautiful hills of Galilee / Rocking chair blues / They'll never keep us down.
LP: .... ROUNDER 0126
MC: .... ROUNDER 0126C

IT'S HARD TO TELL THE SINGER FROM THE SONG.
LP: .... ROUNDER 0226
MC: .... ROUNDER 0226C

Dickens, Little Jimmy

BEST OF THE BEST OF JIMMY DICKENS.
LP: .... GT 0041

I GOT A HOLE IN MY POCKET.
LP: .... REV 3007

STRAIGHT FROM THE HEART (1949-1955).
Tracks: / Sea of broken dreams / Wedding bell waltz / I've just got to see you once more / Rose from a bride's bouquet / Be careful of stones that you throw / That little old country church house / Teardrops (fell like teardrops) / Out of business / My heart's bouquet / Lovin' lies / Ribbon and a rose, A / Bring your broken heart to me.
LP: .... SS 26
MC: .... SSC 26

Dickenson, Peter

RAGS, BLUES & PARODIES.
LP: .... CFRA 134

Dickenson, Vic

BALL OF FIRE (see under Smith, Keith) (Dickenson, Vic & Keith Smith).

ESSENTIAL VIC DICKENSON.
Tracks: / Russian lullaby / Keep out of mischief / Sir Charles at home / Jeepers creepers / I cover the waterfront / Runnin' wild / When you and I were young Maggie / Nice work if you can get it / Old fashioned love / Everybody loves my baby / Suspension blues / You brought a new kind of love to me.
LP: .... VJD 551

JUST FRIENDS.
LP: 2015

TROMBONE CHOLLY.
Tracks: / Long old road / T'aint nobody's business if I do / Trombone cholly / On revival day / Nobody knows you (when you're down and out) / Back water blues / Send me to the electric chair / Do your duty.
LP: .... SNTF 720
MC: .... ZCSN 720

VIC DICKENSON'S QUARTET (Dickenson, Vic Quartet).
LP: .... SLP 4021

YACHT CLUB SWING 1964-1965 (Dickenson, Vic All Stars).
LP: .... HQ 2045

Dickerson, Dwight

SOONER OR LATER (Dickerson, Dwight Trio).
LP: .... DS 792
MC: .... DSC 792

Dickerson, Walt

I HEAR YOU JOHN (Dickerson, Walt & Jimmi Johnson).
LP: .... SCS 1146

SHADES OF LOVE.
LP: .... SCD 17002

VISIONS (Dickerson, Walt & Sun Ra).
LP: .... SCS 1126

Dickie, James F

DICKIE STYLE, THE.
MC: .... CWGR 004

JAMES F DICKIE'S DELIGHTS.
Tracks: / Cairdin o't, The / Highland Donald / Francis Sitwell / Hard is my fate / Good wife admit the wanderer / Dean brig o' Edinburgh, The / Glencoe / Trumpet / Banks / Smith's waltz, The / Millhill's / Laird of Drumblair, The / Baker reel, The / Bonnie lass o' Bon Accord / Peterhead polka, The / Braes o' Auchtertyre, The / Leaving the glen / Miller of drone, The / J.F. Dickie's reel / Bovaglie's plaid / South of the Grampians / Good old John / MacPherson's rant / Madam Frederick / Earl Grey / Whistle o'er the lave o't / White cockade, The.
LP: 12TS 279
MC: .... DUN/JFD 03

Dickie, Neville

EYE OPENER.
LP: .... SOS 1052

NEVILLE DICKIE MEETS FATS, THE LION & THE LAMB.
LP: .... SOS 1176

TAKEN IN STRIDE 2.
LP: .... SOS 1096

Dickie & Red

DICKIE ROCK & RED HURLEY.
MC: .... HTC 8017

Dickies

DAWN OF THE DICKIES.
LP: .... AMLE 68510

GREAT DICTATIONS.
Tracks: / Hideous / You drive me ape (you big gorilla) / Give it back / Paranoid / I'm OK you're OK / Got it at the store / Sound of silence / Banana splits (tra la la song) / Rondo (the midgets revenge) / Nights in white satin / I'm stuck in a pagoda with Tritia Toyota / Manny, Moe and Jack / Fan mail / Attack of the mole men / Gigantor / Eve of destruction.
LP: .... AMA 5236
MC: .... AMC 5236

INCREDIBLE SHRINKING DICKIES.
Tracks: / Give it back / Poodle party / Paranoid / She / Shadow man / Mental ward / Eve of destruction / You drive me ape (you big gorilla) / Waterside / Walk like an egg / Curb job / Shake and bake / Rondo (the midgets revenge).
LP: .... AMLE 64742

LIVE IN LONDON - LOCKED 'N' LOADED.
LP: .... RRLP 137
MC: .... RRLC 137

SECOND COMING.
Tracks: / Hair / Town without pity / Going homo / Booby trap / Caligula / Monkey see, monkey do / Monster Island / Cross-eyed Tammy / Dummy up / Magoomba U / I'm Stan.
LP: .... ENVLP 526
MC: .... TCENV 526

WE AREN'T THE WORLD.
MC: .... A 140

Dickinson, Bruce

MUSIC AND MEDIA INTERVIEW PICTURE DISC.
LPPD: .... MM 1202

TATTOOED MILLIONAIRE (ALBUM).
Tracks: / Son of a gun / Tattooed millionaire / Born in '58 / Hell on wheels / Gypsy road (Dive dive dive) / Dive dive dive / All the young dudes / Lickin' the gun / Zulu Lulu / No lies.
LP: .... EMC 3574
MC: .... TCEMC 3574

Dickinson, Cindy

DELIVERANCE (see People Like Us).

Dickinson, Emily

EMILY DICKINSON - A SELF PORTRAIT (Harris, Julie).
MCSET: 2026

POEMS & LETTERS (Harris, Julie).
MC: 1119

Dickinson, Jimmy

SPRING POEMS.
LP: .... FC 064

Dickinson, John

...PLAYS BALDWIN STUDIO II ORGAN.
LP: .... GRS 1033

Dickinson, Paul

SLEAZY DINNER MUSIC.
LP: .... LRF 106

Dickinson, Peter

PERFECT GALLOWS (Thorne, Stephen).
MC: .... IAB 88102

Dicks

KILL FROM THE HEART.
Tracks: / Anti klan / Bourgeois fascist pig / Rich daddy / No nazis friend / Razor blade dance.
LP: .... SST 017

THESE PEOPLE.
LP: .... VIRUS 43

Dickson, Barbara

AFTER DARK.
Tracks: / Right moment, The / Same sky / Only a dream in Rio / Lush life / I don't believe in you / Caravan / Fortress around your heart / I think it's going to rain today / It's money that I love / Pride (in the name of love) / No milk today / I know him so well.
LP: .... TPD 001
MC: .... TDPC 001

ALL FOR A SONG.
Tracks: / Run like the wind / Caravan song / Answer me / Long and winding road, The / Tonight / With a little help from my friends / January, February / Will you love me tomorrow? / Take good care / I believe in you / Another suitcase in another hall / Surrender to the sun.
LP: .... EPC 10030
MC: 40 10030
LP: .... EPC BD 241
LP: 4630021
MC: 4630024

ANOTHER SUITCASE ANOTHER HALL (OLD GOLD) (See under Julie Covington - Don't Cry For Me).

ANSWER ME.
Tracks: / People get ready / Boys from the man / My man / Lean on me / Goodbye, dreamer / End of the world / Answer me / Goodbye to the cries / From the heart / Let it go / Judgement day / Drift away.
LP: .... SPELP 5
MC: .... SPEMC 5
MC: 3524224

BARBARA DICKSON.
Tracks: / If I ever saw you again / Do right woman / Easy to be hard / I am the great sun / Lullaby for father / Lover's

ghost / You like the sun / Somebody counts on me / Fine flowers in the valley / Something's wrong / Gartan mothers lullaby / Dainty Davie.
LP: . . . . **CN 2058**

BARBARA DICKSON ALBUM.
Tracks: / January, February / In the night / It's really you / Day and night / Can't get by without you / Anytime you're down and out / I'll say it all again / Hello stranger / Goodbye my heart / Plane song / Now i don't know.
LP: **32645**
MC: **40 32645**
LP: . . . . **EPC 84088**

BLOOD BROTHERS (Original London Show).
Tracks: / Narration / Marilyn Monroe / My child / Devil's got your number, The / Easy terms / Just a game / Sunday afternoon / My friend / Bright new day / One summer narration / Saying a word / Miss Jones (sign of the times) / Prison song / Light romance / There's a madman / Tell me it's not true.
LP: . . . . **LLM 3007**
MC: . . . . **LLMK 3007**
LP: . . . . **LIM 101**

COLLECTION: BARBARA DICKSON.
Tracks: / Drift away / Dancing in the street / Stardust / Come rain or come shine / Crying game, The / As time goes by / Fallen angel / Think it over / Will you love me tomorrow / I don't believe in miracles / Take good care / With a little help from my friends / In the night / January February / Stop in the name of love / Little by little in love / My heart lies / I know you know me / Hold on / You know it's over / Tonight.
2LP: . . . . **CCSLP 163**
MC: . . . . **CCSMC 163**

COMING ALIVE AGAIN (ALBUM).
Tracks: / How long / It might be you / Precious cargo / Coming alive again / September song / Dream of you / Every now and then / You're the voice / Letter, The / Give me one good reason / Song for Bernadette.
LP: . . . . **STAR 2349**
MC: . . . . **STAC 2349**

FATE O' CHARLIE, THE (see under Fisher, Archie).

GOLD.
LP: . . . . **ONE 1312**
MC: . . . . **OCE 2312**

HEARTBEATS.
Tracks: / I don't believe in miracles / World without your love / Stop, in the name of love / As time goes by / You don't really know what you want / Tell me it's not true / We were never really out of love / One false move / Crying game, The / Keeping my love / Heartbeat's everything, The / MacCrimmon's lament.
LP: . . . . **EPC 25706**
MC: **40 25706**

HERE WE GO (LIVE ON TOUR).
Tracks: / Caravan song / Answer me / Will you love me tomorrow / MacCrimmon's lament / Stardust / January, February / Drift away / Tonight / Come rain or come shine / Harden my heart / Dancing in the street / He's a rebel / I only want to be with you / You keep me hangin' on / Here we go.
LP: . . . . **EPC 25068**
MC: **40 25086**

I WILL SING.
Tracks: / Somebody counts on me / If I never ever saw you again / Long and lonely winter / Something's wrong / Climb, The / Morning lies heavy, The / Together forever / Do right woman, do right man / Returning / Turn a deaf ear / Gloomy Sunday / Tears of joy / Winter's song / And I will sing.
LP: . . . . **TAB 24**

MORNING COMES QUICKLY.
Tracks: / Deep into my soul / Lover's serenade / Morning comes quickly / It makes me feel good / High tide / Who was it stole your heart away / When you touch me this way / I could fall / There's a party in my heart / Stolen love.
LP: . . . . **SPELP 91**
MC: . . . . **SPEMC 91**
LP: **2394 188**

NOW AND THEN.
MC: . . . . **VSOPMC 166**

RIGHT MOMENT, THE.
Tracks: / Right moment, The / Tenderly / She moved through the fair / Time after time / Follow you, follow me / It's raining again today / Wouldn't it be good? / Boulder to Birmingham / Who are you anyway? / Vanishing days of love, The / Angie baby / Making history / Fine partly cloudy / If you go away.
LP: . . . . **ONE 1335**
MC: . . . . **CE 2335**
MC: . . . . **OCE 2335**

SONGBOOK.
LP: . . . . **NE 1287**

SWEET OASIS.
MC: **40 22160**
LP: . . . . **EPC 432011**

TELL ME IT'S NOT TRUE.
LP: . . . . **LLM 101**

VERY BEST OF BARBARA DICKSON.
LP: . . . . **STAR 2276**
MC: . . . . **STAC 2276**

YOU KNOW IT'S ME.
Tracks: / Think it over / Little by little in love / You know it's me / Hold on / We'll believe in lovin' / Only seventeen / You got me / I know you, you know me / I believe in you / My heart lies.
LP: . . . . **EPC 84551**
MC: **40 84551**

Dickson, Hugh (nar)

BLEAK HOUSE (see under Dickson, Charles (aut)).

MAN WHO COULD WORK MIRACLES, THE (see under Wells, H.G.).

Dictators

BLOOD BROTHERS.
Tracks: / Faster and louder / Baby let's twist / No tomorrow / Minnesota strip, The / Stay with me / I stand tall / Borneo Jimmy / What it is / Slow death.
LP: . . . . **K 53083**

FU 'EM IF THEY CAN'T TAKE A JOKE.**
MC: . . . . **A 102**

MANIFEST DESTINY.
Tracks: / Exposed / Heartaches / Sleepin' with the TV on / Disease / Hey boys / Steppin' out / Science gone too far / Young, fast scientific / Search and destroy.
LP: . . . . **K 53061**

Did Ee Ever Yur Tell?

DID EE EVER YUR TELL? (Recitations) (Various artists).
MC: **45-403**

Diddley, Bo

20TH ANNIVERSARY OF ROCK 'N' ROLL, THE.
Tracks: / Ride the water (part 1) / Not fade away / Kill my body / Drag on / Ride on the water (part 2) / Bo Diddley jam - I'm a man / Hey Bo Diddley / Who do you love / Bo Diddley's a gun slinger / I'm a man.
LP: . . . . **ED 318**

AIN'T IT GOOD TO BE FREE?.
Tracks: / Ain't it good to be free? / Swamp funk.
LP: . . . . **ROSE 34**

BO DIDDLEY BOX SET.
LPS: . . . . **BOX 257**
MCSET: . . . . **TCBOX 257**

BO DIDDLEY - I'M A MAN.
LP: **515027**

BO DIDDLEY IS A GUNSLINGER.
LP: . . . . **NJL 33**

BO DIDDLEY (LP).
Tracks: / Bo Diddley / I'm a man / Bring it to Jerome / Before you accuse me / Hey Bo Diddley / Dearest darling / Hush your mouth / Say bossman / Diddley daddy / Diddy wah diddy / Who do you love.
LP: . . . . **GCH 8026**
MC: . . . . **GCHK 78026**
LP: . . . . **NPL 28026**

BO DIDDLEY RIDES AGAIN.
LP: . . . . **NPL 28029**

BO DIDDLEY'S BEACH PARTY.
Tracks: / Memphis / Gunslinger / Hey Bo Diddley / Old smokey / Bo Diddley's dog / I'm all right / Mr.Custer / Bo's waltz / What's buggin' you / Roadrunner.
LP: . . . . **GCH 8111**
MC: . . . . **GCHK 78111**
LP: . . . . **NPL 28032**

CHESS MASTERS.
Tracks: / Mona / Hey Bo Diddley / Road runner / Bring it to Jerome / Pretty thing / Pills / I'm a man / Hush your mouth / Sax man / Cops and robbers / Mumblin' guitar / Diddley Biddley / Memphis / She's alright / You can't judge a book by the cover / Who do you love.
2LP: . . . . **CXMD 4003**
LP: . . . . **SMR 849**
MC: . . . . **SMC 849**

CHESS MASTERS VOL. 2.
Tracks: / Crackin' up / Blues inst / Great grandfather / You don't love me / What do you know about love / Lazy woman / Come on baby / Dancing girl / Diddy wah diddy / Little girl / Nursery rhyme / Clock strikes twelve / She's fine she's mine / Down home special / Say boss man / Bo meets the monster / Willie & Lillie / Oh yea / Mama keep your big mouth shut / You're looking good / Greatest lover in the world / Let me in / Little girl / Bo's guitar.
2LP: . . . . **CXMD 4009**

EP COLLECTION, THE: BO DIDDLEY.
MC: . . . . **SEEK 321**
LP: . . . . **SEE 321**

GIVE ME A BREAK.
Tracks: / Give me a break.
LP: . . . . **CHECKMATE 1960**

GO BO DIDDLEY.
Tracks: / Crackin' up / I'm sorry / Bo's guitar / Willie and lillie / You don't know me / Say man / Great grandfather / Oh yeah / Don't let it go / Little girl / Dearest darling / Clock struck twelve.
LP: . . . . **GCH 8021**
MC: . . . . **GCHK 78021**

GOT MY OWN BAG OF TRICKS.
2LP: **427011**

HAVE GUITAR, WILL TRAVEL.
Tracks: / She's alright / Cops and robbers / Diddley daddy / Mumblin' guitar / I need you baby / Say man / Back again / Nursery rhyme / I love you so / Spanish guitar / Dancing girl / Come on baby / Run.
LP: . . . . **GCH 8002**
MC: . . . . **GCHK 78002**

HEY, BO DIDDLEY.
Tracks: / Mess around / Somebody's crying / Hong Kong / Can I go home with you / I'm going home / Rhyme song / Cracklin' / Rockin' on.
LP: . . . . **MFM 021**
LP: **2273022**
MC: **2173022**
LP: . . . . **CFRC 507**
MC: . . . . **MCFRC 507**

HIS GREATEST SIDES VOL.1.
Tracks: / Bo Diddley / Pretty thing / Bring it to Jerome / I'm a man / Mona / Diddley daddy / Dearest darling / Who do you love / Roadrunner / Say man / Bo's bounce / You can't judge a book by it's cover / Crackin' up / Hey Bo Diddley.
LP: . . . . **GCH 8005**
MC: . . . . **GCHK 78005**

I'M A MAN.
Tracks: / Bo Diddley / I'm a man / You all green / Mr. Kruschev / Somebody beat me / Tonight is ours / I'm sorry / Little girl.
LP: . . . . **BLM 52004**

IN THE SPOTLIGHT.
Tracks: / Roadrunner / Story of Bo Diddley / Scuttle bug / Signifying blues / Let me in / Limber / Love me / Craw-dad / Walkin' and talkin' / Travelin' west / Deed and deed I do / Live my life.
MC: . . . . **GCHK 78038**
LP: . . . . **GCH 8038**
LP: . . . . **CH 9264**

LIVE '77.
LP: . . . . **FC 009**

LIVING LEGEND.
LP: . . . . **ROSE 188**
MC: . . . . **ROSE 188C**

LONDON BO DIDDLEY SESSIONS, THE.
Tracks: / Don't want no lyin' woman / Bo Diddley / Going down / Make a hit record / Bo Jam / Husband in law / Do the robot / Sneakers on a rooster / Get out of my life.
LP: . . . . **CH 9296**

ROAD RUNNER.
Tracks: / Hey Bo Diddley / Say bossman / Bring it to Jerome / Mona / Before you accuse me / You can't judge a book by the cover / Road runner.
LP: . . . . **BLM 52014**

ROAD RUNNER (INSTANT).
Tracks: / Bo Diddley / I'm a man / Pretty thing / Who do you love / Mona (I need you baby) / Say man / Hush your mouth / Road runner / You can't judge a book by the cover / Cops and robbers / Hey Bo Diddley / Crackin' up / Diddley Daddy / Bring it to Jerome.
MC: . . . . **TCINS 5004**
LP: . . . . **INS 5004**

SUPER BLUES (Diddley, Bo & Muddy Waters).
LP: . . . . **BRP 2012**

TWO GREAT GUITARS (see under Berry, Chuck) (Diddley Bo/Chuck Berry).

WHERE IT ALL BEGAN.
LP: **515012**

Didjits

HEY JUDESTER.
LP: . . . . **TGLP 28**

HORNET PIANTA.
LP: . . . . **TGLP 51**

Die Halbstarken

DIE HALBSTARKEN (Mister Martin's Band).
LP: . . . . **BFX 15329**

Die Hard

DIE HARD 2 (Film soundtrack) (Various artists).
Tracks: / Colonel Stuart: *Kamen, Michael* / General Esperanza: *Kamen, Michael* / Church, The: *Kamen, Michael* / Runaway, The: *Kamen, Michael* / Icicle: *Kamen, Michael* / Terminal, The: *Kamen, Michael* / Baggage handling: *Kamen, Michael* / Annexe skywalk, The: *Kamen, Michael* / Doll, The: *Kamen, Michael* / In the plane: *Kamen, Michael* / Snowmobiles: *Kamen, Michael* / Finlandia: *Kamen, Michael.*
LP: . . . . **VS 5273**
MC: . . . . **VSC 5273**

Die Haut

BURNING THE ICE (Die Haut/Nick Cave).
LP: . . . . **SJAMS 30**

DIE HARD.
LP: . . . . **WFSAF 91**

HEADLESS BODY IN TOPLESS BAR.
LP: . . . . **SF 83**
LP: . . . . **EFA 2683**

Die Hoch-Und...

UNTER DEM DOPPELADLER (Die Hoch-Und Duetschmeister).
LP: **6 26217**
MC: **4 26217**

Die Kreuzen

CENTURY DAYS.
LP: . . . . **TGLP 30**

DIE KREUZEN.
LP: . . . . **TGLP 4**

Die Krupps

METALLE MASCHINEN MUSIK.
LP: . . . . **KRUPPS 1**

Die Poplander

FUNKY ON THE ROCKS.
LP: . . . . **ISST 120**

Die Sache

GIRL WHO STOLE THE EIFFEL TOWER.
LP: . . . . **FABML 10**

Die Todliche Doris

WIE GEHT ES DIR JETZ.
LP: . . . . **WR 33**

Die Warzau

DISCO RIDIDO.
Tracks: / Welcome to America / Jackhammer / Sexus / Free radio Africa / I've got to make sense / Shakedown / Y tagata en situ / Land of the free / Man is meat / Bodybag / Money after all / Strike to the body / National security / Tear it down / Crossburning (part 2).
LP: **839 673 1**
MC: **839 673 4**

Die Zimmermanner

GOETHE.
LP: . . . . **WR 25**

Died Pretty

EVERY BRILLIANT EYE.
LP: . . . . **BEGA 108**
MC: . . . . **BEGC 108**

FREE DIRT.
LP: . . . . **GOES ON 07**
LP: . . . . **CITLP 504**

LOST.
Tracks: / Lost / As must have / Winterland / Crawls away / Towers of strength / Out of my hands / Springenfall / Caesar's cold / One day / Free dirt.
LP: . . . . **CGAS 801**
LP: . . . . **BEGA 101**
MC: . . . . **BEGC 101**

Dieform

POUPEE MECHANIQUE.
LP: . . . . **DFLP 3**

Diego, Don

GIVE IT ALL YOU'VE GOT.
Tracks: / Give it all you've got / My objective / Lonely talking / We still remain friends / Escape / Love is here to stay / Bedroom eyes / Blow / Please make me yours.
LP: . . . . **ULT 4022**
MC: . . . . **ULTMC 4022**

Dieheim, Susan

DESERT EQUATIONS (Dieheim, Susan & Richard Horowitz).
Tracks: / Ishtar / Got away / I'm a man / Tear / Azax attra / Jum jum / Armour / Desert equations.
LP: . . . . **MTM 8**

Diesel

WATTS IN A TANK.
Tracks: / Sausalito summernight / Goin back to China / Alibi / My kind of woman / All because of you / Down in the silvermine / Good mornin' day / Ready

for love / Harness, The / Remember the Romans / Bite back.
LP: . . . . WATTS 1

Diesel, Johnny

JOHNNY DIESEL AND THE INJECTORS (Diesel, Johnny And The Injectors).
Tracks: / Looking for love / Cry in shame / Comin' home / Dry tears / Get ya love / Parisienne hotel / Don't need love / Fire without a flame / Burn / Thang II.
LP: . . . . CHR 1627
MC: . . . . ZCHR 1627

Diesel Park West

DECENCY.
Tracks: / While the world cries decency / Walk with the mountain / Fall to love / Boys on top of the news / Somewhere in the afterglow / Fine Lily fine / I want no mystery / Till the moon struck two / Hot summer water / Safe life, safe times / Clutching at love.
LP: . . . . FOODLP 7
MC: . . . . FOODTC 7

FLIPPED.
Tracks: / Girl with the name, The / Above these things / King fluid / Bent, shattered and blue / Friends and enemies / Endless chains / Find somebody / Lazy me (San Francisco) / Memo from Turner / Mr. Soul (live) / Info freako / No face, no name and no number.
LP: . . . . DPW 1001
MC: . . . . TCDPW 1001

SHAKESPEARE ALABAMA.
Tracks: / Like princes do / All the myths on Sunday / Bell of hope / Out of nowhere / Waking hour, The / When the hoodoo comes / Opportunity crazy / Here I stand / Jackie's still sad / House divided, A / Don't be scared of the night (CD only.) / What about us (CD only.).
LP: . . . . FOOD LP2
MC: . . . . FOOD TC2

Dietrich, Marlene

BEST OF MARLENE DIETRICH.
Tracks: / Ich bin von kopf bis fuss auf liebe eingestellt (Falling in love again (original German version)) / Ich bin die fesch lola / Kinder, heut'abend / Mein blonds baby / Jonny, wenn du geburstag hast / Peter / Wer wird denn weinen / Ich weiss nicht zu wem ich gehore / Blowin' in the wind / Lili Marlene / Allein in einer grossen stadt / Where have all the flowers gone / Sch, kleines baby / Cherchez la rose / Wenn der sommer wider einzicht / Ich werde dick lieben / Die welt war jung / Dejeuner du matin / Wenn die soldaten / Ich hab noch einen koffer in Berlin.
LP: . . . . ED 2606771
MC: . . . . ED 2606774

COMPLETE DECCA RECORDINGS.
LP: . . . . MCA 1501
MC: . . . . MCAC 1501

DIETRICH IN RIO.
Tracks: / Look me over closely / You're the cream in my coffee / My blue Heaven / Boys in the backroom, The / Das lied ist aus / Je tire ma reverance / Alright, okay, you win / Makin' whoopee / I've grown accustomed to her face / One for my baby / Maybe I'll come back / Luar do sertao.
LP: . . . . CBS 32754
MC: 40 32754

ESSENTIAL MARLENE DIETRICH, THE.
Tracks: / Ich bin von kopf bis fuss auf liebe eingestellt (Falling in love again) / Quand l'amour meurt / Give me the man / Leben ohne liebe kannstdu nicht / Mein blondes baby / Allein in einer grossen stadt / Peter / Lola / Wer wird den weinen / Johnny, wenn du geburstag hast / Lili Marlene / Dejeuner du matin / Ou vont les fleurs / Wenn die soldaten / In den kasernen / Und wenn er wiederkommt / Wenn der sommer wieder einzieht (A little on the lonely side) / Blowing in the wind / Der welt war jung (When the world was young) / Where have all the flowers gone / Ich werde dich lieben (Theme for young lovers) / Der trommelmann (The little drummerboy) / Auf der mundharmonika.
MC: . . . . TCEMS 1399
LP: . . . . EMS 1399

IN LONDON.
Tracks: / I can't give you anything but love / Laziest girl in town / Shirc hatan / La vie en rose / Johnny / Go away from my window / Lili Marlene / Allein in einer grossen stadt / Lola / I wish you love / Marie Marie / Honeysuckle rose / Falling in love again.
LP: . . . . FBLP 8103
MC: . . . . ZCFBL 8103

LEGENDARY, LOVELY MARLENE.
Tracks: / Falling in love again / You've got that look / Boys in the backroom, The / I've never been in love before / You go to my head / You do something to me / Illusions / Black market / Lili Marlene / Symphony (Sung in French.) / Another spring, another love / Near you / Kisses sweeter than wine / May I never go home / If he swings by the string / Such trying times / Candles glowing / This world of ours.
LP: . . . . MCL 1685
MC: . . . . MCLC 1685

LEGENDARY MARLENE DIETRICH.
Tracks: / Ich bin von Kopf bis fuss auf Liebe eingestelt / Ich bin die fesche Lola / Wer wird denn weinen / Peter / Allein in einer grossen stadt / Jonny wenn du geburtstag hast / Marie-Marie / Ich hab'noch einen Koffer in Berlin / Und wenn er wiederkommt / Where have all the flowers gone / Lili Marlene / Wenn die Soldaten / Die Antwort weiss ganz allein der Wind / Kinder, heut'abend / Auf der Mundharmonika / Wenn der Sommer wieder einzeiht / Ich werde sich lieben / Paff der Zauberdrachen / Sch... kleines baby / Mutter, hast du mir vergeben.
LP: . . . . NTS 229

LILI MARLENE (CBS).
Tracks: / Lili Marlene / Mean to me / Hobellied / Annie doesn't live here any more / You have my heart / Surrey with the fringe on top / Time on my hands / Taking a chance on love / Must I go / Miss Otis regrets / You have taken my soul / I couldn't sleep a wink last night.
MC: 40 32375
LP: . . . . CBS 32375

LILI MARLENE (EMI).
Tracks: / Lili Marlene / Wer wird denn weinen / In das kasernen / Me in blondes baby / Peter / Allien / Wenn ich mir'was wunschen durfte / Iche bin die fesche lola / Ich bin von kopf bis fuss auf liebe eingestellt (Falling in love again (original German version)) / Wenn die soldaten / Johnny wenn du geburtstag / Ich weiss nicht zu wem ich gehore / Ich hab' noch einen koffer in Berlin / Kinder, heut'abend / Marie-Marie.
LP: 3C 054 46349
MC: 3C 254 46349

LILI MARLENE (NOSTALGIA).
Tracks: / Falling in love again / Ruins of Berlin / Boys in the backroom, The / Lili marlene.
LP: . . . . N 22005

LIVE IN RIO.
LP: . . . . AWS 316

MAGIC OF MARLENE DIETRICH, THE.
Tracks: / Ich bin von kopf bis fuss auf liebe eingestellt (Falling in love again (original German version)) / Wenn die soldaten / Mein blondes baby / Paff, der zauberdrachen (Puff the magic dragon) / Allein in einer grossen stadt / Der trommelmann (the little drummer boy) / Cherche la rose / Where have all the flowers gone / Ich bin die fesch Lola (Lola) / Die antwort weiss ganz allein der wind / Jonny, wenn du geburtstag hast (Johnny) / In den kasernen / Ich weiss nicht zu wem ich gehore / Lili Marlene / Peter / Sagt mir wo die blumen sind (where have all the flowers gone.
LP: . . . . MFP 5790
MC: . . . . TCMFP 5790

MARLENE.
Tracks: / Kinder, heute'abend / Leben ohne liebe kannst du nicht / Falling in love again / Ich bin di fosche Lola / Quand l'amour meurt / Johnny / Mein blondes baby / Wenn die beste freundin / Wenn ich mir'was wunschen durfte / Allein in einer grossen stadt / Ich bin von kopf bis fuss auf liebe eingestellt (Falling in love again (original German version)) / Es liegt in der luft/potpourri / Nimm dich in acht vor blonden frauen / Give me the man.
LP: . . . . AJA 5039
MC: . . . . ZC AJA 5039

MARLENE DIETRICH COLLECTION (20 golden greats).
Tracks: / Lili Marlene / Boys in the backroom, The / Lola / Illusions / Johnny / I've been in love before / Black market / Lazy afternoon / Another spring, another love / Symphonie / You do something to me / Falling in love again / You go to my head / You've got that look / If he swings by the string / This world of ours / Near you / Candles glowing / Kisses sweeter than wine / Such trying times.
LP: . . . . DVLP 2098
MC: . . . . DVMC 2098

MARLENE DIETRICH LEGEND (MYTHOS).
Tracks: / Ich bin von kopf bis fuss auf liebe eingestellt (Falling in love again (original German version)) / Ich bin dei fesche Lola / Wer wird denn weinen / Mein blondes baby / Peter / Allein in einer grossen stadt / Wenn ich mir'was wunschen durfte / Johnny wenn du geburtstag / Marie, Marie / Lili Marlene / Ich weiss nicht, zu wem ich gehore / Ich hab'noch einen koffer in Berlin / Kinder, heut'abend / Wenn die Soldaten / Blowing in the wind / In den Kasernen / Und wenn er wiederkommt / Where have all the flowers gone / Auf der mundharmonika / Little drummer boy / Little on the lonely side, A / Theme for young lovers / Puff, the magic dragon / Hush little baby / Mutter, hast du mir vergeben.
LP: . . . . IC 134 3277/71

MARLENE DIETRICH STORY, THE.
Tracks: / You do something to me / Johnny / You go to my head / Boys in the backroom, The / Another spring, another love / Symphonie / Illusions / Black market / Lola / You've got that look / I've been in love before / Falling in love again / Lili Marlene / La vie en rose / Near you / Such trying times / Candles glowing / This world of ours / Look me over closely / If he swings by the string / Lazy afternoon / Kisses sweeter than wine.
MCSET: . . . . DVREMC 13

Dieval, Jack

ALL THE THINGS YOU ARE.
LP: . . . . VELP 1000

Diez, Frank

CITY LIGHTS (Diez, Frank & Stephan).
LP: . . . . ISST 191

Diez, Stefan

MIRRORS (Diez, Stephan).
LP: . . . . EGO 4008

SUN RIVER (See also under Reiter,Joerg) (Diez, Stefan & Joerg Reiter band).

VISIONS (Diez, Stefan Group).
LP: . . . . ISST 178

Dif Juz

EXTRACTIONS.
Tracks: / Crosswinds / Starting point, A / Love insane / Twin and earth.
LP: . . . . CAD 505

OUT OF THE STREETS.
LP: . . . . CAD 612

OUT OF THE TRESS.
MLP: . . . . MAD 612

WHO SAYS SO?.
Tracks: / Roy's tray / Channel / Song with no name (part 2) / Dub song, The.
LP: . . . . RFM 24

Difference

IS.
LP: . . . . CONTE 115

Difford & Tillbrook

DIFFORD & TILLBROOK.
Tracks: / Action speaks faster / Love's crashing waves / Picking up the pieces / On my mind tonight / Man for all seasons / Hope fell down / Wagon train / You can't hurt the girl / Tears for attention / Apple tree, The.
LP: . . . . AMLX 64985
MC: . . . . CXM 64985

Diga Rhythm Band

DIGA.
Tracks: / Sweet sixteen / Magnificent sevens / Happiness is drumming / Razooli / Tal mala.
MC: . . . . RACS 0101

Digance, Richard

BACKWATER.
LP: . . . . COASTAL 4

COMMERCIAL ROAD.
Tracks: / Suicide Sam / Jungle cup final / East End ding dong / Think of me / Jumping Jack frog / Nightingale sang in Berkeley Square, A / Beauty queen / Goodbye my friend / Goodbye heavyweight Albert / Backstreet international / Jimmy Greaves.
LP: . . . . CHR 1262
MC: . . . . ZCHR 1262

DIGANCE INDULGENCE.
LP: . . . . DAM 004

DRAG QUEEN BLUES.
Tracks: / Drag queen blues / Red lights of Antwerp, The / How the west was lost / England's green and pleasant land / I hear the press gang / Beaver the believer / Teddy bears' picnic / Christopher Robin / Runaway train / Working class millionaire / Migration memoirs / Final bow / Rosemary McLaren of the Strand.
LP: . . . . CFRC 519
MC: . . . . MCFRC 519

HOMEWORK.
LP: . . . . COASTAL 5

HOW THE WEST WAS LOST.
Tracks: / Joe Louis story, The / How the west was lost / Drag queen blues / Working class millionaire / Dear river Thames / Edward Sayer's brass band / Show me the door / I hear the press gang / Bless the evening.
LP: . . . . TRA 289

LIVE AT FAIRFIELD HALLS.
LP: . . . . DAM 011

RICHARD DIGANCE & FRIENDS LIVE AT Q.E. HALL.
Tracks: / Dear Diana / Summertime day in Stratford / Down Petticoat Lane / Drinking with Rosie / Journey of the salmon / Up on the seventh floor / Drag queen blues / Right back where I started / Taken my lifetime away / I want to be there when you make it.
LP: . . . . CHR 1187
MC: . . . . ZCHR 1187

RICHARD DIGANCE IN CONCERT.
Tracks: / I hear the press gang / Drag queen blues / How the west was lost / Show me the door / Working class millionaire / Beaver the believer.
LP: . . . . TRA SAM 35 80

Diggs, David

REAL WORLD.
MC: . . . . PAC 8037
LP: . . . . PA 8037

Digital (label)

DIGITAL B SELECTIONS (Various artists).
LP: . . . . BVPRL 1044

Digital Space

DIGITAL SPACE (London Symphony Orchestra).
Tracks: / Star Wars / Tribute to a bad man / Lady Hamilton / Airport / Things to come / Windjammer / Big Country / Red pony / 49th Parallel / Spitfire prelude and fugue.
2LP: . . . . VCDMM 1000 20

Digital Underground

SEX PACKETS.
LP: . . . . BCM 377 LP
MC: . . . . BCM 377 MC

Dignum, Keith

BY CHANCE IT WAS (Dignum, Keith & Simon Rosser).
LP: . . . . DIN 313

Dikker, Loek

SUMMER SUITE.
Tracks: / Overture / First rain in August / Susan loves the sea / Summer suite / Banana song / Dark tango / Aknathon.
LP: D-003

Dikson, George

MAKOZOUK.
LP: . . . . BMCA 8601

Dilemmas

AND ON THE CONVEYOR BELT TONIGHT.
LP: . . . . PHZA 35

Dillard & Clark

FANTASTIC EXPEDITION OF DILLARD & CLARK.
Tracks: / Out on the side / She darked the sun / Don't come rollin' / Train leaves here this morning / Radio song, The / Git it on brother (git in line brother) / In the plan / Something's wrong / Why not your baby / Lyin' down the middle / Don't be cruel.
LP: . . . . ED 192

THROUGH THE MORNING, THROUGH THE NIGHT.
Tracks: / No longer a sweetheart of mine / Through the morning, through the night / Rocky top / So sad / Corner street bar / I bowed my head and cried holy / Kansas City Southern / Four walls / Polly / Roll in my sweet baby's arms / Don't let me down.
LP: . . . . ED 195

Dillard, Doug

HEARTBREAK HOTEL (Dillard, Doug Band).
LP: . . . . FF 477

HEAVEN.
Tracks: / Stars in my crown / Lord's last supper, The / Heaven / Cast your bread upon the water / Let the light shine down on me / Daniel prayed / Turn your radio / God's record book of life / St.Peter / Singin' all day.
LP: . . . . FF 086

JACK RABBIT.
Tracks: / Hamilton country breakdown / Salty dog blues / Teardrops in my eyes / Ocean of diamonds / Byron's barn / Rolling in my sweet baby's arms / I'll just stay around / Jack Rabbit / Last old shovel / Hickory holler.
LP: . . . . SDLP 018
LP: . . . . FF 208

WHAT'S THAT?.
LP: . . . . FF 377

Dillard, Ricky

AS ALWAYS (see under Farley 'Jackmaster' Funk).

Dillard, Rodney

SILVER DOLLAR CITY.
LP: . . . . FF 369

Dillard, Varetta

DOUBLE CROSSING DADDY.
Tracks: / Them there eyes / Please come back to me / Love and wine / I love you just the same / Getting ready for my daddy / Love / (That's the way) my mind is working / Send me some money / You're the answer to my prayer / I can't stop now / Got you on my mind / Skinny Jimmy / One more time / I don't know what it is but I like it / Scorched / Double crossing daddy.
LP: . . . . RB 106

Dillard-Hartford-Dilla

DILLARD-HARTFORD-DILLARD.
LP: . . . . SNTF 730

GLITTERGLASS FROM THE NASHWOOD HOLLYVILLE STRING.
Tracks: / Don't come rollin' / Cross the border line / Two hits and the joint turned brown / Don't lead me on / Bear creek hop / No end of love / Biggest whatever / Lost in the world / High Dad in the morning / California is nicer than you / Artificial limitations / Get no better.
LP: . . . . FF 036

PERMANENT WAVE.
Tracks: / Break it to me gently / That'll be the day / Same thing (makes you laugh, makes you cry) / Yakety yak / Something's wrong / Boogie on reggae woman / Country boy rock'n'roll / No beer in heaven.
LP: . . . . FF 233

Dillards

COUNTRY TRACKS.
Tracks: / Copperfields / Little Pete / Duelin' banjo / Old home place / Close the door lightly / Doug's tune / Yesterday / Woman turn around / Banjo in the hollow / Brother John / She sang hymns out of tune / I'll fly away / Reason to believe / Lonesome Indian / Hey boys / Nobody knows / Binding the strings / Single saddle / Dooley hickory hollow / I've just seen a face / Ebo walker / Sundown / Rainmaker.
LP: . . . . K 52035

DECADE WALTZ.
LP: . . . . FF 082

DILLARDS VS THE INCREDIBLE L.A. TIME MACHINE.
Tracks: / Gunman's code / Poet, The / Do, Magnolia, do / Annabelle Lee / Softly / Ding dong howdy / Jayne / In one ear / Old Cane press / Let the music flow.
LP: . . . . SNTF 743
LP: . . . . FF 040

HOMECOMING AND FAMILY REUNION.
LP: . . . . FF 215

I'LL FLY AWAY.
Tracks: / I'll fly away / Nobody knows / Hey boys / Biggest whatever / Single saddle / I've just seen a face / Bending the strings / Pictures / Ebo walker / She sang hymns out of tune / Rainmaker / Old man at the mill / Touch her if you can / Woman turn around / Yesterday / Copperfields / West Montana Hanna / Close the door lightly.
LP: . . . . ED 246

Dillinger

BADDER THAN THEM.
Tracks: / Melting pot / Follow fashion / Broken heart / Hearsay / Man Friday / Tallowah / Reggae beat / Disco freak / Remember / Little girlie.
LP: . . . . AMLH 68528

BEST OF DILLINGER (LIVE).
LP: . . . . VSLP 4030
LP: . . . . TRLS 241

BIONIC DREAD.
LP: . . . . ILPS 9455

BLACKBOARD JUNGLE.
LP: . . . . VSLP 5002

CB 200.
LP: . . . . ILPS 9385
MC: . . . . RRCT 30

COCAINE.
Tracks: / Cocaine in my brain / Jah love / Funkey punk / Mickey Mouse crab louse / I thurst / Loving pauper / Flat foot hustlin' / Crabs in my pants / Marijuana in my brain / Cocaine (remix).
LP: . . . . NC 003
MC: . . . . TCNC 003

COCAINE (NEW VERSION).
Tracks: / Cocaine in my brain (acid house mix) / Jah love / Funkey punk / Mickey Mouse crab louse / I thurst / Loving pauper / Flat foot hustlin' / Crabs in my pants / Marijuana in my brain / Cocaine in my brain.
LP: . . . . NC 008
MC: . . . . TCNC 008

CORN BREAD.
LP: . . . . JSLP 0021

KING PHARAOH.
Tracks: / Answer me question / Fernando / Three piece sweet and thing / Check Sister Jane / Know yourself, wicked man / King Pharaoh was a bald head / When the sevens meet / Take care of your wife / War is not the answer / Love is what the world needs.
LP: . . . . BMLP 017
MC: . . . . BMC 017

LIVE AT LONDON (Dillinger/Clint Eastwood).
Tracks: / Send some rain / Tribal war / Musical music.
LP: . . . . DHS 003

MARIJUANA IN MY BRAIN.
LP: . . . . VSLP 4036

TALKIN' BLUES.
Tracks: / African world wide / Truth and rights / Don't take another man's life / Trial and crosses / Jah love / Mind your own business.
LP: . . . . DEAD 1001

TOP RANKING DILLINGER.
LP: . . . . TWS 919

TRIBAL WAR (LP).
Tracks: / Rock to the music / Get on the good side / Super cock / Sex me baby / Soul food / Tribal war / Tallowah / Mr. Flint / Rockers.
LP: . . . . NC 004
MC: . . . . TCNC 004

VERSUS TRINITY CLASH.
LP: . . . . BSLP 1003

Dillon, Dean

SLICK NICKEL.
Tracks: / Hey heart / New never wore off my sweet baby, The / When the feelin's right / I go to pieces / Hard time for lovers / Appalachia got to have you feelin' in my bones / You sure got this ol' redneck feelin' blue / Still got a crush on you / Station to station / Father, Son and Holy Ghost.
LP: C1 48920
MC: C4 48920
LP: 748 920 1
MC: 748 920 4

Dilruba

SHAAL MAR-KAY (LP).
LP: . . . . MUT 1064
MC: . . . . CMUT 1064

Dils

LIVE: DILS.
LP: 51003 1

Dim Subuteo

LAKESIDE.
LP: . . . . REDLP 94

Dimaccio, Christian

CHRISTIAN DIMACCIO.
Tracks: / Hungarian rhapsody no. 2 / Les anges pleurent / Sabre dance / Little white donkey, The / Jeux d'eau / Toccata and fugue in D minor / Flight of the bumble bee / Presto from the sonata, Op 27 No 2 / La campanella.
LP: . . . . MCS 2143

Dimbleby, Richard

VOICE OF RICHARD DIMBLEBY.
LP: 1087

Dimentia 13

DIMENTIA 13.
LP: . . . . MIRLP 116

Dimples

DIMPLES AND FRIENDS.
LP: . . . . MULLP 007

Din A Test Bild

PROGRAMME 3.
LP: . . . . KS 80045

Diner (film)

DINER (1982 film soundtrack) (Various artists).
2LP: 60107.1
MCSET: 90107.4

Dingfelder, Ingrid

FLUTE CONCERTOS (Dingfelder, Ingrid/English Chamber Or./Sir Charles Mackerras).
Tracks: / Flute concerto in D minor Wq.22 / Flute concerto in D major / Flute concerto in G major.
MC: . . . . ZC QS 6012

Dingle's (label)

DINGLE'S REGATTA (Various artists).
LP: . . . . DIN 301

Dingo Girl (show)

DINGO GIRL (Stage show) (Various artists).
LP: . . . . LRF 119

Dinner Ladies

THESE KNEES HAVE SEEN THE WORLD.
LP: . . . . HNBL 1339
MC: . . . . HNBC 1339

Dinning, Judy

WAITING FOR THE CHANGE (Dinning, Judy & Dave Smith).
Tracks: / Fine horseman / Sail far / Love has no pride / Dole queue, The / Man with the child in his eyes, The / Your songs / Young waters / Waiting for the change / Bring the rain / You're a fool / Bonnie ship the Diamond, The.
LP: . . . . RUB 043

Dinning Sisters

DINNING SISTERS-VOL.1.
Tracks: / Sentimental gentleman / Where or when / You're a character, baby / Once in a while / Buttons and bows / Harlem sandman / Beg your pardon / Way you look tonight / Aunt Hagar's blues / Please don't talk about me / Brazil / I love my love / Love on a greyhound bus / San Antonio rose.
LP: 2C 068 54579

DINNING SISTERS-VOL.2.
Tracks: / Lolita Lopaz / My adobe hacienda / Do you love me? / I wonder who's kissing her now / Iggedy song, The / Last thing I want is your pity, The / Bride and groom polka, The / I get blue when it rains / Years and years ago / Fun and fancy free / Melancholy / Wave to me my lady / If I had to live my life over / Oh Monah.
LP: . . . . EMS 1144
MC: . . . . TCEMS 1144

Dinosaur

DINOSAUR.
LP: . . . . HMS 015

Dinosaur Ducks

DINOSAUR DUCKS (Ducktails).
MC: . . . . DIS 025

Dinosaur Jnr

BUG.
LP: . . . . BFFP 31
MC: . . . . BFFP 31C

GREEN MIND.
LP: . . . . BYN 24
MC: . . . . BYN 24C

YOU'RE LIVING ALL OVER ME.
LP: . . . . SST 130
MC: . . . . SSTC 130

Dinosaur Record

DINOSAUR RECORD (Croft, Mike).
LP: . . . . STMP 9017
MC: STMP4 9017

Dinosaurs

DINOSAURS, THE.
Tracks: / Lay back baby / Do I move you? / Resurrection rag / Mona (I need you baby) / Good old rock 'n' roll / Who makes the moves / Strange way / Butcher boy / Fossil fuel (Available on CD only) / Motel party baby (Available on CD only).
LP: . . . . WIK 83

Dinosaurs (film)

DINOSAURS (Film soundtrack) (Various artists).
LP: . . . . C'BUS 213

D'Inverno, Ray

LIVE JAZZ FROM THE SOLENT AREA (see Worlock, Monty and Ray D'Inverno Trios).

Dio

CHRIS TETLEY INTERVIEWS DIO.
LPPD: . . . . CT 1007

DIO: INTERVIEW PICTURE DISC.
LPPD: . . . . BAK 2062

DREAM EVIL.
Tracks: / Night people / Dream evil / Sunset superman / All the fools sailed away / Naked in the rain / Overlove / I could have been a dreamer / Faces in the window / When a woman cries.
LP: . . . . VERH 46
MC: . . . . VERHC 46

HOLY DIVER.
Tracks: / Stand up and shout / Holy diver / Gypsy / Caught in the middle / Don't talk to strangers / Straight through the heart / Invisible / Rainbow in the dark / Shame on the night.
LP: . . . . VERS 5
MC: . . . . VERSC 5
LP: . . . . PRICE 117
MC: . . . . PRIMC 117

INTERMISSION.
Tracks: / King of rock and roll / Rainbow in the dark / Sacred heart / Time to burn / Rock 'n' roll children / We rock.
MLP: . . . . VERB 40
MC: . . . . VERBC 40

LAST IN LINE.
Tracks: / We rock / Last in line / Breathless / I speed at night / One night in the city / Evil eyes / Mystery / Eat your heart out / Egypt-the chains are on.
LP: . . . . VERL 16
MC: . . . . VERLC 16

LOCK UP THE WOLVES.
Tracks: / Wild one / Hey angel / Night music / Evil on Queen Street / Twisted / My eyes / Born on the sun / Between two hearts / Lock up the wolves / Walk on water / Why are they watching me.
LP: 846 033 1
MC: 846 033 4

SACRED HEART.
Tracks: / King of rock and roll / Sacred heart / Another lie / Rock 'n' roll children / Hungry for heaven / Like the beat of a heart / Just another day / Fallen angels / Shoot shoot.
LP: . . . . VERH 30
MC: . . . . VERHC 30

Dio, Ronnie James

CAROLINA COUNTRY BALL.
LP: . . . . LONG 7
MC: . . . . LONGC 7

TRYING TO BURN THE SUN (see under Elf) (Elf & Ronnie James Dio).

Dion

20 GOLDEN GREATS: DION & THE BELMONTS (Dion & The Belmonts).
LP: . . . . NE 1057

20 GREATEST HITS: DION (Dion & The Belmonts).
LP: . . . . BRLP 19
MC: . . . . BRMC 19

ABRAHAM, MARTIN AND JOHN.
Tracks: / Abraham, Martin and John / Purple haze / Tomorrow is a long time / Sonny boy / Dolphins, The / Daddy rollin' (in your arms) / He looks a lot like me / Sun fun song / From both sides now / Sisters of mercy / Loving you is sweeter than ever.
LP: . . . . CH 204

ALONE WITH DION.
Tracks: / Heaven help me / Close your eyes / Fools rush in / My one and only love / Northeast end of the corner / One for my baby / Then I'll be tired of you / Kissin' game, The / Lonely teenager / After the dance / P.S. I love you / Save the last dance for me / Little Miss Blue / Havin' fun.
LP: . . . . CH 115

DION & THE BELMONTS (Dion & The Belmonts).
Tracks: / I wonder why / Teenager in love / Where or when / Runaround Sue / Come go with me / Runaway girl / Born to cry / Majestic / Lonely teenager / Little Diane / Wanderer, The / Love came to me / Sandy / Havin' fun / Little Miss Blue / Lovers who wander / Ruby baby / This little girl / Donna the prima donna / Drip drop.
LP: . . . . ENGY 8

DRIP DROP.
LP: 42917

FABULOUS DION, THE (Dion & The Belmonts).
Tracks: / Runaround Sue / Wanderer, The / Lovers who wander / Little Diane / Love came to me / Lonely teenager / Little Miss Blue / Majestic, The / (I was) born to cry / Sandy / Come go with me / Havin' fun.
MC: . . . . FABC 008

FABULOUS DION & THE BELMONTS, THE (Dion & The Belmonts).
Tracks: / Where on when / Teenager in love, A / I wonder why / No one knows / Don't pity me / Every little thing I do / When you wish upon a star / In the still of the night / I can't go on (Rosalie) / That's my desire / Wonderful girl.
MC: . . . . FABC 002

FIRE IN THE NIGHT (Dion/Streethearts).
Tracks: / Fire in the night / We don't talk anymore / Hollywood / Midnight lover / Street mama / All quiet on 34th Street / You are my star / Poor boy.
LP: . . . . CH 295

GREATEST HITS: DION.
Tracks: / Runaround Sue / Sandy / Lovers who wander / Lonely teenager / Runaway girl / Havin' fun / Little Miss Blue / Queen of the hop / Lonely world / Love came to me / King without a queen / Kissin' game, The / Tonight tonight.
LP: . . . . NL 89006
MC: . . . . NK 89006
LP: . . . . LRSLP 1002
MC: . . . . LRSK 1002

GREATEST HITS: DION & THE BELMONTS (Dion & The Belmonts).
Tracks: / I wonder why / Every little thing I do / No one knows / Funny feeling / Tag along / That's my desire / Don't pity me / Just you / That's how I need you / Teenager in love / Lover's prayer / My day / Where or when / My private joy / In the still of the night / I'm through with love / Will you love me still? / When you wish upon a star.
LP: . . . . LRSLP 1004
MC: . . . . LRSK 1004

HITS (Dion & The Belmonts).
Tracks: / Runaround Sue / Sandy / Teenager in love / Wanderer / Born to cry / Majestic / Don't pity me / Lonely teenager / Lover's prayer / Little Diane / I wonder why / Where or when.
LP: . . . . CHA 176
MC: . . . . CHC 176

I PUT AWAY MY IDOLS.
Tracks: / Here is my servant / Trust in the Lord / Day of the Lord / I put away my idols / Daddy / Give up and surrender / Very soon / He won't tell you / Healing / My prayer for you.
LP: . . . . DAY R 4016
MC: . . . . TC DAY 4016

INSIDE JOB.
Tracks: / I believe / He's the one / Centre of my life / Truth will set you free / Gonna be ready / Old souvenirs / New Jersey wife / Man in the glass / Sweet surrender.
LP: . . . . DAY 4006
MC: . . . . TC DAY 4006

KINGDOM IN THE STREETS.
LP: . . . . DAY R 4032
MC: . . . . DAY C 4032

LOVERS WHO WANDER.
Tracks: / Lovers who wander / Come go with me / King without a queen / So long friend / Twist / Little Diane / Mi muchacha / Stagger Lee / Shout / Tonight, tonight / Born to cry / Queen of the hop / Candy man / Sandy / Lost for sure / Love came to me.
LP: . . . . CH 163

PRESENTING DION & THE BELMONTS (Dion & The Belmonts).
Tracks: / I wonder why / Teen angel / Where or when / You better not do that / Just you / I got the blues / Don't pity me / Teenager in love / Wonderful girl / Funny feeling / I've cried before / That's my desire / No one knows / I can't go on.
LP: . . . . CH 107

RETURN OF THE WANDERER (Dion/ Streethearts).
Tracks: / Lookin' for the heart of Saturday night / Midtown American main street gang / You've awakened something in me / Guitar queen / Pattern of my lifeline, The / (I used to be a) Brooklyn dodger / Sweetheart theme / Power of love within, The / Spanish Harlem incident / Do you believe in magic.
LP: . . . . CH 294

ROCK 'N' ROLL FOREVER (Dion & The Belmonts).
Tracks: / I wonder why / Teenager in love / Wanderer / No one knows / Ruby baby / Drip drop / That's my desire / Where or when / Runaround Sue / Little Diane.
LP: . . . . K 26049
MC: K4 26049

RUNAROUND SUE.
Tracks: / Runaround Sue / Somebody nobody wants / Dream lover / Life is but a dream / Wanderer, The / Runaway girl / I'm gonna make it somehow / Majestic / Could somebody take my place tonight / Little star / Lonely world / In the still of the night / Kansas City / Take good care of my baby.
LP: . . . . CH 148

SO WHY DIDN'T YOU DO THAT THE FIRST TIME? (Dion & The Belmonts).
Tracks: / Wanderer / My private joy / Moon river / Ain't that better baby? / Every little thing I do / We went away / Come take a walk with me / In a room / Lovers who wander / Tag along / Crying / It was never meant to be / Will you love me still? / Teenager in love / That's how I need you / Baby what you want me to do?.
LP: . . . . CH 155

WISH UPON A STAR.
Tracks: / When you wish upon a star / In the still of the night / Lord's prayer / My private joy / My day / Swinging on a star / Every little thing i do / All the things you are / It's only a paper moon / Fly me to the moon / I'm through with love / When the red, red robin comes bob, bob, bobbin' along / September song / Faith.
LP: . . . . CH 138

YO FRANKIE.
Tracks: / King of the New York Streets / And the night stood still / Yo Frankie (she's all right with me) / I've got to get to you / Written on the subway wall / Little star / Drive all night / Always in the rain / Loving you is killing me / Tower of love / Serenade.
LP: 209766
MC: 409766

Dion, Celine

UNISON.
LP: 4672031
MC: 4672034

Diorio, Joe

FEEDLES.
LP: . . . . SJP 146

Dip In The Pool

SILENCE.
LP: . . . . ROUGH 107

Dire Straits

ALCHEMY -- LIVE.
Tracks: / Once upon a time in the west / Expresso love / Private investigations / Sultans of swing / Two young lovers / Telegraph Road / Solid rock / Going home (theme from Local hero) / Romeo and Juliet.
MC: . . . . VERYC 11
2LP: . . . . VERY 11

BROTHERS IN ARMS.
Tracks: / So far away / Money for nothing / Walk of life / Your latest trick / Why worry? / Ride across the river / Man's too strong, The / One world / Brothers in arms.
MC: . . . . VERHC 25
LP: . . . . VERH 25

COMMUNIQUE.
Tracks: / Angel of mercy / Follow me home / Lady writer / News / Once upon a time in the West / Communique / Portobello belle / Single headed sailor / Where do you think you're going? / So far away / Money for nothing / Walk of life / Your latest trick / Why worry? / Ride across the river / Man's too strong, The / One world / Brothers in arms.
LP: 9102 031
MC: 723 1021

DIRE STRAITS.
Tracks: / Down to the waterline / Water of love / Setting me up / Six blade knife / Southbound again / Sultans of swing / In the gallery.
MC: 723 1015
LP: 9102 021

DIRE STRAITS (HALF SPEED MASTER EDITION).
Tracks: / Down to the waterline / Water of love / Setting me up / Six blade knife / Southbound again / Sultans of swing / In the gallery / Wild west end / Lions.
LP: . . . . HS 9102 021

DIRE STRAITS: INTERVIEW PICTURE DISC.
LPPD: . . . . BAK 2018

LOVE OVER GOLD.
Tracks: / Telegraph Road / Private investigations / Industrial disease / It never rains / Love over gold.
LP: 6359 109
MC: 7150 109

MAKING MOVIES.
Tracks: / Tunnel of love / Romeo and Juliet / Skateaway / Expresso love / Les boys / Hand in hand / Solid rock / Down to the waterline / Water of love / Setting me up / Six blade knife / Southbound again / Sultans of swing / In the gallery / Wild West End / Lions.
MC: 7150 034
LP: 6359 034

MAKING MOVIES (HALF SPEED MASTER EDITION).
Tracks: / Tunnel of love / Romeo and Juliet / Skateway / Expresso love / Hand in hand / Solid rock / Les boys.
LP: . . . . HS 6359 034

MONEY FOR NOTHING.
Tracks: / Sultans of swing / Down to the waterline / Portobello belle - live / Twisting by the pool / Romeo and Juliet / Where do you think you're going / Walk of life / Private investigations / Money for nothing / Tunnel of love / Brothers in arms / Telegraph Road - live (remix).
LP: . . . . VERH 64
MC: . . . . VERHC 64

ON EVERY STREET.
Tracks: / Calling Elvis / On every street / When it comes to you / Fade to black / Bug, The / You and your friend / Heavy fuel / Iron hand / Ticket to heaven / My parties / Planet of New Orleans / How long.
LP: 5101601
MC: 5101604

Direct Action

DAMN-AGE.
LP: . . . . EFA 1652

Direct Hits

HOUSE OF SECRETS.
LP: . . . . MAKE 1

Directions

DIRECTIONS (Various artists).
2LP: . . . . INTEL 2

Dirt

NEVER MIND DIRT - HERE'S THE BOLLOCKS.
LP: 221984/7

Dirt Band

AMERICAN DREAM, AN.
LP: . . . . UAG 30271

JEALOUSY.
Tracks: / Jealousy / Too close for comfort / Fire in the sky / Love is the last thing / Crossfire / Circular man / Catch the next dream / So you run / Forget it / Easy slow.
LP: . . . . LBG 30345

MAKE A LITTLE MAGIC.
Tracks: / Make a little magic / Badlands / High school yearbook / Leigh Anne riding alone / Anxious heart / Do it (party lights) / Harmony / Too good to be true / Mullen's farewell to America.
LP: . . . . UAG 30308

Dirty Dancing

DIRTY DANCING (1987 Film Soundtrack) (Various artists).
Tracks: / I've had the time of my life: *Medley, Bill & Jennifer Warnes* / Be my baby: *Ronettes* / She's like the wind: *Swayze, Patrick & Wendy Fraser* / Hungry eyes: *Carmen, Eric* / Stay: *Williams, Maurice & The Zodiacs*/ Yes: *Clayton, Merry* / You don't own me: *Blow Monkeys* / Hey baby: *Channel, Bruce* / Overload: *Zappacosta*/ Love is strange: *Mickey & Sylvia* / Where are you tonight?: *Johnston, Tom* / In the still of the night: *Five Satins.*
LP: . . . . BL 86408
MC: . . . . BK 86408

DIRTY DANCING - LIVE IN CONCERT (Various artists).
Tracks: / Yes: *Clayton, Merry* / Overload: *Clayton, Merry* / Steamroller blues: *Clayton, Merry* / Make me lose control: *Carmen, Eric* / Almost paradise: *Carmen, Eric & Merry Clayton* / Hungry eyes: *Carmen, Eric*/ Get ready: *Contours* / Your love keeps lifting me higher and higher: *Contours* / Cry to me: *Contours*/ Do you love me: *Contours* / Let the good times roll: *Medley, Bill* / Sea cruise: *Medley, Bill* / You've lost that lovin' feeling: *Medley, Bill*/ Old time rock'n'roll: *Medley, Bill* / I've had the time of my life: *Medley, Bill* / I've had the time of my life: *Various artists.*
LP: . . . . BL 90336
MC: . . . . BK 90336

MORE DIRTY DANCING, VOL. 2 (1987 film soundtrack) (Various artists).
Tracks: / I've had the time of my life: *Morris, John Orchestra, The* / Big girls don't cry: *Four Seasons* / Merengue: *Lloyd, Michael & Le Disc* / Some kind of wonderful: *Drifters* / Johnny's mambo: *Lloyd, Michael & Le Disc*/ Do you love me: *Contours* / Love man: *Redding, Otis* / Wipe out: *Surfaris, The* / These arms of mine: *Redding, Otis* / De todo un poco: *Lloyd, Michael & Le Disc* / Cry to me: *Burke, Solomon* / Trot the fox: *Lloyd, Michael & Le Disc* / Will you love me tomorrow: *Shirelles* / Kellerman's anthem: *Emile Bergstein Chorale, The.*
LP: . . . . BL 86965
MC: . . . . BK 86965

Dirty Dingus Magee

DIRTY DINGUS MAGEE (1970 film soundtrack) (Various artists).
LP: . . . . MCA 25095
MC: . . . . MCAC 25095

Dirty Dozen Brass Band

LIVE: MARDI GRAS IN MONTREUX.
LP: . . . . ROUNDER 2052
MC: . . . . ROUNDER 2052C
LP: . . . . REU 1009

MY FEET CAN'T FAIL ME NOW.
Tracks: / Blackbird special / Do it fluid / I ate up the apple tree / Bongo beep / Blue Monk / Caravan / St. James' Infirmary / Li'l Liza Jane / Mary, Mary / My feet can't fail me now.
LP: . . . . GW 3005

NEW ORLEANS ALBUM, THE.
Tracks: / Inside straight / When I'm walking (let me walk) / Hannibal / Don't you feel / My leg / That's how you got killed before / Song for Bob / Monkey, The / Snowball / Me like it like that / Kid Jordan's second line.
LP: 4668941
MC: 4668944

VOODOO.
Tracks: / It's all over now / Oop pop a dah / Moose the mooche / Black drawers, blue piccolo / Voodoo / Gemini rising / Don't drive drunk / Santa Cruz.
LP: 4650971
MC: 4650974

Dirty Dozen (Film)

DIRTY DOZEN (1967 film soundtrack) (Various artists).
Tracks: / Dirty dozen: Main theme: *Various artists* / Building the barracks: *Various artists* / Battle begins: *Various artists* / Girls of the evening: *Various artists* / Dirty dozen, The: *Various artists* / Erinsam: *Various artists* / Mission accomplished: *Various artists* / Bramble bush: *Various artists* / Col. Breed's folly: *Various artists* / Sham Battle, The: *Various artists* / Chateau, The: *Various artists* / Switch-hitters: *Various artists* / Dirty dozen:Finale and end title: *Various artists.*
LP: 4502291
MC: 4502294

DIRTY DOZEN (Film Soundtrack) (Various artists).
Tracks: / Dirty dozen theme: *Various artists* / Building the barracks: *Various artists* / Battle begins: *Various artists* / Girls of the evening: *Various artists* / Dirty dozen: *Various artists* / Einsam: *Various artists*/ Mission accomplished: *Various artists* / Bramble bush: *Various artists* / Col. Breed's folly: *Various artists*/ Sham battle/ Don't sit under the apple tree: *Various artists* / Chateau, The: *Various artists* / Switchhitters: *Various artists* / Finale and end title: *Various artists.*
LP: 2315 049

DIRTY DOZEN/HANNIBAL BROOKS (Film Soundtrack) (Various artists).
Tracks: / Dirty dozen, The (main title): *Various artists* / Building the barracks: *Various artists* / Battle begins: *Various artists* / Girls of the evening: *Various artists* / Dirty dozen, The: *Various artists* / Erinsam: *Siegfried, Sibylle* / Mission accomplished (Destruction of the chateau): *Various artists* / Bramble bush: *Lopez,* Trini / Col. Breed's folly. *Various artists* / Sham battle, The (Interpolating: Don't sit under the...): *Various* artists / Chateau, The: *Various artists* / Switch-hitters: *Various artists* / Dirty dozen, The (finale and end title): *Various artists* / Hannibal Brooks march (main theme): *Various artists* / Journey to Innsbruck: *Various* artists / Peace and understanding: *Various artists* / Hannibal Brooks love theme: *Various artists* (Hannibal Brooks.) / Elephant shake (Lucy's theme): *Various artists* (Hannibal Brooks.) / Respite: *Various artists* / Walk in the woods: *Various artists* / Hannibal's rest: *Various artists* / Tyrolean folk dance: *Various artists*/ Across the river: *Various artists* / Sickness in the family: *Various artists* / Lucy's theme: *Various artists*/ Peace and understanding (reprise): *Various artists* / Approaching the frontier: *Various artists* / Hannibal Brooks love theme (reprise): *Various artists.*
LP: . . . . LPMGM 17
LP: 794 252 1
MC: . . . . TCMGM 17
MC: 794 252 4

Dirty Looks

COOL FROM THE WIRE.
Tracks: / Cool from the wire / It's not the way you rock / Can't take my eyes off you / Oh Ruby / Tokyo / Wastin' my time / Put a spell on you / No brains child / Get it right / It's a bitch / Get off.
LP: . . . . K 781 836 1
MC: . . . . K 781 836 4

DIRTY LOOKS.
Tracks: / They got me covered / Love crimes / You can't love me / Lie to me / Take a life / Let go / 12 o'clock high / You're too old / Accept me / Disappearing / Drop that tan.
LP: . . . . SEEZ 22
MC: . . . . ZSEEZ 22

TURN IT UP.
Tracks: / Daddy's gone / Living alone / Carrie / You've got it / Do we need it / Animal / Turn it up / Deceit / Hit list / Born again / Kiss of death / Time is up / It was.
LP: . . . . SEEZ 38

TURN OF THE SCREW.
Tracks: / Turn of the screw (who's screwing you) / Nobody rides for free / C'mon Frenchie / Take what ya get / Hot flash jelly roll / Slammin' to the big beat.
MC: 7819924
LP: 7819921

Dirty Tricks

HIT AND RUN.
Tracks: / Hit and run / Get out on the street / Gambler, The / Road to Deriabay / I've had these dreams before / Walkin' tall / Last night of freedom / Lost in the past.
LP: 2383 446

Dirty White Boy

BAD REPUTATION.
LP: 8419591
MC: 8419594

Disappointed..

DEAD IN LOVE (Disappointed A Few People).
LP: . . . . BIAS 039

Discharge

DISCHARGE 1980-1986.
LP: . . . . CLAYLP 24

GRAVE NEW WORLD.
LP: . . . . CLAYLP 19

HEAR NOTHING, SEE NOTHING, SAY NOTHING.
Tracks: / Hear nothing, see nothing, say nothing / Nightmare continues, The / Final blood bath, The / Protest and survive / I won't subscribe / Drunk with power / Meanwhile / Hell on earth, A / Cries of help / Possibility of lifes destruction, The / Q - and children? A - and children / Blood runs red, The / Free speech for the dumb / End, The.
LP: . . . . CLAYLP 3

LIVE AT CITY GARDEN.
Tracks: / Warning / Nightmare continues, The / Never again / Blood runs red, The / Protest and survive / State violence state control / More I see, The / Angel burning (encore) / Hear nothing, see nothing, say nothing / Where there is a will / Anger burning / Born to die in the gutter / In defence of our future / Price of silence, The / Decontrol / Blood runs red, The (encore).
LP: . . . . CLAYLP 103

NEVER AGAIN.
Tracks: / Warning / Never again / Hear nothing, see nothing, say nothing / Nightmare continues, The / Where there is a will / Drunk with power / Final blood bath, The / Anger burning / Two monstrous nuclear stockpiles / Price of silence, The / Protest and survive / Born to die in the gutter / Doomsday / More I see, The / State violence/State control / In defence of our future / Decontrol.
LP: . . . . CLAYLP 12

NIGHTMARE CONTINUES, THE.
LP: . . . . CLAYLP 107
MC: . . . . CLAYMC 107

WHY.
Tracks: / Vision of war / Look at tomorrow, A / Maimed and slaughtered / Ain't no feeble bastard / Massacre of innocents (air attack) / Doomsday / Does this system work / Why / Mania for conquest / Is this to be / State violence / State control.
LP: . . . . PLATE 002

Dischord (label)

DISCHORD SINGLES COMPILATION (Various artists).
LP: . . . . DISCHORD 14

Disco

100 ALL TIME CLASSIC DANCE HITS OF THE 1970'S (Various artists).
Tracks: / Shaft, Theme from: *Hayes, Isaac* / That lady: *Isley Brothers* / Move on up: *Mayfield, Curtis* / I'm doing fine now: *New York City* / Mrs Grace: *Tymes* / Family affair: *Sly & the Family Stone* / Groovin' with Mr Bloe: *Mr. Bloe* / Get up I feel like a sex machine: *Brown, James* / I'll take you there: *Staple Singers* / Summer breeze: *Isley Brothers* / Higher and higher: *Wilson, Jackie* / Pick up the pieces: *Average White* Band / Only the strong survive: *Paul, Billy* / Hang on in there baby: *Bristol, Johnny* / I get the sweetest feeling: *Wilson, Jackie* / You can do magic: *Limmie & Family Cooking* / On the pony express: *Johnson, Johnny* & Bandwagon / Backstabbers: *O'Jays* / Walking in rhythm: *Blackbyrds* / Sunshine day: *Osibisa* / Satisfaction guaranteed: *Melvin, Harold & The Bluenotes* / Love train: *O'Jays* / When will I see you again: *3 Degrees* / Rock the boat: *Hues Corporation* / Shame, shame, shame: *Shirly & Company* / Get dancing: *Disco Tex & The Sexolettes* / Ain't gonna bump no more: *Tex, Joe* / Swing your daddy: *Gilstrap, Jim* / Come back and finish what you started: *Knight, Gladys & The Pips* / You'll never find another love like mine: *Rawls, Lou* / Sweet inspiration: *Johnson, Johnny & Bandwagon* / Take good care of yourself: *3 Degrees* / Soul city walk: *Bell, Archie & The* Drells / Be thankful for what you've got: *Devaughan, William* / Lady Marmalade: *Labelle* / Native New Yorker: *Odyssey* / Nice and slow: *Green, Jesse* / I wanna dance wit choo: *Disco Tex & The Sexolettes* / Dr kiss kiss: *5000 Volts* / More more more: *Andrea True Connection* / You to me are everything: *Real Thing* / You don't have to go: *Chi-lites* / Sixty minute man: *Trammps* / First impression: *Impressions* / You little trust maker: *Tymes* / Ride a wild horse: *Clark, Dee* / Gonna get along without you now: *White, Barry* / What it is: *Mimms, Garnet* / This is it: *Moore, Melba* / You're the first, the last, my everything: *White,* Barry / Do the bus stop: *Fatback (Band)* / Never can say goodbye: *Gaynor, Gloria* / Now is the time: *James,* Jimmy & The Vagabonds / Too good to be forgotten: *Chi-lites* / Dolly my love: *Moments (group)* / If I can't have you: *Elliman, Yvonne* / Don't leave me this way: *Melvin, Harold & The Bluenotes* / Let the music play: *White, Barry* / Isn't she lovely: *Parton, David* / Hold back the night: *Trammps* / Shuffle, The: *McCoy, Van* / Walkin' miracle, A: *Limmie & Family Cooking* / There goes my first love: *Drifters* / Sixteen bars: *Stylistics* / I'll go where the music takes me: *James, Jimmy & The Vagabonds* / Sing baby sing: *Stylistics* / You're more than a number in my little red book: *Drifters* / Can't get by without you: *Real Thing* / I'm on fire: *5000 Volts* / Spanish hustle: *Fatback (Band)* / Sad sweet dreamer: *Sweet Sensation* / Hustle, The: *McCoy, Van & Soul City* Symphony / Jack in the box: *Moments (group)* / Ain't no stoppin' us now: *McFadden & Whitehead* / Let's do the latin hustle: *M & O Band* / Get down: *Chandler, Gene* / Shame: *King, Evelyn "Champagne"* / I thought it was you: *Hancock, Herbie* / Strawberry letter 23: *Brothers Johnson* / September: *Earth, Wind & Fire* / High wire: *Carr, Linda* / Ladies night: *Kool & The Gang* / Stuff like that: *Jones, Quincy* / H.A.P.P.Y. radio: *Starr, Edwin* / Ain't we funkin' now: *Brothers Johnson* / Ring my bell: *Ward, Anita* / I will survive: *Gaynor, Gloria* / Got to get you into my life: *Earth, Wind & Fire* / Strutt your funky stuff: *Frantique* / Jack and Jill: *Raydio* / You bet your love: *Hancock, Herbie* / Light my fire: *Stewart, Amii* / Rappers delight: *Sugarhill Gang* / You make me feel: *Sylvester* / Knock on wood: *Stewart, Amii* / I lost my heart to a starship trooper: *Brightman, Sarah* / Contact: *Starr, Edwin* / I love America: *Juvet, Patrick* / Yes sir I can boogie: *Baccara* / In the bush: *Musique*.
LPS: . . . . DHOSLP 100
MCSET: . . . . DHOSMC 100

100 MINUTES OF DISCO DANCE (Various artists).
MC: . . . . ZCTON 129

ATLANTIC DISCO YEARS 1974-70 (See under Atlantic (label)) (Various artists).

BEST DISCO ALBUM IN THE WORLD (Various artists).
Tracks: / Le freak: *Chic* / Knock on wood: *Stewart, Amii* / One way ticket: *Eruption* / Painter man: *Boney M* / I'm every woman: *Khan, Chaka* / One nation under a groove: *Funkadelic* / He's the greatest dancer: *Sister Sledge* / Flashback: *Ashford & Simpson* / Love don't live here anymore: *Rose Royce* / We are family: *Sister Sledge* / I want your love: *Chic* / I can't stand the rain: *Eruption* / Fire: *Pointer* Sisters / Wishing on a star: *Rose Royce* / Young hearts run free: *Staton, Candi* / Weekend: *Jackson, Mick* / You really touched my heart: *Stewart, Amii* / Hooray, hooray, it's a holi holiday: *Boney M.*
LP: . . . . K 58062
MC: K4 58062

BEST OF 12" GOLD VOL.1 (Various artists).
Tracks: / Boogie wonderland: *Earth, Wind & Fire* / Disco nights (rock freak): *G.Q.* / You can do it: *Hudson,* Al & The Partners / I thought it was you: *Hancock, Herbie* / Street life: *Crusaders* / You know how to love me: *Hyman, Phyllis* / It's a disco night (rock don't stop): *Isley Brothers* / Stuff like that: *Jones, Quincy.*
LP: . . . . OG 1401
MC: . . . . OG 2401

BEST OF 12" GOLD VOL.2 (Various artists).
Tracks: / And the beat goes on: *Whispers* / Check out the groove: *Thurston, Bobby* / Music: *Miles, John* / You're lying: *Linx* / Stomp: *Brothers Johnson* / Star: *Earth, Wind & Fire* / You bet you're love: *Hancock, Herbie* / I don't wanna be a freak: *Dynasty.*
LP: . . . . OG 1402
MC: . . . . OG 2402

BEST OF 12" GOLD VOL.3 (Various artists).
Tracks: / Let's groove: *Earth, Wind & Fire* / I'm in love: *King, Evelyn "Champagne"* / Ai no corrida: *Jones, Quincy* / Groove: *Franklin, Rodney* / Funkin' for Jamaica: *Browne, Tom* / Don't stop the music: *Yarbrough & Peoples* / Strut your funky stuff: *Frantique* / Don't push it don't force it: *Haywood, Leon.*
LP: . . . . OG 1403
MC: . . . . OG 2403

BEST OF 12" GOLD VOL.4 (Various artists).
Tracks: / Jump to it: *Franklin, Aretha* / I can make you feel good: *Shalamar* / Put our heads together: *O'Jays* / I've had enough: *Earth, Wind & Fire* / Love come down: *King, Evelyn "Champagne"* / Get down Saturday night: *Cheatham, Oliver* / Crazy: *Manhattans* / It's a love thing: *Whispers.*
LP: . . . . OG 1404
MC: . . . . OG 2404

BEST OF 12" GOLD VOL.5 (Various artists).
Tracks: / Love town: *Newbury, Booker* / Joy: *Band AKA* / Get it right: *Franklin, Aretha* / Stay with me tonight: *Osborne, Jeffrey* / Hi how ya doin'?: *Kenny G.* / I'll be around: *Wells, Terri* / Extraordinary girl: *O'Jays* / Silver shadow: *Atlantic Starr.*
LP: . . . . OG 1405
MC: . . . . OG 2405

BEST OF 12" GOLD VOL.6 (Various artists).
Tracks: / (They long to be) close to you: *Guthrie, Gwen* / You make it heaven: *Wells, Terri* / Serious: *Griffin,* Billy / On the wings of love: *Osborne, Jeffrey* / After the love has gone: *Earth, Wind & Fire* / Secret lovers: *Atlantic Starr* / How 'bout us: *Champaign* / Weekend girl: *S.O.S. Band.*
LP: . . . . OG 1406
MC: . . . . OG 2406

BEST OF 12" GOLD VOL.7 (Various artists).
Tracks: / History: *Mai Tai* / Hangin' on a string: *Loose Ends* / Tell me how it feels: *52nd Street* / Mine all mine: *Cashflow* / Ain't nothin' goin' on but the rent: *Guthrie, Gwen* / Takes a little time: *Total Contrast* / I'll be good: *Rene & Angela* / You and me tonight: *Aurra.*
LP: . . . . OG 1407
MC: . . . . OG 2407

BEST OF 12" GOLD VOL.8 (Various artists).
Tracks: / Grace: *Band AKA* / Can't keep holding on: *Second Image* / Hold me tighter in the rain: *Griffin,* Billy / Nightbirds: *Shakatak* / I specialise in love: *Brown, Sharon* / This beat is mine: *Vicky D.* / So fine: *Johnson, Howard* / Nights over Egypt: *Jones Girls.*
LP: . . . . OG 1408
MC: . . . . OG 2408

BEST OF 12" GOLD VOL.9 (Various artists).
Tracks: / Caravan of love: *Isley-Jasper* / Always and forever: *Heatwave* / Juicy fruit: *Mtume* / Sexual healing: *Gaye, Marvin* / Let's make a baby: *Paul, Billy* / Buttercup: *Anderson, Carl* / New York eyes: *Nicole/Timmy Thomas* / Just be good to me: *S.O.S. Band.*
LP: . . . . OG 1409
MC: . . . . OG 2409

BEST OF 12" GOLD VOL.10 (Various artists).
Tracks: / Let the music play: *Shannon* / Hip hop, be bop: *Man Parrish* / Alice, I want you just for me: *Full Force* / Haunted house of rock: *Whodini* / Body work: *Hot Streak* / Street dance: *Break Machine* / Sexomatic: *Bar-Kays* / Rock it: *Hancock, Herbie.*
LP: . . . . OG 1410
MC: . . . . OG 2410

BEST OF 12" GOLD VOL.11 (Various artists).
Tracks: / Ain't no stoppin' us now: *McFadden & Whitehead* / Ring my bell: *Ward, Anita* / This time baby: *Moore, Jackie* / Can you feel the force: *Real Thing* / Shake your body (down to the ground): *Jacksons* / Time: *Light Of The World* / Turn the music up: *Players Association* / We got the funk: *Positive Force.*
LP: . . . . OG 1411
MC: . . . . OG 2411

BEST OF 12" GOLD VOL.12 (Various artists).
Tracks: / High energy: *Thomas, Evelyn* / Where is my man: *Kitt, Eartha* / You think you're a man: *Divine* / On a crowded street: *Pennington, Barbara* / Light my fire (1985 remix): *Stewart, Amii* / So many men, so little time: *Brown, Miquel* / Can't take my eyes off you: *Boystown Gang* / Y.M.C.A.: *Village People.*
LP: . . . . OG 1412
MC: . . . . OG 2412

BEST OF 12" GOLD VOL.13 (Various artists).
Tracks: / Dancing tight: *Galaxy and Phil Fearon* / I am somebody: *Jones, Glenn* / Your personal touch: *King,* Evelyn "Champagne" / Emergency (dial 999): *Loose Ends* / Encore: *Lynn, Cheryl* / You can't have my love: *Jones Girls* / Tossing and turning: *Windjammer* / You get the best from me (say say say): *Myers, Alicia.*
LP: . . . . OG 1413
MC: . . . . OG 2413

BEST OF 12" GOLD VOL.14 (Various artists).
Tracks: / Love me like this: *Real To Reel* / My love is waiting: *Gaye, Marvin* / Risin' to the top: *Burke,* Keni / Girl from Ipanema: *Gilberto, Astrud* / Does she have a friend: *Chandler, Gene* / Mind blowin' decisions: *Heatwave* / Mellow mellow right on: *Lowrell* / Pillow talk: *Sylvia.*
LP: . . . . OG 1414
MC: . . . . OG 2414

BEST OF 12" GOLD VOL.15 (Various artists).
Tracks: / You gave me love: *Crown Heights Affair* / Casanova: *Coffee* / Never knew love like this before: *Mills,* Stephanie / She's a bad mama jama: *Carlton, Carl* / Burn rubber on me: *Gap Band* / Celebration: *Kool & The Gang* / Southern Freeez: *Freeez* / Walking into sunshine: *Central Line.*
LP: . . . . OG 1415
MC: . . . . OG 2415

BEST OF 12" GOLD, VOL. 16 (Various artists).
Tracks: / Somebody's else's guy: *Brown, Jocelyn* / Thinking of you: *Sister Sledge* / Change of heart: *Change* / Tuch me: *Rae, Fonda* / Who do you love?: *Intruders* / You're the one for me (medley): *Hardcastle, Paul* / Feel so real: *Arrington, Steve* / Say I'm your number one: *Princess.*
MC: . . . . OG 2416

BEST OF 12" GOLD, VOL. 17 (Various artists).
Tracks: / He's the greatest dancer: *Sister Sledge* / Contact: *Starr, Edwin* / I will survive: *Gaynor, Gloria* / Ladies night: *Kool & The Gang* / Get down: *Chandler, Gene* / Good times: *Chic* / Shoulda loved ya, I: *Walden, Narada Michael* / Searching: *Change.*
MC: . . . . OG 2417
LP: . . . . OG 3417

BEST OF TK VOL. 1 (Various artists).
Tracks: / Do what you wanna do: *T-Connection* / One love: *Bee, Celi & The Buzzy Bunch* / That's the way I like it: *K.C. & The Sunshine Band* / Dance across the floor: *Horne, Jimmy 'Bo'* / Get off: *Foxy* / Do ya wanna get funky with me: *Brown, Peter* / Jazz freak: *Reeves, Paulette* / What you won't do for love: *Caldwell, Bobby* / Groove on: *Hale, Willie Beaver* / Rock your baby: *McCrae, George.*
2LP: . . . . ROUS 1041
MCSET: . . . . TCROUS 1041

BOOGIE NIGHTS 1973 - 1980 (Various artists).
Tracks: / Best of my love: *Emotions* / More, more, more: *True, Andrea Connection* / You can do magic: *Limmie* & Family Cooking / I love the nightlife: *Bridges, Alicia* / Gonna get along without you now: *Wills, Viola* / I will survive: *Gaynor, Gloria* / Love train: *O'Jays* / Don't leave me this way: *Melvin, Harold* / Contact: *Starr, Edwin* / Shame: *King, Evelyn "Champagne"* / Boogie nights: *Heatwave* / Blame it on the boogie: *Jacksons* / Celebration: *Kool & The Gang* / It's a disco night (rock don't stop): *Isley Brothers* / Best disco in town: *Ritchie Family* / Ain't gonna bump no more: *Tex, Joe* / Disco lady: *Taylor, Johnny* / Fantasy: *Earth, Wind & Fire* / YMCA: *Village People* / This is it: *Moore, Melba* / What it is: *Mimms, Garnet* / You can do it: *Hudson, Al & The Partners* / Turn the music up: *Players Association* / Use it up, wear it out: *Odyssey.*
MCSET: . . . . OG 2210

DISCO (50 great dancing hits) (Various artists).
2LP: . . . . RML 101
MCSET: . . . . RML 4C101

DISCO BEACH PARTY (Various artists).
2LP: . . . . SMR 8503
MCSET: . . . . SMC 8503

DISCO CLASSICS (Various artists).
2LP: . . . . STAR 2002
MC: . . . . STAC 2002

DISCO DANCE HITS (Various artists).
MC: . . . . ZCTON 115

DISCO DANCER (Various artists).
Tracks: / Love come down: *King, Evelyn "Champagne"* / Walking on sunshine: *Rockers Revenge* / Do it to the music:

Raw Silk / Saddle up: *Christie, David* / Ladies' night: *Kool & The Gang* / Murphy's law: *Cheri*/ Let's funk tonight: *Blue Feather* / Don't walk away: *Four Tops* / Do you wanna funk: *Sylvester* / Message, The: *Grandmaster Flash & The Furious Five* / Perfumed garden: *Rah Band* / Too late: *Junior* / Easier said than done: *Shakatak* / Just an illusion: *Imagination* / Lover in you, The: *Sugarhill Gang* / I can't go for that: *Hall & Oates* / That's when we'll be free: *State Of Grace* / Inside out: *Odyssey*.
LP: . . . . **NE 1190**
MC: . . . . **CE 2190**

DISCO DANCERS VOL.2 (Various artists).
Tracks: / Play that funky music: *Wild Cherry* / Getaway: *Various artists* / Soul city walk: *Bell, Archie* & The Drells / You ought to be havin' fun: *Various artists* / Get you somebody new: *Various artists* / From now on: *Various artists* / Hurt: *Manhattans* / Message in our music: *O'Jays* / Lowdown: *Scaggs, Boz*/ Git it up: *Various artists* / Dance sister dance: *Various artists* / More you do it: *Various artists*/ Movin' in all directions: *Various artists* / Salty tears: *Various artists*.
LP: . . . . **CBS 81816**

DISCO DAZE - DISCO NITES (Various artists).
Tracks: / I feel love: *Summer, Donna* / Contact: *Starr, Edwin* / And the beat goes on: *Whispers* / I owe you one: *Shalamar* / Don't push it don't force it: *Haywood, Leon* / Bourgie bourgie: *Knight, Gladys*/ One nation under a groove: *Funkadelic* / Ain't gonna bump no more: *Tex, Joe* / Southern Freeez: *Freeez*/ Rapper's delight: *Sugarhill Gang* / Stuff like that: *Jones, Quincy* / Searching: *Change* / More more more: *Andrea True Connection* / Rapp payback: *Brown, James* / Intuition: *Linx* / Knock on wood: *Stewart, Amii* / Ain't no stoppin' us now: *McFadden & Whitehead* / Jump to the beat: *Lattisaw, Stacy* / Stomp, The: *Brothers Johnson* / It makes you feel like dancin': *Rose Royce* / Funky town: *Lipps Inc.* / Instant replay: *Hartman, Dan* / Le freak: *Chic* / Somebody help me out: *Beggar & Co* / Ring my bell: *Ward, Anita*/ Get down: *Chandler, Gene* / Lady Marmalade: *Labelle* / Everybody get up: *UK Players* / Can you feel the force: *Four Seasons* / December '63 (oh what a night): *Four Seasons*.
2LP: . . . . **RTL 2056 A/B**
MCSET: . . . . **4CRTL 2056 A/B**

DISCO DIRECTION (Various artists).
Tracks: / Yes sir, I can boogie: *Baccara* / Keep it up: *Olympic Runners* / Native New Yorker: *Odyssey*/ On the road again: *Rogers, D.J.* / Dance and shake your funky tambourine: *Inner City Express* / Turn the beat around: *Robinson, Vicki Sue* / Whispering: *Doctor Buzzards Original Savannah Band* / Make it with you: *Whispers*/ Shame: *King, Evelyn "Champagne"* / Uptown fesitval: *Shalamar* / Star wars theme: *Meco* / Crunch, The: *Rah Band* / Who is gonna love me: *Davison, Alfie* / I'll play the fool: *Doctor Buzzards Original Savannah* Band / Hold tight: *Robinson, Vicki Sue* / Shu' dig dancin' (in my hi-heeled shoes): *Inner City Express* / Funky tropical: *Vanderbilt, Lee* / Whatever it takes: *Olympic Runners* / Sorry I'm a lady: *Baccara* / Close Encounters of the Third Kind suite: *Meco*.
LP: . . . . **PL 42477**
MC: . . . . **PK 42477**

DISCO FRENZY (Various artists).
LP: . . . . **SHM 978**

DISCO INFERNO (Various artists).
MC: . . . . **VCA 045**

DISCO LADY (Various artists).
MC: . . . . **AIM 37**

DISCO LIGHTNING (Various artists).
MC: . . . . **BRC 2520**

DISCO MAGIC (Various artists).
2LP: . . . . **PLD 8015**

DISCO MANIA (Various artists).
MCSET: . . . . **PDC 025**

DISCO NIGHTS (Various artists).
MC: . . . . **BRC 2505**

DISCO PAARRRTY (Various artists).
Tracks: / Let it flow: *Various artists* / For the love of money: *Various artists* / Inside America: *Jones, Juggy* / Breakaway: *Bush, Ernie* / Golden gate get down: *Various artists* / Gotham City: *Various artists*.
LP: . . . . **CLP 540**

DISCO SATURDAY NIGHT (Various artists).
MCSET: . . . . **PLDC 8004**
2LP: . . . . **PLD 8004**

DISCO SIZZLERS (Various artists).
Tracks: / Wings of fire: *Coffey, Dennis* / Devil's gun: *CJ & Co* / Feel the need: *Detroit Emeralds* / Bull, The: *Theodore, Mike Orchestra*.
LP: . . . . **K 50546**

DISCO STARTRACKS (Various artists).
Tracks: / Devils gun: *CJ & Co* / Dance, dance, dance: *Chic* / Pinnochio theory, The: *Bootsy's Rubber Band*/ World I a ghetto, The: *Benson, George* / Belfast: *Boney M* / From now on: *Clifford, Linda* / Do you believe in love at first sight: *Warwick, Dionne* / Love per hour: *Trammps* / Nights on Broadway: *Staton, Candi*/ Waterbed: *Mann, Herbie* / Cosmic wind: *Theodore, Mike Orchestra* / Feel the need: *Detroit Emeralds*/ Disco inferno: *Trammps* / I believe in music: *Mass Production* / I got to have your love: *Fantastic Four*/ Pick up the pieces: *Average White Band* / Free spirit: *Coffey, Dennis* / Wings of fire: *Coffey, Dennis*/ Rubberband man, The: *Detroit Spinners* / It makes you feel like dancin': *Rose Royce*.
LP: **K4 58041**

DISCO SYMPHONY, A (Various artists).
Tracks: / Romeo and juliet: *Various artists* / I hear a symphony: *Various artists* / McArthur Park: *Various artists* / Rhapsody in blue: *Various artists* / Take a ride: *Various artists* / Bee sting: *Various artists*.
LP: . . . . **ETAT 13**

DISCO UK/DISCO USA (Various artists).
Tracks: / Just an illusion: *Imagination* / Rapture: *Blondie* / Gangsters of the groove: *Heatwave* / Do you feel my love?: *Grant, Eddy* / I'm every woman: *Khan, Chaka* / Happy birthday: *Oxygen* / Super Casanova: *Hot Gossip* / I can't stand the rain: *Eruption* / I just wanna (spend some time with you): *Edwards, Alton*/ Ai no corrida: *Jones, Quincy* / So this is romance: *Linx* / Queen of the rapping scene: *Modern Romance*/ I shot the sheriff: *Light Of The World* / Boogie on up: *Rokotto* / Wikka wrap: *Evasions* / British hustle: *Hi Tension* / All American girls: *Sister Sledge* / Roller jubilee: *Di Meola, Al* / You're the one for me: *D-Train* / You bet your love: *Hancock, Herbie* / Taste of bitter love: *Knight, Gladys* / Fungi mama: *Browne, Tom* / Gonna get along without you now: *Wills, Viola* / It's a disco night (rock don't stop): *Isley* Brothers / I want your love: *Chic* / My simple heart: *3 Degrees* / I've got to learn to say no: *Fields*, Richard Dimples / Sign of the times: *James, Bob* / Groove: *Franklin, Rodney* / Hold on to love: *Bristol*, Johnny / Holdin' out for love: *Bofill, Angela* / Keep on dancing: *Gary's Gang* / Light my fire: *Stewart, Amii*.
2LP: . . . . **RTL 2073 A/B**

DISCO YEARS 1974-1979 (Various artists).
LP: **241 677-1**
MC: **241 677-4**

DISCOMANIA/PARTY FEVER (Various artists).
LP: . . . . **TVA 5AB**
MC: . . . . **TVC 5AB**

DISCONIGHTS (Various artists).
MC: . . . . **BRC 2508**

DON'T STOP DANCING (Various artists).
Tracks: / Don't stop till you get enough: *Jackson, Michael* / It's raining men: *Weather Girls* / Doctor doctor: *Thompson Twins* / What do I do?: *Fearon, Phil & Galaxy.* / Your love is king: *Sade* / Just be good to me: *S.O.S. Band* / All night long: *Mary Jane Girls* / Dance hall days: *Wang Chung* / That's the way I like it: *Dead or Alive* / Relax: *Frankie Goes To...* / Street dance: *Break Machine* / Somebody's watching me: *Rockwell* / 99 red balloons: *Nena* / Somebody else's guy: *Brown, Jocelyn* / I am what I am: *Gaynor*, Gloria / To be or not to be (the hitler rap): *Brooks, Mel* / Watching you watching me: *Grant, David* / Do it again, Billie Jean: *Club House*.
LP: . . . . **STAR 2242**
MC: . . . . **STAC 2242**

DOUBLE DECKERS (Various artists).
Tracks: / Just an illusion: *Imagination* / Never let you go: *Savanna* / Just a little bit: *Thompson, Carroll*/ Love you've been fakin': *Index* / Ease your mind: *Touchdown* / Jingo: *Candido* / Feels like I'm in love: *Marie, Kelly* / Love is gonna be on your side: *Firefly* / Do it (till you're satisfied): *B.T.Express*/ Lock it up: *Leprechaun* / Take your time: *Hamilton, Roy* / Nice and slow: *Green, Jesse* / I like plastic: *Raven, Marsha* / I can't turn away: *Savanna* / Puerto Rico: *Decoupage* / I like what you're doing to me: *Young & Co* / You don't like my music: *Kid* / Nice and soft: *Wish* / It's just a groove: *Adams, Glen Affair* / Dancin' and prancin': *Candido*.
2LP: . . . . **RDD 1**

MCSET: . . . . **ZCRDD 1**

GET DOWN ON THE FLOOR (Various artists).
2LP: . . . . **DISC 01**

GROOVES (Various artists).
Tracks: / Groove, The: *Various artists* / Hawkeye: *Various artists* / You got what it takes: *Various artists*/ Give peace a chance: *Various artists* / Check out the groove: *Various artists* / Shadow dancing: *Various artists* / For the public: *Various artists* / Go for it: *Various artists*.
LP: . . . . **CBS 84389**

IN THE GROOVE - THE 12 INCH DISCO PARTY (Various artists).
Tracks: / Last night a DJ saved my life: *Indeep* / Love come down: *King, Evelyn "Champagne"* / Joy: *Band* AKA / Rappers' delight: *Sugarhill Gang* / Sexual healing: *Gaye, Marvin* / Just an illusion: *Imagination*/ Taking a chance on love: *Redd, Sharon* / Twist: *Chill Fac-torr* / Rock the boat: *Forrest* / Hold me tighter in the rain: *Griffin, Billy* / Cash (cash money): *Prince Charles* / Garden party: *Mezzoforte*/ Dancing on the floor: *Third World* / Message, The: *Flash & The Furious Five* / When boys talk: *Indeep*/ Never too much: *Vandross, Luther*.
LP: . . . . **STAR 2228**
MC: . . . . **STAC 2228**

INSTANT REPLAYS (Various artists).
LP: **2480 426**

INTIMATE DISCO (Various artists).
LP: . . . . **E 103**

KEEP ON DANCIN' (Various artists).
Tracks: / Ring my bell: *Various artists* / That's the way I like it: *Various artists* / It's been so long: *Various* artists / Dance with me: *Various artists* / What you won't do for love: *Various artists* / Do what you wanna do: *Various artists* / Loose caboose: *Various artists* / Party boys: *Various artists* / Spank: *Various artists* / Rock your baby: *Various artists* / Get off: *Various artists* / Pease don't go: *Various artists*/ Dance across the floor: *Various artists* / Calypso breakdown: *Various artists* / Tonight is the night part 1: *Various artists* / On fire: *Various artists* / Down on the third time: *Various artists* / Do ya wanna get funky with me: *Various artists*.
LP: . . . . **TKR 54300**
MC: **40 54300**

MAGNET DISCO MAGIC (Various artists).
Tracks: / Move your body: *Various artists* / Hey you should be dancing: *Various artists* / It's uncanny: *Various* artists / All the way in love with you: *Various artists* / Open sesame: *Various artists* / Dancin': *Various* artists / Disco music: *Various artists* / I like it: *Various artists* / Say say say: *Various artists*/ Gimme some: *Various artists* / Rescue me: *Various artists* / Get up and boogie: *Various artists* / Gee baby: *Various artists*.
LP: . . . . **MFP 50454**

MASTER MIXES (Various artists).
Tracks: / Ain't no stoppin' us now: *Enigma (70's)* / Dance on: *Various artists* / Everlasting: *Shampoo*/ Hot picks: *Starshow* / Seasons of gold: *Gidea Park* / Movin' with the times: *Mastergroove* / Platinum pop: *This Years Blonde* / I love music: *Enigma (70's)*.
LP: . . . . **EPC 22138**

MASTERMIXERS (Various artists).
Tracks: / Ain't no stoppin' us now: *Various artists* / Platinum pop: *Various artists* / Everlasting: *Various* artists / Seasons of gold: *Various artists* / Movin' with the times: *Various artists* / Hitpicks: *Various artists* / Dance on: *Various artists* / I love music: *Various artists*.
LP: . . . . **CRX 4**
MC: . . . . **CRXC 4**

MERCURY DANCE CLASSICS (Various artists).
LP: **8840011**
MC: **8840014**

MOVE, GROOVE & NIGHTCLUBBING (Various artists).
2LP: . . . . **MOVE 1**

MUSIC MACHINE (Film soundtrack) (Various artists).
Tracks: / Let me feel your heartbeat: *Various artists* / Disco dancer: *Various artists* / Dilly: *Various* artists / Get the feel right: *Various artists* / Jumping the gun: *Various artists* / Music machine: *Various* artists / Move with the beat: *Various artists* / Music's my thing: *Various artists* / Ready for love: *Various artists*.
LP: . . . . **NH 106**
MC: . . . . **ZC 106**

NON-STOP DISCO CHARTBUSTERS (Various artists).
Tracks: / Brazil: *Various artists* / My way: *Various artists* / Soul Dracula: *Various artists* / Baby do you wanna bump: *Various artists* / Disco hop: *Various artists* / Rock on brother: *Various artists*/ Amor, amor: *Various artists* / Chariot: *Various artists* / Undecided love: *Various artists* / Pretty maid: *Various artists* / Get it together: *Various artists* / Please love me again: *Various artists*.
LP: . . . . **CRLP 508**

ORIGINAL DISCO HITS STORY, THE (Various artists).
Tracks: / Bee sting: *Camouflage* / What's your name, what's your number: *Showdown* / Are you ready: *Rokotto*/ Promise of love: *Delegation* / Delicious: *Duprees* / Your love: *Kissoon, Mac & Katie* / Simplicity: *Tamlins* / Don't okay your rock'n'roll: *Anthony, George* / Back to back: *Federation* / Soul trippin': *Delegation* / Keep doing it (part 1): *Showdown*.
LP: . . . . **ETMP 3**

PRELUDES GREATEST HITS - VOL.I & II (Various artists).
Tracks: / Can you handle it: *Various artists* / Check out the groove: *Various artists* / Your love is a life saver: *Various artists* / You're the one for me: *Various artists* / You'll never know: *Various artists* / Little bit of jazz, A: *Various artists* / Body music: *Various artists* / All my love: *Various artists*.
2LP: . . . . **PHL 22222**
MCSET: **40 22222**

ROLLER DISCO (Various artists).
MC: . . . . **AM 56**

STEPPIN' OUT (Disco's greatest hits) (Various artists).
LP: . . . . **POLS 1005**

THIS IS DISCO! (Various artists).
Tracks: / Hot shot: *Young, Karen* / Is it all over my face: *Loose Joints* / Don't make me wait: *Peech Boys*/ Hard times: *McCall Allie* / Rescue me: *Thomas, Sybil* / Another man: *Mason, Barbara* / Heartbeat: *Gardner, Taana*.
2LP: . . . . **STROBE 1**
MCSET: . . . . **ZCSTROB 1**

TOP TWELVE DISCO SINGLES (Various artists).
LP: . . . . **PKLP 200**

Disco Getter

DISCO, DISCO, DISCO.
Tracks: / Bad girls / Boogie wonderland / Ring my bell / H.A.P.P.Y. radio / Ain't no stoppin' us now / We are family.
LP: . . . . **TSL 101**

Disco Inferno

CLOSE DOORS OPEN WINDOWS.
LP: . . . . **CHE 2**

Disco Scooters

FROM MUD TO THE MOON....
Tracks: / Questionably tortoisehead / Perfect murder / Hey stowaway / Quicksilver / Arable land / From mud to the moon / Hummingbird / Rain rein reign supreme / Some tree talking / I couldn't sing / Rock and roll.
MC: . . . . **DIG 1**

Disco Tex

GET DANCING (Disco Tex & The Sexolettes).
LP: . . . . **CHELV 1003**
MC: . . . . **CHELC 1003**

Discords

SECOND TO NO-ONE.
LP: . . . . **HANG 41 UP**

Discoveries Underwater

DISCOVERIES UNDERWATER (See under Davidson, Howard).

Disember

LIKE AN EVER FLOWING.
LP: . . . . **NB 047LP**
MC: . . . . **NB 047MC**

Disguise

FORTUNE AND FAME.
MC: . . . . **ELY 003**

JOCKY WILSON SAYS.
MC: . . . . **ELY 002**

SECRET'S OUT, THE.
MC: . . . . **ELY 001**

Disharmonic Orchestra

EXPOSITIONSPROPHYLAXE.
LP: **0829811**

SPLIT LP (See under Pungent Stench).

Disirt Tola

DISIRT TOLA.
LP: . . . . **LP 281 832**

Disley, Diz

VIOLINSPIRATION (see under Grappelli, Stephane) (Disley, Diz Trio & Stephane Grappelli).

ZING WENT THE STRINGS (Disley, Diz & The Soho Quintette).
LP: .... **WF 031**

Dislocation Dance

MIDNIGHT SHIFT.
LP: .... **ROUGH 63**

Disney

40 WALT DISNEY ORIGINALS (Various artists).
Tracks: / Mary Poppins: *Various artists* / Bambi: *Various artists* / Snow White: *Various artists* / So dear to my heart: *Various artists* / Summer magic: *Various artists* / Bedknobs and broomsticks: *Various artists*/ Winnie the pooh: *Various artists* / Pinocchio: *Various artists* / Step in time: *Various artists* / Journey: *Various artists* / Jolly holiday: *Various artists* / My own home: *Various artists* / Feed the birds: *Various* artists / Love is a song: *Various artists* / County fair: *Various artists* / Maggie's theme: *Various* artists / Beautiful briny: *Various artists* / Dwarfish yodelling song: *Various artists* / Higitus figitus: *Various artists* / Follow the leader: *Various artists* / Stick to it ivity: *Various artists* / Lavender blue: *Various artists* / You can fly: *Various artists* / Second star to the right: *Various artists* / When you wish upon a star: *Various artists* / Wonderful thing about tiggers: *Various artists* / Ugly bug ball: *Various artists* / Old home guard: *Various artists* / Portobello Road: *Various artists* / Most befudding thing: *Various artists* / Gallant Captain Hook: *Various artists* / Rain, rain, rain came down down down: *Various artists* / Magic song, The: *Various artists* / Madam Mim: *Various artists.*
2LP: .... **PLD 8010**
MCSET: .... **PLDC 8010**

BEST OF DISNEY (Various artists).
Tracks: / Dream is a wish your heart makes, A: *Various artists* (From Cinderella) / When you wish upon a star: *Various* artists (From Pinocchio) / Supercalifragilisticexpialidocious: *Various artists* (From Mary Poppins) / When I see an elephant fly: *Various artists* (From: Dumbo) / I've got no strings: *Various artists* (From: Pinocchio.) / Bella Notte: *Various artists* (From Lady and the Tramp) / Cruella De Ville: *Various artists* (From 101 Dalmations) / Some day my prince will come: *Various artists* (From Snow White.) / Bare necessities: *Various artists* (From Jungle Book.) / Give a little whistle: *Various artists* (From Pinocchio) / Jolly 'Oliday: *Various artists* (From Mary Poppins) / Bibbidi bobbidi boo: *Various artists* (From Cinderella) / Trust in me: *Various artists* (From Jungle Book.) / Second star to the right: *Various artists* (From Peter Pan.) / Little April showers: *Various artists*(From Bambi.) / Spoonful of sugar: *Various artists* (From Mary Poppins.) / He's a tramp: *Various artists* (From Lady and the Tramp.) / Appreciate the lady: *Various artists* (From The Fox and the Hound.) / Chim chim cheree: *Various* artists (From Mary Poppins) / Following the leader: *Various artists* (From Peter Pan.) / I wanna be like you: *Various* artists (From Jungle Book.) / Feeds the birds: *Various artists* (From Mary Poppins.) / Whistle while you work: *Various* artists (From Snow White.) / Look out for Mr. Stork: *Various artists* (From Dumbo.) / Heigh ho: *Various artists*(From Snow White.) / Hi diddle dee dee: *Various artists* (From Pinocchio.) / When you wish upon a star (recap.): *Various artists* (From Pinocchio.).
LP: .... **MFP 5783**
MC: .... **TCMFP 5783**
LP: .... **REH 573**
MC: .... **ZCR 573**

CHIP 'N' DALE (Childrens story book).
MC: .... **DIS 021**

CHRISTMAS FAVOURITES (Various artists).
LP: .... **SHM 939**

CINDERELLA (See Under Cinderella) (Unknown narrator(s)).

CINDERELLA (see under Cinderella (bk)).

CINDERELLA/BABES IN THE WOOD (see under Cinderella (bk)) (Crowther, Leslie (nar)).

DINOSAUR DUCKS (See Under Dinosaur Ducks) (Unknown narrator(s)).

DISNEY CLASSICS FOR CHILDREN (Various artists).
Tracks: / Peer Gynt suite: *Various artists* / In the hall of the mountain king: *Various artists* / Nutcracker suite: *Various artists* / Young persons guide to the orchestra: *Various artists* / Petit suite d'orchestre: *Various artists* / Childrens games: *Various artists* / Marche (trumpet tambour): *Various artists* / Berceuse (la poupee): *Various artists* / Impromptu: *Various artists* / Duo (petit Mari, petit femme): *Various artists* / Galop (le bal): *Various artists* / Mendelssohn violin concerto in E minor: *Various artists* / Grofe Grand Canyon suite: *Various artists* / Swan lake: *Various artists.*
LP: .... **GH 857**

DISNEY HITS (Various artists).
Tracks: / When you wish upon a star: *Sammes, Mike Singers* / Thomas O'Malley cat: *Hilton, Ronnie* / Give a little whistle: *Sammes, Mike Singers* / When I see an elephant fly: *Peterson, Clive* / Who's afraid of the big bad wolf: *Sammes, Mike Singers* / Ugly bug ball, The: *Hilton, Ronnie* / Whistle while you work: *Various artists*/ Winnie the pooh: *Various artists* / Heigh ho: *Various artists* / Siamese cat song: *Sammes, Mike Singers*/ Bare necessities: *Sammes, Mike Singers* / Supercalifragilisticexpialidocious: *Various artists* / Colonel Hathi's march: *Sammes, Mike Singers* / Trust in me: *Curtis, Nick* / That's what friends are for: *Sammes, Mike Singers*/ I wanna be like you: *Sammes, Mike Singers* / Never smile at a crocodile: *Peterson, Clive* / Feed the birds: *Dawn,* Julie / Aristocats, The: *Hilton, Ronnie* / Hi diddle dee dee: *Sammes, Mike Singers* / Ev'rybody wants to be a cat: *Hilton, Ronnie* / My own home: *Heard, Enid* / I've got no strings: *Sammes, Mike Singers.*
MC: .... **HR 8102**
MC: .... **HR 4181024**

DISNEY SPECTACULAR, A (see under Cincinnati Pops Orch).

DISNEY'S ORIGINAL SOUNDTRACK COLLECTION VOL 4 (Various artists).
LP: .... **SHM 909**

DISNEY'S ORIGINAL SOUNDTRACK COLLECTION VOL 3 (Various artists).
LP: .... **SHM 908**

DISNEY'S ORIGINAL SOUNDTRACK COLLECTION VOL 1 (Various artists).
LP: .... **SHM 906**

DISNEY'S ORIGINAL SOUNDTRACK COLLECTION VOL 2 (Various artists).
LP: .... **SHM 907**

DONALD'S POOCH PARLOUR (Various artists).
MC: .... **DIS 026**

GOLDEN HOUR: DISNEY (Various artists).
Tracks: / Whistle while you work: *Various artists* / Heigh ho: *Various artists* / Bare necessities: *Various artists* / Little April showers: *Various artists* / Zip-a-dee-doo-dah: *Various artists* / Spoonful of sugar, A: *Various artists* / Winnie the Pooh: *Various artists* / Ballad of Davy Crockett, The: *Various artists*/ Everybody wants to be a cat: *Various artists* / Bibbidi bobbidi boo: *Various artists* / Mickey's big show: *Various* artists / Donald Duck recites Mary had a little lamb: *Various artists* / Little Boy Blue: *Various artists*/ Clara Cluck song: *Various artists* / Mickey Mouse march: *Various artists* / Who's afraid of the big bad wolf?: *Various artists* / Donald Duck song: *Various artists* / Hi diddle dee dee: *Various artists* / Three caballeros: *Various artists* / He's a tramp: *Various artists* / Feed the birds: *Various artists* / Never smile at a crocodile: *Various artists* / Portobello Road: *Various artists* / Sorcerer's apprentice, The: *Various artists*/ When you wish upon a star: *Various artists.*
LP: .... **GH 856**

GOLDEN HOUR PRESENTS DISNEY TODAY (See under Young Generation for details) (Young Generation/Mike Curb Congregation).

GREAT SONGS FROM DISNEY MOVIES (Various artists).
Tracks: / Funny little bunnies: *Various artists* / Penguin is a very funny creature: *Various artists* / Pied piper: *Various artists* / Grasshopper and the ants: *Various artists* / Rockabye baby: *Various artists* / Wise little hen, The: *Various artists* / Who's afraid of the big bad wolf: *Various artists* / Ferdinand the bull: *Various* artists / Give a little whistle: *Various artists* / When you wish upon a star: *Various artists* / When I see an elephant fly: *Various artists* / Heigh-ho: *Various artists* / I'm wishing: *Various artists* / With a smile and a song: *Various artists* / One song: *Various artists* / Little wooden head: *Various artists*/ Whistle while you work: *Various artists* / Some day my prince will come: *Various artists* / Turn on the old music box: *Various artists* / Love is a song: *Various artists.*
LP: .... **SH 268**

GREATEST HITS: WALT DISNEY (Various artists).
Tracks: / When you wish upon a star: *Various artists* / I've got no strings: *Various artists* / I wanna be like you: *Various artists* / Bare necessities: *Various artists* / Who's afraid of the big bad wolf?: *Various artists*/ When I see an elephant fly: *Various artists* / Ballad of Davy Crockett, The: *Various artists* / Zip a dee doo dah: *Various artists* / Wonderful thing about tiggers: *Various artists* / Spoonful of sugar, A: *Various artists*/ Supercalifragilisticexpialidocious: *Various artists* / Ugly bug ball, The: *Various artists* / Whistle while you work: *Various artists* / Heigh ho!: *Various artists.*
LP: .... **WD 3**
MC: .... **WD 43**

MICKEY MOUSE DISCO (Various artists).
Tracks: / Disco Mickey mouse: *Various artists* / Welcome to Rio: *Various artists* / Greatest band: *Various* artists / Zip a dee do dah: *Various artists* / Macho duck: *Various artists* / Mousetrap: *Various artists*/ Watch out for Goofy: *Various artists* / It's a small world: *Various artists* / Chim chim cheree: *Various artists.*
MC: .... **HSC 3019**
LP: .... **SHM 3019**

MICKEY MOUSE DISCO / MOUSERCISE (Various artists).
2LP: .... **NE 1186 AB**
MCSET: .... **CE 2186 AB**

MORE DISNEY FAVOURITES (Various artists).
Tracks: / Happy mouse: *Various artists* / Ugly bug ball, The: *Various artists* / I wanna be like you: *Various* artists / Give a little whistle: *Various artists* / Siamese cat song: *Various artists* / Wonderful thing about tiggers: *Various artists* / Love is a song: *Various artists* / Supercalifragilisticexpialidocious: *Various* artists / Pink elephants: *Various artists* / You can fly, you can fly: *Various artists* / Oo-de-lally: *Various* artists / Whale of a tale, A: *Various artists* / Thomas O'Malley cat: *Various artists* / Dream is a wish your heart makes, A: *Various artists* / Unbirthday song, The: *Various artists* / Beautiful briny: *Various artists*/ Minnie's yoo-hoo: *Various artists* / Goofy commercials: *Various artists* / End title: *Various artists.*
LP: .... **GH 850**

ORIGINAL SOUNDTRACK PARADE, VOLUME 1 (Various artists).
2LP: .... **PDA 029**

PARADE VOL 2 (Various artists).
Tracks: / Songs from the song of the south: *Various artists* / Aristocats, The: *Various artists* / Dumbo: *Various* artists / Winnie the Pooh: *Various artists* / Snow White and the seven dwarfs: *Various artists* / Alice in Wonderland: *Various artists* / 101 dalmations: *Various artists* / Cinderella: *Various artists.*
2LP: .... **PDA 030**

STAY AWAKE DISNEY (Disney songs) (Various artists).
Tracks: / Opening medley: (I'm getting wet and I don't dare at all): *Various artists* / Hi diddle dee dee: *Nordine, Ken*/ Bill Frisell/Wayne Horvitz / Little April showers: *Merchant, Natalie/Michael Stripe/Mark Bingham & The Roches*/ I wanna be like you (The monkey song): *Los Lobos* / Baby mine: *Raitt, Bonnie/ Was (Not Was)* / Heigh ho (the dwarfs marching song): *Waits, Tom* / Medley two: The darkness sheds its veil: *Various artists* / Stay awake: *Vega, Suzanne* / Little wooden head: *Frisell, Bill/Wayne Horvitz* / Blue shadows on the trail: *Straw, Syd* / Medley three: Three inches is such a wretched height: *Various artists* / Castle in Spain: *Poindexter, Buster & The Banshees* Of Blue / I wonder: *YMA Sumac* / Mickey mouse march: *Neville, Aaron* / Medley four: (All innocent children had better beware): *Various artists* / Feed the birds: *Hudson, Garth* / Whistle while you work: *NRBQ*/ I'm wishing: *Carter, Betty* / Cruella De Ville: *Replacements* / Some day my prince will come: *O'Connor,* Sinead / Medley five: (Technicolour pachyderms): *Various artists* / Pink elephants on parade: *Ra, Sun & His Arkestra*/ Zip-a-dee-doo-dah / Second star to the right: *Taylor, James* / Pinocchio medley (do you see the noses growing?): *Various* artists / Desolation theme: *Nordine, Ken/ Bill Frisell/Wayne Horvitz* / When you wish upon a star: *Starr, Ringo/Herb Alpert.*
LP: .... **AMA 3918**
MC: .... **AMC 3918**

WALT DISNEY STORIES FOR CHILDREN (Various artists).
Tracks: / Peter and the wolf: *Various artists* / Mickey and the beanstalk: *Various artists* / Fee fi fo fum: *Various* artists / My favourite dream: *Various artists* / My what a happy day: *Various artists* / Three little pigs: *Various artists* / Who's afraid of the big bad wolf: *Various artists* / Little engine that could, The: *Various artists.*
LP: .... **GH 858**

WALT DISNEY SUPER SOUNDTRACK ORIGINALS (Various artists).
Tracks: / Supercalifragilisticexpialidocious: *Various artists* / Little April shower: *Various artists* / Thomas O Malley cat: *Various artists* / Once upon a dream: *Various artists* / He's a tramp: *Various artists*/ Chim chim cheree: *Various artists* / Bibbidi bobbidi boo: *Various artists* / I've got no strings: *Various* artists / Whistle while you work: *Various artists* / I wanna be like you: *Various artists* / Bare necessities: *Various artists* / Bella notte: *Various artists* / Trust in me: *Various artists* / Everybody wants to be a cat: *Various artists* / Give a little whistle: *Various artists* / Someone is waiting for you: *Various* artists / Siamese cat song: *Various artists* / Zip a dee doo dah: *Various artists* / When I see an elephant fly: *Various artists* / Spoonful of sugar: *Various artists.*
LP: .... **PLE 7008**
MC: .... **PLC 7008**

WHEN YOU WISH UPON A STAR (16 Disney Favourites) (Various artists).
Tracks: / When you wish upon a star: *Various artists* / Supercalifragilisticexpialidocious: *Various artists* / Dream is a wish your heart makes, (A): *Various artists* / Mickey Mouse march: *Various artists* / Bella notte: *Various* artists / Give a little whistle: *Various artists* / You can fly, you can fly: *Various artists* / Heigh ho: *Various artists* (end s1) / Whistle while you work: *Various artists* / Bibbidi bobbidi boo: *Various artists*/ Alice in wonderland: *Various artists* / Cinderella work song, The: *Various artists* / Ballad of Davy Crockett, The: *Various artists* / Some day my prince will come: *Various artists* / Who's afraid of the big bad wolf (medley): *Various artists* / Ferdinand the bull: *Various artists* / Zip a dee doo dah: *Various artists.*
LP: .... **CBR 1011**
MC: .... **KCBR 1011**

Disney Razors

750 KG MAXIMUM BREAKDOWN.
LP: .... **HT 1**

Disorder

LIVE IN OSLO.
Tracks: / Complete disorder / Daily life / More than fights / Remembrance day / Maternal obsession / Bent edge / Provocated wars / God nose / Education / Driller killer / Prisoners of... / Stagnation / Life / Rampton / After / F**k your nationality / Out of order / Rhino songs.
LP: .... **AARGH 2**

ONE DAY SON, ALL THIS WILL BE YOURS (Disorder & Kaska Process).
LP: .... **AARGH 3**

SINGLES COLLECTION, THE.
LP: .... **12 ORDER 5**

UNDER THE SCALPEL BLADE.
LP: .... **AARGH 1**

VIOLENT WORLD.
LP: .... **AARGH 4**

Disorderlies (film)

DISORDERLIES (1987 Film Soundtrack) (Various artists).
Tracks: / Don't treat me like this: *Anita* / Edge of a broken heart: *Bon Jovi* / Trying to dance: *Kimmel,* Tom / Roller one: *Art Of Noise* / Fat off my back: *Guthrie, Gwen* / Work me down: *Hunter, Laura*/ Baby you're a rich man: *Fat Boys* / I heard a rumour: *Bananarama* / Disorderly conduct: *Latin Rascals*/ Big money: *Cashflow.*
LP: .... **LONLP 46**
MC: .... **LONC 46**

Disruptors

PLAYING WITH FIRE.
LP: .... **RCLP 3**

Dissension

WHY WORK FOR DEATH.
LP: .... **MS 8615**

Dissidenten

ARAB SHADOWS.
Tracks: / Bajka's gnaoui / Inshallah / Allal / Zain / Sahara elektrik / Shadows go arab (remember Hank Marvin).
LP: .... **MASO 33031**

LIFE AT THE PYRAMIDS.
LP: .... **SHAN 64001**
LP: .... **MASO 33037**

SAHARA ELEKTRIK.
Tracks: / Inshallah / Fata Morgana / El moundi / Sahara elektrik / Casablanca.
LP: .... **ORB 004**

MC: . . . . ORBC 004

Dissolution Of Dominic

DISSOLUTION OF DOMINIC BOOT/ DOG IT WAS THAT DIED (see under Stoppard, Tom) (Various artists).

Distance

MOSHI MOSHI.
LP: 6313 143

UNDER THE ONE SKY.
Tracks: / No way out / Leave it up to you / Speech of angels / As you turn away / Give it up / Rescue me / Looking over your shoulder / Every time I stand up / Softly speak / Stand up.
LP: 7599260141
MC: 7599260144

Distant Cousins

DISTANT COUSINS.
LP: . . . . GHETT 002
MC: . . . . GHETTC 002

DISTANT COUSINS (REMIX).
LP: . . . . GHETT 2X
MC: . . . . GHETTC 2X

Distel, Sacha

ADIOS AMIGO.
Tracks: / Adios amigo / Wir konnten freunde sein / Blacky / Eine ist einsam wie du / Traurig schone augen / Ein paar tranen / Marie cherie / Irene von avignon / Der platz neben mir / Unsere sprache ist musik / Ein fraunfreund / Frauen und rosen / Dir frau mit dem einsamen herzeb / Eine tur fiel zu / Deine stimme am telefon / Ich kann dich so schwer vergessen.
LP: . . . . BFX 15310

FROM SACHA WITH LOVE.
Tracks: / Can't smile without you / Chanson d'amour / Don't give up on us / For all we know / How deep is your love / I honestly love you / I'm not in love / If you leave me now / Just the way you are / Killing me softly / Little bit more, A / Love is in the air / Michelle / My eyes adored you / Old fashioned way / Three times a lady / Way we were / When I need you / You make me feel brand new / Your song.
LP: 9198 139

GOLDEN HOUR OF SACHA DISTEL.
LP: . . . . GH 674

LOVE IS ALL.
Tracks: / I thought about you / There's a whole lot of loving / I wouldn't care / How to handle a woman / Madame Louise / We can work it out / Tangerine / I write the songs / Take a look around / Feelings / What I did for love / Love is all.
LP: . . . . NSPL 18504

MORE AND MORE.
LP: . . . . K 46117

MOVE CLOSER.
Tracks: / Move closer / I just called to say I love you / Imagine / To all the girls I've loved before.
LP: . . . . TOWLP 16
MC: . . . . ZCTOW 16

NIGHT AND MUSIC AND YOU, THE.
Tracks: / This guy's in love with you / Feelings / As time goes by / Close to you / If you love me / It's impossible / What I did for love / To wait for love / I can't live my life without you / What now my love / Raindrops keep falling on my head / Beyond the sea / I'll never fall in love again / Autumn leaves / We can work it out / What are you doing the rest of your life.
LP: . . . . NSPL 18606

SACHA DISTEL.
Tracks: / Raindrops keep falling on my head / Darling, je vous aime beaucoup / Sacha's song / Didn't we / That Italian summer / Little green apples / Love is blue / Have I told you lately that I love you / How small we are / Melodie d'amour / Now is now / It can happen to you.
LP: . . . . K 46055
LP: . . . . WS 3003

SACHA DISTEL COLLECTION, THE.
Tracks: / Raindrops keep falling on my head / What now my love? / Can't take my eyes off you / Love is all / We can work it out / Feelings / My cherie amour / How to handle a woman / There's a whole lot of loving / I thought about you / Beyond the sea / I'll never fall in love again / Good life / You are the sunshine of my life / I wish you love / Autumn leaves / What are you doing the rest of your life? / This guy's in love with you / I can't live my life without you / Baby I love you / Tangerine / I write the songs / Yesterday I heard the rain / Love music / What I did for love / Wild world / I thought about you / What am I? / In my quiet world / Half and half (song for Sarah) / Beautiful thing, A / Harmony / She's a woman, it's just a matter of time.
2LP: . . . . PDA 071
MCSET: . . . . PDC 071

Distorted Truth

SMASHED HITS.
LP: . . . . LINKLP 121

Distractions

NOBODY'S PERFECT.
Tracks: / Waiting for Lorraine / Something for the weekend / Boys cry / Sick and tired / Leave you to dream / Louise / Paracetemol paralysis / Fantasy / Nothing / Wonder girl / Untitled / Still it doesn't ring / Looking for a ghost / Valerie.
LP: . . . . ILPS 9604

District Singers

TWELFTH PARTY SING A LONG.
Tracks: / Green grassy slopes / South down militia / Enniskillen dragoons / Ducks of Magheralin / Sash, The / Aughalee heroes / My Aunt Jane / Lily O / Ould Lammas fair / B for Barney / I'll tell me ma / Auld orange flute / My bonnie lies over the ocean / Northern lights of old Aberdeen / End of the road / Orange and blue / Black velvet band / Old mud cabin on the hill / Sprigs of Kilkrea / Wild rover / Love is teasin / Muirsheen durkin / Home boys home / No surrender / Derry's walls / When you and I were young Maggie / Mountains of Mourne / Battle of Garvagh / Star of the County Down / Coortin' in the kitchen / Protestant boys / Scottish soldier, A / Roamin' in the gloamin' / Old rustic bridge / London lights / Twenty one years.
LP: . . . . DULP 11
MC: . . . . CDULP 11

District Six

AKUZWAKALE (LET IT BE HEARD).
Tracks: / Woza wena (a calling to rise) / Skokiaan / Dance of the lions / Owenda / Sivela kude (we come from far) / Ilanga / Akuzwakale (let it be heard).
LP: . . . . D 6001
MC: . . . . DC 6001

LEAVE MY NAME AT THE DOOR.
Tracks: / Leave my name at the door / Nameless one, The / In our hands / Ilanga / Koko / Drums for Nelson / Mangwane.
LP: . . . . WAVE LP 29

TO BE FREE.
Tracks: / Ke a rona (power to the people) / Into the light / Etlon tu / Reasons of the heart / Kwa tebugo (part 2 of songs for Winnie Mandela) / Unity dance (part 3 of songs for Winnie Mandela) / Mbiso / Kalimba (CD only).
LP: . . . . EGED 53
MC: . . . . EGEDC 53

Ditmars, Ivan

5002 PIPES (Ditmars, Ivan/Alex Lasker).
LP: . . . . GNPS 80
MC: GNP5 80

Div

TWIST AND TURN.
LP: . . . . EM 9662

Diva (film)

DIVA (1982 Film Soundtrack) (Various artists).
LP: . . . . SL 9503
MC: . . . . SLC 9503
LP: . . . . PR 2001
MC: . . . . PRC 2001

DIVA SOUNDTRACK (see under Cosma, Vladimir) (Cosma, Vladimir).

Dive

DIVE.
LP: . . . . BR 7007

Divine

BEST OF AND THE REST OF, THE.
Tracks: / Native love / Shake it up / Shoot your shot / Love reaction / Jungle Jezebel / Alphabet rap.
MC: . . . . ARLC 1007

JUNGLE JEZEBEL.
Tracks: / Jungle Jezebel / Shoot your shot / Native love / Kick your butt / Alphabet rap.
LP: . . . . QUELP 2
LP: . . . . OLP 2

MAID IN ENGLAND.
MC: . . . . DTRXC 700
LP: . . . . DTRXLP 700

STORY SO FAR, THE.
LP: . . . . PROTO 3
MC: . . . . ZCPRO 3
LP: . . . . KNOB 3
LP: . . . . REPLAY 3005

Divine Comedy

FANFARE FOR THE COMIC MUSE.
LP: . . . . SETLPM 002

Divine Horsemen

DEVIL'S RIVER.
LP: . . . . ROSE 102

SNAKE HANDLER.
LP: . . . . ROSE 134

Divine Latin Divas

DIVINE LATIN DIVAS (Various artists).
Tracks: / Isadora: *Cruz, Celia* / La bochinchera: *Graciela* / Se formo: *Rivera, Yolanda* / Punto final: *Gil, Blanca Rosa* / Se paso noraida: *Moraida* / Amor y tenacion: *Sophy* / Maria bochaloca: *Silva*, Myrtha / La orquestade mi tierra: *Rivera, Yolanda* / Hacia adelante: *Lupe*, *La* / Me siento guajira: *Lupe*, La / Acuario: *Cruz, Celia* / Mi montuno esta en algo: *Silva, Myrtha* / Estoy a mil: *Graciela* / Camas gemelas: *Gil, Blanca Rosa* / Hasta que se rompa el cuero: *Rivera, Yolanda* / Crystal blue persuasion: *Sophy*/ Como duele eso nene: *Silva, Myrtha* / Ay Jose: *Graciela* / Me cole enel che che: *Noraida* / En la luna: *Sophy*.
MC: . . . . TCHOT 128
LP: . . . . HOT 128

Divine Weeks

THROUGH AND THROUGH.
LP: . . . . ENIG 22061

Divinyls

DESPERATE.
Tracks: / Boys in town / Only lonely / Science fiction / Siren song / Elsie / Only you / Ring me up / Victoria / Take a chance / I'll make you happy.
LP: . . . . CHR 1404
MC: . . . . ZCHR 1404

DIVINYLS, THE.
LP: . . . . VUSLP 30
MC: . . . . VUSMC 30

ESSENTIAL DIVINYLS COLLECTION.
Tracks: / Pleasure and pain / Temperamental / Back to the wall / Only lonely / Don't you go walking / Boys in town / Science fiction / Sleeping beauty / I'll make you happy / Better days (Only on LP and MC) / Heart telegraph (Only on LP and MC) / Dirty love (Only on LP and MC) / Punxsie (Only on CD) / Hey little boy (Only on CD) / Casual encounter (Only on CD).
LP: . . . . CHR 1846
MC: . . . . ZCHR 1846

WHAT A LIFE.
Tracks: / Guillotine day / Pleasure and pain / Don't you go walking / Goodie young / Sleeping beauty / Motion / In my life / Casual encounter / Heart telegraph.
LP: . . . . CHR 1511
MC: . . . . ZCHR 1511

Divorce Me, Darling

DIVORCE ME, DARLING (Original 1965 London cast) (Various artists).
Tracks: / Divorce me darling: Overture: *Various artists* / Here we are in nice again: *Various artists* / Someone to dance with: *Various artists* / Whatever happened to love?: *Various artists* / Lights! Music!: *Various artists*/ On the loose: *Various artists* / Maisie: *Various artists* / Paradise hotel, The: *Various artists* / No harm done: *Various artists* / Together again: *Various artists* / Divorce me darling: *Various artists*/ Here am I (but where's the guy): *Various artists* / Out of step: *Various artists* / You're absolutely me: *Various* artists / Back where we started: *Various artists* / Blondes for danger: *Various artists* / Swing time is here stay: *Various artists* / Divorce me, darling: Finale: *Various artists*.
LP: . . . . TER 1077
MC: . . . . ZCTER 1077
LP: . . . . DS 15009

Dixie Cups

TEEN ANGUISH VOL 1.
LP: . . . . CRM 2004

Dixie Dregs

BEST OF DIXIE DREGS.
LP: . . . . SLAM 2

FREE FALL.
Tracks: / Free fall / Holiday / Hand jig / Moe down / Refried funky chicken / Sleep / Cruise control / Cosmopolitan traveller / Big ditch / Wages of weirdness / Northern lights.
LP: 2429 154

NIGHT OF THE LIVING DREGS.
Tracks: / Punk sandwhich / Country house shuffle / Riff raff, The / Long slow distance / Night of the living dregs / Bash, The / Leprechaun promenade / Patchwork.
LP: 2429 181

UNSUNG HEROES.
Tracks: / Cruise control / Divided we stand / I'll just pick / Day 444 / Rock 'n' roll park / Attila the Hun / Kat food / Go for baroque.
LP: . . . . AL 9548

WHAT IF.
Tracks: / Take it off the top / Odyssey, The / What if / Travel tunes / Ice cakes / Little kids / Gina Lola breakdown / Night meets light.
LP: 2429 165

Dixie Four

CHICAGO SOUTH SIDE (Dixie Four/ Midnight Rounders/State Street Ramblers).
LP: . . . . CI 019

Dixie Hummingbirds

CHRISTIAN TESTIMONIAL, A.
LP: . . . . MCA 28000

DIXIE HUMMINGBIRDS.
Tracks: / Lord come see about me / Two little fishes / Is there anyone in heaven / Search me Lord / I'll be satisfied / Move up a little higher / We shall walk through the valley / You've got to live / What then / Down on me / Dear Lord look down upon me (Track features the Angelic Gospel Singers) / Jesus will answer prayer / Standing out on the highway / In the morning.
LP: . . . . HT 318

Dixie (label)

BEST OF DIXIE RECORDS, VOL.7 (Various artists).
LP: . . . . MILLION 7

BEST OF DIXIE RECORDS, VOL 3 (Various artists).
Tracks: / Three little wishes: *Lee, Jimmie* / Dizzy: *Peters, Pete* / Rockin' in my sweet baby's arms: *Peters*, Pete / Red Rover: *Bragg, Doug* / Pretty little thing: *Bragg, Doug* / Lovin' on my mind: *Bragg, Doug*/ Gotta keep it swinging: *Skelton, Eddie* / Curly: *Skelton, Eddie* / Love you too much: *Skelton, Eddie*/ Rebel's retreat: *Skelton, Eddie* / Handful of love: *Keefer, Lyle* / Blues hanging around: *Kelley, C.*.
LP: . . . . MILLION 3

BEST OF DIXIE RECORDS, VOL 4 (Various artists).
Tracks: / Feel so good: *Carroll, Bill* / Who shot Sam?: *Jones, George Thumper* / This little girl of mine: *Half Brothers* / Way you want it, The: *Meers, Arvil* / Little things you do, The: *Lee, Jimmie* / Never again: *Clayton*, Johnny / Don't tease me: *Pat & Dee* / Little dog blues: *Price, Mel* / Lonesome tavern blues: *Benson, Eddy*.
LP: . . . . MILLION 4

BEST OF DIXIE RECORDS, VOL 5 (Various artists).
Tracks: / I like to go: *McDaniel, Floyd* / Meanest blues: *Thomas, Jake* / Poor boy blues: *Thomas, Jake*/ Concussion: *Holidays* / Big, big man: *Brockman, Danny* / Easy does it: *Couch, Orville* / She told a lie: *Mishoe, Watson* / Teen lover: *Reynolds, Eddy* / What's gonna do now?: *Williams Brothers* / My baby don't want me no more: *Ridings, Jim* / You're gonna pay: *Ridings, Jim* / Ali Baba: *Williams Brothers*.
LP: . . . . MILLION 5

BEST OF DIXIE RECORDS, VOL 6 (Various artists).
Tracks: / Queen from Bowling Green: *Buchanan, Art* / Wonder why: *Buchanan, Art* / It must be me: *Ontario*, Art / Just look, don't touch, she's mine: *Johnson, Dee* / Crazy legs: *Gallegher, Jay* / Steady: *Gallegher*, Jay / Piano polka: *Bailey, M. & D.* / Blue guitar stomp: *Hammock, Ken* / Rock and roll: *White, J.R.*/ Weekend boogie: *Croock, Tom* / I'm your guy: *Johnson, Dee* / Brady and Dunky: *Hanna, Jack*.
LP: . . . . MILLION 6

Dixieaires

LET ME FLY 1948-50.
Tracks: / Will the circle be unbroken? / Poor and needy / I got to stand / If you see my Saviour / Friends let me tell you... / I got a home in that rock / Send me Jesus / God is the greatest creator / Buckle my shoe / Christ ABC / Loose the man / Let me fly / Little wooden church / You better run / I've got an interest over there / Look around you brother.
LP: . . . . HT 317

MY TROUBLE IS HARD.
Tracks: / Old MacDonald had a farm / Joe Louis is a fighting man / Sharp mama / You can't cure the blues / Sun will shine in my back door today, The / Zebedee found the magic stone / My trouble is hard / Pray.
LP: . . . . HT 319

Dixieland Sound

AT THE JAZZBAND BALL.
LP: 1902124

Dixielanders

DIXIELANDERS.
LP: . . . . ZMA 201

Dixon, Bill

LIVE IN NEW MORNING-LEGENDARY PARIS '76 SESSION (Dixon, Bill Trio).
2LP: . . . . LR 412/13

SON OF SISYPHUS.
LP: 1211381
MC: 1211382

WHOOPIN' (See under Winter, Paul) (Dixon, Bill/Paul Winter/Homnick).

Dixon Brothers

DIXON BROTHERS VOL. 3 (Early sacred songs).
LP: . . . . OHCS 178

DIXON BROTHERS VOL. 4.
LP: . . . . OHCS 179

Dixon, Don

MOST OF THE GIRLS LIKE TO DANCE.
Tracks: / Praying Mantis / (You're a) big girl now / Swallowing pride / Wake up / Talk to me / Pocket / Skin deep / Eyes on fire / Girls L.T.D. / Just rites / Ice on the river / Renaissance eyes / Fighting for my life / Southside girl.
LP: . . . . FIEND 60
MC: . . . . FIENDCASS 60

Dixon, Floyd

EMPTY STOCKING BLUES.
Tracks: / Doin' the town / You need me now / Milky white way / Walkin' and talkin' blues / I saw stars / Married woman / Don't cry now baby / Precious Lord / Empty stocking blues / She's understanding / Time and place / Red cherries / I'm so worried / San Francisco blues / Hard living alone / Do I love you.
LP: . . . . KIX 27

HOUSTON JUMP.
Tracks: / Houston jump / Red head 'n' Cadillac / Mississippi blues / Girl fifteen / Sad journey / Tired broke and busted / It's getting foggy / Pleasure days / River, The / Rockin' at home / Come back baby / Roll baby roll / Is it true / Alarm clock blues / I'm ashamed of myself / Tight skirts.
LP: . . . . KIX 11

OPPORTUNITY BLUES.
Tracks: / Dallas blues / Shuffle boogie / Prairie dog hole / Broken hearted / Lovin' / Let's dance / Bad neighbourhood / Blues for Cuba / Real lovin' mama / Telephone blues / Too much jelly roll / Baby lets go down to the woods / Wine wine wine / Moonshine / Ooh little girl / Opportunity blues.
LP: . . . . KIX 1

ROCKIN' THIS JOINT TONITE (See under Thomas, Kid) (Valentine, Kid Thomas, Floyd Dixon & Ace Holder).

Dixon House Band

FIGHTING ALONE.
LP: . . . . INS 2006

Dixon, Jessy

AIN'T GOT TIME TO DIE.
LP: . . . . RMLP 030
MC: . . . . RMC 030

IT'S ALL RIGHT NOW.
Tracks: / I expect to see him / He'll be right there / Father me / I'm satisfied / Hold on / It's all right / Come to me / Lord, You've been so good to me / Born again / He has done great things.
LP: . . . . LS 7045
MC: . . . . LC 7045

SANCTUARY.
LP: . . . . PWRO 1072
MC: . . . . PWCO 1072

SATISFIED (LIVE).
Tracks: / Satisfied / It's so good / Through the blood / I want to get to know you / Heavenly dove / He really didn't have to die / What do you call Him? / I choose to follow you / Jesus is alive and well / Operator.
LP: . . . . LS 7065
MC: . . . . LC 7065

SILENT PARTNER.
LP: . . . . PWRO 1078
MC: . . . . PWCO 1078

WINNING SIDE, THE.
LP: . . . . PWRO 1091
MC: . . . . PWCO 1091

Dixon, Mary

COMPLETE BLUES SESSIONS (See under Bentley, Gladys) (Dixon, Mary & Gladys Bentley).

Dixon, Prince

IT'S A SAD SITUATION.
LP: . . . . JOLIET 5001

Dixon, Reginald

AT THE MOVIES.
Tracks: / Those magnificent men in their flying machines / Love is a many splendoured thing / Green leaves of summer / Hi lili hi lo / Unforgiven, The / Three coins in the fountain / Man and a woman, A / Entertainer, The / Alone / High and mighty / Raindrops keep falling on my head / Big country, The / Speak softly love / Love theme / Friendly persuasion / Good, the bad and the ugly, The.
LP: . . . . OU 2132

AT THE ORGAN OF THE TOWER BALLROOM, BLACKPOOL.
Tracks: / Chattanooga choo choo / Breeze and I / Keep your sunny side up / With sword and lance, march / Gold and silver waltz / Thunder and lightning polka / Forgotten dreams / Spanish gypsy dance / Marche Lorraine / El Abanico / Old comrades / Sons of the brave / Funiculi funiculi / Serenade No. 1 Op. 21 / Colonel Bogey / Eton boating song / Little girl / As time goes by / When I take my sugar to tea / Happy feet / Manhattan / Boo hoo / Le cygne (From Carnival Of The Animals) / Dambusters march / Holiday for strings / By the fireside / Walkin' my baby back home / Five foot two, eyes of blue / Clair de Lune / Country gardens / Ciribiribin / Rustle of spring (fruhlingsrauschen) / Blaze away / Who were you with last night (CD only.) / Side by side (CD only.) / Deep in the heart of Texas (CD only.) / Let me call you sweetheart (CD only.) / Put your arms around me honey (CD only.) / (Gang that sang) heart of my heart (CD only.).
MC: . . . . TCIDL 112

BLACKPOOL NIGHTS.
Tracks: / Chicago / Wyoming / Merry widow selection / Blaze away / Good morning / Sweet Sue / Sympathy / Paradise / Mexicali rose / Wonderful rose / Home / Diane / Whispering / Fascination / Avalon.
LP: . . . . EG 2604781
MC: . . . . EG 2604784

BLAZE AWAY.
MC: . . . . TC ONCR 509

FAREWELL MR BLACKPOOL.
Tracks: / I do like to be beside the seaside / Pigalle / Lullaby of Broadway / Carolina moon / Toot toot tootsie goodbye / Dream of Olwen / South of the border / Stein song, The / Wistful waltz, The / Storm at sea, The / Jack's the lad / Drunken sailor / Anchors aweigh / Skye boat song / Fingal's cave / Imperial echoes / Whispering / Beer barrel polka / Charmaine / Harry Lime theme / Minuet / Darktown strutters' ball / Anniversary waltz / MacNamara's band / I kiss your hand Madame / Happy days are here again / When the saints go marching in / I do like to be beside the seaside.
LP: . . . . SCX 6387

FASCINATING RHYTHM.
MC: . . . . 4 BUR 018
LP: . . . . BUR 018

GREAT ORGAN FAVOURITES.
Tracks: / Samum / Liebesfreud / Finlandia / Music from heaven / Intermezzo / Orpheus in the underworld / Rustle of spring / Andantino in D flat / Trumpet voluntary.
LP: . . . . OU 2166

HOUR OF TOWER BALLROOM FAVOURITES, AN.
Tracks: / Tiger rag / Autumn leaves / Dardanella / Elizabethan Serenade / La paloma / Russian rag / Peanut vendor / Wedding of the painted doll, The / These foolish things / Temptation rag / Sabre dance / Czardas / Sweet and lonely / Canadian capers / Moonlight serenade / Continental, The / Jealousy / 12th Street rag / Deep purple / Cherokee / Toy trumpet, The / Stardust.
MC: . . . . HR 8119
MC: . . . . HR 4181194

ISN'T THIS A LOVELY DAY.
Tracks: / Say it with music / Way you look tonight / C'est si bon / Goodnight Vienna / Sun has got his hat on, The / Shadow waltz / It only happens when I dance with you / Broken doll / When somebody thinks you're wonderful / Cuban love song / Are you lonesome tonight.
MC: . . . . TCNTS 205
LP: . . . . NTS 205

MAGIC OF REGINALD DIXON, THE.
Tracks: / Over the waves / Que sera sera / My resistance is low / At sundown / Dancing with tears in my eyes / Pasadena / Bewitched / Pretty girl is like a melody, A / Is it true what they say about Dixie? / Sweet and lovely / Broadway melody / I can't give you anything but love / Peg o' my heart / Red roses for a blue lady / Sunshine of your smile, The / Second hand Rose / There, I've said it again / Yes sir, that's my baby / This is my lovely day / Shine / You can't stop me from dreaming / When you wore a tulip / Guilty / If you knew Susie / Happy days and lonely nights / On a slow boat to China / Nobody's sweetheart / Shepherd of the hills / Alice blue gown / Bill Bailey, won't you please come home? / Am I wasting my time on you? / My sweetie went away / Oh Johnny, oh Johnny oh / Glad rag doll / Time on my hands / Jeepers creepers / Amazing grace / Old rugged cross, The / I do like to be beside the seaside / Pigalle / Lullaby of Broadway / Carolina moon / Toot toot tootsie / Dream of Olwen / South of the border / Stein song, The / Wistful waltz, The / Storm at sea, The / Life on the ocean wave, A / Jack's the lad / Drunken sailor / Anchors aweigh / Skye boat song / Fingal's cave / Imperial echoes / Whispering / Beer barrel polka / Charmaine / Harry Lime theme / Minuet / Darktown strutters' ball / Anniversary waltz / Macnamara's band / I kiss your hand madame / Happy days are here again / When the saints go marching in / I do like to be beside the seaside.
2LP: . . . . DL 41 1060 3
MC: . . . . DL 41 1060 9
MC: . . . . TCDL 1060

OVER THE WAVES.
Tracks: / Over the waves / Under the linden tree / Continental, The / Peanut vendor / Sophisticated lady / Toy trumpet, The / Sanctuary of the heart / Blaze away / King Cotton / Spartacus love theme / Flea market, The / Cherokee / Tristesse / Wedding of the painted doll, The / Moonlight serenade / Symphonic poem / Samum.
LP: . . . . ONCR 534
MC: . . . . TC ONCR 534

PLAY A SIMPLE MELODY.
Tracks: / Lady in red / Very thought of you / My mother's eyes / Bench in the park / Falling in love again / Over my shoulder / Once in a while / They say it's wonderful / Moonglow / I'm gonna sit right down / Just one of those things.
MC: . . . . TCNTS 183
LP: . . . . NTS 183

RECOLLECTIONS OF THE TOWER, BLACKPOOL (Dixon, Reginald/Ernest Broadbent/Eric Lord).
Tracks: / I do like to be beside the seaside / Happy days are here again / Canadian capers / White cliffs of Dover, The / Tulips from Amsterdam / For you / Keep your sunny side up / Riding on a rainbow / Mozart forty / Vandervalk theme / Jolly brothers, The / Pip.
MC: . . . . AC 199

REGINALD DIXON AT THE WURLITZER ORGAN (Tower Ballroom).
MC: . . . . TCIDL 16

SENTIMENTAL JOURNEY.
MC: . . . . TC OU 2218

SING ALONG AT THE TOWER.
Tracks: / Lily of Laguna / Put your arms around me, honey / Roamin' in the gloamin' / Waiting for the Robert E. Lee / My mammy / Two lovely black eyes / You were meant for me / Gang that sang heart of my heart, The / Mexicali rose / Daddy wouldn't buy me a bow-wow / Swanee / Pack up your troubles in your old kit bag / Maybe it's because I'm a Londoner / Me and my shadow / You made me love you / I belong to Glasgow / Man who broke the bank at Monte Carlo, The / Daisy bell / Five foot two, eyes of blue / I love a lassie / It happened in Monterey / Pretty baby / Memories / Peggy O'Neill / End of the road / When you're smiling / For me and my gal / She's a lassie from Lancashire / Who's sorry now / Oh You beautiful doll / Let the rest of the world go by / Nellie Dean / I'll be your sweetheart / Margie / I wonder who's kissing her now / Avalon / When Irish eyes are smiling / On Ilkley Moor baht'at / In a shanty in old Shantytown / I'm forever blowing bubbles / If you were the only girl in the world / By the light of the silvery moon / Who were you with last night / It's a long way to Tipperary / Sheik of Araby, The / You must have been a beautiful baby / When day is done / Abide with me / I do like to be beside the seaside.
LP: . . . . EMS 106 929 1
MC: . . . . TCEMS 1069294

Dixon, Willie

BIG THREE TRIO, THE.
MC: 4672484

BLUES EVERY WHICH WAY, THE (see under Slim, Memphis.

COLLECTION: WILLIE DIXON (20 Blues Greats).
Tracks: / Little red rooster / Built for comfort / Wang dang doodle / Ain't superstitious / Evil / Walking the blues / Fiery love / Alone / Mannish boy / All aboard / Rock me / I love the life I live / Sugar sweet / Thunderbird / One more / Teenage beat / Snake dancer / Temperature / Rock bottom / Black angel blues.
LP: . . . . DVLP 2092
MC: . . . . DVMC 2092

GINGER ALE AFTERNOON (Film soundtrack).
LP: . . . . VS 5234
MC: . . . . VSC 5234

HIDDEN CHARMS.
LP: . . . . ORELP 515
MC: . . . . OREC 515

WILLIE DIXON BOX SET.
MCSET: . . . . CH 316500

WILLIE'S BLUES (Dixon, Willie & Memphis Slim).
Tracks: / Nervous / Good understanding / That's my baby / Slim's thing / That's all I want baby / Don't you tell nobody / Youth to you / Sittin' and cryin' the blues / Bluit for comfort / I got a razor / Go easy / Move me.
LP: . . . . OBC 501

Diz & The Doormen

CHALK FARM FIESTA.
Tracks: / What have I done to you? / Mardi Gras in New Orleans / She walked right in / Are you going my way? / Swanee River jump / Bluecoat man / Go on, fool / Byrd's bop / Sick and tired / Blow wind blow.
LP: . . . . CH 54

Dizrhythmia

DIZRHYTHMIA.
Tracks: / Dizrhythmia / Standing in the rain / It will only end in tears / Walking on the cracks / 8000 miles / What Katy did next / Grown man, A.
LP: . . . . AN 8727
MC: . . . . ANC 8727

Dizzy

DIZZY (Various artists).
LP: . . . . CE 2458

Dizzy Satellites

CRISIS IN UTOPIA.
LP: . . . . MMLP 007

DIZZNEY WORLD.
Tracks: / (Running at the) speed of life / It's alright / Ballad of hate and revenge / Over under sideways down / Live this life without you / You don't know (how dumb you are) / Everybody needs a kleiner schatzi / Shark fin ride / Time has come (original) / Nothing left to do / E.P couldn't f**k / Pictures of the past.
LP: . . . . MMLP 027

ORBIT DRIVE.
LP: . . . . MMLP 004

D.J. Cheese

COAST TO COAST (see Word of Mouth featuring D.J.Cheese) (D.J. Cheese/ Word Of Mouth).

D.J. Jazzy Jeff

HE'S THE DJ, I'M THE RAPPER (D.J. Jazzy Jeff & Fresh Prince).
Tracks: / D.J. on the wheels / My Buddy / Rhythm Trax / He's The DJ I'm The Rapper / Hip hop dancer's theme / Jazzy's in the house / Human video game.
LP: . . . . HIP 61
MC: . . . . HIPC 61

HOME BASE (D.J. Jazzy Jeff & Fresh Prince).
LP: . . . . HIP 116
MC: . . . . HIPC 116

ROCK THE HOUSE (D.J. Jazzy Jeff & Fresh Prince).
LP: . . . . CHAMP 1004
MC: . . . . CHAMPK 1004

D.J. Quik

QUIK IS THE NAME.
LP: . . . . FILER 402
MC: . . . . FILERCT 402

D.J. Rob

SILK SMOOTH (See under Luv, Monte) (D.J. Rob & Monte Luv).

Djanana, Djuna

NORMAL, NORMAL.
LP: . . . . AMG 012

Django (film)

DJANGO (Original soundtrack) (Various artists).
LP: . . . . IMGM 002

DJANGO SPARA PER PRIMO (HE SHOOTS FIRST) (Original soundtrack) (Various artists).
LP: . . . . IM 012

DJANGO'S REVENGE (Original soundtrack) (Various artists).
LP: . . . . CST 8030

Djavan

BIRD OF PARADISE.
Tracks: / Carnival in Rio / Bird of paradise / Madness / Stephen's

kingdom / Take me / Bouquet / I will I won't / Miss Susanna.
LP: 4611421
MC: 4611424

FLOR DE LIS.
LP: 7702

PUZZLE OF HEARTS.
Tracks: / Corisco / Being cool / Memento / Puzzle of hearts / Vida real / Amazon farewell / Been so blue / Voce bem sabe / Mal de mim / Oceano.
LP: 4669361
MC: 4669364

DMC (label)

DMC-5 (Various artists).
LP: . . . . DMCAST 001

Dmochowski, Jedrez

STALLIONS OF MY HEART.
Tracks: / Golly gosh / Goodbye to today / You are a failure / My guitar / East wind / Part of the world / Ruined city / I'm perfect / I'm sad / Forever / 85 years.
LP: . . . . WHAAM LP 04

D'Molls

D'MOLLS.
LP: 781 791-1

DMZ

DMZ.
Tracks: / Mighty idy / Bad attitude / Watch for me girl / Cinderella / Don't jump me mother / Destroyer / Baby boom / Our of our tree / Borderline / Do not enter / From home.
LP: . . . . SRK 6051

RELICS.
LP: . . . . VOXX 200004

DNA

PARTY TESTED.
Tracks: / Doctor's of the universe / Intellectual freedom for the masses / Rock 'n' roll (part 2) / Song that wrote itself, The / Party tested / Recipe for life, The / What about.
LP: . . . . POLD 5129
MC: . . . . POLDC 5129

D-Nice

CALL ME D-NICE.
LP: . . . . HIP 104
MC: . . . . HIPC 104

Do7 Shirati Luo Jazz

KENYAFRICA (VOL.4).
LP: . . . . PS 33004

Do I Hear A Waltz

DO I HEAR A WALTZ (Original Broadway cast) (Various artists).
LP: . . . . AKOS 2770
MC: . . . . BT 2770

Do Patent Black

DO PATENT BLACK SHOES (Original Broadway cast) (Various artists).
LP: . . . . DP 18852

Do Re Mi

DOMESTIC HARMONY.
Tracks: / Uncle Jim, Theme from / After the volcano / Idiot grin (CD only) / Cuttlefish beach / Warnings moving clockwise / Black crocodiles / Big accident / Racing to zero / New taboos / 1000 mouths / No fury (CD only) / Shake this place (CD only) / Man overboard (12" version) (CD only) / Burning the blues (CD only) / Man overboard.
LP: . . . . V 2367
MC: . . . . TCV 2367
LP: . . . . OVED 246
MC: . . . . OVEDC 246

HAPPIEST PLACE IN TOWN, THE.
Tracks: / Haunt you / King of Moomba / Adultery / Valentine's day / Take me anywhere / Heads will roll / Disneyland / Wild and blue / Desert song, The / Friends like you / That hanging business / Happiest place in town, The.
LP: . . . . V 2467
MC: . . . . TCV 2467

Do The Right Thing

DO THE RIGHT THING (1989 Film Soundtrack) (Various artists).
Tracks: / Fight the power: *Public Enemy* / My fantasy: *Riley, Teddy Featuring Guy* / Party hearty: *E.U.* / Can't stand it: *Steel Pulse* / Prove to me: *Perri* / We love (jingle): *Take 6* / Feel so good: *Perri* / Don't shoot me: *Take 6* / Hard to say: *Perry, Lori & Gerald Alston* / Why don't we try: *John, Keith* / Never explain love: *Jarreau, Al* / Tu y yo: *Blades, Ruben.*
LP: . . . . ZL 72665
MC: . . . . ZK 72665
LP: . . . . MOT 6272

Do They Mean Us?

DO THEY MEAN US? (Various artists).
LP: . . . . PACT 6

D.O.A.

ANCIENT BEAUTY.
MC: . . . . CPH 9004
LP: . . . . PH 9004

BLOODIED BUT UNBOWED.
Tracks: / Everything went black / Prisoner, The / Slumlord / Watcha gonna do? / Two plus two / Smash the state.
LP: . . . . VIRUS 31

COMPANIONS OF THE CRIMSON COLOURED ARK.
MC: . . . . CPH 9009
LP: . . . . PH 9009

LIGHT UPON LIGHT.
LP: . . . . PH 1056
MC: . . . . PH 1056C

MURDER.
LP: . . . . LS 94131

ORNAMENT OF HOPE.
LP: . . . . PH 9000
MC: . . . . PH 9000C

WAR ON 45.
LP: . . . . VIRUS 24

Dobrogosz, Steve

FINAL TOUCH (Dobrogosz, Steve & Berit Andersson).
LP: . . . . DRLP 177

Dobson, Anita

ON MY OWN (LP).
LP: . . . . STAR 2277
MC: . . . . STAC 2277

TALKING OF LOVE.
Tracks: / Talking of love / Last time I made love, The / You can't stay the night / I dream of Christmas / Funny old life ain't it / Let me in (your heart again) / To know him is to love him / Don't fall in love with anybody else / Anyone can fall in love.
LP: . . . . ODN 1007
MC: . . . . TCODN 1007

Dobson, Dobby

SWEET DREAMS.
LP: . . . . SRLLP 2

Dobson, Scott

SON OF GEORDIE.
LP: . . . . MWM 1004

D.O.C.

NO ONE CAN DO IT BETTER.
LP: 7913081
MC: 7913084

Doc Box & B Fresh

DOC BOX & B FRESH.
Tracks: / Time to get smart / Doc's dope jam / Slow love / Nu Jack / I'm a survivor / Doc says dance / She's not my lover / Darlene / Mission impossible, A.
LP: . . . . ZL 72693
MC: . . . . ZK 72693

Doc Dart

PATRICIA.
LP: . . . . VIRUS 079

Doc, John

JOHN DOC AT THE CAROUSEL.
Tracks: / Sweet Caroline / Going nowhere / If / Lyin' eyes / Spanish eyes / My world gets smaller / Love story.
LP: . . . . NEVLP 117

Docherty, Con

CINEMA ORGAN ENCORES.
LP: . . . . DEROY 1106

CINEMA ORGAN FAVOURITES.
LP: . . . . DEROY 856

Docherty, Terry

TELLER OF TALES, THE.
LP: . . . . FE 001

TERRY DOCHERTY COLLECTION, THE.
MC: C2016/C

Docker, Bob

QUINTETTE DU HOT CLUB A'ANGLETERRE.
Tracks: / What this thing called love / Djangology / I'm confessin' / What kind of a friend / Anouman / Sweet Georgia Brown / Baby won't you please come home / Manoir de mes reves / I saw stars / Finesse.
LP: . . . . SPJ 534

Doctor No (film)

DOCTOR NO (Film soundtrack) (Various artists).
Tracks: / James Bond theme: *Various artists* / Kingston calypso: *Various artists* / Island speaks, The: *Various artists* / Under the mango tree: *Various artists* / Jump up: *Various artists* / Doctor No's fantasy: *Various artists* / Boy chase: *Various artists* / Love at last: *Various artists* / Jamaican rock: *Various artists* / Audio bongo: *Various artists* / Twisting with James: *Various artists* / Jamaica jazz: *Various artists.*

LP: . . . . EMS 1265
MC: . . . . TCEMS 1265
LP: 1C 054 82922

Doctor On Approval

DOCTOR ON APPROVAL McConnell, Jean (McConnell, Jean).
MCSET: . . . . SOUND 31

Doctor Snuggles (bk)

ADVENTURES OF DOCTOR SNUGGLES (See under Adventures of ...) (Craven, John (nar)).

Dodd, Dr. Billy

AT GRAND OPERAHOUSE (Dodd, Doctor Billy & His Friends).
LP: . . . . J 162

DOCTOR BILLY DODD & HIS FRIENDS (Dodd, Doctor Billy & His Friends).
LP: . . . . J 130

Dodd, Ken

20 GOLDEN GREATS: KEN DODD.
Tracks: / Tears / Eight by ten / You're my best friend / Just out of reach / Happiness / Remember I love you / More than love / Still / Pianissimo / Love is like a violin / River, The / Promises / Broken hearted / When love's round again / Think of me wherever you are / Matchstalk men and matchstalk cats and dogs / Let me cry on your shoulder / Tears won't wash away my heartache / So deep is the night / It is no secret.
LP: . . . . WW 5098
LP: . . . . STAR 2392
MC: . . . . STAC 2392

FOR SOMEONE SPECIAL.
LP: . . . . SCX 6224

GREATEST HITS: KEN DODD (An Hour of Hits).
Tracks: / Happiness / Love is like a violin / Somewhere my love / River, The / Eight by ten / They didn't believe me / As time goes by / I wish you love / More than ever / So deep is the night / Tears / Still / Broken hearted / She / Old fashioned way, The / For all we know / What a wonderful world / Happy days and lonely nights / Just out of reach / Let me cry on your shoulder / Promises.
MC: . . . . HR 8107
MC: . . . . HR 4181074

HAPPY MOTORING.
MC: . . . . TC-MMC 5006

HITS FOR NOW AND ALWAYS.
LP: . . . . SX 6060

KEN DODD.
Tracks: / Broken hearted / Eight by ten / Try to remember / Beautiful dreamer / Love is like a violin / Story of a starry night / Love me with all your heart / Happiness / Still / Old fashioned way, The / Tears / Think of me (wherever you are) / River, The / She / Tears won't wash away these heartaches / Somewhere my love / What a wonderful world / So deep is the night / When love comes round / Until it's time for you to go / Very thought of you, The / Just out of reach / Only you / I can't begin to tell you.
MC: . . . . TC IDL 21

KEN DODD COLLECTION.
Tracks: / Beautiful dreamer / So deep is the night / Try to remember / Once in a while / Story of a starry night / In the morning / Romantica / Very thought of you, The / If I had my way / Because I love you / When love comes round again / I'm always chasing rainbows / Dancing with tears in my eyes / Four strong winds / Sunrise, sunset / What a wonderful world.
LP: . . . . OU 2077

MORE THAN EVER.
Tracks: / More than ever / Still / River, The / Eight by ten / So deep is the night / Viva Espana / Younger than Springtime / Try to remember / If I had my way / Someone like you / I wonder who's kissing her now / Sunrise, sunset / She / Love me with all your heart / Old-fashioned way, The / For all we know / Beautiful dreamer / Very thought of you, The / Story of a starry night / I don't know why / I'll be seeing you / Dancing with tears in my eyes / One I love belongs to somebody else, The / What a wonderful world.
2LP: . . . . MFP 1021
MCSET: . . . . TCMFP 1021

NOW AND FOREVER.
Tracks: / Now and forever / Perhaps love / Twelfth of never / I wish it could be yesterday today / Scarlet ribbons / Here is my heart / Key, The / Trust in my love / Colours of my life / I thought you loved me / Goodnight my love / One love for me.
LP: . . . . VIR 83002
MC: . . . . ZCVIR 83002

TEARS OF HAPPINESS.
LP: 33SX 1793

VERY BEST OF KEN DODD, THE.
Tracks: / Happiness / Love is like a violin / Somewhere my love / River, The / There are secrets / Eight by ten / Those golden days / Azzuro / Still / Broken hearted / This is our dance / When love comes round again / Pink and pleasant lane, A / Tears.
LP: . . . . MFP 5628
MC: . . . . TCMFP 5628
LP: . . . . MFP 4156281

Doddington, Paula

SEPARATION (Karpf, Eve).
MCSET: . . . . MRC 1042

Dodds, Baby

JAZZ A LA CREOLE DONEWELL (Dodds, Baby Trio).
LP: . . . . GHB 50

Dodds, David

SPORTING DOGS.
MC: 45-126

Dodds, Johnny

BLUE CLARINET STOMP (1926-1928).
Tracks: / Weary blues / New Orleans Stomp / Wild man blues / Melancholy / Come on and stomp, stomp, stomp / After you've gone / Joe Turner blues / When Erastus plays his old kazoo / Blue clarinet stomp / Blue piano stomp / Bucktown stomp / Weary city / Bull fiddle blues / Blue washboard stomp / Sweet Lorraine / Pencil papa / My little Isabel-A / Heah' me talking / Goober dance / Too tight-A.
LP: . . . . VLP 61

BLUE CLARINET STOMP (2).
Tracks: / Blue clarinet stomp (take 1) / Blue clarinet stomp (take 2) / Blue piano stomp / Wolverine blues / Mr Jelly Lord / Bucktown stomp / Weary city / Blue fiddle blues / Blue washboard stomp / Memphis shake / Carpet alley breakdown / Hen party blues / Sweet Lorraine / My little Isobel / Pencil papa / Heah' me talkin' (take 3) / Heah' me talkin' (take 4) / Goober dance / Too tight / Indigo stomp (take 1) / Indigo stomp (take 2).
LP: . . . . NL 82293
MC: . . . . NK 82293

IMMORTAL, THE.
LP: . . . . VLP 48
LP: . . . . M 2002

JAZZ CLASSICS IN DIGITAL STEREO (Johnny Dodds 1923-1929).
LP: . . . . REB 603
MC: . . . . ZCF 603

JIMMIE NOONE & JOHNNY DODDS (See Under Noone, Jimmie) (Dodds, Johnny & Jimmie Noone).

JOHNNY DODDS (1927) (Dodds, Johnny with his Trio).
Tracks: / Weary blues / New Orleans stomp / Wild man blues / Melancholy / Come on and stomp, stomp, stomp / After you've gone / Joe Turner blues / When Erastus plays his old kazoo / Oh Lizzie / Clarinet wobble / New St Louis blues.
LP: . . . . S 808

JOHNNY DODDS (1926-28).
Tracks: / Perdido street blues / Gatemouth / Too tight / Papa dip / Mixed salad / I can't say / Flatfoot / Mad dog / Ballin' the jack / Grandma's ball / My baby / Oriental man / Get 'em again blues / Brush stomp / My girl / Sweep 'em clean / Lady love / Brown bottom Bess.
LP: . . . . S 807

JOHNNY DODDS 1928-29.
LP: . . . . S 848

JOHNNY DODDS VOL 1.
LP: . . . . CJM 32

MYTH OF NEW ORLEANS, THE.
LP: . . . . LPJT 47

STOMP TIME.
Tracks: / Bohunkus blues / Buddy Burton's jazz / East Coast trot / Chicago buzz / Apeman / Your folks / Steal away / Salty dog / Stomp time blues / It must be the blues / Loveless love / 119th Street blues / There'll come a day / Weary way blues / Oriental man / Sock that thing.
LP: . . . . RHA 6024

Dodge, Jim

F U P.
MC: 2029

Dodge, Mary M. (aut)

SILVER SKATES, THE (see under Silver Skates (bk)) (Bloom, Claire (nar)).

Doe, John

MEET JOHN DOE.
LP: 7599242911
MC: 7599242914

Dog Age

GOOD DAY.
LP: . . . . **VOW 016**

Dog Crusoe

DOG CRUSOE, THE (R.M. Ballantyne) (Boland, Arthur).
MCSET: . . . . **COL 3007**

Dog Faced Hermans

EVERYDAY TIMEBOMB.
LP: . . . . **SUK 007**

Dogbowl

TIT (AN OPERA).
Tracks: / On the monkeybars / Starving for love / Obsessed with girls / Oklahoma / Under the water / Girl with the pelican hair, The / Miss you so much (I can die) / Growing up in a wheelchair / Krystellina / When the Romans died / Anastasia / Sex gorillas / Dolphin / Daytime / I had a dream of the plague / Flowers for Katrinka.
LP: . . . . **SDE 023**

Dogger, Bunk

FIRST OFFENCE.
Tracks: / Foolish night, The / French lessons / You know the sandman / Night and day / Smokey Joe's cafe / You did the dirty on Don / (You fell in love with) The bassman / Don't say it never happened / Samba to December / Where do you get your sweetness / Besame mucho / Special, The.
LP: . . . . **PL 25138**
MC: . . . . **PK 25138**

GREAT DETECTIVE.
Tracks: / Women in uniform / Dance music / With one bound he was free / Mobile home / Magazine articles / Send in the clones / Blue movies / People of all nations / Break the spell / Headlining / Please don't tease / Young blood.
LP: . . . . **PL 25298**

Doggett, Bill

14 ORIGINAL GREATEST HITS: BILL DOGGETT.
LP: . . . . **K 5009**

16 BANDSTAND FAVOURITES.
LP: . . . . **SLP 3023**
MC: . . . . **GT 53023**

AS YOU DESIRE ME.
Tracks: / I hadn't anyone till you / Yesterdays / Alone / As time goes by / Dedicated to you / Sweet and lovely / Cottage for sale / As you desire me / Dream / Don't blame me / This love of mine / Fools rush in.
LP: . . . . **SING 523**

BILL DOGGETT.
LP: . . . . **BID 8009**

DAME DREAMING.
Tracks: / Sweet Lorraine / Diane / Dinah / Kamona / Cherry / Cynthia / Jeannine / Tangerine / Nancy / Estrellita / Laura / Marcheta.
LP: . . . . **SING 532**

DANCE A WHILE.
Tracks: / Flying home / Misty moon / Bone tones / Tailor made / Chelsea bridge / Kid from Franklin Street, The / Pied piper of Islip / Passion flower / Song is ended, The / Autumn leaves / How could you? / Smoochie.
LP: . . . . **SING 585**

DOGGETT BEAT FOR HAPPY FEAT, THE.
Tracks: / Soft / And the angels sing / Ding dong / Honey / Easy / Hammerhead / Ram-bunk-shush / Chloe / Hot ginger / King Bee / What a diff'rence a day made / Shinding.
LP: . . . . **SING 557**

EARL BOSTIC/ BILL DOGGET (See under Bostic, Earl).

GOIN' DOGGETT.
Tracks: / Honky tonk (part 1) / Honky tonk (part 2) / Big boy / Slidin' / Buttered popcorn / Backwoods / Slow walk / Quaker city / Night train / Ram-bunk-shush / Peacock alley / Hold it / Rainbow riot.
LP: . . . . **CRB 1094**
MC: . . . . **TCCRB 1094**

MR. HONKY TONK.
LP: **33562**

Doggy Style

LAST LAUGH.
LP: . . . . **NT 891**

Doggy Stylers

UP FROM BEHIND.
Tracks: / Shit / Despair / Wild thing / Mask / Summer of '86 / Life / Happy people / Dead to the world.
LPS: . . . . **DOGGY 286**

Dogmatics

EVERYBODY DOES IT.
LP: . . . . **HMS 049**

THAYER STREET.
LP: . . . . **HMS 003**

Dogs

TOO MUCH CLASS FOR THE NEIGHBOURHOOD.
Tracks: / Shakin' with Linda / Wanderin' / Robin / Most forgotton French boy, The / Gone gone gone / Sandy Sandy / Death Lane / Mad / Too much class for the neighbourhood / Home is where I want to be / Train kept a rollin' / Hesitation / Lonesome Angie / Poisoned town / When I came home.
LP: . . . . **EPC 85241**

Dogs D'Amour

BOOTLEG ALBUM.
Tracks: / Firework girl / Chains / Gold / Pourin' out my heart / Wait until I'm dead / How do you fall in love again? / Kiss this joint / Heroine / Tales of destruction / Dynamite jet saloon / Swingin' the bottle.
LP: . . . . **WOL 7**

DOG'S HITS AND THE BOOTLEG ALBUM.
LP: . . . . **WOL 1020**
MC: . . . . **WOLMC 1020**

ERROL FLYNN.
Tracks: / Drunk like me / Hurricane / Errol Flynn / Princess valium / Trail of tears / Prettiest girl in the world, The / Goddess from the gutter / Satellite kid / Planetary pied piper / Dogs hair / Ballad of Jack / Girl behind the glass.
LP: **8397001**
MC: **8397004**

GRAVEYARD OF EMPTY BOTTLES, A.
MLP: **8391741**
MC: **8390744**

IN THE DYNAMITE JET SALOON.
Tracks: / Debauchery / I don't want you to go / How come it never rains / Last bandit / Medicine man / Gonna get it right / Everything I want / Heartbreak / Billy two rivers / Wait until I'm dead / Sometimes (Only available on CD.) / Kid from Kensington, The (Only available on CD.) / State I'm in, The (Only available on CD.).
MC: . . . . **ZWOL 8**
LP: . . . . **WOL 8**
MC: . . . . **WOLMC 1004**

STRAIGHT.
LP: **8437961**
MC: **8437964**

Dogs In Space (film)

DOGS IN SPACE (1987 Film Soundtrack) (Various artists).
Tracks: / Dog food: *Pop, Iggy* / Dogs in space: *Various artists* / Win, lose: *Olsen, Ollie* / Anthrax: *Gang Of Four* / Skysaw: *Eno, Brian* / True love: *Marching Girls* / Shivers: *Boys Next Door* / Diseases: *Thrush and the Cunts* / Pumping ugly: *Primitive Calculators* / Golf course: *Hutchence, Michael* / Shivers: *Hoy, Marie and friends* / Endless sea: *Pop, Iggy* / Rooms for the memory: *Hutchence, Michael.*
LP: . . . . **CLPX 14**
LP: . . . . **MERH 122**
MC: . . . . **MERHC 122**

Dogwatch

PENFRIEND.
LP: . . . . **BHLP 002**

Doh Albert

COMMENT CA VA.
LP: . . . . **RZ 014**

Doherty, Al

SEEING THE COUNTRY.
Tracks: / Yonder comes a sucker / Alright / Just someone I used to know / Snowbird / Lorna Faye / You cheated me / Welcome to my world / I'm so afraid of losing you again / Shutters and boards / Wildwood flower / Our hearts belong together / Railroad bum / I was raised on country sunshine.
LP: . . . . **FHR 062**

Doherty, Jim

SPONDANCE (A Jazz Ballet) (Doherty, Jim with Louis Stewart & Bob Sheppard).
MC: . . . . **LRCS 10**

Doherty, John

BUNDLE AND GO.
Tracks: / Hudie Gallagher's march / Black mare of Fanad, The / March of the meena toiten bull, The / Kiss the maid behind the bier/The bargain is over / 21 Highland, The / Paps of Glencoe, The / Hare in the corn, The / Knights of St. Patrick / Dispute at the crossroads, The / Roaring Mary - stormy weather / Miss Patterson's slippers / Cat that kittled in Jamie's wig, The / Welcome home royal Charlie / Darby Gallagher / Teelin highland, The / Heathery breeze, The / Monaghan switch, The / Black haired lass, The / Paddy's rambles through the park.
LP: **12TS 398**

JOHN DOHERTY.
LP: . . . . **CEF 072**

JOHNNY DOHERTY.
LP: . . . . **CL 10**

PEDLAR'S PACK.
Tracks: / Stirling Castle / Grey daylight / Blackbird / Atlantic sounds / Moorlough Mary / Postman's knock / Girl's croon / Speaking waltz / Lord of Mayo / McSweeney's reel / Fox-hunt, The / Hare and the hounds, The / Old man rocking the cradle, The / Dark girl dressed in blue / Irish washerwoman, The / Wounded hussar / High level hornpipe / Madam Vanoni / Old hag and the churn, The / Four posts of the bed, The / Three O'Donnells / Welcome home.
MC: **60-074**

STAR OF DONEGAL.
Tracks: / Star, low-level and stepping stones hp / Lough Isle castle / Marry when you're young / Lord Gordon's reel / O'Halloran's reel / Yellow heifer / Cunningham's reel / Heart of my kitty / King of the pipers / Woods of Fanad / Nackers of Nevin / Dear Irish boy / Harvest morning / Napoleon's grand march / Boney crossing the Alps / Haste to the wedding / Bargain is made. the / Welcome home / Bonnie Kate / Salamanca reel / First of May / Boys of the loch / Miss Lyall / Bowing and bagpipes styles / Whistle o'er the lave o't / Dulaman ne beinne buidhe / Shan van vocht / Braes of Maas / Kitty's fancy / McSweeney's lament.
MC: **60-075**

Doherty, Michael

FIDDLER AND THE FAIRY (Doherty, Michael & John).
Tracks: / Flowers of Edinburgh / Little sheep / Paddy's rambles through the park / Easter snow / Fox chase, The / Wee weaver, The / Biddy of Muckross / Poor boy and millionaire's daughter, The / Twisting the hay rope / Girl was too smart for the fiddler, The / St. Colmkille and rope of hay / Peter Street / St. Colmkille and a three-week sleep / Hare and the hounds, The / Foxhunter's, The / St. Colmkille's two curses / McClouds / Broken bridge.
MC: **60-073**

Dojoji

DOJOJI (Dojoji/Lesley Woods).
LP: . . . . **KMH 7091284**

Dokken

BACK FOR THE ATTACK.
Tracks: / Kiss of death / Prisoner, The / Night by night / Standing in the shadows / Heaven sent / Mr. Scary / So many tears / Burning like a flame / Lost behind the wall / Stop fighting love / Cry of the gypsy / Sleepless nights / Dream warriors.
LP: . . . . **EKT 43**
MC: . . . . **EKT 43C**

BEAST FROM THE EAST.
Tracks: / Unchain the night / Kiss of death / Tooth and nail / When Heaven comes down / Standing in the shadows (Not available on CD.) / Into the fire / Sleepless nights (Not available on CD.) / Mr. Scary / Dream warriors / Heaven sent / It's not love / Alone again / Just got lucky / Breaking the chains / In my dreams / Turn on the action (Not available on CD.) / Walk away.
2LP: . . . . **EKT 55**
MC: . . . . **EKT 55 C**

BREAKIN' THE CHAINS.
Tracks: / Breakin' the chains / Seven thunders / I can see you / In the middle / We're illegal / Paris / Stick to your guns / Young girl / Felony / Nightrider.
LP: . . . . **CAL 136**

TOOTH AND NAIL.
Tracks: / Without warning / Tooth and nail / Just got lucky / Heartless heart / Don't close your eyes / When Heaven comes down / Into the fire / Bullets to spare / Alone again / Turn on the action.
LP: **9603761**

UNDER LOCK AND KEY.
Tracks: / Unchain the night / Hunter, The / In my dreams / Slippin' away / Lightning strikes again / It's not love / Jaded heart / Don't lie to me / Will the sun rise? / Till the livin' end.
MC: . . . . **EKT 28 C**
LP: . . . . **EKT 28**

Dokken, Don

UP FROM THE ASHES.
LP: **7599243011**
MC: **7599243014**
MC: . . . . **GEFC 24301**

Dolan, Joe

ALWAYS LOVED YOU.
Tracks: / She doesn't live here anymore / When you walk in the room / Over you / Is it raining in Paris tonight / Once upon a time / Always loved you / Never gonna let you go / Wait 'till the clouds roll by / Never get over you / I tell it like it used to be.
MC: . . . . **HMC 061**

ALWAYS ON MY MIND.
2LP: . . . . **HM 003D**

AT HIS BEST.
MC: . . . . **KMC 60**

CRAZY WOMAN.
Tracks: / Caterina ballerina / Bogie Mame / You belong to me, baby / Crazy woman / If I could put my life on paper / Be my fire / Sister Mary / Lady of the night / Morena / Goodbye Venice goodbye / Fly me Atlantic / My blue tango.
LP: . . . . **NSLP 18503**

GOLDEN HOUR - JOE DOLAN, VOL.1.
LP: . . . . **GH 581**

GOLDEN HOUR - JOE DOLAN, VOL.2.
LP: . . . . **GH 618**

GOLDEN HOUR OF JOE DOLAN, A.
Tracks: / Make me an island / Proud Mary / If you care a little bit about me / Bridge over troubled water / I'll be home in a day or so / Lover come back to me / My way / Love grows / Danny boy (Londonderry air) / You're such a good looking woman / Games people play / Here am I / Can't help falling in love / Something's burning / My first love / Make me act the fool / Wait for me / Love me tonight / You and the looking glass.
MC: . . . . **KGHMC 137**

I NEED YOU.
Tracks: / I need you / Lady in blue / Teresa / You belong to me, baby / Most wanted man in the USA, The / Sister Mary / Make me an island / Hush hush Maria / You're such a good looking woman / Goodbye Venice goodbye / Crazy woman / Sweet little rock 'n' roller.
LP: . . . . **NSPL 18538**

IT'S YOU, IT'S YOU, IT'S YOU..
LP: . . . . **RITZSP 416**
MC: . . . . **RITZSC 416**

LADY IN BLUE.
Tracks: / Sweet little rock 'n' roller / Lady in blue / Sixteen brothers / My darling Michelle / Send an angel of the Lord / Most wanted man in the USA, The / Lady Laura / Anuschka balalaika / Real good woman / Day time night time / Feeling I feel, The / Hush hush Maria.
LP: . . . . **NSPL 18461**

SILENT NIGHT (See under O'Sullivan, Gilbert).

THIS IS MY LIFE.
2LP: . . . . **HM 030D**

TURN OUT THE LIGHT.
LP: . . . . **NSPL 18611**

Dolby, Thomas

ALIENS ATE MY BUICK.
Tracks: / Key to her Ferrari / Airhead / Hot sauce / Pulp culture / My brain is like a sieve / Ability to swing, The / Budapest by blimp / May the cube be with you.
LP: . . . . **MTL 1020**
MC: . . . . **TCMTL 1020**

FIELD WORK (see Sakamoto, Ryuichi) (Dolby, Thomas/Ryuichi Sakamoto).

FLAT EARTH, THE.
Tracks: / Flat earth, The / Screen kiss / Mulu the rain forest / I scare myself / Hyperactive / White City / Dissidents.
LP: . . . . **PCS 240034 1**
MC: . . . . **TCPCS 240034 4**
LP: . . . . **ATAK 93**
MC: . . . . **TCATAK 93**
MC: . . . . **TCTD 1**

GOLDEN AGE OF WIRELESS, THE.
Tracks: / She blinded me with science / Radio silence / Airwaves / Flying north / Weightless / Europa and the pirate twins / Windpower / Commercial break-up / One of our submarines is missing / Cloudburst at Shingle Street.
LP: . . . . **FA 3182**
MC: . . . . **TCFA 3182**
LP: . . . . **VIP 107 607 1**
MC: . . . . **TC VIP 107 607 41**
LP: . . . . **VIP 1001**

GOTHIC (Film soundtrack).
Tracks: / Fantasmagoria / Byronic love / Shelleymania / Mary's theme / Party games / Gipsy girl / Crucifix / Fundamental source, The / Sin and buggery / Impalement / Leech juice / Restless sleep 1,2 & 3 / It's his! / Coitus per stigmata / Once we vowed eternal love / Riddled with guilt / Metamorphosis / Hangman / Beast in the crypt, The / Final seance, The / Funeral by the lake /

No ghosts in daylight / To the grave / Devil is an Englishman, The (Featuring Screamin' Lord Byron) / Skull pulse / Trickle of blood, A.
LP: OVED 229
MC: OVEDC 229
LP: V 2417
MC: TCV 2417

Dolce, Joe

CHRISTMAS ALBUM, THE.
Tracks: / Jingle bell rock / I saw mommy kissing Santa Claus / This time of the year / Silent night / Christmas medley / Twelve days of Christmas, The / Christmas in Australia / Christmas at our house / Blue Christmas / Open up your heart.
LP: BUSLP 1001
MC: ZCBUS 1001

SHADDUP YOU FACE.
Tracks: / If you want to be happy / Reggae Matilda / Shaddup you face / Ain't been missing you / Return (part 1) / Return (part 2) / Ain't no UFO gonna catch my diesel / Stick it out / Blue world / Boat people.
LP: EPC 85109
MC: 40 85109

Dole

SPEED OF HOPE.
LP: BIAS 027

Dolf

TIEN TOFFE GITAARMELBIEEN.
LP: K 031/111

Doll

LISTEN TO THE SILENCE.
Tracks: / One kiss / Zero heroes / Ce soir, cheri / Cinderella with a husky voice / Memories / You used to be my hero / True love / Frozen fire / Carmina / Listen to the silence / Something rare, something beautiful.
LP: BEGA 12

Doll, Andy & Friends

ROCKIN' ROCKIN'.
LP: WLP 8832

Doll By Doll

DOLL BY DOLL.
Tracks: / Figure it out / Caritas / Soon new life / Main travelled roads / Those in peril / I never saw the movie / Perfect romance / Fantastic sensation / Street I love / Be my friend / Up / Bright green field, A.
LP: MAGL 5039
MC: ZCMAG 5039

GRAND PASSION.
Tracks: / Strong hands / Under my thumb / Dancing shoes / Cool skies / Eternal / Lonely kind of show / Natural / Grand passion / City of light / Dawn of the rain girls / Boxers hit harder when women are around / So long, kid.
LP: MAGL 5047
MC: ZCMAG 5047

GYPSY BLOOD.
Tracks: / Teenage lightning / Gypsy blood / Strip show / Human face, The / Hey sweetheart / Binary fiction / Hell games / Highland rain / Endgame / When a man dies.
LP: K 56755

REMEMBER.
Tracks: / Butcher boy / Chances / Sleeping partners / More than human / Lose myself / Janice / Place of love, The.
LP: K 56618
MC: K4 56618

Dollar

DOLLAR ALBUM, THE.
Tracks: / Mirror, mirror / Give me back my heart / Hand held in black and white / Pink and blue / I got your number / Guessing games / Give me some kind of magic / Videotheque / Dangerous blondes / You made me love you / Anyone who's anyone / Second time around.
LP: DTV 1
MC: DTV 41

FLIPHITS (EP).
Tracks: / Shooting star / Who were you with in the moonlight / I wanna hold your hand / Love's gotta hold on me.
MC: RCXK 011

PARIS COLLECTION, THE.
Tracks: / Spring collection - radio, The / Girls are out to get you / Young love / You take my breath away / Love at first sight / Autumn collection - takin' a chance on you, The / Ebony / No man's land / Don't change your life / Heartbeat (love me slowly).
LP: K 58246
MC: K4 58246

SHOOTING STAR.
Tracks: / Overture / Shooting star / Tokyo / Star control / Who were you with in the moonlight / I need your love / Ring / Love's gotta hold on me / Love street.
LP: CAL 111
MC: CAC 111

VERY BEST OF DOLLAR, THE.
Tracks: / Who were you with in the moonlight? / I need your love / Ring, ring / Love's gotta hold on me / Love street / Overture / Shooting star / Tokyo / Star control / I wanna hold your hand.
LP: CAL 3001
MC: CAC 3001

Dollie Deluxe

ROCK V OPERA.
Tracks: / Overture / Zum leiden / Du du du / O Isis and Osiris / Der holle rache / Ach, ich fuhl's / Ein madchen oder weibchen / Finale / Carmen / Gimme some lovin' / Vilja / Whatever you want / Queen of the night / Satisfaction / Caro nome / Sex and drugs and rock and roll.
LP: SPLP 006
MC: SPLC 006

Doll's House

DOLL'S HOUSE, A (See under Ibsen, Henrik) (Ibsen, Henrik (author)).

Dolls Life (show)

DOLLS LIFE, A (Original Broadway cast) (Various artists).
LP: P 18846

Dolly Mixtures

DEMONSTRATION TAPES-.
2LP: GOOD 1

Dolly Sisters

DOLLY SISTERS, THE (1945 film musical soundtrack) (Various artists).
LP: CIF 3010

Dolphin Brothers

CATCH THE FALL.
Tracks: / Catch the fall / Shining / Second sight / Love that you need / Real life, real answers / Host to the holy / My winter / Pushing the river.
LP: V 2434
MC: TCV 2434
MC: OVEDC 350
LP: OVED 350

Dolphin Club

OUT OF THE BLUE.
MC: MVCW 1

Dolphin (label)

BEST OF DOLPHIN: 20 IRISH REQUESTS (Various artists).
MC: DOCS 2019

BEST OF DOLPHIN: FAV. IRISH BALLADS (Various artists).
MC: DOCS 2018

DOLPHIN REBEL SONGS (Various artists).
MC: DOCB 7007

Dolphins Of Hollywood

DOO WOP SESSIONS.
LP: JD 906

Dolphy, Eric

BERLIN CONCERTS.
LP: ENJA 3007 1

CANDID DOLPHY.
Tracks: / Re-incarnation of a love bird / Stormy weather / African lady / Quiet please / Moods in free time / Hazy hues.
LP: CS 9033

COLLECTION: ERIC DOLPHY.
Tracks: / Prophet, The / Like someone in love / Booker's waltz / Bee vamp / Fire waltz.
MC: DVMC 2077

ERIC DOLPHY QUARTET (1961) (Dolphy, Eric Quartet).
LP: JC 107

ERIC DOLPHY & THE CHAMPS ELYSEES ALL STARS (Dolphy, Eric & The Champs Elysees All Stars).
Tracks: / Springtime / GW / 245 / Serene.
LP: WW 016

FIRE WALTZ.
Tracks: / Lautir / Curtsy / Geo's tune / They all laughed / Head shakin' / Dianna / Warm canto / Warp and woof / Fire waltz / Duquility / Thirteen / We diddit / Status seeking.
2LP: PR 24085

IMMORTAL CONCERTS (See under Mingus, Charles) (Dolphy, Eric & Charles Mingus).

LIVE AT GASLIGHT INN (Dolphy, Eric Quintet).
LP: INGO 14

LIVE AT THE FIVE SPOT II.
LP: OJC 247

LOOKING AHEAD (See under McIntyre, Ken) (Dolphy, Eric & Ken McIntyre).

MUSIC MATADOR.
Tracks: / Jitterbug waltz / Music matador / Alone together / Love me.
LP: AFF 47

NEWPORT REBELS (See under Mingus, Charles) (Dolphy, Eric/Charles Mingus/Roy Eldridge/Max Roach/Jo Jones).

OTHER ASPECTS.
Tracks: / Jim Crow / Inner flight 1 / Dolphy'n / Inner flight 2 / Improvisations and tukras.
LP: BT 85131

OUT TO LUNCH.
Tracks: / Hat and beard / Something sweet, something tender / Gazzellioni / Out to lunch / Straight up and down.
LP: BST 84163
MC: 4BN 84163
LP: BNS 40017

QUEST, THE (see Waldron,Mal) (Dolphy, Eric/Mal Waldron).

QUINTET U.S.A..
Tracks: / Miss Ann / Left alone / G.W. / 2.45.
LP: UJ 10

STATUS.
Tracks: / Status seeking / God bless the child / Miss Ann / Laura / Way you look tonight, The / Don't blame me / Don't blame me (take 2) / April fool.
2LP: PR 24070

STOCKHOLM SESSIONS.
LP: ENJA 3055

THREE DOLPHY GROUPS.
LP: UJ 26

VINTAGE DOLPHY.
LP: ENJA 5045

Domani Accadra (film)

DOMANI ACCADRA/STRANA LA VITA (Original soundtrack) (Various artists).
LP: IM 016

Dome

WILL YOU SPEAK THIS WORD?.
LP: U 011

Domeniconi, Carlo

KOYUNBABA.
LP: EULP 1044

Domingo, Placido

ADORO.
LP: CBS 73652
MC: 40 73652

BE MY LOVE.
Tracks: / Granada / Dein ist mein ganzes Herz / Siboney / Because / Magic is the moonlight / Amapola / Mattinata.
LP: 2530700

BE MY LOVE (2).
Tracks: / Be my love / Jealousy tango / Love story / O sole mio / Somewhere over the rainbow / Valencia / La golondrina / Love be my guiding star / Because you're mine / Mamma / El condor pasa / Quiereme mucho / Somewhere my love / En aranjuez con tu amor / La vie en rose / Spanish eyes.
LP: EMTV 54
MC: TCEMTV 54

BELCANTO DOMINGO.
Tracks: / Cavalleria rusticana / Turandot / Lucia di Lammermoor / Un ballo in maschera / Aida / Il travatore.
MC: 4 42954
LP: 6 42954

CON AMORE.
Tracks: / Un uomo tra la folla / Se quel guerrier io fossi / Recitar mentre preso / E lucevan le stelle / Una furtiva lagrima / La donna e mobile / Questa o quella / Che gelida manina / Intanto, amici, qua / La fleur que tu m'avais jetee / De quella pira.
LP: RL 14265
MC: RK 14265

ESSENTIAL DOMINGO.
Tracks: / Questa o quella / Se quel guerrier io fossi / Celeste aida / Fleur que tu m'avais jetee / Donna e mobile / Furtiva lagrima / Nessun dorma / Libiamo ne lieti calici / Ah si, ben mio / Di quella pira / Granada / Mattinata / Catari / Non ti scordar / Marta / Because / Siboney / You are my heart's delight / Be my love.
LP: PDTV 1
MC: PDTVC 1

GOYA...A LIFE IN A SONG (See under Goya).

GREATEST LOVE SONGS.
LP: CBS 44701

IN CONCERT (WITH CARRERAS, PAVAROTTI AND MEHTA) (See under Carreras, Jose).

MAGIC OF PLACIDO DOMINGO, THE (Domingo, Placido and the London Symphony Orchestra).
Tracks: / Martha / L'elisir d'amore / La boheme / Manon / L'Arlesiana / I Pagliacci / La fanciuilla del west / Rigoletto / Le Cid / L'Africana.
LP: CDS 1209
MC: CAM 129

MI QUENOS AIRES QUERIDO.
Tracks: / Mi quenos aires querido / El dia que me quieras.
LP: LOVE 2

MY LIFE FOR A SONG.
Tracks: / I couldn't live without you for a day / Besame mucho / I don't talk to strangers / Follow me / My life for a song / Remembering / Blue moon / Moon river / Autumn leaves / There will be love / Songs of summer, The.
LP: 73683
MC: 40 73683

NESSUM DORMA (FROM TURANDOT) (See under Cobos, Luis) (Domingo, Placido & Luis Cobos).

NESSUN DORMA.
MC: 229242983-4

PERHAPS LOVE (See under Denver, John) (Domingo, Placido & John Denver).
Tracks: / Annie's song / Perhaps love / Yesterday / American hymn, An / He couldn't love you more / Sometimes a day goes by / Time after time / To love / Now while I still remember how / My treasure.
LP: 73592
MC: 40 73592

PLACIDO DOMINGO COLLECTION.
Tracks: / La donna e mobile (Act III) / Che gelida manina / Ah mille vite, si pel cel marmoreo guiro / Dio mi potevi scaguar / Mium mi tema (Act (IV) / Panis angelos / Ave Maria / Hosanna / Agnus dei / Mamma mamma quel vino a genovoso / Dein ist mein ganzes herz / Di quella pira (Act III) / Se quel querrier io fossi / La fleur que tu m'avais jetee / Questa o quella / Dammi Icolori ... recondita armonia / E lucevan le stelle (Act III) / Mon piangere, lu (Act I) / Que tgrouble ionconnu / Va pour kleinzach...il etait un / Allons courage et confiance / Aimis, l'amour tendre et reveur / Donna mon vidi mai / Au fond du temple saint.
2LP: SMR 625
MCSET: SMC 625

PLACIDO DOMINGO SINGS TANGOS.
Tracks: / Caminito / Nostalgias / Volver / Vida mia / Mi buenos / Aires querido / Dia me quieras / Maria / Uno / Alma de Bohemio / Cuesta a bajo.
LP: 2536416
MC: 3336416
LPS: 4138571

PLACIDO DOMINGO SINGS ZARZUELAS.
LP: EL 749 148 1
MC: EL 749 148 4

SAVE YOUR NIGHTS FOR ME.
Tracks: / Love came for me / Save your nights for me / I always believed in love / Love until the end of time / Maria / Great dreamer / If you ever love again / Boats have sailed / Why do all the good times go away / Just a dream away.
LP: FM39866

SONADORES DE ESPANA.
Tracks: / El grito de America / Si you fuera el / Sevilla / Sonadores de Espana / Cancion para una reina / Yo sere tu primer hombre / El necesita ayuda / Dos estamos queriendo.
LP: 4660771
MC: 4660774

SONGS OF ERNESTO LECUONA.
Tracks: / Always in my heart / Siboney / Noche azul / Andalucia / Siempre en mi corazon / Malaguena / Maria la o / Canto karabali / Juventus / Comparsa / Damisela encantadora.
LP: FM 38828
MC: FMT 38828

VIENNA, CITY OF MY DREAMS.
LP: EL 270 408 1
MC: EL 270 408 4

Dominic

DOMINIC.
LP: DSR 9688

READY FOR DOMINIC.
Tracks: / Mini van drama / Year in Jamaica, A / Favour boy George / Football dub / Easy fi come / Let's go and lick some shot / Year in Jamaica (Dub), A / Football story / Ready fi Dominik / Sit on a corner.
LP: ILPS 9893
MC: ICT 9893

Dominic Sonic

COLD TEARS.
LP: CRAM 065
MC: CRAMC 065

Dominican Republic

MERENGUES FROM THE DOMINICAN REPUBLIC (Various artists).
LP: LLST 7351

Dominick & Eugene

DOMINICK & EUGENE (1988 film soundtrack) (Various artists).
LP: 704.540
MC: 704.540C

Dominique

SONGS FROM AROUND THE WORLD.
LP: C 2012

Dominique, Lisa

LISA DOMINIQUE.
LP: ESSLP 148
MC: ESSMC 148

ROCK AND ROLL LADY.
Tracks: / Rock and roll lady / All fall down / Gamble, The / Somebody special / Holding on to your love / Time bomb / Jealous heart / Slow down / One foot back in your door / Trouble.
LP: WKFMLP 117
MC: WKFMMC 117
LPPD: WKFMPD 117

Dominko, Steve

ACCORDION MASTERWORKS.
Tracks: / Hungarian rhapsody no. 2 / Traumerei / Sonata no.7 in D / Fantasia / Poet speaks / Prelude in G minor - English suite no.3 Allemande / Sun will never shine, The / Someone there you know / Little lapwing / Song for dying / Poet, The / After the day / Thank you / I'm over you / Harry's song / Ball and chain / Delph town morn / Blue John's blues.
LP: NEO LP101

Domino, Anna

ANNA DOMINO.
LP: FACT 165
LP: TWI 600

COLOURING THE EDGE AND OUTLINE.
LP: TWI 865

EAST AND WEST.
LP: TWI 182
LP: TWI 187

MYSTERIES OF AMERICA.
LP: TWI 888

THIS TIME.
LP: TWI 777

ZANNA (See under Acker, Luc Van) (Domino, Anna/Luc Van Acker).

Domino, Fats

20 GREATEST HITS.
Tracks: / Blueberry Hill / Be my guest / My girl Josephine / I hear you knocking / Fat man / Blue Monday / Walkin' to New Orleans / Ain't that a shame / My blue Heaven / I want to walk you home / Whole lotta lovin' / Country boy / Let the four winds blow / It keeps rainin' / Jambalaya / I'm ready / Going to the river / I'm walking / Going home / I'm gonna be a wheel someday.
LP: UAS 29967
LP: TW 50032

20 GREATEST HITS: FATS DOMINO (FUN LABEL).
LP: FUN 9011
MC: FUNC 9011

20 GREATEST HITS: FATS DOMINO (MASTERS LABEL).
LP: MA 251185
MC: MAMC 9251185

20 ROCK'N'ROLL HITS: FATS DOMINO.
LP: IC 064 82750

BE MY GUEST.
Tracks: / Blueberry Hill / Whole lotta lovin' / I'm in love again / Blue Monday / I want to walk you home / Ain't that a shame / Be my guest / My girl Josephine / Let the four winds blow / I'm ready.
LP: BDL 1059
MC: BDC 1059

BEST OF FATS DOMINO (LIBERTY).
Tracks: / Blueberry Hill / Ain't that a shame / Please don't leave me / Blue Monday / Fat man / I'm in love again / I'm walking / I'm ready / I'm gonna be a wheel someday / I want to walk you home / Whole lotta lovin' / Be my guest / My girl Josephine / Walkin' to New Orleans / Let the four winds blow / Jambalaya.
LP: EG 2607621
MC: EG 2607624
MC: 16-1

BEST OF FATS DOMINO VOL. 1 (My Blue Heaven).
Tracks: / My blue heaven / Fat man / Please don't leave me / Ain't that a shame / I'm in love again / When my dreamboat comes home / Blueberry Hill / Blue Monday / I'm walkin' / Valley of tears / Big beat, The / Yes my darling / Whole lotta loving / I'm ready / I'm gonna be a wheel someday / I want to walk you home / Be my guest / Walking to New Orleans / Let the four winds blow / What a party.
MC: TCEMS 1381
MC: 792 808 4

BEST OF THE FAT MAN.
MC: U3016-2

BLUEBERRY HILL.
Tracks: / Blue Monday / Whole lotta lovin' / Red sails in the sunset / I'm ready / Jambalaya / Blueberry Hill / Yes it's me, and I'm in love again / Ain't that a shame / I'm in the mood for love / I want to walk you home.
LP: CBR 1003
MC: KCBR 1003
LP: 2236012
MC: 2136012

BLUEBERRY HILL (PICKWICK).
MC: HSC 3404

BLUEBERRY HILL (PICTURE DISC).
LPPD: PD 50001

BLUEBERRY HITS.
MC: 4XLL 8347

BOOGIE WOOGIE BABY.
Tracks: / Rockin' chair / Sometimes I wonder / Nobody loves me / Dreaming / Careless love / I've got eyes for you / Right from wrong / No no baby / My baby's gone / Boogie woogie baby / How long / Rose Mary / Fats Domino blues / What's the matter baby / Stay away / 9th ward blues / Hey la bas boogie.
LP: CHD 140

COLLECTION: FATS DOMINO (DEJA-VU) (20 golden greats).
Tracks: / Blueberry Hill / Blue Monday / So long / Whole lotta loving / Jambalaya / Ballin' the jack / Please don't leave me / When the saints go marching in / Yes it's me and I'm in love again / I'm walking / My blue Heaven / Heartbreak Hill / Walkin' to New Orleans / Let the four winds blow / Kansas City / Why don't you do right? / I'm gonna be a wheel someday / Ain't that a shame / I'm ready / Domino twist.
LP: DVLP 2030
MC: DVMC 2030

EASYRIDING: FATS DOMINO.
Tracks: / Intro. / Blueberry Hill / Jambalaya / Oh, what a price / Domino twist / Let the four winds blow / Whole lotta loving / Blue Monday / I'm walking / Walking to New Orleans / I'm gonna be a wheel someday / I'm in the mood for love / Please don't leave me / Ain't that a shame / So long / My blue Heaven / I want to walk you home / When the saints go marching in.
MC: KNMC 11006
LP: KNLP 11006

FABULOUS MR D, THE.
LP: 2C 068 83296

FAT MAN LIVE, THE.
Tracks: / Fat man / Blueberry hill / Oh, What a price / Domino twist / Let the four winds blow / I'm in the mood for love / Please don't leave me / I'm ready / I'm in love again / Be my guest.
LP: MFM 023

FAT MAN, THE.
Tracks: / I'm gonna be a wheel someday / I want to walk you home / Whole lotta loving / Fat man / Blueberry Hill / Please don't leave me / Blue Monday / Jambalaya / I'm in love again / Be my guest / Red sails in the sunset / Going home.
LP: TOP 110
MC: KTOP 110

FATS DOMINO.
MC: ZCGAS 727
LP: SM 38972

FATS DOMINO (LIVE).
Tracks: / Introduction / Blueberry Hill / Please don't leave me / Domino twist / Let the four winds blow / Whole lotta loving / Blue Monday / You win again / I'm walking / I'm gonna be a wheel someday / I'm in the mood for love / Jambalaya / O what a price / Ain't that a shame / So long / When the saints go marching in / Deep in the heart of Texas.
LP: 824 318-1
MC: 824 318-4

FATS DOMINO (MFP).
Tracks: / Be my guest / Margie / Ain't that a shame / I hear you knocking / When my dreamboat comes home / All by myself / Honey chile / Jambalaya / I'm in love again / What a party / Blueberry Hill / I've been around / My blue Heaven / My girl Josephine / Natural born lover.
LP: MFP 41 5747 1
MC: MFP 41 5747 4
LP: MFP 5747
MC: TC MFP 5747

FATS DOMINO VOL. 1.
LP: SM 3895
MC: MC 3895

FATS DOMINO, VOL. 2.
LP: SM 3896

FATS IS BACK.
LP: 6463 043
MC: 7145 043

GETAWAY WITH FATS DOMINO.
Tracks: / When my dreamboat comes home / Wigs / Trouble in mind / Man that's all / Kansas city / Reelin and rockin / On a slow boat to china / Monkey business / Heartbreak hill / Girl I'm gonna marry, The / Why don't you do right / Ballin' the jack.
LP: CH 90

GOLDEN GREATS: FATS DOMINO.
LP: HMR 9002

GRAFFITI COLLECTION.
MC: GRMC 06

GREATEST HITS: FATS DOMINO.
Tracks: / I'm walking / Blue Monday / Blueberry Hill / When the saints go marching in.
LP: 927 910 1

GREATEST HITS - LIVE.
MCSET: M 10174

HERE STANDS FATS DOMINO.
LP: 2C 068 82621

I MISS YOU SO.
LP: 2C 068 83295

JAMBALAYA.
LP: 20083
MC: 40083

KINGS OF ROCK (see under Kings of ...) (Domino, Fats & Bill Haley).

LET'S DANCE WITH DOMINO.
LP: 2C 068 83031

LIVE AT MONTREUX.
Tracks: / Hello Josephine / I'm in love again / Blueberry hill / Jambalaya / Walking to New Orleans / I'm gonna be a wheel someday / Blue Monday / Mardi gras in New Orleans / Stagger Lee / I want to walk you home / Let the four winds blow / I'm walking / When the saints go marching in / Sentimental journey.
LP: K 50107

LIVE IN CONCERT.
Tracks: / Fat man / Blueberry Hill / Domino twist / What a price / Let the four winds blow / Jambalaya / Honey chile / Red sails in the sunset / Ain't that a shame / So long / Natural born lover / C.C. rider / I'm in the mood for love / I want to walk you home.
LP: CRB 1053

LOT OF DOMINOS, A.
LP: 2C 068 64146

MILLION RECORDS HITS.
LP: 2C 068 83297

MOTIVE SERIES.
Tracks: / My blue Heaven / Blueberry Hill / When the saints go marching in / Deep in the heart of Texas / I left my heart in San Francisco / Blue Monday / You win again / Walking to New Orleans / Mardi Gras in New Orleans / I'm walking / I don't get over it.
LP: 6463 141

MY BLUE HEAVEN.
LP: 20082
MC: 40082

NEW ORLEANS ROCK 'N' ROLL.
LP: PM 1551833

ONLY ROCK AND ROLL.
Tracks: / Fat man / Please don't leave me / All by myself / Ain't it a shame / I can't go on / My blue heaven / When my dreamboat comes home / I'm walkin' / Don't deceive me / Big beat, The / Sick and tired / I'm gonna be a wheel some day / Margie / Li'l Liza Jane / When the saints go marching in / When I was young / Shurah / My girl Josephine.
LP: OFF 6036

REELIN' AND ROCKIN'.
Tracks: / When I'm walking (let me walk) / Kansas City / I'm living right / Land of make believe / Who cares / I'm a fool to care / Love me / Land of a thousand dances / Heartbreak hill / Wigs / Girl I'm gonna marry, The / Something you got / Packin' up / Reelin' and rockin' / Red sails in the sunset.
LP: CRB 1054

ROCK AND ROLLIN'.
Tracks: / Reelin' and rockin' / School days / My ding a ling / Too much monkey business / Memphis, Tennessee / Maybellene / Nadine / Fat man / Blueberry Hill / Oh, what a price / Domino twist / Let the four winds blow / I'm in the mood for love / Please don't leave me / I'm ready / I'm in love again / Be my guest.
LP: 2C 068 62438
LP: 2C 068 83092

ROCK 'N' SLOW.
LP: 1A022 1583481
MC: 1A222 1583484

ROLLIN'.
LP: 269663-1
MC: 269663-4

SINGLES ALBUM.
Tracks: / Blueberry Hill / Be my guest / My girl Josephine / I hear you knocking / Fat man / Blue Monday / Walking to New Orleans / Ain't that a shame / My blue heaven / I want to walk you home / Whole lotta loving / Country boy / Let the four winds blow / It keeps rainin' / Going home / I'm gonna be a wheel someday.
LP: UAG 30254
LP: FA 3046

SLEEPING ON THE JOB.
Tracks: / Sleeping on the job / After hours / When I lost my baby / Something about you baby / Move with the groove / Any old time / Shame on you / I just can't get / Girl I love, The / Love me.
LP: SNTF 793

THIS IS FATS DOMINO.
LP: 2C 068 83298
LP: 2C 068 62383

VERY BEST OF FATS DOMINO, THE (Play It Again).
Tracks: / Blueberry Hill / Ain't that a shame / Fat man.
LP: IC 064 94442
LP: LBS 83331

WALKIN' TO NEW ORLEANS.
LP: PM 1546621

WHAT A PARTY.
LP: PM 1546631

Dominoes

BILLY WARD AND HIS DOMINOES (See under Ward, Billy).

HAVE MERCY, BABY.
Tracks: / Sixty minute man / Chicken blues / You can't keep a good man down / Bells, The / I'd be satisfied / Weeping willow blues / Do something for me / If I never get to Heaven / My baby's 3-D / Pedal pushin' Papa / Don't leave me this way / I am with you / I'm gonna move to the outskirts of town / That's what you're doing to me / Have mercy, baby / I ain't gonna cry for you.
LP: CRB 1095
MC: TCCRB 1095

Dommelvolk

WINTERFOLK 80 (see Battlefield Band).

Domnerus, Arne

A.D. 1980.
Tracks: / Royal Garden blues / Blues for morket och ljuset / If you could see me now / Simbah / My old flame / Tickle toe / Child is born, A / Etyd Kameleont.
LP: PHONT 7529

ALL OF ME (See under Hedenbratt, Sonya) (Domnerus, Arne & Sonya Hedenbratt).

ALLT UNDER HIMMELENS FASTE (See under Hoglund, Ola) (Domnerus, Arne & Ola Hoglund).

ARNE DOMNERUS AND HIS FAVOURITE GROUPS, 1949-50.
LP: DRLP 111

BLUE AND YELLOW - A SWEDISH RHAPSODY.
LP: PHONT 7538

DOWNTOWN MEETING (Domnerus, Arne/ Bengt Hallberg).
Tracks: / Gone with the wind / Embraceable you / On the sunny side of the street / I cover the waterfront / Song from Utanmyra.
LP: PHONT 7518

DUKE'S MELODY (Domnerus, Arne/ Knud Jorgensen).
Tracks: / Black beauty / In a mellow tone / Drop me off in Harlem / Everything but you / I got it bad and that ain't good / Brown skin gal.
LP: PHONT 7533

EVERGREENS (Domnerus, Arne Quartet).
LP: PHONT 7539

FRAGMENT.
Tracks: / Fragment / In a sentimental mood / Avalon / Symphony / My blue Heaven / Lonesome road / Sweet

Lorraine / I poured my heart into a song / Sweet Georgia Brown / C'est si bon.
LP: . . . . PHONT 7536

SWEDISH JINGLES.
Tracks: / Jag vet litet hotel / Sa skimrande var aldrig havet / Allt detta och himlen dartill / Penseer vals / Det regnar pa var karlek / Fjorton ar tror jag visst / Sodermalm / Underbart ar kork / Sillsaltavisan / Don't let it mean goodbye / Truddelutter / Da vantar jag vid vagarna.
LP: . . . . PHONT 7534

Domra, Sydney

MEMORIES OF RUSSIA (Domra, Sydney Ensemble).
LP: . . . . VP 454

Don & Annie

QUEEN OF THE SILVER DOLLAR.
MC: . . . . BBM 139

Don Carlos

DON CARLOS (VIDEO) (see under Verdi (composer) for information).

Don & Dewey

BIM BAM.
Tracks: / Baby gotta party / Sweet talk / Miss Sue / Hey Thelma / Bim bam / Jungle hop / Just a little lovin' / Day by day / Jump awhile / Impossible to say / Jelly bean / Walk alone / Little love.
LP: . . . . CH 151

Don Giovanni (film)

DON GIOVANNI (1979 film soundtrack) (Various artists).
LP: . . . . CBS 73888
MC: 40 73888

DON GIOVANNI (VIDEO) (See under Mozart (composer) for information) (Various artists).

Don Juans

LOVING YOU.
LP: . . . . BLP 007

MORE MONSTER HITS.
LP: . . . . BLP 004

SOLID GOLD.
LP: . . . . BLP 011

Don Quixote (bk)

DON QUIXOTE (Various artists).
MC: . . . . ANV 630

DON QUIXOTE (VIDEO) (see under Kirov Ballet) (Kirov Ballet).

EXPLOITS OF DON QUIXOTE (Miguel De Cervantes) (Quayle, Anthony (nar)).
MC: 1289

Don Slepian

REFLECTIONS.
LP: . . . . SYN 106
MC: . . . . SYNC 106

Donaghadee School

THANK YOU FOR THE MUSIC (Donaghadee Primary School Choir).
Tracks: / Any dream will do / Sleep my little Jesus / Country roads / My way / Hallelujah / There is a green hill far away / Rivers of Babylon / Away in a manger / Mary's boy child / Love comes a tricklin' down / Dust and ashes / Last farewell, The / Thank you for the music.
LP: . . . . STOL 141

Donaghy, Eileen

12 FAVOURITE IRISH SONGS.
Tracks: / Moonshiner / Spinning wheel / Goodbye Mick, goodbye Pat / If I were a blackbird / Three lovely lassies / Slattery's mounted fut / Rose of Mooncoin / Johnny Gray / Dan O'Hara / Castle of Dromore / Do you remember the good old days / Hills of Tyrone.
MC: . . . . CHRL 204

EILEEN DONAGHY ENTERTAINS.
LP: . . . . RGS 3039

GREATEST HITS: EILEEN DONAGHY.
Tracks: / Let Mr. Maguire sit down / Boys from County Mayo / Wee cup of tay.
LP: . . . . G 003

IRELAND'S QUEEN OF SONG.
MC: . . . . CGL 003

IRISH SING ALONG.
Tracks: / If you're Irish come into the parlour. / When Irish eyes are smiling. / With a shillelagh under my arm / Dear little shamrock / Mountains of Mourne / Hannigan's hooley / Phil the Fluter's ball / Cockles and mussels / MacNamara's band / Believe me if all those endearing young charms / Galway Bay / Danny boy / Mother Machree / It's a long way to Tipperary.
MC: 7299672

SOUVENIR OF IRELAND.
LP: . . . . HRL 204

TYRONE'S QUEEN OF SONG.
Tracks: / McCarthy's party / Two little orphans / Little old mud cabin / It's heaven around Galway Bay / Moonshiner / Blarney roses / Goodbye Johnny dear / Doonaree / My home in Mayo / Gentle mother / Moon behind the hill / Boston burglar.
LP: . . . . HRL 195

Donahue, Jerry

BRIEF ENCOUNTERS (Donahue, Jerry & Doug Morter).
LP: . . . . FUN 005

TELECASTING.
LP: . . . . SPIN 118
LP: . . . . UNKNOWN

Donahue, Sam

CONVOY (Donahue, Sam Navy Band).
Tracks: / Convoy / On the sunny side of the street / Deep night / I've found a new baby / I can't give you anything but love / Homeward bound / Lonely nights / Saxophone Sam / Bugle call rag / You was right baby / Moten swing / Just you just me / Gypsy love song / My silent love / Please get us out.
LP: . . . . HEP 2

DOUBLE DATE (Donahue, Sam and Les Brown).
LP: . . . . HEP 14

HOLLYWOOD HOP.
Tracks: / Hollywood hop / Encore essence / St. Louis blues / Dinah / Without a song / Smooth blend / Round the block / Catch as catch can / I cover the waterfront / After you've gone / There'll be some changes made / Exactly like you / Sax a boogie.
LP: . . . . HEP 25

LAST PARTY (Donahue, Sam Navy Band).
Tracks: / World is waiting for the sunrise, The / Dinah / Play fiddle play / Cocktails for two / Mean to me / Last party / Dear Al / Paradise / Melancholy baby heart stood still / C jam blues / Minor de luxe.
LP: . . . . HEP 5

Donal Ring Ceili Band

21ST ANNIVERSARY.
MC: . . . . HSMC 018

COME TO THE CEILE.
MC: . . . . HSMC 048

IRISH JUBILEE.
LP: 815 932 1

WINDING BANKS OF THE LEE.
Tracks: / Polka reel selection / Where the river Shannon flows / Marches / Hornpipe / Winding banks of the Lee / March selection / Mount Cashel brigade / Jackets green / God save Ireland / Whistling Mike / Showman's fancy / Off to California / Planxty O'Rourke / St. Malachy's reel / Drunken piper / Tweed dale reel / Cunning fox, The / Haunting hills / Skibbereeb / Harts jigs / John Joes jig / Tom peoples jigs / O'Donnell Abu / Centenary march / Arsa 'n eireann / Lily McNally McNair / Song of the Clyde / Star of Munster / Belles of St.Louis, The / Kiss the bride / Linen cap / My father's jig / Captain White / Visit to Ireland, A / Health of the ladies / Sweet Marie.
MC: 3 188 108

Donald D

NOTORIOUS.
Tracks: / Notorious / F.B.I. / Who got the gun / Syndicate posse / Letter I'll never send, A / Armed and dangerous / Car chase / Just suck / Lost in a freestyle / On tour / Another night in the Bronx.
LP: 4660871
MC: 4660874

Donald & Lulu

BEAUTIFUL GARDEN (Donald & Lulu with the Wailers).
Tracks: / Just cool runnin's / You'd better believe it / I know you're a child / Lulu, what we gonna do? / Dream of me / Love one another / Marble stones / I never wrote a love song / Destiny / Beautiful garden.
LP: . . . . LP 98101

Donald, Mike

YORKSHIRE SONGS OF THE BROAD ACRES.
Tracks: / Humber fishing boat, The / Fish finger armada / Visions of Cumbria / Bingo in the morning / Whitby smugglers' song / Leeds town / Settle-Carlisle railway / Terrible knitters of Dent / Swaledale leadminers, The / More like Blackpool each day / Land of the old and grey / Steam train.
LP: . . . . FHR 021 S

Donald, Robyn (Author)

BRIDE AT WHANGATAPU (see under Bride at Whangatapu (bk)) (Boyd, Carole (nar)).

Donald, Sheila (nar)

FORGIVING HEART (see under Forgiving Heart).

Donaldson Brothers

SCOTTISH WELCOME, A.
Tracks: / Tally ho twostep / King George V's army / Sheena's wedding / High road to Linton / Plaisir d'amour / John Huband's reel / Bobby McLeod's fancy / Bobby Campbell's reel / Happy haggis, The / Killiecrankie / Bonnie lass o' Fyvie / Muckin' o' Geordie's byre / Haunt of the gnomes, The / Buck o the Cabrach, The / Bonnie Banchory / Willie Merrilees / Kirkwall Bay / Auchtermuchty gala march, The / Madge (Farewell to Scotland) / Duchess tree, The / Our Highland Queen / Triste sourire / Slow airs / Cradle song / Fleur of the Quern / Toot toot tootsie goodbye / Stumbling / Piper's weird, The / Corgarff Castle / Set of jigs / Stoneypath tower / Weaver and his wife, The / Balcomie house / Lamb skinnet.
LP: . . . . GLN 1024

Donaldson, David

ENGLISH LANGUAGE, THE.
LP: . . . . STAG 1
MC: . . . . STAG 41

Donaldson, Eric

KEEP ON RIDING.
LP: . . . . DYLP 3003

KENT VILLAGE.
LP: . . . . DYLP 3013

RIGHT ON TIME.
LP: . . . . DY 3445

Donaldson, James

JUSTIFIED (Donaldson, James Band).
LP: . . . . LKLP 7-6060

Donaldson, John

PAROUSIA.
LP: . . . . PRO 7051

Donaldson, Lou

BLUES WALK.
Tracks: / Move / Masquerade is over, The / Play Ray / Autumn nocturne / Callin' all cats / Blues Walk.
LP: . . . . BST 81593

FORGOTTEN MAN (Donaldson, Lou Quartet).
LP: . . . . SJP 153

HERE 'TIS.
Tracks: / Foggy day / Here 'tis / Cool blues / Watusi jump / Walk wid me.
LP: . . . . BST 84066

LIVE IN BOLOGNA, VOLUME 2 (See under Foster, Herman).

LUSH LIFE.
Tracks: / Sweet slumber / You've changed / Good life / Stardust / What will I tell my heart / It might as well be spring. / Sweet and lovely.
LP: . . . . BST 84254

NATURAL SOUL.
Tracks: / Funky Mama / Love walked in / Spaceman twist / Sow belly blues / That's all / Nice 'n' greasy.
LP: . . . . BST 84108

QUARTET, QUINTET & SEXTET.
Tracks: / If I love again / Down home / Best things in life are free, The / Lou's blues / Cheek to cheek / Sweet ice / Stroller, The / Roccus / Caracas / Moe's bluff / Roccus (alt. take) (CD only.) / Cheek to cheek (alt. take) (CD only.) / Lou's blues (alt. take) (CD only.) / Things we did last summer, The (CD only.) / After you've gone (CD only.).
LP: B1 81537

SWEET POPPA LOU.
Tracks: / Mambo Inn / You'll never know / Mo' Gravy / If I should lose you / Shuckin blues / Don't take your love from me.
LP: . . . . MR 5247

Donaldson, Stephen R.

WHITE GOLD WIELDER.
MC: 1717

Donaldson, Walter

GREATEST SONG HITS OF WALTER DONALDSON.
LP: . . . . MES 7059

Donat, Robert

ROBERT DONAT READS.
MCSET: . . . . SAY 33

Dondadio, Atillio

CAPOLINEA CLUB (Dondadio, Atillio Big Band).
LP: . . . . ISST 150

Doneda, Michel

TERRA.
Tracks: / Le passeur d'etoiles / Vert et jaune / Theatre / Ene maetia / Rose noir / Xorri fourmy / When did you come? / Lile D'Hanako.
LP: . . . . NATO 532

Donegan, Dorothy

BROWN GAL 1946-50 (See under Howard, Camille/Dorothy Donegan etc.) (Donegan, Dorothy/Camille Howard/Lil Armstrong).

EXPLOSIVE, THE.
LP: . . . . AP 209

Donegan, Lonnie

COLLECTION: LONNIE DONEGAN.
Tracks: / Rock Island line / Lost John / Nobody's child / Bring a little water Sylvie / Frankie and Johnny / Cumberland gap / Mule skinner blues / Putting on the style / My Dixie darling / Ham 'n' eggs / Grand Coulee dam / Times are getting hard boys / Long summer day / Does your chewing gum lose it's flavour / Whoa buck / Battle of New Orleans / Fancy talking tinker / Miss Otis regrets / Talking guitar blues / My old man's a dustman / Have a drink on me / Keep on the sunny side / Pick a bale of cotton / This train.
2LP: . . . . CCSLP 223
MC: . . . . CCSMC 223

GOLDEN AGE OF LONNIE DONEGAN VOL.2.
LP: . . . . GGL 0170

GOLDEN AGE OF LONNIE DONEGAN VOL.1.
LP: . . . . GGL 0135

GOLDEN HOUR OF GOLDEN HITS.
MC: . . . . ZCGH 514

GOLDEN HOUR OF GOLDEN HITS, VOL 2.
Tracks: / Mule skinner blues / Pick a bale of cotton / Times are getting hard boys / Sal's got a sugar lip / My dixie darling / Ham 'n' eggs / Lively / Stewball / Fort Worth Jail / Dead or alive / I'm just a rolling stone / Aunt Rhody / Rock o' my soul / Golden vanity / Corina Corina / Seven golden daffodils / Lumbered / Very good year, A.
LP: . . . . GH 565

GOLDEN HOUR OF LONNIE DONEGAN, A.
LP: . . . . KGHMC 129

GREATEST HITS: LONNIE DONEGAN.
MCSET: . . . . DTO 10048

GREATEST HITS: LONNIE DONEGAN (BRAVO LABEL).
MC: . . . . BRC 2530

HIT SINGLES COLLECTION, THE.
Tracks: / Rock Island line / Stewball / Lost John / Railroad Bill / Old Riley / Bring a little water, Sylvie / Dead or alive / Don't you rock me daddy-o / Cumberland Gap / Gamblin' man / Putting on the style / My dixie darling / Jack o' diamonds / Grand Coulee dam / Sally don't you grieve / Betty, Betty, Betty / Lonesome traveller / Tom Dooley / Does your chewing gum lose its flavour? / Fort Worth Jail / Battle of New Orleans / Sal's got a sugar lip / San Miguel / My old man's a dustman / I wanna go home / Lorelei / Lively / Virgin Mary / Have a drink on me / Michael row the boat ashore / Lumbered / Comancheros, The / Party's over, The / Pick a bale of cotton / Lonnie's skiffle party (Parts 1 & 2).
2LP: . . . . PYL 7003
MCSET: . . . . PYM 7003

JUBILEE CONCERT.
Tracks: / Ace in the hole / Isle of Capri / Going home / Shine / Jenny's ball / One sweet letter from you / Hush-a-bye / Bugle call march / Ice cream / John Henry / Take this hammer / Railroad Bill / Tom Dooley / New burying ground / Grand Coulee dam / New York town / Miss Otis regrets / Does your chewing gum lose its flavour? / One night of love / Rock Island line / Gloryland / Corina Corina / Goodnight Irene.
LP: . . . . ICSD 2001
MC: . . . . ZCICSD 2001

LONNIE DONEGAN FILE, THE.
MC: . . . . ZCFLD 011

LONNIE DONEGAN SHOWCASE.
Tracks: / Wabash cannonball / How long how long blues / Nobody's child / I shall not be moved / I'm Alabamy bound / I'm a ramblin' man / Wreck of the old '97 / Frankie and Johnny.
MLP: . . . . NPT 19012

PUTTIN' ON THE STYLE.
Tracks: / Rock Island line / Have a drink on me / Ham 'n' eggs / I wanna go home / Diggin' my potatoes / Nobody's child / Putting on the style / Frankie and Johnny / Drop down baby / Lost John.
LP: . . . . CHR 1158
MC: . . . . ZCHR 1158

RARE AND UNISSUED GEMS.

Tracks: / Cajun Joe / Louisiana moon / There's a big wheel / Fisherman's luck / Lovey told me goodbye / Bad news / Nothing to gain / Five hundred miles / Tiger rag / Keep on the sunny side / Red beret / Kevin Barry / Comancheros, The / Just a-wearyin' for you / Ding ding / Leaving blues.
LP: . . . . BFX 15170

ROCK ISLAND LINE.
Tracks: / My old man's a dustman / Pick a bale of cotton / Bring a little water Sylvie / Cumberland Gap / Michael row the boat ashore / Rock Island line / It takes a worried man / Don't you rock me daddy-o / Does your chewing gum lose its flavour? / Putting on the style / Battle of New Orleans / Have a drink on me.
LP: . . . . FBLP 8071
MC: . . . . ZCFBL 8071

Donkey Cabbages

DONKEY CABBAGES, THE (Various artists).
Tracks: / Donkey cabbages, The: *Various artists* / Drummer, The: *Various artists* / Simeli mountain: *Various artists* / Hop o' my thumb: *Various artists* / Professor know-all: *Various artists.*
MC: . . . . ANV 618

Donkey Show

BALI ISLAND.
LP: . . . . PHZA 26

Donley, Jimmy

GIVE ME MY FREEDOM.
Tracks: / Kickin' my hound around / Come along / Radio jukebox and TV / Please come home / Now I Know / I can't love you / My baby's gone / Shape you left me in / Born to be a loser / Give me my freedom / Baby how long / I'm alone / What must I do / Our love / Child love.
LP: . . . . CR 30265

Donne, John

LOVE POEMS OF JOHN DONNE, THE (Burton, Richard).
MC: 41

Donnelly, Philip

TOWN AND COUNTRY.
Tracks: / Ballad of Robin Wintersmith / Donegal / From Clare to here / Speed of the sound of loneliness / Home is wherever you are / Cajun rock'n'roll stanza / I just kissed a devil last night / Abandoned love / No 1 / Tequila is addictive.
LP: . . . . DUB 1
MC: . . . . DUBC 1

Donnelly, Sean

ON BREEZES FRESH AND FAIR.
LP: . . . . SLP 1011

Donner, Ral

1935-1977: I'VE BEEN AWAY FOR A WHILE.
Tracks: / Memories / So high / Old Shep / Trouble / I need somebody to lean on / Blue moon of Kentucky / My happiness / That's alright mama / I forgot to remember to forget / All shook up / When my blue moon turns to gold again / I'm left you're right she's gone / Heartbreak Hotel / I want you, I need you, I love you / Hound dog / Don't be cruel / Mystery train / Love me tender / Loving you / Got a lot of livin' to do / Jailhouse rock / King Creole / Don't / Precious memories / Wooden heart / Fool such as I, A / One night / I got stung / Stuck on you / It's now or never / White Christmas / Blue Christmas / Girls, girls, girls / Return to sender / Follow the dream / Lawdy Miss Clawdy / Are you lonesome tonight / If I can dream / In the ghetto / Don't cry daddy / Kentucky rain / Separate ways / Mama liked the roses / Viva Las Vegas / 2001 / C.C. rider / Suspicious minds / Lord you gave me a mountain / American trilogy / Can't help falling in love.
2LP: . . . . ND 135

ELVIS PRESLEY SOUND OF, THE.
LP: . . . . LSP 1057

SOUNDS LIKE ELVIS.
LP: . . . . FIRESTAR 1010

YOU DON'T KNOW WHAT YOU GOT.
LP: . . . . NSPL 28269

Donoghue, Breege

BREEGE DONOGHUE & JAMBOREE TOGETHER (Donoghue, Breege & Jamboree).
MC: . . . . GTDC 089

Donoghue, Jim

JIM DONOGHUE.
LP: . . . . LUN 034

Donovan

CATCH THE WIND.
Tracks: / Universal soldier / Little tin soldier / Catch the wind / Candy man / Josie / Colours of Geraldine / War drags on, The / Remember the Alamo.
LP: . . . . SHLP 133
MC: . . . . SHTC 133

COLLECTION: DONOVAN.
Tracks: / Catch the wind / Colours / To try for the sun / Summer day reflection song / Turquoise / Trip, The / Sunshine superman / Ferris wheel / Hey Gyp (dig the slowness) / Museum / Sunny South Kensington / Hurdy gurdy man / Fat angel, The (live) / Hi it's been a long time / Where is she / Changes / Appearances / Cosmic wheels / Lord of the reedy river / I like you / Song for John / There is an ocean.
MC: . . . . CCSMC 276

COLOURS.
Tracks: / Catch the wind / Josie / Ramblin' boy / Donna Donna / Tangerine puppet / Turquoise / Colours / Remember the Alamo / Ballad of a crystal man / Universal soldier / Gold watch blues / Cuttin' out / To try for the sun.
LP: . . . . PYL 7004
MC: . . . . PYM 7004
LP: . . . . FBLP 8074

COSMIC WHEELS.
LP: . . . . EPC 65450

DONOVAN.
MC: C90 5

DONOVAN FILE, THE.
Tracks: / Catch the wind / Why do you treat me like you do? / Remember the Alamo / Cuttin' out / Car car (riding in my car) / Keep on truckin' / Gold watch blues / To sing for you / Josie / You're gonna need somebody on your bond / Tangerine puppet / Donna Donna / Ramblin' boy / Sunny Goodge Street / Oh 'deed I do / Colours / I'll try for the sun / Circus of sour / Summer day reflection song / Candy man / Jersey Thursday / Belated forgiveness plea / Universal soldier / Ballad of a crystal man / Little tin soldier / Ballad of Geraldine, The / War drags on, The / Do you hear me now? / Hey Gyp (dig the slowness) / Turquoise.
2LP: . . . . FILD 004
MC: . . . . ZCFLD 004

DONOVAN IN CONCERT.
LP: . . . . BGOLP 90
MC: . . . . BGOMC 90

DONOVAN RISING.
LP: . . . . PERMLP 2
MC: . . . . PERMMC 2

EP COLLECTION, THE: DONOVAN.
LP: . . . . SEE 300
MC: . . . . SEEK 300

FAIRYTALE.
Tracks: / Colours / I'll try for the sun / Sunny Goodge Street / Oh deed I do / Circus of sour / Summer day reflection song, The / Candy man / Jersey Thursday / Belated of a crystal man / Little tin soldier / Ballad of Geraldine, The.
LP: . . . . NPL 18128
MC: . . . . CLAMC 226

GIFT FROM A FLOWER TO A GARDEN, A.
LP: . . . . NSPL 20000

GOLDEN HOUR OF DONOVAN, A.
Tracks: / Universal soldier / Josie / To sing for you / Donna Donna / Colours / Catch the wind / Candy man / Why do you treat me like you do / Hey gyp (dig the slowness) / I'll try for the sun / Sunny Goodge Street / Little tin soldier / Gold watch blues / Ballad of Geraldine, The / War drags on, The / Turquoise / Jersey Thursday / Ballad of a crystal man / Remember the Alamo / Belated forgiveness plea.
MC: . . . . KGHMC 107
LP: . . . . KGHLP 107

GREATEST HITS AND MORE.
Tracks: / Sunshine superman / Wear your love like Heaven / Jennifer Juniper / Barabajagal (with the Jeff Beck Group.) / Hurdy gurdy man / Epistle to dippy / To Susan on the west coast waiting / Catch the wind / Mellow yellow / There is a mountain / Happiness runs / Season of the witch / Colours / Superlungs/My supergirl / Lalena / Atlantis / Preachin' love (CD only.) / Preachin' love (CD only.) / Poor cow (CD only.) / Teen angel (CD only.) / Aye my love (CD only.).
LP: . . . . EMS 1333
MC: . . . . TCEMS 1333

JENNIFER JUNIPER (See under Singing Corner for details) (Donovan & The Singing Corner).

LADY OF THE STARS.
Tracks: / Lady of the stars / I love you baby / Bye bye girl / Every reason / Season of the witch / Boy for every girl / Local boy chops wood / Sunshine superman / Living for the lovelight / Till I see you again.
LP: . . . . PL 70060
MC: . . . . PK 70060

LOVE IS ONLY FEELING.
LP: . . . . PL 28472

MINSTREL BOY.
Tracks: / Catch the wind / Colours / Josie / Universal soldier / Remember the Alamo / Donna Donna / Ballad of a crystal man.
LP: . . . . DOW 13
MC: . . . . ZCDOW 13

NEUTRONICA.
LP: . . . . PL 28429
MC: . . . . TCPL 28429

OPEN ROAD.
LP: . . . . DNLS 3009

SPOTLIGHT ON DONOVAN.
Tracks: / Catch the wind / Remember the Alamo / To sing for you / Ramblin' boy / I'll try for the sun / Ballad of Geraldine, The / Colours / Josie / Cuttin' out / Gold watch blues / Tangerine puppet / Belated forgiveness plea / Turquoise / Candy man / Circus of sour / Sunny Goodge Street / Jersey Thursday / Hey Gyp (dig the slowness) / Universal soldier / Donna Donna / Little tin soldier / War drags on, The / Ballad of a crystal man / You're gonna need somebody on your bond.
2LP: . . . . SPOT 1017
MCSET: . . . . ZCSPT 1017

SUNSHINE SUPERMAN.
LP: . . . . NPL 18181
LP: . . . . BGOLP 68
MC: . . . . BGOMC 68

TRIP, THE.
Tracks: / Trip, The / Lullaby of the spring / Sunny south Kensington / Sand and foam / Someone singing / Guinevere / Celeste / Widow with a shawl (a portrait) / Writer in the sun / Entertaining of a shy girl / Land of doesn't have to be, The / Skip along Sam / Hampstead incident / Mad John's escape / Three kingfishers / Little boy in corduroy / Isle of Islay / Young girl blues / Museum / As I recall it / Legend of a young girl Linda / House of Jansch / Oh gosh / There was a time.
2LP: . . . . EM 1385
MCSET: TC2EM 1385

UNIVERSAL SOLDIER.
Tracks: / Universal soldier / Josie / Ballad of Geraldine, The / War drags on, The / Colours / Sunny Goodge Street / Turquoise / I'll try for the sun / Hey Gyp (dig the slowness) / Belated forgiveness plea / Candy man / Ballad of a crystal man.
LP: . . . . SPR 8514
MC: . . . . SPC 8514
LP: . . . . MAL 718

UNIVERSAL SOLDIER (DITTO).
MCSET: . . . . DTO 10206

WHAT'S BIN DID AND WHAT'S BIN HID.
LP: . . . . NPL 18117

WORLD OF DONOVAN.
2LP: 66289

Donovan, Jason

BETWEEN THE LINES.
LP: . . . . HF 14
MC: . . . . HFC 14

ESPECIALLY FOR YOU (See under Minogue, Kylie) (Donovan, Jason & Kylie Minogue).

GREATEST HITS: JASON DONOVAN.
MC: . . . . HFC 20
LP: . . . . HF 20

INTERVIEW COMPACT DISC: KYLIE & JASON (See under Minogue, Kylie) (Donovan, Jason & Kylie Minogue).

JASON DONOVAN: INTERVIEW PICTURE DISC.
LPPD: . . . . BAK 2162

TEN GOOD REASONS.
Tracks: / Too many broken hearts / Nothing can divide us / Every day (I love you more) / You can depend on me / Time heals / Sealed with a kiss / Question of pride / If I don't have you / Change your mind / Too late to say goodbye / Especially for you.
LP: . . . . HF 7
MC: . . . . HFC 7

Donovan (Reggae)

BANZANI.
Tracks: / Banzani (own soldier) / Down in the ghetto / Me nuh business / Days of sorrow / Serious man / Devil workshop / I'm not afraid / Crazy daisy / Plantation / Ain't no love at all.
MC: . . . . MCT 1011
LP: . . . . MLPS 1011

Donovan, Tom

SONGS OF DUBLIN.
MC: . . . . EI 805

SONGS OF GALWAY.
MC: . . . . EI 804

SONGS OF KILKENNY (Donovan, Tom & Liam O'Donnell).
LP: . . . . EI 817

SONGS OF ULSTER.
MC: . . . . EI 810

Don't Know Boy

DON'T KNOW BOY, THE (Various artists).
Tracks: / Don't know boy, The: *Various artists* / Comorre the accursed: *Various artists* / North-West wind, The: *Various artists* / Foster brother, The: *Various artists* / King's godson, The: *Various artists* / Tristram and Ysonded: *Various artists.*
MC: . . . . ANV 656

Don't Look Now (film)

DON'T LOOK NOW (1973 film soundtrack) (Various artists).
Tracks: / John's theme: *Various artists* / Candles for Christine: *Various artists* / John's vision: *Various* artists / Through the street: *Various artists* / Dead end: *Various artists* / Christine is dead: *Various* artists / Strange happenings: *Various artists* / Searching for Laura: *Various artists* / Laura comes back: *Various artists* / Laura's theme: *Various artists.*
LP: . . . . TER 1007

Don't Make Waves

DON'T MAKE WAVES (Original soundtrack) (Various artists).
LP: . . . . MCA 25134
MC: . . . . MCAC 25134

Doo Wop

20 GREAT DOOWOP RECORDINGS (Various artists).
Tracks: / Pennies from Heaven: *Skyliners* / Hush-a-bye: *Mystics* / Automobile: *Stickshifts* / Dearest darling: *Smith, Huey "Piano"* / Penalty of love: *Velvetones* / Cool, baby, cool: *Flairs* / Way you look tonight: *Lonely guys, The* / Under stars of love: *Carlos Brothers* / Stay where you are: *Olympics* / Saturday night fish fry: *Blue dots* / These golden rings: *Strangers, The* / Just for you and I: *Supremes* / Why don't you write me: *Jacks* / Love only you: *Meadowlarks* / All I do is rock: *Robins, The* / I believe: *Twilighters* / Please understand: *Milton, Buddy/Twilighters* / Please don't tell 'em: *Blue dots* / Cold chills: *Sounds* / When I fall in love: *Skyliners.*
LP: . . . . DROP 1008
MC: . . . . CROP 1008

CHESS DOO WOP (Various artists).
Tracks: / Let me in: *Sensations* / Peanut butter: *Marathons* / Knee socks: *Ideals* / Sincerely: *Moonglows*/ MTYLTT: *Dream Kings* / I'm so young: *Students* / Long lonely nights: *Andrews, Lee & The Hearts* / False alarm: *Revels* / I'll be home: *Flamingos* / Over the mountain across the sea: *Johnny & Joe* / Happy happy birthday baby: *Tune Weavers.*
LP: . . . . GCH 8101
MC: GCHK78101

CHESS DOO WOP (2) (Various artists).
Tracks: / White cliffs of Dover: *Blue Jays* / Darling I know: *El Rays* / Shoo doo be doo: *Moonlighters*/ Newly weds: *Orchids* / Show me the way: *Five Notes* / Give me (a simple prayer): *Ravens* / Nadine: *Coronets*/ Ding dong: *Quintones* / 4 o'clock in the morning: *Tornados* / I want to love: *Sentimentals* / Teardrops: *Andrews, Lee & The Hearts* / Soft shadows: *Monotones* / I'm so young: *Students* / So far away: *Pastels*/ This broken heart: *Sonics* / False alarm: *Ravels.*
LP: . . . . DET 200

COULD THIS BE MAGIC (Various artists).
Tracks: / Daddy's home: *Various artists* / Gee: *Various artists* / Crying in the chapel: *Various artists*/ Thousand miles away: *Various artists* / Could this be magic: *Various artists* / Sunday kind of love: *Various* artists / Don't say goodnight: *Various artists* / Come back my love: *Various artists* / Tears on my pillow: *Various artists* / See you in September: *Various artists* / I only have eyes for you: *Various artists*/ Maybe: *Various artists* / Million to one: *Various artists* / Sippin' soda: *Various artists.*
LP: . . . . NCP 1001

DANCIN' AND ROMANCIN' (Various artists).
Tracks: / Up on the mountain: *Magnificents* / Down off the mountain: *Magnificents* / You ain't ready: *Flamingos*/ Crazy over you: *Kool Gents* / Feeling alright: *HiLighters* / Stop: *Lyrics* / Get lost: *Rhythm Aces*/ Tears on my pillow: *Eldorados* / Caddy bo: *Magnificents* / Blues in the letter: *Magnificents* / Secret love: *Moonglows* /

For all we know: *Orioles* / Ozeta: *Magnificents* / Hurry home baby: *Flamingos*/ Lonely one, The: *Sherrif & The Ravels* / Now that it's over: *Falcons* / I was wrong: *Moonglows* / Hellow dear: *HiLighters*.
LP: . . . . **CRB 1115**

DON'T STOP ... DOO WOP (Various artists).
LP: . . . . **STAR 2485**
MC: . . . . **STAC 2485**

DOO WOP (Best of Chess/Checker/ Cadet) (Various artists).
Tracks: / Let me in: *Sensations* / Peanut butter: *Marathons* / Knee socks: *Ideals* / Sincerely: *Moonglows*/ M T Y L T T: *Dream Kings* / I'm so young: *Students* / Long lonely nights: *Andrews, Lee & The Hearts*/ False alarm: *Revels* / I'll be home: *Flamingos* / Over the mountain across the sea: *Johnny & Joe* / Happy happy birthday baby: *Tune Weavers* / Been so long: *Pastels* / Tippety top: *Rays* / White cliffs of Dover, The: *Blue Jays*.
LP: . . . . **CXMP 2004**

DOO WOP (Various artists).
Tracks: / Pretty little girl: *Chimes* / Our schooldays: *Monitors* / Bad boy: *Williams, Larry* / Sweet breeze: *Green, Vernon & The Fountains* / Dream girl: *Jessie & Marvin* / Flip: *Marvin, Johnny* / Wheel of fortune: *Four Flames* / Moose on the loose: *Jackson, Roddy* / Cherokee dance: *Landers, Bob* / That mellow saxophone: *Montrell, Roy* / Drunk: *Liggins, Jimmy* / Animal song: *Perry, King* / Cleo: *Hall, Rene* / Traffic song: *Lutcher, Joe*.
LP: . . . . **SNTF 5016**

DOO WOP BALLADS (Various artists).
Tracks: / In the still of the night: *Five Satins* / Oh what a night: *Dells* / Sixteen candles: *Crests*/ My true story: *Passions* / Where or when: *Dion & The Belmonts* / Sincerely: *Moonglows* / For your precious love: *Butler, Jerry & The Impressions* / Earth angel: *Penguins* / Lover's island: *Blue Jays* / Angel baby: *Rosie & The Originals* / Happy, happy birthday baby: *Tune Weavers* / Tonight, tonight: *Mello Kings* / Goodnight sweetheart: *Spaniels* / Gloria: *Passions*.
LP: . . . . **RNLP 70181**
MC: . . . . **RNC 70181**

DOO WOP CLASSICS VOL 1 (Various artists).
LP: . . . . **XELLP 107**
MC: . . . . **XELMC 107**

DOO WOP DELIGHTS (Roots of rock 'n' roll) (Various artists).
LP: . . . . **SJL 1185**

DOO WOP JIVE & STROLL VOL. 1 (Various artists).
LP: . . . . **DJSLP 001**

DOO WOP JIVE & STROLL VOL. 3 (Various artists).
LP: . . . . **DWJS LP 003**

DOO WOP SONS 1954-61 (Music City Records) (Various artists).
LP: . . . . **JD 903**

DOO WOP UPTEMPO (Various artists).
Tracks: / Come go with me: *Del-Vikings* / Rama lama ding dong: *Edsels* / At my front door: *Eldorados*/ Church bells may ring: *Willows* / Buzz buzz buzz: *Hollywood Flames* / I wonder why: *Dion & The Belmonts*/ Unchained melody: *Vito & The Salutations* / Book of love: *Monotones* / Get a job: *Silhouettes* (1958) / When you dance: *Turbans* / Little star: *Elegants* / Step by step: *Crests* / Tonight I fell in love: *Tokens* / Whispering bells: *Del-Vikings*.
LP: . . . . **RNLP 70182**
MC: . . . . **RNC 70182**

DOO WOPS, VOLUME 2 (Various artists).
LP: **1102**

DOO WOPS, VOLUME 3 (Various artists).
LP: **1103**

DOO WOPS, VOLUME 5 (Various artists).
LP: **1105**

DOO WOPS, VOLUME 6 (Various artists).
LP: **1106**

DOOTONE STORY, THE VOL 1 (Various artists).
Tracks: / Ding a ling: *Crescendos* / Baby doll: *Crescendos* / I can't go on: *Milton, Roy & his Orchestra*/ You got me reelin' & rockin': *Milton, Roy & his Orchestra* / My girl: *McCullough, Charles & the Silks* / I got tore up: *Julian, Don & the Meadowlarks* / This must be paradise: *Julian, Don & the Meadowlarks* / Please Mr Jordan: *Duncan, Cleve & the Penguins* / Flee oo wee: *Calvanes* / Wet back hop: *Higgins, Chuck* / Don't you know I love you baby: *Higgins, Chuck* / Boogie woogie teenage: *Meadowlarks* / Be fair: *Pipes...* / Buick '59: *Green, Vernon & the Medallions* / Magic mountain: *Green, Vernon & the Medallions* / Jump and hop: *Romancers*.
LP: . . . . **CHD 242**

DOO-WOP JIVE & STROLL VOL. 2 (Various artists).
LP: . . . . **DJSLP 002**

DOO-WOP OLDTOWN (Various artists).
LP: . . . . **SNTF 820**

DOO-WOP, ROCK, ROCK, ROCK'N'ROLL (Various artists).
LP: **6498 044**

GOLDEN GROUPS VOL.3 (Various artists).
LP: . . . . **ANGLE TONE 5012**

GOLDEN GROUPS VOL.4 (Various artists).
LP: . . . . **CELESTE 5014**

GOLDEN GROUPS VOL.5 (Various artists).
LP: . . . . **HERALD 5015**

GOLDEN GROUPS VOL.6 (Various artists).
LP: . . . . **EMBER 5016**

GOLDEN GROUPS VOL.7 (Various artists).
LP: . . . . **WINLEY 5019**

GOLDEN GROUPS VOL.42 (Best of Lummtone) (Various artists).
LP: . . . . **RELIC 5068**

GOLDEN GROUPS VOL.43 (Best of Combo) (Various artists).
LP: . . . . **RELIC 5069**

GOLDEN GROUPS, VOLUME 44 (Best of Combo, Volume 2) (Various artists).
LP: . . . . **RELIC 5070**

OLDIES BUT GOODIES-DOO WOP STYLE (Various artists).
Tracks: / Blue moon: *Marcels* / Smokey places: *Various artists* / Jerk (The): *Various artists* / Those oldies but goodies: *Various artists* / Earth angel: *Various artists* / Since I don't have you: *Various artists*/ Love potion No.9: *Various artists* / La la la la la: *Various artists* / Lover's island: *Various artists*/ Come go with me: *Various artists* / Needles and pins: *Various artists* / Diamonds and pearls: *Various artists*.
LP: . . . . **TOP 161**
MC: . . . . **KTOP 161**

ORIGINAL CLASSICS: DOO WOP HITS (Various artists).
LP: **522 020**
MC: **722 020**

STREET CORNER MEMORIES (Various artists).
Tracks: / Denise: *Various artists* / Bye bye: *Various artists* / Lovely way to spend an evening, A: *Various* artists / Please write: *Various artists* / Cry and be on my way: *Various artists* / In the beginning: *Various* artists / Little star: *Various artists* / I love you Diane: *Various artists* / Judy: *Various artists*/ Why do kids grow up: *Various artists* / I'll always love you: *Various artists* / Away: *Various artists*/ Jeannie baby: *Various artists* / Candy queen: *Various artists* / Don't worry: *Various artists* / 4 seasons: *Various artists*.
LP: . . . . **CHD 215**

STREET CORNER MEMORIES VOL.1 (Various artists).
Tracks: / Queen of the angels: *Orients, The* / Zoom, zoom, zoom: *Enchords, The* / Gloria: *Passions, The*/ I remember: *Five discs, The* / Angel in my eyes: *Premiere, Ronnie* / Oh melancholy: *Passions, The* / Daddy's going away again: *Harps, The* / Hello dolly: *Vito & The Salutations* / Shrine of St Cecilia: *Bon-Aires*, The / Shouldn't I: *Orients, The* / Just to be with you: *Passions, The* / Hush-a-bye: *Dino & the diplomats*/ You, you my love: *Jo-vals, The* / I can remain truly yours: *Criterions, The* / Wake up: *Elegants* / This is my love: *Passions, The*.
LP: . . . . **CH 205**

VOCAL GROUPS VOL.21 (DOO-WOP) (Various artists).
LP: . . . . **RELIC 5043**

WEST COAST DOOWOP (Various artists).
Tracks: / Oochi pachie: *Maye, Arthur Lee & The Crowns* / Truly: *Maye, Arthur Lee & The Crowns* / Cold chills: *Sounds* / Tell me, thrill me: *Chanters* / She wants to Mambo: *Chanters* / Cool baby cool: *Flairs*/ Hey Rube: *Rocketeers* / Pass the gin: *Meadowlarks* / L-F-M-S-T blues: *Meadowlarks* / Please understand: *Milton, Buddy/Twilighters* / Say another word: *Milton, Buddy/Twilighters* / Real pretty Mama: *Meadowlarks*/ Love only you: *Meadowlarks* / Loop de loop: *Maye, Arthur Lee & The Crowns*.
LP: . . . . **CH 87**

Doobie Brothers

BEST OF THE DOOBIE BROTHERS.
Tracks: / China grove / Long train runnin' / Takin' it to the streets / Listen to the music / Black water / Rockin' down the highway / Jesus is just alright / It keeps you runnin' / South City midnight lady / Take me in your arms / Without you.
LP: . . . . **K 56308**
MC: **K4 56308**

BEST OF THE DOOBIES VOL 2.
Tracks: / Little darling (I need you) / Echoes of love / You belong to me / One step closer / What a fool believes / Dependin' on you / Here to love you / One by one / Real love / Minute by minute.
LP: . . . . **K 56956**
MC: **K4 56956**

BROTHERHOOD.
Tracks: / Something you said / Is love enough / Dangerous / Our love / Divided highway / Under the spell / Excited / This train I'm on / Showdown / Rollin' on.
LP: . . . . **EST 2141**
MC: . . . . **TCEST 2141**

CAPTAIN AND ME, THE.
Tracks: / Natural thing / Long train runnin' / China grove / Dark-eyed Cajun woman / Clear as the driven snow / Without you / South City midnight lady / Evil woman / Busted down around O'Connelly Corners / Ukiah / Captain and me, The.
MC: **K4 46217**
LP: . . . . **K 46217**

CYCLES.
Tracks: / Doctor, The / One chain (don't make no prison) / Take me to the highway / South of the border / Time is here and gone / Need a little taste of love / I can read your mind / Tonight I'm coming through (the border) / Wrong number / Too high a price.
LP: . . . . **EST 2100**
MC: . . . . **TCEST 2100**

DOOBIE BROTHERS.
Tracks: / Nobody / Slippery St. Paul / Greenwood Creek / It won't be right / Travellin' man / Feeling down farther / Master, The / Growin' a little each day / Beehive state / Closer every day / Chicago.
LP: . . . . **K 46090**

FAREWELL TOUR.
Tracks: / Slippery St. Paul / Takin' it to the streets / Jesus is just alright / Minute by minute / Can't let it get away / Listen to the music / Echoes of love / What a fool believes / Black water / You belong to me / Slat key soquel rag / Steamer lane breakdown / South city midnight lady / Olana / Don't start me to talkin' / Long train runnin' / China grove.
LP: **923772 1**

LIVIN' ON THE FAULT LINE.
Tracks: / Nothin' but a heartache / Little darling (I need you) / Livin' on the fault line / Larry the logger two-step / Need a lady / You're made that way / Chinatown / There's a light / You belong to me / Echoes of love.
LP: . . . . **K 56383**
MC: **K4 56383**

MINUTE BY MINUTE.
Tracks: / Here to love you / What a fool believes / Minute by minute / Dependin' on you / Don't stop to watch the wheels / Open your eyes / Sweet feelin' / Streamer lane breakdown / You never change / How do fools survive.
MC: **K4 56486**
LP: . . . . **K 56486**

ONE STEP CLOSER.
Tracks: / Dedicate this heart / Real love / No stoppin' us now / Thank you love / One step closer / Keep this train a rollin' / Just in time / South bay strut / One by one.
LP: . . . . **K 56824**
MC: **K4 56824**

STAMPEDE.
Tracks: / Sweet Maxine / Neal's fandango / Texas lullaby / Music man / Slat key soquel rag / Take me in your arms / I cheat the hangman / Precis / Rainy day crossroad blues / I been workin' on you / Double dealin' four flusher.
LP: . . . . **K 56094**
MC: **K4 56094**

TAKIN' IT TO THE STREETS.
Tracks: / Wheels of fortune / Takin' it to the streets / 8th Avenue shuffle / Losin' end / Rio / For someone special / It keeps you runnin' / Turn it loose / Carry me away.
LP: . . . . **K 56196**

TAKIN' IT TO THE STREETS/LIVIN' ON THE FAULT LINE.
Tracks: / Wheels of fortune / Takin' it to the streets / 8th avenue shuffle / Losin' end / Rio / For someone special / It keeps you runnin' / Turn it loose / Carry me away / Nothin' but a heartache / Little darling (I need you) / Livin' on the fault line / Larry the logger two-step / Need a lady / You're made that way / Chinatown / There's a light / You belong to me / Echoes of love.
MC: . . . . **K 466117**

TOULOUSE STREET.
Tracks: / Listen to the music / Rockin' down the highway / Mamaloi / Toulouse Street / Cotton mouth / Don't start me to talkin' / Jesus is just alright / White sun / Disciple / Snakeman.
LP: . . . . **K 46183**

WHAT WERE ONCE VICES.
Tracks: / Another park, another Sunday / Black water / Daughters of the sea / Down in the track / Eyes of silver / Flying cloud / Pursuit on 53rd street / Road angel / Song to see you through / Spirit / Tell me what you want (and I'll give you what you need) / You just can't stop it.
LP: . . . . **K 56026**
MC: **K4 56026**

Dooleys

6 TRACK HITS: DOOLEYS.
Tracks: / Honey I'm lost / I think I'm gonna fall in love with you / Don't take it lying down / Love patrol / Rose has to die, A / Wanted.
MC: **7SC 5047**

BEST OF THE DOOLEYS.
Tracks: / Wanted / Love of my life / Rose has to die, A / Hands across the sea / Think I'm gonna fall in love with you / Honey I'm lost / Don't take it lyin' down.
LP: . . . . **GTTV 038**
MC: . . . . **GTTC 038**

CHOSEN FEW, THE.
LP: . . . . **GTLP 040**

FULL HOUSE.
Tracks: / Body language / Love patrol / Chosen few / Don't cry for me Argentina / Operator / In a riddle.
LP: . . . . **GTTV 050**
MC: . . . . **GTTC 050**

GREATEST HITS: DOOLEYS.
Tracks: / Wanted / Love of my life / Rose has to die, A / Honey I'm lost / Stand up like a man / What's gonna happen to our love? / Think I'm gonna fall in love with you / Hands across the sea / Don't take it lying down / Sad old Spanish guitar / Stone walls / Don't let me be the last to know.
LP: . . . . **SPR 8519**
MC: . . . . **SPC 8519**

SECRETS.
Tracks: / And I wish / Dancer / Tip of my tongue / What you got / Love trap / Love me love me do / Tokyo feeling / One way loving / In real life / Sooner or later / Will we still be dancing / Secrets.
LP: . . . . **GTLP 048**

Doom

TOTAL DOOM.
LP: . . . . **VILE 011**

WAR CRIMES.
LP: . . . . **VILE 4**

Doonan, John

AT THE FEIS.
Tracks: / Jackie Coleman's reel / Paddy Cavanagh's / John Brennan's / Any old jig will do / Butterfly / Rodney's glory / Idle road, The / Frost is all over, The / Black rogue, The / Spalpeen's lament, The / Kesh, The / Morrison's / Old Joe's / Shannon breeze / Heathery breeze / Green fields of Amerikay / Blackthorn stick / Hurry the dance / Rub the bag / Blackbird, The / Spellan the fiddler / Rights of man, The / Irish washerwoman, The / Father O'Flynn / Lilting fisherman, The.
LP: **12TS 368**

FLUTE FOR THE FEIS.
Tracks: / Sean Maguire's / MacMahon's reel / Hunt, The / Smash the windows / Off she goes / Bonaparte's Retreat / Sport of the chase, The / Flowers of Antrim / Quarrelsome piper, The / An coolin / Fermoy lassies / Sporting Paddy / Dawn / Ace and deuce of pipering, The / Saddle the pony / Shandon bells / Little heathy hill / King of the Fairies, The / Taimse I'm Chadladh / Bonnie Kate / Jenny's chickens.
LP: . . . . **LEA 2043**

Doonican, Val

6 TRACK HITS: VAL DOONICAN.
Tracks: / Leaving on a jet plane / Little arrows / I recall a gypsy woman / Little green apples / Here you come again / You and me against the world.
MC: **7SC 5023**

20 PERSONAL FAVOURITES FOR YOU.

Tracks: / Snowbird / I'm just a country boy / Little green apples / My cup runneth over / You and me against the world / Folks who live on the hill, The / All I ever need is you / Try to remember / Mysterious people / Annie's song / Things / Walking in the sunshine / Morning of my life / He'll have to go / Sing a rainbow / Portrait of my love / Small world / Man chases a girl, A / King of the road / Scarlet ribbons.
LP: . . . . **WW 2001**
MC: . . . . **WW 20014**

BY REQUEST.
Tracks: / Umbrella man / Home town / Underneath the arches / You'll never know / More I see you, The / As time goes by / Very thought of you, The / You are my sunshine / I'll be with you in Apple Blossom time / Whispering / Moonlight and roses / Bye bye blues / My resistance is low / Ole buttermilk sky / Old music master, The / What a difference a day made / But beautiful / When I fall in love / Smilin' through / When you and I were young Maggie / I'll take you home again Kathleen / Galway bay.
LP: . . . . **MFP 5804**
MC: . . . . **TCMFP 5804**

FOCUS ON VAL DOONICAN.
Tracks: / Walk tall / Elusive butterfly / O'Rafferty's motor car / Are you sincere / Memories are made of this / Sing a rainbow / Special years, The / Impossible / Tell me soldier / That's how much I love you / Turn around / I sat back and let it happen / Delaney's donkey / What would I be / Paddy McGinty's goat / Quiet girl, A / Remember me / I gave my love a cherry / I'm just a country boy / I'm gonna get there somehow / Gentle Mary / I still love you / It must be you / Agricultural Irish girl.
2LP: . . . . **FOS 9/10**
MC: . . . . **KFOC 28045**

FORTY SHADES OF GREEN.
LP: . . . . **MFP 5624**
MC: . . . . **TCMFP 5624**

GENTLE SHADES OF VAL DOONICAN.
LP: . . . . **LK 4831**

I LOVE COUNTRY MUSIC.
LP: **9299261**

IMAGES: VAL DOONICAN.
Tracks: / Welcome to my world / Song sung blue / Spanish eyes / Everybody's talkin' / Amazing Grace.
LP: . . . . **WEF 2**
MC: . . . . **CWEF 2**

LUCKY 13 SHADES OF VAL DOONICAN.
LP: . . . . **LK 4648**

MAGIC OF VAL DOONICAN.
LP: **6642 003**

MEMORIES ARE MADE OF THIS.
Tracks: / Walk tall / Special years, The / What would I be / Paddy McGinty's goat / Marvellous toy, The / Delaney's donkey / Memories are made of this / Elusive butterfly / Mysterious people / Two streets / I'm just a country boy / I'm gonna get there somehow / Travelling home / O'Rafferty's motor car.
LP: . . . . **TAB 29**
MC: . . . . **KTBC 29**

MR MUSIC MAN.
Tracks: / Killing me softly with her song / Behind closed doors / That's what friends are for / Annie's song / Thing called love / Morning / All I ever need is you / Until it's time for you to go / Cryin' time / Who's gonna love me now / Can't help falling in love / Love's been good to me.
LP: . . . . **SHM 3067**
MC: . . . . **HSC 3067**

QUIET MOMENTS.
Tracks: / Chanson pour les petits enfants / I never had it so good / My land / Fly away / Follow me / Light the candles / French waltz / Quiet moments / Let's take the long way round the world / Flowers and wine.
LP: . . . . **RCALP 5018**
MC: . . . . **RCAK 5081**

RELAX WITH VAL DOONICAN.
Tracks: / Windmills of your mind / Sunny / First time ever I saw your face, The / Wichita lineman / Stranger on the shore / All my lovin' / Green green grass of home / Story of my life / Here, there and everywhere / Morning has broken / Streets of London / It's impossible / Tie a yellow ribbon / Yesterday / If I were a carpenter / And I love you so / Gentle on my mind / For the good times / My colouring book / I love you because.
LP: . . . . **MFP 5575**
MC: . . . . **TCMFP 5575**

SOME OF MY BEST FRIENDS ARE SONGS.
Tracks: / Some of my best friends are songs.
LP: **6641 607**

SONGBOOK, THE.
Tracks: / Here I go again / Mississippi / Amanda / Me and the elephant / Snowbird / Walk right back / Things / Brown eyes / Country roads / Songs / Walking in the sunshine / Everybody's talkin'.
LP: . . . . **SPR 8503**
MC: . . . . **SPC 8503**

SONGS FROM MY SKETCH BOOK.
Tracks: / My land / Ring of bright water / Memories are made of this / Wonderful world / Spanish lady / Isle Of Innisfree / Beautiful dreamer / Young at heart / Try to remember / Close to you / Little Bridget Flynn / Just the way you are / Sun always shines when you're young, The / Somewhere out there / Stardust (Not on album.) / Deep purple (Not on album.) / September song (Not on album.) / Soon it's gonna rain (Not on album.).
LP: . . . . **PMLP 5014**
MC: . . . . **PMMC 5016**

SOUNDS GENTLE.
LP: . . . . **NSPL 18321**

THIS IS VAL DOONICAN.
LP: **6382 017**

VAL.
LP: . . . . **NSPL 18321**

VAL DOONICAN MUSIC SHOW.
Tracks: / You'll never know / More I see you, The / As time goes by / Very thought of you, The / What a difference a day made / But beautiful / When I fall in love / Smilin' through.
LP: . . . . **REB 510**
MC: . . . . **ZCF 510**

VAL DOONICAN ROCKS BUT GENTLY.
LP: . . . . **NSPL 18204**

VAL SINGS BING.
Tracks: / Pocketful of dreams / Meet the sun halfway / Sing a song of sunbeams / True love / Accentuate the positive / Moonlight becomes you / Irish lullaby / Swinging on a star / Mississippi mud / That sly old gentleman / May I / Beautiful dreamer / Dear hearts and gentle people / Lazy / Gone fishin' / Small fry / Lazybones.
LP: . . . . **INTS 5210**
MC: . . . . **INTK 5210**

VERY BEST OF VAL DOONICAN, THE.
Tracks: / Special years, The / Elusive butterfly / If the whole world stopped loving / Morning / For the good times / First time ever I saw your face, The / Heaven is my woman's love / Now / Paddy McGinty's goat / Walk tall / If I knew then what I know now / What would I be / O'Rafferty's motor car / Marvellous toy / Song sung blue / King of the road / Two streets / I'm just a country boy / Delaney's donkey.
MC: . . . . **MCTC 008**

VERY BEST OF VAL DOONICAN, THE (MFP).
Tracks: / Walk tall / Special years, The / Delaney's donkey / I'm gonna get there somehow / Paddy McGinty's goat / Elusive butterfly / Marvellous toy, The / What would I be? / O'Rafferty's motor car / Memories are made of this / Two streets / If the whole world stopped lovin' / You're the only one / Now / If I knew then what I know now / Ring of bright water / Morning / Heaven is my woman's love / If you could read my mind / I recall a gypsy woman.
LP: . . . . **MFP 41 5681 1**
MC: . . . . **MFP 41 5681 4**

WORLD OF VAL DOONICAN.
Tracks: / Walk tall / Delaney's donkey / Mysterious people / Elusive butterfly / Juice of the barley, The / Cod liver oil / What would I be? / Jarvey was a leprechaun, The / O'Rafferty's motor car / Tender years / Paddy McGinty's goat / Two streets.
LP: . . . . **SPA 3**

WORLD OF VAL DOONICAN: VOL 3.
MC: . . . . **KCSP 79**

Door & The Window

DETAILED TWANG.
LP: . . . . **NB 5**

PERMANENT TRANSCIENCE.
LP: . . . . **NB 2**

Doors

13.
Tracks: / Light my fire / People are strange / Back door man / Moonlight drive / Crystal ship, The / Roadhouse blues / Touch me / Love me two times / You're lost / Hello I love you / Land ho / Wild child / Unknown soldier, The / Little girl.
LP: . . . . **K 42062**
MC: **K4 42062**

ABSOLUTELY LIVE.
Tracks: / Who do you love? / Alabama song / Back door man / Love hides / Five to one / Build me a woman / When the music's over / Close to you / Universal mind / Break on through / Celebration of the lizard / Soul kitchen.
2LP: . . . . **K 62005**
2LP: **2665 002**

ALIVE SHE CRIED.
Tracks: / Gloria / Light my fire / You make me real / Texas radio and the big beat / Love me two times / Little red rooster / Moonlight drive.
LP: **9602691**
MC: **9602694**

AMERICAN PRAYER, AN (Jim Morrison music).
Tracks: / Awake / To come of age / Poet's dreams / World on fire / American prayer, An.
LP: . . . . **K 52111**
MC: **K4 52211**

BEST OF THE DOORS.
Tracks: / Who do you love / Soul kitchen / Hello, I love you / People are strange / Riders on the storm / Touch me / Love her madly / Love me two times / Take it as it comes / Moonlight drive / Light my fire.
LP: . . . . **K 42143**

BEST OF THE DOORS (DOUBLE).
Tracks: / Break on through / Light my fire / Crystal ship, The / People are strange / Strange days / Love me two times / Five to one / Waiting for the sun / Spanish caravan / When the musics over / Hello, I love you / Roadhouse blues / L.A. Woman / Riders on the storm / Touch me / Love her madly / Unknown soldier, The / End, The.
LP: . . . . **EKT 21**
MC: . . . . **EKT 21 C**
LP: **9603451**
MC: **9603454**

CLASSICS.
Tracks: / Strange days / Love her madly / Waiting for the sun / My eyes have seen you / Wild child / Crystal ship, The / Five to one / Roadhouse blues / Land ho / I can't see your face in my mind / Peace frog / Wasp, The / Unknown soldier, The.
LP: . . . . **EKT 9**
MC: . . . . **EKT 9 C**

DOORS.
Tracks: / Break on through / Soul kitchen / Crystal ship, The / Twentieth Century Fox / Alabama song / Light my fire / Back door man / I looked at you / End of the night / Take it as it comes / End, The.
LP: . . . . **K 42012**
MC: **K4 42012**

DOORS IN CONCERT, THE.
LP: . . . . **EKT 88**
MC: . . . . **EKT 88 C**

DOORS: VOL 2.
Tracks: / Hello I love you / Soul kitchen / My eyes have seen you / Running blue / Soft parade, The / Touch me / Crystal ship, The / Wild child / Love street / Horse latitudes / Riders on the storm.
LP: . . . . **K 22008**
MC: **K4 22008**

GREATEST HITS: DOORS.
Tracks: / Hello I love you / Light my fire / People are strange / Love me two times / Riders on the storm / Break on through / Roadhouse blues / Touch me / L.A. woman / Not to touch / Earth, The.
LP: . . . . **K 52254**
MC: **K4 52254**

INTERVIEW WITH JIM MORRISON.
LPPD: . . . . **DOORS 1**

L.A. WOMAN.
Tracks: / Changeling / Love her madly / Cars hiss by my window / L.A. woman / L'America / Hyacinth house / Crawling king snake / Wasp, The / Riders on the storm.
LP: . . . . **K 42090**
MC: **K4 42090**

LIVE AT THE HOLLYWOOD BOWL.
Tracks: / Wake up / Light my fire / Unknown soldier, The / Little games / Hill dwellers, The / Spanish caravan.
LP: . . . . **EKT 40**
MC: . . . . **EKT 40 C**

MORRISON HOTEL.
Tracks: / Roadhouse blues / Waiting for the sun / You make me real / Peace frog / Blue Sunday / Ship of fools / Land ho / Spy, The / Queen of the highway / Indian Summer / Maggie McGill.
LP: . . . . **K 42080**
LP: **EKS7 5007**

MORRISON HOTEL/L.A. WOMAN.
Tracks: / Roadhouse blues / Waiting for the sun / You make me real / Peace frog / Blue Sunday / Ship of fools / Land ho / Spy, The / Queen of the highway / Indian Summer / Maggie McGill / Changeling / Love her madly / Been down so long / Cars hiss by my window / L.A. woman / L'America / Hyacinth house / Crawling king snake / Wasp, The / Riders on the storm.
MC: **K4 62034**

SOFT PARADE.
Tracks: / Tell all the people / Touch me / Shaman's blues / Do it / Easy rider / Wild child / Running blue / Wishful sin / Soft parade, The.
MC: **K4 62040**
LP: . . . . **K 42079**
MC: **K4 42079**

SOFT PARADE/AMERICAN PRAYER.
Tracks: / Tell all the people / Touch me / Shamans blues / Do it / Easy rider / Wild child / Runnin' blue / Wishful sin / Soft parade, The / Awake / To come of age / Poet's dreams / World on fire / American prayer, An.
MC: . . . . **K 462040**

STRANGE DAYS.
Tracks: / Strange days / You're lost / Little girl / Love me two times / Unhappy girl / Horse latitudes / Moonlight drive / People are strange / My eyes have seen you / I can't see your face in my mind / When the music's over.
LP: . . . . **K 42016**
MC: **K4 42016**

WAITING FOR THE SUN.
Tracks: / Hello I love you / Love street / Not to touch / Earth, The / Summer's almost gone / Winter time love / Unknown soldier, The / Spanish caravan / My wild love / We could be so good together / Yes, the river knows / Five to one.
LP: **EKS7 4024**
LP: . . . . **K 42041**
MC: **K4 42041**

WEIRD SCENES INSIDE THE GOLDMINE.
Tracks: / Break on through / Strange days / Shaman's blues / Love street / Peace frog / Blue Sunday / Wasp, The / End of the night / Love her madly / Ship of fools / Spy, The / End, The / Take it as it comes / Running blue / L.A. woman / Five to one / Who scared you? / Don't go no further / Riders on the storm / Horse latitudes / Maggie McGill / You need meat.
2LP: . . . . **K 62009**
MCSET: **K4 62009**

Doowop

VOCAL GROUPS VOL.22 (DOO-WOP)
(Various artists).
LP: . . . . **RELIC 5044**

VOCAL GROUPS VOL.23 (DOO-WOP)
(Various artists).
LP: . . . . **RELIC 5045**

VOCAL GROUPS VOL.24 (DOO-WOP)
(Various artists).
LP: . . . . **RELIC 5046**

VOCAL GROUPS VOL.25 (DOO-WOP)
(Various artists).
LP: . . . . **RELIC 5047**

VOCAL GROUPS VOL.26 (DOO-WOP)
(Various artists).
LP: . . . . **RELIC 5048**

VOCAL GROUPS VOL.27 (DOO-WOP)
(Various artists).
LP: . . . . **RELIC 5049**

Doran, Felix

FOX CHASE.
MC: **30 172**

LAST OF THE TRAVELLING PIPERS, THE.
Tracks: / Mary of Munroe / Green gates, The / Dear Irish boy / Primrose lass, The / Rakish Paddy / Rolandstown churchyard / Ash plant, The / Lark in the morning, The / Fox hunt, The / George White's favourite / Ivy leaf, The / Coolin, The / Boys of the lough / Pigeon on the gate / Miss Monaghan.
LP: **12T 288**

Dore, Charlie

LISTEN.
Tracks: / Listen (I just want you) / Do me a favour / You should hear / Falling / Don't say no / Wise to the lines / I'm over here / Like they do it in America / Sister revenge / Didn't I tell you.
LP: . . . . **CHR 1325**
MC: . . . . **ZCHR 1325**

WHERE TO NOW? (ALBUM).
Tracks: / Pilot of the airwaves / Falling / Sad old world / Where to now? / Sleepless / Fear of flying / Wise owl / Hula valley / Pickin' apples o-sweetheart.

LP: . . . . ILPS 9559

Do-Re-Mi (show)

DO-RE-MI (Original London cast) (Various artists).
Tracks: / Do-re-mi: Overture: *Various artists* / Waiting waiting: *Various artists* / All you need is a quarter: *Various artists* / Take a job: *Various artists* / It's legitimate: *Various artists* / I know about love: *Various artists* / Cry like the wind: *Various artists* / Ambition: *Various artists* / Fire works: *Various* artists / What's new at the zoo?: *Various artists* / Asking for you: *Various artists* / Late, late show, The: *Various artists* / Adventure: *Various artists* / Make someone happy: *Various artists* / All of my life: *Various artists* / Do-re-mi: Finale: *Various artists.*
LP: . . . . TER 1075
MC: . . . . ZCTER 1075

Dorge, Pierre

BALLAD ROUND THE LEFT CORNER.
LP: . . . . SCS 1132

Dorham, Kenny

BUT BEAUTIFUL.
2LP: . . . . M 47036

DEXTER GORDON/KENNY DORHAM (Dorham, Kenny & Dexter Gordon).
Tracks: / Billie's bounce / Just friends / Summertime / Scrapple from the apple.
LP: . . . . JR 159

EASE IT.
Tracks: / Alvars / Stella by starlight / Why not? / Ease it / Samba de Orfeu / East 42nd Street.
LP: . . . . MR 5053

HOT STUFF FROM BRAZIL.
Tracks: / Wee dot / Red door, The / Autumn leaves / Halley's comet / Night in Tunisia / It's alright with me.
LP: . . . . WW 015

KENNY DORHAM/DEXTER GORDON (See under Gordon, Dexter).

MUSIC OF KENNY DORHAM.
LP: . . . . RSR 117

NEW BLUE HORNS (See under Baker Chet) (Dorham, Kenny & Chet Baker).

QUIET KENNY.
LP: . . . . OJC 250

ROUND MIDNIGHT AT THE CAFE BOHEMIA.
Tracks: / Mexico City / Night in Tunisia / Autumn in New York / Hill's edge / Monaco / Round Midnight.
LP: . . . . BST 81524

SCANDIA SKIES.
LP: . . . . SCS 6011

SHADOW OF YOUR SMILE.
LP: . . . . WW 2049

TROMPETA TOCCATA.
Tracks: / Trompeta toccata / Night watch / Mamacita / Fox, The.
LP: . . . . BST 84181

WEST 42ND STREET.
LP: . . . . BLP 60119

WHISTLE STOP.
Tracks: / Philly twist / Buffalo / Sunset / Whistle stop / Sunrise in mexico / Windmill / Dorham's epitaph.
LP: . . . . BLP 4063

Dorman, Harold

MOUNTAIN OF LOVE.
Tracks: / Mountain of love / I'll come running / Sounds like big trouble / Remember me / Is she willing to forget / Do you want to go steady / Mister tears / Love will find a way / Mountain of love (undubbed version) / Moving up to love / Moved to Kansas / Let there be love / Diamond rings / Soda pop baby / Lonely nights / Sweet sweet love (Medley.).
LP: . . . . BFX 15262

Dormannu

RETURN OF QUEBEC.
LP: . . . . JAMS 50

Doro

DORO.
Tracks: / Unholy love / I had too much to dream last night / Rock on / Only you / I'll be holding on / Something wicked this way comes / Rare diamond / Broken / Alive / Mirage.
LP: 846 194 1
MC: 846 194 4

FORCE MAJEURE (Doro & Warlock).
Tracks: / White shade of pale, A / Mission of mercy / Beyond the trees / Hellraiser / Cry wolf / Bis aufs blut / Save my soul / Angels with dirty faces / Hard times / I am what I am / River of tears / Under the gun.
LP: 838 016 1
MC: 838 016 4

RARE DIAMONDS (Doro & Warlock).
LP: 8483531
MC: 8483534

Dorough, Bob

DEVIL MAY CARE.
Tracks: / Old devil moon / It could happen to you / I had the craziest dream / You're the dangerous type / Ow / Polka dots and moonbeams / Yardbird suite / Baltimore oriole / Midnight sun / Johnny one note.
LP: . . . . AFF 176

Dors, Diana

SWINGIN' DORS.
Tracks: / Point of no return / That's how it is / Let there be love / Namely you / Imagination / Roller coaster blues / Gentleman is a dope, The / April heart / In love for the first time / Crazy he calls me / Come by Sunday / Tired of love.
LP: . . . . CFRC 501
MC: . . . . MCFRC 501
LPPD: . . . . CFRP 501

Dorsey Brothers

1935: DORSEY BROTHERS (Dorsey Brothers Orchestra).
LP: . . . . SLP 20

GLENN MILLER MEETS THE DORSEY BROTHERS (Miller, Glenn/Dorsey Brothers).
Tracks: / Boogie woogie / Moonlight serenade / String of pearls / Amapola / Little brown jug / Chattanooga choo choo / Green eyes / In the mood / Serenade in blue / I'm getting married / Over the rainbow / Song of India / So rare / I've got a gal in Kalamazoo / Sunrise serenade.
LP: . . . . XELLP 104
MC: . . . . XELMC 104

HARLEM LULLABY.
LP: . . . . HEP 1006

I'M GETTING SENTIMENTAL.
Tracks: / Lover / Skirts and sweaters / Manhattan / Oh, look at me now / I'm getting sentimental / Most beautiful girl in the world / Panama / Swing low sweet chariot / Tenderly / Door will open, A / Just as though you were here / Let's get away from it all / None but the lonely heart / It never entered my mind / Always in my heart / Everthing happens to me.
MC: 40176
LP: 20176

LEGENDARY DORSEY BROTHERS, THE (Original orchestra 1935).
Tracks: / Don't let it bother you / Sugar foot stomp / Weary blues / By heck / Solitude / Rhythm of the rain / New deal in love, A.
MC: . . . . MRT 40053

LIVE IN THE MEADOWBROOK, 28 OCTOBER 1955 (Dorsey Brothers Orchestra).
LP: . . . . EB 419

MOOD HOLLYWOOD.
LP: . . . . HEP 1005

SPOTLIGHTING THE FABULOUS DORSEYS BROTHERS.
LP: . . . . GOJ 1023

STAGE SHOW '54-5.
LP: . . . . AWE 30
MC: . . . . CAWE 30

YOUNG DORSEY BROTHERS, 1928-30, THE (Dorsey Brothers Orchestra).
Tracks: / Mary Ann / Persian rug / Coquette / Yale blues / Indian cradle song / My melancholy baby / That's my mammy / Dixie dawn / Evening star / Forgetting you / Was it a dream? / 'Round evening / Out of the dawn / Sally of my dreams / She's funny that way / Cross roads / I can make most anything / Spell of the blues / Let's do it / My kinda love / Mean to me / Button up your overcoat / I'll never ask for more / Lover come back to me / Am I blue? / Baby, oh where can you be / Breakaway / Singin' in the rain / Your mother and mine / Maybe, who knows / Can this be love? / Fine and dandy.
2LP: . . . . SHB 67
MC: . . . . TC SHB 67

Dorsey, Gail Ann

CORPORATE WORLD, THE.
Tracks: / Wasted country / If only you / Just another dream / So hard to let you go / Corporate world / No time / S.W.4 / Wishing I was someone else / Carry me off to heaven / Missiles of midnight (On CD and Cassette only.).
LP: . . . . WX 220
MC: . . . . WX 220C

Dorsey, Georgia Tom

COME ON MAMA DO THAT DANCE.
LP: . . . . L 1041

Dorsey, Jack

BIG BAND GOLD (50 years of swing) (Dorsey, Jack Orchestra).
LPS: . . . . RML 107
MCSET: . . . . RML 4C 107

OF CARPENTERS AND KING (Dorsey, Jack Galaxy of Strings).
Tracks: / Superstar / For all we know / Yesterday once more / We've only just begun / Goodbye to love / Ticket to ride / Rainy days and Mondays / Close to you / Hurting each other / Top of the world / Sing / Tapestry / It's too late / Make the night a little longer / I'm into something good / Hey girl / It's going to take some time / Go away little girl / Chains / Up on the roof / When my little girl is smiling / Will you love me tomorrow / It might as well rain until September.
LP: . . . . REH 278

Dorsey, Jimmy

1939: JIMMY DORSEY (Dorsey, Jimmy & His Orchestra).
LP: . . . . CLP 30

CAN ANYONE EXPLAIN?.
Tracks: / Diz does everything / See-saw / I can't get started / McGee's closet / Grand central get away / I'm in love again / Moon of Manakoora / Can anyone explain? / Heatwave / Let's fall in love / Big butter and egg man / This can't be love / Alto tude / Sing a song / Great lie, The.
LP: . . . . F 21030
MC: 40130

CONTRASTS 1945 (Dorsey, Jimmy Orchestra).
LP: . . . . AWE 27

DON'T BE THAT WAY 1935 - 40 (Dorsey, Jimmy & His Orchestra).
LP: . . . . BS 7120
MC: . . . . BS 7120C

DORSEYLAND BAND.
Tracks: / That's a plenty / Basin Street blues / Stars fell on Alabama / Charlie my boy / Beale Street blues / Indiana / Rosetta / Royal Garden blues / Levee blues / Chicago / Way down yonder in New Orleans / Farewell blues.
LP: . . . . HUK 203

EARLY YEARS, THE 1936 - 41 (Dorsey, Jimmy & His Orchestra).
LP: . . . . BS 7104

HEAT WAVE (Dorsey, Jimmy Orchestra).
LP: . . . . GELP 15011

JIMMY DORSEY.
LP: . . . . Q 028

JIMMY DORSEY AND HIS ORCHESTRA 1939/40 (Dorsey, Jimmy & His Orchestra).
Tracks: / Contrasts / Shine on harvest moon / Imagination / Blue Lou / Just for a thrill / Fools rush in / Carolina in the morning / At least you could say hello / Moonlight on the river / I'm stepping out with a memory tonight / Julia / Nearness of you / Shoot the meatball to me Dominick boy / You, you darlin' / Blueberry Hill / Flight of the jitterbug.
LP: . . . . HMP 5042
LP: . . . . HSR 101

JIMMY DORSEY AND HIS ORCHESTRA, VOL. 3 1949-51 (Dorsey, Jimmy Orchestra).
Tracks: / Contrasts / On the Alamo / Stop look and listen / Out of nowhere / Everywhere you go / All of me / In a little Spanish town / Wang wang blues / After I say I'm sorry / Manhattan / Busy signal / Sweet Sue / Perfidia / Undecided / It's a wonderful world.
LP: . . . . HSR 165

JIMMY DORSEY COLLECTION (20 Golden Greats).
Tracks: / Contrasts / Flight of the jitterbug / Fools rush in / Shine on, harvest moon / Moonlight on the river / Blueberry Hill / Carolina in the morning / Imagination / You, you darlin' / Just for a thrill / St. Louis blues / Basin Street blues / Tailspin / Dese, dem, dose / Blue Lou / Julia / Nearness of you, The / Shoot the meatball to me Dominick boy / At least you could say hello / I'm stepping out with a memory tonight.
LP: . . . . DVLP 2063
MC: . . . . DVMC 2063

JIMMY DORSEY & HIS ORCHESTRA (Dorsey, Jimmy & His Orchestra).
Tracks: / Theme / Moonlight serenade / Shine on harvest moon / Comes love / So many times / Dixieland detour / It's funny to everyone but me / Go fly a kite / Pagan love song / Theme - close / Jug music / Where do I go from you / One o'clock jump / As time goes by / I would do anything for you / Jumpin' Jimmy.
LP: . . . . JASM 2513
MC: . . . . JASMC 2513

JIMMY DORSEY & HIS ORCHESTRA, 1944-47 (Dorsey, Jimmy & His Orchestra).
LP: . . . . FH 19

JIMMY DORSEY ORCHESTRA (Dorsey, Jimmy Orchestra).
Tracks: / Wolverine blues / Stuff is here, The / Sandman / Beele / Dorsey stomp / Top hat, white tie and tails / Tap dancer's nightmare / Peanut vendor / Sunset strip / Together / Oh what a beautiful morning / Perdido / I can't believe that you're in love with me / Hi poppin / King Porter stomp.
LP: . . . . QU 028

JIMMY DORSEY, VOL 1, 1935-36.
LP: . . . . AJAX 103

JIMMY DORSEY, VOL 2, 1936.
LP: . . . . AJAX 114

JIMMY DORSEY VOL 2, 1942-44.
Tracks: / Contrasts / Just you, just me / Sowing wild notes / Lord and lady gate / Three little words / Someday sweetheart / I got rhythm / Body and soul / Moonlight on the Ganges / Together / Hit the note / I would do anything for you / Begin the beguine / Sunset strip / All the things you ain't / Grand central get away.
LP: . . . . HSR 153

JIMMY DORSEY, VOL 3, 1936-37.
LP: . . . . AJAX 117

JIMMY DORSEY, VOL 4 1950.
Tracks: / Let's fall in love / Lover / I didn't know what time it was / Them there eyes / Sweet Lorraine / This can't be love / Third man theme / King Porter stomp / It's the dreamer in me / Big butter and egg man / Hello, goodbye, forget it / Fingerbustin'.
LP: . . . . HSR 178

JIMMY DORSEY, VOL 4, 1937-38.
LP: . . . . AJAX 118

JIMMY DORSEY, VOL 5, 1938.
LP: . . . . AJAX 124

JIMMY DORSEY, VOL 6, 1938.
LP: . . . . AJAX 128

JIMMY DORSEY, VOL 7, 1938.
LP: . . . . AJAX 134

JIMMY DORSEY, VOL 8, 1938-39.
LP: . . . . AJAX 141

JIMMY DORSEY, VOL 9, 1939.
LP: . . . . AJAX 148

JIMMY DORSEY, VOL 10, 1939.
LP: . . . . AJAX 156

MOSTLY 1940 (Dorsey, Jimmy Orchestra).
LP: . . . . CLP 46

MUSKRAT RAMBLE (Dorsey, Jimmy & His Dorseylanders).
Tracks: / Muskrat ramble / Royal Garden blues / Sweet Lorraine / Charley my boy / Memphis blues / That's a-plenty / Johnson rag / Wolverine blues / Beale Street blues / Panama / Jazz me blues.
LP: . . . . SWH 22
MC: . . . . CSWH 22

ON THE SUNNY SIDE OF THE STREET (See under Dorsey, Tommy) (Dorsey, Jimmy/ Tommy Dorsey/ Coleman Hawkins).

PENNIES FROM HEAVEN.
Tracks: / It's the natural thing to do / Slap that bass / Love bug will bite you, The / Dorsey Dervish / Pick yourself up / Moon got in my eyes, The / In a sentimental mood / Rap-tap on wood / I love to sing / All you want to do is dance / They can't take that away from me / Serenade to nobody in particular / Let's call a heart a heart / Swingin' the jinx away / Stompin' at the Savoy / After you / Listen to the mockingbird / Pennies from Heaven.
LP: . . . . AJA 5052
MC: . . . . ZC AJA 5052

TOMMY & JIMMY DORSEY ORCHESTRA (See Under Dorsey, Tommy) (Dorsey, Tommy & Jimmy Orchestra).

Dorsey, Lee

ALL WAYS FUNKY.
Tracks: / Hello mama / Hoodlum Joe / Confusion / People sure act funny / Messed around (and fell in love) / Lonely Avenue / What am I living for? / When am I living for / Here comes the hurt again / Ay la ay / Li'l Liza Jane / People gonna talk / My old car / Hello good looking / My babe / Drainin'.
LP: . . . . CRB 1036

AM I THAT EASY TO FORGET?.
Tracks: / Lottie mo / Lover of love / Oo-na-nay / You better tell her / Great googa mooga / As quiet as it's kept / Lonelyology (for your love) / Ride your pony (live) / Coca cola commercial (my old car) / Coca cola commercial (little babe) / Occapella / Sneaking Sally thru the alley / Tears, tears and more tears / Riverboat / Yes we can / Soul mine / If I were a carpenter / Honest I do / Place where we can, A / Can I be the one / Night people / Am I that easy to forget / Before the next teardrop falls / Ya ya

(live) / Working in a coalmine (live) / Lottie mo (live).
2LP: . . . . **CDX 21**

GONH BE FUNKY.
Tracks: / Working in a coalmine / Holy cow / Do-re-mi / Lover was born, A / Give it up / Can you hear me / Freedom for the stallion / Ride your pony / Get out of my life woman / Ya ya / Love lots of lovin' (With Betty Harris.) / Candy yam / Go go girl / You're breaking me up / On your way down / Everything I do gonh be funky.
LP: . . . . **CRB 1001**

NEW LEE DORSEY.
LP: . . . . **SSL 10192**

WORKING IN A COALMINE.
Tracks: / Working in a coalmine / Ya ya / Why wait until tomorrow / Do-re-mi / Ride your pony / Gotta find a job / Holy cow / Get out of my life woman / My old car / Go go girl / Cynthia / Everything I do gonh be funky.
LP: . . . . **TOP 102**

Dorsey, Tommy

16 HITS (Dorsey, Tommy Orchestra/ Frank Sinatra).
LP: . . . . **LPJT 18**

1935 SESSIONS.
LP: . . . . **HDL 103**

1938-1940 (Dorsey, Tommy Orchestra/ Frank Sinatra).
LP: . . . . **SM 3878**
MC: . . . . **MC 3878**

1950-1952 (Dorsey, Tommy & His Orchestra).
Tracks: / Picalily dilly / Let me love you tonight / I kiss your hand Madame / This is romance / Sleepy lagoon / Wagon wheels / Non-drastic / Life is just a bowl of cherries / Sweet Georgia Brown / Bells of St. Mary's / I'm in the mood for love / Shaver's shivers / Maybe / Taking a chance on love / My sweetie went away.
LP: . . . . **SOL 511**

ALL TIME GREATEST HITS, VOLUME 1 (Dorsey, Tommy & Frank Sinatra).
Tracks: / Sky fell down, The / I'll be seeing you / Fools rush in / Imagination / I'll never smile again / Our love affair / Look at me now / Without a song / Lets get away from it all / Blue skies / Street of dreams / Take me / Be careful, it's my heart / These are such things / Light a candle in the chapel.
LP: . . . . **NL 90310**
MC: . . . . **NK 90310**

AT THE FAT MAN'S.
Tracks: / Blue skies / Dawn on the desert / At the Fat Man's / Bingo bango boffo / Marie / Chloe / Well git it / At sundown / Opus one / Candy / Continental / Call you sweetheart / Feels so good / Pussy Willow / Broadcasts from 1945-1948.
LP: . . . . **HEP 9**

BEAT OF THE BIG BANDS (Dorsey, Tommy Orchestra).
Tracks: / Do do do / It started all over again / I dream of you / Moonlight in Vermont / There are such things / Melancholy serenade / Autumn in New York / I should care / This love of mine / Rain.
LP: **32508**

BEST OF TOMMY DORSEY.
Tracks: / Maria / Star dust / Little white lies / I'll never smile again / Yes Indeed / Boogie woogie / Opus one / Song of India / Who / Royal Garden blues / Once in a while / I'm getting sentimental over you.
LP: . . . . **NL 81087**
MC: . . . . **NK 81087**

BIG REUNION PART 1.
LP: . . . . **FH 53**
MC: . . . . **CFH 53**

DORSEY-SINATRA SESSIONS, 1940-42 (Dorsey, Tommy & Frank Sinatra).
Tracks: / Sky fell down, The / Too romantic / Shake down the stars / Moments in the moonlight / I'll be seeing you / Say it / Polka dots and moonbeams / Fable of the rose / This is the beginning of the end / Hear my song, Violetta / Fools rush in / Devil may care / April played the fiddle / I haven't time to be a millionaire / Imagination / Yours is my heart alone / You're lonely and I'm lonely / East of the sun / Head on my pillow / It's a lovely day tomorrow / I'll never smile again / All this and Heaven too / Where do you keep your heart? / Whispering trade winds / One I love, The / Call of the canyon, The / Love lies / I could make you care / World in my arms, The / Our love affair / Looking for yesterday / Tell me at midnight / We three / When you awake / Anything / Shadows on the sand / You're breaking my heart all over again / I'd know you anywhere / Do you know why? / Not so long ago / Stardust / Oh, look at me now / You might have belonged to another / You lucky people / It's always you / I tried / Dolores / Without a song / Do I worry / Everything happens to me / Let's get away from it all / I'd never let a day pass by / Love me as I am / This love of mine / I guess I'll have to dream the rest / You and I / Neiani / Free for all / Blue skies / Two in love / Pale moon / I think of you / How do you do without me? / Sinner kissed an angel, A / Violets for your furs / Sunshine of your smile, The / How about you? / Snootie little cutie / Poor you / I'll take Tallulah / Last call for love / Somewhere a voice is calling / Just as though you were here / Sweet dreams / Take me / Be careful, it's my heart / In the blue of the evening / Dig down deep / There are such things / Daybreak / It started all over again / Light a candle in the chapel.
LPS: . . . . **SD 1000**

FORD V8 SHOWS AT TEXAS CENTENNIAL.
Tracks: / Theme / On the beach at Bali Bali / But definitely / I'm an old cowhand / Ja da / It's a sin to tell a lie / Weary blues / Dancing with you (once in a while) / Big John special / Song of India / Shine on Harvest Moon / Would you? / Happy as the day is long.
LP: . . . . **JASM 2509**
MC: . . . . **JASMC 2509**

FOREVER (Dorsey, Tommy & His Orchestra).
Tracks: / What'll I do / Sweet Sue / Night in Sudan / Too romantic / Say it / Imagination / Devil may care / Swanee river / Yes indeed / Who can I turn to / Embraceable you / Sleepy lagoon / Summertime / Dedicated to you / Will you still be mine / Violets for your furs / Do you know why.
2LP: . . . . **NL 89859**

FRANK SINATRA SINGS THE STANDARDS (Dorsey, Tommy & His Orchestra with Frank Sinatra).
Tracks: / I'll be seeing you / Whispering / Somewhere a voice is calling / Blue skies / Stardust / Without a song / Hear my song, Violetta / Yours is my heart alone / East of the sun / One I love / Let's get away from it all / Fools rush in / I'll never smile again / Polka dots and moonbeams / Imagination / Daybreak / Violets for your furs / Everything happens to me / How about you? / This love of mine.
LP: . . . . **INTS 5098**

FRANK SINATRA WITH THE TOMMY DORSEY ORCHESTRA (Dorsey, Tommy & His Orchestra).
Tracks: / Sinner kissed an angel, A / Polka dots and moonbeams / Fools rush in / Imagination / I could make you care / This love of mine / Without a song / Everything happens to me / Violets for your furs / Sky fell down, The / Be careful, it's my heart / In the blue of the evening.
LP: . . . . **NL 11586**

INDISPENSABLE TOMMY DORSEY, VOL 5/6 (1938-39) (Dorsey, Tommy & His Orchestra).
Tracks: / Cocktails for two / Old black Joe / Down home rag / Hawaiian war chant / Davenport blues / It's all yours / Milenberg joys (parts 1 & 2) / Hold tight / Honolulu / Blue moon / Peckin' with the penguins / Got no time / Little skipper / Our love / Tea for two / By the river Sainte Marie / Asleep or awake / You grow sweeter as the years go by / If you ever change your mind / To you / This is no dream / Marcheta / Lamp is low, The / Dawn on the desert / Why begin again? / Lonesome road / Rendezvous time in Paree / How am I to know? / Is it possible? / Well, all right / La Rosita / All I remember is you.
2LP: . . . . **NL 89589**
MCSET: . . . . **NK 89589**

INDISPENSABLE TOMMY DORSEY VOL 7/8 (Dorsey, Tommy & His Orchestra).
2LP: . . . . **NL 90028**
MC: . . . . **NK 90028**

INDISPENSABLE TOMMY DORSEY, VOL 1/2 (1935-1937) (Dorsey, Tommy & His Orchestra).
Tracks: / Weary blues / I'm getting sentimental over you / Music goes round and around, The / Rhythm in my nursery rhymes / I'm shooting high / Day I let you get away, The / Rhythm saved the world / Stardust / Royal Garden blues / Ja da / At the codfish ball / Mary had a little lamb / You've gotta eat your spinach baby / On the beach at Bali Bali / San Francisco / That's a plenty / After you've gone / Head over heels in love / Sleep / Maple leaf rag / Keepin' out of mischief now / Melody in F / Song of India / Marie / Liebestraum / Mendelssohn's Spring song / Jamming / They can't take that away from me / Humoresque / Beale Street blues / Blue Danube / Dark eyes.
2LP: . . . . **NL 89752**
MCSET: . . . . **NK 89752**

INDISPENSABLE TOMMY DORSEY, VOL 3/4 (1937-38) (Dorsey, Tommy & His Orchestra).
Tracks: / Posin' / That stolen melody / All you want to do is dance / After you / Stardust on the moon / Night and day / Smoke gets in your eyes / Canadian capers / Good-bye Jonah / Big apple, The / Lady is a tramp, The / Tears in my heart / If the man in the moon were a coon / Getting some fun out of life / Nice work if you can get it / Who? / Dipsy doodle, The / Big dipper / Shine on harvest moon / When the midnight choo choo leaves for Alabama / Music, Maestro please / Tisket a tasket, A / Stop beatin' around the mulberry bush / Panama / Washboard blues / Chinatown, my chinatown / Sheik of Araby, The / Copenhagen / Symphony in riffs / Boogie woogie / Tin roof blues / Sweet Sue.
2LP: . . . . **NL 89163**
MCSET: . . . . **NK 89163**

JAMBOREE 1935-6 (Dorsey, Tommy & His Orchestra).
LP: . . . . **HDL 114**
MC: . . . . **CHDL 114**

LITTLE WHITE LIES.
Tracks: / I've got a note / Royal Garden blues / Ja da / Maple leaf rag / Who / Little white lies / Symphony in Riffs / Copenhagen / Old black Joe / Well alright / Back to back / Stomp off.
LP: . . . . **SM 3062**

LIVE AT THE MEADOWBROOK - FEBRUARY 11 1941.
LP: . . . . **FANFARE 29-129**

LIVE IN NEW YORK, 1955-6 (Dorsey, Tommy & Jimmy Orchestra).
Tracks: / I'm getting sentimental over you / My brother is the leader of the band / Teach me tonight / I've got the world on a string / Alexander's ragtime band / Wagon wheels / Don't worry about me / Stereophonic / Always in my heart / Stella by starlight / I'm glad there is you / Bells of St. Mary's / Quiet please.
MC: . . . . **CAWE 37**
LP: . . . . **AWE 37**

MAKING BIG BAND HISTORY (1944).
LP: . . . . **FH 1003**

MAPLE LEAF RAG 1936 - 39 (Dorsey, Tommy & His Orchestra).
LP: . . . . **BS 7116**

ON THE SUNNY SIDE OF THE STREET (Dorsey, Tommy/ Jimmy Dorsey/ Coleman Hawkins).
LP: . . . . **NOST 7653**

ON THE SUNNY SIDE OF THE STREET (SEAR).
LP: . . . . **LPJT 18**
MC: . . . . **MCJT 18**

ONE NIGHT STAND 1940.
LP: . . . . **SH 2001**

REED ALBUM, VOL. 2 (Dorsey, Tommy & Various Artists).
LP: . . . . **MERITT 11**

SENTIMENTAL JOURNEY.
2LP: . . . . **CR 5142**
MCSET: . . . . **CRT 5142**

SINGS THE STANDARDS (Dorsey, Tommy & Frank Sinatra).
Tracks: / I'll be seeing you / Whispering / Stardust / Without a song / Hear my song, Violetta / Yours is my heart alone / East of the sun / One I love (belongs to somebody else), The / Let's get away from it all / Fools rush in / I'll never smile again / Polka dots and moonbeams / Imagination / Daybreak / Violets for your furs / Everything happens to me / How about you / This love of mine / Somewhere a voice is calling / Blue skies.
LP: . . . . **NL 89102**
MC: . . . . **NK 89102**

SOLID SWING.
Tracks: / Chez faire / Capital idea / Swanee River / Continental / Chloe / On the sunny side of the street / Puddle wump / Non drastic / Sweet Georgia Brown / Hollywood hat / Lullaby in boogie / Song of India / Swing to me up in Harlem / Why begin again? / Summertime / At the Fat Man's / Brotherly jump / Harlem express / I'm beginning to see the light / Midriff / Swing high / Dry bones / Another one of them things / Comin' thro' the rye.
LP: . . . . **FH 47**
MC: . . . . **CFH 47**

SONG OF INDIA (Dorsey, Tommy & His Orchestra).
Tracks: / They didn't believe me / Cheek to cheek / Opus one / Tico tico / Blue skies / I'll never smile again / Begin the beguine / There's no you / Midriff / Cuttin' out blues / Pussy willow / Hollywood hat / Then I'll be happy / Lovely weather for ducks / And the angels sing / Somebody loves me / Boogie woogie / Song of India / On the sunny side of the street / Non drastic / Swanee river.
LP: . . . . **DBD 08**
MC: . . . . **DBDC 08**

STORY.
LP: . . . . **BB 12707**

SWING HIGH.
Tracks: / Swing high / Always / Pussy willow / That's it / Swing time up in Harlem / Why begin again / Summertime / At the fat man's / Brotherly jump / Harlem express / I'm beginning to see the light / Midriff / Swing high / Dry bones / Another one of them things / Comin' thro' the rye.
LP: . . . . **F 20127**
LP: **20127**
MC: **40127**

SWINGING BIG BANDS, THE 1937-46 (Dorsey, Tommy & His Orchestra).
Tracks: / Boogie woogie / Copenhagen / Lonesome road / Hawaiian war chant / Sleepy lagoon / L.A. April 1946 / Then I'll be happy / Liebestraum / Song of India / Opus NR / I'm getting sentimental over you / Once in a while / Music, maestro please.
LP: . . . . **SM 3615**

THIS IS TOMMY DORSEY.
2LP: **26 28033**

THIS IS TOMMY DORSEY VOL.2.
2LP: **26 28041**

TOMMY AND JIMMY DORSEY (Dorsey, Tommy & His Orchestra).
LP: . . . . **BO 714**

TOMMY DORSEY.
LP: . . . . **BO 711**

TOMMY DORSEY COLLECTION (20 Golden Greats).
Tracks: / Song of India / Sleepy lagoon / I'm getting sentimental over you / Hawaiian war chant / Boogie woogie / Copenhagen / Then I'll be happy / Liebestraum / Opus one / Lover is blue, A / After all / Polka dots and moonbeams / Fable of the rose / Marie / Deep night / Sky fell down, The / Music, Maestro, please / Do I love you.
LP: . . . . **DVLP 2019**
MC: . . . . **DVMC 2019**

TOMMY DORSEY & COMPANY (Dorsey, Tommy & Company).
LP: . . . . **FH 24**
MC: . . . . **CFH 24**

TOMMY DORSEY & HIS ORCHESTRA (Dorsey, Tommy & His Orchestra).
LP: . . . . **JASM 2523**
MC: . . . . **JASMC 2523**

TOMMY DORSEY & HIS ORCHESTRA.
Tracks: / I'm getting sentimental over you / Maple leaf rag / Melody in F / Marie / Twilight in Turkey / Song of India / Stop, look and listen / Liebestraum / Boogie woogie / Smoke gets in your eyes / Lady is a tramp, The / Who? / Shine on harvest moon / Washboard blues / Chinatown / Davenport blues / Hawaiian war chant / Tin roof blues / Symphony in riffs / Milenberg joys / Stomp it off / Swanee River / Easy does it / On the sunny side of the street / Loose lid special / Minor goes a muggin', The / Blue blazes / At the Fat Man's / Well git it / Chloe / Opus one.
2LP: . . . . **DPM 2026**

TOMMY DORSEY & HIS ORCHESTRA WITH FRANK SINATRA (Dorsey, Tommy & His Orchestra with Frank Sinatra).
Tracks: / Marie / Too romantic / Polka dots and moonbeams / This is the beginning of the end / Hear my song, Violetta / I haven't time to be a millionaire / Head on my pillow / I'll never smile again / One I love, The / Call of the canyon, The / Shadows on the sand / Do you know why / Yearnin' / Not so long ago / Stardust / How am I to know / Look at me now / You lucky people you / Without a song / Everything happens to me / Let's get away from it all / Love me as I am / This love of mine / Blue skies / How do you do without me? / Violets for your furs / How about you / My melancholy baby / Dig down deep / It started all over again / I'll take Tallulah / Song is you, The.
2LP: . . . . **PM 43685**

TOMMY DORSEY IN CONCERT.
LP: . . . . **NL 45154**
MC: . . . . **NK 45154**

TOMMY DORSEY ORCHESTRA (Dorsey, Tommy & His Orchestra).
Tracks: / Jump time / Milenberg joys / Sweet potato / Hawaiian war chant /

Song of India / Blues no more / Swing low sweet chariot / I say I'm sorry / Quiet please / Easy does it / March of the toys / I know that you know.
LP: . . . . **BLJ 8012**

TOMMY DORSEY, VOL. 1.
LP: . . . . **EJLP 01**
MC: . . . . **EJMC 01**

TOMMY DORSEY, VOL. 2.
LP: . . . . **EJLP 09**
MC: . . . . **EJMC 09**

TOMMY & JIMMY DORSEY ORCHESTRA (Dorsey, Tommy & Jimmy Orchestra).
Tracks: / By heck / Stop, look and listen / Milenberg joys / St. Louis blues / Honeysuckle rose / Basin Street blues / Weary blues / Tailspin / That eccentric rag / Dese dem dose / Dippermouth blues.
LP: . . . . **KLJ 20009**

YES INDEED.
Tracks: / Lonesome road (part 1) / Lonesome road (part 2) / Well, all right / Stomp it off / Easy does it / Quiet please / Swing high / Swanee river / Yes, indeed / Loose lid special / Swingin' on nothin' / Moonlight on the Ganges / Well git it / Opus 1 / Chloe / Minor goes muggin', The.
LP: . . . . **NL 90449**
MC: . . . . **NK 90449**

Doss, Tommy

OF THE SONS OF THE PIONEERS.
Tracks: / Call, The / So much to remember / If you would only be mine / I invented the word / Memory, The / Trouble in mind / Rosa / King of the fools / Sing a sad song / I care no more / Every fool has a rainbow.
LP: . . . . **BFX 15225**

D'Ossche, Albert

CROSSOVER (D'Ossche, Albert & Robert Force).
Tracks: / Salvador de Bahia / Spring of '65, The / In the fall / Pokerface smile / Workaday daddy / Tabac allegria / Paradise boy (hush your eyes) / Sing sailor / Krummi (the raven) / Like a ship.
LP: . . . . **SNKF 168**

Dostoevsky, Fyodor

CRIME AND PUNISHMENT (excerpts) (Mason, James (nar)).
MC: **1691**

Dotrice, Michele

NIGHTINGALE, THE (See under Nightingale).

Dotrice, Roy (nar)

BARDELL & PICKWICK.
2LP: . . . . **ZDSW 709/10**

BRIEF LIVES (See under Brief Lives).

READ PETER PAN (Dotrice, Roy and family).
MCSET: . . . . **MCFR 108/9**

READS CHRISTMAS CAROLS.
MCSET: . . . . **MCFR 115/6**

Dotrice, Roy

WATERSHIP DOWN (See under Watership Down).

Dots Will Echo

DOTS WILL ECHO.
Tracks: / Everything in the world / Sandra / Rain / Someday / Dots will echo / Science fiction / She's never lonely / She's a girl / I will too / Heartland / Big jets.
MC: **103102**

Dottsy

TRYIN' TO SATISFY YOU.
Tracks: / Tryin' to satisfy you / Play born to lose again / Everybody's reaching out for someone / Send me the pillow you dream on / It should have been easy / So hard living without you / Here in love / Love is a two way street / Just had you on my mind / If you say it's so / Slip away.
LP: . . . . **PL 42811**

Double

BLUE.
Tracks: / Woman of the world / I know a place / Captain of her heart, The / Your prayer takes me off / Rangoon moon / Urban nomad / Love is a plane / Tomorrow.
LP: . . . . **POLD 5187**
MC: . . . . **POLDC 5187**

DOUBLE.
Tracks: / Fire in disguise / Gliding / Lakes in the desert / Circles prove your love / You don't let me get (close enough) / Silent mountain / Devils ball / Wrong time / Megarhythm dance.
LP: . . . . **POLD 5216**
MC: . . . . **POLDC 5216**

Double Deckers (TV)

DOUBLE DECKERS (Music From TV Soundtrack) (Various artists).
Tracks: / It's a day and a half: *Various artists* / To the countryside: *Various artists* / Good day at Yellowrock: *Various artists* / With a little bit of love: *Various artists* / I gotta get through: *Various artists*/ Get on board: *Various artists* / Life is an wonderful thing: *Various artists* / Grannie's rocking chair: *Various artists* / One man band: *Various artists* / Welcome to the party: *Various artists* / Fat ladies: *Various artists*.
LP: . . . . **EST 672**

Double Exposure

TEN PERCENT.
Tracks: / Ten percent / Gonna give my love away / Everyman / Baby I need your loving / Just can't say hello / My love is free / Pick me.
LP: . . . . **SZS 5503**

Double Happys

HOW MUCH TIME LEFT, PLEASE.
LP: . . . . **ONLYMLP 012**

Double Image

IN LANDS I NEVER SAW.
Tracks: / In lands I never saw / Midnight stardust / Stardust / Orient point / Dusk / K1 / Desert rounds / Woodbell.
LP: . . . . **LPCEL 015**
MC: . . . . **MCCEL 015**

Double Nelson

CEUX QUI L'ONT FAIT.
LP: **360255**

Double Trouble

AS ONE.
LP: . . . . **LUVLP 6**
MC: . . . . **LUVMC 6**

COULDN'T STAND THE WEATHER (See under Vaughan, Stevie Ray).

TEXAS FLOOD (See under Vaughan, Stevie Ray) (Vaughan, Stevie Ray & Double Trouble).

Double Trouble (Film)

DOUBLE TROUBLE (VIDEO) (see under Presley, Elvis) (Various artists).

Douce France

DOUCE FRANCE (Various artists).
2LP: **2C 150 14675/6**

Doucet, Camey

CAJUN GOOD TIME MUSIC.
LP: **6034**
MC: . . . . **6034 TC**

CAJUN GOODIES.
LP: **6028**
MC: . . . . **6028 TC**

CAMEY DOUCET ET MUSIQUE.
LP: **6024**
MC: . . . . **6024 TC**

Doucet, Michael

BELIZAIRE - THE CAJUN (Film soundtrack) (Doucet, Michael & Beausoleil).
LP: . . . . **ARHOOLIE 5038**
MC: . . . . **C 5038**

CAJUN EXPERIENCE (see under Daigle, Paul) (Doucet, Michael/Paul Daigle/Robert Elkins).

CHRISTMAS BAYOU.
Tracks: / We three kings of Orient are / It came upon a midnight clear / Il est ne / Vive le vent / Deck the halls / Little drummer boy / O holy night / Bonne Annee / God rest ye merry gentlemen / Christmas bayou / Please come home for Christmas / Trinquez trinquez / Auld lang syne.
LP: **6064**
MC: . . . . **6064 TC**

DIT BEAUSOLEIL.
LP: . . . . **ARHOOLIE 5025**
MC: . . . . **C 5025**

HOT CAJUN RHYTHM AND BLUES (Doucet, Michael & Cajun Brew).
Tracks: / Wooly bully / Bayou pom pom / Un autre soir ennuyant / Hey good lookin' / Last Wednesday night / Louie Louie / Woman or a man / Pauline / Zydeco boogaloo / Like a real cajun / J'ai passe devant ta porte / Do you want to dance.
LP: . . . . **SPD 1013**

MICHAEL DOUCET & CAJUN BREW (Doucet, Michael & Cajun Brew).
MC: . . . . **ROUNDER 6017C**
LP: . . . . **ROUNDER 6017**

PARLEZ NOUS A BOIRE (Doucet, Michael & Beausoleil).
LP: . . . . **ARHOOLIE 5034**
MC: . . . . **C 5034**

Doucet, Suzanne

IHRE GROSSEN ERFOLGE.
Tracks: / Das geht doch keinen etwas an / Sei doch mein baby (Be my baby) / Schenk mir einen tag mit viel armore / Warte nicht bis morgen / So long, so long / Was fallt dir ein / Okay, ich geh' / Gluck und liebe / Du musst dich entscheiden / Nur aus schaden wird man klug / Oho aha / Das steht in keinem schulbuch / Aber was weiss ich von dir / Geh' nicht am gliuck vorbei.
LP: . . . . **LB 213 005**

ROT WIE RUBIN.
Tracks: / Wenn die nacht ergeht / Allein in einer grossen stadt / Der teddybar / Traume aus papier / Der brief / Mein erster weg / Rot wie rubin / Chantal / Du / Bunter drachen / Irgendein baum / Ein glass, eine flasche.
LP: . . . . **LB 200 007**

Doucet, Tommy

I USED TO PLAY SOME PRETTY TOUGH TUNES.
LP: . . . . **ROUNDER 7010**

Dougall, Robert

BBC STEREO TEST DISC.
LP: . . . . **REC 355**

Doughboys

HAPPY ACCIDENTS.
Tracks: / Countdown / Sorry wrong number / Deep end / Intravenus DeMilo / Happy home / Sunflower honey / Far away / Happy sad day / Wait and see / Every bit of nothing / Dream day / Apprenticeship of Lenny Kravitz, The / Tupperware party.
LP: . . . . **LS 9336 1**

WHATEVER.
LP: . . . . **GOESON 26**

Doughty, Johnny

ROUND RYE BAY FOR MORE (Traditional songs from the Sussex coast).
Tracks: / Herrings' heads / Wreck of the Northfleet, The / When I was single / Golden vanity / Saucy sailor / Baltimore / While going round the Cape / Round Rye Bay for more / Spanish ladies / Sailor's alphabet, The / Mermaid marry me / I'm going to be mother today / Barbara Allen / My boy Billy / Dick Turpin / Let her go back / Rye Harbour girl / Streets of Port Arthur, The.
LP: **12TS 324**

Douglas

BEAUTY REPORTS VOL 1.
2LP: . . . . **SOH 002**

Douglas, Carl

GOLDEN HOUR OF CARL DOUGLAS.
Tracks: / Kung Fu fighting / Witchfinder general / When you got love / Changing times / I want to give you my everything / Dance the Kung Fu / Never had this dream before / I don't care what people say / Blue eyed soul / Girl you're so fine / Run back / Love peace and happiness / I'll be your light / Too hot to handle / What's good for the goose / M.O.R.F. / Green tangerines and wild evergreens / Mistakes of mine / I'll keep lovin' you / Stand up for love.
LP: . . . . **GH 678**
MC: . . . . **ZCGH 67881**

Doûglas, Carol

20 GOLDEN PIECES: CAROL DOUGLAS.
Tracks: / Doctor's orders / Midnight love affair / Light my fire / Burnin' / Night fever / Baby don't let this good love die / We're gonna make it / Dancing queen / All night long / I fell in love with love / Take me (make me lose control) / Hurricane is coming tonight / We do it / I want to stay with you / I'll take a chance on love / Who, what, when, where and why / I've got you on my mind / Boy you know just what I'm after / Friend in need / Will we make it tonight?.
LP: . . . . **BDL 2022**

Douglas, Craig

CRAIG DOUGLAS.
LP: . . . . **BUY 049**

ONLY SIXTEEN.
Tracks: / Our favourite melodies / Time / Hundred pounds of clay / Change of heart, A / Rainbows / Riddle of love / When my little girl is smiling / Pretty blue eyes / No greater love / Girl next door, The / Wish it were me / Sandy / Hello spring / Another you / Teenager in love / Only sixteen / Oh what a day / Dream lover / Ring-a-ding doo.
LP: . . . . **SEE 34**

Douglas, Dev

GUITAR MAGIC.
Tracks: / San Marco / Leaving / Celso / Bendy / Turnip green rag / Tell me / Lonesome / JW 3 / Sunshine in my eyes / Wiggle / Zapata / Toad's tune.
LP: . . . . **MFB 001**

Douglas, George

HOUSE WITH THE GREEN SHUTTERS (Watson, Tom).
MCSET: . . . . **COL 4001**

Douglas Inc. Recipe

MODEST HERITAGE.
Tracks: / Brides ammunition / Muddle / Below the line / Frank Lloyd Wrong / Adult mind, The / How to wear an engine out / Unbridled lullaby / Landed gentry, The / Willow pattern / Young and the ruined, The / Figurehead.
LP: . . . . **SOH 001**

Douglas, Jay

CHANGING CHANNELS.
Tracks: / Emphysema two step / Waltzing on thin ice / Changing channels / Top hat white tie and tails / Freemantle / St. Anne's reel / I was doing all right / (Write it on) the tablet of your heart / Blues in the night / You turned the tables on me.
LP: . . . . **IMCA 5965**
MC: . . . . **IMCAC 5965**

Douglas, Jerry

FLUXEDO.
LP: . . . . **ROUNDER 0112**
MC: . . . . **ROUNDER 0112C**

FLUXOLOGY.
Tracks: / Fluxology / Bill Cheatham / Say a little prayer / C-biscuit / Randy Lynn rag / Wheel hoss / Red Bud rag / Alabama / Dixie hoedown / Blues for Vickie.
LP: . . . . **ROUNDER 0093**
MC: . . . . **ROUNDER 0093C**

UNDER THE WIRE.
Tracks: / T.O.B. / Dhaka rock / Time gone by / Monroe's hornpipe / Before the blues / Trip to Kilkerrin / Grant's corner / Redhill / Two friends / New day, A.
LP: . . . . **IMCA 5675**
MC: . . . . **IMCAC 5675**

Douglas, Joe

VISAGE (Douglas, Joe Trio).
Tracks: / This girl / Promenade / Blue horizons / What do you do? / Visage / Silvana / Into living.
LP: . . . . **SPJ 514**

Douglas, John

HARRIS AND THE MARE (See under Fatal Eggs) (Various artists).

LAZARUS RISING (see under Ringing The Changes) (Various artists).

SCOTTISH LOVE SONGS.
Tracks: / Until my heart stands still / My love is like a red red rose / Culzean Bay / Flow gently sweet Afton / Ye banks and braes / Skye boat song, The / Loch Lomond / Roamin' in the gloamin' / Jean / Down in the glen / Bonnie lass o' Fyvie / Almost like being in love / Heather on the hill / Crooked bawbee.
LP: . . . . **LC 004**
MC: . . . . **LC 004C**

SCOTTISH WELCOME, A.
Tracks: / Mary of Argyll / Tartan, The / Take me back / Lassie come and dance with me / Bonnie Galloway / Will you walk? / Granny's heilan' hame / Dark island / Massacre of Glencoe / Fiona / Fond kiss, A / Roses of Prince Charlie / Scotland the brave / Lochnagar / Dae ye mind? / Road and the miles to Dundee, The.
LP: . . . . **LOCLP 1012**
MC: . . . . **ZCLOC 1012**

Douglas, Johnny

MANY SIDES OF JOHNNY DOUGLAS AND HIS ORCHESTRA, (Douglas, Johnny & His Orchestra).
Tracks: / Feelings / What I did for love / Deep purple / You only live twice / I write the songs / Red roses for a blue lady / Nobody does it better / Shadow of your smile / Aquarius / Hello Dolly / Please / Pennies from Heaven / What are you doing the rest of your life? / Charlie's Angels, Theme from / Railway Children, Theme from / Look of love, The / Calcutta / Too many rings around Rosie / I don't want to walk without you / Dancing queen / You light up my life / You'll never find another love like mine / Tea for two.
2LP: . . . . **CR 066**
MCSET: . . . . **CRT 066**

MORE ROMANCE WITH THE CLASSICS (Douglas, Johnny Strings).
Tracks: / Swan, The / 18th variation from rhapsody on a theme from P / Serenade / Piano concerto no.2, Theme from / Adagio / Romance no.2 / Dreaming / Intermezzo from Cavalleria Rusticana / Swan lake (street scene) / Spring song / Requiem for a love affair /

Moonlight sonata / Symphony No. 5 / Romeo and Juliet / Sonata in D.
LP: . . . . DLCL 105
MC: . . . . DLCT 105

ON SCREEN (Douglas, Johnny Strings).
Tracks: / Days of wine and roses / Gigi / Call me irresponsible / Summer knows, The / Laura / Dungeons and dragons / Like someone in love / Affair to remember, An / Smile / Young at heart / Railway children, The / As time goes by / Dulcima / Somewhere in time / Way we were, The.
MC: . . . . DLCT 110

ON STAGE (Douglas, Johnny Strings).
Tracks: / I could write a book / Bali Ha'i / Tap your troubles away / Hey there / All I ask of you / Ascot Gavotte / If I loved you / Sweetest sound, The / I won't send roses / Stranger in paradise / Where or when / Heather on the hill / I have dreamed / Try to remember / Love changes everything.
MC: . . . . DLCT 109

Douglas, K.C.

BIG ROAD BLUES.
Tracks: / Big road blues / Buck dance / Tore your playhouse down / Whisky headed woman / Catfish blues / Howlin' blues / Kansas City blues / Bottle up and go / K.C. blues / Key to the highway.
LP: . . . . CH 254

COUNTRY BOY, THE.
LP: . . . . ARHOOLIE 1073

MERCURY BOOGIE.
LP: . . . . OL 2812

Douglas, Keith

LOVE WITH STYLE.
LP: . . . . HPLP 001

WHAT THE WORLD NEEDS.
LP: . . . . NCLP 003

Douglas, Mike Stand

MANY SIDES OF MIKE 'STAND' DOUGLAS.
LP: . . . . HMR 9001

Douglas, Mona

REEAGHYN DY VANNIN (Folk songs in Manx Gaelic).
Tracks: / Mona's delight / Arrane y blieeh / Tom the tailor / Arrane y lhondhoo / Manx courting dance / Arrane ny niee / Fairy reel, The / Arrane ny sheeaghyn troailtagh / Widow's house, The / Arrane my vlieaun / Hunt the wren / Hop-tu-naa / Ny kirree fo naghtey / Shiaull ersooyl / Snieu, queeyl, snieu / Te traa goll thie / Reeaghyn dy vannin / Troilt y voidyn moirrey bannee / Yn gulley hesheree / Geay jeh'n aer / Berry dhone / My cailyn veg dhone / Ushag vag ruy / Manx wedding reel / Manx wedding song / Peter O'Tavey (manx wedding dance).
MC: 60-007

Douglas, Shirley

HEART ON THE LOOSE, A.
Tracks: / First time ever I saw your face, The / Snowbird / Greensleeves / Heart on the loose / Right thing to do / Big yellow taxi / You've got a friend / Amazing grace / Try to remember / I'm gonna be a country girl again / Jamie / Everything I own / Wishing and wanting / Nobody knows / If that's what it takes / Until it's time for you to go.
LP: . . . . PRX 17

Douglas Wiggin, Kate

REBECCA OF SUNNYBROOK FARM (Harris, Julie).
MC: . . . . CDL 51637
LP: . . . . TC 1637

Douglas, Wilson

WILSON DOUGLAS.
LP: . . . . ROUNDER 0047

Douleur

COCO.
LP: . . . . TN 592

Doumbe, Jacky

KAPE.
LP: . . . . JDR 013

Doumbia, Nahawa

DIDADI.
Tracks: / Djina Mousso / Banani / Mogoya / Djuguya / Baroo / Neriwe.
LP: . . . . STL 8337

NYAMA TOUTOU.
LP: . . . . STERNS 1033
MC: . . . . STC 1033

Dovells

CAMEO PARKWAY SESSIONS.
Tracks: / Mope itty mope / Bristol stomp / Out in the cold again / Do the continental / Why do fools fall in love / Bristol twistin' Annie / Oh what a night / Gully gully baby / Your last chance / Jitterbug / Kissin' in the kitchen / Save me baby / Short fat Fannie / You can't sit down / Stompin' everywhere / Betty in Bermudas / Dance the frog / Stop monkeying around / No, no, no / Maybellene.
LP: . . . . HAU 8515

Doves

AFFINITY.
LP: . . . . EKT 96
MC: . . . . EKT 96C

Dow, Nick

BURD MARGARET.
Tracks: / Week's work well done / Scarecrow / Tarry trousers / Davy Lowston / Green linnet / Devil and the feathery wife / Lover's ghost / Poor old couple / Fair Rosamond / Burd Margaret / Quaker / Black joker / Jolly bold robber.
LP: . . . . DIN 306

IN RETROSPECT.
MC: . . . . OHMSP 504

MARK UPON THE EARTH, A.
LP: . . . . OHM 107

Dowe, Brent

BUILD ME UP.
LP: . . . . TRLS 76

Dowlais Choir

FAMOUS CHOIRS OF WALES VOL.2 (Dowlais Male Choir).
LP: . . . . SCLP 614

Dowland (composer)

ENGLISH LUTE (Various artists).
LP: . . . . H 71363

Down...

DOWN TO EARTH (Elliot, Emily).
LP: . . . . SDL 301
MC: . . . . CSDL 301

Down Argentine Way

DOWN ARGENTINE WAY (1945 film musical soundtrack) (Various artists).
LP: . . . . HS 5013

Down At The Club

DOWN AT THE CLUB (Various artists).
LP: . . . . FBL 1002

Down By Law (film)

DOWN BY LAW (See under Lurie, John) (Lurie, John).

Down County Boys

BETTER TIMES A' COMING.
LP: . . . . BSS 168

Down Home

DOWN HOME, VOL 2 (Fiddle music) (Various artists).
Tracks: / Hangman's reel, The: *Bain, Aly* / La bastringue: *La Bottine Souriante* / Jack is yet alive: *Anderson, Tom* / Wild rose of the mountain: *Fraley, J.P. & Annadeene* / Uncle Pen: *Monroe, Bill & His Blue Grass Boys*/ Lord MacDonald's reel: *Cremo, Lee & Aly Bain* / Untitled: *Carignan, Jean* / Milk cow blues: *Crow, Alvin*/ Miss Spence's reel: *Lerwick Lounge Ensemble* / Dust bowl children: *Rowan, Peter Band* / Roll her in the Rye grass: *Boys Of The Lough* / Faded love: *Junior Daugherty* / Our Highland queen: *MacNeil, Kyle* / Don't mind the weather: *Ritchie, Jean & Mike Seeger* / Scotland: *Monroe, Bill & His Blue Grass Boys* / Jerry Holland: *Cape Breton Fiddlers* / Scott Skinner selection, The: *Carignan, Jean* / Cape Breton Fiddlers welcome to Shetland: *Hunter, Willie* / Lily Dale: *Junior Daugherty & Aly Bain.*
LP: . . . . LIFL 7012
MC: . . . . LIFC 7012

Down Home Jazzband

YERBA BUENA STYLE.
LP: . . . . SOS 1190

Down & Out In...

DOWN AND OUT IN BEVERLY HILLS (1986 Film Soundtrack) (Various artists).
Tracks: / Great gosh a'mighty: *Little Richard* / Tutti frutti: *Little Richard* / California girls: *Roth, David Lee* / El Tecalitleco: *Mariachi Vargas de Tecalitian* / I love L.A.: *Crawford, Randy* / Down and out in Beverly Hills: *Summers, Andy* / Search for Kerouac: *Summers, Andy* / Nouvelle cuisine: *Summers, Andy*/ Wave hands like clouds: *Summers, Andy* / Mission blues, The: *Summers, Andy* / Jerry's suicide attempt: *Summers, Andy.*
LP: . . . . MCF 3320
MC: . . . . MCFC 3320

Down Town Jazzband

HEAR US TALKIN' TO YA.
LP: . . . . TTD 514

Down Twisted (film)

DOWN TWISTED (1987 film soundtrack) (Various artists).
LP: . . . . STV 81305

Downchild

BLOODRUN HOT.
LP: . . . . LAT 1117

Downes, Geoffrey

LIGHT PROGRAMME, THE.
Tracks: / Ethnic dance / East West / Urbanology / Symphonie electronique / Oceania electronique.
LP: . . . . K 9241561
MC: . . . . K 9241564

Downes, Julia

LET SLEEPING DOGS LIE.
LP: . . . . NAVL 2

Downes, Paul

DANCE WITHOUT MUSIC (Downes, Paul & Phil Beer).
Tracks: / Dance without music / Song, The / Let me play / Somewhere in green / Sunday supplement / Five-poster bed / Take back your pictures / Flower girl / Born again / Friends.
LP: . . . . SFA 046

LIFE GOES ON.
Tracks: / Tall ships / My true love / Price of coal / Plains of Waterloo / Life goes on / Worm forgives the plough / Planxty Hewlett / Sir Richard's song / Friar in the well / Sit you down.
LP: . . . . AVA 109

STILL LIFE.
Tracks: / Same old friends / I could not take my eyes off her / Some words / Did you like the battle? / First time ever I saw your face, The / Still life / Puss 'n' boots / Changeless story, The / You'll be next / Sweet air season / Across the hills.
LP: . . . . SFA 086

Downes, Wray

AU PRIVAVE (Downes, Wray/Dave Young/Ed Bickert).
Tracks: / Anthropology / My romance / I'm hip / Portrait of Jennie / Sweet Georgia Brown / Au privave / Spanish fandango / Yours is my heart alone / Falling in love with love.
LP: 4003

Downing, Big Al

BIG AL DOWNING & THE POE KATS (Downing, Big Al & The Poe Kats).
LP: . . . . JLP 1111

ROCKIN' 'N' ROLLIN'.
Tracks: / Down on the farm / Oh babe / Miss Lucy / Just around the corner / Yes, I'm loving you / Rock 'n' roll boogie / Rock 'n' roll record girl / Piano Nellie / Georgia slop / When my blue moon turns to gold again / It must be love / If I had our love to live over / Please come home / Words of love / Heartbreak Hill / I found someone to love / Story of my life / Saints, The.
LP: . . . . ROLL 2015

Downing, Will

COME TOGETHER AS ONE.
Tracks: / Come together as one / Sake of love / Sometimes I cry / Love call / Love we share, The / Too soon / I'll wait / Rules of love / Test of time / Closer to you / Wishing on a star.
MC: . . . . BRCA 538
LP: . . . . BRLP 538

DREAM FULFILLED, A.
LP: . . . . BRLP 565
MC: . . . . BRCA 565

WILL DOWNING.
Tracks: / In my dreams / Do you? / Free / Love supreme, A (12" & CD single only.) / Security / Set me free / Sending out an SOS / Dancing in the moonlight / Do you remember love?.
LP: . . . . BRLP 518
MC: . . . . BRCA 518

Downliners

SHOWBIZ.
LP: . . . . SKY 301

Downliners Sect

COUNTRY SECT, THE.
LP: . . . . CR 30137

CROSS SECTION.
Tracks: / Little Egypt / One ugly child / Our little rendezvous / Sect appeal / Baby what's on your mind / Cops and robbers / Blood hound / Ballad of the hounds / Rocks in my bed / I got mine / Bad storm coming / I want my baby back again / Now she's dead / Everything I've got to give / Comin' home baby / Why don't you smile now / Outside.
LP: . . . . LIK 10

ROCK SECTS IN, THE.
LP: . . . . CR 30140

SECT, THE.
LP: . . . . CR 30122

Downs & Beer

LIVE IN CONCERT.
Tracks: / Passed you by / List for a sailor / Pavanas / Andalucian gypsies / Cursed Anna / Things we said today / Across the hills / Rough with the smooth / Did you like the battle / Let me play / Both sexes / Them toad suckers / Ode to Billy Joe / Life goes on / Old fiddler / My canary's got circles under his eyes / Nuages / Sweet Georgia Brown / Half asleep / Fox on the run.
LP: . . . . R 005LP

Downsiders

ALL MY FRIENDS ARE FISH.
Tracks: / I wanna drive / Wild honey pie / Old black crow / All my friends are fish / Pony made of ice / Kenny Koughdrop / Waiting for nothing / Feet of clay / She's alright / Ode to Traci.
LP: . . . . SORC 2

Downtown Sisters

NEW HEAVEN (Gospels and Spirituals).
Tracks: / What are they doing in heaven today? / Nothing between / Seeking for me / Shine for Jesus / Never alone / Family prayer / God leads us along / Lily of the valley / I saw the light / Blow ye the trumpet of Zion / I do, don't you / Oh, the joy that came to me.
LP: . . . . SM 3229
MC: . . . . MC 3229

Downtowners

YES I DO.
LP: . . . . PHZA 065

Downy Mildew

BROOMTREE.
Tracks: / Frown song, The / Kitchen, The / Sally (part 3) / Good dream / Hollow girl / Ocean motor kid / Burnt bridges / That's enough of that / Sally (part 2) / Everybody's gone.
LP: . . . . GLALP 025

Doyle, Danny

BORN A RAMBLIN' MAN.
LP: . . . . SOLO 7009

DAISY A DAY, A.
LP: . . . . HPE 638

DANNY DOYLE COLLECTION, VOLUME 1.
LP: . . . . GRLP 002

DANNY DOYLE VOL.1.
LP: . . . . MBR 001

DANNY DOYLE VOL.2.
LP: . . . . MBR 002

GRAND OLE IRISH OPREY.
LP: . . . . BRL 4038

TWENTY YEARS A GROWING.
LP: . . . . TA 3020

VERY SPECIAL LOVE SONG, A.
LP: . . . . BRL 4052

WEST'S AWAKE, THE.
LP: . . . . MBLP 003
MC: . . . . MBC 003

Doyle, Geraldine

STAND ON YOUR MAN.
LP: . . . . LRF 121

Doyle, Jimmy

KINGDOM OF KERRY.
LP: . . . . SHAN 29007

Doyle, Peter

SKIN DEEP.
Tracks: / Skin deep / Harlem dream / Sailor man / Reel back / Way it goes, The / Heart filled up / Rocky lady / One more river / Shangri La.
LP: . . . . PL 25113

D'Oyly Carte

LAST NIGHT COLLECTION, THE.
Tracks: / Yeoman of the guard / Trial by jury / Pirates of Penzance / HMS Pinafore / Iolanthe / Grand duke, The / Princess Ida / Ruddigore / Mikado, The / Gondoliers.
2LP: . . . . CCSLP 228
MC: . . . . CCSMC 228

WORLD OF GILBERT AND SULLIVAN (See under Gilbert & Sullivan) (D'Oyly Carte Opera Company).

Dozier Boys & Others

DOO WOPPIN' THE BLUES.
LP: . . . . RARIN' 777

Dozier, Lamont

BIGGER THAN LIFE.
Tracks: / Bigger than life / Right where I wanna be / On the one / Round trip ticket / Love wars / Scarlett O'Hara / Call the wagon / Nowhere to go but up / Second wind / Hero of my heart.
LP: . . . . FIEND 12

BITTERSWEET.
Tracks: / Boogie business / Love me to the max / True love is bittersweet /

Tough act to follow / I got it all with you / We're just here to feel good / Let your love run free / Fly away little birdsong.
LP: K 56594

RIGHT THERE.
Tracks: / It's the same old song / Right there / Jump right on in / Groovin' on a natural high / Can't get off until the feeling stops / Good eye / With a little bit of mending / In a wild frame of mind / Ain't never loved nobody (like I love you) / Joy.
LP: K 56225

D.P.'s

IF YOU KNOW WHAT I MEAN.
Tracks: / Television romeo / Innocent man, An / Do the works / People on the inside / Born to win / If you know what I mean / Hearts get broken / Answer is a gun / One more pill / Rooftops / City of freaks / You sold me out.
LP: 231 4107

Dr. Alimantado

BEST DRESSED CHICKEN IN TOWN, THE.
Tracks: / Gimme mi gun / Plead I cause / Poison flour / Ride on / Just the other day / Best dressed chicken in town / Unitone skank.
LP: GREL 1
MC: GREEN 1

IN THE MIX.
LP: KM 003
MC: KMC 003

IN THE MIX - PART 2.
LP: KM 005
MC: KMCAS 005

IN THE MIX - PART 3.
LP: KM 007
MC: KMCAS 007

IN THE MIX - PART 5.
LP: KM 010

KING'S BREAD.
LP: ISDA 5000
MC: ISDAMC 5000
MC: ISCA CASS 55

KING'S BREAD DUB.
LP: ISDA 5001

LOVE IS.
LP: KM 001
MC: KMC 001

PRIVILEGED FEW,THE.
LP: KM 009

REGGAE REVUE PART 1.
LP: KM 002
MC: KMC 002

SONS OF THUNDER.
Tracks: / Chant to Jah / Return of Muhammed Ali / Sons of thunder / Dreadlocks dread / Call on Jah / Born for a purpose / Careless Ethiopians repent / Oil crisis / Sitting in the park / Marriage licence.
LP: GREL 22
MC: GREEN 22

Dr. Brent's

DOCTOR BRENT'S BROKEN JOURNEY (see Lester, Jane) (Donald, Sheila (nar)).

Dr. Buzzard's...

DOCTOR BUZZARDS ORIGINAL SAVANNAH BAND.
Tracks: / I'll play the fool / Hard times / Whispering / Cherchez la femme / Se si bon / Sunshower / We got it made / Night and day / You've got something / Betcha the love bug bitcha / Sour and sweet.
LP: PL 11504
LP: RS 1072

MEETS KING PENETT (Doctor Buzzards Original Savannah Band).
Tracks: / Mister Love / Nocturnal interludes / Gigolo and I, The / I'll always have a smile for you / Transistor madness / Future D.J. / Organ grinder's tale, An / Soraya / March of the Nignies / Auf Wiedersehen, Darrio.
LP: PL 12402
MC: PK 12402

Dr. Calculus

DESIGNER BEATNIK.
Tracks: / Blasted with ecstasy / Programme 7. / Moments of being-interlude / Killed by poetry / Man / Dream machine / Candyfloss pink / Just another honey / Designer Beatnik / Perfume from Spain. / Moments of being-reprisal.
LP: XID 14
MC: CXID 14
LP: DIX 45

Dr. Clayton

DOCTOR CLAYTON AND HIS BUDDY, 1935-47.
LP: BD 2062

GOTTA FIND MY BABY.
LP: BT 2005

Dr. Demento

DOCTOR DEMENTO'S DELIGHTS.
Tracks: / Hello muddah hello faddah / Cockroach that ate Cincinnati, The / Get a load of this / Ya wanna buy a bunny? / Eleanor Rigby / They're coming to take me away / Boobs a lot / Ballad of Ben Gay / Who put the benzedrine in Mrs Murphy's ovaltine / If you're a viper / Friendly neighbourhood narco agent.
LP: K 56195

Dr. Detroit (film)

DOCTOR DETROIT (Film soundtrack) (Various artists).
LP: MCF 3175

DOCTOR DETROIT (THEME FROM) (See under Devo) (Devo).

Dr. Ease

PUT YOUR MIND AND BODY AT EASE (Doctor Ease & D.J. Mix).
Tracks: / Make U dance / Can't stand still / Make it last / Get fresh Eastown express / Give the people / Oh girl / Terminator.
LP: BUL 4011
MC: MCBUL 4011

Dr. Feelgood

AS IT HAPPENS.
Tracks: / Take a tip / Every kind of vice / Down at the doctors / Baby Jane / Sugar shaker / Things get better / She's a windup / Ninety nine and a half won't do / Buddy Buddy friends / Milk and alchohol / Matchbox / As long as the price is right / Night time.
LP: UAK 30239

BE SEEING YOU.
Tracks: / Ninety-nine-and-a-half (won't do) / She's a wind up / I thought I had it made / I don't wanna know / That's it I quit / As long as the price is right / Hi rise / My buddy buddy friends / Blues had a baby and they named it rock 'n' roll / Looking back / 60 minutes.
LP: UAS 30123
LP: ED 238
LP: GRAND 14
MC: GRANDC 14

BRILLEAUX.
Tracks: / I love you so you're mine / You've got my number / Big enough / Don't wait up / Get rhythm / Where is the next one? / Play dirty / Grow too old / Rough ride / I'm a real man / Come over here / Take what you can get.
LP: GRAND 04
MC: GRANDC 04

CASE BOOK.
Tracks: / Roxette / Route 66 / She does it right / Riot in cell block 9 / Back in the night / You shouldn't call the doctor / She's a wind up / Looking back / Baby Jane / Milk and alcohol / As long as the price is right / Down at the doctors / Night time / Put him out of your mind / Hong Kong money / Waiting for Saturday night.
LP: LBG 30341

CASE OF THE SHAKES, A.
Tracks: / Jumping from love to love / Going some place else / Best in the world / Punch drunk / King for a day / Violent love / No mo do yakamo / Love hound / Coming to you / Who's winning / Drives me wild / Case of the shakes.
LP: ED 189
LP: UAG 30311
MC: TCUAG 30311
LP: GRAND 10
MC: GRANDC 10

CLASSIC.
Tracks: / Hunting, shooting, fishing / Break these chains / Heartbeat / (I wanna) make love to you / Hurricane / Quit while you're behind / Nothing like it / Spy Vs spy / Highway 61 / Crack me up.
LP: SEEZ 67
MC: ZSEEZ 67
LP: GRAND 11
MC: GRANDC 11

DOCTOR'S ORDERS.
Tracks: / Close but no cigar / So long / You don't love me / My way / Neighbour, neighbour / Talk of the devil / Hit git and split / I can't be satisfied / Saturday night fish fry / Drivin' wheel / It ain't right / I don't worry about a thing / She's in the middle / Dangerous.
LP: LILP 400044
LP: FIEND 29
LP: GRAND 06
MC: GRANDC 06

DOWN BY THE JETTY.
Tracks: / She does it right / Boom boom / More I give, The / One weekend / I don't mind / Twenty yards behind / Keep it out of sight / All through the city / Cheque book / Oyeh / Bony Moronie / Tequila.
LP: ED 160
MC: TCFA 3029
LP: FA 3029
LP: GRAND 05

FAST WOMEN AND SLOW HORSES.
Tracks: / She's the one / Sweet sweet lovin' (gone sour on me) / Trying to live my life without you / Rat race / Baby jump / Crazy about girls / Sugar bowl / Educated fool / Bum's rush / Baby why do you treat me this way? / Beautiful Delilah / Monkey.
LP: TOSS 4
LP: LILP 400062
LP: GRAND 03
MC: GRANDC 03

LET IT ROLL.
Tracks: / Java blues / Feels good / Put him out of your mind / Bend your ear / Hong Kong money / Keeka smeeka / Shotgun / Pretty face / Ridin' on the L & N / Drop everything and run.
LP: UAG 30269
MC: TCK 30269
LP: GRAND 07

LIVE IN LONDON.
Tracks: / King for a day / As long as the price is right / Baby Jane / See you later alligator / You upset me / She does it right / Back in the night.
MC: GRANDC 08
LP: GRAND 08

MAD MAN BLUES.
Tracks: / Dust my broom / Something you got / Dimples / Living on the highway / Tore down / Mad man blues / I've got news for you / My babe / Can't find the lady / Rock me baby.
LP: NOSE 5
LP: GRANDLP 02
MC: GRANDMC 02

MALPRACTICE.
Tracks: / I can tell / Going back home / Back in the night / Another man / Rollin' and tumblin' / Don't let your daddy know / Watch your step / Don't you just know it / Riot in cell block 9 / Because you're mine / You shouldn't call the doctor.
LP: UAS 29880
LP: GRAND 09
MC: GRANDC 09

MUSIC IS MEDICINE.
LP: LR 42.019

ON THE JOB.
Tracks: / Drives me wild / Java blues / Jumping from love to love / Pretty face / Nomo do yakamo / Love hound / Best in the world / Who's winning / Riding on the L'n'N / Case of the shakes / Shotgun blues / Goodnight Vienna.
LP: LBG 30328

PRIMO.
Tracks: / Heart of the city / My sugar turns to alcohol / Going down / No time / World in a jug / If my baby quit me / Primo blues / Standing at the crossroads again / Been down so long / Don't worry baby / Down by the jetty blues / Two times nine.
LP: GRAND 12
MC: GRANDC 12

PRIVATE PRACTICE.
Tracks: / Down at the doctor's / Every kind of vice / Things get better / Milk and alcohol / Night time / Let's have a party / Take a tip / It wasn't me / Greaseball / Sugar shaker.
LP: UAG 30184
LP: GRAND 01
MC: GRANDMC 01

SINGLES (THE UA YEARS).
Tracks: / Roxette / She does it right / Back in the night / Ging back home / Riot in cell block 9 / Sneakin' suspicion / She's a wind up / Baby Jane / Down at the doctors / Milk and alcohol / As long as the price is right / Put him out of your mind / Hong Kong money / No mo do yakamo / Jumping from love to love / Violent love / Waiting for Saturday night / Monkey / Trying to live my life without you / Crazy about girls / My way / Mad man blues / See you later alligator / Hunting shooting fishing / Don't wait up (Not on CD.) / Milk and alcohol (New recipe) (Not on CD.).
2LP: EM 1332
MC: TCEM 1332

SNEAKIN' SUSPICION.
Tracks: / Sneakin' suspicion / Paradise / Nothin' shakin' (but the leaves on the trees) / Time and the devil / Lights out / Lucky seven / All my love / You'll be mine / Walking on the edge / Hey mama keep your mouth shut.
LP: FA 3179
MC: TCFA 3179
LP: GRAND 13
MC: GRANDC 13

STUPIDITY.
Tracks: / I'm talking about you / Twenty yards behind / Stupidity / All through the city / I'm a man / Walking the dog / She does it right / Going back home / I don't mind / Back in the night / I'm a hog for you / Checkin' up on my baby / Roxette.
LP: UAS 29990
LP: ED 2606341
MC: ED 2606344

STUPIDITY PLUS (Live 1976-1990).
Tracks: / I'm talking about you / Twenty yards behind / Stupidity / All through the city / I'm a man / Walking the dog / She does it right / Going back home / I don't mind / Back in the night / I'm a hog for you / Checkin' up on my baby / Roxette / Riot cell block No. 9 / Johnny B. Goode / Take a trip / Every kind of vice / She's a wind up / No mo do yakamo / Love hound / Shotgun blues / King for a day / Milk and alcohol / Down at the doctors.
2LP: EM 1388
MC: TC2EM 1388

WHAT'S UP DOC.
Tracks: / Doctor Feelgood / Bald headed Lena / What's up doc / Right string baby / But the wrong yo-yo / Mister moonlight / I'll give you anything / I'll be home one day / Don't let me catch you wrong / Blang dong / Doctor's boogie, The / Let's have a good time tonight / Same old thing happening, The / My gal Jo / Don't tell me no dirty / Where did you go? / It's a sin to tell a lie.
LP: ED 122

Dr. Hector

HOUSE CALLS (Doctor Hector and the Groove Injectors).
Tracks: / Risky business / Good night for making love / Two strong people / Love crime / Shame, shame, shame / Pickin' the blues / Brick by brick / I wonder where I'm going to sleep tonight? / You can use my shoulder / That's how it will be / Wrong side of love / Infected with love.
LP: KIN 4029
MC: KIN 4029 MC

Dr. Hepcat

JIVE.
LP: CH 171

Dr. Hook

BALLAD OF LUCY JORDAN.
LP: CBS 32087

BEST OF DOCTOR HOOK.
Tracks: / I can't touch the sun / Things I didn't say / Carry me Carrie / When she cries / Kiss it away / Sing me a rainbow / Life ain't easy / Sylvia's mother / Last mornin' / Turn on the world / Ballad of Lucy Jordan / Hey Lady Godiva / Four years older than me / Makin' it natural / Freakers ball / Roland the roadie and Gertrude the groupie / Queen of the Silver Dollar / Cover of the Rolling Stone / Penicillin Penny / Monterey Jack / If I'd only come and gone / Wonderful soup stone.
2LP: CBS 22102

COLLECTION: DOCTOR HOOK.
LP: IC 038 85 156

COUNTRY STORE: DOCTOR HOOK VOL 2.
Tracks: / Sylvia's mother / Sing me a rainbow / Carry me Carrie / Penicillin Penny / Marie Laveux / Cover of the Rolling Stone / Kiss it away / When she cries / Turn on the world / Queen of the silver dollar.
LP: CST 41
MC: CSTK 41

DOCTOR HOOK'S GREATEST HITS.
Tracks: / Sylvia's mother / Cover of the Rolling Stone / Everybody's making it big but me / You make my pants want to get up and dance / Sleeping late / Only sixteen / Walk right in / Millionaire / More like the movies / When you're in love with a beautiful woman / Sexy eyes / If not you / Little bit more, A / Sharing the night together / I don't want to be alone tonight / Better love next time / In over my head / Years from now.
LP: EST 26037
MC: TCEST 26037

GIRLS CAN GET IT.
Tracks: / Girls can get it / Body talking / Hold me like you never had me / Boy talk / Lady sundown / Baby makes her blue jeans talk / Let me drink from your well / When you're 18 / Crazy Rosie / Fire in the night / Devil's daughter / SOS for love.
LP: 822 693 1
MC: 822 693 4

LITTLE BIT MORE, A.
Tracks: / Little bit more, A / When you're in love with a beautiful woman / More like the movies / Radio, The / Up on the mountain / If not you / Jungle to the zoo / Bad eye Bill / What about you / I need the high / Couple more years, A.
LP: FA 41 3106 1
MC: FA 41 3106 4
LP: EST 23795

LIVE IN THE U.K.

Tracks: / You make my pants want to get up and dance / Sexy eyes / Cover of the Rolling Stone / Carry me Carrie / I got stoned and I missed it / When you're in love with a beautiful woman / Ooh-poo-pah-doo / Sylvia's mother.
LP: . . . . MFP 41 5691 1
MC: . . . . MFP 41 5691 4
LP: . . . . EST 26706

LOVE SONGS: DR. HOOK.
LP: . . . . PLAT 3902
MC: . . . . PLAC 3902

MAKIN' LOVE AND MUSIC.
Tracks: / Makin' love and music / Laying too low too long / What a way to go / Sleeping late / Walk right in / Who dat / Let the loose end drag / I'm a lamb / I wanna make the women tremble / Sexy eyes.
MC: . . . . TC EST 11632
LP: . . . . EST 11632

PLAYERS IN THE DARK.
Tracks: / Baby makes her blue jeans talk / Turn on / Lady sundown / I can't say no to her / Loveline / Pity the fool / Chained to your memory / Devil's daughter / Hearts like yours and mine / Fire in the night.
LP: . . . . MERS 002

PLEASURE AND PAIN.
Tracks: / Sharing the night together / Sweetest of all / Storms never last / I don't want to be alone tonight / Knowing she is there / Clyde / When you're in love with a beautiful woman / Dooley Jones / I gave her comfort / You make my pants want to get up and dance.
LP: . . . . ATAK 3
MC: . . . . TCATAK 3
LP: . . . . EAST 11859

RISING.
Tracks: / Girls can get it / Body talking / That didn't hurt too bad / Blown away / SOS for love / Doin' it / Before the tears / Hold me like you never had me / Do you right tonight / 99 and me.
LP: 6302 076

RISING/PLAYERS IN THE DARK.
Tracks: / Girls can get it / Body talking / That didn't hurt too bad / Blown away / SOS for love / Doing it / Before the tears / Hold me like you never had me / Do you right tonight / 99 and me / Baby makes her blue jeans talk / Turn on, The / Lady Sundown / I can't say no to her / Loveline / Pity the fool / Chained to your memory / Devil's daughter / Hearts like yours and mine / Fire in the night.
2LP: 8326111

SHARING THE NIGHT TOGETHER.
MC: 4XL 9042

SOMETIMES YOU WIN.
Tracks: / Better love next time / In over my head / Sexy eyes / Oh Jesse / Years from now / I don't feel much like smilin' / When you're in love with a beautiful woman / What do you want / Love monster / Mountain Mary / Help me mama.
LP: . . . . FA 3012
MC: . . . . TCFA 3012
LP: . . . . EST 12018

SYLVIA'S MOTHER.
Tracks: / I can't touch the sun / Things I didn't say, The / Carry me, Carrie / When she cries / Kiss it away / Sing me a rainbow / Life ain't easy / Sylvia's mother / Last mornin' / Turn on the world.
LP: . . . . CBS 32082
MC: 40 32082
LP: . . . . SHM 3136
MC: . . . . HSC 3136

Dr. Ice

MIC STALKER, THE.
LP: . . . . HIP 86
MC: . . . . HIPC 86

Dr. Jekyll & Mr Hyde

STRANGE CASE OF DR. JEKYLL AND MR. HYDE (See under Stevenson, Robert Louis).

Dr. John

BRIGHTEST SMILE IN TOWN, THE.
Tracks: / Saddled the cow / Boxcar boogie / Brightest smile in town / Waiting for a train / Monkey puzzle / Average kind of guy / Pretty Libby / Marie Le Veau / Come rain or come shine / Suite home New Orleans.
LP: . . . . FIEND 9
MC: . . . . FIENDCASS 9

CITY LIGHTS.
Tracks: / Dance the night away with you / Street side / Wild honey / Rain / Snake eyes / Fire of love / Sonata / He's a hero / City lights.
LP: . . . . AMLJ 732

DOCTOR JOHN PLAYS MAC REBENNACK.
Tracks: / Dorothy / Mac's boogie / Memories of Professor Longhair / Nearness of you / Delicado / Honey dripper / Big Mac / New island midnight / Saints / Pinetop / Silent night (Available on CD only) / Dance a la negres (Available on CD only) / Wade in the water (Available on CD only).
LP: . . . . FIEND 1
MC: . . . . FIENDCASS 1

GRIS GRIS.
Tracks: / Gris gris gumbo ya ya / Danse Kalinda ba doom / Mama roux / Danse fambeaux / Croker courtbullion / Jump sturdy / I walk on gilded splinters.
LP: . . . . AL 3904
LP: . . . . K 40168

GUMBO.
LP: . . . . AL 3901

HOLLYWOOD BE THY NAME.
LP: . . . . BGOLP 62

I BEEN HOODOOD.
Tracks: / Right place wrong time / Same old, same old / Qualified / Travelling mood / Such a night / I been hoodood / Cold, cold, cold / Quitters never win / What comes around (goes around) / (Everybody wanna get rich) rite away / R U 4 real / Can't get enuff / Destively bonnaroo.
LP: . . . . ED 128

IN A SENTIMENTAL MOOD.
LP: . . . . K 9258891
MC: . . . . K 9258894

IN THE NIGHT.
Tracks: / Bald head / Bring your love / Did she mention my name / Go ahead / Grass is greener / I pulled the cover off you two lovers / In the night / Just like America / Tipitina / Zu zu man / Mean cheatin' woman / New Orleans / Shoo-rah / Time has come, The / One night late / Ear is on strike, The.
LP: . . . . TOP 118
MC: . . . . KTOP 118

IN THE RIGHT PLACE.
Tracks: / Right place wrong time / Same old same old / Just the same / Qualified / Travelling mood / Peace brother peace / Life / Such a night / Shoo fly marches on / I been hoodood / Cold cold cold.
LP: . . . . K 50017

LOSER FOR YOU, BABY.
Tracks: / Time had come, The / Loser for you baby / Ear is on strike, The / Little closer to my home, A / I pulled the cover off you two lovers / New Orleans / Go ahead on / Just like a mirror / Bring your love / Bald head.
LP: . . . . THBL 066

MARDI GRAS AT THE MARQUEE (see under Barber, Chris) (Dr. John & Chris Barber).

NIGHT TRIPPER AT HIS BEST.
LP: . . . . BID 8014

ROADHOUSE SYMPHONY (see Crawford, Hank) (Doctor John & Hank Crawford).

SUCH A NIGHT. LIVE IN LONDON.
LP: . . . . SPIN 107
MC: . . . . SPIC 107

TAKE ME BACK TO NEW ORLEANS (see under Barber, Chris) (Dr. John & Chris Barber).

TRIUMVIRATE (see Bloomsfield, Mike) (Doctor John/Mike Bloomsfield/John Hammond).

ZU ZU MAN.
Tracks: / Cat and mouse game / She just a square / Bald headed / In the night / Helping hand / Zu zu man / Mean cheatin' woman / Woman's the root of all evil / Trader John / Shoo-rah / Ti-pi-ti-na / One night late.
LP: . . . . THBL 069

Dr. J.R Cool

COMPLETE STORY OF... (Doctor J.R Cool & The Other Roxannes).
LP: . . . . CLTLM 8271

Dr. Know

WRECKAGE IN FLESH.
Tracks: / War theatre / Mastermind / City wheels / Wreckage / Lake of fire.
LP: . . . . RR 94951

Dr. Mastermind

DOCTOR MASTERMIND.
Tracks: / Domination / Right way, The / Man of the year / We want the world / Control / Abuser / Black leather maniac / I don't wanna die.
LP: . . . . RR 9605

Dr. Mix

1979-1982 (Doctor Mix and The Remix).
LP: . . . . BR 041

WALL OF NOISE.
LP: . . . . ROUGH 6

Dr. Pablo

NORTH OF THE RIVER THAMES (Doctor Pablo & Dub Syndicate).
LP: . . . . ONULP 30

Dr. Phibes

WHIRLPOOL (Doctor Phibes & The House Of Wax Equitations).
LP: . . . . SEEL 002

Dr. Stafford

HE DID IT ALL FOR ME (Doctor Stafford & The Free For All Inspiration Choir).
Tracks: / Faith / He did it all for me / Victory / I know it was the blood / This is the day / Come to the altar / Elevate your minds / Saints / Lord / Hold my hand / I opened my mouth unto the Lord.
LP: . . . . MIR 5001
MC: . . . . ZCMIR 5001

Dr. Strut

DOCTOR STRUT.
Tracks: / Look in your eyes / Granit palace / Canadian star / More stuff / Blowtop / Soul sermonette / Chicken strut / Eddieisms / Who cares / No you came here for an argument.
LP: . . . . STML 12120

STRUTTIN.
Tracks: / Struttin / Acufukture / Blue lodge / CMS / Film city / Commuter rabbit / After / For folon / Nitwit / Nice 'n' sleazy / No, you came here for an argument.
LP: . . . . STML 12132

Dr. Sunshine

SUNNY SONGS FOR CHILDREN.
LP: . . . . KOP 12

Dr. & The Crippens

FIRED FROM THE CIRCUS.
Tracks: / Freak of nature / Billy's dead / Ballad of farmer Vincent, The / Ever been to Utah? / Controlled experiment, A / Something wrong with her / Eat your wheelchair / Ode to a slug / Virgin slugburger / Mr. Creosote / Pneumatic Greek / Eat my dog / Russian roulette / Don't look in the freezer / Tommy backwards / Pink machine gun / Geoffrey's revenge.
LP: . . . . ACHE 014

RAPHANADOSIS.
Tracks: / Garden centre murders, The / Braindead / Epic / I'm so dumb / Henenlotter / Kid with the removable face / Skintight / Jimmy goes to Egypt / Extreme noise T / Bench / Zombies in Disneyland / Elvis shroud, The / My brother is a headcase / Anti Christ on button moon / Greenfinger / 8 years in office / Podbreath / Nightmare on Sesame Street.
LP: . . . . ACHE 18

Dr. & The Medics

I KEEP THINKING IT'S TUESDAY.
Tracks: / Drive he said / Wild flowers / Gorilla / Jack of Kent / When the hammer comes down / Sea of stone / More / Madman of Bernarae / I keep thinking it's Tuesday / Love and everything you eat / I wanna choke on your love / Age of gold / Stare crazy (Only on cassette and CD.).
LP: . . . . MIRF 1024
MC: . . . . MIRFC 1024

LAUGHING AT THE PIECES.
Tracks: / No one loves you when you got no shoes / Kettle on a long chain / Come on call me / Watermelon runaway / Fried egg bad Monday / Spirit in the sky / Lucky Lord Jim / Moon song / Barbara can't dance / Smallness of the mustard pot.
LP: . . . . MIRG 1010
MC: . . . . MIRGC 1010
LPPD: . . . . MIRGP 1010

MUSIC AND MEDIA INTERVIEW PICTURE DISC.
LPPD: . . . . MM 1228

Dr. Who

DOCTOR WHO (Various artists).
Tracks: / Genesis of the daleks: *Various artists* / Slipback: *Various artists.*
MCSET: . . . . ZBBC 1020

DOCTOR WHO (State of decay) (Unknown narrator(s)).
MCSET: . . . . DTO 10517

DOCTOR WHO AND THE PESCATONS (Unknown narrator(s)).
LP: 4144591
MC: 4144594

DOCTOR WHO - THE MUSIC (BBC Radiophonic Workshop).
Tracks: / Tardis / Sea devils, The / Meglos / Kassia's wedding music / Threat of Melkur, The / Exploring the lab / Nyassa is hypnotized / Leisure hive, The / Omega field force / Ergon threat / Termination of the doctor / Banqueting music / TSS machine attacked / Janissary band / Subterranean caves / Requiem / March of the Cybermen / Doctor Who theme.
LP: . . . . REH 462
MC: . . . . ZCR 462

DOCTOR WHO - THE MUSIC VOL 2 (BBC Radiophonic Workshop).
Tracks: / Five doctors, The / King's demon, The / Enlightenment / Warriors of the deep / Awakening, The / Resurrection of the daleks / Planet of fire / Caves of Androzani.
LP: . . . . REH 552
MC: . . . . ZCR 552

DOCTOR WHO'S 25TH ANNIVERSARY ALBUM (Various artists).
Tracks: / Tardis: *Various artists* / Doctor Who theme: *Various artists* / Gavrok's search: *Various artists*/ Child's return, A: *Various artists* / Towers el paradiso: *Various artists* / Burton's escape: *Various artists*/ Drinksmat dawning: *Various artists* / Future pleasure: *Various artists* / Newreel past: *Various artists*/ Sting, The: *Various artists* / 8891 Royale: *Various artists* / White flag: *Various artists* / Guards of silence: *Various artists* / Making of Pex, The: *Various artists* / Cemetery chase: *Various artists*/ Brain, The: *Various artists* / Here's to the future: *Various artists* / Goodbye Doctor: *Various artists*/ Doctor Who: *Various artists.*
LP: . . . . REB 707
MC: . . . . ZCF 707

GENESIS OF THE DALEKS (Unknown narrator(s)).
LP: . . . . REH 364
MC: . . . . ZCR 364

STATE OF DECAY (Baker, Tom).
MC: . . . . PTB 607

Dr. York

NEW.
LP: . . . . SPLP 004
MC: . . . . SPLC 004

RE-NEW.
LP: . . . . YRC 78636
MC: . . . . CYRC 78636

Dr. Zhivago

DOCTOR ZHIVAGO (Film soundtrack) (Jarre, Maurice).
Tracks: / Overture from Dr Zhivago / Lara leaves Yuri / At the student cafe / Komarovsky and Lara's rendezvous / Revolution / Tonya arrives at Varykino / Yuri writes a poem for Lara / Lara's theme.
LP: . . . . CBS 70274
MC: 40 70274

Dr. Zhivago (bk)

DOCTOR ZHIVAGO (Schofield, Paul (nar)).
MC: . . . . TC LFP 7054

Dr. Zhivago (film)

DOCTOR ZHIVAGO (ORIGINAL ISSUE) (Film soundtrack) (Various artists).
LP: . . . . MGM C 8007

Drac

DRAC ATTACK.
LP: . . . . ICH 1013
MC: . . . . ZCICH 1013

Dracula

DRACULA (Narrated by Christopher Lee) (Lee, Christopher).
LP: . . . . NTS 186

DRACULA (see under Stoker, Bram) (Various artists).

Dracula (film)

DRACULA (Original soundtrack) (Various artists).
Tracks: / Four faces of evil: *Various artists* / Fear in the night suite: *Various artists* / She: *Various artists* / Vampire lovers: *Various artists* / Dr Jekyll and Sister Hyde: *Various artists.*
LP: . . . . MCF 3018

DRACULA (Various artists).
LP: 255 087.1
MC: . . . . VSC 5250

Dragnet (film)

DRAGNET (1988 Film Sountrack) (Various artists).
LP: . . . . MCF 3414
MC: . . . . MCFC 3414

Dragon

BODY AND THE BEAT.
Tracks: / Rain / Promises (so far away) / Wilderworld / Cry / Cool down / Body and the beat / Witnessing / Magic / What am I gonna do? / Fool.
MC: . . . . POLDC 5143
LP: . . . . POLD 5143

FALLEN ANGEL.
LP: . . . . FLAG 48
MC: . . . . TFLAG 48

SCREAM OF DEATH.
LP: . . . . FLAG 58
MC: . . . . TFLAG 58

Dragon Den

DRAGON DEN, THE (Childrens story book) (Unknown narrator(s)).
MC: . . . . RWM 003

Dragonette, Jessica

WITH LOVE.
Tracks: / Ay ay ay / Love me tonight / Nevermore / Smoke gets in your eyes / Why do I love you? / Touch of your hand, The / Dream of love / I dream too much / Speak to me of love / Love is the sun / Wanting you / Falling in love with love / You belong to my heart / Make believe / Kiss me again / Give me something to remember you by.
LP: . . . . TOTEM 1029

Dragoni Brothers

EVENING WITH THE DRAGONI BROTHERS.
Tracks: / Lichtensteiner polka / Casatchok / Terang bolan / Loch Lomond / Ye no come back again / Please help me, I'm falling / I love you because / Banks of the Ohio / Londonderry air shake hands with your uncle Mike / Quando, quando, quando / Lemon tree / La paloma / South of the border / Wooden heart / Woodpecker song, The / Rancho grande / Three caballeros / Itsy bitsy / Don't dilly dally / Who were you with / Wish me luck as you wave me goodbye.
LP: . . . . RUB 033
MC: . . . . RUBC 033

Dragons

PARFUMS DE LA REVOLUTION.
LP: 1200 333

Drag's Half Fast

DRAG'S HALF FAST JAZZ BAND (Drag's Half Fast Jazz Band).
LP: . . . . GHB 54

Drake, Nick

BRYTER LAYTER.
Tracks: / Introduction / Hazy Jane 2 / At the chime of the city clock.
LP: . . . . ILPS 9134

FIVE LEAVES LEFT.
Tracks: / Time has told me / River man / Three hours / Day is done / Way to blue / 'Cello song / Thoughts of Mary Jane, The / Man in a shed / Fruit tree / Saturday Sun.
LP: . . . . ILPS 9105

FRUIT TREE.
LP: . . . . HNBL 5302
LPS: . . . . HNBX 5302

HEAVEN IN A WILD FLOWER (Best of Nick Drake).
Tracks: / Fruit tree / Cello song / Thoughts of Mary Jane, The / Northern sky / River man / At the chime of the city clock / Intro / Hazey Jane 1 / Hazy Jane 2 / Pink moon / Road / Which will / Things behind the sun / Time has told me.
LP: . . . . ILPM 9826
MC: . . . . ICM 9826
MC: 842 551 4

PINK MOON.
Tracks: / Pink moon / Place to be / Road / Which will / Horn / Things behind the sun / Know / Parasite / Ride / Harvest breed / From the morning.
LP: . . . . ILPS 9184

TIME OF NO REPLY.
Tracks: / Joey / Clothes of sand / May fair / I was made to love magic / Strange meetings II / Been smoking too long.
LP: . . . . HNBL 1318
MC: . . . . HNBC 1318

Drake, Pete

PETE DRAKE SHOW, THE.
LP: . . . . STOP 1001

STEEL AWAY.
LP: . . . . CGS 8502

Drake, Susan

CAPRICES & FANTASIES (Various artists).
MC: . . . . KA 66340

Drake's Dream (show)

DRAKE'S DREAM (Original cast) (Various artists).
Tracks: / At the court of Queen Elizabeth: *Various artists* / I've always had a dream: *Various artists* / Let's get goin': *Various artists* / When the winds command us away: *Various* artists / She plays a dangerous game: *Various artists* / Between today and tomorrow: *Various artists* / Sedition: *Various artists* / Waiting isn't easy: *Various artists* / Gold: *Various artists* / Nova Albion: *Various* artists / God of the waters: *Various artists* / Spice of life: *Various artists* / Oh Lord protect us: *Various artists* / Fa la la: *Various artists* / Sailing around: *Various artists* / Finale: *Various artists.*
LP: . . . . PTLS 1068

Dramarama

BOX OFFICE BOMB.
Tracks: / Steve & Edie / New dream / Whenever I'm with her / Spare change / 400 blows / Pumpin (my heart) / It's still warm / Out in the rain / Baby rhino's eye / Worse than being by myself / Modesty personified.
LP: . . . . ROSE 138
MC: . . . . ROSE 138C

CINEMA VERITE.
LP: . . . . ROSE 74

Dramatics

DRAMATICS LIVE, THE.
Tracks: / Get up and get down / This guy's in love with you / That's the way I feel about cha / In the rain / Thank you for your love / Respect yourself / Toast to the fool / Whatcha see is watcha get.
LP: . . . . SX 018

NEW DIMENSIONS.
Tracks: / Live it up / Treat me right / I can't stand / She's my kind of girl / It's a dramatic music / I didn't want to loose your love / I believe in you / Night life.
LP: . . . . EST 12205

POSITIVE STATE OF MIND.
LP: . . . . V 3402

SOMEWHERE IN TIME.
Tracks: / Dream lady / Razor blade / One love ago / Show me what you got / When love is over / Somewhere in time / In the rain / I fell for you / Hey you get off my mountain / Girl stop your weeping / Be my girl / Days of yea and nea / Luv's callin' / She's wild.
LP: . . . . F 9642

Dramatis

FOR FUTURE REFERENCE.
Tracks: / Oh 2025 / Human sacrifice / I only find rewind / No-one lives forever / Love needs no disguise / Turn / Take me home / On reflection / Ex luna scientia.
LP: . . . . TRAIN 18

Dramatist Speaks

DRAMATIST SPEAKS, THE (Arnold Wesker) (Arden, John (nar)).
MCSET: . . . . SAY 58

Drame, Adama

AFRICAN PERCUSSION.
Tracks: / B. Mondet / Dougouba dya / Barra / Abounaye / Solo sania / Sabumoya / Badina / Elodie / Layana.
LP: . . . . PS 33525

RHYTHMS OF THE MANDING.
LP: . . . . G 1042
MC: . . . . G 4042

Dransfield, Robin

BOWIN' AND SCRAPIN' (Dransfield, Robin & Barry).
Tracks: / Rattlin' roarin' Willie / Metal man / Fiddler's progress / Who's knows where the time goes / My pagan love / Sheffield hornpipe / Pet of the pipers / Up the aisle (Swedish wedding march) / Wedding song, The / Bridie's wedding / Norwegian wedding march / Wedding Morris / Sandy Bell's / Obliged to fiddle / Planxty Oavy / Spanish cloak, The / Bushes and briars / Swedish air / O'Carolan's concerto / Recitation upon a gentleman sitting on a Cremo / Sally gardens / Conmel races.
LP: 12TS 386

LORD OF ALL I BEHOLD (Dransfield, Robin & Barry).
Tracks: / Faithful Johnny / Bold Nelson's favourite / Who liveth so merry / Adam and the beasts / Lord of all I behold / Paddy Ryan's dream / Still he sings / Bold William Taylor / Just as the tide was flowing / Wild rose, The.
LP: . . . . LER 2026

POPULAR TO CONTRARY BELIEF (Dransfield, Robin & Barry).
LP: . . . . FRR 018

ROUT OF THE BLUES (Dransfield, Robin & Barry).
Tracks: / Rout of the blues, The / Scarborough fair / St. Clement's jig / Huntsman's chorus, The / Nancy / Water o' Tyne, The / Earl of Totnes, The / Tapestry / Trees they do grow high, The / Week before Easter, A / Fair maid walking all in her garden, A / Who's the fool now.
LP: . . . . LER 2011

TIDEWAVE.
Tracks: / Cutty Wren, The / Barley and the rye, The / Fair maids of February / When it's night time in Italy it's Wednesday / Rigs o'rye / Spencer the rover / Tidewave / Cadgwith anthem / I once had a dog / Three muscadets / Mother Nature.
LP: 12TS 414

Draper, Ray

JOHN COLTRANE/RAY DRAPER (see Coltrane, John) (Draper, Ray & John Coltrane).

TUBA JAZZ.
LP: . . . . FS 308

Draper, Rusty

HIS TOP HITS.
MC: 825

Draughtsman's Contract

DRAUGHTSMAN'S CONTRACT, THE (1983 Film Soundtrack) (Various artists).
Tracks: / Queen of the night: *Various artists* / Disposition of the linen, The: *Various artists* / Watery death, A: *Various artists* / Garden is becoming a robe room, The: *Various artists* / Chasing sheep is best left to shepherds: *Various artists* / Eye for optical theory, An: *Various artists* / Bravura in the face of grief: *Various artists.*
LP: . . . . CAS 1158
LP: . . . . SL 9513
MC: . . . . SLC 9513

Draumur, S H

GOD.
Tracks: / Monako Monaco / Helmut a mmotorjoli (bigot on a motorbike) / Kani/ yankee / Engin evintyri (no adventures) / Eg dansa vio lik / I dance with a corpse / Glapur gegn rikinu/crime against the... / Oxnadalsheioi/oxenvalleymoor / Dau hola (a dead hole) / Syrubelio Brennur/ the acidhovel burns / Englarnir (the angels) / Ostur/oysters.
LP: . . . . LKND 002

Drayton, Leslie

LOVE IS A FOUR-LETTER WORD (Drayton, Leslie Orchestra).
Tracks: / Greasy brown paper sack, A / Love is just a four letter word / When will you be mine / You ain't gonna keep me blue / Stormy Monday / What if? / I need your love so bad / Love is just a four letter word (instrumental).
LP: . . . . ER 1003

WHAT IT IS IS WHAT IT IS (Drayton, Leslie & Fun).
Tracks: / What it is is what it is / Sausalito Ferry / I'll take it easy / Comin' at ya / Pershing Square / Brownie points / I'm really gonna miss you.
LP: . . . . ER 1004

Dread, Bobo

GHANA ARMY.
LP: . . . . JESLP 01

Dread, Mikey

BEYOND WORLD WAR III.
LP: . . . . TNT 1

DREAD AT THE CONTROLS.
Tracks: / Everybody needs a proper education / Dread combination / Love the dread / Voice of Jah / Step by step / Walk Rastafari way / King in the ring / Barber saloon.
LP: . . . . TRLS 178
MC: . . . . ZCTRL 178

HAPPY FAMILY.
LP: . . . . RAS 3035
MC: . . . . RASCS 3035

PAVE THE WAY.
LP: . . . . HB 31

PAVE THE WAY PARTS 1 & 2.
Tracks: / Quest for oneness / Nkosi sikelal I'Afrika (dubwise) / Time waster / Relax / Kiss me / Master, The (encore) / Dubmaster / Have you got a minute to spare? / Nowadays youth / Dizzy (herb smoker) / Too many rulers / Paradise / Reggae hit shot / Roots and culture rise again / (Dance) face to face / Knock knock / Ever changing world / Pave the way / Anti-apartheid / (Open the gate) come in / Freedom is coming / Forever and ever / Grove carnival / Enjoy yourself / Kiss me (instrumental).
2LP: . . . . LPDEP 8
MCSET: . . . . CADEP 8

S.W.A.L.K.
LP: . . . . RIDE 10

Dread, Sammy

RAP UP A DRAW.
LP: . . . . SLLP 06

Dread Zeppelin

5,000,000.
Tracks: / Fab (part 1) / Stir it up / Do the claw / When the levee breaks / Misty mountain top / Train kept a rollin' / Nobody's fault (butt-mon) / Big ol' gold belt / Fab (part 2) / Stairway to heaven.
LP: . . . . EIRSA 1057
MC: . . . . EIRSAC 1057

UN-LED-ED.
Tracks: / Black dog / Living loving maid / Bring it on home / Black mountain side / Heartbreaker (at the end of Lonely St) / Your time is gonna come / Whole lotta love / I can't suit you baby / Immigrant song / Moby Dick.
LP: . . . . EIRSA 1042
MC: . . . . EIRSAC 1042

Dreadful Snakes

SNAKES ALIVE.
LP: . . . . ROUNDER 0177
MC: . . . . ROUNDER 0177C

Dream A Little Dream

DREAM A LITTLE DREAM (Various artists).
LP: . . . . YL 0125

Dream Academy

DIFFERENT KIND OF WEATHER, A.
LP: . . . . BYN 23
MC: . . . . BYNC 23

DREAM ACADEMY.
Tracks: / Life in a northern town / Edge of forever, The / Johnny new light / In places on the run / This world / Bound to be / Moving on / Love parade / Party, The / One dream.
LP: . . . . BYN 6
MC: . . . . BYNC 6

REMEMBRANCE DAYS.
Tracks: / Indian Summer / Lesson of love / Humdrum / Power to believe / Hampstead girl / Here / In the hands of love / Ballad in 4/4 / Doubleminded / Everybody's gotta learn sometime / In exile.
LP: . . . . BYN 12
MC: . . . . BYNC 12

Dream Death

JOURNEY INTO MYSTERY.
LP: . . . . NRR 25
MC: . . . . NRC 25

Dream Girls (show)

DREAM GIRLS (Original 1981 Broadway Cast) (Various artists).
Tracks: / Move (you're stepping on my heart): *Various artists* / Fake your way to the top: *Various artists* / Cadillac car: *Various artists* / Ain't no party: *Various artists* / When I first saw you: *Various artists*/ I am changing: *Various artists* / Steppin' to the bad side: *Various artists* / Family: *Various artists*/ I meant you no harm: *Various artists* / Rap, The: *Various artists* / Firing of Jimmy: *Various artists*/ I miss you, old friend: *Various artists* / Dream girls: *Various artists* / Press conference: *Various artists*/ And I'm telling you, I'm not going: *Various artists* / One night only: *Various artists* / Hard to say goodbye: *Various artists* / My love: *Various artists.*
LP: . . . . GEF 85578
MC: 4085578

Dream Glow Collection

DREAM GLOW COLLECTION, THE (See under Barbie).

Dream (Group)

DREAM, THE.
LP: . . . . REVLP 143
MC: . . . . REVMC 143

Dream Of Gerontius

DREAM OF GERONTIUS (Various artists).
LPS: . . . . EX 749 549 1
MCSET: . . . . EX 749 549 4

Dream On (tv)

DREAM ON - WRECK ON THE HIGHWAY (T.V. Sound Tracks) (Various artists).
LP: . . . . REB 769

Dream Syndicate

DAYS OF WINE AND ROSES.
Tracks: / Tell me when it's over / Definately clean / That's what you always say / Then she remembers / Halloween / When you smile / Until lately / Too little, too late / Days of wine and roses.
LP: . . . . SLMP 19
MC: . . . . SLMC 19
LP: . . . . ROUGH 53

DREAM SYNDICATE.
Tracks: / Sure thing / That's what you always say / When you smile / Some kinda itch.
LP: . . . . ZANE 001

GHOST STORIES.
Tracks: / Side I'll never show, The / Loving the sinner, hating the sin / Weathered and torn / I have faith / Black / My old haunts / Whatever you please / See that my grave is kept clean / Someplace better than this / When the curtain falls.
LP: . . . . ENVLP 506
MC: . . . . TCENV 506

LIVE AT RAJI'S.
Tracks: / Still holding on to you / Forest for the trees / Until lately / That's what you always say / Burn / Merrittville / Days of wine and roses, The / Medicine

show, The / Halloween / Boston / John Coltrane stereo blues.
LP: . . . . **ENVLP 531**
LP: . . . . **D FIEND 176**

LIVE AT RAJI'S / GHOST STORIES.
LP: . . . . **FIEND 170**

MEDICINE SHOW.
Tracks: / Still holding on to you / Daddy's girl / Burn / Armed with an empty gun / Bullet with my name on it / Medicine show / John Coltrane stereo blues / Merritville.
LP: . . . . **AMLX 64990**
MC: . . . . **CXM 64990**

OUT OF THE GREY.
Tracks: / Out of the grey / Forest for the trees / 50 in a 25 zone / Boston / Slide away / Dying embers / Now I ride alone / Dancing blind / You can't forget / Blood money (Extra track on cassette only.) / Drinking problem (Extra track on cassette only.).
LP: . . . . **CHR 1539**
MC: . . . . **ZCHR 1539**
LP: . . . . **ZL 71457X**
MC: . . . . **ZK 71457X**

THIS IS NOT THE NEW DREAM SYNDICATE ALBUM.
LP: . . . . **AMLH 12511**

Dream Theater

WHEN DREAM AND DAY UNITE.
Tracks: / Fortune in lies, A / Ytse Jake, The / Light / Status seeker / Killing hand, The.
LP: . . . . **MCF 3445**
MC: . . . . **MCFC 3445**

Dream Warriors

AND NOW THE LEGACY BEGINS.
LP: . . . . **BRLP 560**
MC: . . . . **BRCA 560**

Dreamland Syncopators

TERRITORY JAZZ.
LP: . . . . **SOS 1150**

Dreams & Desires

DREAMS & DESIRES (Various artists).
MC: . . . . **UNKNOWN**

Dreams So Real

ROUGH NIGHT IN JERICHO.
Tracks: / Rough night in Jericho / Heart of stone / Bearing witness / Victim / California / City of love / Open your eyes / Distance / Melanie / Love fall down.
LP: **209457**
MC: **409457**

Dreamscape (film)

DREAMSCAPE (Film soundtrack) (Jarre, Maurice).
LP: . . . . **SONIC 102**

Dreamtime

DREAMTIME (Various artists).
Tracks: / No regrets: *Walker Brothers* / Cherish: *Kool & The Gang* / Arms Of Mary: *Sutherland Brothers* & Quiver / Answer Me: *Dickson, Barbara* / Whistle down the wind: *Heyward, Nick* / Longer: *Fogelberg, Dan*/ Captain of her heart, The: *Double* / How 'bout us: *Champaign* / Everything your heart desires: *Hall & Oates*/ Mandolin wind: *Stewart, Rod* / Dreamtime: *Hall, Daryl* / Lost in love: *Air Supply* / Bridge to your heart: *Wax* / Let it flow: *Clapton, Eric* / Jane: *Jefferson Starship* / Do that to me one more time: *Captain* & Tennille / For ever and ever: *Roussos, Demis* / Gold: *Stewart, John* / What's another year: *Logan, Johnny* / Dream baby: *Orbison, Roy.*
MC: . . . . **STDMC 33**

Dreamtime (Group)

BUNNY UP.
Tracks: / Boys did it / Careful driver / Lend an ear / And so Tibet / Bunny up.
LP: . . . . **AFF 109**

Dreamworld (label)

DREAMWORLD COMPILATION (Various artists).
LP: . . . . **BIG 8**

Drecker, Anneli Marian

KEEP IT UP (See under Y.B.U.) (Y.B.U. Featuring Anneli Marian Drecker).

Dredd Foole

EAT MY DUST (Dredd Foole & The Din).
LP: . . . . **HMS 033**

Dregs

INDUSTRY STANDARD.
LP: **204559**

Dressed To Kill (film)

DRESSED TO KILL (1981 Film Soundtrack) (Various artists).
LP: . . . . **STV 81148**

Dressed Up Animals

DRESSED UP ANIMALS.
Tracks: / Horse with bunders / Turkisches bad / Good morning Mr. King / Cirque / Cat, The / Rooms / Wild flowers sang, The / Entree / Ruinen / Warser aus bomber / Je ne sais rien / Night / Bonga bonga / Mondtanz / Behind you / Dyin' out.
LP: . . . . **DUA 213**

Drew, Kenny

AFTERNOON IN EUROPE (Drew, Kenny Trio).
Tracks: / Golden striker, The / Midnight sun / Jeg gik mig ud en sommerday at hore / Tivoli strool / Ach varmeland,du skona / Afternoon in Paris / Quiet cathedral, The.
LP: . . . . **PL 45373**

ERNIE WILKINS & THE ALMOST BIG BAND/KENNY DREW/ED THIGDEN (See Wilkins, Ernie and The Almost Big Band) (Drew, Kenny & The Almost Big Band/Ed Thigpen/Ernie Wilkins).

MORNING.
LP: . . . . **SCS 1048**

PLAYTIME (See under Vinding, Mads) (Drew, Kenny & Mads Vinding).

PRIZE WINNERS (Drew, Kenny/ Henning/Pedersen/Asmussen/ Thigpen).
Tracks: / Django / Pretty girl / Golgotha / Bridgetown baby / Hush-a-bye / Donna Lee / You are the sunshine of my life / Evening in the park / Careless love.
LP: . . . . **MTX 1001**

THIS IS NEW.
Tracks: / This is new / Carol / It's you or no one / You're my thrill / Little / Paul's pal / Why do I love you.
LP: . . . . **RLP 236**

Drew, Martin

BRITISH JAZZ ARTISTS VOL 3 (Drew, Martin, Band).
LP: . . . . **LAM 003**

Drew, Ronnie

IT'S GUARANTEED RONNIE DREW.
LP: . . . . **DOLM 5021**

RONNIE DREW.
LP: . . . . **RMLP 1017**

Drewo, Carl

SAX MESSAGE.
LP: . . . . **ISST 108**

D.R.I.

22 SONGS.
LP: . . . . **DRR 1983**

CROSSOVER.
LP: . . . . **RR 9620**
MC: . . . . **RR 96204**

DEALING WITH IT.
Tracks: / Snap / Marriage / Counter attack / Nursing home blues / Give my taxes back / Equal people / Bail out / Evil minds / I'd rather be sleeping / Yes ma'am / God is broke / I don't need society / Explorer, The / On my way home / Argument the war / Slit my wrist.
LP: . . . . **ARM 2**
LP: **720691**
LP: . . . . **RR 98981**

DIRTY ROTTEN LP.
LP: . . . . **RR 95551**

FOUR OF A KIND.
Tracks: / All for nothing / Manifest destiny / Gone too long / Do the dream / Shut up / Modern world / Think for yourself / Slumlord / Dead in a ditch / Suit and the guy / Man unkind.
LP: . . . . **RR 9538 1**

THRASH ZONE.
LP: . . . . **RO 9429 1**

Drifterfolk

ALL KINDS OF FOLK.
Tracks: / Coat of many colours / Rambling boy / Evermore the biplane / Ballad of Glencoe / Gallowa' hills, The / Land I love so well, The / Cottonfields / Jinkin' Geordie / Bringing in the sheaves / Highland queen / Goodbye again / Fiddlers green.
LP: . . . . **LILP 5054**

REFLECTIONS.
Tracks: / Piper o'Dundee, The / Tiree love song / Spanish lady / Sheriffmuir / Mursheen Durkin / Streets of London / Reflections / Cam' ye O'er Frae France / Mingulay boat song / Fiery cross, The / Johnnie Cope / Bonnie lass o' Fyvie.
MC: . . . . **LICS 5012**

Drifters

20 GREATEST HITS: DRIFTERS.
LP: . . . . **MA 17983**
MC: . . . . **MAMC 917983**

24 ORIGINAL HITS.
Tracks: / Saturday night at the movies / Dance with me / Some kind of wonderful / When my little girl is smiling / Come on over to my place / Save the last dance for me / At the club / Up on the roof / On Broadway / There goes my baby / I'll take you where the music's playing / Under the boardwalk / Sweet Caroline / I'm free (for the rest of your life) / Kissin' in the back row of the movies / Every night / Like sister and brother / Songs we used to sing, The / There goes my first love / Love games / Love me love the life I lead / If it feels good do it / Blessing in disguise / Down on the beach tonight.
LP: . . . . **K 60106**
MC: **K4 60106**

BEN E KING AND THE DRIFTERS (See under King, Ben E) (King, Ben E. & The Drifters).

BEN E KING & THE DRIFTERS (See also under King, Ben E) (Drifters & Ben E. King).

BEST OF THE DRIFTERS.
Tracks: / Save the last dance for me / Up on the roof / When my little girl is smiling / Dance with me / I've got sand in my shoes / There goes my baby / I'll take you home / Come on over to my place / Under the boardwalk / At the club / This magic moment / (If you cry) true love, true love / I count the tears / Saturday night at the movies / Some kind of wonderful / On Broadwalk.
MC: . . . . **HSC 3310**

COLLECTION: DRIFTERS (2).
Tracks: / Like sister and brother / Every night / You're more than a number in my little red book / Down on the beach tonight / Sweet Caroline (good times never seemed so good) / Hello happiness / There goes my first love / You've got your troubles / Another lovely weekend / Say goodbye to Angelina / Please help me down / Can I take you home little girl? / Kissin' in the back row of the movies / If it feels good do it / Summer in the city / I'm feelin' sad (oh so lonely) / Do you have to go now / Love games / Midnight cowboy / Songs we used to sing, The / I'll get to know your name along the way / Every night is a Saturday night with you / Harlem child / Like a movie I've seen before.
2LP: . . . . **CCSLP 204**
MC: . . . . **CCSMC 204**

DRIFTERS, THE.
Tracks: / Spanish Harlem / This magic moment / Save the last dance for me / Under the boardwalk / Caribbean queen / Penny lover / Wonderful world / Reet petite / Stand by me / Ain't too proud to beg / It's the same old song / Since I lost my baby / I can't help myself / On Broadway / Nothing's gonna change my love for you / (Sittin' on) the dock of the bay.
LP: **510456-4**

DRIFTERS, THE (TELSTAR).
MC: . . . . **STAC 2373**
LP: . . . . **STAR 2373**

DRIFTERS WITH BEN E KING (See also under Ben E King).
LP: . . . . **ENT LP 13032**
MC: . . . . **ENT MC 13032**

GOLDEN HITS: DRIFTERS.
Tracks: / There goes my baby / True love, true love (If you cry) / Dance with me / This magic moment / Save the last dance for me / I count the tears / Some kind of wonderful / Up on the roof / On Broadway / Under the boardwalk / I've got sand in my shoes / Saturday night at the movies.
LP: . . . . **K 40018**
MC: **K4 40018**
LP: **588 103**

GREATEST.
Tracks: / Hello happiness / Kissin' in the back row of the movies / Always something there to remind me / Every night / Sweet Caroline / If it feels good do it / Save the last dance for me / There goes my first love / Like sister and brother / I can't live without you / Harlem child / You've got your troubles / Love games / Down on the beach tonight.
LP: **41 5734 1**
MC: **41 5734 4**
LP: . . . . **MFP 5734**
MC: . . . . **TC MFP 5734**

GREATEST HITS: BEN E KING AND THE DRIFTERS (See under King, Ben E) (King, Ben E. & The Drifters).

GREATEST HITS: DRIFTERS WITH BEN E.KING (Drifters & Ben E. King).
LP: . . . . **FUN 9031**
MC: . . . . **FUNC 9031**

GREATEST HITS LIVE: DRIFTERS.
LP: **20091**
MC: **40091**

JUKE BOX GIANTS.
Tracks: / There goes my baby / This magic moment / Some kind of wonderful / Dance with me / Save the last dance for me / Sweets for my sweet / Saturday night at the movies / I'll take you home / Under the boardwalk / I count the tears / Up on the roof / Please stay / On Broadway / When my little girl is smiling / White Christmas / If you cry-true love.
LP: . . . . **AFEMP 1020**

LIVE AT HARVARD UNIVERSITY.
Tracks: / White Christmas / Lonely winds / Bells of St. Mary's / True love / This magic moment / Up on the roof / Honey love / Under the boardwalk / There goes my baby / Saturday night at the movies / When my little girl is smiling / On Broadway / Save the last dance for me / Money honey.
LP: . . . . **SHLP 124**
MC: . . . . **SHTC 124**

LOVE GAMES.
LP: . . . . **BELLS 246**

SATURDAY NIGHT AT THE CLUB.
Tracks: / Saturday night at the movies / Up in the streets of Harlem / Country to the city / She never talked to me that way / Only in America / Still burning in my heart / Please stay / Up jumped the devil / Be my lady / Rose by any other name / Aretha / Baby what I mean / Beautiful music.
LP: . . . . **SHM 3029**

SAVE THE LAST DANCE FOR ME.
Tracks: / Saturday night at the movies / Come on over to my place / Save the last dance for me / At the club / I count the tears / When my little girl is smiling / Up on the roof / Dance with me / Under the boardwalk / I've got sand in my shoes / There goes my baby / On Broadway / I'll take you home / This magic moment / Some kind of wonderful / I'll take you where the music's playing / If you cry-true love (Extra track on the CD only) / True love (Extra track on the CD only) / Sweets for my sweet (Extra track on the CD only) / Please stay (Extra track on the CD only) / Drip drop (Extra track on the CD only).
LP: **241 121 1**
MC: **241 121 4**
MC: . . . . **ORC 007**

SOME KIND OF WONDERFUL.
Tracks: / This magic moment / I count the tears / Save the last dance for me / Under the boardwalk / Please don't go / Money money / Some kind of wonderful.
LP: . . . . **MFM 026**

STAND BY ME: ULTIMATE COLLECTION, THE (See under King, Ben E) (Drifters & Ben E. King).

THEIR GOES MY BABY.
LP: . . . . **RMB 5636**

THEIR TOP HITS.
MC: **816**

THIS MAGIC MOMENT.
LP: **20094**
MC: **40094**

VERY BEST OF THE DRIFTERS.
LP: . . . . **STAR 2280**
MC: . . . . **STAC 2280**

Driftwood, Jimmie

SONGS OF BILLIE YANK AND JOHNNY REB.
Tracks: / Won't you come along and go / Billy Yank and Johnny Reb / How do you like the army? / On top of Shiloh's Hill / I'm a pome rebel soldier / Giant on the thunderhead, The / Rock of Chickamauga / My blackbird has gone / Oh Florie / When I swim the golden river / Git along little yearlings / Goodbye Reb, you'all come.
LP: . . . . **NL 89994**
MC: . . . . **NK 89994**

Drill

SKIN DOWN.
LP: . . . . **ABT 092**

Drink Small

BLUES DOCTOR, THE.
Tracks: / Tittie man / Little red rooster / So bad / Something in the milk ain't clean / Rub my belly / Baby leave your panties home / Stormy Monday blues / I'm going to move to the outskirts of town / John Henry Ford.
LP: . . . . **ICH 1062**
MC: . . . . **ICH 1062 MC**

ROUND TWO.
Tracks: / D.U.I. / Steal away / Thank you, pretty baby / Don't let nobody know / Widow woman / I'm tired now / Honky tonk / They can't make me hate you / Bishopville women / Can I come over tonight?.
LP: . . . . **ICH 9009**
MC: . . . . **ICH 9009MC**

Drinking Electricity

OVERLOAD.
LP: . . . . **SURLP 001**

Driscoll, Jim (Author)

SHOE PEOPLE (See under Shoe People).

Driscoll, Julie

BEST OF JULIE DRISCOLL.
Tracks: / Let the sun shine in / Road to Cairo / Take me to the water / Save me / Kind of love-in, A / Indian rope man / Why / Break it up / World about colour / This wheels on fire / Tramp.
LP: 2872 114
MC: 3472 114

GREATEST HITS: JULIE DRISCOLL & BRIAN AUGER (Driscoll, Julie & Brian Auger).
2LP: 2664 441
MC: 3578 488

JULIE DRISCOLL & BRIAN AUGER (Driscoll, Julie & Brian Auger).
LP: CR 30200
LP: SPELP 41

LONDON 1964/1967 (see under Auger, Brian) (Driscoll, Julie & Brian Auger).

ROAD TO VAUXHALL 1967-1969, THE (Driscoll, Julie & Brian Auger).
Tracks: / Save me / Kind of love-in, A / Season of the witch / This wheel's on fire / Road to Cairo / I am a lonesome hobo / Tropic of Capricorn / Indian rope man / Save the country / Let the sun shine in / Word about colour, A.
LP: LIK 51
MC: TCLIK 51

THIS WHEEL'S ON FIRE (OLD GOLD) (See under Arthur Brown - Fire for details) (Driscoll, Julie & Brian Auger).

Driscoll, Phil

AMAZING GRACE.
LP: BIRD R 178
MC: BIRD C 178

CELEBRATE FREEDOM.
LP: R 02300
MC: C 02300

CLASSIC HYMNS.
LP: MHR 001
MC: MHC 001

POWER OF PRAISE.
LP: BIRD R 168
MC: BIRD C 168

Drive She Said

DRIVE SHE SAID.
Tracks: / If this is love / Don't you know / Love has no pride / Hold on / I close my eyes / Hard way home / But for you / Maybe it's love / If I told you / As she touches me.
LP: MFN 100
MC: MFNC 100

DRIVIN' SHE SAID.
LP: MFN 118
MC: TMFN 118

D'Rivera, Paquito

CELEBRATION.
Tracks: / Wapango / Magic City (Miami), The / We (to Kristen and me) / Heart of the Kingdom / How many in your party, please? / High tide / "Chick" (For Chick Corea).
LP: 4670811
MC: 4607814

LIVE AT KEYSTONE CORNER.
LP: 25657

MANHATTAN BURN.
Tracks: / Manhattan burn / For Leny / Guataca City / Paquito / Paquito's samba / Feelings of the heart / Two Venzuelan waltzes / Lo Tristano, A / All the things you are.
LP: 4509921

REUNION (D'Rivera, Paquito & Arturo Sandoval).
Tracks: / Mambo influenciado / Reunion / Tanga / Claudia / Friday morning / Part I, II, III / Body and soul / Caprichosos de la habana / Mambo influenciado.
LP: 158051
MC: 158054

WHY NOT?.
LP: 26201
MC: 40.26201

Drivers

SHORT CUTS.
LP: GRK 3301

Drivin'

DRIVIN' EASY (Various artists).
MC: JHC 63

DRIVIN' IN THE VALLEYS (Various artists).
MC: TC MMC 5012

Driving...

DRIVING SOUND OF BRITISH DANCE BANDS (Various artists).
MC: CONE 8

IMPROVE YOUR DRIVING (Various artists).
MC: TC 044

Driving Miss Daisy

DRIVING MISS DAISY (Film Soundtrack) (Zimmer, Hans).
LP: VS5246
MC: VSC5246

Drohar, Tox

NO KIDDING (Drohar, Tox & Charlie Burchell).
LP: WAVE LP 9

Drones

FURTHER TEMPTATIONS.
LP: VRLP 1

Droney, Chris

FLOWING TIDE, THE.
LP: 12TS 503

Droogies

REMEMBER.
LP: NB 015

Droogs

ANTHOLOGY.
LP: MMLP 005

KINGDOM DAY.
LP: PVC 8956
MC: PVCC 8956
LP: MMLP 011

LIVE IN EUROPE 1990.
LP: MMLP 037

MAD DOG DREAMS.
LP: MMLP 026

STONE COLD WORLD.
LP: SPIN 117

Droolian

DROOLIAN.
LP: MOFOCO 090

Drowning By Numbers

DROWNING BY NUMBERS (see under Nyman, Michael) (Various artists).

Drowning Pool

APHONIA.
LP: SAVE 072

SATORI.
LP: WEEAT 004

Drowning Roses

THINGS ARE NOT THE SAME.
LP: WS 034

Dr.'s Children

KING BUFFALO.
LP: UPLP 11M

Dr.'s Mob

HEADACHE MACHINE.
LP: OBGLP 9001

Dr.'s Of Madness

REVISIONISM (Doctors of Madness 1975-78).
Tracks: / Mainlines / Prologue / Waiting / B movie bedtime / In camera / Triple vision / Network / Sons of survival / Marie and Joe / Afterglow / Mitzi's cure / Bulletin.
LP: UNKNOWN

Drugstore Cowboy

DRUGSTORE COWBOY (Film Soundtrack) (Various artists).
Tracks: / For all we know: *Lincoln, Abbey & Geri Allan* / Little things: *Goldsboro, Bobby* / Put a love in your heart: *DeShannon, Jackie* / Psychotic reaction: *Count Five* / Judy in disguise: *Fred, John & His Playboy Band/* Israelites: *Dekker, Desmond & The Aces* / Yesterday's Jones: *Various artists* / Morpheus ascending: *Various artists* / Monkey frenzy: *Various artists* / Wonder waltz: *Various artists* / White gardenia: *Various* artists / Floating hex, The: *Various artists* / Mr F Wadd: *Various artists* / Eligy mirror: *Various* artists / Panda the dog: *Various artists* / Heist and hat: *Various artists* / Strategy song: *Various* artists / Bob's new life: *Various artists* / Clockworks: *Various artists* / Cage iron: *Various artists/* Goonight Nadine: *Various artists.*
LP: PL 83077
MC: PK 83077

Drum Theatre

EVERYMAN.
Tracks: / Home is where the heart is / Eldorado / Reunion / Wide Sargasso Sea / Rhythm of your heart / Living in the past / Children of tomorrow / Moving targets / Once in your lifetime / Runners.
LP: 4502611
MC: 4502614

Drumbeat

DRUMBEAT (Various artists).
LP: NUTM 20

Drummond, Bill

BILL DRUMMOND.
MC: 781 677-4
LP: 781 677-1

MAN, THE.
LP: CRELP 14
MC: CREC 14
LP: CRELP 014

Drummond, Daniel

BLUE HOUR.
LP: DTS 002

Drummond, Don

BEST OF DON DRUMMOND, THE.
LP: SOL 9008

GREATEST HITS: DON DRUMMOND.
Tracks: / Corner stone / Musical communion / Mesopotamia / Cool smoke / Burning torch / Alipang / Don memorial / Stampede / Thorough fare.
LP: TILP 004

Drummond, Ray

TWO OF A KIND (see under Hicks, John) (Drummond, Ray/John Hicks).

Drums (Instruction)

TRICKS OF THE TRADE (DRUMS) (See Under Chimes, Terry) (Chimes, Terry).

Drunk...

DRUNK (Various artists).
LP: MIV 001

Drunken State

KILT BY DEATH.
LP: HMRLP 151
MC: HMRMC 151

Drusky, Roy

ANYMORE.
Tracks: / Anymore / Burning bridges / He had it on his mind / I'd rather loan you out / Almost can't / I wonder where you are tonight / I've got some / Three hearts in a tangle / Another / Alone with you / Before I lose my mind / Swing wide your gate of love.
LP: HAT 3033
MC: HATC 3033

COUNTRY ROSE.
LP: N 23005
MC: 43005

NIGHT FLYING.
LP: BRA 1013
MC: BRC 1013

ROY.
LP: BRA 1009

Dry Branch Fire Squad

ANTIQUES AND INVENTIONS.
LP: ROUNDER 0139
MC: ROUNDER 0139C

BORN TO BE LONESOME.
LP: ROUNDER 0119
MC: ROUNDER 0119C

FANNIN' THE FLAMES.
LP: ROUNDER 0163
MC: ROUNDER 0163C

FERTILE GROUND.
Tracks: / Devil, take the farmer / Darlin' Nellie across the sea / Where we'll never die / Turkey in the straw / There's nothing between us / Love has bought me to dispair / Honest farmer, The / Great Titanic, The / Golden morning / Do you ever dream of me / Old time way, The / Bonaparte's crossing the Rhine.
LP: ROUNDER 0258
MC: ROUNDER 0258C

GOLGOTHA.
LP: ROUNDER 0224
MC: ROUNDER 0224C

GOOD NEIGHBOURS AND FRIENDS.
LP: ROUNDER 0218
MC: ROUNDER 0218C

Dry Cane

WITH COUNTRY IN MIND.
LP: BGC 295
MC: KBGC 295

Dry Throat Five

MY MELANCHOLY BABY - 100% 20'S CHICAGO JAZZ.
LP: SOS 1151

WHO'S BLUE.
LP: SOS 1114

D.S.K

WHAT WOULD WE DO.
LP: HAL 12212

D.T.R.

HOW MANY TIMES.
LP: NG 039

D-Train

D-TRAIN.
Tracks: / You're the one for me / Walk on by / Trying to get over / Lucky day / D train (theme) / Keep on / Love vibration, A / You're the one for me (reprise).
LP: EPC 85683
MC: 40 85683

MUSIC.
Tracks: / Keep giving me love / Shadow of your smile / Are you ready for me / Music / Children of the world / Let me show you / Don't you wanna ride.
LP: PRL 25295

SOMETHING'S ON YOUR MIND.
Tracks: / I treasure your pleasure / Something's on your mind / You're the reason / Hustle and bustle of the city / Thank you / I'll do anything / So far away.
LP: PRSLP 6001
MC: PRSK 6001

YOU'RE THE ONE FOR ME.
Tracks: / You're the one for me / Keep on / Walk on by / I treasure your pleasure / Music / Keep giving me love / Shadow of your smile / Something's on your mind.
LP: ZL 70885
MC: ZK 70885

DT'S

MESSIN' WITH THE BLUES.
LP: MNC 101

Du Maurier, Daphne

FRENCHMAN'S CREEK (Castle, John).
MCSET: CC/021

JAMAICA INN (Eve, Trevor).
MCSET: LFP 7114
MCSET: TCLFP 7114

MY COUSIN RACHEL.
MCSET: 2095

RENDEZVOUS AND OTHER STORIES, THE.
MC: CAB 341

Du Pre, Jacqueline

CELLO CONCERTO (Du Pre, Jacqueline/Halle Orchestra).
LP: ASD 655
MC: TCASD 2746

Du Vin...

EARTHPEOPLE (Du Vin, Du Pain Et Du Boursin).
MLP: SUB 003

Dub Attack

DUB ATTACK 1 (Various artists).
LP: MODUB 1

Dub Master

DUB FROM JAMAICA.
LP: SJ 21

Dub Rockers Delight

DUB ROCKERS DELIGHT.
Tracks: / Leaving dub / Dub glory / Righteous dub / Dub to my woman / Night of dub / Dub softly / Doctor in dub / Bound in dub / Dub in government / Jah in dub.
LP: BMLP 055

Dub Set

FLESH MADE WORLD.
Tracks: / Dice dub disco / Pop roma / Erotica's den / Nameless dread / Vicious affair / Flesh beat fever / Lounge man / Onyeocha onyegee / Ranking jonaow / Risk dub.
LP: 9603471

Dub Sex

PUSH.
Tracks: / Push / Play street / Voice of reason / Kicking the corpse around / Kristallnacht / Splintered / Believe.
MLP: MAN 001

SPLINTERED FAITH.
LP: LPCUT 001

Dub Syndicate

ONE WAY SYSTEM.
MC: A 121

POUNDING SYSTEM.
LP: ONULP 18

STRIKE THE BALANCE.
LP: ONULP 47

TUNES FROM MISSING CHANNEL.
LP: ONULP 38

Dube, Lucky

SLAVE.
LP: SHAN 43060

Dubh Chapter

SILENCE, CUNNING AND EXILE.
LP: EGLP 76
MC: EGMC 76

Dubious Brothers

ABSOLUTE BETHLEHEM.
Tracks: / Englishman's home is his toilet, An / Martin Peters / Falling masonry / Britannia's grand machine / Easter egg remains / South America welcomes the Nazis / Lisa with the Misfits / Old Mother Bordem / Absolute Bethlehem / Could have been.
LP: FFY 008

FORESIGHT SAGA, THE.
LP: GLUTFFY 004

Dublane Organ

GREAT ORGAN MUSIC (Dublane Cathedral Organ).
Tracks: / Opus 4, no 5 in F Major / Opus 7, no 4 in D minor / Voluntary in C major opus 5 no. 2 / Voluntary in A minor.
LP: LILP 5073

Dublin 4 (bk)

DUBLIN 4 (Maeve Binchy) (Binchy, Kate (nar)).
MC: CAB 308

Dublin City Ramblers

BEST OF THE DUBLIN CITY RAMBLERS.
Tracks: / Ferryman, The / Rare ould times / Paddy lie back / O'Carolan's draught / Green hills of Kerry / Mary's song / John O'Dreams / Punch and Judy man / Town of Ballybay, The / Nancy Spain / Belfast mill / Slievenamon / My green valleys / Crack was ninety in the Isle of Man, The.
LP: DOLX 9005
MC: DOCX 9005

BOYS OF THE OLD BRIGADE.
Tracks: / Boys of the old brigade / Three flowers / Over the wall / Broad black brimmer / Lord Inchiquinn / Cliffs of Dooneen / Wrap the green flag 'round me / Reluctant patriot / Gypsy, The / Tricolour ribbon / James Larkin / Lark in the morning, The.
MC: 318803

DUBLIN CITY RAMBLERS.
LP: HPE 610

DUBLIN CITY RAMBLERS IN CONCERT.
MC: RTE 91

FERRYMAN, THE.
Tracks: / Ferryman, The / John O'Dreams / O'Carolan's draught / White man let me go / Frenchman, The / Town of Ballybay, The / Punch and Judy man / My Irish Molly / Belfast mill / Hello friend / Phil's favourites / Rose of Mooncoin.
LP: DOLX 9001
MC: DOCX 9001

FLIGHT OF THE EARLS.
2LP: HM 021D

IRISH REPUBLICAN JAIL SONGS.
MC: DOCB 7021

NATION ONCE AGAIN.
LP: DOLM 5030

RARE OULD TIMES.
Tracks: / Salonika / My green valleys / Nancy Spain / Danny Farrell / Paddy lie back / Phil's march / Rare ould times / "P" it stands for Paddy / Come by the hills / Kidnapped / Crack was ninety in the Isle of Man, The / Mary's song / Punch and Judy man.
LP: DOLM 5025
MC: DOCM 5025

Dublin Town Buskers

DUBLIN TOWN BUSKERS.
LP: EI 801

Dubliners

15 YEARS ON.
LP: CHLP 1025

20 ORIGINAL GREATEST HITS.
LP: CHLP 1028
MC: CHMC 1028

20 ORIGINAL GREATEST HITS VOL.2.
LP: CHLP 1014

20 ORIGINAL GREATEST HITS VOL.3.
LP: CHLP 1015

AT HOME WITH THE DUBLINERS.
LP: EULP 1093
MC: EUMC 1093

AT THEIR BEST.
Tracks: / Wild rover / Easy and slow / Home, boys, home / Chief O'Neill's favourite / Rocky road to Dublin / Leaving of Liverpool / I'll tell my ma / Mason's apron / Foggy dew, The / Old orange flute / Roisin dubh / Holy ground / Nelson's farewell / Twang man, The / Jar of porter / Bonlavogue / Glendalough Saint, The / Air fa la la la lo / Off to Dublin in the green / Sunshine hornpipe / Mountain road, The / Peggy Lettermore / Donegal reel, The / Longford collector, The / Roddy McCorley.
2LP: CR 058
MCSET: CRT 058

BALLADS AND BOOZE.
LP: CHLP 1007

BALLADS ON TAP.
LP: ISLE 3002

BEST OF DUBLINERS (EMI).
Tracks: / Whisky in the jar / Fiddlers green / Town I loved so well / Old triangle / Dirty old town / Wild rover / Wonder horn / Farewell to Carlingford / Lord of dance / Killieburn Brae / Rebellion / Wrap the green flag round me boys / West's awake / Nation once again.
LP: NTS 197
LP: 1A 222 58158
MC: TCNTS 197

BEST OF THE DUBLINERS (HARP).
LP: HPE 649
MC: HPC 649

BEST OF THE DUBLINERS (MFP).
Tracks: / Off to Dublin in the green / Will you come to the bower? / I'll tell me ma / Home, boys, home / Foggy dew, The / Wild rover / Easy and slow / Mason's apron / Nelson's farewell / Glendalough Saint, The / Jar of porter / Seven drunken nights / Whiskey in the jar / Leaving of Liverpool / Seven deadly sins / Sunshine hornpipe / Mountain road, The.
LP: 1A 222-68155
MC: TC-1A 222-68155
LP: 1A02258155
MC: 1A22258155

BEST OF THE DUBLINERS (POLYDOR).
LP: 2459 388
MC: 3192 538

BEST OF THE DUBLINERS (SPOT).
Tracks: / Whiskey in the jar / Fiddlers green / Town I loved so well, The / Old triangle, The / Dirty old town / Wild rover / Wonder horn, The / Farewell to Carlingford / Lord of the dance / Killieburne Brae / Wrap the green flag round / West's awake / Nation once again, A.
LP: SPR 8504
MC: SPC 8504

BEST OF THE DUBLINERS (TRANSATLANTIC).
LP: TRS 105
MC: KTRS 105
LP: TRA 158

BLACK VELVET BAND.
Tracks: / Muirsheen durkin' / Old triangle, The / Paddy's gone to France / Seven drunken nights / Croppy boy, The / Mormon braes / Whiskey on a Sunday / Whiskey in the jar / McAlpines fusiliers / I wish I were back in Liverpool / Many young men of twenty / Rattling, roaring Willie / Kelly, the boy from Killan / Nation once again, A / Galway races / Flop eared mule / Peggy Gordon / Black velvet band / Navvy boots / Maid when you're young / Cork hornpipe / Pipers chair, The / McCafferty / Partin' glass, The.
2LP: VSOPLP 135
MC: VSOPMC 135

COLLECTION: DUBLINERS.
Tracks: / Wild rover / Chief O'Neill's favourite / Glendalough Saint, The / Off to Dublin in the green / Love is pleasing / Nelson's farewell / Monto / Dublin fusiliers / Rocky road to Dublin / Leaving of Liverpool / Old orange flute / Jar of porter / Prefad san ol / High reel / Patriot game / Swallows tail reel / McAlpines fusiliers / Hot asphalt / Within a mile of Dublin / Finnegans wake / Banks of the roses / My love in America / Foggy dew, The / Sea around us, The.
2LP: CCSLP 164
MC: CCSMC 164

COLLECTION: DUBLINERS (CHYME).
MCSET: 35073 6

COLLECTION: DUBLINERS VOLUME 2.
Tracks: / Roddy McCorley / Twwang man, The / Sligo maid/Colonel Rodney / Woman from Wexford / Roisin Dubh / Air fa la la la lo / Peggy Lettermore / Easy and slow / Kerry recruit, The / Donegal reel, The / Longford collector, The / Tramps and hawkers / Home boys home / Sunshine hornpipe / Mountain road, The / Will you come to the bower / I'll tell my ma / Masons apron, The / Holy ground / Boulavogue / Master McGrath / Walking in the dew / Nightingale, The / Sea shanty.
MC: CCSMC 270

DRINKIN' AND COURTIN'.
LP: SMLP 14

DROP OF THE HARD STUFF, A.
LP: MMLP 3

DUBLINERS 25 YEARS CELEBRATION (Dubliners & Pogues).
2LP: SMR 731
MCSET: SMC 731

DUBLINERS BOX SET.
LPS: 31415 3

DUBLINERS DUBLIN, THE.
Tracks: / Finnegan's wake / Raglan Road / Zoological Gardens, The / Honeysuckle (Hornpipe) / Golden Eagle, The (Hornpipe) / Sez she / Three lovely lasses / Johnny Doyle / Weile waile / Bombo Lane / Monto, The (end s1) / Old triangle, The / Dublin jack of all trades, The / Dicey Reilly / Ril gan ainm (Reel) / Shehan's reel (Reel) / Jenny's wedding (Reel) / Ragman's ball, The / Seven drunken nights / Christ Church / Spanish lady / Rare oul' times, The.
LP: HM 088
LP: ESSLP 004
MC: ESSMC 004

DUBLINERS IN CONCERT.
LP: HPE 648
MC: HPC 648

DUBLINERS LIVE.
LP: CHLP 1010

DUBLINERS LIVE.
Tracks: / Finnegan's wake / Fiddle solo / Monto / Dublin fusiliers / Chief O'Neill's favourite / Sea around us, The / McAlpine's fusiliers / Hot asphalt / Glendlock saint / Air fa la la la lo / Peggy Lettermore / Easy and slow / My love is in America / One morning in March / Old orange flute / Leaving of Liverpool.
LP: SPELP 63
MC: SPEMC 63

DUBLINERS NOW.
Tracks: / Farewell to Carlingford / Old triangle, The / Beggarman, The / Matt Hyland / Downfall of Paris, The / Carrickfergus / Lord of the dance / Lifeboat Mona / Farewell to Ireland / Unquiet grave, The / Lord Inchiquinn / Lark in the morning, The / Spanish lady / Foggy dew, The / Kid on the mountain, The / Avondale / Acrobats / Village bells / Blantyre explosion / False hearted lover / Thirty foot trailer / Doherty's reel / Down the broom / Honeymoon reel, The / Parcel o' rogues / Killieburne brae.
2LP: 2681 013

DUBLINERS, THE.
Tracks: / Seven drunken nights / Galway races / Irish navvy / I wish I were back in Liverpool / Zoological gardens / Rising of the moon / Whiskey on a Sunday / Dundee weaver, The / Seven deadly sins / Leaving of Liverpool / Maids when you're young never wed an old man / Dirty old town / Donkey reel / Black velvet band / Pub with no beer, A / Peggy Gordon / Net hauling song / Nancy Whisky / Paddy's gone to France / Skylark / Tibby Dunbar / Go to sea no more.
MC: HR 8166

DUBLINERS, THE (2).
Tracks: / Seven drunken nights / Dirty old town / Peggy Gordon / Galway races / Rattling roaring Willie / I wish I were back in Liverpool / Whiskey on a Sunday / Maids when you're young never wed an old man / I'm a rover / Seven deadly sins / Irish navvy / All for me grog / Rising of the moon / Travelling people, The / Nation once again / Drink it up men / Mushin durkin / Nancy Whiskey / Maid of the sweet brown knowe (CD only.) / Flop eared mule (CD only.) / Quare bungle rye (CD only.).
MC: TCIDL 106
MC: 790 996 4

FAVOURITES.
MC: PLC 5007

GOLDEN FOLK SONGS.
Tracks: / Wild rover / Fiddlers green / Johnston's motor car / Town I loved so well, The / Skibereen / Finnegan's wake / Donegal Danny / Seven drunken nights / Dirty old town / Holy ground / Whiskey in the jar / Ballad of Ronnie's mare.
LP: 2482 259
MC: 3199 189

GREATEST HITS: DUBLINERS (FUN).
Tracks: / Seven drunken nights / Galway races / Rattling roaring Willie / Irish navvy / Muirsheen Durkin / Navvy boots / Mormon braes / Maids when you're young never wed and old man / Peggy Gordon / Whiskey in the jar / Black velvet band / Molly Maguires / Weila weila / All for me grog / Pub with no beer / Leaving of Liverpool / Alabama 58 / McAlpine's fusiliers / Seven deadly sins / Whiskey on a Sunday.
LP: FUN 9033
MC: FUNC 9033

HERE'S THE DUBLINERS.
Tracks: / Maid of the sweet brown knowe / Old alarm clock, The / Colonel Fraser / Rising of the moon / McCafferty / I'm a rover / Maloney wants a drink / Travelling people / Limerick rake / Zoological gardens / Fairmoye lasses and sporting Paddy / Poor Paddy on the railway / Net-hauling song / Nancy Whisky / Many young men of twenty / Paddy's gone to France / Molly Bawn / Dundee weaver, The / Tibby Dunbar / Inniskilling dragoons / Piper's chair, The / Bill Hart's jig / Nights of St Patrick / I wish I were back in Liverpool / Carby O'Leary / Go to sea no more.
2LP: 41 1046 3
MCSET: 41 1046 9

HOME BOYS HOME.
LP: HPE 617

HOMETOWN.
LP: CHLP 1003

I KNOW MY LOVE.
LP: STAL 1015

IN CONCERT.
MC: PLC 5006

IRISH FAVOURITES.
LP: CHLP 1033
LP: CHLP 1034

IRISH REBEL BALLADS.
Tracks: / Johnston's motor car / Ould triangle, The / Four green fields / God save Ireland / Charles Stewart Parnell / Town I loved so well, The / Free the people / Down by the glenside / Boulavogue / Take it down from the mast / Rebel, The / Wrap the green flag 'round me / West's awake / Nation once again, A.
MC: CSDBL 523
LP: SDBL 523

JACK'S HEROES (See under Pogues, The) (Dubliners & Pogues).

LIVE: DUBLINERS.
2LP: CR 5163
MCSET: CRT 5163

LIVE IN CARRE.
Tracks: / Sweets of May / Dicey Riley / Song for Ireland, A / Building up and tearing England down / Dunphy's hornpipe / Leitrim fancy / Down the broom / Dirty old town / Old triangle, The / Whiskey in the jar / Humours of Scariff / Flannel jacket, The / Galway races / Prodigal son / Sick note, The / Wild rover / Seven drunken nights.
LP: 825 681-1
MC: 825 681-4

LUKE KELLY ALBUM, THE (See Kelly, Luke) (Dubliners & Luke Kelly).

LUKE'S LEGACY (See Kelly, Luke) (Dubliners & Luke Kelly).

MORE OF THE HARD STUFF.
LP: MMLP 5

PARCEL OF ROGUES, A.
LP: EULP 1061
MC: EUMC 1061

PRODIGAL SONS.
Tracks: / Building up and tearing England down / Jigs / Newry highwayman / When Margaret was eleven / Prodigal son / Waterford boys / Humours of Scariff / Flannel jacket / Now I'm easy / Hen's march / Song for Ireland / Second world war.
LP: CHLP 1030
LP: POLD 5079

SEVEN DEADLY SINS.
LP: SRS 5101

SEVEN DRUNKEN NIGHTS.
MC: TC ONCR 510
LP: CHLP 1032
MC: TC IDL 6

TOGETHER AGAIN.
Tracks: / Mero / Rare ould times / Spey in spate / Steam packet / Danny Farrell / Song of the iron road / Old man's song / Johnny McGory / Lag's song, The / Sheahan's M1 gig / Band played waltzing Matilda, The / Maid behind the bar, The / Toss the feathers / Parting glass.
LP: CHLP 1012
LP: 2383545

TOWN I LOVED SO WELL, THE.
Tracks: / Donegal Danny / Queen of the fair / Tong by the fire / Fiddlers green / Johnston's motor car / Wonder hornpipe / Jail of Cluan Meala / Town I loved so well, The / Ballad of Ronnie's mare / Three sea captains / Skibereen / Rebellion.
LP: 2384119

VERY BEST OF THE DUBLINERS.
LP: EMC 3091

WILD ROVER, THE.
MC: 495943

Duccia, Ron

MUSIC FROM THE BIG TOMATO.
Tracks: / Monkey jaw-monkey gras / When the hear came down / Bignonia / Waterfall me / Ain't it just like me / Creation suite create yourself / Enter the dream riot act (middle theme) / Trying to sing.
LP: ARM 10

Duchess of Duke Street

DUCHESS OF DUKE STREET (See under Hardwick, Molly).

Duchin, Eddie

EDDIE DUCHIN, NO.2.
LP: GELP 15065

Duck & Cover

DUCK AND COVER (Various artists).
LP: SST 263
MC: SSTC 263

Duck Food

DUCK FOOD.
LP: EMW 5505

Duck & The Ponds

LOST WORLD.
Tracks: / Lost world / Alone / Wild about you / Wrong / On the corner again / Little Eva / Not my scene / Wanna ruin ya.
LP: WIKM 76

Duck You Sucker (film)

DUCK YOU SUCKER (Film Soundtrack) (Various artists).
Tracks: / Duck you sucker - main title: *Various artists* / Love: *Various artists* / Green table: *Various* artists / March of the beggars: *Various artists* / Dead sons: *Various artists* / Addio: *Various artists*/ Jokes on the side: *Various artists* / Mexico and Ireland: *Various artists* / Inventions for John: *Various artists* / Counter revolution: *Various artists* / After the explosion: *Various artists.*
LP: UAS 29345

Duck's Breath Mystery

BORN TO BE TILED.
LP: ROUNDER 3054
MC: ROUNDER 3054C

Ducks Deluxe

DON'T MIND ROCKIN' TONIGHT.
Tracks: / Coast to coast / Fireball / Saratoga Suzie / Don't mind rockin' tonight / Daddy put the bomp / Please, please, please / It's all over now / Love's melody / Two time twister / I fought the law / Paris 9 / My music / Somethings going on / Here comes the night.
LP: NL 71153
MC: NK 71153
LP: PL 25132
MC: PK 25132

LAST NIGHT OF A PUB ROCK BAND.
Tracks: / Fireball / Proud Mary / Evil / Mighty Quinn / Here comes the night / Knockin' on heaven's door / Have you ever seen the rain / Amsterdam dog / Jumpin' in the fire / Run Rudolph run / Teenage head / Coast to coast / Route 66 / Little Queenie / Brown sugar / Midnight rambler / Going down the road.
2LP: BMLP 001

Ducktails

DINOSAUR DUCKS (See Under Dinosaur Ducks) (Unknown narrator(s)).

Dudes (film)

DUDES (1988 film soundtrack) (Various artists).
Tracks: / Rock 'n' roll outlaw: *Keel* / Show no mercy: *W.A.S.P.* / These boots were made for walking: *Megadeth*/ Jesus came driving: *Leather Nun* / Lost highway: *Little Kings* / Amazing grace: *Vai, Steve* / Urban struggle: *Vandals* / Vengeance...: *Steel, Simon and The Claw* / Time forgot you: *Lethal Weapon* / Mountain son: *Jane's Addiction* / Dudes showdown: *Bernstein & Co.*
LP: MCF 3419
MC: MCFC 3419

Dudley, Anne

SONGS FROM THE VICTORIOUS CITY (Dudley, Anne & Jaz Coleman).
Tracks: / Awakening, The / Endless festival / Minarets and memories / Force and fire / Habebe / Ziggarats and Cinnamon / Hannah / Conqueror, The / Survivors tale, A / In a timeless place.
MC: 8470984
LP: 8470981

Dudley, Dave

20 GREAT TRUCK HITS: DAVE DUDLEY.
Tracks: / Six days on the road / Counterfeit cowboy / Rollin' on your track / Me and ole C.B. / Wave at 'em Billy Boy / I have been known not to go home / One more plane / Fireball rolled a seven / Let me dream / Denimus & diamonds / Texas Ruby / Rollin' rig / 1776 / Big stuff / Truckin' dad / Rooster Hill / Been around the Horn / Sentimental journey / My sunny overgrown country town / Sugarland USA.
LP: 7C 062 82631

COLLECTION: DAVE DUDLEY.
LP: IC 028 64521

COUNTRY BEST.
Tracks: / John Henry, No 2 / I'm goin' home / I'm single again / Waterin' hole, The / Roving gambler / Now and then / Yellow rose of Texas / Charlie's shoes / Soldier's spouse lament / Six days on the road / Lookin' south / Place in the sun, A.
LP: BDL 1062

ON THE ROAD.
MC: 0660 324

SIX DAYS ON THE ROAD.
MC: 4XLL 9039

TRUCK SONGS.
Tracks: / Wreck of the old slow binder / Two six packs away / I got lost / Truck drivin' son of a gun / Jack knife / Sugarland USA / Truck driver's waltz / Speed traps, weigh stations and detour signs.
LP: 9279 147
MC: 7259 147

Du-Droppers

BAMBALAM (Best of classical doo wop).
LP: DT 33009

CAN'T DO SIXTY NO MORE.
LP: H 805

DU-DROPPERS, THE.
LP: 33 009

Dudziak, Urszula

MAGIC LADY.
Tracks: / Samba ula / Po tamtej stronie gory / She wants to be free / Wake up call / Papaya / Rosemary's baby / Sorrow is not forever / No else, thank you / Tico tico.
LP: 70081

Duel At Diablo (film)

DUEL AT DIABLO (1965 film soundtrack) (Various artists).
LP: UNKNOWN
MC: MCAC 1436

Duel Of The ... (film)

DUEL OF THE TITANS (Original soundtrack) (Various artists).
LP: PHCAM 06

Duerson, Herve

PIANO OF HERVE DUERSON, THE (Duerson, Herve & Turner Parrish).
LP: BD 2025

Duet Emmo

OR SO IT SEEMS.
LP: STUMM 11

Duff, Mary

LOVE SOMEONE LIKE ME.
Tracks: / Love someone like me / She's got you / Are you teasing me / Crazy / Forever and ever amen / It's not over (if I'm not over you) / Daddy's hands / Pick me up (on your way down) / Dear God / Chicken every Sunday / There won't be any patches in heaven / Do me with love.
LP: RITZLP 0044
MC: RITZLC 0044

WINNING WAYS.
Tracks: / Goin' gone / Yellow roses / Eighteen wheels and a dozen roses / Can I sleep in your arms / Once a day / Does Fort Worth ever cross your mind / One bird on a wing / Just out of reach / Heartaches by the number / I'm not that lonely yet / Come on in / Maggie.
MC: RITZC 051

Duffo

BOB THE BIRDMAN.
LP: DUF 1

DISAPPEARING BOY.
Tracks: / John and Betty go to LA / That kinda guy / Another normal nite / God for the day / Lost in my room / Disappearing boy / Idiot / Duffodil / Mumbo jumbo / After the subsequent inquiry.
LP: PVK 2

DUFFO.
Tracks: / Tower of madness / Chelsea cowgirls / Duff record / Record jerk / Guillotine quickstep / Duffo (I'm a genius) / (We're all) charabancing / I'm not really here / Rise in your levis / Duff odyssey / Dejame joder tu mente / Final brain, The.
LP: BEGA 5
MC: BEGC 5

Duffus, George

STANDING ROOM ONLY.
Tracks: / It's George / Sex equality / Holidays / Ballad of Glencoe / Red cross / Capricorn / David and Goliath / Winning the pools / Earnin' a shillin' / Rubber legs / Scotland's oil / CB mad man.
LP: LILP 5121
MC: LICS 5121

Duffy Brothers

HILLBILLY COUNTRY.
MC: VCA 047

NASSINGTON FLYER (Duffy Brothers & Ron Ryan).
LP: BUFF L-2001

WILD OVER US.
Tracks: / Uncle Pen / Handsome Molly / Bucking mule / Black mountain rag / I wonder if you're lonesome too / I'll be going to Heaven sometime / Can't tell the boys from the girls / Cedar Hill / I'm crying my heart out over you / Wild over me / You've been fooling me baby / This weary heart / Will the circle be unbroken?.
LP: FHR 074

Duffy, Chris

AMBIDEXTROUS- BLUEGRASS, BACH & BEBOP.
LP: LRF 168

BULLANTS IN BUSHLAND.
LP: LRF 122

DOWN YONDER.
LP: LRF 059

KEEP ON PICKIN' (Duffy, Chris & Friends).
LP: LRF 040

SELF PORTRAIT.
LP: LRF 024

Duffy, John

SYMPHONIC DANCES (Heritage: Civilisation and the Jews) (Duffy, John/ Leonard Bernstein).
Tracks: / On the town - dance episodes / Heritage symphonic dances / Heritage fanfare and chorale / Heritage suite for orchestra.
MC: ZC DCA 630
LP: DCA 630

Duffy, Johnny

LIVE FROM LONDON.
LP: NEVLP 110

Duffy, Philip

COLEMAN'S CROSS.
MC: GTDC 030

Duffy, Stephen "Tin

BECAUSE WE LOVE YOU.
Tracks: / Something special / Lot of ink, A / Sunday supplement / Why shouldn't I? / Unkiss that kiss / I love you / When you go to bed / Love station / We'll never argue / Julie Christie.
LP: XID 12
MC: CXID 12

UPS AND DOWNS, THE.
Tracks: / Kiss me / She makes me quiver / Masterpiece, A / But is it art? / Wednesday Jones / Icing on the cake / Darkest blues, The / Be there / Believe in me / World at large alone, The.
LP: XID 5
MC: CXID 5

Duffy, Teresa

DESTINATION DONEGAL.
LP: HRL 142
MC: CHRL 142

Duffy, Waller

CLASSIC COUNTRY GENTS REUNION (Duffy, Waller, Adcock, Gray).
Tracks: / Fare thee well / Stewball / I'll be there in the morning / Champagne breakdown / Here today, gone tomorrow / Gonna get there soon / Hey Lala / Casey's last ride / Wild side of life / Wait a little longer / Say won't you be mine.
LP: SH 3772

Duggan, Jim

WOLVERINE BLUES (See under Riley, Teddy).

Duggan, Larr

PIANO MUSIC FROM THE LAKE STUDIES.
LP: PH 9002

Duhan, Johnny

FAMILY ALBUM.
Tracks: / Room, The / Ordinary town / Trying to get the balanace right / Young mothers / Couple of kids / Cornerstone / Well knit family / We had our trouble then / Storm is passed, The / Voyage, The.
MC: RTMMC 116
LP: RTMLP 116

Duhaney, Rick

ON BROADWAY.
MC: CHV 343

Duhon, Hector

OCTA CLARK/HECTOR DUHON (See under Octa, Clark) (Duhon, Hector & Octa Clark).

Duignan, Packie

MUSIC FROM COUNTY LEITRIM.
Tracks: / Shores of Lough Gowna, The / Rose and the heather, The / Devero the dancer / Connie the soldier / Tailor's thimble, The / Red haired lass, The / Sean Ryan's hornpipe / New found out reel, The / Sporting Paddy / Packie Duigan's reel / Trip to Athlone, The / Hag with the money, The / Castlebar, The / Crowley's reels / Jackie Coleman's reel / Sailor on the rock, The / Bridie Morley / Duigans favourite / Kid on the mountain, The / Highland fling / Mrs. Smullen's reel / House on the hill / Duke of Leinster, The / Dinny Ryan's reels / Tom Ward's downfall / Mullaghnavat reel / Geese in the bog, The / Your jig.
LP: 12TS 339

Duisit, Lorraine

FEATHER RIVER (Duisit, Lorraine & Tom Espinola).
MC: CPH 9012
LP: PH 9012

HAWKS AND HERONS.
LP: FF 308

Duke

BIG BAND AND SMALL.
LP: IAJRC 11

PARTY FOR YUH LIFE.
LP: JWDKE 018

POISON.
LP: JWDKE 002

RETURN OF THE DREAD 1.
LP: DUKE 2
MC: DUKE 2 C

Duke, George

3 (See under Clarke, Stanley) (Clarke, Stanley & George Duke).

1976 SOLO KEYBOARD ALBUM.
Tracks: / Mr. McFreeze / Love reborn / Excerpts from the opera Tzina / Spock gets funky / Pathways / Vulcan mind probe / Dream that ended.
LP: EPC 25021

BRAZILIAN LOVE AFFAIR.
Tracks: / Brazilian love affair / Summer breezin' / Cravo E Canela / Alone / 6 a.m. / Brazilian sugar / Sugar loaf mountain / Love reborn / Up from the sea it arose and ate Rio in one / I need you now / Ao que vai Nascer.
LP: EPC 84311

CLARKE/DUKE PROJECT II (see Clarke, Stanley).

DREAM ON.
Tracks: / Shine on / You / Dream on / I will always be your friend / Framed / Ride on love / Someday / Son of reach for it / Positive energy / Let your love shine.
LP: EPC 85215

FOLLOW THE RAINBOW.
Tracks: / Party down / Say that you will / Funkin' for the thrill / Sunrise / Festival / I'm for real / Straight from the heart / Corina, Corina / Pluck / Follow the rainbow.
LP: EPC 83336

GEORGE DUKE.
Tracks: / Broken glass / I just want to be in your life / Good friends / So mean to me / Stand with your man / Island girl / King for a day / Morning, you and love / I can make it better / African violet.
LP: 9604801
MC: 9604804
LP: EPC 32348

GUARDIAN OF THE LIGHT.
Tracks: / Overture / Light / Shane / Born to love you / Silly fightin' / You / War fugue interlude / Reach out / Give me your love / Stand / Soon / Celebrate / Fly away.
LP: EPC 25262
MC: 40 25262

I LOVE THE BLUES, SHE HEARD MY CRY.
Tracks: / Chariot / Look into her eyes / Sister serene / That's what she said / Mashavu / Rokkinrowl / Prepare yourself / Giant child within us / Someday / I love the blues she heard my cry.
LP: 817 488-1

MASTER OF THE GAME.
Tracks: / Look what you find / Every step I take / Games / I want you for myself / In the distance / I love you more / Dog man / Everybody's talkin'.
LP: EPC 83951

NIGHT AFTER NIGHT.
Tracks: / Miss wriggle / Children of the night / Love ballad / Guilty / Same ole love / Say hello / You are the only one in my life / Brazilian coffee / This lovin' / Mystery eyes.
LP: EKT 52
MC: EKT 52 C

PRIMAL.
Tracks: / Second time around / Night has a thousand eyes / Days of wine and roses / Jeannine / Little girl blue / Secret love.
LP: 5C 064 61170

PROJECT (See under Clarke, Stanley) (Duke, George & Stanley Clarke).

REACH FOR IT.
MC: 4679664

SECRET RENDEZVOUS.
Tracks: / Got to get back to love / Stay awhile / Thinking of you / Secret rendezvous / Take it on / She can wait forever / Better ways / Your life / Ipanema lady.

LP: EPC 26059

SWEET BABY (See under Clarke, Stanley).

THIEF IN THE NIGHT.
LP: EKT 3
MC: EKT 3C

Duke Of Edinburgh

QUESTION OF BALANCE, A (Duke Of Edinburgh, HRH).
MCSET: LFP 7164

Duke Of Wellington

DUKES IN KONZERT, THE (Duke Of Wellington - Regiment 1st Battalion).
LP: MM 0523

DUKES ON PARADE, THE.
LP: MM 0577

DUKES ON THE ROCK, THE (Duke Of Wellington's Regiment).
Tracks: / Gibraltar story / Trumpet filigree / Ja da / Victory beatings / Misty / Sousarama / Chariots of Fire / Drummer's delight / Professionals (theme from) / Concert rock / Regimental march the wellesley.
LP: MM 0595
MC: MMC 0595

STRATFIELD SAYE (Duke Of Wellington's Regiment).
Tracks: / Wellesley / Birdcage walk / Pie Jesu / When Johnny comes marching home / Rock rondo / Golden jubilee / Fanfare and march-Industria Arte Prudentia / Stratfield saye / Wellington / Hazlefax / Eastenders / Sinatra in concert.
MC: ZC BND 1033
LP: BND 1033

Duke, Sister Doris

FUNKY FOX.
Tracks: / I don't believe / You better do it right / No right to cry / Let's try it over / How can you call that love / Losing race / Don't fight the feeling / I'm satisfied / Do it.
LP: MAN 5033

Dukeless Gang

DUKELESS GANG (Dukeless Gang/ Sonny Greer Sextet).
Tracks: / Sleepy baboon / Kansas City caboose (2 takes) / Ration stomp / Helena's dream (2 takes) / Triple play / Why was I born / You're driving me crazy / Key largo / Design for jivin' / Life with fatha / I love my lovin' lover / Blues on my weary mind / Trouble, trouble / I'll get by.
LP: QU 041

Dukes

DUKES.
Tracks: / Hearts in trouble / Leaving it all behind / All in a game / Billy Niles / Crazy fools / Who's gonna tell you / Time on your side / I'll try to help / Heartbreaker.
LP: K 56710

Dukes Of Dixieland

DIXIELAND FAVOURITES.
MC: 4XLL 57001

DUKES OF DIXIELAND.
MC: ZCGAS 714

Dukes Of Hazzard (tv

DUKES OF HAZZARD (TV Soundtrack) (Various artists).
Tracks: / Good ol' boys: *Booke, Sorrell* / Laughing all the way to the bank: *Booke, Sorrell* / Duellin' Dukes: *Booke, Sorrell* / General Lee: *Cash, Johnny* / Flash: *Best, James* / Up on Cripple Creek: *Wopat, Tom* / Cover girl eyes: *Kershaw, Doug* / Keep between them ditches: *Kershaw, Doug* / Ballad of the General Lee: *Kershaw, Doug* / In the driver's seat: *Schneider, John* / Down home, American girl: *Bach, Catherine*.
LP: SCT 85593
MC: 40 85593

STORIES FROM THE DUKES OF HAZZARD (Various artists).
LP: SPR 8550
MC: SPC 8550

Dukes Of Stratosphear

25 O'CLOCK.
Tracks: / 25 o'clock / Bike ride to the moon / My love explodes / What in the world...?? / Your gold dress / Mole from the ministry, The.
LP: WOW 1
MC: WOWC 1

PSONIC PSUNSPOT.
Tracks: / Vanishing girl / Have you seen Jackie? / You're a good man Albert Brown (curse you red / Collideascope / You're my drug / Shiny cage / Brainiac's daughter / Affiliated, The / Pale and precious.
LP: V 2440
MC: TCV 2440

Dukov, Bruce

DEPARTURES.
Tracks: / Viva Vivaldi / Sad song rondo / Sleepy shores / Unaccompanied cello suite No 1 / Bailero / For Kriesler's sake / Heart-throb romance / Could it be magic? / Meow ski / Variegated Maria, A.
LP: BS 73680
MC: 40 73680

Dulcimer

DULCIMER.
Tracks: / Sonnet to the fall / Pilgrim from the city / Morman's casket / Ghost of the wandering minstrel boy / Gloucester City / Starlight / Caravan / Lisa's song / Time in my life / Fruit of the musical tree / While it lasted / Suzanne.
LP: SEE 266

Dulfer, Candy

LILY WAS HERE (OST) (See under 'Lily Was Here').

SAXUALITY.
Tracks: / Pee wee / Saxuality / So what? / Jazzid / Heavenly city / Donja / There goes the neighbourhood / Mr Lee / Get the funk / House is not a home, A.
LP: PL 74661
MC: PK 74661
MC: PK 75111

Dulkas

KURIYAN KUR KURIYAN.
LP: MUT 1096
MC: CMUT 1096

Dum Dum Score

AUDIO SHEEP.
LP: NMW 003

Dumas, Alexandre

COUNT OF MONTE CRISTO (Jordan, Louis).
LP: TC 1554
MC: CDL 51554

COUNT OF MONTE CRISTO (Daneman, Paul (nar)).
MC: BKK 403

THREE MUSKETEERS, THE (children's classics) (Unknown narrator(s)).
MC: PLBC 78

THREE MUSKETEERS, THE (chapters 1-5) (York, Michael (nar)).
MC: 1692

Dumas, Tony

NO LIMIT (see Pepper, Art).

Dumbo (Film)

DUMBO (Childrens story book) (Unknown narrator(s)).
MC: DIS 019

DUMBO (Film soundtrack) (Various artists).
Tracks: / Look out for Mr. Stork: *Various artists* / Casey Junior: *Various artists* / It's a circus day again: *Various artists* / Dumbo: *Various artists* / Pink elephants on parade: *Various artists* / Dumbo and Timothy: *Various artists* / Pyramid of elephants: *Various artists* / Dumbo disgraced: *Various artists* / When I see an elephant fly: *Various artists* / Dumbo's triumph: *Various artists* / Finale: *Various artists* / Song of the roustabouts: *Various artists*.
LP: REC 542
MC: ZCM 542
LP: DQ 1204

DUMBO (Various artists).
LP: D 324
MC: D 3DC

Dummer, John

HOUSEWIVES CHOICE (See under April, Helen) (Dummer, John & Helen April).

Dummies

DUMMIES, THE.
LP: QUEST 4

Dumptruck

FOR THE COUNTRY.
Tracks: / Island / 50 miles / Friends / Carefree / Brush me back / Hung out on a line / Going nowhere / For the country / Dead weight / Wire / Barking up the wrong tree.
LP: ZL 71492
MC: ZK 71492

POSITIVELY.
Tracks: / Back where I belong / Secrets / Nine people / Autumn lights / Winter / Alone / Seven steps / Change / Walk into mirrors / Ethics.
LP: ZL 71272
MC: ZK 71272

Dumpy's Rusty Nuts

GET OUT ON THE ROAD.
LP: METALP 118

HOT LOVER.

LP: GAS 4010

SOMEWHERE IN ENGLAND.
LP: GAS 4013
LP: LDLP 101

Dunbar, Aynsley

BLUE WHALE.
Tracks: / Willing to fight / Willie the pimp / It's your turn / Days / Going home.
LP: CR 30142

Dunbar, Sly

SLY, WICKED AND SLICK.
Tracks: / Rasta fiesta / Sesame street / Lover's bop / Senegal market / Mr. Music / Queen of the minstrels / Dirty Harry / Oriental taxis.
LP: FL 1042

SLY-GO-VILLE.
Tracks: / Slippin' into darkness / Gonna love you / Battle of Jericho, The / Inner city blues / If you want it / River Nigger / Hot you're hot / Un metred taxi.
LP: ILPS 9673
MC: ICT 9673

Dunbar, Ted

JAZZ GUITARIST.
Tracks: / Winding blues / Total conversation / Trees and grass and nice things / Nica's dream / Hi-fly / Bougie / Epistrophy.
LP: XAN 196

OPENING REMARKS.
LP: X 155

Dunbar, Valerie

BLUE EYES.
Tracks: / Blue eyes crying in the rain / Old rugged cross, The / Amazing grace / Bless this house / If I had my way / Twelfth of never / True love / Beautiful dreamer / Pal of my cradle days / Silver threads among the gold / Somewhere my love / Another year passes (Anniversary song) / I'd rather die young / Morning has broken / When I grow too old to dream / Loves old sweet song / Now is the hour.
LP: KLP 40
MC: ZCKLP 40

CALLING ME HOME.
Tracks: / Proud lion rampant, The / Bless this house / Lovely Stornoway / Cailin mo ruin-sa / Northern lights of old Aberdeen / Love me tender / These are my mountains / Memories/I'll be your sweetheart / Let the rest of the world go by / When I grow too old to dream / La vie en rose / Carnival is over, The / Back to Bonnie Scotland/Wild mountain thyme / Come by the hills/Back to bonny Scotland / Calling me home / Draem Angus / Farewell my love / Coorie doon.
LP: ITV 464
MC: KITV 464

FLOWER OF SCOTLAND.
Tracks: / How great Thou art / Flower of Scotland / Loch Lomond / Thistle of Scotland / Bluebells of Scotland / Uist tramping song / Scotland forever / There was a man / Bonnie Scotland I adore thee / Where were you, Lord? / Down in the glen / David / Eternally / Till the boys come home / Roses of Picardy / Goodbye.
LP: KLP 46
MC: ZCKLP 46

FOR MY AIN FOLK.
Tracks: / For my ain folk / Morning has broken / Rothesay Bay / John Anderson my Jo / Bright eyes / Ca' the yowes / When I grow too old to dream / Loves old sweet song / Now is the hour / No more / Lochnagar / Tobermory Bay / Lark in the clear air / Road and miles to Dundee / Scotland I'm coming home / Brahm's cradle song / Scotland you're a lady.
LP: KLP 21
MC: ZCKLP 21

I'LL SAY FAREWELL.
Tracks: / Massacre of Glencoe / Old Scots mother mine / Old rustic bridge / Scotland the brave / My love is like a red red rose / Galway Bay / Believe me if all those endearing young charms / When Irish eyes are smiling / How can you buy Killarney / Will ye no come back again / I'll say farewell / Twelfth of never / Hundred thousand welcomes / Take me back / Keep right on to the end of the road / Soft Lowland tongue of the border / Mull of Kintyre / Somewhere my love.
LP: KLP 35
MC: ZCKLP 35

LEGENDS OF SCOTLAND.
MC: ZCCLS 708

OLD RUGGED CROSS.
LP: KLP 63
MC: ZCKLP 63

PORTRAIT OF VALERIE DUNBAR, A.
Tracks: / Ye banks and braes / Aye waukin' o / Auld hoose, The / Last rose of summer / Sweetest of all / Ae fond kiss / I'd rather die young / Eriskay love lilt / Rowan tree / Lochinver / Beautiful dreamer / Dark island.
LP: KLP 15
MC: ZCKLP 15

RELAX WITH.
Tracks: / Tighnabruaich (home to the Kyles) / Wee hoose among the heather / It is no secret / Always / Misty islands of the highlands / You'll never walk alone / Mother's prayer, A / Amazing grace / Bonnie wells o' Wearie / This is my song / Man's a man, A / We'll meet again.
LP: KLP 52
MC: ZCKLP 52

ROSE.
LP: KLP 57
MC: ZCKLP 57

SCARLET RIBBONS.
MC: ZCKLP 69

SINGS SACRED.
Tracks: / Whispering hope / Holy City, The / Just a closer walk with thee / Blessed assurance / Rock of ages / Why me Lord / Precious Lord take my hand / Abide with me / In the sweet bye and bye / Beautiful Isle of somewhere / Battle hymn of the republic.
LP: ITV 421
MC: KITV 421

Duncan, Alex

IT'S A VET'S LIFE.
MC: SOUND 4

TO BE A COUNTRY DOCTOR.
MC: SOUND 8

VET HAS NINE LIVES, THE.
MC: SOUND 40

Duncan, Bryan

STRONG MEDICINE.
LP: ART R 4602
MC: ART C 4602

WHISTLIN' IN THE DARK.
LP: ART R 4600
MC: ART C 4600

Duncan, Daryll

HEAVEN.
Tracks: / Boomerang / Phone / James Brown / Best friend / My dream / One touch / Heaven / Girlfriend.
LP: ZL 72624
MC: ZK 72624

Duncan, Hank

PIANO SOLOS.
LP: 88 UR 001

Duncan, Hugo

16 BEST OF HUGO DUNCAN.
Tracks: / Gypsy, The / Village where I went to school / Answer to everything, The / Dear oul Donegal / Home town on the Foyle / Home to Mayo / My own peculiar way / Catch me if you can / Rose of Killarney / Dear old Galway town / Village of Astee, The / Misty rolling Midlands / Ring your mother wore / Limerick you're a lady / Cottage on the old Dungannon road / If those lips could only speak.
LP: PHL 497
MC: CPHL 497

BY SPECIAL REQUEST.
Tracks: / Barney Brannigan / Old claddagh ring / Funny face / Bold O'Donaghue / Shutters and boards / Mary from Dungloe / My lovely Irish rose / We stood at the altar / Moonshine / Road by the river / Marriage / Kingdom I call home / Old mud cabin on the hill / I love you still.
LP: DHL 718
MC: CDHL 718

COME DOWN THE MOUNTAIN KATIE DALY.
Tracks: / Come down the mountain Katie Daly / Heart you break may be your own, The / Sun in the morning, The / My Kathleen / Band of gold / Sweetest of all / O'Hara from Tara / We're gonna go fishin' / Fields of Athenry / Fairy reel, The / Home to Mayo / If I didn't have a dime / I'll forgive and try to forget / I wonder could I live there anymore.
LP: DHL 715
MC: CDHL 715

HITS OF HUGO DUNCAN, THE.
Tracks: / Dear God / Cry cry again / Almost persuaded / Old bog road / Angel Judy / Pain of loving you / Heartaches by the number / Cinderella / Three leaf shamrock / Tall men / Two of the usual / Eileen O'Grady.
LP: PHL 407
MC: CPHL 407

IF I HAD TO DO IT AGAIN.
Tracks: / If I had to do it again / Village in County Tyrone / Golden jubilee / From the candy store on the corner to the chapel on the hill / Road to Kildare / Westmeath bachelor / Golden dreams / Donegal rose / Think of me when you're lonely / Come back home to Erin /

Moonlight in Mayo / No tears my lady / Little country town in Ireland / You seldom come to see me anymore.
LP: . . . . DHL 716

IF WE ONLY HAD OLD IRELAND OVER HERE.
Tracks: / If we only had old Ireland over here / Gypsy, The / Happy anniversary / If those lips could only speak / Cottage on the old Dungannon road / My mother's birthday today / When you and I were young, Maggie / Catch me if you can / When the fields are white with daisies / Wedding song, The / Any Tipperary town / Broken engagement / Two loves / Dear old Galway town.
LP: . . . . DHL 702
MC: . . . . CDHL 702

IRELAND'S FAVOURITE SINGER.
Tracks: / Brady of Strabane / After all these years / Village of Astee, The / Nancy Miles / My Eileen is waiting for me / You can't break a broken heart / Old Dungarvan Oak / You're as welcome as the flowers in May / I will love you all my life / Veil of white lace / Pictures from the past / Rose of Killarney / I love you the best of all / Misty rollin' Midlands.
LP: . . . . DHL 711
MC: . . . . CDHL 711

IRELAND'S OWN (IRISH REQUESTS).
LP: . . . . PHL 490

IRISH COUNTRY.
Tracks: / By the light of the silvery moon / Sweet forget me not / Part of me / Boyle in the Co. Roscommon / Two little girls in blue / Clock in the tower, The / Little town in the ould County Down / Back home to Glenamaddy / Home to Donegal / Old pals are always the best / Black sheep / I can't help it / Old cross of Arboe / Killarney in my dreams.
MC: . . . . CDHL 719

IRISH FAVOURITES.
MC: . . . . CDHL 490

IRISH REQUESTS.
Tracks: / Village where I went to school / Dear old Galway town / Stone outside Dan Murphy's door, The / Eileen O'Grady / Old bog road / Misty rollin' midlands / Take me back to the castlebar / Pretty girl from Omagh / Long before your time / Slievenamon / Do you want yer oul lobby washed down / Home town on the Foyle / My Eileen is waiting for me / Catch me if you can.
MC: . . . . CPHL 490

ISLE OF INNISFREE.
Tracks: / Isle of Innisfree / Pretty Kitty Kelly / Talk back tremblin' lips / Stone outside Dan Murphy's door, The / Long before your time / Nora Malone / I love you more and more every day / Patsy McCann / Jody and the kid / Me and Bobby Magee / If I had my life to live over / Daddy Frank.
LP: . . . . PHL 473
MC: . . . . CPHL 473

LAND WE LOVE SO WELL, THE.
MC: . . . . CDSBL 522

MOST REQUESTED SONGS.
Tracks: / Mary Ann regrets / Boston burglar / My own peculiar way / Do you want yer oul lobby washed down? / Town I loved so well, The / Kentucky in the morning / Take me back to Castlebar / Village where I went to school / I'll take you home again, Kathleen / Galway shawl / Cottage on the borderline / Dear old Donegal.
LP: . . . . PHL 478
MC: . . . . CPHL 478

WEDDING SONG, THE.
Tracks: / Ring your mother wore / Home town on the Foyle / My wild Irish rose / Rose of Castlerea / Blacksmith / Pretty little girl from Omagh / Limerick, you're a lady / Wedding song, The / Take good care of her / Old flames / Keeps right on a hurtin' / Old house / 40 miles from Poplar Bluff / Answer to everything, The.
MC: . . . . CDHL 707
LP: . . . . DHL 707

Duncan, Johnny (1)

GREATEST HITS: JOHNNY DUNCAN.
Tracks: / Stranger / Sweet country woman / Atlanta Georgia stray / She can put her shoes under my bed / Come a little bit closer / Song in the night / It couldn't have been any better / Jo and the cowboy / Thinkin' of a rendezvous / Scarlet water.
LP: . . . . CBS 83486

NICE 'N' EASY (Duncan, Johnny/Janie Fricke).
Tracks: / He's out of my life / Nice 'n' easy / There's nothing stronger than our love / Baby / Loving arms / Come a little bit closer / It couldn't have been any better / Atlanta Georgia stray / Thinkin' of a rendezvous / Stranger.
LP: . . . . CBS 85111

Duncan, Johnny (2)

LAST TRAIN TO SAN FERNANDO (Duncan, Johnny & The Blue Grass Boys).
Tracks: / Last train to San Fernando / Itching for my baby / Geisha girl / Jig along home / Railroad, steamboat, river and canal / I heard the bluebirds sing / Git along home Cindy / Raise a ruckus tonight / Rockabilly baby / Detour / Which way did he go / Blue, blue heartaches / Footprints in the snow / My little baby / Yellow moon / Pan American / I'm movin' on / Dang me.
LP: . . . . BFX 15169

WORLD OF COUNTRY MUSIC VOL 2 (Duncan, Johnny & The Blue Grass Boys).
Tracks: / Mustang prang / Life can be beautiful / Hello heartache / If it feels good, do it / Wild side of life / Just for what I am / Salty dog blues / Just a little lovin' / Footprints in the snow / Blue, blue heartaches / Someone to give my love to / Hey good lookin' / I can't help it / Jambalaya / Smoke, smoke, smoke / Tom Dooley / Last train to San Fernando / Mustang prang (revisited).
LP: . . . . SPA 295

Duncan, Kenny

DANCING THROUGH SCOTLAND.
LP: . . . . DS 040

Duncan, Lesley

EVERYTHING CHANGES.
Tracks: / My soul / Broken old doll / Serf, The / Hold on / Everthing changes / Love melts away / Sam / You / Watch the tears / We'll get by.
LP: . . . . GML 1007

MAYBE IT'S LOST.
Tracks: / Sky's on fire, The / Maybe it's lost / Slipping sidesways / Living it all again / Another rainy day / Ride on the wind / Let it roll / Walk in the sea / Falling like a leaf / Don't worry about it / Drift away.
LP: . . . . GML 1019

MOON BATHING.
Tracks: / I can see where I'm going / Heaven lady step lightly / Wooden spoon / Pick up the phone / Helpless / Fine friends / Jumped right in the river / Rockin' chair.
LP: . . . . GML 1017

Duncan, Rob

TOUCH OF CLASS.
Tracks: / In your eyes / Mandy / Funny / Unchained melody / She believes in me / Three times a lady / When I fall in love / Love is a many splendoured thing / New York, New York / American trilogy.
LP: . . . . KPM 2
MC: . . . . TCKPM 2

Duncan, Sammy

SWINGIN' JAZZ (Duncan, Sammy & His All-Stars).
LP: . . . . J 84

WHEN THE SAINTS GO MARCHING IN (Duncan, Sammy & His All-Stars).
LP: . . . . J 118

WHEN YOU'RE SWINGING (Duncan, Sammy & His All-Stars).
LP: . . . . J 119

Duncan Sisters

DUNCAN SISTERS, THE.
Tracks: / Sadness in my eyes / Outside love / Rock along slowly / Boys will be boys / Love is on the way / You give me such a feeling.
LP: . . . . EMLP 4001

Duncans

GONNA STAY IN LOVE.
LP: . . . . MAL 7405

Dundas, David

VERTICAL HOLD.
Tracks: / It ain't so easy / Doing the best I can / Guy the gorilla / Lady you are my only worry / Gimme a little bit / When I saw you today / Radio fun / Never surrender / Twelve-bar blues / America.
LP: . . . . CHR 1197

Dundee Strathspey...

BOWS AND STRINGS, BUTTONS AND KEYS (Dundee Strathspey & Reel Society).
LP: . . . . WGR 047
MC: . . . . CWGR 047

FIDDLE ME JIG (Dundee Strathspey & Reel Society).
MC: . . . . LICS 5199

Dune (Film)

DUNE (1985 film soundtrack) (Various artists).
Tracks: / Dune: *Various artists* / Dune prologue: *Various artists* / Dune main title: *Various artists*/ Robot fight: *Various artists* / Leto's theme: *Various artists* / Box, The: *Various artists* / Floating fat man, The: *Various artists* / Trip to Arrakis: *Various artists* / First attack: *Various artists* / Phrophecy theme: *Various artists* / Dune (desert home): *Various artists* / Paul meets Chani: *Various artists*/ Prelude (take my hand): *Various artists* / Paul takes the water of life: *Various artists* / Big battle, The: *Various artists* / Paul kills Feyd: *Various artists* / Final dream: *Various artists* / Take my hand: *Various artists*.
LP: 823 770-1
MC: 823 770-4

Dune Trilogy Soundbook

DUNE TRILOGY SOUNDBOOK (See under Herbert, Frank).

Dunham, Andrew

DETROIT BLUES (Vol.2 1948-49) (Dunham, Andrew & Friends).
Tracks: / Wife lovin' blues / Stranger in your town / I tried / Waterlee blues / Single man blues / Thanksgiving blues / Big chested mama blues / Stormy weather blues / When I'm gone / Pay day blues / Christmas blues / Brown skinned woman / Cottonfield blues / 3 cent stamp blues.
LP: . . . . KK 7423

Dunham, Sonny

1943-1944 (Dunham, Sonny & His Orchestra).
LP: . . . . CLP 85

HALF PAST JUMPING TIME (Dunham, Sonny & His Orchestra).
LP: . . . . GELP 15008

SONNY DUNHAM ON THE AIR (Dunham, Sonny & His Orchestra).
Tracks: / Mocassin Glide / Besame mucho / Shoo shoo baby / Old acquaintance / Holiday for strings / When they ask about you / I'll be around / Don't worry mom / You're blase / Body and soul / Do nothing till you hear from me / With a sweetheart like you / Matinee at the meadowbrook / Blue moon.
LP: . . . . AIRCHECK 25

SONNY DUNHAM ORCHESTRA (Dunham, Sonny & His Orchestra).
LP: . . . . GELP 15044

Dunkley, Errol

DARLING OOH.
Tracks: / You never know / Movie star / Created by the father / Little way different, A / Like to be boosted / Darling ooh / Baby I love you / You're gonna need me / I'm not the man for you / It was nice while it lasted.
LP: . . . . TRLS 179
LP: . . . . ATLP 116
MC: . . . . MCAT 116

PROFILE: ERROL DUNKLEY.
LP: . . . . TDWD 16

SPECIAL REQUEST.
LP: . . . . CARLP 1

Dunlap, Gene

IT'S JUST THE WAY I FEEL.
Tracks: / Rock radio / Before you break my heart / I got you / Love dancin' / Title track / Should i take her back, should i let her go / Surest things can change.
LP: . . . . EST 12130

PARTY IN ME.
Tracks: / Party in me / Jam city / Something special / This one's on me / Take my love / Our moments together / Something inside my head / Corner pocket / There will never be another.
LP: . . . . EST 12190

Dunloy Accordion Band

MARCHING TO CHURCH.
Tracks: / It is no secret / As we are known / When the roll is called up yonder / There's a Saviour / Glory to His name / Coming home / All the way to Calvary / Guide me o thou great Jehovah / Labour on / I am thine o Lord / I have a song / I'm redeemed / Pass me not / Come to the saviour / Soldier's dream / Complete in Him / Shanghai / Heather glen hiking song, The / There is a fountain / Windsor castle / Hill of Glenore / Shear water grove / At the cross.
MC: . . . . COB 4003

Dunn, Bill

THANK GOD I AM FREE.
Tracks: / Blue skies / Thank God I am free / Day by day / There is a river / Touching Jesus / Jesus, use me / There's coming a day / Burdens are lifted at Calvary / Let me touch Him.
LP: . . . . PC 435

Dunn, George

GEORGE DUNN.
LP: . . . . LEE 4042

Dunn, Holly

BLUE ROSE OF TEXAS, THE.
Tracks: / Are you ever gonna love me? / Most of all, Why? / No one takes the train anymore / Sometime today / If I'd never loved you / You're still keeping me up at night / Thunder and lightnin' / Blue rose of Texas, The / There goes my heart again / There's no heart so strong.
LP: . . . . K 9259391
MC: . . . . K 9259394

Dunn, Johnny

DOC COOK DREAMLAND ORCHESTRA (See under Cook, Doc).

JOHNNY DUNN'S ORIGINAL JAZZ HOUNDS 1923-27 (Dunn, Johnny Original Jazz Hounds).
LP: . . . . VLP 11

Dunn, Kevin

C'EST TOUJOURS LA MEME GUITAR.
LP: . . . . PRESS 2007

JUDGEMENT OF PARIS, THE (Dunn, Kevin & Regiment of Women).
Tracks: / Creep, The / Tootsie (part 1) / Private sector / 911 / Grovinezza / 20,000 years in Sing Sing / Tootsie (part 2) / Saturn / A.G..
LP: . . . . ARM 3

TANZFELD.
Tracks: / Nam / Clear title / You better move / Burning love '81 / 5.9148 / Louie, Louie / Giovinezza / Nadine / Something new to get upset about.
LP: . . . . P 4007

Dunn, Mike

FREE YOUR MIND.
Tracks: / Born 2 B house / Hold on / Free your mind / Word to the mutha / I'll see you through / Give me your love / Born this way / Everything must change / Dream, A / Groove, A.
LP: . . . . LUVLP 8

Dunne, Pecker

TINKER MAN, THE.
MC: . . . . MB LP 1018

Dunning, Brian

ALONE TOGETHER (see under Stewart, Louis) (Dunning, Brian & Louis Stewart).

Dunphy, Sean

20 IRISH GREATS.
LP: . . . . DOLS 2001

BANSHEE.
LP: . . . . DOL 1010

BEST OF SEAN DUNPHY.
LP: . . . . DOLB 7003

BEST OF SEAN DUNPHY, VOLUME 2.
LP: . . . . DOLB 7013

IRISH SINGALONG.
Tracks: / Claddagh Ring / Rose of Arranmore / If we only had old Ireland over here / Stone outside Dan Murphy's door, The / Parting glass, The / Master McGrath / Reilly's daughter / Dicey Riley / Whiskey in the jar / Goodbye Mick, goodbye Pat / Nightingale, The / Back velvet band / Boston burglar / Goodbye Johnny dear / God be with you, Kerry / Shall my soul pass through old Ireland / Limerick City / Rafferty's motor car / Slattery's mounted fut / Agricultural Irish girl / Muirsheen Durkin.
LP: . . . . DOLS 2011
MC: . . . . DOCS 2011

JUST SEAN.
LP: . . . . DOLB 7014

THRU OLD IRELAND.
LP: . . . . DOLS 1009
MC: . . . . DOCS 1009

Dunphy, Tom

VERY BEST OF TOM DUNPHY.
LP: . . . . STAL 1049

Dunsany, Baron

BOOK OF WONDER.
MC: . . . . CDL 51693

Dunvant Male Choir

POWER AND GLORY, THE.
Tracks: / Soldiers'chorus / Sarah / Lord's prayer, The / Amazing Grace / My old Kentucky home / Close thine eyes / Soldiers' farewell / Bandit's chorus (From 'Ernani').
LP: . . . . GRALP 9
MC: . . . . GRTC 9

Dunwich Horror (Film)

DUNWICH HORROR, THE (1970 film soundtrack) (Various artists).
LP: . . . . VC 81103

Dunwich Story (Film)

DUNWICH STORY, THE (Film soundtrack) (Various artists).
LP: . . . . VOXX 200063

Duo Greco

BOUZOUKI AT THE BRIDGE.
MC: **00781**

Duo, Joanne

TOGETHER.
LP: . . . . **ERON 009**

Duodecima

MUSIC FOR TWO GUITARS.
LP: . . . . **OP 8201**

Dupe, Mo

GRATITUDE (see Ade, King Sunny) (Dupe, Mo/King Sunny Ade).

Dupont, Martin

HOT PARADOX.
LP: . . . . **AA 32004**

Dupree, Champion Jack

1940-50.
LP: . . . . **BOB 14**

1944-1945: THE OTHER TAKES.
Tracks: / She makes good jelly / Rum cola blues / Lovers Lane / Black wolf / Outside man, The / Forget it mama / You've been drunk / G.R. boogie / Santa Claus blues / Love strike blues / Wet deck mama / Big legged mama / I'm a doctor for waman.
LP: . . . . **KK 801**

BACK HOME IN NEW ORLEANS.
Tracks: / When I'm drinkin' / Lonesome bedroom / I don't know / Calcutta / Freedom / My woman left me / Broken hearted / Way down / Blind man / No future.
LP: . . . . **BB 9502**

BEST OF THE BLUES.
LP: . . . . **SLP 4010**
LP: . . . . **SLP 151**

BLUES FOR EVERYONE.
2LP: . . . . **GD 0037**
MCSET: . . . . **GD 5037**

BLUES FOR EVERYONE (BELLAPHON).
LP: . . . . **BID 8020**

BLUES OF CHAMPION JACK DUPREE, THE.
LP: . . . . **SLP 240**

CHAMPION JACK DUPREE 1944-1945.
Tracks: / Rum cola blues / She makes good jelly / Johnson Street boogie woogie / I'm going down with you / F.D.R. blues / God bless our new president / Gin mill sal / County jail special / Fisherman's blues / Lover's lane / Black wolf / Walkin' by myself / Outside man / Forget it mama / You've been drunk / Santa Claus blues.
LP: . . . . **RP 701**

FROM NEW ORLEANS TO CHICAGO.
Tracks: / Third degree / T.V. mama / He knows the rules / Ain't it a shame / Ooh-la-la / (Going down to) big leg Emma's / Won't be a fool no more / Take it slow and easy / She's all in my life / Poor poor me / Pigfoot and a bottle of beer / Down the valley / Too early in the morning / Shim-sham-shimmy.
LP: . . . . **CCR 1009**

HAPPY TO BE FREE.
LP: . . . . **GNPS 10005**

I'M GROWING OLDER EVERY DAY (See under Blues Roots Volume 6).

INCREDIBLE CHAMPION JACK DUPREE, THE.
Tracks: / Big fat mama / 41 Highway / Old woman blues / President Kennedy blues / I'm goin' to look the world over / Poor boy blues / Miss Ada blues / Gravier Street special / You're so fine / Rock me, mama / Don't worry / Driving me mad.
LP: . . . . **SNTF 614**

JUBILEE ALBUM.
Tracks: / Freedom / Ramblin' boogie / Jump for Jack / Nobody loves me / Blues for champ / Married man / I hate to be alone / When Victoria Spivey was living / Rocky Mountain / New York City / Move me, baby / Shineberger boogie / Thank you, God / Happy birthday / Rockin' the house / One more time / Blues ad lib, The / Bye bye blues / Mother in law / Georgina / One scotch, one bourbon, one beer.
2LP: . . . . **BMLP 2074**

JUNKER BLUES 1940-41.
LP: . . . . **TM 807**

LEGACY OF THE BLUES VOL. 3 (See under Legacy of the Blues).

ROCKIN' THE BOOGIE.
Tracks: / My baby's coming back / Rockin' the boogie / I don't know / You better kick the habit / I had that dream / I hate to be alone / Be a man / Old old woman / Good Lord born on Christmas Day / Baby please don't go.
LP: . . . . **BMLP 058**

RUN A LITTLE BOOGIE 1945-53.
LP: . . . . **KK 7401**

SHAKE BABY SHAKE.
Tracks: / Ups, The / Lonely road blues / Story of my life / When I get married / Dirty woman / Old time rock'n'roll / Down the lane / Rocky mountain / Just like a woman / Shake baby shake / Wrong woman, The / You're always cryin' the blues / Woman trouble again / My baby's like a clock / Hello darlin' / Lollipop baby.
LP: . . . . **DT 33007**

TRICKS, THE.
LP: **512502**
LP: . . . . **GNPS 10001**

TROUBLE, TROUBLE.
LP: . . . . **SLP 4139**

WON'T BE A FOOL NO MORE.
Tracks: / Third degree / T.V. mama / He knows the rules / Ain't it a shame? / Ooh-la-la / Big leg Emma's / Won't be a fool no more / Calcutta blues / Take it slow and easy / She's all in my life / Poor poor me / 24 hours / Pigfoot and a bottle of beer / Down in the valley / Too early in the morning / Shim-sham-shimmy.
LP: . . . . **SEE 44**

Dupree, Cornell

GUITAR GROOVE.
Tracks: / Staying alive I & 2 / Boogie nights / Shake it well / How deep is your love / Lovely day / Slip slidin' away / It's so easy.
LP: . . . . **TOP 167**
MC: . . . . **KTOP 167**

TEASIN'.
Tracks: / Teasin' / Blue nocturne / Jamaican lady / Feel all right / How long will it last / What would I do without you / Okie Dokie stomp / Plain Ol'blues.
LP: . . . . **K 50071**

Dupree, Robbie

ROBBIE DUPREE.
Tracks: / Steal away / I'm no stranger / Thin line / It's a feeling / Hot rod hearts / Nobody else / We both tried / Love is a mystery / Lonely runner.
LP: . . . . **K 52235**

STREET CORNER HEROES.
Tracks: / Street corner heroes / Desperation / Brooklyn girls / All night long / Free fallin' / I'll be the fool again / Are you ready for love / Saturday night / Missin' you / Long goodbye.
LP: . . . . **K 52290**

Dupree, Simon

AMEN (Dupree, Simon & The Big Sound).
Tracks: / Kites / Like the sun like the fire / Sleep / For whom the bell tolls / Broken hearted pirates / Minutes of your love / Lot of love, A / Love / Get off my Bach / There's a little picture playhouse / Day time / Night time / I see the light / What is soul / Amen / Who cares / She gave me the sun / Thinking about my life / It is finished / I've seen it all before / You need a man / Reservations.
LP: . . . . **CM 109**
MC: . . . . **CMK 109**

SIMON DUPREE & THE BIG SOUND (Dupree, Simon & The Big Sound).
Tracks: / Kites / Like the sun like the fire / Sleep / For whom the bell tolls / Broken hearted pirates / Sixty minutes of your love / Love / Get off my Bach / There's a little picture playhouse / Day time, night time / I see the light / What is soul / Amen / Who cares / She gave me the sun / Thinking about my life / It is finished / I've seen it all before / You need a man / Reservations.
LP: . . . . **NUTM 32**

WITHOUT RESERVATIONS (Dupree, Simon & The Big Sound).
Tracks: / Without reservations.
LP: . . . . **PCS 7029**

Duran Duran

ARENA.
Tracks: / Is there something I should know? / Hungry like the wolf / New religion / Save a prayer / Wild boys / Seventh stranger, The / Chauffeur, The / Union of the snake / Planet Earth / Careless memories.
LP: . . . . **DD 2**
MC: . . . . **TCDD 2**
LP: . . . . **ATAK 125**
LP: . . . . **EX 2603081**
MC: . . . . **EX 2603084**
MC: . . . . **TCATAK 125**
LP: . . . . **FA 3225**
MC: . . . . **TCFA 3225**

BIG THING.
Tracks: / Big thing / I don't want your love / All she wants is / Too late Marlene / Drug (It's just a state of mind) / Do you believe in shame? / Palomino / Interlude one / Land / Flute interlude / Edge of America, The / Lake shore driving.
LP: . . . . **DDB 33**
MC: . . . . **TCDDB 33**
LP: . . . . **ATAK 148**
MC: . . . . **TCATAK 148**

DECADE.
Tracks: / Planet earth / Girls on film / Hungry like the wolf / Rio / Save a prayer / Is there something I should know / Union of the snake / Reflex, The / Wild boys / View to a kill, A / Notorious / Skin trade / I don't want your love / All she wants is.
LP: . . . . **DDX 10**
MC: . . . . **TCDDX 10**

DURAN DURAN.
Tracks: / Girls on film / Planet earth / Anyone out there / To the shore / Careless memories / Night boat / Sound of thunder, The / Friends of mine / Tel Aviv.
LP: . . . . **EMC 3372**
MC: . . . . **TCEMC 3372**
LP: . . . . **FA 3185**
MC: . . . . **TCFA 3185**

DURAN DURAN: INTERVIEW PICTURE DISC.
LPPD: . . . . **BAK 2002**

LIBERTY.
Tracks: / Violence of summer (love's taking over) / Liberty / Hothead / Serious / All along the water / My Antarctica / First impressions / Read my lips / Can you deal with it / Venice drowning / Downtown.
LP: . . . . **PCSD 112**
MC: . . . . **TCPCSD 112**

NOTORIOUS.
Tracks: / Notorious / American science / Skin trade / Hold me / Vertigo (do the demolition) / So misled / Meet el Presidente / Winter marches on / Proposition / Matter of feeling, A.
LP: . . . . **DDN 331**
MC: . . . . **TCDDN 331**

RIO.
Tracks: / Rio / My own way / Lonely in your nightmare / Hungry like the wolf / Hold back the rain / New religion / Last chance on the stairway / Save a prayer / Chaffeur, The.
LP: . . . . **EMC 3411**
MC: . . . . **TCEMC 3411**
LP: . . . . **ATAK 149**
MC: . . . . **TCATAK 149**

SEVEN AND THE RAGGED TIGER.
Tracks: / Reflex, The / New moon on Monday / I'm looking for cracks in the pavement / I take the dice / Of crime and passion / Union of the snake / Shadows on your side / Tiger tiger / Seventh stranger, The.
LP: . . . . **EMC 1654541**
MC: . . . . **TCEMC 1654544**
LP: . . . . **FA 3205**
MC: . . . . **TCFA 3205**

Duran, Eddie

LET THERE BE LOVE (see Bell, Dee).

ONE BY ONE (see Bell, Dee) (Duran, Eddie & Dee Bell).

Duran, Eleanor

BRANDENBURG BOOGIE (Duran, Eleanor with Grappelli, Holloway, Walley & Ganley).
Tracks: / Brandenburg boogie / Jesu, joy of man's desiring / Groovy gavotte (1) / Fascinating fugue / Groovy gavotte (II) / Sleeper's awake / Aria / D minor double / Minuet / Jig / Air on a G string / Groovy gavotte (III) / Sicilienne / Funky flute.
LP: . . . . **EMD 5536**
MC: . . . . **TCEMD 5536**

NORWEGIAN WOOD (see Grappelli, Stephane) (Duran, Eleanor & Stephane Grappelli).

VIVA ELENA.
Tracks: / Song of the Andes / La paloma / River song / Black orpheus theme / Brazilian serenade / Guantanamera / Mexican hat dance / Mary Rose / La cucaracha / Walaychu / Totoras / Cielito lindo / Benedito pretinho / Inca dance / Frog song.
LP: . . . . **RCALP 6030**
MC: . . . . **RCAK 6030**

Durante, Jimmy

BING CROSBY WITH SPIKE JONES & JIMMY DURANTE (see Crosby, Bing) (Durante, Jimmy, Bing Crosby, Spike Jones).

ON THE RADIO.
LP: . . . . **MR 1080**

START OF EACH DAY (Durante, Jimmy, Bing Crosby, Spike Jones).
MC: . . . . **JSP 701**

Durbin, Deanna

BEST OF DEANNA DURBIN.
Tracks: / It's raining sunbeams / My own / Spring in my heart / One fine day / Love is all / Perhaps / Last rose of summer / Can't help singing / Blue Danube dream / Californ-i-ay / Because / Turntable song, The / Spring will be a little late this year / Home sweet home / Waltzing in the clouds / Ave Maria.
LP: . . . . **MCL 1634**
MC: . . . . **MCLC 1634**

BEST OF DEANNA DURBIN, VOL 2.
Tracks: / Any moment now / Kiss me again / La estrellita (my little star) / Love's old sweet song / Loch Lomond / When the roses bloom again / Bacio, The (The kiss) / Silent night / My hero / Musetta's waltz song / Old folks at home / Poor butterfly / Cielito lindo / Annie Laurie / O come all ye faithful / Allelujah.
LP: . . . . **MCL 1729**
MC: . . . . **MCLC 1729**

CAN'T HELP SINGING.
Tracks: / Waltzing in the clouds / It's raining sunbeams / Blue Danube dream / When April sings / It's only love / Love at last / Always / Brindisi / Beneath the lights of home / Something in the wind / Can't help singing / Les filles de cadiz / More and more / One fine day / Amapola / Perhaps.
LP: . . . . **MFP 50559**
MC: . . . . **TCMFP 50559**

DEANNA DURBIN COLLECTION (20 Golden Greats).
Tracks: / Going home / Ave Maria / Carousel in the park / Largo al factotum / One night of love / Waltz song from Romeo and Juliet / Can't help singing / It's raining sunbeams / Spring will be a little late this year / Viennese waltz / I love to whistle / Blue Danube dream / One fine day / You're as pretty as a picture / Because / Granada / La capinera (the wren) / Waltzing in the clouds / Last rose of summer.
LP: . . . . **DVLP 2091**
MC: . . . . **DVMC 2091**

FAVOURITES.
Tracks: / My hero / Can't help singing / Kiss me again / Turntable song, The / Always / When April sings / Amapola / Lover / Danny boy / Because / Spring will be a little late this year / You wanna keep your baby looking right.
LP: . . . . **MOIR 206**
MC: . . . . **CMOIR 206**

LEGENDARY, THE.
MC: . . . . **MRT 40041**

MOVIE SONGS.
Tracks: / Lover / Danny boy / In the spirit of the moment / When you're away / Russian medley / Night and day / Spring in my heart / Prince, The / Old refrain, The / Moonlight bay / I'll take you home again Kathleen.
LP: . . . . **MCL 1668**
MC: . . . . **MCLC 1668**

SONGS OF THE SILVER SCREEN.
Tracks: / One night of love / My heart is singing / You're as pretty as a picture / Mighty like a rose / Give me a little kiss / Granada / Carousel in the park / Waltz song from Romeo and Juliet / La capinera (the wren) / Goodbye / I love to whistle / Going home / With a heart that's free / Largo al factotum / Seguidilla / Serenade to the stars, A / Chapel bells / When I sing / Viennese waltz.
LP: . . . . **MCG 6007**
MC: . . . . **MCGC 6007**

Durbridge, Francis

PAUL TEMPLE AND THE CONRAD CASE (Various artists).
MCSET: . . . . **ZBBC 1032**

Duren, Van

STARING AT THE CEILING.
Tracks: / Chemical fire / This love inside / Oh babe / Waiting / Grow yourself up / Guaranteed / Positive / New Year's Eve / So good to me / Yellow light / For a while / Stupid enough / Love that I love.
LP: . . . . **SHY 8530**

Durham, Bobby

WHERE I GREW UP.
Tracks: / Where I grew up / Several hearts / I drove here there / Cheap hotels / You gotta have a licence / If you count goodbye / Dance real slow / Playboy / Let's start a rumour today / Comin' back.
LP: . . . . **FIEND 110**

Durham Cathedral Choir

CHRISTMAS CAROLS FROM DURHAM CATHEDRAL.
Tracks: / Lo, He comes with clouds descending / Drop down, ye heavens / There is no rose of virtue / Cherry tree carol, The / All this night / Jesus sweet and Mary / When Jordan hushed / Once

in Royal David's city / Welcome Yule / Love came down at Christmas / I wonder as I wander / I saw three ships / Little Jesus, sweetly sleep / Away in a manger / O come all ye faithful.
LP: . . . . MVP 800
MC: . . . . MVPC 800

DURHAM CATHEDRAL CHOIR.
Tracks: / My beloved spake / Christe jesu, pastor bone / When Mary thro' the garden went / Let me know mine end / Sweet was the song / I will lift up mine eyes / Thou, O God, art praised in Sion / Still throned in heaven / Ave Maria / Te deum (Collegium Regale).
MC: . . . . HAC 832

NEARER, MY GOD, TO THEE.
Tracks: / Holy, holy, holy / Not for our sins alone / For the beauty of the earth / Alone with none but thee / Nearer, my God, to thee / By gracious powers / Lord, thou hast told us / Jesus shall reign / Ring Christ, ring Mary / Come, my way / Awake, our souls / Keep me / O God of grace / King of glory / Jesu, lover of my soul / Lord of beauty / When I survey / Ye that know the Lord.
MC: . . . . HAC 852

Durham, John (aut)

APACHE MOON (See under Apache Moon) (Horne, David (nar)).

Durkin, Kathy

MEMORIES.
2LP: . . . . HM 032D

MOONLIGHT REFLECTIONS.
Tracks: / Midnight to moonlight / Tie that binds, The / Clock in the tower, The / Love makes the world go round / Mama's angels / Rose, The / Anger and tears / Flight of Earls / Water is wide, The / Way back home, The / Boulder to Birmingham / As I leave behind Neidin / Jones on the jukebox / Blue Kentucky girl / Jigs / Save the last dance for me.
LP: . . . . HM 056

Durno, Duncan

HILLS OF CULDRAIN.
Tracks: / Buchan ploorman, The / Waddin' o' McPhee / Drumdelgie / Livetside / Gartley.
MC: . . . . CWGR 093

Durocs

DUROCS.
Tracks: / Hog wild / Lie to me / Don't let the dream die / We do good together / No fool no fun / It hurts to be in love / Seeker / True love / One day at a time / Saving it all up for Larry.
LP: . . . . EST 11981

Durrell, Gerald

MY FAMILY & OTHER ANIMALS (Harper, Gerald).
MCSET: . . . . LFP 7318

Durutti Column

ANOTHER SETTING.
LP: . . . . FACT 74

CIRCUS AND BREAD.
Tracks: / Pauline / Tomorrow / Dance II / For Hilary / Street fight / Royal Infirmary / Black horses / Dance I / Blind elevator girl / Osaka.
LP: . . . . FBN 36
MC: . . . . FBNC 36

GUITAR AND OTHER MACHINES, THE.
Tracks: / Miracle of love / Price of love, The / Heart has it's reasons / Alone in the night / Lover's story / Take me home.
LP: . . . . FACT 204
MC: . . . . FACT 204C
DAT: . . . . FACT 204 DT

L.C..
LP: . . . . FACT 44
MC: . . . . FACT 44C

LIVE AT THE BOTTOM LINE.
MC: . . . . A 152

OBEY THE TIME.
LP: . . . . FACT 274
MC: . . . . FACT 274C

RETURN OF THE DURUTTI COLUMN.
LP: . . . . FACT 14
MC: . . . . FACT 14 C

VALUABLE PASSAGES.
Tracks: / Sketch for summer / Conduct / Sketch for winter / Lips that would kiss / Belgian friends / Danny / Piece for out-of-tune piano / Never know / Jacqueline / Missing boy / Prayer / Spent time / Without mercy stanzas 2-8 12-15 / Room / Blind elevator girl / Tomorrow / LFO MOD.
MC: . . . . FACT 164 C

VINI REILLY.
LP: . . . . FACT 244
MC: . . . . FACT 244 C
DAT: . . . . FACT 244 D

WITHOUT MERCY.
LP: . . . . FACT 84
MC: . . . . FACT 84 C

Dury, Ian

4,000 WEEKS HOLIDAY (Dury, Ian & The Music Students).
Tracks: / Inspiration / Friends / Tell your daddy / Peter the painter / Ban the bomb / Percy the poet / Very personal / Take me to the cleaners / Man with no face / Really glad you came.
LP: . . . . POLD 5112
LP: . . . . PIPLP 004
MC: . . . . PIPMC 004

APPLES.
LP: . . . . WX 326
MC: . . . . WX 326C

DO IT YOURSELF.
Tracks: / In betweenies / Quiet / Don't ask me / Sink my boats / Waiting for your taxi / This is what we find / Uneasy sunny day hotsy totsy / Mischief / Dance of the screamers / Lullaby for Francies.
LP: . . . . SEEZ 14
LP: . . . . FIEND 133
MC: . . . . FIENDCASS 133

GREATEST HITS:IAN DURY.
Tracks: / What a waste / Reasons to be cheerful - part 3 / Wake up and make love with me / There ain't half been some clever bastards / Hit me with your rhythm stick / Razzle in my pocket / Sex and drugs and rock and roll / In betweenies / Common as muck / Sweet Gene Vincent / I want to be straight / You'll see glimpses.
LP: . . . . FA 3031
MC: . . . . TCFA 3031

HANDSOME (See under Kilburn & The High Roads) (Kilburn & The High Roads With Ian Dury).

IAN DURY AND THE BLOCKHEADS.
Tracks: / Intro / Wake up and make love with me / Clevor Trever / If I was with a woman / Billericay dickie / Quiet / My old man / Spasticus autisticus / Plaistow Patricia / There ain't half been some clever bastards / Sweet Gene Vincent / What a waste / Hit me with your rhythm stick / Blockheads.
LP: . . . . FIEND 777
MC: . . . . FIENDCASS 777

JUKE BOX DURY.
Tracks: / What a waste / Reasons to be cheerful - part 3 / Wake up and make love with me / There ain't half been some clever bastards / Hit me with your rhythm stick / Razzle in my pocket / Sex and drugs and rock and roll / In betweenies / Common as muck / Sweet Gene Vincent / I want to be straight / You'll see glimpses.
LP: . . . . SEEZ 41
MC: . . . . ZSEEZ 41

LAUGHTER (Dury, Ian & The Blockheads).
Tracks: / Superman's big sister / Pardon, The / Delusions of grandeur / Yes and no / Dance of the crackpots / Over the points / Take your elbow out of the soup... / Uncoolohol / Hey hey take me away / Manic depression / Oh Mr. Peanut / F**king Ada.
LP: . . . . SEEZ 30
MC: . . . . ZSEEZ 30

LORD UPMINSTER.
Tracks: / Funky disco bops / Body song / Lonely town / Trust is a must / Red letter / Girls watching / Wait for me / Spasticus Autisticus.
LP: . . . . POLD 5042
LP: . . . . PIPLP 005
MC: . . . . PIPMC 005

NEW BOOTS AND PANTIES (Dury, Ian & The Blockheads).
Tracks: / Sweet Gene Vincent / Wake up and make love with me / I'm partial to your Abracadabra / My old man / Billericay Dickie / Clevor Trever / If I was with a woman / Plaistow Patricia / Blockheads / Blackmail man.
LP: . . . . FIEND 63
MC: . . . . FIENDCASS 63
MC: . . . . ZSEEZ 4
LP: . . . . SEEZ 4

SEX AND DRUGS AND ROCK AND ROLL (Dury, Ian & The Blockheads).
Tracks: / Hit me with your rhythm stick / I want to be straight / There ain't half been some clever bastards / What a waste / Common as muck / Reasons to be cheerful / Sex and drugs and rock and roll / Supermans big sister / Razzle in my pocket / You're more than fair / In betweenies / You'll see glimpses.
LP: . . . . XFIEND 69
MC: . . . . FIENDCASS 69

Duskin, Big Joe

CINCINNATI STOMP.
LP: . . . . ARHOOLIE 1080

DON'T MESS WITH THE BOOGIE MAN.
LP: . . . . SPD 1017
MC: . . . . SPDC 1017

Dust

DUST.
LP: . . . . BBLP 1

Dust Devils

GUTTERLIGHT.
LP: . . . . CONCORD 008

RHENYARD'S GRIN.
Tracks: / Encient / Life garden / Lost divide, The / Hard rough force / Mouth full of stars / Dirt of days / In it's own light / Pressed / Another hilt / Real hate work.
LP: . . . . CONCORDE 9

Dusty, Slim

AUSTRALIA IS HIS NAME.
LP: . . . . PH 1119
MC: . . . . PH 1119C

PUB WITH NO BEER (OLD GOLD) (see under King, Solomon) (Various artists).

Dusty & the Dinosaurs

ADVENTURES OF DUSTY AND THE DINOSAURS (See under Adventures of...) (Newman, Nannette (nar)).

Dutch Swing College

40 YEARS, 1945-1985, AT ITS BEST.
LP: . . . . TTD 616

BAND'S BEST, THE.
Tracks: / Way down yonder in New Orleans / Weary blues / South / Doctor Jazz / I've found a new baby / Alexander's ragtime band / King Porter stomp / Buddy's habits / Quena blues / Besame mucho / Wilhelm Tell / Tennessee waltz rock / Mack the knife / Milenberg joys / At the jazz band ball / Fidgety feet / Royal Garden blues / Basin Street blues / Ice cream / See see rider / Tiger rag / When the saints go marching in / Big butter and egg man / High society / I wish I could shimmy like my sister Kate / Clarient marmalade / Struttin' with some barbecue / Please don't talk about me when I'm gone.
LP: 6601 024
MC: 7588 024

DIGITAL ANNIVERSARY.
Tracks: / Bourbon Street parade / Wabash blues / Caribbean parade / Is it true what they say about Dixie? / Clarinet games / Saturday night is the loneliest night of the week / Coal black shine / Third Street blues / Gladiolus rag / Columbus stockade blues / Devil in the moon / Original Dixieland one-step.
LP: 824 585 1
MC: 824 585 4

DIGITAL DATE.
Tracks: / That's a plenty / I remember Johnny / Stockyards strut / I'm coming Virginia / Chimes blues / (Back home again in) Indiana / Sweetie dear / Somewhere somehow / Alabama jubilee / Murkeys / Tat da da strain / That's my desire / Lulu's back in town / Crazy sticks / When my sugar walks down the street / Kaper's up / South Rampart Street parade / Jamaican brew.
LP: 8340871
MC: 8340374

DIGITAL DIXIE.
Tracks: / Way down yonder in New Orleans / Kneedrops / West End blues / At a Georgia camp meeting / I want a little girl / China boy / Creole belles / Sugar / Kazoo / Down home rag / On Green Dolphin Street / Everybody loves my baby.
LP: 6433 472
MC: 7111 472

DUTCH SAMBA.
Tracks: / Corro / Velas blancas / Girl from Ipanema / Samba de Orfeu / Menina flor meditacao / Manana / Corcovado / Poinciana / Samba de Quena / Eso es el Amor / La adelita.
LP: . . . . TTD 552

DUTCH SWING COLLEGE BAND (Best of Dixieland).
LP: 838 765 1

JUBILEE CONCERT.
MC: 7588 003
LP: 6601 003

MUSIC FOR THE MILLIONS.
Tracks: / Ice scream / Memphis blues / Take your pick / Just a closer walk with thee / Tennessee waltz rock / March of the Indians / Marina / I ain't gonna give nobody none of my jelly roll / Black and tan fantasy / Tiger rag / You don't know how much you suffer / High society.
LP: 6375 463
MC: 7174 463

ON TOUR.
LP: 9279 368
MC: 7259 368

WHEN THE SWING COMES MARCHING IN.
Tracks: / High school cadets / High society / Swanee / Liberty bell / Copenhagen / Stars and stripes forever / Anchors aweigh / Original Dixieland one-step / Semper Fidelis / Ory's Creole trombone / Sensation rag / Officer of the day.
LP: 6375 424
MC: 7174 424

Duteil, Yves

YVES DUTEIL.
LP: 2C 070 14836

Duval, Frank

WHEN YOU WERE MINE.
Tracks: / When you were mine / Face to the wind / Galaxis zena / It seems to be a dream (BMW theme) / Element / Fight in myself / When he left her.
LP: 6.26555
MC: 4.26555

Du-val, Raye

BOPPIN' WITH A BAD BAD GIRL (Duval, Raye & the Rockmates).
Tracks: / Boppin' with a bad bad girl / Put on your dancing shoes.
MC: . . . . QUCS 1

VIVE ROCK'N'ROLL.
LP: . . . . LP 1932/4AC
MC: . . . . LS 1932/4AC

Duvall, Huelyn

CHALLENGE MASTERS, THE.
Tracks: / Comin' or goin' / Boom boom baby / Pucker paint / Juliet / Friday night on a dollar bill / You knock me out / Danny Wolfe / Teen queen (take 11) / Teen queen (Take 12) / Three months to kill / Hum-m-m-dinger / Fool's hall of fame (take 11) / Little boy blue.
LP: . . . . BFX 15200

HUELYN DUVALL (Duvall, Huelyn & The Tight Strings).
Tracks: / Life begins at 4 o'clock / Just me and you baby / Blue eyed baby / So help me gal / Beautiful dreamer / Whole lotta shakin' goin' on / Lonely / Double talkin' baby / Com'n or go'n / Teen queen / Hum-dinger / Susie's house / Does she love me / Double talkin' baby.
LP: . . . . WLP 8864

MORE.
Tracks: / Three months to kill / Juliet / My girl / Blue lotta blue / Why tell me, baby? / So help me, gal / Rocking and rehearsing / Remember last night / Got a little girl / It's no wonder / When the party's over / Little blue boy.
LP: . . . . WLP 8880

TODAY AND YESTERDAY.
Tracks: / Blue lotta blue / It's no wonder / Got a little girl / Susie's house / Party doll / Lawdy Miss Clawdy / Pucker paint / Lotta lovin' / Hey Brutus / Friday night on a dollar bill / Brown eyes / Teen queen / Can't go away / Humdinger / These children / Be bop a lula.
LP: . . . . WLP 8923

Duvant Male Choir

WITH A VOICE OF SINGING.
Tracks: / With a voice of singing / Nant y mynydd / God's choir / Goodnight / My love is like a red rose / Roman war song, A / Morte Christe / When I survey the wondrous cross / Song of freedom / De animals a-comin'.
LP: . . . . NTS 175

Dvorak (composer)

CELLO CONCERTO IN B MINOR, OP 104 (Various artists).
MC: 4250204

DVORAK (Various artists).
MC: . . . . DLCMC 216

DVORAK NEW WORLD SYMPHONY (Brahms Academic Festival Overture) (London Philharmonic Orchestra).
Tracks: / Symphony no.9 (Dvorak) ('New World') / Academic Festival Overture.
MC: . . . . ZC QS 6037

DVORAK SLAVONIC DANCES (Various artists).
LP: . . . . REH 731
MC: . . . . ZCR 731

LIEBESTRAUM (See under Liebestraum) (London Symphony...).

MAGIC OF ROMANTICISM (See under Magic of romanticism) (Various orchestras).

OVERTURES (See also Suppe, Berlioz) (Ljubljana Symphony Orchestra/ Nanut).

SERENADE FOR STRINGS IN E (Directed by Jaime Laredo) (Scottish Chamber Orchestra).
Tracks: / Serenade for strings in E, Opus 22 (Dvorak) / Romance in F minor, Opus 11 (Dvorak) / Siegfried Idyll (Wagner).
MC: . . . . CIMPC 928

SERENADES FOR STRINGS (See under Tchaikovsky for full details) (English String Orchestra, conducted by William Boughton).

SYMPHONY NO.8 (DVORAK) in G major (Royal Liverpool Philharmonic Orchestra/London Philharmonic O).
Tracks: / Symphony No.8 op.88 / Carnival overture op. 92.
MC: . . . . **ZC QS 6006**

SYMPHONY NO.9 (DVORAK) (From the New World) (Various artists).
LP: **4273461**
MC: **4273464**

SYMPHONY NO.9/CARNIVAL OVERTURE (Vienna Philharmonic Orchestra).
MC: **4278054**

SYMPHONY NO 9 (DVORAK) (San Francisco Symphony Orchestra).
MC: **426 073-4**

SYMPHONY NO. 9 (NEW WORLD) (Vienna State Opera Orchestra).
MC: . . . . **VETC 6510**

WIND AND STRING SERENADES (Northern Sinfonia of England).
Tracks: / Serenade for strings op. 22 / Serenade for wind op. 44.
MC: . . . . **ZC QS 6002**

Dvorin, Miriam

YIDDISH SONGS.
LP: . . . . **ARHOOLIE 3019**

Dwarves

HORROR STORIES.
LP: . . . . **VOXX 200037**

Dwyer, Finbarr

BEST OF FINBARR DWYER.
MC: . . . . **COX 1011**

FINBARR DWYER (Irish traditional accordionist).
MC: . . . . **COX 1004**

IRELAND'S CHAMPION ACCORDIONIST.
MC: . . . . **COX 1032**

IRELAND'S OWN TRADITIONAL ACCORDIONIST.
MC: . . . . **COX 1016**

TRADITIONAL MUSIC.
LP: . . . . **OLP 1004**

Dyall, Valentine

ECHOES FROM THE MACABRE (Echoes from the macabre).
MC: . . . . **CAB 008**

HOUSE OF THE SEVEN FLIES (See under House of the seven flies).

TALES OF TERROR.
MC: . . . . **P 90009**

Dyani, Johnny

BORN UNDER THE HEAT (Dyani, Johnny Mbizo).
LP: . . . . **DRLP 68**

JOHN DYANI WITH JOHN TCHICAI & DUDU PUKWANA.
LP: . . . . **SCS 1098**

MUSIC FOR XABA.
LP: . . . . **SNTF 642**

MUSIC FOR XABA VOL.2.
Tracks: / Mad high / Mighty blues / Dear Africa / Makaya Makaya Makaya / Witchdoctor's son.
LP: . . . . **SNTF 824**

REJOICE - AFRICAN JAZZ (Dyani, Johnny/Mongezi Fena/Okay Temiz).
LP: . . . . **SGC 1017**

WITCHDOCTOR'S SON, TOGETHER.
Tracks: / Together / Johnny's kwela / Marabi soweto / High priest / Kalahari / Crossroads / Tula tula.
LP: . . . . **SGC 1016**

Dyer, Johnny

JOHNNY DYER AND THE L.A.JUKES (Dyer, Johnny & the L.A. Jukes).
LP: . . . . **MB 1004**

Dying Inside

DYING INSIDE (Silverberg, Robert).
MC: . . . . **CDL 51612**

Dying To Meet..

DYING TO MEET YOU (See under Gill, B.M.) (Gill, B.M.).

Dyke & The Blazers

SO SHARP.
Tracks: / Funky Broadway (part 1) / Funky Broadway (part 2) / Uhh (part 1) / Runaway people / We got more soul / It's your thing / Shot gun Slim / So sharp / Let a woman be a woman - let a man be a man / You are my sunshine / Funky walk (part 2) / Wrong house, The.
LP: . . . . **KEND 004**

Dylan, Bob

ANOTHER SIDE OF BOB DYLAN.
Tracks: / All I really want to do / Black crow blues / Spanish Harlem incident / Chimes of freedom / I shall be free / To Ramona / Motorpsycho nightmare / My back pages / I don't believe you / Ballads in plain D / It ain't me babe.
LP: **32034**
MC: **40 32034**
LP: . . . . **BPG 62429**

AT THE BUDOKAN.
Tracks: / Mr. Tambourine man / Shelter from the storm / Love minus zero / No limit / Ballad of a thin man / Don't think twice, it's alright / Maggie's farm / One more cup of coffee / Like a rolling stone / I shall be released / Is your love in vain? / Going going gone / Blowin' in the wind / Just like a woman / Oh, sister / Simple twist of fate / All along the watchtower / I want you woman / Oh, sister / All I really want to do / Knockin' on heaven's door / It's alright ma / Forever young / Times they are a changin'.
2LP: . . . . **CBS 96004**
MC: **40 96004**

BASEMENT TAPES.
Tracks: / Odds and ends / Orange juice blues (blues for breakfast) / Million dollar bash / Yaroo Street scandal / Goin' to Acapulco / Kate's been gone / You ain't goin' nowhere / Don't ya tell Henry / Nothing was delivered / Open the door, Homer / Long distance operator / This wheel's on fire / Lo and behold / Bessie Smith / Clothes line saga / Apple suckling tree / Mrs. Henry / Tears of rage / Too much of nothing / Yea, heavy and a bottle of bread / Ain't no more cane / Crash on the levee (down in the flood) / Ruben Remus / Tiny Montgomery.
LP: . . . . **CBS 88147**
MC: **40 88147**

BEFORE THE FLOOD.
Tracks: / Most likely you'll go your way and I'll go mine / Lay lady lay / Rainy day women Nos 12 & 35 / Knockin' on Heaven's door / It ain't me babe / Ballad of a thin man / Up on Cripple Creek / I shall be released / Endless highway / Night they drove old Dixie down, The / Stagefright / Don't think twice / Just like a woman / It's alright, ma (I'm only bleeding) / Shape I'm in, The / When you awake / Weight, The / All along the watchtower / Highway '61 revisited / Like a rolling stone / Blowin' in the wind.
2LP: . . . . **CBS 22137**
MCSET: **40 22137**
2LP: . . . . **IDBD 1**

BEST OF BOB DYLAN.
LP: . . . . **SM 4123**

BIOGRAPH.
Tracks: / Lay lady lay / If not for you / Times they are a-changin' / Blowin' in the wind / Masters of war / Percy's song / Like a rolling stone / Subterranean homesick blues / Mr. Tambourine man / It ain't me babe / Million dollar bash / It's all over now baby blue / Positively 4th Street / Heart of mine / I believe in you / Time passes slowly / Forever young / Baby let me follow you down / I'll be your baby tonight / I'll keep it with mine / Times they are a-changin' / Lonesome death of Hattie Carroll / Mixed-up confusion / Tombstone blues / Groom's still waiting at the altar / Most likely you'll go your way and I'll go mine / Jet pilot / Lay down your weary tune / I don't believe you (she acts like we never have met) / Visions of Johanna / Every grain of sand / Quinn the Eskimo / Dear landlord / You angel you / To Ramona / You're a big girl now / Abandoned love / Tangled up in blue / Can you please crawl out of your window? / Isis / Caribbean wind / Up to me / Baby I'm in the mood for you / I wanna be your lover / I want you / On a night like this / Just like a woman / Romance in Durango / Senor (tales of Yankee power) / Gotta serve somebody / I shall be released / Knockin' on Heaven's door / All along the watchtower / Solid rock.
LPS: . . . . **CBS 66509**
MCSET: **40 66509**

BLONDE ON BLONDE.
Tracks: / Rainy day women Nos 12 & 35 / Pledging my time / Visions of Johanna / One of us must know / I want you / Stuck inside a mobile with the Memphis blues again / Leopardskin pillbox hat / Just like a woman / Most likely you'll go your way and I'll go mine / Temporarily like Achilles / Absolutely sweet Marie / Fourth time around / Obviously five believers / Sad eyed lady of the Lowlands.
2LP: . . . . **CBS 22130**
MCSET: **40 22130**
2LP: . . . . **DDP 66012**

BLOOD ON THE TRACKS.
Tracks: / Tangled up in blue / Simple twist of fate / You're a big girl now / Idiot wind / You're gonna make me lonesome when you go / Meet me in the morning / Lily Rosemary and the jack of hearts / If you see her / Say hello / Shelter from the storm / Buckets of rain.
LP: . . . . **CBS 69097**
MC: **40 69097**

BLOWIN' IN THE WIND.
LP: . . . . **PLP 38**
MC: . . . . **PMC 38**
LP: **2215551**
MC: **2115551**

BOB DYLAN.
Tracks: / She's no good / Talkin' New York blues / In my time of dying / Man of constant sorrow / Fixing to die blues / Pretty Peggy-O / Highway 51 blues / Gospel plow / Baby let me follow you down / House of the Rising Sun / Freight train blues / Song to Woody / See that my grave is kept clean.
LP: **32001**
MC: **40 32001**
LP: . . . . **BPG 62022**

BOB DYLAN SONGBOOK (See Under Bob Dylan Songbook) (Various artists).

BOOTLEG SERIES, THE VOLUMES 1-3 (Rare and Un-released (1961-1991)).
Tracks: / Hard times in New York Town (Live in a Minnesota hotel room (20/11/61)) / He was a friend of mine (Out-take from the album Bob Dylan (20/11/61)) / Man on the street (Out-take from the album Bob Dylan (22/11/61)) / No more auction block (Live at The Gaslight Cafe, Greenwich Village, New York City (1962)) / House carpenter (Out-take from the album Freewheelin' Bob Dylan (19/3/62)) / Talkin' Bear Mountain picnic massacre blues (Out-take from the album Freewheelin' Bob Dylan (25/4/62)) / Let me die in my footsteps (Out-take from the album Freewheelin' Bob Dylan (25/4/62)) / Rambling, gambling Willie (Out-take from the album Freewheelin' Bob Dylan (24/4/62)) / Talkin' Hava negeilah blues (Out-take from the album Freewheelin' Bob Dylan (25/4/62)) / Quit your low down ways (Out-take from the album Freewheelin' Bob Dylan (9/7/62)) / Worried blues (Out-take from the album Freewheelin' Bob Dylan (9/7/62)) / Kingsport Town (Out-take from the album Freewheelin' Bob Dylan (14/11/62)) / Walkin' down the line (Publishing demo for Witmark Publishing Company (1963)) / Walls of red wing (Out-take from the album Freewheelin' Bob Dylan (24/2/63)) / Paths of victory (Out-take from the album Times They Are A-Changin' (12/8/63)) / Talkin' John Birch paranoid blues (Live at Carnegie Hall (26/10/63)) / Who killed Davey Moore? (Live at Carnegie Hall (26/10/63)) / Only a hobo (Out-take from the album Times They Are A-Changin' (12/8/63)) / Moonshiner (Out-take from the album Times They Are A-Changin' (12/8/63)) / When the ship comes in (Piano demo for Witmark Music Publishing Company (1962)) / Time they are a changin', The (Piano demo for Witmark Music Publishing Company (1963)) / Last thoughts on Woody Guthrie (Poem recited live at Town Hall (12/4/63)) / Seven curses (Out-take from the album Times They Are A-Changin' (6/8/63)) / Eternal circle (Out-take from the album Times They Are A-Changin' (24/10/63)) / Suze (The cough song) (Out-take from the album Times They Are A-Changin' (24/10/63)) / Mama you been on my mind (Out-take from the album Bringing It All Back Home (9/6/64)) / Farewell, Angelina (Out-take from the album Bringing It All Back Home (13/1/65)) / Subterranean homesick blues (Alternate acoustic version (13/1/65)) / If you gotta go, go now (Or else you got to stay all night) (Out-take from the album Bringing It All Back Home (15/1/65)) / Sitting on a barbed wire fence (Out-take from the album Highway 61 Revisited (15/6/65)) / Like a rolling stone (Rehearsal in studio (15/6/65)) / It takes a lot to laugh, it takes a train to c (Alternate version (15/6/65)) / I'll keep it with mine (Rehearsal in studio (27/1/66)) / She's your lover now (Out-take from the album Blonde On Blonde (21/1/66)) / I shall be released (Out-take from the album Basement Tapes (1967)) / Santa-Fe (Out-take from the album Basement Tapes (1967)) / If not for you (Alternate version (1/5/70)) / Wallflower (Studio recording (4/11/71)) / Nobody 'cept you (Out-take from the album Planet Waves (2/11/73)) / Tangled up in blue (Original New York studio session for Blood On The Tracks (16/9/74)) / Call letter blues (Out-take from the album Blood On The Tracks (16/9/74)) / Idiot wind (Original New York session for Blood On The Tracks (16/9/74)) / If you see her, say hello (Original New York studio session for Blood On The Tracks (16/9/74)) / Golden loom (Out-take from the album Desire (30/7/75)) / Catfish (Out-take from the album Desire (28/7/75)) / Seven days (Live performance, Tampa, Florida (21/4/76)) / Ye shall be changed (Out-take from the album Slow Train Coming (2/5/79)) / Every grain of sand (Publishing demo for Special Rider Music (23/9/80)) / You changed my life (Out-take from the album Shot Of Love (23/4/81)) / Need a woman (Out-take from the album (4/5/81)) / Angelina (Out-take from the album Shot Of Love (4/5/81)) / Someone's got a hold of my heart (Early version of the song 'Tight connection to my heart' (25/4/83)) / Tell me (Out-take from the album Infidels (21/4/83)) / Lord protect my child (Out-take from the album Infidels (3/5/83)) / Foot of pride (Out-takefrom the album Infidels (25/4/83)) / Blind Willie McTell (Out-take from the album Infidels (5/5/83)) / When the night comes falling from the sky (Original version (19/2/85)) / Series of dreams (Out-take from the album Oh Mercy (23/3/89)).
LPS: **4680861**
MCSET: **4680864**

BRINGING IT ALL BACK HOME.
Tracks: / Subterranean homesick blues / She belongs to me / Maggie's farm / Love minus zero / Outlaw blues / On the road again / Bob Dylan's 15th dream / Mr. Tambourine man / Gates of Eden / It's alright, ma (I'm only bleeding) / It's all over now, baby blue.
LP: . . . . **CBS 32344**
MC: **40 32344**
LP: . . . . **BPG 62515**

DESIRE.
Tracks: / Hurricane / Isis / Mozambique / One more cup of coffee / Oh sister / Joey / Romance in Durango / Black diamond Bay / Sara.
LP: . . . . **CBS 32570**
MC: **40 32570**
LP: . . . . **CBS 86003**

DON'T THINK TWICE.
LP: **2215531**
MC: **2115531**

DOWN IN THE GROOVE.
Tracks: / Let's stick together / When did you leave heaven? / Sally Sue Brown / Death is not the end / Had a dream about you, baby / Ugliest girl in the world / Silvio / Ninety miles an hour (down a dead end street) / Shenandoah / Rank strangers to me.
LP: **4602671**
MC: **4602674**

DYLAN.
Tracks: / Lily of the west / Can't help falling in love / Sarah Jane / Ballad of Ira Hayes, The / Mr. Bojangles / Mary Ann / Big yellow taxi / Fool such as I, A / Spanish is the loving tongue.
LP: . . . . **CBS 32286**
MC: **4032286**

DYLAN AND THE DEAD (Dylan, Bob/ Grateful Dead).
Tracks: / Slow train / I want you / Gotta serve somebody / Queen Jane approximately / Joey / All along the watchtower / Knockin' on heavens door.
LP: **4633811**
MC: **4633814**

EMPIRE BURLESQUE.
Tracks: / Tight connection to my heart (has anybody seen my love?) / Seeing the real you at last / I'll remember you / Clean cut kid / Emotionally yours / Dark eyes / Something's burning baby / Never gonna be the same again / Trust yourself / When the night comes / Falling from the sky.
LP: . . . . **CBS 86313**
MC: **40 86313**
MC: **4678404**

FREEWHEELIN' BOB DYLAN, THE.
Tracks: / Blowin' in the wind / Girl from the North Country / Masters of war / Down the highway / Bob Dylan's blues / Hard rain's gonna fall / Don't think twice / Bob Dylan's dream / Oxford Town / Talking World War III blues / Corina Corina / Honey, just allow me one more chance / I shall be free.
LP: . . . . **CBS 62193**
MC: **40 62193**
LP: . . . . **BPG 62193**
LP: **323901**
MC: **323904**

GREATEST HITS: BOB DYLAN.
Tracks: / Blowin' in the wind / It ain't me babe / Times they are a-changin' / Mr. Tambourine man / She belongs to me / It's all over now, baby blue / Subterranean homesick blues / One of us must know / Like a rolling stone / Just like a woman / Rainy day women Nos 12 & 35 / I want you.
LP: . . . . **CBS 62847**
MC: **40 62847**
LP: **4609071**
MC: **4609074**

LP: . . . . SBPG 62847

GREATEST HITS, VOL 2: BOB DYLAN.
Tracks: / I want you / One of us must know / Gates of Eden.
LP: 62911

GREATEST HITS, VOL 3: BOB DYLAN.
Tracks: / Positively 4th Street / One too many mornings.
LP: 63111

HARD RAIN'S A-GONNA FALL, A.
Tracks: / Maggie's farm / One too many mornings / Stuck inside a mobile with the Memphis blues again / Oh sister / Lay lady lay / Shelter from the storm / You're a big girl now / I threw it all away / Idiot wind.
LP: . . . . CBS 32308
MC: 40 32308
LP: 2215541
MC: 2115541
LP: . . . . CBS 86016

HE WAS A FRIEND OF MINE.
LP: . . . . PLP 39
MC: . . . . PMC 39

HIGHWAY '61 REVISITED.
Tracks: / Like a rolling stone / Tombstone blues / It takes a lot to laugh, it takes a train to cry / From a Buick 6 / Ballad of a thin man / Queen Jane approximately / Highway '61 revisited / Just like Tom Thumb's blues / Desolation Row.
LP: . . . . CBS 62572
MC: 40 62572
LP: . . . . BPG 62572
LP: 4609531
MC: 4609534

HISTORICAL ARCHIVES VOL.1.
Tracks: / Man on the street / He was a friend of mine / Talkin' Bear Mountain picnic massacre blues / Song to Woody / Car car / Pretty Polly two trains runnin' / Ramblin' on my mind.
LP: . . . . GILP 1
MC: . . . . GIMC 1

HISTORICAL ARCHIVES VOL.2.
Tracks: / Rocks and gravels / Quit your low down ways / He was a friend of mine / Let me die in my footsteps / Death of Emmett Till, The / Stealin' / Hiram Hubbard / Blowin' in the wind.
LP: . . . . GILP 2
MC: . . . . GIMC 2

INFIDELS.
Tracks: / Jokerman / Sweetheart like you / Neighbourhood bully / License to kill / Man of peace / Union sundown / I and I / Don't fall apart on me tonight.
LP: . . . . CBS 25539
MC: 40 25539
LP: 4607271
MC: 4607274

JOHN WESLEY HARDING.
Tracks: / John Wesley Harding / As I went out one morning / I dreamed I saw St. Augustine / Drifter's escape / All along the watchtower / I am a lonesome hobo / Ballad of Frankie Lee and Judas Priest / Dear landlord / I pity the poor immigrant / Wicked messenger / Down along cove / I'll be your baby tonight.
LP: . . . . CBS 63252
MC: 40 63252
LP: . . . . SBPG 63252
LP: 4633591
MC: 4633594

KNOCKED OUT LOADED.
Tracks: / You wanna ramble / They killed him / Driftin' too far from shore / Precious memories / Maybe someday / Brownsville girl / Got my mind made up / Under your spell.
LP: . . . . CBS 86326
MC: 40 86326
MC: 4670404

LIVE DYLAN WITH THE BAND - ROYAL ALBERT HALL '66, THE.
LP: . . . . BGLP 001

MORE BOB DYLAN'S GREATEST HITS.
Tracks: / Watching the river flow / Don't think twice / It's alright / Lay lady lay / Stuck inside a mobile with the Memphis blues again / I'll be your baby tonight / All I really want to do / My back pages / Maggie's farm / Tonight I'll be staying here with you / Positively 4th Street / All along the watchtower / Mighty Quinn, The / Just like Tom Thumb's blues / Hard rain's gonna fall / If not for you / New morning / Tomorrow is a long time / When I paint my masterpiece / I shall be released / You ain't goin' nowhere / Down in the flood.
2LP: . . . . CBS 67238/9
MC: 40 67239

NASHVILLE SKYLINE.
Tracks: / Girl from the north country (With Johnny Cash) / Nashville skyline rag / To be alone with you / I threw it all away / Peggy Day / Lay lady lay / One more night / Tell me that it isn't true / Country pie / Tonight I'll be staying here with you.
LP: 32675
MC: 40 32675
LP: . . . . CBS 63601

NEW MORNING.
Tracks: / If not for you / Day of the locusts / Time passes slowly / Went to see the gypsy / Winterlude / If dogs run free / New morning / Sign in the window / One more weekend / Man in me, The / Three angels / Father of night.
LP: . . . . CBS 32267
LP: . . . . CBS 69001
MC: 4032267

OH MERCY.
Tracks: / Political world / Where teardrops fall / Ring them bells / Man in the long black coat / Most of the time / What good am I? / Disease of conceit / What was it you wanted / Shooting star.
LP: 4658001
MC: 4658004

PAT GARRET AND BILLY THE KID (Film soundtrack).
Tracks: / Pat Garret and Billy the Kid (Main title) / Workin' for the law (Cantina theme) / Billy 1 / Bunkhouse theme / River theme / Turkey chase / Knockin' on Heaven's door / Pat Garret and Billy the Kid (Final theme) / Billy 4 / Billy 7.
LP: . . . . CBS 32098
MC: 40 32098
LP: . . . . CBS 69042

PLANET WAVES.
Tracks: / On a night like this / Going going gone / Tough mama / Hazel / Something there is about you / Forever young / Dirge / You angel you / Never say goodbye / Wedding song, The.
LP: . . . . CBS 32154
MC: 40 32154
LP: . . . . ILPS 9261

PRESS CONFERENCES '86'.
LPPD: . . . . HEARTS OF 5

REAL LIVE.
Tracks: / Highway '61 revisited / Maggie's farm / I and I / License to kill / It ain't me babe / Tangled up in blue / Masters of war / Ballad of a thin man / Girl from the North Country / Tombstone blues.
LP: . . . . CBS 26334
MC: 40 26334

SAVED.
Tracks: / Satisfied mind / Saved / Covenant woman / What can I do for you / Solid rock / Pressing on / In the garden / Saving grace / Are you ready.
LP: . . . . CBS 32742
LP: . . . . CBS 86113
MC: 4032742

SELF PORTRAIT.
Tracks: / All the tired horses / Alberta no.1 / I've forgotten more than you'll ever know / Days of '49 / Early morning rain / In search of little Sadie / Let it be me / Woogie boogie / Belle Isle / Living the blues / Like a rolling stone / Copper kettle / Gotta travel on / Blue moon / Boxer, The / Mighty Quinn, The / Take me as I am / It hurts me too / Minstrel boy / She belongs to me / Wigwam / Alberta no.2.
LP: 4601121
LP: . . . . CBS 66250
MC: 4601124

SHOT OF LOVE.
Tracks: / Shot of love / Heart of mine / Property of Jesus / Lenny Bruce / Watered-down love / Dead man, dead man / In the Summertime / Trouble / Every grain of sand.
LP: . . . . CBS 85178
LP: 85178
MC: 4678394

SLOW TRAIN COMING.
Tracks: / Gotta serve somebody / Precious angel when you gonna wake me up / I believe in you / Slow train / Gonna change my way of thinkin' / Do right to me baby / When he returns / Man gave names to all the animals / Changing of the guard / New pony / No time to think / Baby stop crying / Is your love in vain / Senor / True love tends to forget / We better talk this over / Where are you tonight / Journey through dark heat.
LP: . . . . CBS 32524
MC: 40 32524

SONGS OF BOB DYLAN, THE (See under Songs of Bob Dylan) (Various artists).

STREET LEGAL.
Tracks: / Changing of the guard / New pony / No time to think / Baby stop crying / Is your love in vain? / Senor (tales of Yankee power) / True love tends to forget / We better talk this over / Where are you tonight? / Journey through dark heat.
LP: . . . . CBS 86067
MC: 40 86067

TIMES THEY ARE A-CHANGIN', THE.
Tracks: / Times they are a-changin' / Ballad of Hollis Brown, The / With God on our side / One too many mornings / North Country blues / Only a pawn in their game / Boots of Spanish leather / When the ship comes in / Lonesome death of Hattie Carroll / Restless farewell.
MC: 40 22147
LP: 32021
MC: 40 32021
LP: . . . . BPG 62251

UNDER THE RED SKY.
Tracks: / Wiggle wiggle wiggle / Under the red sky / Unbelievable / Born in time / TV talkin' song / 10,000 men / 2x2 / God knows / Handy Dandy / Cat's in the well.
LP: 4671881
MC: 4671884

Dyna Tones

LIVE IT UP.
LP: . . . . ROUNDER 9005
MC: . . . . ROUNDER 9005C

SHAMELESS.
Tracks: / Heartbreak radio / Italian shoes / Take the heat / Lean your love on me / Back for a taste of your love / Beware / Old habits die hard / Can't give you up / Shake sherry / Just like that.
LP: . . . . K 925672 1
MC: . . . . K 925672 4

TOUGH TO SHAKE.
LP: . . . . ROUNDER 9000
MC: . . . . ROUNDER 9000C

Dynamic Govenors

TURNIN' TABLES.
Tracks: / Turnin' tables.
LP: . . . . SEX 071

Dynamic Superiors

YOU NAME IT.
Tracks: / Stay away / Looking away / Many, many changes / Before the street lights come on / I can't stay away / If I could meet you / I can't afford to be poor.
LP: . . . . STML 12051

Dynamite Band

ROCKIN' IS OUR BUSINESS.
Tracks: / Big beat, The / Tonight's the night / Red for danger / Hot footin' / Hot banana / I want you to be my baby / Rockin' is our business / Latin time / Tribute to Bill Haley / Hor rod / Let em' one / Take one.
LP: . . . . CH 53

Dynarock

DYNAROCK (Various artists).
LP: . . . . SHM 3115

Dynasty

ADVENTURES IN THE LAND OF MUSIC.
Tracks: / Adventures in the land of music / I've just begun to love you / Groove control / Take another look at love / Day and night / Do me right / Something to remember / Ice breaker.
LP: . . . . SOLA 3

RIGHT BACK AT CHA.
Tracks: / Right back at cha / Check it out / Strokin / Only one, The / Questions / Does that ring a bell / Straight out / That's the way I feel about you / I can't stop loving you / All's fair in love and war.
LP: . . . . K 52419

SECOND ADVENTURE, THE.
Tracks: / Here I am / Pain, got a hold on me / Man in love, A / Give your love to me / You're my angel / Love in the fast lane / Revenge / Give it up for love / High time / That loving feeling.
LP: . . . . K 52306

YOUR PIECE OF THE ROCK.
Tracks: / You piece of the rock / I don't want to be a freak / Satisfied / When you feel like giving love / It's still a thrill.
MLP: . . . . FL 13398

Dynes, Sean

PADDY'S GREEN SHAMROCK SHORE.
LP: . . . . HRL 113
MC: . . . . CHRL 113

Dyoxen

FIRST AMONG EQUALS.
LP: . . . . ATV 17

D.Y.S.

FIRE AND ICE.
LP: . . . . TG 2981

Dysart & Dundonald

PIPE BANDS OF DISTINCTION.
MC: . . . . ZCMON 803

SKIRL O' THE PIPES (Dysart & Dundonald Pipe Band).
Tracks: / My land / Balkan hills / Wexford hornpipe / Wings / Doctor Thompson / Games day at Aboyne / Crooked bawbee / Princes Street Gardens / Desperate battle of the birds / Drum fanfare / Within a mile of Edinburgh toon.
LP: . . . . LILP 5051
MC: . . . . LICS 5051

SUPREME CHAMPIONS (Dysart & Dundonald Pipe Band).
Tracks: / Drunker piper, The / H.L.I. hornpipe / Highland brigade at Magersfontein, The / Mull of Kintyre / Flora Graham / Cock o' the North / Laird of Drumblair, The / Saffron kilt / Entry into crater / Killiecrankie / Martyrdom.
LP: . . . . LILP 5019
MC: . . . . LICS 5019

WORLD BEATERS (Dysart & Dundonald Pipe Band).
LP: . . . . GLN 1007

WORLD CHAMPIONS (Dysart & Dundonald Pipe Band).
2LP: . . . . LILP 5090
MC: . . . . LICS 5090

WORLD CHAMPIONS (STATE).
2LP: . . . . ETMPO 11/12/13

Dyson, Ronnie

MORE YOU DO IT, THE.
Tracks: / Song for you / Close to you / More you do it, The / You set my spirits free / You and me / Love won't let me wait / Lovin' feeling / Won't you come stay with me / Jive talkin'.
LP: . . . . CBS 81676

Dzata

UNDERGROUND.
LP: . . . . DHILP 10001

Dzikunu, George

KPANLOGO.
MC: . . . . BIP 401

SOCIAL & CEREMONIAL DANCE MUSIC OF GHANA.
MC: . . . . BIPMAR 001

Dzintars

SONGS OF AMBER.
Tracks: / Blow wind blow / Breaking flax / Sun moves quickly, The / Sleep my child / Song of the wind / Autumn landscape / Tomtit's message, The / Where have you been, brother? / Orphan girl in white / Di raike / Christmas masquerade / Oi hanuke / So silent is the Ukranian night / Forest shook from dancing, The.
MC: . . . . RACS 0130

E, Eazy

SEE ALL RECORDINGS (See Under Eazy E).

E Power Biggs

SCOTT JOPLIN RAGS.
LP: . . . . CBS 60269

Eager, Allen

RENAISSANCE.
Tracks: / Just you just me / For all we know / Room service blues / Equinoxe / I should care / Ladybird.
LP: . . . . UP 27 09

Eager, Vince

20 YEARS ON.
LP: . . . . NEVLP 143

Eagle Brass Band

LAST OF THE LINE, THE.
LP: . . . . GHB 170

Eagles

BEST OF THE EAGLES.
Tracks: / Tequila sunrise / Lyin' eyes / Take it to the limit / Hotel California / Life in the fast lane / Heartache tonight / Long run, The / Take it easy / Peaceful, easy feeling / Desperado / Best of my love / One of these nights / New kid in town.
LP: . . . . EKT 5
MC: . . . . EKT 5 C

DESPERADO.
Tracks: / Doolin Dalton / 21 / Out of control / Tequila sunrise / Desperado / Certain kind of fool / Outlaw man / Saturday night / Bitter Creek.
LP: . . . . K 53008
MC: K4 53008

DESPERADO/ONE OF THESE NIGHTS.
Tracks: / Doolin Dalton / Twenty one / Out of control / Tequila sunrise / Desperado / Certain kind of fool / Doolin Dalton (instrumental) / Outlaw man / Saturday night / Bitter creek / Desperado (reprise) / One of these nights / Too many hands / Hollywood waltz / Journey of the sorcerer / Lyin' eyes / Take it to the limit / Visions / After the thrill is gone / I wish you peace.
MC: K4 62033

EAGLES.
Tracks: / Take it easy / Witchy woman / Chug all night / Most of us are sad / Nightingale / Train leaves here this morning / Take the devil / Earlybird / Peaceful easy feeling / Trying / Doolin Dalton / Twenty one / Out of control / Tequila sunrise / Desperado / Certain kind of fool / Outlaw man / Saturday night / Bitter creek.
LP: . . . . K 53009
MC: K4 53009

EAGLES LIVE.
Tracks: / Hotel California / Heartache tonight / I can't tell you why / Long run, The / New kid in town / Life's been good / Seven bridges road / Wasted time / Take it to the limit / Doolin Dalton / Desperado / Saturday night / All night long / Life in the fast lane / Take it easy.
LP: . . . . K 62032
MC: K4 62032

GREATEST HITS: EAGLES VOL.2.
Tracks: / Hotel California / Heartache tonight / Seven bridges road / Victim of love / Sad cafe, The / Life in the fast lane / I can't tell you why / New kid in town / Long run, The / After the thrill is gone.
LP: 9602051
MC: 9602054

HOTEL CALIFORNIA.
Tracks: / Hotel California / New kid in town / Life in the fast lane / Wasted time / Wasted time (reprise) / Pretty maids all in a row / Try and love again / Last resort, The / Victim of love.
LP: . . . . K 53051
MC: K4 53051

HOTEL CALIFORNIA/LONG RUN, THE.
Tracks: / Hotel California / New kid in town / Life in the fast lane / Wasted time / Wasted time (reprise) / Victim of love / Pretty maids all in a row / Try and love again / Last resort, The / Long run, The / I can't tell you why / In the city / Disco strangler, The / King of Hollywood / Heartache tonight / Those shoes / Teenage jail / Greeks don't want no freaks, The / Sad cafe, The.
MCSET: 9602754

LONG RUN, THE.
Tracks: / Long run, The / I can't tell you why / In the city / Disco strangler, The / King of Hollywood / Heartache tonight / Those shoes / Teenage jail / Greeks don't want no freaks, The / Sad cafe, The.
LP: . . . . K 52181
MC: K4 52181

ON THE BORDER.
Tracks: / Already gone / You never cry like a lover / Midnight flyer / My man / On the border / James Dean / 01 55 / Is it true / Good day in hell / Best of my love.
LP: . . . . K 43005
MC: K4 43005
LP: . . . . SYL 9016

ONE OF THESE NIGHTS.
Tracks: / One of these nights / Too many hands / Hollywood waltz / Journey of the sorcerer / Lyin' eyes / Take it to the limit / Visions / After the thrill is gone / I wish you peace.
LP: . . . . K 53014
MC: K4 53014
LP: . . . . SYLA 8759

THEIR GREATEST HITS 1971-1975.
Tracks: / Take it easy / Witchy woman / Lyin' eyes / Already gone / Desperado / One of these nights / Tequila sunrise / Take it to the limit / Peaceful easy feeling / Best of my love.
LP: . . . . K 53017
MC: K4 53017

TRYING TO GET TO YOU.
Tracks: / What a crazy feeling / Trying to get to you / Don't you wanna be mine / Such a fool / I told myself / Do you need me (like I need you) / Please, please / Just right / I stole a rose.
LP: . . . . BF 15232

Eagles (60's)

SMASH HITS (MARCH OF THE EAGLES).
Tracks: / March of the Eagles / Dance on / Lonely bull, The / Desperados, The / Scarlett O'Hara / Stranger on the shore / Al di la / Exodus / Johnny's tune / Bristol express / Pipeline / Some people / Old Ned (theme from Steptoe and son) / Maigret, Theme from / Happy Joe (Theme from Comedy Playhouse) / Special agent / Hava nagila / Suki yaki / Desafinado / Theme from Station Six Sahara / Wishin' and hopin' / Come on baby (to the Floral Dance) / Moonstruck (Available on CD only) / Andorra (Available on CD only) / Theme to Oliver Twist (Available on CD only) / Telstar (Available on CD only).
LP: . . . . SEE 277

Eaglesham, Bobby

WEATHER THE STORM.
Tracks: / Weather the storm / Helen of Kirkconnel / Tramps and hawkers / Bonnie George Campbell / Rowan tree / Planxty Irwin (on 12" only.) / Cock o' the north / Athole highlanders, The / Shearing, The / She moved through the fair / Redundant Mr. Brown, The / Soor milk cairt / Curwen jig / Without me just with you.
LP: . . . . FE 033

Eaglin, Snooks

BABY YOU CAN GET YOUR GUN.
Tracks: / You give me nothing but the blues / Oh sweetness / Lavinia / Baby you can get your gun / Drop the bomb / That certain door / Mary Joe / Nobody knows / Pretty girls everywhere.
LP: . . . . FIEND 96
LP: . . . . BT 1037
MC: . . . . BT 1037C

BLUES FROM NEW ORLEANS VOL 2 (Various artists).
LP: . . . . SLP 140

DOWN YONDER.
Tracks: / Down yonder / No more doggin' / Talk to your daughter / Going to the river / Oh red / Yours truly / Travelling mood / St. Pete Florida blues / Teeny bit of your love, A / Mustang Sally / Let the four winds blow / San Jose.
LP: . . . . SNTF 752
LP: . . . . GNPS 10023

LEGACY OF THE BLUES VOL. 2 (See under Legacy of the Blues).

NEW ORLEANS 1960-62.
LP: . . . . SG 709 04

OUT OF NOWHERE.
Tracks: / Oh lawdy, my baby / Lipstick traces (on a cigarette) / Young girl / Out of nowhere / You're so fine / Mailman blues / Well-a, well-a, baby-la / Kiss of fire / It's your thing / Playgirl / West side baby / Cheetah.
LP: . . . . FIEND 146

PORTRAITS IN BLUES VOL. 1.
LP: . . . . SLP 146

POSSUM UP A SIMMON TREE.
LP: . . . . ARHOOLIE 2014

Eanes, Jim

BLUEGRASS BALLADS.
Tracks: / Where the cool water flows / Orchids of love / Just for you / Legend of the girl / On the cliff / If I had my time to live over / Sally's the girl for me / I'll pretend it's raining / Rose garden waltz / Sleeping where the roses grow / Baby blue eyes / All the good times are past and gone / Kentucky bluegrass angels.
LP: . . . . REBEL 1643
MC: . . . . REBEL 1643C

LET HIM LEAD YOU.
Tracks: / Welcome in / Crown of thorns / Jesus is my guiding light / Mother taught me how to pray / In his arms I'm not afraid / Coming of the Lord / Little house of prayer / Old Satan / Let him lead you / Candle song / When they ring those golden bells / Take me home blessed Jesus.
LP: . . . . REBEL 1673

REMINISCING.
LP: . . . . REBEL 1653
MC: . . . . REBEL 1653C

Ear Damage

PROGRESS OF HUMANITY.
Tracks: / Progress of humanity / Hunter, The / Blind hatred / Your God is dead / Police patrol / Ignorance / Red white and blue / Emotions not allowed / Burn in hell? / Skateboard blues / Euthanasia / Civielebescherming / Not normal / Radioactive future / Fashion parade.
LP: . . . . HH 009

Ear Trumpet

BRING ON THE DIRT.
LP: . . . . DTS 001

Earby Band

EARBY BAND.
Tracks: / Nibelungen / Cavatina / Nightingale / All creatures great and small / We've only just begun / Dominique / Amazing grace / In Dublin's fair city / I don't know how to love him / Copacabana / Feelings / Cowshed capers.
LP: . . . . CAS LP 012

Earcom

EARCOM 2 (See under Joy Division) (Various artists).

Eardley, Jon

JON EARDLEY-MICK PYNE (Eardley, Jon/Mick Pyne).
Tracks: / Crazy rhythm / Basin Street blues / Emily / My funny valentine / You don't know what love is / My old flame / You'd be so nice to come home to / Nightingale sang in Berkeley Square, A.
LP: . . . . SPJ LP 16

NAMELY ME.
Tracks: / Andree / Namely me / Sabam / Laugh little boy / Konigawenz / Bell and bugle / Horshoe curve.
LP: . . . . SPJ LP 17

STABLEMATES (see Haig, Al) (Eardley, Jon & Al Haig).

Earekson, Joni

JONI'S KIDS (I've Got Wheels).
LP: . . . . WST 9642

JONI'S SONG.
Tracks: / My little tune / Journeys end / Part you wrote for me / I am willing, Lord / Father lift me up / It is well with my soul / Lord you've given me so much / Joni's waltz / I am a servant / We are the reason.
LP: . . . . WST 9610
MC: . . . . WC 9610

LET GOD BE GOD.
Tracks: / I can (written by Claire Cloninger/Lynn Keesecker) / Your faithfulness / Praise song medley (Exalt His Name together/We have come/O Lord our Lord/Praise to the Lord) / Strength of the Lord / Be a window / I want to be your friend / Let God be God / Just to know / Hymn medley (I need You every hour/Precious Lord/Abide with me) / Although there were times I've stepped out of His will.
LP: . . . . WST R 9087
MC: . . . . WST C 9087

SPIRIT WINGS.
LP: . . . . WST 9621
MC: . . . . WC 9621

Earl, Ronnie

I LIKE IT WHEN IT RAINS.
LP: . . . . AN 002

PEACE OF MIND (Earl, Ronnie & the Broadcasters).
Tracks: / I want to shout about it / I wish you could see me now / Peace of mind / T Bone boogie / Wayne's blues / Bonehead too / More than I deserve / Can't keep from cryin' / I cried my eyes out / No use crying / Stickin' / Wayward angel (Only on CD).
LP: . . . . FIEND 169

RONNIE EARL AND THE BROADCASTERS (Earl, Ronnie & the Broadcasters).
LP: . . . . BT 1023

SMOKING (Earl, Ronnie & the Broadcasters).
LP: . . . . SPIN 205

SOUL SEARCHIN' (With Jerry Portnoy) (Earl, Ronnie & the Broadcasters).
LP: . . . . BT 1042
MC: . . . . BT 1042C

THEY CALL ME MR EARL (Earl, Ronnie & the Broadcasters).
LP: . . . . SPIN 125
LP: . . . . BT 1033
MC: . . . . BT 1033C

Earland, Charles

COMING TO YOU LIVE.
Tracks: / Cornbread / Take me to heaven / Good question / I will never tell / Zee funkin' space / It's the woman in you / Coming to you live / Spend the night with me.
LP: . . . . CBS 84815

IN THE POCKET.
Tracks: / Tackhead / In the alley / Grant's groove / Ballad for Mom / Good date, A.
LP: . . . . MR 5240

INFANT EYES.
Tracks: / We are not alone / Blues for Rudy / Thang, The / Infant eyes / Is it necessary?.
LP: . . . . MR 5181

MAMA ROOTS (see Coleman, George) (Earland, Charles & George Coleman).

PLEASANT AFTERNOON.
LP: . . . . MR 5201

Earle, Steve

COPPERHEAD ROAD.
Tracks: / Copperhead Road / Snake oil / Back to the wall / Devil's right hand / Johnny come lately / Even when I'm blue / You belong to me / Waiting on you / Once you love / Nothing but a child.
LP: . . . . MCF 3426
MC: . . . . MCFC 3426
LP: . . . . UNID 7280

EARLY TRACKS.
Tracks: / Nothin' but you / If you need a fool / Continental railway blues / Open up your door / Breakdown lane / Squeeze me in / Annie, is tonight the night / My baby worships me / Cadillac / Devil's right hand.
LP: 4508731
MC: 4508734

EXIT O.
Tracks: / Nowhere road / Sweet little '66 / No. 29 / Angry young man / San Antonio girl / Rain came down, The / I ain't ever satisfied / Week of living dangerously, The / I love you too much / It's all up to you.
LP: . . . . MCF 3379
MC: . . . . MCFC 3379
MC: . . . . MCLC 1904

GUITAR TOWN.
Tracks: / Guitar town / Goodbye's all we've got left / Hillbilly highway / Good

ol' boy (getting tough) / My old friend the blues / Someday / Think it over / Fearless heart / Little rock 'n' roller / Down the road / Good ol' boy (getting tough).

LP: MCF 3335

MC: MCFC 3335

HARD WAY, THE (Earle, Steve & the Dukes).

Tracks: / Other kind, The / Promise you anything / Esmerelda / Hopeless romantics / This highway / Billy Austin / Justice in Ontario / Have mercy on me / When the people find out / Country girl / Regular guy / West Nashville.

LP: MCG 6095

MC: MCGC 6095

SHUT UP AND DIE LIKE AN AVIATOR.

LP: MCA 10315

MC: MCAC 10315

Earls, Jack

LET'S BOP.

Tracks: / Let's bop / Slow down / My gal Mayann / Sign on the dotted line / Crawdad hole / They can't keep me from you / Hey Slim / Take me to that place / Fool for loving you, A / Hey Jim / When I dream / Crawdad hole / If you don't mind / They can't keep me from you.

LP: BFX 15273

Early B

FOUR WHEEL NO REAL.

LP: Unknown

GHOSTBUSTERS.

LP: Unknown

JOSEY WALES MEETS EARLY B (see Wales,Josey/Early B) (Early B/Josey Wales).

MY FRIENDS CIRCLE JAMAICA (Early B & Malibu).

LP: DSR 6876

REALLY REALLY.

LP: Unknown

SUNDAY DISH.

LP: Unknown

Early Sixties...

EARLY SIXTIES POP NUMBER ONES VOL.1 (OLD GOLD) (See Under 60's) (Various artists).

Earth & Fire

EARTH AND FIRE.

Tracks: / Memories / Seasons / Ruby is the one / Wild and exciting / Invitation / Storm and thunder / Maybe tomorrow, maybe tonight / Love of life / Only time will tell / Thanks for the love / What difference does it make / 78th Avenue / Smile / Green Park Station.

LP: 810510 1

MC: 810510 4

Earth Girls Are Easy

EARTH GIRLS ARE EASY (1989 film soundtrack) (Various artists).

LP: 925835 1

MC: 925835 4

Earth Messengers

IVORY TOWERS.

Tracks: / Hey love / Burning reggae / Parting / Ivory towers / Happiness / Contentment / Freedom for the blackman / Mad mad world / Conspirers / Reunite Jamaica / Cold blooded murders.

MC: MCT 1015

LP: MLPS 1015

Earth Opera

GREAT AMERICAN EAGLE TRAGEDY, THE.

Tracks: / Home to you / Mad Lydia's waltz / Alfie Finney / Sanctuary from the law / All Winter long / American eagle tragedy, The / Roast beef love / It's love.

LP: ED 215

Earth, Wind & Fire

ALL'N'ALL.

Tracks: / Serpentine fire / Fantasy / In the marketplace (interlude) / Jupiter / Love's holiday / Brazilian rhyme / I'll write a song for you / Master mind / Runnin' / Brazilian rhyme (interlude) / Be ever wonderful.

LP: CBS 32266

MC: 40 32266

LP: CBS 86051

BEST OF EARTH, WIND AND FIRE VOL. 2, THE.

Tracks: / Turn on (the beat box) / Let's groove / After the love has gone / Fantasy / Devotion / Serpentine fire / Love's holiday / Boogie wonderland / Saturday nite / Mighty mighty.

MC: 4632004

BEST OF EARTH, WIND AND FIRE VOL 1, THE.

Tracks: / Got to get you into my life / Fantasy / Saturday night / Love music / Getaway / That's the way of the world / September / Shining star / Reasons / Sing a song.

LP: CBS 32536

MC: 40 32536

LP: CBS 83284

COLLECTION: EARTH, WIND AND FIRE.

LP: NE 1322

MC: CE 2322

EARTH, WIND AND FIRE (CBS).

LPS: CBS 66350

EARTH, WIND AND FIRE (PICKWICK).

LP: SSP 3078

FACES.

Tracks: / Let me talk / Turn it into something good / Pride / You / Sparkle / Back on the road / Song in my heart / You went away / Love goes on / Sailaway / Take it to the sky / Win or lose / Share your love / In time / Faces.

2LP: CBS 88498

MC: 40 88498

GRATITUDE.

Tracks: / Introduction medley / Africano/Power / Yearnin' learnin' / Devotion / Sun goddess / Reasons / Sing a message to you / Shining star / New world symphony / Sunshine / Sing a song / Gratitude / Celebrate / You can't hide love.

2LP: CBS 22129

HEAD TO THE SKY.

Tracks: / Evil / Jeep your head to the sky / Build your nest / World's a masquerade / Clover / Zanzibar / Turn it into something good / You / Sparkle / Back on the road / Song in my heart / You went away / And love goes on / Sailaway / Take it to the sky / Win or lose / Share your love / In time / Faces / Got to get you into my life.

LP: CBS 32017

MC: 40 32017

HERITAGE.

Tracks: / Interlude / Soweto / Takin' chances / Heritage / Good time / Interlude / Body wrap / Anything you want / Interlude / Bird / Wanna be the man / Interlude / Close to home / Daydreamin' / King of the groove / I'm in love / For the love of you / Gotta find out / Motor / Interlude / Faith / Welcome / Soweto (reprise).

LP: 4662421

MC: 4662424

I AM.

Tracks: / In the stone / Can't let go / After the love is gone / Let your feelings show / Boogie wonderland / Star / Wait / Rock that / You and I.

MC: 40 32656

LP: CBS 32656

LP: CBS 86084

LAST DAYS AND TIME.

Tracks: / Time is on your side / They don't see / Make it with you / Power / Remember the children / Where have all the flowers gone / I'd rather have you / Mom.

LP: CBS 31761

MC: 40 31761

OPEN OUR EYES.

LP: CBS 32033

POWER LIGHT.

Tracks: / Fall in love with me / Spread your love / Side by side / Straight from the heart / Speed of love / Freedom of choice / Something special / Hearts to heart / Miracles.

LP: CBS 25120

RAISE.

Tracks: / Let's groove / Lady sun / You are a winner / My love / Evolution orange / Kalimba tree / I've had enough / Wanna be with you / Changing times.

MC: 40 32809

LP: CBS 32809

LP: CBS 85272

SPIRIT.

Tracks: / Getaway / On your face / Imagination / Spirit / Saturday nite / Earth, wind and fire / Departure / Biyo / Burnin' bush.

LP: SHM 3133

LP: CBS 81451

THAT'S THE WAY OF THE WORLD.

LP: CBS 32054

TOUCH THE WORLD.

Tracks: / System of survival / Evil Roy / Thinking of you / You and I / Musical interlude new horizons / Money tight / Every now and then / Touch the world / Here today and gone tomorrow / Victim of the modern heart.

LP: 4604091

MC: 4604094

Earthquake

8.5.

Tracks: / Finders keepers / Little Cindy / And he likes to hurt you / Savin' my love / Girl named Jesse James / Motivate me / Hit the floor / Same old story / Don't want to go back.

LP: BSERK 5

LEVELLED.

Tracks: / Lovin' cup / Emma / Kicks / Trainride / Nothing personal / Street fever / Julie Anne / Upstairs.

LP: BSERK 7

ROCKING THE WORLD.

Tracks: / Route 66 / Power glide slide / Friday on my mind / Mr. Security / Sitting in the middle of madness / Tin soldier / Head held high / Ma ma am belle.

LP: BSERK 3

Earthquake Album

EARTHQUAKE ALBUM, THE (See under Rock Aid Armenia) (Various artists).

Earthquake (film)

EARTHQUAKE (Film Soundtrack) (Various artists).

MC: VSC 5262

Earth's Answer

EARTH'S ANSWER (Various artists).

LP: LPCEL 016

MC: MCCEL 016

Earthshaker

EARTH SHAKER.

LP: MFN 13

FUGITIVE.

LP: MFN 21

MC: TMFN 21

MIDNIGHT FLIGHT.

LP: MFN 37

East

EAST (Various artists).

LP: GOOD 1

East Coast Offering

ALOHA (see Eyermann,Tim & East Coast Offering) (East Coast Offering & Tim Eyermann).

EAST COAST OFFERING.

Tracks: / Don't take your love away / Mr. Peanut / Dartangnon / Window shopping / Corilla / You and me / K.C.'s head / Funke monke.

LP: MCF 3234

MC: MCFC 3234

East European Folk

EAST EUROPEAN FOLK MUSIC.

MC: GB 004

East Of Croydon

EAST OF CROYDON (Various artists).

LP: SHAK 1

East Of Eden

SNAFU.

Tracks: / Have to whack it up / Leaping beauties for Rudy / Marcus junior / Xhorkham / Ramadhan / In the snow for a blow / Better git it in your soul / Uno transito clapori / Gum Arabic / Confucius / Nymphenburger / Habibi baby / Boehm constrictor / Beast of Sweden / Traditional.

LP: SML 1050

WORLD OF EAST OF EDEN.

Tracks: / Nymphenburger / Leaping beauties for Rudy / Marcus junior / Ramadhan (Medley) / In the snow for a blow / Better git it in your soul / Northern hemisphere / Gum Arabic / Confucius / Isadora / Jig a jig.

LP: SPA 157

East Of Java

IMP AND THE ANGEL, THE.

LP: PLASLP 18

East Side Stompers

ALGIERS STRUT 1985.

Tracks: / Bourbon Street parade / Curse of an aching heart, The / China boy / Flat foot / Algiers strut / Stevedore stomp / Savoy blues / Coney Island washboard / Double dare you / Tuxedo rag / Freddie Moore rag / Chimes blues.

LP: LC 37

ORIGINAL EAST SIDE STOMPERS, THE.

LP: LC 21S

East Side Torpedoes

COAST TO COAST.

Tracks: / Face it where it stands / Better the devil I know / Bebop / Medley, The / On such a night as this / That's all I need / Coast to coast / Pick everybody up / East end, west end / 67 97 / Sweet memory.

LP: VALP 102

Eastenders

EASTENDERS SING-A-LONG (Various artists).

Tracks: / Hello, hello, who's your lady friend: *Various artists* / Man who broke the bank at Monte Carlo, The: *Various artists* / Ship ahoy: *Various artists* / It's a long way to Tipperary: *Various artists* / I do like to be beside the seaside: *Various artists* / Pack up your troubles in your old kit bag: *Various artists* / Goodbye Dolly Gray: *Various artists* / Don't dilly dally on the way: *Various artists* / Run rabbit run: *Various artists* / Wot'cher (knocked 'em in the Old Kent Road): *Various artists* / Waiting at the church: *Various artists* / Strollin': *Various artists* / Underneath the arches: *Various artists* / Home town: *Various artists* / Lily of Laguna: *Various artists* / On mother Kelly's doorstep: *Various artists* / I'm forever blowing bubbles: *Various artists*/ Barrow boy song, The: *Various artists* / Lambeth walk: *Various artists* / Nice cup of tea, A: *Various artists*/ Daddy wouldn't buy me a bow-wow: *Various artists* / I'm Henery the eighth I am: *Various artists* / Boiled beef and carrots: *Various artists* / Any old iron: *Various artists* / My old man's a dustman: *Various artists*/ I've got a lovely bunch of coconuts: *Various artists* / Knees up Mother Brown: *Various artists* / Give my regards to Broadway: *Various artists* / Are you from Dixie: *Various artists* / If you knew Susie: *Various artists*/ Maybe it's because I'm a Londoner: *Various artists* / Hold your hand out you naughty boy: *Various artists* / Who were you with last night: *Various artists* / How ya gonna keep 'em down on the farm: *Various artists* / Baby face: *Various artists* / Four leaf cloveer: *Various artists* / Toot, toot, tootsie goodbye: *Various artists*/ Somebody stole my gal: *Various artists* / Put your arms around me honey: *Various artists* / Oh Johnny, oh Johnny oh: *Various artists* / Yes sir, that's my baby: *Various artists* / For me and my gal: *Various artists*/ Shine on Harvest moon: *Various artists* / Who's sorry now: *Various artists* / You made me love you: *Various* artists / It had to be you: *Various artists* / Some of these days: *Various artists* / Alabamy bound: *Various* artists / Waiting for the Robert E. Lee: *Various artists* / When you're smiling: *Various artists* / California here I come: *Various artists* / Swanee: *Various artists* / Roll out the barrel: *Various artists* / Row row row: *Various artists* / She'll be coming round the mountain: *Various artists*.

LP: MFP 5779

MC: TCMFP 5779

MC: ZCF 586

LP: REB 586

Easter, David

AND I DREAM (See under O'Connor, Hazel) (Easter, David/ Hazel O'Connor).

Easter Parade

EASTER PARADE (Film soundtrack) (Various artists).

Tracks: / Steppin' out with my baby: *Various artists* / Fella with an umbrella, A: *Various artists* / Shaking the blues away: *Various artists* / Medely: *Various artists* / Couple of swells, A: *Various artists* / It only happens when I dance with you: *Various artists* / Better luck next time: *Various artists* / Easter parade: *Various artists*.

LP: CBS 70288

MC: 40 70288

EASTER PARADE/SINGING IN THE RAIN (See Singing in the rain) (Various artists).

SINGIN' IN THE RAIN/EASTER PARADE (see under Singin' in the rain) (Various artists).

Easter & The Totem

SUM IS GREATER THAN THE PARTS.

Tracks: / Modern romantic / At full stretch / Dreams in isolation / Irritant urge / We fade / Distant generations / Stripped down / Acid reign / Days after.

LP: TOTEM 1

Easterhouse

CONTENDERS.

LP: ROUGH 94

MC: ROUGHC 94

WAITING FOR THE REDBIRD.

LP: ROUGH 124

MC: ROUGHC 124

Easterling, Skip

TAKING INVENTORY.

Tracks: / I'm your hoochie coochie man / Ooh poo pah doo / Little wonderful girl / Don't let him (come between us) / Pennsylvania coalyard blues / Run along to mama / All for you / Grass looks greener, The / Just one more time / Too weak to break the chains / I'm your man / I don't know / Travellin' mood / How can I forget / I'll be standing by / Keep the fire burning.

LP: CRB 1171

MC: TCCRB 1171

Eastern Dark

GIRLS ON THE BEACH (WITH CARS).
LP: DAMP 100

LONG LIVE THE NEW FLASH.
LP: GOES ON 06

Eastley, Max

NEW AND REDISCOVERED INSTRUMENTS (Eastley, Max/David Toop).
Tracks: / Hydrophone / Metallophone / Elastic aerophone / Centriphone / Do the bathosphere / Divination of the bowhead whale / Chairs story.
LP: OBS 4

Eastman Marimba Band

EASTMAN MARIMBA BAND.
LP: SRI 75108

Eastman Symphonic Wind

MARCHING ALONG.
LP: SRI 75004

Eastman-Dryden

CHANSONETTE.
Tracks: / Sometime / L'amour toujours/ l'amour / Glorianna / Firefly / Vagabond King / Adieu / High jinks / Katinka.
LP: ABQ 6562

VICTOR HERBERT SOUVENIR.
Tracks: / Suite of serenades / Karma / Souvenir / Badinage / Panamericana / 22nd regiment march / Mile modiste / Naughty Marietta / Fortune teller.
LP: ABQ 6529

Eastman-Rochester Pops

MALAGUENA.
LP: SRI 75097

MUSIC OF COLE PORTER (see Fennell,Frederick & Eastman Rochester Orch. (Eastman Rochester Orchestra/ Frederick Fennell).

Easton, Elliot

CHANGE NO CHANGE.
Tracks: / Tools of your labour / Like a wheel / Shayla / Help me / New for me / I want you / Hard way, The / Fight my way to love / Change / Wide awake.
LP: 960393 1

Easton, Sheena

BEST KEPT SECRET.
Tracks: / Telefone / I like the fright / Almost over you / Devil in a fast car / Don't leave me this way / Let sleeping dogs lie / With her radio / Just one smile / Sweet talk / Best kept man.
LP: EMC 1077951

DO YOU.
Tracks: / Do it for love / Don't break my heart / Magic of love / Don't turn your back / Jimmy Mack / Can't wait 'till tomorrow / Young lions / Kisses / Money back guarantee / When the lightening strikes again.
LP: EMC 3505

FOR YOUR EYES ONLY (Best of Sheena Easton).
Tracks: / 9 to 5 / For your eyes only / Take my time / When he shines / Modern girl / Just another broken heart / Wind beneath my wings / Machinery / We've got tonight / Strut / Ice out in the rain (remix) (Leeson/Vale.) / Telefone (Long distance love affair) / Almost over you / I wouldn't beg for water / One man woman / You could have been with me / Swear / Sugar walls.
LP: EMC 3556
MC: TCEMC 3556

LOVER IN ME, THE.
Tracks: / Lover in me, The / 101 / Cool love / Days like this / No deposit, no return.
LP: MCA 42249
MC: MCGC 6036
LP: MCG 6036

MADNESS, MONEY AND MUSIC.
Tracks: / Weekend in Paris / Are you man enough / I wouldn't beg for water / There when I needed you / Wind beneath my wings / Machinery / Ice out in the rain / I don't need your word / Madness, money and music / You do it / In the Winter / Please don't sympathise.
LP: EMC 3414
MC: TCEMC 3414

NO SOUND BUT A HEART.
Tracks: / Eternity / Still willing to try / Still in love / Wanna give my love / Last to know, The / No sound but a heart / What if we fall in love / No ordinary love / Floating hearts.
LP: EMC 3536
MC: TCEMC 3536

PRIVATE HEAVEN, A.
Tracks: / Strut / Sugar walls / Hungry eyes / Hard to say it's over / Love and affection / Back in the city / You make me nervous / All by myself / Double standard.
LP: SHEEN 1
MC: TC SHEEN 1

TAKE MY TIME.
Tracks: / Don't send flowers / Cry / Take my time / When he shines / One man woman / Prisoner, The / 9 to 5 / So much in love / Voice on the radio / Calm before the storm / Modern girl / No-one ever knows.
LP: ATAK 64
MC: TCATAK 64
LP: EMC 3354

WHAT COMES NATURALLY.
LP: MCA 10131
MC: MCAC 10131

YOU COULD HAVE BEEN WITH ME.
Tracks: / Little tenderness, A / Savoir faire / Just another broken heart / I'm not worth the hurt / You could have been with me / Letter from Joey, A / Telephone lines / Johnny / Trouble in the shadows / Isn't it so.
LP: MFP 41 5670 1
MC: MFP 41 5670 4
LP: EMC 3378

Easton, Ted

KIDNEY STEW (Easton, Ted & His Band).
LP: CLP 57

PEANUTS HUCKO WITH TED EASTON'S BAND (Easton, Ted & His Friends).
LP: CLP 21

SALUTE TO SATCHMO (Easton, Ted & His Friends).
LP: CLP 12

East-West Trading

EAST-WEST TRADING (Various artists).
Tracks: / We are very good friends: *East-West Trading Company (label)* / Johnny: *East-West Trading Company (label)*/ Alvi and the Alvietters: *East-West Trading Company (label)* / Obsession: *Camp Sophisto* / Skyliner: *Die Zwei* / Gummitwist: *Der Plan* / Grenze: *Hirnheimer* / Saigon dep lam: *Hat Voi* / Mosche bildt njet: *Strafe Feur Rebellion* / Weil die moral schlaeft: *Die Zimmermanner.*
LP: EWLP 1

Eastwood, Clint

MAKE MY DAY (see Sheppard, T.G.) (Eastwood, Clint & T.G. Sheppard).

Eastwood, Clint

AFRICAN YOUTH.
LP: TWS 33

BEST OF CLINT EASTWOOD.
LP: VSLP 5001

CLINT EASTWOOD LIVE IN LONDON.
LP: DHS 3

DEATH IN THE ARENA.
LP: CHA LP 003

JAH LIGHTS SHINING.
LP: VSLP 4034

LOVE AND HAPPINESS.
LP: BV 1001

SEX EDUCATION.
Tracks: / On the continent / Sidekick / Sweet sweet Jamaica / Whole heap a gal in a de dance / Sex education (me go deh already) / Blues night / Watch yourself Mr. Newspaperman / Lend me one a fi your girlfriend / Brother man / I'm a family man.
LP: GREL 11

STOP THAT TRAIN (Eastwood, Clint & General Saint).
Tracks: / Stop Jack / True vegetarian / Everything crash / Monkey man / H.A.P.P.Y. / Stop that train / Vote for me / Nuclear crisis / Rock with me / Shame and scandal.
LP: GREL 53
MC: GREEN 53

TWO BAD DJ'S (Eastwood, Clint & General Saint).
Tracks: / Can't take another world war / Another one bites the dust / Talk about run / Sweet sweet Matilda / Special request to all prisoner / Dance have fi nice / Gal pon the front line / Jack Spratt / Tribute to General Echo / Hey Mr. DJ.
LP: GREL 24
MC: GREEN 24

Eastwood, Kevin

BLUE MOON.
LP: NRLD 005

Easwaran, Eknath

MEDITATION.
LP: ARHOOLIE 9001

Easy Action

EASY ACTION.
Tracks: / Rocket ride / Mental dance / End of the line / Don't cry don't crack / Another Saturday night / Round round round / We go rocking / Let's lose control / Rock things out / Number one / Rock on rockers.
LP: 923973 1

Easy Club

ALTERNATIVE MEDICINE.
LP: RELS 479
MC: RECS 479

EASY CLUB, THE.
LP: ABB 1001

SKIRLIE BEAT.
Tracks: / Auchengeich / Euphemia / To India / Skirlie beat / Heilanman's umbrella, The / First time ever I saw your face, The / Doon in the wee room / Song of the clyde / Shipyard, The.
LP: RELS 483
MC: RECS 483

Easy Listening

50 ORCHESTRAL FAVOURITES (Various artists).
Tracks: / What the world needs now is love: *Goodwin, Ron & His Orchestra* / Love story theme: *Manuel & The Music of the Mountains* / She: *Pourcel, Franck & His Orchestra* / Girl from Ipanema: *Love, Geoff & His Orchestra & Singers*/ Aces high: *Goodwin, Ron & His Orchestra* / Sunrise, sunset: *Manuel & The Music of the Mountains* / Snowbird: *Franck Pourcel & His Orchestra* / Laura: *Love, Geoff & His Orchestra & Singers* / 633 Squadron: *Goodwin, Ron* & His Orchestra / Spanish eyes: *Manuel & The Music of the Mountains* / El condor pasa: *Franck Pourcel & His Orchestra*/ Shadow of your smile: *Love, Geoff & His Orchestra & Singers* / Where eagles dare, Theme from: *Goodwin, Ron* & His Orchestra / Autumn leaves: *Manuel & The Music of the Mountains* / Forever and ever: *Franck Pourcel & His Orchestra*/ Chariots of fire: *Love, Geoff & His Orchestra* / Legend of the glass mountain: *Goodwin, Ron & His Orchestra*/ Somewhere my love: *Manuel & The Music of the Mountains* / Let it be: *Franck Pourcel & His Orchestra* / Tonight: *Love, Geoff & His Orchestra* / Do you know the way to San Jose?: *Goodwin, Ron & His Orchestra* / Spanish Harlem: *Manuel & The Music of the Mountains* / Leaving on a jet plane: *Franck Pourcel & His Orchestra* / Portrait of my love: *Love, Geoff & His Orchestra* / Raindrops keep falling on my head: *Goodwin, Ron & His Orchestra* / Moon River: *Manuel & The Music of the Mountains* / Bridge over troubled water: *Franck Pourcel & His Orchestra* / Misty: *Love,* Geoff & His Orchestra / Tara theme: *Goodwin, Ron & His Orchestra* / Ebb tide: *Manuel & The Music of the Mountains*/ Make it easy on yourself: *Franck Pourcel & His Orchestra* / Love letters: *Love, Geoff & His Orchestra* / This guy's in love with you: *Goodwin, Ron & His Orchestra* / Fools rush in: *Manuel & The Music of the Mountains* / White rose of Athens, The: *Manuel & The Music of the Mountains* / Godfather love theme: *Pourcel, Franck & His Orchestra*/ When I fall in love: *Love, Geoff & His Orchestra* / Limelight: *Goodwin, Ron & His Orchestra* / Stardust: *Manuel* & The Music of the Mountains / On a clear day: *Pourcel, Franck & His Orchestra* / Time for us, A: *Love, Geoff* & His Orchestra & Singers / Bali Ha'i: *Manuel & The Music of the Mountains* (Not on CD.) / Around the world: *Love,* Geoff & His Orchestra / Magnificent Seven, The: *Goodwin, Ron & His Orchestra* / Girl with misty eyes, The: *Goodwin,* Ron & His Orchestra / Desafinado: *Love, Geoff & His Orchestra* / Elizabethan serenade: *Goodwin, Ron & His Orchestra*/ Walk on by: *Goodwin, Ron & His Orchestra.*
MCSET: TR 1566

100 MINUTES OF EASY LISTENING INSTRUMENTALS (Various artists).
MC: ZCTON 125

BEST OF THE JAMESON COLLECTION, THE (Various artists).
MC: HSC 663

EASY LISTENING BEATLES (Various artists).
Tracks: / Hey Jude: *Conniff, Ray* / Fool on the hill: *Faith, Percy Orchestra* / Yesterday: *Conniff, Ray*/ Eleanor Rigby: *Mathis, Johnny* / Something: *Nero, Peter* / Long and winding road, The: *Kostelanetz, Andre*/ Michelle: *Kostelanetz, Andre* / Ob la di ob la da: *Nero, Peter* / Let it be: *Vale, Jerry.*
LP: CBS 32664
MC: 40 32664

FEELIN' FINE (Various artists).
MC: GM 0214

FEELINGS (Various artists).
MC: GM 0226

GREEN GREEN GRASS OF HOME (Various artists).
MCSET: WW 6048

IMAGES (18 beautiful instrumentals) (Various artists).
Tracks: / What a feeling: *Royal Philharmonic Orchestra* / Up where we belong: *Royal Philharmonic Orchestra* / Greatest love of all, The: *Royal Philharmonic Orchestra* / All time high: *Royal Philharmonic Orchestra* / It might be you: *Royal Philharmonic Orchestra* / Memory: *Royal Philharmonic Orchestra* / Woman: *London Symphony Orchestra*/ And I'm telling you I'm not going: *Royal Philharmonic Orchestra* / Woman in you, The: *Royal Philharmonic Orchestra*/ America: *Royal Philharmonic Orchestra* / Dynasty, Theme from: *Royal Philharmonic Orchestra* / You've lost that loving feeling: *London Symphony Orchestra* / Loving Walter: *Royal Philharmonic Orchestra* / All creatures great and small: *Pearson, Johnny Orchestra* / Simon and Simon, Theme from: *Royal Philharmonic Orchestra* / Spy ship, Theme from: *Royal Philharmonic Orchestra* / Bridge over troubled water: *Royal Philharmonic Orchestra* / Terrahawks, Theme from: *Royal Philharmonic Orchestra.*
LP: NE 1254
MC: CE 2254

IMAGES SAMPLER (Various artists).
Tracks: / Chi mai: *Shadows* / Lonely shepherd, The: *Zamfir, Gheorghe* / Memory: *Wunderlich, Klaus* / Air on a G string: *Loussier, Jacques* / Malaguena of lecuona: *Martin, Juan* / I will return: *Springwater*/ Stranger on the shore: *Bilk, Acker* / Concierto de Aranjuez: *De Angelis, Nicolas* / Cavatina: *Williams, John* / Girl from Ipanema: *Jobim, Antonio Carlos* / Rondo russo: *Stenberg, Berdien* / Song for guy: *John, Elton.*
MC: KNMC 16001

INTERNATIONAL STARS OF TALK OF THE TOWN (Various artists).
2LP: DUO 117
LP: NTSA 501

IT'S ALL FOR YOU (Various artists).
MCSET: WW 6043

JUKE BOX COLLECTION - THIS IS MY SONG (Popular 60's ballad hits) (Various artists).
Tracks: / This is my song: *Clark, Petula* / Let it be me: *Everly Brothers* / Something's gotten hold of my heart: *Pitney, Gene* / Make me an island: *Dolan, Joe* / Anyone who had a heart: *Warwick, Dionne* / Detroit City: *Jones, Tom* / Michelle: *Overlanders* / What a wonderful world: *Armstrong, Louis* / If I only had time: *Rowles, John* / And the heaven's cried: *Newley, Anthony* / You'll answer to me: *Laine, Cleo* / Let the heartaches begin: *Baldry, Long John* / Mama: *Francis, Connie* / Single girl: *Posey, Sandy.*
LP: OG 1711
MC: OG 2711

LOVE IS ON THE AIR TONIGHT (Various artists).
Tracks: / Love is on the air tonight: *Powell, Dick* / When love comes swingin along: *Bowlly, Al* / Blue moon: *Crosby, Bob* / Cheek to cheek: *Baker, Kenny (1)* / If I had you: *Edwards, Cliff* / When did you leave heaven?: *Martin, Tony* / Beloved: *Lattimore, Harlan* / I owe you: *Regan, Phil* / Prisoner of love: *Combo, Russ* / Maybe I'm wrong again: *Crosby, Bing* / Long ago and far away: *Clark, Buddy* / Red sails in the sunset: *Ross, Lanny* / It's a sin to tell a lie: *Tracy, Arthur* / Sunday in the park: *Crumit, Frank* / Daydreaming (all night long): *Vallee, Rudy* / Everything I have is yours: *Austin, Gene* / You're the only star in my blue heaven: *Todd, Dick* / Goodnight sweet dreams, goodnight: *Como, Perry.*
LP: CHD 156
MC: MCHD 156

MAGIC MOMENTS (CBS) (Various artists).
Tracks: / Just walking in the rain: *Ray, Johnnie* / Blame it on the bossa nova: *Gorme, Eydie* / It's only a paper moon: *Sinatra, Frank* / I feel pretty: *Day, Doris* / Secret love: *Day, Doris* / Orange blossom time: *Crosby, Bing* / Some enchanted evening: *Clooney, Rosemary* / I could have danced all night: *Clooney, Rosemary* / Pennies from Heaven: *Bennett, Tony* / Jezebel: *Laine, Frankie* / Whatever will be will be: *Doris Day* / If I were a rich man: *Topol* / Misty: *Garner, Erroll* / Standing on the corner: *Four Lads* / Cry: *Ray, Johnnie*/ I'm gonna wash that man right out of my hair: *Holliday, Judy* / Party's over, The: *Holliday, Judy.*
LP: 54680
MC: 40 54680

MAGIC MOMENTS (MFP) (Various artists).
Tracks: / Magic moments: *Como, Perry* / Catch a falling star: *Como, Perry* / Shadow of your smile: *Damone, Vic* /

Light my fire: *Feliciano, Jose* / You win again: *Pride, Charley* / Make it with you: *Jones, Jack*/ Make the world go away: *Arnold, Eddy* / Without you: *Nilsson (Harry)* / We used to: *Parton, Dolly* / Distant drums: *Reeves, Jim* / That old feeling: *Benton, Brook* / Moon river: *Mancini, Henry* / Moonlight serenade: *Miller, Glenn* / Cry me a river: *Cooke, Sam* / Stormy weather: *Horne, Lena* / Solitude: *Ellington, Duke*.
LP: . . . . **MFP 5780**
MC: . . . . **TCMFP 5780**

MAGIC MOMENTS (STARBLEND) (Various artists).
Tracks: / Magic moments: *Como, Perry* / Volare: *Martin, Dean* / Heartaches by the number: *Mitchell, Guy*/ Hey there: *Clooney, Rosemary* / Love letters in the sand: *Boone, Pat* / Que sera sera: *Day, Doris* / Just walking in the rain: *Ray, Johnnie* / Passing strangers: *Eckstine, Billy & Sarah Vaughan* / Answer me: *Whitfield*, David / Man that got away, The: *Garland, Judy* / Walk hand in hand with me: *Martin, Tony* / Fever: *Lee*, Peggy / No other love: *Hilton, Ronnie* / Wanted: *Martino, Al* / Story of my life: *Holliday, Michael*/ But not for me: *Fitzgerald, Ella* / Stranger in paradise: *Bennett, Tony* / On the street where you live: *Damone*, Vic / Rock and roll waltz: *Starr, Kay* / Woman in love, A: *Laine, Frankie* / Portrait of my love: *Monro*, Matt / Around the world: *Crosby, Bing* / My prayer: *Platters* / You belong to me: *Stafford, Jo* / Island in the sun: *Belafonte, Harry* / Wedding bells: *Fisher, Eddie* / Mountain greenery: *Torme, Mel*/ Softly softly: *Murray, Ruby*.
2LP: . . . . **SLTD 17**
MC: . . . . **SLTK 17**

MELODIES FOR YOU (VOLUME 1) (Various artists).
LP: . . . . **MOR 502**

MEMORIES ARE MADE OF THIS (Various artists).
LP: . . . . **RTL 2062**
MC: **4CRTL 2062**

MISS YOU (Various).
Tracks: / I'll never mention your name / Dear Mom / Goodnight sweetheart / Goodnight soldier / Wish you were waiting for me / Miss you / Waitin' for the train to come in / Light a candle in the chapel / Wait for me Mary / I left my heart at the stage door canteen.
MC: . . . . **K 1010**

MISTY WATER-COLOUR MEMORIES (Various artists).
Tracks: / As time goes by: *Various artists* / Both sides now: *Various artists* / Sailing by: *Various artists*/ Cavatina: *Various artists* / Goodbye to love: *Various artists* / Bright eyes: *Various artists* / Ways to say goodbye: *Various artists* / Witchcraft: *Various artists* / I'm not in love: *Various artists* / Solitaire: *Various artists* / Baby I'm a want you: *Various artists* / Go, before you break my heart: *Various* artists / Eden grove: *Various artists* / Leaving: *Various artists* / Just the way you are: *Various artists*/ Someone to watch over me: *Various artists* / Strangers in the night: *Various artists* / Summer knows, The: *Various artists* / Hill Street blues: *Various artists* / Way we were, The: *Various artists*.
LP: . . . . **REC 472**
MC: . . . . **ZCM 472**
MC: . . . . **HSC 649**

MOMENTS (Various artists).
Tracks: / Sentimental journey: *Day, Doris* / There, I've said it again: *Damone, Vic* / As time goes by: *Lee*, Peggy / Fools rush in: *Benton, Brook* / Moonlight serenade: *Miller, Glenn* / Taking a chance on love: *Shore*, Dinah / You'll never know: *Mancini, Henry* / Love letters: *Cole, Nat King* / Time after time: *Wilson*, Nancy / They can't take that away from me: *Astaire, Fred* / Hello young lovers: *Como, Perry* / There are such things: *Vaughan, Sarah* / Love is a many splendoured thing: *Four Aces* / True love: *Crosby, Bing & Rosemary* Clooney / That ole devil called love: *Holiday, Billie* / Stranger in paradise: *Bennett, Tony* / Nevertheless: *Mills Brothers* / Tenderly: *Clooney, Rosemary* / I'll be seeing you: *Sinatra, Frank* / Every time we say goodbye: *Fitzgerald, Ella*.
LP: . . . . **STAR 2342**
MC: . . . . **STAC 2342**

MOONLIGHT & ROSES (Various artists).
Tracks: / Moonlight and roses: *Reeves, Jim* / Look of love, The: *Simone, Nina* / Send me some lovin': *Cooke*, Sam / In the ghetto: *Parton, Dolly* / Unchained melody: *Belafonte, Harry* / I only have eyes for you: *Horne*, Lena / And I love her: *Feliciano, Jose* / Joanne: *Nesmith, Michael* / And I love you so: *Como, Perry*/ Harry: *Howe, Catherine* / Time after time: *Damone, Vic* / Someone to watch over me: *Jones, Salena* / Boquet of roses: *Arnold, Eddy* / More than in love: *Robbins, Kate* / Just between you and me: *Pride, Charley*/ I made it through the rain: *Kenny, Gerard*.
LP: . . . . **MFP 5817**
MC: . . . . **TCMFP 5817**

MUSIC ON THE MOVE (20 EASY LISTENING FAVOURITES) (Various artists).
MC: . . . . **INTK 9004**

NICE 'N' EASY (Various artists).
Tracks: / In the mood: *Various artists* / I'd like to teach the world to sing: *Various artists* / Chirpy chirpy cheep cheep: *Various artists* / Aquarius: *Various artists* / Mozart 40: *Various artists* / Tweedle Dee, Tweedle Dum: *Various artists* / Puppet on a string: *Various artists* / Secret love: *Various artists* / Brand new key: *Various artists* / Strangers in the night: *Various artists* / Brazil: *Various artists*/ Chattanooga choo choo: *Various artists* / Guantanamera: *Various artists* / Easy to remember: *Various artists*/ Moonlight serenade: *Various artists* / Misty: *Various artists* / Amazing grace: *Various artists* / Man and a woman, A: *Various artists* / Till: *Various artists* / Raindrops keep falling on my head: *Various artists*/ Love story theme: *Various artists* / Lara's theme: *Various artists* / It's impossible: *Various artists*/ Adios: *Various artists*.
2LP: . . . . **TIMD 1**
MCSET: . . . . **TIMDC 1**

OSCAR WINNING SONGS (Various artists).
Tracks: / For all we know: *Mantovani* / Love is a many splendoured thing: *Mantovani* / Que sera sera: *Mantovani*/ Way you look tonight, The: *Mantovani* / Over the rainbow: *Mantovani* / Three coins in the fountain: *Mantovani*/ Never on Sunday: *Mantovani* / Lullaby of Broadway: *Heath, Ted* / Baby it's cold outside: *Heath, Ted*/ Call me irresponsible: *Chacksfield, Frank Orchestra* / Last time I saw Paris, The: *Chacksfield, Frank Orchestra*/ Continental, The: *Greenslade, Arthur* / Way we were: *Candler, Norman* / Raindrops keep falling on my head: *Aldrich, Ronnie*.
LP: . . . . **UNKNOWN**

RITZ RADIO FAVOURITES (VOLUME 2 - EASY LISTENING (Various artists).
LP: . . . . **RITZSP 412**
MC: . . . . **RITZSC 412**

SATURDAY SIDE OF DAVID JACOBS (Various artists).
LP: . . . . **REH 675**
MC: . . . . **ZCR 475**

SATURDAY SIDE OF DAVID JACOBS (Various artists).
Tracks: / Come back to me: *Various artists* / Folks who live on the hill, The: *Various artists* / I won't send roses: *Various artists* / Taking a chance on love: *Various artists* / Do I love you because you're beautiful?: *Various artists* / Guess who I saw today: *Various artists* / Pleasure of her company: *Various artists*/ My favourite things: *Various artists* / You've got possibilities: *Various artists* / I'm through with love: *Various* artists / So rare: *Various artists* / If love were all: *Various artists* / I get along without you very well: *Various artists* / This is it: *Various artists* / Best thing for you, The: *Various artists* / Change partners: *Various artists* / On the street where you live: *Various artists*.
LP: . . . . **REH 475**

SHOW SIDE OF DAVID JACOBS (Various artists).
Tracks: / Pleasure of your company, The: *Various artists* / I'm going back: *Various artists* / Consider yourself: *Various artists* / Woman from the man (who has everything): *Various artists* / Half a sixpence: *Various artists*/ One: *Various artists* / Willkommen: *Various artists* / Someone nice like you: *Various artists* / For once in your life: *Various artists* / Some of us belong to the stars: *Various artists* / Take a little one step: *Various artists* / Hey there: *Various artists*.
LP: . . . . **REH 523**
MC: . . . . **ZCR 523**

SOFT AND EASY Various artists (Various artists).
Tracks: / Some enchanted evening: *Mantovani* / Summertime: *Chacksfield, Frank & His Orchestra* / Nights in white satin: *Muller, Werner & His Orchestra* / Elvira Madigan: *Aldrich, Ronnie* / It must be him: *Larcarnge, Maurice*/ Summer place, A (theme from): *Mantovani* / Love me tonight: *Muller, Werner & His Orchestra* / Sweet gingerbread man: *Larcarnge, Maurice* / It's impossible: *Aldrich, Ronnie* / No other love: *Mantovani* / Close to you: *Chacksfield, Frank & His Orchestra* / Auf wiederseh'n sweetheart: *Muller, Werner & His Orchestra* / Midnight cowboy: *Aldrich, Ronnie* / What are you doing the rest of your life?: *Larcarnge, Maurice* / Man and a woman, A: *Chacksfield*, Frank & His Orchestra / Strangers in the night: *Mantovani* / Forgotten dreams: *Muller, Werner & His Orchestra*/ Man without love, A: *Aldrich, Ronnie* / Stranger on the shore: *Chacksfield, Frank & His Orchestra* / If you go away: *Larcarnge, Maurice* / Meditation: *Muller, Werner & His Orchestra* / I've grown accustomed to her face: *Mantovani*/ Windmills of your mind: *Larcarnge, Maurice* / Trains and boats and planes: *Chacksfield, Frank & His Orchestra*.
2LP: . . . . **DPA 3021/2**
MC: . . . . **KDPC 28039**

SOFT AND EASY, VOL.4 (Various artists).
Tracks: / Shadow of your smile: *Various artists* / When you wish upon a star: *Various artists* / Sweet and lovely: *Various artists* / Song sung blue: *Various artists* / Sweet Leilani: *Various artists* / Petite fleur: *Various artists* / I love you so: *Various artists* / Way you look tonight: *Various artists* / Once upon a summertime: *Various artists* / Candlelight waltz: *Various artists* / As tears go by: *Various artists*/ Tenderly: *Various artists* / I pretend: *Various artists* / Love me tender: *Various artists* / Just the way you are: *Various artists* / Candle in the wind: *Various artists* / Best thing that ever happened to me: *Various* artists / Who can I turn to: *Various artists* / How deep is your love: *Various artists* / She: *Various* artists / In the gentle hours: *Various artists* / Cast your fate to the wind: *Various artists* / Love in the open air: *Various artists* / Put your head on my shoulder: *Various artists* / Mahogany, Theme from: *Various artists* / I'm stone in love with you: *Various artists* / You'll never get to heaven: *Various artists*.
2LP: . . . . **DPA 3091**

SOFT AND EASY, VOL 2 Various artists (Various artists).
Tracks: / Born free: *Mantovani* / Folks who live on the hill, The: *Chacksfield, Frank & His Orchestra* / Send in the clowns: *Mantovani* / To wait for love: *Chacksfield, Frank & His Orchestra* / Seasons in the sun: *Botticelli* Orchestra / La mer: *Chacksfield, Frank & His Orchestra* / Scarborough fair: *Chacksfield, Frank & His Orchestra*/ If I only had time: *Larcarnge, Maurice* / Love is blue: *Mantovani* / For all we know: *Mantovani* / To sir with love: *Aldrich, Ronnie* / Fly me to the moon: *Mantovani* / Plaisir d'amour: *Larcarnge, Maurice*/ Both sides now: *Mantovani* / Air that I breathe, The: *Botticelli Orchestra* / Moon river: *Chacksfield, Frank* & His Orchestra / Way we were, The: *Aldrich, Ronnie* / Michelle: *Larcarnge, Maurice* / Killing me softly with his song: *Botticelli Orchestra* / Goin' out of my head: *Aldrich, Ronnie* / Wichita lineman: *Chacksfield, Frank* & His Orchestra / Light my fire: *Muller, Werner & His Orchestra* / Good life: *Aldrich, Ronnie* / Something stupid: *Larcarnge, Maurice* / My Cherie amour: *Larcarnge, Maurice* / Looking through the eyes of love: *Botticelli Orchestra* / First time ever I saw your face, The: *Aldrich, Ronnie* / Magic moments: *Aldrich, Ronnie*.
2LP: . . . . **DPA 3037/8**
MC: . . . . **KDPC 28064**

SOUNDS BEAUTIFUL (Various artists).
LP: . . . . **WW 1004**
MC: . . . . **WW 10044**

SOUNDS SENTIMENTAL (Various artists).
Tracks: / None but the lonely heart: *Various artists* / This nearly was mine: *Various artists* / My funny valentine: *Various artists* / Moon river: *Various artists* / Those were the days: *Various artists* / Green leaves of summer: *Various artists* / She's leaving home: *Various artists* / I'll never fall in love again: *Various* artists / Try to remember: *Various artists* / Bridge over troubled water: *Various artists* / Everyone's gone to the moon: *Various artists* / yesterday: *Various artists* / No other love: *Various artists* / For all we know: *Various artists*.
LP: . . . . **MOR 26**

THEMES ALBUM, THE (Various artists).
Tracks: / Bolero: *Hartley, Richard* / Thorn birds - love theme: *Martin, Juan & Royal Philharmonic Orchestra* / Educating Rita: *Musicale* / Only he has the power to move me: *Musicale* / Way he makes me feel, The: *Musicale*/ Who pays the ferryman: *Musicale* / Bird of paradise: *Musicale* / Reilly, ace of spies - theme: *Olympic Orchestra*/ Woman: *London Symphony Orchestra* / Nights in white satin: *London Symphony Orchestra* / Take that look off your face: *London Symphony Orchestra* / She's out of my life: *London Symphony Orchestra* / Arthur's theme: *London* Symphony Orchestra / Country diary of an Edwardian lady: *Central Concert Orchestra* / Greatest love of all, The: *Royal* Philharmonic Orchestra / Terms of endearment: *Royal Philharmonic Orchestra* / It might be you: *Royal Philharmonic* Orchestra / Up where we belong: *Royal Philharmonic Orchestra* / All time high: *Royal Philharmonic Orchestra*/ Champions: *Royal Philharmonic Orchestra* / Thorn birds: *Royal Philharmonic Orchestra* / Loving Walter: *Royal* Philharmonic Orchestra / Memory: *Royal Philharmonic Orchestra* / Major Yeates' fancy: *De Danann* / Hill street blues: *Hinde, Derek Quartet* / Jewel in the crown: *Fenton, George Orchestra* / Derry air, The: *Coulter, Phil* Orchestra / Winds of war, The: *Nuremberg Symphony Orchestra* / Chariots of fire: *Masterworks* / Cacharpaya: *Incantation*.
2LP: . . . . **ONE 1257**
MC: . . . . **OCE 2257**

THEMES AND SCREENS (Various artists).
Tracks: / Somewhere my love: *Mathis, Johnny* / Godfather love theme: *Williams, Andy* / What I did for love: *3 Degrees* / Aquarius: *Mathis, Johnny* / Tomorrow: *Rawls, Lou* / How deep is your love: *Mathis, Johnny*/ Evergreen: *Lewis, Ramsey* / Maria: *Williams, Andy* / Climb every mountain: *Bennett, Tony* / Wouldn't it be loverly: *Conniff, Ray* / Memory: *Mathis, Johnny* / Windmills of your mind: *Paul, Billy* / I don't know how to love him: *Conniff, Ray* / Born free: *Barry, John* / Up where we belong: *Lewis, Ramsey* / Last of the summer wine: *Hazelhurst, Ronnie*.
LP: . . . . **WW 2009**
MC: . . . . **WW 20094**

THEMES - ROMANTIC (Various artists).
LP: . . . . **ADL 512**
MC: . . . . **ADK 512**

THIS IS EASY LISTENING (Various artists).
MC: . . . . **CMOIR 115**

THIS IS EASY LISTENING 2 (Various artists).
MC: . . . . **CMOIR 507**

TOP 25 FROM YOUR HUNDRED BEST TUNES (Various artists).
2LP: . . . . **HBT 1**
MC: . . . . **KHBT 1**

ULTIMATE SELECTION (Various artists).
Tracks: / To all the girls I've loved before: *Various artists* / Isn't she lovely: *Various artists* / Let's do it (soap theme): *Various artists* / Star trek: *Various artists* / I won't send roses: *Various artists*/ Just for you: *Various artists* / When Mabel comes in the room: *Various artists* / I wanna be like you: *Various* artists / I just called to say I love you: *Various artists* / Memory: *Various artists* / Music maestro please: *Various artists* / How about you: *Various artists* / Let me call you sweetheart: *Various artists* / Bring me sunshine: *Various artists* / Sheik of Araby, The: *Various artists* / Swinging safari: *Various artists*/ Ballin' the jack: *Various artists* / Orchids in the moonlight: *Various artists* / Moonlight lady: *Various artists* / But beautiful: *Various artists* / Air that I breathe, The: *Various artists*.
MC: . . . . **CSUS 20**

UNFORGETTABLE MELODIES (Various artists).
Tracks: / Bridge over troubled water: *Goodwin, Ron & His Orchestra* / Never on a Sunday: *Love, Geoff & His Orchestra*/ Honeymoon song: *Manuel & The Music of the Mountains* / Snowbird: *Pourcel, Franck & His Orchestra* / What the world needs now is love: *Goodwin, Ron & His Orchestra* / Moon river: *Manuel & The Music of the Mountains* / True love: *Love, Geoff & His Orchestra* / Godfather love theme: *Pourcel, Franck & His Orchestra* / Misty: *Love*, Geoff & His Orchestra / Fool on the hill: *Goodwin, Ron & His Orchestra* / Spanish Harlem: *Manuel & The Music* of the Mountains / Forever and ever: *Pourcel, Franck & His Orchestra* / Spartacus love theme: *Love, Geoff & His Orchestra*/ Love story theme: *Goodwin, Ron & His Orchestra* / Autumn leaves: *Manuel & The Music of the Mountains* / She: *Pourcel, Franck & His Orchestra* / Ballade pour Adeline: *Love, Geoff & His Orchestra* / Walk on by: *Goodwin*, Ron & His Orchestra / White rose of Athens, The: *Manuel & The Music of the Mountains* / Blue moon: *Pourcel, Franck* & His Orchestra / Walk in the Black Forest, A: *Love, Geoff & His Orchestra* / Rhapsody on a theme by Paganini: *Goodwin*, Ron & His Orchestra / Waltz from serenade for strings: *Manuel & The Music of the Mountains* /

Summertime: *Pourcel, Franck & His Orchestra* / When I fall in love: *Love, Geoff & His Orchestra* / Elizabethan serenade: *Goodwin, Ron & His Orchestra* / Shadow of your smile: *Manuel & The Music of the Mountains* / On a clear day: *Pourcel, Franck & His Orchestra*.
2LP: . . . . **DL 1120**
MC: . . . . **TCDL 1120**

VELVET WATERS 18 instrumentals of peace & tranquility (Various artists).
Tracks: / Elizabethan serenade: *Bilk, Acker* / Ballade pour Adeleine: *Clayderman, Richard* / Long road, The: *Knopfler, Mark* (Theme from 'Cal') / Power of love, The: *Bilk, Acker* / Whiter shade of pale, A: *Shadows* / Alamo Bay, Theme from: *Cooder, Ry* / Waterfalls: *Riverside Strings* / Intermezzo from Cavalleria Rusticana (Theme from Raging Bull) / Scarborough Fair: *Williams, John* / Peaceful the night / Concierto de Aranjuez: *De Angelis, Nicolas* / Song of joy: *Clayderman, Richard* / Brahms' waltz: *Bilk, Acker* / Sleepy shores: *Riverside Strings* / Going home: *Shadows* / Over the sea to Skye: *Williams, John* / Ebb tide: *Riverside Strings* / Clair de Lune: *Various artists*.
2LP: . . . . **SMR 8507**
MCSET: . . . . **SMC 8507**

VERY THOUGHT OF YOU (Various artists).
Tracks: / Gigi: *Various artists* / Mon dimenticar: *Various artists* / Mam'selle: *Various artists* / Live for life: *Various artists* / Very thought of you: *Various artists* / Autumn in London town: *Various artists*/ Autumn leaves: *Various artists* / Romance: *Various artists* / If you go away: *Various artists* / Stronger than us: *Various artists* / Pavane: *Various artists* / Somewhere my love: *Various artists* / Unforgettable: *Various artists* / Al di la: *Various artists* / I'll never fall in love again: *Various artists* / Symphony: *Various artists*.
LP: . . . . **BM 3002**

Easy Rider (film)

EASY RIDER (Film soundtrack) (Various artists).
Tracks: / Pusher, The: *Steppenwolf* / Born to be wild: *Steppenwolf* / Weight, The: *Band* / I wasn't born to follow: *Byrds* / If you want to be a bird: *Holy Modal Rounders* / Don't Bogart me: *Fraternity of Man*/ If six was nine: *Hendrix, Jimi Experience* / Kyrie Eleison Mardi Gras: *Electric Prunes* / It's alright, ma (I'm only bleeding): *McGuinn, Roger* / Ballad of Easy Rider: *McGuinn, Roger*.
LP: . . . . **MCL 1647**
MC: . . . . **MCLC 1647**
LP: . . . . **CLALP 139**
MC: . . . . **CLAMC 139**
LP: . . . . **SSL 5018**

Easy Riders Jazz Band

RED WING (Easy Riders Jazz Band and Kid Thomas and Sammy Rimington).
LP: . . . . **GHB 189**

Easybeats

BEST OF THE EASYBEATS.
LP: . . . . **RNLP 124**

EASY AS CAN BE.
LP: . . . . **FC 019**

FRIDAY ON MY MIND.
LP: . . . . **FC 014**

FRIDAY ON MY MIND (OLD GOLD) (See under Zombies/She's not there(Old Gold).

Eat

SELL ME A GOD.
MC: **838 944 4**
LP: **838 944 1**

Eat The Rich (film)

EAT THE RICH (1987 film soundtrack) (Various artists).
Tracks: / Eat the rich: *Motorhead* / Terrorists: *Brint, Simon* / Nosher in the bar: *Eccleston, Danny*/ Arriba salsa: *Brint, Simon* / Doctor Rock: *Motorhead* / On the road: *Motorhead* / Car approach: *Brint, Simon* / Pistol in my pockets: *Various artists* / Orgasmatron: *Motorhead* / Bess: *Wurzel* / End title: *Eccleston, Danny*.
LP: . . . . **MOMENT 108**
MC: . . . . **MOMENTC 108**

Eater

HISTORY OF EATER VOL.1.
LP: . . . . **EAT 1**

Eather, Rod

BACK TO EARTH.
LP: . . . . **LRF 085**

Eating Raoul (film)

EATING RAOUL (1983 Original soundtrack) (Various artists).
LP: . . . . **STV 81164**

Eaton, Chris

VISION.
LP: . . . . **RRA R 0013**
MC: . . . . **RRA C 0013**

Eaton, Cleveland

BAMA BOOGIE WOOGIE.
Tracks: / Bama boogie woogie / West coast disco / Funky funky music / Pure love / Whammy omy / Flying high / Chitown theme / Funky cello.
LP: . . . . **MLP 3001**

KEEP LOVE ALIVE.
Tracks: / Birmingham train / I'm lonely tonight / Burnin' / I don't know / Get off / Flyin' high / Free at last / Keep love alive.
LP: . . . . **MLP 3008**

Eazy-E

EAZY-DUZ IT.
LP: . . . . **SL 57100**
MC: . . . . **BRCA 535**
LP: . . . . **BRLP 535**
MC: . . . . **ICM 2070**

E.B.C.

PIPING UP.
Tracks: / Chariots of fire / Bulgarian suite / Midnight blue / German folk songs medley / Journey to Scotland / Mary Scott / Flower of Yarrow, The / Tribute to Ireland, A / Amazing grace / Hotteterre suite / Scotland The Brave medley / Jesu joy of man's desiring / Ode to joy.
LP: . . . . **LILP 5178**
MC: . . . . **LICS 5178**

Eberhart, Richard

RICHARD EBERHART READING.
MC: **1243**

Ebony Quartet

FLYING HOME.
Tracks: / Benny Goodman suite / Bagatelle / Canonic suite / Brimpton suite / Variations on a theme of Pagnini.
LP: . . . . **MRF 85078**

E.C.

FATHERS HAVE A HOME SWEET HOME (E.C. & Orna Ball).
LP: . . . . **ROUNDER 0072**

Eccles, Clancy

FATTY FATTY (Eccles, Clancy & Friends).
LP: . . . . **TRLS 262**

PRESENTS HIS REGGAE REVUE.
LP: . . . . **HB 71**

Echo Base

BUY ME.
Tracks: / Puppet at the go-go / Peteri / Peoples world / Genius+soul=jazz / Lenny Bruce / City streets / Street called lonely / Free your mind / Out of reach.
LP: . . . . **LPDEP 9**
MC: . . . . **CADEP 9**

Echo & the Bunnymen

CROCODILES.
Tracks: / Going up / Stars are stars / Pride / Monkeys / Crocodiles / Rescue / Villiers Terrace / Pictures on the wall / All that jazz / Happy death man / Do it clean (Only on import LP.).
LP: . . . . **KODE 1**
MC: . . . . **CODE 1**

ECHO AND THE BUNNYMEN.
Tracks: / Game, The / Over you / Bedbugs and ballyhoo / All in your mind / Bombers bay / Lips like sugar / Lost and found / New direction / Bue blue ocean / Satellite / All my life.
LP: . . . . **WX 108**
MC: . . . . **WX 108C**

ECHO & THE BUNNYMEN: INTERVIEW PICTURE DISC.
LPPD: . . . . **BAK 2010**

HEAVEN UP HERE.
Tracks: / Show of strength / With a hip / Over the wall / It was a pleasure / Promise, The / Heaven up here / Disease, The / All my colours / No dark things / Turquoise days / All I want.
LP: . . . . **KODE 3**
MC: . . . . **CODE 3**

OCEAN RAIN.
Tracks: / Silver / Nocturnal me / Crystal days / Yo yo man / My kingdom / Thorn of crowns / Killing moon / Seven seas.
LP: . . . . **KODE 8**
MC: . . . . **CODE 8**

PORCUPINE.
Tracks: / Cutter, The / Back of love / My white devil / Clay / Porcupine / Heads will roll / Ripeness / Higher hell / Gods will be gods / In bluer skies.
LP: . . . . **KODE 6**
MC: . . . . **CODE 6**

REVERBERATION.
LP: . . . . **KODE 14**
MC: . . . . **CODE 14**

SONGS TO LEARN AND SING (The Singles Album).
Tracks: / Rescue / Puppet, The / Do it clean / Promise, The / Back of love / Cutter, The / Never stop / Killing moon / Silver / Seven seas / Bring on the dancing horses / Pride (On cassette only.) / Simple stuff (On cassette only.) / Read it in books (On cassette only.) / Angels and devils (On cassette only.).
LP: . . . . **KODE 13**
MC: . . . . **CODE 13**

Echoes Of Greece

ECHOES OF GREECE (See Under Greece) (Various artists).

Ecklund, Peter

PAUL LOCKHEART WITH PETER ECKLUND & FRIENDS (see under Lockheart, Paul) (Ecklund, Peter and Paul Lockheart).

PETER ECKLUND AND THE MELODY MAKERS (Ecklund, Peter & The Melody Makers).
LP: . . . . **SOS 1175**

Eckstine, Billy

BILLY ECKSTINE AND QUINCY JONES (Eckstine, Billy & Quincy Jones).
MC: **8325924**

BLOWING THE BLUES AWAY (Eckstine, Billy & His Orchestra).
LP: . . . . **ST 1015**

GOLDEN HOUR: BILLY ECKSTINE.
Tracks: / Just a little lovin' / What the world needs now is love / My Cherie amour / Taste of my tears, The / Remembering / I am yours / Maybe this time / Sophisticated lady / We've only just begun / Make it with you / If she walked into my life / Very thought of you, The / Loving arms / All in love is fair / Walk a mile in my shoes / Feel the warm / Mixed-up girl.
LP: . . . . **GH 842**

GREATEST HITS: BILLY ECKSTINE.
Tracks: / I apologise / Love me or leave me / St. Louis blues / Here comes the blues / Life is just a bowl of cherries / Tenderly / Taking a chance on love / Everything I have is yours / How high the moon / Laura / You're driving me crazy / No one but you / I left my hat in Haiti / As long as I love.
LP: . . . . **SPELP 64**
MC: . . . . **SPEMC 64**

I AM A SINGER.
LP: . . . . **KIM 1**

IMAGINATION.
Tracks: / It was so beautiful / I gotta right to sing the blues / Love is just around the corner / I don't stand a ghost of a chance / Faded summer love, A / What a little moonlight can do / Imagination / Lullaby of the leaves / I cover the waterfront / I wished on the moon / That's all.
LP: . . . . **MOIR 129**
MC: . . . . **CMOIR 129**

IRVING BERLIN SONGBOOK, (THE) (see Vaughan, Sarah) (Eckstine, Billy & Sarah Vaughan).

MR. B AND THE BAND - SAVOY SESSIONS.
Tracks: / Lonesome lover blues / Last night / Cottage for sale / I love the rhythm in a riff / Prisoner of love / It ain't like that / I'm in the mood for love / You call it madness / All I sing is the blues / Long long journey / I only have eyes for you / You're my everything / Jitney man / Blue / Second balcony jump / Tell me pretty baby / Love is the thing / Without a song / Cool breeze / Don't take you love from me / Oop bop sh'bam, the things you are / Jelly jelly / My silent love / Time on my hands / All the things you are / In a sentimental mood / Blues for sale / Serenade in blue / Solitude / Sophisticated lady.
2LP: . . . . **WL 70552**

ONCE MORE WITH FEELING.
LP: . . . . **FS 134**

SOMETHING MORE.
Tracks: / Something more / All in love is fair / Mixed-up girl / Song for you, A / Remembering / Sophisticated lady / Feel the warm / Think about things / Very thought of you, The / Thank you for the moment / Maybe this time, Mister / You've gone and got the blues.
LP: . . . . **STAXL 5007**
MC: . . . . **STAXK 5007**

STORMY MONDAY BLUES (See Basie, Count) (Eckstine, Billy & Count Basie).

TOGETHER (Eckstine, Billy Big Band).
Tracks: / Blowin' the blues away (Instrumental number.) / Deed I do (Vocal number.) / I wanna talk about you (Vocal number.) / Together (Vocal number.) / Mean to me (Vocal number.) / Without a song (Vocal number.) / Mr. Chips (Instrumental number.) / Airmail special (Instrumental number.) / Don't blame me (Vocal number.) / If that's the way you feel (Vocal number.) / Opus X (Instrumental number.) / Love me or leave me (Instrumental number.).
LP: . . . . **SPJ 100**

Eclectricity

LANGUAGE OF THE HEART.
LP: . . . . **FF 281**

Eclipse First

ECLIPSE FIRST.
LP: . . . . **IR 012**
MC: . . . . **IRC 012**

NAMES AND PLACES (Eclipse First & Scotrail Vale Of Athol Pipe Band).
MC: . . . . **IRC 013**

Econochrist

RUINATION.
LP: . . . . **VSR 8**

Ecosse, Kevin

DAYS OF LIFE, THE.
Tracks: / Days of life, The / Summer rain / Thought you didn't love me / Now / She'll never know / Perfect day / Something / What makes life worth living / Be anything / We've gotta try.
LP: . . . . **SLVR 101**
MC: . . . . **TCSLVR 101**

Eddie, John

JOHN EDDIE.
Tracks: / Dream house / Pretty little rebel / Hide out / Just some guy / Please Jodi / Cool walk / Jungle boy / Stranded / Waste me / Romance / Buster / Living doll.
LP: . . . . **CBS 26853**
MC: **40 26853**

Eddie & Sugar Lou...

EDDIE & SUGAR LOU'S HOTEL TYLER ORCHESTRA 1929-31 (Eddie & Sugar Lou's Hotel Tyler Orchestra).
LP: **E-1012**

Eddie & Sunshine

PERFECT STRANGERS.
LP: . . . . **SURLP 006**

Eddie & The Cruisers

EDDIE AND THE CRUISERS (1983 film soundtrack) (Various artists).
Tracks: / On the dark side: *Various artists* / Tender years: *Various artists* / Runaround Sue: *Various artists*/ Down on my knees: *Various artists* / Hang up my rock 'n' roll shoes: *Various artists* / Wild summer nights: *Various artists* / Boardwalk angel: *Various artists* / Betty Lou's got a new pair of shoes: *Various artists* / Those oldies but goodies(remind me of you): *Various artists* / Season in hell: *Various artists*.
LP: . . . . **SCT 25702**
MC: **40 25702**

EDDIE AND THE CRUISERS II (Eddie lives) (Various artists).
Tracks: / Runnin' thru the fire: *Various artists* / Open road: *Various artists* / Emotional storm: *Various artists* / Garden of Eden: *Various artists* / Some like it hot: *Various artists* / Just a matter of time: *Various artists* / Maryia: *Various artists* / Pride and passion: *Various artists* / NYC song: *Various artists*/ (Keep my love) alive: *Various artists*.
LP: **8420461**
MC: **8420464**

Eddie & The Hot Rods

FISH 'N' CHIPS.
Tracks: / Fish 'n' chips / Wide eyed kids / You better run / Time won't let me / Unfinished business / Another party / This is today / Farther on down the road / Call it quits / We want mine.
LP: . . . . **EMC 3344**

LIFE ON THE LINE.
LP: . . . . **ILPS 9509**

ONE STORY TOWN.
LP: . . . . **WF 023**

TEENAGE DEPRESSION.
LP: . . . . **ILPS 9457**

THRILLER.
Tracks: / Power and the glory / Echoes / Media messiahs / Circles / He does it with mirrors / Strangers on the pay phone / Out to lunch / Breathless / Take it or leave it / Living dangerously.
LP: . . . . **ILPS 9563**

Eddie & The Tide

GO OUT AND GET IT.
Tracks: / What love is all about / Runnin' wild, runnin' free / Looking for excitement / It's a gift / Call my name / One in a million / Just need a little rock / Go out and get it / This could be the one / This girl.
LP: **790 289-1**

Eddy, Duane

BEST OF DUANE EDDY.
Tracks: / Ballad of Paladin / Boss guitar / Guitar man / High noon / Rebel rouser / Deep in the heart of Texas.
LP: . . . . CDS 1109
LP: . . . . NML 1012
MC: . . . . ZCNML 1012

DANCE WITH THE GUITAR MAN.
Tracks: / Rebel rouser / Play me like you play your guitar / Lonely one, The / Movin' 'n' groovin' / Cannonball / Yep / Ramrod / Ring of fire / Ragbone / 40 miles of bad road / Dance with the guitar man / Peter Gunn / Because they're young / Some kinda earthquake / Dixie / Shazam / Kommotion / Trambone / Bonnie come back / Detour.
LP: . . . . ARA 1004
MC: . . . . ARAC 1004
LP: . . . . RD 7545

DUANE EDDY.
Tracks: / Kickin' ashphalt / Rockestra theme (Recorded in England) / Theme for something really important (Recorded in England) / Spies / Blue city / Trembler, The (Recorded in England) / Los Campaneros / Lost innocence / Rockabilly holiday (Recorded in England) / Last look back.
LP: . . . . EST 2034
MC: . . . . TCEST 2034

DUANE EDDY COLLECTION.
Tracks: / High noon / Unchained melody / Moon river / Hi lili hi lo / Love me tender / Boss guitar / Guitar man / Rebel rouser / Deep in the heart of Texas.
2LP: . . . . PDA 043
MCSET: . . . . PDC 043

FABULOUS DUANE EDDY, THE.
Tracks: / I'm walking / Twistin' 'n' twangin' / Soldier boy / Raunchy / Last date / He's so fine / Summer place, A (theme from) / Son of rebel rouser / Mr. Guitar man / More / Walk right in / Roughneck / Moonshot / Joshin' / Stranger on the shore / Sugarfoot rag / Please help me, I'm falling / All you gave to me / Country twist / Weary blues / Wildwood flower / Making believe / Window up above / Crazy arms / Have you ever been lonely? / Satisfied mind, A / Wild westerner / Precious memories / Peace in the valley / Waltz of the wind.
2LP: . . . . CR 065
MCSET: . . . . CRT 065

FOREVER.
Tracks: / (Dance with the) guitar man / Peppermint twist / Raunchy / Moanin' 'n' twistin' / Wild Watusi / Summer place, A (theme from) / Water skiing / Sugar foot rag / Twangsville / Let's twist again / Bali Ha'i / He's so fine / Deep in the heart of Texas / Wake ballet, The / Boss guitar / Rumble / Scrape, The / Walk right in / Lonely boy, lonely guitar / New hully gully / Moon river / Guitar'd and feathered / Rebel rouser / Your baby's gone surfin' / Mr. Guitar man / Ballad of Paladin / Shindig / Secret love / Twist, The.
2LP: . . . . NL 89246
MCSET: . . . . NK 89246

GUITAR MAN.
Tracks: / (Dance with the) guitar man / Fireball mail / Lonely boy, lonely guitar / Your baby's gone surfin' / Wildwood flower / Boss guitar / Rebel rouser / Ballad of Paladin / Deep in the heart of Texas / Tequila / Stranger on the shore / Swingin' shepherd blues.
LP: . . . . MFP 5777
MC: . . . . TCMFP 5777

GUITAR MAN, THE (20 classic tracks).
LP: . . . . PFP 1000
MC: . . . . PFC 1000

HAVE TWANGY GUITAR WILL TRAVEL.
LP: . . . . HAW 2160

LEGEND OF ROCK.
Tracks: / Movin' 'n' groovin' / Up and down / Rebel rouser / Drivin' home / Mason Dixon line / Cannon ball / Lonely one, The / Walker, The / Forty miles of bad road / Fuzz / Yep! / Some kinda earthquake / Because they're young / Quiet three, The / Bonnie come back / Shazam! / Secret seven, The / Kommotion / Peter Gunn / Dixie / Ring of fire / Ramrod / Rebel walk / My blue Heaven.
2LP: . . . . DLL 5003/4

MILLION DOLLARS WORTH OF TWANG.
LP: . . . . HAW 2325

MILLION DOLLARS WORTH OF TWANG VOL.2.
LP: . . . . HAW 2435

MOVIN' 'N' GROOVIN'.
Tracks: / Peter Gunn / Rebel rouser / Three thirty blues / Movin' 'n' groovin' / Forty miles of bad road / Shazam! / Some kinda earthquake / Only child / Blueberry Hill / Hard times / Avenger, The / Because they're young.
LP: . . . . ZGW 105

PETER GUNN (see under Art Of Noise) (Eddy, Duane and the Art Of Noise).

REBEL ROUSIN'.
Tracks: / This guitar was made for twangin' / Night train / One lonely girl / Batman daydream / American patrol / Wicked woman from Wickenburg / Crying again / Green berets, The / Bye bye blues / Groovy kind of love / Wishing on a star / Monday Monday / Roarin' / Sunset stripper / Evening glow.
LP: . . . . MFLP 031

SHAZAM.
Tracks: / Dance with the guitar man / Peter Gunn / Because they're young / Some kinda earthquake / Dixie / Shazam / Kommotion / Trambone / Bonnie come back / Detour (end s1) / Rebel rouser / Play me like you play your guitar / Lonely one, (The) / Movin' and groovin' / Cannonball / Yep / Ramrod / Ring of fire / Ragbone / Forty miles of bad road.
LP: . . . . PMP 1000
MC: . . . . PMPK 1000

SONGS OF OUR HERITAGE.
LP: . . . . HAW 2285

TOKYO HITS.
LP: . . . . SJET 7915

TWANGIN THE GOLDEN HITS.
LP: 26 21194
MC: . . . . TC 26 21194

TWANG'S THE THANG, THE.
LP: . . . . HAW 2236

TWANGY GUITAR - SILKY STRINGS.
LP: . . . . RD 7510

TWANGY PEAKS.
Tracks: / Trash / Puddin' / Moovin' n groovin' / Choo choo a go go - toot toot / Just to satisfy you / Around the block in 80 day (march in 'A') / Cottonmouth / If you've seen one you've seen 'em all / South Phoenix / Dream lover / Busted / I'm blue / Don't think twice / House of the rising sun / It ain't me babe / Not the loving kind / She belongs to me / All I really want to do / Houston / Love minus zero/No limit / Mr. Tambourine man / Blowin' in the wind / Swing low sweet chariot / Eve of destruction.
MC: . . . . TCEMS 1405

TWENTY TERRIFIC TWANGIES.
Tracks: / Guitar man / Deep in the heart of Texas / Stretchin' out / Blue eyes crying in the rain / Feud, The / Ballad in A / Backward swan / Our day will come / Blowin' up a storm / Ballad of Paladin / Boss guitar / Jerky jalopy / Rebel rouser / Country twist / Sunday morning rain / Miriam / Twangsville / Peppermint twist / Saints and sinners / Last dance.
LP: . . . . NL 89318
MC: . . . . NK 893138
LP: . . . . INTS 5056

TWISTIN' AND TWANGIN'.
LP: . . . . RD 27264

Eddy Duchin Story

EDDY DUCHIN STORY (Film soundtrack) (Various artists).
Tracks: / To love again: *Various artists* (Based on Chopin's E Flat Nocturne.) / Manhattan: *Various artists* / Shine on harvest moon: *Various artists* / It must be true: *Various artists* / Whispering: *Various artists*/ Dizzy fingers: *Various artists* / You're my everything: *Various artists* / Chopsticks: *Various artists*/ On the sunny side of the street: *Various artists* / Brazil: *Various artists* / La vie en rose: *Various artists.*
LP: . . . . MCL 1666
MC: . . . . MCLC 1666

Eddy, Nelson

20 GOLDEN HITS: NELSON EDDY & JEANETTE MACDONALD (Eddy, Nelson/Jeanette MacDonald).
Tracks: / Indian love call / Stranger in Paradise / Tit willow / Shenandoah / Tramp, tramp, tramp.
LP: . . . . N 22009
MC: . . . . N 42009

CHASE AND SANBORN RADIO SHOW.
LP: . . . . JN 113

DESERT SONG, THE.
LP: . . . . JN 116

GREATEST HITS : NELSON EDDY.
Tracks: / Tramp tramp tramp / Rose Marie / Mounties / At the Balalaika / Song of the Volga boatmen / Short'n'in bread / Stouthearted men / I'll see you again / Lover come back to me / My hero / I married an angel.
LP: 32312

JEANETTE MACDONALD AND NELSON EDDY (See Macdonald, Jeanette) (Eddy, Nelson and Jeanette MacDonald).

LEGENDARY (Eddy, Nelson and Jeanette MacDonald).
Tracks: / Indian love call / Rose Marie / Italian Street song / Ah - sweet mystery of life / I'm falling in love with someone / Sweetheart waltz / Will you remember / Tramp, tramp, tramp along the highway / Wanting you / Rosalie / Giannina mia / Stouthearted men / Beyond the blue horizon / Song of love / I'll see you again.
LP: . . . . PL 12468
MC: . . . . PK 12468

LOVE'S OLD SWEET SONG.
Tracks: / When I grow too old to dream / Rose Marie / 'Neath the southern moon / Deep river / Perfect day, A / Rosary, The / Thy beaming eyes / Sylvia / Dusty road / Auf wiedershehen / Smilin' through / Ah sweet mystery of life / Love's old sweet song / At dawning / Oh promise me / Hills of home / Mounties, The / Trees / Dream, A / Through the years.
LP: . . . . CHD 150
MC: . . . . MCHD 150

NELSON EDDY AND ILONA MASSEY (Eddy, Nelson and Ilona Massey).
LP: . . . . JN 126

NELSON EDDY: ON THE AIR.
Tracks: / On the great come and get it day / Romance / 'Neath the southern moon / Lover / When day is done / Indian love call / Blind ploughman, The / Shortnin' bread / It's a grand night for singing / In the still of the night / It ain't necessarily so / Get happy / Where or when / Come to the Mardi Gras.
LP: . . . . TOTEM 1035

OPERATIC RECITAL.
LP: . . . . JN 114

PHANTOM OF THE OPERA.
LP: JN124

RADIO SHOWS.
LP: . . . . JN 121

WITH FRIENDS.
2LP: . . . . JN 128

Edelhagen, Kurt

BIG BAND HITS.
Tracks: / Jumpin' at The Woodside / String of pearls / Carioca / Mood indigo / Cherokee.
LP: 2459 254
MC: 3146 254

KURT EDELHAGEN AND HIS ORCHESTRA.
LP: . . . . GELP 15017

PORTRAIT: KURT EDELHAGEN.
Tracks: / Hawaiian war chant / Down by the riverside / Sleepy lagoon / You're driving me crazy / By the time I get to Phoenix.
LP: 2664 286

SWINGTIME.
Tracks: / Goody goody / Sweet Sue / St. Louis blues / Organ grinder's swing / Harlem / Bugle call rag / Alexander's ragtime band / Back bay shuffle.
LP: 2459 253
MC: 3146 253

Edelman, Randy

CARE BEARS TO THE RESCUE (See under Care Bears).

KINDERGARTEN COP (Film Soundtrack).
LP: . . . . VS 5305
MC: . . . . VSC 5305

ON TIME.
Tracks: / Nobody made me / Please don't stop remembering / Dinner for two at Su Wing Wu / Round fourteen / Turn around / Half heaven half heartache / Tried and true / Thanksgiving prayer / Katie go / Pretty girls / Wings (London to LA).
LP: . . . . TRAIN 20
MC: . . . . SHUNT 20

PRIME CUTS.
Tracks: / Bluebird / Pistol packin' melody / I'm a dancer / Where did we go wrong / Stan the pantsman / You are the sunlight, I am the moon / Woman on your arm / Isn't it a shame / Everybody wants to call you sweetheart / June lullaby.
LP: . . . . BT 448

RANDY EDELMAN AND HIS PIANO.
LP: . . . . VCLP 2
MC: . . . . ZCVCL 2

SWITCH OF THE SEASONS.
Tracks: / Concrete and clay / Weekend in New England / Uptown uptempo woman.
LP: . . . . VCLP 010
MC: . . . . ZCVCL 010

UPTOWN, UPTEMPO - THE BEST OF RANDY EDELMAN.
Tracks: / Concrete and clay / Fresh outa love / You're the one / Slippin' away / Woman on your arm, The / Don't let go of me / Can't it all be love? / Uptown, uptempo woman / Night has a thousand eyes, The / You / Weekend in New England / Take my hand / Pistol packin' melody / Blue Street.
MC: . . . . T 601

YOU'RE THE ONE.
Tracks: / Don't let go of me / You can always buy her pearls / If this is love / Thirty years old / Night music / You're the one / Time changes people / Potato in the rain, A / My heart got in the way / All along the Rhine.
LP: . . . . BT 581

Eden

LIGHT BETWEEN WORLDS, THE.
MLP: . . . . NISHI 209

Eden, Dorothy

VOICE OF THE DOLLS, THE (Narrated by Rowena Cooper).
MC: . . . . CAB 322

Eder, Linda

VIENNA.
Tracks: / As the river runs / From this moment on / Every little thing / Love is forever / After all / Rescue me / I never knew love could be like this / Little bit of heaven, A / Before I fall / Vienna.
LP: . . . . PL 74330
MC: . . . . PK 74330

Edge, Damon

ALLIANCE.
LP: . . . . ROSE 51

GRAND VISIONS.
LP: . . . . ROSE 90

WIND IS TALKING, THE.
LP: . . . . ROSE 64

Edge (Group)

COMPLETE WORKS OF....
Tracks: / Watching you / Edge theme / Weekend return / Wallflowers / Winning streak / Isn't it strange / Hanging man / American excess / I'm cold / Friday the 17th / I give up / Let go / Take off / Here and now / Next in line / New world / Downhill / Macho man.
LP: . . . . EDGE 1

SQUARE 1.
Tracks: / Edge theme / Wallflowers / Isn't it strange / Weekend return / Hanging man / Winning streak / Friday the 17th / I give up / Take off / Here and now / Next in line / New world.
LP: . . . . FLAK 102

UNEASY PEACE.
Tracks: / When you're down the only way is up / Martha's lament / Uneasy peace / Danielle and the holy tree.
LP: . . . . CSLP 1

Edge (U2 Guitarist)

CAPTIVE (1986 film soundtrack) (Edge & Sinead O'Connor).
Tracks: / Rowena's theme / Heroine (theme from 'Captive') / One foot in heaven / Strange party, The / Hiro's theme 1 / Drift / Dream theme, The / Djinn / Island / Hiro's theme 2.
LP: . . . . V 2401
MC: . . . . TCV 2401
LP: . . . . OVED 257
MC: . . . . OVEDC 257

SNAKE CHARMER (See under Jah Wobble) (Edge/Jah Wobble/Holger Czukay).

Edgerton, Andy

COUNTRY WORLD OF....
MC: . . . . SPVP 173C

Edifanko

EDIFANKO-THE PACESETTERS (Edifanko African Super Band).
Tracks: / Nka bom / Something legeh-o / Gbenta / Blinking eyes / Moonlight Africa / Daa edifanko.
LP: . . . . EGED 12

Edinburgh...

EDINBURGH MILITARY TATTOO 1974 (Various artists).
LP: . . . . MFP 50429

EDINBURGH MILITARY TATTOO 1980 (Various artists).
LP: . . . . GLN 1020

Edinburgh, Eddie

EDDIE EDINBURGH & HIS NEW ORLEANS WILD CATS.
LP: . . . . VLP 38

Edinburgh Military

CORNEMUSE ECOSSAISE (Various artists).
Tracks: / Massed pipes and drums march: *Various artists* / Country dance: *Various artists* / Grand march: *Various* artists / Set dance: *Various artists* / Pipe

major march: *Various artists* / Quick march: *Various artists*/ Piper dance: *Various artists* / Pipes and drums in Kathmandou: *Various artists* / Scottish dance: *Various* artists / Royal Scots polka: *Various artists* / Drummers call: *Various artists* / Hills of Glenorchy: *Various* artists / Greenwood side: *Various artists* / Slow march: *Various artists* / Banks of Allan, The: *Various* artists / Amazing grace: *Various artists* / Auld Lang Syne: *Various artists* / Military fanfare: *Various artists* / Black bear, The: *Various artists* / Fanfare Drawbridge: *Various artists*.
MC: ARN 433229

Edinburgh Military

EDINBURGH MILITARY TATTOO (Various artists).
LP: GLN 1026

Edison, Harry Sweets

BEST OF HARRY EDISON.
Tracks: / Edison's lights / Ain't misbehavin' / Avalon / E / Miz Kitty's blues / Feelings / My ideal / Simply sweets.
LP: 231 0847
MC: K10 847

BLUES FOR BASIE.
Tracks: / Blues for Piney Brown / Blues for the blues / Blues for Basie / Gee baby ain't I good to you / You're getting to be a habit with me / Taste on the place / Moonlight in Vermont.
LP: 2332 082

EDISON, DAVIS & BOONE (Edison, Harry Sweets, Eddie Lockjaw Davis & Richard Boone).
LP: SLP 271

EDISON'S LIGHTS.
Tracks: / Edison's lights / Ain't misbehavin' / Avalon / E / Helena's theme / Homegrown / Spring is here / On the trail.
LP: 2310 780
MC: K10 780

HARRY 'SWEETS' EDISON & EDDIE 'LOCKJAW' DAVIS (Edison, Harry Sweets & Eddie 'Lockjaw' Davis).
LP: SLP 276

INVENTIVE MR EDISON, THE (Edison, Harry Sweets Quartet).
LP: FS 50

JUST FRIENDS (see Sims,John Haley/ Harry "Sweets" Edison) (Edison, Harry Sweets and John Haley Sims).

MEETING IN STOCKHOLM (Edison, Harry Sweets & Claes Crona).
LP: BRLP 001

OPUS FUNK VOL. 2 (Edison, Harry Sweets & Eddie 'Lockjaw' Davis).
LP: SLP 4025

OSCAR PETERSON AND HARRY EDISON (see Peterson, Oscar) (Edison, Harry Sweets and Oscar Peterson).

SIMPLY SWEETS (Edison, Harry 'Sweets' & Eddie 'Lockjaw' Davis).
Tracks: / Dirty butt blues / Feelings / One for the Count / My ideal / Simply sweets / Opus funk / Lax / Miz Kitty's blues.
LP: 231 0806
MC: K10 806

SWEET TRACKS (Edison, Harry Sweets & Jimmy Forrest).
Tracks: / Pussy Willow / Centerpiece / Indiana / If I had you / Jive at five / Imagination / Louisiana / Candy / Harriet / Sweetnings / Paradise / It happened in Monterey / Angel eyes / Sweet cakes / It's easy to remember / Twenty forty / There is no greater love / Tea for two / They can't take that away from me / Candid sweets / Ain't misbehavin' / I'm confessin' / Blue skies / Witchcraft.
LP: VJD 547

SWINGER, THE.
Tracks: / Pussy Willow / Nasty / Thought of you, The / Stroller, The / Sunday / Fairground.
LP: 2304 538

TOGETHER (See also Williams, Joe) (Edison, Harry Sweets & Joe Williams).

Edison Lighthouse

LOVE GROWS (WHERE MY ROSEMARY GOES) (OLD GOLD) (See under Honeycombs/Have I the right).

Edith Et Marcel (film)

EDITH ET MARCEL (1983 motion picture soundtrack) (Various artists).
Tracks: / La vie en rose: *Various artists* / Un homme comme les autres: *Various artists* / L'effet qu'tu m'fais: *Various artists* / C'est peut etre ca: *Various artists* / Je t'ai dans la peau: *Various artists* / Medley d'Edith et Marcel: *Various artists* / Avant toi (versailles): *Various artists* / Le fanion de la legion: *Various* artists / La Marseillaise: *Various artists* / Qu'est ce qu'on attend: *Various artists* / Pour etre heureux: *Various artists* / Insensiblement: *Various artists* / C'est un gars: *Various artists* / La priere: *Various* artists / Viens au creux de mon epaule: *Various artists* / Avant toi (Versailles): *Various artists* / Le chant d'amour: *Various artists* / Bal dans ma rue: *Various artists* / Le diable de la bastille: *Various artists*/ Margot coeur gros: *Various artists* / Comme moi: *Various artists* / C'est marveilleux (du film): *Various artists* / La fould: *Various artists* / L'homme que J'aimerai: *Various artists* / Je n'attendais que toi: *Various* artists / La mer: *Various artists* / Le club des sanc: *Various artists* / La mort de Cerdan: *Various artists* / Combat de boxe: *Various artists* / Avec toi: *Various artists*.
2LP: DUO 131
MCSET: TCDUO 131

Edith Strategy

EDITH STRATEGY.
LP: ABB 19

Editions EG (label)

ANGELS IN THE ARCHITECTURE (Various artists).
Tracks: / Gunfighter, The: *Budd, Harold* / Plateaux of mirror, The: *Budd, Harold & Brian Eno* / Place in the wilderness, A: *Eno, Roger* / Split seconds: *Bruford, Bill & Patrick Moraz* / Kliene blume irgendwo: *Roedelius, Hans Joachim*/ Delta rain dream: *Hassell, Jon/Brian Eno* / Distant village: *Brook, Michael* / Prelude and yodel: *Penguin Cafe Orchestra* / Sound of someone you love, The: *Penguin Cafe Orchestra* / Europe 80-1: *Manzanera, Phil* / 1988: *Fripp, Robert* / Chords that bind, The: *Fripp, Robert* / Meditation II: *Laraaji*.
MC: EGEDC 47
LP: EGED 47

Edmonds, Frances (aut)

ANOTHER BLOODY TOUR (See under Another Bloody Tour).

Edmonds, Noel

NOEL'S FUNNY PHONE CALLS.
Tracks: / Telephone engineer, The / Mickey mouse phone / American parking ticket / Playing cricket in prison / Booking a band to play in the nude / Telephone consumer service / Spanish holiday / Pony trekking in Wales / New driving test with extras, The / Emergency stop, The / Wrong highway code, The / Going into hospital / Launderette / Unusual gift, The / Robin Cousins fit it / Haggis shooting.
LP: REC 433
MC: ZCM 433

NOEL'S FUNNY PHONE CALLS VOL.2.
Tracks: / Ceiling, The / Washing machine, The / Impressionist, The / Lady rowers / Molecatcher / Registration plates / Cosmetic surgery / Shocking telephone, The / Crutches / Netball knickers / Mrs. Cockshot / DIY traffic lights / Siamese cat meeting, The.
LP: REC 456
MC: ZCM 456

NOEL'S FUNNY PHONE CALLS VOL.3.
Tracks: / Streaker / Nude choir, The / Polish cooker / Arab and the oranges, The / Water hoarding / Lost teeth / Vocalist required for "pelvic thrust" / Flying nuns, The / Bubble car / Thai beatle, The / R.A.F. pass / Pigeon fancier, The / Malcolm the puffin / Birth film, The.
LP: REC 488
MC: ZCM 488

Edmunds, Dave

BEST OF DAVE EDMUNDS.
Tracks: / Deborah / Girls talk / I knew the bride / A1 on the jukebox / Race is on, The / I hear you knocking / Almost saturday night / Sabre dance / Queen of hearts / Crawling from the wreckage / Here comes the weekend / Trouble boys / Ju ju man / Singing the blues / Born to be with you.
LP: SSK 59413
MC: SK4 59413

CLASSIC TRACKS 1968/1972 (Love sculpure).
Tracks: / I hear you knocking / You can't catch me / In the land of the few / Farandole / Summertime / Blues helping / Stumble, The / Down down down / Seagull / Sabre dance / Outlaw blues / Promised land.
LP: FA 413 138 1
MC: FA 413 138 4
LP: OU 2047

CLOSER TO THE FLAME.
Tracks: / King of love / Don't talk to me / Every time I see her / Closer to the flame / Stockholm / Fallin' through a hole / Never take the place of you / I got your number / Sincerely / Test of love.
LP: EST 2113
MC: TCEST 2113
LP: ATAK 172
MC: TCATAK 172

COMPLETE EARLY EDMUNDS, THE.
Tracks: / Morning dew / It's a wonder / Brand new woman / Stumble, The / 3 o'clock blues / I believe to my soul / So unkind / Summertime / On the road again / Don't answer the door / Wang-dang-doodle / Come back baby / Shake your hips / Blues helping / In the land of the few / Seagull / Nobody's talking / Farandole / You can't catch me / Mars / Sabre dance (single version) / Sabre dance / Why / People people / Think of love / Down down down / I hear you knocking / Hell of a pain / It ain't easy / Promised land, The / Dance dance dance / (I am) a lover not a fighter / Egg or the hen / Sweet little 'n' roller / Outlaw blues / Black Bill / Country roll / I'm comin' home / Blue Monday / I'll get along.
MCSET: TCEM 1406

D.E.7.
Tracks: / From small things, big things come / Me and the boys / Bail you out / Generation rumber / Other guy's girls / Warmed over kisses / Deep in the heart of Texas / Louisiana man / Paula meet Jeanne / Oe more night / Dear dad.
LP: FA 4130901
MC: TCFA 41 30904
LP: SPART 1184
MC: TCART 1184

EARLY WORKS 1968/72.
Tracks: / Sabre dance / Think of love / River to another day / Brand new woman / Farandole / You can't catch me / In the land of the few / Stumble / Wang dang doodle / I believe to my soul / So unkind / On the road again / Shake your hips / Blues helping / Down down down / I hear you knocking / Hell of a pain / It ain't easy / Promised land / Black Bill / I'm coming home / Egg or the hen / Sweet little rock 'n' roller / Outlaw blues / Blue Monday / I'll get along.
2LP: 2 C 15099546/7

GET IT.
Tracks: / Get out of Denver / I knew the bride / Back to schooldays / Here comes the weekend / Worn out suits, brand new pockets / Where or when / Ju ju man / Get it / Let's talk about us / Hey good lookin' / What did I do last night / Little darlin' / My baby left me.
LP: SSK 59404

I HEAR YOU ROCKIN'.
Tracks: / I hear you knocking / Down down down / Hell of a pain / It ain't easy / Country roll / Dance, dance, dance / Lover not a fighter / Egg or the hen / Sweet little rock 'n' roller / Outlaw blues / Blue Monday / Black Bill / I'll get along / Promised land / Sabre dance.
LP: 208228
MC: 408228

INFORMATION.
Tracks: / Slipping away / Don't you double / I want you bad / Wait / Watch on my wrist, The / Shape I'm in, The / Information / Feel so right / What have I got to do to win / Don't call me tonight / Have a heart.
LP: 205348
MC: 405348

ORIGINAL ROCKPILE, THE (Volume II).
Tracks: / I hear you knocking / Down down down / Hell of a pain / It ain't easy / Country roll / Dance, dance, dance / Lover not a fighter / Egg or the hen / Sweet little rock 'n' roller / Outlaw blues / Blue Monday / Black Bill / I'll get along / Promised land / I'm comin' home / Sabre dance.
LP: EMS 1126
MC: TCEMS 1126

REPEAT WHEN NECESSARY.
Tracks: / Girls talk / Crawling from the wreckage / Black lagoon / Sweet little Lisa / Dynamite / Queen of hearts / Home in my hand / Goodbye Mr. Good Guy / Take me for a little while / We were both wrong / Bad is bad.
LP: SSK 59409
MC: SK4 59409

RIFF RAFF.
Tracks: / Something about you / Breaking out / Busted loose / Far away / Rules of the game / Steel claw / S.O.S. / Hang on / How could I be so wrong / Can't get away.
LP: 206396

ROCKPILE.
Tracks: / Down down down / I hear you knocking / Sweet little rock 'n' roller.
LP: 5 C 038 93282

SINGLES A'S & B'S (Edmunds, Dave & Love Sculpture).
Tracks: / I hear you knocking / Blue Monday / Down down down / Brand new woman / Black Bill / Wang dang doodle / Morning dew / Seagull / People, people / Sabre dance / Stumble, The / In the land of the few / It's a wonder / River to another day / It ain't easy / I'll get along / Country roll / I'm coming home / Think of love / Farandole.
MC: TCSHSM 2032
LP: SHAM 2032
LP: SEE 282

SUBTLE AS A FLYING MALLET.
Tracks: / Baby I love you / Leave my woman alone / Maybe da doo ron ron / Let it be me / No money down / Shot of rhythm and blues, A / Billy the Kid / Born to be with you / She's my baby / I ain't never / Let it rock.
LP: INTS 5131
MC: INTK 5131
LP: PL 25129
MC: PK 25129

TRACKS ON WAX 4.
Tracks: / Trouble boys / Never been in love / Not a woman, not a child / Television / What looks best on you / Readers wives / Deborah / Thread your needle / A1 on the jukebox / It's my own business / Heart of the city.
LP: SSK 59407
MC: SK4 59407

TWANGIN'....
Tracks: / Something happens / It's been so long / Singing the blues / I'm gonna start living again if it kills me / Almost Saturday night / Cheap talk, patter and jive / You'll never get me up / I'm only human / Race is on, The / Baby let's play house.
LP: SSK 59411
MC: SK4 59411

Eduboy

ONYE MA ECHI.
LP: HBP 101

Educating Rita (film)

EDUCATING RITA (See under Hentschel, David) (Hentschel, David).

Education

MUSIC TIME (Music from BBC Schools TV series) (Various artists).
LP: REC 362

Edward II

LET'S POLKA STEADY (Edward II & The Red Hot Polkas).
Tracks: / Dawn run / Little left Lew / Swiss boy / 79th Highlanders farewell to Gibraltar / Blue blue morning / Another fine mess / Walls of Butlins, The / Mr Prime's polka / 3 hand reel / Sophie Bourbon's hornpipe.
LP: COOK 007
MC: COOKC 007

TWO STEPS TO HEAVEN (With the Mad professor) (Edward II & The Red Hot Polkas).
Tracks: / Bjorn again polka / Swing easy / Untitled polka / Steamboats, The / Lover's two step / Pomp and pride / Queen's jig / Cliffhanger / Staffordshire hornpipe / Jenny Lind / Stack of wheat (CD only.) / Brimfield hornpipe (CD only.) / Swedish polka (CD only.) / Two step to heaven (CD only.).
LP: COOK 019
MC: COOKC 019

Edward II (King)

EDWARD II (see under Marlowe, Christopher) (Various artists).

Edward, Jim

JIM EDWARD, MAXINE & RONNIE BROWN (Edward, Jim/Maxine & Ronnie Brown).
LP: HAT 3090
MC: HATC 3090

Edward, John

BLUE RIDGE (Edward, John & The Seldom Scene).
Tracks: / Don't this road look rough and rocky / How long have I been waiting for you / Blue ridge / Seven daffodils / Sunshine / Only a hobo / God gave you to me / Little hands / I don't believe I'll stay here anymore / Don't crawfish me baby.
LP: SH 3747
MC: ZCSH 3747

Edwards, Alf

FIRST PERSON (Edwards, Alf Concertina/Swarbrick, Dave).
Tracks: / Four drunken maidens / St. James's hospital / Kelly gang, The / I wish my love / Jack Orion / Lover's ghost, The / Rocking the cradle / Drover's dream, The / Short jacket and white trousers / Sovay, the female highwayman / Reynardine / Farewell Nancy / Fanny Blair / Shickered as he could be.
LP: 12T 118

Edwards, Bill

COUNTRY SOUNDS.
LP: . . . . **LKLP 6581**

Edwards, Charles

GOOD ROCKIN' CHARLES.
LP: . . . . **MR.BLUES 7601**

Edwards, Cliff

CLIFF EDWARDS & HIS HOT COMBINATION (Edwards, Cliff & His Hot Combination).
LP: . . . . **FV 203**

FASCINATIN' RHYTHM.
Tracks: / Fascinating rhythm / Object of my affection, The / Down home in Tennessee / Georgia on my mind / Ain't misbehavin' / Me and my shadow / Mean to me / It all depends on you / Back in your own back yard / Sunday / I can't get the one I want / St Louis blues / Waiting for the Evening Mail / It all belongs to me / You're driving me crazy / Just you, just me / Say it again / Little you, a little me, A / After you've gone.
LP: . . . . **TOTEM 1045**

HOTTEST MAN IN TOWN, THE.
Tracks: / That's my weakness now / Sing a happy little thing / I'll see you in my dreams / My red hot gal / I can't give you anything but love / He's the hottest man in town / Who takes care of the caretaker's daughter? / It had to be you / Paddlin' Madelin' home / Just like a melody out of the sky / Halfway to heaven / Singin' in the rain / Fascinating rhythm / Reaching fo. someone (and not finding anyone there) / Mary Ann / Anything you say / Singing a song to the stars / It goes like this, that funny melody / If you could land her on the old veranda / Hang on to me / Stack o lee.
LP: . . . . **AJA 5010**
MC: . . . . **ZC AJA 5010**

I WANT A GIRL (Edwards, Cliff (Ukelele Ike)).
Tracks: / I want a girl / For me and my gal / Toot, toot, tootsie / When my sugar walks down the street / I want to call you sweet mama / Yaaka hula hickey dula / Good little me, bad little you / Somebody stole my gal / Mandy / Margie / If you knew Susie / K-K-K-Katy / My little girl / Mary Ann / Paddlin' Madelin' home / Walkin' my baby back home / Sleepy time gal.
LP: . . . . **TOTEM 1014**

I'M A BEAR IN A LADY'S BOUDOIR.
LP: . . . . **L 1047**

SHAKIN' THE BLUES AWAY.
Tracks: / Singin' in the rain / Shakin' the blues away / Alabamy bound / I feel like a feather in the breeze / Everybody step / Indiana / I found a new baby / I'm gonna sit right down & write myself a letter / Yes Sir, thats my baby / Way down yonder in New Orleans / There'll be some changes made / Blues my naughty sweetie gives to me, The / Darktown strutters' ball / My baby don't mean maybe / Hang on to me / When you wore a tulip.
LP: . . . . **TOTEM 1005**

Edwards, David

DAVID EDWARDS.
Tracks: / Best friend / Rather be wrong / Commercial suicide / Nagging optimism / Hollywood high / Getaway / Kicks / Disposable love / Tongue is a fire, The / Don't ever say / Not going to fall away / Song of wholeness.
LP: . . . . **MYR 1100**
MC: . . . . **MC 1100**

Edwards, Dennis

COOLIN' OUT.
Tracks: / Try a little tenderness / State of limbo / No such thing / Amanda / Why do people fall in love / Givin' so much / Coolin' out / Breakin' loose / Wrap you.
LP: . . . . **ZL 72390**
MC: . . . . **ZK 72390**

DON'T LOOK ANY FURTHER.
Tracks: / I'm up for you / Don't look any further / (You're my) aphrodisiac / Can't fight it / Another place in time / Shake hands (come out dancin') / I though I could handle it / Just like you / Let's go up.
LP: . . . . **ZL 72148**
MC: . . . . **ZK 72148**
LP: . . . . **WL 72625**
MC: . . . . **WK 72625**

Edwards, Dorothy

ALL ABOUT MY NAUGHTY LITTLE SISTER (Kendall, Felicity (nar)).
MC: . . . . **TC LFP 7013**
MCSET: . . . . **LFP 7334**

EQUALITY OF LOVE.
MCSET: . . . . **MRC 1031**

MORE NAUGHTY LITTLE SISTER STORIES (See also Maggie McCarthy).
MC: **881727**

Edwards, Eddie

EDDIE EDWARDS ORIGINAL DIXELAND JAZZ BAND.
LP: **6.26170**

Edwards, Hank

I'M SO LONESOME I COULD CRY.
Tracks: / I'm so lonesome I could cry / I watched my dreamworld crumble like clay / Everybody's rockin' / Settin' the woods on fire / There'll be no teardrops tonight / Alabama jailhouse / Live and let live / What's the matter with the mill / Teenage boogie / Letters have no arms / I'm blue, I'm lonesome / Long gone lonesome blues.
LP: . . . . **SJLP 576**

REAL THING, THE.
LP: . . . . **SJLP 586**

Edwards, Jackie

BEFORE THE NEXT TEARDROP FALLS.
LP: . . . . **TWS 928**

COME TO ME SOFTLY.
LP: . . . . **TDWD 10**

LET'S FALL IN LOVE.
LP: . . . . **TDWD 3**

ORIGINAL MR.COOL RULER, THE.
Tracks: / Do it sweet / Angel of love / My lady.
LP: . . . . **VSLP 4019**

SINCERELY.
LP: . . . . **TRLS 158**

Edwards, Jonathan

DARLENE REMEMBERS DUKE, JONATHAN PLAYS FATS (9"Great songs murdered by the non-great") (Edwards, Jonathan & Darlene).
Tracks: / Honeysuckle rose / I'm gonna sit right down and write myself a letter / Ain't misbehavin' / Black and blue / Keepin' out of mischief now / I've got a feeling I'm falling / Do nothing till you hear from me / Take the 'A' train / I'm beginning to see the light / Sophisticated lady / Don't get around much anymore / Mood indigo.
LP: . . . . **COR 117**

JONATHAN & DARLENE EDWARDS IN PARIS ("Grammy Award-winning comedy album") (Edwards, Jonathan & Darlene).
Tracks: / I love Paris / Valentine / Boulevard of broken dreams / La vie en rose / River Seine, The / April in Paris / Poor people of Paris, The / Last time I saw Paris, The / Autumn leaves / Paris in the spring / Mademoiselle de Paris / Darling, je vous aime beaucoup.
LP: . . . . **COR 103**

PIANO ARTISTRY OF JONATHAN EDWARDS, THE ("Jonathan and Darlene's original masterpiece") (Edwards, Jonathan & Darlene).
Tracks: / It might as well be spring / Poor butterfly / Autumn in New York / Nola / Stardust / It's magic / Sunday, Monday or always / Jealousy / Cocktails for two / Dizzy fingers / Three coins in the fountain / You're blase.
LP: . . . . **COR 104**

SING ALONG WITH JONATHAN & DARLENE EDWARDS ("Only the chorus is for real") (Edwards, Jonathan & Darlene).
Tracks: / Alabamy bound / By the light of the silvery moon / Be my little baby bumble bee / Pretty baby / For me and my gal / Tiptoe through the tulips / That certain party / Object of my affection, The / Moonlight bay / Five foot two, eyes of blue.
LP: . . . . **COR 120**
LP: . . . . **INTS 5100**
MC: . . . . **INTK 5100**

SONGS FOR SHEIKS AND FLAPPERS ("Jonathan and Darlene loose in the Roaring Twenties") (Edwards, Jonathan & Darlene).
Tracks: / Crazy words, crazy tune / Moonlight on the Ganges / Deep purple / Carioca / Button up your overcoat / Who? / Why was I born? / I wanna be loved by you / Flapperette / Varsity drag.
LP: . . . . **COR 122**

Edwards, Rupie

DUB CLASSIC.
LP: . . . . **SUC 175**

HIT PICK VOL.1.
LP: . . . . **SUCCESS 176**

IRE FEELINGS.
Tracks: / Wanderer, The / Dub master / Rasta Dreadlocks / Free the wind / Wandering dub / Feeling horn / Dub master special / Spangy / Rasta Dreadlocks dub / What can I do / Feeling time / Ten dread commandment.
LP: . . . . **TRLS 281**
MC: . . . . **TELS 280**
LP: . . . . **CTLP 106**

LET THERE BE VERSION.
LP: . . . . **TRLS 280**

PLEASURE AND PAIN.
Tracks: / Sometime / Just when I decide to change / I believe in you / I won't forget you / Your eyes are dreaming / Oh Donna / Sincerely / Blue moon / Vow, The / Goodnight my love / Dream dream dream / This is my story.
LP: . . . . **SUCCESS 188**

Edwards, Sandra

DON'T LOOK ANY FURTHER (see Walker,Bryon) (Edwards, Sandra/Bryon Walker).

Edwards, Teddy

GOOD GRAVY (Edwards, Teddy Quartet).
LP: . . . . **SJP 139**

OUT OF THIS WORLD (Edwards, Teddy Quartet).
LP: . . . . **SCS 1147**

TEDDY'S READY!.
Tracks: / Blues in G / Scrapple from the apple / What's new / You name it / Take the 'A' train / Sermon / Higgins hideaway.
LP: **1007 583**
LP: . . . . **COP 003**

Edwards, Terry

MARTY ROBBINS SONGBOOK.
Tracks: / Big iron / Cool water / Devil woman / Streets of Laredo / El Paso / Singing the blues / Story of my life.
MC: . . . . **AIM 112**

SLIM WHITMAN SONGBOOK (VOL.2), THE.
Tracks: / Tell me / Tumbling tumbleweeds / We stood at the altar / Love sick blues / Mockin' Bird Hill.
MC: . . . . **AIM 116**

Edwards, Tibby

FLIP, FLOP AND FLY.
Tracks: / Flip flop and fly / Play it cool man play it cool / There ain't no better time / Shift gears / You made a believer out of me / Long time ago, A / C'est si tout / It'll be a long long time / Too proud to wear your name / Try to understand / Just a few more tears / What has become of you / Mine forever / If you love me (let me know) / That's how I was lost / Cry cry darlin'.
LP: . . . . **BFX 15180**

Edwards, Tommy

HIS TOP HITS.
MC: **826**

IT'S ALL IN THE GAME (See under Marvin Rainwater - Whole Lotta Woman).

Eek-A-Mouse

ASSASSINATOR.
Tracks: / Assassinator / Gunshot a cry / Crimes / Born traveller / Peeni walli / Triple love / Safari / Bad friday / Posse / Some a holla some a bawl.
LP: . . . . **RAS 3006**
LP: . . . . **GREL 86**
MC: . . . . **GREEN 86**

EEK A MOMICS.
LP: . . . . **RAS 3033**

KING AND I.
Tracks: / Skull ah sea side / Juicy juicy & weedle weedle / Now I know / Fry dumpling / Me did deh deh / Macho man / I like them all / Mi beetheren roach / It was my land.
LP: . . . . **OSLP 1001**
LP: . . . . **RAS 3016**

MICHIGAN & SMILEY LIVE AT REGGAE SUNSPLASH.
LP: . . . . **VSLP 8906**
LP: . . . . **RS 8914**

MOUSE AND THE MAN, THE.
Tracks: / Hitler / Stadium hot / Struggle / Mouse and the man, The / Modelling queen / Terrorists in the city / Schoolboy / Sexy girl / Pretty city / Maybe lady.
LP: . . . . **GREL 56**
MC: . . . . **GREEN 56**

MOUSEKETEER.
Tracks: / Queen Elizabeth / Star, daily news or cleaner / Atlantis lover / Palaving / Treason / Anarexol / Chip out / Wild like a tiger / Don't run and cry / How I got my name.
LP: . . . . **GREL 65**
MC: . . . . **GREEN 65**

SKIDIP.
Tracks: / Sensee party / Looking sexy / Modelling queen / You na love reggae music / Always on my mind / Do you remember / Skidip / Na make mi girl go away / Fat and slim / Where is my baby.
LP: . . . . **GREL 41**
MC: . . . . **GREEN 41**

VERY BEST OF EEK-A-MOUSE, THE.
Tracks: / Anarexol / Star daily news or cleaner / Noah's ark / Terrorists in the city / Peeni walli / Wild like a tiger / Wa do dem / Assassinator / Christmas a come.
LP: . . . . **GREL 105**
MC: . . . . **GREEN 105**

WA DO DEM.
Tracks: / Ganja smuggling / Long time ago, A / Operation eradication / There's a girl in my life / Slowly but surely / Wa do dem / Lonesome journey / I will never leave my love / Noahs ark / Too young to understand.
LP: . . . . **GREL 31**
MC: . . . . **GREEN 31**

E.F. Band

DEEP CUT.
LP: . . . . **CULP 2**

LAST LAUGH IS ON YOU.
LP: **6362 076**

Effervescent Elephant

SOMETHING TO SAY.
LP: . . . . **EELP 009**

Egan, Joe

M.A.P..
LP: . . . . **ARL 5052**

OUT OF NOWHERE.
Tracks: / Back on the road / Ask for no favours / Natural high / Why let it bother you / Last farewell, The / Freeze / Pride / No time for sorrow / Leaving it all behind / Out of nowhere.
LP: . . . . **ARL 5021**

STUCK IN THE MIDDLE (see Rafferty, Gerry) (Egan, Joe & Gerry Rafferty).
LP: . . . . **AMLH 64708**

Egan, Mark

TOUCH OF LIGHT, A.
LP: . . . . **GR 9572**
MC: . . . . **GRC 9572**

Egan, Seamus

SEAMUS EGAN.
LP: . . . . **SHAN 29020**

Egan, Walter

HI FI.
Tracks: / I can't wait / That's that / Little miss it's you / Man B. Goode / I do / Hi fi love / Hurt again / Drive away / Love at last / Like you do / You're the one / Bad news.
LP: **2310673**

LAST STROLL.
Tracks: / Baby let's run away / Y me? / Tuesday Weld / Bad attitude / Fall for you / First date, last date / Heart / Chaminade / Motel broken hearts / Waitin' for the rain.
LP: . . . . **HOG 3**

Egan, Willie

GOING BACK TO LOUISIANA.
Tracks: / Fannie Mae / I'm walking / Careless love / Junco partner / It's all right / Tra-la-la / Chicken shack boogie / Ya ya / Tro / Don't blame it on me / She's gone away / Wear your black dress.
LP: . . . . **CH 95**

ROCK 'N' ROLL FEVER 1955-58.
LP: . . . . **KK 7404**

WILLIE EGAN & HIS FRIENDS.
LP: . . . . **RELIC 8002**

Egg

SEVEN IS A JOLLY GOOD TIME.
Tracks: / Bulb / While growing my hair / I will be absorbed / Fugue in D minor / They laughed when I sat down at the piano / Song of McGillicudie the pusillanimous, The ((see recording notes)) / Boilk / You are all princes / Symphony No.2 (Movements 1 & 2, blane, movement 4) / Seven is a jolly good time.
LP: . . . . **SEE 47**

E(gg)clectic 1

FRIED EGG COLLECTION, A.
LP: . . . . **FRY 2**

Eggs Is Eggs

EGGS IS EGGS (See under Bangers & Mash (tv)).

Eggs Over Easy

GOOD 'N' CHEAP.
Tracks: / Party party / Arkansas / Henry Morgan / Factory / Face down in the meadow / Home to you / Song is born of riff and tongue / Don't let nobody / Runnin' down to Memphis / Pistol on a shelf / Night flight.
LP: . . . . **ED 199**

Egypt

CRAZY HORSES.
Tracks: / Gallows wait, The / On the road / Richard III / Tower, The / Metal ships / Find a way / Crazy horses.
LP: . . . . **HTDLP 1**
MC: . . . . **HTDMC 1**

Egypt (Country)

ANCIENT EGYPT (Various artists).
LP: . . . . **LLST 7347**
MC: . . . . **LLCT 7347**

L'ART DU KANOUN EGYPTIEN (Various artists).
LP: . . . . **UNKNOWN**

L'ORDRE CHAZILI D'EGYPTE (Musique Soufi vol.4) (Various artists).
Tracks: / Al-dhikr (recitation des textes sacres du dhik: *Various artists* / Insad (recitation des poemes): *Various artists*.
LP: . . . . **ARN 33658**

L'ORDRE CHAZILI D'EGYPTE (Musique soufi vol.5) (Various artists).
Tracks: / L'Insad de la vie du prophete Mohammad: *Various artists*.
LP: . . . . **ARN 33659**

Egyptian (film)

EGYPTIAN, THE (1954 film soundtrack) (Various artists).
Tracks: / Prelude: *Various artists* / Her name was merit: *Various artists* / Pharoah Akhnaton, The: *Various* artists / Nefer Nefer Nefer: *Various artists* / Lotus pool, The: *Various artists* / Valley of the kings: *Various* artists / At the tomb of Amenhotep: *Various artists* / Maryrdom of merit, The: *Various artists* / Death of Akhnaton, The: *Various artists* / Horemheb, the new pharoah: *Various artists* / Exile and death: *Various artists*.
LP: . . . . **MCA 1523**
MC: . . . . **MCAC 1523**
MC: . . . . **VSC 5258**

Eh, Geoff Mann Band

MINISTRY OF THE INTERIOR.
LP: . . . . **GRUB 21**
MC: . . . . **TGRUB 21**

Ehrlich, Marty

PLIANT PLIANT.
LP: . . . . **ENJA 5065**

Ehrling, Thore

MINNS MED.
LP: . . . . **NOST 7656**

Ehrlinger, Hans

TAKE THE CHANCE FOR A DANCE (Ehrlinger, Hans & His Orchestra).
LP: . . . . **ISST 102**

TROMBONE TALK (Ehrlinger, Hans & His Orchestra).
LP: . . . . **ISST 122**

Eide, Khalifa Ould

MOORISH MUSIC FROM MAURITANIA (Eide, Khalifa Ould & Dimi Mint Abba).
MC: . . . . **WCC 019**

Eider, Max

BEST KISSER IN THE WORLD.
Tracks: / My other life / Sensitive touch / Bel Aire home / Rosemary / It has to be you / Quiet lives / Raking up leaves / Sense of motion / Let somebody down / Perfect companion.
LP: . . . . **ZL 71428**
MC: . . . . **ZK 71428**

Eieio

LAND OF OPPORTUNITY.
Tracks: / This time / Hello heartache / Get back to Arkansas / Tear it down / Me and Jesus Christ / Go West young man / Every word true / White lines, blue sky, black top / Blue mountain top / Middle of November.
LP: . . . . **FIEND 56**
MC: . . . . **FIENDCASS 56**

THAT LOVING THANG.
Tracks: / Hey Cecelie / Words falling down / Crack crack crack / Ya ya love / Andy Warhol's dead but I'm not / That love thang / Sea of light / Where you go / Gonna get gone / Across the tracks / Brother Michael.
LP: . . . . **FIEND 117**

Eikhard, Shirley

TAKING CHARGE.
Tracks: / Roll that rock / You're my weakness / Something that lasts / I get so jealous / Secrets / Night of no return / Someone else / While we're still young / It's understood / Pray for rain.
LP: . . . . **YL 0110**

Einstein

THEORY OF EMCEES SQUARED, THE.
LP: . . . . **STEIN 1**
MC: . . . . **STEIN 1 C**

Einsturzende Neubauten

2 + 4.
MC: . . . . **A 133**

FUNF AUF DER NACHT OBEN OFFENEN RICHTERSKALA.
LP: . . . . **BART 332**
MC: . . . . **BART 332C**

HAUS DER LUEGE.
Tracks: / Prolog / Feurio! / Ein Stuhl in der Hoelle / Haus der luege / Epilogue / Hirnlego / Schwindel / Der Kuss.
LP: . . . . **BART 333G**

HOUSE OF LIES.
LP: **BART333**
MC: **BART333C**

KOLLAPS.
LP: . . . . **EFA 2517**

PICTURE OF PATIENT O.T. (Zeichnungen des patienten O.T.).
LP: . . . . **SBVART 2**

STRATEGIES AGAINST ARCHITECTURE.
LP: . . . . **STUMM 14**

Eitzel, Mark

SONGS OF LOVE.
Tracks: / Firefly / Channel No. 5 / Western sky / Blue and grey shirt / Gary's song / Outside this bar / Room above the club / Last harbour / Kathleen / Crabwalk / Jenny / Take courage / Nothing can bring me down.
LP: . . . . **FIEND 213**

Ejected

SPIRIT OF REBELLION.
LP: . . . . **CITY 007**

TOUCH OF CLASS, A.
LP: . . . . **CITY 003**

Ek, Lars

DIZZY ACCORDION.
Tracks: / Vision of love / Mariposita / Thoughts of love / Dizzy accordion / Coquette polka / Jolly caballero / Atacka Marschen / Yodelling accordion / Jularboglade / Dansar shottis / Sambo hambo / Waltz grundstrom.
LP: . . . . **AIR 1012**

LARS EK IN DISNEYLAND.
LP: . . . . **SPMC 3005**
MC: . . . . **Unknown**

LARS EK PLAYS FROSINI.
Tracks: / Dizzy fingers / Vieni amore / Bel fiore / Varserenade / Bel viso / La mariposita / Hot fingers / Olive blossoms / Jolly caballero / Musette masuka / Love smiles / Through the park.
LP: . . . . **LPRP 56**

LARS EK'S HOT TRIO.
Tracks: / Raggin' the scale / Echo mazurka / Voss on the rocks / Fors majeur.
LP: . . . . **EKLP 8501**
MC: . . . . **UNKNOWN**

Ekland, Britt

TRUE BRITT Britt Ekland reads from her autobiography.
MCSET: . . . . **SAY 3**

El Cid (film)

EL CID (1961 film soundtrack) (Various artists).
Tracks: / El Cid overture: *Various artists* / Prelude: *Various artists* / Palace music: *Various artists* / Fight for Calahorra: *Various artists* / 13 knights: *Various artists* / Farewell: *Various artists* / Intermezzo: *Various artists* / El Cid march, The: *Various artists* / Twins, The: *Various artists* / Battle of Valencia: *Various artists* / Cid's death, The: *Various artists* / Legend and epilogue, The: *Various artists*.
LP: . . . . **LPMGM 5**
MC: . . . . **TCMGM 5**
LP: **793 301 1**
MC: **793 301 4**

EL CID (Film soundtrack) (Various artists).
LP: . . . . **MCA 25005**
MC: . . . . **MCAC 25005**
LP: **2353 046**

El Dorado (Film)

EL DORADO (1988 film soundtrack) (Various artists).
LP: . . . . **A 342**
MC: . . . . **C 342**
LP: . . . . **LAALP 1007**

El Gran Combo

15 GRANDS SUCCES.
LP: . . . . **LPGS 034**

El Greco (film)

EL GRECO (Original soundtrack) (Various artists).
LP: . . . . **SP 8061**

El Hamid, Hmaoui Abd

LA FLUTE DE L'ATLAS.
Tracks: / Takadoum / Golia, El / El Hanane / Kasbah / Lamarsah / Maname, El / Acharbil / Ouahdania / Bent Sahrah / Sambra.
LP: . . . . **ARN 33336**
MC: . . . . **ARN 433336**

LA FLUTE ORIENTALE.
Tracks: / Layali et Maghreb / Ennakhil / El ouahm / Ghouroub / El hob / El amal / Jabalia / Hazina / Koutoubia / Nagmat et hayat / Ghariba / Atlas.
LP: . . . . **ARN 30104**

El Mondao

FLAMENCO TOTAL.
LP: . . . . **EULP 1089**
MC: . . . . **EUMC 1089**

El Mubarak, Abdel Aziz

ABDEL AZIZ EL MUBARAK.
Tracks: / Tahrimni minnak / Ahla eyyoun / Ah'laa jarah / Tarig ash-shoag / Bitgooli la.
LP: . . . . **ORB 023**
MC: . . . . **ORBC 023**

STRAIGHT FROM THE HEART.
LP: . . . . **WCB 010**

El Pili

FLAMENCO (See under Montoya, Carlos) (El Pili & Carlos Monotya).

El Rayo X

VERY GREASY (See under Lindley, David).

Elder, Michael

ALIEN EARTH, THE.
MCSET: . . . . **COL 2019**

NOWHERE ON EARTH.
MCSET: . . . . **COL 2023**

Eldon, Jim

I WISH THERE WERE NO PRISONERS.
LP: . . . . **SD 002**

Eldorados

BIM BAM BOOM.
LP: . . . . **CRB 1022**

Eldridge, Roy

ARCADIA BALLROOM 39.
LP: . . . . **JA 14**

ART FORD'S JAZZ PARTY (October 1958).
LP: . . . . **AFJP 7**

BEST OF ROY ELDRIDGE.
Tracks: / Recado bossa nova / Sweethearts on parade / Willow,weep for me / Gofor / I want a little girl / That thing / All of me / Bye bye blackbird.
LP: **231 0857**
MC: **K10 857**

BODY AND SOUL AT THE BAYOU CLUB: VOL 2 (see Hawkins, Coleman) (Eldridge, Roy & Coleman Hawkins).

DALE'S WAIL.
Tracks: / Little jazz / Wrap your troubles in dreams / Roy's riff / Rockin' chair / Love for sale / Man I love, The / Oscar's arrangement / Dale's wail / Somebody loves me / Willow weep for me / I can't get started / When it's sleepy time down South / Don't blame me / Feeling a draft / Echoes of Harlem / When your lover has gone / Blue moon / Stormy weather / Sweethearts on parade / Foggy day / If I had you / I only have eyes for you / Sweet Georgia Brown / Song is ended.
2LP: **2632081**

EARLY YEARS, THE.
LP: . . . . **CBS 88585**

EUROPEAN CONCERT (see Hawkins, Coleman) (Eldridge, Roy & Coleman Hawkins).

GREAT ENGLISH CONCERT, THE (See Hawkins, Coleman) (Eldridge, Roy/ Coleman Hawkins/Stan Getz).

HAPPY TIME.
Tracks: / Sweethearts on parade / Willow weep for me / Makin' whoopee / Gee baby ain't I good to you / All of me / I want a little girl / On the sunny side of the street / I can't get started / Stormy Monday / Let me off uptown.
LP: **231 0746**
MC: **K10 7**

HAWK & ROY (see Hawkins, Coleman) (Eldridge, Roy & Coleman Hawkins).

HEAT'S ON, THE (Eldridge, Roy/ Howard McGhee).
LP: . . . . **ESQ 307**

JAZZ MATURITY...WHERE IT'S COMING FROM (See under Gillespie, Dizzy for details) (Eldridge, Roy & Dizzy Gillespie).

KRUPA YEARS 1941-2 (Sideman 1940).
LP: . . . . **MERITT 502**

KRUPA YEARS, THE.
LP: . . . . **NOST 7642**

LITTLE JAZZ.
Tracks: / King David / It don't mean a thing / Wrap your troubles in dreams / Undecided / Ain't no flies on me / Man I love, The / Easter parade / Wild driver / If I had you / Nuts / Someone to watch over me / Goliath / Bounce / I remember Harlem / Baby, don't do me like that / Une petite laitue / L'Isle Adam / Black and blue / Tue disais quetu m'aimais / Oh shut up / Hollywood pastime / I'd love him so / Heat is on, The / Wild man blues / Fire works.
2LP: . . . . **VJD 533**

LITTLE JAZZ LIVE IN 1957.
Tracks: / Sweet Georgia Brown / Embraceable you / Lover come back to me / Little jazz / Rockin' chair / Lady be good / Soft wind / Perdido / Long blues, The.
LP: . . . . **EB 408**

LITTLE JAZZ SPECIAL.
LP: . . . . **QUEEN 066**

LITTLE JAZZ & THE JIMMY RYAN ALL-STARS (Eldridge, Roy & The Jimmy Ryan All-Stars).
Tracks: / Between the Devil and the deep blue sea / St. James' Infirmary / Beale Street blues / Black and blue / Sing, sing, sing / Wynola / Cute / Bourbon Street / All of me / Last call at Jimmy Ryan's.
LP: **231 0869**
MC: **K10 869**

NIFTY CAT, THE.
Tracks: / Jolly Hollis / Cotton / 5400 North / Ball of fire / Wineola / Nifty cat, The.
LP: . . . . **NW 349**

ONE IS NEVER TOO OLD TO SWING (Eldridge, Roy & Tiny Grimes).
Tracks: / Romance without finance / West End Phil / T'ain't what you do (it's the way that you do it) / Food for thought / One is never too old to swing / In a swinging groove / Downtown sound, The / Frantic.
LP: . . . . **SNTF 736**
MC: . . . . **ZCSN 736**

OSCAR PETERSON AND ROY ELDRIDGE (see Peterson, Oscar) (Eldridge, Roy and Oscar Peterson).

PORTRAITS IN JAZZ (Eldridge, Roy/ Richie Kamuca).
LP: . . . . **PUMPKIN 107**

RARE BROADCASTS.
Tracks: / Goof and I, The / Undecided / Heat is on, The / I remember / Interview / Lady Brown.
LP: . . . . **D 1010**

ROY ELDRIDGE.
LP: . . . . **GNPS 9009**

ROY ELDRIDGE 1957.
LP: . . . . **AA 514**

ROY ELDRIDGE 1935-40.
LP: . . . . **TAX 8020**

ROY ELDRIDGE AT JERRY NEWMAN'S.
Tracks: / Sweet and brown / Body and soul / Lemon house / Jazz rose / Sweet Lorraine / I can't give you anything but love / I surrender, dear (Two takes.) / Way you look tonight (Three takes.) / Rags (Two takes.).
LP: . . . . **XAN 186**

ROY ELDRIDGE FOUR.
Tracks: / Between the Devil and the deep blue sea / Gofor / I surrender, dear / Joie de Roy / Perdido / Bye bye blackbird.
LP: **2308 203**
MC: . . . . **K 08 203**

TIPPIN' OUT.
2LP: . . . . **AFSD 1016**

TRUMPET SUMMIT (see Clayton, Buck) (Eldridge, Roy/Buck Clayton).

UNE PETITE LAITUE.
LP: . . . . **JL 92**
LP: **500092**

WHAT'S IT ALL ABOUT?.
Tracks: / I still love him so / Heat's on, The / That thing / Recado bossa nova / Melange.
LP: **231 0766**
MC: **K10 766**

Eleanor Rigby

CENSORSHIP.
Tracks: / Think for yourself / Getting thru the day / Over and over / 1995 / I want to sleep with you / Play with fire / Mod girls / Censorship / More than the truth / Love on the phone / For the video.
LP: . . . . **WSR 001**

Electribe 101

ELECTRIBAL MEMORIES.
Tracks: / Talking with myself / Lipstick on my lover / You're walking (peeping Tom mix) / Inside out / Diamond dove / Heading for the night / Tell me when the fever ended / Talking 2 / Electribal memories / You're walking (corporate def mix) / Talking with myself (Frankie Knuckles mix 12") / Tell me when the fever ended (Larry Heard mix).
LP: **8429651**
MC: **8429654**

Electric Banana
SEVENTIES, THE.
LP: .... NOTT 001

SIXTIES, THE.
LP: .... NOTT 003

Electric Bluebirds
ELECTRIC BLUEBIRDS, THE.
LP: .... SPRAY 105
MC: .... CSPRAY 105

Electric Boys
FUNK O-METAL CARPET RIDE.
Tracks: / Psychedelic eyes / All lips 'n' hips / Change, The / If I had a car / Captain of my soul / Rags to riches / Cheek to cheek / Electrified / Who are you / Into the woods.
LP: 846 055 1
MC: 846 055 4

Electric Chairs
ELECTRIC CHAIRS.
Tracks: / Eddie and Sheena / Bad in bed / Hot blood / Worry wart / 28 Model T / Out of control / Max's / On the crest / Plain of Nazca / Big black window / Take it / Rock and roll / Ressurection.
LP: .... LONG 1

Electric Circus
HELLO.
Tracks: / Vermillion / Clouds sail by / Rhythm and rhyme / Opal / Envelop / Kamarac / Some thoughts / Snow.
LP: .... VE 25
MC: .... TCVE 25

Electric Dreams (film)
ELECTRIC DREAMS (1984 film soundtrack) (Various artists).
Tracks: / Electric dreams: *Arnold, P.P.* / Video: *Lynne, Jeff* / Dream, The: *Culture Club* / Duel, The: *Moroder, Giorgio* / Now you are mine: *Terry, Helen* / Love is love: *Culture Club* / Chase runner: *Heaven 17* / Let it run: *Lynne, Jeff* / Madeline's theme: *Moroder, Giorgio* / Together in electric dreams: *Moroder, Giorgio & Philip Oakey*.
LP: .... V 2318
MC: .... TCV 2318

Electric Flag
GROOVIN' IS EASY.
Tracks: / Spotlight / I was robbed last night / I found out / Never be lonely again / Losing game / My baby wants to test me / I should have left her / You don't realise / Groovin' is easy.
LP: .... THBL 1.006

TRIP, THE (Film soundtrack).
Tracks: / Peter's trip / Joint passing / Psyche soap / M 23 / Synesthesia / Little head, A / Hobbitt / Inner pocket / Fewghh / Green and gold / Other Ed Norton, The / Flash, bam pow / Home room / Peter gets off / Practice music / Fine jung thing / Senior citizen / Gettin' hard.
LP: .... ED 211

Electric Horseman
ELECTRIC HORSEMAN, THE (Film soundtrack) (Various artists).
Tracks: / Midnight rider: *Nelson, Willie* / My heroes have always been cowboys: *Nelson, Willie* / Mamas don't let your babies grow up to be...: *Nelson, Willie* / Hands on the wheel: *Nelson, Willie* / Electro-phantasma: *Various artists* / Rising star: *Various artists* / Electric horseman: *Various artists* / Tumbleweed morning: *Various artists* / Disco magic: *Various artists* / Freedom: *Various artists* / Epilogue: *Various artists*.
LP: .... JS 36327
MC: .... JST 36327
LP: 70177
MC: 40 70177

Electric Prunes
I HAD TOO MUCH TO DREAM LAST NIGHT.
LP: .... REP 24033

LONG DAY'S FLIGHT.
Tracks: / Ain't it hard / Little Olive / I had too much to dream (last night) / Luvin' / Get me to the world on time / Are you lovin' me more (but enjoying it less) / Bangles / Train for tomorrow / Sold to the highest bidder / Try me on for size / Doctor Do-Good / Hideaway / Great banana hoax, The / Children of rain / Antique doll / I happen to love you / Long days flight / You never had it better.
LP: .... ED 179
MC: .... CED 179

Electric Sun
EARTHQUAKE.
Tracks: / Electric sun / Lilac / Burning wheels turning / Japanese dream / Sundown / Winter days / Still so many lives away / Earthquake.
LP: 0060 196

FIRE WIND.
Tracks: / Cast away your chains / Indian dawn / I'll be loving you always / Fire wind / Prelude in space minor / Just another rainbow / Children of the sea / Chaplin and I / Enola Gay / Tune of Japan / Attack / Lament.
LP: 0060 378

Electric Toilet
IN THE HANDS OF KARMA.
LP: .... PSYCHO 8

Electro Hippies
ELECTRO HIPPIES LIVE.
LP: .... VILE 013

ONLY GOOD PUNK IS A DEAD ONE, THE.
Tracks: / Faith / Acid rain / Run Ronald / Scum / B.P. / Unity / Terror eyes / So wicked / Profit / Freddy's revenge / Mistake / Things of beauty / Protest / Gas Joe Pearce / Lies / Tortured tears / D.I.Y. nor D.R.I / Suck / Deception.
LP: .... VILE 002

PLAY LOUD OR DIE.
Tracks: / Acid rain / Wings of death / Theme toon / Reaper, The / Profit from death / Run Ronald / Terror eyes / Am I punk yet? / Vivisection / Horns of Hades, The.
LP: .... NECRO 1

Electronic
DRIVING SYNTHESISER SOUNDS (Hi-tec sounds for the 90's) (Various artists).
MC: .... CONE 10

SYNTHESIS VOL.1 (Electronic Synthesizer Sound Productions).
MC: .... ESSP S1

SYNTHESIS VOL.2 (Electronic Synthesizer Sound Productions).
MC: .... ESSP S2

SYNTHESIS VOL.3 (Electronic Synthesizer Sound Productions).
MC: .... ESSP S3

Electronic Art
INQUIETUDE.
LP: .... GR 7003

Electronic (group)
ELECTRONIC.
MC: .... FACT 290C
LP: .... FACT 290

Electronic Moods
ELECTRONIC MOODS (Various artists).
LP: .... NE 1373
MC: .... CE 2373

Electronicas
BIRD DANCE, THE.
LP: 6435 093
MC: 7106 093

Electropathics
BATTERIES NOT INCLUDED.
LP: .... GUM 001

Electrophon
FURTHER THOUGHTS ON THE CLASSICS.
Tracks: / Arrival of the Queen of Sheba, The / Girl with the flaxen hair, The / Flight of the bumble bee / None but the weary heart / Allegro / Greensleeves / Sabre dance / Skaters waltz / Serenade / Moto perpetuo / Anitra's dance / Hall of the mountain king.
LP: 2482 335

Electropop Trax
SUBTLE HINTS.
LP: .... SANE 001

Elektro Robotik Dub...
STRIKTY AUTOMATIK (Elektro Robotik Dub Orchestra).
LP: .... ARILP 16

Element Of Crime
TRY TO BE MENSCH.
Tracks: / No good anymore / She'll never die / You shouldn't be lonely / As long as I love you / Don't you smile / Something was wrong / Beware of strangers / He's gone / Last dance / Nervous and blue.
LP: 831 787-1
MC: 831 787-4

Elements
BLOWN AWAY.
LP: .... PJ 88029
MC: .... PJC 88029

ELEMENTS.
LP: .... P 2002

ESSENTIAL FIRMAMENT & THE ELEMENTS (See Essential Firmament) (Elements/Essential Firmament).

ILLUMINATION.
Tracks: / Hymnalayas / Walk in / Mandela / Illumination / Seeker, The / One thousand words / Go ahead Stan / Sunken cathederal / Saturn return / Bali.
LP: .... PL 83031
MC: .... PK 83031

LIBERAL ARTS.
Tracks: / Amberlinn / Liberal arts / Underwater / American hope / Quetico / Coral canyon / Oslo / SB 206 / Michele's dance.
LP: .... PL 83058
MC: .... PK 83058

SPIRIT RIVER.
LP: .... PL 83089
MC: .... PK 83089

Elen, Gus
YOU HAVE MADE A NICE OLD MESS OF IT.
Tracks: / Golden dustman, The / E dunno where 'e are / Mrs. Carter / If it wasn't for the 'ouses in between / Meriah / 'Arf a pint of ale / Pavement artist, The / Wait till the work comes round / Publican, The / Coster's pony, The / Dick Whittington - a parody / Nature's made a big mistake / Don't stop my 'arf a pint o' beer / I'm going to settle down / Pretty little villa down at Barking.
LP: 12TS 396

Eley, B
VOICE (see under Tippetts, J).

Elf
CAROLINA COUNTRY BALL (see under "Dio, Ronnie James").

ELF.
LP: .... CBS 26910
MC: 40 26910

TRYING TO BURN THE SUN (Elf & Ronnie James Dio).
LP: .... LONG 8
MC: .... LONGC 8

Elfman, Danny
BATMAN 2 (See Under Films).

DICK TRACY (ORIGINAL FILM SCORE) (See under Dick Tracy).

EDWARD SCISSORHANDS (See Under Edward Scissorhands).

MUSIC FROM A DARKENED THEATRE.
Tracks: / Pee Wee's big adventure / Batman / Dick Tracy / Beetlejuice / Nightbreed / Darkman / Back to school / Midnight run / Wisdom / Hot to trot / Big top Pee Wee / Simpsons, The / Alfred Hitchcock presents: The jar / Tales from the crypt / Face like a frog / Forbidden zone / Scrooged.
MC: .... MCAC 10065

Elgar (composer)
CONCERTO FOR CELLO AND ORCHESTRA IN E MINOR Conducted by Rafael Fruhbeck (London Symphony Orchestra).
Tracks: / Concerto for cello and orchestra in E minor / Fantasia on a theme by Thomas Tallis / Fantasia on greensleeves (Williams).
MC: .... CIMPC 930

DREAM OF GERONTIUS, THE conductor: Richard Hickox (London Symphony Orchestra).
2LP: .... DRBD 2014
MCSET: .... DBTD 2014

ELGAR CELLO CONCERTO (Royal Philharmonic Orchestra).
LP: .... RPO 8012
MC: .... ZC RPO 8012

ENIGMA VARIATIONS & FALSTAFF (Various artists).
MC: 4251554

ENIGMA VARIATIONS/FALSTAFF SYMPHONIC STUDY (Montreal Symphony Orchestra).
Tracks: / Enigma variations, op 36 / Falstaff - Symphonic study in C minor, op 68.
MC: 4302414

SPIRIT OF ENGLAND, THE (London Symphony Chorus/Northern Sinfonia).
Tracks: / Spirit of England / Give unto the Lord (Psalm 29) / O hearken thou / Snow / Land of hope and glory.
LP: .... EL 749 481-1
MC: .... EL 749 481-4

WAND OF YOUTH SUITES 1-2 (London Philharmonic Orchestra).
LP: .... EMX 2148
MC: .... TCEMX 2148

WORLD OF ELGAR (Various artists).
Tracks: / Pomp and circumstance march No. 1 in D major: *Various artists* / Serenade in E minor for strings, op 20: *Various artists* / There is sweet music: *Various artists* / Salut d'amour: *Various artists* / Introduction and allegro: *Various artists* / Pomp and circumstance march No. 4 in G major: *Various artists* / Nimrod (variation IX from Enigma variations): *Various artists* / Give unto the Lord: *Various artists* / Dream of Gerontius, The - But hark a great mysterious...: *Various artists* (...harmony - Praise to the holiest in the height.).
MC: 4300944

Elgart, Charlie
BALANCE.
Tracks: / On the breeze of a shadow / My sentiments exactly / Balance / Bryanna / Sight unseen / Goodbye my friend / Sundance.
LP: .... PL 83068
MC: .... PK 83068

SIGNS OF LIFE.
Tracks: / Float / Sojourn / This thing we share / Signs of life / I cry for you / When I'm with Stu / Summer dusk, A.
LP: .... PL 83045
MC: .... PK 83045

Elgart, Larry
HOOKED ON SWING (Elgart, Larry & His Manhattan Swing Orchestra).
Tracks: / Hooked on swing / Hooked on big bands / Hooked on a star / Hooked on Astaire / Hooked on the blues / Hooked on Broadway.
LP: .... RCALP 6051
MC: .... RCAK 6051

Elgart, Les
LES ELGERT AND HIS ORCHESTRA 1946 (Elgart, Les & His Orchestra).
LP: .... CLP 126

Elgin Strathspey
STRINGS O'MORAY (Elgin Strathspey & Reel Society).
Tracks: / March/Strathspey & Reel / Highland Schottische / Weaving set / Andy Ross two-step, The / Slow air / Pipe marchse / Waltzes / Reels (a trip to Bavaria) / Marches / Tom Burns polka, The / Slow air (2) / March/Strathspey & Reel (2) / John Huband's dancing fingers / Moray jigs / Bothy ballads / Reels.
LP: .... ITV 408
MC: .... KITV 408

Elias, Eliane
AMANDA (see Brecker, Randy) (Elias, Elaine/ Randy Brecker).

CROSS CURRENTS (BLUE NOTE).
Tracks: / Hallucinations / Cross currents / One side of you / East coasting / Coming and going (Vou ali e ja volta) / Campari and soda / Beautiful love / Impulsive / When you wish upon a star.
LP: B1 48785

ILLUSIONS (BLUE NOTE).
Tracks: / Choro / Through the fire / Illusions / Sweet Georgie Fame / Locomotif / Iberia / Falling in love with love / Chan's song.
LP: .... BLJ 46994

SO FAR SO CLOSE.
Tracks: / At first sight / Bluestone / Barefoot / Straight across (to Jaco) / Two way street / With you in mind / So far so close / Nightimer / Still hidden.
LP: B1 91411
LP: 791 411 1

Elias Hulk
UNCHAINED.
Tracks: / Anthology of dreams / Nightmare / Been around too long / Yesterday's trip / We can fly / Free / Delhi blues / Ain't got you.
LP: .... SEE 286

Eliclean Namanono,
AMALABI ZULU TRADITIONAL.
LP: .... ELP 2003

Elimhlophe, Ihashi
BAMBELELA.
Tracks: / Bambelela / Ukhalelani / Izidumo / Amathunz amnyama / Udlame / Indizamshini / Sizokushaya ngengoma / Velani obala / Ngiboniseni emhlabeni.
LP: .... TUS 8008
MC: .... TUS 8008MC

Eliot, George
MILL ON THE FLOSS, THE (Bloom, Claire (nar)).
MC: 1568

MILL ON THE FLOSS, THE (Atkins, Eileen).
MCSET: CC/009

SILAS MARNER (Dench, Judi).
MCSET: .... SAY 5
MCSET: .... ARGO 1136

SILAS MARNER (Rathbone, Basil (nar)).
MCSET: 2024

Eliot, T.S.
FAMILY REUNION.
MCSET: 0308

LOVE SONG OF J. ALFRED PRUFROCK, THE.
MC: 1045

MURDER IN THE CATHEDRAL (Pasco, Richard & The Royal Shakespeare Company).
MCSET: . . . . SAY 26

MURDER IN THE CATHEDRAL.
MCSET: 330

OLD POSSUM'S BOOK OF PRACTICAL CATS (Gielgud, Sir John (nar)).
MC: 1713

WASTE LAND (Guinness, Alec).
MCSET: . . . . SAY 25

WASTE LAND & OTHER POEMS.
MC: 1326

Eliovson, Steve

DAWN DANCE.
LP: . . . . ECM 1198

Elixir

ELIXIR.
LP: . . . . GM 003

LETHAL POTION.
LP: . . . . SONICLP 9

Elizabeth 1

ELIZABETH 1- 1533/1603 Various artists (Vahey, Robert).
MC: . . . . HM 007

FIRST QUEEN ELIZABETH (history for ages 8+) (Unknown narrator(s)).
MC: . . . . PLBH 101

Elizalde, Fred

VOLUME 2 1927-33.
MC: . . . . UNKNOWN

VOLUME 4 1927-33.
MC: . . . . NEO 929

Elkin, Greta

MARRIED AND THE FREE, THE.
LP: . . . . RBA 1001

MOCKIN' BIRD, THE.
LP: . . . . RBA 132

Elkins, Robert

CAJUN EXPERIENCE (See under Daigle, Paul) (Elkins, Robert/Paul Daigle/Michael Douchet).

LA LUMIERE DANS TON CHASSIS (see Daigle, Paul) (Elkins, Robert/ Paul Daigle/ Cajun Gold).

Ellboj, Lulle Och Hans

MODERN DANSMUSIK (Ellboj, Lulle Och Hans Orkester 1944-46).
LP: . . . . DRLP 40

Ellegaard, Mogens

ELEGANT ELLEGAARD.
Tracks: / Partita piccola / In the zoo / Toccata and fugue in D min. / Toccata No.1 / Italian concerto (1st Movement.) / Histoires (La marchant d'eau, le meneuse de tortues d'or).
LP: . . . . LP 3004

MADE IN DENMARK.
Tracks: / Toccata no. 2 / Six arabesques / How to play in D-major without caring about it / Sonata for accordion / Invention for accordion.
LP: TPLP-51

PLASTICITY.
Tracks: / Plasticity / Sonata in A minor / Invention / Le coucou.
LP: . . . . TFP 07 EP

Ellert

WHEN THE NIGHT BEGINS.
LP: . . . . PL 71702

Elli & Jacno

TOUT VA SAUTER.
LP: . . . . ILPS 9688

Ellie & The Hagwitch

ELLIE AND THE HAGWITCH (See under Cresswell, Helen) (Cresswell, Helen).

Elliman, Yvonne

I DON'T KNOW HOW TO LOVE HIM (See under Head, Murray).

YVONNE.
Tracks: / Love pains / Savannah / Cold wind across my heart / Greenlight / Everything must change / How long / Hit the road Jack / Sticks and stones / Rock me slowly / I'm gonna use what I got to get what I need / Nowhere to hide.
LP: . . . . RSS 16

Ellington, De Lange

NEWPORT 1958 (Ellington, De Lange & Mills).
LP: 84408
MC: 40 84408

NUTCRACKER SUITE (Ellington, De Lange & Mills).
LP: 84413

Ellington, Duke

1ST ANNUAL CONNECTICUT JAZZ FESTIVAL (Ellington, Duke orchestra & friends).
LP: . . . . IAJRC 45

1943:VOL. 1 (World Broadcasting Service) (Ellington, Duke And His Orchestra).
LP: . . . . CLP 101

1943:VOL. 2 (World Broadcasting service) (Ellington, Duke And His Orchestra).
LP: . . . . CLP 102

1943:VOL. 3 (World Broadcasting Service) (Ellington, Duke And His Orchestra).
LP: . . . . CLP 103

1943:VOL. 4 (World Broadcasting Service) (Ellington, Duke And His Orchestra).
LP: . . . . CLP 104

1943:VOL. 5 (World Broadcasting Service) (Ellington, Duke And His Orchestra).
LP: . . . . CLP 105

1945:VOL. 6 (Ellington, Duke And His Orchestra).
LP: . . . . CLP 106

1945:VOL. 7 (Ellington, Duke Orchestra).
LP: . . . . CLP 107

1945:VOL. 8 (Ellington, Duke & His Famous Orchestra).
LP: . . . . CLP 108

1945:VOL. 9 (Ellington, Duke Orchestra).
LP: . . . . CLP 109

1953 PASADENA CONCERT, THE.
Tracks: / Tattooed bride, The / Diminuendo and crescendo in blue / Hawk talks, The / Monologue / St. Louis blues / VIP's boogie / Without a song / Do nothing till you hear from me / Street blues / Perdido / Ellington medley.
LP: . . . . NP 708
MC: . . . . ZCNCP 708
LP: 500201

1954 LOS ANGELES CONCERT.
LP: 500 207

1927-30 (Ellington, Duke Orchestra).
LP: . . . . LPJT 35

1928-33.
Tracks: / Black beauty / Sweet mama / When you're smiling / Admiration / Accordion Joe / Home again blues / Moon over Dixie / Baby when you aint there / Anytime, anyday, anywhere / Delta bound / Eerie moan / Bundle of blues.
LP: . . . . SM 3081

1931-39 VOL 2.
LP: . . . . LPJT 42

1927-1934 JAZZ CLASSICS IN DIGITAL STEREO (1927-1934).
Tracks: / Jubilee stomp / Blues with a feeling / Hop head / What can a poor fellow do / Chicago stompdown / Black beauty / Hot and bothered / Misty morning / Mooche, The / Paducah / East St. Louis toodle-oo / Creole love call / Fast and furious / Solitude / Stompy Jones / Live and love tonight.
LP: . . . . REB 643
MC: . . . . ZCF 643

AFRO-BOSSA (Ellington, Duke And His Orchestra).
Tracks: / Afro-bossa / Purple gazelle / Absinthe / Moonbow / Sempre amore / Silk lace / Tigress / Angu / Volupte / Bonga pyramid / Eighth veil, The.
LP: . . . . DS 871

AGE OF ELLINGTON, THE.
Tracks: / Take the 'A' train / I got it bad (and that ain't good) / Sophisticated lady / Perdido / Solitude / Cottontail / Concerto for Cootie (Do nothin' till you hear from me) / Mood indigo / C-jam blues / Prelude to a kiss / Caravan / Things ain't what they used to be / Don't get around much anymore / Jump for joy / Chelsea Bridge / Black and tan fantasy / East St. Louis toodle-oo / Creole love call / Transblucency / Jack the bear / Harlem air shaft / Sepia panorama / Conga brava / Rockabye river / Blood count / Raincheck / Lotus blossom / Twitch, The / New world a coming / Black, brown and beige / Perfume suite, The / David danced before the Lord with all his might.
LPS: . . . . PL 42086

ALL STAR ROAD BAND VOL.1 (Ellington, Duke And His Orchestra).
Tracks: / Take the 'A' train / Such sweet thunder / Frustration / Cop out / Perdido / Mood indigo / Bassment / Sophisticated lady / Stardust / Jeeps blues / All of me / Diminuendo and crescendo in blue / I got it bad and that ain't good / On the sunny side of the street.
2LP: . . . . ASLD 850
MC: . . . . ZCASD 850

ALL STAR ROAD BAND VOL.2 (Ellington, Duke And His Orchestra).
Tracks: / Mood indigo / Satin doll / Happy go lucky local / Things ain't what they used to be / Do nothing till you hear from me / Guitar amour / Summertime / C-jam blues / Silk lace / I got it bad and that ain't good / Isfahan / Timon of Athens / Tutti for cootie / Stompin' at the Savoy / Jeep's blues / I can't stop loving you / Diminuendo and crescendo in blue.
2LP: . . . . ASLD 853
MC: . . . . ZCASD 853

ANATOMY OF A MURDER.
LP: 84411

AND HIS MOTHER CALLED HIM BILL (Ellington, Duke And His Orchestra).
Tracks: / Boo-dah / U.M.M.G. / Blood count / Smada / Rock skipping at the Blue Note / Raincheck / Midriff (CD only) / My little brown book / Lotus blossom / Snibor / After all / All day long / Daydream / Intimacy of the blues, The / Charpoy.
LP: . . . . NL 89166
MC: . . . . NK 89166
LP: . . . . LSA 3073

AND THE ELLINGTONIANS.
Tracks: / Cat walk / Moonlight fiesta / She / Happening, The / Swamp drums / Sultry serenade / Indian Summer / Britt and butter blues / Caravan / Alternate / Hoppin' John / Jumpin' with symphony Sid / New piano roll blues, The / Perdido / Take the 'A' train / Oscalypso / Blues for Blanton / Things ain't what they used to be / Make no mistake / In a blue summer garden / Cottontail / Flamingo / Bang up blues / "C" Jam blues / Johnny come lately / Great times.
2LP: . . . . VJD 525
2LP: 400019

ART OF DUKE ELLINGTON (Great Paris concert).
Tracks: / Kinda Dukish / On the sunny side of the street / Star crossed lovers / All of me / Asphalt jungle, The / Concerto for Cootie (Do nothin' till you hear from me) / Tutti for cootie / Suite Thursday / Perdido / Eighth veil, The / Rose of the Rio Grande / Cop out / Bula / Jam with Sam / Happy go lucky local / Local / Tone parallel to Harlem.
LP: . . . . K 60044

AT CARNEGIE HALL NOV 23 1946 (Ellington, Duke Orchestra).
Tracks: / Eighth veil, The / Golden feather / Flippant flurry / Golden cress / Unbooted character, The / Sultry sunset / Deep south suite.
LP: . . . . QU 018

AT HIS VERY BEST.
Tracks: / Jack the Bear / Concerto for Cootie (Do nothin' till you hear from me) / Harlem air shaft / Across the track blues / Chloe / Royal Garden blues / Warm valley / Koko / Black, brown and beige / Creole love call / Transblucency.
LP: . . . . LSA 3071

AT NEWPORT.
Tracks: / Newport jazz festival suite / Festival junction / Blues to be there / Newport up / Jeep's Blues / Diminuendo And Crescendo In Blues.
LP: 84403
LP: 4509861
MC: 4509864

AT NEWPORT (II).
LP: 84420

AT SOUTHLAND AND COTTON CLUB.
LP: . . . . CC 16

AT TANGLEWOOD - JULY 15, 1956 VOL.2 (Ellington, Duke Orchestra).
LP: . . . . QU 050

AT TANGLEWOOD - JULY 15, 1956 VOL.1 (Ellington, Duke Orchestra).
Tracks: / Newport jazz festival suite / Festival junction / Blues to be there / Newport up / Hawk talks, The / Prelude to a kiss / I got it bad and that ain't good / La Virgen de la Macarena / Black and tan fantasy / Harlem air shaft / Clarinet melodrama / Theme for Trambean / Sophisticated lady / Take the 'A' train.
LP: . . . . QU 049
LP: . . . . QUEEN 049

AT THE BAL MASQUE.
Tracks: / Satin doll / Lady in red, The / Indian love call / Donkey serenade, The / Gypsy love song / Laugh, clown, laugh / Alice blue gown / Who's afraid of the big bad wolf? / Got a date with an angel / Poor butterfly / Satan takes a holiday / Peanut vendor.
LP: 84409
LP: . . . . CBS 21144
MC: 40 21144

AT THE COTTON CLUB.
LP: . . . . TAX 8001

AT THE COTTON CLUB-1939 (Ellington, Duke And His Orchestra).
Tracks: / East St. Louis toodle-oo / Jig walk / In a sentimental mood / I'm slapping Seventh Avenue with the sole of my shoe / Alabamy home / If you were in my place / I've got to be a home / I've got to be a rug cutter / Lost in meditation / Oh, babe, maybe someday / Everyday / Azure / Carnival in Caroline / Dinah's in a jam / Frolic Sam.
LP: . . . . SM 3111

AT THE HURRICANE CLUB VOL. 1.
LP: . . . . HC 6001

AT THE HURRICANE CLUB VOL. 2.
LP: . . . . HC 6002

BACK TO BACK (Ellington, Duke/ Johnny Hodges).
Tracks: / Weary blues / St. Louis Blues / Loveless love / Royal Garden blues / Wabash blues / Basin Street blues / Beale street blues.
MC: 3113 087
LP: 2304 503

BAND SHORTS (Ellington, Duke And His Orchestra).
Tracks: / Black and tan fantasy / Duke steps out / Black beauty / Cotton club stomp / Hot feet / Same train / Lightnin' / Rockin' in rhythm / Stormy weather / Bugle call rag.
LP: . . . . MTLP 1005

BERNE LEIGHTON PLAYS DUKE ELLINGTON AT JIMMY WES (See under Leighton, Bernie).

BEST OF DUKE ELLINGTON (JOKER) 1927 - 1941.
Tracks: / East St. Louis toodle-oo / Black and tan fantasy / Creole love call / Mooche, The / Mood indigo / Rockin' in rhythm / Echoes of the jungle / Harlem speaks / Caravan / Conga brava / Cottontail / Take the 'A' train.
LP: . . . . SM 3056

BEST OF DUKE ELLINGTON (MUSIDISC) 1942-46 (Ellington, Duke And His Orchestra).
Tracks: / Frankie and Johnny / Diminuendo and crescendo in blue / In the shade of the old apple tree / Harlem airshift / Creole love call / It don't mean a thing / Kissing bug / Prelude to a kiss / Jam-a-ditty / Beautiful Indians: Hiawatha/Minnehaha / Happy go lucky local / Overture to a jam session / Blue skies (Trumpet no end) / Magenta haze / Golden feather / Sultry sunset / Flippant flurry.
2LP: . . . . ALB 130

BEST OF DUKE ELLINGTON (PABLO).
Tracks: / Bateau / Sophisticated lady / Goof, The / Black butterfly / Mendoza / Layin' on mellow / Sunset and the mocking bird (From Queen's suite.) / Lightning bugs and frogs (From Queen's suite.) / Le sucrier velours (From Queen's suite.) / Northern lights (From Queen's suite.) / Single petal of a rose (From Queen's suite.) / Apes and peacocks (From Queen's suite.).
LP: 231 0845
MC: K10 845

BLACK, BROWN AND BEIGE.
LP: 84406
LP: . . . . MES 7077

BLACK, BROWN AND BEIGE (The 1944-46 Band Recordings).
Tracks: / Work song / Come Sunday / Blues, The / Three dances / I ain't got nothin' but the blues / I'm beginning to see the light / Don't you know I care (or don't you care to) / I didn't know about you / Carnegie blues / Blue cellophane / Mood to be woo'd / (All of a sudden) My heart sings / Kissing bug / Everything but you / (Otto make that) Riff staccato / Prelude to a kiss / Caravan / Black and tan fantasy / Mood indigo / In a sentimental mood / It don't mean a thing / Sophisticated lady / Tonight I shall sleep (with a smile on my face / I let a song go out of heart / Solitude / Black beauty / Every hour on the hour (I fall in love with you) / Balcony serenade / Dancers in love / Coloratura / Things ain't what they used to be / Tell ya what I'm gonna do / Come to baby do / I'm just a lucky so and so / Long, strong and consecutive / Wonder of you, The / Rockabye river (hop, skip and jump) / Suddenly it jumped / Transbluecency / Just squeeze me (but tease me) / Gathering in a clearing, A / You don't love me no more / Pretty woman / Hey baby / Back home again in Indiana / Blue is the night / Lover man / Just you, just me / Beale Street blues / My honey's lovin' arms / Memphis blues / I don't stand a ghost of a chance with you / St. Louis blues / Swamp fire / Royal Garden blues / Esquire swank / Midriff.
LPS: . . . . PL 86641

BLACK BUTTERFLY.
Tracks: / Happy reunion / Chinoiserie / Hank Cinq / Star crossed lovers / Such sweet thunder / Perdido / Black butterfly / In a sentimental mood / Mood indigo / I'm beginning to see the light / I got it bad and that ain't good / Just squeeze me / It don't mean a thing / Solitude.
LP: . . . . **BLM 52041**

BLANTON-WEBSTER YEARS, THE (Ellington, Duke And His Orchestra).
Tracks: / You, you darlin' / Jack the bear / Koko / Morning glory / So far, so good / Conga brava / Concerto for Cootie (Do nothin' till you hear from me) / Me and you / Cottontail / Never no lament / Dusk / Bojangles / Portrait of Bert Williams, A / Blue goose / Harlem air shaft / At a Dixie roadside diner / All too soon / Rumpus in Richmond / My greatest mistake / Sepia panorama / There shall be no night / In a mellow tone / Five o'clock whistle / Warm valley / Flaming sword, The / Jumpin' punkins / Across the track blues / John Hardy's wife / Blue serge / After all / Chloe / Bakiff / Are you sticking? / I never felt this way before / Just a sittin' and a rockin' / Giddybug gallop, The / Sidewalks of New York, The / Chocolate shake / Flamingo / I got it bad (and that ain't good) / Clementine / Brown skin gal / Girl in my dreams tries to look like you, The / Jump for joy / Moon over Cuba / Take the 'A' train / Five o'clock drag / Rocks in my bed / Blip blip / Chelsea Bridge / Raincheck / What good would it do? / I don't know what kind of blues I got / Perdido / C jam blues / Moon mist / What am I here for? / I don't mind / Someone / My little brown book / Main stem / Johnny come lately / Hayfoot strawfoot / Sentimental lady / Sip of the lip, A (can sink a ship) / Sherman shuffle.
LPS: . . . . **PL 85659**
MCSET: . . . . **PK 85659**

BLUE ROSE (See under Clooney, Rosemary) (Ellington, Duke & Rosemary Clooney).

BLUES IN ORBIT.
Tracks: / Blues in orbit / Track 360 / Villes ville is the place, man / Brown penny / Three J's blues / Smada / Pie eyes blues / C jam blues / Sweet and pungent / In a mellow tone / Sentimental lady / Blues in blueprint / Swingers get the blues too / Singer's jump, The.
LP: **84307**
LP: **4608231**
MC: **4608234**

BRAGGIN' IN BRASS 1936-39.
LP: . . . . **TAX 8010**

BRUNSWICK SESSIONS VOL.1 (1932-35).
Tracks: / It don't mean a thing / Lazy rhapsody / Blue tune.
LP: . . . . **CAH 3001**

BRUNSWICK SESSIONS VOL.2 (1932-35).
Tracks: / Clouds in my heart / Ducky wucky / Jack cocktail / Lightnin' / Stars / Any time, any day, any where / Anywhere / Doin the new low down / I must have that man / Happy as the day is long.
LP: . . . . **CAH 3002**

BRUNSWICK SESSIONS VOL.3 (1932-35).
Tracks: / Get yourself a new broom / Bundle of blues / Sophisticated lady / I'm satisfied / Saddest tale / Sumpin' about rhythm / Margie lets have a jubilee / Harlem speaks / Farewell Blues.
LP: . . . . **CAH 3003**

CARNEGIE HALL CONCERT (Ellington, Duke & His Famous Orchestra).
LP: . . . . **MVS 2004**

CARNEGIE HALL CONCERTS (DECEMBER 1947).
Tracks: / New look / Blue serge / Triple play / Harlem airshift / Wonderlust / Junior hop / Jeep's blues / Squatty roo / Mood to be wooed / Mella brava / Kickapoo joy juice jolt / On a turquoise cloud / Bakiff / Liberian suite / Cottontail / East St. Louis / Toodle-oo / Echoes of Harlem / Black and tan fantasy / Things ain't what they used to be / Basso profundo / New York City blues / Clothed woman.
2LP: . . . . **PR 24075**

CARNEGIE HALL CONCERTS (DECEMBER 1944).
Tracks: / Blutopia / Midriff / Creole love call / Suddenly it jumped / Pitter panther patter / It don't mean a thing / Perfume suite / Black, brown and beige / Things ain't what they used to be / Mood to be wooed / Blue cellophane / Blue skies / Frankie & Johnny.
2LP: . . . . **PR 24073**

CARNEGIE HALL CONCERTS (JANUARY 1946).
Tracks: / Caravan / In a mellow tone / Solid old man / Black, brown and beige / Rugged romeo / Sono / Air conditioned jungle / Pitter panther patter / Take the 'A' train / Magenta haze / Diminuendo in blue/transluency / Crescendo in blue / Suburbanite / I'm just a lucky so and so / Riffin' drill / Tonal group.
2LP: . . . . **PR 24074**

CLASSIC TRANSCRIPTIONS.
Tracks: / West Indian pancake / Love and I / John Hardy's wife / Clementine / Love like this can't last / After all / Girl of my dreams / Jumpin' punkins / Frankie and Johnny / Flamingo / It's sad but true / Mooche, The / Ring dem bells / Frustration / Coloratura / Rose of the Rio Grande / Love you madly / Take the 'A' train / Tone parallel to Harlem / Duet / Bounce / I hear a rhapsody / Madame will drop her shawl / Frenesi / Until tonight.
2LP: . . . . **AFSD 1032**

COMPLETE ELLINGTON 1947/52.
LPS: **66607**

COMPLETE LOUIS ARMSTRONG-DUKE ELLINGTON SESSIONS (See under Armstrong, Louis) (Ellington, Duke & Louis Armstrong).

CONCERT IN THE VIRGIN ISLANDS (Ellington, Duke And His Orchestra).
Tracks: / Island virgin / Virgin jungle / Fiddler on the diddle / Jungle kitty / Things ain't what they used to be / Big fat Alice's blues / Chelsea Bridge / Opener, The / Mysterious chick / Barefoot stomper / Fade up.
LP: . . . . **DS 841**
MC: . . . . **DSC 841**

CONCERT OF SACRED MUSIC.
Tracks: / In the beginning, God / Tell me it's the truth / Come Sunday / Will you be there? / Ain't but the one / New world a-coming / David danced before the Lord with all his might.
LP: . . . . **PL 43663**

CONCERTS IN CANADA.
LP: . . . . **E 87**

COSMIC SCENE, THE.
LP: **84407**

COTTON CLUB DAYS.
Tracks: / Creole love call / Blues I love to sing / Black and tan fantasy / East St. Louis toodle-oo / Black beauty / Mooche, The / Cotton Club stomp / Misty morning / Duke steps out / Shout 'em aunt Tillie / Mood indigo / Old man blues.
LP: . . . . **CL 89801**
MC: . . . . **CK 89801**

COTTON CLUB STOMP (1937-39).
LP: . . . . **TAX 8012**

CRUISIN' WITH CAB (1939-1940) (Ellington, Duke Orchestra & Cab Calloway).
MC: . . . . **UMK 99004**

DANCE DATE (Airforce USA March 1958).
LP: **JC004**

DANCE DATE (2) (Air Force 1960).
LP: . . . . **UJ 27**

DIGITAL DUKE.
Tracks: / Solitude / Sophisticated lady / Prelude to a kiss / Perdido / Take the 'A' train / Do nothing till you hear from me / Jeep's blues / In a mellow tone / Cottontail / Satin doll / Mood indigo / Birmingham breakdown / 22 cent's stomp.
LP: . . . . **GRP 91038**
MC: . . . . **GRPM 91038**
DAT: . . . . **GRT 9548**

DRUM IS A WOMAN, A.
LP: **84405**

DUKE.
LP: . . . . **VS 81007**

DUKE:- 1956 TO 1962 VOL.1 (Ellington, Duke And His Orchestra).
Tracks: / Black and tan fantasy / A-flat minor / Suburban beauty / Cafe au lait / West Indian dance / Cop out / Allah-bye / Piano improvisations (parts 1-4) / Commercial time / Mood indigo / Willow weep for me / Mood indigo (II) / Where or when / All the things you are / Night and day / Slamar in D flat / Track 360 / Jones / Lullaby of Birdland / Feet bone / Red carpet / Satin doll / When I trilly with my filly / Anatomy of a murder.
2LP: . . . . **CBS 88653**
MC: **40 88653**

DUKE:- 1956 TO 1962 VOL.2 (Ellington, Duke And His Orchestra).
Tracks: / Brown penny / Pie eyes blues / Sentimental lady / Sweet and pungent / Swinger's jump, The / Lullaby of Birdland / Dreamy sort of thing / Wailer, The / Asphalt jungle, The / Lotus blossom / Matumbe / Just a sittin' and a rockin' / Tulip or turnip? / Jingle bells / One more once / Blues in Hoss's flat / Asphalt jungle theme-Pt 1, Pt 3 / Bon amour / Paris blues- Parts 1-3 / Turkish coffee.
2LP: . . . . **CBS 88654**
MC: **40 88654**

DUKE:- 1956 TO 1962 VOL.3 (Ellington, Duke And His Orchestra).
Tracks: / If you were in my place / Just a sittin' and a rockin' / Pomegranate / Rock city rock / Your love has faded / My heart, my mind, my everything / Together / Duke's place / Hand me down love / Walkin' and singin' the blues / I can't give you anything but love / To know you is to love you / Lonely one, The / Lost in loveliness / I'm just a lucky so and so / One more once / Day in, day out / Why was I born? / Love you madly / Where in the world? / Moulin Rouge.
2LP: . . . . **CBS 26306**
MC: **40 26306**

DUKE ELLINGTON (On various discs 1945-46).
Tracks: / Perfume suite (Recorded at the 400 Club, New York, 7 April 1945.) / Under the balcony (Recorded at the 400 Club, New York, 7 April 1945.) / Strange feeling (Recorded at the 400 Club, New York, 7 April 1945.) / Dancers in love (Recorded at the 400 Club, New York, 7 April 1945.) / Coloratura (Recorded at the 400 Club, New York, 7 April 1945.) / Diminuendo in blue (Recorded at the 400 Club, New York, 1 August 1945.) / Crescendo in blue (Recorded at the 400 Club, New York, 1 August 1945.) / In the shade of the old apple tree (Recorded at the Zanzibar Club, New York, 14 November 1945.) / Esquire swank (Recorded at the Philharmonic Auditorium, Los Angeles, 17 January, 1946.) / Frankie and Johnny (Recorded at the Philharmonic Auditorium, Los Angeles, 26 December, 1945.) / Sultry sunset (Recorded at Carnegie Hall, New York, 23 November 1946.) / Take the 'A' train / C jam blues / On the sunny side of the street / Caravan / I got it bad and that ain't good / Sophisticated lady / I let a song go out of my heart / Don't get around much anymore / Solitude / Rockin' in rhythm.
LP: . . . . **BLJ 8018**
LP: . . . . **KLJ 20003**
MC: . . . . **ZCGAS 749**

DUKE ELLINGTON (1941).
LP: **99003**

DUKE ELLINGTON (1927-30).
LP: . . . . **S 1231**

DUKE ELLINGTON (1946-47).
Tracks: / Magenta haze (Recorded in New York, 28 March 1946.) / Eighth veil, The (Recorded in New York, 28 March 1946.) / Transblucency (Recorded in New York, 28 March 1946.) / Embraceable you (Recorded in New York, 28 March 1946.) / Hey baby (Recorded in Hollywood, 11 July 1946.) / Come rain or come shine (Recorded in Hollywood, 11 July 1946.) / Overture to a jam session (Recorded in New York, 7 January 1947.) / Jam-a-ditty (Recorded in New York, 7 January 1947.) / Frustration (Recorded in New York, 10 June 1947.) / Azalea (Recorded in New York, 10 June 1947.) / Orchids for madam (Recorded in New York, 10 June 1947.).
LP: . . . . **QU 036**

DUKE ELLINGTON AND FRIENDS (Compact/Walkman jazz) (Ellington, Duke & Friends).
Tracks: / Take the 'A' train / Caravan / Mood indigo / I let a song go out of my heart / Prelude to a kiss / Satin doll / Stompy Jones / I got it bad (and that ain't good) / Don't get around much anymore / It don't mean a thing.
MC: **833 291-4**

DUKE ELLINGTON AND HIS FAMOUS ORCHESTRA.
MC: . . . . **UMK 99003**

DUKE ELLINGTON AND HIS ORCHESTRA (1940-41) (Ellington, Duke and his orchestra).
Tracks: / Stomp caprice / Bugle breaks / You and I / Have you changed? / Raincheck / Blue serge / Moon mist / I don't want to set the world on fire / Easy Street / Perdido.
LP: . . . . **SM 3120**

DUKE ELLINGTON AND JOHN COLTRANE (Ellington, Duke/John Coltrane).
Tracks: / In a sentimental mood / Take the Coltrane / Big Nick / Stevie / My little brown book / Angelica / Feeling of jazz, The.
LP: . . . . **JAS 4**
MC: . . . . **JAS C4**

DUKE ELLINGTON AND ORCHESTRA (Ellington, Duke Orchestra).
LP: . . . . **EJLP 04**
MC: . . . . **EJMC 04**

DUKE ELLINGTON AND ORCHESTRA (1946) (Ellington, Duke And His Orchestra).
Tracks: / Take the 'A' train / Crosstown / Passion flower / Magenta haze / Everything goes / Eighth veil, The / Riff'n'drill / Blue abandon / Transblucency / Rugged romeo / Jennie / Sono / Jeep is jumpin'.
LP: . . . . **HSR 125**

DUKE ELLINGTON AND ORCHESTRA, VOL. 2 (1946) (Ellington, Duke Orchestra).
Tracks: / Rockabye river / Pretty woman / Gathering in a clearing, A / You don't love me no more / Tip toe topic / Just squeeze me / Perdido / Hey baby / Suddenly it jumped / Come rain or come shine / Fickle fling / 9:20 special / One o'clock jump.
LP: . . . . **HSR 126**

DUKE ELLINGTON AND REX STEWART (1943-46) (Ellington, Duke & Rex Stewart).
LP: . . . . **AA 501**

DUKE ELLINGTON AND THE SMALL GROUPS.
LP: . . . . **LPJT 70**

DUKE ELLINGTON AT CARNEGIE HALL (23/11/46).
LP: . . . . **QUEEN 017**

DUKE ELLINGTON COLLECTION (20 golden greats).
Tracks: / Take the 'A' train / I got it bad and that ain't good / Things ain't what they used to be / Black and tan fantasy / Creole love call / Mooche, The / El Gato / Rockin' in rhythm / Hawk talks, The / East St. Louis toodle-oo / Cotton Club stomp / Saratoga swing / Jungle nights in Harlem / Koko / Do nothing till you hear from me / Harlem air shaft / C jam blues / Chloe / Just a sittin' and a rockin' / Across the track blues.
LP: . . . . **DVLP 2014**
MC: . . . . **DVMC 2014**

DUKE ELLINGTON CONCERT (1953).
LP: . . . . **GNPS 9045**
MC: **GNP5 9045**

DUKE ELLINGTON DANCE (1958).
LP: . . . . **UJ 16**

DUKE ELLINGTON & HIS FAMOUS ORCHESTRA (1932-38).
LP: . . . . **SWINGFAN 1001**

DUKE ELLINGTON & HIS FAMOUS ORCHESTRA (Ellington, Duke and his orchestra/Johnny Hodges).
Tracks: / My heritage / Happy go lucky local / Soda fountain rag / What's you gonna do when the bed breaks down? / My people / Blues, The / Rockin' in rhythm / My mother and my father / Impressions of the Far East / Bluebird of Delhi / David danced before the Lord with all his might / Banquet / Skinipoop / Jam with Sam / Take the 'A' train.
LP: . . . . **RARITIES 29**

DUKE ELLINGTON & HIS ORCHESTRA 1939-40/CRUISIN' WITH CAB (Ellington, Duke & Cab Calloway).
MC: . . . . **UMK 99004**

DUKE ELLINGTON IN LONDON (1958).
2LP: . . . . **E 88**

DUKE ELLINGTON MEETS COLEMAN HAWKINS (Ellington, Duke & Coleman Hawkins).
Tracks: / Limbo jazz / Mood indigo / Ray Charles's place / Wanderlust / You dirty dog / Self portrait (of the bean) / Jeep is jumpin' / Recitic, The.
LP: . . . . **JAS 1**
MC: . . . . **JAS C1**
LP: . . . . **AS 26**
MC: . . . . **ASC 26**

DUKE ELLINGTON (OCTOBER 20, 1945).
LP: . . . . **QUEEN 006**

DUKE ELLINGTON ORCHESTRA.
Tracks: / How blue can you be? / Ultra blue / Teardrops in the rain / Time on my hands / Koko / Honeysuckle rose / Perdido / Air conditioned jungle / Waitin' for the train to come in / I'd do it all over again / If I loved you / Fancy dance / Homesick, that's all / Blues on the double.
LP: . . . . **QU 006**
LP: . . . . **GM 7705**

DUKE ELLINGTON PRESENTS... (Big band bounce and boogie) (Ellington, Duke And His Orchestra).
Tracks: / Summertime / Laura / I can't get started / My funny Valentine / Everything but you / Frustration / Cottontail / Daydream / Deep Purple / Indian Summer / Blues.
LP: . . . . **AFS 1013**
MC: . . . . **TCAFS 1013**

DUKE ELLINGTON VOL.1.

LP: . . . . T 1001

DUKE ELLINGTON VOL.2.
LP: . . . . T 1003

DUKE ELLINGTON: VOL.4.
LP: . . . . FDC 1023

DUKE ELLINGTON: VOL. 2, 1944-46.
LP: . . . . FDC 1011

DUKE ELLINGTON, VOL. 3 (1946) (Ellington, Duke Orchestra).
Tracks: / Unbooted character, The / Suburbanite, The / Indiana / Moon mist / In a jam / On the Alamo / I can't believe that you're in love with me / Tea for two / Just you, just me / Someone / Double ruff / Flower is a lovesome thing, A / Mooche, The.
LP: . . . . HSR 127

DUKE ELLINGTON: VOL. 3, 1945-47.
LP: . . . . FDC 1013

DUKE ELLINGTON, VOL. 4 (1947) (Ellington, Duke Orchestra).
Tracks: / Golden cress / Flippant flurry / Jam-a-ditty / Fugueaditty / Happy go lucky local / Overture to a jam session / Sultry sunset / Beale Street blues / Memphis blues / St. Louis Blues / Who struck John?.
LP: . . . . HSR 128

DUKE ELLINGTON, VOL. 5 (1947) (Ellington, Duke Orchestra).
Tracks: / Swamp fire / How high the moon / Blue Lou / Violet blue / Royal Garden blues / Jumpin' punkins / Park at 106th / Frustration / Blue is the night / Jump for joy / Far away blues / Embraceable you / Frisky / Take the 'A' train.
LP: . . . . HSR 129

DUKE ELLINGTON WITH ALICE BABS AND NILS LINDBERG (Ellington, Duke, Alice Babs & Nils Lindberg).
LP: . . . . PHON 11

DUKE FEATURES HODGES.
Tracks: / Ring dem bells / Daydream / Jump for joy / Warm valley / Rockabye river / Whispering grass / Mood to be wooed, The / Jeep is jumpin' / Sentimental lady / I don't mind / Passion flower / Hop, skip and jump.
LP: . . . . UJ 35

DUKE IS ON THE AIR: VOLUME 1, THE (Ellington, Duke And His Orchestra).
Tracks: / Bensonality / All of me / Bakiff / Hawk talks, The / Do nothing till you hear from me / VIP's boogie / Jam with Sam / Just a sittin' and a rockin' / Mood indigo / Tulip or turnip / Ting a ling / Flamingo / Rockin' in rhythm / Sophisticated lady / Take the 'A' train / Flying home.
LP: . . . . AIRCHECK 4

DUKE IS ON THE AIR: VOLUME 2, THE (Ellington, Duke And His Orchestra).
Tracks: / Blue cellophane / Frustration / I'm beginning to see the light / Just a sittin' and a rockin' / Trumpets no end / Midriff / Candy / Black, brown and beige / Accentuate the positive / Way low.
LP: . . . . AIRCHECK 29

DUKE'S BIG FOUR (Ellington, Duke Quartet).
Tracks: / Cottontail / Blues, The / Hawk talks, The / Prelude to a kiss / Love you madly / Just squeeze me / Everything but you.
LP: 2310 703
MC: K10 703

DUKE,THE 1940.
2LP: . . . . AA 520/521

EARLY CLASSICS VOL.1, THE.
MC: . . . . NEO 725

EARLY CLASSICS VOL.2, THE.
LP: . . . . NEO 726

EARLY CLASSICS VOL.3 (1926-28).
MC: . . . . NEO 758

EARLY ELLINGTON.
Tracks: / Black and tan fantasy / Creole love call / East St. Louis toodle-oo / Black beauty / Mooche, The / Flaming youth / Ring dem bells / Old man blues / Mood indigo / Rockin' in rhythm / Creole rhapsody / Creole rhapsody (part 2) / Echoes of the jungle / Daybreak express / Stompy Jones / Solitude.
LP: . . . . NL 86852
MC: . . . . NK 86852

ELEGANT MR ELLINGTON, THE.
LP: . . . . SWH 4
MC: . . . . CSWH 4

ELLA AND DUKE AT THE COTE D'AZUR (see under Fitzgerald, Ella) (Ellington, Duke and Ella Fitzgerald).

ELLINGTON, DUKE & HIS ORCHESTRA.
LP: . . . . SLP 4003

ELLINGTON MOODS.
LP: 500061

ELLINGTON SUITES, THE.
Tracks: / Sunset and the mocking bird (From Queen's suite.) / Lightning bugs and frogs (From Queen's suite.) / Le sucrier velours (From Queen's suite.) / Northern lights (From Queen's suite.) / Single petal of a rose (From Queen's suite.) / Apes and peacocks (From Queen's suite.) / Fanfare (From Goutelas suite.) / Goutelas / Get with it ness (From Goutelas suite.) / Something (From Goutelas suite.) / Having at it (From Goutelas suite.) / Uwis (From Uwis suite.) / Klop (From Uwis suite.) / Loco madi (From Uwis suite.).
LP: 231 0762
MC: K10 762

ELLINGTON TRAIN, THE.
LP: . . . . E 30 885

ELLINGTON UPTOWN.
LP: 84309

ESSENTIAL DUKE ELLINGTON VOL.1 (1924-27).
LP: . . . . VLP 71

ESSENTIAL DUKE ELLINGTON VOL.2 (1927).
LP: . . . . VLP 72

ESSENTIAL DUKE ELLINGTON VOL.3 (Instrumentals 1927-1928).
Tracks: / Red hot band / Doin' the frog / Sweet mama / Stack o lee blues / Bugle call rag / Got everything but you / Jubilee stomp / Harlem twist / Take it easy / Black beauty / Jubilee stomp (II) / Yellow dog blues / Tishomingo blues / Diga diga doo / Doin' the new low down / Swampy river / Mooche, The.
LP: . . . . VLP 73

ESSENTIAL DUKE ELLINGTON VOL.4 (1928-29).
LP: . . . . VLP 74

ESSENTIAL DUKE ELLINGTON VOL.5.
LP: . . . . VLP 75

ESSENTIAL, THE.
MC: 4671464

EVENING WITH THE DUKE (Ellington, Duke Orchestra).
LP: . . . . GOJ 1003

FABULOUS FORTIES, THE.
Tracks: / Bojangles / People will say, The / Five o'clock drag / Johnny come lately / Tonight I shall sleep / Wait for me, Mary / It's been so long / Blue skies / Don't get around much anymore / Altitude / I don't want anybody at all / Things ain't what they used to be / April in Paris / Whispering grass / Just a sittin' and a rockin' / Theme and intro.
LP: . . . . RARITIES 56
LP: . . . . LPJT 66

FABULOUS FORTIES VOL.2, THE.
Tracks: / C jam blues / Sophisticated lady / I can't give you anything but love / It don't mean a thing / On the sunny side of the street / Moon mist / Theme and intro / Happy-go-lucky local / Jungle / Frantic fantasy / In a sentimental mood / Mood indigo / Hiawatha / Warm valley / Frustration / Air conditioned jungle / Caravan / Solitude / Don't get around much anymore.
LP: . . . . RARITIES 59

FANTASTIC.
LP: . . . . FJL 27161(2)

FAR AWAY STAR (see under Babs, Alice) (Ellington, Duke, Alice Babs & Nils Lindberg).

FARGO ENCORES.
LP: . . . . NOST 7636

FEELING OF JAZZ, THE.
LP: . . . . BLP 60123

FESTIVAL SESSION (Ellington, Duke And His Orchestra).
Tracks: / Idiom '59 (parts 1-3) / Things ain't what they used to be / Launching pad / Perdido / Cop out extension / Duael fuel (parts 1-3).
LP: . . . . CBS 21137
MC: 40 21137

FIVE HORN GROVE (Ellington, Duke and his trumpets).
LP: 500094

GIANTS, 3 (Ellington, Duke with Holiday, Billie and Louis Armstrong).
LP: . . . . GOJ 1008
MC: . . . . GOJC 1008

GIRL'S SUITE (Ellington, Duke Orchestra).
Tracks: / Girls / Mahalia / Peg o' my heart / Juanita / Sylvia / Lena / Girl's suite / Dinah / Clementine / Diane / Under the balcony / Strange feeling / Dancers in love / Coloratura.
LP: . . . . CBS 85933

GOIN' UP (Ellington, Duke Orchestra).
Tracks: / Coca cola theme & intro / Perdido / Hayfoot strawfoot / Don't get around much anymore / Coca cola commercial / Going up / Things ain't what they used to be / Take the 'A' train / After a while / I ain't got nothin' but the blues / Riff staccato / I didn't know about you / Main stem.
LP: . . . . D 1011

GOLDEN DUKE.
Tracks: / Jam-a-ditty / Diminuendo in blue / Magenta haze / Blue skies / Hiawatha (Duke Ellington swings Hiawatha on Golden Duke.) / Minnehaha / Overture to a jam session / Flippant flurry / Golden feather / Tulip or turnip / It shouldn't happen to a dream / Sultry sunset / Happy-go-lucky local / Cottontail / C jam blues / Flamingo / Bang up blues / Tonk / Johnny come lately / In a blue summer garden / Great times / Perdido / Take the 'A' train / Oscalypso / Blues for Blanton.
2LP: . . . . PR 24029

GREAT DUKE ELLINGTON, THE (Premier label).
Tracks: / Take the 'A' train / I got it bad and that ain't good / Perdido / Mood indigo / Black and tan fantasy / Twitch / Solitude / Do nothin' til you hear from me / Mooche / Sophisticated lady / Creole love call.
LP: CBR1009

GREAT REUNION (See Armstrong, Louis) (Ellington, Duke & Louis Armstrong).

GREAT TIMES (Ellington, Duke & Billy Strayhorn).
LP: . . . . OJC 108

GREATEST HITS: DUKE ELLINGTON.
Tracks: / Take the 'A' train / Sophisticated lady / Caravan / Perdido / Prelude to a kiss / C jam blues / Mood indigo / Mooche, The / Satin doll / Solitude.
LP: . . . . CBS 21059
MC: 40 21059

HARLEM (Ellington, Duke And His Orchestra).
Tracks: / Blow by blow / Caravan / Satin doll / Harlem / Things ain't what they used to be / All of me / Prowling cat, The / Opera, The / Happy reunion / Tutti for cootie.
LP: 230 8245
MC: . . . . K 08 245

HOLLYWOOD BOWL CONCERT, THE.
Tracks: / Blutopia / Overture to a jam session / Mooche, The / Jumpin' punkins / Ring dem bells / Beale Street blues / Memphis blues / St. Louis blues / Golden feather / Air conditioned jungle / Golden cress / Diminuendo in blue / Translucency / Crescendo in blue.
LP: . . . . UJ 01

HOLLYWOOD BOWL CONCERT: VOL 2.
Tracks: / Come Sunday / Blues, The / Emancipation celebration / Dancers in love / Frankie and Johnny / Take the 'A' train / Moon mist / Jam-a-ditty / Minnehaha / Hiawatha.
LP: . . . . UJ 03

HOT FROM HARLEM (1927-1930) (Ellington, Duke And His Orchestra).
Tracks: / Black and tan fantasy / Chicago stompdown / Sweet mama / Bugle call rag / Take it easy / Jubilee stomp / Harlem twist / Black beauty / Swamp river / Mooch / Move over / Hot and bothered / Misty mornin' / Syncopated shuffle / Big house blues / Ring dem bells / Three little words / Old man blues / Sweet chariot / Mood indigo / Rockin' in rhythm.
2LP: . . . . SHB 58

HOT FROM THE COTTON CLUB.
Tracks: / Mooche, The / Harlem twist / Hot and bothered / Diga diga doo / Black beauty / Mood indigo / Ring dem bells / Doin' the new low down / Black and tan fantasy / Jungle jamboree / Big house blues / Old man blues / Rockin' in rhythm / Blues with a feeling / Misty mornin' / Goin' to town.
LP: . . . . EG 2605671
MC: . . . . EG 2605674

IMMORTAL DUKE ELLINGTON & HIS ORCHESTRA (Broadcasts 1940/41) (Ellington, Duke And His Orchestra).
Tracks: / Grievin' / Gal from Joe's, The / Day in, day out / I don't want to set the world on fire.
LP: 20805

IN A MELLOTONE.
Tracks: / Take the 'A' train / Portrait of Bert Williams, A / Main stem / Just a settin' and a rockin' / I got it bad (and that ain't good) / Perdido / Blue serge / Flaming sword, The / In a mellow tone / Cottontail / I don't know what kind of blues I got / Rumpus in Richmond / All too soon / Sepia panorama / Rocks in my bed / What am I here for?.
LP: . . . . LSA 3069

IN CONCERT AT THE PLEYEL PARIS VOL.2 (1958).
Tracks: / El Gato / Take the 'A' train / M.B. blue / VIP boogie / Jam with Sam / Stompy Jones / Hi fi fo fun / Medley / Hawkes talks.
MC: . . . . CAWE 39

IN SWEDEN (1958).
LP: . . . . CAH 4001

IN THE UNCOMMON MARKET.
Tracks: / Bula / Silk Lace / Asphalt jungle, The / Star crossed lovers / Getting sentimental over you / E.S.P. (extra sensory perception) / Paris blues / Shepherd, The (first concept) / Kinda Dukish.
LP: 230 8247
MC: . . . . K 8247

INCOMPARABLE, THE.
LP: . . . . DBD 11
MC: . . . . DBDC 11

INDIGOS.
LP: 4633421
MC: 4633424
LP: 82682

INDISPENSABLE DUKE ELLINGTON VOLS.9-10 (The small groups).
Tracks: / Daydream / Good Queen Bess / That's the blues, old man / Junior hop / Without a song / My Sunday gal / Mobile Bay / Linger awhile / Charlie the Chulo / Lament for Javanette / Lull at dawn, A / Ready Eddy / Dear old Southland / Solitude / Some Saturday / Subtle slough / Menelik the lion of Judah / Poor bubber / Squattyroo / Passion flower / Things ain't what they used to be / Going out the back way / Brown suede / Noir blue / C jam blues / June / Frankie and Johnny / Jumpin' room only / Tonk / Drawing room blues.
2LP: . . . . NL 89582
MCSET: . . . . NK 89582

INDISPENSABLE DUKE ELLINGTON VOLS 1-2 (1927 - 29).
Tracks: / Creole love call / Blues I love to sing / Black and tan fantasy / Washington wobble / Harlem river quiver / East St. Louis toodle-oo / Blue bubbles / Black beauty / Jubilee stomp / Got everything but you / Flaming youth / Saturday night function / Doin' the voom voom / Harlemania / Dicty glide, The / Hot feet / Sloppy Joe / Stevedore stomp / Cotton Club stomp / Mississippi dry / Duke steps out / Haunted nights / Swanee shuffle / Breakfast dance / Jazz lips / Mooche, The / High life / Misty mornin' / Saratoga swing.
2LP: . . . . NL 89749
MCSET: . . . . NK 89749
2LP: . . . . PM 43687

INDISPENSABLE DUKE ELLINGTON VOL.7-8.
2LP: . . . . NL 89274
MC: . . . . NK 89274

INDISPENSABLE DUKE ELLINGTON VOLS. 5-6.
Tracks: / Koko (II) / Bojangles (II) / Pitter panther patter (II) / Body and soul (take 2) / Sophisticated lady (II) / Jack the bear / Koko / Morning glory / Conga brava / Concerto for Cootie (Do nothin' till you hear from me) / Bojangles / Cottontail / Never no lament / Dusk / Portrait of Bert Williams, A / Blue goose / Harlem air shaft / At a Dixie roadside diner / All too soon / Rumpus in Richmond / Sepia panorama / In a mellow tone / Five o'clock whistle / Warm valley / Across the track blues / Chloe / Sidewalks of New York, The / Pitter panther patter / Body and soul / Sophisticated lady / Mr. J.B. Blues.
2LP: . . . . NL 89750
MCSET: . . . . NK 89750
2LP: . . . . PM 45352

INDISPENSABLE DUKE ELLINGTON VOLS. 3-4.
Tracks: / Stompy Jones / Solitude / Blue feeling / Ebony rhapsody / Live and love tonight / I met my Waterloo / My old flame / Troubled waters / Double check stomp / Sweet dreams of love / Jungle nights in Harlem / Shout 'em Aunt Tillie / Aunt Tillie / Ring dem bells / Old man blues / Nine little miles from Ten Ten Tennessee / When a black man's blue / Mood indigo / Rockin' in rhythm / Creole rhapsody (parts 1 & 2) / Limehouse blues / Echoes of the jungle / It's glory / Mystery song, The / Dinah / Bugle call rag / Dallas doings / Sweet jazz o'mine / Rude interlude / Dear old Southland / Daybreak express / Delta serenade.
2LP: . . . . NL 89762
2LP: . . . . PM 43697
MCSET: . . . . NK 89762

INDISPENSABLE DUKE ELLINGTON, VOLS.11-12 (1944-46).
Tracks: / I'm beginning to see the light / Black, brown and beige - i) Work song / Black, brown and beige - ii) Come Sunday / Black, brown and beige - iii)

The blues / Black, brown and beige - iv) Three dances / Carnegie blues / Mood to be wooed, The / (Otto make that) riff staccato / Prelude to a kiss / Caravan / Black and tan fantasy / Mood indigo / In a sentimental mood / It don't mean a thing / Sophisticated lady / Tonight I shall sleep / I let a song go out of my heart / Solitude / Black beauty / Perfume suite -i) Balcony serenade / Perfume suite - ii) Strange feeling / Perfume suite - iii) Dancers in love / Perfume suite - iv) Coloratura / Time's a wastin' / Rockabye river / Suddenly it jumped / Transblucency / Just squeeze me / Gathering in a clearing, A / Beale Street blues / Memphis blues / St. Louis blues / Swamp fire / Royal Garden blues.
2LP: . . . . **NL 89972**
MC: . . . . **NK 89972**

INTIMACY OF THE BLUES (Ellington, Duke-Small Bands).
Tracks: / Combo suite / Intimacy of the blues, The / Out south / Tell me 'bout my baby / Kentucky Avenue / Near North / Soul country / Noon morning / Rockochet / Tippy-toeing through the jungle garden / Just a sittin' and a rockin' / All too soon.
LP: . . . . **F 9640**

INTIMATE DUKE ELLINGTON.
Tracks: / Moon maiden / Edward the first / Symphonette / Intimate interlude / Some summer fun / Layin' on mellow / Eulb / Tenz / I got it bad and that ain't good / Sophisticated lady / Edward the second.
LP: **2310 787**
MC: **K10 787**

ISFAHAN.
Tracks: / Satin doll / Isfahan / Diminuendo and crescendo in blue / Jeep's blues / Pyramid / La plues belle / Africaine.
LP: . . . . **BLM 52031**

JAM-A-DITTY (Ellington, Duke Orchestra).
LP: . . . . **JJ 602**

JAZZ CLASSICS IN DIGITAL STEREO (Swing 1930-1938).
Tracks: / Rockin' in rhythm / It don't mean a thing / Baby, when you ain't there / Bugle call rag / Blue harlem / Jazz cocktail / Lightnin' / Slippery horn / Drop me off at Harlem / Bundle of blues / Jive stomp / Dear old Southland / Saddest tale / Truckin' / Clarinet lament / Echoes of Harlem / In a jam / Stepping into swing society.
LP: . . . . **REB 686**
MC: . . . . **ZCF 686**

JAZZ COCKTAIL (Ellington, Duke And His Orchestra).
Tracks: / Stevedore stomp / Creole love call / It don't mean a thing / Hot and bothered / Rose room / Old man blues / Jungle nights in Harlem / Tiger Bay / Sweet jazz o' mine / Mood indigo / Sing you sinners / Limehouse blues / Double check stomp / Swing low / Jazz cocktail / Creole rhapsody.
LP: . . . . **AJA 5024**
MC: . . . . **ZC AJA 5024**

JAZZ FESTIVAL JAZZ (see under Clayton, Buck for media details) (Ellington, Duke and Buck Clayton).

JAZZ OF WORLD WAR 2.
Tracks: / Creole love call / It don't mean a thing / Harlem air shaft / Kissing bug / Prelude to a kiss / Ring them bells / Diminuendo and crescendo in blue / In the shade of the old apple tree / Frankie and Johnny.
LP: . . . . **SM 3134**

JAZZ PARTY.
LP: **4600591**
MC: **4600594**
LP: **84410**

JAZZ TIME VOL.14.
LP: **502714**

JEEP IS JUMPIN', THE.
Tracks: / East St. Louis toodle-oo / Creole love call / Stompy Jones / Jeep is jumpin' / Jack the bear / In a mellow tone / Koko / Midriff / Stop look and listen / Unbooted character, The / Lonesome lullaby / Upper Manhattan medical group.
LP: . . . . **AFF 91**

JIMMY BLANTON YEARS.
Tracks: / Koko / Blue goose / So far so good / Cottontail / Concerto for Cootie (Do nothin' till you hear from me) / Jack the bear / Boy meets horn / Sgt was shy, The / Ring dem bells / Chelsea Bridge / Jive rhapsody / Jumpin' punkins / Frankie and Johnny / Take the 'A' train.
LP: . . . . **QU 007**
LP: . . . . **QUEEN 007**

JOHN COLTRANE AND DUKE ELLINGTON (see under Coltrane,John) (Ellington, Duke and John Coltrane).

JUMP FOR JOY.
LP: **26012**
MC: **46012**

JUMPIN'.
Tracks: / Newport Jazz Festival suite / Jeep's blues / Take the 'A' train / Diminuendo and crescendo in blue / Segue in 'C' / Battle royal / Jumpin' at the woodside.
MC: . . . . **ELITE 014MC**

JUNGLE NIGHTS IN HARLEM.
LP: . . . . **NL 82499**
MC: . . . . **NK 82499**

JUNGLE TRIANGLE.
Tracks: / Caravan / Jungle triangle / Sentimental lady / Guitar amour / El viti / Passion flower / Agra / What am I here for? / Flirtibird.
LP: . . . . **BLM 52021**

L.A. CONCERT (1954).
LP: . . . . **GNPS 9049**
MC: **GNP5 9049**

LEGENDARY DUKE ELLINGTON, THE.
LP: . . . . **SLDO 930**
LP: . . . . **VG SLD903**

LIVE AT STUTTGART VOL.1.
LP: . . . . **EB 411**

LIVE AT THE CLUB ZANZIBAR.
Tracks: / Take the 'A' train / Wonder of You, The / Riff 'n' Drill / Last time I saw you / How Deep Is The Ocean / Every hour on the hour (I fall in love with you) / Harlem air shaft / Light / Tell it to a star / I ain't got nothin' but the blues.
LP: . . . . **GOJ 1020**
MC: . . . . **GOJC 1020**

LIVE: DUKE ELLINGTON.
2LP: . . . . **AFFD 28**

LIVE FROM HOTEL SHERMAN, CHICAGO VOL.1.
LP: . . . . **JS 704**

LIVE IN PARIS.
Tracks: / Deep purple / All of me / What else can you do with a drum / Harlem air shaft / Such sweet thunder / Stompy Jones / Things ain't what they used to be / Fe fi fo fum / El gato.
LP: . . . . **AWE 19**
MC: . . . . **CAWE 19**

LOUIS ARMSTRONG AND DUKE ELLINGTON VOL 1 (See under Armstrong Louis) (Ellington, Duke & Louis Armstrong).

LOUIS ARMSTRONG & DUKE ELLINGTON VOL.1 (Ellington, Duke & Louis Armstrong).
Tracks: / It don't mean a thing / Solitude / Don't get around much anymore / I'm beginning to see the light / Just squeeze me / Do nothing till you hear from me / I got it bad and that ain't good / Azalea.
LP: . . . . **JR 114**

MAGENTA HAZE.
Tracks: / Feeling of jazz, The / Magenta haze / Dancers in love / I'm gonna go fishin' / Rockin' in rhythm / Mr. Gentle and Mr. Cool / Smada / Jump for joy / Things ain't what they used to be.
LP: . . . . **BLM 52011**

MARCH 27TH, 1959.
Tracks: / Fat mouth / Lost in the night / Little John's tune / Frou frou / Dankworth Castle / Moonstone / Night stick / Lullaby for dreamers / She was a tinkling thing / Jamaica tomboy / Still water / Jet strip.
LP: . . . . **JV 101**

MASTERPIECES BY... (Ellington, Duke And His Orchestra).
LP: **84415**
MC: **40 84415**

MASTERS OF JAZZ.
LP: . . . . **CL 42237**

MASTERS OF JAZZ VOL.6 (Ellington, Duke And His Orchestra).
LP: . . . . **SLP 4106**

MEMORIAL.
2LP: **400029**

MIDNIGHT IN PARIS.
LP: **84414**

MONKEY JUNGLE.
Tracks: / Monkey jungle / Fleurette Africaine (the African flower) / Very special / Warm valley / REM blues / Little Max, A / Wig wise / Switchblade / Caravan / Backward country boy blues / Solitude.
LP: . . . . **BT 85129**
LP: **785 129 1**
LP: . . . . **BNP 25113**

MUSIC IS MY MISTRESS.
Tracks: / C jam blues / All of me / Black and tan fantasy / Danske onje (Danish eyes) / Queenie pie reggae / Azure / Jack the bear / Sweet Georgia Brown / Flower is a lovesome thing, A / Music is my mistress suite.
MC: . . . . **MMD 20185Y**
LP: . . . . **MMC 40185Z**

MY PEOPLE (Ellington, Duke And His Orchestra).
Tracks: / Ain't but the one / Will you be there? / Come Sunday / David danced before the Lord with all his might / My mother and my father / Montage / My people / Blues ain't / Workin' blues / My man sends me / Jail blues / Lovin' lover / King fit the battle of Alabam' / What colour is virtue?.
LP: . . . . **SM 3257**

NEVER BEEN RELEASED, RECORDINGS 1965-1972.
Tracks: / Old circus train, The / Swamp goo / Trombone buster / Bourbon street jingling / Jollies / Mellow ditty / To know you is to love you / Naidni remmus / Prowling cat, The / Madiera / Thanks for the beautiful land / Charpoy / Portrait of Louis Armstrong / Girdle hurdle / Sans snyphelle / Woods.
LP: **820 835-2**

NEW ORLEANS SUITE.
Tracks: / Blues for New Orleans / Bourbon Street jingling jollies / Portrait of Louis Armstrong / Thanks for the beautiful land on the delta / Portrait of Wellman Braud / Second line / Portrait of Sidney Bechet / Aristocracy a la Jean Lafitte / Portrait of Mahalia Jackson.
LP: . . . . **K 50403**

NIGHT TRAIN.
LP: **20132**
MC: **40132**

NUTCRACKER SUITE (Ellington, Duke And His Orchestra).
Tracks: / Nutcracker suite / Peer Gynt suite No. 1 / Peer Gynt suite No. 2.
LP: . . . . **CBS 61899**
LP: . . . . **BBL 7418**

OKEH ELLINGTON, THE.
MC: **4669644**

ON THE AIR (Ellington, Duke And His Orchestra).
Tracks: / Harlem speaks / Caravan / One, two, button your shoe / Sophisticated lady / Rockin' in rhythm / East St. Louis toodle-oo / Grievin' / Little Posey / Gal from Joe's, The / Tootin' through the roof / Day in, day out / Merry go round.
LP: . . . . **BDL 1046**
MC: . . . . **AJKL 1046**

ONE NIGHT STAND.
LP: . . . . **JLP 1023**

PARIS JAZZ PARTY.
LP: . . . . **AFF 57**

PIANO IN THE BACKGROUND (Ellington, Duke And His Orchestra).
LP: **84418**

PIANO IN THE FOREGROUND (Ellington, Duke And His Orchestra).
LP: **84419**

PIANO REFLECTIONS.
Tracks: / Who knows? / Retrospective / B flat blues / Passion flower / Dancers in love / Reflections in D / Melancholia / Prelude to a kiss / In a sentimental mood / Things ain't what they used to be / All too soon / Janet / Kinda Dukish / Night time / December blue (CD only.).
LP: **2M 056 80802**
MC: **2M 256 80802**

PIANO REFLECTIONS (1953) (Ellington, Duke Trio).
LP: . . . . **S 1346**

POPULAR DUKE ELLINGTON, THE.
Tracks: / Take the 'A' train / I got it bad and that ain't good / Perdido / Mood indigo / Black and tan fantasy / Twitch / Solitude / Do nothing till you hear from me / Mooche, The / Sophisticated lady / Creole love call.
LP: . . . . **NL 89095**
MC: . . . . **NK 89095**
LP: **9LSA 3072**
LP: . . . . **INTS 5006**

RAINBOW ROOM BROADCASTS (1967) (Ellington, Duke Octet).
Tracks: / Satin doll / Mood indigo / Take the 'A' train / Passion flower / Sophisticated lady / Things ain't what they used to be / Tricky's lick / Blues / Solitude / Daydream / Caravan.
LP: . . . . **UJ 15**

RAREST OF ALL RARE PERFORMANCES VOL 1.
LP: . . . . **KLJ 20034**

REFLECTIONS IN ELLINGTON.
LP: . . . . **EV 3005**

REPLAY ON DUKE ELLINGTON.
LP: . . . . **FEDB 5020**
MC: . . . . **FEDC 5020**

ROCKIN' IN RHYTHM (Ellington, Duke Orchestra).
Tracks: / Shoe shine boy / Trumpet in spades / Solitude / Happy as the day is long / Cootie's concerto / In a jam / Uptown beat / Yearning for love / Love is like a cigarette / Exposition swing / Show boat shuffle / Barney's concerto / It was a sad night in Harlem / East St. Louis toodle-oo / Mooche, The / It don't mean a thing / Rockin' in rhythm / Black and tan fantasy.
LP: . . . . **AJA 5057**
MC: . . . . **ZC AJA 5057**

ROCKIN' IN RHYTHM (2) (Affinity label) (Ellington, Duke And His Orchestra).
Tracks: / Rockin' in rhythm / Mood indigo / Double check stomp / Awful sad / Yellow dog blues / Louisiana / Black and tan fantasy / Creole rhapsody (parts 1 & 2) / Immigration blues / East St. Louis toodle-oo / New Orleans low down / Rent party blues / Cotton club stomp No. 1 / Home again blues / Sweet Mama / Harlem flat blues / Jungle Jamboree.
LP: . . . . **AFS 1034**

ROYALTY.
Tracks: / Mooche, The / Someone / I can't believe that you're in love with me / Indiana / Fickle fling / One o'clock jump / Tip toe topic / Tea for two / Gathering in a clearing, A / Suddenly it jumped.
LP: . . . . **ALEB 2310**
MC: . . . . **ZCALB 2310**
LP: . . . . **FEDB 5027**

SEATTLE CONCERT, THE.
Tracks: / Skin deep / How could you do a thing like that to me? / Perdido / Caravan / Harlem / Hawk talks, The / Ellington medley / Jam with Sam.
LP: . . . . **NL 90071**

SERENADE TO SWEDEN.
Tracks: / Take the 'A' train / Taffy twist / Black and tan fantasy / Stompy Jones / Sophisticated lady / C jam blues / Serenade / Boo-dah / I let a song go out of my heart.
LP: . . . . **BLM 52001**
MC: . . . . **BLM 52001C**

SHOWCASE.
Tracks: / Satin doll / C Jam blues / In a sentimental mood.
LPS: . . . . **PM 155189-3**

SIDE BY SIDE (Ellington, Duke/Johnny Hodges).
Tracks: / Stompy Jones / Squeeze me / Big shoe / Going up / Just a memory / Let's fall in love / Ruin / Bend one / You need go rock.
LP: **8215781**
MC: **8215784**

SOLOS, DUETS AND TRIOS.
Tracks: / Tonk / Frankie and Johnny / Dear old Southland / Pitter panther patter (take 1) / Body and soul (take 1) / Body and soul (take 3) / Sophisticated lady (take 2) / Mr J.B. blues (take 2) / Drawing room blues / Jumpin' room only / Solitude / Pitter panther patter (take 2) / Body and soul (take 2) / Sophisticated lady (take 1) / Mr J.B. Blues (take 1).
LP: . . . . **NL 82178**
MC: . . . . **NK 82178**

SONGBOOK 2 (see Vaughan, Sarah) (Ellington, Duke and Sarah Vaughan).

SOPHISTICATED LADY (16 Ellington Classics) (Ellington, Duke And His Orchestra).
Tracks: / Take the 'A' train / Perdido / In a mellow tone / Happy go lucky local / Sophisticated lady / I got it bad and that ain't good / Mood indigo / It don't mean a thing / Things ain't what they used to be / I let a song go out of my heart / Something to live for / Black beauty / Caravan / Dancers in love / Solitude / Black and tan fantasy.
LP: . . . . **CBS 25742**
LP: **25742**
MC: **40 25742**

SOPHISTICATED LADY (2).
MC: **771502**

SOUNDTRACK (Ellington, Duke and Bessie Smith).
LP: . . . . **SLP 702**

SOUTHLAND CAFE (1940) (See under Basie, Count) (Ellington, Duke & Count Basie).

S.R.O.
Tracks: / Take the 'A' train / I got it bad and that ain't good / Things ain't what they used to be / West Indian pancake / Black and tan fantasy / Creole love call / Mooche, The / Soul call / El gato / Open house / Rockin' in rhythm / Jam with Sam / Adlib on Nippon / C jam blues / Hawk talks, The.
MC: . . . . **MC 7680**

STEREO AIR FORCE DANCE VOL. 2 (1958).
LP: . . . . **UJ 34**

STEREO EXCURSION WITH DUKE ELLINGTON 1953-73.

LP: . . . . E 86

STOCKHOLM CONCERT (1966) (see Fitzgerald, Ella) (Ellington, Duke and Ella Fitzgerald).

STUDIO RECORDINGS VOL.1 (1937-47).
LP: . . . . UTD 2002

STUDIO RECORDINGS VOL.2 (1947-9).
LP: . . . . UTD 2003

STUDIO RECORDINGS VOL.3 (1926-52).
LP: . . . . UTD 2004

STUDIO RECORDINGS VOL.4 (1947-51).
LP: . . . . UTD 2005

STUDIO RECORDINGS VOL.5 (1929-56).
LP: . . . . UTD 2006

STUDIO RECORDINGS VOL.6 (1930-58).
LP: . . . . UTD 2007

STUDIO RECORDINGS VOL.7 (1929-62).
LP: . . . . UTD 2008

STUDIO RECORDINGS VOL.8 (1933-1967) (Ellington, Duke And His Orchestra).
LP: . . . . UTD 2009

SWEET THUNDER.
LP: 2673721
MC: 2673724

SYMPHONIC ELLINGTON.
LP: . . . . TR 529

TAKE THE 'A' TRAIN.
Tracks: / Take the 'A' train / Black and tan fantasy / Mood indigo / Skin deep / Satin doll / St. Louis blues / Diminuendo in blue / Crescendo in blue / Fat mouth / Lost in the night / Little John's tune / Lullaby for dreamers / Night stick.
LP: 20024
MC: 40024

TENDERLY (Ellington, Duke And His Orchestra).
Tracks: / Nutcracker suite overture / Such sweet thunder / Black and tan fantasy / Creole love call / Mooche, The / Tulip or turnip / Tenderly / All of me / Jeeps blues.
LP: . . . . SHLP 110
MC: . . . . SHTC 110

THIS ONE'S FOR BLANTON (Ellington, Duke/Ray Brown).
Tracks: / Do nothing till you hear from me / Pitter panther patter / Things ain't what they used to be / Sophisticated lady / See see rider / Fragmented suite for piano and bass.
LP: 231 0721
MC: K10 721

THREE SUITES, THE.
MC: 4679134

TOGETHER FOR THE FIRST TIME (See under Armstrong, Louis) (Ellington, Duke & Louis Armstrong).

TRANSCRIPTION YEARS, THE.
LP: . . . . S 1388

TRANSCRIPTION YEARS VOL.1 (1941-45).
LP: . . . . TAX 8037

TREASURY SHOW VOL.1.
Tracks: / Take the 'A' train / Blutopia / Midriff / Creole love call / Suddenly it jumped / Frustration / I'm beginning to see the light / Love / Perfume suite / Violence / Dancers in love / Coloratura / Air conditioned jungle / I ain't got nothin' but the blues / Subtle slough / Passion flower.
LP: . . . . NOST 7621

TREASURY SHOW VOL.2.
Tracks: / Take the 'A' train / Mood to be wooed / If you are but a dream / Riff staccato / I'm beginning to see the light / Black brown and beige / Stomp look and listen / Frantic fantasy / It don't mean a thing / Sentimental lady.
LP: . . . . NOST 7622

TREASURY SHOW VOL.3.
Tracks: / Take the 'A' train / Midriff / Carnegie blues / Someone / My little brown book / Kissing bug / Ring dem bells / I'm beginning to see the light / Black brown and beige / Candy / Teardrops in the rain / Accentuate the positive / Way low.
LP: . . . . NOST 7623

TREASURY SHOW VOL.4.
Tracks: / Blutopia / Clementine / Sentimental journey / I got it bad and that ain't good / Three cent stomp / Black and tan fantasy / Blue skies / Passion flower / Air conditioned jungle / Frantic fantasy / I'm beginning to see the light / Main stem / Everything but you / Carnegie blues / Jump for joy / Things ain't what they used to be / Take the 'A' train / My heart sings.
LP: . . . . NOST 7624

TREASURY SHOW VOL.5.
Tracks: / Take the 'A' train / Carnegie blues / Riff staccato / All at once / Yesterdays / I kiss your kiss / Accentuate the positive / Blue cellophane / Prelude to a kiss / Caravan / Sophisticted lady / I'm beginning to see the light / Solitude / I ain't got nothin' but the blues / I don't mind / Jeep is jumpin'.
LP: . . . . NOST 7631

TREASURY SHOW VOL.6.
Tracks: / Take the 'A' train / Teardrops in the rain / Everything but you / Perdido / If you are but a dream / Pitter panther patter / Emancipation celebration / I should care / In a sentimental mood / It don't mean a thing / Solitude / I'm beginning to see the light / Bond promo / Subtle slough / C jam blues / Don't you know I care / Stomp look and listen / Things ain't what they used to be.
LP: . . . . NOST 7632

TREASURY SHOW VOL.7.
Tracks: / Take the 'A' train / Sugar hill penthouse / Suddenly it jumped / Candy / Friend of yours, A / Kissing bug / Hollywood hangover / Laura / In the shade of the old apple tree / Frankie and Johnny / I'm beginning to see the light / Bond promo / Midriff / I ain't got nothin' but the blues / My honey's loving arms / Rockin' in rhythm.
LP: . . . . NOST 7633

TREASURY SHOW VOL.8.
Tracks: / Take the 'A' train / Mood to be wooed, The / Jack the bear / More I see you, The / Way low / Blues on the double / Summertime / Come Sunday / Light / I'm beginning to see the light / On the Alamo / Carnegie blues / Riff staccato / Blue skies / Things ain't what they used to be / Moon maiden / Edward the first / Symphonette / Intimate interlude / Some summer fun / Layin' on mellow / Eulb / Tenz / I got it bad and that ain't good / Sophisticated lady / Edward the second.
LP: . . . . NOST 7634

TRIBUTE TO DUKE (See under Tribute To ...) (Various artists).

TWO GREAT CONCERTS IN EUROPE.
Tracks: / Take the 'A' train / Caravan / Do nothing till you hear from me / Fancy dance / Hawk talks, The / Swamp drum / Main stem / Tattooed bride / Threesome / Take the 'A' train (version) / Satin doll / Sophisticated lady / Meow, shorted encore / I got it bad and that ain't good / Harmong in Harlem / Things ain't what they used to be / Perdido / New concerto for Cootie, The / Carolina shout / Take the 'A' train.
MC: 302282

UNDOCUMENTED ELLINGTON, THE.
LP: . . . . UTD 2001

UNFORGETTABLE DUKE ELLINGTON, THE.
Tracks: / H'ya Sue / It's mad mad mad / You gotta crawl before you walk / Brown Penny / Boogie bop blues / Three cent stomp / Progressive gavotte / Take it easy / Singing in the rain / Don't get around much anymore / I can't believe that you're in love with me.
MCSET: . . . . DTO 10045

UNKNOWN SESSION.
Tracks: / Everything but you / Black beauty / All too soon / Something to live for / Mood indigo / Creole blues / Don't you know I care / Flower is a lovesome thing / Mighty like the blues / Tonight I shall sleep / Dual highway / Blues.
LP: . . . . CBS 82819

UNUSUAL ELLINGTON, THE.
Tracks: / Stomp look and listen / Warm valley / Sultry serenade / Hiya Sue / Passion flower / Primping for the prom / Cobb's tune / Coffee and kisses / Easy to love / Change my ways / Liza / Body and soul.
LP: . . . . NOST 7614

UP IN DUKE'S WORKSHOP.
Tracks: / Blem / Goof, The / Love is just around the corner / Bateau / Wanderlust / Neo-Creole / Black butterfly / Mendoza.
LP: 231 0815
MC: K10 815

UPTOWN.
Tracks: / Take the 'A' train / Mooche, The / Tone parallel to Harlem / Perdido / Controversial suite part 1 / Before my time / Controversial suite part 2 / Skin deep.
LP: 4608301
MC: 4608304

VIP (Rare live performances).
LP: . . . . SWH 28

WASHINGTON D.C. ARMORY CONCERT, THE.
Tracks: / Perdido / All the things you are / Just squeeze me / La virgen de la Macarena / Happy go lucky local / Tone parallel to Harlem / Take the 'A' train / John Sander's blues.
LP: . . . . NOST 7611

WASHINGTON WOBBLE.
LP: . . . . SVL 206

WAY LOW - LANGLEY FIELDS BROADCAST (1942-1943) (Ellington, Duke Orchestra).
LP: . . . . D 1015

WEST COAST TOUR.
LP: . . . . JAZ 2010
MC: . . . . ZCJAZ 2010

Ellington, Lance

PLEASURE AND PAIN.
LP: . . . . AMA 7049
MC: . . . . AMC 7049

Ellington, Mercer

STEPPIN' INTO SWING SOCIETY (Ellington, Mercer & His Orchestra).
Tracks: / Steppin' into swing society / Frolic Sam / Ruint / Be patient / Gal from Joe's, The / Indelible / Broadway babe / Black butterfly / Got my foot in the door / If you were in my place / Yearning for love / Afternoon moon / Black and tan fantasy / Maroon / Azure / Mood indigo.
LP: . . . . AFF 194

Ellington, Ray

GOON SHOW HITS (Ellington, Ray Quartet).
Tracks: / Framed / Three bears, The / I've got a gal in Kalamazoo / Signora-Bueno sera (medley) / Lady's in love with you, The / Little girl / That's my girl / Teddy bears' picnic / Ol' man river / Miss Otis regrets / Old Mother Hubbard / My very good friend the milkman / It's a sin to tell a lie / I want a little girl / From this moment on.
LP: . . . . REC 172

Elliot, Derek

YORKSHIRE RELISH (Elliot, Derek & Dorothy & Nadine).
LP: . . . . TSR 025

Elliot, Don

MELLOPHONE.
LP: . . . . FS 200

Elliot, Richard

INITIAL APPROACH.
LP: 3283 1

TAKE TO THE SKIES.
Tracks: / I'm loving you / Take to the skies / When a man loves a woman / In your arms / Down to the keys / Broadwalk walk / In the name of love / Grip, The / Moonlight in your eyes / 4.00 a.m..
LP: . . . . ENVLP 527
MC: . . . . TCENV 527
LP: . . . . INTM 73348
LP: 773 348 1

Elliott, Bern

BEAT YEARS, THE (Elliott, Bern & The Fenmen).
Tracks: / Money / Nobody but me / New Orleans / Chills / I can tell / Do the mashed potatoe / Please Mr. Postman / Shake sherry shake / Talking about you (live) / Everybody needs a little love / Shop around / Little Egypt (live) / Good times / What do you want with my baby / Guess who / Make it easy on yourself / Forget her / Voodoo woman / Lipstick traces (on a cigarette) / Be my girl / Rag doll / I've got everything you need babe / Every little day now.
LP: . . . . SEE 239

Elliott, Jack

JACK ELLIOTT OF BIRTLEY.
LP: . . . . LEA 4001

KEROUAC'S LAST DREAM.
LP: . . . . FF 4005

MULESKINNER.
Tracks: / San Francisco bay blues / Ol' Riley / Boll weevil / Bed bug blues / New York town / Old blue / Grey goose / Mule skinner blues / East Texas talking blues / Cocaine / Dink's song / Black baby / Salt dog.
LP: 12T 106

ROLL ON BUDDY.
Tracks: / Rich and rambling boy / Buffalo skinners / I wish I was a rock / It's hard ain't it hard / All around the water tank / Mother's not dead / East Virginia blues / Old bachelor, The / Danville girl / State of Arkansas / Death of Mr.Garfield / Roll on Buddy.
LP: 12T 105

TALKING DUST BOWL.
Tracks: / Pretty boy Floyd / Roll in my sweet baby's arms / Tom joad / Riding in my car / Grand Coulee dam / East Virginia blues / South coast / Tramp on the street / Cuckoo, The / Talking dustbowl blues / New York Town / So long (it's been good to know you) / Railroad Bill / Talking Columbia blues / Last letter, The / This land is your land.
LP: . . . . WIK 86

TALKING WOODY GUTHRIE.
Tracks: / Talking Columbia blues / Pretty Boy Floyd / Ludlow massacre / Talking miner blues / Hard travellin' / So long, it's been good to know you / Talking dustbowl blues / 1913 / Massacre / Rambling blues / Talking sailor blues.
LP: 12T 93

Elliott, Mike

AT LAST IT'S MIKE ELLIOTT.
Tracks: / Pseudosciences / Bio-rhythms / Willy trapping / T.V. adverts / Breasts for men / Trip to France / Grammar schoolboy / St. Tupperware / Cow turd pie / Makin' me happy.
LP: . . . . RUB 044
MC: . . . . RUBC 044

OUT OF THE BROWN.
Tracks: / Just a word in your ear / Talking crap / Cushie butterfield / True and woeful story of a woman undone, A / Thank you Lord / Red badge of carrots, A / Brown ale crazy / He was a rover / Ferret's magic / Lav story / Joseph / Mary and the bairn / Commercial break.
LP: . . . . RUB 025

Ellis, Alton

25TH SILVER JUBILEE.
LP: . . . . SKYLP 46
MC: . . . . SKYCAS 46

ALTON AND HORTENSE ELLIS (Ellis, Alton & Hortense).
LP: . . . . HB 64

BEST OF ALTON ELLIS.
LP: . . . . CSL 8019

CONTINUATION.
LP: . . . . AT 0051

DAY DREAMING.
LP: . . . . SCLP 009

HERE I AM.
LP: . . . . ANG 005LP

JUBILEE VOL.2.
LP: . . . . SKYLP 53
MC: . . . . SKYCAS 53

LOVE TO SHARE.
LP: . . . . TDWD 6

MY TIME IS THE RIGHT TIME.
LP: . . . . TRLS 282

STILL IN LOVE.
Tracks: / Still in love / Rock steady / Change of plan / Breaking up / Play it cool / Reggae with you.
LP: . . . . HRLP 708

SUNDAY MORNING.
LP: . . . . POSL 3423

Ellis, Anita

ANITA ELLIS SINGS WITH THE MICHAEL ELLIS ORCHESTRA (Ellis, Anita & The Michael Ellis Orchestra).
LP: . . . . AP 38

Ellis, Beggs & Howard

HOMELANDS.
Tracks: / Where did tomorrow go? / Bad times / Two lonely hearts / Hungry man / Ju ju goodbye / Say a prayer / Why does living become a crime / Big bubbles, no troubles / Homeland / I would die for you.
LP: . . . . PL 71885
MC: . . . . PK 71885

Ellis, Bobbie

UNDER BEACON'S BROW.
LP: . . . . FE 008

Ellis, Chris

VOCAL WITH HOT ACCOMPANIMENT.
LP: . . . . DM 15

Ellis D

FREE YOUR MIND.
LP: . . . . XLLP 101

Ellis, Don

HOW TIME PASSES.
Tracks: / How time passes / Sallie / Simplex one, A / Waste / Improvisational suite.
LP: . . . . CS 9004

LIVE AT MONTREUX.
Tracks: / Open wide / Loneliness / Future feature / Go no go / Sporting dance / Niner two.
LP: . . . . K 50496

OUT OF NOWHERE.
LP: . . . . CS 9032

Ellis, Ellie

BREATH OF FRESH AIR, A (Ellis, Ellie & Sara Grey).

Tracks: / Going to Little Creek / Big Liza / Wintry winds / Freighting from Wilcox to Globe / Jolly raftsman / Lake of the Coagama / Boatman / Sandy river belle / Going out West this fall / Turtle dove / Train on the island / Cole Younger / Sally in the garden / Frosty morning / Rowley's tax list / Lonesome roving wolves / Some little bug / Parting friends.
LP: FE 031

MAKING THE AIR RESOUND (See under Grey, Sara for details) (Ellis, Ellie & Sara Grey).

Ellis, Herb

DOGGIN' AROUND (Ellis, Herb & Red Mitchell).
LP: CJ 372
MC: CJ 372C

GREAT GUITARS (See under Byrd, Charlie) (Ellis, Herb with Charlie Byrd and Barney Kessel).

GREAT GUITARS AT THE WINERY (See Kessel, Barney) (Ellis, Herb with Charlie Byrd and Barney Kessel).

HELLO HERBIE (See under Peterson, Oscar) (Ellis, Herb & Oscar Peterson).

HERB MIX.
Tracks: / It's a small world after all / Tenderly / Girl from Ipanema / It could happen to you / Deep / Moonlight in Vermont / Give my regards to Broadway / Way we were, The / Preacher, The.
LP: CJ 181

SOFT AND MELLOW.
LP: CJ 77

TRIO (See under Alexander, Monty) (Ellis, Herb & Monty Alexander).

TRIPLE TREAT (See under Alexander, Monty) (Ellis, Herb & Monty Alexander & Ray Brown).

TRIPLE TREAT II (See Alexander, Monty) (Ellis, Herb & Monty Alexander & Ray Brown).

TRIPLE TREAT III (see under Alexander, Monty) (Ellis, Herb & Monty Alexander & Ray Brown).

TWO FOR THE ROAD (Ellis, Herb & Joe Pass).
Tracks: / Love for sale / Am I blue? / Seven come eleven / Guitar blues / Lady be good / Cherokee (concept 1) / Cherokee (concept 2) / Gee baby ain't I good to you / Try a little tenderness / I found a new baby / Angel eyes.
LP: 231 0714
MC: K10 714

Ellis, Hortense

JAMAICAS FIRST LADY OF SONG.
LP: TWS 918

REFLECTIONS.
Tracks: / Reflections / Unexpected places / You're gonna make me love somebody else / Somebody help me.
LP: UAG 30272

Ellis, John

BIRLIN SPORRANS.
Tracks: / Broon's reel / Boston two step / Angus Lawrie Medley / Scottish waltz selection / Eva three step / Fiddle hornpipes / Strathspeys and reels / Two 4/4 marches / Two pipe reels / Gay gordons / Royal visit, The (jigs) / Highland medley, A / Pipe hornpipes / Circassian circle / Gaelic waltz / 2/4 march and reels / Highland schottische / Pipe medley.
LP: LILP 5183
MC: LICS 5183

FIRE IN THE KILT (Ellis, John & His Highland Country Band).
LP: LILP 5158
MC: LICS 5158

JOHN ELLIS AND HIS HIGHLAND COUNTRY BAND (Ellis, John & His Highland Country Band).
LP: WGR 057
MC: CWGR 057
LP: LILP 5107
MC: LICS 5107

REEL KICK, A (Ellis, John & His Highland Country Band).
Tracks: / Gates of Edinburgh, The / Quaker jig / Gaelic waltz / Polka / Eight men of Moidart / March Strathspey and Reel / Highland Schottische / Pipe tunes / Hornpipes / Pipe marches.
LP: LILP 5120
MC: LICS 5120

Ellis, John Fury

MICROGROOVE MAXI.
Tracks: / Babies in jars / Curve of the earth / Amazaface / Hit man / Hollow Graham.
LP: HAI 203

Ellis, Leonard

CIRCLE OF DREAMS.
MC: C 123

Ellis, Red

FIRST FALL OF SNOW.
LP: OHCS 322

Ellis, Segar

SEGAR ELLIS CHOIRS OF BRASS (1937).
LP: QRS 2408

Ellis & The Crew

SHAKA.
LP: DA 102

Ellis, Tinsley

FANNING THE FLAMES.
LP: AL 4778

GEORGIA BLUE.
Tracks: / Can't you lie / You picked a good time / Crime of passion / Double eyed whammy / Look ka py py / Free manwells / Texas stomp / I've made nights by myself / Hot potato / She wants to sell my monkey / As the years go passing by / Lucky lot.
LP: AL 4765

Ellis, Tony

BABA TUNDE.
Tracks: / Spaceman / Nothing from nothing / Change will come.
LP: 2480 640

DIXIE BANNER.
LP: FF 444

Ellis, Vivian

THREE BY VIVIAN ELLIS (Original cast recordings) (Various artists).
Tracks: / I want to see the people happy: *Various artists* / London Town: *Various artists* / Who's the lady: *Various* artists / Let us go down the river: *Various artists* / Other men: *Various artists* / Love me not: *Various* artists / Tough at the top: *Various artists* / I'm on fire: *Various artists* / Blood and iron: *Various* artists / Interlude: *Various artists* / I don't want to marry: *Various artists* / I feel a new fellow: *Various* artists / I wish I could sing: *Various artists* / Really a rather nice man: *Various artists* / Muffin man: *Various artists* / All the ladies are lovely: *Various artists* / England is a lovely place: *Various artists*/ This is not the end: *Various artists* / And so to bed: *Various artists* / Bartholomew Fair: *Various artists*/ Amo amas: *Various artists* / Gaze not on swans: *Various artists* / Lov me little, love me long: *Various artists* / Sarabande: *Various artists* / Beauty retire: *Various artists* / Oaths: *Various artists*.
LP: SH 339

Ellison, Lorraine

LORRAINE ELLISON.
Tracks: / Walk around heaven / Country woman's prayer / Do better than you're doin' / If only I could see him / No relief / I'll fly away / Road I took to you, The / Stormy weather / Many rivers to cross.
LP: K 46296

PHILADELPHIA'S QUEEN OF SOUL.
Tracks: / Stay with me baby / Good love / No matter how it all turns out / Heart and soul / Heart be still / When love flies away / Try (just a little bit harder) / I want to be loved / You really got a hold on me / He's my guy / He ain't heavy he's my brother / Many rivers to cross.
LP: K 52630

STAY WITH ME.
Tracks: / Only your love / Try (just a little bit harder) / I'm gonna cry 'till my tears run dry / I want to be loved / Hurt came back again, The / Stay with me / You don't know nothing about love / You're easy on my mind / No matter how it all turns out / Good love / Heart be still.
LP: BMLP 025

Elman, Ziggy

1947: ZIGGY ELMAN (Elman, Ziggy & His Orchestra).
LP: CLP 70

Elmer Gantry (film)

ELMER GANTRY (Original soundtrack) (Various artists).
LP: MCA 39070
MC: MCAC 39070

Elms, Stewart

TAKE A WALK WITH ME.
Tracks: / Take a walk with me / Another chance / First time / Bar room blues / F T A S F J B.
MC: MOCHTC 1

E.L.O.

BALANCE OF POWER.
Tracks: / Heaven only knows / So serious / Getting to the point / Secret lives / Is it alright / Sorrow about to fall / Without someone / Calling America / Endless lies / Send it.
LP: EPC 26467
MC: 40 26467
MC: 4685764

COLLECTION: ELECTRIC LIGHT ORCHESTRA.
LP: IC 028 05698

DISCOVERY.
Tracks: / Shine a little love / Confusion / Need her love / Diary of Horace Wimp / Last train to London / Midnight blue / On the run / Wishing / Don't bring me down.
LP: 4500831
MC: 4500834
LP: JETLX 500
LP: JETLX 500

EARLY ELO (1971-1973).
Tracks: / 10538 overture / Look at me now / Nellie takes her bow / Battle of Marston Moor / 1st movement / Mr Radio / Manhattan rumble (49th street massacre) / Queen of the hours / Whispers in the night / Roll over Beethoven / In old England town / Momma / From the sun to the world / Kuiama / Showdown / Baby I apologize / Auntie / My woman / Bev's trousers.
MC: TCEM 1419

ELDORADO.
Tracks: / Eldorado overture / Can't get it out of my head / Boy blue / Laredo tornado / Poorboy (The Greenwood) / Mister kingdom / Nobody's child / Illusions in G Major / Eldorado / Eldorado (finale).
LP: K 56090

ELECTRIC LIGHT ORCHESTRA.
LP: SHVL 797
LP: FA413084-1

ELECTRIC LIGHT ORCHESTRA VOL.2.
Tracks: / In old England town (boogie no.2) / Momma / Roll over Beethoven / From the sun to the world (boogie No.2) / Kuiama.
LP: FA 3003
MC: TCFA 3003
LP: SHVL 806

FACE THE MUSIC.
Tracks: / Fire on high / Waterfall / Nightrider / Poker / Strange magic / Down home town / One summer dream.
LP: EPC 32544
MC: 40 32544

FIRST MOVEMENT.
Tracks: / First movement / Look at me now / 10538 Overture / Queen of the hours / Battle of Marston Moor, The / Mr. Radio / Kuiama / Roll over Beethoven / From the sun to the world / Momma / In old England town / Showdown.
LP: EMS 1128
MC: TCEMS 1128

GREATEST HITS: ELECTRIC LIGHT ORCHESTRA.
Tracks: / Telephone line / Evil woman / Livin' thing / Can't get it out of my head / Showdown / Turn to stone / Rockaria / Sweet talkin' woman / Ma ma ma belle / Strange magic / Mr. Blue sky.
LP: 4503571
MC: 4503574
LP: JETLX 525

LIGHT SHINES ON, THE.
Tracks: / Roll over Beethoven / In old England town (Instrumental.) / Look at me now / Momma / Showdown / Mr. Radio / Battle of Marston Moor, The / Whisper in the night / 10538 Overture.
LP: SHSM 2015
MC: TCSHSM 2015

LIGHT SHINES ON, THE, VOL.2.
Tracks: / 10538 overture / First movement / In old England town / Manhattan rumble / From the sun to the world / Kuiama / Nellie takes her bow / Queen of the hours / Roll over Beethoven.
LP: SHSM 2027

LIVE AT LONG BEACH.
LP: 32700

MILESTONES.
Tracks: / 10538 overture / Look at me now / Nellie takes her bow / Battle of Marston Moor, The / First movement / Mr. Radio / Manhattan rumble / Queen of the hours / Whisper in the night / In old England town / Mama / Roll over Beethoven / From the sun to the world / Kuiama.
2LP: 5C 138 52658/59

NEW WORLD RECORD, A.
Tracks: / Tightrope / Telephone line / Rockaria / Mission (A new world record) / So fine / Livin' thing / Above the clouds / Do ya / Shangri-la.
LP: JET 32545
MC: 40 32545
LP: UAG 30017
LP: 902198 1
MC: 902198 4

NIGHT THE LIGHT WENT OUT, THE.
Tracks: / Daybreaker / Showdown / Day tripper / 10538 Overture / Mik's solo / Orange blossom special / In the hall of the mountain king / Great balls of fire / Roll over Beethoven.
LP: EPC 32700
MC: 40 32700

ON THE THIRD DAY.
Tracks: / Ocean break-up / King of the universe / Bluebird is dead / Oh no, not Susan / New world rising / Queen break-up / Daybreaker / Ma ma ma belle / Dreaming of 4,000 / In the hall of the mountain king.
LP: JETLP 202
MC: JETCA 202
LP: K 56021

OUT OF THE BLUE.
Tracks: / Turn to stone / It's over / Sweet talkin' woman / Across the border / Night in the city / Starlight / Jungle / Believe me now / Steppin' out / Standing in the rain / Summer and lightning / Mr. Blue sky / Sweet is the night / Whale, the / Wild West hero.
2LP: 4508851
MCSET: 4508854
2LP: JETDP 400
2LP: UAR 100

SECRET MESSAGES.
Tracks: / Secret messages / Loser gone wild / Take me on and on / Bluebird / Four little diamonds / Stranger / Danger ahead / Letter from Spain / Train of gold / Rock 'n' roll is king.
MC: JETLC 527
LP: JETLX 527
MC: 4624874

THREE LIGHT YEARS.
MCSET: JET BX1

TIME.
Tracks: / Prologue / Twilight / Yours truly 2095 / Ticket to the moon / Way life's meant to be, The / Another heart beats / Rain is falling / From the end of the world / Lights go down, The / Here is the news / Twenty first century man / Hold on tight / Epilogue.
LP: 4602121
MC: 4602124
LP: JETLP 236

VERY BEST OF ELO.
LP: STAR 2370
MC: STAC 2370

XANADU (See under Newton-John, Olivia) (Newton-John, Olivia & ELO).

E.L.O. Part 2

ELO (PART 2).
LP: STAR 2503
MC: STAC 2503

Eloy

CODENAME WILDGEESE (Film soundtrack).
Tracks: / Patrol, The / Hong Kong (theme 1) / Hit and run / Queen of rock 'n' roll / Destiny / Discovery / Jukebox / Deadlock / Cha-shoen / Sabotage / On the edge / Long goodbye / Face to face / Revenge / Hong Kong (theme 2).
LP: MILCH 014

COLOURS.
LP: IC 064 45936

INSIDE.
LP: 1C 064 29479

LIVE: ELOY.
Tracks: / Poseidon's creation / Incarnation of Logos / Sun song / Dance in doubt and fear / Mutiny / Gliding into light and knowledge / Inside / Atlantis agony at June 5th / 8498, 13 p.m. Gregorian earthtime.
LP: IC 164 32934/35'

METROMANIA.
LP: HMILP 21
MC: HMIMC 21

PERFORMANCE.
Tracks: / In disguise / Shadow and light / Surrender / Heartbeat / Fools / Broken frame.
LP: HMILP 12
MC: HMIMC 12
LPPD: HMIPD 12

PLANETS.
Tracks: / Introduction / On the verge of darkening lights / Point of no return / Mysterious monolith / Queen of the night / At the gates of dawn / Sphinx / Carried by cosmic winds.
LP: HMILP 1
LPPD: HMIPD 1
MC: HMIMC 1
LP: IC 064 46483

RA.
LP: REVLP 120
MC: REVMC 120

TIME TO TURN.
Tracks: / Through a sombre galaxy / Behind the walls of imagination / Illuminations / Time to turn / End of an odyssey / Flash, The / Say, is it really true?.

LP: . . . . HMILP 3
MC: . . . . HMIMC 3
LP: . . . . IC 064 46548

Elrick, George

WHEN YOU'RE SMILING (Elrick, George & His Band).
Tracks: / When you're smiling / Me myself and I / I love to whistle / Paradise street / Nice cup of tea, A / Boo hoo / You can't stop me from dreaming / Number one honeymoon lane / Bank of sunshine / Feather in her tyrolean hat.
LP: . . . . GCE 1

Elsdon, Alan

JAZZ JOURNEYMEN.
Tracks: / Lord Randal / Saturday afternoon blues / Diga diga doo / There's yes yes in your eyes / Panama rag / Four or five times / Two deuces / Come back, sweet Papa / Lovely Rita, meter maid / Satisfaction.
LP: . . . . BLP 12163

Elton, Ben

MOTORMOUTH.
LP: . . . . BENLP 1
MC: . . . . BENMC 1

MOTORVATION.
LP: 836 652-1
MC: 836 652-4

Elves & The Shoemaker

ELVES AND THE SHOEMAKER, THE (well loved tales age up to 9).
MC: . . . . PLB 63

ELVES AND THE SHOEMAKER, THE.
MC: . . . . STC 307A

Elvin, Simon

SOMEWHERE IN TIME.
Tracks: / Another land / Caught in the clouds / His love / Lifetime / Somewhere in time / King for a day / Stepping in time with you / Need in me, The / Eye for an eye / This one love / Love will take me home.
LP: . . . . MYRR 1234
MC: . . . . MYRC 1234

Elvira Madigan (film)

ELVIRA MADIGAN (1987 film soundtrack) (Various artists).
LP: . . . . ASD 2465
MC: . . . . TCASD 2465

Elvis Hitler

DISGRACELAND.
LP: . . . . GWLP 37

Ely Cathedral Choir

SERVICE HIGH AND ANTHEMS CLEAR.
Tracks: / Exultate Deo / Blessed be the God and Father / Evening canticles in B flat / Come, Holy Ghost / I was glad / Evening canticles in G / O thou, the central orb.
MC: . . . . KH 88006

Ely, Joe

DIG ALL NIGHT.
Tracks: / Settle for love / For your love / My eyes got lucky / Maybe she'll find me / Drivin' man / Dig all night / Grandfather blues / Jazz street / Rich man, poor boy / Behind the bamboo shade.
LP: . . . . FIEND 130

DOWN ON THE DRAG.
Tracks: / Fools fall in love / B.B.Q. and foam / Standin' at the big hotel / Crazy lemon / Crawdad train / In another world / She leaves you where you are / Down on the drag / Time for travelin' Maria.
LP: . . . . MCG 3532

HI-RES.
LP: . . . . MCF 3214
MC: . . . . MCFC 3214

JOE ELY.
LP: . . . . MCL 1604
MC: . . . . MCLC 1604

LIVE AT LIBERTY LUNCH.
Tracks: / Me and Billy the kid / Are you listening Lucky? / Grandfather blues / B.B.Q. and foam / Row of dominoes / Dallas / Where is my love / She gotta get the gettin' / Drivin' to the poorhouse / Cool rockin' Loretta / Musta notta gotta lotta / Letter to L.A. / If you were a bluebird.
LP: . . . . MCG 6113
MC: . . . . MCGC 6113

LIVESHOTS.
LP: . . . . MCF 3064

LORD OF THE HIGHWAY.
Tracks: / Lord of the highway / (Don't put a) lock on my heart / Me and Billy The Kid / Letter to L.A. / No rope, Daisy-o / Thinks she's French / Everybody got hammered / Are you listening Lucky ? / Row of dominoes / Silver City.
LP: . . . . FIEND 101

MILKSHAKES AND MALTS.
Tracks: / She never spoke Spanish to me / Boxcars / West Texas waltz / Down on the drag.
LP: . . . . SSAD 05

MUSTA NOTTA GOTTA LOTTA.
LP: . . . . MCF 3099

WHATEVER HAPPENED TO MARIA.
LP: . . . . SSAD 007

Ely, Pat

COUNTRY TRACKING.
Tracks: / Good old days / Blue eyes crying in the rain / Red necks, white socks and blue ribbon beer / Waiting for a train / In the middle of nowhere / Johnny Cash medley / Pinto the wonder horse is dead / You're gonna wonder about me / They're all going home but one / I took a memory to lunch / You remember me / Soft lights and hard country music.
LP: . . . . PHL 411
MC: . . . . CPHL 411

MY DONEGAL SHORE.
Tracks: / Newport town / Nancy Miles / Galtee mountain boy / Galway shawl / Rose of Castlerea / Boys from County Armagh / Old rustic bridge / Shanagolden / Boys from County Mayo / My lovely Rose of Clare / My Donegal shore / Town I loved so well, The.
LP: . . . . DOLS 2013
MC: . . . . DOCS 2013

MY FAVOURITE IRISH SONGS.
Tracks: / Rose of Mooncoin / Pretty little girl from Omagh.
LP: . . . . HRL 136
MC: . . . . CHRL 136

Embatta, Marc

HIDDEN PASSIONS.
LP: . . . . MMLP 015

Emblow, Jack

ALABAMY BOUND (Emblow, Jack & His Riverboat Collection).
LP: . . . . MTS 16

AROUND THE WORLD (Emblow, Jack & The French Collection).
LP: . . . . DS 065

BEST OF JACK EMBLOW (Emblow, Jack & The French Collection).
MC: . . . . CMTS 10

ENJOY YOURSELF VOL.1.
Tracks: / Whistle medley / Happy talk / Smile / Under the roofs of Paris / Blowin' bubbles / Sophie's choice / Enjoy yourself / Frenesi / Numero / Nola / Bring me sunshine.
LP: . . . . MTS 1

ENJOY YOURSELF VOL.2.
Tracks: / J'attendrai / Tango musette / Tango of the bells / Canadian capers / Five foot two / Good morning / Irish medley / Singing piano / Call you sweetheart / Summer holiday / Spread a little happiness / Rumba cassis / Tonight / Sleepy time gal.
LP: . . . . MTS 6

FLYING HIGH (Emblow, Jack & Tony Compton Trio).
Tracks: / Come fly with me / Days of wine and roses / Sophisticated lady / Autumn leaves / Sunshine of my life / Out of nowhere / Quiet nights / Undecided / Matchmaker / Satin doll / I'm old fashioned / 'S wonderful / Sky lark.
LP: . . . . AFA 871
MC: . . . . AFAC 871

FRENCH CONNECTION, THE.
LP: . . . . MTS 23

I LOVE PARIS.
Tracks: / I love Paris / Milord#People of Paris / April in Paris / C'est si bon / La ronde / I wish you love / 'Allo 'allo / Chanson d'amour / Mam'selle#Autumn leaves / Umbrellas of Cherbourg / Boom / Louise / My prayer.
LP: . . . . MTS 11

Embrace

EMBRACE.
LP: . . . . DISCHORD 24

Embryo

AFRICA.
LP: 003036

OPAL.
LP: . . . . MASO 33046

ROCK SESSIONS.
LP: 0201.109

Emerald

DOWN TOWN.
LP: . . . . MEGATON 0011

Emerald Forest (film)

EMERALD FOREST (1985 film soundtrack) (Various artists).
LP: . . . . CST 8008
LP: . . . . STV 81244
MC: . . . . CTV 81244

Emerald Isle Singers

MEMORIES OF IRELAND.
LP: . . . . TA 3015

Emerald Vein

LAND OF THE LIVING.
LP: . . . . SUB 3302231

Emerald Web

CATSPAW.
LP: . . . . SYN 100
MC: . . . . SYNC 100

Emerson, Billy

CRAZY 'BOUT AUTOMOBILES (Emerson, Billy 'The Kid').
Tracks: / Every woman I know likes an automobile / Tomorrow never comes / Don't start me to lying / If you won't stay home / Don't be careless / Do the chicken / Somebody show me (the way to go home) / Pleasure's all mine, The / Do yourself a favour / You never miss the water.
LP: . . . . CFM 602

LITTLE FINE HEALTHY THING (Emerson, Billy 'The Kid').
LP: . . . . CR 30187

Emerson, Keith

BEST REVENGE (Film soundtrack).
LP: . . . . CHORD 001

CHRISTMAS ALBUM, THE.
LP: . . . . KEITHLP 1
MC: . . . . KEITHMC 1

EMERSON COLLECTION, THE.
Tracks: / Inferno / Mater Teneberarun / Starship / Chic Charni / Dreamer, The / Playing for keeps / Orchestral suite from best revenge / Bach before the mast/ Hello sailor / Salt cay / Prelude to Candice / Candice / Nighthawks.
LP: . . . . CHORD ESP/1

HARMAGEDDON/CHINA FREE FALL (Emerson, Keith/Derek Austin).
Tracks: / Theme of Floi / Joe and Michiko / Children of the light / Funny's skate state / Zamedy stomp / Challenge of the psionic fighters / China free fall / Main title / Eight man visions / Magic garden / Summer palace / Space reality / Canton stadium / Chinese star 3.
LP: . . . . CHORD 003

HONKY (Original soundtrack).
LP: . . . . CHORD 002

HONKY TONK TRAIN BLUES.
Tracks: / Honky tonk train blues.
LP: . . . . K 13513

INFERNO (Original soundtrack).
Tracks: / Inferno / Rose's descent into the cellar / Taxi ride, The / Library, The / Sarah in the library vaults / Bookbinder's delight / Rose leaves the apartment / Rose gets it / Elisa's story / Cat attic attack, A / Kazanians tarantella / Mark's discovery / Mater tenebrarum / Inferno (finals) / Cigarettes, ices, etc..
LP: . . . . K 50753
LP: . . . . CIA 5022
MC: . . . . CIAK 75022

KEITH EMERSON WITH THE NICE (See under Nice) (Emerson, Keith/ Nice).

MURDEROCK (Film soundtrack).
LP: . . . . CHORD 004

NIGHTHAWKS (Film soundtrack).
LP: . . . . MCA 1521
MC: . . . . MCAC 1521
LP: . . . . MCF 3107
MC: . . . . MCFC 3107

Emerson, Lake & Palmer

BEST OF EMERSON, LAKE AND PALMER, THE.
Tracks: / Hoe down / Lucky man / Karn evil 9 / Trilogy / Fanfare for the common man / Still...you turn me on / Tiger in the spotlight / Jerusalem / Peter Gunn.
LP: . . . . K 50757
MC: K4 50757

BRAIN SALAD SURGERY.
Tracks: / Jerusalem / Toccata / Still...you turn me on / Benny the bouncer / Karn evil 9 / First impression (part 1) / First impression / Second impression / Third impression.
LP: . . . . K 53501
MC: K4 53501

EMERSON, LAKE AND PALMER.
Tracks: / Barbarian, The / Take a pebble / Knife edge / Three fates, The / Clotho / Lachesis / Auropos / Tank / Lucky man.
LP: . . . . K 43503
MC: K4 43503
LP: . . . . ILPS 9132

EMERSON, LAKE AND PALMER IN CONCERT.
Tracks: / Introductory fanfare / Peter Gunn / Tiger in the spotlight / C'est la vie / Enemy god, The / Knife edge / Piano concerto no.1 / Pictures at an exhibition.
LP: . . . . K 50652
MC: K4 50652

LOVE BEACH.
Tracks: / All I want is you / Love beach / Taste of my love / Gambler, The / For you / Canario / Memoirs of an officer and a gentleman / Prologue / Education of a gentleman, The / Love at first sight / Letters from the front / Honourable company.
LP: . . . . K 50552
MC: K4 50552

PICTURES AT AN EXHIBITION.
Tracks: / Promenade / Gnome, The / Sage, The / Old castle, The / Blues variation / Hut of baba yaba,The / Curse of Baba Yaga, The / Great gate of Kiev, The / End, The - nutrocker.
LP: . . . . K 33501
MC: K4 33501
LP: . . . . HELP 1

TARKUS.
Tracks: / Tarkus / Eruption / Stones of years / Iconoclast / Mass / Manticore / Battlefield / Aquatarkus / Jeremy Bender / Bitches crystal / Only way, The / Infinite space (conclusion) / Time and a place, A / Are you ready Eddy?.
LP: . . . . K 43504
MC: K4 43504
LP: . . . . ILPS 9155

TRILOGY.
Tracks: / Endless enigma, The (part 1) / Fugue / Endless enigma, The (part 2) / From the beginning / Sheriff / Hoe down / Trilogy / Living sin / Aboddon's bolero.
LP: . . . . K 43505
MC: K4 43505
LP: . . . . ILPS 9186

WELCOME BACK.
Tracks: / Hoe down / Jerusalem / Toccata / Tarkus / Tarkus (conclusion) / Take a pebble / Piano improvisation / Jeremy Bender / Sheriff / Karn evil 9.
LP: . . . . K 63500
MC: K4 63500

WORKS: EMERSON, LAKE AND PALMER.
Tracks: / Piano concerto no. 1 / Lend your love to me tonight / C'est la vie / Hallowed be thy name / Nobody loves you like I do / Closer to believing / Enemy god, The / L.A. nights / New Orleans / Bach two part invention in D minor / Food for your soul / Tank / Fanfare for the common man / Pirates.
2LP: . . . . K 80009
MCSET: K4 80009

WORKS VOL 2.
Tracks: / Tiger in the spotlight / When the apple blossoms bloom in the windmills of your mind / I'll be your valentine / Bullfrogs / Brain salad surgery / Barrelhouse shake down / Watching over you / So far to fall / Maple leaf rag / I believe in Father Christmas / Close but not touching.
LP: . . . . K 50422
MC: K4 50422

Emerson, Lake & Powell

EMERSON LAKE AND POWELL.
Tracks: / Mars the bringer of war / Score / Learning to fly / Miracle / Touch and go / Love blind / Step aside / Lay down your guns.
LP: . . . . POLD 5191
MC: . . . . POLDC 5191

Emery, Dick

IF YOU LOVE HER.
Tracks: / If you love her.
LP: 7N 17644

Emery, Jon

HILLYBILLY ROCK'N'ROLL.
Tracks: / Hillbilly rock'n'roll / Brown boots / Bring back love / Delmore trilogy / Delmore blues / Fast freight train / Endless river / Hillbilly jukebox / Beer thirty / Dutchess / Strangers in the dark / Long train home / Rockin' Rhonda.
LP: . . . . BFX 15208

EMF

SCHUBERT DIP.
Tracks: / Children / Long Summer days / When you're mine / Travelling not running / I believe / Unbelievable / Girl of an age / Admit it / Lies / Longtime / Live at the Bilson.
LP: . . . . PCS 7353
MC: . . . . TCPCS 7353

EMI Comedy Classics

AT THE DROP OF A HAT/AT THE DROP OF ANOTHER HAT (Flanders & Swann).
Tracks: / Transport of delight / Song of reproduction / Gnu song, The / Design for living / Je suis le tenebreux / Songs for our time / Song of the weather, A / Reluctant cannibal, The / Greensleeves / Misalliance / Madeira M'dear / Hippopotamus song, The / Gas-man cometh, The / Sounding brass / Los olvidados / In the desert / Ill wind / First and second law / All gall / Horoscope / Friendly duet / Bedstead men / By air /

Slow train / Song of patriotic prejudice / Hippo encore.
MCSET: . . . . ECC 2

CHEEKY CHAPPIE, THE (Miller, Max).
Tracks: / Mary from the dairy (entry) / She shall have music / Cheeky chappie tells one / Cheeky chappie tells a few / Cheeky chappie tells a few more / Lulu / Cheeky chappie tells a few more / Hiking song, The / Mary from the dairy (exit) / Max gets ideas on courting (Sitting in the park with Sarah) / More about courting and married life / Max, always an artist, is now a painter (Cheeky chappie) / Max in an air raid (I never slept a wink all night) / New kind of old fashioned girl, A / Cheeky chappie picks from the white book and the blue book / Cheeky chappie goes on picking 'em, The / Is there no end to his cleverness? / What Ju Ju wants, Ju Ju must have / Sitting in the old armchair / Stringing along with you / Jean Carr asks some questions but Max knows all the answers / Max gives Jean some chocolates / Hiking song, The / All good things come to an end / Grand old man, The / Max tells of his first ARP experience / Max is now a swimming instructor ... (...but is never out of his depth) / Max sings of some of the girls he has met ... (...and tells of some his father knew!!) / Max tells one and then becomes Max with the flashing eyes... (...and charming smile) / Mary from the dairy (entry) / When we go on our honeymoon / Cheeky chappie tells one / Cheeky chappie tells a few / Cheeky chappie tells a few more / I thought we came here to pick some flowers / Mary from the dairy / All because I rolled my eyes / Cheeky chappie concludes / Mary from the dairy (exit) / Ain't love grand / Every Sunday afternoon / Old oak tree, The / Everything happens to me / Cheeky chappie tells some / Passing the time away / Chats on etiquette and manners / he tells some more / Down where the rambling roses grow / I don't like the girls / All good stuff, lady / Mary Ann / At the bathing parade / I never thought that she'd do that to me / Mary from the dairy.
MCSET: . . . . ECC 10

COLLECTION OF SPIKES, A (Milligan, Spike).
Tracks: / Q 5 piano tune, The / Ning nang nong / Python, The / Silly old baboon / Call up / Purple aeroplane / Another lot / Sewers of the strand, The / Frank J. Itchikutchi / Brass band samba / My darling little baby / Nothing at all / I've got a photograph of you / Postman's knock / Sex, food and a pig / Wormwood scrubs tango / Cougher royal / Morning in Puckoon / Tower bridge / Word power / You gotta go oww! / Escape / Fun, fun, fun / Wish I knew / Father Rudden / Silent night / Hit parade / RAF interview / Underneath it all / Good King Eccleslas / Q8 theme / Finale / Q8 theme reprise / Will I find my love today / After lights out / Ning nang nong / I'm walking out with a mountain / Woe is me / Puckoon flyer, The / My September love / Hippo rhinostricow / Power of licorice, The / Have they gone / Australia.
MCSET: . . . . ECC 11

FAREWELL TO THE NORTH ENCLOSURE (Boyce, Max).
Tracks: / Sospan fach / I am an entertainer / I wandered lonely / I gave my love a debenture / Slow, men at work / Pontypool front row, The / Sospan fach / Divine intervention, The / Ode to Barry Island / Incredible plan, The / I was there interpolating brief extrac from 'Delilah' / Day that Gareth was dropped, The / Childhood memories / What does she know about music? / Y deryn pur (gentle bird) / 100,000,000,000 green bottles / French trip interpolating 'The Stripper' / Day we lost to England, The / Paul Ringer's song interpolating 'Captain Beaky' / Tarquin's letter / Oggie song, The / Farewell to the north enclosure / Play off - brief extract only from 'Hyms and Arias'.
MCSET: . . . . ECC 8

GOON SHOWS VOL.1 (Goons).
Tracks: / Tales of old Dartmoor / Tale of men's shirts / Dishonoured / Scarlet capsule, The.
MCSET: . . . . ECC 4

GOON SHOWS VOL. 2 (Goons).
Tracks: / China story / Macreekie rising of '74 / Six Charlies in search of an author / Insurance - the white man's burden.
MCSET: . . . . ECC 6

GOON SHOWS VOL. 3 (Goons).
Tracks: / Missing No. 10 Downing Street, The / Red fort, The / Foiled by President Fred / Robin Hood and his merry men.
MCSET: . . . . ECC 9

LAUREL & HARDY (Laurel & Hardy).
Tracks: / Introduction including the cuckoo song / Fresh fish / Victims of the depression / Furniture payment / Let me call you sweetheart / What flavours have you / Higher endeavours / Mistaken identity / Trail of the lonesome pine (Featuring Chill Wills) / Long distance / Oh Gaston / Stagecoach manners / At the ball (Featuring the Avalon Boys.) / New recruits, The including the cuckoo song / There's a dollar / Hard boiled eggs including in the good old summertime / Where were you born / United we stand / Annual convention / We're going now / Way down south including I want to be in Dixie / Introduction including the cuckoo song / Turn on the radio / Ever as you and I / Clean sweep, A / Future Mrs. Hardy, The / Every cloud has a silver lining / Lazy moon / When the cat's away / Danger by clockwork / Food for thought / Court again / Dual deceit including Honolulu baby & Sons of the desert / Goodbye.
MCSET: . . . . ECC 13

NIGHTCLUB YEARS (1964-1968) (Allen, Woody).
MCSET: . . . . ECC 3

PETER SELLERS COLLECTION (Sellers, Peter).
Tracks: / Any old iron / Hard days night, A / Common entrance (Not on CD.) / My old dutch (Not on CD.) / Can't buy me love (Not on CD.) / Thank heaven for little girls (Not on CD.) / All the things you are / We'll let you know (Not on CD.) / Wouldn't it be loverly (Not on CD.) / In a free state / Peter Sellers sings Rudolph Friml / Goodness gracious me / So little time / Puttin' on the smile (Not on CD.) / Trumpet volunteer, The / I'm so ashamed (Not on CD.) / She loves you (inspired by Dr. Strangelove) / Unchained melody / Peter Sellers sings George Gershwin / Dance with me, Henry / Critics, The (Not on CD.) / Why worry? (Not on CD.) / Grandpa's grave (Not on CD.) / Boiled bananas and carrots (Not on CD.) / We need the money (Not on CD.) / Never never land / Suddenly it's folk song / Auntie Rotter / Bangers and mash / Conversation No. 1 (a right bird) / Help (Not on CD.) / Singin' in the rain (Not on CD.) / Party political speech / House on the Rue Sichel ((Some voices inspired by the film 'Soft Beds, Hard bath) Not on CD.) / Dipso calypso / Face to face (Not on CD.) / Balham - gateway to the South / I haven't told her, she hasn't told me (Not on CD.).
MCSET: . . . . ECC 5

SONGS AND MONOLOGUES OF JOYCE GRENFELL, THE (Grenfell, Joyce).
Tracks: / Opening numbers / Nursery school / Joyful noise / picture postcard / What shall I wear / Visitor / Dear Francois / Nursery school (flowers) / I'm going to see you today / Shirley's girlfriend "picnic" / Oh Mr. Du Maurier / Writer of children's books / Olde tyme dancing / Telephone call / Bring back the silence / Old girls' school re-union / Three brothers / Nicodemus / Hostess, The / Lally Tullet / Hymn / Wrong songs for wrong singers (or songs to make you sick) / Wedding is on Saturday, The / Fan / I wouldn't go back / Thursdays / Duet / Nursery school (going home) / Slow down.
MCSET: . . . . ECC 18

STANLEY HOLLOWAY (Holloway, Stanley (nar)).
Tracks: / Pick up tha' musket / 'Alt who goes theer? / Beat the retreat on thy drum / One each a piece all round / Sam's medal / Old Sam's party (Part 1) (Humorous monologue.) / Old Sam's party (Part 2) (Humorous monologue.) / Marksman Sam / Sam drummed out / Sam's sturgeon (Acc. Wolseley Charles.) / Old Sam's Christmas pudding (Acc. Leo Conriche.) / Sam goes to it (W.T. Best at the piano.) / Three Ha'pence a foot (Wolseley Charles at the piano.) / Many happy returns (Wolseley Charles at the piano.) / With her head tucked underneath her arm / Beefeater, The / Jubilee sovereign / 'Ole in the ark, The / Lion and Albert, The (Acc Wolseley Charles.) / Albert comes back (Acc Wolseley Charles.) / Albert and the 'eadsman (Acc Wolseley Charles.) / Albert evacuated (Acc Leo Conriche) / Gunner Joe (Acc. Wolseley Charles.) / Runcorn ferry (Acc. Wolseley Charles.) / Jonah and the grampus (Acc. Wolseley Charles.) / Parson of puddle, The (Wolseley Charles, piano.) / Recumbent posture (Acc. Leo Conriche.) / My missus (Acc. Leo Conriche.) / Brahn boots (Acc. Leo Conriche.) / Up 'ards (W.T. Best at the piano.) / Guarding the gasworks (W.T. Best at the piano.) / No like-a-da war (W.T. Best at the piano.) / Petticoat Lane (From the film 'Hello London'.) / Sing a song of London / Tommy the whistler (Acc. orchestra and Tony Osborne.) / Comedy tonight.
MCSET: . . . . ECC 16

TURNED OUT NICE AGAIN (40 Formby Favourites).
Tracks: / Riding in the T.T. races / George Formby medley part 1 / George Formby medley part 2 / When I'm cleaning windows / Sitting on the sands / Dare devil Dick / Lancashire toreador, The / When we feather our nest / Leaning on a lamp post / With my little stick of Blackpool rock / Window cleaner, The (No. 2) / Does your dream book tell you that / Like the big pots do / Mother what'll I do now / In my little snapshot album / I blew a little blast on my whistle / Our Sergeant Major / Frigid air Fanny / Swing it George part 1 / Swing it George part 2 / Turned out nice again / Hill Billy Willie / Lancashire hot pot swingers / Grandad's flanelette nightshirt / Mr. Wu';s a window cleaner now / Oh don't the wind blow cold / I'm the ukelele man / Bless 'em all / Guarding home of the Home Guards / Hi-tiddley-hi-ti-island / You'd be far better off in a home / Emperor of Lancashire, The / Auntie Maggie's remedy / Frank on his tank / Katy-did, Katy didn't / Andy and the handy man / Thirsty thirsty sailors / Bunty's such a big girl now / Our Fanny's gone all Yankee / She's got two of everything.
MCSET: . . . . ECC 20

WE'LL GATHER LILACS (Hinge & Bracket).
Tracks: / Sing heigh to you (From act two 'Patience') / Zigeuner (From 'Bitter Sweet') / Fold your wings (from 'Glamorous Night') / We'll gather lilacs (From 'Perchance To Dream') / Poor wand'ring one (From Act I of the 'Pirates Of Penzance') / Regular royal queen, A (Act I finale from 'The Gondoliers') / If only he'd looked my way (From 'Gay's The Word') / Cat duet, The (Duetto buffo di gue gatti) / Keep the homefires burning / Land of hope and glory / Blameless dances (Duet from act II of 'Ruddigore') / Liste des vins / Hail men o'wars / Tripping hither, tripping thither (From 'Iolanthe') / Highwayman love (From 'Perchance To Dream') / Elopement, The (From 'Perchance To Dream') / Gangway.
MCSET: . . . . ECC 15

Emil

STAMMER.
MC: . . . . BI-JOOP 012

Emils

FIGHT TOGETHER.
LP: . . . . WEBITE 25
LP: 081249

Emily

RUB AL KHALI.
LP: . . . . EVERY 3

TO THE GLORY OF GOD.
LP: . . . . KLO 42

Emma (book)

EMMA (See under Austen, Jane) (Scales, Prunella (nar)).

EMMA (See under Austen, Jane) (Lapotaire, Jane).

EMMA VOL. 1 (See under Austen, Jane) (Rees, Angharad (nar)).

EMMA VOL. 2 (See under Austen, Jane) (Rees, Angharad (nar)).

Emmanuelle (film)

EMMANUELLE (1974 film soundtrack) (Various artists).
Tracks: / Emmanuelle in the mirror: *Various artists* / Emmanuelle song (French vocal version): *Various artists* / Emmanuelle in Thailand: *Various artists* / Emanuelle steps out: *Various artists* / Emmanuelle theme: *Various* artists / Night club: *Various artists* / Emmanuelle swims: *Various artists* / Emmanuelle in Thailand (variation): *Various artists* / Emmanuelle theme (instrumental): *Various artists* / Emmanuelle song (English vocal version): *Various artists* / Emmanuelle theme (instrumental variation): *Various artists* / Mood: *Various artists* / Emmanuelle theme (uptemp): *Various artists* / Opium den: *Various artists* / Rape sequence: *Various artists* / Cigarette act: *Various artists*.
LP: . . . . K 56084

EMMANUELLE 2 (1976 film soundtrack) (Various artists).
Tracks: / Love of loving: *Various artists* / Fantasies of Emmanuelle: *Various artists* / Jade garden, The: *Various* artists / Emmanuelle 2: *Various artists* / Emmanuelle's lesson of love: *Various artists* / Arrival of Emmanuelle, The: *Various artists* / Meeting in Bali: *Various artists* / a: *Various artists.*
LP: . . . . K 56231

EMMANUELLE 4 (Original Soundtrack) (Magne, Michael).
LP: 66084
MC: 76084

Emma's War (film)

EMMA'S WAR (1987 film soundtrack) (Various artists).
Tracks: / Emma's theme: *Williams, John (Guitarist)* / My devotion: *Geraldo & His Orchestra* / Emma's theme (part 2): *Williams, John (Guitarist)* / I'll never smile: *Geraldo & His Orchestra* / Revelation: *Williams, John* (Guitarist) / Our love affair: *Roy, Harry & His Orchestra* / Understanding: *Williams, John (Guitarist)* / So easy to love: *Baker, Josephine* / Readjusting: *Williams, John (Guitarist)* / You're the top: *Merman, Ethel*/ Garden music: *Williams, John (Guitarist)* / Emma's war: *Williams, John (Guitarist)* / Quintet in A: *Various artists.*
LP: . . . . MOMENT 106
MC: . . . . MOMENTC 106

Emmerdale Farm

EMMERDALE FARM CHURCH ALBUM (Emmerdale Farm Church Choir).
Tracks: / Guide me o thou great Jehovah / Lord of tomorrow / Praise my soul / Dear Lord and Father / Following on / When I survey / Lord's my shepherd, The / Don't close the door / All things bright and beautiful / Love / Day thou gavest, Lord is ended, The / Emmerdale prayer.
LP: . . . . EER 053
MC: . . . . EEC 053

Emmery, H

FREE FAIR (See Van Denbroeck, R) (Emmery, H/R. Van Denbroeck).

Emmons, Buddy

BUDDIES (See under Spicher, Buddy) (Emmons, Buddy & Buddy Spicher).

BUDDY EMMONS SINGS BOB WILLS.
Tracks: / Deep in the heart of Texas / Bottle baby boogie / Boot heel drag / Deep water / I need you / New road under my wheels / Roley poley / If no news is good news / Four, five times / Twinkle, twinkle little star / Time changes everything / End of the line.
LP: . . . . SDLP 033

MINORS ALOUD.
Tracks: / Scrapple from the apple / Compared to what.
LP: . . . . FF 088
LP: . . . . SNTF 799

SINGS BOB WILLIS.
Tracks: / Deep in the heart of Texas / Bottle baby boogie / Boot heel drag / Deep water / I needed you / New road under my wheels / Roly poly / If no news is good news / Four, five times / Twinkle twinkle little star / Time changes everything / End of the line.
LP: . . . . FF 017
LP: . . . . SNTF 706

STEEL GUITAR.
Tracks: / Indian killed the woodcock / Sugar foot rag / Wild mountain thyme / Orange blossom special / Nothing was delivered / Rose in Spanish Harlem / Top heavy / Canon in D major.
LP: . . . . FF 007
LP: . . . . SNTF 708

Emotions

EMOTIONS (AIM label) (Various artists).
MC: . . . . AIM 12

Emotions & Cancer

EMOTIONS AND CANCER (Leshan, Lawrence).
MC: . . . . PT 29

Emotions (group)

COME INTO OUR WORLD.
Tracks: / What's the name of you love / 'Cause I love you / On and on / I should be dancing / Come into my world / Where is your love / Movie / Yes I am / Layed back.
LP: 83483

FLOWERS.
Tracks: / Flowers / Best of my love / I don't want to lose your love / Me for you / You've got the right to know / We go through changes / Special part / No plans for tomorrow / How can you stop loving someone / God will take care of you.
LP: . . . . UNKNOWN

IF I ONLY KNEW.
Tracks: / Supernatural / Good times / Miss your love / If I only knew then / Just a girl in town / Shine your love on me / Giving you all I got / Closer to you / Eternally.
LP: . . . . ZL 72371
MC: . . . . ZK 72371

REJOICE.
LP: . . . . UNKNOWN

Emperor Beaver

POLLUTION (See under Orbitone).

Emperor & The

EMPEROR AND THE NIGHTINGALE, THE.
Tracks: / Emperor and the nightingale, The / Master thief, The / Three oranges, The / Three musicians, The / Fox, the cat and the dog, The.
MC: . . . . **ANV 650**

EMPEROR AND THE NIGHTINGALE, THE.
MC: . . . . **PLB 238**

Emperor's New Clothes

EMPEROR'S NEW CLOTHES (Asher, Jane (nar)).
MC: . . . . **LPMC 210**

EMPEROR'S NEW CLOTHES, THE.
Tracks: / Emperor's new clothes, The / Salt, pepper and mustard / Kastchey the deathless / John and Jane / Shortshanks and sturdy-oh.
MC: . . . . **ANV 651**

EMPEROR'S NEW CLOTHES, THE (Hans Christian Andersen) (Gielgud, Sir John & Mark Isham).
MC: . . . . **WT 0719**

EMPEROR'S NEW CLOTHES, THE (Well Loved Tales Up to Age 9).
MC: . . . . **PLB 50**

Empire

EXPENSIVE SOUND.
Tracks: / Safety / Him or me / All These Things / New emotion / Strand, The / Empire / Hot seat / Electric guitar / Turn it round / Today / Expensive sound.
LP: . . . . **ROUTE 001**

WHO STARTS THE STOPPING IT?.
Tracks: / This my word / My imagination / All of the places / Love like a brother / Talk free / Who starts the stopping it? / Tears / Higher and higher / Precious love / This way / Southwinds (Only on CD.) / Behind closed doors (Only on CD.) / Big city (Only on CD.).
LP: . . . . **PCS 7323**
MC: . . . . **TCPCS 7323**

Empire Brass...

BACH FESTIVAL.
MC: . . . . **EL 747 395 4**

FIREWORKS.
MC: . . . . **EL 749 277 4**

JOY TO THE WORLD (Music of Christmas).
Tracks: / Joy to the world / Holly and the ivy, The / Away in a manger / It came upon a midnight clear / O little town of Bethlehem / Good Christian men, rejoice / First Noel, The / Hark the herald angels sing / Angels we have heard on high / God rest ye merry gentlemen / Lo, how a rose e'er blooming / Make a joyful noise / O come, o come Emmanuel / Deck the halls / Good King Wenceslas / What child is this / Silent night / O tannenbaum / O holy night / O come all ye faithful.
MC: . . . . **EL 7490974**

Empire Movie Music

EMPIRE MOVIE MUSIC COLLECTION (See Under Films) (Various artists).

Empire of the Sun (bk)

EMPIRE OF THE SUN (J.G. Ballard) (Irons, Jeremy (nar)).
MCSET: **0600558703**

Empire Of The Sun

EMPIRE OF THE SUN (1987 film soundtrack) (Various artists).
Tracks: / Suo Gan: *Various artists* / Cadillac of the skies: *Various artists* / Jim's new life: *Various artists*/ Lost in the crowd: *Various artists* / Imaginary air battle: *Various artists* / Liberation:exsultate justi: *Various artists* / Return of the city,The: *Various artists* / British Grenadiers, The: *Various artists* / Toy planes, home and hearth: *Various artists* / Streets of Shangai,The: *Various artists* / Pheasant hunt, The: *Various artists* / No road home/seeing the bomb: *Various artists* / Exsultate justi: *Various artists.*
LP: . . . . **K 925668 1**
MC: . . . . **K 925668 4**

Empire State (film)

EMPIRE STATE (1987 film soundtrack) (Various artists).
Tracks: / Vicious games: *Yello* / Summerland: *State Project* / Heavens above: *Communards* / Empire state: *State Project* / Argument: *State Project* / Dance floor: *State Project* / Lobby, The: *State Project*/ Hollywood bar: *State Project* / Ship of fools: *Chaos 808* / Murder: *New Order* / Money: *Money.*
LP: . . . . **STATELP 1**
MC: . . . . **STATETC 1**

Empire Strikes Back

EMPIRE STRIKES BACK (Film soundtrack) (Various artists).
Tracks: / Imperial march: *Various artists* (Darth Vaders March) / Yoda's theme: *Various artists* / Asteroid field, The: *Various artists* / Han Solo and the princess: *Various artists* / Empire strikes back, The: Finale: *Various* artists / Training of a Jedi knight, The: *Various artists* / Yoda and the force: *Various artists* / Duel, The: *Various artists* / Battle in the snow, The: *Various artists.*
LP: . . . . **RSS 023**
MC: . . . . **TRSS 023**
LP: **827580.1**
MC: **827580.4**
LP: **2394 276**
LP: **2394 257**
MC: **3216 257**

EMPIRE STRIKES BACK, THE (Film Soundtrack) (Various artists).
Tracks: / Asteroid field, The: *Various artists* / Battle in the snow, The: *Various artists* / Duel, The: *Various* artists / Han Solo and the princess: *Various artists* / Imperial march: *Various artists* / Star wars: *Various* artists / Training of a Jedi Knight: *Various artists* / Yoda and the force: *Various artists* / Yoda's theme: *Various artists* / Finale: *Various artists.*
LP: . . . . **D 451**
MC: . . . . **D 151DC**

STORY OF THE EMPIRE STRIKES BACK (Various artists).
LP: . . . . **D 62102**

Empty Pocket

PAINTED LADY.
Tracks: / Kings own deer, The / Painted lady / Erin my country / My son John / Trees they grow high, The / Last folk song, The / Rocky road to Dublin, The / John Barleycorn / Babe I bruise so easy / Moon rakers / Ye knights of the round table / Spinning wheel / Give it steam.
MC: . . . . **BH 8803 C**

Empty Quarter

DELIRIUM.
LP: . . . . **AMA 24**

En Vogue

BORN TO SING.
LP: **7567820841**
MC: **7567820844**

Enchantment

JOURNEY TO THE LAND OF ENCHANTMENT.
Tracks: / Future gonna get you / Magnetic feel / Anyway you want it / Love melodies / Oasis of love / I wanna boogie / Fun / Let me entertain you / Forever more / Where do we go from here / Journey.
LP: . . . . **FL 13269**

Encircled Sea (film)

ENCIRCLED SEA (Film Soundtrack) (Various artists).
Tracks: / Water's edge, The: *Various artists* / Earth, fire and water: *Various artists* / Heart of the Mediterranean, The: *Various artists* / Fishermen, The: *Various artists* / Shipbuilders: *Various artists* / Navigators, The: *Various artists* / Great exchange, The: *Various artists* / Gateways and haven: *Various artists* / Theatre of war: *Various artists* / Sea of belief: *Various artists.*
MC: . . . . **FILMC 076**

End

GUSTO.
LP: . . . . **GUSTLP 1**
MC: . . . . **GUSTMC 1**

End Of The... (bk)

END OF THE TETHER, THE (Joseph Conrad) (Andrews, Harry (nar)).
MCSET: **418 003-4**

Endgames

BUILDING BEAUTY.
Tracks: / Love cares / Universe won't mind, The / Ecstasy / Miracle in my heart / Love building beauty / Desire / Waiting for another chance / Searching for love / Both of us.
LP: . . . . **V 2287**
MC: . . . . **TCV 2287**

Endle St Cloud

THANK YOU ALL VERY MUCH.
Tracks: / Piano a tempo: 21 street corner preacher / Piano scherzo: 40 who would you like to be / Piano tranquillo: 30 this is love / Piano allegretto: 16 professor black / Piano diminuendo: 22 / Piano agitato: 33 laughter / Piano adagio: 39 Jessica / Piano conbrio: 12 come through / Piano andante: 47 like a badge / Piano Temeramente: 21.
LP: . . . . **LIK 34**

Endless Games

ENDLESS GAMES, THE (See under Morricone, Ennio) (Morricone, Ennio).

Endless Love (film)

ENDLESS LOVE (Original soundtrack) (Various artists).
Tracks: / Endless love: *Various artists* / Dreaming of you: *Various artists* / I was made for lovin' you: *Various artists* / Dreamin': *Various artists.*
MC: **7141 182**
LP: **6337 182**

Endresen, Sidsel

SO I WRITE.
LP: . . . . **ECM 1408**
MC: **8417764**

Endsley, Melvin

I LIKE YOUR KIND OF LOVE.
Tracks: / I like your kind of love / Is it true / I got a feeling / Keep a lovin' me, baby / Let's fall out of love / Just want to be wanted / I ain't gettin' nowhere with you / Hungry eyes / Loving on my mind / Lonely all over again / There's bound to be / Gettin' used to the blues / Bringin' the blues to my door / I'd just be fool enough.
LP: . . . . **BFX 15275**

Enemies- A Love Story

ENEMIES- A LOVE STORY (Film soundtrack) (Various artists).
Tracks: / Herman: *Various artists* / Tamara: *Various artists* / In the wood: *Various artists* / Masha: *Various artists* / Third wife, A: *Various artists* / Kertchmar Country Club: *Various artists* / Rumba, The: *Various artists* / Baby Masha: *Various artists.*
LP: . . . . **VS 5253**
MC: . . . . **VSC 5253**

Enemies Of The State

ENEMIES OF THE STATE (Various artists).
LP: . . . . **IN 12**

Enemy

GATEWAY TO HELL, THE.
LP: . . . . **FALL LP 015**

LAST BUT NOT LEAST.
LP: . . . . **ASS 12**

Enemy Mine (film)

ENEMY MINE (1986 film soundtrack) (Various artists).
Tracks: / Fryine IV: *Jarre, Maurice* / Relationship: *Jarre, Maurice* / Small drac, The: *Jarre, Maurice*/ Crater, The: *Jarre, Maurice* / Birth of Zammia: *Jarre, Maurice* / Spring: *Jarre, Maurice* / Scavengers: *Jarre, Maurice* / Davidges lineage: *Jarre, Maurice* / Football game: *Jarre, Maurice* / Before the enemy empire: *Jarre, Maurice.*
LP: . . . . **CST 8011**
MC: . . . . **CSTC 8011**
MC: . . . . **CTV 81271**
LP: . . . . **TER 1112**

Enemy Within

TOUCH OF SUNBURN.
Tracks: / All quiet / Chinese white boy / Rock and roll feeling / Doctor / Four minute melody / Post modern blues / Eprom song / Intensity of vision / Camel's eye blues / Way you dance / End zone / Nietzche's ass.
LP: . . . . **RL 067**
MC: . . . . **CRL 0067**

TWO GREENS MAKE A BLUES (See Under Green, Peter) (Enemy Within, Peter Green & Mick Green).

Energy

ENERGY (Various artists).
LP: . . . . **LELEP 1003**
MC: . . . . **CELEP 1003**

Energy Orchard

ENERGY ORCHARD.
LP: . . . . **MCG 6083**
MC: . . . . **MCGC 6083**

Engbarth, Gerhard

BLUES VOM FRIEDEN (Engbarth, Gerhard with Louisiana Red).
LP: . . . . **LR 44.011**

Engel, Detlef

MISTER BLUE.
Tracks: / Einen engel ohne flugel / Traumen (Immer nur traumen) / Mister Blue / Komm zu mir, darling / Isabella / Zieg' mir bei nacht die sterne / Wenn du nicht bei mir bist / Schnek mir doch ein bild von dir / Oh, I love you (never let me go) / So klar wei die sterne / Ich such' ein herz / Rock a hula baby / Vier kleine schuhe / War nur der and're nicht gekonnen / Ich bin nicht so wie alle anders / Sweety-sleepy melodie.
LP: . . . . **BFX 15054**

Engelhardt, Toulouse

TOULOUSIONS.
LP: . . . . **SBR 4203**

England

ALL ROUND ENGLAND AND BACK AGAIN (ENGLISH CUSTOM (Various artists).
Tracks: / Furry dance and hal-an-tow, The: *Various artists* / Hobby horse day: *Various artists* / Oak apple / garland day: *Various artists* / Whit Monday Morris, The: *Various artists* / Horn dance, The: *Various artists*/ Soul cakers, The: *Various artists* / Plough jags, The: *Various artists* / Easter Jolly Boys, The: *Various artists* / Wassailers: *Various artists* (Wassailers - Charlie Bate, Padstow, Cornwall...Fred Adams, Minehead & Ca).
LP: . . . . **SDL 332**
MC: . . . . **CSDL 332**

ANTHOLOGY OF ENGLISH SONG (Various artists).
MC: . . . . **NVLC 107**

COUNTRY GARDENS (Various artists).
Tracks: / Wasps, The (overture): *Various artists* / Rhosymedre: *Various artists* / Capriol suite: *Various artists* / Summer night on the river: *Various artists* / Song before sunrise: *Various artists* / Country gardens: *Various artists* (Morris Dance Tune.) / Mock morris: *Various artists* / Shepherd's hey: *Various artists*/ Cherry ripe: *Various artists* / Petite suite de concert No.s 1 & 2: *Various artists* / Three dances from "Nell Gwyn": *Various artists* / In the country: *Various artists* (From "Meadow to Mayfair") / Chanson de matin: *Various artists* / Salut d'amour: *Various artists.*
MC: **TC2MOM 123**
MC: . . . . **LZ 762 529 4**

ENGLISH MUSIC HERITAGE (Various artists).
MC: . . . . **AMP 020**

ENGLISH SPORTING BALLADS (Various artists).
Tracks: / Eccles wake: *Various artists* / Bonnie Beeswing: *Various artists* / Ballad of Trubshaw and Green, The: *Various artists* / Great foot race, The: *Various artists* / Newcastle wakes: *Various artists* / Charcoal black and the bonny greu: *Various artists* / Sayer's and Heenan's great fight: *Various artists* / Boat race, The: *Various artists* / White hare of Howden, The: *Various artists* / Noble fox hunting, The: *Various artists*/ Alnwick football song: *Various artists* / Bullard's song, The: *Various artists.*
LP: . . . . **BRO 128**
MC: . . . . **KBRO 128**

SOUNDS AND SONGS OF LONDON (Various artists).
LP: . . . . **EMS 1055881**
MC: . . . . **TCEMS 1055884**

SOUNDS OF ENGLAND, THE Various artists (Various artists).
Tracks: / White cliffs of Dover, The: *Lynn, Vera* / Run rabbit run: *Roy, Harry & His Orchestra* / English country garden: *Morris Concert Band* / Maybe it's because I'm a Londoner: *Flanagan & Allen* / Jerusalem: *Band of HM Royal Marines* / Widecombe Fair: *Spinners* / We'll gather lilacs: *Ziegler, Anne & Webster Booth* / Mad dogs and Englishmen: *Coward, Noel* / Lambeth walk: *Munro, Ronnie & His Orchestra* / Standard of St George, The: *Band of HM Royal Marines* / Nightingale sang in Berkeley Square, A: *Lynn, Vera* / When the boat comes in: *Moorhouse, Alan* / I do like to be beside the seaside: *Dixon, Reginald* / Sun has got his hat on, The / Wish me luck as you wave me goodbye: *Fields, Gracie* / Greensleeves: *Morris Concert Band* / I leave my heart in an English garden: *Booth, Webster* / Life on the ocean wave, A: *Band of HM Royal Marines* / We'll meet again: *Lynn, Vera* / Underneath the arches: *Flanagan & Allen* / Blaydon races: *Spinners* / Look for the silver lining: *Matthews, Jessie*/ Early one morning: *G.U.S. Footwear Band* / Stately homes of England, The: *Coward, Noel* / Colonel Bogey: *Band of HM Royal Marines* / To be a farmer's boy: *Spinners* / There'll always be an England: *Lynn, Vera* / Land of hope and glory: *Central Band of the RAF.*
2LP: . . . . **DL 1131**
MC: . . . . **TCDL 1131**

WORLD OF ENGLAND, THE (Various artists).
Tracks: / This royal throne of Kings (from Richard II): *Various artists* / Orb and sceptre Coronation march - excerpt: *Various artists* / O peaceful England: *Various artists* / Shepherd's dance: *Various artists* / English rose: *Various artists* / Pastoral dance: *Various artists* / Scarborough Fair: *Various artists* / Early one morning: *Various artists* / Floral dance, The: *Various artists* / Oranges and lemons: *Various artists*/ Knightsbridge march: *Various artists* / Strawberry Fair: *Various artists* / Eton boating song: *Various artists*/ Sussex by

the sea: *Various artists* / Greensleeves: *Various artists* / Pomp and circumstance march no.1: *Various artists*.
LP: . . . . **SPA 190**

England, Colin

COLIN ENGLAND.
Tracks: / I've got what you need / She blew my mind / Say you love me / I need your love / Try me (try my love) / To love her / What should I do / Change / Don't tell me why / Always / Don't tell me why (inst.) (CD only.).
LP: . . . . **ZL 72745**
MC: . . . . **ZK 72745**

England Dan

DOCTOR HECKLE AND MR. JIVE (England Dan/John Ford Coley).
Tracks: / Hollywood heckle and jive / What can I do with this broken heart / Another golden oldie for Wendy / Broken hearted me / Children of the half light / Rolling fever / Love is the answer / Only matter of time / Caught up in the middle / Running after you / What's forever for.
LP: . . . . **K 50602**

DOWDY FERRY ROAD (England Dan/John Ford Coley).
LP: . . . . **K 50362**

I HEAR THE MUSIC (England Dan/John Ford Coley).
Tracks: / Used to you / Tell her hello / New Jersey / Idolizer / Simone / I hear the music / Legendary captain / Miss me / Pilot / Carry on.
LP: . . . . **AMLH 64613**

NIGHTS ARE FOREVER (England Dan/John Ford Coley).
Tracks: / I'd really love to see you / Tonight / I'll stay / Westward wind / Long way home / There'll never be another for me / Nights are forever without you / It's not the same / Showboat gambler / Prisoner, The / Everything's gonna be alright.
LP: . . . . **K 50297**

SOME THINGS DON'T COME EASY (England Dan/John Ford Coley).
LP: . . . . **K 50470**

England Football Team

THIS TIME (WE'LL GET IT RIGHT) (England World Cup Squad 1982).
Tracks: / This time / England we'll fly the flag / Head over heels / We are the champions / Bulldog Bobby / Grandstand / Land of hope and glory / Abide with me / Road to Spain / Back home / You'll never walk alone / Can't get a ticket for the world cup / Match of the day / World of sport theme / National anthem / This time we'll get it right.
LP: . . . . **NE 1169**
MC: . . . . **CE 2169**

WORLD BEATERS DING THE WORLD BEATERS (England World Cup Squad 1970).
LP: . . . . **NSPL 18337**

WORLD CUP PARTY.
Tracks: / Rule Britannia ((medley also includes: There'll always be an England, Floral dance, Bl) / When we are far from home / Whatever will be will be ((Medley also includes: Wonderful Copenhagen, Tulips from Amsterdam, Ed) / Yellow rose of Texas ((Medley also includes: The lion sleeps tonight, Carolina in the mornin) / Barbados ((Medley also includes: Rivers of Babylon, Caribbean queen, Copacabana)) / Chicago ((Medley also includes: Figaro, Lady of Spain, Give my regards to broad) / We've got the whole world at our feet / Happy wanderer, The ((Medley also includes: Waltzing Matilda, Una Paloma blanca, Volare, Y) / South of the border ((Medley also includes: Spanish eyes, Isle of Capri, Auf wiederseh'n swe) / On a slow boat to China ((Medley also includes: Arrivederci Roma, C'est si bon, Trail of the lo).
MC: . . . . **TCSCX 6703**
LP: . . . . **SCX 6703**

WORLD IN MOTION (see under New Order) (England World Cup Squad 1990/New Order).

England Swings

ENGLAND SWINGS (Various artists).
MC: . . . . **KNMC 15008**

England Under Snow

CONVERSATIONS.
Tracks: / First / Strawberry / Paris / Meadow / Mersey / Petula / Ride / Five / Ice / Arthur / Edward / Jacqueline / Seaside / Waltz / Castles / Tango / Turkey / Sewing / Hornpipe / Polonaise / Barn / Goodbye.
LP: . . . . **OPUS 1**

CONVERSATIONS (PART 2).
Tracks: / Forget / Home / Relax / Banana / Hate / Gardening / Seven / Proud / Spain / Funk / Sad / Mirror / Umbrella / E / Boogie / Rock / Chocolates / China / Passion / Lawn / Swing / Pain / Gold / Class / Woman / Woman (II) / Horses / Psycho / Last.
LP: . . . . **OPUS 2**

Englands Glory

LEGENDARY LOST RECORDINGS.
Tracks: / Devotion / Wide waterway, The / City of fun / First time I saw you, The / Broken arrows / Bright lights / It's been a long time / Guest, The / Peter and the pets / Showdown.
LP: . . . . **TOCK 4**

Engleman, Harry

KEYS TO ROMANCE.
LP: . . . . **DTL 3014**

TANGO TIME (Engleman, Harry & His Tango Orchestra).
LP: . . . . **DTL 3009**

English

ENGLISH (COURSE) (see under G.C.S.E Packs) (Longman/Pickwick Pass Packs).

English Air

SPACE IN BETWEEN, THE.
Tracks: / Koln Square / Dancer / Sound as a bell / Song for Davie / Pedro and the bat / Space inbetween, The / Time and again / Willows in the wind / Brassic tapestry / River flows on.
LP: . . . . **DCLP 1**

English, Barbara Jean

EXPERIENCE.
LP: . . . . **BLUEBJLP 1**

English Brass Ensemble

LYRIC BRASS.
LP: . . . . **DCA 660**
MC: . . . . **ZCDCA 660**

English Chamber

CELEBRATION: FOR FLUTE AND ORCHESTRA.
LP: . . . . **DCA 652**
MC: . . . . **ZC DCA 652**

FLUTE CONCERTOS (See under Dingfelder, Ingrid) (English Chamber Orchestra/Ingrid Dingfelder).

MONSIGNOR QUIXOTE SUITE (TV soundtrack).
Tracks: / Monsignor Quixote / Rocinante / Streets of Toboso, The / Twilight in La Mancha / Companeros / Windmills or giants / Let me feel temptation / Dulcinea / Adventures in the mind / In a certain village / Thoughts of a distant friend.
LP: . . . . **RBLP 1010**
MC: . . . . **ZCRB 1010**

SUMMER (THE LAST MOVEMENT) (see under Kennedy, Nigel) (Kennedy, Nigel & English Chamber Orchestra).

VIVALDI: THE FOUR SEASONS (Handel: Water Music).
Tracks: / Four seasons, The (Vivaldi) / Water music suite no.1 in F major (Handel).
MC: . . . . **ZC DCA 579**

WHITE CLIFFS OF DOVER, THE (See under Buchanan, Isobel) (English Chamber Orchestra/Isobel Buchanan).

English Chorale

CAROLS FOR CHRISTMAS.
Tracks: / O come all ye faithful / While shepherds watched their flocks by night / We three kings of Orient are / God rest ye merry gentlemen / Il dulce jubilo / Silent night / Good King Wenceslas / O little town of Bethlehem / In the bleak mid winter / First Noel, The / Once in royal David's city / Away in a manger / Hark the herald angels sing.
LP: . . . . **FA 3170**
MC: . . . . **TCFA 3170**
LP: . . . . **WHS 3170**
LP: . . . . **WHS 4131701**

GOLDEN GOSPEL.
Tracks: / Rivers of Babylon / He's got the whole world in his hands / Amazing Grace / Down by the riverside / Oh happy day / Michael row the boat ashore / Swing low sweet chariot.
2LP: . . . . **WW 5131/2**
MCSET: . . . . **WW 45131/2**

NATIONWIDE CAROLS.
Tracks: / Dream of Christmas, A / Innkeeper's song / Folksong, A / Postage Stamp Gardens / December town / Welcome to the world / Mary's song / Listen / Country boy's carol, A / Lullaby / Go there, go there / Camel boogie woogie.
LP: . . . . **WRD 3001**
MC: . . . . **TC WRD 3001**

English Country Blues

HOME AND DERANGED (English Country Blues Band).
LP: . . . . **FMSL 2004**
MC: . . . . **FMSC 3004**

NO RULES (English Country Blues Band).
LP: . . . . **DIN 323**

English Dogs

FORWARD INTO BATTLE.
LP: . . . . **ASS 20**

INVASION OF THE PORKY MEN.
LP: . . . . **CLAYLP 10**

WHERE LEGEND BEGAN.
LP: . . . . **FLAG 4**

English Electric

LANDING LIGHTS (See Under Tyla, Sean) (English Electric & Sean Tyla).

English Evenings

AFTER DARK.
LP: . . . . **GCB 1**
MC: . . . . **GCBC 1**

English Folk...

ENGLISH FOLK SONGS FROM 17TH AND 18TH CENTURIES (Broadside Band).
LP: . . . . **HM 1039**

English Guitar Quartet

BAROQUE GUITAR QUARTETS.
MC: . . . . **CSDL 386**

ROMANTIC GUITAR QUARTETS.
Tracks: / Song without words No.45 (Mendelssohn) (Op.102 No.3) / Song without words No. 7 (Mendelssohn) (Op.30 No.1) / Song without words No.35 (Mendelssohn) (Op.67 No.5) / Song without words No.44 (Mendelssohn) (Op.102 No.2) / Song without words No.21 (Mendelssohn) (Op.53 No.3) / Mazurka No.35 (Chopin) (Op.56 No.3) / Mazurka No.37 (Chopin) (Op.59 No.2) / Mazurka No.32 (Chopin) (Op.50 No.3) / Notturno (Borodin) (from Second String Quartet) / Arpeggione sonata (3 tracks: Allegro Moderato, Adagio & Allegretto).
MC: . . . . **CSDL 379**

English, Joe Band

WHAT YOU NEED.
LP: . . . . **MYR R 1213**
MC: . . . . **MYR C 1213**

English, Junior

IN LOVING YOU.
LP: . . . . **BS 036**

JACK THE RIPPER.
LP: . . . . **FORM 1093**

LOVERS KEY.
LP: . . . . **BR 1010**

WIN SOME, LOSE SOME.
Tracks: / Never win, never lose / Tell me baby / I bet you'll never be sorry / Stay a bit longer / I'll never fall in love again / Humanity / Dance with me / In loving you / Run girl / After tonight / I never see luxury / Girl you've changed your ways.
LP: . . . . **BS 41012**

English Literature

ENGLISH LITERATURE (COURSE) (See under G.C.S.E. Packs) (Longman/Pickwick Pass Packs).

English Monarchs

ENGLISH MONARCHS (line of succession).
MC: . . . . **WHC 004**

English National Opera

GLORIANA (See under Gloriana).

IN CONCERT.
LP: . . . . **LKLP 6398**

English Sinfonia

ENTENTE CORDIALE (Conducted by Sir Charles Groves).
Tracks: / Masques et bergamasques Opus 112 (Faure) / Overture (Faure) / Menuet (Faure) / Gavotte (Faure) / Pastorale (Faure) / Chanson de nuit / Chanson de matin / Pavane, Opus 50 (Faure) / On hearing the first cuckoo in Spring (Delius) / Pavane pour une infante defunte (Ravel) / Capriol suite for strings (Warlock) / Banks of Green Willow, The / Gymnopedie.
MC: . . . . **CIMPC 926**

English Songs

TREASURY OF ENGLISH SONGS (Various artists).
2LP: . . . . **EX 2909113**
MCSET: . . . . **EX 2909115**

English String

CELLO CONCERTOS (See under Haydn for full details).

COMPLETE WORKS FOR STRING ORCHESTRA (See under Elgar for full details).

MUSIC FOR STRING ORCHESTRA (See under Bartok for full details).

ORCHESTRAL WORKS (See under Finzi for full details).

SERENADES FOR STRINGS (See under Tchaikovsky for full details).

English With A Dialect

ENGLISH WITH A DIALECT.
LP: . . . . **REC 173**
MC: . . . . **ZCM 173**

English With An Accent

ENGLISH WITH AN ACCENT.
LP: . . . . **REC 166**
MC: . . . . **ZCM 166**

Englund, Ernie

HIS TRUMPET & THE VISBY BIG BAND.
LP: . . . . **PHONT 7567**

VISBY DOMKYRKA (Englund, Ernie and Ola Hoglund).
LP: . . . . **FLC 5071**

Englund, Lasse

ANCHOR (Englund, Lasse and Palle Mikelborg).
LP: . . . . **AM 62**

Enid

AERIE FAERIE NONSENSE.
Tracks: / Prelude / Mayday galliard / Ondine / Childe Roland / Fand: first movement / Fand: second movement.
LP: . . . . **ENID 6**
LP: . . . . **EG 2603241**

FAND SYMPHONIC TONE POEM.
LP: . . . . **ENID 9**

IN THE REGION OF THE SUMMER STARS.
Tracks: / Fool / Falling tower, The / Death, the reaper / Lovers / Devil / Sun / Last judgement / In the region of the Summer stars.
LP: . . . . **ENID 7**
LP: . . . . **EG 2603231**

LIVE AT HAMMERSMITH, VOL. 1.
LP: . . . . **ENID 1**

LIVE AT HAMMERSMITH, VOL. 2.
LP: . . . . **ENID 2**

LOVERS AND FOOLS.
Tracks: / Fantasy on Scarborough fayre / Hall of mirrors / Sheets of blue / Lovers, The / Evensong / Bright star / Flame of power, The / Fool / Falling tower, The / Something wicked this way comes / Summer / Flood, The / In the region of the Summer stars.
2LP: . . . . **DOJOLP 24**
MC: . . . . **DOJOTC 24**

RHAPSODY IN ROCK.
Tracks: / God save the Queen / Dies Irae / Song of Fand, The / Punch and Judy man / Humoresque / Cortege / Wild things / Sanctus / Hall of mirrors / Dreamer, The.
2LP: . . . . **NSPD 18619**

SALOME.
Tracks: / O Salome / Streets of blue / Change, The / Jack, The / Flames of power.
LP: . . . . **ENID 10**

SEED AND THE SOWER, THE.
Tracks: / Children crossing / Bar of shadow, A / La rage / Longhome / Earth born.
LP: . . . . **ENID 11**

SIX PIECES.
Tracks: / Sanctus / Once she was / Ring master / Punch and Judy man / Hall of mirrors / Dreamer / Joined by the heart (pt. 1) (CD only.).
LP: . . . . **ENID 4**
MC: . . . . **ZCN 116**
LP: . . . . **NH 116**

SOMETHING WICKED THIS WAY COMES.
Tracks: / Raindown / Jessica / And then there was none / Evensong / Bright star / Song for Europe / Something wicked this way comes.
LP: . . . . **ENID 3**

SPELL, THE.
Tracks: / Winter "The key" / Spring / Summer / Autumn "Veni creator spiritus" (Come creative spritus) / Elephants never die / Sentimental side of Mrs James (For the family and friends of Mark.) / Fand ((Live Hammersmith 1979). (CD only).).
LP: . . . . **ENID 8**

TOUCH ME.
Tracks: / Humouresque / Cortege / Elegy (touch me) / Gallevant / Albion fair / Joined by the heart.
LP: . . . . **NSPH 18593**
MC: . . . . **ZCP 18593**
LP: . . . . **ENID 5**

Enigma (70's)

AIN'T NO STOPPIN' US NOW.
Tracks: / I love music / Turn the music up / Shake your body / Lovely one / Celebration / Can you handle it / It's a love thing / Stomp / Don't stop til you get enough / Let's all chant / Casanova / Is it

love you're after? / Boogie wonderland / Lover's holiday / I shoulda loved ya / Make that move / Instant replay / Hot stuff / Cuba / I haven't stopped dancing yet / Viva Espana / Hasta la vista / Une paloma blanca / One for you one for me / Rasputin / Painter man / Brown girl in the ring / Rivers of Babylon / Figaro / Singin in the rain / Copacabana / El bimbo / Summer of 42 / Da doo ron ron / Que sera mi vida / Born to be alive / D.I.S.C.O. / Ain't no stoppin' us now / Le freak / In the forest / Do you feel my love / Master blaster / Rapture / Oops upside your head / Car wash / Hi ho silver lining / Jump to the beat / Baby love / Ring my bell / Use it up wear it out / Mysteries of the world / Feel the need / Love train / Somebody help me out / Hustle, The / I will survive / Ain't no stoppin' us now / Funkercize lesson 1 / Good time / Dance, dance, dance / Everybody dance / My forbidden lover / Lost in music / Feet keep dancin' / He's the greatest dancer / I'm coming out / Upside down / My old piano / Spacer / We are family / Funkercize II.
LP: . . . . **CRX 1**

Enigma (90's)

MCMXC CD.
LP: . . . . **LPVIR 1**
MC: . . . . **MCVIR 1**

Enigma (film)

ENIGMA (1982 film soundtrack) (Various artists).
Tracks: / Enigma: main titles: *Various artists* / Alex goes home: *Various artists* / Love theme: *Various* artists / Crossing the frontier: *Various artists* / Escape from Schiller's resturant: *Various artists* / Gasthaus theme, The: *Various artists* / Russian Christmas time: *Various artists* / Christmas carol: *Various artists*/ Centra builing fire, The: *Various artists* / Karen's arrest: *Various artists* / Dimitri's discovery and farewell: *Various artists* / Enigma: End titles: *Various artists.*
LP: . . . . **TER 1027**

Enjoy, Enjoy, Enjoy

ENJOY ENJOY ENJOY (Various artists).
LP: . . . . **NYL 500**

Enjoy-Story Of Rap

ENJOY-STORY OF RAP SET (See Under Rap) (Various artists).

Ennemis Intimes (film)

ENNEMIS INTIMES (INTIMATE ENEMIES) (Original soundtrack) (Various artists).
LP: . . . . **A 350**

Ennis, Ethel

THIS IS ETHEL ENNIS.
Tracks: / He loves me / Occasional man, An / Dear friend / Nobody told me / As you desire me / Joey, Joey, Joey / Moon was yellow (and the night was young) / Who will buy? / Night club / Love don't turn away / Starry eyed and breathless / When did I fall in love.
LP: . . . . **NL 90043**
MC: . . . . **NK 90043**

Ennis, Seamus

40 YEARS OF IRISH PIPING.
LP: . . . . **FRR 001/2**
LP: . . . . **SIF 1000**

BEST OF IRISH PIPING.
MC: . . . . **TA 1002/9**

FEIDHLIM TONN RI'S CASTLE (King of Ireland's son).
MC: **4CC 19**
LP: . . . . **CC 19**

MUSIC AT THE GATE.
Tracks: / Leprechaun / On the banks of the roses / Groves medley / Molly Bawn / Praties, they are small, The / New Demesne, The / Bonnie boy is young, The / Whistling thief / Trip over the mountain / Brian O'Linn / Captain Wedderburn's courtship / Mountain dew / Uncle Rat went out to ride / Boyne hunt / Fairy lullaby, A / Ould orange flute / Calm Avonree / Cucanandee / Old woman wrapped up in a blanket, The / Lord Gregory / Brown thorn, The / Football crazy / Red herring, The.
MC: **60-079**

PURE DROP,THE.
LP: . . . . **TARA 1002**
MC: **4TA 1002**

SEAMUS ENNIS.
LP: . . . . **LEA 2003**

UILEAN PIPES - THE FOX CHASE.
LP: . . . . **TARA 1009**
MC: **4TA 1009**

WANDERING MINSTREL,THE.
Tracks: / Wandering minstrel / Jackson's morning brush / Boys from Blue Hill / Dunphy's hornpipe / Glen Nephin cuckoo / Little fair cannavans, The / Frieze britches / Flags of Dublin, The / Wind that shakes the barley, The / Little stack of barley, The / Hornpipe / New Demesne, The / Blackbird, The / Gillian's apples / Walls of Liscarroll, The / Stone in the field, The / Molly o'Malone / Kiss the maid behind the barrel / Happy to meet and sorry to part.
LP: **12TS 250**

Ennis, Skinnay

SKINNAY ENNIS, 1947-48.
Tracks: / Got a date with an angel / Heart of stone / Moon is low, The / Remember me / La vie en rose / Lamplight / Stella by starlight / All of me / Little bit independent, A / My number one dream came true / That's my desire / I wanna be loved / Rain / Easy to love / Same old dream, The / Ain'tcha ever comin' back.
LP: . . . . **HSR 164**

Ennis, Tom

JAMES MORRISON AND TOM ENNIS (Ennis, Tom & James Morrison).
Tracks: / Money musk / Johnny, will you marry me / Keel row, The / Bags of spuds / Temple house / Pigeon on the gate / Job of journeywork / Girl that broke my heart, The / Galway, The / Kildare fancy, The / New steamboat / Bucks of Oranmore, The / Gardiner's daughter / Trip to the cottage / Limestone rock / Flowers of spring / Maid behind the bar, The / Trim the velvet / Paddy in London / Butcher's march / Sligo Bay / Curlew hills / Peach blossoms / Frieze breeches.
LP: . . . . **12 TS 390**

Eno, Brian

ANOTHER GREEN WORLD.
Tracks: / Sky saw / Over fire island / St. Elmo's fire / In dark trees / Big ship, The / I'll come running / Another green world / Sombre reptiles / Little fishes / Golden hours / Becalmed / Zawinul/Lava / Everything merges with the night / Spirits drifting.
LP: . . . . **EGLP 21**
MC: . . . . **EGMC 21**
LP: **2302 069**

APOLLO (Atmospheres and Soundtracks).
Tracks: / Under stars / Secret place, The / Matta / Signals / Ending (ascent), An / Under stars II / Drift / Silver morning / Deep blue day / Weightless / Always returning / Stars.
LP: . . . . **EGLP 53**
MC: . . . . **EGMC 53**

BEFORE AND AFTER SCIENCE.
Tracks: / No one receiving / Spider and I / Through hollow lands / By this river / Julie with ... / Here he comes / King's lead hat / Energy fools the magician / Kurt's rejoinder / Backwater.
LP: **2302 071**
LP: . . . . **EGLP 32**
MC: . . . . **EGMC 32**

BEGEGNUNGEN (Eno/Mobius/ Rodelius/Plank).
LP: . . . . **SKY 095**

BRIAN ENO BOX SET (Another green world/Before & after science/Apollo).
MCSET: . . . . **EGBM 7**

DISCREET MUSIC.
Tracks: / Discreet music 1 & 2 / Fullness of wind (part 1) / French catalogues (part 2) / Brutal adour (part 3).
LP: . . . . **EGED 23**
MC: . . . . **EGEDC 23**

FOURTH WORLD MUSIC (see under Hassell, Jon).

HERE COME THE WARM JETS.
Tracks: / Needles in the camel's eye / Paw paw negro blowtorch, The / Baby's on fire / Cindy tells me / Driving me backwards / On some faraway beach / Black Frank / Dead finks don't talk / Some of them are old / Here come the warm jets.
MC: . . . . **EGMC 11**
LP: . . . . **EGLP 11**
LP: **2302 063**
LP: . . . . **ILPS 9268**

MORE BLANK THAN FRANK.
Tracks: / Here he comes / Everything merges with the night / On some faraway beach / I'll come running (to tie your shoe) / Taking tiger mountain / Backwater / St. Elmo's fire / No one receiving / Great pretender, The / King's lead hat / Julie with ... / Back in Judy's jungle.
LP: . . . . **EGLP 65**
MC: . . . . **EGMC 65**

MUSIC FOR AIRPORTS.
Tracks: / 1/1 / 2/1 / 1/2 / 2/2.
LP: . . . . **EGED 17**
MC: . . . . **EGEDC 17**
LP: . . . . **AMB 001**
MC: . . . . **AMBC 1**

MUSIC FOR FILMS.
Tracks: / M386 / Aragon / From the same hill / Inland sea / Two rapid formations / Slow water / Sparrow fall 1 / Sparrow fall 2 / Sparrow fall 3 / Quartz / Events in dense fog / There is nobody / Patrolling wire borders / Task force / Strange light / Final sunset / Measured room, A / Alternative 3.
LP: **2310 623**
LP: . . . . **EGED 5**
MC: . . . . **EGEDC 5**

MUSIC FOR FILMS VOL.2.
LP: . . . . **EGED 35**
MC: . . . . **EGEDC 35**

MY LIFE IN THE BUSH OF GHOSTS (Eno, Brian & David Byrne).
Tracks: / America is waiting / Mea culpa / Help me somebody / Regiment / Jezebel spirit / Moonlight in glory / Come with us / Carrier, The / Secret life / Mountain of needles / Very, very hungry.
LP: . . . . **EGLP 48**
MC: . . . . **EGMC 48**

ON LAND.
Tracks: / Lizard point / Lost day, The / Tal coat / Shadow / Lantern marsh / Unfamiliar wind (Leeks hills) / Clearing, A / Dunwich Beach, Autumn 1960.
LP: . . . . **EGED 20**
MC: . . . . **EGEDC 20**

PEARL, THE (See under Budd, Harold) (Eno, Brian & Harold Budd).

PLATEAUX OF MIRRORS (See under Budd, Harold) (Eno, Brian & Harold Budd).

TAKING TIGER MOUNTAIN BY STRATEGY.
Tracks: / Burning airlines give you so much more / Back in Judy's jungle / Fair lady of Limbourg, The / Mother whale eyeless / Great pretender, The / Third uncle / Put a straw under baby / True wheel, The / China my china / Taking tiger mountain.
LP: . . . . **EGLP 17**
MC: . . . . **EGMC 17**
LP: **2302 068**

THURSDAY AFTERNOON.
Tracks: / Thursday afternoon.
LP: . . . . **EGLP 64**

VOICES (Eno, Brian and Roger Eno).
Tracks: / Place in the wilderness, A / Day after, The / At the water's edge / Grey promenade / Paler sky, A / Through the blue / Evening tango / Recalling winter / Voices / Old dance, The / Reflections on I.K.B..
LP: . . . . **EGED 42**
MC: . . . . **EGEDC 42**

WORKING BACKWARDS 1983-1973 (11 record set).
LPS: . . . . **EGBS 2**

WRONG WAY UP (Eno, Brian/John Cale).
LP: . . . . **LAND 12**
MC: . . . . **LANDC 12**

Eno, Roger

BETWEEN TIDES.
Tracks: / Out at dawn / Field of gold / Prelude for St John / Ringinglow / Frost, The / One gull / Silent hours, The / Between tides / Winter music / While the city sleeps / Sunburst / Autumn / Almost dark.
LP: . . . . **LAND 001**

VOICES (See under Eno, Brian) (Eno, Brian and Roger Eno).

Enola Gay (film)

ENOLA GAY (1980 film soundtrack) (Various artists).
LP: . . . . **STV 81149**

Enormous Crocodile

ENORMOUS CROCODILE, THE (Roald Dahl) (Blake, Roger (nar)).
MC: **00 102211 3**

Enos The Clown

BAALGAD (See under Brown, Dennis) (Enos The Clown & Dennis Brown).

Enriquez, Bobby

CONCERTS BY THE SEA.
LP: . . . . **GNPS 2179**
MC: **GNP5 2179**

CONCERTS BY THE SEA II.
LP: . . . . **GNPS 2183**
MC: **GNP5 2183**

ESPANA.
Tracks: / Andalucia / Cordoba / Alhambra / Gitanerias / Malaguena / Jamaica farewell / Nightingale / Angelitos negros / Old bird, The.
LP: . . . . **N 5019**
MC: . . . . **ZCN 5019**
LP: . . . . **GNPS 2155**
MC: **GNP5 2155**

LIVE IN TOKYO.
Tracks: / Killer Joe / Airegin / After hours / Meditation / Misty / Groovin' high / Ain't misbehavin' / Holiday for strings / Donna Lee / Sweet Georgia Brown / Emily / Anthropology / Yellow days / Memories of you / Salambit / Confirmation.
LP: . . . . **N 6552**
LP: . . . . **GNPS 2161**
MC: **GNP5 2161**

LIVE IN TOKYO II.
LP: . . . . **GNPS 2168**
MC: **GNP5 2168**

PRODIGIOUS PIANO.
LP: . . . . **GNPS 2151**
MC: **GNP5 2151**

WILD MAN, THE.
Tracks: / Sweet Georgia Brown / Emily / Anthropology / Georgia on my mind / Yellow days / Memories of you / Salambit / Confirmation.
LP: . . . . **NCP 1005**
LP: . . . . **GNPS 2144**
MC: **GNP5 2144**

Ensemble de Bruxelles

FRENCH SONGS VOL 1 (see under Farley, Carole) (Ensemble de Bruxelles/ Carole Farley/Orch. Symph. de la RTBF).

Ensemble Musica

MUSIQUE TRADITIONALE DU CHILI.
MC: **824744**

Enter The Dragon

ENTER THE DRAGON (Film soundtrack) (Various artists).
Tracks: / Sampans: *Various artists* / Monk, The: *Various artists* / Gentle softness, The: *Various artists*/ Big battle, The: *Various artists* / Han's island: *Various artists* / Human fly: *Various artists* / Bamboo bird cage: *Various artists* / Broken mirrors: *Various artists* / Enter the dragon: *Various artists.*
LP: . . . . **K 46275**

Entertainment ...

ENTERTAINMENT ON THE THEME OF THE MONARCHY, AN (see under Hollow crown) (Various artists).

Entertainment USA (tv)

ENTERTAINMENT USA (THEME FROM) (See under King, Jonathan 'I'll slap your face') (King, Jonathan).

VERY BEST OF ENTERTAINMENT USA (Various artists).
LP: . . . . **UPTVR 1**

Entombed

LEFT HAND PATH.
LP: . . . . **MOSH 21**
MC: . . . . **MOSH 21 MC**

Entwistle, John

TOO LATE THE HERO.
Tracks: / Try me / Talk dirty / Love bird / Sleeping man / I'm coming back / Dancing master / Fallen angel / Love is a heart attack / Too late the hero.
LP: . . . . **K 99179**
MC: **K4 99179**

Enuff Z Nuff

ENUFF Z NUFF.
Tracks: / New thing / Fly high Michelle / In the groove / For now / I could never be without you / She wants more / Hot little summer girl / Little indian angel / Kiss the clown / Finger on the trigger.
LP: **K791 262 1**
MC: **K791 262 4**

STRENGTH.
MC: **7567916384**
LP: **7567916381**

Envy

AIN'T IT A SIN.
Tracks: / Ain't it a sin? / I believe in you / Heartache / Lie here waiting / Wait on you / You're so hot / All the reasons / I see the light / I'm not your lover / Hurt me.
LP: . . . . **K 790 605 1**
MC: . . . . **K 790 605 4**

Enya

CELTS, THE.
Tracks: / Celts, The / Aldebaran / I want tomorrow / March of the celts / Deireadh an tuath / Sun in the stream / To go beyond / Fairytale / Epona / Triad: St. Patrick cu chulainn oisin / Portrait / Boadicea / Bard dance / Dan y dwr / To go beyond (2).
LP: . . . . **REB 605**
MC: . . . . **ZCF 605**

ENYA: INTERVIEW PICTURE DISC.
LPPD: . . . . **BAK 2152**

FROG PRINCE, THE (See under Frog Prince, The).

WATERMARK.
Tracks: / Watermark / Cursum perfico / On your shore / Storms in Africa / Exile / Miss Clare remembers / Orinoco flow / Evening falls / River / Longships / Na

laetha geal m'oige / Storms in Africa (part II).
LP: . . . . WX 199
MC: . . . . WX 199 C

Epic Poems

EPIC POEMS (Powell, Robert (nar)).
Tracks: / How Horatius held the bridge / Elegy written in a country churchyard / John Gilpin / Hiawatha's wooing / Hiawatha's departure / Pied piper / Lepanto / Jackdaw of Rheims / Rhyme of the ancient mariner, The / Revenge-a ballad of the fleet / Armada - a fragment / Ballad of the East and West, The / Sicilian's tale, King Robert / Morte d'Arthur.
MCSET: . . . . ZBBC 1026

Epidemic

TRUTH OF WHAT WILL BE, THE.
LP: . . . . CORE 4

Epidemics

EPIDEMICS, THE.
Tracks: / Never take no for an answer / What would I do without you / Situations / You don't love me anymore / Love is alright / You can be anything / No cure / Don't I know you / Give an inch / Full moon.
LP: . . . . ECM 1308

Episode Six

PUT YOURSELF IN MY PLACE.
Tracks: / Put yourself in my place / That's all I want / I hear trumpets blow / True love is funny that way / Here, there and everywhere / Mighty Morris Ten / I will warm your heart / Incense / Love-hate-revenge / Baby baby baby / Morning dew / Sunshine girl / I can see through you / When I fall in love.
LP: . . . . PYL 6026
MC: . . . . PYM 6026

E.P.M.D.

BUSINESS AS USUAL.
Tracks: / I'm mad / Hardcore / Rampage / Manslaughter / Jane 3 / For my people / Mr Bozack / Gold digger / Give the people / Rap is outta control / Brothers on my jock / Underground / Hit squad heist / Funky piano.
LP: 4676971
MC: 4676974

STRICTLY BUSINESS.
LP: . . . . LPRE 82006
LP: . . . . SBUKLP 1

UNFINISHED BUSINESS.
LP: . . . . SBUKLP 8
MC: . . . . SBUKMC 8

Eppler, Alex

BARINYA (THE LADY).
LP: . . . . FF 285

Equale Brass

CABARET.
LP: 45014

Equality Of Love

EQUALITY OF LOVE (See under Edwards, Deirdre) (Edwards, Deirdre).

Equals

6 TRACK HITS.
Tracks: / Baby come back / Softly softly / Viva Bobby Joe / I won't be there / Black skinned blue eyed boys / Michael and his slipper tree.
MC: 7SC 5007

20 GREATEST HITS: EQUALS.
LP: 20050
MC: 40050

20 GREATEST HITS: EQUALS (2).
Tracks: / Baby come back / Black skinned blue eyed boys / Police on my back / Viva Bobby Joe / Good times / Butterly red white and blue / Give love a try / You've got too many boyfriends / Michael and the slipper tree / Hold me closer / I get so excited / Softly softly / Soul groovin' / Happy Birthday girl / I won't be there / Rub a dub / Giddy up.
LP: 226 201 5
MC: 216 201 5

ALL THE HITS PLUS MORE.
LP: . . . . PRST 001
MC: . . . . ZPRST 001

BABY COME BACK.
LP: . . . . PLP 27
MC: . . . . PMC 27

BEST OF THE EQUALS.
Tracks: / Baby come back / Giddy up a ding dong / Soul groovin' / Give love a try / I get so excited / You got too many boyfriends / I won't be there / Laurel and Hardy / Police on my back / Good times are gone forever / Butterfly red white and blue / Hold me closer.
LP: . . . . JOYS 137
LP: 20048
MC: 40048

DOIN THE 45S.
Tracks: / Baby come back / Gigolo Sam / Rub-a-dub-dub / Soul brother Clifford / Blue skinned blue eyed boys / Viva Bobby Joe / Michael and his slipper tree / I can see but you don't know / Happy birthday girl / Softly softly.
LP: 20047
MC: 40047
LP: . . . . RHAS 9017

EQUALS EXPLOSION.
LP: . . . . PTLS 1015

GREATEST HITS: EQUALS.
MC: . . . . DSK 122

PROFILE: EQUALS.
Tracks: / Baby come back / Giddy up a ding dong / Viva Bobby Joe / I get so excited / Police on my back / I won't be there / Hold me closer / Michael and his slipper tree / Soul brother Clifford / Rub-a-dub-dub / Another sad and lonely night / My life ain't easy.
LP: 6.24605
MC: CL4 24605

UNEQUALLED EQUALS.
LP: . . . . PTL 1006

Equators

HOT.
Tracks: / Rescue me / Age of 51 / If you need me / More than a person / Rankin' discipline / Mr. Copper / Nightmare / Where did Johnny go / There is someone / Learn my lesson / Feeling high.
LP: . . . . SEEZ 35

Eraserhead (film)

ERASERHEAD (1978 film soundtrack) (Various artists).
LP: . . . . VIRUS 30
LP: . . . . SP 70027
MC: . . . . CS 70027

Erasure

CHORUS.
LP: . . . . STUMM 95
MC: . . . . CSTUMM 95

CIRCUS, THE (ALBUM).
LP: . . . . STUMM 35
MC: . . . . CSTUMM 35

ERASURE: INTERVIEW PICTURE DISC.
LPPD: . . . . BAK 2161

ERASURE MEGAMIX (See under Drop The Bomb).

INNOCENTS, THE.
Tracks: / Little respect, A / Ship of fools / Phantom bride / Chains of love / Hallowed ground / 65,000 / Heart of stone / Yahoo! / Imagination / Witch in the ditch / Weight of the world.
LP: . . . . STUMM 55
MC: . . . . CSTUMM 55

TWO RING CIRCUS.
LP: . . . . STUMM 35 R
MC: . . . . CSTUMM 35 R

WILD.
LP: . . . . STUMM 75
MC: . . . . CSTUMM 75

WONDERLAND.
LP: . . . . STUMM 25
MC: . . . . CSTUMM 25

Erazerhead

RUMBLE OF THE EAST, THE.
Tracks: / Martian girl / Apeman / No one sees me now / She can dance / Next dance / I hate you / Teenager in love.
LP: . . . . SHARP 105

SHELLSHOCKED 1980-4.
LP: . . . . SHARP 025

TAKE ME TO YOUR LEADER.
LP: . . . . SHARP 017

Erfolg, Rudolf Wurther

RUDOLF WURTHER ERFOLG.
Tracks: / Carmen-fantasie - solo / La campanella (solo) / Variationen uber 'komm lieber mai' - orch. / Variation ein russisches volksleid / Variation uber russische volkslied - solo / Ouverture uber zwei finnische themen - orch..
LP: . . . . HS 053

Eric B & Rakim

FOLLOW THE LEADER.
Tracks: / Follow the leader / Microphone fiend / Lyrics of fury / Eric B never scared / Just a beat / Put your hands together / To the listeners / No competition / R, The / Musical massacre / Beats for the listeners.
LP: . . . . MCG 6031
MC: . . . . MCGC 6031

LET THE RHYTHM HIT 'EM.
Tracks: / Let the rhythm hit 'em / No omega / Ghetto, The / Step back / Eric B make my day / Run for cover / Untouchable / Mahogany / Keep 'em eager / Set 'em.
LP: . . . . MCG 6097
MC: . . . . MCGC 6097

PAID IN FULL.
Tracks: / I' ain't no joke / Eric B - is on the cut / My melody / I know you got soul / Move the crowd / As the rhyme goes on / Chinese arithmetic / Eric B for president / Extended beat / Paid in full / Eric B is on the cut / Paid in full.
LP: . . . . BRLP 514
MC: . . . . BRCA 514
MC: . . . . ICM 2007
LP: . . . . BWAY 4005
MC: 842 589 4

Eric & The Good...

FUNKY (Eric & The Good Good Feeling).
LP: . . . . EQNLP 1
MC: . . . . EQNMC 1

Eric The Viking (film)

ERIC THE VIKING (Film soundtrack) (Various artists).
LP: . . . . SNTF 1023

Erickson, Rod

SHE TAUGHT ME TO YODEL.
LP: . . . . GNPS 2105

Erickson, Roky

CASTING THE RUNES.
LP: . . . . TOCK 7
LPPD: . . . . TOCK 7P

CLEAR NIGHT FOR LOVE.
LP: . . . . ROSE 69

DON'T SLANDER ME.
Tracks: / Don't slander me / Haunt / Crazy crazy mama / Nothing in return / Burn the flames / Click your fingers applauding the play / If you have ghosts / Bermuda / You drive me crazy / Can't be brought down / Starry eyes / Damn thing, The / Sputnik.
LP: . . . . FIEND 86

GREMLINS HAVE PICTURES.
Tracks: / Night of the vampire / Interpreter / Song to Abe Lincoln / John Lawman / Anthem / Warning / Sweet honey pie / I am / Cold night for alligators / Heroin / I have always been here before / Before in the beginning.
LP: . . . . FIEND 66

HOLIDAY INN TAPES.
LP: . . . . FC 030

I THINK OF DEMONS (Erickson, Roky & The Aliens).
Tracks: / Two headed dog / I think of demons / I walked with a zombie / Don't shake me Lucifer / Night of the vampire / Bloody hammer / White faces / Cold night for alligators / Creature with the atom brain / Mine mine mind / Stand for the fire / Wind and more, The.
LP: . . . . ED 222
LP: . . . . CBS 84463

LIVE AT THE RITZ, 1987.
LP: . . . . FC 046

OPENERS.
LP: . . . . TOCK 10

TRIBUTE TO ROKY ERICKSON (WHERE THE PYRAMID) (Various artists).
MC: 7599264224

TWO HEADED DOG.
Tracks: / Two headed dog.
LP: . . . . FC 038

Ericson, Rolf

OH PRETTY LITTLE NEIDA.
LP: . . . . FLC 5003

STOCKHOLM SWEETNIN'.
LP: . . . . DRLP 78

Erin Ceili Band

PRIDE OF ERIN CEILI BAND.
LP: . . . . SOLP 1036

Erin's Green Shore

SINGING AND DANCING.
LP: . . . . SDBL 512

Erinsaga

ERINSAGA (See under Kiernan, Ken for details) (Kiernan, Ken/Ger MacDonald).

Erlando, Juan

ERLANDO AND HIS NEW LATIN BAND (Erlando, Juan/New Latin Band).
LP: . . . . ISST 190

JUAN ERLANDO AND THE NEW LATIN BAND.
LP: . . . . ISST 147

Ermoll, Serge

JUNGLE JUICE.
LP: . . . . LRF 193

Erney, Dewey

BEAUTIFUL FRIENDSHIP, A (Erney, Dewey & Ron Eschete).
Tracks: / For all we know / My romance / Love is here to stay / Long ago and far away.
LP: . . . . DS 881

SECOND SET, THE (Erney, Dewey & Ron Eschete).
LP: . . . . SG 5003

Erotic Dreams

EROTIC DREAMS (Various artists).
LP: . . . . SHM 3100
MC: . . . . HSC 3100

Erraji, Hassan

IA DOUNIA (Erraji, Hassan & Arabesque With Sabra).
LP: . . . . TUG 002
MC: . . . . TUGC 002

NIKRIZ (Erraji, Hassan & Hassan Arabesque).
LP: . . . . TUG 001
MC: . . . . TUGC 001

Errosion

MORTAL AGONY.
LP: . . . . WEBITE 36

Erskine, Peter

MOTION POET.
Tracks: / Erskoman / Not a word / Hero with a thousand faces / Dream clock / Exit up right / New regalia, A / Boulez / Mysery man, The / In walked Maya.
LP: . . . . INLP 803

PETER ERSKINE.
Tracks: / Leroy Street / E.S.P. / All's well that ends / Coyote blues / In statu nascendi / Change of mind / My ship.
LP: 1014 010

Erstrand, Lars

LARS ERSTRAND AND FOUR BROTHERS (Erstrand, Lars & Four Brothers).
LP: . . . . OP 8402

MINE FOREVER (Erstrand, Lars Trio).
LP: . . . . PHM 1010

TRIBUTE TO BENNY GOODMAN (See Peanuts Hucko) (Erstrand, Lars, Peanuts Hucko & Billy Butterfield).

TWO SIDES OF LARS ERSTRAND.
LP: . . . . OP 8302

Eruption

ERUPTION.
Tracks: / I can't stand the rain / Movin' / I'll take you there / Computer love / Way we were, The / Do you know what it feels like / Be yourself / I can't carry on / Wayward love / Party party.
LP: . . . . K 50454

LEAVE A LIGHT.
Tracks: / Leave a light / Sweet side / Up and away / Left me in the rain / Valley of the dolls / One way ticket / Hey there lonely girl / No good searchin' / Fire is gone / I can't stand the rain.
LP: . . . . K 50632

Ervin, Booker

BOOK COOKS.
Tracks: / Blue book, The / Git it / Little Jane / Book cooks, The / Largo / Poor butterfly.
LP: . . . . AFF 88

FREEDOM AND SPACE SESSIONS.
Tracks: / Lunar tune / Dry me not / Day to mourn / Grant's stand / Stella by starlight / Al's in / Mojo / I can't get started / Number two / Second 2 / There is no greater love.
2LP: . . . . PR 24091

LAMENT FOR BOOKER ERVIN.
LP: . . . . ENJA 2054

SONG BOOK, THE.
LP: . . . . PR 7318

SOULFUL SAXES (See under Kirk, Roland) (Kirk, Roland & Booker Ervin).

THAT'S IT.
Tracks: / Mojo / Uranus / Poinciana / Speak low / Booker's blues / Boo.
LP: . . . . CS 79014

Ervin, Frankie

DRAGNET BLUES.
LP: . . . . JD 902
LP: EA902

Erwin, Randy

COWBOY RHYTHM.
Tracks: / Cowboy rhythm / Long gone lonesome blues / Bring it on down to my house / Cowboy night herd song / In the jailhouse now.
LP: . . . . HLD 006

TILL THE COWS COME HOME.
LP: . . . . HLDM 001

Erwin, Trudy

BING AND TRUDY ON THE AIR (See under Crosby, Bing) (Erwin, Trudy & Bing Crosby).

Escalation

ESCALATION/GALILEO (See under Galileo for details) (Morricone, Ennio).

Escalators

MOVING STAIRCASES.
Tracks: / Day the sun burned down, The / Sloane rangers / Video club / Flanders fields / Young men / Cut up / Eskimo rock / Slumberland / Dog eats robot / Camden crawl / Survivalists / Starstruck / Monday.
LP: . . . . **WIKM 15**

Escape Club

WHITE FIELDS.
Tracks: / Push, The / Sound of the city / Fall / Where angels cry / I will be there / Blood and water / Hard way, The / White fields / Rescue me / Slow train.
LP: . . . . **PCS 7304**
MC: . . . . **TCPCS 7304**

WILD WILD WEST.
Tracks: / Wild wild west / Jealousy / Shake for the sheik / Walking through walls / Longest day, The / Who do you love? / Staring at the sun / Only the rain / Goodbye Johnny Ray / Working for the fat man.
LP: **255630 1**
MC: **255630 4**

Escape From New York

ESCAPE FROM NEW YORK (1981 film soundtrack) (Various artists).
LP: . . . . **TER 1011**
MC: . . . . **CTV 81134**
MC: . . . . **CL 0004**

Eschete, Ron

BEAUTIFUL FRIENDSHIP, A (See under Erney, Dewey) (Erney, Dewey & Ron Eschete).

Escorts

FROM THE BLUE ANGEL.
Tracks: / Dizzy Miss Lizzy / All I want is you / One to cry, The / Tell me baby / I don't want to go without you / Don't forget to write / C'mon home baby / You'll get no lovin' that way / Let it be me / Mad mad world / From head to toe / Night time.
LP: . . . . **FORD 1**

FROM THE CARIBBEAN.
LP: . . . . **LR 44.004**

Escovedo, Pete

MISTER E.
Tracks: / Whatcha gonna do? / Tassajara / Un poquito / Let's wait awhile / Gingerbread girl / Caribe / Take some time / Doctor Macumba / Mister E / D..:n - the beginning.
LP: . . . . **CR 5005**
MC: . . . . **CRC 5005**

YESTERDAY'S MEMORIES - TOMORROW'S DREAMS.
Tracks: / Charango sunrise / Moving pictures / Azteca Mozambique / Ah ah / Cueros / Modern dance / Zina's Zamba / Yesterday's memories, tomorrow's dreams / Revolt.
LP: . . . . **CR 5002**
MC: . . . . **CRC 5002**

Es-Feiv

COWS IN MOTION.
LP: . . . . **ROCK 3347**

Eshelman, Dave

DEEP VOICES (Eshelman, Dave Jazz Garden Big Band).
LP: . . . . **SB 2039**

Eskovitz, Bruce

WINDFALL.
Tracks: / Funk / Gettin' it / Sweet home / Q the chase / Groove chic / Latin fever / Troll / Variations on an Autumn theme.
LP: . . . . **OUTSTANDING 34**

ESP Is Alive & Well

ESP IS ALIVE AND WELL (Krippner, Stanley).
MC: . . . . **PT 30**

Espionage

E.S.P..
Tracks: / I couldn't get to sleep last night / In the name of love / It's Easter / Make it on a love / Deliver me / Couldn't hold back the tears / Cinema magic / Always / Turn around / Imagination.
LP: . . . . **EKT 10**

ESPIONAGE.
Tracks: / Sound of breaking hearts / Your love's for sale / Great escape / Freedom / Miracles / Living under rocks / Good things don't go on forever / I never meant to make you cry / Can't you feel my heartbeat / Ships across the night / One night stand.
LP: . . . . **AMLX 64935**

Espitalier, George

ESPITALIER AND HIS FOLKGROUP.
Tracks: / Reel / Krezbube / Tambourin / Malaguena / Hederit / Kiruna-melodie / Heidschnuck / Dalarna lok / Schlauer bauer / Makedonka / Cathrineta / Mariuca / Oro / Kasanka / Bauernquadrille / Sailor marimba / Sailor step / Lutt Anna.
LP: **099 095**

Esplin, Joss

SCOTLAND PAST AND PRESENT.
Tracks: / Bonnie Dundee / Flight from Culloden / Nicky Tams / Skyline of Skye / Bonnie lass o' Fyvie / Lassie wi the yellow coatie / Braes o' Killecrankle, The / Menzles tree, The / Cam ye by Atholl / My bonnie Maureen / Massacre of glencoe / Lassie come and dance with me / Come by the hills / Scotland tomorrow.
MC: . . . . **CJW 006**

Esposito, Joe

SOLITARY MEN (See Moroder, Giorgio) (Esposito, Joe & Giorgio Moroder).

Esquerita

BEST OF ESQUERITA.
LP: . . . . **FC 053**

ESQUERITA.
Tracks: / Hey Miss Lucy / She left me crying / Hole in my heart / Believe me when I say rock 'n' roll is here to stay / I need you / Why did it take you so long / Get back baby / I'm batty over Hatty / Gettin' plenty lovin'.
LP: . . . . **PM 1550791**
LP: . . . . **SSL 6037**
MC: . . . . **TCSSL 6037**

ROCKIN' THE JOINT.
Tracks: / Rockin' the joint / Esqurita and the voola / Laid off / Oh baby / Sarah Lee / I live the life I love / Katie Mae / Wait a minute baby / Good golly Annie Mae / Found her / I live the life I love (2) / This thing called love / Baby come back / You can't pull me down / Please come home / Just another lie.
LP: . . . . **OFF 6001**

VINTAGE VOOLA (Rare unissued acetates).
LP: **202**

Esquire

ESQUIRE.
Tracks: / To the rescue / Sunshine / Knock twice for heaven / Up down turnaround / Blossom time / Hourglass / Moving together / Silent future / Special greeting / What you've been saying.
LP: **9241011**
MC: **9241014**

Esquire Jazz...

ON THE AIR 1944 (Esquire Jazz All Stars).
Tracks: / Esquire bounce / Rockin' chair / Basin street blues / I'll get by / Rachel's dream / Tea for two / Get happy / My silent love / Surrey with the fringe on top / Esquire blues / Honeysuckle rose.
LP: . . . . **AIRCHECK 27**

Essence

ECSTACY.
LP: . . . . **CHIME 039 S**
MC: . . . . **CHIME 039 C**

NOTHING LASTS FOREVER.
LP: . . . . **CHIME 0114S**
MC: . . . . **CHIME 0114C**

PURITY.
LP: . . . . **CHIME 0011 S**

Essential Bop

FLICK WAS BOSS, THE.
LP: . . . . **TSA 1001**
LP: . . . . **TOCK 11**

Essential Classics

ESSENTIAL CLASSICS (Various artists).
MCSET: **4315414**
2LP: **4315411**

Essential Death ...

ESSENTIAL DEATH AND HORROR (1 AND 2) (See under Sound Effects) (Various artists).

Essential Firmament

ESSENTIAL FIRMAMENT AND THE ELEMENTS.
LP: . . . . **P 2202**

Essential Logic

BEAT RHYTHM NEWS.
LP: . . . . **ROUGH 5**

Essential Sound

ESSENTIAL SOUND EFFECTS (See under Sound Effects) (Various artists).

Essex, David

6 TRACK HITS.
Tracks: / Rollin stone / Ooh darlin / America / Stay with me baby / Turn me loose / Cool out tonight.
MC: **7SC 5017**

ALL THE FUN OF THE FAIR.
LP: . . . . **CBS 69160**

BE-BOP THE FUTURE.
Tracks: / Totally secure / Sunday papers / Magician / Politician / Sunshine girl / Be bop a lula / Life support system / Show girls / Silly little baby running / Pick up the future.
LP: **635 906 4**

CENTRE STAGE.
Tracks: / 42nd Street‡Lullaby of Broadway / Summertime / Corner of the sky / Tahiti / Bright eyes / Pinball wizard / Ghost buster / I wanna be like you / Phantom of the opera / Save the people / I dreamed a dream / Out here on my own.
LP: . . . . **ONE 1333**
MC: . . . . **OCE 2333**

COLLECTION: DAVID ESSEX.
Tracks: / Lamplight / Ocean girl / On and on / Rock on / Tell him no / Window / I know / America / Gonna make you a star / Bring in the sun / Ooh darling / Stardust / Streetfight / Turn me loose / For Emily / We all insane.
2LP: . . . . **PDA 069**
2LP: . . . . **CCSLP 248**
MC: . . . . **CCSMC 248**

DAVID ESSEX.
LP: **32439**
MC: **40 32439**
LP: **69088**

DAVID ESSEX ALBUM.
LP: **10011**

GOLD AND IVORY.
LP: **86038**

GREATEST HITS: DAVID ESSEX.
LP: . . . . **CBS 32237**

HOLD ME CLOSE.
Tracks: / Hold me close / You / I know / Dance little girl / Coming home / Gold and ivory / Lamplight / Gonna make you a star / If I could / Thank you very much / Bring in the sun / Ooh love on and on / Cool out tonight.
LP: . . . . **CBS 31763**

HOT LOVE.
Tracks: / Hot love / I luv ya / Talking with your body / Zebra kid / Heart on my sleeve / Reality / Rock 'n' roll me / Cold as ice / Swim against the flow / On my bike.
LP: **6359 017**

IMPERIAL WIZARD.
Tracks: / Are you still my true love / Call on me / Goodbye first love / I forgot to forget you / Imperial wizard / Let it flow / Oh what a circus / Oh what a feeling / Ships that pass in the night / 20 flights up / Won't change me now.
LP: **6359 017**
LP: **9109616**

MUTINY.
LP: . . . . **MERH 30**
MC: . . . . **MERHC 30**

ON TOUR.
LP: **9500**

OUT ON THE STREET.
LP: **86017**

ROCK ON.
Tracks: / Rock on / Zone, The.
LP: **65823**

SILVER DREAM RACER.
Tracks: / Dunes, The / Silver dream machine / Looking for something / Bike, The / Where is love? / When I'm dancing / Suzuki warlord / Sea of love / I think I'll always love you / Race, The.
LP: . . . . **ERB 7**
MC: . . . . **ERBC 7**
LP: **9109634**
LP: . . . . **MERB 7**
MC: **7231 447**

STAGE STRUCK.
Tracks: / No substitute / Oh la baby blonde / You're so fierce / Me and my girl (night clubbing) / You don't know like I know / Call me your lover / Sweethearts / Romance / Verity / Secondhand love / Sleeping with the director / Stage struck.
LP: . . . . **MERS 4**
MC: . . . . **MERSC 4**

THIS ONE'S FOR YOU.
Tracks: / Secret habit / Look at your face / Alice / Victim / Look at them laughing / Danze musik / Don't you go / Welcome / This one's for you / Falling angels riding / Friends.
LP: . . . . **MERH 57**

TOUCHING THE GHOST.
Tracks: / Touching the ghost / Missing you (magic) / Sun ain't gonna shine anymore, The / Look at the sun shining / Heartbeats like a drum / They're doing it again / River, The / Masterpiece or fake / Forever and a day / Rock on.
LP: . . . . **LAMPLP 1**
MC: . . . . **LAMPMC 1**

VERY BEST OF DAVID ESSEX.
Tracks: / Gonna make you a star / Rock on / Oh what a circus / Heart on my sleeve / No substitute / Silver dream machine / Rollin' stone / Hold me close / Me and my girl (night clubbing) / Brave new world / Hot love / Lamplight / If I could / Imperial wizard / Ships that pass in the night / Stardust.
LP: . . . . **TVA 4**
MC: . . . . **TVC 4**

WHISPER.
Tracks: / Whisper / You're in my heart / Down again / Fishing for the moon / Ears of the city, The / Love, oh love / Moonlight dancing / Love is a stranger / Winter's tale, A / Two runaways.
LP: . . . . **MERH 34**

Essig, David

WHILE LIVING IN THE GOOD YEARS.
LP: . . . . **AP 041**

Essous

LILY GERMAINE.
LP: **19759**

Establishment

BAD CATHOLICS.
LP: . . . . **SPIN 992**

Estefan, Gloria

ANYTHING FOR YOU (Estefan, Gloria and Miami Sound Machine).
Tracks: / Betcha say that / Let it loose / Can't stay away from you / Give it up / Surrender / Rhythm is gonna get you / Love toy / I want you so bad / 1-2-3 / Anything for you / Rhythm is gonna get you (12" version) (Only on CD.) / Betcha say that (12" version) (Only on CD.).
LP: **4631251**
MC: **4631254**

CUTS BOTH WAYS.
Tracks: / Ay ay, I / Here we are / Say / Think about you / Nothin' oye mi canto / Don't wanna lose you / Get on your feet / Your love is bad for me / Cuts both ways.
LP: **4651451**
MC: **4651454**

EXITOS DE GLORIA ESTEFAN.
Tracks: / Renacer / Conga / No sera facil / Dr. Beat / Regresa a mi / No ti olvidare / Dingui-li bangui / No me vuelvoa ennamorar / Si voy a perderte / Oye mi canto.
LP: **4675201**
MC: **4675204**

GLORIA ESTEFAN - THE 12" TAPE.
Tracks: / Oye mi canto (hear my voice) / Bady boy / Get on your feet / Rhythm is gonna get you.
MC: **4689894**

INTO THE LIGHT.
Tracks: / Coming out of the dark / Seal our fate / What goes around / Nayib's song (I am here for you) / Remember me with love / Heart with your name on it / Sex in the '90s / Close my eyes / Language of love / Light of love / Can't forget you / Live for loving you / Mama you can't go / Desde la oscuridad.
LP: **4677821**
MC: **4677824**

LET IT LOOSE (Estefan, Gloria/Miami Sound Machine).
Tracks: / Betcha say that / Let it loose / Can't stay away from you / Give it up / Surrender / Rhythm is gonna get you / Love toy / I want you so bad / 1-2-3 / Anything for you.
LP: **4509101**
MC: **4509104**

Estelle, Don

COOL WATER (See under Davies, Windsor) (Estelle, Don & Windsor Davies).

PAPER DOLL (See under Davies, Windsor) (Estelle, Don & Windsor Davies).

SING LOFTY (Estelle, Don & Windsor Davies).
LP: . . . . **EMC 3102**

SINGS SONGS FOR CHRISTMAS.
Tracks: / Prelude / First Nowell, The / Winter wonderland / Song for Christmas / God rest ye merry gentlemen / Rudolf the red nosed reindeer / In the bleak mid winter / Silver bells / Sleigh ride / Rocking carol / Little donkey / Silent night / Do you hear what I hear / Auld lang syne.
LP: . . . . **SHM 3015**

TIME AFTER TIME.
Tracks: / Time after time / Bright eyes / More than a bedroom thing / For no reason at all / Folks who live on the hill / Pretend / Still dream of you / Every time we say goodbye / Music / Hatcheck girl from Reno / Only the lonely / Sad eyes / Girl from the Fairisle / Swinging on a star / Kiss in your eyes, The / Hard to say goodbye / Only me / Old Shep / Restless wind / Crying game, The.
LP: . . . . **UAG 30265**

WHISPERING GRASS (OLD GOLD) (See under Davies, Windsor) (Estelle, Don & Windsor Davies).

WITH A SONG IN MY HEART.
LP: LR 1002
MC: LRK 1002

Estes, Sleepy John

1929-30 SESSIONS.
LP: RSE 4

BLUES OF SLEEPY JOHN ESTES I.
LP: S 1219

BLUES OF SLEEPY JOHN ESTES II.
LP: S 1220

BROKE AND HUNGRY.
LP: DL 608

BROWNSVILLE BLUES.
LP: DL 613

ELECTRIC SLEEP.
LP: DS 619
LP: DL 619

LEGEND OF....
LP: DL 603

LIVE IN AUSTRIA, 1966 (Estes, Sleepy John and Yank Rachell).
LP: WOLF 120 913

SOUTHERN BLUES.
LP: WOLF 120.916

Estonian Singers &...

BEST LOVED ESTONIAN SONGS (Estonian Singers & Orchestra).
LP: ALP 112

Estragon, Vladimir

THREE QUARKS FOR MISTER MARK.
LP: 807 803

Estus, Deon

MY GUY, MY GIRL (see Stewart, Amii/ Deon Estus) (Estus, Deon/Amii Stewart).

SPELL.
LP: 835 713 1
MC: 835 713 4

E.T.

E.T. (Disney storyteller version) (Various artists).
LP: D 456

E.T. (1982 film soundtrack) (Various artists).
LP: MCA 37264
MC: MCAC 37264

E.T. -- THE EXTRATERRESTRIAL (Film soundtrack) (Various artists).
Tracks: / Three million light years from home: *Various artists* / Abandoned and pursued: *Various artists* / E.T.'s halloween: *Various artists* / Flying: *Various artists* / E.T. (phone number): *Various artists* / Over the moon: *Various artists* / Adventure on Earth: *Various artists*.
LP: MCL 1878
MC: MCLC 1878

E.T. - THE EXTRATERRESTRIAL (Narrated by Michael Jackson) (Jackson, Michael).
LP: CA 70000
MC: CAC 70000

Etant Donnes

AURORE.
LP: TO 16

ROYAUME.
Tracks: / Royaume / Matin / Quatre / Bleu.
LP: TOUCHTONE 2

Eternal Triangle

TOUCH AND LET GO.
LP: SITU 9

Eternal Wind

TERRA INCOGNITA.
LP: FF 422

WASULU - 'WORLD' FUSION.
LP: FF 481

Eternity

WAU'S VOLUME 1.
LP: GEEA 002
MC: GEEAC 002

Ethereal

ETHEREAL COUNTERBALANCE.
LP: W 012

Etheridge, Melissa

BRAVE AND CRAZY.
Tracks: / No souvenirs / Brave and crazy life / You used to love to dance / Angels, The / You can sleep while I drive / Testify / Let me go / My back door / Skin deep / Royal station 4/16.
MC: ICT 9939
LP: ILPS 9939

MELISSA ETHERIDGE.
Tracks: / Similar features / Chrome plated heart / Like the way I do / Precious pain / Don't need / Late September dogs, The / Occasionally / Watching you / Bring me some water / I want you.
LP: ILPS 9879
MC: ICT 9879

Ethiopia

ETHIOPIAN URBAN AND TRIBAL MUSIC VOLUME 1 (Mindanoo mistiru) (Various artists).
LP: LLST 7243

ETHIOPIAN URBAN AND TRIBAL MUSIC VOLUME 2 (Gold from wax) (Various artists).
LP: LLST 7244

MUSIC OF ERITREA (Various artists).
LP: TGM 103

MUSIC OF THE CENTRAL HIGHLANDS VOLUME 1 (Various artists).
LP: TGM 101

MUSIC OF THE DESERT NOMADS VOLUME 2 (Various artists).
LP: TGM 102

MUSICA DELL'ETIOPIA (Various artists).
LP: VPA 8230

Ethiopians

CLASSIC TRACKS (See under Gardner, Boris) (Ethiopians/Boris Gardner).

OPEN THE GATE OF ZION.
LP: GG 0012

ORIGINAL REGGAE HIT SOUNDS.
Tracks: / Free man / Train to Skaville / Engine 54 / Come on now / Train to glory / Whip / Everything crash / Things a get bad to worse / Well red / One / Hong Kong flu / Gun man / What a fire / Woman capture man / Feel the spirit / Drop him / Good ambition / No baptism / Selah / Pirate / Word is love.
LP: TRLS 228
MC: ZCTRL 228

SLAVE CALL.
LP: TWS 15
LP: RRTG 7716
MC: RRTGC 7716

Ethnic Heritage

LIVE FROM STOCKHOLM - ANCESTRAL SONG.
LP: SHLP 108

Etkind, Annabel

NEW ROMANCE, A.
Tracks: / Oxygene / Bright eyes / Vienna / Bach prelude no.1 / Rachmaninov 2nd piano concerto.
LP: LEG 14
MC: LEGC 14

Eton Crop

IT'S MY DOG, MAESTRO.
LP: GGAGG 2

UNDERWATER MUSIC GOES ON, THE.
LP: CJ 332
MC: CJC 332
LP: CALCLP 033

YES PLEASE, BOB.
LP: CALCLP 013

Ettaswell Brass Band

SOUNDING BRASS.
Tracks: / Lohengrin - prelude to Act III / Angelique / Hello goodbye / Priere a Notre Dame / Lincolnshire poacher / Nimrod / Sounding brass / Eleanor Rigby / Spring theme / March from second suite in F / Silver threads among the gold / Australasian, The.
LP: NSPL 18610

Etting, Ruth

AMERICA'S RADIO SWEETHEART.
LP: SH 2033

KEEP SWEEPING THE COBWEB.
MC: 045

ON THE AIR: RUTH ETTING.
Tracks: / Dancing with tears in my eyes / Whose honey are you? / I'm facing the music / Zing went the strings of my heart / Shine on harvest moon / Tormented / You / Somebody loves me / You took me out of this world / This is the night / He's funny that way / By the light of the silvery moon / Do you ever think of me? / All of me.
LP: TOTEM 1018

RUTH ETTING VOL.8 - 1932-1933.
Tracks: / All of me / Home / Love you funny thing / Can't we talk it over / Happy go lucky you / Hold me / You've got me crying again / Take me in your arms / Try a little tenderness / It was So Beautiful.
MC: NEO 959

RUTH ETTING VOL 5. (1929-1930).
Tracks: / Right kind of man, the / More than you know / I'm yours / Dancing with tears in my eyes / It happened in Monterey / Ten cents a dance / Kiss waltz, The / I remember you from somewhere.
MC: NEO 942

RUTH ETTING VOL. 6.
Tracks: / Just a little closer / Were you sincere / Out of nowhere / Say a little prayer for me / I'll be blue just thinking of you / Body and soul / Faithfully yours / There ought to be moonlight saving time / Now that you're gone / Guilty / Falling in love again.
MC: NEO 943

RUTH ETTING VOL 7 (1931-1932).
Tracks: / Faded summer love, A / Goodnight sweetheart / Too late / Cuban love song / When were alone / Love letters in the sand / Nevertheless / If I didn't have you / Voice in the old village choir, The.
MC: NEO 944

TEN CENTS A DANCE.
Tracks: / Ten cents a dance / Button up your overcoat / Funny, dear, what love can do / But I do, you know I do / Mean to me / I'm yours / If I could be with you one hour tonight / Don't tell him what happened to me / Body and soul / Sam, the old accordion man / Dancing with tears in my eyes / Hello baby / What wouldn't I do for that man? / Could I, certainly could / Kiss waltz, The / Shakin' the blues away / You're the cream in my coffee / Lonesome and sorry / Laughing at life / Love me or leave me.
LP: AJA 5008
MC: ZC AJA 5008

E-Types

E-TYPES VS MYSTIC TIDE (E-Types/ Mystic Tide).
LP: EVA 12037

Eubanks, Kevin

FACE TO FACE.
Tracks: / Face to face / That's what friends are for / Essence / Silent waltz / Moments aren't moments / Wave / Relaxin' at Camarillo / Ebony surprise / Trick bag.
LP: GRP 91029
MC: GRPM 91029

GUITARIST.
Tracks: / Novice bounce, The / Inner-vision / Yesterdays / Evidence / Urban heat / Thumb, The / Blues for Wes / Untitled shapes / Blue in green.
LP: E 0213

HEAT OF HEAT, THE.
Tracks: / Receipt please (On CD only) / Heat of heat, The / Palace of the seven jewels / First things first / Nardis / In a few / Sorrir - smile / Soujorn / Third interior.
LP: GRP 91041
MC: GRPM 91041

OPENING NIGHT.
Tracks: / Opening nights / Shades of black / Navigator, The / Thought about thinking / In flight from Omelas / Place before you've been, A / Vera's isle / To be continued.
LP: GRP 91013
MC: GRPM 91013
LP: GRPA 1013
MC: GRPC 1013

PROMISE OF TOMORROW.
Tracks: / Angel with the blues / Promise of tomorrow / This place in time / Eyes of a lost child / Cullerton Street / Hope / Haze / He smiled the sea / Passage of the prince / In a sentimental mood.
LP: GRP 96041
MC: GRP 96044

SEARCHER, THE.
LP: GRP 95801
MC: GRP 95804

SHADOW PROPHETS.
LP: GRP 91054
MC: C 1054

SUNDANCE.
LP: A 1008
MC: C 1008

Eubanks, Robin

DIFFERENT PERSPECTIVES.
LP: 8344241

Eugene, Wendell

WENDELL EUGENE AND FRIENDS (Eugene, Wendell, Teddy Riley, Michael White, Kid Sheik Cola).
LP: LPS 4
MC: TCS 4

WEST INDIAN BLUES (Eugene, Wendell New Orleans Band 1968).
Tracks: / Everybody loves somebody / West Indies blues / Muskrat ramble / Blues / Liza Jane / Pagan love song / Should I / Bourbon Street parade / Boogie / I can't give you anything but love / China boy / Exactly like you / Fidgety feet.
LP: NOLA LP 20
LP: LPS 8

Euripides

MEDEA (Anderson, Dame Judith).
MCSET: 0302

Eurogliders

ABSOLUTELY.
Tracks: / Can't wait to see you / City of soul / What kind of fool / So tough / We will together / Absolutely / Jesse / Moving away / Enough love / We will together (in twelve inch mix on cassette.).
LP: CBS 26784
MC: 40 26784

Euro-k

EURO-K.
Tracks: / Brother man / I don't sleep / Inner city blues / Friday nite / She's a... / Subtle party / Let us get back... (to what we call...) / Mr Do / Soul power 1990 / Life (ain't it funky).
LP: FILER 278

Europe

CHRIS TETLEY INTERVIEWS EUROPE.
LPPD: CT 1002

EUROPE.
Tracks: / In the future to come / Female / Seven doors hotel / King will return, The / Boyazant / Children of the time / Words of wisdom / Paradise beach / Memories.
LP: CHORD 008
MC: CHORDTC 008

EUROPE: INTERVIEW PICTURE DISC.
LPPD: BAK 2041

FINAL COUNTDOWN, THE.
Tracks: / Love chaser / On the loose / Heart of stone / Time has come / Final countdown, The / Cherokee / Ninja / Danger on the track / Rock the night / Carrie.
LP: 4624991
LP: EPC 26808
MC: 40 26808
LP: 4663281
MC: 4663284

OUT OF THIS WORLD.
Tracks: / Superstitious / Let the good times rock / Open your heart / More than meets the eye / Coast to coast / Ready or not / Sign of the times / Just the beginning / Never say die / Lights and shadows / Tower's callin' / Tomorrow.
LP: 4624491
MC: 4624494

WINGS OF TOMORROW.
Tracks: / Stormwind / Scream of anger / Open your heart / Treated bad again / Aphasia / Wings of tomorrow / Wasted time / Lyin' eyes / Dreamer / Dance the night away.
LP: 4602131
MC: 4602134

Europe, Jim

1907-1919 (Europe, Jim & Arthur Pryor Bands).
LP: SDL 221

European Classic...

THAT'S LIKE IT OUGHT TO BE (European Classic Jazz Trio).
LP: SOS 1142

WHIP ME WITH PLENTY OF... (European Classic Jazz Trio).
LP: SOS 1070

European Concert...

MOZART MAGIC (European Concert Orchestra).
MC: TCMOZ 1

European Jazz Ensemble

AT THE PHILHARMONIC COLOGNE.
LP: A 800-1
MC: A 800-4

European Jazz Quartet

LIVE AT MOERS FESTIVAL '77.
LP: RING 01018

European Jazz Quintet

EUROPEAN JAZZ QUINTET.
LP: EGO 4012

European Tales

FAVOURITE EUROPEAN TALES (Hepburn, Katharine).
MC: LFP 41 7180 5

European Toys

NINE MEN APPLAUDING.
LP: NCHLP 4

Europeans

LIVE.
Tracks: / Typical / American people / Joining dots / Innocence / Spirit of youth / Going to work / A.E.I.O.U / Animal song / Tunnel vision / Falling.
LP: SCOT 1

RECURRING DREAMS.
Tracks: / 1,001 arguments / Home town / Burning inside you / You don't want me

(in your life) / Writing for survival / Love has let me down / Don't give your heart to anybody / Acid rain.
LP: .... AMA 5034
MC: .... AMC 5034

VOCABULARY.
Tracks: / Animal song / A.E.I.O.U. / Voice on the telephone / American people / Falling / Recognition / Innocence / Spirit of youth / Modern homes / Kingdom come.
LP: .... AMLX 68558

Eurovision Song

EUROVISION SONG CONTEST WINNERS 1956-81 (Various artists).
2LP: 2675 221
MC: 3577 364

Eurythmics

1984 - FOR THE LOVE OF BIG BROTHER (Film soundtrack).
Tracks: / I did it just the same / Sexcrime (nineteen eighty-four) / For the love of big brother / Winston's diary / Greetings from a dead man / Julia / Doubleplusgood / Ministry of love / Room 101.
LP: .... OVED 207
MC: .... OVEDC 207
LP: .... V 1984

BE YOURSELF TONIGHT.
Tracks: / It's alright (baby's coming back) / Would I lie to you / There must be an angel (playing with my heart) / I love you like a ball and chain / Sisters are doin' it for themselves / Conditioned soul / Adrian / Here comes that sinking feeling / Better to have lost in love than never to have loved at all.
LP: .... PL 70711
MC: .... PK 70711
LP: .... NL 74602
MC: .... NK 74602

EURYTHMICS BOX SET.
MCSET: .... NK 74384

EURYTHMICS: INTERVIEW PICTURE DISC.
LPPD: .... BAK 2128

GREATEST HITS: EURYTHMICS.
Tracks: / Love is a stranger / Sweet dreams / Who's that girl ? / Right by your side / Here comes the rain again / There must be an angel (playing with my heart) / Sisters are doin' it for themselves / It's alright (baby's coming back) / When tomorrow comes / You have placed a chill in my heart / Sex crime (1984) / Thorn in my side / Don't ask me why / Angel (Track on cassette/ CD only.) / Would I lie to you ? (Track on cassette/ CD only.) / Missionary man (Track on cassette/ CD only.) / I need a man (Track on cassette/ CD only.) / Miracle of love (Track on cassette/ CD only.).
LP: .... PL 74856
MC: .... PK 74856

IN THE GARDEN.
Tracks: / English summer / Belinda / Take me to your heart / She's invisible now / Your time will come / Caveman head / Never gonna cry again / All the young people (of today) / Sing sing / Revenge.
LP: .... PL 70006
MC: .... PK 70006
LP: .... RCALP 5061
LP: .... NL 75036
MC: .... NK 75036

MUSIC AND MEDIA INTERVIEW PICTURE DISC.
LPPD: .... EU 1015

REVENGE.
Tracks: / Let's go / Take your pain away / Little of you, A / Thorn in my side / In this town / I remember you / Missionary man / Last time, The / When tomorrow comes / Miracle of love, The.
LP: .... PL 71050
MC: .... PK 71050

SAVAGE.
Tracks: / Beethoven (I love to listen to) / I've got a lover back in Japan / Do you want to break up? / You have placed a chill in my heart / Shame / Savage / I need a man / Put the blame on me / Heaven / Wide eyed girl / I need you / Brand new day.
LP: .... PL 71555
MC: .... PK 71555

SWEET DREAMS (ARE MADE OF THIS).
Tracks: / Love is a stranger / I've got an angel / Wrap it up / Could give you a mirror / Walk, The / Sweet dreams (are made of this) / Jennifer / Somebody told me / This city never sleeps / This is the house.
LP: .... PL 70014
MC: .... PK 70014
LP: .... NL 71471
MC: .... NK 71471
LP: .... RCALP 6063

TOUCH.
Tracks: / Here comes the rain again / Regrets / Right by your side / Cool blue / Who's that girl? / First cut, The / Aqua / No fear, no hate, no pain (no broken hearts) / Paint a rumour.
LP: .... PL 70109
MC: .... PK 70109
LP: .... NL 90369
MC: .... NK 90369

TOUCH DANCE (7 Track Mini Album).
Tracks: / First cut, The / Cool blue / Paint a rumour / Regrets / First cut, The (instrumental) / Cool blue (instrumental) / Paint a rumour (instrumental).
MLP: .... PG 70354
MC: .... PH 70354

WE TOO ARE ONE.
Tracks: / We too are one / King and Queen of America, The / (My my) baby's gonna cry / Don't ask me why / Angel / Revival / You hurt me (I hate you) / Sylvia / How long? / When the day goes down.
LP: .... PL 74251
MC: .... PK 74251

Eustace, Frances

BASSOON COLLECTION (Eustace Frances & ensemble).
MC: .... CSAR 35

Evan, Lurie

HAPPY HERE.
LP: .... TWI 574

Evans, Bill

ALTERNATIVE MAN.
Tracks: / Alternative man, The / Path of least resistance / Let the juice loose / Gardiners garden / Survival of the fittest / Jo Jo / Cry in her eyes, The / Miles away / Flight of the falcon.
LP: .... BT 85111
MC: .... TCBT 85111

AT THE MONTREUX JAZZ FESTIVAL.
Tracks: / One for Helen / Sleeping bee / Mother of pearl / Nardis / O loves you Porgy / Touch of your lips, The / Embraceable you / Some day my prince will come / Walkin' up / Quiet now.
LP: 2304152

AUTUMN LEAVES.
Tracks: / Emily / There will never be another you / Stairway to the stars / Some day my prince will come / Blue in green / Round midnight / Autumn leaves.
LP: .... CJZ LP 7
LP: .... LOP 14069
LP: .... LPPS 111 11

BILL EVANS (Compact/Walkman jazz).
Tracks: / I believe you / Spartacus (love theme) / Granados / My foolish heart / I loves you Porgy / How about you / I've got you under my skin / Round midnight / Elsa / Sleeping bee / Pavane / Little Lulu.
MC: 831 366-4

BILL EVANS - A TRIBUTE (Various artists).
LP: .... PA 8028

BILL EVANS GOLDEN TRIO (Evans, Bill Golden Trio).
Tracks: / Come rain or come shine / Autumn leaves (mono) / Autumn leaves (stereo) / Witchcraft / When I fall in love / What is this thing called love / Spring is here / Some day my prince will come / Blue in green / Peri's scope / Nardis / Israel / I wish I knew / Sweet and lovely / How deep is the ocean / Haunted heart / Beautiful love / Elsa / Boy next door, The / My foolish heart / My romance / Some other time / Solar / Gloria's step / My man's gone now / All of you / Alice in Wonderland / Porgy / Milestones / Detour ahead / Waltz for Debbie / Jade visions.
LP: .... RIV 4000

BILL EVANS LIVE IN PARIS, 1965.
LP: .... RJ 503

BILL EVANS TRIO AT SHELLEY'S MANNEHOLE (Evans, Bill Trio).
Tracks: / Isn't it romantic / Boy next door, The / Wonder why / Swedish pastry / Love is here to stay / Blues in F / 'Round midnight / Stella by starlight.
LP: .... OJC 263

BILL EVANS WITH SYMPHONY ORCHESTRA.
LP: 8219381
MC: 8219384

CALIFORNIA HERE I COME.
Tracks: / California here I come / Polka dots and moonbeams / Turn out the stars / Stella by starlight / You're gonna hear from me / In a sentimental mood / G waltz / On Green Dolphin Street / Gone with the wind / If you could see me now / Alfie / Very early / Round midnight / Emily / Wrap your troubles in dreams.
2LP: 811 674-1

COLLECTION: BILL EVANS.
Tracks: / Autumn leaves / Waltz for Debbie / Milestones / My romance / All of you / Alice in Wonderland / Time remembered / My foolish heart / My man's gone now / Detour ahead / Solar / Gloria's step.
MC: .... DVMC 2042

CONSECRATION VOL 1 (Evans, Bill Trio).
Tracks: / You and the night and the music / Emily / Two lonely people, The / I do it for your love / Re: person I knew / Polka dots and moonbeams / Knit for Mary F / Someday my prince will come.
LP: .... SJP 331

CONSECRATION VOL 2 (Evans, Bill Trio).
Tracks: / Tiffany / My foolish heart / Days of wine and roses / Your story / Turn out the stars / Like someone in love / My romance.
LP: .... SJP 332

EVERYBODY DIGS BILL EVANS.
Tracks: / Minority / Young and foolish / Lucky to be me / Night and day / Epilogue / Tenderly / Peace piece / What is there to say? / Oleo.
LP: .... RSLP 291

HIS LAST CONCERT IN GERMANY.
LP: .... WW 0022

IN YOUR OWN SWEET WAY.
LP: .... AFF 58

INTERMODULATION (Evans, Bill & Jim Hall).
LP: 833 771 1
MC: 833 771 4

IT HAPPENED IN PESCARA 1969-89 (Evans, Bill/Art Pepper).
2LP: 214W 100/101

LIVE IN EUROPE.
Tracks: / How my heart sings / Time to remember / Twelve-toned tune / Waltz for Debbie / Stella by starlight / Some day my prince will come / Round midnight.
LP: .... UJ 24

LIVE IN PARIS 1972 VOL 1.
Tracks: / Re person I knew / Gloria's step / Waltz for Debbie / Turn out the stars / Two lonely people / What are you doing the rest of your life.
LP: .... FC 107

LIVE IN PARIS VOL.1.
LP: .... FC 125

LIVE IN PARIS VOL.2.
Tracks: / Twelve tone tune / Sugarplum / Quiet now / Very early / Autumn leaves / Time remembered / My romance / Some day my prince will come.
LP: .... FC 114

LIVING ON THE CREST OF A WAVE.
Tracks: / Reef carnival / When it's a good thing / Dawn / Young and old / Past thoughts / Living on the crest of a wave.
LP: 9603491

MONTREUX 2.
MC: .... CTK 9511

MY ROMANCE.
LP: .... ZET 702

NEW JAZZ CONCEPTIONS.
Tracks: / I love you / Five / I got it bad and that ain't good / Conception / Easy living / Displacement / Speak low / Waltz for Debbie / Our delight / My romance / No cover, no minimum (2 takes).
LP: .... OJC 025

PARIS CONCERT, THE (EDITION ONE).
Tracks: / I do it for your love / Quiet now / Noelle's theme / My romance / I loves you Porgy / Up with the lark / All mine / Beautiful love.
LP: .... E 0164

PORTRAIT IN JAZZ.
Tracks: / Come rain or come shine / Autumn leaves / Witchcraft / When I fall in love / Peri's scope / What is this thing called love? / Spring is here / Some day my prince will come / Blue in green.
LP: .... OJC 088

QUIET NOW.
Tracks: / Very airy / Sleeping bee / Quiet now / Turn out the stars / Autumn leaves / Nardis.
LP: .... AFF 73

RE: PERSON I KNEW.
Tracks: / Re: Person I knew / Sugar plum / Alfie / T.T.T. / Excerpt from Dolphin dance / Very early / 34 skidoo / Emily / Are you all the things?.
LP: .... F 9608

SYMBIOSIS.
LP: .... MPS 68 052

TIME REMEMBERED.
LP: 68150

TOGETHER AGAIN (See under Bennett, Tony).

TRIO'64 (Evans, Bill Trio).
Tracks: / Little Lulu / Sleeping bee / Santa Claus is coming to town / I'll see you again / For Heaven's sake / Dancing in the dark / Everything happens to me.
LP: 815 057-1

TRIO '65 (Evans, Bill Trio).
Tracks: / Israel / Elsa / Round midnight / Our love is here to stay / How my heart sings / Who can I turn to / Come rain or come shine / If you could see me now.
LP: 2304517

TRIO/DUO.
Tracks: / Little Lulu / Sleeping bee / Always / Santa Claus is coming to town / I'll see you again / For Heaven's sake / Dancing in the dark / Everything happens to me / I've got you under my skin / My man's gone now / Turn out the stars / Angel face / Jazz samba / All across the city.
LP: 2632 054

UNDERCURRENT (EMI) (Evans, Bill Trio).
LP: B1 90583

UNDERCURRENT (MEMOIR) (Evans, Bill & Jim Hall).
Tracks: / My funny valentine / I hear a rhapsody / Dream gypsy / Romain / Skating in Central Park / Darn that dream / My funny valentine (alt. take) (CD only.) / Stairway to the stars (CD only.) / I'm getting sentimental over you (CD only.) / Romaine (alt. take) (CD only.).
LP: .... MOIR 504
MC: .... CMOIR 504

WE WILL MEET AGAIN.
LP: .... WB 56807

WHAT'S NEW ? (Evans, Bill & Jeremy Steig).
LP: 2304 285

WITH SYMPHONY ORCHESTRA (Evans, Bill Trio).
Tracks: / Granados / Valse / Prelude / Time remembered / Pavane / Elegie / My bells / Blue interlude.
LP: 230 452-5
MC: 8219834
LP: 8219831

YOU'RE GONNA HEAR FROM ME.
Tracks: / You're gonna hear from me / Waltz for Debbie / Time remembered / Emily / Some day my prince will come / Round midnight / Nardis / Who can I turn to / Love is here to stay.
LP: .... MX 9164

Evans, Dale

GOOD LIFE, THE (see Rogers,Roy/Dale Evans) (Evans, Dale/Roy Rogers).

Evans, Dave

BLUEGRASS MEMORIES.
LP: .... REBEL 1630
MC: .... REBELMC 1630

CLOSE TO HOME (Evans, Dave & River Bend).
Tracks: / Another night / I'll just pretend / Second handed flowers / Last public hanging in West Virginia, The / Salt Creek / Rovin' gambler / Wild Bill Jones / Meet me by the moonlight / I just got wise / Home sweet home / Why don't you tell me so / Father's table grace.
LP: .... REBEL 1639

FEW MORE SEASONS, A.
LP: .... REBEL 1608
MC: .... REBELMC 1608

GOIN' ROUND THIS WORLD.
LP: .... REBEL 1602

POOR RAMBLER.
LP: .... REBEL 1616

SAD PIG DANCE.
Tracks: / Stagefright / Chaplinesque / Train and the river, The / Veronica / Captain / Knuckles and buster / Mole's moan / Gentle man / Sad pig dance / Raining cats and dogs / Braziliana / Sun and moon / Steppenwolf / Morocco John / Sneaky.
LP: .... SNKF 107
LP: .... KM 120

TAKE A BITE OUT OF LIFE.
Tracks: / Keep me from the cold / Whistling milkman / Illustrated man / You and me / Insanity rag / Every bad dog / Take a bit out of life / Willie me / You're wrong / Sunday is beautiful / Tear away / Lucky me / I'm all right.
LP: .... SNKF 122
LP: .... KM 134

Evans, Doc Jazzband

AT THE GAS LIGHT.
LP: .... AP 95

DOWN IN JUNGLE TOWN.
LP: .... AP 4
LP: .... AP 8

Evans, Dr. Christopher

DREAMS AND DREAMING (See under Psychology).

Evans, Frank

FRANK EVANS.
Tracks: / Waltz for Django / Andalucia / Dear Bill / Soiree / Autumn leaves / What's new / Angel eyes / Misty / Manoir de mes reves / All the things you are.
LP: . . . . **BB 102**

NOCTUARY.
Tracks: / Nuages / Child is born, A / Send in the clowns / Wave / What are you doing the rest of your life / Gymnopedie / Round midnight / Song is you, The / Body and soul.
LP: . . . . **BB 101**

Evans, George

GREAT FOR DANCING (Evans, George & His Symphony of Saxes).
MC: . . . . **MWMC 1034**
LP: . . . . **MWM 1034**

Evans, Gil

AT THE PUBLIC THEATRE VOL.2.
LP: . . . . **BKH 526**

BIG BAND LUMIERE (Evans, Gil & Laurent Cugny).
LP: **836 401-1**

BLUES IN ORBIT.
LP: . . . . **ENJA 3069**

BRITISH ORCHESTRA, THE.
Tracks: / Hotel me / Friday thirteenth / London / Little wing.
LP: . . . . **MOLE 8**

BUD AND BIRD (Evans, Gil & The Monday Night Orchestra).
2LP: . . . . **K 19 P 6455**

CARNEGIE HALL 1961 (See under Davis, Miles) (Evans, Gil & Miles Davis).

FAREWELL (Evans, Gil & The Monday Night Orchestra).
LP: . . . . **K 28P 6486**

GIL EVANS LIVE.
Tracks: / Angel / Parabola / Orange was the colour / Silk blue / Stone free / Fugue / Cheryl / Birdhead / Relaxing at Carnarillo.
LP: . . . . **PL 25209**

GUITAR FORMS (See under Burrell, Kenny) (Evans, Gil & Kenny Burrell).

LITTLE WING.
LP: . . . . **RK 23578/13**

LIVE 1976.
LP: . . . . **ZET 714**

LIVE AT SWEET BASIL (Evans, Gil & The Monday Night Orchestra).
Tracks: / Parabola / Voodoo chile / Orange was the colour of her dress, then silk blue / Prince of darkness / Blues in C / Cheryl / Bird feathers / Relaxin' at Camarillo / Goodbye pork pie hat / Up from the skies.
LP: . . . . **K 23P 6355**

LIVE AT SWEET BASIL. VOL.2 (Evans, Gil & The Monday Night Orchestra).
2LP: . . . . **K 19P 6421**

LIVE AT THE PUBLIC THEATRE VOL.1.
LP: . . . . **BKH 525**

MILES DAVIS ALL STARS & GIL EVANS (see Davis, Miles) (Evans, Gil & Miles Davis).

OUT OF THE COOL.
Tracks: / La Nevada / Where flamingos fly / Bilbao song / Stratusphunk / Sunken treasure.
LP: . . . . **JAS 52**
MC: . . . . **JAS C52**
LP: . . . . **AS 4**
MC: . . . . **ASC 4**

PACIFIC STANDARD TIME.
2LP: . . . . **BND 4024**

PARABOLA.
LP: . . . . **HDLP 31/32**

PARIS BLUES.
LP: . . . . **OWLL 049**
MC: . . . . **OWLM 749**

PRIESTESS.
LP: . . . . **AN 8717**
MC: . . . . **ANC 8717**

REST OF GIL EVANS LIVE AT THE RFH 1978.
LP: . . . . **MOLE 3**

THERE COMES A TIME (Evans, Gil Orchestra).
Tracks: / King Porter stomp / Thre comes a time / Makes her move / Little wing / Meaning of the blues / Aftermath the fourth movement / Children of the fire / Anita's dance.
LP: . . . . **PL 11057**

Evans, Guy

DOLPHINS (see under Potter, Nic).

LONG HELLO 2 (see under Potter, Nic).

LONG HELLO, THE VOL 4.
LP: . . . . **HAI 101**

Evans, Joe

TWO POOR BOYS (Evans, Joe & Arthur McClain).
LP: . . . . **BD 616**

Evans, Margie

ANOTHER BLUES DAY.
LP: . . . . **LR 42.060**

MISTREATED WOMAN.
LP: . . . . **LR 42.050**

WE SHALL WALK THROUGH THE VALLEY IN PEACE (see under Grundy, Ricky) (Evans, Margie/Ricky Grundy & Williams Family).

Evans, Maureen

EVEN I DO.
LP: . . . . **LPM 46**

LIKE I DO.
LP: . . . . **TREASURE 46**

Evans, Paul

HELLO THIS IS: PAUL EVANS.
Tracks: / Build an ark / Rosemaria / Hello this is Joanie / Disneyland daddy / Half man, half music / What's a nice guy like me / Lullaby tissue papar co. / Mack the knife / I'm giving up my baby / First time I've had second thoughts.
LP: . . . . **POLS 1008**

PAUL EVANS SINGS THE FABULOUS TEENS.
LP: . . . . **SKYLINE 1382**

Evans, Terry

LIVE AND LET LIVE (See under King, Bobby) (Evans, Terry & Bobby King).

SEEING IS BELIEVING (See King, Bobby) (Evans, Terry & Bobby King).

Evans, Tony

10 DANCE CHAMPIONSHIPS (Evans, Tony & His Orchestra).
Tracks: / Cheek to cheek / Dancing with you in my arms / Dearly beloved / In dreams a memory / Adios muchachos / Cavatina / Who's taking you home / Very thought of you, The / Kiss me honey / And I love you so / Spanish eyes / Sucu sucu / Spanish matador / Johnson rag.
LP: . . . . **TE 1006**

ARTISTRY IN SWING (Evans, Tony & His Orchestra).
LP: . . . . **TE 3031**
MC: . . . . **CTX 3031**

BALLROOM DANCING CHAMPION STYLE (Evans, Tony & His Orchestra).
LP: . . . . **RIM 3004**

BROADWAY GOES LATIN Seqence Dance music (Evans, Tony & His Orchestra).
LP: . . . . **TE 1020**

CHA CHA CARNIVAL.
LP: . . . . **TE 1023**
MC: . . . . **CTX 1023**

DANCE IN THE OLD FASHIONED WAY (Evans, Tony & His Orchestra).
LP: . . . . **TE 1001**

DANCE WITH ME (Evans, Tony & His Orchestra).
LP: . . . . **TE 1013**
MC: . . . . **CTX 1013**

GENTLE ON MY MIND (Evans, Tony & His Orchestra).
Tracks: / Here, there and everywhere / Witchita lineman / By the time I get to Phoenix / Hey Jude / Gentle on my mind / For once in my life / Once more / Ob la di ob la da / Impossible dream, The / Last waltz, The / Look of love, The / Dancing with a dream.
LP: . . . . **TE 1009**
MC: . . . . **VCA 004**

HEY, LOOK ME OVER (Evans, Tony & His Orchestra).
LP: . . . . **TE 1019**

I'M IN THE MOOD FOR DANCING (Evans, Tony & His Orchestra).
LP: . . . . **TE 1004**

IN TIJUANA (Evans, Tony & His Orchestra).
Tracks: / Brasilia / So what's new / Spanish flea / Breakthrough / Gringo / Do you know the way to San Jose / Tijuana taxi / Little brown jug / Raindrops keep falling on my head / Everybody's talkin' / Place in the sky, A / Come back and shake me.
LP: . . . . **ELITE 7071**

IT'S MY PARTY (Evans, Tony & His Orchestra).
Tracks: / Can can / Cokey cokey / Agadoo / Knees up mother Brown / Auld lang syne.
LP: . . . . **PTE 5054**
MC: . . . . **PTX 5054**

JIVE ALIVE (Evans, Tony & His Orchestra).
LP: . . . . **PTE 5051**

KEEP ON DANCING (Evans, Tony & His Orchestra).
LP: . . . . **PTE 5052**

MAY I HAVE THE NEXT DREAM (Evans, Tony & His Orchestra).
Tracks: / Mr. Sandman / Pretend / Every dream / Roses of Picardy / I dont want to walk without you / May I have the next dream / Hasta luego / I wonder who's kissing her now / Song of my life, The / Mexican hat dance / Ole guapa / Golden tango.
LP: . . . . **TE 1007**
MC: . . . . **CTX 1007**

MERRY CHRISTMAS (Evans, Tony & His Orchestra).
LP: . . . . **TE 1015**
MC: . . . . **CTX 1015**

NO TIME LIKE OLD TIME (Evans, Tony & His Orchestra).
LP: . . . . **TE 1005**
MC: . . . . **CTX 1005**

PLAYS THE DANCE CLUB (Evans, Tony & His Orchestra).
LP: . . . . **TE 1012**

RISE (Evans, Tony & His Orchestra).
LP: . . . . **TE 1021**

ROARIN' RAGTIME (Evans, Tony & His Orchestra).
Tracks: / Bugle call rag / Mississippi rag / Tiger rag / Barnsley chop rag / Johnson rag / Alexander's rag / Cincinnati rag / 12th Street rag / Greengate rag / Russian rag / Maple leaf rag.
LP: . . . . **STE 3032**
MC: . . . . **CXT 3032**

ROMANTIC LATIN BY ROMANA (Evans, Tony & His Orchestra).
LP: . . . . **VA 3**

SENTIMENTAL OVER YOU (Evans, Tony Orchestra & Chorus).
LP: . . . . **TE 1022**

SHALL WE DANCE (Evans, Tony & His Orchestra).
Tracks: / Shall we dance / You do something to me / Stay as sweet as you are / For you are beautiful / First day of spring / Answer me / Mardi gras cha cha / Wheels cha cha / Forever and ever / So near to you / Moonlight serenade / Sol-y-mar samba.
LP: . . . . **TE 1010**

SIMPLY BEAUTIFUL (Evans, Tony & His Orchestra).
LP: . . . . **TE 1018**

SPANISH FIRE-WONDERFUL WORLD OF TANGOS (Evans, Tony & His Orchestra).
LP: . . . . **TE 1014**
MC: . . . . **CTX 1014**

SPRING.
LP: . . . . **EMI TE1016**

TOGETHER FOREVER (Evans, Tony Orchestra & Chorus).
LP: . . . . **TE 1024**

TOUCH OF CLASS FOR YOUR DANCING OR LISTENING PLEASURE (Evans, Tony & His Orchestra).
LP: . . . . **TEVOL 1**

UK MODERN BALLROOM CHAMPIONSHIPS IN SEQUENCE (Evans, Tony & His Orchestra).
LP: . . . . **TE 1003**

WONDERFUL WORLD OF FOXTROTS (Evans, Tony & His Orchestra).
LP: . . . . **TE 1011**

WONDERFUL WORLD OF QUICKSTEPS (Evans, Tony & His Orchestra).
LP: . . . . **TE 1017**

WONDERFUL WORLD OF WALTZES (Evans, Tony & His Orchestra).
LP: . . . . **TE 1016**
MC: . . . . **CTX 1016**

WORLD LATIN CHAMPIONSHIPS (Evans, Tony & His Orchestra).
LP: . . . . **TE 1002**

WORLD MODERN BALLROOM CHAMPIONSHIPS (Evans, Tony & His Orchestra).
LP: . . . . **TE 1008**

Evans/Zager

IN THE YEAR 25-25 (see Zager).

Eve of St. Venus (bk)

EVE OF ST. VENUS/NOTHING LIKE THE SUN (Burgess, Anthony (aut)).
MC: **1442**

Evelyn, Anthony

ASSASSIN, THE (Pickles, Carolyn).
MCSET: . . . . **CAB 296**

Evening Falls

EVENING FALLS (Various artists).
Tracks: / Songbird: *Various artists* / All I ask of you: *Various artists* / Going home (theme from Local Hero): *Various artists* / Chi mai: *Various artists* / Harry's game (theme from): *Various artists* / Picnic at hanging rock: *Various artists* / Song for Guy: *Various artists* / Pachelbel canon: *Various artists* / Orinoco flow: *Various artists* / Edge of darkness: *Various artists* / Bilitis: *Various artists* / Silhouette: *Various artists* / Evening falls: *Various artists* / Brothers in arms: *Various artists.*
LP: . . . . **STAR 2350**
MC: . . . . **STAC 2350**

Evening With...

EVENING WITH ALAN JAY LERNER (Various artists).
LP: . . . . **ENCORE 2**
MC: . . . . **ENCOREC 2**

Event

EVENT, THE.
LP: . . . . **VOXX 200059**

Ever Ready Band

COMMEMORATION (Ever Ready Band/ Hammond Sauce Works Band).
Tracks: / Grand march from Aida / Lost chord, The / North east fantasy / Air from Suite No. 3 (In D) / Pomp and circumstance march no.1 / Marche slave / Summertime / Ballet music from William Tell / Deep harmony / Hallelujah chorus.
LP: . . . . **PRL 016**
MC: . . . . **CPRL 016**

EVER READY BAND (Cond. by Squadron Leader Eric Banks M.B.).
LP: . . . . **DS 017**

EVER READY BAND PLAYS PATRICK MOORE.
Tracks: / March of the centaurs / Ariadne / Penguin parade / Triumphal march / King Neptune / Sunrise polka / Intermezzo / Vienna clouds / Herald.
LP: . . . . **TB 3017**

Everage, Dame Edna

DAME EDNA EVERAGE PARTY EXPERIENCE.
Tracks: / Bad / When will I be famous / Layla (alias Edna) / I should be so lucky / Locomotion, The / Bad 'nice' reprise / Walzing Matilda / Twist, The / Venus / Like a virgin / Girls just want to have fun / Venus (reprise) / Shout (part 1) / Shout (Part 2) / I got you babe (who needs you babe) / I wanna dance with somebody / Stop in the name of love / Dancing in the street / I wanna dance with somebody (reprise) / Neighbours / Leader of the pack / It's my party.
LP: . . . . **MOOD 7**
MC: . . . . **MOODC 7**

LAST NIGHT OF THE POMS (Everage, Dame Edna & Carl Davis).
LP: . . . . **EDNA 81**

Everett, Betty

1957 - 1961 (Everett, Betty & Lillian Offitt).
Tracks: / Tell me darling / I'll weep no more / Killer diller / My life depends on you / My love / Ain't gonna cry / Oh mama / Will my man be home tonight / Man don't work / My man is a lover / Troubles / Shine on.
LP: . . . . **FLY 589**

DELICIOUS TOGETHER (Everett, Betty & Jerry Butler).
LP: . . . . **JOY 123**

JERRY AND BETTY (Everett, Betty & Jerry Butler).
LP: . . . . **CRM 2022**

Everett, Kenny

CAPTAIN KREMMEN (Greatest Adventure Yet).
LP: . . . . **CBS 84761**

KENNY EVERETT NAUGHTY JOKE BOX.
LP: . . . . **LAXLP 101**
MC: . . . . **LAXC 101**

KREMMEN THE MOVIE (Various artists).
Tracks: / Call for Kremmen: *Various artists* / Q's theme: *Various artists* / Pretty Pauline: *Various artists*/ Announcer: *Various artists* / Kremmen and Q: *Various artists.*
LP: . . . . **EMC 3342**
MC: . . . . **TCEMC 3342**

Everett Shock

GHOST BOYS.
LP: . . . . **SST 182**
MC: . . . . **SSTC 182**

Everette, Leon

LEON EVERETTE'S GREATEST HITS.
Tracks: / Giving up easy / Don't feel like the lone ranger / I love that woman (like

the devil loves sin) / I don't want to lose / Over / If I keep on going crazy / Hurricane / Midnight rodeo / Don't be angry / Just give me what you think is fair / Soul searching / Shadows of my mind / My lady loves me (just as I am) / Lady she's right / I could'a had you / Shot in the dark.
LP: . . . . **NL 90010**
MC: . . . . **NK 90010**

THIS IS LEON EVERETTE.
Tracks: / If I keep on going crazy / Over / I love that woman / It's not supposed to be that way / This moment of love / Giving up easy / I don't want to lose / Champagne dreams / Shadows of my mind / Don't feel like the Lone Ranger / Hurricane / Make me stop loving her / Betty Ruth / Don't be angry / Feelin's right / Midnight rodeo / Let me apologise / Think it over / Running on love / If you're serious about cheating.
LP: . . . . **INTS 5211**

Everhart, Bob

COUNTRY.
LP: . . . . **WRS 162**

Everill, Joyce

GRANNY'S BUTTON BOX.
Tracks: / Memories / Granny's button box / Schoolday ruminations / Fishy story, A / Torry skipper, A / Fishwife in the green, A / Castlegate yestreen / Cocky Hunter's store / Seterday's penny / Divi day / Washin' day / Summers remembered / Doon the sanny dee / Mind yer mainners / Somebidy chappin' at the door / By Royal appointment / Standin' in the lobby / I kent best / Ca' canny noo / Laddie, far hae ye been / Baby-sitter, The / Progress? / Exile's return, The / Torry then / Children on the shore / His will -nae mine / Woman of the year.
MC: . . . . **ACLMC 2**

Everlast

FOREVER EVERLASTING.
LP: **7599260974**
MC: **7599260972**

Everlasting love

EVERLASTING LOVE (Various artists).
MC: . . . . **ASK 783**

Everly Brothers

6 TRACK HITS: EVERLY BROTHERS.
Tracks: / All I have to do is dream / Wake up little Susie / Bye bye love / Bird dog / Problems / Till I kissed you.
MC: **7SC 5000**

20 GOLDEN LOVE SONGS: EVERLY BROTHERS.
LP: . . . . **MA 5785**
MC: . . . . **MAMC 95785**

20 GREATEST HITS: EVERLY BROTHERS.
LP: . . . . **MA 3785**
MC: . . . . **MAMC 93785**

ALL THEY HAD TO DO WAS DREAM.
LP: . . . . **RNLP 214**

BEAT AND SOUL.
Tracks: / Love is strange / Money / What am I living for / High heel sneakers / C.C. rider / Lonely avenue / Man with money / People get ready / My babe / Walking the dog / I almost lost my mind / Girl can't help it, The.
LP: . . . . **ROLI 319**

BEST OF THE EVERLY BROTHERS (CREOLE).
MC: **16-24**

BEST OF THE EVERLY BROTHERS (WB).
LP: **923994 1**
MC: **923994 4**

BORN YESTERDAY.
Tracks: / Amanda Ruth / I know love / Born yesterday / These shoes / Arms of Mary / That uncertain feeling / Thinking 'bout you / Why worry / Abandoned love / Don't say goodnight / Always drive a Cadillac / You send me.
LP: . . . . **MERH 80**
MC: . . . . **MERHC 80**

BOTH SIDES OF AN EVENING.
Tracks: / My mammy / Muskrat / My gal Sal / My grandfather's clock / Bully of the town / Chloe / Mention my name in Sheboygan / Hi lili hi lo / Wayward wind / Don't blame me / Now is the hour / Little old lady / When I grow too old to dream / Love is where you find it.
LP: . . . . **ROLI 315**

BYE BYE LOVE.
LP: . . . . **ENT LP 13025**
MC: . . . . **ENT MC 13025**

CATHY'S CLOWN.
Tracks: / Crying in the rain / Lucille / Cathy's clown / Don't blame me / Walk right back / That's old fashioned / So sad / Temptation / Ebony eyes / I'm not angry / Muskrat / How can I meet her?.
LP: . . . . **SHM 3030**

COLLECTION: EVERLY BROTHERS.
Tracks: / Problems / When will I be loved / This little girl of mine / Be bop a lula / Leave my woman alone / Roving gambler / Lightning express / Rockin' alone in an old rockin' chair / Like strangers / Wake up little Susie / Devoted to you / Bird dog / Rip it up / Brand new heartache / Should we tell him / Keep a knockin' / Put my little shoes away / Kentucky / Long time gone / Down in the willow garden / Take a message to Mary / Maybe tomorrow / Since you broke my heart / Let it be me.
2LP: . . . . **CCSLP 139**
MC: . . . . **CCSMC 139**

DATE WITH THE EVERLY BROTHERS, A.
Tracks: / Made to love / That's just too much / Stick with me baby / Baby what you want me to do / Sigh cry almost die / Always it's you / Love hurts / Lucille / So how come / Donna Donna / Change of heart, A / Cathy's clown.
LP: . . . . **ROLI 314**

EB 84/BORN YESTERDAY.
Tracks: / On the wings of a nightingale / Danger danger / Story of me / I'm takin' my time / First in line / Lay, lady, lay / Following the sun / You make it seem so easy / More than I can handle / Asleep / Amanda Ruth / I know love / Born yesterday / These shoes / Arms of Mary / Uncertain feeling / Thinkin' 'bout you / Why worry? / Abandoned love / Don't say goodnight / Always drive a Cadillac / You send me.
2LP: **8321731**

EVERLY BROTHERS.
LP: . . . . **RNLP 211**
LP: **1 A022 58092**
MC: **1 A222 58092**

EVERLY BROTHERS SHOW.
Tracks: / Mama tried / Kentucky / Bowling green / Till I kissed you / Wake up little Susie / Cathy's clown / Bird dog / Mabellene / Lord of the manor / I wonder if I care as much / Love is strange / Let it be me / Give peace a chance / Rock and roll music / End, The / Aquarius / If I were a carpenter / Price of love, The / Thrill is gone, The / Games people play / Baby what you want me to do / All I have to do is dream / Walk right back / Suzie Q / Hey Jude.
2LP: . . . . **K 66003**

EVERLY BROTHERS SING GREAT COUNTRY HITS.
Tracks: / Oh lonesome me / Born to lose / Just one time / Send me the pillow that you dream on / Release me / Please help me, I'm falling / I walk the line / Lonely street / Silver threads and golden needles / I'm so lonesome I could cry / Sweet dreams / This is the last song I'm ever going to sing.
LP: . . . . **ROLI 320**

EVERLY BROTHERS, THE (MERCURY).
Tracks: / On the wings of a nightingale / Danger danger / Story of me / I'm taking my time / First in line / Lay lady lay / Following the sun / You make it seem so easy / More than I can handle / Asleep.
LP: . . . . **MERH 44**
MC: . . . . **MERHC 44**
LP: . . . . **PRICE 110**
MC: . . . . **PRIME 110**

EVERLY BROTHERS, THE (WARNER BROS).
Tracks: / Gone gone gone / So how come (no one loves me) / Always its you / Silver threads and golden needles / That'll be the day / All I have to do is dream / Made to love / That's just too much / Memories are made of this / Oh boy / Change of heart, A / Ain't that loving you baby.
LP: . . . . **K 26010**
MC: **K4 26101**

FABULOUS EVERLY BROTHERS, THE.
Tracks: / Bye bye love / Wake up little Susie / All I have to do is dream / Bird dog / Problems / ('Til) I kissed you / Let it be me / When will I be loved / Take a message to Mary / Claudette / Poor Jenny / Devoted to you.
MC: . . . . **FABC 006**

FABULOUS STYLE OF THE EVERLY BROTHERS.
LP: . . . . **RNLP 213**
LP: . . . . **HAA 2266**

GOLDEN HITS: EVERLY BROTHERS.
Tracks: / That's old fashioned (that's the way love should be) / How can I meet her? / Crying in the rain / I'm not angry / Don't blame me / Ebony eyes / Cathy's clown / Walk right back / Lucille / So sad to watch good love go bad / Muskrat / Temptation.
LP: . . . . **K 46005**
MC: **K4 46005**

GONE GONE GONE.
Tracks: / Lonely island / Facts of life / Ain't that loving you baby / Love is all I need / Torture / Drop out, The / Radio and TV / Honolulu / It's been a long dry spell / Ferris wheel / Gone gone gone.
LP: . . . . **ROLI 316**

GREATEST HITS: EVERLY BROTHERS (ASTAN).
LPPD: . . . . **AR 30046**

GREATEST HITS: EVERLY BROTHERS (DITTO).
Tracks: / All I have to do is dream / Wake up little Susie / When will I be loved? / Be bop a lula.
MCSET: . . . . **DTO 10054**

GREATEST HITS: EVERLY BROTHERS (PICKWICK).
Tracks: / Bye bye love / I wonder if I care as much / Wake up little Suzie / Maybe tomorrow / This little girl of mine / Should we tell him / All I have to do is dream / Claudette / Bird dog / Devoted to you / Problems / Love of my life / Take a message to Mary / Poor Jenny / Till I kissed you / Oh what a feeling / Let it be me / Since you broke my heart / When will I be loved / Be bop a lula / Like strangers / Brand new heartache / I'm here to get my baby out of jail / Lightning express.
2LP: . . . . **PDA 063**

GREATEST HITS: EVERLY BROTHERS VOL 1.
LP: . . . . **SHM 3161**
MC: . . . . **HSC 3161**

GREATEST HITS: EVERLY BROTHERS VOL 2.
Tracks: / Take a message to Mary / Poor Jenny / Till I kissed you / Oh what a feeling / Let it be me / I'm here to get my baby out of jail / When will I be loved? / Be bop a lula / Like strangers / Brand new heartache / Since you broke my heart / Lightning express.
LP: . . . . **SHM 3168**
MC: . . . . **HSC 3168**

GREATEST RECORDINGS.
Tracks: / Wake up little Susie / Problems / Take a message to Mary / I wonder if I care as much / Poor Jenny / Love of my life / Bird dog / Like strangers / Hey doll baby / Leave my woman alone / Till I kissed you / Claudette / Should we tell him / All I have to do is dream / Rip it up / When will I be loved / Bye bye love / Let it be me.
LP: . . . . **CHA 194**
MC: . . . . **CHC 194**

IN GERMANY AND ITALY.
LP: . . . . **LSP 1056**

IN OUR IMAGE.
Tracks: / Leave my girl alone / Chained to a memory / I'll never get over you / Doll house is empty, The / Glitter and gold / Power of love, The / Price of love, The / It's all over / I used to love you / Lovely Kravezit / June is as cold as December / It only cost a dime.
LP: . . . . **ROLI 318**

IN THE STUDIO.
Tracks: / Leave my woman alone / Hey doll baby / I wonder if I care as much / Wake up little Susie / Maybe tomorrow / All I have to do is dream / Like strangers / Poor Jenny / Oh true love / Till I kissed you / Love of my life / When will I be loved / Should we tell him / Kentucky.
LP: . . . . **CH 159**

INSTANT PARTY.
Tracks: / Jezebel / Oh mein papa / Step it up and go / True love / Bye bye blackbird / Trouble in mind / Love makes the world go round / Long lost John / Autumn leaves / Party's over, The / Ground hawg / When it's night time in Italy.
LP: . . . . **ROLI 321**
LP: . . . . **WM 4061**

IT'S EVERLY TIME.
Tracks: / So sad / Just in case / Memories are made of this / That's what you do to me / Sleepless nights / What kind of girl are you / Oh true love / Carol Jane / Some sweet day / Nashville blues / You thrill me / I want you to know.
LP: . . . . **ROLI 313**
LP: . . . . **WM 4006**

LIVING LEGENDS.
LP: . . . . **WW 5027**

LOVE HURTS.
Tracks: / All I have to do is dream / Till I kissed you / So sad / Let it be me / Problems / Love of my life / No one can make my sunshine smile / Devoted to you / Take a message to Mary / When will I be loved? / Love hurts / Walk right back / Memories are made of this / Like strangers / Brand new heartache / Since you broke my heart / Love is strange / Crying in the rain / Donna Donna / Cathy's clown.
LP: . . . . **NE 1197**
MC: . . . . **CE 2197**

NEW ALBUM, THE.
Tracks: / Silent treatment / Dancing on my feet / Gran Mamou / Burma shave / Nancy's minuet / He's got my sympathy / Little Hollywood girl / Omaha / Empty boxes / I can't say goodbye to you / Nothing matters but you / When snowflakes fall in the summer / I'll see your light / Why not?.
LP: . . . . **K 56415**

NICE GUYS.
Tracks: / Trouble / What about me / Eden to Cainin / Chains / Meet me in the bottom / In the good old days / Nice guys / Stained glass morning / Dancing on my feet / Mr. Soul / Don't you even try / Kiss your man goodbye.
LP: . . . . **MFLP 1.028**
MC: . . . . **MFC 1.028**

ORIGINAL GREATEST HITS.
LP: **66255**

PASS THE CHICKEN AND LISTEN.
Tracks: / Lay it down / Husbands and wives / Woman don't you try to tie me down / Sweet memories / Ladies love outlaws / Not fade away / Watchin' it go / Paradise / Somebody nobody knows / Good hearted woman / Nickel for the fiddler, A / Rocky top.
LP: . . . . **ED 319**

PERFECT HARMONY.
Tracks: / Bye bye love / I wonder if I care / Wake up little Susie / This little girl of mine / All I have to do is dream / Claudette / Bird dog / Problems / Devoted to you / Take a message to Mary / Poor Jenny / ('Til) I kissed you / Let it be me / Like strangers / When will I be loved / Cathy's clown / Always its you / So sad (to watch good love go bad) / Lucille / Don't blame me / Walk right back / Ebony eyes / Temptation / Stick with me baby / Muskrat / That's old fashioned (that's the way love) / How can I meet her? / Don't ask me to be friends / True love (from High Society) / Crying in the rain / No one can make my sunshine smile / (So it was - so it is) So it will always be / Girl sang the blues, The / Gone, gone, gone / Ferris wheel / That'll be the day / Price of love, The / I'll never get over you / Love is strange / Love hurts / Dancing in the street / Bowling green / It's my time / Oh boy / Air that I breathe, The / Sweet grass county Montana / God bless older ladies / Snowflake bombadier / Yesterday just passed my way again / Since you broke my heart / Love at last sight / Brother juke box / On the wings of a nightingale / Lay lady lay / Why worry / Born yesterday / Arms of Mary / Ride the wind / Don't worry baby.
LPS: . . . . **EVYLP 47004**
MCSET: . . . . **EVYMC 47004**

PROFILE: EVERLY BROTHERS.
LP: **6.24003**
MC: **CL4 24003**

PURE HARMONY.
Tracks: / Bye bye love / Like strangers / Oh what a feeling / Bird dog / I wonder if I care as much / Take a message to Mary / All I have to do is dream / Wake up little Susie / Devoted to you / Maybe tomorrow / Love of my life / Till I kissed you / Since you broke my heart / Let it be me.
LP: . . . . **CH 118**

REUNION ALBUM.
2LP: . . . . **IMDP 1**
MC: . . . . **IMDK 1**

RIP IT UP.
Tracks: / Rip it up / Leave my woman alone / Hey doll baby / Brand new heartache / Problems / Be bop a lula / Poor Jenny / This little girl of mine / Claudette / Should we tell him? / When will I be loved? / Keep a knockin'.
LP: . . . . **CH 64**

RIP IT UP/PURE HARMONY.
Tracks: / Rip it up / Leave my woman alone / Hey doll baby / Brand new heartache / Problems / Be bop a lula / Poor Jenny / This little girl of mine / Claudette / Should we tell him / When will I be loved / Keep a knockin' / Bye bye love / Like strangers / Oh what a feeling / Bird dog / I wonder if I care as much / Take a message to Mary / All I have to do is dream / Wake up little Susie / Devoted to you / Maybe tomorrow / Love of my life / (Til) I kissed you / Since you broke my heart / Let it be me.
MCSET: . . . . **CHC 804**

ROCK 'N' ROLL FOREVER.
Tracks: / Wake up little Susie / Bird dog / Good golly Miss Molly / Oh Boy / Donna Donna / Lucille / Gone gone gone / Walk right back / Bye bye love / That'll

be the day / Slippin' and slidin' / Price of love, the.
LP: . . . . K 26063
MC: K4 26063

ROCK 'N' SOUL.
Tracks: / That'll be the day / So fine / Maybellene / Dancing in the street / Kansas City / I got a woman / Love hurts / Slippin' and slidin' / Suzie Q / Hound dog / I'm gonna move to the outskirts of town / Lonely weekends.
LP: . . . . ROLI 317

ROCKING IN HARMONY.
Tracks: / Wake up little Susie / Devoted to you / This little girl of mine / Like strangers / Roving gambler / Leave my woman alone / Bird dog / Long time gone / Problems / When will I be loved / I'm here to get my baby out of jail / Be bop a Lula.
LP: . . . . GEM 002
MC: . . . . GEMC 002

ROOTS (EDSEL).
LP: . . . . ED 203

ROOTS (ROLLERCOASTER).
Tracks: / Mama tried / Less of me / T for Texas / I wonder if I care as much / Ventura Boulevard / Shady grove / Illinois / Living too close to the ground / You done me wrong / Turn around / Sing me back home.
LP: . . . . ROLI 322

SINGLES SET.
LPS: . . . . SET 1

SO MANY YEARS.
LP: 260 471 1
MC: 260 471 4

SOME HEARTS.
Tracks: / Some hearts / Ride the wind / Can't get over it / Brown eyes / Julianne / Don't worry baby / Be my love again / Angel of the darkness / Three bands of steel / Any single solitary heart.
LP: 832 520 1
MC: 832 520 4

SONGS OUR DADDY TAUGHT US.
Tracks: / Roving gambler / Down in the willow garden / Long time gone / Lightning express / That silver haired daddy of mine / Who's gonna shoe your pretty little feet? / Barbara Allen / Oh so many years / I'm here to get my baby out of jail / Rockin' alone in an old rockin' chair / Kentucky / Put my little shoes away.
LP: . . . . CH 75

SUSIE Q.
Tracks: / Love with your heart / How can I meet her / Nothing but the best / Sheik of Araby, The / To show I love you / Susie Q / Am abend auf der heide / Sag su wiedersehen / When snowflakes fall in the summer / Little Hollywood girl / He's got my sympathy / Silent treatment, The.
LP: . . . . MFLP 052
MC: . . . . MFC 052

TWO YANKS IN ENGLAND.
Tracks: / Somebody help me / So lonely / Kiss your man goodbye / Signs that will never change / Like everytime before / Pretty flamingo / I've been wrong before / Have you ever loved somebody / Collector, The / Don't run and hide / Fifi the flea / Hard, hard year.
LP: . . . . ED 297

VERY BEST OF THE EVERLY BROTHERS VOL.2.
Tracks: / Cathy's clown / Price of love, The / Muskrat / Temptation / Love is strange / So sad (to watch good love go bad) / So it will always be / Cryin' in the rain / Walk right back / Lucille / Ebony eyes / No one can make my sunshine smile / How can I meet her / Don't blame me / Gone gone gone / Ferris wheel.
MC: . . . . PWKMC 4028

VERY BEST OF THE EVERLY BROTHERS (FUN (HOLLAND)).
LP: . . . . FUN 9024
MC: . . . . FUNC 9024

VERY BEST OF THE EVERLY BROTHERS (HALLMARK).
LP: . . . . SHM 3246
MC: . . . . HSC 3246

VERY BEST OF THE EVERLY BROTHERS, THE (WARNER BROS.).
Tracks: / Bye bye love / ('Til) I kissed you / Wake up little Susie / Crying in the rain / Walk right back / Cathy's clown / Bird dog / All I have to do is dream / Devoted to you / Lucille / So sad to watch good love go bad / Ebony eyes.
LP: . . . . K 46008
MC: K4 46008

WALK RIGHT BACK WITH THE EVERLYS.
Tracks: / Walk right back / Crying in the rain / Wake up little Susie / Love hurts / Till I kissed you / Love is strange / How can I meet her? / Temptation / Don't blame me / Cathy's clown / So sad to watch good love go bad / Bird dog / No one can make my sunshine smile / Ferris wheel / Price of love, The / Muskrat / Ebony eyes / Bye bye love.
LP: . . . . K 56168
MC: K4 56168

WARNER BROS. YEARS VOL.1, THE.
Tracks: / It's been nice / No one can make my sunshine smile / Nancy's minuet / I'm afraid / Girl who sang the blues / Don't forget to cry / Ring around my Rosie / Don't ask me to be friends / So it always will be / Whatever happened to Judy / Love her / Hello Amy / You're the one I love / You're my girl.
LP: . . . . CH 272

WARNER BROTHERS YEARS VOL.2, THE.
Tracks: / Lord of the manor / My little yellow bird / Cuckoo bird / I'm on my way home again / Carolina in my mind / Yves / Human race / Give me a sweetheart / Don't let the whole world know / Follow me / Love of the common people / You're just what I was looking for today / It's my time / Milk train.
LP: . . . . CH 281

Everly, Don

BROTHER JUKE BOX.
Tracks: / Love at last sight / So sad to watch good love go bad / Letting go / Since you broke my heart / Never like this / Deep water / Yesterday just passed my way again / Oh I'd like to go away / Oh what a feeling / Turn the memories loose again / Brother juke box.
LP: . . . . SDLP 002
MC: . . . . SDC 002

Everly, Phil

LOUISE.
Tracks: / Louise / Sweet Suzanne / She means nothing to me / Man and a woman, A / Who's gonna keep me warm / One way love / Sweet pretender / Better than now / Oh baby oh / God bless older ladies / Never gonna dream again / I'll mend your broken heart / When I'm dead and gone.
LP: . . . . MFLP 053
MC: . . . . MFC 053

PHIL EVERLY.
Tracks: / She means nothing to me (Featuring Cliff Richard with Phil Everly) / I'll mend your broken heart (Featuring Cliff Richard with Phil Everly) / God bless older ladies / Sweet pretender / Never gonna dream again / Better than now / Woman and a man / Louise / When I'm dead and gone / Sweet Suzanne / Oh baby oh (you're the star).
LP: . . . . EST 27670
MC: . . . . TC EST 27670

Everton Football Club

SOUVENIR ALBUM.
LP: . . . . EG 2403901
MC: . . . . EG 2403904

Every Mothers

EVERY MOTHERS NIGHTMARE.
Tracks: / Hard to hold / Bad on love / Love can make you blind / Dues to pay / Lord willin' / Ez come, ez go / Walls come down / Listen up / Long haired country boy / Nobody knows.
LP: 210921
MC: 410921

Every New Dead Ghost

NEW WORLD, A.
LP: . . . . PLASLP 024

RIVER OF SOULS.
LP: . . . . PLASLP 19
MC: . . . . PLASMC 19

Every Which Way But

EVERY WHICH WAY BUT LOOSE (Film soundtrack) (Various artists).
Tracks: / Every which way but loose: *Rabbitt, Eddie* / Send me down to Tucson: *Tillis, Mel* / I seek the night: *Locke, Sandra* / Coca cola cowboy: *Tillis, Mel* / Monkey see, monkey do: *Crofford, Cliff* / Salty dog blues (instrumental): *Various artists* / I'll wake you up when I get home: *Rich, Charlie* / Red eye special: *Collins, Larry* / Eastwood's alley walk: *Various artists* / Behind closed doors: *Rich, Charlie* / I can't say no to a truck drivin' man: *Chase, Carol* / Under the double eagle (instrumental): *Various artists* / Bikers theme (instrumental): *Various artists* / Don't say you don't love me no more: *Locke, Sandra* / Six pack to go, A: *Thompson, Hank* / Overture (instrumental): *Various artists.*
LP: . . . . K 52119

Everybody Wins

EVERYBODY WINS (Film soundtrack) (Various artists).
Tracks: / Seduced: *Redbone, Leon* / Warm beginning, A: *Isham, Mark* / Burning amongst the gravestones: *Isham, Mark* / Dark tabernacle: *Isham, Mark* / One step away from a dream: *Isham, Mark* / Tip of the iceberg, The: *Isham, Mark* / Frozen moment, A: *Isham, Mark* / Major could help, The: *Isham, Mark* / Polly wolly doodle: *Redbone, Leon* / Don't buy the nightmare: *Isham, Mark* / Two moments alone: *Isham, Mark* / Question of elocution, A: *Isham, Mark* / Question is reasked, The: *Isham, Mark* / Everything is possible: *Isham, Mark* / No high like a true confession: *Isham, Mark* / Time bomb on a motorcycle: *Isham, Mark* / On top of the mountain: *Isham, Mark* / Hot time in the old town tonight, A: *Redbone, Leon* / Final summation: *Isham, Mark* / Sympathy and acknowledgement: *Isham, Mark.*
LP: . . . . V 2619
MC: . . . . TCV 2619

Everybody's All

EVERYBODY'S ALL AMERICAN (1988 film soundtrack) (Various artists).
LP: . . . . C 11 G 91184
MC: . . . . C 41 G 91184

Everybody's Gotta...

EVERYBODY'S GOTTA LEARN SOMETIME (See Under International Hostage Release) (Various artists).

Everyday Heroics of

EVERYDAY HEROICS OF LIVING & DYING (Becker, Ernest).
MC: . . . . PT 41

Everyday People

YOU WASH, I'LL DRY.
Tracks: / Make him wait / Headline news / I guess it doesn't matter / More than a friend / Good as gold / This kind of woman / Second nature / Place in the sun / I've been there / All I see / Let somebody love you.
LP: . . . . SBKLP 4
LP: 794 425 1
MC: . . . . SBKTC 4
MC: 794 425 4

Everyday Stories

EVERYDAY STORIES NO.1.
MC: . . . . AC 107

EVERYDAY STORIES NO.2.
MC: . . . . AC 108

Everyman Band

EVERYMAN BAND.
LP: . . . . ECM 1234

WITHOUT WARNING.
Tracks: / Patterns which connect / Talking with himself / Multibluetonic blues / Celebration / Trick of the wool / Huh what he say / Al ur.
LP: . . . . ECM 1290

Everything But The

BABY THE STARS SHINE BRIGHT.
Tracks: / Come on home / Don't leave me behind / Country mile, A / Cross my heart / Don't let the teardrops rust your shining heart / Careless / Sugar Finney / Come hell or high water / Fighting talk / Little Hitler.
LP: . . . . BYN 9
MC: . . . . BYNC 9

EDEN.
Tracks: / Each and everyone / Bittersweet / Tender blue / Another bridge / Spice of life / Dust bowl / Crabwalk / Even so / Frost and fire / Fascination / I must confess / Soft touch.
LP: . . . . BYN 2
MC: . . . . BYNC 2

IDLEWILD.
Tracks: / Love is here where I live / These early days / Oxford Street / Night I heard Caruso sing, The / Goodbye Sunday / Shadow on a harvest moon / Blue moon rose / Tears all over town / Lonesome for a place I know / Apron strings / I don't want to talk about it.
LP: . . . . BYN 16
MC: . . . . BYNC 16

LANGUAGE OF LIFE, THE.
LP: . . . . BYN 21
MC: . . . . BYNC 21

LOVE NOT MONEY.
Tracks: / When all's well / Ugly little dreams / Shoot me down / Are you trying to be funny / Sean / Ballad of the times / Anytown / This love (not for sale) / Trouble and strife / Angel / Heaven help me (Available on cassette only) / Kid (Only on cassette.).
LP: . . . . BYN 3
MC: . . . . BYNC 3

Eviction

WORLD IS HOURS AWAY, THE.
LP: . . . . ZORRO 14

Evidence

SEE YOU LATER.
Tracks: / Later / Kinacho / Sleeping city / Salsa differente / Golden road / East St. Louis toodle-oo.
LP: . . . . TRIO 301
MC: . . . . TRIOC 301

Evie

CHRISTMAS, A HAPPY TIME.
LP: . . . . WST 9651

CHRISTMAS MEMORIES.
Tracks: / Come on ring those bells / Some children see Him / One small child / No room (medley) / Have you any room for Jesus? (medley) / Silent night / What child is this? / Thousand candles, A / Away in a manger / Mary's boy child / Holy night / Christmas, a happy time / First Noel, The / Joy to the world / Shiloh has come / Christmas gospel, The (medley) (Silent night#Jesus, Name above all names#The Name of Jesus) / Tiny baby, A / O little town of Bethlehem / O come, o come Emmanuel / Hark the herald angels sing / O come all ye faithful.
LP: . . . . WST R 9689
MC: . . . . WST C 9689

COME ON RING THOSE BELLS.
Tracks: / Come on ring those bells / Away in a manger / No room / Have you any room? / Mary's boy child / Silent night / O holy night / What child is this? / Some children see Him / One small child.
LP: . . . . WST 9574

EVIE.
Tracks: / My tribute / Sweet, sweet song of salvation / Blood will never lose its power, The / Movin' in the spirit / Would you? / Praise the Lord, He never changes / One more day / Say "I do" / On the wings of a snow white dove / I surrender all / I need Thee every hour.
LP: . . . . WST 9520
MC: . . . . WC 9520

EVIE AGAIN.
Tracks: / Sunday morning / Clean before my Lord / Give yourself to Jesus / Someone who can / Have Thine own way / Welcome back to Jesus / Stop, look and listen / That day is coming closer / All the time in the world / Jesus loves me / And oh how He loves you and me.
LP: . . . . WST 9529
MC: . . . . WC 9529

FAVOURITES VOL. 1.
Tracks: / My tribute / Praise the Lord, He never changes / Say "I do" / Clean before my Lord / Jesus loves me / And oh how He loves you and me / Name of Jesus, The / Give them all to Jesus / Part the waters / Broken up people / Born again / Mirror.
LP: . . . . WST 9597
MC: . . . . WC 9597

GENTLE MOMENTS.
Tracks: / Give them all to Jesus / Part the waters / You got the power / I don't have to worry / Meet me here / Pass it on / Broken up people / Waiting / For baby (for Bobbie) / Shepherd of love.
LP: . . . . WST 9562
MC: . . . . WC 9562

LITTLE SONG OF JOY FOR MY LITTLE FRIENDS, A.
Tracks: / Step into the sunshine / Why complain? / Tree song / His will / All day song / I am safe / Jesus, I believe what You said / It's not just a story / Will the circle be unbroken? / This little light of mine / Creature praise / Into my heart.
LP: . . . . WST 9582
MC: . . . . WC 9582

MIRROR.
Tracks: / Mirror / Lord, send that morning / If heaven never was promised to me / Jesus was there all the time / Now is the time / He loves me / Four feet eleven / Praise you just the same / Born again / Just because I asked.
LP: . . . . WSB 8735

NEVER THE SAME.
Tracks: / Live for Jesus / Hold on / Special delivery / Never the same again / This life / Shine / At the River of Jordan / Don't run from reality / Home / You have everything in your hands / Jesus, I love You.
LP: . . . . WST 9593
MC: . . . . WC 9593

UNFAILING LOVE.
Tracks: / How I love you, Lord / Bind us together / Cross where Jesus gave his life, The / Be still / I love my Jesus / Unfailing love / Picture of you / All the glory / You gave a song / Lord's prayer, The.
LP: . . . . WST 9612
MC: . . . . WC 9612

WHEN ALL IS SAID AND DONE.
LP: . . . . WST R 9682

MC: . . . . **WST C 9682**

Evil Dead (Film)

EVIL DEAD II (1987 film soundtrack) (Various artists).
Tracks: / Behemoth: *Various artists* / Book of evil, The: *Various artists* / Fresh panic (other side of your dream): *Various artists* / Putrified forest under her skin: *Various artists*.
LP: . . . . **TER 1142**
MC: . . . . **ZCTER 1142**

Evil Dead (Group)

RISE ABOVE.
LP: **507577**

Evil Under The Sun

EVIL UNDER THE SUN (Featuring the music of Cole Porter) (Various artists).
LP: . . . . **INTS 5225**
MC: . . . . **INTK 5225**

Evita (show)

EVITA (1978 Original London cast) (Various artists).
Tracks: / Requiem for Evita: *Various artists* / Oh what a circus: *Various artists* / On this night of a thousand stars: *Various artists* / Eva and Magaldi: *Various artists* / Eva, beware of the city: *Various artists*/ Buenos Aires: *Various artists* / Goodnight and thank you: *Various artists* / Lady's got potential, The: *Various* artists / Charity concert: *Various artists* / I'd be surprisingly good for you: *Various artists* / Another suitcase in another hall: *Various artists* / Dangerous Jade: *Various artists* / New Argentina, A: *Various* artists / On the balcony of the Casa Rosada: *Various artists* / Don't cry for me Argentina: *Various artists*/ High flying, adored: *Various artists* / Rainbow high: *Various artists* / Rainbow tour: *Various artists*/ Actress hasn't learned the lines (you'd like to hear), The: *Various artists* / And the money kept rolling in (and out): *Various artists* / Santa Evita: *Various artists* / Waltz for Eva and Che: *Various artists* / She is a diamond: *Various artists* / Dice are rolling: *Various artists* / Eva's sonnet: *Various artists* / Eva's final broadcast: *Various artists* / Montage: *Various artists* / Lament: *Various artists* / Cinema in Buenos Aires 26 July 1952, A: *Various artists* / Art of the possible: *Various artists* / Peron's latest flame: *Various artists*.
LP: . . . . **MCG 3527**
MC: . . . . **MCGC 3527**

EVITA (Original Broadway cast) (Various artists).
Tracks: / Don't cry for me Argentina: *Various artists* / Another suitcase in another hall: *Various artists* / On the night of a thousand stars: *Various artists* / And the money kept rolling in (and out): *Various artists*/ Buenos Aires: *Various artists* / High flying, adored: *Various artists* / Dangerous jade: *Various artists*.
2LP: . . . . **MCDW 453**

EVITA (1976 Studio recording) (Various artists).
Tracks: / Cinema in Buenos Aires 26 July 1952, A: *Various artists* / Requiem for Evita/Oh what a circus: *Various artists*/ On this night of a thousand stars: *Various artists* / Buenos Aires: *Various artists* / Goodnight and thank you: *Various artists* / Lady's got potential, The: *Various artists* / Charity concert/I'd be surprising: *Various* artists / Another suitcase in another hall: *Various artists* / Dangerous Jade: *Various artists* / New Argentina, A: *Various artists* / On the balcony of the Casa Rosada: *Various artists* / High flying, adored: *Various artists*/ Rainbow high: *Various artists* / Rainbow tour: *Various artists* / Actress hasn't learned the lines, The: *Various* artists / And the money kept rolling in (and out): *Various artists* / Santa Evita: *Various artists* / Waltz for Eva and Che: *Various artists* / She is a diamond: *Various artists* / Dice are rolling/Eva's sonet: *Various artists* / Eva's final broadcast: *Various artists* / Montage: *Various artists* / Lament: *Various artists*.
2LP: . . . . **MCX 503**
MC: . . . . **MCXC 503**

EVITA SELECTION FROM THE MUSICAL (Various artists).
LP: **2384 096**

EVITA/JESUS CHRIST SUPERSTAR (Various artists).
Tracks: / Cinema in Buenos Aires 26 July 1952, A: *Various artists* / Requiem for Evita: *Various artists* / Oh, what a circus: *Various artists* / On this night of a thousand stars: *Various artists* / Eva and Magaldi: *Various* artists / Eva beware of the city: *Various artists* / Buenos Aires: *Various artists* / Goodnight and thank you: *Various artists* / Lady's got potential, The: *Various artists* / Charity concert: *Various artists*/ I'd be surprisingly good for you: *Various artists* / Another suitcase in another hall: *Various artists* / Dangerous Jade: *Various artists* / New Argentina, A: *Various artists* / On the balcony of the Casa Rosada: *Various artists*/ Don't cry for me Argentina: *Various artists* / High flying, adored: *Various artists* / Rainbow high: *Various* artists / Rainbow tour: *Various artists* / Actress hasn't learned the lines (you'd like to hear), The: *Various* artists / And the money kept rolling in (and out): *Various artists* / Santa Evita: *Various artists* / Waltz for Eva and Che: *Various artists* / She is a diamond: *Various artists* / Dice are rolling: *Various artists*/ Eva's sonnet: *Various artists* / Eva's final broadcast: *Various artists* / Montage: *Various artists* / Lament: *Various artists* / Heaven on their minds: *Various artists* / Everything's alright: *Various artists*/ This Jesus must die: *Various artists* / Hosanna: *Various artists* / Simon Sealnotes: *Various artists*/ I don't know how to love him: *Various artists* / Gethsemane: *Various artists* / Pilate's dream: *Various* artists / King Herod's song: *Various artists* / Could we start again please: *Various artists* / Trial before Pilate: *Various artists* / John 19:41: *Various artists* / Forty one: *Various artists*.
MCSET: . . . . **MCA 2 114**

Ewans, Kai

DANISH JAZZ VOL.1.
LP: . . . . **SLP 410**

Ewart, Douglas

JILA (See under Lewis, George) (Ewart, Douglas & George Lewis).

Ewell, Don

DENVER CONCERT (Ewell, Don & Barbara Dane).
LP: **PUMPKIN120**

DON EWELL AND BARBARA DANE (Ewell, Don & Barbara Dane).
LP: . . . . **PUMPKIN 120**

DON EWELL AND HIS ALL STARS (Ewell, Don, Conger and Thompson).
LP: . . . . **J 29**

DON EWELL QUINTET (Ewell, Don Quintet).
LP: . . . . **J 69**

IN NEW ORLEANS.
LP: . . . . **GHB 30**

IN NEW ORLEANS (Ewell, Don & Herb Hall Quartet).
LP: . . . . **NOR 7209**

JAZZ ON A SATURDAY AFTERNOON.
LP: . . . . **SLP 502**

PIANO SOLOS.
LP: . . . . **88 UR 002**

TOGETHER (Ewell, Don/Bob Green).
LP: . . . . **JCE 84**

YELLOW DOG BLUES (Ewell, Don Quintet).
LP: . . . . **AP 66**

Ewing, Maria

FROM THIS MOMENT ON (Ewing, Maria & The Royal Philharmonic Orchestra).
Tracks: / Cole Porter sequence / More than you know / All the things you are / Yesterdays / But beautiful / As time goes by / It never was you / Come rain or come shine / When the sun comes out / Man that got away, The / One for my baby, and one more for the road / Spring is here / Gerswhin sequence.
MC: . . . . **MCC 18**

Ewing, Skip

WILL TO LOVE, THE.
Tracks: / Will to love, The / Please don't leave me now / If a man could live on love alone / Karen / Door, The / It wasn't his child / It's you again / Age doesn't matter at all / Ain't that the way it always ends / She's makin' plans.
LP: . . . . **MCA 42301**

Ewok Adventures (film)

EWOK ADVENTURES, THE (Original soundtrack) (Various artists).
LP: . . . . **STV 81281**

Ex

AURAL GUERRILLA, THE.
LP: . . . . **EX 36**

HANDS UP YOU'RE FREE.
LP: . . . . **EX 35**

JOGGERS AND SMOGGERS.
LP: . . . . **EX 40**

Ex Cathedra

CHRISTMAS MUSIC BY CANDLELIGHT.
Tracks: / Videte miraculum / Hymn to the virgin, A / Allelujah, a new work is come on hand / Song of the nuns of Chester / There is no rose / Gaudete natus est / Bethlehem down / Benedicamus domino / How shall I fitly meet thee / Riu riu chiu el lobo rabioso / Away in a manger / When Jesus our lord.
LP: . . . . **APS 320**

Excalibur

BITTER END, THE.
LP: . . . . **QUEST 5**

ONE STRANGE NIGHT.
Tracks: / Una notte strana / Lights go down, The / Round and round / Early in the morning / Running scared / Fight / Waiting / Frozen promises / Carole Ann / Death's door.
LP: . . . . **ATV 10**

Excalibur (Film)

EXCALIBUR (Original soundtrack) (New Philharmonic Orchestra/Sir Adrian Boult).
Tracks: / Ride of the Valkyries / Funeral march / Prelude to Tristan and Isolde / O fortuna.
LP: . . . . **ILPS 9682**
MC: . . . . **ICT 9682**

Excel

JOKES ON YOU, THE.
Tracks: / Drive / Shadow wind / Fired (you're) / Tapping the source / Resentment / Seeing insane / My thoughts / Never denied / Message in a bottle / Given question / Stranger, The / Blaze some hate (Only on CD.).
LP: . . . . **CARLP 7**
MC: . . . . **CARC 7**

Excelsior Brass Band

EXCELSIOR BRASS BAND.
LP: . . . . **WIZARD 3**

Excerpts From

EXCERPTS FROM CHRISTMAS STORIES (see under Dickens, Charles) (Williams, Emlyn (nar)).

Exciter

HEAVY METAL MANIAC.
Tracks: / Holocaust / Heavy metal maniac / Mistress of evil / Rising of the dead / Cry of the banshee / Stand up and fight / Iron dogs / Under attack / Blackwitch.
LP: . . . . **RR 9710**

LONG LIVE THE LOUD.
LP: . . . . **MFN 47**

OTT.
LP: **084602**

UNVEILING THE WICKED.
LP: . . . . **MFN 61**
MC: . . . . **TMFN 61**

VIOLENCE AND FORCE.
LP: . . . . **MFN 17**

Excruciation

LAST JUDGEMENT.
LP: . . . . **CM 002**

E-X-E

SICKER THAN I THOUGHT.
LP: . . . . **PRL 70101**

STRICKEN BY MIGHT.
LP: . . . . **AXISLP 2**

Executioner

BREAK THE SILENCE.
LP: . . . . **NRR 24**
MC: . . . . **NRC 24**

IN THE NAME OF METAL.
LP: . . . . **GWD 90538**
MC: . . . . **GWC 90538**

Executive Slacks

FIRE AND ICE.
MC: . . . . **CAVE 009**

NAUSEA.
LP: . . . . **SAVE 004**

YOU CAN'T HUM WHEN YOU'RE DEAD.
LP: . . . . **SAVE 003**

Exeter Cathedral

EVENSONG AT EXETER CATHEDRAL (Exeter Cathedral Choir).
Tracks: / Locus Iste / Versicles and responses / Christ is made the sure foundation (Plainsong.) / Psalm 84 / First lesson / Magnificat / Nunc dimittis in D / Second lesson / Creed / Lesser litany / Lord's prayer, The / Responses and collects / Blessed city, heavenly Salem (Anthem.) / Prayers / Ye watchers and ye holy ones / Flourish for an occasion.
LP: . . . . **ACA 544**
MC: . . . . **CACA 544**

Exhibit B

PLAYING DEAD.
LP: . . . . **EXBLP 1**

Exile

ALL THERE IS.
Tracks: / How could this go wrong / All there is / Too proud to cry / Part of me that needs you most / Destiny / Being in love with you is easy / Let's do it again / Come on over.
LP: . . . . **SRAK 535**

EXILE.
Tracks: / Take me to the river / Woke up in love / Red dancing shoes / We've still got love / I just came back to break my heart again / This could be the start of something good / After all these years / High cost of leaving / I don't want to be a memory / Here I go again.
LP: . . . . **EPC 25809**
MC: **40 25809**

GREATEST HITS: EXILE.
Tracks: / Woke up in love / I don't want to be a memory / Give me one more chance / She's a miracle / Hang on to your heart / Girl can't help it, The / I could get used to you / Crazy for your love / Super love / Kiss you all over.
LP: . . . . **EPC 57089**
MC: **40 57089**

HANG ON TO YOUR HEART.
Tracks: / Promises promises / I could get used to you / Hang on to your heart / She likes her lovin' / Music / I got love (super duper love) / It'll be me / Practice makes perfect / She's too good to be true / Proud to be her man.
LP: . . . . **EPC 26617**
MC: **40 26617**

I LOVE COUNTRY.
Tracks: / Super love / I could get used to you / Hang on to your heart / It'll be me / Proud to be her man / Woke up in love / I don't want to be a memory / Red dancing shoes / Here I go again / Give me one more chance / She's a miracle / Crazy for your love / Comin' apart at the seams / You make it easy / Take me to the river / Kiss you all over / Dancing the night away / Ain't no sunshine / If you ever change your mind / It's like we never said goodbye / Blue side, The / Little bit of rain, A / Love crazy love / Tennessee / Half the way / Lean on me / You never gave up on me / Crying in the rain / Woman in me, The / Same old story / Livin' in these troubled times / Miss the Mississippi and you.
LP: **4510071**
MC: **4510074**

Exiles

FREEDOM COME ALL YE.
Tracks: / Ballad of accounting / Moving on song, The / We're only over here for exploration / Thank Christ for Christmas / Pigeon / Pound a week rise, The / Freedom, come all ye / For a' that and a' that / Arthur MacBride / Willie Brennan / Wae's me for Prince Charlie / La pique / Van Diemans land / Twa recruiting sergeants.
LP: **12T 143**

HALE AND THE HANGED, THE.
Tracks: / Jolly beggar / Fair flower of Northumberland, The / Corner house, The / Sally gardens / Laird o' the windy wa', The / Dainty Davie / Le reel du pendu / Queen Eleanor's confession / Plooman laddie, The / Shoals of herring / Coolin, The / I walked up to her / Rocky road to Dublin / Wee weaver, The / Battle of Harlaw, The / I will lay ye doon, love / Planxty Davis.
LP: **12T 164**

SENSE IN WHAT THEY'RE..., THE.
LP: . . . . **WANDA LP1**

Exises

EXISES.
LP: . . . . **MEGATON 0016**

Exit

MONEY TO BURN.
LP: . . . . **LD 5014**
MC: . . . . **LDC 5014**

Exit 13

CELIA'S LAST WEDNESDAY.
LP: . . . . **LOS 001**

Exit Condition

DAYS OF WILD SKIES.
LP: . . . . **COX 027**

Exit (film)

EXIT (See under Tangerine Dream) (Tangerine Dream).

Exit Out

PERUSE PRANKSTER.
LP: . . . . **SF 025**

Ex-Mortis

IMMORTALITY'S END.
LP: . . . . **CCG 011**

Exodus

BONDED BY BLOOD.
Tracks: / Bonded by blood / And then there were none / Metal command / No love / Strike of the beast / Exodus / Lesson in violence, A / Piranha / Deliver us to evil.
LP: . . . . **MFN 44**

MC: . . . . TMFN 44

FABULOUS DISASTER.
LP: . . . . MFN 90
MC: . . . . TMFN 90
LPPD: . . . . MFN 90P

IMPACT IS IMMINENT.
Tracks: / Impact is imminent / A.W.O.L. / Lunatic parade, The / Within the walls of chaos / Objection overruled / Only death decides / Heads they win (tails you lose) / Changing of the guard / Thrash under pressure.
LP: . . . . EST 2125
LP: 790 379 1
MC: . . . . TCEST 2125
MC: 790 379 4

PLEASURES OF THE FLESH.
Tracks: / Deranged / Parasite / Faster than you'll ever live to be / 30 seconds / Chemi-kill / Till death do us part / Brain dead / Pleasures of the flesh / Seed of late / Choose your weapon.
LP: . . . . MFN 77
MC: . . . . TMFN 77
LPPD: . . . . MFN 77P

Exodus (Film)

EXODUS (1961 motion picture soundtrack) (Various artists).
Tracks: / Exodus: *Various artists* / Summer in Cyprus/Escape: *Various artists* / Ari: *Various artists*/ Karen: *Various artists* / Valley of Jezreel: *Various artists* / Fight for survival: *Various artists*/ In Jerusalem: *Various artists* / Brothers: *Various artists* / Conspiracy: *Various artists* / Prison break: *Various artists* / Dawn: *Various artists* / Fight for peace: *Various artists* / Hatikvah: *Various artists.*
LP: 4502341
MC: 4502344

EXODUS (ORIGINAL ISSUE) (Film soundtrack) (Various artists).
LP: . . . . RD 27210

EXODUS/CAST A GIANT SHADOW (Various artists).
Tracks: / Cast a giant shadow (prologue): *Various artists* (Cast A Giant Shadow.) / Land of hope: *Various artists*(Cast A Giant Shadow.) / War in the desert: *Various artists* (Cast A Giant Shadow.) / Magda: *Various artists* (Cast A Giant Shadow.) / Cast a giant shadow: *Various artists* (Cast A Giant Shadow.) / Love me true: *Various artists*(Cast A Giant Shadow. Vocal by Vince Hill.) / Road to Jerusalem, The: *Various artists* (Cast A Giant Shadow.) / Gathering of the forces, The: *Various artists* (Cast A Giant Shadow.) / Victory on the beach: *Various artists* (Cast A Giant Shadow.) / Garden of Abu Gosh: *Various artists* (Cast A Giant Shadow.) / Cast a giant shadow (finale): *Various artists*(Cast A Giant Shadow. The Zemel choir.) / Exodus: *Various artists* (Theme from) / Summer in Cyprus: *Various artists*(Exodus.) / Escape: *Various artists* (Exodus.) / Ari: *Various artists* (Exodus.) / Karen: *Various artists*(Exodus.) / Valley of Jezreel: *Various artists* (Exodus.) / Fight for survival: *Various artists* (Exodus.) / Brothers: *Various artists* (Exodus.) / Conspiracy: *Various artists* (Exodus.) / Prison break: *Various artists* (Exodus.) / Dawn: *Various artists* (Exodus.) / Fight for peace: *Various artists* (Exodus.) / Hatikvah: *Various artists*(Exodus.).
LP: . . . . LPMGM 11
LP: 794 286 1
MC: . . . . TCMGM 11
MC: 794 286 4

Exodus Supreme

STEPPIN' IN THE FUTURE.
LP: 52 123EP

Exon Singers

EXON SINGERS.
LP: . . . . APS 309

Exorcist

NIGHTMARE THEATRE.
LP: . . . . RR 9700

Expectant Father

EXPECTANT FATHER (From the book by Betty Parsons) (O'Sullivan, Richard).
LP: . . . . LEG 5

Expectant Mother

EXPECTANT MOTHER (Esther Rantzen talks to Betty Parsons) (Rantzen, Esther).
LP: . . . . LEG 4

Experiment In Terror

EXPERIMENT IN TERROR (Original soundtrack) (Various artists).
LP: . . . . NL 45964

Experiments With Ice

EXPERIMENTS WITH ICE.
LP: . . . . EX 001

Explainer

POSITIVE VIBRATIONS.
LP: . . . . VSLP 4003
MC: . . . . VSMC 003

STOP THE TUGGING.
LP: . . . . ECR 3029

Exploding White Mice

EXPLODING WHITE MICE.
LP: . . . . NORMAL 119

IN A NEST OF VIPERS.
LP: . . . . BTA 010
LP: . . . . GPR 115

Exploited

DEATH BEFORE DISHONOUR.
LP: . . . . JUST 6

EXPLOITED ON STAGE.
LP: . . . . EXPLP 2001

HORROR EPICS.
Tracks: / Horror epics / Don't forget the chaos / Law and order / I hate you / No more idols / Maggie / Dangerous vision / Down below / Treat you like shit / Forty odd years ago / My life.
LP: . . . . DOJOLP 37
LP: . . . . KOMA 788012
MC: . . . . AMOK 788012
MC: . . . . DOJOTC 37

INNER CITY DECAY.
LP: . . . . WAT 1

LET'S START A WAR (SAID MAGGIE ONE DAY).
Tracks: / Let's start a war / Insanity / Safe below / Eyes of the vulture / Should we can't we / Rival leaders (re-mix) / God save the Queen / Psycho / Kid ology / False hopes / Another day to go nowhere / Wankers.
LP: . . . . PAX 18
LP: . . . . DOJOLP 10
MC: . . . . DOJOTC 10

LIVE AND LOUD.
LP: . . . . LINK LP 018

LIVE AT THE WHITEHOUSE.
LP: . . . . SDLP 2

LIVE, LEWD LUST.
LP: . . . . SLAM 7

LIVE ON THE APOCALYPSE NOW TOUR 1981.
LP: . . . . APOCA 2

MASSACRE, THE.
LP: . . . . JUST 15
MC: . . . . TJUST 15

ON STAGE.
Tracks: / Cop cars / Crashed out / Dole Q / Dogs of war / Army life / Out of control / Ripper / Mod song / Exploited / Barmy army / Royalty / Sex and violence / Punks not dead / I believe in anarchy.
LP: . . . . DOJOLP 9
MC: . . . . DOJOTC 9

PUNKS NOT DEAD.
Tracks: / Punks not dead / Mucky pup / Cop cars / Free flight / Army life / Blown to bits / Sex and violence / SPG / Royalty / Dole Q / Exploited barmy army / Ripper / Out of control / Son of a copper / I believe in anarchy.
LP: . . . . SEC 1
MC: . . . . TSEC 1
LP: . . . . LINK 065
LP: . . . . RR 9995

PUNKS NOT DEAD/TROOPS OF TOMORROW.
MCSET: . . . . RR 49651

TOTALLY EXPLOITED.
Tracks: / Punk's not dead / Army life / F**k a mod / Barmy army / Dogs of war / Dead cities / Sex and violence / Yops / Daily news / Dole Q / Believe in anarchy / God save the queen / Psycho / Blown to bits / Insanity / SPG / Jimmy Boyle / U.S.A. / Attack / Rival leaders.
LP: . . . . DOJOLP 1
MC: . . . . DOJOTC 1

TROOPS OF TOMORROW.
Tracks: / Jimmy Boyle / Daily news / Disorder / Alternative / Rapist / Troops of tomorrow / UK 82 / Sid Vicious was innocent / War / They won't stop / So tragic / Germs / U.S.A..
LP: . . . . SEC 8
MC: . . . . CQ 2
MC: . . . . TSEC 8
LP: . . . . LINK 066
LP: . . . . RR 9981
LP: . . . . SLAM 8

Exploits of Don...

EXPLOITS OF DON QUIXOTE (see under Don Quixote) (Quayle, Anthony (nar)).

Explorers

EXPLORERS, THE.
Tracks: / Lorelei / Breath of life / Venus de Milo / Soul fantasy / Prussian blue / Two worlds apart / Robert Louis Stevenson / You go up in smoke / Ship of fools.
LP: . . . . V 2341
MC: . . . . TCV 2341
LP: . . . . TRL 041
MC: . . . . TCTRL 041
LP: . . . . OVED 185
MC: . . . . OVEDC 185

Explorers (film)

EXPLORERS (1986 film soundtrack) (Various artists).
LP: . . . . MCA 6148
MC: . . . . MCAC 6148
MC: . . . . VSC 5261

Export

EXPORT.
Tracks: / Fast lane to your heart / Wheeler dealer / Too much in love with you / Lovin' you baby / You're my best friend / Someone, somewhere / Light in the dark / I'm sorry.
LP: . . . . VICE 1

Expose

EXPOSURE.
Tracks: / Come go with me / Let me be the one / Exposed to love / Seasons change / Extra extra / Point of no return / Love is our destiny / I know you know / You're the one I need / December.
LP: 208147
MC: 408147

WHAT YOU DON'T KNOW.
Tracks: / What you don't know / Stop, look, listen and think / Tell me why / Let me down easy / Still hung up on you / Your baby never looked good in blue / Now that I've found you / Love don't hurt (until you fall) / Didn't it hurt to hurt me? / Walk along with me.
LP: 210062
MC: 410062

Ex-Post-Facto

SHE'LL RAPE THE WORLD.
LP: . . . . PS 2

Exposure

OUT OF THE DARK INTO THE LIGHT.
LP: . . . . ABT 002

WILD.
LP: . . . . STATLP 19
MC: . . . . STATC 19

Expressions

EXPRESSIONS (Various artists).
LP: . . . . NE 1307
MC: . . . . CE 2307

Exq's

RIS'X.
Tracks: / Ris'x.
LP: . . . . ANT 008

Extra Hot Sauce

TACO OF DEATH.
Tracks: / Taco of death / Hairpie / Tony's dilemma / I need a job / Extreme hatred / Hommina hommina hommina / Passive terrorism / Aids / Paranoid / Clueless f**ks / Caucasian beat boss / Communication breakdown / Lookout for the cheeba man / Freebird.
LP: . . . . VILE 008
LP: . . . . ARENA 1005

Extras

EXTRA FUNKY.
LP: . . . . DF 3001

Extreme

EXTREME.
Tracks: / Little girls / Wind me up / Kid ego / Watching waiting / Mutha (don't wanna go to school today) / Teachers pet / Big boys don't cry / Smoke signals / Flesh and blood / Rock a bye bye.
LP: . . . . AMA 5238
MC: . . . . AMC 5238

EXTREME II PORNOGRAFFITTI.
LP: 3953131
MC: 3953134

Extreme Noise Terror

COMPLETE PEEL SESSIONS: EXTREME NOISE TERROR.
Tracks: / False profit / Use your mind / Human error / Only in it for the music / Subliminal music / Punk, fact and fiction? / Deceived / Another nail in the coffin / Carry on screaming / Conned thru life / Work for never / 3rd world genocide / I am a bloody fool / In it for life / Shock treatment.
MLP: . . . . SFPMA 208
MC: . . . . SFPMC 208

EAR SLAUGHTER (See under Chaos UK) (Chaos UK & Extreme Noise Terror).

FILTHKICK - IN IT FOR LIFE.
LP: . . . . SINK 1

HOLOCAUST IN YOUR HEAD.
Tracks: / Statement / Take the strain / Show us you care / Use your mind / If your only in it for / Deceived / Conned thru life / Innocence to ignorance / Another nail in the coffin.
LP: . . . . HURT 1

Extreme Prejudice

EXTREME PREJUDICE (1987 film soundtrack) (Various artists).
Tracks: / Arrivals: *Various artists* / Cash: *Various artists* / Set-up, The: *Various artists* / Dust: *Various artists* / Identities: *Various artists* / Extreme prejudice: *Various artists* / Plan, The: *Various artists* / To Mexico: *Various artists* / No friendlies: *Various artists* / They didn't care: *Various artists*/ Funeral, The: *Various artists* / Deal, A: *Various artists.*
LP: . . . . FILM 011
MC: . . . . FILMC 011

Extremes (Film)

EXTREMES (Film Soundtrack Excerpts) (Various artists).
Tracks: / Ear ago, An: *Various artists* / Great Lager Street: *Various artists* / Box man: *Various artists*/ Black rose: *Various artists* / Refrigerated warmth: *Various artists* / Let your love run through: *Various artists* / Hit it: *Various artists* / Surely: *Various artists* / Am I not like other birds of prey: *Various artists* / I'm a perfectly happy man: *Various artists* / Words unspoken: *Various artists* / Elvish queen: *Various artists* / We gotta watch out: *Various artists.*
LP: . . . . SML 1095

Exumer

POSSESSED BY FIRE.
LP: 10005

RISING FROM THE SEA.
LP: 082566
LP: 6435123

Eydie & Steve

SING THE GOLDEN HITS.
LP: . . . . JASM 1517

Eye Hate God

IN THE NAME OF SUFFERING.
LP: . . . . SPASM 003

Eye Of The Needle

EYE OF THE NEEDLE (1982 film soundtrack) (Various artists).
LP: . . . . TER 1010

Eye To Eye

EYE TO EYE.
Tracks: / Hunger pains / Life in motion / Nice girls / More hopless knowledge / Progress ahead / Physical attraction / Time flies / On the mend.
LP: K56940

Eyeless in Gaza

BACK FROM THE RAINS.
Tracks: / Between these dreams / Twilight / Back from the rains / Lie still, sleep long / Catch me / Evening music / She moved through the fair / Sweet life longer / New love here / Welcome now / Your rich sky / Flight of swallows / My last lost melody / New risen / Bright play of eyes / Scent on evening air / Drumming the beating heart.
LP: . . . . BRED 69
MC: . . . . CBRED 69

CAUGHT IN A FLUX.
LP: . . . . BRED 18

DRUMMING THE BEATING HEART.
Tracks: / Transience blues / Ill wind blows / One by one / Picture the day / Dreaming at rain / Two / Veil like calm / Throw a shadow / Pencil sketch / At arms length / Lights of April / Before you go.
LP: . . . . BRED 36

KODAK GHOSTS RUN AMOK - 1980-1986.
Tracks: / Kodak ghosts run amok / Invisibility / No noise / Others / Pencil sketch / Veil like calm / Bright play of eyes / New risen / No perfect stranger / Sunbursts in / Welcome now / New love here / Back from the rains.
LP: . . . . BRED 73
MC: . . . . CBRED 73

PALE HANDS I LOVE SO WELL.
LP: . . . . U 004

PHOTOGRAPHS AS MEMORIES.
Tracks: / Seven years / Fixation / Looking daggers / From A to B / Clear cut apparently / Speech rapid fire / John of Patmos / Knives replace air / Faceless / In your painting / Keepsake / Whitewash / No noise.
LP: . . . . BRED 13

RUST RED SEPTEMBER.
Tracks: / Changing stations / Pearl and pale / New risen / September hills / Taking steps / Only whispers / Leaves are dancing / No perfect stranger / Corner of dusk / Bright play of eyes / Stealing Autumn.
LP: . . . . BRED 50
MC: . . . . CBRED 50

Eyermann, Tim

ALOHA (Eyermann, Tim & East Coast Offering).
LP: . . . . **IC 1095**

Eyes

BLINK.
Tracks: / 19th nervous breakdown / Immediate pleasure, The / I wanna be your man / When the night falls / Good day sunshine / Please don't cry / My degeneration / Man with money / You're too much / I'm rowed out.
LP: . . . . **KIRI 028**

SCENE BUT NOT HEARD.
LP: . . . . **MARI 038**

Eyes Of Laura Mars

EYES OF LAURA MARS (1978 film soundtrack) (Various artists).
LP: . . . . **CBS 70163**
MC: **40 70163**

Eyes of Mind

TALES OF THE TURQUOISE UMBRELLA.
LP: . . . . **VOXX 200016**

Eyes On You

RECEIVED WITH THANKS.
Tracks: / Lost / Independence day / Until I die / For me / South Africa / Chances you missed.
LP: . . . . **GURT 19**

Eyuphuro

MAMA MOSAMBIKI.
Tracks: / Samukeha (the nostalgic man) / Mwanuni (the bird) / Akakswela (love is so bewildering) / We awaka (you are mine) / Kihiyeny (leave me alone) / Nifungo (the key of the house) / Oh mama (oh mother) / Nuno maalani (single mother of a single mother.
LP: . . . . **RWLP 10**
MC: . . . . **RWMC 10**

Ezell, Will

PITCHIN' BOOGIE.
LP: . . . . **OL 2830**

PITCHIN' BOOGIE 1927-29.
LP: . . . . **OL 2331**

Ezintabeni

AMASWAZI EMVELO.
LP: . . . . **ERT 1003**

Ezo

EZO.
Tracks: / House of 1,000 pleasures / Flashback heart attack / Mr. Midnight / Here it comes / I walk alone / Destroyer / Big changes / Kiss of fire / Desiree.
LP: **9241431**
MC: **9241434**

FIRE FIRE.
Tracks: / Love junkie / Fire fire / Burn down the night / Back to zero / She's ridin' the rhythm / Million miles away / Night crawler / Wild talk / Black moon / Cold blooded / Streetwalker.
LP: . . . . **K 9242301**
MC: . . . . **K 9242304**

Ezrin, Arlene

DEADLY DEVELOPMENTS/THE BOOK OF HELL.
MC: . . . . **NF 6**

Ezy Meat

ROCK YOUR BRAINS.
LP: . . . . **ES 0002**

Fab (label)

FABULOUS COMPILATION (Various artists).
LP: . . . . . **FABL 007**

Fabares, Shelly

SHELLY.
LP: . . . . . **CP 426**

THINGS WE DID LAST SUMMER.
LP: . . . . . **SCP 431**

Fabian

FABULOUSLY GRATEFUL.
LP: . . . . . **CHL 5025**

TEEN KINGS (Fabian & Frankie Avalon).
Tracks: / String along / About this thing called love / Got the feeling / Long before / Kissin' and twistin' / Tiger / Just ask your heart / Gingerbread / Why / Venus / Teacher's pet / Boy without a girl.
LP: . . . . . **GEM 008**
MC: . . . . . **GEMC 008**

TIGER, THE.
LP: . . . . . **CHL 5026**

Fabian (Reggae)

IT'S NOT ENOUGH (See under Papa San) (Fabian (Reggae) & Papa San).

Fables Of Aesop

FABLES OF AESOP, THE.
Tracks: / Hare and the tortoise, The / Wolf in sheep's clothing, The / Lion and the mouse, The.
MC: . . . . . **AC 111**

Fabrizio, Mario

MOVEMENT IN THE SKY.
LP: . . . . . **ARL 5017**

Fabulous Baker Boys

FABULOUS BAKER BOYS - SOUNDTRACK (See under Grusin, Dave) (Various artists).

Fabulous Five

JAMAICAN WOMAN.
Tracks: / Jamaican woman.
LP: . . . . . **STAGE 007**

MILES AND MILES OF MUSIC.
LP: . . . . . **Unknown**

Fabulous Singlettes

STOP, IN THE NAME OF LOVE (Live from The Piccadilly).
LP: . . . . . **SCENE 13**
MC: . . . . . **SCENEC 13**

Fabulous Thunderbirds

BUTT ROCKIN'.
Tracks: / I believe I'm in love / One's too many / Give me all your lovin' / Roll roll roll / Cherry pink and apple blossom white / I hear you knocking / Tip on in / I'm sorry / Mathilda / Tell me why / On orbit.
LP: . . . . . **CHR 1319**
MC: . . . . . **ZCHR 1319**

FABULOUS THUNDERBIRDS, THE.
Tracks: / Wait on time / Scratch my back / Rich woman / Fulltime lover / Pocket rocket / She's tuff / Marked deck / Walkin' to my baby / Rock with me / C-boy's / Blues / Let me in.
LP: . . . . . **CHR 1250**

HOT NUMBER.
Tracks: / Stand back / Hot number / Wasted tears / It comes to me naturally / Love in common / How do you spell love / Streets of gold / Sofa circuit / Don't bother tryin' to steal her love / It takes a big man to cry.
LP: **4509491**
MC: **4509494**

PORTFOLIO.
Tracks: / Crawl, The / She's tuff / Scratch my back / Tip on in / That's enough of that stuff / Full time lover / Sugar-coated love / Wait on time / Los Fabulosos Thunderbirds / I'm a good man if you treat me right / You ain't nothin' but fine / Walkin' to my baby / Marked deck / Learn to treat me right / I believe I'm in love / How do you spell love / Mathilda / One's too many / Dirty work / Can't tear it up enuff / Cherry pink and apple blossom white / Monkey, The / Give me all your lovin' / Diddy wah diddy / My babe / Roll roll roll.
LP: . . . . . **CNW 2**
MC: . . . . . **ZCNW 2**

POWERFUL STUFF.
Tracks: / Rock this place / Knock yourself out / Mistake number 1 / One night stand / Emergency / Powerful stuff / Close together / Now loosen up baby / She's hot / Rainin' in my heart.
LP: **4633821**
MC: **4633824**

T-BIRD RHYTHM.
Tracks: / Can't tear it up enuff / How do you spell love / You're humbuggin' me / My babe / Neighbour tend to your business / Monkey, The / Diddy wah diddy / Lover's crime / Poor boy / Tell me (pretty baby) / Gotta have some- just got some.
LP: . . . . . **CHR 1395**
MC: . . . . . **ZCHR 1395**

TUFF ENUFF.
Tracks: / Tuff enuff / Tell me / Look at that / Two time my lovin' / Amnesia / Wrap it up / True love / Why get up / I don't care / Down at Antones.
LP: . . . . . **EPC 26883**
MC: **40 26883**

WHAT'S THE WORD.
Tracks: / Running shoes / You ain't nothin' but fine / Low down woman / Extra Jimmies / Sugar coated love / Last call for alcohol / Crawl, The / Jumping bad / Learn to treat me right / I'm a good man if you treat me right / Dirty work / That's enough of that stuff / Los Fabulosos Thunderbirds.
LP: . . . . . **CHR 1287**
MC: . . . . . **ZCHR 1287**

Fabvre, Harry

DISCREET AGENT.
Tracks: / Discreet agent, The / Rendezvous by the Seine / Spy who had her hair cut short, The / Handsome young man, The / Arrival in Paris / Empty rooms / Velous insomniac, The / Agent assasinated, The.
LP: . . . . . **TMLP 30**

DISCREET AGENT, THE.
LP: . . . . . **MSR 4**

Face Dancer

ABOUT FACE.
Tracks: / My girl / Forever beach / Treat me right / Pamela / I won't let you go / Shakin' it / Gotta get out / Everytime we kiss / How to be a man / Hard day's night, A / Love me do / She loves me / Please please me.
LP: . . . . . **EST 12082**

Face To Face

CONFRONTATION.
Tracks: / Tell me why / Confess / Why do I say / Too late / 4th watch, The / Walk into the fire / When time stands still / Shake the world / Boy like you, A / America's dream.
LP: . . . . . **EPC 26705**
MC: **40 26705**

FACE TO FACE.
Tracks: / Out of my hands / Face in front of mine / Pictures of you / Over the edge / Under the gun / 10-9-8 / Don't talk like that / Heaven on earth / Wreckless heart.
LP: . . . . . **EPC 25978**

ONE BIG DAY.
MC: . . . . . **MERHC 126**
LP: . . . . . **MERH 126**

Face To Face (film)

FACE TO FACE (FACCIA A FACCIA) (Original Soundtrack) (Various artists).
LP: . . . . . **IM 004**

Faces

BEST OF THE FACES, THE.
Tracks: / Flying / Around the plynth / Nobody knows / Three button hand me down / Sweet Lady Mary / Maybe I'm amazed / Had me a real good time / Miss Judy's farm / Memphis / Too bad / Stay with me / That's all you need / Cindy incidentally / Ooh la la / Flags and banners / Borstal boys / I wish it would rain / Pool hall Richard / You can make me dance, sing or anything / It's all over now.
LP: . . . . . **RVLP 3**

FACES FEATURING ROD STEWART (Faces & Rod Stewart).
Tracks: / Cindy incidentally / On the beach / Glad and sorry / Maybe I'm amazed / Shake shudder shiver / I feel so good / If I'm on the late side / Three button hand me down / Ooh la la / Looking out the window / Devotion / Had me a real good time.
LP: . . . . . **SSP 3074**
MC: . . . . . **SSC 3074**

FIRST STEP.
Tracks: / Wicked messenger / Devotion / Shake shudder shiver / Stone / Around the plynth / Flying / Pinapple and the monkey / Nobody knows / Looking out the window / Three button hand me down.
LP: . . . . . **ED 240**
LP: . . . . . **K 46053**
LP: . . . . . **XED 240**
LP: . . . . . **WS 3000**

FIRST STEP / LONG PLAYER.
Tracks: / Wicked messenger / Devotion / Shake, shudder, shiver / Stone / Around the plynth / Pineapple and the monkey / Nobody knows / Looking out the window / Three button hand me down / Bad 'n' ruin / Tell everyone / Sweet Lady Mary / Richmond / Maybe I'm amazed / Had me a real good time / One the beach / I feel so good / Jerusalem.
2LP: . . . . . **K 66027**

LONG PLAYER.
Tracks: / Bad 'n' ruin / Tell everyone / Sweet Lady Mary / Richmond / Maybe I'm amazed / Had me a real good time / On the beach / I feel so good / Jerusalem.
LP: . . . . . **K 46064**
LP: . . . . . **W 3011**

NOD'S AS GOOD AS A WINK TO A BLIND HORSE, A.
Tracks: / Miss Judy's farm / You're so rude / Love lived here / Last orders please / Stay with me / Debris / Memphis / Too bad / That's all you need.
LP: . . . . . **K 56006**
MC: **K4 56006**

OOH LA LA.
Tracks: / Silicone grown / Cindy incidentally / Flags and banners / My fault / Borstal boys / Fly in the ointment / If I'm on the late side / Glad and sorry / Just another honky / Ooh la la.
LP: . . . . . **K 56011**

OVERTURE & BEGINNERS (see under Stewart, Rod) (Faces & Rod Stewart).

Facial Expression

WINDMILL RUN, THE.
LP: . . . . . **LRF 116**

Fact

AS A MATTER OF.......FACT.
LP: . . . . . **SKULL 8364**

Faction

BAG.
LP: . . . . . **TMLP 29**

HEAVEN.
LP: . . . . . **TMLP 056**

Factory (Group)

BLACK STAMP.
LP: . . . . . **COB 37010**

Factory (label)

FACTORY BENELUX GREATEST HITS (1983) (Various artists).
LP: . . . . . **FBN 27**

FACTORY QUARTET (Various artists).
MC: . . . . . **FACT 24 C**

Factory Sample

FACTORY SAMPLE, A (See under Joy Division) (Various artists).

Fad Gadget

FIRESIDE FAVOURITES.
LP: . . . . . **STUMM 3**

GAG.
LP: . . . . . **STUMM 15**
MC: . . . . . **CSTUMM 15**

INCONTINENT.
Tracks: / Blind eyes / Swallow it / Saturday night special / Incontinent / Manual dexterity / Innocent bystanders / King of the flies / Diminished responsibility / Plain clothes.
LP: . . . . . **STUMM 6**
MC: . . . . . **CSTUMM 6**

UNDER THE FLAG.
LP: . . . . . **STUMM 8**
MC: . . . . . **CSTUMM 8**

Fad, J.J.

SUPERSONIC - THE ALBUM.
Tracks: / Supersonic / Blame it on the muzick / Eenie meenie beats / Let's get hyped / Is it love / Way out / In the mix / My dope intro / Time tah get stupid.
LP: **790 959-1**
MC: **790 959-4**

Faddis, Jon

JON AND BILLY (Faddis, Jon & Billy Harper).
LP: . . . . . **BKH 532**

LEGACY.
Tracks: / West end blues / Little jazz / Night in Tunisia / Instigator, The / Things to come / Child is born, A / Li'l darlin' / Whisper not.
LP: . . . . . **CJ 291**
MC: . . . . . **CJC 291**

OSCAR PETERSON AND JON FADDIS (see Peterson, Oscar) (Faddis, Jon & Oscar Peterson).

YOUNG BLOOD.
LP: **231 0765**
MC: **K10 765**

Fadela, Chaba

HANA, HANA (Fadela, Chaba & Cheb Sahraoui).
Tracks: / Hana hana / Ha rai / Ma nesbarchi / Nghir menek / Randjouh / Hadek mi andi.
MC: . . . . . **MCT 1005**
LP: . . . . . **MLPS 1005**

MAGOUITE OUALOU.
MC: . . . . . **MCPE 1209**

YOU ARE MINE.
MC: . . . . . **ICT 9915**
LP: . . . . . **ILPS 9915**

Fagen, Donald

COLLECTION: BECKER/FAGEN (See under Becker, Walter) (Fagen, Donald & Walter Becker).

EARLY YEARS, THE (see Becker, Walter) (Fagen, Donald & Walter Becker).

NIGHTFLY, THE.
Tracks: / New frontier / I.G.Y. / Green Flower Street / Ruby baby / Maxine / Walk between raindrops / Goodbye look, The / Night fly.
LP: . . . . . **W 3696**
MC: . . . . . **W 3696 4**
CD: **923696 1**

Fagin, Joe

BEST OF AUFWIEDERSEHEN PET (Fagin, Joe & Dave Mackay).
MC: . . . . . **AZAUF 2**
LP: . . . . . **AUF 2**

LOVE HANGS BY A THREAD.
LP: . . . . . **TOWLP 6**
MC: . . . . . **ZCTOW 6**

Fahey, John

AMERICA.
Tracks: / Voice of the turtle, The / Waltz that carried us away and then a mosquito came / Knoxville blues / Mark.
LP: . . . . . **SNTF 628**

BEST OF JOHN FAHEY 1959-1977.
Tracks: / Sunflower river blues / St. Louis blues / Poor boy / When the springtime comes again / Some summer day / Spanish dance / Take a look at that baby / I'm going to do all I can for my Lord / Last steam engine train / In Christ there is no East or West / Give me cornbread when I'm hungry / Dance of the inhabitants of the palace of King Philip XIV / Revolt of the Dyke Brigade / On the sunny side of the ocean / Spanish two step.
MC: . . . . . **ZCTKM 6004**
LP: . . . . . **TKMLP 6004**

BLIND JOE DEATH VOL.1.
Tracks: / On doing an evil deed blues / St. Louis blues / Poor boy / Uncloudy day / Desperate man blues / Sun gonna shine in my back door / Some day blues / Sligo river blues / I'm gonna do all I can for my Lord / John Henry / In Christ there is no East or West / Transcendental waterfall, The.
LP: . . . . . **SNTF 607**

CHRISTMAS ALBUM.
Tracks: / Joy to the world / What child is this? / Hark the herald angels sing / O come all ye faithful / Auld Lang Syne /

Bells of St. Mary's / Good King Wenceslas / We three kings of Orient are / God rest ye merry gentlemen / First Noel, The / Christ's saints of God fantasy / It came upon a midnight clear / Go I will send thee / Lo how a rose e'er blooming / Silent night, holy night.
LP: . . . . SNTF 702

CHRISTMAS GUITAR.
LP: . . . . V 002
MC: . . . . V 002C

DEATH CHANTS.
Tracks: / John Henry variations / Downfall of the Adelphi Roling grist mill, The / Take a look at that baby / Dance of the inhabitants of the palace of King Philip XIV / America / Episcopal hymn / Sunflower river blues / When the springtime comes again / Stomping tonight on the Pennsylvania / Albamam border / Some summer day / On the beach at Waikiki / Spanish dance.
LP: . . . . SNTF 608

FARE FORWARD VOYAGERS.
Tracks: / When the fire and the Rose are one / Thus Krishna on the Battlefield / Fare forward voyagers.
LP: . . . . SNTF 656

I REMEMBER BLIND JOE DEATH.
Tracks: / Evening mysteries of Ferry Street / You'll find her name written there / Minutes seem like hours, hours seem like days / Are you from Dixie / Minor blues, A / Steel guitar rag / Nightmare / Summertime / Let me call you sweetheart / Unknown tango / Improv in E minor / Lava on Waikiki / Gaucho.
LP: . . . . REU 1025

LEO KOTTKE WITH PETER LANG & JOHN FAHEY (see Kottke, Leo with Peter Lang & John Fahey).

LET GO.
LP: . . . . V 008
MC: . . . . V 008C

LIVE IN TASMANIA.
Tracks: / On the sunny side of the ocean / Tasmanian two step / Tiger / Approaching of the disco void / Waltzing Matilda / Fahey establishes raport with the Tasmanians / Disertation on 'Obscurity', A / Spoken / Steamboat gwine 'Round de bend' / Indian Pacific RR blues.
LP: . . . . SNTF 861

OF RIVERS AND RELIGION (Fahey, John & His Orchestra).
Tracks: / Steamboat gwine 'round de bend / Deep river / Dixie pig Bar-B-Q blues / Texas and pacific blues / Funeral song for Mississippi / By the side of the road / Lord have mercy / Song / Ol man river.
LP: . . . . ED 216

OLD FASHIONED LOVE.
Tracks: / In a Persian market / Jaya shiva shankaram / Marilyn / Assassination of Stefan Grossman, The / Old fashioned love / Boodle am shake / Keep your lamp trimmed and burning / I saw the light shining 'round and 'round.
LP: . . . . SNTF 688
MC: . . . . SHMC 99001

POPULAR SONGS OF CHRISTMAS AND NEW YEAR.
LP: . . . . VR 012
LP: . . . . V 012
MC: . . . . V 012C

RAILROADS 1.
Tracks: / Frisco leaving Birmingham / Oneonta / Summer cat by my door / Steve Talbot on the keddie wye / Afternoon espee through salem / Enigmas and perplexities of the Norfolk and Western / Charlie Becker's meditation / Imitation train whistles / Life is like a mountain railroad / Delta dog through the book of revelation.
LP: . . . . TKMLP 6005
MC: . . . . ZCTKM 6005

RAIN FORESTS, OCEANS AND OTHER THEMES.
LP: . . . . V 019
MC: . . . . VRC 019

REQUIA / THE YELLOW PRINCESS.
Tracks: / Requiem for John Hurt / Requiem for Russell Blaine Cooper / When the catfish is in bloom / Requiem for Molly (parts 1 to 4) / Fight on, Christians, fight on / Yellow Princess, The / View (east from the top of the Riggs Road) / B and O trestle / Lion / March for Martin Luther King / Singing bridge of Memphis, Tennessee, The / Dance of the inhabitants / Charles A. Lee - in memoriam / Irish setter / Commemorative transfiguration and communion at Magruder Park.
2LP: . . . . VSD 55/56

TRANSFIGURATION OF BLIND JOE DEATH, THE.
Tracks: / Beautiful Linda Getchell / Orinda-moraga / I am the resurrection / On the sunny side of the ocean / Tell her to come back to me / My station will be changed after a while / 101 is a hard road to travel / How green was my valley / Bicycle built for two / Death of the Clayton Peacock / Brenda's blues / Old southern medley / Come back baby / Poor boy / St. Patrick's hymn.
LP: . . . . TKMLP 6003
MC: . . . . ZCTKM 6003
LP: . . . . SNTF 744

Fahey, Warren

BILLY OF TEA (Fahey, Warren & Larrikins).
LP: . . . . LRF 028

BUSH TRADITIONS.
LP: . . . . LRF 07

LIMEJUICE AND VINEGAR (Fahey, Warren & Larrikins).
LP: . . . . LRF 159

Fahnbulleh, Miatta

MIATTA.
Tracks: / Jungle music / Bird song / Mr. Fine / I need you now / Wah gee da tebo / Ain't no way for a woman / Lullaby.
LP: . . . . EMC 3294

Fahres, Michael

PIANO, HARFE.
Tracks: / Ship of fools / Piano / Harfe.
LP: . . . . ECM 1281

Fahrt Art Trio

JOE DE SWIMMER.
LP: . . . . LR 171

Faine Jade

INTROSPECTION: A FAINE JADE RECITAL.
LP: . . . . PSYCHO 13

Fair Isle Folk

SHAMROCK AND THE ROSE, THE.
Tracks: / Raglan Road / Water is deep, The / Anne Devlin / Star of the County Down / Britches full of stitches and Mike / Hollow rock waltz / Shamrock and the rose, The / Jennifer gentle / Tram workers / Candlelight and wine / Right all right / Newfoundland / Rooster, The.
LP: . . . . DOLS 2017
MC: . . . . DOCS 2017

Fair, Jad

JAD FAIR & DANIEL JOHNSTONE (Fair, Jad & Daniel Johnstone).
LP: . . . . JAD 9 1
MC: . . . . JAD 9 4

ROLL OUT THE BAND (Fair, Jad & Kramer).
LP: . . . . BLP 60903

Fairchild, Barbara

ANSWER GAME, THE (Fairchild, Barbara & Billy Walker).
Tracks: / Bye, bye, love / If we take our time / Somewhere between leaving and gone / Answer game, The / Let me be the one / You've still got it baby / Deep purple / Broken trust / Over my head in love with you / Love's slipping through our fingers.
LP: . . . . INTS 5124
MC: . . . . INTK 5124

MISSISSIPPI.
Tracks: / Mississippi / Let me love you once before you go / Under your spell again / You are always there / Touch my heart / Cheatin' is / Music of love, The / Did it rain? / What you left my memory / Let Jesse rob this train.
LP: . . . . CBS 82020

Fairchild, Rev.C.L.

TESTIMONY.
Tracks: / Christ my hope / Lord hold my hand / You've been so good / You've got the power / Praise His name / For my life / You don't know / Everlasting love.
LP: . . . . MIR 4017
MC: . . . . MIR 4017MC

Fairclough, Gordon

HERE COMES CHARLIE MOON (See under Hughes, Shirley).

Fairer Sax

DIVERSIONS WITH THE FAIRER SAX.
Tracks: / Arrival of the Queen of Sheba, The / Sixteenth century dances / Fugue in D minor (Bach) / Aria (From suite No.3 Bach) / Moment musicale (Schubert) / Something doing (Joplin).
LP: . . . . SDL 365
MC: . . . . CSDL 365

Fairey Engineering

BEST OF THE FAIREY BAND (Fairey Engineering Works Band).
Tracks: / Entry of the gladiators / Spring / Hungarian dance no. 5 / Believe me if all those endearing young charms / Fairies of the waters / Fame and glory / Our boys will shine tonight / William Tell (Finale.) / To a wild rose / Thunder and lightning polka / When the saints go marching in / Famous British marches.
LP: . . . . LSA 3279

CHAMPION BRASS (Fairey Engineering Works Band).
Tracks: / King Cotton / Perpetuum mobile / Send in the clowns / Lohengrin - intro. to Act 3 / Girl I left behind me, The / If / Queen of Sheba, The / Can can, The / Don't cry for me Argentina / Polly wolly doodle / Hustle, The / Peace / Fanfare and soliloquy.
LP: . . . . REC 302
MC: . . . . ZCM 302

FAIREY ENGINEERING WORKS BAND (Fairey Engineering Works Band).
Tracks: / Hungarian march / Chanson hindoue / Cossack ride and slavonic dance / Serenade / Le carnaval Romain overture / Arnhem march / Du bist die ruh / You are my life / Salamanca / Concert variations / Heroic march from Epic Symphony.
LP: . . . . SB 342

SOUVENIR OF MEMORIES (Fairey Engineering Works Band).
Tracks: / Marching with Sousa / Serenade from String Quartet in F / Oh my beloved Father / Donnauwellen / Three musketeers / Radetzky march / Romanza / Andante cantabile / Les preludes.
LP: . . . . NTS 167

Fairfield Parlour

FROM HOME TO HOME.
LP: . . . . BFT 003LP

Fairground Attraction

AY FOND KISS.
Tracks: / Jock O'Hazeldean / Walkin' after midnight / Trying times / Winter rose / Allelujah (live) / Watching the party / Game of love / You send me / Mystery train / Do you want to know a secret? / Cajun band / Ay fond kiss.
LP: . . . . PL 74596
MC: . . . . PK 74596

FIRST OF A MILLION KISSES.
Tracks: / Smile in a whisper, A / Perfect / Moon on the rain / Find my love / Fairground attraction / Wind knows my name, The / Clare / Comedy waltz / Moon is mine, The / Station Street / Whispers / Allelujah / Falling backwards (Only on CD.) / Mythology (Only on CD.).
LP: . . . . PL 71696
MC: . . . . PK 71696

Fairground Organs

FAIRGROUND ORGANS FROM THE THURSFORD COLLECTION.
Tracks: / Entry of the Toreador / Neues leben / Kaiser Freidrich / Merry widow selection / In Munchen steht ein Hofbrauhaus / Lily the pink / Beer barrel polka / Gallop / Vater rheim / Florentiner marsch / Espana / Stars and stripes forever / Petite waltz / Canadian capers / Destiny / Gladiator's return.
LP: . . . . OU 2228

Fairman, Blain (nar)

MONKEY PUZZLE (See under Gosling, Paula).

NOT-JUST-ANYBODY FAMILY, THE (see under Not Just Anybody... (bk)).

Fairport Convention

ANGEL DELIGHT.
Tracks: / Lord Marlborough / Sir William Gower / Bridge over the river Ash / Wizard of the wordly game / Journeyman's grace, The / Angel delight / Banks of the sweet primroses / Instrumental medley / Bonnie black hare / Sickness and diseases.
LP: . . . . ILPS 9162

A.T.2..
MC: . . . . WRC 001

BONNY BUNCH OF ROSES.
Tracks: / Adieu adieu / Bonnie bunch of roses, The / Eynsham poacher, The / General Taylor / James O'Donnell's jig / Last waltz, The / Poor ditching boy, The / Royal selleccion number 13 / Run Johnny run.
LP: 9102 015
LP: . . . . WR 011
MC: . . . . WRC 011
MC: . . . . HACS 70167

EXPLETIVE DELIGHTED.
LP: . . . . WR 009
MC: . . . . WRC 009

FAIRPORT CONVENTION.
Tracks: / Time will show the wiser / I don't know where I stand / Decameron / Jack o' diamonds / Portfolio / Chelsea morning / Sun shade / Lobster, The / It's alright ma, it's only witchcraft / One sure thing / M.I. breakdown.
LP: 238 404 7
MC: 835 230 4

FAIRPORT CONVENTION 9.
Tracks: / Hexhamshire lass, The / Polly on the shore / Brilliancy medley and Cherokee shuffle, The / To Althea from prison / Tokyo / Bring 'em down / Big William / Pleasure and pain / Possibly parsons green.
LP: . . . . ILPS 9246

FAREWELL, FAREWELL.
Tracks: / Matty groves / Orange blossom special / John Lee / Bridge over the river Ash / Sir Patrick Spens / Mr. Lacey / Walk awhile / Bonnie black hare / Journeyman's grace / Meet on the ledge.
LP: . . . . GAMA 1

FIVE SEASONS, THE.
LP: . . . . RUE 005
MC: . . . . RUEMC 005

FULL HOUSE.
Tracks: / Walk awhile / Dirty linen / Sloth / Sir Patrick Spens / Flatback caper / Doctor of physick / Flowers of the forest.
LP: . . . . ILPS 9130
LP: . . . . HNBL 4417
MC: . . . . HNBC 4417

GLADYS LEAP.
LP: . . . . WR 007
MC: . . . . WRC 007
LP: . . . . V 023
MC: . . . . VRC 023

HEYDAY (BBC Radio Sessions).
LP: . . . . HNBL 1329
MC: . . . . HNBC 1329

HISTORY OF FAIRPORT CONVENTION, THE.
Tracks: / Meet on the ledge / Fotheringay / Mr. Lacey / Book song / Sailor's life / Si tu dois partir / Who knows where the time goes / Matty Groves / Crazy man Michael / Now be thankful (Medley) / Walk awhile / Sloth / Bonnie black hare / Angel delight / Bridge over the river Ash / John Lee / Breakfast in Mayfair / Hanging song / Hen's march / Four poster bed, The.
LP: . . . . ICD 4
MC: . . . . ICM 2073

HOUSE FULL (Live in L.A.).
Tracks: / Sir Patrick Spens / Banks of the sweet primroses / Toss the feathers / Sloth / Staines morris / Matty grows / Mason's apron / Battle of the Somme.
LP: . . . . HNBL 1319
MC: . . . . HNBC 1319
LP: . . . . HELP 28

IN REAL TIME.
LP: . . . . ILPS 9883
MC: . . . . ICT 9883
MC: . . . . ICM 2026
MC: 846 559 4

JOHN BABBACOME LEE.
LP: . . . . ILPS 9176

LIEGE AND LIEF.
Tracks: / Come all ye / Reynardine / Matty groves / Farewell farewell / Deserter, The / Lark in the morning, The (medley) / Tamlin / Crazy man Michael / Rakish paddy / Foxhunters jigs / Toss the feathers.
LP: . . . . ILPM 9115
MC: . . . . ICM 9115
LP: . . . . ILPS 9115
MC: 842 608 4

LIVE: FAIRPORT CONVENTION.
Tracks: / Matty Groves / Rosie / Fiddlestix / John the gun / Something you got / Sloth / Dirty linen / Down in the flood / Sir B MacKenzie.
LP: . . . . ILPS 9285

MOAT ON THE LEDGE.
LP: . . . . WR 001

MOAT ON THE LEDGE: LIVE AT BROUGHTON CASTLE.
MC: SP5 1052

RED AND GOLD.
Tracks: / Set me up / Red and gold / Battle, The / London river / Noise club, The / Beggars song, The / Dark eyed Molly / Open the door Richard.
LP: . . . . RUE 002
MC: . . . . RUEMC 002

RISING FOR THE MOON.
Tracks: / Rising for the moon / Restless / White dress / Let it go / Stranger to himself / What is true? / Iron lion / Dawn / After halloween / Night-time girl / One more chance.
LP: . . . . ILPS 9313

ROSIE.
Tracks: / Rosie / Matthew, Mark Luke and John / Knights of the road / Peggy's pub / Plainsman, The / Hungarian rhapsody / My girl / Me with you / Hen's march / Furs and feathers.
LP: . . . . ILPS 9208

THIRD LEG, THE.
MCSET: . . . . UNKNOWN

TIPPLERS' TALES.

Tracks: / Ye mariners all / Jack O'Rion / Banruptured / Hair of the dogma, The / Three drunken maidens / Reynard the fox / Widow of Westmorland, The / John Barleycorn.
LP: . . . . BGOLP 72
MC: . . . . BGOMC 72

UNHALFBRICKING.
Tracks: / Genesis hall / Si tu dois partir / Autopsy / Cajun woman / Who knows where the time goes / Percy's song / Million dollar bash / Sailor's life.
LP: . . . . ILPS 9102
LP: . . . . CGLP 4418
MC: . . . . CGC 4418

WHAT WE DID ON OUR HOLIDAYS.
Tracks: / Fotheringay / Mr. Lacey / Book song / Lord is in this place, The / No man's land / I'll keep it with mine / Eastern rain / Nottamun town / Tale in hard time / She moved through the fair / Meet me on the ledge / End of a holiday.
LP: . . . . ILPS 9092
LP: . . . . CGLP 4430
MC: . . . . CGC 4430

Fairweather, Digby

GOING OUT STEPPIN'.
Tracks: / She's funny that way / Jeepers creepers / Moanin' in the mornin' / Run rabbit run / Small fry / Looking at you / Going out steppin' / Very thought of you / If I had rhythm in my nursery rhymes / Blues for the depression / What a little moonlight can do / As long as I love.
LP: . . . . BLP 12190

HAVIN' FUN.
Tracks: / Indiana / Georgia on my mind / It don't mean a thing / I've got the world on a string / Sing / Cherokee / Some of these days / Moon country / At sundown / Black butterfly / Havin' fun.
LP: . . . . BLP 12175

SONGS FOR SANDY.
Tracks: / Prologue / Sandy and Al / Singing away the cold in Edinburgh / Hi-life in Hampstead / Sandy's blues / Requiem for a weeping willow / Singing away the cold in Edinburgh (reprise) / It's always Fairweather / Pal Sandy / Rosetta / Blue turning grey over you / One for Sandy.
LP: . . . . HEP 2016

VELVET.
LP: . . . . BLP 12187

Fairweather-Low, Andy

6 TRACK HITS: ANDY FAIRWEATHER-LOW.
Tracks: / Wide-eyed and legless / Reggae tune / Spider jiving / La booga rooga / Dancing in the dark / My bucket's got a hole in it.
MC: 7SC 5038

MEGA-SHEBANG.
Tracks: / Night time djuke-ing / Hard hat boogie / Whole lotta someday / Fool 4 some, A / Bingerama / Let ya beedle lam bam / Leave it out / 3 step shuffle / Hello Josephine / Psyche out.
LP: . . . . K 56832
MC: K4 56832

SPIDER JIVING.
Tracks: / Spider jiving / Drowning on dry land / Keep on rocking / Same old story / I ain't no mountain / Everyday I die / Light is within / Reggae tune / Standing on the water / Mellow down / Dancing in the dark.
LP: . . . . MFP 50440

Fairy Stories/ Tales

BEDTIME FAIRY STORIES (Unknown narrator(s)).
MCSET: . . . . DTO 10534

DICK WHITTINGTON & HIS CAT & OTHER TALES (Bloom, Claire (nar)).
MC: 1091

FAIRY STORIES (Lancaster, Ann).
Tracks: / Tinder box, The / Princess and the golden ball, The / Hansel and Gretel / Thumbelina / Babes in the wood / Rumpelstiltskin.
MCSET: . . . . DTO 10010

FAIRY TALES (see under Jones, Terry).

FAIRY TALES FOR YOU (Unknown narrator(s)).
MCSET: . . . . DTO 10533

GREAT FAIRY TALES OF THE WORLD (Unknown narrator(s)).
MCSET: . . . . DTO 10578

MORE WELL-LOVED FAIRY STORIES.
MC: . . . . TC LFP 7056

MY FAVOURITE FAIRY STORIES Read by Nanette Newman,Richard Norman,Judi Dench,Pete Murray (Various artists).
MC: . . . . TC-LFP 7003

YOUR FAVOURITE FAIRY STORIES
Adapted by Richard Baldwyn (Craig, Wendy / Richard Briers).
Tracks: / Cinderella / 3 little pigs / Rapunzel / Goldilocks and the three bears / Snow White and the seven dwarfs / Jack & the beanstalk / Gingerbread man / Dick Whittington / Beauty and the beast / Hansel and Gretel / Little Red Riding Hood (story) / Rumpelstiltskin / Hare and the hedgehog / Sleeping beauty.
MCSET: . . . . LFP 7262
MCSET: . . . . TCLFP 7262

Faith

LIVE FAITH.
LP: . . . . DOVE 50

Faith, Adam

20 GOLDEN GREATS: ADAM FAITH.
LP: . . . . WW 5113

ADAM.
LP: . . . . PMC 1128

ADAM FAITH.
LP: . . . . PMC 1162

ADAM FAITH SINGLES COLLECTION (His Greatest Hits).
Tracks: / Got a heartsick feeling / What do you want? / Poor me / Someone else's baby / When Johnny comes marching home / Made you / How about that / Who am I? / Easy going me / Don't you know it? / Time has come, The / Lonesome / As you like it / Don't that beat all / What now / First time / We are in love / Message to Martha, A / Someone's taken Maria away / Cheryl's goin' home.
LP: . . . . EMS 1350
MC: . . . . TCEMS 1350

BEAT GIRL (SOUNDTRACK) (See under Barry, John) (Various artists).

BEST OF ADAM FAITH.
Tracks: / What do you want? / Easy going me / As you like it / We are in love / Someone's taken Maria away / First time / Don't that beat all? / Message to Martha / Mix me a person / Someone else's baby / Time has come, The / Poor me / Baby take a bow / Cheryl's goin' home.
LP: 41 5735 1
MC: 41 5735 4

BEST OF ADAM FAITH (2).
Tracks: / What do you want / Poor me / Someone else's baby / Johnny comes marching home / Made you / How about that / Lonely pup (in a christmas shop) / This is it / Who am I? / Easy going me / Don't you know it / Time has come, The / Lonesome / As you like it / Don't that beat all / What now / Walkin' tall / First time / We are in love / If he tells you (CD only.) / I love being in love with you (CD only.) / Message to Martha (Kentucky bluebird) / Stop feeling sorry for yourself (CD only.) / Someone's taken Maria away (CD only.) / Cheryl's goin' home.
LP: . . . . MFP 5849
MC: . . . . TC-MFP 5849

EP COLLECTION, THE: ADAM FAITH.
LP: . . . . SEE 298
MC: . . . . SEEK 298

FAITH ALIVE (Faith, Adam & The Roulettes).
Tracks: / Lady oh lady / High heel sneakers / Talk about love / Look out baby / Everybody's talking 'bout a thing / Night time is the right time / Little Queenie / Hey little lovin' girl / Hey baby / I can't think of anyone else / You can't blame him / Heartbreak Hotel / I need your lovin'.
LP: C5-515
MC: C5K-515
LP: . . . . PMC 1249

I SURVIVE.
Tracks: / I survived / I believe in love / Honey / Foreign lady / Change / Maybe / Never say goodbye / Goodbye / In your life / Star song.
LP: . . . . K 56054

NOT JUST A MEMORY.
Tracks: / We are in love / If he tells you / I love being in love with you / Stop feeling sorry for yourself / Message to Martha / Someone's taken Maria away / Cheryl's goin' home / I don't need that kind of lovin' / First time / Here's another day / When Johnny comes marching home / Lonesome / Easy going me / This is it / As you like it / What now? / Brother heartache and sister tears / If ever you need me / Just mention my name / Only one such as you / I'm used to losing you / Who am I? / Don't you know it?.
LP: . . . . CM 121

Faith Brothers

EVENTIDE.
Tracks: / Eventide / Sunday (rebel soul) / Whistling in the dark / Tradesman's entrance, The / Storyteller / Daydreamers philosophy, A / Easter parade / Dust in the soul / Victoria green / Secret heart / Sleepwalker, The.
LP: . . . . XID 15
MC: . . . . CXID 15
LP: . . . . SIRENLP 1

HUMAN SOUND, A.
Tracks: / With no constitution but my own / That's just the way it is with me / Saint of contradiction / You can't go home again / Isolato / Dancing with Peter Pan's shadow / Consider me / Welcome pain, A / May your children speak well of your mother tongue / Boy and the river, A.
LP: . . . . SRNLP 9
MC: . . . . SRNMC 9
MC: . . . . CXID 18
LP: . . . . XID 18

Faith, George

HAPPY ANNIVERSARY.
LP: . . . . TRACK 1004

ON MY OWN (See under Baines, Murray) (Baines, Murray & George Faith).

SINGS FOR LOVERS ONLY.
Tracks: / Need to belong to someone / Look through your window / I want to be with you / Diana / It's been a long long time / I won't cry / Confidential / Vow, The / Wide awake in a dream.
LP: . . . . HLP 017

STRAIGHT TO THE HEART.
LP: . . . . EADLP 1005

TO BE A LOVER (HAVE MERCY).
MC: . . . . RRCT 31

TOGETHER FOREVER (See under Baines, Murray) (Baines, Murray & George Faith).

Faith Global

SAME MISTAKES,THE.
LP: . . . . SURLP 003

Faith No More

INTERVIEW, THE.
MC: . . . . MBAK 6020

INTRODUCE YOURSELF.
Tracks: / Faster disco / Anne's song / Introduce yourself / Chinese arithmetic / Death march / We care a lot / R N' R / Crab song / Blood / Spirit.
LP: . . . . SLAP 21
MC: . . . . SMAC 21

LIVE AT THE BRIXTON ACADEMY.
Tracks: / Epic / From out of nowhere / We care a lot / Falling to pieces / Real thing, The / Warriors / Zombie eaters / Edge of the world / Grade, The (Only on MC and CD.) / Cowboy song (Only on MC and CD.).
LP: 828 238 1
MC: 828 238 4

REAL THING, THE.
Tracks: / From out of nowhere / Epic / Falling to pieces / Surprise, you're dead / Zombie eaters / Real thing, The / Underwater love / Morning after, The / Woodpecker from Mars / War pigs (Only on cassette and CD.) / Edge of the world (Only on cassette and CD.).
LP: 828 154 1
MC: 828 154 4
LPPD: 828 217 1

WE CARE A LOT.
LP: . . . . MDR 1

Faith Over Reason

EYES WIDE SMILE.
LP: . . . . ABB 027

Faith, Percy

IMAGES: PERCY FAITH.
Tracks: / How can I be sure / Never can say goodbye / If / Without you / Fool on the hill, The / Good morning starshine / Funny girl / Angel of the morning / This guy's in love with you / Windmills of your mind / Here, there and everywhere / Gypsies, tramps and thieves / Spinning wheel / First time ever I saw your face, The.
MC: . . . . KNMC 16011

MOODS (Faith, Percy & His Orchestra).
Tracks: / Summer Place, A theme from / Aquarius / Romeo and Juliet love theme / Good morning, starshine / Song sung blue / Amazing grace / Day by day / Candy man / Godfather love theme / How can I be sure? / Conquistador.
MCSET: . . . . DTO 10042

VIA MEXICO.
LP: . . . . CBS 54937
MC: 40 54937

Faithful Breath

GOLD 'N' GLORY.
LP: . . . . SKULL 8335
MC: . . . . TAPE 78335

Faithful Harmonizers

FAITHFUL HARMONIZERS.
MC: . . . . GVMMC 209

Faithfull, Marianne

AS TEARS GO BY.
Tracks: / Come and stay with me / Last thing on my mind / Cockleshells / Tomorrow's calling / Something better / Sunny Goodge Street / Is this what I get for loving you? / As tears go by / Reason to believe / Sister morphine / House of the Rising Sun / Sha-la-la song / Sally / Free and easy / Yesterday.
LP: . . . . TAB 13

BLAZING AWAY.
Tracks: / Les prisons du roi / Guilt / Sister Morphine / Why'd ya do it? / Ballad of Lucy Jordan / Blazing away / Broken English / Strange weather / Working class hero / As tears go by / When I find my life / Times Square / She moved through the fair.
MC: . . . . ICT 9957
LP: . . . . ILPS 9957

BROKEN ENGLISH.
Tracks: / Working class hero / What's the hurry / Ballad of Lucy Jordan / Why d'ya do it / Broken English / Witches' song / Guilt / Brain drain.
LP: . . . . ILPM 9570
MC: . . . . ICM 9570
LP: . . . . M 1
LP: . . . . ILPS 9570
MC: 842 355 4

CHILD'S ADVENTURE, A.
LP: . . . . ILPM 9734
MC: . . . . ICM 9734
LP: . . . . ILPS 9734
MC: 811 310 4

COME MY WAY.
Tracks: / Come my way / Jabberwock / Portland town / House of the rising sun / Spanish is a loving tongue / Fare thee well / Lonesome traveller / Down in the salley garden / Mary Ann / Full fathom five / Four strong winds / Black girl / Once I had a sweetheart / Bells of freedom / Blowin' in the wind / Et maintenant (what now my love) / That's right baby / Sister morphine.
LP: . . . . LK 4688

DANGEROUS ACQUAINTANCES.
LP: . . . . ILPS 9648
MC: . . . . ICT 9648
MC: . . . . ICM 2029
MC: 846 560 4

DREAMIN' MY DREAMS.
LP: . . . . NEL 6007

FAITHLESS.
LP: . . . . CLALP 148
MC: . . . . CLAMC 148

MARIANNE FAITHFULL.
Tracks: / Come and stay with me / If I never get to love you / Time takes time / He'll come back to me / Downtown / Plaisir d'amour / Can't you hear my heartbeat? / As tears go by / Paris belles / They never will leave you / What have they done to the rain? / In my time of sorrow / What have I done wrong? / I'm a loser.
LP: . . . . NEL 6012
LP: . . . . DOA 3
LP: . . . . LK 4689

MUSIC FOR THE MILLIONS.
Tracks: / Yesterday / Sunny Goodge Street / Coquillages / Blowin' in the wind / Counting / Come and stay with me / Monday Monday / Summer nights / What have I done wrong / Go away from my world / Sister morphine.
LP: 8102281
MC: 8102284

RICH KID BLUES.
Tracks: / Rich kid blues / Long black veil / Sad Lisa / It's all over now, baby blue / Southern butterfly / Chords of fame / Visions of Johanna / It takes a lot to laugh, it takes a train to cry / Beware of darkness / Corina Corina / Mud slide Slim / Crazy lady blues / All I want to do in life / I'll be your baby tonight / Wait for me down by the river / That was the day / This time / Way you want me to be, The / Dreamin' my dreams / Wrong road again / Fairytale hero / Vanilla O'Lay / Lady Madelaine / Honky tonk angels.
2LP: . . . . CCSLP 107
MC: . . . . CCSMC 107

STRANGE WEATHER.
Tracks: / Stranger intro / Boulevard of broken dreams / I ain't goin' down to the well no more / Yesterdays / Sing of judgement / Strange weather / Love life and money / I'll keep it with mine / Hello stranger / Penthouse serenade / As tears go by / Stranger on earth, A.
LP: . . . . ILPS 9874
MC: . . . . ICT 9874
MC: . . . . ICM 2028
MC: 842 593 4

SUMMER NIGHTS.
Tracks: / Summer nights / What have they done to the rain / Plaisir d'amour / Young girl blues / First time ever I saw your face / Paris bells / I'm the loser / Monday, monday / This little bird / Ne me quitte pas / Scarborough Fair.
LP: . . . . TAB 78

WORLD OF MARIANNE FAITHFULL.
Tracks: / As tears go by / This little bird / Summer nights / Scarborough fair / Monday, Monday / Come and stay with me / Is this what I get for loving you? / Yesterday / Tomorrow's calling / In my time of sorrow / Go away from my world.
LP: . . . . SPA 17

Falay, Maffy

AT FREGATTAN (Falay, Maffy & Sevda).
LP: . . . . SNTF 665

WE SIX (Falay, Maffy Sextet).
LP: . . . . PHONT 7576

Falco

EINZELHAFT.
LP: . . . . AMLH 68550

EMOTIONAL.
Tracks: / Kiss of Kathleen Turner, The / Kamikaza Cappa / Crime time / Cowboyz and indianz / Coming Home / Star of moon and sun, The / Les nouveaux riches / Sound of Musik, The / Emotional (New York mix English version) / Emotional (Continental version).
LP: . . . . WX 75
MC: . . . . WX 75C

FALCO 3.
Tracks: / Rock me Amadeus / America / Tango the night / Munich girls(looking for love) / Jeanny / Vienna calling / Manner des westens (Translation:Any kind of land.) / Nothin' sweeter than arabia / Macho macho / It's all over now baby blue / Jeanny (German version).
LP: . . . . AMA 5105
MC: . . . . AMC 5105

JUNGE ROEMER.
Tracks: / Junge roemer / Tut ench amon / Brillantin' brutal / Iher tochter / No answer / Nut mit dir / Hoch wie nie / Steuermann / Kann denn liebe sunde sein.
LP: . . . . AMLX 68566

WEINER BLUT.
LP: . . . . K 255397-1
MC: . . . . K 255397-4

Falco, Tav

BEHIND THE MAGNOLIA CURTAIN.
LP: . . . . FC 029

NOW (Falco, Tav & The Panther Burns).
MC: . . . . C 37

RED DEVIL.
LP: . . . . ROSE 140

RETURN OF THE BLUE PANTHER (Falco, Tav & The Panther Burns).
LP: . . . . ROSE 215

SUGAR DITCH.
LP: . . . . ROSE 73

TONIGHT IN MEMPHIS (Falco's Panther Burns, Tav).
LP: . . . . ROSE 185

WORLD WE KNEW, THE (Falco, Tav & The Panther Burns).
LP: . . . . ROSE 113
MC: . . . . ROSE 113C

Falcon, Billy

FALCON AROUND.
LP: . . . . MCF 3065

PRETTY BLUE WORLD.
Tracks: / Power windows / Heaven's highest hill / What she will / Pretty blue world / Die twice / Still got a prayer / Not funny anymore / My new girlfriend / This burning love / Gettin' married in the morning / Oh boy.
LP: 8488001
MC: 8488004

Falcon, Joseph

LIVE AT A CAJUN DANCE.
LP: . . . . ARHOOLIE 5005
MC: . . . . C 5005

Falcon & the...(film)

FALCON AND THE SNOWMAN (1985 film soundtrack) (Various artists).
Tracks: / Psalm 121 - flight of the falcon: *Metheny, Pat* / Daulton Lee: *Metheny, Pat* / Chris: *Metheny, Pat* / This is not America: *Metheny, Pat & David Bowie* / Extent of the life: *Metheny, Pat* / Level of description, The: *Metheny, Pat* / Capture: *Metheny, Pat* / Epilogue (psalm 121): *Metheny, Pat.*
LP: . . . . EJ 2403051
MC: . . . . EJ 2403054
LP: . . . . FAL 1

THIS IS NOT AMERICA (See under Bowie, David) (Bowie, David/Pat Metheny Group).

Falcons

FALCONS' STORY, PART 3.
LP: . . . . RELIC 8010

I FOUND LOVE.
LP: . . . . RELIC 8006

YOU'RE SO FINE.
LP: . . . . RELIC 8005

Falk, Dieter

INSTRUMENTAL JOURNEY.
LP: . . . . MYR R 1237
MC: . . . . MYR C 1237

TODAY.
LP: . . . . MYRR 1243
MC: . . . . MYRC 1243

Falkirk Youth Theatre

WE'LL GO WHERE THE MUSIC TAKES US.
Tracks: / I'll go where the music takes me / Rivers of Babylon / There is love / With a little help from my friends / Goodbye to love / Gonna build a mountain / Mull of Kintyre / I write the songs / Skye boat song / Give me the chance / Singing the blues / Thank you for the music / Your hand in mine / Rhythm of life.
LP: . . . . MOR 523

Fall

45 84 89 (A' sides).
LP: . . . . BEGA 111
MC: . . . . BEGC 111

B SIDES.
LP: . . . . BEGA 116
MC: . . . . BEGC 116

BEND SINISTER.
Tracks: / R.O.D. / Doctor Faustus / Shoulder pads / Mr. Pharmacist / Gross chapel / U.S. 80's - 60's / Terry Waite sez / Bournemouth runner / Riddler / Shoulder pads 2.
LP: . . . . BEGA 75
MC: . . . . BEGC 75

DRAGNET.
LP: . . . . SFAL 4

EXTRICATE.
Tracks: / Sing Harpy / I'm Frank / Bill is dead / Black monk theme (pt I) / Popcorn double feature / Telephone thing / Hilary / Chicago now / Littlest rebel, The / And therein... / Black monk theme (pt II) (Available CD and cassette only) / Arms control poseur (Available CD and cassette only) / British people in hot weather (Available CD and cassette only) / Extricate (Available CD and cassette only).
LP: 842 204 1
MC: 842 204 4

FALL LIVE (Totalle's Turns).
LP: . . . . ROUGH 10

FRENZ EXPERIMENT.
Tracks: / Frenz / Carry bag man / Get a hotel / Victoria / Athlete cured / In these times / Steak place, The / Bremen nacht / Guest informant / Oswald defence lawyer.
LP: . . . . BEGA 91
MC: . . . . BEGC 91

GROTESQUE.
LP: . . . . ROUGH 18

HEX ENDUCTION HOUR.
Tracks: / Classical, The / Hip priest / Mere pseud mag ed / Winter 2 / Who makes the nazis / And this day / Jawbone and the air rifle / Fortress/Deer park / Winter (hostel maxi) / Just step s'ways / Iceland.
LP: . . . . LILP 400126
LP: . . . . KAM 005

HIP PRIESTS AND KAMERADS.
LP: . . . . SITU 13
MC: . . . . SITC 13
LP: . . . . SITL 13
MC: . . . . SITLC 13

HIT THE NORTH (PART 2).
Tracks: / Hit the north (part 2) / Australians in Europe (Only on 12" version.) / Northerners in Europe (Only on 12" version.).
MCSET: . . . . BEG 200 C

I AM KURIOUS ORANJ.
Tracks: / Overture from 'I am kurious oranj' / Dog is life / Jerusalem / Kurious oranj / Wrong place right time / Win fall CD / Van plague / Bad news girl.
LP: . . . . BEGA 96
MC: . . . . BEGC 96

LIVE AT THE WITCH TRIALS.
LP: . . . . SFLP 1

PALACE OF SWORDS REVERSED.
LP: . . . . COG 1
MC: . . . . CCOG 1

PERVERTED BY LANGUAGE.
LP: . . . . LILP 400116
LP: . . . . ROUGH 62
MC: . . . . ROUGHC 62

ROOM TO LIVE.
LP: . . . . LILP 400109

SEMINAL LIVE.
LP: . . . . BBL 102
MC: . . . . BBLC 102

SHIFT WORK.
MC: 8485944
LP: 8485941

SLATES.
Tracks: / Older lover, An / Slates / Leave the capitol / Prole art threat.
MLP: . . . . RT 071

THIS NATION'S SAVING GRACE.
Tracks: / Mansion / Bombast / Barmy / What you need / Spoilt Victorian child / L.A. / Gut of the quantifier / My new house / Paintwork / I am Damo Suzuki / To Nkroachment : Yarbles.
LP: . . . . BEGA 67
MC: . . . . BEGC 67
LP: . . . . BBL 67
MC: . . . . BBLC 67

WONDERFUL AND FRIGHTENING WORLD OF THE FALL.
LP: . . . . BBL 58
MC: . . . . BBLC 58
LP: . . . . BEGA 58
MC: . . . . BEGC 58

Falla Trio

VIRTUOSO MUSIC FOR THREE GUITARS.
LP: . . . . CC 2007

WEST SIDE STORY/PULCINELLA/JAZZ SONATA.
LP: . . . . CC 2013
MC: . . . . CC 2013 C

Fallen Angels

FALLEN ANGELS.
LP: . . . . FALL LP 023
MC: . . . . FALL CLP 023

IN LOVING MEMORY.
LP: . . . . FREUD 12

SIX POINT SIX.
LP: . . . . HB 2001

WHEEL OF FORTUNE.
LP: . . . . FREUD 23

Falling Towards

FALLING TOWARDS ENGLAND (see under James, Clive) (James, Clive).

Fallon, Roisin

COUNTRY & IRISH.
MC: . . . . GTDC 023

YOU'RE STILL THE ONLY ONE I'LL EVER LOVE.
MC: . . . . GTDC 102

Fallout

BUTCHERY.
LP: . . . . FLP 2

False Prophets

FALSE PROPHETS.
LP: . . . . VIRUS 48

IMPLOSION.
LP: . . . . VIRUS 58

Faltskog, Agnetha

EYES OF A WOMAN.
Tracks: / One way love / Eyes of a woman, The / Just one heart / I won't let you go / Angels cry / Click track / We should be together / I won't be leaving you / Save me / I keep turning off lights / We move as one.
LP: . . . . EPC 26446

FRIDA & AGNETHA - AFTER ABBA (See under Frida for details) (Agnetha & Frida).

I STAND ALONE.
Tracks: / Last time, The / Little white secrets / I wasn't the one (who said goodbye) / Love in a world gone mad / Maybe it was magic / Let it shine / We got a way / I stand alone / Are you gonna throw it all away / If you need somebody tonight.
LP: . . . . WX 150
MC: . . . . WX 150C

WRAP YOUR ARMS AROUND ME.
Tracks: / Heat is on, The / Can't shake loose / Shame / Stay / Once burned, twice shy / Mr. Persuasion / Wrap your arms around me / To love / I wish tonight could last forever / Man / Take good care of your children / Stand by my side.
LP: . . . . EPC 25505
MC: 40 25505

Fame

FAME (Film Soundtrack) (Various artists).
Tracks: / Out here on my own: *Cara, Irene* / Hot lunch jam: *Cara, Irene* / Dogs in the yard: *McCrane, Paul* / Red light: *Clifford, Linda* / Is it okay if I call you mine?: *McCrane, Paul* / Never alone: *Contemporary* Gospel Chorus / Ralph and Monty (dressing room piano): *Gore, Michael* / I sing the body electric: *Various artists* / Fame: *Cara, Irene.*
LP: . . . . SPELP 82
MC: . . . . SPEMC 82
LP: 2479 253
MC: 3216 265

FAME-MUSIC & SONGS FROM (Famous D.dance school choir & orchestra) (Various artists).
Tracks: / I can do anything better than you can: *Various artists* / We got the power: *Various artists* / Out here on my own: *Various artists* / Mannequin: *Various artists* / Starmaker: *Various artists* / Step up to the mike: *Various artists* / Hi fidelity: *Various artists* / It's Sonata Mozart: *Various artists* / Show must go on: *Various artists.*
LP: . . . . MFP 4156341
MC: . . . . TCMFP 4156344

Fame, Georgie

20 BEAT CLASSICS.
Tracks: / Yeh yeh / Getaway / Do-re-mi / My girl / Sweet things / Point of no return / Get on the right track baby / Baby / Ride your pony / Moody's mood for love / Funny how time slips away / Sunny sitting in the park / Green onions / In the meantime / Papa's got a brand new bag / Blue Monday / Pride and joy / Pink champagne / Let the sun shine in / I love the life I live.
LP: . . . . SPELP 45
MC: . . . . SPEMC 45
LP: . . . . RSX 1

BACK AGAIN (Fame, Georgie/Blue Flames).
LP: . . . . NE 1372
MC: . . . . CE 2372

BALLAD OF BONNIE AND CLYDE.
LP: . . . . SHLP 149
MC: . . . . SHTC 149

CLOSING THE GAP.
Tracks: / Give a little more / Run away with me / I love Jamaica / Eros hotel / Everything I own / Lean on me / Upright / Bring back my love.
MC: . . . . ZCN 137
LP: . . . . N 137

COOL CAT BLUES.
Tracks: / Cool cat blues / Every knock is a boost / You came a long way from St. Louis / Big brother / It should have been me / Yeah yeah / Moondance / Cats eyes / I love the life I live / Survival / Little pony / Rocking chair.
MC: . . . . VBR 20434

FAME AT LAST.
LP: 33SX 1638

FIRST THIRTY YEARS, THE.
Tracks: / Do the dog / Yeh yeh / Getaway / Ballad of Bonnie and Clyde / Rosetta / Daylight / Samba (toda menina baiana) / In crowd, The / C'est la vie / Fully booked / That ol' rock and roll / Sitting in the park / Do-re-mi / Like we used to be / Sunny / Seventh son / Ali shuffle / Hurricane, The / Moody's mood for love / Dawn yawn / Mellow yellow / Woe is me / Funny how time slips away / Old music master, The.
2LP: . . . . VSOPLP 144
MC: . . . . VSOPMC 144

GEORGIE FAME WITH ALAN PRICE (Fame, Georgie/Alan Price).
MCSET: . . . . DTO 10069

GEORGIE FAME/LENA ERICSON/LASSE SAMUELSON (Fame, Georgie/Lena Ericson/Lasse Samuelson).
LP: . . . . FLC 5091
MC: . . . . FLCK 15901

HALL OF FAME.
LP: . . . . SX 6120

IN GOODMAN'S LAND (Fame, Georgie/Sylvia Vrethammar).
Tracks: / Flying home / Makin' whoopee / King Porter stomp / Limehouse blues / Just one of those things / Don't be that way / Alexander's ragtime band / Sweet Georgia Brown / You turned the tables on me / Airmail special / Memories of you / In Goodmansland medley.
LP: . . . . SNTF 908

IN HOAGLAND 81 (See under Ross, Annie) (Fame, Georgie/Annie Ross).

LIVE AT MONTREUX: GEORGIE FAME (see under Hudik big band/Georgie Fame/Bengt A.Wallin (Fame, Georgie/Bengt A. Wallin/ Hudik big band).

MY FAVOURITE SONGS (Fame, Georgie/Blue Flames).
Tracks: / Rosetta / Ballad of Bonnie and Clyde / Barefootin' / That old rock 'n' roll / Get away / Yeh yeh / Bring it on home

to me / Saturday night fish fry / Someday / Lawdy Miss Clawdy.
LP: LF6 25646
MC: PF4 25646

NO WORRIES (Fame, Georgie & The Australian Blue Flames).
Tracks: / Lady be good / Ole buttermilk sky / Eros Hotel / Little Samba / It ain't right / On a misty night / Cats' eyes / Parchman farm / Zulu / Saturday night fish fry / Try na get along with the blues / Yeh yeh / Get away.
LP: . . . . FLC 5099
MC: . . . . FLCK 5099

RHYTHM AND BLUES AT THE FLAMINGO CLUB.
Tracks: / Night train / Let the good times roll / Do the dog / Eso beso / Work song / Parchman farm / You can't sit down / Humpty Dumpty / Shop around / Baby please don't go.
LP: . . . . SPELP 80
MC: . . . . SPEMC 80

RIGHT NOW.
Tracks: / Different dream / Funny how tiem slips away / Little samba / I'm in love with ya baby / Ollie's party / Eros Hotel / 'Cross a lazy afternoon / Country girl / Don't you worry 'bout a thing / Too shy to say / Zulu / Last song, The.
LP: . . . . NSPH 18600

SOUND VENTURE.
LP: . . . . SX 6076

SWEET THINGS.
LP: . . . . SX 6043

SWINGING ON A STAR (see Boulaye, Patti & Georgie Fame) (Fame, Georgie/ Patti Boulaye).

THAT'S WHAT FRIENDS ARE FOR.
Tracks: / Maybe tomorrow / Lovely day / L in L.A. / You / I don't care who I can dance with / That's what friends are for / Don't hit me when I'm down / Sitting in the park / If I didn't mean you well / Cat's eyes.
MC: . . . . ZCN 119
LP: . . . . N 119

TOGETHER (see Price, Alan) (Fame, Georgie/Alan Price).

TWO FACES OF FAME.
LP: . . . . SBPG 63018

Famille Verret

JULES VERRET: VOL. 1.
LP: . . . . PH 2007

Family

ANYWAY.
Tracks: / Good news bad news / Willow tree / Holding the compass / Strange band part of the load / Normans lives and ladies.
LP: . . . . K 54002
LP: . . . . SEE 245
LP: . . . . RSX 9005

BANDSTAND.
Tracks: / Burlesque / Bolero babe / Coronation / Dark eyes / Broken nose / My friend the sun / Glove, The / Ready to go / Top of the hill.
LP: . . . . K 54006
LP: . . . . SEE 241

BEST OF FAMILY.
Tracks: / Burlesque / My friend the sun / Chase, The / Old songs new songs / Part of the load / In my own time / It's only a movie / Sweet desiree / Sat'd'y barfly / Children / No mules fool / Weaver's answer, The.
LP: . . . . K 54023
LP: . . . . SEE 330
MC: . . . . SEEK 330

FAMILY ENTERTAINMENT.
Tracks: / Weaver's answer, The / Observations from a hill / Hung-up down / Summer '67 / How-hi-the-li / Second generation woman / From the past archives / Dim / Processions / Face in the crowd / Emotions.
LP: . . . . K 44069
LP: . . . . SEE 200
MC: . . . . SEEK 200
LP: . . . . RSLP 6340

FAMILY IN CONCERT.
MC: . . . . WINCMC 001

FAMILY, THE.
Tracks: / High fashion / Mutiny / Screams of passion, The / Yes / River run dry / Nothing compares 2 U / Susannah's clothes / Desire.
LP: 925322 1

FEARLESS.
LP: . . . . K 54003

IT'S ONLY A MOVIE.
LP: . . . . RA 58501

IT'S ONLY A MOVIE/FEARLESS.
Tracks: / It's only a movie / Leroy / Buffet tea for two / Boom bang / Boots'n'roots / Banger / Sweet Desiree / Suspicion / Check out / Between blue and me / Sat'd'y barfly / Larf and sing / Spanish tide / Save some for thee / Take your partners / Children / Crinkly grin / Blind / Burning bridges.
2LP: . . . . TFOLP 22
MC: . . . . TFOMC 22

MUSIC IN A DOLL'S HOUSE.
Tracks: / Chase, The / Mellowing grey / Never like this / Me my friend / Hey Mr. Policeman / See through windows / Variation on a theme of hey Mr. policeman / Winter / Old songs new songs / Variation on the theme of the breeze / Variation on a theme of me my friend / Peace of mind / Voyage / Breeze, The / 3 x time.
LP: . . . . K 44057
LP: . . . . SEE 100
MC: . . . . SEEK 100
LP: . . . . RLP 6312

OLD SONGS, NEW SONGS.
Tracks: / Hung up down / Today / Observations from a hill / Good friend of mine / Drowned in wine / Peace of mind / Home town / Cat and the rat, The / No mule's fool / See through windows / Weaver's answer, The.
LP: . . . . K 34001

RISE - VERY BEST OF FAMILY.
Tracks: / Burlesque / In my own time / Weaver's answer, The.
LP: . . . . BEC 777

SONG FOR ME, A.
Tracks: / Drowned in wine / Some poor soul / Love is a sleeper / Stop for the traffic / Wheels / Song for sinking lovers / Hey let it rock / Cat and the rat, The / 93's OK J / Song for me, A.
LP: . . . . SEE 240
LP: . . . . RSLP 9001

WILDEBEEST.
LP: . . . . PGLP 002

Family Brown

FAVOURITES.
Tracks: / You're the light / Lovin' fool / I'm available / Family love / Stay with me / Amazing grace / Juke box lover / Love was on our side / Heaven's just a sin away / Feeling's too strong / How great thou art / Poor mans crown.
LP: . . . . PL 10360

NOTHING REALLY CHANGES.
Tracks: / Sing a family song / Coat of many colours / Family circle / Nothing really changes / Momma was a fighter / Careless hands / But its cheating / It's really love this time / Ribbon of gold / One day at a time / Another broken hearted melody / Antique / Sing a song of love / Old rugged cross.
LP: . . . . RCALP 5021

Family Fodder

ALL STYLES.
Tracks: / Disarm completely / Winter song / Malfunction / Ectasy harmony / Falling in love again / Mack the Knife / Windmills of your mind.
2LP: . . . . FREUD 02

GREATEST HITS: FAMILY FODDER.
LP: . . . . CRAM 016

MONKEY BANANA KITCHEN.
LP: . . . . FRESH LP 3

Family Love

STAY WITH ME (see under Redrose ,Anthony).

TEAZER (see under Redrose, Anthony).

Family Ness (tv)

FAMILY NESS: ELSPETH & ANGUS BUY A PUPPY.
MC: . . . . TTS 9841

FAMILY NESS: ELSPETH & ANGUS MEET THE NESSIES.
MC: . . . . TTS 9842

FAMILY NESS: ELSPETH & ANGUS MEET THE PROFESSOR.
MC: . . . . TTS 9843

FAMILY NESS, (THE) (Various artists).
Tracks: / Angus and Elspeth meet the Loch Ness monster: *Various artists* / Angus and Elspeth buy a puppy: *Various artists* / Speedy-ness saves the day: *Various artists* / Ferocious-ness loses his roar: *Various artists* / Clever-ness helps with the homework: *Various artists* / Professor Dumkopf gets stuck in a bubble: *Various artists*/ Ferocious-ness and the look-alike contest: *Various artists* / Professor Dumkopf and his amazing cannonball: *Various artists* / Baby-ness and the Mayor's statue: *Various artists* / Clever-ness and the curling championship: *Various artists*.
LP: . . . . REC 530
MC: . . . . ZCM 530

FAMILY NESS: THE NESSIES HELP WITH HOMEWORK.
MC: . . . . TTS 9844

Family Stand

CHAIN.
Tracks: / Ghetto heaven / Only / Ovasaxed / Last temptation, The / Avenue lust / Twisted / In Summer I fall / Sweet liberation / Chain / Little white, little black lies.
LP: . . . . WX 349
MC: . . . . WX 349 C

Famous...

FAMOUS FAIRY TALES (Reid, Beryl (nar)).
MC: . . . . P 90031

FAMOUS FIVE Various Artists.
LP: . . . . STMP 28

Famous Collection

FAMOUS COLLECTION VOL.1 (Les Paul Trio/ Carmen Cavallaro/ Spike Jones).
LP: . . . . VDL 1009

FAMOUS COLLECTION VOL.2 (Louis Jordan/ Benny Goodman/ Milt Herth).
LP: . . . . VDL 1010

Famous Five..

ALL RECORDINGS (see under Blyton, Enid (aut)).

Famous Jazz Singers

FAMOUS JAZZ SINGERS VOL.3 (See Under Jazz...) (Various artists).

FAMOUS JAZZ SINGERS VOL. 1 (See Under Jazz...) (Various artists).

FAMOUS JAZZ SINGERS VOL. 2 (See Under Jazz...) (Various artists).

Famous Overtures

FAMOUS OVERTURES Various artists (Various artists).
Tracks: / Egmont: *Various artists* / Fidelio: *Various artists* / Leonora: *Various artists* / William Tell: *Various artists* / Marriage of Figaro, The: *Various artists* / Die Fledermaus: *Various artists*/ Die meistersinger: *Various artists*.
MCSET: . . . . DTO 10030

Famous Potatoes

BORN IN A BARN.
LP: . . . . WF 046

IT WAS GOOD FOR MY OLD MA.
MC: . . . . WF 018 C
LP: . . . . WF 018

SOUND OF THE GROUND, THE.
LP: . . . . WF 028
MC: . . . . WF 028 C

Famous Rays

ENDING BEGINNING.
LP: . . . . MOULT 1

Famous Southern

MOVIN' ON (see under Lane, Steve) (Famous Southern Stompers/Steve Lane).

Fanchette, Sterge

RUSSIAN SONGS AND ROMANCES.
LP: . . . . SYS 110
MC: . . . . CSYS 110

Fancy

FANCIES AND GOODNIGHTS (Collier, J.) (Price, Vincent).
MC: . . . . CP 1652

Fane, Little Billy

FROM QUAY TO COAST.
LP: . . . . MWM SP 7
MC: . . . . MWM CSP 7

GEORDIE'S HEAR.
LP: . . . . MWM SP 6

Fang

MI GA SFAFAS A.
Tracks: / Blood pudding / You suck / Damaging dose / Puff the magic dragon / F.*.*.K Y.O.U. / Severed by war / Hitch a ride / House wrecking party / Fistfull of wicked women / Lolita.
LP: . . . . BITE 29

SPUN HELGA.
LP: . . . . WEBITE 17

Fania Allstars

AT YANKEE STADIUM.
LP: . . . . SLP 476

BAMBOLEO.
Tracks: / Bamboleo / Siento / Smooth operator / Quiero saber / Ljobi djoba / Don't you worry about a thing.
LP: . . . . HOT 119
MC: . . . . TCHOT 119

LIVE: FANIA ALLSTARS.
LP: . . . . SLP 00477

LO QUE PIDE LA GENTE.
LP: . . . . SLP 629

SALSA MADNESS (See Under Cruz, Celia) (Fania Allstars & Celia Cruz).

VIVA LA CHARANGA.
LP: . . . . JM 640

Fankhauser, Merrell

FAPARDOKLY.
LP: . . . . TOCK 3

MAUI ALBUM, THE.
LP: . . . . RECK 10

MESSAGE TO THE UNIVERSE.
LP: . . . . OBGLP 9002

THINGS (Frankhauser, Merrell).
Tracks: / Things / Girl / What does she see in you? / Lost in the city / Your painted lives / Drivin' sideways / In a minute not too soon / Visit with Ashiya / Big gray sky / Rich man's fable / Ice cube island / Madame Silky / I'm flying home.
LP: . . . . TSSLP 2

Fanshawe (Composer)

AFRICAN SANCTUS.
LP: 655 800-1

AFRICAN SANCTUS (Ambrosian Singers).
MC: 426055-4

Fantasia (Film)

FANTASIA (Original soundtrack) (Various artists).
Tracks: / Pastoral symphony (no.6 in F): *Various artists* / Rite of spring, The: *Various artists* / Dance of the hours: *Various artists* / Night on bald mountain: *Various artists* / Ave Maria: *Various artists* / Toccata and fugue in D minor: *Various artists* / Sorcerer's apprentice: *Various artists*.
2LP: . . . . D 104
MCSET: . . . . D 104 VC
2LP: . . . . REQ 537
MCSET: . . . . ZCQ 537

FANTASIA (1940 Film Soundtrack) (Various artists).
Tracks: / Toccata and fugue in D minor: *Various artists* / Sorcerer's apprentice, The: *Various artists* / Nutcracker suite (part 1): *Various artists* / Nutcracker suite (part 2): *Various artists* / Night on a bare mountain: *Various artists* / Ave Maria: *Various artists*.
MC: 4178514

Fantasist (film)

FANTASIST, THE (1987 film soundtrack) (Various artists).
Tracks: / More passionate than we are: *Various artists* / Up on the roof: *Quinn, Paul* (Performed by: Paul Quinn) / Another day comes another day goes: *Dee, Kiki* / Living in a world turned upside down: *Private Lives* (Performed by: Private Lives) / I'll do it all again: *Heffernen, Honor* (Performed by: Honor Heffernan) / Fantasist, The: *Various artists* / Temple of Venus: *Various artists* / Childhood story: *Various artists* / Clocks: *Various artists*/ Rooftops: *Various artists* / Discovery: *Various artists*.
LP: . . . . PTLS 1085

Fantastic Baggys

SURFIN' CRAZE.
Tracks: / Tell 'em I'm surfin' / Surfin' craze / Let's make the most of summer / Anywhere the girls are / Big gun board / Alone on the beach / Debbie be true / This little woodie surfin' craze / When surfers rule / Surfer boy's dream come true / It was I / Wax up your board / Summer means fun / Surfin's back again / Surf impersonations.
LP: . . . . ED 118

Fantastic Four

GOT TO HAVE YOUR LOVE.
Tracks: / She'll be right for me / Mixed up moods and attitudes / There's no fire down below / Ain't been good to you / Cash money / I got to have all the love you got.
LP: . . . . K 50415

Fantastic Mr.Fox

FANTASTIC MR. FOX (see Dahl, Roald) (Dahl, Roald (aut)).

Fantastic Something

FANTASTIC SOMETHING.
Tracks: / Night we flew out of the window, The / Melancholy bay / Drawing rooms / Picking up little adventures / Angels took over the train, The / Sleeping in your white valleys / Perfect Napoleon / Garden city / In houses by the port / Hurt kingdoms.
LP: . . . . BYN 4
MC: . . . . BYNC 4

Fantastic Violinaires

SING WITH THE ANGELS (See under Blair, Robert) (Fantastic Violinaires/ Robert Blair).

TALK TO JESUS.
LP: . . . . MAL 04389

Fantasticks (show)

FANTASTICKS (1960 Original Broadway cast) (Various artists).

Tracks: / Try to remember: *Various artists* / Much much more: *Various artists* / Metaphor: *Various artists*/ Never say no: *Various artists* / It depends on what you pay: *Various artists* / You wonder how these things begin: *Various artists* / Soon It's gonna rain: *Various artists* / Rape ballet, The: *Various artists* / Happy ending: *Various artists* / This plum is too ripe: *Various artists* / I can see it: *Various artists* / Plant a radish: *Various artists* / Round and round: *Various artists* / There is a curious paradox: *Various artists* / They were you: *Various artists* / Try to remember (Reprise): *Various artists*.
LP: . . . . TER 1099
MC: . . . . ZCTER 1099

Faoi Lan Tseoil

NA HANCAIRI.
MC: . . . . GTDC 022

Far Corporation

DIVISION ONE.
Tracks: / Stairway to heaven / You are the woman / One of your lovers / Live inside your dreams / Johnny don't go the distance / Fire and water / If you could see you through my eyes / Rock 'n' roll connection.
LP: 207390
MC: 407390

Far From The..(bk)

FAR FROM THE MADDING CROWD (see Hardy, Thomas) (Thorne, Stephen).

Far pavillions (tv)

FAR PAVILIONS (TV Soundtrack) (Various artists).
Tracks: / Branding, The: *Various artists* / Making of an officer, The: *Various artists* / Prayer: *Various* artists / Belinda's waltz: *Various artists* / Journey to the north: *Various artists* / Fight in pass: *Various* artists / Wedding procession: *Various artists* / Evening ride: *Various artists* / Cave scene: *Various* artists / Sunset procession: *Various artists* / Bhithor: *Various artists* / Farewell my own: *Various* artists / Mission to Kabul: *Various artists* / Wally laid to rest: *Various artists* / Death of Rana - Rescue: *Various artists* / Two souls into one: *Various artists* / Sunset vow and end title: *Various artists*.
LP: . . . . CDL 1464
MC: . . . . ZCDL 1464

Farafina

BOLOMAKOTE.
LP: . . . . VBR 20261

Farah, Ardeshir

GUITARRAS (See under Strunz, Jorge).

Faraway Stars

UNDER THE SUN.
LP: . . . . RUN 1002

Farber, Mitch

STARCLIMBER.
Tracks: / Starclimber / Lonely promises / Chooser, The / Sky dance / Monuments / Time line.
LP: . . . . MR 5276

Fardon, Don

INDIAN RESERVATION.
Tracks: / Indian reservation / Gimme gimme good lovin' / Letter, The / Treat her right / I'm alive / Follow your drum / Delta queen / Running bear / Belfast boy / Take a heart / Lola / It's been nice loving you / Hudson Bay / On the beach / Tobacco Road / California maiden / Coming on strong / Mr. Station Master / Miami sunset / Riverboat.
LP: . . . . GNPS 2044
LP: C5-540

Fardon, Lee

GOD GIVEN RIGHT, THE.
Tracks: / God given right / She rains / Dreaming still / Turn out the light / Window display.
LP: . . . . AUL 720

SAVAGE ART OF LOVE, THE.
LP: . . . . CHORD 007

STORIES OF ADVENTURE.
Tracks: / Fast at 17 / Strange kinda love / Don't wanna be me / I mean it this time / Sleepwalking / I don't know how to touch you anymore / Mystery lover.
LP: . . . . AUL 713

Farenholtz, Peter

RAGTIME SOLO.
LP: . . . . WAM/N No.2

Farewell To Arms

FAREWELL TO ARMS (Original soundtrack) (Various artists).
LP: . . . . AUSLP 1014

Farewell To..(film)

FAREWELL TO THE KING (1989 Film Soundtrack) (Poledouris,Basil).
LP: . . . . A 375
MC: . . . . C 375

Fargo, Donna

QUEENS OF COUNTRY (see under Parton, Dolly) (Fargo, Donna/Dolly Parton).

SHAME ON ME.
Tracks: / Shame on me / Ragamuffin man / Loving you / Happy together / Do I love you / Gone at last / That was yesterday / Dee dee / Time / Kirksville, Missouri / Race is on, The.
LP: . . . . K 56442

Fargo, Wells

WHO'S BUYING.
LP: . . . . BSS 352

Farina, Mimi

SOLO.
LP: . . . . PH 1102
MC: . . . . PH 1102C

Farina, Richard

BEST OF MIMI & RICHARD FARINA (Farina, Richard & Mimi).
LP: . . . . VNP 6402

Farka, Ali

ALI FARKA TOURE.
Tracks: / Timbarma / Singya / Nawiye / Bakoytereye / Kadi kadi / Yulli / Bakoye / Amandrai.
LP: . . . . WCB 007
MC: . . . . WCC 007

Farley, Carole

CAROLE FARLEY SINGS PROKOFIEV (see under Prokofiev) (Farley, Carole/ Roger Vignoles).

FRENCH SONGS VOL 1 (Farley, Carole/Orchestre Symph.d.l.RTBF/ Ensemble d.Bruxelles).
Tracks: / Chanson Perpetuelle (Chausson) / Cinq melodies (Duparc) / Quatre melodies (Satie) / Bonne Chanson (Faure) (Song cycle).
LP: . . . . DCA 605
MC: . . . . ZC DCA 605

JOSE SEREBRIER, VOL 1.
LP: . . . . DCA 612
MC: . . . . ZC DCA 612

Farlow, Tal

AUTUMN IN NEW YORK.
Tracks: / Strike up the band / Have you met Miss Jones? / Cherokee / Autumn in New York.
LP: 2304 321

CHROMATIC PALETTE.
LP: . . . . CJ 154

COOKIN' ON ALL BURNERS.
Tracks: / You'd be so nice to come home to / If I should lose you / I've got the world on a string / Love letters / Lullaby of the leaves / I thought about you / I wished on the moon / Why shouldn't I? / Just friends.
LP: . . . . CJ 204

LEGENDARY TAL FARLOW, THE.
Tracks: / You stepped out of a dream / When your lover has gone / I got it bad and that ain't good / When lights are low / Who cares? / I can't get started / Prelude to a kiss / Everything happens to me.
LP: . . . . CJ 266

ON STAGE (Farlow/Norvo/Jones/ Brown/Hanna).
LP: . . . . CJ 143

RED NORVO TRIO (Farlow, Tal & Charles Mingus).
Tracks: / Swedish pastry / Take 1 / I can't believe you're in love with me / Time and tide / Those little white lies / Prelude to a kiss / Move / Godchild take 2 / September song / This can't be love (take 1) / I'm yours / I get a kick out of you / Zing went the strings of my heart / Cheek to cheek / Night and day / Godchild / Mood indigo / This can't be love (take 2) / If I had you / Deed I do / I'll remember April / This can't be love (master) / I've got you under my skin / Have you met Miss Jones.
LP: . . . . SJL 2212

RETURN OF TAL FARLOW, THE.
Tracks: / Straight No Chaser / Darn That Dream / Summertime / Sometime Ago / I'll Remember April / My Romance / Crazy she calls it.
LP: . . . . PR 7732
MC: . . . . PRC 7732

SWINGING GUITAR OF TAL FARLOW, THE.
Tracks: / Taking a chance on love / Yardbird suite / You stepped out of a dream / They can't take that away from me / Like someone in love / Meteor / I love you.
LP: 2304 211

Farlowe, Chris

14 THINGS TO THINK ABOUT.
LP: . . . . IMLP 005

ART OF CHRIS FARLOWE, THE.
LP: . . . . IMLP 006

BORN AGAIN (Farlowe, Chris/ Thunderbirds).
Tracks: / Into the night / Starting all over again / Lonely eyes / One night stand / Ain't got no money / I'm yours / I've been born again / Living ain't easy without you / Never too old / End of the line / I stayed away too long.
LP: . . . . BNLP 001
MC: . . . . BNLPC 001
LP: . . . . PHZA 028
MC: . . . . PHZC 028

BUZZ WITH THE FUZZ (Farlowe, Chris/ Thunderbirds).
Tracks: / Reelin' and rockin' / Voodoo / I remember / Push push / Itty bitty pieces / Girl trouble / Just a dream / What you gonna do / Hound dog / Hey hey hey / Buzz with the fuzz / You're the one / They call it stormy Monday (part 1) / They call it stormy Monday (part 2).
LP: . . . . LIK 16

CHRIS FARLOWE & THE THUNDERBIRDS (Farlowe, Chris/ Thunderbirds).
Tracks: / They call it stormy Monday (part 1) / Reelin' and rockin' / Just a dream / Hey hey hey / Hound dog / They call it stormy Monday (part 2) / What you gonna do? / I remember / Itty bitty pieces / Girl trouble / Puss puss / Voodoo.
LP: . . . . CR 30021

GREATEST HITS: CHRIS FARLOWE.
Tracks: / Satisfaction / Ride on, baby / What becomes of the broken hearted? / Fool, The / Think / Handbags and gladrags / Paint it black / Yesterday's papers / In the midnight hour / Reach out I'll be there / Moaning / Out of time.
LP: . . . . IML 2002

MR.SOULFUL.
Tracks: / Think / It was easier to hurt her / Fool, The / I'm free / Handbags and gladrags / In the midnight hour / I've been lovin' you too long / Reach out I'll be there / Mr. Pitiful / Paint it black.
LP: . . . . SHLP 156
MC: . . . . SHTC 156

OUT OF THE BLUE.
Tracks: / I ain't superstitious / Gambler's blues / Them that's got (I ain't got nothin' yet) / Ain't no love in the heart of the city / It's all wrong / Key to my kingdom / Thrill is gone, The / Watch your step / All the way lover / Standing on shakey ground.
LP: . . . . THBL 024
LP: 825 543-1

OUT OF TIME.
LP: . . . . IML 1002

OUT OF TIME - PAINT IT BLACK.
LP: . . . . CR 30020

Farm

INTERVIEW.
LP: . . . . OTM 002

PASTURES OLD AND NEW.
LP: . . . . REFIRELP 3

SINFUL (2) (See Under Wylie, Pete) (Farm & Pete Wylie).

SPARTACUS.
MC: . . . . MILKMC 1
LP: . . . . MILKLP 1

Farmer, Art

ART FARMER QUINTET (Farmer, Art Quintet).
LP: . . . . OJC 241

ART FARMER SEPTET (Farmer, Art Septet).
LP: . . . . OJC 054

ARTWORKER.
LP: . . . . ORL 8293

BIG BLUES (Farmer, Art & Jim Hall).
Tracks: / Whisper not / Child is born, A / Big blues / Pavane for a dead princess.
LP: . . . . CTI 7083

CRAWL SPACE.
LP: . . . . CTI 9008

ELOQUENT.
Tracks: / Cascavelo / Day after / Con fab / Gap sealer / Cocodrilo / Whole tone stomp.
LP: 5C 064 61176

FOOLISH.
Tracks: / Larry's delight / Al-leu-cha / D's dilemma / In a sentimental mood / Foolish memories / Farmer's market.
LP: . . . . LR 45008

INTERACTION (Farmer, Art, Quartet, featuring Jim Hall).
Tracks: / Days of wine and roses / By myself / My little suede shoes / Embraceable you / My kinda love / Sometime ago.
LP: . . . . K 50728

MANHATTAN (Farmer, Art Quintet).
LP: . . . . SN 1026

MEET THE JAZZTET (Farmer, Art & Benny Golson).
Tracks: / Serenata / It ain't necessarily so / Avalon / I remember Clifford / Blues march / It's alright with me / Park Avenue petite / Mox Nix / Easy living / Killer Joe.
LP: . . . . GCH 8092
MC: . . . . GCHK 78092

ON THE ROAD.
Tracks: / Downwind / My funny valentine / Namely you / What am I here for / I can't get started / Will you still be mine.
LP: . . . . COP 009

PORTRAIT OF ART FARMER.
Tracks: / Back in the cage / Stablemates / Very thought of you, The / And now.... / Nita / By myself / Too late noe / Earth.
LP: . . . . COP 029
LP: . . . . COP 029
LP: . . . . S 7554

SING ME SOFTLY OF THE BLUES (Farmer, Art Quartet).
Tracks: / Sing me softly of the blues / A.D. infinitum / Petite belle / Tears / I waited for you / Ore for Majid.
LP: . . . . K 50725

SLEEPING BEE, THE.
LP: . . . . SNTF 715
MC: . . . . ZCSN 715

SOMETHING YOU GOT.
LP: . . . . CTI 9016

TWO TRUMPETS (Farmer, Art & Donald Byrd).
LP: . . . . OJC 018

WARM VALLEY.
Tracks: / Moose the mooche / And now there's you / Three little words / Eclipso / Sad to say / Upper Manhattan medical group / Warm valley.
LP: . . . . CJ 212
MC: . . . . CJC 212

WHEN FARMER MET GRYCE (Farmer, Art & Gigi Gryce).
Tracks: / Night at Tony's, A / Blue concept / Stupendous - lee / Deltitnu / Capri / Blue lights / Infant's song / Social call.
LP: . . . . OJC 072

WORK OF ART, A.
Tracks: / She's funny that way / Love walked in / Change partners / Red cross / You know I care.
LP: . . . . CJ 179

YAMA (Farmer, Art/Joe Henderson).
LP: . . . . CTI 9019

Farmer, Mylene

AINSI SOIT JE.
MC: 835 564 4
LP: 835 564 1

Farmer's Boys

GET OUT AND WALK.
Tracks: / Matter of fact / Probably one of the best investments... / More than a dream / Woke up this morning / Way you made me cry / Promise you can't keep / Soft drink / Wailing wall / For you / Torn in two / Who needs it.
LP: . . . . EMC 1077991

WITH THESE HANDS.
Tracks: / In the country / I built the world / Sport for all / Art gallery / Something from nothing / Phew wow / All of a sudden / Heartache / Walkabout / Whatever is he like.
LP: . . . . FBLP 2
MC: . . . . TC FBLP 2

Farmstead

SHEEP AND THE HAY, THE.
Tracks: / Sheep and the hay, The / Chickens in the garden / Three airs / Lord George / Western breeze / Three peaks, The / Sleeping lion / Huntsman's chorus, The / Line o'er the fell, The / Turning of the year / Morris jig / Roving fiddler, The / Song of the Yorkshire Dales.
LP: . . . . FE 005

Farner, Mark

JUST ANOTHER INJUSTICE.
LP: . . . . RO 9033
MC: . . . . CO 9033

MARK FARNER.
Tracks: / Dear Miss Lucy / Street fight / Easy breezes / Social disaster / He let me love / You and me baby / Second chance to dance / Lorraine / Lady luck / Ban the man.
LP: . . . . K 50419

Farnham, Allen

FIFTH HOUSE.
Tracks: / Fifth house / It's not always where you think it is / You stepped out of a dream / You know I care / Speak no evil / Colin (Only on CD.) / Now he sings, now he sobs / Despair / Hadd bone (Only on CD.) / Pine Hollow Road.

MC: . . . . CJ 413 C

Farnham, John

AGE OF REASON.
Tracks: / Age of reason / Blow by blow / Listen to the wind / Two strong hearts / Burn down the night / Beyond the call / We're no angels / Don't tell me it can't be done / Fire / Some do, some don't / When the war is over (CD only) / It's a long way to the top if you wanna... (CD only).
LP: . . . . **PL 71839**
MC: . . . . **PK 71839**

CHAIN REACTION.
Tracks: / That's freedom / In days to come / Burn for you / See the banners fall / I can do anything / All our sons and daughters / Chain reaction / In your hands / New day / Time has come, The / First step / Time and money.
MC: . . . . **PK 74768**
LP: . . . . **PL 74768**

UNCOVERED.
Tracks: / Matilda / She says to me / Jillie's song / Infatuation / On my own / Back to the backwoods / I never did get through / Please don't ask me / She's everywhere / Help.
MC: . . . . **NK 74742**

WHISPERING JACK.
Tracks: / Pressure down / You're the voice / One step away / Reasons / Going, going, gone / No one comes close / Love to shine / Trouble / Touch of paradise / Let me out.
LP: . . . . **PL 71224**
MC: . . . . **PK 71224**

Farnon, Robert

AT THE MOVIES (Farnon, Robert & his Orchestra).
Tracks: / Moment I saw you, The / Early one morning / Best things in life are free, The / Wouldn't it be loverly / How beautiful is night / You're the cream in my coffee / Pictures in the fire / I guess I'll have to change my plan / Great day / When I fall in love / Melody fair / Just imagine / Lady Barbara / Trolley song, The / Way we were, The / Sunny side up.
LP: . . . . **SIV 1111**
MC: . . . . **CSIV 1111**

MELODY FAIR.
Tracks: / Journey into melody / Tangerine / Jumping bean / Nearness of you, The / Dancing in the dark / Very thought of you, The / Melody fair / Moonlight becomes you / Love walked in / British grenadiers, The / Portrait of a flirt / Georgia on my mind / Reflections in the water / Secret love / Can I forget you / Where or when / My foolish heart / You're the cream in my coffee / You and the night and the music / Comin' thro' the rye / My love is like a red red rose.
LP: . . . . **PLE 526**

Farouz, Rita

BREAKING THOSE WALLS.
Tracks: / Breaking those walls / Moment of truth / Making life / Game, The / Slave of time / Slowdown / Mirror of love / Roxanne / Last of the great pretenders / Rain, The.
LP: **6.26432**
MC: **4.26432**

Farr Bros.

TEXAS CRAPSHOOTER.
LP: . . . . **JEMF 107**

Farr, Gary

DEM BONES.
LP: . . . . **EVA 12041**

LONDON 1964-1965 (Farr, Gary & The T-Bones).
Tracks: / How many more times / I'm a lover not a fighter / Dearest darling / You don't love me / Quit teasing me baby / Louisiana red / Oh baby, baby / C.C. rider / Get the money / Yes I do, I feel alright.
LP: . . . . **CR 30015**

ONE MORE CHANCE (Farr, Gary & The T-Bones).
Tracks: / I'm a lover not a fighter / Won't you give him one more chance / Get the money / Indeed I do / Louisiana red / You don't love me / Quit teasing me baby / Oh baby baby / Feel alright / C.C. rider / Dearest darling / How many more times / Hamish's express relief / Give all she's got / Don't stop & stare / Jump back / Got love if you want it.
LP: . . . . **LIK 11**

Farr, Jimmy

BEST BY FARR (Farr, Jimmy & His Orchestra).
LP: . . . . **CLP 26**

Farr, Richard

FARR COUNTRY.
Tracks: / Let the rest of the World go by / Della and the dealer / Tonight / Bottle let me down, The / It's four in the morning / Lucille / My way of life / Walk on by / Buck's polka / Guilty / How can I write on paper what I feel in my heart / Your my best friend / Send me the pillow that you dream on / Take these chains from my heart / Jealous heart / Someday you'll want me to want you.
LP: . . . . **KLP 25**
MC: . . . . **ZCKLP 25**

Farrar, John

HANK MARVIN AND JOHN FARRAR (see under Marvin, Hank) (Farrar, John & Hank Marvin).

JOHN FARRAR.
Tracks: / Reckless / Tell someone who cares / Can't hold back / Gettin' loose / Cheatin' his heart out again / Recovery / It'll be me babe / Falling / From the heart.
LP: . . . . **CBS 84324**

Farrell, Al

LIVE IN KANSAS CITY (Farrell, Al & Crescent City Statement).
MC: . . . . **STC 1001**

Farrell & Farrell

MANIFESTO.
LP: . . . . **SR R 2074**

Farrell, Robert

THIS IS MY COUNTRY (Farrell, Robert & Ringing World).
LP: . . . . **RW 1**

Farrell, Timothy

MUSIC FROM THE ROYAL WEDDINGS.
Tracks: / Wedding march / Minuet from 'Berenice' / Bridal march / Trumpet tune and air / Air from 'The water music' / Furique a la cigue / Toccata in F / First movement from Concerto in F major / Jesu joy of man's desire / Radetsky march / Toccata from Symphony No. 9.
LP: . . . . **ETMP 14**

Farren, Mick

MONA.
LP: . . . . **PSYCHO 20**

Farriers

BRUMMAGEM BALLADS (Farriers/ Kempion).
Tracks: / I can't find Brummagem / New navigation, The / Tom King / Opening of Birmingham & Liverpool Railway / Norton new bell wake / Birmingham On Sea / Birmingham Jack of all trades / Scot and Granby / Birmingham omnibus, The / Humphrey Hardfeature's description of cast iron inventions / Cockney's trip to Brummagem, The / When Birmingham is a seaport town / Slap bum tailor, The / Rigs of Birmingham, The / Armourer's widow, The.
LP: . . . . **BRO 119**
MC: . . . . **KBRO 119**

Farris, Rev. Lonnie

REV. LONNIE FARRIS 1962.
LP: . . . . **ELE 3-200**

Farrow, Gene

MOVE YOUR BODY.
MC: . . . . **TCMAGL 5024**

Farthest Shore

FARTHEST SHORE (see Le Guin, Ursula) (Hood, Morag).

Fascinating Aida

BUNCH OF OLD SEQUINS, A.
LP: . . . . **CAST 9**
MC: . . . . **CASTC 9**

SWEET F.A..
Tracks: / Herpes tango, The / Sloane Rangers / Saturday night / Time / My favourite tool / Moscow, Moscow / Sid / Song of the despairing sales assistant / Kay, why? / Jogging song / Bunker lullaby / Cheque book journalism.
LP: . . . . **REB 567**
MC: . . . . **ZCF 567**

Fashek, Majek

I AND I EXPERIENCE.
LP: . . . . **CBS N 1003**

PRISONER OF CONSCIENCE.
Tracks: / Send down the rain / Let righteousness cover the Earth / Genesis / Hey Mr. Morning / Prisoner of conscience / Redemption song / Afrikans keep your culture / I've got the feeling / Police brutality.
MC: . . . . **MCT 1030**
LP: . . . . **MLPS 1030**

Fashion

FABRIQUE.
Tracks: / Move on / Love shadow / Streetplayer / Dressed to kill / You only left your picture / Something in your picture / It's alright / White stuff / Do you wanna make love / Slow blue.
LP: . . . . **SPART 1185**
MC: . . . . **TCART 1185**

HEIGHT OF FASHION, THE.
Tracks: / Move on / Love shadow / Street player - mechanik / Dressed to kill / You only left your picture / Something in your picture / It's alright / White stuff / Do you wanna make love / Slow blue / Mutant love / Love shadow smokey dialogue / Street mechanik / Do you wanna make love (at 5.00 am) / You only left your picture (reggae reprise).
MC: **410626**

PRODUCT PERFECT.
LP: . . . . **FML 1**

TWILIGHT OF IDOLS.
Tracks: / Eye talk / Dreaming / Hit girl / Trader / You in the night / Delirious / Hurricane / Too much too soon / Slow down / Twilight of idols.
LP: . . . . **EPC 25909**

Fashion In Shrouds

FASHION IN SHROUDS, THE (See Under Radio Collection) (Various artists).

Fasoli, Claudio

LIDO.
LP: . . . . **SN 1071**

Fast Eddie

CHRISTMAS CLASSICS (See under Filthy Phil for details) (Fast Eddie & Filthy Phil).

JACK TO THE SOUND.
LP: . . . . **DJART 902**
MC: . . . . **ZCART 902**

MOST WANTED.
LP: **466 024 1**
MC: **466 024 4**

POCKETFUL OF BLUES.
LP: . . . . **NIXON 7**

Fast Forward (film)

FAST FORWARD (1984 film soundtrack) (Various artists).
LP: **925263 1**
MC: **925263 4**

Fast Product (label)

FAST PRODUCT - THE FIRST YEAR (Various artists).
Tracks: / Never been in a riot: *Various artists* / Heart and soul: *Various artists* / 32 weeks: *Various artists*/ Adultery: *Various artists* / Horror show: *Various artists* / Being boiled: *Various artists* / Circus of death: *Various artists* / All time low: *Various artists* / Where to now: *Various artists* / Love like anthrax: *Various artists* / Armalite rifle: *Various artists* / Damaged goods: *Various artists* / I'll have to dance then: *Various artists* / Where were you: *Various artists*.
LP: . . . . **EMC 3312**
MC: . . . . **TCEMC 3312**

Fastbacks

AND HIS ORCHESTRA.
LP: . . . . **SUBORG 008**

VERY VERY POWERFUL MOTOR.
LP: . . . . **BLATLP 1**

Faster Pussycat

FASTER PUSSYCAT.
Tracks: / Don't change that song / Bathroom wall / No room for emotion / Cathouse / Babylon / Smash alley / Shooting you down / City has no heart / Ship rolls in / Bottle in front of me.
LP: **9807301**
MC: **9807304**

FASTER PUSSYCAT: INTERVIEW PICTURE DISC.
LPPD: . . . . **BAK 2127**

WAKE ME UP WHEN IT'S OVER.
Tracks: / Where there's a whip there's a way / Crying shame / Little dove / House of pain / Pulling the weeds / Poison ivy / Gonna walk / Slip of the tongue / Tattoo / Ain't no way.
LP: . . . . **EKT 64**
MC: . . . . **EKT 64 C**

Fastest Bat

COLD HAILY WINDY NIGHT.
Tracks: / Corn rigs / Roll the woodpile / Shores of Old Blighty, The / Jim Jones / Leaking whippet (immortal at last) / "P" it stands for Paddy / Cold haily windy night / Brisk young widow / Standing down in New York / Jig (four poster bed).
LP: . . . . **HUMAN LP 2**

Fastest Guitar Alive

FASTEST GUITAR ALIVE, THE (1966 film soundtrack) (Various artists).
LP: . . . . **MCA 1437**
MC: . . . . **MCAC 1437**

FASTEST GUITAR ALIVE/YOUR CHEATIN' HEART (Film Soundtracks) (Various artists).
Tracks: / Whirlwind: *Various artists* (Fastest Guitar Alive.) / Medicine man: *Various artists* (Fastest Guitar Alive.) / River: *Various artists* (Fastest Guitar Alive.) / Fastest guitar alive, The: *Various artists* (Fastest Guitar Alive.) / Rollin' on: *Various artists* (Fastest Guitar Alive.) / Pistolero: *Various artists* (Fastest Guitar Alive.) / Good time party: *Various artists* (Fastest Guitar Alive.) / Heading South: *Various artists* (Fastest Guitar Alive.) / Best friend: *Various artists* (Fastest Guitar Alive.) / There won't be many coming home: *Various artists*(Fastest Guitar Alive.) / Your cheatin' heart: *Various artists* (Your Cheatin' Heart.) / Hey good lookin': *Various* artists (Your Cheatin' Heart.) / I saw light: *Various artists* (Your Cheatin' Heart.) / Jambalaya: *Various artists*(Your Cheatin' Heart.) / Ramblin' man: *Various artists* (Your Cheatin' Heart.) / I'm so lonesome I could cry: *Various* artists (Your Cheatin' Heart.) / Jambalaya: *Various artists* (Your Cheatin' Heart.) / Cold cold heart: *Various* artists (Your Cheatin' Heart.) / Kaw-liga: *Various artists* (Your Cheatin' Heart.) / I couldn't help it: *Various* artists (Your Cheatin' Heart.) / Hey good lookin': *Various artists* (Your Cheatin' Heart.) / Long gone lonesome blue: *Various artists* (Your Cheatin' Heart.) / You win again: *Various artists* (Your Cheatin' Heart.).
LP: . . . . **LPMGM 18**
LP: **794 274 1**
MC: . . . . **TCMGM 18**
MC: **794 274 4**

Fastway

ALL FIRED UP.
Tracks: / All fired up / Misunderstood / Steal the show / Station / Non stop love / Hurtin' me / Tell me / Hung up on love / Stranger / Telephone / If you could see me.
LP: . . . . **CBS 25958**

BAD BAD GIRLS.
Tracks: / I've had enough (Only on CD.) / Bad bad girls / All shook up / Bod rock / Miles away / She won't rock (Only on CD.) / No repair / Death of me / Cut loose / Lucky to lose / Big beat no heart.
MC: . . . . **LLK 130**
LP: . . . . **LLP 130**

FASTWAY.
Tracks: / Easy livin' / Feel me touch me / All I need is your love / Another day / Heft / We become one / Give it all you got / Say what you will / You got me runnin' / Give it some action.
LP: **25359**

ON TARGET.
LP: . . . . **GWLP 22**
MC: . . . . **GWTC 22**
LP: . . . . **RR 9562 1**

TRICK OR TREAT (See under 'Trick Or Treat').

WORLD WAITS FOR YOU, THE.
Tracks: / Waiting for the roar / Girl / Back door man / Doin' just fine / World waits for you, The / Kill me with your heart / Tired of your love / Change / Move over / Little by little / Rock on.
LP: . . . . **CBS 26654**
MC: **40 26654**

Fat Boys

BIG AND BEAUTIFUL.
Tracks: / Sex machine / Go for it / Breakdown / Double-O Fat Boys / Big and beautiful / Rapp symphony (In C minor) / Beatbox part 3 / In the house / Beatbox is rockin'.
LP: **253077 1**
MC: **253077 4**

COMING BACK HARD AGAIN.
LP: . . . . **URBLP 13**
MC: . . . . **URBMC 13**

CRUSHIN'.
Tracks: / Crushin' / Protect yourself / Rock ruling / Making noise / Boys will be boys / Falling in love / Fat Boys dance / Wipe out / Between the sheets / Hell, no.
LP: . . . . **URBLP 3**
MC: . . . . **URBMC 3**

FAT BOY'S.
LP: **251987 1**
MC: **251987 4**

FAT BOYS ARE BACK, THE.
Tracks: / Fat Boys are back, The / Don't be stupid / Human beatbox part II / Yes, yes, y'all / Hard core reggae / Pump it up / Fat Boys scratch / Rock and roll.
LP: **252368 1**
MC: **252368 4**

FAT BOYS: INTERVIEW PICTURE DISC.
LPPD: . . . . **BAK 2117**

KRUSH ON YOU.
Tracks: / Sex machine / Jailhouse rap / Human beatbox / Fat Boys scratch / Fat Boys / Human beatbox part II / Beat box part III / Hard core reggae / In the house / Fat Boys are back, The / Big and beautiful / Can you feel it? / Pump it up / Don't you dog me / Don't be stupid / Chillin' with the refrigerator.
2LP: . . . . **BLATLP 8**

MC: . . . . BLATMC 8

ON AND ON.
LP: 838 867 1
MC: 838 867 4

Fat & Frantic

AGGRESSIVE SUNBATHING.
LP: . . . . FATLP 2
MC: . . . . TCFATLP 2

BIG HATS AND SMALL HEADS.
MC: . . . . FILBY 2

LIVE AT THE WONKY DONKEY.
MC: . . . . FATC 6

QUIRK.
Tracks: / Too late / Last night my wife hoovered my head / Rise up / Who's your friend Eddy? / I don't want to say goodbye / Africa / It's you / If I could be your milkman / Aggressive sunbathing / Senator's daughter / I'm sorry / I wish / Darling Doris / River, A.
LP: . . . . FATLP 7
MC: . . . . FATMC 7
LP: 5018524 01101
MC: 5018524 01104

WAXING A HOTTIE.
MC: . . . . TCFATLP 1

Fat Lady Sings

TWIST.
LP: . . . . WX 418
MC: . . . . WXMC 418

Fat Larry's Band

BEST OF FAT LARRY'S BAND - BRIGHT CITY LIGHTS.
Tracks: / Centre city / Fascination / We just can't get it together / Boogie town / Looking for love / Close encounters of a funky kind / Last chance to dance / Hey Pancho, it's disco.
LP: . . . . FT 564

BREAKIN' OUT.
Tracks: / Act like you know / Traffic stoppers / Zoom / House party / Breakin' out / Be my lady / Golden moment / Video.
LP: . . . . OVED 64
MC: . . . . OVEDC 64
LP: . . . . V 2229

FEEL IT.
Tracks: / Feel it / Nightime boogie / Down on the avenue / Music makers / Center city / Fascination / Life of an entertainer / We just want to play for you.
LP: . . . . K 50330

NICE.
LP: . . . . OMN LP 1

STAND UP.
Tracks: / Party after midnight / Can't keep my hands to myself / Play with me / Stand up / You've waited too long / Dirty words / You gotta help yourself.
LP: . . . . F 9699

STRAIGHT FROM THE HEART.
Tracks: / Straight from the heart / Imagination / Stubborn kind of fellow / Always / Kilowatt / Tune me up / In my song / Don't let it go to your head / Hitman.
LP: . . . . V 2289
MC: . . . . TCV 2289

Fat Man Ridim Section

KING OF LOVE.
LP: . . . . CSLP 0013

Fatal Attraction

FATAL ATTRACTION (Original Soundtrack) (Various artists).
Tracks: / Fatal attraction: *Various artists* / Following Dan: *Various artists* / Madness: *Various artists*/ Where is Ellen?: *Various artists* / Beth: *Various artists* / Confrontation: *Various artists*.
LP: . . . . GNPS 8011
MC: GNP5 8011

FATAL ATTRACTION (film soundtrack) (Various artists).
Tracks: / Fatal attraction: *Various artists* / Following Dan: *Various artists* / Madness: *Various artists*/ Where is Ellen: *Various artists* / Beth: *Various artists* / Confrontation: *Various artists*.
LP: . . . . PYL 6035
MC: . . . . PYM 6035

Fatal Beauty (film)

FATAL BEAUTY (1988 Film Soundtrack) (Various artists).
Tracks: / Make it my heart: *Allen, Donna* / Just that type of girl: *Madam X* / Casanova: *Levert* / Edge of love: *Howard, Miki* / Criminal: *Shannon* / Red hot: *Gibson, Debbie* / Didn't I blow your mind: *System*/ Sin city: *War*.
LP: . . . . K 781 809 1
MC: . . . . K 781 809 4

Fatal Charm

ENDANGERED SPECIES.
LP: . . . . CAL 218

THIS STRANGE ATTRACTION.
LP: . . . . FATAL 001

Fatal Eggs (play)

FATAL EGGS, THE/HARRIS AND THE MARE (Dramatised by Arthur Samuels).
MC: . . . . NF 5

Fatal Flowers

FATAL FLOWERS.
Tracks: / Billy / Crying over sin / Midnight train / Rip off / Fatal flower / We thought they loved you.
LP: 240700 1

YOUNGER DAYS.
Tracks: / Deep inside / Good enough / Ballroom / Nowhere to lay my head / Younger days / Well baby / Gimme some truth / Blackspot / For Christ's sake / Here's your song.
LP: 242045 1
MC: 242045 4

Fatala

FATALA.
Tracks: / Timini / Maane / Seoroba / Limbadji Toko / Soisisa / Yekeke / Gongoma times / Boke (n'yaraloum-ma) / Sohko.
LP: . . . . WOMAD 011
MC: . . . . WOMCAS 11

Fatback (Band)

14 KARAT.
Tracks: / Lets do it again / Angel / Backstrokin' / Concrete jungle / Without your love / Gotta get my hands on some (money) / Your love is strange / Lady groove / Chillin' out.
LP: 2391 493

BEST OF THE FATBACK BAND.
Tracks: / Spanish hustle / Yum, yum / Wicky wacky / Party time / Put your love / Trompin' / (Are you ready) do the bus stop / Keep on stepping / Disco crazy / Boogie with Fatback / Night fever.
LP: 2391 246

BRIGHT LIGHTS, BIG CITY.
Tracks: / Freak the freak the funk / Let me do it to you / Big city / Boogie woogie / Hesitation / Wild dreams.
LP: 239 138 7

FATBACK BAND "LIVE".
LP: . . . . STL 12
MC: . . . . STC 12

GREATEST HITS: FATBACK.
Tracks: / Wicky wacky / Bus stop / Is this the future / I found lovin' / Backstrokin'.
LP: . . . . TANLP 4
MC: . . . . ZCTAN 4

GREATEST, THE.
LP: . . . . CHELP 1
MC: . . . . ZCHE 1

IS THIS THE FUTURE?.
Tracks: / Is this the future? / Double love affair / Spread love / Funky aerobics (Body movement) / Up against the wall / Finger lickin' good / Sunshine lady / Girl is fine.
LP: . . . . POLD 5108

KEEP ON STEPPIN'.
Tracks: / Mister bass man / Stuff / New York style / Love / Can't stop the flame / Wicky wacky / Feeling / Keep on stepping / Breaking up with someone you love is hard to do.
LP: . . . . SEW 001
MC: . . . . SEWC 001

MAN WITH THE BAND.
LP: . . . . SEW 036

NIGHT FEVER.
Tracks: / Night fever / Little funky dance, A / If that's the way you want it / Joint (you and me), The / Disco crazy / Booty, The / No more room on the dancefloor / December 1963 (oh what a night).
LP: . . . . SEW 008
MC: . . . . SEWC 008

NYCNYUSA.
LP: . . . . SEW 030
MC: . . . . SEWC 030

ON THE FLOOR.
LP: . . . . SP 16736

PHOENIX.
Tracks: / Drum song / I love you so / Jump up baby jump up / Big brother / You've got that magic / Call out my name / Lover man / Just be my love.
LP: 7901681

RAISING HELL.
LP: . . . . SEW 028
MC: . . . . SEWC 028
LP: 2391203

SO DELICIOUS.
Tracks: / Girls on my mind / Go out with a bang / Lover under cover / Sequence 96 / Let's play tonight / She's a go-getter / So delicious / Evil.
LP: 790253 1
MC: 790253 4

TASTY JAM.
Tracks: / Take it any way you want it / Wanna dance / Keep your fingers out of the jam / Kool whip / High steppin' lady / Get ready for the night.
LP: 2391 512

TONITE'S ALL NIGHT PARTY.
LP: . . . . STL 16
MC: . . . . STC 16

WITH LOVE.
Tracks: / He's a freak undercover / Rastajam / I love your body language / I found lovin' / I wanna be your lover / Please stay.
LP: . . . . SEW 024
MC: . . . . REWC 024

YUM YUM.
Tracks: / Yum yum (gimme some) / Trompin' / Let the drums speak / Put the funk on you / Feed me your love / (When you wanna boogie) boogie with Fatback / Got to learn how to dance / If you could turn into me / (Hey) I feel real good.
LP: . . . . SEW 016
MC: . . . . SEWC 016

Fate

CRUISING FOR A BRUISING.
Tracks: / Beneath da' coconuts / Love on the rox / Knock on wood / Lovers / Dead boy, cold meat / Babe, you got a friend / Lock you up / Cupid shot me / Diamond in the rough / Send a little money.
LP: . . . . EMC 3550
MC: . . . . TCEMC 3550

MATTER OF ATTITUDE, A.
Tracks: / Won't stop / Hard as a rock / I can't stand losing you / Point of no return / Hunter, The / Summer love / Farrah / Get up and go / Limbo a go go / Do it.
LP: . . . . EMC 3537
MC: . . . . TCEMC 3537

Fates

FURIA.
LP: . . . . HAG 1

Fates Warning

AWAKEN THE GUARDIAN.
Tracks: / Sorceress / Valley of the dolls / Fata Morgana / Guardian / Prelude to ruin / Giants love / Time long past / Exodus.
LP: . . . . RR 9660

NIGHT ON BROCKEN.
LP: . . . . RR 9823 1

NO EXIT.
LP: . . . . RR 95581

SPECTRE WITHIN, THE.
LP: . . . . RR 9737

Fathead

BAD BOY SKANKING (see Yellowman).

DIVORCED (see Yellowman) (Fathead/ Yellowman).

Father Abraham

FATHER ABRAHAM IN SMURFLAND.
LP: . . . . SMURF 1

Father Brown..

FATHER BROWN (See Under Radio Collection) (Various artists).

MORE FATHER BROWN STORIES (Hawthorne, Nigel (nar)).
MCSET: . . . . ARGO 1268

SCANDAL OF FATHER BROWN, THE (G.K. Chesterton).
MCSET: . . . . CAT 4027

THREE FATHER BROWN STORIES (G.K Chesterton) (Hawthorne, Nigel (nar)).
MCSET: . . . . ARGO 1007

Father Is Away ...

FATHER IS AWAY ON A BUSINESS TRIP (1987 film soundtrack) (Various artists).
LP: . . . . A 279

Father M.C.

FATHER'S DAY.
LP: . . . . MCA 10061
MC: . . . . MCAC 10061

Father & Son (tv)

FATHER AND SON (VATER UND SOHNE) (Original soundtrack) (Various artists).
LP: . . . . ACH 013

Father Xmas & Tuffty

READ, LISTEN & LEARN.
MC: . . . . BBM LB 4

Fathers & Daughters

CHERISH THE LADIES ARTISTS.
LP: . . . . SHAN 79054

Fathers & Sons

FATHERS AND SONS.
Tracks: / Twelve's it / Joy forever / Nostalgic / Impressions / Futuristic / Lush life / Jug ain't gone / Time marches on / I can't get started / Tribute to our fathers.
LP: . . . . CBS 85786

SOUL STIRRERS (Soul Stirrers and the Original Blind Boys).
LP: . . . . SF 1001

Fatima Mansions

AGAINST NATURE.
LP: . . . . KWLP 11

VIVA DEAD PONIES.
LP: . . . . RAR 10242
MC: . . . . RARC 10242

Fatool, Nick

SPRING OF '87 (Fatool, Nick Jazzband).
LP: . . . . J 158

Fat's Garden

BURIED IN EDEN.
LP: . . . . TWI 896

Fats, Happy

CAJUN & COUNTRY SONGS (Fats, Happy & Alex Broussard).
LP: 6005

FAIS DO DO BREAKDOWN (See under Sonnier, Lee) (Fats, Happy & Lee Sonnier).

Fattburger

ONE OF A KIND.
Tracks: / 59th Street Bridge Song / Park Lane / Yum yum / Auto bahn / Fattburger / One of a kind / I knew that.
LP: . . . . GBJ 2001

TIME WILL TELL.
Tracks: / Who put the meat in my bed / Oh girl / Amazon / For the father / Monica / Time will tell / Any two can play / Golden girl / Flirtin' / Back to Jersey.
LP: . . . . INTM 73503
LP: 773 503 1

Faubert, Shane

KALKARA.
Tracks: / I wanna hide / It's not enough (for Nick) / Unknown sky of blue / (East) Now I know (West) / Will you be there tomorrow / I'll be waiting / Lifeline / Into the wind / Take your time / Just a girl / Home / Flow my tears.
LP: . . . . MMLP 029

Faulkner, John

KIND PROVIDENCE.
LP: . . . . SIF 1064
MC: . . . . CSIF 1064

Faure (Composer)

FAURE VIOLIN CONCERTO (Orquesta Filarmonica de la Ciudad de Mexico).
Tracks: / Violin concerto (Faure) (Allegro only; work not completed. This is the world premiere recording.) / Berceuse (Faure) / Elegie (Faure) / Masques et bergamasques overture (Faure) / Shylock nocturne (Faure) / Pelleas et Melisande suite (Faure).
LP: . . . . DCA 686
MC: . . . . ZC DCA 686

VIOLIN SONATAS (FAURE/DEBUSSY/ FRANCK) (Various artists).
MC: 4218174

Faure, Mike

VOICE OF THE WIND.
MC: . . . . ZPREC 794

Faust

FAUST.
LP: . . . . RR 1

MUNICH AND ELSEWHERE.
LP: . . . . RR 25

ONE.
LP: . . . . RRA 1

SO FAR.
LP: . . . . RR 2
LP: . . . . RRA 2

Faux, George

TIME FOR A LAUGH AND A SONG.
LP: . . . . HAR 006
MC: . . . . HARC 006

Faverin, Julian Jay

WAITERS ON THE DANCE.
Tracks: / Child of the evening (I & II) / Stranger and death of aida / Dance of the golden flamingos / Lylle / Soldiers of time.
LP: . . . . TOCK 2

Favourite...

FAVOURITE FAIRY STORIES Various artists.
Tracks: / Pied piper / Puss 'n' boots / Cinderella / Snow White.
LP: . . . . SPR 8520
MC: . . . . SPC 8520
MC: . . . . VCA 106

Favourite Classics

FAVOURITE CLASSICS (London Festival Orchestra).

MC: . . . . KH 88030

Favourite Encores ...

FAVOURITE ENCORES FOR STRING QUARTET (Delme string quartet).
MC: . . . . KH 88038

Favourite Hymns

FAVOURITE HYMNS (See Under Hymns...) (Various artists).

Favourite Rupert...

FAVOURITE RUPERT STORIES (See under Ruper Bear (bk)) (Bennett, Judy (nar)).

Favourites of the...

FAVOURITES OF THE PHILHARMONIC: VOL 2 Various orchestras (Various Orchestras).
Tracks: / Fidelio overture opus 72b / Midsummer nights dream overture opus 21 / Ruy blas overture opus 95 / Night on the bare mountain / Marche from 'le coq d'or / Turkish march from 'the ruins of Athens' / Prelude to Act III Lohengrin / Emperor waltz opus 437 / Perpetuum mobile / Champagne polka / Annen polka / Thunder and lightning polka / Danse macabre opus 40 / Prelude a l'apres midi d'un faune / Hungarian march / Marche joyeuse.
2LP: . . . . MFP 1036
MCSET: . . . . TCMFP 1036

Favre, Pierre

DRUM CONVERSATION.
LP: . . . . CAL 30 606

SINGLE DRUMS (Favre, Pierre Ensemble).
LP: . . . . ECM 1274

Favre, Pierre & Tamia

DE LA NUIT .... LE JOUR.
Tracks: / Ballade / Wood song / Maroua / De la nuit .... le jour / Mit sang und klang / Yemanja.
LP: . . . . ECM 1364

Fawcett & Kazakov

VIRTUOSISSIMI.
Tracks: / Thieving magpie overture / La cumparsita / Carnival of Venice / Dringo's serenade / Spic and span / Toccata and fugue in D minor / Ukranian folk variations / Russian comic dancing songs.
LP: . . . . CAM 200

Fawcett, Pearl

ACCORDION TAPESTRY.
Tracks: / Marriage of Figaro / Badinerie / William Tell / Minuet from Berenice / Hungarian dance no. 5 / Scherzetto / Dance of the comedians / Durand's first waltz / Allegro / Dance of the hours / Turkish march / Prelude.
LP: . . . . CA 100

MUSETTE PARISIENNE.
Tracks: / Caravelle / Piccolino polka / Le poussin / Tinarella / Douce souvenance / Perlina / Musette Parisienne / Clockwork polka / Letizia / Tippi / Silhouettes de Paris / Geraldine.
LP: . . . . CA 102

MUSIC ON THE MOVE.
Tracks: / Muzurka / Sleepy blues / Carnival of Venice / Boogie etc.
MC: . . . . CAC MM 1

Fawkes, Wally

HUMPHREY LYTTELTON & HIS BAND (See under Lyttelton, Humphrey) (Fawkes, Wally & Humphrey Lyttelton & His Band).

JUICY AND FULL TONED.
Tracks: / Sheik of Araby / Summertime / Monday date / Fishmouth / Exactly like you / That's what it's all about / Lullaby of the leaves / Bodgers blues / Polka dot rag / Mobile blues / Avalon / Lazy bones / Petite fleur / Baby Brown.
LP: . . . . LA 5012
MC: . . . . LA 5012C

OCTOBER SONG (Fawkes, Wally & Friends).
Tracks: / Avalon / Rent party blues / Lucky duck / Dallas blues / Viper mad.
LP: . . . . CLGLP 010

WALLY FAWKES AND THE RHYTHM KINGS (Fawkes, Wally & The Rhythm Kings).
LP: . . . . SOS 1060

WALLY FAWKES NEO-TROGLODYTES (Fawkes, Wally & The Neo-Troglodytes).
LP: . . . . DCS 33001

WHATEVER NEXT (Fawkes, Wally & Soho Shakers).
LP: . . . . SOS 1144

Fawlty Towers (tv)

FAWLTY TOWERS 1 (Various artists).
MCSET: . . . . ZBBC 1006

FAWLTY TOWERS 2 (Various artists).
MCSET: . . . . ZBBC 1015

FAWLTY TOWERS: A LA CARTE (Various artists).
LP: . . . . REB 484
MC: . . . . ZCF 484

FAWLTY TOWERS: AT YOUR SERVICE (Various artists).
LP: . . . . REB 449
MC: . . . . ZCF 449

FAWLTY TOWERS: EXTRACTS, VOL 1 (Various artists).
LP: . . . . REB 377
MC: . . . . ZCF 377

FAWLTY TOWERS: SECOND SITTING (Original cast) (Various artists).
LP: . . . . REB 405
MC: . . . . ZCF 405

Fax

FAX.
LP: . . . . BTEL 1

Faye, Alice

ALICE FAYE: ON THE AIR.
Tracks: / Hats off / Sittin' up, waiting for you / You're getting to be a habit with me / Gather lip rouge while you may / Weep no more / You've got everything / Dinah / Young and healthy / Ooh, I'm thinking / Man Harlem / My, oh my / Happy as the day is long / I've got the world on a string / You're an old smoothie / Shuffle off to buffalo.
LP: . . . . TOTEM 1011

ALICE FAYE: ON THE AIR: VOL 2.
Tracks: / Oh my / Honeymoon Hotel / How'm I doin' / You're gonna lose your gal / Sittin' up, waitin' for you / Shuffalo off to Buffalo / Foolin' with another woman's man / Nasty man / Key to my heart / I didn't know you'd get that way / According to the moonlight / Now it can be told / So help me.
LP: . . . . TOTEM 1032

ALICE FAYE & PHIL HARRIS (Two Complete Radio Broadcasts) (Faye, Alice & Phil Harris).
Tracks: / Volunteer firemen, The / Tonsilectomy, The.
LP: . . . . LP 101

ALICE FAYE & THE SONGS OF HARRY WARREN.
LP: . . . . CT 6004

ALL THE GANG'S HERE (Original soundtrack) (Faye, Alice/Miranda Goodman).
LP: . . . . CIF 3003

IN HOLLYWOOD.
Tracks: / Nasty man / Here's the key to my heart / Yes to you / According to the moonlight / Speaking confidentially / I've got my fingers crossed / I'm shooting high / Spreadin' rhythm around / Goodnight my love / This year's kisses / Slumming on Park Avenue / I've got my love to keep me warm / Never in a million years / It's swell of you / There's a lull in my life / Wake up and live.
LP: . . . . CBS 32316
MC: 40 32316
LP: . . . . ACL 3068

ON THE AIR 1933-84.
LP: . . . . SH 2020

THIS YEARS KISSES.
Tracks: / Oh I didn't know you'd get that way / I'm shooting high / One never knows, does one? / You can't have everything / You've got to eat your spinach, baby / Got my mind on music / It's swell of you / Now it can be told / He ain't got rhythm / You turned the tables on me / Never in a million years / Sing, baby, sing / Please pardon us, we're in love / I love to ride the horses on a merry-go-round / Danger, love at work / Whose baby are you / Slumming on Park Avenue / Who stole the jam? / When I'm with you / This year's kisses.
LP: . . . . CMS 001
MC: . . . . CMSC 001

Faye, Frances

CAUGHT IN THE ACT VOL. 2.
LP: . . . . GNPS 92

FRANCES FAYE - CAUGHT IN THE ACT.
LP: . . . . GNPS 41

I'M WILD AGAIN.
LP: . . . . FS 251

Faye, Glenda

FLATPICKIN' FAVORITES.
LP: . . . . FF 432

Fayte, Kevin

RIDIN' IN ROCKET (Fayte, Kevin & Rocket 8).
LP: . . . . NERD 024

Fazarro, Susan

FINE AND MELLOW (Fazarro, Susan & Richard Stoker).
Tracks: / Ain't misbehavin' / Bread and gravy / My house is small / Fine and mellow / Sophisticated lady / Deed I do / Heart and soul / What are you doing with the rest of your life / Cry me a river / It's alright with me / Good morning heartache / Nearness of you / Night and day.
LP: EAT1/81LP

Fazzini, Tom

NECK TO NECK.
LP: . . . . JOHN 21:18

Fean, Johnny

LAST BANDITS IN THE WORLD (See under Sudden, Nikki) (Fean, Johnny, Nikki Sudden, Simon Carmody).

Fear Is The Key (film)

FEAR IS THE KEY (Film Soundtrack) (Budd, Roy & His Orchestra).
Tracks: / Main theme / Car chase / Lousiana ferry / Hostage escapes / Bayou blues / Swamp / In search of the key / Breakout / Oil rig / From sea bed to surface.
LP: . . . . NSPL 18398

Fear Of Darkness

VIRGIN LAND, THE.
LP: . . . . EMLP 3

Fearing, Stephen

BLUE LINE.
LP: . . . . RUE LP 003
MC: . . . . RUE MC 003

Fearless Iranians From

DIE FOR ALLAH.
Tracks: / Die for Allah / Deathwish / What's the news / Life inside Iran / F.I.F.H. / Iranians on bikes / Simple Life / Chant / Ultraviolence / Inro.
LP: . . . . TAKE 1

Fearon, Phil

PHIL FEARON & GALAXY (Fearon, Phil & Galaxy.).
LP: . . . . ENCL 2

THIS KIND OF LOVE (Fearon, Phil & Galaxy.).
LP: . . . . ENCL 4

Feast Of...

FEAST OF TRADITIONAL MUSIC & SONG, VOL.2 (Various artists).
MC: . . . . GTDC 034

Feather

CHEN YOU LIPS.
Tracks: / Gaviota / On Green Dolphin Street / Gee I missed you today / Morning / Beautiful / Mulega day / Out of the night / Chen you lips / Follow your road.
LP: . . . . DS 867

GOIN' THROUGH CHANGES.
LP: . . . . DS 821

ZANZIBAR.
Tracks: / Zanzibar / Joy spring / It's all we do / Passe / High butterfly / Alicia / Nica's dream / My desiree / Cascade of the seven waterfalls.
LP: . . . . DS 903

Feather, Leonard

LEONARD FEATHER PRESENTS.
LP: . . . . VSOP 12

PRESENTS 'JAZZ FROM 2 SIDES'.
LP: . . . . VL 5

Feather, Lorraine

SWEET LORRAINE.
LP: . . . . CJ 78

Feathers, Charlie

ALL TORE UP.
Tracks: / Bottle to the baby / I can't hardly stand it / One hand loose / Everybody's lovin' my baby / Dinky John / South of Chicago / Corina, Corina / Defrost your heart / Running around / I've been deceived / Wild of side, The / Don't you know / Where's she at tonight.
LP: . . . . Z 2008

HONKY TONK MAN.
LP: . . . . ROSE 144

JUNGLE FEVER.
LP: . . . . KAY 5045

LEGENDARY 1956 DEMO SESSION, THE.
Tracks: / Bottle to the baby / So ashamed / Frankie and Johnny / Honky tonk kind / Frankie and Johnny (take 5) / So ashamed (take 4) / Honky tonk kind (take 4 and false starts) / Bottle to the baby (take 2).
LP: . . . . ZZ 1001

LIVING LEGEND, THE.
LP: . . . . REDITA 107

NEW JUNGLE FEVER.
LP: . . . . ROSE 117

ROCKABILLY'S MAIN MAN.
Tracks: / Peepin' eyes / I've been deceived / Defrost your heart / Wedding gown of white / Mad at you / I forgot to remember to forget / Uh huh honey / Mound of clay / Send me the pillow that you dream on / Tongue tied Jill / Gone gone gone / Two to choose.
LP: . . . . CR 30161

WILD WILD PARTY.
LP: . . . . RSRLP 1014

Federal Music Society

COME AND TRIP IT (Hyman, Dick & Schwarz, Gerard & Their Orchestra's).
Tracks: / Prima donna waltz / Jenny Lind polka / Minuet and gavotte / Country fiddle music / Natilie polka-mazurka / Flying cloud / Victoria gallop / Flirt polka, The / La sonnambula / Eliza Jane McCue / Blaze-away / Hiawatha / Sweet man.
LP: . . . . NW 293

Federal Sampler

FEDERAL SAMPLER / KING (See under King / Federal Sampler) (Various artists).

Federal State

N: EURO.
LP: 081115

Federation of S.A.

SOUTH AFRICAN TRADE UNION WORKER CHOIRS (Members).
LP: . . . . ROUNDER 5020
MC: . . . . ROUNDER 5020C

Fedora (film)

FEDORA (1978 film soundtrack) (Various artists).
LP: . . . . STV 81108

Feds (film)

FEDS (1988 Film Soundtrack) (Edelman, Randy).
LP: . . . . UNKNOWN
MC: . . . . UNKNOWN

Feedback (Label)

FEEDBACK (Various artists).
LP: . . . . FEEDBACK 001

Feedtime

COOPER S.
LP: . . . . ROUGHUS 039

SUCTION.
LP: . . . . DYL 5

Feeley, John

CELTIC CLASSICS.
LP: . . . . KLP 235

Feelies

CRAZY RHYTHMS.
Tracks: / Boy with the perpetual nervousness / Fa ce-la / Loveless love / Forces at work / Original love / Everybody's got something to hide / Moscow nights / Raised eyebrows / Crazy rhythms.
LP: . . . . SEEZ 20
MC: . . . . ZSEEZ 20
LP: . . . . LILP 400168

GOOD EARTH, THE.
LP: . . . . ROUGH 104

ONLY LIFE.
Tracks: / Only life / Too much / Deep fascination / Higher ground / Undertow, The / For a while / Final world, The / Too far gone / Away / What goes on.
LP: . . . . AMA 5214
MC: . . . . AMC 5214
LP: 7502 15214 1

Feezey, John

JOHN FEEZEY.
LP: . . . . CEF 109

Feidman, Giora

MAGIC OF THE KLEZMER, THE (Feidman, Giora & The Feidman Ensemble).
LP: . . . . DCD 4005

Feinstein, Michael

ISN'T IT ROMANTIC.
Tracks: / Isn't it romantic / Where do you start / Fine romance, A / I can dream, can't I / You're an education / My favourite year / No other love / I wanna be loved / How about you / I'll get by / Wasn't it romantic / I'll be seeing you.
LP: . . . . K 9607921
MC: . . . . K 9607924

MGM ALBUM, THE.
LP: 9608931
MC: 9608934

OVER THERE.
Tracks: / Over there / Oh how I hate to get up in the morning / Would you rather be a Colonel with an eagle on your shoulder / Good morning, Mr Zip-Zip-Zip / Good-bye Broadway, hello France / Keep the home fires burning / Sister Susie's sewing shirts for soldiers / Just a baby's prayer at twilight / It's a long way to Tipperary / Roses of Picardy / How'ya gonna keep 'em down on the farm / I want to hear a Yankee doodle tune /

When day is done / Two hearts swing in three-quarter time / Yours in my heart alone / Vienna, my city of dreams / Gigolette / Galatea / Advice to young girls / To each his own / Sufficient lover / Each time I see a maiden fair / Rider's song / Parting song / Beautiful child.
MC: . . . . **EG 763 282 4**

SINGS IRVING BERLIN.
Tracks: / Let me sing and I'm happy / Change partners / Puttin' on the Ritz / When the midnight choo choo leaves for Alabam / Better luck next time / I'm putting all my eggs in one basket / What chance have I with love / Looking at you (across the breakfast table) / Just one way to say I love you / Let's have another cup of coffee / I say it's spinach and the hell with it / Say it isn't so / Alexander's ragtime band.
LP: . . . . **K 9607441**
MC: . . . . **K 9607444**

Felder, Don

AIRBORNE.
Tracks: / Bad girls / Winners / Haywire / Who tonight / Never surrender / Asphalt jungle, The / Night owl / Still alive.
LP: **960 295-1**
MC: **960 295-4**

Felder, Wilton

GENTLE FIRE.
Tracks: / Gentle fire / Driftin' on a dream / Only for those who care / I got to feel like you do / Summer nights in Rio / Somewhere in my past.
LP: . . . . **MCF 3167**
MC: . . . . **MCFC 3167**

INHERIT THE WIND.
LP: . . . . **MCG 4013**

INHERIT THE WIND (OLD GOLD) (See under Crusaders (Streetlife)).

SECRETS (featuring Bobby Womack/ Alltrinna Grayson).
Tracks: / Secrets / (No matter how high I get) I'll still be looking / La luz / Truth song, The / I found you.
LP: . . . . **MCF 3237**
MC: . . . . **MCFC 3237**

WE ALL HAVE A STAR.
Tracks: / We all have a star / I know who I am / Why believe / Cycles of time, The / Let's dance together / My name is love / You and me and ecstasy.
LP: . . . . **MCL 1652**
MC: . . . . **MCLC 1652**

Feldman, Victor

BIG BANDS, VOL 2 (Ninetet and Quintet).
Tracks: / Blues in two modes / Jennie / One momentum / Karen / Woodwork / It ain't necessarily so / Short circuit.
LP: . . . . **JASM 2003**

IN LONDON VOL.1.
Tracks: / Jackpot / Karen / You are too beautiful / You are my heart's delight / Minor and the major / Toff / Wilbert's tune.
LP: . . . . **JASM 2023**

ROCKAVIBABE.
Tracks: / Rockavibabe / Your smile / Quietly / I love Lucy / Brazilian fire / Minor catastrophe / Crazy chicken / Seven steps to heaven.
LP: . . . . **DJF 20491**

SECRET OF THE ANDES.
LP: . . . . **PA 8053**

SUITE SIXTEEN.
Tracks: / Ca baletto / Elegy / Suite sixteen / Sonar / Big top / Duffle coat / Brawl for all / Sunshine on a dull day / Maenya.
LP: . . . . **COP 038**

THOU SWELL (see Deucher, Jimmy) (Feldman, Victor/Jimmy Deucher/Alan Clare/Tony Kinsey).

TO CHOPIN WITH LOVE (Feldman, Victor Trio).
LP: . . . . **PA 8056**

TRANSATLANTIC ALLIANCE.
Tracks: / Four / Gipsy, The / Get up / Stomp / Wail / Together / Darn that dream / I surrender, dear / I've lost your love / Wailing wall.
LP: . . . . **JASM 2002**

VIC FELDMAN (Feldman, Vic and Mallets A Fore Thought).
LP: . . . . **VSOP 13**

YOUNG VIC, THE (Studio Recordings, Vol. 1).
Tracks: / Mop mop / Ladybird / Quaternity / Moonlight in Vermont / Gone with the wind / Ego / Jolly Rogers / Evening in Paris / Kashmir / Pakistan / Harem scarem / Monkey business / Serenade in blue / For you alone / Body and soul.
LP: . . . . **ESQ 327**

Feldman, Zev

ZEV FELDMAN & ANDY STATMAN (Feldman, Zev & Andy Statman).
LP: . . . . **SHAN 21002**

Felice, John

NOTHING PRETTY (Felice, John & The Lowdowns).
Tracks: / Don't be telling me / Ain't we having fun / I'll never sing that song again / Not the one / Perfect love / Nowadaze kids / Nothing pretty / Dreams / Don't make me wait / Can't play it safe.
LP: . . . . **ROSE 141**

Feliciano, Jose

10 TO 23.
Tracks: / Amor jibaro / First of May / Windmills of your mind, The / By the time I get to Phoenix / Miss Otis regrets / Little red rooster / She's a woman / Lady Madonna / Rain / Gotta get a message to you / Hey Jude.
LP: . . . . **SF 7946**
MC: . . . . **VCS 67236**

ALIVE, ALIVE O.
Tracks: / Hi heel sneakers / Rain / Malaguena / El jinete / Nobody knows you when you're down and out / Maracangalha / Eve of destruction / Menuet in G / Saved by the bell / Old rivers / Tip toe through the tulips / Guantanamera / No dogs allowed / Mama don't allow it / Don't let the sun catch you crying / Day tripper / Day in the life, A / Felicidade / Samba de Orfeu / Manha de carnaval / California dreamin' / Light my fire / La entrada de bilboa (Battle of Entrada).
2LP: **26 28007**
2LP: . . . . **SF 8084**

BAG FULL OF SOUL, A.
LP: **26 21193**

BEST OF JOSE FELICIANO.
Tracks: / Light my fire / California dreamin' / And the sun will shine / Windmills of your mind / Miss Otis regrets / Rain / First of May / Guantanamera / Che sara / Destiny / Suzie Q / High heel sneakers / Cico and the man, Theme from / Hitchcock railway / Malaguena / No dogs allowed.
LP: . . . . **NL 89561**
MC: . . . . **NK 89561**

BY DESIGN (See under Schuur, Diane) (Feliciano, Jose & Diane Schuur).

ENCORE - JOSE FELICIANO'S FINEST PERFORMANCES.
Tracks: / Hi heel sneakers / Rain / Pegao / Susie Q / Wichita lineman / California dreamin' / Hitchcock railway / Destiny / Nature boy / Malaguena / Life is that way / Light my fire.
LP: . . . . **SF 8188**
LP: **2C 21119**

ESCENAS DE AMOR.
Tracks: / Samba pa ti / Aranjuez mon amour / Volvere alguna vez / No I lay sombra que me cubra (the only woman) / Malas costumbres / La balada del pianista / Para decir adios / Todo el mundo te ama (everybody loves me) / Y I loy se que volvere (I'm coming home again) / Ahora si quiero amar (I wanna be where you are).
LP: . . . . **STML 12176**
MC: . . . . **CSTML 12176**

FANTASTIC FELICIANO.
LP: . . . . **NL 43867**

FELICIANO.
Tracks: / California dreamin' / Light my fire / Don't let the sun catch you crying / In my life / Nena, Nana / There's always something there to remind me / Just a little bit of rain / Sunny / Here, there and everywhere / Last thing on my mind / And I love her.
LP: . . . . **NL 89845**
MC: . . . . **NK 89845**
LP: . . . . **SF 8044**

FIREWORKS.
LP: . . . . **SF 8124**

I'M NEVER GONNA CHANGE.
Tracks: / Never gonna change / Vienna nights / Love is not a war / Into the night / Ibiza / Heart don't change my mind / Puerto Rican feeling / Cielito lindo / Through whatever / Living in a world.
LP: . . . . **SCX 6718**
MC: . . . . **TCSCX 6718**

JOSE FELICIANO.
Tracks: / I wanna be where you are / I second that emotion / Ain't that peculiar / Let's make love over the telephone / Everybody loves me / Free me from my freedom / Find yourself / Drought is over, The.
LP: . . . . **STML 12161**
MC: . . . . **CSTML 12161**

LIGHT MY FIRE.
LP: **26 21116**

LIGHT MY FIRE (The Best Of...).
Tracks: / Light my fire / Sunny / California dreamin' / You're no good / Norwegian wood / Always something to remind me / Hey Jude / Yesterday / Don't let the sun catch you crying / Don't think twice it's alright / Here, there and everywhere / Nature boy / Day in a life, A / Masters of war / Let it be.
MC: . . . . **KAZ MC 20**

LOS EXITOS DE.
Tracks: / Volvere alguna vez / Eterno amor / Samba pa ti / Me enamore / Paso la vida pensando / Ay carino / Para decir adios / La balada del pianista / Todo bolvio a comenzar / Malas costumbres.
LP: . . . . **ZL 72296**
MC: . . . . **ZK 72296**

PORTRAIT: JOSE FELICIANO.
Tracks: / Light my fire / Nature boy / Don't let the sun catch you crying / Suzie Q / No dogs allowed / Destiny / And the sun will shine / Fire works / California dreamin' / Que sera / Norwegian wood / Windmills of your mind / Hitchcock railway / Rain / First of May / Duelin' banjo.
LP: . . . . **STAR 2256**
MC: . . . . **STAC 2256**

ROMANCE IN THE NIGHT.
Tracks: / Lonely teardrops / If you have a heart / Taking it all in stride / Let's find each other tonight / One night / So into you / Play me / I feel fine / I feel fine / Cuidado / Romance in the night.
LP: . . . . **STML 12185**
MC: . . . . **CSTML 12185**

SINGS AND PLAYS THE BEATLES.
Tracks: / Hey Jude / Norwegian wood / She came in through the bathroom window / Blackbird / Yesterday / Here, there and everywhere / Help / She's a woman / Let it be / Lady Madonna / In my life / And I love her / Day tripper / Day in the life, A.
LP: . . . . **NL 89715**
MC: . . . . **NK 89715**

SPANISH PORTRAIT, A.
LP: . . . . **NL 89347**
MC: . . . . **NK 89347**

STEPPIN' OUT.
Tracks: / Everyday / Steppin' out / Tenderly / Burnin' / Lovers' vows / Softly, as I leave you / Somewhere over the rainbow / Descarga / I carnival / Slipping away.
LP: **2600 714 9**
MC: **4600 714 9**

Feline Groove

FELINE GROOVE.
LP: . . . . **RAZM 48**

Feline, Regine

AFRIK MISIK.
LP: . . . . **TSHI 004**

Felix, Julie

BLOWIN' IN THE WIND.
LP: . . . . **DID 714**

CHANGES.
LP: . . . . **TL 5368**

FOLK DOUBLE (Felix, Julie/Foggy Dew-O).
MCSET: . . . . **DTO 10257**

HOT CHOCOLATE.
LP: . . . . **GULP 1032**

Felix, Lennie

PIANO SOLOS.
LP: . . . . **88 UR 003**

Felling Male Voice

VOICES OF THE TYNE.
Tracks: / Battle hymn of the Republic / Balm in Gilead / What you gonna call yo pretty little baby / Don't let the river run dry / Sound an alarm / Kumbaya / Every time I feel the Spirit / Last words of David / Ol' ark's a-movering / Isle of Mull / One world / Turtle dove / Lord is my light, The / Calvary.
LP: . . . . **MWM 1028**

Fellow Travellers

NO EASY WAY.
LP: . . . . **OK 33010**
MC: . . . . **OK 33010MC**

Fellows, Susannah

IGGIE'S HOUSE (see under Iggie's House (bk)).

Felt

BUBBLEGUM PERFUME.
Tracks: / I will die with my head in flames / I didn't mean to hurt you / Autumn / There's no such thing as victory / Final resting place of the ark, The / Don't die on my doorstep / Book of swords / Gather up your wings and fly / Bitter end / Voyage to illumination / Stained glass windows / Space blues / Be still / Magellan / Sandmans on the rise again / Wave crashed on my doorstep / Declaration / Darkest ending, The / Rain of crystal spires / Ballad of the band.
LP: . . . . **CRELP 69**
MC: . . . . **CCRE 69**

CRUMBLING THE ANTISEPTIC BEAUTY.
Tracks: / Evergreen dazed / Fortune / Birdman / Cathedral / I worship the sun / Templeroy.
LP: . . . . **BRED 25**

FOREVER BREATHES THE LONELY WORD.
LP: . . . . **CRELP 011**

GOLDMINE TRASH.
Tracks: / Something sends me to sleep / Trails of colours dissolve / Dismantled king is off the throne / Penelope tree / Sunlight bathed the golden glow / Crystal ball / Day the rain came down, The / Fortune / Vasco da Gama / Primitive painters.
LP: . . . . **BRED 79**
MC: . . . . **CBRED 79**

IGNITE THE SEVEN CANNONS.
Tracks: / My darkest night will shine / Day the rain came down, The / Scarlet servants / I don't know which way to turn / Primitive painters / Textile ranch / Black ship in the harbour / Elegance of an only dream / Serpent shade / Caspian see / Southern state tapestry / Roman litter / Sempiternal darkness / Spanish house / Imprint / Sunlight bathed the golden glow / Vasco da Gama / Crucifix heaven / Dismantled King is off the throne / Crystal ball / Whirlpool vision of shame.
LP: . . . . **BRED 65**

LET THE SNAKES CRINKLE THEIR HEADS TO DEATH.
LP: . . . . **CRELP 009**

ME AND A MONKEY ON THE MOON.
Tracks: / Can't make love / Mobile shack / Free / Budgie jacket / Cartoon sky / New day dawning / August path / Never let you go / Hey sister / Get out of my mirror.
LP: . . . . **ACME 24**
MC: . . . . **ACME 24 C**

PICTORIAL JACKSON REVIEW.
LP: . . . . **CRELP 030**

POEM OF THE RIVER.
LP: . . . . **CRELP 017**

SPLENDOUR OF FEAR, THE.
Tracks: / Red Indians / World is soft as lace / Optimist and the poet / Mexican bandits / Stagnant pool / Preacher in New England.
LP: . . . . **BRED 57**
MC: . . . . **CBRED 57**
LP: . . . . **IMCA 1635**

STRANGE IDOLS PATTERN & OTHER SHORT STORIES.
Tracks: / Roman litter / Sempiternal darkness / Spanish house / Imprint / Sunlight bathed the golden glow / Vasco da Gama / Crucifix heaven / Dismantled king is off the throne / Crystal ball / Whirlpool vision of shame.
LP: . . . . **BRED 63**

TRAIN ABOVE THE CITY.
LP: . . . . **CRELP 035**

Felts, Narvel

NARVEL FELTS STORY.
LP: . . . . **SKYLINE 1880**

RADIO ROCKABILLIES (Felts, Narvel & Jerry Mercer).
LP: . . . . **RSRLP 1016**

TEEN'S WAY, A (Felts, Narvel & The Rockets).
Tracks: / I'm headin' home / Foolish thoughts / Cry, baby, cry / Vada Lou / Little girl step this way / Rocket ride / Why don't you love me / Remember me / Come back baby / Fool in Paradise, A / Lonely river / Kiss me baby / Your touch / Your first broken heart / Teen's way, A / Dream world / Lonesome feeling.
LP: . . . . **BFX 15242**

Femme Fatale

FEMME FATALE.
Tracks: / Waiting for the big one / Falling in and out of love / Back in your arms again / Rebel / Fortune / If / Touch and go / Heat the fire / Cradle's rockin'.
LP: . . . . **MCF 3433**
MC: . . . . **MCFC 3433**

Fender, Freddy

20 GREATEST HITS.
Tracks: / Before the next teardrop falls / Wasted days and wasted nights / You'll lose a good thing / Almost persuaded / She's about a mover / Lovin' cajun style / Man can cry, A / Crazy baby / I'm leaving it (all) up to you / Rains came, The / Wild side of life / Silver wings /

Enter my heart / What I'd say / Sweet summer day / Mathilda / Running back / Going out with the tide / Baby I want to love you / Girl who waits on tables.
LP: 20017
MC: 40017
MC: 2630014
LP: 2630011

BEFORE THE NEXT TEARDROP FALLS.
Tracks: / Before the next teardrop falls / Mathilda / Loving cajun style / What'd I say / Sweet Summer day / Silver wings / Running back / Enter my heart / Going out with the tide / Baby I want to love you.
LP: SDLP 1020

BEFORE THE NEXT TEARDROP FALLS (2).
Tracks: / Coming home soon / Just because / Mean woman blues / Something on your mind / Only one / Since I met you baby / Before the next teardrop falls / Wasted days and wasted nights / La Bamba / Ooh poo pah doo / Rains came, The / Wild side of life.
LP: TOP 170
MC: KTOP 170

BEST OF FREDDY FENDER.
Tracks: / Before the next teardrop falls / Wasted days and wasted nights / I can't put my arms / Wild side of life / Vaya con dios / Livin' it down / I love my Rancho Grande / We'll take our last walk tonight / Sugar coated love / Rains came, The / Matilda, Matilda / Don't do it darling / If you don't love me (why don't you just leave me alone) / You'll lose a thing / 50's medley.
LP: MCL 1809
MC: MCLC 1809

COUNTRY STORE: FREDDY FENDER.
MC: CSTK 47

CRAZY BABY.
Tracks: / Crazy baby / Wasted days and wasted nights / What's I say / Something on your mind / Loving cajun / Style / Mean woman / La bamba / Get out of my life woman / Only one / Coming home soon / Before the next teardrop falls / Since I met you baby / Wild side of life / Rains came, The / Mathilda / You'll loose a good thing / Just because / Black shirt / You made a fool / Coming 'round the mountain.
LP: SMT 012
MC: SMTC 012

EARLY YEARS 1959-1963.
Tracks: / I'm gonna leave / Wasted days & wasted nights / Mean woman / Crazy baby / Wild side of life / You're something else for me / Going out with the tide / San Antonio rock / Louisiana blues / Since I met you baby / Little mama / You told me you loved me / I can't remember when I didn't love you / Only one / Find somebody new / Roobie doobie.
LP: KK 7437

Fendermen

MULE SKINNER BLUES.
LP: MG 1240

Fenhoulet, Paul

STAIRWAY TO THE STARS (Fenhoulet, Paul & Skyrockets Dance Orchestra).
Tracks: / Stairway to the stars / Saturday night jump / No love no nothing / Heavy gang / I'll keep you in my heart / California sunbeam / October mood / My heart tells me / I get up every morning / Money is the root of all evil / Once upon a wintertime / It's alright / Guilty / Lullaby moderne / Rickety rickshaw man / I fall in love with you every day / Sooner or later / Bayswater bustle / Bow bells / Sentimental journey.
LP: SVL 161

Fenix Jazz Band

GRANDPA'S SPELLS.
LP: SOS 1129

Fennel Symphonic Winds

BROADWAY MARCHES.
LP: SRI 75115

Fennell, Frederick

MUSIC OF COLE PORTER (Fennell, Frederick & Eastman Rochester Orchestra).
Tracks: / Begin the beguine / I've got you under my skin / Night and day / Anything goes.
LP: SRI 75110

PLAY GERSHWIN (Fennell, Frederick & His Orchestra).
LP: SRI 75127

PLAY LEROY ANDERSON (Fennell, Frederick & His Orchestra).
Tracks: / Irish suite / Serenata / Sandpaper ballet / Forgotten dreams / Trumpeter's lullaby / Sleigh ride / Penny-whistle song / Bugler's holiday.
LP: SRI 75013

Fenner

FENNER.
MC: BBM LB 3

Fenton, George

HANDFUL OF DUST (Fenton, George/ Incantation).
LP: LPLTD 071
MC: MCLTD 071

LONG WALK HOME, THE (Film Soundtrack).
LP: VS 5304
MC: VSC 5304

Fenton, Shane

I'M A MOODY GUY (Fenton, Shane & The Fentones).
Tracks: / I'm a moody guy / Five foot two / Eyes of blue / Why little girl / It's all over now / It's gonna take magic / Cindy's birthday / Too young for sad memories / Fallen leaves on the ground / You're telling me / Walk away / Don't do that / I'll know / Fool's paradise, A / You need love / Somebody else not me / I ain't got nobody / Hey, Miss Ruby / Hey Lulu / I do do you / Breeze and I / Fool's paradise, A.
LP: CM 102
MC: CMK 102

Fents

OTHER SIDE.
LP: PC 88031
MC: PCC 88031

Fenwick, Ray

FORCEFIELD III (see under Bonnet, Graham) (Fenwick, Ray/Graham Bonnet/Cozy Powell/Jan Akkerman).

Ferber, Edna

SHOWBOAT & THE GAY OLD DOG.
MC: 1719

Ferbos, Lionel

JAZZ BAND BALL (Ferbos, Lionel and his New Orleans Serenaders).
Tracks: / Jazz band ball / Somewhere over the rainbow / Shake it and break it / Bogalusa strut / Pretty baby / Once in a while / Sobbin' blues / Let me call you sweetheart.
LP: LPS 18

Ferez, Earl

ARTISTRY IN HAMMOND.
Tracks: / I'll get by / It had to be you / Me and my shadow / Manhattan / Sleepy time girl / Song is ended, The / Lullaby of the leaves / Back in your own back yard / Five foot two, eyes of blue / How deep is the ocean / After you've gone / Blue skies / In a Spanish town / You wear my ring / I'll see you in my dreams / Moonlight and roses.
LP: PRX 3

Fergus, Winston

I WILL SING.
LP: JDP 002

Ferguson, Allyn

PICTURES AT AN EXHIBITION FRAMED IN JAZZ.
LP: DS 810

WITH THE CHAMBER JAZZ SEXTET (Ferguson, Allyn & Kenneth Patchen).
LP: DS 858

Ferguson, Craig

BIG STOATIR, A.
MC: 843 432 4
LP: 843 432 1

MENTAL...BING HITLER IS DEAD?.
Tracks: / Thor / Scandinavians / Turkey in the Eurovision song contest / Explorers / Philosophers and sex / Advertising and sex / Wrestling round 1 / Scotland hooch och aye / Wrestling round 2 / Meaningless songs / Compendium of games, The / Scary television / Bite.
LP: 837 643-1
MC: 837 643-4

Ferguson, Dave

SOMEWHERE OVER THE RAINBOW.
LP: BD 002

Ferguson, Horace

SINCE THE ADDICT.
Tracks: / Jah order / Great stone / Sensi addict / Tranquilizer / Gazuma / Slave / Tickle me / Hunts bay / Kic out / Bossman.
LP: UJLP 001

Ferguson, Jay

ALL ALONE IN THE END ZONE.
Tracks: / Snakes on the run / Turn it up / Medicated goo / Madam Doktor / All alone in the end zone / Cinnamon City / To the island / Hit and run / Everybody goes from here / Time and time again.
LP: K 53040

REAL LIFE AIN'T THIS WAY.
Tracks: / Shakedown cruise / No secrets / Real life ain't this way / Davey / Turn yourself in / Do it again / Paying time / Too late to save your heart / Let's spend the night together / Have you seen your mother, baby, standing in the shadow / Standing in the shadow / City of angels.
LP: K 53086

THUNDER ISLAND.
Tracks: / Soulin' / Happy birthday baby / Losing control / Cozumel / Nightshift / Babylon / Live is cold / Happy too / Magic moments.
LP: K 53066

Ferguson, Jennifer

HAND AROUND THE HEART.
LP: AM 1005

Ferguson, Max

WHERE DO WE GO FROM HERE?/ LAST VISIT.
MC: NF 2

Ferguson, Maynard

BEST OF MAYNARD FERGUSON.
Tracks: / Gonna fly now / McArthur Park / Star Trek / Birdland / Give it one / Stella by starlight / Battlestar Galactica / Pagliacci / Main title (theme from Star Wars) / Airegin.
LP: CBS 84200

BIG BOP NOUVEAU.
Tracks: / Blue birdland / Cherokee / Caught in a current / But beautiful / Cruisin' for a bluesin'.
LP: INTM 73390
LP: 773 390 1

BODY AND SOUL.
Tracks: / Expresso / Body and soul / M.O.T. / Mira Mira / Last dive / Beautiful hearts / Central Park.
LP: BKH 50101
MC: BKHMC 50101

CHAMELEON.
MC: 4670914

CONDUCTS THE BIRDLAND DREAMBAND VOL.1/2.
Tracks: / Wailing boat, (The) / Somebody wants me down there / Maynard the fox / Blue Birdland / Great guns / Lady bug / More west / Stillwater stomp / That Jones boy / Button nose / Little girl Kimbi / Straight up / Cervezita / Mogo / Sleep softly / Geller's cellar / Free Lee / Say it with trumpets / Everybody moan / Tell me funky / You said it / Early hours / Nightmare Alley.
2LP: PM 43841

HIGH VOLTAGE.
LP: ENVLP 517
MC: TCENV 517

HOLLYWOOD.
Tracks: / Don't stop till you get enough / Deja vu / Hollywood / Nine to five / For your eyes only / Here today / Portuguese love / Touch and go.
LP: CBS 85503

MAYNARD '61.
Tracks: / Ole / New blue / Blues for Kapp (AKA Coldwater Canyon blues) / Ultimate rejection / Pharaoh, The / Goodbye / Saturday night (is the loneliest night of the week) (CD only.) / This is my lucky day (CD only.) / Go East, young man (CD only.).
LP: ROU 1010
LP: 793 900 1

MAYNARD '62.
Tracks: / Have you met Miss Jones? / Maria / Zip'n'zap / Lazy afternoon / Go East young man / This my lucky day / 'X' stream / Four / Pretty little Nieda / 'Round about the blues.
LP: FS 364

MAYNARD FERGUSON AND HIS ORIGINAL DREAMBAND (Ferguson, Maynard & His Original Dreamband).
LP: AR 104

MESSAGE FROM BIRDLAND.
LP: FS 228

MESSAGE FROM NEWPORT, A (Ferguson, Maynard Orchestra).
Tracks: / Fugue, The / Fan it, Janet / Waltz, The / Tag team / And we listened / Slide's derangement / Frame for the blues / Humbug / Three little foxes.
LP: FS 104
LP: ROU 1004
LP: 793 272 1

NEWPORT SUITE.
LP: FS 94

SI SI M. F. (Ferguson, Maynard & His Orchestra).
Tracks: / What'll I do / Early hours / Morganpoint / Si si M.F. / Great guns / My sweetie went away she didn't say where when / Almost like being in love / Mimi / Morgan's organ / Born to be blue / Straight out / For the cats (CD only.) / Vignette (CD only.) / New bag blues (CD only.) / Easy chair (CD only.) / Animated suspension (CD only.).
LP: ROU 1025
LP: 795 334 1
LP: FS 84

STRAIGHT AWAY JAZZ THEMES.
Tracks: / Straightaway / Apprehension / Mambo la mans / Cocky Scott / Up shift / Last lap / Melancholia / Pit stop / Stroking / After the race.
LP: FS 365

SWINGING MY WAY THROUGH COLLEGE.
LP: FS 320

THREE KENTON'S BE BOPPERS GROUPS 1947-50 (Ferguson, Maynard / Vido Musso / Eddie Safranski).
LP: UJ 36

TRUMPETS OUT FRONT (Ferguson, Maynard & Herb Pomeroy).
Tracks: / Fugue / Fan it Janet / Waltz / Tag team / And we listened / Slide's derangement / Frame for the blues / Humbug / Three little foxes / Bluegrass / Wolafunt's lament / Jack Spratt / Aluminium baby / It's sandman / Our delight / Theme for Terry / No one will room with me / Feather merchant / Bit man / Less talk.
2LP: VJD 567
MCSET: ZCVJD 567

TWO'S COMPANY (Ferguson, Maynard/Conner, Chris).
LP: FS 93

Fermanagh Ceili Band

FERMANAGH CEILI BAND.
MC: COX 1030

Fermor, Patrick Leigh

BETWEEN THE WOODS AND THE WATERFRONT (Adamson, Raymond).
MC: IAB 88101

Fernandel

FELICIE AUSSI.
2LP: 2C 178 15408/09

Fernandez, Tony

ZODIAQUE (See under Wakeman, Rick) (Fernandez, Tony & Rick Wakeman).

Fernandez, Wilhelmenia

GERSHWIN SONGS.
Tracks: / Fascinating rhythm / I'll build a stairway to paradise / They all laughed / Man I love, The / 'S wonderful / By Strauss / Love is here to stay / Embraceable you / Someone to watch over me / Strike up the band / But not for me / Soon.
LP: A 215

NEGRO SPIRITUALS.
Tracks: / My lord what a mornin' / Oh what a beautiful city / His eye is on the sparrow / He's gone away / You can tell the world / Got the whole world in his hands / Ev'ry time i feel the spirit / Were you there / Witness / Sometimes i feel like a motherless child / Honor, honor / Ride on king jesus / Lords prayer.
LP: A 192

SINGS GEORGE GERSHWIN.
MC: C 215

Fernest & Thunders

FERNEST & THE THUNDERS.
LP: LP 5005

ZYDECO THUNDER.
LP: GB 1001

Ferns, Peter

STREETS OF BELFAST.
MC: ERON 029 CA

Ferrante & Teicher

TWIN PIANOS OF FERRANTE & TEICHER.
Tracks: / Misty / I'm in the mood for love / I left my heart in San Francisco / Autumn leaves / Love is blue / More / I've grown accustomed to her face / Charade / Wives and lovers / Godfather love theme / Moonlight in Vermont / Love is a many splendoured thing / I'll be seeing you / Days of wine and roses / My funny valentine / I could have danced all night / What kind of fool am I? / Till.
MC: EE 260 1444

Ferrara, Peter

KING KONG (see under Pickett, Bobby 'Boris') (Ferrara, Peter/Bobby Pickett).

Ferrars, Elizabeth

MARCH HARE MURDERS, THE (see under March Hare Murders (bk)) (Bron, Eleanor (nar)).

Ferrat, Jean

LA CHANSON FRANCAISE.
LP: 920493

Ferre, Boulou

TRINITY.
LP: SCS 1171

Ferrer, Jose

WOMAN (See Under Clooney, Rosemary - Man).

Ferrer, Violeta

FEDERICO GARCIA LORCA II.
Tracks: / Son de Negros en Cuba / Asesinato / Oda al rey de harlem / Oda a Walt Whitman / Omega / Hida de Nueva York / Cafe cantante / Romance somnambulo / Postal a Luis Bunuel / Luna y panorama de los insectos / Romance de la pena negra / Pequeno poema infinito / Romance de la luna / Luna / Cometa / LLuvia.
LP: .... **NATO 124**

POEMAS DE FEDERICO GARCIA LORCA.
Tracks: / Zorongo / Romance de la guardia civil Espaniola / Danza (en el huerto de la petenera) / Prendimiento de Antonio el Cambrio en el Camino de Sevilla / Muerte de Antonio el Cambrio / El grito / Reyerta / La guitarra / LLanto por Ignacio Sanchez Mejias / El Silencio.
LP: .... **NATO 7**

Ferret, Sarane

TRIBUTE TO DJANGO (Ferret, Sarane & Matelo).
LP: .... **FC 124**

Ferrier, Al

BOPPIN' TONIGHT (See under Storm, Warren) (Ferrier, Al/Warren Storm).

DIXIE.
LP: .... **LP 8708**

FROM 1955-1975 -THE SOUND OF ROCKABILLY.
LP: .... **SHOWTIME 1000**

LET'S GO BOPPIN' TONIGHT.
Tracks: / Blues stop knocking / She left me / Honey baby / I'm the man / Love me baby / Indian rock and roll / You win again / Hey baby / Send her back / Gunsmoke / Chrisholm trail rock.
LP: .... **FLY 597**

Ferrier, Kathleen

SINGER AND PERSON, THE.
LP: .... **REGL 368**
MC: .... **ZCF 368**

WORLD OF KATHLEEN FERRIER.
LP: .... **SPA 172**

WORLD OF KATHLEEN FERRIER (2).
Tracks: / Blow the wind southerly (Trad. arr. Whittaker.) / Keel row, The (Trad. arr. Whittaker.) / Ma bonny lad (Trad. arr. Whittaker.) / Go not happy day (Bridge, Tennyson) / Come you not from Newcastle (Trad. arr. Britten.) / Kitty my love (Trad. arr. Hughes.) / Art thou troubled? (Rodelinda) / Ombra mai fu (Handel) (Serse) / What is life? (Gluck) (Orfeo ed Euridice) / Woe unto them (Mendelssohn) (Elijah) / O rest in the Lord (Mendelssohn) (Elijah) / Have mercy, Lord, on me (St Matthew Passion) / Gretchen am Spinnrade (Schubert) / Die junge Nonne (Schubert) / An die musik / Der Musensohn (Shubert).
MC: **4300964**

Ferry Across The

FERRY ACROSS THE MERSEY (FILM SOUNDTRACK) (See under Gerry & The Pacemakers) (Gerry & the Pacemakers).

Ferry, Bryan

ANOTHER TIME, ANOTHER PLACE.
Tracks: / In crowd, The / Smoke gets in your eyes / Walk a mile in my shoes / Funny how time slips away / You are my sunshine / (What a) wonderful world / It ain't me babe / Finger poppin' / Help me make it through the night / Another time, another place.
LP: **2302 047**
MC: **3100 347**
LP: .... **EGLP 14**
MC: .... **EGMC 14**
LP: .... **ILPS 9284**

BETE NOIRE.
Tracks: / Limbo / Kiss and tell / New town / Day for night / Zamba / Right stuff, The / Seven deadly sins / Name of the game / Bete noire.
LP: .... **V 2474**
MC: .... **TCV 2474**

BOYS AND GIRLS.
Tracks: / Sensation / Slave to love / Don't stop the dance / Waste land, A / Windswept / Chosen one, The / Valentine / Stone woman / Boys and girls.
LP: .... **EGLP 62**
MC: .... **EGMC 62**

BRIDE STRIPPED BARE, THE.
Tracks: / Sign of the times / Can't let go / Hold on I'm coming / Same old blues / When she walks in the room / Take me to the river / What goes on / Carrickfergus / That's how strong my love is / This island Earth.
LP: .... **EGLP 36**
MC: .... **EGMC 36**
LP: .... **POLD 5003**
MC: .... **POLDC 5003**

BRYAN FERRY BOX SET (These Foolish Things/Let's Stick Together/ Boys.
MCSET: .... **EGBM 5**

BRYAN FERRY: INTERVIEW PICTURE DISC.
LPPD: .... **BAK 2036**

IN YOUR MIND.
Tracks: / This is tomorrow / All night operator / One kiss / Love me madly again / Tokyo Joe / Party doll / Rock of ages / In your mind.
LP: .... **EGLP 27**
MC: .... **EGMC 27**
LP: **2302 055**
MC: **3100 055**

LET'S STICK TOGETHER.
Tracks: / Let's stick together / Casanova / Sea breezes / Shame shame shame / 2HB / Price of love, The / Chance meeting / It's only love / You go to my head / Re-make/Re-model / Heart on my sleeve.
LP: .... **EGLP 24**
MC: .... **EGMC 24**
LP: **2302 045**
MC: **3100 345**
LP: .... **ILPSX 1**

STREET LIFE (Greatest Hits) (Ferry, Bryan & Roxy Music).
Tracks: / Virginia Plain / Hard rain's gonna fall / Pyjamarama / Do the Strand / These foolish things / Street life / Let's stick together / Smoke gets in your eyes / Love is the drug / Sign of the times / Dance away / Angel eyes / Oh yeah / Over you / Same old scene / Midnight hour, The / More than this / Avalon / Slave to love / Jealous guy.
LP: .... **EGTV 1**
MC: .... **EGMTV 1**

THESE FOOLISH THINGS.
Tracks: / Hard rain's gonna fall / River of salt / Don't ever change / Piece of my heart / Baby I don't care / It's my party / Don't worry baby / Sympathy for the devil / Tracks of my tears / You won't see me / I love how you love me / Loving you is sweeter than ever / These foolish things.
LP: .... **EGLP 9**
MC: .... **EGMC 9**
LP: .... **ILPS 9249**

ULTIMATE COLLECTION (Ferry, Bryan & Roxy Music).
Tracks: / Let's stick together ('88 remix) / In crowd, The / Angel eyes / He'll have to go / Tokyo Joe / All I want is you / Jealous guy / Price of love, The / Don't stop the dance / Love is the drug / This is tomorrow / Slave to love / Help me / Avalon / Dance away.
LP: .... **EGTV 2**
MC: .... **EGMTV 2**

Feso Trombone

FREEDOM TRAIN.
Tracks: / Freedom train.
LP: .... **ADRY 4**
LP: .... **ANT 026**

Fessor's Big City Band

FEELIN' GOOD.
LP: .... **SLP 426**

HAMBA NAMI.
LP: .... **SLP 261**

HOT BISCUITS.
LP: .... **SLP 406**

JUNGLE BLUES.
LP: .... **SLP 440**

LIVE.
LP: .... **SLP 424**

STOLEN SUGAR.
LP: .... **SLP 427**

THIRD FLOOR RICHARD.
LP: .... **SLP 433**

WILD BILL DAVISON.
LP: .... **SLP 421**

Fessor's Danish Jazz

FESSOR'S NIGHTHAWKS (see under Cheatham, Doc) (Cheatham, Doc/John Williams/Herb Hall).

Fessors Session Boys

GEORGE KELLY & AL VASEY/ FESSOR'S SESSION BOYS (See under Kelly, George) (Fessors Session Boys/ George Kelly & Al Vasey).

Festa New Orleans

ASCONA.
LP: .... **FESTA 934**

Festival de Musique

FESTIVAL DE MUSIQUE ACADIENNE '81 LIVE (Various artists).
LP: **6046**
MC: .... **6046 TC**

Festival (Group)

EVITA.
Tracks: / Buenos Aires / I'd be surprisingly good for you / Don't cry for me Argentina / High flying, adored / Rainbow high / She is a diamond.
LP: .... **RSS 18**

Fetchin' Bones

CABIN FLOUNDER.
LP: .... **DBAT 77**

Fettig, Mary

IN GOOD COMPANY.
Tracks: / Danza / Some other time / Alice in Wonderland / We'll be together again / Scrapple from the apple / Morning / All of you / Young and foolish / Secret love.
LP: .... **CJ 273**

Fettlers

PRIDE OF THE NORTH.
LP: .... **TSR 037**

Fetus Productions

ENVIRONMENTAL.
LP: .... **FETUS 4**

Feud

TO LOAD BUT ONCE.
LP: .... **FEUD 1**

Fever Tree

SAN FRANCISCO GIRLS.
Tracks: / Imitation situation / Where do you go? / San Francisco girls / 99 and one half / Man who paints the pictures (Parts 1 & 2) / Filigree and the shadow / Sun also rises, The / Day tripper (Medley) / Nowadays Clancy can't even sing / Unlock my door / Come with me / Peace of mind / Death is the dancer / We can work it out (Medley).
LP: .... **SEE 71**

Feverhouse (film)

FEVERHOUSE (See under Biting Tongues) (Various artists).

Feyer, George

ESSENTIAL COLE PORTER, THE.
LP: .... **VSD 93**

Fflaps

AMHERSAIN.
LP: .... **PROBE 21**

MAILROD.
LP: .... **PROBE 28**

F.F.W.

WEIRDELIC.
LP: .... **MFN 115**
MC: .... **TMFN 115**

Fiahlo, Fransico

O FADOAL LATINO.
LP: .... **EULP 1075**
MC: .... **EUMC 1075**

Fialka, Karel

HUMAN ANIMAL.
Tracks: / Sun In My Eyes / Hey Matthew / You be the judge / Undercurrents / City, The / Eyes Have it, The.
LP: .... **MIRF 1036**
MC: .... **MIRFC 1036**

STILL LIFE.
Tracks: / Eyes have it, The / People are strange / File in forget / Cost / Rough and ready / Armband / Still life / Good, the bad and the ugly, The / Appointment in Samarra.
LP: .... **BLUP 5003**

Fiat Lux

HIRED HISTORY.
Tracks: / Secrets / Photograph / Blue emotion / Comfortable life / Sleepless nightmare / Aqua vitae.
LP: **8216371**
MC: **8216374**

Fiction Brothers

THINGS ARE COMING MY WAY.
LP: .... **FF 204**

Fiction Factory

ANOTHER STORY.
Tracks: / Another story / Standing at the top of the world / Not the only one / All for you / Lose your heart in nature / No time / Power room, The / Make believe / Time is right / Victoria victorious.
LP: .... **FONDL 2**
MC: .... **FONDC 2**

THROW THE WARPED WHEEL OUT.
Tracks: / Feels like heaven / Heart and mind / Hanging gardens, The / All or nothing / Hit the mark / Ghost of love / Tales of tears / First step / Warped wheel, The.
LP: .... **CBS 32778**
MC: **40 32778**

Fiddle

DOWN HOME, VOL 1 (Fiddle music) (Various artists).
Tracks: / Hangman's reel, The: *Bain, Aly* / Da tushker: *Lerwick Lounge Ensemble* / Howling at the moon: *Rowan, Peter Band* / Glencoe: *MacMaster, Buddy* / British American polka, The: *Carignan, Jean* / Big yellow moon: *Neely, Bill* / Arkansas traveller: *Jarrell, Tommy* / Jim Anderson's delight: *Hunter, Willy & Aly Bain*/ Right or wrong: *Junior Daugherty* / Spey in spate, The: *Cape Breton Fiddlers* / Pine county breakdown: *Monroe, Bill & His Blue Grass Boys* / Alexanders hornpipe: *Boys Of The Lough* / L'isle des voyageurs: *La Bottine Souriante*/ Tom and Jerry: *O'Connor, Mark* / Darlin' Corey: *Seeger, Mike* / My lily: *Holland, Jerry & Aly Bain*/ Gardenia waltz, The: *Gimble, Johnny* / Mrs Hamilton Of Pencaitland: *Hunter, Willie* / Susan Anna: *Jarrell, Tommy* / Shoot out: *O'Connor, Mark & Aly Bain*.
LP: .... **LIFL 7011**
MC: .... **LIFC 7011**

ENGLISH FIDDLE PLAYERS (Various artists).
MC: .... **PLC 077**
LP: .... **PLR 077**

FIDDLE & BANJO BLUEGRASS (Various artists).
Tracks: / Low down Billy: *Various artists* / Talkin' fiddlin' blues: *Various artists* / Ole Joe Clark: *Various artists* / Party time: *Various artists* / Fire in the mountain: *Various artists* / Billy low ground: *Various artists* / 8th of January: *Various artists* / Baby Sue: *Various artists* / Runnin' wild: *Various artists*/ Banjo pickin' time: *Various artists* / Orange blossom hoedown: *Various artists* / Cacklin' hen, The: *Various artists* / Feeling bad: *Various artists* / Wildwood flower: *Various artists* / Weepin' willow: *Various artists* / Mockingbird, The: *Various artists* / String time: *Various artists* / Honeysuckle: *Various artists*/ Lonesome road: *Various artists*.
LP: .... **ARN 33717**
MC: .... **ARN 433717**

FIDDLE FEVER (Various artists).
LP: .... **FF 247**

FIDDLE SWING (Various artists).
LP: .... **KK 7451**

FIDDLE TUNES FOR BANJO (Various artists).
LP: .... **ROUNDER 0124**
MC: .... **ROUNDER 0124C**

FIDDLE TUNES VOL.2 (Various artists).
LP: .... **ROUNDER 0058**

FIDDLER'S COMPANION (Various artists).
Tracks: / Shakin' o' the pocky: *Various artists* / Firth House: *Various artists* / Well may Charley wear the crown: *Various artists* / Donald MacLean's farewell to Oban: *Various artists* / Gin ye kiss my wife: *Various artists*/ Robert Innes of Sterling University: *Various artists* / Methlick style: *Various artists* / Merrily danced the quaker's wife: *Various artists* / Balmoral Castle: *Various artists* / Da sixereen: *Various artists* / Mr. A.G. Wilken's favourite: *Various artists* / Earl Haig: *Various artists* / Chapel Keithack: *Various artists*/ Muir O'Gellan: *Various artists* / Gicht Castle: *Various artists*.
LP: .... **GLN 1023**

FIDDLERS HALL OF FAME (Various artists).
LP: .... **SLP 209**
MC: .... **GT 5209**

GOLDEN FIDDLE AWARDS 1979 (Various artists).
LP: .... **EPC 61998**

WALTZ OF THE WIND (Various artists).
LP: .... **FF 303**

Fiddler of the Reels

FIDDLER OF THE REELS (Hardy, Thomas) (Morant, Richard).
MC: .... **TTC/TH 03**

Fiddler on the Roof

FIDDLER ON THE ROOF (1971 Film Soundtrack) (Various artists).
Tracks: / Prologue and 'Tradition' and main title: *Various artists* / If I were a rich man: *Various artists* / Sabbath prayer: *Various artists* / To life: *Various artists* / Miracle of miracles: *Various artists* / Tevye's dream: *Various artists* / Sunrise sunset: *Various artists* / Wedding celebration and the bottle dance: *Various artists* / Do you love me?: *Various artists* / Far from the home I love: *Various artists* / Chava ballet sequence: *Various artists* / Anatevka: *Various artists* / Finale: *Various artists* / Matchmaker, matchmaker: *Various*

artists / Bottle dance: *Various artists* / Now I have everything: *Various artists.*
MC: **2TCK 60011**
LP: . . . . **UAD 60011**
LP: **2621147**
2LP: . . . . **UAD 60011/2**

FIDDLER ON THE ROOF (Original Broadway cast - 1964) (Various artists).
Tracks: / Tradition: *Various artists* / Matchmaker, matchmaker: *Various artists* / If I were a rich man: *Various* artists / Sabbath prayer: *Various artists* / Sunrise, Sunset: *Various artists* / To life: *Various artists*/ Miracle of miracles: *Various artists* / Tevye's dream: *Various artists* / Now I have everything: *Various* artists / Do you love me?: *Various artists* / Far from the home I love: *Various artists* / Anatevka: *Various artists.*
LP: . . . . **BL 1093**

FIDDLER ON THE ROOF (1967 Original London cast) (Various artists).
Tracks: / Tradition: *Various artists* / Matchmaker, matchmaker: *Various artists* / If I were a rich man: *Various* artists / Sabbath prayer: *Various artists* / To life: *Various artists* / Miracle of miracles: *Various* artists / Tevye's dream: *Various artists* / Sunrise, sunset: *Various artists* / Bottle dance: *Various* artists / Now I have everything: *Various artists* / Do you love me: *Various artists* / Far from the home I love: *Various artists* / Anatevka: *Various artists.*
LP: . . . . **CBS 31519**
MC: . . . . **PST 30742**

FIDDLER ON THE ROOF (ORIGINAL ISSUE) (London cast) (Various artists).
LP: . . . . **SBPG 70030**

Fiddler's Dram

FIDDLER'S DRAM.
LP: . . . . **DID 711**
MC: . . . . **DIDC 711**

TO SEE THE PLAY.
Tracks: / Jack in London City / Song of victory / Song of the blackbird / Day trip to Bangor / Flash lad / Ythanside / Keyhole in the door / Walney Island cockfight / Two brothers / Peel the tatties / False knight on the road / Nottingham goose fair.
LP: . . . . **DIN 304**

Fiddlers Three Plus

FIDDLERS THREE PLUS TWO VOL. 1.
LP: . . . . **LOCLP 1035**

FIDDLERS THREE PLUS TWO VOL. 2.
Tracks: / Isle of Skye / Scottish legacy / Dean Brig Reel, The / Green shades of gask / Loch of the rising mist / Cutty Sark / Sarah / Echoes of Oban / Fairy dance, The / Mason's apron / Kilt is my delight, The / Thistle hornpipe / Dancing feet / Galley watch / Morning fair / Kildare fancy, The / Hamilton house.
LP: . . . . **LOCLP 1041**
MC: . . . . **ZCLOC 1041**

Fiddy, John

EXTRACTING THE DIGITAL (See under Fisher, Tony) (Fiddy, John & Tony Fisher).

IMAGINATIONS (Fiddy, John & orchestra).
LP: . . . . **ISST 137**

Fidelio

FIDELIO (VIDEO) (see under Mozart (composer)) (Various artists).

FIDELIO (VIDEO) (see under Mozart (composer)) (Various artists).

Fidelio Quartet

TIPPETT.
LP: . . . . **GSGC 7057**
MC: . . . . **ZCGC 7057**

Fiedler, Arthur

ARTHUR FIEDLER & THE BOSTON POPS ORCHESTRA.
Tracks: / Popcorn / Amazing grace / Everything is beautiful / Help me make it through the night / Song sung blue / Those were the days / Serenade / Spring song / Minuet / Intermezzo / Dreams / Eleanor Rigby / Ob la di ob la da / Hey Jude / Michelle / I want to hold your hand / Yesterday / Love is a many splendoured thing / September song / Days of wine and roses / Stardust / I left my heart in San Francisco / Shadow of your smile.
2LP: . . . . **CR 071**
MCSET: . . . . **CRT 071**

PLAY GERSHWIN.
Tracks: / Girl crazy suite / Wintergreen for president / Three preludes / Second rhapsody / Overtures from Oh Kay / Funny face / Let 'em eat cake / Of thee I sing.
LP: **4118351**
LP: . . . . **PFS 4438**

SATURDAY NIGHT FIEDLER (Fiedler, Arthur & The Boston Pops Orchestra).
Tracks: / Stayin' alive / Night fever / Manhattan skyline / Night on disco mountain / Disco inferno / Bachmania.
LP: . . . . **BDL 1032**

SONG AFTER SUNDOWN, A (see under Getz, Stan) (Fiedler, Arthur & Stan Getz).

WHITE CHRISTMAS (Fiedler, Arthur & The Boston Pops Orchestra).
Tracks: / Christmas festival / Sleighride / Jesu, joy of man's desiring / Shepherd's pastorale / Sheep may safely graze / Hallelujah chorus / Waltz of the flowers / Musical sleighride / White Christmas / Santa Claus is coming to town / Rudolph the red nosed reindeer.
LP: . . . . **DG 419414 1**

Field, Billy

BAD HABITS.
Tracks: / Bad habits / Good golly me / You weren't in love with me / Baby I'm easy for it / Never be blue / Since I found out / You'll call it love / Celebrity Lane / Single man / If I was a millionaire.
LP: . . . . **CBS 856749**

Field (film)

FIELD, THE (Film Soundtrack) (Various artists).
LP: . . . . **VS 5292**
MC: . . . . **VSC 5292**

Field, Graham

AGONY (See under Fletcher, Babs) (Field, Graham & Babs Fletcher).

Field Guide To...

FIELD GUIDE TO THE MAMMAL VOICES OF EUROPE.
2LP: . . . . **RFLP 5016/5017**

Field, Keith

ANOTHER HANDFUL OF SONGS (See under Morgan, Maria) (Field, Keith & Maria Morgan).

HANDFUL OF SONGS, A (See Morgan, Maria) (Field, Keith & Maria Morgan).

Field Mice

COASTAL.
LP: . . . . **SARAH 606**
MC: . . . . **SARAH 606MC**

SKYWRITING.
Tracks: / Triangle / Clearer / Below the stars / Canada / It isn't forever / Humblebee.
LP: . . . . **SARAH 601**

SO SAID KAY.
MLP: . . . . **SARAH 38**

Field Of Dreams (film)

FIELD OF DREAMS (1989 Film Soundtrack) (Various artists).
Tracks: / Cornfield: *Various artists* / Deciding to build the field: *Various artists* / Shoeless Joe: *Various* artists / Timeless street, The: *Various artists* / Old ball players: *Various artists* / Drive home, The: *Various* artists / Field of dreams: *Various artists* / Library, The: *Various artists* / Moonlight Graham: *Various* artists / Night mists: *Various artists* / Doc's memories: *Various artists* / Place where dreams come true: *Various artists* / End credits: *Various artists.*
MC: . . . . **BK 90386**
LP: . . . . **BL 90386**
LP: **3060.1**
MC: **3060.4**

Field, Paul

DIFFERENT YET THE SAME.
LP: . . . . **MYR R 1121**
MC: . . . . **MYR C 1121**

RESTLESS HEART.
Tracks: / Rock with the best of them / Radio / Has to be you, has to be me / Solo / Positive / Storm is over, The / Fair fight / Stranger in your eyes / Just around the corner / You're the one / Nearly midnight / Restless heart.
LP: . . . . **MYR 1117**
MC: . . . . **MC 1117**

VISIONS.
2LP: . . . . **MYX 1191**
MCSET: . . . . **MCD 1191**

Fielding, Henry

JOSEPH ANDREWS (Massey, Daniel (nar)).
MCSET: **418 162-4**

Fielding, Jerry

SWINGIN' IN HI-FI (Fielding, Jerry & His Orchestra).
Tracks: / Smack dab in the middle / If I may / Razzle dazzle / Fish roll / Boss is home, The / Ooo wee / Burn that candle / Look out / Turkish torture / Heavy Henry's first flirtation / Doll face / South wind.
LP: . . . . **JASM 1025**

Fields, Alvin

SPECIAL DELIVERY.
Tracks: / Special delivery / Anyway you like it / All in the name of love / All that I am / Lucky number seven / Share my dream / Fire of life / Punk funk.
LP: . . . . **AMLH 64890**

Fields, Gracie

AMAZING GRACIE.
Tracks: / Reviens / Punch and Judy show, The / Gracie's Christmas party / My Ohio home / Our avenue / When the fields are white with daises, I'll return / Would a manx cat wag it's tail? / Home sweet home / Looking on the bright side of life / They all make love but me / Clatter o' clogs / Life's desire / I took my harp to a party / Just one more chance / In my little bottom drawer / Isle of Capri / Mockingbird went cuckoo / Sing as we go / My blue Heaven / We're living at the cloisters / Take a look at mine / Like the big pots do / Serenade / Singin' in the bathtub.
LP: . . . . **SVL 170**
MC: . . . . **CSVL 170**

AMAZING GRACIE FIELDS.
LP: . . . . **MES 7079**

BEST OF HER BBC BROADCASTS.
Tracks: / Sally / Roses of Picardy / When I grow too old to dream / Walter, Walter lead me to the altar / Wish me luck as you wave me goodbye / Thanks to the nation / I love the moon / Rochdale hounds, The / Co-op shop / Old violin, An / Sing as we go / Mockin' Bird Hill / Oh I never cried so much / So in love / At the end of the day / Land of hope and glory / Volare.
LP: . . . . **REGL 380**
MC: . . . . **ZCF 380**

BIGGEST ASPIDISTRA IN THE WORLD.
LP: . . . . **MCL 1806**

CLASSIC YEARS IN DIGITAL STEREO.
Tracks: / Sally / Clatter o' clogs / Dicky bird hop, The / Singin' in the bathtub / Ring down the curtain / Little pudden basin / Nowt about owt / Will you love me when I'm mutton / She's one of those old fashioned ladies / Biggest aspidistra in the world, The / I took my heart to a party / Ee, by gum / Pass, shoot, goal / Fall in and follow / She fought like a tiger for 'er 'onour / You've got to be smart to be in the ... / Let's all go posh / Smile when you say goodbye.
LP: . . . . **REB 690**
MC: . . . . **ZCF 690**

FOCUS ON GRACIE FIELDS.
MC: . . . . **KFOC 28073**

GOLDEN AGE OF..., THE.
Tracks: / There's a cabin in the pines / Whiskers and all / Punch and Judy show, The / Rochdale hounds, The / May morning / Out in the cold / I can't remember / Sally / Stormy weather / Fall in and follow the band / Happy ending / My lucky day / Heaven will protect an honest girl / Sing as we go / Love is everywhere / Mrs. Binn's twins / Danny boy / Grandfather's bagpipes / Annielaurie / Wish me luck as you wave me goodbye.
LP: . . . . **GX 41 2530 1**
MC: . . . . **GX 41 2530 4**

GOLDEN YEARS, THE.
LP: . . . . **WW 5007**

GRACIE FIELDS.
Tracks: / Take me to your heart again / Sing a we go / September song / Mrs Binngs's twins / Around the world / You didn't want me when you had me / Kerry dance, The / Little donkey / Ugly duckling / Mary's boy child / Home / Photograph of mother's wedding group, The / Scarlet ribbons (for her hair) / We've got to keep up with the Jones / Lord's prayer, The / Far away / He forgot to come back / My favourite things / Twelfth of never, The / Singing in the bathtub / Stop and shop in the Co-op shop / Biggest aspidistra in the world, The / Ave Maria / Sally.
MC: . . . . **HR 8186**

GRACIE FIELDS STORY, THE.
Tracks: / Sally / My blue Heaven / Because I love you / Isle of Capri / I'm a dreamer / 'Ee by gum / One night of love / Wish me luck as you wave me goodbye / Sing as we go / Serenade / In my little bottom drawer / Looking on the bright side of life / Mrs. Binn's twins / House is haunted, The / Ave Maria / Little old lady / Around the world / Kerry dance, The / I took my harp to a party / Take me to your heart again / Photograph of Mother's wedding group, The / Scarlet ribbons / Do-re-mi / Lord's prayer, The / Little donkey / We've got to keep up with the Joneses / Go away from my window / Song of the mountains / Biggest Aspidistra in the world, The / How are things in Glocca Morra? / You're breaking my heart / Now is the hour.
2LP: . . . . **EMSP 333**

ISLE OF CAPRI.
Tracks: / There's a lovely lake in London / Isle of Capri / South American Joe / Mockingbird went cuckoo, The / Keeping up with the Joneses / Cherie / In my little bottom drawer / I'm ninety nine today / Sally / Sing as we go / Roll along prairie moon / One of the little orphans of the storm / Just one more chance / Winter draws on / Red sails in the sunset / What can you give a nudist on his ... / Love, life and laughter / I took my harp to a party.
LP: . . . . **JOY'D 287**

LAST CONCERT IN AMERICA.
LP: . . . . **AEI 2123**

LAUGHTER AND SONG.
Tracks: / Charmaine / Because i love you / My blue Heaven / House is haunted, The / Dancing with tears in my eyes / Home / I'm playing with fire / Take a good look at mine / How deep is the ocean / Play to me gypsy / Say it isn't so / You're driving me crazy / I lift up my finger and say tweet tweet / One little hair on his head, The / Fred Fannakapan / Heaven will protect an honest girl / Little pudden basin / Photograph of mother's wedding group / Sitting on a five bar gate / He forgot to come back / Will you love me when I'm mutton.
LP: . . . . **SH 510**
MC: . . . . **TCSH 510**

LIFE IS A SONG.
Tracks: / Life is a song / Words are in my heart, The / Lullaby of Broadway / Red sails in the sunset / Have you forgotten so soon / Desert song, The / Ah sweet mystery of life / Greatest mistake of my life / It looks like rain in Cherry Blossom Lane / Bluebird of happiness / He wooed her and wooed her and wooed her / Come back to Sorrento / It began with a tango / For ever and ever / Honey child / You're too dangerous cherie / Somewhere, somehow, someday / Papa won't you dance with me / Serenade of the bells / Au revoir.
LP: . . . . **RFL 36**

QUEEN OF HEARTS - BEST OF 1930S.
Tracks: / Queen of hearts / First time I saw you, The / It looks like rain in Cherry Blossom Lane / Did your mother come from Ireland? / One of the little orphans of the storm / Song in your heart, A / Gypsy lullaby / In the chapel in the moonlight / We're all good pals together / When my dreamboat comes home / September in the rain / Little old lady / Giannina mia / Clogs and shawl / Would you? / My love for you / Laughing Irish eyes / Where is the sun? / When the harvest moon is shining / Feather in her Tyrolean hat, A / Organ, the monkey and me, The / Smile when you say goodbye.
LP: . . . . **CHD 144**
MC: . . . . **MCHD 144**

SALLY.
Tracks: / Sally / Sing as we go / Red sails in the sunset / One of the little orphans of the storm / There's a lovely lake in London / Isle of Capri / We've got to keep up with the Joneses / In my little bottom drawer / Roll along prairie moon / It looks like rain in Cherry Blossom Lane / Greatest mistake of my life / I never cried so much in all my life / Smile when you say goodbye / I haven't been the same girl since / You haven't altered a bit / Did your mother come from Ireland / Turn 'Erbert's face to the wall mother / When I grow too old to dream.
LP: . . . . **BUR 001**
MC: . . . . **4 BUR 001**

SING AS WE GO (ALBUM).
Tracks: / Sally / My blue heaven / I'm a dreamer (aren't we all) / Lancashire blues / Three green bonnets / He forgot to come back / My lucky day / I took my harp to a party / House is haunted, The / In my little bottom drawer / Happy ending / Ave Maria / Sing as we go / I never cried so much in all my life / Love is everywhere / Woodpecker song, The / Umbrella man, The / Wish me luck.
LP: . . . . **SH 520**
LP: **794 322 1**
MC: . . . . **TCSH 520**

THAT OLD FEELING.
Tracks: / Sweetest song in the world, The / Turn 'Erbert's face to the wall mother / Home / Remember me? / Round the bend of the road / Will you remember? / When I grow too old to dream / That old feeling / Fred Fannakapan / My first love song / Walter, Walter, lead me to the altar / Goodnight my love / Red sails in the sunset / Ah sweet mystery of life / Smilin' through / Giannina mia / There's a lovely lake in London / We've got to keep up with the Joneses / I never cried

so much in all my life / First time I saw you, The / Fall in and follow the band / Sally.
LP: AJA 5062
MC: ZC AJA 5062

THIS IS.
Tracks: / Sally / My blue Heaven / Isle of Capri / I'm a dreamer / Sing as we go / Ee by gum / Serenade / Little old lady / Wish me luck as you wave me goodbye / Scarlet ribbons / Little donkey.
LP: THIS 8

VERY BEST OF GRACIE FIELDS, THE (20 Great Songs).
MC: PLAC 28

WORLD OF GRACIE FIELDS.
Tracks: / Sally / Come back to Sorrento / Walter / Heaven will protect an honest girl / Bless this house / Shall I be an old man's darling / At the end of the day / Little old lady / Rochdale hounds, The / Count your blessings / He's dead but he won't lie down / O my beloved father / Now is the hour.
LP: SPA 82

WORLD OF VOL.1.
MC: KCSP 82

Fields, Judy

HALFWAY TO PARADISE.
LP: V 1036 1

Fields Of The Nephilim

DAWNRAZOR.
Tracks: / Intro / Slow kill / Volcane / Vet for the insane / Dust / Reanimator / Dawnrazor / Sequel, The / Power (Cassette and CD only.) / Preacher man (Cassette and CD only.) / Secrets (CD only.) / Tower (CD only.).
LP: SITUP 18
MC: SITCP 18
LP: SITL 18
MC: SITLC 18

EARTH INFERNO.
LP: BEGA 117
MC: BEGAC 117

ELIZIUM.
LP: BEGA 115
MC: BEGC 115

NEPHILIM, THE.
Tracks: / Endemoniada / Celebrate / Watchman, The / Moonchild / Chords of souls / Last exit for the lost / Phobia.
MC: SITC 22
LP: SITU 22

RETURNING TO GEHENNA.
LP: SF 008
LP: SF 008CV

Fields, Richard

DARK GABLE.
Tracks: / Shake em down / Make my dreams come true / I'd really love to see you tonight / Star I've always wanted to be / She's a bad lil lady / Don't give up too soon / One special one / You sure know how to give a party / I won't rush you.
LP: PL 85582
MC: PK 85582

DIMPLES.
Tracks: / I like your loving / Let me take you in my arms tonight / Let the lady dance / Lovely lady / In the still of the night / She's got papers on me / I've got to learn to say no / Earth angel / Don't ever take your love.
LP: EPC 85345

GIVE EVERYBODY SOME.
Tracks: / People treat you funky / Butter / Wish somebody loved me / Don't ever stop chasing your dreams / You shouldn't have made it so good / Let it all hang out / You send me / Moody's mood for love / Goodbye you, hello her.
LP: EPC 252 26

MMM....
Tracks: / Jazzy lady / Your wife is cheatin' on us / Dear Mr God / Woman let me into your life / Dog or a hog / We've gotta stop meeting like this / Don't turn your back on my love / I need you so.
LP: PL 85169
MC: PK 85169

MR. LOOK SO GOOD.
Tracks: / If it ain't one thing ...it's another / After I put my lovin' on you / Baby work out / Mr. Look so good / Taking applications / Freak on the side / Sincerely / Lady is bad.
LP: EPC 85693

TELLIN IT LIKE IT IS.
Tracks: / Tell it like it is / You're everything I want in a woman / Hooked on your lovin' / Stand up on it / Never gonna let the sweet get sour / Dor or hog / I won't rush you / I can't live with or without you / Do you belong to the dope man.
LP: 4600021
MC: 4600024

Fields, Shep

1947: SHEP FIELDS (Fields, Shep & His Rippling Rhythm Orchestra).
LP: CLP 38

RIPPLING RHYTHMS 1936 - 42 (Fields, Shep & His Orchestra).
Tracks: / Gone with the wind / I surrender, dear / Cecilia / Jersey bounce / I found a million dollar baby / Secret / Us on a bus / Star is born, A / Daydreams come true at night / When the mush begins to rush down father's vest / Sleepy moon / Little old lady.
LP: BS 7138
MC: BS 7138C

SHEP FIELDS 1942-44.
Tracks: / Fire dance / Sophisticated lady / Skylark / American patrol / Heavenly isn't it / Autumn nocturne / Shakey / Stormy weather / Things ain't what they used to be / Little pink elephants / Harlem nocturne / Moon is low, The / If I had you / Lover's lament / 1600 by the clock / Sheik of Araby.
LP: HSR 160

SHEP FIELDS AND ORCHESTRA 1947-51.
LP: CLP 133

SHEP FIELDS VOL 2, 1940 (Fields, Shep & His Rippling Rhythm Orchestra).
Tracks: / Imagination / They ought to write a book / Cecilia / Concert to the stars / Let there be love / Charming little faker / It never entered my mind / Country garden / Shake down the stars / From another world / Gavotte in G / A vous tout de vey, a vous?.
LP: HSR 179

Fieldwork

SHARPEN THE SICKLE.
LP: MEK 3

SUNFISHING.
MC: UNKNOWN

Fierce Heart

FIERCE HEART.
Tracks: / Echoes / Fierce heart / Out for blood / Lion's share / Search and destroy / Heroes / Never gonna make me cry / Bad Maureen / Loose lips.
LP: POLD 5184
MC: POLDC 5184

Fiery Dragon

FIERY DRAGON, THE/THE BOOK OF BEASTS (See under Nesbitt, E) (Bliss Caroline/Peter Bartlett).

Fiesta Vellenanta

FIESTA VELLENANTA (Various artists).
Tracks: / Triste despedida: *Chimenti, Rusbell & Orlando Jimenez* / La envidiosa: *Ossa, Julia De La* / Puno molio: *Ossa, Julia De La* / Camino verde: *Blanco, Morgan* / Lo mas sabroso: *Pedrozo, Jimmy & Ariza, Franklin*/ Maria Elena: *Sanchez, Joaquin y su conjunto* / Tu cosita: *Sanchez, Joaquin y su conjunto* / Ahora y siempre: *Tobio, Luis & Iguita, Vincente* / Bella cascada: *Tobio, Luis & Iguita, Vincente* / Sirvientas modernas: *Pedrozo, Jimmy* / El loro: *Pedrozo, Jimmy* / India matea: *Duran, Miguel y su conjunto* / Apariencia: *Barranquilla vallenata.*
LP: ORB 011

Fiestas

OH SO FINE.
Tracks: / So fine / Dollar bill / That was me / Mr. Dillon, Mr. Dillon / Come on and love me / Mexico / Last night I dreamed / Lawman / Our anniversary / Railroad song / Try it one more time / Mama put the law down / Fine as wine / You can be my girlfriend / Anna / I'm your slave.
LP: CH 173

Fifteen Rabbits

FIFTEEN RABBITS (Felix Salten - Celebration of life).
MC: CDL 51635

Fifth Angel

FIFTH ANGEL.
LP: RR 96881

Fifty...

50 FABULOUS MILLION SELLERS (Various artists).
LP: WW 1003
MC: WW 10034

Fifty Four Forty

SHOW ME.
Tracks: / One day in your life / Get back down / Walk in line / Standing in the way / Everyday / What's in a name / One gun / Come here / All the love is gone / Show me.
LP: 925572 1
MC: 925572 4

Fifty Two Pick Up

52 PICK UP (1987 film soundtrack) (Various artists).
LP: STV 81300

Figgis, Mike

STORMY MONDAY (See under Stormy Monday) (King, B.B. & Mike Figgis).

Figgy Duff

AFTER THE TEMPEST.
LP: CM 023

FIGGY DUFF.
LP: DIN 326

Figures On A Beach

STANDING ON CEREMONY.
Tracks: / No stars / Glamour of motion, The / Feel the mood / Angels working overtime / Rhythm / Elvis' house / Pagan gift, A / Paris / State of emergency / Delirium / Big top.
LP: 925596 1
MC: 925596 4

Fiji

20 GOLDEN SONGS OF FIJI VOL.2 (Various artists).
LP: VP 424
MC: VPS 424C

Filarfolket

LIVE: FILARFOLKET.
LP: TIMP 1
LP: AM 49

SMUGGLE.
LP: TIMP 2

File

CAJUN DANCE BAND.
LP: FF 418

Filipinos

SUMMERTIME.
LP: TWIST 001

Filippini, Rocco

HAYDN 'LONDON' TRIOS 1-3/PIANO TRIOS 15 & 16 (see under Haydn (composer)) (Nicolet, Aurele & Christiane /Rocco Filippini/Bruno Canino).

Filleul, Peter

MARKSMAN, THE (see under Thompson, Richard) (Filleul, Peter/ Richard Thompson).

Fillmore

LAST DAYS, THE.
2LP: K 66013

Film 90

FILM 90 (See Themes and Dreams: Johnny, Pearson) (Pearson, Johnny Orchestra).

Film Scores

GREAT AMERICAN FILM SCORES (Various artists).
LP: ERS 6506

MUSIC FROM THE FILMS OF RAINER WERNER FASSBINDER (Original film scores) (Various artists).
Tracks: / Berlin Alexanderplatz: *Various artists* / Marriage of Maria Braun, The: *Various artists* / Mother Kuster's trip to heaven: *Various artists* / Bolweiser: *Various artists* / Fox and his friends: *Various artists*/ Despair: *Various artists* / I only want you to love me: *Various artists* / Satan's brew: *Various artists*/ Whity: *Various artists* / Gods of the plague: *Various artists* / Querelle: *Various artists* / Lola: *Various artists* / Third generation, The: *Various artists* / Veronika voss: *Various artists* / Lili Marlene: *Various artists.*
LP: TER 1085

TOP FILM HITS (See under Top Film Hits) (Various artists).

Film Star Parade

FILM STAR PARADE (Various artists).
Tracks: / I wanna be loved by you: *Kane, Helen* / Please: *Crosby, Bing* / Ich bin von kopf bis fuss auf liebe eingestellt: *Dietrich, Marlene* (Falling in love again (original German version)) / My wife is on a diet: *Cantor, Eddie*/ You're always in my arms: *Daniels, Bebe* / Living in clover: *Buchanan, Jack* / Let me sing and I'm happy: *Jolson, Al* / What'll I do?: *Pidgeon, Walter* / Dance of the cuckoos: *Laurel & Hardy* / Eadie was a lady: *Merman, Ethel* / All I need is just one girl: *MacMurray, Fred* / Love, your magic spell is everywhere: *Swanson, Gloria*/ Sweet music: *Astaire, Fred & Adele* / I could make a good living at that: *Formby, George* / Don't tell him what's happened to me: *Bankhead, Tallulah* / My rock-a-bye baby: *Moore, Grace* / (I'd like to be) A bee in your boudoir: *Rogers, Charles 'Buddy'* / Love me tonight: *MacDonald, Jeanette/Maurice Chevalier.*
LP: AJA 5020
MC: ZC AJA 5020

Films

4 ALFRED HITCHCOCK FILMS (See under Ketcham, Charles) (Ketcham, Charles & Utah Symphony Orchestra).

4 ALFRED HITCHCOCK FILMS (See under Ketcham, Charles) (Ketcham, Charles & Utah Symphony Orchestra).

2001: A SPACE ODYSSEY (Film soundtrack) (Various artists).
Tracks: / Also sprach Zarathustra: *Various artists* / Requiem for soprano, mezzo soprano...: *Various artists*(...two mixed choirs and orchestra) / Lux Aeterna: *Various artists* / Blue Danube: *Various artists* / Gayane ballet suite: *Various artists* / Atmospheres: *Various artists* / Blue Danube: *Various artists* / Also sprach Zarathustra: *Various artists.*
LP: LPMGM 6
MC: TCMGM 6
LP: 793 302 1
MC: 793 302 4
LP: MGM CS 8078
LP: 2315 034

ADVENTURES IN BABYSITTING (See under 'Night on the town'(USA title)) (Various artists).

AFTER DARK MY SWEET (Film Soundtrack) (Various artists).
Tracks: / Suite I - After dark my sweet: *Jarre, Maurice* / Suite II - Collie and Fay: *Jarre, Maurice* / Suite III - Uncle Bud: *Jarre, Maurice* / Suite IV - The kidnapping: *Jarre, Maurice.*
LP: VS 5274
MC: VSC 5274

ALEXANDERS RAGTIME BAND (Film soundtrack) (Various artists).
LP: HS 406

ALMOST AN ANGEL (Film Soundtrack) (Various artists).
LP: VS 5307
MC: VSC 5307

ANTHONY ADVERSE (Composed by Erich Wolfgang Korngold) (Various artists).
MC: VSC 5285

AROUND THE WORLD IN 80 DAYS (Film soundtrack) (Various artists).
LP: MCA 37986
MC: MCAC 37986

BACK DRAFT (Original Soundtrack) (Various artists).
LP: A 807
MC: AC 807

BATMAN 2 (Film Soundtrack) (Various artists).
Tracks: / Batman theme: *Elfman, Danny* / First confrontation: *Elfman, Danny* / Clown attack: *Elfman, Danny*/ Roasted dude: *Elfman, Danny* / Descent into mystery: *Elfman, Danny* / Joker's poem, The: *Elfman, Danny*/ Charge of the Batmobile: *Elfman, Danny* / Up the cathedral: *Elfman, Danny* / Final confrontation: *Elfman, Danny* / Roof fight: *Elfman, Danny* / Flowers: *Elfman, Danny* / Batman to the rescue: *Elfman, Danny*/ Photos: *Elfman, Danny* / Beautiful dreamer: *Elfman, Danny* / Bat cave, The: *Elfman, Danny* / Love theme: *Elfman, Danny* / Attack of the batwing: *Elfman, Danny* / Waltz to the death: *Elfman, Danny* / Finale: *Elfman, Danny.*
LP: WX 287
MC: WX 287C

BEN HUR (Film soundtrack) (Various artists).
Tracks: / Ben Hur prelude: *Various artists* / Adoration of the Magi, The: *Various artists* / Roman march: *Various* artists / Friendship: *Various artists* / Love theme from Ben Hur: *Various artists* / Burning desert, The: *Various artists* / Rowing of the galley slaves, The: *Various artists* / Naval battle: *Various artists*/ Return to Judea: *Various artists* / Victory parade: *Various artists* / Mother's love, The: *Various artists*/ Lepers search for the Christ: *Various artists* / Procession to Calvary, The: *Various artists* / Miracle and finale, The: *Various artists.*
LP: LPMGM 8
MC: TCMGM 8
MC: 793 304 4

BEST FILM MUSIC OF GEORGES DELERUE VOL 1 (Various artists).
LP: A 319
MC: C 319

BEST FILM MUSIC OF GEORGES DELERUE VOL 2 (Various artists).
LP: A 320
MC: C 320

BEST OF GENE KELLY -- FROM MGM FILMS (See under Kelly, Gene) (Kelly, Gene).

BEST REVENGE (See under Emerson, Keith) (Various artists).

BIRD (FILM) (See under Parker, Charlie) (Parker, Charlie).

BODY PARTS (Composed by Loek Dikker) (Various artists).
LP: . . . . **VS 5337**
MC: . . . . **C 5537**

CHANSONS POUR FELLINI (Film Soundtrack) (Various artists).
MC: . . . . **C 330**

CHORUS LINE (Original Film Soundtrack) (Various artists).
Tracks: / I hope I get it: *Various artists* / Who am I anyway?: *Various artists* / I can do that: *Various* artists / At the ballet: *Various artists* / Surprise, Surprise: *Various artists* / Nothing: *Various artists*/ Let me dance for you: *Various artists* / Dance:ten looks three: *Various artists* / One(rehearsal and finale versions): *Various artists* / What I did for love: *Various artists* / Looks:three: *Various artists*.
LP: . . . . **CANH 11**
MC: . . . . **CANHC 11**

CINE MOVIE (Various artists).
Tracks: / Psycho prelude: *Various artists* / De lift (ending): *Various artists* / Elephant man theme, The: *Various* artists / Enchantment At Tugu: *Various artists* / Russian Christmas Theme: *Various artists* / Vivement dimanche: *Various artists* / La notte: *Various artists* / Days of heaven: *Various artists* / North by North West theme: *Various artists* / Von Kern's Attack: *Various artists* / Suite Pour Choeur Et Orchestre: *Various artists*/ Le Reve I: *Various artists* / Train ride to Brooklyn: *Various artists* / Garcon: *Various artists* / Folie douce: *Various artists* / My name is nobody (theme): *Various artists*.
LP: . . . . **A 289**
MC: . . . . **C 289**

CINEMA HITS ALBUM, THE (Various artists).
LP: . . . . **TVLP 9**
MC: . . . . **ZCTV 9**

CINEMA OF THE '80S (Various artists).
MC: . . . . **C 394**

CINEMA WEEKEND (Various artists).
Tracks: / 2001: *Various artists* / Platoon: *Various artists* / Elephant man: *Various artists* / Diva: *Various artists* / Children of a lesser god: *Various artists* / Untouchables, The: *Various artists* / Dangerous moonlight: *Various artists* / Excalibur: *Various artists* / Death in Venice: *Various artists*/ Room with a view: *Various artists* / Barry Lyndon: *Various artists* / Amadeus: *Various artists*.
MC: **4213974**

CITIZEN KANE (London Philharmonic Orchestra).
Tracks: / Citizen Kane:Overture / Jane Eyre / Devil and Daniel Webster, The: Sleigh-ride / Snows of Kilimanjaro, The: Interlude / Jason and the argonauts / Citizen Kane:Variations / Citizen Kane:Ragtime / Citizen Kane:Finale / Swing your partners / Memory waltz, The.
MC: **4178524**

CITY SLICKERS (Original Soundtrack).
LP: . . . . **VS 5321**
MC: . . . . **VSC 5321**

CLASSIC BRITISH FILM MUSIC (Various artists).
MC: . . . . **FILMC 072**

CLASSIC BRITISH FILM THEMES OF THE '40'S & '50'S (Various artists).
Tracks: / Way to the stars, The: *Various artists* / Cornish rhapsody: *Various artists* / Voice in the night, A: *Various artists* / Warsaw concerto: *Various artists* / Dream of Olwen: *Various artists* / Saga of Odette, The: *Various artists* / Carriage and pair: *Various artists* / Long forgotten melody: *Various artists*/ Portrait of Clare: *Various artists* / Beggar's theme, The: *Various artists*.
LP: . . . . **SH 384**
MC: . . . . **TC SH 384**
LP: . . . . **GX 2551**
MC: . . . . **TCGX 2551**

CLASSIC FILM SCORES BY ALFRED NEWMAN (Various artists).
Tracks: / Captain from Castile: *Various artists* / How to marry a millionaire: *Various artists* / Wuthering heights: *Various artists* / Down to the sea in ships: *Various artists* / Bravados: *Various artists* / Anastasia: *Various artists* / Best of everything, The: *Various artists* / Airport: *Various artists* / Song of Bernadette: *Various artists* / Robe: *Various artists*.
LP: . . . . **GL 43437**
MC: . . . . **GK 43437**

CLASSIC FILM SCORES BY BERNARD HERRMANN (Various artists).
Tracks: / Citizen Kane: *Various artists* / On dangerous ground: *Various artists* / Beneath the 12 mile reef: *Various artists* / Hangover square: *Various artists* / White witch doctor: *Various artists*.
LP: . . . . **GL 43444**
MC: . . . . **GK 43444**

CLASSIC FILM SCORES BY DIMITRI TIOMKIN (Various artists).
Tracks: / Lost horizon: *Various artists* / Guns of Navarone: *Various artists* / Big sky: *Various artists*/ Fourposter: *Various artists* / Friendly persuasion: *Various artists* / Search for paradise: *Various artists*.
LP: . . . . **GL 43445**
MC: . . . . **GK 43445**

CLASSIC FILM SCORES BY FRANZ WAXMAN (Various artists).
Tracks: / Sunset Boulevard: *Various artists* / Prince Valient: *Various artists* / Place in the sun: *Various* artists / Bride of Frankenstein: *Various artists* / Old acquaintance Rebecca: *Various artists* / Philadelphia story: *Various artists* / Taras Bulba: *Various artists*.
LP: . . . . **GL 43442**
MC: . . . . **GK 43442**

CLASSIC FILM SCORES BY MAX STEINER (Various artists).
Tracks: / Gone with the wind: *Various artists* / Now voyager: *Various artists* / Saratoga trunk: *Various* artists / Charge of the Light Brigade: *Various artists* / Four wives: *Various artists* / Big sleep: *Various* artists / Johnny Belinda: *Various artists* / Since you went away: *Various artists* / Informer, The: *Various artists* / Fountainhead: *Various artists*.
LP: . . . . **GL 43447**
MC: . . . . **GK 43447**

CLASSIC FILM SCORES BY MIKLOS ROZSA (Various artists).
Tracks: / Spellbound: *Various artists* / Red house: *Various artists* / Thief of Baghdad: *Various artists*/ Lost weekend: *Various artists* / Four feathers: *Various artists* / Double indemnity: *Various artists*/ Knights of the round table: *Various artists* / Jungle book: *Various artists* / Ivanhoe (overture): *Various artists*.
LP: . . . . **GL 43443**
MC: . . . . **GK 43443**

CLASSIC FILM SCORES FOR BETTE DAVIS (Various artists).
Tracks: / Now voyager: *Various artists* / Dark victory: *Various artists* / Stolen life: *Various artists*/ Private lives of Elizabeth and Essex: *Various artists* / Mr Skeffington: *Various artists* / In this, our life: *Various artists* / All about Eve: *Various artists* / Jezebel: *Various artists* / Beyond the forest: *Various artists* / Juarez: *Various artists* / Letter: *Various artists* / All this and heaven too: *Various artists*.
LP: . . . . **GL 43436**
MC: . . . . **GK 43436**

CLASSIC FILM SCORES FOR ERROL FLYNN (Various artists).
Tracks: / Captain Blood: *Various artists* / Adventures of Don Juan: *Various artists* / Sea hawk: *Various* artists / They died with their boots on: *Various artists* / Dodge city: *Various artists* / Objective Burma: *Various artists* / Sun also rises: *Various artists* / Robin Hood: *Various artists*.
LP: . . . . **GL 43444**
MC: . . . . **GK 43444**
MC: . . . . **GK 80912**

CLASSIC FILM SCORES FOR HUMPHREY BOGART (Various artists).
Tracks: / Casablanca: *Various artists* / Passage to Marseille: *Various artists* / Treasure of the Sierra Madre: *Various artists* / Big sleep: *Various artists* / Two Mrs Carrolls: *Various artists* / Caine Mutiny: *Various* artists / To have and have not: *Various artists* / Sabrina: *Various artists* / Virginia city: *Various artists* / Key Largo: *Various artists*.
LP: . . . . **GL 43439**
MC: . . . . **GK 43439**

CLASSIC FILM SCORES OF ERICH WOLFGANG KORNGOLD (Various artists).
Tracks: / Elizabeth and Essex: *Various artists* / Prince and the pauper: *Various artists* / Anthony Adverse: *Various* artists / Sea wolf: *Various artists* / Deception: *Various artists* / Another dawn: *Various artists*/ Of human bondage: *Various artists* / Sea hawk: *Various artists* / Adventures of Robin Hood: *Various artists*/ Juarez: *Various artists* / King's row: *Various artists* / Constant nymph, The: *Various artists* / Captain Blood: *Various artists* / Between two worlds: *Various artists* / Deception: *Various artists* / Devotion: *Various artists* / Escape me never: *Various artists*.
LP: . . . . **GL 43446**
MC: . . . . **GK 43446**

CLASSIC MIKLOS ROZSA, THE (Various artists).
Tracks: / El Cid: *Nuremberg Symphony Orchestra* / Coronation: *Nuremberg Symphony Orchestra* / Story of three loves, The: Boccaccio march: *Nuremberg Symphony Orchestra* / Story of three loves, The (Finale): *Nuremberg Symphony Orchestra*/ Lost weekend, The (Love theme): *Nuremberg Symphony Orchestra* / King of Kings (Entr'acte): *Nuremberg Symphony Orchestra*/ Dead men don't wear plaid (Finale): *Nuremberg Symphony Orchestra* / Ben Hur: *Nuremberg Symphony Orchestra* / Private life of Sherlock Holmes: *Nuremberg Symphony Orchestra* / Strange love of Martha Ivers, The (Prelude): *Nuremberg* Symphony Orchestra / Strange love of Martha Ivers, The (love themes): *Nuremberg Symphony Orchestra* / Mayflower, the: *Nuremberg Symphony Orchestra* / Quo vardis domine: *Nuremberg Symphony Orchestra*.
2LP: **TER2 1135**
MC: . . . . **ZCTER 1135**
2LP: . . . . **CST 80272**

CLASSIC MOVIE MUSIC VOL 1 (Various artists).
Tracks: / Platoon: *Various artists* / Apocalypse Now: *Various artists* / Bostonians, The: *Various artists*/ Testimony: *Various artists* / Amadeus: *Various artists* / Out of Africa: *Various artists* / Brief Encounter: *Various artists*.
LP: . . . . **AVM 1006**
MC: . . . . **AVMC 1006**

CLASSIC MOVIE MUSIC VOL 2 (Various artists).
Tracks: / Trading Places: *Various artists* / 49th Parallel: *Various artists* / Eddie Duchin Story: *Various artists* / Story of Three Lovers: *Various artists* / Slaughterhouse 5: *Various artists*.
LP: . . . . **AVM 1015**
MC: . . . . **AVMC 1015**

CLASSIC MOVIE MUSIC VOL 3 (Various artists).
Tracks: / Raging Bull, Theme from: *Various artists* (Intermezzo from Cavalleria Rusticana) / Room With a View: *Various* artists / Manhattan: *Various artists* / Lonely Passion of Judith Hearne, The: *Various artists* / 2001: *Various artists* / Fantasia: *Various artists*.
LP: . . . . **AVM 1026**
MC: . . . . **AVMC 1026**

CLASSIC THEMES FOR CLASSIC FILMS (Various artists).
Tracks: / Apocalypse now: *Various artists* / Barry Lyndon: *Various artists* / Clockwork orange, A: *Various* artists / Gallipoli: *Various artists* / Elephant man: *Various artists* / Deer hunter: *Various artists*/ Diva: *Various artists* / Kramer vs Kramer: *Various artists* / Ordinary people: *Various artists* / 10: *Various artists* / Raging bull: *Various artists* / 2001: *Various artists*.
MCSET: . . . . **MGT 39495**

CLASSICS II (Various artists).
Tracks: / Excalibur: *Various artists* / Platoon: *Various artists* / Elephant Man: *Various artists* / Witches of Eastwick, The: *Various artists* / French Lieutenant's Woman, The: *Various artists* / Barry Lyndon: *Various* artists / Children of a Lesser God: *Various artists* / Untouchables, The: *Various artists* / Hannah and Her Sisters: *Various artists* / Ordinary People: *Various artists* / 10: *Various artists*.
MC: **4212604**

CLASSICS III (Various artists).
MC: **4212694**

CLOSE ENCOUNTERS OF THE THIRD KIND/STAR WARS (Composer: Charlie Gerhardt) (Various artists).
LP: . . . . **RL 12698**

CODENAME WILDGEESE (See under Eloy) (Eloy).

COMMITMENTS, THE (Film Soundtrack) (Various artists).
LP: . . . . **MCA 10286**
MC: . . . . **MCAC 10286**

COMPANY OF WOLVES (film '81 soundtrack) (Various artists).
LP: . . . . **TER 1094**

CRY BABY (Original Film Soundtrack) (Various artists).
Tracks: / King cry baby: *Intveld, James* / Doin' time: *Intveld, James* / Please, Mr. Jailer: *Sweet, Rachel*/ Teardrops are falling: *Intveld, James* / Mister Sandman: *Baldwin & The Whiffles* / Bad boy: *Jive Bombers*/ I'm so young: *Students* / I'm a bad bad girl: *Little Esther* / Cherry: *Jive Bombers* / Sh boom: *Baldwin* & The Whiffles / Teenage prayer, A: *Sweet, Rachel* / Cry baby: *Honey Sisters* / Nosey Joe: *Jackson, Bull* Moose / High school hellcats: *Intveld, James* / Flirt, The: *Shirley & Lee* / My heart goes: *Brown, Nappy*/ Jungle drums: *Bostic, Earl* / Rubber biscuit: *Chips*.
LP: . . . . **MCG 6089**
MC: . . . . **MCGC 6089**

CRY FREEDOM (1987 film soundtrack) (Various artists).
Tracks: / Crossroads-a dawn raid: *Various artists* / Gumboots: *Various artists* / Black township: *Various artists* / Shebeen Queen: *Various artists* / Asking for trouble: *Various artists* / Dangerous country: *Various artists* / Mortuary,The: *Various artists* / Funeral, The: *Various artists* / Detention: *Various artists*.
LP: . . . . **MCG 6029**
MC: . . . . **MCGC 6029**

DARKMAN (Film Soundtrack) (Elfman, Danny).
Tracks: / Darkman (main titles) / Woe, the darkman... woe / Rebuilding / Failure / Love theme / Julie transforms / Rage / Peppy science / Creating Pauley / Double durante / Plot unfolds (dancing freak), The / Carnival from Hell / Julie discovers Darkman / High steel / Finale from Darkman / Darkman (end credits).
LP: . . . . **MCA 10094**
MC: . . . . **MCAC 10094**

DEAD AGAIN (Composed by Patrick Doyle) (Various artists).
LP: . . . . **VS 5339**
MC: **C5339**

DESPERATELY SEEKING SUSAN/ MAKING MR RIGHT (1987 film soundtracks) (Various artists).
LP: . . . . **STV 81320**
MC: . . . . **CTV 81320**

DICK TRACY (Film soundtrack) (Various artists).
Tracks: / Dick Tracy (theme): *Various artists* / After the 'kid': *Various artists* / Crime spree: *Various* artists / Breathless theme: *Various artists* / Big boy, bad boy: *Various artists* / Tess' theme: *Various* artists / Slimy D.A.: *Various artists* / Breathless comes on: *Various artists* / Meet the blank: *Various* artists / Story unfolds, The: *Various artists* / Tess' theme (reprise): *Various artists* / Chase, The: *Various artists* / Showdown (reunited): *Various artists* / Dick Tracy (finale): *Various artists*.
LP: **7599262361**
MC: **7599262364**

DIVA COLLECTION (Various artists).
Tracks: / Can't help lovin' dat man: *Gardner, Ava* / My heart tells me: *Grable, Betty* / Then it isn't love: *Lombard*, Carol / I don't know why: *Bacall, Lauren & Bing Crosby* / Ramona: *Del Rio, Dolores* / It's oh so quiet: *Hutton*, Betty / Heatwave: *Monroe, Marilyn* / Goodnight my love: *Faye, Alice* / Paradise: *Lamour, Dorothy*/ Reckless: *Harlow, Jean* / I never knew heaven could speak: *Crawford, Joan* / Amado mio: *Hayworth, Rita*/ Love: *Swanson, Gloria* / Mambo bacan: *Loren, Sophia* / They're either too young or too old: *Davis, Bette*/ What do I care?: *Bankhead, Tallulah* / I'm in the mood for love: *West, Mae* / Ain't there anyone here for love?: *Russell, Jane* / Ich bin die fesche Lola: *Dietrich, Marlene* / Chica chica boom chic: *Miranda, Carmen*.
LP: . . . . **DVLP 2118**
MC: . . . . **DVMC 2118**

D.O.A. (Film Soundtrack) (Jankel, Chas).
LP: **704.610**

DOCTOR ZHIVAGO/RYAN'S DAUGHTER (Various artists).
Tracks: / Dr Zhivago overture: *Various artists* (Doctor Zhivago) / Doctor Zhivago (main title): *Various artists*(Doctor Zhivago) / Lara leaves Yuri: *Various artists* (Doctor Zhivago) / At the student cafe: *Various artists*(Doctor Zhivago) / Komarovsky and Lara's rendezvous: *Various artists* (Doctor Zhivago) / Revolution: *Various artists*(Doctor Zhivago) / Lara's theme: *Various artists* (Doctor Zhivago) / Funeral, The: *Various artists* (Doctor Zhivago) / Sventytski's waltz: *Various artists* (Doctor Zhivago) / Yuri escapes: *Various artists* (Doctor Zhivago) / Tonya arrives at Varykino: *Various artists* (Doctor Zhivago) / Yuri writes a poem for Lara: *Various artists* (Doctor Zhivago) / Ryan's daughter (main title): *Various artists* (Ryan's daughter) / Major, The: *Various artists* (Ryan's daughter) / You don't want me then: *Various artists* (Ryan's daughter) / Michael's theme: *Various artists* (Ryan's daughter) / Ride through the woods: *Various artists* (Ryan's daughter) / Obsession: *Various artists* (Ryan's daughter) / Shakes, The: *Various artists* (Ryan's daughter) / Rosy on the beach: *Various artists* (Ryan's daughter) / Song of the Irish rebels: *Various artists* (Ryan's daughter) / Rosy and the schoolmaster: *Various artists* (Ryan's daughter) / Michael shows

Randolph his strange treasure: *Various artists* (Ryan's daughter) / Rosy's theme: *Various artists*(Ryan's daughter).
LP: **LPMGM 3**
MC: **TCMGM 3**

DRIVIN' MOVIE THEMES (Various artists).
MC: **TC-MMC 5015**

DROID WORLD (Various artists).
LP: **D 453**
MC: **D 153DC**

DUTCH (Original Soundtrack) (Various artists).
LP: **VS 5336**
MC: **C5336**

DYING YOUNG (Composed by Kenny G - Original Soundtrack) (Various artists).
LP: **211952**
MC: **411952**

EDWARD SCISSORHANDS (Film Soundtrack) (Elfman, Danny).
Tracks: / Edward Scissorhands (main titles) / Story time / Castle on the hill / Cookie factory / Edwardo the barber / Etiquette lesson / Ballet de suburbia (suite) / Death / Final confrontation / Edward Scissorhands (finale) / Farewell / Ice dance / Home sweet home / Esmeralda / Helst / Rampage / Plot unfolds / Edward Scissorhands (end credits) / Beautiful new world / With these sands.
MC: **MCAC 10133**

EIGHTEEN TV/FILM THEMES (Various artists).
Tracks: / To have and to hold: *Stock, Catherine* / Me and my girl: *Skellern, Peter* / Cats eyes: *Kongos*, John / Two of us, The: *Silsoe* / Aztec gold: *Silsoe* / Walk on: *New Horizon* / Tales of the unexpected: *Grainer, Ron Orchestra* / Cavatina: *Williams, John* / Prospects: *Made in England* / Dempsey and Makepeace: *Various artists* / Woman of substance: *Various artists* / Reilly: *Various artists* / Anna of the five towns: *Various artists* / All passion spent: *Various artists* / Onedin line, The: *Various artists* / Love for Lydia: *Various artists* / Lillie: *Various artists* / Monsignor Quixote: *Various artists.*
LP: **FEDM 1**
MC: **CFEDM 1**

EMPIRE MOVIE MUSIC COLLECTION (Various artists).
Tracks: / On Earth as it is in heaven: *London Philharmonic Orchestra* / Last Emperor (main title): *Byrne, David*/ Merry Christmas Mr Lawrence: *Sakamoto, Ryuichi* / Black rain suite: *Zimmer, Hans* / Looks like a tablecloth: *Martinez, Cliff* / Homeboy: *Clapton, Eric* / C'est le vent Betty: *Yared, Gabriel* / Key, The: *Fenton, George* / Etude: *Oldfield, Mike* / Call to arms, A: *Horner, James* / Les modernes: *Krause, Steven.*
LP: **VMM 1**
MC: **TCVMM 1**

EPIC FILM SCORES (Various artists).
Tracks: / King of Kings main theme: *Various artists* / Nativity: *Various artists* / Miracles of Christ: *Various artists* / Salome's dance: *Various artists* / Way of the cross: *Various artists* / Resurrection and finale: *Various artists* / Ben Hur love theme: *Various artists* / Victory parade: *Various artists* / Miracle and finale: *Various artists* / El Cid overture: *Various artists* / Palace music: *Various artists* / Legend and epilogue, The: *Various artists.*
LP: **VC 81104**

EPIC FILM SCORES (Various artists).
Tracks: / Ben Hur prelude: *Various artists* / Ben Hur love theme: *Various artists* / Parade of the charioteers: *Various artists* / Mother's love, The: *Various artists* / El Cid overture: *Various artists* / El Cid love theme: *Various artists* / El Cid march: *Various artists* / King of Kings nativity: *Various artists* / Way of the cross, The: *Various artists* / Pieta: *Various artists* / King of Kings theme: *Various artists*/ Quo vadis triumphal march: *Various artists* / Quo vadis love theme: *Various artists* / Domine: *Various artists.*
LP: **CN 7013**

FABULOUS BAKER BOYS, THE (1989 Film Soundtrack) (Various artists).
Tracks: / Makin' whoopee: *Pfeiffer, Michelle* / My funny valentine: *Pfeiffer, Michelle* / Do nothin' till you hear from me: *Ellington, Duke* / Moonglow: *Goodman, Benny.*
LP: **GRP 20021**
MC: **GRP 20024**

FALLING IN LOVE (1985 Film Soundtrack) (Grusin, Dave).
LP: **GRPA 9522**
DAT: **GRT 9522**

FELLINI FILM THEMES (Various artists).
Tracks: / Amarcord: *Various artists* / Juliet of the spirits: *Various artists* / 8-1/2: *Various artists*/ La dolce vita: *Various artists* / Satyricon Roma: *Various artists* / White sheik: *Various artists* / I vitelloni: *Various artists* / Il bidone: *Various artists* / Nights of Cabiria: *Various artists* / La strada: *Various artists.*
LP: **HNBL 9301**
MC: **HNBC 9301**

FELLINI/ROTA (Film Soundtracks: Music From the Films of Felli (Various artists).
Tracks: / White Sheikh, The: *Various artists* / I vitelloni: *Various artists* / La strada: *Various artists*/ Swindle (il bidone), The: *Various artists* / La notti di cabiria: *Various artists* / La dolce vita: *Various* artists / 8/1/2: *Various artists* / Juliet of the spirits: *Various artists* / Toby Dammit - The clowns: *Various* artists / Satyricon-roma: *Various artists* / Amarcord: *Various artists* / Il casanova (o venezia, venaga): *Various artists* / Il casanova (pin penin): *Various artists* / Orchestra rehearsal: *Various artists.*
LP: **FILM 004**
MC: **FILMC 004**

FILM 81 (Various artists).
LP: **73634**
MC: **40 73634**

FILM MUSIC OF DIMITRI TIOMKIN (Various artists).
Tracks: / Roman Empire overture: *Tiomkin, Dimitri* / Pax Romana: *Tiomkin, Dimitri* / Guns of Navarone: *Tiomkin,* Dimitri / Wild is the wind: *Tiomkin, Dimitri* / Rhapsody of steel: *Tiomkin, Dimitri* / President's country: *Tiomkin, Dimitri.*
MC: **JST 44370**
LP: **DKP 9047**

FILM MUSIC OF FRANZ WAXMAN, THE (Queensland Symphony Orchestra).
LP: **704.320**

FILM MUSIC OF JOHN BARRY (16 Great themes) (Various artists).
Tracks: / Born free: *Various artists* / Lion in Winter, The: *Various artists* / Wrong box, The: *Various artists*/ Ipcress file, The: *Various artists* / Thunderball: *Various artists* / Whisperers, The: *Various artists*/ Goldfinger: *Various artists.*
MC: **JST 44376**

FILM MUSIC OF LEE HOLDRIDGE, THE (Various artists).
Tracks: / Wizards and warriors: *London Symphony Orchestra* / Splash: *London Symphony Orchestra* / Great whales, The: *London Symphony Orchestra* / Heming way play - Parisian sketch: *London Symphony Orchestra* / Going home: *London* Symphony Orchestra / Journey, The: *London Symphony Orchestra* / Beastmaster suite, The: *London Symphony Orchestra*/ Music for strings: *London Symphony Orchestra* / East of Eden (suite): *London Symphony Orchestra.*
LP: **704.290**
MC: **C704.290**

FILM MUSIC OF SIR WILLIAM WALTON (London Philharmonic Orchestra).
Tracks: / Henry V (suite) / Battle of Britain / Troilus and Cressida / As You Like It / History of English Speaking Peoples.
LP: **EL 270591-1**
MC: **EL 270591-4**

FILM MUSIC VOL 2 (Various artists).
LP: **DKP 9042**

FIRESTARTER (Film Soundtrack - Composed by Tangerine Dream) (Various artists).
Tracks: / Crystal voice: *Various artists* / Testlab: *Various artists* / Escaping point: *Various artists*/ Burning force: *Various artists* / Shop territory: *Various artists* / Out of the heat: *Various artists*/ Run, The: *Various artists* / Charly the kid: *Various artists* / Rainbirds move: *Various artists* / Between realities: *Various artists* / Flash final: *Various artists.*
LP: **MCF 3233**
MC: **MCFC 3233**
LP: **MCA 6131**
MC: **MCAC 6131**
MC: **VSC 5251**

FOUR MUSKETEERS AND OTHER SCORES (See under Four Musketeers...) (Various artists).

FREDDY'S DEAD - THE FINAL NIGHTMARE (Composed by Brian May - Original Soundtrack) (Various artists).
LP: **VS 5333**
MC: **VSC 5333**
LP: **ZORRO 33**

GANGSTERS AND GOOD GUYS (Various artists).
Tracks: / Public enemy, The: *Various artists* / Petrified forest, The: *Various artists* / Each dawn I die: *Various* artists / High sierra: *Various artists* / Angels with dirty faces: *Various artists* / Key Largo: *Various* artists / White heat: *Various artists* / Roaring 20's, The: *Various artists* / Big sleep: *Various artists*/ Maltese Falcon: *Various artists* / To have and have not: *Various artists* / Across the Pacific: *Various artists* / Treasure of the Sierra Madre: *Various artists* / Casablanca: *Various artists.*
LP: **PL 70566**
MC: **PK 70566**

GARBO (Soundtracks Of Various MGM Films) (Various artists).
Tracks: / Foreward: *Pidgeon, Walter* / Grand Hotel: *Garbo, Greta & John Barrymore* / Queen Christina: *Garbo,* Greta & John Gilbert / Camille: *Garbo, Greta & Robert Taylor* / Conquest: *Garbo, Greta & Charles Boyer* / Ninotchka: *Various artists* / Susan Lennox, her rise and fall: *Garbo, Greta & Clark Gable* / Anna Christie: *Garbo, Greta & Marie Dressler* / Anna Karenina: *Garbo, Greta & Frederick March* / Mata Hari: *Various artists.*
LP: **2353 059**

GHAZALS FROM FILMS VOLUME 2 (Various artists).
LP: **CDPMLP 5348**

GHOSTBUSTERS 2 (Various artists).
LP: **MCG 6056**
MC: **MCGC 6056**

GOLDEN AGE OF CLASSIC BRITISH FILM THEMES OF 40' (Various artists).
Tracks: / Way to the stars, The: *Two Cities Symphony Orchestra* (Conducted by Charles Williams. Composer: Brodszky. Themes from the film) / Cornish rhapsody: *London Symphony Orchestra* (From 'Love Story'. Conducted by Hubert Bath. Composer: Hubert Bath) / Voice in the night, A: *Queen's Hall Light Orchestra* (Theme from 'Wanted for Murder'. Conducted by Charles Williams. Composer:) / Warsaw concerto: *London Symphony Orchestra* (Recorded from the soundtrack of the RKO film 'Dangerous Moonlight'. Cond) / Dream of Olwen and incidental music, The: *Williams, Charles and His Orchestra* (From the Edward Dryhurst film 'While I Live'. Composer: Charles Williams) / Mansell concerto, The: *Williams, Charles and His Orchestra* (From the Associated British-Bow Bells film 'The Woman's Angle'.) / Saga of Odette, The: *Williams, Charles and His Orchestra*(From the Wilcox-Neagle production 'Odette'. Composer: A Collins.) / Carriage and Pair: *Williams, Charles and His Orchestra*(From the film 'So Long At The Fair'. Composer: Benjamin Frankel.) / Long forgotten melody: *Williams, Charles and His Orchestra*(From the film 'So Long At The Fair'. Composer: Benjamin Frankel.) / Portrait of Clare: *Williams, Charles and His Orchestra*(From the film 'Portrait of Clare'. Transcribed and arranged from Schuman) / Beggar's theme, The: *Williams, Charles and His* Orchestra (Featured in the film 'The Last Holiday'. Composer: Chagrin.) / Voice in the night, A: *Queen's Hall Light Orchestra*(Theme from 'Wanted for Murder'. Conducted by Charles Williams. Composer:).
LP: **GX 41 2551**
MC: **TCGX 2551**

GOLDEN AGE OF HOLLYWOOD STARS (Various artists).
Tracks: / Don Juan: *Various artists* / Jazz singer, The: *Various artists* / Little Caesar: *Various artists*/ Public Enemy, The: *Various artists* / Gold diggers of 1933: *Various artists* / I'm a fugative from a chain gang: *Various artists* / Captain Blood: *Various artists* / Misummer night's dream, A: *Various artists* / Adventures of Robin Hood: *Various artists* / Jezebel: *Various artists* / Dark victory: *Various artists* / Angels with dirty faces: *Various artists* / Maltese Falcon: *Various artists* / Sea hawk, The: *Various artists*/ King's row: *Various artists* / High sierra: *Various artists* / Now, Voyager: *Various artists* / Arsenic and old lace: *Various artists* / Mildred Pierce: *Various artists* / Big sleep: *Various artists* / White heat: *Various artists.*
2LP: **USD 311**

GOLDEN SONGS FROM THE SILVER SCREEN (Various artists).
MC: **TCMFP 50453**
LP: **MFP 50453**

GOLDEN SONGS OF STAGE AND SCREEN (Various artists).
Tracks: / Around the world in: *Monro, Matt* (From Around The World In Eighty Days.) / Somewhere my love: *Dodd, Ken*(Lara's theme from Dr. Zhivago.) / Evergreen: *Love, Geoff & His Orchestra & Singers* (From A Star Is Born.) / Day by day: *Laine, Cleo* (From Godspell.) / Summer knows, The: *Gillies, Stuart* (From the summer of '42.) / Send in the clowns: *Love, Geoff & His Orchestra & Singers* (From A Little Night Music.) / Edelweiss: *Hill, Vince* (From The Sound Of Music.) / Somewhere: *Bassey, Shirley* (From West Side Story.) / Long ago: *Love, Geoff & His Orchestra & Singers*(From No No Nannette) / People: *Bassey, Shirley* (Funny girl.) / Don't cry for me Argentina: *Love, Geoff & His Orchestra & Singers* (From Evita.) / Soliloquy: *Hill, Vince* / Where do I begin: *Love, Geoff & His Orchestra & Singers*(From Love Story.) / Gonna build a mountain: *Monro, Matt* / Alfie: *Black, Cilla* (From Alfie.) / How to handle a woman: *Young, Robert* (From Camelot.) / Sunrise, sunset: *Dodd, Ken* (From Fiddler On The Roof.).
MC: **HR 8139**

GOLDEN THEMES OF HOLLYWOOD (Various artists) (Various artists).
Tracks: / Around the world in 80 days: *Various artists* / Picnic: *Various artists* / Sparatcus - love theme: *Various* artists / Robe - love theme: *Various artists* / Magnificent obsession: *Various artists* / Madame X - Swedish rhapsody: *Various artists* / Tammy - main title and Tammy: *Various artists* / Eddy Duchin story - To love again: *Various artists* / Anastasia: *Various artists* / Imitation of life - To whom the bells toll: *Various artists*/ Love theme - From here to eternity: *Various artists.*
LP: **CPS 78**

GOLDEN VOICES FROM THE SILVER SCREEN VOL 3 (Various artists).
Tracks: / Dhoondo dhoondo re: *Mangeshkar, Lata* / Saqiya aaj mujhe: *Bhosle & Chorus, Asha* / Satyam shivam (part 1): *Mangeshkar, Lata* / Ab reat guzarne vali: *Mangeshkar, Lata* / Leke pahla ahla pyar: *Bhosle/Begum/Rafi*/ Hondton pe aisi: *Mangeshkar/Bupinder* / Salam e ishq: *Mangeshkar, Lata* / Aaj ki raat: *Bhosle & Chorus,* Asha / Satyam shivam (part 2): *Mangeshkar, Lata* / Jean Pehchaan no: *Rafi, Mohammed* / Toote na dil toote na: *Mukesh.*
LP: **ORBAD 059**

GOLDEN VOICES FROM THE SILVER SCREEN VOL.2 (Various artists).
LP: **ORBAD 056**

GOLDEN VOICES FROM THE SILVER SCREEN VOL.1 (Various artists).
LP: **ORBAD 054**

GREAT BALLS OF FIRE (Film Soundtrack) (Various artists).
LP: **839 516 1**
MC: **839 516 4**

GREAT CINEMA THEMES (Various artists).
Tracks: / '2001': *Various artists* / Clockwork orange, A: *Various artists* / La traviata: *Various artists*/ Apocalypse now: *Various artists* / Death in Venice: *Various artists* / Elvira madigan: *Various artists.*
LPS: **4138731**

GREAT FILM CLASSICS VOL.2 (Various artists).
LP: **2535469**

GREAT FILM COMPOSERS (Various artists).
LP: **2489 123**

GREAT FILM MUSIC (Various artists).
Tracks: / Spitfire prelude & fugue: *Various artists* / Henry V: *Various artists* / Richard II: *Various artists*/ Escape me never: *Various artists* / Oliver twist: *Various artists* / 49th parallel: *Various artists*/ Things to come: *Various artists.*
LP: **4118371**

GREAT HOLLYWOOD MUSICALS (Various artists).
LP: **ACH 023**
MC: **CCH 023**

GREAT MGM STARS: GENE KELLY (See under Kelly, Gene) (Kelly, Gene).

GREAT MGM STARS: HOWARD KEEL (See under Keel, Howard) (Keel, Howard).

GREAT SCREEN LOVERS COLLECTION (Various artists).
Tracks: / Who is there among...?: *Nicholson, Jack* / Chattanooga choo choo: *Power, Tyrone* / Louise: *Chevalier,* Maurice / Manhattan: *Rooney, Mickey* / Let's do it: *Coward, Noel* / Foolish pride: *Mitchum, Robert*/ Puttin' on the Ritz: *Gable, Clarke* / Two of us, The: *Curtis, Tony & Gloria De Haven* / Let's make love: *Montand,* Yves / Day after day: *Stewart, James* / Did I remember?: *Grant, Cary* / Kashmiri love song: *Valentino,* Rudolph / Pillow talk: *Hudson, Rock* / Mary's a grand old name: *Cagney, James* / Woman in love: *Brando,* Marlon & Jean Simmons / As

long as there is music: *Sinatra, Frank* / Chico's choo choo: *Wagner, Robert & Debbie* Reynolds / Lover come back to me: *Various artists* / All I do is dream of you: *Kelly, Gene* / Gotta bran' new suit: *Astaire & Fabray*.
LP: . . . . **DVLP 2117**
MC: . . . . **DVMC 2117**

GREAT WARNER BROTHERS LOVE THEMES (Various artists).
Tracks: / Summer place, A (theme from): *Various artists* / Klute: *Various artists* / Thief who came to dinner: *Various artists* / Lovers must learn: *Various artists* / Love is never out of style: *Various artists*/ Parrish: *Various artists* / Hotel: *Various artists* / Summer of '42: *Various artists* / Bullitt: *Various* artists / Enter the dragon: *Various artists* / Petulia: *Various artists* / Madwoman of Chaillot: *Various artists* / Private lives of Elizabeth and Essex: *Various artists*.
LP: . . . . **K 26122**
MC: **K4 26122**

GREAT WARNER BROTHERS SPECTACULARS (Various artists).
Tracks: / Towering inferno: *Various artists* / Battle of the bulge: *Various artists* / Damned, The: *Various* artists / Swarm: *Various artists* / Sea hawk: *Various artists* / Private lives of Elizabeth and Essex: *Various artists*.
LP: . . . . **K 26121**
MC: **K4 26121**

GREAT WESTERN FILM THEMES (Various artists).
Tracks: / Magnificent seven, The: *Various artists* / March of the horse soldiers: *Various artists* / Joe Bass and the scalphunters: *Various artists* / Big country: *Various artists* / High noon: *Various artists* / Duel at Diablo: *Various artists* / Return of the seven: *Various artists* / Way west: *Various artists*/ Wonderful country: *Various artists* / Hour of the gun: *Various artists* / Unforgiven: *Various artists*/ Green leaves of summer: *Various artists* / McLintock: *Various artists* / Hallelujah trail: *Various artists*.
LP: . . . . **SLS 50425**
MC: . . . . **TCT 50425**

GREAT WESTERN FILM THEMES COLLECTION (Various artists).
Tracks: / Magnificent Seven, The: *Various artists* / Big Country, The: *Various artists* / Scalphunters, The: *Various* artists / One-eyed Jacks: *Various artists* / High Noon: *Various artists* / Way West, The: *Various artists*/ Duel at Diabola: *Various artists* / Wonderful country, The: *Various artists* / Hour of the gun: *Various* artists / Unforgiven, The: *Various artists* / Alamo, The: *Various artists* / McLintock: *Various artists*/ Katherine: *Various artists* / Good, the bad and the ugly, The: *Various artists* / How the West was Won: *Various* artists / Big Gundown: *Various artists* / Hang 'em High: *Various artists* / Young Billy Young: *Various* artists / Fistful of dollars: *Various artists* / For a few dollars more: *Various artists* / Misfits, The: *Various artists* / True Grit: *Various artists* / Navajo Joe: *Various artists* / Professional gun: *Various artists* / Streets of Laredo: *Various artists*.
2LP: . . . . **UAD 60079/80**

GREAT WESTERN MOVIE THEMES (Various artists).
MC: . . . . **VCA 102**

GREAT WESTERN THEMES (Various artists).
Tracks: / Gunlaw: *Various artists* / Maverick: *Various artists* / Rawhide: *Various artists* / Laramie: *Various artists* / Bonanza: *Various artists* / Boots and saddles: *Various artists* / Call of the faraway hills, The: *Various artists* / Last round-up, The: *Various artists* / Wagon train: *Various artists* / Bronco: *Various artists* / Deputy, The: *Various artists* / Cheyenne: *Various artists* / Wells Fargo: *Various* artists / High noon: *Various artists* / Wyatt Earp: *Various artists* / Sugarfoot: *Various artists*/ Chaquito: *Various artists* / Good, the bad and the ugly, The: *Various artists* / Big country, The: *Various artists* / Cascading strings: *Various artists* / Raindrops keep fallin' on my head: *Various artists*.
MCSET: . . . . **DTO 10200**

GREAT WESTERN THEMES (see under Great western themes) (Various artists).

GREATEST MOVIE THEMES (Various artists).
MC: . . . . **AIM 38**

GREATEST WESTERN THEMES,THE (Various artists).
Tracks: / Good, the bad and the ugly, The: *Various artists* / Ghost riders in the sky: *Various artists* / Fistful of dollars: A: *Various artists* / Man who shot Liberty Valance, The: *Various artists* / Hanging tree, The: *Various* artists / Streets of Laredo: *Various artists* / Hang 'em high: *Various artists* / High Chaparral: *Various* artists / Bonanza: *Various artists* / For a few dollars more: *Various artists* / Big country, The: *Various artists* / Magnificent seven, The: *Various artists* / Shenandoah: *Various artists* / Red River Valley: *Various artists* / Once upon a time in the west: *Various artists*.
LP: . . . . **ONE 1279**
MC: . . . . **OCE 2279**

HALLOWEEN (Film soundtrack) (Various artists).
LP: . . . . **CL 0008**
MC: . . . . **CTV 81176**

HALLOWEEN 2 (Film soundtrack) (Various artists).
LP: . . . . **CL 0009**
LP: . . . . **STV 81152**
LP: . . . . **CST 8040**
MC: . . . . **CTV 81152**

HALLOWEEN 3 (Film soundtrack) (Various artists).
LP: . . . . **VS 5243**
MC: . . . . **VSC 5243**
LP: . . . . **MCA 6115**

HALLOWEEN 4 (Film soundtrack) (Various artists).
LP: . . . . **VS 5205**
MC: . . . . **VSC 5205**

HALLOWEEN 5 (Film soundtrack) (Various artists).
Tracks: / Romeo Romeo: *Becca* / Dancin' on Churchill: *Churchill* / Sporting woman: *Diggy/Chosak/Clark*/ Shape also rises, The: *Howarth, Alan* / First victim: *Howarth, Alan* / Tower farm: *Howarth, Alan* / Trapped: *Howarth, Alan* / Jailbreak: *Howarth, Alan* / Anything for money: *DVB* / Second time around: *Rhythm* Tribe / Halloween 5 - the revenge: *Howarth, Alan* / Evil child must die: *Howarth, Alan* / Stranger in the house: *Howarth, Alan* / Stop the rage: *Howarth, Alan* / Attic, The: *Howarth, Alan* / Halloween finale: *Howarth, Alan*.
LP: . . . . **VS 5239**
MC: . . . . **VSC 5239**

HELLO DOLLY (Original film soundtrack) (Various artists).
Tracks: / Just leave everything to me: *Various artists* / It takes a woman: *Various artists* / Put on your Sunday clothes: *Various artists* / Ribbons down my back: *Various artists* / Dancing: *Various artists* / Before the parade passes by: *Various artists* / Elegance: *Various artists* / Love is only love: *Various artists*/ Hello, Dolly: *Various artists* / It only takes a moment: *Various artists* / So long dearie: *Various artists*/ Finale: *Various artists*.
LP: **810 368-1**
MC: **810 368-4**

HOLLYWOOD SOUNDSTAGE, VOL. 1 (Various artists).
MC: . . . . **VSC 5301**

HOT SHOTS (By Sylvester Levay) (Various artists).
LP: . . . . **VS 5338**
MC: . . . . **VSC 5338**

HUDSON HAWK (Film Soundtrack) (Various artists).
LP: . . . . **VS 5323**
MC: . . . . **VSC 5323**

I'M GONNA GIT YOU SUCKA (Various artists).
Tracks: / I'm gonna git you sucka: *Gap Band* / Clean up your act: *Jackson, Jermaine* / He's a fly guy: *Mayfield, Curtis* / If ever a love there was: *Four Tops/Aretha Franklin* / Magic man: *Holiday, Jennifer*.
LP: **209622**
MC: **409622**

IMMORTAL FILM MUSIC OF MIKLOS ROZSA (Various artists).
Tracks: / Young Bess: *Various artists* / Lust of life: *Various artists* / Lady Hamilton: *Various artists*/ Asphalt jungle, The: *Various artists* / Thief of Baghdad, The: *Various artists* / Lydia: *Various artists*/ Killers: *Various artists* / Time to love and a time to die, The: *Various artists* / Lost weekend: *Various artists*.
LP: . . . . **MOIR 101**
MC: . . . . **CMOIR 101**

JACOB'S LADDER (Original soundtrack) (Various artists).
LP: . . . . **VS 5291**
MC: . . . . **VSC 5291**

JAMES BOND 007 (See under Shaw, Roland) (Shaw, Roland Orchestra).

JAMES BOND:GREATEST HITS (Various artists).
Tracks: / James Bond theme: *Norman, Monty & Studio Orchestra* / Kingston calypso: *Norman, Monty & Studio Orchestra*/ Under the mango tree: *Norman, Monty & Studio Orchestra* / From Russia with love: *Monro, Matt* / Goldfinger: *Bassey*, Shirley / 007: *Barry, John & Studio Orchestra* / Thunderball: *Jones, Tom* / You only live twice: *Sinatra*, Nancy / On her Majesty's secret service: *Barry, John & Studio Orchestra* / We have all the time in the world: *Armstrong*, Louis / Diamonds are forever: *Bassey, Shirley* / Live and let die: *McCartney, Paul & Wings* / Just a closer walk with thee: *Dejan, Harold A. "Duke" & The Olympia Brass Band* / New second line: *Dejan, Harold A. "Duke" & The* Olympia Brass Band / Bond meets Solitaire: *Martin, George & Studio Orchestra* / Man with the golden gun, The: *Lulu*/ Bond '77: *Hamlisch, Marvin & Studio Orchestra* / Moonraker: *Bassey, Shirley* / For your eyes only: *Easton, Sheena* / Nobody does it better: *Simon, Carly*.
LP: . . . . **EMTV 007**
MC: . . . . **TCEMTV 007**

KENTUCKIAN, THE AND OTHER FILM THEMES (See under Kentuckian) (Various artists).

KENTUCKIAN, THE AND OTHER FILM THEMES (Various artists).
Tracks: / Kentuckian, The: *Various artists* / Down to the sea in ships: *Various artists* / Day the earth stood still: *Various artists* / In love and war: *Various artists* / Sunrise at Campobello: *Various artists*.
LP: . . . . **ERS 6506**

KING AND I, THE (Film Soundtrack) (Various artists).
Tracks: / I whistle a happy tune: *Various artists* / My lord and master: *Various artists* / Hello, young lovers: *Various artists* / March of the Siamese children: *Various artists* / Puzzlement, A: *Various artists* / Getting to know you: *Various artists* / We kiss in a shadow: *Various artists* / I have dreamed: *Various artists*/ Shall I tell you what I think of you?: *Various artists* / Something wonderful: *Various artists* / Song of the King: *Various artists* / Shall we dance?: *Various artists* / Something wonderful: *Various artists* (finale).
LP: . . . . **SLCT 6108**
MC: . . . . **TCSW 740**

KING OF KINGS/GREATEST STORY EVER TOLD (See under King of Kings) (Various artists).

LA BAMBA (2) (More Music from the Film) (Various artists).
Tracks: / Ready Teddy: *Little Richard* / Chantilly lace: *Big Bopper* / Tweedlee dee: *Various artists*/ Don't you just know it?: *Smith, Huey & The Clowns* / Betty Jean: *Berry, Chuck* / La Bamba: *Valens, Ritchie*/ Sleepwalk: *Santo & Johnny* / Over the mountain across the sea: *Johnnie & Joe* / For your precious love: *Butler*, Jerry & The Impressions / This I swear: *Skyliners* / Smoke gets in your eyes: *Platters* / Donna: *Valens, Ritchie*.
MC: . . . . **LONC 56**
LP: . . . . **LONLP 56**

LABYRINTH (Film Soundtrack) (Various artists).
Tracks: / Underground: *Bowie, David* / Into the labyrinth: *Various artists* / Magic dance: *Bowie, David*/ Sarah: *Various artists* / Chilly down: *Various artists* / Hallucination: *Various artists* / As the world falls down: *Bowie, David* / Goblin battle, The: *Various artists* / Within you: *Various artists* / Thirteen o'clock: *Various artists* / Home at last: *Various artists* / Underground (reprise): *Bowie, David*.
LP: . . . . **AML 3104**
MC: . . . . **TCAML 3104**

LAST VALLEY, THE (Film Soundtrack) (Various artists).
Tracks: / Last valley, The (main title): *Various artists* / Last valley: *Various artists* / Shrine: *Various* artists / Evening song: *Various artists* / Plague pit: *Various artists* / Village attack: *Various artists*/ Children's song: *Various artists* / Attack at Rheinfelden: *Various artists* / Last valley, The part 2 (main title): *Various artists* / Last valley: *Various artists* / Christmas song, The: *Various artists* / Witch burning: *Various artists* / Offertory chant: *Various artists* / Vogel leaves the valley: *Various artists*/ Death of the captain/ End title: *Various artists*.
LP: . . . . **SPB 1027**

LEADING LADIES FROM AROUND THE WORLD (Various artists).
LP: . . . . **A 510**
MC: . . . . **C 510**

LICENCE TO KILL (Film soundtrack) (Various artists).
Tracks: / Licence to kill: *Various artists* / Dirty love: *Various artists* / If you asked me to: *Various* artists / His funny valentine: *Various artists* / Ninja: *Various artists* / Wedding party: *Various artists*/ Pam: *Various artists* / James and Felix on their way to church: *Various artists* / Sanchez is in the Bahamas (Shark fishing): *Various artists* / Licence revoked: *Various artists*.
LP: . . . . **MCG 6051**
MC: . . . . **MCGC 6051**

LOST HORIZON (Various artists).
Tracks: / Lost horizon suite: *Various artists* / Guns of Navarone (prelude): *Various artists* / Big sky, The (prelude): *Various artists* / Forest at night (nocturne): *Various artists* / Wide Missouri, The (epilogue): *Various artists*/ Fourposter, The (overture): *Various artists* / Friendly persuasion (love scene in the barn): *Various artists*/ Search for paradise (choral finale): *Various artists*.
MC: . . . . **GK 91669**

LUNATIC (Various artists).
LP: . . . . **MLPS 1086**
MC: . . . . **MCT 1086**

MIDNIGHT COWBOY (Film Soundtrack) (Barry, John).
Tracks: / Everybody's talkin' / Joe Buck rides again / Famous myth, A / Fun City / He quit me man / Jungle gym at the zoo / Midnight cowboy / Old man Willow / Florida fantasy / Tears and joys / Science fiction / Everybody's talkin'.
LP: . . . . **LBR 1036**

MIKLOS ROZSA: CHAMBER MUSIC (Various artists).
LP: . . . . **CN 6001**

MORE AMADEUS (Various artists).
LP: . . . . **LONLP 7**
MC: . . . . **LONC 7**

MOVIE BUSTERS (Various artists).
Tracks: / Ghostbusters: *Various artists* / Footloose: *Various artists* / Chariots of fire: *Various artists*/ Arthur's theme: *Various artists* / Flashdance... what a feeling: *Various artists* / Love on the rocks: *Various* artists / E.T., Theme from: *Various artists* / It might be you: *Various artists* / Eye of the tiger: *Various* artists / Maniac: *Various artists* / Against all odds: *Various artists* / Let's hear it for the boy: *Various* artists / Up where we belong: *Various artists* / For your eyes only: *Various artists* / Carol Anne's theme: *Various artists* / Terms of endearment: *Various artists*.
LP: . . . . **BER 001**
MC: . . . . **KBER 001**

MOVIE COLLECTION (Various artists).
2LP: **2675178**

MOVIE GREATS (Various artists).
Tracks: / Jaws: *Various artists* / Flying (theme from E.T.): *Various artists* / Axel F: *Various artists*/ Back to the future: *Various artists* / Somewhere in time: *Various artists* / Fletch theme: *Various artists*/ Entertainer, The: *Various artists* (from "The Sting") / Overture (from: Jesus Christ Superstar): *Various artists*/ Love story theme: *Various artists* / River, The: *Various artists* / Main title: *Various artists* (From the film 'Out of Africa'.) / Over the moon (E.T. the Extra-Terrestial): *Various artists*.
LP: . . . . **MCL 1860**
MC: . . . . **MCLC 1860**

MOVIE MASTERS (16 original soundtrack recordings) (Various artists).
Tracks: / Godfather, The: *Various artists* / Great Gatsby: *Various artists* / Oh what a lovely war: *Various* artists / Odd couple: *Various artists* / Chinatown: *Various artists* / Borsalino: *Various artists*/ Nashville: *Various artists* / Love story: *Various artists* / Serpico: *Various artists* / Song of Norway: *Various artists* / Ten commandments: *Various artists* / Dove: *Various artists* / Easy rider: *Various artists* / Shaft in Africa: *Various artists*.
LP: . . . . **ABCL 5205**

MOVIE MONDO (Various artists).
LP: . . . . **WIK 90**

(MOVIE MUSICALS 1927-1936) (Classic Years in Digital Stereo) (Various artists).
Tracks: / Fine romance, A: *Astaire, Fred & Ginger Rogers* / Three little words: *Ellington, Duke* / My mammy: *Jolson*, Al / My man: *Brice, Fanny* / What would you do: *Chevalier, Maurice* / Beyond the blue horizon: *McDonald*, Joe / I love you so much that I hate you: *Swan Song* / It's only a paper moon: *Edwards, Cliff* / I'm no angel: *West, Mae* / 42nd Street: *Keeler, Ruby/Dick Powell* / Learn to croon: *Crosby, Bing* / On the good ship lollipop: *Temple, Shirley* / Okay toots: *Cantor, Eddie* / Lulu's back in town: *Powell, Dick* / Old man river: *Robeson, Paul* / Bojangles of Harlem: *Astaire, Fred*.
LP: . . . . **REB 654**
MC: . . . . **ZCF 654**

MOVIE MUSICALS 1930-1938 (Classic years in digital stereo) (Various artists).

Tracks: / Broadway melody: *Various artists* / Everybody sing: *Various artists* / Let's sing again: *Various* artists / Rose Marie: *Various artists* / Some of these days: *Various artists* / I'm putting all my eggs in one basket: *Various artists* / About a quarter to nine: *Various artists* / Lullaby of Broadway: *Various artists*/ Swing me an old fashioned song: *Various artists* / Yours and mine: *Various artists* / Little Broadway: *Various artists* / Dear Mr. Gable: *Various artists.*
LP: . . . . **REB 767**
MC: . . . . **ZCF 767**

MOVIE THEMES (Various artists).
Tracks: / Way we were, The: *Webb, Roger* / Honeymoon song: *Manuel & The Music of the Mountains* / Miss Marples theme: *Goodwin, Ron & His Orchestra* / Beyond tomorrow: *King, Denis & His Orchestra* / Princess Leia's theme: *Love,* Geoff & His Orchestra / James Bond theme: *Pourcel, Franck & His Orchestra* / 633 Squadron: *Goodwin, Ron & His* Orchestra / It's only a paper moon: *Webb, Roger* / Close Encounters of the Third Kind: *Love, Geoff & His Orchestra*/ Evergreen: *Manuel & The Music of the Mountains* / Chinatown, Theme from: *King, Denis & His Orchestra* / You're the one that I want: *Love, Geoff & His Orchestra.*
MC: . . . . **EE 260 093 4**

MOVIE WONDERLAND (Various artists).
MC: . . . . **BRC 2512**

MUSIC FOR SHAKESPEAREAN FILMS (Royal Liverpool Philharmonic Orchestra).
Tracks: / Richard III / Shakespeare suite / Funeral march (from Hamlet) / Henry V (suite).
LP: . . . . **EL 270118-1**
MC: . . . . **EL 270118-4**

MUSIC FROM 3 SERGIO CORBUCCI WESTERNS (Various artists).
LP: . . . . **IMGM 009**

MUSIC FROM GREAT AUSTRALIAN FILMS (Australian Broadcasting Comm. Philharmonic Orch.).
Tracks: / Newsfront / Gallipoli / My brillant career / Tall timbers / Cathy's child / Eliza Frazer / Breaker morant / Chant of Jimmy Blacksmith / Picture show man / Picnic at Hanging Rock / Mango tree, The / Dimboola / Caddie.
LP: . . . . **SBL 12582**
MC: . . . . **SBLC 12582**

MUSIC FROM THE DEAD ZONE 2 (Various artists).
LP: . . . . **DMCDZ 002**

MUSIC FROM THE FILMS OF FRANCOIS TRUFFAUT VOL 1 (Various artists).
LP: . . . . **A 220**
MC: . . . . **C 220**

MUSIC FROM THE FILMS OF JAMES DEAN (Various artists).
Tracks: / Rebel without a cause: *Various artists* / East of Eden: *Various artists* / Giant (There's never been anyone else but you): *Various artists* / There's never been anyone else but you: *Various artists.*
LP: . . . . **SLS 50420**

MUSIC FROM THE HORROR FILMS OF DARIO ARGENTO (Various artists).
LP: . . . . **CIA 5009**
MC: . . . . **CIAK 75009**

MUSIC FROM THE MOVIES (Various artists).
Tracks: / Warsaw concerto: *Various artists* / Dream of Olwen: *Various artists* / Spellbound concerto: *Various artists* / Cornish rhapsody: *Various artists* / Rhapsody in blue: *Various artists.*
LP: . . . . **ASD 3862**
LP: **CFP4 14493 1**
MC: **CFP4 14493 4**

MUSIC FROM THE PASOLINI FILMS (Various artists).
LP: **803 072**

MUSIC FROM THE REPUBLIC STUDIO SERIALS (Various artists).
LP: . . . . **STV 81250**

MUSIC TO BE MURDERED BY (Hitchcock, Alfred).
LP: . . . . **SL 5183**

MUSIQUE DE FILM (FILM MUSIC) (Various artists).
LPS: . . . . **PM 2901573**

NAKED GUN 2 AND A HALF, THE - THE SMELL OF FEAR (Film Soundtrack) (Various artists).
LP: . . . . **VS 5331**
MC: . . . . **VSC 5331**

NIGHTHAWKS (See under 'Nighthawks') (Emerson, Keith).

OKLAHOMA (Film Soundtrack) (Various artists).
Tracks: / Oklahoma overture: *Various artists* / Oh what a beautiful morning: *Various artists* / Surrey with the fringe on top: *Various artists* / Kansas City: *Various artists* / I can't say no: *Various artists* / Many a new day: *Various artists* / People will say we're in love: *Various artists* / Poor Jud is dead: *Various* artists / Out of my dreams: *Various artists* / Farmer and the cowman: *Various artists* / All er nothin': *Various artists* / Oklahoma: *Various artists.*
LP: . . . . **LCT 6100**
MC: . . . . **TCSW 595**

OMEN 4 (Composed by Jonathan Sheffer) (Various artists).
LP: . . . . **VS 5318**
MC: . . . . **VSC 5318**

OMEN AND OTHER THEMES, THE (Film Soundtracks: 50 Years Of Classic Horror) (Various artists).
Tracks: / Omen suite: *Various artists* / She suite: *Various artists* / Rosemary's baby suite: *Various artists*/ Doctor Jekyll & Mr. Hyde suite: *Various artists* / King Kong suite: *Various artists* / Vampire lovers suite, The: *Various artists* / Fear in the night suite: *Various artists* / Exorcist II suite: *Various artists*/ Hellraiser suite: *Various artists* / Doctor Jekyll & Sister Hyde suite: *Various artists.*
LP: . . . . **FILM 017**
MC: . . . . **FILMC 017**

ONLY THE LONELY (Various artists).
LP: . . . . **VS 5324**
MC: . . . . **VSC 5324**

ORIGINAL SOUNDTRACKS FROM JACQUES TATI'S FILMS (Various artists).
LP: **8122 311**
MC: **8122 314**

OSCAR (Film Soundtrack) (Various artists).
LP: . . . . **VS 5313**
MC: . . . . **VSC 5313**

OUT FOR JUSTICE (Film Soundtrack) (Various artists).
Tracks: / Don't stand in my way: *Allman, Greg* / Shake the firm: *Cool J.T.* / Temptation: *Belmont James,* Teresa / When the night comes down: *Smallwood, Todd* / One good man: *Armstrong, Kymberli* / Puerto Riqueno: *Jimenez, Michael* / Bad side of town: *Ball, Sherwood* / Bigger they are, The: *Cool J.T..*
LP: . . . . **VS 5317**
MC: . . . . **VSC 5317**

OUT OF AFRICA (Film soundtrack) (Various artists).
Tracks: / I had a farm in Africa: *Various artists* / I'm better at hello (Karen's theme I): *Various artists* / Have you got a story for me: *Various artists* / Concerto for clarinet in A (K 622): *Various artists* / Safari: *Various artists* / Karen's journey: *Various artists* / Siyawe: *Various artists* / Flying over Africa: *Various artists* / I had a compass from Denys (Karen's theme II): *Various artists* / Alone on the farm: *Various* artists / Let the rest of the world go by: *Various artists* / If I know a song from Africa (Karen's theme III): *Various artists* / You are Karen (end theme): *Various artists* / Music of goodbye: *Various artists.*
LP: . . . . **MCF 3310**
MC: . . . . **MCFC 3310**

PAINT YOUR WAGON (Film Soundtrack) (Various artists).
Tracks: / I'm on my way: *Various artists* / I still see Elisa: *Various artists* / First thing you know, The: *Various* artists / Hand me down that can o' beans: *Various artists* / They call the wind Maria: *Various artists* / Million miles away behind the door: *Various artists* / There's a coach comin' in: *Various artists* / Whoop-ti-ay (shivaree): *Various artists* / I talk to the trees: *Various artists* / Gospel of no name city, The: *Various* artists / Best things: *Various artists* / Wand'rin' star: *Various artists* / Gold fever: *Various artists*/ Finale: *Various artists.*
LP: . . . . **MCL 1667**
MC: . . . . **MCLC 1667**

PARTY PARTY (Film soundtrack) (Various artists).
Tracks: / Party party: *Costello, Elvis* / Run Rudolph run: *Edmunds, Dave* / No woman, no cry: *Black, Pauline*/ Yakety yak: *Bad Manners* / Elizabethan reggae: *Bad Manners* / Tutti frutti: *Sting* / Need your love so bad: *Sting* / No feelings: *Bananarama* / Band of gold: *Modern Romance* / Little town flirt: *Altered Images* / Man who sold the world, The / Auld lang syne: *Chas & Dave.*
LP: . . . . **SHM 3157**
MC: . . . . **HSC 3157**
LP: . . . . **AMLH 68551**

PORTRAIT OF ALFRED HITCHCOCK AND OTHER FILM THEMES (London Philharmonic Orchestra).
Tracks: / Le 7 voyage Sinbad (the 7th voyage of Sinbad) / Psychose (psycho) / Pas de printemps pour Marnie / La mort aux trousses (north by northwest) / Sueurs froides / Mais qui a tue Harry (The trouble with Harry) / Voyage au centre de la terre / Le jour ou la terre s'arreta / Fahrenheit 451 / L'Ile mysterieuse / Jason and the Argonauts / Voyages de Gulliver (Gulliver's travels).
LP: **414 296-1**

PUMP UP THE VOLUME (Original Soundtrack) (Various artists).
LP: . . . . **MCG 6121**
MC: . . . . **MCGC 6121**

QUERELLE (Film Soundtrack, Composed by: Peter Raben) (Various artists).
LP: . . . . **SL 9509**
MC: . . . . **SLC 9509**

RAGE IN HARLEM, A (Film Soundtrack) (Various artists).
LP: . . . . **VS 5325**
MC: . . . . **VSC 5325**

RED HEAT (Film Soundtrack, Composer: James Horner) (Various artists).
Tracks: / Main title: *Horner, James* / Russian streets: *Horner, James* / Cleanhead bust: *Horner, James*/ Victor escapes: *Horner, James* / Tailing kat: *Horner, James* / Hospital chase: *Horner, James* / Hotel: *Horner, James* / Bus station: *Horner, James* / End credits: *Horner, James.*
LP: . . . . **V 2558**
MC: . . . . **TCV 2558**
LP: **790989.1**
MC: **790989.4**

RETURN OF THE MUSKETEERS (Film Soundtrack,Composed by:Jean Petite Claude) (Various artists).
LP: . . . . **ETKLP 287LP**
MC: . . . . **ETKY 287C**

RETURN TO OZ (Film soundtrack, Composed by: David Shire) (Various artists).
LP: . . . . **SONIC 113**

ROBIN HOOD - PRINCE OF THIEVES (Film Soundtrack) (Various artists).
LP: **511050-1**
MC: **511050-4**

ROMANCE OF THE MOVIES (Various artists).
Tracks: / Last tango in Paris: *Various artists* / Look of love, The: *Various artists* / More: *Various artists*/ Cabaret: *Various artists* / Casino Royale: *Various artists* / Last horizon: *Various artists* / Love story (where do I begin): *Various artists* / Bless the beasts and children: *Various artists* / Getaway love theme: *Various artists* / Windmills of your mind: *Various artists* / Man and a woman, A: *Various artists* / Raindrops keep falling on my mind: *Various artists.*
LP: . . . . **SPR 8546**
MC: . . . . **SPC 8546**

RUSSIA HOUSE, THE (Film Soundtrack) (Various artists).
Tracks: / Katya: *Various artists* / Russia House (introductions): *Various artists* / Conversation, The: *Various* artists / Training: *Various artists* / Katya and Barley: *Various artists* / First name, Yakov: *Various* artists / Bon voyage: *Various artists* / Meeting, The: *Various artists* / I'm with you: *Various artists*/ What is this thing called love?: *Various artists* / Alone in the world: *Various artists* / Gift, The: *Various* artists / Full marks: *Various artists* / Barley's love: *Various artists* / My only country: *Various artists*/ Crossing over: *Various artists* / Deal, The: *Various artists* / Family arrives, The: *Various artists.*
MC: . . . . **MCAC 10136**

SCANDAL (Film Soundtrack) (Various artists).
Tracks: / Nothing has been proved: *Springfield, Dusty* / Apache: *Shadows* / What do you want: *Faith, Adam*/ Dreamin': *Burnette, Johnny* / Jambalaya: *Domino, Fats* / Those lazy hazy crazy days of summer: *Cole, Nat* King / Come softly to me: *Fleetwoods* / Only sixteen: *Douglas, Craig* / You make me feel so young: *Riddle,* Nelson / Una furtiva lagrima: *L'Elixir D'Amour-Donizetti* / Twist, The: *Checker, Chubby* / Three steps to heaven: *Cochran, Eddie* / My kind of girl: *Monro, Matt* / Miss Jamaica: *Cliff, Jimmy* / African waltz: *Dankworth, John & His Orchestra* / Goodness gracious me: *Sellers, Peter/ Sophia Loren* / I remember you: *Ifield,* Frank / Do you want to know a secret: *Kramer, Billy J.* / Johnny remember me: *Leyton, Johnny* / Scandal (Love theme): *Davis, Carl.*
LP: . . . . **PCS 7331**
MC: . . . . **TCPCS 7331**

SCI - FI MUSIC FESTIVAL (Various artists).
Tracks: / Hunger, The: *Various artists* / Videodrome: *Various artists* / Friday the 13th: *Various artists*/ Brainstorm: *Various artists.*
LP: . . . . **A 263**
MC: . . . . **C 263**

SCREEN MUSIC FOR LOVERS (Various artists).
LP: . . . . **SX 007**

SEA HAWK (Composed by Erich Wolfgang Korngold) (Various artists).
Tracks: / Sea hawk, The: *New York Philharmonic Orchestra* / Of human bondage: *New York Philharmonic Orchestra*/ Between two worlds: *New York Philharmonic Orchestra* / Constant nymph, The: *New York Philharmonic Orchestra*/ Kings row: *New York Philharmonic Orchestra* / Deception: *New York Philharmonic Orchestra* / Devotion: *New* York Philharmonic Orchestra / Anthony adverse: *New York Philharmonic Orchestra* / Escape me never: *New York Philharmonic Orchestra.*
MC: . . . . **GK 87890**

SECRET OF MY SUCCESS, THE (Original Soundtrack) (Various artists).
Tracks: / Secret of my success, The: *Night Ranger* / Sometimes the good guys finish first: *Benatar, Pat* / I burn for you: *Peck, Danny and Nancy Shanks* / Riskin' a romance: *Bananarama* / Gazebo: *Foster, David* / Price of love, The: *Daltrey, Roger* / Water fountain: *Foster, David* / Don't ask the reason why: *Restless Heart*(Co-produced by Tim DBois and Scott Hendricks) / Themes: *Foster, David* / Heaven and the heartaches: *Taxxi.*
LP: . . . . **MCF 3380**
MC: . . . . **MCFC 3380**

SEX, LIES AND VIDEOTAPE (Film Soundtrack) (Various artists).
Tracks: / Garbage: *Mangini, Mark* / Looks like a tablecloth: *Martinez, Cliff* / Take my shirt off: *Martinez,* Cliff / Are you comfortable: *Martinez, Cliff* / Here we go: *Martinez, Cliff* / What other men: *Martinez,* Cliff / Sniff the jacket: *Martinez, Cliff* / You've got a problem: *Martinez, Cliff* / I'm gonna drawl: *Martinez, Cliff.*
LP: . . . . **V 2604**
MC: . . . . **TCV 2604**

SGT. PEPPER'S LONELY HEARTS CLUB BAND (Film Soundtrack) (Various artists).
2LP: . . . . **AMLZ 66600**

SHAFT'S BIG SCORE (Various artists).
Tracks: / Blowin' your mind: *Various artists* / Other side: *Various artists* / Smart money: *Various artists*/ First meeting: *Various artists* / Ashby - Kelly man: *Various artists* / Don't misunderstand: *Various artists*/ Move on in: *Various artists* / Symphony for shafted souls (big chase): *Various artists* / Take off: *Various* artists / Dance of the cars water ballet part 1: *Various artists* / Dance of the cars water ballet part 2: *Various artists* / Call and response: *Various artists* / Last amen: *Various artists.*
MC: **3110 073**
LP: **2315 115**

SHE DEVIL (Film Soundtrack) (Various artists).
Tracks: / I will survive: *Sa-Fire* / You can have him: *Carmel* / C'mon and get my love: *D Mob* / Always: *Kimmel, Tom* / You're the devil in disguise: *Presley, Elvis* / Party up: *Checker, Chubby* / Tren d'amour: *Stewart, Jermaine* / That's what I call love: *Ceberano, Kate* / Tied up: *Yello* / It's getting hot: *Fat Boys.*
LP: **841 583 1**
MC: **841 583 4**

SILENCE OF THE LAMBS (Film Soundtrack) (Various artists).
LP: . . . . **MCA 10194**
MC: . . . . **MCAC 10194**

SOAPDISH (Film Soundtrack) (Various artists).
LP: . . . . **VS 5322**
MC: . . . . **VSC 5322**

SOME KIND OF WONDERFUL (Film soundtrack) (Various artists).
Tracks: / Do anything: *Shelley, Peter* / Brilliant mind: *Furniture* / Cry like this: *Blue Room* / I go crazy: *Flesh For Lulu* / She loves me: *Duffy, Stephen "Tin Tin"* / Hardest walk: *Jesus & Mary Chain* / Shyest time, The: *Apartments* / Miss Amanda Jones: *March Violets* / Can't help falling in love: *Lick The Tins*/ Turn to the sky: *March Violets* / Dr. Mabuse: *Propaganda.*
LP: . . . . **MCF 3365**
MC: . . . . **MCFC 3365**

SOMEWHERE IN TIME (Film Soundtrack) (Various artists).
Tracks: / Somewhere in time: *Various artists* / Old man, The: *Various artists* / Journey back in time, The: *Various artists* / Day together, A: *Various artists* / Rhapsody on a theme of Paganini: *Various artists* / Is he the one?: *Various artists* / Man of my dreams, The: *Various artists* / Return to the present: *Various artists*/ Somewhere in time: *Various artists.*
LP: . . . . **MCF 3333**
MC: . . . . **MCFC 3333**

SONGS FROM FELLINI FILMS (Ranierei, Katyna).
2LP: . . . . **A 329.330**
MCSET: . . . . **C 329/330**

SONGS FROM JANE POWELL'S FILMS (Various artists).
LP: . . . . **CC 100.4**

SOUND AND THE FURY, THE (Composed by Alex North, Original Soundtrack) (Various artists).
MC: . . . . **VSC 5297**

SOUNDS SUPERNATURAL (Various artists).
Tracks: / Satan speaks: *Various artists* / Dr Jekyll and Mr Hyde: *Various artists* / Rosemary's baby: *Various* artists / King of kings: *Various artists* / Seventh victim: *Various artists* / Exorcist 2: *Various artists*/ Heretic: *Various artists* / Omen: *Various artists.*
MC: **4212674**

SPELL BOUND (Various artists).
Tracks: / Red house, The (suite): *Various artists* / Thief of Baghdad, The (The love of the princes: *Various artists*/ Lost weekend, The (suite): *Various artists* / Four feathers, The (sunstroke): *Various artists* / Four feathers, The (river journey): *Various artists* / Double indemnity (Mrs Dietrichson): *Various artists* / Double indemnity (The conspiracy): *Various artists* / Knights of the round table: *Various artists* / Jungle book, The (song of the jungle): *Various artists* / Spellbound (the dream sequence): *Various artists* / Spellbound (the mountain lodge): *Various artists* / Ivanhoe (overture): *Various artists.*
MC: . . . . **GK 80911**

STATE OF GRACE (Film Soundtrack) (Various artists).
Tracks: / Hell's kitchen: *Various artists* / Park Ave.: *Various artists* / Shootout, The: *Various artists*/ Hundred yard dash: *Various artists* / State of grace: *Various artists* / New Jersey: *Various artists*/ Mott Street: *Various artists* / Confrontation: *Various artists* / Finn: *Various artists* / Terry Noonan: *Various artists* / St. Patrick's day: *Various artists* / Backroom, The: *Various artists* / Jackie's death: *Various artists* / Terry and Kate: *Various artists* / Kitchen, The: *Various artists* / Bronx drug deal: *Various artists* / Murder in Matty's bar: *Various artists* / First date, The: *Various artists.*
MC: . . . . **MCAC 10019**

STING,THE (Film Soundtrack) (Various artists).
Tracks: / Solace: *Various artists* / Entertainer, The: *Various artists* / Easy winners: *Various artists*/ Pineapple rag: *Various artists* / Gladiolus rag: *Various artists* / Merry go round music: *Various artists*/ Listen to the mockingbird: *Various artists* / Darling Nellie Gray: *Various artists* / Turkey in the straw: *Various artists* / Ragtime dance: *Various artists* / Hooker's hooker: *Various artists* / Luther: *Various artists*/ Glove, The: *Various artists* / Little girl: *Various artists.*
LP: . . . . **MCL 1735**
MC: . . . . **MCLC 1735**
LP: . . . . **MCF 2537**

STREETS OF FIRE (Film Soundtrack) (Various artists).
LP: . . . . **MCF 3221**
MC: . . . . **MCFC 3221**

TEENAGE MUTANT HERO TURTLES II (The Secret of the Ooze) (Various artists).
Tracks: / Awesome (You are my hero): *Ya Kid K* / Ninja rap: *Vanilla Ice* / Find the key to your life: *Dennis*, Cathy & David Morales / Moov: *Tribal House* / (That's your) consciousness: *Hartman, Dan* / This world: *Magnificent* VII / Creatures of habit: *Spunkadelic* / Back to school: *Fifth Platoon* / Cowabunga: *Orchestra On The Half Shell* / Tokka and rahzar: *Orchestra On The Half Shell* / Monster mix, The: *Orchestra On The Half Shell.*
LP: . . . . **SBKLP 14**
MC: . . . . **SBKTC 14**

TEENAGE MUTANT NINJA TURTLES (Various artists).
Tracks: / This is what we do: *M.C. Hammer* / Spin that wheel: *Hi Tek 3 featuring Ya Kid K* / Family: *Riff*/ 9.95: *Spunkadelic* / Turtle power: *Partners In Kryme* / Let the walls come down: *Kemp, Johnny* / Every heart needs a home: *St. Paul* / Shredder's suite: *Various artists* / Splinter's tale I & II: *Various artists*/ Turtle rhapsody: *Orchestra On The Half Shell.*
LP: . . . . **SBKLP 6**
LP: **791 066 1**
MC: . . . . **SBKTC 6**
MC: **791 066 4**
LPS: . . . . **SBKLPBOX 6**
MCSET: . . . . **SBKTCBOX 6**

TERMINATOR 2: JUDGEMENT DAY (Film Soundtrack) (Various artists).
LP: . . . . **VS 5335**
MC: . . . . **VSC 5335**

THANK YOUR LUCKY STARS (Film Soundtrack) (Various artists).
LP: . . . . **SH 2012**
LP: . . . . **CC 100/8**

THEIR FIRST FILMS (Various artists).
Tracks: / St Louis Blues: *Various artists* / You Rascal You: *Various artists* / Shine: *Various artists*/ Harlem Camp Meeting: *Various artists* / Zaz-Zuh-Zah: *Various artists* / Lady with the fan, The: *Various* artists / I Love A Parade: *Various artists* / Hotcha razz ma tazz: *Various artists* / Long about midnight: *Various artists* / Jitterbug: *Various artists.*
LP: . . . . **MTLP 022**

THELMA AND LOUISE (Film Soundtrack) (Various artists).
LP: . . . . **MCA 10239**
MC: . . . . **MCAC 10239**

THING, THE (Film Soundtrack) (Morricone, Ennio).
MC: . . . . **VSC 5278**

THIRD MAN, THE (Music From Various Classic Films) (Various artists).
Tracks: / Third man, Theme from: *Various artists* / Charade: *Various artists* / Mondo Cane: *Various artists*/ Good, the bad and the ugly, The: *Various artists* / Sandpiper: *Various artists* / Never on Sunday: *Various* artists / Big country, The: *Various artists* / Born free: *Various artists* / Breakfast at Tiffany's: *Various* artists / Umbrellas of Cherbourg: *Various artists* / Alfie: *Various artists* / Summer place, A (theme from): *Various artists* / Spellbound: *Various artists* / Zorba the Greek: *Various artists.*
MC: **4212644**

THOROUGHLY MODERN MILLIE (Film soundtrack) (Various artists).
Tracks: / Thoroughly modern Millie: *Various artists* / Baby face: *Various artists* / Do it again: *Various* artists / Poor butterfly: *Various artists* / Stumbling: *Various artists* / Japanese sandman: *Various* artists / Tapioca: *Various artists* / Jewish wedding song: *Various artists* / Rose of Washington Square: *Various* artists / Overture: Orchestra: *Various artists* / Jimmy: *Various artists* / Jazz baby: *Various artists*/ Intermission: *Various artists* (Medley.) / Thoroughly modern Millie (reprise): *Various artists* / Exit music: *Various artists.*
LP: . . . . **MCL 1723**
MC: . . . . **MCLC 1723**

THOROUGHLY MODERN MILLIE (ORIGINAL ISSUE) (Film soundtrack) (Various artists).
LP: . . . . **STA 8685**

THOUSANDS CHEER (Film soundtrack) (Various artists).
LP: . . . . **HS 409**

TWILIGHT ZONE - THE MOVIE (Film soundtrack) (Various artists).
LP: **923887 1**

UP THE ACADEMY (Film soundtrack) (Various artists).
Tracks: / Kicking up a fuss: *Blow Up* / Beat the devil: *Blow Up* / X offender: *Blondie* / Roadrunner: *Richman, Jonathan & Modern Lovers* / We gotta get out of here: *Hunter, Ian* / Coquette: *Cheeks* / Bony moronie: *Cheeks* / We live for love: *Benatar, Pat* / Bad reputation: *Hagar, Sammy* / Midnight rendevous: *Babys.*
LP: . . . . **EST 12091**
MC: . . . . **TC EST 12091**

VAMP (Film soundtrack) (Various artists).
LP: . . . . **STV 81288**
MC: . . . . **CTV 81288**

WALTON FILM MUSIC (London Philharmonic Orchestra).
Tracks: / Henry V suite / Battle of Britain / Battle in the air / March and Siegfried / Troilus and Cressida (interlude) / As you like it / History of the English speaking peoples (march.
LP: . . . . **EL 270591-1**
MC: . . . . **EL 270591-4**

WESTERN FILM WORLD OF DIMITRI TIOMKIN, THE (Various artists).
Tracks: / Giant: Prelude: *London Studio Symphony Orch.* / Red River: Prelude: *London Studio Symphony Orch.* / Wagon train: *London Studio Symphony Orch.* / Red River crossing: *London Studio Symphony Orch.* / Challenge and finale, The: *London Studio Symphony Orch.* / Duel in the Sun: Prelude and legend: *London Studio Symphony Orch.*/ Buggy ride,The: *London Studio Symphony Orch.* / Trek to the sun/ Love-death and finale: *London Studio Symphony Orch.*/ High Noon: *London Studio Symphony Orch.* / Clock and the showdown, The: *London Studio Symphony Orch.* / High noon: *London Studio Symphony Orch.* / Night passage: Follow the river: *London Studio Symphony Orch.* / Rio Bravo: DeGuella: *London Studio Symphony Orch.* / Love theme: *London Studio Symphony Orch.* / Rio Bravo: Main titles: *London Studio Symphony Orch..*
LP: . . . . **DKP 9002**

WHAT A CRAZY WORLD (Film soundtrack) (Brown, Joe & The Bruvvers).
Tracks: / What a crazy world we're livin' in / Layabout's lament, A / I sure know a lot about love / Bruvvers / Oh, what a family / Alfred Hichins / Sally Ann / Wasn't it a handsome punch-up / Please give me a chance / Independence / I feel the same way too / Just you wait and see / Things we never had.
LP: . . . . **PLE 512**

WHITE CHRISTMAS (Original soundtrack) (Various artists).
Tracks: / Count your blessings instead of your sheep: *Various artists* / Old man, The: *Various artists* / Sisters: *Various artists* / Best things happen while you're dancing: *Various artists* / Snow: *Various artists*/ Mandy: *Various artists* / Choreography: *Various artists* / Gee, I wish I was back in the army: *Various artists*/ Love, you did'nt do right by me: *Various artists* / What can you do with a general: *Various artists* / White Christmas (finale): *Various artists.*
LP: . . . . **MCL 1777**
MC: . . . . **MCLC 1777**

WINDS OF WAR (Film soundtrack) (Various artists).
Tracks: / Winds of war, The: Main title: *Various artists* / Nazi generals meet with Hitler: *Various artists* / Rosenthal: *Various artists* / Prelude to pug's bombing mission: *Various artists* / Byron and Natalie: *Various* artists / Through Poland to a Jewish village: *Various artists* / Refugees on the road: *Various artists* / Nazis victorious(Bombing of London): *Various artists* / Rhoda and Kirby: *Various artists* / Byron and Natile's wedding: *Various artists* / Pug at the Rusian front: *Various artists* / Danger! Neutrals at the train station: *Various artists* / Pug and Pamela(in love in London): *Various artists* / Pearl harbour/ A day of infamy: *Various artists* / Henry family theme: *Various artists* / Winds of war,The: End title: *Various artists.*
LP: . . . . **TER 1070**
MC: . . . . **ZCTER 1070**

WIZARD OF OZ (Various artists).
MC: . . . . **CMR 1109**

WIZARD OF OZ, THE (Original soundtrack) (Various artists).
Tracks: / Wizard of Oz (main title): *Various artists* / Dialogues: *Various artists* / Over the rainbow: *Various* artists / Dialogues: *Various artists* / Munchkin land: *Various artists* / Ding dong the witch is dead: *Various* artists / Follow the yellow brick road: *Various artists* / If I only had a brain: *Various artists* / We're off to see the wizard: *Various artists* / If I only had a heart: *Various artists* / We're off to see the wizard: *Various artists* / If I only ad the nerve: *Various artists* / We're off to see the wizard: *Various artists*/ If I were king of the forest: *Various artists* / Courage: *Various artists* / Dialogues: *Various artists*/ Ding dong the witch is dead: *Various artists* / Dialogues: *Various artists* / Home sweet home: *Various artists*/ Over the rainbow: *Various artists.*
LP: . . . . **LPMGM 7**
MC: . . . . **TCMGM 7**
LP: **793 303 1**
MC: **793 303 4**

YOUNG EINSTEIN (Original Soundtrack) (Various artists).
Tracks: / Rock and roll music: *Serious, Yahoo* / Rock and roll music: *Mental As Anything* / Music goes round my head: *Saints* / Who can you trust?: *Yahoo & Lulu* / Dumb things: *Kelly, Paul & The Messengers* / Hungry town: *Big Pig* / Great southern land: *Icehouse* / Great big brain: *Song Company* / Tasmanian, The: *Serious*, Yahoo / I hear motion: *Models* / Theory of relativity: *Serious, Yahoo* / At first sight: *Stems* / Fist full of scientists: *Lime Spiders* / Weirdo libido: *Lime Spiders* / Young Einstein pacifist: *Serious, Yahoo.*
LP: . . . . **AMA 3929**
MC: . . . . **AMC 3929**

YOUNG SOUL REBELS (Original Soundtrack) (Various artists).
LP: . . . . **BLRLP 10**
MC: . . . . **BLRMC 10**

ZABRISKIE POINT (Original Soundtrack) (Various artists).
Tracks: / Heat beat, pig meat: *Pink Floyd* / Brother Mary: *Kaleidoscope* / Dark star (excerpt): *Grateful* Dead / Crumbling land: *Pink Floyd* / Tennessee waltz: *Page, Patti* / Sugar babe: *Youngbloods* / Love scene: *Garcia, Jerry* / I wish I were a single girl again: *Holcomb, Roscoe* / Mickey's tune: *Kaleidoscope*/ Dance of death: *Fahey, John* / Come in Number 51, your time is up: *Pink Floyd.*
LP: . . . . **MCA 25032**
MC: . . . . **MCAC 25032**
LP: . . . . **GO 2029**
MC: . . . . **TCGO 2029**
MC: **794 217 4**

Filmtracks

FILMTRACKS-BEST OF BRITISH FILM MUSIC (Various artists).
Tracks: / Chariots of Fire: *Vangelis* / Wall, The: *Pink Floyd* / Going Home (Theme from Local Hero): *Knopfler*, Mark / Passage to India: *Jarre, Maurice* / Killing Fields, The: *Oldfield, Mike* / Dance With a Stranger: *Wilson*, Mari / Merry Christmas, Mr Lawrence: *Sakamoto, Ryuichi* / Honorary Consul, The: *Williams, John* / Long Road, The (Theme from Cal): *Knopfler, Mark* / Joy (Theme from Comfort and Joy): *Knopfler, Mark* / Chain, The: *Dickson*, Barbara / Freedom (Theme from Water): *Connolly, Billy* / Always Look on The Bright Side of Life: *Idle, Eric*/ Company of Wolves: *Various artists* / Another Country: *Various artists* / Bostonians, The: *Various artists*/ Champions: *Various artists* / Passage to India, A: *Various artists* / Heat and Dust: *Various artists*/ Gandhi: *Various artists* / Another Time, Another Place: *Various artists* / Return of the Soldier: *Various* artists / Gregory's Girl: *Various artists* / Death on the Nile: *Various artists* / Murder on the Orient Express: *Various artists.*
LP: . . . . **YEAR 1**
MC: . . . . **YEARMC 1**

Filmtrax II

FILMTRAX II (Various artists).
Tracks: / O mio Babbino caro: *Various artists* / Prick Up Your Ears: *Various artists* / My Beautiful Laundrette: *Various artists* / Mona Lisa: *Various artists* / Emma's War: *Various artists* / High Season: *Various* artists / Defence of the Realm: *Various artists* / Fourth Protocol: *Various artists* / Personal Services: *Various artists* / Half Moon Street: *Various artists* / Legend: *Various artists* / Letter to Brezhnev: *Various artists* / Indian Summer: *Various artists* / Withnail & I: *Various artists* / Mission, The: *Various artists* / Zina: *Various artists* / Chain, The: *Various artists* / Empire State: *Various artists.*
LP: . . . . **MOMENT 107**
MC: . . . . **MOMENTC 107**

Filthy Christians

MEAN.
LP: . . . . **MOSH 17**
MC: . . . . **MOSH 17 MC**

Filthy Phil

CHRISTMAS CLASSICS (Filthy Phil & Fast Eddie).
LP: . . . . **RRLP 124**

Final Assault

MESSENGER OF GOD.
LPPD: . . . . **A 26**

Final Conflict

ASHES TO ASHES.
LP: . . . . **PUS 0012-13**

Final Countdown

FINAL COUNTDOWN (For your ears only) (Various artists).
Tracks: / Introduction: *Bushido* / Fusillade III: *Attrition* / Almost virgin: *Credit* / Into the waves: *Attrition* / Till the stars fall: *Badland* / Aggression (Frontline Assembly): *Frontline Assembly* / Question of time: *Bushido* / And the Lord said "Rise": *Ka-Spel, Edward* / Pas de plaisanterie: *Pritchard, Bill*/ Rising tide, The: *All Singing All Dancing* / Paper house: *Beautiful Pea Green Boat* / Greek street: *Pritchrad*, Bill / Why can't I: *Intimate Obsessions* / Nostalgia: *Konstruktivitis* / I love your suit: *Turner, Simon* Fisher / What are these words: *Credit* / Erebus to Hades:

Intimate Obsessions / And she laughed too: *Beautiful* Pea Green Boat / Recalled to life: *Bushido* / Time and time again: *Bushido* / Grains of time, The: *All* Singing All Dancing / Paintbox: *Tragic Venus* / Dejeuner sur l'herbe: *Pritchard, Bill* / Entrails: *Jung Analysts* / Day I was born: *Attrition*.
LP: . . . . NIXON 4
2LP: . . . . TMLP 17/18

FINAL COUNTDOWN, THE (Various artists).
MC: . . . . STAC 2431
LP: . . . . STAR 2431

Final Exam
FINAL EXAM, THE (Original soundtrack) (Various artists).
LP: . . . . AEI 3105

Final Takes
FINAL TAKES (Various artists).
LP: . . . . FLY 594

Final Teaze
FINAL TEAZE, THE (Various artists).
LP: . . . . FINALLP 42

Finally Sunday
FINALLY SUNDAY (VIVEMENT DIMANCHE) (Film soundtrack) (Various artists).
LP: . . . . A 213

Finch, Horace
CINEMA ORGAN ENCORES VOL 1.
LP: . . . . DEROY 951

CINEMA ORGAN ENCORES VOL 2.
LP: . . . . DEROY 1120

CINEMA ORGAN ENCORES VOL. 3.
LP: . . . . DEROY 1235

Finchampstead Church
MARK ROBSON (see under Robson, Mark) (Finchampstead Church Choristers/Mark Robson).

Finchley Boys
PRACTICE SESSIONS.
LP: . . . . EVA 12033

Findask
BETWEEN THE WHITE LINES.
LP: . . . . TP 014

WAITING FOR A MIRACLE.
LP: . . . . TP 026
MC: . . . . CTP 026

Findlater, John
LOVER'S STONE (Findlater, John & Ethel).
Tracks: / Four Maries, The / Jim Blakeley / Half past ten / Poor old maid / Andrew Ross / Mary in the silvery tide / Two soldiers / Nelly Gordon / Ship's carpenter, The / Binnorie-o / Hammers of Syradale / Wexford murder / Maid of the cowdie an' knowes / Captain on the sea / Mistletoe bough, The / Lord Lovel / Laird O' drum, The / Ploughboys dream.
MC: 60-063

Fine Arts Brass...
LIGHTER SIDE OF FINE ARTS BRASS ENSEMBLE, THE (Fine arts brass ensemble).
MC: . . . . CSDL 381

PASTIME WITH GOOD COMPANY (Fine arts brass ensemble).
LP: . . . . MMLP 1026
MC: . . . . HMC 1026

Fine Hunting Day
FINE HUNTING DAY, A Various artists (Various artists).
LP: . . . . LEE 4056

Fine Mess
FINE MESS, A (Film soundtrack) (Various artists).
Tracks: / Fine mess, A: *Temptations* / Walk like a man: *Mary Jane Girls* / Easier said than done: *DeBarge, Chico* / Can't help falling in love: *McVie, Christine* / Slow down: *Vera, Billy & the Beaters* / Love's closing in: *Jameson, Nick* / Wishful thinking: *Robinson, Smokey* / Moving so close: *Second Generation* / I'm gonna be a wheel someday: *Los Lobos* / Stan & Ollie: *Mancini, Henry*.
2LP: . . . . ZL 72440
MC: . . . . ZK 72440

Fine Night For Dying
FINE NIGHT FOR DYING, A (see under Higgins, Jack (author)).

Fine Young Cannibals
FINE YOUNG CANNIBALS.
Tracks: / Johnny come home / Blue / Suspicious minds.
LP: . . . . LONLP 16
MC: . . . . LONC 16

RAW AND THE COOKED, THE.
Tracks: / She drives me crazy / Good thing / I'm not the man I used to be / I'm not satisfied / Tell me what / Don't look back / It's OK (It's alright) / Don't let it get you down / As hard as it is / Ever fallen in love (with someone you shouldn't've).
LP: 828 069 1
MC: 828 069 4

RAW AND THE REMIX, THE.
Tracks: / She drives me crazy (David Z 12" version) / I'm not satisfied (New York rap version) / Good thing (12" version) / Johnny come home (Mark Moore 12" version) (The mix with no beard on CD.) / I'm not the man I used to be (Jazzie B & Nellee Hooper ver.) / She drives me crazy (Monie love remix) / I'm not satisfied (Matt Dike remix) / It's OK (It's alright) (Ploeg club mix) / I'm not the man I used to be (Smith & Mighty version) / Johnny takes a trip / Tired of getting pushed around (Mayhem rhythm remix) (Not on LP.) / Don't look back (12" version) (Not on LP.).
LP: 828 221 1
MC: 828 221 4

Fine Young Things
CANDY MAN.
LP: . . . . KEV 2
MC: . . . . KEVM 2

Finegan, Bill
DIRECTIONS IN MUSIC (see under Sauter, Eddie) (Finegan, Bill & Eddie Sauter).

RETURN OF THE DOODLETOWN FIFERS (See under Sauter, Eddie).

Finesse & Synquis
SOUL SISTERS.
LP: . . . . MCA 42177

Finest Hour Of Sixties
FINEST HOURS OF SIXTIES PUNK various artists (Various artists).
LP: . . . . EVA 12039

Finger, Peter
ACOUSTIC ROCK GUITAR.
LP: . . . . UNKNOWN

BOTTLENECK GUITAR SOLOS.
Tracks: / Blues for the Rhine / Rattlesnake shake / Newborn yet to come / Fox hunt, The / Homecoming / Dancing in the street / Barn dance / Night falls while the days breaks / Told you so / Desert trot / Tribute to a jelly roll baker / Karen's blues / Second love / Hard road to the left / Trans European express / Don't cry for your baby.
LP: . . . . SNKF 105

Finger Snappers
FINGER SNAPPERS Various artists (Various artists).
Tracks: / You never fail to amaze me: *Various artists* / Be that way sometime: *Various artists* / I'm gonna love you: *Various artists* / Give in to the power of love: *Various artists* / Say something nice to me: *Various* artists / Couldn't last a day without your love: *Various artists* / It takes love: *Various artists* / Permanent vacation: *Various artists* / I need a love: *Various artists* / Feel good all over: *Various artists* / I'm doing the best I can: *Various artists* / Shame shame shame: *Various artists* / Can't live without you: *Various artists* / You're gone: *Various artists.*
LP: . . . . LPSS 106

Fingerpicking...
ADVANCED FINGERPICKING GUITAR TECHNIQUES Anthology (Various artists).
LP: . . . . KM 147

FINGERPICKING GUITAR TECHNIQUES (Grossman, Stefan).
LP: . . . . KM 112

Fingerprintz
BEAT NOIR.
LP: . . . . V 2201

VERY DAB, THE.
Tracks: / Close circuit connection / Fingerprintz / Wet job / Punchy Judy / Temperamental / Hey Mr. Smith / Tough luck / Invisible seams / On the hop / Beam me up Scotty.
LP: . . . . V 2119

Fingers
REMEMBER MINGUS.
Tracks: / Anthropology / Mood indigo / Remember Mingus / Tears inside / Alice's wonderland.
LP: . . . . SPJ 521

Fingers Inc.
ANOTHER SIDE.
Tracks: / Decision / Bye bye / Never no more lonely / Shadows / Another side / So glad / I'm strong / Love of my own / Distant planet / Feeling sleazy / Music take me up / Mystery friend / Mysteries of love / Path, A / Bring down the walls / Can you feel it.
LP: . . . . FING 1
MC: . . . . CFING 1

Fingers, Johnny
40 ACCORDION FAVOURITES.
LP: . . . . UNKNOWN

Fings Ain't Wot...
FINGS AIN'T WOT THEY USED T'BE (1959 Original London cast) (Various artists).
Tracks: / Fings ain't wot they used t'be: Overture: *Various artists* / G'night dearie: *Various artists* / Fings ain't wot they used t'be: *Various artists* / Layin' abaht: *Various artists* / Where it's hot: *Various artists*/ Ceiln's comin' dahn, The: *Various artists* / Contempery: *Various artists* / Entr'acte: *Various artists*/ Cochran will return: *Various artists* / Polka dots: *Various artists* / Meatface: *Various artists* / Where do little girls go?: *Various artists* / Big time: *Various artists* / Carve up: *Various artists*/ Cop a bit of pride: *Various artists* / Student ponce, The: *Various artists.*
LP: . . . . TER 1047
MC: . . . . ZCTER 1047

FINGS AIN'T WOT THEY USED T'BE (ORIGINAL ISSUE) (London cast) (Various artists).
LP: . . . . LK 4346

Fini Tribe
GROSSING 10K.
LP: . . . . TPLP 24
MC: . . . . TPLP 24 MC

NOISE LUST AND FUN.
LP: . . . . FTLP 001

Finians Rainbow (show)
FINIANS RAINBOW (Reprise Repertory Theatre).
Tracks: / Overture / This time of the year / How are things in Glocca Morra? / If this isn't love / Look to the rainbow / Something sort of grandish / Old devil moon / Necessity / When I'm not near the girl I love / When the idle poor become the idle rich / Begat, The / How are things in Glocca Morra (reprise) / That great come and get it day.
LP: . . . . K 54112

FINIANS RAINBOW (1948 Original Broadway cast) (Various artists).
MC: . . . . PST 04062
MC: . . . . GK 81057
MC: . . . . JST 04062

FINIANS RAINBOW (Original Broadway cast) (Various artists).
LP: . . . . PS 2080
MC: . . . . PST 2080

Fink, Cathy
CATHY FINK & DUCK DONALD (Fink, Cathy & Duck Donald).
LP: . . . . FF 053

DOGGONE MY TIME.
Tracks: / Where the west begins / I'm so lonesome I could cry / Cuckoo, The / Sara McCutcheon / Cat's got the measles, The / Coal mining woman / Monkey medley / Midnight prayerlight / No tell motel, The / When it's darkness on the delta / Cottonpatch rag / Coming home / Little Billy Wilson / Shenandoah Falls / My old Kentucky home.
LP: . . . . SH 3783
MC: . . . . SH 3783C

GRANDMA SLID DOWN THE MOUNTAIN.
LP: . . . . ROUNDER 8010
LP: 8010
MC: . . . . ROUNDER 8010C

LEADING ROLE.
LP: . . . . ROUNDER 0223
MC: . . . . ROUNDER 0223C

WHEN THE RAIN COMES DOWN.
LP: . . . . ROUNDER 8013
MC: . . . . ROUNDER 8013C

Finland
KAUSTINEN FOLK MUSIC FESTIVAL 1990.
MC: . . . . BHC 9130

Finlay, Karen
TRUTH IS HARD TO SWALLOW, THE.
LP: . . . . PWAI 069

Finn, Fred
FRED FINN & PETER HORAN.
LP: . . . . LUN 035

Finn, Mickey
HONKY TONK PIANO (Finn, Mickey/ Tiny Little).
2LP: . . . . GNPS 2-2127
MCSET: GNP5 2-2127

Finn, Tim
BIG CANOE, THE.
Tracks: / Are we one or are we two? / Spiritual hunger / Don't bury my heart / Timmy / Water into wine / Hyacinth / Big canoe / So deep / No thunder/No fire/No rain / Carve you in marble.
LP: . . . . OVED 221
MC: . . . . OVEDC 221

ESCAPADE.
Tracks: / Fraction too much friction / Staring at the embers / Through the years / Not for nothing / In a minor key / Made my day / Wait and see / Below the belt / I only want to know / Growing pains.
LP: . . . . EPC 25812

TIM FINN.
Tracks: / Young mountain / Not even close / How'm I gonna sleep / Parihaka / Tears inside / Birds swim fish fly / Suicide on Downing St / Show a little mercy / Crescendo / Been there, done that.
LP: . . . . EST 2088
MC: . . . . TCEST 2088

Finnegan
EASY WE EASY (Finnegan & Junior Rankin).
Tracks: / What a gwan / Tell me why / Dem a draw card / Easy we easy / News headlines / Do what you doing / Stop study evil / Trodding the biscayne.
LP: . . . . CSLP 23

Fintl
TERJE RYPDAL (see under Rypdal) (Fintl/Rypdal/Garbarek).

Fintry Style
PUTTING ON THE STYLE.
Tracks: / Old rustic bridge / Bonnie lass o' Fyvie / Bunch of violets blue / Kirkwall Bay / Take me back / Rose of mooncoin / Lovely Leitrim / Slievenamon / Village where I went to school / Rose of allandale / Love song of the waterfall / Millers cave / Isle of Innisfree / Wabash cannonball / Among the wicklow hills / Tinkers lullaby / She taught me how to yodel.
MC: . . . . ZCKBP 504

Fiol, Henry
SONERO.
LP: . . . . EWV 19
MC: . . . . TCEWV 19

Fiona
BEYOND THE PALE.
Tracks: / Tragedy / Hopelessly love you / Living in a boy's world / Thunder and lightning / Tender is the heart / Running out of night / In my blood / He's on my side / You better wait / Keeper of the flame.
LP: 781 639-1
MC: 781 639-4

FIONA.
Tracks: / Hang your heart on mine / Talk to me / You're no angel / Rescue you / James / Love makes you blind / Over now / Na na song.
LP: 781 242-1
MC: 781 242-4

HEART LIKE A GUN.
LP: . . . . K 781 903-1
MC: . . . . K 781 903-4

Fiorillo, Elisa
ELISA FIORILLO.
Tracks: / You don't know / How can I forget you / Gimme special love / Forgive me for dreaming / Do something foolish / Little too good to me / More Than Love / Heading for a heartache / Lover's prayer / Two Times Love.
LP: . . . . CHR 1608
MC: . . . . ZCHR 1608

Fire
MAGIC SHOEMAKER.
LP: . . . . SEE 294

Fire Brigade
OLD SOAKS AND NEW FLAMES.
LP: . . . . BLP 009

Fire Escape
PSYCHOTIC REACTION.
LP: . . . . GNPS 2034

Fire & Grace
FIRE AND GRACE (Various artists).
LP: . . . . IR 013LP
MC: . . . . IR 013MC

Fire Hydrant Men
MISSED IT BY THAT MUCH.
LP: . . . . NCHLP 3

Fire & Ice
UNCHANGED LOVE.
LP: . . . . FELP 12

Fire Merchants
IGNITION.
LP: . . . . MD 94351

Fire Next Time
NORTH AND SOUTH.
Tracks: / Fields of France / Can't forgive / Stay with me now / Supasave / We've lost too much / Too close / St. Mary's steps / Following the hearse / North and South.

LP: . . . . FNTLP 1
MC: . . . . FNTMC 1

Fireball XL5

GO FOR IT.
LP: . . . . NWLP 1003

Fireballs

HERE ARE THE FIREBALLS.
LP: . . . . Unknown

VAQUERO.
LP: . . . . RS 643

Firebird

GAME, THE.
Tracks: / Hurt a heart / Raphaello / Make a fresh start / Back on the road / Put off till tomorrow / Game, The / Sing Gaudete / Watching the night / Sometimes / Lady of the night.
LP: . . . . R 009LP

Firebird (book)

FIREBIRD, THE (Unknown narrator(s)).
MC: . . . . PLB 213

Firebirds

JOURNEY TO ZOAR (see Lasha, Prince) (Firebirds & Prince Lasha).

Firefall

ELAN.
Tracks: / Strange way / Sweet and sour / Wrongside fo town / Count your blessings / Get you back / Anymore / Baby / Goodbye, I love you / Winds of change.
LP: . . . . K 50494

FIREFALL.
Tracks: / It doesn't matter / Love isn't all / Livin' ain't livin' / No way out / Dolphin's lullaby / Cinderella / Sad ol' love song / You are the woman / Mexico / Do what you want.
LP: . . . . K 50260

LUNA SEA.
Tracks: / So long / Just remember I love you / Sold on you / Someday soon / Just think / Getaway / Only a fool / Head on home / Piece of paper / Even Steven.
LP: . . . . K 50355

Firefox

FIRE FOX.
Tracks: / We just wanna dance / Come and teke my lovin' / Action speaks louder than words / Stand up (for what you believe in) / Fire / Round trip ticket / You make me feel brand new / Fire down below.
LP: 781 270-1
MC: 781 270-4

Firehose

FROM OHIO.
LP: . . . . SST 235
MC: . . . . SST 235 C

IF'N.
Tracks: / Sometimes / Honey please / For the singer of REM / Anger.
LP: . . . . SST 115

RAGIN' FULL ON.
Tracks: / Under the influence / Locked in / Brave captain / Under the influence of meat puppets / Chemical wire / Another theory shot to shit on your ....
LP: . . . . SST 079

Firehouse

FIREHOUSE.
Tracks: / Rock on the radio / All she wrote / Shake and tumble / Don't treat me bad / Oughta be a law / Lover's lane / Home is where the heart is / Don't walk away / Seasons of change / Overnight sensation / Love of a lifetime / Helpless.
LP: 4674411
MC: 4674414

Firehouse Five

GOOD TIME JAZZ (Firehouse Five Plus Two).
Tracks: / Runnin' wild / Five foot two, eyes of blue / When you wore a tulip (and I wore a red red rose) / I can't give you anything but love / Swanee River / Alabama jubilee / Muskrat ramble / That's a plenty / Frankie and Johnny / Yes sir, that's my baby / Tiger rag / Sheik of Araby, The / California here I come / Isle of Capri / Everybody loves my baby / St. Louis blues / Just a stomp at twilight / Sweet Georgia Brown / Doctor Jazz / 12th Street rag.
LP: . . . . MFP 50533
MC: . . . . TCMFP 50533

Fireman Sam (bks)

ADVENTURES OF FIREMAN SAM, THE (Alderton, John (nar)).
MC: 00 1041339

FIREMAN SAM.
Tracks: / Fireman Sam / Pontpandy bus, The / Person in charge is Officer Steele, The / Bella and her cat, Rosa / Elvis cooks the lunch / Dilys always knows / Sarah and James / Naughty Norman Price / Inventing shed, The / Snow Business suite, The / Snowy morning - here comes Trevor, A / Elvis helps out / Great sledge race, The / Jupiter to the rescue / Four steps to safety / Another mince pie / Christmas tree / Lights out.
MC: . . . . HSC 654

SAM SMELLS A RAT (Alderton, John (nar)).
MC: 00 103455 3

SAM TO THE RESCUE (Childrens story book) (Unknown narrator(s)).
MC: . . . . RWM 005

SAM'S BUMPER JUMPER (Alderton, John (nar)).
MC: . . . . 0 00 102180 X

SAM'S NIGHT WATCH (Alderton, John (nar)).
MC: 00 1034561

SAM'S RABBIT RESCUE (Alderton, John (nar)).
MC: 0 00 102179 6

Fireparty

FIRE PARTY.
LP: . . . . DISCHORD 28

Firewalker

FIREWALKER (1987 film soundtrack) (Various artists).
LP: . . . . STV 81303

Firewater

BRAND NEW VINTAGE.
Tracks: / Crazy / Almost Saturday night / Sea of heartbreak / Lonely road cafe / Whisky drinking man / Driving my life away.
LP: . . . . SDLP 031
MC: . . . . SDC 031

Firm

SERIOUS FUN.
LP: . . . . NE 1387
MC: . . . . CE 2387

Firm (rock)

FIRM.
Tracks: / Closer / Make or break / Someone to love / Together / Radioactive / You've lost that lovin' feeling / Money can't buy satisfaction / Midnight moonlight / Satisfaction guaranteed.
LP: 781 239-1
MC: 781 239-4

MEAN BUSINESS.
Tracks: / Fortune hunter / Cadillac / All the kings horses / Live in peace / Tear down the walls / Dreaming / Free to live / Spirit of love.
LP: . . . . WX 43
MC: . . . . WX 43 C

Firma

FIRMA.
LP: . . . . GILP 888

First Anansi Story

FIRST ANANSI STORY, THE (Various artists).
Tracks: / First Anansi story, The: *Various artists* / How bear learned to swim: *Various artists* / How Anansi got his limp: *Various artists* / How crab got his shell: *Various artists* / Only birds may fly: *Various artists* / Tiger's stew: *Various artists* / Anansi's birthday: *Various artists*.
MC: . . . . ANV 632

First Battalion Glos

GLORIOUS GLOSTERS, THE.
Tracks: / Southfield / Warning / Folk song suite / Contrasts / This night the stars / Song of Gloucestershire / Intermezzo from 1st suite in E flat / Roads go down, The / Three English dances / Glorious Glosters, The / Kinnegad slashers.
LP: . . . . RSK 109
MC: . . . . RSKC 109

First Blood

FIRST BLOOD (1982 Film Soundtrack) (Various artists).
LP: . . . . TER 1038

First Brass

FIRST BRASS.
LP: . . . . LPNU 1580
MC: . . . . MCNU 1584

First British ...

FIRST BRITISH R & B FESTIVAL, FEBRUARY 28TH 1964 An historic artefact (Various artists).
Tracks: / Introduction by Bob Wooler: *Davis, Spencer R & B Quartet* / Dimples: *Road Runners* / You can make it if you try: *Road Runners* / Mary Ann: *Road Runners* / Bright lights big city: *Stewart, Rod* / 2.19 blues: *Baldry, Long John* / Night time is the right time: *Davis, Spencer R & B Quartet* / Slow walk: *Williamson*, Sonny Boy & The Yardbirds / Pontiac blues: *Williamson, Sonny Boy & The Yardbirds* / Lonesome cabin: *Williamson*, Sonny Boy & The Yardbirds / Bye bye bird: *Williamson, Sonny Boy & The Yardbirds* / Got my mojo working: *All Star Jam*.
LP: . . . . LIK 54

First British Corps...

ALLIANCE PARADE.
LP: . . . . DR 8

First Call

EVENING IN DECEMBER, AN.
LP: . . . . DAY R 4037
MC: . . . . DAY C 4037

SOMETHING TAKES OVER.
LP: . . . . DAY R 4161
MC: . . . . DAY C 4161

UNDIVIDED.
LP: . . . . DAY R 4038
MC: . . . . DAY C 4038

First Choice

HOLD YOUR HORSES.
Tracks: / Let me down easy / Good morning midnight / Great expectations / Hold your horses / Love thang / Double cross.
LP: . . . . SSLP 1514

SUPREME DOUBLE HEADER, THE (See under Royal Delite) (First Choice/ Royal Delite).

First Circle

BOYS NIGHT OUT.
Tracks: / Working up a sweat / Miracle worker / In the name of love / Dream you came back / Get off it / Can't find a love / You're on my mind / Boy's night out.
LP: . . . . AML 3118
MC: . . . . TCAML 3118

First Cut

FIRST CUT- THE OXFORD SOUND various artists (Various artists).
LP: . . . . WF 100

First Edition

FIRST EDITION (Various artists).
LP: . . . . EGED 15

First Fragile Sampler

FIRST FRAGILE SAMPLER, THE various artists (Various artists).
MC: . . . . FC 08

First Frames

FIRST FRAMES (Various artists).
Tracks: / Introduction: *Lynn, Ian* / Do you see: *Lynn, Ian* / Seven bridges: *Lynn, Ian* / First love: *R.M.S.* / Life on the farm: *20th Century Blues* / Horses of steam: *Armstrong, Herbie* / Ravel: *Allair, John* / Since I fell for you: *Allair, John* / Gentle giant: *Paragonne* / Mister Yang: *Sunwind* / Naledi's dreamsong: *Defries, David* / First finale: *Lynn, Ian* / First touch: *Argent, Rod* / Celebration: *Lynn, Ian*.
MC: . . . . TCMMC 1001

First Great Train ...

WILD ROVERS AND THE FIRST GREAT TRAIN ROBBERY (See under Wild Rovers) (Various artists).

First House

CANTILENA.
Tracks: / Cantilena / Underfelt / Dimple / Sweet Williams / Low-down (toytown) / Hollyhocks / Madeleine after prayer / Shining brightly / Jay-tee / Pablo.
LP: . . . . ECM 1393

ERINDIRA.
Tracks: / Day away, A / Innocent erendira / Journeyers to the east, The / Bracondale / Grammenos / Stranger than paradise / Bridge call / Doubt / Further away.
LP: . . . . ECM 1307

First Impressions

FIRST IMPRESSIONS (Original Broadway cast) (Various artists).
LP: . . . . AOS 2014

First Ladies

FIRST LADIES OF COUNTRY MUSIC (Various artists).
MC: . . . . AM 67

FIRST LADIES OF COUNTRY MUSIC (Various artists).
Tracks: / Snowbird: *Murray, Anne* / Different drum: *Ronstadt, Linda* / Hand that rocks the cradle, The: *Colter, Jessi* / Simple little words: *Various original artists* / Coat of many colours: *Peppers, Nancy* / Reuben James: *Jackson, Wanda* / Pinkerton's flowers, The: *Montgomery, Melba* / Someday soon: *Gayle, Crystal* / 57 chevrolet: *Spears, Billie Jo* / Get on my love train: *La Costa* / Ode to Billy Joe: *Gentry, Bobbie* / Queen of the house: *Miller, Jody* / Delta dawn: *Reddy, Helen* / Lesson in leavin', A: *West, Dottie* / Mercy: *Shepard, Jean* / Angel of the morning: *Newton, Juice*.
LP: . . . . MFP 41 5687-1

FIRST LADIES OF COUNTRY, VOL.II (Various artists).
Tracks: / But love me: *Various artists* / Other side of me, The: *Various artists* / Your good girl's gonna go bad: *Various artists* / Would you lay with me (in a field of stone): *Various artists* / Takin' it easy: *Various* artists / Blue side, The: *Various artists* / When I fall in love: *Various artists* / My elusive dreams: *Various* artists / Loving arms: *Various artists* / Wrap your love all around your man: *Various artists* / Half the way: *Various artists* / Womanhood: *Various artists* / Best of my love: *Various artists* / Enough of each other: *Various artists* / Hard times: *Various artists* / Angel in your arms: *Various artists* / Miss the Mississippi and you: *Various artists* / Pass me by: *Various artists* / Help me make it through the night: *Various artists* / Sea of heartbreak: *Various artists*.
LP: . . . . CBS 85442

First Ladies Of

FIRST LADIES OF COUNTRY (See Under Country...) (Various artists).

First Light

FIRST LIGHT.
Tracks: / Don't be mistaken / Explain the reason / Daybreak / I don't care / Horse with no name, A / AM / She's a mystery / Time machine.
LP: 8132 241

YOU HAD IT ALL.
Tracks: / Right or wrong / Illusion / You had it all / Winner / You and me / Loving you / So easy / No way out / I'll write again / Don't push me.
LP: . . . . SGTLP 1
MC: . . . . SGTMC 1

First Love

FIRST LOVE various artists (Various artists).
2LP: . . . . ADEP 41

First of Folklore

FIRST OF FOLKLORE.
Tracks: / Liverpool Lou / I never will marry / England's motorway.
LP: . . . . HRL 104

First Of The Few

FIRST OF THE FEW (1942 film soundtrack) (London Philharmonic Orchestra).
LP: . . . . ED 291129 1
MC: . . . . ED 291129 4

First Offence

FIRST OFFENCE.
LP: . . . . OTH 11

First Quest

FIRST QUEST (Various artists).
2LP: . . . . DRAGON 1
MC: . . . . DRAGON C 1

First Revolution

NEW ORLEANS GOSPEL -RHYTHM & BLUES.
Tracks: / Anonymous love / It's gonna rain / Down by the riverside / Please remember me / There's room at the cross / Mary don't you weep / I'm gonna serve the Lord.
LP: . . . . LPS 24

RUNNING FOR JESUS (New Orleans Gospel) (First Revolution Singers Of New Orleans).
MC: . . . . 504 TCS 101G

First Sessions

FIRST SESSIONS 1949/50 (Various artists).
2LP: . . . . PR 24081

First Songs

FIRST SONGS FOR BABY (Various artists).
MC: . . . . PLB 261

First story in the

FIRST STORY IN THE WORLD, THE (Various artists).
Tracks: / First story in the world: *Various artists* / Four men: *Various artists* / Building of the temple, The: *Various artists* / Coloured coat, The: *Various artists* / Tables are turned, The: *Various artists*.
MC: . . . . ANV 608

First Sunday Singalong

FIRST SUNDAY SINGALONG (Various artists).
MC: . . . . MMC 0183

First Ten Years

FIRST TEN YEARS, THE (Various artists).
Tracks: / Bricklayer's beautiful daughter: *Ackerman, William* / White rain: *Grassi de, Alex* / Colors/Dance: *Winston*, George / Angel's flight: *Shadowfax* / Bradley's dream: *Story, Liz* / Afternoon postlude soliloquy: *Hecht*, Daniel / 2nd gymopedie (1888): *Quist*,

Bill / Homefeild suite: *Qualey, David* / Rickover's dream: *Hedges, Michael* / Variations on clair de lune: *Basho, Robbie* / Oristano sojourn: *Cossu, Scott* / Clockwork: *Grassi* de, Alex / Peace: *Winston, George* / Aerial boundaries: *Hedges, Michael* / Egrets: *Montreux* / On the threshold of liberty: *Isham, Mark* / Welcoming: *Manring, Michael* / 19a, The: *Nightnoise* / Montana half light: *Aaberg, Philip* / Shadowdance: *Shadowfax* / Pittsburgh 1901: *Isham, Mark* / Calling, The: *Stein & Walder* / Gwenlaise: *Cossu, Scot/Friesen, Eugene* / Dolphins: *Marshall, Mike & Darol Anger* / Wishing well: *Schonherz & Scott* / Theme for Naomi Uemura: *Aaberg, Philip* / Toys not ties: *Nightnoise/* Close cover: *Mertens, Wim* / To the well: *Mathieu, W.A.* / Hot beach: *Interior* / New waltz: *Dalglish, Malcolm* / Processional: *Ackerman, William* / Woman at the well: *Story, Tim*.
MCSET: . . . . **WT 1095**

First Term at (bk)

FIRST TERM AT MALORY TOWERS
(see under Blyton, Enid (aut)).

First Words

FIRST WORDS (Childrens story book) (Unknown narrator(s)).
MC: . . . . **RWM 001**

Fisc

HANDLE WITH CARE.
Tracks: / Come run riot / Won't let go / Love fight / Hold your head up / Let me leave / Live it up / Lover under attack / Handle with care / Got to beat the clock / Speed limit 55?.
LP: . . . . **MFN 91**

Fischer Choir

40 YEARS OF THE FISCHER CHOIR.
Tracks: / Radetzky marsch / Adieu mein kleiner gardeoffizier / Gefangenchor aus "nabucco" / Triumph march / Matrosenchor aus "der fliegende Hollander" / Grob is dien name / Madonna aus Peru / Frieden / Das wandern ist des mullers lust / Wem gott will rechte gunst erweisen / Alle vogel sind schon da / Heimatmelodie / Finkensalzer / Im schosten weisengrunde / Andulka.
LP: **827 474-1**
MC: **827 474-4**

GLORY HALLELUJA.
Tracks: / Glory halleluja / Exodus / River Kwai / Song of joy / Marchen aus der kinderzeit / Schiwago melodie / Elizabethan serenade.
LP: **2872 136**
MC: **3472 136**

MUSIC FOR THE MILLIONS.
Tracks: / La paloma / Schon ist es auf der welt zu sein / Plaisir d'amour / Mein vater war ein wandersmann / Tritsch tratsch polka / Stenka rasin / Mit der troika in die grosse stad / Spanish eyes / Gluhwurmchenidyll / Donauwalzer / Bruilofskoor vit, lohengrin / Wenn wirheut auseinandergehen.
LP: **815321 1**
MC: **815321 4**
LP: **2372 091**
MC: **3151 091**

SENSATIONAL FISCHER CHOIR.
Tracks: / Brazil / Amazing grace / Song of joy / Y viva Espana / Somewhere my love / Elizabethan serenade / Cossack patrol / When the saints go marching in / Black eyes / La paloma / Drunken sailor / Radetzky march / Exodus song / Moscow nights.
LP: **2489 540**

SENSATIONAL VOL 2.
Tracks: / Una paloma blanca / Katiushka / Volga boatmen / Wooden heart / Spanish eyes / Lili Marlene / Land of hope and glory / Rosamunde / Plaisir d'amour / Glory halleluja / Fernando / Griechischer wein / Two guitars / Kalinka.
LP: **2371881**

Fischer, Clare

ALONE TOGETHER.
Tracks: / Yesterdays / Tahila / Touch of your lips, The / Everything happens to me.
LP: . . . . **DS 820**

AND SOMETIMES VOICES (Fischer, Clare & Salsa Picante & Two Plus Two).
Tracks: / Malibu glide / Country / Canto / Shake out all those blues / One night (in a dream) / Renacimiento / La ronde / Como come.
LP: . . . . **DS 852**
MC: . . . . **DSC 852**

BY AND WITH HIMSELF (Clare Fischer Plays Piano).
Tracks: / Giant steps / Jeru / Counterall / Fugue / Turn out the stars / Last night when we were young / Mememto.
LP: . . . . **DS 934**

CRAZY BIRD (Fischer, Clare & Salsa Picante).
Tracks: / Bernie's tune / Where are the children? / Serenidade / La mucura / Pajaro loco / Solar patrol / Canto Africano / Pavillion.
LP: . . . . **DS 914**
MC: . . . . **DSC 914**

DUALITY (Fischer, Clare Big Band).
Tracks: / Come Sunday / This is always / Old folks.
LP: . . . . **DS 807**

EASY LIVIN'.
Tracks: / In your own sweet way / Glad to be unhappy / Aquarius / My pretty girl / Kerry dancer / Goodbye / I'll take romance / Easy living.
LP: . . . . **REV 2**

EXTENSION (Fischer, Clare Orchestra, featuring Jerry Coker).
Tracks: / Ornithology / Quiet dawn / Bittersweet / Igor / Extension / Coker's blues / Running mate / Soloette / Passacaglia / Canto Africano.
LP: . . . . **DS 902**

FREE FALL (Fischer, Clare & His Latin Jazz Sextet/2 + 2 Plus).
Tracks: / Samba Claro / Novios / Blues bossa / Night we called it a day, The / You and I.
LP: . . . . **DS 921**
MC: . . . . **DSC 921**

GREAT WHITE HOPE.
Tracks: / After you've gone / Autumn leaves / Western airlines / Fuzz blues / Music of the spheres / You call it madness / C minor theme.
LP: . . . . **REV 13**

JAZZ SONG.
Tracks: / Spring is here / Suerte / Here's that rainy day / Moon mist / Autumn lines / Love locked out / Serenidade / Just friends.
LP: . . . . **REV 31**

LEMBRANCAS (REMEMBRANCES).
Tracks: / C.P. (Charlie Palmieri) / Fina / Coco B. / Curumim / Endlessly / On Green Dolphin Street / Xapun / Gilda / Pan pipe dance / And miles to go / Strut, The (CD only.).
MC: . . . . **CJP 404C**

MACHACHA (IMPORT) (Fischer, Clare & Salsa Picante).
LP: . . . . **DS 835**
MC: . . . . **DSC 835**

ONE TO GET READY.
Tracks: / Liz Anne / In memoriam: J.F.K. and R.F.K. / You stepped out of a dream / Lover man / Free ways.
LP: . . . . **REV 6**

RECLAMATION ACT OF 1972.
Tracks: / Blues reclaimed, The / Soon / Sometimes I feel this way / Meade Lux Lewis, I love you / Pensativa / W.P.A. work chant.
LP: . . . . **REV 15**

REPORT OF THE SYMPOSIUM ON RELAXED IMPROVISATION VOLUME 1 (see Marsh, Warne) (Fischer, Clare/ Warne Marsh/Gary Foster).

SALSA PICANTE.
LP: . . . . **DS 817**
MC: . . . . **DSC 817**

STARBRIGHT (Fischer, Clare & Gary Foster).
Tracks: / Cherokee / Some day my prince will come / Brazilian waltz / Bluesome / Starbright / I love you / If you could see me now / Slippin' at Bells.
LP: . . . . **DS 885**
MC: . . . . **DSC 885**

STATE OF HIS ART.
Tracks: / Duke, The / Some day my prince will come / Woodyn' you? / Free improvisation / Basic blues / Proto-blues / Phrygian blues / Out-of-tempo blues.
LP: . . . . **REV 26**

T' DA-A-A-A-A (Fischer, Clare & Yamaha Quartet).
Tracks: / Soon / Round midnight / Lennie's pennies / Blues in F / Crystal sunrise.
LP: . . . . **REV 23**

WHOSE WOODS ARE THESE?.
Tracks: / Blues trilogy / Basic blues / Blues in G / Blues bossa / If / Da vida bel / Long time ago, A / Free prelude / Lennie's pennies.
LP: . . . . **DS 880**
MC: . . . . **DSC 880**

Fischer, Lisa

SO INTENSE.
LP: **7559608891**
MC: **7559608894**

Fischer, Lou

ROYAL STREET (Fischer, Lou Rehearsal Band).
LP: . . . . **SB 2012**

Fischer-Z

FISHES HEAD.
Tracks: / Say no / Masquerade / It could be you / Sticky business / Huba / Oh mother / Just words / It's only a hurricane / She said / Ho ho ho.
LP: **209772**
MC: **409772**

GOING DEAF FOR A LIVING.
Tracks: / Room service / So long / Crazy girl / No right / Going deaf for a living / Pick up, slip up / Crank / Haters / Four minutes in Durham (with you) / Limbo.
LP: **1A 038 15753**
MC: **1A 238 1575384**
LP: . . . . **UAG 30295**

GOING RED FOR A SALAD (UA years 1979-1982).
Tracks: / So long / Acrobats / Worker, The / Wax dolls / Remember Russia / Going deaf for a living / Room service / Pretty paracetamol / Marliese / You'll never find Brian here / Berlin / Battalions of strangers / Bathroom scenario / Wristcutters lullaby / Crazy girl / One voice (CD only.) / Involuntary movement (CD only.) / Mayday Mayday (CD only.) / I smelt roses (in the underground) (CD only.) / Limbo.
LP: . . . . **GO 2030**
MC: . . . . **TCGO 2030**

RED SKIES OVER PARADISE.
Tracks: / Berlin / Marliese / Red skies over paradise / In England / You'll never find Brian here / Battalions of strangers / Song and dance brigade / Writer, The / Bathroom scenario / Wristcutters lullaby / Cruise missiles / Luton to Lisbon / Multinationals bite.
LP: . . . . **LBG 30326**

REVEAL.
Tracks: / Perfect day / Leave it to the businessmen to die young / I can't wait that long / Tallulah tomorrow / Realistic man / Fighting back the tears / Big drum / Heartbeat / It takes love / So far / Marguerite (Extra track on CD only.).
LP: **208620**
MC: **408620**

WORD SALAD.
Tracks: / Pretty paracetamol / Acrobats / Worker, The / Spiders / Remember Russia / French let her, The / Lies / Wax dolls / Headlines / Nice to know / Billy and the motorway police / Lemmings.
LP: . . . . **UAG 30232**

Fish

VIGIL IN THE WILDERNESS OF MIRRORS.
Tracks: / Vigil / Big wedge / State of mind / Company, The / Gentleman's excuse me, A / Voyeur, The (I like to watch) (Not on album.) / Family business / View from the hill / Cliche.
LP: . . . . **EMD 1015**
MC: . . . . **TCEMD 1015**
LPPD: . . . . **EMPD 1015**

Fish Called Wanda

FISH CALLED WANDA, A (Original Soundtrack) (Various artists).
LP: . . . . **A 376**
MC: . . . . **C 376**

Fish Co

BENEATH THE LAUGHTER.
Tracks: / Beneath the laughter / Never feel alone / Two on the street / Across table / Miss Esther Lauden / Seventies children / Harbour mouth / Sail away / Super heroes.
LP: . . . . **PC 114**

Fish Out Of Water

RED SUNSET.
LP: . . . . **SR 001**
MC: . . . . **SR 001C**

Fish & Roses

WE ARE HAPPY TO SERVE YOU.
LP: . . . . **HMS 130**

Fish, the Tree,...

FISH, THE TREE, THE BIRD AND THE BELL, THE (Various artists).
Tracks: / Prospect street: *Big Dish* / Broke away (live): *Wet Wet Wet* / Real McCoy (live): *Silencers/* Jamie Foyers (live): *Gaughan, Dick* / Glasgow Barrowlands, The: *Reader, Eddi* / Regret: *Blue Nile* / Jocelyn Square: *Love & Money* / River, The: *Martyn, John* / Southside: *Texas (Group)* / Are you ready to be heartbroken (live): *Cole, Lloyd* / Christmas and Glasgow: *Deacon Blue* / Mother Glasgow (live): *Hue & Cry*.
LP: **4678801**
MC: **4678804**

Fishbone

FISHBONE.
Tracks: / Ugly / Another generation / Modern industry / Party at ground zero / V.T.T.O.T.F.D.G.F. / Lyin' ass bitch.
LP: . . . . **CBS 20529**

REALITY OF MY SURROUNDINGS, THE.
Tracks: / Fight the youth / If I were a ....I'd / So many millions / Asswhippin' / Housework / Deathmarch / Behaviour control technician / Pressure / Junkies prayer / Prayer to the junkiemaker / Everyday sunshine / Naz-tee may'en / Babyhead / Those days are gone / Sunless Saturday.
LP: **4676151**
MC: **4676154**

TRUTH AND SOUL.
Tracks: / Freddie's dead / Ma and pa / Might long way / Pouring rain / Deep inside / Question of life / Bonin' in the boneyard / One day / Subliminal fascism / Slow bus movin' (Howard beach party) / Ghetto soundwave / Change.
LP: **4611731**
MC: **4611734**

Fisher, Archie

FATE O' CHARLIE, THE (Fisher, Archie & Barbara Dickson).
LP: . . . . **LER 3002**

SUNSET'S I'VE GALLOPED INTO... (Fisher, Archie/Garnet Rogers).
Tracks: / Ashfields and Brine / Yonder banks / Shipyard apprentice, The / Cuillins of Home / Southside blues / Silver coin / Prescence, The / Gunsmoke and whiskey / Bill Hosie / I wandered by a brookside / Merry England / Great North road / Eastfield / Black horse, The / All that you ask.
LP: . . . . **TRAX 020**
MC: . . . . **CTRAX 020**

WILL YE GANG, LOVE.
LP: **12TS 277**

Fisher, Cilla

BALCANQUHAL (Fisher, Cilla & Artie Trezise).
LP: . . . . **LER 2100**

CILLA AND ARTIE (Fisher, Cilla & Artie Trezise).
Tracks: / Norland wind / Beggarman, The / What can a young lassie / Fisher lassies / Generations of change / Fair maid of London Town / Wicked wife, The / Gypsy laddie, The / Blue bleezin' blind drunk / John Grumlie / Jeannie C, The.
LP: **12TS 405**

CILLA FISHER & ARTIE TREZISE (Fisher, Cilla & Artie Trezise).
LP: . . . . **ALLP 205**

FOR FOUL DAY AND FAIR (Fisher, Cilla & Artie Trezise).
LP: . . . . **KAC 1**

REACHING OUT (Fisher, Cilla & Artie Trezise).
LP: . . . . **KOP 17**
MC: . . . . **KOP 17C**

SONGS OF THE FISHING.
LP: . . . . **KOP 11**

Fisher, Eddie

AS LONG AS THERE'S MUSIC.
Tracks: / I'll buy you a star / You are too beautiful / I am in love / Best thing for you, The / Time on my hands / I'll see you again / As long as there's music / You're my girl / In love in vain / I wish I were in love again / Close as pages in a book / There but for you go I.
LP: . . . . **NL 90066**
MC: . . . . **NK 90066**

EDDIE FISHER'S GREATEST HITS.
Tracks: / Outside of Heaven / Everything I have is yours / Downhearted / I'm walking behind you / Wish you were here / Oh mein papa / I need you now / Wedding bells / Cindy Oh Cindy / Anytime / Heart / Trust in me / Lady of Spain / Tell me why / I'm yours / Thinking of you / Fanny.
LP: . . . . **INTS 5094**
MC: . . . . **INTK 5094**

GREATEST HITS: EDDIE FISHER.
Tracks: / Outside of heaven / Everything I have is yours / Downhearted / I'm walking behind you / Wish you were here / Oh mein papa / I need you now / Wedding bells / Cindy Oh Cindy / Anytime / Heart / Trust in me / Lady of Spain / Tell me why / I'm yours / Thinking of you / Fanny.
LP: . . . . **NL 89414**
MC: . . . . **NK 89414**

POP SINGERS ON THE AIR (See under Pop Singers On The Air) (Various artists).

Fisher Family

FISHER FAMILY, THE.
Tracks: / Come all ye fisher lassies / Schooldays over / Rigs o' Rye / Donalogue / For our lang biding here / Joy of my heart / Hey ca'through / What's poor Mary weeping for / Bonnie lass o'Ballochmyle / I am a miller tae ma trade / Birkin tree, The / I am a free born man / Aince upon a time.

LP: 12T 137

Fisher, Morgan

IVORIES.
LP: . . . . SBR 1LP

LOOK AT LIFE.
Tracks: / Lord of the full moon / Happy again / Mount Fuji / Time and tide / Pastorale / Meeting and merging / Samba de Carnaval / Heart to heart / Summer holidays / Erik.
LP: . . . . BRED 64
MC: . . . . CBRED 64

SEASONS.
Tracks: / Time of the season / Geneva / Take a heart / Taste of honey, A / Un homme et une femme / Coloured rain / Kites / Silent zone / May this be love / World at one, The.
LP: . . . . BRED 54

Fisher, Ray

BONNIE BRIDE.
LP: . . . . LER 2038

Fisher, Sonny

TEXAS ROCKABILLY.
Tracks: / Rockin' daddy / Hold me baby / Sneaky Pete / Rockin' and rollin' / Pink and black / I can't lose / Hey mama / Little red wagon.
LP: . . . . CH 14

TEXAS ROCKABILLY TEAR UP.
Tracks: / Driving my life away / Sweet sixteen / You're right / Raining in my heart / Truckstop baby / Shake it around / I'm flying in / Rockabilly tonight / I miss you Elvis / On the road again.
LP: . . . . MFM 005

Fisher, Tony

EXTRACTING THE DIGITAL (Fisher, Tony & John Fiddy Enterprise).
LP: . . . . ISST 117

Fisherfolk

BE LIKE YOUR FATHER.
LP: . . . . CR 1019
MC: . . . . CT 2019

CELEBRATE THE WHOLE OF IT.
LP: . . . . CR 1010
MC: . . . . CT 2010

COME AND WORSHIP.
LP: . . . . MS 003
MC: . . . . MSC 003

CRY HOSANNA.
LP: . . . . CR 1023
MC: . . . . CT 2023

GOD MAKE US YOUR FAMILY.
MC: . . . . CT 2016
LP: . . . . CR 1016

IN THE PRESENCE OF YOUR PEOPLE.
Tracks: / Song of greeting / Isn't it good / God's love for you today / I am a rock / Lord for evermore / Sing praise to the Lord / Wells of salvation.
LP: . . . . CR 1024
MC: . . . . CT 2024

JOY IN THE MORNING.
MC: . . . . CT 2028
LP: . . . . CR 1028

JOY OF CHRISTMAS, THE.
Tracks: / Ding dong merrily on high / Joy to the world / Silent night / Hallelujah chorus / Sing joyfully.
LP: . . . . CR 1027
MC: . . . . CT 2027

LOVE DIVINE.
LP: . . . . CR 1018
MC: . . . . CT 2018

MORE SONGS FROM SOUND OF LIVING WATERS/FRESH SOUNDS.
Tracks: / Jesus is Lord / Spirit is a-movin', The / Lord is a great and mighty King, The / What could be better? / Let us break bread together.
MC: . . . . CT 2020
LP: . . . . CR 1020

O FOR A THOUSAND TONGUES.
Tracks: / Awake, awake, to love and work / O for a thousand tongues to sing / Glory to God in the high / Glory be to Jesus / Jesus shall reign.
MC: . . . . CT 2021

ON TIPTOE.
Tracks: / Listen can't you hear / On tiptoe / Come, Lord Jesus / We will sing to the Lord our God / Never in my life / Hallelujah, His blood avails for me.
LP: . . . . CR 1004
MC: . . . . CT 2004

PEACE WITH THE FATHER.
LP: . . . . MS 002
MC: . . . . MSC 002

REJOICE WITH THE FISHERFOLK.
Tracks: / This is the day / Come and go with me / Something in my heart / Thank you thank you Jesus / I must have Jesus / Oh how good is the lord / There's a river of life / Spirit of the living god.
MC: . . . . CT 2017
LP: . . . . CR 1017

SING PRAISE WITH THE FISHERFOLK.
LP: . . . . CR 1031
MC: . . . . CT 2031

SING THE WORD WITH THE FISHERFOLK.
Tracks: / Ho everyone that thirsteth / Wherever two or more / Thou wilt keep him in perfect peace / Complete in him / Joy in the lord / My soul doth magnify the lord / New commandment, A.
MC: . . . . CT 2011
LP: . . . . CR 1011

SONGS FROM FRESH SOUNDS.
Tracks: / Come to the waters / I heard the voice / Bless you Jesus / O magnify the Lord / Steadfast love of the Lord, The / My song is love unknown.
LP: . . . . CR 1006
MC: . . . . CT 2006

SONGS FROM SOUND OF LIVING WATERS.
Tracks: / Seek ye first / We see the Lord / Fear not, rejoice and be glad / How sweet the Name / Jesus is a friend of mine / Butterfly song, The / Let us give thanks.
MC: . . . . CT 2002
LP: . . . . CR 1002

SPECTRUM.
Tracks: / We really want to thank You, Lord / Do you know? / Celebration song / Seek ye first / We see the Lord.
LP: . . . . CR 1029
MC: . . . . CT 2029

SUN'S GONNA SHINE, THE.
Tracks: / Jesus we're so glad / I woke up this morning / Dance the dance of life / Light of the world / Good evening father / We have another world in view / Day by day.
LP: . . . . CR 1025
MC: . . . . CT 2025

SWEET WATER.
Tracks: / Sweet water / There's a river of life / Come go with me to that land / What a great thing it is / Jesus how lovely you are.
LP: . . . . CR 1026
MC: . . . . CT 2026

THIS IS THE DAY.
Tracks: / This is the day / Good morning Jesus / Jesus Jesus is my Lord / Just as I am / They that wait upon the Lord.
LP: . . . . CR 1022
MC: . . . . CT 2022

WAKE UP TO SING THE PRAISE OF JESUS.
LP: . . . . CR 1015
MC: . . . . CT 2015

WILLING TO ROW.
Tracks: / Wings as the eagle / To whom shall we go / Hang in there Job / Lord of life / Jesus is the answer.
LP: . . . . CR 1030
MC: . . . . CT 2030

WITH THANKGIVING.
LP: . . . . MS 001
MC: . . . . MSC 001

WORSHIP WITH THE FISHERFOLK.
Tracks: / Jesus Christ is risen today / Joy of the Lord, The / Jesus took my burdens / Praise him / I want to live for Jesus / Here comes Jesus / Alleluia / My song is love unknown.
LP: . . . . CR 1007
MC: . . . . CT 2007

Fishin' In My Pond

FISHIN' IN MY POND (Various artists).
LP: . . . . FLY 582

Fisk, Nicholas

TRILLIONS (See also Steve Hodgson).
MCSET: CC/039
MC: 882146

Fisk, Steve

ONE MORE VALLEY.
MC: . . . . KC 016

Fist

BACK WITH A VENGEANCE.
Tracks: / Feeling's right, The / Dog soldier / All I can do / Turn the hell on / Devil rise / S.S.Giro / Going wild tonight / Too hot / Lost and found.
LP: . . . . NEAT 1003

TURN THE HELL ON.
LP: . . . . MAF 3082

Fistful Of Dollars

FISTFUL OF DOLLARS, A (Lure of the West, The) (Various artists).
Tracks: / Fistful of Dollars: *Various artists* / Magnificent Seven, The: *Various artists* / Rawhide: *Various* artists / Ghost Riders in the Sky: *Various artists* / High Chaparral: *Various artists* / Good, the Bad and the Ugly, The: *Various artists* / Bonanza: *Various artists* / Streets of Laredo: *Various artists* / Man Who Shot Liberty Valance, The: *Various artists* / Big Country, The: *Various artists*.
LP: . . . . OCN 2020WL
MC: . . . . OCN 2020WK

FISTFUL OF DOLLARS/FOR A FEW DOLLARS MORE (Original soundtracks) (Various artists).
LP: . . . . CDS 1052
MC: . . . . CAM 411
LP: . . . . NL 70391
MC: . . . . NK 70391

Fistful Of Dynamite

FISTFUL OF DYNAMITE, A (Original Soundtrack) (Various artists).
LP: . . . . NL 70223

Fistful Of Pussies

FISTFUL OF PUSSIES, A (Various artists).
Tracks: / Repo man: *Various artists* / Mystery street: *Various artists* / Alley cat king: *Various artists*/ Spy catcher: *Various artists* / Brand new cadillac: *Various artists* / No dog: *Various artists* / Hangman's noose: *Various artists* / Go gorilla: *Various artists* / Cyclonic: *Various artists* / I knew sky: *Various* artists / My brain is in the cupboard above the kitchen sink: *Various artists* / Surf city: *Various artists*/ I get so excited: *Various artists* / Rumble in the jungle: *Various artists* / Six brides for Jerry Lee: *Various* artists / Holy hack Jack: *Various artists* / 13 lines: *Various artists* / Boneshaker baby: *Various artists*/ She's gone: *Various artists* / Thee holy jukebox: *Various artists*.
LP: . . . . GRAM 36
LP: . . . . CGRAM 36

Fitchet, Angus

FITCHET'S FANCY (Fitchet, Angus & His All Star Scottish Band).
LP: . . . . GLN 1025

LEGENDARY ANGUS FITCHET, THE.
Tracks: / Jigs / Barn dance / Scottish waltz / Two step / Violin solo / Polka / Selected reels.
LP: . . . . LOCLP 1024
MC: . . . . ZCLOC 1024

Fi-Tones

PRESENTING THE FI-TONES.
LP: . . . . ANGLE TONE 5010

Fits

FACT OR FICTION (MINI LP).
MLP: . . . . FIT 003

YOU'RE NOTHING YOU'RE NOWHERE.
Tracks: / Nothing and nowhere / Too many rules / Disease / Man at dawn / Cats dinner / Prostitute / Make's me wanna / I don't need it / Time is right / You named us / Jumpin Jack Flash / Listen to me / Straps.
LP: . . . . ABOUT 6
MC: . . . . CARB 6

Fitzcaraldo (film)

FITZCARALDO (See under Popul Vuh) (Popul Vuh).

Fitzgerald, Ella

16 ORIGINAL HITS: ELLA FITZGERALD.
MC: . . . . MC 1629

ALL THAT JAZZ.
Tracks: / Dream a little dream of me / My last affair / Baby don't you quit now / Oh look at me now / Jersey bounce / When your lover has gone / That ole devil called love / All that jazz / Just when we're falling in love / Good morning heartache / Little jazz / Nearness of you, The.
MC: . . . . PBDC 006

ANTONIO CARLOS JOBIM SONGBOOK, THE.
Tracks: / Somewhere in the hills / Girl from Ipanema / Dindi / Off key / Water to drink / Triste / How insensitive / He's a carioca / Felicidade / This love that I've found / Dreamer / Quiet nights of quiet stars / Bonita / One-note samba / Wave / Don't ever go away / Song of the jet / Useless landscape.
2LP: 263 0201
MCSET: . . . . K 30 201

AT THE MONTREUX JAZZ FESTIVAL 1975.
Tracks: / Caravan / Satin doll / Teach me tonight / Wave / It's alright with me / Let's do it / How high the moon / Girl from Ipanema / T'aint nobody's business if I do.
LP: 2310 751
MC: K10 751

AT THE OPERA HOUSE.
Tracks: / It's alright with me / Don'cha go 'way mad / Bewitched, bothered and bewildered / Stompin' at the Savoy / These foolish things / Ill wind / Goody goody / Moonlight in Vermont / Lady be good.
LP: 8215541

AT THE SOUTHLAND OF BOSTON (Fitzgerald, Ella/Chick Webb).
Tracks: / Let's get together / Poor little rich girl / New moon and an old serenade / Breaking 'em down / If I didn't care / Stars and stripes forever / I never knew Heaven could speak / My wild Irish rose / Chew, chew, chew, chew (your bubble gum) / Blue Lou / Deep in a dream / One o'clock jump / That was my heart.
LP: . . . . BLJ 8010

BASIN STREET BLUES.
LP: . . . . VS 3406
MC: . . . . VSK 3406

BEST OF ELLA FITZGERALD.
Tracks: / Tisket a tasket, A / Stairway to the stars / Into each life some rain must fall / Paper moon / Flying home / I love you (for sentimental reasons) / Lady be good / How high the moon / Basin Street blues / My one and only love / I've got the world on a string / Walkin' by the river / Lover come back to me / Mixed emotions / Smooth sailing / If you can't sing it you'll have to swing it / I wished on the moon / That old black magic / It's too soon to know / Tender trap, The.
LP: . . . . MCL 1611
MC: . . . . MCLC 1611

BEST OF ELLA FITZGERALD (2).
Tracks: / Dreamer / Fine and mellow / Street of dreams / This love that I've found / How long has this been going on / You're blase / Honeysuckle rose / I'm walking / I'm getting sentimental over you / Don't be that way.
LP: . . . . PEM 001
MC: . . . . PEMC 001

BEST YEARS OF ELLA FITZGERALD.
Tracks: / Tisket a tasket, A / Take another guess / I've got a guy / Gotta pebble in my shoe / Undecided / Chew, chew, chew, chew (your bubble gum) / You'll have to swing it / Big boy blues / Dedicated to you / This time it's for real.
LP: . . . . SM 3054

BEWITCHED.
Tracks: / Bewitched / Begin the beguine / My funny valentine / 'S wonderful / Let's do it / Manhattan / Night and day.
MC: 2475 233
LP: 3236 233

BILLIE, ELLA, LENA, SARAH (See under Holiday, Bille for details) (Various artists).

CAB, ELLA & CHICK (See under Calloway, Cab) (Fitzgerald, Ella/Cab Calloway/Chick Webb).

CHEEK TO CHEEK (See under Armstrong, Louis) (Fitzgerald, Ella & Louis Armstrong).

CLASSY PAIR, A (Fitzgerald, Ella/Count Basie).
Tracks: / I'm getting sentimental over you / Organ grinder's swing / Just a sittin' and a rockin' / My kind of trouble is you / Ain't misbehavin' / Some other spring / Teach me tonight / Don't worry 'bout me / Honeysuckle rose / Sweet Lorraine / Please don't talk about me when I'm gone.
MC: K12 132
LP: 231 2132

COLE PORTER SONG BOOK VOLS. 1 AND 2.
Tracks: / All through the night / Anything goes / Miss Otis regrets / Too darn hot / In the still of the night / I get a kick out of you / Do I love you / Always true to you in my fashion / Let's do it / Just one of those things / Every time we say goodbye / All of you / Begin the beguine / Get out of town / I am in love / From this moment on / I love Paris / You do something to me / Ridin' high / Easy to love / It's alright with me / Why can't you behave / What is this thing called love / You're the top / Love for sale / It's de-lovely / Night and day / Ace in the hole / So in love / I've got you under my skin / I concentrate on you / Don't fence me in.
2LP: 2683 044

COLE PORTER SONGBOOK VOL.1.
MC: 311 205 4

COLE PORTER SONGBOOK VOL.2.
MC: 311 205 5

DIGITAL III AT MONTREUX (Fitzgerald, Ella/Count Basie/Joe Pass).
Tracks: / I can't get started / Good mileage / Ghost of a chance / Flying home / I cover the waterfront / Li'l darlin' / In your own sweet way / Oleo.
LP: 230 8223
MC: . . . . K 08 223
LP: . . . . D 230 8223

EASY LIVIN (Fitzgerald, Ella & Joe Pass).
LP: 231 0921

MC: K10 921

ELLA A NICE.
Tracks: / Night and day / Get out of town / Easy to love / You do something to me / Body and soul / Man I love, The / Porgy / Bossa scene, The / Girl from Ipanema / Fly me to the moon / O nosso amor / Cielito lindo / Magdalena / Aqua de beber / Summertime / They can't take that away from me / Mood indigo / Do nothing till you hear from me / It don't mean a thing / Something / St. Louis blues / Close to you / Put a little love in your heart.
LP: **230 8234**
MC: **K 08 234**

ELLA AND DUKE AT THE COTE D'AZUR (Fitzgerald, Ella/Duke Ellington).
2LP: **833 562 1**

ELLA AND HER FELLAS.
Tracks: / You won't be satisfied (until you break my heart) / That's the way it is / Stone cold dead in the market (he had it done coming) / I gotta have my baby back / Sentimental journey / Frim fram sauce / It's only a paper moon / Dream a little dream of me / Baby it's cold outside / Tisket a tasket, A / Would you like to take a walk / Don'cha go way mad.
LP: **MCL 1705**
MC: **MCLC 1705**

ELLA AND LOUIS (Fitzgerald, Ella & Louis Armstrong).
Tracks: / Can't we be friends? / Isn't this a lovely day / Moonlight in Vermont / They can't take that away from me / Under a blanket of blue / Foggy day, A / Tenderly / Stars fell on Alabama / Nearness of you, The / April in Paris / Cheek to cheek.
LPS: **2615 034**
LP: **ENT LP 13023**
MC: **ENT MC 13023**
LP: **825 373-1**
MC: **825 373-4**

ELLA AND OSCAR (Fitzgerald, Ella & Oscar Peterson).
Tracks: / Mean to me / How long has this been going on / When your lover has gone / More than you know / There's a lull in my life / Midnight sun / I hear music / Street of dreams / April in Paris / Hear music.
LP: **2310 759**
MC: **10 759**

ELLA AT THE OPERA HOUSE.
LP: **33X 10126**

ELLA & BASIE (Fitzgerald, Ella/Count Basie).
Tracks: / Honeysuckle rose / Deed I do / Into each life some rain must fall / Them there eyes / Dream a little dream of me / Tea for two / Satin doll / I'm beginning to see the light / Shiny stockings / My last affair / Ain't misbehavin' / On the sunny side of the street.
LP: **2304 049**
MC: **3113 108**

ELLA & ELLIS (Fitzgerald, Ella/Ellis Larkin).
Tracks: / I'm glad there is you / What is there to say / People will say we're in love / Please be kind / Until the real thing comes along / Makin' whoopee! / Imagination / Stardust / My heart belongs to daddy / You leave me breathless / Baby, what else can I do / Nice work if you can get it / Someone to watch over me / My one and only (what am I gonna do) / But not for me / Looking for a boy / I've got a crush on you / How long has this been going on / Soon / Maybe.
LP: **MCL 1775**
MC: **MCLC 1775**

ELLA FITZGERALD (Compact/Walkman jazz).
Tracks: / Goody goody / Rough ridin' / Boy from Ipanema, The / Sweet Georgia Brown / Duke's place / Misty / Somebody loves me / How high the moon.
MC: **831 367-4**

ELLA FITZGERALD AND LOUIS ARMSTRONG (2) (Compact/Walkman Jazz) (Fitzgerald, Ella & Louis Armstrong).
Tracks: / They can't take that away from me / Gee baby ain't I good to you / I won't dance / It ain't necessarily so / Fine romance, A / Stompin' at the Savoy / Foggy day, A / Don't be that way / Summertime / Cheek to cheek / Can't we be friends / Let's call the whole thing off.
MC: **835 313-4**

ELLA FITZGERALD AND LOUIS ARMSTRONG (see Armstrong, Louis) (Fitzgerald, Ella & Louis Armstrong).

ELLA FITZGERALD AND THE CHICK WEBB ORCHESTRA (Fitzgerald, Ella & The Chick Webb Orchestra).
Tracks: / Blue Lou / Cryin' mood / Clap hands, here comes Charlie / I've got a guy / Strictly jive / Just a simple melody / Holiday in Harlem / Rock it for me / Harlem congo / Midnight in Harlem / Spinnin' the web / Chew, chew, chew, chew (your bubble gum) / I let a tear fall in the river / Sugar pie.
LP: **SM 3613**

ELLA FITZGERALD COLLECTION (20 Golden Greats).
Tracks: / Lover come back to me / Just one of those things / Angel eyes / My heart belongs to daddy / Good enough to keep / I'm beginning to see the light / Sophisticated lady / I can't give you anything but love / Cryin' mood / Just a simple melody / Ella / Tisket a tasket, A / I found a yellow basket / Dedicated to you / I've got a guy / Gotta pebble in my shoe / Undecided / Chew, chew, chew, chew (your bubble gum) / This time it's for real / You'll have to swing it.
LP: **DVLP 2004**
MC: **DVMC 2004**

ELLA FITZGERALD (ENTERTAINERS).
LP: **ENT LP 13008**
MC: **ENT MC 13008**

ELLA FITZGERALD & HER ORCHESTRA LIVE (From Roseland ballroom) (Fitzgerald, Ella/her Famous Orchestra).
LP: **20804**

ELLA FITZGERALD LIVE (Compact/Walkman jazz).
Tracks: / Oh lady be good / Summertime / Honeysuckle Rose / Body and soul / Squeeze me / These foolish things / Stompin' at the Savoy.
MC: **833 294-4**

ELLA FITZGERALD SINGS THE JOHNNY MERCER SONGBOOK.
Tracks: / Too marvellous for words / Early Autumn / Day in, day out / Laura / This time the dream's on me / Skylark / Single-O / Something's gotta give / Travelling light / Midnight sun / Dream / I remember you / When a woman loves a man / Let's begin / Fine romance, A / All the things you are / I'll be hard to handle / You couldn't be cuter / She didn't say yes / I'm old fashioned / Remind me / Way you look tonight / Yesterdays / Can't help lovin' dat man / Why was I born?.
MC: **TWOMC 11**

ELLA FITZGERALD SONGBOOK, THE.
Tracks: / Begin the beguine / Every time we say goodbye / Fascinating rhythm / Stormy weather.
LPS: **ALBUM 58**
MCSET: **CASSETTE 58**

ELLA FITZGERALD STORY, THE.
Tracks: / You'll have to swing it / Big boy blues / Take another guess / Dedicated to you / Cryin' mood / Just a simple melody / Holiday in Harlem / I've got a guy / Tisket a tasket, A / Ella / Gotta pebble in my shoe / I let a tear fall in the river / I found my yellow basket / Undecided / Chew, chew, chew, chew (your bubble gum) / Vote for Mr. Rhythm / Everybody step / It's foxy / Lover come back to me / Angel eyes / I'm beginning to see the light / My heart belongs to daddy / Just one of those things / I can't give you anything but love, baby / Sophisticated lady.
MCSET: **DVREMC 05**

ELLA FITZGERALD VOL.1.
LP: **LOP 14,015**
LP: **ST 1006**

ELLA FITZGERALD VOL.2.
LP: **LOP 14088**

ELLA FITZGERALD'S CHRISTMAS.
Tracks: / O holy night / It came upon a midnight clear / Hark the herald angels sing / Away in a manger / Joy to the world / First noel, The / O come all ye faithful / Sleep, my little Jesus / Angels we have heard on high / O little town of Bethlehem / We three kings / God rest ye merry gentlemen.
MC: **C4 94452**
MC: **794 452 4**

ELLA IN LONDON.
Tracks: / Sweet Georgia Brown / They can't take that away from me / Every time we say goodbye / It don't mean a thing / You've got a friend / Lemon drop / Very thought of you, The / Happy blues / Man I love, The.
LP: **2310 711**
MC: **K10 711**

ELLA IN ROME.
LP: **835 454 1**

ELLA LOVES COLE.
Tracks: / I get a kick out of you / Down in the depths / At long last love / I've got you under my skin / So near and yet so far / All of you / Without love / My heart belongs to Daddy / Love for sale / Just one of those things / I concentrate on you / Anything goes / C'est magnifique.
LP: **K 40450**

ELLA & RAY (Fitzgerald, Ella & Ray Brown).
Tracks: / Ool-ya-koo / Love that boy / Mr. Paganini / Too soon to know / I never knew / How high the moon / Heatwave / Old Mother Hubbard / Pop goes the weasel / Flying home.
LP: **BLJ 8035**

ELLA SINGS GERSHWIN.
Tracks: / Someone to watch over me / My one and only (what am I gonna do) / But not for me / Looking for a boy / Nice work if you can get it / Oh lady be good / I've got a crush on you / How long has this been going on / Maybe / Soon / I'm just a lucky so and so / I didn't mean a word I said.
LP: **MCL 1820**
MC: **MCLC 1820**
LP: **LA 8648**

ELLA SINGS GERSHWIN VOL.5.
LP: **CLP 1353**

ELLA SWINGS LIGHTLY.
Tracks: / Little white lies / You hit the spot / What's your story, morning glory? / Just you, just me / As long as I live / Teardrops from my eyes / Gotta be this or that / Moonlight on the Ganges / My kinda love / Blues in the night / If I were a bell / You're an old smoothie / Little Jazz / You brought a new kind of love to me / Knock me a kiss / 720 in the books.
LP: **2304 134**

ELLA (VERVE).
Tracks: / Sweet and lovely / Let's fall in love / Makin' whoopee / That old feeling / I remember you / Moonlight serenade / Gone with the wind / Can't we be friends / Out of this world / My old flame / East of the sun / Lullaby of Broadway.
LP: **2352 170**

ELLA VOL.2 (Lady Be Good).
LP: **SM 3975**
MC: **MC 3975**

ELLA VOL. 1 (Mr. Paganini).
LP: **SM 3974**
MC: **MC 3974**

ELLA WITH... (Fitzgerald, Ella/Savoy 8/Benny Goodman/Chick Webb/Mills Bros).
Tracks: / All over nothing at all / If you ever should leave / It's my turn now / Everyone's wrong but me / Bei mir bist du schon / Little bit later on, A / I want to be happy / Hallelujah! / Crying my heart out for you / You'll have to swing it / Holiday in Harlem / Cryin' mood / Devoting my time / Rock it for me / Darktown strutters' ball / Sing me a swing song / Vote for Mr. Rhythm / Just a simple melody / Swinging on the reservation / Under the spell of the blues / I got the spring fever blues / Rhythm and romance / If dreams come true / Take another guess / Dipsy doodle, The / I've got a guy / When I get low I get high / Did you mean it? / Dedicated to you / Big boy blues / Goodnight my love.
2LP: **AJD 055**
MCSET: **ZC AJD 055**

EVENING AT THE HOLLYWOOD BOWL, AN (See under Peterson, Oscar) (Fitzgerald, Ella & Oscar Peterson).

FINE AND MELLOW.
Tracks: / Fine and mellow / I'm just a lucky so and so / Ghost of a chance / Rockin' in rhythm / I'm in the mood for love / Round midnight / I can't give you anything but love / Man I love, The / Polka dots and moonbeams.
LP: **2310 829**
MC: **K10 828**

FIRST LADY OF SWING.
LP: **ENT LP 13034**
MC: **ENT MC 13034**

FITZGERALD AND PASS...AGAIN (Fitzgerald, Ella & Joe Pass).
Tracks: / Ain't got nothing but the blues / T'is autumn / My old flame / That old feeling / Rain / I didn't know about you / You took advantage of me / I've got the world on a string / All too soon / One I love, The / Solitude / Nature boy / Tennessee waltz / One-note samba.
LP: **231 0772**
MC: **K10 772**

FOR THE LOVE OF ELLA.
2LP: **841 766 1**
MCSET: **841 766 4**

FOREVER YOUNG VOL.1.
Tracks: / My melancholy baby / All my life.
LP: **ST 1006**

FOREVER YOUNG VOL.2.
LP: **ST 1007**

GEORGE GERSHWIN SONG BOOK, THE.
Tracks: / Sam and Delilah / But not for me / My one and only / Let's call the whole thing off / I've got beginner's luck / Lady be good / Nice work if you can get it / Things are looking up / Just another rhumba / How long has this been going on? / 'S wonderful / Man I love, The / That certain feeling / By Strauss / Who cares? / Someone to watch over me / Real American folk song / They all laughed / Looking for a boy / My cousin from Milwaukee / Somebody from somewhere / Foggy day, A / Clap yo' hands / For you, for me, for evermore / Stiff upper lip / Strike up the band / Soon / I've got a crush on you / Bidin' my time / Aren't you kind of glad we did? / Of thee I sing / Half it dearie blues, The / I was doing it right / He loves and she loves / Love is sweeping the country / Treat me rough / Love is here to stay / Slap that bass / Isn't it a pity / Shall we dance? / Love walked in / You've got what gets me / They can't take that away from me / Embraceable you / I can't be bothered now / Boy, what love has done to me / Fascinating rhythm / Oh so nice / Lorelei / Let's kiss and make up / I got rhythm.
LP: **VRV 9**
MC: **VRVC 9**

GERSHWIN SONGBOOK 1.
Tracks: / Sam and Delilah / But not for me / My one and only / Let's call the whole thing off / Beginner's luck / Embraceable you / Lady be good / Nice work if you can get it / Things are looking up / Just another rhumba / How long has this been going on? / I can't be bothered now / 'S wonderful / Man I love, The / That certain feeling / By Strauss / Someone to watch over me / Real American folk song / Funny face / They all laughed / My cousin in Milwaukee / Somebody from somewhere / They can't take that away from me / Let's kiss and make up.
2LP: **2682 004**

GET HAPPY.
Tracks: / Somebody loves me / Cheerful little earful / You make me feel so young / Beat me daddy, eight to the bar / Like young / Cool breeze / Moonlight becomes you / Blue skies / You turned the tables on me / Gypsy in my soul / Goody goody / St. Louis blues.
LP: **813 391-1**

GOLDEN GREATS: ELLA FITZGERALD.
Tracks: / Tisket a tasket, A / Stairway to the stars / It's only a paper moon / That old black magic / Tender trap, The / Into each life some rain must fall / Flying home / (I love you) for sentimental reasons / O lady be good / How high the moon / Basin Street blues / My one and only love / I've got the world on a string / Walkin' by the river / Lover come back to me / Mixed emotions / Smooth sailing / (If you can't sing it) you'll have to swing it / I wished on the moon.
LP: **MCM 5009**
MC: **MCMC 5009**

GREATEST HITS 2.
LP: **33005**
MC: **63005**

GREATEST HITS: ELLA FITZGERALD.
LP: **33004**
MC: **63004**

HELLO DOLLY.
Tracks: / Hello Dolly / People / Sweetest sounds, The / Can't buy me love / Miss Otis regrets / My man / How high the moon / Volare / Thrill is gone, The / Memories of you / Lullaby of the leaves / Pete Kelly's blues.
LP: **MOIR 128**
MC: **CMOIR 128**

HELLO LOVE.
Tracks: / You go to my head / Willow weep for me / I'm through with love / Spring will be a little late this year / Everything happens to me / Lost in a fog / I've grown accustomed to his face / I'll never be the same / So rare / Tenderly / Stairway to the stars / Moonlight in Vermont.
LP: **MOIR 124**
MC: **CMOIR 124**

INCOMPARABLE ELLA, THE.
Tracks: / Lady is a tramp, The / Manhattan / Very thought of you / From this moment on / I've got you under my skin / Foggy day / With a song in my heart / Cheek to cheek / I've got a crush on you / Night and day / Every time we say goodbye / It's only a paper moon / I get a kick out of you / I got rhythm / My funny valentine / That old black magic.
LP: **POLTV 9**

IRVING BERLIN SONGBOOK, THE.
Tracks: / Let's face the music and dance / You're laughing at me / Let yourself go / You can have him / Puttin' on the Ritz /

Get thee behind me, Satan / Alexander's ragtime band / Top hat, white tie and tails / How about me? / Cheek to cheek / I used to be colour blind / Lazy / How deep is the ocean? / All by myself / You forgot to remember / Blue skies / Supper time / How's chances? / Heatwave / Isn't this a lovely day / You keep coming back like a song / Reaching for the moon / Slumming on Park Avenue / Song is ended, The / I'm putting all my eggs in one basket / Now it can be told / Always / It's a lovely day today / Change partners / No strings / I've got my love to keep me warm.
2LP: **2683 027**

IT HAPPENED ONE NIGHT (see under Parker, Charlie) (Fitzgerald, Ella/Dizzy Gillespie/Charlie Parker).

JEROME KERN/JOHNNY MERCER SONGBOOKS, THE.
Tracks: / Let's begin / Fine romance, A / All the things you are / I'll be hard to handle / You couldn't be cuter / She didn't say yes / I'm old fashioned / Remind me / Way you look tonight / Yesterdays / Can't help lovin' dat man / Why was I born? / Too marvellous for words / Early Autumn / Day in, day out / Laura / This time the dream's on me / Skylark / Single-o / Something's gotta give / Travellin' light / Midnight sun / Dream / I remember you / When a woman loves a man.
2LP: **2610 025**

LADY TIME.
Tracks: / I'm walking / All or nothing at all / I never had a chance / I cried for you / What will I tell my heart? / Since I fell for you / And the angels sing / I'm confessin' / Mack the knife / That's my desire / I'm in the mood for love.
LP: **231 0825**
MC: **K10 825**

L'ART VOCAL VOLUME 5: LA SELECTION 1935-1939 (See Under L'Art Vocal).

LIKE SOMEONE IN LOVE.
Tracks: / There's a lull in my life / More than you know / What will I tell my heart? / I never had a chance / Close your eyes / We'll be together again / Then I'll be tired of you / Like someone in love / Midnight sun / I thought about you / You're blase / Night wind / What's new? / Hurry home / How long has this been going on?.
LP: **2352 097**

LIVE AT CARNEGIE HALL (5/7/73).
LP: . . . . **CBS 88621**

LOVE SONGS: ELLA FITZGERALD.
Tracks: / I can't get started / It might as well be spring / You'll never know / I wished on the moon / Please be kind / Someone to watch over me / My one and only love / I'm glad there is you / Angel eyes / Walkin' by the river / How long has this been going on / Old devil moon / Baby doll.
LP: . . . . **MOIR 111**
MC: . . . . **CMOIR 111**

LOVER COME BACK TO ME.
LP: **2M 056 64868**
MC: **2M 256 64868**

LULLABIES OF BIRDLAND.
Tracks: / Lullaby of Birdland / Rough ridin' / Angel eyes / Smooth sailing / Lady be good / Later / Ella hums the blues / How high the moon / Basin Street blues / Airmail special / Flying home.
LP: . . . . **JASM 1027**

NICE WORK IF YOU CAN GET IT (Fitzgerald, Ella/Andre Previn).
Tracks: / Let's call the whole thing off / How long has this been going on / Who cares / I've got a crush on you / Someone to watch over me / Embraceable you / They can't take that away from me / Foggy day, A / But not for me / Nice work if you can get it.
LP: **231 2140**
MC: . . . . **K 12 140**

PERFECT MATCH, A (Fitzgerald, Ella/Count Basie).
Tracks: / Please don't talk about me when I'm gone / Sweet Georgia Brown / Some other spring / Make me rainbows / After you've gone / Round midnight / Fine and mellow / You've changed / Honeysuckle rose / St. Louis blues / Basella.
LP: **231 2110**
MC: . . . . **K 12 110**

PETE KELLY'S BLUES (see Lee, Peggy) (Fitzgerald, Ella & Peggy Lee).

PORGY & BESS (see under Armstrong, Louis) (Fitzgerald, Ella & Louis Armstrong).

PORTRAIT OF ELLA FITZGERALD, A.
Tracks: / Mack the knife / But not for me / Begin the Beguine / Manhattan / Every time we say goodbye / Desafinado / Embraceable you / Moonlight in Vermont / How high the moon / Someone to watch over me / Lullaby of Broadway / Very thought of you, The / Where or when / Georgia on my mind / Foggy day, A / Can't buy me love.
LP: . . . . **SMR 847**
MC: . . . . **SMC 847**

RAREST OF ALL RARE PERFORMANCES VOL 1.
LP: . . . . **KLJ 20032**

RAREST, THE 1936-39.
Tracks: / Vote for Mr. Rhythm / Everybody step / Swinging on the reservation / I got the spring fever blues / I'm just a jitterbug / It's foxy / If dreams come true / F.D.R. Jones / Love, you're just a laugh / Pack up your sins and go to the devil / I love each move you make / I can't stop loving you.
LP: . . . . **SM 3281**
MC: . . . . **MC 3281**

RHYTHM IS MY BUSINESS.
LP: **2304 558**

ROCK IT FOR ME, 1937 (See under Holiday, Billie) (Fitzgerald, Ella/Billie Holiday).

RODGERS AND HART SONGBOOK.
Tracks: / Have you met Miss Jones? / You took advantage of me / Ship without a sail / To keep my love alive / Dancing on the ceiling / Lady is a tramp, The / With a song in my heart / Manhattan / Johnny One Note / I wish I were in love again / Spring is here / It never entered my mind / This can't be love / Thou swell / My romance / Where or when / Little girl blue / Give it back to the Indians / Ten cents a dance / There's a small hotel / I didn't know what time it was / Everything I've got / I could write a book / Blue room / My funny valentine / Betwitched / Mountain greenery / Wait till you see her / Lover / Isn't it romantic? / Here in my arms / Blue moon / My heart stood still / I've got five dollars.
2LP: **2683 053**

SENTIMENTAL JOURNEY.
Tracks: / Sentimental journey / Dream a little dream of me / Someone to watch over me.
LP: . . . . **SHM 3232**
MC: . . . . **HSC 3232**

SINGS CHRISTMAS.
Tracks: / O holy night / It came upon a midnight clear / Hark the herald angels sing / First Noel, The / Silent night / O come all ye faithful / Sleep my little Jesus / O little town of Bethlehem / We three kings of Orient are / God rest ye merry gentlemen.
LP: . . . . **MFP 5587**
MC: . . . . **TCMFP 5587**

SINGS RODGERS AND HART VOL 2.
MC: **3112015**

SINGS THE GEORGE AND IRA GERSHWIN SONGBOOK.
LPS: **2615 063**

SPEAK LOVE.
Tracks: / Speak low / Come love / There's no you / I may be wrong but I think you're wonderful / At last / Thrill is gone, The / Gone with the wind / Blue and sentimental / Girl talk / Georgia on my mind.
LP: **2310 888**

SPECIAL MAGIC OF ELLA FITZGERALD & LOUIS (Fitzgerald, Ella & Louis Armstrong).
MC: **3113168**

SPECIAL MAGIC OF ELLA FITZGERALD.
Tracks: / Rough ridin' / Sweet Georgia Brown / This year's kisses / You brought a new kind of love to me / Beat me daddy, eight to the bar / Angel eyes / Stella by starlight / Like young / You turned the tables on me / Cry me a river / Broadway / Matchmaker, matchmaker / Round midnight / Gypsy in my soul.
LP: **2317 145**

STOCKHOLM CONCERT, 1966 (Fitzgerald, Ella/Duke Ellington).
Tracks: / Imagine my frustration / Duke's place / Satin doll / Something to live for / Wives and lovers / So dance samba / Let's do it / Lover man / Cottontail.
LP: **230 8242**
MC: . . . . **K 8242**

SUNSHINE OF YOUR LOVE.
Tracks: / Hey Jude / Sunshine of your love / This girl's in love with you / Watch what happens / Alright, OK you win / Give me the simple life / Useless landscape / Old devil moon / Don'cha go 'way mad / House is not a home, A / Trouble is a man / I love you madly.
LP: **8212901**

SWEET AND HOT.
Tracks: / Thanks for the memory / It might as well be spring / You'll never know / I can't get started / Moanin' low / Taking a chance on love / That old black magic / Old devil moon / Lover come back to me / Between the Devil and the deep blue sea / You'll have to swing it.
LP: . . . . **JASM 1045**

SWINGING CHRISTMAS.
Tracks: / Jingle bells / Winter wonderland / Santa Claus is coming to town.
LP: **2304 445**

TAKE LOVE EASY (Fitzgerald, Ella & Joe Pass).
Tracks: / Take love easy / Once I loved / Don't be that way / You're blase / Lush life / Foggy day, A / Gee baby ain't I good to you / You got to my head / I want to talk about you.
LP: **231 0702**
MC: **K10 702**

THANKS FOR THE MEMORY.
Tracks: / That old black magic / You'll never know / It might as well be spring / I can't get started / It's only a paper moon / Oh lady be good / You'll have to swing it / My one and only love / Lover come back to me / Tisket a tasket, A / I wished on the moon / How high the moon / Flying home / Moanin' low / Taking a chance on love / Thanks for the memory.
LP: . . . . **PLAT 305**
MC: . . . . **PLAC 305**

THANKS FOR THE MEMORY (PICKWICK) (50th Anniversary Collection).
Tracks: / I'm beginning to see the light / Nice work if you can get it / My heart belongs to daddy / Guy is a guy, A / Happy talk / Crying in the chapel / That old black magic / My man / How high the moon / Oh, lady be good / I'm gonna wash that man right outta my hair / Can't help lovin' dat man / It might as well be spring / Imagination / Thanks for the memory.
LP: . . . . **SHM 3302**
MC: . . . . **HSC 3302**

THAT OLD ELLA MAGIC.
Tracks: / Tisket, a-tasket, A / Hard hearted Hannah / Angel eyes / But not for me.
LP: . . . . **MFP 5623**
MC: . . . . **TCMFP 5623**

THESE ARE THE BLUES.
LP: **829 536 1**
MC: **829 536 4**

VERY THOUGHT OF YOU.
LP: . . . . **CN 2087**
MC: **CN4 2087**

WEBB ON THE AIR.
LP: . . . . **JAZ 2021**
MC: . . . . **ZCJAZ 2021**

WHISPER NOT.
LP: **2304 393**

WITH CHICK WEBB.
LP: **20077**
MC: **40077**

WITH THE TOMMY FLANAGAN TRIO (Fitzgerald, Ella & Tommy Flanagan Trio).
Tracks: / Too close for comfort / I ain't got nothin' but the blues / My man / Come rain or come shine / Day by day / Ordinary fool / One-note samba / I let a song go out of my heart / Billie's bounce / You are the sunshine of my life.
LP: **2308 206**
MC: . . . . **K 08 206**

Fitzgerald, Kathleen

BEST OF KATHLEEN FITZGERALD WITH RICHARD & BARNEY.
Tracks: / Beautiful Bundoran / Moonlight in Mayo / My Dublin Bay / Shawl of Galway Grey / Shamrock from Glenore / Slieve Gallion Braes / Let him go, let him tarry / Ar shiul measc na sleibhte dtir chonaill / Old refrain / Star of Donegal / Shall my soul pass through old Ireland.
LP: . . . . **HRL 172**
MC: . . . . **CHRL 172**

HILLS OF DONEGAL, THE.
Tracks: / If we only had old Ireland over here / Dear little shamrock / Hills of Donegal.
LP: . . . . **HRL 153**
MC: . . . . **CHRL 153**

KATHLEEN FITZGERALD SINGS.
Tracks: / My lovely Irish rose / Meetings of the waters / Dan O'Hara / Spinning wheel / Lovely lough gil / Terry / Three lovely lassies / It's heaven around Galway Bay / Kitty of Coleraine / Moonlight in Mayo / Killarney / Beautiful Bundoran.
MC: **823 481-4**

Fitzgerald, Patrick

DRIFTING INTO SILENCE.
LP: . . . . **HIM 009**

GIFTS AND TELEGRAMS.
LP: . . . . **RF 8**

GRUBBY STORIES.
Tracks: / As ugly as you / Nothing to do / All my friends are dead now / Adopted girl / Don't tell me because I'm young / When I get famous / Little fishes / Lovers' pact / All the years of trying / But not anymore / Suicidal wreck / My secret life / Conventions of life / Parentgames / No fun football / Make it safe / Your hero.
LP: **2383533**

Fitzgerald, Paul

QUIET WATER (Fitzgerald, Paul & Mark Flanagan).
MC: . . . . **C 132**

SPIRIT CATCHER (Fitzgerald, Paul & Mark Flanagan).
MC: . . . . **C 136**

Fitzgerald, Richard

RICHARD FITZGERALD (Fitzgerald, Richard Ceili Band).
LP: . . . . **ZMAL 701**

RICHARD FITZGERALD CEILI BAND (Fitzgerald, Richard Ceili Band).
MC: . . . . **GTDC 077**

SOUND OF RICHARD FITZGERALD (Fitzgerald, Richard Ceili Band).
LP: . . . . **ZMAL 0370**

Fitzpatrick, Gene

EMERALD SMILE, THE.
Tracks: / Emerald smile, The / First and last three minutes, The / Growing up / Message and movies / Belfast / S-S-Sixties, The / Love and marriage / I wish I was eighteen again / Cally out / Room service / Vindaloo victims / And visitors / Touch of the master's hand, The / It's the way we talk / Bit of a ballot, A / Priests / Penance / And Burton's bible / Take me drunk I'am home / When I leave the world behind / Wish I was 18 again.
LP: . . . . **DHL 704**
MC: . . . . **CDHL 704**
MC: . . . . **TVDHL 704**

FITZ OF LAUGHTER.
Tracks: / Medical mirth / Kids crack.
LP: . . . . **PHL 450**
MC: . . . . **CPHL 450**

LIVE AT THE GROUP THEATRE.
Tracks: / Kingdom I call home / Meet Gene Fitzpatrick / Couple of countrymen, A / Nurse nurse / Keeping fit / Let's talk about love / Road block / Yard men, The / Scots, The / Air pocket / Mug shots / Court cases / Stoneface / Hot breakfast / Look no jacket / No hope / In the jungle / In the carry out / Kamikaze / Jimmy quit the drinking / Out on the town / Happy birthday / Absent friends / Going home / At the zoo / Jaws / Meet his reverence / Ian and Gerry / Hee haw / Jailhouse mouse / Ian and the cardinal / Holy coke / Landlady / Last dance / Lovely eyes / Look no glass / Ian's above / Hot line / Centre forward, The / Finale.
LP: . . . . **PHL 434**
MC: . . . . **CPHL 434**

Fitzroy, Eddie

COMING UP STRONG.
Tracks: / Watch deh / Jah sun / Coming up strong / Motherless children / Love the people want / Chant dem rasta / Easy rider / Father / Princess Black / Sow your corn.
LP: . . . . **SP 999**

Fitzroy, Edi

ECLIPSE.
LP: . . . . **RAS 3041**

Fitzsimmons, A.

MAGEEAN/FITZSIMMONS (See under Mageean, J & A) (Fitzsimmons, A & J. & A. Mageean).

Fitzsimmons, Eddie

WELCOME TO THE COUNTRY.
MC: . . . . **FACS 011**

Fitzwilly

FITZWILLY (Original soundtrack) (Various artists).
LP: . . . . **MCA 25098**
MC: . . . . **MCAC 25098**

Five A Slide

FIVE A SLIDE Various artists (Various artists).
LP: . . . . **AP 180**

Five Bands That ...

FIVE BANDS THAT CHANGED THE WORLD (Various artists).
LP: . . . . **FH 12-004**

Five Blind Boys...

FIVE BLIND BOYS OF ALABAMA (Five Blind Boys Of Alabama).
Tracks: / I want my crown / What more can Jesus do / Don't wonder about him / I've an interest over there / Death has taken mother home / What manner of man is this / Living on Mother's prayer / Honey in the rock / Jesus won't deny me / Anyhow / Blessed be the name / Good religion / No more tears no more dying / Come over here / Canaan's land / Leave your burden there.
LP: . . . . **HT 315**

Five Children & It

FIVE CHILDREN AND IT (see Nesbitt, E) (Donald, Sheila (nar)).

Five Corners

FIVE CORNERS (1988 film soundtrack) (Various artists).
LP: . . . . **STV 81354**
MC: . . . . **CTV 81254**

Five Easy Pieces

FIVE EASY PIECES (Film Soundtrack) (Various artists).
Tracks: / Stand by your man: *Various artists* / Raffle of a dog: *Various artists* / Freeway dialogue: *Various* artists / Chopin's Fantasy in F minor op.49: *Various artists* / Oil field dialogue: *Various artists* / Bach's Chromatic fantasy and fugue: *Various artists* / Recording studio dialogue: *Various artists* / D I V O R C E: *Various* artists / Dialogue in Rayette's house: *Various artists* / Where there's a fire in your heart: *Various artists*/ On the road: *Various artists* / Motel dialogue: *Various artists* / Mozart's E flat major concerto K 271: *Various* artists / Chopin's prelude in E minor op.28 no.4: *Various artists* / Mozart's fantasy in D minor K.397: *Various* artists / Bobby's monologue with his father: *Various artists* / Bobby and Rayette in the car: *Various artists*/ Don't touch me: *Various artists*.
LP: **70091**

Five Guys Named Moe

FIVE GUYS NAMED MOE.
Tracks: / Selfish days / Eyes like thunder / Good news / What Fran says / Beneath the willow / Pieni suomalainen / Breathing / If I were a man / She's on a mountain / Loud tie / Fairvan.
LP: . . . . **PL 74606**
MC: . . . . **PK 74606**

Five Hand Reel

BUNCH OF FIVES, A.
Tracks: / I'll lay you down / Man from God knows where / Maggie Lauder / Satan will appear / House of airlie / Paddy's green shamrock / Land o' the leal.
LP: **12TS 406**

EARL O MORAY.
Tracks: / My love is like a red red rose / Sheriff Muir / Child on the road, The / Bonnie Earl O'Moray, The / Trooper and the maid, The / Beef can close, The / Jackson and Jane / Freedom come all ye.
LP: . . . . **PL 25150**
MC: . . . . **PK 25150**

FIVE HAND REEL.
Tracks: / Both sides of the Forth / Death of Arhyll, The / Kempy's hat / Knight and the shepherd's daughter, The / Sliave Gallion braes / Wee german lairdy / Maid of Listowel, The / When a man's in love / Frankie's dog.
LP: . . . . **CRO 211**
MC: . . . . **CROC 211**
MC: . . . . **CROC 212**
LP: . . . . **PL 25065**
MC: . . . . **PK 25065**

FOR 'A THAT.
Tracks: / Bratach bana / Pinch of snuff / Man's a man for a' that, A / Haughs o' Cromdale / Ae fond kiss / P stands for Paddy / Cruel brother, The / Carrickfergus / Lochanside / Jig of Slurs, The / Linda Brechin's / Marquis of Tullybardine, The.
LP: . . . . **CRO 212**
LP: . . . . **PL 25066**
MC: . . . . **PK 25066**

NOTHING BUT THE BEST.
Tracks: / Bonnie Earl O'Moray, The / Bratach bana / P stands for Paddy / Both sides of the Forth / Carrickfergus / My love is like a red red rose / Freedom come-all-ye / Knight and the shepherd's daughter / Sheriff Muir / Frankie's dog.
LP: . . . . **PL 25267**

Five Harmaniacs

FIVE HARMANIACS.
LP: . . . . **PURITAN 3004**

Five Keys

14 ORIGINAL GREATEST HITS:FIVE KEYS.
LP: . . . . **K 5013**

BEST OF CLASSIC DOOWOP VOL.2 (Five Keys/Nitecaps).
Tracks: / I'll follow you / When will my troubles end / Lawdy Miss Mary / Teeth and tongue will get you hung / Sweet thing / Kiss and a vow, A / Tough mama / Be my girl / Snap crackle and pop / Bamboo rock 'n' roll / You're gonna be sorry / You may not know / In each corner of my heart / Let me know tonight / Oh you sweet girl.
LP: . . . . **DET 33010**

FIVE KEYS, THE.
LP: . . . . **BID 8038**

IT'S A GROOVE.
Tracks: / Hucklebuck with Jimmy / How do you expect me to / Old MacDonald had a farm / Why oh why / Serve another round / I'm so high / Glory of love / Rockin' & cryin' blues / She's the most / From the bottom of my heart / Close your eyes / Now don't that prove I love you / That's right / Out of sight, out of mind / My pigeon's gone.
LP: . . . . **CRB 1040**

Five On A Hike (bk)

FIVE ON A HIKE TOGETHER (see under Blyton, Enid (aut)) (Bennett, Judy (nar) & Charles Collingwood (nar)).

Five Or Six

THRIVING AND HAPPY LAND, A.
LP: . . . . **FRIZBEE 2**

Five Pennies

FIVE PENNIES, THE (Film soundtrack) (Various artists).
LP: . . . . **HAU 2189**

Five Red Caps

FIVE RED CAPS-VOL.2 1943-1946 (It's so good).
Tracks: / It's so good / Gabriel's band / I learned a lesson / Atlanta G.A. / Boogie woogie ball / I'm crazy 'bout you / In the quiet of the dawn / Grand Central station / Sugar lips / Strictly on the safety side / Somebody's lyin' / Mama put your britches on / Was it you / There's a light on the hill.
LP: . . . . **KK 799**

LENOX AVENUE JUMP.
Tracks: / Boogie woogie on a Saturday night / It's got a hole in it / Get off that kick / Mary had a little jam / Don't fool with me / Just for you / Mama put your britches on / Lenox Avenue jump / Boogie woogie ball / Tuscaloosa / No fish today / That's the stuff / Monkey and the baboon / Boogie beat'll getcha.
LP: . . . . **KK 779**

Five Royales

17 ORIGINAL GREATEST HITS:FIVE ROYALES.
LP: . . . . **K 5014**

DEDICATED TO YOU.
Tracks: / Think / Someone made you for me / Just as I am / Don't be ashamed / Come on and save me / I'd better make a move / Dedicated to the one I love / Right around the corner / Say it / Messin' up / Tears of joy / Thirty second lover.
LP: . . . . **SING 580**

FIVE ROYALES, THE.
Tracks: / I know it's hard but it's fair / Miracle of love / My sugar sugar / When you walked through the door / School girl / Get something out of it / Tell me you care / Wonder where your love has gone / It hurts inside / Mine forever more / One mistake / Women about to make me go crazy.
LP: . . . . **BID 8039**
LP: . . . . **SING 678**

REAL THINGS, THE.
LP: . . . . **H 802**

ROOTS OF SOUL.
Tracks: / Tell the truth / Don't let it be in vain / Slummer the slum, The / I'm with you / I'm gonna run it down / Devil with the rest / You didn't learn it at home / Mohawk squaw / How I wonder / When I get like this / I ain't getting caught / Right around the corner / I could love you if you let me / Come on and save me / Get something out of it / Think.
LP: . . . . **CRB 1096**

SING BABY DON'T DO IT.
LP: . . . . **RELIC 8015**

SING FOR YOU.
Tracks: / Your only love / Real thing, The / Don't let it be in vain / Do the cha cha cherry / Double or nothing / Mohawk squaw / How I wonder / I need your lovin' baby / Feeling is real, The / Tell the truth / My wants for love / Slummer the slum, The / Do unto you / I ain't getting caught / When I get like this / Monkey hips and rice.
LP: . . . . **SING 616**

SING THE LAUNDROMAT BLUES.
LP: . . . . **RELIC 8016**

Five Satins

GREATEST HITS: FIVE SATINS.
LP: . . . . **EMBER 5009**

GREATEST HITS OF THE FIVE SATINS VOL.2.
LP: . . . . **EMBER 5013**

Five Smith Brothers

MR & MRS SMITH'S FIVE LITTLE BOYS.
Tracks: / Blaydon races / Geordie haud the bairn / Keep your feet still / Lambton worm, The / Cushie butterfield / On Ilkley moor baht'at / O my Jock Mackay / Hannigan's hooley / Gordon for me, A / After the wedding at Donnegal Bay / Patsy Fagan / As Irish as Dublin Town / Galway bay / Star o' Rabbie Burns, The / Guid new year, A / Eileen O'Grady / I'll take you home again Kathleen.
LP: . . . . **MWM 1020**
MC: . . . . **MWMC 1020**

MR & MRS SMITH'S FIVE LITTLE BOYS-VOL 2.
Tracks: / Shoemaker's serenade, The / Cobbler, The / Hopscotch polka / Sunshine of your smile, The / Goodnight Irene / Thing, The / When I leave the world behind / Sipping cyder by the Zuyder Zee / My mothers eyes / Silver threads among the gold / In the cool cool cool of the evening / Kiss for every candle, A / Barefoot days / Rose in a garden of weeds, A / Underneath the arches / Blue eyes / Smokin' and a-dreamin'.
LP: . . . . **MWM 1023**
MC: . . . . **MWMC 1023**

Five Star

BETWEEN THE LINES.
Tracks: / Somewhere somebody / Whenever you're ready / Strong as steel / Read between the lines / Live giving love / Ain't watcha do / Made out of love / You should have waited / Knock twice / Hard race.
LP: . . . . **PL 71505**
MC: . . . . **PK 71505**

FIVE STAR.
LP: **4667041**
MC: **4667044**

GREATEST HITS: FIVE STAR.
Tracks: / Can't wait another minute / Whenever you're ready / Rain or shine / Find the time / System addict / Stay out of my life / Let me be the one / Rock my world / With every heartbeat (CD only.) / Slightest touch, The / All fall down / If I say yes / Somewhere somebody / R.S.V.P. / Strong as steel / Love take over / Another weekend / Something about my baby (CD only.).
LP: . . . . **PL 74080**
MC: . . . . **PK 74080**

GREATEST HITS: FIVE STAR.
Tracks: / Rain or shine / R.S.V.P. / Can't wait another minute / System addict / Hide and seek / All fall down.
MC: . . . . **THPA 1231**

LUXURY OF LIFE.
Tracks: / Love take over / All fall down / Let me be the one / System addict / Hide and seek / R.S.V.P. / Now I'm in control.
LP: . . . . **PL 70735**
MC: . . . . **PK 70735**
MC: . . . . **NK 74515**

MUSIC AND MEDIA INTERVIEW PICTURE DISC.
LPPD: . . . . **MM 1203**

ROCK THE WORLD.
Tracks: / Free time / Physical attraction / Someone's in love / There's a brand new world / Rescue me / Another weekend (Friday night mix) / Rock my world (Extra-terrestrial mix).
LP: . . . . **PL 71747**
MC: . . . . **PK 71747**

SILK AND STEEL.
Tracks: / Can't wait another minute / Find the time / Rain or shine / If I say yes / Please don't say goodnight / Stay out of my life / Are you man enough / Show me what you've got for me / Slightest touch, The / Don't you know I love you.
LP: . . . . **PL 71100**
MC: . . . . **PK 71100**

Fivepenny Piece

EVENING WITH THE FIVEPENNY PIECE, AN.
Tracks: / Five merry minstrels / Gather in the mushrooms / Black pud stud / Streets of London / Polar bear / Saturday cowboys / Lunatic song / Give us a smile George / What can you do when your clogs let water in / Johnny Beggar / Seth Davey / Liverpool lullaby / I'm in love with... / Up North / Early in the morning.
LP: **6382154**

FIVEPENNY PIECE.
Tracks: / Watercolour morning / Ee by gum / Pete was a lonely mongrel dog who lived in central Wigan / Down our street / King Cotton / Mi grandfather's day (CD only.) / Stories from the wishing well / Gradely prayer / Gotta get away / Tell you owt / Mountain climber (CD only.) / Spanish holiday / I don't know if I wanna go home / Tuppence change / Fred Fannakapan / Stalybridge station / Homemade brew / Winter sun / Molly Kershaw / Stalybridge market / Watering can (CD only.) / Where there's muck there's brass / Sail away tin soldier (CD only.) / Big Jim.
MC: . . . . **TCIDL 113**

KING COTTON.
LP: . . . . **EMC 3129**

LIFE IS A GAME OF CHANCE.
Tracks: / Buggerlugs love sugar butty / Dear Albert / Dutchman / Four strong winds / I like the working class / Let me down easy / Life is a game of chance / Matchstalk men / Miss Prim and Proper / Our corner shop's a supermarket now / Up North / When granny sang me songs.
LP: **9109234**

MAKING TRACKS.
LP: . . . . **SCX 6536**

PEDDLERS OF SONG.
Tracks: / Take me with you / Simon Gavin / Going nowhere / Willie Pollard / Your song / River / Flamingo / Union silver / Amore / Lady lovely lady / Peddler of songs / I'll be still in love with you.
LP: . . . . **SCX 6607**

THIS IS FIVEPENNY PIECE.
Tracks: / Save your last kiss for me / Two soldiers / Fishin' / Gotta get away / Ashton Mashers / Stories from the wishing well / Journeys of my mind, The / Miss Nightingale / Rainbow / Spanish holiday / Mountain climber / Diddler's three, The / Mi granny / Brown photographs / Water colour morning / Hiking / Land of the musical telephone / Reflections of Emily / Take me with you.
LP: . . . . **THIS 21**

VERY BEST OF FIVEPENNY PIECE, THE.
Tracks: / Watercolour morning / Stalybridge market / Ee by gum / Where there's muck there's brass / My brudda Sylvest / I'm powfagged / King Cotton / Affluence / Man like thee, A / Big Jim / Gradely prayer / Down our street / Watering can / Teacher / Weight watchers / They tell us owt / Stalybridge Station / Bantam cock / Fred Fannackapan / Wish you were here.
LP: . . . . **SCX 6612**

Fixed Up

VITAL HOURS.
LP: . . . . **NOSE 13**

Fixx

CALM ANIMALS.
Tracks: / I'm life / Driven out / Subterranean / Precious stone / Gypsy feet / Calm animals / Shred of evidence / Flow / World weary / Cause to be alarmed.
LP: . . . . **PL 88566**
MC: . . . . **PK 88566**

INK.
Tracks: / All is fair / How much is enough / No one has to cry / Crucified / Falling in love (Not on album.) / Shut it out / Still around / All the best things / Yesterday, today / One jungle / Climb the hill / Make no plans (CD only.).
LP: . . . . **EMC 3589**
MC: . . . . **TCEMC 3589**

PHANTOMS.
Tracks: / Lose face / Less cities more moving people / Sunshine in the shade / Women on a train / Wish / Lost in the battle over seas / Question / In suspense / Facing the wind / Are we ourselves / I will / Phantom living.
LP: . . . . **FX 1003**
MC: . . . . **FXC 1003**

REACH THE BEACH.
Tracks: / One things lead to another / Sign of fire, The / Running / Saved by zero / Opinions / Reach the beach / Changing / Liner / Privilege / Outside.
LP: . . . . **FX 1002**
MC: . . . . **FXC 1002**

SHUTTERED ROOM.
Tracks: / Some people / Stand or fall / Cameras in Paris / Shuttered room / Fool, The / Lost planes / I live / Sinking island / Time in a glass / Red skies.
LP: . . . . **FX 1001**
MC: . . . . **FXC 1001**

WALKABOUT.
Tracks: / Secret separation / Built for the future / Treasure it / Chase the fire / Can't finish / Walkabout / One look up / Read between the lines / Sense the adventure / Camphor.
LP: . . . . **FX 1004**
MC: . . . . **FXC 1004**

Fjedur

LANGE, LEVE, LIVET.
LP: . . . . FLC 5067

Fjellgaard, Gary

HEART OF A DREAM.
LP: . . . . SVLP 9211
MC: . . . . SVMC 9411

NO TIME TO LOSE.
LP: . . . . SVLP 9203
MC: . . . . SVMC 9403

F***k Your Dreams...

F*K YOUR DREAMS, THIS IS HEAVEN** (Various artists).
LP: . . . . CRAM 048

Flack, Roberta

BEST OF ROBERTA FLACK.
Tracks: / Killing me softly with his song / Closer I get to you, The / You've got a friend / Feel like makin' love / Will you love me tomorrow / Where is the love? / First time ever I saw your face, The / Back together again / If I ever see you again / You are my heaven / Jesse.
LP: . . . . K 50840
MC: K4 50840

BLUE LIGHTS IN THE BASEMENTS.
Tracks: / Why don't you move in with me / Closer I get to you, The / Fine fine day, A / This time I'll be sweeter / 25th of last December / After you / I'd like to be baby to you / Soul deep / Love is the healing / Where I'll find you.
MC: K4 50440
LP: . . . . K 50440

BORN TO LOVE (Flack, Roberta & Peabo Bryson).
Tracks: / Tonight, I celebrate my love / Blame it on me / Heaven above / Born to love / Maybe / I just came here to dance / Comin' alive / You're lookin' like love to me / Can we find love again.
LP: . . . . EST 7122841
MC: . . . . TCEST 7122844
LP: . . . . ATAK 2
MC: . . . . TCATAK 2

CHAPTER TWO.
Tracks: / Reverend Lee / Do what you gotta do / Just like a woman / Let it be me / Gone away / Until it's time for you to go / Impossible dream, The / Business goes on as usual.
LP: . . . . K 40097

FEEL LIKE MAKIN' LOVE.
Tracks: / Feeling that glow / I wanted it too / I can see the sun in late December / Some gospel according to Mathew / Feel like makin' love / Mr. Magic / Early every midnight / Old heart break top ten / She's not blind.
LP: . . . . K 50049

FIRST TAKE.
Tracks: / Compared to what / Angelitos negros / Our ages or our hearts / I told Jesus / Hey, that's no way to say goodbye / First time ever I saw your face, The / Trying times / Ballad of the sad young man.
LP: . . . . K 40040
MC: K4 40040

FIRST TAKE / CHAPTER TWO.
Tracks: / Compared to what / Angelitos negros / Our ages or our hearts / First time ever I saw your face, The / Trying times / Ballad of the sad young man / Do what you gotta do / Just like a woman / Let it be me / Gone away until it's time / Impossible dream, The / Business goes on as usual.
2LP: . . . . K 60062

FIRST TIME I EVER SAW YOUR FACE.
Tracks: / Killing me softly / First time ever I saw your face / Will you still love me tomorrow / Bridge over troubled water / To love somebody / Sunday & sister Jones / Sweet bitter love / Let them talk / See you then / Go up Moses.
LP: . . . . SHM 3022

GREATEST HITS: ROBERTA FLACK.
Tracks: / Tonight, I celebrate my love / Feel like makin' love / Killing me softly with his song / You've got a friend / Closer I get to you, The / Will you love me tomorrow / Maybe / Where is the love? / First time ever I saw your face, The / Jessie / If ever I see you again / You're lookin' like love to me / Don't make me wait too long / You are my Heaven / Heaven above me / Back together again.
LP: . . . . NE 1269
MC: . . . . CE 2269

HEAVEN ABOVE ME (See Bryson, Peabo) (Flack, Roberta & Peabo Bryson).

I'M THE ONE.
Tracks: / I'm the one / Till the morning comes / Love and let love / Never loved before / In the name of love / Ordinary man / Making love / Happiness / My love for you.
LP: . . . . K 50890

KILLING ME SOFTLY.
Tracks: / Killing me softly with his song / Jesse / No tears (In the end) / I'm the girl / River / Conversation love / When you smile / Suzanne.
LP: . . . . K 50021
MC: K4 50021

LIVE - AND MORE (Flack, Roberta & Peabo Bryson).
Tracks: / Only Heaven can wait / You are my Heaven / Make the world stand still / Feel the fire / Killing me softly with his song / More than everything / Feel like makin' love / When will I learn? / Back together again / Love in every season / I believe in you / God don't like ugly / If only for one night / Love is a waiting game / Reachin' for the sky / Don't make me wait too long.
2LP: . . . . K 60155
MC: K4 60155

NO ONE EMOTION (See under Benson, George) (Flack, Roberta/George Benson).

OASIS.
Tracks: / Oasis / Something magic / Uh uh ooh ooh look out (here it comes) / And so it goes / Shock to my system / You know what it's like / You who brought me love / And so it goes (reprise) / My someone to love / (His name) Brazil.
LP: . . . . WX 229
MC: . . . . WX 229 C

ROBERTA FLACK.
Tracks: / What a woman really means / You are everything / Independent man / If ever I see you again / And the feeling's good / Knowing that we're made for each other / Come share my love / Baby I love you so / When it's over.
LP: . . . . K 50495
MC: K4 50495

ROBERTA FLACK, FEATURING DONNY HATHAWAY (Flack, Roberta & Donny Hathaway).
Tracks: / Only heaven can wait / God don't like ugly / You are my heaven / Disguises / Don't make me wait too long / Back together again / Stay with me / Only Heaven can wait / God don't like ugly / You are my Heaven / Disguises / Don't make me wait too long / Back together again / Stay with me.
LP: . . . . K 50696
MC: K4 50696

TONIGHT I CELEBRATE MY LOVE FOR YOU (DOUBLE A) (See under Bryson, Peabo) (Flack, Roberta & Peabo Bryson).

Flacke, Nils

NILS FLACKE IN BREADTH.
Tracks: / United nations polka / Allevalsen springtime / Snickerpelles waltz / Jugansbo-hambo / Intermezzo / Stars and stripes / Waltz accordia / Hopsassa promenade rhythm / Indo waltz / March gall rini / Internationalen.
LP: . . . . P 002

Flag Of Democracy

23.
Tracks: / Geisha / 13 years / Dekcuf Ruoy / Aberration / Doors o' reception / Teen beat / Going going gone / Love songs III / Brain dead / Non stop weekend / 40oz of manhood / I don't know / All that you need / This beautiful place / Out to get you / Pop goes the weasel / Green pepper blues.
LP: . . . . BORE 8902

SHATTER YOUR DAY.
Tracks: / Houses's made for mannequins / Love song II / Metal plate / Kid called me / Shatter your day / Family knows, The / Science patrol / Mad house / Carousel / Everything's OK / Cheap alcohol / Hoe down / Shadows of children / Serene danker / Guimo's theme / Black light.
LP: . . . . WETLP 002

Flagrant Desir

FLAGRANT DESIR (1987 film soundtrack) (Various artists).
LP: . . . . A 255

Flags Of Dublin

FLAGS OF DUBLIN (Various artists).
Tracks: / Do you want any more?: *Various artists* (Paddy Glackin fiddle/Mick Gavin flute/Michael o'Brien uilleann pipes - i) / Gallowglaes, The: *Various artists* (Paddy Glackin fiddle/Mick Gavin flute/Michael o'Brien uilleann pipes - i) / Silver spear: *Various artists* (Paddy Glackin fiddle/Mick Gavin flute/Michael o'Brien uilleann pipes - i) / Flax in bloom: *Glackin,* Paddy (Paddy Glackin fiddle/Mick Gavin flute/Michael o'Brien uilleann pipes - i) / Unidentified fling: *Various artists*(Paddy Glackin fiddle/Mick Gavin flute/Michael o'Brien uilleann pipes - i) / Blackthorn: *Various artists* (Paddy Glackin fiddle/Mick Gavin flute/Michael o'Brien uilleann pipes - i) / Lucky in love: *Gavin, Mick* (Paddy Glackin fiddle/Mick Gavin flute/Michael o'Brien uilleann pipes - i) / Flags of Dublin: *Various artists* (Paddy Glackin fiddle/Mick Gavin flute/Michael o'Brien uilleann pipes - i) / Dublin reel: *Various artists* (Paddy Glackin fiddle/Mick Gavin flute/Michael o'Brien uilleann pipes - i) / Gold ring, The: *Various artists* (Paddy Glackin fiddle/Mick Gavin flute/Michael o'Brien uilleann pipes - i) / Paddy O'Rafferty: *O'Brien, Michael* (Paddy Glackin fiddle/Mick Gavin flute/Michael O'Brien uilleann pipes - i) / Unidentified reel: *Various artists* (Paddy Glackin fiddle/Mick Gavin flute/Michael O'Brien uilleann pipes - i) / Cow that ate the blanket, The: *Gavin, Mick* (Paddy Glackin fiddle/Mick Gavin flute/Michael O'Brien uilleann pipes - i) / Rodney's glory: *Glackin,* Paddy (Paddy Glackin fiddle/Mick Gavin flute/Michael O'Brien uilleann pipes - i) / Coppers and brass: *Various artists*(Paddy Glackin fiddle/Mick Gavin flute/Michael O'Brien uilleann pipes - i) / Lark in the morning, The: *Various artists*(Paddy Glackin fiddle/Mick Gavin flute/Michael O'Brien uilleann pipes - i) / Rakish Paddy: *Various artists* (Paddy Glackin fiddle/Mick Gavin flute/Michael O'Brien uilleann pipes - i) / Castle Kelly: *O'Brien, Michael* (Paddy Glackin fiddle/Mick Gavin flute/Michael O'Brien uilleann pipes - i) / Jackson's reel: *Various artists* (Paddy Glackin fiddle/Mick Gavin flute/Michael O'Brien uilleann pipes - i) / Dunmore lasses: *Various artists* (Paddy Glackin fiddle/Mick Gavin flute/Michael O'Brien uilleann pipes - i) / Monaghan: *Various artists* (Paddy Glackin fiddle/Mick Gavin flute/Michael O'Brien uilleann pipes - i) / Kiss the maid behind the barrel: *Gavin, Mick* (Paddy Glackin fiddle/Mick Gavin flute/Michael O'Brien uilleann pipes - i) / Captain Rock: *Various artists* (Paddy Glackin fiddle/Mick Gavin flute/Michael O'Brien uilleann pipes - i) / Miller's daughter: *Various* artists (Paddy Glackin fiddle/Mick Gavin flute/Michael O'Brien uilleann pipes - i) / Ballyoran: *O'Brien, Michael* (Paddy Glackin fiddle/Mick Gavin flute/Michael O'Brien uilleann pipes - i) / Reavy's reel: *Glackin, Paddy* (Paddy Glackin fiddle/Mick Gavin flute/Michael O'Brien uilleann pipes - i).
LP: 12TS 383

Flaherty, Liam

ECSTASY OF ANGUS, THE.
2LP: . . . . CCT 15/16

Flairck

FLAIRCK.
Tracks: / East-West express / Some phoney symphony / Butterfly / Circus / Doubles / Playing with Sofia / Aoife / Steam engine waltz / Lady's variations.
LP: . . . . POLD 5081

FLAIRCK LIVE.
Tracks: / Oost-west express ((Time 8.20)) / De Stoomwals ((Time: 6.35)) / Aoife ((Time: 6.45)) / Variaties opus en dame ((Time: 19.35)).
LP: 810 819-1
MC: 810 819-4
2LP: 2646103

SLEIGHT OF HAND.
Tracks: / At the blacksmith's hands / Sleight of hand / Behind the glass curtain / Trick of the night, A / Walk upon dreams / Seven card tango / Thin air, The / Lady shuffles, The / At the blacksmith's hands-part 2.
LP: . . . . SCX 6704
MC: . . . . TCSCX 6704

VARIATIONS ON A LADY.
Tracks: / Aoife / Prelude in Sofia / April 3rd / Odd waltz / Variations on a lady / Double.
LP: 2480 508

Flambards

FLAMBARDS (TV Soundtrack) (Various artists).
LP: 9109226
MC: 7231452

Flame

FLAME.
Tracks: / On the strength / Show and tell / Lifetime groove / Satisfied / House is surrounded, The / One way lover / Holiday / Come and get it.
LP: 4658441
MC: 4658444

FLAME, THE (2).
Tracks: / This time tomorrow / X-streams / Stella / Last day of Summer, The / Fever / Joe Lean / Tears of an oyster / Patrick and Anne / Snake talk / Move the moon / Trucks (Not on album.) / Fishing for wreaths (Not on album.) / Love won't sit down (CD only.).
LP: . . . . NERVLP 1
MC: . . . . NERVMC 1

SNAKE TALK (See Under Perkins, Jonathan) (Flame & Jonathan Perkins).

Flame Groove

FLAME GROOVE (Various artists).
LP: . . . . MELTLP 4

Flame Trees Of Thika

FLAME TREES OF THIKA, THE (TV soundtrack) (Various artists).
LP: . . . . EMC 3385
MC: . . . . TCEMC 3385

Flamenco...

BEST OF FLAMENCO (Various artists).
LP: . . . . EULP 1158
MC: . . . . EUMC 1158

EARLY CANTE FLAMENCO VOL.1 (Various artists).
LP: . . . . FL 9001

EARLY CANTE FLAMENCO VOL.2 (Various artists).
LP: . . . . FL 9039

FESTIVAL FLAMENCO GITANO VOL.1 (Various artists).
Tracks: / Rumba gitana: *Various artists* / Mirabras: *Various artists* / Guajiras: *Various artists* / Tientos: *Various artists* / Rumba gitana (2): *Various artists* / Fandangos: *Various artists* / Rumbo gitana (3): *Various artists* / Fandangos (2): *Various artists* / Bulerias: *Various artists* / Panaderos flamencos: *Various artists* / Rumba gitana (4): *Various artists.*
LP: . . . . LR 44.003

FESTIVAL FLAMENCO GITANO VOL.2 (Various artists).
LP: . . . . LR 44.007

FESTIVAL FLAMENCO GITANO VOL.3 (Various artists).
LP: . . . . LR 44.015

FLAMENCO (Various artists).
LP: 843620 1
MC: 843620 4

FLAMENCO ESPANOL (Various artists).
Tracks: / El yunque: *Various artists* / Se elevo mi amour & en las salinas de Cadiz: *Various artists* / Los marismenos: *Various artists* / Porque la quiero & ese lunes en el rocio: *Various artists* / Cantores de hispalis: *Various* artists / A nuestro aire & salsa, compas y palmas & cantare: *Various artists* / Los romeros de la puebla: *Various* artists / Tengo en mi casa un tambor: *Various artists* / La casada infiel & cantaora: *Various artists* / Terremoto de jerez: *Various artists* / Paco de antequera: *Various artists* / Eista en el barrio santiago: *Various artists*/ Amina: *Various artists* / Leyes gitanas: *Various artists* / Amigos de gines: *Various artists* / El adios & ole que arte & mananitas de mayo: *Various artists.*
LP: 8214871

FLAMENCO GUITAR, MUSIC OF (See under Pena, Paco) (Pena, Paco).

GREAT SINGERS OF FLAMENCO VOL2 (Pepe de la Matrona).
LP: . . . . LDX 74829
MC: K4 74829

GREAT SINGERS OF FLAMENCO VOL1 (El nino de Almaden).
LP: . . . . LDX 74830
MC: K4 74830

Flamin' Groovies

BUCKETFUL OF BRAINS.
LP: . . . . UNKNOWN

GROOVIES GREATEST, THE.
LP: . . . . K 925 948 1
MC: . . . . K 925 948 4

JUMPIN IN THE NIGHT.
Tracks: / Please please me / Next one crying / Down down down / Tell me again / Absolutely sweet Marie / You're a wonderful one / Jumpin' in the night / Yes I am / 19th nervous breakdown / Boys / 5D first plane home / Ladyfriend / In the USA.
LP: . . . . SRK 6067

NOW.
Tracks: / Feel a lot better / Between the lines / Ups and downs / There's a place / Take me back / Reminiscing / Good laugh man / Each my baby / House of blue lights / All I wanted / Blue turns to grey / When I heard your name / Move it / Don't put me on.
LP: . . . . SRK 7059

ONE NIGHT STAND.
LP: . . . . ABCLP 10

ROAD HOUSE.
LP: . . . . ED 183
MC: . . . . CED 183

ROCKFIELD SESSIONS.
LP: . . . . COLLECT 2

SHAKE SOME ACTION.

Tracks: / Shake some action / Sometimes / Yes it's true / St. Louis blues / You tore me down / Please please girl / Let the boy rock 'n' roll / Don't you lie to me / She said yeah / I'll cry alone / Misery / I say her / Teenage confidential / I can't hide.
LP: .... SRK 6021

STILL SHAKIN.
Tracks: / Teenage head / Evil hearted Ada / Comin' after me / Have you seen my baby / Walking the dog / Doctor Boogie / Keep a knockin' / Shakin' all over / That'll be the day / Louie Louie / My girl Josephine / Around and around / Rockin' pneumonia and the boogie woogie flu / Going out theme.
LP: 2522621
MC: 2522624

SUPERGREASE.
LP: .... SK 12226

SUPERSNAZZ.
LP: .... ED 173

TEENAGE HEAD (DOJO).
Tracks: / Teenage head / 32-02 / Evil hearted Ada / Doctor Boogie / Whisky woman / High flyin' baby / City lights / Have you seen my baby? / Yesterday's numbers.
LP: .... DOJOLP 58

Flaming Ember

WEST BOUND NO.9.
LP: .... HDH LP 008

Flaming Lips

HEAR IT IT.
LP: 2173 1

TAKING DRUGS.
2LP: .... KAR 008

TELEPATHIC SURGERY.
Tracks: / Drug machine / Michael time to wake up / Miracle on 42nd Street / UFO story / Shaved gorilla / Begs and achin' / Right now / Hare Krishna stomp wagon / Chrome plated suicide / Redneck school of technology / Spontaneous combustion of John / Last drop of morning dew, The.
LP: .... ENVLP 523
MC: .... TCENV 523

UNCONSCIOUSLY SCREAMING.
LP: .... EFA 4063

Flaming Mussolinis

CHARMED LIFE.
Tracks: / Two mountains high / Different kind of love / Over and over / Invisible man, The / Girl on a train / Jonestown / Other side of the world / Wild time / Ghost of love / Goodbye Rachel.
LP: 4601591
MC: 4601594

JANK MAMBA A.K.A.
Tracks: / Animal tactics (7" version) / Rumble / Standing in your light / Time and prize / Animal tactics (extended) / Way things are, The / Show me something / Young hearts wear scarlet (Live: Recorded noise from tape source.).
LP: .... DOJOLP 44

WATCHING THE FILM.
Tracks: / My Cleopatra / Horror show / Catholic wedding / Ember days / Dangerous persuasion / Swallow Glass / Landslide / Holding sand / Long way to fall, A / Masuka Dan.
LP: .... PRT 26828
MC: 40 26828

Flamingo Kid

FLAMINGO KID (1985 film soundtrack) (Various artists).
Tracks: / Breakaway: *Various artists* / (Love is like a) heatwave: *Various artists* / He's so fine: *Various* artists / One fine day: *Various artists* / Stranger on the shore: *Various artists* / Runaround Sue: *Various* artists / Good golly Miss Molly: *Various artists* / Money (Thats what I want): *Various artists* / It's alright: *Various artists* / Finger poppin' time: *Various artists* / Get a job: *Various artists* / Boys will be boys: *Various artists.*
LP: .... ZL 72370
MC: .... ZK 72370

Flamingos

CHESS SESSIONS, THE.
LP: .... DET 201

REQUESTFULLY YOURS.
LP: .... END LP 308

SERENADE.
LP: .... END LP 304

Flanagan & Allen

BEST OF FLANAGAN AND ALLEN.
Tracks: / Underneath the arches / Music Maestro please / Home town / Maybe it's because I'm a Londoner / Umbrella man / How do you do Mr. Right / Home is where your heart is / Friendly Street / Just for laughs / Strollin' / Nice people / Hey neighbour / Free / On the other side of town / Galloping major, The / Goodbye Sue / Wanderer (Early chorus successes) / Dreaming (Early chorus successes) / Where the arches used to be / Can't we meet again (Early chorus successes) / Million tears, A (Early chorus successes) / Underneath the arches (Early chorus successes).
LP: .... ONCR 513
MC: .... TC ONCR 513

UNDERNEATH THE ARCHES.
Tracks: / Run rabbit run / Miss you / Smiths and the Jones, The / In a little rocky valley / Two very ordinary people / Down every street / Flying through the rain / F.D.R. Jones / On the outside looking in / Roll on tomorrow / There's a boy coming home on leave / Shine on harvest moon / We'll smile again / Underneath the arches.
LP: .... CN 2054
MC: CN4 2054
MC: .... TCDL 1209

WE'LL SMILE AGAIN.
Tracks: / We're gonna hang out the washing on the Siegfried line / Let's be buddies / If a grey-haired lady says 'How's yer father?' / Don't ever walk in the shadows / Smiths and the Jones, The / I'm nobody's baby / Yesterday's dreams / There's a boy coming home on leave / Why don't you fall in love with me? / F.D.R. Jones / Don't believe everything you dream / What more can I say? / Run, rabbit, run / We'll smile again.
LP: .... ACL 1196

YESTERDAY'S DREAMS.
Tracks: / Yesterday's dreams / Sierra Sue / What more can I say / Don't ever walk in the shadows / I don't want to walk without you / Run, rabbit, run / Round the back of the arches / Down Forget-Me-Not Lane / Dreaming / I'm nobody's baby / Let's be buddies / Hang out the washing on the Siegfried Line / Why don't you fall in love with me / If a grey-haired lady says "how's yer father" / Don't believe everything you dream / Miss you / Underneath the arches.
LP: .... RFL 9

Flanagan Brothers

IRISH DELIGHT, AN.
Tracks: / Paddy in London / Paddy Ryan's dream / Beggarman song, The / An carrowath / Longdance / No name / My Aunt Jane / Rakes of mallow / New Irish barn dance, The / One step / Irish boy, The / Irish delight / Auld blackthorn, The / My Irish Molly O / Old fashioned waltz medley / Highland fling / Bandy legged mule, The / Sprig of shillelagh / Exhibitioned hornpipe / Blackbird, The.
LP: 12TS 365

NIGHT PAT MURPHEY DIED, THE.
LP: .... SHAN 33005

Flanagan, Mark

QUIET WATER (see under Fitzgerald, Paul) (Flanagan, Mark & Paul Fitzgerald).

SPIRIT CATCHER (see under Fitzgerald, Paul) (Flanagan, Mark & Paul Fitzgerald).

Flanagan, Mikey

LONE SHANAKYLE.
Tracks: / Lone Shanakyle / Michael Power / Clare to the front / Cattle drive / Lie like a frog / Oak tree / Thousands are sailing / Patrick O Donnell / Poor old Granuaile / Father Tom O' Neill / William O'Brien from Tipperary / Lilt.
LP: .... OAS 3013

Flanagan, Ralph

ON THE BEAT.
LP: .... GELP 15043

Flanagan, Tommy

ALONE TOO LONG (Music for piano).
Tracks: / Parisian thoroughfare / In your own sweet way / Like a butterfly / Billie Holiday medley / Alone too long / Maybe September / Strollin / Here's that rainy day.
LP: .... YX 7523

AND A LITTLE PLEASURE (See under Montrose, J R).

BALLADS AND BLUES.
LP: .... ENJA 3031

BEST OF TOMMY FLANAGAN.
Tracks: / All day long / U.M.M.G. / Intimacy of the blues, The / Main stem / Star crossed lovers / Jump for joy / Woodyn' you / Blue bossa.
LP: 231 0854
MC: K10 854

CATS, THE (Flanagan, Tommy, John Coltrane, Kenny Burrell).
Tracks: / Minor mishap / How long has this been going on / Eclipso / Solacium / Tommy's time.
LP: .... OJC 079

CONFIRMATION.
LP: .... ENJA 4014

DREAM COMES TRUE, A (See under Terry, Lilian) (Flanagan, Tommy & Lilian Terry).

ECLYPSO.
LP: .... ENJA 2088

HOME COOKING (Flanagan, Tommy/ Nisse Sandstrom/Red Mitchell).
Tracks: / I remember you / Painter's blues / Karen / I could happen to you / Minor mishap / Way you look tonight / Indian Summer.
LP: .... PHONT 7530

I'M ALL SMILES (see Jones, Hank) (Flanagan, Tommy & Hank Jones).

IN STOCKHOLM 1957.
LP: .... DRLP 87

JAZZ POET.
Tracks: / Raincheck / Lament / Willow weep for me / Caravan / That tired routine called love / Glad to be happy / St Louis blues / Mean streets.
LP: .... SJP 301
MC: .... MCSJP 301

MAGNIFICENT TOMMY FLANAGAN, THE.
LP: .... PRO 7059

NIGHTS AT THE VANGUARD.
LP: .... UP 27 29

SOMETHING BORROWED, SOMETHING BLUE.
LP: .... GXY 5110

SUPER JAZZ TRIO, THE (Flanagan, Tommy and Reggie Workman and Joe Chambers).
LP: .... PL 45367

SUPER SESSION.
LP: .... ENJA 3059

THREE FOR ALL (see Woods, Phil) (Flanagan, Tommy/Red Mitchell/Phil Woods).

TOGETHER (Flanagan, Tommy & Kenny Barron).
Tracks: / Dig / If I should lose you / Stella by starlight / I can't get started / Darn that dream / Way you look tonight.
LP: .... YX 7544

TOKYO RECITAL (Flanagan, Tommy Trio).
Tracks: / All day long / U.M.M.G. / Something to live for / Main stem / Daydream / Intimacy of the blues, The / Caravan / Chelsea Bridge / Take the 'A' train.
LP: 231 0724
MC: K10 724

TOMMY FLANAGAN THREE.
Tracks: / Barbados / Some other spring / Easy living / Star crossed lovers / Jump for joy / Woodyn' you? / Blue bossa.
LP: 2308 202
MC: .... K 08 202

WITH THE TOMMY FLANAGAN TRIO (see Fitzgerald, Ella) (Flanagan, Tommy Trio & Ella Fitzgerald).

YOU'RE ME (Flanagan, Tommy/ Red Mitchell).
Tracks: / You're me / Darn that dream / What am I here for / When I have you / All the things you are / Milestones / Whisper not / There'll never be another you.
LP: .... PHONT 7528

Flanders & Swann

AT THE DROP OF A HAT.
Tracks: / Transport of delight / Song of reproduction / Gnu song, The / Design for living / Je suis le tenebreux / Songs of our time / Philogical waltz / Satellite moon / Happy song / Song of the weather / Reluctant cannibal, The / Greensleeves / Misalliance / Madeira, m'dear? / Hippopotamus song, The.
LP: .... ONCR 511
MC: .... TC ONCR 511

AT THE DROP OF A HAT/AT THE DROP OF ANOTHER HAT (see under EMI Comedy Classics).

AT THE DROP OF ANOTHER HAT.
Tracks: / Gas-man cometh, The / Sounding brass / Los Olividados / In the desert / Ill wind / First and second law / All Gall / Horoscope / Friendly duet / Bedstead men / By air / Slow train / Song of patriotic prejudice / Hippo encore.
LP: .... ONCR 512
MC: .... TC ONCR 512

AT THE DROP OF ANOTHER HAT (ORIGINAL ISSUE) (London cast).
LP: .... PMC 1216

BESTIARY OF FLANDERS AND SWANN.
Tracks: / Warthog, The (The hog beneath the skin) / Sea horse, The / Chameleon, The / Whale, The (Moby Dick) / Sloth, The / Rhinoceros, The / Twosome-Kang and Jag / Dead ducks / Elephant / Armadillo, The / Spider, The / Threesome (the duck billed platypus) / Hummingbird (The portuguese man of war) / Wild bear, The / Ostrich, The / Wompom, The.
LP: .... ONCR 527

TRIED BY THE CENTRE COURT.
Tracks: / Twice shy / Commonwealth fair / P**P*B****B**D****** / Too many cookers / Vanessa / Tried by the centre court / Paris / Eine kleine nachtmusik cha cha cha / Hundred song / Built-up area / In the bath / Sea fever / Youth of the heart / Food for thought / Bed.
LP: .... NTS 116

Flappers, Vamps...

FLAPPERS, VAMPS AND SWEET YOUNG THINGS (Various artists).
Tracks: / I'm gonna meet my sweetie now: *Green, Jane* / Am I blue?: *Holman, Libby* / Dangerous Nan McGrew: *Kane,* Helen / Maybe, who knows?: *Smith, Kate* / Do do do: *Lawrence, Gertrude* / Blues have got me, The: *Harris,* Marion / New kind of man with a new kind of love for me: *Seely, Blossom* / Please don't talk about me when I'm gone: *Hunt, Mildred* / I'll get by: *Stanley, Aileen* / Why am I so romantic?: *Roth, Lilian* / You wouldn't fool me, would you?: *Hanshaw, Annette* / If your kisses can't hold the man you love: *Tucker, Sophie* / Red hot moma: *Brox Sisters* / Moanin' low: *Morse, Lee* / It all belongs to me: *Etting, Ruth* / Blues in my heart: *Keller,* Greta / Do something: *O'Neal, Zelma* / You remind me of a naughty springtime cuckoo: *Morgan, Helen* / Red hot Henry Brown: *Young, Margaret* / Ya gotta know how to love: *Walker, Esther.*
LP: .... AJA 5015
MC: .... ZC AJA 5015

Flare Groove

FLARE GROOVE (Various artists).
Tracks: / Loose booty: *Henderson, Willie* / Funky judge, The: *Bull & the Matadors* / Make me believe in you: *Jo,* Patti / Fat man / You are the one: *AM FM* / Do bad: *Burks, Donny* / I'll bake me a man: *Acklin, Barbara* / Loose hips: *Eliminators* / Keep on dancing: *Cash, Alvin* / It's your thing: *Moorer, Betty* / If she won't (find someone who will): *Dorsey, Lee* / Wiggler (the worms don't know): *Gibson, Billy* / If it's good for you (it's good for me) (part 1): *Bo, Eddie.*
LP: .... KENT 078

Flash

NO POINT OF REFERENCE.
Tracks: / Grand prix / Hey you / Sweet pretender / Rock 'n' roll heart / No more love, no more lies / Hot tonight / Black Jack / I need it / Modern lover / Is it true.
LP: .... FP 01

Flash Company

FLASH COMPANY (Various artists).
Tracks: / Bold Princess Royal, The: *Various artists* / Seventeen come Sunday: *Various artists* / Rap a tap tap: *Various artists* / Song of the thrush, The: *Various artists* / Gypsy's warning, The: *Various artists*/ Barbara Allen: *Various artists* / Faithful sailor boy, The: *Various artists* / Flash company: *Various artists*/ Wheel you're rambulator: *Various artists* / Go and leave me if you wish it: *Various artists* / John Barleycorn: *Various artists* / Hares on the mountain: *Various artists* / Knife in the window, The: *Various artists.*
LP: .... FE 050
LP: 12TS 243
MC: .... FE 050 C

Flash Company Inc

CASTLE KEEP.
LP: .... PLR 067

Flash Gordon

FLASH GORDON (Unknown narrator(s)).
MCSET: .... DTO 10522

FLASH GORDON (See under Queen) (Queen).

Flash of '29

FLASH OF '29 Portrait in music of 1929 (Various artists).
Tracks: / Some of these days: *Various artists* / If I had a talking picture of you: *Various artists* / Messa stomp: *Various artists* / Louise: *Various artists* / Dinah: *Various artists* / Button up your overcoat: *Various* artists / Honey: *Various artists* / Won't you get off it, please?: *Various artists* / Muskrat ramble: *Various* artists / After you've gone: *Various artists* / Black and blue: *Various artists* / When you're smiling: *Various* artists / Wang wang blues: *Various artists* / I'm a dreamer, aren't we all?: *Various artists* / Everybody loves my baby: *Various artists* / Bashful baby: *Various artists.*
LP: .... NOST 7608

MC: . . . . NOST 8608

Flash & The Pan

FLASH & THE PAN.
Tracks: / African shuffle / And the band played on / California / First and last / Hey, St. Peter / Hole in the middle / Lady killer / Man in the middle / Man who knew the answer / Walking in the rain.
LP: . . . . ENVY 6

HEADLINES.
Tracks: / Jetsetters' ball / Don't vote / Waiting for a train / War games / Where were you? / Love is a gun / Up against the wall / Psychos in the street / Hey Jimmy / Phil the Creole.
LP: . . . . ENVY 3001
MC: . . . . ENCAS 3001

LIGHTS IN THE NIGHT.
Tracks: / Media man / Headhunter / Restless / Welcome to the universe / Make your own cross / Lights in the night / Captain beware / Atlantis calling.
LP: . . . . ENVY 11

NIGHTS IN FRANCE.
Tracks: / Money don't lie / Nights in France / Ayla / Yesterday's gone / Drawn by the light / Hard livin' / Saviour man / Bones.
LP: 4602241
MC: 4602244

PANORAMA.
LP: . . . . EASLP 100

Flash tracks

FLASH TRACKS Various artists (Various artists).
Tracks: / Fame: *Cara, Irene* / Take a chance with me: *Roxy Music* / Stool pigeon / Mama used to say: *Junior/* Do you wanna funk: *Sylvester with Patrick Cowley* / Invitations: *Shakatak* / Me and my girl (night clubbing): *Essex, David* / Weave your spell: *Level 42* / Walking on sunshine: *Rockers Revenge* / Dear John: *Status* Quo / Do you really want to hurt me?: *Culture Club* / Just what I always wanted: *Wilson, Mari* / Zoom: *Fat* Larry's Band / Night train: *Visage* / Mad world: *Tears For Fears* / Da da da: *Trio* / Shy boy: *Bananarama/* Love is a stranger: *Eurythmics* / Feel me: *Blancmange* / Starmaker: *Kids From Fame.*
LP: . . . . PTVL 1

Flashback '67

FLASHBACK '67 (Various artists).
2LP: . . . . R 109/110
MCSET: . . . . C 105

Flashbacks

FLASHBACKS VOL. 1 (Various artists).
LP: . . . . SNTF 780

FLASHBACKS VOL. 2 (Various artists).
LP: . . . . SNTF 829

FLASHBACKS VOL. 3 (Various artists).
LP: . . . . SNTF 867

FLASHBACKS VOL. 4 (Various artists).
LP: . . . . SNTF 893

Flashbax

FLASHBAX (Various artists).
2LP: . . . . CR 116
MCSET: . . . . CRT 116

Flashdance

FLASHDANCE (1983 film soundtrack) (Various artists).
Tracks: / Flashdance... what a feeling: *Cara, Irene* / He's a dream: *Shandi* / Flashdance love theme: *St.* John, Helen / Manhunt: *Kamon, Karen* / Lady, lady, lady: *Esposito, Joe* / Imagination: *Branigan, Laura/* Romeo: *Summer, Donna* / Seduce me tonight: *Cycle V* / I'll be here where the heart is: *Carnes, Kim/* Maniac: *Sembello, Michael.*
LP: . . . . PRICE 111
MC: . . . . PRIMC 111
LP: . . . . CANH 5
MC: . . . . CANHC 5

Flashpoint

FLASHPOINT (See under Tangerine Dream) (Tangerine Dream).

Flat Foot Stompers

FLAT FOOT STOMPERS & FRIENDS VOL 2 (Various artists).
LP: . . . . TTD 529

Flat Stanley (bk)

FLAT STANLEY (Jeff Brown) (Healy, David (nar)).
MCSET: CC/011

Flatischler, Reinhard

MEGADRUMS.
Tracks: / Transformation / Ektalpuri / Worldcomparsa / Whales in Tibet / Drummers circle / Call, The / Swinging kangoguis.
LP: . . . . VBR 2033 1
MC: . . . . VBR 2033 4

Flatlanders

ONE MORE ROAD.
Tracks: / You've never seen me cry / Dallas / Tonight I think I'm gonna go downtown / She had everything / Bhagavan decreed / Rose from the mountain / Down in my hometown / One road more / Waitin' for a train / Hello stranger / One day at a time / Stars in my life / Not so long ago / I know you / Heart you left behind, The / Jole Blon / Keeper of the mountain.
LP: . . . . CRM 2038

Flatmates

LOVE AND DEATH.
Tracks: / I could be in Heaven / Tell me why / I don't care / Life of crime / On my mind / So in love with you / Happy all the time / You're gonna cry / Shimmer / Heaven knows / Don't say if / Is it me? / Thinking of you / Love cuts / My empty head / This thing called love / Never coming down / Turning you blue / When I'm with you.
LP: . . . . SUBORG 14

Flatpickin'

FLATPICKIN' GUITAR FESTIVAL Various original artists (Various artists).
Tracks: / Paddy on the swingpipe: *Various artists* / Soldiers' joy: *Various artists* / Hippodrome reel: *Various* artists / Shebean an she mor: *Various artists* / Beaumont rag: *Various artists* / Dusty Miller: *Various* artists / Indian killed the woodcock: *Various artists* / Groves of Slaney, The: *Various artists* / Iron gate, The: *Various artists* / Kitchen girl, The: *Various artists* / El chicken real: *Various artists* / Alabama jubilee: *Various artists* / Merrily kiss the quaker: *Various artists* / Glentannan slide: *Various artists/* Sheik of Araby, The: *Various artists* / Pigeon on the gate: *Various artists* / Swinging on a gate: *Various* artists / Sheehan's reel: *Various artists* / Green fields of America: *Various artists* / Texas gales: *Various artists.*
LP: . . . . SNKF 124

Flatt, Lester

BLUE RIDGE CABIN HOME (Flatt, Lester & Earl Scruggs).
Tracks: / Blue ridge cabin home / Don't let your deal go down / Some old day / I'll never shed another tear / I'll take the blame / Six white horses / Hundred years from now / On my mind / Shuckin' the corn / Let those brown eyes smile at me / No mother in this world / I won't be hanging around.
LP: . . . . CCS 102
LP: . . . . P 14370

DON'T GET ABOVE YOUR RAISIN' (Flatt, Lester & Earl Scruggs).
LP: . . . . SS 08
MC: . . . . SSC 08

FANTASTIC PICKIN' (Flatt, Lester & Nashville Grass).
Tracks: / Roanoke / Cannon ball blues / When it's lamplighting time in the valley / Two in the morning / Old spinning wheel / Peacock rag / Drive time / In the garden / Nashville wagoner / When I saw sweet Nellie home / Fiddlin' cricket / Last waltz, The.
LP: . . . . CMH 6232

FLATT AND SCRUGGS (Flatt, Lester & Earl Scruggs).
Tracks: / I'll go stepping too / Dear old Dixie / No doubt about it / You put me on my feet / Before I met you / Foggy mountain special / Till the end of the world rolls round / What's good for you / Who knows right from wrong / Cabin in the hills.
LP: . . . . CBS 25018

GOLDEN ERA, THE (Flatt, Lester & Earl Scruggs).
LP: . . . . SS 05
MC: . . . . SSC 05

GOLDEN HITS (Flatt, Lester & Earl Scruggs).
LP: . . . . PO 297

GOLDEN YEARS, THE (Flatt, Lester & Earl Scruggs).
LP: . . . . CCS 101

HEAVEN'S BLUEGRASS BAND (Flatt, Lester & Nashville Grass).
Tracks: / Dixie flyer / Home without love is just a house / Great big woman / Night Daddy passed away, The / You know you caused it all by telling lies / House of bottles and cans, The / Heaven's bluegrass band / Ten years of heartaches / Love me Lorena / Gone with the delta queen / I'm gonna sit down beside my Jesus.
LP: . . . . CMH 6207

LESTER AND MAC (Flatt, Lester & Mac Wiseman).
Tracks: / You're the best of all the leading / Homestead on the farm / Now that you have me / Will you be loving another man / Sweetheart you done me wrong / Your love is like a flower / Bluebirds singing for me, The / Jimmy Brown the newsboy / I'll never love another.
LP: . . . . HAT 3065
MC: . . . . HATC 3065

LESTER FLATT'S BLUEGRASS FESTIVAL (Flatt, Lester & Nashville Grass).
Tracks: / Why did you wander / Columbus stockade blues / Down the road / Jimmie Brown the newsboy / Before I met you / Backin' to Birmingham / Martha White theme / Roll in sweet baby's arms / She's my little Georgia rose / Tennessee mountain home / Panhandle county / When I stop dreaming / Georgia cotton / Ugly girl, The / I don't love nobody / I know what it means to be lonesome / We'll meet again, sweetheart / Joshua / Little Lewis wildwood flower / Dim light, thick smoke / Goin' up Cripple Creek / Til the end of the world rolls round / Randy Lynn rag / Hot corn, cold corn / Get in line, brother / Will the circle be unbroken.
2LP: . . . . CMH 9009

LESTER RAYMOND FLATT.
Tracks: / Come back darling / Wreck of old '97 / Some old day / Listen to my mockingbird / When it's time for the whippoorwill to sing / Down the road / I won't care / It was only the wind / My cabin in Caroline / Sleep with one eye open / Foggy mountain chimes / That old book of mine.
LP: . . . . FF 015

LIVE AT THE BLUEGRASS FESTIVAL.
Tracks: / Foggy mountain breakdown(Instrumental) / Lost all my money / Homestead on the farm / Rawhide(Instrumental) / Wabash cannonball / Orange blossom special (instrumental) / Nine pound hammer / Flint hill special (instrumental) / Get in line brother / Blue moon of Kentucky / Will you be loving another man / Little cabin on the hill / Salty dog blues / Dig a hole in the meadow / Cumberland gap.
LP: . . . . NL 84071
MC: . . . . NK 84071

LIVE BROADCAST (Flatt, Lester & Earl Scruggs).
LP: . . . . SH 2104

LIVING LEGEND, A (Flatt, Lester & Nashville Grass).
Tracks: / I don't care anymore / It's too late now / Shuckin' the corn / Legend of the Johnson mountain boys / Please don't wake me / Good times are past and gone / Don't drink that mash and talk that trash / Why don't you tell me so / Gonna have myself a ball / Ballad of Jed Clampett / Why did you wander / Regina / I'll be the life of Riley / Foggy mountain special / We can't be darlings anymore / I still miss someone / Black eyed Susan Brown / If I wander back tonight / Bummin' and old freight train / Thinking about you.
2LP: . . . . CMH 9002

MERCURY SESSIONS VOL. 1 (Flatt, Lester & Earl Scruggs).
LP: . . . . SS 18
MC: . . . . SSC 18

MERCURY SESSIONS VOL. 2 (Flatt, Lester & Earl Scruggs).
Tracks: / My little girl in Tennessee / Will the roses bloom / I'll never shed another tear / Bouquet in heaven / Cabin in Caroline / I'll never love another / God loves his children / Pain in my heart / Baby blue eyes / Doing my time / Preaching, praying, singing / Why don't they tell me so / Foggy mountain breakdown / I'm going to make heaven my home.
LP: . . . . SS 19
MC: . . . . SSC 19

PICKIN' TIME (Flatt, Lester & Nashville Grass).
Tracks: / Uncle Billy play your fiddle for me / Pickin' time / Cabin on the hill / Bluegrass shuffle / Goin' up on black mountain / I love you until I am dizzy / We don't care what Mama allow / If you ain't tried it don't knock it / On my mind / I'll be all smiles tonight / Auction sale / Little brown church.
LP: . . . . CMH 6226

YOU CAN FEEL IT IN YOUR SOUL (Flatt, Lester & Earl Scruggs).
LP: . . . . CCS 111
MC: . . . . CCS 111MC

Flaubert, G.

MADAME BOVARY (Worth, Irene).
MC: . . . . CDL 51664

Flavin, Mick

DUET ALBUM (See Under Begley, Philomena) (Flavin, Mick & Philomena Begley).

I'M GONNA MAKE IT AFTER ALL.
2LP: . . . . HM 026D

INTRODUCING MICK FLAVIN.
Tracks: / Dream of me / Who will I be lovin' / Leaving on her mind / Precious jewel / Come back today / Tipperary, so far away / Gone gone gone / After the fire is gone / Never was a fool / Little bitty heart.
LP: . . . . IHLP 09
MC: . . . . IHMC 09

MICK FLAVIN IN CONCERT.
MC: . . . . RITZRC 501

TRAVELLIN' LIGHT.
Tracks: / Jennifer Johnson and me / Blue blue day / Hard times lovin' can bring / Where have all the lovers gone / Home to Donegal / Old side of town, The / Roads and other reasons / Travellin' light / There is no other way / Rarest flowers, The.
MC: . . . . RITZLC 0053

YOU'RE ONLY YOUNG ONCE.
2LP: . . . . HM 044D

Fleadh Night

FLEADH NIGHT (Various artists).
MC: . . . . CT 104

Fleck, Bela

CROSSING THE TRACKS.
LP: . . . . ROUNDER 0121
MC: . . . . ROUNDER 0121C

DEVIATION (Fleck, Bela & The New Grass Revival).
LP: . . . . ROUNDER 0196
MC: . . . . ROUNDER 0196C

DOUBLE TIME.
LP: . . . . ROUNDER 0181
MC: . . . . ROUNDER 0181C

DRIVE.
Tracks: / Whitewater / Slipstream / Up and around the bend / Natchez trace / See rock city / Legend, The / Lights of home, The / Down in the swamp / Sanctuary / Open road, The.
LP: . . . . ROUNDER 0255
MC: . . . . ROUNDER 0255C

INROADS.
LP: . . . . ROUNDER 0219
MC: . . . . ROUNDER 0219C

NATURAL BRIDGE.
Tracks: / Punch drunk / Flexibility / Dawg's due / Daybreak / Bitter gap / October winds / Crossfire / Applebutter / Old hickory waltz / Rock road / Natural bridge suite.
LP: . . . . ROUNDER 0146
MC: . . . . ROUNDER 0146C

Flederman

AUSTRALIAN MUSIC.
LP: . . . . LRF 156

Fledgling Spy

FLEDGLING SPY, THE (Book One Of The Secret Pilgrim) (Le Carre, John).
MCSET: . . . . LFP 7517

Flee-Rekkers

JOE MEEK'S FABULOUS FLEE REKKERS.
LP: C5 564

Fleets In

FLEETS IN, THE (1942 film musical soundtrack) (Various artists).
LP: . . . . HS 405

Fleetwood Mac

ALBATROSS (Fleetwood Mac & Christine Perfect).
Tracks: / Albatross / Rambling pony / I believe my time ain't long / Doctor Brown / Stop messin' around / Love that burns / Jigsaw puzzle blues / Need your love tonight / I'd rather go blind / Crazy 'bout you baby / And that's saying a lot / I'm on my way / No road is the right road / Let me go (leave me alone) / I'm too far gone to turn around / When you say.
LP: . . . . CBS 31569
MC: 40 31569

BARE TREES.
Tracks: / Child of mine / Ghost, The / Homeward bound / Sunny side of heaven / Bare trees / Sentimental lady / Danny's chant / Spare me a little of your love / Dst / Thoughts on a grey day.
LP: . . . . K 44181

BEHIND THE MASK.
LP: . . . . WX 335
MC: . . . . WX 335C

BLACK MAGIC WOMAN.
Tracks: / Black magic woman / Coming home / Lazy poker blues / Something inside of me / Evenin' boogie / If you be my baby / Without you / Rockin' boogie / Need your love so bad / Rollin' man / Dust my broom / I've lost my baby / Big boat, The / Shake your moneymaker / Sun is shining, The / Last night.
LP: . . . . CBS 31798

BLUES COLLECTION, THE.

2LP: . . . . CCSLP 216
MC: . . . . CCSMC 216

BLUES YEARS, THE.
Tracks: / My heart beat like a hammer / Merry go round / Long grey mare / Hell hounds on my trail / Shake your money maker / Looking for somebody / No place to go / My baby's good to me / I loved another woman / Cold black night / World keep on turning, The / Got to move / Stop messin' around / Coming home / Rollin' man / Dust my broom / Love that burns / Doctor Brown / Need your love tonight / If you be my baby / Evenin' boogie / Lazy poker blues / I've lost my baby / Trying so hard to forget / I believe my time ain't long / Ramblin' pony / Black magic woman / Sun is shining, The / Need your love so bad / Albatross / Jigsaw puzzle blues / Man of the world / Someone's gonna get their head kicked in tonite / Watch out / Worried dream / Fleetwood Mac / First train home / Drifting / Mean old fireman / Allow me one more show / Just the blues / Big boat, The / I'd rather go blind / Watch out (2nd version) / Homework / I can't hold out / Like it this way / Last night / I'm worried / Words in a tangle.
LPS: . . . . ESBLP 138

BOSTON LIVE.
Tracks: / Oh well / Like it this way / World in harmony / Only you (end s1) / Black magic woman / Jumping at shadows / Can't hold on.
LP: . . . . CLALP 152
MC: . . . . CLAMC 152
LP: . . . . IMPL 400129

CERULEAN.
Tracks: / Madison blues / Sandy Mary / Stranger blues / Great balls of fire / Jenny Jenny / Got to move / Oh baby / Teenage darling / Loving kind / Tutti frutti / Rattlesnake shake / Keep a knockin' / Red hot mama / Green manalishi.
2LP: . . . . HAI 300
MC: . . . . HAC 300

COLLECTION: FLEETWOOD MAC.
Tracks: / Shake your moneymaker / Long grey mare / I loved another woman / Got to move / World keep on turning / Black magic woman / Need your love so bad / Doctor Brown / Need your love tonight / Love that burns / Lazy poker blues / Dust my broom / Drifting / Fleetwood Mac / Love that woman / I've lost my baby / Man of the world / Someone's gonna get their head kicked in tonight / Watch out / Homework / Rockin' boogie / Jigsaw puzzle blues / Albatross.
2LP: . . . . CCSLP 157
MC: . . . . CCSMC 157

FLEETWOOD MAC.
Tracks: / Monday morning / Warm always / Blue letter / Rhiannon / Over my head / Crystal / Say you love me / Landslide / I'm so afraid / World turning / Sugar daddy.
LP: . . . . K 54043
MC: K4 54043

FLEETWOOD MAC (1ST LP).
LP: . . . . BPG 763200

FLEETWOOD MAC: INTERVIEW PICTURE DISC.
LPPD: . . . . BAK 2126

FLEETWOOD MAC LIVE.
Tracks: / Monday morning / Say you love me / Dreams / Oh well / Over and over / Sara / Not that funny / Never going back again / Landslide / Fireflies / Over my head / Rhiannon / Don't let me down again / One more night / Go your own way / Don't stop / I'm so afraid / Farmer's daughter, The.
2LP: . . . . K 66097
MC: K4 66097

FUTURE GAMES.
Tracks: / Woman of 1000 years / Morning rain / What a shame / Future games / Sands of time / Sometimes / Lay it all down / Show me a smile.
LP: . . . . K 44153

GREATEST HITS: FLEETWOOD MAC (CBS).
Tracks: / Greem Manalishi, The / Oh well, part 1 / Oh well, part 2 / Shake your moneymaker / Need your love so bad / Rattlesnake shake / Dragonfly / Black magic woman / Albatross / Man of the world / Stop messin' around / Love that burns.
LP: 4607041
MC: 4607044

GREATEST HITS: FLEETWOOD MAC (WEA).
Tracks: / As long as you follow / No questions asked / Rhiannon / Don't stop / Go your own way / Hold me / Everywhere / Gypsy / Say you love me / Dreams / Little lies / Sara / Tusk / Oh Diane (Only on CD and cassette.) / Big love (Only on CD and cassette.) / You make loving fun (Only on CD and cassette.) / Seven wonders (Only on CD and cassette.).
LP: . . . . WX 221
MC: . . . . WX 221 C

GREATEST HITS LIVE: FLEETWOOD MAC.
MC: 2648214
LP: 2648217

HEROES ARE HARD TO FIND.
Tracks: / Heroes are hard to find / Coming home / Angel / Bermuda Triangle / Come a little bit closer / She's changing me / Bad loser / Silver heels / Prove your love / Born enchanter / Safe harbour.
LP: . . . . K 54026
MC: K4 54026

HISTORY OF FLEETWOOD MAC: VINTAGE YEARS.
Tracks: / Black magic woman / Coming home / Rambling pony / Something inside of me / Dust my broom / Sun is shining, The / Albatross / Just the blues / Evenin' boogie / Big boat, The / Jigsaw puzzle blues / I've lost my baby / Doctor Brown / Need your love so bad / Looking for somebody / Need your love tonight / Shake your moneymaker / Man of the world / Stop messin' around / Rollin' man / If you be my baby / Lazy poker blues / Trying so hard to forget.
2LP: . . . . CBS 22122

JUMPING AT SHADOWS.
LP: . . . . V 020
MC: . . . . VRC 020

KILN HOUSE.
Tracks: / This is the rock / Station man / Blood on the floor / Hi ho silver / Jewel eyed Judy / Buddy's song / Earl Gray / One together / Tell me all the things you do / Mission bell.
LP: . . . . K 54001
LP: . . . . RSLP 9004

LIKE IT THIS WAY.
Tracks: / Lazy poker blues / Something inside of me / Evening boogie / Rockin' boogie / Dust my broom / Rollin' man / Merry go round / Hellbound on my trail / Last night / Need your love tonight / Rambling pony / I can't hold out / Like it this way / Home work / Cold black night / Big boat, The / Just the blues / Dragonfly / Trying so hard to forget.
MC: . . . . ELITE 008 MC

LIVE: FLEETWOOD MAC(IMPORT).
LP: . . . . BRLP 16
MC: . . . . BRMC 16

LONDON LIVE '68.
Tracks: / Got to move / I held my baby last night / My baby's sweet / My baby's a good un / Don't know which way to go / Buzz me / Dream, The / World keeps turning, The / How blue can you get / Bleeding heart.
LP: . . . . THBL 1.038
MC: . . . . THBC 1.038

LOOKING BACK AT FLEETWOOD MAC.
Tracks: / Albatross / Looking for somebody / My baby's good to me / I loved another woman / If you be my baby / Without you / Jigsaw puzzle blues / Black magic woman / Need your love so bad / Love that burns / My heart beats like a hammer / I believe my time ain't long / Shake your money maker / World keep on turning, The / Stop messin' around / Coming home.
LP: . . . . SHM 3268
MC: . . . . HSC 3268

MAN OF THE WORLD (OLD GOLD)
(See under Humble Pie/Natural born budgie).

MIRAGE.
Tracks: / Love in store / Can't go back / That's alright / Book of love / Gypsy / Only over you / Empire State / Straight back / Hold me / Oh Diane / Eyes of the world / Wish you were here.
LP: . . . . K 569 52
MC: . . . . K 456 952

MISTER WONDERFUL.
Tracks: / Stop messin' round / Coming home / Rollin' man / Dust my broom / Love that burns / Doctor Brown / Need your love tonight / If you be my baby / Evenin' boogie / Lazy poker blues / I've lost my baby / Trying so hard to forget.
LP: . . . . ESSLP 010
MC: . . . . ESSMC 010
LP: 763205

MYSTERY TO ME.
Tracks: / Emerald eyes / Believe me / Just crazy love / Hypnotised / Forever / Keep on going / City, The / Miles away / Somebody / Way I feel, The / Good things come to those who wait / Why?.
LP: . . . . K 44248
LP: . . . . MSX 2279

OH WELL.
LP: 264 824 1
MC: 264 824 4

ORIGINAL FLEETWOOD MAC, THE.
LP: . . . . ESSLP 026
MC: . . . . ESSMC 026

PENGUIN.
Tracks: / Remember me / Bright fire / Dissatisfied / I'm a road runner / Derelict, The / Revelation / Did you ever love me / Night watch, The / Caught in the rain.
LP: . . . . K 44235

PETER GREEN'S FLEETWOOD MAC.
LP: . . . . IMLP 400216

PIOUS BIRD OF GOOD OMEN, THE.
Tracks: / Need your love so bad / Coming home / Rambling pony / Big boat, The / I believe my time ain't long / Sun is shining, The / Albatross / Black magic woman / Just the blues / Jigsaw puzzle blues / Looking for somebody / Stop messin' around / Stop messin' around.
LP: . . . . CBS 32050
LP: 763215

RUMOURS.
Tracks: / Secondhand news / Dreams / Never going back again / Don't stop / Go your own way / Songbird / Chain, The / You make loving fun / I don't want to know / Oh daddy / Gold dust woman.
LP: . . . . K 56344
MC: K4 56344

RUMOURS AND FLEETWOOD MAC.
Tracks: / Second hand news / Dreams / Never going back again / Don't stop / Go your own way / Songbird / Chain, The (Theme for BBC tv's Grand Prix) / You make loving fun / I don't want to know / Oh Daddy / Gold dust woman / Monday morning / Warm ways / Blue letter / Rhiannon / Over my head / Crystal / Say you love me / Landslide / World turning / Sugar daddy / I'm so afraid.
MC: K4 66103

TANGO IN THE NIGHT.
Tracks: / Big love / Seven wonders / Everywhere / Caroline / Tango in the night / Mystified / Little lies / Family man / Welcome to the room...Sara / Isn't it midnight? / When I see you again / You and I (part 2).
LP: . . . . WX 65
MC: . . . . WX 65C

THEN PLAY ON.
Tracks: / Coming your way / Closing my eyes / Fighting for Madge / When you say / Show biz blues / Underway / One sunny day / Although the sun is shining / Rattlesnake shake / Without you / Searching for Madge / My dream / Like crying / Before the beginning.
LP: . . . . K 44103
MC: K4 44103
LP: . . . . RSLP 9000

TUSK.
Tracks: / Over and over / Ledge, The / Think about me / Save me a place / Sara / What makes you think you're the one? / Storms / That's all for everyone / Not that funny / Sisters of the moon / Angel / That's enough for me / Brown eyes / Never make me cry / I know I'm not wrong / Honey hi / Beautiful child / Walk a thin line / Tusk / Never forget.
2LP: . . . . K 66088
MC: K4 66088

Fleetwood, Mick

I'M NOT ME (Fleetwood, Mick Zoo).
Tracks: / Angel come home / You might need somebody / Tonight / I want you back / I'm not me / State of the art / Tear it up / This love / I give / Just because / Put me right.
LP: . . . . PL 84652

VISITOR, THE.
Tracks: / Rattlesnake shake / You weren't in love / O Niamali / Super brains / Don't be sorry just be happy / Walk a thin line / Not fade away / Cassiopeia surrender / Visitor, The / Ammele (Come show me your heart).
LP: . . . . RCALP 5044
MC: . . . . RCAK 5044
LP: . . . . PIPLP 020
MC: . . . . PIPMC 020

Fleetwood, Susan

FIFTH CHILD, THE (See also Doris Lessing).

Fleming, Chuck

SHAKE LOOSE THE BORDER (Fleming, Chuck & Gerry Kaley).
LP: . . . . CRO 209
MC: . . . . CROC 209

Fleming, Ian

CHITTY CHITTY BANG BANG (Gingold, Hermione).
MC: 1390

DIAMONDS ARE FOREVER (Ogilvy, Ian).
MCSET: . . . . LFP 7172

FROM RUSSIA WITH LOVE.
MC: . . . . LFP 41 7196 5

GOLDFINGER.
MC: 41 7226 5

LIVE AND LET DIE.
MC: . . . . LFP 41 7166 5

ON HER MAJESTY'S SECRET SERVICE.
MCSET: . . . . CAB 291

Flesh

FLESH.
LP: . . . . JAMS 9

Flesh & Blood

READ, WHITE AND BLUE.
LP: . . . . K 781 957 1
MC: . . . . K 781 957 4

Flesh & Blood (Film)

FLESH AND BLOOD (1985 film soundtrack) (London Symphony Orchestra).
LP: . . . . VS 1012
LP: . . . . STV 81256
MC: . . . . CTV 81256

Flesh Eaters

DESTROYED BY FIRE - GREATEST HITS.
Tracks: / See you in the bone yard / Cyrano / Dominoes / Impossible crime / Secret life / Hard road to follow / Wedding dice, The / Pony dress / We'll never die / Digging my grave / Lake of burning fire.
LP: . . . . FC 025

LIVE: THE FLESH EATERS.
LP: . . . . HMS 124 1

MINUTE TO PRAY A SECOND TO DIE, A.
LP: . . . . IRC 007

Flesh For Lulu

BIG FUN CITY.
LP: . . . . STATLP 28
MC: . . . . STATC 28

BLUE SISTERS SWING.
LP: . . . . RIB 3

FLESH FOR LULU.
Tracks: / Restless / Dog dog dog / Huena / Coming down / Jigsaw puzzle / Subterraneans / Brainburst / Peace and love / So strong / Heavy heavy angel.
LP: . . . . POLD 5165

LONG LIVE THE NEW FLESH.
Tracks: / Lucky day / Postcards from paradise / Hammer of love / Siamese twist / Sooner or later / Good for you / Crash / Way to go / Sleeping dogs / Dream on cowboy.
LP: . . . . BEGA 82
MC: . . . . BEGC 82
LP: . . . . BBL 82
MC: . . . . BBLC 82

PLASTIC FANTASTIC.
Tracks: / Decline and fall / House of cards / Time and space / Every little word / Slowdown / Highwire / Slide / Day one / Choosing you / Stupid on the street / Avenue / Plastic fantastic.
LP: . . . . BEGA 100
MC: . . . . BEGC 100

Fleshtones

BLAST OFF.
MC: . . . . A 107
LP: . . . . DANLP 039

FLESHTONES.
Tracks: / Hex breaker / Deep in my heart / What so new / Screaming skull / Wheelman / New scene / Right side of a good thing / Brainstorm / This house is empty / Want / Burnin' hell.
LP: . . . . SP 70605

FLESHTONES VS. REALITY.
LP: . . . . EM 9634

POWERSTANCE.
Tracks: / Armed and dangerous / I'm still thirsty / Waiting for a message / Let it rip / Three fevers / Living legends / I can breathe / Mod teepee / House of rock / Irresistible / Candy ass.
LP: . . . . WIK 99
MC: . . . . WIKC 99

ROMAN GODS.
LP: . . . . SP 70018

Fleshtones Present...

BIG BANG THEORY (Various artists).
LP: . . . . ROSE 137

Fletch

FLETCH (1985 film soundtrack) (Various artists).
Tracks: / Fletch theme: *Faltermeyer, Harold* / Diggin' in: *Faltermeyer, Harold* / Exotic skates: *Faltermeyer*, Harold / Running for love: *Faltermeyer, Harold* / Bit by bit: *Mills, Stephanie* / Fletch, get outta town: *Hartman, Dan* / Name of the game: *Hartman, Dan* / Running for love:

Farnham, John / Letter to both sides, A: *Fixx* / Is it over?: *Wilde, Kim*.
LP: . . . . **MCF 3284**
MC: . . . . **MCFC 3284**

Fletcher, Bud

ANOTHER TRIP TO THE OUTHOUSE.
LP: **111**

BEST OF BUD FLETCHER AT THE OUTHOUSE.
LP: **131**
MC: . . . . **131 TC**

MORE OF BUD FLETCHER AND CYPRIENNE ROBESPIERRE (Fletcher, Bud/Cyprienne Robespierre).
LP: **102**

STANDING ROOM ONLY AT THE OUTHOUSE.
LP: **125**

Fletcher, Cyril

ADVENTURES OF ALICE IN WONDERLAND, THE.
LP: . . . . **CF 223**

Fletcher, Guy

BERTHA (See under Television).

Fletcher, Vo

ENGLISH AIR (Fletcher, Vo and Rachel).
LP: . . . . **PAR 1001**

Fleury Trio

CONCERT BY THE FLEURY TRIO, A.
LP: . . . . **AP 53**

Flex Your Head

FLEX YOUR HEAD Various bands (Various artists).
LP: . . . . **DISCHORD 7**

Flicks

GO FOR THE EFFECT.
Tracks: / Sortin' it out / Scared of the night / Gypsy woman / Close to you / Flames are burning / I want to leave you behind / Happy this morning / Light to follow / Love me tenderly / Tonite's alright / Queen of the roadsters / Rock'n'roll band.
LP: . . . . **ARL 5024**

Flies

GET BURNED.
LP: . . . . **HMS 046**

GET WISE.
LP: . . . . **HMS 013**

Flies On Fire

FLIES ON FIRE.
LP: . . . . **K 791 284 1**
MC: . . . . **K 791 284 4**

STONES.
Tracks: / Anything goes / Baptise me over Elvis Presley's grave / C'mon / Smalltown / Underground / Long gone dead / Salvation boulevard / You can't go back / Not for long / Since you been gone / Let it roll.
LP: . . . . **UNKNOWN**

Flight Of The Condor

FLIGHT OF THE CONDOR (T.V. soundtrack) (Guamary).
Tracks: / Floreo de Llamas / Mi raza / Inti illimani / Alturas / De terciopelo negro / Dolencias / A vos te h'ai pesar / Sicuriadas / Danza de Los Quechuas / Papel de plata / Volando / La mariposa / Tema de la Quebrada de Humahuaca / Vasija de barro / Huajra / Lonquita / Llanto de mi madre / Calambito temucano.
LP: . . . . **REB 440**
MC: . . . . **ZCF 440**

Flight Of The Doves

FLIGHT OF THE DOVES (Film Soundtrack) (Various artists).
Tracks: / Theme from Flight of the doves: *Various artists* / Walkin' down O'Connell Street: *Various artists* / Here comes the hawk: *Various artists* / Runaways: *Various artists* / Fiddler at the fair: *Various artists*/ You don't have to be Irish to be Irish: *Various artists* / In search of a dream: *Various artists* / Drop o' the Irish (smuggler's in the cemetary): *Various artists* / Far off place: *Various artists* / Doves in flight: *Various artists* / Hawk on the hunt: *Various artists* / Little boy, little girl: *Various artists*.
LP: . . . . **SKL 5093**

Flights Of Fancy

FLIGHTS OF FANCY (Beautiful Sound of the Panpipes) (Various artists).
Tracks: / Light of experience: *Various artists* / El condor pasa: *Various artists* / Picnic at hanging rock (theme): *Various artists* / Cacharpaya: *Various artists* / First time ever I saw your face, The: *Various artists*/ Godfather, The: *Various artists* / Endless love: *Various artists* / True: *Various artists* / Bluebird: *Various artists* / Do you know where you're going to: *Various artists* / And I love her: *Various artists*/ Tara's theme: *Various artists* / Once upon a time in the west: *Various artists* / Flame Trees of Thika: *Various* artists / Feelings: *Various artists* / True love ways: *Various artists* (CD only.) / Why can't it wait 'till morning: *Various artists* (CD only.).
MC: . . . . **TCMFP 5896**

Flightt, K.C.

IN FLIGHT.
Tracks: / Planet E / Let's get jazzy / Summer madness / Bass line / Let's go / Jazz player / Fantasy / She's sexxy / Your place or mine / It goes like this / Africa / Let's get jazzy (dope mix) (on cassette and CD only).
LP: . . . . **PL 90390**
MC: . . . . **PK 90390**

Flindt, Lennart

ONLY LOVE IS THE WAY (Flindt, Lennart Trio).
LP: . . . . **MLP 15659**

Flint, Berni(e)

I DON'T WANT TO PUT A HOLD ON YOU.
LP: . . . . **EMC 3184**

JUST LIKE A MOVIE.
Tracks: / Beautiful loser / Dance with me / Just like a woman / Here / Hold out / Rocky racoon / Caroline and me / Only me / Dusk till dawn / I'll have to say I love you in a song / Let me be the wind in your sail / Too late / Father and son.
LP: . . . . **EMC 3297**

Flint, J.C. Band

WHEN THE WINTER IS OVER.
MC: . . . . **MR 1020**

Flint, Tim

ICE CASTLES.
LP: . . . . **GRS 1163**

Flintlock

HOT FROM THE LOCK.
LP: . . . . **PLP 8309**

ON THE WAY.
LP: . . . . **PLP 8307**

STAND ALONE.
Tracks: / Stand alone / You're like a magnet / Fool's a winner / Neerodavi' blues / Tokyo / Let it be me / Don't drink the water / On my own again / End of time.
LP: . . . . **PLP 8312**

TEARS N CHEERS.
LP: . . . . **PLP 8310**

Flint's Holiday

FLINT'S HOLIDAY (See under Action Force (tv)).

Flintstones

BRONTONAPPERS, THE.
MC: . . . . **PLBF 282**

FRED THE FISHERMAN (Unknown narrator(s)).
MC: . . . . **PLBF 283**

Flipenstein

FLIPENSTEIN (Various).
LP: . . . . **PRO 7063**

Flippen, Jay C.

JAY C. FLIPPEN 1926-27 (Flippen, Jay C. & His Gang).
LP: . . . . **FV 204**

Flipper

BLOWING CHUNKS.
MC: . . . . **A 126**

GONE FISHIN'.
LP: . . . . **SAVE 017**

PUBLIC FLIPPER LIMITED.
Tracks: / Nuru nuru / Hard cold world / I'm fighting / Games gotta price, The / Love canal / Oh oh ay oh / We don't understand / If I can't be drunk / Sex bomb / Brainwash / Shy / Southern California / Life / Wheel, The / Flipper blues.
LP: . . . . **SAVE 015/016**

Flips

LESS IS MORE.
LP: . . . . **CHIME 9M**

WHATS IN THE BRIGHT PINK BOX?.
LP: . . . . **FF 457**

Flirts

FLIRTS.
Tracks: / Jukebox / Boy crazy / On the beach / Passion / We just want to dance / Calling all boys / Jungle rock / I only want to be with you / Surf's up.
LP: . . . . **QUELP 1**

QUESTIONS OF THE HEART.
Tracks: / All you ever think about is sex / Daddy I'm not a baby / Boys on the beach / My boyfriend is a marine / Just another kiss / Special angel / Motorama(turn up the radio) / Forgive / Like a thief in the night / After midnight.
LP: **4502791**
MC: **4502794**

Flitox

GET HOMME EST MORT.
LP: . . . . **JHL 107**

Flo & Eddie

MOVING TARGETS.
Tracks: / Moving targets / Mama, open up / Love you gave away / Hot / Best friends / Best possible me / Keep it warm / Guns / Elanore / Sway when you walk.
LP: . . . . **CBS 81509**

Float Up CP

KILL ME IN THE MORNING.
LP: . . . . **ROUGH 77**

Floaters

FLOATERS.
LP: . . . . **ABCL 5229**

Flock

FLOCK.
LP: . . . . **CBS 63733**

Flock Of Seagulls

BEST OF A FLOCK OF SEAGULLS.
Tracks: / I ran (so far away) / Space age love song / Telecommunication / More you live, the more you love, The / Nightmares / Wishing (if had a photograph of you) / It's not me talking / Transfer affection / Who's that girl (she's got it) / D.N.A. I ran.
LP: . . . . **HIP 41**
MC: . . . . **HIPC 41**

COLLECTION OF TEN 12" SINGLES.
Tracks: / Telecommunication / Intro / Modern love / You can run / D.N.A. I ran / Pick me up / Space age love song / Windows / Wishing (if I had a photograph of you) / Committed / Nightmares / Rosenmontag / Transfer affection / I ran (so far away) (live) / It's not me talking / Tanglimara / Never again (the dancer) / Living in Heaven / More you live, the more you love, The / Lost control.
LP: . . . . **AFLOCK 1**

DREAM COME TRUE.
LP: . . . . **HIP 32**
MC: . . . . **HIPC 32**

FLOCK OF SEAGULLS, A.
LP: . . . . **HOP 201**
LPPD: . . . . **HOPX 201**

LISTEN.
LPPD: . . . . **HIPX 4**
LP: . . . . **HIP 4**

STORY OF A YOUNG HEART, THE.
LP: . . . . **HIP 14**

Floor Kiss

GOODNIGHT MOON.
LP: . . . . **ID 16**

Floorshakers

NORTHERN FLOORSHAKERS (Various artists).
Tracks: / Hide nor hair: *Grant, Earl* / Soul self satisfaction: *Jackson, Earl* / Call me: *Bishop, Eddie*/ Something beautiful: *Mandolph, Magaret* / Gonna be a big thing: *Sapphires* / Like Adam and Eve: *Reflections*/ Up and over: *Traynor, Jay* / Darkest days: *Lee, Jackie* / I'm gonna love you a long long time: *Patti & The* Emblems / I'm not built that way: *Hesitations* / You've been a long time coming: *Braithwaite, Mitchell* / Pennygold: *Stevens, Lindy* / Determination: *Parrish, Dean* / All of a sudden: *Williams, Jeanette*.
LP: . . . . **KENT 007**

Flophouse

FLOPHOUSE.
LP: . . . . **HEY 015 1**
MC: . . . . **HEY 015 4**

Flora The Red Menace

FLORA THE RED MENACE (Original off-Broadway cast (1987 revival)) (Various artists).
Tracks: / Prologue / Unafraid: *Various artists* / Street song I: *Various artists* / Kid herself, The: *Various* artists / All I need is one good break: *Various artists* / Not every day of the week: *Various artists* / Street song II: *Various artists* / Sign here: *Various artists* / Street song III: *Various artists* / Quiet thing, A: *Various artists* / Flame: *Various artists* / Not every day of the week (reprise): *Various artists*/ Street song IV: *Various artists* / Dear love: *Various artists* / Keepin' it hot: *Various artists* / Street song V: *Various artists* / Express yourself: *Various artists* / Where did everybody go?: *Various artists*/ Street song VI: *Various artists* / You are you: *Various artists* / Joke, The: *Various artists* / Quiet thing, A (reprise): *Various artists* / Sing happy: *Various artists* / Closing scene: *Various artists*.
LP: . . . . **TER 1159**
MC: . . . . **ZCTER 1159**

Floren, Myron

ACCORDION MAN.
Tracks: / Dance of the comedians / Yesterday / Bem-te-atrevido / Lost chord, The / Accordion man polka / Tiger rag / Stardust / Blue tango / How great thou art / God bless America.
LP: **R.8199**

Florence, Bob

DREAM (see Sommers,Joanie) (Florence, Bob & Joanie Sommers).

LIVE AT CONCERT BY THE SEA (Florence, Bob Big Band).
LP: . . . . **TR 523**
MC: . . . . **TRC 523**

MAGIC TIME (Florence, Bob Limited Edition).
Tracks: / Magic time / Double barrel blues / Industrial strength stomp, The / Rhythm and blues / Bluephoria / Sailing.
LP: . . . . **TR 536**

STATE OF THE ART (Florence, Bob Limited Edition).
Tracks: / Just friends / Moonlight serenade / Silky / Crunch, The / Stella by starlight / All the things you are / Mr. Paddington / BBC / Auld lang syne.
LP: **C5-533**
LP: . . . . **USA 589**

TRASH CAN CITY (Florence, Bob Limited Edition).
Tracks: / Willowcrest / Flight of fancy / Jewels / Babbling brook, The.
LP: . . . . **TR 545**
MC: . . . . **TRC 545**

WESTLAKE (Florence, Bob Big Band).
LP: . . . . **DS 832**
MC: . . . . **DSC 832**

Flores, Rosie

ROSIE FLORES.
Tracks: / Crying over you / Lovin' in vain / Heart beats to a different drum / Somebody loses, somebody wins / Turn around / Midnight to moonlight / God may forgive you (but I won't) / Blue side of town / Heartbreak train / I gotta know.
LP: . . . . **K 925626 1**
MC: . . . . **K 925626 4**

Floria, Cam

COME BLESS THE LORD (Floria, Cam's Continentals).
Tracks: / Love, joy, peace / All day song / Bubbling / His banner over me is love / I love the Father / I love you with the love of the Lord / This is my commandment / God is so good / Oh, river of God / Peace like a river / Peace / Hallelujah, I'm gonna sing / Canaan's land / Joy is the flag / Come into His presence / Beautiful music / Come bless the Lord / Bless the Lord / Thy word have I hid in my heart / Lord thy God, The / This is the day / Steadfast love of the Lord, The / Beloved, let us one another / Lord's my shepherd, The / In all thy ways / Keep on asking / Teach me Lord to wait / And ye shall know the truth / Titus 3:5 / It is no longer I that liveth / If you delight yourself / I saw the Lord / Many mansions / I came to praise the Lord / Praise Him / Great is the Lord / Thy loving kindness / Clap your hands / He that overcomes / Where the spirit of the Lord is / Sweet, sweet spirit / Rejoice in the Lord always / Joy of the Lord, The / Spring up, O well / For those tears I died / Jesus, You are my friend / Bless that wonderful name / Now let us sing / Under the blood / Oh, the blood of Jesus / Oh, how I will praise you / Praise to thee, Jesus / Blessed be the name / Jesus is the sweetest name I know / Jesus, Jesus, Jesus / Sing alleluia to the Lord / O come, let us adore Him / We worship and adore Thee / Thou art worthy / Here comes Jesus / I believe in Heaven / He's the saviour of my soul / Oh, how I love Jesus / To me His name is so wonderful / Every knee shall bow / He is Lord.
LP: . . . . **WST 9578**
MC: . . . . **WC 9578**

COME PRAISE AND BLESS THE LORD (Floria, Cam's Continentals).
Tracks: / Praise and rejoice / Sing a new song / Make a joyful noise / Rejoice / I will enter His gates with thanksgiving / Horse and rider, The / Jehovah Jireh / I've got confidence / This is the confidence / Law of the Lord, The / He is my everything / Come go with me to that land / Give me oil in my lamp / Greater is He / Greater and greater / In the name of Jesus / Lift Jesus higher / Sea walker, The / In my Father's house / Joy is flowing / Oh how He loves you and me / Sweet Jesus / Rest of my life, The / My soul doth magnify the Lord / How great thou art / How great is our God / Ha, la, la, la / Al, le, le / Hal-le-lu-u-u-jah / Bless His holy name / I will bless thee, o Lord / Kumbaya / Into thy presence / We have come into His house / Bind us together / Ho, ho, ho, hosanna / Joy

unspeakable / I will bless the Lord at all times / Praise the name of Jesus / Blessed assurance / Praise Him, praise Him / Wonderful words of life / Tell me the old, old story / More about Jesus / What a wonderful Saviour / I will sing of the mercies of the Lord / My redeemer / Jesus paid it all / Amazing grace / Saved, saved / I stand amazed / To God be the glory / I will sing the wondrous story / O for a thousand tongues to sing.
LP: WST 9595
MC: WC 9595

SING IT WITH LOVE (Floria, Cam's Continentals).
Tracks: / Sing it with love / Ordinary people / Spirit of God descend upon my heart / Every time I feel the Spirit / Just a closer walk with thee / I'm gonna sing (when the Spirit says sing) / I have decided to follow Jesus / I am your servant / Bread upon the waters / Give them all to Jesus / I wanna be ready / Solid rock, The / Rock-a-my-soul / Jesus is the rock / Communion song / He's alive.
LP: WST 9585
MC: WC 9585

SKY SHALL UNFOLD, THE.
Tracks: / One more song for you / Because of who I am / Trumpet of Jesus, The / O Buddha / Little child / We are climbing / We are the reason / You know that I do / He's as close as the mention of His name / Praise the Lord / We shall behold Him.
LP: WST 9609
MC: WC 9609

Florida Sun

FLORIDA SUN ALBUM.
Tracks: / Hurt / If dreams come true / Cry / You belong to me.
LP: TMB 117
MC: TMBC 117

Flory, Chris

FOR ALL WE KNOW.
Tracks: / Soft winds / Tain't me / Avalon / Tenderly / Close your eyes / Lee's blues / It had to be you / For all we know / Airmail special / Ninth Avenue shuffle / Lullaby of the leaves.
MC: CJ 403C

Flory, Med

JAZZ WAVE (Flory, Med & His Orchestra).
LP: FS 107

Flotsam & Jetsam

DOOMSDAY FOR THE DECEIVER.
LPPD: 722081P
MC: RR 96834
LP: RR 9683

NO PLACE FOR DISGRACE.
Tracks: / No place for disgrace / Dream of death / N.E.T. / Escape from within / Saturday night's alright for fighting / Hard on you / I live you die / Misguided fortune / T.A.A.B. / Jones, The.
LP: RR 95491
MC: RR 95494

WHEN THE STORM COMES.
Tracks: / Master sleeps, The / Deviation / No more fun / 6, six, VI / E.M.T.E.K. / K.A.B. / Burned device / October thorns / Suffer the masses / Greed / Scars.
LP: MCG 6084
MC: MCGC 6084

Flotsam & Jetsam (2)

FLOTSAM AND JETSAM.
LP: SYO 14

Flour

FLOUR.
LP: TGLP 33

Flourgan

COUNT OUT.
LP: GREL 134

DOLLARS TALK (See under Ninja Man) (Flourgan & Ninja Man).

JUMP SPREAD OUT (See under Daddy Lizard) (Flourgan/Daddy Lizard).

RED DRAGON VS. FLOURGON.
LP: LP 005

Flouride, Klaus

BECAUSE I SAY SO.
LP: VIRUS 67

Flower

HOLOGRAM SKY.
LP: SR 40069421

Flower And Adolescent

FLOWER AND ADOLESCENT (Various artists).
MC: HRP 7304

Flower Drum Song

FLOWER DRUM SONG (1960 Original London cast) (Various artists).
Tracks: / Overture: *Various artists* / You are beautiful: *Various artists* / Hundred million miracles, A: *Various* artists / I enjoy being a girl: *Various artists* / I am going to like it here: *Various artists* / Like a god: *Various artists* / Chop suey: *Various artists* / Don't marry me: *Various artists* / Grant Avenue: *Various* artists / Love look away: *Various artists* / Fan tan Fannie: *Various artists* / Gliding through my memoree: *Various artists* / Other generation, The: *Various artists* / Sunday: *Various artists* / Finale: *Various artists.*
LP: TER 1060
MC: ZCTER 1060

FLOWER DRUM SONG (Original Broadway cast) (Various artists).
LP: PS 2009
MC: PST 2009

FLOWER DRUM SONG (ORIGINAL ISSUE) (Broadway cast) (Various artists).
LP: ABL 3302

FLOWER DRUM SONG (ORIGINAL ISSUE) (London cast) (Various artists).
LP: CLP 1359

Flower, E

ART OF MINSTREL (see under Best, Martin) (Flower, E & Martin Best).

Flower, Robin

BABIES WITH GLASSES (Flower, Robin & The Bleachers).
LP: FF 428

FIRST DIBS.
LP: FF 326

GREEN SNEAKERS.
LP: FF 273

Flowered Up

LIFE WITH BRIAN, A.
Tracks: / Sunshine / Take it / Mr Happy reveller / Hysterically blue / It's on / Silver plan / Phobia / Egg rush / Doris... is a little bit partial / Crackerjack.
LP: 8282441
MC: 8282444

Flowerpot Men

LET'S GO TO SAN FRANCISCO.
Tracks: / Let's go to San Francisco (Part two) / Walk in the sky, A / Am I losing you / You can never be wrong / Man without a woman, A / In a moment of madness / Young birds fly / Journeys end / Mythological Sunday / Blow away / Piccolo man / Let's go to San Francisco / Silicon City.
LP: 6 26179
MC: 4 26179
LP: C5-526

Flowers

FLOWERS IN THE DESERT (Various artists).
LP: VS 2010

Flowers & Frolics

SOLD OUT.
LP: BR 6

Flowers From the ...

FLOWERS FROM THE DOCTOR (Lucilla Andrews) (Clarke, Marie).
MCSET: SOUND 16

Flowers, Herbie

LITTLE POTTY.
Tracks: / Whale / Lonely me, I'm alone again / Don't take my bass away / People of mine / Big George / I want to be with you / Floral dance / Burlington Bertie / Sorry sad and no / Flanker / Mr. Moonlight / Just for you.
LP: NTS 216

Flowers In The Attic

FLOWERS IN THE ATTIC (1988 film soundtrack) (Various artists).
LP: STV 81358

Flowmasters

ENERGY DAWN.
LP: XLEP 103

Flowmotion

FLOWMOTION (Various artists).
LP: FM 001

Floy Joy

INTO THE HOT.
Tracks: / Burn down a rhythm / Baby you know I... / Holiday / Until you come back to me / Operator / East side west side / Into the hot / Mission / Sebastopol / Age of reason, Theme from.
MC: OVEDC 178
LP: V 2319
LP: OVED 178

WEAK IN THE PRESENCE OF BEAUTY.
Tracks: / Weak in the presence of beauty / Friday night / Penny in my pocket / Too drunk to funk / Ask the lonely / Chinese a go go / Crackdown / Walking in the night / This is my time / It makes no difference to me.
LP: V 2368
MC: TCV 2368
LP: OVED 247
MC: OVEDC 247

Floyd

LITTLE MAN, THE.
LP: PACT 8

Floyd, Bobby

SECRET LOVER (see under Baines, Murray) (Baines, Murray & Bobby Floyd).

Floyd, Eddie

FLASHBACK.
Tracks: / Flashback / Love's gonna get to you / From your head to your toes / Soul is back again / She likes the soaps / You don't say no / Pretty girls / Gonna satisfy you / Daddy's coming home.
LP: WIL 3005
MC: ZCWIL 3005

KNOCK ON WOOD.
LP: SD 07714
LP: 589-006

KNOCK ON WOOD - THE BEST OF EDDIE FLOYD.
Tracks: / Knock on wood / Raise your hand / Big bird / On a Saturday night / Things get better / Love is a doggone good thing / I've never found a girl / Consider me / Bring it on home to me / I've got to have your love / Blood is thicker than water / Baby lay your head down / Too weak to fight / Oh how it rained / Why is the wine sweeter (on the other side) / Soul Street / Don't tell your mama (Available on CD only) / Girl, I love you (Available on CD only) / People get it together (Available on CD only) / Something to write home about (Available on CD only) / Check me out (Available on CD only) / Stealing love (Available on CD only).
LP: SX 010
MC: SXC 010

Floyd Lloyd Seivright

MANGO BLUES.
LP: 101 LP5

Floyd's Cajun Fais Do

FLOYD'S CAJUN FAIS DO DO (See Under Cajun...) (Various artists).

Fluid

FLUID.
LP: FLUID LP

FREAK MAGNET.
LP: EFA 4476

ROADMOUTH.
LP: EFA 4489

Flute Indienne

EL CONDOR PASA.
LP: 2M 056 95465
MC: 2M 256 95465

Fluters Five

O'CAROLAN'S RECEIPT FOR DRINKING.
Tracks: / Orange and green / Night rider / Fairy reel, The / Planxty Irwin / Planxty O'Connor / Ar eireann ni n eosfainn ceh t / O'Carolan's receipt for drinking / Slane / Planxty Browne / St. Mary's / Church Street / O'Rourke's noble feast / Spanish cloak, The / Tabhair dom do lamh / Ramelton / Planxty Maguire / O'Carolan's concerto / South wind / Drops of brandy.
LP: OAS 3032

Flutes Grecques

LES FLUTES GRECQUES (Various artists).
Tracks: / Omorfoula: *Various artists* / Zonaradikos: *Various artists* / Air pour kanonaki: *Various artists*/ Kostantis: *Various artists* / Solo pour floghera et santouri: *Various artists* / Tzivaeri: *Various artists*/ Air pastoral: *Various artists* / Slow Pentozalis: *Various artists* / Air pour gaida solo: *Various artists*/ Kalamatianos takis: *Various artists* / Paidushka: *Various artists* / Bals de Smyrne: *Various artists.*
LP: ARN 33286
MC: ARN 433286

Flux Of Pink Indians

STRIVE TO SURVIVE CAUSING THE LEAST SUFFERING POSSIBLE.
Tracks: / Progress / They lie, we die / Myxomatosis / Is there anybody there? / Fun is over, The / Song for them / Charity hilarity / Some of us scream / Some of us shoot / Take heed / T.V. dinners / Tapioca sunrise.
LP: SDL 8
LP: TPLP 2

TREAT.
Tracks: / Flux 1 / Uncarved block / Value of nothing, The / Youthful immortal / Just is / Children who know / Backword / Footprints in the snow / Nothing is not done / Stonecutter, The.
LP: TPLP 3

UNCARVED BLOCK.
LP: TPLP 1

Fly (film)

FLY II, THE (1988 film soundtrack) (Various artists).
Tracks: / Fly II, The: *Various artists* / Fly variations: *Various artists* / Spider and the fly, The: *Various* artists / Fly march, The: *Various artists* / Bay 17 mysteries: *Various artists* / What's the magic word: *Various* artists / Come fly with me: *Various artists* / Musica domestica metastasis: *Various artists* / More is coming: *Various artists* / Accelerated Brundle disease: *Various artists* / Bartok barbaro: *Various artists* / Dad: *Various artists.*
LP: VS 5220
MC: VSC 5220

FLY, THE (1986 film soundtrack) (Various artists).
Tracks: / Main title: *Various artists* / Last visit, The: *Various artists* / Phone call: *Various artists*/ Ronnie calls back: *Various artists* / Particle magazine: *Various artists* / Ronnie's visit: *Various artists*/ Fingernails, The: *Various artists* / Creature, The: *Various artists* / Maggot, The/Fly graphic: *Various* artists / Ultimate family, The: *Various artists* / Plasma pool: *Various artists* / Stathis entera: *Various* artists / Seth goes through: *Various artists* / Jump, The: *Various artists* / Armwrestle, The: *Various* artists / Stairs, The: *Various artists* / Baboon teleportation: *Various artists* / Steak montage: *Various artists* / Success with baboon: *Various artists* / Finale: *Various artists.*
LP: TER 1120
MC: ZCTER 1120

Flyaway (book)

FLYAWAY (BOOK) (Desmond Bagley) (Barron, Keith (nar)).
MCSET: ZC SWD 361

Flyin' Saxophones

THOSE FLYIN', JUMPIN' AND GRUNTIN' SAXOPHONES Various artists (Various artists).
Tracks: / Blow, Illinois, blow: *Jacquet, Illinois* / Illinois blows the blues: *Jacquet, Illinois* / Still flyin': *Cobb, Arnett* / Cobb's idea: *Cobb, Arnett* / Queen bee blues: *Vinson, Eddie* / Jump and grunt: *Vinson,* Eddie / Old maid boogie: *Vinson, Eddie* / Kidney stew: *Vinson, Eddie* / Lavender coffin: *Thomas, Joe*/ Backstage at the Apollo: *Thomas, Joe* / Every man to his own profession: *Jordan, Louis* / Chicky Mo, Craney Crow: *Jordan, Louis* / Coleslaw: *Jordan, Louis* / My baby says yes: *Crosby, Bing & Louis Jordan* / Your socks don't match: *Crosby, Bing & Louis Jordan.*
LP: QU 058

Flyin' Turkey

IRON PRESCRIPTION.
LP: GS 2310

Flying Burrito

BURRITO DELUXE.
Tracks: / Lazy days / Image of me, The / High fashion queen / If you gotta go, go now / Man in the fog / Farther along / Older guys / Cody, Cody / God's own singer / Down in the churchyard.
LP: ED 194

DIM LIGHTS, THICK SMOKE AND LOUD MUSIC.
Tracks: / Train song / Close up the honky tonks / Sing me back home / Tonight the bottle let me down / Your angel steps out of heaven / Crazy arms / Together again / Honky tonk women / Green green grass of home / Dim lights / Bony Moronie / To love somebody / Break my mind / Dim lights, thick smoke and loud music.
LP: ED 197

FROM ANOTHER TIME.
Tracks: / Diggi diggi li / Wheels / Dim light thick smoke / Faded love / Devil in disguise / Building fires / Non soir blues / White line fever / Sin City / She thinks I still care / Why baby why / Close up the honky tonks.
MC: SDC 072
LP: CDLP 072

GILDED PALACE OF SIN, THE.
Tracks: / Christine's tune / Sin city / Do right woman, do right man / Dark end of the street / My uncle / Wheels / Juanita / Hot burrito no.1 / Hot burrito no.2 / Do you know how it feels / Hippie boy.
LP: ED 191
MC: CED 191

HOLLYWOOD NIGHTS 1979-1981.
Tracks: / She belongs to everyone but me / Somewhere tonight / Baby, how'd we ever get this way / Too much honky tonkin' / My abandoned heart / She's a friend of mine / Louisiana / Why must the ending always be so sad / That's when you know it's over / She's a hell of a deal

/ Another shade of grey / Damned if I'll be lonely tonight / If something should come between us / Run to the night / Coast to coast / Closer to you / True love never runs dry / Tell me it ain't so.
LP: . . . . **SDLP 067**

LAST OF THE RED HOT BURRITOS.
Tracks: / Devil in disguise / Six days on the road / My uncle / Dixie breakdwon / Don't let your deal go down / Orange blossom special / Ain't that a lot of love / High fashion Queen / Don't fight it / Hot burrito no.2 / Losing game.
LP: . . . . **AMLS 64343**

LIVE FROM TOKYO.
Tracks: / Big bayou / White line fever / Dim lights / Thick smoke / There'll be no teardrops tonight / Rollin' in my sweet baby's arms / Hot burrito no.2 / Colorado / Rocky top / Six days on the road / Truck drivin' man.
LP: . . . . **SDLP 025**

SLEEPLESS NIGHTS.
LP: . . . . **AMLH 64578**

Flying Colour

FLYING COLOUR.
LP: . . . . **FLP 1022**

Flying Column

FOUR GREEN FIELDS.
Tracks: / Old maid in a garret / Castle of Dromore, The / Legion of the rearguard / Song of the dawn / Four green fields / Roisin dubh / Sam Hall / Dirty old town / Madame Bonaparte / Johnston's motor car / Boolavogue / Golden jubilee.
LP: . . . . **BER 008**
MC: . . . . **KBER 008**
LP: . . . . **GES 1059**
MC: . . . . **KGEC 1059**

Flying Down To Rio

FLYING DOWN TO RIO (1933 film musical soundtrack) (Various artists).
LP: . . . . **CIF 3004**

FLYING DOWN TO RIO/CAREFREE (Original soundtrack) (Various artists).
LP: . . . . **SH 2010**
MC: . . . . **CSH 2010**

Flying Emus

LOOK OUT BELOW.
LP: . . . . **LRF 166**

Flying Lizards

FLYING LIZARDS.
Tracks: / Summertime blues / Money / TV.
LP: . . . . **V 2150**

FOURTH WALL.
LP: . . . . **V 2190**

TOP TEN.
Tracks: / Tutti frutti / Sex machine / What's new pussycat / Whole lotta shakin' goin' on / Purple haze / Great balls of fire / Dizzy Miss Lizzy / Suzanne / Then he kissed me / Tears.
LP: . . . . **STATLP 20**
MC: . . . . **STATC 20**

Flying Padovanis

THEY CALL ME CRAZY.
Tracks: / Rattleshake / Lies / Three for trouble / Wipe out / They call him crazy / No place to hide / Last bullet / Murder / Bumble bee / Caravan.
LP: . . . . **RAZ 25**

Flying Pickets

BEST OF THE FLYING PICKETS.
Tracks: / Only you / I heard it through the grapevine / Tears of a clown, The / You've lost that lovin' feelin' / Sealed with a kiss / Only the lonely / Space oddity ('Live') / Who's that girl / When you're young and in love / Groovin' / Summertime / Masters of war / I got you babe ('Live') / Summer in the city / Higher and higher / Get off my cloud.
MC: . . . . **VVIPC 111**

FLYING PICKETS LIVE AT THE ALBANY EMPIRE.
LP: . . . . **AVMLP 1**
MC: . . . . **ZCAVM 1**

LIVE.
Tracks: / Remember this / When you're young and in love / Last round up in Deptford / Buffalo soldier / Sun ain't gonna shine / Psycho killer / Space oddity / Broken English / So close / Reds under your beds / Only you / Higher and higher / Disco down (Cassette only) / I got you babe (Cassette only) / Wide boy (Cassette only).
LP: . . . . **DIX 19**
MC: . . . . **CDIX 19**
LP: . . . . **XID 3**
MC: . . . . **CXID 3**

LOST BOYS.
Tracks: / Remember this / I heard it through the grapevine / Disco down / So close / Tears of a clown / When you're young and in love / You've lost that lovin' feeling / Psycho killer / Wide boy / Factory / Monica engineer / Only you / Masters of war / Who's that girl.
LP: . . . . **DIX 4**
MC: . . . . **CDIX 4**

Flying Saucers

AT THE PICKETTS LOCK.
Tracks: / R.O.C.K. / You're my sunshine / Apron strings / Good golly Miss Molly / I'm goin' home / Miss Froggie / Rock and roll boogie / Flea brain / Hey bop a rebop / Washing machine boogie.
LP: . . . . **CFM 104**

FLYING TONIGHT.
Tracks: / Bop a Lena / Honey bush / Unchained melody / Bring my baby back / Baby's leaving town / Loverboy / Baby blue / Rock with me baby / Wedding of love / Let's rock / She's gonna break your heart / So long / I lost my heart / Rockin' & rollin' on a Saturday night.
LP: . . . . **EMC 3401**

KEEP ON COMIN'.
LP: . . . . **CR 30207**

MINI LP COLLECTION.
LP: . . . . **MLP 8417**

PLANET OF THE DRAPES.
LP: . . . . **NEVLP 114**
LP: . . . . **LP 8703**

SOME LIKE IT HOT.
Tracks: / Some like it hot / Head on down / Bye bye baby / Dream is just a dream / Rockabilly love affair / Lonely willow / Just my size / All by myself / Up above our heads / Hold me, hug me, rock me / You took my heart away / Love me like you did last night / Baby don't make me mad / Old black Joe.
LP: . . . . **EMC 3366**

Flying Saucers (2)

FLYING SAUCERS ROCK'N'ROLL (Various artists).
LP: . . . . **CFM 503**

Flynn, Errol

ERROL FLYNN ALBUM, THE.
Tracks: / They died with their boots on / Gentleman Jim (Radio versions).
LP: . . . . **CT 7003**

Flynn, Noel

MEMORIES OF IRELAND.
MC: . . . . **GTDC 015**

Flys

FLYS BUZZ BACK.
LP: . . . . **SEE 304**

OWN.
Tracks: / Let's drive / Energy boy / Fascinate me / Talking to the wall / 16 down / Fortunes / Night creatures / When 2 & 5 make 9 / Undercover agent zero / Cheap days / Walking the streets / Through the windscreen / Freezing / Frenzy is 23.
LP: . . . . **EMC 3316**

FM

CITY OF FEAR.
Tracks: / Krakow / Power / Truth of consequences / Lost and found / City of fear / Surface to air / Up to you / Silence / Riding the thunder / Nobody at all.
LP: . . . . **LOGO 1031**

INDISCREET.
Tracks: / That girl / Other side of midnight, The / Love lies dying / I belong to the night / American girls / Hot wired / Face to face / Frozen heart / Heart of the matter.
LP: . . . . **PRT 26827**
MC: **40 26827**
LP: **4663391**
MC: **4663394**

TOUGH IT OUT.
Tracks: / Tough it out / Bad luck / Everytime I think of you burning my ... / Obsession / Don't stop / Someday / Dream that died, The.
LP: **4655891**
MC: **4655894**

FM (Film)

FM (1978 film soundtrack) (Various artists).
Tracks: / Life in the fast lane: *Eagles* / Do it again: *Steely Dan* / Lido shuffle: *Scaggs, Boz* / It keeps you runnin': *Doobie Brothers* / Your smiling face: *Taylor, James* / Life's been good: *Walsh, Joe*/ We will rock you: *Queen* / FM (reprise): *Steely Dan* / Night moves: *Seger, Bob* / Fly like an eagle: *Miller, Steve* / Cold as ice: *Foreigner* / Breakdown: *Petty, Tom* / Bad man: *Meisner, Randy*/ Tumbling dice: *Ronstadt, Linda* / Poor poor pitiful me: *Ronstadt, Linda* / Livingston Saturday: *Buffett, Jimmy* / There's a place: *Fogelberg, Dan* / Way you are, The: *Joel, Billy*.
2LP: . . . . **MCLD 621**
MCSET: . . . . **MCLDC 621**
2LP: . . . . **MCSP 284**

FN Guns

GOOD SHOT.
Tracks: / Don't cross the line / She goes on / SOS for love / Hero, The / I am the walrus / All the night / Until I do / Can't see it no way / Teenage rampage.
LP: . . . . **RUMLP 003**

NIGHTMARE.
LP: . . . . **SKULL 8355**

Fochabers Fiddlers

FOCHABERS FIDDLERS, VOLUME II.
Tracks: / Mrs. H.L.MacDonald of Dunach / Skyeman's jig, The / Auld noost, The / MacLeod of Mull / Earl Grey / Da saandie burn reel / Fear a' bhata / Lilydale / Father John MacMillan of Barra / Crossing the minch / Helen Black of Inveran / Four poster bed, The / Drummond Castle / Lamb skinnet / Stool of repentance, The / Athole highlanders, The / Coleburn, The / Paddy's leather breeches / Ale is dear, The / High road to Linton / Willie's gane tae Melville Castle / Chapel Keithack.
MC: . . . . **CWGR 128**

FOCHERBERS FIDDLERS.
MC: . . . . **CWGR 118**

Focus

FOCUS.
Tracks: / Russian roulette / King kong / Le tango / Indian Summer / Beethoven's revenge / Ole Judy / Who's calling.
LP: **824 524 1**

FOCUS 2.
LP: **5C 038 24385**

FOCUS 3.
Tracks: / Round goes the gossip / Love remembered / Sylvia / Carnival fugue / Focus III / Answers? Questions. Answers? Questions / Anonymus II / Elspeth of Nottingham / House of the king.
2LP: **2383 016**
2LP: **2659 016**

FOCUS AT THE RAINBOW.
LP: **5C 038 24939**
LP: **2442 118**

FOCUS ON FOCUS.
LP: **5C 050 26233**

GREATEST HITS: FOCUS (Moving Waves).
Tracks: / Focus / Moving waves / Focus II / Tommy / Hocus pocus / House of the King / Sylvia / Janis.
LP: . . . . **FA 41 3112 1**
MC: . . . . **FA 41 3112 4**

HAMBURGER CONCERTO.
2LP: **1A 128 25693/4**
2LP: **2442 124**

HOUSE OF THE KING.
LP: **5C 034 25130**

MOVING WAVES.
Tracks: / Hocus pocus / Le clochard (bread) / Janis / Moving waves / Focus II / Eruption.
LP: **2931 002**

MOVING WAVES (COMPILATION).
2LP: **5C 180 52636/37**

Focus On Fusion

FOCUS ON FUSION (Various artists).
Tracks: / Brazilian skies: *Summers, Bill* / African bird: *Opa* / Roll with the punches: *Rushen, Patrice*/ 2 for 1: *Pleasure* / Los conquestadores chocolates / Moondreams: *Purim, Flora* / Rio: *Glenn, Roger*/ Novo ano: *Lawrence, Azar*.
LP: . . . . **BGP 1004**
MC: . . . . **BGPC 1004**

FOCUS ON FUSION VOL.2 (Various artists).
Tracks: / Love Samba: *McCoy Tyner Quartets* / Festival: *De Souza, Raul* / Visions: *Gasca, Luis* / Friday night funk for Saturday night brothers: *Bryant, Rusty* / Up the street, round the corner...: *Burrell, Kenny* / Montevideo: *Opa*.
LP: . . . . **BGP 1009**

Focus (Various)

FOCUS (Various artists).
Tracks: / Overture on a spiritual: *Various artists* / Divertissment: *Various artists* / Musikk for saxofon og accordeon: *Various artists* / Ayres Danzas: *Various artists* / Air for two: *Various artists* / Modal music: *Various artists* / Symphonietta voor acc orkest: *Various artists*.
LP: . . . . **KS 20 7055**

Foden Motor Works Band

FODEN MOTOR WORKS BAND.
Tracks: / Knight on the road / New world fantasy / Skye boat song / Vilanelle / Finale / Girl with the flaxen hair, The / Music / Paris le soir / Famous British marches.
LP: . . . . **GRS 1087**

FODEN MOTOR WORKS BAND NO.2.
Tracks: / Intrada and scherzo (rhapsodic symphony) / Shylock / Eugene Onegin / Pride of youth / Oberon / Threnody / Jenny Jones / Sylvia.
LP: . . . . **SB 341**

WORLD OF BRASS BANDS.
MC: . . . . **KCSP 20**
LP: . . . . **SPA 20**

Foden O.T.S. Band

ENGLISH HERITAGE SERIES-ELGAR: VOL.3.
Tracks: / Four pieces from 'Wand of youth' / Salut d'amour / Serenade opus 20 / Pomp and circumstance march nos.1-5.
LP: . . . . **EHS 003D**
MC: . . . . **CEHS 003D**

Foehner, Gale

RHYMES IN RAGTIME.
LP: . . . . **SOS 1023**

Foetus

NAIL (Scraping Foetus Off The Wheel).
LP: . . . . **WOMB FIP 4**
MC: . . . . **WOMB CFIP4**

SINK.
LP: **WOMBINC6**
MC: **WOMBINC6C**

THAW (Foetus Interuptus).
LP: . . . . **WOMBFIP 5**
MC: . . . . **WOMBFIP 5C**

Fog

FOG, THE (1979 film soundtrack) (Various artists).
LP: . . . . **CST 8002**
LP: . . . . **STV 81191**
MC: . . . . **CTV 81191**

Fogelberg, Dan

EXILES.
Tracks: / Exiles / What are you doing / Lonely in love / Seeing you again / She don't look back / Way it must be, The / Hearts in decline / It doesn't matter / Our last farewell.
LP: **4504911**
MC: **4504914**

GREATEST HITS: DAN FOGELBERG.
Tracks: / Power of gold, The / Heart hotel / Hard to say / Missing you / Longer / Missing you / Make love stay / Leader of the band / Run for the roses / Same old lang syne.
LP: . . . . **EPC 32653**
MC: **40 32653**

HIGH COUNTRY SNOWS.
Tracks: / Down the road / Mountain pass / Sutter's mill / Wolf creek / High country snows / Outlaw / Shallow rivers / Go down easy / Think of what you've done / Wandering sheperd / Higher you climb, The.
LP: . . . . **EPC 26274**

HOME FREE.
Tracks: / To the morning / Stars / More than ever / Be on your way / Hickory groove / Long way home / Anyway I love you / Wysteria / River / Looking for a lady.
LP: . . . . **EPC 31847**

PHOENIX.
Tracks: / Tullamore dew / Phoenix / Gypsy wind / Last to know, The / Face the fire / Wishing on the moon / Heart hotel / Longer / Beggar's game / Along the road.
LP: . . . . **EPC 83317**
MC: **40 83317**

WILD PLACES, THE.
Tracks: / Aurora nova / Wild places, The / Forefathers / Song of the sea / Anastasia's eyes / Blind to the truth / Lovers in a dangerous time / Rhythm of the rain / Rain / Bones in the sky / Spirit trail, The / Ever on.
LP: **4670061**
MC: **4670064**

WINDOWS AND WALLS.
Tracks: / Language of love / Windows and walls / Loving cup / Tucson, Arizona / Let her go / Sweet magnolia / Believe in me / Gone too far.
LP: . . . . **EPC 25773**

Fogerty, John

BLUE RIDGE RANGERS.
LP: **1061150**

CENTERFIELD.
Tracks: / Old man down the road, The / Rock and roll girls / Big train / I saw it on T.V. / Mr. Greed / Searchlight / Centerfield / I can't help myself / Zanz kant danz.
LP: **925203 1**
MC: **925203 2**

EYE OF THE ZOMBIE.
Tracks: / Eye of the zombie / Goin' back home / Headlines / Knockin' on your door / Change in the weather / Wasn't that a woman / Violence is golden / Soda pop / Sail away.

LP: 925449 1
MC: 925449 4

JOHN FOGERTY.
Tracks: / Rockin' all over the world / You rascal you / Wall, The / Travellin' high / Lonely teardrops / Almost Saturday night / Where the river flows / Sea cruise / Dream song / Flying away / Comin' down the road / Ricochet.
LP: . . . . FACE 507
MC: . . . . FACC 507

Foggy

IT'S FOGGY AGAIN.
Tracks: / One more time / Ballad of Tracy and Margaret, The / Song to Lawrence Stephen / Oh what a shame / Airport story / One for the money / Wortley's song / Me and Bobby McGhee / Sail on your memories / End of the line / Give my regards to Dublin / Old days.
LP: . . . . LKLP 6385

Foggy Dew

FOGGY DEW (Suffolk and Essex folksingers) (Various artists).
Tracks: / Foggy dew, The: *Various artists* / Cunning cobbler, the: *Various artists* / Georgie: *Various artists*/ Barbara Allen: *Various artists* / Wild rover: *Various artists* / Blow the candle out: *Various artists*/ Oak and the ash, The: *Various artists* / Larks they sang so melodious, The: *Various artists* / Sylvia: *Various* artists / Young British water man: *Various artists* / Mary across the wild moor: *Various artists* / Dog and gun: *Various artists* / Butcher and cobbler: *Various artists* / Down in Cimred garden: *Various artists*/ Nobleman's lady: *Various artists* / Sweet William: *Various artists* / Tree in the wood, The: *Various artists*/ Foggy dew (second version): *Various artists.*
MC: 60-040

Foghat

BEST OF FOGHAT, THE.
LP: . . . . NEDLP 141
MC: . . . . NEDMC 141

ENERGIZED.
Tracks: / Honey, hush / Step outside / Golden arrow / Home in my hand / Wild cherry / That'll be the day / Fly by night / Nothin' I won't do.
LP: . . . . K 55500

FOGHAT.
Tracks: / I just want to make love to you / Trouble trouble / Leavin' again / Fools hall of fame / Sarah Lee / Highway (killing me) / Mabellene / Hole to hide in / Gotta get to know you.
LP: . . . . K 45503

FOGHAT 2.
Tracks: / Ride ride ride / Feel so bad / Long way to go / It's too late / What a shame / Helping hand / Road fever / She's gone / Couldn't make her stay.
LP: . . . . K 45514

FOGHAT (LIVE).
Tracks: / Fool for the city / Home in my hand / I just want to make love to you / Road fever / Honey hush / Slow ride.
LP: . . . . K 55518
LP: . . . . NEXLP 112
MC: . . . . NEXMC 112

FOOL FOR THE CITY.
Tracks: / Fool for the city / My babe / Slow ride / Terraplane blues / Save your loving (for me) / Drive me home / Take it or leave it.
LP: . . . . K 55507

GIRLS TO CHAT AND BOYS TO BOUNCE.
Tracks: / Second childhood / Wide boy / Love zone.
LP: . . . . AALP 3578
MC: . . . . BKR 3578

NIGHTSHIFT.
Tracks: / Drivin' wheel / Don't run me down / Burning the midnight oil / Nightshift / Hot shot love / Take me to the river / I'll be standing by.
LP: . . . . K 55511

ROCK AND ROLL OUTLAWS.
Tracks: / Eight days on the road / Hate to see you go / Dreamer / Trouble in my way / Rock and roll outlaws / Shirley Jean / Blue spruce woman / Chateau lafitte '59 boogie.
LP: . . . . K 55502

TIGHT SHOES.
Tracks: / Stranger in my home town / Loose ends / Full time lover / Baby can I change your mind / Too late the hero / Dead end street / Be my woman / No hard feelings.
LP: . . . . ILPS 9637

Fold

FOLD.
LP: . . . . FN 62

Foley, Connie

16 BEST IRISH BALLADS.
LP: . . . . CSDBL 507

IRISH PUB SING A LONG.
LP: . . . . HRL 112
MC: . . . . CHRL 112

ISLE OF INNISFREE.
LP: . . . . SOLP 1021
MC: . . . . COX 1021

SING AN IRISH REBEL SONG.
LP: . . . . CSDBL 504

SING AN IRISH SONG.
LP: . . . . HRL 184
MC: . . . . CHRL 184

SINGING THROUGH IRELAND.
Tracks: / Isle of Innisfree / Cottage by the Lee.
LP: . . . . HRL 119
MC: . . . . CHRL 119

THREE LEAF SHAMROCK.
MC: . . . . COB 4017

WILD COLONIAL BOY.
Tracks: / That old Irish mother of mine / Home to Mayo.
LP: . . . . SOLP 1018
MC: . . . . COX 1018

Foley, Ellen

ANOTHER BREATH.
Tracks: / Boys in the attic / Johnny and Mary / Another breath / Let me be the one you love / Read by lips / Nightline / Come to me / Run for my life / Come and get these memories / Spy in the house of love.
LP: . . . . EPC 25258
MC: 40 25258

NIGHT OUT.
Tracks: / We belong to the night / What's a matter baby / Stupid girl / Night out / Thunder and rain / Sad song / Young lust / Hideaway / Don't let go.
LP: . . . . EPC 83718

SPIRIT OF ST. LOUIS.
Tracks: / Shuttered palace / Torchlight / Beautiful waste of time / Death of the psychoanalyst of Salvador Dali / M.P.H. / My legionnaire / Theatre of cruelty / How glad I am / Phases of travel / Game of a man / Indestructible / In the killing hour.
LP: . . . . EPC 84809

Foley, George

I LOVE IT.
LP: . . . . SOS 1088

Foley, Red

COMPANY'S COMING.
LP: . . . . HAT 3122

RED AND ERNIE (Foley, Red & Ernest Tubb).
Tracks: / Tennessee border (no.2) / Goodnight Irene / Hillbilly fever (no.2) / Don't be ashamed of your age / It's a mileage that's slowin' us down / Double datin' / No help wanted (No.2) / Too old to cut the mustard / Kentucky waltz / I'm in love with Molly / Strange little girl / You're a real good friend.
LP: . . . . HAT 3000
MC: . . . . HATC 3000

RED FOLEY SHOW, THE.
LP: . . . . HAT 3016
MC: . . . . HATC 3016

RED FOLEY STORY, THE.
Tracks: / Chattanooga shoeshine boy / Blues in my heart / Salty dog rag / Old Shep / Tennessee Saturday night / Hominy grits / Tennessee polka / Hearts of stone / Nobody / Tennessee Border / M-i-s-s-i-s-s-i-p-p-i / Steal away / Old pappy's new banjo / Peace in the valley / Satisfied mind, A / I'll be a sunbeam / My God is real / Beyond the sunset / Should you go first / Take my hand, precious Lord / Just a closer walk with thee / God walks these hills with me / Jesus loves me / He'll understand and say well done.
2LP: IMCA2 4053

TENNESSEE SATURDAY NIGHT.
Tracks: / Tennessee Saturday night / Plantation boogie / Hot dog rag / Hillbilly fever / Freight train boogie / Pinball boogie / Milkbucket boogie / Hoot owl boogie / Hobo boogie / Night train to Memphis / Shake a hand / Hearts of stone / Crawdad song / Rockin' 'n' reeling crazy little guitar man / Sugarfoot rag / Hot rod race / Kentucky fox chase.
LP: . . . . CR 30230

Folk

40 FOLK FAVOURITES (Various artists).
2LP: . . . . PLD 8013

A SOLDIER'S LIFE FOR ME Folk songs of Great Britain vol.8 (Various artists).
Tracks: / List, bonny laddie: *Strachan, John* / Swansea barracks: *Tanner, Phil* / Dying soldier, The: *Doran*, Mary / Willie o' Reilly: *Cinnamond, Robert* / Banks of the Nile: *Richards, Sidney* / Bonnets o'blue: *Matthew*, Jean / Recruiting song, The: *Rew, William* / William Taylor: *Covill, Harold* / Johnny Harte: *Maguire*, Mrs. / Soldier and the sailor, The: *Lenox, Arthur* / Bold General Wolfe: *Scarce, Bob* / Muddley barracks: *Brightwell, Jumbo* / Handsome Polly-o: *Moran, Thomas* / Deadly wars, The: *Robertson, Jeannie* / McCafferty: *Reilly, Peter* / Drink old England dry: *Haxey Carol Singers* / Prince Charlie Stuart: *Bright Tunney* / My son Tim: *Walsh, Timothy* / Napoleon Bonaparte: *Cinnamond, Robert* / Bonnie bunch of roses, The: *Holmes, Louise* / Napoleon's dream: *Larner, Sam* / Forfar soldier, The: *McBeath, Jimmy.*
LP: 12T 196

ALL ROUND MY HAT (Songs of False Love and True) (Various artists).
Tracks: / All round my hat: *Various artists* / Blacksmith courted me, A: *Various artists* / Bonnie labouring boy, The: *Various artists* / Cuckoo, The: *Various artists* / Deep in love: *Various artists* / Deluded lover: *Various artists* / Blackwater side: *Various artists* / False bride, The: *Various artists* / False young man, The: *Various artists* / Forsaken mother and child: *Various artists* / Going to mass last Sunday: *Various* artists / Green bushes: *Various artists* / Green grass it grows bonny: *Various artists* / Health to all true lovers: *Various artists* / Sheffield park: *Various artists* / Iron door: *Various artists* / Locks and bolts: *Various artists* / Darling ploughman boy: *Various artists* / Nobleman's wedding: *Various artists*/ Our wedding day: *Various artists* / Seeds of love: *Various artists* / Yon green valley: *Various artists.*
MC: 60-015

ALL THE FOLK THAT FITS (Various artists).
2LP: 2668 026
MCSET: 3571 016

ALL TOGETHER LIKE THE FOAKS O'SHIELDS (Various artists).
LP: . . . . GVR 222

AMERICAN AUTHENTIC SQUARE DANCES (Various artists).
LP: . . . . MS 15

ANOTHER FEAST OF IRISH FOLK (Various artists).
Tracks: / Rare ould times: *Doyle, Danny* / Do you want yer oul lobby washed down: *Crowley, Jimmy & Stokers Lodge*/ Glenbeigh hornpipe: *Various artists* / Mountain lark: *Various artists* / Musical priest, The: *Various artists*/ Tipping it up to Nancy: *Moore, D* / Kid on the mountain, The: *Various artists* / An phis fhliuch (slip jigs): *Planxty* / Boys of Killybegs: *Makem, Tommy* / Thios chios na tra domh: *Clannad* / Lannigan's ball: *Bards*/ Snowy breasted pearl, The: *Wolfetones* / Green fields of France: *Fureys* / Boys of Fairhill: *Crowley, Jimmy*/ Seven drunken nights: *Dubliners* / Pretty Peg: *Various artists* / Craig's pipes: *Bothy Band* / Shipward slips: *Fureys* / Johnny Cope: *Planxty* / Weila weila waile: *Dubliners.*
LP: 290 401 6
MC: 316 311 6

ANTHOLOGY OF SWEDISH FIDDLE MUSIC (Various artists).
LP: . . . . SNTD 201

AS I ROVED OUT (Songs of Courtship) (Various artists).
Tracks: / As I roved out: *Various artists* / Blackberry grove: *Various artists* / Bonnie wee window: *Various* artists / Ca' the yowes: *Various artists* / Colin and Phoebe: *Various artists* / Come write me down: *Various* artists / Country courtship: *Various artists* / Easter snow: *Various artists* / Greasy cook: *Various* artists / Greenwood laddie: *Various artists* / Harry the tailor: *Various artists* / Lion's den: *Various* artists / Long and wishing eye: *Various artists* / Madam will you walk: *Various artists* / Mountain streams: *Various artists* / Next Monday morning: *Various artists* / No sir: *Various artists* / Old grey beard: *Various artists* / Ploughboy, The: *Various artists* / Queen among the heather: *Various artists* / Spotted cow: *Various artists* / When a man's in love: *Various artists* / Young Roger esq.: *Various artists.*
MC: 60-013

AUSTRIA FOLKLORE (Various artists).
MC: 299426

BBC'S FOLK ON 2 PRESENTS NORTHUMBRIAN FOLK (Various artists).
Tracks: / Northwalbottle rapper sword dance, The: *Monkseaton morris men* / Morpeth rant: *Oselton, Dennis & Archie* Bertram / Border shepherd, A: *Bertram, Archie* / College valley hunt, The: *Davenport, Bob/Marsden Rattlers*/ Bobby Shaftoe: *Washington greys* / Cushie butterfield: *Washington greys* / Lambton worm, The: *Marsden rattlers*/ Chevy Chase: *Ross, Colin* / Blow the wind southerly: *Norman, Anne* / Sea lore: *Davenport, Bob* / Story of Grace Darling, The: *White, Kate (Mrs.)* / My bonnie lad: *Davenport, Bob* / Keel row, The: *Norman, Anne*/ Keel row, The: *Adamson, Edith carillon* / Hadrian's wall: *Dobson, Scott* / Keep your feet still Geordie Hinny: *Davenport, Bob/ Marsden Rattlers* / Durham miners gala, The: *Elliot, John* / In the bar room: *Elliots of Birtley*/ Water o' Tyne, The: *Norman, Anne* / Wor nanny's a mazer: *Marsden rattlers* / Dan Leno's hornpipe: *Ellwood, Johnson* / Blaydon races: *Davenport, Bob/Marsden Rattlers.*
LP: . . . . REC 118

BEST OF BRITISH ENCHANTED EVENINGS (Various artists).
Tracks: / Girls girls girls: *Various artists* / Mandy: *Various artists* / Silver lady: *Various artists*/ Gondoliers: *Various artists* / Love is in the air: *Various artists* / I knew the bride: *Various artists*/ Nice and slow: *Various artists* / Feel the need in me: *Various artists* / Who's gonna love me: *Various artists*/ Bullshipper, The: *Various artists* / Stone in love with you: *Various artists* / Some enchanted evening: *Various artists* / Tonights the night: *Best of British....*
LP: . . . . SFA 110

BEST OF BRITISH FOLK (Various artists).
Tracks: / Streets of London: *McTell, Ralph* / Net hauling song: *Campbell, Ian Folk Group* / Drag queen blues: *Digance, Richard* / Rosemary Lane: *Jansch, Bert* / Market song: *Pentangle* / Shoeshine boy: *Humblebums*/ Travel away: *Humblebums* / Up to now: *Dransfields* / Dear River Thames: *Digance, Richard* / Lover for all seasons, A: *Oldfield, Sally & Mike* / You ought to know: *Johnstons* / If it wasnae for your wellies: *Connolly*, Billy / Skye boat song: *McCalmans* / Noah and the rabbit: *Renbourn, John & Bert Jansch* / Sir Gavin Grimbold: *Gryphon* / Cod liver oil and orange juice: *Imlach, Hamish* / Ive's horizon: *Giltrap, Gordon* / Marie's Wedding (musical appreciation): *Connolly, Billy* / Gingerbread man: *Story Teller* / Byker Hill: *Swarbrick, Dave*/ Martin Carthy / Ungodly, The: *Decameron (bk)* / Hermit, The: *Renbourn, John* / Mary Skeffington: *Rafferty, Gerry* / Spiral staircase: *McTell, Ralph* / Light flight: *Pentangle.*
2LP: . . . . CR 052
MCSET: . . . . CRT 052

BEST OF BRITISH FOLK (See under British Folk) (Various artists).

BEST OF BRITISH FOLK (CASTLE) (Various artists).
Tracks: / Light flight: *Pentangle* / Travel away: *Humblebums* / My friend up the road: *Digance, Richard*/ Byker Hill: *Swarbrick, Dave/Martin Carthy* / Spiral staircase: *McTell, Ralph* / Continental trailways bus: *Johnstons*/ Streets of London: *McTell, Ralph* / Mary Skeffington: *Rafferty, Gerry* / Rosemary Lane: *Jansch, Bert*/ White house blues: *Renbourn, John* / If it wasnae for your wellies: *Connolly, Billy* / Up to now: *Dransfields*/ Join us in our game: *Mr. Fox* / Easy street: *James, John/Pete Berryman* / All in a dream: *Tilston, Steve*/ Sir Gavin Grimbold: *Gryphon* / Ungodly, The: *Decameron (bk)* / Gingerbread man: *Story Teller* / Lover for all seasons, A: *Sallyangie* / Boxing match, The: *Black Country Three* / Mouse and crow: *Pegg, Caroline*/ Dear River Thames: *Digance, Richard* / After the dance: *Jansch, Bert/ John Renbourn* / Maid that's deep in love: *Pentangle.*
2LP: . . . . CCSLP 222
MC: . . . . CCSMC 222

BEST OF BRITISH FOLK VOL. 2 (Various artists).
2LP: . . . . CR 5164
MCSET: . . . . CRT 5164

BEST OF ENGLISH FOLK (Various artists).
MC: . . . . ASK 766

BEST OF ENGLISH FOLK MUSIC (Various artists).
LP: . . . . SAM 001
MC: . . . . KSAM 001

BEST OF SCOTTISH FOLK (Various artists).
MC: . . . . ASK 765

BEST OF WELSH FOLK (Various artists).
LP: . . . . 1278 H

BEST OF:CARLISLE'S FOLK WORKSHOP (Various artists).
LP: . . . . FE 002

BETTER CLASS OF FOLK (Various artists).
Tracks: / Ensemble: *Various artists* / If you want to see the General: *Davidson, Billy* / Shores of Sutherland: *Whellans, Mike* / Wars o' Germany, The: *Barty, Allan* / Aunque me des: *MacKintosh, Iain* / Glasgow that I used to know, The: *Behan, Dominic* / Liverpool Lou: *Davidson, Billy* / Scottish Sabbath, The: *Whellans, Mike* / Ballad of San Stone: *Barty, Allan* / Sunshine hornpipe: *MacKintosh, Iain* / Humours of Glendart: *MacKintosh,* Iain / Ballad of Joe Hill: *Behan, Dominic* / Spanish lady: *Various artists* / Good ship Reuben James, The: *Various artists.*
LP: . . . . **LILP 5022**

BITTER WITHY SAMPLER (Various artists).
LP: . . . . **NEVLP 005**

BLACK VELVET BAND (Songs of news and sensation) (Various artists).
Tracks: / Black velvet band: *Various artists* / Blackberry fold: *Various artists* / Brennan on the moor: *Various* artists / Derry gaol: *Various artists* / Donnelly and Cooper: *Various artists* / Epsom races: *Various* artists / Erin go bragh: *Various artists* / Folkestone murder, The: *Various artists* / Heenan and Sayers: *Various artists* / Jack Hall: *Various artists* / Lakes of Shillin: *Various artists* / Morrissey and the Russian sailor: *Various artists* / Newlyn town: *Various artists* / Oxford girl: *Various artists* / Parcel in an apron: *Various artists* / Poison in a glass of wine: *Various artists* / Polly Vaughan: *Various artists*/ Spencer the rover: *Various artists* / Standing stones ballad: *Various artists* / Sweet Fanny Adams: *Various artists* / Sylvia or female highwayman: *Various artists* / Three jolly sportsmen: *Various artists.*
MC: **60-029**

BLACKBIRDS AND THRUSHES (Songs of seduction) (Various artists).
Tracks: / Blackbirds and thrushes: *Various artists* / Blow the candle out: *Various artists* / Bold English navvy, The: *Various artists* / Coachman's whip: *Various artists* / Firelock style: *Various artists* / Foggy dew, The: *Various artists* / Game of cards, The: *Various artists* / Aylesbury girl, The: *Various artists* / London tinker: *Various artists* / Knife in the window, The: *Various artists* / Dainty Doonby: *Various artists*/ Ball of yarn: *Various artists* / Long peggin' awl: *Various artists* / Magpie's nest, The: *Various artists*/ Maid of Australia: *Various artists* / Nightingales sing: *Various artists* / Nutting girl, The: *Various artists*/ Overgate, The: *Various artists* / Barley straw: *Various artists* / Rolling in the dew: *Various artists*/ She was a rum one: *Various artists* / Three maidens a milking did go: *Various artists* / Up to the rigs of London town: *Various artists* / New mown hay: *Various artists.*
MC: **60-017**

BROADSIDE - SONGS OF THE NORFOLK BROADS (Various artists).
MC: . . . . **TC 0016**

BRONGL - EIN ROYND (Various artists).
LP: . . . . **HJF 8**

BUTTER'D PLEASE (Yorkshire country dances. Fiddle, accordion etc.) (Various artists).
MC: **60-211**

CAN YOU POOKER ROMANY? (Various artists).
MC: **60-441**

CAPE BRETON SYMPHONY FIDDLE VOL 1 (Various artists).
Tracks: / An t each ruadh: *North Shore Singers* / Coilsfield house: *MacInnis* / Hi hin thog lad amach: *MacLean*/ Glencoe march: *Various artists* / Sandpoint, The: *Various artists* / No name: *Various artists* / Mo nighean donn as boidhche: *Various artists* / Captain Campbell: *Various artists* / Marnoch strathspey: *Various* artists / Mrs. General Campbell: *Various artists* / Allt a'ghobhainn: *Various artists* / Sandy McIntyre's trip to Boston: *Various artists* / Sir Reginald MacDonald: *Various artists* / Dan J Campbell's reel: *Various* artists / Port a beul: *Various artists* / Maili dhonn, bhoidheach dhonn: *Various artists* / Mo ghaol air aird a chuan, The: *Various artists* / Sir Thomas Sinclair Ray: *Various artists* / Highlander's farewell: *Various* artists / Miss Lyle's strathspey: *Various artists* / Miss Lyl'es reel: *Various artists* / Sandy is my darling: *Various artists* / Bonnie Annie: *Various artists* / O a hu a nighean dubh, nighan donn: *Various artists*/ Paddy's resource: *Various artists* / Flowers of Edinburgh: *Various artists* / Na h igheagan donna, boidheach: *Various artists* / Ma bhuannaich thus nighean ghrinn: *Various artists.*
LP: **12TS 353**
LP: . . . . **WGR 031**
MC: . . . . **CWGR 031**

CHANNEL ISLANDS FOLK MUSIC 1 (Guernsey & Sark) (Various artists).
MC: **60-213**

CHANNEL ISLANDS FOLK MUSIC 2 (Various artists).
MC: **60-214**

CHERISH THE LADIES (Various artists).
Tracks: / Callan lassies: *Various artists* / Flowing bowl: *Various artists* / Donegal jig: *Various artists*/ Cherish the ladies: *Various artists* / Scully Casey's: *Various artists* / O'Bryne's: *Various artists*/ Boys of the 25: *Various artists* / Farrel O'Gerbhaigh: *Various artists* / Dark slender boy: *Various artists*/ Bonnie Prince Charlie: *Various artists* / Dairy maid: *Various artists* / Heathery breeze: *Various artists*/ Dublin reel: *Various artists* / Trip to Athlone: *Various artists* / Gold ring, The: *Various artists*/ Murphy's: *Various artists* / O'Rourke's: *Various artists* / Pinch of snuff: *Various artists* / Hewlett: *Various artists* / Sonny Mazurka: *Various artists* / Churn of buttermilk: *Various artists* / O'Kennedy's: *Various artists* / Tom Ward's down fall: *Various artists.*
LP: . . . . **SOLP 1043**

CHILD BALLADS 1, THE (Folk songs of Great Britain vol.4) (Various artists).
Tracks: / Elfin knight, The: *Copper, Bob & Ron* / False knight on the road: *Quinn, Frank* / Lady Isabel and the elf knight: *Jordan, Fred* / Twa sisters, The: *Strachan, John* / Lord Randal: *Various artists* / Edward: *Various artists* / King Orfeo: *Stickle, John* / Cruel mother: *Moran, Thomas* / Broomfield wager: *Poacher,* Cyril / Captain Wedderburn's courtship: *Ennis, Seamus* / Twa brothers, The: *Stewart, Lucy* / Lord Bateman: *Moran, Thomas/Jeannie Robertson* / Lord Thomas and fair Ellen: *Murray, Jessie* / Lord Lovel: *Findlater, Mrs.* Ethel / Lord Gregory: *Cronin, Elizabeth* / Barbara Allen: *Various artists* / George Collins: *White, Enos*/ Cruel Lincoln: *Butcher, Ben* / Prickly bush, The: *Scaddon, Julia.*
LP: **12T 160**

CHILD BALLADS 2, THE (Folk songs of Great Britain vol.5) (Various artists).
Tracks: / Royal forester: *Strachan, John* / Baffled knight, The: *Bishop, Emily* / Johnnie Cock: *Strachan,* John / Robin Hood and Little John: *Strachan, John* / Jew's garden, The: *Costello, Cecilia* / Battle of Harlaw, The: *Stewart, Lucy* / Four Maries, The: *Robertson, Jeannie* / Gypsy laddie, The: *Various artists* / Georgie: *Cox, Harry* / Dowie dens of Yarrow, The: *Stewart, Davie* / Grey cock, The: *Costello, Cecilia* / Henry Martin: *Tanner, Phil* / Lang Johnnie More: *Strachan, John* / Willie's fate: *Robertson, Jeannie* / Our goodman: *Various artists* / Farmer's cursed wife, The: *Moran, Thomas* / Jolly beggar, The: *Robertson, Jeannie*/ Auld beggar man, The: *Chambers, Maggie & Sarah* / Keach in the creel, The: *Gallagher, Michael* / Golden vanity: *Cameron, Bill* / Trooper lad, The: *McBeath, Jimmy.*
LP: **12T 161**

COMBOLAND (Various artists).
LP: . . . . **SPIN 209**

COME ALL YOU COAL MINERS (Various artists).
MC: **60-511**
LP: . . . . **ROUNDER 4005**

CONTEMPORARY FOLK GUITAR (Various artists).
Tracks: / Willoughby's farm: *Various artists* / Gardener, The: *Jansch, Bert* / Fast approaching: *Giltrap,* Gordon / McGee's rag: *Pearse, John* / Death of Clayton Peacock, The: *Pearse, John* / Day at the seaside: *Renbourn,* John / Goodbye pork pie hat: *Pentangle* / Guitar train: *Pearse, John* / Stepping stones: *Jansch, Bert/John* Renbourn / Wino and the mouse: *McTell, Ralph* / Tinker's blues: *Jansch, Bert* / I am the resurrection: *Fahey,* John / Judy: *Renbourn, John* / Rizrak laru: *McTell, Ralph* / Ive's horizon: *Giltrap, Gordon* / Angie: *Various artists* / Tonia's waltz: *Various artists* / McGee's rag: *Various artists* / Hair across the Frets: *Various artists* / Vestapol: *Various artists* / Judy: *Various artists* / Trout joins the cavalry: *Various* artists / Marigold chrome: *Various artists* / Red's favourite: *Various artists* / Georgeman's junction: *Various* artists / Guitar train: *Various artists* / Rock salmon suite: *Various artists* / Wormwood tangle: *Various artists* / Miss Heather Rosemary Sewell: *Various artists* / Lucifers cage: *Various artists* / Black scrag: *Various artists* / Tinker's blues: *Various artists* / Nefarious doings: *Various artists* / Bach goes to town: *Various artists* / Pavana Anna Bannana: *Various artists* / Fast approaching: *Various artists* / And the dog was sleeping in the corner: *Various artists* / Sweet gypsy rose: *Various artists* / No exit: *Various artists.*
2LP: . . . . **CR 055**
MCSET: . . . . **CRT 055**

COUNTRY DANCES (Various artists).
LP: . . . . **UD 301447**

COUNTRY SPEECH, SONGS AND DANCES (Various artists).
MC: **45 410**

CREAM OF THE CROP (Various artists).
LP: . . . . **RL 332**

CUT AND DRY DOLLY (Collection of Northumbrian pipe tunes) (Various artists).
Tracks: / Sunderland lasses: *Various artists* / Lads of Alnwick, The: *Various artists* / All the night I lay with jockey: *Various artists* / Peacock followed the hen, The: *Various artists* / Jack Layton: *Various artists*/ Green breckons: *Various artists* / Bob and Jones: *Various artists* / Kiss her under the coverlet: *Various* artists / Cuckold came out of the amrey: *Various artists* / Cuddly claw'd her: *Various artists* / Holme's fancy: *Various artists* / Stagshaw bank fair: *Various artists* / Lasses pass the brandy: *Various artists*/ Cut and dry Dolly: *Various artists* / John Fenwick's the flower among them: *Various artists* / Over the border: *Various artists* / Pheasant's dance: *Various artists* / Rusty gully: *Various artists* / Keelman over the land: *Various artists* / I saw my love come passing by me: *Various artists* / My laddie sits o'er late up: *Various artists* / Shew's the way to Wallington: *Various artists* / Drops of brandy: *Various artists.*
LP: **12TS 278**

DEVON TRADITION (Various artists).
Tracks: / Exmoor ram, The: *Various artists* / Molecatcher, The: *Various artists* / When I was a young man: *Various* artists / Tuning: *Various artists* / Barbara Allen: *Various artists* / Head a nodding: *Various artists*/ Thrashing machine, The: *Various artists* / Sweet Willie: *Various artists* / Navvy boots: *Various artists*/ Leg o' the Mallard, The: *Various artists* / Royal comrade: *Various artists* / Three men went a hunting: *Various* artists / Farmer in Leicester, The: *Various artists* / Seven nights drunk: *Various artists* / Remington greatmeat pie, The: *Various artists* / Up the green meadows: *Various artists* / Rattling Irish boy: *Various artists*/ Mortal unlucky old chap: *Various artists.*
LP: **12TS 349**

DIDDLE DADDLE (Mouth music of Britain) (Various artists).
MC: **60-301**

DOG BIG AND DOG LITTLE (Various artists).
LP: . . . . **CC 51**
MC: **4CC 51**

DOWN AT THE OLD SHIP (Saturday night sing-song) (Various artists).
Tracks: / Nutting girl, The: *Various artists* / When Paddy stole the rope: *Various artists* / Blackbird, The: *Various artists* / Dolphin, The: *Various artists* / M-o-n-e-y: *Various artists* / Nancy of Yarmouth: *Various* artists / Newlyn town: *Various artists* / Flash company: *Various artists* / Sailor and his true love, A: *Various* artists / Maggie May: *Various artists* / Broomfield wager: *Various artists* / Maid and the magpie, The: *Various* artists / Poaching song: *Various artists* / Jones's ale: *Various artists* / Bold General Wolfe: *Various artists* / Health to the Barley Mow: *Various artists.*
MC: **60-036**

DOWNSTAIRS AT KENNEDY'S (Aba Daba) (Various artists).
Tracks: / Overture: *Lowe, Simon* / Cast on: *Williams, Bronwen/Jim McManus/Chris Owen* / Behind the headlines: *Williams, Bronwen* / Lord Chancellor's nightmare, The: *McManus, Jim* / Purdah: *Williams, Bronwen & Chris Owen*/ Jim sits it out: *McManus, Jim* / Week's good cause - help the aged: *McManus, Jim & Bronwen Williams* / Vicar, The: *Owen, Chris* / Right hon. member for Barnet and Finchley: *Williams, Bronwen* / Man and a woman, A: *Williams,* Bronwen & Chris Owen / Policeman's lot, A: *McManus, Jim* / Spinning the drum: *McManus, Jim & Chris Owen* / Miss Muffett: *Williams, Bronwen* / Outward bound: *Owen, Chris* / I always thought she loved me: *McManus, Jim*/ Coronation Road: *Williams, Bronwen/Jim McManus/Chris Owen* / Cast off: *Williams, Bronwen/Jim McManus/Chris Owen.*
MC: . . . . **TT 007**

DRONES AND THE CHANTERS, THE (Various artists).
LP: . . . . **CC 11**
MC: **4CC 11**

DRUMMERS FANFARE (Various artists).
Tracks: / Drum fanfare: *Shotts & Dykehead Caledonia Pipe Band* / Selection: *Cook, Arthur* / March strathspey and reel: *Kilpatrick, Jim* / Selection: *Ward, Eric* / Selection: *Kilpatrick, Jim* / March strathspey and reel: *Houlden, Jackie* / March strathspey and reel: *Cook, Arthur* / Selection: *Houlden, Jackie* / March strathspey and reel: *Ward, Eric.*
LP: . . . . **LILP 5174**
MC: . . . . **LICS 5174**

DUNHILL FOLK-ROCK VOL.2 (Various artists).
Tracks: / This is what I was made for: *Iguanas* / Let's live for today: *Grassroots* / You're a lonely girl: *Grassroots*/ Skateboard craze: *Willie & the Wheels* / Strange young girls: *Mamas & Papas* / No salt on her tail: *Mamas* & Papas / This precious time: *McGuire, Barry* / California dreamin': *McGuire, Barry* / Don't you wonder: *M.F.Q.*/ Night time girl: *M.F.Q.* / How many guys: *Black, Terry* / Ashes have turned: *Yester, Jerry* / Penny arcade: *Group, Thomas* / Secret agent man: *Blaine, Hal* / No more running around: *Lamp of Childhood.*
LP: . . . . **WIK 77**

EAR TO THE GROUND (Various artists).
Tracks: / Own Sammy Shuttleworth: *Warcaba, Kay & Phil Wood* / Blue eyed stranger: *Banana Barn Dance Band* / Banbury bill: *Banana Barn Dance Band* / Raynard the fox: *Prince Of Wales Rattlers* / Captain Pouch: *Marson, Stuart*/ Up & down again: *Loake, Andrew* / Farmers anthem: *Prince Of Wales Rattlers* / Over the Lancashire hills: *Marson,* Stuart / Bad eye Bill: *Banana Barn Dance Band* / Close to the wind: *Marson, Stuart* / Licenced saloon, The: *Prince Of Wales Rattlers* / Millers reel, The: *Warcaba, Kay & Phil Wood* / Old french: *Warcaba, Kay & Phil* Wood / Men of worth: *Plews, Bob* / Nagasaki: *Banana Barn Dance Band* / Drowsy Maggie: *Banana Barn Dance Band* / Mason's apron: *Banana Barn Dance Band.*
MC: . . . . **BEC 101**

EARL SOHAM SLOG (Various artists).
LP: **12TS 374**

EARLY SHAKER SPIRITUALS (Various artists).
LP: . . . . **ROUNDER 0078**

ECHO US DE BERGE (Various artists).
MC: **299400**

EDINBURGH FESTIVAL FRINGE 1976 (Various artists).
LP: . . . . **SFA 058**
LP: . . . . **SZLP 2149**

ELLIPSIS (Various artists).
LP: . . . . **FF 339**

ENGLISH CANALS (Various artists).
MC: . . . . **KBRO 118**
LP: . . . . **BRO 118**

ENGLISH COUNTRY MUSIC (Various artists).
Tracks: / Bluebell polka: *Various artists* / Foggy dew, The: *Various artists* / Sailor cut down in his prime, The: *Various artists* / Untitled polka: *Various artists* / Off she goes: *Various artists* / Red wing: *Various artists* / Believe me if all those endearing young charms: *Various artists* / Johnny's so long at the fair: *Various artists* / Wild Colonial boy: *Various artists* / Jenny Lind: *Various artists* / Girl I left behind me, The: *Various artists* / Peggy Wood: *Various artists* / When there isn't a girl about: *Various artists*/ Schottisches: *Various artists* / Washing day: *Various artists* / Old Mrs Huddledee: *Various artists*/ Cat's got the measles, The: *Various artists* / Waltz Vienna, The: *Various artists* / Four hand reel: *Various artists* / Soldiers joy: *Various artists* / Shepherds hey: *Various artists.*
LP: **12T 296**

ENGLISH COUNTRY MUSIC FROM EAST ANGLIA (Various artists).
Tracks: / Woods: *Various artists* / Gay ladies polka: *Various artists* / Old Joe the boat is going over: *Various artists* / Untitled polka: *Various artists* / Step dance tune: *Various artists* / Dulcie belle: *Various* artists / Yarmouth breakdown: *Various artists* / Italian waltz: *Various artists* / Polka: *Various artists*/ Yarmouth hornpipe: *Various artists* / On the green: *Various artists* / Oyster girl, The: *Various artists*/ On parade: *Various artists* /

Waltz for the veleta: *Various artists* / Step dance tune: *Various artists*/ Oh Joe the boat is going over: *Various artists* / Barn dance tune: *Various artists* / Sheringham breakdown: *Various* artists / Nutting girl, The: *Various artists* / Jack's the lad: *Various artists* / Red wing: *Various artists* / Heel and toe polka: *Various artists*.
LP: **12TS 229**

ENGLISH FOLK DANCES (Various artists).
LP: . . . . **CLP 3754**

ENGLISH FOLK DANCES FOR YOUNG PEOPLE (Various artists).
Tracks: / Brighton camp: *Various artists* / Haste to the wedding: *Various artists* / Durham reel: *Various* artists / Ribbon dance: *Various artists* / Sicilian circle: *Various artists* / Lucky seven: *Various artists*/ Goddesses: *Various artists* / Pat-a-cake polka Galopede: *Various artists* / Bonnets so blue: *Various artists*/ We won't go home till morning: *Various artists* / Christchurch bells: *Various artists* / Flowers of Edinburgh: *Various artists* / Butterfly: *Various artists* / Tom Pate: *Various artists* / Thady you gander: *Various artists* / Rose tree, The: *Various artists*.
LP: . . . . **CLP 3753**

ENGLISH FOLK SONGS (A selection from the Penguin book) (Various artists).
Tracks: / When I was young: *Various artists* / Gaol song, The: *Various artists* / Whale catchers: *Various* artists / Young and single sailor: *Various artists* / False bride, The: *Various artists* / Ratcliffe highway: *Various artists* / Grey cock, The: *Various artists* / Basket of eggs: *Various artists* / One night as I lay on my bed: *Various artists* / Banks of Green Willow, The: *Various artists* / All things are quite silent: *Various artists* / Banks of Newfoundland: *Various artists*.
LP: . . . . **FE 047**
MC: . . . . **FE 047C**

ENGLISH GARLAND (Topic sampler no.8) (Various artists).
Tracks: / Robin Hood and the tanner: *Harris, Roy/Notts Alliance & Roger Watson* / Breakdown, The: *High Level Ranters*/ Blanchland races: *High Level Ranters* / Six jolly miners: *Arthur, Dave & Toni* / Snow it melts the soonest, The: *Briggs, Anne* / Fox jumps over the parson's gate, The: *Bellamy, Peter* / Molecatcher, The: *Wrigley, Bernard*/ Thousands or more: *Oak* / Barley and the rye, The: *Bellamy, Peter with Barry Dransfield fiddle* / Cuckoo, The: *Briggs, Anne* / Lark in the morning, The: *Arthur, Dave & Toni with Barry Dransfield Fiddle* / Gee whoa, Dobbin: *Wrigley, Bernard & Wilf Darlington* / Jack the horse courser: *Wrigley, Bernard & Wilf Darlington* / Roving round the County Tyrone: *Webb, Peta* / Bonnie green woods, The: *Harris, Roy & Muckram Wakes* / Hexhamshire lass, The: *Gelfellon, Tom & The High Level Ranters* / Scan's polkas: *Oak*.
LP: **12TS 221**

ENGLISH MELODEON PLAYERS (Various artists).
LP: . . . . **PLR 073**
MC: . . . . **PLC 073**

ENGLISH REBEL SONGS (Various artists).
LP: . . . . **MEK 006**

ETERNAL WIND (Various artists).
LP: . . . . **FF 348**

EUROPEAN FOLK SONGS (Various artists).
LP: . . . . **IC 057-99832**

EVENING WITHOUT (Various artists).
LP: . . . . **ORA 006**
MC: . . . . **TORA 006**

FAIR GAME AND FOUL (Folk songs of Great Britain vol.7) (Various artists).
Tracks: / Northamptonshire poacher: *Baldry, Jim* / Jimmy Raeburn: *Murray, Jessie* / Drumhullogan's bottom: *Moran, Thomas* / Sweet Fanny Adams: *Vincent, Vashti* / Sylvia: *Walsh, Timothy* / Young Willie: *McCuskey, Paddy*/ Lakes of Shillin: *Reynolds, Mary* / Brennan on the moor: *Cinnamond, Robert* / Butcher boy: *Robertson, Jeannie*/ Three jolly sportsmen: *Scarce, Bob* / Jack Hall: *Endacott, Jack* / Standing stones, The: *Findlater, John* & Ethel / Polly Vaughan: *Cox, Harry* / Lion's den: *Maguire, Mrs.* / Van Diemans land: *McBeath, Jimmy*/ Blind man he can see, The: *Connors, Mary/Paddy Doran* / Oxford City: *Doran, Mary* / Erin go bragh: *Strachan, John* / Derry Gaol: *Maken, Sarah* / Newlyn Town: *Scarce, Bob*.
LP: **12T 195**

FAMILY REQUESTS (Various artists).
Tracks: / Pal of my cradle days: *Breen, Ann* / Two loves: *Duncan, Hugo* / You're my best friend: *Quinn, Brendan*/ Mother's love's a blessing, A: *Teamwork* / Spinning wheel: *Margo* / Molly darling O: *Bell, Crawford*/ Old rustic bridge: *Breen, Ann* / When you were sweet sixteen: *Woods, Pat* / Sunset years of life, The: *Teamwork*/ Back home again: *Quinn, Brendan* / Catch me if you can: *Duncan, Hugh* / There's a family Bible on the table: *Margo* / When you and I were young, Maggie: *Duncan, Hugo* / Bunch of violets blue: *Breen, Ann*.
LP: . . . . **PHL 465**
MC: . . . . **CPHL 465**

FAR CANADIAN FIELDS Various artists (Various artists).
LP: . . . . **LEE 4057**

FAREWELL NANCY (Various artists).
Tracks: / Wilde goose: *Various artists* / Lovely Nancy: *Campbell, Ian* / Nightingale, (The): *Tawney, Cyril*/ Heave away, my Johnny: *Various artists* / Row, bullies, row: *Various artists* / Fireship, (The): *Tawney, Cyril* / Tom's gone to Hilo: *Various artists* / Ship in distress: *Killen, Louis* / Lowlands low: *Various* artists / One morning in spring: *Tawney, Cyril* / Hilo Johnny Brown: *Various artists* / Poor old horse: *Various* artists / Bold Princess Royal, The: *Killen, Louis* / Billy boy: *Davenport, Bob* / Bold Benjamin, The: *Tawney, Cyril* / Hog eye man, The: *Various artists* / Goodbye, fare thee well: *Various artists*.
LP: **12T 110**

FEAST OF IRISH FOLK (Various artists).
Tracks: / Cliffs of Dooneen: *Planxty* / Wind in the willows: *Bread & Fishes* / Nancy Spain: *Moore, Christy*/ Clare to here: *Furey's/D.Arthur* / Town I loved so well, The: *Coulter, P* / Tebhair dom de lamh: *Wolftones*/ Only our rivers: *Planxty* / Rambling Irishman: *De Danann* / Lonesome boatman, The: *Furey's/ D.Arthur*/ Yarmouth town: *Planxty* / Silver in the stubble: *Dublin City Ramblers* / Fiddlers green: *Wolftones*/ Bunch of thyme: *Moore, Christy* / Shores of Lough Bran, The: *De Danann* / Gentle Annie: *Makem, Tommy*/ Banks of Claudy, The: *Munroe*.
LP: **2475605**
MC: **3236605**

FEED THE FOLK (Various artists).
LP: . . . . **FTF 1**
LP: . . . . **FT 01**
MC: . . . . **FTP 01**

FELLSIDE FOLK FAVOURITES (Various artists).
Tracks: / Peace egging: *Various artists* / Banks of red roses, The: *Various artists* / Demon lover: *Various* artists / Sailor and the string: *Various artists* / Johnnie laddie: *Various artists* / Willy's lyke wake: *Various artists* / Gypsy laddie, The: *Various artists* / Rambler gambler: *Various artists* / Mowing the barley: *Various artists* / Shearing, The: *Various artists* / Weaver and the factory maid: *Various artists*/ Clear away the morning dew: *Various artists* / Dives and Lazarus: *Various artists* / Lovely Joan: *Various artists* / Shallow Brown: *Various artists*.
MC: . . . . **FSC 4**

FELLSIDE INSTRUMENTAL SAMPLER VOL.1 (Various artists).
Tracks: / Professor Blackie: *Various artists* / Snot rag: *Various artists* / Bratach bana: *Various artists*/ Highland Donald: *Various artists* / Black bear, The: *Various artists* / Red joak: *Various artists* / Dipper of stars: *Various artists* / Shepton mallet hornpipe: *Various artists* / Dorset four hand reel: *Various* artists / Farewell to whiskey: *Various artists* / Cantsfield polka: *Various artists* / Dovecote Park: *Various* artists / Rab's wedding: *Various artists* / Loop to Lee: *Various artists* / Cameron highlanders, The: *Various* artists / Fiddlers joy: *Various artists* / Caddam Woods: *Various artists* / Glafis, The: *Various artists*/ Alabama jubilee medley: *Various artists* / Hesleyside reel,: *Various artists* / Sally in the garden: *Various artists* / Frosty morning: *Various artists* / Cunnla medley: *Various artists* / Jenny Bell: *Various artists*/ Herd on the hill: *Various artists* / Galloping trots: *Various artists*.
MC: . . . . **FSC 3**

FELLSIDE SONG SAMPLER VOL.1 (Various artists).
Tracks: / Rob Roy: *Various artists* / Bushes and briars: *Various artists* / Female drummer: *Various artists*/ Bonnie lass among the heather: *Various artists* / Chelsea quarters: *Various artists* / Farewell dearest Nancy: *Various artists* / Roll the woodpile down: *Various artists* / Sedgefield fair: *Various artists* / Reedy river: *Various artists* / Ford o' Kabul river: *Various artists*/ Helen of Kirkconnel: *Various artists*/ Boomers story: *Various artists* / From a princess to a beggarman: *Various artists* / Clear the track: *Various artists* / Bushman's story: *Various artists* / Parting friends: *Various artists*.
MC: . . . . **FSC 2**

FESTIVAL AT BLAIRGOWRIE (Various artists).
Tracks: / Festival o'Blair, The: *Stewart, Belle* / I am a miller tae ma trade: *Stewart, Davie* / Irthing water hounds, The: *Various artists* / Old man come courting me, An: *Various artists* / My Johnny: *Various artists*/ Bellingham boats: *Various artists* / Smash the windows: *Various artists* / My old man: *Various artists*/ Puppet on a string: *Various artists* / Nam shuidh so gad chuimhneachadh: *Various artists* / Bas an eich (The poor horse buried at sea): *Various artists* / Nucan bhalallan (The whales of Balallon): *Various artists* / MacCrimmon's lament: *Various artists* / Berryfields o'Blair, The: *Various artists*.
LP: **12T 181**

FESTIVAL FOLK VOL.1 (Various artists).
MC: . . . . **RTE 66**

FESTIVAL FOLK VOL.2 (Various artists).
MC: . . . . **RTE 77**

FESTIVAL FOLK VOL.3 (Various artists).
MC: . . . . **RTE 86**

FOLK AT THE BLACK HORSE (Various artists).
Tracks: / Stanton drew: *Various artists* / Jock Stewart: *Various artists* / I like to rise: *Various artists*/ Carrickfergus: *Various artists* / Doffin mistress: *Various artists* / Arthur McBride: *Various artists*.
LP: . . . . **ERON 012 LP**
MC: . . . . **ERON 012 CA**

FOLK DANCES (Various artists).
Tracks: / Dorset triumph: *Various artists* (CD only.) / Double schottische: *Various artists* / Stoke Golding country dance: *Various artists* / Tom Pate: *Various artists* / Three meet: *Various artists* (CD only.) / Cumberland reel: *Various artists* (CD only.) / Bonnie breast knot: *Various artists* / Circle waltz: *Various artists*/ Pop goes the weasel: *Various artists* / Galopede: *Various artists* / Bonnets so blue: *Various artists*/ Buttered peas: *Various artists* / Huntsman's chorus: *Various artists* / Meeting six: *Various artists*/ Brass nuts: *Various artists* (CD only.) / Flowers of Edinburgh: *Various artists* / Christchurch bells: *Various* artists / Corn rigs: *Various artists* / Rifleman, The: *Various artists* / Cottagers, The: *Various artists*/ Vermont tempest: *Various artists* / Double quadrille: *Various artists*.
MC: . . . . **TCEMS 1387**

FOLK FESTIVAL OF THE BLUES (Various artists).
Tracks: / Wee baby blues: *Various artists* / Sitting and thinking: *Various artists* / Worried blues: *Various* artists / Bring it on home: *Various artists* / Sugar mama: *Various artists* / Clouds in my heart: *Various* artists / May I have a talk with you: *Various artists* / Got my mojo working: *Various artists* / Don't know which way to go: *Various artists* / Nineteen years old: *Various artists*.
LP: . . . . **GCH 8004**
MC: . . . . **GCHK 78004**
LP: . . . . **CXMP 2006**

FOLK FRIENDS (Various artists).
LP: . . . . **FF 3001/2**

FOLK HERITAGE (Various artists).
MC: . . . . **MCTC 043**

FOLK MASTERS (Various artists).
MC: . . . . **ARLC 1017**

FOLK MUSIC (1) (Various artists).
MC: **D58005**

FOLK MUSIC (2) (Various artists).
MC: **D58003**

FOLK MUSIC OF BULGARIA (Various artists).
LP: **12T 107**

FOLK MUSIC OF NORWAY (Various artists).
LP: **12TS 351**

FOLK ROOTS VOL. II (Various artists).
LP: . . . . **FMSL 2013**

FOLK SONGS (1) (Topic sampler No.1) (Various artists).
Tracks: / Heave away my Johnny: *Killen, Louis/chorus* / Stewball: *Lloyd, A. L.* / Cutty Wren, The: *Campbell*, Ian Folk Group / Let no man steal your thyme: *Cameron, Isla* / Doctor Gilbert: *Various artists* (Michael Gorman: fiddle, Margaret Barry: banjo.) / Blow the man down: *Corbett, Harry H./chorus* / Jug of punch: *McPeake Family*/ Up the raw: *Killen, Louis* (Colin Ross: whistle.) / Donal Don: *Kent, Enoch* / My bonny bonny boy: *Briggs, Anne* / Miners dances: *Celebrated working man's band* / Johnny Cope: *MacColl, Ewan*.
LP: . . . . **TPS 114**

FOLK SONGS (2) (Topic sampler No.2) (Various artists).
Tracks: / Whip jamboree: *Spinners* / Hedgehog pie: *Handle, Johnny* (Tom Gilfellon: guitar, Colin Ross: whistle.) / Sailor cut down in his prime, The: *Kelly, Stan* / Fair Rosamund: *West, Hedy* / Fourpence a day: *MacColl*, Ewan / Master McGrath: *Behan, Dominic* (Ralph Rinzler: mandolin, Peggy Seeger: guitar.) / Buy broom besoms: *Campbell*, Ian Folk Group / Overlander, The: *Lloyd, A. L.* / Broom o'the Cowdenknowes: *Watersons* / Rambleaway: *Collins, Shirley* / Buck dancer's choice: *Paley, Tom* / Night visiting song: *Fisher, Ray & Archie*.
LP: . . . . **TPS 145**

FOLK SONGS (6) (Topic sampler No.6) (Various artists).
Tracks: / Brave wolfe: *Various artists* / Pace egging song: *Various artists* / Droylsden wakes: *Various artists*/ John Barleycorn: *Various artists* / Bonnie ship the Diamond, The: *Various artists* / Blackleg miner: *Various* artists / Jolly waggoners: *Various artists* / Trimdon grange explosion, The: *Various artists* / Sweet primroses: *Various artists* / White cockade, The: *Various artists*.
LP: . . . . **TPS 201**

GAELIC FOLK SONGS (Various artists).
Tracks: / Am bratch bana: *Various artists* / Eilean mo chridh: *Various artists* / Muile ghradhach: *Various* artists / Oran luathaidh: *Various artists* / Soraidh leis an ait': *Various artists* / An crann ceusaidh: *Various* artists / Tuireadh iain ruaidh: *Various artists* / Mi lee m'uilnn: *Various artists* / Chairstion: *Various* artists / Gur boidheach na gillean: *Various artists* / Taladh: *Various artists* / An seann mharaiche: *Various artists*.
LP: . . . . **LILP 5048**
MC: . . . . **LICS 5048**

GAME AS NED KELLY (Various artists).
LP: . . . . **LRF 050**

GAS MARK 5 (Various artists).
LP: . . . . **FESTIVAL 2**

GEORGE DAVIS IS INNOCENT O.K. (Various artists).
Tracks: / These are more enlightened days: *Various artists* / Lags song, The: *Various artists* / They couldn't find the right man: *Various artists* / Ilford film: *Various artists* / Old Bailey lady: *Various artists*/ Statistics never need to tell the truth: *Various artists* / Sgt. Matthews: *Various artists* / All along the East End: *Various artists* / Identification: *Various artists* / Headingley song The: *Various artists* / Ballad of the East End: *Various artists* / Cut and dried: *Various artists* / Ballad of George Davis: *Various artists*/ George Davis protest song: *Various artists* / Identification song: *Various artists*.
LP: . . . . **SFA 054**

GIRL FROM DONEGAL (10 original hits from home) (Various artists).
MC: . . . . **CHR 10**

GOING DOWN THE VALLEY (Various artists).
Tracks: / I truly understand, you love another man: *Roark, Shortbuckle and Family* / Old Joe Clark: *Jarrell, Ben*(Accompanied by DaCosta Woltz's Southern Broadcasters.) / Billy Grimes, The Rover: *Shelor Family, The* / George Washington: *Pope's Arkansas Mountaineers* / Little Maud: *Lam, Bela and His Greene County Singers* / Cotton-eyed Joe: *Carter* Brothers & Son, / Going down the valley: *Stoneman, Ernest V. and His Dixie Mountaineers* / Cottage door, The: *Perry County Music Makers, The* / Carve that possum: *Macon, Uncle Dave and His Fruit Jar Drinkers* / Molly put the kettle on: *Tanner, Gid & His Skillet Lickers* / Milwaukee blues: *Poole, Charlie and the North Carolina Ramblers* / Corina, Corina: *Ashley & Abernathy* / Katy dear (silver dagger): *Callahan Brothers, The* / New salty dog, A: *Allen* Brothers, The / Nancy Jane: *Fort Worth Doughboys, The* / Sweet rose of heaven: *Taylor-Griggs Louisiana Melody Makers* / Banjo pickin' girl: *Coon Creek Girls* / Little Maggie: *Mainer, Wade, Zeke Morris and Steve Ledford*.
LP: . . . . **NW 236**

GOING UP CAMBORNE HILL (Folksongs from Cornwall) (Various artists).
Tracks: / Going up Camborne Hill: *Various artists* / Padstow: *Various artists* / Sweet nightingale: *Various artists* / It rains, it hails: *Various artists* / Holly tree carol: *Various artists* / Hal-an-tow: *Various* artists / John the bone: *Various artists* / Where are you going to my

pretty maid: *Various artists* / Cornish miner's song, The: *Various artists* / Tree on the hill: *Various artists* / Billy boy: *Various artists*/ Treble-tailed gypsy-o: *Various artists* / Cadgwith anthem: *Various artists* / Cluster of nuts: *Various artists*/ Old grey duck: *Various artists* / As I sat on a sunny bank: *Various artists* / Fisherman's hymn: *Various artists* / While shepherds watched their flocks by night: *Various artists* / Old King Cole: *Various artists*/ Lamorna wet wet wet: *Various artists* / Truro wassail songs: *Various artists*.
MC: **60-010**

GOLDEN MUSIC BOX FAVOURITES (Various artists).
Tracks: / Home sweet home: *Various artists* / Love's old sweet song: *Various artists* / In the gloaming: *Various* artists / My wild Irish rose: *Various artists* / Listen to the mockingbird: *Various artists* / Hearts and flowers: *Various artists* / Robin Adair: *Various artists* / Narcissus: *Various artists* / Juanita: *Various* artists / Last rose of summer: *Various artists* / Old folks at home: *Various artists* / Annie Laurie: *Various* artists / Lorely: *Various artists* / My old Kentucky home: *Various artists* / Silver threads among the gold: *Various artists* / Santa Lucia: *Various artists* / Glow worm: *Various artists* / Heart that once thru, The: *Various artists* / Tarra's Hall: *Various artists*.
LP: . . . . **AB 5**
MC: . . . . **AB-C 5**

GOOD BLOW OUT FOR FOURPENCE, A (Various artists).
LP: **12TS 782**
LP: **12TMH 782**

GOOD OLD WAY (British folk music today) (Various artists).
LP: **12TS 412**
LP: . . . . **TPS 8412**

GREAT ACOUSTICS (Various artists).
LP: . . . . **PH 1101**
MC: . . . . **PH 1101C**

GREAT MEAT PIE, THE (Various artists).
Tracks: / Merry maids of York, The: *Brewhouse Brass* / Great meat pie, The: *Artisan* / Lord Bateman: *Miles, Dick* / T'owd Weaver: *Palmer, Roy* / Lancashire Morris: *Murfitt, Adrian* / Shamrock Shore: *Miles, Dick*/ Green bushes: *Witcham Toll* / Lady Franklin's lament: *Artisan* / Highland Mary: *Jerrom, Ren & Ron Adkin*/ Bonnie underneath her apron, The: *Palmer, Roy* / Plains of Waterloo, The: *Witcham Toll* / Golden glove, The: *Lyons, Philip & Phillipa* / Bold Turpin hero: *Miles, Dick* / Gentle shepherd: *Brewhouse Brass*.
LP: . . . . **BH 8907**

GREATEST FOLK SINGERS OF THE SIXTIES (Various artists).
Tracks: / You were on my mind: *Ian & Sylvia* / Now that the buffalo's gone: *Sainte-Marie, Buffy* / Walk right in: *Rooftop Singers* / East Virginia: *Baez, Joan* / Old Blue: *Houston, Cisco* / I feel like I'm fixin' to die rag: *Country Joe & The Fish* / John Henry: *Odetta* / Pack up your sorrows: *Farina, Richard* / Greenland whale fisheries: *Collins, Judy & Theodore Bikel* / Well, well, well: *Gibson, Bob & Hamilton Camp* / Rambling boy: *Paxton, Tom* / La Bamba: *Feliciano, Jose* / Virgin Mary had one son: *Baez, Joan & Bob Gibson* / Salty dog blues: *Flatt, Lester & Earl Scruggs* / Blowin' in the wind: *Dylan, Bob* / There but for: *Ochs, Phil*/ Violets of the dawn: *Anderson, Eric* / Sitting on top of the world: *Watson, Doc* / Travelling riverside: *Hammond, John* / House of the Rising Sun / Crazy words, crazy tune: *Kweskin, Jim & The Jug Band* / Candy man: *Hurt, Mississippi* John / Erie Canal: *Weavers* / Wish I had answered: *Staple Singers* / Ballad of Springhill: *Seeger, Peggy* & Ewan MacColl / Mellow down easy: *Butterfield, Paul* / I got it: *Chambers Brothers* / Whistling gypsy: *Makem, Tommy* / I got it: *New Lost City Ramblers* / Paper of pins: *Brand, Oscar & Jean Ritchie* / East Virginia blues: *Seeger, Pete*.
2LP: . . . . **VSD 17**

GREATEST FOLK SINGERS OF THE SIXTIES (Various artists).
LP: . . . . **VNP 5317**
MC: . . . . **VNP 6317**

GREEN GROW THE LAURELS (Country singers from the south) (Various artists).
Tracks: / Green grows the laurel: *Fuller, Louise* / Rich lady gay, The: *Upton, Harry* / Wexford town: *Haynes, Mary Ann* / Aylesbury girl, The: *Goodban, Jack* / Tree in the wood, The: *Newman, George Tom* / I am a donkey driver: *Upton, Harry* / Molecatcher, The: *Fuller, Louise* / Hopping down in Kent: *Fuller, Louise* / Shannon frigate, The: *Goodban, Jack* / Young Maria: *Fuller, Louise* / Colour of amber: *Haynes, Mary Ann* / Banks of the sweet Dundee: *Upton, Harry* / Single life: *Upton, Harry* / Woman's work is never done: *Upton, Harry*.
LP: **12TS 285**

GUINNESS RECORD OF IRISH BALLADS (See under Ireland) (Various artists).

GUINNESS RECORD OF IRISH BALLADS VOL.2 (See under Ireland) (Various artists).

GUINNESS RECORD OF IRISH BALLADS VOL.3 (See under Ireland) (Various artists).

GUINNESS RECORD OF IRISH BALLADS, VOL 4 (See under Ireland) (Various artists).

HEARTBEAT (Various Roots & Folk Music) (Various artists).
LP: . . . . **SPD 1029**
MC: . . . . **SPDC 1029**

I'LL TAKE YOU HOME (10 original hits from home) (Various artists).
MC: . . . . **CHR 03**

IN COMES I' TOM FOOL (Various artists).
MC: **30 105**

IN THE SWISS MOUNTAINS (Various artists).
MC: **299408**

INNSBRUCK, THE BEAUTIFUL ALPINE CITY (Various artists).
MC: **299425**

INTERNATIONAL FOLKLORE FESTIVAL (Various artists).
LP: . . . . **ARN 33735**

JACK OF ALL TRADES (Folksongs of Great Britain vol.3) (Various artists).
Tracks: / Jovial tradesmen, The: *Copper, Bob & Ron* / Roving journey man, The: *Doran, Paddy* / Candlelight fisherman, The: *Hammond, Phil* / Canny shepherd laddies, The: *White, Jimmy* / Dairy maid, The: *Maguire, John* / Green brooms: *McDonagh, Sean* / Gruel: *McBeath, Jimmy* / Jug of punch: *Quinn, Edward* / Gresford disaster, The: *Cosgrove, Mrs. A.* / Jolly miller: *Strachan, John* / Irish washerwoman, The: *McDonald, John* / Fagan the cobbler: *Richardson, Whickets* / Ould piper, The: *Mc Peake, Frank* / Sweep, chimney sweep: *Copper, Bob & Ron*/ Mason's apron: *White, Agnes & Bridie* / Rhynie: *Tunney, John* / Wee weaver, The: *Doherty, John* / Jim the Carter lad: *Goodfellow, Jack* / Drumdelgie: *Stewart, Davie* / Merry haymakers, The: *Copper, Bob & Ron*/ I'll mend your pots and kettles: *Ennis, Seamus*.
LP: **12T 159**
MC: **60-021**

KINGS OF RAGTIME GUITAR (Various artists).
LP: . . . . **L 1044**

KINGSBRIDGE FAIR (Song competition) (Various artists).
Tracks: / Flags are flying: *Various artists* / In old Kingsbridge town: *Various artists* / Good old Kingsbridge Town: *Various artists* / Time for Kingsbridge fair: *Various artists* / Kingsbridge Fair welcomes you, me dear: *Various artists* / Sun is up, The: *Various artists* / Old Kinsbridge Town (winners): *Various artists*/ Going to Kingsbridge Fair: *Various artists* / Come with me: *Various artists* / Kingsbridge Fair week: *Various* artists / Doin' the Kingsbridge rag: *Various artists* / East Hallington handbell ringers: *Various artists*/ Adjudication speech: *Various artists* (Spoken word).
MC: **45-088**

LAKELAND COLLECTION (Various artists).
Tracks: / Huntsman's chorus: *Various artists* / Lammerside: *Various artists* / It's no but me: *Various artists*/ Fine hunting day: *Various artists* / Lish young buy a broom: *Various artists* / Shades o' John Peel: *Various* artists / John Peel: *Various artists* / Keswick driver, The: *Various artists* / Northern lass: *Various* artists / Eskdale and Ennerdale hunt song: *Various artists* / Line o'er the fell, The: *Various artists* / Lakeland pubs: *Various artists* / Dunmail: *Various artists* / Canny Cumberland: *Various artists* / One horned sheep: *Various artists*.
MC: . . . . **FSC 1**

LARK IN THE CLEAR AIR (Various artists).
LP: **12TS 230**

LARK RISE TO CANDLEFORD (A country tapestry) (Various artists).
Tracks: / Girl I left behind me, The: *Various artists* / Lemady/arise and pick a posy: *Various artists* / All of a row: *Various artists* / Tommytoes: *Various artists* / John Dory: *Various artists* / Witch Elder: *Various artists* / Abroad for pleasure: *Various artists* / Day Thou gavest, Lord is ended, The: *Various artists*/ Battle of the Somme: *Various artists* / Grand circle dance, The: *Various artists* / Speed the plough: *Various* artists / Snow falls: *Various artists* / Cart music: *Various artists* / Holly and the ivy, The: *Various* artists / Postman's knock: *Various artists* / Hunt music: *Various artists* / Scarlet and the blue: *Various artists* / Dare to be a Daniel: *Various artists* / Jacob's well: *Various artists*.
LP: . . . . **CDS 4020**
LP: . . . . **CHC 73**
MC: . . . . **CHCMC 73**

MAGICAL MULL (Various artists).
MC: . . . . **MR 1001**

MASTERS OF THE FOLK GUITAR (Various artists).
LP: . . . . **ALLP 248**

MATCHBOX DAYS (British folk blues '67-70) (Various artists).
LP: . . . . **FMSL 2016**

MAYPOLES TO MISTLETOE (Various artists).
LP: . . . . **LER 2092**

MELODEON GREATS (Various artists).
LP: **12TS 376**

MEN BEHIND THE WIRE (Various artists).
LP: . . . . **CROL 3001**

MIDSUMMER NIGHT FEST (Folk music & dances) (Various artists).
LP: . . . . **ALP 109**

MIRI IT IS (Various artists).
LP: . . . . **PLR 043**

NEW ROOTS (Various artists).
Tracks: / Get rhythm: *Various artists* / I ain't ever satisfied: *Various artists* / Lost and found: *Various* artists / Hearts of olden glory: *Various artists* / Hush little baby: *Various artists* / Turning of the tide: *Various artists* / Love like a rock: *Various artists* / Wholly humble heart: *Various artists* / Don't be afraid of the dark: *Various artists* / Good tradition: *Various artists* / Bjorn again polka: *Various artists*/ Road to Ballyalla, The: *Various artists* / Carrickfergus: *Various artists* / Like the weather: *Various artists*/ Streets of Bakersfield: *Various artists* / If I had a boat: *Various artists*.
2LP: . . . . **SMR 972**
MC: . . . . **SMC 972**

NICHT AT THE BOTHY (Various artists).
MC: . . . . **CWGR 054**

NIGHT AT THE AULD MEAL MILL 1984 (Various artists).
LP: . . . . **WGR 076**
MC: . . . . **CWGR 076**

NIGHT AT THE AULD MEAL MILL 1985 (Various artists).
LP: . . . . **WGR 087**
MC: . . . . **CWGR 087**

NIGHT AT THE AULD MEAL MILL 1986 (Various artists).
MC: . . . . **CWGR 105**

NIGHT AT THE AULD MEAL MILL 1987 (Various artists).
MC: . . . . **CWGR 112**

NIGHT AT THE AULD MEAL MILL 1988, A (Various artists).
MC: . . . . **CWGRTV 9**

NORTH COUNTRY RANTS & REELS Border folk dances by traditional players (Various artists).
MC: **60-121**

OUR FOLK HERITAGE (Various artists).
LP: . . . . **LER 2087**

'OWDHAM 'EDGE Song and verse from Lancashire (Various artists).
LP: **12T 204**

PACKMEN'S BLUE RECORD (Various artists).
LP: . . . . **FE 010**

PADDY IN THE SMOKE (Various artists).
LP: **12T 176**

PENNYWHISTLERS (Various artists).
LP: . . . . **H 72007**

PLAY ANOTHER BEFORE YOU GO (Various artists).
Tracks: / I'm Henry the eighth I am: *Champion, Harry* / Cover it over quick, Jemima: *Champion, Harry* / Girls I left behind me: *Tilley, Vesta* / I'll show you around Paree: *Tilley, Vesta* / I wanted a wife: *Sheridan,* Mark / One of the boys: *Sheridan, Mark* / I may be a millionaire: *Stratton, Eugene* / Send for John Willie: *Formby, George* / Playing the game in the west: *Formby, George* / They're all single at the seaside: *Retford,* Ella / Molly Malone: *Retford, Ella* / We all go the same way home: *Whittle, Chas R.* / Play us another before you go: *Whittle, Chas R.* / Mr. & Mrs. Smith: *Mayne, Clarice*.
LP: **12TMH 781**

PROSPECT OF SCOTLAND Topic sampler no.5 (Various artists).
LP: . . . . **TPS 169**

RAGLAN ROAD (Various artists).
LP: . . . . **LRF 132**

RAVE ON (Various artists).
Tracks: / Rave on: *Steeleye Span* / Ploughboy and the cockney, The: *Hart, Tim & Maddy Prior* / Westron wynde: *Hart, Tim & Maddy Prior* / Banks of the Bann: *Collins, Shirley* / Cold haily windy night: *Steeleye Span*/ Let no man steal your thyme: *McDonald, Shelagh* / Lovely on the water: *Steeleye Span* / Just as the tide was flowing: *Collins, Shirley* / Cannily, cannily: *Hart, Tim & Maddy Prior* / Matt Hyland: *Carthy, Martin*/ Of all the birds: *Hart, Tim & Maddy Prior* / Bank, The: *Carthy, Martin & Dave Swarbrick* / Marrowbones: *Steeleye Span*.
LP: . . . . **CREST 17**

REVIVAL IN BRITAIN VOL. 1 (Various artists).
Tracks: / O'Rourke: *McGinn, Matt* / Under alow the ground: *McGinn, Matt* / Can o' tea: *McGinn, Matt*/ Mambo: *McGinn, Matt* / Rum'll hae to do today: *McGinn, Matt* / Tam the toff: *McGinn, Matt* / I'll give you your whiskey back again: *McGinn, Matt* / Haunted single end, The: *McGinn, Matt* / My father was born a Hebrew: *McGinn, Matt* / This is your land: *McGinn, Matt* / They'll neither work nor want: *McGinn, Matt* / My uncle Dan: *McGinn, Matt* / Liverpool town: *Kelly, Stan* / Old Mark II, The: *Kelly, Stan* / Farewell to the monty: *Handle, Johnny* / Gaffer's bait, The: *Handle, Johnny* / Stoneman's lament, The: *Handle, Johnny* / Collier lad is a canny lad, The: *Handle, Johnny* / College valley hunt, The: *Rogerson, Alan* / Christmas comes but once a year: *Kent, Enoch* / Man in charge of the knob, The: *Kent, Enoch* / Our commonwealth brothers: *Kent, Enoch*/ No room at the inn: *Parker/ Charles*.
MC: . . . . **CTRAX 033**

RIVERS OF DELIGHT (Various artists).
LP: . . . . **H 71360**

ROUNDER FOLK VOLUME 1 (Various artists).
LP: . . . . **AN 04**
MC: . . . . **ANC 04**

ROUNDER FOLK VOLUME 2 (Various artists).
MC: . . . . **ANC 05**
LP: . . . . **AN 05**

SAILORMEN AND SERVINGMAIDS Folk songs of Great Britain vol.6 (Various artists).
Tracks: / Paddy West: *Walsh, Timothy* / Liverpool packet, The: *Barber, Billy* / Green banks of Yarrow, The: *Maguire,* Mrs. / Our gallant ship: *Howell, William* / Alehouse, The: *Cronin, Elizabeth* / Rosemary land: *Laurenson,* Bruce / Ratcliffe highway: *Baldry, Jim* / Lowlands of Holland, The: *Tunney, Paddy* / Quaker, The: *Dorchester mummers* / Beninn a' cheathaich: *McNeil, Flora* / Whale fishery, The: *Hamon, Philip/Hilary Carre* / Grey silkie, The: *Sinclair, John* / Warlike seamen: *Copper, Bob & Ron* / Boat that brought me, The: *Moran, Thomas*/ Handsome cabin boy, The: *Robertson, Jeannie* / Unst boat song, The: *Stickle, John* / Smacksman, The: *Larner,* Sam / Sweet Willie: *Smith, Lal* / Campanero: *Cameron, Bill* / Andrew Ross: *Findlater, John & Ethel*/ Bold Princess Royal, The: *Adams, Ned* / Boatie rows, The: *Murray, Jessie* / Our ship is ready: *Cinnamond, Robert* / Nancy of Yarmouth: *Ling, Fred*.
LP: **12T 194**

SANDY BELL'S CEILIDH (Various artists).
Tracks: / An comhra donn/the galway/ the strand: *Various artists* / John Barleycorn: *Various artists* / Lea rig, The: *Various artists* / Cruel brother, the: *Various artists* / Lowlands away: *Various artists* / Sandy Bell's man: *Various artists* / Kirsteen: *Various artists* / Crossing the Minch: *Various artists* / Johnny Sangster: *Various artists* / Sleepy toon: *Various artists* / Doon in the wee room: *Various artists* / Jigs: *Various artists* (The lilting fisherman / Lough Gowna / Sweet Biddy Daly).
MC: . . . . **CTRAX 015**

SCAPA FLOW Instrumental music: Orkney (Various artists).
Tracks: / Scapa Flow: *Various artists* / Bruces's march: *Various artists* / Rendell and grimsetter polkas: *Various* artists / Barony, The: *Various artists* / House on the hill: *Various artists* / Red house, The: *Various* artists / Four posts of the bed, The: *Various artists* / 4-some

reel: *Various artists* / Rory O'More: *Various* artists / Shepherd's wife, The: *Various artists* / Kissin' dance (or Babbity Bowster): *Various artists* / Victoria waltz: *Various artists* / Greeny Hill harch: *Various artists* / Drunken piper: *Various artists*/ King William's march: *Various artists* / Cliff: *Various artists* / Miss Brown's hornpipe: *Various artists*/ Arthur's seat: *Various artists* / Eugene Stratton: *Various artists* / Banks hornpipe: *Various artists*/ Two quadrille tunes: *Various artists* / Ninepins: *Various artists* / Paddy Carter (polka-mazurka): *Various* artists / Venus polka: *Various artists* / Morning star, The: *Various artists* / Kitty, my navel: *Various* artists / Maggie: *Various artists* / Money musk: *Various artists* / Iron man: *Various artists* / Archie O'Lambholm: *Various artists* / Quickstep: *Various artists* / House of skene, The: *Various artists*/ 4 stringer, The: *Various artists* / McDonald Black: *Various artists*.
MC: **60-064**

SEODA CEOIL (Various artists).
LP: . . . . **CEF 018**

SHANTY MEN (Various artists).
Tracks: / Epilogue: *Various artists* / Prelude: *Various artists* / Walk me out in the morning dew: *Various artists*.
LP: . . . . **GVR 201**

SHEPWAY FOLK (Various artists).
Tracks: / Keys of Canterbury: *Various artists* / Mandy: *Various artists* / Congo river: *Various artists*/ Flowers of Scotland: *Various artists*.
LP: . . . . **ERON 003 LP**
MC: . . . . **ERON 003 CA**

SHROPSHIRE IRON Life & Times (folk songs of Shropshire) (Various artists).
Tracks: / Most extraordinary district in the world: *Various artists* / Shropshire iron: *Various artists* / Abraham darby: *Various artists* / Simple life of a quaker, The: *Various artists* / Success to all these learned men: *Various artists* / Lament for darby: *Various artists* / Boys of bedlam: *Various artists* / Bedlam jig: *Various* artists / John Wilkinson: *Various artists* / Furnaceman's life, A: *Various artists* / Bridge of iron, A: *Various* artists / Colebrook dale: *Various artists* / Pride of Englishmen, The: *Various artists* / Contemplate good fortune: *Various artists*.
LP: . . . . **FE 071**
MC: . . . . **FE 071 C**

SILVER BOW: SHETLAND FOLK FIDDLING (Various artists).
LP: . . . . **PH 2019**

SILVER DARLINGS, THE Harness and friends (Various artists).
MC: . . . . **MR 1017**

SING, SAY & PLAY (Various artists).
Tracks: / Blacksmith's daughter, The: *Various artists* / Ratcliffe highway: *Various artists* / Barn dance, The: *Various artists* / Cock o' the North: *Various artists* / London prentice boy, The: *Various artists* / Next tune tonight, The: *Various artists* / Turkey in the straw: *Various artists* / Banks of the Nile: *Various* artists / Out with my gun in the morning: *Various artists* / Old country waltz: *Various artists* / Pigeon on the gate: *Various artists* / Strolling down to Hastings: *Various artists* / Fellow who played the trombone, The: *Various artists* / Sailors hornpipe medley: *Various artists* / Oak and the ash, The: *Various artists*/ Jolly tinker: *Various artists* / Two step: *Various artists* / Yarmouth hornpipe: *Various artists* / Parson's creed (recitation), The: *Various artists* / Marrowbones: *Various artists* / Golden slippers: *Various* artists / Chinaman's song, The: *Various artists* / Old brown in the rose and crown: *Various artists* / Red river valley: *Various artists* / Polka medley: *Various artists*.
LP: **12TS 375**

SINGING & DANCING FROM ERIN GREEN'S SHORE (Various artists).
LP: . . . . **CSDBL 512**

SKARA BRAE (Various artists).
LP: . . . . **CEF 031**

SONGS FOR PEACE (Various artists).
LP: . . . . **ROUNDER 4015**
MC: . . . . **ROUNDER 4015C**
LP: . . . . **FF 4010**

SONGS OF CEREMONY Folk songs of Great Britain vol.8 (Various artists).
Tracks: / Cornish wassail song: *Various artists* / New'r even's song: *Various artists* / Mari lwyd ceremony, The: *Various artists* / Joys of Mary, The: *Various artists* / Holly and the ivy, The: *Various artists* / Twelve days of Christmas, The: *Various artists* / Bitter withy: *Various artists* / As I sat on a sunny bank: *Various* artists / Singing of the travels, The: *Various artists* / Drivers and lazarus: *Various artists* / Gower wassail: *Various artists* / Taladh an leinibh Iosa: *Various artists* / St. Clemennts song, The: *Various artists*/ Shrove Tuesday song, The: *Various artists* / Cherry tree carol, The: *Various artists* / Sommerset wassail song: *Various artists* / Hunting the wren: *Various artists* / Cheshire souling song: *Various artists* / Six jolly miners: *Various artists* / John Barleycorn: *Various artists* / Hal-an-tow: *Various artists* / Huntingdonshire may carol: *Various artists* / Cornish May carol: *Various artists*.
LP: **12T 197**

SONGS OF COURTSHIP Folk Songs Of Great Britain Vol.1 (Various artists).
Tracks: / Green grows the laurel: *Robertson, Jeannie* / False bride, The: *Copper, Bob* / Our wedding day: *McPeake*, Francis / When a man's in love: *Tunney, Paddy* / Ailein Duinn: *McNeill, Flora* / Bonnie Kate: *Whyte*, Agnes / Old grey beard newly shaven: *Robertson, Jeannie* / Coolin': *Taylor, Paddy* / Shule aroon: *Cronin*, Elizabeth / Mountain streams, The: *Tunney, Paddy* / Brown thorn, The: *Ennis, Seamus* / As I roved out: *Ennis*, Seamus / Magpie's nest, The: *Kelly, Jane* / Casadh ant sugain: *O'Sullivan, Maire* / Girl was too smart for the fiddler, The: *Doherty, Michael* / My darling ploughman boy: *McPeake, Jimmy & Francis* / I'm a young bonnie lassie: *Wood, Blanche* / No, John, no: *Various artists* / Cois abhainn na sead: *Ni cheochain, Marie* / Bogie's bonnie belle: *Stewart, Davie*.
LP: **12T 157**

SONGS OF SEDUCTION Folk songs of Great Britain Vol.2 (Various artists).
Tracks: / Nutting girl, The: *Poacher, Cyril* / Bonnie wee lassie who never said no, The: *Robertson, Jeannie* / Bundle and go: *Doherty, John* / Blow the candle out: *Gilhanie, Jimmie* / Foggy dew, The: *Hammond, Phil*/ Toorna ma goon: *McBeath, Jimmy* / Rolling in rye grass: *Taylor, Paddy* / Jolly tinker: *Moran, Thomas*/ Long peggin' awl: *Cox, Harry* / Thrashing machine, The: *O'Neil, Anne* / Rigs of London town, The: *Wills*, Charlie / Wind blew the bonnie lassie's plaidie awa',The: *Various artists* (Jimmy McBeath/Duncan Burke bagpipes/ Jeannie Robertson) / Cunning cobbler, The: *Spicer, George* / Dublin City: *Ennis, Seamus* / Light dragoon, The: *List*, Harry / Orkney style of courtship, The: *Findlater, John* / Cuckoo's nest, The: *Various artists* (Jeannie Robertson/John Maguire tin whistle/John Strachan) / Soldier and the lady, The: *Cantwell, Raymond & Frederick* / Behind the bush in the garden: *Ennis, Seamus* / Never wed an old man: *Robertson, Jeannie* / Maid of Australia: *Cox, Harry* / Merchant's son and the beggar's daughter, The: *Stewart, Davie* / Bold English navvy, The: *Smith, Lal* / Cruisin' round Yarmouth: *Cox, Harry*.
LP: **12T 158**

SONGS OF THE ANIMALS & OTHER MARVELS Vol. 10 (Various artists).
LP: **12T 198**

SONGS OF THE WORKING PEOPLE (Various artists).
LP: . . . . **FF 483**

SONGS & SOUTHERN BREEZES (Country singers from Hampshire & Sussex) (Various artists).
Tracks: / Bonnie bunch of roses, The: *Gillette, Noah* / Epsom races: *Attrill, George* / Banks of the Mossom, The: *Various artists* / False Lanky: *Fosbury, George* / Cruel Lincoln: *Butcher, Ben* / Silver pin, The: *Chapman, Mrs.* / Chiner's song, The: *Bond, Frank* / God bless the master: *Bond, Frank* / Prickle holly bush, The: *Hewitt, Fred* / Three maidens a milking did go: *Hewitt, Fred* / Her servant man: *Stone, Gladys* / Rolling in the dew: *Johnson, Leslie* / Sheffield Park: *Butcher, Ben* / George Collins: *White, Enos* / Streams of lovely Nancy, The: *Brown, Victor Turp* / As broad as I was walking: *Brown, Victor Turp* / Six jolly miners: *Brown, Victor Turp*.
LP: **12T 317**

SONGS, STORIES & TUNES FROM THE CENTRAL COUNTIES (Various artists).
Tracks: / Dudley boys, The: *Wide Midlands* / When shall we get married, John: *Wide Midlands* / Slap bum tailor, The: *Wide Midlands* / Swaggering boney: *Wide Midlands* / Black joke, The: *Wide Midlands* / Stop that clock: *Wide Midlands* / Early in the morning: *Wide Midlands* / When you get up in the morning: *Wide Midlands*/ Jolly Joe the collier's son: *Wide Midlands* / Owd never could: *Wide Midlands* / I can't find Brummagem: *Wide Midlands* / Birmingham Jack of all trades: *Wide Midlands* / Nailmakers' strike, The: *Wide Midlands* / Old miner, The: *Wide Midlands* / Birmingham Sally: *Wide Midlands* / Buffoon: *Wide Midlands* / Staffordshire hornpipe: *Wide Midlands* / Aye for Saturday night: *Wide Midlands* / Aston Villa supporter, The: *Wide Midlands* / Motor trade workers: *Wide Midlands*.
LP: **12TS 210**

SOUTHWEST VIRGINIA FIELD RECORDINGS VOL.1 (Various artists).
LP: . . . . **ROUNDER 0057**

SPINNING WHEEL, THE 10 original hits from home (Various artists).
MC: . . . . **CHR 05**

SQUARE ROOTS (Various artists).
LP: . . . . **FROOT 001**
MC: . . . . **FROOTC 001**

STEAM BALLADS (Various artists).
Tracks: / Navvy on the line: *Various artists* / Bold navvies: *Various artists* / Paddy works on the railway: *Various* artists / Newcastle and Shields railway: *Various artists* / Johnny Green's trip to see the Manchester railway: *Various* artists / Birmingham and Liverpool railway: *Various artists* / Iron horse: *Various artists* / Oxford and Hampton railway, The: *Various artists* / Cockney's trip to Brummagem, The: *Various artists* / Wonderful effects of the Leicester railway: *Various artists* / Cosher Bailey: *Various artists* / Moses of the mail: *Various artists*/ Fireman's growl: *Various artists*.
LP: . . . . **BRO 121**
MC: . . . . **KBRO 121**

STREETS OF GLASGOW (Various artists).
LP: **12TS 226**

SUPER HIT PARADE OF FOLK MUSIC (Various artists).
Tracks: / Holzhackerbaum-jodler: *Hellwig, Maria & Margot* / Harmonika-Hansi: *Medium Terzett* / Lieder, die von herzen kommen: *Pat & Paul* / Veteranenmarsch: *Mosch, Ernst & his Original Egerland Musicians* / Alpski-schwung: *Alpenoberkrainer* / Appenzeller jodler: *Bauer, Uschi*.
LP: **6.26345**
MC: **4.26345**

SWEDISH FIDDLE MUSIC (Various artists).
LP: . . . . **SNTF 740**

TAP ROOTS (Various artists).
LP: . . . . **FROOT 002**
MC: . . . . **FROOTC 002**

TEXAS CZECH-BOHEMIAN BANDS, THE (1928-1958) (Various artists).
LP: . . . . **FL 9031**

THREE SWEDISH FIDDLERS (Various artists).
LP: . . . . **SHAN 21001**

TIROLER-ABEND (Various artists).
MC: **299422**

TOMORROW WE PART (Various artists).
LP: . . . . **BRO 133**
MC: . . . . **KBRO 133**

TOWN I LOVE SO WELL (10 original hits from home) (Various artists).
MC: . . . . **CHR 11**

TRADITIONAL SONGS AND MUSIC (Various artists).
LP: . . . . **LLST 7356**

TRAMSHED FOREVER (Various artists).
2LP: . . . . **SFAX 111**

TRAVELLING FOLK (Various artists).
LP: . . . . **ERON 006 LP**
MC: . . . . **ERON 006 CA**

TRIBUTE TO WOODY GUTHRIE, A (Various artists).
LP: **64 861**

TRIP TO HARROGATE (Various artists).
LP: . . . . **TSR 027**

TWENTY BEST OF TODAY'S FOLK MUSIC (Various artists).
LP: . . . . **EULP 1071**
MC: . . . . **EUMC 1071**

UKRAINIAN-AMERICAN FIDDLE & DANCE MUSIC I (Various artists).
LP: . . . . **FL 9014**

UKRAINIAN-AMERICAN FIDDLE & DANCE MUSIC II (Various artists).
LP: . . . . **FL 9015**

UNCLE MORT'S NORTH COUNTRY (Various artists).
MCSET: . . . . **ZBBC 1103**

UNCLE MORT'S SOUTH COUNTRY (Various artists).
MCSET: . . . . **ZBBC 1176**

UP LIKE THE SWALLOW (Various artists).
LP: . . . . **BRO 131**
MC: . . . . **KBRO 131**

VIENNESE FOLK MUSIC (Various artists).
2LP: **DP6 28034**

VILLAGE I WAS BORN 10 original hits from home (Various artists).
MC: . . . . **CHR 08**

WEED A RARE BATCH (Various artists).
LP: . . . . **ST 107**

WHEN SHEEPSHEARING'S DONE: SONGS FROM SOUTHERN E (Various artists).
LP: **12T 254**

WHERE WAS BUTLER? (Various artists).
LP: . . . . **FL 9048**

WHERE WOULD YOU RATHER BE TONIGHT (Various artists).
Tracks: / Passed you by: *Beer, Phil/ Mike Oldfield* / Weaver and the factory maid, The: *Steeleye Span* / Y420 Q/A: *Baynham, Grant* / Same old man: *Arizona Smoke Revue* / When Dracula went to...: *Barker, Les* / Fast lane down: *Metsers, Paul* / Tortoise: *Thackeray, Jake* / Quazi be good: *Benns, Jon/ Fairport* / Jimmy's song: *Taylor, Allan* / Electric guitar: *Hutchings, Ashley* / Black is the colour: *Simpson/Radcliffe* / When all is said and done: *Coppin, Johnny* / Nelson monologue, The: *Woolley, Shep* / Where would you rather be tonight: *Silver, Mike*.
LP: . . . . **A40111 M**

WOODSTOCK MOUNTAINS (Various artists).
LP: . . . . **SNTF 767**
LP: . . . . **ROUNDER 3018**
MC: . . . . **ROUNDER 3018C**

WORLD OF FOLK VOL 2 (Various artists).
LP: . . . . **SPA 307**

Folk 77

TRY TO REMEMBER.
Tracks: / Song for a winter's night / I dreamed you / New world in the morning / I love one day at a time / Thank you for the music / Bye bye love / I've got a winner in the goldrush / Music speaks louder than words / If I fell / Try to remember / Sound of silence / Hallelujah.
LP: . . . . **FBR 0847**

Folk Blues..

AMERICAN FOLK BLUES FESTIVAL (Various artists).
2LP: . . . . **ALB 125**

AMERICAN FOLK BLUES FESTIVAL (Various artists).
2LP: . . . . **LR 42.013**

AMERICAN FOLK BLUES FESTIVAL 1970 (Various artists).
2LP: . . . . **LR 42.021**

AMERICAN FOLK BLUES FESTIVAL 1966, VOL 2 (Various artists).
LP: **855 126**

AMERICAN FOLK BLUES FESTIVAL 1966, VOL 1 (Various artists).
LP: **855 114**

AMERICAN FOLK BLUES FESTIVAL 1964 (Various artists).
Tracks: / I'm trying to make London my home: *Various artists* / Dissatisfied: *Various artists* / Every time I get to drinking: *Various artists* / Ain't it a pity: *Various artists* / Baby please don't go: *Various artists*/ I'm a tearing little Daddy: *Various artists* / Cotton pickin' blues: *Various artists* / No title boogie: *Various artists* / Slip in mules: *Various artists* / Dust my broom: *Various artists*.
LP: . . . . **LR 42024**

AMERICAN FOLK BLUES FESTIVAL 1983 (Various artists).
2LP: . . . . **LR 42.063**

AMERICAN FOLK BLUES FESTIVAL 1985 (Various artists).
LP: . . . . **LR 42.065**

AMERICAN FOLK BLUES FESTIVAL 1982 (Various artists).
2LP: . . . . **LR 42.052/053**

AMERICAN FOLK BLUES FESTIVAL 1981 (Various artists).
LP: . . . . **LR 42.022**

AMERICAN FOLK BLUES FESTIVAL 1962 (Various artists).
Tracks: / We're gonna rock: *Various artists* / I wanna see my baby: *Various artists* / I'm in love: *Various* artists / I'm crazy 'bout you baby: *Various artists* / Stewball: *Various artists* / Let's make it baby: *Various* artists / Shake it baby: *Various artists* / Right time, The: *Various artists* / Hey baby: *Various artists*/ Love my baby: *Various artists* / Crying at the station: *Various artists* / Bye bye baby: *Various artists*.
LP: . . . . **LR 42017**

AMERICAN FOLK BLUES FESTIVAL 1972 (Various artists).
2LP: . . . . **LR 42.018**

AMERICAN FOLK BLUES FESTIVAL 1963 (Various artists).
Tracks: / Wish me well: *Various artists* / I have no friends: *Various artists* / Sittin' and cryin' the blues: *Various artists* / Crazy for my baby: *Various artists* / Grant Spivey: *Various artists* / Matt's guitar boogie: *Various artists* / I don't know: *Various artists* / Sonny Boy's harmonica blues: *Various artists*/ It's too late to cry: *Various artists* / Had my fun: *Various artists* / Five long years: *Various artists*/ Bye bye blues: *Various artists*.
LP: . . . . **LR 42023**

BEST OF THE AMERICAN FOLK BLUES FESTIVALS (1963-1967) (Various artists).
Tracks: / I'm tearing little daddy: *Various artists* / First time I met the blues: *Various artists* / Hound dog: *Various artists* / Five long years: *Various artists* / Dust my broom: *Various artists* / King of the world: *Various artists* / I'm trying to make London my home: *Various artists* / Rock island line: *Various artists*/ Come on back home: *Various artists* / Vietnam blues: *Various artists* / Aberdeen Mississippi blues: *Various artists* / Ain't it a pity: *Various artists*.
LP: . . . . **LR 42.066**

Folk Devils

GOODNIGHT IRONY.
LP: . . . . **SITUP 19**
MC: . . . . **SITCP 19**

Folk Hymnal

SINGALONG.
Tracks: / They'll know we are Christians by our love / Kumbaya / Yesterday, today and tomorrow / Where is this old world a goin? / I was in His mind / I know where I'm going / Come and praise the Lord our King / Angel rolled the stone away, The / Thank you / Let the whole world know / Happiness is the Lord / Heaven came down and glory filled my soul / He keeps me singing a happy song / Higher hands / This I believe / I have decided to follow Jesus / Somebody touched me / Wondrous love / That's the way to find happiness / Doxology.
LP: . . . . **PC 746**

Folk Synth Orchestra

FOLK SYNTH ORCHESTRA.
LP: . . . . **AMLP 856**

Folk Tales

FOLK TALES OF THE TRIBES OF AFRICA (Kitt, Eartha).
MC: **1267**

Folklore

FAVOURITE IRISH BALLADS.
MC: . . . . **GTDC 042**

GALWAY RACES, THE.
MC: . . . . **GTDC 028**

ROOM FOR COMPANY.
Tracks: / Famine Ethiopia / S.O.S..
LP: . . . . **BSS 211**

Folksongs In Welsh

FOLKSONGS IN WELSH (See under Cleaver, Emrys for details) (Cleaver, Emrys).

Folkways

OTHER NAME, THE.
LP: . . . . **FHR 029**

Folkways (Compilation)

FOLKWAYS: A VISION SHARED (See under Vison Shared, A) (Various artists).

Follett, Ken

KEY TO REBECCA, THE (Quayle, Anthony (nar)).
MCSET: . . . . **LFP 7198**

Follies

FOLLIES (1987 Original West End London cast) (Various artists).
LP: . . . . **ENCORE 3**
MC: . . . . **ENCOREC 3**

FOLLIES (1985 Lincoln Center revival cast) (Various artists).
Tracks: / Follies: Overture: *Various artists* / Beautiful girls: *Various artists* / Don't look at me: *Various artists* / Waiting for the girls upstairs: *Various artists* / Rain on the roof: *Various artists* / Ah, Paree: *Various artists* / Broadway baby: *Various artists* / Road you didn't take, The: *Various artists* / In Buddy's eyes: *Various artists* / Who's that woman?: *Various artists* / I'm still here: *Various artists*/ Too many mornings: *Various artists* / Right girl, The: *Various artists* / One more kiss: *Various artists*/ Could I leave you?: *Various artists* / Loveland: *Various artists* / You're gonna love tomorrow/ Love will see us through: *Various artists* / Buddy's blues: *Various artists* / Losing my mind: *Various artists* / Story of Lucy and Jessie, The: *Various artists* / Live, laugh, love: *Various artists* / Follies: Finale: *Various artists*.
2LP: . . . . **BL 87 128**
MCSET: . . . . **BK 87 128**

FOLLIES (1971 Original Broadway cast) (Various artists).
Tracks: / Prologue - beautiful girls: *Various artists* / Don't look at me: *Various artists* / Waiting for the girls upstairs: *Various artists* / Ah Paris, Broadway baby: *Various artists* / Road you didn't take, The: *Various artists* / In Buddy's eyes: *Various artists* / Who's that woman: *Various artists* / I'm still here: *Various* artists / Too many mornings: *Various artists* / Right girl, The: *Various artists* / Could I leave you?: *Various* artists / You're gonna love tomorrow (love will see us through): *Various artists* / God-why-don't-you-love-me blues, The: *Various artists* / Losing my mind: *Various artists* / Story of Lucy and Jessie: *Various artists*/ Live, laugh, love: *Various artists* / Love will...: *Various artists*.
LP: . . . . **EMS 1250**
MC: . . . . **TC EMS 1250**
MC: **92094.4**

FOLLIES, SCANDALS AND OTHER DIVERSIONS (Various artists).
LP: . . . . **NW 215**

Follow That Girl

FOLLOW THAT GIRL (Original London cast) (Various artists).
LP: . . . . **AEI 1121**

FOLLOW THAT GIRL (ORIGINAL ISSUE) (London cast) (Various artists).
LP: . . . . **CLP 1366**

Follow The Boys

FOLLOW THE BOYS (Original soundtrack) (Various artists).
LP: . . . . **HS 5012**

Follow The Fleet

FOLLOW THE FLEET (1936 film musical soundtrack) (Various artists).
LP: . . . . **SH 2099**

Follow The Star

FOLLOW THE STAR (Various artists).
LP: **6382 120**

Fonda, Henry (nar)

OX-BOW INCIDENT (see under Ox-Bow Incident (bk)).

Fonda, Jane

JANE FONDA WORKOUT (Various artists).
Tracks: / Warm-up: *Various artists* / Biceps curls: *Various artists* / Push ups: *Various artists* / Standing stretches: *Various artists* / Buttocks extension: *Various artists* / Lower body stretches: *Various artists*/ Upright rows: *Various artists* / Lateral raises: *Various artists* / Aerobics: *Various artists* / Lunges, quad stretch: *Various artists* / Abdominals: *Various artists*.
LP: . . . . **K 925851 1**
MC: . . . . **K 925851 4**

JANE FONDA'S WORKOUT RECORD (Various artists).
Tracks: / Can you feel it?: *Various artists* / In your letter: *Various artists* / Stomp: *Various artists*/ Bridge over troubled water: *Various artists* / Night (feel like getting down): *Various artists* / Bricklayer's beautiful daughter, The: *Various artists*.
LP: . . . . **CBS 88581**
MC: **40 88581**

JANE FONDA'S WORKOUT RECORD FOR PREGNANCY, BIRTH & RECOVERY (Various artists).
Tracks: / On posture: *Fonda, Jane* / Breathing: *Fonda, Jane* / Warm-up: *Fonda, Jane* / Daily exercise routine: *Fonda, Jane* / Pregnancy workout, The: *Fonda, Jane*.
2LP: . . . . **CBS 88620**
MCSET: **40 88620**

WORKOUT RECORD NEW AND IMPROVED (Various artists).
Tracks: / Wanna be startin' something: *Jackson, Michael* / Keep the fire burning: *REO Speedwagon* / Rhythm, part 1: *Correa, Dean* / Dance for me: *Correa, Dean* / Megatron man: *Cowley, Patrick* / Do you wanna funk: *Sylvester*/ One hundred ways: *Jones, Quincy & James Ingram* / X-cit-mental: *Correa, Dean*.
2LP: . . . . **CBS 88640**
MCSET: **40 88640**

Fong, Oden

COME FOR THE CHILDREN.
Tracks: / Mask, The / Natural man / Crazy voices / White eagle / Selfish man / Again and again / Ready to fly / Come for the children / She begins to dance.
LP: . . . . **MM 0051**
MC: . . . . **TC MM 0051**

Fonseca

MELODIES FROM PORTUGAL.
LP: . . . . **EULP 1087**
MC: . . . . **EUMC 1087**

Fontaine, Claudia

WARM LOVE (See under Beatmasters for details).

Fontaine, Eddie

NOTHIN' SHAKIN'.
LP: **33.102**

ROCK WITH ME.
Tracks: / Hey Marie, rock with me / Cool it baby / One and only / Honky tonk man / Who's Eddie / Just tryin' / Don't ya know / Nothin' shakin' / Run Elmer run / Fun lovin' / Years before, The / You can't see the sun when you're crying / Into each life some rain must fall.
LP: . . . . **CR 30266**

Fontana, Carl

GREAT FONTANA, THE.
LP: . . . . **UP 27 28**

Fontana, Wayne

GAME OF LOVE (Fontana, Wayne & the Mindbenders).
Tracks: / Game of love / She's got the power / You don't know me / Git it / Jaguar and the thunderbirds / Certain girl, A / One more time / Um, um, um, um, um, um / Where have you been? / Keep your hands off my baby / Too many tears / Girl can't help it, The / Cops and robbers / I'm gonna be a wheel someday / Since you've been gone / It's just a little bit too late.
LP: **8322601**
MC: **8322604**

WAYNE FONTANA & THE MINDBENDERS.
LP: . . . . **TL 5230**

Fontane Sisters

ROCK AGAIN LOVE.
Tracks: / Rock love / Fool around / You're mine / Listen to your heart / Ragtime rock'n'roll / Old piano roll blues, The / Rollin' stone / Still / Chanson d'amour / Got you on my mind / You always hurt the one you love / Lonesome lover blues / I understand / If I could be with you.
LP: . . . . **CR 30257**

ROCK LOVE.
Tracks: / Seventeen / I'm sticking with you / Please don't leave me / I'm in love again / Playmates / Hearts of stone / Love like a fool / You are my sunshine / Eddie my love / Billy Boy / Rock 'n' rolla / Daddy o / Jealous heart / Most of all / Banana boat song / Echoes of love.
LP: . . . . **CR 30229**

Fontenot, Allen

CAJUN HONKY TONK SONGS.
LP: **11012**
MC: . . . . **11012 TC**

Fontenot, Canray

CANRAY FONTENOT & CARRIER BROS. (Fontenot, Canray & Carrier Bros.).
LP: . . . . **ARHOOLIE 5031**

Fonteyn, Margot

DAME MARGOT FONTEYN (Fonteyn, Dame Margot).
MCSET: . . . . **SAY 6**

Food For Millions

FOOD FOR MILLIONS (See under UNESCO reports).

Foodband

FOODBAND.
Tracks: / Lovelight / You gave your love away / Running through the alley / I'm cruisin' tonight / Send me up to Mona / Workin' for the sunshine / It's so hard / Nothin' better / Starlight.
LP: . . . . **TRIX 10**

Fool Britannia

FOOL BRITANNIA (Various artists).
LP: . . . . **CEL 902**

Fool For Love

FOOL FOR LOVE (1986 film soundtrack) (Various artists).
LP: . . . . **MCA 6156**
MC: . . . . **MCAC 6156**

Fool Proof

NO FRICTION.
LP: **188804 1**
MC: **188804 4**

Fools

SOLD OUT.
Tracks: / Night out / Fine with me / Don't tell me / Sold out / Sad story / Mutual of Omaha / It's a night for beautiful girls / Spent the rent / Easy for you / I won't grow up.
LP: . . . . **AML 3008**

Fools Dance

FOOLS DANCE.
Tracks: / Sa'ha / Don Diddy song, The / Priest hole, The / Happy families / Waiting (at the sky lab landing bay) / I'm so many (talk talk).
MLP: . . . . **TURN 19**

Foort, Reginald

KEEP SMILING.
Tracks: / Keep smiling / ABC march, The / Serenade / Skaters waltz, The / Whistler and his dog, The / Whistle while you work / Some day my prince will come / I'm wishing / Heigh-ho / With a smile and a song / Dwarf's yodel song / Destiny waltz / Sanctuary of the heart / In a Persian market / In a monastery garden / In a Chinese temple garden / Bells across the meadow / Vision of Fuji-San etc, The / Majesty of the Mountain Fuji-San, The / Lone vision, The / Dance of the Japanese actors / Apotheosis of the lone vision / By the blue Hawaiian waters etc / Hula dance / Kanaka lover appears, The / Song of the hula dancer / Dance of the betrothal ceremony.
LP: . . . . **SH 338**
MC: . . . . **TC SH 338**

Football

CELTIC SOUVENIR Highlights 1965-1970.
LP: . . . . **QP 3/70**

CUP WINNERS CUP-1971 Chelsea v Real Madrid.
LP: . . . . **QP 8/71**

EUROPEAN CUP FINAL-1968 (Manchester United v Benfica).
LP: . . . . **QP 12/73**

EUROPEAN CUP FINAL-1977 (Liverpool v Borrusia MGB).
LP: . . . . **QP 24/77**

EUROPEAN CUP FINAL-1978 (Liverpool v Bruges).
LP: . . . . **QP 27/78**

EUROPEAN CUP FINAL-1981 (Liverpool v Real Madrid).
LP: . . . . **QP 37/81**

EUROPEAN CUP FINAL-1982 (Villa-The Champions of Europe).
LP: . . . . **QP 39/82**

EUROPEAN CUP FINALS-1979 AND 1980 (Nottingham forest's double).
LP: . . . . **QP 33/80**

F.A. CUP FINAL-1970 Chelsea v Leeds.
LP: . . . . **QP 4/70**

F.A. CUP FINAL-1971 Arsenal v Liverpool.
LP: . . . . **QP 7/71**

F.A. CUP FINAL-1972 Arsenal v Leeds.
LP: . . . . **REC 122**

F.A. CUP FINAL-1974 Liverpool v Newcastle.
LP: . . . . **QP 15/74**

F.A. CUP FINAL-1975 West Ham v Fulham.
LP: . . . . **QP 17/75**

F.A. CUP FINAL-1976 Southampton v Manchester United.
LP: . . . . **QP 19/76**

F.A. CUP FINAL-1977 Manchester United v Liverpool.
LP: . . . . **QP 23/77**

F.A. CUP FINAL-1978 Ipswich v Arsenal.
LP: . . . . **QP 26/78**

F.A. CUP FINAL-1979 Arsenal v Manchester.
LP: . . . . **QP 29/79**

F.A. CUP FINAL-1980 West Ham v Arsenal.
LP: . . . . **QP 31/80**

LEAGUE CHAMPIONSHIP 1979-80 SEASON Liverpool.
LP: . . . . **QP 32/80**

LEAGUE CHAMPIONSHIP 1980-81 SEASON Aston Villa.
LP: . . . . **QP 36/81**

LEAGUE CUP FINAL-1971 Tottenham Hotspurs v Aston Villa.
LP: . . . . **QP 6/71**

LEAGUE CUP FINAL-1972 Stoke City v Chelsea.
LP: . . . . **QP 9/72**

LEAGUE CUP FINAL-1973 Tottenham Hotspurs v Norwich.
LP: . . . . **QP 10/73**

LEAGUE CUP FINAL-1974 Wolves v Manchester city.
LP: . . . . **QP 14/74**

LEAGUE CUP FINAL-1975 Aston Villa v Norwich.
LP: . . . . **QP 16/75**

LEAGUE CUP FINAL-1976 Manchester city v Newcastle.
LP: . . . . **QP 18/76**

LEAGUE CUP FINAL-1977 Aston Villa v Everton.
LP: . . . . **QP 22/77**

LEAGUE CUP FINAL-1978 Nottingham Forest v Liverpool.
LP: . . . . **QP 25/78**

LEAGUE CUP FINAL-1979 Nottingham Forest v Southampton.
LP: . . . . **QP 28/79**

LEAGUE CUP FINAL-1980 Wolves v Nottingham Forest.
LP: . . . . **QP 30/80**

LEAGUE CUP FINAL-1981 (Liverpool v West Ham).
LP: . . . . **QP 34/81**

LEAGUE CUP FINAL-1982 (Liverpool v Tottenham Hotspur).
LP: . . . . **QP 38/82**

OFFICIAL MUSIC - MEXICO '86 (Various artists).
Tracks: / Opus one(Canada): *Various artists* / Opus two(Morocco,Algeria): *Various artists* / Opus three(Spain,Portugal): *Various artists* / Opus four(Russia,Poland,Hungary,Bulgaria): *Various artists* / Opus five(Italy,France): *Various artists* / Opus six(England,Scotland,N.Ireland): *Various artists* / Opus seven(S.Korea,Iraq): *Various artists*/ Opus eight(Belgium,Denmark,Germany): *Various artists* / Opus nine (Brazil,Argentina,Paraguay,Uruguay): *Various artists*/ Goodbye Mexico: *Various artists*.
LP: . . . . **MTM 021**

SCOTTISH CUP-1976 (Rangers v Hearts).
LP: . . . . **QP 20/76**

UEFA CUP-1976 (Liverpool v Bruges).
LP: . . . . **QP 21/76**

WORLD CUP FINALS-1966 & 1970 HIGHLIGHTS.
LP: . . . . **QP 5/70**

WORLD CUP SOUVENIR ALBUM (Various artists).
LP: . . . . **KBLP 502**
MC: . . . . **ZCKBP 502**

Footloose

FOOTLOOSE (1986 film soundtrack) (Various artists).
Tracks: / Footloose: *Loggins, Kenny* / Let's hear it for the boy: *Williams, Deniece* / Almost paradise: *Wilson, Ann & Mike Reno* / Holding out for a hero: *Tyler, Bonnie* / Dancing in the street: *Shalamar* / I'm free (heaven helps the man): *Loggins, Kenny* / Somebody's eyes: *Bonoff, Karla* / Girl gets around, The: *Hagar, Sammy*/ Never: *Moving Pictures*.
LP: . . . . **CBS 70246**
LP: **4630001**
MC: **4630004**
MC: **40 70246**

Footstompers

FOOTSTOMPERS (Various artists) (Various artists).
Tracks: / Like one: *Carter, Jean* / Take away the painstain: *Austin, Patti* / Ten shades of blue: *Spindles*/ You should o' held on: *7th Avenue Aviators* / You don't love me anymore: *Caswell, Johnny* / Tears (nothing but tears): *Roye, Lee* / I surrender: *Holman, Eddie* / You've been away: *Parker, Rubin* / Larue: *Edmund Jr., Lada* / I'll always need you: *Barry, Len* / Playin' hide and seek: *Regan, Eddie* / Soul symphony: *Sons of Moses* / We go together: *August & Duneen* / Cracked up over you: *White, Danny*.
LP: . . . . **KENT 017**

For A Few Dollars More

FOR A FEW DOLLARS MORE (Film soundtrack) (Morricone, Ennio).
LP: **26 21208**

FOR A FEW DOLLARS MORE/ FISTFUL OF DOLLARS (See under Fistful of dollars) (Various artists).

For A Few Pussies More

FOR A FEW PUSSIES MORE (Various artists).
LP: . . . . **GRAM 29**

For Collectors Only

FOR COLLECTORS ONLY (Various artists).
Tracks: / Not me baby: *Silhouettes* / Hey girl (where are you going): *Topics, The* / Sweet magic: *Servicemen, The* / What a love this is (oh, oh, oh): *Revlons, The* / Baby I dig you: *Anderson, Gene & The Dynamic Psychedelics*/ I must love you: *Timothy Wilson* / Too much of a good thing: *Ambassadors* / Something is bad: *Nomads*/ Nothing can compare to you: *Velvet Satins, the* / I don't like to lose: *Group, The* / Try my love: *Sequins, The* / Meet me halfway: *Lillie Bryant* / My life with you: *Traditions* / You didn't have to leave: *Ellusions*.
LP: . . . . **LPSS 102**
MC: . . . . **CLPSS 102**

For Dancers...

FOR DANCERS ALSO (Various artists).
Tracks: / Lay this burden down: *Love, Mary* / If I could turn back the hands of time: *Garrett, Vernon* / Beauty is just skin deep: *Turner, Ike & Tina* / My baby needs me: *Baker, Yvonne* / Good taste of love: *Monday, Danny* / Can it be me: *Williams, Mel* / Wanting you: *Bee, Jimmy* / Take your shoes off (part II): *Booker T & The MG's* / Hole in the wall: *Other Bros* / Talkin' woman: *Fulson, Lowell* / Everybody needs love: *Gauff, Willie & The Love Brothers* / Running out: *Garrett, Vernon* / Country girl: *Otis, Johnny Show* / What kind of man are you: *Day, Jackie* / I'm in your hands: *Love, Mary*.
LP: . . . . **KENT 002**

FOR DANCERS ALWAYS (Various artists).
Tracks: / You turned my bitter into sweet: *Love, Mary* / Let me know: *Love, Mary* / Lay this burden down: *Love, Mary* / I'm in your hands: *Love, Mary* / I can feel your love: *Taylor, Felice* / Baby, without you: *Monday, Danny* / Good taste of love: *Monday, Danny* / Your love has made me a man: *Hutch, Willie* / I'm so thankful: *Ikettes* / In the sunshine: *Marvellos* / Before it's too late: *Day, Jackie* / What kind of man are you?: *Day, Jackie* / I can't believe what you say: *Turner, Ike & Tina* / Gimme gimme: *Hill, Z.Z.* / Baby I'm sorry: *Hill, Z.Z.* / You just cheat and lie: *Hill, Z.Z.* / My aching back: *Fulson, Lowell* / Talkin' woman: *Fulson, Lowell* / Come back baby: *Young, Tami* / I've been taken for a ride: *Saints* / Dancing fast, dancing slow: *Intentions* / If I could turn back the hands of time: *Garrett, Vernon* / Running out: *Garrett, Vernon* / Beauty is just skin deep: *Sweethearts* / My baby needs me: *Baker, Yvonne* / Can it be me: *Williams, Mel* / Wanting you: *Bee, Jimmy* / Take your shoes off: *Booker T Averham & The Mustangs* / Hole in the wall: *Other Brothers* / Everybody needs love: *Gauff, Willie & The Love Brothers* / Country girl: *Johnny Otis Show*.
MC: . . . . **KENC 805**

FOR DANCERS ONLY (Various artists).
Tracks: / You turned my bitter into sweet: *Love, Mary* / I can feel your love: *Taylor, Felice* / Baby, without you: *Monday, Danny* / Your love has made me a man: *Hutch, Willie* / I'm so thankful: *Ikettes* / In the sunshine: *Marvellos* / Before it's too late: *Day, Jackie* / I can't believe what you say: *Turner, Ike & Tina* / Gimme gimme: *Hill, Z.Z.* / My aching back: *Fulson, Lowell* / Come back baby: *Young, Tami* / I've been taken for a ride: *Saints* / Dancing fast, dancing slow: *Intentions* / Baby, I'm sorry: *Hill, Z.Z.* / Let me know: *Love, Mary* / If you just cheat and lie: *Hill, Z.Z.*.
LP: . . . . **KENT 001**

For Lovers Only

FOR LOVERS ONLY (Various artists).
Tracks: / Total eclipse of the heart: *Tyler, Bonnie* / Sorry seems to be the hardest word: *John, Elton* / Forever autumn: *Hayward, Justin* / Can't get used to losing you: *Beat* / Cry me a river: *Wilson, Mari* / What becomes of the broken hearted?: *Ruffin, Jimmy* / Without you: *Nilsson (Harry)* / I'm not in love / Words: *Tremeloes* / Hard to say I'm sorry: *Chicago* / Being with you: *Robinson, Smokey* / Touch me in the morning: *Ross, Diana* / Dancing tight: *Galaxy* / High life: *Modern Romance* / Love come down: *King, Evelyn "Champagne"* / Happening, The: *Ross, Diana & The Supremes* / Three times a lady: *Commodores* / Just the way you are: *Joel, Billy*.
LP: . . . . **RTL 2093**
MC: . . . . **4C RTL 2093**

For Me & My Gal

FOR ME AND MY GAL (Film soundtrack) (Various artists).
LP: . . . . **STK 107**

For Sentimental

FOR SENTIMENTAL REASONS 1942-49 (Various artists).
Tracks: / Golden earrings: *Lee, Peggy* / Manana: *Lee, Peggy* / I love you for sentimental reasons: *Cole, Nat King* / Christmas song, The: *Cole, Nat King Trio* / Blue moon: *Various artists* / Again: *Various artists* / Tampico: *Kenton, Stan & His Orchestra* / Tree in the meadow, A: *Whiting, Margaret* / Long ago and far away: *Stafford, Jo* / Dream: *Pied Pipers* / Hurry on down: *Lutcher, Nellie* / Personality: *Mercer, Johnny & The Pied Pipers* / On the Atchison, Topeka and Santa Fe: *Mercer, Johnny & The Pied Pipers* / Buttons and bows: *Dinning Sisters* / Cow-cow boogie: *Slack, Freddie & His Orch.* / Temptation: *Ingle, Red & The Natural Seven*.
LP: . . . . **MOIR 502**
MC: . . . . **CMOIR 502**

For The Good Times

FOR THE GOOD TIMES (Various artists).
Tracks: / Star dust: *Various artists* / Very special love song, A: *Various artists* / I don't know why (I just do): *Various artists* / Please help me, I'm falling: *Various artists* / Near you: *Various artists* / Things I might have been, The: *Various artists* / Sweet music man: *Various artists* / Me and the elephant: *Various artists* / True love ways: *Various artists* / Faded love: *Various artists* / Always: *Various artists* / My happiness: *Various artists* / Most beautiful girl, The: *Various artists* / But love me: *Various artists* / Thing called love, A: *Various artists* / Here we are: *Various artists* / Miss the Mississippi and you: *Various artists* / Best of my love: *Various artists* / Only the lonely know: *Various artists* / For the good times: *Various artists*.
LP: . . . . **EPC 25035**

For Those I Loved

FOR THOSE I LOVED (Original soundtrack) (Various artists).
Tracks: / For those I love: *Various artists* / First love: *Various artists* / Insurrection march: *Various artists* / Past, The: *Various artists* / Melody mansion: *Various artists* / Treblinka: *Various artists* / Escape: *Various artists* / Zofia: *Various artists* / Deportation: *Various artists* / Cafe Sztuka: *Various artists* / Ghetto uprising, The: *Various artists* / Fire: *Various artists* / Hope and the future: *Various artists*.
LP: . . . . **REH 518**
MC: . . . . **ZCR 518**

FOR THOSE I LOVED - VOL.2 (Various artists).
LP: **803 073**
MC: **804 073**

For Whom The Bell

FOR WHOM THE BELL TOLLS (1943 film soundtrack) (Various artists).
LP: . . . . **DUN 112**

For Your Eyes Only

FOR YOUR EYES ONLY (Film soundtrack) (Various artists).
MC: . . . . **TCLBG 30337**
LP: . . . . **LBG 30337**

Forbert, Steve

ALIVE ON ARRIVAL.
Tracks: / Goin down to Laurel / Steve Forbert's midsummer nights toast / Thinkin / What kind of guy / It isn't gonna be that way / Big city cat / Grand central station / March 18, 1977 / Tonight I feel so far away from home / Settle down / You can not win if you do not play.
MC: **40 32053**
LP: . . . . **EPC 83308**

JACK RABBIT SLIM.
LP: . . . . **EPC 83879**

LITTLE STEVIE ORBIT.
Tracks: / Get well soon / Cellophane city / Song for Carmelita / Laughter Lou / Song for Katrina / One more glass of beer / Lucky / Rain / I'm an automobile / Schoolgirl / If you gotta ask you'll never know / Lonely girl / Visitor.
LP: . . . . **EPC 84501**

STEVE FORBERT.
Tracks: / He's gotta live up to his shoes / Ya ya / When you walk in the room / Listen to me / Oh so close / You're darn right / Prisoner of stardom / On the beach / Lost / It takes a whole lotta help / Beautiful Diana.
LP: . . . . **EPC 85297**

STREETS OF THIS TOWN.
Tracks: / Running on love / Don't tell me I know / I blinked once / Mexico / As we live and breathe / On the streets of this town / Hope, faith and love / Perfect stranger / Wait a little longer / Search your heart.
MC: . . . . **WX 167C**
LP: . . . . **WX 167**
MC: . . . . **GEFC 24194**

Forbes, Bryan

ENDLESS GAME.
MC: . . . . **TTDMC 407**

Forbes, Roy

LOVE TURNS TO ICE.
LP: . . . . **FF 499**

Forbes, Sandy

NIGHTINGALE SANG IN BERKELEY SQUARE, A.
Tracks: / You'd be so nice to come home to / Nightingale sang in Berkeley Square, A / Jersey bounce / Room five hundred and four / Tag und nacht / Run rabbit run / White cliffs of Dover, The / Que reste t'il de nos amours / Blues in the night / Deep purple / Cherokee / Seule ce soir / Begin the beguine / Lambert's nachtlokal / Tuxedo junction / Last time I saw Paris, The / Deep in a dream / It's a lovely day today.
MC: . . . . **HSC 659**

Forbidden

FORBIDDEN EVIL.
LP: . . . . **FLAG 27**
MC: . . . . **TFLAG 27**

Forbidden Broadway

FORBIDDEN BROADWAY (Original Broadway cast) (Various artists).
LP: . . . . **SBL 12585**
MC: . . . . **SBLC 12585**

Forbidden Planet

FORBIDDEN PLANET (Original soundtrack) (Various artists).
LP: . . . . **GNPSPR 001**
MC: **GNP5PR 001**

Forbidden Zone

FORBIDDEN ZONE (Original soundtrack) (Various artists).
LP: . . . . **STV 81170**
MC: . . . . **VSC 5268**

Force

FORCE.
Tracks: / New frontiers / Eye to eye / No fixed emotion / Amigo / Change your heart / Tomorrow may never come / All too much / Turn to love / All alone / I hear the sound / Shout.
LP: **790555 1**
MC: **790555 4**

SET ME FREE.
LP: . . . . **HMRLP 16**
MC: . . . . **HMRMC 16**

Force 10

FORCE 10.
Tracks: / Watanabe / Hypnotised / I feel so amused / Pictures (of my favourite things) / Mountain of love / Show me your love / Bastinado / My future / I'll see you.
LP: . . . . **K 56932**

Force Dimension

DEUS EX MACHINA.
LP: . . . . **KK 049**

Force Fed

CLAUSTROPHOBIA.
LP: . . . . **FACE 008**

Force M.D.'s

LOVE LETTERS.
Tracks: / Tears / Forgive me girl / Itchin' for a scratch.
LP: . . . . **ILPS 9820**

TENDER LOVE.
Tracks: / One plus one / Tears / Uh oh / Here I go again / Chillin' / Tender love / Will you be my girlfriend? / Walking on air / Force MD's meet The Fat Boys / Smoke on the water / Shine it on me.
LP: . . . . **ILPS 9837**
MC: . . . . **ICT 9837**

TOUCH AND GO.
Tracks: / Love is a house / Would you love me? / Touch and go / Couldn't care less / Your love drives me crazy / Midnite lover / Take your love back / Sweet dreams.
LP: . . . . **WX 134**
MC: . . . . **WX 134 C**
LP: **254 889 1**
MC: **254 889 4**

Force Of Music

LIBERATED DUB.
Tracks: / Moonlight city / Baktu / Waterhouse / Marverly / Riverton city / Cockburn pen / Bell rock / Whitewing walk / Tower hill / Central village.
LP: . . . . **UAS 30229**

Forced Entry

FORCED ENTRY.
LP: . . . . **ATOMH 004**

Forcefield

FORCEFIELD.
Tracks: / Set me free / Best shot / Runaway / Sunshine of your love / Shine it on me / Whole lotta love / Black cat / White room / You really got me / Fire in the city / Keep on running / Smoke on the water.
LP: . . . . **PTLS 1088**

MC: . . . . PTLC 1088

FORCEFIELD IV (Various artists).
MC: . . . . PCOM 1110

TALISMAN, THE.
Tracks: / Talisman, The / Year of the dragon / Tired of waiting for you / Heartache / Good is good / Carrie / Without your love / I lose again / Mercenary, The / Black night (Only on CD.) / I lose again (instrumental version) (Only on CD.).
LP: . . . . PTLS 1095
MC: . . . . PTLC 1095

Forces Favourites

END CONSCRIPTION CAMPAIGN OF S. AFRICA (Various artists).
LP: . . . . ROUNDER 4023
MC: . . . . ROUNDER 4023C

Forcione, Antonio

CELEBRATION (see Niebla, Eduardo) (Forcione, Antonio/Eduardo Niebla).

Forces Of Music

KING AND QUEEN DUB.
LP: . . . . TWLP 1017

Ford, Adrian

ADRIAN FORD'S ORCHESTRA (Ford, Adrian & His Orchestra).
LP: . . . . ANTEATER 006

Ford, Charles

REAL CHARLES FORD BAND, THE.
LP: . . . . ARHOOLIE 4005

REUNION, A (Ford, Charles Band).
LP: . . . . BR 101

Ford, Clinton

CLINTON FORD.
LP: . . . . PS 40021

Ford, Emile

VERY BEST OF EMILE FORD & THE CHECKMATES (Ford, Emile & The Checkmates).
LP: . . . . SEE 309
MC: . . . . SEEK 309

Ford, Frankie

LET'S TAKE A SEA CRUISE WITH....
Tracks: / Sea cruise / Alimony / I want to be your man / It must be jelly / Watchdog / What's going on? / Roberta / I'm worried over you / You talk too much / Hour of need / If you've got troubles / Cheatin' woman.
LP: . . . . CH 67

NEW ORLEANS DYNAMO.
Tracks: / Don't drop it / Certain girl, A / Sick and tired / Whisky heaven / Fine thang / Don't you know Yockomo? / That's right / Lipstick traces (on a cigarette) / Rockin' behind the Iron Curtain / Yours truly / I wanna walk you home / Bony Moronie.
LP: . . . . CH 116

Ford, Gerry

ALL OVER AGAIN.
Tracks: / If I had to do it all over again / After all these years / Till it snows in Mexico / They call him boxcar / There I go dreaming again / I always get it right / Till I'm too old to die young / True true love never dies / I never once stopped loving you / Jesus, I need to talk to you / Dim the lights and pour wine / Your love.
LP: . . . . TT 108
MC: . . . . CTT 108

BETTER MAN.
Tracks: / On second thought / If tomorrow never comes / Somebody up there / What God has joined together / It don't hurt to dream / Fourteen minutes old / Better man, A / It's our anniversary / Lonely farmer's daughter / Alone / Don't play faded love.
LP: . . . . TT 117
MC: . . . . CTT 117

FAMILY BIBLE.
Tracks: / Family bible / Who will sing for me / Lord I'd forgotten / One of these days / Someone is looking for someone like you / He took your place / What God has joined together / Jesus I need to talk to you / Just a closer walk with thee / 'Til I'm too old to die young / Gone away.
MC: . . . . CTT 116

LET'S HEAR IT FOR THE WORKING MAN.
Tracks: / Let's hear it for the working man / Goodbye / I'll be there (if you ever want me) / Roads and other reasons / Storms never last / I wish that I had loved you better / Slippin' away / I came so close to calling you last night / Drink it down lady / I'm getting better / Sweet dreams / Freedom highway.
LP: . . . . BRA 1016
MC: . . . . BRC 1016

MEMORY MACHINE.
Tracks: / Memory machine / There goes my everything / Teddy bear song, The / Daisy a day / Rainbows and roses / I love love songs / Lonesome medley / I will love you all my life / Everything's a waltz / I wouldn't change you if I could / Make the world go away / Daddy's farm.
MC: . . . . CTT 102

ON THE ROAD.
Tracks: / On the road to loving me again / Teardrop on a rose / I want you back again / It wasn't me who said I owned a goldmine / Ruby, don't take your love to town / Blue eyes crying in the rain / She loves my troubles away / Lord I'd forgotten / One of these days / Great mail robbery, The / Heartache following me, A / Easy.
LP: . . . . BRA 1010
MC: . . . . BRC 1010

STRANGEST THINGS HAVE HAPPENED.
Tracks: / I wish that I could fall in love today / Forgiving you was easy / Even cowgirls get the blues / You make me feel like a man / Slowly but surely / I have you / Stranger things have happened / Storms of life, The / Anger and tears / Excuse me (I think I've got a heartache) / Life turned her that way / Carmen.
MC: . . . . CTT 110

THANK GOD FOR RADIO.
Tracks: / Thank God for radio / I don't care / What is love? / Are you teasing me? / Who will sing for me / Let the rest of the world go by / I'll never need another you / Amazing love / Got no reason now for going home / This working mans got you / Have you ever been lonely / Someone is looking for someone like you.
LP: . . . . TT 103
MC: . . . . CTT 103

Ford, Jed

I WONDER WHAT SHE'S DOING NOW.
LP: . . . . SRTZ 75346

IS ANYONE GOIN' TO SAN ANTONE.
LP: . . . . SRTM 73325

JED FORD.
MC: . . . . VCA 075

Ford, Ken

CANADIAN PACIFIC (Ford, Ken/Billie).
MC: . . . . VCA 039

COUNTRY STARS (Ford, Ken/Billie).
LP: . . . . SBOL 4025

I DON'T WANT TO CRY (Ford, Ken/ Billie).
LP: . . . . LKLP 6370

KEN AND BILLIE FORD (Ford, Ken/ Billie).
MC: . . . . VCA 083

REMEMBER THE ALAMO (Ford, Ken/ Billie).
LP: . . . . SDLA 4002
MC: . . . . VCA 088

Ford, Lita

DANCIN ON THE EDGE.
LP: . . . . VERL 13
MC: . . . . VERLC 13

LITA.
Tracks: / Back to the cave / Can't catch me / Blueberry / Kiss me deadly / Falling in and out of love / Fatal passion / Under the gun / Broken dreams / Close my eyes forever.
LP: . . . . PL 86397
MC: . . . . PK 86397

LITA FORD: INTERVIEW PICTURE DISC.
LPPD: . . . . BAK 2133

OUT FOR BLOOD (Ford, Lita Band).
Tracks: / Out for blood / Stay with me baby / Just a feeling / Ready willing and able / Die for me only / Rock 'n' roll made what I am today / If you can't live with it / On the run / Any way that you want me / I can't stand it.
LP: . . . . MERL 26
MC: . . . . MERLC 26

STILETTO.
Tracks: / Your wake up call / Dedication / Lisa / Big gun / Bad boy / Cherry red / Hungry / Stiletto / Ripper, The / Only women bleed / Aces and high / Outro.
LP: . . . . PL 82090
MC: . . . . PK 82090

Ford, Lynn

GIVE ME A CHANCE.
LP: . . . . CPL 101

Ford, Pennye

PENNYE.
Tracks: / I feel the music / Uh, oh I made a mistake / Change your wicked ways / Serious love / Don't you know I love you / Ready for love / Dangerous / Never let you go.
LP: . . . . PL 89449
MC: . . . . PK 89449

Ford, Ricky

3 R'S, THE (see Rodney,Red/Richie Cole/Ricky Ford) (Ford, Ricky/Red Rodney/Richie Cole).

FLYING COLORS.
Tracks: / Jordanian walk / Chelsea Bridge / Take the Coltrane / Bye-ya / Olympic glaze / Portrait of Mingus / Flying color.
LP: . . . . MR 5227

INTERPRETATIONS.
Tracks: / Interpretations, opus 5 / Moon mist / Seabea / Fix or repair / Daily / Lady A / Bostonova / Dexter.
LP: . . . . MR 5275

LOXODONTA AFRICANA (The Jazz Sound).
Tracks: / Loxodonta Africana / UCIL / Blues Peru / Dexter / My romance / One up one down / Aerolinos.
LP: . . . . NW 204

MANHATTAN BLUES.
Tracks: / In walked Bud / Misty / Ode to crispus attacks / Bop nouveau / My little strayhorn / Manhattan blues / Half nelson.
LP: . . . . CS 9036

MANHATTAN PLAZA.
Tracks: / Fadism / Afternoon in New York / Diane's melody / Ceal's place / On the Plaza / If you could see me now / Olean visit.
LP: . . . . MR 5188

SHORTER IDEAS.
Tracks: / Yes or no / Miyako / Dance cadaverous / Pinocchio / Tabloid blues / Wolf trap / Happy reunion.
LP: . . . . MR 5314

Ford, Robben

ROBBEN FORD.
LP: . . . . K 925647 1
MC: . . . . K 925647 4

TALK TO YOUR DAUGHTER.
Tracks: / Talk to your daughter / Wild about you (can't hold out much longer) / Help the poor / Ain't got nothing but the blues / Born under a bad sign / I got over it / Revelation / Getaway / Can't let her go.
LP: 925647 1
MC: 925647 4

Ford, Rosemarie

I WANNA DANCE WITH SOMEBODY.
Tracks: / I wanna dance with somebody / Miss you like crazy / I've had the time of my life / How am I supposed to live without out / If love is forever / Get here / 1-2-3 / If I were your woman / Crazy for you / Too little too late / Another day in paradise / Hold out for love.
LP: . . . . ADD 26
MC: . . . . ZDD 26

Ford, Sugar Ray

EXOTIC HOTSHOTS (Ford, Sugar Ray & The Hotshots).
Tracks: / Mambo rock / She is the most / Rock around the island / Oop pop a da / Caldonia / Big fat lie / Rumba chile / Two eyes / No more / Cool it baby / If love is a fortune.
LP: . . . . WIK 37

Ford, Tennessee Ernie

CAPITOL COLLECTORS SERIES: TENNESSEE ERNIE FORD.
Tracks: / Tennessee border No. 1 / Country junction / Smokey Mountain boogie / Mule train / Anticipation blues / Cry of the wild goose / I'll never be free / Ain't nobody's business / Shot gun boogie / Tailor made woman / I'm a bad man / Strange little girl, The / Mister and Mississippi / Kissin' bug boogie / Blackberry boogie / Hog-tied over you / I don't know / Hey Mr. Cotton picker / Celebration / Catfish boogie / Honeymoon's over, The / River of no return / Ballad of Davy Crockett, The / His hands / Sixteen tons / Nine pound hammer / That's all / In the middle of an island / Hicktown.
MC: C4 95291

COUNTRY COLLECTION.
MC: . . . . KNMC 13056

FARMYARD BOOGIE (Ford, Tennessee Ernie & Friends).
Tracks: / Hey Mr. Cotton Picker / Tennessee local / Celebratin' / I'm hog tied over you / Ain't gonna let it happen no more / Rock city boogie / I'll never be free / Stack o lee / Milk 'em in the morning / Kiss me big / Tailor made woman / Ain't nobody's business / Everybody's got a girl but me / Snowshoe Thompson / Anticipation blues / Feed 'em in the morning blues / Kissin' bug boogie / Don't start courtin' in a hot rod / My hobby / False hearted girl.
LP: . . . . SEE 262

FORD FAVOURITES.
Tracks: / Watermelon song, The / One suit / Have you seen her / Call me darling / That's all / Sixteen tons / River of no return / You don't have to be a baby to cry / First born / Give me your word.
LP: . . . . HAT 3051
MC: . . . . HATC 3051

HE TOUCHED ME.
Tracks: / Glory to His name / He'll understand and say "Well done" / I will sing of my Redeemer / Am I a soldier of the Cross? / Since Jesus came into my heart / He touched me / Almighty Father, strong to save / We're marching to Zion / He leadeth me / Evening prayer, An.
LP: . . . . WST 9579
MC: . . . . WC 9579

OL' ROCKIN' ERN.
Tracks: / Milk 'em in the morning blues / Catfish boogie / Anticipation blues / Country junction / Shotgun boogie / She's my baby / Blackberry boogie / Kiss me big / Ain't nobody's business / Smokey mountain boogie / I ain't gonna let it happen no more / Lord's lariat, The.
LP: . . . . HAT 3040
MC: . . . . HATC 3040

SIXTEEN TONS.
Tracks: / Milk 'em in the morning blues / Country junction / Smoky mountain boogie / Anticipation blues / Mule train / Cry of the wild goose / My hobby / Feed 'em in the morning blues / Shot gun boogie / Tailormade woman / You're my sugar / Rock City boogie / Kissin' bug boogie / Hey good lookin' / Hambone / Everybody's got a girl but me / Snow shoe Thompson / Blackberry boogie / Hey Mr. Cotton Picker / Kiss me big / Catfish boogie / Ballad of Davy Crockett, The / Sixteen tons / Rovin' gambler / Black eyed Susan Brown.
MC: 1A220 1583344
LP: . . . . HAT 3118
MC: . . . . HATC 3118

SUNDAY'S STILL A SPECIAL DAY.
Tracks: / Turn your radio on / Holy holy holy / Name of Jesus, The / Holy Holy / Reach out to Jesus / Put your hand in the hand / Jesus I come / May I introduce you to a friend / I've found a friend / Goodnight and good morning / Sunday's still a special day / Break thou the bread of life / Come, ye thankful people, come / My tribute / Crown him with many crowns / Face to face / Won't be long / When I reach that city / Saved by grace / I wish we'd all been ready.
LP: . . . . WRD 3009
MC: . . . . TCWR 3009

SWEET HOUR OF PRAYER.
MC: 4XL 9169

SWING WIDE YOUR GOLDEN GATE (Ford, Tennessee Ernie & The Jordanaires).
Tracks: / Swing wide your golden gate / How big is God? / Just a little while / Mansion over the hilltop / I like the old time way / What would you give in exchange? / Bring back the springtime / Unclouded day, The / Room at the cross / One day at a time.
LP: . . . . WST 9588
MC: . . . . WC 9588

TELL ME THE OLD, OLD STORY.
Tracks: / Tell me the old, old story / Send the light / When we all get to Heaven / Let others see Jesus in you / Stand up for Jesus / Only believe / Yield not to temptation / Are you washed in the blood? / Standing on the promises / Revive us again.
LP: . . . . WST 9598
MC: . . . . WC 9598

THERE'S A SONG IN MY HEART.
Tracks: / I'll fly away / His hands / I'll be a friend to Jesus / If I could hear my mother pray again / Ol' wooded brook, The / Leavin' on my mind / Operator (give me Jesus on the line) / Jesus paid it all / Handshakes and smiles / He knows what I need / Amazing grace.
LP: . . . . WST 9622
MC: . . . . WC 9622

VERY BEST OF TENNESSEE ERNIE FORD.
Tracks: / Sixteen tons / Kentucky waltz / Blackberry boogie / River of no return / Milk 'em in the morning blues / Bright lights and blonde haired women / Tennessee local / Ballad of Davy Crockett, The / Shot gun boogie / Give me your word / Feed 'em in the morning blues / Stack-o-lee / Anticipation blues / You don't have to be a baby to cry / Mule train / Old rugged cross, The.
LP: . . . . MFP 5611

Ford, Tommy

MODEL T.
Tracks: / Tommy Ford reel / George Bell polka / Slow air / Shufflin' Sammy / Continental caprice / Jigs selection / Bonnie lass o' Bon Accord / Jolson medley / Waltz time / Slow air march and

reel / Two step / Barn dance - Fiona and Bill / Pentland slopes / Dublane medley.
LP: . . . . LILP 5124
MC: . . . . LICS 5124

Forde, Ben

LIGHTS OF HOME, THE.
Tracks: / Walk beside me / What a friend we have in Jesus / Lights of home, The / Living sermon for thee, A / Speak louder / Let the spirit work in silence / Give it away / Jesus took my burdens / Who at my door is standing / Because he lives / Each step I take / Will you be ready.
LP: . . . . PC 446

SUPREME SACRIFICE, THE.
Tracks: / Only a prayer away / Give me a heart like thine / Brighten the corner where you are / What a day that will be / Just a closer walk with thee / Hold the fort / Supreme sacrifice, The / I'm going higher some day / Sweet by and by / I believe in a hill called Mount Calvary / Build me a cabin.
LP: . . . . PC 428

Forder, Timothy

BILL THE MINDER.
Tracks: / Old Crispin / King, The / Navigator, The / Aunt Galladia / Respectable gentleman, The / Chloe / Doctor, The / Sicilian cleaning lady, The / Button crane of Bararoo, The / Waiter, The / Bosworth.
MC: . . . . TS 349

Fordham, Julia

JULIA FORDHAM.
Tracks: / Happy ever after / Comfort of strangers, The / Few too many / Invisible war / My lover's keeper / Cocooned / Where does the time go? / Woman of the 80's / Other woman, The / Behind closed doors / Unconditional love.
LP: . . . . CIRCA 4
MC: . . . . CIRC 4
LP: . . . . JULIA 4
MC: . . . . JULIAC 4

PORCELAIN.
Tracks: / Lock and key / Porcelain / Girlfriend / For you only for you / Genius / Did I happen to mention / Towerblock / Island / Your lovely face / Prince of peace.
LP: . . . . CIRCA 10
MC: . . . . CIRC 10

Foreigner

AGENT PROVOCATEUR.
Tracks: / Tooth and nail / That was yesterday / I want to know what love is / Growing up the hard way / Reaction to action / Stranger in my own house / Love in vain / Down on love / Two different worlds / She's too tough.
LP: 781 999-1
MC: 781 999-4

DOUBLE VISION.
Tracks: / Hot blooded / Blue morning, blue day / You're all I am / Back where you belong / Love has taken it's toll / Double vision / Tramontane / I have waited so long / Lonely children / Spellbinder.
LP: . . . . K 50476
MC: K4 50476

FOREIGNER.
Tracks: / Feels like the first time / Cold as ice / Starrider / Headknocker / Damage is done / Long long way from home / Woman oh woman / At war with the world / Fool for the anyway / I need you.
LP: . . . . K 50356
MC: K4 50356

HEAD GAMES.
Tracks: / Dirty white boy / Love on the telephone / Women I'll get even with you / Seventeen / Head games / Modern day / Blinded by science / Do what you like / Rev on the red line.
LP: . . . . K 50561
MC: K4 50651

INSIDE INFORMATION.
Tracks: / Heart turns to stone / Can't wait / Say you will / I don't want to live without you / Night to remember, A / Inside information / Beat of my heart / Face to face / Out of the blue / Counting every minute.
LP: . . . . WX 143
MC: . . . . WX 143 C

RECORDS.
Tracks: / Cold as ice / Double vision / Head games / Waiting for a girl like you / Feels like the first time / Urgent / Dirty white boy / Jukebox hero / Long long way from home / Hot blooded.
LP: . . . . A 0999
MC: . . . . A 0999 4

Forest, Andy J.

ANDY J FOREST AND THE SNAPSHOTS (Andy J Forest & the Snapshots).
LP: . . . . AP 026

HOG WILD.
LP: . . . . AP 036

Forest City Joe

MEMORY OF SONNY BOY (Forest City Joe/Rocky Fuller).
Tracks: / Special delivery man / Shady lane woman / Woman on every street, A / Sawdust bottom / Ash Street boogie / Mean mistreatin' woman / Lonesome day blues / Memory of Sonny Boy / Soon one morning / Rock me baby (come on baby now) / Under a neon sign / Catch me a freight train / Looking for the mail man / The moon won't go down / Gonna leave this town / Raining and storming.
LP: . . . . GCH 8112

Forest, Earl

EARL FOREST AND THE BEALE STREETERS (Forest, Earl/Bobby Bland/Johnny Ace).
Tracks: / Whoopin' and hollerin' / Pretty Bessie / I.O.U. blues / Lovin' blues / Fifty-three / Rock the bottle / Baby baby / How can you have been so mean / Out on a party / Ohh ohh wee / My kind of girl / Oh why / Your kind of love / Keep that monkey off me / Got a feelin' / I'm your boy.
LP: . . . . CHD 220

Forest of Dean

FOREST TALK (Various artists).
MC: . . . . CSDL 316

Forester, C.S.

HUNTING THE BISMARCK.
MC: . . . . LFP 41 7156-5

Foretich, Herman

FORETICH FOUR (Foretich, Herman Four).
LP: . . . . J 144

HERMAN FORETICH AND THE ATLANTA SWING QUARTET (Foretich, Herman & The Atlanta Swing Quartet).
LP: . . . . AP 124

Forever

FOREVER AND EVER.
Tracks: / Wicked bitch / D.B.L. / Sail on / Just to live / I'm lost / No chance / Cry for life / Enter eternity / Harsh reality.
LP: . . . . HMUSA 66

Forever Country

FOREVER COUNTRY (Various artists).
2LP: . . . . IMP 93
MCSET: . . . . IMPC 93

Forever & Ever

FOREVER AND EVER (18 Songs from the heart) (Various artists).
Tracks: / Gambler, The: *Rogers, Kenny* / True love ways: *Holly, Buddy* / You're breaking my heart: *Rose Marie* / What a wonderful world: *Armstrong, Louis* / When your old wedding ring was new: *Longthorne, Joe* / Love letters: *Lester, Ketty* / Something's gotten hold of my heart: *Pitney, Gene* / It's only make believe: *Twitty, Conway* / Wind beneath my wings: *Greenwood, Lee* / Long arm of the law: *Rogers, Kenny* / Sweet dreams: *Cline, Patsy* / You're my best friend: *Williams, Don* / If I were you: *Judds* / Someone loves you honey: *Pride, Charley* / Jackson: *Sinatra, Nancy & Lee Hazelwood* / Just beyond the moon: *Ritter, Tex* / Dedicated to the one I love: *Mamas & Papas* / Moonlight and roses: *Reeves, Jim.*
LP: . . . . PLAT 3906
MC: . . . . PLAC 3906

Forever Everlasting

FOREVER.
Tracks: / Syndicate soldier / What is this? / I got the knack / Everyone / Pass it on / Speak no evil / Rhythm, The / On the edge / Goodbye / Never missin'.
LP: 9260071
MC: 9260074

Forever Gene Vincent

FOREVER GENE VINCENT (Various artists).
Tracks: / Bring it on home: *Various artists* / Rose of love, The: *Various artists* / Hey hey hey: *Various artists* / Party doll: *Various artists* / Say mama: *Various artists* / Black leather rebel: *Various artists* / Right now: *Various artists* / Rocky road blues: *Various artists* / Dance to the bop: *Various artists* / Be bop boogie: *Various artists* / Lotta lovin': *Various artists.*
LP: . . . . MFLP 049
MC: . . . . MFC 049

Forever Gold

FOREVER GOLD (Various artists).
LP: . . . . IMP 90
MCSET: . . . . IMPC 90

Forgiving Heart

FORGIVING HEART (Olive Baxter) (Donald, Sheila (nar)).
MCSET: . . . . CLT 1003

Forman, Bruce

BRUCE FORMAN 20-20.
LP: . . . . MR 5273

DYNAMICS (Forman, Bruce & George Cables).
LP: . . . . CJ 279

FULL CIRCLE (Forman, Bruce Quintet).
Tracks: / Marshal arts / Helen's song / On the sunny side of the street / Skylark / Circular / Giant steps / Desert rain / Summertime.
LP: . . . . CJ 251

IN TRANSIT.
LP: . . . . MR 5299

PARDON ME (Forman, Bruce Quartet).
LP: . . . . CJ 368
MC: . . . . CJ 368 C

RIVER JOURNEY.
Tracks: / River journey / Simple waltz, A / Two bits / St. Thomas / Chances / I just got back in town / Nature boy.
LP: . . . . MR 5251

Formative Years

FORMATIVE YEARS: A TRIBUTE TO BENNY GOODMAN (Various artists).
Tracks: / That's a plenty: *Goodman, Benny* / Clarinetitis: *Goodman, Benny* / Wolverine Blues: *Goodman, Benny* Boys / Room 1411: *Goodman, Benny Boys* / Blue: *Goodman, Benny Boys* / Crazy 'bout my gal: *Mills, Irving* & His Hotsy Totsy Gang / Railroad man: *Mills, Irving & His Hotsy Totsy Gang* / Carolina in the morning: *Nichols, Red & Orchestra* / How come you do me like you do?: *Nichols, Red & Orchestra* / Basin Street blues: *Charleston* Chasers / I gotta right to sing the blues: *Goodman, Benny & His Orchestra* / Your mother's son in law: *Goodman, Benny & His Orchestra* / Georgia jubilee: *Goodman, Benny & His Orchestra* / Junk man: *Goodman, Benny & His Orchestra* / Ol' pappy: *Goodman, Benny & His Orchestra* / Moonglow: *Goodman, Benny & His Orchestra* / Nitwit serenade: *Goodman, Benny & His Orchestra* / Bugle call rag: *Goodman, Benny & His Orchestra.*
LP: . . . . RAL 508

Formby, George

ALL THE HITS.
MCSET: . . . . DTO 10204

CHIP OFF THE OLD BLOCK, A (Formby, George, Senior & Junior).
Tracks: / Twice nightly / Then we all went marching in / Looking for mugs in the Strand / All of a sudden it struck me / Did you see the crowd in Piccadilly? / I had my hand in my pocket at the time / Bells were ringing, The / Standing at the corner of the street / All going back / John Willie's jazz band / I was always a willing young lad / I parted my hair in the middle / Man was a stranger to me, The / John Willie, come on / Rolling around Piccadilly / In the Congo.
LP: . . . . AJA 5003
MC: . . . . ZC AJA 5003

EASY GOING CHAP.
Tracks: / Pleasure cruise / You can't stop me from dreaming / You're a li-a-ty / Noughts and crosses / It ain't nobody's business what I do / Goody goody / I like bananas / Biceps, muscle and brawn / I'm a froggie / Radio bungalow town / I don't like / Wunga bunga boo / Somebody's wedding day / Tan-tan-tivvy tally ho / My little goat and me / Five and twenty years / Like the big pots do / My plus-fours / Ring your little bell (Ting, ting) / Farmer's boy, A / Trailing around in a trailer / Easy going chap.
LP: . . . . CMS 003
MC: . . . . CMSC 003

FORMBY AT WAR - LIVE.
MC: . . . . KGRS 1224

GEORGE FORMBY.
Tracks: / Isle of Man / Hi tiddly hi ti island / Blue eyed blonde next door / Lancashire hot pot swingers / Left hand side of Egypt, The / Oh don't the wind blow cold? / Bless 'em all / I'd do it with a smile / Barmaid at the Rose and Crown / Ordinary people / I'm saving up for Sally / Pleasure cruise / On the beat / Hitting the high spots now / I always get to bed by half past nine / On the Wigan boat express.
LP: . . . . SH 151

LEANING ON A LAMP POST.
Tracks: / When I'm cleaning windows / Fanlight Fanny / Chinese laundry blues / My ukelele / Baby / I do do things I do / Sunbathing in the park / I went all hot and cold / Fiddler kept on fiddling, The / Let's all go to Reno / Leaning on a lamp post / Auntie Maggie's remedy / I told my baby with the ukulele / Believe it or not / In a little Wigan garden / Levi's minkey Mike / She's never been seen since then / Wedding of Mr. Wu, The / If you don't want the goods, don't maul 'em / There's nothing proud about me / Madam Moscovitch / As the hours and the days and the weeks / Why don't women like me / Running round the fountains in Trafalger Squar / Sitting on the ice in the ice rink / I could make a good living at that / John Willie at the license office / Come hither with your zither / Do de o do / John Willie's jazz band / Swimmin' with the wimmin' / You can't keep a growing lad down / Old kitchen kettle, The / Best of schemes, The / John Willie goes carolling.
2LP: . . . . RECDL 4
MCSET: . . . . RECDC 4

LEANING ON A LAMP POST (MFP).
Tracks: / Leaning on a lamp post / Mother, what'll I do now? / Auntie Maggie's remedy / Grandad's flannelette nightshirt / In my little snapshot album / With my little bit of Blackpool rock / Window cleaner, The / Window cleaner, The (No.2) / Mr. Wu's a window cleaner now / Our Sergeant Major / Lancashire toreador, The / I'm the ukelele man / Riding in the T.T. races / Oh dear Mother / Bell bottom George / Count your blessings and smile / Frigid air Fanny / You'll be far better off in a home / It's turned out nice again / It's in the air / They can't fool me / Wash house at the back, The / I blew a little blast on my whistle / Hindoo man.
2LP: . . . . MFP 1032
MCSET: . . . . TCMFP 1032

MAN WITH THE UKELELE.
LP: . . . . SH 126

TURNED OUT NICE AGAIN (See under EMI Comedy Classics).

VERY BEST OF GEORGE FORMBY, THE (20 great songs).
MC: . . . . PLAC 29

WINDOW CLEANER, THE (see under Penrose, Charles).

WITH MY UKELELE.
Tracks: / Chinese laundry blues / I told my baby with my ukelele / Baby / Sunbathing in the park / Leaning on a lamp post / She's never been seen since then / When i'm cleaning windows / Wedding of Mr.Wu / Do de o do / If you don't want the goods don't maul em / Fiddler kept on fiddling, The / There's nothing proud about me / Believe it or not / I went all hot and cold / I do do things I do / In a little Wigan garden / As the hours and the days and the weeks.
LP: . . . . RFL 8

WORLD OF GEORGE FORMBY, THE.
Tracks: / When I'm cleaning windows / Why don't women like me? / You can't keep a growing lad down / Swimmin' with women / Old kitchen kettle, The / With my little ukelele in my hand / Chinese laundry blues / Sitting on the ice in the ice rink / Running around the fountains in Trafalgar Squa / Fanlight Fanny / It's no use looking at me / Leaning on a lamp post.
LP: . . . . SPA 50
MC: . . . . KCSP 50

Formell, Juan

SANDUNGUERA (Formell, Juan & Los Van Van).
LP: 15943

Formula

FORMULA (1982 film soundtrack) (Various artists).
LP: . . . . STV 81153

Formula Thirty

FORMULA THIRTY (Various artists).
Tracks: / Honky tonk women: *Rolling Stones* / Maggie May: *Stewart, Rod* / All right now: *Free* / Keep on running: *Davis, Spencer Group* / Virginia plain: *Roxy Music* / Layla: *Derek & The Dominoes* / Hi ho silver lining: *Beck, Jeff* / Come on Eileen: *Dexy's Midnight Runners* / Satisfaction: *Rolling Stones* / Rockin' all over the world: *Status Quo* / You ain't seen nothing yet: *Bachman-Turner Overdrive* / Call me: *Blondie* / Substitute: *Who* / Sha-la-la-la-lee: *Small Faces* / She's not there: *Zombies* / Whiter shade of pale, A: *Procul Harum* / Let's spend the night together: *Rolling Stones* / Love is the drug: *Roxy Music* / Nutbush city limits: *Ike & Tina Turner.*
2LP: . . . . PROLP 4
MCSET: . . . . PROMC 4

FORMULA THIRTY 2 (Various artists).
Tracks: / I want to break free: *Queen* / I'm still standing: *John, Elton* / All night long: *Rainbow (Group)* / Oliver's army: *Costello, Elvis* / 2-4-6-8 motorway: *Robinson, Tom* / Rollin' home: *Status Quo* / More than this: *Roxy Music* / Vienna: *Ultravox* / Walk of life: *Dire Straits* / In a big country: *Big Country (group)* / Who are you: *Who* / Shout: *Tears For Fears* / I love the sound of breaking glass: *Lowe,* Nick / Hit me with your rhythm stick: *Dury, Ian* / I don't like

Mondays: *Boomtown Rats* / Video killed the radio star: *Buggles*.
LP: . . . . PROLP 9
MC: . . . . PROMC 9

Formula V

ON THE RISE.
LP: . . . . MAL 7433

Fornaciari, Zucchero

BLUES.
Tracks: / Blue's introduction / Con le mani / Pippo / Dune mosse / Bambino lo, bambino tu (legenda) / Non ti sopporto piu / Senza una donna / Hey man / Solo una sana E consapevole libidine / Salva Il Giovane Dallo lo stress E dall'azione cattolica / Hai scelto me.
LP: 833 077-1
MC: 833 077-4

Forrest

FORREST.
Tracks: / One lover / Feel the need in me / Could this be love / Just let it happen / Hand it over / Dancing with my shadow / Comin' up / I want you / Rock the boat / I just want to love you.
LP: . . . . CBS 25579
MC: 40 25579

Forrest, Helen

DICK HAYMES AND HELEN FORREST (see Haymes, Dick & Helen Forrest) (Forrest, Helen & Dick Haymes).

NOW AND FOREVER.
Tracks: / I've heard that song before / I don't want to walk without you / Happiness is a thing called Joe / But not for me / I cried for you / I had the craziest dream / You made me love you / I didn't want to do it / You'll never know more than you know.
LP: . . . . ST 225
LP: . . . . ST 129

SOMETHING TO REMEMBER YOU BY (see Haymes, Dick & Helen Forest) (Forrest, Helen & Dick Haymes).

SUNNY SIDE OF THE STREET, THE.
LP: . . . . AP 47

Forrest, Jimmy

ALL THE GIN IS GONE.
LP: . . . . DL 404

BLACK FORREST.
LP: . . . . DS 427

HEART OF THE FORREST.
LP: . . . . PA 8021

LIVE IN CHICAGO (Forrest, Jimmy & Al Grey).
LP: . . . . AVIVA 6002

OUT OF THE FORREST.
LP: . . . . OJC 097

SIT DOWN AND RELAX.
Tracks: / Tuxedo / Moonglow / Rocks in my bed / Organ grinder's swing / Tin tin deo / Moon was yellow and the night was cold.
LP: . . . . PR 7235

SOUL BATTLE (See under Nelson, Oliver) (Nelson, Oliver/Jimmy Forrest/ King Curtis).

SWEET TRACKS (see Edison, Harry) (Forrest, Jimmy & Harry Edison).

Forrester, Helen

THREE WOMEN OF LIVERPOOL.
MC: . . . . SOUND 34

Forrester, Howdy

RED APPLE RAG (See under Baker, Kenny) (Baker, Kenny & Howdy Forrester).

Forrester Sisters

ALL I NEED.
LP: . . . . K 9257791
MC: . . . . K 9257794

PERFUME, RIBBONS, AND PEARLS.
Tracks: / 100% chance of blue / Heartache headed my way / Back into my arms again / Somebody's breakin' a heart / That's easy for you to say / Blame it on the moon / Lonely alone / Heartless night / You were the one / Drawn to the fire.
LP: . . . . K 925411 1
MC: . . . . K 925411 4

SINCERELY.
LP: 925746 1
MC: 925746 4

YOU AGAIN.
Tracks: / That's what your love does to me / (I'd choose) you again / Before you / Too many rivers / My mothers eyes / Sooner or later / I can't lose what I never had / Lyin' in his arms again / Down the road / Wrap me up.
LP: 925571 1
MC: 925571 4

Forsey, Keith

DYNAMITE.
Tracks: / Take me to the pilot / Give me the right / Don't be shy / Can't you see it / Hold on / Dynamite / Seventeen / Thin ice / School girls / Romeo.
LP: . . . . CAL 133

Forster, E.M. (Author)

PASSAGE TO INDIA (Kingsley, Ben).
MCSET: . . . . SAY 115
MCSET: . . . . ARGO 1064

ROOM WITH A VIEW, A (Dench, Judi).
MCSET: 418 153-4
MCSET: . . . . ARGO 1082

Forster, Robert

DANGER IN THE PAST.
Tracks: / Baby stones / Leave here satisfied / Is this what you call change / Danger in the past / Justice / River people, The / Heart out to tender / Dear black dream / I've been looking for somebody.
LP: . . . . BEGA 113
MC: . . . . BEGC 113

Forsyte Saga

FORSYTE SAGA, THE (See under City of Birmingham Symphony Orch.) (City Of Birmingham Symphony Orchestra).

Forsyth, Bruce

BOTH SIDES OF BRUCE.
Tracks: / Go on and take a bow / Answer me / You'll never find another love like mine / Always wear your love for me / Kissing in the cactus / This song is just for you / Make your own sunshine / You make me feel brand new / Let's fall in love / I wonder who's kissing her now / Song and dance man / Life is the name of the game / Startime / Just in time / It's never too late / Nellie Dean / Misty / Singin' in the rain / Raindrops keep falling on my head / Generation game / Laughing policeman, The / Requests at the piano / Mini medley / Impressions / Question time / Goodnight.
2LP: . . . . K 66053

BRUCE FORSYTH ALBUM.
Tracks: / All I want / My favourite lady / Behind closed doors / Too much I'm in love / They call it love / Send in the clowns / Funny kind of a day / Sandra / Sing baby sing / You and me against the world / Love's theme / Piano.
LP: . . . . K 56166

Forsyth, Frederick

DEVIL'S ALTERNATIVE, THE (Egan, Peter).
MCSET: . . . . LFP 7361

FOURTH PROTOCOL, THE (Dance, Charles).
MCSET: . . . . LFP 7190
MCSET: . . . . LFP 4171905

ODESSA FILE, THE (Allen, Patrick (nar)).
MC: . . . . TC-LFP 7030

ODESSA FILE, THE (RE-ISSUE).
MC: . . . . CAB 333

SHEPHERD, THE (Powell, Robert (nar)).
MC: . . . . PTB 600

Fort Saganne

FORT SAGANNE (Original soundtrack) (London Symphony Orchestra).
LP: . . . . A 238
MC: . . . . C 238

Fort Valley Blues

GEORGIA 1941-43.
LP: . . . . FLY 250

Fort Worth...

FORT WORTH SHUFFLE 1958-64 (Various artists).
LP: . . . . KK 7426

Forties...

FABULOUS '40'S VOL 1 (Various artists).
LP: 27006
MC: 47006

FABULOUS '40'S VOL 2 (Various artists).
LP: 27007
MC: 47007

FABULOUS '40'S VOL 3 (Various artists).
LP: 27008
MC: 47008

Fortran 5

BLUES, THE.
LP: . . . . STUMM 079
MC: . . . . STUMMC 079

Fortress

FORTRESS.
LP: . . . . A 29

HANDS IN THE TILL.
Tracks: / Back on the path / Breakin free / Carry me back / Comin after you / Hands in the till / How do I exist / Kisses / Lets do it again / Mystery / Requiem.
LP: . . . . K 50782
MC: K4 50782

Fortunate Sons

KAREZZA.
LP: . . . . KIRI 093

RISING.
LP: . . . . KIRI 050

Fortune Tellers

FORTUNE TOLD FOR FREE.
LP: . . . . ROSE 82

MUSICK WITHOUT TEARS.
LP: . . . . ROSE 114

Fortunes

BEST OF THE FORTUNES.
LP: 1A 022 58227
MC: 1A 222 58227

GREATEST HITS: FORTUNES.
MC: . . . . ASK 775

GREATEST HITS: FORTUNES (IMPORT).
LP: . . . . BRLP 27
MC: . . . . BRMC 27

HIT COLLECTION, THE.
LP: . . . . VCL 3
MC: . . . . ZCVCL 3

MUSIC FOR THE MILLIONS.
Tracks: / You've got your troubles / This golden ring / Maria / Is it really worth your while / Things I should have known / I've got to go / Here it comes again / You gave me somebody to love / Looking through the eyes of love / Am I losing my touch / Silent street / Someone to care.
LP: 8200051
MC: 8200054

REMEMBERING.
Tracks: / Caroline / If you don't want me now / If we lived on top of a mountain / You can have her / This empty place / Our love has gone / Come on girl / Coloured lights / I like the look of you / Truly yours / Time to be going / You've got your troubles.
LP: . . . . REM 2

Forty 45's

FORTY 45'S (Various artists).
2LP: . . . . PYL 7007
MCSET: . . . . PYM 7007

Forty Christmas Carols

40 CHRISTMAS CAROLS (Various artists).
Tracks: / Once in Royal David's city: *Various artists* / Away in a manger: *Various artists* / Zither carol: *Various* artists / Cherry tree carol, The: *Various artists* / First nowell, The: *Various artists* / As Joseph was a-walking: *Various artists* / Torches: *Various artists* / Past three o'clock: *Various artists* / See, amid the winter's snow: *Various artists* / Welcome yule: *Various artists* / Adam lay ybounden: *Various artists* / Here is the little door: *Various artists* / Spotless rose, A (Howells): *Various artists* / Patapan: *Various artists*/ All God's chillun: *Various artists* / Mary had a baby: *Various artists* / Little David, play your harp: *Various* artists / Holly and the ivy, The: *Various artists* / Ding dong merrily on high: *Various artists* / O come, all ye faithful: *Various artists* / Christmas is coming: *Various artists* / O little town of Bethlehem: *Various* artists / Tomorrow shall be my dancing day: *Various artists* / Little drummer boy: *Various artists* / Rocking: *Various artists* / When Christ was born of Mary free: *Various artists* / Shepherd's pipe carol, The: *Various* artists / King Jesus hath a garden: *Various artists* / Little road to Bethlehem, The: *Various artists* / Boar's head carol: *Various artists* / Good King Wenceslas: *Various artists* / Silent night: *Various artists*/ In the bleak mid winter: *Various artists* / While shepherds watched their flocks: *Various artists* / We three kings: *Various artists* / Holy boy, The: *Various artists* / Lully, lulla, thou little tiny child: *Various* artists / God rest ye merry gentlemen: *Various artists* / Hark the herald angels sing: *Various artists* / Puer nobis: *Various artists*.
2LP: . . . . LPB 820
MC: . . . . LPBC 820

Forty Golden Country

40 GOLDEN COUNTRY HITS - VOL.2 (Various artists).
LP: DS6 28532
MC: CS4 28532

Forty Minutes Of

FORTY MINUTES OF DAYLIGHT (Various artists).
LP: . . . . LD 5007

Forty Non Stop...

40 NON STOP ROCK 'N' ROLL SMASH HITS (Various artists).
2LP: . . . . MFP 1022
MCSET: . . . . TCMFP 1022

40 NON-STOP PARTY HITS (Various artists).
2LP: . . . . PLD 8014

Forty Oldies ...

FORTY OLDIES BUT GOODIES (Various artists).
2LP: . . . . PLD 8003

Forty Show Stoppers

40 SHOW STOPPERS (Various artists).
2LP: . . . . MFP 1019
MCSET: . . . . TCMFP 1019

Forty Solid Gold...

40 SOLID GOLD HITS (Various artists).
2LP: . . . . PLD 8005
MCSET: . . . . PLDC 8005

Forty Years On (bk)

FORTY YEARS ON (Alan Bennett).
MC: . . . . ZCF 504

FORTY YEARS ON/A WOMAN OF NO IMPORTANCE (Alan Bennett Double Bill) (Gielgud, Sir John/Patricia Routledge (nars)).
MCSET: . . . . ZBBC 1029

Forty-Nine Minute...

49 MINUTE TECHNICOLOUR DREAM, THE (Rubble Four) (Various artists).
Tracks: / Black mass: *Jason Crest* / Wedding of Ramona Blair: *Mirage* / Baby your phrasing is bad: *Caleb*/ Flight from Ashiya: *Kaleidoscope* / Matramonial fears: *Cymbaline* / On the beach: *Finders Keepers* / Cooks of cake and kindness: *Californians* / Strange things are happening: *Rings & Things* / Butterfly: *Fox* (Band) / 3:30 a.m.: *Unit 4 + 2* / Dream for Julie, A: *Kaleidoscope* / Come alive: *Tempus Fugit* / Golden glass: *Misunderstood*.
LP: . . . . KIRI 027

Forty-One Degrees

OPEN HEART.
LP: 41-001

Forward

FORWARD (Various artists).
Tracks: / Another one bites the dust: *Eastwood, Clint & General Saint* / Wa-do-dem: *Eek-A-Mouse* / Diseases: *Michigan* & Smiley / Gun man: *Prophet, Michael* / Fattie boom boom: *Ranking Dread* / Born for a purpose: *Dr. Alimantado*/ Bathroom sex: *General Echo* / War: *Wailing Souls* / Yellowman get's married: *Yellowman* / Fat she fat: *Holt, John*.
LP: . . . . GREL 60
MC: . . . . GREEN 60

Forward Motion

BERKLEE TAPES, THE.
LP: . . . . HEP 2026

PROGRESSIONS.
LP: . . . . HEP 2033

Forward Reggae

FORWARD REGGAE Volume 1 (Various artists).
LP: . . . . JALP 001

FORWARD REGGAE Volume 2 (Various artists).
Tracks: / Welding: *I-Roy* / Fade away: *Byles, Junior* / What good am I: *London, Jimmy* / Come softly: *Wilson, Delroy* / Hey girl: *Mighty Diamonds* / Without you in my life: *Davis, Ronnie* / I'm your puppet: *London, Jimmy* / Rock children: *Bryan, Rad* / Hurt me: *Taylor, Tyrone* / Stay a little bit longer: *Davis, Ronnie* / Love affairs: *Poppin, Keith* / Something strange: *Washington, Norman T.*.
LP: . . . . UNKNOWN

Foster, Al

MOREOVER (see under Jones, Hank) (Foster, Al/Hank Jones/Eddie Gomez).

Foster & Allen

AFTER ALL THESE YEARS.
LP: . . . . RITZLP 0032
MC: . . . . RITZLC 0032
MC: . . . . RITZSC 420

AT THE TOP.
LP: . . . . RITZSP 410
MC: . . . . RITZSC 410
LP: . . . . CMLP 1005

BLACKSMITH, THE.
LP: . . . . CMRLP 1003

BUNCH OF THYME.
LP: . . . . RITZLP 0003
MC: . . . . RITZLC 0003
MC: . . . . RITZSC 408

BUNCH OF THYME (SINGLE).
Tracks: / Bunch of thyme.
LP: . . . . RITZLP 0005

CHRISTMAS ALBUM.
MC: . . . . STAC 2459
LP: . . . . STAR 2459

FOSTER & ALLEN.
2LP: . . . . CMCSB 004

FOSTER & ALLEN CHRISTMAS COLLECTION.
LP: . . . . SMR 995
MC: . . . . SMC 995

FOSTER & ALLEN SELECTION, THE.
LP: . . . . RITZLP 0008
MC: . . . . RITZLC 0008
MC: . . . . RITZSC 409

I WILL LOVE YOU ALL OF MY LIFE.
LP: . . . . RITZLP 0015
MC: . . . . RITZLC 0015
MC: . . . . RITZSC 419

LOVE SONGS: FOSTER & ALLEN (The very best of Foster & Allen Volume 2).
MC: . . . . RITZLC 0036
LP: . . . . RITZLP 0036

MAGGIE.
LP: . . . . RITZLP 0012
MC: . . . . RITZLC 0012
MC: . . . . RITZSC 418

REFLECTIONS.
Tracks: / Truelove / Ramblin' rose / I love you because / Goodnight Irene / Annie's song (instrumental) / Old love, An / Away to Mary Anne / Mary of Argyll / Tennessee waltz / Could I have this dance / Part of me will always be in love with you / Last thing on my mind / Edelweiss / Life in the Finland woods / Scarlet ribbons / Rose of Tralee, The / All the days of my life / No more good times / Now is the hour.
LP: . . . . SMR 739
MC: . . . . SMC 739
LP: . . . . HSM 739

REMEMBER YOU'RE MINE.
Tracks: / Silver threads among the gold / Wild rover / Remember you're mine / Hills of Connemara / Golden years / First house in Connaught, The / Donegal reel, The / From the candy store on the corner (to the..) / Stone outside Dan Murphy's door, The / Rose of my heart / Woman in the bed, The / Once upon a time / My lovely rose of Clare / On the mountain / Tobin's favourite / More than yesterday / Ballad of Dawn Run, The / Sorrento thoughts.
LP: . . . . SMR 853
MC: . . . . SMC 853

REMINISCING.
Tracks: / Nobody's darlin' but mine / Somewhere my love / Old Shep / Sweetest of all / Fraulein / Moonshiner / Sunshine of your smile, The / Sitting alone in an old rocking chair / Wild side of life / Old loves never die / Sweet by and by / Old pals / If we had old Ireland here / I wish I was eighteen again / She sang the melody / Pub with no beer, A / Long before your time / Mira, The.
2LP: . . . . SMR 623
MCSET: . . . . SMC 623
LP: . . . . HSM 623

SOUVENIRS.
MCSET: . . . . STAC 2457
LP: . . . . STAR 2457

THEIR GREATEST HITS.
Tracks: / After all these years / Old rustic bridge by the mill, The / Red river valley / Wild rover, The / Silver threads among the gold / Jacqueline waltz / I will love you all my life / If we had old Ireland here / Gentle Annie / Somewhere my love / Maggie / If those lips could only speak / Cottage by the sea / Drink up the cider / When I dream / Come back Paddy Reilly to Ballyjamesduff / Molly my lovely Molly / I still love you / Oslo waltz, The / I'll never stop wanting you / Old flames / Mull of Kyntre, The / Blind, The / To remind I love you / Seven wonders of Fore, The / Golden years / Bluebell polka / Rose of Allendale, The / Black sheep / Bunch of thyme / Stone outside Dan Murphy's door, The / Rose of Mooncoin / Dawn run / I'll take you home again Kathleen / Courtin' in the kitchen / Benbulden of Sligo / Now is the hour / Green willow / Mrs Kenny's waltz.
LP: . . . . SMR 989
MC: . . . . SMC 989

VERY BEST OF FOSTER & ALLEN, THE.
Tracks: / Buch of thyme / Old flames / Maggie / I will love you all my life / Blacksmith / Oslo waltz.
LP: . . . . RITZLP TV 1
MC: . . . . RITZLC TV 1

WORLDS OF MICK FOSTER & TONY ALLEN, THE.
Tracks: / Love letters in the sand / He'll have to go / Forgiving you was easy / My own peculiar way / Little bitty tear, A / Someone like you / Pearly shells / Anna Marie / Blue side of lonesome, The / Turn out the lights / Don't be angry / I would like to see you again / Beneath still waters / Song for a winters night / Sing me the old songs / Haste to the wedding / Donie's fancy / Molly Bawn / Bluebell polka / Clock in the tower, The / High level, The / Gentle maiden, The / Those endearing young charms / Come back Paddy Reilly to Ballyjamesduff / Moon behind the hill / I'll forgive and I'll try to forget / You're as welcome as the flowers in May / Staten Island / Lady Nicknack / Green hills of Ireland, The / Kerry slides / Fairy reel, The / She's a lassie from Lancashire / I'll be your sweetheart / In the shade of the old apple tree / When I grow too old to dream / Black sheep / Snow in summer waltz.
2LP: . . . . SMR 861
MCSET: . . . . SMC 861

Foster, Chris

ALL THINGS IN COMMON.
LP: 12TS 391

LAYERS.
Tracks: / Ranter, The / Coast of Peru, The / Worcester City / Glastonbury town / Lady Maisry / Jack the sailor lad / Golden glove, The / When a man's in love / Buxton lass, The / Flower of serving men, The / Banks of Newfoundland / Black fox, The / Low down in the broom / Grey cock, The / Pigeon on the gate / Unicorns / King John and the Abbot of Canterbury / Jump at the sun / Working chap, The / When this old hat was new / World turned upside down, The.
LP: 12TS 329

Foster, Chuck

1945-1946 (Foster, Chuck & His Orchestra).
LP: . . . . CLP 68

CHUCK FOSTER, 1940.
Tracks: / Oh, you beautiful doll / Friendly tavern polka / My sister and I / You tell me your dream / Dixie girl / Knee deep in stardust / Sunshine of my heart / No foolin' / Little brown jug / Little bit south of North Carolina, A / Dark eyes / Dream affair, A / These things you left me / Listen to my heart / I've been drafted / Goodbye now.
LP: . . . . HSR 115

CHUCK FOSTER, VOL 2 1938-39.
Tracks: / I get along without you very well / Only when you're in my arms / Romance runs in the family / Red skies in the night / Good for nothin' / Little Sir Echo / I found my yellow basket / This night will be my souvenir / Are there any more at home like you / Ain't ya got no romance / Little skipper / Horray for spinach / How strange / Sing a song of sunbeams.
LP: . . . . HSR 171

LONG OVERDUE (Foster, Chuck & Pete Christlieb).
LP: . . . . SB 2023

MUSIC IN THE FOSTER FASHION (Foster, Chuck & His Orchestra).
Tracks: / Oh you beautiful doll / Little girl / Shake down the stars / I've told every little star / Give a little whistle / Glow worm / How high the moon / Angel / Let there be love / Isle of May / Five foot two, eyes of blue / Singing hills, The / I've got my eyes on you / Majorette / Love song of Renaldo / Too romantic / Where was I? / It's a blue world.
LP: . . . . AIRCHECK 22

Foster, David

DAVID FOSTER.
Tracks: / St. Elmo's Fire love theme / Color Purple (Main title) / Flight of the snowbirds / All that my heart can hold / Best of me, The / Tap Dance / Who's gonna love you tonight / Elizabeth / Playing with fire / Saje.
LP: 781 642-1
MC: 781 642-4

SONGWRITERS FOR THE STARS 2 (Foster, David/Barry Mann/Cynthia Weil).
Tracks: / After the love is gone / Simone / Look what you've done to me / It's not what you're looking for / Nothing you can do about it / You've lost that lovin' feeling / Just once / Here you come again / Late at night / On Broadway.
LP: 6327 079

SYMPHONY SESSIONS.
Tracks: / Piano concerto in G / Time passing / Firedance / Water fountain / Morning to morning / Ballet / Conscience / Just out of reach / Winter games / We were close.
LP: 781 799-1
MC: 781 799-4

Foster, Frank

2 FRANKS PLEASE (Foster, Frank/ Frank Wess).
2LP: . . . . SJL 2249

FRANKLY SPEAKING (Foster, Frank & Frank Weiss).
Tracks: / When did you leave heaven? / Up and coming / One morning in May / Two Franks / This is all I ask / Blues backstage / An' all such stuff as'dat / Summer knows, The.
LP: . . . . CJ 276

MANHATTAN FEVER (Foster, Frank/ Loud Minority).
Tracks: / Thruway traffic / Four five six / Manhattan fever / Marie Jean.
LP: . . . . YX 7521

SHINY STOCKINGS (Foster, Frank/ Loud Minority).
Tracks: / Shiny stockings / Love scene / Tomorrow's blues today / Day spring / Hills of the north rejoice.
LP: . . . . YX 7545

TWO FOR THE BLUES (Foster, Frank/ Frank Wess).
Tracks: / Two for the blues / Nancy / Send in the clowns / Your beauty is a song of love / But for the likes of you / Spring can really hang you up the most / Time for love, A / Heat of winter / Bay street.
LP: 231 0905
MC: K10 905

Foster, Gary

GRAND CRU CLASSE.
Tracks: / Tune for a lyric / Morning star / You stepped out of a dream / Duke, The / Samba de Elencia / Everything I love.
LP: . . . . REV 19

REPORT OF THE SYMPOSIUM ON RELAXED IMPROVISATION VOLUME 1 (see Marsh, Warne) (Foster, Gary/ Warne Marsh/Clare Fischer).

STARBRIGHT (see Fischer, Clare).

SUBCONSCIOUSLY.
Tracks: / All of me / Pensativa / What is this thing called love / I'll close my eyes / Liz Anne / In memoriam: J.F.K. and R.F.K. / Elegy / Wistful samba / Peri's scope.
LP: . . . . REV 5

Foster, Gina

EVERYTHING I WANT.
Tracks: / Everything I want / Here I am / So in love / Cry in vain / Love is a house / Love is in my system / One kiss / Contact / Take me away.
LP: . . . . PL 74192
MC: . . . . PK 74192

Foster, Herman

LIVE IN BOLOGNA VOLUME 2 (Foster, Herman & Lou Donaldson Quartet).
LP: . . . . SJP 207

ONE AND ONLY, THE (Herman Foster Trio).
LP: . . . . SJP 201

Foster, Ian

IAN FOSTER.
Tracks: / Out for the count / Heaven (sent your love to me) / This time / We've lost this feeling / Tell me it's true / You make all the right moves / Ooh wee baby.
LP: . . . . MCA 42002
LP: . . . . MCF 3399
MC: . . . . MCFC 3399

Foster & Lloyd

VERSION OF TRUTH.
Tracks: / Is it love? / I wishdaida run into you / Side of the road / Lonesome run / Workin' on me / Version of the truth / Leavin' in your eyes / It's a done deal / All said and done / Whoa.
LP: . . . . PL 90487
MC: . . . . PK 90487

Foster, Michael

DANCING ACCORDION.
Tracks: / Showmans fancy / Paddy the dandy / My home / Sweets of May (Jigs.) / Irish polka / Bridge Jig / Oslo road Waltzes / Beer barrel polka / Bag of Spuds / Sally gardens.
LP: . . . . DOLB 7029
MC: . . . . DOCB 7029

Foster, Mo

BEL ASSIS.
Tracks: / Light in your eyes / Walk in the country, A / Gaia / Crete re-visited / So far away / Analytical engine / Pump II / Jaco / Bel assis / And then there were ten / Nomad.
MC: . . . . TCMMC 1013
LP: . . . . LPMMC 1013

Foster, Ronnie

DELIGHT.
Tracks: / Argentina / You're the one / We as love / Let me in your life / Feet / When will I write you a song? / Delight / I've got your love.
LP: . . . . CBS 83776

LOVE SATELLITE.
Tracks: / Why don't you look inside / Soft heart / Happy song / Shooting star / Midnight plane / I want to bring my love home / Easier said than done / Nassau day / Love satellite.
LP: . . . . CBS 83037

Foster, Teddy

MELODY MAN 1936-37.
Tracks: / Melody man / Sing, sing, sing / Skeleton in the cupboard, The / Harlem / Jerry the junker / Where the lazy river goes by / When a lady meets a gentleman down south / Breakfast in Harlem / St. Louis blues / Sugar rose / Pennies from Heaven / T'ain't no use / With a banjo on my knee / Rhythm's OK in Harlem, The / Poor Dinah / Take another guess.
LP: . . . . HQ 3020

Fotheringay

FOTHERINGAY (Fotheringay with Sandy Denny).
Tracks: / Nothing more / Sea, The / Ballad of Ned Kelly, The / Winter winds / Peace in the end / Way I feel, The / Pond and the stream, The / Too much of nothing / Banks of the Nile.
LP: . . . . HNBL 4426
MC: . . . . HNBC 4426
LP: . . . . ILPS 9125

Foul Play

FOUL PLAY (Film soundtrack) (Various artists).
LP: . . . . ARTY 160
MC: . . . . TCARTY 160

Foundation

FLAMES.
LP: . . . . ILPS 9896

HEART FEEL IT.
MC: . . . . MCT 1014
LP: . . . . MLPS 1014

Foundation... (bk)

FOUNDATION - PSYCHOHISTORIANS (Shatner, William (nar)).
LP: . . . . TC 1508
MC: . . . . CDL 51508

Foundations

BACK TO THE BEAT.
Tracks: / Baby now that I've found you / Build me up buttercup / Back on my feet again / Any old time (you're lonely and sad) / In the bad bad old days (before you loved me) / Born to live and born to die / I can take or leave your loving / Stop her on sight (S.O.S).
LP: . . . . DOW 7
MC: . . . . ZCDOW 7

BEST OF THE FOUNDATIONS.
Tracks: / Baby now that I've found you / Back on my feet again / Tomorrow / Harlem shuffle / Mr. Personality man / I can take or leave your loving / Let the heartaches begin / Am I groovin' you / That same old feeling / Any old time (you're lonely and sad) / Build me up buttercup / In the bad bad old days (before you loved me) / Born to live and born to die / Waiting on the shores of nowhere / Come on back to me / Jerkin' the dog / Take away the emptiness too / My little chickadee / Love is alright / We are happy people.
LP: . . . . PYL 4003
MC: . . . . PYM 4003

GOLDEN HOUR OF THE FOUNDATIONS GREATEST HITS.
Tracks: / Baby now that I've found you / Back on my feet again / Tomorrow / Harlem shuffle / Mr. Personality man / I can take or leave your loving / Let the heartaches begin / Am I groovin' you / That same old feeling / Any old time (you're lonely and sad) / Build me up buttercup / In the bad bad old days (Before you loved me) / Born to live and born to die / Waiting on the shores of nowhere / Come on back to me / Jerkin' the dog / Take away the emptiness too / My little chickadee / Love is alright / We are happy people.
MC: . . . . KGHMC 104

Foundry Bar Band

FOUNDRY BAR BAND, THE.
Tracks: / Auchmithie / Hot punch / O nach aghmhor / Guise o'tough, The / Out on the ocean / Roxburgh castle / Mrs. H.L.MacDonald of Dunach / Grant Farquharson of Inveravon / Catherine Street / Rhodesian regiment, The / Tramps and Hawkers / Wee tod.
LP: . . . . SPR 1007
MC: . . . . SPRC 1007

ON THE ROAD WITH......
LP: . . . . SPR 1012
MC: . . . . SPRC 1012

ROLLING HOME.
MC: . . . . SPRC 1026

Fountain, Pete

ALIVE IN NEW ORLEANS.
LP: . . . . FA 7706

SUPER JAZZ 1 (Fountain, Pete & Al Hirt).
2LP: . . . . **MNT 22009**

Fountainhead

BURNING TOUCH.
Tracks: / Open up / Feel it now / So good now (with you) / When the lifeline begins / Rhythm / Sometimes / Seeing is believing / Faraway / Take my life.
LP: . . . . **WOL 3**

VOICE OF REASON.
Tracks: / Someone like you / Angel / Still dreaming / Price you've got to pay / This generation / Future days / Driving in my car / Nowhere train, The / Step by step / Rain came down, The / So good now (Extra track on CD.) / Sometimes (Extra track on CD.).
LP: . . . . **WOL 5**
MC: . . . . **ZWOL 5**
MC: . . . . **ZWOL 3**

Fountains Of... (bk)

FOUNTAINS OF PARADISE (Arthur C Clarke).
MC: **1606**

Four 20th Century

499 2139 (4992139).
Tracks: / Skip the beat / Sure fire / Distant drums / Audio audio / Career girls / Carscape / Go steady / Kicking up a fuss / Sex object / Green glass green / Alice in Wonderland / King's new clothes, The / Tircky girls / Feeling hard.
LP: . . . . **DIAL 1**

Four Aces

BEST OF THE FOUR ACES (CREOLE).
MC: **16-3**

BEST OF THE FOUR ACES (MCA).
Tracks: / Three coins in the fountain / Tell me why / Heart / Perfidia / World outside, The / It's no sin / Garden in the rain / Mr. Sandman / Stranger in Paradise / Gang that sang heart of my heart / Heart and soul / Woman in love / Rock 'n' roll rhapsody / Melody of love / Friendly persuasion / Love is a many splendoured thing.
LP: . . . . **MCL 1687**
MC: . . . . **MCLC 1687**

GOLDEN GREATS: FOUR ACES.
Tracks: / Love is a many splendoured thing / Three coins in the fountain / Mr. Sandman / Woman in love / Stranger in Paradise / Tell me why / Heart / Perfidia / World outside, The / (It's no) sin / Garden in the rain / Gang that sang heart of my heart, The / Heart and soul / Melody of love / Friendly persuasion.
LP: . . . . **MCM 5014**
MC: . . . . **MCMC 5014**

THEIR HITS (see Four lads) (Four Aces & Four Lads).

Four Big Guitars From

THAT'S COOL, THAT'S TRASH.
Tracks: / That's cool, that's trash / Groovus / Sunburn / Rebel - Johnny Yuma, The / (Ghost) riders in the sky / Eyes of Texas, The / High tide in hub city / Alamo beach / Absorber, The / Woo-hoo / Holiday for Hoss / Guitarget / Neanderthal / Hardy Street.
LP: . . . . **FIEND 68**
MC: . . . . **FIENDCASS 68**
LP: . . . . **ROSE 89**

TRASH, TWANG AND THUNDER.
Tracks: / Boomerang / Breaker / Lost Inca / Shanghai cobra / Guitar army / Chainsaw / Ride of the ruthless / Bulldoggin boogie / Strained / Do the dootz / Good, the bad and the ugly, The / Riot at Huntsville.
LP: . . . . **FIEND 40**

Four Brothers

BROS.
Tracks: / Rudo chete / Nhamo / Munondizvidza / Wakazvarwa / Ngatipindukewo / Zuro chisara / Vabereki / Kutambura chete / Chenjerera ngozi.
LP: . . . . **COOK 023**
MC: . . . . **COOKC 023**

MAKOROKOTO.
Tracks: / Makorokoto / Rugare / Wapenga nayo bonus / Ndakatadzeiko / Sara Tasangana / Pamusoroi / Nhaka yemusiiranwa / Uchandifunga / Guhwa uri mwana waani / Ndakatambura / Vimbayi (CD only.) / Rumbidzai (CD only.) / Rudo imoto (CD only.) / Pasi pano pane zviedzo (CD only.) / Siya Maishoko ababa namai (CD only.) / Siya zviriko (CD only.).
LP: . . . . **COOK 014**
MC: . . . . **COOKC 014**
LP: . . . . **BAKE 004**
MC: . . . . **BAKEC 004**

Four Bucketeers

FOUR BUCKETEERS.
LP: . . . . **BUCK 1**

Four Champions

TRADITIONAL IRISH ACCORDION SESSION.
MC: . . . . **COX 1027**

Four Dragon Stories

FOUR DRAGON STORIES (see Nesbitt, E) (Guthrie, Gwyneth).

Four Feathers

FOUR FEATHERS (see Mason, A.E.W) (Heller, Martin (nar)).

Four Freshmen

LIVE AT BUTLER UNIVERSITY (Four Freshmen & The Stan Kenton Orchestra).
Tracks: / There will never be another you / After you / Byrd Avenue / Surfer girl / Girl talk / When the feeling hit you / Walk on by / What are you doing the rest of your life? / Brand new key / Teach me tonight / Beautiful friendship, A / Summer has gone / Hymn to her / Come back to me / It's not unusual / Coming round the mountain / Walk softly / Artistry in rhythm.
LP: . . . . **JAS 203**
2LP: . . . . **STD 1059**
MC: . . . . **STC 1059**

STARS IN OUR EYES.
Tracks: / Shangri-la / Sentimental me / Standing on the corner / Lamplighter's serenade, The / Teach me tonight / Tom dooley / Opus one / I thought about you / Love is a many splendoured thing / Green fields / In apple blossom time / Imagination.
LP: . . . . **EMS 1152**
MC: . . . . **TCEMS 1152**

VOICES IN FUN.
Tracks: / I want to be happy / Ole buttermilk / I can't give you anything but love / You make me feel so young / Save the bones for Henry Jones / Swinging on a star / On sunny side of the street / Manana / On the Atchison, Topeka and Santa Fe / Aren't you glad you're you / Happy talk / Accentuate the positive.
LP: . . . . **EMS 1131**
MC: . . . . **TCEMS 1131**

Four Giants Of Swing

FOUR GIANTS OF SWING:'S WONDERFUL.
LP: . . . . **FF 035**

Four Girls

FOUR DECADES OF JAZZ (Various artists).
2LP: . . . . **X 5001**

FOUR FROM THE MADDING CROWD... (Various artists).
Tracks: / We love the moon: *Royal Family & The Poor* / Dog star: *Royal Family & The Poor* / Recalled to life: *Bushido* / Chance meeting: *Bushido* / Time: *Bushido* / Machima: *Intimate Obsessions* / Baruch: *Intimate Obsessions* / Confessions of: *Intimate Obsessions* / Lonely heart dance: *Ohama Meets Dania* / Take me dancing: *Ohama Meets Dania*.
LP: . . . . **TMLP 16**

FOUR GIRLS (North, Alex).
LP: . . . . **VC 81074**

FOUR STAR COUNTRY (Various artists).
LP: . . . . **NE 1278**
MC: . . . . **CE 2278**

FOUR STAR SHOWCASE (Various artists).
LP: . . . . **RSLP 1**

FOUR TRADITIONAL FAIRY TALES (Various artists).
LP: . . . . **TMP 9005**
MC: **TMP4 9005**

Four Interns

I'M TROUBLED.
LP: . . . . **RF 1400**

Four Jills In A Jeep

FOUR JILLS IN A JEEP (Original soundtrack) (Various artists).
LP: . . . . **HS 407**

Four Lads

GREATEST HITS.
LP: . . . . **CBS 32410**

THEIR HITS (Four Lads & Four Aces).
MC: **815**

Four Lanes Male Choir

SING WE FOR PLEASURE.
LP: . . . . **BURL 014**

Four Of Us

SONGS FOR THE TEMPTED.
Tracks: / Drag my bad name down / Fool for temptation / Mary / One strong hammer / Jolene / Lightning Paul / I just can't get enough / Washington down / Kill you / Home is where the heart is / Love with Christine.
LP: **4653481**
MC: **4653484**

Four Pennies

TWO SIDES OF FOUR PENNIES.
LP: . . . . **BL 7642**

Four Seasons

BIG ONES, THE.
LP: **6336-208**

EDIZIONE D'ORO.
LP: **6640-002**

FOUR SEASONS STORY.
2LP: . . . . **DAPS 1001**

FRANKIE VALLI & THE FOUR SEASONS (see under Valli, Frankie) (Four Seasons & Frankie Valli).

GREATEST HITS: FOUR SEASONS.
Tracks: / Big girls don't cry / Sherry / Why do fools fall in love / Stay / Merlena / Gypsy woman / Book of love / Oh what a night / Who loves you.
LP: . . . . **ZL 71923**
MC: . . . . **ZK 71923**
LP: . . . . **NE 942**

HELICON.
Tracks: / If we should lose our love / Let's get it right / Long ago / Rhapsody / Helicon / Down the hall / Put a little away / New York street song (no easy way) / I believe in you.
LP: . . . . **K 56350**

REUNITED LOVE (see under Valli, Frankie) (Four Seasons & Frankie Valli).

SHERRY.
LP: . . . . **SL 10033**

WHO LOVES YOU.
Tracks: / Who loves you / Silver star / Storybook lovers / Harmony, perfect harmony / Mystic Mr Sam / December '63 (oh what a night) / Slip away / Emily's.
MC: **K4 56179**
LP: . . . . **K 56179**

Four Sherlock

FOUR SHERLOCK HOLMES STORIES (see under Sherlock Holmes) (Hardy, Robert (nar)).

Four Stars

DANCE.
LP: . . . . **TAN 7009**

Four Symphonic

FOUR SYMPHONIC WORKS BY DUKE ELLINGTON (Various artists).
Tracks: / Harlem: *Various artists* / Three black kings: *Various artists* / New world a comin': *Various artists*/ Black, brown and beige: *Various artists*.
LP: . . . . **MMC 40176M**

Four Tops

20 GOLDEN GREATS: FOUR TOPS.
Tracks: / Reach out I'll be there / Walk away Renee / Standing in the shadows of love / Seven rooms of gloom / I can't help myself / It's the same old song / Bernadette / Baby, I need your loving / What is a man? / Do what you gotta do / It's all in the game / River deep, mountain high / Still water / If I were a carpenter / Loving you is sweeter than ever / You keep running away / Yesterday's dreams / I'm in a different world / You gotta have love in your heart / Simple game.
LP: . . . . **EMTV 26**
MC: . . . . **CMTV 26**

ANTHOLOGY - FOUR TOPS (LP).
Tracks: / Baby I need your loving / Without the one you love / Ask the lonely / I can't help myself / It's the same old song / Something about you / Shake me wake me / Loving you is sweeter than ever / Reach out I'll be there / Standing in the shadows of love / I got a feeling / Bernadette / Seven rooms of gloom / (You keep) running away / Walk away Renee / If I were a carpenter / Yesterdays dreams / I'm in a different world / Can't seem to get you out of my mind / It's all in the game / Still water (Pre-computerised listing shows two tracks: Still water(love) and Still w) / River deep, mountain high / Just seven numbers / In these changing times / I can't quit your love / (It's the way) nature planned it / You gotta have love in your heart / What is a man? / Do what you gotta do / MacArthur Park part 2 / Simple game / So deep within you / Hey man (medley) / We gotta get you a woman.
2LP: . . . . **TMSP 6013**
MCSET: . . . . **CTMSP 6013**
2LP: . . . . **ZL 72352**

AT THE TOP.
Tracks: / H.E.L.P. / Bits and pieces / Seclusion / Put it on the news / This house / Just in time / Inside a brokenhearted man / When your dreams take wings and fly.
LP: . . . . **ABCL 5262**

BACK WHERE I BELONG.
LP: . . . . **STML 12197**
MC: . . . . **CSTML 12197**

BEST OF THE FOUR TOPS.
Tracks: / Reach out I'll be there / Walk away Renee / Standing in the shadows of love / Seven rooms of gloom / I can't help myself / It's the same old song / Bernadette / Baby, I need your loving / What is a man? / Do what you gotta do / It's all in the game / River deep, mountain high / Still water / If I were a carpenter / Loving you is sweeter than ever / You keep running away / Yesterday's dreams / I'm in a different world / You gotta have love in your heart / Simple game.
LP: . . . . **NE 1160**
MC: . . . . **CE 2160**

FABULOUS FOUR TOPS, THE.
Tracks: / I can't help myself / I got a feeling / Your love is amazing / Yesterday's dreams / I'm grateful / Little green apples.
LP: . . . . **TMS 3502**
MC: . . . . **TMC 3502**

FOUR TOPS.
Tracks: / Baby I need your loving / Without the one you love / Where did you go / Ask the lonely / Your love is amazing / Sad souvenirs / Don't turn away / Tea house in China Town / Left with a broken heart / Love has gone / Call on me.
LP: . . . . **STMS 5033**
MC: . . . . **CSTMS 5033**

FOUR TOPS LIVE!.
LP: . . . . **STML 11041**

FOUR TOPS ON TOP.
LP: . . . . **TML 11037**

FOUR TOPS STORY 1964-72.
Tracks: / Baby I need your loving / Without the one you love / Ask the lonely / I can't help myself / It's the same old song / Something about you / Shake me wake me / Loving you is sweeter than ever / Yesterday's dream / I'm in a different world / What is a man / Do what you gotta do / It's all in the game / Still water / Just seven numbers / Reach out I'll be there / Standing in the shadows of love / Bernadette / 7 rooms of gloom / I'll turn to stone / You keep running away / Walk away Renee / If I were a carpenter / In these changing times / MacArthur Park / Simple game / I can't quit your love / Nature planned it / River deep, mountain high / You gotta have love in your heart.
2LP: . . . . **TMSP 1124**
2LP: . . . . **TMSP 11241/2**

GREATEST HITS: FOUR TOPS.
Tracks: / Baby I need your loving / It's the same old song / Reach out, I'll be there / Ask the lonely / Standing in the shadows of love / Loving you is sweeter than ever / I can't help myself / Without the one you love / Seven rooms of gloom / Something about you / Bernadette / Shake me, wake me (when it's over).
LP: . . . . **WL 72280**
MC: . . . . **WK 72280**
LP: . . . . **STML 11061**
LP: . . . . **MCL 1675**

GREATEST HITS: FOUR TOPS VOL.2.
LP: . . . . **STML 11195**

HEART 'N' SOUL.
MC: . . . . **KNMC 12065**

HITS OF GOLD.
Tracks: / Standing in the shadows of love / Key, The / Seven rooms of gloom / Where did you go / Look of love, The / Honey / Loving you is sweeter than ever / I'm grateful / Sunny / This guy's in love with you / Daydream believer / Light my fire.
LP: . . . . **TMS 3514**
MC: . . . . **TMC 3514**

HOT NIGHTS.
Tracks: / Hot nights / Red hot love / I believe in you and me / Let's jam / We got bus'ness / This is love / So up for you / Livin it up too much / Four of us, The.
LP: . . . . **ZL 72480**

INDESTRUCTIBLE.
Tracks: / Indestructible / Loco in Acapulco / Sun ain't gonna shine, The / Let's jam / Change of heart / When you dance / If ever a love there was / Next time / Are you with me / I'm only wounded.
LP: **208840**
MC: **408840**
LP: **211567**
MC: **411567**

IT'S ALL IN THE GAME.
MC: . . . . **TCMFP 50416**
LP: . . . . **MFP 50416**

KEEPER OF THE CASTLE.
LP: . . . . **ABCL 5023**

LIVE: FOUR TOPS.

Tracks: / Introduction / It's the same old song / It's not unusual / Baby, I need your loving / Reach out I'll be there / I'll turn to stone / I left my heart in San Francisco / You can't hurry love / Ask the lonely / Climb every mountain / Girl from Ipanema / If I had a hammer / I can't help myself / I like everything about you.
LP: . . . . STMS 5087
MC: . . . . CSTMS 5087

MAGIC.
Tracks: / I can feel the magic / Don't tell me that it's over / Sexy ways / Easier said than done / Don't turn away / I'm ready for love / Again / Remember me / Maybe tomorrow.
LP: . . . . ZL 72301
MC: . . . . ZK 72301

MAGNIFICENT 7, THE (See under Supremes for details) (Four Tops & The Supremes).

MAIN STREET PEOPLE.
Tracks: / I just can't get you out of my mind / It won't be the first time / Sweet understanding love / Am I not my brothers keeper / Are you man enough / Whenever there's blue / Too little, too late / Peace of mind / One woman man / Main street people.
LP: . . . . CRB 1129

ONE MORE MOUNTAIN.
Tracks: / Sad hearts / One more mountain to climb / Givin' it up / I believe in you and me / I'm the one / Keep on lightin' my fire / Nobody's gonna love you like I do / Dream on / Whatever it is.
LP: . . . . CANS 3
MC: . . . . CANSC 3

REACH OUT.
Tracks: / Reach out I'll be there / Walk away Renee / Seven rooms of gloom / If I were a carpenter / Last train to Clarksville / I'll turn to stone / I'm a believer / Standing in the shadows of love / Bernadette / Cherish / Wonderful baby / What else is there to do (but think about you).
LP: . . . . STMS 5004
MC: . . . . CSTMS 5004
LP: . . . . WL 72067
MC: . . . . WK 72067
LP: . . . . STML 11056

RIVER DEEP MOUNTAIN HIGH (See under Supremes).

SECOND ALBUM.
Tracks: / I can't help myself / Love feels like fire / Is there anything that I can do? / Something about you / It's the same old song / Helpless / Just as long as you need me / Darlin' / I hum our song / I like everything about you / Since you've been gone / Stay in my lonely arms / I'm grateful.
LP: . . . . STMS 5077
MC: . . . . CSTMS 5077

STILL WATERS RUN DEEP.
Tracks: / Still water / Reflection / It's all in the game / Everybody's talkin' / Love is the answer / I wish I were your mirror / Elusive butterfly / Bring me together / L.A. (my town) / Still water.
LP: . . . . STMS 5063
MC: . . . . CSTMS 5063
LP: . . . . STML 11149
MC: . . . . WK 72734

SUPER HITS.
Tracks: / Reach out I'll be there / I can't help myself / Walk away Renee / Standing in the shadows of love / Seven rooms of gloom / It's the same old song / What is a man? / Bernadette / If I were a carpenter / It's all in the game / Do what you gotta do / Still water / Loving you is sweeter than ever / Yesterday's dreams / You keep running away / I'm in a different world / Simple game.
LP: . . . . STMA 8024
MC: . . . . CSTMA 8024

THEIR GREATEST HITS.
LP: . . . . STAR 2437
MC: . . . . STAC 2437

TONIGHT.
Tracks: / When she was my girl / Don't walk away / Tonight / I'm gonna love you / Who's right, who's wrong / Let me set you free / Something to remember / From a distance / All I do / I'll never ever leave again.
LP: 6480 059
MC: 7190 058
LP: 836 967 1
MC: 836 967 4

YESTERDAY'S DREAMS.
LP: . . . . STML 11087

YOU GOTTA HAVE LOVE IN YOUR HEART (See under Supremes).

Four & Twenty...

FOUR & TWENTY NURSERY RHYMES VOL.1 (Various artists).
LP: . . . . UNKNOWN

Four Vagabond

YESTERDAY'S MEMORIES.
LP: . . . . RELIC 8012

Four X

BALLET DANCER.
LP: . . . . APK 9

Four Yn Y Bar

BYTH ADRA.
LP: . . . . 1308 M

NEWID CYNEFIN.
LP: . . . . SAIN 1392 M

Fourgiven

VOILA.
LP: . . . . LOLITA 5048

Fourmost

FIRST AND FOREMOST.
LP: . . . . BGOLP 51

MOST OF THE FOURMOST, THE.
Tracks: / Hello little girl / I'm in love / Here, there and everywhere / Till you say you'll be mine / Something got a hold on me / You got that way / Girl can't help it, The / In crowd, The / Baby sittin' boogie / Heebie jeebies / Girls girls girls / Auntie Maggie's remedy / How can I tell her / Just in case / Yakety yak / Turn the lights down / Little loving, A.
LP: . . . . CM 104
MC: . . . . CMK 104

Foursome For Brass

FOURSOME FOR BRASS (Various artists).
Tracks: / Foursome for brass: *Various artists* / Eriskay love lilt: *Various artists* / Fancy's knell: *Various* artists / Alla burlesca: *Various artists* / Mary: *Various artists* / Foresters sound the cheerful horn: *Various artists* / Concordia: *Various artists* / Butterfly caprice: *Various artists.*
LP: . . . . SDL 254
MC: . . . . CSDL 254

Fourteen Bites..

14 BITES OF BUN AND CHEESE (Various artists).
LP: . . . . BMLP 28

Fourth Folly

FOURTH FOLLY (see Treves, Katherine) (McBain, Rose).

Fourth Man

FOURTH MAN, THE (Original soundtrack) (Various artists).
LP: . . . . STV 81222

Fourth Protocol (film)

FOURTH PROTOCOL (Film soundtrack).
Tracks: / Fourth protocol / Gorvoshin, Karpov, Borisov / Petrovsky, Preston / Berenson / Mr. Ross, Telecommunications / Disc, The, Gregorio, Glasgow docks / Uranium uranium, how about a drink... / Windows / Vasilievna / Detonator / Zero time / Before I go, kill her, I feel lucky / Traffic jam / Attic, The / Explosions, The / Going home (end titles).
LP: . . . . MOMENT 109
MC: . . . . MOMENTC 109

Fourth To Deal

FOURTH TO DEAL Various artists (Various artists).
LP: . . . . ARKLP 2

Fourway Cross

ON THE OTHER HAND.
LP: . . . . SAVE 78

SHIMMER.
LP: . . . . MOTIV 005

Fowler, T.J.

EARLY DETROIT RNB (Fowler, T.J. & His Band).
Tracks: / T.J. boogie / What's the matter now / Midnight clipper (part 1) / Midnight clipper (part 2) / Harmony grits / Red hot blues / Hot sauce / Blue lullaby / Night crawler / Fowler's boogie / Back biter / Wine cooler / Camel walk / Gold rush / Queen, The / Tell me what's the matter.
LP: . . . . OFF 6044

Fowley, Kim

FRANKENSTEIN AND MONSTER BAND.
LP: . . . . SNTF 918

HOLLYWOOD CONFIDENTIAL.
LP: . . . . GNPS 2132
MC: GNP5 2132

LIVING IN THE STREETS.
Tracks: / Motor boat / 25 hours a day / Big bad Cadilac / Man without a country / California summertime / Hollywood nights / Born to make you cry / Thunder road / Summertime frog / Love bomb / Living in the streets / Sex dope and violence.
LP: . . . . SNTF 755

SNAKE DOCUMENT MASQUERADE 1980-1989.
Tracks: / Run for your life / Black Christmas / Stranded in the future / Don't feed the animals / Saga of Hugo X / Physical lies / Snake document masquerade 1980-1989 / Lost like a lizard in the snow / Searching for a human in tight blue jeans / Waiting around for the next ten years.
LP: . . . . ILPS 9572

SUNSET BOULEVARD.
LP: . . . . ILP 002

VAMPIRES FROM OUTERSPACE.
LP: 400 330

Fowlkes, Curtis

BROKEN NIGHT (See Nathanson, Roy) (Fowlkes, Curtis/Roy Nathanson).

DERANGED AND DECOMPOSED (See under Nathanson, Roy) (Nathanson, Roy & Curtis Fowlkes & The Jazz Passengers).

Fox

FOX, THE (see under Lawrence, D.H.) (Massey, Anna (nar)).

Fox (Band)

FOX.
LP: . . . . GTLP 001

SET ME FREE.
LP: . . . . MAL 7432

Fox, Bob

NOWT SO GOOD'LL PASS (Fox, Bob & Stu Luckley).
Tracks: / Bonnie Gateshead lass, The / Reynard the fox / Gypsey Davey / Beggin', The / Bonnie at morn / Row between the cages / Sally Wheatley / Sandgate lass on the ropey banks, The / Isle of Islay / Doodle let me go.
LP: . . . . RUB 028
MC: . . . . RUBC 028

WISH WE NEVER HAD PARTED (Fox, Bob & Stu Luckley).
Tracks: / Sally Gee / Two magicians / Shores of Old Blighty, The / I once loved a lass / Iron road, The.
LP: . . . . CRO 204
MC: . . . . CROC 204

Fox, Charles

SEASONS.
Tracks: / Seasons / My fair share / Killing me softly with his song / And the feeling's good / Ready to take a chance again / Reflections / Elusive blue / I need you now / Pachelbel canon.
LP: . . . . RCALP 5055
MC: . . . . RCAK 5055

Fox, John

FAIREST ISLE (Fox, John Singers).
Tracks: / Last rose of summer / Scarborough fair / Here's to the maiden of bashful fifteen / David of the white rock / It was a lover and his lass / Golden slumbers / Bonnie Mary of Argyle / Fairest isle / John Peel / Greensleeves / Billy boy / Three ravens.
LP: . . . . REC 287

GERSHWIN'S GREATEST HITS (Fox, John & The Radio Orchestra).
Tracks: / Love walked in / Our love is here to stay / Lady be good / Someone to watch over me / I got rhythm / Summertime / Strike up the band / Fascinating rhythm / Foggy day in London town, A / Embraceable you / Somebody loves me / 'S wonderful.
LP: . . . . REC 320

SAILING BY (Fox, John Orchestra).
Tracks: / Sailing by / Clair / We'll gather lilacs / Make it with you / Last waltz, The / London pride / Here, there and everywhere / Sleepy lagoon / This is my lovely day / Roses of Picardy / Garden in the rain / Day by day.
LP: . . . . REC 280

Fox, Roy

AT MONSEIGNEUR RESTAURANT, PICCADILLY (Fox, Roy & His Band).
Tracks: / Whispering / Minnie the moocher / Kicking the gong around / Jig time / I got rhythm / Nobody's sweetheart / Georgia on my mind / Yes yes / Old man of the mountain, The / If I didn't have you / How'm I doin' / She didn't say yes / You're my everything / Oh Monah.
LP: . . . . ACL 1172

BANDS THAT MATTER, THE.
Tracks: / Londonola, The / Build a little home / June in January / May 1 / Lovable / Jungle drums / Goodnight Vienna / Living in clover / Corina, Corina / Japanese sandman / Everything I have is yours / Drowsy blues / What a perfect combination / Goodnight lovely little lady.
LP: . . . . ECM 2045

FOX FAVOURITES (Fox, Roy & His Orchestra).
Tracks: / Keep young and beautiful / Black eyed Susan Brown / I cover the waterfront / Over my shoulder / Maybe I'm wrong again / You ought to be in pictures / Sweet and hot / Every little moment / When the robin sings his song again / Blue moments / Without that certain thing / We've got to put that Sun back in the sky / Rhythm lullaby / Everything stops for tea.
LP: . . . . JASM 2019

GOLDEN AGE OF ROY FOX.
Tracks: / Love is a dancing thing / Play orchestra play / Let's face the music and dance / South sea island / Whispering / Night is young / Love and learn / I've got beginners luck / I've got my love to keep me warm / 50000000 robins can't be wrong / Can i forget you / Things are looking up / Roses in december / You leave me breathless / You went to my head / If it rains who cares.
LP: . . . . GX 41 2528
MC: . . . . GX 41 2528 4

I'LL STRING ALONG WITH YOU.
2LP: . . . . SVLD 004
MC: . . . . CSVLD 004

INVITATION TO A DANCE (Fox, Roy & His Band).
Tracks: / Swaller tail coat / True / One morning in May / Drowsy blues / Fair and warmer / You oughta be in pictures / Jungle drums / Soon / I'll string along with you / I saw stars / What a difference a day made / I'm in love / Out in the cold again / Dream man (make me dream some more) / I've got an invitation to a dance / If the moon turns green / Accent on youth / San Felipe / Do you ever have a feeling you're flying / Echo of a song, The.
LP: . . . . SVL 179
MC: . . . . CSVL 179

RISE 'N' SHINE (Fox, Roy Orchestra).
Tracks: / Rise 'n' shine / It's been so long / Your heart and mine / Quicker than you can say Jack Robinson / Miracles sometimes happen / Saddle your blues to a wild mustang / Moon for sale / Bird on the wing / Star and the rose, The / You / You do the darndest things, baby / Carelessly / It's the natural thing to do / Moon got in my eyes, The / Let's call the whole thing off / They can't take that away from me / Whispers in the dark / Too marvellous for words / That old feeling / Stop, you're breaking my heart.
LP: . . . . SVL 197
MC: . . . . CSVL 197

ROY FOX, 1928-32 (Fox, Roy & Al Bowlly).
Tracks: / Cuddle up a little closer / Masquerade / Moochi, The / Mam'selle / Peanut vendor / I got rhythm / Somebody loves you / Life is just a bowl of cherries.
LP: . . . . HQ 3026

ROY FOX AND HIS BAND (Fox, Roy & His Band featuring Al Bowlly).
Tracks: / Ya got love / Betty co-ed / Maybe it's love / Oh Monah / I'd rather be a beggar with you / That lindy hop / One more time / Smile darn ya, smile / Thank you father / Your forgot your gloves / Roll on, Mississippi, roll on / Bathing in the sunshine / Ten cents a dance / Between the Devil and the deep blue sea / My temptation / Sing another chorus please / You forgot your gloves.
LP: . . . . JOYD 266
MC: . . . . TCJOYD 266

ROY FOX AND HIS BAND: VOLUME 2 (Fox, Roy & His Band).
Tracks: / You're telling me / My romance / Roll on, Kentucky moon / I don't want to go to bed / What would happen to me? / Love, you funny thing / Lady I love, The / Time alone will tell / When the waltz was through / Guilty / Goodnight Vienna / Stardust / Blue moon in the sky / Echo of a song, The / Put that sun back in the sky.
LP: . . . . JOY'D 275
MC: . . . . TC JOY'D 275

ROY FOX AND HIS ORCHESTRA (1938) (Fox, Roy & His Orchestra).
Tracks: / Nice work if you can get it / Gypsy in my soul / Who? / College swing / Let's all dance / Rockin' the town / Meanest thing you ever did, the / What a fool I've been / I double dare you / You took the words right out of my heart / Rhythm in me, the / Mamma, I wanna make rhythm / Me, myself and I / You appeal to me / Rosalie / Love walked in / You went to my head / Sweet someone / Just a simple melody / Snake charmer / It's the natural thing to do.
LP: . . . . HAL 9

ROY FOX & HIS ORCHESTRA, 1936-1938 (Fox, Roy & His Orchestra).

Tracks: / Love is a dancing thing / Play, orchestra, play / But where are you? / Let's face the music and dance / South sea island magic / Did your mother come from Ireland? / What will I tell my heart? / I've got my love to keep me warm / Things are looking up / Roses in December / Dearest love / I could use a dream / I fall in love with you every day / You leave me breathless / It rains, who cares? / Rose Marie / Calling me home / Miller's daughter, Marianne / Merry-go-round, The / Broken down / Night is young and you're so beautiful, The / Where are you? / Gone with the wind / Can I forget you? / When the sun says goodnight to the mountain / You do the darndest things baby / Baby / Love and learn / I've got beginner's luck / You went to my head / Fifty million robins can't be wrong / Whispering / Alone / Music goes round and around, The / Sweetheart, let's grow old together / Cheek to cheek / On Treasure Island / Poor little Angeline / It's a sin to tell a lie / Is it true what they say about Dixie? / Ramona / Wedding of the painted doll, The / Dancing with tears in my eyes / Goodnight sweetheart / Let's put out the lights / Stormy weather / Isle of Capri / When I grow too old to dream / Alone / September in the rain.
2LP: SHB 33

STRICTLY INSTRUMENTAL (Fox, Roy & His Orchestra).
Tracks: / I got rhythm / Black eyes / Way down yonder in New Orleans / You're the cream in my coffee / Lady be good / Birth of the blues / Happy feet / Mean to me / That's a plenty / Someday, sweetheart / Everybody loves my baby / On the sunny side of the street / Tiger rag / Let's do it / Impressions of Harlem / China boy / Chicago / Ain't she sweet / Congo / Mr. Sweeney's learned to swing / Song of India.
MC: CHAL 1
LP: HAL 1

TEN CENTS A DANCE.
Tracks: / Maybe it's love / One more time / Peanut vendor / Lady play your mandolin / Dancing through the ages (part 1) / My sweet Virginia / Between the devil and the deep blue sea / What made you so adorable / Thank you father / Hurt / Ten cents a dance / Writing a letter to you / That Lindy hop / Dancing through the ages (part 2) / If I have to go on without you / Ya got love / Betty loved / Bathing in the sunshine.
LP: BUR 015
MC: 4 BUR 015

THIS IS ROMANCE (At the Kit Cat Restaurant 1933) (Fox, Roy & Kit-Cat Band).
Tracks: / Look what you've done / There's a ring around the Moon / Girl in the little green hat / This is romance / Something came and got me in the spring / That's what life is made of / Oh Johanna / Without that certain thing / Blue moments / Happy and contented / Louisiana lullaby / My hat's on the side of my head.
LP: SVL 166
LP: JOYD 285

THIS IS ROY FOX.
Tracks: / Singin' in the rain / Bye bye blackbird.
LP: HAL 7
MC: CHAL 7

WHISPERING (Fox, Roy & His Band).
Tracks: / Whispering / Out of nowhere / We'll all go riding on a rainbow / I wished on the moon / Lazy day / Cobra and the flute, The / My sweet / Truckin' / It must be true / To be worthy of you / All I do is dream of you / In the middle of a kiss / Poor kid / Alexander's ragtime band / I'm gonna get you / La majestica / You didn't know the music (I didn't know the words) / Little man you've had a busy day.
LP: RFL 13

Fox, Samantha

GREATEST HITS: SAMANTHA FOX.
MC: THPA 1233

HITS COLLECTION: SAMANTHA FOX.
Tracks: / Touch me (I want your body) / Hot for you / I promise you / Best is yet to come, The / True devotion / Baby I'm lost for words / Naughty girls / Hold on tight / One in a million / That sensation / I surrender (to the spirit of the night) / Confession / It's only love / Do ya do ya (wanna please me).
LP: SHM 3284
MC: HSC 3284

I WANNA HAVE SOME FUN.
Tracks: / I wanna have some fun / Next to me / You started something / Out of your hands / One in a million / Love house / Ready for this / Hot for you / Confession / Walking on air.
LP: HIP 72
MC: HIPC 72

I WANNA HAVE SOME FUN (SINGLE).
Tracks: / I wanna have some fun / Out of our hands / Love don't grow on trees.
MC: FOXYC 12

JUST ONE NIGHT.
LP: HIP 112
MC: HIPC 112

ROCKING WITH MY RADIO.
LPPD: GENSF 1

SAMANTHA FOX.
Tracks: / (I can't get no) satisfaction / I surrender (to the spirit of the night) / I promise you / Naughty girls / True devotion / Nothing's gonna stop me now / If music be the food of love / That sensation / Dream city / Best is yet to come, The.
LP: HIP 48
MC: HIPC 48
LPPD: HIPO 48

SAMANTHA FOX: INTERVIEW PICTURE DISC.
LPPD: BAK 2098
LPPD: BAK 2023

SAMANTHA FOX: INTERVIEW PICTURE DISC, VOL 2.
LPPD: BAK 2055

TOUCH ME (I WANT YOUR BODY).
Tracks: / Touch me (I want your body) / I'm all you need / Suzie, don't leave me with your boyfriend / Wild kinda love / Hold on tight / Do ya do ya (wanna please me) / Baby I'm lost for words / It's only love / He's got sex / Drop me a line / Tonights the night.
LP: HIP 39
MC: HIPC 39

TOUCH ME (SPECIAL EDITION).
Tracks: / Touch me / I'm all you need / Suzie, don't leave me with your boyfriend / Wild kinda love / Hold on tight / Do ya do ya (wanna please me) / Baby I'm lost for words / It's only love / It's got sex / Drop me a line / Tonight's the night.
LP: HIP R39
MC: HIP RC39

Fox & The Hound

FOX AND THE HOUND (Film soundtrack) (Various artists).
Tracks: / Best of friends: *Various artists* / Lack of education: *Various artists* / Huntin' man: *Various artists* / Goodbye may seem forever: *Various artists* / Appreciate the lady: *Various artists*.
LP: D 383
MC: D 27DC
LP: REC 576
MC: ZCM 576

Fox (TV Series)

FOX (See under Blake, Peter) (Blake, Peter).

Foxes

FOXES (Original motion picture soundtrack) (Various artists).
LP: 6685 051
MC: 7599 051

Foxton, Bruce

TOUCH SENSITIVE.
LP: 206251

Foxx, Inez & Charlie

MOCKINGBIRD (Best of Inez & Charlie Foxx).
Tracks: / Mockingbird / Searching for my C.C. / Broken hearted fool / My momma told me / Don't do it no more / I wanna see my baby / If I need anyone / Here we go round the mulberry bush / Hurt by love / Sitting hero / La dee dah I love you / I fancy you / Down by the seashore / Ask me / Confusion / Jaybirds.
LP: SSL 6000
MC: TCSSL 6000

Foxx, John

GARDEN, THE.
Tracks: / Europe after the rain / Systems of romance / When I was a man and you were a woman / Dancing like a gun / Pater Noster / Night suit / You were there / Fusion / Walk away / Garden, The / Fission.
LP: OVED 47
MC: OVEDC 47
LP: V 2194

GOLDEN SECTION, THE.
Tracks: / My wild love / Someone / Your dress / Sitting at the edge of the world / Like a miracle / Hidden man / Running across thin ice with tigers / Ghosts on water / Twilight's last gleaming / Endlessly.
LP: V 2233
MC: TCV 2233
LP: OVED 120
MC: OVEDC 120

IN MYSTERIOUS WAYS.
Tracks: / Stars on fire / Lose all sense of time / What kind of girl / Shine on / Enter the angel / In mysterious ways / This side of paradise / Stepping softly / Morning glory / Enter the angel 2.
LP: V 2355
MC: TCV 2355
LP: OVED 189
MC: OVEDC 189

METAMATIC.
Tracks: / Plaza / He's a liquid / Underpass / Metal beat / No-one driving / New kind of man, A / Blurred girl / 030 / Tidal wave / Touch and girl.
LP: OVED 46
MC: OVEDC 46
LP: V 2146

Foxx, Red

OPEN THE DOOR RICHARD! (Foxx, Red/Dusty Fletcher).
LP: SJL 1181

Foxy

HOT NUMBERS.
Tracks: / Headhunter / Devil boogie / Give me a break / Nobody will ever take me away from you / Chicapbon chicapbon / Hot numbers / Lady / Give me that groove / Lady of the streets.
LP: TKR 83353

PARTY BOYS.
Tracks: / Girls / Let's be bad tonight / Sambambe Rio / I belong to you / She's so cool / Rrrrock / Fantasy / Pensando en ti / Party boys.
LP: TKR 83384

Foyer Des Arts

EIN KUSS IN DER IRRTUMSTAVERNE.
LP: EFA 4528

Fra Lippo Lippi

IN SILENCE.
LP: U 003

LIGHT AND SHADE.
Tracks: / Angel / Freedom / Don't take away the light / Beauty and madness / Home / Light and shade / Some people / Crazy wisdom / Stardust motel / In difference.
LP: V 2442
MC: TCV 2442

NOW AND FOREVER.
MC: U 005

SMALL MERCIES.
LP: U 017

SONGS.
Tracks: / Come Summer / Shouldn't have to be like that / Even tall trees bend / Just like me / Leaving / Regrets / Every time I see you / Crash of light / Distance between us, The / Coming home.
LP: V 2375
MC: TCV 2375

Fractured

NO PEACE FOR THE WICKED.
Tracks: / Honest lovin' / Chauffeur driven limousine / Dark blue sea / Kisses sweeter than wine / Girl on the corner / Gamblin' man / Sold my secret / Big John.
LP: NOSE 17

Fraggle Rock

FRAGGLE ROCK (T.V. soundtrack).
Tracks: / Fraggle rock / Follow me / Convincing John / Doozer knitting song / Do it on my own / Wemblin' fool / Why? / Lost and found / Working / Travelling Matt / Catch the tail by the tiger / Dum of a son of a gun / Brave boy jump up / Muck and goo / Friendship song / Fraggle rock rock / Beetle song / Easy is the only way to go / Our melody.
LP: PL 70221
MC: PK 70221

IF I WERE KING OF THE UNIVERSE.
MC: LL 41 8035 4

TALE OF TRAVELLING MATT, THE.
MC: LL 41 8033 4

WHAT DO DOOZERS DO.
MC: LL 41 8034 4

WHAT'S A FRAGGLE.
MC: LL 41 8036 4

Frampton, Peter

6 TRACK HITS: PETER FRAMPTON.
Tracks: / Show me the way.
MC: 7SC 5039

ART OF CONTROL.
LP: AMLH 64905

BEST OF FRAMPTON COMES ALIVE.
LP: SHM 3165
MC: HSC 3165

BREAKING ALL THE RULES.
Tracks: / You kill me / Friday on my mind / Lost a part of you / Breaking all the rules / I don't wanna let you go / Rise up / Wasting the night away / Going to L.A..
LP: AMLK 63722

FRAMPTON COMES ALIVE.
Tracks: / Something's happening / Doobie wah / Show me the way / It's a plain shame / All I want to be (is by your side) / Wind of change / Baby, I love your way / I wanna go to the sun / Penny for your thoughts / I'll give you money / Shine on / Jumpin' Jack Flash / Lines on my face / Do you feel like we do?.
2LP: AMLM 63703
MCSET: CLM 63703

I'M IN YOU.
LP: AMLK 64039

PREMONITION.
Tracks: / Stop / Hiding from a heartache / You know so well / Premonition / Lying / Moving a mountain / All eyes on you / Into view / Call of the wild.
LP: OVED 220
MC: OVEDC 220

WHERE I SHOULD BE.
Tracks: / I can't stand it no more / Got my feet back on the ground / Where I should be / Everything I need / May I baby / You don't know like I know / She don't reply / We've just begun / Take me by the hand / It's a sad affair.
LP: AMLK 63710

Fran & Anna

INCREDIBLE FRAN & ANNA, THE.
LP: NB 113

LOVE FROM FRAN AND ANNA.
Tracks: / Donald, where's yer troosers / Just a wee deoch and doris / Scotland the brave / Flower of Scotland / Amazing grace / My bonnie lies over the ocean / Hava nagila / Rusty old halo.
LP: NM 1

Franc, Rene

BLACK STICK.
LP: WAM/O No.4

France

GREAT FRENCH STARS OF THE 30'S (Various artists).
Tracks: / Paris, je t'aime d'amour: *Chevalier, Maurice* / C'est si facile de vous aimer: *Baker, Josephine* / Boum: *Trenet, Charles* / Il n'est pas distingue: *Piaf, Edith* / Ignace: *Fernandel* / C'est vrai: *Mistinguett*/ Si tu m'aimes: *Sablon, Jean* / En Septembre sous la pluie: *Marjane, Leo* / Amapola: *Rossi, Tino* / Quand un vicomte: *Hildegarde* / Swing guitar: *Reinhardt, Django/Stephane Grappelli* / Melancolie: *Sablon, Jean*/ Et voila, voila les hommes: *mirielle* / Vous valez mieux qu'un sourire: *Chevalier, Maurice* / La musique vient par ici: *Ventura, Ray & His Collegians* / Chez moi: *Boyer, Lucienne* / Je chante: *Trenet, Charles* / C'est un nid charmant: *Baker, Josephine* / Berceuse de Jocelyn: *Rossi, Tino* / La java de cezique: *Piaf, Edith*/ Oh que j'aime Paris: *Mistinguett*.
LP: CHD 157
MC: MCHD 157

MAGIC OF PARIS (Various artists).
Tracks: / Sous le ciel de Paris: *Various artists* / J'aime Paris au mois de Mai: *Various artists* / Parisse: *Various* artists / Paris, tu m'as pris dans tes bras: *Various artists* / Pigalle: *Various artists* / Rue des Blancs Manteaux: *Various artists* / Menilmontant: *Various artists* / Sous les toits de Paris: *Various artists*/ A Paris: *Various artists* / Champs Elysee: *Various artists* / J'ai deux amours: *Various artists* / Song from Moulin Rouge: *Various artists* / A Paris dans chaque faubourg: *Various artists* / Paris je t'aime d'amour: *Various artists*.
LP: NTS 227
MC: TCNTS 227

PARIS AFTER DARK (Various artists).
Tracks: / La mer: *Trenet, Charles* / Hymne a l'amour: *Piaf, Edith* / J'attendrai: *Rossi, Tino* / Ma Tonkinoise: *Baker, Josephine* / Valentine: *Chevalier, Maurice* / Je cherche un millionaire: *Mistinguett* / Embrasse-moi cherie: *Delyle, Lucienne* / Pigalle: *Ulmer, Georges* / Le chaland qui passe: *Gauty, Lys* / Sur ma vie: *Les Compagnons De La Chanson* / La vie en rose: *Piaf, Edith* / Parlez-moi d'amour: *Boyer, Lucienne* / Ces petites choses: *Sablon, Jean* / Mon homme: *Mistinguett* / J'ai deux amours: *Baker, Josephine* / Boum: *Trenet, Charles* / La java bleue: *Frehel* / Le fiacre: *Sablon, Jean* / Les trois cloches: *Piaf, Edith et Les Compagnons De La Chansons* / C'est a Capri: *Rossi, Tino*.
LP: EMS 1296
MC: TCEMS 1296

PARIS BLUES (French 'Realist Singers' 1926-1958) (Various artists).
Tracks: / Les amants d'un jour: *Piaf, Edith* (Orchestra: Robert Chauvigny) / Ou sont tous mes amants?: *Frehel*(With orchestra) / La rue de Notre Amour: *Damia* (Orchestra: Pierre Chagnon) / C'est mon gigolo: *Delyle, Lucienne*(Orchestra: Aime Barelli) /

Dans la rue des Blancs Manteaux: *Greco, Juliette* (Orchestra: P. Arimi.) / Tel qu'il est: *Frehel* (Maurice Alexander & His Orchestra) / La serenade due pave: *Buffet, Eugenie* (With chorus & orchestra.) / La chanson de Margaret: *Montero, Germaine* (Philippe Gerard Ensemble) / Pars piano: *George, Yvonne* (Georges Van Parys) / Au bal de la chance: *Piaf, Edith* (Orchestra: Robert Chauvigny.) / La complainte de la butte: *Vaucaire, Cora* (Orchestra: Francois Rauber.) / Sombre Dimanche: *Damia* (With Russian chorus.) / Le Noel de la rue: *Piaf, Edith* (With the Raymond Saint-Paul Chorus.) / Lili Marlene: *Solidor, Suzy* (Orchestra: Georges Briez) / Mon amant de St Jean: *Delyle, Lucienne* (Orchestra: Aime Barelli) / Sarah: *Lasso, Gloria* (Orchestra: Franck Pourcel.) / Le chant des partisans: *Sablon, Germaine* (Orchestra: Guy Luypaerts.) / La chanson de Catherine: *Piaf, Edith* (Orchestra: Robert Chauvigny) / La chanson des fortifs: *Frehel* / La fille de Londres: *Montero, Germaine* (M. Philippe-Gerard & His Ensemble).
LP: . . . . **EMS 1397**
MC: . . . . **TCEMS 1397**

PARIS BY NIGHT (Various artists).
Tracks: / Milord: *Piaf, Edith* / Douce France: *Trenet, Charles* / Briu d'amour: *Alexander, Maurice* / Sur les quais du vieux Paris: *Delyle, Lucienne* / Vieni vieni: *Rossi, Tino* / Seule ce soir: *Marjane, Leo* / J'aime Paris au mois de mai: *Aznavour, Charles* / Puisque vous partez en voyage: *Sablon, Mireille & Jean* / Moulin rouge: *Les Compagnons De La Chanson* / A Paris dans chaque faubourg: *Gauty, Lys* / Sur le pont d'Avignon: *Sablon, Jean* / Ou est-il donc?: *Frehel* / Ma Louise: *Chevalier, Maurice* (Film Chanson De Paris.) / La clocher de mon coeur: *Busch, Eva* / Nuages: *Reinhardt, Django* / Depuis que les bals sont fermes: *Damia* / Que reste-t-il de nos amours?: *Trenet, Charles* / Ma cabane au Canada: *Renaud, Line* / Un seul couvert, please, James: *Sablon, Jean* / Bal dans ma rue: *Piaf, Edith*.
LP: . . . . **EMS 1363**
MC: . . . . **TCEMS 1363**

SONGS AND DANCE FROM NORMANDY (Various artists).
Tracks: / Branle de village: *Various artists* / Mon pere avait un petit bois: *Various artists* / Sophie Dondon: *Various artists* / Le loup: *Various artists* / La lurette: *Various artists* / La lauriette: *Various artists* / Mardi gras: *Various artists* / A moi la vache a Biron: *Various artists* / Cousine, cousin: *Various artists* / Branle gay: *Various artists* / Par devant derriere: *Various artists* / En revenant de Paris: *Various artists* / Contredanse: *Various artists* / Le tour du moulin: *Various artists* / Noel: *Various artists* / Un jour dans la prairie: *Various artists* / Les fetus: *Various artists*.
LP: . . . . **ARN 33539**

SOUVENIR DE PARIS (The Great French Stars) (Various artists).
Tracks: / C'est un p'tit rien: *Mistinguett & Jean Gabin* / Tango de Marilou: *Rossi, Tino* / Si, j'etais Blanche: *Baker, Josephine* / Oui, papa: *Chevalier, Maurice* / Parlez-moi d'amour: *Boyer, Lucienne* / St. Louis blues: *Ventura, Ray & Ses Collegiens* / Plaisir d'amour: *Printemps, Yvonne* / Pauvre grand: *Frehel* / Vous avez: *Sablon, Jean* / Le fiancre: *Guilbert, Yvette* / Plus rien, je n'ai plus rien qu'un chien: *Sablon, Jean* / Ca c'est Paris: *Mistinguett* / Ca c'est fou: *Alibert* / Le chaland qui passe: *Gauty, Lys* / Valentine: *Chevalier, Maurice* / C'est mon gigolo: *Damina* / La petite Tonkinoise: *Baker, Josephine* / Couche dans le foin: *Pills & Tabet* / Papa n'a pas voulou: *Mireille* / La Marseillaise: *Thill, Georges*.
LP: . . . . **AJA 5028**
MC: . . . . **ZC AJA 5028**

France Joli

FRANCE JOLI.
Tracks: / Come to me / Let go / Don't stop dancing / Playboy.
LP: . . . . **ARL 5046**

TONIGHT.
Tracks: / This time / When love hurts inside / Tonight / Stoned in love / Heart to break the heart / Feel like dancing / Tough luck.
LP: . . . . **ARL 5060**

Frances Concert

BEST OF FRANCES CONCERT COMPILATION (Various artists).
LP: . . . . **FC 130**

Francia, Paul

MORTAR FIRE - NORMANDY TO GERMANY 1944-45.
MC: . . . . **STD 001**

Francie & Josie

FRANCIE AND JOSIE.
Tracks: / Hallawreer / Where the sourocks meet the heather / I'm glad that I was born in Glasgow / My love / Wachlin' hame / La di da / We'd rather be here with you / Camalachie / Hee drum ho drum ragtime / I should have listened to Grannie / Glasgow underground, The / Glasgow highland games, The / So long it's been good to know you / We're no awa' tae bide awa'.
LP: . . . . **LBLP 2004**
MC: . . . . **ZCLBP 2004**

Francis, Bob

THIS IS MY LIFE.
Tracks: / Disco in Brazil / This is something new to me / I'm a fool for love / Something's gotta give / Tell her it's snowing / This is my life / My prayer / We talk we speak / Symphony of love / Without a song / Dancing with the lights down low.
LP: . . . . **PKL 5581**

Francis, Brenda

MY NUMBER ONE (See under La Compagnie) (Francis, Brenda & La Compagnie).

Francis, Connie

24 GREATEST HITS.
MC: . . . . **PLAC 3910**

AMONG MY SOUVENIRS.
Tracks: / My happiness / Stupid Cupid / Let's have a party / Valentino / Among my souvenirs / Who's sorry now? / Plenty good lovin' / Mama / Carolina moon / Lipstick on your collar / Everybody's somebody's fool / My heart has a mind of its own.
LP: **825 799-1**
MC: **825 799-4**
LP: . . . . **STAR 2393**
MC: . . . . **STAC 2393**

CONNIE FRANCIS.
Tracks: / Delilah / Les bicyclettes de Belsize / Don't say a word / Kiss me goodbye / Three good reasons / Mr. Love / It's not unusual / Last waltz, The / What's wrong with my world / Lifetime of love / What the world needs now / Promises, promises / Do you know the way to San Jose / Trains & boats & planes / Make it easy on yourself / Alfie / This girl's in love with you / I say a little prayer / Wanting things / Walk on by / Magic moments / Blue on blue / Don't make me over.
2LP: **2675180**

CONNIE FRANCIS IN DEUTSCHLAND (The Complete German, Dutch & Swedish Connie).
Tracks: / Die liebe ist ein seltsames spiel / Ich komm' nie mehr von dir los / Ich denk an dich / Immer und uberall / Wenn ich traume / Niemand / Mein Herz weiss genau was es will / Shoner fremder Mann / Ene Insel fur Zwei / Oh, I like it / Darlin' meine liebe / Mond von Mexico / Lili Marlene / Weine nicht um mich / Einmal komm' ich wieder / Paradiso / lu' mir nicht weh / Immer wenn's am schonsten ist / Colombino / Das ist zuviel (too many rules) / Nino / Alle jungen leute / Wenn du gehst / Die nacht ist mein / Mein schiff fahrt zu dir / Barcarole in der Nacht / Perlen der Sudsee / Ein boy fur mich (kiss 'n' twist) / Gondola D'amore / Jedes Boot hat seinen Hafen / Ich bin allein / Ich geb' 'ne Party heut' Nacht / Meinen Sunny krieg ich nie mehr wieder / Du musst blieben, Angelino / Napoli / Abends in der Mondscheinallee / Jede Liebe geht einmal zu Ende / Hast du Heimweh / Abschiedsmelodie / I inmal wirst du kommen / Weekend boy / Ich war gerne verliebt / Denk nicht an die and're / Immer geht's im Kreis herum / Mein Herz wird warten / Komm zu mir, Joe / Der mond war schuld daran / Sternenmelodie / Blaue Nacht am Hafen / Er ist mein / Jonny der Schweiger / Eines I ages wird er bei mir sein / Mein Herz ruft nach dir / Keine liebe ohne tranen / Alte liebe rostet nicht / Das soll nie mehr vorubergeh'n / Es ist so schon, dass es dich gibt / Jeder traum ist einmal ausgetraumt / Meine Reise ist zu Ende / Lass mich bei dir sein / Canzone di Napoli / Schade um die schon Zeit / Scharze Augen / Er war nur ein Marchenerzahler / Sing von Liebe, Balalaika / Ende gut, alles gut / Traumboot / Goodbye mama / Oh blieb bei mir / Wenn du in meinen traumen bei mir bist / Malaguena / Deine Liebe / Heisser sand / Fur immer / Zorba's l anz / Drei Munzen im Brunnen / Oh mein papa / Sag, weiss du denn was liebe ist / Vaya Con Dios / Romantica / Sonnenschein, uberall nur Sonnenschein / Keep smiling / Jedem Abend folgt ein Morgen / Du sagst goodbye / Strand der Tausend Lieder / Happy girl / Ich zahl die Stunden / Lissabon / Lass mir die bunten Traume / Fahr hinaus mit den Sternen / Blauer wind / Buona sera / Es begann in einer kleinen Bar / Gino / Meine Welt beginnt bei dir / Traume und Tranen / Moderne Marchen / Gitarren der Liebe / Lovin' man / Liebe / Er nennt mich Spatz oder Schatz / Auch ein Star weint aus Liebe / Regen in der nacht / Hier wie dort, morgen wie heute / Heut fiel auf einmal Schnee / Das regenlied / Erinnerung / Bis wir uns Kussten / Regenbogenland / Was ich bin, das bin ich alleine durch dich / Ich bin allein (2) / Barcarole in der Nacht (2) / Perlen der Sudsee (2) / Die nacht ist mein (2) / Blaue Nacht am Hafen (2) / Mack the knife / Bacarole in der Nacht (3) / Gino / Danke schon / Jij bent niet van mij (Dutch) / Pretty little baby (2) / Pretty little baby / Mister twister / Wozu ist Liebe gut / Die lieber gehn'mir niemals aus / Only a woman / Esist niemals zu spat / Das spiel der spiele / Ich bin dein Schatten.
LPS: . . . . **BFX 15305-9**

CONNIE FRANCIS & PETER KRAUS - VOL.1 (Francis, Connie & Peter Kraus).
Tracks: / Oh I like it ((Previously unissued)) / Schreib mire eine (Send a picture postcard) / Mission bell / Das haben die madchen gern / Susi sagt es gabi / Honeymoon / Keine nacht kann ich schlafen / Par le monde (Honey moon) / Gondola d'amore / Oh so wunderbar (wunderbar wie du) / Columbino / Alright, okay you win / Ich denk an dich (I think of you.) / Doll doll dolly / Ich komm' nie mehr von dir los (Many tears ago.) / Comme un tigre.
LP: . . . . **BFX 15061**

CONNIE FRANCIS & PETER KRAUS - VOL.2 (Francis, Connie & Peter Kraus).
Tracks: / Darlin' meine liebe / Twenty four hours (Ich denk an dich) / Mondschein und liebe (Sweet love) / Everybody else but me / Sag mir was du denkst / Je pense a toi / Ein rendezvous mit dir / C'est toi la plus belle / Niemand / Wenn ich traume (Where the boys are) / Alle jungen leute / Das ist zuviel (too many rules) / Immer und uberall / Immer wenn's am schonsten ist / Weine nicht um mich / Ein boy fur mich (kiss 'n' twist).
LP: . . . . **BFX 15062**

CONNIE'S GREATEST HITS.
Tracks: / Someone else's boy / Who's sorry now / Stupid cupid / Plenty good lovin' / My happiness / Lipstick on your collar / Many tears ago / My heart has a mind of its own / Everybody's somebody's fool / Among my souvenirs / Let's have a party / Looking for love / Don't break the heart that loves you / Mr. Twister / Frankie / Robot man.
LP: **831 994 1**
MC: **831 994 4**

CONNIE'S GREATEST HITS (MGM).
LP: . . . . **MGM C 831**

COUNTRY STORE: CONNIE FRANCIS.
Tracks: / Your cheatin' heart / Oh lonesome me / She'll have to go / I don't hurt anymore / Bye bye love / I walk the line / I don't wanna play house / I can't stop loving you / There'll be no teardrops tonight / Please help me, I'm falling / Heartaches by the number / How's the world treating you / I'm movin' on / (I'd be a) legend in my own time.
LP: . . . . **CST 56**
MC: . . . . **CSTK 56**

GREATEST HITS: CONNIE FRANCIS VOLS.1 & 2.
Tracks: / Who's sorry now / Stupid cupid / Plenty good lovin' / My happiness / Lipstick on your collar / Many tears ago / My heart has a mind of its own / Everybody's somebody's fool / Among my souvenirs / Carolina moon / Mama / Where the boys are / Frankie / Vacation / If I didn't care / Together / I'm sorry I made you cry / When the boy in your arms / Teddy / If my pillow could talk / Fallin' / You're gonna miss me / Valentino / Happy days and lonely nights / Secondhand love / Drownin' my sorrows / He's my dreamboat / My child / Don't break the heart that loves you / Jealous heart / Robot man.
2LP: **262 403 8**
MCSET: **327 130 5**

ICH GEB'NE PARTY HEUT'NACHT.
Tracks: / Ich geb'ne party heut'nacht (Let's have a party.) / Weekend boy / Ich war / Gerne verliebt (Looking for love) / Komm zu mir, Joe / Nino / Meinen sunny Krieg ich nie mehr wielder / Jedes boot hat seinen hafen / Abschiedsmelodie / Oh blieb bei mir (Previously unissued.) / Denk nicht an die and're / Sternenmelodie / Keine liebe ohne tranen / Jeder traum ist einmal ausgetraumt / Traumboot / Mein herz ruft nach dir (My heart cries for you) / Blauer wind (Previously unissued.).
LP: . . . . **BFX 15137**

I'M ME AGAIN - SILVER ANNIVERSARY ALBUM.
Tracks: / I'm me again / Milk and honey / Lincoln street chapel / No sun today / What good are tears / Comme ci comme ca / Where the boys are / Don't break the heart that loves you / My happiness / I don't want to walk without you / White cliffs of Dover, The / Cry.
LP: **2315426**

LEGEND IN HER TIME - THE COUNTRY HITS.
MC: **8477514**

LOVE SONGS: CONNIE FRANCIS.
Tracks: / Who's sorry now / Carolina Moon / Jealous heart / He thinks I still care / Fallin' / I don't hurt anymore / Bye bye love / When the boy in your arms / My heart has a mind of its own / Half as much / Make it easy on yourself / Walk on by / Oh lonesome me / Among my souvenirs.
MC: **CN4 2098**
LP: . . . . **CN 2098**

LOVE'N'COUNTRY.
Tracks: / My happiness / This girl's in love with you / I'm sorry I made you cry / What's wrong with my world / I'm a fool to care / Please help me, I'm falling / Many tears ago / I can't stop loving you / You always hurt the one you love / Look of love, The / If I didn't care / Breaking in a brand new broken heart / If you ever change your mind / Send me the pillow that you dream on / Everybody's somebody's fool / My heart cries for you.
LP: . . . . **CN 2081**
MC: **CN4 2081**

MY SOUVENIRS.
LP: . . . . **ADAH 437**
MC: . . . . **ADAHC 437**

PORTRAIT OF A SONG STYLIST.
Tracks: / Come rain or come shine / All by myself / Song is ended, The / Moon river / Mack the knife / Love is a many splendoured thing / True love / All the way / Second time around / Lili Marlene / Milord / Am I blue / La vie en rose / Take me to your heart again / Fascination.
LP: . . . . **HARLP 108**
MC: . . . . **HARMC 108**

ROCK 'N' ROLL MILLION SELLERS.
Tracks: / Heartbreak hotel / Tweedle dee / I almost lost my mind / I hear you knocking / Just a dream / Don't be cruel / Lipstick on your collar / Sincerely / Ain't that a shame / Silhouette / I'm walking / It's only make believe.
LP: . . . . **LSP 1061**
LP: **831 995-1**
MC: **831 995-4**
LP: . . . . **MGM C 804**

SINGS GREAT COUNTRY HITS.
LP: . . . . **SPELP 62**
MC: . . . . **SPEMC 62**

TWENTY ALL-TIME GREATS.
Tracks: / Who's sorry now? / Stupid Cupid / My happiness / Everybody's somebody's fool / Carolina moon / Plenty good lovin' / Where the boys are / Robot man / When the boy in your arms / Mama / Lipstick on your collar / Among my souvenirs / Many tears ago / Breaking in a brand new broken heart / Vacation / Together / Jealous heart / You always hurt the one you love / My heart has a mind of its own / My child.
LP: **239 129 0**
MC: **317 729 0**

VERY BEST OF CONNIE FRANCIS.
Tracks: / Who's sorry now? / Stupid Cupid / Carolina moon / Mama / My happiness / Lipstick on your collar / Everybody's somebody's fool / Among my souvenirs / Many tears ago / Lili Marlene / La Bamba.
2LP: **2670 168**

Francis, Dick (author)

BOLT (Havers, Nigel).
MCSET: . . . . **LFP 7306**

BREAK IN (Havers, Nigel).
MCSET: . . . . **LFP 7260**
MCSET: . . . . **TCLFP 7260**

DANGER, THE (Pigott-Smith, Tim (nar)).
MCSET: . . . . **LFP 7182**
MCSET: . . . . **LFP 4171825**

EDGE, THE (Marinker, Peter (nar)).
MCSET: . . . . **LFP 7424**

ENQUIRY/BONECRACK (Various artists).
MCSET: . . . . **ZBBC 1055**

HIGH STAKES (Bolam, James (nar)).
MCSET: . . . . **LFP 7358**

HOT MONEY (Cazenove, Christopher).
MCSET: . . . . **LFP 7326**

LONGSHOT (see under Longshot) (Branagh, Kenneth).

ODDS AGAINST (Powell, Robert (nar)).
MCSET: **CC/029**

PROOF (Dance, Charles).
MCSET: . . . . **LFP 7214**
MCSET: . . . . **LFP 417214 5**

STRAIGHT (McCorkindale, Simon).
MCSET: . . . . **LFP 7457**

Francis, Donovan

WORLD POWER.
Tracks: / New York / Illusion / Rainbow country / Lover's quarrel / Busy street / World power / Human bomb / Easy mi idren / Evil eyes / Abas apartheid.
MC: . . . . **ICT 9909**
LP: . . . . **ILPS 9909**

Francis, Jan (nar)

BALLET SHOES (See under Ballet Shoes).

FIVE ON A TREASURE ISLAND (see under Blyton, Enid (aut).

SECRET ISLAND, THE (see under Blyton, Enid (aut)).

Francis, Joe

EVERY STEP OF THE WAY.
Tracks: / Let's face the music and dance / Where do you start / Nobody loves you quite like me / Play it again Sam / One word / I wonder who's kissing her now / Moments like this / Let's fall in love / Dancing in the dark / Gentle touch, The / Every step of the way / Just in time (Only on CD.).
LP: . . . . **PL 74166**
MC: . . . . **PK 74166**

Francis, Morris

FUN IN ACADIANA.
LP: **1018**
MC: . . . . **1018 TC**

Francis, Panama

EVERYTHING SWING (Francis, Panama & The Savoy Sultans).
LP: . . . . **ST 233**

GROOVING (Francis, Panama & The Savoy Sultans).
LP: . . . . **ST 218**

PANAMA FRANCIS ALL STARS 1949 (Various artists).
LP: . . . . **KK 813**

Francis, Syd

SOMETHING SPECIAL.
LP: . . . . **SRTZ 78393**

Francis, Winston

JUST ONE (Francis, Winston Cobra).
LP: . . . . **TWLP 1011**

MR. FIXIT.
LP: . . . . **CSL 8018**

Francis X

SOUL INCEST (Francis X & The Bushmen).
LP: . . . . **REV LP 84**

Francisco, Don

HIGH PRAISE.
Tracks: / Worship the King / I will rejoice / Speak peace to my heart / Come Holy Spirit / I will praise You / Help me worship / To God / Through all my days / Lord of your church / No better place.
LP: . . . . **SR R 8100**
MC: . . . . **SR C 8100**

ONE HEART AT A TIME.
LP: . . . . **MYR 1195**
MC: . . . . **MC 1195**

POWER, THE.
LP: . . . . **SRR 8097**
MC: . . . . **SRC 8097**

Franck, Albert

UN PARISIEN A PARIS.
LP: . . . . **ROSE 236**
MC: . . . . **ROSK 236**

Franck (Composer)

STRING QUARTET IN D Ravel/String Quartet in F (Fitzwilliam String Quartet).
MC: **4254244**

Franco

A NAIROBI.
LP: . . . . **POP 033**
MC: . . . . **C 1020**

BOIS NOIR.
MC: . . . . **C 1021**

CHEZ RHYTHMES ET MUSIC A PARIS (Franco Et Le TPOK Jazz).
LP: . . . . **POP 32**

FRANCO AND JOLIE DETTA (Franco & Jolie Detta).
LP: . . . . **ESP 8427**

LA VIE DES HOMMES.
LP: . . . . **CHOC 006**
MC: . . . . **C 1018**

MARIO.
LP: . . . . **CHOC 005**

OM NA WAPI (Franco : Rochereau).
LP: . . . . **SHAN 43024**
MC: . . . . **SHANC 43024**

ORIGINALITE.
LP: . . . . **RETRO 2**

SPECIAL 30 ANS (Franco & Simaro).
LP: . . . . **CHOC 007**
MC: . . . . **C 1026**

Franco, Gian

SEA, THE (Franco, Gian Reverberi).
LP: . . . . **PRIM 6001**
MC: . . . . **ZPRIM 6001**

Franco & Josky

CHOC, CHOC, CHOC 3.
LP: . . . . **CHOC 003**

Francois, Claude

ALBUM SOUVENIR.
Tracks: / Le telephone pleure / Nina nanna / Fille sauvage / Le mal aime / La plus belle fille du monde / C'est toujours le meme refrain / La musique Americaine / Toi et moi contre le monde entier / Six jours sur la route / Le chanteur malheureux / Soudain il ne reste qu'une chanson / Le spectacle est termine / Le lundi au soleil / Dis-lui pour moi / On ne choisit pas / Belinda / Part ca la vie est belle, A / Je viens diner ce soir / Chanson populaire d'Azerbaidjan / Je t'embrace / Gens qui pleurent, gens qui rient / Sha-la-la / J'ai encore ma maison / Notre dernier chanson ensemble.
LP: **4505191**
MC: **4505194**

Francour, Chuck

UNDER THE BOULEVARD LIGHTS.
Tracks: / Under the boulevard lights / Wild one / Magician politician / Don't call me / Over the line / Don't be cruel / Easy street / Down in the alley / Alibis / Back on the avenue.
LP: . . . . **AML 3013**

Frank, Anne

DIARY OF ANNE FRANK, THE (Bloom, Claire (nar)).
MC: . . . . **CDL 51522**

Frank Chickens

CLUB MONKEY.
LP: . . . . **STIR 2**
MC: . . . . **STIRC 2**

GET CHICKENIZED.
Tracks: / We say you say / Sacred marriage / Street angels, Tokyo / Two little ladies / Solid life / Japanese girl / Island inside island / Young summer / Chicken ondo / Yellow toast.
LP: . . . . **STIR 1**

WE ARE FRANK CHICKENS.
Tracks: / Cheeba cheeba chimpira / Mothra / Green banana / Madam fatal / We are Ninja / Yellow detective / Shellfish bamboo / Pikadon / We are Frank Chickens / Sake ballad.
LP: . . . . **KAZ LP 2**
MC: . . . . **KAZ MC 2**

Frank, Ed

NEW NEW ORLEANS MUSIC, VOL. 1 (Frank, Ed Quintet).
LP: . . . . **ROUNDER 2065**
MC: . . . . **ROUNDER 2065C**

Frank, Jackson C.

JACKSON AGAIN.
LP: . . . . **BCLP 4**

Frank, Stanley

PLAY IT TILL IT HURTS.
Tracks: / Rocco's girl / Rock crazy baby / We want a war / Sister delight / Nylon meat dreams / Love like a hammer / I am the law / Dying to live / Good lovin' / Hot on you / Reeling to the rock / Waiting for the big time.
LP: . . . . **AMLH 64828**

Franke, Bob

FOR REAL.
LP: . . . . **FF 368**

LOVE CAN'T BE BITTER ALL THE TIME.
LP: . . . . **FR 116**

Franke, Rennee

DING DONG BOOGIE.
Tracks: / Ding dong boogie / Bimmelbahn boogie (choo choo boogie) / Sailors boogie / Columbus boogie / Krahwinkel boogie / Der kuck-kuck swing / Botch-a-me (emglisch) / Der teddy mit dem dudelsack / Musikverrucko (crazy man crazy) / Dreissig tassen kaffee / Mr. Patton aus Manhattan (see you later alligator) / Das ist der richt'ge rhythmus fur die jungen madchen schuhpu / Gerne mocht ich kussen (botch a me) / Mi no mei och.
LP: . . . . **BFX 15223**

Frankenstein

FRANKENSTEIN (Powell, Robert (nr)).
MC: . . . . **SQRL 31**

FRANKENSTEIN (horror classics for ages 7-12) (Unknown narrator(s)).
MC: . . . . **PLB 126**

FRANKENSTEIN (Mason, James (nr)).
LP: . . . . **TC 1541**
MC: . . . . **CDL 51541**

Frankie Goes To...

FRANKIE GOES TO HOLLYWOOD: INTERVIEW PIC DISC (Frankie Goes To Hollywood).
LPPD: . . . . **BAK 2009**

LIVERPOOL.
LP: . . . . **ZTTIQ 8**
MC: . . . . **ZCIQ 8**

MUSIC AND MEDIA INTERVIEW PICTURE DISC.
LPPD: . . . . **FG 1017**

POWER OF LOVE.
Tracks: / Power of love, The.
MC: . . . . **CTIS 105**

RELAX.
Tracks: / Relax / One September Monday.
MC: . . . . **CTIS 102**

TWO TRIBES (Frankie Goes To Hollywood).
Tracks: / Two tribes (carnage mix) (Available on 12" only.).
MC: . . . . **CS 784**

WELCOME TO THE PLEASURE DOME.
Tracks: / World is my oyster, The / Welcome to the pleasure dome / Relax / War / Two tribes / Happy hi / Born to run / Wish the lads were here (inc. ballad of '32) / Krisco kisses / Black night white light / Only star in heaven, The / Power of love, The / Bang.....
LP: . . . . **ZTTIQ 1**
MC: . . . . **ZCIQ 1**

Frankie & Knockouts

FRANKIE & THE KNOCKOUTS.
Tracks: / Come back / Sweetheart / She's a runner / You're my girl / One four all / Tonight running into the night / Tell me why / Annie goes Hollywood / Don't stop.
LP: . . . . **RCALP 5026**

Frankins...(bk)

FRANKINS, THE - PROLOGUE AND TALE (see under Chaucer, Geoffrey) (Frankins...).

Franklin, Alan

BLUES CLIMAX, THE (Franklin, Alan Explosion).
LP: . . . . **PSYCHO 18**

Franklin, Aretha

20 GREATEST HITS: ARETHA FRANKLIN.
LP: . . . . **K 2411352**

ALMIGHTY FIRE.
Tracks: / Almighty fire (woman of the future) / Lady lady / More than just a joy / Keep on loving you / I needed you baby / Close to you / No matter who you love / This you can believe / I'm your speed.
LP: . . . . **K 50445**

AMAZING GRACE.
2LP: **2-906**

ARETHA.
Tracks: / Jimmy Lee / I knew you were waiting (for me) (duet with George Michael) / Do you still remember? / Jumpin' Jack Flash / Rockalott / Angel cries. An / He'll come along / If you need my love tonight (duet with Larry Graham.) / Look to the rainbow.
LP: **208020**
MC: **408020**
LP: . . . . **SPART 1147**
MC: . . . . **TCART 1147**
LP: **208883**
MC: **408883**

ARETHA (CBS).
Tracks: / Won't be long / Over the rainbow / Love is the only thing / Sweet lover / All night long / Who needs you / Right now / Are you sure / Maybe I'm a fool / It ain't necessarily so / Blue by myself / Today I sing the blues.
LP: . . . . **CBS 32408**
MC: **40-32408**

ARETHA IN PARIS.
LP: **SD8207**

ARETHA NOW.
LP: **588-114**

ARETHA'S GOLD.
Tracks: / I never loved a man (the way I love you) / Do right woman, do right man / Respect / Doctor Feelgood / Baby, I love you / (You make me feel like) a natural woman / Chain of fools / Since you've been gone (sweet sweet baby) / Ain't no way / Think / You send me / House that Jack built, The / I say a little prayer / See-saw.
LP: . . . . **K 40036**

ARETHA'S GREATEST HITS.
Tracks: / Spanish Harlem / Chain of fools / Don't play that song / I say a little prayer / Doctor Feelgood / Let it be / Do right woman, do right man / Bridge over troubled water / Respect / Baby I love you / (You make me feel like) a natural woman / I never loved a man (the way I love you) / You're all I need to get by / Call me.
LP: . . . . **K 40279**
MC: **K4 40279**

BEST OF ARETHA FRANKLIN.
Tracks: / Chain of fools / I say a little prayer / You make me feel like a natural woman / Think / Rock steady / Until you come back to me / Respect / Spanish Harlem / Doctor Feelgood / Do right woman, do right man / I never loved a man (the way I love you) / Save me.
LP: **780 169-1**
MC: **780 169-4**

CHICAGO GOLDEN YEARS.
LP: **515007**

COLLECTION: ARETHA FRANKLIN.
Tracks: / Walk on by / It ain't necessarily so / What a difference a day made / Once in a lifetime (live) / Over the rainbow / You made me love you / Say it isn't so / Unforgettable / My guy / Exactly like you / Try a little tenderness / I'm sitting on top of the world / Skylark / Solitude / Where are you / Love for sale (live) / Swanee / I surrender dear / Look for the silver lining / Lover come back to me / Make someone happy / Ol' man river / I apologise.
2LP: . . . . **CCSLP 152**
MC: . . . . **CCSMC 152**

ELECTRIFYING/SOUL SISTER.
2LP: . . . . **CBS 22188**

FIRST 12 SIDES,THE.
Tracks: / Won't be long / Over the rainbow / Love is the only thing / Sweet lover / All night long / Who needs you / Right now / Are you sure / Maybe I'm a fool / It ain't necessarily so / (Blue) by myself / Today I sing the blues.
LP: **65482**
MC: **4065482**

FIRST LADY OF SOUL.
2LP: . . . . **SMR 8506**
MCSET: . . . . **SMC 8506**

GET IT RIGHT.
Tracks: / Get it right / Pretender / Every girl (Wants my guy) / When you love me like that / I wish it would rain / Better friends than lovers / I've got your love / Giving in.
LP: **205544**
MC: **405544**

GREATEST HITS: ARETHA FRANKLIN (1960-1965).
Tracks: / Soulville / Lee Cross / Skylark / Take it like you give it / Try a little tenderness / Take a look / Runnin' out of fools / Sweet bitter love / Rockabye your baby with a Dixie melody / Cry like a baby / God bless the child.
LP: **4506261**
MC: **4506264**

I NEVER LOVED A MAN THE WAY I LOVE YOU.
LP: **SD8139**
LP: **587-006**

JUMP TO IT.
Tracks: / Jump to it / Love me right / If she don't want your lovin' / This is for real / It's just for love / I wanna make it up to you / It's your thing / Just my day dream / Get it right.
LP: **204742**
MC: **404742**
LP: **209060**
MC: **409060**

LA DIVA.
Tracks: / Ladies only / It's gonna get a bit better / What if I should ever need you / Honey I need your love / I was made for you / Only star / Reasons why / You brought me back to life / Half a love / Feeling, The.
LP: . . . . **K 50637**

LADY SOUL.
LP: . . . . **SD 08176**
LP: **588-099**

LEGENDARY QUEEN OF SOUL.
Tracks: / Mockingbird / How glad i am / Walk on by / You'll lose a good thing / Every little bit hurts / I can't wait until i see my baby's face / You made me love you / Nobody like you / Rough lover / Lee cross / Runnin' out of fools / Won't be long / Until you were gone / Blue holiday / One room paradise / Cry like a baby / Can't you just see me / Two sides of love / I won't cry anymore / I'll keep on smiling.
2LP: . . . . **CBS 22112**

LET ME IN YOUR LIFE.
Tracks: / Let me into your life / Every natural thing / Ain't nothing like the real

thing / I'm in love / Until you come back to me / Masquerade is over, The / With pen in hand / Oh baby / Eight days on the road / If you don't think / Song for you, A.
LP: . . . . K 50031

LOVE ALL THE HURT AWAY.
Tracks: / You can't always get what you want / Hold on I'm coming / It's my turn / Living in the streets / Love all the hurt away / There's a star for everyone / Truth and honesty / Search on / Whole lot of me / Kind of man.
LP: . . . . SPART 1170
MC: . . . . TCART 1170

NEVER GROW OLD (Franklin, Aretha & Reverend Franklin).
Tracks: / Mother loves her children / I will trust in the Lord / Old ship of Zion (parts 1 & 2) / Never grow old / I'm going through (parts 1 & 2) / Precious Lord (part 1 & 2) / You grow closer.
LP: . . . . GCH 8014
MC: . . . . GCHK 78014

ONE LORD, ONE FAITH, ONE BAPTISM.
Tracks: / Walk in the light / Prayer invitation by Rev Cecil Franklin / Introduction by Rev Jesse Jackson / Jesus hears every prayer / Surely God is able / Lord's prayer, The / Oh happy day / We need power / Speech by Rev Jesse Jackson / Ave Maria / Introduction by Rev Jaspar Williams / Higher ground / Prayer invitation by Rev Donald Parsons / I've been in the storm too long / Packing up, getting ready to go.
LP: 208715
MC: 408715

SISTERS ARE DOIN IT FOR THEMSELVES (See under Eurythmics) (Eurythmics & Aretha Franklin).

SO SWELL.
LP: 226 2525
MC: 216 2525

SOUL SENSATION (Franklin, Aretha/ Percy Sledge).
Tracks: / Day is passed and gone / He will wash you as white as snow / While the blood runs warm / Yield not to temptation / He's alright / Jesus on the mainline / This little light of mine / Make it last / When a man loves a woman / Walkin' in the sun / Warm and tender love / Good love, The / Out of left field / Behind closed doors / Just out of reach / I believe you / Take time to know her.
MC: . . . . BMDC 001

SOUL SURVIVOR.
Tracks: / Day is passed and gone / He will wash you as white as snow / While the blood runs warm / Yield not to temptation / He's alright / Jesus on the mainline / This little light of mine.
LP: . . . . BMM 004

SPARKLE.
Tracks: / Sparkle / Giving him something he can feel / Hooked on your love / Look into your heart / I get high / Jump / Loving you baby / Rock with me.
LP: . . . . K 56248

SWEET PASSION.
Tracks: / Break it to me gently / When I think about you / What I did for love / No one could ever love you more / Tender touch / Touch me up / Sunshine will never be the same / Meadows of a springtime / Mumbles / I've got the music in me / Passion.
LP: . . . . K 50368

TEN YEARS OF GOLD.
Tracks: / I never loved a man (the way I love you) / Respect / Baby, I love you / (You make me feel like) A natural woman / Think / See-saw / Spanish harlem / Rock steady / Daydreaming / Angel / Until you come back to me / Something he can feel.
MC: K4 50328
LP: . . . . K 50328

THROUGH THE STORM.
Tracks: / Gimme your love / He's the boy / It ain't never gonna be / Think / Mercy / It isn't, it wasn't, it ain't never gonna be / Through the storm / If ever a love there was.
LP: 209842
MC: 409842
LP: . . . . AL 8572

WHAT YOU SEE IS WHAT YOU SWEAT.
Tracks: / Everyday people / Everchanging time / What you see is what you sweat / Mary goes round / I dreamed a dream / Someone else's eyes / Doctor's orders / You can't take me for granted / What did you give / Everyday people (remix).
LP: 211724
MC: 411724

WHO'S ZOOMIN' WHO?.
Tracks: / Freeway of love / Another night / Sweet bitter love / Who's zoomin' who? / Sisters are doin' it for themselves / Until you say you love me / Push / Ain't nobody ever loved you / Integrity.
LP: 207202
MC: 407202
LP: 209053
MC: 409053

YEAH.
Tracks: / This could be the start of something / Once in a lifetime / Misty / More / There is no greater love / Muddy water / If I had a hammer / Impossible / Today / Today I love everybody / Without the one you love / Trouble in mind / Love for sale.
LP: . . . . CBS 21066
MC: 40 21066

Franklin, Phil

PHIL FRANKLIN JAZZ BAND (Franklin, Phil Jazz Band).
LP: . . . . TTD 501

Franklin, Rex

COUNTRY WORLD OF....
MC: . . . . SPVP 171C

Franklin, Rodney

DIAMOND INSIDE OF YOU.
Tracks: / Malibu shuffle / Gotta give it up / Stop to love / Woman of the world / Shasta wind / Woogie / Turn to love / Mediterranean shore / Interlude / Diamond inside of you.
LP: . . . . PL 83038
MC: . . . . PK 83038

ENDLESS FLIGHT.
Tracks: / Dance tonight / Cancion para mi mama / Vibrations / Benetta / Morning light / Endless flight / Mansaje de Dios / Return to the source / Hill Street blues.
LP: . . . . CBS 84945

IT TAKES TWO.
Tracks: / Motion / Look what's showing through / Broken wings / Eagle and the Condor, The / It takes two / Rollin' in our love / My wish / Let there be piece.
LP: . . . . CBS 26992
MC: 40 26992

LEARNING TO LOVE.
Tracks: / Enuff is enuff / That's the way I feel about love / Sunshine / Don't wanna let you go / Sailing / Genesis / New day / Nature's way / Early morning / Let there be light / Learning to love.
LP: . . . . CBS 85978

RODNEY FRANKLIN.
Tracks: / Windy City / Life moves on / In the centre / I like the music / Awakening / Make it hot / Theme for Jackie / On the oath / Creation.
LP: . . . . CBS 84528

SKYDANCE.
Tracks: / Fiesta / Destiny / Song for you, A / Children / One from the heart / Skydance.
LP: . . . . CBS 26399

STREET LANGUAGE.
Tracks: / Let freedom ring / Ballad of fat Eddie / When I'm free again / She loves the jerk / When the blue hour comes / Oh King Richard / Looking for you / Stay (don't be cruel) / Best I can / Past like a mast.
LP: . . . . CBS 57021
MC: 40 57021

YOU'LL NEVER KNOW.
Tracks: / Felix Leo / God bless the blues / Watcher / Journey / Groove / You'll never know / Return / Parkay man.
LP: . . . . CBS 83812

Franko, Frankie

FROM N.O. TO CHICA (See Jones, Richard).

Franko, Mladen

SUMMER SERENADE (Franko, Mladen & dreamland strings).
LP: . . . . ISST 139

Franks, Michael

ART OF TEA.
Tracks: / Nightmoves / Egg plant / Monkey see, Monkey do / St. Elmo's fire / Don't know why I'm so happy I'm sad / Jive / Popsicle toes / Mr. Blue / Sometimes I just forget to smile.
LP: . . . . K 54048
MC: K4 54048

BLUE PACIFIC.
LP: 7599261831
MC: 7599261834

CAMERA NEVER LIES.
Tracks: / Face to face / I surrender / Camera never lies, The / Lip service / When I think of us / Island life / Now you're in my dreams / Doctor Sax / Innuendo.
LP: . . . . K 925570 1
MC: . . . . K 925570 4

OBJECTS OF DESIRE.
Tracks: / Jealousy / Ladies night / No deposit love / Laughing gas / Wonderland / Tahitian moon / Flirtation / Love duet / No one but you.
LP: . . . . K 56973
MC: K4 56973

PASSION FRUIT.
Tracks: / Alone at night / Never satisfied / Amazon / Now that your joysticks broke / Sunday morning here with you / Never say die / Rainy night in Tokyo / Tell me all about it / When Sly calls / How the garden grows.
LP: 923962 1

SKIN DIVE.
Tracks: / Read my lips / Let me count the ways / Your secret's safe with me / Don't be shy / When I give my love to you / Queen of the underground / Now I know why they call it falling / Please don't say goodnight / When she is mine.
LP: . . . . K 925275 1

Franks, Preston

ZYDECO, VOL.2 (Franks, Preston/Sam Ambrose).
LP: . . . . ARHOOLIE 1090

Frannie

ROCK 'N' ROLL FROM THE 50'S.
LP: . . . . EULP 1002

Frantic (Film)

FRANTIC (Film soundtrack) (Various artists).
Tracks: / I'm gonna lose you: *Simply Red* / Frantic: *Various artists* / On the roofs of Paris: *Various artists*/ One flugel horn: *Various artists* / Six short interludes: *Various artists* / Nocturne for Michel: *Various* artists / In the garage: *Various artists* / Paris project, The: *Various artists* / Sadly nostalgic: *Various artists* / Frantic: *Various artists.*
LP: 9607821
MC: 9607824

Frantic Five

DON LANG GETS THE BUG (see under Lang, Don) (Frantic Five/Don Lang).

Frantic Flintstones

NIGHTMARE ON NERVOUS.
Tracks: / Hellfire / Monte Carlo or bust / 44 / Please cool baby / Oh baby oh baby / Alley cat king / Gone gone well gone / Red chevy / Ring ring ringin' / What the hell / Sugar daddy / Frantic Flintstones.
LP: . . . . NERD 034

RAUCOUS RECORDINGS VOLUME 1, THE.
LP: . . . . RAUCLP 3

YABBA DABBA DOO.
LP: . . . . ROCK 2229

Frantique

FRANTIQUE.
Tracks: / Disco dancer / Getting serious / Night people / These days / Strut your funky stuff.
LP: . . . . PIR 83784

STRUT YOUR FUNKY STUFF (OLD GOLD) (See under Franklin, Rodney/ Groove, The).

Franzella Quintette

IN A MIST.
LP: BH7.701

Fraser

ARCHAEOLOGY.
LP: . . . . AH 008

Fraser, Alasdair

PORTRAIT OF A SCOTTISH FIDDLER.
LP: . . . . WGR 063
MC: . . . . CWGR 063

SKYEDANCE (Fraser, Alasdair & Paul Machlis).
LP: . . . . CUL 101
MC: . . . . CULC 101

Fraser, Alison

COMING HOME (Fraser, Alison).
MC: . . . . PMB 015

Fraser, Antonia

JEMIMA SHORE'S FIRST CASE AND OTHER STORIES.
MC: . . . . CAB 340

Fraser, Dean

MOONLIGHT.
LP: . . . . GREL 154

RAW SAX.
LP: . . . . GREL 129
MC: . . . . GREEN 129

Fraser Highlanders

HIGHLANDERS PIPE BAND.
Tracks: / Fairview cottage / Mason's apron / Resolis / Struan Robertson / Ness pipers / Little cascade, The / Jimmie Findlater / Lochanside / Fair maid of Barra, The / Clumsy lover / Lagan love / Nameless / Silver spear / Summertime / Rocking the baby / Haste to the wedding / Farewell to the creeks / Scotland the brave / Wings / Rowan tree / Murdo's wedding / Cameronian rant.
LP: . . . . LILP 5131
MC: . . . . LICS 5131

LIVE IN CONCERT IN IRELAND.
Tracks: / Lord Lovat's lament / Beverley's wedding / Ishabel T MacDonald / Catrina Baker / Gordon MacRae's favourite / Cliffs of Dooneen / Brig gen Ronald Cheape of Tiroran / Laggan love song / Lament for the children / Up to the line / John MacColl's farewell to the Scottish / Farewell to Erin / Journey to Skye / Mason's apron, The / Fair maid of Barra, The.
2LP: . . . . LDDL 8003
MCSET: . . . . LDDC 8003

Fraser, Liz

MOON AND THE MELODIES, THE (See under Budd, Harold) (Various artists).

Fraser, Simon

NOUS SOMMES PRETS (Fraser, Simon University Pipe Band).
Tracks: / Children / Cameronian rant / MacAllisters dirk / All through the night / Willie Davie / Linen cap / Ms. Joy Cairns / Kitchen piper / Muldron glen / Streaker / Arniston castle.
LP: . . . . LILP 5140
MC: . . . . LICS 5140

Frat Rock

FRAT ROCK VOL.1 (Various artists).
Tracks: / Louie Louie: *Kingsmen* / Wooly bully: *Sam The Sham & The Pharaohs* / Double shot of my baby's love: *Swingin' Medallions* / Nobody but me: *Human Beinz* / Twist and shout: *Isley Brothers* / Hang on sloopy: *McCoys* / Wild thing: *Troggs* / I want candy: *Strangeloves* / Little Latin Lupe Lu: *Righteous Brothers*/ Keep on dancing: *Gentrys* / Wipe out: *Surfaris* / Shout: *Dyna Tones.*
LP: . . . . RNLP 70136
MC: . . . . RNC 70136

FRAT ROCK VOL.2 (Various artists).
Tracks: / Dance to the music: *Sly & the Family Stone* / Gimme some lovin': *Spencer Davis group* / Tequila: *Champs*/ What kind of fool do you think I am: *Deal, Bill & The Rhondells* / Just like me: *Revere, Paul & Raiders* / La bamba: *Valens, Ritchie* / Little bit o'soul: *Music Explosion* / I fought the law: *Fuller, Bobby Four*/ Farmer John: *Premiers* / La la la la la: *Blendells* / Peanut butter: *Marathons* / Reelin' and rockin': *Berry, Chuck.*
LP: . . . . RNLP 70183
MC: . . . . RNC 70183

FRAT ROCK VOL 3 (Various artists).
Tracks: / Surfin' bird: *Trashmen* / Do you wanna dance: *Shannon, Del* / Shakin' all over: *Guess Who*/ Liar liar: *Castaways* / Dirty water: *Standells* / Barbara Ann: *Beach Boys* / Land of a thousand dances: *Cannibal & The Head Hunters* / Whittier boulevard: *Midniters* / What'd I say (part 1): *Charles, Ray* / Shake a tail feather: *Five Du-Tones* / Jolly green giant: *Kingsmen* / Johnny B. Goode: *Berry, Chuck.*
LP: . . . . RNLP 70184
MC: . . . . RNC 70184

Frawzies & Scrumpy

FOOD AND DRINK.
MC: 45-404

Frazer, Dean

BIG BAD SAX.
Tracks: / Big bad sax / Dean is clean / East of Dub City / Far west / Ain't no more sax around / Raw deal / Full moon / Don't run / Old time sax / Champagne reggae.
LP: . . . . SPLP 5
MC: . . . . SPLC 5

DANCE HALL SAX.
LP: . . . . BTRLP 005

DEAN FRAZER.
LP: . . . . WKS 011

LITTLE LOVE, A (See under Porter, Hugh) (Frazer, Dean/Hugh Porter).

SINGS AND BLOWS.
Tracks: / Falling in love / Jamaican lady / Girlfriend / Magnet and steel / Voyage to Atlantis.
LP: . . . . GREL 113
MC: . . . . GREEN 113

STEALING LOVE ON THE SIDE (See under Davis, Carlene for details) (Frazer, Dean/Carlene Davis).

Frazer, Grant

MY LAND IS SCOTLAND.
LP: . . . . NEVLP 160
MC: . . . . NEVC 160

ONE HUNDRED THOUSAND WELCOMES.

Tracks: / Hundred thousand welcomes, A / Bonnie Scotland / Come by the hills / Leaving Lismore / Sound of the West, The / Kirsteen / My love is like a red red rose / Westering home / Skye boat song / I belong to Glasgow / Mull of Kintyre / Mist covered mountains / Mull of the cool high Ben Moore / How can you buy Killarney / Star o' Rabbie Burns, The / Legend of Scotland / Mary of Skye / Marching through the heather / Johnny Lad / Flower of Scotland.
LP: BGC 348
MC: KBGC 348

Frazer, Phillip

BLOOD OF THE SAINT.
Tracks: / Blood of the saint.
LP: SCLP 0124

Frazier, Calvin

CALVIN FRAZIER & SAM PITMAN 1938 Detroit (Frazier, Calvin/Sam Pitman).
LP: FLY 542

Frazier Chorus

SUE.
Tracks: / Dream kitchen / 40 winks / Sloppy heart / Sugar high / Typical / Little chef / Storm / Ha ha happiness / Living room / Forgetful / Shi-head.
LP: V 2578
MC: TCV 2578

Frazier, Rob

CUT IT AWAY.
LP: LS 7076
MC: LC 7076

THIS TOWN.
LP: LS R 7081
MC: LS C 7081

Freak Beat Fantoms

FREAK BEAT FANTOMS (Rubble thirteen) (Various artists).
LP: KIRI 102

Freak Show

FREAK SHOW.
LP: AUL 735

Freaks

IN SENSURROUND.
Tracks: / Freak out in the freakhouse / (Livin' in a) warzone / Inside of my mind / Teen queen / Time won't heal / Tag / Green silver / Lost and found / Potter's field / Me am bizarro / Succubus.
LP: R 33/8924

Freberg, Stan

BEST OF STAN FREBERG.
MC: 4XL 9444

CAPITOL YEARS, THE: STAN FREBERG (The best of Stan Freberg).
Tracks: / Yellow rose of Texas / St. George and the dragonet / Sh'boom / Rock island line / Tele-vee-shun / Rock around Stephen Foster / Wun'erful, wun'erful / Little blue riding hood / Heartbreak hotel / Quest for Bridey Hammerschlaugen / Great pretender, The / I've got you under my skin / Old payola roll blues / Green Christmas / Banana boat song.
LP: EMS 1321
MC: TCEMS 1321

CHILD'S GARDEN OF FREBERG, A.
Tracks: / St. George and the Dragonet / C'est si bon / Try / Wild-screen mama blues / Heartbreak hotel / Rock around Stephen Foster / Yellow rose of Texas / John and Marsha / Great pretender, The / That's my boy / Rock Island line / Sh'boom.
LP: JAS 301
MC: JAS C301

Fred & Dread

IRON WORKS.
LP: SHAKA 875

Fred, John

BEST OF JOHN FRED AND THE PLAYBOYS (Fred, John & The Playboys).
LP: JIN 9027
MC: JIN 9027 TC

Freddie & The Dreamers

BEST OF FREDDIE AND THE DREAMERS.
Tracks: / I'm telling you now / Playboy / If you've got a minute, baby / Short shorts / Over you / I understand / If you gotta make a fool of somebody / Do the Freddie / What have I done to you / Don't make me cry / You were made for me / I don't love you anymore / Tell me when / Just for you / Little you, A / I just don't understand / I'm a hog for you baby / Johnny B. Goode / I love you baby / It doesn't matter anymore.
LP: C5-503
MC: C5K 503
LP: 038 065 66

EP COLLECTION, THE: FREDDIE & THE DREAMERS.
LP: SEE 299
MC: SEEK 299

FREDDIE & THE DREAMERS.
LP: 33SX 1577
LP: 1A 052 06566

HITS OF FREDDIE & THE DREAMERS, THE.
LP: 1A046 1065661

Freddy The Detective

FREDDY THE DETECTIVE (Walter R. Brooks) (Carroll, Pat (nar)).
MC: CP 1698

Frederick, Jeffrey

SPIDERS IN THE MOONLIGHT.
LP: ROUNDER 3015

Fredericks, Goldman

C'EST PAS D'L'AMOUR (Fredericks, Goldman, Jones).
Tracks: / C'st pas d'l'amour / Vivre cent vies (A hundred lives) / Ne en 17 a Leidenstadt (Born 1917 in Leidensta / Un, deux, trois / Tu manques / Je l'aime aussi / Chanson d'amour / A nos actes manques (to the deeds we missed) / Peurs / Nuit.
LP: 4685131
MC: 4685134

Fredriksson, Borje

FREDRIKSSON SPECIAL.
LP: DRLP 167

Free

ALL RIGHT NOW.
LP: ILPTV 2
MC: ICTV 2

COMPLETELY FREE.
LP: ILPS 9719

FIRE AND WATER.
Tracks: / Oh I wept / Remember / Heavy load / Fire and water / Mr. Big / Dont say you love me / All right now.
LP: ILPM 9120
MC: ICM 9120
LP: ILPS 9120
MC: 842 556 4

FREE AT LAST.
Tracks: / Catch a train / Soldier boy / Magic ship / Sail on / Travelling man / Little bit of love, A / Guardian of the Universe / Child / Goodbye.
LP: ILPS 9192

FREE LIVE.
Tracks: / All right now / I'm a mover / Be my friend / Fire and water / Ride on pony / Mr. Big / Hunter, The / Get where I belong.
LP: ILPS 9160

FREE STORY, THE.
MC: ZCID 104
2LP: ISLD 4

FREE STORY, THE (2).
LP: ILPS 9945
MC: ICT 9945

FREE'N'EASY.
Tracks: / Hunter, The / Wishing well / Fire and water / Travellin' in style / Bodie / Walk in my shadow.
LP: ILPS 9453

HEARTBREAKER.
Tracks: / Wishing well / Come together in the morning / Travellin' in style / Heartbreaker / Muddy water / Common mortal man / Easy on my soul / Seven angels.
LP: ILPS 9217
MC: ICT 9217

HIGHWAY.
Tracks: / Highway song / Stealer, The / On my way / Be my friend / Sunny day / Ride on pony / Love you so / Bodies / Soon I will be gone.
LP: ILPS 9138

I'LL BE CREEPIN'.
Tracks: / I'll be creepin' / Songs of yesterday / Lying in the sunshine / Trouble on double time / Mouthful of grass / Woman / Free me / Broad daylight / Mourning sad morning.
LP: ILPS 9104

TONS OF SOBS.
Tracks: / Over the green hills (part 1) / Worry / Walk in my shadow / Wild Indian woman / Going down slow / I'm a mover / Hunter, The / Moonshine sweet tooth / Over the green hills (Part 2).
LP: ILPS 9089

Free Fair

FREE FAIR, VOL.2.
LP: SJP 141

Free For All

FREE FOR ALL (Various artists).
LP: HR 9458 1

Free Hot Lunch

PENGUIN LOVE.
LP: FF 410

Free Spirit

MUSIC FOR DULCIMER.
LP: FF 4008

Free Spirit (Rock)

FREE SPIRIT (Various artists).
Tracks: / I want it all: *Queen* / If I could turn back time: *Cher* / Poison: *Cooper, Alice* / Talking to myself: *Terraplane* / It must have been love: *Roxette* / Need you tonight: *INXS* / Touch: *Noiseworks*/ Best, The: *Tyler, Bonnie* / You took the words right out of my mouth: *Meatloaf* / You give love a bad name: *Bon Jovi* / How can we be lovers?: *Bolton, Michael* / I don't love you anymore: *Quireboys* / Carrie: *Europe*/ Black velvet: *Myles, Alannah* / (I just) died in your arms: *Cutting Crew* / Flame, The: *Cheap Trick*/ Living years, The: *Mike & The Mechanics.*
LP: MOOD 16
MC: MOODC 16

Free Zone

MAMMON.
LP: CHEEPL 007

Freed, Alan

ALAN FREED'S ROCK & ROLL DANCE PARTY, VOL 3.
LP: WINS 1012

ALAN FREED'S ROCK & ROLL DANCE PARTY, VOL.2.
LP: WINS 1011

ALAN FREED'S ROCK & ROLL DANCE PARTY, VOL 4 (Various artists).
LP: WINS 1013

ALAN FREED'S ROCK & ROLL DANCE PARTY, VOL.1.
Tracks: / Right now right now / Only you / Up and down / Rock around the clock / Slow boat to monaco / Rock n roll boogie / Teen rock / See you later alligator / Teener's canteen / Great pretender, The / Grey bear / Take one.
LP: JASM 1036
LP: WINS 1010

ALAN FREED'S ROCK & ROLL DANCE PARTY, VOL.5.
LP: WINS 1014

Freedom Fire

FREEDOM FIRE (Various artists).
Tracks: / Thuto kelefa: *Various artists* / Izulu elimnyama: *Various artists* / Nginokuthulu: *Various artists*/ Ikhaya lami: *Various artists* / Amaqhawe omgoashivo: *Various artists* / Madiyisa mbitsij: *Various artists*/ Mme ngwana walla: *Various artists* / Asambeni sonke: *Various artists* / Sondelani ku jesu: *Various artists*/ Sakhala isigimci: *Various artists* / Mashaba: *Various artists* / Yeso: *Various artists* / Lenyalo: *Various artists* / Masole a banana: *Various artists* / D D special: *Various artists.*
LP: EWV 17
MC: TCEWV 17

Freedom Music

FREEDOM MUSIC (Various artists).
LP: WOW 003
MC: WOWC 003

Freedom Principle

FREEDOM PRINCIPLE (See under Acid Jazz) (Various artists).

Freedom Songs

14 FREEDOM SONGS OF IRELAND (Various artists).
Tracks: / Little Armalite: *Various artists* / Bogside volunteers: *Various artists* / Follow me up to Carlow: *Various artists* / Whack for the diddle: *Various artists* / Down by Liffey Side: *Various artists* / Sea around us: *Various artists* / Free Belfast: *Various artists* / Four green fields: *Various artists* / Right you are: *Various artists* / Erin go bragh: *Various artists* / Ricochet: *Various artists* / Rubber bullets: *Various artists* / Song of the dawn: *Various artists* / Smashing of the van: *Various artists.*
LP: CSDBL 516
LP: SDBL 516

FREEDOM SONGS (A young choir from Uppsala) (Various artists).
LP: PHONT 7531

Freedom Sons

REBEL SONGS OF IRELAND.
LP: CSDBL 517

Freedom To Party

FREEDOM TO PARTY (Various artists).
LP: MODEM 1048
MC: MODEMC 1048

Freeez

ANTI-FREEEZ.
Tracks: / Flying high / Alone / Southern Freeez / One to one / Fly by night / Roller chase / Caribbean winter.
LP: BEGA 53
MC: BEGC 53

GONNA GET YOU.
Tracks: / We've got the juice / Can't keep my love / Love's gonna get you / Pop goes my love / I.O.U. / Freezin' / Can you / Watch me.
LP: BEGA 48
MC: BEGC 48

IDLE VICE.
Tracks: / VIPs / Other side, The / Within these walls / Volunteers / Train of thoughts / Naked as a razor / That beats my patience / One second chance / Spy of Baghdad.
LP: BEGA 62
MC: BEGC 62

SOUTHERN FREEEZ.
Tracks: / Marpose / Caribbean winter / Easy on the onions / Sunset / Flying high / Southern Freeez / Rollerchase / First love / Finale.
LP: BEGA 22
MC: BEGC 22

Freeflight

BEYOND THE CLOUDS.
LP: PA 8075

JAZZ, THE (Classical Union).
LP: PA 8042
MC: PAC 8042

SOARING.
LP: PA 8050

Freel, Brian

TORC.
Tracks: / King of rock 'n' roll / It's your life / Why my girl? / Torc / Higher power / Hang on / Nightrider / Everybody gets somewhere.
LP: BRM 0001

Freelove, Laurie

SMELLS LIKE TRUTH.
Tracks: / Smells like truth / Eyes / Arms of a dream / (If you) walk away awhile / Heaven on earth / Haunted / White hall / Oh my heart / Getting close / Song to the siren.
LP: CHEN 20
MC: ZCHEN 20

Freeman, Alan

BY INVITATION ONLY (Alan Freeman's pop pickers) (Various artists).
Tracks: / Whole lotta love: *Led Zeppelin* / It's only rock 'n' roll: *Rolling Stones* / Love the one you're with: *Stills, Stephen* / Pick up the pieces: *Average White Band* / Expecting to fly: *Buffalo Springfield* / World became the world, The: *PFM* / Rock and roll: *Heavy Metal Kids* / Yours is no disgrace: *Yes* / Nes perce: *Wally* / First time ever I saw your face, The: *Flack, Roberta* / Karn evil 9: *Emerson, Lake & Palmer*/ Sound chaser: *Yes* / Immigrant song: *Led Zeppelin* / Angie: *Rolling Stones* / Only you and I know: *Delaney & Bonnie* / Is it only love: *Pretty Things* / Somewhere: *Franklin, Aretha.*
LP: K 60112

Freeman, Bobby

DO YOU WANNA DANCE?.
LP: JGM 1086

Freeman, Bud

BUCK CLAYTON, HOT LIPS PAGE & BUD FREEMAN (See under Clayton, Buck) (Freeman, Bud/Hot Lips Page/ Bud Freeman).

BUD FREEMAN.
LP: MES 7022

BUD FREEMAN & FAMOUS CHICAGOANS.
LP: SFR 742

BUD FREEMAN & HIS ALL STARS (Freeman, Bud & His All Stars).
LP: SWH 32

BUD FREEMAN TAPES, THE (Freeman, Bud with the Cambridge City Jazzband).
Tracks: / Hindustan / Once in a while / Wolverine blues / Sunday / 'S wonderful / Tea for two / That's a plenty / I found a new baby.
LP: PLJ 001

BUD FREEMAN WITH THE BOB BARNARD JAZZBAND (Freeman, Bud with the Bob Barnard Jazzband).
LP: S 1367

CHICAGO.
Tracks: / Saturday night fish fry / Meet you in San Juan / Basin Street blues / Chicago / School days / All by myself / Loveless love / One for the money.
LP: BLP 30108

CHICAGOANS IN NEW YORK.
LP: . . . . DC 12009

CHICAGO-STYLED, 1935-40, VOL 1.
LP: . . . . S 1216

COMMODORE STYLE (Freeman, Bud & George Wettling).
LP: 6.25894

COMPLETE BUD FREEMAN.
LP: . . . . J 165

DOLPHIN HAS A MESSAGE, THE.
LP: . . . . JSP 1011

KEEP SMILIN' AT TROUBLE.
Tracks: / Keep smilin' at trouble / Sail fish, The / What is there to say / Oh baby / Big boy / That da da strain / Wailing blues / Copenhagen / As long as I live / Sensation rag / Sunday / Satanic blues / Buzzard, The / I need some pettin' / Fidgety feet / Tillie's downtown now / Tia juana / Susie.
LP: . . . . AFS 1036

LAST NIGHT WHEN WE WERE YOUNG.
LP: . . . . BLP 30189

STOP LOOK AND LISTEN TO BUD FREEMAN (Freeman, Bud/various).
Tracks: / Newport news / At sundown / Exactly like you / Let's do it / But not for me / Stop, look and listen / Hanid / Dave's blues / I remember you / Perdido / You took advantage of me.
LP: . . . . AFF 112

SUPERBUD (Freeman, Bud & The Keith Ingham Trio).
LP: . . . . 77 S 55

SWINGING TENORS (Freeman, Bud & Eddie Miller).
LP: . . . . AFF 64

THREE'S NO CROWD (Freeman, Bud Trio).
Tracks: / You took advantage of me / Three's no crowd / I got rhythm / Keep smiling at trouble / At sundown / My honey's loving arms / I don't believe it / Three little words / Swingin' without Mazz / Blue room / Exactly like you.
LP: AG6 24061

TWO BEAUTIFUL (Freeman, Bud & Buddy Tate).
LP: . . . . CLP 69

Freeman, Chico

DESTINY'S DANCE.
LP: 1014 008

GROOVIN' LATE (Live At Ronnie Scotts (2)).
Tracks: / Going places / Groovin' late / Free association / In a sentimental mood / What if / Traveller,The.
MC: . . . . ESMMC 018

LUMINOUS (Freeman, Chico & Arthur Blythe).
Tracks: / Footprints / Luminous / Naima's love song / Avotja.
LP: . . . . JHR 010

MORNING PRAYER.
LP: . . . . IN 1063

MYSTICAL DREAMER (Freeman, Chico & Brainstorm).
Tracks: / Footprints / Did I say anything, prelude / On the Nile / Sojourn / Mystical dreamer, The / I'll be there / Did I say anything (CD only.).
LP: 70061

NO TIME LEFT (Freeman, Chico Quartet).
LP: . . . . BSR 0036

PIED PIPER, THE.
LP: . . . . BKH 50801
MC: . . . . BKHMC 50801

SEARCH, THE.
LP: . . . . IN 1059

SPIRIT SENSITIVE.
LP: . . . . IN 1045

SWEET EXPLOSION (Freeman, Chico & Brainstorm).
Tracks: / Peaceful heart / Exotic places / Afro tang / My heart / Pacifica 1 / Pacifica 2 / Pacifica 3 / Read the signs / On the Nile.
LP: 70101

TALES OF ELLINGTON.
LP: . . . . BKH 537

TANGENTS.
Tracks: / Tangents / Sir Tashi and the Yetti / Ballad for Hakima / Fifty Tenth street / Computerised indifference / Sangoma and Nelly / You are the one / Spook and fade.
LP: 9603611

TRADITION IN TRANSITION.
Tracks: / Jackie-ing / Free association / Mys-Story / Talkin' trash / Each one teach one / At a glance / Trespasser / In spirit / Prayer.
LP: . . . . K 52412

Freeman, Doug

DOUG FREEMAN & DON LANGE (Freeman, Doug & Don Lange).
LP: . . . . FF 011

Freeman, George

BIRTH SIGN.
LP: . . . . DS 424

NEW IMPROVED FUNK.
LP: . . . . PLEO 22

Freeman, Kookie

SWINGING MIDDLE OF THE ROAD.
LP: . . . . ISST 145

Freeman, Louise

LISTEN TO MY HEART.
Tracks: / When push comes to shove / Save your love / Nothin's gonna win me (but love) / Love is gone / Back in stride / I don't want to talk about it / Fever / Unchained melody.
LP: . . . . ICH 1111
MC: . . . . ICH 1111MC

Freeman, Russ

NOCTURNAL PLAYGROUND.
Tracks: / Nocturnal playground / Polo in the Palisades / What she really wants / Jamaican nights / Easter Island / Moving violation / Amelia / Paradise cove.
LP: . . . . CHAMP 1011
MC: . . . . CHAMPK 1011

QUARTET: RUSS FREEMAN AND CHET BAKER (Freeman, Russ and Chet Baker).
LP: . . . . FS 88

Freeman, Stan

NOT A CARE IN THE WORLD.
LP: . . . . AP 202

Freeman, Von

HAVE NO FEAR.
LP: . . . . N 6

SERENADE AND BLUES.
Tracks: / Serenade in blue / After dark / Time after time / Von Freeman's blues / I'll close my eyes.
LP: . . . . N 11

VON FREEMAN.
Tracks: / I'll close my eyes / Young and foolish / Bye bye blackbird.
LP: D-002

YOUNG AND FOOLISH (Freeman, Von Quartet).
Tracks: / I'll close my eyes / Young and foolish / Bye bye blackbird.
LP: . . . . AFF 184

Freeway

FREEWAY.
Tracks: / I love the music / Greatest song / Sarah girl / Lost in a dream / Loose in Harlem / Don't drop it / I'm in love / London rush / Sweet Ann / Fool, fool, fool / You better get ready.
LP: . . . . TXS 131

Frehley, Ace

ACE FREHLEY SOLO ALBUM.
LP: 6399083

Frehley's Comet

FREHLEY'S COMET.
Tracks: / Rock soldiers / Breakout / Into the night / Something moved / We got your rock / Love me right / Calling to you / Dolls / Stranger in a strange land / Fractured too.
LP: 781 749-1
MC: 781 749-4

LIVE PLUS ONE.
Tracks: / Rip it out / Breakout / Something / Something moved / Rocket ride / Words are not enough.
MC: . . . . K 781 826 4
LP: . . . . K 781 826 1

SECOND SIGHTING.
Tracks: / Insane / Time ain't runnin' out / Dancin' with danger / It's over now / Loser in a fight / Juvenile delinquent / Fallen angel / Separate / New kind of lover / Acorn is spinning, The.
LP: 781 862-1
MC: 781 862-4

TROUBLE WALKING.
Tracks: / Shot full of rock / Do ya / Five card stud / Hide your heart / Lost in limbo / Trouble walkin' / 2 young 2 die / Back to school / Remember me / Fractured III.
LP: 782042 1
MC: 782042 4

Freiberg, David

BARON VON TOLLBOOTH AND THE CHROME NUN (Freiberg, David & Grace Slick & Paul Kantner).
Tracks: / Ballad of the chrome nun / Fat / Flowers of the night / Walkin' / Your mind has left your body / Across the board / Harp tree lament / White boy / Fishman / Sketches of China.
LP: BFL1 0148

Freiheit

FANTASY.
Tracks: / Keeping the dream alive / Kissed you in the rain / Diana / Land of fantasy, The / Moonlight / Tears are a girls best friend / So good / Forever and a day / Poor little boy / On the run to be free.
LP: 4624821
MC: 4624824

Freiwillige

IN DIXIELAND.
LP: . . . . CALCLP 042

ORIGINAL GASMAN BAND.
LP: . . . . SBR 36LP

PARTY.
LP: . . . . SBR 030LP

Frempong, Thomas

ANANSI SHUTTLE.
LP: . . . . ASR 5010
MC: . . . . CASR 5010

AYE YI.
LP: . . . . ASR 2010

French

FRENCH (COURSE) (See under GCSE packs) (Longman/Pickwick Pass Packs).

French Accordion

FRENCH ACCORDION (Various artists).
Tracks: / La java: *Various artists* / C'es un mauvais garcon: *Various artists* / Las plus bath de javas: *Various* artists / Ca gaze: *Various artists* / Aubade d'oiseaux: *Various artists* / Le gros Lulu: *Various artists*/ La panse: *Various artists* / La goualante du pauvre Jean: *Various artists* / Suois le ciel de Paris: *Various* artists / Fais gaffe: *Various artists* / Java te revoila: *Various artists* / Rue de Lappe: *Various artists*/ La mattchiche: *Various artists* / La java des dockers: *Various artists* / La marche le gosses: *Various artists*/ Le denicheur: *Various artists* / Ca tourne rond: *Various artists* / Padam padam: *Various artists* / Accordeon: *Various artists* / Passe musette: *Various artists.*
2LP: 2664 337
MCSET: 3578 337

MUSETTE DE PARIS.
Tracks: / Sous le ciel de Paris / Pigalle / Du bon musette / La Seine / Parlez-moi d'amour / C'est si bon / Les majorettes / Milord / Petite fleur / Le gamin de Paris / Les mots d'amour / Domino / La vie en rose.
LP: 8127391
MC: 8127394

French Cut

FRENCH CUT (Various artists).
Tracks: / French cut: *Lyrical* / Corporate: *Lady B* / Sweet sweet truny: *Z., Patrick* / Old time thing: *Tupa Lion* / No darkness tonight: *Molly* / Glamour girl: *Ranks, Nardo* / Knock knee boogie: *Tenor Cat* / Peace: *Shields, Shaba* / Duppy de pon dem: *Bengi* / French cut (dub): *Various artists.*
LP: . . . . DSR 5043

French Folk Songs

AU BORD D'UNE FONTAINE (French folk songs: Channel Islands) (Various artists).
Tracks: / Au bord d'une faintaine: *Various artists* / Au logis de mon pere: *Various artists* / Belle rose: *Various* artists / Bitchon-bitchet: *Various artists* / Le bon maraim: *Various artists* / La fille de l'avocat: *Various* artists / J'ai perdu ma femme: *Various artists* / Jean, petit, coq: *Various artists* / Jean, petit, Jean: *Various artists* / Ma mere m'envoie-t-au marche: *Various artists* / Madeleine: *Various artists* / Malbrouck: *Various artists* / Marguerite se promene: *Various artists* / Mon buonhomme est bein malade: *Various artists*/ Mon il me marie: *Various artists* / Mon pere m'a donne-z-un mari: *Various artists* / Le petit couturier: *Various* artists / Le petit navire: *Various artists* / Si j'avais les souliers: *Various artists* / Les trois demoiselles et le cordonnier: *Various artists* / Les troisjeunes soldats: *Various artists* / Trois jeunes tambours: *Various artists* / Ver-du-ron, ver-du-ro-net'o: *Various artists* / Le vingt-cinquieme du mois d'Octobre: *Various artists.*
MC: 60-012

French, Frith...

INVISIBLE MEANS (French, Frith, Kaiser & Thompson).
LP: . . . . FIEND 199

LIVE, LOVE, LARF, LOAF (French, Firth, Kaiser, Thompson).
Tracks: / Wings a la mode / Killerman gold posse / Where's the money / Hai sai oji-san / Drowned dog black night / Surfin' USA / Blind step away, A / Second time, The / Tir-nan darag / Disposable thoughts / Bird in god's garden lost and found.
LP: . . . . FIEND 102

French Lieutenant's

FRENCH LIEUTENANT'S WOMAN (Film soundtrack) (Various artists).
LP: . . . . SL 6106
MC: . . . . SLC 6106
LP: . . . . DRG 6106
MC: . . . . DRGC 6106

French, Robert

FAVOURITE, THE.
LP: . . . . Unknown

ROBERT FRENCH MEETS ANTHONY JOHNSON (French, Robert & Anthony Johnson).
LP: . . . . Unknown

SHOWCASE.
LP: . . . . PROG 001

STUMBLING BLOCK (See under Ninja Man) (French, Robert & Ninja Man).

WONDERING.
LP: . . . . BMLP 008

French Rockin Boogie

FRENCH ROCKIN' BOOGIE (Lanor sides) (Various artists).
LP: . . . . KK 7447

French Toast

FRENCH TOAST.
Tracks: / Why not? / Joe Cool / Ion you / B.A. express / Butter (tribute to Quentin Jackson) / Calentado, man-part 2 of the 'suite sandrine".
LP: . . . . K 28P 6302

Frenchman's Creek

FRENCHMAN'S CREEK (Various artists).
2LP: . . . . ZBBC 1106

FRENCHMAN'S CREEK (see Du Maurier, Daphne) (Castle, John).

Frenzy

BEST OF FRENZY.
LP: . . . . RAGELP 107

CLOCKWORK TOY.
LP: . . . . NOSE 8

HALL OF MIRRORS.
LP: . . . . NERD 016

LIVE AT THE 100 CLUB.
Tracks: / Misdemeanor / Love is the drug / House on fire / Howard Hughes / Hunt, The / Clockwork toy / Migrain / It's all over now / Robot riot.
LP: . . . . NERD 033

NOBODY'S BUSINESS.
LP: . . . . PLAT 1001

SALLY'S PINK BEDROOM.
Tracks: / Red book, The / Sign of the times / Hunt, The / Game of love / Satisfaction / House of fire / Like father, like son / Man at the top / Blue eyes / Jump the gun / Gotta go / Run to you.
LP: . . . . NOSE 19

THIS IS THE FIRE.
MLP: . . . . RAGELP 1

Fresh Claim

HUDS CONTINENTAL.
MC: . . . . PCN 127

NO CLAIMS BONUS (LIVE).
Tracks: / Enough is enough / Rely on me / Love and rockets / Sunday morning dawn / Strong enough to see / Troubled vision / Izabella / Soon it will be night.
MC: . . . . PCN 125

ODD ONE OUT.
Tracks: / Strong enough to see / There's someone loving you / Sunday morning dawn / Yesterday's hero / Enough is enough / Visions never sleep.
MC: . . . . PCN 121

Fresh, Doug E

OH MY GOD.
LP: . . . . LTLP 3
MC: . . . . ZCTLP 3

WORLD'S GREATEST ENTERTAINER, THE (Fresh, Doug E & Get Fresh Crew).
LP: . . . . F 9658

Fresh 'N' Up

FRESH 'N' UP (Various artists).
LP: . . . . FULP 1
MC: . . . . ZUFU 1

Fresh New Beats

FRESH NEW BEATS (Various artists).
Tracks: / Show, The: *Various artists* ((Special 'Get Fresh' "Gadget" mix)) / (Nothing serious) Just buggin': *Various* artists / Pee wee's dance (extended version): *Various artists* / Eric B. for President: *Various artists* / All the way to heaven (extended version): *Various artists* / Bassline: *Various artists* / Bite this (extended version): *Various artists* / Who me?: *Various artists* / We work hard

(full version): *Various artists* / (Bang zoom) Let's go go (extended version): *Various artists*.
LP: .... **CTLP 1**
MC: .... **ZCTLP 1**

Fresh Prince

HE'S THE DJ, I'M THE RAPPER (see under DJ Jazzy Jeff) (Fresh Prince/DJ Jazzy Jeff).

ROCK THE HOUSE (See also under DJ Jazzy Jeff) (Fresh Prince/DJ Jazzy Jeff).

Fresh Selection

FRESH SELECTION (Various artists).
LP: .... **FRESH LP8**

Freshies

WE'RE LIKE YOU (See under Sievey, Chris).

Freud

FREUD (Film soundtrack) (Various artists).
LP: .... **CT 6019**

Freud, James

BREAKING SILENCE.
Tracks: / Modern girl / Television's hungry, The / Saviours, The / Enemy lines / Butane babies / Star to star / 19 again / No more telephone / Automatic crazy / Blue moon.
LP: .... **CAL 134**

Freudiana

FREUDIANA (Various artists).
Tracks: / Nirvana principle, The: *Various artists* / Fruediana: *Various artists* (Lead vocal: Eric Woolfson.) / I am a mirror: *Various artists* (Lead vocal: Leo Sayer.) / Little Hans: *Various artists* (Lead vocal: Graham Dye.) / Dora: *Various artists* (Lead vocal: Eric Woolfson.) / Funny you should say that: *Various artists* (Lead vocal: Flying Pickets.) / You're on your own: *Various artists* (Lead vocal: Kiki Dee.) / Far away from home: *Various* artists (Lead vocal: Flying Pickets.) / Let yourself go: *Various artists* (Lead vocal: Eric Woolfson.) / Beyond the pleasure principle: *Various artists* / Ring, The: *Various artists* (Lead vocal: Eric Stewart.) / Sects therapy: *Various artists* (Lead vocal: Frankie Howerd.) / No one can love you better than me: *Various artists* (Lead vocal: Kiki Dee/Marti Webb/Gary Howard/Eric Woolfson.) / Don't let the moment pass: *Various artists* (Lead vocal:Marti Webb.) / Upper me: *Various artists* (Lead vocal:Eric Stewart.) / Freudiana: *Various artists* / Destiny: *Various artists*(Vocals: Chris Rainbow.) / There but for the grace of God: *Various artists* (Lead vocal: John Miles.).
2LP: .... **EN 5012**
MCSET: .... **TCEN 5012**

Freund, Siamund

SEE EMILY PLAY.
Tracks: / Song for Bodil / See Emily play / Under control / Don't buy me / Safest place, The / We'll meet again / Touch the spot / Deep edged.
LP: .... **ANT 075**

Freur

DOOT DOOT.
Tracks: / Doot doot / Runaway / Riders in the night / Film of the same name (theme from) / Tender surrender / Matters of the heart / My room / Whispering steam machine / All too much.
LP: .... **CBS 25522**
MC: **40 25522**

Frey, Glenn

ALLNIGHTER, THE.
Tracks: / Allnighter, The / Sexy girl / I got love / Somebody else / Lover's moon / Smuggler's blues / Let's go home / Better in the USA / Living in darkness / New love.
LP: .... **MCF 3277**
MC: .... **MCFC 3277**

NO FUN ALOUD.
Tracks: / I found somebody / One you love, The / Partytown / I volunteer / I've been born again / Sea cruise / That girl / All those lies / She can't let go / Don't give up.
LP: .... **K 52395**
MC: **K4 52395**

SOUL SEARCHING.
Tracks: / Livin' right / True love / I did it for your love / Working man / Two hearts / Some kind of blue / Can't put out this fire / Let's pretend we're still in love / Soul searching / It's your life.
LP: .... **MCF 3429**
MC: .... **MCFC 3429**

Fricke, Janie

AFTER MIDNIGHT.
Tracks: / Are you satisfied / I hurt / I don't like being lonely / Teach me how to forget / If I didn't care / Baby you're gone / My eternal flame / Nobody ever loved me so good / From time to time / I won't be easy.
LP: **4504861**
MC: **4504864**

BLACK AND WHITE.
Tracks: / Till I can't take it anymore / He's breathing down my neck / Take me like a vacation / Nothing left to say / Comin' apart at the seams / Always have always will / Don't put it past my heart / When a woman cries / He's making a long short story / I'd take you back again.
LP: .... **CBS 57022**
MC: **40 57022**

COUNTRY STORE: JANIE FRICKE.
Tracks: / Please help me, I'm falling / Loving arms / Blue sky shining / Got my mojo working / Tell me a lie / Do me with love / Your hearts not in it / It ain't easy bein' easy (Only on CD.) / Don't worry 'bout me baby (Only on CD.) / If you could see me now / Lonely people / But love me / Come a little bit closer / Cry / Enough of each other / Homeward bound / When I fall in love (Only on CD.) / Till I can't take it anymore (Only on CD.).
LP: .... **CST 13**
MC: .... **CSTK 13**

FIRST WORD IN MEMORY.
Tracks: / Talkin' through / First word in memory is me / One way ticket / First time out of the rain / Love like ours / Your heart's not in it / First time out of the rain / Love like ours / In between the heartache / Another man like that / Without each other / Take it from the top.
LP: .... **CBS 26101**

FROM THE HEART.
Tracks: / But love me / Fallin' for you / My world begins and ends with you / Cool September / When I fall in love / Pass me by / Gonna love ya / Some fools don't ever learn / One piece at time / This ain't Tennessee and he ain't you.
LP: .... **CBS 84130**

I'LL NEED SOMEONE TO HOLD ME WHEN I CRY.
Tracks: / I'll need someone to hold me when I cry / Enough of each other / Going through the motions / Pride / Down to my last broken heart / Cry / Every time a teardrop falls / It's raining too / I just can't fool my heart / Blue sky shining.
LP: **84729**

IT AIN'T EASY.
Tracks: / He's a heartache / Who better than an angel / It ain't easy bein' easy / Too hard on my heart / Little more love / Love have mercy / Tell me a lie / You don't know love / Heart to heart talk / Tryin' to fool a fool.
LP: .... **CBS 85983**

IT'S A CHEATING SITUATION (See under Bandy, Moe) (Fricke, Janie & Moe Bandy).

JANIE FRICKE: I LOVE COUNTRY.
Tracks: / Please help me, I'm falling / He's a heartache / Walking a broken heart / Pride / But love me / Homeward bound / Cry / Do me with love / Always / She's single again.
LP: **54948**
MC: **40 54948**

LABOR OF LOVE.
Tracks: / Love is one of those words / Give 'em my number / What are you doing here with me / Last thing that I didn't do, The / Walking on the moon / Feeling is believing / I can't help the way I don't feel / No ordinary memory / One of those things / My old friend the blues.
LP: **4657911**
MC: **4657914**

LOVE LIES.
Tracks: / If the fall don't get you / Have I got a heart / How do you fall out of love / Love lies / Tell me a lie / Let's stop talkin' about it / Lonely people / Walkin' a broken heart / I've had all the love I can stand / Where's the fire.
LP: .... **CBS 25551**

LOVE NOTES.
Tracks: / I'll love away your troubles for awhile / Somewhere to come when it rains / River blue / Let's try again / Let me love you good-bye / Love is worth it all / You're the one I love / Playin' hard to get / Stirrin' up feelin's / Got my mojo working.
LP: .... **CBS 32768**
MC: **40 32768**
LP: .... **CBS 83543**

SADDLE THE WIND.
Tracks: / Sugar moon / I'll walk before I'll crawl / Heart / I'm not that good at goodbye / Don't touch me / Where does love go / If I were only her tonight / Healing hands of time / Crazy dreams / Saddle the wind.
LP: **4651281**
MC: **4651284**

SINGER OF SONGS.
Tracks: / I loved you all the way / We could have been the closest of friends / You changed my life in a moment / No one's ever gonna love you / I believe in you / Please help me, I'm falling / What're you doing tonight / Week-end friend / Baby it's you / I think I'm fallin' in love.
LP: .... **CBS 32078**
LP: .... **CBS 83154**

SLEEPING WITH YOUR MEMORY.
Tracks: / Do me with love / Homeward bound / Love me / Don't worry 'bout me baby / Sleeping with your memory / Heart / Always / If you could see me now / There's no future in the past / Midnight words.
LP: .... **CBS 85309**

VERY BEST OF JANIE FRICKE, THE.
LP: .... **CBS 26671**
MC: **40 26671**

Fricker, Thomas

SUMMER OF ROSES.
LP: .... **SFA 041**

Friction

REPLICANT WALK.
LP: .... **EMY 109**

Friction Groove

BLACK BOX, THE.
Tracks: / Time bomb / Family affair / Kiss, The / Smouldering / Never mind love / School bully / On the wall / Black box / Infalliblle system / Somebody to love.
LP: **781 262-1**
MC: **781 262-4**

Frida

FRIDA & AGNETHA - AFTER ABBA (Frida & Agnetha).
MCSET: .... **DTO 10301**

SHINE.
Tracks: / Shine / One little lie / Face / Twist in the dark / Slowly / Heart of the country / Come to me / Chemistry tonight / Don't do it / Comfort me.
LP: .... **EPC 26178**

SOMETHING'S GOING ON.
Tracks: / Tell me it's over / I see red / I got something / Strangers / To turn the stone / I know there's something going on / Threnody / Baby don't you cry no more / Way you do / You know what I mean / Here we'll stay.
LP: .... **EPC 85966**

Friday, Gavin

EACH MAN KILLS THE THING HE LOVES.
Tracks: / Each man kills the thing he loves (Only on 12" and CD single.) / He got what he wanted / Tell tale heart / Man of misfortune / Apologia / Rags to riches / Dazzle and delight / Next thing to murder, The / Next / Love is just a word / You take away the sun / Another blow on the bruise / Death is not the end.
MC: .... **ICT 9925**
LP: .... **ILPS 9925**

Friday On My Mind

FRIDAY ON MY MIND (see under Rediscover Series) (Various artists).

Friday Rock Show

FRIDAY ROCK SHOW (Various artists).
Tracks: / What you're doing to me: *Spider* / Don't you ever leave me: *Diamond Head* / Eye of the storm: *Sweet* Savage / Dance of the music: *Last Flight* / One helluva night: *Demon* / Edge of the world: *Black Axe*/ Belfast: *Witchfynde* / Cuttin' loose: *Xero*.
LP: .... **REH 426**
MC: .... **ZCR 426**

Friday The 13th

FRIDAY THE 13TH, PART 1,2,& 3 (Original film soundtrack) (Various artists).
LP: .... **GR 1030**
LP: .... **FMC 10**

FRIDAY THE 13TH: THE TV SERIES (Various artists).
LP: .... **GNPS 8018**
MC: **GNP5 8018**

Fridges

AUDITIONING FOR WHIMMIN.
LP: .... **PLASLP 015**

Friedman, David

DOUBLE IMAGE.
LP: .... **ENJA 2096**

Friedman, Dean

DEAN FRIEDMAN.
Tracks: / Company / Ariel / Solitaire / Woman of mine / Song for my mother / Letter, The / I may be young / Humor me / Funny papers / Love is not enough.
LP: .... **LSLP 6008**

DEAN FRIEDMAN/ WELL WELL SAID THE ROCKING CHAIR (Two albums on one CD).
MC: .... **WIKDC 98**

RUMPLED ROMEO.
Tracks: / First date / McDonald's girl / Are you ready yet / Hey Larry / Love is real / Buy my baby a car / Special effects / I depend on you, Jesus / Marginal middle class / I will never leave you.
LP: .... **EPC 85670**

VERY BEST OF DEAN FRIEDMAN.
MC: .... **MCTC 036**

WELL WELL SAID THE ROCKING CHAIR.
LP: .... **LSLP 6019**

Friedman, Don

FUTURES PASSED (Friedman, Don Quartet).
LP: .... **ENJA 2068**

HOT KNEPPER AND PEPPER.
Tracks: / Audobon / I'm getting sentimental over you / Hellure / Groovin' high / Alfie / Laura / Prelude to a kiss / I got it bad and that ain't good / Beautiful love.
LP: .... **PRO 7036**

OF THE WIND'S EYE (Friedman, Don Quartet).
LP: .... **ENJA 3089**

REFLEXIONEN LIVE (See under Reflexionen) (Friedman, Don Quartet).

Friedman, Marty

DRAGON'S KISS.
LP: .... **RR 9529 1**
MC: .... **RR 9529 4**

Friel, Pat

HUMOURS OF WESTPORT.
MC: .... **GTDC 056**

Friend from England

FRIEND FROM ENGLAND, A (Anita Bruckner) (Lunghi, Cherie (nar)).
MC: .... **CAB 335**

Friendly Persuasion

FRIENDLY PERSUASION (Original soundtrack) (Various artists).
LP: .... **STV 81165**

Friends

LET'S GET AWAY FROM IT ALL.
Tracks: / Let's get away from it all.
LP: .... **SUML 003**

ROADS LEADING EVERYWHERE.
LP: .... **SUML 005**

SONGS WITHOUT TEARS.
LP: .... **SUML 6**

Friends Again

TRAPPED AND UNWRAPPED.
Tracks: / Lucky star / Sunkissed / Lullaby no.2 / Vaguely yours / Skip the gold rush / Tomboy / State of art / Swallows in the rain / South of love / Old flame / Honey at the core / Moon 3.
LP: **8368951**
MC: **8368954**
LP: .... **MERL 43**

Friends Again

FRIENDS AGAIN (Various artists).
Tracks: / I recall a gypsy woman: *Williams, Don* / Jolene: *Parton, Dolly* / Right time of the night: *Warnes*, Jennifer / I'll never fall in love again: *Gentry, Bobbie* / Gentle on my mind: *Campbell, Glen* / Why have you left the one you left me for?: *Gayle, Crystal* / Sexy eyes: *Various artists* / It doesn't matter anymore: *Ronstadt*, Linda / Desperado: *Spears, Billie Jo* / Lady: *Rogers, Kenny* / Coat of many colours: *Parton, Dolly*/ Stay young: *Williams, Don* / Rhinestone cowboy: *Campbell, Glen* / Talking in your sleep: *Gayle, Crystal*/ Little bit more, A: *Various artists* / When will I be loved?: *Ronstadt, Linda* / Your good girl's gonna go bad: *Spears, Billie Jo* / All I have to do is dream: *Campbell, Glen & Bobbie Gentry*.
LP: .... **LPIMP 8**
MC: .... **TCIMP 8**

Friends (Film)

FRIENDS (Film soundtrack) (Various artists).
Tracks: / Friends: *Various artists* / Honey roll: *Various artists* / Variations on Michelle's song: *Various* artists / Day in the country, A: *Various artists* / Four moods: *Various artists* / Seasons reprise: *Various* artists / Variations on friends theme (The first kiss): *Various artists* / Can I put you on: *Various artists*/ Michelle's song: *Various artists* / I mean't to do my work today (a day in the country): *Various artists*.
LP: .... **MCL 1749**
MC: .... **MCLC 1749**
LP: .... **SPFL 269**

Friends & Lovers

FRIENDS AND LOVERS (Various artists).
Tracks: / Can't be with you tonight: *Boucher, Judy* / On my own: *Labelle, Patti & Michael McDonald* / All cried out: *Moyet, Alison* / Always and forever: *Heatwave* / How 'bout us: *Champaign* / When a man loves a woman: *Sledge, Percy* / Heartbreaker: *Warwick, Dionne* / Greatest love of all, The: *Benson, George* / Every loser wins: *Berry, Nick* / Coming round again: *Simon, Carly* / Kiss and say goodbye: *Manhattans* / Stand by me: *King, Ben E.* / Right moment, The: *Dickson, Barbara* / Don't wanna go home alone: *Nicholas, Paul* / Always there: *Webb, Marti with the Simon May Orchestra* / Nikita: *John, Elton*.
LP: . . . . **NE 1352**
MC: . . . . **CE 2352**

Friends Of Fats

FRIENDS OF FATS (Various artists).
LP: . . . . **CI 007**

Friendship

FRIENDSHIP.
Tracks: / Bullet train / Tighten up / Situation / Let's not talk about it / Here today...here tomorrow / Waterwings / Real thing, The.
LP: . . . . **K 52185**

Frier, Tich

GOING STRAIGHT.
LP: . . . . **CM 014**

Friesen, David

AMBER SKIES (Friesen, David/Chic Corea/Paul Horn/Airto).
LP: . . . . **UNKNOWN**

PATHS BEYOND TRACING.
LP: . . . . **SCS 1138**

Fright Night

FRIGHT NIGHT (Film soundtrack) (Various artists).
Tracks: / Fright Night: *J.Geils Band* / You can't hide from the beast inside: *Autograph* / Good man in a bad time: *Hunter, Ian* / Rock myself to sleep: *April Wine* / Let's talk: *Devo* / Armies of the night: *Sparks* / Give it up: *King, Evelyn "Champagne"* / Save me tonight: *White Sister* / Boppin' tonight: *Fabulous Fontaines* / Come to me: *Fiedel, Brad*.
LP: . . . . **EPC 70270**
MC: **40 70270**

Frightwig

PHONESEXY.
Tracks: / A.M.X. '89 / Public baths / I support you / I wanna live / Just one look / Frightwig luvs ya baby.
LP: . . . . **TUPLP 014**

Frighty

LIFE (Frighty & Colonel Mite).
LP: . . . . **FILER 282**
MC: . . . . **FILERCT 282**

Fripp, Robert

BEWITCHED (Fripp, Robert & Andy Summers).
LP: . . . . **EGLP 56**

EVENING STAR (Fripp, Robert & Brian Eno).
Tracks: / Wind on water / Evening star / Evensong / Wind on wind / Index of metals, An.
LP: . . . . **EGED 3**

EXPOSURE.
Tracks: / Breathless / Chicago / Disengage / Exposure / First inaugural address to the I.A.C.E. Sherbourne House / Here comes the flood / I may not have had enough of me but I've had enough of you / Mary / North star / NY3 / Urban landscape / Water music 1 / You burn me up I'm a cigarette / Preface / Postscript / Haaden two / Water music 2.
LP: . . . . **EGLP 41**
MC: . . . . **EGMC 41**

GOD SAVE THE KING.
Tracks: / God save the King / Under heavy manners / Heptaparaparshinokh / Inductive resonance / Cognitive dissonance / Dislocated / H.G.Wells / Eye needles / Trap.
LP: . . . . **EGED 9**
MC: . . . . **EGEDC 9**

I ADVANCE MASKED (See also Summers, Andy) (Fripp, Robert & Andy Summers).

LET THE POWER FALL (An album of Frippertronics).
Tracks: / 1984 / 1985 / 1986 / 1987 / 1988 / 1989.
LP: . . . . **EGED 10**

NETWORK.
Tracks: / North Star (Vocal-Daryl Hall) / Water music 1 (Taped voice-J.G. Bennett) / God save the King / Under heavy manners (Vocal-David Byrne) / Here comes the flood (Vocal-Peter Gabriel).
MC: . . . . **EGMMC 4**

NO PUSSY FOOTING (Fripp, Robert & Brian Eno).
Tracks: / Heavenly music corporation, The / Swastika girls.
LP: . . . . **EGED 2**

ROBERT FRIPP AND THE LEAGUE OF CRAFTY GUITARISTS.
Tracks: / Guitar craft theme 1: Invocation / Tight muscle party at love beach / Chords that bind, The / Guitar craft theme 3: Eye of the needle / All or nothing (2) / Crafty march / Guitar craft theme 2: Aspiration / All or nothing (1) / Circulation / Fearful symmetry, A / New world.
LP: . . . . **EGED 43**
MC: . . . . **EGEDC 43**

UNDER HEAVY MANNERS.
LP: . . . . **EGLP 45**
MC: . . . . **EGMC 45**

Frisaura, Lorraine

BE HAPPY FOR ME.
Tracks: / Things to do / All I've been looking for / I don't wanna go / Part of me / It's really alright / Next time, The / No thanks / Jimmy Mack / Nothing's the same / I'm still here.
LP: . . . . **PL 13034**

Frisco Jazz Band

GOOD MAN IS HARD TO FIND, A.
LP: . . . . **DC 12005**

Frisell, Bill

BEFORE WE WERE BORN.
Tracks: / Before we were born / Pip squeak / Hard plains drifter / Steady girl / Some song and dance / Goodbye / Lone ranger, The.
LP: . . . . **K 960843 1**
MC: . . . . **K 960843 4**

IN LINE.
Tracks: / Start / Throughout / Two arms / Shorts / Smile on you / Beach, The / In line / Three / Godson song.
LP: . . . . **ECM 1241**

LOOKOUT FOR HOPE (Frisell, Bill Band).
Tracks: / Lookout for hope / Little brother Bobby / Hangdog / Remedios / Beauty, The / Lonesome / Melody for Jack / Hackensack / Little bigger / Animal race, The / Alien prints (for D Sharpe).
LP: . . . . **ECM 1350**

NEWS FOR LULU (see under Zorn, John) (Zorn, John/Bill Frisell/George Lewis).

RAMBLER.
Tracks: / Tone, The / Music I heard / Rambler / When we go / Resistor / Strange meeting / Wizard of odds.
LP: . . . . **ECM 1287**

WORKS: BILL FRISELL.
Tracks: / Monica Jane / Beach, The / When we go throughout / Black is the colour of my true love's hair / Wizard of odds / Conception vessel / Etude.
LP: **8372731**

Frishberg, Dave

LET'S EAT HOME.
Tracks: / Brenda Starr / Let's eat home / Mr. George / Matty / Mooche, The / I was ready / Strange music / Ship without a sail, A / Lookin' good / Underdog, The.
MC: . . . . **CJ 402C**

Frith, Fred

NOUS AUTRE (Frith, Fred & Rene Luiser).
LP: . . . . **VICT 01**

TECHNOLOGY OF TEARS.
LP: . . . . **RECREC 20**

Frizzell, Lefty

20 GOLDEN HITS OF LEFTY FRIZZELL.
MCSET: . . . . **GTV 15595**

HIS LIFE HIS MUSIC.
Tracks: / I love you a thousand ways / If you've got the money, I've got the time / Shine, shave, shower (It's Saturday) / Cold feet / Don't think it ain't been fun, dear / When payday comes around / My baby's just like money / Look what thoughts will do / You want everything but me / I want to be with you always / Give me more of your kisses / How long will it take (to stop loving you) / Always late (with your kisses) / Mom and Dad's waltz / You can go on your way now / Treasure / Untold - blue yodel No 6 / Travellin' blues / My old pal / Blue yodel no. 2 (My Lovin' gal Lucille) / Lullaby-Yodel Brakeman's blues / My rough and rowdy ways / I love you (though you're no good) / It's just you / (Darling now) you're here, so everythings alright / I've got reasons to hate you / Don't stay away / If you can spare the time (I won't miss the money) / King without a queen / Forever and always / I know you're lonesome (while waiting for me) / Lost love blues / That's me without you / I won't be good for nothin / If I lose you (I'll lose my world) / I'm an old old man (trying to live while I can) / You're just mine (only in my dreams) / I'll try / (Honey,baby,hurry) Bring your sweet self back to me / Time changes things / All of me, loves all of you / California blues / Never no mo' blues / We crucified our Jesus / When it comes to measuring love / Sleep, baby sleep / I'm lonely and blue / Before you go, make sure you know / Two friends of mine (in love) / Hopeless love / Then I'll come back to you / Tragic letter, The / Two hearts broken now / You can always count on me / I've been away way too long / Run 'em off / Darkest moment (it's just before the light of day), The / You're too late / My little her and him / I love you mostly / You're there, I'm here / Let it be Mama / Making believe / Moonlight, darling and you / I'll sit alone and cry / Forest fire (is in your heart), A / Sweet lies / You're tomorrows will never come / It gets late so early / I'm lost between right and wrong / Promises (promises, promises) / My love and baby's gone / Today is that tomorrow (I dreamed of yesterday) / First to have a second chance / These hands / You can't divorce my heart / Treat her right / Heart's highway / I'm a boy left alone / Just can't live that fast anymore / Waltz of the angels, The / Lullaby waltz / Glad I found you / Now that you are gone / From an angel to a devil / Lover by appointment / Sick, sober and sorry / No one to talk to but the blues / Is it only that you're lonely / Mailman, bring me no more blues / You've still got it / Tell me dear / To stop loving you means cry / Torch within my heart, The / Time out for the blues / Why should I be lonely / Signed, sealed, delivered, I'm yours / Nobody knows but me / Silence release me / You're humbuggin' me / She's gone / Cigarettes and coffee / I need your love / If you're ever lonely darling / Sin will be the chaser for the wine / Knock again true love / Long black veil / One has been to another / Farther than my eyes can see / My blues will pass / Ballad of the blue and grey / That's all I can remember / So what let it rain / What you gonna do Leroy / I feel sorry for me / Heaven's plan / Looking for you / Stranger / Few steps away, A / Forbidden lovers / Just passing through / That reminds me of you / Don't let her see me cry / Through the eyes of a fool / James River / Preview of coming attractions / Lonely heart / What good did you get out of breaking my heart / When it rains the blues / I'm not the man I'm supposed to be / Saginaw Michigan / There's no food in the house / Rider, The / Nester, The / I was coming home to you / Hello to him (goodbye to me) / I can tell / Make that one for the road a cup of coffee / Gator hollow / I cost too much to die / She's gone, gone, gone / Running into memories of you / Confused / How far down can I go / It's bad (when it's that away) / I don't trust you anymore / Little unfair, A / Woman let me sing you a song / Preparations to be blue / Looks good on you / Mama / Writing on the wall / I just couldn't see the forest (for the trees) / Everything keeps coming back (but you) / Heart (don't love her anymore) / You don't have to be present to win / Song from a lonely heart, A / You gotta be puttin' me on / Get this stranger out of me / Money tree / Hobo's pride / When the rooster leaves the yard / Anything you can spare / Only way to fly / Prayer on your lips is like freedom in your hands, A / Little ole wine drinker me / Almost persuaded / You ever been untrue / If you've got the money, I've got the time / When the grass grows green again / Marriage bit, The / Wasted way of life / Keep them flowers watered while I'm gone / Article of life, An / Honky tonk hill / Baby is a tramp / She brought love sweet love / Watermelon time in Georgia / I must be getting over you / Out of you / Three cheers for the good guys / Honky tonk stardust cowboy / What am I gonna do / You babe / Down by the railroad tracks / Let me give her the flowers / If I had half the sense a fool was born with / Somebody's words / Lucky arms / True love needs to be in touch / My house is your honky tonk / I buy the wine / If she just helps me get over you / Falling railroad lady / I can't get over you, to save my life / I never go around mirrors / That's the way love goes / She found the key / I wonder who's building the bridge / My washing room / I'm gonna hang out my mind today / Sittin' and thinkin' / I'm not that good at goodbye / Yesterday just passed my way again / Life's like poetry / Bridges to burn / Honey baby, you were wrong / Please be mine / Dear blue eyes / I'm yours if you want me / I'll be a bachelor till I die / Yesterday's mail (live) / Stay all night, stay a little longer / Somebody's pushing / Things / Woodchopper's ball.
LPS: . . . . **BFX 15100/15**

HONKY TONKIN'.
LP: . . . . **FLY 596**

LEFTY FRIZZELL.
Tracks: / I love you a thousand ways / Cold feet / I want to be with you always / Mama / I'm an old, old man trying to love while I can / Forever / Heart's highway / King without a queen / No one to talk to.
LP: . . . . **CBS 25017**

LEFTY FRIZZELL GOES TO NASHVILLE.
Tracks: / It's lonely and blue / It gets so late so early / Lost love blues / Sweet lies / Two broken hearts now / Tragic letter, The / Lullaby waltz / How far down can I go / Stranger / Little ole wine drinker me / Get this stranger out of me / Hello to him (goodbye to me) / Almost persuaded.
LP: . . . . **SS 16**

LEGENDARY LAST SESSIONS, THE.
Tracks: / I can't get over you to save my life / I never go around mirrors / If I had half the sense (A fool was born with) / Somebody's words / Lucky arms / That's the way love goes / If she just helps me get over you / I buy the wine / Let me give her the flowers / Railroad lady / Lifes's like poetry / She's found the key / Falling / I'm not that good at goodbye / My house is your honky tonk / Yesterday just passed my way again / Sittin' and thinkin' / My wishing room / I love you a thousand ways.
2LP: **IMCA2 4161**

TREASURES UNTOLD.
Tracks: / Shine shave shower (it's Saturday) / It's just you / How long will it take (to stop loving you) / Run 'em off / Now that you are gone / If you can spare the time / Look what thoughts will do / My baby's just like money / Time changes everything / Waltz of the winds / Then I'll come back to you / Treasure untold.
LP: . . . . **SS 11**

Froboess, Conny

CONNY ROCKT.
Tracks: / Glockergiesser rock / Sunshine / Blue jean boy / Auch du hast dein schicksal in der hand / Diana / I love you baby / Schicke schicke schuh / Teenager Susan / Lippenstift am jacket / Little girl / Billy Jack and Joe / Jolly joker / Hey boys / How do you do / Mister music / Ob 15 ob 16 ob 17 jahre alt / Holiday in Honolulu.
LP: . . . . **BFX 15049**

WEN DIE CONNY MIT DEM PETER (Froboess, Conny/Peter Kraus).
Tracks: / Teenager melodie / Ich denk an dich / Hey boys / How do you do / Sugar baby / Ich mocht mit dir traumen - teenager melodie / Jolly joker.
LP: . . . . **BFX 15328**

Froese, Edgar

AGES.
Tracks: / Metropolis / Era of the slaves / Tropic of Capricorn / Nights of automaticwoman / Icarus / Children's deeper study / Ode to Granny A / Pizarro and Atahuallpa / Golgatha and the circle closes.
2LP: . . . . **VD 2507**

AQUA.
Tracks: / Upland / Panorphelia / NGC / Aqua.
LP: . . . . **OVED 20**
LP: **0060 404**

AQUA (AMBIENT BOX SET) (See under Ambient).

EPSILON IN MALAYSIAN PALE.
Tracks: / Epsilon in Malaysian pale (Continuous track) / Maroubra bay (Continuous track).
LP: . . . . **OVED 22**

KAMIKAZE.
Tracks: / Videophonic / Vitamin C / Krismopompas / Police disco / Intuition / Police therapy centre / Blue panther / Snake bath / Unexpected death / Flying kamikaze / Tower block / 31st floor, The.
LP: . . . . **OVED 125**
LP: . . . . **V 2255**

MANCULA TRANSFER.
Tracks: / OS 452 / Af 765 / Pa 701 / Quantas 611 / If 810.
LP: **0060 008**

PINNACLES.
Tracks: / Specific gravity of smile / Light cone, The / Walkabout / Pinnacles.
LP: . . . . **OVED 144**

SOLO.
Tracks: / Drunken Mozart in the desert / IF 810 / Tropic of Capricorn / Epsilon in

Malaysian pale / PA 701 / Stuntman / O5 452 / Pizarro and Atahuallpa / NGC.
LP: . . . . **OVED 69**

SOLO 1974-1979.
LP: . . . . **V 2197**

STUNTMAN.
Tracks: / Stuntman / It would be like Samoa / Detroit snackbar dreamer / Drunken Mozart in the desert / Dali-esque sleep fuse, A / Scarlet score for Mescalero.
LP: . . . . **OVED 21**
LP: . . . . **V 2139**

Frog Prince (film)

FROG PRINCE, THE (Film soundtrack) (Enya).
LP: . . . . **ISTA 10**
MC: . . . . **ICT 10**

Froggatt, Raymond

STAY WITH ME.
Tracks: / I will stay with you / Sometimes people get hurt / Festival of fools / Goodbye in a letter / Naz, The / Bandman / High as Georgia pines / It's only the memories / Fools rush in / Smile and a song, A.
LP: . . . . **DSM 002**

WHY.
LP: . . . . **MMLP 1032**

Froggits

START FROM SCRATCH.
LP: . . . . **TMB 114**
MC: . . . . **TMBC 114**

Frogs

IT'S ONLY RIGHT AND NATURAL.
LP: . . . . **HMS 169 1**
MC: . . . . **HMS 169 4**

Frogs, Freddy

AT MY FRONT DOOR.
LP: . . . . **NERD 013**

Frohliche Blasmusik

FROHLICHE BLASMUSIK (German brass band).
LP: **2418 634**
MC: **3190 634**

From...

FROM BROMLEY WITH LOVE (Various artists).
LP: . . . . **ALT 007 A**

FROM BRUSSELS WITH LOVE (Various artists).
LP: . . . . **TWI 1007**

FROM FINLAND WITH LOVE (Various artists).
Tracks: / Hei lumpun lumpun: *Various artists* / Miss soutaen tuulessa (summer wedding): *Various artists* / Vanhus ja talvi: *Various artists* / Kapakkalaulajatar: *Various artists* / Kavattunnelmia: *Various artists* / Karajalan kunnailla: *Various artists* / Tyttojen: *Various artists* / Plylpyppy: *Various artists* / Tammerkoski: *Various artists* / Kirje sielta: *Various artists* / Tuo suru jonka sain: *Various artists* / Syysillan tuuli: *Various artists* / Yolintu: *Various artists* / Sininen ja volkoinen: *Various artists* / El porompompero: *Various artists.*
LP: . . . . **ALP 103**

FROM KONGA TO ZION (Various artists).
LP: . . . . **HB 17**

FROM L A TO L A (Various artists).
LP: . . . . **JSP 1066**

FROM SEWINGSHIELDS TO GLENDALE (Various artists).
LP: . . . . **MWM 1033**
MC: . . . . **MWMC 1033**

FROM SWING TO BE-BOP (Various artists).
LPS: . . . . **PM 45350**

FROM ZE TO ETERNITY (Various artists).
Tracks: / Be bop kid: *Various artists* / Sweetheart: *Various artists* / Twist: *Various artists* / Cry for love: *Various artists* / Heatwave: *Various artists* / Contort yourself: *Various artists* / Disco clone: *Various artists* / Baby you can drive my car: *Various artists* / There but for the grace of God: *Various artists*/ Darrio: *Various artists.*
LP: . . . . **IRSP 9**

From Bam Bam

FROM BAM BAM TO CHERRY OH BABY (Various artists).
LP: . . . . **TRL 51**

From Beyond

FROM BEYOND Original soundtrack (Various artists).
LP: . . . . **ENIGMA 32401**

From Boogie To Bop

FROM BOOGIE TO BOP 1939-1956 (See Under Jazz...) (Various artists).

From Erin's green

FROM ERIN'S GREEN SHORE: TOPIC SAMPLER, NO 4 (Various artists).
Tracks: / Zoological gardens: *Behan, Dominic & John Hasted* / Cunnla: *Heaney, Joe* / Our ship is ready: *Barry, Margaret* / Boys from Blue Hill: *Gorman, Michael & Margaret Barry* / Rollicking boys around Tandaragee: *Tunney, Paddy* / Will ye go, lassie, go?: *McPeake Family* / Castle of Drumboe: *Behan, Dominic & John Hasted* / Chater's song, The: *Clancy, Willie* / Song of the dawn: *Kearney, Arthur* / My Lagan love: *Barry, Margaret* / Maguire's favourite: *Gorman, Michael.*
LP: . . . . **TPS 168**

From Hi-Tension

FROM HI-TENSION TO INFINITY (Various artists).
Tracks: / Let me feel it: *Gilles, Samantha* / Love and devotion: *Bow, Michael* / Flashlight on a disconight: *Rofo*/ Midnight lover: *Bianca* / I want you: *Rofo* / Love gun: *Special Touch* / One more time: *Bianca*/ One shot so hot: *Bow, Michael* / You've got to move on: *Rofo* / Now is the time: *Paparazzi* / S.T.O.P.: *Gilles, Samantha* / Beach love: *Rofo.*
LP: . . . . **PAPX 102**

From Lizzie With...

FROM LIZZIE WITH LOVE (Sixteen seductive love songs) (Various artists).
Tracks: / Stay on these roads: *A-Ha* / Sign your name: *D'arby, Terence Trent* / Paradise: *Sade* / Piano in the dark: *Russell, Brenda* / There's nothing better than love: *Hines, Gregory* / I'll always love you: *Dayne,* Taylor / Dreaming: *Goldsmith, Glen* / Wonderful tonight: *Clapton, Eric* / He ain't heavy, he's my brother: *Medley, Bill* / Time will ease: *Jackson, Paul* / With a little help from my friends: *Wet Wet Wet.*
LP: . . . . **SMR 864**
MC: . . . . **SMC 864**

From Memphis To...

FROM MEMPHIS TO NEW ORLEANS 1930-36 (Various artists).
LP: . . . . **BD 2056**

From Route 66

FROM ROUTE 66 TO THE FLAMINGO (Various artists).
Tracks: / I can't stand it: *Soul Sisters* / Hurt by love: *Foxx, Inez & Charlie* / You can't sit down: *Upchurch,* Phil Combo / Sticks: *Adderley, Cannonball Quartet* / I got a woman: *McGriff, Jimmy* / I know: *George,* Barbara / Let the good times roll: *Shirley & Lee* / Think about the good times: *Soul Sisters* / Loop de loop: *Soul Sisters* / Little bitty pretty one: *Harris, Thurston* / Googa mooga: *Roach, Freddie* / Little bit of soap, A: *Mimms, Garnet* / Quiet place, A: *Mimms, Garnet* / Discotheque USA: *McGriff, Jimmy* / Soul serenade: *Curtis, King.*
LP: . . . . **SSL 6034**
MC: . . . . **TCSSL 6034**

From Russia With Love

FROM RUSSIA WITH LOVE (James Bond Original Soundtrack) (Various artists).
Tracks: / James Bond is back - opening titles: *Various artists* / James Bond theme: *Various artists* / Tania meets Klebb: *Various artists* / Meeting in St. Sophia: *Various artists* / Golden horn, The: *Various artists*/ Girl trouble: *Various artists* / Bond meets Tania: *Various artists* / 007: *Various artists* / Gypsy camp: *Various artists* / Death of Grant: *Various artists* / From Russia with love: *Monro, Matt* / Spectre island: *Various artists* / Guitar lament: *Various artists* / Man overboard: *Various artists* / James Bond with bongos: *Various artists* / Stalking: *Various artists* / Leila dances: *Various artists* / Death of Kerim: *Various artists* / 007 takes the lektor: *Various artists.*
LP: . . . . **EMS 1267**
MC: . . . . **TCEMS 1267**
LP: **1C 054 82931**

FROM RUSSIA WITH LOVE (Original film soundtrack).
LP: . . . . **IC 054 82931**

From San Antonio...

FROM SAN ANTONIO TO THE GULF OF MEXICO (Various artists).
LP: . . . . **BLP 702**

From The...

FROM THE FIFTIES: VOL 1 (Various artists).
LP: . . . . **KLJ 20030**

FROM THE FIFTIES: VOL 2 (Various artists).
LP: . . . . **KLJ 20031**

FROM THE FORTIES: VOL 1 (Various artists).
LP: . . . . **KLJ 20027**

FROM THE FORTIES: VOL 2 (Various artists).
LP: . . . . **KLJ 20028**

FROM THE HOUSE OF LORDS (Rubble Nine) (Various artists).
Tracks: / House of Lords: *Various artists* / Colliding minds: *Sugar Battle* / I'm not your stepping stone: *Ice* Doves, The / Workshop of my mind: *Glass keys, The* / Living colours: *Black atlas, The* / Slow patience: *Attractions*/ Last mile, The: *Sleepeaters* / Dear Prudence: *Time Machine* / Summer evening: *Wedding* / Mad Elaine: *Roland, Paul* / Father's name is dad: *Fading dream, The.*
LP: . . . . **KIRI 065**

FROM THE IRISH TRADITION: VOL 3 (Various artists).
MC: . . . . **CDTC 003**

FROM THE IRISH TRADITION: VOL 1 (Various artists).
MC: . . . . **CDTC 001**

FROM THE IRISH TRADITION: VOL 2 (Various artists).
MC: . . . . **CDTC 002**

From The Hip

FROM THE HIP (Original soundtrack) (Various artists).
LP: . . . . **STV 81309**

From The New World

FROM THE NEW WORLD (American folk-rock) (Various artists).
Tracks: / You pretty fool: *Webs* / Ring around the Rosie: *Shaggs* / I'm not the same: *Corporate Image*/ Forever eyes: *Peabody* / When Johnny comes ...: *Sheppards* / Hold on: *Uncle Sam & The War Machine* / In his shadow: *Penthouse Five* / All I really wanna do: *Evil Incorporated* / Girl you can depend on, A: *Palace* Guard / Take a giant step: *Fountain Of Youth* / All night long: *Palace Guard* / They just don't care: *Christopher* & The Chaps / Baby you come ...: *Peppermint Trolley Co.* / I feel teardrops: *Onion Ring* / I ask you why: *Dave & The Customs* / How she's hurtin' me: *Jagged Edge* / How many times: *Chozen Ones.*
LP: . . . . **STZ 5004**

From the Tatra

FROM THE TATRA MOUNTAINS (Classic Polish/American recordings from the 1920's) (Various artists).
LP: . . . . **MS 45007**

From The Vaults

FROM THE VAULTS (Various artists).
Tracks: / Nobody but you: *Temptations* / Take me where you go: *Ross, Diana & The Supremes* / Cry: *Monitors*/ Sweeter as the days go by: *Gaye, Marvin* / I should have known better: *Marvellettes* / What more could a boy ask for?: *Spinners* / It's fantastic: *Miracles* / Drop in the bucket: *Wells, Mary* / Lonely heart and lonely eyes of lonely me: *Knight, Gladys & The Pips* / Undecided lover: *Reeves, Martha.*
LP: . . . . **STMS 5080**
MC: . . . . **CSTMS 5080**
LP: . . . . **STMT 9001**

Front

FRONT, THE.
Tracks: / Fire / Sunshine girl / Pain / Sweet addiction / (Segue) / Ritual / Le motion / Sister moon / In the garden / Violent world / Sin.
LP: **4661431**
MC: **4661434**

Front 242

FRONT BY FRONT.
Tracks: / Until death us do part / Circling overland / In rhythms beliben / Felines / First in, first out / Blend the strengths / Headhunter V.30 / Work 01 / Terminal state / Welcome to paradise.
LP: . . . . **RRELP 007**
MC: . . . . **RREMC 007**
DAT: . . . . **RREDT 007**

GEOGRAPHY.
Tracks: / Operating tracks / With your cries / Art and strategy / Geography II / U men / Dialogue / Least inkling / GVDT / Geography 1 / Black, white, blue / Kinetics / Kampferereit.
LP: . . . . **MK 001**
MC: . . . . **MK 001MC**

NO COMMENT.
Tracks: / Commando mix / S. fr. nomenklatura pt 1/2 / Deceit / Lovely day / No shuffle / Special forces.
LP: . . . . **MK 002**
MC: . . . . **MK 002MC**

OFFICIAL VERSION.
Tracks: / What you have is what you get / Re-run / Television station / Agressive due / Masterhit pt.1 / Slaughter / Quite unusual / Red team / Agressive angst / Masterhit pt.2.
LP: . . . . **RRELP 5**
MC: . . . . **RREMC 5**

TYRANNY FOR YOU.
LP: . . . . **RRE LP 11**
MC: . . . . **RRE MC 11**

Front Porch String

FRONT PORCH STRING BAND.
Tracks: / If you're ever in Oklahoma / Heart against the winds / Living in our country world / Come unto me / Girl I love, The / Singer, The / Go my way / Hills of Alabama / Back to my love / Grant's mill / Wabash cannonball.
LP: . . . . **REBEL 1624**
MC: . . . . **REBEL 1624C**

Front Street Gaities

FRONT STREET GAITIES (US cast) (Various artists).
LP: . . . . **AEI 1133**

Frontline

FRONTLINE - SAMPLER 1 (Various artists).
Tracks: / Right time, The: *Mighty Diamonds* / Natty rebel: *U-Roy* / Declaration of rights: *Clarke, Johnny*/ Don't touch I man locks: *I-Roy* / Looks is deceiving: *Gladiators* / Great Psalms, The: *U-Roy* / Civilization: *Hudson, Keith* / Know yourself mankind: *Gladiators* / Africa: *Mighty Diamonds* / Freedom fighters: *Washington, Delroy.*
LP: . . . . **C 1521**

FRONTLINE - SAMPLER 2 (Various artists).
Tracks: / Jah works: *Gladiators* / Natty dread upon a mountain top: *U-Brown* / I love you so: *Twinkle Brothers*/ Foggy road: *Prince Far-I* / Mr. Bassie: *Dunbar, Sly* / Sister Bella: *Prince Hammer* / Make a truce: *Althia & Donna* / Dread beat and blood: *Johnson, Linton Kwesi* / Rub-a-dub style: *Ranking Trevor* / Holy Mount Zion: *Culture* / Tribute to Steve Biko: *Zukie, Tappa* / Love we a deal with: *Big Youth* / Jordan river: *I-Roy* / Cocaine: *Jah Lloyd.*
LP: . . . . **FLB 3001**

FRONTLINE - SAMPLER 3 (Various artists).
Tracks: / Lonely girl: *Isaacs, Gregory* / Mr. Music: *Dunbar, Sly* / 4000 years: *Mighty Diamonds* / Fire in a wire: *I-Roy* / Jahovah: *Twinkle Brothers* / Get ready: *Gladiators* / I got to tell you goodbye: *U-Roy*/ I tried: *Culture* / Ogun dub: *Prince Far-I & The Arabs* / South African enlistment: *Abyssinians.*
LP: . . . . **FLB 3002**

Frontline Assembly

CAUSTIC GRIP.
LP: . . . . **TMLP 50**

CORROSION.
Tracks: / Lurid sensation / Right hand of heaven / Concussion / On the cross / Conflict / Controversy / Dark dream / Wrack, The (part 2).
LP: . . . . **TMLP 21**

DISORDER.
LP: . . . . **TMLP 24**

FRONTLINE ASSEMBLY.
LP: . . . . **ST 7547**

GASHED SENSES AND CROSSFIRE.
Tracks: / No limit / Hypocrisy / Prayer / Big money / Sedation / Anti social / Shut down / Digital tension dimension / Fools game.
LP: . . . . **TMLP 31**

INITIAL COMMAND.
Tracks: / Initial command.
LP: . . . . **KK 001**

STATE OF MIND.
MC: . . . . **A 180**

Frosini, Pietro

BEST OF PIETRO FROSINI (Various artists).
Tracks: / Jolly Caballero: *Various artists* / Love smiles, skippin' along: *Various artists* / Serenata Primaverile: *Various artists* / Swedish Italian Mazurka: *Various artists* / Rag in D Minor: *Various artists* / Olive blossoms: *Various artists* / Hot points: *Various artists* / Carmelita: *Various artists* / Bel viso: *Various artists* / La Mariposita: *Various artists* / Dizzy accordion: *Various artists.*
LP: **BLU-247**

Frost, Frank

FRANK FROST.
LP: . . . . **JEWEL 5013**

HEY BOSS MAN (Frost, Frank with the Night Hawks).
LP: . . . . **CRM 2011**

RIDE WITH YOUR DADDY TONIGHT.
Tracks: / My back scratcher / Never leave me at home / Harpin' on it / Things you do, The / Feel good babe / Pocket full of money / Ride with your Daddy tonight / Got my Mojo working / Janie on

my mind / Harp and soul / Didn't mean no harm / Pretty baby / Five long years.
LP: . . . . CRB 1103

Frost, Robert

ROAD NOT TAKEN, THE.
MC: 1060

Frozen Ghost

FROZEN GHOST.
Tracks: / Should I see / Promises / Yum bai ya / Beware the masque / Love like fire / End of the line / Time is the answer / Love without lies / Soldiers cry / Truth in lies.
LP: 254565 1
MC: 254565 4

Frozen Gold

GO TO HELL.
LP: . . . . GOLD 1

Frugivores

NEW AGE SONGS.
LP: . . . . NAGE 13
MC: . . . . NAGEC 13

Fruit Bats

7 SISTERS.
LP: . . . . NCHLP 14

Fruit Machine (film)

FRUIT MACHINE (See under Zimmer, Hans) (Various artists).

Fruit Of The...

FRUIT OF THE ORIGINAL SIN (Various artists).
2LP: . . . . TWI 035

Fruits of Passion

FRUITS OF PASSION.
Tracks: / Everything (I ever wanted) / Take what you want / Devotion / Kiss me / Bring it down / Love's glory / Truthful / Don't hold your breath / No more tears / Pride.
LP: . . . . XID 16
MC: . . . . CXID 16
LP: . . . . SIRENLP 3

Fruko

GODFATHER OF SALSA, THE.
MC: . . . . MCT 1022
LP: . . . . MLPS 1022

Fruscella, Tony

DEBUT.
LP: . . . . SPJ 126

FRU AND BREW (Fruscella, Tony/Brew Moore).
Tracks: / Sometimes I'm happy / Blue Lester / Hackensack / Imagination / Donna.
LP: . . . . SPJ 151

Fry, Albert

MAIDIN LUAN CINCISE.
LP: . . . . CEF 026

Fry, Steve

THY KINGDOM COME.
LP: . . . . SP R 1182
MC: . . . . SP C 1182

Frye, Velma

TO SOMEONE.
LP: . . . . FF 498

Frying High

PRIMUS.
LP: 210898
MC: 410898

FSK

CONTINENTAL BREAKFAST.
LP: . . . . CALCLP 016

F.U.A.L.

F.U.A.L..
Tracks: / 20 years on? / Follow me / Yes you! / Reaction of a closed mind / Dead clergymen / Soft drinks / Unhappy families / Suffer little children / Stop f*****g about / Curse of macha / Never make a statement / And the birdie sang / Rest in pieces.
LP: . . . . COX 018

Fuel

BACK OF THIS BEYOND, THE.
Tracks: / Age and present past / Heaven's 7th palace / Copper Davidfield, A / In the land of Prestor John / Philomel / Wind rose / Charon / White water shroud / Myrida streams / Sacred blue / Winter fair.
LP: . . . . NISHI 203

Fugard, Athol

BLOOD KNOT (Various artists).
MCSET: 0362

Fugazi

FUGAZI.
LP: . . . . DISCHORD 30
MC: . . . . DISCHORD 30C

MARGIN WALKER.
LP: . . . . DISCHORD 35
MC: . . . . DISCHORD 35C

REPEATER.
LP: . . . . DISCHORD 44

STEADY DIET OF NOTHING.
LP: . . . . DISCHORD 60
MC: . . . . DISCHORD 60C

Fugis

FUGIS (Various artists).
Tracks: / Jah man: *Campbell, Errol* / Jah man dub: *Campbell, Errol* / Sun is shining: *Matumbi, Bagga* / Shining is shining: *Matumbi, Bagga* / November: *Tomm, Sonny* / November dub: *Tomm, Sonny* / Cry: *Angelique* / Cry dub: *Angelique* / Lili twill: *Raaw* / Jah find Babylon guilty: *Brown, Junior* / Babylon in a dub: *Brown, Junior*.
LP: . . . . TEMPL 003

Fugitive from Love

FUGITIVE FROM LOVE (Ashwell, Julia).
MC: 85 1001

Fuglar, Fagrir

VEDURLOG (Fuglar, Fagrir/Karsten Vogel).
LP: . . . . HJF 11

Fugs

GOLDEN FILTH.
Tracks: / Slum goddess / CCD / How sweet I roamed / I couldn't get high / Saran wrap / I want to know / Home made / Nothing / Supergirl.
LP: . . . . ED 217

IT CRAWLED INTO MY HAND, HONEST.
Tracks: / Crystal liason / Rameses II is dead, my love / Burial waltz / Wide wide river / Life is strange / Johnny Pissoff meets the red angel / Marijuana / Leprechaun / When the mode of the music changes / Whimpers from the jello / Divine toe (part 1) / We're both dead now, Alice / Life is funny / Grope need (part 1) / Tuli, visited by the ghost of Plontinus / More grope need (grope need part 2) / Robinson Crusoe / National Haiku contest / Divine toe (part 2) / Irene / Claude Pelieu & JJ Lebel....
LP: . . . . XED 181
MC: . . . . CED 181

NO MORE SLAVERY.
LP: . . . . ROSE 79

REFUSE TO BE BURNT-OUT.
LP: . . . . ROSE 56

STAR PEACE.
LP: . . . . ROSE 115

TENDERNESS JUNCTION.
Tracks: / Turn on, tune in, drop out / Garden is open, The / Hare Krishna / War song / Fingers of the sun / Knock knock / Wet dream / Exorcising the evil spirits / Dover beach / Aphrodite mass.
LP: . . . . ED 298

Fuhrs & Frohling

AMMERLAND.
LP: 0060 105

DIARY.
Tracks: / Late in the evening / All hallows eve dream / On my pillow / Prelude / Back and again / Aogo / China puppet / Green Island / Mind games.
LP: 0060 333

Fujikawa, Mayumi

TWO VIOLIN SONATAS, THE (see under Prokofiev) (Fujikawa, Mayumi/ Craig Sheppard).

Fuknotz

LET'S PLAY SCRATCH'N'SNIFF WITH GRANDPA'S BUTT.
Tracks: / Scratch'n'sniff with Grandpa's butt / Batfag / Gopher holes / Feedback in Em / Seasons in da scum / Hyman munster / Penis gunis / Fuk u, I ain't Ghandi / Monster fuk / Sunfability / Are you dirty? / Camel balls.
LP: . . . . WH 008

Fukumura, Hiroshi

HUNT UP WIND.
LP: . . . . IC 6067

Full Circle (film)

FULL CIRCLE (See under Towns, Colin) (Towns, Colin).

Full Faith

DEBUT (Full Faith & Credit Big Band).
LP: . . . . PA 8001

JAZZFAIRE (Full Faith & Credit Big Band).
LP: . . . . PA 8003

Full Force

FULL FORCE.
Tracks: / Alice I want you just for me / Unselfish lover / Please stay / United / Girl if you take me home / Dream believer, The / Half a chance / Man upstairs, The / Let's dance against the wall.
LP: . . . . CBS 26595
MC: 40 26595

FULL FORCE GET READY 1 TIME.
Tracks: / Unfaithful / Never had another lover / Old flames never die / Child's play (part 1) / So much / Chain me to the night / Body heavenly / Love scene / Child's play (part 2) / Temporary love thing.
LP: . . . . CBS 57051
MC: 40 57051

GUESS WHO'S COMIN' TO THE CRIB?.
Tracks: / Take care of homework / Love is for suckers (like me and you) / All in my mind / 3 o'clock...school's out! / Child's play (part 3) / Full Force git money $ / Your love is so def / Katty women / Low blow Brenda / Black radio.
LP: 4602661
MC: 4602664

SIRLING COOKE FORCE, THE.
LP: . . . . EBON 3

SMOOVE.
Tracks: / Don't waste my time / Ain't my type of hype / Friends B-4 lovers / All I wanna do / 4-U Full Force's mellow medley / La la means I love you / Love on a two way street / Distant lover / In like with you / It's been a long time / Kiss those lips / Smoove / Make love to my mind / Man upstairs, The (On cassette only.) / That's how I'm lovin' (On cassette only.).
LP: 4654371
MC: 4654374

Full Head Of Steam

FULL HEAD OF STEAM, A (Various artists).
Tracks: / These my dreams are yours: *Almond, Marc* / Out of nowhere: *Diesel Park West* / Name, The: *Syndicate*/ Candlestick park: *Goodbye Mr. Mackenzie* / Turn it over: *Manyika, Zeke* / Ignition: *Wild Weekend* / I walk alone: *Bliss* / That way: *Neighbourhood* / Family: *New Model Army* / In the sun: *Crazyhead*.
LP: . . . . FHOSLP 1
MC: . . . . FHOSTC 1

Full House

FULL HOUSE (Various artists).
Tracks: / I love you, Samantha: *Howard, Johnny* / Jeanie with the light brown hair: *McVay, Ray* / Shenandoah: *McVay, Ray* / Fascination: *Turner, Ken* / Easy to love: *Howard, Johnny* / On the street where you live: *McVay, Ray* / I get a kick out of you: *McVay, Ray* / Dreamin': *Pearce, Monty & Bryan Smith* / Jealousy: *Turner, Ken* / Delilah: *Pearce, Monty & Bryan Smith* / Just the way you are: *McVay, Ray* / All of you: *Howard, Johnny* / Feelings: *Ross, Andy* / Non dimentica: *Smith, Bryan* / Smile: *Smith, Bryan*.
LP: . . . . DS 057

Full Metal Jacket

FULL METAL JACKET (Original soundtrack) (Various artists).
Tracks: / Full metal jacket: *Various artists* / Hello Vietnam: *Various artists* / Chapel of love: *Various* artists / Wooly bully: *Various artists* / I like it like that: *Various artists* / These boots are made for walking: *Various artists* / Suffrin' bird: *Various artists* / Marines' hymn, The: *Various artists* / Transition: *Various artists* / Parris Island: *Various artists* / Ruins: *Various artists* / Leonard: *Various artists*/ Attack: *Various artists* / Time suspended: *Various artists* / Sniper: *Various artists*.
LP: 925613 1
MC: 925613 4

Full Moon

FULL MOON.
LP: . . . . LUNAR 13

LIVE ENCOUNTER, THE.
LP: . . . . LUNAR 014

Full Swing

END OF THE SKY.
LP: . . . . YL 9999

IN FULL SWING.
LP: . . . . YL 0109

Full Time Men

YOUR FACE, MY FIST.
LP: . . . . ROSE 149

Fuller, Blind Boy

1935-1940.
Tracks: / Baby you gotta change your mind / Baby I don't have to worry / Looking for my woman / Precious lord / Jesus is a holy man / Bye bye baby / You got to have your dollar / Shake that shimmy / Truckin' my blues away.
LP: . . . . BOB 12
LP: . . . . BC 11

BLIND BOY FULLER AND BROWNIE MCGHEE 1936-41 (Fuller, Blind Boy & Brownie McGhee).
Tracks: / Black and tan / Red's got the piccolo blues / If you don't give me what I want / Black bottom blues / Me and my dog / Picking up tomatoes / Money spending woman / Double trouble.
LP: . . . . FLY 105

BLUE AND WORRIED MAN.
Tracks: / I'm a good stem winder / It doesn't matter, baby / Jivin' Big Bill blues / Blue and worried man / Woman you better wake up / You can't hide from The Lord / Twelve gates to the city / Baby, you gotta change your mind / You got to have your dollar / Bye bye baby / No stranger now / Must have been my Jesus / Jesus is a holy man.
LP: . . . . TM 801

DEATH VALLEY.
LP: . . . . OL 2809

EAST COAST PIEDMONT BLUES.
MC: 4679234

GREAT CAROLINA BLUESMAN.
LP: . . . . OT 1202

ON DOWN 1937-40.
LP: . . . . PY 1811

SHAKE THAT SHIMMY 1935-36.
LP: . . . . PY 1807

TRUCKIN' MY BLUES AWAY.
LP: . . . . L 1060

Fuller, Bobby

BOBBY FULLER INSTRUMENTAL ALBUM.
LP: . . . . LP 8504

I FOUGHT THE LAW (OLD GOLD) (See under Valens, Ritchie).

LIVE AGAIN.
LP: . . . . EVA 12046

MEMORIES OF BUDDY HOLLY.
LP: . . . . LP 8407

Fuller, Curtis

ALL STAR SEXTETS.
2LP: . . . . SJL 2239

BLUESETTE.
LP: . . . . WL 70502

CURTIS FULLER MEETS ROMA JAZZ TRIO (Fuller, Curtis & Roma Jazz Trio).
LP: . . . . SJP 204

FIRE AND FILIGREE.
LP: . . . . BH 7007

FOUR ON THE OUTSIDE.
Tracks: / Four on the outside (Adams plays baritone sax.) / Kathy (Adams plays baritone sax.) / Hello, young lovers (Adams plays baritone sax.) / Little dreams (Adams plays baritone sax.) / Ballad for Gabe-Wells (Adams plays baritone sax.) / Corrida del terro (Adams plays baritone sax.).
LP: . . . . SJP 124

GIANT BONES 80 (see under Winding, Kai) (Fuller, Curtis/Kai Winding).

NEW TROMBONE.
Tracks: / Vonce and 5 / Transportation blues / Namely you / What is this thing called love?.
LP: . . . . OJC 077

ONE MORE MEMORY (see Golston,Benny Quintet with Curtis Fuller) (Fuller, Curtis with Benny Golston Quintet).

WITH FRENCH HORNS.
LP: 1902112

Fuller, Jesse

FRISCO BLUES.
LP: . . . . ARHOOLIE 2009

JAZZ FOLKSONGS,SPIRITUALS & BLUES.
LP: 1010 031

JESSE FULLER.
2LP: . . . . CHD 226

MOVE ON DOWN THE LINE.
Tracks: / Move on down the line / Stealing / Ninety-nine years and one dark day / Animal fair / Sleeping in the midnight cold / Stack o lee / Railroad worksong / Lining up the track / Hanging 'round a skin game / Railroad blues / San Francisco Bay blues.
LP: 12T 134

SAN FRANCISCO BAY BLUES.
Tracks: / San Francisco Bay blues / Jesse's new midnight special / Morning blues / Little black train / Midnight cold / Whoa mule / John Henry / I got a mind to ramble / Crazy about a woman (you're no good) / Where could I go but to the Lord / Stealin' back to my old time used to be / Brown skin gal.
LP: 1010 051
LP: . . . . CH 226

Fuller, Johnny

FOOLS PARADISE.
LP: . . . . DD 4304

FULLER'S BLUES.
LP: . . . . DD 4311

Fullerton College

LOVE YA (Fullerton College Jazz Band).
LP: . . . . AM 17

PRIMARILY JAZZ (Fullerton College Jazz Band).
Tracks: / Licks and tricks / Shadow of a doubt / Four play / Shuffle this / Bop brothers' beach party / Say it, Roger / Why not? / Morning sun.
LP: . . . . AM 13

TIME TRIPPING (Fullerton College Jazz Band).
Tracks: / Straight tone and strive ahead / Sienna / Cozumel rendezvous / Umpire strikes back, The / Battle of the bop brothers / Soft summer breeze / Beach bum memories / Yo mombo.
LP: . . . . AM 10

UNFORGETTABLE (Fullerton College Big Band).
Tracks: / In the mood / Sweet Georgia Brown / Easy living / Some day my prince will come / That's all and more / But beautiful.
LP: . . . . AM 15

Fulson, Lowell

BABY WON'T YOU JUMP WITH ME.
2LP: . . . . IG 407/408
MCSET: . . . . IGC 407/408

BLUE DAYS, BLACK NIGHTS.
Tracks: / Talkin woman / Black nights / Sittin' here thinkin / Little angel / Shattered dreams / I found love / Hustler's game / Get your game uptight / Tramp / Back to Chicago / Everyday / Funky broadway.
LP: . . . . CH 184

BLUES GOT ME DOWN, THE.
LP: . . . . DD 4306

CHICAGO GOLDEN YEARS.
2LP: 427007

HUNG DOWN HEAD.
LP: . . . . BRP 2031

I DON'T KNOW MY MIND.
Tracks: / Kansas City / Drifting blues / I cried like a baby / I want affection not protection / Don't make promises / Blood sweat and tears / You're gonna miss me / Let me ride in your automobile / Gettin' drunk / Walk on / Sweetest thing / Come back baby / Your woman / You don't know my mind.
LP: . . . . BFX 15279

IN A HEAVY BAG.
LP: . . . . JEWEL 5003

IT'S A GOOD DAY.
LP: . . . . ROUNDER 2088
MC: . . . . ROUNDER 2088C

I'VE GOT THE BLUES.
Tracks: / Teach me / I've got the blues / Every second a fool is born / Searchin' out / Crying won't help you / Last one to know, The / Sleeper / Man on the run / Don't destroy me / Cheatin' woman / Do you feel it? / Lonesome Christmas, parts 1 & 2.
LP: . . . . TOP 178
MC: . . . . KTOP 178

LOWELL FULSON.
Tracks: / Want to know / Lonely hours / Loving you / It's a long time / Rollin' blues / Love 'n' things / Swingin' party / Took a long time / Love grows cold / Hung down head / Some day baby / That's alright / I want to make love to you / Rock this morning.
LP: . . . . CXMD 4052
MC: . . . . ZCCXD 4052

LOWELL FULSON 1946/57 (Giant of the blues guitar).
Tracks: / Television blues / Katie Lee blues / Fulson boogie / Tell me baby / 9.30 shuffle / Thinking blues / My gal at eight / Black widow spider / My baby / Let's live right / Guitar shuffle / Blues never fail / I believe I'll give it up / You've gotta reap / Please don't go / Don't drive me baby.
LP: . . . . BB 302

LOWELL FULSON AND HIS GUITAR.
LP: . . . . ARHOOLIE 2003

MAN OF MOTION.
LP: . . . . CRB 1018

OL' BLUES SINGER, THE.
LP: . . . . JETLP 9

THINK TWICE BEFORE YOU SPEAK.
Tracks: / Parachute woman / I'm tough / Think twice before you speak / Well oh well / Come back, baby / Sinner's prayer / One-room country shack / Meet me in the bottom / Come on / You're gonna miss me.
LP: . . . . JSP 1082

Fulton, Bill

BAKER'S DOZEN.
Tracks: / Tuxedo Junction / Hey little dog / Taste of honey, A / Autumn leaves / Speckled hen / Runaway nun / In a shanty in old Shantytown / Lazy baker in sunshine / One-note samba / Marching song / Dindi / Bebop blues / Ivy toccata.
LP: . . . . REL 458

Fulton, David

DON'T ASK.
LP: . . . . ST 7535

LIKE CHIGNIK.
LP: . . . . ST 7519

Fumblebum Agency

DORIC-VISION SONG CONTEST, THE.
Tracks: / Fumblebum entry / Aboyne Entry / Cults entry / Drumoak entry / Drom o'Wartle entry / Castlegate entry / Inverurie entry / Stonehaven entry / Newmacher entry / Turriff entry.
MC: . . . . CWGRTV 5

Fun At One

FUN AT ONE (Comedy from Radio 1) (Various artists).
LP: . . . . REB 371
MC: . . . . ZCF 371

MORE FUN AT ONE (Various artists).
LP: . . . . REB 399

Fun Boy Three

BEST OF FUN BOY THREE.
LP: . . . . CHR 1459
MC: . . . . ZCHR 1459

FUN BOY THREE.
Tracks: / Sanctuary / Way on down / Lunatics, The / Life in general (Lewe in Algemeen) / Faith hope and charity / Funrama 2 / Best of luck mate / T'aint what you do (it's the way that you do it) / Telephone always rings, The / I don't believe it / Alone.
LP: . . . . CHR 1383
MC: . . . . ZCHR 1383
LP: . . . . FA 41 3115 1
MC: . . . . FA 41 3115 4
LP: 204513

WAITING.
Tracks: / Murder, she said / More I see (the less I believe / Going home / We're having all the fun / Farmyard connection / Tunnel of love / Our lips are sealed / Pressure of life / Things we do / Well fancy that.
LP: . . . . CHR 1417
MC: . . . . ZCHR 1417

Fun Lovers

JOYRIDE.
LP: . . . . REBEL 1009

Fun On The Frets

FUN ON THE FRETS (Early jazz guitar) (Various artists).
LP: . . . . L 1061

Fun While It Lasted

FUN WHILE IT LASTED (Various artists).
LP: . . . . ONLYLP 006

Fun With Music

ADVENTURES OF AMERICAT (Various artists).
MC: . . . . TCFWM 8

ATISHOO OF LIES (Witch's Revenge) (Various artists).
MC: . . . . TCFWM 14

BEETHOVEN'S BIRTHDAY PARTY (Various artists).
MC: . . . . TCFWM 2

CHOU-CHOU'S BIRTHDAY MUSIC (Various artists).
MC: . . . . TCFWM 7

CINDERELLA (Various artists).
MC: . . . . TCFWM 17

KING WHO BROKE HIS PROMISE (A Spooky Halloween/Farewell Little Princess) (Various artists).
MC: . . . . TCFWM 1545474

KING WHO BROKE HIS PROMISE (Spooky Halloween/Farewell, Little Princess) (Various artists).
MC: . . . . TCFWM 18

MAN WHO NEVER WAS, THE (The Prince and the Magic Feather) (Various artists).
MC: . . . . TCFWM 16

MAN WHO NEVER WAS/PRINCE AND THE MAGIC FEATHER (Various artists).
MC: . . . . TCFWM 1545464

MANDY AND THE MAGIC BUTTERFLY (Various artists).
MC: . . . . TCFWM 12

MOZART, THE MIRACLE MAESTRO (Various artists).
MC: . . . . TCFWM 15

MR. HANDEL'S FIREWORKS PARTY (Various artists).
MC: . . . . TCFWM 19

MUSICAL JOURNEY TO THE MOON, A (Various artists).
MC: . . . . TCFWM 11

MYSTERY OF THE SPANISH GARDEN (Freedom Flag/Sad Dance) (Various artists).
MC: . . . . TCFWM 1545484

NURSE GOOSE AND THE MAGIC DOORS (Fawn and the Otter/ Chickabiddy) (Various artists).
MC: . . . . TCFWM 1545444
MC: . . . . TCFWM 5

NUTCRACKER, THE (Various artists).
MC: . . . . TCFWM 13

ONCE UPON THE THAMES (Various artists).
MC: . . . . TCFWM 1

PAPA HAYDN'S SURPRISE (Various artists).
MC: . . . . TCFWM 6

PHANTOM OF THE LAKE (Various artists).
MC: . . . . TCFWM 1545494

ROMEO AND JULIET (Story of the Ballet) (Various artists).
MC: . . . . TCFWM 1545414
MC: . . . . TCFWM 10

SEASONS GREETINGS FROM VIVALDI (Various artists).
MC: . . . . TCFWM 9

SINBAD AND THE WIZARD EAGLE (Various artists).
Tracks: / Sinbad and the wizard eagle: *Various artists.*
MC: . . . . TCFWM 1545404
MC: . . . . TCFWM 4

SLEEPING BEAUTY, THE (Various artists).
MC: . . . . TCFWM 20

SLEEPING BEAUTY, THE (The Story of the Ballet) (Various artists).
MC: . . . . TCFWM 1545424

SWAN LAKE (Story of the Ballet) (Various artists).
MC: . . . . TCFWM 3

WITCH'S REVENGE/ATISHOO OF LIES (Various artists).
MC: . . . . TCFWM 1545434

Fundamental Frolics

FUNDAMENTAL FROLICS (Various artists).
LP: . . . . REB 435

Fundamental Hymnal

FUNDAMENTAL HYMNAL (Various artists).
LP: . . . . SAVE 79

Fundeburgh, Anson

BLACK TOP BLUES-A-RAMA, LIVE AT TIPITINA'S VOL.1 (Fundeburgh, Anson & The Rockets).
LP: . . . . BT 1044
MC: . . . . BT 1044C

RACK 'EM UP.
Tracks: / Tell me what I have done wrong / Since we've been together / Rack 'em up / Mama and poppa / 20 miles / Hold that train, conductor / I'm your professor / I'll keep on trying / All your love / Are you out there? / (Woman who only drinks) lemonade, A / Meanstreak.
LP: . . . . FIEND 147

SHE KNOCKS ME OUT (Fundeburgh, Anson & The Rockets).
LP: . . . . BT 1022

SINS (With Sam Myers) (Fundeburgh, Anson & The Rockets).
Tracks: / Man needs his loving / I'll be true / Don't want no leftovers / Walked all night / My kind of baby / Changing neighbourhoods / I can't stop loving you / Chill out / My heart / Trying to make you mine / Sleeping in the ground / Hard hearted woman.
LP: . . . . FIEND 104
LP: . . . . BT 1038
MC: . . . . BT 1038C

TALK TO YOU BY HAND (Fundeburgh, Anson & The Rockets).
Tracks: / Talk to you by hand / Tore up / Come on / I found a new love / How long? / That will never do / Nobody but you / This should go on forever / Walking Doctor Bill / All my love in vain / I was fooled / Red hot mama.
LP: . . . . KK 777
LP: . . . . BT 1001

Funeral Nation

STATE OF INSANITY.
LP: . . . . CCG 012

Funhouse

GENERATION GENERATOR.
LP: . . . . HMUSA 160
MC: . . . . HMAMC 160

Funhouse of Fear

FUNHOUSE OF FEAR (See under Batman (bk).

Funk

GOGO CRANKIN' (Various artists).
Tracks: / Meet me at the go-go: *Hot Cold Sweat* / Let's get small: *Trouble funk* / We need some money: *Brown, Chuck & Soul Searchers* / Ohh la la la: *E.U.* / Drop the bomb: *Various artists* / Good to go: *Various artists* / Somebody's ringin' that door bell: *E.U.* / Say what: *Trouble Funk.*
LP: . . . . DCLP 100
MC: . . . . DCCA 100

GO-GO-THE SOUND OF WASHINGTON DC various artists (Various artists).
LP: . . . . BOMB 1
MC: . . . . KBOMB 1

HITS FROM THE HOUSE OF SHAKA (Various artists).
LP: . . . . SHAKA 857

JBS FUNKY PEOPLE (Various artists).
Tracks: / Gimme some more: *J.B.'s* / Pass the peas: *J.B.'s* / Think (about it): *Collins, Lyn* / Givin' up food for funk (part 1): *J.B.'s* / Mama feel good: *Collins, Lyn* / Hot pants: *J.B.'s* / Rock me again & again & again.....: *Collins, Lyn* / Damn right, I am somebody (part 1): *Wesley, Fred & The J.B.'s* / Take me just as I am: *Collins, Lyn* / If you don't get it the first time...: *Wesley, Fred & The J.B.'s* / Party (part 1): *Maceo & The Macks* / It's not the express it's the JBs monaurail (part 1): *Fred & The New JB's.*
LP: . . . . URBLP 10
MC: . . . . URBMC 10

MESSAGE, THE (Rare groove 2) (Various artists).
Tracks: / I don't know if I can make it: *Smith, Dawson* / Mama's got the wagon: *Murray, Mickey* / Mr. Bump Man (give me a hand): *Beavers, Jackie* / Bra: *Cymande* / Keep on dancing: *Cash, Alvin* / Thank you for letting me be myself again: *Maceo & All The Kings Men* / Check your bucket: *Bo, Eddie* / Brothers on the slide: *Cymande*/ Mr. Brown: *African Music Machine* / Fug: *Cymande.*
LP: . . . . CRB 1188
MC: . . . . TCCRB 1188

MUTANT DISCO (Various artists).
Tracks: / Me no pop I: *Coati Mundi* / Cowboys and gangsters: *Various artists* / Contort yourself: *White, James* / Maladie d'amour: *Various artists* / Wheel me out: *Various artists.*
LP: . . . . ISSP 4001

P.FUNK (Various artists).
LP: . . . . PFUNK 1
MC: . . . . ZCFUNK 1

STAX FUNK - GET UP AND GET DOWN (Various artists).
Tracks: / Shaft, Theme from: *Hayes, Isaac* / Castle of joy: *Fat Larry's Band* / What goes around (must come around): *Sons Of Slum* / Dark skin woman: *Rice, Sir Mack* / Whatcha see is whatcha get: *Dramatics* / Son of Shaft: *Bar-Kays* / Dryer Part 1, The: *Johnson, Roy Lee & The Villagers* / Cool strut: *Hayes, Bernie* / Mr. Big Stuff: *Knight, Jean* / Funkasize you: *Sho Nuff* / Holy ghost: *Bar-Kays* / Men, The (Theme from): *Hayes,* Isaac / Circuit's overloaded: *Foxx, Inez & Charlie* / FLB: *Fat Larry's Band* / Black: *Mar Keys* / Get up and get down: *Dramatics* / Moving on: *Dynamic Soul Machine* / Dark skin woman Part 1 & 2: *Rice, Sir* Mack (Available on CD and cassette only) / You chose me: *Sho Nuff* (Available on CD and cassette only) / Men, The (Theme from): *Hayes, Isaac* (Available on CD and cassette only) / Dryer Part 2, The: *Johnson, Roy Lee & The Villagers*(Available on CD and cassette only) / Cool strut: *Hayes, Bernie* (Available on CD and cassette only).
LP: . . . . SX 020
MC: . . . . SXC 020

THAT'S FUNK, VOL.2 (Various artists).
LP: 6 25635
MC: 425635

Funk & Blues

FUNK AND BLUES 1956-1967 (Blue Note 50th anniversary collection vol. 3) (Various artists).
Tracks: / Senor blues: *Silver, Horace* / Song for my father: *Silver, Horace* / Moanin': *Blakey, Art/Jazz* Messengers / Back at the chicken shack: *Smith, Jimmy (USA)* / Cristo redentor: *Byrd, Donald* / Blue bossa: *Henderson, Joe/Kenny Dorham* / Funjii mama: *Mitchell, Blue* / Sidewinder, The: *Morgan, Lee* / Alligator Boogaloo: *Donaldson, Lou.*

2LP: BST2 92471
MC: TCBST2 92471

Funk In Yo Face

FUNK IN YO FACE (Various artists).
LP: 241 675-1
MC: 241 675-4

Funk Inc

ACID INC - THE BEST OF FUNK INC.
Tracks: / Chicken lickin' / Sister Jane / Jung bongo / Where are we going / Smokin' at Tiffany's / Kool's back again / Give me your love / Let's make love and stop the war.
LP: . . . . BGP 1011
MC: . . . . BGPC 1011

Funk 'n' Soul

FUNK 'N' SOUL REVOLUTION (Various artists).
Tracks: / Somebody touch me (in the right place): *Knight, Boobie & The Uni* / Ali shuffle: *Cash, Alvin* / Give it up: *Eliminators* / (For God's sake) give more power to the people: *Chi-lites* / Work work work: *B W & The* Next Edition / South African man: *Bohannon (Hamilton)* / Foot stompin' music: *Bohannon (Hamilton)* / How can you say goodbye: *Quails, Sidney Joe* / Boo on you (shakin' the baby's shoes): *Jones, Chuck & Company* / Let me down easy: *Rare Pleasure* / I ain't got nobody: *Sly & the Family Stone* / Sweeping your dirt under my rug: *Bailey, Ann* / This time around: *Soul* / There it is: *Davis, Tyrone.*
LP: . . . . KENT 051

Funkadelic

AMERICA EATS ITS YOUNG.
LP: SEW2 029
MC: . . . . SEWC 2 029

COSMIC SLOP.
LP: . . . . SEW 035
MC: . . . . SEWC 035

ELECTRIC SPANKING OF WAR BABIES.
Tracks: / Electric spanking of war babies / Electro-cuties / Funk gets stronger / Brettino's bounce / She loves you / Shockwaves / Oh, I / Icka-prick.
LP: . . . . K 56874

FREE YOUR MIND AND YOUR ASS WILL FOLLOW.
Tracks: / Free your mind and your ass will follow / Friday night, August 14th / Funky dollar bill / I wanna know if it's good to you / Some more / Eulogy and light.
LP: . . . . SEW 012
MC: . . . . SEWC 012

FUNKADELIC.
Tracks: / Mommy, what's a Funkadelic? / I bet you / Music for my mother / I got a thing, you got a thing, everybody's got a thing / Good old music / Quality and satisfy / What is soul?.
LP: . . . . SEW 010
MC: . . . . SEWC 010

HARDCORE JOLLIES.
Tracks: / Osmosis phase one / Comin' round the mountain / Smokey / If you got funk, you got style / Hardcore jollies / Terribitus phase two / Soul mate / Cosmic stop / You scared the lovin outta me / Adolescent funk.
LP: . . . . K 56299

MAGGOT BRAIN.
Tracks: / Maggot brain / Can you get to that / Hit it and quit it / You and your folks, me and my folks / Super stupid / Back in our minds / Wars of Armageddon.
LP: . . . . SEW 002
MC: . . . . SEWC 002

ONE NATION UNDER A GROOVE (LP).
Tracks: / One nation under a groove / Groovallegiance / Who says a funk band can't play rock / Promentalshitbackwashipsychosisenema squad / Into you / Cholly / Lunchmeataphobia / P.E. squad / Doodoo chasers / Maggot brain.
LP: . . . . K 56539

STANDING ON THE VERGE OF GETTING IT.
LP: . . . . SEWA 040
MC: . . . . SEWC 040

UNCLE JAM WANTS YOU.
Tracks: / Freak of the week / (Not just) knee deep / Uncle Jam / Field manoeuvers / Holly wants to go to California / Foot soldiers.
LP: . . . . K 56712

Funkapolitan

FUNKAPOLITAN.
Tracks: / Run run run / Illusions / War / If only / In the crime of life / Behold the super ace / There it is again / As time goes by.
LP: . . . . SH 8548

Funkin Marvellous

FUNKIN MARVELLOUS (Various artists).
LP: . . . . MARV 1000
MC: . . . . MARVC 1000

Funky

FUNKY (Various artists).
LP: 6498 141
MC: 7133 141

Funky Alternatives

FUNKY ALTERNATIVES VOL.4 (Various artists).
LP: . . . . CPRODLP 009

FUNKY ALTERNATIVES VOL.5 (Various artists).
LP: . . . . CPRODLP 012

FUNKY ALTERNATIVES (VOL. 1) (Various artists).
MC: . . . . CPRODMC 001
LP: . . . . CPRODLP 001

FUNKY ALTERNATIVES (VOL. 2) (Various artists).
LP: . . . . CPRODLP 002

Funky Five

N.O. TEA PARTY (Various).
LP: . . . . NOLA LP 18

Funky Nor JB

MAKE ME A PALLET ON THE FLOOR.
LP: . . . . HERWIN 301

Funky Party

FUNKY PARTY (Various artists).
Tracks: / Party time: *Blow, Kurtis* / She talks to me with her body: *Bar-Kays* / Style: *Cameo* / You can't run from my love: *Mills, Stephanie* / Ms. Got the body: *Con Funk Shun* / Feels so good: *Yarbrough & Peoples* / Early in the morning: *Gap Band* / I'm out to catch: *Haywood, Leon* / Can you feel the groove tonight?: *Con Funk Shun* / Party night: *Yarbrough & Peoples.*
MC: 822 335-4

Funky Punany

FUNKY PUNANY (Ten cuts of the "Stopper" rhythm) (Various artists).
LP: . . . . FADLP 019

Funny Bones (bk)

FUNNY BONES (Janet & Allan Ahlberg).
MC: 0 00 102197 4

Funny Commercials...

FUNNY COMMERCIALS & OTHER RADIO FLUFFS (Various artists).
LP: . . . . LP 1901

Funny Face

FUNNY FACE (Original Soundtrack Recording) (Various artists).
LP: . . . . DS 15001

Funny Feeling

FUNNY FEELING (Various artists).
LP: . . . . BSLP 1024

Funny Feet

FUNNY FEET (Various artists).
MC: . . . . ST 3632

Funny Girl

FUNNY GIRL (Film soundtrack) (Various artists).
Tracks: / Funny girl overture: *Various artists* / I'm the greatest star: *Various artists* / If a girl isn't pretty: *Various artists* / Roller skate rag: *Various artists* / I'd rather be blue over you (than happy with somebody else): *Various artists* / His love makes me beautiful: *Various artists* / People: *Various artists* / You are woman: *Various artists* / Don't rain on my parade: *Various artists* / Sadie Sadie: *Various artists* / Swan, The: *Various artists* / Funny girl: *Various artists* / My man: *Various artists* / Finale: *Various artists.*
LP: 70 044
LP: 4665281
MC: 4665284

FUNNY GIRL - ORIGINAL BROADWAY CAST (Original Broadway cast) (Various artists).
Tracks: / Funny girl overture: *Various artists* / If a girl isn't pretty: *Various artists* / I'm the greatest star: *Various artists* / Cornet man: *Various artists* / Who taught her everything: *Various artists* / His love makes me beautiful: *Various artists* / I want to be seen with you tonight: *Various artists* / Henry Street: *Various artists* / People: *Various artists* / You are woman: *Various artists* / Don't rain on my parade: *Various artists* / Sadie Sadie: *Various artists* / Find yourself a man: *Various artists* / Rat-tat-tat-tat: *Various artists* / Who are you now: *Various artists* / Music that makes me dance, The: *Various artists* / Finale: *Various artists.*
LP: . . . . EG 2605681
MC: . . . . EG 2605684

FUNNY GIRL (ORIGINAL ISSUE) (Film soundtrack) (Various artists).
LP: . . . . W 2059

Funny Lady

FUNNY LADY (Original soundtrack) (Various artists).
LP: ALB6 8347
MC: ACB6 8347

Funny Man

FUNNY MAN (Various artists from the 20's & 30's) (Various artists).
LP: . . . . SH 396
MC: . . . . TC SH 396

Funny Thing

FUNNY THING HAPPENED... (..on the way to the Forum) (Various artists).
Tracks: / Funny thing happened... overture: *Various artists* / Comedy tonight: *Various artists* / Love, I hear: *Various artists* / Lovely: *Various artists* / Pretty little picture: *Various artists* / Everybody ought to have a maid: *Various artists* / I'm calm: *Various artists* / Impossible: *Various artists* / Bring me my bride: *Various artists* / That dirty old man: *Various artists* / That'll show him: *Various artists* / Lovely (2): *Various artists* / Funeral sequence and dance: *Various artists* / Comedy tonight (2): *Various artists.*
LP: . . . . EMS 1240
MC: . . . . TC EMS 1240
LP: . . . . OCR 3
MC: . . . . OCRC 3
LP: . . . . DS 15028

Furay, Richie

I'VE GOT A REASON.
Tracks: / Look at the sun / We'll see / Starlight / Gettin' through / I've got a reason / Mighty maker / You're the one I love / Still rolling stones / Over and over again.
LP: . . . . MYR 1105
MC: . . . . MC 1105
LP: . . . . K 53043

SEASONS OF CHANGE.
Tracks: / Hallelujah / Endless flight / Yellow moon rising / Seasons of change / My Lord and my God / Rise up / Promise of love / Home to my Lord / For the prize / Through it all.
LP: . . . . MYR 1119
MC: . . . . MC 1119

Furey, Finbar

LOVE LETTERS.
Tracks: / Miss you nights / First time ever I saw your face, The / Something / Love me tender / Rose, The / Darlin' / Love letters / I'll have to say I love you in a song / You needed me / My Lagan love / Wonderful tonight / Sailing / Railway Square / Song for while I'm away, A.
LP: 211156
MCSET: 411156

TRADITIONAL IRISH PIPE MUSIC.
MC: . . . . ASK 767

Furey, Ted

TOSS THE FEATHERS.
LP: . . . . SOLP 1020

TRADITIONAL FIDDLE.
MC: . . . . COX 1020

Fureys

AT THE END OF THE DAY (Fureys & Davey Arthur).
Tracks: / Perfect day / Come by the hills / Morning has broken / Love is pleasing / Twelfth of never / Annie's song / Old house / All through the night / Bless this house / Smiling through / Bright eyes / Wait till the clouds roll by / Bonnie Mary of Argyle / Sally gardens / Last rose of summer / Amazing grace / At the end of the day.
LP: . . . . ONE 1310
MC: . . . . OCE 2310

BEST OF THE FUREYS AND DAVEY ARTHUR (Fureys & Davey Arthur).
Tracks: / When you were sweet 16 / Maggie / Morning has broken / Twelfth of never / Annie's song / I'll take you home again Kathleen / Love is pleasin' / Beautiful dreamer / Bonnie Mary of Argyle / Just a song at twilight / Bless this house / I'll be your sweetheart / Last rose of summer / If I had my life to live over / Wait till the clouds roll by / Scarlet ribbons / Perfect day, A / When I grow too old to dream / Come by the hills / Anniversary waltz.
MC: . . . . MCTC 010

COLLECTION: FUREYS (Furey, Finbar & Eddie).
Tracks: / Rakish Paddy / Hag with the money, The / Bill Hart's favourite / Dance around the spinning wheel / Fin's favourite / Spanish cloak, The / Young girl milking the cow, The / Piper in the meadow straying / Castle terrace / Madam Bonaparte / Grahams flat / Fox chase, The / McShane / Colonel Fraser / Lonesome boatman, The / Carron Lough bay / Come by the hills / Sliabh na mban / Flowers in the valley, The / Pigeon on the gate / Eamonn an chnuic (Ned of the hills) / This town is not their own / Rocking the baby.
2LP: . . . . CCSLP 165
MC: . . . . CCSMC 165

COLLECTION: FUREYS AND DAVEY ARTHUR (Fureys & Davey Arthur).
Tracks: / Paddy in Paris / Reason I left Mullingar, The / Mountains of Mourne, The / Irish eyes / Who do you think you are? / Lovers / Ted Furey's selection / Evening falls / Night Ferry / Portland town / Ned of the hill / October song / Leaving Nancy / Garrett Barry's jig / Sitting alone / Big ships / From where I stand / Morning cloud*New copperplate etc. / Dreaming my dreams / Lament / I'll be there / First leaves of Autumn.
2LP: . . . . CCSLP 231
MC: . . . . CCSMC 231

EMIGRANT (Furey Brothers & Davey Arthur).
LP: 2904 009

FINBAR AND EDDIE FUREY.
Tracks: / Graham's flat / Leezie Lindsay / Piper through the meadow straying / Curragh of Kildare, The / Eamonn an chnuic (ned of the hills) / Town is not your own, This / Rocking the baby / Spanish cloak, The / Come by the hills / Sliabh na mban / Dainty Davie / Tattered Jack Welch / Flowers in the valley, The / Pigeon on the gate / Lonesome boatman, The / Carron lough bay / Prickly bush, The / Bogie's bonnie belle / Fox chase, The / Bill Hart's favourite / Dance around the spinning wheel / Let me go to the mountains / McShane / Colonel Fraser.
2LP: . . . . CR 053
MCSET: . . . . CRT 053
LP: . . . . HPE 654
MC: . . . . HPC 654

FIRST LEAVES OF AUTUMN, THE.
LP: . . . . RITZLP 0039
MC: . . . . RITZLC 039

FUREYS & DAVEY ARTHUR,THE (Fureys & Davey Arthur).
MC: . . . . ARANC 003

FUREY'S FINEST, THE.
LP: . . . . STAR 2311
MC: . . . . STAC 2311
LP: . . . . HSTAR 2311
MC: . . . . HSTAC 2311

FUREYS IN CONCERT, THE (Furey Brothers & Davey Arthur).
LP: . . . . RITZLP 0025
MC: . . . . RITZLC 0025
MC: . . . . RTE 71

GOLDEN DAYS (Fureys & Davey Arthur).
LP: . . . . NE 1283
MC: . . . . OCE 2283
LP: . . . . ONE 1283

GREEN FIELDS OF FRANCE.
MC: . . . . BAN 1001

MORNING ON A DISTANT SHORE.
LP: 2904 010

SCATTERING, THE (Fureys & Davey Arthur).
Tracks: / Tara Hill / Setting, The / When I leave behind Neidin / Sometimes / Railway hotel / Lonely in London / Euston station / If you should go / I will love you till I die / I'll always love you / We dreamed our dreams / Old bog road.
LP: . . . . HM 047
LP: 210.294
MC: 410.294

SOUND OF,THE (Fureys & Davey Arthur).
Tracks: / Green fields of France / Gypsy Davey / Reason I left Mullinger,The / Clare to here / Ask me father / Finbar Dwyers / Old oak tree, The / Lark on the strand, The / Her father didn't like me anyway. / Shipyard slips / Leaving Nancy / O'Carolans tribute / Roster,The / Night ferry / Lament / Beer, beer, beer / Lonesome boatman, The.
LP: 2490 160
MC: 3184119
LP: . . . . RGLP 11

STEAL AWAY (Fureys & Davey Arthur).
LP: . . . . RITZLP 0014

TOWN IS NOT THEIR OWN, THE.
LP: . . . . HPE 613

WHEN YOU WERE SWEET SIXTEEN (Fureys & Davey Arthur).
Tracks: / Green fields of France / When you were sweet sixteen / My love is like a red red rose / Anniversary song / I will love you everytime / Yesterdays people / Lonesome boatman,The / Old man,The / Oh Babushka / Belfast mill / Siege of a nation / Yesterdays men.
LP: . . . . RITZLP 0004
MC: . . . . RITZLC 0004

LP: . . . . CLALP 171
MC: . . . . CLAMC 171

Furio De Castri

THINGS.
LP: . . . . IJC 002

Furious Fish...

FURIOUS FISH ON THE LOOSE (Various artists).
LP: . . . . FFLPS 001

Furlong, Michael

BREAKAWAY.
LP: . . . . MFN 79

USE IT OR LOSE IT.
Tracks: / Careless / Use it or lose it / Head on rock 'n' roll / Back to the wall / On the firing line / Right-a-way / Don't start lovin' me / Two hearts / I've got news for you / Don't gimme the biz.
LP: 780181 1

Furniss, Paul

VANITY FAIR (With the Eclipse Valley Five-1974).
LP: . . . . S 1368

Furniture

FOOD, SEX AND PARANOIA.
Tracks: / One step behind you / Slow motion kisses / Swing tender / Taste of you, A / Plot to kiss what was, A / On a slow fuse / Subway to the beach / Song for a doberman / Love me / Friend of a friend / Hard to say.
LP: 210377
MC: 410377

FURNITURE SCRAPBOOK, THE.
LP: . . . . SURLP 013
MC: . . . . SURMC 013

WHEN THE BOOM WAS ON.
LP: 4C 1

WRONG PEOPLE,THE.
LP: . . . . SEEZ 64
MC: . . . . ZSEEZ 64

Furtado, Tony

SWAMPED.
Tracks: / John Henry / Swamped / Glory at the meeting house / Old homestead waltz / Daddio / Crossing at the Severn / Celtic medley / Broken pledge, The / Golden eagle hornpipe / Blues for Alice / Salutations.
LP: . . . . ROUNDER 0277
MC: . . . . ROUNDER 0277C

Further Railway

FURTHER RAILWAY STORIES (See under Railway Stories) (Rushton, Willie (nar)).

Fury, Billy

BILLY.
Tracks: / We were meant for each other / How many nights, how many days / Willow weep for me / Bumble bee / She cried / Let me know / Chapel on the hill, The / Like I've never been gone / Million miles from nowhere, A / I'll show you / Our day will come / All my hopes / One stop from heaven / One kiss / Hard times (no one knows better than I) / (Here I am) broken hearted / I'll never fall in love again / Kansas city / Go ahead and ask her / What am I gonna do.
LP: . . . . LK 4533

BILLY.
LP: . . . . BGOLP 17

BILLY FURY.
Tracks: / Cross my heart / King for tonight / What do you think you're doing of / All I wanna do is cry / I'll never fall in love again / Didn't see the real thing come along / If I lose you / Alright, goodbye / Where do you run / Away from you / She so far she's in / Baby what you want me to do / Talkin' in my sleep / Running around / You don't know / Last kiss, The / What am I gonna do / Gonna type a letter / Don't knock upon my door / Nothin' shakin' / Go ahead and ask her / Glad all over.
MC: . . . . SPC 8573
LP: . . . . SEE 32
LP: . . . . BGOLP 18

BILLY FURY HIT PARADE, THE.
Tracks: / Maybe tomorrow / Colette / That's love / Thousand stars, A / Halfway to paradise / Jealousy / I'd never find another you / Last night was made for love / Once upon a dream / Because of love / Like I've never been gone / When will you say 'I love you'? / In summer / Somebody else's girl / Do you really love me too? / I will / It's only make believe / Lost without you / In thoughts of you / Run to my lovin' arms.
LP: . . . . TAB 37
MC: . . . . KTBC 37

BILLY FURY STORY.
Tracks: / Maybe tomorrow / Margo / Don't knock upon my door / That's love / My advice / Phone call / You don't know / Turn my back on you / Don't say it's over / Since you've been gone / It's you I need / Alright goodbye / Don't leave me this way / Wondrous place / Don't worry / Halfway to paradise / I love how you love me / Candy kisses / When will you say 'I love you'? / Kansas City / Hippy hippy shake / Glad all over / Nothin' shakin' / It's only make believe / Baby you want me to do / In thoughts of you.
2LP: . . . . DPA 3033
MC: . . . . KDPC 8059

COLLECTION: BILLY FURY.
Tracks: / Don't leave me this way / Margo / Colette / I love how you love me / Halfway to paradise / Nobody's child / Hippy hippy shake / Push push / Gonna type a letter / In thoughts of you / When will you say I love you / In summer / Kansas City / Glad all over.
2LP: . . . . CCSLP 160
MC: . . . . CCSMC 160

EP COLLECTION, THE: BILLY FURY.
Tracks: / Turn your lamp down low / Don't walk away / You're having the last dance with me / Wondrous place / What am I living for / That's enough / You got me dizzy / Saved / Keep away / My Christmas prayer / I can feel it / I love how you love me / Would you stand by me / Margo / Play it cool / Don't jump / Please don't go / What did I do / I'll never quite get over you / Nobody's child.
LP: . . . . SEE 59
MC: . . . . SEEK 59

HALFWAY TO PARADISE.
Tracks: / Halfway to paradise / Don't worry / You're having the last dance with me / Push push / Fury's tune / Talkin' in my sleep / Stick around / Thousand stars, A / Cross my heart / Comin' up in the world / He will break your heart / Would you stand by me.
LP: . . . . BGOLP 19
LP: . . . . ACL 1083

IN THOUGHTS OF YOU (The best of Billy Fury).
Tracks: / It's only make believe / Jealousy / Thousand stars, A / Push push / Angel face / I will / Letter full of tears / I'll never quite get over you / In thoughts of you / Wondrous place / Nobody's child / Kansas City / Candy kisses / Glad all over / If I lose you / Give me your word.
MC: . . . . PWKMC 4053P

LOVING YOU.
Tracks: / Sheila / Maybe baby / Lazy life / I'm gonna love you too / In my room / All the way to the USA / Loving you / Your words / Suzanne in the mirror / Well alright / I love you / Lyanna.
LP: . . . . MFLP 1027
MC: . . . . MFC 1027

MEMORIES.
Tracks: / I will / Like I've never been gone / Last night was made for love / I'm lost without you / When will you say 'I love you'? / Run to my lovin' arms / It's only make believe / Maybe tomorrow / In thoughts of you / Give me your word / That's love / Once upon a dream / Colette / Wondrous place / Thousand stars, A / I'd never find another you / Fool's errand / Jealousy / Somebody else's girl / Halfway to Paradise.
LP: . . . . NE 1227
MC: . . . . CE 2227

MISSING YEARS (1967-1980), THE.
Tracks: / Wondrous place / She loves somebody / Paper aeroplanes / Do my best for you / Spider and the fly, The / Silly boy blue / Fascinating candle flame / I saw the light / Bye bye / Hurtin' is loving / Lady / I call for my Rose / Let me go my way / It just don't matter now / Break my heart in two.
LP: . . . . BUSLP 1003
MC: . . . . ZCBUS 1003

ONLY ONE, THE.
Tracks: / Be mine tonight / No trespassers / Love or money / Love sweet love / Let me go, lover / Devil or angel / Don't tell me lies / Deborah / This little girl of mine / I'm telling you / Someday.
LP: . . . . POLD 5069
MC: . . . . POLDC 5069

SOUND OF FURY, THE.
Tracks: / That's love / My advice / Phone call / You don't know] / Turn my back on you / Don't say it's over / Since you've been gone / It's you I need / Alright goodbye / Don't leave me this way.
LP: . . . . LF 1329

STICKS AND STONES.
Tracks: / Sticks and stones / Driving nicely / Going back to Germany / Certain things / Any morning now / Come outside and play / Baby get yourself together / I'll go along with it / Easy living / Day by day / Dreaming of St Louis / Phonebox.
LP: . . . . MFLP 2029

WE WANT BILLY! (Fury, Billy & The Tornados).
Tracks: / Sweet little sixteen / Baby come on / That's alright / Wedding bells / Sticks and stones / Unchain my heart / I'm movin' on / Just because / Halfway to Paradise / I'll never find another you / Once upon a dream / Last night was made for love / Like I've never been gone / When will you say 'I love you'?.
LP: . . . . TAB 62
MC: . . . . KTBC 62
LP: . . . . LK 4548

WORLD OF BILLY FURY, VOL.1.
Tracks: / Halfway to Paradise / Because of love / In summer / Nobody's child / Thousand stars, A / Magic eyes / I'd never find another you / Last night was made for love / Like I've never been gone / Once upon a dream / Push push / Letter full of tears.
LP: . . . . SPA 575
MC: . . . . KCSP 575

WORLD OF BILLY FURY, VOL.2.
Tracks: / Je.lousy / Do you really love me too? / C..lette / If I lose you / This diamond ring / I'm lost without you / I will / Play it cool / Twist kid, The / Somebody else's girl / I've got a horse / Give me your word / I'll never quite get over you / Run to my lovin' arms.
MC: . . . . KCSP 188
LP: . . . . SPA 188

Fury (Film)

FURY, THE (Various artists).
Tracks: / Fury, The (the main title): *Various artists* / Vision on the stairs: *Various artists* / Gillian's escape: *Various artists* / Death on the carousel: *Various artists* / For Gillian: *Various artists* / Hester's theme and the house,: *Various artists* / Search for Robin, The: *Various artists* / Gillian's vision: *Various artists* / Fury, The (end titles): *Various artists* / Epilogue: *Various artists.*
MC: . . . . VSC 5264

Furyo

FURYO.
Tracks: / Gold of our loves / Vultures / In the arena / Monster of a thousand / Opera in the air.
LP: . . . . GRAM 12

Fuse

FUSE II - WORLD DANCE MUSIC (Various artists).
LP: . . . . NR 0005L

FUSE - WORLD DANCE MUSIC (Various artists).
Tracks: / Yassassin (wild assassin mix): *Harrow, David* / Encantador: *I Loca!* / Radio morocco: *Pulse 8*/ Teus quay ana: *Paradise* / Jihad: *Mahatma T* / Ah kudia: *Sapna* / Shanti: *Mahatma T* / O'dhe o'dhe: *Sapna.*
LP: . . . . NR 0001L

Fuse One

FUSE ONE (Various artists).
Tracks: / Grand prix: *Various artists* / Waterside: *Various artists* / Sunshine lady: *Various artists*/ To whom all things concern: *Various artists* / Double steal: *Various artists* / Friendship: *Various artists*/ Taxi blues: *Various artists.*
LP: 2406 012

FUSE ONE - THE COMPLETE RECORDINGS (Various artists).
MC: . . . . CIJD 40140F

SILK.
Tracks: / Silk / In celebration of the human spirit / Sunwalk / Hot fire.
LP: . . . . CTI 9006

Future Shock

FUTURE SHOCK (Various artists).
Tracks: / Move in rhythm: *Various artists* / Sympathy (don't be taken in): *Various artists* / You're without sound: *Various artists* / Human factor, The: *Various artists* / Shangri-la: *Various artists* / Head in the clouds: *Various artists* / Choreography: *Various artists* / Them or me: *Various artists* / True colours: *Various* artists / Where have I seen you: *Various artists* / After-image: *Various artists* / Gimmick: *Various* artists / I don't know: *Various artists* / Hey disco Joe: *Various artists* / Immortal in mirrors: *Various artists* / T.V. me: *Various artists.*
LP: . . . . THBL 012

Future Tense

FUTURE TENSE (Various artists).
LP: . . . . TMLP 15

Future World Moves

VOICE OF AUTUMN.
LP: . . . . FWM 001

Futurism & Dada...

FUTURISM & DADA REVIEWED (Various artists).
LP: . . . . SUB 33014 19

Fuzzbox

BIG BANG.
Tracks: / Pink sunshine / Jamaican sunrise / Versatile for discos and parties / Self / Do you know / Fast forward futurama / Walking on thin ice / International rescue / Irish bride / Beauty.
LP: . . . . WX 282
MC: . . . . WX 282C

Fuzztones

CREATURES THAT TIME FORGET.
LP: . . . . MMLP 020

IN HEAT.
Tracks: / In heat / Chedenne rider / Black box / It came in the mail / Heathen set / What you don't know / Nine months later / Everything you got / Shame on you / Me Tarzan, you Jane / Hurt on hold / Charlotte's remains.
LP: . . . . SITU 23
MC: . . . . SITUC 23

LEAVE YOUR MIND AT HOME-LIVE.
LP: . . . . MIRLP 105

LIVE IN EUROPE.
LP: . . . . MMLP 006

LYSERGIC EMANATIONS.
Tracks: / 1-2-5 / Gotta get some / Ward 81 / Radar eyes / Cinderella / Highway 69 / Just once / Living sickness / She's wicked.
LP: . . . . ABCLP 4
LPPD: . . . . ABCLP 4P

Fuzzy Mountain String

FUZZY MOUNTAIN STRING BAND.
LP: . . . . ROUNDER 0010

SUMMER OAKS AND PORCH.
LP: . . . . ROUNDER 0035

F.X. (film)

F/X: MURDER BY ILLUSION (Original soundtrack) (Various artists).
LP: . . . . STV 81276
MC: . . . . CTV 81276

Fyfe, Will

12 & A TANNER A BOTTLE.
MC: . . . . SEV 12

Fylde Coast Jazzmen

RUNNING WILD.
Tracks: / Indiana / Big butter and egg man / In a mellow tone / Royal Garden blues / Bourbon Street parade / Mood indigo / Running wild / Doctor Jazz / Tiger rag.
LP: . . . . FHR 088

G

G A'S

EMOTIONAL WARFARE.
Tracks: / Devastated / Outside / Possessions / Finger / Love bites / Losing my patience / Definitely a lie / Wasted passion / Burning inside / Treatment.
LP: . . . . POLS 1052

IS IT GOOD TO YOU.
LP: . . . . EXLP 3

G. Band

PARIS MATCH.
Tracks: / Love street / Lay your love on me / I really didn't love her at all / She was alright / Hard to settle down / Almost American / It's alright / You never walk out on your baby / Look what you've been missing / Sympathy for the devil.
LP: . . . . CBS 81717

Gaberlunzie

FREEDOM'S SWORD.
Tracks: / Freedom's sword / Dainty Davie / Johnny Cope / Jamie Allen / Cam ye o'er frae France / Schiehallion / Duncrievie / Lassie wi the yellow coatie / Rattlin' roarin' Willie / Bannockburn / Kismuil's galley / Boys from Blue Hill / Parcels of rogues / Scotland will rise again / Great white sheep, The / Busk busk bonnie lassie / Gaberlunzie man, The.
LP: . . . . LOCLP 1005
MC: . . . . ZCLOC 1005

HIGHLAND LINES.
MC: . . . . ZCLOC 1056

LEGENDS OF SCOTLAND.
MC: . . . . ZCCLS 710

SCOTLAND AGAIN.
Tracks: / Scotland tomorrow / Massacre of Glencoe / Glasgow Dan / Edmonton Scottish / Gypsy rover, The / Follow the blackbird / Morning song / Band played waltzing Matilda, The / Happy hooligans / Glenfarg bull / Scotland again.
LP: . . . . KLP 12
MC: . . . . ZCKLP 12

SCOTS WHA'HAE.
MC: . . . . ZCLOC 1043

SUPERSTITION.
Tracks: / Superstition / Barnyards of Delgaty / Menzies tree / Willie John McMenemy / Ye banks and braes / Don't bury me before the battle / Haughs o' Cromdale / Auld folk, The / Cam ye by Atholl / Bonnie Dundee / Spirit of the eagle / Bonnie Argylls, The / Leaving Loch Broom.
LP: . . . . KLP 34

TAKE THE ROAD.
Tracks: / Smuggler's road / Witch / Jackson's bottle of claret / Rakes of kildare / Drunken piper / Bottom of the punchbowl / Pheasants cock / Humours of cleish / '45 / Black Jack Davy / Auld man of benarty.
LP: . . . . KLP 50

TRAVELLING MAN, THE.
Tracks: / Twa recruiting sergeants / Bonnie lass o' Fyvie / Pear tree, The / Follow the ploo / Donnie Macphail / Broom o'the Cowdenknowes / Sam the skull / Hercules the bear / Blind Angus of the hill / Air fa la la la lo / Burghead sands / Scotland owns me / Exile, The / Long distance travelling man.
LP: . . . . KLP 22
MC: . . . . ZCKLP 22

WIND AND WATER, TIME AND TIDE.
Tracks: / Mormond braes / Kishorn commandos / Back o' beyond / Morris's march / Weavers, The / Sleepy toon / This land is your land / Men from the rigs / Bodie's bonny bell / Come by the hills / Remember John Maclean / Kissing in the dark / Muckin' o' Geordie's byre / Tarry arry arry / Lion on the gold.
LP: . . . . KLP 45
MC: . . . . ZCKLP 45

Gable, Bill

THERE WERE SIGNS.
Tracks: / Go ahead and run / Who becomes the slave / All the posters come down / Three levels of Nigeria, The / Cape Horn / High trapeze / There were signs / Letting the jungle in / Leaving Venice to the rain.
LP: 209 759
MC: 409 759

Gable, Eric

CAUGHT IN THE ACT.
LP: D1 75603

Gabor, B.B.

B.B.GABOR.
Tracks: / Metropolitan life / Consumer / Soviet jewelry / Laser love / All the time / Moscow drug club / Underground world / Hunger, poverty and misery / Ooh mama / Big yellow taxi.
LP: . . . . BLUP 5004

Gabriel, Peter

BIRDY (Film soundtrack).
Tracks: / At night / Floating dogs / Quiet and alone / Close up (from 'Family snapshot') / Slow water / Dressing the wound / Birdy's flight (from 'Not one of us') / Slow marimbas / Heat, The (from 'Rhythm of the heat') / Sketchpad with trumpet and voice / Under lock and key (from 'Wallflower') / Powerhouse at the foot of the mountain (from 'San Jacinto').
LP: . . . . CAS 1167
MC: . . . . CASMC 1167
LP: . . . . OVED 283
MC: . . . . OVEDC 283

MUSIC AND MEDIA INTERVIEW PICTURE DISC.
LPPD: . . . . PG 1014

PASSION (Music for the Last Temptation Of Christ).
Tracks: / Feeling begins, The / Gethsemane / Of these, hope / Lazarus raised / Of these hope (reprise) / In doubt / Different drum, A / Zaar / Troubled / Open / Before night falls / With this love / Sandstorm / Stigmata / Passion / Disturbed / With this love / It is accomplished / Wall of breath / Promise of shadows / Bread and wine.
2LP: . . . . RWLP 1
MC: . . . . RWMC 1

PETER GABRIEL 1.
Tracks: / Moribund the burgermeister / Solsbury Hill / Modern love / Excuse me / Humdrum / Slowburn / Waiting for the big one / Down the dolce vita / Here comes the flood.
LP: . . . . CHC 39
MC: . . . . CHCMC 39

PETER GABRIEL 1/PETER GABRIEL 2.
Tracks: / Moribund the burgermeister / Solsbury Hill / Modern love / Excuse me / Humdrum / Slowburn / Waiting for the big one / Down the dolce vita / Here comes the flood / On the air / D.I.Y. / Mother of violence / Wonderful day in a one-way world, A / White shadow / Indigo / Animal magic / Exposure / Flotsam and jetsam / Prospective / Home sweet home.
MCSET: . . . . CASMC 102

PETER GABRIEL 2.
Tracks: / On the air / D.I.Y. / Mother of violence / Wonderful day in a one-way world, A / White shadow / Indigo / Animal magic / Exposure / Flotsam and jetsam / Perspective / Home sweet home.
LP: . . . . CHC 24
MC: . . . . CHCMC 24

PETER GABRIEL 3.
Tracks: / Intruder / No self control / I don't remember / Family snapshot / And through the wire / Games without frontiers / Not one of us / Lead a normal life / Biko.
LP: . . . . CDS 4019
MC: . . . . CDSMC 4019

PETER GABRIEL 4.
Tracks: / Rhythm of the heat, The / San Jacinto / I have the touch / Family and the fishing net, The / Shock the monkey / Lay your hands on me / Wallflower / Kiss of life.
LP: . . . . PG 4
MC: . . . . PGMC 4

PETER GABRIEL: INTERVIEW PICTURE DISC.
LPPD: . . . . BAK 2015

PLAYS LIVE.
Tracks: / San Jacinto / Solsbury hill / No self control / Shock the monkey / I don't remember / Humdrum / On the air / Biko / Rhythm of the heat, The / I have the touch / Not one of us / Family snapshot / D.I.Y. / Family and the fishing net, The / Intruder / I go swimming.
2LP: . . . . PGDL 1
MCSET: . . . . PGDMC 1

SO.
Tracks: / Red rain / Sledgehammer / Don't give up / That voice again / In your eyes / Mercy street / Big time / We do what we're told (Milgram's 37) / This is the picture (excellent birds) (CD & cassette only).
LP: . . . . PG 5
MC: . . . . PGMC 5

Gabusi Ensemble

LES, COMORES (Ensemble Gabusi Des Iles).
Tracks: / Tari / Gabusi / Sambe / Ndzedze / Debe / Firimbi / Danse Biyaya / Chigoma / Yimbiyo / Nkandza.
LP: . . . . ARN 33769
MC: . . . . ARN 433769

Gad, Pablo

HARD TIMES.
LP: . . . . FORM 1099

TRAFALGAR SQUARE.
LP: . . . . BS 1038

Gadd Gang

HERE AND NOW.
Tracks: / I can't turn you loose / My girl / Them changes / Soul serenade / Things ain't what they used to be / Che ore so / Signed, sealed, delivered (I'm yours) / Whiter shade of pale, A.
LP: 4610011
MC: 4610014

Gadd, Steve

GADDABOUT.
Tracks: / Gaddabout / My little brother / Montauk moon / Duke, The / Lucky 13 / Leavin' tomorrow.
LP: . . . . K 28P 6314

Gaddis, Mark

POINT OF REFUGE.
Tracks: / Keeper / Can't find a reason / Say you'll stay / Black and white / When love says no / It's love that I feel / Drift away / Point of refuge / Don't go looking for love / Silhouette of darkness.
LP: . . . . OV 1741

Gaddy, Bob

BICYCLE BOOGIE.
LP: . . . . BLP 109

RIPPING AND RUNNING WITH.
Tracks: / Come on little children / Operator / I love my baby / Rip and run / Woe woe is me / What would I do / Paper lady / Out of my name / I'll go my way / Things that I used to do / What wrong did I do / Girl who promises / Forgive me / Take my advice / Stormy Monday blues / Till the day I die.
LP: . . . . CH 164

Gadfly (film)

GADFLY, THE (Film soundtrack) (Various artists).
Tracks: / Gadfly, The: Overture: *Various artists* / Contradance: *Various artists* / National holiday: *Various* artists / Gadfly, The: Prelude and waltz: *Various artists* / Galop: *Various artists* / Gadfly, The: Introduction into the dance: *Various artists* / Romance: *Various artists* / Gadfly, The: Interlude: *Various artists*/ Nocturne: *Various artists* / Scene: *Various artists* / Gadfly, The: Finale: *Various artists.*
LP: . . . . CFP 4144631
MC: . . . . CFP 4144634

Gadgets

BLUE ALBUM, THE.
LP: . . . . PLASLP 16
LP: . . . . GLALP 006
MC: . . . . GLAMC 006

FRUIT OF AKELDAMA.
LP: . . . . PLASLP 007

GADGETREE.
LP: . . . . PLASLP 013

INFANTREE/FRUITS OF AKELDAMA.
LP: . . . . PLASLP 012

LOVE, CURIOSITY, FRECKLES AND DOUBT.
LP: . . . . PLASLP 014

Gadney, Reg

FAVOURITE COUNTRY LOVE SONGS.
MC: . . . . BBM 113

Gaelforce Orchestra

FROM HIGHLANDS TO LOWLANDS.
Tracks: / Maciain of Glencoe / Dream Angus / Ca' the ewes / Crimond / Green grow the rushes-o / Mingulay boat song, The / Aye waukin' o / Queen's Maries, The / Mo mathair (my mother) / Bluebells of Scotland / Jock O'Hazeldean / Cradle song / Proud lion rampant, The / Old Scots songs, The.
LP: . . . . LILP 5191

FROM THE GREEN ISLAND TO THE LAND OF THE EAGLE.
Tracks: / Green Island / Pat Murphy's meadow / Meeting of the waters, The / After all these years / Rose of Tralee, The / My cavan girl / Danny boy / Song for Ireland / Boolavogue / Flight of Earls / Little grey home in the west / Banks of my own lovely Lee, The / Green glens of Antrim / Shores of Americay, The.
LP: . . . . LILP 3004

PLAY THE MELODIES OF IRELAND.
Tracks: / Galway bay / Fields of Athenry / Town I loved so well, The / Rose of Mooncoin / Slievenamon / Mountains of Mourne / Molly Malone / Carrickfergus / She moved through the fair / Mary from Dungloe / Rare aul' times, The / Spancil Hill.
LP: . . . . LRIR 3001
MC: . . . . LRIC 3001

PLAY THE MELODIES OF SCOTLAND.
Tracks: / Dark Lochnagar / Ye banks and braes / Mary of Argyll / Dark island / Dumbarton's drums / Amazing grace / Flower of Scotland / Scots wha' hae / Old rustic bridge / Always Argyll / Rowan tree / Will ye no' come back again / Down in the glen / My ain folk / An eriskay love lilt / Farewell my love (Only on CD.).
LP: . . . . LILP 5153
MC: . . . . LICS 5153
LP: . . . . LDOM 9010

SCOTLAND AGAIN.
Tracks: / Skye boat song / Loch Lomond / Westering home / Red red rose / Glencoe / Flowers of the forest / Mull of Kintyre / Bonnie lass O'Ballochmyle / Scotland again / Star o' Rabbie Burns, The / Annie Laurie / Man's a man, A / Auld lang syne.
LP: . . . . LILP 5169
MC: . . . . LICS 5169

SCOTLAND FOREVER.
Tracks: / Scotland forever / Loch tay boat song / Calling me home / Scotland for me / Ae fond kiss / Culloden / John Anderson, my Jo / Highland cathedral / Mull of the cool bens / Bonnie Galloway / Scotland my home / Flower o' the quern / Land for all seasons, A / Scotland yet.
LP: . . . . LILP 5179
MC: . . . . LICS 5179

Gaetano

100% ZOUK.
LP: . . . . LA 9003

Gagnon, Andre

IMAGINATION.
Tracks: / Endless rest / Unforgettable / Flashback / Wow / Nelligan / Snow on Kamouraska / Ta samba / Raindrops on my window.
LP: . . . . PFS 4384

Gaiety Orchestra

MAGIC OF VIENNA.
LP: . . . . NSPH 6

Gaillard, Slim

ANYTIME, ANYPLACE, ANYWHERE.
Tracks: / How high the moon / Anytime, anyplace, anywhere / I can't get started / Slim's jam No.2 / Everything's OK in the UK / Music goes round and around, The / Satin doll / Honeysuckle rose.
LP: . . . . HEP 2020

AT BIRDLAND: SLIM GAILLARD.
Tracks: / Flat foot floosie No 1 / Cement mixer / Imagination / Sabroso / Flat foot floosie No 2 / Lady be good / Fine and dandy / Serenade in sulpher / Serenade in vout.
LP: . . . . HEP 21

CEMENT MIXER PUT-TI PUT-TI.
LP: . . . . FL 9038

CHICKEN RHYTHM VOL.2.
LP: . . . . OFF 3055

LAUGHING IN RHYTHM, 1945-51.

LP: . . . . OFF 3050

OPERA IN VOUT.
LP: 2304 554

ROOTS OF VOUTY.
Tracks: / Slim's jam / I don't know why / Dizzy boogie / School kids' hop / Poppity pop / Chicken rhythm / Riff City / Mean mama blues / Peanut vendor / Mean pretty mama / Santa Monica jump.
LP: . . . . PUT 01

SLIM GAILLARD, HELEN HUMES & WILD BILL MOORE (Gaillard, Slim/ Helen Humes/Wild Bill Moore).
LP: . . . . SJL 2242

TUTTI FRUTTI.
LP: . . . . ST 1018
MC: . . . . SC 1018

VOUTEST, THE.
Tracks: / Tee say malee / Gaillard special / Dynamite / Yep roc heresy / Poppity pop / Gaillard special no. 2 / Bow tie Jim / Eastwood, Voutwood / Ya ha ya / Dunkin bagel / Laguna / Gaillard special no. 3 / Cement mixer.
LP: . . . . HEP 28

Gailmor, Jon

DIRT.
LP: . . . . PH 1092

Gainen, Maury

JAZZ SUNRISE.
Tracks: / Jazz sunrise / To the sea / In a sentimental mood / Out of the night came you / Night has a thousand eyes, The / Three for Bob / Little Linda / Mr. Wind / Spring can really hang you up the most.
LP: . . . . DS 855

Gaines, Earl

YEARNING AND BURNING.
Tracks: / Certain girl, A / I'll take care of you / If you want what I got / Been so long / Taking all the love I can / Trust in me / Keep your mind on me / Turn on your lovelight / Hymn no. 5 / Nine pound steel / It takes you / I can't face it / Thats how strong my love is / Since i've lost you / Yearning and burning / You're the one.
LP: . . . . CRB 1142

Gaines, Grady

FULL GAIN w. Roy Gaines (Gaines, Grady & The Texas Upsetters).
Tracks: / Mr Blues in the sky / I've been out there / If I don't get involved / Full gain / Shaggy dog / Soul twist / If I loved you a little less / Your girlfriend / Stealing love / There is something on your mind / Gangster of the blues / Miss Lucy Brown.
LP: . . . . BT 1041
MC: . . . . BT 1041C
LP: . . . . FIEND 148
MC: . . . . FIENDCASS 148

Gaines, Roy

GAINELINING.
Tracks: / First rule of cheating / Lowdown and funky / Baby, what you want me to do? / It's too late, brother / It came on time / Hell of a night tonight / Houston, Texas / Short-haired woman / Roy's new 6 am 3 o'clock blues / Okie dokie stomp.
LP: . . . . RL 035

Gaines, Steve

ONE IN THE SUN.
Tracks: / Give it to get it / It's alright / Black jack David / On the road / One in the sun / Talkin' about love / Nothin' is now / Take my time / Summertime's here.
LP: . . . . WKFMLP 136
MC: . . . . WKFMMC 136

Gainsbourg, Serge

AUX ARMES ET CAETERA.
Tracks: / Javanaise remake / Aux armes et caetera / Les locataires / Des laids des laids / Brigade des stups / Vielle canaille / Lola Rastaquouere / Relax baby be cool / Daisy Temple / Eau et gaz a tous les etages / Pas long feu / Marilou reggae dub.
LP: . . . . ILPS 9581

JE T'AIME MOI NON PLUS.
LP: . . . . DN 2002

Gaither, Bill

20 BEST-LOVED GOSPEL SONGS: BILL GAITHER (Gaither, Bill Trio).
Tracks: / He touched me / Get all excited / Rejoice, you're a child of the King / My faith still holds / Thank God for the promise of spring / Longer I serve Him, The / It's no wonder / I came to praise the Lord / Plenty of room in the family / Blessed Jesus / I could never out-love the Lord / God gave the song / That's what Jesus means to me / Walk on the water / Resurrection morn / Contented / Waters are troubled, The / All my hopes / I believe what the Bible says / I believe it.
LP: . . . . PC 321

BLESS THE LORD WHO REIGNS IN BEAUTY.
Tracks: / Perfect heart, A / Lord is my light, The / I have decided / Sanctus / Majesty / Yes / Right place, right time / God hath provided a Lamb / Resurrection / I then shall live.
LP: . . . . WST 9617
MC: . . . . WC 9617

ESPECIALLY FOR CHILDREN (Gaither, Bill Trio).
Tracks: / Hello / I've got a friend / I wonder how it felt / God can / You're something special / Sing with us / Jesus loves the little children / I'd like to teach the world to sing / Only a boy named David / Shadrach, Meshach and Abednego / All night, all day / Safe am I / God is watching over you / This little light of mine / God thought of everything / That's him / Sunday school song parade / Everybody ought to go to Sunday school / Heavenly sunshine / Be careful, little hands, what you do / Happy day express, The / I have the joy / A-B-C-D-E-F-G / For God so loved the world / Oh how I love Jesus / Into my heart.
LP: . . . . PC 779

HE TOUCHED ME (Gaither, Bill Trio).
Tracks: / He touched me / I will serve Thee / Longer I serve Him, The / Broken pieces / All my hopes / I believe it / He was there every time / One of those days / It's no wonder / Now I have everything / I believe what the Bible says.
LP: . . . . PC 737

LEROY'S BUDDY 1935-41.
LP: . . . . PY 1804
LP: . . . . DLP 508

LEROY'S BUDDY 1936-39.
Tracks: / Pins & needles / Curbstone blues / Too many women / Gravel in my bed / I just keep on worryin' / Another big leg woman.
MC: . . . . NEO 852

LIVE ACROSS AMERICA (Gaither, Bill Trio).
Tracks: / Praise for the Lord / Feeling at home in the presence of the Lord / Let's just praise the Lord / This is the time I must sing / Something beautiful / I just feel that something good is about to happen / Difference is in me, The / Tell it to a few close friends / We are persuaded / Things I must tell the children / Because He lives / Praise you / Precious Jesus / I am loved / Your first day in Heaven / Rejoice, you're a child of the King / Plenty of room in the family / Family of God, The / He touched me / Old rugged cross made the difference, The / I believe in a hill called Mount Calvary / Get all excited / Church triumphant, The / It is finished.
LP: . . . . WSX 9605
MC: . . . . WC 9605

VERY BEST OF THE VERY BEST (Gaither, Bill Trio).
Tracks: / I am loved / There's something about that name / Joy comes in the morning / Plenty of room in the family / Family of God, The / Church triumphant, The / God gave the song / He touched me / I am a promise / I will serve thee / Jesus is Lord / King is coming.
LP: . . . . WST 9592
MC: . . . . WC 9592

WE ARE PERSUADED (Gaither, Bill Trio).
Tracks: / We are persuaded / Praise you / I do believe / My father's angels / Seek and you shall find / Because He lives / All the time / Heavens declare the glory of God, The / Two prayers / I will go on.
LP: . . . . WST 9599
MC: . . . . WC 9599

Gaizmauskas, Yurgis

RUSSIAN SONGS & DANCES (YURGIS GAIZMAUSKAS).
MC: . . . . SM 00144

Gala Performance

FORTY GALA PERFORMANCES (Various artists).
2LP: . . . . PLD 8006

GALA PERFORMANCE (Various artists).
LP: . . . . PLE 7005

Galactic Cowboys

GALACTIC COWBOYS.
LP: . . . . DGC 24324
MC: . . . . DGCC 24324

Galante, Marie

BAN BOU LA.
LP: . . . . PV 9396

Galas, Diamanda

DIVINE PUNISHMENT, THE.
LP: . . . . STUMM 27

LITANIES OF SATAN.
LP: . . . . ISO 001

SAINT OF THE PIT.
LP: . . . . STUMM 33

YOU MUST BE CERTAIN OF THE DEVIL.
Tracks: / Swing low sweet chariot / Let's not chat about despair / You must be certain of the devil / Malediction / Double barrel prayer / Birds of death / Let my people go / Lord's my shepherd, The.
LP: . . . . STUMM 46

Galaxie 500

ON FIRE.
LP: . . . . ROUGH 146
MC: . . . . ROUGHC 146

THIS IS OUR MUSIC.
LP: . . . . ROUGH 156
MC: . . . . ROUGHC 156

TODAY.
Tracks: / Flowers / Pictures / Parking lot / Don't let our youth go to waist / Temperature's rising / Oblivious / It's getting late / Instrumental / Tugboat / King of Spain (CD only.) / Crazy (CD only.).
LP: . . . . AU 002
LP: . . . . M 8905

Galbraith, Art

ART GALBRAITH.
LP: . . . . ROUNDER 0133

SIMPLE PLEASURES.
LP: . . . . ROUNDER 0157

Galbraith, Charlie

PORTRAIT OF CHARLIE GALBRAITH.
Tracks: / Jeepers creepers / Lover come back to me / Days of wine and roses / I surrender dear / Limehouse blues / Stars fell on Alabama / I'll remember April / Struttin' with some barbeque.
LP: . . . . PLR 006

Gale, Arlyn

BACK TO THE MIDWEST NIGHT.
Tracks: / Back to the midwest night / Take the night flight / Tiger on the lawn / Sunrise on sunset / Ronee / Suspicious fires / She's alright / Halfway to hell.
LP: . . . . ABCL 5216

Gale, Eric

BEST OF ERIC GALE.
Tracks: / Ginseng woman / Let me slip it to you / Multiplication / Trio / De rabbit / Lookin' good / Red ground / Oh Mary don't you weep.
LP: . . . . CBS 84201

BLUE HORIZON.
Tracks: / Blue horizon / Wait until the city sleeps / When Tokyo / Mako d'amour / Clock a pa / Call me at the same number / 97th and Columbus.
LP: . . . . K 52349

ISLAND BREEZE.
Tracks: / Boardwalk / We'll make it / My momma told me so / Island breeze / I know that's right.
LP: 9601981

PART OF YOU.
Tracks: / Lookin' good / Nesumi / Holding on to love / Let me slip it to you / Lookin' good / Trio.
LP: . . . . CBS 83464
MC: 40 83464

TOUCH OF SILK.
Tracks: / You got your life in my hands / Touch of silk / War paint / Once in a smile / With you I'm born again / Au privave / Lie to love.
LP: . . . . CBS 84509
MC: 40 84509

Gale, Warren

BEBOP AND BEYOND.
Tracks: / Longhorn / On a misty night / Moon Magic / Super trouper / Evidence / Monk's mood / One for all.
LP: . . . . CJ 244

Gale, Wilson & Co

GIFT WRAPPED.
MC: . . . . JETCA 223
LP: . . . . JETLP 223

Galica, Divina

FIT TO SKI.
MC: . . . . MCFR 103

PREHISTORIC SCANDINAVIA.
LP: 136 1031

SONGS AND DANCES OF EASTERN INDIANS.
LP: . . . . NW 337

TURTLE DANCE SONGS.
LP: . . . . NW 310

Galileo (film)

GALILEO/ESCALATION (Film soundtrack) (Various artists).
LP: . . . . RP 017

Galimir Quartet

RAVEL (see under Debussy).

Gall, France

BABACAR.
Tracks: / Papillo de nuit / Babacar / Ella elle l'a / La chasons d'azima / C'est ba que tu sois la / Dancing brave / J'irai ou tu iras / Evidemment / Urgent d'attendre.
LP: 2420961
MC: 2420964

TOUR DE FRANCE.
Tracks: / Urgent d'attendre / Amor tambien / Evidemment / Big fat mama / Debranche / Il jouait du piano debout / Hong Kong star / J'irai ou tu iras / Resiste.
LP: 2442141
MC: 2442144

Gallagher, Brian

COMING HOME.
LP: . . . . YL 0126

Gallagher, Bridie

GIRL FROM DONEGAL.
Tracks: / Girl from Donegal / Take this message darling / Two little orphans / Goodbye Johnny / My mother's last goodbye / Irish jaunting car / My lovely Irish Rose / When will you marry me Johnny / Tumbledown shack in Athlone / Faithful Sailor boy, the / Killarney and you / Road by the river / Hills of Donegal / I'll forgive but I'll never forget / Boys from County Armagh / Rose of Kilkenny / Lovely Derry on the banks of the Folye / Cottage by the lee / Homes of Donegal.
MC: . . . . 4 HOM 002

LIGHTS OF HOME, THE.
MC: . . . . CWGR 113

TODAY.
LP: . . . . RBA 107

Gallagher & Lyle

BREAKAWAY.
Tracks: / Breakaway / Stay young / I wanna stay with you / Heart on my sleeve / Fifteen summers / Sign of the times / If I needed someone / Storm in my soul / Rockwriter / Northern girl.
LP: . . . . AMLH 68348
MC: . . . . CAM 68348
LP: . . . . SPR 8545
MC: . . . . SPC 8545

GALLAGHER & LYLE.
Tracks: / Mrs. Canatelli's / City and surburban blues / Caledonia steam packet co. / To David, Charlie & Ian / Broken wings / Coat for the spring / Great Australian dream / Rock 'n' roll hero / Greenfingers / Comfort and joy / Of a moment / Desiderata.
LP: . . . . AMLS 68125

HEART ON MY SLEEVE (The Very Best Of).
LP: 3971231
MC: 3971234

LAST COWBOY.
Tracks: / Keep the candle burning / Song and dance man / Acne blues / I'm amazed / King of the silents / Rain / We / Mhairu / Villain of the peace / Last cowboy, The.
LP: . . . . AMLH 68237

LONESOME NO MORE.
Tracks: / Believed in you / Concrete and steel / Deja vu / Diamonds / Fool for your love / Lay me down and die / Let go / Mexico / Missing you / Partners / Wheels / Wide wide world.
LP: 9109628

LOVE ON THE AIRWAVES.
Tracks: / Love on the airwaves / Runaway / Every little teardrop / I had to fall in love / Street boys / Never give up on love / Dude in the dark / Head talk / Call for the captain / It only hurts when I laugh.
LP: . . . . AMLH 64620
LP: . . . . MFP 50497

WILLIE & THE LAP DOG.
Tracks: / Willie / Home / Give a boy a break / Sittin' down music / Among the birks / Jesus save me / S.S.Man / Hotel Constantine / Lap dog, The / Harmonium / Thoughts from a station.
LP: . . . . AMLS 68148

Gallagher, Rory

AGAINST THE GRAIN.
Tracks: / Let me in / Cross me off your list / Ain't too good / Souped up Ford / Bought and sold / I take what I want / Lost at sea / All around man / Out on the Western Plain / At the bottom.
LP: . . . . CHR 1098
MC: . . . . ZCHR 1098
LP: . . . . CLALP 233
MC: . . . . CLAMC 233

BEST OF RORY GALLAGHER AND TASTE (Gallagher, Rory & Taste).
Tracks: / Blister on the moon / Hail / Born on the wrong side of time / Dual

carriageway pain / Same old story / On the boards / See here / I'll remember / Sugar mama (Live) / Sinner boy (Live) / I feel so good (Live) / Catfish / I'm movin' on / What's going on / Railway and gun / Morning sun / Eat my words.
LP: . . . . MACH 10D

BLUEPRINT.
Tracks: / Walk on hot coals / Daughter of the Everglades / Banker's blues / Hands off / Race the breeze / Seventh son of a seventh son / Unmilitary two step / If I had a reason.
LP: . . . . CHR 1253
MC: . . . . ZCHR 1253
LP: 2383-189

CALLING CARD.
Tracks: / Do you read me / Country mile, A / Moonchild / Calling card / I'll admit your gone / Secret agent / Jacknife beat / Edged in blue / Barley and grape rag.
LP: . . . . CHR 1124
MC: . . . . ZCHR 1124
LP: . . . . ESSLP 143
MC: . . . . ESSMC 143

DEFENDER.
Tracks: / Kickback City / Loan shark blues / Continental op / I ain't no saint / Failsafe day / Road to hell / Doing time / Smear campaign / Don't start me to talkin' / Seven days / Seems to me (Available on CD and cassette only) / No peace for the wicked (Available on CD and cassette only).
LP: . . . . XFIEND 98
MC: . . . . FIENDCASS 98

DEUCE.
Tracks: / Used to be / I'm not awake / Don't know where I'm going / Maybe I will / Whole lot of people / In your town / Should've learnt my lesson / There's a light / Out of my mind / Crest of a wave.
MC: . . . . ZCHR 1254
LP: . . . . CHR 1254
LP: 2383-076

FRESH EVIDENCE.
LP: . . . . CAPOLP 14
MC: . . . . CAPOMC 14

IN THE BEGINNING (Vocal and guitar).
Tracks: / Wee wee baby / How many more years / Take it easy baby / You've go to pay / Worried man / Norman invasion / Pardon me mister.
LP: . . . . GES 1110

IRISH TOUR '74....
Tracks: / Cradle rock / I wonder who (who's gonna be your sweet man) / Tattoo'd lady / Too much alcohol / As the crow flies / Million miles away, A / Walk on hot coals / Whose that comin' / Stomping ground / Just a little bit.
2LP: . . . . CTY 1256
MCSET: . . . . ZCTY 1256
2LP: . . . . DFIEND 120
MCSET: . . . . FIENDCASS 120
2LP: 2659 031

JINX.
Tracks: / Big guns / Bourbon / Double vision / Devil made me do it, The / Hellcat / Signals / Jinxed / Easy come, easy go / Ride on red, ride on / Loose talk.
LP: . . . . FIEND 126
MC: . . . . FIENDCASS 126
LP: . . . . CHR 1359
MC: . . . . ZCHR 1359

LIVE IN EUROPE.
Tracks: / Messin' with the kids / Laundromat / I could've had religion / Pistol slapper blues / Going to my home town / In your town / Bullfrog blues.
LP: . . . . CHR 1257
MC: . . . . ZCHR 1257
LP: 2383-112

LIVE IN EUROPE/STAGE STRUCK.
Tracks: / Messin' with the kid / Laundromat / I could've had religion / Pistol slapper blues / Going to my home town / In your town / Bullfrog blues / Shinkicker / Wayward child / Brute force and ignorance / Moonchild / Follow me / Bought and sold / Last of the independants, The / Shadow play.
2LP: . . . . TFOLP 20
MC: . . . . TFOMC 20

PHOTO-FINISH.
Tracks: / Shin kicker / Brute force and ignorance / Cruise on out / Cloak and dagger / Overnight bag / Shadow play / Mississippi sheiks, The / Last of the independants, The / Fuel to the fire.
LP: . . . . CHR 1170
MC: . . . . ZCHR 1170

RORY GALLAGHER.
Tracks: / Laundromat / Just the smile / I fall apart / Wave myself goodbye / Hands up / Sinner boy / For the last time / It's you / I'm not surprised / Can't believe it's true.
LP: . . . . CHR 1258
MC: . . . . ZCHR 1258
LP: 2383-044

RORY GALLAGHER (PICKWICK).
Tracks: / Sinner boy / Crest of a wave / I fall apart / Used to be / I'm not awake yet / For the last time / There's a light / Don't know where I'm going / Just the smile / Hands up.
LP: . . . . SHM 3041
MC: . . . . HSC 3041

STAGE STRUCK.
Tracks: / Shin kicker / Wayward child / Brute force and ignorance / Moonchild / Follow me / Bought and sold / Last of the independants, The / Shadow play.
LP: . . . . CHR 1280
MC: . . . . ZCHR 1280

TATTOO.
Tracks: / Tattoo'd lady / Cradle rock / 20:20 vision / They don't make them like you any more / Livin' like a trucker / Sleep on a clothes-line / Who's that coming / Million miles away, A / Admit it.
MC: . . . . ZCHR 1259
LP: . . . . CHR 1259
LP: 2383 230

TATTOO/BLUEPRINT.
Tracks: / Tattoo'd lady / Cradle rock / 20:20 vision / They don't make them like you any more / Livin' like a trucker / Sleep on a clothes line / Who's that coming / Million miles away / Admit it / Walk on hot coals / Daughter of the Everglades / Banker's blues / Hands off / Race the breeze / Seventh son of a seventh son / Unmilitary two step / If I had a reason.
2LP: . . . . TFOLP 21
MC: . . . . TFOMC 21

TOP PRIORITY.
Tracks: / Follow me / Philby / Wayward child / Keychain / At the depot / Bad penny / Just hit town / Off the handle / Public enemy no.1.
LP: . . . . CHR 1235
LP: . . . . FIEND 123
MC: . . . . FIENDCASS 123
MC: . . . . ZCHR 1235

Gallant, Patsy

PATSY.
Tracks: / O Michel / It'll all come around / Slow down / Let me free your love / Best of the woman in me / Lost you to L.A. / Party baby / Te caliente / We'll find a way / Love affair.
LP: . . . . MLP 3004

Gallay, Jean F

DOUZE CAPRICE POUR COR.
LP: . . . . TWI 755

Gallery

GALLERY.
LP: . . . . ECM 1206

Galliano

IN PURSUIT OF THE 13TH NOTE.
LP: 8484931
MC: 8484934

Galliard Brass

CAROLS FOR BRASS.
Tracks: / Joy to the world / Rejoice and be merry (Gallery carol) / It came upon a midnight clear / O come, all ye faithful / Once in royal David's city / Deck the halls / Wexford carol, The / Ding dong merrily on high / Hosanna to the Son of David / Rejoice in the Lord always / Queum vidistis pastores / Boston and Judea / Puer natus in Bethlehem / Hodie Christus natus est / Hosanna to the Son of David / In dulci jubilo.
LP: . . . . DCA 527
MC: . . . . ZC QS 6035

Gallivan, Joe

EXPRESSION TO WINDS (Gallivan, Joe & Charles Austin).
LP: . . . . SB 6

Galloping Green

DUBLIN MILLENNIUM.
Tracks: / Calm before the storm / Long boats / Dubh Linn / Clontarf / Tailors hall / Liberties hornpipes / Arthur Guinness / Mine's a pint / Laochra / Millennium waltz / Dublin in shawls / Within a mile of Dublin / Dublin porter / Dublin reel.
LP: . . . . RGLP 8
MC: . . . . RGMC 8

Galloway, Jim

BOJANGLES.
LP: . . . . HEP 2008

METRO STOMPERS.
Tracks: / Blues my naughty sweetie gives to me.
LP: 4002

THOU SWELL (Galloway, Jim Quartet & Jay McShann).
Tracks: / Thou swell / Someone to watch over me / Wrap your troubles in dreams / Black butterfly / Sweet Sue / I've got the world on a string / Just a gigolo / Humoresque / I only have eyes for you.
LP: 4011

THREE IS COMPANY.
Tracks: / Minor drag / Lulu's back in town / Sunday morning / Buddy Bolden's blues / I'd climb the highest mountain / Let's get away from it all / Everything I've got.
LP: 2007

Galloway, Leata

NAKED TRUTH, THE.
Tracks: / With every beat of my heart / Fascination / Shades of blue / Heartache (don't discriminate) / Cry me a river / One of these nights / You'll never get to heaven / I'm scared of you / Naked truth, The.
LP: 4625821
MC: 4625824

Gallowglass Ceili Band

25TH ANNIVERSARY ALBUM.
LP: . . . . STAL 1042

GALLOWGLASS CEILI BAND.
Tracks: / Jackets green / Bold fejan man, The / Bridge of Athlone / Trip to the cottage / Kingston hornpipe, The / Flowers of Antrim / Humours of Tulla / Bird in the tree / Sailor's cravat, The / Garden of daisies, The / Down the brae / O'Brien of Arra / Johnny Cope / Sackow's jig / Lark on the strand, The / Father Kelly's reel / Showman's fancy.
MCSET: . . . . DTO 10009

IRISH DANCING TIME.
MC: . . . . CMCS 1024

OLD BOG ROAD, THE.
MC: . . . . CMCS 1027

WILD COLONIAL BOY.
LP: . . . . ERIN 201
MC: . . . . ERINC 201
LP: . . . . CMCS 1025

Gallow's Pole

GALLOW'S POLE.
LP: . . . . A 7886

Galper, Hal

IVORY FOREST.
LP: . . . . ENJA 3053

NATURALLY.
LP: . . . . BKH 529

NO METHOD (See under Goodwin, Bill) (Galper, Hal/ Bill Goodman/ Billy Peterson).

NOW HEAR THIS.
LP: . . . . ENJA 2090

PORTRAIT: HAL GALPER TRIO (Galper, Hal Trio).
Tracks: / After you've gone / Giant steps / In your own sweet way / I'll be seeing you / What is this thing called love / I didn't care / I should care.
LP: . . . . CJ 383

SPEAK WITH A SINGLE VOICE (Galper, Hal Quintet).
LP: . . . . ENJA 4006

WINDOWS (Galper, Hal & Lee Konitz).
LP: . . . . SCS 1057

Galsworthy, John

IN CHANCERY (Forsyte saga Pt.2) (Horden, Sir Michael).
MCSET: . . . . LFP 7250
MCSET: . . . . TCLFP 7250

MAN OF PROPERTY, THE (Forsyte saga) (Hordern, Sir Michael).
MCSET: . . . . LFP 41 7234 5
MCSET: . . . . LFP 7234

SILVER SPOON, THE Forsyte saga, The - vol. 5 (Jarvis, Martin (nar)).
MCSET: . . . . LFP 7397

SWAN SONG Forsyte saga vol. 6 (Jarvis, Martin (nar)).
MCSET: . . . . LFP 7427

TO LET (Forsyte saga pt.3) (Horden, Sir Michael).
MCSET: . . . . LFP 7292

WHITE MONKEY, THE Forsyte saga - part four (Jarvis, Martin (nar)).
MCSET: . . . . LFP 7367

Galt, John

ANNALS OF THE PARISH (Sheddon, John).
MCSET: . . . . COL 4505

Galway, James

ANNIE'S SONG.
MC: . . . . GK 60747

CHRISTMAS CAROL.
LP: . . . . RL 85888
MC: . . . . RK 85888

CORIGLIANO FLUTE CONCERTO.
LP: . . . . RL 86602
MC: . . . . RK 86602

ENCHANTED FOREST, THE (Melodies of Japan).
Tracks: / Enchanted forest / Lyrical shortpiece / Nakasendo (The old road) / Zui zui zukkorobashi (Children's play song) / Star children / Song of the deep forest (Improvisation) / Tokuyama lullaby / Hietsuki bushi (Love song) / Usuhiki uta (Song of the mill) / Love song / Echoes / Song of clay / Harukoma (Spring horse-dance) / Sakura (Cherry blossom) / Romantic world.
MC: . . . . RK 87893

EXCEPTIONAL TALENT OF..., THE.
Tracks: / Concerto for flute and orchestra no. 1 in G / Concerto for flute and orchestra no. 2 in D / Minuet and badinerie / Clair de lune / Syrinx / Little shepherd, The / Moto perpetuo op. 11 / Concerto in E major op. 8 / Spring (Four seasons) / Dance of the blessed spirits from Orpheus / Sonatina for flute and piano Opus 13 / Adagio.
2LP: . . . . PDA 077
MCSET: . . . . PDC 077

GREATEST HITS: JAMES GALWAY.
Tracks: / Annie's song / Thorn birds / Memory (from Cats) / Danny boy / Perhaps / Kanon in D / Pink panther, The / Sabre dance / Clair de lune.
LP: . . . . RL 87778
MC: . . . . RK 87778

IN THE PINK (Galway, James & Henry Mancini).
Tracks: / Pink panther / Thorn birds / Breakfast at Tiffany's / Penny whistle jig / Crazy world / Pie in the face polka / Baby elephant walk / Two for the road / Speedy Gonzales / Molly McGuires / Cameo for flute / Days of wine / Roses / Charade / Moon River.
LP: . . . . RL 85315
MC: . . . . RK 85315

JAMES GALWAY COLLECTION.
Tracks: / Annie's song / I started a joke / Sometimes when we touch / Song of the seashore / Cherry blossom time / Brian Boru's march / Belfast hornpipe / Le basque / Carnival is over, The / Clair de lune / Berceuse (Dolly suite) / I know now (From 'Robert & Elizabeth') / Consuelo's love theme / Schon rosemarin / Les millions d'arlequin / 'Suite of three pieces' Waltz from Op 16 / Hora staccato / Arrival of the Queen of Sheba, The / Pachelbel canon / Four season, winter slow movement, The / Minuet and Badinerie / Minute waltz / Tambourin / Flight of the bumble bee / Moto perpetuo op. 11 / Drifting dreaming / Dance of the Blessed Spirits from Orpheus / Scherzo from 'A Midsummer Nights Dream' / Fantaisie for flute and orchestra / Variations on a theme by Rossini.
2LP: . . . . STAR 2224
MC: . . . . STAC 2224

JAMES GALWAY PLAYS SONGS FOR ANNIE.
LP: . . . . RL 25163

JAMES GALWAY & THE CHIEFTANS IN IRELAND (Galway, James & Chieftans).
Tracks: / Roche's favourite / Down by the Sally Gardens / She moved through the fair / O'Carolan's concerto / Danny boy / Crowley's reel / Avondale / Up and about / Humours of Kilfenora / Carrickfergus.
LP: . . . . RL 85798
MC: . . . . RK 85798

MAGIC FLUTE OF JAMES GALWAY.
LP: LRL1 5131
MC: . . . . PK 70260

MAN WITH THE GOLDEN FLUTE.
LP: . . . . LRL 15127

MERCADANTE FLUTE CONCERTOS.
LP: . . . . RL 87703
MC: . . . . RK 87703

NOCTURNE.
Tracks: / Clair De Lune / Nocturne in E flat, Op.9 No.2 / Dreamers / Pan and the birds / Meditation / Berceuse (the firebird) / Berceuse (Dolly suite) / En bateau (petite suite) / Nocturne / Nocturne No.5 in B flat / Consolation No.3 / Morning - Peer Gynt suite No.1.
LP: . . . . RS 9012
MC: . . . . RK 9012

OVER THE SEA TO SKYE (Galway, James & Chieftans).
Tracks: / Carolan's quarrel with the landlady / Three hornpipes / Eugene Stratton / Banks, The / Arthur Seat / Over the sea to Skye / A slip and double jig / Cath cheim an fhia / Rowan tree, The / Bonnie Prince Charlie / Lilliburlero / Dark island / Skibbereen / Fanfare, A / Last rose of summer / Dance in the morning early / Three sea captains, The / Full of joy (Chinese folk tune) / Solo salutes (Finale).
LP: . . . . RL 60424
MC: . . . . RK 60424

PACHELBEL CANON, THE.
Tracks: / Pachelbel canon / I started a joke / Jamaican rhumba / I know now / 2,000 weeks / Carnival is over, The /

Rush theme / Molly on the shore / Waltzing Matilda / Silver stars are in the sky, The / Long white cloud, The / Thredbo suite / Sleigh ride to Thredbo / Air from the high mountain / Waiata poi.
LP: RCALP 6011
MC: RCAK 6011

PLAY SONGS FOR ANNIE.
Tracks: / Le basque / Bachianas brasileiras No.5 / Liebesfreud / Dolly-berceuse / Allegro (in an 18th century drawing room) / Annie's song / Tambourin / La plus que lente / Brian Boru's march / Belfast hornpipe / Spanish love song / Carmen fantasy.
LP: RL 70257
MC: RK 83061
LP: RL 83061

SERENADE.
MC: RK 60033
LP: RL 60033

SOMETIMES WHEN WE TOUCH (Galway, James & Cleo Laine).
Tracks: / Drifting dreaming / Title track / Play it again sam / Skylark / How where when? / Fluter's ball / Consuelo's love theme / Keep loving me / Anyone can whistle / Still was the night / Lo here the gentle lark / Like a sad song.
LP: RL 25296
LP: INTS 5229

SONGS OF THE SEASHORE.
Tracks: / Oboro Tsukiyo (misty moon night) / Hana (cherry blossom time) / Komorebi - Introduction (Sunlight shining through the trees) / Kojo no tsuki / Hamabe no uta / Itsuki no komoriuta (Lullaby) / Komorebi - coda (sunlight shining through the trees) / Aka tombo / Yoi mach igusa (the evening primrose) / Sakura-gai no uta (song of the seashore) / Farusato (my home land) / Habu n minato (The port of Habu) / Yashi No Mi (the coconut shell).
LP: NL 70117
MC: NK 70117
LP: INTS 5230
LP: RL 25253

SONGS OF THE SOUTHERN CROSS.
Tracks: / Waita poi / I started a joke / Jamaican rhumba / 2000 weeks / I know now / Waltzing Matilda / Molly on the shore / Carnival is over, The / Silver stars are in the sky / Long white cloud / Thredbo suite / Sleigh ride to Thredbo / Air from the high mountain / Rush (theme from).
LP: RL 25316

WAYWARD WIND, THE.
Tracks: / Homecoming / Don't it make my brown eyes blue / Duelin banjos / Shenandoah / Montana skies / Piper piper / Wayward wind / Winter sunset / Drifter / Smokey pines / Shaman (medicine man) dreams.
LP: PL 70118
MC: PK 70118
LP: RCALP 6053

Gambale, Frank

BRAVE NEW GUITAR.
LP: UNKNOWN

PRESENT FOR THE FUTURE.
LP: UNKNOWN

Gambetta, Beppe

DIALOGUES.
LP: HF 005

Gamble, Paddy

KILLEAVY'S PRIDE.
Tracks: / Killeavy's pride / Master McGrath / Cassie Stones / My heather belle / Banks of the sweet Dundee / Bonnie bunch of roses, The / Seven years I'm apprentice bound / Jack the charmer / When first to Armoy / Bonnie Kellswater.
LP: OAS 3011

Gambler

LOVE AND OTHER CRIMES.
Tracks: / Something crazy / It never felt like this / Even a loser / Dirty Susie / Double indemnity / Head hunter / She's my girl / Hotline / Life on the line / I put my love.
LP: AML 3010

TEENAGE MAGIC.
LP: AML 3005

Gambler (show)

GAMBLER,THE (Original London cast) (Various artists).
Tracks: / Get yer life: *Various artists* / Loach's song: *Various artists* / Horse race, The: *Various artists*/ Barmaid's song: *Various artists* / Ten thousand quid: *Various artists* / Lullaby: *Various artists* / Danny's song: *Various artists* / Greyhound race: *Various artists* / I've sailed through hell: *Various artists*/ Craps: *Various artists* / Easy: *Various artists* / Shaking in the shadows: *Various artists*.
LP: SCENE 3
MC: SCENEC 3

Game Set & Match (tv)

GAME SET AND MATCH (T.V. soundtrack) (Various artists).
LP: CHR 1692
MC: ZCHR 1692

Game Theory

BIG SHOT CHRONICLES.
LP: 3210 1

LOLITA NATION.
LP: 3280 1

TWO STEPS FROM THE MIDDLE AGES.
Tracks: / Room for one more, honey / What the whole world wants / Picture of agreeability / Amelia have you lost / Rolling with the moody girls / Wyoming / In a delorean / You drive / Leilian / Wish I could stand or have / Don't entertain me twice / Throwing the election / Initiations week.
LP: ENVLP 507
MC: TCENV 507

Gamil, Soliman

ANKH.
LP: TO 14

EGYPTIAN MUSIC.
LP: TO 7
LP: HNBL 1359
MC: HNBC 1359

Gamma

GAMMA 3.
Tracks: / What's gone is gone / Right the first time / Moving violation / Mobile devotion / Stranger / Condition yellow / Modern girl / No way out / Third degree.
LP: K 52355

GAMMA I.
Tracks: / Thunder and lightning / I'm alive / Razor king / No tears / Solar heat / Ready for action / Wish I was / Fight to the finish.
LP: K 53163

GAMMA II.
Tracks: / Meanstreak / Four horsemen / Dirty city / Voyager / Something in the air / Cat on a leash / Skin and bone / Mayday.
MC: K4 52245
LP: K 52245

Gamma Ray

HEAVEN CAN WAIT.
Tracks: / Heaven can wait (new version) / Sail on / Who do you think you are / Lonesome stranger, The / Mr. Outlaw.
MLP: NUK 1515

Gammer

ROCKET TICKET (Gammer & His Familiars).
Tracks: / Before the break / Put me in the ad on TV / Rocket ticket / Too much too soon / Market place / Cars and my relations / Ghosts won't get in the way / You're a screwball / Then we can dry each others eyes / Motorbike motorway.
LP: GAMMERL 4

WON'T LOOK OUT (Gammer & His Familiars).
LP: GAMMERL 3

Gammon, Patrick

DON'T TOUCH ME.
Tracks: / This shit is bad / Don't touch me / Cop an attitude / My island / Yo' Chevy / Infatuation / My song in G / First time for surprise / Later for love.
LP: STML 12119

Ganbara

BANAN BANAN.
LP: ELKAR 113

Ganderton, Ron

GUITAR STAR (Ganderton, Ron & Sounds Ceremony).
LP: RING 001

Gandhi

HIS LIFE AND PHILOSOPHY.
LP: REH 466
MC: ZCR 466

Gandhi (Film)

GANDHI (Original soundtrack) (Various artists).
LP: RCALP 6062
MC: RCAK 6062

Ganelin Trio

ANCORA DA CAPO.
LP: LR 108

ANCORA DA CAPO (2).
LP: LR 109

BALTIC TRIANGLE.
LP: LR 125

CON AFFETTO.
LP: LR 137

CON AMORE.
LP: LR 147

CON FUOCO.
LP: LR 106

GANELIN TRIO.
LP: LR 168

GREAT CONCERTS OF NEW JAZZ.
2LP: LR 400/401

GREAT CONCERTS OF NEW JAZZ VOL. 2.
2LP: LR 410/11

INVERSO.
LP: LR 140

LIVE IN EAST GERMANY.
LP: LR 102

NEW WINE.
LP: LR 112

STRICTLY FOR OUR FRIENDS.
LP: LR 120

VIDE.
LP: LR 117

Gang Green

ANOTHER WASTED NIGHT.
Tracks: / Another wasted night / Skate to hell / Last chance / Alcohol / Have fun / 19th hole, The / Skate hate / Let's drink some beer / Protect and serve / Another bomb / Voices carry / Sold out Alabama.
LP: FH 12-002
LP: 086 401

CAN'T LIVE WITHOUT IT.
Tracks: / Let's drink some beer / Bartender / Lost chamber / We'll give it to you / We can do / Have fun / Last chance / Just one bullet / Born to rock / Rabies / Voices carry / Sold out / Bedroom of doom / Bomb / Alcohol.
LP: RR 93801
MC: RR 93804

I81B4U.
LP: RR 9500 1
MC: RR 9500 4
LP: RAZD 39

OLDER ... BUDWEISER.
LP: EM 94641
MC: EM 94644
LP: LM 9464 1

YOU GOT IT.
LP: RR 9591
MC: RR 4951 1

Gang Of Four

AT THE PALACE.
Tracks: / We live as we dream alone / History is not made by great men / Silver lining / History of the world / I love a man in a uniform / Paralysed / Is it love / Damaged goods / At home he's a tourist / I will be a good boy / Call me up (If I'm home).
LP: MERL 51

BRIEF HISTORY OF THE 20TH CENTURY (The EMI Compilation).
Tracks: / At home he's a tourist / Damaged goods / Ntur's not in it (Not on LP.) / Not great men / Anthrax / Return the gift / It's her factory (Not on LP.) / What we all want (live) / Paralysed / Hole in the wallet, A (Not on LP.) / Cheeseburger (Not on LP.) / To hell with poverty / Capital (it fails us now) / Call me up (If I'm home) / I will be a good boy / History of the world / I love a man in a uniform / Is it love / Woman town / We live as we dream, alone.
LP: EMC 3583
MC: TCEMC 3583

ENTERTAINMENT.
Tracks: / Ether / Naturals not in it / Not great man / Damaged goods / Return the gift / Guns before butter / I found that essence rare / Glass / Contract / At home he's a tourist / 5-45 / Love like anthrax.
LP: ATAK 41
MC: TCATAK 41
LP: EMC 3313

HARD.
Tracks: / Is it love / I flee / Silver lining / Woman town / Man with a good car / It don't matter / Arabic / Piece of my heart / Independence.
LP: EMC 1652191

PEEL SESSIONS:GANG OF FOUR (ALBUM) (Complete sessions 1979-1981).
LP: SFRLP 107
MC: SFRC 107

SOLID GOLD.
Tracks: / Paralysed / What we all want / If i could keep it myself / Outside the trains don't run on time / Why theory? / Cheeseburger / Republic / In the ditch / Hole in the wallet, A / He'd send in the army.
LP: EMC 3364

SONGS OF THE FREE.
Tracks: / Call me up (If I'm home) / I love a man in a uniform / Muscle for brains / It is not enough / Life it's a shame / I will be a good boy / History of the world / We live as we dream, alone / Of the instant.
LP: EMC 3412

YOU CATCH UP WITH HISTORY (1978-1983).
Tracks: / Love like anthrax / Damaged goods / At home he's a tourist / Ether / Naturals not in it / Return the gift / Guns before butter / I found that essence rare / To hell with poverty (CD only.) / Paralysed (CD only.) / Outside the trains don't run on time / Call me up (If I'm home) / I love a man in a uniform / I will be a good boy / What we all want / Woman town / Armalite rifle (CD only.) / Is it love.
LP: GO 2028
MC: TCGO 2028

Gangs All Here (film)

GANGS ALL HERE, THE (Original Soundtrack) (Various artists).
LP: SH 2009

Gangstarr

STEP IN THE ARENA.
Tracks: / Name tag (Premier and The Guru) / Step in the arena / Form of intellect / Execution of a chump (No more Mr. Nice Guy Pt. 2) / Who's gonna take the weight? / Beyond comprehension / Check the technique / Love sick / Here today, gone tomorrow / Game plan / Take a rest / What you want this time? / Street ministry / Just to get a rep / Say your prayers / As I read my S-A / Precisely the right rhymes / Meaning of the name, The.
LP: CTLP 21
MC: ZCTLP 21

Gangster Fun

COME SEE COME SKA.
LP: SKAR 009

Gangsters

GANGSTERS, THE.
LP: BEAT 2

Gangsters Of House

STREETS OF CHICAGO.
LP: HTPA 10

Gangway

SITTING IN THE PARK.
MC: LONC 61
LP: LONLP 61

TWIST, THE.
LP: IRMG 10

Gant, Cecil

CECIL BOOGIE.
LP: FLY 4714

I'M STILL SINGING THE BLUES TODAY.
LP: OL 8004

KILLER DILLER BOOGIE.
LP: PY 1816

ROCK LITTLE BABY.
LP: FLY 4714

ROCK THIS BOOGIE.
Tracks: / Cecil boogie / Hit that jive Jack / Hogan's alley / I gotta gal / Boogie blues / Little baby you're running wild / Long distance / Am I to blame / Rock the boogie / Blues in LA / Cecil boogie No. 2 / What's on your worried mind / Stuff you gotta watch / Syncopated boogie / Time will tell / Cecil's mop top.
LP: KK 7413

Gants

I WONDER.
LP: KIRI 067

Gap Band

BEST OF THE GAP BAND.
Tracks: / Oops upside your head / Early in the morning / Yearning for your love / Outstanding / Burn rubber on me / Can't get over you / You dropped a bomb on me / Someday / Party train.
LP: JABH 15
MC: JABHC 15
LP: 824343 1
MC: 824343 4

GAP BAND 2.
Tracks: / Steppin' out / No hiding place / I don't believe you want to get up and dance / Who do you call / You are my high / Party lights / Boys are back in town.
LP: 9111062

GAP BAND 3.
Tracks: / When I look in your eyes / Yearning for your love / Burn rubber on me / Nothin' comes to sleepers / Are you living / Sweet Caroline / Humpin' / Way / Gash gash gash.
LP: 6337110

GAP BAND 4.
Tracks: / Early in the morning / Seasons no reason to change / Lonely like me / Outstanding / Stay with me / You

dropped a bomb on me / I can't get over you / Talkin' back.
LP: . . . . MERS 6
MC: . . . . MERSC 6
LP: . . . . FL 89476
MC: . . . . FK 89476

GAP BAND 6.
Tracks: / Beep a freak / Don't you leave me / Disrespect / Sun don't shine everyday / Video junkie / Weak spot / I believe / I found my baby.
LP: . . . . FL 89476

GAP BAND 7.
LP: . . . . FL 85714
MC: . . . . FK 85714

GAP BAND 8.
Tracks: / Big fun / I can't live without your love / Get loose, get funky / Don't take it away / Going in circles / Keep holding on / I'll always love you / Bop-b-da-b-da-da (that's how music came about) / I owe it to myself.
LP: . . . . FL 89992
MC: . . . . FK 89992

OUTSTANDING (OLD GOLD) (See under Yarbrough & Peoples/Don't stop...).

ROUND TRIPP.
Tracks: / All of my love / Addicted to your love / We can make it alright / It's our duty / Wednesday lover / I like it / I'm dreaming / Antidote (to love) / No easy out / Jam / Let's talk about love.
LP: . . . . EST 2116
MC: . . . . TCEST 2116

V-JAMMIN'.
Tracks: / Where are we goin / Shake a leg / I'm ready if you're ready / Jammin' in America / Smile / Party train / Jam the motha' / I expect more / You're something special / Someday.
LP: . . . . TEL 2

Garage

2ND PSYCHO-ATTACK OVER EUROPE (Various artists).
Tracks: / I've got the edge: *Meteors* / Listen to what Archie sez: *Archie* / Little Red Riding Hood: *P.O.X.*/ Smell of Kat: *Stringbeans* / Cat, The: *Sunny Domestozs* / Turkey dance: *Pharaohs* / Ride on: *Dazzlers*/ Take a look: *Roughnecks* / Nobody's business: *Frenzy* / Warpath: *Archie* / Torment: *Torment*/ Scum of the neighbourhood: *Batmobile* / Nighttime syndicate: *P.O.X.* / Hard times: *Roughnecks* / Get away off my brain: *Dazzlers*.
LP: KIX4U 3337
LP: . . . . ROCK 3337

BEST OF PEBBLES (Various artists).
LP: . . . . TAKE 1

CAVEMAN - BEST OF PEBBLES VOL.3 (Various artists).
LP: . . . . TAKE 003

ENGLISH FREAKBEAT VOL.1 (Various artists).
LP: . . . . AIP 10039

ENGLISH FREAKBEAT VOL.3 (Various artists).
LP: . . . . AIP 10048

ENGLISH FREAKBEAT VOL.4 (Various artists).
LP: . . . . AIP 10051

I WAS A TEENAGE CAVEMAN (Raw savage sixties) (Various artists).
LP: . . . . TC 1966

MAJOR BILL TAPES - VOL.2 (The Fort Worth scene) (Various artists).
LP: . . . . WIK 59

MAJOR BILL'S TEXAS ROCK 'N' ROLL (Various artists).
Tracks: / Cross-eyed Mary: *Various artists* / Somebody help me: *Various artists* / Gonna come a time: *Various artists* / Last kiss, The: *Various artists* / Fannie Mae: *Various artists* / Honky tonk man: *Various artists*/ Wayward wind: *Various artists* / No: *Various artists* / Baby you're mine: *Various artists* / Evil doll: *Various artists* / Out here in the country: *Various artists* / Squirm: *Various artists*.
LP: . . . . SNTF 807

NUGGETS VOL.1 (Various artists).
Tracks: / Dirty water: *Standells* / Pushin' too hard: *Seeds* / Psychotic reaction: *Count Five* / Let's talk about girls: *Chocolate Watch Band* / Friday on my mind: *Easybeats* / I see the light: *Five Americans*/ Why pick on me: *Standells* / Little girl: *Syndicate Of Sound* / Pleasant Valley Sunday: *Monkees* / Lies: *Knickerbockers* / Laugh laugh: *Beau Brummels* / Wild thing: *Troggs* / Heaven and hell: *Easybeats*/ Valleri: *Monkees* / Open my eyes: *Nazz* / Just a little: *Beau Brummels* / Can't seem to make you mine: *Seeds* / Journey to the centre of the mind: *Amboy Dukes*.
LP: . . . . RNLP 025

NUGGETS VOL.2 Punk (Various artists).
LP: . . . . RNLP 026

NUGGETS VOL.3 Pop (Various artists).
LP: . . . . RNLP 027

NUGGETS VOL.4 Pop part 2 (Various artists).
LP: . . . . RNLP 028

NUGGETS VOL.5 Pop part 3 (Various artists).
LP: . . . . RNLP 29

NUGGETS VOL.6 Pop part 2 (Various artists).
LP: . . . . RNLP 30

NUGGETS VOL.7 (Early San Francisco) (Various artists).
LP: . . . . RNLP 31

NUGGETS VOL.8 Northwest (Various artists).
LP: . . . . RNLP 70032

NUGGETS VOL.9 Acid rock (Various artists).
LP: . . . . RNLP 70033

NUGGETS VOL.10 Folk-rock (Various artists).
LP: . . . . RNLP 70034

NUGGETS VOL.11 Pop (Various artists).
LP: . . . . RNLP 70035

NUGGETS VOL.12 Punk (Various artists).
LP: . . . . RNLP 70036

PEBBLES BOX, THE (Various artists).
LPS: . . . . BOXX 1

PEBBLES VOL.1 (Various artists).
LP: . . . . BFD 5016

PEBBLES VOL.2 (Various artists).
LP: . . . . BFD 5019

PEBBLES VOL.3 (Various artists).
LP: . . . . BFD 5020

PEBBLES VOL.4 (Various artists).
LP: . . . . BFD 5021

PEBBLES VOL.11 (Various artists).
LP: . . . . AIP 10001

PEBBLES VOL.12 (Various artists).
LP: . . . . AIP 10002

PEBBLES VOL.13 (Various artists).
LP: . . . . AIP 10013

PEBBLES VOL.14 (Various artists).
LP: . . . . AIP 10016

PEBBLES VOL.15 (Various artists).
LP: . . . . AIP 10018

PEBBLES VOL.16 (Various artists).
LP: . . . . AIP 10023

PEBBLES VOL.17 (Various artists).
LP: . . . . AIP 10032

PEBBLES VOL.18 (Various artists).
LP: . . . . AIP 10033

PEBBLES VOL.19 (Various artists).
LP: . . . . AIP 10034

PEBBLES VOL.20 (Various artists).
LP: . . . . AIP 10035

PEBBLES VOL.22 (Various artists).
LP: . . . . AIP 10037

PEBBLES VOL.23 (Various artists).
LP: . . . . AIP 10040

PEBBLES VOL.24 (Various artists).
LP: . . . . AIP 10043

PEBBLES VOL.25 (Various artists).
LP: . . . . AIP 10042

PEBBLES VOL 26 (Various artists).
LP: . . . . AIP 10044

PEBBLES VOL 27 (Various artists).
LP: . . . . AIP 10045

PEBBLES VOL 28 (Various artists).
LP: . . . . AIP 10046

PEBBLES VOL 29 (Various artists).
LP: . . . . AIP 10047

PSYCHOTIC REACTIONS Early American Rock Groups (Various artists).
Tracks: / Psychotic reaction: *Various artists* / Bend me shape me: *Various artists* / Kind of a drag: *Various artists* / Time won't let me: *Various artists* / Like to get to know you well: *Various artists* / One toe over the line: *Various artists* / In a gadda-da-vida: *Various artists* / Liar liar: *Various artists* / Mercy,mercy,mercy: *Various artists* / Let it all hang out: *Various artists* / Incense and peppermints: *Various artists* / They're gonna get you: *Various artists*.
LP: . . . . TOP 153
MC: . . . . KTOP 153

RAW CUTS (Various artists).
LP: . . . . CRIMLP 129

RAW CUTS 2 - SWEDISH GARAGE BANDS (Various artists).
LP: . . . . CRIMLP 132

RAW CUTS 3 - GERMAN UNDERGROUND (Various artists).
LP: . . . . RAW 003

RAW CUTS 4 - AUSTRALIAN NITRO (Various artists).
LP: . . . . RAW 004

RAW CUTS 5 - SWEDISH BEAT 2 (Various artists).
LP: . . . . RAW 005

RAW CUTS 6 (American psych) (Various artists).
LP: . . . . RAW 006

RAW CUTS 7 - UK GARAGE DISEASE (Various artists).
LP: . . . . RAW 007

RAW CUTS - BEGINNERS GUIDE TO GARAGE FRENCH (Various artists).
LP: . . . . CRIMLP 119

SONGS WE TAUGHT THE FUZZTONES (32 garage classics) (Various artists).
LP: . . . . MMLP 66002

SOUND OF GARAGE, VOL. 3 (Various artists).
LP: . . . . RAID 505
MC: . . . . ZCRAID 505

STARS ON PSYCHO (Various artists).
LP: . . . . ROCK 3348

TEXAS FLASHBACKS VOL.1 (Various artists).
LP: . . . . TEXAS 1

TEXAS FLASHBACKS VOL.2 (Various artists).
LP: . . . . TEXAS 2

TEXAS FLASHBACKS VOL.3 (Various artists).
LP: . . . . TEXAS 3

TEXAS FLASHBACKS VOL.4 (Various artists).
LP: . . . . TEXAS 4

TEXAS FLASHBACKS VOL.5 (Various artists).
LP: . . . . TEXAS 5

TEXAS FLASHBACKS VOL.6 (Various artists).
LP: . . . . TEXAS 6

TRANSWORLD PUNK RAVE UP 1964-66 (Various artists).
LP: . . . . TW 64

TWISTED TEENAGE SCREAMING FUZZBUSTER (Various artists).
LP: . . . . ISR 004

Garbarek, Jan

AFRIC PEPPERBIRD (see under Rypdal) (Garbarek/Rypdal).

AFTENLAND.
LP: . . . . ECM 1169

ALL THOSE BORN WITH WINGS.
Tracks: / Last clown, The / Yellow fever / Soulful Bill / La divetta / Cool train / Loop, The.
LP: . . . . ECM 1324

ESOTERIC CIRCLE.
Tracks: / Traneflight / Rabalder / Esoteric circle / VIPs / S.A.S. 644 / Nefertiti / Gee / Karin's mode / Breeze ending.
LP: . . . . FLP 41031

EVENTYR.
LP: . . . . ECM 1200

FOLK SONGS (Garbarek/ Haden/ Gismonti).
LP: . . . . ECM 1170

I TOOK UP THE RUNES.
Tracks: / Gula gula / Molde canticle (parts 1-5) / His eyes were suns / I took up the runes / Buena hora, buenos vientos.
LP: . . . . ECM 1419
MC: 8438504

LEGENDS OF THE SEVEN DREAMS.
Tracks: / He comes from the North / Aichuri, the song man / Tongue of secrets / Brother wind / It's name is secret road / Send word / Voy cantado / Mirror store.
LP: . . . . ECM 1381
MC: 8373444

LISTEN TO THE GRAY VOICE.
LP: . . . . ECM 1294

MAGICO (See under Haden, Charlie) (Garbarek/ Haden/ Gismonti).

PATHS, PRINTS.
LP: . . . . ECM 1223

ROSENSFOLE (Garbarek, Jan/Maria Buen-Garnas).
LP: . . . . ECM 1402
MC: 8392934

SART (see under Rypdal) (Garbarek/ Rypdal/Stenson).

TERJE RYPDAL (see under Rypdal) (Garbarek/Rypdal/Fintl).

WAYFARER.
Tracks: / Gesture / Wayfarer / Gentle / Pendulum / Spor / Singsong.
LP: . . . . ECM 1259

WORKS: JAN GARBAREK.
Tracks: / Folk songs (From Folk Songs ECM 1170) / Skirk and hyl (From Dansere ECM 1075) / Passing (From Places ECM 1118) / Selje (From Tryptykon ECM 1029) / Viddene (From Dis ECM 1093) / Snipp, snapp, snute (From Eventyr ECM 1200) / Beast of Kommodo (From Afric Pepperbird ECM 1007) / Svevende (From Dansere ECM 1075).
LP: 8232661

Garber, Jan

JAN GARBER, 1939-41.
Tracks: / My dear / It's a wonderful world / Rose room / Tumbling tumbleweeds / Do you ever think of me / Oh what you said / Siren's song, The / Lady be good / Stardust / Because of you / Birth of the blues / I hear a rhapsody / Whispering / Love song of Renaldo / Somebody loves me / I'll see you in my dreams.
LP: . . . . HSR 130
LP: . . . . HMP 5053

JAN GARBER AND ORCHESTRA 1944 (Garber, Jan & His Orchestra).
LP: . . . . CLP 99

JAN GARBER AND ORCHESTRA PLAY 22 BIG BAND RECORDINGS (Garber, Jan & His Orchestra).
LP: . . . . HSR 403

JAN GARBER, VOL 2, 1946-47.
Tracks: / My dear / S'wonderful / You turned the tables on me / You're blase / At sundown / My melancholy baby / I love my baby / Blue / Should I? / Lovely to look at / Do I worry / From Monday on / Kashimiri love song / I can't believe that you're in love with me / Tea for two / Three little words / Just friends / My dear (spoken closing theme).
LP: . . . . HSR 155

UNCOLLECTED JAN GARBER AND HIS ORCHESTRA (Tommy Traynor, Vol 3) (Garber, Jan & His Orchestra).
Tracks: / Who / Maria Elena / Things we did last summer, The / Paper moon / More than you know / Bye bye blues / Dancing in the dark / Prisoner of love / Diane / Old buttermille sly / Over the rainbow / Cherokee.
LP: . . . . HUK 204

Garber, Lloyd

ENERGY PATTERNS.
Tracks: / Bumble bee / Painted fortune teller at the B.W.L.T / Trip / I am I am / Prepared / Energy patterns / Voyage of the desert weirdo / Hatful of wertmuller.
LP: . . . . SERIES 001
LP: . . . . ONARI 001

Garbutt, Vin

ESTON CALIFORNIA.
Tracks: / Bantry bay / Den toppede hone / Land of three rivers, The / Gentle Annie / Hornpipes / Belfast, The / Japanese, The / Hartlepool monkey, The / Tonto McGuire / Ring of iron, The / Skibereen / Their Ulster peace / Tear the calico / Providence / Water o' Tyne, The.
LP: 12TS 378

KING GOODEN.
LP: . . . . LER 2102

LITTLE INNOCENTS.
Tracks: / Royal blackbird, The / Fear of imperfection, The / Lynda / Calum more / Coalman, The / Leslie / Dormanstown Jimmy / If / Blue sunset / Little innocents.
LP: 12TS 428

SHY TOT POMMY.
LP: . . . . CM 024
MC: . . . . CMC 024

TOSSIN' A WOBBLER.
Tracks: / Man of the earth / Legend of Roseberry / Long note, The / Lads of Laois / Le reel Jeune Marie / Photographic memory / Yorkshire volunteers' farewell to the good folks of Stockton / Push about the Jorum / St. Helena's march / Carrigdhoun / Fremantle doctor / One-legged beggar, The / They don't write 'em like that any more.
LP: 12TS 385

VALLEY OF TEES, THE.
LP: . . . . LER 2078

YOUNG TIN WHISTLE PEST,THE.
LP: . . . . LER 2081

Garcia, Jerry

ALMOST ACOUSTIC (Garcia, Jerry Acoustic Band).
Tracks: / Swing low, sweet chariot / Blue yodel no. 9 (Standing on the corner) / I'm troubled / Oh babe, it ain't no lie / Casey Jones / Ripple / Deep elem blues

/ I'm here to get my baby out of jail / Girl at the crossroads bar, The / Diamond Joe / Spike diver blues (Available on CD only) / I've been all around this world (Available on CD only) / Oh, the wind and the rain (Available on CD only) / Gone home (Available on CD only).
LP: . . . . GDV 4005
MC: . . . . GDTC 4005

COMPLIMENTS OF GARCIA.
Tracks: / Let it rock / That's what love will make us do / Turn on the bright lights / What goes around / Mississippi moon / Hunter gets captured by the game, The / Russian lullaby / He ain't give you none / Let's spend the night together / Midnight town.
LP: . . . . GDV 4011
MC: . . . . GDTC 4011

HOOTEROLL (Garcia, Jerry & Howard Wales).
LP: . . . . RACS 0052

JERRY GARCIA BAND.
Tracks: / Way you do the things you do, The / Waiting for a miracle / Simple twist of fate / Get out of my life / My sister and brothers / I shall be released / Dear Prudence / Deal / Stop that train / Senor (tales of Yankee power) / Evangeline / Night they drove old Dixie down, The / Don't let go / That lucky old sun / Tangled up in blue.
MC: 504284

OLD AND IN THE WAY (Garcia, Jerry/ David Grisman/Peter Rowan).
Tracks: / Pig in a pen / Midnight moonlight / Old and in the way / Knockin' on your door / Hobo song, The / Panama red / Wild horses / Kissimmee kid / White dove / Land of the Navajo.
LP: . . . . SH 3746
MC: . . . . ZCSH 3746

REFLECTIONS.
Tracks: / Might as well / Mission in the rain / They love each other / I'll take a melody / It must have been the roses / Tore up (over you) / Catfish John / Comes a time.
LP: . . . . GDV 4008
MC: . . . . GDTC 4008

RUN FOR THE ROSES.
Tracks: / Run for the roses / I saw her standing there / Without love / Midnight getaway / Leave the little girl alone / Valerie / Knockin' on Heaven's door.
LP: 1204973

WHEEL, THE.
Tracks: / Deal / Sugaree / Late for supper / Eep hour / Odd little place, An / Bird song / Loser / Spidergawd / To lay me down / Wheel, The.
LP: . . . . GDV 4003
MC: . . . . GDTC 4003

Garcia, Jose Luis

VIVALDI: THE FOUR SEASONS (Handel: Water music)(see under English Chamber Orchestra) (Garcia, Jose Luis/ English Chamber Orchestra).

Garcia, Renee

LIVING IN THE VERTICAL.
LP: . . . . RRA R 0027
MC: . . . . RRA C 0027

Garcia, Russell

I LEAD A CHARMED LIFE.
LP: . . . . DS 814

JOHNNY EVER GREEN'S, THE (Garcia, Russell Orchestra).
Tracks: / Body and soul / Who do you think you are / Living in dreams / Out of nowhere / I wanna be loved / Steam is on the beam, The / Trembling of a leaf / Easy come, easy go / I cover the waterfront / Coquette / You're mine you / Not bad / Hello, my lover, goodbye / There's a ring around the Moon / I'm yours / With you, with me.
LP: . . . . FS 240

VARIATIONS FOR FLUGELHORN, STRING QUARTET, BASS AND DRUMS.
LP: . . . . TR 522

Garden, Bill

BILL GARDEN'S HIGHLAND FIDDLE ORCHESTRA (Garden, Bill & His Highland Fiddle Orchestra).
Tracks: / Porteau blanc (The French Canadian Special.) / Snowshoers reel (The French Canadian Special.) / Quintuplets reel (The French Canandian Special.) / Masons apron (Stings to The bow (Reels & Jigs).) / Fairy dance, The (Stings to The bow (Reels & Jigs).) / De'il amang the tailors / Blackthorn stick / Roaring jelly / Brumley brae / Bonnie Mary of Argyle (Slow Air Strathspey & Reel.) / Highland whiskey (Slow Air Strathspey & Real.) / Laird of Drumblair, The (Slow Air Strathspey & Reel.) / Kate Dalrymple (Slow Air Strathspey & Reel.) / Jans dance (Hornpipes.) / Mathematician, The (Hornpipes.) / High level, The (Hornpipes.) / Reel of Tulloch, The / Comin' thro' the rye (The Robert Burns Waltz.) / Scots wha' hae (The Robert Burns Waltz.) / Ye banks and braes (The Robert Burns Waltz.) / Maries wedding (March, Strathspey and Reel.) / Vist tramping songs (March, Strathspey and Reel.) / Marquis of Huntly, The (March, Strathspey and Reel.) / Scotland the brave (March, Strathspey and Reel.) / Phil the fluter's ball (The Scots and Irish (Reels 7 Jigs).) / Flannel jacket, The (The Scots and Irish (Reels 7 Jigs).) / March hare (The Scots and Irish (Reels 7 Jigs).) / Mrs. McLeod (The Scots and Irish (Reels 7 Jigs).) / Speed the plough (The Scots and Irish (Reels 7 Jigs).) / Rollicking Irishman (The Scots and Irish (Reels 7 Jigs).) / Pet of the pipers (The Scots and Irish (Reels 7 Jigs).) / Irish washerwoman, The (The Scots and Irish (Reels 7 Jigs).) / Rowan tree (The Scots and Irish (Reels 7 Jigs).) / Jigtime (Polka.) / McFlannels / Para Handy (Polka.) / Turkey in the straw (The country hoedown.) / Arkansas traveller (The country hoedown.) / Smiths reel (The country hoedown.) / Orange blossom special (The country hoedown.) / Road and the miles to Dundee, The (The intercity waltz.) / Northern lights of old Aberdeen (The intercity waltz.) / I belong to Glasgow (The intercity waltz.) / Lady Madeline Sinclair (Schottische Reel.) / Jelly bawbee (Schottische Reel.) / Lord Moira (Schottische Reel.) / Orange and blue (Schottische Reel.) / Drunken piper (Schottische Reel.) / Roamin' in the Gloamin' (Sir Harry Lauder selection.) / I love a lassie (Sir Harry Lauder selection.) / Stop your ticklin' Jock (Sir Harry Lauder selection.) / Wee Deoch an' Doris (Sir Harry Lauder selection.).
LP: . . . . ITV 423
MC: . . . . KITV 423

COUNTRY GOLD HITS.
Tracks: / Today I started loving you again / Jambalaya / Maggie (when you and I were young) / Ramblin' rose / Please help me, I'm falling / Married by the Bible / Wild side of life / Make the world go away / Sea of heartbreak / Your cheatin' heart / Green green grass of home / Release me / Behind closed doors / It's four in the morning.
LP: . . . . BGC 266
MC: . . . . KBGC 266

IOLAIRE (Garden, Bill Fiddle Orchestra).
MC: . . . . KITV 514

Garden Gang

GERTRUDE GOOSEBERRY & BELINDA BLACKCURRENT (Unknown artist(s)).
MC: . . . . PLB 135

PAM PARSNIP & LAWRENCE LEMON (Unknown artist(s)).
MC: . . . . PLB 144

PATRICK PEAR & COLIN CUCUMBER (Unknown artist(s)).
MC: . . . . PLB 133

PEDRO PEPPER & THE CHERRY TWINS (Unknown artist(s)).
MC: . . . . PLB 132

PERCIVAL PEA & POLLY POMEGRANATE (Unknown artist(s)).
MC: . . . . PLB 141

PETER POTATO & ALICE APPLE (Unknown artist(s)).
MC: . . . . PLB 134

ROBERT RASPBERRY & GRACE GRAPE (Unknown artist(s)).
MC: . . . . PLB 131

SHEILA SHALLOT & BENNY (Unknown artist(s)).
MC: . . . . PLB 142

SIMON SWEDE & AVRIL APRICOT (Unknown artist(s)).
MC: . . . . PLB 143

WEE WILLIE WATER MELON & BETTY BEETROOT (Unknown artist(s)).
MC: . . . . PLB 140

Garden Of The

GARDEN OF THE FINZI-CONTINIS (Film Soundtrack) (Various artists).
Tracks: / Micol's theme: *Various artists* / Tennis match: *Various artists* / Giorgio and Micol (love theme): *Various* artists / Persecution: *Various artists* / Garden of the Finzi-Continis: *Various artists* / Meeting at Easter: *Various artists* / Declaration of war: *Various artists* / Leaving for Genoble: *Various artists* / Giorgio's delusion: *Various artists* / Garden of the Finzi-Continis: *Various artists* / Villa: *Various artists*/ Childhood memories: *Various artists* / Garden of the Finzi-Continis (finale): *Various artists* / Micol's theme (reprise): *Various artists*.
LP: . . . . SF 8289

Garden Party

GARDEN PARTY, THE (see Mansfield, Katherine) (Ashcroft, Peggy).

Garden, Stephen Lee

INTRODUCING STEPHEN LEE GARDEN.
Tracks: / Love changes everything / Anthem / Born to be me / Can't stay away from you / Way you look tonight, The / Will you love me tomorrow / Missing you / Music of the night, The / Through the eyes of love / Music and you / Stardust / Story of my life, The / Running with the night / Lovely day.
LP: . . . . MODEM 1038
MC: . . . . MODEMC 1038

Gardening By Moonlight

METHOD IN THE MADNESS.
Tracks: / Method in the madness / Letters / Diction and fiction / Whistling in the dark / Weights and measures / Strange views / Chance / Strange news / Method again.
LP: . . . . INTO 2

Gardiner, Boris

EVERYTHING TO ME.
Tracks: / Wrong end of the rainbow / All in my dreams / Last night / I'm falling in love / Next to you / Jean / Cara mia / I want to wake up with you / Let's make it tonight.
LP: . . . . BGLP 1
MC: . . . . BGMC 1

FRIENDS AND LOVERS (see under Guthrie, Gwen) (Gardiner, Boris & Gwen Guthrie).

IT'S NICE TO BE WITH YOU.
LP: . . . . PKL 2000

LET'S TAKE A HOLIDAY.
LP: . . . . WKS 009
MC: . . . . WKSC 009

SOULFUL EXPERIENCE.
LP: . . . . DY 3321

Gardner, Freddy

1935-37.
LP: . . . . HQ 3018

FREDDY GARDNER AND SWING ORCHESTRA 1937-9 (Gardner, Freddy & His Swing Orchestra).
Tracks: / I want to be happy / Limehouse blues / I double dare you / That old feeling / Can't stop me from dreamin' / Hold tight / Music maestro please / It's de-lovely.
LP: . . . . HQ 3027

MUSIC MAESTRO PLEASE (Gardner, Freddy & His Swing Orchestra).
Tracks: / Music maestro please / Dipsy doodle / Limehouse blues / Nobody's sweetheart / Bugle call rag / My sweetie went away / You can't stop me from dreaming / I double dare you / Jeepers creepers / They say / Hold tight, hold tight / Snake charmer, The / Tiger rag / Dinah / Temptation rag / Have you got any castles, baby? / Tom, Tom, the piper's son / I want to be happy.
LP: . . . . RFL 44

Gardner, Joanna

JOANNA GARDNER.
Tracks: / I never thought / We can make it / Special feelings / Friday night / Watching you / I could never love another like you / Pick up the pieces / Spooky.
LP: . . . . POLD 5178

Gareth Of Orkney

GARETH OF ORKNEY.
MC: . . . . ANV 612

Garfield

AM I COOL OR WHAT? (Various artists).
Tracks: / Shake your paw: *Temptations* / I love it when I'm naughty: *Labelle, Patti* / Fat is where it's at: *Anderson*, Carl / Long 'bout midnight: *Cole, Natalie* / Nine lives: *Pointer Sisters* / Here comes Garfield: *Rawls*, Lou / Next to you I'm even better: *Schuur, Diane* / Spare time: *Benoit, David* / Up on a fence: *Goyette, Desiree* / Monday morning blues: *King, B.B.*.
LP: . . . . GRP 96411
MC: . . . . GRP 96414

Garfield, Leon

GHOST DOWNSTAIRS, THE.
MCSET: 086 222 044X

Garfunkel, Art

ANGEL CLARE.
Tracks: / Travelin' boy / Down in the willow garden / I shall sing / Old man / Feuilles-oh / Do space men pass dead souls on their way to.. / All I know / Harry was an only child / Woyaya / Barbara Allen / Another lullaby.
LP: . . . . CBS 69021
LP: . . . . CBS 32076

ANIMALS CHRISTMAS,THE.
Tracks: / Annunciation,The / Creatures of the field,The / Just a simple little tune / Decree, The / Incredible phat / Friendly beasts, The / Song of the camels, The / Words from an old Spanish Carol / Carol of the birds / Frog,The / Herod / Wild geese, The.
LP: . . . . CBS 26704
MC: 40 26704

ART GARFUNKEL.
LPS: . . . . CBS 66351

ART GARFUNKEL ALBUM, THE.
Tracks: / Bright eyes / Breakaway / Heart in New York, A / I shall sing / 99 miles from L.A. / All I know / I only have eyes for you / Watermark / Sometimes when I'm dreaming / Travellin boy / Same old tears on a new background,The / (What a) wonderful world / I believe / Scissors cut.
LP: . . . . CBS 10046
MC: 40 10046
LP: 4663331
MC: 4663334

BREAKAWAY.
Tracks: / I believe / Rag doll / Breakaway / Disney girls / My little town / Waters of March / I only have eyes for you / Looking for the right one / 99 miles from L.A. / Same old tears on a new background / Breakaway / Stay young / Heart on my sleeve / Fifteen summers / Sign of the times / If I needed someone / Storm in my soul / Rockwriter / Northern girl.
LP: . . . . CBS 32574
MC: 40 32574
LP: . . . . CBS 86002
LP: 902199 1
MC: 902199 4

FATE FOR BREAKFAST.
Tracks: / In a little while / Since I don't have you / I know / Sail on a rainbow / Miss you nights / Bright eyes / Finally found a reason / Beyond the tears / Oh how happy / When someone doesn't want you / Take me away.
LP: . . . . CBS 86082

LEFTY.
Tracks: / This is the moment / I have a love / So much in love / Slow breakout / Love is the only chain / When a man loves a woman / I wonder why / King of Tonga / If love takes you away / Promise, the.
LP: 4606941
MC: 4606944

SCISSORS CUT.
Tracks: / Scissors cut / Heart in New York, A / Up in the world / Hang on in / So easy to begin / Can't turn my heart away / French waltz / Romance / In cars / That's all I've got to say (Theme from 'the last unicorn').
LP: . . . . CBS 85259
MC: 40 85259

WATERMARK.
Tracks: / Crying in my sleep / Marionette / Shine it on me / Watermark / Saturday suit / All my loves laughter / What a wonderful world / Mr. Shuck'n'jive / Paper chase / She moved through the fair / Someone else / Wooden planes / (What a) wonderful world.
LP: 4503781
MC: 4503784
LP: . . . . CBS 86054
MC: 40 86054

Gargleblud

HOWLINYOWLINSCREAMINESS.
LP: . . . . BLUD 001

Gargoyle Sox

HEADLESS HORSEMEN.
LP: . . . . SAVE 025

Gargoyles

MRS TWO DINNERS.
LP: . . . . JRRLP 001

SOD THE AQUARIUM.
LP: . . . . JRRLP 005

STEAM FLAPPER.
Tracks: / Ferry across the Humber / Me and Ted / Fancy rubber things / Every body loves the gasman / Magnificent church, The / Reverend Prentis / Bancy bancy / Man called tuppence, A / Dead men's boots / Mister Punch / Madmen.
LP: . . . . JRRLP 007

Gargoyles S.F.

DOWN ON YOU.
MLP: . . . . YEAH-HUP 017

Garioch Blend

DANCERS DELIGHT.
LP: . . . . CDR 002

Garland, Hank

GUITAR GENIUS (Garland, Hank/Grady Martin/Les Paul).
Tracks: / E string rag / Guitar shuffle / I'm movin' on / Hillbilly express / Third

man, Theme from / Low down Billy / Doll dance / Slewfoot rag / Blue skies / Guitar boogie / Steel guitar rag / Dark eyes / Sioux city Sue / Hot lips / Pork chop stomp / Diesel smoke, dangerous curves.
LP: . . . . CR 30243

Garland, Judy

ALL ALONE.
Tracks: / Man that got away, The / For me and my gal / Trolley song, The / Swanee / I'm nobody's baby / After you've gone / Alexander's ragtime band / Over the rainbow / I feel a song coming on / Rockabye your baby with a Dixie melody / I'm always chasing rainbows / All alone.
LP: . . . . MTM 025

BEST OF JUDY GARLAND.
Tracks: / On the Atchison, Topeka & The Santa Fe / I'm always chasing rainbow / But not for me / Meet me in St. Louis / For me and my gal / In between / Dear Mr. Gable / F.D.R. Jones / Embraceable you / Trolley song / I got rhythm / Boy next door, The / Zing went the strings of my heart / When you wore a tulip / I'm nobody's baby / Over the rainbow.
LP: . . . . MCL 1630

BEST OF JUDY GARLAND (2).
Tracks: / Summer stock / Broadway melody / Good old Summertime, The / Meet me in St Louis / Till the clouds roll by / Harvey girls.
LP: . . . . MCA 25165
MC: . . . . MCAC 25165

BING, BOB AND JUDY (See under Crosby, Bing) (Garland, Judy, Bing Crosby, Andrews Sisters).

BING CROSBY, JUDY GARLAND AND THE ANDREWS SISTERS (see Crosby, Bing) (Garland, Judy, Bing Crosby, Andrews Sisters).

CAPITOL YEARS, THE: JUDY GARLAND.
Tracks: / That's entertainment / You made me love you / For me and my girl / Trolley song, The / Man that got away, The / Lucky day / I can't give you anything but love / Zing went the strings of my heart / I hadn't anyone till you / Come rain or come shine / Shine on harvest moon / Some of these days / My man / I don't care / Do I love you / If I love again / Old devil moon / This is it / Do it again / Who cares / Over the rainbow.
LP: . . . . EMS 1347
MC: . . . . TCEMS 1347

CHASING RAINBOWS.
Tracks: / I never knew / Oceans apart / Love / But not for me / Embraceable you / Over the rainbow / Blues in the night / How about you / Poor little rich girl / No lover no nothing / For me and my gal / Trolley song, The / This heart of mine / You made me love you.
MCSET: . . . . CRT 121

COLLECTION: JUDY GARLAND.
Tracks: / Man that got away, The / Swanee / I'm nobody's baby / After you've gone / Alexander's ragtime band (Irvin Berlin Copyright control.) / Over the rainbow / I feel a song coming on / Rockabye your baby with a Dixie melody / I'm always chasing rainbows / From this moment on / Sweet little Alice Blue gown / Sweet danger / This can't be love / Never will I marry / I'm old fashioned / Old devil moon / Fly me to the moon / That's entertainment / More / Chicago / Battle hymn of the republic / Come rain or come shine / Smile / I can't give you anything but love / Hey look me over.
2LP: . . . . CCSLP 129
MC: . . . . CCSMC 129

FOR COLLECTORS ONLY: LIVE, 1962.
LP: . . . . PARAGON 1002

GARLAND AT THE GROVE.
Tracks: / Trolley song, The / Over the rainbow / When you're smiling / Zing went the strings of my heart / Purple people eater / You made me love you / For me and my gal / When the sun comes out / Rockabye your baby with a Dixie melody / After you've gone / Pretty girl milking her cow, A / Swanee.
LP: . . . . CAPS 2600071
MC: . . . . TCCAPS 2600074

GOLDEN GREATS: JUDY GARLAND.
Tracks: / On the Atchison, Topeka and Santa Fe / I'm always chasing rainbows / But not for me / Meet me in St Louis / For me and my gal / In between / You made me love you / F.D.R. Jones / Trolley song, The / Embraceable you / Boy next door, The / Zing went the strings of my heart / I got rhythm / When you wore a tulip / I'm nobody's baby / Over the rainbow.
LP: . . . . MCM 5023
MC: . . . . MCMC 5023

GREAT GARLAND DUETS, THE.
LP: . . . . PARAGON 1001

GREAT MGM STARS: JUDY GARLAND.
Tracks: / Over the rainbow / I don't care / Meet me tonight in dreamland / Play that barbershop chord (With the King's Men) / Put your arms around me honey / Merry Christmas / Love of my life / Be a clown / You can do no wrong / Look for the silver lining / Who? / Get happy / (Howdy neighbour) happy harvest / Friendly star / If you feel like singing, sing / Johnny one note / I wish I were in love again / Couple of swells, A / Fella with an umbrella, A / I love a piano / Better luck next time / Easter parade / When the midnight choo choo leaves for Alabama.
LP: . . . . LPMGM 29
LP: 795 856 1
MC: . . . . TCMGM 29
MC: 795 856 4

HITS OF A LEGEND.
LP: 22004
MC: 42004

I COULD GO ON SINGING (Original soundtrack).
Tracks: / I could go on singing / Overture / Hello bluebird / I am the Monarch of the sea (From H.M.S. Pinafore.) / It never was you / By myself / Helicopter ride / Interlude / Matt's dilemma.
LP: . . . . EMS 1288
MC: . . . . TCEMS 1288

JUDY AT CARNEGIE HALL.
Tracks: / When you're smiling / Almost like being in love (medley) (Includes: Almost like being in love/This can't be love/You go to my head) / Who cares? / Puttin' on the Ritz / How long has this been going on / Just you, just me / Man that got away, The / San Francisco / That's entertainment / Come rain or come shine / You're nearer / Foggy day, A / If love were all / Zing went the strings of my heart / Stormy weather / You made me love you (medley) (Includes: You made me love you/For me and my gal/The trolley song.) / Rockabye your baby with a Dixie melody / Over the rainbow / Swanee / After you've gone / Chicago / Trolley song, The (overture) / Over the rainbow (overture) (Not available on CD.) / Man that got away, The (overture) / This can't be love (medley) / Do it again (Not on CD.) / You go to my head / Alone together / I can't give you anything but love.
2LP: . . . . EM 2604323
MCSET: . . . . EM 2604325

JUDY AT CARNEGIE HALL.
LP: . . . . W 1569

JUDY GARLAND.
LP: . . . . LOP 14 116
MC: . . . . LCS 14116
LP: . . . . HDY 1952
MC: . . . . ZCHDY 1952
MC: . . . . MRT 40033

JUDY GARLAND COLLECTION (DEJA VU) (20 Golden Greats).
Tracks: / Over the rainbow / Moon river / When you're smiling / Ol' man river / I've got my love to keep me warm / Fly me to the moon / Get happy / Give my regards to Broadway / Rockabye your baby with a Dixie melody / Hey look me over / Johnny One Note / As long as he needs me / I don't care / Puttin' on the Ritz / Alexander's ragtime band / Nearness of you, The / They can't take that away from me / Just in time / After you've gone / Almost like being in love.
LP: . . . . DVLP 2002
MC: . . . . DVMC 2002

JUDY GARLAND: HER GREATEST HITS.
Tracks: / Get happy / Johnny one note / Friendly star / Over the rainbow / They can't take that away from me / Give my regards to broadway / Alexander's ragtime band / Almost like being in love / This can't be love / You go to my head / Who cares / Just in time / Man that got away, The.
2LP: . . . . ALB 224

JUDY GARLAND STORY, THE.
Tracks: / Over the rainbow / Rockabye your baby with a Dixie melody / Johnny One Note / Get happy! / Alexander's ragtime band / Give my regards to Broadway / They can't take that away from me / When you're smiling / Just in time / Stormy weather / Ol' man river / As long as he needs me / Moon river / Almost like being in love / San Francisco / Smile / Fly me to the moon / More / I've got my love to keep me warm / Nearness of you, The / Hey look me over / After you've gone / You made me love you / For me and my gal / Trolley song, The.
MCSET: . . . . DVREMC 07

JUDY GARLAND: VOL 1.
MC: . . . . ZCGAS 707

JUDY GARLAND: VOL 2.
MC: . . . . ZCGAS 708

JUDY GARLAND: VOL 3.
MC: . . . . ZCGAS 734

JUDY GARLAND:VOL 4.
MC: . . . . ZCGAS 743

JUDY IN LOVE.
Tracks: / Zing went the strings of my heart / I can't give you anything but love / This is it / More than you know / I am loved / I hadn't anyone till you... / I concentrate on you / I'm confessin' / Do I love you? / Do it again / Day in, day out.
LP: 2C 068 54573
LP: . . . . PM 1545734

JUDY (PATHE MARCONI).
Tracks: / Come rain or come shine / Just imagine / I feel a song coming on / Last night when we were young / Life is just a bowl of cherries / April showers / Maybe I'll come back / Dirty hands, dirty face / Lucky day / Memories of you / Any place I hang my hat is home.
LP: . . . . PM 1547701
MC: . . . . PM 1547704

LAST CONCERT 20-7-68.
LP: . . . . PARAGON 1003

LETTER, THE (Garland, Judy with John Ireland).
Tracks: / Beautiful trouble / Love in the village / Charley's blues / Worst kind of man, The / That's all there is, there isn't any more / Love in Central Park / Red balloon / Fight, The / At the stroke of midnight / Come back.
MC: . . . . EG 2606024

LITTLE GIRL BLUE.
Tracks: / Zing went the strings of my heart / Little girl blue / Lucky day / I can't give you anything but love / Puttin' on the Ritz / It never was you / After you've gone / You'll never walk alone / That's entertainment / Happiness is a thing called Joe / Come rain or come shine / April showers / Rock a bye your baby with a dixie melody / More than you know / I gotta right to sing the blues / Over the rainbow.
LP: PCD-2-1223

LIVE AT THE LONDON PALLADIUM (Garland, Judy & Liza Minnelli).
Tracks: / Over the rainbow / What now, my love / Liza (all the clouds will roll away) / Travellin' life, The / Smile / Man that got away, The / Gypsy in my soul / Hello Dolly / Together (wherever we go) / We could make such beautiful music / Bob White / Hooray for love / After you've gone / By myself / 'S wonderful / How about you / Lover come back to me / You and the night and the music / It all depends on you / Who's sorry now / How could you believe me when I said I loved you... (Full title: How could you believe me when I said I loved you when you kn) / Take me along / If I could be with you one hour tonight / Tea for two / Who / They can't take that away from me / My mammy / Make someone happy / Never will I marry / Music that makes me dance, The / When the saints go marching in / He's got the whole world in his hands / Swanee / Chicago / Over the rainbow / San Francisco / Pass that peace pipe.
2LP: . . . . EM 1249
MCSET: . . . . TCEM 1249

LIVE IN PERSON.
MCSET: . . . . DTO 10091

MAGIC OF JUDY GARLAND, THE.
Tracks: / I never knew (I could love anybody) / On the sunny side of the street / F.D.R. Jones / But not for me / I'm always chasing rainbows / Our love affair / Old black magic, The / Pretty girl milking her cow, A / On the Atchison, Topeka and Santa Fe / Embraceable you / Zing went the strings of my heart / I'm nobody's baby.
LP: . . . . MCL 1821
MC: . . . . MCLC 1821

ON THE RADIO.
MC: . . . . MR 1040

OVER THE RAINBOW.
Tracks: / Over the rainbow / Foggy day, A / Make someone happy / What'll I do? / Man that got away, The / Couple of swells, A / I'm always chasing rainbows / How about me? / Free and easy / Alexander's ragtime band.
LP: . . . . PHX 1008
LPPD: . . . . AR 30064
LP: . . . . MFP 50555

OVER THE RAINBOW (ENTERTAINERS).
LP: . . . . ENT LP 13049
MC: . . . . ENT MC 13049

RECITAL.
Tracks: / April showers / Rockabye your baby with a Dixie melody (Orchestra conducted by Freddie Martin.) / Alone together (Orchestra conducted by Jack Marshall.) / That's entertainment (Orchestra conducted by Jack Marshall.) / Chicago (Orchestra conducted by Mort Lindsey.) / Zing went the strings of my heart (Orchestra conducted by Freddie Marshall.) / When you're smiling (Orchestra conducted by Mort Lindsey.) / Come rain or come shine (Orchestra conducted by Nelson Riddle.) / Just you just me (Orchestra conducted by Jack Marshall.) / Medley (Medley: 'You made me love you', 'For me and my gal', 'The trolley song'.) / Over the rainbow (Chorus & orchestra conducted by Jack Catheart.) / Swanee (Orchestra conducted by Freddy Martin).
LP: 2604091
MC: 2604094

SHOWSTOPPERS.
MC: 4XL 9598

STAR IS BORN, A (Film soundtrack).
Tracks: / Gotta have me go with you / Man that got away, The / Born in a trunk / I'll get by / You took advantage of me / Black bottom / Peanut vendor / My melancholy baby / Swanee / Here's what I'm here for / It's a new world / Someone at last / Lose that long face.
LP: . . . . CBS 32499
MC: 40 32499
LP: 31695

TWO COMPLETE PROGRAMS (See under Crosby, Bing) (Garland, Judy, Bing Crosby, Andrews Sisters).

UNFORGETTABLE: JUDY GARLAND (16 Golden Classics).
Tracks: / Medley / For me and my gal / Trolley song, The / Swanee / I'm nobody's baby / Alexander's ragtime band / Over the rainbow / I feel a song coming on / Rockabye your baby with a Dixie melody / Medley (A) Almost like being in love / Medley (B) This can't be love / Fly me to the moon / That's entertainment / Chicago / Battle hymn of the republic / Come rain or come shine / Smile / I can't give you anything but love / Hey look me over.
LP: . . . . UNLP 001
MC: . . . . UNMC 001

WIT AND WONDER OF....
LP: . . . . SL 5179

YOUNG JUDY GARLAND, THE.
Tracks: / Stompin' at The Savoy / Swing Mister Charlie / All God's chillun got rhythm / Everybody sing / You can't have everything (From the 20th Century Fox film You Can't Have Everything.) / Cry baby cry / It never rains but it pours (From the MGM film Love Finds Andy Hardy.) / Ten pins in the sky (From the MGM film Listen Darling.) / Swanee / How about you? (From the MGM film Babes on Broadway.) / Bidin' my time (From the MGM film Girl Crazy.) / Poor little rich girl (From the musical On With the Dance.) / I never knew / Fascinating rhythm / Friendship / Buds won't bud.
LP: . . . . MCL 1731
MC: . . . . MCLC 1731

Garland, Phil

HUNGER IN THE AIR (Songs of old New Zealand).
LP: . . . . LRF 191

Garland, Red

ARTISTRY IN JAZZ.
LP: . . . . SJP 179

BRIGHT AND BREEZY.
LP: . . . . OJC 265

CROSSINGS.
LP: . . . . GXY 5106

FEELIN' RED.
Tracks: / It's alright with me / You better go now / On a clear day / Going home / Second time around / I wish I knew / Cherokee.
LP: . . . . MR 5130

GROOVY (Garland, Red Trio).
LP: . . . . OJC 061

I LEFT MY HEART.
Tracks: / Will you still be mine / Please send me someone to love / Bye bye Blackbird / Body and soul / Bag's Groove / I left my heart in San Francisco.
LP: . . . . MR 5311

MOODSVILLE 6 (Garland, Red Trio).
LP: . . . . OJC 224

RED ALERT.
LP: . . . . GXY 5109

RED GARLAND'S PIANO.
Tracks: / Please send me someone to love / Stompin' at The Savoy / Very thought of you, The / Almost like being in love / If I were a bell / I know why / But not for me / I can't give you anything but love.
LP: . . . . OJC 073

SAYING SOMETHING.
Tracks: / Undecided / What is there to say / Two bass hit / Billie's bounce / Soft

winds / Solitude / Lazy Mae / On Green Dolphin Street / If you could see me now.
2LP: . . . . **PR 24090**

STEPPING OUT.
Tracks: / Yours is my heart alone / You stepped out of a dream / I wish I knew / Have you met Miss Jones / Daahound / Here's that rainy day.
LP: . . . . **GXY 5129**

Garlow, Clarence

BON TON ROOLA.
Tracks: / Cry cry baby / I'll never hold it against you / Foggy blues / If I keep on worrying / You gonna get old / New bon ton roola / I called you up daddy / Let me be your Santa Claus / Sound the bell / Carry on / I'm just a cry cry baby.
LP: . . . . **FLY 586**

Garner, Erroll

1945.
LP: . . . . **ZET 713**

ART TATUM AND ERROLL GARNER (See under Tatum, Art) (Garner, Erroll & Art Tatum).

AT THE PIANO.
Tracks: / Caravan / No greater love / Avalon / Lullaby of Birdland / Memories of you / Will you still be mine.
LP: . . . . **BVL 040**
LP: **62311**

BEST OF COMPACT JAZZ.
MC: **830 695 4**

CLOSEUP IN SWING.
LP: . . . . **NL 89431**
LP: . . . . **BBL 7579**

COMPACT JAZZ: ERROLL GARNER.
Tracks: / Misty / Oh lady be good / Begin the beguine.
MC: **831 695-4**

COMPLETE SAVOY SESSIONS 1 (1945 - 49).
Tracks: / Play fiddle play / Dark eyesky / Laff slam laff / Jumpin' at the deuces / Laura / Stardust / Somebody loves me / Back home again in Indiana / I cover the waterfront / It's easy to remember / Penthouse serenade / Love walked in / September song / Body and soul.
LP: . . . . **WL 70521**
MC: . . . . **WK 70521**

COMPLETE SAVOY SESSIONS 2 (1949).
2LP: . . . . **WL 70542**
MCSET: . . . . **WK 70542**

COMPLETE SAVOY SESSIONS 3.
Tracks: / This can't be love / Man I love, The / Moonglow / I want a little girl / She's funny that way / Until the real thing comes along / Confessin' / Stormy weather / On the sunny side of the street / Rosalie / Everything happens to me / Stairway to the stars.
LP: . . . . **WL 70833**
MC: . . . . **WK 70833**

CONCERT BY THE SEA.
Tracks: / I'll remember April / Teach me tonight / Mambo Carmel / It's alright with me / Red top / April in Paris / They can't take that away from me / Where or when / Erroll's theme.
MC: **4062310**
LP: **4510421**
MC: **4510424**

CONCERT GARNER, THE.
LP: . . . . **JG 008**

DREAMY.
LP: **84267**

EASY TO LOVE.
LP: **8329941**

ELF, THE.
Tracks: / Cover the waterfront / Love walked in / I don't stand a ghost of a chance / Indiana / Somebody loves me / Body and soul / Penthouse serenade / Undecided / Red sails in the sunset / I can't believe that you're in love with me / Stompin' at the Savoy / Stardust / More than you know / Over the rainbow / Laura / This can't be love / Man I love, The / Moonglow / I want a little girl / It's easy to remember / Goodbye / She's funny that way / Until the real thing comes along / Confessin' / Stormy weather / I surrender dear / I'm in the mood for love / All of me.
LP: . . . . **SJL 2207**

ENCORES IN HI FI.
Tracks: / Moonglow / Sophisticated Lady / Robbins' nest / Creme De Menthe / Humouresque / How high the moon / Fancy / Groovy day / Man I love, The.
LP: . . . . **CBS 21134**
MC: **40 21134**

ERROLL GARNER AND ART TATUM VOL.1 (Garner, Erroll & Art Tatum).
LP: . . . . **KLJ 20020**

ERROLL GARNER COLLECTION (20 golden greats).
Tracks: / Misty / Girl from Ipanema / Rosalie / I'm in the mood for love / All of me / September song / Stardust / Body and soul / I only have eyes for you / There will never be another you / Man I love, The / It's easy to remember / On the sunny side of the street / This can't be love / Red sails in the sunset / All the things you are / She's funny that way / Over the rainbow / Until the real thing comes along / Stormy weather.
LP: . . . . **DVLP 2016**
MC: . . . . **DVMC 2016**

ERROLL GARNER GEMS.
Tracks: / Laura / Indiana / I'm in the mood for love / Way you look tonight / Penthouse serenade / Frenesi / Play, piano, play / Body and soul / I cover the waterfront / Oh lady be good / Mean to me / Easy to love.
LP: . . . . **CBS 21062**
MC: **40 21062**

ERROLL GARNER PLAYS GERSHWIN AND KERN.
Tracks: / Strike up the band / I got rhythm / Foggy day, A / Can't help lovin' dat man / Ol' man river / Fine romance, A / Love walked in / Someone to watch over me / Lovely to look at / Only make believe.
LP: . . . . **BDL 4004**
MC: . . . . **BDC 4004**

ERROLL GARNER: VOL 1.
Tracks: / Body and soul / All of me / More than you know / Penthouse serenade / I only have eyes for you / September song / Red sails in the sunset / I can't believe that you're in love with me / Stardust / All the things you are / On the sunny side of the street.
LP: . . . . **SM 3718**
MC: . . . . **MC 3718**

ERROLL GARNER: VOL 2.
LP: . . . . **SM 3719**

GEMINI.
Tracks: / How high the moon / It could happen to you / Gemini / When a gypsy makes his violin cry / Tea for two / Something / Eldorado / These foolish things.
LP: . . . . **BDL 4007**
MC: . . . . **BDC 4007**

GREAT GARNER, THE.
Tracks: / Way you look tonight / Turquoise / Pavanne / Impressions / Confessin' / I may be wrong / Skylark / Summertime / Flamingo / Reverie / Blue and sentimental / I can't give you anything but love.
LP: **50243**

JAZZ TIME VOL.7.
LP: **502707**

KING OF THE JAZZ PIANO.
Tracks: / Moonglow / Stardust / Confessin' / Over the rainbow / All of me / I surrender dear / Undecided / Stormy weather / Stompin' at the savoy / I'm in the mood for love / Red sails in the sunset / I can't believe you're in love with me.
LP: . . . . **MTM 011**

LIVE: ERROLL GARNER TRIO (Garner Trio, Erroll).
Tracks: / Theme...Tippin' out and introduction / Just too marvellous for words / Misty / Stompin' at the Savoy / 7-11 jump, The / Lover / I'll remember April / Dreamin' / Passin' through / Two handed blues / I only have eyes for you / Theme...Tippin' out / It's alright with Met / Where or when / Tea for three.
LP: . . . . **EB 404**

LONG AGO AND FAR AWAY.
Tracks: / When Johnny comes marching home / It could happen to you / I don't know why / It could happen to you (2) / My heart stood still / When you're smiling / Long ago and far away / Poor butterfly / Spring is here / Petite waltz / Petite waltz bounce / Lover / How high the moon / People will say we're in love / Laura / I cover the waterfront / Penthouse serenade.
LP: **4606141**

MISTY.
Tracks: / Misty / Very thought of you, The / It might as well be spring / Dreamy / I didn't know what time it was / Moment's delight / On the street where you live / Other voices / This is always / Solitaire / St. Louis blues / Summertime / 'S wonderful / Easy to love / Way you look tonight / I'm in the mood for love.
LP: . . . . **CBS 32260**
MC: **40-32260**

MISTY/CONCERT BY THE SEA.
Tracks: / Misty / Very thought of you, The / It might as well be spring / Dreamy / I didn't know what time it was / Moment's delight / On the street where you live / Other voices / This is always / Solitaire / St. Louis blues / Summertime / 'S wonderful / Easy to love / I'll remember April / Teach me tonight / Mambo Carmel / Autumn leaves / It's alright with me / Red top / April in Paris / They can't take that away from me / How could you do a thing like this to me? / Where or when / Erroll's theme / Way you look tonight / I'm in the mood for love.
2LP: . . . . **CBS 22185**
MCSET: **40 22185**

MOONGLOW.
LP: . . . . **PM 1652401**
MC: **1652404**

MOST HAPPY PIANO.
Tracks: / But not for me / Alexander's ragtime band / Time on my hands / Girl of my dreams / Mambo 207 / Way back blues / Ol' man river / Full moon and empty arms / Passing through.
LP: **4503061**
MC: **4503064**

NIGHT AT THE MOVIES, A.
Tracks: / You made me love you / As time goes by / Sonny boy / Charmaine / I found a million dollar baby / I'll get by / Three o'clock in the morning / Stella by starlight / Jeannine / Schoner gigolo, armer gigolo / How deep is the ocean? / It's only a paper moon / Paramount on parade.
LP: . . . . **BDL 4005**

OTHER VOICES.
Tracks: / Misty / Very thought of you,The / It might as well be spring / Dreamy / I didn't know what time it was / Moment's delight / On the street / Where you live / Other voices / This is always / Solitaire.
LP: . . . . **CBS 32736**
MC: **40 32736**

OVERTURE TO DAWN.
Tracks: / I hear a rhapsody / You were born to be kissed / Overture to dawn / Autumn mood / Erroll's concerto / Floating on a cloud / I surrender dear / I got rhythm / On the sunny side of the street / Yesterdays / Fast company / Duke for dinner / Fighting cocks, The / Erroll's reverie / Lick and a promise, A / All the things you are / Gas light / Opus 1 / Clock stood still, The.
LPS: . . . . **OFF 3016-3**

PLAY PIANO, PLAY.
Tracks: / Play piano, play / Love is the strangest game / Blues Garni / Don't worry 'bout me / Loose nut / Love for sale / Frankie and Johnny / Sloe gin fizz / Pastel / Trio.
LP: . . . . **SPJ 129**

PLAY PIANO, PLAY (2).
2LP: **400028**

QUARTET.
LP: . . . . **SM 3911**
MC: . . . . **MC 3911**

RELAXIN'.
LP: **500117**

ROMANTIC AND SWINGING.
Tracks: / That old feeling / Lady be good / Exactly like you / I'll never smile again / Love in bloom / Solitaire / All of a sudden / Misty / You are my sunshine / St. James' Infirmary.
LP: **9279 113**
MC: **7259 113**

SAVOY COMPLETE VOLUME 2.
LP: . . . . **NL 70542**
MC: . . . . **NK 70542**

SHADOW OF YOUR SMILE.
Tracks: / Shadow of your smile / Girl from Ipanema / Misty / There will never be another you / Variations on misty / Yesterdays / I'll remember April / Tell it like it is.
LP: . . . . **LPUP 5115**

STARDUST.
LP: **20105**
MC: **40105**

THAT'S MY KICK.
LP: . . . . **NL 89433**

Garnett, Carlos

BLACK LOVE.
LP: . . . . **MR 5040**

Garon, Jesse

CABINET FULL OF CURIOSITIES, A (Garon, Jesse & The Desperadoes).
LP: . . . . **SPEEDLP 111**
LP: . . . . **FFUS 3302**

HOLD ME NOW (Garon, Jesse & The Desperadoes).
LP: . . . . **AGAP 001**

RAIN FELL DOWN, THE (See under Desperadoes).

Garrett, Amos

AMOS BEHAVIN'.
LP: . . . . **SPL 1053**

GEOFF MULDAUR & AMOS GARRETT (see under Muldaur, Geoff) (Garrett, Amos & Geoff Muldaur).

GO CAT GO.
LP: . . . . **WF 006**
LP: . . . . **FF 226**

Garrett, Kenny

AFRICAN EXCHANGE STUDENT.
MC: **75678215644**

GARRETT FIVE.
Tracks: / Feeling good / But beautiful / Computer 'G' / Lee Hall's blues / Odoriko / Little Dixie / Little melonae / La bamba / Tokyo tower / United we waltz.
LP: **K28P 6494**

INTO (Featuring Woody Shaw) (Garrett, Kenny Quintet).
LP: . . . . **CRISS 1014**

Garrett, Leif

CAN'T EXPLAIN.
Tracks: / Bare trees / You had to go and change on me / Stuck in the middle with you / Gimme gimme good lovin' / Love's so cruel / I can't explain / Bits and pieces / Thoughts / Run run run / Rowena / Stop in the name of love.
LP: . . . . **K 50758**

FEEL THE NEED.
Tracks: / I was made for dancin' / Groovin' / Forget about you / Once a fool / Fun, fun, fun / Sheila / When I think of you / This time / Living without your love / Feel the need.
LP: . . . . **K 50535**

LEIF GARRETT.
Tracks: / Wanderer / California girls / Put your head on my shoulder / I wanna share a dream with you / Johnny B. Goode / Runaround Sue / That's all / Bad to me / Surfin' USA.
LP: . . . . **K 50429**

SAME GOES FOR YOU.
Tracks: / Same goes for you / Memorize your number / Kicks / Little things that you do / When I think of you / Singin' in the rain / Hungry for your love tonight / Guilty / I was looking for someone to love / Give in / If I were a carpenter / Moonlight dancin'.
LP: . . . . **K 50677**

Garrett, Siedah

KISS OF LIFE.
Tracks: / K.I.S.S.I.N.G. / Refuse to be loose / Innocent side / Night of no return / Kiss of life / Groove of midnight / Ruby diamond / Baby's got it bad / Nobody does me.
LP: . . . . **WX 175**
MC: . . . . **WX 175C**

Garrett,Tommy

FIFTY GUITARS OF TOMMY GARRETT, THE.
MC: . . . . **EE 2601434**

Garrick, Michael

KRONOS.
LP: . . . . **HEP 2013**

YOU'VE CHANGED.
Tracks: / You've changed / Rhythm a ning / Like someone in love / Soft awakening.
LP: . . . . **HEP 2011**

Garrie & The Roosters

SHAKE IT DOWN.
LP: . . . . **WKFMLP 54**

Garson, Michael

OXNARD SESSIONS.
LP: . . . . **RR 37**

SERENDIPITY.
LP: . . . . **RR 20**

Garthwaite, Terry

HAND IN GLOVE.
Tracks: / If you can't love me / You don't know happiness / Some other spring / Bye bye moondance / You're fine / What's the matter with love / Here today / Ticket to Chicago.
LP: . . . . **FT 554**

Garve, Andrew

VERY QUIET PLACE, A.
MCSET: . . . . **CAT 4028**

Garvey, Keith

TALES OF MY UNCLE HARRY.
LP: . . . . **LRF 045**

Garvey, Marcus

TRIBUTE TO MARCUS GARVEY (See under Reggae) (Various artists).

Garvey, Nick

BLUE SKIES.
Tracks: / So slow / Think tough / Take a look over my shoulder / Emotional ammunition / Looking at you / Skin / Play the game / Humming / Sometimes / Don't you know? / Now is the time.
LP: . . . . **V 2231**

Garvin, Rex

SOCK IT TO 'EM JB (see under Curtis,King "Memphis soul stew").

Gary, John

SINCERELY YOURS.
Tracks: / Love me with all your heart / Yours / In the still of the night / It's magic / September song / Georgia on my mind / Don't blame me / All the things you are / I'll be seeing you / Shadow of your smile / Stella by starlight / Softly as I leave you.
LP: . . . . NL 89471
MC: . . . . NK 89471

Gary's Gang

KEEP ON DANCING.
Tracks: / Showtime / Party tonight / Do it at the disco / Let's lovedance tonight / Keep on dancing / You'll always be my everything.
LP: . . . . CBS 83583

Gash

GASH.
LP: . . . . MLCR 109

Gaskell, Elizabeth

COUSIN PHYLLIS (Branagh, Kenneth).
MCSET: CC/027

CRANFORD (Scales, Prunella (nar)).
MCSET: 418 018-4

Gaskin

END OF THE WORLD.
Tracks: / Sweet dream maker / Victim of the city / Despiser / Burning alive / Day thou gavest, Lord is ended, The / End of the world / On my way / Lonely man / I'm no fool / Handful of reasons.
LP: . . . . ABOUT 4

NO WAY OUT.
Tracks: / Dirty money / Freeman / Just like a movie star / Say your last word / Broken up / Ready for love / Come back to me / High crime zone / No way out.
MC: . . . . CARB 8

Gaslini, Giorgio

SCHUMANN REFLECTIONS.
Tracks: / Von fremden landern un menschen / Kuriose geschichte / Hasche-mann / Schmann reflections / Bittendes kind / Gluckes genius / Wichtige begebenheit / Traumerei / Am kamin / Ritter vom steckenpferd / Fast zu ernst / Furchtenmachen / Kind im einschlummern / De ditcher spricht.
LP: . . . . SN 1120

Gasparyan, Djivan

I WILL NOT BE SAD IN THIS WORLD.
LP: . . . . LAND 006
MC: . . . . LANDC 006

Gaston, Bill

WINTER AND THE WHITE WITCH.
MC: . . . . SOUND 27

Gastunk

UNDER THE SUN.
LP: . . . . PUS 0012-19

Gatecrashers

ALTOGETHER NOW.
LP: . . . . JBLP 303

TOO SHORT FOR A QUIFF.
LP: . . . . FER 015

Gateley, Sid

PARTY DANCES 70'S STYLE (Gateley, Sid & His Music).
LP: . . . . RES 001

Gatemouth

BOGALUSA BOOGIE MAN.
LP: 90035

Gates, David

DAVID GATES - FIRST.
MC: . . . . K 442150

FALLING IN LOVE AGAIN.
Tracks: / Can I call you / Where does love go / 20th century man / She was so young / Silky / Falling in love again / Starship ride / Chingo / Sweet desire.
MC: . . . . K 452206

FIRST.
Tracks: / Sail around the world / Sunday rider / Soap (I use the) / Suite: Clouds, rain / Help is on the way / Ann / Do you believe he's coming / Sight and sound / Lorilee.
LP: . . . . K 42150

GOODBYE GIRL.
Tracks: / Goodbye girl / Took the last train / Overnight sensation / California lady / Ann / Drifter / He don't know how to love you / Clouds suite / Lorilee / Part time love / Sunday rider / Never let her go.
MC: . . . . K 452091
LP: . . . . K 52091

NEVER LET HER GO.
Tracks: / Never let her go / Angel / Playin' on my guitar / Watch out / Part-time love / Chain me / Light of my life / Someday / Greener days / Strangers.
LP: . . . . K 52012

TAKE ME NOW.
Tracks: / It's you / Take me now / She's a heartbreaker / This could be forever / Come home for Christmas / Still in love / Vanity / Nineteen on the Richter scale / Lady Valentine / It's what you say.
LP: . . . . SPART 1175

Gateway Jazz Band

GATEWAY JAZZ BAND WITH GEORGE CHISHOLM (Gateway Jazz Band & George Chisholm).
Tracks: / Struttin' with some barbecue / Nobody knows you (when you're down and out) / Ain't misbehavin' / Creole love call / Sweet Georgia Brown / Shine / I got it bad and that ain't good / Surrey with the fringe on top / Black and blue / Just a closer walk with thee.
LP: . . . . FE 016

LIVE JAZZ FROM THE SOLENT AREA.
MC: . . . . VOL 4

Gathering

GATHERING.
LP: . . . . PROMLP 101

Gathering Peascods

GATHERING PEASCODS (Period dances).
MC: 30-322

Gathorne-Hardy,

CYRIL BONHAMY AND THE GREAT DRAIN ROBBERY See also Hugh Laurie.
MC: 2CCA 3058

Gatlin, Larry

GREATEST HITS: GATLIN BROTHERS.
MC: . . . . SPC 8576

GREATEST HITS: LARRY GATLIN.
Tracks: / Broken lady / Night time magic / Sweet Becky Walker / I just wish you were someone I love / Delta duet / I don't wanna cry / Do it again tonight / Bigger they are, harder they fall / Statues without hearts / Heart / Love is just a game.
LP: . . . . CBS 32129
LP: . . . . MNT 83665

HELP YOURSELF (Gatlin, Larry & The Gatlin Brothers Band).
Tracks: / Take me to your lovin' place / It don't get no better than this / Must be all the same to you / Until she said goodbye / I still don't love you anymore / Help yourself to me / Wind is bound to change / Straight to my heart / Daytime heroes / Songwriter's trilogy.
LP: . . . . CBS 84730
MC: 40 84730

LARRY GATLIN (I love country).
Tracks: / All the gold in California / Denver / Houston / Indian Summer / Sure feels like love / Midnight choir / We're number one / Nothing but your love matters / Almost called her baby / Indian Summer.
LP: 4504271
MC: 4504274

LARRY GATLIN AND THE GATLIN BROTHERS.
LP: . . . . UVL 78003

PURE 'N' SIMPLE (Gatlin, Larry/Gatlin Bros. Band/Roy Orbison/Barry Gibb).
LP: . . . . UVL 42277
MC: . . . . UVLC 42277

SMILE (Gatlin, Larry & The Gatlin Brothers).
Tracks: / Runaway go home / One on one / Say / I saved your place / Everytime freedom changes hands / Can't stay away from her fire / Get me into this love, Lord. / I'd throw it all away / Nothing but your love matters / Indian Summer.
LP: . . . . CBS 26621
MC: 40 26621

STRAIGHT AHEAD (Gatlin, Larry & The Gatlin Brothers Band).
Tracks: / All the gold in California / Piece by piece / Way I did before / Can't cry anymore / Gypsy flower child / We're number one / Taking somebody with me when I fall / How much is man supposed to take / Hold me closer / Midnight choir.
LP: . . . . CBS 84057
MC: 40 84057

SURE FEELS LIKE LOVE (Gatlin, Larry/Gatlin Bros. Band/Roy Orbison/Barry Gibb).
Tracks: / Sure feels like love / Almost called her baby / Anything but leavin' / What a wonderful way to die / Easy on the eye / Luau / Only been wounded / Whole wide world stood still / Somethin' like each other's arms / Home is where the healin' is.
LP: . . . . CBS 85982

Gator (film)

GATOR (Original soundtrack) (Various artists).
LP: . . . . MCA 25014
MC: . . . . MCAC 25014

Gatton, Danny

DANNY GATTON.
MC: 7559610324

Gaudin Fair Organ

ALL THE FUN OF THE FAIR-VOL 1.
Tracks: / Temptation rag / Puppet on a string / Alexander's ragtime band / Winchester Cathedral / Hello Dolly / Cheek to cheek / Get me to the church on time / Waiting for the Robert E. Lee / Carolina in the morning / Pretty baby / Toot toot tootsie goodbye / I'm sitting on top of the world / I'm looking over a four leaf clover / Chinatown, my Chinatown / Baby face / Chitty chitty bang bang / On Mother Kelly's doorstep / Half a sixpence / Buona sera / Harry Lime theme / I've got a lovely bunch of coconuts / Seventy-six trombones / I wonder who's kissing her now / Moonlight bay / On the Mississippi / Back home in Tennessee / When the midnight choo choo leaves for Alabam' / Where the black-eyed Susans grow.
LP: . . . . JOYS 168

ALL THE FUN OF THE FAIR-VOL 2.
Tracks: / Soldiers in the park / Soldiers of the Queen / Irish jig / At the Balalaika / Down the Mall / Over the waves / World war one medley / If those lips could only speak / Down at the old Bull and Bush / Beer beer glorious beer / Man who broke the bank at Monte Carlo, The / Did your mother come from Ireland / Whatever will be will be.
LP: . . . . JOYS 217

COME TO THE FAIR.
Tracks: / Colonel Bogey / King Cotton / Estudiantina / Tulips from Amsterdam / Knightsbridge / Piccolo polka / Around the world / Thin red line, The / Light of foot / Charmaine / Cuckoo waltz / With sword and lance / Children of the regiment / Drink drink brother drink / Hop scotch polka.
LP: . . . . JOYS 167

COME TO THE FAIR - VOL.2.
Tracks: / Roses of Picardy / Out of town / Lara's theme / Java / Kiss in the dark / Happy days and lonely nights / It goes like this (that funny melody) / Swedish rhapsody / One summer night / Vienna, city of my dreams / La ronde / Moonlight and roses / Celebrating / Diamonds are a girl's best friend.
LP: . . . . JOYS 216

Gaugers

BEWARE OF THE ABERDONIAN.
Tracks: / Young Jackie / Cruel brother, The / Monymusk lads / Keys to the cellar, The / Go to Berwick, Johnnie / Lass o' the Moorland hills, The / Bonnie lass o' Anglesey, The / Sleep sound in the morning / Donald blue / Aberdonian, The / Lochaber no more / Minister's sheep, The / Bogie bonnie belle / Ewie wi' the crookit horn / Jolly shepherd, The / Polly Stewart / Scrankly black farmer, The.
LP: 12TS 284

Gaughan, Dick

CALL IT FREEDOM.
LP: . . . . CM 041

COPPERS AND BRASS (Scots & Irish Dance Music on Guitar).
Tracks: / Coppers and brass / Gander in the pratie hole / O'Keefe's / Foxhunter's, The / Flowing tide, The / Fairies hornpipe / Oak tree, The / Music in the glen / Planxty Johnson / Gurty's frolics / Spey in spate, The / Hurricane / Alan MacPherson of Mosspark / Jig of slurs, The / Thrush in the storm, The / Flogging reel pipes / Ask my father / Lads of Laois / Connaught heifers, The / Bird in the bush, The / Boy in the gap, The / MacMahon's reel / Strike the gay harp / Shores of Lough Gowna, The / Jack broke da prison door / Donald blue / Wha'll dance wi' wattie.
LP: 12TS 315

DIFFERENT KIND OF LOVE SONG, A.
LP: . . . . CM 017
MC: . . . . CMC 017

GAUGHAN.
Tracks: / Bonnie Jeannie O'Bethelnie / Bonnie lass among the heather / Crooked Jack / Recruited colliers, The / Pound a week rise, The / My Donald / Willie o' Winsbury / Such a parcel of rogues in a nation / Gillie Mor.
LP: 12TS 384

HANDFUL OF EARTH.
Tracks: / Erin go bragh / Now westlin' winds / Craigie Hill / World turned upside down, The / Snows they melt the soonest, The / Lough Erne / First kiss at parting / Scojun waltz / Randers hopsa / Song for Ireland, A / Workers' song, The / Both sides of the Tweed.
LP: 12TS 419

KIST OF GOLD.
LP: . . . . LER 2103

NO MORE FOREVER.
LP: . . . . LER 2072

PARALLEL LINES (Gaughan, Dick & Andy Irvine).
LP: . . . . FF 4007

SONGS FOR PEACE (Gaughan, Dick & Leon Rosselson).
LP: . . . . FF 4010

SONGS OF EWAN MACCOLL (Gaughan, Dick, Dave Burland & Tony Capstick).
Tracks: / Ballad of accounting / Moving on song, The / Jamie Foyers / Freeborn man / Manchester rambler, The / Schooldays end / Thirty foot trailer / Big hewer, The / First time ever I saw your face, The.
LP: . . . . RUB 027
LP: . . . . CRO 215
MC: . . . . CROC 215

WOODY LIVES.
Tracks: / Hard travellin' / Vigilante man / Deportees (plane wreck at Los Gatos) / Do-re-mi / Tom Joad / This land is your land / Pretty boy Floyd / Philadelphia lawyer / Pastures of plenty / Will you miss me.
LP: . . . . CRO 217
MC: . . . . CROC 217

Gaultier, Jean Paul

AOW TOU DOU ZAT.
Tracks: / Don't do that / Noisy / Do / It's crazy with an accordian / What will I do with that / Do it again / How to do that (in a new way) / Technic idea / Jaques Lacan deconstuction mix / Rai it / How to drum it / How to mix that.
LP: 838 271 1
MC: 838 271 4

Gauthe, Jacques

CASSOULET STOMP (Gauthe, Jacques & His Creole Rice Jazzband).
LP: . . . . SOS 1170

RIZ A LA CREOLE (Gauthe, Jacques & His Creole Rice Jazzband).
LP: . . . . GHB 179

Gavin, Catherine

SNOW MOUNTAIN (Hood, Morag).
MCSET: . . . . COL 4501

Gavin, Frankie

FRANKIE GAVIN & ALEC FINN (Gavin, Frankie & Alec Finn).
LP: . . . . SHAN 29008

FRANKIE GOES TO TOWN.
LP: . . . . BKLP 1
MC: . . . . BKMC 1

UP AND AWAY.
LP: . . . . CEF 103

Gavioli Fair Organ

BIOSCOPE MEMORIES.
Tracks: / Midnight cakewalk ball / Row row row / My mother's rosary / Battle Connecticut march / Boston waltz / Ching chong / Sunny side up / Back to Caroline / 99 out of 100 / Tell me that you love me / Our director / Espana / My croony melody.
LP: . . . . SDL 318
MC: . . . . CSDL 318

FAIRGROUND MELODIES.
Tracks: / Cows may come cows may go / Dear old girl / Tipperary / King of the air / Dream of fairies / Dublin bay / Years years ago / Washington post / Skaters' waltz / California and you / Semper fidelis.
LP: 15-61

Gawain & The Green

GAWAIN & THE GREEN KNIGHT (Various artists).
Tracks: / Gawain and the green knight: *Various artists* / Lancelot on the quest: *Various artists*.
MC: . . . . ANV 606

GAWAIN & THE GREEN KNIGHT & THE PEARL (Various artists).
MC: 1192

Gay 90's

GAY 90'S, THE (Musical Boxes/Pianolas) (Various).
Tracks: / Last rose of summer / Old folks at home / Home, sweet home / Holy City, The / Soldiers of the Queen / I wish I was in Dixie / Love's old sweet song / Daisy Bell / Queen of the earth / Birdseller, The / Starlight, starbright / Whisper, and I shall hear / Tom Titt.
LP: . . . . SDL 312
MC: . . . . CSDL 312

Gay Divorcee (musical)

GAY DIVORCEE/TOP HAT (Film soundtracks) (Various artists).
LP: STK 105

Gaye Bykers On Acid

CANCER PLANET MISSION.
LP: NBX 001
MC: NBX 001MC

DRILL YOUR OWN HOLE.
Tracks: / Motorvate / Call me a liar / All hung up / Zen express / World war 7 blues / Git down / After blow there's suck / So far out / Drive in salvation / T.V.cabbage.
LP: V 2478
MC: TCV 2478

GROOVEDIVESOAPDISH.
MC: DRY 002
LP: MLP 002

STEWED TO THE GILLS.
Tracks: / It is are you? / Better off dead / M.A.D. / Hot thing / Testicle of God (and it was good) / Ill / Mass gyrate (Only on CD and cassette.) / Harmonious murder / Shoulders / Hair of dog / Sade dude / Teeth / Floydrix / Bedlam a go go (Only on CD and cassette.) / Fairway to heaven / It is are you (concept reprise).
LP: V 2579
MC: TCV 2579

Gaye, Marvin

18 GREATEST HITS: MARVIN GAYE.
Tracks: / I heard it through the grapevine / Let's get it on / Too busy thinking about my baby / How sweet it is (to be loved by you) / You're all I need to get by / Got to give it up / You are everything / Can I get a witness / I'll be doggone / What's going on / Abraham, Martin and John / It takes two / Stop look, listen to your heart / Chained / Trouble man / You ain't livin' till you're lovin' / Onion song, The / Wherever I lay my hat (that's my home).
LP: WL 72645
MC: WK 72645

ANTHOLOGY - MARVIN GAYE (Volumes 1 & 2).
Tracks: / Chained / End of our road, The / Mercy me / Inner city blues / Trouble man / Distant lover / After the dance / Once upon a time / Forever / It takes two / If this world were mine / Stubborn kind of fellow / Hitch hike / Pride and joy / Can I get a witness / What's the matter with you baby (with Mary Wells.) / You're a wonderful one / Try it baby / Baby don't you do it / What good am I without you (with Kim Weston.) / How sweet it is to be loved by you / Pretty little baby / Ain't that peculiar / Ain't no mountain high enough (with Tammi Terrell.) / One more heartache / Take this heart of mine / Your precious love (with Tammi Terrell.) / Little darling (I need you) / Your unchanging love / If this world were mine (with Tammi Terrell.) / You / If I could build my whole world around you (with Tammi Terrell.) / Ain't nothing like the real thing (with Tammi Terrell.) / How can I forget / Heaven sent you, I know (with Kim Weston.) / I heard it through the grapevine / Good lovin' ain't easy to come by / Too busy thinking about my baby / That's the way love is / You're all I need to get by (with Tammi Terrell.) / What's going on / Mercy, mercy me / Save the children / You're the man (part 1) / Let's get it on / Come get to this / I want you / Got to give it up.
2LP: TMSP 1128
2LP: ZL 72156

BEST OF MARVIN GAYE.
Tracks: / I heard it through the grapevine / Too busy thinking about my baby / That's the way love is / Abraham, Martin and John / What's going on? / Inner city blues / Mercy mercy me / Let's get it on / Come get to this / You sure love to ball / I want you / After the dance / Come live with me angel / Save the children.
LP: STML 12042
MC: CSTML 12042
LP: ZL 72029
MC: ZK 72029
LP: WL 72612
MC: WK 72612

DIANA & MARVIN (Gaye, Marvin & Diana Ross).
Tracks: / You are everything / Love twins / Don't knock my love / You're a special part of me / Pledging my love / Just say just say / Stop, look, listen (to your heart) / I'm falling in love with you / My mistake (was to love you) / Include me in your life.
LP: STMS 5001
MC: CSTMS 5001
LP: WL 72066
MC: WK 72066
LP: STMA 8015

DREAM OF A LIFETIME.
Tracks: / Sanctified lady / Savage in the sack / Masochistic beauty / It's madness / Ain't it funny? / Symphony / Life's opera / Dream of a lifetime.
MC: 40 26239
LP: CBS 26239

EARLY YEARS 1961-1964.
Tracks: / Can I get a witness? / I'm crazy 'bout my baby / Pride and joy / Got to get my hands on some lovin' / One of these days / You're a wonderful one / Hitch hike / Try it, baby / Stubborn kind of fellow / I'm yours, you're mine / Never let you go / Taking my time / Wherever I lay my hat / Let your conscience be your guide / Mister Sandman / It hurt me too.
LP: STMR 9004
MC: CSTMR 9004

EASY (Gaye, Marvin & Tammi Terrell).
Tracks: / Good Lovin ain't easy to come by / California soul / Love woke me up this morning / This poor heart of mine / I'm your puppet / Onion soup / What you gave me / Baby I need your loving / I can't believe you love me / How you gonna keep it / More,more,more / Satisfied feeling.
LP: WL 72507
MC: WK 72507

GREATEST HITS: MARVIN GAYE.
Tracks: / I heard it through the grapevine / Let's get it on / Too busy thinking about my baby / How sweet it is to be loved by you / You're all I need to get by / Got to give it up / You are everything / Midnight lady / Sexual healing / What's going on? / Abraham, Martin and John / It takes two / Stop, look, listen (to your heart) / My love is waiting / Onion song, The / Wherever I lay my hat.
LP: STAR 2234
MC: STAC 2234

GREATEST HITS: MARVIN GAYE (TAMLA).
LP: STML 11065

GREATEST HITS:MARVIN GAYE & TAMMI TERRELL (Gaye, Marvin & Tammi Terrell).
Tracks: / Your precious love / Ain't no mountain high enough / You're all I need to get by / Ain't nothing like the real thing / Good livin' ain't easy to come by / If this world were mine / Onion song, The / I could build my whole world around you / Keep on lovin' me, honey / What you gave me / You ain't livin' till you're lovin' / Hold me, oh my darling.
LP: STMS 5066
MC: CSTMS 5066
LP: STML 11153
MC: CSTML 11153
LP: WL 72103
MC: WK 72103

HERE MY DEAR.
Tracks: / Here my dear / I met a little girl / When did you stop loving me, when did I stop loving you? / Anger / Funky space reincarnation / You can leave but it's goin' to cost you / Falling in love again / Is that enough? / Everybody needs love / Time to get it together / Sparrow, The / Anna's song.
2LP: TMSP 6008
MCSET: CTMSP 6008

HITS OF MARVIN GAYE.
Tracks: / I heard it through the grapevine / Abraham, Martin and John / What's going on? / Inner city blues / That's the way love is / How sweet it is to be loved by you / Mercy mercy me / Too busy thinking about my baby / You / Your unchanging love / Chained / How can I forget? / End of our road, The / Little darling (I need you).
LP: STML 11201
LP: ZL 72216

HOW SWEET IT IS (TO BE LOVED BY YOU).
Tracks: / You're a wonderful one / How sweet it is (to be loved by you) / Try it baby / Baby don't you do it / Need your lovin' (want you back) / One of these days / No good without you / Stepping closer to your heart / Need somebody / Me and my lonely room / Now that you've won me / Forever.
LP: MFP 50423

I HEARD IT THROUGH THE GRAPEVINE.
Tracks: / You / Tear it down / Chained / I heard it through the grapevine / At last / Some kind of wonderful / Loving you is sweeter than ever / Change what you can / It's love I need / Every now and then / You're what's happening (in the world now) / There goes my baby.
MC: WK 72374
LP: WL 72374

I WANT YOU.
Tracks: / I want you / Come live with me angel / Angel / After the dance (Instrumental.) / Feel all my love inside / I wanna be where you are / All the way round / Since I had you / Soon I'll be loving you again / I want you (intro jam) / After the dance (plus instrumental).
LP: STML 12025
LP: WL 72027

IN OUR LIFETIME.
Tracks: / Praise / Life is for learning / Love party / Funk me / Far cry / Love me now or love me later / Heavy love affair / In our lifetime.
LP: STML 12149
MC: CSTML 12149

LET'S GET IT ON.
Tracks: / Let's get it on / Please don't stay (once you go away) / If I should die tonight / Keep gettin' it on / Distant lover / You sure love to ball / Just to keep you satisfied / Come get to this.
LP: STMS 5034
MC: CSTMS 5034
LP: WL 72085
MC: WK 72085
LP: STMA 8013

LIVE AT THE LONDON PALLADIUM.
Tracks: / You're all I need to get by (with Florence Lyles.) / Ain't nothing like the real thing (with Florence Lyles.) / Your precious love (with Florence Lyles.) / It takes two (with Florence Lyles.) / Ain't no mountain high enough (with Florence Lyles.) / Intro theme / All the way round / Since I had you / Come get to this / Let's get it on / Closing theme / Got to give it up / Ain't that peculiar / You're a wonderful one / Stubborn kind of fellow / Pride and joy / Little darling (I need you) / I heard it through the grapevine / Hitch hike / You / Too busy thinking about my baby / How sweet it is to be loved by you / Inner city blues / God is love / What's going on? / Save the children.
LP: WL 72213
MC: WK 72213

LOVE MAN.
Tracks: / Ego tripping out / Life's a game of give and take / Life is now in session / I offer you nothing but love / Just because you're so pretty / Dance 'n' be happy / Funk me, funk me, funk me / Love's plea.
LP: STML 12126

LOVE SONGS: MARVIN GAYE & SMOKEY ROBINSON (Gaye, Marvin & Smokey Robinson).
LP: STAR 2331
MC: STAC 2331

MAGIC OF MARVIN GAYE, THE.
Tracks: / How sweet it is to be loved by you / Little darling (I need you) / Take this heart of mine / One more heartache / Night life / One for my baby.
LP: TMS 3508
MC: TMC 3508

MARVIN GAYE.
Tracks: / Let's get it on / You are everything / It takes two / Too busy thinking 'bout my baby / What's going on / You're all I need to get by / That's the way love is / Midnight lady / I heard it through the grapevine / Sexual healing / Abraham, Martin and John / Onion song / How sweet it is (to be loved by you) / Got to give it up / Sanctified lady / My love is waiting / Stop, look, listen / Wherever I lay my hat.
MC: STAC 2427
LP: STAR 2427

MARVIN GAYE AND HIS GIRLS.
Tracks: / Once upon a time / What's the matter with you, baby? / It's got to be a miracle (this thing called love) / It takes two / Your precious love / Good lovin' ain't easy to come by / You're all I need to get by / You ain't livin' till you're lovin' / What good am I without you? / I want you around / Deed I do / Together.
LP: STMS 5088
MC: CSTMS 5088
LP: WL 72115

MARVIN GAYE: LIVE.
Tracks: / Beginning, The / Introduction / Overture / Trouble man / Inner city blues / Distant lover / Jan / Fossil medley (I'll be doggone) / Try it baby / Can I get a witness? / You're a wonderful one / Stubborn kind of fellow / How sweet it is to be loved by you / Let's get it on / What's going on?.
LP: STMS 5035
MC: CSTMS 5035
LP: SHM 3209
MC: HSC 3209
LP: WL 72086
MC: WK 72086

MIDNIGHT LOVE.
Tracks: / Joy / My love is waiting / Midnight lady / Sexual healing / Rockin' after midnight / Til tomorrow / Turn on some music / Third world girl.
LP: CBS 32776
MC: 40 32776
LP: CBS 85977

MOTOWN REMEMBERS MARVIN GAYE.
Tracks: / I heard it through the grapevine / World is rated X / Lonely lover / Just like a man / I'm going home / No greater love / Dark side of the world / Loving and affection / I'm in love with you / That's the way it goes / Baby I'm glad that things worked out so well / Baby don't you leave me.
LP: ZL 72463
MC: ZK 72463

M.P.G..
Tracks: / Too busy thinking about my baby / This magic moment / That's the way love is / End of our road, The / Seek and you shall find / Memories / Only a lonely man would know / It's a bitter pill to swallow / More than a heart can stand / Try my true love / I got to get to California / It don't take much to keep me.
LP: STMS 5064
MC: CSTMS 5064

MUSICAL TESTAMENT 1964/1984.
Tracks: / Crossroads / Right on / After the dance / Try it baby / I heard it through the grapevine / Loving and affection / Parting of the ways, A / Just to keep you satisfied / When did you stop loving me, when did I stop loving you / Distant lover / Anger / Witness to love, A / Baby don't you do it / Little darling I need you / Lonely lover / That's the way love is / Dark side of the world / End of our road, The / Introspection / Star spangled banner, The / Save the children / Wholy, holy / His eye is on the sparrow / Life is a gamble / If I should die tonight.
2LP: ZL 72639
MC: ZK 72639

POPS, WE LOVE YOU (See under Ross, Diana) (Ross, Diana/Stevie Wonder/ Marvin Gaye/Smokey Robinson).

ROMANTICALLY YOURS.
Tracks: / More / Why did I choose you / Maria / Shadow of your smile / Fly me to the moon / I won't cry anymore / Just like / Walking in the rain / I live for you / Stranger in my life / Happy go lucky.
LP: CBS 26783
MC: 40 26783
LP: CBS MG 241

TRIBUTE TO THE GREAT NAT KING COLE, A.
Tracks: / Nature boy / Ramblin' rose / Too young / Pretend / Straighten up and fly right / Mona Lisa / Unforgettable / To the ends of the earth / Sweet Lorraine / It's only a paper moon / Send for me / Calypso blues.
MC: WK 72210

TROUBLE MAN (Film soundtrack).
Tracks: / Trouble man main theme (2) / 'T' plays it cool / Poor Abbey Walsh / Break in (police shoot big) / Cleo's apartment / Trouble man / Trouble man, Theme from / 'T' stands for trouble / Trouble man main theme (1) / Life is a gamble / Deep in it / Don't mess with Mr. T / There goes mister 'T'.
LP: STMS 5065
MC: CSTMS 5065
LP: WL 72215
MC: WK 72215

UNITED (Gaye, Marvin & Tammi Terrell).
Tracks: / Ain't no mountain high enough / You got what it takes / I could build my whole world around you / Something stupid / Your precious love / Hold me oh my darling / Two can have a party / Little ole boy, little ole girl / If this world were mine / Sad wedding / Give a little love / Oh how I'd miss you.
LP: STMS 5036
MC: CSTMS 5036
LP: WL 72211
MC: WK 72211

WHAT'S GOING ON?.
Tracks: / What's going on? / What's happening brother / Flyin' high / Save the children / God is love / Mercy mercy me / Right on / Wholly holy / Inner city blues.
LP: WL 72611
MC: WK 72611

YOU ARE EVERYTHING (See under Ross, Diana) (Gaye, Marvin & Diana Ross).

YOU'RE ALL I NEED (Gaye, Marvin & Tammi Terrell).
Tracks: / Ain't nothing like the real thing / Keep on lovin' me, honey / You're all I need to get by / Baby dontcha worry / You ain't livin' till you're lovin' / Give in, you just can't win / When love comes knocking at my heart / I can't help but love you / That's how it is (since you've been gone) / I'll never stop loving you, baby / Memory chest.
LP: STMS 5005
MC: CSTMS 5005
MC: WK 72208

Gaylads

UNDERSTANDING.
Tracks: / Love and understanding / May be for long / Peculiar man / Little candle / Love is gone / I.N.R.I..
LP: . . . . . UAG 30236

Gayle, Crystal

6 TRACK HITS.
Tracks: / If you ever change your mind / Blue side, The / Ain't no sunshine / Lovin' in these troubled times / Dancing the night away / I just can't leave your love alone.
MC: 7SC 5048

20 LOVE SONGS.
Tracks: / Hello I love you / Cry me a river / Dreaming my dreams with you / Someday soon / I'll do it all over again / I wanna come back to you / Somebody loves you / It's alright with me / Coming closer / Don't it make my brown eyes blue? / When I dream / I'll get over you / Heart mender / Funny / I still miss someone / Talking in your sleep / Right in the palm of your hand / Beyond you / Going down is slow / Woman's heart, (is a handy place to be) (CD only.).
LP: . . . . . MFP 5629
MC: . . . . . TCMFP 5629
LP: . . . . . MFP 415 629 1
MC: . . . . . TCMFP 4156294

AIN'T GONNA WORRY.
Tracks: / Everybody's reaching out for someone / It ain't gonna worry my mind / Just an old love / Just like the blues / Whenever it comes to you / Never ending song of love / Once in a very blue moon / More than love / What he's doing now / Faithless love.
MC: C4 94301
MC: 794 301 4

BEST OF CRYSTAL GAYLE.
Tracks: / Cry / Turning away / Baby what about you / Straight to the heart / Till I gain control again / Only love can save me now / Long and lasting love, A / Our love is on the faultline / I don't wanna lose your love / Sound of goodbye, The.
LP: . . . . . K 925622 1
MC: . . . . . K 925622 4

CAGE THE SONGBIRD.
Tracks: / Sound of goodbye, The / I don't wanna lose your love / Me against the night / Cage the songbird / Turning away / Come back / Victim of a fool / You made a fool of me / On our way to love / Take me home.
LP: 923958 1
MC: 923958 4

COLLECTION: CRYSTAL GAYLE (CBS).
Tracks: / Half the way / Ready for the times to get better / Other side of me, The / Hollywood / Blues side, The / Crying in the rain / Why have you left the one you left me for? / Livin' in these troubled times / Don't go, my love / Don't it make my brown eyes blue / Talking in your sleep / Woman in me, The / If you ever change your mind / Keepin' power / Same old story, same old song / Love, crazy love / Miss the Mississippi and you / Dancing the night away / Too many lovers / What a little moonlight can do.
LP: . . . . . CBS 25169
MC: 40 25169

COLLECTION: CRYSTAL GAYLE (KNIGHT).
MC: . . . . . KNMC 13052

COUNTRY GIRL.
Tracks: / Why have you left the one you left me for? / Wrong road again / When I dream / They come out at night / Wayward wind / You never miss a real good thing ('til he says goodbye) / Forgettin' 'bout you / I'll do it all over again / Someday soon / Ready for the times to get better / I still miss someone / Sweet baby on my mind / Somebody loves you / We should be together / River road / This is my year for Mexico.
LP: . . . . . MFP 41 5693 1
MC: . . . . . MFP 41 5693 4
MC: . . . . . TCMFP 5693

COUNTRY STORE: CRYSTAL GAYLE VOL.2.
Tracks: / Keepin' power / Same old story, same old song / Crying in the rain / It's like we never said goodbye / Livin' in these troubled times / Blue side, The / Other side of me, The / Too many lovers / What a little moonlight can do / Love crazy love / Half the way / You never gave up on me / Lean on me / Take it easy / Miss the Mississippi and you / Woman in me, The / If you ever change your mind.
LP: . . . . . CST 40
MC: . . . . . CSTK 40

CRYSTAL.
Tracks: / I'll do it all over again / On my soul / Ready for the times to get better / Come home Daddy / One more time / You never miss a real good thing / Right in the palm of your hand / Forgettin' 'bout you / Let's do it right / I'm not so far away.
LP: . . . . . GO 2009

CRYSTAL CHRISTMAS.
Tracks: / White Christmas / Oh holy night / Winter wonderland / I'll be home for Christmas / Have yourself a merry little christmas / Rudolph the red nosed reindeer / Little drummer boy / Christmas songs, The / Jingle bells / Silver bells / Silent night.
LP: 925508 1

CRYSTAL GAYLE.
Tracks: / Wrong road again / Woman's heart / Hands / When I dream / Beyond you / Loving you so long now / Gonna lay me down beside my memories / You / This is my year for Mexico / Counterfeit love.
LP: . . . . . LBR 1014

CRYSTAL GAYLE (CAPITOL).
MC: 4XL 9019

HOLLYWOOD/TENNESSEE.
Tracks: / Keepin' power / Woman in me / Ain't no sunshine / You never gave up on me / Hollywood / Lovin' in these troubled times / Love crazy love / Lean on me / Crying in the rain / Tennessee.
LP: . . . . . CBS 85171

I LOVE COUNTRY.
LP: 4510001

I'VE CRIED THE BLUE RIGHT OUT OF MY EYES.
LP: . . . . . MFP 50398

LOVE SONGS: CRYSTAL GAYLE.
Tracks: / Other side of me, The / I just can't leave your love alone / What a little moonlight can do / It's like we never said goodbye / You've almost got me believin' / Help yourselves to each other / If you ever change your mind / Miss the Mississippi and you / Don't go, my love / Too many lovers / Half the way / Blue side, The.
LP: . . . . . SHM 3125
MC: . . . . . HSC 3125

LOVE SONGS: CRYSTAL GAYLE (LIBERTY).
Tracks: / Hello I love you / Cry me a river / Dreaming my dreams with you / Some day soon / I'll do it all over again / I wanna come back to you / Somebody loves you / It's alright with me / Coming closer / Don't it make my brown eyes blue / When I dream / I'll get over you / Heart mender / Funny / I still miss someone / Talking in your sleep / Right in the palm of your hand / Beyond you / Going down slow / Woman's heart.
LP: . . . . . LBR 1044

MISS THE MISSISSIPPI.
Tracks: / Half the way / Other side for one more,The / Room for one more, honey / Don't go my love / Dancing the night away / It's like we never said goodbye / Blue side, The / Little bit of rain, A / Danger zone / Miss the Mississippi and you.
LP: . . . . . CBS 32767
MC: 40 32767
LP: . . . . . CBS 86102

MOST BEAUTIFUL SONGS OF CRYSTAL GALE, THE.
LP: 022 58165
MC: 222 58165

NOBODY WANTS TO BE ALONE.
Tracks: / Long and lasting love, A / Tonight, tonight / Nobody wants to be alone / Love does that to fools / Coming to the dance / You were there for me / Touch and go / Someone like you / New way to say I love you, A / God bless the child.
LP: 925154 1
MC: 925154 4

NOBODY'S ANGEL.
Tracks: / Nobody's angel / Prove me wrong / Tennessee nights / When love is new / Hopeless romantic / Love found me / Heat / After the best / Love may find out.
LP: 925706 1
MC: 925706 4

SINGLES ALBUM: CRYSTAL GAYLE.
Tracks: / Somebody loves you / Wrong road again / I'll get over you / High time / Ready for the times to get better / You never miss a real good thing (till he says goodbye) / River road / Don't it make my brown eyes blue / When I dream / Talking in your sleep / Why have you left the one you left me for / All I wanna do in life / We should be together / Too deep for tears.
LP: . . . . . ATAK 1
MC: . . . . . TCATAK 1
LP: . . . . . UAG 30287
MC: . . . . . TCK 30287

SOMEBODY LOVES YOU.
Tracks: / Before I'm fool enough / I'll get over you / Sweet baby on my mind / I want to lose me in you / High time / Wrong road again / Somebody loves you / What you've done for me / Coming closer / Dreaming my dreams with you / What I've been needin' / They come out at night.
MC: 4XL 9021
LP: . . . . . GO 2023

STRAIGHT TO THE HEART.
Tracks: / Straight to the heart / Cry / Take this heart / Little bit closer, A / Do I have to say goodbye / Deep down / Crazy in the heart / Only love can save me now / Nobody should have to love this way / Lonely girl.
MC: 925405 1

TALKING IN YOUR SLEEP.
Tracks: / Don't it make my brown eyes blue / All I wanna do in life / Paintin' this old town blue / I want to lose me in you / Your old cold shoulder / Green door / When I dream / It's alright with me / Before I'm fool enough / Gonna lay me down beside my memories / Your kisses will / One more time / Lay back lover / You / Let's do it right / Restless / Too deep for tears / Too good to throw away / Loving you so long now / Talking in your sleep.
LP: . . . . . EMS 1289
MC: . . . . . TCEMS 1289

THESE DAYS.
Tracks: / Too many lovers / If you ever change your mind / Ain't no love in the heart of the city / Same old story / Help yourselves to each other / Take it easy / I just can't leave your love alone / You've almost got me believin' / Lover man / What a little moonlight can do.
LP: . . . . . CBS 84529

TRUE LOVE.
Tracks: / Our love is on the faultline / Deeper in the fire / Till I gain control again / Baby what about you? / You bring out the lover in me / Take me to the dance / True love / Everything I own / Let your feelings show / Easier said than done / He is beautiful to me.
LP: . . . . . E 0222
MC: . . . . . E 02224

WE MUST BELIEVE IN MAGIC.
Tracks: / Don't it make my brown eyes blue / I wanna come back to you / River road / It's alright with me / Going down slow / All I wanna do in life / Make a dream come true / Green door / We must believe in magic.
MC: . . . . . TCK 30108
LP: . . . . . UAG 30108
LP: . . . . . GO 2016

WE SHOULD BE TOGETHER.
LP: . . . . . UAG 30256

WOMAN IN ME, THE.
LP: . . . . . SHM 3166
MC: . . . . . HSC 3166

Gaylor, Hal

TRIO, THE (Gaylor, Hal, Walter Norris, Billy Bean).
Tracks: / Grooveyard / Smoke gets in your eyes / End of a love affair, The / Scramble / Out front / Che-low / For heaven's sake / D & D.
LP: . . . . . RSLP 380

Gaylords

THEIR TOP HITS.
MC: 823

Gaynair, Wilton

BLUE BOGEY (Gaynair, Wilton 'Bogey').
Tracks: / Wilton's mood / Deborah / Joy spring / Rhythm / Blues for Tony / Way you look tonight.
LP: . . . . . JASM 2016

Gaynor, Gloria

GLORIA GAYNOR (ECSTASY).
Tracks: / Runaround love / Mack side / Stop in the name of love / Tease me / America / For you my love / Love me real / Even a fool would let go.
LP: . . . . . XTLP 1
MC: . . . . . XTCC 1

GLORIA GAYNOR (POLYDOR).
Tracks: / Let me know (I have a right) / Say somethin' / You took me in again / Don't stop us / Tonight / Can't fight the feelin' / Midnight rocker / One number one.
LP: 2391426

GREATEST HITS: GLORIA GAYNOR.
Tracks: / I will survive / Never can say goodbye / Reach out I'll be there / Casanova Brown / We can start all over again / I've got you under my skin / If you want it / Do it yourself / Let me know (I have a right) / Honeybee / All I need is your sweet lovin' / Be mine / Most of all / Walk on by / How high the moon.
LP: 248 257 3
MC: 319 257 3

HEART AND SOUL OF GLORIA GAYNOR.
Tracks: / Never can say goodbye / All I need is your sweet lovin' / Anybody wanna party? / Let's mend what's been broken / Ain't no bigger fool / Substitute / Reach out (I'll be there) / How the moon / Honey bee / Walk on by / Let's make a deal / (If you want it) do it yourself / Let me know (I have a right) / I will survive.
MC: . . . . . KNMC 12058

I AM GLORIA GAYNOR.
Tracks: / I am what I am / Chain of whispers / Strive eeny meeny macker rack / Bullseye / Only in a love song / I've been watching you / More than enough.
LP: . . . . . CHR 1466
MC: . . . . . ZCHR 1466

I KINDA LIKE ME.
Tracks: / I kinda like me / Fingers in the fire / Let's mend what's been broken / Yesterday we were like buddies / I can stand the pain / I love you 'cause / When you get around to it / Chasin' me into somebody else's arms / Story of the Jones, The.
LP: 2391 514

LOVE TRACKS.
Tracks: / Stoplight / Anybody wanna party / Please, be there / Goin' out of my head / I will survive / You can exit / I said yes / Substitute.
LP: 2391 385

NEVER CAN SAY GOODBYE.
Tracks: / Honey bee / Never can say goodbye / Reach out and touch (somebody's hand) / I'll be there / All I need is your sweet lovin' / Searchin' / We belong together / False alarm / Real good people.
LP: 2315 321
LP: 2482 476

POWER OF,THE.
Tracks: / Don't you dare call it love / Eye of the tiger / Heat is on, The / Every breath you take / Feel so real / Broken wings / Power of love, The.
2LP: . . . . . SMR 618
MCSET: . . . . . SMC 618

STORIES.
Tracks: / Ain't no bigger fool / I let love slip right through my hands / On a diet of you / Lock me up / All my life / Don't read me wrong / Luckiest girl in the world / Make me yours.
LP: 2391 457

Gayten, Paul

CHESS KING OF NEW ORLEANS.
Tracks: / You better believe it / Mother Roux / Down boy / Nervous boogie / For you my love / Sweeper, The / Music goes round and round / Windy / Get it / Tickle toe / Hot cross buns / Hunch, The.
LP: . . . . . CH 9294

CREOLE GAL (Gayten, Paul & Annie Laurie).
Tracks: / Your hands ain't clean / True / Peter blues and Jasper too / I still love you / One sweet letter from you / Hey little girl / Annie's blues / Gayten's nightmare / Creole gal / My rough and ready man / You ought to know / Cuttin' out / I ain't gonna let you in / Broadway's on fire / Goodnight Irene / Cow cow blues / Nervous blues.
LP: . . . . . KIX 8

Gazarian, Ani

AMAZING ANNO DAZUMAL, THE.
Tracks: / My sister / Eine ballonfahrt / Edelweiss / Liten Karin / Marche langue docienne / La noce au bobosses / Le cake walk / Wiener mad'in / Tramway / Svenska dagbladets Bostonvals / Dans le bles / Mitt soderfjas / Une fleur / For d'amour.
LP: . . . . . PHONT 7515

Gazebo

GAZEBO.
Tracks: / Lunatic / Love in your eyes / London Paris / Masterpiece / I like Chopin / Wrap rock / Midnight cocktail / Gimmick.
LP: . . . . . BABLP 4000
MC: . . . . . ZCBAB 4000

Gazza

LET'S HAVE A PARTY (Gazza & Friends).
Tracks: / Fog on the Tyne (revisited) / 70's soul medley / Elvis Presley medley / Classical house / Geordie boys / Motown magic moments / Gilbert O'Sullivan greats / All you need is love.
LP: . . . . . ZL 74857
MC: . . . . . ZK 74857

G.B. Rockers

WHEN YOU'RE HOT YOU'RE HOT.
LP: . . . . . RUN 1001

G.B.H.

CITY BABIES REVENGE.
LP: . . . . . CLAYLP 8

LP: CLAYCLP 8
LP: RR 9877

CITY BABY ATTACKED BY RATS.
Tracks: / Boston babies / Sick boy / Slit your own throat / Willie Whitelaw's willie / Big women / Heavy discipline / Bellend bop / Self destruct / No survivors / Passenger on the menu.
LP: CLAYLP 4
LP: RR 9949
MC: CLAYMC 4

CITY BABY ATTACKED BY RATS/ LEATHER, BRISTLESS...
MCSET: RR 49643

CLAY YEARS 81-84, THE.
LP: CLAYLP 21
MC: CLAYMC 21

DIPLOMATIC IMMUNITY.
LP: CLAYLP 106
MC: CLAYMC 106

DRIVEN TO DEATH.
LP: CLAYLP 105

FRIDGE TOO FAR, A.
Tracks: / Go home / Twenty floors below / Checking out / Needle inna haystack / See you bleed / Pass the axe / Crossfire / Captain Chaos / Fist of regret / Nocturnal journal.
LP: JUST 13

FROM HERE TO REALITY.
LP: JUST 16
MC: TJUST 16

LEATHER, BRISTLES NO SURVIVORS AND SICK BOYS.
LP: RR 9935
LP: CLAYLP 5
MC: CLAYMC 5

LEATHER BRISTLES STUDS ACNE.
LP: PLATE 3
MC: PLATEMC 3

MIDNIGHT MADNESS AND BEYOND.
LP: JUST 2
MC: TJUST 2

NO NEED TO PANIC.
LP: JUST 7

NO SURVIVORS.
Tracks: / Sick boy / Maniac / Time bomb / Necrophilia / I am the hunted / Generals / Catch 23 / Give me fire / City baby attacked by rats / No survivors / Alcohol / Bell end stop.
LP: CLAYLP 102

G.C.E. O Level...

ENGLISH LANGUAGE Study guide.
MC: TD 03

ENGLISH LITERATURE Henry IV part 1.
MC: TD 01

ENGLISH LITERATURE Macbeth.
MC: TD 05

ENGLISH LITERATURE Romeo and Juliet.
MC: TD 07

ENGLISH LITERATURE Midsummer night's dream, A.
MC: TD 08

FRENCH.
MC: TD 11

MATHEMATICS.
MC: TD 09

SPANISH.
MC: TD 02

G-Clefs

I UNDERSTAND (OLD GOLD) (See under Paris Sisters - I love the way).

G.C.S.E. Packs

ART & DESIGN (Longman/Pickwick Pass Packs).
MC: PASS 11

BIOLOGY (COURSE) (Longman/ Pickwick Pass Packs).
MCSET: PASS 10

BUSINESS STUDIES (COURSE) (Longman/Pickwick Pass Packs).
MCSET: PASS 01

CHEMISTRY (COURSE) (Longman/ Pickwick Pass Packs).
MCSET: PASS 06

COMPUTER STUDIES (Longman/ Pickwick Pass Packs).
MC: PASS 13

CRAFT, DESIGN & TECHNOLOGY (Longman/Pickwick Pass Packs).
MC: PASS 15

ECONOMICS (Longman/Pickwick Pass Packs).
MC: PASS 20

ENGLISH (COURSE) (Longman/ Pickwick Pass Packs).
MCSET: PASS 07

ENGLISH LITERATURE (COURSE) (Longman/Pickwick Pass Packs).
MCSET: PASS 05

FRENCH (COURSE) (Longman/ Pickwick Pass Packs).
MCSET: PASS 04

GEOGRAPHY (COURSE) Longman/ Pickwick "Pass Packs" (Longman/ Pickwick Pass Packs).
MCSET: PASS 03

HOME ECONOMICS (COURSE) (Longman/Pickwick Pass Packs).
MCSET: PASS 09

HUMAN BIOLOGY (Longman/Pickwick Pass Packs).
MC: PASS 19

MATHEMATICS (COURSE) (Longman/ Pickwick Pass Packs).
MCSET: PASS 08

PHYSICS (COURSE) Longman/ Pickwick "Pass Pack" (Longman/ Pickwick Pass Packs).
MCSET: PASS 02

RELIGIOUS STUDIES (Longman/ Pickwick Pass Packs).
MC: PASS 17

SCIENCE (Longman/Pickwick Pass Packs).
MC: PASS 16

SOCIAL & ECONOMIC HISTORY (Longman/Pickwick Pass Packs).
MC: PASS 14

TYPEWRITING (Longman/Pickwick Pass Packs).
MC: PASS 18

WORLD HISTORY (Longman/Pickwick Pass Packs).
MC: PASS 12

Gear Daddies

LETS GO SCARE AL.
LP: 8434291
MC: 8434294

Gebruder Enger

SKANDAL.
LP: SKY 024

Gedda, Nicolai

TENOR - SPRINGTIME IN SONG (Live in Concert).
LP: GLS 8007

Geddes, Graham

AT HOME WITH GRAHAM GEDDES.
LP: WGR 077
MC: CWGR 077

BLOOMS OF BON-ACCORD, THE (Geddes, Graham & His Scottish Dance Band).
MC: CWGR 048

LOCHNAGAR (Geddes, Graham & David Morrice).
MC: CWGR 137

SEVEN THISTLES (Geddes, Graham & His Scottish Dance Band).
LP: WGR 020
MC: CWGR 020

STEP IN TIME, A (Geddes, Graham & His Band).
MC: CWGR 107

Gee, H

AFTER MIDNIGHT.
LP: SV 002

Gee, Matthew

JAZZ BY GEE.
LP: RLP 221

Gee Mr. Tracey

HARMONY'RHAPSODY'DESTINY'..
LP: NCHMLP 11

SHOOTMETHATSHERBERT.
LP: NCHMLP 5

Geekais

NINCOMPOOP.
LP: STELLP 1

Geesin, Ron

AS HE STANDS.
LP: RON 28

BODY, THE (see under Waters, Roger) (Geesin, Ron & Roger Waters).

ELECTROSOUND.
LP: KPM 1102

PATRUNS.
LP: RON 31

RIGHT THROUGH.
LP: RON 323

Geet

NO PROBLEM.
LP: SSRLP 5099

Gehrman, Shura

FAIR MAID OF THE MILL, THE (See under Schubert for full details).

MAN WHO STEALS THE FLAME, THE (See under Schubert for full details).

Geils, J.

FREEZE FRAME.
Tracks: / Freeze frame / Rage in the cage / Centerfold / Do you remember when / Insane / Insane again / Flamethrower / River blindness / Angel in blue / Piss on the wall.
LP: AML 3020

J. GEILS BAND.
Tracks: / Wait / Cruisin' for a love / Serves you right to suffer / First I look at the purse / On borrowed time / Sno-cone / Ice breaker / Hard drivin' man / Homework / What's your hurry / Pack fair and square.
LP: ED 300

J. GEILS LIVE.
Tracks: / Southside shuffle / Back to get ya / Shoot your shot / Musta got lost / Where did our love go / Truck drivin' man / Love itis / Intro / Houseparty / So sharp / Detroit breakdown / Chimes / Sno-cone / Wait / Raise your hand / Start all over / Give it to me.
LP: K 60115

LADIES INVITED.
LP: K 40536

LIVE - FULL HOUSE.
Tracks: / First I look at the purse / Homework / Pack fair and square / Whammer jammer / Hard drivin' man / Serves you right to suffer / Cruisin' for a love / Looking for a love.
LP: K 40426

LOVE STINKS.
LP: 2C 070 86971

MONKEY ISLAND.
Tracks: / Surrender / You're the only one / I do / Somebody / I'm falling / Monkey island / I'm not rough / So good / Wreckage.
LP: K 50381

SANCTUARY (Geils, J. Band).
Tracks: / I could hurt you / One last kiss / Take it back / Sanctuary / Teresa / Wild man / I can't believe you / I don't hang around much anymore / Jus' can't stop me.
LP: AMLH 2004

SHOWTIME (Geils, J. Band).
Tracks: / Jus' can't stop me / Just can't wait / Till the walls come tumblin' down / Sanctuary / I'm falling / Love rap / Love stinks / Stoop down 39 / I do / Centerfold / Land of a thousand dances.
LP: AML 3028

YOU'RE GETTING EVEN WHILE I'M GETTING OLD (Geils, J. Band).
LP: EJ 2402401

Geiser

COMPILATION.
LP: ENIG 32511

Geisha

PHANTASMAGORIA.
Tracks: / You got what it takes / Shock rock school / Gangland sector 21 / Alive and scratching / Claws of sin / Underworld / S & M youth.
LP: HMILP 88

Geissler, Ladi

ROCK GUITAR OF LADI GEISLER.
Tracks: / Lonely guitar / Navajo / Geisterreiter (ghost riders in the sky) / Red river rock / Little darlin' / Banana boat song / Dreaming guitar / Ladi's guitar boogie / Stormy night guitar / Tomahawk / Helena / Wheels / Amazonas paddleboat / Little geisha / Indigo / Yellow bird.
LP: BFX 15363

Gelato, Ray

RAY GELATO'S GIANTS OF JIVE (Gelato, Ray's Giants of Jive).
Tracks: / Sing sing sing / T'ain't what you do (it's the way) / Please Mr. Policeman / Late night blues / Eel, The / Baby it's cold outside / On the sunny side of the street / Flying home / All the jive is gone / Big fat mamas are back in style again / It don't mean a thing / Perdido.
LP: BLUH 006

Geldof, Bob

DEEP IN THE HEART OF NOWHERE.
Tracks: / This is the world calling / In the pouring rain / Love like a rocket / Words from heaven / Deep in the heart of nowhere / Pulled apart by horses (Extra track on cassette and compact disc only.) / When I was young / This heartless heart / Night turns to day / Beat of the night / Good boys in the wrong (Extra track on cassette and compact disc only) / I cry too / August was a heavy month / Truly truly blue (Extra track on cassette and compact disc only.).
LP: BOBLP 1
MC: BOBMC 1

VEGETARIANS OF LOVE.
Tracks: / Gospel song, A / Great song of indifference, The / Big romantic stuff / Chains of pain, The / No small wonder / Let it go / Love or something / Thinking voyager 2 type things / Crucified me / Rose at night, A / Walking back to happiness / End of the world.
LP: 846 250 1
MC: 846 250 4

Geller, Herb

BIRDLAND STOMP.
Tracks: / Birdland stomp / Come rain or come shine / Our love is here to stay / Princess,The / Summer serenade / Confirmation.
LP: ENJA 5019

FIRE IN THE WEST.
LP: FS 139

RHYME AND REASON (Geller, Herb Octet).
Tracks: / Rhyme and reason (our birthday party) / Sudden senility.
LP: DS 874

STAX OF SAX (Geller, Herb Quintet).
LP: FS 101

WEST COAST SCENE.
2LP: UNKNOWN

Gellgud, Sir John

WORLD OF, THE (See under Ashcroft, Peggy) (Ashcroft, Peggy).

Gem Lucky Jazz

KENYAFRICA (VOL.2).
LP: PS 33002

Gemini

GEMINI.
LP: POLD 5189
MC: POLDC 5189

Gendall, Richard

CANOW KERNOW Folksoungs in Cornish.
Tracks: / Bryn cambron / Can cala me / Can wassel / Dus ha my a gan dhys / An eos whek / Glaw, keser, ergh ow-cl yma / Ma grun war'n gelynen / Hal-an-tow / Jowan bon / Trelawny / An wedhen war an vre / Nancy Hegar / Map ker dew / Carol an mysyow / An gewndryas / An edhen olow / Mar ughul yn an gwyth / Dowrow nantyan / A, pyth yn henna war dha ben? / Helghya arscott a detcott.
MC: 60-009

LUL-HA-LAY (26 songs in Cornish).
MC: 90-125

Gene & Eunice

THIS IS MY STORY.
LP: PM 1561361

Gene Loves Jezebel

DISCOVER.
Tracks: / Heartache / Over the rooftops / Kicks / White horse / Wait and see / Desire / Beyond doubt / Sweetest thing / Maid of Sker / Brand new moon.
LP: BEGA 73
MC: BEGC 73

HOUSE OF DOLLS, THE.
Tracks: / Gorgeous / Motion of love, The / Set me free / Suspicion / Every door / 20 killer hurts / Treasure / Message / Drowning crazy / Up there.
LP: BEGA 87
MC: BEGC 87

IMMIGRANTS.
LP: SITU 14
MC: SITC 14
LP: SITL 14

KISS OF LIFE.
Tracks: / Jealous / Kiss of life / Szyzygy / Tangled up in you / Evening star / It'll end in tears / Why can't I / Walk away / Two shadows / I die for you.
LP: BEGA 109
MC: BEGC 109

PROMISE.
Tracks: / Screaming for Emmalie / Bread from heaven / Wraps and arms / Upstairs / Psychological problems / Scheming / Influenza / Punch drunk.
LP: SITU 7
LP: SITL 7

Gene Syndrome

DELICIOUS, THE.
LP: SYNLP 01

General, Bob

MAKE UP YOUR MIND (See under Sparks, Trevor) (General, Bob & Trevor Sparks).

General Echo

12" OF PLEASURE.
Tracks: / Lorna she love young boy banana / It's my desire to set your crutches on fire / Me know everything about she pum pum / Old man love

young gal vegie / This are the cockie tribulation / Bathroom sex / This a loves corner / Love me waist don't bother me face / Love bump / She have a pair of headlamp breast.
LP: . . . . GREL 15

General Levy

WILD ANIMAL (See under Junior Dan) (General Levy & Junior Dan).

General Mickey (show)

GENERAL MICKEY (Original soundtrack) (Various artists).
Tracks: / We're the future: *Various artists* / Now this is a character: *Various artists* / General Mickey: *Various* artists / Can't call you my baby: *Various artists* / When you're bad: *Various artists* / Strangest stranger: *Various artists* / Why don't you look at me?: *Various artists* / We will move the world: *Various artists*/ I believe in him: *Various artists* / We wanna see more of you: *Various artists* / Hard times blues: *Various artists* / Edge of darkness: *Various artists* / Nothing's that simple: *Various artists* / Cell with no key: *Various artists* / Why did I go?: *Various artists* / We don't want him here: *Various artists* / We will move the world (reprise): *Various artists* / Why is life?: *Various artists* / Now this is a character (reprise): *Various artists* / General Mickey (reprise): *Various artists*.
MC: . . . . JM 1

General, Mikey

SOUND BOY BURIAL (General, Mikey & Andrew Paul).
LP: . . . . DIGLP 001

General Prince

PEOPLE.
LP: . . . . MOLPS 118

General Prologue (bk)

GENERAL PROLOGUE, THE / PARDONER'S TALE, THE (see under Chaucer, Geoffrey (aut)).

GENERAL PROLOGUE, THE / REEVE'S TALE, THE (see under Chaucer, Geoffrey (aut)).

General Public

ALL THE RAGE.
Tracks: / Hot you're cool / Tenderness / Anxious / Never you done that / Burning bright / As a matter of fact / Are you leading me on? / Day to day / Where's the line / General Public.
LP: . . . . V 2324
MC: . . . . TCV 2324
LP: . . . . OVED 180
MC: . . . . OVEDC 180

HAND TO MOUTH.
Tracks: / Come again / Faults and all / Forward as one / Murder / Cheque in the post / Too much or nothing / Love without the fun / In conversation / Never all there / Cry on your own shoulder.
LP: . . . . OVED 226
MC: . . . . OVEDC 226

General Strike

DANGER IN PARADISE.
MC: . . . . TO 2

General T

SHOWCASE (General T/Sister Candy/ Colonel Flux).
LP: RM004

General Trees

EVERYTHING SO-SO.
LP: . . . . BLSCLP 010

GHOST RIDER.
LP: . . . . Unknown

KINGSTONIAN MAN.
Tracks: / Kingstonian man / Ready fe talk to them / Family ram / Mr. Belly / Nuh money nuh run / Move up and down / Hero life / Plan your family / Any pint bottle - 40 cents / Horseman style.
LP: . . . . CSLP 26
MC: . . . . ZCSLC 26

LIVE: TIGER MEETS GENERAL TREES (See Tiger) (General Trees & Tiger).

NEGRIL.
LP: . . . . SDR 7596

NUFF RESPECT.
LP: . . . . SHAN 43046
MC: . . . . SHANC 43046

RAGGA RAGGA RAGAMUFFIN.
LP: . . . . RRTG 7702
MC: . . . . RRTGC 7702

TIGER MEETS GENERAL TREES (See under Tiger).

YOUNGER HORSEMAN, THE.
LP: . . . . Unknown

Generation

GENERATION, A/CANAL/ASHES AND DIAMONDS (See Canal) (Various artists).

Generation Band

CALL OF THE WILD.
LP: . . . . PA 202

Generation X

BEST OF GENERATION X.
LP: . . . . CHR 1521
MC: . . . . ZCHR 1521

GENERATION X.
Tracks: / One hundred punks / Listen / Ready steady go / Kleenex / Promises, promises / Day by day / Invisible man, The / Kiss me deadly / Too personal / Valley of the dolls / Running with the boss sound / Night of the cadillacs / Friday's angels / King rocker / Wild youth / Dancing with myself / Triumph / Revenge / Youth youth youth / From the heart.
LP: . . . . CHR 1169
MC: . . . . ZCHR 1169

GENERATION X LIVE.
LP: . . . . JOCKLP 11

KISS ME DEADLY.
Tracks: / Dancing with myself / Untouchables / Happy people / Heaven's inside / Triumph / Revenge / Stars look down / What do you want? / Poison / Oh Mother.
LP: . . . . CHR 1327
MC: . . . . ZCHR 1327

ORIGINAL GENERATION X.
LP: . . . . JOCK LP 9

VALLEY OF THE DOLLS.
Tracks: / Running with the boss sound / Night of the Cadillacs / Paradise west / Friday's angels / King rocker / Valley of the dolls / English dream / Love like fire / Prime of Kenny Silvers.
LP: . . . . CHR 1193
MC: . . . . ZCHR 1193

Generic

L.P. (Generic/Mortal Terror).
LP: . . . . COX 010

Genesis

ABACAB.
Tracks: / No reply at all / Me and Sarah Jane / Keep it dark / Dodo / Lurker / Man on the corner / Who dunnit? / Like it or not / Another record / Abacab.
LP: . . . . CBR 102
MC: . . . . CBRC 102
MC: . . . . OVEDC 344

AND THEN THERE WERE THREE.
Tracks: / Scenes from a night's dream / Snowbound / Ballad of big / Burning rope / Deep in the motherlode / Down and out / Follow you follow me / Lady lies, The / Many too many / Say it's alright Joe / Undertow.
LP: . . . . CDS 4010
MC: . . . . CDSMC 4010
MC: . . . . OVEDC 368

DUKE.
Tracks: / Behind the lines / Duchess / Guide vocal / Man of our times / Misunderstanding / Heathaze / Turn it on again / Alone tonight / Cul-de-sac / Please don't ask / Duke's end / Duke's travels.
LP: . . . . CBR 101
MC: . . . . CBRC 101
MC: . . . . OVEDC 345
LP: . . . . OVED 345

FOXTROT.
Tracks: / Watcher of the skies / Time table / Get 'em out by Friday / Can-utility and the coastliners / Horizon / Supper's ready.
LP: . . . . CHC 38
MC: . . . . CHCMC 38
LP: . . . . CAS 1058

FOXTROT/TRESPASS.
Tracks: / Time table / Get 'em out by friday / Can-utility and the coastliners / Horizon / Supper's ready / Lover's leap / Guaranteed eternal sanctuary man, The / Ikhnaton and Itsacon and their band of merry men / How dare I be so beautiful / Willow farm / Apocalypse in 9/8 / Dancing with the moonlit knight / I know what I like (in your wardrobe) / More fool me / Battle of Epping forest, The / Firth of fifth / After the ordeal / Cinema show, The / Aisle of plenty / Watchers of the skies.
MCSET: . . . . CASMC 112

FROM GENESIS TO REVELATION.
LP: 621580

GENESIS.
Tracks: / Mama / Illegal alien / That's all / Taking it all too hard / Just a job to do / Home by the sea / Second home by the sea / It's gonna get better / Silver rainbow.
LP: . . . . GENLP 1
MC: . . . . GENMC 1

GENESIS: 9 ALBUM BOX SET.
LPS: . . . . GENBOX 1V
LPS: . . . . GENBOX 1B

GENESIS: INTERVIEW PICTURE DISC.
LPPD: . . . . BAK 2008

GENESIS LIVE.
Tracks: / Watcher of the skies / Get em out by Friday / Knife / Return of the giant hogweed / Musical box.
LP: . . . . CLASS 1
LP: . . . . CHC 23
MC: . . . . CHCMC 23

INVISIBLE TOUCH.
Tracks: / Invisible touch / Tonight tonight tonight / Land of confusion / In too deep / Anything she does / Domino-part 1 (in the glow of the night) / Domino-part 2 (the last domino) / Throwing it all away / Brazilian.
LP: . . . . GENLP 2
MC: . . . . GENMC 2

LAMB LIES DOWN ON BROADWAY, THE.
Tracks: / Lamb lies down on Broadway, The / Riding the scree / In the rapids / It / Fly on a windshield / Broadway melody of 1974 / Cuckoo cocoon / In the cage / Grand parade of lifeless packaging, The / Back in N.Y.C. / Hairless heart / Counting out time / Carpet crawlers, The / Chamber of 32 doors, The / Lilywhite lilith / Waiting room / Anyway / Here comes the supernatural anaesthetist / Lamia, The / Silent sorrow in empty boats / Colony of slippermen (The arrival) / Colony of slippermen (A visit to the doctor) / Colony of slippermen (The-Raven) / Ravine.
2LP: . . . . CGS 101
MC: . . . . CGSMC 101

NURSERY CRYME.
Tracks: / Musical box, The / For absent friends / Return of the giant hogweed, The / Seven stones / Harold the barrel / Harlequin / Fountain of Salmacis, The.
LP: . . . . CHC 22
MC: . . . . CHCMC 22
LP: . . . . CAS 1052

ROCK ROOTS.
Tracks: / Silen sun, The / That's me / Where the sour turns to sweet / In the beginning / Fireside song / Serpent, The / Am I very wrong? / In the wilderness / Conqueror, The / In hiding / One day / Window / In limbo / Silent sun / Place to call my own, A / Winter's tale, A / One eyed hound.
LP: . . . . ROOTS 1
MC: . . . . KRTC 1

SECONDS OUT.
Tracks: / Squonk / Carpet crawlers, The / Robbery, assault and battery / Afterglow / Firth of fifth / I know what I like / Lamb lies down on Broadway, The / Musical box, The (closing section) / Supper's ready / Cinema show, The / Dance on a volcano / Los Endos.
2LP: . . . . GE 2001
MC: . . . . GEMC 2001

SELLING ENGLAND BY THE POUND.
Tracks: / Dancing with the moonlit knight / I know what I like (in your wardrobe) / Firth of fifth / More fool me / Battle of Epping Forest, The / After the ordeal / Cinema show, The / Aisle of plenty.
LP: . . . . CHC 46
MC: . . . . CHCMC 46
LP: . . . . CAS 1074

SILENT SUN, THE.
Tracks: / Silent sun, The / That's me / Fireside song / Serpent, The / In the wilderness / In hiding / In limbo / Place to call my own, A / Winter's tale, A / One eyed hound.
LP: 624359

SOUR TURNS TO SWEET.
LP: . . . . MACM 4
MC: . . . . MACK 4

THREE SIDES LIVE.
Tracks: / Behind the lines / Duchess / Me and Sarah Jane / Follow you follow me / One for the vine (NOT on CD) / Fountain of Salmacis, The (NOT on CD) / Watcher of the skies (NOT on CD) / Turn it on again / Dodo / Abacab / Misunderstanding / In the cage (medley) / Afterglow / Paperlate (CD only) / You might recall (CD only) / Me and Virgil (CD only) / Evidence of Autumn (CD only) / Open door (CD only).
MC: 7 565008
2LP: . . . . GE 2002
MC: . . . . GEMC 2002
2LP: 6 650008

TRESPASS.
Tracks: / Looking for someone / White mountain / Visions of angels / Stagnation / Dusk / Knife.
LP: . . . . CHC 12
MC: . . . . CHCMC 12

TRICK OF THE TAIL, A.
Tracks: / Dance on a volcano / Entangled / Squonk / Mad man moon / Robbery, assault and battery / Ripples / Trick of the tail, A / Los Endos.
LP: . . . . CDS 4001
MC: . . . . CDSMC 4001
LP: . . . . OVED 306
MC: . . . . OVEDC 306

TWO GREAT POP CLASSICS.
2LP: 832176 1

WHEN THE SOUR TURNS TO SWEET ("Genesis To Revelation").
Tracks: / Silent sun / That's me / Where the sour turns to sweet / In the beginning / Fireside song / Serpent, The / Am I very wrong / In the wilderness / Conqueror, The / In hiding / One day / Window / In limbo / Silent sun / Place to call my own, A / Winter's tale, A / One eyed hound.
LP: . . . . MACHM 4
LPPD: . . . . MACHMP 4

WIND AND WUTHERING.
Tracks: / Eleventh Earl of Mar / One for the vine / Your own special way / Wot gorilla? / All in a mouse's night / Blood on the rooftops / Unquiet slumbers for the sleepers / In that quiet earth / Afterglow.
LP: . . . . CDS 4005
MC: . . . . CDSMC 4005
LP: . . . . OVED 332
MC: . . . . OVEDC 332

Genesis (film)

GENESIS (See under Ravi Shankar) (Shankar, Ravi).

Genesis Gospel Singers

N'TUTU.
Tracks: / Momma mo akoma n'tutu / Me myame ao me nyame / Noah nda no / Monyi nyame aye / Okwamb I / Onyame begye wayey I (part 1) / Agya onyame / Onyame begye waye I (part 2) / Akri stofo nyinaa Monico / Awurade mefere wda gye / Mfa yie yo nkame nyame / N'Tutu.
LP: . . . . ADRY 5

Genesis, Lee

I WANNA DO IT (see Scandal) (Genesis, Lee & Scandal).

Genetics Of

GENETICS OF ENVIRONMENT Eysenck, Proff. H.J (Eysenck, Proff. H.J.).
MC: . . . . PT 33

Geney, Michel & Claude

MUSETTE EN FLEUR.
Tracks: / Musette en fleur / Bocage Printanier / Schneewaltzer / Festival Fisa / Rose Champetre / Accordeon joyeux / Rapide digitale / La savoyarde / Echo champetre / Musette en montagne / Sur les deux rives / Verte valle.
LP: 742068
MC: . . . . Unknown

Genocide

BLACK SANCTUARY.
LP: . . . . KRK 1004

IMAGES OF DELUSION.
LP: . . . . SAP 2 12

SUBMIT TO GENOCIDE.
LP: . . . . NRR 30
MC: . . . . NRC 30

Genova, Jackie

WORK THAT BODY.
LP: . . . . ILPS 9732
MC: . . . . ICT 9732

WORK THAT BODY INTO SKI SHAPE.
Tracks: / Warm up / Aerobics for skiers / Strengthening and fatigue-resisting exercises / Cool down.
MC: . . . . ICT 4749

Genova Jazzband

GENOVA JAZZBAND AND GEORGE MASSO 1986 (Genova Jazzband/ George Masso).
LP: . . . . FDC 3004

Gentle Faith

GENTLE FAITH.
LP: . . . . HS 27

Gentle Giant

CIVILIAN.
MC: . . . . ZCHR 1285
LP: . . . . CHR 1285

FREE HAND.
Tracks: / Just the same / On reflection / Free hand / Time to kill / His last voyage / Talybont / Mobile.
LP: . . . . CHR 1093
MC: . . . . ZCHR 1093

GREATEST HITS: GENTLE GIANT.
LP: 6381 045
MC: 7215 045

INTERVIEW.
Tracks: / Interview / Give it back / Design / Another show / Empty city, The / Timing / I lost my head.
LP: . . . . CHR 1115

MC: . . . . ZCHR 1115

LIVE - PLAYING THE FOOL.
Tracks: / Just the song / Proclamation / On reflection / Excerpts from Octopus / Funny ways / Runaway / Experience / So sincere / Freehand / Breakdown in Brussels / Peel the paint / I lost my head.
2LP: . . . . CTY 1133
MC: . . . . ZCTY 1133
LP: . . . . ESSLP 006

MISSING PIECE, THE.
Tracks: / Two weeks in Spain / I'm turning around / Betcha thought we couldn't do it / Who do you think you are / Mountain time / As old as you're young / Memories of old days / Winning / For nobody.
LP: . . . . CHR 1152
MC: . . . . ZCHR 1152

OCTOPUS.
Tracks: / Advent of panurge, The / Raconter troubadour / Cry for everyone / Knots / Boys in the band / Dog's life / Think of me with kindness / River.
LP: 6 360080
MC: 7 138046

Gentlemen Prefer

GENTLEMEN PREFER BLONDES (Original Broadway cast) (Various artists).
LP: . . . . AOS 2310
MC: . . . . BT 2310

GENTLEMEN PREFER BLONDES (Original London cast) (Various artists).
Tracks: / Overture: *Ainsworth, Alyn & Orch.* / It's high time: *Hart, Griffin & Co* / Bye bye baby: *Bryan*, Dora Stewart / Little girl from little rock, A: *Bryan, Dora Stewart* / I love what i'm doing: *Hart, Anne and Boys*/ Just a kiss apart: *Palmer, Robin* / Sunshine: *Bryan, Middleton & co* / Mamie is mimi: *Walsh, Cole & Tye*/ You kill me: *Stern, Gerald and Showgirls* / You say you care: *Hart, Anne & R. Palmer* / Diamonds are a girl's best friend: *Bryan, Dora* / Homestick blues: *Byran/Hart* / Au revoir babies: *Au revoir babies* / Keeping cool: *Hart, A, Bessie & Co* / Button up: *Bryan, D, Stewart, D & Co.*
LP: . . . . TER 1059
MC: . . . . ZCTER 1059

Gentlemen Without

TRANSMISSIONS.
Tracks: / Buddha's monkey / Eons roll by / Earth love / Islands of the future / Transmissions / Rains of terror / Unconditional love / Uchu o mamoro / Time (the clock song) / Earthlings.
LP: . . . . AMA 5204
MC: . . . . AMC 5204

Gentles, Bill

I WANT TO BE LOVED.
LP: . . . . JALP 005

Gentry, Bobbie

ALL I HAVE TO DO IS DREAM (See under Campbell, Glen) (Gentry, Bobbie & Glen Campbell).

BEST OF BOBBIE GENTRY.
Tracks: / I'll never fall in love again / Mississippi delta / Raindrops keep falling on my head / Son of a preacher man.
LP: . . . . 048 CRY 81802

BOBBIE GENTRY & GLEN CAMPBELL (Gentry, Bobbie & Glen Campbell).
LP: . . . . ST 2928

TOUCH 'EM WITH LOVE.
LP: . . . . EST 155

Gents

WAITING TO BE SEEN.
LP: . . . . PSM 10

Geordie

GEORDIE FEATURING BRIAN JOHNSON (Geordie Featuring Brian Johnson).
Tracks: / All because of you / Keep on rockin / Natural born loser / Rocking with the boys / Going down / Black cat woman / Electric lady / Can you do it / Don't do that / Ain't it just like a woman / Hope you like it / Fire queen / Mercenary man / Treat her like a lady.
LP: . . . . RBMP 5001

NO SWEAT.
Tracks: / No sweat / This time / Move away / Time to run / So you lose again / Rock & Roll / Oh no / Hungry / We make it rock.
LP: . . . . NEAT 1008

George, Catherine

RELUCTANT PARAGON (see under Reluctant Paragon) (Boyd, Carole (nar)).

George, Doctor David

VOICES OF DOCTOR DAVE.
LP: . . . . MAL 7425

George & Earl

GOING STEADY WITH THE BLUES.
Tracks: / Your highstone ways / Fifty-fifty honky tonkin' / Hi there sweet thing / I'm just passin' through / I guess you don't care / Flutter bug / Sundown train, The / Don't add an ex to your name / If you got anything good (you better save it save it) / Sweet little Miss Blue eyes / Can I / I don't know nothing about nothing / Don't fix up the doghouse / I'll keep your name on file / Gold wedding band / Goin' steady with the blues.
LP: . . . . BFX 15173

George, Jean Craighead

JULIE OF THE WOLVES (Worth, Irene).
MC: 1534

George, Lowell

THANKS I'LL EAT IT HERE.
Tracks: / What do you want the girl to do / Honest man / Two trains / Can't stand the rain / Cheek to cheek / Easy money / 20 million things / Find a river / Himmler's ring.
LP: . . . . K 56487
MC: K4 56487

George M (show)

GEORGE M (Original Broadway Cast) (Various artists).
LP: . . . . PS 3200
MC: . . . . PST 3200

George & Martha

ANOTHER HEAD.
LP: . . . . COLP 001

George, Robin

DANGEROUS MUSIC.
Tracks: / Heartline / Spy / No news is good news / French kisses / Stolen from my heart / Shout / Showdown / Hitlist / Shoot on sight / Don't turn away.
LP: . . . . BRON 554
MC: . . . . BRONC 554

George, Sophia

FRESH.
LP: . . . . WINLP 1

George, Susan

TRIP I FORGANNWG Mabsant (George, Susan & Stuart Brown).
Tracks: / Pan oeddwn ar ddydd yn cyd-rhodio / Difyrrwch gwyr trelai / Cefn mabli / Glyn cynon / LLwydcoed / Can y cardi / Emyn y glowr / Pris y glo / Ymdaith gwyr cyfarthfa / Mwynen merthyr / Difyrrwch dic dywyll / Baledwyr Merthyr / Can y wech awr / Ffarwel i langyfelach lon.
MC: 60-054

George, Wally

WAL-LY WAL-LY.
LP: . . . . RNEP 612

Georgia Grinders

GEORGIA GRINDERS AND JIM SNYDER (Georgia Grinders & Jim Snyder).
LP: . . . . SOS 1068

Georgia Mass Choir

HOLD ON HELP IS ON ITS WAY.
LP: . . . . SL 7098

WE'VE GOT THE VICTORY.
2LP: . . . . SGL 7093
MC: . . . . SGLC 7093

Georgia Melodians

GEORGIA MELODIANS 1924 VOL.1, THE.
LP: . . . . FG 402

GEORGIA MELODIANS 1924-6 VOL.2, THE.
LP: . . . . FG 405

Georgia Satellites

GEORGIA SATELLITES.
Tracks: / Keep your hands to yourself / Railroad steel / Battleship chains / Red lights / Myth of love, The / I can't stand the pain / Golden lights / Over and over / Nights of mystery / Every picture tells a story.
LP: 9604961
MC: 9604964

GEORGIA SATELLITES: INTERVIEW PICTURE DISC.
LPPD: . . . . BAK 2112

IN THE LAND OF SALVATION AND SIN.
Tracks: / I dunno / Bottle o' tears / All over but the crying / Shake that thing / Six years gone / Games people play / Another choice / Bring down the hammer / Slaughter house / Stellazine blues / Sweet blue midnight / Days gone by / Crazy Dan takes five.
LP: . . . . EKT 62
MC: . . . . EKT 62C

KEEP THE FAITH.
LP: . . . . SPRAY 301
MC: . . . . CSPRAY 301

OPEN ALL NIGHT.
Tracks: / Open all night / Sheila / Whole lotta shakin' goin' on / Cool inside / Don't pass me by / Mon cheri / Down and down / Dunk 'n' dine / Baby so fine / Hand to mouth.
LP: . . . . EKT 47
MC: . . . . EKT 47C

Georgia Sea Island

GEORGIA SEA ISLAND SONGS (Various artists).
Tracks: / Moses: *Davis, John* (With Peter Davis/Bessie Jones/Henry Morrison/Willis Proctor.) / Kneebone: *Armstrong, Joe* (With: Jerome Davis/ John Davis/Peter Davis/Bessie Jones/ Henry Morrison/Wi) / Sheep, sheep, don't you know the road: *Jones*, Bessie (With: John Davis/Peter Davis/Henry Morrison/Willis Proctor.) / Live humble: *Davis, John* (With: Joe Armstrong/ Jerome Davis/Peter Davis/Bessie Jones/Henry Morrison) / Daniel: *Proctor, Willis* (With: Joe Armstrong/Jerome Davis/John Davis/Peter Davis/Bessie Jones/Hen) / O Death: *Jones, Bessie* (With: Joe Armstrong/Jerome Davis/ John Davis/Peter Davis/Henry Morrison/W) / Read 'em John: *Davis, John* (With: Joe Armstrong/Jerome Davis/Peter Davis/Bessie Jones/Henry Morrison) / Beulah land: *Davis, John* (With: Bessie Jones/Henry Morrison/Nat Rahmings(drums)/Alberta Ramsy/ Emma) / Buzzard lope, The: *Jones*, Bessie (With: Joe Armstrong/Jerome Davis/John Davis/Peter Davis/Henry Morrison/W) / Raggy Levi: *Davis, John* (With Peter Davis/Bessie Jones/Henry Morrison/Willis Proctor.) / Ain't I right: *Morrison, Henry* (With: Joe Armstrong/ Jerome Davis/John Davis/Peter Davis/ Bessie Jones/Wil) / See Aunt Dinah: *Jones, Bessie* (With: John Davis/Henry Morrison/Nat Rahmings(drums)/Albert Ramsy/Emma Ra) / Walk, Billy Abbot: *Proctor, Willis* (With: Joe Armstrong/ Jerome Davis/ John Davis/Peter Davis/ Bessie Jones/He) / Reg'lar reg'lar rollin' under: *Jones, Bessie* (With: John Davis/ Bessie Jones/Henry Morrison/Nat Rahmings(drums)/Alberta) / Pay me: *Armstrong, Joe* (With Jerome Davis/ John Davis/Peter Davis/Bessie Jones/ Henry Morrison/Wil) / Carrie Belle: *Davis*, John (With Joe Armstrong/ Jerome Davis/Peter Davis/Bessie Jones/Henry Morrison/) / Laz'rus: *Morrison, Henry* (With: John Davis/Peter Davis/Besie Jones/Willis Proctor.) / Titanic, The: *Jones, Bessie* (With: John Davis/Henry Morrison/Nat Rahmings(drums)/Alberta Ramsy/ Emma R).
LP: . . . . NW 278

Georgia Tom

ACCOMPIANIST, THE.
LP: . . . . BD 2061

Georgiades, Michael

NATURAL PROGRESSIONS (see Leadon, Bernie) (Georgiades, Michael/ Bernie Leadon).

Georgians

GEORGIANS WITH FRANK GUARENTE 1922-3.
MC: . . . . VC 12

Georgie & Jackie

SING JUST FOR YOU.
LP: . . . . GJLP 1307

Georgio

SEXAPPEAL.
Tracks: / Sexappeal / Lovers Lane / 1/4 2 9 / Menage a trois / Tina Cherry / Hey u / I won't change.
LP: . . . . ZL 72583
MC: . . . . ZK 72583

Geraldine

IT'S ONLY LOVE.
Tracks: / Run wild, run free / Is my love in vain / Here I go again / Thank you for tonight / Love is just a moment away / Heart of Africa, The / Heart of Africa, The / It's only love / Black Jack / I'm still in love with you / Only a woman can / Will you go, Lassie go.
LP: . . . . MAGL 5055
MC: . . . . ZCMAG 5055

LOVE ME TENDER.
Tracks: / Love me tender (Elvis Presley/ Vera Matson) / You light up my life (J.Brooks) / He was beautiful (Robbins Music) / Hopelessly devoted to you (J.Farrar) / Tammy (Livingston/Evans) / Nobody does it better (M.Hamlisch/ C.Bayer-Sager) / True love (Cole Porter) / Ben (W.Scharf/D.Black) / I will wait for you (M.Legrand/N.Gimbel) / Jean (R.McKuen) / Secret love (S.Fain/ P.Webster) / Sunshine on my shoulders (Denver/Taylors/Kniss).
LP: . . . . MAGL 5068
MC: . . . . ZCMAG 5068

Geraldo

GERALDO & AL BOWLLY (See under Bowlly, Al) (Geraldo & Al Bowlly).

GERALDO AND HIS MUSIC WITH CYRIL GRANTHAM.
Tracks: / What's the reason / What a difference a day made / Rose in her hair, The / Too beautiful for words / Geraldo nights / Outside of you / Bonjour Mam'selle / Sorrento by the sea / Whispering trees / My heart jumped over the moon / Paris in the spring / With all my heart and soul / Moon was yellow, The / Rose of Italy / There's a bit of Paree in you / Chestnut man / Where an old Spanish town used to be.
LP: . . . . BUR 021
MC: . . . . 4 BUR 021

GERALDO AND HIS ORCHESTRA (Geraldo & His Orchestra).
Tracks: / Let the people sing / Jealousy / You're as pretty as a picture / Deep purple / It's de-lovely / You're a sweet little headache / In the blue of the evening / Sunday, monday or always / I want to be in dixie / Blues in the night / Russian salad / Don't sit under the apple tree / I'm old fashioned / My guy's come back / Shoo-shoo baby / Moonlight mood.
LP: . . . . SH 215

GERALDO: THE MAN AND HIS MUSIC (Geraldo & His Orchestra).
Tracks: / British Grenadiers, The / But not for me / Oh baby mine / Lisa / Ding dong the witch is dead / After you get what you want you don't want it / Cottontail / On the waterfront / Clock on the wall / Jungle mambo / April in Portugal / I lived when I met you / Velvet glove, The / Look out the window / Love me always / Latin lady / Hi lili hi lo / Shifting, whispering sands.
LP: . . . . PLE 511
MC: . . . . TC-PLE 511

GERRY'S MUSIC SHOP (Geraldo & His Orchestra).
Tracks: / Nice work if you can get it / Mardi gras / Sunset in Vienna / Foggy day / You turned the tables on me / Lonely troubadour / Does your heart beat for me / When the sun says "goodnight" to the mountain / Sweet Louise / "Swing Time" melody / My cabin of dreams / Celebratin' / Melody of love / To Mary with love / When evening comes / Music shop.
LP: . . . . RFL 2

GOLDEN AGE OF GERALDO.
LP: . . . . GX 41 2540 1
MC: . . . . GX 41 2540 4

HEART AND SOUL (Geraldo & His Orchestra).
Tracks: / Heart and soul / World is waiting for the sunrise / Two sleepy people / How do you do Mr. Right / And the angels sing / Same old story / What goes up must come down / Two dreams met / I miss you in the morning / I'd know you anywhere / How beautiful you are / My heart is taking lessons / Where or when / Deep in a dream / I hear a dream / Thanks for everything / Room 504 / Could be / When the sun comes out / Between a kiss and a sigh.
LP: . . . . SVL 153

JEALOUSY (Geraldo & His Gaucho Tango Orchestra).
Tracks: / I could be happy with you / You could never be true / My sunshine is you / Jealousy / Reginello / For you, just you, my baby / Three little times / Let me be your Carmen / Little Lady / Tonight I'm going to be gay / Dream tango, The / O cara mia / Two tears / Rosita / Old Spanish tango, An / Yira yira.
LP: . . . . JOYD 276

MEMORIES OF GERRY (Geraldo & His Orchestra).
LP: . . . . OLD 4
MC: . . . . COLD 4

MILESTONES OF MELODY (Irving Berlin introduces) (Geraldo & His Concert Orchestra).
Tracks: / Alexander's ragtime band / Everybody's doin' it, you'd be suprised / All by myself / It's a lovely day tomorrow / Say it isn't so / Top hat white day / Cheek to cheek / Saw the sea / Let yourself go / I'd rather lead a band / But where you are / Slumming on Park Avenue / This years kisses / I've got my love to keep me warm / You're laughing at me / Girl on the police gazette, The.
LP: . . . . RD 3

PENNY SERENADE (Geraldo & His Orchestra).
Tracks: / Penny serenade / Continental / Stormy weather / Nobody's sweetheart / Love in bloom / It's a sin to tell a lie / Pennies from Heaven / Star fell out of heaven / At the cafe continental / Scrapin' the toast / Robins and roses / One, two, button your shoe / I get a kick

out of you / Fine romance, A / You're a sweet little headache / Goodnight my love.
LP: . . . . JOYD 278
MC: . . . . TC JOY'D 278

SERENADE IN THE NIGHT (Geraldo, His Gaucho Tango Orchestra & Monte Rey).
Tracks: / Te quiere dijiste / Serenade in the night / Melody of love / Noche de reves / Let us be sweethearts over again / No more you / You needn't have kept it a secret / Waltz of the gipsies / When the sun says goodnight to the mountain / Lady of Spain / Margarita / Sunset in Vienna / At the balalaika / Dolores / Red roof of Brittany / Our song / Pour que? / If the world were mine.
LP: . . . . RFL 43

SINCERELY YOURS (Geraldo & His Orchestra).
LP: . . . . RFL 16

TAKE THE 'A' TRAIN (Geraldo & His Dance Orchestra).
Tracks: / Rose of Washington Square / How about you? / Flamingo / He's my guy / Lonesome road / Smoke gets in your eyes / I'll get by / Take the 'A' train / Don't get around much anymore / Keep your sunny side up / I'm so all alone / Zoot suite / Concerto for drums / I cover the waterfront / Hey good lookin' / Ragtime cowboy Joe / I'm ridin' for a fall / I dream of Jeannie with the light brown hair / Kentucky / G'bye now.
LP: . . . . AJA 5051
MC: . . . . ZC AJA 5051

TIP-TOP TUNES.
Tracks: / In a little Spanish town / Nearness of you (Featuring Carole Carr) / Top hat / Autumn concerto (Featuring Roy E) / Hallelujah (Featuring Carole Carr) / Signature tune / My heart stood still / There's a small hotel (Featuring Dick Ja) / Heather on the hill (Featuring Neville Williams and Joy Hoodles) / Rockin' through Dixie / Nature boy (Featuring Archie Lewis) / What is this thing called love? / I'm on a see-saw (Featuring Dick Ja) / So many times have I cried over you (Featuring Derrick Francis) / When Johnny comes marching home / Begin the beguine / Isle of Innisfree (Featuring Bob Dale) / Arkansas traveller.
LP: . . . . CHD 135
MC: . . . . MCHD 135

UNISSUED RECORDINGS (Geraldo & His Orchestra).
LP: . . . . HAL 14

Gerber, Mike

PASSION FLOWER.
LP: . . . . SNTF 931

Gerechtigkeits Liga

HYNOYISCHER EXISTENZIALISMUS (Gerechtigkeits Liga (Justice League)).
LP: . . . . SER 06

Geremia, Paul

I REALLY DON'T MIND LIVIN'.
LP: . . . . FF 270

MY KINDA PLACE.
LP: . . . . FF 395

Gerhard, Wolfgang

JAZZ MEETS FLAMENCO.
Tracks: / Jazz meets flamenco / Spain / Wolkentanz / Solea por bulerias / Tientos y tangoes / Nena.
LP: 813 425-1

German Folk Music

SUPER HIT PARADE.
LP: 819 392-1
MC: 819 392-4

Germany

MUSIK AUS BAYERN - MUSIQUE BAVAROISE (Various artists).
Tracks: / Tiroler holzhacker buam: *Various artists* / Ich hab'dich gern: *Various artists* / Waldler-Marsch: Various artists / Prima: *Various artists* / Prima potpourri: *Various artists* / Lili Marlene: *Various artists*/ Beliebt und bekannt: *Various artists* / Appenzeller Jodler: *Various artists* / Alte Kameraden: *Various artists*/ Flascher wein: *Various artists* / Unter maibaum: *Various artists* / Auf der Wies'n: *Various artists*/ Polka Perlen: *Various artists* / Blaue Augen: *Various artists* / Bayruscher Defilier Marsch: *Various artists*.
LP: . . . . ARN 33629

Germinal

DIN.
LP: . . . . LATEX 2

Germino, Mark

CAUGHT IN THE ACT OF BEING OURSELVES.
Tracks: / From the Brooklyn Bridge / Third coast rag / Propaganda requiem in A minor / Rex Bob Lowenstein / Intermission at the Belcourt Twin / Backstreet Mozart / Teasin' me do / Diamonds are out, rubies are in / Caught in the act of being ourselves.
LP: . . . . PL 86608
MC: . . . . PK 86608

LONDON MOON AND BARNYARD REMEDIES.
Tracks: / Political / Oriental drag / Barnyard (rhapsody in brown) / God ain't no stained glass window / Sally Baker's (low tar) dream / Broken man's lament / We got away / Immigrant shuffle.
LP: . . . . PL 85852
MC: . . . . PK 85852
LP: . . . . NL 90446
MC: . . . . NK 90446

RADARTOWN (Germino, Mark & The Sluggers).
Tracks: / Radartown / Let freedom ring (Vol. 4, 5, and 6) / Leroy and Bo's totalitarian showdown / Unionville / Economics (of the rat and snake) / She's a mystery / Pandora's boxcar blues / Exalted rose / Burning the firehouse down / Serenade of Red Cross / Rex Bob Lowenstein.
MC: . . . . PK 90550

Germs

GERMICIDE.
MC: . . . . A 108

Gerrard, Alice

HAZEL DICKENS AND ALICE GERRARD (See under Hazel & Alice) (Gerrard, Alice & Hazel Dickens).

Gerry & the Pacemakers

20 YEAR ANNIVERSARY ALBUM.
Tracks: / Oh my love / I like it / Don't let the sun catch you cryin' / How do you do it? / You'll never walk alone.
LP: . . . . DEB 1101
MC: . . . . DEBC 1101

BEST OF GERRY & THE PACEMAKERS.
Tracks: / I like it / You're the reason / I'm the one / It's gonna be alright / Away from you / How do you do it? / Walk hand in hand / I'll be there / Shot of rhythm and blues, A / Ferry 'cross the Mersey / You'll never walk alone / Don't let the sun catch you cryin' / Where have you been all of my life? / Think about love / Jambalaya / Chills / Why oh why / My babe.
LP: . . . . NUT 10
MC: . . . . TCNUT 10
MC: 4XL 9382

COLLECTION: GERRY & THE PACEMAKERS.
2LP: . . . . CCSLP 247
MC: . . . . CCSMC 247

EP COLLECTION, THE: GERRY & THE PACEMAKERS.
Tracks: / How do you do it? / Away from you / I like it / Chills / You'll never walk alone / Shot of rhythm and blues, A / You've got what I like / I'm the one / Don't let the sun catch you crying / Where have you been all my life / Maybellene / You're the reason / It's gonna be alright / I'll wait for you / Ferry 'cross the Mersey / You win again / Reelin' and rockin' / Whole lotta shakin' goin' on / Skinny Lizzie / My babe / What'd I say.
LP: . . . . SEE 95
MC: . . . . SEEK 95

FERRY ACROSS THE MERSEY (1964 film soundtrack).
Tracks: / It's still rock and roll to me / I'm the one / Unchained melody / Roll over Beethoven / Imagine / Running man / Just the way you are / How do you do it? / Ferry 'cross the Mersey.
LP: . . . . SHLP 102
MC: . . . . SHTC 102
LP: . . . . BGOLP 10
LP: 33SX 1676

GERRY AND THE PACEMAKERS.
MC: 807
LP: 1A 052 06474

HIT SINGLES ALBUM.
Tracks: / You'll never walk alone / How do you do it / Away from you / I like it / Baby you're so good to me / It's happened to me / It's all right / I'm the one / You've got what I like / Don't let the sun catch you crying / Show me that you care / It's gonna be alright / It's just because / Ferry cross the Mersey / You you you / I'll be there / I am your driver / Fine line / Face to face / Shatterproof / Shine shine / Lesson in love / One night (for lovers) / Stay alone / Temptation / She says / Hunter, The.
LP: . . . . EMS 1125
MC: . . . . TCEMS 1125

HOW DO YOU LIKE IT.
Tracks: / Shot of rhythm and blues / Where have you been / Pretend / You'll never walk alone / You're the reason / You can't fool me / Summertime / Jambalaya / Here's hoping / Maybellene / Wrong yo yo, The / Chills / Don't you ever / Slow down.
LP: 33SX 1546
LP: . . . . BGOLP 57

VERY BEST OF GERRY & THE PACEMAKERS.
Tracks: / How do you do it? / I like it / It's gonna be alright / I'll be there / Girl on a swing / Come back to me / When, oh when? / Don't let the sun catch you cryin' / You'll never walk alone / I'm the one / Walk hand in hand / La la la / It's alright / Give all your love to me / Hallelujah I love her so / Ferry 'cross the Mersey.
LP: . . . . MFP 41 5654 1
MC: . . . . MFP 41 5654 4
MC: . . . . TCMFP 5654

YOU'LL NEVER WALK ALONE.
MC: 1A 220 1583244

Gershwin Broadway

GERSHWIN BROADWAY OVERTURES (Buffalo Philharmonic Orchestra).
Tracks: / Funny face / Girl crazy / Strike up the band / Of thee I sing / Let 'em eat cake / OH Kay!.
LP: . . . . CBS 76632

Gershwin (Composer)

50TH ANNIVERSARY (Various artists).
Tracks: / Rhapsody in blue: *Gershwin, George* / American in Paris, An: *Gershwin, George* / Three preludes: *Gershwin, George* / Sweet and lowdown: *Gershwin, George* / That certain feeling: *Gershwin, George* / Looking for a boy: *Gershwin, George* / Do, do, do: *Gershwin, George* / When do we dance?: *Gershwin, George* / Someone to watch over me: *Gershwin, George* / Clap yo' hands: *Gershwin, George* / Maybe: *Gershwin, George* / My one and only: *Gershwin, George* / 'S wonderful: *Gershwin, George* / Funny face: *Gershwin, George* / I'll build a stairway to paradise: *Whiteman, Paul orchestra/Bix Beiderbecke/Bing Crosby* / Somebody loves me: *Columbia Dance Orchestra*/ Lady be good: *Hylton, Jack & His Orchestra* / Fascinating rhythm: *Savoy Hotel Orpheans* / That certain feeling: *Mackey, Percival Orchestra* / Looking for a boy: *Mackey, Percival Orchestra* / Clap yo' hands: *Wolfe, Roger* Kahn Orchestra / Do, do, do: *Olsen, George Orchestra* / Someone to watch over me: *Olsen, George Orchestra*/ My one and only: *Johnson, Johnny & His Statler Pennsylvanians* / Man I love, The: *Rich, Fred/Hotel Astor Orchestra*/ I got rhythm: *Rich, Fred/ Hotel Astor Orchestra* / Oh gee, oh joy: *Selvin, Ben Orchestra* / 'S wonderful: *Cotton*, Billy London Savana Band / Liza: *Ipana Troubadors* / Strike up the band: *Lown, Bert & His Biltmore Hotel Orchestra*/ Embraceable you: *Arden, Victor/Phil Ohman Orchestras* / Delishous: *Shilkret, Nat & His Orchestra*.
2LP: . . . . HDD 001
MCSET: . . . . CHDD 001

AMERICAN IN PARIS (Utah Symphony Orchestra).
MC: . . . . VETC 6518

GEORGE GERSHWIN COLLECTION (16 golden greats) (Various artists).
Tracks: / Rhapsody in blue: *Gershwin, George & Paul Whiteman* / Fascinating rhythm: *Astaire, Fred & George Gershwin*/ Love walked in: *Various artists* / Swanee: *Jolson, Al* / Summertime: *Bailey, Mildred* / I got rhythm: *Waller, Fats* / Foggy day, A: *Shaw, Artie* / Porgy: *Holiday, Billie* / Our love is here to stay: *Various artists* / Someone to watch over me: *Fitzgerald, Ella* / Embraceable you: *Vaughan, Sarah* / It ain't necessarily so: *Robeson, Paul* / They can't take that away from me: *Garland, Judy* / Do it again: *Monroe, Marilyn*/ Lady be good: *Gillespie, Dizzy*.
LP: . . . . DVLP 2105
MC: . . . . DVMC 2105

GERSHWIN'S BEST (Various artists).
MC: . . . . BESC 1001
LP: . . . . BES 1001

GERSWHIN'S GREATEST HITS (Various artists).
MC: 40 79024

GOLDEN AGE OF GEORGE GERSHWIN (Various artists).
Tracks: / Delishious: *Savoy Hotel Orpheans with Jack Plant* / Bidin' my time: *Savoy Hotel Orpheans with The Carlyle* Cousins / Let's call the whole thing off: *Savoy Hotel Orpheans with Carroll Gibbons, Anne Lerner* / Shall we dance?: *Savoy Hotel Orpheans with Carroll Gibbons, Anne Lerner* / Nice work if you can get it: *Savoy Hotel Orpheans with George* Melacrino / Strike up the band: *Savoy Hotel Orpheans with Anne Lenner* / They can't take that away from me: *Fox, Roy & His Orchestra* / Things are looking up: *Fox, Roy & His Orchestra* / They all laughed: *Hall, Henry & The Dance* Orchestra with Leslie Douglas / Slap that bass: *Six Swingers with Sam Costa* / Beginner's luck: *Six Swingers with* Sam Costa / Foggy day, A: *Loss, Joe & His Band with Chick Henderson* / Love is here to stay: *Harris, Jack & His Orchestra* / Love walked in: *Harris, Jack & His Orchestra* / Rhapsody in blue: *Roy, Harry & His Orchestra*.
LP: . . . . GX 41 2524-1
MC: . . . . GX 41 2524-4
LP: . . . . GX 2557
MC: . . . . TCGX 2557

GREAT BRITISH DANCE BANDS PLAY GEORGE GERSHWIN (See under Dance Bands...) (Various artists).

HITS OF GEORGE GERSHWIN (50th Anniversary album) (Various artists).
LP: . . . . HDL 112
MC: . . . . CHDL 112

PLAYS GERSHWIN.
MC: . . . . ORC 015

PORGY AND BESS (Various artists).
LPS: . . . . PORGY 1
LPS: . . . . EX 749 568 1
MCSET: . . . . TCPORGY 1
MCSET: . . . . EX 749 568 4

PORTRAIT OF GEORGE GERSHWIN (BBC Philharmonic Orchestra).
LP: . . . . PREC 5010
MC: . . . . ZPREC 5010

RHAPSODY IN BLUE (Various artists).
MC: 4278064

RHAPSODY IN BLUE (2) (Various artists).
Tracks: / Rhapsody in blue: *Various artists* / Piano concerto in F: *Various artists* / Rhapsody on a theme of Paganini (Rachmaninov): *Various artists*.
MC: 769 113 4

SELECTIONS FROM... (Gershwin, George & Kurt Weill).
LP: . . . . MRS 904

SONG IS...GERSHWIN, THE (Gershwin 50th Anniversary Tribute) (Various artists).
Tracks: / I got rhythm: *Waller, Fats* / Man I love, The: *Welch, Elisabeth* / Half of it dearie blues, The: *Astaire*, Fred / Oh lady be good: *Hylton, Jack & His Orchestra* / Little jazz bird: *Hylton, Jack & His Orchestra* / Do what you do: *O'Neal, Zelma* / Funny face: *Smith, Jack* / My one and only: *Gershwin, George* / I found a four leaf clover: *Hart, Audrey/ Irene/Charles* / Nashville nightingale: *Waring's Pennsylvanians* / Sweet and low down: *Selvin, Ben Orchestra* / That certain feeling: *Selvin, Ben Orchestra* / Liza: *Jolson, Al* / When do we dance: *Gershwin, George* / Someone to watch over me: *Lawrence, Gertrude* / 'S wonderful: *Winter, Marius* B Dance Band / Fascinating rhythm: *Edwards, Cliff* / I'll build a stairway to paradise: *Whiteman, Paul & His Orchestra*/ I got plenty o' nuttin': *Tibbett, Lawrence*.
LP: . . . . AJA 5048
MC: . . . . ZC AJA 5048

TWO SIDES OF GEORGE GERSHWIN, THE.
Tracks: / Rhapsody in blue / Three piano preludes / Andante from Rhapsody in blue / American in Paris, An / Sweet and low down / That certain feeling / Looking for a boy / When do we dance? / Do do do / Someone to watch over me / Clap yo' hands / Maybe / My one and only / 'S wonderful / Funny face.
LP: . . . . HDL 101
MC: . . . . CHDL 101

Gerty, Ric

BITTEN ZUM TANZ-IN STRICT TEMPO RHYTHM.
LP: F669.115

DANCE AROUND THE CLOCK-IN STRICT TEMPO RHYTHM.
LP: . . . . VM 16029

Get On This

GET ON THIS (See Under Dance) (Various artists).

Get Right With God

GET RIGHT WITH GOD (See Under Gospel...) (Various artists).

Get Smart

GET SMART.
LP: . . . . NERD 027

Getz, Stan

ANNIVERSARY.
LP: 8387691
MC: 8387694

ANOTHER WORLD.
Tracks: / Pretty city / Keep dreaming / Sabra / Anna / Another world / Sum, sum / Willow weep for me / Blue serge /

Brave little Pernille / Club Seven and other places.
LP: . . . . CBS 88315

APASIANADO.
LP: 3952971
MC: 3952974

AT STORYVILLE '51 (Getz, Stan Quintet).
Tracks: / Thou swell / Song is you, The / Parker 51 / Mosquito knees / Budo / Pennies from Heaven.
LP: 500079

AUTUMN LEAVES.
LP: . . . . WW 2046

BEST OF STAN GETZ.
Tracks: / Times lie / La fiesta / Street tattoo / Ligia / Don't cry for me Argentina / Club 7 and other wild places / Skylark.
LP: . . . . CBS 84236

BILLY HIGHSTREET.
LP: 838 771 1
MC: 838 771 4

BOSSA NOVA YEARS.
LPS: 823 611-1
MCSET: 823 611 4

CHILDREN OF THE WORLD.
Tracks: / Don't cry for me Argentina / Children of the world / Livin' it up / Street tattoo / Hop scotch / On rainy afternoons / You, me and the spring / Summer poem / Dreamer / Around the day in eighty worlds.
LP: . . . . CBS 83642

COMMUNICATIONS.
LP: 837 437 1
MC: 837 437 4

COOL JAZZ.
Tracks: / S'cool boy / Prelude to a kiss / I only have eyes for you / Ack, varmeland du skona / Night and day / Flamingo / Don't get scared / I'm getting sentimental over you / On the Alamo / You go to my head / Strike up the band / Out of nowhere / S'wonderful / Best thing for you, The / Fools rush in / Sometimes I'm happy.
LP: . . . . OFF 3022

DIZ AND GETZ (See under Gillespie, Dizzy) (Getz, Stan & Dizzy Gillespie).

DOLPHIN,THE.
Tracks: / Time for love, A / Joy Spring / Dolphin, The / Close enough for love (Theme for the film 'Agatha').
LP: . . . . CJ 158

EARLY DAYS, THE (SCANDINAVIA) (Getz, Stan & Oscar Pettiford).
Tracks: / Out of nowhere / Yesterdays / Fireplace blues / My funny valentine / Laverne walk / I remember Clifford / Stuffy.
LP: . . . . RARITIES 53

EARLY DAYS, VOL 2 (SCANDINAVIA).
Tracks: / Bound to be blue / Ack varmeland du Skona / Amore / Move / Spring can really hang you up the most / I like to recognise the tune / Land's end / Love walked in.
LP: . . . . RARITIES 64

EARLY GETZ (Getz, Stan & Friends).
Tracks: / Michelle / T. & S. / Terry's tune / Cuddles / Speedway / Battleground / Four and one Moore / Five brothers / Skull buster / Ante room / Pennies from Heaven / Poop deck / Marcia / Pinch bottle / Earless engineering / Be still / TV / Short P not LP / I've got you under my skin / What's new / You stepped out of a dream / My old flame / Lady in red, The / Signal / Lee / 'Round midnight / Motion.
2LP: . . . . PR 24088

FOR MUSICIANS ONLY (Getz, Stan, Sonny Stitt and Dizzy Gillespie).
LP: 837 435 1

GETZ AU GO GO.
Tracks: / Singing song, The / Telephone song / One mote samba / Only trust your heart / Corcovado / It might as well be Spring / Eu e voce / Summertime / Six mix pix flix / Here's that rainy day.
LP: 2304 173
MC: 311 200 8

GETZ-GILBERTO COLLECTION (20 Golden Greats) (Getz, Stan & Joao Gilberto).
Tracks: / It might as well be Spring / Corcovado / Here's that rainy day / Samba da minha terra / Un abraco no bonfa / One-note samba / Stan's blues / Tonight I shall sleep / Telephone song / Only trust your heart / O pato / Rosa Moreno / Singing song, The / Voce e eu / Grandfather's waltz / Meditation / Six mix pix flix / They all fall in love / All God's chillun got rhythm.
LP: . . . . DVLP 2024
MC: . . . . DVMC 2024

GETZ-GILBERTO STORY, THE (Getz, Stan & Joao Gilberto).
Tracks: / Diaper pin / Interlude on bebop / Stan's mood / Always / Night and day / I got it bad and that ain't good / Pot luck / All God's chillun got rhythm / They all fall in love / East of the sun (and west of the moon) / Telephone song, The / Eu e voce / Singing song, The / Corcovado / Only trust your heart / It might as well be Spring / One note samba / Here's that rainy day / Tonight I shall sleep / Stan's blues / Grandfather's waltz.
MCSET: . . . . DVREMC 17

GILBERTO AND GETZ (see Gilberto, Astrud) (Getz, Stan & Astrud Gilberto).

GREAT ENGLISH CONCERT, THE (See Hawkins, Coleman) (Getz, Stan/ Coleman Hawkins/Roy Eldridge).

HIGHLIGHTS.
MCSET: 8474304

IT MIGHT AS WELL BE SPRING.
Tracks: / On the Alamo / Gone with the wind / Yesterdays / Sweetie pie / You go to my head / Hershey bar / Tootsie roll / Strike up the band / Imagination / For stompers only / Navy blue / Out of nowhere / S' wonderful / Penny / Split kick / It might as well be Spring / Best thing for you / Melody express / Yvette / Potter's luck / Song is you / Wildwood / Lullaby of Birdland / Autumn leaves / Fools rush in / These foolish things.
2LP: . . . . VJD 573

JAZZ SAMBA (Getz, Stan & Charlie Byrd).
LP: . . . . SULP 9013
LP: 810 061-1
MC: 810 061-4

JAZZ SAMBA ENCORE (Getz, Stan & Luis Bonfa).
Tracks: / Sambalero / So danco samba / O morro noa tem vez / Insensatez / Samba de duas notas / Mania de Maria / Saudade vem correndo / Um abraco no Getz / Ebony samba / Menina flor.
LP: . . . . V 68523

JAZZ SUMMET (Getz, Stan and Dave Brubeck).
2LP: 400015

LET THERE BE LOVE (see Bell, Dee) (Getz, Stan/Dee Bell).

LINE FOR LYONS (Getz, Stan & Chet Baker).
Tracks: / Just friends / Stella by starlight / Airegin / My funny valentine / Milestones / Dear old stockholm / Line for lyons.
LP: . . . . SNTF 899

LIVE AT THE VILLAGE VANGUARD.
Tracks: / Feather merchant / Polka dots and moonbeams / Jordu / Is it true what they say about Dixie? / Time after time / To the ends of the earth / Stars fell on Alabama.
LP: . . . . INGO 1

LYRICAL STAN GETZ, THE.
Tracks: / Willow weep for me / La fiesta / Captain Marvel / Ligia / Misty / Lover man (oh where can you be).
LP: 4608191
MC: 4608194

MIDEM - LIVE,'80 (Getz, Stan, Paul Horn and Mike Carson).
Tracks: / Heartplace / Kali-au / Chappaqua / Nature boy / Impromptu / Samba de Orfeu / Work song.
LP: . . . . GATE 7004
MC: . . . . CGATE 7004

MOONLIGHT IN VERMONT (Getz, Stan & Johnny Smith).
Tracks: / Moonlight in Vermont / Taboo / Tenderly / Jaguar / Stars fell on Alabama / Where or when / Foggy day, A / I didn't know what time it was / It might as well be spring / On the Alamo / Lullaby of Birdland / These foolish things / Autumn leaves / Imagination / Dear old Stockholm / When I fall in love / Nearness of you, The / Satin doll / Deep purple / Sentimental journey.
LP: . . . . VJD 539

OPUS DE BOP.
LP: . . . . WL 70516

PEACOCK (Getz, Stan & Jimmy Rowles).
Tracks: / I'll never be the same / Lester left town / Body and soul / What am I here for / Serenade to Sweden / Chess players / Mosaic / Peacocks / My buddy / Hour of parting / Rose Marie / This is all I ask / Skylark / Would you like to take a walk.
LP: . . . . CBS 21138

POETRY (Getz, Stan & Albert Dailey).
Tracks: / Confirmation / Child is born, A / Tune up / Lover man / Night in Tunisia / Spring can really hang you up the most / Round midnight.
LP: 9603701

PORTRAITS (Getz, Stan Quartet).
Tracks: / Sweet rain / Wee / Lush life / Night time street / La fiesta.
LP: . . . . LPPS 111 09

PURE GETZ (Getz, Stan Quartet).
Tracks: / On the up and up / Blood count / Very early / Sippin' at bells / I wish I knew / Come rain or come shine / Tempus fugit.
LP: . . . . CJ 188
MC: . . . . CJC 188

ROOST YEARS, THE (The Best of Stan Getz).
Tracks: / Gone with the wind / Yesterdays / Hershey Bar / Imagination / Split kick / It might as well be Spring / Parker '51 / Signal / Everything happens to me / Budo / Potter's luck / Wild wood / Autumn leaves / Lullaby of Birdland / Moonlight in Vermont / Sometimes I'm happy.
MC: . . . . TCROU 1047

SERENITY.
LP: 838 770 1
MC: 838 770 4

STAN GETZ.
Tracks: / Lover come back to me / Yesterdays / There will never be another you / How high the moon / Strike up the band / Get happy / Dear old Stockholm / Pernod.
LP: . . . . QU 013
LP: . . . . SM 3967

STAN GETZ (Compact/Walkman Jazz).
MC: 831 368-4

STAN GETZ AND FRIENDS Compact/ Walkman jazz (Getz, Stan & Friends).
Tracks: / Desafinado / Corcovado (Quiet nights) / Moonlight in Vermont / So danc, O samba / Summertime / One note samba / Manha de carmava / How insensitive / O grande amor / O pato (The duck) / Here's that rainy day / Girl from Ipanema, The.
MC: 835 317 4

STAN GETZ AND JOAO GILBERTO (Getz, Stan & Joao Gilberto).
Tracks: / Girl from Ipanema / Doralice / Para vachuchar / Meu coracao / Desafinado / Corcovado / So dance smba / O grande amor / Vivo sohando.
LP: 230 407 1

STAN GETZ AND MILES DAVIS (Getz, Stan & Miles Davis).
LP: . . . . KLJ 20013

STAN GETZ AT STORYVILLE.
2LP: . . . . VJD 554

STAN GETZ AT STORYVILLE VOL. I.
Tracks: / Thou swell / Song is you, The / Mosquito knees / Pennies from Heaven / Move / Parker 51.
LP: . . . . ROU 1016
LP: 794 505 1

STAN GETZ AT STORYVILLE VOL. II.
Tracks: / Hershey bar / Rubberneck / Signal / Everything happens to me / Jumping with symphony Sid / Yesterdays / Budo.
LP: . . . . ROU 1017

STAN GETZ & BOB BROOKMEYER (Getz, Stan & Bob Brookmeyer).
Tracks: / Minuet circa / Who could care? / Nice work if you can get it / Thump, thump, thump! / Nightingale sang in Berkeley Square, A / Love jumped out.
LP: 8133 591

STAN GETZ IN PARIS 1956.
LP: . . . . FS 7

STAN GETZ IN PARIS 1958.
LP: . . . . ROYALLD 4002

STAN GETZ IN STOCKHOLM.
Tracks: / Honeysuckle rose (take 2) / They can't take that away from me / Topsy / Celebrating (Janne's blues) (take 2) / Cabin in the sky (take 2) / Speak low (take 5) / Stockholm street (take 2) / Bengt's blues (take 2) / Gold rush / Stockholm street / Cabin in the sky (rehearsal take) / Cabin in the sky / Celebrating (Janne's blues) / Speak low (take 3) / Like someone in love / Like someone in love (take 2) / Gold rush.
2LP: . . . . DRLP 157/158

STAN GETZ (PRESTIGE).
Tracks: / Five brothers / Battle of the saxes / Preservation / Crazy chords / Introit / Long Island sound / Indian Summer / There's a small hotel / Too marvellous for words / Wrap your troubles in dreams / My old flame / Lady in red, The / Ginza samba / I've grown accustomed to her face / For all we know / Crow's nest / Liz Anne / Big bear / My buddy.
2LP: . . . . PR 24019

STAN GETZ QUARTET AND SHELLY MANNE QUINTET (Getz, Stan Quartet & Shelly Manne Quintet).
Tracks: / Some blues (bronx blues) / Polka dots & moonbeans / Theme / Jordu / Lover man / Ain't you a mess / Theme - introduction / Dart game, The / Parthenia / B's flat / Gem from tiffany, A / Little girl blue / Lover come back to me.
LP: . . . . EB 407

STAN GETZ SPECIAL, VOL 2.
Tracks: / Everything happens to me / I'll remember April / Strike up the band / All God's chillun got rhythm / Love walked in / We'll be together again.
LP: . . . . FC 5012
LP: . . . . RARETONE 5002

STEAMER, THE.
Tracks: / Blues for Mary Jane / There will never be another you / You're blase / Too close for comfort / Like someone in love / How about you?.
LP: 2304 533

STOCKHOLM CONCERT.
LP: . . . . SNTF 1019

SWEET RAIN.
Tracks: / Litha / O grande amor / Sweet rain / Con Alma / Windows / There will never be another you.
LP: 2317.115

TENDERLY.
MC: 771510

TWO SIDES OF STAN GETZ.
LP: . . . . UJ 33

VOYAGE.
Tracks: / I wanted to say / I thought about you / Yesterdays / Dreams / Falling in love / Voyage.
LP: . . . . BKH 51101
MC: . . . . BKHMC 51101

WEST COAST JAZZ.
LP: 2304 330

WITH EUROPEAN FRIENDS.
Tracks: / All God's chillun got rhythm / Broadway / Ladybird / Dear old Stockholm / East of the sun / They all fall in love / Theme for Manuel / Our kind of sabi.
MC: . . . . MC 7679

YESTERDAYS.
Tracks: / Sweetness / Long Island sound / Yesterdays / Strike up the band / Pernod / Get happy / Dear old Stockholm.
LP: . . . . BLJ 8036

Geyer, Renee

SING TO ME.
Tracks: / Without love / All my love / Woman in love / Everyday of the week / Sing to me / Telling it like this / Fever / Guess who I saw today / Faithful love / Memory.
LP: 252139 1

G-Force (Gary Moore)

G-FORCE.
Tracks: / White knuckles / Rockin' and rollin' / She's got you / I look at you / Because of your love / You kissed me sweetly / Hot gossip / Woman's in love / Dancin'.
LP: . . . . CLALP 212
MC: . . . . CLAMC 212

G.G.F.H.

ECLIPSE.
LP: . . . . KTB 2
MC: . . . . KTB 2MC

Ghana

DANCE MUSIC AND SONGS OF GHANA (Various artists).
LP: . . . . H 72082

DRUMS OF WEST AFRICA (Ritual music of Ghana) (Various artists).
LP: . . . . LLST 7307
MC: . . . . LLCT 7307

GHANA- MUSIC OF THE NORTHERN TRIBES (Various artists).
LP: . . . . LLST 7321
MC: . . . . LLCT 7321

MUSIC OF GHANA (Kpanlogo party) (Various artists).
LP: . . . . LLST 7251

SOUNDS OF WEST AFRICA (The kora and the xylophone) (Various artists).
LP: . . . . LLST 7308

Ghandi

WORDS OF GANDHI, THE (Kingsley, Ben).
MC: 1740

Ghettovetts

MISSIONARIES MOVING.
Tracks: / Go down / Now take your balls / Death command / Dead men tell no tales / Lecture.
LP: . . . . BRLP 521
MC: . . . . BRCA 521

Ghiglioni, Tiziana

SOUNDS OF LOVE.
Tracks: / Beautiful singing / My old flame / All of me / Ruby my dear / Naima / Sound of love / I remember you / My funny valentine / Straight no chaser.
LP: . . . . SN 1056

Ghosh, Jnan Prakash

DRUMS OF INDIA VOL 1.
LP: . . . . ECSD 2362

Ghosh, Pannalal

GURU SHISHYA PARAMPARA, THE (Ghosh, Pannalal & Vijay Rao).
MC: .... TCS 7452

RG YAMAN/SHREE.
LP: .... ECSD 1252
MC: .... TC 6103

Ghost

FOR ONE SECOND.
LP: .... KIRI 077

Ghost Boast

GHOST BOAST (See under Bangers & Mash (tv)).

Ghost Dance

STOP THE WORLD.
LP: .... CHR 1706
MC: .... ZCHR 1706

Ghost (Film)

GHOST (Original Soundtrack).
LP: .... A 620
MC: .... C 620

Ghost & Mrs.Muir

GHOST AND MRS.MUIR, THE (Film Soundtrack) (Various artists).
LP: 704.340
MC: .... C 704.304

Ghost Stories

GHOST STORIES (see under James, M.R.) (Horden, Sir Michael).

Ghost Story (film)

GHOST STORY (Film Soundtrack) (Various artists).
MC: .... VSC 5259

Ghostbusters (film)

GHOSTBUSTERS (Original Soundtrack) (Various artists).
Tracks: / Ghostbusters: *Parker, Ray Jnr.* / Cleanin' up the town: *Bus Boys* / Savin' the day: *Alessi*/ In the name of love: *Thompson Twins* / I can wait forever: *Air Supply* / Hot night: *Branigan, Laura*/ Magic: *Smiley, Mick* / Ghostbusters (main title theme): *Bernstein, Elmer* / Dana's theme: *Bernstein, Elmer*.
LP: 208720
MC: 408720
LP: 206559
MC: 406559

Ghostly Tales

GHOSTLY TALES (mystery & adventure for ages 7-12) (Unknown narrator(s)).
MC: .... PLB 211

Ghostriders

TRUE CONFESSIONS.
LP: .... CCD 03

Ghosts In The Machine

GHOSTS IN THE MACHINE (CHANNEL 4 TV) (See under Karn, Mick 'Titles') (Karn, Mick).

Ghoul

FOX MACHINE.
LP: .... FH 1023
MC: .... FH 12037

Ghoulies

DOGGED BY DOGMA.
LP: .... LA 01

GI Blues

G.I.BLUES (See under Presley, Elvis) (Various artists).

Giancarlo, Nicolai

GOCCIE (Giancarlo, Nicolai Trio).
LP: .... LR 139

Giant

LAST OF THE RUNAWAYS.
Tracks: / I'm a believer / Innocent days / I can't get close enough / I'll see you in my dreams / No way out / Shake me up / It takes two / Stranger to me / Hold back the night / Love welcome home / Big pitch, The.
LP: .... AMA 5272
MC: .... AMC 5272

Giant (Film)

GIANT (Film Soundtrack) (Various artists).
MC: 92056.4

Giant Sand

BALLAD OF A THIN LINE MAN.
Tracks: / Thin line man / All along the watchtower / Graveyard / Body of water / Last legs / You can't put your arms around a memory / Hard man to get to know / Who am I? / Chill outside / Desperate man.
LP: .... ZONG 013

LONG STEM RANT.
Tracks: / Unfinished love / Sandman / Bloodstone / Searchlight / Smash jazz / Sucker in a cage / Patsy does Dylan / It's long 'bout now / Lag craw / Loving cup / Paved road to Berlin / Anthem / Picture shows / Drum and guitar / Get to leave / Searchlight cha cha (Available on CD only) / Return of the big red guitar (Available on CD only) / Stuck dog (Available on CD only) / Real gone blue guitar (Available on CD only) / Jig's up, The (Available on CD only).
LP: .... FIEND 164

LOVE SONGS: GIANT SAND.
Tracks: / Wearing the robes of Bible black / One man's woman / No man's land / Mad dog a man / Fingernail moon, barracuda and me / Mountain of love / Almost the politician's wife / Doors, The / Love like a train / Is that all there is.
LP: .... FIEND 129

STORM.
Tracks: / Town where no town belongs / Back to black and grey / Bigger than that / Right makes right / Three sixes / Replacement, The / Storm / Was is a big word / Town with little or no pity / Weight, The.
LP: .... FIEND 115

VALLEY OF RAIN.
Tracks: / Down on town / Love's no answer / Black venetian blind / Curse of a thousand flames / Artists / Man of want / Valley of rain / Tumble and tear / October anywhere / Barrio / Death, dying and channel 5 / Torture of love.
LP: .... ZONG 008
MC: .... ZONG CASS 008
LP: .... ROSE 84

Giant Steps

BOOK OF PRIDE.
Tracks: / Steamy / Another lover (the world don't need) / Into you / Golden hours / Do you still care / Same planet, different world / Book of pride / End of the war / Dance away / Dream wonderful.
LP: .... AMA 5190
MC: .... AMC 5190

Giants

GIANTS (Various artists).
LP: .... MCF 3058

Giants Of...

GIANTS OF JAZZ AND BLUES (See Under Jazz...) (Various artists).

GIANTS OF JAZZ IN BERLIN (See Under Jazz) (Various artists).

GIANTS OF JAZZ, THE (See Under Jazz...) (Various artists).

GIANTS OF ROCK & ROLL (See Under Rock & Roll...) (Various artists).

TRIBUTE TO GEORGE GERSHWIN, A (See Under Jazz...) (Various artists).

Gibb, Andy

FLOWING RIVERS.
Tracks: / I just wanna be your everything / Thicker than water.
LP: 2394 183

GREATEST HITS: ANDY GIBB.
Tracks: / I just want to be your everything / Thicker than water / Shadow dancing / Everlasting love / Don't throw it all away / Time is time / Me / Will you love me tomorrow / After dark / Desire.
LP: 2394 287
MC: 3216 287

SHADOW DANCING.
Tracks: / Shadow dancing / Why / Fool for a night / Melody / I go for you / Good feeling / Waiting for you / Everlasting love.
LP: .... RSS 1
LP: 2394 202

Gibb, Barry

HAWKS (Film soundtrack) (See under Hawks).

HAWKS LOST.
LP: 837 264 1

NOW VOYAGER.
Tracks: / I am your driver / Fine line / Face to face / Shatterproof / Shine shine / Lesson in love / One night for lovers / Stay alone / Temptation / She says / Hunter.
LP: .... POLH 14

Gibb, Robin

HOW OLD ARE YOU.
Tracks: / Juliet / How old are you / In and out of love / Kathy's gone / Don't stop the night / Another lonely night in New York / Danger / He can't love you / Hearts on fire / I believe in miracles.
LP: POLD5099

SECRET AGENT.
Tracks: / Boys (do fall in love) / In your diary / Rebecca / Secret agent / Living in another world / X-ray eyes / King of fools / Diamonds.
LP: .... POLD 5142

WALLS HAVE EARS.
LP: 827 592-1
MC: 827 592-4

Gibbons, Carroll

BODY AND SOUL (Gibbons, Carroll & Savoy Hotel Orpheans).
Tracks: / Body and soul / I don't know why (I just do) / She's funny that way / I apologise / Who am I? / Mean to me / Faded summer love, A / Sweet and lovely / Mona Lisa / Moonbeam dance / There's a time and place for everything / You're blase / Reaching for someone (and not finding anyone there) / Alone with my dreams / Oh Monah.
LP: .... JOY 268
MC: .... TC-JOY B 268

BRIGHTER THAN THE SUN (Gibbons, Carroll & Savoy Hotel Orpheans).
Tracks: / You're gonna lose your gal / One morning in May / May I? / Beat O' my heart / So help me / I saw stars / For all we know / All my life / You're the kind of a baby for me / Kiss by kiss / Sailin' on the Robert E. Lee / One hour with you / What makes you so adorable / By special permission of the copyright owners / After tonight we say goodbye / I wish I knew a bigger word than love / What more can I ask / Brighter than the sun / It's gonna be you / Oceans of time.
LP: .... SVL 174
MC: .... CSVL 174

CARROLL GIBBONS STORY (Carroll Gibbons & Savoy Hotel Orpheans).
Tracks: / Mama's gone goodbye / Where'd you get those eyes? / Garden in the rain / Can't we talk it over? / When we're alone / I'll never be the same / Isn't it romantic? / I guess I'll have to change my plan / Shuffle off to Buffalo / On the air / Living in dreams / Easy come, easy go / Piccolino, The / Broadway rhythm / I got a feelin' you're foolin' / These foolish things / Midnight in Mayfair / Goodnight my love / There's a lull in my life / So rare / Can I forget you? / Folks who live on the hill, The / Foggy day, A / Remember me / Sing my heart / There goes my dream / I don't want to talk without you / I'll get by / Don't you know I care / It was swell while it lasted / Moment I saw you, The.
2LP: .... SH 167/8
MCSET: .... TC2 SH 167/8

CARROLL RE-CALLS THE TUNES.
Tracks: / Lady is a tramp, The / Sweet Sue / California here I come / Babette / I can't give you anything but love / Dinah / Ain't misbehavin' / Stormy weather / Exactly like you / Oh me, oh my / They didn't believe me / Cheek to cheek / In the still of the night / Two sleepy people / Rosalie / Solitude / Time on my hands / Manhattan holiday / Bubbling over / I cried for you / Somebody loves me / These foolish things / I'll see you in my dreams / Diane / I'll see you again / Kiss me again / Alice blue gown / Speak to me love / Marcheta / Honeysuckle rose / I've got a feeling I'm falling / Keepin' out of mischief now / Summer rain / Smoke gets in your eyes / Way you look tonight / Moonbeams dance / I want the waiter.
LP: .... SH 509
MC: .... TCSH 509

DANCING IN THE DARK (Gibbons, Carroll & Savoy Hotel Orpheans).
Tracks: / What a life / Dancing in the dark / Sweet and lovely / Keepin' out of mischief now / Actions speak louder than words / My silent love / I heard / Bidin' my time / I wanna be loved / Great big bunch of you / As time goes by / Snuggled on your shoulder / All of a sudden / Old man of the mountain, The / Love me tonight / Blues in my heart / Goopy Geer (He plays piano and he plays by ear) / With love in my heart.
LP: .... SVL 157
MC: .... CSVL 157

GOLDEN AGE OF CARROLL GIBBONS, THE (Gibbons, Carroll & The Savoy Hotel Orpheans).
Tracks: / On the air / Dancing in the dark / Home / Tony's wife, with thee I swing / I double dare you / Sixty seconds got together / I have eyes / Wishing / Nightingale sang in Berkeley Square, A / I'm nobody's baby / Room 504 / Come happy day / Let's be sensible / When day is done / I'm going to get lit up when the lights go up in London.
LP: .... GX 412 526-1
MC: .... GX 412 526-4

I SAW STARS.
2LP: .... SVLD 001
MCSET: .... CSVLD 001

MUSIC MAESTRO PLEASE.
Tracks: / You were there / Play, orchestra, play / There isn't any limit to my love / This'll make you whistle / Did you mean it? / I'm in a dancing mood / I've got my love to keep me warm / This year's kisses / Too marvellous for words / It looks like rain in Cherry Blossom Lane / Foggy day, A / Nice work if you can get it / With a smile and a song / One song / Love walked in / Love is here to stay / Music, maestro, please / It's de-lovely / My heart is taking lessons / On the sentimental side.
LP: .... SVL 200
MC: .... CSVL 200

ON THE AIR (Gibbons, Carroll & The Savoy Hotel Orpheans).
Tracks: / On the air / Have you met Miss Jones / Comes love / Stairway to the stars / What's new / My heart belongs to Daddy / I don't want to set the world on fire / F.D.R. Jones / Shake down the stars / Accentuate the positive / Tomorrow's sunrise / Cynthia's in love / Over Wyoming / Silver wedding waltz / Francesca / Wandering along / I can dream, can't I / So ends my search for a dream.
LP: .... PLE 513
MC: .... TC-PLE 513

ON THE AIR (The Hartley's Jam Broadcasts 1943-45) (Gibbons, Carroll & The Boyfriends Featuring Anne Lenner).
Tracks: / Who? / Smoke gets in your eyes / Don't let it bother you / I saw stars / Messengers / Walking the chalk line / I'll see you again / Love is in the air / Coffee in the morning / Tea for two / Continental, The / Lost in a fog / Take a number from one to ten / If the moon turns green / Straight from the shoulder / You turned your head / Other peoples babies / Dinah / What a difference a day made / Pardon my southern accent / Heatwave.
LP: .... SH 360
MC: .... TCSH 360

ON THE WIRELESS AT 7 PM EACH THURSDAY (Hartley's Jam broadcasts).
Tracks: / My lips and your lips / You've got to admit / I'm so misunderstood / Swing on the gait / Life of the party / While there's a 'you' about / Love is just around the corner / Say when / Needle in a haystack / Wrapped around your finger / Body and soul / You fit into the picture / College rhythm / Blue moon / I got rhythm / In my country that means love.
LP: .... SH 519
LP: 794 321 1
MC: .... TCSH 519
MC: 794 321 4

ON YOUR TOES 34/35.
Tracks: / Rise 'n' shine / Never in a million years / Couple of April fools, A / When did you leave heaven / In the still of the night / Goodnight angel / Juba, The / Touch of your lips, The / Let's put our heads together / Fatal fascination.
LP: .... SCS D-01

SUNRISE SERENADE.
MC: .... CMOIR 302

TOO MARVELLOUS FOR WORDS.
Tracks: / Too marvellous for words / Night is young and you're so beautiful, The / Seal it with a kiss / Here comes the sandman / Goodnight my love / Foggy day, A / I don't want to make history / Never gonna dance / Take my heart / I stumbled over love / This years kisses / Moon got in my eyes / Nice work if you can get it / Roses in December / Can I forget you / You're not the kind / Remember me? / Put me behind bars.
LP: .... BUR 016
MC: .... 4 BUR 016

Gibbons, Leroy

FOUR SEASON LOVER.
Tracks: / Missing you / For seasonal lover / This magic moment / Build up the vibes / Lover's question / Why are you going? / Cupid / Spread out / Samfire girl / She's my baby.
LP: .... SPLP 6
MC: .... SPLC 6

Gibbons, Stella (aut)

COLD COMFORT FARM (see under Cold Comfort Farm (bk)) (Margolyes, Miriam (nar)).

COLD COMFORT FARM (see under Cold Comfort Farm (bk)) (Scales, Prunella (nar)).

Gibbons, Steve

BEST OF STEVE GIBBONS BAND (Gibbons, Steve Band).
Tracks: / Tulane / Johnny Cool / Down in the bunker / Mr. Jones / Eddy Vortex / No spitting on the bus / Watching the river flow / Git it / He gave his life to rock'n'roll / Rollin' / Tupelo Mississippi flash.
LP: 2384 110

CAUGHT IN THE ACT (GIBBONS) (Gibbons, Steve Band).
LP: 2478 112

DOWN IN THE BUNKER.
LP: .... RAZ 35
MC: .... RAZK 35

MAINTAIN RADIO SILENCE.

LP: . . . . LUSLP 8

ON THE LOOSE.
Tracks: / Down the road apiece / Chuck in my car / Absolutley gone / Love part one / Trucker / On the loose / To be alone with you / Love 'n' peace / Like a rolling stone.
LP: . . . . MFLP 041

ROLLIN' ON (Gibbons, Steve Band).
Tracks: / Wild flowers / Light up your face / Now you know me / Mr. Jones / Till the well runs dry / Tulane / Cross me over the road / Till the well runs dry / Low down man / Right side of heaven / Rollin' on / Please don't say goodbye / Tupelo Mississippi flash / Rounden.
LP: 2383 433

SAINTS AND SINNERS (Gibbons, Steve Band).
Tracks: / B.S.A / Loving me loving you / Till I waltz again with you / American rock 'n' roll / Biggles flys undone / Social dance / Somebody stole my synthesizer / Home from home / Fiction factory / Rugged rock.
LP: . . . . RCALP 6017
MC: . . . . RCAK 6017

STEVE GIBBONS- LIVE.
LP: 088829

STREET PARADE (Gibbons, Steve Band).
Tracks: / Street parade / A to Z / Human race / Graffiti man / Sonny Day & the Tropics / Blue lagoon / I'm a man / British rock'n'roll / New romance / Abracadabra / Fair play / Saturday night / Midnight moon.
LP: . . . . RCALP 5005

Gibbs, Joe

AFRICAN DUB (1) (Gibbs, Joe/ Professionals).
Tracks: / African dub / Universal dub / Midnight movie / Getto shank / Lime key rock / Lovers serenade / Treasure dub / Schooling the beat / Campus rock / Half ounce / Worrier / East Africa.
LP: . . . . LIP 10
LP: . . . . JGMLP 15

AFRICAN DUB (2) (Gibbs, Joe/ Professionals).
Tracks: / Chapter two / Angola crisis / Outrage / My best dub / Heavy duty dub / Mackarus serenade / Marriguna affair, The / Peeping Tom / Idlers rest / Third world / Musical arena / Jamaican grass.
LP: . . . . LIP 11
LP: . . . . JGMLP 014

AFRICAN DUB (5).
LP: . . . . JGMLP 017

MAJESTIC DUB (Gibbs, Joe/ Professionals).
Tracks: / Ten commandments / Majestic dub / Social justice / Kings of the dub / Bionic encounter / Edward the eighth / International treaty / Martial law / Nations of dub / Embargo.
LP: . . . . LASL 3
LP: . . . . BMLP 022

REGGAE TRAIN, THE 1968 - 1971 (Gibbs, Joe & Friends).
LP: . . . . TRLS 261

Gibbs, Kevin

CHRISTMAS PRESENCE (Gibbs, Kevin Trio).
Tracks: / God rest ye merry gentlemen / Christmas song, The / Deck the halls / Have yourself a merry little Christmas / Sleigh ride / Silent night / What child is this? (Greensleeves) / Oh Christmas tree.
MC: . . . . CJ 432 C

Gibbs, Mike

BIG MUSIC (Gibbs, Mike Orchestra).
Tracks: / Wall to wall / Pride aside / Kosasa / Almost ev'ry day / Watershed / Mopsus / Adult / Pride outside.
LP: . . . . VE 27
MC: . . . . TCVE 27

Gibbs, Terri

I'M A LADY.
LP: . . . . MCF 3132

TURN AROUND.
LP: . . . . CAA R 0014
MC: . . . . CAA C 0014

Gibbs, Terry

CHICAGO FIRE (Gibbs, Terry & Buddy De Franco).
Tracks: / Rockin' in rhythm / Please send me someone to love / Sister Sadie / This is always / Cherokee / Giant steps / Bopstacle course / Stella by starlight / 52nd Street theme.
LP: . . . . C 14036

FEBRUARY 19TH, 1963 (Family Album) (Gibbs, Terry Quartet).
Tracks: / Button up your lips / Up at Logue's place / One for my uncle / Ballad for Barbara / Sherry bossa nova / El cheapo / Henny time / Many moons ago / Better to be rich than poor / Sunny girl / S'all right with me / Half stuie.
LP: . . . . JV 110
LP: 500072
LP: . . . . JL 72

JAZZ PARTY - FIRST TIME TOGETHER (Gibbs, Terry & Buddy De Franco).
LP: . . . . PA 8011
MC: . . . . PAC 8011

TAKE IT FROM ME (Gibbs, Terry Quartet).
Tracks: / Take it from me / El Fatso / OGE / Pauline's place / 8lb 10oz / Gee dad, it's a deacan / All the things you are / Honeysuckle rose.
LP: . . . . JAS 60
MC: . . . . JAS C60

TERRY.
Tracks: / Temporary / Tremendez / Old man Newman / What ho / Fatty / Baby doll / Peaches / Jazz mambo / Where are you / That feeling / Love is just around the corner / Trotting.
LP: . . . . JASM 1005

TERRY GIBBS AT THE PIANO.
LP: . . . . FS 217

Gibson, Banv

BANV GIBSON ON TOUR.
LP: . . . . J 154

JAZZ BABY (Gibson, Banv & NOR Hot Jazz).
LP: . . . . SOS 1073

Gibson Brass Band

NON-UNION MUSICIANS OF NEW ORLEANS (Louisiana Vol. 1).
LP: . . . . GHB 215

NON-UNION MUSICIANS OF NEW ORLEANS (Louisiana Vol. 2).
LP: . . . . GHB 216

Gibson Brothers

BIG PINE BOOGIE.
LP: . . . . HMS 119-1

CUBA.
Tracks: / Cuba / Oh what a life / West Indies / Better do it Salsa / You / Que sera mi vida.
LP: . . . . ILPS 9579
MC: . . . . ICT 9579

DEDICATED FOOL.
LP: . . . . HMS 141 1
MC: . . . . HMS 141 4

ON THE RIVIERA.
Tracks: / Metropolis / Mariana / All I ever want is you / Good girl bad boy / Latin America / Dancin' the mambo / Fly away.
MC: . . . . ZCI 9620
LP: . . . . ILPS 9620

QUARTIER LATIN.
Tracks: / Quartier latin / Limbo / I left my heart in Jamaica / Sheela / 'A' train to Bombay / Caribbean concerto / Paranoi / I, I, I love you / Baisers sales.
LP: . . . . EPC 85468

Gibson, Clifford

BEAT YOU DOING IT.
LP: . . . . L 1027

Gibson, Debbie

ANYTHING IS POSSIBLE.
MC: . . . . WX 399C
LP: . . . . WX 399

DEBBIE GIBSON: INTERVIEW PICTURE DISC.
LPPD: . . . . BAK 2150

ELECTRIC YOUTH.
Tracks: / Who loves ya baby / Lost in your eyes / Love in disguise / Helplessly in love / Silence speaks (a thousand words) / Should've been the one / Electric youth / No more rhyme / Over the wall / We could be together / Shades of the past.
LP: . . . . WX 231
MC: . . . . WX 231 C

OUT OF THE BLUE.
Tracks: / Out of the blue / Staying together / Only in my dreams / Foolish beat / Red hot / Wake up to love / Shake your love / Fallen angel / Play the field / Between the lines.
LP: . . . . K 781 780 1
MC: . . . . K 781 780 4

Gibson, Don

15 GREAT HITS.
LP: . . . . CL 42838
MC: . . . . CK 42838

20 OF THE BEST: DON GIBSON.
Tracks: / Oh lonesome me / I can't stop loving you / Blue blue day / Gonna give myself a party / Look who's blue / Who cared for me / Lonesome old house / Don't tell me your troubles / Just one time / Far far away / Sweet dreams / (I'd be a) legend in my own time / What about me / Sea of heartbreak / Lonesome number one / I can mend your broken heart / Watch you're going / Yes I'm hurting / I think it's best to forget me / Same old trouble, The.
LP: . . . . INTS 5184
LP: . . . . NL 89089
MC: . . . . NK 89089
MC: . . . . INTK 5184

COLLECTION: DON GIBSON.
Tracks: / Oh lonesome me / Snap your fingers / Just one time / Take these chains from my heart / Sweet dreams / Release me / Blue blue day / Funny, familiar forgotten feelings / Kaw-liga / There goes my everything / Touch the morning / Too soon to know / Cold cold heart / I'm all wrapped up in you / You've still got a place in my heart / Sweet sensuous sensation / Why you been gone so long / I can't stop loving you / Lonesome number one / You win again / Mansion on the hill / (I'd be a) legend in my own time / Yesterday just passed my way again / Fan the flame feed the fire.
2LP: . . . . CCSLP 158
MC: . . . . CCSMC 158

COUNTRY NUMBER ONE.
MC: . . . . WW 4 5079

DON GIBSON & LOS INDIOS TABAJARAS (Gibson, Don & Los Indios Tabajaras).
Tracks: / I can't tell my heart that / Cryin' heart blues / My adobe hacienda / Address unknown / That's how it goes / When will this end / So how come (no one loves me) / What about me / I couldn't care less / Same old trouble, The / Hurting inside / Fireball mail / Above and beyond / Camptown races.
LP: . . . . BFX 15193

EARLY DAYS, THE.
Tracks: / Automatic mama / Why am I so lonely / I lost my love / Cloudy skies / Dark future / Blue million tears, A / Just let me love you / Roses are red / Red lips white lies and blue hours / I love no one but you / Caroline breakdown / Wigglewag.
LP: . . . . BFX 15196

FAMOUS COUNTRY MUSIC MAKERS.
Tracks: / Oh lonesome me / I can't stop loving you / Blue blue day / Give myself a party / Look who's blue / Who cares (for me) / Lonesome old house / Don't tell me your troubles / I'm movin' Juston / One time / Far, far away / Sweet dreams / What about me / Sea of heartbreak / Lonesome number one / I can mend your broken heart / Head over heels in love with you / Anything new gets old (except my love for you) / Again / Watch where you're going / Born loser / (Yes) I'm hurting / Funny familiar, forgotten feelings / All my love / It's a long long way to Georgia / Solitary / I will always / There's a story (goin 'round).
2LP: . . . . PL 42002

LEGEND IN HIS OWN TIME.
Tracks: / Give myself a party / I can't stop loving you / Oh lonesome me / I let her get lonely / Just one time / Don't tell me your troubles / I think it's best (to forget me) / Sea of heartbreak / Same old trouble, The / Lonesome number one / I can mend your broken heart / Blue dream / It's a sin / Baby we're really in love / Sweet dreams / Hurting inside / Far far away / World is waiting for the sunrise, The / What about me? / What's the reason I'm not pleasing you? / Big hearted me / (I'd be a) legend in my own time / Foolish me / My tears don't show / Next voice you hear, The / Again / Time hurts (as well as it heals) / Maybe tomorrow.
2LP: . . . . CR 063
MCSET: . . . . CRT 063

ROCKIN' ROLLIN' GIBSON VOL.1.
Tracks: / Pretty rainbow (Previously unissued.) / Sittin' here cryin' / I love you still / I can't leave / Tell it like it is (1st recording) (Previously unissued.) / Oh lonesome me / Blue blue day / If you don't know it / Even tho' / Didn't work out, did it / Sea of heartbreak / Who cares? (Previously unissued.) / Sweet sweet girl (Previously unissued.) / Don't tell me your troubles (Previously unissued.) / Far far away / I sat back and let it happen (Previously unissued.).
LP: . . . . BFX 15089

ROCKIN' ROLLIN' GIBSON VOL.2.
Tracks: / Just one time / Lonesome old house / Who cares / Sweet sweet girl / Won't cha come back to me / I know the score (Previously unissued.) / Tell it like it is (2nd recording) (Previously unissued.) / Look who's blue / Don't tell me your troubles / Everybody but me / Cute little girls / Why don't you love me / Let's fall out of love (Previously unissued.) / Lonesome number one / I'm movin' on / Bad, bad day.
LP: . . . . BFX 15097

SEA OF HEARTBREAK (OLD GOLD) (See Hank Locklin - Please Help Me I'm Falling).

SINGS COUNTRY FAVOURITES.
Tracks: / Green green grass of home / There goes my everything / Release me / I heard that lonesome whistle blow / Cold cold heart / Kaw-liga / She even woke me up to say goodbye / Sea of heartbreak / My elusive dreams / You win again / I love you because / Window shopping / (I'd be) a legend in my time / Too soon to know / Take these chains from my heart / Lonesome number one / Sweet dreams / I can't stop loving you / Oh, lonesome me / Funny, familiar, forgotten feelings.
MC: . . . . PWKMC 4049
LP: . . . . PWKS 4049

THAT GIBSON BOY.
Tracks: / Even tho' / It's my way / Midnight / As much / Do you think / Didn't work out, did it? / Won't cha' come back to me / I wish it had been a dream / Ages and ages ago / Almost / It has to be / Foggy river.
LP: . . . . NL 90002
MC: . . . . NK 90002

YOU WIN AGAIN.
Tracks: / I heard that lonesome whistle blow / You win again / Cold cold heart / Mansion on the hill / Take these chains from my heart / Kaw-liga / Window shopping / My heart would know / Crazy heart / On the banks of the old pontchartrain.
LP: . . . . SDLP 023
MC: . . . . SDC 023

Gibson, Harry

BOOGIE WOOGIE IN BLUE (Gibson, Harry "Hipster").
Tracks: / Barrelhouse boogie / Stop that dancin' up there.
LP: . . . . MVS 2003

EVERYBODY'S CRAZY BUT ME (Gibson, Harry "Hipster").
LP: . . . . PRO 7042

Gibson, John

CHANGE OF HEART.
Tracks: / Yah mo B there / Wall, The / Friend in you / Change of heart / Lost inside of you / Man overboard / Child without a name / Too tough / Technology man.
LP: . . . . RO 9032
MC: . . . . CO 9032

Gibson, Lacy

SWITCHY TITCHY.
LP: . . . . BM 9002

Gibson, Mel

MY COUSIN RACHEL (See also Daphne Du Maurier).

Gibson, Steve

BLUEBERRY HILL (Gibson, Steve & The Red Caps).
Tracks: / Scratch an' you'll find it / You can't see the sun when you're crying / Jack you're dead / I want a roof over my head / Blueberry Hill / Three dollars and ninety eight cents / Why don't you love me / Two little kisses / Thing, The / I went to your wedding / Truthfully / Danny boy.
LP: . . . . H 806

Gidea Park

GIDEA PARK.
Tracks: / California gold / Don't worry baby / Beach boy gold / Summer girls / Happy birthday Brian Wilson / Seasons of gold / My Maria / Lolita / Baby come back.
LP: . . . . POLP 102

Gielgud, Sir John

AGES OF MAN (See under Ages of Man).

BLEAK HOUSE (see under Dickens, Charles (aut)).

BRIDESHEAD REVISITED (see under Brideshead Revisited).

EMPEROR'S NEW CLOTHES, THE (See under Emperor's New Clothes) (Gielgud, Sir John & Mark Isham).

FORTY YEARS ON/A WOMAN OF NO IMPORTANCE (see under Forty Years On (bk)) (Gielgud, Sir John/Patricia Routledge (nars)).

PILGRIM'S PROGRESS, THE (see under Pilgrim's Progress (bk)).

SIR JOHN GIELGUD - HIS GREATEST ROLES.
Tracks: / Hamlet speech / Richard II / King Lear / Tempest, The / Forty years on / No mans land / Ode to the west wind.
LP: . . . . REGL 351
MC: . . . . ZCF 351

Gift Of Music

GIFT OF MUSIC (Various artists).
Tracks: / When I need you: *Various artists* / Feelings: *Various artists* / I'm stone in love with you: *Various artists* / One day in your life: *Various artists* / I will survive: *Various artists* / When you're in love with a beautiful woman: *Various artists* / For your eyes only: *Various artists* / You don't bring me flowers: *Various artists* / Misty blue: *Various artists* / Bridge over troubled water: *Various artists.*
LPS: IMP 92
MCSET: IMPC 92

Gifts of Legends

GIFTS OF LEGENDS Ayrton, Michael (Ayrton, Michael).
MC: SS 115

Giger, Paul

CHARTRES (SOLO VIOLIN).
LP: ECM 1386

Giggetty

BLACK COUNTRY TIME.
Tracks: / Black Country time / Maggie May / Lullaby / Streets of London / Geordie / Misty Midlands morning / Penny for the guy / Lord of the dance / Severn Valley railway / Animals lament / Black Country historian / Isiah's rhubarb wine / Cottonfields.
LP: REVLP 1

Gigi (musical)

GIGI (Film Soundtrack) (Various artists).
Tracks: / Overture: *Various artists* / Thank Heaven for little girls: *Various artists* / Parisians: *Various* artists / Waltz at Maxim's: *Various artists* / Night they invented champagne, The: *Caron, Leslie/Louis Jordan/Hermione* Gingold / I remember it well: *Various artists* / Say a prayer for me tonight: *Various artists* / I'm glad I'm not young anymore: *Various artists* / Gigi: *Various artists* / Finale: *Various artists.*
LP: CBS 70277
MC: 40 70277
LP: MGM C 770

GIGI (Original London Cast) (Various artists).
Tracks: / Paris is Paris again: *Various artists* / It's a bore: *Various artists* / Earth and other minor things, The: *Various artists* / Thank heaven for little girls: *Various artists* / She's not thinking of me: *Various* artists / Night they invented champagne, The: *Various artists* / I remember it well: *Various artists* / Gigi: *Various artists* / Gigi: Entr'acte: *Various artists* / Contract, The: *Various artists* / I'm glad I'm not young anymore: *Various artists* / Wide wide world: *Various artists* / Gigi: Finale: *Various artists.*
LP: GIGI 1
MC: GIGI C 1

GIGI (Film Soundtrack) (Various artists).
Tracks: / Overture: *Various artists* / Thank heaven for little girls: *Various artists* / It's a bore: *Various artists* / Parisians: *Various artists* / Waltz at Maxim's (she is not thinking of me): *Various artists* / Night they invented champagne: *Caron, Leslie/Louis Jordan/Hermione Gingold* / I remember it well: *Various artists* / Say a prayer for me tonight: *Various artists* / I'm glad I'm not young anymore: *Various artists* / Gigi: *Various artists* / Finale - thank heaven for little girls: *Various artists.*
MC: 3110 041
LP: 2353 037

GIGI (Original Broadway cast) (Various artists).
Tracks: / Overture: *Orchestra* / Thank Heaven for little girls: *Drake, Alfred* / It's a bore: *Drake, Alfred* & Daniel Massey / Earth and other minor things, The: *Wolfe, Karin* / Paris is Paris again: *Drake, Alfred/* She is not thinking of me: *Various artists* / I remember it well: *Drake, Alfred & Maria Karnilova* / Night they invented champagne, The: *Karnilova, Maria, Daniel Massey, Karin Wolfe* / Gigi: *Massey, Daniel (nar)* / Contract, The: *Morehead, Agnes* / In this wide, wide world: *Wolfe, Karin* / I'm glad I'm not young anymore: *Drake, Alfred/* Finale: *Orchestra* / Thank Heaven for little girls (reprise): *Drake, Alfred.*
LP: NL 80404
MC: NK 80404

GIGI/AN AMERICAN IN PARIS (Various artists).
Tracks: / Gigi overture: *Various artists* (Gigi) / Thank heaven for little girls: *Various artists* (Gigi) / It's a bore: *Various artists* (Gigi) / Parisians, The: *Various artists* (Gigi) / Waltz at Maxim's (She is not thinking of me): *Various artists* (Gigi) / Night they invented champagne, The: *Caron, Leslie/Louis Jordan/Hermione Gingold*(Gigi) / I remember it well: *Various artists* (Gigi) / Say a prayer for me tonight: *Various artists* (Gigi) / I'm glad I'm not young anymore: *Various artists* (Gigi) / Gigi finale: *Various artists* (Gigi) / 'S wonderful: *Various* artists (An American In Paris) / Love is here to stay: *Various artists* (An American In Paris) / I'll build a stairway to paradise: *Various artists* (An American In Paris) / I got rhythm: *Various artists* (An American In Paris) / American in Paris ballet, An: *Various artists* (An American In Paris).
LP: LPMGM 1
MC: TCMGM 1
LP: 793 296 1
MC: 793 296 4

Gigli, Benjamino

BENJAMINO GIGLI.
LP: RHA 6017

CENTENARY TRIBUTE (1921-30).
LP: CHD 170
MC: MCHD 170

GIGLI FAVOURITES.
Tracks: / Del tempio al limitar / Una furtiva lagrima / M'apparitutt'amor / Mi batte il cor...OParadiso / Colenne in quest'ora / Recitar...vesti la giubba / Intanto amici, qua / In un coupe...mimi, tu piu non torni / Donna non vidi mai / Recondita armonia / E lucevan le stelle / Serenata / Notturno d'amore / Musica proibita / Quanno 'a femmena vo' / Funiculi funicula / Addio a Napoli.
LP: CHD 149
MC: MCHD 149

GREAT VOICES OF THE CENTURY.
Tracks: / Quando nascesti tu / Vanto lo pur / A casinha pequenina / Mimosa / Addio fugir mi lascia / Vedilo piango / Laggiu nelle nebbe remote / O osurdato nnammurato / Dimmi tu primavera / Una casetta in campagna / Merce merce / Esculate and dio mi potevi scaglia / Liriam / Questa o quella / O sole mio / Non ti scorda di me / Dormi dormi / Piscatore e pusilico / Speech by Gigli.
LP: GVC 500

Gigolo, Tony

AIN'T IT GOOD TO YA.
LP: 5525

ICE.
LP: FS 78722

Gil, Gilberto

MINHA IDEOLOGIA NOITE NEON.
Tracks: / Minha ideologia, minha religiao / Nos barracos da cidade (barracos) / Roque santeiro, o rock / Seu Olhar / Febril / Touches pas mon pote / Logos versus logo / Oracao pela libertacao da Africa do sul / Cliche do cliche / Casinha feliz / Duas luas.
LP: 253045 1

NIGHTINGALE.
Tracks: / Sarara / Goodbye my girl / Ella / Here and now / Balafon / Alapala / Maracatus Atomico / Move along with me / Nightingale / Samba de Los Angeles.
LP: K 52120

O ETERNO DEUS MU DANCA.
LP: 2566201
MC: 2566204

RACA HUMANA.
Tracks: / Extra II / Felix por um triz / Pessoa nefasta / Tempo rei / Vamos fugir / A mao da limpeza / Indigo blue / Vem morena / A raca humana.
LP: 252112 1

REALCE.
LP: 250038 1

RIO ZONE.
LP: A 352

SOY LOCO POR.
LP: BR 4000

Gilbert, Andrew

WONDERLAND BY NIGHT (Plays the Kawai 900 Organ).
Tracks: / Danke schon / Love me tender / Wonderland by night / How can I tell you / Shadow of your smile / Riders in the sky / September in the rain / You make me feel brand new / Red Sarafan, The / Ave Maria / Don't it make my brown eyes blue / I can't give you anything but love / Bali Ha'i.
LP: GRS 1108

Gilbert, Ann

IN A SWINGIN' MOOD.
LP: FS 176

Gilbert, B.C.

EIGHT TIME (See under Lewis, G. for information) (Gilbert, B.C. / G. Lewis).

Gilbert, Bruce

SHIVERING MAN, THE.
LP: STUMM 39

SONGS FOR FRUIT.
LP: STUMM 77

THIS WAY TO THE SHIVERING MAN.
Tracks: / Work for 'do you me? I did' / Hommage / Shivering man, The / Here visit / Epitaph for Henran Brenlar / Angelfood.
LP: STUMM 18

Gilbert, Jacqueline

CHEQUERED SILENCE, A (see under Chequered Silence) (Boyd, Carole (nar)).

Gilbert & Lewis

MZUI (Gilbert, Lewis & Mills).
Tracks: / Mzui Pt. 1 / Mzui Pt. 2.
LP: BRED 27

Gilbert, Paul & Racer

STREET LETHAL (see Racer X, with Paul Gilbert).

Gilbert & Sullivan

BEST OF GILBERT AND SULLIVAN, THE (Excerpts From) (Various artists).
Tracks: / Mikado, The: *Various artists* / Gondoliers: *Various artists* / Iolanthe: *Various artists* / Pirates of Penzance, The: *Various artists* / HMS Pinafore: *Various artists.*
MC: TC2MOM 106
MC: LZ 762 531 4

D'OYLY CARTE 1875-1975 (Various artists).
LP: TXS 113

GILBERT AND SULLIVAN GALA (Various artists).
LP: EL 2701701
MC: EL 2701704

GILBERT & SULLIVAN DUETS (Various artists).
LP: ASD 4392
MC: TCCASD 4392

GILBERT & SULLIVAN FAVOURITES (Various artists).
MC: TC2MOM 114

GILBERT & SULLIVAN GALA, A (D'Oyly Carte Opera Company).
LP: TAB 41
MC: KTBC 41

GILBERT & SULLIVAN OVERTURES AND EXCERPTS (Various artists).
2LP: WGAS 6750
MCSET: ZCGS 6750

GILBERT & SULLIVAN SPECTACULAR (Gondoliers/Pirates of Penzance/Mikado) (Various artists).
LP: SPR 8536
MC: SPC 8536

GILBERT & SULLIVAN SPECTACULAR English chorale (London Concert Orchestra).
Tracks: / Sunny Spanish shores, The / In enterprise of martial kind / Take a pair of sparkling eyes / On the day when I was wedded / Small titles and orders / Finale - one more Gondoleri / Poor wand'ring one / When a felon's not engaged / Stay Frederick stay / Hail men o wars / I'm called little buttercup / When I was a lad / Never mind the why and wherefore / Wand'ring minstrel I, A / As someday it may happen / Sun whose rays, The / Here's a how de do / On a tree by a river / There is beauty in the bellow / Finale - For he's gone and married Yum Yum.
LP: ETMP 15

GONDOLIERS, THE (D'Oyly Carte Opera Company).
2LP: SKL 5277/8
MCSET: 4172544
2LP: 4172541

GONDOLIERS/COX & BOX (D'Oyly Carte Opera Company).
LPS: SKL 4138/40

GONDOLIERS/RUDDIGORE (EXCERPTS) (Various artists).
2LP: WGAS 6751
MCSET: ZCGS 6751

HEYDAY OF GILBERT & SULLIVAN (Various artists).
2LP: EX 2904803

HMS PINAFORE (Various artists).
2LP: SXLP 30088/9

HMS PINAFORE (D'Oyly Carte Opera Company).
2LP: 4142831
MCSET: 4142834

HMS PINAFORE/PIRATES OF PENZANCE (EXCERPTS) (Various artists).
MCSET: DTO 10011

HMS PINAFORE/YEOMAN OF THE GUARD (Various artists).
2LP: EX 749 594 1
MCSET: EX 749 594 4

IF PATRIOTIC SENTIMENT (D'Oyly Carte Opera Company).
MC: KCSP 515
LP: SPA 515

IOLANTHE (D'Oyly Carte Opera Company).
2LP: DPA 3055/6

IOLANTHE (D'Oyly Carte Opera Company).
2LP: SKL 51889
MCSET: K2C 35
2LP: SKL 4119/20
MCSET: 4141454

IOLANTHE/PATIENCE (Various artists).
2LP: EX 749 597 1
MCSET: EX 749 597 4

MIKADO, THE (D'Oyly Carte Opera Company).
2LP: DPA 3049/50
2LP: SKL 4006/7
MCSET: 4143414
2LP: 4143411

MIKADO, THE (Various artists).
2LP: EX 7496961
MCSET: EX 7496964

MIKADO, THE (D'Oyly Carte Opera Company).
MC: ZCTER 1178

MIKADO, THE (TV Cast with Groucho Marx) (Various artists).
LP: AOL 5480

MIKADO, THE (HIGHLIGHTS) (English National Opera) (Various artists).
LP: TER 1121
MC: ZCTER 1121

MORE GILBERT & SULLIVAN FAVOURITES (Various artists).
MC: TC2MOM 124

PATIENCE (D'Oyly Carte Opera Company).
2LP: SKL 4146/7
MCSET: 4144294
2LP: DPA 3063/4

PIRATES OF PENZANCE (D'Oyly Carte Opera Company).
2LP: DPA 3051/2

PIRATES OF PENZANCE (Various artists).
2LP: SKL 4925/6

PIRATES OF PENZANCE, THE (D'Oyly Carte Opera Company).
LP: 4142861
MC: 4142864

PIRATES OF PENZANCE, THE (D'Oyly Carte Opera Company).
MCSET: ZCTER 1177

PRINCESS IDA (Various artists).
2LP: DPA 3053/4
2LP: SKL 47079
MCSET: 4144264

RUDDIGORE (D'Oyly Carte Opera Company).
2LP: SKL 4504/5
2LP: DPA 3061/2
MCSET: 4173554

RUDDIGORE/PIRATES OF PENZANCE (Various artists).
2LP: EX 749 693 1
MCSET: EX 749 693 4

SAVOY OPERA VOL. 1 Pirates of Penzance/Iolanthe/H.M.S. Pinafore (D'Oyly Carte Opera Company).
LPS: 9 BB 156/161

SAVOY OPERA VOL. 2 Yeoman of the Guard/Mikado/Gondoliers (D'Oyly Carte Opera Company).
LPS: 9 BB 162/167

SORCERER, THE (D'Oyly Carte Opera Company).
2LP: SKL 48256
MCSET: 4143444

SULLIVAN HIGHLIGHTS (Various artists).
Tracks: / Mikado: *Various artists* / Yeoman of the guard: *Various artists* / Iolanthe: *Various artists/* Gondoliers: *Various artists* / Pirates of Penzance: *Various artists* / HMS Pinafore: *Various artists.*
MC: TCCFP 40238

SULLIVAN OVERTURES (Sargent, Sir Malcolm/Pro Arte Orchestra).
Tracks: / Mikado / Sorcerer / Gondoliers / Patience / Iolanthe / Pirates of Penzance / Ruddigore / HMS Pinafore / Cox and Box / Princess Ida / Yeomen of the guard.
LP: CFP 4529
MC: TCCFP 4529
MC: TCCFP 4145294

TRIAL BY JURY (Various artists).
2LP: SXDW 3034

WORLD OF GILBERT AND SULLIVAN (D'Oyly Carte Opera Company).
MC: 4300954

WORLD OF GILBERT & SULLIVAN - VOL.3 (D'Oyly Carte Opera Company).
LP: SPA 147

WORLD OF GILBERT & SULLIVAN - VOL.1 (D'Oyly Carte Opera Company).
MC: KCSP 28
LP: SPA 28

WORLD OF GILBERT & SULLIVAN - VOL.2 (D'Oyly Carte Opera Company).
MC: KCSP 29
LP: SPA 29

YEOMEN OF THE GUARD, THE (Various artists).
2LP: SKL 4624/5

YEOMEN OF THE GUARD/BALLET SUITE (Various artists).
MC: K157 K22

YEOMEN OF THE GUARD/ GONDOLIERS (EXCERPTS) (Various artists).
Tracks: / Man who would woo a fair maid, A: *Gilbert & Sullivan*.
MCSET: DTO 10067

YEOMEN OF THE GUARD/TRIAL BY JURY (D'Oyly Carte Opera Company).
2LP: SKL 4809
MCSET: 4173584

Gilbert, W.S.

BAB BALLADS AND CAUTIONARY VERSES, THE (Holloway, Stanley & Joyce Grenfell).
MC: 1104

GOLDEN SLUMBERS.
MC: 1399

Gilberto, Astrud

ASTRUD GILBERTO.
MC: ZCGAS 737

ASTRUD GILBERTO (Verve/Walkman jazz).
MC: 831 369 4

BEST OF ASTRUD GILBERTO.
Tracks: / Stay / Call me / Meditation / Light of my life / How insensitive / It might as well be spring / Here's that rainy day / Agua de beber / Beach samba / One note samba / My foolish heart / Certain smile, A / Girl from Ipanema / Shadow of your smile.
LP: 2482 559
MC: 3201 729
LP: 825 791-1
MC: 825 792-4

ESSENTIAL ASTRUD GILBERTO.
Tracks: / Take me to Aruanda / Bim bom / So nice (summer samba) / One note samba / O Ganso / Tristeza / Fly me to the moon / It might as well be spring / Manha de carnaval / Girl from Ipanema / Meditation / O morro nao tem vez / Corcovado / Certain smile, A / Beach samba / Agua de beber / Goodbye sadness.
LP: VRV 6
MC: VRVC 6

GILBERTO.
MC: 8230094
LP: 8230091

GIRL FROM IPANEMA, THE (See under Getz, Stan for details) (Gilberto, Astrud & Stan Getz).

GIRL FROM IPANEMA, THE (BBC LABEL).
LP: PREC 5009
MC: ZPREC 5009

LOOK TO THE RAINBOW.
Tracks: / Berimbau / Once upon a summertime / Felicidade / I will wait for you / Frevo / Maria Quiet (Marie Moita) / Look at the rainbow / Bim bom / Lugar bonito / El preciso aprender a ser so (learn to live alone).
LP: 8215561
MC: 8215564

MUSIC FOR THE MILLIONS.
Tracks: / Once I loved / Auga de beber / Meditation / And roses and roses / How insensitive / O morro / Dindi / Photograph / Dreamer / So tinha de ser com voce / All that's left is to say goodbye.
LP: 817 852-1
MC: 817 852-4

ONCE UPON A SUMMERTIME.
Tracks: / One note samba / Meditation / My foolish heart / Berimbau / Frevo / Once upon a summertime / How insensitive / Stay / Light my fire / Call me / I will wait for you / She's a carioca.
LP: 2352 172

SHADOW OF YOUR SMILE.
Tracks: / Shadow of your smile / Fly me to the moon / Gentle rain, The / Who can I turn to / Day by day.
LP: 2304 540

THAT GIRL FROM IPANEMA, THE.
Tracks: / Girl from Ipanema / Meu piao / Far away / We'll make today last night again / Black magic / All I've got / Love for sale / Wanting you / Puppy song, The / Mamae eu quero / Chica chica boom chic.

LP: PHX 1022
LP: ARTL 705

THIS IS ASTRUD GILBERTO.
LP: 825 064-1

Gilberto, Joao

BRASIL.
LP: 6328 382

GILBERTO AND JOBIM.
Tracks: / Manha de Carnaval / O pato / Corcovado / Trevo de quarto folhas / Un abraco no bonfa / Se e tarde me pardoa / Discussao / A felicidade / Amor certinho / Outra vez / Samba de una nota so / Doralice / So em teus bracos / Meditacao / Felicidade.
LP: 3C 054 81353
MC: 3C254 81353

JOAO & ASTRUD GILBERTO MEET STAN GETZ (Gilberto, Joao/Astrud Gilberton/Stan Getz).
LP: ENT LP 13051
MC: ENT MC 13051

Gilder, Nick

FREQUENCY.
Tracks: / You really rock me / Time after time / Metro jets / Electric love / Brightest star / Watcher of the night / Worlds collide / Hold on me tonight / Into the 80's.
LP: CHR 1219

ROCK AMERICA.
Tracks: / Rock America / I've got your number / 20th century girls / Catch 22 / Wild ones / On the beat / Night comes down / Lady you're a killer / One of the crowd.
LP: NBLP 7243

Gildo, Rex

GEH NICHT VORBEI.
Tracks: / Geh nicht vorbei (walk on by) / Speedy Gonzales / Oh oh candy lips / Liebe kaelter als eis (devil in disguise) / Leider leider (dear one) / Sieben wochen nach Bombay (I'm gonna get married) / Rexy zaehl auf mich (count on me) / Das ende der liebe (tell Laura I love her) / Denk an mich in der ferne (put your head on my / Du eine (dear someone) / Ich moecht in deinen armen sein / Glueck gohoert dazu / Du nennist alle maenner / Darling (you call everybody darling) / Dein zu sein (we got love) / Wenn es sein muss kann ich treu sein / Lass mich gehn (turn me loose).
LP: BFX 15090

Giles, Chris

CHRIS GILES PLAYS THE WERSI GALAXY.
Tracks: / Shaft, Theme from (Theme from "Shaft".) / Even now / At the sign of the swingin' cymbal / Ballade pour Adeline / Fanfare for the common man / Overture poet and peasant / Soul limbo / Romance / Bel viso / L'amour de plein ete / Rinky dink / Hooked on romance.
LP: GRS 1122

Giles, Giles & Fripp

CHEERFUL INSANITY OF.....
Tracks: / Saga of Rodney Toady, The / North meadow / Newly weds / One in a million / Call tomorrow / Digging my lawn / Little children / Crukster, The / Thursday morning / Just George / How do they know / Elephant song, The / Sun is shining, The / Suite No.1 / Erudite eyes.
LP: EGED 16

Gilfellon, Tom

IN THE MIDDLE OF THE TUNE.
Tracks: / Banks of red roses, the / Boys of Ballysadare, The / Worker's song, The / Celebrated working man / Uncle Albert's last heroic farewell to the world / Lady Ann Montgomery (Reel.) / Wind that shakes the barley, The / Foxhunter's, The (Reel.) / Snow it melts the soonest, The / Bonnie Gateshead lass, The / Thomas Friel's jig (Jig.) / Battering ram, The / Two sisters, The / Row in the gutter, The / Fiery clockface, The / Johnny Miner.
LP: 12TS 282

LOVING MAD TOM.
LP: LER 2079

Gilgamesh

ANOTHER FINE TUNE YOU GOT ME INTO.
Tracks: / Bobberty theme from something else; waiting / Darker, brighter / Waiting / Play time / Underwater song / Foel'd again / T.N.T.F.X..
LP: CRL 5009

Gill, B.M.

DYING TO MEET YOU.
MCSET: CAB 299

Gill, Earl

ENCHANTMENT.
Tracks: / Western echoes / Luke Kelly - a tribute / Songs of love / Lloyd Webber - show stoppers / Emigration / My Ireland / Eamonn an chnuic (Ned of the hills) / Love thee dearest / Danny boy / Chuilfhionn (the cualann), An / Power of love, The / Panis Angelicus / You'll never walk alone / South Pacific medley, The.
LP: HM 55

Gill, John

FINGER BUSTER.
LP: SOS 1066

Gill, Johnny

CHEMISTRY.
Tracks: / Half crazy / Can't wait till tomorrow / Don't take away my pride / One small light / Way that you love me, The / Because of you / Chemistry / I found love.
LP: 790250 1

JOHNNY GILL.
Tracks: / Rub you the right way / Wrap my body tight / Never know love / Lady Dujour / Giving my all to you / My my my (reprise) / Fairweather friend / Feels so much better / My my my / Just another lonely night / Let's spend the night / Wrap my body tight (Jazzie B 12" remake version) (Only on CD and cassette.) / My my my (live) (Only on CD and cassette.).
MC: ZK 72698
LP: ZL 72698
MC: ZK 72747

PERFECT COMBINATION (See under Lattisaw, Stacy).

WHERE DO WE GO FROM HERE (See also Lattisaw,Stacy) (Gill, Johnny & Stacy Lattisaw).

Gill, Vince

VINCE GILL.
LP: PL 89567
MC: PK 89567

WHEN I CALL YOUR NAME.
Tracks: / Never alone / Sight for sore eyes / Oh girl / Oklahoma swing / When I call your name / Ridin' the rodeo / Never knew lonely / We won't dance / We could have been / Rita Ballou.
LP: MCA 42321

Gillan

ACCIDENTALLY ON PURPOSE (Gillan & Roger Glover).
Tracks: / Clouds and rain / Evil eye / She took my breath away / Dislocated / Via Miami / I can't dance to that / Can't believe you wanna leave / Lonely Avenue / Telephone box / I thought no / Cayman Island (CD only) / Purple people eater (CD only) / Chet (CD only).
LP: V 2498
MC: TCV 2498

CHILD IN TIME.
Tracks: / Lay me down / You make me feel so good / Shame / My baby loves me / Down the road / Child in time / Let it slide.
LP: 2490 136

CLEAR AIR TURBULENCE.
Tracks: / Clean air turbulence / Five moons / Money lender / Over the hill / Goodhand Liza / Angel Manchenio.
LP: OVED 76
MC: OVEDC 76
LP: VM 4

DOUBLE TROUBLE.
Tracks: / I'll rip your spine out / Restless / Men of war / Sunbeam / Nightmare / Hadely bop bop / Life goes on / Born to kill / No laughing in Heaven / No easy way / Trouble / Mutually assured destruction / If you believe me / New Orleans.
2LP: VGD 3506
MC: VGDC 3506

FUTURE SHOCK.
Tracks: / Future shock / Night ride out of Phoenix / Ballad of the Lucitania Express, The / No laughing in Heaven / Sacre bleu / New Orleans / Bite the bullet / If I sing softly / Don't want the truth / For your dreams / One for the road (Only on CD.) / Bad news (Only on CD.) / Take a hold of yourself (Only on CD.) / M.A.D. (Only on CD.) / Maelstrom (Only on CD.) / Trouble (Only on CD.) / Your sisters on my list (Only on CD.) / Handles on her hips (Only on CD.) / Higher and higher (Only on CD.) / I might as well go home (mystic) (Only on CD.).
MC: TCV 2196
LP: OVED 74
MC: OVEDC 74
LP: VK 2196

GLORY ROAD.
Tracks: / Unchain your brain / Are you sure / Time and again / No easy way / Sleeping on the job / On the rocks / If you believe me / Running, white face, city boy / Nervous / Your mother was right (Only on CD.) / Red watch (Only on CD.) / Abbey of Thelema (Only on CD.) / Trying to get to you (Only on CD.) / Come tomorrow (Only on CD.) / Dragons tongue (Only on CD.) / Post-fade brain damage (Only on CD.).
LP: OVED 49
MC: OVEDC 49
LP: V 217,1

LIVE AT READING ROCK FESTIVAL 1980.
LP: FRSLP 002
MC: FRSMC 002

LIVE AT THE BUDOKAN.
Tracks: / Clear air turbulence / My baby loves me / Scarabus / Money lender / Twin exhausted / Over the hill / Child in time / Smoke on the water / Mercury high / Woman from Tokyo.
2LP: VGD 3507
MCSET: VGDC 3507

LIVE AT THE BUDOKAN (HARDROCK BOX SET) (See under Hard Rock).

MAGIC.
Tracks: / What's the matter / Bluesy blue sea / Caught in a trap / Long gone / Driving me wild / Demon driver / Living a lie / You're so right / Living for the city / Demon driver (reprise) / Breaking chains (Only on CD.) / Fiji (Only on CD.) / Purple sky (Only on CD.) / South Africa (Only on CD.) / John (Only on CD.) / South Africa (12" extended version) (Only on CD.) / Helter skelter (Only on CD.) / Smokestack lightning (Only on CD.).
LP: OVED 75
MC: OVEDC 75
LP: V 2238

MR.UNIVERSE.
Tracks: / Mr. Universe / Second sight / Secret of the dance / She tears me down / Roller / Vengeance / Puget sound / Dead of night / Message in a bottle / Fighting man / On the rocks (Only on CD.) / Bite the bullet (Only on CD.) / Mr Universe (version) (Only on CD.) / Vengeance (Only on CD.) / Smoke on the water (Only on CD.) / Lucille (Only on CD.).
LP: ACRO 3
LP: FA 3057

SCARABUS.
Tracks: / Scarabus / Twin exhausted / Poor boy hero / Mercury high / Pre-release / Slags to bitches / Apathy / Mad Elaine / Country lights / Fool's mate / My baby loves me (live).
LP: OVED 77
MC: OVEDC 77
LP: VM 3

TROUBLE (The best of Gillan).
Tracks: / Trouble / New Orleans / Fighting man / Living for the city / Helter skelter / Mr. Universe / Telephone box / Dislocated / Sleeping on the job / No laughing in heaven / Nightmare / Restless / Purple sky / Born to kill / Smoke on the water.
MC: VVIPC 113

VERY BEST OF GILLAN.
MC: MCTC 032

WHAT I DID ON MY VACATION.
Tracks: / On the rocks / Scarabus / Puget sound / Mad Elaine (NOT on CD) / Time and again (NOT on CD) / Vengeance (NOT on CD) / No easy way / If I sing softly / I'll rip your spine out / New Orleans / Mutually assured destruction / Unchain your brain (NOT on CD) / You're so right / No laughing in Heaven (NOT on CD) / Long gone / If you believe me / Trouble / Bluesy blue sea / Lucille.
2LP: DIXD 39
MCSET: CDIXD 39

Gillan, Ian

GARTH ROCKET & THE MOONSHINERS (VIDEO) (See under Rocket, Garth) (Rocket, Garth & The Moonshiners).

GILLAN (Gillan, Ian Band).
LP: STI 80000

LIVE AT THE RITZ '89 (See under Rockett, Garth) (Rockett, Garth & The Moonshiners).

NAKED THUNDER.
Tracks: / Gut reaction / No good luck / Sweet Lolita / Moonshine / Love gun / Talking to you / Nothing but the best / Nothing to lose / Long and lonely ride / No more can on the Brazos.
LP: 9031718991
MC: 9031718994

Gillan, Pauline

HEARTS OF FIRE (Gillan, Pauline Band).
LP: AMP 8

ROCKS ON! (Gillan, Pauline & Paul Dean).

Tracks: / Riders in the night / Sunshine of your love / Love sting / Black night / On the road again / Light my fire / Rocks on / Hole, The / Running wild / If you gotta make a fool of somebody / Angel lover.
LP: . . . THBL 014

Gillespie, Dana

BELOW THE BELT.
Tracks: / Lovin' machine / Come on / Sixty minute man / Ugly papa / On hour mama / Below the belt / My man stands out / It ain't the meat / Joe's joint / Don't you make me high / Empty bed blues / Horizontal boogie.
LP: . . . CH 126

DANA GILLESPIE'S BLUE JOB.
Tracks: / Lotta what you got, A / Sailor's delight / Big 10-inch record / King size papa / Organ grinder / Wasn't that good / Play with my poodle / Too many drivers / Nosey Joe / Diggin' my potatoes / Main line baby / Snatch it grab it.
LP: . . . CH 62

SWEET MEAT.
Tracks: / Three hundred pounds of joy / Pencil thin papa / Fat Sam from Birmingham / Big fat mamas are back in style again / Long lean baby / Tall skinny papa / Sweets / Fat meat is good meat / Meat on teir bones / Sweet meat / Meat balls / Built for comfort.
LP: . . . BLUH 007

Gillespie, Dizzy

20 GOLDEN PIECES: DIZZY GILLESPIE.
Tracks: / Night and day / Man I love, The / When it's sleepy time down South / Sweet and lovely / Very thought of you, The / Jealousy / Blue and sentimental / My old flame / Pennies from Heaven / Blue moon / Blue 'n' boogie / Hot house / Groovin' high / Dizzy atmosphere / All the things you are / Things to come / Emanon / Ray's idea / Our delight / Good dues blues.
LP: . . . BDL 2006
MC: . . . BDC 2006

1948-52 (Gillespie, Dizzy Big Band).
Tracks: / Cubana be, Cubana bop / Groovin' high / Candido bongos / On the sunny side of the street / Ooh-shoo-be-doo-bee.
LP: . . . QU 045

1948-53.
LP: . . . VG 502002

AFRO-CUBAN BOP (Gillespie, Dizzy & His Orchestra).
Tracks: / Oop-pop-a-da / One bass hit / Guarachi guaro / Relaxin' at Camarillo / I should care / Squirrel, The / Dizzier and dizzier / Taboo.
LP: . . . BLJ 8028

AFRO-CUBAN JAZZ MOODS (Gillespie, Dizzy & Machito).
Tracks: / Oro, incienso y mirra / Calidoscopico / Pensativo / Exuberante.
LP: . . . 2310 771
MC: . . . K10 771

ALTERNATE BLUES (see under Clark, Terry) (Gillespie, Dizzy/Clark Terry/ Freddie Hubbard/Oscar Peterson).

ANONYMOUS MR. GILLESPIE, THE.
Tracks: / My melancholy baby / Cherokee / You're only happy when I'm blue / Ten lessons with Timothy / Who / Way you look tonight, The / Why do I love you / All the things you are / Night and day / Weeping Willie / Everytime I think of you / Baranco boogie / Shades of twilight / Once in a lovetime / Worried life / Empty bed blues.
LP: . . . OFF 3032

AT DOWNBEAT CLUB, SUMMER 47.
LP: . . . JG 1010

AT NEWPORT.
LP: . . . 2304 348

AT THE MONTREUX JAZZ FESTIVAL 1975 (Gillespie, Dizzy Big Seven).
Tracks: / Lover come back to me / What's new? / Cherokee.
LP: . . . 2310 749
MC: . . . K10 749

BEBOP ENTERS SWEDEN 1947-49 (Gillespie, Dizzy Big Band).
LP: . . . DRLP 34

BEST OF DIZZY GILLESPIE.
Tracks: / Unicorn / Free ride / Pensavito / Exuberante / Behind the moonbeam / Shim-sham-shimmy.
LP: . . . 231 0855
MC: . . . K10 855

BIG BAND 1968.
LP: . . . BEP 509

BIRK'S WORKS.
Tracks: / Birk's works / Good bait / Oop-pop-a-da / Woodyn' you / Champ, The / I can't get started / Caravan.
LP: . . . D 1019

BODY AND SOUL (Gillespie, Dizzy & His Orchestra).
Tracks: / Rhumbop concerto / Relaxin' at Camarillo / Guarachi guaro / Soulphony in three hearts / Love me or leave me (Vocals: Sarah Vaughan) / Body and soul (Vocals: Sarah Vaughan) / Oop-pop-a-do / Ool-ya-koo / I'm beboppin' too.
LP: . . . BDL 1057
MC: . . . BDC 1057

BOP SESSION, THE (Gillespie, Dizzy/ Sonny Stitt/John Lewis/Max Roach).
Tracks: / Blues 'n' boogie / Confirmation / Groovin' high / Loverman / All the things you are / Ladybird.
LP: . . . SNTF 692
MC: . . . ZCSN 692

CHAMP 1951-1952, THE.
Tracks: / Champ, The / Birk's works / Caravan / Time on my hands / On the sunny side of the street / Tin tin deo / Stardust / They can't take that away from me / Bluest blues / Swing low sweet Cadillac / Ooh-shoo-be-doo-bee.
LP: . . . JA 5183

CHARLIE PARKER & DIZZY GILLESPIE (See under Parker, Charlie) (Gillespie, Dizzy & Charlie Parker).

CHARLIE PARKER, MILES DAVIS & DIZZY GILLESPIE, VOL 2 (see Parker, Charlie) (Gillespie, Dizzy/Charlie Parker/ Miles Davis).

CLOSER TO THE SOURCE.
Tracks: / Could it be you / It's time for love / Closer to the source / You're No.1 in my book / Iced tea / Just before dawn / Textures.
LP: . . . 781 646-1
MC: . . . 781 646-4

COMPLETE PLEYEL CONCERT.
2LP: . . . 429002

CONCERT - MASSEY HALL, TORONTO (15 May 1953). (Gillespie, Dizzy & Charlie Parker).
Tracks: / Perdido / Salt peanuts / All the things you are / Wee / Hot house.
LP: . . . SM 3784
MC: . . . MC 3784

CONFIRMATION (Gillespie, Dizzy & Sonny Berman).
Tracks: / Confirmation / Diggin' for Diz / Dynamo / When I grow too old to dream / Round midnight / Nocturne / Curbstone scuffle / Woodchopper's holiday / Somebody loves me / Blue serge.
LP: . . . SPJ 132

DEEGEE DAYS (Savoy Sessions).
Tracks: / Tin tin deo / Birk's works / We love to boogie / Lady be good / Champ, The / I'm in a mess / School days / Swing low sweet cadillac / Bopsie's blues / I couldn't beat the rap / Caravan / Nobody knows / Bluest blues / On the sunny side of the street / Stardust / Time on my hands / Blue skies / Umbrella man / Confessin' / Ooh-shoo-be-doo-bee / They can't take that away from me.
2LP: . . . WL 70517
2LP: . . . SJL 2209

DIGITAL AT MONTREUX 1980.
Tracks: / Christopher Columbus / I'm sitting on top of the world / Manteca / Get the booty / Kisses.
LP: . . . D 2308 226
MC: . . . K 08 226

DIZ DELIGHTS (Gillespie, Dizzy & His Orchestra).
Tracks: / 52nd Street theme / Night in Tunisia / Anthropology / Ow / Oop-pop-a-da / Two bass hit / Stay on it / Woodyn' you / Cool breeze / Manetca / Good bait / Ool-ya-koo.
LP: . . . CL 89804
MC: . . . CK 89804

DIZZY (Gillespie, Dizzy Big 7).
LP: . . . GNPS 9028

DIZZY... (Live at Carnegie Hall 1947) (Gillespie, Dizzy & His Legendary Big Band).
LP: . . . AR 110

DIZZY GILLESPIE....
LP: . . . LPPS 111 14

DIZZY GILLESPIE (1946-1949).
Tracks: / Manteca / Good bait / Ool-ya-koo / 52nd Street theme / Night in Tunisia / Ol' man rebop / Anthropology / Owl / Oop-pop-a-da / Cool breeze / Cubana be, Cubana bop / Minor walk / Guarachi guaro / Duff capers / Lover come back to me / I'm beboppin' too / Overtime / Victory ball / Swedish suite / St. Louis blues / Katy mo' meat / Jumpin' with Symphony Sid / In the land of oobla-dee.
2LP: . . . NL 89763
MCSET: . . . NK 89763
2LP: . . . PM 42408

DIZZY GILLESPIE (1948-1953).
LP: . . . 502002

DIZZY GILLESPIE AND CHARLIE PARKER (Gillespie, Dizzy & Charlie Parker).
LP: . . . 2M 056 64847
MC: . . . 2M 256 64847

DIZZY GILLESPIE AND HIS BAND IN CONCERT (Gillespie, Dizzy & His Band).
LP: . . . GNPS 23

DIZZY GILLESPIE AND HIS ORCHESTRA (Gillespie, Dizzy & Orchestra).
LP: . . . LPJT 37

DIZZY GILLESPIE AND THE DOUBLE SIX OF PARIS.
LP: . . . 6337 203

DIZZY GILLESPIE COLLECTION (20 Golden Greats).
Tracks: / Oo-shoo-be-do-be / I can't get started / Tin tin deo / On the sunny side of the street / Oop bop sh'bam / Lady be good / My man / Embraceable you / Ray's idea / Blue 'n' boogie / Swing low sweet Cadillac / That's Earl's brother / Things to come / One bass hit / This is happiness / Our delight / Emanon / Groovin' high / Dizzy atmosphere / Salt peanuts.
LP: . . . DVLP 2028
MC: . . . DVMC 2028

DIZZY GILLESPIE JAM.
Tracks: / Girl of my dreams / Get happy / Once in a while / But beautiful / Here's that rainy day / Champ, The.
LP: . . . 2308 211
MC: . . . K 08 211

DIZZY GILLESPIE MEETS PHIL WOODS QUARTET.
LP: . . . SFP 250
LP: . . . SJP 250

DIZZY GILLESPIE (MERCURY) (Compact/Walkman Jazz).
MC: . . . 832 574-4

DIZZY GILLESPIE QUINTET IN EUROPE (Gillespie, Dizzy Quintet).
Tracks: / Lady be good / No greater love / Mooche, The / Night in Tunisia / Long, long summer.
LP: . . . UJ 30

DIZZY GILLESPIE SEXTET (Gillespie, Dizzy Sextet).
LP: . . . 429 002

DIZZY GILLESPIE VOL1.
Tracks: / Emanon / Ool-ya-koo / 'Round midnight / Stay on it / Good bait / One bass hit / I can't get started / Manteca.
LP: . . . JR 120

DIZZY GILLESPIE VOL 2.
Tracks: / Champ, The / Tin tin deo / They can't take that away from me / Good bait / Mon homme / Bluest blues / Birk's works / On the sunny side of the street / Swing low sweet Cadillac / School days / Shoo-be-doo-be-doo.
LP: . . . JR 137

DIZZY GILLESPIE VOL 3.
Tracks: / Oop-pop-a-da / Round midnight / Algo bueno / I can't get started / Two bass hit / Good bait / Afro-Cuban suite / Ool-ya-koo / Things to come.
LP: . . . JR 141

DIZZY GILLESPIE'S BIG FOUR.
Tracks: / Frelimo / Hurry home / Russian lullaby / Be bob (Dizzy's fingers) / Birk's works / September song / Jitterbug.
LP: . . . 2310 719
MC: . . . K10 719

DIZZY ON THE FRENCH RIVIERA.
LP: . . . TIME 09
MC: . . . TIMEC 09

DIZZY'S DELIGHT.
LP: . . . LP 4

DIZZY'S PARTY.
Tracks: / Dizzy's party / Shim-sham-shimmy / Harlem samba / Land of milk and honey.
LP: . . . 231 0784
MC: . . . K10 784

ELECTRIFYING EVENING.
Tracks: / Kush / Salt peanuts / Night in Tunisia / Mooche, The.
LP: . . . 2304 349

ENDLESSLY.
LP: . . . MCA 42153
MC: . . . MCAC 42153

ENDURING MAGIC.
Tracks: / Blue 'n' boogie / Thrill is gone, The / Yale blue blues / Take the 'A' train / Love for sale / Street of dreams / Jew's harp.
LP: . . . BKH 51801

FREE RIDE.
Tracks: / Unicorn / Incantation / Wrong number / Free ride / Ozone madness / Love poem for Donna / Last stroke of midnight.
LP: . . . 231 0794

MC: . . . K10 794

GIANTS OF JAZZ (Gillespie, Dizzy, Art Blakey & Thelonious Monk).
Tracks: / Straight, no chaser / Thelonious / Sweet and lovely / Don't blame me / I'll wait for you / Epistrophy.
LP: . . . GW 3004

GIFTED ONES, THE (See Basie, Count) (Gillespie, Dizzy & Count Basie).

GILLESPIE JAM SESSIONS, THE.
2LP: . . . 2610 023

GOOD BAIT.
Tracks: / Good bait / Algo bueno / Minor walk / Half nelson / Cool breeze / Squirrel, The / Oop-pop-a-da / S'posin' / Taboo.
LP: . . . SPJ 122

GREAT DIZZY GILLESPIE, THE.
Tracks: / Blue 'n' boogie / Groovin' high / Dizzy atmosphere / All the things you are / Salt peanuts / Hot house / Oop bop sh'bam / That's Earl's brother / Our delight / One bass hit / Things to come / Ray's idea.
LP: . . . SM 3541

GROOVIN' HIGH (Gillespie, Dizzy & His Sextets).
LP: . . . MVS 2009

IN CONCERT 1956.
LP: . . . AR 111

IN THE BEGINNING.
Tracks: / Blue 'n' boogie / Groovin' high / All the things you are / Dizzy atmosphere / Salt peanuts / Shaw 'nuff / Lover man / Hot house / One bass hit / Oop bop sh'bam / Hand fulla gimme / That's Earl, brother / Things to come / Good dues blues / Our delight / Ray's idea / Emanon / He beeped when he shoulda bopped / I waited for you / Nice work if you can get it / She's gone again / Thinking of you.
2LP: . . . PR 24019

INCREDIBLE.
LP: . . . 5C 064 99400

IT HAPPENED ONE NIGHT (See under Fitzgerald, Ella) (Gillespie, Dizzy/Ella Fitzgerald/Charlie Parker).

JAZZ MATURITY...WHERE ITS COMMING FROM (Gillespie, Dizzy/Roy Eldridge).
LP: . . . 231 0816
MC: . . . K10 816

JAZZ TIME VOL.5.
LP: . . . 502705

JUST BOP (Gillespie, Dizzy Sextet).
LP: . . . QU 039

LEGENDARY, THE.
2LP: . . . 400018

LIVE: AT BIRDLAND 1956 (Gillespie, Dizzy Big Band).
LP: . . . LP 46-146

LIVE AT THE SHRINE AUDITORIUM (Gillespie, Dizzy Big Band).
LP: . . . QU 003

LIVE AT THE VILLAGE VANGUARD.
LP: . . . BNS 40035

MILES DAVIS, DIZZY GILLESPIE & CHARLIE PARKER (see Davis, Miles) (Gillespie, Dizzy/Charlie Parker/Miles Davis).

MONTEREY 1961.
LP: . . . JL 90

NEW FACES.
Tracks: / Birk's works / Lorraine / Tin tin deo / Tenor song / Every morning / Ballad / Fiesta mojo.
LP: . . . GRP 91012
MC: . . . GRPM 91012
LP: . . . GRPA 1012

NIGHT IN TUNISIA.
LP: . . . JJ 606

N.Y.C. 1952.
Tracks: / Champ, The / Good bait / Tin tin deo / Perdido.
LP: . . . LPPS 111 10

ONE BASS HIT (Gillespie, Dizzy & His Orchestra).
LP: . . . MVS 2010

ONE NIGHT IN WASHINGTON.
Tracks: / Afro suite / Hob nail boogie / Caravan / Tin tin deo / Ups 'n' downs / Wild bills boogie.
LP: . . . 9603001

OO POP A DA (Gillespie, Dizzy Quartet).
LP: . . . AFF 142

OOP-BOP SH'BAM.
Tracks: / I waited for you / Groovin' high / Oop-pop-a-da / Cool breeze / Stay on it / Ladybird / Wouldn't you? / Two bass hit / Oop bop sh'bam / Hot house / Ray's idea / Pan dameronium.
LP: . . . NOST 7629

OSCAR PETERSON AND DIZZY GILLESPIE (see Peterson, Oscar) (Gillespie, Dizzy & Oscar Peterson).

PARIS CONCERT.
LP: . . . . GNPS 9006

PASADENA 1948 (Legendary Big Band Concerts).
LP: 500060

PHOENIX JAZZ FIFTH ANNIVERSARY ALBUM (see Harris, Bill) (Gillespie, Dizzy/Bill Harris/Eddie Costa/Coleman Hawkins).

PLAYS AND RAPS IN HIS GREATEST CONCERT.
LP: . . . . D 2620 116
MC: K20 116

PLEYEL CONCERT 1953.
Tracks: / Champ, The / Tin tin deo / They can't take that away from me / Good bait / Bluest blues / Birks works / I can't get started / On the sunny side of the street / Mon homme / Swing low sweet Cadillac / School days / Oo-shoo-be-do-be.
LP: 509173

PORTRAIT OF DUKE ELLINGTON, A (Gillespie, Dizzy & His Orchestra).
Tracks: / In a mellow tone / Things ain't what they used to be / Serenade to Sweden / Chelsea Bridge / Upper Manhattan medical group / Do nothing till you hear from me / Caravan / Sophisticated lady / Johnny come lately / Perdido / Come Sunday.
LP: 817 107-1

PROFESSOR BOP.
Tracks: / Blue 'n' boogie / Groovin' high / Dizzy atmosphere / All the things you are / Hot house / Oop bop sh'bam / Our delight / Things to come / Ray's idea / Emanon / Good dues blues.
LP: . . . . ATS 11
MC: . . . . TCATS 11

SMALL COMBOS.
LP: . . . . LPJT 32

SMALL GROUPS, 1945-46, THE.
Tracks: / Melancholy baby / On the Alamo / Cherokee / Blue 'n' boogie / One bass hit / Ooh bob sh'bam / Handful of gimme / That's Earl's brother / Groovin' high / All the things you are / Dizzy atmosphere / Salt peanuts / Shaw 'nuff / Lover man.
LP: . . . . LP 2

SUMMERTIME (Gillespie, Dizzy & Mongo Santamaria).
Tracks: / Virtue / Afro blue / Summertime / Mambo Mongo.
LP: D230 8229
MC: . . . . K 08 229

SWEET SOUL.
LP: . . . . GSLP 7025
LP: 2M 056 64825
MC: 2M 256 64825

SWING LOW SWEET CADILLAC.
Tracks: / Swing low sweet Cadillac / Mas que nada / Something in your smile / Kush / Bye.
LP: . . . . JAS 5
MC: . . . . JAS C5
LP: . . . . AS 9149
MC: . . . . ASC 9149

TENDERLY.
MC: 771508

Gillespie, Hugh

CLASSIC RECORDINGS OF IRISH TRADITIONAL FIDDLE MUSIC.
Tracks: / Dowd's favourite / McKenna's farewell / Master Crowley's reels / Irish mazurka, The / Jenny's welcome to Charlie / Master Crowley's favourites / Finnea lassies / Gurren's castle / Girl that broke my heart, The / Dick Cosgrove's reels / Farewell to Leitrim / Tom Steele / Jackson's favourite / Kips / Paddy Finley's fancy / Joe O'Connell's dream / Versevanna / Donegal traveller, The / Miss Ontgomery / Mountain stream / Parker's fancy / Contentment is wealth / Finley's jig / Dowd's number nine / Jacksons.
LP: 12TS 364

Gillespie, Jon

TAM LIN (see Armstrong, Frankie) (Gillespie, Jon/Frankie Armstrong/Brian Pearson/Blowzabella).

Gillespie, Rhondda

DUETS ALBUM, THE (see under Weatherburn, Robert) (Gillespie, Rhondda & Robert Weatherburn).

Gillett, Belinda

WHO WANTS TO LIVE FOREVER? (See under Meeson, Ian) (Gillett, Belinda & Ian Meeson).

Gilley, Mickey

20 GOLDEN SONGS.
LP: 20113
MC: 40113

DOWN THE LINE.
LP: . . . . CR 30192

FROM PASADENA WITH LOVE.
Tracks: / Still care about you / Keepin' on / That's how it's got to be / I miss you so / Just out of reach / Grapevine / Fraulein / No greater love / Boy who didn't pass / I ain't going home.
LP: . . . . SDLP 1016
MC: . . . . SDC 1016

I LOVE COUNTRY.
Tracks: / Headache tomorrow or a headache tonight / Power of positive drinking, The / City lights / Lonely nights / Lawdy Miss Clawdy / Stand by me / True love ways / Talk to me / Tears of the lonely.
LP: 4504321
MC: 4504324
MC: . . . . ZCGAS 713

MICKEY AT GILLEY'S.
LP: . . . . CMLF 1012

PUT YOUR DREAMS AWAY.
Tracks: / Talk to me / Don't you be foolin' with a fool / I really don't want to know / If I can't hold her on the outside / Put your dreams away / Honky tonkin' / Rocky road to romance.
LP: . . . . EPC 85851

ROCKIN' ROLLIN' PIANO.
LP: . . . . MINOR 1006

THAT'S ALL THAT MATTERS TO ME.
Tracks: / That's all that matters to me / Blues don't care who's got 'em / More I turn the bottle up / Jukebox argument / Million dollar memories / Blame lies with me / True love ways / Lyin' again / So easy to begin / Headache tomorrow or a headache tonight.
LP: . . . . EPC 84391

TOO GOOD TO STOP NOW.
Tracks: / Too good to stop now / Make it like the first time / Shoulder to cry on / When she runs out of fools / Right side of the wrong bed / Everything I own / Reminders / You can lie to me tonight / I'm the one mama warned you about / Quittin' time.
LP: . . . . EPC 26070

Gillies, Alasdair

ALL MY LIFE'S A CIRCLE.
Tracks: / Song of the Mira / When I come home the first time / Mountains of Mourne / Unicorn / Island Moon / Leezie Lindsay / Touch the wind / Let Mr. Maguire sit down / Youth of the heart, The / Give me your hand / Sligo town / All my life's a circle.
LP: . . . . BGC 328
MC: . . . . KBGC 328

AMONG MY SOUVENIRS.
Tracks: / Take me home / I dream of Jeannie with the light brown hair / Among my souvenirs / I will love you all my life / Tak a dram / Scarlet ribbons / Scotland my home / Banners of Scotland, The / Bonnie Mary of Argyle / Say you'll stay until tomorrow / Beautiful dreamer / More than yesterday / Maggie / Messin' about on the river.
LP: . . . . ITV 416
MC: . . . . KITV 416

BY COOL SILOAM.
LP: . . . . BGC 237

FAREWELL MY LOVE.
MC: . . . . ZCPKB 5567

LIVE AT EDEN COURT THEATRE, INVERNESS.
Tracks: / Let's have a ceilidh / Highland gentleman, A / Inverary Inn / Nobody loves like a Skyeman / Westering home / Marie's wedding / Uist tramping song / Stornoway / Loch Maree islands / Take the boat over to Skye / Centipede / An cluinn thu mi mo nighean donn / Gentle Annie / Politician / Our ain fireside / High level hornpipe / Hebridean melody / Morag of Dunvegan / Lovely Stornoway / Lochindaal / Cailin mo ruin-sa / Dancing in Kyle / Granny's heilan' hame / Farewell my love / Scotland the brave / Will ye no come back again.
2LP: . . . . BGC 239
MC: . . . . KBGC 239

SCOTCH ON THE ROCKS.
Tracks: / Scotch on the rocks / Lonely scapa flow / Broken down house / O Vancouver / Tobermory Bay / Always have a friend / Dark island / Those brown eyes / Whistling gypsy / Flora / Bonnie wee window / Time.
LP: . . . . PKL 5556
MC: . . . . ZCPKB 5556

SCOTTISH TRILOGY.
LP: . . . . BGC 311

SILVER AND GOLD.
Tracks: / Buaim a'choirce (Islay repear's song) / Suas leis a'ghaidhlig (exalt the Gaelic language) / Taladh chriosda (the Christ child lullaby) / Nam aonar le mo smaointean (alone with my thoughts) / An fhaidhir mhuileach (the mull fair) / Cumha mhic criomain (Mac Crimmon's lament) / Medley (foal hill, filoro, last night) / Psalm 65 / Mhnathan a ghlinne so (women of this Glen) / Muile nam fuar-bheann mor (mull of the cold high mountains) / No chailin dileas sonn (my dark haired maid) / Oidhche mhath leibh (goodnight to you).
LP: . . . . ITV 365
MC: . . . . KITV 365

WALTZING ROUND SCOTLAND.
Tracks: / Clans are gathering, The / Sons of Glencoe, The / Laird of Cockpen, The / Ae fond kiss / Ceilidh place / Bonnie naver bay / Waters of Kylesku / Granny's heilan' hame / Westering home / Soft lowland tongue o' the borders / Bonnie galloway / Old Scots mother mine / My ain folk / Scottish trilogy - Scotland again / Flower of Scotland / Scots wha' hae / Flower o' the quern / Mairi's song / Come by the hills / Song of the sea / Dark island / Bonnie Scotland I adore thee / Old Scottish waltz / Rowan tree.
LP: . . . . BGC 297
MC: . . . . KBGC 297

Gillies, Anne Lorne

BELOVED SCOTLAND.
Tracks: / Loch Maree / Ye banks and braes / Bunch of thyme / Lea rig, The / Come to the hills / My ain folk / Wild mountain thyme / Rowan tree / Whistle and I'll dance / Aye waukin' o / Canadian exile song / Our ain fireside.
LP: . . . . LOCLP 1026
MC: . . . . ZCLOC 1026

HILLS OF LORNE, THE.
Tracks: / Hills of Lorne, The / Dark island / I know a lad / Banks of Sicily / Salt sea wine / Glencoe / Think of me / Land for all seasons, A / Sandy at sunset / Bonnie Galloway / Dumbarton's drums / Dark Lochnagar / Golden wedding ring / Farewell my love.
LP: . . . . LOCLP 1008
MC: . . . . ZCLOC 1008

LEGENDS OF SCOTLAND.
Tracks: / Ae fond kiss / Jock O'Hazeldean / Coille'n Fhasaich / Aye waukin' o / Canadian exile song / Our ain fireside / Parcel o' rogues / Wae's me for Prince Charlie / Orain luaidh / Dark Lochnagar / Hills of Lorne, The / Dumbarton's drums.
MC: . . . . ZCLLS 709

MILESTONE.
Tracks: / Parcel o' rogues / Fond kiss, A / My fiddle and me / Rattlin' roarin' Willie / Smile in your sleep / Scotland again / Jock O'Hazeldean / Road to Drumleman / Leave them a flower / Wae's me for Prince Charlie / High Germany / South wind / Bonnie lass o' Fyvie.
LP: . . . . LOCLP 1019
MC: . . . . ZCLOC 1019

SINGS...THE SONGS OF THE GAEL.
Tracks: / Am bauchaille ban / Ho ro chall eile / Nah uainairantulaich / Cumha iain ghairbh ratharsair / Allt an t-siucair / Griogal cirdhe / Coille'n fhasaich / Gur moch rinn mi dusgadh / Mo dhomhnallan fhin / Nach forach mi gadchaoineach / Orain luaidh / Iain glinn cuaich / A fhleasgaicha chuildualaich / A chuairt shamhraidh.
LP: . . . . LOCLP 1014
MC: . . . . ZCLOC 1014

Gills, Johnny

BIG CITY BLUES (Gills, Johnny California Sunset Five).
LP: . . . . SOS 1157

DOWN HOME BLUES.
LP: . . . . SOS 1126

I LOST MY HEART (Gills, Johnny Original Sunset Five).
LP: . . . . SOS 1094

SOME SWEET DAY (Vol 1).
LP: . . . . SOS 1156

Gillum, Bill 'Jazz'

JAZZ GILLUM 35-47.
LP: . . . . DLP 522

JAZZ GILLUM 1935-46.
LP: . . . . BOB 4

JAZZ GILLUM 1938-47.
Tracks: / It sure had a kick / Maybe you'll love me too / Tell me, mama / Little woman / 5 feet 4 / What a gal / Water pipe blues / She belongs to me / Boar hog blues / You are doing me wrong / You're tearing my playhouse down / I couldn't help it / Talking to myself / Muddy pond blues / War time blues / Blues what am.
LP: . . . . TM 808

ME AND MY BUDDY 1938-42.
LP: . . . . BT 2013

ROLL DEM BONES 1938-49.
LP: . . . . WBJ 002

Gilmer, Jimmy

SUGAR SHACK.
LP: . . . . DOT 25545

Gilmore, Gene

GENE GILMORE AND 5 BREEZES 1939-40 (Gilmore, Gene & 5 Breezes).
LP: . . . . BD 2065

Gilmore, Jimmie Dale

AFTER AWHILE.
MC: 7559611484

Gilmore, John

BLOWING IN FROM CHICAGO (see Jordan, Clifford) (Gilmore, John/Clifford Jordan).

Gilmore, Otis Elevator

CINCINNATI'S FINEST - 1959-67.
LP: . . . . FLY 623

Gilmore, Peter (nar)

LORNA DOONE (see under Lorna Doone (bk)).

Gilmour, David

ABOUT FACE.
Tracks: / Until we sleep / Murder / Love on the air / Blue light / Out of the blue / You know I'm right / Cruise / Let's get metaphysical / Near the end / All lovers are deranged.
LP: . . . . FA 3173
MC: . . . . TCFA 3173
LP: . . . . SHSP 2400791
MC: . . . . TCSHSP 2400794

DAVID GILMOUR.
Tracks: / Mihalis / There's no way out of here / Cry from the street / So far away / Short and sweet / Raise my rent / No way / Definitely / I can't breathe anymore.
LP: . . . . FA 4130791
MC: . . . . TCFA 41 30791
LP: . . . . SHVL 817

Gilmour, Jimmie Dale

FAIR AND SQUARE.
Tracks: / Honky tonk masquerade / Don't look for a heartache / Trying to get to you / Singing The Blues / Just a wave, not the water / All Grown Up / 99 holes / Rain just falls / White freightliner blues.
LP: . . . . FIEND 113

JIMMIE DALE GILMOUR.
Tracks: / Honky tonk song / Doors are open wide, The / See the way / Beautiful rose / Dallas / Up to you / Red chevrolet / Deep Eddy blues / That hardwood floor / When the nights are cold.
LP: . . . . FIEND 145

TWO ROADS (See under Hancock, Butch).

Gilmour, Jon

GONNA DIE WITH A SMILE IF IT KILLS ME.
LP: . . . . PHILO 1095
MC: . . . . PH 1095C

Gilson, Jef

SOUL OF AFRICA (see under Singer, Hal) (Jef Gilson & Hal Singer).
LP: . . . . LDX 74556

Gilstrap, Jim

SWING YOUR DADDY.
LP: . . . . CHELV 1005
MC: . . . . CHELC 1005

Giltrap, Gordon

AIRWAVES.
Tracks: / Black lightning / El Greco / Heroes / Haunted heart / Rainbells / Dreamteller / Reaching out / Sad skies / Air waves / Empty / Lake Isle / Lost love.
LP: . . . . GIL 2

ELEGY.
LP: . . . . MODEM 1001
MC: . . . . MODEMC 1001

FEAR OF THE DARK.
Tracks: / Roots (part one and two) / Nightrider / Inner dream / Weary eyes / Fast approaching / Melancholy lullaby / Fear of the dark / Visitation.
LP: . . . . TRIX 7
MC: . . . . ZCTRIX 7

LIVE: GORDON GILTRAP.
Tracks: / Awakening / Robes and crowns / Quest / Deserter, The / Fast approaching / Catwalk blues / Roots 1 & 2 / Nightrider / Inner dream / Fear of the dark / Visitation / Heartsong / Lucifer's cage.
LP: . . . . ICS 1001

MATTER OF TIME, A (Giltrap, Gordon & Martin Taylor).
MC: . . . . CASSGP 007

MIDNIGHT CLEAR, A.
LP: . . . . MODEM 1006
MC: . . . . MODEMC 1006

ONE TO ONE.
LP: . . . . NP 002
MC: . . . . NP 002MC

PEACOCK PARTY.
Tracks: / Headwind - the eagle / Magpie rag / Hocus pocus / Turkey trot - a country bluff / Tailor bird / Black rose - the raven / Birds of a feather / Jester's jig / Gypsy Lane / Party piece / Chanticleer / Dono's dream.
LP: GIL 1
MC: GILK 1
LP: PRST 507
MC: ZPRST 507

PERILOUS JOURNEY.
Tracks: / Quest / Deserter, The / Morbio gorge / Heartsong / Reflections and despair / Cascade / To the high throne / Vision.
LP: TRIX 4
MC: ZCTRIX 4

PERILOUS JOURNEY/ELEGY.
MC: ZPRIM 850

PLATINUM COLLECTION.
Tracks: / Heartsong / Price of experience, The / Vision / Inner dream / Night / Revelation / Awakening / From the four winds / Lucifer's cage / Night rider / Morbio gorge / Deserter, The / Oh well / Tyger, The / Echoing green, The / Pastoral / Fast approaching / O Jerusalem / Fear of the dark / Quest / Cascade / Reflections and despair / Visitation / Weary eyes.
LP: PLAT 1005
MC: ZCPLT 1005

VISIONARY.
Tracks: / Awakening / Robes and crowns / From the four winds / Lucifer's cage / Revelation / Price of experience, The / Dance of Albion, The / Tyger, The / Echoing green, The / London / Night.
LP: TRIX 2
MC: ZCTRIX 2

VISIONARY/FEAR OF THE DARK.
LP: ZPRIM 851

Giltrap, Joe

PLACE IN YOUR HEART (ISLAND), A (See Under Palmer, Joe) (Giltrap, Joe & Joe Palmer).

Gilvray, Frances

INTO THE LIGHT (Gilvray, Frances & Mick Burke).
LP: COASTAL 1

Gimble, Johnny

HONKY TONK HITS.
2LP: CMH 9038
MC: CMHC 9038

ON THE ROAD AGAIN (See also Nelson, Willie) (Gimble, Johnny & Willie Nelson).

STILL SWINGIN' (Gimble, Johnny & The Texas Swing Pioneers).
LP: CMH 9020
MC: CMHC 9020

TEXAS FIDDLE COLLECTION, THE.
LP: CMH 9027
MC: CMHC 9027

Gimell

1585 - 1985.
LP: 15851
MC: 15851T

Gin on the Rocks

COOLEST GROOVE.
LP: 087625

Gina & The Strollers

HARD UP AND RESTLESS.
Tracks: / Not fade away / My heart is aching / This little girl / Please don't leave me / It ain't easy / Harp attack / Hard up and restless / Blues stay away / Lond black hair / Baby please don't go / I'm so lonely tonight / Thunder and lightning / Barbara Ann.
LP: MFLP 070

Gina X

NICE MOVER.
Tracks: / Nice mover / No G.D.M. / Plastic surprise box / Casablanca / Be a boy / Exhibitionism / Black sheep / Do it yourself.
LP: STATLP 30
LP: EMC 3314

X-TRAORDINAIRE (Gina X Performance).
Tracks: / Strip tease / Do it yourself / Opposite numbers / Cologne intime / Weekend twist / Vendor's box / Ciao Caruso.
LP: EMC 3336

YINGLISH.
LP: STATLP 21
MC: STATC 21

Ginger Ale Afternoon

GINGER ALE AFTERNOON (See under Dixon, Willie) (Dixon, Willie).

Ginger, Debbie

DOLLY PARTON'S GREATEST HITS.
MC: BBM 115

Ginger & Fred (film)

GINGER AND FRED (Film Soundtrack) (Various artists).
LP: A 284
MC: C 284

Ginger Tree (tv)

GINGER TREE, THE (Various artists).
MCSET: ZBBC 1130

Gingerbread Boy...

GINGERBREAD BOY, THE (well loved tales up to age 9) (Unknown narrator(s)).
MC: PLB 90

Gingerbread Man

GINGERBREAD MAN (Unknown narrator(s)).
MC: STC 305

GINGERBREAD MAN, THE (Hampshire, Susan).
MC: 3605

Gingold, Hermione

LA GINFOLD.
LP: MRS 902

Ginsberg, Allen

HOWL.
Tracks: / Howl / Sunflower Sutura, The / Footnote to howl / Supermarket, A / In California / Organ Music / Transcription / In the back of the real / America.
LP: BGP 1018

LION FOR REAL, THE.
Tracks: / Scribble / Xmas gift / Lion for real, The / Shrouded stranger, The / Cleveland, the flats / Stanzas - written at night in Radio City / Hum bom / Guru / C'mon Jack / Gregory Corso's story / End, The / Sunset / Krai majales / Ode to failure.
MC: ANC 8750
LP: AN 8750

WORLDS GREATEST POETS (America today).
LP: PRCS 115

Giorbino, Anthony

ART OF LETTING GO, THE.
LP: SBR 20 LP

Giordano, Steve

DAYBREAK.
Tracks: / Daybreak / Stages / Prissy / Moment's notice / Summer landscape.
LP: MR 5211

Gipsy Fire

GIPSY FIRE.
MC: INT 445149

Gipsy Kings

ALLEGRIA.
Tracks: / Tena tinita / La dona / Sueno / Un amor / Pharoan / Recuerda / Allegria / Solituda / Djobi, djoba / Papa, no pega la mama / Tristessa.
LP: 631 345 0
MC: 720 045 0
LP: 4667621
MC: 4667624

ESTE MUNDO.
Tracks: / Baila me / Sin ella / Habla me / Lagrimas / Oy / Mi vida / El mauro / Non Volvere / Furia / Oh mai / Ternuras / Ests mundo.
LP: 4686481
MC: 4686484

GIPSY KINGS.
Tracks: / Tu quieres volver / Moorea / Bem, bem, Maria / Un amor / Inspiration / Mi minera, A / Djobi djoba / Faena / Quiero saber / Amor amor / Duende.
LP: PEM 155011
MC: PEM 155014
LP: STAR 2355
MC: STAC 2355
LP: A1 LP 1003
MC: A1 C 1003

LUNA DE FUEGO.
LP: 834 164 1
MC: 834 164 4
LP: 4667631
MC: 4667634

MOSAIQUE.
MC: STAC 2398
LP: STAR 2398

Giraffe In Flames

GIRAFFE IN FLAMES (Various artists).
LP: AAZ 1

Girard, Adele

MERRY CHRISTMAS.
Tracks: / O holy night / Angels we have heard on high / Away in a manger / We three kings of Orient are / First Noel, The / God rest ye merry gentlemen / It came upon a midnight clear / Do you hear what I hear / O Christmas tree / Sleigh ride / Winter wonderland / What child is this? / Silver bells / Good King Wenceslas / Hark the herald angels sing / Carol of the bells / O little town of Bethlehem / Jingle bells / Silent night.
LP: TOTEM 1024

Girard, Chuck

CHUCK GIRARD.
Tracks: / Rock and roll preacher / You ask me why / Evermore / Quiet hour / Everybody knows for sure / Galilee / Tinagera / Lay your burden down / Slow down / Sometimes allelujah.
LP: MYR 1025
MC: MC 1025

GLOW IN THE DARK.
Tracks: / Anthem / Callin' you / I remember / Return / I know a lady / No, no, you're not afraid / Somethin' supernatural / When I was ready to listen / So thankful (song for Easter morning) / Old Dan Cotton.
LP: MYR 1050
MC: MC 1050

NAME ABOVE ALL NAMES, THE.
LP: MYR 1177
MC: MC 1177

STAND, THE.
Tracks: / Soldier / Home for good / Busy day / Bordertown / Witness / Fold, The / Stand, The / Racin' like the wind / Child come home.
LP: MYR 1089
MC: MC 1089

TAKE IT EASY.
Tracks: / Take a hand / Love is alive / Little people / Full immersion ocean water baptism by the sea / Without your love / Our lives are in your hands / His word is still His promise / Song for a Christian wedding / Wings of mercy / All I want.
LP: MYR 1077
MC: MC 1077

WRITTEN ON THE WIND.
Tracks: / Spirit wind / Mary's song / Thank you Lord / Plain ol' Joe / Harvest time / Fool for Jesus / Hear the angels sing / Peace in the valley / Warrior.
LP: MYR 1065
MC: MC 1065

Girl

BLOOD, WOMEN, ROSES.
LP: 33PROD 4

SHEER GREED.
Tracks: / Hollywood tease / Things you say, The / Lovely Lorraine / Strawberries / Little Miss Ann / Doctor Doctor / Do you love me / Take me dancing / What's up / Passing clouds / My number / Heartbreak America.
LP: JETLP 224
MC: JETCA 224

WASTED YOUTH.
Tracks: / Thru' the twilight / Old dogs / Ice in the blood / Wasted youth / Standard romance / Nice 'n' nasty / McKitty's back / 19 / Overnight angels / Sweet kids.
LP: JETLP 238

Girl Can't Help It

GIRL CAN'T HELP IT, THE (Film soundtrack) (Various artists).
LPPD: PD 1050

Girl Crazy (musical)

GIRL CRAZY (Film soundtrack) (Various artists).
LP: HS 5008

GIRL CRAZY (Studio Cast) (Various artists).
LP: COS 2560

Girl From ...

GIRL FROM THE CANDLE-LIT BATH (Scales, Prunella (nar)).
MC: CAB 016

Girl From Ipanema

GIRL FROM IPANEMA (See under Jobim, Antonio Carlos) (Jobim, Antonio Carlos).

Girl Groups

DETROIT GIRL GROUPS (Various artists).
LP: RELIC 8004

GIRL GROUPS (Various artists).
LP: 6498 032
MC: 7133 032

GIRL GROUPS OF THE 60'S (Various artists).
MC: GM 0213

GIRL GROUPS OF THE MOTORCITY (Various artists).
LP: MOTCLP 22

GIRLS (Various artists).
LP: ROCK 9001

GIRLS CAN'T HELP IT (Various artists).
LP: RNLP 024

GIRLS WITH GUITARS (Various artists).
Tracks: / Can't you hear my heartbeat: *Goldie & The Gingerbreads* / Time to say goodnight: *Martells* / Don't stop now: *Kittens* / I've been crying: *St. John, Barry* / Oo-chang-a-lang: *Orchids* / Now I know: *Beat* Chics / Dat's love: *Vernon Girls* / Bread and butter: *St. John, Barry* / Give me rhythm and blues: *Mysteries....* / I'll come running over: *Lulu* / You just gotta know my mind: *Gillespie, Dana* / Grumbling guitar: *Other* Two / 'Round about way: *Kittens* / That's why I love you: *Goldie & The Gingerbreads* / Say it again: *Chimes* / Love is gonna happen to me: *Marsden, Beryl*.
LP: ACT 012

GOLDEN GIRLS OF THE 60'S (Various artists).
MC: PLAC 344

GOLDEN HOUR OF GOLDEN GIRLS, A (Various artists).
MC: KGHMC 155

LES GIRLS! (Various artists).
Tracks: / Private number: *Grimes, Carol* / Shame shame shame: *Thomas, Irma* / Little bell: *Dixie Cups* / Easier to say than do: *Lavette, Betty* / I'm just a down home girl: *Ad Libs* / Harper Valley PTA: *Riley, Jeannie C.* / Letter full of tears: *Knight, Gladys* / My baby specializes: *Grimes, Carol* / Piece of my heart: *Lavette, Betty* / Boy from New York City: *Ad Libs* / If you should ever leave me: *Driscoll, Julie* / I need a man: *Pittman, Barbara* / Past, present and future: *Shangri-Las* / Love me or leave me: *Simone, Nina* / Getting mighty crowded: *Everett, Betty* / Ride your pony: *Harris, Betty* / Another boy like mine: *Dixie* Cups / Lady Marmalade: *Thomas, Irma* / It's in his kiss: *Everett, Betty* / Heaven only knows: *Shangri-Las* / Little girl blue: *Simone, Nina* / Girl most likely, The: *Riley, Jeannie C.*
2LP: CR 105
MCSET: CRT 105

LOOKIN' FOR BOYS (19 Girl classic's from the 60's) (Various artists).
LP: XSLP 102

STOP LOOK & LISTEN (Various artists).
Tracks: / Stop, look & listen: *Les Girls!* / Kiss & tell: *Julie & The Desires* / He's just a playboy: *Carroll,* Bernadette / Your big mistake: *Delrons* / Heading for a heartbreak: *Cheese Cakes* / Let me get close to you: *Warren, Beverly* / My block: *Four Pennies* / When the boy's happy (the girl's happy too): *Four Pennies* / He's my dream boy: *Antoinette, Marie* / If I knew then what I know now: *Four Pennies* / Love me like you're gonna lose me: *Chiffons* / When the boy's happy (the girl's happy too): *Chiffons* / I believe they're all talking about me: *Dawn* / Whenever a teenager cries: *Jeans* / Shy guy: *Charmers* / He's an angel: *Summits* / How can I be sure: *Dennis, Gloria*.
LP: ACT 001

WHERE THE GIRLS ARE (Various artists).
Tracks: / Sneaky Sue: *Lace, Patty & The Petticoats* / Sh-down down song, The: *Ginger Snaps & Dandee Dawson* / Please don't kiss me again: *Charmettes* / Baby that's me: *Cake* / Thank you for loving me: *Various artists* / We'll start the party again: *Peters, Bernadette* / Let's break up for a while: *Sapphires* / In his car: *Ward,* Robin & The Rainbows / Ain't that love: *Berry, Dorothy* / Hey boy: *Crampton Sisters* / Everything: *Orlons, The* / Come on baby: *Bon Bons* / Revolution: *Rachel & The Revolvers* / I want you to be my boyfriend: *Various artists* / It hurts to be sixteen: *Chandler, Barbara* / Our day will come: *Ruby & The Romantics*.
LP: KENT 016

Girl Groups (film)

GIRL GROUPS: THE STORY OF A SOUND (Film Soundtrack) (Various artists).
Tracks: / Leader of the pack: *Shangri-Las* / Stop in the name of love: *Ross, Diana & The Supremes* / Give him a great big kiss: *Shangri-Las* / My guy: *Wells, Mary* / You should have seen the way he looked at me: *Dixie* Cups / Come see about me: *Ross, Diana & The Supremes* / Will you love me tomorrow: *Shirrelles, The* / Needle in a haystack: *Velvelettes* / Dancing in the street: *Reeves, Martha & The Vandellas* / My boyfriend's back: *Angels* / Baby love: *Ross, Diana & The Supremes* / Remember (walking in the sand): *Shangri-Las* / Please Mr. Postman: *Marvelettes* / Someday we'll be together: *Ross, Diana & The Supremes* / Back in my arms again: *Ross, Diana & The Supremes* / Chapel of love: *Dixie Cups*.
LP: STMR 9020
MC: CSTMR 9020
LP: WL 72140

Girl Guides

COME ON AND SING.
MC: MRMC 024

SING FOR JOY.
Tracks: / Let it be / Family of man / Black and white.
LP: . . . . REC 328
MC: . . . . ZCM 328

Girl In Pink Tights

GIRL IN PINK TIGHTS, THE (Original Broadway cast) (Various artists).
LP: . . . . AOL 4890

Girl Of The Great

GIRL OF THE GREAT MOUNTAIN, THE.
Tracks: / Girl of the great mountain / Bear woman and the little Navaho / Black bull and the magic drum / Magic bag of Golden Eagle / Sleeper of the cave of darkness / Three brothers.
MC: . . . . ANV 635

Girl Talk (1)

GIRL TALK (Various artists).
Tracks: / Marie Celeste: *Various artists* / Lemon tarts: *Various artists* / Marvellous boy: *Various artists*/ Libera me: *Various artists* / Oh Constance: *Various artists* / Man of mine: *Various artists* / Perfect dear: *Various artists* / Rave up: *Various artists* / Curtain: *Various artists* / Camera loves me, The: *Various artists* / Goodbye again: *Various artists*.
LP: . . . . ACME 20

Girl Trouble

HIT IT OR QUIT IT.
LP: . . . . NBT 3303

Girl Who Pretended...

GIRL WHO PRETENDED TO BE A BOY (Fullerton, Fiona).
MC: . . . . LP 204
MC: . . . . LPMC 203

Girl With The ...

GIRL WITH THE GOLDEN HAIR (See under Barbie (bk).

Girlfriend (film)

GIRLFRIEND, THE (Original cast) (Various artists).
MC: . . . . ZCTER 1148
LP: . . . . TER 1148

Girls About Town

GIRLS ABOUT TOWN (Various artists).
Tracks: / You're so fine: *Berry, Dorothy* / He's got your number: *Demures* / Change, The: *Eady, Ernestine*/ Bad trouble: *Big Maybelle* / Better be ready: *Annette* / Sweet & lovely: *Candy & The Kisses* / I want to get married: *Delicates* / Comin' down with love: *Delicates* / You don't love me anymore: *Dodds, Nella*/ Little girl lost: *Brown, Maxine* / Girl is not a girl, A: *Shirelles* / You won't be there: *Teardrops...*/ Let me down easy: *Toys* / Boy I love, The: *Medina, Renee* / Nothing to write home about: *Francettes*/ Muscle bustle: *Loren, Donna*.
LP: . . . . ACT 006

Girls At Our Best

PLEASURE.
LP: . . . . RVLP 1

Girls Girls Girls

GIRLS GIRLS GIRLS (FILM) (Film soundtrack) (See under Presley, Elvis) (Presley, Elvis).

Girls Just Wanna ...

GIRLS JUST WANNA HAVE FUN (Film Soundtrack) (Various artists).
LP: . . . . MERH 72
MC: . . . . MERHC 72

Girlschool

CHEERS YOU LOT.
Tracks: / C'mon let's go / Race with the devil / Wildlife / Screaming blue murder / Please don't touch / Breakout / Emergency / Yeah right / Bomber / Demolition boys / Take it from me / Tush.
LP: . . . . METALPM 127

DEMOLITION.
Tracks: / Demolition boys / Not for sale / Race with the devil / Take it all away / Nothing to lose / Breakdown / Midnight ride / Emergency / Baby doll / Deadline.
LP: . . . . BRON 525

HIT AND RUN.
Tracks: / Hit and run / C'mon let's go / Hunter / Victim / Kick it down / Following the crowd / Tush / Watch your step / Back to start / Yeah right / Future flash.
LP: . . . . BRON 534

NIGHTMARE AT MAPLE CROSS.
MC: . . . . GWTC 2
LP: . . . . GWLP 2

PLAY DIRTY.
Tracks: / Going under / High and dry / Play dirty / 20th century boy / Breaking all the rules / Burning in the heat / Surrender / Rock me shock me / Running for cover / Breakout.
LP: . . . . BRON 548

RACE WITH THE DEVIL.
Tracks: / 1-2-3-4 rock and roll / Furniture fire / Take it all away / Kick it down / Midnight ride / Race with the devil / Play dirty / Yeah right / Emergency / Breakout (Knob in the media) / Flesh and blood / Tush / Don't stop / Future flash / Rock me shock me / Screaming blue murder / Wild life / Bomber / Nothing to lose / Live with me / Like it like that / Tonight / Take it from me.
LP: . . . . RAWLP 013
MC: . . . . RAWTC 013

SCREAMING BLUE MURDER.
Tracks: / Screaming blue murder / Live with me / Take it from me / Wildlife / Turns your head around / Don't call it love / Hell razor / When your blood runs cold you got me / Flesh and blood.
LP: . . . . BRON 541
MC: . . . . BRONC 541

ST. VALENTINES DAY MASSACRE (See under Headgirl) (Girlschool & Motorhead).

TAKE A BITE.
Tracks: / Action / Girls on top / Fox on the run / Tear it up / Love at first bite / Up all night / Don't walk away / Head over heels / This time / Too hot too handle.
LP: . . . . GWLP 21
MC: . . . . GWTC 21
LP: . . . . RR 9513 1
LP: . . . . GWC 21

Giscombe, Junior

STAND STRONG.
LP: . . . . MCG 6105
MC: . . . . MCGC 6105

Giselle (Ballet)

GISELLE (See under Kirov Ballet) (Kirov Ballet).

Gish, Lillian

TALE OF THE SHINING PRINCESS, THE.
MC: 1707

Gismonti, Egberto

DANCA DAS CABECAS.
MC: 3101089

DANCA DOS ESCARVOS.
LP: . . . . ECM 1387

DUAS VOZES (Gismonti, Egberto & Nana Vasconcelos).
Tracks: / Rio De Janeiro / Tomarapeba / Dancando / Fogueira / Bianca / Don Quixote / O dia / A noite.
LP: . . . . ECM 1279

FOLK SONGS (See under Garbarek, Jan) (Gismonti/ Haden/ Garbarek).

MAGICO (See under Haden, Charlie) (Gismonti/ Haden/ Garbarek).

SANFONA.
LP: . . . . ECM 1203

WORKS: EGBERTO GISMONTI.
Tracks: / Loro / Gismonti / Mauro senise / Zeca assumpcao / Nene raga / Vasconcelos / Colin Walcott / Ciranda nordestina / Magico / Garbarek / Charlie Haden / Maracutu / Nene salvador.
MC: 3100 391
LP: 8232691

Gist

EMBRACE THE HERD.
LP: . . . . ROUGH 25

Giuffre, Jimmy

AD LIB (Giuffre, Jimmy Three).
LP: 2304 490

EASY WAY, THE (Giuffre, Jimmy Three).
Tracks: / Easy way, The / Mack the knife / Come rain or come shine / Careful / Ray's time / Dream, A / Off centre / Montage / Time enough.
LP: 2304 491

FOUR BROTHERS.
Tracks: / Do it / All for you / I only have eyes for you / Four brothers / Sultana / Nutty pine / Wrought iron / Someone to watch over me / Ring-tail monkey / Ironic.
LP: . . . . AFF 70

JIMMY GIUFFRE IN CONCERT (Giuffre, Jimmy Trio).
Tracks: / Flight / Goodbye / Used to be hiptus / Venture / This time, this time.
LP: . . . . UJ 18

JIMMY GIUFFRE QUARTET IN PERSON (Giuffre, Jimmy Quartet).
Tracks: / Quiet time / Crab, The / My funny valentine / We see / What's new? / Two for Timbuctu.
LP: 2304 492

TANGENTS IN JAZZ.
LP: . . . . AFF 60

TENORS WEST (Giuffre, Jimmy & The Marty Paich Octet).
LP: . . . . GNPS 9040

THESIS (Giuffre, Jimmy Three).
LP: 2304 499

WEST COAST SCENE (Giuffre, Jimmy & The Marty Paich Octet).
Tracks: / There's no you / Dragon / Shorty George / Paichence / At the Mardi Gras / Take the 'A' train / Ballet du bongo / Line for Lyons / Jacqueline / Con spirito / On Green Dolphin Street / I'm also a person / I had the craziest dream / Arrivederci / Brown cow / Anyhow / Julie is her name / Aplomb / Sunset eyes / Tenors west.
2LP: . . . . VJD 536

Giuffria

GIUFFRIA.
Tracks: / Do me right / Don't tear me down / Lonely in love / Turn me on / Awakening, The / Call to the heart / Dance / Trouble again / Line of fire / Out of the blue (too far gone).
LP: . . . . MCL 1844
MC: . . . . MCLC 1844
LP: . . . . MCF 3244
MC: . . . . MCFC 3244

SILK AND STEEL.
Tracks: / No escape / Love you forever / I must be dreaming / Girl / Change of heart / Radio / Heartache / Lethal lover / Tell it like it is / Dirty secrets.
LP: . . . . IMCA 5742
MC: . . . . IMCAC 5742

Give My Regards ...

GIVE MY REGARDS TO BROAD STREET (See under McCartney, Paul) (McCartney, Paul).

Glackin, Kevin

NA SAIGHNEAIN (Glackin, Kevin & Seamus).
LP: . . . . CEF 140

Glackin, Paddy

DOUBLIN (Glackin, Paddy & Paddy Keenan).
LP: . . . . TA 2007
MC: 4TA 2007

HIDDEN GROUND (Glackin, Paddy & Jolyon Jackson).
LP: . . . . TA 2009
MC: 4TA 2009

PADDY GLACKIN.
LP: . . . . CEF 060

Glad

ROMANS.
MC: . . . . C 02507

Gladiators

DREADLOCKS THE TIME IS NOW (See also under Reggae).

DREADLOCKS THE TIME IS NOW.
MC: . . . . FLC 9001

GLADIATORS.
Tracks: / Oh what a joy / Good music / Hello Carol / I feel like a star / Man who's strong / Duppy conqueror / Disco reggae / Come take my hand / Behind closed doors / Mine for all time.
LP: . . . . V 2161

NATURALITY.
Tracks: / Naturality / Struggle / Write to me / Counting my blessing / Get ready / Praises to the most high / Nyahbingi marching on / Dry your weeping eyes / Greatest love / Exodus.
LP: . . . . FL 1035

SERIOUS THING.
LP: . . . . NH 308

SWEET SO TILL.
LP: . . . . FL 1048

SYMBOL OF REALITY.
LP: . . . . NH 305

VITAL SELECTION.
Tracks: / Naturality / Hearsay / Looks is deceiving / Chatty chatty mouth / Pocket money / Hello Carol / Stick a bush / Write to me / We'll find a blessing / Dreadlocks the time is now.
LP: . . . . VX 1003

Gladstone, Neal

SLEEP NEAT.
LP: . . . . F 28
MC: . . . . C 28

Glahe, Will

GOLD ALBUM.
LP: 6 28582
MC: 4 28582

GOLDEN WIL GLAHE ALBUM.
Tracks: / FFeuert los / Tanzended finger / Kuckuckswaltzer (Cuckoo waltz) / Am abend auf der heide / Leitmeritzer schutzenmarsch / Melodie in F / Huckepack alter kameraden / Quecksilver polka / Kie dorfmusik / Sous les ponts de Paris / Da capo / Der ziegenbock / Wiener praterleben / So sind wir / Gerburtstags standchen / Daar bij die molen / Liechtensteiner polka / Di schlittsschuhlaufer / Im gansmarsch / Krakowac / Mit musick geht alles besser / Night and day / Paris canaille / Jetzt trink'n ma noch a flascherl wien / Spatzenkonzert / Bohmisch polka / Grillenhockzeit.
2LP: . . . . DP 6.28582
MCSET: . . . . CT 4.28582

IN BAVARIA.
Tracks: / Liechtensteiner polka / Beer barrel polka / Skaters waltz / Clarinet polka / Gold and silver waltz / Auf wiederseh'n sweetheart / In Munchen steht ein Hofbrauhaus / Hoop dee doo / Wenzel polka / Pennsylvania polka / Vienna, city of my dreams / Forever and a day.
LP: . . . . DGS 4

MEIN LEBEN MIT DEM AKKORDEON (My Life With The Accordion).
Tracks: / Tanzende finger / Wien bleibt wein / Kuckuckswaltzer (Cuckoo waltz) / Kinderfest-polka (Childrens festival polka) / C'est si bon / Klarinetten-polka (Clarinet polka) / Krakowac / Finken-waltzer / Lieber nachbar (Dear neighbour) / Wettspiele / Rosamunde / Herz-Schmerz polka / Im Ganse marsch / Horst du mein heimliches Rufen / Souvenir de Suisse / etc.
LP: 6.26421
MC: 4.26421

Glam Rock

GLAM CRAZEE (Various artists).
Tracks: / Ballroom blitz: *Sweet* / Tiger feet: *Mud* / Mama weer all crazee now: *Slade* / Metal guru: *T. Rex* / See my baby jive: *Wizzard* / Angel face: *Glitter Band* / Rock'n'roll (part 2): *Glitter, Gary* / New York groove: *Hello* / My coo ca choo: *Stardust, Alvin* / Son of my father: *Chicory Tip*/ School's out: *Cooper, Alice* / Saturday night's all right for fighting: *John, Elton* / Stay with me: *Faces*/ Virginia Plain: *Roxy Music* / This town ain't big enough for both of us: *Sparks* / Roll away the stone: *Mott The Hoople* / All because of you: *Geordie* / I can do it: *Rubettes* / Can the can: *Quatro, Suzi* / I love rock'n'roll: *Arrows* / Let's swing again (glam mix): *Jive Bunny*.
MC: . . . . VTMC 1
LP: . . . . VTLP 1

GLAM SLAM (Various artists).
Tracks: / Devil gate drive: *Quatro, Suzi* / Ballroom blitz: *Sweet* / Blockbuster: *Sweet* / Schools out: *Cooper, Alice* / All the young dudes: *Mott The Hoople* / Bye bye baby: *Bay City Rollers* / Hot love: *T. Rex* / Get it on: *T. Rex* / Do you wanna touch me: *Glitter, Gary* / Rock'n'roll: *Glitter, Gary* / Mama weer all crazee now: *Slade*.
2LP: . . . . NE 1434
MC: . . . . CE 2434

GREAT GLAM ROCK EXPLOSION, THE (Various artists).
LP: . . . . BIFF 3

Glamour Girls

GLAMOUR GIRLS, THE (Various artists).
LP: 32002
MC: 62003

Glaser Brothers

AT THE COUNTRY STORE (see under Tompall & The Glaser Brothers) (Glaser Brothers, The & Tompall).

LOVIN' HER WAS EASIER (Tompall & The Glaser Brothers).
Tracks: / Lovin' her was easier / Busted / Feeling the weight of my chains / Just one time / Last thing on my mind / United we fall / Drinkin' them beers / Trying to outrun the wind / Mansion on the hill.
LP: . . . . K 52331

MORE OF TOMPALL & THE GLASER BROTHERS (Tompall & The Glaser Brothers).
Tracks: / Sweet love me good woman / Home's where the hurt is / Woman, woman / Molly darling / Wicked California / Gonna miss me / Rings / Phoney world / Gone girl / Gone on the other hand / Moods of Mary / Loving you again / Pretty eyes / Blue Ridge Mountain.
LP: 2391 487

Glaser, Jim

COUNTRY STORE: JIM GLASER.
Tracks: / Love of my woman, The / You were gone before you said goodbye / Past the point of no return / It's not easy / Merry go round / Tough act to follow / Early morning love / I'll be your fool tonight / In another minute / If I don't love you / Those days.
LP: . . . . CST 16
MC: . . . . CSTK 16

MAN IN THE MIRROR.
Tracks: / When you're not a lady / You're gettin' to me again / You got me running / Pretend / Woman, woman / I'd

love to see you again / Close friends / If I could only dance with you / Let me down easy / Stand by the road / Man in the mirror.
LP: . . . . **IMCA 5636**
LP: . . . . **RANGE 7003**

PAST THE POINT OF NO RETURN.
Tracks: / Merry-go-round / Those days / Tough act to follow / Love of my woman, The / Early morning love / You were gone before you said goodbye / I'll be your fool tonight / Past the point of no return / In another minute / It's not easy / If I don't love you.
LP: . . . . **IMCA 5612**

Glaser, Tompall

COUNTRY STORE: TOMPALL GLASER (Glaser, Tompall & the Glaser Brothers).
Tracks: / Gentle on my mind / We live in two different worlds / When it goes, it's gone girl / Good hearted woman / Time changes everything / Broken down momma / I can't remember / Wild side of life / Faded love / Hunger, The / Take the singer with the song / If I'd only come and gone / Charlie / Lay down beside me.
LP: . . . . **CST 27**
MC: . . . . **CSTK 27**

NIGHTS ON THE BORDERLINE.
Tracks: / Night on the border / Mamma don't let you big boy play outside / I cried a mile (for every inch I laughed) / Put another log on the fire / Up where we belong / I don't care anymore / Auction, The / Lovely Lucy / Streets of Baltimore / Till the right one comes along.
LP: . . . . **IMCA 39051**
MC: . . . . **IMCAC 39051**

Glasgow, Alex

NORTHERN DRIFT (Glasgow, Alex & Henry Livings).
Tracks: / Festival time / I wrote a sonnet once / Budding gardeners No 1 / Nigel / Sammy Bell / Butcher, The / Keep your 'and on your 'apenny / Aesop / Freezer song, The / Budding gardeners No 2 / Dark shirt, A / R.I.P. / Maggie Gee / Our Harold / As soon as this pub closes.
LP: . . . . **MWM 1018**

NOW AND THEN.
Tracks: / Dance ti thi daddy / My dad / Ma bonny lad / When it's ours / Sally Wheatley / Geordie broon / Keep your feet still Geordie Hinny / Geordie the professional / Sunsets bonny lad, The / Water o' Tyne, The / Any minute now / Wor Nanny's a mazer / And I shall cry again / Cushie Butterfield / In my town / Oh dear what mun I de.
LP: . . . . **MWM 1011**
MC: . . . . **MWMC 1011**

SONGS OF ALEX GLASGOW.
Tracks: / Close the coalhouse door / Standing at the door / Socialist ABC, The / 20 long weeks / Little cloth cap / As soon as this pub closes / Paradise flat / Jack and Jill / Proper man, A / Saturday afternoon / All in a day / Grandad.
LP: . . . . **MWM 1006**
MC: . . . . **MWM C106**

SONGS OF ALEX GLASGOW, VOL. 2.
Tracks: / Turning the clock back / Maggie Gee / Lovely little Lucy / My daddy is a left-wing intellectual / Mary Baker city mix / Sexpertise / Nigel / Candidate / Mary Jane beware / Time enough tomorrow / Liverpool lad / Sammy Bell / Dorothy / Aubrey St John / Keep your 'and on your 'apenny / Harlequin, The / Englishman / How different from the home-life of our own dear Queen.
LP: . . . . **MWM 1009**

SONGS OF ALEX GLASGOW, VOL. 3 (Glasgow, Alex & the Northern Sinfonia Orchestra).
Tracks: / My love and I / Little Tommy yesterday / My little Johnnie-O / Escalator / Festival time / Eyes / Wild Utopian dream, A / Junior reporter, The / Mummy says / Xanadu / Mr. Henderson / Hands / Million miles away, A.
LP: . . . . **RUB 030**

Glasgow Caledonian

FIDDLES GALORE (Glasgow Caledonian Strathspey & Reel Society).
Tracks: / Golden fiddle march / Reels medley / Barn dance / Gaelic waltzes / March Stratspey and reel / Hebridean waltz / Scottish waltz medley / Jigs medley.
LP: . . . . **LILP 5060**

IN CONCERT (Glasgow Caledonian Strathspey & Reel Society).
Tracks: / O'Kane's march / Mrs. E.M.Ross's welcome to Kiltarility cottage / Smith's a gallant fireman / Merry lad's O' Foss, The / Haste to the wedding / Stool of repentance / Jig of slurs, The / Father O'Flynn / My home / Queen Maries, The / Bonnie wells o' Wearie / Sound of the sea, The / Bonniest lass in awe the world,The / Mermaids song, The / Conundrum, The / James Stephen / Princess Margaret / Elizabeth Adair / Maryhill highlanders, The / Norman Whitelaw / Rose of Allandale / Annie Laurie / Bonnie Galloway / Rowan tree / Star o' Rabbie Burns, The / Battle of the Somme / Earl Mansfields march / Leaving port Askaig / Glasgow highlanders / Stumpie / William McDonald black / Lady Charlotte Campbell / Gentle maiden, The / Come back to Erin / Mountains of Mourne / Forty shades of green / Earl of Cromartie, The / Jolly beggarman / Blackbear, The / Mrs. Hamilton of Pencaitland / Ronas Voe / Norven house / Katie stammers / Sunset over Foula / Shetland fiddlers society, The / Pipe Major J.K.Cairns / Glasgow week in Hamburg / Always welcome / Jackie Coleman's reel / Sheehan's reel / Trip to Windsor, A.
LP: . . . . **LILP 5137**
MC: . . . . **LICS 5137**

Glasgow, Deborahe

DEBORAH GLASGOW.
LP: . . . . **GREL 135**
MC: . . . . **GREEN 135**

Glasgow Gaelic...

GAELIC GALORE (Glasgow Gaelic Musical Association).
Tracks: / Tuireadh nan treun / 'S olc a dh' fhag an uiridh mi / O hi ri ri, tha e tighinn / Maighdeanan na h-airidh / Tir an airm / Seoladh dhachaidh / An ataireachd ard / Allt an t-siucair / An ubhal as airde / Nuair bha mi og / Strathspey and reel / O righ nan dul / 'S cian bho dh'fhag mi leodhas / An t-Iarla diurach / Cathair a chulchinn / Cearcall a chuain / Oran an lennaibh og / Och nan och, tha mi fo mhulad / Caberfeidh.
LP: . . . . **LILP 5193**
MC: . . . . **LICS 5193**

Glasgow Hebridean

GLASGOW HEBRIDEAN CHOIR.
LP: . . . . **AKH 002**

Glasgow Islay...

IT'S GOODBYE TO CARE (Glasgow Islay Gailic Choir).
Tracks: / Moladh na Iandaidh / Muile nam fuar-bheann mor (mull of the cold high mountains) / Tuireadh nan treun / Eilean mo chridh / Miann an eilthirich / Leann bhaile chaquil / Puirt a beul / Cearcall a' chuain / Thug mi gaol do'n fhest bhan / Rosan an leth-bhaile / Gaol na h-oighe / Psalm 65 / Odche mhath leibh.
LP: . . . . **LOCLP 1025**
MC: . . . . **ZCLOC 1025**

Glasgow Orpheus Choir

GLASGOW ORPHEUS CHOIR.
Tracks: / All in the April evening / Peat fire smooring prayer / Ae fond kiss / Bonnie Dundee / Ellan vannin / Jesu, joy of man's desiring / Hark hark the echo falling / Orlington / Crimond / Eriskay love lilt / Ca' the yowes / Dashing white sergeant / Cloud capp'd towers, The / Bluebird, The / Faery song, The / Belmont hymn.
LP: . . . . **SRS 5124**

Glasgow Phoenix Choir

GLASGOW PHOENIX CHOIR.
Tracks: / Mice and men / Johnnie cope / I know where I'm going / Dance to your daddy / Kaleenka / Eriskay love lilt / Ride the chariot / Isle of Mull / Dashing white sergeant / O Mary don't you weep / Bonnie Earl O'Moray, The / Caller herring / Brigg Fair / Deep river / Quodlibet / Iona boat song / Far away.
LP: . . . . **LIDL 6018**
MC: . . . . **LIDC 6018**

INSPIRATIONAL BEST, THE.
Tracks: / O love that wilt not let me go / O perfect love / When I survey the wondrous cross / Were you there / What a friend we have in Jesus / Guide me o thou great Jehovah / Abide with me / Onward Christian soldiers / O what can little hand do / Day thou gavest, Lord is ended, The / Lord's my shepherd, The / O for a closer walk with God / Worship the Lord / O send thy light forth / O light of life / Ye gates lift up your heads / All people that on earth do dwell / O God of Bethel / Glory be to God.
LP: . . . . **TWE 6002**
MC: . . . . **TC TWE 6002**

WITH VOICES RISING.
Tracks: / Scots wha hae / In the Wheatfield / When the Saints go marching in / Annie Laurie / Time for man go home / Brother James' air / Shenandoah / John Anderson my Jo / Tumbalalaika / Little cherry tree / Corn rigs / Dream angus / Death o death oh me lawd / Loch Lomond / Campbells are coming, The / All my trials / Lament of Mary Queen Of Scots / Battle of the republic.
MC: . . . . **LIDC 6030**

Glasgow Police

...MARCH PAST.
Tracks: / Sheiling, The / H.L.I. hornpipe / Mill in the glen, The / Blackhorn stick, The / White cockade, The / MacKenzie highlanders / Memorial bells of Inverary / Captain C.R. Lumsden / Sweet maid of Mull, The / Heights of casino / Men of Argyle, The / Rose among the heather, The / Captain Horne / MacKay from Skye / Shoals of herring / Shores of Loch Bee, The / Murdo's wedding / Woe's me for Prince Charlie / Slainte Mhath / Battle of Waterloo / Dalnahessaig / Keel row, The / Highland wedding reel, The / Rachael Rae / H.M.S. Renown / Ronnie Lawrie's rant / Major Moir of Villaveque / I lo'ed nae a lassie but ane / Campbeltown Loch / Major A.C.W. Ray's farewell / Major Bobby / Muir of Ord, The / Dream Angus / Blackbird hornpipe, The / Campbeltown kiltie ball / Miller o'Drone / Braes o' mar / Circassian circle / Petronella / Old rigged ship, The / Dreaming of Islay / Friendly piper, The.
LP: . . . . **SZLP 2148**

SCOTLANDS BEST VOLUME 11 (Glasgow Police Pipe Band).
Tracks: / 6/8 marches / Strathspeys and reels / 51st Highland Division / Flett from Flotta / Bonnie Prince Charlie / H.L.I. hornpipe / Minnie Hynd / Barbara's jig / I see mull land of my youth / Oh, Mairi / Hi ro hirum / Dancing feet / Nameless / Alex McDonald / Polkas / Airs / Strathconnon / Captain Horne / Retreats airs / Scots wha' hae.
MC: . . . . **KBER 021**

Glasgow Sings Along

GLASGOW SINGS ALONG (Lou Grant).
Tracks: / I Belong To Glasgow / Glasgow underground, The / I'm glad that I was born in Glasgow / When I Leave Old Glasgow Behind.
MC: . . . . **KITV 447**

Glasgow Skye Pipe...

MEN FROM SKYE, THE (Glasgow Skye Pipe Band Association).
Tracks: / Killiecrankie / Rowan tree / Bonnie Galloway / By cool Siloam's shady rill / Day thou gavest, Lord is ended, The / Ae fond kiss / Man's a man, A / My love she's but a lassie yet / Duncan Gray / Spinning wheel / Miss Virginia Thomson's fancy / Highland wedding / Blair Drummond / Lexie McAskill / Gipsy's warning, The / Busancy / Far o'er struy / Dark island / Paddy leather breeches / Curlew, The / Scotland the brave / Heilan Laddie / Breton melody / Man from Skye, The / Miller of Drone, The / Campbeltown kiltie ball / Ale is dear, The / Highland laddie / Skyeman's jig / Dumbarton's drums / Keel row, The / Dalnahessaig / Rose amang the heather / High road to Linton / Kate Dalrymple / Fairy dance, The / Mrs. MacLeod of Raasay / Frank Thomson / John Gordon of Drumvie / Green hills of Tyrol / When the battle is over / Lochanside / Going home.
LP: . . . . **LBLP 2003**
MC: . . . . **ZCLBP 2003**

Glasgow &

GLASGOW & STRATHCLYDE UNIVERSITY OTC PIPE BAND (Glasgow & Strathclyde University OTC Pipe Band).
MC: . . . . **LICS 5082**

Glass Axe

GLASS AXE/WICKED PRINCE, THE (Dotrice, Michele).
MC: . . . . **LP 201**
MC: . . . . **LPMC 201**

Glass, Dudley

SONGS OF BRER RABBIT (see under Brer Rabbit).

Glass (label)

FIFTY THOUSAND GLASS FANS CAN'T BE WRONG (Various artists).
LP: . . . . **GLALP 019**

Glass Menagerie (film)

GLASS MENAGERIE, THE (Film Soundtrack) (Various artists).
LP: . . . . **MCA 6222**
MC: . . . . **MCAC 6222**

Glass Museum

GLASS MUSEUM.
LP: . . . . **RGMLP 10021**

Glass, Philip

1000 AIRPLANES ON THE ROOF.
Tracks: / 1000 airplanes on the roof / City walk / Girlfriend / My building disappeared / Screens of memory / What time is grey? / Labyrinth / Return to the hive / Three truths / Encounter / Grey cloud over New York / Where have you been as the doctor / Normal man running, A.
LP: . . . . **VE 39**
MC: . . . . **TCVE 39**

DANCE PIECES.
Tracks: / In the upper room / Dance / Glasspieces.
LP: . . . . **FM 39539**
MC: . . . . **FMT 39539**

GLASSWORKS.
Tracks: / Opening / Floe / Slands / Rubric / Facades / Closing.
LP: . . . . **CBS 73640**
MC: **40 73640**

KOYAANISQATSI (Film soundtrack).
Tracks: / Opening / Vessels / Cloud / Pruitt egoe 5.15 / Closing.
LP: . . . . **ISTA 4**
MC: . . . . **ICT 4**
MC: . . . . **ICM 2036**
MC: **814 042 4**

MUSIC IN 12 PARTS.
Tracks: / Music in 12 parts - Part 1 / Music in 12 parts - Part 2.
MC: . . . . **TCA 2010**
LP: . . . . **CA 2010**

MUSIC IN 12 PARTS (Performed by the ensemble).
Tracks: / Music in 12 parts - parts 1-12.
LPS: . . . . **VEBX 32**
MCSET: . . . . **TCVBX 32**

NORTH STAR.
Tracks: / Etoile polaire (North star) / Victor's lament / River run / Mon pere, mon pere / Are years what? (for Marianne Moore) / Lady Day / Ange des orages / Ave / Ik-ook / Montage.
LP: . . . . **OVED 151**
MC: . . . . **OVEDC 151**

PASSAGES (Glass, Philip & Ravi Shankar).
Tracks: / Offering / Channels and winds / Meetings along the edge / Sadhanipa / Ragas in minor scale / Prashanti.
LP: **210947**
MC: **410947**

PHOTOGRAPHER, THE.
Tracks: / Gentleman's honor, A / Act II / Gentleman's honor, A (instrumental) / Act III.
LP: **25480**
MC: **40 25480**

POWAQQATSI (Film soundtrack).
LP: . . . . **K 979192 1**
MC: . . . . **K 979192 4**

SOLO MUSIC.
LP: . . . . **SHAN 83515**

SONGS FROM LIQUID DAYS.
Tracks: / Changing opinion / Lightning / Freezing / Liquid days (part 1) / Open the kingdom (liquid days part 2) / Forgetting.
LP: . . . . **FM 39564**
MC: . . . . **FMT 39564**

Glass Tiger

DIAMOND SUN.
Tracks: / Diamond sun / Far away from here / I'm still searching / Lifetime of moments, A / It's love U feel / My song / Watching worlds crumble / Send your love / Suffer in silence / This island earth.
LP: . . . . **MTL 1021**
MC: . . . . **TCMTL 1021**

SIMPLE MISSION.
Tracks: / Blinded / Animal heart / Let's talk / Where did our love go / My town / Rhythm of your love / Spanish slumber / Simple mission / Stand or fall / Rescued (by the arms of love) / One to one / One night alone / (She said) love me like a man.
LP: . . . . **MTL 1061**
MC: . . . . **TCMTL 1061**

THIN RED LINE, THE.
Tracks: / Thin red line, The / Don't forget me when I'm gone / Closer to you / Vanishing tribe / Looking at a picture / Secret / Ancient evenings / Ecstasy / Someday / I will be there / You're what I look for.
LP: . . . . **MTL 1003**
MC: . . . . **TCMTL 1003**

Glassfield, Chris

ISLAND.
MC: . . . . **C 130**

OF DREAMS UNDONE.
MC: . . . . **C 156**

Glasso, Michael

SCENES.
Tracks: / Scene I / Scene II / Scene III / Scene IV / Scene V / Scene VI / Scene VII / Scene VIII / Scene IX.
LP: . . . . **ECM 1245**

Glaxo Babies

NINE MONTHS TO THE DISCO.
Tracks: / Maximum sexual joy / This is your vendetta / Seven days / Electric

church / Nine months to the disco / Promised land / Tea master & the assasin / Free dem cells / Dinosaur disco meets the swampstomp / Conscience / Slim / Shake.
LP: HB 2

PUT ME ON THE GUEST LIST.
Tracks: / Avoiding the issue / Because of you / This is your life / Police state / Who killed Bruce Lee? / Stay awake / She went to pieces / Burning / Flesh / Puppet patrol.
LP: HBM 3

Glazunov (composer)

SYMPHONY NO.3 (GLAZUNOV) (Unknown).
Tracks: / Symphony no.3 (Glazunov).
LP: DCA 581
MC: ZC DCA 581

SYMPHONY NO.6 (GLAZUNOV) (London Symphony Orchestra/Royal Philharmonic Orchestra).
Tracks: / Symphony no.6 (Glazunov) / Serenades (the 2) (Glazunov) / Triumphal march (Glazunov).
LP: DCA 699
MC: ZC DCA 699

Gleason, Jackie

JACKIE GLEASON PLAYS ROMANTIC JAZZ.
Tracks: / I've got my eyes on you / Lady is a tramp, The / There'll be some changes made / My blue Heaven / Soon / Petite waltz / Love next / How about you? / Crazy rhythm / Don't blame me / Best things in life are free, The / Who cares? / I never knew / Most beautiful girl in the world, The / You can't pull the wool over my eyes.
MC: PM 1552954
LP: PM 1552951

MUSIC TO MAKE YOU MISTY/NIGHT WINDS.
Tracks: / It all depends on you / Man I love, The / I hadn't anyone till you / When your lover has gone / Tenderly / Dark is the night (c'est fini) / Say it isn't so / I guess I'll have to change my plans / It happened in Monterey / You were meant for me / Prelude to a kiss / Thinking of you / When you're away / What can I say after I say I'm sorry / Love letters in the sand / You are too beautiful / Touch of your lips, The / Sleepy time gal / Good night, sweet nightingale / Memories of you / Love locked out / I apologise / Dancing with tears in my eyes / Thousand goodnights, The.
MC: C 492088

SILK'N'BRASS.
Tracks: / One of those songs / Girl from Ipanema / It's such a happy day / Everything's coming up roses / Real live girl / Starry eyed and breathless / You're nobody till somebody loves you / Begin to love / Shangri-la / If I ruled the world / Somebody else is taking my place.
LP: EMS 1182
MC: TCEMS 1182

SONGS AND STORY OF JACKIE GLEASON.
2LP: IC 134 85230/1

TORCH WITH THE BLUE FLAME, THE.
Tracks: / Let's face the music and dance / Just in time / But beautiful / Love letters / My heart reminds me / Again / I've grown accustomed to her face / Careless / My silent love / Fascination / Alone in the crown / Time.
LP: EMS 1136
MC: TCEMS 1136

Glen, Mayson Orchestra

BENNY'S THEME (see under Henry, Paul).

Glenaruel Scottish...

REELIN' 'N' RAMBLIN' (Glendaruel Scottish Dance Band).
Tracks: / Hoop her and grid her / Rev de Musetta / Boston two step / Dunoon barn dance / Carse of Stirling / Gay Gordons / Fairly shot of her / Scottish waltz medley / Happy returns / Duff house.
LP: LILP 5046

SCOTTISH COUNTRY DANCE (Glendaruel Scottish Dance Band).
LP: LILP 5098

Glenn, Garry

FEELS GOOD TO FEEL GOOD.
Tracks: / Do you have to go? / Torch for you / Running away / Out of a dream / I'm still waiting / Feels good to feel good / Lonely nights / Can't get enough of love / Love makes it right.
LP: ZL 72617
MC: ZK 72617

G.G..
LP: PPO 2012

Glenn, Glen

EVERYBODY'S MOVIN' AGAIN.
Tracks: / Down the line / Come on / Flip flop and fly / Jack and Jill boogie / I sure do love you baby / Mean woman blues / Rock 'n' roll Ruby / Bony Moronie / Rockin' around the mountain / Why don't you love me? / Ugly and slouchy / You win again / Everybody's movin' again / Sick & tired.
LP: CH 105

GLEN GLENN STORY, THE.
Tracks: / If I had me a woman / One cup of coffee / Hold me baby / Baby let's play house / Laurie Ann / Be bop a lula / Kitty Kat / Everybody's movin' / Shake, rattle and roll / Treat me nice / Blue jeans / I got a woman / Kathleen.
LP: CH 57

ROCKABILLY LEGEND.
Tracks: / Everybody's movin' / One cup of coffee / Kathleen / I'm glad my baby's gone / Would ya / Laurie Ann / I'll never stop loving you / Blue jeans and a boys shirt / I didn't have the sense to go / I saw my castles fall today / Alone with you / Crazy arms / It rains rain / Folsom prison blues/Hey porter/I walk the line / Baby, I don't care / Mean woman blues.
LP: SJLP 572

ROCKABILLY REUNION (See under Maddox, Rose) (Glenn, Glen/Rose Maddox).

Glenn, John

ALONE WITH YOU.
MC: TAC 117

BACK AGAIN (Glenn, John & Mainliners).
LP: MYLP 5003

BEST OF JOHN GLENN.
Tracks: / Blue Ridge mountain turning green / Boys from County Armagh / Keep on the sunny side / Sunny side of the mountain / Your my best friend / Turn out the light (love me tonight) / Annabelle Lee / Call me darling / Say you're gone / Let's turn back the years / Couple more years, A / Little country town in Ireland / Before this day ends / Town of Galway.
LP: PHL 451
MC: CPHL 451

COUNTRY STAR (Glenn, John & Mainliners).
Tracks: / Keep on the sunny side / Ghost story / Bob Wills is still the king / Rainbow at midnight / Lone Lyville / Say your gone / Can you hear the Robin sing / Lets turn back the years / Boys from County Armagh / This is my year for Mexico / Can I sleep in your arms / Call me darling / Don't wait until the last minute to pray / I keep looking for tomorrow.
LP: PHL 432
MC: CPHL 432

LITTLE COUNTRY TOWN IN IRELAND (Glenn, John & Mainliners).
Tracks: / Little country town in Ireland / Somebody to love / Old mud cabin on the hill / September in Miami / Last date / Love me like I love you / Couple more years, A / Queen of our town / Feeling better / Velvet wallpaper / House without love / Before this day ends / Colour of the blues / That's why I am walking / Gone away / Barney McShane / IOU.
LP: PHL 433
MC: CPHL 433

MAKE MINE COUNTRY STYLE (Glenn, John & Mainliners).
Tracks: / There's a bluebird singing / She's in love with a rodeo man / Half as much / Leona / Streets of San Francisco / Arkensaw river / Ghost of Jim Bob Wilson / I need someone to hold me when I cry / Deep deep down / Farewell to Galway / All over again / I never had a thing that ain't been used.
LP: PHL 435
MC: CPHL 435

SUNNYSIDE OF THE MOUNTAIN (Glenn, John & Mainliners).
Tracks: / Sunny side of the mountain / Turn out the light (love me tonight) / Who will I be lovin' / Drink up and go home / Annabelle Lee / Blue Ridge Mountain turning green / Picture from lifes other side, A / Sunset & Vine / You're my best friend / More than words can tell / I think it's time she learned / Bury me beneath the willow / Noreen bawn / Sweet Charlotte Ann.
LP: PHL 431
MC: CPHL 431

Glenn, Lloyd

AFTER HOURS.
LP: PM 154661
LP: OL 8002

BLUE IVORIES.
Tracks: / Pinetop's boogie woogie / Blue ivories / In the mood / Topsy / Swing time shuffle / Hep cat shuffle / Now is the time / Jungletown jubilee / Night time / Savage boy / Boogie woogie on St. Louis blues / Blues / Ugh.
LP: RJ 203

BLUES AND BOOGIE.
LP: 33563

TEXAS MAN.
Tracks: / Texas man / All alone blues / Advice to a fool / Still my love is your / Midnight boogie / Brazos bottom / Dedicated to you / Honky tonk train blues / Joymakers boogie / It moves me / Angora / Levee blues / Stranger / It's you I'm thinking of / Cute-tee / Where or when.
LP: JB 608

Glenn Miller Story

GLENN MILLER STORY (See under Miller, Glenn) (Various artists).

Glenside Ceile Band

GLENSIDE CEILE BAND.
MC: ASK 768
MC: PLC 5002

Glimmer

GLIMMER Various artists.
MC: BBM LB 1

Glindeman, Ib

IB GLINDEMAN AND HIS DANISH BIG BAND (Glindeman, Ib.and his Danish big band).
LP: BBILP 2704

Gline, Bob

FEELINGS AT CHRISTMAS (Gline, Bob & Clare Mance).
LP: LPNCL 3
MC: CNCL 3

Glinn, Lillian

COLUMBIA BLUES ISSUES 1927-29.
Tracks: / All alone and blue / Come home Daddy / Man I love is worth talkin' about / Doggin' me blues / Brown skin blues / Best friend blues / Lost letter blues / Packing house blues / Shake it down / I'm a front door woman with a back door man / Where have all the black men gone? / Atlanta blues / All the week blues / Wobble it a little / Daddy / Black man blues.
LP: VLP 31

LILLIAN GLINN AND MAE GLOVER (1929-31) (Glinn, Lillian & Mae Glover).
LP: BD 2009

Glitter Band

GALAXY OF GLITTERING HITS, A.
LP: BIFF 5

GREATEST HITS: GLITTER BAND.
LP: BELLS 264

HEY!.
LP: BELLS 241

HITS COLLECTION.
LP: GRAB 1
MC: GRABMC 1

LIVE AT THE MARQUEE.
LP: QUEST 7

ROCK 'N' ROLL DUDES.
LP: BELLS 253

Glitter, Gary

6 TRACK HITS: GARY GLITTER.
Tracks: / Rock and roll / Always yours / I'm the leader of the gang / I love you love me love / Remember me this way / I didn't know I loved you till I saw you rock'n'roll.
MC: 7SC 5002

ALIVE AND KICKING.
LP: APK 7
MC: APKC 7

ALWAYS YOURS.
Tracks: / Intro / Rock and roll / Do you want to touch? / Always yours / Hello I'm back / Leader of the gang / I belong to you / I love, you love, me love / Oh no / I'm not just a pretty face / When I'm on, I'm on / Wild horses.
LP: DOJOLP 20
MC: DOJOTC 20

BACK AGAIN - THEIR VERY BEST (Glitter, Gary & Glitter Band).
Tracks: / Hello hello I'm back again / Do you wanna touch me (oh yeah) / I'm the leader of the gang / Rock 'n' roll part 2 / I love you love me love / Always yours / Remember me this way / Love in the sun / Angel face / People like you, people like me / Tears I cried, The / Goodbye my love / Just for you.
MC: PWKMC 4052

BOYS WILL BE BOYS.
Tracks: / Crash crash / Lets get sexy / Dance me up / When I'm on, I'm on / Another rock'n'roll Christmas / Shout shout shout / If you want me / Hair of the dog / Boys will be boys / Close to you.
LP: 206687
MC: 406687

C'MON C'MON (The Gary Glitter Party Album).
LP: STAR 2310
MC: STAC 2310

GARY GLITTER'S GANGSHOW.
Tracks: / Rock 'n' roll (part II) / I didn't know I loved you till I saw you rock 'n' roll / When I'm on I'm on / Do you wanna touch me / Alright with the boys / Hello hello, I'm back again / Shake it up / Always yours / Frontier of style / Only way to survive, The / Rock 'n' roll (part I) / Good rockin' tonight / Baby, let's play house / Be bop a lula / Another rock'n'roll Christmas / I love you love me love / Leader of the gang.
2LP: CCSLP 234
MC: CCSMC 234

GARY GLITTER'S GOLDEN GREATS.
Tracks: / Rock and roll (part 1) / Always yours / Baby, please don't go / Hello hello, I'm back again / Wanderer / I'm the leader of the gang (I am) / I love you love me love / Rock and roll (part 2) / I didn't know I loved you till I saw you rock'n'roll / Lonely boy / Do you wanna touch me / Oh Yes you're beautiful / Rock on / Remember me this way.
LP: GTLP 021

GLITTER.
LP: BELLS 216

GREATEST HITS: GARY GLITTER.
LP: BELLS 262

LEADER, THE.
Tracks: / Rock and roll / Always yours / Baby please don't go / Hello hello I'm back again / Wanderer / I'm the leader of the gang (I am) / I love you love me love / I didn't know I loved you till I saw you rock'n'roll / Rock on / Do you wanna touch me / Oh yes you're beautiful / Remember me this way.
LP: EPC 32200
MC: 40 32200
LP: GTLP 046

REMEMBER ME THIS WAY.
LP: BELLS 237

TOUCH ME.
LP: BELLS 222

Glo Friends

GLO BUG (up to age 6) (Unknown narrator(s)).
MC: PLBG 202

GLO BUTTERFLY (up to age 6) (Unknown narrator(s)).
MC: PLBG 184

GLO CRICKET (up to age 6) (Unknown narrator(s)).
MC: PLBG 183

GLO WORM (up to age 6) (Unknown narrator(s)).
MC: PLBG 203

Global Music...

GLOBAL MUSIC - MADE IN MANCHESTER (Various artists).
MC: UNKNOWN

Globe Unity Orchestra

GLOBE UNITY ORCHESTRA.
LP: JAPO 60039

Gloria

AT HER BEST.
LP: HPE 608

GLORIA.
LP: RRL 8012

MISSISSIPPI.
LP: HPE 645

ONE DAY AT A TIME & OTHER SONGS.
LP: BT 300
MC: BTC 300

PRETTY BROWN EYES.
MC: MB LP 1023

Glorious Bank Robbers

DYNAMITE SEX DOZE.
LP: 107011
MC: 107014

Glorious Gospel

GLORIOUS GOSPEL (See Under Gospel...) (Various artists).

Glory

SKINS 'N' PUNKS VOL 3 (Glory/ Magnificent).
LP: OIR 009

Glory Bells

CENTURY RENDEZVOUS.
Tracks: / Flight back home / Wardrummer / Big thunder / My life / After twelve / Indian rainsong / Sweet Irene / Five foxes / In the attic.
LP: THBL 023

Glory (film)

GLORY (Film soundtrack) (Various artists).

Tracks: / Call to arms, A: *Various artists* / After antietam: *Various artists* / Lonely Christmas: *Various* artists / Forming the regiment: *Various artists* / Whipping, The: *Various artists* / Burning the town of darien: *Various artists* / Brave words: *Various artists* / Braver deeds: *Various artists* / Year of jubilee, The: *Various artists* / Preparations for battle: *Various artists* / Charging for wagner: *Various artists* / Epitaph: *Various artists* / Glory (closing credits): *Various artists*.
MC: . . . . TCV 2614
LP: . . . . V 2614

Glory Of The ...

GLORY OF THE MUSIC HALL, THE VOL 1 (See Under Music Hall) (Various artists).

Glory Of The...(bk)

GLORY OF THE GARDEN, THE (see under Chaucer, Geoffrey (aut)).

Glory Of Xmas

GLORY OF XMAS, THE (See Under Christmas...) (Various artists).

Glosters Regt. Band

GLOSTERS (28TH/61ST) REGT BAND & CORPS OF DRUMS (Glosters (28th/61st) Regt Band & Corps of Drums).
Tracks: / Army of the Nile / Banditenstreiche / On parade / Salamanca day / Royal standard / Elephantine / Children of the regiment / Wellington / Variations on a Korean folk song / Hands across the sea / Colonel Robin Grist / Regimental marches.
LP: . . . . MM 0586
MC: . . . . MC 0586

Gloucester Cathedral

CAROLS FOR CHRISTMAS (Gloucester Cathedral Choir).
LP: . . . . MVP 807

Glove

BLUE SUNSHINE.
Tracks: / Like an animal / Looking glass girl / Sex-eye-make-up / Blues in drag, A / Mr. Alphabet says / Punish me with kisses / Green city, This / Orgy / Perfect murder / Relax.
LP: . . . . SHELP 2
MC: . . . . SHEMC 2
LP: 8150191
MC: 8150194

Glover, Danny

BRER RABBIT (See under Brer Rabbit) (Glover, Danny & Taj Mahal).

Glover, John

MIDNIGHT OVER ENGLAND.
Tracks: / Limits of your love / Tired of being alone / Little England / Where do we stand / Out in the jungle / You are what you are / How long / Tears don't become you / Do it again / Crazy pages / Midnight over England.
LP: . . . . TRIX 9

Glover, Roger

ACCIDENTALLY ON PURPOSE (See under Gillan) (Glover, Roger & Ian Gillan).

BUTTERFLY BALL, THE.
LP: . . . . LONG 9
MC: . . . . LONGC 9

BUTTERFLY BALL, THE/WIZARD'S CONVENTION (1974 film musical) (Glover, Roger & Guests).
Tracks: / Dawn / Get ready / Saffron dormouse and Lizzy bee / Harlequin hare / Old blind mole / Magician moth / No solution / Behind the smile / Fly away / Aranea / Sitting in a dream / Waiting / Sir Maximus mouse / Dreams of Sir Bedivere / Together again / Watch out for the bat / Little chalk blue / Feast, The / Love is all / Homeward / Craig song, The / When the sun stops shining / Loose ends / Money to burn / Who's counting on me / Make it soon / Until tomorrow / Light of my life / She's a woman / Swanks and swells.
2LP: . . . . VSOPLP 139
MC: . . . . VSOPMC 139

DISLOCATED (See under Gillan) (Glover, Roger & Ian Gillan).

MASK, THE.
Tracks: / Divided word / Getting stranger / Mask, The / Fake it / Dancin' again / Remote / Hip level / Don't look down.
LP: . . . . POLD 5139

SHE TOOK MY BREATH AWAY (See under Gillan) (Glover, Roger & Ian Gillan).

Glover, Tony

ASHES IN MY WHISKEY (Glover, Tony & Dave Ray).
LP: . . . . ROUGH 152
MC: . . . . ROUGHC 152

Gluck, Harry

HEY BABY.
Tracks: / Hey baby / Let's think about living / Love my life away / Who could be bluer / Blue moon / I feel so bad / I got a funny feeling / Poor me / White for you and blue for me.
LP: . . . . BFX 15067

Gluck, Jeremy

I KNEW BUFFALO BILL.
Tracks: / Looking for a place to fall / Too long / Gone free / Hymn / Time undone / Gallery wharf / Four seasons of trouble / All my secrets.
LP: . . . . SHARP 037
MC: . . . . SHARP 037C

Glyder

GLYDER.
Tracks: / It doesn't matter anymore / She left me at the station / Good to be alive / 'Cause I loved you / Too far / Tomorrow still comes / Treat me nice / See it now / Long fight / Love gave me everything / Simple song / 'Cause I loved you (reprise).
LP: . . . . K 56167

GMC

FOOT ON THE ROCK (see under God, Mother & Country).

Gnomes

GHOST OF BLACKLAKE, THE (Unknown narrator(s)).
MC: . . . . PLBG 287

SPECIAL PRESENT, THE (Unknown narrator(s)).
MC: . . . . PLBG 286

Go Ahead

BALLROOM STOMPERS, THE.
LP: . . . . FABL 012

Go Go Lorenzo

ALL RECORDINGS (see under Davis Pinckney Project) (Go Go Lorenzo/Davis Pinckney Project).

Go Into Your Dance

GO INTO YOUR DANCE/ WUNDERBAR (Film soundtracks) (Various artists).
LP: . . . . SH 2030

Go Johnny Go (film)

GO JOHNNY GO (Film soundtrack) (Various artists).
LP: . . . . JN 5705

Go Team

ARCHER COME SPARROW.
MC: . . . . KC 017

DONNA PARKER POP.
MC: . . . . KC 005

LIVE IN WASHINGTON.
LP: . . . . KC 006

YOUR PRETTY GUITAR.
MC: . . . . KC 004

Go West

BANGS AND CRASHES.
Tracks: / We close our eyes (total overhang mix) / Man in my mirror / Goodbye girl / S.O.S. (perpendicular mix) / Eye to eye (the horizontal mix) / Ball of confusion (Recorded live at Hammersmith Odeon.) / Call me - the indiscriminate mix / Haunted / Missing person (Recorded live at Hammersmith Odeon.) / Don't look down (statospheric mix) / One way street (From the film Rocky IV.) / Innocence (desperation mix).
LP: . . . . CHRD 1495
MC: . . . . ZCHRD 1495

DANCING ON THE COUCH.
LP: . . . . CDL 1550
MC: . . . . ZCDL 1550

GO WEST.
Tracks: / We close our eyes / Don't look down / Call me / Eye to eye / Haunted / S.O.S. / Goodbye girl / Innocence / Missing persons.
LP: . . . . CHR 1495

Goat

AS YOU LIKE.
Tracks: / Don't cry / Fallen over you / Mother / Zombie break out / D'ya like it / How long?.
LP: . . . . BBL 110
MC: . . . . BBLC 110

MEDICATION TIME.
LP: . . . . BEGA 119
MC: . . . . BEGAC 119

Go-Betweens

16 LOVERS LANE.
Tracks: / Love goes on / Quiet heart / Love is a sign / You can't say no forever / Dive for your memory / Devil's eye, The / Streets of your town / Clouds / Was there anything I could do / I'm alright.
MC: . . . . BEGC 95
LP: . . . . BEGA 95

1978-1990.
LP: . . . . BEGA 104
MC: . . . . BEGC 104

BEFORE HOLLYWOOD.
Tracks: / Bad debt follows you / Two steps step out / Before Hollywood / Dusty in here / Ask / Cattle and cane / By chance / As long as that / On my block / That way.
LP: . . . . ROUGH 54

LIBERTY BELLE AND THE BLACK DIAMOND EXPRESS.
Tracks: / Spring rain / Ghost and the black hat / Wrong road, The / To reach me / Twin layers of lightning / In the core of a flame / Head full of steam / Bow down / Palm down / Apology accepted.
LP: . . . . BEGA 72
MC: . . . . BEGC 72
LP: . . . . BBL 72
MC: . . . . BBLC 72

METAL AND SHELLS.
Tracks: / Part company / Batchelor kisses / Cattle and cane.
LP: . . . . PVC 8942

SEND ME A LULLABY.
LP: . . . . ROUGH 45

SPRING HILL FAIR.
Tracks: / Bachelor kisses / Five words / Old way out ,The / You've never lived / Part company / Slow slow music / Draining the pool for you / River of money / Unkind & unwise / Man o'sand to girl o'sea.
LP: 925179 1

TALLULAH.
Tracks: / Right here / You tell me / Someone else's wife / I just get caught out / Cut it out / House that Jack Kerouac built / Bye bye pride / Spirit of a vampyre / Clarke sisters, The / Hope then strife.
LP: . . . . BEGA 81
MC: . . . . BEGC 81
LP: . . . . BBL 81
MC: . . . . BBLC 81

Goblin

DAWN OF THE DEAD (See under Dawn Of The Dead - Film Soundtrack).

GREATEST HITS: GOBLIN.
LP: . . . . ORL 8305
MC: . . . . ORK 78305

Goblin Market (show)

GOBLIN MARKET (Original Broadway cast) (Various artists).
LP: . . . . TER 1144
MC: . . . . ZCTER 1144

God

FOR LOVERS ONLY.
Tracks: / For lovers only.
LP: . . . . YEAHHUP 002

SWEET LIFE.
Tracks: / See smoke smell fire / Finger, The / Settling down / Lust / Wimps / Teste marce / Stomping ground / Sack B / So be it / Asset of punishment, The.
LP: . . . . K 031/110

God Emperor...

GOD EMPEROR OF DUNE Herbert, Frank (Herbert, Frank (aut)).
MC: . . . . CDL 51694

God Said

OFF THE PLOT.
Tracks: / Slip into gear / House G / Absurdly obsessed / Thousand tears, A / Reunion / Man who said yes, The / Out of time / Hear them / Slowly.
LP: . . . . TMLP 25

God Told Me To

GOD TOLD ME TO / RING OF BRIGHT WATER (See under 'Ring of bright water' for details) (Cordell, Frank).

Godard Ca Vous Chante?

GODARD CA VOUS CHANTE? (Various artists).
Tracks: / Sonate en re mineur: *Godard Ca Vous Chante?* / Godard: *Godard Ca Vous Chante?* / Chest: *Godard* Ca Vous Chante? / Respect: *Godard Ca Vous Chante?* / Du cote des peudecerfs: *Godard Ca Vous Chante?* / La croisiere immobile: *Godard Ca Vous Chante?*.
LP: . . . . NATO 634

Godard, Vic

RETROSPECTIVE, A (1977-81) (Godard, Vic & The Subway Sect).
LP: . . . . ROUGH 56

SONGS FOR SALE (Godard, Vic & The Subway Sect).
Tracks: / I'm in love / Crazy, crazy / Mr. Bennett / What's your name / Nola's salon / Be your age / Moving bed / Swing gently / Stamp of a vamp / Love for sale / Dilletante / Just in time / No style.
LP: . . . . SH 8549
MC: . . . . KSAC 8549

TROUBLE.
LP: . . . . ROUGH 86

WHAT'S THE MATTER BOY.
Tracks: / Birth and death / Stand back / Watching the devil / Enclave / Out of touch / Vertical integration / Split up the money / Stool pigeon / Double negative / Exit no return / Empty shell / Make me sad / View.
LP: . . . . MCL 1697
MC: . . . . MCLC 1697

Godden, Rumer (author)

GREENGAGE SUMMER, THE (York, Susannah).
MCSET: . . . . ZC SWD 363

Godding, Brian

SLAUGHTER ON SHAFTESBURY AVENUE.
LP: . . . . RECK 16

Goddo

PRETTY BAD BOYS.
LP: . . . . LAT 1120
MC: . . . . CAT 1120

Godfather (film)

GODFATHER SUITE, THE (Music from the Godfather Trilogy) (Various artists).
LP: . . . . FILM 077
MC: . . . . FILMC 077

GODFATHER, THE (Film Soundtrack) (Various artists).
Tracks: / Godfather waltz, The: *Various artists* / I have but one heart: *Various artists* / Pickup, The: *Various* artists / Connie's wedding: *Various artists* / Halls of fear, The: *Various artists* / Sicillian pastorale: *Various artists* / Godfather, Love theme: *Various artists* / Godfather waltz, The: *Various artists* / Appollonia: *Various artists* / New godfather, The: *Various artists* / Baptism: *Various artists* / Godfather finale, The: *Various artists*.
LP: . . . . FILM 032
MC: . . . . FILMC 032
LP: . . . . SPFA 7003

GODFATHER, THE PART III (Film Soundtrack) (Various artists).
Tracks: / Godfather part III main title: *Various artists* / Godfather waltz, The: *Various artists* / Marcia Religioso: *Various artists* / Michael's letter: *Various artists* / Immigrant, The: *Various artists* / Godfather part III love theme: *Various artists* / Godfather waltz, The (2): *Various artists* / To each his own: *Various artists* / Vincent's theme: *Various artists* / Altobella: *Various artists* / Godfather intermezzo: *Various artists* / Sicilian medley: *Various artists* / Promise me you'll remember (love theme): *Various artists* / Preludio and Siciliano: *Various artists* / A case amiche: *Various artists* / Preghiera: *Various artists* / Godfather finale, The: *Various artists* / Coda: The Godfather finale: *Various artists*.
LP: 4678131
MC: 4678134

Godfathers

BIRTH SCHOOL WORK DEATH.
Tracks: / Birth, school, work, death / Tell me why / It's so hard / 'Cause I said so / Strangest boy / S.T.B. / Just like you / Obsession / Love is dead / When am I coming down / If I only had time.
LP: 4605831
MC: 4605834

HIT BY HIT.
LP: . . . . GFTRLP 010
MC: . . . . GFTRC 010

MORE SONGS ABOUT LOVE AND HATE.
Tracks: / She gives me love / Those days are over / How low is low? / Pretty girl / This is your life / I'm lost and then I'm found / I don't believe in you / Life has passed us by / Walking talking Johnny Cash blues / Halfway paralysed / Another you.
LP: 4633941
MC: 4633944

UNREAL WORLD.
Tracks: / Unreal world / Don't let me down / King of misery / Believe in yourself / I'll never forget / What's his name / How does it feel to feel / Drag me down again / Something good about you / I love what's happening to me / This is war.
LP: 4669521
MC: 4669524

Godflesh

GODFLESH.
LP: . . . . FLESHLP 1

PURE.
LP: . . . . MOSH 032
MC: . . . . MOSH 032MC

STREETCLEANER.
MC: . . . . MOSH 15 MC
LP: . . . . MOSH 15

TINY TEARS.
LP: TINY 1

Godiego

MONKEY (Music from the TV series).
Tracks: / Birth of the Odyssey / Monkey magic / Fool / Asiatic fever / Dragons and demons / Celebration / Gandhara / Steppin' into your world / Flying / Havoc in heaven / We're heading out West to India / Thank you baby.
LP: REB 384

Godley & Creme

BIRDS OF PREY.
Tracks: / My body the car / Worm and the rattlesnake / Cat's eyes / Samson / Save a mountain for me / Madame guillotine / Woodwork / Twisted nerve / Out in the cold.
LP: POLD 5070

CONSEQUENCES.
LP: CONS 017

FREEZE FRAME.
Tracks: / Englishman in New York / Random brainwave / I pity inanimate objects / Freeze frame / Clues / Brazilia / Mugshots / Get well soon.
LP: SPELP 30
LP: POLD 5027

GOODBYE BLUE SKY.
Tracks: / H.E.A.V.E.N. / Little piece of Heaven, A / Don't set fire (to the one I love) / Golden ring / Crime and punishment / Big bang, The / 10,000 angels / Sweet memory / Airforce one / Last page of history / Desperate times.
LP: POLH 40
MC: POLHC 40

HISTORY MIX, THE.
Tracks: / Wet rubber soup / Cry / Expanding business / Dare you' man The / Hum drum boys in Paris / Mountain tension.
LP: POLH 22
MC: POLHC 22

ISMISM.
Tracks: / Snack attack / Under your thumb / Joey's camel / Problem - ready for Ralph / Wedding bells / Lonnie / Sale of the century / Party.
LP: POLD 5043
LP: 2383 618

"L".
LP: 9109 611

MUSIC FROM CONSEQUENCES.
Tracks: / Burial scene / Cool, cool, cool / Five o'clock in the morning / Flood / Honolulu / Lost weekend / Rosie / Sailor / Sleeping earth / When things go wrong.
LP: 910 961 5

Gods

BEST OF THE GODS.
Tracks: / Real love guaranteed / Farthing man / Penny dear / Lovely Anita / Momma I need / Candlelight / Radio show / Hey bulldog / Maria / Yes I cry / Candles getting shorter / Looking glass / Somewhere in the street / Towards the skies / Misleading colours.
LP: C5-537

God's Gift

FOLIE A QUATRE.
MC: PS 007

God's Kitchen

BOY WHO LOVED AEROPLANES, THE.
Tracks: / Stop that for a start / Brillant blonde / Boy who loved aeroplanes, The / Black rain / Muswell Hill.
MC: GKMC 1

God's Little Monkeys

LIP.
MC: COOKC 043
LP: COOK 043

NEW MAPS OF HELL.
Tracks: / Pay that money down / Hangman Botha / Underneath the arches / Sound out the symbols / Minister for motivation / New Year's honours / Sea never dry / Tory heart / Where were you / New statesman / Gas town / Whistle, daughter, whistle.
LP: COOK 022
MC: COOKC 022

Gods Must Be Crazy

GODS MUST BE CRAZY (Film soundtrack) (Various artists).
LP: STV 81243

Gods & Ungods

GODS AND UNGODS OF IRELAND.
MC: ANV 603

Godspell (musical)

GODSPELL (American Cast Recording) (Various artists).
Tracks: / Prepare ye the way of the lord: *Various artists* / Save the people: *Various artists* / Day by day: *Various* artists / Learn your lessons well: *Various artists* / Bless the Lord: *Various artists* / All for the best: *Various artists* / All good gifts: *Various artists* / Light of the world: *Various artists* / Turn back, o man: *Various artists* / Alas for you: *Various artists* / By my side: *Various artists* / We beseech thee: *Various artists* / On the willows: *Various artists* / Finale: *Various artists* / Day by day/ Prepare ye (reprise): *Various artists*
LP: SBLL 146

GODSPELL (Original soundtrack) (Various artists).
LP: ALB 6
MC: ACB 6 8337

GODSPELL (London cast) (Various artists).
Tracks: / Prepare ye the way of the Lord: *Various artists* / Save the people: *Various artists* / Day by day: *Various* artists / Learn your lessons well: *Various artists* / Bless the Lord: *Various artists* / All for the best: *Various artists* / All good gifts: *Various artists* / Light of the world: *Various artists* / Turn back o man: *Various artists* / Alas for you: *Various artists* / By my side: *Various artists* / We beseech thee: *Various artists* / On the willows: *Various artists* / Finale: *Various artists* / Day by day/Prepare ye (reprise): *Various artists.*
LP: BELLS 203

GODSPELL (Various artists).
Tracks: / Prepare ye the way of the Lord: *Various artists* / Save the people: *Various artists* / Day by day: *Various* artists / Learn your lessons well: *Various artists* / Bless the Lord: *Various artists* / All for the best: *Various artists* / All good gifts: *Various artists* / Light of the world: *Various artists* / Turn back o' man: *Various artists* / Alas for you: *Various artists* / By my side: *Various artists* / We beseech thee: *Various artists* / On the willows: *Various artists* / Finale: *Various artists* / Day by day/ Prepare ye (reprise): *Various artists.*
LP: SRS 5153

GODSPELL (BROADWAY CAST) (Various artists).
LP: ALB 6
MC: ACB6 8304

JESUS CHRIST SUPERSTAR / GODSPELL (See under Jesus Christ Superstar) (Various artists).

Godwin, Peter

CORRESPONDENCE.
Tracks: / Baby's in the mountain / Art of love / Window shopping / Soul to soul / Young pleasure / Dancer / Correspondence / Over 21 / Soul of love.
LP: POLD 5114

DANCE EMOTIONS.
Tracks: / Emotional disguise / Torch songs / French emotions / Images of Heaven / Cruel heart / Luxury.
LP: 2478 169

Godz

I'LL GET YOU ROCKIN'.
LP: HMUSA 48

NOTHING IS SACRED.
Tracks: / Gotta muv / Festyvul season / Rock yer sox auf / I'll bi yer luv / Luv kage / He's a fool / 714 / Hey mama / Snakin' / I don't wanna go home.
LP: XL 13072

POWER ROCK FROM USA.
Tracks: / go away / Baby, I love you / Guaranteed / Gotta keep a runnin' / Under the table / Cross country / Candy's going bad.
LP: XL 13051
MC: XK 13051

Goebbels, Heiner

MAN IN THE ELEVATOR, THE (Goebbels, Heiner & Heiner Muller).
LP: ECM 1369

Goffin, Louise

THIS IS THE PLACE.
Tracks: / In the mood / Banging on a brand new drum / 5th of July / Deep kiss / Bridge of sighs / So many summers gone / Carnival / All it takes / Ghosts on the High Street / Send a message.
LP: WX 136
MC: WX 136C

Goffin/King

GOFFIN AND KING (See under 60's).

Go-Go's

BEAUTY AND THE BEAT.
Tracks: / Our lips are sealed / How much more? / Tonight / Lust to love / This town / We got the beat / Fading fast / Automatic / You can't walk in your sleep / Skidmarks on my heart / Can't stop the world.
LP: SP 70021
MC: CS 70021

GO-GO'S GREATEST HITS.
LP: 3953331
MC: 3953334

TALK SHOW.
Tracks: / Head over heels / Turn to you / You thought / Beneath the blue sky / Forget that day / I'm the only one / Yes or no / Capture the light / I'm with you / Mercenary.
LP: IRSA 7041
MC: IRSC 7041

VACATION.
LP: SP 70031

Going Home

GOING HOME (See under Payton, K.M.) (Peyton, K.M.).

Going Places

GOING PLACES (Beggars Mantle).
MC: KITV 436

Going Steady (film)

GOING STEADY (Film soundtrack) (Various artists).
LP: WW 5078

Going Straight (tv)

GOING STRAIGHT (THEME) (See under Barker, Ronnie).

Golbey, Brian

COUNTRY MUSIC STORY.
MC: AMP 023

LAST TRAIN SOUTH (Golbey, Brian & Nick Strutt).
Tracks: / Days of the railroad / I'm bound to ride a boxcar / Rancho grande / Faded love / Yellow rose of Texas / Last train south / Texas when I die / Jimmie's Texas blues / Last cowboy, The / South of the border / Black smoke.
LP: WF 011

WHEN THE DEALINGS DONE (Golbey, Brian & Pete Stanley).
LP: WF 002

Gold

GOLD LIVE FROM MOSCOW.
Tracks: / 2001 / Mony mony / I will survive / Rockin' all over the world / United we stand / Midnight light / Disco USSR / Gamblin man / Here we go again / Twist and shout / All you need is love / Ob la di ob la da / Hi ho silver lining / Harlequin.
LP: PRX 14

Gold, Andrew

ALL THIS AND HEAVEN TOO.
Tracks: / How can this be love? / Oh Urania / Still you linger on / Never let her slip away / Always for you / Thank you for being / Friend, A / Looking for my love / Genevieve / I'm on my way / You're free.
LP: K 53072
MC: K4 53072

ANDREW GOLD.
Tracks: / That's why I love you / Heartaches / Love hurts / Resting in your arms / I'm a gambler / Endless flight / Hang my picture straight / Ten years behind me / I'm coming home.
LP: K 53020

WHAT'S WRONG WITH THIS PICTURE.
Tracks: / Hope you feel good / Passing thing / Do wah diddy diddy / Learning the game / Angel woman / Must be crazy / Lonely boy / Firefly / Stay / Go back home again / One of them is me.
LP: K 53052

WHIRLWIND.
Tracks: / Kiss this one goodbye / Sooner or later / Leave her alone / Little company / Brand new face / Whirlwind / Nine to five / Stranded on the edge / Make up your mind.
LP: K 52219
MC: K4 52219

Gold, Angie

ANGIE GOLD.
Tracks: / Lucky in love / Who am I kidding / No alibi / Please tell me what your thinking / Red light / Every home should have one / Nobody said it's over / Love's fool / Can't dance / Flavour of the month.
LP: KR 25055

Gold, Brian & Tony

POISON (see under Brown, Dennis) (Gold, Brian & Tony/Dennis Brown).

Gold Diggers (film)

GOLD DIGGERS (Film soundtrack) (Cooper, Lindsay).
LP: SP 0617

Gold, Frankincense...

BUTTERFIELD DOWN (Gold, Frankincense & Disc Drive).
LP: NB 001

LIFECYCLE (Gold, Frankincense & Disc Drive).
LP: WIND 2

WHERE DO WE DRAW THE LINE (Gold, Frankincense & Disc Drive).
Tracks: / Where do we draw the line / Prequest / Wallpaper / Loop the loop / African dust, The / Churn / Airburst / Orienteering / Butterside downs / Railway children, The.
LP: VILEPOP 001

Gold, Harry

BOUNCING BACK (Gold, Harry & His Pieces Of Eight).
Tracks: / Bouncing back / Ostrich walk / Look at em doing it / Little rock getaway / Temptation blues / Panama rag / I wanna be like you / Since my best gal turned me down / Meander in the minor / Honky tonk train blues / Birth of the blues / There'll be some changes made / Dixieland shuffle / Tiger rag.
LP: LA 5011
MC: LA 5011 C

DIXIE (Gold, Harry & His Famous Pieces Of Eight).
Tracks: / If you wore a tulip / Blue and brokenhearted / Dixie / After you've gone / Rosie / Sensation rag / Walk right back / Ostrich walk / At the jazz band ball / Basin Street blues / Old man time / Copenhagen.
LP: HQ 3001

LIVE IN LEIPZIG (Gold, Harry & His Pieces Of Eight).
Tracks: / Dixieland jamboree / Davenport blues / That's a plenty / Blue / Riverboat shuffle / At the jazz band ball / Paper doll / Farewell blues / Maryland / Jazz me blues / Some of these days / Big chief battle axe.
MC: LA 5003C
LP: LA 5003

OCTAGONAL GOLD (Gold, Harry & His Pieces Of Eight).
Tracks: / If you knew Susie / Mississippi mud / Ory's Creole trombone / Stumbling / You turned the tables on me / Washington and Lee swing / I want a big butter and egg man / Poor butterfly / That da da strain / Watford Gap / Ida, sweet as apple cider / Dippermouth blues.
LP: BLP 12118

Golden Age of...

GOLDEN AGE OF BLACK MUSIC (See Under Soul...) (Various artists).

GOLDEN AGE OF CHICAGO BLUES (See Under Blues...) (Various artists).

Golden Bough

BEYOND THE SHADOWS.
LP: EULP 1092
MC: EUMC 1092

BOATMAN'S DAUGHTER.
LP: EULP 1037
MC: EUMC 1037

FAR FROM HOME.
LP: EULP 1065
MC: EUMC 1065

FLIGHT OF FANTASY.
LP: EULP 1045
MC: EUMC 1045

WINDING ROAD.
LP: EULP 1051
MC: EUMC 1051

WINTER'S DANCE.
LP: EULP 1046
MC: EUMC 1046

Golden Child (film)

GOLDEN CHILD (Film Soundtrack) (Various artists).
Tracks: / Best man in the world: *Wilson, Ann* / Deeper love: *Morgan, Meli'sa* / Love goes on (theme from the Golden child): *Ashford & Simpson* / Shame on you: *Davis, Martha* / Body talk: *Ratt* / Chosen one, The: *Jackson, Marlon* / Sardo and the child: *Colombier, Michael* / Golden love: *Colombier, Michael* / Confrontation: *Colombier, Michael.*
LP: EST 2030
MC: TCEST 2030

Golden Classics

GOLDEN CLASSICS (Various artists).
2LP: RML 100
MCSET: RML 4C100

Golden Dawn

POWER PLANT.
Tracks: / Evolution / This way please / Starvation / I'll be around / Seeing is believing / My time / Nice surprise / Everyday / Tell me why / Reaching out to you.
LP: LIK 24

Golden Eagle Gospel...

GOLDEN EAGLE GOSPEL SINGERS, 1937-40 (Golden Eagle Gospel Singers).

LP: . . . . ELE 4-200

Golden Eagle Jazz Band

GOLDEN EAGLE JAZZ BAND.
LP: . . . . SOS 1192

YOUNG WOMAN (see under Morris, Chris).

Golden Eagles

LIGHTNING AND THUNDER (Golden Eagles & Monk Boudreaux).
LP: . . . . ROUNDER 2073
MC: . . . . ROUNDER 2073C

LIGHTNING AND THUNDER Live at the H & R Bar, New Orleans.
Tracks: / Shotgun Joe / Little Liza Jane / Two way e way / Shallow water, oh mama / Shotgun Joe / Sew-sew-sew / Indian red / Hold 'em Joe / Little Liza Jane.
LP: . . . . FIEND 118

Golden Earring

2ND LIVE.
LP: 2625 042
MC: 3500 130

CUT.
Tracks: / Devil made me do it, The / Future, The / Baby dynamite / Last of the Mohicans / Lost and found / Twilight zone / Chargin' up my batteries / Secrets.
LP: 6302 224
MC: 7144 224

GOLDEN EARRING LIVE.
Tracks: / Candy's going bad / She flies on strange wings / Mad love's comin' / Eight miles high / Vanilla queen / To the hilt / Fighting windmills / Con man / Radar love / Just like Vince Taylor.
LP: 2625 034
LP: . . . . SPELP 44

GRAB IT FOR A SECOND.
Tracks: / Movin' down life / Against the grain / Grab it for a second / Cell 29 / Roxanne / Leather / Temptin' / U-turn time.
LP: 2310 639

GREATEST HITS: GOLDEN EARING.
2LP: 2664 440
MC: 3578 487

GREATEST HITS: GOLDEN EARRING VOL.3.
Tracks: / Radar love / She flies on strange wings / Instant poetry / Ce soir / Movin' down life / Bombay / Weekend love / Sleepwalking / Against the grain / I do rock 'n' roll / Long blond animal / No for an answer.
LP: 2311 094
MC: 3100 609

MOONTAN.
Tracks: / Radar love / Candy's going bad / Vanilla queen / Big tree, blue sea / Are you receiving me?.
LP: 2406 112
MC: 3191 112

NORTH SOUTH EAST WEST.
LP: . . . . CAL 204
MC: . . . . CAC 204

SWITCH.
Tracks: / Plus minus absurdio / Love is a rodeo / Switch, The / Kill me / Tons of time / Daddy's gonna save my soul / Troubles and hassles / Lonesome DJ.
LP: 2872 104
MC: 3472 104

TO THE HILT.
LP: 248 033-1

Golden Echoes

HEAVEN ON MY MIND.
LP: . . . . ROUNDER 2002

Golden Fiddle

BEST OF THE GOLDEN FIDDLE OCHESTRA (Fifty Fiddle Favourites).
LP: . . . . PLAT 15
MC: . . . . PLAC 15

GOLDEN FIDDLE ORCHESTRA, THE.
LP: . . . . LILP 5118
MC: . . . . LICS 5118

MAGIC OF THE FIDDLE.
Tracks: / Bonnie Dundee / Geordies byre / Pibroch O'Donald Dhy / Bugle horn, The / Ken Muirs on and away / Midlothian pipe band / Cock o' the north / Roxburgh castle / Kiss me quick / Tone, The / McKenzie of Coull / Storrier's hornpipe / Kirks hornpipe / Caddam Woods / He's o'er the hills / John Grumlie / Craighill / Merrily danced the quakers' wife / Middling thank you / Teviot Brig / Wild rose of the mountains / Miss Betsy Robertson / Rose among the heather / Green grow the rushes-o / Cameron's got his wife again / Wind that shakes the barley, The / Calum Donaldson / Hamilton rant / Far frae hame / Mickie Ainsworth / De'il amang the tailers / Soldier's joy / Mason's apron / Fairy dance, The / High road to Linton / Mrs. Macleod / Drunken piper / Back o'Benachie / Greenwood side / Hunters hill / Brochan lom / Braes of Tullymet / Lad wi' the plaidie, The / Castles in the air / Lord Moira / Gay Gordons / Glen Livet / Laird of Drumblair, The / MacKenzie hay / MacKenzie Fraser / Angus Campbell.
LP: . . . . TOPS 130

Golden Fox

GOLDEN FOX (Valentine, Anthony).
MCSET: . . . . LFP 7529

Golden Gate Quartet

GOLDEN GATE QUARTET 1937-9.
LP: . . . . SM 4043

JUBILEE.
LP: 60558
MC: . . . . C 60558

NEGRO SPIRITUALS.
Tracks: / Rock my soul / Joshua fit de battle of Jerico / Sometimes I feel like a motherless child / Hard trials and great tribulations / Jezebel / Only believe / Michael / Didn't it rain / Nobody knows the trouble I've seen / Put your hand / Down by the riverside / When saints go marching in.
LP: . . . . B 90069

NO. 1'S (GREATEST HITS), THE.
LP: 60587
MC: . . . . C 60587

SPIRITUALS.
Tracks: / King of kings / Old time religion / Take my hand precious Lord / My Lord, what a morning / Precious memories / For the rest of my life / Casey Jones / Somebody's knocking at your door / Rocks don't fall on me / Roll Jordan roll / Skip to my lou / When they ring the golden bells / Peace in the valley.
LP: 3C 054 10534
MC: 3C 254 10534

Golden Goose

GOLDEN GOOSE, THE (well loved tales age up to 9) (Unknown narrator(s)).
MC: . . . . PLB 57

Golden Horde

CHOCOLATE BISCUIT CONSPIRACY, THE.
LP: . . . . NOSE 7

DIG THAT CRAZY GRAVE.
LP: . . . . CALCLP 051

IN REALITY.
Tracks: / In reality.
LP: . . . . MB 6

RUCTIONS, DESTRUCTION....
MC: . . . . CALC 051C
LP: . . . . CALC 051

Golden Hour of...

GOLDEN HOUR OF IRISH SHOWBAND HITS (See Under Irish...) (Various artists).

Golden Lady (film)

GOLDEN LADY (Film soundtrack) (Various artists).
Tracks: / We had it all: *Blonde On Blonde* / Dahlia: *Blonde On Blonde* / Sophisticated like you: *Blonde On Blonde* / Woman is free: *Blonde On Blonde* / Golden lady: *3 Degrees* / Golden lady's theme: *Aznavour, Charles* / Fly me till I die: *Aznavour, Charles* / Praxis: *Aznavour, Charles* / Just making love: *Aznavour, Charles* / We had it all: *Aznavour, Charles*.
LP: . . . . ARL 5019

Golden Oldies...

GOLDEN OLDIES (Various artists).
MC: 4510014

Golden Palaminos

BLAST OF SILENCE.
LP: . . . . CELL 6127
MC: . . . . CELL 6127C

DEAD HORSE, A.
LP: . . . . CEL 6138
MC: . . . . CELC 6138

GOLDEN PALAMINOS.
LP: . . . . CEL 6662

VISIONS OF EXCESS.
LP: . . . . CEL 6118

Golden Seal (film)

GOLDEN SEAL, THE (Film soundtrack) (Various artists).
Tracks: / Letting go: *Golden Seal (film)* / Story begins, The: *Golden Seal (film)* / Voyage to Dutch: *Golden* Seal (film) / Legend, The: *Golden Seal (film)* / Williwa: *Golden Seal (film)* / Bridge, The: *Golden Seal* (film) / Face to face: *Golden Seal (film)* / Frolic, The: *Golden Seal (film)* / Swimming lessons: *Golden* Seal (film) / Close call: *Golden Seal (film)* / Choice, The: *Golden Seal (film)* / You're safe now: *Golden Seal (film)* / Goodbye: *Golden Seal (film)*.
LP: . . . . CLTLP 351
MC: . . . . ZCCLT 351

Golden Soul

GOLDEN SOUL (See Under Soul...) (Various artists).

Golden Star

BHANGRA '88.
LP: . . . . SSRLP 5074
MC: . . . . SC 5074

DHOOTAKADA BAI DHOOTAKADA.
LP: . . . . SSRLP 5109
MC: . . . . SC 5109

ESPECIALLY FOR YOU.
LP: . . . . SSRLP 5095
MC: . . . . SC 5095

FAST FORWARD.
LP: . . . . SSRLP 5091
MC: . . . . SC 5091

I LOVE GOLDEN STARBHANGRA.
LP: . . . . SSRLP 5069
MC: . . . . SC 5069

UPFRONT.
LP: . . . . SC 5084

Golden Strings

MY LIFE IS LIKE A STANLEY KNIFE (see Buy Off The Bar/Golden Strings).

Golden Themes...

GOLDEN THEMES FROM MGM CLASSIC FILMS (See Under Films) (Various artists).

Golden Turkey Album

GOLDEN TURKEY ALBUM, THE (Various artists).
LP: . . . . RNLP 307

Golden Years...

GOLDEN YEARS OF THE 50'S, VOL 3, THE (See Under 50's) (Various artists).

GOLDEN YEARS OF THE 60'S, VOL. 3, THE (See Under 60's) (Various artists).

GOLDEN YEARS OF THE 70'S, VOL. 3, THE (See under 70's) (Various artists).

Goldenthal, Elliot

PET SEMATARY (See under Pet Sematary).

Goldfinger (film)

GOLDFINGER (Original Film Soundtrack) (Various artists).
Tracks: / Goldfinger: *Various artists* / Golden girl: *Various artists* / Alpine Drive - Auric's factory: *Various* artists / Death of Tilley: *Various artists* / Odd Jobb's pressing engagement: *Various artists* / Laser beam, The: *Various artists* / Bond back in action again: *Various artists* / Pussy Galore's flying circus: *Various* artists / Teasing the Korean: *Various artists* / Gassing the gangsters: *Various artists* / Dawn raid on Fort Knox: *Various artists* / Arrival of the bomb and countdown: *Various artists* / Death of Goldfinger: *Various artists*.
LP: . . . . SLS 50172

GOLDFINGER (Film soundtrack) (Various artists).
Tracks: / Goldfinger: *Bassey, Shirley* / Into Miami: *Barry, John* (0.54) / Golden girl: *Barry, John*(2.03) / Alpine drive - Auric's factory: *Barry, John* (3.15) / Death of Tilley: *Barry, John* (1.58) / Oddjob's pressing engagement: *Barry, John* (3.05) / Laser beam, The: *Barry, John* (2.47) / Bond back in action again: *Barry*, John (2.29) / Pussy Galore's flying circus: *Barry, John* (2.40) / Teasing the Korean: *Barry, John* (2.12) / Gassing the gangsters: *Barry, John* (1.03) / Dawn raid on Fort Knox: *Barry, John* (6.43) / Arrival of the bomb and countdown: *Barry, John* (3.36) / Death of Goldfinger: *Barry, John* (2.34).
LP: 261077 1
MC: 261077 4
LP: . . . . EMS 1266
MC: . . . . TCEMS 1266
LP: . . . . DS 2610771

GOLDFINGER (Film soundtrack) (Various artists).
LP: . . . . ULP 1076

Goldie, Don

JAZZ EXPRESS.
LP: . . . . J 135

Goldilocks...

GOLDILOCKS.
MC: . . . . STC 008
MC: . . . . STC 304C

GOLDILOCKS AND THE THREE BEARS (Unknown narrator(s)).
MC: . . . . STK 006

GOLDILOCKS AND THE THREE BEARS.
Tracks: / Goldilocks and the three bears (Read by Dorit Wells.) / Sleeping beauty (Read by Peter Bartlett.) / Cock, the mouse and the little red hen, The (Read by Barbara Bliss.) / Hansel and Gretel (Read by Barbara Bliss.) / Little Red Riding Hood (story).
MC: . . . . TS 339

GOLDILOCKS & OTHER FAVOURITE STORIES (for children aged 3-7).
MC: . . . . VCA 601

GOLDILOCKS & THE THREE BEARS (well loved tales age up to 9) (Unknown narrator(s)).
MC: . . . . PLB 53

GOLDILOCKS & THE THREE BEARS (Bloom, Claire (nar)).
MC: 1392

Goldilocks (show)

GOLDILOCKS (SHOW) Original Broadway cast (Various artists).
LP: . . . . COS 2007

Goldman Band

PRIDE OF AMERICA.
Tracks: / Governor's own, The / Boston commandery / Pathfinder of Panama, The / Gate city / His excellency / Chimes of liberty / Bonnie Annie Laurie / President's march, The / Our Director / Pride of America / Tabasco / Revival march / Grandioso / My Maryland / On Jerry shore / Gardes du corps / Serenade, The / Sesquicentennial march.
LP: . . . . NW 266

Goldman, Jean-Jacques

ENTRE GRIS CLAIR ET GRIS FONCE.
Tracks: / A quoi tu sers? / Il changeait la vie / Tout petit monde / Entre gris clair et gris fonce / La bas / C'est ta chance / Des bouts de moi / Fais des bebes / Puisque tu pars / Filles faciles / Je commence demain / Elle a fait un bebe toute seule / Quelque part, quelqu'un / Qu'elle soit elle / Doux / Reprendre c'est voler / Il y a / Peur de rien / Il me restera / Appartenir.
LP: 4604041
MC: 4604044

TRACES.
Tracks: / C'est ta chance / Elle a fait un bebe toute seule / Intro - A quoi tu sera / Long is the road / Il y a / Puisque tu pars / Reprendre c'est voler / Peur de rien blues / Doux / Il changeait la vie / Medley.
LP: 4634261
MC: 4634264

Goldrick, Michael

CHAMPION OF THE WORLD.
MC: . . . . BIP 801

Goldsboro, Bobby

BEST OF BOBBY GOLDSBORO.
Tracks: / Honey / Little things / Summer (the first time) / Hello summertime.
LP: 1A 222 58138
MC: . . . . TC 1A 222 58138

GOLDEN HITS.
MC: 4XLL 9171

GREATEST HITS: BOBBY GOLDSBORO (2).
Tracks: / Honey / With pen in hand / Mississippi delta queen / See the funny little clown / Voodoo woman / Autumn of my life / Watchin' Scotty grow / Little things / Hello summertime / Broomstick cowboy / Butterfly for Bucky / Summer (the first time).
LP: . . . . SLS 50421

GREATEST HITS: BOBBY GOLDSBORO (PREMIER).
Tracks: / Honey / Straight life / With pen in hand / Muddy Mississippi line / Blue Autumn / Little things / Summer (the first time) / Watchin' Scotty grow / See the funny little clown / Broomstick cowboy / It's too late / Autumn of my life / Hello summertime / I'm a drifter.
LP: . . . . PMP 1008
MC: . . . . PMPK 1008

SUMMER (THE FIRST TIME).
Tracks: / Summer (the first time) / Marlena / He's part of us / L and N don't stop here anymore, The / Brand new kind of love / Sing me a smile / Mississippi delta queen / I can see clearly now / She / Killing me softly with her song / Spread my wings and fly / If'n I was God (from the film Tom Sawyer) / Summer(The first time).
LP: . . . . SLS 50405

VERY BEST OF BOBBY GOLDSBORO, THE.
Tracks: / Honey / Straight life / With pen in hand / Muddy Mississippi line / Blue Autumn / Little things / Summer (the first time) / Watchin' scotty grow / See the funny little clown / Cowboy and the lady, The / Broomstick cowboy / It's too late / Autumn of my life / Hello summertime / I'm a drifter / Love divine / Payin' for the good times / Street dancin'.
LP: C5-534
MC: C5K-534

Goldsbury, Mack

ANTHROPOLOGIC.
Tracks: / Anthropology / Rain garden / It's only a paper moon / Be my love / Crossing over.
LP: . . . . MR 5194

Goldsmith, Glen

WHAT YOU SEE IS WHAT YOU GET.
Tracks: / What you see is what you get / What you see is what you get (corrosive) / I won't cry / Save a little bit / Dreaming / Undercover / Gone too far / Shame / Keep in touch / Rhythm of romance / Shadow of doubt.
LP: . . . . PL 71750
MC: . . . . PK 71750

Goldsmith, Jerry

ISLANDS IN THE STREAM (See under Islands In The Stream).

KING SOLOMONS MINES (See under King Solomons Mines).

LEVIATHAN (See under Leviathan (Film).

RUSSIA HOUSE, THE (See Under Russia House).

SLEEPING WITH THE ENEMY (See Under Sleeping With The ...) (Various artists).

SOUNDTRACKS OF JERRY GOLDSMITH WITH THE PHILHAR (Goldsmith, Jerry with the Philharmonia).
Tracks: / Blue Max, The / Man from UNCLE, The / Doctor Kildare / Room 222 / Waltons, The / Barnaby Jones / Masada / Gremlins suite / Sand pebbles / Chinatown / Patch of blue poltergeist, A / Pappillon / Wind and the lion / Generals, The / Lionheart.
LP: 8207571
MC: 8207574

WILD ROVERS AND THE FIRST GREAT TRAIN ROBBERY (See under Wild Rovers) (Various artists).

Goldsmith, Oliver

VICAR OF WAKEFIELD, THE (Jacobi, Derek (nar)).
MCSET: 418 174-4

Goldstein, Gil

WRAPPED IN A CLOUD.
Tracks: / Sands of time / Wishing well / Finding your own way / Singing rhythm / Wrapped in a cloud / Beantown (revisited).
LP: . . . . MR 5229

Goldthorp, Mark

FLIGHT COMMANDER SOLITUDE AND THE... (Goldthorp, Mark & Simon Hinkler).
LP: . . . . GDLP 3

G'Ole (film)

G'OLE (See under Wakeman, Rick) (Film soundtrack) (Wakeman, Rick).

Golf Omnibus

GOLF OMNIBUS (Cadell, Simon).
MCSET: . . . . ZBBC 1160

Golgotha

UNMAKER OF WORLDS.
LP: . . . . CMGLP 003

Golson, Benny

... WITH BOBBY TIMMONS (Golson, Benny/Guerin, Roger).
LP: . . . . FS 187

BENNY GOLSON'S NEW YORK SCENE.
Tracks: / Something in B flat / Step lightly / Blues it / Capri / Whisper not / Just be myself / You're mine you.
LP: . . . . COP 043

BLUES ON DOWN.
2LP: . . . . M 47048

CALIFORNIA MESSAGE.
LP: . . . . SFP 177

GROOVIN' WITH GOLSON.
LP: . . . . OJC 226

ONE MORE MEMORY (Golson, Benny Quintet with Curtis Fuller).
LP: . . . . SJP 180

PARIS/NEW YORK 1958.
LP: . . . . SW 8418

STARDUST (Golson, Benny & Freddie Hubbard).
Tracks: / Stardust / Double bass / Gipsy jingle-jangle / Povo / Love is a many splendoured thing / Sad to say / Far away.
MC: . . . . CC 23

THIS IS FOR YOU JOHN.
Tracks: / Jam the avenue / Greensleeves / Origin / Change of heart / Times past (this is for you, John) / Page 12 / Vilia.
LP: . . . . SJP 235

TIME SPEAKS.
Tracks: / I'll remember April / Time speaks / No dancin' / Jordu / Blues for Duane / Theme for Maxine.
LP: . . . . SJP 187

Goltz, Michael

POETRY VOL 2.
LP: . . . . ISST 171

POETRY-GUITAR BALLADS.
LP: . . . . ISST 119

Golub, Jeff

UNSPOKEN WORDS.
LP: 139008-1
MC: 139008-4

Gomez, Eddie

DOWN STRETCH.
LP: . . . . BKH 531

GOMEZ (Gomez, Eddie & Chick Corea).
Tracks: / Dabble vision / Santurce / Japanese waltz / Zimmermann (for Toru Takemitsu) / Mez-ga / Ginkakuji / Pops and Alma / Row, row, row your tones / We will meet again.
MC: . . . . CC 17

MEZGO.
Tracks: / Me too / Capricious fantasy / Puccini's walk / Delgado / Caribbean morning / Scott David / Cello sonata in G Minor / 1st movement.
LP: . . . . EPC 57084
MC: 40 57084

MOREOVER (see under Jones, Hank) (Gomez, Eddie/Hank Jones/Al Foster).

POWER PLAY.
Tracks: / Power play / Loco motive / Mel / Spanish flower / Mr. Go / Amethyst / W.110th.St / Forever.
LP: 4611841
MC: 4611844

STREET SMART.
Tracks: / Street smart / Lorenzo / I'caramba / It was you all along / Blues period / Double entendre / Carmen's song / Bella horizonte / Besame mucho.
LP: 4662251
MC: 4662254

Gomez, Jill

CABARET CLASSICS (Gomez, Jill with John Constable).
MC: . . . . DKPC 9055

SOUTH OF THE BORDER...DOWN MEXICO WAY.
MC: . . . . KA 66500

Gomez, Ray

VOLUME.
Tracks: / Make your move / U.S.A / Waiting for the big time / West side boogie / Summer in the city / Love at first sight / World will keep on turning / Blues for Mez.
LP: . . . . CBS 84134

Gomm, Ian

GOMM WITH THE WIND.
Tracks: / Hold on / Hooked on love / Sad affair / Black and white / Come on / Airplane / 24 hour service / That's the way I rock'n'roll / Dirty lies / You can't do that / Chicken run / Another year.
LP: . . . . DAI 1

IMAGES: IAN GOMM.
Tracks: / It's got to be magic / Little lost lamb / Lego / Modern soul / State I'm in, (The) / Cheap hearts hurt / Play on / Just images / What makes a man a... / T.V. times / That girl / Beauty and the beast / Cry myself to sleep / Keep on dancing.
LP: . . . . LIK 4

SUMMER HOLIDAY.
Tracks: / Hooked on love / Sad affair / Black and white / Come on / Hold on / Airplane / Images / Twenty four hour service / That's the way I rock'n'roll / Dirty lies / You can't do that / Chicken run / Another year / Going through the motions.
LP: . . . . ALBG 100

VILLAGE CHOICE, THE.
LP: . . . . ALB 112

Gonads

LIVE AND LOUD.
LP: . . . . LINK LP 049

LIVE:THE OFFICIAL BOOTLEG.
2LP: . . . . SYNDLP 8

REVENGE OF THE GONADS, THE.
LP: . . . . LINK LP 085

Gondoliers

GONDOLIERS, THE (see under Gilbert & Sullivan).

Gone

LET'S GET REAL, REAL GONE FOR A CHANGE.
LP: . . . . SST 061

Gone To Earth

FOLK IN HELL.
LP: . . . . PROBE 6

VEGETARIAN BULLFIGHTER.
LP: . . . . PROBE 15
MC: . . . . PROBE 15C

Gone With The Wind

GONE WITH THE WIND (Soundtrack recording) (Various artists).
LP: . . . . DUN 108

GONE WITH THE WIND (Original London cast) (Various artists).
LP: . . . . AEI 1113

GONE WITH THE WIND (Film soundtrack) (Various artists).
Tracks: / Main title: *Various artists* / Scarlett and Rhett's first meeting: *Various artists* / Ashley and Scarlett: *Various artists* / Mammy: *Various artists* / Christmas during the war in Atlanta: *Various artists* / Atlanta in flames: *Various artists* / Reconstruction: *Various artists* / Ashley returns to Tara from the war prison: *Various* artists / Scarlett makes her demands of Rhett: *Various artists* / Scarlett's fall down the staircase: *Various artists* / Bonnie's fatal pony ride: *Various artists* / Finale: *Various artists.*
LP: . . . . CBS 70283
MC: 40 70283
LP: 2353 031

GONE WITH THE WIND (Film soundtrack) (Various artists).
Tracks: / Main title: *Various artists* / Barbecue at twelve oaks: *Various artists* / Ball, The: *Various artists*/ Ashley and Scarlett: *Various artists* / Mammy: *Various artists* / Christmas in Atlanta: *Various artists*/ Fall of the South: *Various artists* / Intermission music: *Various artists* / Sherman's march through Georgia: *Various artists* / Ashley returns to Tara from the war: *Various artists* / Scarlett and Rhett at Tara: *Various* artists / Belle Watling: *Various artists* / Rhett and Bonnie: *Various artists* / Scarlett's fall - Rhett's remorse: *Various artists* / Bonnie's death: *Various artists* / Finale: *Various artists.*
LP: 817 116 1
MC: 9676.4
MC: . . . . GK 80452
MC: 817 116 4
LP: . . . . MGM CS 8056

GONE WITH THE WIND (Original Drury Lane Cast) (Various artists).
Tracks: / Overture - Today's the day: *Various artists* / We belong to you: *Various artists* / Tara: *Various* artists / Two of a kind: *Various artists* / Blissful Christmas/ Home again: *Various artists* / Lonely stranger: *Various artists* / Time for love: *Various artists* / Which way is home: *Various artists* / How often, how often: *Various artists* / If only: *Various artists* / Southern lady: *Various artists* / Marrying for fun: *Various artists* / Blueberry blue: *Various artists* / Strange and wonderful: *Various artists* / Little wonders: *Various artists* / Bonnie gone: *Various artists* / It doesn't matter now/ Finale: *Various artists.*
LP: . . . . SCXA 9252

Gonella, Nat

CRAZY VALVES (Gonella, Nat & His Georgians).
Tracks: / How'm I doin? / Capri caprice / Skeleton in the cupboard, The / I can't dance / Crazy valves / Bessie couldn't help it / Take another guess / Nagasaki / Just a crazy song / Sheik of Araby, The / Tiger rag / Copper coloured gal / Ol' man mose / Trumpetuous / I'm gonna clap my hands / Makin' a fool of myself / 'Bill' Tell / Georgia on my mind.
LP: . . . . AJA 5055
MC: . . . . ZC AJA 5055

GEORGIA ON MY MIND (Gonella, Nat & His Georgians).
Tracks: / E flat blues / Tiger rag / Wabash blues / Someone stole Gabriel's horn / Ol' man Mose / Bye bye blues / Jeepers creepers / Spooky takes a holiday / Flat foot Floogie / Mahogany Hall stomp / When you're smiling / You must have been a beautiful baby / I must see Anne tonight / Just a kid named Joe / Georgia on my mind.
LP: . . . . SH 369
LP: . . . . RFL 12

GOLDEN AGE OF NAT GONELLA.
LP: . . . . GX 41 2536 1
MC: . . . . GX 41 2536 4

HOLD TIGHT.
Tracks: / Music maestro please / 'Tain't what you do / Limehouse blues / Ain't cha comin' out / I'd like to see Samoa of Samoa / Corrigan hop, The / Flat foot floogee / I go for that / Wacky dust / Swing, swing, swing daughter swing / Hold tight / Spider and the fly, The / There's a hole in the old oaken bucket / My Swiss hilly billy / Tea for two / Tisket a tasket, A.
MC: . . . . CMOIR 303

HOW'M I DOIN'? (Gonella, Nat & His Georgians).
Tracks: / How'm I doin'? / Mama don't allow it / Blue turning grey over you / Lazy rhythm / Fan it / You rascal you / Get hot / Kicking the gong around / Bye bye blues / Music goes round and around, The / Confessin' / Somebody stole Gabriel's horn / Lady be good / His old cornet / How long how long blues / I want to be happy / Sweet music man / Ol' man river / Swingin' to those lies (it's a sin to tell a l.
LP: . . . . OLD 11
MC: . . . . COLD 11

MISTER RHYTHM MAN (Gonella, Nat & His Georgians).
Tracks: / Don't let your love go wrong / Moonglow / Troublesome trumpet / Dinah / Let him live / Oh mo'nah / Georgia on my mind / Sing / E flat blues / Georgia's a gorgeous gal / Basin Street blues / I'm gonna wash my hands of you / Mister rhythm man / Stardust / Earful of music / Down at uncle Bill's / Smoke rings / Beale Street blues / Rockin' chair / I heard / St Louis blues / Runnin' wild / Rhythm is our business / Breakin' the ice.
LP: . . . . EG 2601881
MC: . . . . EG 2601884

NAT GONELLA AND HIS TRUMPET.
Tracks: / Georgia on my mind / Sweet Sue / Moon country / Nobody's sweetheart / Troublesome trumpet / I heard / That's my home / When you're smiling / Rockin' chair / I can't believe that you're in love with me / Stormy weather / I can't dance / Carolina.
LP: . . . . ACL 1241

NAT GONELLA SCRAPBOOK, THE.
Tracks: / Gotta pebble in my shoe / Solitude / Blue skies / Begin the beguine / If I didn't care / This night / Ain't cha comin' out / T'aint what you do (it's the way that you do it) / He stole my heart away / Louis blues / Meet me down in sunset valley / Harlem speaks / Tiger rag / Never break a promise / Music maestro please / On the sentimental side / Spider and the fly, The.
LP: . . . . JOY 284

NAT GONELLA STORY.
Tracks: / Georgia on my mind / Wild man blues / Bessie couldn't help it / Miss Otis regrets (she's unable to lunch today) / Them there eyes / O Mo'nah / Nagasaki / Honeysuckle rose / Just a kid named Joe / Ain't misbehavin' / Stompin' at the Savoy / It's a pair of wings for me / Don't get around much anymore / Five minutes more.
LP: . . . . NTS 146

NAT GONELLA VOL 1 (1934-1935).
Tracks: / Sweet Sue / Georgia on my mind / E flat blues / Breakin' the ice / Nagasaki / Hesitation blues / Sensation / Truckin'.
MC: . . . . NEO 951

NAT GONELLA VOL. 2 - 1932-1935.
Tracks: / I can't believe that you're in love with me / I heard / Rockin' chair / When you're smiling / Oh Peter / Star dust / That's my home / Stormy weather / Nobody's sweetheart / I got ants in my pants / Carolina.
MC: . . . . NEO 956

NATURALLY GONELLA.
Tracks: / Yeah man / Truckin' / Hot lips / Sheik of Araby, The / Black coffee / Blow, Gabriel, blow / Capri caprice / Oh Peter (you're so nice) / Georgia rockin' chair / Lazy river / Sweet and hot / Pidgin English hula / Squareface / Japanese sandman / Ghost of Dina / Jig time / Gonna wed that gal o' mine / Peanut vendor / Sophisticated lady.
LP: . . . . CHD 129

RUNNING WILD (Gonella, Nat & His Georgians).
LP: . . . . HQ 3003

YEAH MAN (1935-1937).
Tracks: / Georgia rockin' chair / St. Louis blues / Yeah man / Mahogany hall stomp / I'm getting sentimental over you / Japanese sandman / I'm gonna kiss myself goodbye / Big apple / Whatcha gonna do when there ain't no swing? / Swingin' the jinx away / Someday, sweetheart / I don't like / Peckin' / Farewell blues / You can't swing a love song / Taint good (like a nickel made of wood).
LP: . . . . HQ 3019

Gong

ANGELS EGGS.
Tracks: / Other side of the sky / Sold to the highest Buddha / Castle in the clouds / Prostitute poem / Givin my luv to you / Selene / Flute salad / Oily way / Outer temple / Inner temple / Love is how you

make it / I never gild before / Eat that phonebook code.
LP: .... CR 30219

BREAKTHROUGH.
LP: .... EULP 1053
MC: .... EUMC 1053

CAMEMBERT ELECTRIQUE.
Tracks: / Radio gnome-predection / You can't kill me / I've bin stone before / Mister Long Shanks: O Mother:I am your fantasy / Dynamite: I am your animal / Wet cheese delirium / Squeezing sponges over policemen's heads / Fohat digs holes in space / And you tried so hard / Tropical fish: Selene / Gnome the second.
LP: .... CRM 2003
MC: .... TCCRM 2003
LP: .... C 1520

EXPRESSO 2.
Tracks: / Heavy tune / Golden dilemma / Sleepy / Soli / Boring / Three blind mice.
LP: .... OVED 65

FLYING TEAPOT.
Tracks: / Radio gnome invisible / Pot head pixies, The / Octave doctors and the crystal machine, The / Zero the hero and the witches spell / Witches song I am your pussy.
LP: .... CR 30202
MC: .... TCCR 30202

GAZEUSE.
Tracks: / Expresso / Night illusion / Percolations (part 1) / Percolations (part 2) / Shadows of / Mireille / Esnuria.
LP: .... OVED 18

HISTORY AND THE MYSTERY OF THE PLANET GONG, THE.
Tracks: / Concert intro / Captain Shaw and Mr. Gilbert / Love makes sweet music / D.L.T.interview / Riot 1968 / Dreaming it / I feel so lazy / And I tried so hard / Radio gnome pre-mix / Pot head pixies / Majick brother / Line up / Clarence in Wonderland / Breakthrough interview / Where have all the hours gone / Gong poem / Dey a goddess / Opium for the people / Red alert / 13/8 / Gliss-u-well / Future, The / Dream, The / Chernobyl rain / Let me be one.
LP: .... DMLP 1018

LIVE ETC.
Tracks: / You can't kill me / Zero the hero and the witches spell / Flying teapot / Dynamite: I am your animal / 6/8 / Est-ce que je suis / Ooby-scooby doomsday or the D-day DJ's got the / Radio gnome invisible / Oily way / Outer temple / Inner temple / Where have all the flowers gone / Isle of everywhere, The / Get it inner / Master Builder / Flying teapot (reprise).
2LP: .... VGD 3501

MAGICK BROTHER.
Tracks: / Mystic sister: Magick brother (Composer: Gilli Smyth.) / Magick brother / Glad to say to say (Composer: Gilli Smyth.) / Rational anthem (Composer: Gilli Smyth.) / Chainstore chant: pretty Miss Titty (Composer: Gilli Smyth.) / Pretty miss titty / Fable of a Fredfish (Composer: Gilli Smyth.) / Hope you feel O.K. / Ego (Composer: Gilli Smyth.) / Gong song (Composer: Gilli Smyth.) / Princess dreaming (Composer: Gilli Smyth.) / 5 & 20 schoolgirls (Composer: Gilli Smyth.) / 'Cos you got green hair (Composer: Gilli Smyth.).
LP: .... AFF 4

RADIO GNOME INVISIBLE, PART 1 (The flyting teapot).
Tracks: / Radio gnome invisible / Flying teapot / Pothead pixies, The / Octave doctors and the crystal machine, The / Zero the hero and the witches spell / Witches song I am your pussy.
LP: .... OVED 14

RADIO GNOME INVISIBLE, PART 2 (Angel's Egg).
Tracks: / Other side of the sky / Sold to the highest Buddha / Castle in the clouds / Prostitute poem / Givin' my luv to you / Selene / Flute salad / Oily way / I never gild before / Eat that phonebook code / Outer temple / Inner temple / Percolations / Love is how you make it.
LP: .... OVED 15

SHAMAL.
Tracks: / Wingful of eyes / Chandra / Bambooji / Cat in Clark's shoes / Mandrake / Shamal.
LP: .... OVED 17

YOU.
Tracks: / A.P.H.P's advice / Thoughts for nought / Magick mother invocation / Master builder / Sprinkling of clouds, A / Perfect mystery / Isle of everywhere, The / You never blow your trip forever.
LP: .... OVED 16

Gong Maison

GONG MAISON.
LP: .... DMLP 1024

Gonnella, Ron

BURN'S NIGHT.
Tracks: / Bonnie wee thing / O wert thou in the cauld blast / Awa' wi' your witchcraft o'beauty's alarms / I am my Mammy's wee bairn / Aye waukin' o / Does the Haughty Gaul invasion threaten / Phillis the Fair / My wife's a winsome wee thing / O a' the airts / Flow gently sweet Afton / There was a lass and she was fair / Man's a man for a' that, A.
LP: .... LILP 5070
MC: .... LICS 5070

FIDDLE AND PIPE FAVOURITES.
MC: .... KITV 510

FIDDLE GEMS.
Tracks: / Well may my true love arrive / Rebel war song / Well may Charlie wear the crown / Sitting in the stern of the boat / Beauty of the north, The / Good wife admit the wanderer / Fall of the foyers / Archibald MacDonald of Keppoch / Huntly's wedding medley / Hymn to the saviour / My wife is forever storming at me / Caledonia's wail for Niel Gow.
LP: .... LILP 5044
MC: .... LICS 5044

FIDDLERS FANCY.
Tracks: / Bonnie lass o' Bon Accord / Donald MacPherson lament / Miss Gordon of Park / Chapel Keithack / Cradle song / Dumbarton castle / Corgarff castle / Music o'spey, The / Lady Niven Lumsden of Achindoir / Mr. Morison of Bognie / Roseacre / Sandy's goat / Weeping birches of Kilmorach.
LP: .... LILP 5017
MC: .... LICS 5017

PLAYS THE FIDDLES OF GOW, MARSHALL & SKINNER.
LP: .... WGR 028
MC: .... CWGR 028

RON GONNELLA'S INTERNATIONAL FRIENDSHIP FIDDLE.
Tracks: / BBC echoes / Cape Breton ceudh / Hector MacAndrews favourites / Congratulations all round / Sounds of Strathearn / Touch of Gaelic, A / Bonnie Dundee / Boston tea party / Jimmy Shand special / Strathspey king and friends, The / Scottish dance music corner / Canadian connection, The / Fiddlers two / My friend Adam Rennie / New York, New York / Music of William Marshall, The.
MC: .... KITV 453

SCOTTISH FIDDLE MASTER.
Tracks: / Family favourites / Lilt of the Lowes / Kintyre airs / Flavour of the fiddle / Border love song, A / Over the Isles to America / MacKintosh medley / Lowland folk / Royal Deeside jigs / Border airs.
MC: .... LICS 5099
LP: .... LILP 5099

TRIBUTE TO NEIL GOW.
Tracks: / Atholl volunteers march, The / Nathaniel Gow's lament for the death of his / Prince Charlie's quickstep / Cam ye by Atholl / Dunkeld volunteers, The / Lady Anne Hope's favourite / Miss Margaret Brown's favourite / Niel Gow's compliments returned to Mr Marshall / Earl of Dalhousie's happy return to Scotland / Flora MacDonald's lament / Lady Mary Haye's scotch measure / Caller herring / Lady Dorothea Stewart (Murray's wedding jig) / Miss Lucy Johnston's compliments to Niel Gow.
LP: .... LILP 5085
MC: .... LICS 5085

Gonsalves, Paul

CLEOPATRA FEELIN' JAZZY.
Tracks: / Action in Alexandria / Cleo's asp / Cleopatra's lament.
LP: .... JAS 47
MC: .... JAS C47

DUKE ELLINGTON & PAUL GONSALVES (See Ellington, Duke) (Gonsalves, Paul & Duke Ellington).

IT DON'T MEAN A THING IF IT AIN'T GOT THAT SWING (see under Hines, Earl) (Gonsalves, Paul & Earl Hines).

JUST A-SITTIN' AND A-ROCKIN' (Gonsalves, Paul & Ray Nance).
Tracks: / BP blues / Lotus blossom / Don't blame me / Just a sittin' and a rockin' / Hi ya, Sue / Angel eyes / I'm in the market for you / Tea for two.
LP: .... BLP 30138

MEXICAN BANDIT MEETS PITTSBURGH PIRATE (Gonsalves, Paul & Roy Eldridge).
Tracks: / 1.5400 North / I cover the waterfront / C jam blues / Body and soul / It's the talk of the town / Somebody loves me.
LP: .... F 9646
MC: 5F 9646

RARE PAUL GONSALVES SEXTET IN EUROPE 1963 (Gonsalves, Paul Sextet).
LP: .... JC 109

TELL IT THE WAY IT IS.
Tracks: / Tell it the way it is / Things ain't what they used to be / Duke's place / Impulsive / Rapscallion in Babs Canyon / Body and soul.
LP: .... JAS 27
MC: .... JAS C27

Gonzales, Charlie

CHARLIE GONZALES 1950-51.
Tracks: / Hi-yo Silver / Such a darn fool over you / Hey must I tell / I'm through with you / It's all my fault / I'm free / Every dog has it's day / Let me make love to you.
LP: .... KK 810

Gonzales, Dennis

NAMESAKE (Gonzales, Dennis New Dallas Quartet).
LP: .... SHLP 106

STEFAN (Gonzales, Dennis New Dallas Quartet).
LP: .... SHLP 101

Gonzalez

GONZALEZ.
LP: .... SWK 2001

MOVE IT TO THE MUSIC.
Tracks: / Love it / People's party / Livin' in the light of your love / Take me the way / Ain't no way to treat a lady / Love is like a slave / Dance machine / Move it to the music.
LP: .... SWK 2003

Gonzalez, Celina

FIESTA GUAJIRA.
Tracks: / Yo sol el punto cubano / Muero de olivdo / Santa Barbara / Oye mi le lo ley / Guajiro Guarachero / Paisajes naturales / El refran se te Olivdo / Aguacero aguacerito / Mi tierra es asi.
LP: .... WCB 006

Gonzalez, Jerry

YA YO ME CURE.
LP: .... AMCL 1001

Goo Brothers

YUAN (Goo Brothers & Shung Tian).
Tracks: / Dancing and singing in the village / Soldiers of the long march / Step by step / Fishing by lamplight / Three kingdoms / Evening song / Training horses on the Mongolian grassland / Springtime on Parmir Mountains / My second life / One flower / Dream of the red mansion, The.
LP: .... RWLP 11
MC: .... RWMC 11

Goo Goo Dolls

HOLD ME UP.
LP: .... AFTER 8

JED.
Tracks: / Out of sight / No way out / Down on the corner / Road to Salinas / Misfortune / Gimme shelter / Up yours / Sex maggot / Had enough / Em elbmuh / Artie / James Dean.
LP: .... RO 94771

Gooch, John

AS TIME GOES BY.
Tracks: / As time goes by / Dischopin / Manhattan / Chi mai / Girl talk / Liebestraum / Hazurre / Brendan's theme / September song / Tea for two / Mon amour / Laura / Je voulais (te dire que je t'attends) / You're my everything / Whispering (on 12" only) / Shine on harvest moon.
LP: .... PRX 24

Good Brothers

DELIVERING THE GOODS.
LP: .... SVLP 9205
MC: .... SVMC 9405

Good Companions (show)

GOOD COMPANIONS, THE (Original London cast) (Various artists).
LP: .... DS 15020

Good & Gone

METHIL BOX.
LP: .... RADGE 2

Good Missionaries

FIRE FROM HEAVEN.
LP: .... DLP 04

SCARS ON SUNDAY (See under Alternative TV).

Good Morning Babylon

GOOD MORNING BABYLON (Film Soundtrack) (Various artists).
LP: .... A 300
MC: .... C 300

Good Morning Vietnam

GOOD MORNING VIETNAM (Film Soundtrack) (Various artists).
Tracks: / Nowhere to run: *Reeves, Martha* / I get around: *Beach Boys* / Game of love: *Fontana, Wayne & the Mindbenders* / Sugar and spice: *Searchers* / Liar liar: *Castaways* / Warmth of the sun: *Beach Boys*/ I got you: *Brown, James* / Baby please don't go: *Them* / Danger heartbreak dead ahead: *Marvelettes*/ Five o'clock world: *Vogues* / California sun: *Rivieras* / What a wonderful world: *Armstrong, Louis.*
LP: .... AMA 3913
MC: .... AMC 3913

Good News

GOOD NEWS (See Under Gospel...) (Various artists).

Good News (Film)

GOOD NEWS (Film soundtrack) (Various artists).
LP: .... STK 111

Good Ol' Persons

ANYWHERE THE WIND BLOWS.
Tracks: / Anywhere the wind blows / Wildflowers / Danny J, The / Dreaming in three quarter time / Waterbound / Hamsters in the pantry / Suffer the consequences / Walkin' the floor over you / Waking up alone / La arboleda / Think about me.
LP: .... F 38
MC: .... C 38

I CAN'T STAND TO RAMBLE.
Tracks: / I can't stand to ramble / Kissing comes easy / Broken tie / Itzbin reel / You don't miss your water / I will arise / Get up and go to work / In dreams / I'm satisfied with you / Not this time / China camp Ellie / Open your heart.
LP: .... F 17

OLD-TIME BLUEGRASS MUSIC.
LP: .... BAY 208

PART OF A STORY.
Tracks: / Broken hearted lover / Easy substitute / My my my / I don't hurt anymore / It's gonna rain / You're a flower / Crossing the Cumberlands / It seems there's nothing I can do / This young boy / Part of a story.
LP: .... F 26
MC: .... C 26

Good Old Bad Old ...

GOOD OLD BAD OLD DAYS (Original London cast) (Various artists).
Tracks: / Good old bad old days: *Various artists* / Fool who dared to dream: *Various artists* / Wisdom of the world: *Various artists* / Thanks giving day: *Various artists* / Today/ tomorrow/ yesterday: *Various artists*/ It's a musical world: *Various artists* / I do not love you: *Various artists* / Cotton pickin' moon: *Various* artists / Good things in life, The: *Various artists* / People tree: *Various artists* / We've got a cure for everything on Broadway: *Various artists* / Good old bad old days - finale: *Various artists.*
LP: .... EMA 751

GOOD OLD BAD OLD DAYS, THE (Original London cast) (Various artists).
LP: .... AEI 1116

Good Old Days (tv)

GOOD OLD DAYS, THE (Various artists with Leonard Sachs) (Various artists).
Tracks: / Hello hello who's your lady friend: *Various artists* / Moonlight bay: *Various artists* / Mary: *Various* artists / Don't dilly dally on the way: *Various artists* / By the light of the silvery moon: *Various artists*/ Row row row: *Various artists* / If those lips could only speak: *Various artists* / Trifling occurrences: *Various* artists / Hold your hand out you naughty boy: *Various artists* / Robert E. Lee, The: *Various artists* / Toot toot toosie goodbye: *Various artists* / Are you from Dixie: *Various artists* / Little Annie Rooney: *Various* artists / Down at the old Bull and Bush: *Various artists* / K-K-K-Katy: *Various artists* / Who were you with last night: *Various artists* / Cherry ripe: *Various artists* / Don't you think he's mad: *Various artists*/ Paradise for two, A: *Various artists* / Oh Oh Antonio: *Various artists* / I'll be your sweetheart: *Various* artists / Has anybody here seen Kelly?: *Various artists* / Till we meet again: *Various artists* / Down at the old Bull and Bush: *Various artists* / Here we are, here we are: *Various artists.*
LP: PKL5534

Good Question

GOOD QUESTION.
Tracks: / Got a new love / Body contact / Dance with me / One on one / Listen to your heart / Private property / Real love / Mysterious lady / Like an explosion / One more time.
LP: 925743 1
MC: 925743 4

Good Rats

FROM RATS TO RICHES.
Tracks: / Taking it to Detroit / Just found me a lady / Mr. Mechanic / Dear Sir let me / Victory in space / Coo coo coo blues / Don't hate the ones who bring you rock and roll / Could be tonight / Local zero.
LP: RAD 5

Good Rockin' Charles

GOOD ROCKIN' CHARLES.
LP: R 7601

Good Shepherds

ONE.
Tracks: / Wedding song, The / Cain.
LP: SHEPHERDS 001C
LP: CONCORD 14

Good, the Bad & the

GOOD, THE BAD AND THE UGLY (IMPORT) (Film soundtrack) (Various artists).
Tracks: / Good, the bad and the ugly, The: *Various artists* / Sundown, The: *Various artists* / Strong, The: *Various* artists / Desert, The: *Various artists* / Carriage of the spirits, The: *Various artists* / Marcia: *Various* artists / Story of a soldier: *Various artists* / Marcia without hope: *Various artists* / Death of a soldier, The: *Various artists* / Ecstacy of gold, The: *Various artists* / Trio, The: *Various artists* (Main title theme).
LP: 5C 062 90960

GOOD, THE BAD AND THE UGLY, THE (Film soundtrack) (Various artists).
LP: SULP 1197

GOOD, THE BAD AND THE UGLY, THE (Film Soundtrack) (Various artists).
Tracks: / Good, the bad and the ugly, The: *Various artists* / Sundown, The: *Various artists* / Strong, The: *Various* artists / Desert, The: *Various artists* / Carriage of the spirits, The: *Various artists* / Marcia: *Various* artists / Story of a soldier: *Various artists* / Marcia without hope: *Various artists* / Death of a soldier, The: *Various artists* / Ecstasy of gold: *Various artists* / Trio, The: *Various artists* (Main title theme).
LP: EG 2605821
MC: EG 2605824

Goodacre, Tony

25TH ANNIVERSARY: TONY GOODACRE.
Tracks: / Everyday love / Love me tender / Blue Hawaii / California cottonfields / Through the eyes of love / I'd love to lay down / Why me lord / Another long day / Desert blues / Mr. Ting-a-ling...pick me up on the way / Wait a moment, Wendy / Honey girl / Worried man blues (medley) / Midnight special (medley) / Cottonfields / Freight train / Wabash cannonball / Putting on the style / Rock Island line.
LP: STON 8108
MC: CSTON 8108

GRANDMA'S FEATHER BED.
Tracks: / Grandma's feather bed / Idaho / Out and free / Streets of London / When a woman leaves home / Morning past the night before, The / Jimmie the kid / That's you and me / Kelly's wife / Old shep / All that glitters / Key, The / Nashville rail.
LP: SBOL 4021
MC: COB 4021

MR COUNTRY MUSIC.
Tracks: / My music city friends / Do you know you are my sunshine / Old rugged cross, The / Susan Flowers / My elusive dreams / Mr. Country music...bird on the wing / Blue eyes crying in the rain / Merry go round of love / China doll / My little son / Dear old sunny south by the sea.
LP: SBOL 4029
MC: COB 4029

RECORDED LIVE IN ILKLEY.
Tracks: / Country music in my soul / Red river valley / Mermaid, The / Back home again / Great El Tigre, The / Triad / I love you because / One day at a time / Railroad bum / Lord made a hobo out of me, The / Slowly / What's wrong with the way that we're doing it now / Forty shades of green / Letter edged in black / Travelling blues / Tenessee border / Rose of San Antone (instrumental).
LP: STON 8003
MC: CSTON 8003

RED ROSES.
Tracks: / Red roses for a blue lady / Walking the floor / Funny face / Sail away / There'll never be anyone else but you / Country boy / Lucy ain't your loser looking good / Before I met you / Annie's song / Saginaw Michigan / If heaven ain't a lot like Dixie / Roses in the winter / Old flame.
LP: STON 8301
MC: CSTON 8301

ROAMIN' ROUND IN NASHVILLE.
Tracks: / Canadian Pacific / Peach picking time in Georgia / Welcome to my world / Country hall of fame / Abilene / Golden rocket / There goes my everything / I wonder where you are tonight / Jody and the kid / Satin sheets / Year that Clayton Delaney died, The / Why should I be so lonely / Don't it make you wanna go home / Your cheatin' heart.
LP: SBOL 4019
MC: COB 4019

SYLVANTONE SHOWCASE, THE (Goodacre, Tony/Jeannie Dee/Stu Page/Remuda/Geoff Ashford).
Tracks: / Don't play me no love songs / Your leaving song / Me or the bottle / Rags to riches / We belong together / Country picker / You'll be home / Radio nights / My name is Billy / One of a kind / Love made a fool / Falling apart at the seams / Artist, The / Texas music.
LP: STON 8504
MC: CSTON 8504

THANKS TO THE HANKS.
Tracks: / Thanks to the Hanks / And thanks to George Hamilton VI / Wild side of life / From here to there to you / Pan American / Rockin' rollin' ocean / My front door is open / Fool such as I, A / We're gonna go fishing / Blackboard of my heart / Teardrops on a rose / Last ride, The / Send me the pillow that you dream on / Standing on the outside / This song is just for you / I don't hurt anymore / Blues come around, The.
LP: SBOL 4024
MC: COB 4024

TONY GOODACRE COLLECTION, THE.
Tracks: / Nashville marathon / It's almost tomorrow / Girl I used to know, A / Workin' my way through a heartache / Have I told you lately that I loved you / Down in Waikiki / I wonder who's kissing her now / Man in the sky / Woman's touch, A / No tomorrow for yesterdays dreams / Place in the choir / Mockin' Bird Hill / You've made my life complete / Country music is my life / Ain't got nothing to wear.
LP: STON 8607
MC: CSTON 8607

WRITTEN IN BRITAIN.
Tracks: / Written in Britain / Let me be there / Call of the wild / Last farewell, The / Let's live the good life again / Turn me round / Mississippi fireball... ten guitars / Ballad of a young woman / World of our own, A / Come back to me / Yesterday / You do love me don't you.
LP: SBOL 4027
MC: COB 4027

YOU'VE MADE MY LIFE COMPLETE.
Tracks: / You've made my life complete / Burn Atlanta down / Railway bridge at Crewe, The / I love you in an old fashion way / High on your love / Bingo Bill...country music is my life / It's not the end of the world / Load of bread, A (a jug of wine) / Only way to say goodbye, The / International ambassador country music / Show me a sign.
LP: SBOL 4043
MC: COB 4043

Goodall, Med

EMERGENCE.
MC: C 145

INNOCENCE.
MC: C 157

KINDRED SPIRITS.
MC: C 165

Goodbye Mr Chips

BOYFRIEND, THE/GOODBYE MR. CHIPS (See under Boyfriend) (Various artists).

GOODBYE MR CHIPS (Original cast recoding featuring John Mills) (Various artists).
Tracks: / Roll call: *Various artists* / Fill the world with love: *Various artists* / Would I had lived my life then: *Various artists* / Schooldays: *Various artists* / That's a boy: *Various artists* / Where did my childhood go?: *Various artists* / Boring: *Various artists* / Take a chance: *Various artists* / Walk through the world: *Various artists* / When I am older: *Various artists* / Miracle: *Various artists* / Day has a hundred pockets, The: *Various artists* / You and I: *Various artists* / What a lot of flowers: *Various artists*/ When I was younger: *Various artists* / Goodbye, Mr Chips: *Various artists*.
LP: TER 1025
MC: ZCTER 1025

GOODBYE MR CHIPS (See Hilton, James) (Sheddon, John).

GOODBYE MR CHIPS (Original soundtrack) (Various artists).
LP: MCA 39066
MC: MCAC 39066

Goodbye Mr. Mackenzie

FISH HEADS AND TALES.
Tracks: / Amsterdam / Somewhere in China / Calton Hill (Not on CD) / Secrets (Not on CD) / Face to face / Sick of you / Green turn red / Pleasure search / Mystery train / Knockin' on Joe (live) / Strangle your animal (CD only.) / Hear comes Deacon Brodie (live) (CD only.).
LP: CAPS 2001
MC: TCCAPS 2001

GOOD DEEDS AND DIRTY RAGS.
Tracks: / Open your arms / Wake it up / His masters voice / Goodwill city / Candlestick Park / Goodbye Mr. Mackenzie / Rattler, The / Dust / You generous thing you / Good deeds / Amsterdam (CD only.) / Calton Hill (CD only.) / Secrets (CD only.) / Knockin' on Joe (CD only.) / Strangle (On free single only.) / Extended strangle (On free single only.) / Secrets (live) (On free single only.) / Green turn red (live) (On free single only.).
MC: TCEST 2089
LP: EST 2089

HAMMER AND TONGS.
Tracks: / Blacker than black / Bold John Barley Corn / Diamonds / Burning / Shoo fly / Sick baby / Down to the minimum / She's strong / Love child / Tongue tied.
LP: PCS 7345
MC: TCPCS 7345
LP: RAR 10227
MC: RARC 10227

Goodfellas (film)

GOODFELLAS (Original Soundtrack) (Various artists).
Tracks: / Rags to riches: *Bennett, Tony* / Sincerely: *Moonglows* / Speedo: *Cadillacs* / Stardust: *Ward, Billy* / Look in my eyes: *Chantels* / Life is but a dream: *Harptones* / Remember (walkin' in the sand): *Shangri-Las*/ Baby I love you: *Franklin, Aretha* / Beyond the sea: *Darin, Bobby* / Sunshine of your love: *Cream* / Mannish boy: *Waters, Muddy* / Layla (piano edit): *Derek & The Dominoes*.
LP: 7567821521
MC: 7567821524

Goodhand-Tait, Phillip

TEACHING AN OLD DOG NEW TRICKS.
Tracks: / Teaching an old dog new tricks.
LP: CHR 1146

Goodies

GOODIES GREATEST.
Tracks: / Funky gibbon / Black pudding Bertha / Father Christmas do not touch me / Nappy love / Rock with a policeman / I'm a teapot / Spring spring spring / Good ole country music / Wild thing / In betweenies / M.I.C.K.E.Y. M.O.U.S.E. / Cricklewood / Man's best friend is his duck / Melody park / Charles Aznovoice / Last chance dance / Taking my oyster for walkies / Baby samba / Rastashanty / Make a daft noise for Christmas.
LP: NTS 233
LP: BRADL 1012

NEW GOODIES LP.
LP: BRADL 1010

Gooding, Cuba

LOVE DANCER.
Tracks: / Disco royale / Trust me / I'm yours now / Hey, the party's in here / Dance floor lover / Tell me how long it's been / Running man.
LP: STML 12113

Goodland, David

CASTLE OF YEW, THE (see under Castle of Yew).

Goodland, Norman

MY OLD CHAP.
Tracks: / Cuckoo be come / I thank ee, Lard / I do luv ee / Poacher, (The) / When zun de dip.
LP: SDL 320
MC: CSDL 320

Goodluck, John

MONDAY'S CHILDE.
LP: TSR 028

SPEED THE PLOUGH.
Tracks: / Cowboy, The / Jack the sailor lad / Me and me dog / Smugglers boy, The / Jimmy Allen / Rufford Park poachers / Stormy weather / Cod banging / Greasy cook / Then up be doing / Candlelight fisherman, The / Speed the plough / Battle of sole bay.
LP: SFA 047

SUFFOLK MIRACLE, THE.
LP: TSR 015

Goodman, Benny

20 GREATEST HITS: BENNY GOODMAN.
LP: 20121
MC: 40121

20 GREATEST HITS (MASTERS).
LP: U 50042

1938 CARNEGIE HALL JAZZ CONCERT.
Tracks: / Don't be that way / One o'clock jump / Sensation rag / I'm coming, Virginia / When my baby smiles at me / Shine / Blue reverie / Life goes to a party / Honeysuckle rose / Body and soul / Man I love, The / Avalon / I got rhythm / Blue skies / Loch Lomond / Blue room / Swingtime in the Rockies / Bei mir bist du schon / China boy / Stompin' at The Savoy / Dizzy spells / Sing, sing, sing / Big John special.
2LP: 66202

AIRCHECKS/RHYTHMAKERS (Goodman, Benny & Charlie Barnet).
LP: IAJRC 8

ALL OF ME.
Tracks: / In the mood / Yam, The / Moten swing / Begin the beguine / Blue Hawaii / All of me / Hartford stomp / Trees / Clap hands, here comes Charlie / Sly mongoose / Hot foot shuffle / Hold tight.
LP: INT 127 034
MC: CAS 427 034

ALL THE CATS JOIN IN.
Tracks: / Clarinade / All the cats join in / Mad boogie / Remember / Somebody stole my gal / Darktown strutters' ball / Lucky / Rattle and roll / Body and soul / Lady be good.
LP: FH 37
MC: CFH 37
LP: BDL 1056
MC: BDC 1056

ALL THE CATS JOINED IN (VOL.2).
Tracks: / Not mine / You're easy to dance with / Why don't you do right? / Mission to Moscow / Fascinating rhythm / Rattle and roll / All the cats join in / Fly by night / Darktown strutters' ball / Six flats unfurnished / After you've gone / Clarinade / Lucky (you're right, I'm wrong) / Swing angel / Oh, baby / Put that kiss back where you found it.
LP: 4611001
MC: 4611004

ALTERNATE GOODMAN, THE VOL. 1 (Jumpin' at the woodside).
LP: NOST 7606

ALTERNATE GOODMAN, THE VOL. 2 (Flying home).
Tracks: / I've been there before / Homeward bound / Make with the kisses / Soft winds / Darn that dream / Beyond the moon / I'm confessin' / Squeeze me / King Porter stomp / I can't love you anymore / Nostalgia / Nobody / Man I love, The / Henderson stomp / Benny rides again / Cabin in the sky.
LP: NOST 7610

ALTERNATE GOODMAN, THE VOL. 3 (Frenesi).
Tracks: / Frenesi / Hard to get / Moonlight on the Ganges / Yes my darling daughter / I'm always chasing rainbows / Somebody stole my gal / Let the doorknob hitcha / I hear a rhapsody / Corn silk / Birds of a feather / Breakfast feud / Gone with what draft / I'm not complaining / Time on my hands / You're dangerous / Memory of a rose.
LP: NOST 7612

ALTERNATE GOODMAN, THE VOL. 4 (Jenny).
Tracks: / This is new / Jenny / Perfidia / Bewitched / Afraid to say hello / Lazy river / Scarecrow / Yours / You lucky people / Oh, look at me now / Take it / Solo flight / Good enough to keep / Amapola / Intermezzo / Fiesta in blue.
LP: NOST 7615

ALTERNATE GOODMAN, THE VOL. 5 (The Earl) (Goodman, Benny & His Orchestra).
Tracks: / Cherry / Good evenin' good lookin' / Something new / I found a million dollar baby / Don't be that way / When the sun comes out / Smoke gets in your eyes / Tuesday at ten / Soft as spring / Down, down, down / Pound Ridge / Elmer's tune / Clarinet a la King / My old flame / How deep is the ocean? / Earl, The.
LP: NOST 7616

ALTERNATE GOODMAN, THE VOL. 6 (Clarinet a la king).
Tracks: / This autumn / That's the way it goes / Clarinet a la King / I'm here / Shady ladybird / Buckle down Winsocki / Let's do it / I'll get by / If I had you / Limehouse blues / Someone else is taking my place / Somebody nobody

loves / How long has this been going on? / That did it, Marie / Winter weather.
LP: . . . . NOST 7617

ALTERNATE GOODMAN, THE VOL. 7 (Royal flush).
Tracks: / Everthing I love / Someone's rocking my dreamboat / Let's give love a chance / Not mine / Not a care in the world / You don't know what love is / Where or when / On the sunny side / Royal flush / When / On the sunny side of the street / Dear old Southland / At the darktown strutters' ball / Zoot suite / String of pearls / My little cousin / Ramona.
LP: . . . . NOST 7620

ALTERNATE GOODMAN, THE VOL. 8 (Dance and swing with Benny Goodman).
Tracks: / Let's dance / Don't be that way / You was right, baby / Seven come eleven / Come to baby, do / Lucky / It's the talk of the town / Somebody stole my gal / Rattle and roll / Who's sorry now? / Ain't misbehavin' / And the angels sing / All the cats join in / I got the sun in the morning / Sing, sing, sing.
LP: . . . . NOST 7603

ALTERNATE GOODMAN, THE VOL. 9.
LP: . . . . NOST 7648

ALTERNATE GOODMAN, THE VOL. 10 (Gotta be this or that).
LP: . . . . NOST 7650

ALTERNATE GOODMAN, THE VOL. 11 (I got rhythm).
LP: . . . . NOST 7652

ALTERNATE GOODMAN, THE VOL. 12 (Oh lady be good).
LP: . . . . NOST 7654

AVALON - THE SMALL BANDS.
Tracks: / Avalon / Handful of keys / Man I love, The / Smiles / Liza / Where or when / Vieni, vieni / I'm a ding dong daddy (from Dumas) / Sweet Lorraine / Blues in your flat, The / Sugar / Dizzy spells / Opus 1/2 / I must have that man / Sweet Georgia Brown / 'S wonderful / Pick-a-rib (part 1) / Pick-a-rib (part 2) / I cried for you / I know that you know / Opus 3/4.
LP: . . . . NL 82273
MC: . . . . NK 82273

BASIN STREET BLUES.
LP: 20084
MC: 40084

BASLE, SWITZERLAND, 1959.
LP: . . . . AR 108

BENNY GOODMAN, 1937-38.
LPS: 2615 060

BENNY GOODMAN.
MC: . . . . ZCJC 835

BENNY GOODMAN (1943).
LP: . . . . QUEEN 042

BENNY GOODMAN (Compact/ Walkman Jazz).
Tracks: / Stealin' apples / Moonglow / I want to be happy / I found a new baby / Where or when / I would do most anything for you / Lady be good / Don't be that way.
MC: 8205434

BENNY GOODMAN, 1938.
Tracks: / Don't be that way / House hop / Sampson stomp / I can't give you anything but love / I've found a new baby / One o'clock jump / I let a song go out of my heart / Jazz me blues / King Porter stomp / I never knew / Flat foot floogie / Diga diga doo / Shine on harvest moon.
LP: . . . . QU 060

BENNY GOODMAN, 1939.
LP: . . . . TAX 8021

BENNY GOODMAN 1939, VOL. 2.
LP: . . . . TAX 8033

BENNY GOODMAN, 1943.
LP: . . . . Q 042

BENNY GOODMAN, 1946.
LP: . . . . UNKNOWN

BENNY GOODMAN, 1937-38 (Goodman, Benny & His Orchestra).
Tracks: / Blue Hawaii / Veni, veni / All of me / Yam, The / Moten swing / Clap hands, here comes Charlie / Hartford stomp / Trees / Begin the beguine / Sly mongoose / Hot foot shuffle / Hold tight.
LP: . . . . JA 5114

BENNY GOODMAN AND HIS ORCHESTRA 1935 - 1939 (Goodman, Benny & His Orchestra).
LP: . . . . LPJT 38

BENNY GOODMAN (BLU-DISC).
LP: . . . . T 1002

BENNY GOODMAN COLLECTION (20 Golden Greats).
Tracks: / Let's dance / Bugle call rag / King Porter stomp / St. Louis blues / Stealin' apples / Stompin' at the Savoy / Dinah / Alexander's ragtime band / Dear old Southland / Get happy / Body and soul / Christopher Columbus / One o'clock jump / Chloe / Rosetta / My melancholy baby / Sometimes I'm happy / Three little words / I want to be happy / Goodbye.
LP: . . . . DVLP 2011
MC: . . . . DVMC 2011

BENNY GOODMAN, HIS STARS AND HIS GUESTS (1939-41).
Tracks: / I cried for you / Lady be good / Opus one/two / Memories of you / Lamp is low, The / Gone with "what" wind / Jack hits the road / Southpaw serenade / Fiesta in blue / There'll be some changes made / Chonk, Charlie, chonk / Superman / Flying home / Rose room / Let the doorknob hitcha.
LP: . . . . QU 016

BENNY GOODMAN IN HI-FI.
Tracks: / Let's dance / Jumpin' at The Woodside / Stompin' at The Savoy / What can I say, after I say I'm sorry? / When I grow too old to dream / Get happy / You brought a new kind of love to me / Rock rimmon / Somebody stole my gal / Blue Lou / Sent for you yesterday / You're a sweetheart / Big John special / Jersey bounce / Airmail special / Ain't misbehavin' (CD only.) / Slipped disc (CD only.) / Rose room (CD only.) / I would do anything for you (CD only.).
LP: . . . . ED 2604261
MC: . . . . ED 2604264

BENNY GOODMAN (JAZZ REACTIVATION).
LP: . . . . JR 155

BENNY GOODMAN (LIVE IN LAS VEGAS) (December 31, 1966) (Goodman, Benny Sextet).
Tracks: / Sweet Georgia Brown / Rose room / Airmail special / Memories of you.
LP: . . . . SG 8010

BENNY GOODMAN (LOTUS).
LP: . . . . LOP 14,081

BENNY GOODMAN ON THE AIR 1940 (Goodman, Benny & His Orchestra).
Tracks: / Let's dance / Big John special / Hour of parting / Seven come eleven / Where do I go from you? / Goodbye / These foolish things / After you've gone / Board meeting / Six appeal / Stardust / Goodbye / Idaho.
LP: . . . . AIRCHECK 16

BENNY GOODMAN ON THE AIR VOL 3 (Goodman, Benny & His Orchestra).
Tracks: / Stompin' at the Savoy / Louise / Bugle call rag / Love me or leave me / Lady's in love with you, The / Without a song / Memories of you / And the angels sing / King Porter stomp / Jumpin' at the woodside / There'll be some changes made / China boy / Class of '39, The / Wrappin' it up / Goodbye / Moonlight serenade / Mozart matriculates / Stealin' apples / Pic-a-rib / One o'clock jump.
LP: . . . . AIRCHECK 34

BENNY GOODMAN ON THE AIR VOL 2 (Goodman, Benny & His Orchestra).
Tracks: / Don't be that way / Louise Tobin blues / Make believe / Sheik of Araby, The / Alexander's ragtime band / It's never too late / Sent for you yesterday / Goodbye / Let's dance / Blue skies / If you ever change your mind / Russian lullaby / Boy meets horn / I got rhythm / Sugar foot stomp / Three little words / Don't worry 'bout me / In a little spanish town / Tea for two / Indianapolis speedway race.
LP: . . . . AIRCHECK 32

BENNY GOODMAN ORCHESTRA AND GROUPS (Goodman, Benny & His Orchestra).
Tracks: / Blue Hawaii / Veni, veni / All of me / Yam, The / Moten swing / Clap hands, here comes Charlie / Sly mongoose / Hot foot shuffle / Hold tight / Hartford stomp / Begin the beguine / September song / World is waiting for the sunrise / Bill Bailey won't you please come home / I want to be happy / Runnin' wild / Mission to Moscow / Clarinet a la King / King Porter stomp / World is waiting for the sunrise / Poor butterfly / Let's dance / I walk with you / Yesterday / Great day / Shadow of your smile / Airmail special / String of pearls.
LP: . . . . KLJ 20005

BENNY GOODMAN PLAYS CLASSICS.
2LP: 6 48262
MCSET: 4 48262

BENNY GOODMAN PLAYS GERSHWIN.
Tracks: / I got rhythm / Man I love, The / Nice work if you can get it / Who cares? / How long has this been going on? / Love walked in / Embraceable you / Liza / Fascinating rhythm / Oh lady I love / Lady be good / Somebody loves me.
LP: . . . . CBS 21064
MC: 40 21064

BENNY GOODMAN STORY, THE.
Tracks: / Blue skies / King Porter stomp / Goodbye / Stompin' at the Savoy / Get happy / Christopher Columbus / St. Louis blues / Alexander's ragtime band / Dear old Southland / So rare / Big John special / I've got my love to keep me warm / Smiles / Chloe / I got rhythm / Don't be that way / One o'clock jump / My melancholy baby / Whispering / Bach goes to town (a fugue in swing tempo) / If dreams come true / AC/DC current / Bugle call rag / Don't be that way / Sing, sing, sing.
MCSET: . . . . DVREMC 08

BENNY GOODMAN SWINGS.
LP: . . . . PM 155 1563

BENNY GOODMAN - THE KING SWING (December 8, 1973).
Tracks: / Avalon / Lady be good / After you've gone / That's a plenty.
LP: . . . . SG 8006

BENNY GOODMAN TODAY.
2LP: . . . . DDS 3

BENNY GOODMAN TRIO PLAYS.... (Fletcher Henderson Fund WNEW New York 1951) (Goodman, Benny Trio).
LP: . . . . M 8041

BENNY GOODMAN VOL.1.
Tracks: / Sweet Georgia Brown / Broadway / Blue room.
LP: . . . . BO 704
MC: . . . . CIJ 20142 F
LP: . . . . CIJ 40142 A

BENNY GOODMAN VOL.2 (Big band).
LP: . . . . T 1004

BENNY GOODMAN VOL.3.
LP: . . . . T 1006

BENNY GOODMAN VOL.4.
LP: . . . . T 1009

BENNY GOODMAN VOL.5 (Small group).
LP: . . . . T 1011

BENNY GOODMAN VOL.6 (Smallgroup 1939/45).
LP: . . . . T 1012

BENNY GOODMAN: VOLUME 2 (Goodman, Benny & His Orchestra).
Tracks: / Can't we be friends? / Bugle call rag / Indiana / I surrender, dear / Life is a song / Sweet little you / Between the Devil and the deep blue sea / Royal Garden blues / Sweet and lovely / Three little words / Sugar foot stomp / When we're alone / There must have been a devil in the Moon / Restless.
LP: . . . . BO 718
LP: . . . . JA 5152

BENNY GOODMAN - WHEN SWING WAS KING.
Tracks: / Johnny One Note / That foolish feeling / More than you know / Camel hop / Big John Special / Lullaby in rhythm.
LP: . . . . SG 8004

BENNY GOODMAN WITH RED NICHOLS' ORCHESTRA (Goodman, Benny & Red Nichols).
Tracks: / How come you do me like you do? / Making faces at the man in the moon / East St. Louis toodle-oo.
LP: . . . . V 5001

BENNY GOODMANS 1934 BILL DODGE ALLSTAR RECORDINGS.
2LP: . . . . CLP 111/112

BENNY RIDES AGAIN.
Tracks: / Mission to Moscow / Benny rides again / Earl, The / Oh baby / Fascinating rhythm / Everything I've got / Whispering / All the things you are / You do something to me / It could happen to you / Stereo stomp.
LP: . . . . GCH 8096

BENNY'S BOP.
Tracks: / Mary's idea / Bye bye blues bop / There's a small hotel / Blue views / I can't give you anything but love / You took advantage of me / Where oh where has my little dog gone / Pepper (Patsy's idea) / String of pearls / I'll see you in my dreams / Undercurrent blues.
LP: . . . . HEP 36

BEST OF BENNY GOODMAN.
Tracks: / Don't be that way / Sing, sing, sing / And the angels sing / Loch Lomond / King Porter stomp / Stompin' at The Savoy / One o'clock jump / After you've gone / Goodnight my love / Goodbye.
MC: . . . . NK 89323
LP: . . . . NL 89323
LP: . . . . INTS 5079

BEST OF NEWHOUSE (Camel Caravan broadcasts 1938-39).
Tracks: / One o'clock jump / Moonglow / Stardust / Lullaby in rhythm / Alexander's ragtime band / Shine on harvest moon / Diga diga doo / I know that you know / I've found a new baby / Swingtime in the Rockies / Clarinet marmalade / I hadn't anyone till you / Minnie the moocher's wedding day / Dinah / Runnin' wild / Sugar foot stomp / Honeysuckle rose / Shine / You're driving me crazy / Sing, sing, sing / Dizzy spells / Smoke house / It had to be you / Bach goes to town / I'm a ding dong daddy / Whispering / Undecided / Sent for you yesterday / Kingdom of swing / Who'll buy my bublitchki? / Goodbye.
2LP: . . . . NOST 7625/26

BEST OF, THE.
LP: . . . . SM 3973/2

BIG BAND 1936-1939.
LP: . . . . SM 3870
MC: . . . . MC 3870

BIG BAND EUROPE (Benny Goodman vol. 3).
Tracks: / Pennies from Heaven / Fine romance, A.
MC: . . . . CIJ 20157Z
LP: . . . . CIJ 40157Y

BIG CITY SWING.
Tracks: / Let's dance / Roll 'em / Don't be that way / Stompin' at The Savoy / And the angels sing / Why don't you do right? / String of pearls / Where or when / Jersey bounce / Poor butterfly / Please don't talk about me when I'm gone / How high the moon.
LP: . . . . TAB 5

BREAKFAST BALL, 1934 (Goodman, Benny & His Orchestra).
Tracks: / Georgia jubilee / Junk man / Ol' pappy / Emaline / I ain't lazy, I'm just dreaming / As long as I live / Moon glow / Breakfast ball / Take my word / It happens to the best of friends / Nitwit serenade / Bugle call rag / Learning / Stars fell on Alabama / Solitude / I'm getting sentimental over you / I'm a hundred per cent for you / Cokey / Like a bolt from the blue / Music hall rag.
LP: . . . . SVL 172
MC: . . . . CSVL 172

CAMEL CARAVAN BROADCASTS 1938 (Goodman, Benny & His Orchestra).
LP: . . . . LP 1019

CAMEL CARAVAN BROADCASTS, VOL 2 (Goodman, Benny & His Orchestra).
LP: . . . . LP 1020

CAMEL CARAVAN BROADCASTS, VOL 3 (Goodman, Benny & His Orchestra).
LP: . . . . LP 1021

CAMEL CARAVAN BROADCASTS/ CAFE ROUGE (Goodman, Benny & His Orchestra).
LP: . . . . JASM 2518
MC: . . . . JASMC 2518

CAMEL CARAVAN, VOL. 1.
Tracks: / Let's dance / I can't give you anything but love / Hurry home / Songwriter's story, The / You must have been a beautiful baby / Honky tonk train blues / Cuckoo in the clock / Roll 'em / Goodbye / Let's dance / Sweet Sue / Could be / Softly as in a morning sunrise / Ciribiribin / I have eyes / Umbrella man / Sent for you yesterday / Goodbye.
LP: . . . . GOJ 1030

CAMEL CARAVAN, VOL. 2.
LP: . . . . GOJ 1033

CAMEL CARAVAN, VOL. 3 (One o' clock jump).
LP: . . . . GOJ 1036

CAMEL CARAVAN, VOL. 4.
Tracks: / Louise / I'm forever blowing bubbles / That sly old gentleman / Opus 3/4 / Kingdom of swing / Hold tight / I found a new baby / Honeysuckle rose / Tears from my inkwell / Estrellita / Pinetops boogie woogie / Sing sing sing / Don't worry 'bout me.
LP: . . . . GOJ 1039

CARNEGIE HALL ENCORE.
LP: . . . . SG 8020

CHARLIE CHRISTIAN WITH BENNY GOODMAN SEXTET AND ORCHESTRA (See under Christian, Charlie) (Goodman, Benny & His Orchestra).

CLARINET A LA KING (CBS).
Tracks: / How deep is the ocean / Zaggin' with Zig / It never entered my mind / Henderson stomp / Superman / Yes, my darling daughter / Bewitched / Scarecrow / Solo flight / Cherry / I found a million dollar baby / When the sun comes out / Pound ridge / Earl, The / Caprice XXIV Paganini / Clarinet a la king.
LP: 4608291
MC: 4608294

CLARINETITIS.

Tracks: / Clarinetitis / After a while / Dinah / Jazz holiday, A / Jungle blues / Sheik of Araby, The / Shimme-sha-wabble / How come you do me like you do? / Blue / Muskrat ramble / Room 1411 / That's a-plenty / Indiana / Shirt-tail stomp / Sugar / Crazy 'bout my gal / Woverine blues / Railroad man.
LP: . . . . AFS 1018
MC: . . . . TCAFS 1018

CLASSICS IN JAZZ.
LP: . . . . S 1381

COMMAND PERFORMANCE.
Tracks: / I'm just wild about Harry / Stealin' apples / Improvisation / Why don't you do right.
LP: . . . . SWH 46
MC: . . . . CSWH 46

COMPLETE SMALL COMBINATIONS VOLS.1/2 (1935-1937).
Tracks: / After you've gone / Body and soul / Who? / Someday, sweetheart / China boy / More than you know / All my life / Lady be good / Nobody's sweetheart / Too good to be true / Moonglow / Dinah / Vibraphone blues / Sweet Sue / My melancholy baby / Tiger rag / Stompin' at the Savoy / Whispering / Ida sweet as apple cider / Tea for two / Runnin' wild / Avalon / Handful of keys / Man I love, The / Exactly like you.
2LP: . . . . NL 89753
MCSET: . . . . NK 89753

COMPLETE SMALL COMBINATIONS VOLS.3/4 (1937-1939).
Tracks: / Sugar / Dizzy spells / Opus 1/2 / I must have that man / Sweet Georgia Brown / 'S wonderful / Pick-a-rib (parts 1 & 2) / I cried for you (2 takes) / I know that you know - 2 / Opus 3/4 / Smiles / Liza / Where or when / Silhouetted in the moonlight / Vieni, vieni / I'm a ding dong daddy / Bei mir bist du schon (parts 1 & 2) / Sweet Lorraine / Blues in your flat, The (3 Takes).
2LP: . . . . NL 89754
MCSET: . . . . NK 89754

COMPOSITIONS AND COLLABORATORS (collectors' edition).
LP: . . . . CBS M 42227

DURING THE FABULOUS FIFTIES.
LP: . . . . GOJ 1010

ELLA WITH (see under Fitzgerald, Ella) (Goodman, Benny/his orch/Ella Fitzgerald/MillsBros/Chick Webb).

ESSENTIAL, THE.
MC: 4671514

FAMOUS LIVE BROADCASTS 1937/44 (Goodman, Benny & His Orchestra).
Tracks: / Let's dance / Memories of you / Bugle call rag.
LP: 20807

FASCINATING RHYTHM.
LP: 500202

GET HAPPY.
Tracks: / Hooray for love / Get rhythm in your feet / Blue skies / Jingle bells / Santa Claus came in the spring / Goodbye / Yankee Doodle never went to town / No other one / Eeny meeny miney mo / Basin Street blues / It's been so long / Stompin' at the Savoy / Goody goody / Breakin' in a pair of shoes / Get happy / Christopher Columbus / I know that you know / Star dust / You can't pull the wool over my eyes / Glory of love.
LP: . . . . SVL 185
MC: . . . . CSVL 185

GOODMAN ON THE AIR.
Tracks: / Airmail special / After you've gone / Flying home / Slipped disc / Clarinade / Oomph fah fah / Clarinet a la King / It's only a paper moon / Rachel's dream / Something new / Tiger rag / Rattle and roll / Rose room / King Porter stomp.
LP: . . . . NOST 7605

GOODMAN TOUCH, THE.
LP: . . . . S 1380

GREATEST HITS: BENNY GOODMAN.
LP: 33006
MC: 63006

HALL OF FAME: BENNY GOODMAN & HIS ORCHESTRA (Goodman, Benny & Orchestra).
Tracks: / In the mood / Yam / Moten swing / Clap hands, here comes Charlie / Blue Hawaii / Vieni vieni / All of me / Hartford stomp / Trees / Begin the beguine / Sly mongoose / Hot foot shuffle / Hold tight.
LP: . . . . BLPS 20151

HALLELUJAH 1944-46.
LP: . . . . SG 8016

HISTORY OF JAZZ.
Tracks: / Sometimes I'm happy / Basin Street blues / Stompin' at The Savoy / Swingtime in the Rockies / Pick yourself up / He ain't got rhythm / Roll 'em / One o'clock jump / Ooh, oh boom / Undecided / And the angels sing / Jumpin' at The Woodside.
LP: . . . . SM 3057

INDISPENSABLE BENNY GOODMAN VOL. 3/4 (1936-37) (Goodman, Benny & His Orchestra).
Tracks: / T'ain't no use / Bugle call rag / Jam session / Goodnight my love / (Oh yes) take another guess / Did you mean it? / When you and I were young, Maggie / Swing low sweet chariot / He ain't got rhythm / I want to be happy / Chloe / Rosetta / Peckin' / Can't we be friends? / Sing,Sing,Sing & Christopher columbus / When it's sleepy time down South / Roll 'em / Changes / Bob White / Sugar foot stomp / I can't give you anything but love / Minnie the moocher's wedding day / Let that be a lesson to you / Popcorn man / Loch Lomond / Camel hop / True confession / Life goes to a party / It's wonderful / Thanks for the memory / If dreams come true / Sweet stranger.
2LP: . . . . NL 89756
MC: . . . . NK 89756

INDISPENSABLE BENNY GOODMAN VOL. 5/6 (1938-39) (Goodman, Benny & His Orchestra).
Tracks: / Don't be that way / One o'clock jump / Please be kind / Ti-pi-tin / Oooooh-boom / Always and always / Make believe / Blue room / Lullaby in rhythm / I never knew / Sweet Sue / Feeling high and happy / Why'd ya make me fall in love? / Big John special / Wrappin' it up / Flat foot floogie / Margie / Russian lullaby / Bumble bee stomp / Topsy / Smoke house / My honey's loving arms / Farewell blues / It had to be you / Louise / Whispering / Bach goes to town (a fugue in swing tempo) / I'll always be in love with you / Undecided / And the angels sing / Sent for you yesterday / Kingdom of swing / Pick-a-rib.
2LP: . . . . NL 89587
MC: . . . . NK 89587

INDISPENSABLE BENNY GOODMAN VOLS. 1/2 (1935-36) (Goodman, Benny & His Orchestra).
Tracks: / Blue skies / Dear old Southland / Sometimes I'm happy / King Porter stomp / Between the devil and the deep blue sea / Mad house / If I could be with you one hour tonight / When Buddha smiles / Stompin' at the Savoy / Breakin' in a pair of shoes / I hope Gabriel likes my music / Mutiny in the parlour / I'm gonna clap my hands / Swing is here / Get happy / Christopher Columbus / I know that you know / Stardust / You forgot to remember / House hop / I would do anything for you / I've found a new baby / Swingtime in the Rockies / Pick yourself up / Down south camp meeting / St. Louis blues / Love me or leave me / Bugle call rag (2 takes) / Organ grinder's swing / Riffin' at the Ritz / Somebody loves me.
2LP: . . . . NL 89755
MCSET: . . . . NK 89755

JAM.
Tracks: / I want to be happy / When you're smiling / Rachel's dream / Jam on the brakes / Sunny side of the streets / Rose room / Moonglow / Sing, sing, sing.
LP: . . . . SWH 37
MC: . . . . CSWH 37

JAM SESSION (Goodman, Benny, All Stars).
MCSET: . . . . DTO 10250

JAZZ CLASSICS IN DIGITAL STEREO (Benny Goodman 1934-1938).
Tracks: / Nitwit serenade / Music hall rag / Dear old Southland / Breakin' in a pair of shoes / Christopher Columbus / Bumble bee stomp / Smoke house / Farewell blues / Cokey / Blue skies / Mad house / Get happy / Bugle call rag / Topsy / My honey's lovin' arms.
LP: . . . . REB 759
MC: . . . . ZCF 759

JUMPIN' AT THE WOODSIDE (The alternate Goodman, Vol 1).
Tracks: / Jumpin' at The Woodside / There'll be some changes made / Stealin' apples / Comes love / Bolero blues / What's new? / Spring song / Night and day / Blue orchids / One sweet letter / Boy meets horn / I didn't know what time it was / Love never went to college / Scatterbrain / Down by the old mill stream.
LP: . . . . GOJ 1042
MC: . . . . GOJC 1042

KING OF SWING 1958-67.
Tracks: / September song / World is waiting for the sunrise, The / Bill Bailey, won't you please come home? / I want to be happy / Runnin' wild / Mission to Moscow / Clarinet a la King / King Porter stomp / Poor butterfly / World is waiting for the sunrise, The / Let's dance / I walk with you / Great day / Shadow of your smile / Airmail special / String of pearls / Avalon / It's alright with me / Whispering / Diga diga doo / After you've gone / Where or when / I got rhythm / These foolish things / That's a plenty / Slipped disc / I can't give you anything but love / Sheik of Araby, The / There'll be some changes made / I've found a new baby.
LP: . . . . MTM 020
LP: 66420
2LP: . . . . ALB 246

KING OF SWING (ACCORD).
MC: 300152

KING OF SWING (PICKWICK).
MC: . . . . HSC 3273

KING OF SWING, THE (ENTERTAINERS).
LP: . . . . ENT LP 13022
MC: . . . . ENT MC 13022

KING OF SWING, THE (GIANTS OF JAZZ).
LP: . . . . LPJT 34
LP: . . . . GOJ 1017

KING PORTER STOMP.
Tracks: / Someday, sweetheart / Mad house / Sandman / If I could be with you one hour tonight / When Buddha smiles / Hunkadola / I'm living in a great big way / Dixieland band / Japanese Sandman / You're a heavenly thing / Restless / Always / Ballad in Blue / Dear old Southland / Sometimes I'm Happy / King Porter stomp / Between the devil and the deep blue sea / After you've gone / Body and Soul.
LP: . . . . SVL 176
MC: . . . . CSVL 176

KING PORTER STOMP (DANCE BAND DAYS).
LP: . . . . DBD 02
MC: . . . . DBDC 02

KING PORTER STOMP, VOL. 1.
LP: . . . . SM 3971

LEGENDARY PERFORMER, A.
Tracks: / Don't be that way / One o'clock jump / Loch Lomond / After you've gone / Sing, sing, sing / Stompin' at the savoy / Goodnight my love / King Porter stomp / Avalon / And the angels sing / Bei mir bist du schon / Goodbye.
LP: . . . . PL 12470
MC: . . . . PK 12470

LET'S DANCE (Goodman, Benny & His Orchestra).
Tracks: / Blue Hawaii / Vieni, vieni / All of me / Yam, The / Moten swing / Clap hands, here comes Charlie / Sly mongoose / Hot foot shuffle / Hold tight / Hartford stomp / Trees / Begin the beguine / Let's dance / I know that you know.
LP: . . . . BLJ 8013
LP: . . . . MM 20112 Z
MC: . . . . MMC 40112 Y

LET'S DANCE (EMI (EUROPE)).
LP: . . . . 2 M 056 64869
MC: . . . . 2 M 256 64869

LIVE AT BASIN STREET (Benny Goodman vol 2).
Tracks: / Let's dance / Memories of you / Airmail special.
MC: . . . . CIJ 20156 F
LP: . . . . CIJ 40156 A

LIVE AT CARNEGIE HALL (40th Anniversary concert).
Tracks: / Let's dance / I've found a new baby / Send in the clowns / Loch Lomond / Stardust / I love a piano / Roll 'em / King Porter stomp / Rocky raccoon / Yesterday / That's a plenty / How high the moon / Moonglow / Oh lady be good / Jersey bounce / Someone to watch over me / Please don't talk about me when I'm gone / Benny Goodman Medley / Sing, sing, sing and Christopher Columbus / Goodbye.
2LP: 4509831
MCSET: 4509834
MCSET: . . . . KDBC 3/4
2LP: . . . . DBC 3/4

LIVE AT THE INTERNATIONAL WORLD EXHIBITION (Brussels 1958: Unissued Recordings) (Goodman, Benny & His Orchestra).
Tracks: / Let's dance / When you're smiling / Sent for you yesterday (and here you come today) / Pennies from Heaven / Goin' to Chicago / Soon / Who cares / Deed I do / I hadn't anyone till you / I've got you under my skin / There no fool like an old fool / Sometimes I'm happy / Oh boy I'm lucky / Song is ended, The / I'm coming Virginia / Fine romance, A / Harvard blues / If I had you / Goodbye theme.
LP: . . . . AWE 36
MC: . . . . CAWE 36

LONDON DATE.
LP: . . . . SON 011

MANHATTAN MEMORIES.
MC: . . . . SLC 61095

MEMORIAL.
LP: . . . . AWE 23
MC: . . . . CAWE 23

MEMORIES OF THE SIXTIES (Goodman, Benny & His Orchestra).
Tracks: / You've made me so very happy / Romeo and Juliet love theme / Good morning, starshine / I'll never fall in love again / Both sides now / Watch what happens / Monday, Monday / Bluesette / Aquarius / Up, up and away / Spinning wheel / Windy.
LP: . . . . BDL 1038
MC: . . . . AJKL 1038

MORE OF THE FABULOUS FIFTIES.
LP: . . . . GOJ 1011

NIGHT WITH BENNY GOODMAN, A.
Tracks: / Blue skies / With all my heart / Walk, Jenny, walk / Rosetta / Bugle call rag / Thanks a million / Truckin' / Alamo, The / Eeny meeny miney mo / Mad house.
LP: . . . . BLJ 8026

O'CLOCK JUMP Vol. 2.
LP: . . . . SM 3972

OH MR GOODMAN.
LP: . . . . SWH 3
MC: . . . . CSWH 3

ORCHESTRA AND GROUPS.
LP: . . . . RARITIES 21

ORCHESTRAS AND GROUPS (2).
Tracks: / Poor butterfly / Avalon / It's alright with me / Whispering / Diga diga doo / Where or when / I got rhythm / These foolish things / That's a plenty / Slipped disc / After you've gone / Body and soul / China boy / I can't give you anything but love / Sheik of Araby, The / There'll be some changes made / I've found a new baby.
LP: . . . . RARITIES 30

ORIGINAL SOUNDS OF THE SWING ERA VOL.6.
LP: . . . . CL 05515
LP: 26 28130

PERMANENT GOODMAN, THE (Portrait of music 1926-45).
LPS: . . . . NOST 7659-61

RARE BROADCASTING TRANSCRIPTIONS, 1935 (Goodman, Benny & His Orchestra).
Tracks: / I know that you know / Changes / Yes, we have no bananas / I never knew / Stompin' at The Savoy / Farewell blues / Pardon my love / St. Louis blues / Jingle bells / Rosetta / King Porter stomp / Stardust / If I could be with you / Poor butterfly.
LP: . . . . JA 5151

REHEARSAL SESSIONS 1940.
LP: . . . . VA 7997

RIFFIN' AT THE RITZ (Goodman, Benny & His Orchestra).
Tracks: / St. Louis blues / Love me or leave me / Moon glow / Dinah / Exactly like you / Vibraphone blues / When a lady meets a gentleman down south / You're giving me a song and a dance / Organ grinder's swing / Peter Piper / Riffin' at the Ritz / Alexander's ragtime band / Somebody loves me / Tain't no use / Bugle call rag / Jam session / Goodnight my love / Take another guess / Did you mean it? / Sweet Sue, just you.
LP: . . . . SVL 203
MC: . . . . CSVL 203

ROLL 'EM (Goodman, Benny/Sid Catlett).
2LP: . . . . HR 5004/5

ROLL 'EM (Goodman, Benny, All Stars).
Tracks: / Airmail special / Don't be that way / Between the devil and the deep blue sea / Flying home / Roll 'em boogie.
LP: . . . . SWH 7
MC: . . . . CSWH 7

ROLL 'EM VOL.1.
LP: 4600621
MC: 4600624

ROYAL FLUSH (ASTAN).
LP: 20085
MC: 40085

SECOND CARNEGIE HALL JAZZ CONCERT 6 OCTOBER 1939.
LP: . . . . EB 401

SELECTET (Goodman, Benny(Quintet & Sextet)).
LP: . . . . SWH 17

SESSION (Goodman, Benny, All Stars).
Tracks: / Go, Margot, go / Get happy / Raising the riff / Billie's bounce / Ten-bone / Honeysuckle rose / Slipped disc / Breakfast feud.
LP: . . . . SWH 24
MC: . . . . CSWH 24

SEXTET.
LP: 4504111
MC: 4504114

SING ME A SWING SONG.
Tracks: / You forgot to remember / Walk, Jennie, walk / China boy / More than you know / All my life / Oh, lady be good / Nobody's sweetheart / Too good to be true / Sing me a swingsong (and let me dance) / I would do anything for you / These foolish things / In a sentimental mood / I've found a new baby / Swingtime in the Rockies / House hop / There's a small hotel / You turned the tables on me / Here's love in your eyes / Pick yourself up / Down South camp meeting.
LP: . . . . **SVL 192**
MC: . . . . **CSVL 192**

SLIPPED DISC.
LP: **4633371**
MC: **4633374**

SMALL GROUPS 1941/45.
LP: **4633411**
MC: **4633414**

SMALL GROUPS (1947-49).
LP: . . . . **S 1364**

SMALL GROUPS, VOLUME 1.
Tracks: / Softly as in a morning sunrise / Umbrella man / I've found a new baby / Deep purple / Exactly like you / Pagan love song / Opus 3-4 / Chicago / Lady be good / Old-fashioned love / Memories of you / Wishing.
LP: . . . . **GOJ 1034**

SO RARE (Goodman, Benny & Tommy Dorsey).
LP: . . . . **JA 49**

STARS FELL ON ALABAMA (Goodman, Benny & Orchestra).
2LP: . . . . **SVLD 005**
MC: . . . . **CSVLD 005**

STOMPIN' AT THE SAVOY.
LP: . . . . **JJ 609**

SWING WITH BENNY GOODMAN AND HIS ORCHESTRA.
LP: **21124**
MC: **40 21124**

SWINGIN' THROUGH THE YEARS.
LP: . . . . **GOJ 1005**
MC: . . . . **GOJC 1005**

S'WONDERFUL SWING.
Tracks: / Seven come eleven / Great day / Lonely moments / Oh baby / Moon-faced and starry-eyed / Cu-tu-gu-ru / 'S wonderful / Linda / Clarinet a la King / Maybe you'll be there / Mahzel / Sing, sing, sing.
LP: . . . . **FH 23**
MC: . . . . **CFH 23**

THIS IS BENNY GOODMAN.
Tracks: / King Porter stomp / Sometimes I'm happy / When Buddha smiles / Stompin' at the Savoy / I know that you know / These foolish things / Down South camp meeting / You turned the tables on me / Moonglow / Goodnight my love / Never should have told you / Sing, sing, sing / Changes / Afraid to dream / Avalon / Sugarfoot Stomp / Don't be that way / One o'clock jump / I let a song go out of my heart / And the Angels sing.
2LP: . . . . **NL 89224**
MC: . . . . **NK 89224**

THIS IS BENNY GOODMAN VOL 1.
2LP: **26 28035**

THIS IS BENNY GOODMAN VOL 2.
2LP: **26 28040**

TOGETHER AGAIN (Quartet reunion).
Tracks: / Who cares / Dearest / Seven come eleven / I've found a new baby / Somebody loves me / I'll get by / Say it isn't so / Runnin' wild / I got it bad and that ain't good / Four once more.
LP: . . . . **NL 89304**
MC: . . . . **NK 89304**

UNFORGETTABLE BENNY GOODMAN.
LP: . . . . **UNLP 018**
MC: . . . . **UNMC 018**

UNHEARD BENNY GOODMAN, THE - VOL.9, 1947-1955.
LP: . . . . **T 1016**

UNHEARD BENNY GOODMAN, THE - VOL.8, 1936-1955.
LP: . . . . **T 1015**

UNHEARD BENNY GOODMAN, THE - VOL.7, 1941-1942.
LP: . . . . **T 1014**

UNISSUED RADIO MATERIAL (1943) (Goodman, Benny & His Orchestra).
Tracks: / Sugar foot stomp / Sweet Georgia Brown / Mission to Moscow / You're driving me crazy / Henderson stomp / Do nothing till you hear from me / Lady be good / Don't be that way / Stealin' apples / I'm just wild about Harry / Minnie's in the money / I'm here / Honeysuckle rose / Seven come eleven.
LP: . . . . **QU 042**

V DISCS 1943/44.
LP: . . . . **AA 509**

WAR YEARS, 1943/44/45.
Tracks: / Stealin' apples / After you've gone / Three little words / Minnie's in the money / I've found a new baby / Mission to Moscow / Mr. Five by five / Gotta be this or that / Seven come eleven / Frenesi / Every time / Downhearted blues / Airmail special / World is waiting for the sunrise, The.
LP: . . . . **JA 5226**

WAR YEARS, THE (1942-45).
LP: . . . . **AA 510**

WHEN BUDDHA SMILES.
Tracks: / Music Hall rag / Always / Blue skies / Down home rag / Ballad in blue / Devil and the deep blue sea / Mad house / Down South Camp meeting / Can't we be friends / Sugarfoot stomp / Big John special / Jumpin' at the woodside / Night and day / Board meeting / When Buddha smiles / Take another guess / Roll 'em / Don't be that way / Wrappin' it up / Stealin' apples / Honeysuckle rose / Zaggin' with zig.
LP: . . . . **AJA 5071**
MC: . . . . **ZC AJA 5071**

Goodman, Jerry

ARIEL.
Tracks: / Going on 17 / Tears of joy / Lullaby for Joey / Topanga waltz / Broque / Rockers / Once only.
LP: **209.961**
MC: **409.961**

IT'S ALIVE.
Tracks: / Goin' on / Tears of joy / Too cool / Endless / November / Topanga waltz / I hate you / Orangutango / Outcast islands / Heart's highway / Perry Mason (theme from).
LP: **209642**
MC: **409642**

LIKE CHILDREN (See under Hammer, Jan) (Goodman, Jerry & Jan Hammer).

ON THE FUTURE OF AVIATION.
Tracks: / On the future of aviation / Endless November / Outcast islands / Orangutango / Waltz of the windmills / Sarah's lullaby.
LP: **209.958**
MC: **409.958**

Goodman, Steve

SAY IT IN PRIVATE.
Tracks: / I'm attracted to you / You're the girl I love / Video tape / There's a girl in the heart of Maryland / Two lovers / Is it true what they say about Dixie / Weary blues from waitin' / Daley's gone / My old man / Twentieth century is almost over, The.
LP: . . . . **K 53067**

WORDS WE CAN DANCE TO.
Tracks: / Roving cowboy / Tossin' and turnin' unemployed / Between the lines / Old fashioned / Can't go back / Banana republic / Death of a salesman / That's what friends are for / Story of love.
LP: . . . . **K 53038**

Goodnight Stories (bk)

GOODNIGHT STORIES.
MCSET: . . . . **DTO 10505**

Goodrum, Randy

SOLITARY NIGHTS.
Tracks: / It's like you never left at all / Software / Mr. Sandman / Holdin' out for love / Silhouette / Dolph / Solitary nights / Lady in the doorway, The / Little Bird / So soft your goodbye.
LP: . . . . **GRP 91019**
MC: . . . . **C 1019**

Goodson, Ida

IDA GOODSON SINGS AND PLAYS CHURCH MUSIC FROM THE SOUTH.
LP: . . . . **CLPS 1015**

Goodwin, Jim

JIM GOODWIN AND FRIENDS.
LP: . . . . **BR 4**

Goodwin, Ken

MAKE SOMEONE HAPPY.
Tracks: / Ukelele man / Keep your heart / Sweet little headache / April love / Say it every day / Sweet lady.
LP: . . . . **PRX 15**
MC: . . . . **TC PRX 15**

MERRY CHRISTMAS, DARLING.
Tracks: / Merry Christmas, darling / Round and round the Christmas tree / Secret of Christmas, The / And the bells rang / Littlest angel, The / We wish you a merry Christmas / When a child is born / We wish you the merriest / White Christmas / Story of Christmas, The / Settle down / Thank you for loving me.
LP: . . . . **PRX 11**

Goodwin, Mabel

"JAN STEWER" RECITATIONS.
MC: **30-413**

Goodwin, Myles

MYLES GOODWIN.
Tracks: / Veil of tears / Do you know what I mean / Caviar / Sonya / Head on / Face the storm / Frank Sinatra can't sing / Giving it up (for your love) / Are you still loving me / Mama won't say (it's good).
LP: . . . . **K 781 821 1**
MC: . . . . **K 781 821 4**

Goodwin, Ron

ADVENTURE AND EXCITEMENT (Goodwin, Ron & His Orchestra).
Tracks: / Adventures Of Black Beauty, Theme from / Battle Of Britain / Trap / Lawrence of Arabia / First of the few, The / Ben Hur / Big Country, The / Magnificent seven, The / Headless horseman / Lara's theme / Music of Richard Rodgers / Carousel waltz (From Oklahoma) / Oklahoma / Galloping Home (Theme from - The adventures of Black Beauty -) / Those magnificent men in their flying machines / Luftwaffe march / 633 Squadron / Lancelot and Guinevere / Where eagles dare, Theme from / Monte Carlo Or Bust.
LP: . . . . **EMS 1244**
MC: . . . . **TCEMS 1244**

CHRISTMAS WONDERLAND (Goodwin, Ron & His Orchestra).
Tracks: / White Christmas / Rudolph the red nosed reindeer / Silent night / Sleigh ride / Little donkey / Have yourself a merry little Christmas / Carol of the drum / Jingle bells / Mary's boy child / Winter wonderland / Brahms' lullaby / Christmas tree / Carols medley.
LP: . . . . **ED 2607281**
MC: . . . . **ED 2607284**

DRAKE 400 (CONCERT SUITE).
Tracks: / Prelude from beauty and the beast / Candleshoe / Festival time / Amazing grace / Force 10 from Navarone / Minuet in blue / Spaceman and King Arthur, The / Girl with misty eyes, The / Auld lang syne.
LP: . . . . **LBRD 001**
MC: . . . . **LBTD 001**

FIRE AND ROMANCE (Goodwin, Ron & His Orchestra).
Tracks: / Baby elephant walk / Days of wine and roses / Charade / Moon river / Dream of Olwen / Operation crossbow (theme) / Elizabethan serenade / Intermezzo / Prelude / Love theme / Parade of the charioteers / Cornish rhapsody / Miss Marple's theme / Song of the high seas / Zorba's dance / She loves you / Eleanor Rigby / Yesterday / All my loving / Hey, Jude / E.T., Theme from / Skyliner / Bilitis / High noon / Marie / (Po atarau) now is the hour.
MC: . . . . **TCEMS 1320**

LEGEND OF THE GLASS MOUNTAIN (Goodwin, Ron & His Orchestra).
Tracks: / Legend of the glass mountain / Dream of Olwen / Intermezzo from escape to happiness / Way to the stars, Theme from / Warsaw concerto / Spitfire prelude and fugue / Limelight / Rhapsody on a theme by Paganini / Moulin Rouge / Cornish rhapsody.
LP: . . . . **THIS 25**
MC: . . . . **TCTHIS 25**
LP: . . . . **TWO 220**

LOVE ALBUM, THE.
LP: **41 5709 1**
MC: **41 5709 4**

MY KIND OF MUSIC (Goodwin, Ron & Bournemouth Symphony Orch).
Tracks: / Trap, The (London marathon theme) / Here where you are / Kojak / Hill Street Blues / Star Trek / Dynasty / Dallas / Here's that rainy day / Tribute to Miklos Rosza, A / Ben Hur (Love theme) / Red house, The / Four feathers, The / Parade of the Charioteers / Trolley song / Zip a dee doo dah / Someday my prince will come / I wanna be like you / Little April shower / When you wish up on a star / Caravan - the girl from Corsica / Stephen Foster tribute / Oh Susanna / Swannee River / Beautiful dreamer / Camptown races / Drake 400 suite / Battle finale.
LP: . . . . **LBRD 025**
MC: . . . . **LBTD 025**

PROJECTIONS (Goodwin, Ron with Royal Philharmonic Orchestra).
Tracks: / Memories of Ingrid Bergman / E.T., Theme from / High noon / Bilitis / Chariots of fire / On golden pond / Clash of loyalties / It can't be wrong / Zorba's dance.
LP: . . . . **EMS 197 7691**

RON GOODWIN AND BOURNEMOUTH S.O..
Tracks: / Drake 400 suite / Prelude from 'Beauty and the beast' / Festival Time / Candleshoe / Amazing grace / Force 10 from Navarone / Minuet in blue / Spaceman and King Arthur / Girl with the misty eyes / Auld lang syne.
LP: . . . . **ABRD 1014**

RON GOODWIN CONDUCTS THE NEW ZEALAND SYMPHONY OR (Goodwin, Ron & The New Zealand Symphony Orchestra).
Tracks: / Carnival / Sophisticated lady / Skyliner / Moonlight serenade / Marie / Begin the beguine / Aotearoa (land of the long white cloud) / Milford Sound / Picnic at Rotorua / Earsnslaw steam theme / A and P Show, The / Po atarau (Now is the hour).
LP: . . . . **EJ 2601721**
MC: . . . . **EJ 2601724**

RON GOODWIN PLAYS BACHARACH AND DAVID.
Tracks: / This guy's in love with you / I'll never fall in love again / Wives and lovers / One less bell to answer / Look of love, The / I say a little prayer / Raindrops keep falling on my head / What the world needs now is love / Do you know the way to San Jose? / Alfie / Close to you / Walk on by.
MC: . . . . **E 2600924**

SOUNDS SUPERB (Goodwin, Ron & His Orchestra).
Tracks: / 633 Squadron / Elizabethan serenade / Clair de lune / Song of the high seas / Trap / Those magnificent men in their flying machines / Limelight / London serenade / Sunrise serenade / Girl with a dream / Under the linden tree / Girl from Corsica / Headless horseman / Of human bondage / Miss Marple theme / Operation Crossbow / March from serenade for strings / Romanoff and Juliet / Prairie serenade / Waltz serenade / India / Puppet serenade / Elizabeth and Essex love theme / Serenade to a double scotch.
2LP: . . . . **MFP 1025**

Goofus Five

GOOFUS FIVE 1924-5, THE.
LP: . . . . **FJ 118**

Goombay Dance Band

BORN TO WIN.
Tracks: / Santorini goodbye / Take me down to the Caribbean / Little blue canary / Caribbean dreams / Carry the load / Golden veil / Jericho / Tel Aviv / If you ever fall in love / Slavery / Song for tomorrow.
LP: . . . . **EPC 25077**

GOOMBAY DANCE BAND.
Tracks: / Seven tears / Sun of Jamaica / Rain / We'll ride the waves together.
MC: . . . . **EPC A 40 2624**

SEVEN TEARS.
Tracks: / Seven tears / Cherokee / Rain / Child of the sun / Under the sun, moon and stars / Guantanamera / My bonny / Marrakesh / Magician / Eldorado / Ave Maria / Montezume / We'll ride the wave together / Sun of Jamaica.
LP: . . . . **EPC 85702**

SUN OF JAMAICA.
Tracks: / Sun of Jamaica / Under the sun, moon and stars / Land ho / Child of the sun / Fly flamingo / Eldorado / Rain / King of Peru / Alicia / Day after day / Paradise of joy / Aloha-oe / Until we meet again.
LP: . . . . **EPC 84951**

Goonies (film)

GOONIES (Film Soundtrack) (Various artists).
Tracks: / Goonies 'r' good enough: *Lauper, Cyndi* / Eight arms to hold you: *Good Squad* / Love is always: *Bailey, Philip* / I got nothing: *Bangles* / 14K: *Marie, Teena* / Wherever you're goin' (it's alright): *REO Speedwagon*/ She's so good to me: *Vandross, Luther* / What a thrill: *Lauper, Cyndi* / Save the night: *Williams, Joseph*/ Goonies: *Grusin, Dave.*
LP: . . . . **EPC 70264**
MC: **40 70264**

Goons

BEST OF THE GOON SHOWS VOL.2.
LP: . . . . **PMC 1129**

BEST OF THE GOON SHOWS VOL. 1.
Tracks: / Missing No 10 Downing Street, The / Red fort, The.
LP: . . . . **EMC 3062**
MC: . . . . **TCEMC 3062**
LP: . . . . **PMC 1108**

DARK SIDE OF THE GOONS.
Tracks: / Boiled bananas and carrots / Any old iron / You gotta go now / Will I find my lover today? / Heart of a clown / Fuller's earth / Faith can move mountains / Wormwood Scrubs tango / One love, one lifetime / My September love / Wish I knew / My old dutch / Putting on the smile / I'll make you mine / Postman's knock / Drop of the hard stuff / I'm so ashamed / Here is my heart.
LP: . . . . **OU 2232**
MC: . . . . **TC OU 2232**

FIRST MEN ON THE GOON.

Tracks: / Foiled by president Fred / Robin Hood and his merry men.
LP: NTS 170
MC: TCNTS 170

GOON SHOW CLASSICS (Volume 5).
MCSET: ZBBC 1133

GOON SHOW CLASSICS (Volume 2).
MCSET: ZBBC 1016

GOON SHOW CLASSICS (Volume 1).
MCSET: ZBBC 1007

GOON SHOW CLASSICS (Volume 4).
MCSET: ZBBC 1048

GOON SHOW CLASSICS (Volume 3).
MCSET: ZBBC 1047

GOON SHOW CLASSICS, VOL 1.
Tracks: / Dreaded batter pudding hurler of Bexhill-on-Sea, The / History of Pliny the Elder, The.
LP: REB 177
MC: RMC 4010

GOON SHOW CLASSICS, VOL 2.
Tracks: / Jet-propelled guided NAAFI, The / Evils of Bushey Spon, The.
LP: REB 213
MC: RMC 4026

GOON SHOW CLASSICS, VOL 3.
Tracks: / Lurgi strikes Britain / International Christmas pudding, The.
LP: REB 246
MC: RMC 4046

GOON SHOW CLASSICS, VOL 4.
Tracks: / Napoleon's piano / Flea, The.
LP: REB 291
MC: ZCF 291

GOON SHOW CLASSICS, VOL 5.
Tracks: / Treasure in the lake, The / Greenslade story, The.
LP: REB 339
MC: ZCF 339

GOON SHOW CLASSICS, VOL 6.
Tracks: / Wings over Dagenham / Rent collectors, The.
LP: REB 366
MC: ZCF 366

GOON SHOW CLASSICS, VOL 7.
Tracks: / Man who never was, The / Case of the missing CD plates, The.
LP: REB 392
MC: ZCF 392

GOON SHOW CLASSICS, VOL 8.
Tracks: / World War 1 / Nasty affair at the Burami oasis.
LP: REB 422
MC: ZCF 422

GOON SHOW CLASSICS, VOL 9.
Tracks: / Call of the West / Last smoking Seagoon, The.
MC: ZCF 444
LP: REB 444

GOON SHOW CLASSICS, VOL 10.
Tracks: / Whistling spy enigma, The / I was Monty's treble.
LP: REB 481
MC: ZCF 481

GOON SHOW CLASSICS, VOL 11.
Tracks: / Shifting sands / 1985.
LP: REB 565
MC: ZCF 565

GOON SHOW GREATS.
Tracks: / Tales of old Dartmoor / Dishonoured (Parts 1 and 2) / Six Charlies in search of an author.
MC: TCPMC 7179
LP: PMC 7179

GOON SHOW, THE.
Tracks: / White man burden / China story.
LP: MFP 415650-1
MC: TCMFP 415650-4

GOON SHOWS, THE (see under EMI Comedy Classics).

HOW TO WIN AN ELECTION.
LP: AL 3464

LAST GOON SHOW OF ALL.
LP: REB 142
MC: REMC 142

Goose Girl

GOOSE GIRL, THE (well loved tales age up to 9) (Unknown narrator(s)).
MC: PLB 130

Gorby, Sarah

INDOUBLIABLES CHANTS DU GHETTO DE SARAH GORBY.
Tracks: / Rifkale / S'brent bridelecht / Moide ani / Kinderlech / Dain mame kimt nit zurich / Geien sei in shvarze raien / Dos ingele igt farbrent / Mach she daine eigalech tzu.
LP: ARN 34357

RUSSUE ETERNELLE (Russian and gypsy songs) (Gorby, Sarah & Orchestra).
Tracks: / Poi Poi / Vidou v polie / Ogonki daliokie / Dva Boitza / Tcudo, Tcudesa / Ne govorite mne o niom / Jizn tziganskaia / Rouki / Kalinka / Menia ti vovse ne lioubila / Toska po rodine / Govoriat, Govoriat.
LP: ARN 33185

Gord, Gerry

WITH LOVE.
Tracks: / With love / Other side of the morning / Funny face / In crowd, The / If you've got ten minutes / Country music will live on / Once in a lifetime thing / What's really on your mind / Somebody loves you honey / Memory before my time / What will you do / Another blue day.
LP: GES 5017

Gordon, Curtis

ROCK ROLL JUMP AND JIVE.
Tracks: / Draggin' / Rock roll jump and jive / I'm sitting on top of the world / Mobile Alabama / Cry cry / Sixteen / Please baby please / I wouldn't / Play the music louder / Baby please come home / So tired of crying / Too young to know / Out to win your heart / One blue moon one broken heart / Don't trade / Hey Mr. Sorrow.
LP: BFX 15181

YOU AIN'T SEEN NOTHING YET.
Tracks: / Rompin' and stompin' / Caffeine and nicotine / Baby, baby me / Tell 'em no / Divided heart / Little Bo Peep / I'd like to tell you / You crazy, crazy moon / I'd do it for you / You ain't seen nothing yet / If you tell me one more lie / Greatest sin, The / Rocky road of love / What's a little pride / Where'd ja get so much of / I just don't love you anymore.
LP: BFX 15238

Gordon, Dagger

HIGHLAND MANDOLIN.
Tracks: / Hen's march / Archibald MacDonald of Keppoch / Ardross Hall (Medley.) / Song for Julie / Forbes Morrison / Prince Charlie's quickstep / Shandwick stone / Leaving Ardtornish / Cross Ross walk / Pipe Major Donald MacLean of Lewis / Inchindown jig / Grand pair of boots, The / Hunt for the septic / Round room / Sweep.
MC: DAG 1

Gordon, Dexter

AFTER MIDNIGHT (Film Soundtrack).
LP: SCS 1226

BEST OF DEXTER GORDON (Blue Note years).
Tracks: / It's you or no one / Society red / Smile / Cheesecake / Three o'clock in the morning / Soy califa / Don't explain / Tanya (CD only.).
LP: B1 91139
MC: B4 91139

BLUES AND BALLADS.
LP: SNTF 639

BLUES WALK.
Tracks: / Like someone in love / Body and soul / There will never be another you / Blues walk.
LP: BLP 30157

BOTH SIDES OF MIDNIGHT.
LP: BLP 60103

BOUNCIN' WITH DEX.
LP: SCS 1060

CHARLIE PARKER MEMORIAL (Gordon, Dexter & Lee Konitz).
Tracks: / Billie's bounce / Just friends / Scrapple from the apple / Summertime / Ornithology / Groovin' high / Yardbird suite / Now's the time / Parker's mood / Disappointed/Oh lady be good.
2LP: GCH 2-6026
MCSET: GCHK 2-6026

CHASE, THE.
Tracks: / Chase, The / Mischievous lady / Lullaby in rhythm / Horning in / Chromatic aberration / Talk of the town / Blues bikini / Ghost of a chance / Sweet and lovely / Duel.
LP: SPJ 130

CLUBHOUSE.
Tracks: / Hanky panky / I'm a fool to want you / Devilette / Clubhouse / Jodie / Lady Iris B.
LP: LBR 1022

DADDY PLAYS THE HORN.
Tracks: / Daddy plays the horn / Confirmation / Number four / Darn that dream / Autumn in New York / You can depend on me.
LP: AFF 103

DEXTER BLOWS HOT AND COLD.
Tracks: / Silver plated / Cry me a river / Rhythm mad / Don't worry 'bout me / I hear music / Bonna Rue / I should care / Blowin' for Dootsie / Tenderly.
LP: BOP 006

DEXTER GORDON QUARTET (Gordon, Dexter Quartet).
LP: ZET 705

DEXTER GORDON/KENNY DORHAM (See under Dorham, Kenny) (Gordon, Dexter & Kenny Dorham).

DEXTER: THE DIAL SESSIONS.
LP: SLP 814

DOIN' ALRIGHT.
Tracks: / I was doin' alright / You've changed / For regulars only / Society red / It's you or no one / For regulars only (alternate version) / I want more (Not on album.).
MC: 4BN 84077
LP: BST 84077
LP: BNS40014

FOR ALL WE KNOW.
LP: 2273232
MC: 2173232

GETTIN' AROUND.
Tracks: / Manha de carnaval / Who can I turn to? / Heartaches / Shiny stockings / Everybody's somebody's fool / Le coiffeur / Very saxily yours / Flick of a trick.
LP: BST 84204

GO.
Tracks: / Cheesecake / Guess I'll hang my tears out to dry / Second balcony jump / Love for sale / Where are you? / Three o'clock in the morning.
LP: BST 84112
MC: 4BN 84112
LP: BNS 40032

GOTHAM CITY.
Tracks: / Hi-fly / Nightingale sang in Berkeley Square, A / Blues walk / Gotham City.
LP: CBS 84825

GREAT ENCOUNTERS.
Tracks: / Blues up and down / Cake / Diggin in' / Ruby, my dear / It's only a paper moon.
LP: 83643

HUNT, THE (see Gray, Wardell) (Gordon, Dexter & Wardell Gray).

I WANT MORE.
LP: SCC 6015

LIVE AT THE AMSTERDAM PARADISO.
Tracks: / Fried bananas / What's new / Good bait / Rhythm-a-ning / Willow weep for me / Junior / Scrapple from the apple / Closing announcement / Introduction.
2LP: AFFD 27

LIVE: DEXTER GORDON AND SONNY GREY (With the Georges Arvanitas Trio) (Gordon, Dexter & Sonny Grey).
Tracks: / Caloon blues / Fried bananas / No matter how / Dexter leaps out.
LP: SPJ LP 10

LONG TALL DEXTER.
Tracks: / Blow Mr. Dexter / Dexter's deck / Dexter's cuttin' out / Dexter's minor mad / Long tall Dexter / Dexter rides again / I can't escape from you / Dexter digs in / Settin' the pace / So easy so easy / Dexter's riff / Dexter's mood / Dextrose index / Dextivity / Wee dot / Lion roars / After hours bop.
LP: SJL 2211

MANHATTAN SYMPHONIE.
Tracks: / As time goes by / Moment's notice / Tanya / Body and soul / LTD.
LP: CBS 83184

MONTMARTRE COLLECTION, VOL 1.
Tracks: / Sonnymoon for two / For all we know / Devilette / Doxy.
LP: BLP 30102

MORE THAN YOU KNOW.
LP: SCS 1030
MC: SCM 51030

MOVE.
Tracks: / Move / As time goes by / Stranger in town / Yardbird suite / Guilty / Mischievous lady / Lullaby in rhythm / Chromatic aberration / Talk of the town / Ghost of a chance / Sweet and lovely / Blues in Teddy's flat / Intersection / Mop mop / Stardust.
LP: SPJ 133

MPS JAZZ TIME VOL 12 (Gordon, Dexter & Slide Hampton).
Tracks: / My blues / You don't know what love is / New thing / What's new / Shadow of your smile / Day in Vienna, A.
LP: 5C 064 60411

NIGHTS AT THE KEYSTONE.
Tracks: / Sophisticated lady / It's you or no one / Antabus / Easy Living / Tangerine / More than you know / Come rain or come shine.
2LP: BST2 85112
MCSET: TCBST2 85112

ONE FLIGHT UP.
Tracks: / Tanya / Coppin' the haven / Darn that dream / King Neptune (CD only.).
LP: BST 84176

OTHER SIDE OF ROUND MIDNIGHT, THE.
Tracks: / Round midnight / Berangere's nightmare / Call sheet blues / What is this thing called love.. / Tivoli / Society red / As time goes by / It's only a paper moon.
LP: BST 85135

OUR MAN IN PARIS.
Tracks: / Scrapple from the apple / Willow weep for me / Stairway to the stars / Night in Tunisia / Our love is here to stay / Like someone to love / Broadway.
LP: BST 84146
MC: 4BN 84146

POWER.
Tracks: / Montmartre / Sticky wicket / Ladybird / Rainbow people / Stanley the steamer / Those were the days / Fried bananas / Meditaion / Boston Bernie.
2LP: PR 24087

ROUND MIDNIGHT (OST) (See under Gordon, Dexter).

SAVOY MASTER TAKES 1945-47.
Tracks: / Dexter's cuttin' out / Dexter's Minor Mad / Long tall Dexter / Dexter rides again / I can't escape from you / Dexter digs in / Settin' the pace / So easy / Dexter's riff / Dexter's mood / Dextrose / Index / Dextivity / Blow Mr. Dexter / Dexter's Deck.
LP: WL 70814
MC: WK 70814

SOMETHING DIFFERENT.
LP: SCS 1136

SOPHISTICATED GIANT.
Tracks: / Laura / Moontrane, The / Red top / Fried bananas / You're blase / How insensitive.
LP: 4503161
MC: 4503164

STRINGS AND THINGS.
LP: SCS 1145

SWINGIN' AFFAIR, A.
Tracks: / Soy Califas / Don't explain / You stepped out of a dream / Backbone, The / Until the real thing comes along, (It will have to do) / McSplivens.
LP: BST 84133

SWISS NIGHTS VOL.3.
LP: SCS 1110

TAKE THE A TRAIN.
Tracks: / But not for me / Take the A train / For all we know / Blues walk / I guess I'll have to hang my tears out to dry / Love for sale.
LP: BLP 60133

Gordon, Frank

CINEMA ORGAN ENCORES.
LP: DEROY 1372

Gordon, Hannah (nar)

ANIMALS OF FARTHING WOOD (See under Animals of Farthing...).

SECRET GARDEN, THE (see under Secret Garden).

Gordon, Harry

HARRY GORDON.
LP: SNECKY 1

Gordon Highlanders

GORDON HIGHLANDERS, THE.
LP: 6 21321

PRIDE O' THEM A', THE.
LP: DR 4
MC: CDR 4

Gordon, Jimmie

JIMMIE GORDON 1934-41.
LP: BD 2075

MISSISSIPPI MUDDER (1934-141).
LP: DLP 515

Gordon, Joe

CROOKIT BAWBEE (Gordon, Joe & Sally Logan).
Tracks: / Ballad of the slippy stone, The / Mother's love's a blessing, A / Old rustic bridge / My wee laddie / Two loves / Dumbarton's drums / Crooked bawbee / Spinning wheel / Auld meal mill, The / Road and the miles to Dundee, The / If you will marry me / Granny's heilan' hame.
LP: KLP 51
MC: ZCKLP 51

END OF A PERFECT DAY, THE (Gordon, Joe & Sally Logan).
Tracks: / Loves old sweet song / Beautiful Isle of somewhere / Old rugged cross, The / Until it's time for you to go / Memories / Heaven's just a sin away / Garden, The / You needed me / Mother of mine / Everybody wants to go to heaven / You're free to go / Keep on the sunny side.
LP: KLP 33
MC: ZCKLP 33

FAVOURITES (Gordon, Joe & Sally Logan).
Tracks: / Somebody else is taking my place / Silver threads among the gold / In the gloaming / My prayer / Will you always call me sweetheart / Words / Anniversary waltz / It's only a hole in the wall / If I had my way / If I could only make you care / Poor blind boy / Daddy's little girl.
LP: . . . . **KLP 27**
MC: . . . . **ZCKLP 27**

JOE GORDON & SALLY LOGAN (Gordon, Joe & Sally Logan).
Tracks: / Snowbird / Sunshine of your smile, The / Valley where the Leven flows, The / Silver threads among the gold / Ooor ain fireside / Don't ever leave me / Love is a beautiful song / We'd better bide a wee / Granny Fraser's flitting / House with the spire, The / Dreaming of home / Auld Scots sangs, The / I adore thee.
LP: . . . . **LILP 5032**

LOOKIN' GOOD.
LP: **1007 597**

MOONLIGHT AND ROSES (Gordon, Joe & Sally Logan).
Tracks: / Moonlight and roses / Whispering hope / My happiness / Old fashioned mother of mine / Island of dreams / When I leave the world behind / September song / My heart cries for you / Beautiful dreamer / Let the rest of the world go by / To him we're all the same / When you were sweet sixteen.
LP: . . . . **NA 106**
MC: . . . . **NC 106**

TOGETHER (Gordon, Joe & Sally Logan).
Tracks: / Where has all the love gone / I can wait until forever / Faraway land / Just out of reach / Why did you make me care / If I will marry me / Songs my mother used to sing / Bonnie Aberdeen / It is no secret / Dark Lochnagar / Bright shining light o' the moon, The / Ribbon of darkness.
LP: . . . . **LILP 5053**
MC: . . . . **LICS 5053**

Gordon, Michael

FEELING OF LOVE.
Tracks: / Nobody else but you / I don't wanna lose your love / Everything or nothing / Ready and waiting for you / You're the only one for me / Come around and give me your love / Magic feeling / What am I to say / Turn out the lights.
LP: . . . . **FADLP 006**
MC: . . . . **FADC 006**

MASTER PERFORMANCE VOL 1: THE PIANO OF MICHAEL GORDON.
Tracks: / Ballade pour Adeline / Concerto No. 1 for piano / Veronique / Yesterday / Bird of paradise / One summer day.
MC: . . . . **AIM 97**

Gordon, Peter

INNOCENT.
Tracks: / Day the devil comes to getcha / Romance / Double / That hat / St. Cecilia / Afternoon drive / Diamond Lane / Announcement / Psycho / Heaven.
LP: . . . . **FM 42098**
MC: . . . . **FMT 42098**

OTELLO.
MC: . . . . **A 150**

Gordon, Richard

DOCTOR AT LARGE (Nedwell, Robin).
MC: . . . . **CAB 004**

Gordon, Rob

COMPLETE CALEDONIAN BALL (Gordon, Rob & His Band).
Tracks: / Circassian circle / Brisk young lad / Byron strathspey / Saltire society reel / Hebridean weaving lilt / Johnnie Walker / Crammond Bridge / Silver star, The / Cumberland reel / New Scotia quadrille / Dundee whaler, The / Bannetstane, The / Lomond waltz / Angus reel, The / Belle of Bon Accord / Rab the ranter / C'est l'amour / Wind on Loch Fyne / Seton's ceilidh band / New petronella / Bonnie lass o' Bon Accord / Bank Street reel / Joe McDiarmid's jig / Broon's reel / Rothesay rant.
2LP: . . . . **LDDL 8005**
MCSET: . . . . **LDDC 8005**

FOURTH CALEDONIAN BALL (Gordon, Rob & His Band).
Tracks: / Ellwyns fairy glen / Neil Gows' farewell to whiskey / Polworth on the green / Pipers cave, The / Welcome to Queens cross / Cupar barn dance / Off she goes in the north / Heather hills / Mrs. Blairs jig / Seann truibhs willican / My dearie / Miss Laura Andrews / Miss Graham of inchbrakie / Reels of five / Jim McCabe / Jim Douglas / Maxwells rant / Lass of gowrie / Maggie Lauder / Waltz country dance / Come o'er the stream / Green grow the rushes-o / Laird of Cockpen, The / Sound the pibroch / Tribute to the borders / Daggs of graighouse / Shetland Boston, The / Farmers jamboree, The / Garry Strathspey / Jigtime polka, The / Teviot Brig / Queenie of Larkhill / Gowan hill / Margaret cooks fancy.
LP: . . . . **FE 029**

Gordon, Robert

ARE YOU GONNA BE THE ONE?.
Tracks: / Are you gonna be the one / She's not mine anymore / Someday, someway / Standing on the outside of her door / Look who's blue / Too fast to live, too young to die / Lover boy / Drivin' wheel / Take me back / But, but.
LP: . . . . **RCALP 5033**
MC: . . . . **RCAK 5033**

BAD BOY.
Tracks: / Sweet love on my mind / Worrying kind / Bad boy / Picture of you / Torture / Crazy man crazy / Born to lose / Nervous / Uptown / Is it wrong / Need you.
MC: . . . . **PK 13523**
LP: . . . . **PL 13523**

LIVE AT THE LONE STAR.
LP: . . . . **ROSE 173**
MC: . . . . **ROSE 173C**

ROCK BILLY BOOGIE.
Tracks: / Rock Billy boogie / Love my baby / I just found out / All by myself / Black slacks / Catman / It's only make believe / Wheel of fortune / Am I blue / Walk on by / I just met a memory / Blue Christmas.
LP: . . . . **PL 13294**

Gordon, Roscoe

BEST OF ROSCO GORDON: VOL 1.
Tracks: / Booted / Why do I love you baby / Throwing my money away / Ouch pretty baby / Saddled the cow and milked the horse / Two kinds of woman / New Orleans wimmen / Whiskey made me drunk / Don't have to worry 'bout you no more / Blues for my baby / No more doggin' / Are you gonna be the one / Just in from Texas / Miserable old feeling / Lucille (looking for my baby).
LP: . . . . **CH 26**

KEEP ON DIGGIN'.
Tracks: / Booted / Love you 'til the day I die / Rosco's boogie / Cold cold winter / What you got on your mind / Tomorrow may be too late / Hey fat girl / Wise to you baby / T-Model boogie / Three cent love / Keep on diggin' / Too many women / Bad dream / Girl to love, A / Dilly bop / Little bit of magic.
LP: . . . . **RB 103**

KEEP ON ROLLING.
LP: . . . . **REDITA 131**

LEGENDARY SUN PERFORMERS.
Tracks: / Let's get height / Real pretty mama / T-Model boogie / Doctor Blues / Just love me baby / Bop with me baby / Decorate the counter / Love for you baby / That's what you do to me / Tired of living / If you don't love me baby / Dream on baby / Do the bop Sally Jo.
LP: . . . . **CR 30133**

MEMPHIS MASTERS, THE.
Tracks: / She rocks me / Tell me, tell me baby / That gal of mine / So tired / Dime a dozen / Run to me baby / Kickin' the boogie / Rosco's boogie / Bye bye woman / New remedy for love, A / City woman / You can't treat me right / Cold cold winter / Ouch pretty baby.
LP: . . . . **CH 51**

NO MORE DOGGIN'.
Tracks: / No more doggin' / Just a little bit / What you do to me / Going home / Fool in love / Dapper dan / You keep me locked up / Surely i love you / Every night of the week / What i wouldn't do / Let em try / Sit right here / My chick / Jelly, jelly / New orleans l.a..
LP: . . . . **CRB 1044**

ROSCOE ROCKS AGAIN.
Tracks: / Chicken, The / Hello baby / Kansas City / I don't wanna die / I got so many women / Darling I really love you / Shoobie oobie / 3 o'clock blues.
LP: . . . . **JSP 1052**

Gordon, Roxy

CRAZY HORSE NEVER DIED.
LP: . . . . **SSAD 06**

Gordon, Steve

DANCE OF FLIES (Gordon, Steve & John Shanahan).
LP: . . . . **SFA 077**

Gordon, Vin

WAY OVER YONDER.
LP: . . . . **JGML 6042**

Gore

CRUEL PLACE, THE.
Tracks: / Breeding, The / Cruel place, The / Garden of evil / Death has come.
LP: . . . . **MD 7905**

HEART GORE.
LP: . . . . **EXACT 028**

MEAN MAN'S DREAM.
LP: . . . . **CALCLP 029**

Gore, Lesley

DER ERSTE TANZ.
Tracks: / Der erste tanz / Hab ich das verdient / Sieben girls / Little, little liebling / Goodbye, Tony / Musikant / Nur du ganz allein / So sind die boys alle.
LP: . . . . **BF 15264**

GOLDEN HITS: LESLEY GORE.
LP: **810370 1**
MC: **810370 4**

Gore, Martin L

COUNTERFEIT.
Tracks: / Compulsion / In a manner of speaking / Smile in the crowd / Gone / Never turn your back on mother earth / Motherless child.
MLP: . . . . **STUMM 67**
MC: . . . . **CSTUMM 67**

Gorehounds

HALLOWEEN EVERYWHERE.
LP: . . . . **THORN 003**

Gorilla Biscuits

START TODAY.
Tracks: / New direction / Degradation / Forgotten / Start today / First failure / Time flies / Stand still / Good intentions / Things we say / 2 sides / Competition / Cats and dogs.
MC: **086 103**

Gorillas In The Mist

GORILLAS IN THE MIST (Film soundtrack) (Various artists).
LP: . . . . **MCA 6255**
MC: . . . . **MCAC 6255**

Gorka, John

JACK'S CROWS.
Tracks: / Silence / Treasure Islands / Jack's crows / Houses in the fields / Mercy of the wheels, The / Good Semper fi / Where the bottles break / Night is a woman / I'm from New Jersey / My new neighbour / Ballad of Jamie Bee, The / You're on your way.
MC: **103092**

Gorky Park

GORKY PARK.
Tracks: / Bang / Try to find me / Hit me with the news / Sometimes at night / Peace in our time / My generation / Within your eyes / Child of the wind / Fortress / Danger.
LP: **838 628 1**
MC: **838 628 4**

Gorky Park (film)

GORKY PARK (Film Soundtrack) (Various artists).
Tracks: / Main title: *Various artists* / Following Kirwill: *Various artists* / Irina's theme: *Various artists*/ Following KGB: *Various artists* / Chase through the park: *Various artists* / Arkady and Irina: *Various artists*/ Faceless bodies: *Various artists* / Irina's chase: *Various artists* / Sable shed, The: *Various artists*/ Airport farewell: *Various artists* / Releasing the sables/ End title: *Various artists*.
LP: . . . . **TER 1086**
MC: . . . . **CTV 81206**

Gorl, Robert

NIGHTFUL OF TENSION.
LP: . . . . **STUMM 16**
MC: . . . . **CSTUMM 16**

Gorman, Michael

BONNIE KATE.
Tracks: / Gannon's slip-jig / Merry sisters, the / Farrel Gurney / Doctor Gilbert / Jolly Tinker / Miss McCloud's and variations / Barn dance / Polka mazurka / Varsoviana / Valeta lancers (five figures) / Talk about life, music, Sligo, Gannon etc. (Spoken word) / O'Dwyer's HP / Alphabic method of notation, the (Spoken word) / Types of dances (Spoken word) / Bonnie Kate (variations) / Tell her I am kid on the mountain.
MC: **60-077**

HER MANTLE SO GREEN (See under Barry, Margaret) (Gorman, Michael & Margaret Barry).

Gorman, Micheal

MOUNTAIN ROAD: IRISH REELS AND JIGS.
MC: **60-169**

Gorme, Eydie

COME IN FROM THE RAIN.
Tracks: / Since I fell for you / Breaking up is hard to do / You're nobody till somebody loves you / Come in from the rain / Send in the clowns / What'll I do / God bless the child / First time / Round midnight / But he was good for me.
LP: . . . . **PRCV 123**
MC: . . . . **TC PRCV 123**

EYDIE GORME VAMPS THE ROARING 20'S.
Tracks: / When the red, red robin comes bob, bob, bobbin' along / Who's sorry now? / Toot toot tootsie goodbye / My man / Singin' in the rain / Chicago / I wanna be loved by you / My buddy / Tiptoe through the tulips / Let's do it / Button up your overcoat / Back in your own back yard.
LP: . . . . **MOIR 103**
MC: . . . . **CMOIR 103**

GREATEST HITS: EYDIE GORME.
Tracks: / If he walked into my life / Amor / What did I have that I don't have / I wish you love / Sabor a mi / Blame it on the bossa nova / Softly, as I leave you / Mas amor / Matchmaker, matchmaker / Don't go to strangers.
LP: **32420**

I STILL BELIEVE IN LOVE (see Lawrence, Steve) (Gorme, Eydie & Steve Lawrence).

ON STAGE.
Tracks: / Taking a chance on love / Just one of those things / You turned the tables on me / But not for me / Get out of town / Alright, OK you win / I got lost in his arms / Better luck next time / I'm in luck / I'm shooting high / You're getting to be a habit with me / One for my baby.
LP: . . . . **JASM 1509**

OUR LOVE IS HERE TO STAY (Gorme, Eydie & Steve Lawrence).
Tracks: / Rhapsody in blue / Fascinating rhythm / I got rhythm / Foggy day, A / Looking for a boy / Somebody loves me / Oh lady be good / How long has this been going on / Love walked in / Soon / They can't take that away from me / Let's call the whole thing off / It ain't necessarily so / Mine / Do-do-do / Please do it again / I've got a crush on you / Embraceable you / Someone to watch over me / Summertime / Bess, you is my woman now / I love you Porgy / American in Paris, An / Tra-la-la / Nice work if you can get it / 'S wonderful / Man I love, The / Bidin' my time / They all laughed / But not for me / Who cares? / Love is sweeping the country / Of thee I sing / Fidgety feet / Isn't it a pity / He loves and she loves / For you, for me, for evermore / Love is here to stay.
2LP: . . . . **UAD 60141/2**

SINGS SHOW STOPPERS.
Tracks: / Johnny One Note / I Don't Care / You're Just In Love / My Funny Valentine / You Can't get a man with a gun / Always True To You In My Fashion / Guys And Dolls / I can't say no / Hello Young Lovers / Thou swell / I'm Gonna wash That Man Right Out Of My hair / Baubles, bangles and beads.
LP: . . . . **MOIR 121**
MC: . . . . **CMOIR 106**

TOMAME O DEJAME.
Tracks: / Sabras que te quiero / Dime / Esta tarde vi llover / Erus tu / Sgae / Quiereme mucho / Tomame o dejame / Muy amigos / Hay muy pocos / Te sigo amamndo / Si vuelves tu.
LP: . . . . **PRCV 128**

Gornack Bros

REFUND.
Tracks: / God bless the medicine man / Marm / Judas / When love kills / Two black swans / Still / Three living meet the three dead, the / I want to live / Devil rides a harpt / Love you hide away, The / You don't have to know / I'm not gonna be yours.
LP: . . . . **SBR 15LP**

Gorp

WILD WALK SIDEWAYS.
LP: . . . . **PLATTER 001**

Gosdin, Vern

THERE IS A SEASON.
Tracks: / Turn, turn, turn (to everything there is a season) / Love me right to the end / How can I believe you (when you'll be leaving me)? / Slow-healing heart / I can tell by the way you dance / What would your memories do? / Slow-burning memory / Dead from the heart on down / Stone-cold heart / I've got a heart full of you.
LP: . . . . **CLTLP 352**
MC: . . . . **ZCCLT 352**

Gosling, Paula

MONKEY PUZZLE (Fairman, Blain (nar)).

MC: IAB 88082

Gospel..

18 REQUESTED GOSPEL SONGS (Various artists).
MC: CHRL 177
LP: HRL 177

20 GOSPEL GREATS (Various artists).
LP: DROP 1017
MC: CROP 1017

20 GOSPEL SONGS (Various artists).
Tracks: / Where the soul never dies: *Bell, Crawford* / Upper room, The: *Locklin, Hank* / It is no secret: *Wells, Tracy* / Holy Bible: *Lynam, Ray* / Royal telephone: *McFarland, Billy* / I love you Jesus: *Wells, Tracy*/ Three rusty nails: *Abraham, Ivan* / One day at a time: *Wells, Tracy* / In the garden: *Bell, Crawford*/ I'm using my bible for a road map: *Greer, John* / Soft and tenderly: *Bell, Crawford* / Last look at Momma: *Locklin, Hank* / How great thou art: *Kelley* / Dear God: *Duncan, Hugo* / Old rugged cross, The: *McFarland, Billy*/ Family Bible: *Margo* / If Jesus came to your house: *Abraham, Ivan* / What a friend we have in mother: *Breen, Ann* / Precious memories: *Bell, Crawford* / Dust on the Bible: *Greer, John*.
MC: CHRL 214

20 GOSPEL SONGS FROM N. IRELAND (Various artists).
Tracks: / What a friend we have in Jesus: *Greer, John* / Old account, The: *Nabney, Joe* / One day at a time: *Leon*/ Dust on mother's Bible: *Anderson, Jim* / Kneel at the cross: *Harbour Lights* / Whispering hope: *Greer, John*/ On a tree at Calvary: *Abraham, Ivan* / In my heart there is a melody: *Nabney, Joe* / Mother of a wandering boy: *Bell, Crawford* / On a tree at Calvary: *Abraham, Ivan* / Whispering hope: *Greer, John* / In my heart there is a melody: *Nabney, Joe* / Mother of a wandering boy: *Bell, Crawford* / His banner over me is love: *Bell* Sisters / Just a closer walk with thee: *Wells, Tracy* / Turn your radio on: *Harbour Lights* / He the pearly gates will open: *Wright, Jim* / Mama sang a song: *Bell, Crawford* / Pull for the shore: *Nabney, Joe* / Trouble in amen corner: *Greer, John* / Spring of living waters: *Harbour Lights* / Life's railway to Heaven: *Wells, Tracy* / Over the deadline: *Wright, Jim* / Stone was rolled away, The: *Abraham, Ivan*.
MC: CHRL 216

ALL MY APPOINTED TIME (Various artists).
Tracks: / Standing by the bedside of a neighbour: *Acapella Gospel Golden Gate Quartet* (Full title of group: Forty Years Of Acappella Gospel Golden Gate Quartet) / Listen to the lambs: *Acapella Gospel Golden Gate Quartet* (Full title of group: Forty Years Of Acappella Gospel Golden Gate Quartet) / Precious Lord: *Kings Of Harmony* / God shall wipe all tears away: *Kings Of Harmony* / I'm bound for Canaan land: *Blue Jay Singers* / Standing out on the highway: *Blue Jay Singers*/ Well well well: *Soul Stirrers* / I'm gonna tell God: *Soul Stirrers* / Here I am, do Lord send me: *Peach, Georgia &* the Harmonaires / Where the sun will never go down: *Peach, Georgia & the Harmonaires* / Lord will make a way, The: *Griffin, Bessie* / Any stars in my crown: *Golden Harps* / I'll make it somehow: *Golden Harps*/ They led my Lord away: *Williams, Marion* / All my appointed time: *Williams, Marion*.
2LP: ST 114

BLACK GOSPEL (Various artists).
MC: C 223

BLACK GOSPEL (MCA) (Various artists).
2LP: MCLD 614
MCSET: MCLDC 614

BLESS MY BONES (Memphis Gospel Radio: The Fifties) (Various artists).
LP: ROUNDER 2063
MC: ROUNDER 2063C

CHICAGO GOSPEL PIONEERS (Various artists).
LP: SF 1004

CLEVELAND GOSPEL (Various artists).
Tracks: / Need Jesus on my journey: *Friendly Brothers* / You can't thumb a ride: *Friendly Brothers* / You can't win: *Friendly Brothers* / Ten commandments: *Friendly Brothers* / I thank you Jesus: *Shield Brothers* / Saviour don't pass me: *Shield Brothers* / Won't you hear me pray: *Shield Brothers* / Pray every step: *Elite* Jewels / Going to move: *L & N Gospel Singers* / You been so good: *L & N Gospel Singers* / Ride on King Jesus: *Elite Jewels* / Standing on the rock: *Elite Jewels* / I'm going through: *Angels Of Harmony* / Now Lord: *Angels Of Harmony* / Do not pass me by: *Kings Of Harmony* / Jesus is everything: *Kings Of Harmony*.
LP: HT 316

DETROIT GOSPEL (Various artists).
LP: HT 311

EVERYTIME I FEEL THE SPIRIT (Various artists).
LP: SH 9102

FAMOUS SPIRITUAL & GOSPEL FESTIVAL 1965 (Various artists).
LP: LR 44.005

GET RIGHT WITH GOD (Hot Gospel 1947-53) (Various artists).
Tracks: / Tree of life, The: *Powers, Prophet* / Blood done signed my name: *Radio Four* / I got good religion: *National Independent Gospel Singers* / Tell me why you like Roosevelt: *Jackson, Otis*.
LP: KK 7417

GET RIGHT WITH GOD VOL 2 (Various artists).
LP: KK 7424

GOD GIVE ME LIGHT 1927-31 (Various artists).
LP: HER 203

GOLDEN AGE OF GOSPEL SINGING (Various artists).
LP: FL 9046

GOSPEL AT CHRISTMAS (Various artists).
LP: MAL 04404

GOSPEL CANNONBALL (Various artists).
Tracks: / Gospel cannonball: *Various artists* / Lesson is love, The: *Various artists* / If God for us: *Various* artists / Our God reigns: *Various artists* / His name is Wonderful: *Various artists* / Singleminded message, A (To a double minded man): *Various artists* / Search me, O God: *Various artists* / Stop look and listen: *Various artists* / Not enough: *Various artists* / Best, The: *Various artists*.
LP: MM 0126
MC: TC MM 0126

GOSPEL CARAVAN (Various artists).
LP: AV 4705
MC: AV 5705

GOSPEL COLLECTION (Gospels and spirituals) (Various artists).
Tracks: / Take my mother home: *Belafonte, Harry* / I'm glad salvation: *Jackson, Mahalia* / Gospel train: *Golden* Gate Quartet / Every time I feel the spirit: *Robeson, Paul* / Lord's Prayer, The: *Vaughan, Sarah* / I believe: *Jackson, Mahalia* / What more can my Jesus do?: *Mitchell's Christian Singers* / I'm on my way: *Golden Gate* Quartet / Motherless child: *Vaughan, Sarah* / Move on up a little higher: *Jackson, Mahalia* / Didn't my Lord deliver Daniel?: *Robeson, Paul* / My mother died a-shoutin': *Mitchell's Christian Singers* / Go tell it on the mountain: *Jackson, Mahalia* / Rock Daniel: *Tharpe, Sister Rosetta*.
LP: DVLP 2116
MC: DVMC 2116

GOSPEL PIANO AND GUITAR CLASSICS 1926-30 (Various artists).
LP: BD 2003

GOSPEL SHIP (Various artists).
Tracks: / Amazing Grace: *Various artists* (Howard Adams leading the congregation of the Thornton Regular Baptist Ch) / Poor Pilgrim: *Various artists* / Testimony: *Various artists* / Why must I wear this shroud?: *Various artists*(Congregation of the Thornton Regular Bapist Church.) / When Jesus Christ was here on Earth: *Various artists* / Old gospel ship, The: *Various artists* / When the stars begin to fall: *Various artists* / Hick's Farewell: *Various artists*/ See that my grave is kept clean: *Various artists* / I am a poor way faring stranger: *Various artists* / Little family, The: *Various artists* / Jim and Me: *Various artists* / Airplane ride, The: *Various artists* / Guide me o thou great Jehovah: *Various artists* (lke Caudill leading the congregation of the Mount Olivet Regular Baptist) / Testimony of pioneer religion: *Various artists*.
LP: NW 294

GOSPEL SONGS (Various artists).
MC: GM 0202

GOSPEL WARRIORS (Various artists).
LP: SF 1003

GOSPELS AND SPIRITUALS (Various artists).
LPS: C 84-3 BOX 3

GOTHAM GOSPEL VOL. 1 (Various artists).
LP: KK 812

GOTHAM GOSPEL VOL. 2 (Various artists).
Tracks: / Gospel train: *Harmony Kings* / Down on my knees: *Harmony Kings* / I'm a pilgrim: *Harmony Kings*/ Do you know him: *Harmony Kings* / Jesus is my only friend: *Harmony Kings* / Call him anytime: *Various artists*/ Jezebel: *Various artists* / When I take vacation: *Mount Eagle 4tet* / He's a friend: *Mount Eagle 4tet*/ No Jim Crow in heaven: *Capitol City 4tet* / Lord send mother: *Capitol City 4tet* / Found no friend: *Bunn, Allen/Tarheel Slim* / Get on road to glory: *Bunn, Allen/Tarheel Slim* / I'll be satisfied: *Various artists*.
LP: KK 825

GREAT LADIES OF GOSPEL (Various artists).
LP: SC 7095

GREATEST GOSPEL HITS VOL 1 (Various artists).
LP: MALP 6004
MC: MALC 6004

I BELIEVE (20 All-Time Gospel Greats) (Various artists).
Tracks: / Family bible: *Gray, Claude* / Put your hand in the hand: *Anderson, Lynn* / How great thou art: *Worth,* Marion / Peace in the valley: *Price, Kenny* / Old rugged cross, The: *Philips, Bill* / Keep on the sunny side: *Lee, Wilma & Stoney Cooper* / Family who prays shall never part, The: *Louvin, Charlie* / Lord, I'm coming home: *Collins, Tommy* / Swing low, sweet chariot: *Cash, Johnny* / I believe: *Wynette, Tammy* / Wings of a dove: *Husky, Ferlin* / Oh happy day: *Statler Brothers* / You gotta climb: *Robbins, Marty* / I'll fly away: *Bowes,* Margie / Will the circle be unbroken: *Miller, Ned* / I saw the light: *Philips, Bill* / Amazing grace: *Warner,* Mack / In the sweet bye and bye: *Kilgore, Merle* / Where no one stands alone: *Various artists* / What a friend we have in Jesus: *Helms, Bobby*.
LP: PAST 3

JUBILEE TO GOSPEL (Black Religious music 1921-53) (Various artists).
LP: JEMF 108

NEW ORLEANS GOSPEL QUARTETS 1947-1956 (Various artists).
LP: HT 306

NEWARK GOSPEL GROUPS various Gospel groups (Various artists).
LP: HT 324

NO NAME GOSPEL SINGERS (Various artists).
MC: GVMMC 207

PREACHIN' THE GOSPEL - HOLY BLUES (Various artists).
MC: 4678904

SING A GOSPEL SONG (Various artists).
LP: HRL 214

SOUL OF BLACK MUSIC - GOSPEL SCENE (Various artists).
2LP: 426001

SOUL OF BLACK MUSIC VOL 1 (Various artists).
Tracks: / Borrowed time: *Various artists* / Gamblin' man: *Various artists* / Jesus you've been good: *Various* artists / Going home to get my crown: *Various artists* / I'm going to serve Jesus: *Various artists* / Grandma's hands: *Various artists* / I'll be satisfied: *Various artists* / Lord I've done what you told me to do: *Various* artists / I'm holding on: *Various artists* / What am I going to do: *Various artists* / Won't it be grand: *Various artists* / My soul: *Various artists* / I've already been to the water: *Various artists* / Sleep on mother: *Various artists*.
LP: SNTF 795

SOUL OF BLACK MUSIC VOL 2 (Various artists).
Tracks: / Ezekiel: *Various artists* / Nobody's fault but mine: *Various artists* / Stop by: *Various artists*/ He's working it out: *Various artists* / May the work I've done speak for me: *Various artists* / What about me: *Various artists* / New walk: *Various artists* / When we got to heaven: *Various artists* / I love to praise Him: *Various artists* / Stand by me: *Various artists* / Everyday will be Sunday: *Various artists* / Through it all: *Various artists* / How much do I owe: *Various artists* / Walk through the valley: *Various artists*.
LP: SNTF 796

SOUL STIRRERS: A TRIBUTE TO SAM COOKE Various artists (Various artists).
Tracks: / My loved ones: *Various artists* / Striving: *Various artists* / Hello sunshine: *Various artists*/ That's heaven to me: *Various artists* / Farther along: *Various artists* / Slow train: *Various artists*/ Don't move that mountain: *Various artists* / God is standing by: *Various artists* / Peace in the valley: *Various artists* / Son,The: *Various artists* / Heaven is my home: *Various artists*.
LP: GCH 8086
MC: GCHK 78086

STORM IS PASSING BY (Early post-war gospel) (Various artists).
MC: GVMMC 203

TEN YEARS OF BLACK COUNTRY RELIGION 1926-36 (Various artists).
LP: L 1022

WAY DOWN DEEP IN MY SOUL (Various artists).
LP: SH 9103

WHAT MORE D'YA WANT Gospel rarities 1926-1930 (Various artists).
LP: ELE 5-200

WHITE GOSPEL Early 1950's (Various artists).
LP: KK 315
LP: KK 815

Gospel At Colonus

GOSPEL AT COLONUS, THE (Original Broadway cast) (Various artists).
Tracks: / Live where you can: *Various artists* / Stop do not go on: *Various artists* / How shall I see you through my tears: *Various artists* / Voice foretold prayer, A: *Various artists* / Never drive you away: *Various artists*/ Numberless are the world's wonders: *Various artists* / Lift me up (like a dove): *Various artists* / Sunlight of no light: *Various artists* / Eternal sleep: *Various artists* / Lift him up: *Various artists* / Now let the weeping cease: *Various artists*.
LP: 925182 1
MC: 925182 4

Gospel Choralettes

WITHOUT YOU LORD.
Tracks: / Rejoice and be glad / Higher ground / Without you Lord / Good news / Standing on the promises / Hold on / I must tell Jesus / Bled and He died (just for me).
LP: MIR 5016
MC: MIR 5016MC

Gospel Christian

ACAPELLA SINCE 1929.
MC: GVMMC 212

CATCH THE AIR.
MC: GVMMC 215

Gospel Keynotes

FROM THE HEART.
LP: MAL 4430
MC: MALC 4430

GOING BACK WITH THE LORD.
LP: MAL 4423
MC: MALC 4423

SATAN IS ON THE LOOSE.
LP: MAL 04416

Gospel Miracles

JOY.
LP: MIR 5008
MC: ZCMIR 5008

Gospel Music Workshop

LIVE IN ST.LOUIS.
LP: MALP 7096

Gospel Road (film)

GOSPEL ROAD, THE (Film soundtrack) (Cash, Johnny).
2LP: CBS 68253

Gossip Girls

LILAC DREAMS.
LP: NCHMLP 2

Gotham

GOTHAM.
LP: LSLP 1

Gothenburg Brass Band

GOTHENBURG BRASS BAND.
Tracks: / Prelude for an occasion / Liten marsch / Born free / Year of the dragon / Swedish folk-songs / Shepherd's song / Gonna fly now / Old Fabodpsalm.
LP: PRL 032D
MC: CPRL 032D

Gothic

GOTHIC (see under Dolby, Thomas) (Various artists).

Gothic (film)

GOTHIC (see under Dolby, Thomas) (Dolby, Thomas).

Gothic Slam

JUST A FACE.
LP: RO 94741

KILLER INSTINCT.
LP: RR 9554 1

Gothique

KRISTIANA.
MC: C 004

Gott, Karel

STOWAWAYS ON THE ARK (see under Stowaways on the ark).

Gottlieb, Danny

WHIRLWIND.
LP: K 7815981
MC: K 7815984

Gottsching, Manuel

E2 E4.
LP: INT 200004

Goudge, Elizabeth

WHITE WITCH, THE (Guthrie, Gwyneth).
MCSET: COL 2022

Goudreau, Barry

BARRY GOUDREAU.
Tracks: / Hard luck / Nothin' to lose / What's a fella to do / Mean woman blues / Leavin' tonight / Dreams / Life is what you make it / Sailin' away / Cold cold wind.
LP: PRT 84449

Gould, Kevin

CLEAR VISION.
Tracks: / All I really want / I'm going home / Tongue, The / You are everything / Seed song / Agape / Father's love / Feel the music you play / I've got a song / We believe in love.
LP: PC 122

Goulder, Dave

MAN WHO PUT THE ENGINE IN THE CHIP SHOP.
Tracks: / Race to the North / Station people / Settle & Carlisle / Ais gill / Train / Man who put the engine in the chip shop, The / Eight freight blues / In the sidings now / Big Bertha / Dinosaur the railway left behind, The / Narrow gauge / Last train.
LP: FE 065
MC: FE 065 C

REQUIEM FOR STEAM (Railway songs).
LP: BB 00 04

Gouldman, Graham

ANIMALYMPICS.
LP: 9109 630
MC: 7231 443

Goulet, Robert

AS TIME GOES BY.
LP: MOIR 117

CLOSE TO YOU.
Tracks: / Atlantic City / It's impossible / What I did for love / Something to believe in / This masquerade / Time for us, A / If ever I would leave you / Where do I begin? / Way we were, The / You light up my life.
LP: PRCV 125
MC: TC PRCV 125

ROBERT GOULET: GREATEST HITS.
Tracks: / If ever I would leave you / Begin to love / This is all I ask / Summer sounds / Real live girl / What kind of fool am I / My love forgive me / Ciao compare / Autumn leaves / Fortissimo / Imossible dream.
LP: CBS 32258
MC: 40 32258

SINCERELY YOURS.
Tracks: / I talk to the trees / Nearness of you / Tonight / Another time another place / Poinciana / Ebb tide / Moon was yellow / You stepped out of a dream / Two people / Maria / Gigi / Stella by starlight.
LP: CBS 32374

Goupil, Augie

TAHITIAN SWING 1935-37 (Goupil, Augie & His Royal Tahitians).
LP: HT 322

TAHITIAN SWING 1936-38 (Goupil, Augie & His Royal Tahitians).
LP: HQ 2073

Goutier, Alain

PARIS EN AUTOMNE (see Reininger, Blaine) (Goutier, Alain/Blaine Reininger).

Govan Gaelic Choir

GOVAN GAELIC CHOIR.
LP: LILP 5020

Govan, James

I'M IN NEED.
Tracks: / Jealous kind, The / Uphill climb / Tell you about my girl / Starting all over again / Oh what a price / Help me in need / Love (I thought I would never find love) / Don't give up the ship / You left the water running / We had it all.
LP: CRB 1162
MC: TCCRB 1162

Govenek Choir

SONGS OF HOPE.
MC: SENC 1085

Government Issue

BOYCOTT STAB.
LP: FOY 002

CRASH.
LP: WEBITE 42

FINALE.
LP: B 00613

FUN JUST NEVER STOPS, THE.
LP: FOY 017

GOVERNMENT ISSUE 5TH.
LP: FOY 024

YOU.
LP: 081275

Gowan

GOWAN.
Tracks: / Jet white / Keep up the fight / Live in / Come a little closer / Make it alone / Oceania / Send me energy / I'm not involved / I was only looking / Victory.
LP: CBS 25128
MC: 40 25128

STRANGE ANIMAL.
Tracks: / Cosmetics / Desperate / City of the angels / Walking on air / Burning torches of hope / Keep the tension on / Guerilla soldier / You're a strange soldier / Criminal mind.
LP: CBS 26493
MC: 40 26493

Gowland, Mox

MASTERCLASS HARMONICA BLUES.
LP: JTL 1

Goya, Francis

DE MOOISTE GITAARSUCCESSEN VAN FRANCIS GOYA.
LP: 022 58246
MC: 222 58246

QUIET MOMENTS (Goya, Francis & His Orchestra).
Tracks: / For your eyes only / One day I'll go away / Bright eyes / Image / Crying / Song for Guy / Feelings / I'm not in love / Just when I need you most.
2LP: STD 10
MCSET: STDK 10

THIS IS FRANCIS GOYA.
LP: 830 828 1
MC: 830 828 4

Goya (show)

GOYA - LIFE IN A SONG, A (Stage show) (Various artists).
Tracks: / Overture: *Various artists* / Espana: *Various artists* / Astounding romantic adventures of Goya, The: *Various artists* / In the middle of the 18th century: *Various artists* / Girl with a smile: *Various artists*/ Till I loved you: *Various artists* / Picture it: *Various artists* / I will paint sounds: *Various artists*/ Viva Espana: *Various artists* / Once a time I loved you: *Various artists* / I stand alone: *Various artists*/ Dog in the quicksand: *Various artists* / Moving on: *Various artists* / Bon soir: *Various artists* / Finale: *Various artists.*
LP: 4632941
MC: 4632944

Goyeneche, Roberto

TANGOS DEL SUR.
LP: A 516
MC: C 516

Goykovich, Dusko

AFTER HOURS.
LP: ENJA 2020

CELEBRATION (Goykovich, Dusko Quartet).
LP: HH 1003

G.Q.

DISCO NIGHTS.
LP: ARTY 169

FACE TO FACE.
Tracks: / Shake / You put some love in my life / Shy baby / Sad girl / I love the skin (you are in) / Boogie shoogie feelin' / Dark side of the sun / Face to face / You've got the floor.
LP: SPART 1163

TWO.
LP: SPART 1116

Grab Me A Gondola

GRAB ME A GONDOLA (Original London cast) (Various artists).
LP: AEI 1119

Grable, Betty

FILM, TELEVISION.
LP: CC 100/5

RARE RECORDINGS (1930-70).
LP: SH 2014

Grace

BEST OF GRACE.
MC: BOCAS 1315

BUNCH OF GRACE, A.
MC: KMC 115

GRACE.
LP: MCF 3102

GRACE LIVE.
LP: CLAYLP 2

HIS GRACE ALIVE O'.
MC: SOLO 7007

HIS GRACE AT HARVEST.
MC: SOLO 7010

TWO SIDES OF GRACE.
MC: RTE 94

Grace, Brendan

BOTTLER THE ALUMINIUM ALBUM.
LP: STAR 2325

Grace, John

PRIVATE PARTS.
Tracks: / Red haired Mary / Hole in the elephant's bottom, The / Carrickfergus / When the old Duncow caught fire / She was poor but she was honest / Prize winning Hereford bull / Old Riley's daughter / Chandler's shop, The / Farmer's boy / Seven golden daffodils / Brian Boru / Late last night / Sail away.
LP: SFA 098

STORIES AND SONGS OF PORTLAND BILL, THE.
Tracks: / Guided tour, The / Gone fishin' / Beachcombing / Kite flying / Football / Foggy day, The / Bad dogger / Garden party.
MC: TS 346

WAYFARER (Grace, John & Nick Kier).
MC: MR 1016

Graces

PERFECT VIEW.
LP: AMA 5265
MC: AMC 5265

Gracie, Charlie

AMAZING GRACIE.
LP: CR 30211

BEST OF CHARLIE GRACIE.
LP: REV 3005

CHARLIE GRACIE'S EARLY RECORDINGS.
LP: Unknown

LIVE AT THE STOCKTON GLOBE AUGUST 26TH 1957.
Tracks: / Ko ko mo (I love you so) / Long tall Sally / Trying / Tutti frutti / Flip flop and fly / Sway / Hound dog / Guitar boogie / Butterfly / Ninety nine ways / I love you so much it hurts / Fabulous.
LP: ROLL 2005

ROCKIN' PHILADELPHIA.
Tracks: / Heart like a rock / You mostest girl / Too much monkey business / Love doll / Rockin' the boogie / Little John's gone / Fabulous / Train down to hell / Dirty dog / My baby loves me.
LP: MFM 004

Gracious

GRACIOUS.
LP: BGOLP 34

Graduate

ACTING MY AGE.
Tracks: / Elvis should play Ska / Watching your world / Love that is bad / Julie Julie / Bad dreams / Acting my age / Sick and tired / Ever met a day / Dancing nights / Sut up.
MLP: DOW 452
MC: ZCDOW 452
LP: PART 001
MC: ZCPAR 001

Graduate (film)

GRADUATE, THE (see under Simon & Garfunkel) (Simon & Garfunkel).

Graebe, Martin

JACK-IN-THE-GREEN.
Tracks: / As I sailed / Lavender express / Daniel's duck / Tale of Neddy Niblem and Biddy Flynn / Honiton lace / Eight set's song / Harry the hawker / Under the drooping willow / Bird starver's cry, The / November drinking song / Knocker-up woman, The / Newton fair / Peter's private army / Shropshire Union Canal, the / Plymouth galleon, the.
MC: 60-049

Graffiti Bridge (film)

GRAFFITI BRIDGE (OST) (See under 'Prince' for details) (Prince).

Graham, Billy

CRUSADE MEMORIES VOL.2 (Various artists).
LP: TWE 6016

WELCOME TO MISSION ENGLAND.
LP: WST 9655
MC: WC 9655

Graham Central Station

AIN'T NO BOUT A DOUBT IT.
Tracks: / Jam, The / Your love / It's alright / I can't stand the rain / Ain't nothing but a Warner Brothers party / Ole Smokey / Easy rider / Water luckiest people.
LP: K 56147

GRAHAM CENTRAL STATION.
Tracks: / We've been waiting / It ain't no fun to me / Hair / We be's getting down / Tell me what it is / Can you handle it / People / Why / Ghetto, The.
LP: K 46286
LP: K 56062

NOW DO YOU WANNA DANCE.
Tracks: / Happ-e 2 -c-u-a-ginn / Now do u wanta dance / Last train / Love and happiness / Earthquake / Crazy chicken / Stomped beat up and whooped / Lead me on / Saving my love for you / Have faith in me.
LP: K 56359

Graham, D'ancey

ALLUMA.
LP: SHLP 100

Graham, Davey

ALL THAT MOODY.
Tracks: / Finger buster / Blue raga / To find the sun / Tristano, etc / Anji / Travelling man / Sunshine raga / Kim / Jenra / La Morena / Preacher blues.
MC: ERON 007 CA
LP: ERON 007 LP

COMPLETE GUITARIST, THE.
Tracks: / Lord Mayo / Lord Inchiquinn / Lashtail's room / Ein feste burg / Road to Lisdoonvarna, The / Renaissance piece / Hardiman the fiddler / Sarah / Frieze britches / Blues for Gino / Hunter's purse, (The) / Prelude from the suite in D minor / Fairies hornpipe / Forty-ton parachute / Gold ring, (The) / Down ampney / Banish misfortune.
LP: SNKF 138

DANCE FOR TWO PEOPLE.
Tracks: / Dance for two people / Bloody fields of Flanders, The / Indian piece / Lute prelude / She moved through the Bizarre / Minuets I & II / Reng / Breathe on me breath of God / El cafe de Chinitas / Happy meeting in glory / Farewell to the creeks / Yemeni tagsim / Mna na Heireann / Kim / Lady Hunsdon's puffe / Wash nha home / Two hymns / Uskudar.
LP: KM 161
LP: SNKF 158

FOLK BLUES AND ALL POINTS IN BETWEEN.
Tracks: / Leaving blues / Cocaine / Rock me baby / Moanin' / Skillet / Ain't nobody's business / Maajun (a taste of Tangier) / I can't keep from crying sometimes / Going down slow / Better git it in your soul / Freight train blues / Both sides now / No preacher blues / Bad boy blues / I'm ready / Hoochie coochie man / Blue raga.
LP: SEE 48

GODINGTON BOUNDARY.
LP: PTLS 1039

IRISH REELS, JIGS, HORNPIPES & AIRS (Graham, Dave/Dave Evans/Dan Ar Brass/Duck Baker).
LP: SNKF 153

Graham, David

DANCETIME AT THE TOWER.
LP: GPR 19

DAVID GRAHAM PLAYS THE BLACKPOOL TOWER WURLITZER....
LP: GPR 21
MC: KGPR 21

WISH YOU WERE HERE.
LP: GRS 1149

Graham, Eve

WOMAN OF THE WORLD.
Tracks: / All the money in the world / We got tonight / Give us time / Real to reel / Chanson pour les petits enfants / Woman of the world / Falling in love again / Just a smile / Evergreen / Black widow spider / Leaving it all / Woman in love.
LP: ACLP 007

Graham, George

ALL THE RIGHT STUFF.
Tracks: / Pretty / Good bad case of you / 18th Century shuffle / Hunk o' funk / Walkin' with pops / Breezy.
LP: OUTSTANDING 49

Graham, Jaki

BREAKING AWAY.
Tracks: / Set me free / Breaking away / Still in love / Love under moonlight / Lets get blue (Duet with Derek Bramble.) / Stop the world / Luv 2 much / Love of your life, The / Closest one, The (Duet with Derek Bramble.) / Step right up / Mated (Duet with David Grant.) / Love me tonight.
LP: EMC 3514
MC: TCEMC 3514

FROM NOW ON.
Tracks: / From now on / Provocative / Better part of me / Faking the feeling / I still run to you / Baby don't you want me /

I want to thank you (Heavenly Father) / First in line / Every little bit hurts / Nobody's fool (CD only.).
LP: EMC 3560
MC: TCEMC 3560

HEAVEN KNOWS.
Tracks: / Round and around / Heaven knows / Could it be I'm falling in love / I fell for you / Hold on / Facts of love / You're mine / Loving you / What's the name of your game / Stay the way you are.
LP: FA 3181
MC: TCFA 3181
LP: JK 1
MC: TC JK 1

LIVING FOR YOU (See under Hardcastle, Paul) (Graham, Jaki & Paul Hardcastle).

MATED (see Grant, David) (Graham, Jaki & David Grant).

Graham, John (nar)

ALADDIN AND ALI BABA (See under Aladdin... (bk).

FUTURE FEAR (See under Morris, James D - Future Fear).

HANDS OFF/THE MONKEY'S PAW.
MC: NF 10

LOVE AND THE LONELY DIE/THE BODY SNATCHERS.
MC: NF 3

Graham, Kenny

BATTLE ROYAL (see Scott, Ronnie) (Graham, Kenny & Ronnie Scott).

CARIBBEAN SUITE/AFRO KADABRA.
Tracks: / Jump for Joe / Night in Tunisia / Take the 'A' train / Flamingo / Keni B'sindika / Afro-Kadabra / Mango walk / Bongo chant / Saga boy / Dance of the zombies / Wha' huppin' sah? / Tempo medio lento / Beguine / Haitian ritual.
LP: ESQ 329

MANGO WALK.
LP: ESQ 308

Graham, Larry

FIRED UP.
Tracks: / What we all need is more love / For your love / Nobody's gonna steal you away / That's why I love you / How does it feel / Let's go / Cruisin' / Tearing out my heart / Fired up / Love all the hurt away.
LP: 925307 1
MC: 925307 4

JUST BE MY LADY.
Tracks: / Just be my lady / Loving you is beautiful / Guess who / Our love keeps growing strong / Can't nobody take your place / No place like home / Baby you are my sunshine / I just love you / Feels like love / Remember when.
LP: K 56909

ONE IN A MILLION YOU.
Tracks: / One in a million you / Stand up and shout about love / Sweetheart / There's something about you / Forever yours / I'm so glad it's summer again / When we get married / Time for you and me / I just can't stop dancing / Sunshine love and music.
LP: K 56843

SOONER OR LATER.
Tracks: / Sooner of later / Still thinkin' of you / Don't stop when you're hot / You're my girl / I feel good / Walk baby walk / Let me come into your life / Hold up your hand / Easy love.
LP: K56992

Graham, Len

AFTER DAWNING (See under Holmes, Hoe) (Graham, Len & Hoe Holmes).

DO ME JUSTICE.
LP: CC 37

SKYLARK.
LP: CC 46
MC: 4CC 46

WIND AND WATER (Traditional Songs, Ballads and Lilts).
Tracks: / My parents reared me tenderly / Maggie Picken / Sean O'Duibhir a Ghleanna / County Mayo, The / Star of Moville, The / Green fields of Amerikay / Western winds / Paidin o' Raibheartaigh / My Willie o / Daniel O'Connell and his steam engine / Rights of man, The / One morning in May / Knight templar's dream, The.
LP: 12TS 334

YE LOVERS ALL.
LP: CC 41
MC: 4CC 41

Graham, Lou

LONG GONE DADDY.
LP: KK 835

Graham, Vanessa

SUCH MEN ARE DANGEROUS.
MCSET: MRC 1043

Grahame, Kenneth

HOME SWEET HOME (Wind in the willows characters).
MCSET: 00 103 209 7

OPEN ROAD, THE (Wind in the Willows characters).
MCSET: 00 103 210 0

RELUCTANT DRAGON, THE (Karloff, Boris (nar)).
MC: 1074

RELUCTANT DRAGON, THE (With Tarka the otter by Williamson) (Horden, Sir Michael).
MCSET: SAY 70

WIND IN THE WILLOWS.
Tracks: / Wind in the willows (Theme.) / On the river / Ducks ditty / Open road, The / Mr. Toad - the motorist / Wild wood, The / Mr. Badger / Dulce domum / Further adventures of toad, The / Hero's song, A / When the toad came home / Battle, The / Wind in the willows.
LP: RBDLP 1150
MC: ZCRBD 1150

WIND IN THE WILLOWS (Bennett, Alan (nar)).
MCSET: ZBBC 1072

WIND IN THE WILLOWS.
MCSET: SAY 8
MCSET: ARGO 1124

WIND IN THE WILLOWS (Duncan, Frank).
MC: P 90022

WIND IN THE WILLOWS (children's classics) (Unknown narrator(s)).
MC: PLBC 85

WIND IN THE WILLOWS, THE (Unknown narrator(s)).
MCSET: DTO 10566

WIND IN THE WILLOWS, THE (Williams, Kenneth (nar)).
MCSET: LFP 7041
MCSET: LFP 4170415

WIND IN THE WILLOWS: THE RIVER BANK (See also John Braddeley).
MC: 00 102118 4

WIND IN THE WILLOWS: THE WILD WOOD (See also Braddeley, John).
MC: TTS 9835
MC: 00 102117 6

Grahame, Laurie

PARENT'S SURVIVAL GUIDE (Steed, Maggie).
MCSET: ZBBC 1070

Grahamophones

MAD DOGS AND ENGLISHMEN.
LP: PTLS 1097
MC: PTLC 1097

PUDSEY'S PICNIC (see under Hunniford, Gloria) (Dalby, Graham/ Grahamophones/Gloria Hunniford/ Adrian Love).

WE'RE TOPS ON SATURDAY NIGHT.
Tracks: / Chinese laundry blues / Blue moon / We're tops on Saturday night / I would sooner be a crooner / Isn't this a lovely day / Who stole my heart away / Nobody's sweetheart / You rascal you / Stars fell on Alabama / When can I have a banana again / Room with a view / Deep purple / Puttin' on the ritz / Mr. Wu's xylophone blues.
LP: PTLS 1086
MC: PTLC 1086

Grain Aid

GRAIN-AID (Various artists).
MC: MMATT 19

Grainer, Ron

TALES OF THE UNEXPECTED & OTHER THEMES (Grainer, Ron Orchestra).
Tracks: / Tales of the unexpected / I've danced with a man / Born and bred / Malice aforethought / Joe 90 / Touch of velvet / Sting of brass / Doctor Who / Rebecca (love theme from) / When love grows cold / Paul Temple / Six by six.
LP: RKLB 1003

Grainger (composer)

GRAINGER PLAYS GRAINGER & GRIEG.
LP: RL 10168

MUSIC OF PERCY GRAINGER (Various artists).
MCSET: TCSLS 5249

ONE MORE DAY.
LP: LRF 034

ROOM MUSIC TIT BITS AND....
MC: RK 25198
LP: RL 25198

SALUTE TO PERCY GRAINGER (Various artists).
LP: SXL 6410
MC: 4251594

Grainger, Richard

DARKLANDS.
Tracks: / Give us a job / Farewell to Angus / Whalerman's lament / Evergreen / Grey cock, The / Chemical worker's song, The / Born today / Barricades / Lowlands of Holland, The / Old pubs, The / Last light on the row / Darklands.
LP: FSLP 8
MC: FSMC 8

HERBS ON THE HEART.
Tracks: / Whitby whaler / Princess to a beggarman / Death of Nelson / Weaver and the factory maid, The / Isles of Shetland, The / Teeside and Yorkshire / Faithful sailor boy / Every time / Willie o' Reilly / Days at the end.
LP: FE 038
MC: FE 038 C

HOME ROUTES (Grainger, Richard & Dick Miles).
LP: BHL 9008
MC: BHC 9008

Gramatsky, Hardie

LITTLE TOOT STORIES (Conreid, Hans).
MC: 1528

Gramm, Lou

FOREIGNER IN A STRANGE LAND.
LP: THBL 065

LONG HARD LOOK.
Tracks: / I'll come running / Heart and soul / One dream / Warmest rising sun / Hangin' on my hip / Word gets around / I'll know when it's over / Lightnin' strikes again.
LP: WX 228
MC: WX 228 C

READY OR NOT.
LP: K 781 728 1
MC: K 781 728 4

Grammacks

ROOTS CARIBBEAN ROCK (Grammacks feat. Jeff Joseph).
Tracks: / Roots caribbean rock / News and politiks / Reggae rhythm / Party party / Who's that lady / Debar debar / I'm a winner / Hot music.
LP: 8219151
MC: 8219154

Grammy R & B Songs

GRAMMY R AND B SONGS 1960'S-1970'S (See Under Rhythm and Blues) (Various artists).

Grammy Winners

GRAMMY WINNERS (Various artists).
Tracks: / Copacabana: *Various artists* / Just the way you are: *Various artists* / Hotel California: *Various* artists / Killing me softly with his song: *Various artists* / I honestly love you: *Various artists* / This masquerade: *Various artists* / You light up my life: *Various artists* / Love will keep us together: *Various artists* / First time ever I saw your face, The: *Various artists* / You've got a friend: *Various artists*.
LP: SX 7010

Granata, Rocco

MARINA.
Tracks: / Marina / Donna / Te quiero / Gute nacht / Germania / Buona notte / Irena / Ma nuela / Ein Italiano / Alles war schon / Oh oh Rosi / Guten abend / E Primavera.
LP: BFX 15134

Grand Chinese

CHINESE FLUTE CONCERTOS.
LP: LLST 7372

Grand Daddy I.U.

SMOOTH ASSASSIN.
LP: 7599263411
MC: 7599263414

Grand Dominion Jazz

AIN'T NOBODY GOT THE BLUES LIKE ME.
Tracks: / Old folks at home / Ain't nobody got the blues like me / Bedelia / Snag it / Worn out blues / Panama / Yearning (just for you) / Saratoga swing / Joe Avery's piece / Trog's blues / Georgia grind.
LP: SOS 1189

COME BACK, SWEET PAPA.
Tracks: / One sweet letter from you / Ponchatrain / Perdido St blues / Make me a pallet on the floor / Bogalusa strut / Come back, sweet papa / Friendless blues / Martha / J'ai de la fievre / Minor drag, The.
LP: T 106

DON'T GIVE UP THE SHIP.
LP: SOS 1139

GRAND DOMINION JAZZ BAND, THE.
LP: GHB 174

Grand Funk Railroad

CAUGHT IN THE ACT.
Tracks: / Introduction / Footstompin' music / Rock and roll / Soul / Closer to home / Heartbreaker / Some kind of wonderful / Shinin' on the locomotion / Black licorice / Railroad, The / We're an American band / T.N.U.C / Inside looking out / Gimme shelter.
2LP: E STSP 15

COLLECTION: GRAND FUNK RAILROAD.
LP: IC 038 80456

GRAND FUNK LIVES.
Tracks: / Good times / Queen bee / Testify / Can't be with you tonight / No reason why / We gotta get out of this place / Y.O.U. / Stuck in the middle / Greed of man / Wait for me.
LP: K 99191

LIVE ALBUM: GRAND FUNK RAILROAD.
Tracks: / Are you ready (Introduction) / Paranoid / In need / Heartbreaker / Inside looking out / Words of wisdom / Mean mistreater / Mark say's alright / T.N.U.C. / Into the sun.
2LP: ESTDW 1/2

WHAT'S FUNK.
Tracks: / Rock and roll American style / Nowhere to run / Innocent / Still waitin' / Borderline / El Salvador / It's a man's world / I'm so true / Don't lie to me / Life in outer space.
LP: 923 750 1

Grand Hotel

DO NOT DISTURB.
Tracks: / Stranger in a strange town / Atmosphere / Light years away / Do not disturb / Reach for the light / Somebody please / No dice / Low life / Secret life.
LP: CBS 83134

Grand, Johnny

PARADE OF BROKEN HEARTS.
Tracks: / Parade of broken hearts / Casey's last ride / Cookie and Lila / Lookin' out my back door / Sweet memories / Everybody wants to be somebody / Wanna be a star / Today I started loving you again / Let me be there / Hello heartache / We're all goin' nowhere / Teach your children.
LP: LILP 5066

Grand Mal

BINGE PURGE.
LP: FOY 016

Grand Mamou Orchestra

CAJUNS VOL 2.
Tracks: / Bayou pom pom / Callcashieo waltz / V'tait au bal ce soir / Valse de meche / Fifi Ponchot / Country gentleman / La fille de la veuve / Flame de fer / Grand prairie waltz.
LP: SNTF 644

Grand Man

GRAND MAN Catherine Cookson (Jameson, Susan (nar)).
MC: CAB 006

Grand Mixer

GRAND MIXER CUTS IT UP (see Infinity feat. Grand Mixer) (Grand Mixer/ Infinity).

Grand, Otis

ALWAYS HOT! (Grand, Otis & the Dance Kings).
LP: SPD 1019
MC: SPDC 1019

Grand Prix

FIRST ALBUM, THE.
Tracks: / Waiting for the night / Day in the life, A / Thinking of you / Mama says / Which way did the wind blow / Westwind / Next to you / You know it can be / Feel like I do / Very last time (dreamer), The.
LP: PL 25321
MC: PK 25321

SAMURAI.
Tracks: / Give me what's mine / Shout / 50/50 / Here we go again / Countdown to zero / Somewhere tonight / High time / Never before / Freedom / Samurai.
LP: CHR 1430
MC: ZCHR 1430

THERE FOR NONE TO SEE.
Tracks: / Heaven to hell / Troubador / Take a chance / Paradise / Keep on believing / Taking your life away / Runaway / Tough of the track / Atlantis / Relay.
LP: RCALP 6027
MC: RCAK 6027

Grand Prix (Film)

GRAND PRIX (Film soundtrack) (Various artists).

LP: MCA 25101
MC: MCAC 25101

Grand Slam (film)

GRAND SLAM (AD OGNI COSTO) (Film soundtrack) (Various artists).
LP: SP 8021

Grandfather Mountain

GRANDFATHER MOUNTAIN GALA.
Tracks: / O my America / Military / St. Bernards Waltz / Grandfather mountain / Strathspey Medley / Minuet / Jig Medley / Reel medley / Eva three step / Waltz / Gala night / Blgeddie reel, The.
LP: LGMHG 86/1
MC: GMHG 86/1

Grandmaster Flash

BA DOP BOOM BANG.
LP: K 9607231
MC: K 9607234

BEST OF GRANDMASTER FLASH ....
MCSET: IED 33

GREATEST MESSAGES (Grandmaster Flash & The Furious Five).
Tracks: / Message, The / Survival (message II) / Freedom / Flash to the beat / Jesse / White lines (don't don't do it) / New York, New York / Internationally known / Birthday party / Adventures of Grandmaster Flash on the wheels of steel / It's nasty (Only on cassette.) / Scorpio (Only on cassette.).
MC: ZCSH 5552
LP: SHLP 5552

MESSAGE, THE (Grandmaster Flash & The Furious Five).
Tracks: / She's fresh / It's nasty (genius of love) / Scorpio / It's a shame / Dreamin / You are / Message, The / Adventures of Grandmaster Flash on the wheels of steel.
LP: SHLP 1007
MC: ZCSH 1007

ON THE STRENGTH (Grandmaster Flash & The Furious Five).
Tracks: / Gold / Cold in effect / Yo baby / On the strength / King, The / Fly girl / Magic carpet ride / Leave here / This is where you got it from / Boy is dope, The / Back in the old days of hip-hop (Only on cassette and CD.).
LP: K 9607691
MC: K 9607694

SOURCE, THE.
Tracks: / Street scene / Style (Peter Gunn theme)MS thang / P.L.U. (peace, love and unity) / Throwin' down / Behind closed doors / Larry's dance theme (part2) / Lies / Fastest man alive / Freelance.
LP: 9604761
MC: 9604764

THEY SAID IT COULDN'T BE DONE (Grandmaster Flash & The Furious Five).
Tracks: / Girls love the way he spins / Joint is jumpin, The / Rock the house / Jailbait / Sign of the times / Larry's dance theme / Who's the lady? / Alternate groove / Paradise.
LP: 9603891
MC: 9603894

Grandmaster Melle Mel

STEP OFF (Grandmaster Melle Mel & The Furious Five).
LP: SGLP 9001

STEPPING OFF (Grandmaster Melle Mel & The Furious Five).
Tracks: / Pump me up / Step off / We don't work for free / White lines / Jesse / Message II (survival) / Megamelle mix.
MC: ZCSH 5555
LP: SHLP 5555

WHITE LINES (DON'T DO IT) (see under Grandmaster Flash).

WORK PARTY (Grandmaster Melle Mel & The Furious Five).
Tracks: / Hustlers convention / Yesterday / At the party / White lines (don't don't do it) (on 12" only) / We don't walk for free / Truth, The / World War III / Can't keep runnin away / New adventures of Grandmaster, The.
LP: SHLP 5553
MC: ZCSH 5553

Grandmaster Richie

JESSE (see under Grandmaster Melle Mel).

Grandmothers

LOOKING UP GRANNY'S DRESS.
LP: 6 25048

Grandpa Jones

FAMILY ALBUM.
Tracks: / Old mountain dew / Muleskinner blues / Banks of the Ohio / Cannon ball blues / Falling leaves / Pig in the pen / Nellie Bly / The flowers of Edinburgh / There'll come a time / Autoharp concerto / Blind girl, The / My pretty quadroon / I gave my love a cherry / Billy Richardson's last ride / 10th of November / Clear in the kitchen / Red haired boy / Autoharp trilogy / Let him go, God bless him / Down home waltz / Who will sing for me / Ramona's choice / Over the waterfall / Johnson boys, The.
2LP: CMH 9015

GRANDPA JONES STORY.
Tracks: / Sweet dreams of Kentucky / My Carolina sunshine girl / Jesse James / Raining here this morning / Eight more miles to Louisville / Tragic romance / Kentucky / Old rattler / Mountain Laurel / I'm on my way back home / Sweeping through the gates / There's a hand that's a waiting / Old camp meeting time / Closer to God than ever before / I'll meet you in the morning / You'll make our shack a mansion / Dark as a dungeon / I'm on my way somewhere / Rosalee / Gone home.
2LP: CMH 9007
MC: CMHC 9007

Granelli, Larry

ONE DAY AT A TIME.
LP: ITMP 970055

Graney, Dave

MY LIFE ON THE PLAINS.
LP: FIRELP 20

Grange Hill Cast

GRANGE HILL - THE ALBUM.
Tracks: / You know the teacher (smash head) / Girls like to do it too / School love / No supervision at break / Biology / Just say no / Don't stop / Lad's medley / I don't like Mondays / Girl's medley / Girls just wannt to have fun / Greatest love of all, The / That's what friends are for.
LP: REB 609
MC: ZCF 609

Granny Reardun

GRANNY REARDUN (Garner, Alan (nar)).
LP: ZDSW 725

Granpa

GRANPA (FILM) (See under Blake, Howard).

Grant, Amy

AGE TO AGE.
Tracks: / In a little while / I have decided / I love a lonely day / Don't run away / Fat baby / Sing your praises to the Lord / El-Shaddai / Raining on the inside / Got to let it go / Arms of love.
LP: MYR 1124
MC: MC 1124

AMY GRANT.
LP: MYR 1164
MC: MC 1164

AMY GRANT IN CONCERT VOLS.1&2.
Tracks: / Beautiful music / Giggle / Old man's rubble / Never give you up / Mimi's house / Father's eyes / Faith walking people / Walking away with you / Mountain top / All I ever have to be / Singing a love song / Don't give up on me / I'm gonna fly / Too late / So glad / You gave me love / Fill me with your love / What a difference you've made / If I have to die / That's the day / Look what has happened to me / Keep it on going / Nobody loves me like you.
2LP: MYD 1120
MCSET: MCD 1120

CHRISTMAS ALBUM, A.
Tracks: / Tennessee Christmas / Hark the herald angel sing / Preiset dem Konig (Praise the King) / Emmanuel / Little town / Christmas hymn / Love has come / Sleigh ride / Christmas song, The / Heirlooms / Mighty fortress, A / Angels we have heard on high.
LP: MYR 1155
MC: MC 1155

COLLECTION: AMY GRANT.
Tracks: / Old man's rubble / My father's eyes / El Shaddai / Stay for a while / Find a way / Angels / Love can do / Sing your praises to the Lord / Thy word / Emmanuel.
LP: MYR R 1219
MC: MYR C 1219

FATHER'S EYES.
LP: MYR 1165
MC: MC 1165

HEART IN MOTION.
LP: 3953211
MC: 3953214

LEAD ME ON.
Tracks: / 1974 / Lead me on / Shadows / Saved by love / Faithless heart / What about the love / If these walls could speak / All right / Sure enough / Say once more / Wait for the healing (Only on CD.) / If you have to go away.
LP: AMA 5199
MC: AMC 5199
LP: MYR R 6871
MC: MYR C 6871

NEVER ALONE.
Tracks: / Look what has happened to me / So glad / Walking away with you / Family / Don't give up on me / That's the day / If I have to die / All I ever have to be / It's a miracle / Too late / First love / Say once more.
LP: MYR 1098
MC: MC 1098

NEXT TIME I FALL, THE (See under Cetera, Peter) (Grant, Amy and Peter Cetera).

STRAIGHT AHEAD.
LP: MYR 1159
MC: MC 1159

UNGUARDED.
Tracks: / Love of another kind / Find a way / Everywhere I go / I love you / Stepping in your shoes / Fight / Wise up / Who to listen to / Sharayah / Prodigal.
LP: AMA 5060
MC: AMC 5060
LP: MYR 1183
MC: MC 1183

Grant, Angus

HIGHLAND FIDDLE.
Tracks: / Pipe Major Sam Scott / Portree Bay / Flower o' the quern / Mrs. H.L.MacDonald of Dunach / J.F. MacKenzie / Captain MacDiarmid / Mo Mhathair / Laura Andrews / Goatherd, The / Curlew, (The) / Millicent's favourite hornpipe / Harvest home / Stirling Castle / MacKinnon's reel / Dargai / Kilworth Hills / Loch Maree / Neil Gows' lament for his second wife / Marquis of Huntly's farewell / Marquis of Tullibardine / Marquis of Lorne / Minstrel's favourite hornpipe, The / Iain Ghlinn Cuaich / Seann Drochaid / Miss Addy / Lady Montgomery / Da mirrie boys of Greenland / Leveneep head / Willafjord / Forneth house / Clan MacColl / Cameron's got his wife again / Jock Wilson's ball.
LP: 12TS 347

Grant, Bill

BILL GRANT AND DELIA BELL (Grant, Bill & Delia Bell).
LP: REB 1593

CHEER OF THE HOMEFIRES (See under Bell, Delia) (Grant, Bill & Delia Bell).

FEW DOLLARS MORE, A (See under Bell, Delia) (Grant, Bill & Delia Bell).

FOLLOWING A FEELING (See under Bell, Delia) (Grant, Bill & Delia Bell).

ROLLIN' (Grant, Bill & Delia Bell).
Tracks: / Rollin' / No one else / Only you / Take my hand and tell me / Bluest girl in town, The / Goin' to see my Jesus / Girl at the crossroads bar, The / Moods of a fool, The / Rock pile, The / Stone walls and steel bars / Memories in the fall / I am the man, Thomas.
LP: REB 1604

Grant, David

ANXIOUS EDGE.
LP: BRLP 552
LP: 846 843 1
MC: BRCA 552
MC: 846 843 4

CHANGE.
Tracks: / Before too long / Change / Touch, The / Take us back / Ultimate love / Emblems / Thank you / Under one flag.
LP: POLH 37
MC: POLHC 37

DAVID GRANT.
Tracks: / Rock the midnight / Love will find a way / Wrap yourself around me / Stop and go / Organise / In the flow of love / Holding on / Watching you, watching me / You are all.
LP: CHR 1448
MC: ZCHR 1448

HOPES AND DREAMS.
Tracks: / Where our love begins / Turn around / Hopes and dreams / Take my heart / So excited / Could it be I'm falling in love / Crime of passion / Cool September / Love is alive / How many times.
LP: CHR 1483
MC: ZCHR 1483

Grant, Della

LISTEN.
Tracks: / Watch your step / Proud to be black / All I need is jah, jah love / Somebody killed my friend / Consider the children / How do I love you / What can we do / Afrikan princess / Capricorn woman.
LP: RG 409

Grant, Eddy

ALL THE HITS.
LP: NE 1284
MC: CE 2284

BORN TUFF.
Tracks: / Dance party / Next time around / Come along to my place / Melody of the night / Born tuff / Blood money / Village life / Funny little groove / In L.A. / She's standing at the corner.
LP: ICELP 6002
MC: ICEK 6002

CAN'T GET ENOUGH.
LP: ICELP 5002
MC: ICEK 5002
LP: ICEL 21

FILE UNDER ROCK.
Tracks: / Harmless piece of fun / Don't talk to strangers / Hostile country / Win or lose / Gimme hope Jo'Anna / Another riot / Say hello to Fidel / Chuck (is the king) / Long as I'm wanted by you / Put a hold on it.
LP: PCS 7320
MC: TCPCS 7320
LP: FA 3232
MC: TCFA 3232

GOING FOR BROKE.
Tracks: / Romancing the stone / Boys in the street / Come on let me know / Till I can't take love no more / Political bassa bassa / Telepathy / Only heaven knows / Ire Harry / Rock you good / Blue wave.
LP: ICELP 6001
MC: ICEK 6001

KILLER ON THE RAMPAGE.
Tracks: / Electric Avenue / I don't wanna dance / It's all in you / War party / Funky rock 'n' roll / Too young to fall / Latin love affair / Another revolutionary / Drop baby drop / Killer on the rampage.
LP: ICELP 3023
MC: ICEK 3023

LIVE AT NOTTING HILL.
Tracks: / Say I love you / Jamaican child / Neighbour, neighbour / Cockney black / Curfew / My turn to love you / Hello Africa / Walking on sunshine / Living on the frontline.
LP: ICELP 22
MC: ICEK 22
LP: ICELP 5005

LOVE IN EXILE.
Tracks: / My turn to love you / Feel the rhythm / Use it or lose it / Nobody's got time / Preachin' genocide / Exiled / Everybody dance.
LP: ICE 19

WALKING ON SUNSHINE (Very Best Of Eddy Grant).
Tracks: / I don't wanna dance / Gimme hope Jo'anna / Electric Avenue / Living on the frontline / Do you feel my love / Till I can't take love no more / Walking on sunshine / Baby come back / Romancing the stone / Can't get enough of you / Harmless piece of fun / Put a hold on it.
LP: PCSD 108
MC: TCPCSD 108

WALKING ON SUNSHINE.
Tracks: / Walk on sunshine / Living on the frontline / Frontline symphony / My love my love / Just imagine I'm loving you / Dancing in Guyana / Say I love you / We are.
LP: ICELP 5001
MC: ICEK 5001
LP: ICE 4
MC: TCPCSD 108

Grant, Gogi

GRANTED.... IT'S GOGI.
Tracks: / By myself / Day you came along, The / That's my desire / No fool like an old fool / I'm a dreamer, aren't we all / Don't be that way / I'm getting sentimental over you / I wished on the moon / Bibbidi bobbidi boo / Would I love you / I'm confessin' / You're getting to be a habit with me.
LP: NL 90044
MC: NK 90044

WELCOME TO MY HEART.
LP: FS 162

Grant, Lou

LOU GRANT PRESENTS PARTY TIME IN SCOTLAND.
Tracks: / Going down the water / Scotland the brave / My Bonnie lies over the ocean / I belong to Glasgow / Cock o the North / Catch me if you can / Coming round the mountain / Song of the Cly / Green oak tree / Flower of Scotland (Includes the track: Scots wha hae) / I love you because / Star o' Rabbie Burns, The / Scotch on the rocks / In dear old Glasgow toon.
LP: ITV 468
MC: KITV 468

LOU GRANT SINGS YOUR RADIO FAVOURITES.
Tracks: / Candy kisses / Five little fingers / Just loving you / Jean / No one will ever know / Rose of Tralee, The / Careless hands / When I leave the world behind / Yer mither / When the gold in

your hair turns to silver / Still / Turn your radio on / We will make love / Tribute to Jock Stein, A.
LP: . . . . **BGC 419**
MC: . . . . **KBGC 419**

Grant, Manson

AWARD WINNERS (Grant, Manson & The Dynamos Showband).
Tracks: / Heartaches by the number / I won't go huntin' with you Jake / Weatherman, The / Legend in my time, A.
MC: . . . . **CWGRTV 2**
LP: . . . . **WGRTV 2**

COUNTRY STARS (Grant, Manson & The Dynamos Showband).
LP: . . . . **WGR 038**
MC: . . . . **CWGR 038**

COUNTRYWIDE REQUESTS (Grant, Manson & The Dynamos).
LP: . . . . **WGR 070**
MC: . . . . **CWGR 070**

HAPPY HEART (Grant, Manson & The Dynamos).
LP: . . . . **WGR 085**
MC: . . . . **CWGR 085**

MANSON GRANT & THE DYNAMOS SHOWBAND (Grant, Manson & The Dynamos Showband).
LP: . . . . **WGR 007**
MC: . . . . **CWGR 007**

ON THE COUNTRY TRAIL.
LP: . . . . **WGR 065**
MC: . . . . **CWGR 065**

SING ANOTHER SONG (Grant, Manson & The Dynamos).
LP: . . . . **WGR 019**
MC: . . . . **CWGR 019**

Grant, Rudy

HARRISONS CAVE, BARBADOS.
LP: . . . . **CSEA 1 LP**

SOCA FOR LOVERS.
LP: . . . . **SEA 3LP**

SOCA FOR LOVERS VOL. 1.
LP: . . . . **SEA 1LP**

SOCA FOR LOVERS VOL. 2.
LP: . . . . **SEA 4LP**
MC: . . . . **SEA 4CASS**

Grant, Russell

ZODIAC JUKEBOX.
Tracks: / No matter what sign you are / Soldier / Bulls / Man who got no sign, The / Bad moon rising / You're so vain / Doctor sketch / Gimme little sign / Edge of the universe / Ghosts / Zodiac cafe / Aquarius / Puck's soliloquy.
LP: . . . . **REH 491**

Grant, Tom

EDGE OF THE WORLD.
MC: **8430114**

Granz, Norman

JAM SESSION NUMBER 3.
LP: **2304 421**

Grapes Of Wrath

NOW AND AGAIN.
Tracks: / All the things I wasn't / What was going through my head / Do you want to tell me? / Most, The / I'm gone / Blind / Stay / I can tell / Not the way it is / Hiding / Time is here, The / ...But I guess we'll never know.
LP: . . . . **EST 2118**
MC: . . . . **TCEST 2118**

SEPTEMBER BOWL OF GREEN.
LP: . . . . **NTL 30004**

Grapes Of Wrath (book)

GRAPES OF WRATH (Steinbeck, John (author)).
LP: . . . . **TC 1570**
MC: . . . . **CDL 51570**

Grappelli, Stephane

50TH ANNIVERSARY CONCERT (see Reinhardt, Django) (Grappelli, Stephane/Django Reinhardt).

80.
LP: . . . . **B 90104**
MC: . . . . **MB 990104**

AFTERNOON IN PARIS.
Tracks: / Autumn leaves / This can't be love / Time after time / Undecided / You were only passing by / Tangerine / Chicago / Manoir de mes reves / Daphne / Misty / Afternoon in Paris.
LP: . . . . **MPS 68 156**

AT THE WINERY VOL.2.
Tracks: / You are the sunshine of my life / Love for sale / Angel's camp / Willow weep for me / Chicago / Talking a chance on love / Minor swing / Let's fall in love / Just you, just me.
LP: . . . . **CJ 139**

BEST OF STEPHANE GRAPPELLI.
Tracks: / It don't mean a thing / I remember Django / Little star / Tournesol / Improvisation on prelude in E minor / Two cute / This can't be love / I can't believe that you're in love with me / Sweet Georgia Brown / Gershwin medley.
LP: . . . . **INT 147 013**

BEST OF STEPHANE GRAPPELLI (BLACK TULIP).
MC: **48052**

COLLECTION: STEPHANE GRAPPELLI.
MC: . . . . **CCSMC 274**

DJANGO REINHARDT WITH STEPHANE GRAPPELLI (see Reinhardt, Django) (Grappelli, Stephane/Django Reinhardt).

FASCINATING RHYTHM.
LP: **26013**
MC: **46013**

FEELING AND FINESSE.
Tracks: / Django / Nuages / Alabamy bound / You better go now / Daphne / Le tien / Minor swing / Makin' whoopee / How about you / Soft winds.
LP: **790 140-1**

FOR ALL SEASONS (see under Menuhin, Yehudi).

GIANTS, THE (Grappelli, Stephane/Earl Hines).
Tracks: / Fine and dandy / Over the rainbow / Manhattan / Moonlight in Vermont / I can't get started / You took advantage of me / Sometimes I'm happy.
LP: . . . . **BLP 30193**

GOLDEN HOUR OF STEPHANE GRAPPELLI.
MC: . . . . **KGHMC 111**
MC: . . . . **ZCGH 650**

HOMAGE TO DJANGO.
Tracks: / Sweet Sue / Tears / Avalon / Manoir de mes reves / Clopin clopant / Daphne / Swing guitars / Are you in the mood? / I wonder where my baby is tonight.
LP: . . . . **SM 3510**
MC: **401202**

HOMAGE TO DJANGO, VOL 2.
Tracks: / Djangology / Sweet chorus / Swing '39 / Oriental shuffle / Minor swing / Venez donc chez moi / Nuages / I saw stars / Fantasie / Dark eyes.
LP: . . . . **SM 3511**

HOT CLUB DE FRANCE (Grappelli, Stephane/Django Reinhardt).
MCSET: . . . . **DTO 10245**
LPS: **99001**

I GOT RHYTHM (Grappelli, Stephane/Hot Club).
Tracks: / Dinah / I'm confessin' / Tiger rag / Heavenly music / Someday, sweetheart / Stephane Blues / When I look at you / After you've gone / Star eyes / Stephane's tune / Don't you know I care / Sweet Sue / Jive bomber / Weep no more / My lady / Liza (all the clouds will roll away) / Three o'clock in the morning / Folks who live on the hill, The / That old black magic / Noel brings the swing / It's a hap-hap-happy day / I got rhythm / My heart tells me / Bluebirds in the moonlight / Oh Johnny, oh Johnny oh / I never mention your name / Oh lady be good / You made me love you / Alexander's ragtime band / Playmates / In the mood / Ting a ling / Oh by jingo, oh by gee / Sheik of Araby, The / I said no / Scatterbrain / Rose room / This can't be love / I can't believe that you're in love with me / Misty / Tea for two / After you've gone.
2LP: . . . . **RECDL 12**
MCSET: . . . . **RECDC 12**
2LP: . . . . **BLP 30158**
MCSET: . . . . **BLP 30158C**

I HEAR MUSIC.
Tracks: / Tea for two / Danny boy / Let's do it / Dear Ben / I hear music / Dany / Smoke gets in your eyes / Body and soul / Gary / Flowers for Kenny.
LP: . . . . **INTS 5047**
MC: . . . . **INTK 5047**

I REMEMBER DJANGO (Grappelli, Stephane/Barney Kessel).
Tracks: / I remember Django / Honeysuckle rose / I can't get started / What a difference a day made / More than you know / Et maintenant / I found a new baby / It's only a paper moon.
LP: . . . . **BLP 30101**

IMPROVISATIONS.
Tracks: / Body and soul / Fascinating rhythm / My funny valentine.
2LP: . . . . **BARC 96069/70**

INTIMATE.
LP: **2273032**
MC: **2173032**

JEALOUSY (Hits Of The Thirties) (Grappelli, Stephane/Yehudi Menuhin).
Tracks: / Jealousy / Blue room / Fine romance, A / Billy / Love is here to stay / Aurore / Pick yourself up / Night and day / I can't believe that you're in love with me / These foolish things / Errol / Lady be good / Jermyn Street / Cheek to cheek / Cheek to cheek / Lady is a tramp, The.
MC: . . . . **TCCFP 4576**

JUST ONE OF THOSE THINGS.
Tracks: / Cheek to cheek / Are you in the mood? / Just one of those things / There's a small hotel / Pent-up house / I'll remember April / Surrey with the fringe on top / I get a kick out of you / Blue moon / Them there eyes / I can't give you anything but love / How high the moon / Waltz du passe / My one and only love.
LP: . . . . **EMD 143 643 1**
MC: . . . . **TCEMD 1436434**

JUST ONE OF THOSE THINGS (BLACK LION).
Tracks: / Just one of those things / Misty / More / Que rest et il de nos amours? / Don't get around much anymore / Them there eyes / Honeysuckle rose.
LP: . . . . **BLP 30152**

LIVE IN SAN FRANCISCO (Grappelli, Stephane & His Trio).
Tracks: / I got rhythm / Fascinating rhythm / Let's fall in love / Swing '42 / Honeysuckle Rose / You are the sunshine of my life / Minor swing / Here, there and everywhere / St. Louis blues / Them there eyes / After you've gone.
LP: . . . . **BKH 51601**

MAGIC OF STEPHANE GRAPPELLI, THE.
LP: . . . . **SPR 8563**
MC: . . . . **SPC 8563**

MEETS THE RHYTHM SECTION.
Tracks: / Love for sale / Perugia / Two cute / Fascinating rhythm / Parisian thoroughfare / Improvisation on prelude in E minor / Wave / Hallelujah.
LP: . . . . **BLP 30183**

MENUHIN AND GRAPPELLI PLAY... (see under Menuhin, Yehudi) (Grappelli, Stephane/Yehudi Menuhin).

MY OTHER LOVE.
MC: **40 46257**

NORWEGIAN WOOD (Grappelli, Stephane/Elena Duran).
Tracks: / Yesterday / All my loving / Eleanor Rigby / Norwegian wood / Can't buy me love / Here, there and everywhere / Michelle / Hey Jude / Long and winding road, The / Hard day's night, A.
LP: . . . . **RCALP 6007**
MC: . . . . **RCAK 6007**

ON THE ROAD AGAIN (see Brewer, Teresa) (Grappelli, Steph./Teresa Brewer).

OSCAR PETERSON & STEPHANE GRAPPELLI (see Peterson, Oscar) (Grappelli, Stephane Quartet/Oscar Peterson).

PARIS ENCOUNTER (Grappelli, Stephane/Garry Burton).
Tracks: / Daphne / Blue in green / Falling grace / Here's that rainy day / Coquette / Sweet rain / Night has a thousand eyes, The / Arpege / Eiderdown.
LP: . . . . **K 40378**

PARISIAN THOROUGHFARE.
Tracks: / Love for sale / Perugia / Two cute / Parisian thoroughfare / Improvisation on prelude in E minor / Wave / Hallelujah.
LP: . . . . **BLM 51502**

PLAYS GERSHWIN.
MC: **402052**

PLAYS JEROME KERN (Grappelli, Stephane & His Trio).
LP: . . . . **GRP 91032**
MC: . . . . **GRPM 91032**

REUNION, THE (Grappelli, Stephane/George Shearing).
Tracks: / I'm coming Virginia / Time after time / La chanson de rue / Too marvellous for words / It don't mean a thing / Makin' whoopee / After you've gone / Flamingo / Star eyes / Folks who live on the hill, The.
LP: **8218681**
LP: . . . . **MPS 68 162**

RHYTHM IS OUR BUSINESS (see Reinhardt, Django) (Grappelli, Stephane/Django Reinhardt).

SKOL (See under Peterson, Oscar) (Grappelli, Steph./Oscar Peterson/Joe Pass).

SPECIAL STEPHANE GRAPPELLI (1947-1961).
Tracks: / Qui, pour vous revoir / Tea for two / Pennies from Heaven / Can't help lovin' dat man / Girl in Calico, A / World is waiting for the sunrise, The / I can't recognize the tune / You took advantage of me / Folks who live on the hill / Looking at you / Swing 39 / Belleville / Manoir de mes reves / Djangology / Have you met Miss Jones? / This can't be love / Alemberts / Marno / Blue moon (With Sextette Pierre Spiers.) / Foggy day in London town, A (With Sextette Pierre Spiers.).
MC: . . . . **TCEMS 1365**

STARDUST.
LP: . . . . **BLP 60117**

STEPHANE GRAPPELLI (Compact/Walkman Jazz) (Grappelli, Stephane & His Trio).
Tracks: / Djangology / I'm coming Virginia / Misty / Shine / Blues for Django and Stephane / Chicago / Makin' whoopee / Hot lips.
MC: **831 370-4**

STEPHANE GRAPPELLI 1973.
Tracks: / It don't mean a thing / I've got the world on a string / What are you doing the rest of your life? / Birth of the blues / Opportunity / Just a gigolo / Didn't we? / Crazy rhythm / It might as well be spring / Emotion / Three little words / Avalon.
LP: . . . . **NSPL 18403**

STEPHANE GRAPPELLI IN CONCERT.
Tracks: / Just one of those things / Misty / More / Que reste t'il de nos amours / Don't get around much anymore / Them there eyes / Honeysuckle rose.
LP: . . . . **BLP 12183**

STEPHANE GRAPPELLI LIVE AT THE CARNEGIE HALL.
Tracks: / I can't give you anything but love / As time goes by / Crazy rhythm / Golden green / Chattanooga choo choo / Blues in B for BT / Nuages.
LP: . . . . **ASLP 1001**
MC: . . . . **ZCAS 1001**

STEPHANE GRAPPELLI PLAYS COLE PORTER.
Tracks: / It's alright with me / You're the top / Anything goes / In the still of the night / You've got a thing / Miss Otis regrets / I've got you under my skin / Love for sale / Easy to love / You'd be so nice to come home to / Let's do it / My heart belongs to daddy.
2LP: . . . . **ALB 240**

STEPHANE GRAPPELLI PLAYS GERSHWIN.
MC: **402054**

STEPHANOVA.
Tracks: / Tune up / Thou swell / Norwegian dance / Fulton Street samba / My foolish heart / Lover / Way you look tonight / Stephanova / Smoke rings and wine / Tangerine / Waltz for Queenie / Sonny boy.
LP: . . . . **CJ 225**
MC: . . . . **CJC 225**

STRUTTIN' OUT (see Reinhardt, Django) (Grappelli, Stephane/Django Reinhardt).

SWINGING AFFAIR (Grappelli, Stephane/Django Reinhardt).
Tracks: / I wonder where my baby is tonight / If I had you / Hungaria / Tornerai / After you've gone / It had to be you / Tea for two / Dinah / Body and soul / Time on my hands / Stardust / Margie / Henderson stomp / You're the cream in my coffee.
LP: . . . . **MOR 530**

TALK OF THE TOWN, THE.
Tracks: / Talk of the town / Amanda / Stardust / Can't help lovin' dat man / We'll be together again / Nature boy / Nearness of you, The / Tournesol / Greensleeves / You go to my head.
LP: . . . . **BLP 30165**

TEA FOR TWO (Grappelli, Stephane/Yehudi Menuhin).
Tracks: / Crazy rhythm / Man I love, The / Tea for two / Air on a shoestring / Foggy day, A / Viva Vivaldi / My funny valentine / Limehouse blues / Thou swell / Yesterdays / Between the Devil and the deep blue sea.
LP: . . . . **EMD 5530**
MC: . . . . **TCEMD 5530**

TIVOLI GARDENS, COPENHAGEN (Grappelli, Stephane/Joe Pass/Niels Pedersen).
Tracks: / It's only a paper moon / Time after time / Let's fall in love / Crazy rhythm / How deep is the ocean? / I'll remember April / I can't get started / I get a kick out of you.
LP: **2308 220**
MC: . . . . **K 08 220**

TOGETHER (see Reinhardt, Django) (Grappelli, Steph./Django Reinhardt/Eddie South).

TOGETHER AT LAST (Grappelli, Steph./Vassar Clements).
LP: . . . . **FF 421**

TOP HAT (Grappelli, Stephane/Yehudi Menuhin).
Tracks: / Puttin' on the Ritz / Way you look tonight / He loves and she loves / Isn't this a lovely day / Piccolino / Alison / Change partners / Top Hat / They can't take that away from me / Continental / They all laughed / Amanda / Funny face / Carioca.
LP: . . . . **EMD 5539**

TRIBUTE TO DJANGO.
LP: . . . . **B 90103**
MC: . . . . **MB 90103**

TWO OF A KIND (See under Asmussen, Svend) (Grappelli, Steph./Svend Asmussen).

TWO-FER, A (Grappelli, Stephane/Hank Jones).
Tracks: / Thou swell / These foolish things / September in the rain / You better go now / Hallelujah / Yesterdays / Mellow grapes / I'll never be the same.
LP: . . . . **MR 5287**

VENUPELLI BLUES (Grappelli, Steph./Joe Venuti).
Tracks: / I can't give you anything but love / My one and only love / Undecided / Venupelli blues / I'll never be the same / Tea for two.
LP: **260 229-1**
LP: . . . . **AFF 29**

VINTAGE 1981.
Tracks: / If I had you / I can't get started / Blue moon / But not for me.
LP: . . . . **CJ 169**

VIOLIN SUMMIT.
LP: **8213031**

VIOLINS NO END (Grappelli, Stephane/Stuff Smith).
Tracks: / Don't get around much anymore / Chapeau blues / No points today / Lady is a tramp, The / Desert sands / How high the moon / Moonlight in Vermont.
LP: **2310 907**
MC: **K10 907**

VIOLINSPIRATION (Grappelli, Stephane/Diz Disley Trio).
Tracks: / Lover come back to me / Sweet Lorraine / Shine / Solitude / Ain't misbehavin / Souvenir de villinger / Hot lips / My heart stood still / Nearness of you, The / Joy / Nightingale sang in Berkely square,A / Cherokee / Lover man.
LP: . . . . **MOIR 110**
MC: . . . . **CMOIR 110**
LP: . . . . **MPS 68 058**

YOUNG DJANGO.
Tracks: / Djangology / Sweet chorus / Minor swing / Are you in the mood / Galerie St. Hubert / Tears / Swing guitars / Oriental shuffle / Blues for Django and Stephane.
LP: . . . . **MPS 68 230**

Grass Roots (reggae)

GRASS ROOTS VOLUME 1.
LP: . . . . **LALP 009**

Grasso, Frank

FRANK GRASSO BIG BAND (Grasso, Frank Big Band).
LP: . . . . **SJP 226**

Grassroots

SONGS OF OTHER TIMES (see under Sloan, P.F.) (Grass Roots/P.F. Sloan)).

Grassroots (bluegrass)

FEELING SO BLUEGRASS.
Tracks: / Raymond's breakdown / Fox on the run / Walking in Jerusalem / Ashes of love / Rebel soldier / Bird dog / Teach your children / Roll on Ohio river / Siver nicholette waltz / Pan American.
LP: . . . . **KO 1002**

Grateful Dead

AMERICAN BEAUTY.
Tracks: / Box of rain / Friend of the Devil / Operator / Sugar magnolia / Ripple / Brokedown palace / Till the morning comes / Attic of my life / Truckin.
LP: . . . . **K 46074**
MC: **K4 46074**

ANTHEM OF THE SUN.
Tracks: / That's it for the other one / Cryptical envelopment / Quadlibet / For tender feet / Faster we go, the rounder we get, The / We leave the castle / Alligator / Caution (do not stop on the tracks).
LP: **K2 46021**

AOXOMOXOA.
Tracks: / St. Stephen / Dupree's diamond blues / Rosemary / Doin' that rag / Mountains of the moon / China cat sunflower / What's become of the baby cosmic Charlie.
LP: . . . . **K 46027**
MC: . . . . **K 446027**

BEST OF GRATEFUL DEAD, THE.
Tracks: / Golden road (to unlimited devotion), The / Truckin / Rosemary / Sugar magnolia / St. Stephen / Uncle John's band / Casey Jones / Mexicali blues / Turn on your lovelight / One more saturday night / Friend of the devil.
LP: . . . . **K 56024**

BLUES FOR ALLAH.
Tracks: / Help on the way / Slipknot / Franklin's tower / King Solomon's marbles: (Part 1) - Stronger than / King Solomon's marbles: (Part 2) - Milkin' the turkey / Music never stopped, The / Crazy fingers / Sage and spirit / Blues for Allah / Sand castles and glass camels / Unusual occurrences in the desert.
LP: . . . . **UAS 29895**
LP: . . . . **GDV 4001**
MC: . . . . **GDTC 4001**

BUILT TO LAST.
Tracks: / Foolish heart / Just a little light / Built to last / Blow away / Standing on the moon / Victim or the crime / We can run / Picasso moon / I will take you home.
LP: **210326**
MC: **410326**

DEAD SET.
Tracks: / Samson and Delilah / Friend of the devil / New minglewood blues / Deal / Candy man / Little red rooster / Loser / Passenger / Feel like a stranger / Franklin's tower / Rhythm devils / Space / Fire on the mountain / Greatest story ever told / Brokedown.
2LP: . . . . **DARTY 11**

DEADICATED (See under Indie) (Various artists).

DYLAN AND THE DEAD (See under Dylan, Bob).

EUROPE 72.
Tracks: / Cumberland blues / He's gone / He's gone / One more saturday night / Jack straw / You can win again / China cat sunflower / Sunflower / I know you rider / Brown eyed woman / Hurts me too / Ramblin' rose / Sugar magnolia / Mr. Charlie / Tennessee Jed / Truckin' / Epilogue / Prelude.
2LP: . . . . **K 66019**

FROM THE MARS HOTEL.
Tracks: / U.S. blues / Unbroken chain / Scarlet begonias / Money money / China doll / Loose Lucy / Pride of cucamonga / Ship of fools.
LP: . . . . **GDV 4007**
MC: . . . . **GDTC 4007**
LP: . . . . **K 59302**

GO TO HEAVEN.
Tracks: / Far from me / Althea / Feel like a stranger / Alabama getaway / Don't ease me in / Easy to love you / Lost sailor / Saint of circumstance.
LP: . . . . **SPART 1115**

GRATEFUL DEAD.
Tracks: / Golden road (to unlimited devotion) / Beat it on down the line / Good morning little schoolgirl / Cold rain and snow / Sitting on top of the world / Cream puff war / Morning dew / New, new Minglewood blues / Viola Lee blues.
LP: . . . . **ED 221**

GRATEFUL DEAD: INTERVIEW PICTURE DISC.
LPPD: . . . . **BAK 2148**

GRATEFUL DEAD LIVE.
Tracks: / Bertha / Mama tried / Big railroad blues / Playing in the band / Wharf rat / Not fade away / Goin' down the road feeling bad / Other one, The / Me and my Uncle / Big boss man / Me and Bobby McGee / Johnny B. Goode.
2LP: . . . . **K 66009**

IN THE DARK.
Tracks: / Touch of grey / Hell in a bucket / When push comes to shove / West LA fadeaway / Tons of steel / Throwing stones / Black muddy river.
LP: **208564**
MC: **408564**
LP: **211145**

LIVE DEAD.
Tracks: / Dark star / Death don't have no mercy / Feedback / And we bid you goodnight / St. Stephen / Eleven / Turn on your love / Light.
2LP: . . . . **K 66002**

ONE FROM THE VAULT.
LPS: **CDV3 4015**
MCSET: **GDTC3 4015**

RECKONING.
Tracks: / Dire wolf / Race is on, The / Oh babe / It ain't no lie / It must have been the roses / Dark hollow / China doll / Been all around this world / Monkey and the engineer / Jack-a-roe / Deep elem blues / Cassidy / To lay me down / Rosalie McFall / Road again, The / Bird song / Ripple.
2LP: . . . . **DARTY 9**

SHAKEDOWN STREET.
Tracks: / Good lovin' / France / Shakedown Street / Serengetti / Fire on the mountain / I need a miracle / From the heart of me / Stagger Lee / All new minglewood blues / If I had the world to give.
LP: . . . . **ARTY 159**

SKELETONS FROM THE CLOSET.
Tracks: / Golden road (to unlimited devotion), The / Truckin' / Rosemary / Sugar magnolia / St. Stephen / Uncle John's band / Casey Jones / Mexicali blues / Turn on your lovelight / One more Saturday night / Friend of the devil / Don't fall in love (rock 'n' roll) / Do you believe? / Creeper, The / Wednesday / Remember (walking in the sand) / Call your name / Take you home / Halloween / Rollercoaster / Blizzard / On the run.
LP: . . . . **THBL 018**
MC: . . . . **THBC 018**

STEAL YOUR FACE.
Tracks: / Promised land / Cold, rain and snow / Around and around / Stella blue / Mississippi half-step uptown toodeloo / Ship of fools / Beat it on down the line / Big river / Black-throated wind / U.S. blues / El Paso / Sugaree / It must have been the roses / Casey Jones.
2LP: . . . . **UAD 60131/2**
LP: **GDV2 4006**
MC: . . . . **GDTC 4006**

TERRAPIN STATION.
Tracks: / Estimated prophet / Dancing in the street / Passenger / Samson and Delilah / Sunrise / Lady with the fan, The / Terrapin station / Terrapin / Terrapin transit / At a siding / Terrapin fever / Refrain.
LP: **201190**
MC: **401190**
LP: . . . . **SPARTY 1016**

WAKE OF FLOOD/ FROM MARS HOTEL.
Tracks: / Mississippi half-step uptown toodeloo / Let me sing your blues away / Row Jimmy / Stella blue / Here comes sunshine / Eyes of the world / Weather report / Suite (Prelude Part 1; Part 2 - Let it grow) / U.S. blues / China doll / Unbroken chain / Loose Lucy / Scarlet begonias / Pride of Cucamonga / Money, money / Ship of fools.
2LP: . . . . **UDM 103/4**

WAKE OF THE FLOOD.
Tracks: / Mississippi half step uptown toodeloo / Row Jimmy / Here comes sunshine / Weather report / Let me sing your blues away / Stella blue / Eyes of the world.
LP: . . . . **GDV 4002**
MC: . . . . **GDTC 4002**

WHAT A LONG STRANGE TRIP IT'S BEEN (Best of Grateful Dead, The).
Tracks: / New New Minglewood blues / Cosmic Charlie / Truckin' Black Peter / Born cross-eyed / Riddle / Doin' that rag / Dark star / High time / New speedway boogie / St. Stephen / Jack Straw / Me and my uncle / Tennessee Jed / Cumberland blues / Playing in the band / Brown eyed woman / Ramble on Rose.
2LP: . . . . **K 66073**

WITHOUT A NET (Live).
Tracks: / Feel like a stranger / Mississippi half step / Mexicali blues / Cold rain and snow / Walkin' blues / Althea / Cassidy / Bird song / Let it grow / Playing in the band / China cat sunflower / I know you rider / Victim or the crime / Other one, The / Wharf rat / Help on the way / Franklin's tower / One more Saturday night.
2LP: **303935**
MCSET: **503935**

WORKINGMAN'S DEAD.
Tracks: / Uncle John's band / High time / Dire wolf / New speedway boogie / Cumberland blues / Black Peter / Easy wind / Casey Jones.
LP: . . . . **K 46049**
MC: **K4 46049**
LP: . . . . **WS 1869**

Graupner

GRAUPNER.
LP: . . . . **ANTAR 8**

Grauzone

GRAUZONE.
Tracks: / Film 2 / Schlachtet / Hinte den bergen / Maikaefer flieg / Marmelade und himbeereis / Wuetendes glas / Kaelte kriecht / Kunstgewerbe / Der weg zu zweit / In der nacht.
LP: . . . . **EMC 3408**

Gravedigger

HEAVY METAL BREAKDOWN.
LP: . . . . **N 0007**

WAR GAMES.
LP: . . . . **N 0034**

WITCH HUNT.
LP: . . . . **N 0020**

Gravelle, Eirlys

DANIEL.
Tracks: / Daniel.
MC: . . . . **POPDY CP2**

Gravenites, Nick

MONKEY BUSINESS (Gravenites Nick/John Cipollina Band).
LP: . . . . **WIKM 29**

Graves

WE'RE GONNA HAVE A BALL.
LP: . . . . **CCLP 102**

Graves, Josh

DAD THE DOBRO MAN (Graves, Josh & Billy Troy).
Tracks: / Don't let the stars get in your eyes / Cory belle / In the jailhouse now / Elareeb / She's loving me blind / Doin' my time / Come walk with me / Dad the dobro man / All for the love of a girl / Coal field march / Harvest of my heart / California blues.
LP: . . . . **CMH 6264**
MC: . . . . **CMH 6264C**

KING OF THE DOBRO.
LP: . . . . **CMH 6252**

SING AWAY THE PAIN.
Tracks: / I'm gonna sing away the pain tonight / Movin' South / Calico gypsy / Evelina / Good time Charlie's got the blues / Lay down Sally / Brand new Carroll County blues / I still get funny when it rains / Easy money / Easin' down the turnpike / Crazy mama / Uncle Josh plays 'lectrified dobro.
LP: . . . . **CMH 6233**
MC: . . . . **CMH 6233C**

SWEET SUNNY SOUTH (Graves, Josh/Bobby Smith & Boys From Shiloh).
Tracks: / Dixieland for me / Jennifer waltz / Take me back to the sweet sunny South / Juarez / Head over heels in love with you / Crossin' the rockies / Mississippi flood / On my mind / Trouble in mind / Starlight waltz / Pleasant valley.
LP: . . . . **CMH 6209**
MC: . . . . **CMH 6209C**

Graves, Robert (aut)

CLAUDIUS THE GOD (see under Claudius The God (bk)) (Jacobi, Derek (nar)).

GREEN-SAILED VESSEL, THE.
LP: . . . . **CCT 14**

I CLAUDIUS (Jacobi, Derek (nar)).
MCSET: . . . . **SAY 16**
MCSET: . . . . **ARGO 1022**

ROBERT GRAVES READS.
MC: **1066**

Graves, Roosevelt

ROOSEVELT GRAVES.
LP: . . . . **WSE 110**

Gravestone

BACK TO ATTACK.
LP: **941 306**

CREATING A MONSTER.
LP: **805 033**

Gravine, Anita

DREAM DANCING.
LP: . . . . **PRO 7074**

I ALWAYS KNEW.
LP: . . . . **ST 255**

Grawe, George

SIX STUDIES FOR PIANO SOLO.
LP: . . . . **WW 012**

Gray, Barry

NO STRINGS ATTACHED.
Tracks: / Thunderbird / Captain Scarlet / Hijacked / Aqua Marina / Stingray / Mysterons / Joe 90 / Parker - well done.
LP: . . . . **DOW 3**
MC: . . . . **ZCDOW 3**
MC: . . . . **CLAMC 204**

THUNDERBIRDS ARE GO (See under Thunderbirds Are Go).

Gray, Bruce

BRUCE GRAY'S VINTAGE JAZZBAND 1973.
LP: . . . . **S 1418**

Gray, David

ARMCHAIR MELODIES (Gray, David/Tommy Tycho).
LP: . . . . **NE 927**

Gray, Dobie

LONDON BOYS (See under Small Faces) (Gray, Dobie/Small Faces/Byrds/David Bowie).

SINGS FOR 'IN' CROWDERS THAT GO 'GO-GO'.

Tracks: / The 'in' crowd / Blue ribbons (for her curls) / Monkey jerk / Walk with love / Look at me / Be a man / No room to cry / Out on the floor / See you at the 'go-go' / Mr Engineer / In Hollywood / Broken in two / That's how you treat a cheater / Feeling in my heart.
LP: **KENT 071**

Gray, Dolores

WARM BRANDY.
Tracks: / Shangri la / Penthouse serenade / You're getting to be a habit with me / Kiss me / How long has this been going on / Close your eyes / You go to my head / Do do do / Speak low / Don't blame me / Isn't it romantic / You're my thrill.
LP: **PM 155 300 1**
MC: **PM 155 300 4**

Gray, Glen

1939: GLEN GRAY (Gray, Glen & The Casa Loma Orchestra).
LP: **CLP 36**

1940: GLEN GRAY AND THE CASA LOMA ORCHESTRA (Gray, Glen and the Casa Loma Orchestra).
LP: **CLP 61**

GLEN GRAY, 1943-46.
Tracks: / Sitting on the third rail / Blule rhapsody / Don't take your love from me / Fifth Avenue sax / From the blue / Flat third jive / Dancing on the ceiling / Featuring the boys / Maybe / Lion and the mouse, The / I don't care who knows / Who ray / After you've gone / Savage / If I love again / Hold the phone.
LP: **HSR 120**

GLEN GRAY & CASA LOMA ORCHESTRA (HINDSIGHT) (1939-40) (Gray, Glen and the Casa Loma Orchestra).
Tracks: / Smoke rings / Wrap your troubles in dreams / Hindustan / Hour of parting / It's funny to everyone but me / Sometimes I'm happy / No-name jive / Meet me tonight in dreamland / Memories of you / What's the matter with me / Little brown jug / In the mood / Tuxedo Junction / Day in, day out / High society / Sassin' the boss.
LP: **HSR 104**

GLEN GRAY & THE CASA LOMA ORCHESTRA (JASMINE) (Gray, Glen & The Casa Loma Orchestra).
Tracks: / Theme - introduction / Lovely come back / Should I / Sheik of Araby, The / Chant of the jungle / Zonky / I never knew / I found a new baby / I got rhythm / Closing / Way down yonder in New Orleans / Truckin' / Weary blues / Walking the dog / I may be wrong / My blue Heaven / Dardanella / Farewell blues / Theme - close.
LP: **JASM 2516**
MC: **JASMC 2516**

GLEN GRAY & THE CASA LOMA ORCHESTRA, 1943-46 (Gray, Glen & The Casa Loma Orchestra).
Tracks: / Sitting on a third rail / Blue rhapsody / Don't take your love from me / Fifth Avenue sax / From the blue / Flat third jive / Dancing on the ceiling / Featuring the boys / Maybe / Lion and the mouse, The / I don't care who knows / If I love again / Who Ray / After you've gone / Savage / Hold the phone.
LP: **HMP 5050**

JONAH JONES QUARTET/GLEN GRAY & THE CASA LOMA OR (See under Jones, Jonah) (Gray, Glen & Jonah Jones).

MOONGLOW 1930 - 36 (Gray, Glen & His Orchestra).
LP: **BS 7126**

ONE NIGHT STAND WITH GLEN GRAY & CASA LOMA ORCHESTRA (Gray, Glen & The Casa Loma Orchestra).
LP: **SH 1005**

SHALL WE SWING (Gray, Glen & The Casa Loma Orchestra).
LP: **ST 1055**

SOLO SPOTLIGHT (Gray, Glen & The Casa Loma Orchestra).
Tracks: / Golden earrings / Street of dreams / Blue star (The Medic theme) / My foolish heart / Love letters / Around the world in 80 days / Was I to blame for falling in love with you / Stella by starlight / Beautiful love / When I fall in love / I don't stand a ghost of a chance with you / Love me.
LP: **EMS 1147**
MC: **TCEMS 1147**

SOUNDS OF THE GREAT BANDS IN LATIN (Gray, Glen & The Casa Loma Orchestra).
Tracks: / String of pearls / Lean baby / Take the 'A' train / Casa Loma stomp / Stardust / No name jive / Frenesi / Collaboration / Mole, The / Early Autumn / King Porter stomp.
LP: **EMS 1303**
MC: **TCEMS 1303**

SWING GOES ON, VOL 1.
Tracks: / Bugle call rag / Symphony in riffs / Floyd's guitar blues / Well git it / Opus one / Two o'clock jump / Swingin' the blues / New no-name jive / 720 in the books / Uptown blues / Baubles, bangles and beads / Night train / Dippermouth blues / Flying home.
LP: **IC 054 52710**

SWINGIN DECADE (Gray, Glen & The Casa Loma Orchestra).
Tracks: / Apple honey / Midnight sun / Mission to Moscow / Harlem Nocturne / Jack the bear / Champ, The / Blues Rhapsody / Malibu / Opus one / Sherwood Forest / Oh what a beautiful morning / Intermission riff.
LP: **EMS 1133**
MC: **TCEMS 1133**

THEMES OF THE GREAT BANDS (Gray, Glen & The Casa Loma Orchestra).
Tracks: / Let's dance / Getting sentimental over you / Redskin rhumba / Moonlight serenade / Leap frog / I can't get started / Nightmare / Ciribiribin / Blue flame / Quaker city / Tuxedo Junction / Artistry in rhythm.
LP: **2C 068 54574**

Gray, Gregory

THINK OF SWANS.
Tracks: / Life of Reilly / James Bond / Speechless / Life and times / Books to read twice / Johnny Purify / Sensual / Charlie gets hurt / Strawberries / Seatown.
LP: **CBS 26655**
MC: **40 26655**

Gray, Hebbie

SOUND OF HEBBIE GRAY.
MC: **CJW 015**

Gray, Henry

LUCKY MAN.
LP: **BP-2788**

Gray, Jerry

BIG DANCE TONIGHT (Gray, Jerry & His Orchestra).
Tracks: / Thou swell / Swanee / Champagne boogie / Off limits / Way you look tonight / Off the wall / Adios / Darktown strutters' ball / Kettle drum hop / Oomp-chuck / Coronado cruise / Baby's lullaby.
LP: **JASM 1039**

UNCOLLECTED(1952), THE.
LP: **HUK 212**

Gray, Mark

FEELING INSIDE,THE.
Tracks: / Please be love / She will / You're the reason / Born to be a music man / Strong heart dance with me / Back when love was enough / I need you again / Walking after midnight / That feeling inside.
LP: **CBS 26694**
MC: **40 26694**

MAGIC.
Tracks: / It ain't real if it ain't you / Wounded hearts / Whatever happened to the good old days / Lean on me / Till her heartbreak is over / Left side of the bed / Sun don't shine on the same folks all the time / If all the magic's gone / Till you and your lover are lovers again / Fire from a friend.
LP: **CBS 25838**

THIS OL' PIANO.
Tracks: / Diamond in the dust / Twenty years ago / You're gonna be the last love / This ol' piano / I guess you must have touched me just right / Smooth sailing / Dixie girl / Lonely people / It's got to be you / Sometimes when we touch.
LP: **CBS 26149**

Gray Matter

FOOD FOR THOUGHT.
Tracks: / Retrospect / Oscars eye / Fill a void / Give me a clue / Gray matter / Caffeine blues / Crisis and compromise / Flash in time / Phobies / I am the walrus.
LP: **DISCHORD 48**

Gray, Owen

BATTLE OF THE GIANTS, ROUND 1 (Gray, Owen & Pluggy Satchmo).
LP: **STLP 1010**

CUPID.
LP: **SMLP 12-153**

DREAMS OF OWEN GRAY.
LP: **TRLS 150**
LP: **BMLP 017**

FORWARD ON THE SCENE.
LP: **TWLP 4**

HIT AFTER HIT VOL 2.
LP: **CGLP 014**

HIT AFTER HIT: VOL 4.
LP: **STLP 1013**

INSTANT RAPPORT.
LP: **BFMLP 107**

LITTLE GIRL.
LP: **STLP 1032**

OLDIES BUT GOODIES (Gray, Owen & Delroy Wilson).
LP: **STLP 1007**
MC: **VSMC 007**

OWEN GRAY MEETS MAX ROMEO (Gray, Owen & Max Romeo).
LP: **VSLP 5004**

OWEN SINGS BOB MARLEY.
LP: **SRLLP 007**

READY, WILLING AND ABLE.
LP: **PHLP 0015**
MC: **PHLC 0015**

ROOM AT THE TOP.
LP: **WENLP 3028**

STAND BY ME.
LP: **Unknown**

WATCH THIS SOUND.
MC: **SKYCAS 52**
LP: **SKYLP 52**

Gray, Simon

BUTLEY.
MCSET: **0362**

Gray, Wardell

1947-52.
LP: **LPJT 27**

ALUMNI MASTERS, THE (Gray, Wardell & Ben Webster).
Tracks: / Jumpin' at The Woodside / Golden bullet / How high the moon / One o'clock jump / Cottontail / Audiology / Honeysuckle rose / Loverman / Main stem.
LP: **BLJ 8038**

CENTRAL AVENUE.
Tracks: / Twisted / Twisted (unissued take) / Easy living / Southside / Southside (unissued take) / Sweet Lorraine / Scrapple from the apple / Move / Siner kissed an angel, A / Blue gray / Grayhound / Teadin' / April skies / Bright boy / Jackie / Farmer's market / Sweet and lovely / Lover man (oh where can you be) / Man I love, The / Lavonne / So long, Broadway / Paul's case.
LP: **PR 24062**

CHASE, THE (see under Gordon, Dexter) (Gray, Wardell & Dexter Gordon).

HUNT, THE (Gray, Wardell & Dexter Gordon).
2LP: **SJL 2222**

LIVE JAM SESSION AT TRADEWINDS.
Tracks: / Out of nowhere / Strike up the band / Pennies from Heaven.
LP: **JAM 103**

SWEDISH PASTRY (See under Hasselgard, Stan) (Gray, Wardell/Stan Hasselgard).
LP: **DRLP 16**

THIN MAN MEETS FAT BOY (Gray, Wardell/Don Lamphere Quintet).
LP: **MLP 1981**

THIN MAN MEETS FAT BOY VOL. 2 (Gray, Wardell/Don Lamphere Quintet).
LP: **MLP 1982**

THIN MAN MEETS MAD LAD (Gray, Wardell/Leo Parker Quartet).
LP: **MLP 1983**

WARDELL GRAY.
Tracks: / Bebop / Hot house / Groovin' high / King, The / It serves me right / Little dog / Spasmodic / X-1 / Good bait / C jam blues / How high the moon.
LP: **SPJ 134**

WARDELL GRAY AND THE BIG BANDS.
Tracks: / Let's get started / Blue keys / Straight life / Now that you're mine / Bamby / At El Grotto / Nonchalant man / Blues for sale / Having a wonderful wish / Hucklebuck, The / Egg head / Nails / Little pony / Jeep is jumpin' / Caxton Hall swing / For europeans only.
LP: **OFF 3029**

Graye, Tony

OH GEE (Graye, Tony Quartet/Quintet).
Tracks: / These foolish things / 'S wonderful / Hey Dot / Lover man / Oh gee / I remember you / Night and day / Slowly with expression / I know you want to do it.
LP: **ZMS 2001**

Grayson, Kathryn

20 GOLDEN FAVOURITES: KATHRYN GRAYSON.
Tracks: / Make believe / Daybreak / Voice of spring / Romance / Tales from the Vienna Woods / Someday / Let there be music / Take a chance on romance / Time after time / Thine alone / Love is where you find it / They didn't believe me / Were thine that special face / Jealousy / Can't help lovin' dat man / Hi lili hi lo / Both sides now / Scarborough fair / Smoke gets in your eyes / What is youth?.
LP: **BDL 2043**

Grayzell, Rudy

LET'S GET WILD.
LP: **LP 1321**

Grease

GREASE (Film soundtrack) (Various artists).
Tracks: / Grease: *Valli, Frankie* / Summer nights: *Travolta, John & Olivia Newton John* / Hopelessly devoted to you: *Newton-John, Olivia* / Sandy: *Travolta, John* / Look at me, I'm Sandra Dee: *Channing, Stockard* / Greased lightning: *Travolta, John* / It's raining on prom night: *Bullens, Cindy* / You're the one that I want: *Travolta, John & Olivia Newton John* / Beauty school drop-out: *Avalon, Frankie* / Alone at the drive in movie: *Watts, Ernie* / Blue moon: *Sha Na Na* / Rock 'n' roll is here to stay: *Sha Na Na* / Those magic changes: *Sha Na Na* / Hound dog: *Sha Na Na* / Born to hand jive: *Sha Na Na* / Tears on my pillow: *Sha Na Na* / Mooning: *Bullens, Cindy* / Freddy my love: *Bullens, Cindy* / Rock 'n' roll party queen: *St. Louis, Louis* / There are worst things I could do: *Channing, Stockard* / Look at me I'm Sandra Dee (reprise): *Newton-John, Olivia* / We go together: *Travolta, John & Olivia Newton John* / Love is a many splendoured thing: *Studio Orchestra* / Grease (reprise): *Valli, Frankie*.
2LP: **SPDLP 4**
MCSET: **351 701 5**
2LP: **RSD 1001**
MCSET: **817 998-4**
2LP: **817 998-1**

GREASE 2 (Film soundtrack) (Various artists).
Tracks: / Back to school again: *Four Tops* / Cool rider: *Pfeiffer, Michelle* / Score tonight: *T-Birds & Pink Ladies* / Girl for all seasons: *Teefy, Maureen/ Lorna Luft/Alison Price/Michelle Pfeiffer* / Do it for our country: *Frechette, Peter* / Who's that guy?: *Cast* / Prowlin': *T-Birds* / Reproduction: *Hunter, Tab* / Charades: *Caulfield, Maxwell* / Turn back the hands of time: *Caulfield, Maxwell & Michelle Pfeiffer* / Rock a hula: *Cast* / We'll be together: *Caulfield, Maxwell*.
LP: **RSD 5020**
MC: **TRSD 5020**

Grease Band

AMAZING GREASE.
Tracks: / New morning / Dwoogie blue Monday / Reminiscing / Mandolin song / Honky tonk angels / Rock 'n' roll rodeo / Pontardawe.
LP: **CR 30166**

Great Blues Guitarists

GREAT BLUES GUITARISTS - STRING DAZZLERS (See Under Blues...) (Various artists).

Great Bluesmen

GREAT BLUESMEN/NEWPORT (See Under Blues...) (Various artists).

NEWPORT (See Under Blues...) (Various artists).

Great Bone

OSSIFIED.
MC: **SLOB 005**

THOSE DAYS OF YORG.
MC: **SLOB 003**

Great British...

GREAT BRITISH PSYCHEDELIC TRIP VOL. 3 (See Under Psychedelic...) (Various artists).

GREAT BRITISH PSYCHEDELIC TRIP VOL. 2 (See Under Psychedelic) (Various artists).

GREAT BRITISH PSYCHEDELIC TRIP VOL. 1 (See Under Psychedelic) (Various artists).

Great British Aircraft

GREAT BRITISH AIRCRAFT (See under Aircraft Sounds) (Various).

Great Caruso (film)

GREAT CARUSO (Film soundtrack) (See under Lanza, Mario) (Lanza, Mario).

GREAT CARUSO, THE (see under Caruso, Enrico) (Various artists).

Great Chaquito...

LATIN CLASSICS VOL.1 (Great Chaquito Big Band).
MC: **8460514**

Great Classical

GREAT CLASSICAL MASTERPIECES: SPRING (Various artists).
LP: ONE 1291
MC: OCE 2291

GREAT CLASSICAL MASTERPIECES: SUMMER (Various artists).
LP: ONE 1292
MC: OCE 2292

Great Egg Race

GREAT EGG RACE (THEME FROM) (See under Denton, Richard) (Denton, Richard).

Great Escape (bk)

GREAT ESCAPE, THE (Paul Brickhill) (Todd, Richard (nar)).
MCSET: LFP 7148
MCSET: LFP 4171485

Great Escape (film)

GREAT ESCAPE (Film Soundtrack) (Various artists).
Tracks: / Main title: *Various artists* / Premature plans: *Various artists* / Cooler and Mole: *Various artists*/ Blythe: *Various artists* / Discovery: *Various artists* / Various troubles: *Various artists* / On the road: *Various artists* / Betrayal: *Various artists* / Hendley's risk: *Various artists* / Road's end: *Various artists* / More action: *Various artists* / Chase, The: *Various artists* / Finale: *Various artists.*
LP: SLS 50177

GREAT ESCAPE, THE (Film soundtrack) (Various artists).
LP: LN 10284
MC: L4N 10284

Great Expectations

GREAT EXPECTATIONS (see under Dickens, Charles) (Jeffrey, Peter (nar)).

GREAT EXPECTATIONS (see Dickens, Charles) (Jarvis, Martin (nar)).

Great Film Themes

GREAT FILM THEMES (See Under Films...) (Various artists).

Great Glam Rock ...

GREAT GLAM ROCK EXPLOSION, THE (See Under Glam Rock) (Various artists).

Great Guitars

STRAIGHT TRACKS.
Tracks: / I'm putting all my eggs in one basket / Clouds / Gravy waltz / Um abraco no bonfa / Little rock getaway / It might as well be Spring / Kingston cutie / Favela.
MC: CJ 421 C

Great Hitchcock

GREAT HITCHCOCK MOVIE THRILLERS (London Philharmonic Orchestra).
Tracks: / Psycho / Marnie / North by Northwest / Vertigo / Trouble with Harry, The: Portait of Hitch.
MC: 4178474

Great Jazz...

GREAT JAZZ LEGENDS (See Under Jazz...) (Various artists).

Great Jazz Trio

CHAPTER 11.
LP: 6315 069

STANDARD COLLECTION.
Tracks: / Autumn in New York / Caravan / 'S wonderful / Our love is here to stay / Someone to watch over me / Isn't it romantic / Embraceable you / In a sentimental mood / Satin doll / Lush life / Sophisticated lady / Take the 'A' train / Blue monk / Ruby my dear / Monk's dream / Monk's mood.
MC: CC 18

Great Kat

BEETHOVEN ON SPEED.
Tracks: / Beethoven on speed / Flight of the bumble-bee / Funeral march / God / Sex and violins / Gripping obsession / Worshipping bodies / Total tyrant / Ultra-dead / Revenge of the mongrel / Kat abuse / Made in Japan / Beethoven mosh (5th symphony) / Paganini's 24th caprice / Guitar concerto in blood minor / Bach to the future; for geniuses only..
LP: RO 93731
MC: RO 93734

WORSHIP ME OR DIE.
LP: RR 9589

Great Leap Forward

DON'T BE AFRAID OF CHANGE.
LP: CULP 1

SEASON 87-88.
LP: CU 003

Great Moghuls (film)

GREAT MOGHULS (Film Soundtrack) (Various artists).
LP: FILM 064
MC: FILMC 064

Great Moments...

GREAT MOMENTS IN JAZZ (See Under Jazz...) (Various artists).

Great Movie

GREAT MOVIE SOUNDTRACKS (See Under Films...) (Various artists).

GREAT MOVIE SOUNDTRACKS VOL II (See Under Films...) (Various artists).

Great Musicals

GREAT MUSICALS (See under London Festival Orch) (London Festival Orchestra).

Great Ormond St Hosp.

SONGS FOR THE WISHING WELL (Various artists).
MCSET: DTO 10584

Great Outdoors

MAKING ALLOWANCES FOR THE JARGON.
LP: GODLP 1

Great Outdoors (Film)

GREAT OUTDOORS (Film Soundtrack) (Various artists).
Tracks: / Land of a thousand dances: *Elwood Blues Revue/Wilson Pickett* / Hot fun in the summertime: *Elwood Blues* Revue/Sam Moore/Oren Roberts / Big country: *Walsh, Joe* / Unbearable: *Wonder Stuff* / Cabin fever: *Wilcox, David* / Big bear: *Bomb The Bass* / Beaver patrol: *Pop Will Eat Itself* / Hot weasel: *Elwood Blues Revue/Peter Aykroyd* / Hey cowboy: *Newman, Thomas & The Lazy* / Dragboat: *Elwood Blues Revue.*
LP: 781 859-1
MC: 781 859-4

Great Plains

BEFORE WE STOPPED TO THINK.
LP: SR 0387

COLORIZED.
Tracks: / Exercise / Serpent mound / Way she runs a fever, The / Rutherford B Hayes / End of the seventies / Dick Clark / Love to the third power / Lincoln logs / Same moon / Letter to a fanzine / It's dying / War, The / Violent gesture / Before we stopped to think.
LP: SORC 6

NAKED AT THE BUY, SELL AND TRADE.
LP: HMS 048

SUM THINGS UP.
LP: SR 1087

Great Radio Stars Of

GREAT RADIO STARS OF THE 30'S VOL.1 (See Under Radio) (Various artists).

Great Rock'n'Roll

GREAT ROCK'N'ROLL SWINDLE, THE (see under Sex Pistols) (Film soundtrack) (Sex Pistols).

Great Society

CONSPICUOUS ONLY IN IT'S ABSENCE (Great Society with Grace Slick).
LP: CBS 31800
MC: 40 31800

GREAT SOCIETY.
Tracks: / Sally go' round the roses / Didn't think so / Grimly forming / Somebody to love / Father Bruce / Outlaw blues / Often as I may / Arbitration / White rabbit / That's how it is / Darkly smiling / Nature boy / You can't cry / Daydream nightmare / Everybody knows / Born to be burned / Father.
2LP: DED 280

LIVE AT THE MATRIX.
2LP: DED 208

Great Songs...

GREAT SONGS FROM MGM CLASSIC FILMS, VOL 1 (See Under Films...) (Various artists).

Great Sopranos

GREAT SOPRANOS OF OUR TIME (Various artists).
LP: EMX 2099
MC: TCEMX 2099

Great Spanish Tenors

GREAT SPANISH TENORS (Domingo/ Carreras/Kraus).
LP: EL 7499291
MC: EL 7499294

Great Swing Sax

GREAT SWING SAX (See Under Jazz...) (Various artists).

Great Tenors

GREAT TENORS OF OUR TIME (Various artists).
LP: EMX 2114
MC: TCEMX 2114

Great Train Robbery

(FIRST) GREAT TRAIN ROBBERY, THE (1978 film soundtrack) (Various artists).
LP: MCA 25102
MC: MCAC 25102

Great Trumpets

CLASSIC JAZZ TO SWING (See Under Jazz) (Various artists).

Great Vocalists

GREAT VOCALISTS, THE.
LPS: C 10-3 BOX 3

Great Waltz (musical)

GREAT WALTZ, THE (1934 US Cast recording) (Various artists).
LP: AEI 1153

GREAT WALTZ, THE (Original London Cast) (Various artists).
Tracks: / Overture: *Various artists* / Waltz with wings: *Various artists* / I'm in love with Vienna: *Various* artists / My philsophy of life: *Various artists* / Love and gingerbread: *Various artists* / Teeter-totter me: *Various artists* / Where would I be: *Various artists* / Of men and violins: *Various artists* / Artist's life, An: *Various artists* / Enchanted wood: *Various artists* / At Dommayer's: *Various artists* / Gypsy told me, A: *Various artists* / Tritschtratsch polka: *Various artists* / No two ways: *Various artists*/ I hate music: *Various artists* / Blue Danube: *Various artists.*
LP: SCX 6429

GREAT WALTZ, THE (Film soundtrack) (Various artists).
Tracks: / Crystal and gold: *Various artists* / Nightfall: *Various artists* / Warm: *Various artists* / Wine, women and song: *Various artists* / Love is music: *Various artists* / Louder and faster: *Various artists*/ With you gone: *Various artists* / Through Jetty's eyes: *Various artists* / Say yes: *Various artists*/ Six drinks: *Various artists* / Schani gives chase: *Various artists* / Who are you: *Various artists*/ Great waltz in Boston (Blue Danube): *Various artists.*
LP: STK 109
MC: 3110 090
LP: 2315 130

Great Western...

GREATEST WESTERN THEMES,THE (See under Films...) (Various artists).

Great White

GREAT WHITE.
Tracks: / Out of the night / Stock it / Substitute / Bad boys / On your knees / Streetkiller / No better than hell / Hold on / Nightmares / Dead end.
LP: AML 240 087 1
MC: TC AML240 087 4

HOOKED.
Tracks: / Call it rock 'n' roll / Original Queen of Sheba, The / Cold hearted lovin' / Can't shake it / Lovin' kind / Heartbreaker / Congo square / South bay cities / Desert moon / Afterglow.
LP: EST 2138
MC: TCEST 2138

ONCE BITTEN.
Tracks: / Lady red light / Gonna getcha / Rock me / All over now / Fast road / What do you do (live) / Face the day (US radio blues version) / Gimme some lovin'.
LP: EST 2039
MC: TCEST 2039
LP: ST 12565
LP: FA 3252
MC: TCFA 3252

RECOVERY: LIVE.
Tracks: / Immigrant song / Rock and roll / Money (that's what I want) / Red house / I don't need no doctor / Shot in the dark / What do you do / Gonna getcha / All over now.
LP: ATAK 130
MC: TCATAK 130
LP: EMS 1302
MC: TCEMS 1302

TWICE SHY.
Tracks: / Move it / Heart the hunter / Highway nights / Angel song, The / Mista bone / Baby's on fire / House of broken love / She only / Once bitten twice shy / Wasted rock ranger.
LP: ESTX 2096
MC: TCESTX 2096
LP: 790 640 1
MC: 790 640 4
LP: EST 2096
MC: TCEST 2096
LP: 792 743 1
MC: 792 743 4

TWICE SHY/LIVE AT THE MARQUEE (Special Edition - Free Bootleg).
Tracks: / Move it / Heart the hunter / Highway nights / Angel song, The / Bitch / It's only rock 'n' roll / Women / Mista bone / Baby's on fire / House of broken love / She only / Once bitten twice shy / Wasted rock range / Shot in the dark / What do you do / Gonna getcha / Money / All over now / Is anybody there / Face the day / Rock me.
2LP: 793 636 1
2LP: ESTS 2096
MC: TCESTS 2096

Greater St. Stephen

GOD'S GOT THOSE HEALING HANDS (Greater St. Stephen Baptist Church B.C. Mass Choir).
Tracks: / Healing hands / Jesus is the light / I keep praying / Rejuvenate me / Yet will I trust / Thank you / Remember God / Stand still / I am healed.
LP: GCR 4035
MC: GCR 4035MC

Greater Than One

ALL THE MASTERS LICKED ME.
LP: SER 10

DANCE OF THE COWARDS.
Tracks: / Now is the time / Song for England / Truth, The / Kunst gleich kapital / All the masters licked you / Dance of the cowards / All men are boys / I know everything.
LP: KGKLP 001

FORCE.
LP: TORSO 33149

G-FORCE.
LP: KGKLP 002

LONDON.
2LP: KGKLP 2

Greatest Boogie Woogie

GREATEST BOOGIE WOOGIE PERFORMANCES Vol. 2.
LP: SM 3904

GREATEST BOOGIE WOOGIE PERFORMANCES.
LP: SM 3905-2

GREATEST BOOGIE WOOGIE PERFORMANCES Vol. 1.
LP: SM 3903

Greatest Folk Singers

GREATEST FOLK SINGERS OF THE SIXTIES (See Under Folk...) (Various artists).

Greatest Gospel Gems

GREATEST GOSPEL GEMS VOLS 1 AND 2 (See Under Gospel...) (Various artists).

Greatest Ragtime

GREATEST RAGTIME OF THE CENTURY (See Under Jazz...) (Various artists).

Greatest Show on Earth

HORIZONS.
Tracks: / Sunflower morning / Angelina / Skylight man / Day of the lady / Real cool world / I fought for love / Horizons / Again and again.
LP: EMS 2600001

Greatest Story Ever

GREATEST STORY EVER TOLD, THE (Film soundtrack) (Various artists).
LP: MCA 39057
MC: MCAC 39057

KING OF KINGS/THE GREATEST STORY EVER TOLD (see under King Of Kings) (Various artists).

Greatest Years

GREATEST YEARS OF ROCK'N'ROLL (See Under Rock'n'Roll) (Various artists).

Greaves, Dennis

JUMP (Greaves, Dennis & The Truth).
Tracks: / Wings of a prayer / Throwing it all away / Shadow on the sun / Let freedom reign / God gave rock 'n' roll to you / Tug of war / Prisoner of love / Jealous man / Listening to the rain again / Straight to my heart.
LP: EIRSA 1003
MC: EIRSAC 1003

Greaves John

KEW RHONE (See Under Blegvad, Peter) (Greaves John/Peter Blegvad).

Greaves, Nigel (nar)

SECRET OF KELLY'S MILL, THE (see under Secret of Kelly's... (bk).

Grebenshikov, Boris

RADIO SILENCE.
Tracks: / Radio silence / Postcard / Wind, The / Winter / That voice again / Young lions / Fields of my love / Death of King Arthur / Real slow today / Mother / China.
LP: 4650381
MC: 4650384

SUBWAY CULTURE (See under Kuryokhin, Sergey) (Grebenshikov, Boris & Sergey Kuryokhin).

Greco, Buddy

AT MISTER KELLY'S.
Tracks: / Welcome to Mr Kelly's / But not for me / They can't take that away from me / Polka dots and moonbeams / They didn't believe me / Foggy day, A / Here I am in love again / My baby just cares for me / My ship / Dancing on the ceiling / Will you still be mine? / One for my baby / Nearness of you, The / Give me the simple life.
LP: . . . . **JASM 1013**

FOR ONCE IN MY LIFE.
Tracks: / In the still of the night / More I see you, The / What now my love? / Moment truth, The / Tenderly (Instrumental.) / Very thought of you, The / Satin doll / Sherry / Lady is a tramp, The / I didn't know what time it was / Look of love, The / Watch what happens / Day in the life of a fool, A / For once in my life / I had a ball.
LP: . . . . **BDL 1034**

GREATEST HITS: BUDDY GRECO.
Tracks: / Lady is a tramp, The / My kind of girl / Around the world / Like young / Roses of Picardy / Taking a chance on love / To be or not to be in love / Mr. Lonely / Ain't she pretty / At long last love / But not for me / You're nobody 'til somebody loves you.
LP: . . . . **CBS 32522**

MOVING ON (It's Magic).
Tracks: / Movin' on / Legacy / Hungry tears / Touch me in the morning / Me and Mrs Jones / Love won't let me wait / Ready for your love / It's magic / You better go now / Neither one of us / Teach me tonight / Georgia Road.
LP: . . . . **PREC 5007**
MC: . . . . **ZCPREC 5007**

Greco, Juliette

DISQUE D'OR.
LP: . . . . **PM 240 141 1**
MC: . . . . **PM 240 141 4**

Greece

BEST OF GREECE VOL. II (Various artists).
LP: . . . . **EULP 1159**
MC: . . . . **EUMC 1159**

ECHOES OF GREECE (Various artists).
Tracks: / To tragoudi tou gero nafti: *Various artists* (The old sailor's song.) / Peripatos: *Various artists*(Promenade.) / To domatio enos pediou: *Various artists* (A child's room.) / Andreas Zeppos: *Various artists* / Ena koritsi apo tin Alexandria: *Various artists* (A girl from Alexandria.) / I ora tou apocheretismou: *Various artists*(The hour of farewell.) / Epimoni: *Various artists* (Insistence.) / Ta evghenika pedia: *Various artists* (The polite children.) / Ena dilino: *Various artists* (One afternoon.) / O palios dromos: *Various artists* (The old street.) / Sto Hatzikiriakio: *Various artists* (In Hatzikiriakio.) / Otan anapsoun I foties: *Various artists* (When the fires will be on.) / Milisse mou: *Various artists* (Speak to me.) / Yioussouroum: *Various artists* (CD only.) / E hartaeti: *Various artists* (Kites. CD only.) / Astrologia: *Various artists* (Astrology. CD only.).
MC: . . . . **TCEMS 1372**

GOLDEN DANCES 1928-34, THE (Smyrnaic/Rebetic songs & dances) (Various artists).
LP: . . . . **FL 9033**

GOLDEN SOUVENIRS FROM GREECE (Various artists).
Tracks: / Siko horepse sirtaki: *Mouzas & Lignos* / Ximeroni: *Mitropanos, Dimitris* / Zorbas dance: *Zambetas, George* / 'Kyra Giorgena: *Mitropanos, Dimitris* / Odos oniron: *Marinella* / Pente pente deca: *Athenians*/ Ta pedia tou pirea: *Mouskouri, Nana* / Mil-lisse mou: *Karatzas, Sofoulis* / Yioussouroum: *Zambetas, George*/ O kaymos: *Leandros, Vicky* / Strose to stroma sou yia thio: *Mouzas & Lignos* / Dirlada: *Marinella*.
LP: **9279 223**
MC: **7259 223**

GRECE ETERNELLE (Various artists).
Tracks: / Zonarathiko: *Various artists* / Hier ou avant-hier je suis passe: *Various artists* / La femme rousse du pasteur: *Various artists* / Uncle Mathios: *Various artists* / Les bruits de chaines: *Various artists*/ Les lamentations: *Various artists* / Aman gkel aman: *Various artists* / Au revoir chere mere: *Various artists*/ Votre mouchoir cher John: *Various artists* / Allant a Rhodes: *Various artists* / 45 artisans: *Various artists*/ O Maranton: *Various artists* / Zeimbekiko de Smyrne: *Various artists*.
LP: . . . . **ARN 33303**

GREECE IS.. (Popular & Folk Dances) (Various artists).
LP: **062 7007**
MC: . . . . **TC 062 7007**

GREEK BOUZOUKEE (Various artists).
LP: . . . . **H 72004**

GREEK FOLK MUSIC (Various artists).
LP: . . . . **LLST 7188**

GREEK MUSIC FROM THE ISLE OF CRETE (Various artists).
LP: . . . . **LLST 7293**
MC: . . . . **LLCT 7293**

MAGIC OF GREECE, THE (Various artists).
Tracks: / Siko horepse syrataki: *Various artists* / Pai-pai: *Various artists* / Mithikes: *Various artists*/ Play bouzouki: *Various artists* / Simera: *Various artists* / Ta pedia tou pirea: *Various artists* / Milisse mou: *Various artists* / Perdika: *Various artists* / Corfu kefi: *Various artists* / Who pays the ferryman: *Various artists* / Zorba's dance: *Various artists* / Lotus eaters: *Various artists* / Matia vourko meni: *Various artists* / O horos tou sekana: *Various artists*.
MC: . . . . **TCNTS 207**
LP: . . . . **NTS 207**

MEMORIES OF GREECE (Various artists).
MC: . . . . **BRC 2529**

SOUL OF GREECE (Various artists).
LP: . . . . **ADL 503**
MC: . . . . **ADK 503**

SPOTLIGHT ON GREECE (Various artists).
LP: **6641986**

VARIOUS DANCE SONGS & MELODIES (folk music from Greece) (Various artists).
LP: **12TS 231**

VIRTUOSO CLARINET OF GREECE, THE (Various artists).
LP: . . . . **CEL 011**
MC: . . . . **MC CEL 011**

Green, Al

AL GREEN GETS NEXT TO YOU.
Tracks: / I can't get next to you / Are you lonely for me baby / God is standing by / Tired of being alone / I'm a ram / Drivin' wheel / Light my fire / You say it / Right now right now / All because.
LP: . . . . **HIUKLP 403**

BELLE ALBUM, THE.
Tracks: / Belle / Loving you / Feels like summer / Georgia boy / I feel good / All in all / Chariots of fire / Dream.
LP: . . . . **HIUKLP 421**
LP: . . . . **HLP 6004**

BEST OF AL GREEN.
LP: . . . . **HIUKLP 425**

CALL ME.
Tracks: / Call me / Have you been making out OK? / Stand up / I'm so lonesome I could cry / Your love is like the morning sun / Here I am / Funny how time slips away / You ought to be with me / Jesus is waiting.
LP: . . . . **SHU 8457**
LP: . . . . **HIUKLP 409**

COVER ME GREEN.
Tracks: / I want to hold your hand / My girl / The letter / Light my fire / I say a little prayer / Summertime / Get back / For the good times / Oh pretty woman / I'm so lonesome I could cry / Lean on me / Unchained melody / Ain't no mountain high enough / People get ready / Amazing grace.
LP: . . . . **HIUK 107**

CREAM OF AL GREEN.
Tracks: / Tired of being alone / Love and happiness / Here I am / I feel good / Call me / Unchained melody / I stand accused / I can't get next to you / Let's stay together / How can you mend a broken heart? / You ought to be with me / Belle / Let's get married / Look what you done for me / I'm still in love with you.
LP: . . . . **HLPC 101**
MC: . . . . **ZCHLP 101**

EXPLORES YOUR MIND.
Tracks: / Sha-la-la / Take me to the river / God blessed our love / City, The / One night stand / I'm hooked on you / Stay with me forever / Hangin' on / School days.
LP: . . . . **SHU 8479**
LP: . . . . **HIUKLP 413**

FULL OF FIRE.
Tracks: / There's no way / I'd fly away / Full of fire / Together again / Soon as I get home / Let it shine / Glory, glory / That's the way it is / Always.
LP: . . . . **HIUKLP 417**

GOING AWAY.
Tracks: / Going away / True love / He is the Light / I feel like going on / Be with me, Jesus / You brought the sunshine / Power / Building / Nearer my God to thee.
LP: . . . . **AMA 5102**
MC: . . . . **AMC 5102**

GREATEST HITS.
Tracks: / Let's stay together / I can't get next to you / You ought to be with me / Look what you done for me / Let's get married / Tired of being alone / Call me / I'm still in love with you / Here I am (come and take me) / How can you mend a broken heart.
LP: . . . . **HIUKLP 425**
MC: . . . . **HIUKCASS 425**
LP: **6.22217**
MC: **CT4 22217**
LP: . . . . **SHU 8481**

GREEN IS BLUES.
Tracks: / One woman / Talk to me / My girl / Letter, The / I stand accused / Gotta find a new world / What am I gonna do with myself / Tomorrow's dream / Get back baby / Summertime.
LP: . . . . **HIUKLP 401**

HAVE A GOOD TIME.
Tracks: / Keep me cryin' / Smile a little bit more / I tried to tell myself / Something / Truth marches on, The / Have a good time / Nothing takes the place of you / Hold on forever.
LP: . . . . **HIUKLP 419**

HIGHER PLANE.
Tracks: / Higher plane / People get ready / By my side / Spirit might come - on and on / Where love rules / Amazing grace / His name is Jesus / Battle hymn of the Republic.
LP: . . . . **HIUKLP 431**
LP: . . . . **HLP 6006**
MC: . . . . **ZCHLP 6006**

HI-LIFE - THE BEST OF AL GREEN.
Tracks: / Let's stay together / Tired of being alone / Sha-la-la / Look what you done for me / How can you mend a broken heart / Living for you / Take me to the river / I can't get next to you / I'm still in love with you / Let's get married / Belle / L-O-V-E.
MC: . . . . **CE 2420**
LP: . . . . **NE 1420**

I GET JOY.
LP: **395 228-1**
MC: **395 228-4**

I'M STILL IN LOVE WITH YOU.
Tracks: / I'm still in love with you / I'm glad you're mine / Love and happiness / What a wonderful thing love is / Simply beautiful / Oh pretty woman / For the good times / Look what you done for me / One of these good old days.
LP: . . . . **HIUKLP 407**
LP: . . . . **SHU 8443**

IS LOVE.
Tracks: / L-O-V-E (love) / Rhymes / Love sermon, The / There is love / Could I be the one / Love ritual / I didn't know / Oh me, oh my (dreams in my arms) / I gotta be more (take me higher) / I wish you were here.
LP: . . . . **HIUKLP 415**

LET'S STAY TOGETHER.
Tracks: / Let's stay together / I've never found a girl / You're leaving / It ain't no fun to me / Talk to me, talk to me / Old time lovin' / Judy / What is this feelin' / Tomorrow's dream / How can you mend a broken heart / La la for you / Let's stay together.
LP: . . . . **HU 8430**
LP: . . . . **HIUKLP 405**

LIVIN' FOR YOU.
Tracks: / Living for you / Home again / Free at last / Let's get married / So good to be here / Sweet sixteen / Unchained melody / My God is real / Beware.
LP: . . . . **HIUKLP 411**

LORD WILL MAKE A WAY, THE.
Tracks: / Lord will make a way, The / Pass me not / Too close / Highway to Heaven / Saved / None by the righteous / In the holy name of Jesus / I have a friend above all others.
LP: . . . . **HIUKLP 433**
LP: . . . . **MYR 1109**
MC: . . . . **MC 1109**

LOVE RITUAL.
Tracks: / Love ritual / So good to be here / Ride Sally ride / Surprise attack / Love is real / I think it's for the feeling / Up above my head / Strong as death / Mimi / I want to hold your hand.
LP: . . . . **HIUKLP 443**
MC: . . . . **HIUKCASS 443**

PRECIOUS LORD.
Tracks: / Precious Lord / What a friend we have in Jesus / Old rugged cross, The / Morning star / How great Thou art / Glory to His name / Rock of ages / In the garden / Hallelujah.
LP: . . . . **HLP 6007**
LP: . . . . **HIUKLP 429**

PUT A LITTLE LOVE IN YOUR HEART (See under Lennox, Annie) (Green, Al & Annie Lennox).

SOUL SURVIVOR.
Tracks: / Everything's gonna be alright / Jesus will fix it / You know and I know / So real to me / Introduction - soul survivor / Soul survivor / You've got a friend / He ain't heavy, he's my brother / 23rd Psalm.
LP: . . . . **AMA 5150**
MC: . . . . **AMC 5150**

SPOTLIGHT ON AL GREEN.
Tracks: / Tired of being alone / Take me to the river / Living for you / Let's get married / Love ritual / School days / Let's stay together / How can you mend a broken heart? / Call me (come back home) / You ought to be with me / Here I am (come and take me) / Oh me, oh my (dreams in my arms) / Sha-la-la / Oh pretty woman / Love and happiness / I can't get next to you / For the good times / L.O.V.E. / I'm still in love with you / Look what you done for me / I stand accused / Unchained melody / Belle / To sir with love.
2LP: . . . . **SPOT 1016**
MCSET: . . . . **ZCSPT 1016**

TAKE ME TO THE RIVER (Greatest Hits Vol. 2).
Tracks: / Drivin' wheel / I've never found a girl / Love and happiness / Living for you / Sha-la-la / L-O-V-E / One woman / Take me to the river / Rhymes / Oh me, oh my (dreams in my arms) / Glory, glory / Full of fire / Keep me cryin' / Belle.
LP: . . . . **HIUKLP 438**
MC: . . . . **HIUKCASS 438**

TOKYO - LIVE.
Tracks: / Love / Tired of being alone / Let's stay together / How can you mend a broken heart? / All 'n' all / God blessed our love / You ought to be with me / For the good times / Belle / Sha-la-la / Let's get married / Dream / I feel good / Love and happiness.
2LP: . . . . **HCD 5001**
MCSET: . . . . **ZHCD 5001**
2LP: **8302ML2**

TRUST IN GOD.
Tracks: / Don't it make you wanna go home / No not one / Trust in God / Lean on me / Ain't no mountain high enough / Up the ladder to the roof / Never met nobody like you / Holy spirit / All we need is a little more love.
LP: . . . . **HIUKLP 423**

WHITE CHRISTMAS.
Tracks: / White Christmas / Christmas song, The / Winter wonderland / I'll be home for Christmas / Jingle bells / What Christmas means to me / Oh holy night / Silent night / It feels like Christmas.
LP: . . . . **XHIUKLP 437**

YOU SAY IT.
Tracks: / You say it / I'll be standing by / True love / Right now, right now / Memphis Tennessee / I'm a ram / Listen / Baby what's wrong with you / Ride Sally ride / Eli's game / Sweet song / Everything to me / Starting all over again.
LP: . . . . **HIUKLP 144**

Green, Benny

BEBOP REVISITED, VOL 4 (See under Moody, James) (Green, Benny & James Moody).

BLOWS HIS HORN.
LP: **1902113**

CONNECTION, THE.
2LP: . . . . **UNKNOWN**

JUGGIN' AROUND (See under Ammons, Gene) (Green, Benny/Gene Ammons).

SWINGS THE BLUES.
Tracks: / Been walkin' / Blue mambo / Love at last / Penthouse blues / Hop, skip and jump / Bun dance, A / Pennies from Heaven / Change up blues.
LP: . . . . **FS 389**

TROMBONE BY THREE (See under Johnson, J J).

Green, Bob

TOGETHER (see under Ewell,Don) (Green, Bob/Don Ewell).

Green Bullfrog

FROM THE DEEP.
Tracks: / My baby left me / Marking time / Lawdy Miss Clawdy / By bullfrog / I want you / I'm a free man now / Walk a mile in my shoes / Lovin' you is good....
LP: . . . . **SEE 227**

Green, Bunky

PLACES WE'VE NEVER BEEN.
Tracks: / East and west / April green / Command module / Only in seasons / Places we've never been / Tension and release / Little girl, I'll miss you.

LP: . . . . VSD 79425

Green, Candy

LADY IN RED.
LP: . . . . JSP 1022

Green Card (film)

GREEN CARD (Film Soundtrack) (Various artists).
LP: . . . . VS 5309
MC: . . . . VSC 5309

Green, Carl

THING IS... (Green, Carl & The Scene).
Tracks: / Competition time / Fresh start / Strange affair of Grant, The / Ladies before gentlemen / Rodo do do / It's platonic / Girl by a river / Murder at Tudor Close / Sky at night, The.
LP: . . . . RCALP 6008
MC: . . . . RCAK 6008

Green, Danny

NIGHT DOG.
Tracks: / Ask her / Blue lady / Stand with the best / Good time don't come for free / Final showdown / Dreamin' again / She don't want a lover / Take me to the islands / Slave trader / Three angels.
LP: . . . . ABCL 5259

Green, Dave

I SING THE SONGS.
Tracks: / Way we were, The / Impossible dream, The / I couldn't live without your love / Hawaiian wedding song / Without you / Exodus / I sing the songs / You are the sunshine of my life / For the good times / I will drink the wine / Send in the clowns / My way.
LP: . . . . SRTM CUS051

Green, Freddie

NATURAL RHYTHM (Green, Freddie/Al Cohn).
Tracks: / Up in the blues / Down for double / Back and forth / Free and easy / Learnin' the blues / Feed bag / Something's gotta give / Easy does it / Little red / Swinging back / Date with Ray, A / When you wish upon a star / Doggin' around / Jump the blues away / Jack's kinda swing / Natural thing to do, The / A.C. meets Osie / Baby please / 9:20 Special / Pick a dilly / Count me in / Freddie's tune.
LP: 208980
MC: 408980

RHYTHM WILLIE (See Ellis, Herb) (Green, Freddie & Herb Ellis).

Green, Garland

JUST WHAT THE DOCTOR ORDERED.
LP: . . . . KENT 097

Green, Gary

FAVOURITE SONGS OF IRELAND (Green, Gary & Steve Mack).
MC: . . . . GTDC 043

Green, George

JAMMIN' THE BOOGIE (Green, George & Bob Hall).
LP: . . . . BLP 12146

Green, Grant

BORN TO BE BLUE.
Tracks: / Some day my prince will come / Born to be blue / If I should lose you / Back in your own back yard / My one and only love / Count every star / Born to be blue (CD only.) / Cool blues (CD only.) / Outer space (CD only.).
LP: . . . . BST 84432
MC: 4BN 84432

GRANT GREEN.
Tracks: / Reaching out / Our Miss Brooks / Flick of a prick, A / One for Blena / Baby you should know it / Falling in love with love.
LP: . . . . BLP 60129

GRANTSTAND.
Tracks: / Grantstand / My funny valentine / Blues in Maude's flat / Old folks / Green's greenery.
LP: . . . . BST 84036
LP: . . . . BST 84086

IDLE MOMENTS.
Tracks: / Idle moments / Jean De Fleur / Django / Nomad.
LP: . . . . BST 84154

IRON CITY.
Tracks: / Iron city / Black Orpheus / Old man (let my people go) / High heel sneakers / Motherless child / Work song.
LP: . . . . MR 5120

LAST SESSION.
Tracks: / Wave / Just the way you are / Easy / Empanada / Night time in the switching yard / Three times a lady.
LP: . . . . ATS 9
MC: . . . . TCATS 9

Green Grass Cloggers

THROUGH THE EARS.
LP: . . . . ROUNDER 0228
MC: . . . . ROUNDER 0228C

Green Howards

GREEN HOWARDS, XIX (Green Howards Regimental Band).
Tracks: / Fanfare / Olav V / World cup march, The / Bosun's fancy / High on a hill / On her Majesty's secret service / Burlesk for band / Luftwaffe march / On Richmond Hill / Baht'at / Berliner luft / Helter skelter / Tiger rag / Hip flask / Regt. slow march Maria Theresa / Quick march bonnie English rose.
LP: . . . . MM 0591
MC: . . . . MMC 0591

Green Ice (film)

GREEN ICE (Original film soundtrack) (Various artists).
Tracks: / Si si: *Various artists* / Beach chase: *Various artists* / Holbrooks house (green ice theme): *Various artists* / Floating (Cloouhopper theme): *Various artists* / Emerald guitars: *Various artists* / Emerald vault: *Various artists* / Water bottle, The: *Various artists* / Noche de amour: *Various artists* / Colombia: *Various artists* / Tenderness: *Various artists* / Showdown: *Various artists* / Showdown: *Various artists* / Cloudhoppers: *Various artists* / Churchyard: *Various artists* / Mines, The: *Various artists*/ Sol y sombra: *Various artists* / Miomi arrival: *Various artists* / Emerald waltz: *Various artists* / Si si reprise: *Various artists*.
LP: . . . . POLS 1031
MC: . . . . POLSC 1031

Green, Jack

HUMANESQUE.
Tracks: / Murder / So much / Valentina / Babe / Can't stand it / I call, no answer / Life on the line / 'Bout that girl / Thought it was easy / Factory girl / This is japan.
LP: . . . . RCALP 5004

LATEST GAME.
Tracks: / Sweet Lover / Latest game / Television / Loving & knowing / You didn't have to love me / American fool / Win your love / Right now / Difficult to cure / I've had enough.
LP: . . . . REVLP 87
MC: . . . . REVMC 87

Green, Jesse

NICE AND SLOW.
Tracks: / Nice and slow / You came you saw you conquered / Greatest love / Don't knock my love / You're a miracle / Highwaves of the sea / Flip / You are the star / Let's get it on / Easy / Don't let me down.
LP: . . . . EMC 3164

Green, Keith

COLLECTION: KEITH GREEN.
Tracks: / Rushing wind / You put this love in my heart / Grace by which I stand / You / Your love broke through / He'll take care of the rest / Lies / Sheep and the goats, The / Asleep in the light / Soften your heart / How can they live without Jesus? / This is the day / Scripture in song / This is my commandment / Rejoice in the Lord always / Clap your hands / Spring up, O well.
LP: . . . . BIRD 133
MC: . . . . TC BIRD 133
MC: . . . . SPC 1146

FOR HIM WHO HAS EARS TO HEAR.
Tracks: / You put this love in my heart / I can't believe it / Because of you / When I hear the praises start / He'll take care of the rest / Your love broke through / No one believes in me anymore (Satan's boast) / Song to my parents (I only want to see you there) / Trials turned to gold / Easter song.
LP: . . . . BIRD 112
MC: . . . . TC BIRD 112

I ONLY WANT TO SEE YOU THERE.
LP: . . . . BIRD 143
MC: . . . . TC BIRD 143

JESUS COMMANDS US TO GO.
LP: . . . . BIRD 161
MC: . . . . TC BIRD 161

MINISTRY YEARS, VOL. 2.
MC: . . . . SP C 1170

NO COMPROMISE.
Tracks: / Soften your heart / Make my life a prayer / Dear John letter (to the Devil) / How can they live without Jesus? / Asleep in the light / My eyes are dry / You! / I don't wanna fall away from you / Strained glass / To obey is better than sacrifice / Victor, The / Altar call.
LP: . . . . BIRD 118
MC: . . . . TC BIRD 118

PRODIGAL SON, THE.
LP: . . . . BIRD 149
MC: . . . . TC BIRD 149

SO YOU WANNA GO BACK TO EGYPT.
LP: . . . . BIRD 139
MC: . . . . TC BIRD 139

SONGS FOR THE SHEPHERD.
Tracks: / How majestic is thy name / You are the one / O Lord our God / Promise song, The / Jesus is Lord / Draw me / Lord's my shepherd, The / Until that final day / I will give thanks to the Lord (Psalm 9) / There is a Redeemer / Glory Lord Jesus.
LP: . . . . BIRD 140
MC: . . . . TC BIRD 140

Green, Lee

BLUES AND BARREL HOUSE PIANO 1927-37.
LP: . . . . BD 609

LEE GREEN 1929-37.
LP: . . . . BD 2050

SOMEBODY'S PRAYING, LORD (Green, Lee with Lafayette Leake).
LP: . . . . LR 44.013

Green, Lil

FOREMOTHERS, VOLUME 5.
MC: . . . . RC 1310

Green, Lloyd

GREEN VELVET.
Tracks: / Rainbows and roses / Heartbreak Tennessee / Motel time again / Seven days of crying (makes one weak) / Almost persuaded / Green velvet / Touch my heart / Show me the way to the circus / Cave, The / Bridge washed out, The.
LP: . . . . PRCV 112

LLOYDS OF NASHVILLE.
LP: . . . . RRL 8013

STAINLESS STEEL.
Tracks: / Edgewater beach / Desperado / Kiss the moonlight / My love / Stainless steel / Little bit more, A / Twilight dew / Feelings / You and me.
LP: . . . . NSPL 28249

STEEL RIDES.
Tracks: / Sally G / Coconut Grove / Steelin' away / Canadian sunset / Spirit of '49 / San Antonio rose / I can help / Crying time / Seaside / Phase phive / Lutetia.
LP: . . . . MNT 81245

STEELIN' FEELIN'S.
LP: . . . . CMLF 1010

SWEET CHEEKS.
Tracks: / Sweet cheeks / Green strings / Skillet lickin' / Drifter's polka / Funny bunny / Red eye / Pickin' pot pie / Lovin' machine, The / Pedal pattle / Little darlin'.
LP: . . . . PRCV 103

TEN SHADES OF GREEN.
LP: . . . . CMLF 1001

Green, Michael

SETTLIN' UP THE SCORE (Green, Michael & Bob Guida).
MC: . . . . GVMMC 202

Green, Mick

PAINKILLER.
Tracks: / Painkiller / Burning rubber / Dead city / Chicken / Make it easy / Shakin' all over.
LP: . . . . THBM 004

TWO GREENS MAKE A BLUES (See Under Green, Peter) (Green, Mick, Peter Green & The Enemy Within).

Green On Red

BEST OF GREEN ON RED.
LP: . . . . WOL 1021
MC: . . . . WOLMC 1021

GAS FOOD LODGING.
Tracks: / That's what dreams / Black river / Hair of the dog / This I know / Fading away / Easy way out / Sixteen ways / Drifter, The / Sea of Cortez / We shall overcome.
LP: . . . . ZONG 005
MC: . . . . ZONGCASS 005
LP: . . . . ROSE 65

GRAVITY TALKS.
Tracks: / Gravity talks / Old chief / 5 easy pieces / Deliverance / Over my head / Snake bite / Blue paradise / That's what you're here for / Brave generations / Abigail's ghost / Cheap wine / Nar colepsy.
LP: . . . . SLMP 16
MC: . . . . SLMC 16

GREEN ON RED.
Tracks: / Death and angels / Hair and skin / Black night / Illustrated crawling / Aspirin / Lost world / Apartment 6.
LP: . . . . ZANE 002

HERE COME THE SNAKES.
Tracks: / Keith can't read / Morning blue / Broken radio / Tenderloin / D.T. blues / Rock 'n' roll disease / Zombie for love / Change / Way back home.
LP: . . . . RED 093
MC: . . . . REDC 093
LP: . . . . RTD 85
LP: 8392941
MC: 8392944

KILLER INSIDE ME, A.
Tracks: / We ain't free / Clarkesville / Mighty gun / Jamie / Whispering wind / Ghost hand / Sorry Naomi / No man's land / Track you down (his master's voice) / Born to fight / Killer inside me.
LP: . . . . GORLP 1
MC: . . . . GORMC 1

LITTLE THINGS IN LIFE - 1987-91.
MC: . . . . MCTC 037

LIVE AT THE TOWN & COUNTRY CLUB.
LP: 841 013-0
MC: 841 013-4

NO FREE LUNCH.
LP: . . . . MERM 78
MC: . . . . MERMC 78

SCAPEGOATS.
LP: . . . . WOL 1001
MC: . . . . WOLMC 1001

THIS TIME AROUND.
LP: 841 248 1
MC: 841 248 4
LP: 841 720 1
MC: 841 519 4
LP: 841 519 1
MC: . . . . WOLMC 1019

Green Pajamas

GHOSTS OF LOVE.
LP: . . . . BLP 4033

SUMMER OF LUST.
LP: . . . . BAKTUN 1

Green, Peter

BACKTRACKIN'.
Tracks: / In the skies / Fool no more / Tribal dance / Just for you / Born on the wild side / Proud pinto / Shining star / Slaybo day / Indian lover / Carry my love / Corner of my mind / Cryin' won't bring you back / Little dreamer / Momma don't cha cry / Baby when the sun goes down / Born under a bad sign / Walkin' the road / Loser two times / What am I doing here / Big boy now / Time for me to go / It's gonna be me / You won't see me anymore / Bad bad feeling.
2LP: . . . . TRKLP 101
MCSET: . . . . TRKMC 101

BLUE GUITAR.
Tracks: / Gotta see her tonight / Last train to San Antone / Woman don't / Whatcha gonna do? / Walkin' the road / Apostle / Fool no more, A / Loser two times / Slabo day / Crying won't bring you back.
LP: . . . . CRX 5
MC: . . . . CRXC 5

CASE FOR THE BLUES, A.
LP: . . . . NTFL 2001

COME ON DOWN.
LP: . . . . HMS 031

END OF THE GAME, THE.
Tracks: / Bottoms up / Timeless time / Descending scale / Burnt foot / Hidden depth / End of the game, The.
LP: . . . . K 44106

IN THE SKIES.
Tracks: / In the skies / Slabo day / Fool no more, A / Funky chunk / Tribal dance / Seven stars / Just for you / Proud pinto / Apostle.
LP: . . . . PULS 101

KOLORS.
Tracks: / What am I doing here? / Bad bad feeling / Big boy now / Black woman / Bandit / Same old blues / Liquor and you / Gotta do it with me / Funky jam.
LP: . . . . HED 2
MC: . . . . HEDC 2

LEGEND.
Tracks: / Touch my spirit / Six string guitar / Proud pinto / Clown, The / You won't see me anymore / Long way from home / Little dreamer (Available on CD only) / In the skies / Rubbing my eyes / What am I doing here? / Corner of my mind / Carry my love / Bandit / White skies.
LP: . . . . CRX 12
MC: . . . . CRXC 12

LITTLE DREAMER.
Tracks: / Loser two times / Momma don't cha cry / Born under a bad sign / I could not ask for more / Baby when the sun goes down / Walkin' the road / One woman love / Cryin' won't bring you back / Little dreamer.
LP: . . . . PVLS 102

WATCHA GONNA DO?.
Tracks: / Gotta see her tonight / Promised land / Bullet in the sky / Give me back my freedom / Last train to San Antone / To break your heart / Bizzy Lizzy / Lost my love / Like a hot tomato / Head against the wall.

LP: .... PET 1

WHITE SKY.
Tracks: / Time for me to go / Shining star / Clown, The / White sky (love that evil woman) / It's gonna be me / Born on the wild side / Falling apart / Indian lover / Just another guy.
LP: 6 25155
LP: .... HED 1
MC: .... HEDC 1

Green, Phil

ROMANTIC SOUND OF THE 20'S (Green, Phil Orchestra).
Tracks: / I'll get by / My blue heaven / April showers / Blue skies / Whispering my melancholy baby / You were meant for me / Rock a bye your baby with a Dixie melody / Should I? / When day is gone / I can't give you anything but love / If I had you / Rose room / Funny face / Tea for two / I cried for you / Room with a view, A / If I had my way / Let me sing and I'm happy / Goodnight sweetheart.
LP: .... ETMP 4

ROMANTIC SOUND OF THE 30'S (Green, Phil Orchestra).
Tracks: / Over the rainbow / You are my lucky star / They can't take that away from me / Temptation / Night and day / Foggy day, A / Love for sale / Am I blue / Begin the beguine / Fine romance, A / I've got you under my skin / Let's face the music and dance / Touch of your lips, The / September song / Just one of those things / Time on my hands / Isn't this a lovely day / Penthouse serenade / You and the night and the music / In a sentimental mood.
LP: .... ETMP 5

ROMANTIC SOUND OF THE 40'S, THE (Green, Phil Orchestra).
Tracks: / Laura / Nearness of you, The / Sand in my shoes / Tenderly / Long ago and far away / That old black magic / Stella by starlight / They say it's wonderful / Girl that I marry, The / La mer / So in love / Bewitched / All the things you are / In the still of the night / On the Isle Of May / Tangerine / Dearly beloved / Out of my dreams / I remember you / How are things in Glocca Morra.
LP: .... ETMP 6

ROMANTIC SOUNDS OF YESTERDAY VOL 3, THE (Green, Phil Orchestra).
Tracks: / On a clear day you can see forever / Bali Ha'i / On the street where you live / Misty / They didn't believe me / Spanish eyes / Lara's theme / Blue dawn / Michelle / Impossible dream, The / I've grown accustomed to her face / Willow weep for me / Just in time / Music of the angels / Alice blue gown / You'll never know / Dream a little dream of me / I get a kick out of you / Easy to love / It only happens when I dance with you.
LP: .... ETMP 13

ROMANTIC SOUNDS OF YESTERDAY VOL 2, THE (Green, Phil Orchestra).
Tracks: / People / Love walked in / Climb every mountain / Manhattan / Moon river / C'est magnifique / Allagheny river waltz / Why do I love you / My funny valentine / Tiara tahiti / Yesterday / Body and soul / Change partners / Can I forget you? / Fly me to the moon / Singing rain, The / Sunrise sunset / Trade winds / Someday I'll find you / Strangers in paradise.
LP: .... ETMP 12

ROMANTIC SOUNDS OF YESTERDAY, VOL 1, THE (Green, Phil Orchestra).
Tracks: / Gigi / Hello young lovers / You're just in love / Autumn leaves / Paris in the Spring / Soliloquy / Summer place, A / Shadow of your smile, The / Quiet night of quiet stars / Dream / Sound of music / I could have danced all night / It might as well be Spring / Out of nowhere / My silent love / Do I hear a waltz? / Love is lue / Look for the silver lining / Love is a stranger / Folks who live on the hill, The.
LP: .... ETMP 11

Green River

DRY AS A BONE.
Tracks: / Unwind / This town / Baby takes / P.C.C. / Ozzie.
LP: .... TUPLP 17

REHAB DOLL.
LP: .... EFA 4465
LP: .... GR 0031

Green, Ruby

PANIC WHEN THE SUN GOES DOWN (See under Katzman, Nick) (Green, Ruby & Nick Katzman).

Green Rushes

GREEN RUSHES - THE QUIET MAN (see Walsh, Maurice) (Adair, Peter).

Green, Steve

FIND US FAITHFUL.
LP: .... SP R 1164
MC: .... SP C 1164

FOR GOD AND GOD ALONE.
LP: .... WING R 530
MC: .... WING C 530

HE HOLDS THE KEY.
LP: .... WING R 528
MC: .... WING C 528

JOY TO THE WORLD.
Tracks: / Joy to the world / Silent night / Hark the herald angels sing / O come, o come Emmanuel / Thou didst leave Thy throne / Angels from the realms of glory / O come all ye faithful / Birthday of a King / O holy night / Christmas once again / Messiah medley / Rest.
LP: .... WING R 532
MC: .... WING C 532

STEVE GREEN.
MC: .... TC WING 526

Green, Urbie

BLUES AND OTHER SHADES OF GREEN (Green, Urbie Quintet).
LP: .... FS 61

MESSAGE, THE (Green, Urbie And His Orchestra).
LP: .... FS 178

Green Willow Band

COTSWOLD MUSIC.
Tracks: / Three meet / Billy Johnson's Ball / Forester, The / Evesham stick dance / Bourton six / May Day song / Napoleons retreat / Worcester hornpipe / Hunting the squirrel / Greensleeves / Barley mow, The / Sicilian peasant turnpike gate / German clockmender / Lemmie's hornpipe / Bill the weaver / Slave, The / Bugle horn, The / Slow quickstep / Haste to the wedding / Wassailing song, The.
LP: .... SFA 115

Greenberg, Rowland

HOW ABOUT YOU.
Tracks: / Seven up / I don't stand a ghost of a chance / Have you met Miss Jones / Georgia on my mind / Stella by starlight / Gone with the wind / Basin Street blues / Strike up the band / On the sunny side of the street / Taps Miller / Sweet & lovely.
LP: .... GMLP 55

Greenbriar Boys

BEST OF THE GREENBRIAR BOYS (Greenbriar Boys feat. John Herald).
LP: .... VLP 79317
MC: .... VMC 79317

Greene, Graham

DREAM OF A STRANGE LAND (Burden, Hugh (nar)).
MC: .... TTC/GG 03

END OF THE AFFAIR (Glover, Julian/ Kika Markham).
MCSET: .... ZBBC 1068

STAMBOUL TRAIN (McDowall, Roddie).
MCSET: 2099

VISIT TO MORIN, A (Burden, Hugh (nar)).
MC: .... TTC/GG 02

Greene, Jack

GREATEST HITS: JACK GREENE.
LP: .... GT 0096

GREATEST HITS: JACK GREENE & JEANNIE SEELY (Greene, Jack/Seely, Jeannie).
LP: .... GT 0092

Greene, Joe

HIGH COUNTRY (See under Baker, Kenny) (Baker, Kenny & Joe Greene).

Greene, Richard

DUETS.
LP: .... ROUNDER 0075

RAMBLIN'.
LP: .... ROUNDER 0110
MC: .... ROUNDER 0110C

Greene, Sarah (nar)

FIVE GO TO MYSTERY MOOR (see under Blyton, Enid (aut)).

FIVE ON FINNISTON FARM (see under Blyton, Enid (aut)).

Greene String Quartet

MOLLY ON THE SHORE.
LP: .... HNBL 1333
MC: .... HNBC 1333

Greenfield, Dave

FIRE AND WATER (Greenfield, Dave & Jean Jacques Burnel).
Tracks: / Liberation / Rain & dole & tea / Vladimir and Sergei / Le soir / Trois pedophiles pour Eric Sabir / Dino rap / Nuclear power (yes please) Detective Prive / Consequences.
LP: .... EPC 25707
MC: 40 25707

Greengage Summer

GREENGAGE SUMMER, THE (See under Godden, Rumer (author)).

Greenhill, Mitch

STORM COMING (Greenhill, Mitch & Mayne Smith).
LP: .... BAY 215

Greenidge, Robert

MAD MUSIC (See also Utley, Michael) (Greenidge, Robert & Michael Utley).
Tracks: / Conchita pan classique / Sunshine / Coco loco / Hibiscus / Conchita / Pan classique in B minor (mad music) / African friend / Funk on steel / Shango.
LP: .... IMCA 5695
MC: .... IMCAC 5695

UTLEY JUBILEE (Greenidge, Robert & Michael Utley).
LP: .... IMCA 42045
MC: .... IMCAC 4205

Greenpeace

GREENPEACE: THE ALBUM (Various artists).
LP: .... FUND 1
MC: .... ZC FUND 1

Greenslade

BEDSIDE MANNERS ARE EXTRA.
Tracks: / Bedside manners are extra / Pilgrims progress / Time to dream / Drum folk / Sunkissed you're not / Chalkhill.
LP: .... K 46259

CACTUS CHOIR.
Tracks: / Pedro's party / Gettysburg / Swings and roundabouts / Time takes my time / Forever and ever / Cactus choir / Country dance / Finale.
LP: .... K 56306

GREENSLADE.
Tracks: / Feathered friends / English western, An / Drowning man / Temple song / Melange / What are you doin' to me / Sundance.
LP: .... K 46207

SPY GLASS GUEST.
Tracks: / Spirit of the dance / Little red fry up / Rainbow / Siam seesaw / Joie de vivre / Red light / Melancholic race / Theme for an imaginary western.
LP: .... K 56055

TIME AND TIDE.
Tracks: / Animal farm / Newsworth / Time / Tide / Catalan / Flatery stakes, The / Waltz for a fallen idol / Ass's ears, The / Doldrums / Gangsters.
LP: .... K 56126

Greenslade, Arthur

ABBA'S GREATEST HITS (Greenslade, Arthur & Orchestra).
Tracks: / Fernando / S.O.S. / My love, my life / Dancing queen / Hasta manana / Mamma mia / Money, money, money / Knowing me, knowing you / I do, I do, I do / Honey honey / When I kissed the teacher / Waterloo.
LP: .... PL 13036

COUNTRY STRINGS (Greenslade, Arthur & Orchestra).
Tracks: / One day at a time / Lucille / You needed me / Duelling Banjos / Welcome to my world / Blue eyes crying in the rain / Devil went down to Georgia, The / For the good times / Stand by your man / What I've got in mind / Convoy / Don't it make my brown eyes blue.
LP: .... CFRC 502
MC: .... MCFRC 502

Greenslade, Dave

PENTATEUCH, THE.
Tracks: / Intriot / Moondance / Beltempest / Glass / Three brides / Birds and bats and dragonflies / Nursery hymn / Minstrel / Fresco / Kashrinn / Barcarolle / Dry land / Forest kingdom / Vivat regina / Scream but not heard / Mischief / War / Lament for the sea / Miasma generator / Exile / Jubilate / Tiger the dove.
2LP: .... EMSP 332

Greensleeves

GREENSLEEVES (Various artists).
Tracks: / Fantasia on 'Greensleeves': *Various artists* / Lark ascending, The: *Various artists* / English folk song suite: *Various artists* / Walk to the paradise garden, The: *Various artists* (from 'A Village Romeo & Juliet'.) / On hearing the first cuckoo in spring: *Various artists* / Shropshire lad, A: *Various artists* / Banks of Green Willow, The: *Various artists* / Serenade for strings Opus 20: *Various artists*.
MC: TC2MOM 104
MC: .... LZ 762 527 4

Greenway

SERIOUS BUSINESS.
Tracks: / In the danger zone / Right track / Playin' to win / Serious business / I can't hold back / Let it go / R U ready for love / I believe in you / It's alright / I can't say no.
LP: .... K 781 872 1
MC: .... K 781 872 4

Greenwell, Peter

PETER GREENWELL IN CABARET.
LP: .... SR 305

Greenwillow (show)

GREENWILLOW (Original Broadway cast) (Various artists).
LP: .... P 13974
MC: .... BT 13974

Greenwood, Joan (nar)

ALICE IN WONDERLAND (see under Carroll, Lewis).

Greenwood, Lee

GREATEST HITS: LEE GREENWOOD.
Tracks: / Fool's gold / Somebody's gonna love you / It turns me inside out / She's lying / Dixie road / Ain't no trick (It takes magic) / Ring on her finger, time on her hands / I.O.U. / Going, going, gone. / God bless the U.S.A..
LP: .... IMCA 5582

IF ONLY FOR ONE NIGHT.
Tracks: / If only for one night / Opinion on love / We fell in love anyway / Comin' apart at the dreams / 'Til then / I go crazy / I love the way he left you / Any way the law allows / My heart is on the line / Home to Alaska.
LP: .... MCA 42300
MC: .... MCAC 42300

INSIDE OUT.
LP: .... MCF 3157

LOVE WILL FIND IT'S WAY TO YOU.
Tracks: / Love will find it's way to you / Look what we made (when we made love) / Silver saxophone / Gonna leave the light on / Heartbreak radio / Just another somebody's body / Didn't we / Mornin' ride / From now on / Little red caboose.
LP: .... IMCA 5770
MC: .... IMCAC 5770

SOMEBODY'S GONNA LOVE YOU.
Tracks: / I.O.U. / Somebody's gonna love you / Going, going, gone / Call it what you want to (It's still love) / Barely holding on / Love won't let us say goodbye / Ladies love / Wind beneath my wings / Think about the good times / Someone who remembers.
LP: .... MCF 3186
MC: .... MCFC 3186

STREAMLINE.
Tracks: / Streamline / Lonely people / I don't mind the thorns (If you're the rose) / Hearts aren't meant to break (They're meant to love) / Little at a time, A / Breakin' even / Don't underestimate my love for you / Same old song / Will to love,The / Leave my heart the way you found it.
LP: .... IMCA 5622

WIND BENEATH MY WINGS, THE.
Tracks: / You've got a good love comin' / I found love in time / I don't want to wake you / Love me like I'm leavin' tonight / Worth it for the ride / Wind beneath my wings / Two heart serenade / I.O.U. / Fools' gold / Even love can't save us now.
LP: .... MCF 3228
MC: .... MCFC 3228

Greer, John

BEST OF JOHN GREER VOL 1.
Tracks: / All I have to offer you is me / Crystal chandeliers / Jack to a king / Don't let me cross over / I threw away the rose / Sing me back home / Swingin' doors / Streets of Baltimore / Letter edged in black / Fraulein / Broken engagement / Mama tried / Silver haired daddy of mine / Teardrop on a rose.
LP: .... HRL 147
MC: .... CHRL 147

COUNTRY HALL OF FAME.
Tracks: / Help me make it through the night / I threw away the rose / So afraid of losing you / Fraulien / Letter edged in black / Did she mention my name / Country hall of fame / Almost persuaded / Streets of Baltimore / She's mine / Fugitive, The / Me and Bobby McGee.
MC: .... CT 121

COUNTRY REQUESTS.
Tracks: / You're my best friend / Among the Wicklow hills / Truck drivin' man / Sing me back home / Silver sandals / Broken engagement / Day the blizzard hit our town, The / Country music has gone to town / Able bodied man / Soldier's last letter / Two little orphans / Swingin' doors / Five little fingers / Once again.
LP: .... HRL 123

COUNTRY SIDE OF JOHN GREER.

Tracks: / Mamma tried / Blue side of lonesome / Today I started lovin' you again / Suny side of my life, The / Teardrop on a rose / Farmer's daughter, The / Jambalaya / Good old country music / Cover mama's flowers / Santa and the kids / Silver haired daddy of mine / Pass me by / Crystal chandeliers / Try it, you'll like it.
LP: . . . . . STOL 126
MC: . . . . . CT 126

HITS OF JOHN GREER.
Tracks: / Teddy bear / Dust on the bible / Love's gonna live here again / Singin' on a Sunday / If teardrops were pennies / Good old country music / Marriage CB way (Romance on the airwaves) / Coat of many colours / Silver sandals / Truck drivin' man / Keep it country / Roses for Mama.
LP: . . . . . PHL 438
MC: . . . . . CPHL 438

IRISH SONGS, COUNTRY STYLE.
Tracks: / Boys from County Armagh / Let us sing of dear old Ireland / Little country town in Ireland / Forty shades of green / Any Tipperary town / Green green grass of home / Isle of Innisfree / Gentle mother / Galway bay / Danny boy / Irish eyes / I'll settle for old Ireland.
LP: . . . . . PHL 426
MC: . . . . . CPHL 426

JOHN GREER'S COUNTRY & WESTERN HITS.
Tracks: / Two loves / All I have to offer you is me / Jack to a king / Lonely music / Most of the time / Coat of many colours / When two worlds collide / 21 years / Pub with no beer / Don't let me cross over / Jeannie Norman / If teardrops were pennies / Crown of thorns / Rocking alone in an old rocking chair.
LP: . . . . . CHRL 109

KEEP IT COUNTRY.
Tracks: / Keep it country / Hank William's guitar / Branded man / So much for me so much for you / Don't squeeze my Sharmon / I'll tell you where to go / Hear the family sing / Red rose from blue side of town / Okie from Muskogee / She just loved the cheatin' out of me / Love gonna live here again / Holding things together.
LP: . . . . . PHL 402
MC: . . . . . CPHL 402

MY MOTHER PRAYED FOR ME.
Tracks: / Jesus take a hold / If Jesus came to your house / Family who prays shall never part, The / Great speckled bird, The / What a friend we have in Jesus / Wait a little longer dear Jesus / I saw the light / When you get to heaven / If I were alone with God / Flowers, the sunset, the trees, The / On the wings of a dove / Take time out for Jesus / I'm using my buble for a roadmap / My mother prayed for me.
LP: . . . . . HRL 144
MC: . . . . . CHRL 144

OLD COUNTRY CHURCH.
Tracks: / Old country church / It is no secret / Church in the wildwood, The / Family bible / Mother went a walkin' / This world is not my home / Trouble in Amen Corner / Kneel down and pray / When the roll is called up yonder / Good folks in my life, The / When God comes and gathers his jewels / Old rugged cross, The / Lay your mighty hand on me / Dust on the bible.
LP: . . . . . HRL 126

R&B IN NEW YORK CITY.
Tracks: / Woman is a five letter word / Tell me so / Got you on my mind / Let me hold you / You played on my piano / Lonesome and blue / I need you / I'll never let you go / I'm the fat man / Beginning to miss you / Rhythm in the breeze / Drinkin' fool / Getting mighty lonesome for you / Too long / Come back Maybeline / Night crawlin'.
LP: . . . . . OFF 6026

ROSES FOR MAMA.
Tracks: / What's wrong with the way that we're doing it now / Roots of my raising / Shindig in the barn / Nothing sure looked good on you / Each season changes you / My daddy's eyes / Roses for Mama / That's what makes a country sing / Honky tonk blues / D.J cried, The / We sure danced us some good'uns / I gotta thing about trains.
LP: . . . . . PHL 423
MC: . . . . . CPHL 423

SINGIN' ON A SUNDAY.
Tracks: / Whispering hope / Help me understand / Hear the family sing / Supper time / Precious memories / Shall we gather at the river? / No earthly God / Singin' on a Sunday / That's where I learned to pray / Childhood memories / In the sweet bye and bye.
LP: . . . . . PHL 424
MC: . . . . . CPHL 424

SINGS COUNTRY.
Tracks: / Two loves / From a jack to a king / Pub with no beer.
LP: . . . . . HRL 109

SOMEWHERE BETWEEN.
Tracks: / New patches / Somewhere between / Reasons / I still believe in waltzes / Old time sake / You sure make cheatin' seem easy / One I'm holding now / God must be a cowboy at heart / Promise, The / Forget me not.
LP: . . . . . HAW 091

THAT'S COUNTRY.
Tracks: / That's only / Charlie's angel / I made the prison band / My last day / Mom & dad waltz / Rooftop lullaby / Sing me a song papa / Sundown in Nashville / Last country song, The.
LP: . . . . . RBA 1002

WHAT A FRIEND WE HAVE IN JESUS.
Tracks: / What a friend we have in Jesus / Just a little longer please, Jesus / On the wings of a dove / Family who prays shall never part, The / Kneel down and pray / Shall we gather at the river? / Whispering hope / In the sweet bye and bye / It is no secret / Old rugged cross, The / Church in the wildwood, The / When the roll is called up yonder.
LP: . . . . . PHL 459
MC: . . . . . CPHL 459

Greger, Max

CLASSICS FOR DANCING.
Tracks: / Pizzicati / Cha-cha-cha / Melodie in F / Mozart symphony no.40 / Furst igor ballet music / Liszt liebestraum / Offenbach barcarole / Mozart eine kleine nachmusik / Afforderung zum tanz / Poeme langsamer / Carmen / Chopin etude langsamer / Dvorak humoreske / Strauss vienna / Brahms' ungarisc her tanz no.5.
LP: 817 857-1
MC: 817 857-4

DANCE APPEAL.
Tracks: / Rock around the clock / La Paloma / True love / Greensleeves / Night fever / Stayin alive / Dancing in the city / Ma Baker.
LP: 2872 170
MC: 3472 170

EMOTIONS OF LOVE.
Tracks: / Emotions of love / Do you really want to hurt me / Hard to say I'm sorry / It's raining again / Words / Major Tom (Vollig losgelost) / Tu, soltanto tu / Adios amor / Save your love / Arrivederci Claire / Heartbreaker / Amore mio.
LP: 811 761-1
MC: 811 761-4

EUROPEAN JAZZ SOUNDS (Greger, Max & His Orchestra).
Tracks: / Discussion / Bluer than blue / Revelation / You're the one / Sax life / Carrera / Portrait in smoke / Meet BB / M G blues / Boomerang.
LP: 829 257-1

HALLO MAX.
LP: 829 126.1

MAX GREGER.
Tracks: / Little brown jug / Don't sit under the apple tree / Sun valley jump / American patrol / Sunrise serenade / Stairway to the stars / At last / Tuxedo Junction / Pennsylvania 65000 / Chattanooga choo choo / I know why / Nightingale sang in Berkeley square, A / In the mood / Blue skies / Johnson rag / It happened in Sun valley / Sonata / Song of the volga boatmen / Ida, sweet as apple cider / Bugle call rag / Anvil chorus / Tiger rag / Serenade in blue / String of pearls / St. Louis blues march / Moonlight serenade.
LP: 2482 583
MC: 3201 425

MAXIMUM (Greger, Max Big Band).
Tracks: / Salute to Miles / Bossa flute / Piece for two / One for Cann / Senor Bailey / Falling in love / Early blues / Take the 'A' train.
LP: 825 703-1

SUPERB DANCE MIX.
Tracks: / Playa blanca / Jenseits Von Eden / Abschied ist ein schares schwert / To all the girls I've loved before / Ci Sara / Die sonne und du / Footloose / Wake me up before you go go / Memories / Self-control / High on emotion / Mexican flavour / Rio Chico / Dream waltz / B.R. boogie.
MC: 823 687-4
LP: 823 687-1

TANZEN '87.
LP: 831 079.1

WIJ DANSEN VOL 7.
Tracks: / Foxtrot - some girls / Quickstep - humoreske / Engelse wals - feeling groovy / Tango - Rico Chico / Slow fox - banks of Ohio / Weense wals - wiener blut / Cha cha cha - Africa / Cha cha cha - Michaela / Rumba - melodie / Samba - matrimony / Disco-cha-cha - ring my bell / Jive - let's jive.
LP: 823 440-1
MC: 823 440-4

WIJ DANSEN VOL 8.
Tracks: / Cha cha cha - un deux trois / Cha cha cha - one way ticket / Rumba - ein bischen frieden / Samba - un poco rio / Jive - baby Jane / Rock 'n' roll - rock a beatin' boogie / Rock around the clock / Quickstep - hip hap hop / Foxtrot (Aufforderung zum tanz) / Engelse wals - love forever / Tango - Carmen / Slow fox - Road to romance / Weense wals - Daisy waltz / My Bonnie.
LP: 823 441-1
MC: 823 441-4

Gregg, Christina

MUSIC 'N' MOTION.
LP: . . . . . WW 5041

Gregg, Hubert

SONG FROM ME TO YOU, A (Hubert Gregg sings Hubert Gregg).
Tracks: / I wonder if you know what it means / It was never like this / Somebody is banging on the ceiling / From the French / Marie Louise / Things are never going to be different / Maybe it's because I'm a Londoner / I wasn't there / I'm going to get lit up / What do you do / Nothing in E flat / Je ne sais pas pourquoi / By kind permission of you / Best time to see a city, The / I love you for that / It's been a lovely day.
LP: . . . . . PRCV 137
MC: . . . . . TCPRCV 137

THANKS FOR THE MEMORY (Gregg, Hubert & Patricia Kirkwood).
LP: . . . . . REC 283

Gregorian Chant

GREGORIAN CHANT (Capella Antiqua Munchen).
Tracks: / Grates nunc omnes reddamus Domino Deo / La et abundus exsultet fidelis chorus / Stans a longe publicanus / Lauda, sion, salvatorem / Victimae paschali laudes / Zima vetus expurgetur / Summi triumphum regis / Omnes gentes, plaudite / Veni, sancte spiritus / Dies irae / Rex caeli, Domine maris / Mundi aetate octava.
MC: . . . . . GK 71953

SOLESMES ABBEY RECORDINGS.
MC: 200894

Gregoris

GREGORIS TRAVELLING.
LP: . . . . . SNTF 900

WHEREVER I WANDER I LONG FOR GREECE.
Tracks: / Heaven and sea / Byzantio / Black horse on the naked mountain / Great uprising / Here are the Balkans / Love is pain / Zeibeckiko / Agion oros / Hymn.
LP: . . . . . SNTF 888

Gregor-Smith, Bernard

RACHMANINOV AND CHOPIN CELLO SONATAS (Gregor-Smith, Bernard/ Yolande Wrigley).
Tracks: / Cello sonata (Rachmaninov) (in G minor) / Cello sonata (Chopin) (in G minor).
LP: . . . . . DCA 672
MC: . . . . . ZC DCA 672

Gregory, Billy

IT'S A BLUESY DAY.
LP: . . . . . AP 008

Gregory, Bryn

BRYN GREGORY AND THE CO-STARS.
LP: . . . . . RAZS 17

Gregory, John

DETECTIVES, THE (Gregory, John Orchestra).
Tracks: / Banacek / Cannon / Columbo / Griff / Harry O / Kojak / McCloud / McMillan and wife / Policewoman / Rockford files / Six million dollar man / Streets of San Francisco / S.W.A.T. / Sweeney.
LP: . . . . . SON 030

DYNAMIC SOUND OF JOHN GREGORY.
MC: 8428334

I WRITE THE SONGS (Gregory, John and his cascading strings).
Tracks: / La mer / My cherie amour / Night and day / Fool on the hill.
LP: . . . . . AKM 1001

Gregory, Michael

WHAT TO WHERE.
Tracks: / Jubilee / One / Still waiting / Heart of happiness / Superstitious game / Last home at / Where / What / Falling down / Fan the flame / Slow burn (there's more) / Elan.
LP: . . . . . PL 83023

Gregson, Clive

MISCHIEF (See Collister, Christine) (Gregson, Clive & Christine Collister).

STRANGE PERSUASIONS.
Tracks: / Summer rain / Jewel in your crown / I still see her face / Home is where the heart is / Play the fool / Poor relation / This town / Safety net, The / American car / I fell apart.
LP: . . . . . FIEND 45
MC: . . . . . FIENDCASS 45

WELCOME TO THE WORKHOUSE.
LP: . . . . . SPD 1026
MC: . . . . . SPDC 1026

Gregson & Collister

CHANGE IN THE WEATHER, A (Gregson, Clive & Christine Collister).
Tracks: / Blessing in disguise / Voodoo doll / This is the deal / Jumped up madam / My blue suede shoes / How weak I am / Blues on the run / Talent will out.
LP: . . . . . SPD 1022
MC: . . . . . SPDC 1022

HOME AND AWAY (Gregson, Clive & Christine Collister).
Tracks: / It's all just talk / Mama tried / Home is where the heart is / All the time in the world / Unlucky in love / Matchbox / When my ship comes in / I heard it through the grapevine / Chase the dragon / As lovers do / All because of you / Northern soul / Tough and go / Slow down / I'm blowing away.
LP: . . . . . COOK 003
LP: . . . . . BAKE 002
MC: . . . . . BAKEC 002

LOVE IS A STRANGE HOTEL.
Tracks: / For a dancer / Move away Jimmy Blue / How men are / Love is a strange hotel / Even a fool would let go / One step up / Things we do for love / Lonesome whistle / Same situation / Always better with you / Today I started loving you again / Most beguiling eyes, The.
MC: . . . . . SPDC 1035
LP: . . . . . SPD 1035

Gregson, John

WINGS OF SOUND (Gregson, John and his orchestra).
LP: . . . . . GREG 1

Greinke, Jeff

PLACES OF NOTILITY.
LP: . . . . . ST 7530

TIMBRAL PLANES.
Tracks: / Timbral planes / Slow fall / Rift / Splash and thunder / Glacial return / Rolling black cloud / Waiting, The / In cages / River's edge / Upon reflection.
LP: . . . . . ST 7549

Greko, Keith

LAST TRAIN OUTTA FLAGSTAFF.
LP: . . . . . VL 4

Gremlins (film)

GREMLINS (Film soundtrack) (Various artists).
LP: . . . . . RESLD 1
MC: 4054685
LP: . . . . . GEF 54685

GREMLINS 2 (Film Soundtrack) (Various artists).
Tracks: / Just you wait: *Various artists* / Gizmo escapes: *Various artists* / Leaky faucet: *Various artists*/ Cute ...: *Various artists* / Pot luck: *Various artists* / Visitors, The: *Various artists* / Teenage mutant gremlins: *Various artists* / Keep it quiet: *Various artists* / No rats: *Various artists* / Gremlin pudding: *Various artists* / New trends: *Various artists* / Gremlin credits: *Various artists*.
LP: . . . . . VS 5269
MC: . . . . . VSC 5269

Grenadier Guards

BEST OF BRITISH, THE.
LP: . . . . . DJM 6000
MC: . . . . . DMC 6000

BRITISH GRENADIERS, THE (Grenadier Guards Band).
Tracks: / British grenadiers, The / Scipio / 1st battalion bugle call / Queens company, The / 2nd battalion bugle call / Nilimegen / 3rd battalion bugle call / Inkerman / Rule Brittania / Grenadiers march / Duke of York's march / Duke of Gloster's march / Belle isle / Portsmouth / Grenadiers march, The / Wargramer grenadier march / Last post / Grenadier's return / Reveille / Musick marziale.
LP: . . . . . BND 1038
MC: . . . . . ZC BND 1038

CHRISTMAS FROM THE GUARDS.
LP: . . . . . PRD 2010
MC: . . . . . PRD 4 2010

DRUMS AND FIFES (Combined corps of drums 1st/2nd Batallion).

Tracks: / Ye Bitish Grenadiers / Girl I left behind me, The / Flag & Empire / Romantica / Prince Rupert's march / See the conquering hero comes / Precision in percussion.
LP: . . . . BND 1012
MC: . . . . ZC BND 1012

FOCUS ON THE GRENADIER GUARDS.
2LP: . . . . FOS 47/48

MARCH SPECTACULAR.
Tracks: / British Grenadiers, The / Through bolts and bars / Army and marine / Dunedin / Carry on / Bond of friendship / King's troop / Trafalgar / Furchtlos und treu / Red men's march / Ein andere / Dunedin / Badenviller / Scipio / Carry on / Bond of friendship / Independentia / King's troop / Luftwaffe march / Imperial echoes / Admiral of the air / Grenadiers march.
LP: . . . . BND 1006
MC: . . . . ZC BND 1006

MARCHING THROUGH THE YEARS (Band of the Grenadier Guards).
Tracks: / Children of the regiment / Admiral of the air / Washington grays / Bridge too far, A / Army and Marine / In the Dolomites / In storm and sunshine / Kennebec / Marching through the years / Birdcage walk / Red Men's march, The / Man O'Brass / Raiders of the Lost Ark / Piper in the meadow / True comrades in arms / Robinson's grand entree / Independentia / On the square.
LP: . . . . GRALP 19
MC: . . . . GRTC 19

MARCHING WITH THE GRENADIER GUARDS.
Tracks: / British Grenadiers, The / Tour of duty / Imperial echoes / Zapfenstreich nr.1 / Old comrades / Scipio march / Blaze away / Troop 'Les Huguenots' / Hands across the sea / Colonel Bogey / Grenadiers slow march / Liberty bell / Purple pageant, The / Radetzky march / Duke of York slow march, The / Europe United / Coronation bells / New colonial march, The.
LP: . . . . GUARDS 1
MC: . . . . TCGUARDS 1

NATIONAL ANTHEMS OF THE WORLD.
LP: . . . . MOR 504

NEW WORLD SALUTE (Grenadier Guards & Gordon Highlanders).
LP: . . . . BND 1052
MC: . . . . ZC BND 1052

ON STAGE.
Tracks: / Fanfare - stage presence / Full speed ahead / Grenadiers waltz, The / Overture on themes of Offenbach / Love changes everything / Carnival of Venice / Debutante, The / Prelude to romance / Send in the clowns / Portrait in time, A / Me and my girl / March and dance of the comedians / Les miserables / Spanish rhapsody - fiesta / March - Atlantis (Tape only.) / Three bavarian dances (Tape only.).
MCSET: . . . . BNC 63006

QUEEN'S BIRTHDAY, THE (see Saint John's School Choir/Band of the Grena (Band Of The Grenadier Guards/Saint John's School Choir).

TERCENTENARY GALA CONCERT.
Tracks: / Windsor flourish, A / Polovtsian dances / Grenadiers, The / Soldiers' chorus (From the Decemberists) / Battle hymn / Man o'brass / Grenadiers march / Armenian dances / It's a grand night for singing / British Grenadiers, The.
LP: . . . . PRM 105D
MC: . . . . CPRM 105D

WORLD OF SOUSA MARCHES, THE (Grenadier Guards Band).
LP: . . . . SPA 404
MC: . . . . KCSP 404

WORLD OF THE GRENADIER GUARDS.
LP: . . . . SPA 248

WORLD'S GREATEST MARCHES, THE.
MC: . . . . PRD 42004

YANKEE DOODLE DANDY (Grenadier Guards Band).
Tracks: / American patrol / Cole Porter-A symphonic portrait / Alouette / Sidewalks of New York, The / Stars and stripes forever / Shenandoah / U.S.A. services marches.
LP: . . . . DR 106

Grenfell, Joyce

COLLECTION: JOYCE GRENFELL.
Tracks: / I'm going to see you today / Encores / Picture postcard / Dear Francois / Old girls' school reunion / Re-union / Joyful noise / Nursery school - flowers / Rime / Three brothers / Shirley's girlfriend / Fanfare / Oh, Mr. Du Maurier / Boat train / I wouldn't go back / Old Joe Clarke (Songs my mother taught me) / Step light lady / All the pretty little horses / Nursery school - Free activity period / Olde tyme dancing.
LP: . . . . OU 1249
MC: . . . . TCOU 1249

GEORGE DON'T DO THAT.
MC: . . . . TCSRS 5199
LP: . . . . SRS 5199

JOYCE GRENFELL REQUESTS THE PLEASURE.
Tracks: / How was it for you / Life's rich pageant / Christmas carol / Joyce Grenfell requests the pleasure / Vintage Archers / Diary of a nobody, A / Clinging to the wrecking / Tales from a long room / Just Williams / Plain tales from Raj / Epic poems / Perfect spy, A.
MCSET: . . . . ZBBC 1049

JOYCE GRENFELL TALKING.
LP: . . . . HIFLY 34

KEEPSAKE.
Tracks: / Mad about the boy / Sigh no more / Ziguener / I'd follow my secret heart / Parisian Pierrot / Some day I'll find you / Matelot / I'll see you again / Useful and acceptable gifts / Keepsake / Maud / Yellow rose of Texas / All the pretty little horses / I don't 'arf love you / Narcissus / If love were all / Some day I'll find you / Matelot / Party's over, The / I'm going to see you today / Drifting / There's nothing new to tell you / Village mother, The / American mother.
LP: . . . . SH 507
MC: . . . . TCSH 507

NEW JOYCE GRENFELL COLLECTION.
MC: . . . . TC2 DUO 128

RE-JOYCE.
Tracks: / Opera interval / American mother / Old girls' school reunion / I'm going to see you today / Committee / Useful and acceptable gifts / Hymn / Security song / Shirley's girlfriend / I like life / First flight / Maud / Life and literature / Nursery school / Three brothers / Terrible worrier, A / Narcissus / Time.
LP: . . . . EMS 1305
MC: . . . . TCEMS 1305

SECOND COLLECTION, THE.
Tracks: / Opening numbers / Nursery school 'Going home time" / Hymn / Wedding is on Saturday, The / If love were all / Thursdays / Fan / Slow down / Bring back the silence / Shirley's girlfriend / Wrong songs for wrong singers (or songs to make you sick) / Telephone call / Hostess, The / London Scottish / Lally Tullet / Party's over, The.
LP: . . . . ONCR 524
MC: . . . . TC ONCR 524

SONGS AND MONOLOGUES OF JOYCE GRENFELL, THE (See under EMI Comedy Classics).

Gresley Male Voice

BEGONE DULL CARE.
LP: . . . . BNB 2005

Grey, Al

AL GREY AND JESPER THILO QUINTET (Grey, Al & Jesper Thilo Quintet).
LP: . . . . SLP 4136

AL GREY'S ALL STARS.
LP: . . . . TP 3001

BASIC GREY.
Tracks: / Things ain't what they used to be / Open wider please / I got it bad and that ain't good / Don't get around much anymore / How come you do me like you do / Bluish grey / Elder, The / Bewitched / Kenie-Konie / Bluish grey / Wild deuce / Green dolphin street / Bantu / Melba's blues / Nothing but the truth / Three-fourth blues / Just waiting / R.B.Q / Minor on top / Africa lady / Hi fly.
2LP: . . . . GCH 2-6030

GET IT TOGETHER Live at The Pizza Express (Grey,Al & Tony Coe).
LP: . . . . PE 5504

JUST JAZZ (See under Tate, Buddy) (Grey, Al & Buddy Tate).

LIVE AT RICKS (See under Forrest, Jimmy) (Grey, Al & Jimmy Forrest).

LIVE AT THE 1990 CONCORD JAZZ FESTIVAL (See Under McConnell, Rob) (Grey, Al & Rob McConnell & Benny Powell).

LIVE IN CHICAGO (see Forrest, Jimmy & Al Grey) (Grey, Al & Jimmy Forrest).

THINGS ARE GETTING BETTER ALL THE TIME (see Johnson, J.J.) (Grey, Al & J.J. Johnson).

Grey, Blind Arvella

BLUES FROM MAXWELL STREET.
LP: . . . . C 5527

Grey Fox (film)

GREY FOX, THE (Film Soundtrack) (Various artists).
Tracks: / Grey Fox, The (main titles): *Chieftains* / Oyster bed sequence: *Chieftains* / Country store sequence: *Chieftains* / Ride to Kamloops: *Chieftains* / Meeting tram at Ducks Siding: *Chieftains* / Chase, The: *Chieftains* / End title: *Chieftains* / Sweet Betsy from Pike: *Farnsworth, Richard.*
LP: . . . . SL 9515
MC: . . . . SLC 9515

Grey, Mark

SOMETIMES WHEN WE TOUCH (see under Wynette, Tammy) (Grey, Mark/ Tammy Wynette).

Grey Matter

TAKE IT BACK.
LP: . . . . DISCHORD 21

Grey Parade

REASON, THE.
Tracks: / Crocodile tears / Flags are burning / Each time we touch / Empty room / Reason / Winter / Exteriors / Chosen few / Impressions of Africa / Heaven and hell.
LP: . . . . GREY 1

Grey, Sara

MAKING THE AIR RESOUND (Grey Sara & Ellie Ellis).
Tracks: / Bayou Sara / Goodnight loving trail / Dear honey / Little birdie / Washington's march / Waiting for Nancy / Love was the price / Old granite state, The / Knoxville girl / Aragon mill / New wood / Cobweb of dreams / Bull at the wagon / Light from the lighthouse / Friends and neighbours.
LP: . . . . FE 039

PROMISES TO KEEP.
LP: . . . . HAR 011
MC: . . . . HARC 011

YOU GAVE ME A SONG (Grey Sara & Ellie Ellis).
LP: . . . . GVR 231

Grey, Sonny

LIVE: DEXTER GORDON & SONNY GREY (see Gordon, Dexter) (Grey, Sonny & Dexter Gordon).

Grey, Zane

THUNDER MOUNTAIN.
MCSET: . . . . CAB 256

Greyhound

BLACK AND WHITE.
Tracks: / Black and white / Dream lover / Stand for our rights / Jamaica rum / Sky high / Wily / Only love can win / Mango rock / Unchained melody / Hold on to your happiness / Wappadusa / Some dark city.
LP: . . . . TRLS 27
LP: C5-539

Greystoke...(film)

GREYSTOKE - LEGEND OF TARZAN (Film soundtrack) (Various artists).
LP: 925120 1

Gribbin, Tom

SON OF LIGHTNING.
Tracks: / Train to Dixie / Waymore's blues / Saltwater gypsy / Champagne ladies / Son of lightning / Guns of Brixton / Honky tonk blues / Johnny deepwater / Big rig / To be your man.
LP: . . . . CRLP 1001

USEPPA ISLAND RENDEVOUS (Gribbin, Tom & The Saltwater Band).
Tracks: / My images come / Gospel rock / Sad cafe / Time will tell / Out of my hands / Rich in the blues / Love you too / Fisherman's prayer / What am I supposed to do / Salty dog cracker man.
LP: . . . . RANGE 7002

Grid

ELECTRIC HEAD.
LP: . . . . WX 342
MC: . . . . WX 342 C

Grief

GRIEF, THE.
LP: . . . . NT 12

HUIS CLOS.
LPS: . . . . NT 15

KITTYSTRA QUATRE.
LP: . . . . DANLP 014

Grieg (composer)

GRIEG'S BEST (Various artists).
LP: . . . . BES 1008
MC: . . . . BESC 1008

HOLBERG SUITE & OTHERS (Berlin Philharmonic Orchestra).
MC: 4278084

HOMAGE TO GRIEG (see under Homage to Grieg) (Various artists).

INCIDENTAL MUSIC TO PEER GYNT (Various artists).
LP: . . . . ASD 1434401
MC: . . . . TCCASD 1434404

PEER GYNT - SIGURD JORSALFAR Five songs (London Symphony Orchestra).
MC: 4255124

PEER GYNT SUITES NOS. 1 & 2 Lyric suite (Gothenburg Symphony Orchestra).
MC: 4278074

PIANO CONCERTO IN A MINOR (Concertgebouw Orchestra Amsterdam).
MC: 426 079-4

Grieg, Stan

BLUES EVERY TIME.
Tracks: / Love for sale / Honky tonk train blues / Take five / Willlow weep for me / Five o'clock blues / Air to The Duke / Mop mop.
LP: . . . . CLGLP 004
MC: . . . . ZCLG 004

Grier, David

FREEWHEELING.
LP: . . . . ROUNDER 0250

Grier, Jimmy

12 RADIO BROADCASTS OF 1940'S (Grier, Jimmy & Orchestra).
LP: . . . . GL 6015

JIMMIE GRIER, 1935-36.
Tracks: / Varsity drag / You're my everything / One I love, The / Every little moment / You are my lucky star / Chicago / Goofus / Lady be good / Darktown strutters ball / Music goes 'round and 'round, The / Blues my naughty sweetie gives to me / Canadian capers / Let's sing about something / Hollywood at vine / My rhythm mood / Stompin' at the Savoy.
LP: . . . . HSR 177

Grierson, Jimmy

SERIES OF LONG JUMPS.
LP: JETLP225

Griff, Zaine

ASHES AND DIAMONDS.
Tracks: / Tonight / Run / Ashes and diamonds / Secret pleasures / She's my man / Things you say / Scandinavian / Orient / Iron curtain / Ta cigarette apres l'amour.
LP: . . . . K 56834

FIGURES.
Tracks: / Proud ones / Vanishing men / Flowers / Hot / Fahrenheit / 451 / Figures / Stranger / Time stands still / 83rd and 4th / Chance of a dance / Beating of wings.
LP: . . . . POLD 5061

Griffin, Angee

GENTLE (IMPORT).
LP: . . . . SL 7000

Griffin, Annette

SONGS FROM ASHFORD CASTLE.
MC: . . . . GTDC 007

Griffin, Billy

BE WITH ME.
Tracks: / Be with me / Stone's throw from heaven, A / Hold me tighter in the rain / Love is not a word / Beat is getting stronger / 2nd day love story / Breaking out / Understand.
LP: . . . . CBS 85591

RESPECT.
Tracks: / Respect / Don't stop lovin' me / Serious / Save your love for me / Don't ask me to be friends / So many ways / Hit me with the beat / Dreaming.
LP: . . . . CBS 25697

SYSTEMATIC.
Tracks: / Systematic / If i ever lose this heaven / Waiting to touch / This ain't puppy love / Electrified / Everybody needs somebody / Easy thing to say / Can't keep running away.
LP: . . . . CBS 26449

Griffin Brothers

RIFFIN' WITH THE GRIFFIN BROTHERS ORCHESTRA (Griffin Brothers Orchestra).
Tracks: / Little red rooster / Weepin' and cryin' / Griff's boogie / Blues all alone / Teaser / Pretty baby / Blues with a beat / Stubbon as a mule / I wanna go back / I'm gonna jump in the river / Comin' home / Tra-la-la / Shuffle bug / Ace in the hole / Hot pepper / It'd surprise you.
LP: . . . . CHD 136

Griffin, Clive

INSIDE OUT.
LP: 8484531
MC: 8484534

STEP BY STEP.
LP: 836 737 1

MC: 836 737 4

Griffin, James

CURE FOR SNAKEBITE, A (Griffin, James & The Subterraneans).
LP: . . . . CLP 12

IMMIGRANT TANGO (Griffin, James & The Subterraneans).
LP: . . . . CHASE 2

Griffin, John 'Jarfly'

SOUTHBOUND TRAIN.
LP: . . . . LR 44.010

Griffin, Johnny

BLOWING SESSION, A.
Tracks: / Way you look tonight / Ball bearing / All the things you are / Smoke stack.
LP: . . . . BLP 1559
LP: B1 81559

CAT, THE.
MC: . . . . ANC 8762

CONGREGATION.
Tracks: / Congregation, The / Latin quarter, The / I'm glad there is you / Main spring / It's you or no one.
LP: . . . . BLP 1580

FLY MISTER FLY With the Joe Morris Orchestra.
LP: . . . . BP 504

FULL HOUSE (see Montgomery,Wes) (Griffin, Johnny & Wes Montgomery).

GRIFF AND LOCK (Griffin, Johnny & Eddie Lockjaw Davis).
LP: . . . . OJC 264

INTRODUCING JOHNNY GRIFFIN.
Tracks: / Mil dew / Chicago calling / These foolish things / Boy next door, The / Nice and easy / It's alright with me / Lover man / Way you look tonight / Cherokee.
LP: . . . . BST 81533

JAMFS ARE COMING, THE (Griffin, Johnny and Art Taylor Quartet).
LP: . . . . SJP 121

JOHNNY GRIFFIN.
LP: . . . . HLL 101/10

JOHNNY GRIFFIN MEETS DEXTER GORDON (Griffin, Johnny and Dexter Gordon).
LP: . . . . ORL 8247

JOHNNY GRIFFIN SEXTET (Griffin, Johnny Sextet).
Tracks: / Stix' trix / What's new / Wooding you / Johnny G.G / Catharsis.
LP: . . . . RLP 264

LITTLE GIANT, THE.
Tracks: / Catharsis / What's new / Hot sausage / Woodyn' you / Where's your overcoat boy / Little John / 63rd Street theme / Playmates / Message / Kerry dancers / Black is the colour of my true loves hair / Green grow the rushes-o / Londonderry air.
2LP: . . . . M 47054

MAN I LOVE, THE.
Tracks: / Man I love, The / Hush-a-bye / Blues for Harvey / Masquerade is over, The / Sophisticated lady / Wee.
LP: . . . . BLP 60107

NYC UNDERGROUND.
Tracks: / Yours is my heart alone / Few words from Johnny Griffin / Alone again / Let me touch it / Sophisticated lady / Rhythm-a-ning.
LP: . . . . GXY 5132

SWINGIN', THE.
Tracks: / Foot patting / Please send me someone to love / Turk's Bolero, The / Deep eight / Handful of soul, A / Jamfs are coming, The / Lady heavy bottom's house.
LP: . . . . GATE 7020
MC: . . . . CGATE 7020

TOUGHEST TENORS (Griffin, Johnny & Eddie Lockjaw Davis).
Tracks: / Tickle toe / Save your love for me / Funky fluke / Epistrophy / Well you needn't / I mean you / Good bait / Walkin' / Blues up and down / Camp meeting / Blue Lou / How am I to know / Tin tin deo.
LP: . . . . M 47035

YOU LEAVE ME BREATHLESS.
Tracks: / Rhythm-a-ning / Old folks / Wee / You leave me breathless / Leave me alone blues.
LP: . . . . BLP 30134

Griffin, Vincent

TRADITIONAL FIDDLE MUSIC FROM COUNTY CLARE.
Tracks: / Fahey's 1 & 2 / Paddy Fahey's / Cliffs of Moher, The / Paddy Ryan's dream / Mammy's pet / Martin Rocheford's / Sligo maid, The / New century, The / Cuckoo, The / Coleman's / Lord McDonald's / Ballinasloe fair / Reefs, The / McFadden's favourite / New year's in, The / Youghal quay / Se bhfath mo bhfuartha (The cause of my sorrow) / Lord Gordons / Doctor Gilbert / Queen of May, The / Trip to Sligo, The / Garrett Barry's / Night in Ennis, The / Maid behind the bar, The / Crowley's / Lady Ann Montgomery / Down the broom / Gatehouse maid, The.
LP: 12TS 338

Griffith, Nanci

LAST OF THE TRUE BELIEVERS.
Tracks: / Last of the true believers, The / Love at the five and dime / St. Olav's gate / More than a whisper / Banks of the old Pontchartrain / Looking for the time / Goin' gone / One of these days / Love's found a shoulder / Fly by night / Wing and the wheel.
LP: . . . . REU 1013
MC: . . . . REUC 1013
MC: . . . . CPH 1109
LP: . . . . PH 1109

LATE NIGHT GRANDE HOTEL.
LP: . . . . MCA 10304
MC: . . . . MCAC 10304

LITTLE LOVE AFFAIRS.
LP: . . . . MCF 3413
MC: . . . . MCFC 3413

LONE STAR STATE OF MIND.
Tracks: / Lone star state of mind / Cold hearts, closed minds / From a distance / Beacon Street / Nickel dreams / Sing one for sister / Ford econoline / Trouble in the fields / Love in a memory / Let it shine on me / There's a light beyond these woods.
LP: . . . . MCF 3364
MC: . . . . MCFC 3364

ONCE IN A VERY BLUE MOON.
Tracks: / Ghost in the music / Love is a hard waltz / Roseville fair / Mary and Omie / Friend out in the madness / I'm not drivin' these wheels / Ballad of Robin Winter-Smith / Daddy said / Once in a very blue moon / Year down in New Orleans / Spin on a red brick floor.
LP: . . . . PH 1096
MC: . . . . PH 1096C
LP: . . . . MCG 6054
MC: . . . . MCGC 6054
MC: . . . . MCLC 1759

ONE FAIR SUMMER EVENING.
Tracks: / Once in a very blue moon / Looking for the time / Deadwood, South Dakota / More than a whisper / Wing and the wheel / Spin on a red brick floor / Roseville fair / Workin' in corners.
LP: . . . . MCF 3435
MC: . . . . MCFC 3435

STORMS.
LP: . . . . MCG 6066
MC: . . . . MCGC 6066

THERE'S A LIGHT BEYOND THESE WOODS.
Tracks: / Michael's song / West Texas sun / Dollar matinee / Alabama soft spoken blues / Song for remembered heroes / There's a light beyond these woods / Montana backroads.
LP: . . . . PH 1097
MC: . . . . PH 1097C
LP: . . . . MCG 6052
MC: . . . . MCGC 6052

Griffiths, Albert

COUNTRY LIVING (Griffiths, Albert & The Gladiators).
LP: . . . . REU 1003
LP: . . . . HB 36

GLADIATORS IN STORE FOR YOU.
Tracks: / Give It Up / New York / Make it work / Vitamin A & C / Clean hands / Careless gun / On TV / Merciless Pay / Holy hill, The / Instore for you.
LP: . . . . HB 41

Griffiths, Dave

PIGEONS ON MY BRAIN.
LP: . . . . FR 131

Griffiths, Derek

HEADS & TAILS.
LP: . . . . REC 379
MC: . . . . ZCM 379

Griffiths, Hugh

MEMORIES.
LP: . . . . BMLP 018

MOTHER AFRICA.
Tracks: / Happy go lucky girl / 400 years / Ghetto children / Mother Africa / Reggae rock steady / Tender touch / African dreams / Darker days.
LP: . . . . WRLP 0102

MR WALKER.
LP: . . . . VSLP 2007

Griffiths, Marcia

CAROUSEL.
Tracks: / Electric boogie (radio mix) / Groovin' / Carousel / One who really loves you, The / Electric boogie (dub mix) / Do unto others / All over the world / Sugar shack / Money in the bank.
MC: . . . . MCT 1024
LP: . . . . MLPS 1024

I LOVE MUSIC.
LP: . . . . MMLP 004

MARCIA.
LP: . . . . DGLP 7
MC: . . . . DGLC 7

MUSIC FOR THE WORLD (see Marley, Rita) (Griffiths, Marcia, R. Marley & J. Mowatt).

NATURALLY.
LP: . . . . SKYLP 9

ROCK MY SOUL.
LP: . . . . PRLP 29

STEPPIN'.
MC: . . . . SHMC 44007

SWEET BITTER LOVE.
Tracks: / First time ever I saw your face, The / Play me / There's no me without you / I'd rather be lonely / Gypsy man / Sweet bitter love / Here I am baby / Everything I own / Green grasshopper / Children at play.
LP: . . . . TRLS 94

Griffiths, Marcus

THRILL OF VICTORY, THE.
LP: . . . . GALP 006

Griffiths, Roni

RONI GRIFFITHS.
Tracks: / Love is the drug / Breakin' up (Best part of) / That's rock'n'roll / Desire / Voodoo man / Heart on the line / Take me out.
LP: . . . . VSD 79435

Grifters (film)

GRIFTERS, THE (See under Bernstein, Elmer) (Bernstein, Elmer).

Grill, Rob

UPROOTED.
Tracks: / Feel the heat / God help the man / Have mercy / Rockin' on the road again / Strangers / Rock sugar / When will it be / Open up your heart / Where were you when I needed you.
LP: 9111005

Grills, Lucky

TRUE BLUE COMEDY VOL 1 (Hard up for sex).
MCSET: . . . . PLAC 471

TRUE BLUE COMEDY VOL 2 (Red hot & very blue).
MCSET: . . . . PLAC 472

TRUE BLUE COMEDY VOL 3 (True blue Aussie).
MCSET: . . . . PLAC 473

Grim

FACE OF BETRAYAL.
LP: . . . . CHEM 107
MC: . . . . CHEM 107C

Grim Reaper

FEAR NO EVIL.
LP: . . . . EBON 32

SEE YOU IN HELL.
LP: . . . . EBON 16

Grim Tales...

GRIM TALES FROM THE SCOTS (see Scot, Stevenson & Hogg) (Sheddon, John).

Grimes, Carol

CAROL GRIMES.
Tracks: / I've been used / Number one (In my heart) / You make my life / Up hill peace of mind / I betcha didn't know that / Brand new tomorrow / My baby specializes / That's the time / I feel like going home / Private number / Dynamite / No more tears.
LP: . . . . CR 30164

EYES WIDE OPEN.
LP: . . . . TM 9
MC: . . . . ZCTM 9

Grimes, Tammy (nar)

JENNY AND THE CAT CLUB/JENNY'S FIRST PARTY (See under Jenny & the Cat (bk)).

WHEN JENNY LOST HER SCARF/ JENNY'S ADOPTED BROTHER (See under When Jenny Lost (bk)).

Grimes, Tiny

EARLY-MID 1950S (Grimes, Tiny & His Friends).
Tracks: / Movin' out today / Things got tough again / Long lean and lanky / Keep me with you / I'm in love with you / Do you really love me / Start talking baby / I'll never let you go / I'm a wine drinker / I love to make love / I want a present for Xmas / I can't go on / Call of the wild.
LP: . . . . KK 821

FRANKIE AND JOHNNY BOOGIE.
LP: 33712

LOCH LOMOND (Grimes, Tiny & His Rockin' Highlanders).
Tracks: / Blue harlem / Flying high / That old black magic / Profoundly blue / Boogie woogie barbecue / Annie Laurie / Nightmare blues / Hot in Harlem / Loch Lomond / Midnight special / Jumpin' at Gleason's / Jealousy / Begin the beguine / Sidewalks of New York, The / Man I love, The / Sanctifying the blues.
LP: . . . . KM 706

ONE IS NEVER TOO OLD TO SWING (see under Eldridge, Roy) (Grimes, Tiny & Roy Eldridge).

PROFOUNDLY BLUE.
LP: . . . . MR 5013

ROCK THE HOUSE (Grimes, Tiny & His Rockin' Highlanders).
LP: . . . . ST 1016

TINY GRIMES VOLUME 1 (1949-1952).
Tracks: / Tiny's jump / Hey Now / Why did you waste my time / St. Louis Blues / Drinking beer / My baby's left me / Frankie and Johnnie Boogie-1 / Hey Mr. J.B. / Battle of the mass / I'm in love with you baby / My baby's cool / Hawaiian boogie / No hug no kiss / Frankie and Johnnie boogie-2.
LP: . . . . KK 804

TINY GRIMES VOLUME 2 (1949-55) (Instrumentals).
LP: . . . . KK 817

TINY'S BOOGIE Rockin' & sockin' 1948-50.
LP: . . . . OL 8009

Grimethorpe Colliery

AGE OF SELF, THE (see White, Robert) (Grimethorpe Colliery Band/Robert White).

BAND OF THE YEAR.
Tracks: / March "The Nybbs" / Lark in the clear air / Waltz from the sleeping beauty / Cleopatra / Sarie marais / March from Suite no.1 in E flat major, Op 28 / Intermezzo from "Cavalleria Rusticana" / Trumpet voluntary.
LP: . . . . PL 25048
MC: . . . . PK 25048

CLASSIC BRASS.
Tracks: / Florentiner march / William Tell overture / Sweet Georgia Brown / Serenade / Sugar blues / Mr. Jums / Valdres march / MacArthur Park / Gymnopedie no.1 / Mr. Lear's carnival / Misty / Procession to the Minster / Irish tune from County Derry ((Danny boy). CD only.) / Finale from Faust (CD only.).
LP: . . . . MFP 5860
MC: . . . . TCMFP 5860

CLASSICS FOR BRASS.
LP: . . . . SXL 6820

FIREBIRD.
Tracks: / Midnight sleighride / On with the motley / Songs of the quay / In a sentimental mood / Pictures at an exhibition / Festive prelude, A / Scherzo / Berne patrol / Why did I choose you / Firebird.
LP: . . . . PRL 010
MC: . . . . CPRL 010

GRIMETHORPE COLLIERY BAND.
Tracks: / Believe me if all those endearing young charms / Torramawakefield / Concert variations / Festival overture / Brassmen's holiday / Pandora / Pionciana / Goodbye to love / Haryjanos.
LP: . . . . LKLP 6482

GRIMETHORPE SPECIAL.
LP: . . . . HEAD 14

KING SIZE BRASS.
Tracks: / Big G / Bobby Shaftoe / Ballad for trombone / All creatures great and small / Ticket to ride / La belle Americaine / Simoraine / Holiday for strings / Blaythorne suite / Mozart rondo / Dunlapps creek / Simple gifts / Superman.
LP: . . . . PRL 004
MC: . . . . CPRL 004

POP GOES THE POST HORN.
LP: . . . . GRS 1022

Grimm

FAIRY TALES.
Tracks: / Rumpelstiltskin / Little red cap / Nose, The / Tom Thumb / Elves and the shoemaker, The / Peter and the goatherd / Golden goose, The / Travelling musicians, The / Rose-bud / Wolf and the seven little goats, The / Valiant tailor, The / Grateful beasts, The / Three children of fortunes, The / Hans in luck.
MCSET: 414 706-4

FOUR OF YOUR FAVOURITE STORIES FROM...
LP: . . . . TMP 9009
MC: TMP4 9009

GRIMM BROTHERS FAIRY TALES VOL 2 (Gordon, Hannah (nar)).
LP: . . . . P 0052

GRIMM BROTHERS FAIRY TALES VOL 1 (Gordon, Hannah (nar)).
LP: . . . . P 0051

GRIMMS FAIRY TALES (Hancock,Sheila).
MC: . . . . TCLFP 417124-5

GRIMMS FAIRY TALES.
MC: . . . . STC 013

GRIMM'S FAIRY TALES.
Tracks: / Rumpelstiltskin / Little Red-Cap / Nose, The / Tom Thumb / Elves and the shoemaker, The / Peter and goatherd / Golden goose, The / Travelling musicians, The / Rose-Bud / Wolf and the seven little goats / Valiant tailor, The / Grateful beasts, The / Three children of fortune, The / Hans in luck.
MCSET: . . . . ARGO 1196

GRIMMS FAIRY TALES VOL 1.
MC: . . . . VCA 107

MORE GRIMM'S FAIRY TALES.
Tracks: / Cinderella / Four accomplished brothers, The / Old Mother Frost / Little farmer, The / Goose girl, The / Wonderful musician, The / King grisly - beard / Hansel and gretel / Queen bee / Twelve dancing princesses, The / Tom tit and the bear, The / Little brother and sister, The.
MCSET: 414 715-4

RUMPELSTILTSKIN: THE FLYING TRUNK (Ogilvy, Ian).
MC: . . . . LPMC 208

SNOW WHITE AND ROSE RED.
Tracks: / Snow White and Rose Red / Little grey goose, The / Soldier boy.
LP: . . . . TMP 9006

Grind (show)

GRIND (Original Broadway cast) (Various artists).
Tracks: / This must be the place: *Various artists* / Cadava: *Various artists* / Sweet thing like me, A: *Various artists* / I get myself out: *Various artists* / My daddy always taught me to share: *Various artists* / All things to one man: *Various artists* / Line, The: *Various artists* / Katie, my love: *Various artists* / Grind, The: *Various artists* / Yes, ma'am: *Various artists* / Why, mama, why: *Various artists* / This crazy place: *Various artists* / From the ankles down: *Various artists* / Who is he: *Various artists* / Never put it in writing: *Various artists* / I talk, you talk: *Various artists* / Timing: *Various artists*/ These eyes of mine: *Various artists* / New man: *Various artists* / Down: *Various artists* / Century of progress, A: *Various artists* / Finale: *Various artists.*
LP: . . . . TER 1103
MC: . . . . ZCTER 1103

Grinder

DAWN FOR LIVING.
LP: 083853

DEAD END.
Tracks: / Agent orange / Blade is back, The / Just another scar / Why / Dead end / Inside / Total control / Train raid.
LP: 083 861

NOTHING IS SACRED.
Tracks: / Drifting for 99 seconds / Hymn for the isolated / Spirit of violence, The / Nothing is sacred / None of the brighter days / Superior being / Dear Mr. Sinister / Pavement tango / Nothing song, The / NME.
LP: . . . . NO 1651
MC: . . . . NO 1654

Grindsman

BABY FATHER (See under Hicky, Don) (Grindsman & Don Hicky).

Grine, Janny

LIKE THE WIND.
LP: . . . . BIRD 164
MC: . . . . TC BIRD 164

Gringos Locos

GRINGOS LOCOS.
Tracks: / Higher than high / Sweet little sisters / Jealousy / Mountain / I ain't braggin' / Mean rock 'n' roller / Susie / Shout / Bad lucks lament / Tough kid / Blues, The.
LP: . . . . DIGLP 35
MC: . . . . DIGMC 35
MC: 834 204 4

PUNCHDRUNK.
LP: . . . . K 781 988 1
MC: . . . . K 781 988 4

Grip

BE YOURSELF.
Tracks: / Crush on you / Two hearts / Rain comes down / Baby blue / Ballad of Vera Daydream, The / Bet your gonna lose her / She walks out / We don't want it / Be yourself / Great balls of fire (live).
LP: . . . . RAZ 29

Grippe, Ragner

SAND.
LP: . . . . SHAN 83518

Grisman, David

ACOUSTIC CHRISTMAS.
LP: . . . . ROUNDER 0190
MC: . . . . ROUNDER 0190C

DAVID GRISMAN QUINTET.
LP: . . . . F 5
MC: . . . . C 5

DAVID GRISMAN ROUNDER ALBUM.
Tracks: / Hello / Sawing on the strings / Waiting on Vasser / I ain't broke but I'm badly bent / Op 38 / Hold to God's unchanging hand / Boston boy / Cheyenne / Til the end of the world rolls around / You'll find her name written there / On and on / Bob's Brewin / So long.
LP: . . . . ROUNDER 0069
MC: . . . . ROUNDER 0069C

EARLY DAWG.
LP: . . . . SH 3713
MC: . . . . ZCSH 3713

HERE TODAY (Grisman, David/Various Artists).
LP: . . . . ROUNDER 0169
MC: . . . . ROUNDER 0169C

HOME IS WHERE THE HEART IS.
Tracks: / True life blues / Down in the willow garden / My long journey home / Little Willie / Highway of sorrow / Sophronie / My aching heart / Close by / Feast here tonight / Leavin' home / Little cabin home on the hill / I'm comin' back / But I don't know when / Salty Dawg blues / If I lose / Sad and lonesome day / My little Georgia rose / Foggy mountain top / I'm my own grandpa / Pretty Polly / Home is where the heart is / Nine pound hammer / Memories of mother and day / Teardrops in my eyes / House of gold.
2LP: . . . . ROUNDER 0251/2
MCSET: . . . . ROUND 0251/2

MANDOLIN ABSTRACTIONS (Grisman, David & Andy Statman).
LP: . . . . ROUNDER 0178
MC: . . . . ROUNDER 0178C

OLD AND IN THE WAY (see Garcia, Jerry) (Grisman, David/Jerry Garcia).

Griswalds

WHO FRAMED THE GRISWALDS?.
LP: . . . . NERD 047

Gritzbach, George

ALL AMERICAN SONG.
LP: . . . . FF 353

SWEEPER.
Tracks: / Sweeper & the debutante / Moon shepherd stride / Over the river / Poor boy / Out of the game / Mr. Fats sad surprise / Long as it's green / Duck in a peacock flock / Delia / Cemetery weather / If by chance / Buddy Bolden.
LP: . . . . SNKF 157

Grobschnitt

BALLERMAN.
2LP: 0021 050

ILLEGAL.
LP: 0060 365

MERRY GO ROUND.
LP: 0060 024

RAZZIA.
LP: 0060 510

ROCKPOMMELS LAND.
LP: 0060 041

SOLAR MUSIC-LIVE.
LP: 0060 139

Grofe (composer)

GRAND CANYON SUITE AND PORGY AND BESS (London Festival Orchestra).
MC: 4255084

Grogan, Ali

LLIW HEULWEN.
LP: . . . . 1305 M

Grogan Brothers

LAKES NEAR KILLALOE, THE.
MC: . . . . GTDC 081

Grolnick, Don

HEARTS AND NUMBERS.
Tracks: / Pointing at the moon / More pointing / Pools / Regrets / Four sleepers, The / Human bites / Act natural / Hearts and numbers.
LP: . . . . VBR 20161

Gronenthal, Max

WHISTLING IN THE DARK.
Tracks: / Sailfish / Still I wonder / You / Lookin' for a girl / Get it straight / I know you're in there / Sonya / I can't leave the city / All the time / Faded satin lady.
LP: . . . . CHR 1231

Groove Farm

PLUG.
Tracks: / I'm never going to fall in love again / Please don't make me unhappy / Number one / No one like you / Corrupt / Discotheque / Forever is a long time / I don't blame you / World would die for you / It's not that I can't it's just / It might mean that much to you ... / Drag me under / I don't like you (but I can't get ...) / Plug.
LP: . . . . RAVE 005LP

Groove Juice Special

GROOVE JUICE COMIN' TO TOWN.
LP: . . . . BEAR 29
MC: . . . . BEARMC 29

HIT THAT JACK JIVE.
Tracks: / Five guys named Moe / Hit that jive Jack / You run your mouth I'll run my business / Three handed woman / Moten swing / Sat night fish fry.
LP: . . . . G 101

Groove Train

ALVIN IS KING.
LP: . . . . SUBORG 009

Grooveyard

AT HOME WITH THE GROOVEYARD.
LP: . . . . PLAYD 003-12

Groovy Tunes

GROOVY TUNES.
LP: . . . . HS 010

Groovy, Winston

AFRICAN GIRL.
Tracks: / African girl / Moving on / You keep me hangin' on / From we met / Please don't go / Lay back in the arms of someone / Girl, without you / So in love with you / All because of you / Give me time / Please don't make me cry / Am I a dreamer / Oh little darling / Dear mama / Black hearted woman / Midnight train / Can't stand the morning / Anything goes with me / Old rock and roller / Don't wanna hear that song again / Sea of dreams.
LP: . . . . BMLP 013
MC: . . . . BMC 013

FREE THE PEOPLE.
LP: . . . . PMLP 1028

PLEASE DON'T MAKE ME CRY.
LP: . . . . WGLP 005
MC: . . . . WGC 005

Grosmont Handbell

GROSMONT HANDBELL RINGERS.
Tracks: / Isle of Capri / Music box dancer / Flow gently sweet Afton / Swallows return when willows are green / Long, long ago.
MC: . . . . CSDL 298

Gross, Helen

HELEN GROSS WITH CLIFF JACKSON (Gross, Helen/Jackson, Cliff/ Fuller, Bob).
LP: . . . . DLP 542

Gross, Henry

I KEEP ON ROCKIN'.
LP: . . . . SNTF 990
MC: . . . . ZCSN 990

SHE'S MY BABY.
Tracks: / She's my baby / Searching for my baby / Light the moon / This car / Thing worth having, A / Mariane / I can't stop my heart / Knock knocking / Do you have to / Ruby tonight.
LP: . . . . SNTF 1008

Grossman, Stefan

ANTHOLOGY: STEFAN GROSSMAN.
Tracks: / Hot dogs / Blues jumped the rabbit / Hi dum diddle / Morning comes / Satisfied and ticked too / Alibi / Candy man / Fat man / Teddy Roosevelt / Blues for Mr. Sam / Those lazy blues / Twelve string medley / Little Sally Water / Lena Anne / Danish drone / Matesa.
LP: . . . . MTRA 2015

AUNT MOLLY'S MURRAY FARM.
Tracks: / Aunt Molly's Murray Farm / Foregone conclusion / Religious trainfare blues / See see rider / Delilah / Sideways nowhere bound / Special rider blues / Wall hollow blues / Cow cow's 4-4 waltz / Dallas rag / All my friends are gone / Number one / Money's all gone / Big road blues / Roberta.
LP: . . . . SNTF 640

BOTTLENECK SERENADE.
Tracks: / Tightrope / Lullaby for Anna / Bottleneck serenade / First time I ever saw your face / Birdnest two step / Dance of the blind Minotaur / Tomorrow / Working on the new railroad / Concrete parachute / For Elvie / Delta side of 1928 / Friends forever.
LP: . . . . TRA 293

COUNTRY BLUES GUITAR.
Tracks: / Special rider blues / Pallet on your floor / New pony blues / One kind favor / Hollerin' for my crow Jane / Hard time killin' floor blues / If you haven't any hay get on down the road / Ragtime mama blues / Some day baby / Yonder comes the blues / Weeping willow / Brownsville blues.
LP: . . . . SNKF 129

GRAMERCY PARK SHEIK.
Tracks: / Little Rock blues number two / Lena Anne / Hans Fried / Crow black squall / Gentle joys, gentle sorrows / Requiem for Patrick Kilroy / Not you or I my dear / Mississippi blues number two / Cross-eyed blues / Irene's sleepy lullaby / You'd best be gentle.
LP: . . . . SNTF 627

HOT DOGS.
LP: . . . . TRA 257 80

HOW TO PLAY BLUES GUITAR.
LP: . . . . SNKF 150
LP: . . . . KM 109

HOW TO PLAY BLUES GUITAR VOL.2.
Tracks: / Man of my own / Rainy day blues / Strange city streets / Easy street / Nobody's fault but mine / Come back baby / Moon goin' down / Motherless children / Wake up Mama / Morning blues / Pallet on your floor / Jubilee jamboree / Good morning little school boy.
LP: . . . . SNKF 148
LP: . . . . KM 151

HOW TO PLAY RAGTIME GUITAR.
LP: . . . . KM 115

KICKING MULE (Grossman, Stefan & John Renbourn).
Tracks: / Snap a little owl / Bermuda triangle exit / Charles Mingus, Theme from / Shoes of the fisherman's wife are some jive ass slippers / Luckett Sunday / Why a duck / Drifter, The / Looper's corner / Luke's little summer / Spirit levels / Way she walks, The / Woman from Donori.
LP: . . . . SNKF 139

SHINING SHADOWS.
LP: . . . . SHAN 95002

THREE KINGDOMS (See under Renbourn, John) (Grossman, Stefan & John Renbourn).

THUNDER ON THE RUN.
Tracks: / Thunder on the run / Assassination of John Fahey, The / From Berne to Perth / Sergeant Early's dream / Red haired boy / Blind Mary / Callaghan's hornpipe / Pretty girl milking a cow / Peak's puzzle / Kicking up the dust / St. Andrews / Fiddler's contest / Silver swan / Billy in the lowgrounds / Greenfields of America.
LP: . . . . SNKF 170

UNDER THE VOLCANO.
LP: . . . . SNKF 161
LP: . . . . KM 162

YAZOO BASIN BOOGIE.
Tracks: / Adam's voice / Tickle dew / Dallas rag / I'm so glad / Katz rag / Texas lemon flavour rag / Sunday rag / Pigtown fling / Red pepper rag / House carpenter / Maple leaf rag / Colored aristocracy / Slow blues in C / Aurora's powder rag / County line / Last of Callahan / Dervish boogie / Yazoo basin boogie.
LP: . . . . SNKF 134
LP: . . . . KM 102

Grossman, Steve

TERRA FIRMA.
LP: . . . . PM 012

WAY OUT WEST VOL.1.
LP: . . . . VPA 176

WAY OUT WEST VOL. 2.
LP: . . . . VPA 183

Grossmith, G & W

DIARY OF A NOBODY, THE (Lowe, Arthur).
MCSET: . . . . ZBBC 1023

DIARY OF A NOBODY, THE.
MCSET: . . . . SAY 76

Grosswendt, Martin

DOG ON A DANCE FLOOR.
LP: . . . . PH 1041

Grosvenor Myer,

BUTTER AND CHEESE AND ALL.
MC: . . . . BH 8904 C

Grosz, Marty

ACOUSTIC GUITAR DUETS (Grosz, Marty & Wayne Wright).
LP: . . . . AVIVA 6000

CHICAGO 1957 (Grosz, Marty & His Honoris Causa Jazz Band).
LP: . . . . CI 008

DICK WELLSTOOD AND MARTY GROSZ (Grosz, Marty/Dick Wellstood).

LP: . . . . AVIVA 6001

MARTY GROSZ AND HIS BLUE ANGELS (Grosz, Marty & His Blue Angels).
LP: . . . . AVIVA 6004

MARTY GROSZ AND THE KEEPERS OF THE FLAME (Grosz, Marty & The Keepers Of The Flame).
LP: . . . . SOS 1158

MARTY GROSZ AND WAYNE WRIGHT (Grosz, Marty & Wayne Wright).
LP: . . . . AVIVA 6003

SINGS OF LOVE (Grosz, Marty/Tiny Signa).
LP: . . . . SLP 8080

Groucutt, Kelly

KELLY.
Tracks: / Am I a dreamer / Oh little darling / Dear mama / Black hearted woman / Midnight train / Can't stand the morning / Anything goes with me / Old rock & roller / Don't wanna hear that song again / Sea of dreams.
LP: . . . . RCALK 3063
LP: . . . . RCALP 3063

Ground Zero

PINK.
LP: . . . . REFLEX M

Groundhogs

BACK AGAINST THE WALL.
Tracks: / Back against the wall / No to submission / Blue boar blues / Waiting in the shadows / Ain't no slaver / Stick to your grass / In the meantime / 54156.
LP: . . . . DMLP 1014

BLACK DIAMOND.
LP: . . . . UA 29994

BLUES OBITUARY.
LP: . . . . BGOLP 6

CROSSCUT SAW.
LP: . . . . UA 29917

GROUNDHOGS BEST 1969-1972.
Tracks: / Groundhog / Strange town / Bog roll blues / You had a lesson / Eccentric man / Earth is not room enough / BDD / Split part 1 / Cherry red / Mistreated / 3744 James Road / Soldier / Sad is the hunter / Garden / Split part 4.
MC: . . . . BGLDMC 1
2LP: . . . . BGLDLP 1
MC: 2TCK 60063

HOG WASH.
LP: . . . . BGOLP 44
LP: . . . . UA 29419

HOGGIN' THE STAGE.
LP: . . . . PSYCHO 24

HOGS ON THE ROAD.
Tracks: / Groundhogs, The / Hogs in the road / Express man / Strange town / Eccentric man / 3744 James Road / I want you to love me / Split IV / Soldier / Back against the wall / Garden / Split / Waiting in the shadows / Light my light / Me and the devil / Mistreated / Ground hogs blues / Cherry red.
2LP: . . . . DMLP 1016

MOVING FAST, STANDING STILL.
Tracks: / Hunt (part 1), The / Hunt (part 2), The / Hunt (part 3), The / Hunt (part 4), The / Ain't gonna cry no more / 3 x 7 / Morning eyes / Dog me bitch / T.S instrumental / You don't love me / Razors edge / I Confess / Born to be with you / One more chance / Someone to love me / Protector / Superseded / Moving fast, standing still / I Want you to love me / When you gotta a good friend.
LP: . . . . RAWLP 021
MC: . . . . RAWTC 021

NO SURRENDER.
Tracks: / Razors edge / 3744 James Road / Superseded / Light my light / One more chance / Garden / Split Pt. 2 / Eccentric man (CD only.) / Strange town (CD only.) / Cherry red (CD only.).
LP: . . . . HTDLP 2

RAZOR'S EDGE.
LP: . . . . QUEST 1
LP: . . . . BUT 005

SCRATCHING THE SURFACE.
LP: . . . . BGOLP 15

SOLID.
LP: . . . . WWA 004

SPLIT.
Tracks: / Split (part one) / Cherry red / Year in the life, A / Junkman groundhog / Split (part two) / Split (part three) / Split (part four).
LP: . . . . ATAK 73
MC: . . . . TCATAK 73
LP: . . . . LBR 1017
LP: . . . . LBG 83401
LP: . . . . BGOLP 76

THANK CHRIST FOR THE BOMB.
Tracks: / Strange town / Darkness is no friend / Soldier / Thank Christ for the bomb / Ship on the ocean / Garden / Status people / Rich man,poor man / Eccentric man.
LP: . . . . FA 41 3152 1
MC: . . . . TCFA 3152
LP: . . . . LBS 83295
LP: . . . . BGOLP 67

WHO WILL SAVE THE WORLD?.
LP: . . . . UAG 29237
LP: . . . . BGOLP 77

Grove, Fred

SANACO.
MC: . . . . SOUND 26

Growling Tiger

HIGH PRIEST OF MI-MINOR (Knockdown calypso).
LP: . . . . ROUNDER 5006

GRP (label)

ALL RECORDINGS (See under Jazz).

Grubbs, Earl

NEPTUNE (Grubbs, Earl & Carl).
LP: . . . . MR 5195

Grumbleweeds

BEST OF THE GRUMBLEWEEDS.
LP: . . . . REH 372
MC: . . . . ZCR 372

LET THE GOOD TIMES ROLL.
Tracks: / Let the good times roll / Dizzy / Womans intuition / Let your love flow / Rose has to die, A / Little bit wiser,A / Hands across the sea / One little smile / Party times / More I see you, The / Whispers / Hold out / Live it down / All for the sake of rock'n'roll.
LP: . . . . NE 1336
MC: . . . . CE 2336

WORRAVAGORRINMEPOCKIT.
LP: . . . . MFP 50525

Grummit, John

FREE TO FLY (Grummit, John & Maureen).
MC: . . . . JM 1

Grundy, Ricky

WE SHALL WALK THROUGH THE VALLEY IN PEACE (Grundy, Ricky & The Williams Family).
LP: . . . . LR 44.014

Gruntz, George

THEATRE (Gruntz, George Concert Jazz Band '83).
Tracks: / El chancho / In the tradition of Switzerland / No one can explain it / Holy grail of jazz and joy.
LP: . . . . ECM 1265

Grupo Raiz

AMANECERES.
Tracks: / El vuelo de la parina / Me matan si no tradajo / El mayor / Bailecito de la pena / Vaya un pecado / Los mapuches / El guillatun / Arauco tiene una pena / Segun el favor del viento / Victor Jara / Tema de la quebrada de San Lorenzo / Los Palafitos / Amaneceres.
LP: . . . . MFS 812
MC: 51 812

POR AMERICA DEL CENTRO - VOL.2.
Tracks: / Dove, The / Voice, The / Between the seasons / Ana Maria / Seven stars / Urgent song for Nicaragua / For central America / El Caracol / Chief O'Neill's favourite / Son to Fonseca / Song in solidarity with El Salvador.
LP: . . . . MFS 818

Gruppo Sportivo

BACK TO '78.
Tracks: / Hey girl / Bernadette / P.S. 78 / Tokyo / I said no / Real teeth / Are you ready / Booby trap boogie / Blah blah magazines / One way love / I'm a rocket / Shave / Pogo never stops / Bottom of the class / Single.
LP: . . . . EPC 83263

Grusin, Dave

CINEMAGIC.
Tracks: / Actor's life, An / It might be you / Heaven can wait / On golden pond / Condor (three days of the Condor) / Heart is a lonely hunter / Opening theme (From Goonies.) / Champ, The (theme from) / Mountain dance (CD only) / Letting go (CD only) / PLO camp entrance (*= Bonus track on CD only) / Little drummer girl (Bonus track on CD only).
LP: . . . . GRP 91037
MC: . . . . GRPM 91037
DAT: . . . . GRT 9547

COLLECTION: DAVE GRUSIN.
LP: . . . . GR 95791
MC: . . . . GR 95794

DAVE GRUSIN AND NY-LA DREAM BAND (Grusin, Dave & NY-LA Dream Band).
Tracks: / Shuffle city / Count down / Serengeti walk / Champ, The (theme from) / What matters most / Three days of the condor.
LP: . . . . GRP 91001
MC: . . . . GRPM 91001

DISCOVERED AGAIN.
LP: . . . . ST 500
LP: . . . . LAB 5

FLIP OF THE COIN (Grusin, Dave & Stanley Turrentine).
Tracks: / Don't touch / It's gotta be me / Same old me / Flip of the coin / Love's finally found me / Brown eyed woman / Ma cherie amour / Yesterme yesteryou yesterday / Wedding bell blues.
LP: . . . . MAN 5008

GRUSIN COLLECTION, THE.
LP: . . . . GRP 95791
MC: . . . . GRP 95794

HARLEQUIN (Grusin, Dave & Lee Ritenour).
Tracks: / Harlequin / Early A.M. attitude / San Y Sidro / Before it's too late / Cats of Rio / Grid lock / Silent message / Bird, The.
LP: . . . . GRP 91015
MC: . . . . GRPM 91015
LP: . . . . GRPA 1015

HAVANA (FILM SOUNDTRACK) (See under Havana).

KALEIDOSCOPE.
LP: . . . . 20 AP 1423

LIVE IN JAPAN.
Tracks: / Modaji / Trade winds / Shamballa / Friends and strangers / Band introduction / Uh oh / Don and Dave / Captain caribe.
LP: 209339
MC: 409339

MIGRATION.
LP: . . . . GRP 95921
MC: . . . . GRP 95924

MOUNTAIN DANCE.
Tracks: / Rag bag / Friends and strangers / City lights / Rondo-"if you hold out your hand" / Thanksong / Capitain Caribe / Either way / Mountain dance.
LP: . . . . GRP 91018
LP: . . . . GRP 5010
MC: . . . . C 1018

NIGHT LINES.
Tracks: / Secret place / Night-lines / Kitchen dance / Somewhere between old and New York / Bossa barbeque / Power Wave / Thankful 'n' thoughtful / St. Elsewhere / Haunting me.
2LP: . . . . GRP 91006
MC: . . . . GRPC 1006

ONE OF A KIND.
Tracks: / Modaji / Heart of the lonely hunter / Catavento / Montage / Playera.
LP: . . . . GRP 91011
MC: . . . . GRPM 90101

OUT OF THE SHADOWS.
Tracks: / Last train to Paradiso / She could be mine / Crystal morning / Five brothers / Athem internationale / Serengeti walk / Hokkaido / Sweetwater nights.
LP: 204719

STICKS AND STONES (Grusin, Dave & Don).
LP: . . . . GRP 91051
MC: . . . . GRPM 91051

SUPER LIVE 2 (Grusin, Dave/Lee Ritenour/Chick Corea).
LP: . . . . A 1650
MC: . . . . C 1650

Grusin, Don

RAVEN.
Tracks: / Flight of the raven / Two lives / Hip hop be bop / Oracle / Outback oasis / Light in the window / Zuma noon / Un beijo (A kiss) / Graffiti-bird / Highline / Catwalk.
LP: . . . . GRP 96021
MC: . . . . GRP 96024

ZEPHYR.
Tracks: / Zephyr / Tonight, pure love / Still good lookin' / Anoranza / Hardwood / Storyteller / Chico / Tribe / Last train / Hattie-Mae (Dance all day).
LP: . . . . GRP 96441
MC: . . . . GRP 96444

Gryce, Gigi

RAT RACE BLUES.
Tracks: / Rat race blues / Strange feeling / Boxer's blues / Blues in bloom / Monday through Sunday.
LP: . . . . OJC 081

SIGNALS (Gryce, Gigi/Duke Jordan/Hal Overton).
LP: . . . . SJL 2231

WHEN FARMER MET GRYCE (see Farmer, Art) (Gryce, Gigi & Art Farmer).

Gryphon

MIDNIGHT MUSHRUMPS.
Tracks: / Midnight mushrumps / Ploughboys dream / Last flash of gaberdine tailor, The / Gulland rock / Dubbel dutch / Ethelion.
LP: . . . . CFRC 518

GTR

GTR.
Tracks: / When the heart rules the mind / Hunter, The / Here I wait / Sketches in the sun / Jekyll and Hyde / You can still get through / Reach out (never say no) / Toe the line / Hackett to bits / Imagining.
LP: 207716
MC: 407716
LP: 208980
MC: 408980

Guacaran, Mario

HARPE INDIENNE - FIESTA LLANERA AU VENEZUELA (Guacaran, Mario/Los Quirpa/Los Caracas).
Tracks: / Numero uno / El alcaraban / Torrealbara / Concierto en la Llanura / Despertar / Golpe tocuyano / Seis por derecho / Carnaval / Noche de luna / Guadalajara / El gavilan / Pajarillo.
LP: . . . . ARN 30093

Guadalcanal Diary

2 X 4.
Tracks: / Litany / Under the yoke / Get over it / Little birds / Things fall apart / Let the big wheel roll / Where angels fear to tread / Newborn / Winds of change / Say please / 3 a.m. / Lips of steel.
LP: 9607521
MC: 9607524

FLIP FLOP.
Tracks: / Look up / Likes of you, The / Whisky talk / Everything but good luck / Fade out / Always Saturday / Happy home / Pretty is as pretty does / Ten laws / Vista.
LP: . . . . K 9608481
MC: . . . . K 9608484

JAMBOREE.
Tracks: / Pray for rain / Cattle prod / Jamboree / Fear of God / Man hunt / Spirit train / Lonely street / Country club gun / Trouble / Michael rockefeller / Please stop me / I see more / Dead eyes.
LP: 9604781
MC: 9604784

WALKING IN THE SHADOW OF THE BIG MAN.
Tracks: / Trail of tears / Fire from heaven / Sleepers awake / Gilbert takes the wheel / Ghost on the road / Watusi rodeo / Why do the heathen rage? / Pillow talk / Walking in the shadow of the big man / Kumbaya.
LP: . . . . EKT 13
LP: . . . . HYBLP 2

Guana Batz

BEST OF THE BATZ.
Tracks: / King rat / Nightmare fantasy / I'm on fire / You're my baby / Dynamite / Radio sweetheart / Streetwise / Please give me something / Seethrough / Baby blue eyes / Rock this town / Loan shark / Spy catcher / Bring my cadillac back.
LP: . . . . WRONG 001

ELECTRA GLIDE IN BLUE.
LP: . . . . SERV 009

HELD DOWN AT LAST.
LP: . . . . NOSE 4

LIVE OVER LONDON.
LP: . . . . NOSE 14

LOAN SHARKS (LP).
LP: . . . . NOSE 10
MC: . . . . KOSE 10

ROUGH EDGES.
Tracks: / Streetwise / One night / Fight back / Love generator / Rocking with Ollie Vee / You can run / Open your mouth / Rocking on creek road / Spy catcher / Bring my cadillac back / Two shadows.
LP: . . . . NOSE 20
MC: . . . . KOSE 20

Guaraldi, Vince

FLOWER IS A LOVESOME THING, A (Guaraldi, Vince & Trio).
LP: . . . . OJC 235

Guard, Charles

AVENGING AND BRIGHT.
LP: . . . . CC 26
MC: 4CC 26

Guardian

FIRST WATCH.
Tracks: / I'll never leave you / Mystery man / Livin' for the promise / Miracle / Saints battalion / Kingdom of rock / Good life / One of a kind / World without love / Rock in victory.
LP: . . . . RR 94401

Guardian Angels

GUARDIAN ANGELS, THE.
LP: . . . . GHR 1496
MC: . . . . ZGHR 1496

Guards Spectacular

SCARBOROUGH FAIR.
LP: . . . . PGT 1001

Guarnieri, Johnny

JOHNNY GUARNIERI PLAYS FATS WALLER.
LP: . . . . TJZ 1002

SUPERSTRIDE.
LP: . . . . TJZ 1001

Gubara, Mohamed

SOUNDS OF SUDAN VOL. 3.
LP: . . . . WCB 005

Guedon, Henri

L'OPERA TRIANGULAIRE (Guedon, Henri & L'Orchestra Du Havre).
LP: 15996

Guest Of Honour (bk)

GUEST OF HONOUR/CARMILLA.
MC: . . . . NF 9

Guest Stars

GUEST STARS, THE.
Tracks: / Northern lights / You can't weep over it / Valentine's day / Tin can alley / I know I know / Wake it up / Latierra y el sol cupido.
LP: . . . . GS 10
MC: . . . . GSC 10

LIVE IN BERLIN.
LP: . . . . ES 2033
MC: . . . . GS 12C

OUT AT NIGHT.
Tracks: / Montezuma's mother / Miles apart / Amy's bounce / What means love / Wind is getting angry, The / Song of the bridge / Uranus in jeopardy / Birds of a feather.
LP: . . . . GS 11
MC: . . . . GSC 11

Guetary, Georges

GEORGES GUETARY.
LP: 2C 178 15414/15

Guibert, Bod

LA GUIBA.
LP: . . . . BG 016

Guida, Bob

SETTLIN' UP THE SCORE (See under Green, Michael) (Guida, Bob/Michael Green).

Guide To Better...

GUIDE TO BETTER LISTENING, A (Narrators:Peter Goodchild & Caroline Grant).
LP: . . . . PFFS 1

Guido Toffolettis

LIVE AT THE CITY HALL CAFE.
LP: . . . . AP 053

NO COMPROMISE.
LP: . . . . AP 048

Guidon

BRIDGE TO ETERNITY.
LP: . . . . GUID 001

Guidoni, Jean

CRIME PASSIONNEL (Music by Astor Piazzolla).
Tracks: / Le haut mur / Masque noir / Coups de coeur / Solo / Weidmann / Qui crie / Lames / Fleurs fanees / Mandatt d'amener / Les draps blancs.
LP: 6313 305
MC: 7200 305

Guiglielmo Tell

GUIGLIELMO TELL (See Under Rossini (composer)) (Various artists).

Guilbeau, Gib

TOE TAPPIN' MUSIC.
LP: . . . . SHILOH 4085

Guild Of...

BY BEAT OF DRUM (Guild of Ancient Fifes & Drums).
Tracks: / Drummers call / Drum demonstration / English march / 1775 medley / Chester Castle / Downfall of Paris / To danton me / Rogues march / Grenadiers march / See the conquering hero comes / Toledo / It's a long way to Tipperary / San Lorenzo / Wondermarsch / Basle drum and fife display / Der morgenstreich / Sans Gene / Come lasses and lads / Glopfgaisht / Stenlemmer / Windschi / Dtitt vars / Arabi / Guards, The / Der vaudois / S'laggerli.
LP: . . . . BND 1044
MC: . . . . ZC BND 1044

Guildford Cathedral

CHRISTMAS CAROLS FROM GUILDFORD CATHEDRAL.
Tracks: / Once in royal David's city / God rest ye merry gentlemen / While shepherds watched their flocks by night / See, amid the winter's snow / As with gladness men of old / First Noel, The / Hark the herald angels sing / It came upon a midnight clear / Silent night / Good King Wenceslas / O little town of Bethlehem / O come all ye faithful.
LP: . . . . MFP 51 5723-1
MC: . . . . MFP 51 5723-4
LP: . . . . MFP 5723
MC: . . . . TC MFP 5723
LP: . . . . MFP 1104

EVENING AT GUILDFORD CATHEDRAL, AN.
LP: . . . . WST R 9705
MC: . . . . WST C 9705

Guildhall Strings

TIPPETT - BRITTEN.
MC: . . . . RK 87846

Guill, Gene

THREE BONES AND A QUILL.
LP: . . . . FS 117

Guillory, Chuck

GRAND TEXAS.
LP: . . . . ARHOOLIE 5039
MC: . . . . C 5039

Guillory, Isaac

SOLO.
LP: . . . . GRAF 1

Guinn

GUINN.
Tracks: / Dreamin' / Open your door / I can't live without you / Slow down / Sincerely / People will be people / Give everything you got for love.
LP: . . . . ZL 72418
MC: . . . . ZK 72418

Guitar

20 GREAT GUITAR INSTRUMENTALS (Various artists).
Tracks: / Nut rocker: *Shades* / Rawhide: *Geezers* / Jupiter stroll: *Meteors* / Fat back: *Wray, Link*/ Please please me: *Wray, Link* / Napoleon solo, The: *Meteors* / Run chicken run: *Milkshakes* / Lynch mob: *Shades* / Jack the ripper: *Milkshakes* / Getaway: *Rodgers, Kid & The Henchmen* / Little deuce coupe: *Defenders* / Stick shift: *Raiders* / Fast freight: *Allens, Arvee* / Swinging the rock: *Holloway, Alden* / Tuff: *Smith, Bill Combo* / Frisky: *Millsap, Bob* / Meanwhile: *Heap, Jimmy* / Thumbs guitar boogie: *Bill Wimberley band* / Steamboat blues: *Steve Diver One Man Band* / Steve's guitar parody: *Steve Diver One Man Band.*
LP: . . . . DROP 1006
MC: . . . . CROP 1006

BOSS TWANG (Various artists).
Tracks: / Twangin' fool: *Hightower, Dean* / Duanes stroll: *Keymen* / Fool's blues, A: *Casey, Al* / Juice: *Casey, Al* / Freight train: *Eddy, Duane* / 5.17: *Eddy, Duane* / Put a little love in your heart: *Eddy*, Duane / Something: *Eddy, Duane* / Boss: *Rumblers* / Thing, The: *Blattner, Jules* / Nut cracker: *Nimble*, Jack B. & The Quicks / Never on Sunday: *Nimble, Jack B. & The Quicks* / Guitar boogie: *Wilcox, Harlow* / Raunchy: *Wilcox, Harlow* / Groovy grubworm: *Wilcox, Harlow* / Goodnight sweetheart: *Hightower, Dean.*
LP: . . . . CR 30254
MC: . . . . TCCR 30254

CONTEMPORARY GUITAR ALBUM (Various artists).
LP: . . . . TRS 5001
MC: . . . . KTRS 5001

CONTEMPORARY GUITAR WORKSHOP (Various artists).
LP: . . . . SNKF 143

ELITE SYNCOPATION (Advanced finger picking guitar techniques) (Various artists).
Tracks: / Maple leaf rag: *Various artists* / Solace a Mexican serenade: *Various artists* / Monparaeil (none to equal): *Various artists* / Favourite, The: *Various artists* / Strenuous life, The: *Various artists* / Rosebud march, The: *Various artists* / Eugenia: *Various artists* / Weeping willow: *Various artists* / Scott Joplin's new rag: *Various artists* / Elite syncopations: *Various artists.*
LP: . . . . SNKF 135

FAMOUS GUITARS - ACOUSTIC COLOURS (Various artists).
Tracks: / Rio Ancho: *Lucia, Paco De* / El baile de Luis Alonso: *Various artists* / Malaguena: *Garcia, Pato*/ Samba triste: *Powell, Baden* / Short tales of the black forest: *McLaughlin, John* / Asturias: *Romero, Pepe*/ Bolero: *Coryell, Larry* / Ritual fire dance: *Presti, Ida and Alexandre Lagoya* / Guardian angel: *De Lucia, Paco.*
LP: 814 022 1
MC: 814 022 4

GUITAR ALBUM (Various artists).
LP: . . . . CBS 32097
MC: 40 3297

GUITAR AND THE GUN VOL 2 (Various artists).
LP: . . . . ADRY 6

GUITAR DOWN UNDER (Various artists).
LP: . . . . LRF 056

GUITAR FAVOURITES (Various artists).
MC: TC2MOM 117

GUITAR GOLD (Various artists).
LP: . . . . EGS 45002
MC: . . . . EC/EGS /4/5002

GUITAR SAMPLER VOL. 2 (Various artists).
Tracks: / Momentary change of heart, A: *DeGrassi, Alex* / Deep at night: *DeGrassi, Alex* / Sunday on the violet sea: *Torn, David* / Lion of Boaz: *Torn, David* / Ritual dance: *Hedges, Michael* / If I needed someone: *Hedges, Michael* / Selene: *Manring, Michael* / Red right returning: *Manring, Michael* / Sweet pea: *Andress, Tuck* / Betcha by golly, wow: *Andress, Tuck.*
MC: . . . . WT 1106

GUITAR SPEAK (Various artists).
Tracks: / No limit: *Lee, Alvin* / Prisoner, The: *California, Randy* / Western flyer: *Johnson, Eric* / Let me out 'a here: *West, Leslie* / Blood alley 152: *Montrose, Ronnie* / Sharp on attack: *Howe, Steve*/ Sphinx: *Manzanera, Phil* / Sloe moon rising: *Derringer, Rick* / Danjo: *Haycock, Pete* / Urban strut: *Hunter, Steve* / Captain Zlogg: *Marvin, Hank* / Strat a-various: *Kreiger, Bobby.*
LP: . . . . ILP 033
MC: . . . . ILPC 033

GUITAR SPEAK II (Various artists).
Tracks: / Miranha: *Iommi, Tony* / Stelph: *Akkerman, Jan* / Feeding on fear: *Mankey, James* / Prisoner of love: *Truth* / All alone with friends: *Marvin, Hank* / Shame: *Trower, Robin* / Babylon: *Marino, Frank* / Snake bite: *Mandel, Harvey* / Sonic blue: *Bourelly, Jean-Paul* / Head the ball: *Marsden, Bernie.*
LP: . . . . EIRSA 1025
MC: . . . . EIRSAC 1025

GUITAR SPECTACULAR (Various artists).
MC: . . . . AM 8

GUITAR SPECTRUM (Various artists).
Tracks: / Don't cry for me Argentina: *Various artists* / Fields: *Various artists* / Fascinating rhythm: *Various* artists / Etoile: *Various artists* / Norwegian Wood: *Various artists* / Scarborough Fair: *Various artists*/ Heigh Ho: *Various artists* / Nuages: *Various artists* / Lisbeth: *Various artists* / Jesus Christ Superstar: *Various artists.*
MC: . . . . ZCP 18608
LP: . . . . NSPL 18608

GUITAR STAR Anthology (Various artists).
Tracks: / Hard times: *Young, Mighty Joe* / Guitar star: *Young, Mighty Joe* / Say your leaving: *Robinson*, Fenton / Directly from my heart: *Robinson, Fenton* / Somebody loan me a dime: *Various artists* / Blues get off my shoulder: *Parker, Bobby* / You got what it takes: *Parker, Bobby* / Bloody tears: *Littlejohn, Johnny*/ Do Uncle Willies dance: *Walker, Homer Junior* / Move back baby: *Walker, Homer Junior* / Out of bad luck: *Magic Sam* / She belongs to me: *Magic Sam* / Rock alley: *Bates, Lefty 'Guitar'* / Background: *Bates, Lefty 'Guitar'* / Rambling woman: *Big Moose* / Rockin': *Bennett, Wayne.*
LP: . . . . RL 017

GUITAR THE PIANO AND YOU (Various artists).
Tracks: / Cupid: *Various artists* / South of the border: *Various artists* / Brazil: *Various artists*/ I'm happy just to dance with you: *Various artists* / It's my turn: *Various artists* / Perhaps, perhaps perhaps: *Various artists* / I made it through the rain: *Various artists* / What kind of fool: *Various artists*/ Love will keep us together: *Various artists* / Fascination: *Various artists* / So far away: *Various artists*/ Sexy eyes: *Various artists* / Imagine: *Various artists* / Quiet nights of quiet stars: *Various artists*/ Put your head on my shoulder: *Various artists* / She's out of my life: *Various artists* / Feelings: *Various* artists / Besame mucho: *Various artists* / Morning train: *Various artists* / Crying: *Various artists*/ Maria Elena: *Various artists* / Strangers in the night: *Various artists* / Intermezzo: *Various artists*/ Man and a woman, A: *Various artists* / Desafinado: *Various artists* / California girls: *Various artists*/ Green eyes: *Various artists* / Tangerine: *Various artists.*
2LP: . . . . CR 032
MCSET: . . . . CRT 032

GUITAR WARS (Various artists).
Tracks: / Lady of the eighties: *Various artists* / Walks like a lady: *Various artists* / Born to be wild: *Various* artists / Green manalishi: *Various artists* / Well all right: *Various artists* / South station blues: *Various artists* / I'm a king bee: *Various artists* / Rockin' LA: *Various artists.*
LP: . . . . CBS 25025

GUITAR WIZARDS 1926-35 (Various artists).
LP: . . . . L 1016

JUST GUITARS (Various artists).
LP: . . . . CBS 25946
MC: 40 25946

Guitar Gable

COOL, CALM, COLLECTED.
Tracks: / This should go on forever / Goodbye baby / Life problem / Congo mombo / Have mercy on me / String bean' / Walking in the park / Please operator / Mary Lou / No matter who / Walking with the King / Irene / Long way from home / Cool calm collected.
LP: . . . . FLY 599

Guitar Nubbit

RE-LIVING THE LEGEND.
LP: . . . . MB 12-01

Guitar Orchestra

GUITAR ORCHESTRA, THE.
Tracks: / Really? / Pernod for the bamboo man, A (aperitif) / First kiss, The / Closer to the heart / Ocean / Pernod for the bamboo man, A.
MC: . . . . PRKMC 6

Guitar Pete's Axe

DEAD SOLDIER'S REVENGE.
Tracks: / Won't ease up / Dead soldier's revenge / Road warrior / Shattered paradise / Satan's sister / Ball breaker / Thirsty for blood / Gutter rat / Diggin' for gold.
LP: . . . . HMUSA 31

NITEMARE.
LP: . . . . FLAME 003

Guitar Slim

ATCO SESSIONS.
LP: 81760-1

BATTLE OF THE BLUES (Guitar Slim & Earl King).
Tracks: / Certainly all / Going down slow / Stand by me / You give me nothing but the blues / You're gonna miss me / I wanna love a you / I got sumpin' for you / Reap what you sow / I'm your best bet baby / Mothers love, A / Eating and sleeping / No one but me / Funny face / Sittin' and wondering / What can I do? / Till I say well done.
LP: . . . . CHD 189

CAROLINA BLUES (Guitar Slim & Jelly Belly).
LP: . . . . ARHOOLIE 2005

GREENSBORO ROUNDER.
LP: . . . . FLY 538

RED CADILLAC AND CRAZY CHICKS.
LP: . . . . CG 709-08
LP: . . . . SG 709-08

THINGS THAT I USED TO DO, THE.
Tracks: / Well I done got over it / Trouble don't last / Guitar Slim / Story of my life / Letter to my girlfriend / Reap what you sow / Later for you baby / Things that I used to do / Quicksand / Bad luck blues / Think it over / Our only child / I got sumpin' for you / Sufferin' mind / Twenty five lies / Something to remember you by.
LP: . . . . CHD 110

Guitars Unlimited

GUITARS UNLIMITED.
LP: . . . . SNTF 923

THREE FOR THE ROAD.
LP: . . . . SNTF 1006

Gulda, Friedrich

MUSIC OF OUR TIME.
2LP: . . . . MPS 88 050

Gulezyan, H Aram

EXOTIC MUSIC FOR THE OUD (see Arabia).

OUD, THE (see Arabia).

Gulgowski, Wlodek

HOME.
LP: . . . . AMLP 5001

Gullin, Lars

IN CONCERT (Gullin, Lars Quintet).
LP: . . . . SLP 432

LARS GULLIN VOL.1, 1955/56.
Tracks: / Danny's dream / Igloo / Lars meets Jeff / Cool blues / Brash lover

man / I'll remember April / Fedja / Ma / Perntz.
LP: .... DRLP 36

LARS GULLIN VOL.3, 1954/55.
LP: .... DRLP 127

LARS GULLIN VOL. 4, 1959-60.
LP: .... DRLP 156

LARS GULLIN-VOL.2, 1953.
LP: .... DRLP 75

Gulliver's Travels

GULLIVER IN LILLIPUT (Duncan, Frank).
MC: .... P 90034

GULLIVER'S TRAVELS (see Swift, Jonathan) (Various artists).

GULLIVER'S TRAVELS & OTHER FAVOURITE STORIES For children aged 5 - 9.
MC: .... VCA 612

HOUYHNHNMS, THE (Gulliver's travels) (Redgrave, Sir Michael).
MC: 1099

Gulyayeu, Yuri

FOLK SONGS.
MC: .... SM 00173

Gumdrop

GUMDROP Biro, Val (Brairs, Richard).
MC: .... CS 009

Gun

RACE WITH THE DEVIL (OLD GOLD) (See Ram Jam - Black Betty for details).

Gun (2)

TAKING ON THE WORLD.
Tracks: / Better days / Feeling within, The / Inside out / Money (Everybody loves her) / Taking on the world / Shame on you / Can't get any lower / Something to believe in / Girls in love / I will be waiting.
LP: .... AMA 7007
MC: .... AMC 7007

Gun Club

BIRTH, THE DEATH, THE GHOST, THE.
LP: .... ABCLP 1
MC: .... KAS 1

DANSE KALINDA BOOM (Live in Pandoras Box).
LP: .... MD 7979

FIRE OF LOVE.
Tracks: / Sex beat / Preaching the blues / Promise me / She's like heroin to me / For the love of Ivy / Fire spirit / Ghost on the highway / Jack on fire / Black train / Cool drink of water / Goodbye Johnny / Walking with the beast.
LP: .... ROSE 8
LP: .... BEGA 37
MC: .... BEGC 37

LAS VEGAS STORY.
Tracks: / Las Vegas story, The / Walking with the beast / Eternally is here / Stranger in our town / My dreams / Creator has a master plan, The / My mans gone now / Bad America / Moonlight hotel / Give up the sun.
LP: .... CHR 1477

LOVE SUPREME LIVE MATERIAL '82.
LP: .... OFFENCE 9002

MIAMI.
Tracks: / Carry home / Like calling up thunder / Brother and sister / Run through the jungle / Devil in the woods / Texas serenade / Watermelon man / Bad Indian / John Hardy / Fire of love / Sleeping in blood city / Mother of earth.
LP: .... CHR 1398

MOTHER JUNO.
Tracks: / Bill Bailey won't you please come home / Thunderhead / Lupita screams / Yellow eyes / Breaking hands / Araby / Hearts / My cousin Kim / Ports of souls.
LP: .... REDLP 084
MC: .... REDC 084

TWO SIDES OF THE BEAST.
Tracks: / Sex Beat (Live) / Walking with the beast / Like calling up thunder / Mother of earth run through the jungle / Eternally is here / Las Vegas Story, The / Death party (12" version) / Seven miles with the devil (live) / Bo Diddley's a gunslinger (live) / Preaching blues (live) / Goodbye Johnny (live) / Going down the red river (live).
LP: .... DOJOLP 8

Gunn, Douglas

CAROLAN AGUS CEOLTA (Gunn, Douglas Ensemble).
LP: .... CEF 077

Gunning, Sarah Ogun

GIRL OF CONSTANT SORROW, A.
Tracks: / Loving Nancy / Old Jack frost / May I go with you, Johnny / Hand of God on the wall, The / Girl of constant sorrow, A / Down on the picket line / I hate the company bosses / I'm going to organize / Christ was a wayworn traveller / Why do you stand / Dreadful memories / Old southern town / I have letters from my father / Captain Devin / Gee whiz what they done to me / Davy Crockett / Battle of Mill Spring / Just the same today / Sally / Oh death.
LP: 12T 171

SILVER DAGGER, THE.
LP: .... ROUNDER 0051

Guns For San Sebastian

GUNS FOR SAN SEBASTIAN (Film soundtrack) (Various artists).
LP: .... MCA 25103
MC: .... MCAC 25103

Guns 'n' Roses

APPETITE FOR CONVERSATION (Interview picture disc).
LPPD: .... BAK 6001
MC: .... MBAK 6001

APPETITE FOR DESTRUCTION.
Tracks: / Welcome to the jungle / It's so easy / Nightrain / Out ta get me / Mr. Brownstone / Paradise city / My Michelle / Think about you / Sweet child o' mine / You're crazy / Anything goes / Rocket queen.
LP: .... WX 125
MC: .... WX 125C
MC: .... GEFC 24148
LP: .... GEF 24148

BAD BOYS.
LP: .... POW 005

GUNS 'N' ROSES.
Tracks: / It's so easy (live) / Shadow of your love (live) / Move to the city (live) / Knockin' on heaven's door (live) / Whole lotta Rosie (live).
MLP: .... P 6270

GUNS 'N' ROSES: INTERVIEW PICTURE DISC.
LPPD: .... CT 1013

GUNS 'N' ROSES: INTERVIEW PICTURE DISC.
LPPD: .... BAK 2079

LIES, THE SEX, THE VIOLENCE, THE SHOCKING TRUTH,.
Tracks: / Reckless life / Patience / Nice boys / Used to love her / Move to the city / You're crazy / Mama kin / One in a million.
LP: .... WX 218
MC: .... WX 218 C
MC: .... GEFC 24198
LP: .... GEF 24198

USE YOUR ILLUSION VOL.1.
LP: .... GEF 24415
MC: .... GEFC 24415

USE YOUR ILLUSION VOL.2.
LP: .... GEF 24420
MC: .... GEFC 24420

Guns of Navarone (bk)

GUNS OF NAVARONE, THE (Alistair MacLean) (Allen, Patrick (nar)).
MC: .... LFP 41 7150 5

Guns of Navarone

GUNS OF NAVARONE, THE (Various artists).
Tracks: / First of the few, The: *Various artists* / Bridge on the river Kwai, The: *Various artists* / Guns of Navarone: *Various artists* / Victory at sea: *Various artists* / 633 Squadron: *Various artists* / Longest day, The: *Various artists* / Western approaches: *Various artists* / Great escape, The: *Various artists*/ Mrs. Miniver: *Various artists*.
MC: 4178534

Gunson, David

WHAT GOES UP MIGHT COME DOWN.
Tracks: / Rollin' in my sweet baby's arms / Down, down, down.
MC: .... BBMC 00 12
LP: .... BB 00 12

Gunter, Arthur

BLACK AND BLUES.
LP: .... LP 8017

Gunter, Hardrock

BOOGIE WOOGIE ON A SATURDAY NIGHT.
Tracks: / Won't ease up / Dead soldier's revenge / Road warrior / Shattered paradise / Satan's twister / Ball breaker / Thirsty for blood / Gutter rat / Diggin' for gold.
LP: .... CR 30228

Gurdev & Raj

PUNJABI MUNDDA PAAVEY BHANGRA.
Tracks: / Kurri jaandi walaiti disco punjabi mundda paavey bhangra / Akhh da ishara maar gidde wich nachie kurri / Gaddi jat di jaandi toorran pat di / Saahnun nach ke dakha mutyare / Dudh vee naku ghee vee naklee / Veer daivin tun sab nu rabba / Mitran di awaajsun ke / Nashe di ae laur dooja sohriyan da pind / Billo waikh ke gulabi mukh tera.
MC: .... TCIRH 1002

Gurdjieff The Man

GURDJIEFF THE MAN (Bennett, J.G).
MC: .... SS 124

Gurkhas

GURKHAS,THE.
Tracks: / Green hills of Tyrol / Scotland the brave / Rowan tree / Highland laddie / Circassian circle / Skye boat song / Mairi's wedding / Westering home / Morag of Dunvegan / Paddy's leather breeches / Cock o' the north / Black bear, The.
LP: .... PRM 102
MC: .... CPRM 102

Guru Guru

DANCE OF THE FLAMES.
Tracks: / Dagobert Duck's 100th birthday / Girl from Hirschhorn, The / Day of time stop, The / Dance of the flames / Samba das rosas / Rallulli / At the juncture of light and dark / God's endless love for men.
LP: .... K 50044

HOT ON SPOT/IN BETWEEN (Guru Guru & Ultrepe).
LP: .... UD 024

Guru Guru Sun Band

HEY DU.
LP: 0060 187

Guru Josh

INFINITY.
Tracks: / Warehouse requiem / Whose law (is it anyway) / Powerforce / Move your body / E minor dim 7 / Lift up your arms / Wanderer, The / Infinity / Crave it.
LP: .... PL 74701
MC: .... PK 74701

Guru Wierdbrain

WEIRD WEIRD WORLD.
LP: .... HWLP 8505

Gurus Disciples &...

GURUS DISCIPLES & ASHRAMS (Brent, Peter).
MC: .... SS 122

Gurvitz, Adrian

CLASSIC.
Tracks: / No fears in the night / Living ain't easy without you / Hello New York / Your dream / Classic / Breakdown / No one can take your place / End the story.
LP: .... SRAK 547

IL ASSASSINO.
LP: .... JETLP 226

KICK OFF YOUR MUDDY BOOTS.
LP: .... THS 15

G.U.S. Band

BANDOLOGY (G.U.S. Footwear Band).
Tracks: / Bandology / Concert march- Cockleshell heroes / Mary Poppins / Slavonic rhapsody No.2 / Tit-larks / Amparita roca / Paso doble / Congratulations / Who would true valour see, Hymn / Punchinello / Overture from the Arcadians / Les preludes, symphonic poem no 3 / Coronation Street / Beautiful Colorado / No hiding place March / Praise my soul the King of Heaven.
LP: .... OU 2179

BEST OF BRASS (G.U.S. Footwear Band).
Tracks: / Zampa / Anchors aweigh / March / Morning papers / Op 279 Waltz / Spanish gypsy dance / Post horn polka / Pomp and circumstance march no.1 / Knightsbridge March / Poet and peasant / Overture / March of the cobblers / Waltzing with Sullivan / Pirates of Penzance / Galop / Abide with me.
LP: .... SRS 5033

CELEBRATION GOLDEN JUBILEE (G.U.S. Footwear Band).
Tracks: / Jubilee overture / One fine day / Celebration / Harmonious blacksmith, The / Finale from "Checkmate" / Fanfare and ceremonial prelude / Londonderry air / Cornet carillon / Flying Dutchman, The.
LP: .... BBRD 1019
MC: .... BBTD 1019

CHAMPIONSHIP BANDSTAND.
Tracks: / Thunder and lighting polka / Silver threads / Florentine march / Little Lisa / Endearing young charms / Marinarella / Number one / Facilita / Brass band boogie / Pendine / Horbury / James Cook, circumnavigator.
LP: .... ONCR 514

GOING HOME (G.U.S. Footwear Band).
Tracks: / Aida / Going home / Galloping home / Bass in the ballroom / Hark, hark my soul / Scheherazade / Festivities at Baghdad, the sea / Totem pole / Bless this house / Piper in the meadow / Greensleeves / How sweet the name of Jesus sounds / Resurgam.
LP: .... TWOX 1039

G.U.S. BAND.
Tracks: / Rhapsody in blue / When the saints go marching in / Sarabande en bleu / Saint Louis blues / I loves you porgy / Three songs of the south / DL blues / Blues in the night / Nobody knows the trouble i've seen / G.U.S. Band.
LP: .... BBRD 1015
MC: .... BBTD 1015

LAND OF HOPE & GLORY (G.U.S. Footwear Band).
Tracks: / Soldiers chorus / Student marching song / Drinking song / Romberg / Pilgrims' chorus (from 'Tannhauser') / Lost chord, The / Jerusalem / Mine eyes have seen the glory (battle hymn of the Republic) / Cavalry of the Steppes / David of the White Rock / Anvil chorus / Abide with me / Land of hope and glory.
LP: .... SCX 6406

QUARTETS FOR BRASS (G.U.S. Band Quartet).
Tracks: / Elegy and Rondo / Fancy's knell / Alla burlesca / Lully's march / Purcell's song / Rameau's tambourin / Handel's air / Bach's badinerie / Corelli's dance / Couperin's lullaby / Loeilly's jig.
LP: .... PRL 003
MC: .... CPRL 003

TRIBUTE TO ERIC BALL, A.
Tracks: / Symphonic march / October festival / Free fantasia / Symphonic suite for brass band / Festival music overture / Romance / Impromptu / Festival prelude from Fantasia celebration / Fantasy: the English maiden / Spring humoreske from three songs without words / Tone Poem: Resurgam (I shall rise again).
LP: .... TB 3021

Gustafsson, Rune

HIMSELF.
LP: .... SNTF 637

JUST THE WAY YOU ARE (Gustafsson, Rune & Niels-Henning Orsted-Pederson).
Tracks: / Just the way you are / Laverne walk / What are you doing the rest of your life / Slipped disc / Thrill is gone, The / Latin turkey / Seven steps to heaven / Alice in wonderland / How insensitive / Hot house / Jitterbug waltz.
LP: .... SNTF 869

MOVE.
LP: .... GNPS 2118

STRING ALONG WITH BASIE.
Tracks: / Splanky / After supper / Topsy man / TV time / Cute / Satin doll / Whirly bird / Shiny stockings / Teach me tonight.
LP: 500013
LP: .... SNTF 1005

SWEETEST SOUNDS, THE (Gustafsson, Rune & Zoot Sims).
LP: .... SNTF 819

Guthrie, Arlo

ALICE'S RESTAURANT (Film soundtrack) (See under Alice's Restaurant).

ARLO GUTHRIE.
Tracks: / Won't be long / Presidential rag / Deportees (Plane wreck at Los Gatos) / Children of Abraham / Nostalgia rag / When the cactus is in bloom / Me and my goose / Bling blang / Go down Moses / Hard times / Last to leave.
LP: .... K 54019

ARLO GUTHRIE & PETE SEEGER IN CONCERT (Guthrie, Arlo & Pete Seeger).
Tracks: / Way out there / Yodelling / Roving gambler / Don't think twice / Declaration of independence / Get up and go / City of New Orleans / Estadio Chile / Guantanamera / On a Monday / Presidential rag / Walkin' down the line / Well may the world go / Henry my son / Mother, The queen of my heart / Deportees (Plane wreck at Los Gatos) / Joe Mill / May there always be sunshine / Joe Hill / Three rules of discipline and the eight rules of attention / Stealin' / Golden vanity / Lonesome valley / Quite early morning / Sweet Rosyanne.
2LP: .... K 64023

BEST OF ARLO GUTHRIE.
Tracks: / Alice's restaurant massacre / Gabriels mothers highway ballad / 16 blues / Coopers lament / Motor cycle song / Coming into Los Angeles / Last train / City of New Orleans / Darkest hour / Last to leave.
LP: .... K 56431
MC: .... K 456 431

HOBO'S LULLABY.

Tracks: / Anytime / City of New Orleans / Lightning bar blues / Shackles and chains / 1913 massacre / Somebody turned on the light / Ukelele Lady / When the ship comes in / In maple (20 per cent) rag / Days are short / Hobo's lullaby.
LP: . . . . **K 44169**

LAST OF THE BROOKLYN COWBOYS.
LP: . . . . **K 44236**

OUTLASTING THE BLUES.
Tracks: / Prologue / Which side / Wedding song / World away from me / Epilogue / Telephone / Sailing down / This golden river / Carry me over / Underground / Drowning man / Evangelina.
LP: . . . . **K 56658**

POWER OF LOVE.
Tracks: / Power of love, The / Oklahoma nights / If I could only touch your life / Waimanalo blues / Living like a legend / Give it all you got / When I get to the border / Jamaica farewell / Slow boat / Garden song.
LP: . . . . **K 56910**

Guthrie, Gwen

GOOD TO GO LOVER.
Tracks: / Close to you / Outside in the rain / Good to go lover / You touch my life / Ain't nothin' goin' on but the rent / I still want you / Stop holding back / Passion eyes.
LP: . . . . **POLD 5201**
MC: . . . . **POLDC 5201**

GWEN GUTHRIE.
MC: . . . . **ICT 9690**
LP: . . . . **ILPS 9699**

JUST FOR YOU.
Tracks: / Put your love in control / Love in moderation / Just for you / I gotta have you / Feel it no more / Oh Donny no / Joy riders / Thrill me.
LP: . . . . **BRLM 505**
MC: . . . . **BRCM 505**
LP: . . . . **BRLP 505**
MC: . . . . **BRCA 505**

LIFELINE.
Tracks: / Destiny / Too many fish in the sea / Rockin' chair / What would I do without you / Bye bye lover / Don't take your love from me / Can't love you tonight / Once more with feeling / Send me somebody.
LP: . . . . **WX 154**
MC: . . . . **WX 154 C**

PADLOCK.
Tracks: / Peanut butter prelude / Hopscotch / Seventh heaven / Getting hot / Getting hot / Peanut butter / Padlock.
LP: . . . . **IMA 2**
MC: . . . . **IMC 2**

PORTRAIT: GWEN GUTHRIE.
Tracks: / Peanut butter / Seventh heaven / You're the one / Family affair / Hopscotch / Younger than me / Padlock / Oh what a life.
LP: . . . . **ILPS 9758**
MC: . . . . **ICT 9758**

TICKET TO RIDE.
Tracks: / Ticket to ride / Peek-a-boo / Younger than me / Oh what a life / It should have been you / You're the one / Family affair / Seventh heaven.
LP: . . . . **BRLP 516**
MC: . . . . **BRCA 516**

Guthrie, Jack

JACK GUTHRIE & HIS GREATEST SONGS.
LP: . . . . **HAT 3095**
MC: . . . . **HATC 3095**

Guthrie, Robin

MOON AND THE MELODIES, THE (See under Budd, Harold).

Guthrie, Woody

COLUMBIA RIVER COLLECTION.
LP: **12T 448**
LP: . . . . **ROUNDER 1036**
MC: . . . . **ROUNDER 1036C**

DUST BOWL BALLADS.
LP: . . . . **ROUNDER 1040**
MC: . . . . **ROUNDER 1040C**
LP: . . . . **FH 5212**

IT TAKES A LOT OF PEOPLE (See under Long, Larry) (Long, Larry).

LEGENDARY PERFORMER, A.
Tracks: / Great dust storm, The / I ain't got no home / Talking dust bowl blues / Vigilante man / Dust can't kill me / Dust pneumonia blues / Pretty boy Floyd / Blowin' down this road / Tom Joad (part 1) / Tom Joad (part 2) / Dust bowl refugee / Do re mi / Dust bowl blues / Dusty old dust (so long it's been good to know).
LP: . . . . **PL 12099**
MC: . . . . **PK 12099**

LIBRARY OF CONGRESS RECORDINGS VOL.2.
LP: . . . . **ROUNDER 1042**
MC: . . . . **ROUNDER 1042C**

LIBRARY OF CONGRESS RECORDINGS VOL. 1.
LP: . . . . **ROUNDER 1041**
MC: . . . . **ROUNDER 1041C**

LIBRARY OF CONGRESS RECORDINGS VOL.3.
LP: . . . . **ROUNDER 1043**
MC: . . . . **ROUNDER 1043C**

POOR BOY.
Tracks: / Baltimore to Washington / Little black train / Who's going to shoe your pretty feet / Slip knot / Poor boy / Mean talking blues / Stepstone / Bed on the floor / Little darlin' / Miner's song / Train blues / Danville girl no.2 / Ride old paint.
LP: . . . . **TRS 113**

SONGS FROM BOUND TO GLORY.
Tracks: / Gypsy Davey / Jesus Christ / Pastures of plenty / Columbus Georgia stockade / So long (It's been good to know you) / Howidido / Pretty boy Floyd / Hard travellin' / Better world / This land is your land.
LP: . . . . **K 56335**

STRUGGLE.
Tracks: / Struggle blues / Dollar down, A / Get along little doggies / Hang knot / Waiting at the gate / Dying miner, The / Union burying ground / Lost John / Buffalo / Pretty boy Floyd / Ludlow massacre / 1913 massacre.
LP: . . . . **FA 2485**
LP: . . . . **SPD 1034**
MC: . . . . **SPDC 1034**

THIS LAND IS YOUR LAND.
LP: . . . . **FTS 31001**

WOODY GUTHRIE.
Tracks: / More perty gals / Gypsy Davey / Pretty boy Floyd / Poor boy / Hey Lolly Lolly / Lonesome day / Rangers command / Ain't gonna be treated this way / Buffalo skinners / Hard, ain't it hard / Worried man blues.
LP: . . . . **CW 129**

WOODY GUTHRIE COLLECTION (20 golden greats).
Tracks: / House of the Rising Sun / John Henry / More pretty girls than one / Danville girl no.2 / Hard travellin' / Poor boy / Baltimore to Washington / Bed on the floor / Dig my life away / Buffalo skinners / Hard, ain't it hard? / Gypsy Davey / Little darlin' / I ride an old paint / Bury me beneath the willow / Sourwood Mountain / Oregon trail, The / Boll weevil blues / Mean talking blues.
LP: . . . . **DVLP 2128**
MC: . . . . **DVMC 2128**

WOODY GUTHRIE SINGS FOLK SONGS VOL.2 (Guthrie, Woody/Cisco Houston/Sonny Terry).
LP: . . . . **FA 2484**

WOODY GUTHRIE SINGS FOLKSONGS OF LEADBELLY.
LP: . . . . **FA 2483**

WOODY GUTHRIE VOL. 1.
LP: . . . . **SM 3960**
MC: . . . . **MC 3960**

Gutter Brothers

ISOMETRIC BOOGIE.
Tracks: / Everlasting shining peace of mind / Bubbling under, boiling over / Live and learn / Hand jive / Blow away / Fat cadillac / Frame, The / Still waiting / Where do they keep the water? / Kiss.
MC: . . . . **FLAB 515-001C**
LP: . . . . **FLAB 515 001A**

Gutterboy

GUTTERBOY.
LP: **7599242821**
MC: **7599242824**

Guttersnipes

POOR DRESS UP, THE.
Tracks: / Funny old world / Forgotten men / Sale of the century / Addicted to love / On fire / Hate game, The / Time of our lives / Guns and rockets / Today / They're telling me.
LP: . . . . **RAZ 42**

Guy

FUTURE, THE.
LP: . . . . **MCG 6119**
MC: . . . . **MCGC 6119**

GUY.
LP: . . . . **MCG 6043**
MC: . . . . **MCGC 6043**
LP: . . . . **MCA 42176**

IMPROVISATIONS ARE FOREVER NOW (see under Riley) (Guy/Riley/Wachsmann).

Guy, Barry

APPLICATION, INTERACTION AND... (see Stevens, John) (Guy, Barry/John Stevens/Trevor Watts).

ENDGAME (Guy, Barry & Howard Riley & John Stevens & Trevor Watts).
LP: . . . . **JAPO 60028**

ISKRA 1903 (see under Rutherford, Paul) (Guy, Barry/Paul Rutherford/Derek Bailey).

NO FEAR (see Stevens, John) (Guy, Barry/John Stevens/Trevor Watts).

ODE FOR JAZZ ORCHESTRA (Guy, Barry & The London Jazz Comp Orchestra).
2LP: . . . . **INCUS 6/7**

SOLO BRASS IMPROVISATIONS.
LP: . . . . **INCUS 22**

Guy, Buddy

BUDDY GUY.
Tracks: / Broken hearted blues / I got my eyes on you / First time I met the blues / Let me love you baby / Hard but fair / When my left eye jumps / Stone crazy / No lie / Stick around / My time after awhile / Leave my girl alone / My Mother.
LP: . . . . **CXMP 2010**

CHESS MASTERS.
Tracks: / Broken hearted blues / I got my eyes on you / First time I met the blues / Let me love you baby / Hard but fair / When my left eye jumps / Stone crazy / No lie / Stick around / My time after awhile / Leave my girl alone / My mother.
LP: . . . . **GCH 8013**
MC: . . . . **GCHK 8013**

CHICAGO GOLDEN YEARS.
2LP: **427006**

DAMN RIGHT, I'VE GOT THE BLUES.
Tracks: / Damn right, I've got the blues.
LP: . . . . **ORELP 516**
MC: . . . . **OREMC 516**

DJ PLAY MY BLUES.
Tracks: / Good news / Blues at my babies house / She suits me to a T / Just teasin' / All your love / D.J play my blues.
LP: . . . . **JSP 1042**

DOLLAR DONE FELL, THE.
LP: . . . . **JSP 1009**

DRINKIN' TNT 'N' SMOKIN' DYNAMITE (Guy, Buddy & Junior Wells).
Tracks: / Ah'w baby / Everything gonna be alright / How can one woman be so mean / Checking on my baby / When you see the little tears from my eyes / My younger days.
LP: . . . . **RL 034**
LP: **BP-1182**
LP: . . . . **SNTF 920**

FINAL TAKES, THE (See Rush, Otis) (Guy, Buddy & Otis Rush).

GOT TO USE YOUR HOUSE.
LP: **2005**

HOLD THAT PLANE.
Tracks: / Watermelon man / I'm ready / You don't love me / Hello San Francisco / Hold that plane / My time after a while / Come see about me.
LP: . . . . **VNP 5315**
MC: . . . . **VNP 6315**

HOT AND COOL.
Tracks: / I got my eyes on you / Things I used to do, The / (You give me) Fever / 24 hours of the day / I had a dream last night / Hold that plane / Man and the blues, A / Sweet little angel / Worry, worry.
LP: . . . . **VSD 79290**

I AIN'T GOT NO MONEY (Guy, Buddy/Blue Charlie/Joe Johnson).
LP: . . . . **FLY 620**

I LEFT MY BLUES IN SAN FRANCISCO.
Tracks: / Keep it to yourself / Crazy love / I suffer with the blues / When my left eye jumps / Buddy's groove / Going home / She suits me to a tee / Leave my girl alone / Too many ways / Mother-in-law / Every girl I see.
LP: . . . . **CH 9262**

I WAS WALKING THROUGH THE WOODS.
LP: . . . . **BRP 2030**

IN THE BEGINNING.
Tracks: / Sit and cry / Try to quit you baby / You sure can't do / This is the end / Broken hearted blues / Slop around / First time / I got my eyes on you / Stone crazy / Skippin (Inst) / When my left eye jumps / Treasure untold, The / My time after awhile / I dig your wig.
LP: . . . . **RL 001**

MESSIN' WITH THE BLUES (VIDEO) (See Under Water, Muddy) (Waters, Muddy, Buddy Guy & Junior Wells).

ORIGINAL BLUES BROTHERS - LIVE (Guy, Buddy & Junior Wells).
Tracks: / Buddy's blues / Blue Monday / Everyday I have the blues / Woman blues / Satisfaction / Messin' with the kid / No use cryin' / Just to be with you / Junior's shuffle / Out of sight.
LP: . . . . **BMLP 1007**

PHIL GUY (see Guy, Buddy) (Guy, Buddy & Phil).

STONE CRAZY.
Tracks: / Slop around / Broken hearted blues / I got my eyes on you / First time I met the blues / Let me love you baby / I got a strange feeling / Hully gully / Ten years ago / Watch yourself / Stone crazy / Hard but fair / Baby (baby, baby) / When my left eye jumps / That's it no lie / Every girl I see / Leave my girl alone / She suits me to a tee / Mother in law blues / Going home / I suffer with the blues.
LP: . . . . **AL 4723**

TEN BLUE FINGERS.
Tracks: / Girl you're nice and clean / Garbage man blues / Tell me what's inside of you / You can make it if you try / Have you ever been lonesome / She winked her eye.
LP: . . . . **JSP 1085**

Guy Called Gerald

AUTOMANIKK.
Tracks: / To the otherside / Automanikk / Eyes of sorrow (viv version) / Stella / Untitled / FX (mayday upgrade) / Emotions electric 2 / I feel rhythm / Blame the artist / I won't give in.
LP: **4664821**
MC: **4664824**

HOT LEMONADE.
LP: . . . . **RA 001**
MC: . . . . **TAC 1**

Guy, Phil

BAD LUCK BOY (Guy, Phil & Buddy).
Tracks: / Bad luck boy / Money / Breaking out on top / Mellow down / Cold feeling / Comin' on.
LP: . . . . **JSP 1061**

DOUBLE DYNAMITE: MISSISSIPPI & CHICAGO BLUES (See also McDowell, Fred) (Guy, Phil & McDowell, Mississippi Fred).

I ONCE WAS A GAMBLER.
LP: . . . . **JSP 1114**

IT'S A REAL MUTHA FUCKA.
Tracks: / Tina Nu / Steppin out / Where can I go / Good things / Stone crazy / It's a real mutha.
LP: . . . . **JSP 1094**

PHIL GUY (See under Guy, Buddy) (Guy, Phil & Buddy).

RED HOT BLUES OF PHIL GUY.
Tracks: / Love is like quicksand / Blues with a feeling / Skin and bones / Winehead / Texas flood / Red dress / Garbage man blues.
LP: . . . . **JSP 1047**

TOUGH GUY (Guy, Philip & The Chicago Machine).
Tracks: / Inlation / You made your move too soon / Frosty / She's fine / Like ice around my heart / Feeling sexy / Chicken shack / Down home blues.
LP: . . . . **RL 062**

Guys & Dolls

BEST OF GUYS & DOLLS.
Tracks: / Only loving does it / You don't have to say you love me / Let's make love / We're changing / Don't make me over / If you love me let me go / There's a whole lot of loving / Deeper and deeper / Just loving you / Son Caliu / I've been loving you / Angel of the morning.
LP: . . . . **SPR 8544**
MC: . . . . **SPC 8544**

GUYS & DOLLS.
LP: . . . . **MAG 5005**

SPOTLIGHT ON GUYS & DOLLS.
Tracks: / You don't have to say you love me / I've been loving you / Killing me softly with his song / (Last night) I didn't get to sleep at all / Son Caliu / If only for the good times / There's a whole lot of loving / Don't pull your love / Bye bye rainy days / Lovely lady / Starlight, starbright / Rescue me / Only loving does it / Never an everyday thing / Angel of the morning / Remembered memory / Perfectly well / You're my world / Love train / Don't make me over / Just loving you / How can loving you be wrong / I must go home alone / Something's gotten hold of my heart.
2LP: . . . . **SPOT 1022**
MCSET: . . . . **ZCSPT 1022**

THERE'S A WHOLE LOT OF LOVING.

LP: . . . . SSP 3076

Guys & Dolls (Musical)

GUYS & DOLLS (Reprise Repertory Theatre) (Reprise Repertory Theatre).
Tracks: / Overture / Fugue for tinhorns / I'll know / Oldest established craps game in New York / Bushel and a peck, A / Guys and dolls / If I were a bell / I've never been in love before / Take back your mink / More I cannot wish you / Adelaide's lament / Luck be a lady / Sue me / Sit down you're rockin' the boat / Guys and dolls (reprise).
LP: . . . . **K 54113**

GUYS & DOLLS (London revival cast) (Various artists).
Tracks: / Runyonland music: *Various artists* / Fugue for tinhorns: *Various artists* / Follow the fold: *Various* artists / Oldest established craps game in New York: *Various artists* / I'll know: *Various artists* / Bushel and a peck, A: *Various artists* / Adelaide's lament: *Various artists* / Guys and dolls: *Various artists*/ If I were a bell: *Various artists* / My time of day: *Various artists* / I've never been in love before: *Various* artists / Take back your mink: *Various artists* / Adelaide's lament (reprise): *Various artists* / More I cannot wish you: *Various artists* / Craps shooter's ballet, The: *Various artists* / Luck be a lady: *Various artists*/ Sue me: *Various artists* / Sit down you're rockin' the boat: *Various artists* / Marry the man today: *Various artists* / Guys and dolls (reprise): *Various artists.*
LP: . . . . **CDL 1388**
MC: . . . . **ZCDL 1388**

GUYS & DOLLS (Film soundtrack) (Various artists).
LP: . . . . **MPT 3**

GUYS & DOLLS (Original Broadway Cast) (Various artists).
Tracks: / Runyonland music: *Various artists* / Fugue for tinhorns: *Various artists* / Follow the fold: *Various* artists / Oldest established craps game in New York: *Various artists* / I'll know: *Various artists* / Bushel and a peck, A: *Various artists* / My time of day: *Various artists* / Adelaide's lament: *Various artists*/ Guys and dolls: *Various artists* / If I were a bell: *Various artists* / I've never been in love before: *Various* artists / Take back your mink: *Various artists* / More I cannot wish you: *Various artists* / Luck be a lady: *Various artists* / Sue me: *Various artists* / Sit down you're rockin' the boat: *Various artists* / Marry the man today: *Various artists* / Guys and dolls (reprise): *Various artists.*
LP: . . . . **SHM 3201**
MC: . . . . **HSC 3201**
LP: . . . . **MCL 1659**
MC: . . . . **MCLC 1659**

Gwalarn, Groupe

GWALARN - ECOUTEZ, JEUNES ET VIEUX.
Tracks: / Karantez ha Karantez / Da vrest zo deut ur vatimant / Me garje bout / Ton fulup / Ur paotr bihan a Blougerne / Castle Kelly / O tistrein eus a blouneour trez / Selaouit koz ha yaouank / Marc'heg an nevez amzer / Planedenn / Karantez-vro.
LP: . . . . **ARN 33726**

Gwalia Male Choir

TRAVELLING.
Tracks: / Yankee doodle / Rose of Tralee, The / Marching song / Nant y mynydd / Stodole pumpa / Eriskay love lilt / Heimat / Long day closes, The / Down among the dead men / Chocoloza / Das Morgenrot / La vergine / Silver birch, The / Steal away / Nos a bore / Calm is the sea / Nava Nagila.
LP: . . . . **GRALP 15**
MC: . . . . **GRTC 15**

Gwar

HELL-O.
Tracks: / Time for death / Americanized / Slutman city / War toy / Pure as the artic snow / Gwar theme / Ollie North / U ain't shit / Black and huge / A.E.I.O.U. / I'm in love with a dead dog / World o' filth / Captain crunch / Je m'appelle J. Cousteau / Bone meal / Techno's song / Rock'n'roll party theme.
LP: . . . . **SDE 8910**
LP: . . . . **SHIMMY 010**

SCUMDOGS OF THE UNIVERSE.
LP: . . . . **MASLP 001**
MC: . . . . **MASMC 001**

Gwendal

GWENDAL.
2LP: . . . . **PM 1728913**
MC: . . . . **PM 1728919**

Gwerz

AUDELA.
LP: . . . . **BUR 821**

Gwigwi's Band

KWELA.
LP: . . . . **77 AFRO 101**

Gwillan's Harp

GWILLAN'S HARP Ursuala K LeGuin - Spoken word.
LP: . . . . **TC 1556**
MC: . . . . **CDL 51556**

Gypsy

GYPSY (Various artists).
LP: . . . . **ADL 504**
MC: . . . . **ADK 504**

GYPSY SONGS AND MUSIC (Various artists).
MC: . . . . **C 295**

Gypsy Baron

GYPSY BARON (Various artists).
LP: **6.21286**
MC: **CH4 21286**

Gypsy Kyss

WHEN PASSION MURDERED INNOCENCE.
Tracks: / When passion murder innocence.
LP: **942210**

Gypsy Queen

GYPSY QUEEN.
Tracks: / Love is strange / I can't help it / Radio / Hey (are you ever satisfied) / Leave us alone / Don't rush me / Love is a shadow / I still care / Who are you? / She wants to ... / Love is strange (remix) / Where does our love go.
LP: . . . . **LOPL 500**
MC: . . . . **LOPC 500**

Gypsy Rose

PREY.
Tracks: / Poisoned by love / Crawlin' / Borderline / Blood 'n' sweat / Love me or leave me / Make me do anything you want / Shiver then shake / Wild reaction / Don't turn your back on me now / Highway-one-way.
LP: . . . . **PL 90530**
MC: . . . . **PK 90530**

Gypsy (Show)

GYPSY (Original Broadway Cast) (Various artists).
LP: . . . . **PS 32607**
MC: . . . . **PST 32607**

Gypsy Songs & Music

SONGS OF THE OPEN ROAD (Gypsies,travellers & country singers) (Various artists).
LP: **12T 253**

TRAVELLING SONGSTER (An Anthology from Gypsy Singers) (Various artists).
Tracks: / Small birds whistle, The: *Travelling Songster* / Sheepfold, The: *Travelling Songster* / One penny: *Travelling* Songster / Basket of eggs: *Travelling Songster* / Pony march: *Travelling Songster* / Whistling rufus: *Travelling* Songster / Tuning: *Travelling Songster* / Green bushes: *Travelling Songster* / Irish girl, The: *Travelling* Songster / Raking the hay: *Travelling Songster* / Moon shines bright, The: *Travelling Songster* / Father had a knife: *Travelling Songster* / Jew's garden, The: *Travelling Songster* / Step dance tune: *Travelling Songster*/ Turning: *Travelling Songster* / Sweet William: *Travelling Songster* / Johnny Abourne: *Travelling Songster*/ Died for love: *Travelling Songster* / Captain thunderbold: *Travelling Songster* / Cock o' the north: *Travelling Songster* / Flowers of Edinburgh: *Travelling Songster* / Girl I left behind me, The: *Travelling Songster.*
LP: **12TS 304**

Gyson, Brion

DREAM MACHINE.
LP: . . . . **KK 015**

Gyuto Monks

FREEDOM CHANTS FROM THE ROOF OF THE WORLD.
Tracks: / Yamantaka / Mahakala / Number 2 for Gaia.
MC: . . . . **RACS 0113**

H2O

FAITH.
Tracks: / Success / Dream of sleep / Who'll stop the rain / Just outside of heaven / Action / Sundays are blue / All that glitters / Another face / It's in you.
LP: PL 70107
MC: PK 70107

H Block

H BLOCK (Various artists).
LP: HBLP 001

H Factor

H FACTOR.
LP: EIRSA 1029
MC: EIRSAC 1029

Ha Ha Ha

UP AND DOWN.
Tracks: / Up and down / Resuene / Al aire / El Dron / Guadiana / Del Cerro / Mi tierra / Boabdil / A Mandeli.
LP: Unknown

Habichuela, Pepe

A MANDELI.
Tracks: / Resuene / Al aire / El dron / Guadiana / Del cerro / Mi tierra / Boabdil / A mandeli / Mandeli, A.
LP: HNBL 1315
LP: V 2514
MC: TCV 2514
LP: HNBL 6302

Habit

MEDICINE MAN.
Tracks: / Lucy / Medicine man / Build it up / Starlight / Anonymous / Love for keeps / Heaven must be playing games / Get back / Shotgun city / Never street.
LP: V 2531
MC: TCV 2531

Hackberry Ramblers

FIRST RECORDINGS 1935-48.
MC: C 0127

LOUISIANA CAJUN MUSIC.
LP: ARHOOLIE 5003
MC: C 5003

Hacker, Alan

BRAHMS CLARINET TRIO AND SONATAS (see under Brahms (Composer)) (Hacker, Alan/Jennifer Ward Clarke/Richard Burnett).

CLARINET COLLECTION (Hacker, Alan/Richard Burnett).
Tracks: / She moved through the fair / Sinfonia from 'Su le sponde del Tebro' (A. Scarlatti) / L'hiver (Telemann) / March by Mr. Handel / Adagio cantabile (Vanhal) / Minuet from Divertimento K439b (Mozart) / Variations for clarinet and piano Opus 33 (Weber) / Duo for clarinet and piano opus 15 (Burgmuller) / Phantasy pieces opus 73 (Schumann) / Romanza from 'La forza del destino' (Verdi) / Macedonian folk tune.
LP: SAR 10
MC: CSAR 10

HACKER ILK.
LP: NATO 214

Hacker, Marilyn

POETRY AND VOICE OF MARILYN HACKER.
LP: TC 1501

Hackett, Bobby

AT NICK'S 1944 (Hackett, Bobby & His Orchestra).
LP: 6.26171

BIG 'T' S JAZZ / GOTHAM JAZZ SCENE (see under Teagarden, Jack) (Hackett, Bobby & Jack Teagarden).

BOBBY HACKETT & HIS ORCHESTRA 1943 (Hackett, Bobby & His Orchestra).
LP: J 111

BOBBY HACKETT'S SEXTET (Hackett, Bobby Sextet).
Tracks: / Bill Bailey won't you please come home / Sentimental blues / Deed I do / Struttin' with some barbecue / Swing that music / S'wonderful / Fidgety feet / There'll never be another you / String of pearls / There'll be some changes made / Sign off.
LP: SLP 4059

BUTTERFLIES AIRS.
LP: HD 6617

HOLLYWOOD BOWL CONCERT, 1963 (See under Teagarden, Jack) (Hackett, Bobby & Jack Teagarden).

IN A MELLOW MOOD.
Tracks: / Stars in my eyes / In a sentimental mood / All through the night.
LP: PM 155 297 1
MC: PM 155 297 4

JAM SESSION (see Condon, Eddie) (Hackett, Bobby/Eddie Condon).

JAZZ FROM THE RUSTIC LODGE, VOL 1 (Hackett, Bobby & Red Allen).
LP: JASS 16
MC: JASS 16C

JAZZ ULTIMATE (Hackett, Bobby & Jack Teagarden).
Tracks: / Indiana / Oh baby / It's wonderful / I found a new baby / Sunday / Baby won't you please come home / Everybody loves my baby / Mama's gone goodbye / Way down yonder in New Orleans / 55th and Broadway / 'S wonderful.
LP: EMS 1134
MC: TCEMS 1134

JULY 25TH, 1960.
Tracks: / David and Goliath / Swing low sweet chariot / I'm climbing up the mountain / Nobody knows the trouble I've seen / When the saints go marching in / Heaven's full of joy / Golden gate / Way up there / Balm in Gilead / Steal away / Better be ready / Bye and bye.
LP: JV 108

LIVE FROM MANASSAS (Hackett, Bobby, Vic Dickenson, Maxine Sullivan).
LP: J 76

LIVE FROM THE VOYAGER ROOM (Hackett, Bobby & His Jazz Band).
Tracks: / Allahandra / It's all in your mind / Perdido / Spain / Stardust / Clark and Madison / Cottontail / Fidgety feet / It don't mean a thing / Swing 39 / Handel with Cary / Christopher Columbus.
LP: SS 108

LIVE FROM THE VOYAGER ROOM - VOL.2.
Tracks: / Lullaby in rhythm / Holiday hop / I'm beginning to see the light / Cornet chop suey / Ill wind / Swiss criss / Lady with the lavender hair, The / Poor butterfly / Whisper not / Morning aire / Seal, The / I guess I'll go back home / Zig zag.
LP: SS 113

MELODY IS A MUST, VOL 1 (Live at the Roosevelt Grill).
LP: PHONT 7571

MELODY IS A MUST, VOL 2 (Live at the Roosevelt Grill).
LP: PHONT 7572

RARE ITALIAN DATES/LIVE AT LOUISIANA DATES 1971 (Hackett, Bobby & Albert Nicholas).
LP: FDC 3001

Hackett, Steve

BAY OF KINGS.
Tracks: / Bay of kings / Journey, The / Kim / Marigold / St Elmo's fire / Petropolis / Second chance / Cast adrift / Horizons / Black light / Barren land, The / Calmaria.
LP: LMGLP 3000
MC: ZCLGP 3000
LP: STL 10
MC: STC 10
LP: SCD 10

CURED.
Tracks: / Hope I don't wake / Picture postcard / Can't let go / Air-conditioned nightmare / Funny feeling / Cradle of swans, The / Overnight sleeper / Turn back time.
LP: CHC 21
MC: CHCMC 21
LP: CDS 4021

DEFECTOR.
Tracks: / Steppes, The / Time to get out / Slogans / Leaving / Two vamps as guests / Jacuzzi / Hammer in the sand / Toast / Show, The / Sentimental.
LP: CHC 15
MC: CHCMC 15
LP: CDS 4018

HIGHLY STRUNG.
Tracks: / Casino royale / Cell 151 / Always somewhere else / Walking through walls / Give it away / Weightless / Group therapy / India rubber man / Hackett to pieces.
LP: CHC 40
MC: CHCMC 40
LP: HACK 1

MOMENTUM.
LP: STL 15
MC: STC 15

PLEASE DON'T TOUCH.
Tracks: / Narnia / Carry on up the vicarage / Racing in A / Kim / How can I? / Icarus ascending / Hoping love will last / Land of a thousand autumns / Please don't touch / Voice of Necam, The.
LP: CDS 4012
LP: CHC 48

SPECTRAL MORNINGS.
Tracks: / Everyday / Virgin and the gypsy, The / Red flower of Tachai blooms everywhere, The / Clocks - The angel of Mons / Ballad of the decomposing man / Lost time in Cordoba / Tigermoth / Spectral mornings.
LP: CDS 4017
LP: CHC 67
MC: CHCMC 67

TILL WE HAVE FACES.
Tracks: / Let me count the ways / Doll that's made in Japan / Myopia / What's my name / Rio connection, The / Taking the easy way out / When you wish upon a star / Duel / Matilda Smith-Williams' home for the aged.
LP: LMGLP 4000
MC: ZCLMG 4000
LP: STL 11
MC: STC 11

VOYAGE OF THE ACOLYTE.
Tracks: / Ace of wands / Hands of the priestess-part 1 / Tower struck down, A / Hands of the priestess-part 2 / Hermit, The / Star of Sirius / Lovers, The / Shadow of the Hierophant.
LP: CHC 47
LP: CAS 1111

VOYAGE OF THE ACOLYTE/PLEASE DON'T TOUCH.
Tracks: / Ace of wands / Hands of the priestess-part 1 / Tower struck down, A / Hands of the priestess-part 2 / Hermit, The / Star of Sirius / Lovers, The / Shadow of the Hierophant / Narnia / Carry on up the vicarage / Racing in A / Kim / How can I? / Hoping love will last / Land of a thousand Autumns / Please don't touch / Voice of Necam, The / Icarus ascending.
MCSET: CASMC 105

Hackney 5-0

BETWEEN THE FLOORS.
LP: CHIME 0018

MILLSTONE.
LP: CHIME 0113S

Hackney Empire

ON STAGE PLEASE AT THE HACKNEY EMPIRE Various artists (Various artists).
Tracks: / Overtures and beginners: That's entertainment: *Royal Artillery Orchestra* / One of the ruins (that Cromwell knocked about a bit): *Mansfield, Elizabeth* / Flanagan: *Manners, Margery* / Only a bird in a gilded cage: *Manners, Margery* / (Last of the) Gaiety Girls, The: *Wells, Billy* / Joshua: *Windsor, Barbara* / London medley, A: *Kane, Joy/Sylvia Young's Young 'uns* (Any old iron#Maybe it's because I'm a Londoner#Lambeth Walk) / Burlington Bertie: *Stables, Maggie* / Sand of the desert (medley): *Cox Twins and Pauline* (Sand dance, The#Sheik of Araby#Egyptian ballet) / Underneath the arches: *Crowther, Leslie & Bernie Winters* (end s1) / Sally: *Pollard, Su (aut)* / Songs from the shows (medley): *Arden-Griffith, Paul* (Dames#Youre getting to be#On the street where#Tonight#Thats entertainmt.) / Cavatina: *Weedon, Bert* / Rock 'n' roll medley: *Weedon, Bert* (Guitar boogie shuffle#What'd I say#Shake rattle#Blue suede shoes#&2) / Songs from Broadway: *Howard, Joyce* (Broadway baby#Nobody does it like me#Razzle dazzle#If my friends could..) / What is a mummy, daddy?: *Trinder, Tommy* / There's no business like show business (Finale): *Royal Artillery Orchestra*.
LP: PRCV 138
MC: TC-PRCV 138

Hadden, Rothfield &

WHEN THESE SHOES WERE NEW.
Tracks: / Captain Ward / Gadie rins, The / Fiddle tunes / Take me out drinking / Postman song, The / Texas gals / Cleator moor / Bury me beneath the willow / Ballad of Willie Moor / Bad girl.
LP: LIFL 7005
MC: LIFC 7005

Haddix, Travis

WINNERS NEVER QUIT.
Tracks: / Homeslice / Bag lady / She's not the kind of girl / Better than nothing / Winners never quit / Something in the milk ain't clean / Beggin' business / Abused / Someone to love / I'm mean.
LP: ICH 1101
MC: ICH 1101 MC

Haden, Carl

CARL HADEN'S SUMMA CUM LAUDE ORCHESTRA (Haden, Carl Summa Cum Laude Orchestra).
LP: J 152

Haden, Charlie

AS LONG AS THERE'S MUSIC (Haden, Charlie/ Hampton Hawes).
LP: AH 4

BALLAD OF THE FALLEN.
Tracks: / El Segardors / If you want to write me / Ballad of the fallen / Grandola vila morena / Introduction to people / People united will never be defeated / Silence / Too late / La pasionaria / La santa espina.
LP: ECM 1248

CLOSENESS.
Tracks: / Ellen David / O.C. / For Turiya / For a free Portugal.
LP: AMLJ 710

FOLK SONGS (See under Garbarek, Jan) (Haden/ Garbarek/ Gismonti).

GOLDEN NUMBER, THE.
LP: AMLJ 727

IN THE YEAR OF THE DRAGON (See Under Allen, Geri) (Haden, Charlie/ Geri Allen/ Paul Motian).

LIBERATION MUSIC ORCHESTRA.
Tracks: / Introduction, The / Song of the united front / El quinto regimento / Los cuatro generals (the four generals) / Ending of the first side, The / Song for Che / War orphans / Interlude / Circus 68, 69 / We shall overcome.
LP: JAS 55
MC: JAS C55
LP: MCA 39125

QUARTET WEST.
LP: 831 673-1
MC: 831 673-4

Hades

IF AT FIRST YOU DON'T SUCCEED.
LP: RR 95331

RESISTING SUCCESS.
Tracks: / On to Iliad / Legal tender / Sweet revenge / Nightstalker / Resist success / Widows mite / Cross, The / Masque of the red death.
LP: RR 9598

Hadidjah, Idhah

TONGGERT.
Tracks: / Tonggert / Bayu bayu / Mahoni / Hiji / Catetan / Arum / Bandung / Daun / Pulus / Keser / Bojong / Serat / Sahara.
LP: K 979173 1
MC: K 979173 4

Hadley, Bob

RAVEN.
Tracks: / Wreck of the last steam engine train / Day after pay day / Come all ye fair and tender maidens / Chorale from Beethoven's ninth symphony / Harvest time / Sue / Summer and fall / First snowfall / Reflections on English bay.
LP: SNKF 109
LP: KM 113

TUNES FROM THE WELL.
Tracks: / Dragonfly / Romantic Logician, The / Cripple creek / Wizard's wine, The / Your smile is like a theorem / Lynn Canyon creek / Bob sled / Coocoo, The / I bid my heart be still (Scottish medley) / Wild mountain thyme / John Henry / Farrell's farewell / New boots.
LP: SNKF 126
LP: KM 103

Haeffner, Nick

GREAT INDOORS.
Tracks: / You know I hate nature / Sneaky mothers, The / Master, The / Earth movers, The / Furious table / Breaths / Back in time for tea / Steel grey / Great outdoors, The / Don't be late / Don't be late reprise / Mean Guitar / Master (Single Mix), The / Back in time for tea (single mix).
LP: . . . . **KIRI 071**

Hafler Trio

BAG OF CATS, A.
LP: **SPL001**

BANG AN OPEN LETTER.
LP: . . . . **DVR 4**

BEN RACH AB SHALOSHTEM YECHAUD THAUBODO (Hafler Trio/ Dari, Luciano).
LP: . . . . **EEE 001**

CONTACT.
LP: . . . . **TO 17**

INPOUTOF.
LP: . . . . **KK 008**

KUKLOS (Hafler Trio/Touch).
MC: . . . . **T 33.9**

MASTURBATORIUM.
LP: . . . . **TOUCHTONE 1**

THIRSTY FISH, A.
2LP: . . . . **TO 9**

THREE WAYS OF SAYING TWO (Netherland lectures).
LP: . . . . **CHARM 3**

Hag

HAG (Various artists).
Tracks: / Trouble: *Spatula. Flick* / Eternal damnation: *Who's In The Kitchen* / More: *Swis* / Surviving to breed: *Salad From Atlantis* / Uncle Pig's...: *First men in space* / Southern life: *Cropdusters* / What the...: *Regular Guys* / From within: *Fence* / Lillie: *How Many Beans Make 5?* / She's on fire: *Electric Circus* / Government health: *Cement garden.*
LP: . . . . **HAGLP 1**

Hagar, Sammy

BEST OF SAMMY HAGAR, THE.
LP: . . . . **WX 291**
MC: . . . . **WX 291C**

CENTRE HOLE.
Tracks: / Red / Catch the wind / Cruisin' and boozin' / Free money / Rock 'n' roll weekend / Fillmore shuffle / Hungry / Pits / Love has found me / Little star / eclipse.
LP: . . . . **EST 11599**

COLLECTION: SAMMY HAGAR.
LP: . . . . **IC 038 82216**

DANGER ZONE.
Tracks: / Love or money / 20th century man / Miles from boredom / Mommy says / In the night / Iceman / Bad reputation / Heartbeat / Run for your life / Danger zone.
LP: . . . . **EST 12069**

LOOKING BACK.
Tracks: / I'll fall in love again / There's only one way to rock / Heavy metal / Remember the heroes / Baby's on fire / Three lock box / Two sides of love / I can't drive 55 / I don't need love / Voa.
LP: **9241271**
MC: **9241274**

LOUD AND CLEAR.
Tracks: / Rock 'n' roll weekend / Make it last / Reckless / Turn up the music / I've done everything for you / Young girl blues / Bad motor scooter / Space station no. 5.
LP: . . . . **EST 25330**

MUSICAL CHAIRS.
Tracks: / Turn up the music / It's gonna be alright kid / You make me crazy / Reckless / Try / Don't stop me now / Straight from the hip kid / Hey boys / Someone out there / Crack in the world.
LP: . . . . **GO 2021**

NINE ON A TEN SCALE.
Tracks: / Keep on rockin' / Urban guerilla / Flamingos fly / China / Silver lights / All American / Confession (please come back) / Young girl blues / Rock 'n' roll Romeo.
LP: . . . . **FA 3068**
MC: . . . . **TCFA 3068**
LP: . . . . **GO 2017**

RED ALERT, DIAL NINE.
Tracks: / Red / Cruisin' and boozin' / Turn up the music / Reckless / This planet's on fire / Urban guerilla / Trans Am / Miles from boredom / 20th century man / Space station no.5 / I've done everything for you / Young girl blues.
LP: . . . . **EST 26882**

SAMMY HAGAR.
Tracks: / Red / Catch the wind / Cruisin' and boozin' / Free money / Rock'n'roll weekend / Fillmore shuffle / Hungry / Pits / Love has found me / Little star / Eclipse.
LP: . . . . **GO 2007**

SAMMY HAGAR (GEFFEN).
Tracks: / When the hammer falls / Hands and knees / Give to live / Boy's night out / Returning home / Standin' at the same old crossroads / Privacy / Back into you / Eagle's fly / What the world needs now is love.
LP: . . . . **WX 114**
MC: . . . . **WX 114C**

STANDING HAMPTON.
Tracks: / There's only one way to rock / Baby's on fire / Can't get loose / I'll fall in love again / Heavy metal / Baby it's you / Surrender / Inside lookin' in / Sweet hitchhiker / Piece of my heart.
LP: **9020061**
MC: **9020064**
LP: . . . . **GEF 85456**

STREET MACHINE.
Tracks: / Never say die / This planet's on fire (burn to hell) / Wounded in love / Falling in love / Growing pains / Child to man / Trans am (Highway wonderland) / Feels like love / Plain Jane.
LP: . . . . **REV LP 72**
LP: . . . . **EST 11983**

THREE LOCK BOX.
Tracks: / Three lock box / Remote love / Remember the heroes / Your love is driving me crazy / In the room / Rise of the animal / I wouldn't change a thing / Growing up / Never give up / I don't need love.
LP: **9020211**
MC: **9020214**
MC: **4024254**

THROUGH THE FIRE (Hagar, Schon, Aaronson, Shrieve).
Tracks: / Top of the rock / Missing you / Animation / Valley of the kings / Giza / Whiter shade of pale, A / Hot and dirty / He will understand / My home town.
LP: . . . . **GEF 25893**

VOA.
Tracks: / I can't drive 55 / Swept away / Rock is in my blood / Two sides of love / Dick in the dirt / Voa / Don't make me wait / Burnin' down the city.
LP: **9240431**
MC: **9240434**

Hagen, Nina

NINA HAGEN.
Tracks: / Move over / Super freak family / Love heart attack / Hold me / Las Vegas / Live on Mars / Dope sucks / Only seventeen / Where's the party / Ave Maria.
LP: **838 505 1**
MC: **838 505 4**

NINA HAGEN BAND (Hagen, Nina Band).
Tracks: / TV glotzer / Rangehn / Unbeschreiblich / Auf'm bahnhof zoo / Naturtrane / Superboy / Heiss / Fisch im Wasser / Auf'm friedhof / Der spinner / Pank.
LP: . . . . **CBS 83136**

NUNSEXMONKROCK.
Tracks: / Antiworld / Smack Jack / Taitschi-tarot / Dread love / Future is now / Born in Xixax / Iki maska / Dr. Art / Cosma shiva / UFO.
LP: . . . . **CBS 85774**

STREET.
Tracks: / Blumen fur die damen / Divine love, sex and romance / Ruler of my heart / Nina 4 president / Keep it live / Berlin / In my world / Gretchen / Erfurt and Gera / All 4 franckie.
MC: **8487164**
LP: **8487161**

UNBEHAGEN.
Tracks: / African reggae / Alptraum / Wir leben immer noch / Wenn ich ein Junge war / Hermann hiess er / Auf'm rummel / Wau wau / Fall in love mit mir / No way.
LP: . . . . **CBS 84159**

Haggard, H Rider

KING SOLOMON'S MINES (Young, John).
MCSET: . . . . **COL 2003**

KING SOLOMON'S MINES (Anderson, Miles).
MCSET: **414 724-4**
MCSET: . . . . **ARGO 1190**

Haggard, Merle

25TH ANNIVERSARY ALBUM: MERLE HAGGARD.
Tracks: / Please Mr. DJ / I wonder what she'll think / Life's like poetry / Holding things together / I've done it all / Home is where a kid grows up / Girl turned ripe, The / Irma Jackson / White man singing the blues / Love and honor / I'm gonna break every heart I can / Farmer's daughter, The / Wine take me away / I wonder where I'll find you at tonight / Someone told my story / After loving you / Working man can't get nowhere today, A / I can't hold myself in line / Way it was in '51, The / Silver wings.
LP: . . . . **EMS 1313**
MC: . . . . **TCEMS 1313**

5.01 BLUES.
Tracks: / Broken friend / Someday we'll know / Sea of hearbreak / If you want to be my woman / Somewhere down the line / Losin' in Las Vegas / Wouldn't that be something / Better love next time / Thousand lies ago, A / 5.01 blues.
LP: **4651841**
MC: **4651844**

AMBER WAVES OF GRAIN.
Tracks: / Amber waves of grain / Tulare dust / Mama tried the farmer's daughter / Okie from Muskogee / I wish things were simple / Working man's blues / Always late with your kisses / American waltz.
LP: . . . . **EPC 26811**
MC: **40 26811**

BACK TO THE BAR ROOMS.
Tracks: / Misery and gin / Back to the bar rooms again / Make-up and faded blue jeans / Ever changing woman / Easy come easy go / I don't want to sober up tonight / Can't break the habit / Out paths may never cross / I don't have any more love songs / Leonard / I think I'll just stay here and drink.
LP: . . . . **MCF 3089**

BEST OF MERLE HAGGARD, THE.
LP: **1A 220 1583354**

BIG CITY.
Tracks: / Big city / My favourite memory / Good old American guest / I think I'm gonna live forever / This song is mine / Stop the world / Are the good times really over / You don't have very far to go / I always get lucky with you / Texas fiddle song.
LP: . . . . **EPC 85303**

BRANDED MAN.
Tracks: / My friends are gonna be strangers / Swinging doors / Bottle let me down, The / I'm a lonesome fugitive / I threw away the rose / Branded man / Sing me back home / Legend of Bonnie and Clyde, The / Mama tried / I take a lot of pride in what I am / Hungry eyes / Working man blues / Okie from Muskogee / Street singer / Jesus take a hold / I can't be myself / Sidewalks of Chicago / Soldier's last letter / Someday we'll look back / Here comes the freedom train.
LP: . . . . **EG 2605291**
MC: . . . . **EG 2605294**

CAPITOL COUNTRY CLASSICS.
Tracks: / Fightin' side of me, The / Daddy Frank / Carolyn / Grandma Harp / It's not love but it's not bad / I wonder if they ever think of me / Everybody had the blues / If we can make it through December / Things aren't funny anymore / Old man from the mountain / Kentucky gambler / Always wanting you / Movin' on / It's all in the movies / Roots of my raising / Cherokee maiden.
LP: . . . . **CAPS 1034**
MC: . . . . **TCCAPS 1034**

CHILL FACTOR.
Tracks: / Chill factor / Twinkle, twinkle lucky star / Man from another time / We never touch at all / You babe / Thanking the good Lord / After dark / 1929 / Thirty again / I don't have any love around / More than this old heart can take.
LP: **4607831**
MC: **4607834**

COUNTRY LEGEND.
MC: . . . . **PLAC 358**

COUNTRY STORE: MERLE HAGGARD.
Tracks: / There, I've said it again / Poncho and Lefty / I think I'm gonna live forever / Are the good times really over / That's the way love goes / Still water runs the deepest / Silver eagle / Yesterday's wine / Big city / You take me for granted / For all I know / I'm gonna plant me a bed of roses / Going where the lonely go / Natural high / Old flames (Only on CD.) / To all the girls I've loved before (Only on CD.) / Stop the world (Only on CD.) / Okie from Muskogee (Only on CD.).
LP: . . . . **CST 15**
MC: . . . . **CSTK 15**

EPIC COLLECTION (RECORDED LIVE).
Tracks: / Honky tonk night time man / Old man of the mountain, The / Holding things together / Sing a sad song / Every fool has a rainbow / Blue yodel no. 2 (My lovin' gal Lucille) / Trouble in mind / Things aren't funny anymore / Strangers / I always get lucky with you / Working man blues.
LP: . . . . **EPC 25806**
MC: **40 25806**

FAMILY BIBLE, THE.
MC: **4XL 9290**

FRIEND OF CALIFORNIA, A.
LP: **26876**
MC: **40 26876**

GOING WHERE THE LONELY GO.
Tracks: / Going where the lonely go / Why am I drinkin / If I left it up to you / I won't give up my train / Someday you're gonna need your friends again / Shopping for dresses / You take me for granted / Half a man / For all I know / Nobody's darlin but mine.
LP: . . . . **EPC 25024**

GREATEST HITS:MERLE HAGGARD.
Tracks: / I think I'll just stay here and drink / I'm always on a mountain when I fall / Red bandana / Way I am, The / It's been a great afternoon / Ramblin' fever / Misery and gin / My own kind of hat / If were not back in love by Monday / Rainbow stew.
LP: . . . . **IMCA 5386**

HEART TO HEART (Haggard, Merle & Leona Williams).
Tracks: / Heart to heart / Let's pretend we're married tonight / You can't break the chains of love / Waltz across Texas / We're strangers again / Waitin' on the good life to come / Don't ever let your lover sleep alone / It's cold in California / I'll never be free / Sally let your bangs hang down.
LP: . . . . **MERL 29**
MC: . . . . **MERLC 29**

I'M A LONESOME FUGITIVE.
Tracks: / I'm a lonesome fugitive / All of me belongs to you / House of memories / Life in prison / Whatever happened to me / Drink up and be somebody / Someone told my story / If you want to be my woman / Mary's mine / Skid Row / My rough and rowdy ways / Mixed up mess of a heart.
LP: . . . . **SEE 49**
MC: . . . . **SEEK 49**

I'M ALWAYS ON A MOUNTAIN WHEN I FALL.
Tracks: / I'm always on a mountain when I fall / It's been a great afternoon / Love me when you can / There won't be another now / Don't you ever get tired (of hurting me) / Life of a rodeo cowboy / There ain't no good chain gang / Dream, The / Immigrant, The / Mama I've to go to Memphis.
LP: . . . . **MCF 2848**

IT'S ALL IN THE GAME.
Tracks: / Let's chase each other around the room / Place to fall apart / It's all in the game / Lonely little hotel room / I never go home anymore / All I want to do is sing my song / Natural high / Thank heaven for little girls / To all the girls I've loved before / You nearly lose your mind.
LP: . . . . **EPC 26071**

IT'S ALL IN THE MOVIES.
Tracks: / It's all in the movies / Nothing's worse than comes / After loving you / Stingeree / I know an ending when it comes / This is the song we sing / Living with the shades pulled down / Hag's Dixie blues / Let's stop pretending / Cotton patch blues / Seeker, The.
LP: . . . . **ST 11483**

JUST BETWEEN THE TWO OF US (See under Owens, Bonnie) (Haggard, Merle & Bonnie Owens).

KERN RIVER.
Tracks: / Kern River / Old flames / There, I've said it again / You don't love me anymore / Natural high / Big butter and egg man / Ridin' high / There's somebody else on your mind / I wonder where I'll find you at tonight / There won't be another now / Old watermill.
MC: **40 26432**

LAND OF MANY CHURCHES, THE (Haggard, Merle/Carter Family).
2LP: . . . . **HAT 3097/8**
MCSET: . . . . **HATC 3097/8**

LEGEND OF BONNIE AND CLYDE, THE.
LP: . . . . **HAT 3075**
MC: . . . . **HATC 3075**

LEGENDARY, THE.
MC: **4XL 8354**

MERLE HAGGARD (I love country).
Tracks: / Place to fall apart, A / Someday when things are good / Stop the world / Big city / Kern River / Reasons to quit / Natural high / Yesterday's wine / My favourite memory.
LP: . . . . **CBS 54944**
LP: . . . . **EPC 54944**
MC: **40 54944**

MERLE HAGGARD COLLECTION, THE.
Tracks: / Cherokee maiden / Roots of my raising / It's all in the movies / Movin'

on / Always wanting you / Kentucky gambler / Old man from the mountain / Things aren't funny anymore / If we make it through December / Everybody's had the blues / I wonder if they ever think of me / It's not love (but it's not bad) / Grandma Harp / Carolyn.
MC: . . . . **KNMC 13058**

MERLE HAGGARD SINGS COUNTRY FAVOURITES.
Tracks: / She thinks I still care / Mom and dad's waltz / Making believe / Moanin' the blues / Lovesick blues / Blues stay away from me / You've still got a place in my heart / Right or wrong / Mule skinner blues / Green green grass of home / Folsom Prison blues / Walking the floor over you / Son of Hickory Holler's tramp, The / Long black limousine / San Antonio rose / Take me back to Tulsa / Waiting for a train / This cold war / Little ole wine drinker me / Today I started loving you again.
LP: . . . . **EMS 1253**
MC: . . . . **TCEMS 1253**

MY FAREWELL TO ELVIS.
LP: . . . . **IMCA 924**

OKIE FROM MUSKOGEE - LIVE.
Tracks: / Opening introduction and theme / Mama tried / No hard times / Silver wings / Swinging doors / I'm a lonesome fugative / Sing me back home / Branded man / In the arms of love / Workin' man blues / Introduction to "Hobo Bill" / Hobo Bill's last ride / Billy overcame his size / If I had left it up to you / White line fever / Blue rock / Okie from Muskogee.
LP: . . . . **ST 384**

PONCHO AND LEFTY.
Tracks: / Poncho and Lefty / It's my last day / My Mary / Half a man / No reason to quit / Still water runs the deepest / M 4 life's been a pleasure / All the soft places to fall / Opportunity to cry.
LP: . . . . **EPC 85754**
MC: **40 85754**

PRIDE IN WHAT I AM (Haggard, Merle & the Strangers).
Tracks: / I take a lot of pride in what I am / Who'll buy the wine / Day the rains came, The / It meant goodbye to me when you said hello to him / I can't hold myself in line / I'm bringin' home good news / Keep me from cryin' today / I just want to look at you one more time / Somewhere on skid row / I'm free / California blues / I think we're livin' in the good old days.
LP: . . . . **SKAO 168**

RAINBOW STEW.
Tracks: / Misery and gin / I think I'll just stay here and drink / Back to the bar rooms again / Our paths may never cross / Running kind, The / I'm a lonesome fugitive / Rainbow stew / Blue yodel no. 9 (Standing on the corner) / Dealing with the devil / Fiddle breakdown / Sing me back home.
MC: . . . . **MCFC 3131**
LP: . . . . **MCF 3131**

RAMBLIN' FEVER.
Tracks: / Ramblin' fever / When my blue moon turns to gold again / Ghost story / Set me free / Love somebody to death / If we're not back in love by Monday / I think it's gone forever / Ain't your memory got no pride at all / My love for you / Last letter, The.
LP: . . . . **MCA 2267**

SALUTES THE GREATS.
Tracks: / Way it was in '51, The / Moanin' the blues / My heart would know / Lovesick blues / I saw the light / San Antonio rose / Take me back to Tulsa / Brain cloudy blues / Right or wrong / Stay a little longer / Mule skinner blues / My rough and rowdy ways / Waitin' for a train / Peach picking time down in Georgia / Train whistle blues / Mom and dad's waltz / It meant goodbye to me when you said hello to him / I'm an old old man (tryin' to live while I can) / I never go around mirrors / Goodbye lefty.
2LP: . . . . **SLB 8137**

SERVING 190 PROOF.
Tracks: / Footlights / Got lonely too early this morning / Heaven was a drink of wine / Driftwood / I can't get away / Red bandana / My own kind of hat / I must have done something bad / I didn't mean to love you / Sing a family song / Roses in winter.
LP: . . . . **MCL 1608**
MC: . . . . **MCLC 1608**
LP: . . . . **MCF 3002**

SING ME BACK HOME.
Tracks: / Sing me back home / I'm a lonesome fugitive / Where does the good times go / Green green grass of home.
MC: **4XL 9028**

SONGS FOR THE MAMA THAT TRIED.
Tracks: / When God comes and gathers his jewels / Supper time / He walks with me / Softly and tenderly / Why me / Where no one stands alone / One day at a time / What a friend we have in Jesus / Swing low sweet chariot / Old rugged cross, The / Keep on the sunny side.
LP: . . . . **IMCA 5250**

SONGWRITER.
Tracks: / Footlights / It's been a great afternoon / My own kind of hat / Life's just not the way it used to be / I think I'll just stay here and drink / Ramblin' fever / Make up and faded blue jeans / Red bandana / From Graceland to the promise land / Rainbow stew.
LP: . . . . **IMCA 5698**

STRANGERS.
LP: . . . . **HAT 3133**
MC: . . . . **HATC 3133**

SWINGING DOOR.
Tracks: / Swinging doors / If I could be him / Longer you wait, The / I'll look over you / I can't stand me / Girl turned ripe, The / Bottle let me down, The / No more you and me / Someone else you've known / High on a hilltop / This town ain't big enough for the both of us / Shade tree.
LP: . . . . **SEE 68**

TASTE OF YESTERDAY'S WINE, A (Haggard, Merle & George Jones).
Tracks: / Yesterday's wine / After I sing all my songs / I think I've found a way (to life without you) / Brothers / Mobile Bay / C.C. Waterback / Silver Eagle must've been drunk / I haven't found her yet / No show Jones.
LP: . . . . **EPC 25012**
MC: **40 25012**
LP: . . . . **SHM 3177**
MC: . . . . **HSC 3177**

THAT'S THE WAY LOVE GOES.
Tracks: / What am I gonna do / Bed of roses / Someday when things are good / That's the way love goes / Carryin' fire / Don't seem like we've been together all our lives / If you hated me / Love will find you / Last boat of the day / I think I'll stay.
LP: . . . . **EPC 25573**

TO ALL THE GIRLS I'VE LOVED BEFORE.
Tracks: / My favourite memory / Reasons to quit / You take me for granted / That's the way love goes / Are all good times really over / Big city / Poncho and Lefty / What am I gonna do / Old flames / Going where the lonely go / Let's chase each other around the room / Natural high / Place to fall apart, A / To all the girls I've loved before / It's all in the game / Stop the world.
LP: . . . . **PMP 1003**
MC: . . . . **PMPK 1003**

WALKING THE LINE (Haggard, Merle, George Jones, Willie Nelson).
Tracks: / I gotta get drunk / No show Jones / Pancho & Lefty / Yesterday's wine / Half a man / Big butter and egg man / Heaven or hell / Midnight rider / Are the good times really over / Drunk can't be a man, A.
LP: **4505761**
MC: **4505764**

Haggart, Bob

MAXINE SULLIVAN WITH THE BOB HAGGART QUINTET (See Maxine Sullivan) (Haggart, Bob/Maxine Sullivan).

PORTRAIT OF BIX, A.
LP: . . . . **J 149**

WORLDS GREATEST JAZZ BANDS (See under Lawson, Yank) (Haggart, Bob & Yank Lawson).

Haggart, Lawson

1951/52 (Haggart, Lawson Jazz Band).
LP: . . . . **M 8040**

Hague, Mel

MEL HAGUE LIVE.
Tracks: / Ruby don't take your love to town / Please don't bury me / Everything big in Texas / Good hearted woman / Dreaming my dreams / Boy named Sue, A / I wore out my knees loving you / You're the only good thing / Fifteen beers ago / Give my love to Rose / Old Joe / Another night's done and gone / Little ole wine drinker me.
LP: . . . . **LKLP 6364**

MERRY GO ROUND.
LP: . . . . **LKLP 6558**

OLD GRAVEL BOOTS.
Tracks: / Door is always open, The / Running close behind you / Please remind me / I think I'm being taken for a ride / Couple more years, A / I'm gonna be a truck / Long haired country boy / If I needed you / I read it in rolling stone / Groover, The / Nothing to say.
LP: . . . . **LKLP 6270**

WINNER, THE.
LP: . . . . **LKLP 6023**

Hahn, Jerry

JERRY HAHN QUINTET (Hahn, Jerry Quintet).
LP: . . . . **ARHOOLIE 8006**

Haider, Hans

LAUTARRE MAL 2.
LP: . . . . **EULP 1016**

RENAISANCE AND BAROCK.
LP: . . . . **EULP 1028**

Haider, Joe

JOE HAIDER.
LP: . . . . **CAL 30 618**

Haig, Al

BE BOP KEYBOARD MASTERS (See Be-bop Keyboard Masters).

EXPRESSLY ELLINGTON (Haig, Al Quartet).
Tracks: / Just squeeze me / Body and soul / I let a song go out of my heart / Lush life / Perdido / I got it bad and that ain't good / Flamingo / Sophisticated lady.
LP: . . . . **SPJ LP 20**

INVITATION (Haig, Al Trio).
Tracks: / Holy Land / Enigma / Invitation / Sawbo City blues / If you could see me now / Sambalhasa / Daydream / Linear.
LP: . . . . **AH 4**

JAZZ WILL-O'-THE-WISP (Haig, Al Trio).
LP: . . . . **FS 197**

MANHATTAN MEMORIES (Haig, Al Trio & Quartet).
LP: . . . . **SB 1008**

MEETS THE MASTER SAXES, VOL 1.
Tracks: / Light grey / Stoned / Matter and mind / Toup, The / Shawn / Hot halavah / Bopel-ground / Cobblestones / Prelude to a kiss / Boppin' in B flat / Man with a horn / Sophisticated lady / Rifftide / Stuffy.
LP: . . . . **SPJ 139**

MEETS THE MASTER SAXES, VOL 2.
Tracks: / Pardon my bop, 1, 2, 3 / As I live and I bop / Interlude on bebop / Diaper pin / Diaper pin 2 / Frosty / Deedle / In the merry land of bop / Pogo stick / Alleytalk / Way you look tonight / If love is trouble / Hee haw / Laughing boy.
LP: . . . . **SPJ 140**

MEETS THE MASTER SAXES, VOL 3.
Tracks: / Donna Lee / East of the sun / Sweet miss / Long Island sound / Medicine man / Passport to Pimlico / T'ain't no use / Sinbad the tailor / Haig 'n' Haig / Always / Bopelbaby / Talk a little bop.
LP: . . . . **SPJ 143**

PIANO INTERPRETATIONS.
LP: . . . . **SB 1001**

PORTRAIT OF BUD POWELL, A.
LP: . . . . **IP 7707**

QUINTET OF THE YEAR REVISITED.
Tracks: / Birk's works / I mean you / Bag's groove / Epistrophy / Lover man / Night in Tunisia.
LP: . . . . **SPJ LP 23**

SERENDIPITY.
LP: . . . . **IP 7713**

SOLITAIRE.
Tracks: / Lament / Joanne / Summertime / Bess, you is my woman now / In your own sweet way / Never let me go / Here's that rainy day / Don't you know I care.
LP: . . . . **SPJ LP 14**

SPECIAL BREW (Haig, Al & Jimmy Raney 4).
Tracks: / Freedom jazz dance / We'll be together / Marmaduke / Dolphin dance / Blues for Alice / Shaw 'nuff / Don't you know I care / Just friends.
LP: . . . . **SPJ LP 8**

STABLEMATES (Haig, Al & Jon Eardley).
Tracks: / Tangerine / Speak low / Round midnight / Love walked in / Embraceable you / Don't blame me.
LP: . . . . **SPJ LP 11**

Haig, Paul

EUROPEAN SUN.
Tracks: / Running away / Chance / Justice / Swinging for you / Shining hour / Fear and dancing / Psycho San Jose / Ghost rider / Torchomatic / Executioner, The / Painless song.
LP: . . . . **TWI 829**

PAUL HAIG.
Tracks: / Something good / True blue / Communication / Swinging for you / Time of her time / Faithless / Times can change / Turn the vision / Sooner or later / Chained / Ideal of living (Only on CD.).
LP: . . . . **CIRCA 7**
MC: . . . . **CIRC 7**

RHYTHM OF LIFE.
Tracks: / Adoration / Stolen love / In the world / Justice / Blue for you / Never give up / Work together / Heaven sent / Don't rush in.
LP: . . . . **ILPS 9742**
MC: . . . . **ICT 9742**

SENSE OF FUN.
LP: . . . . **LPOPA 003**

WARP OF PURE FUN, THE.
LP: . . . . **TWI 669**

Haigh, Robert

THREE SEASONS ONLY (Haigh, Robert & Sema).
LP: . . . . **LR 102**

VALENTINE.
LP: . . . . **UD 026**

Hail Variety

HAIL VARIETY various artists (Various artists).
LP: . . . . **HRH 4**
MC: . . . . **ZCHRH 4**

Hailey, Arthur & John

FLIGHT INTO DANGER (Albert, Edward).
MCSET: . . . . **LFP 7290**

Hailwood, Mike

MY TWELVE T.T. WINS.
LP: . . . . **SSLP 580**

Hain, Kit

SCHOOL FOR SPIES.
LP: . . . . **MERS 32**
MC: . . . . **MERSC 32**

SPIRITS WALKING OUT.
Tracks: / Force grown / I'm the one who's with you / Uninvited guests / Aaron awaking again / Look for you / Danny / Spirits walking out / Parting would be painless / You are the one.
LP: . . . . **SML 1122**
MC: . . . . **KSCM 1122**

Haines, Alan

KING ARTHUR AND HIS KNIGHTS.
MC: . . . . **TS 334**

Haines, Denis

LISTENING PRINCIPLE, THE.
Tracks: / Curtain / Home and away / Softly the morning comes / Isolation / Over the wall / Strangelands / Take me home / Creation / Curtain (reprise).
LP: . . . . **KNEWL 03**
MC: . . . . **KNEWMC 03**

Hair

HAIR (London cast) (Various artists).
Tracks: / Aquarius: *Edward, Vince & The Company* / Donna: *Tobias, Oliver & The Company* / Sodomy: *Feast,* Michael & The Company / Coloured spade: *Straker, Peter & The Company* / Ain't got no: *Feast, Michael/Peter Straker/ Joanne* White/The Company / Air: *Kendrick, Linda & The Company* / I got life: *Nicholas, Paul & The Company* / Hair: *Nicholas, Paul/Oliver Tobias/The Company* / My conviction: *Forray, Andy* / Easy to be hard: *Leventon, Annabel* / Frank Mills: *Kristina, Sonja* / Where do I go?: *Nicholas, Paul & The Company* / Electric blues: *Gulliver,* John/Rohan McCullough/Andy Forray/Jimmy Winston / Black boys: *Kelly, Colette/ Rohan McCullough/Lucy Fenwick* / White boys: *Hunt, Marsha/Ethel Coley/ Joanne White* / Walking in space: *Company* / Able baby: *Straker, Peter/ Limbert* Spencer/Leighton Robinson / Three five zero zero: *Company* / What a piece of work is man: *Edward, Vince & Leighton* Robinson / Good morning, starshine: *Various artists* / Bed, The: *Company* / Let the sun shine in: *Various artists.*
LP: **583 043**
LP: **2459361**

HAIR (Various artists).
Tracks: / Hair: *Various artists* / Sodomy: *Various artists* / I got life: *Various artists* / Aquarius: *Various artists* / Let the sun shine in: *Various artists* / Where do I go: *Various artists* / Frank Mills: *Various artists* / Donna: *Various artists* / Coloured spade: *Various artists* / Black boys: *Various artists* / White boys: *Various artists* / My conviction: *Various artists.*
LP: . . . . **BD 3008**

HAIR (Original Broadway cast) (Various artists).
Tracks: / Aquarius: *Various artists* / Donna: *Various artists* / Hashish: *Various artists* / Sodomy: *Various artists* / Coloured spade: *Various artists* / Manchester, England: *Various artists* / I'm black: *Various artists* / Ain't got no: *Various artists* / Air: *Various artists* / Initials: *Various artists*/ I got life: *Various artists* / Hair: *Various artists* / My conviction: *Various artists* / Don't put it

down: *Various artists* / Frank Mills: *Various artists* / Be in: *Various artists* / Where did I go?: *Various artists* / Black boys: *Various artists* / White boys: *Various artists* / Easy to be hard: *Various artists* / Walking in space: *Various artists* / Abie baby: *Various artists* / Three five zero zero: *Various* artists / What a piece of work is man: *Various artists* / Good morning starshine: *Various artists* / Flesh failures (let the sunshine in): *Various artists.*
LP: BL 89084
MC: BK 89084
LP: SF 7959

HAIR (Film soundtrack) (Various artists).
Tracks: / Aquarius: *Various artists* / Sodomy: *Various artists* / Donna: *Various artists* / Hashish: *Various artists* / Coloured spade: *Various artists* / Manchester, England: *Various artists* / Abie baby: *Various artists* / Fourscore: *Various artists* / I'm black: *Various artists* / Ain't got no air: *Various* artists / Party music: *Various artists* / My conviction: *Various artists* / I got life: *Various artists*/ Frank Mills: *Various artists* / Hair: *Various artists* / L.J.B: *Various artists* / Hare Krishna: *Various* artists / Electric blues: *Various artists* / Old fashioned melody: *Various artists* / Where do I go: *Various* artists / Black boys: *Various artists* / White boys: *Various artists* / Walking in space: *Various artists*/ Easy to be hard: *Various artists* / 3-5-0-0: *Various artists* / Good morning starshine: *Various artists*/ What a piece of work is man: *Various artists* / Somebodyto love: *Various artists* / Don't put it down: *Various artists* / Flesh failures: *Various artists* / Let the sun shine in: *Various artists.*
2LP: BL 83274
MCSET: BK 83274

HAIR (Original Off Broadway Cast) (Various artists).
Tracks: / Ain't got no....I got life: *Various artists* / Air: *Various artists* / Going down: *Various artists*/ Hair: *Various artists* / Dead end: *Various artists* / Frank Mills: *Various artists* / Hare Krishna: *Various artists* / Where do I go: *Various artists* / Electric blues: *Various artists* / Easy to be hard: *Various artists* / Manchester: *Various artists* / White boys black boys: *Various artists* / Walking in space: *Various artists* / Aquarius: *Various artists* / Good morning starshine: *Various artists* / Exanplanetooch: *Various artists* / Climax: *Various artists.*
LP: INTS 1133

Hair Disco ...

DISCO SPECTACULAR (Various artists).
Tracks: / Aquarius: *Various artists* / Let the sun shine in: *Various artists* / Where do I go: *Various artists*/ Easy to be hard: *Various artists* / Good morning starshine: *Various artists.*
LP: PL 13356
MC: PK 13356

Haircut 100

PAINT AND PAINT.
Tracks: / Fish in a bowl / Immaterial / So tired / Hidden years / 40-40 home / High noon / Too up too down / Benefit of the doubt / Prime time / Where do you run to now / Infatuation.
LP: HCLP 1

PELICAN WEST.
Tracks: / Favourite shirts (boy meets girl) / Love plus one / Lemon firebrigade / Marine boy / Milk film / Kingsize / Fantastic day / Baked beans / Snow girl / Love's got me in triangles / Surprise me again / Calling Captain Autumn.
LP: HCC 100
MC: TCHC 100
LP: FA 413092-1
MC: TCFA 41 30924

Hairspray

HAIRSPRAY (Film soundtrack) (Various artists).
Tracks: / Hairspray: *Sweet, Rachel* / Madison time, The: *Bryant, Ray* / I'm blue (the gong-gong song): *Ikettes*/ Mama didn't lie: *Bradley, Jan* / Town without pity: *Pitney, Gene* / Roach, The: *Gene & Wendell* / Foot stompin': *Flares* / Shake a tail feather: *Five Du-Tones* / Bug, The: *Dallman, Jerry/Knightcaps* / You'll lose a good thing: *Lynn, Barbara* / I wish I were a...: *March, Peggy* / Nothing takes the place of you: *McCall, Toussaint.*
LP: IMCA 6228
MC: IMCAC 6228

Hairston, Curtis

CURTIS HAIRSTON.
Tracks: / Chillin' out / Let's make love tonight / You're my shining star / Hold on (for me) / All we have is love / Take charge / Morning after, the / Let me change your mind.

LP: 781 693-1
MC: 781 693-4

Haiti

FOLK MUSIC FROM HAITI (Various artists).
LP: LLST 7340
MC: LLCT 7340

KONBIT: BURNING RHYTHMS OF HAITI (Various artists).
Tracks: / Rit komesyal (commercial rhythm): *Various artists* / Libete (liberty): *Magnum Bond* / Rebati kay-la (rebuild the house): *Various artists* / San nou ki la (my blood): *Neville Brothers* / Ayiti pa fore (Haiti is not a forest): *Various artists* / Vaksine (vaccinate): *Sanba Yo* / Mario, Mario: *Various artists* / Raraman: *Various artists* / Konbit (working together): *Neville Brothers/Les Freres Pa* / Tchoul No 3 (The kept man No. 3): *Various artists.*
LP: AMA 5281
MC: AMC 5281

MERINGUES AND FOLK BALLADS OF HAITI.
LP: LLST 3740

RITUAL DRUMS OF HAITI Voodoo trance magic (Various artists).
LP: LLST 7279
MC: LLCT 7297

TOTO BISSAINTHE CHANTE HAITI (Benait, Marie-Claude/Miriam Matheus).
Tracks: / Soley danmbalab / Papaloko / Ibo ogoun / Papadanmbalah / Lamize pa dous / Dey / Rasanbleman.
LP: ARN 33380
MC: ARN 433380

Hakim, Omar

RHYTHM DEEP.
Tracks: / Crucial 2 groove / Rhythm deep / Real side, The / Love is here to stay / Tears / Isolated lonely / Take my heart / Amethyst secrets / Angel delight / Constructive criticism / Sun always shines / Mystic's glance.
LP: GRP 95851
MC: GRP 95854

Hakim, Sadik

CRUCIAL TO GROOVE.
LP: A 4007
MC: C 4007

SONNY STITT MEETS SADIK HAKIM (See Stitt, Sonny) (Hakim, Sadik & Sonny Stitt).

Hakon Graf

HIDEAWAY.
MC: SRLP 107C

Haland, Bjoro

MY NASHVILLE ALBUM.
Tracks: / Catfish John / Storms never last / Nickels and dimes / If I can't have all of you / Just call me lonesome / Arizona whiz, The / Some day my day will come / I'll go somewhere and sing my song again / What can I do to get me back on your mind / I've already loved you in my mind / Am I that easy to forget.
LP: KLP 26
MC: ZCKLP 26

TO MY FRIENDS.
Tracks: / Kissed by the rain and warmed by the sun / Little miracle, A / Please change your mind / Little ole dime / Forget me not / Am I losing you / Country is / Blue eyes crying in the rain / Some broken hearts never mend / Love or something like it / Talking walls, The / One day at a time.
LP: KLP 20
MC: ZCKLP 20

Halcox, Pat All Stars

SEVENTH AVENUE.
Tracks: / Flinstones / Blue and sentimental / I'm gonna lock my heart / China boy / I wanna little girl / What's the racket / Jeepers creepers / You took advantage of me / Three for the blues / Dusk.
LP: PLJ 002

Halcyon Dance

MY BLUE HEAVEN.
LP: HAL 10

Hale, Binnie

GOLDEN AGE OF BINNIE HALE AND BOBBIE HOWES (Hale, Binnie & Bobby Howes).
LP: GX 412542-1
MC: GX 412542-4

Hale, Corky

CORKY HALE PLAYS GERSHWIN AND DUKE.
LP: GNPS 9035

HARP BEAT.
Tracks: / Nothing higher / Paradise / Roof garden / So much in love / Up in smoke / I'm the one / Yesterdays / Best thing.

LP: AFF 150
MC: TCAFF 150

Hale, Jo Jo

OUT THE OTHER SIDE.
LP: OAK 005
MC: OAK 005 C

Hale, Richard

TOGETHER (Hale, Richard and Maureen Hart).
LP: KLP 48
MC: CKLP 48

Hale, Willie Beaver

BEAVER FEVER.
Tracks: / Thank you for my life / Don't get tired of me / I feel like crying / Party times / Groove on / Katy / Pearl.
LP: TKR 83392

Haley, Alex

TELLS THE STORY OF HIS SEARCH FOR ROOTS.
2LP: K 66057

Haley, Bill

6 TRACK HITS (Haley, Bill & The Comets).
Tracks: / Whole lotta shakin' goin' on / Rock around the clock / Shake, rattle and roll / Kansas city / Me and Bobby McGee / Rip it up.
MC: 7SC 5012

20 GOLDEN PIECES: BILL HALEY (Haley, Bill & The Comets).
Tracks: / Saints rock 'n' roll / Razzle dazzle / Blue comet blues / Skokiaan / Shake, rattle and roll / ABC boogie / See you later alligator / Rip it up / Caravana a go-go / Whole lotta shakin' goin' on / How many? / Land of a thousand dances / Skinny Minnie / Harlem nocturne / Justine / Seventh son / Mohair Sam / New Orleans / High heel sneakers / Rock around the clock.
LP: BDL 2002

20 GREATEST HITS: BILL HALEY & HIS COMETS (Haley, Bill & The Comets).
Tracks: / Rock around the clock / See you later alligator / Shake, rattle and roll / Johnny B. Goode / Lucille.
LP: FUN 9013
MC: FUNC 9013

20 GREATEST HITS: BILL HALEY & THE COMETS (Haley, Bill & The Comets).
Tracks: / Rock around the clock / Shake, rattle and roll / Kansas city / Razzle dazzle / Guitar boogie / Rip it up / See you later alligator.
LP: 2636741
MC: 2636744

BEST OF BILL HALEY (Haley, Bill & The Comets).
MC: 16-5

BIGGEST HITS (Haley, Bill & The Comets).
MC: ZCSNB 9945

BILL HALEY & HIS COMETS (Haley, Bill & The Comets).
MC: ZCGAS 747

BILL HALEY & HIS COMETS (Haley, Bill & The Comets).
Tracks: / Rock around the clock / Fool such as I, A / I got a woman / Goofin' around / Miss you / Rockin' rollin' rover / Calling all comets / Don't knock the rock / Shake, rattle and roll / Forty cups of coffee / Dinah / ABC boogie / Tonights the night / Razzle dazzle / Birth of the boogie / R-O-C-K / Rip it up / Dim, dim the lights / Two hound dogs / Mary Mary Lou / Burn that candle / Thirteen women / Vive la rock and roll / Rockin' through the rye / It's a sin / Billy Goat / Blue comet blues / Hot dog buddy buddy / Move it on over / See you later alligator.
MCSET: CRT 015

BILL HALEY RARITIES.
LP: A 98100

BOOGIE WITH BILL (Haley, Bill & The Comets).
Tracks: / See you later alligator / ABC boogie / Altar of love / Don't mess around with my love / Helena / I've got news for you / Rock around the clock / Panic / Wobble, The / This is goodbye / Train of sin / Skokiaan.
LP: TOP 114
MC: KTOP 114

COLLECTION: BILL HALEY (20 rock 'n' roll greats).
Tracks: / Rock around the clock / Shake, rattle and roll / Mambo rock / Rockin' rollin' rover / Teenager's mother / Razzle dazzle / Don't knock the rock / Saints rock 'n' roll / Rip it up / Hot dog Buddy Buddy / ABC boogie / R-O-C-K / Forty cups of coffee / Rockin' through the rye / See you later alligator / You hit the wrong note, billy goat / Rock-a-beatin' boogie / Burn that candle / Rudy's rock / Thirteen women.

LP: DVLP 2069
MC: DVMC 2069

ELVIS PRESLEY WITH BILL HALEY (See under Presley, Elvis) (Haley, Bill & Elvis Presley).

EVERYONE CAN ROCK 'N' ROLL (ALBUM) (Haley, Bill & The Comets).
Tracks: / Hail, hail rock'n'roll / Jim Dandy / That's how I got to Memphis / Juke box cannonball / Let the good times roll again / God bless rock 'n' roll / Everyone can rock'n'roll / Battle of New Orleans / I need the music / Heartaches by the number / Tweedle Dee / So right tonight.
LP: SNTF 808

GOLDEN COUNTRY ORIGINS.
Tracks: / Yodel your blues away / Rovin' eyes / Rose of my heart / Yodeller's lullaby / Candy and women / Foolish question / Covered wagon rolled right along, The / Wreck on the highway / Behind the eight ball / My mom heard me crying / Within this broken heart of mine / Cotton haired gal.
LP: ROL 1300

GOLDEN GREATS: BILL HALEY.
Tracks: / Rock around the clock / Shake, rattle and roll / See you later alligator / Rock-a-beatin' boogie / Rip it up / Forty cups of coffee / Two hound dogs / Rudy's rock / Thirteen women / Saints rock 'n' roll / Don't knock the rock / Mambo rock / Corina Corina / Calling all Comets / Skinny Minnie / Rockin' through the rye / ABC boogie / Razzle dazzle / R-O-C-K / Burn that candle.
LP: MCM 5004
MC: MCMC 5004

GOLDEN HITS (Haley, Bill & The Comets).
Tracks: / Rock around the clock / Burn that candle / Forty cups of coffee / Two hound dogs / Rudy's rock / Shake, rattle and roll / Rip it up / Rock-a-beatin' boogie / Thirteen women / Saints rock 'n' roll / See you later alligator / Don't knock the rock / Mambo rock / Corina Corina / Calling all Comets / Skinny Minnie / Rockin' through the rye / ABC boogie / Razzle Dazzle / R-O-C-K.
LP: MCL 1778
MC: MCLC 1778

GOLDEN HITS/ROCK AROUND THE CLOCK.
Tracks: / Rock around the clock / Shake, rattle and roll / ABC boogie / You hit the wrong note Billy goat / Thirteen women / Tonight's the night / Razzle dazzle / Two hound dogs / Dim dim the lights / Happy baby / Birth of the boogie / Rockin' rollin' rover / Mambo rock / Hide and seek / Rock-a-beatin' boogie / Burn that candle / Forty cups of coffee / Rudy's rock / Rip it up / Saints rock 'n' roll / See you later alligator / Don't knock the rock.
MCSET: MCA 2 118

GREATEST HITS: BILL HALEY & THE COMETS (Haley, Bill & The Comets).
Tracks: / Rock this joint tonite / Rock-a-beatin' boogie / Skinny Minnie / Razzle dazzle / Rudy's rock / See you later alligator / When the saints go marching in / Framed / Shake, rattle and roll / Rip it up / Crazy man crazy / Rock around the clock.
LP: 2459 413
MC: 3192 626

HIER BIN ICH- HIER BLEIB ICH... UND ABENDS IN DIE SCALA Original film music (see Valente, Caterina/Bill Haley) (Various artists).

HILLBILLY HALEY.
Tracks: / Within this broken heart of mine / Wreck on the highway / Behind the eight ball / Life of the party / I should write a song about you / My mom heard me crying / My dream / Red river valley / Yodeller's lullaby / Yodel your blues away / This is the thanks I get / Cold cold heart / Boquet of roses / All I need is some more loving / Covered wagon rolled right along, The / Rose of my heart / Cotton haired gal / Candy and women / Rovin' eyes / Foolish questions.
LP: ROLL 2007

JUST ROCK AND ROLL.
Tracks: / I'm walking / High heel sneakers / Blue suede shoes / Tossin' and turnin' / Flip, flop and fly / Whole lotta shakin' goin' on / C.C. rider / Lawdy Miss Clawdy / Bring it on home to me / Personality / Crazy man crazy / Rock and roll music.
LP: SNTF 645

KINGS OF ROCK (see under Kings of ...) (Haley, Bill & Fats Domino).

LIVE IN SWEDEN (Haley, Bill & The Comets).
MC: ZCSND 9989

MR. ROCKIN' ROLLIN' (Essential Bill Haley, The) (Haley, Bill & The Comets).

Tracks: / Rock around the clock / Thirteen women / Shake, rattle and roll / ABC boogie / Mambo rock / Razzle dazzle / R-O-C-K / Rock-a-beatin' boogie / Saints rock 'n' roll / Burn that candle / See you later alligator / Rudy's rock / Hot dog buddy buddy / Rockin' through the rye / Teenager's mother / Rip it up / Don't knock the rock / Forty cups of coffee / You hit the wrong note Billy goat / Rockin' rollin' rover / Beak "speaks", The / Move it one over / Rock the joint / Skinny Minnie / Lean Jean / Joey's song / Whoa Mabel / Ooh look-a-there, ain't she pretty / Skokiaan / Green door / Yeah, she's evil / How many?.
2LP: . . . . CDX 5
MC: . . . . TCCDX 5

ORIGINAL HITS 1954-57 (Haley, Bill & The Comets).
Tracks: / Rock around the clock / Rock the joint / Saints rock 'n' roll / Mambo rock / Rockin' rollin' rover / Don't knock the rock / Calling all Comets / Rockin' through the rye / Choo choo ch' boogie / Razzle dazzle / Rudy's rock / Hot dog buddy buddy / Rocking little tune / R-O-C-K.
LP: . . . . SHM 3207
MC: . . . . HSC 3207

RIP IT UP, ROCK'N'ROLL (Haley, Bill & The Comets).
Tracks: / Rock around the clock / Saints rock'n'roll / You hit the wrong note billy goat / Goofin' around / Thirteen women (and only one man in town) / Caldonia / Shake, rattle and roll / Choo choo ch' boogie / Burn that candle / Happy baby / Hook, line and sinker / Rock Lomond / See you later alligator / Mambo rock / Dim, dim the lights / Lean Jean / Tonight's the night / Calling all Comets / Rip it up / Hide and seek / Mary Lou / Teenage mothers / Move it on over / Vive la rock'n'roll.
2LP: . . . . VSOPLP 116
MC: . . . . VSOPMC 116

R-O-C-K (Haley, Bill & The Comets).
Tracks: / Ooh, look-a-there ain't she pretty? / Dim dim the lights / Burn that candle / R-O-C-K / I got a woman / Farewell, so long, goodbye / ABC boogie / I'll be true / Dance with a dolly / Mohair Sam.
LP: . . . . SNTF 710

ROCK AND ROLL (Haley, Bill & The Comets).
LP: . . . . GNPS 2077
MC: GNP5 2077

ROCK AROUND THE CLOCK.
Tracks: / Rock around the clock / Shake, rattle and roll / Saints rock 'n' roll / Love letters in the sand / Rock the joint / Flip flop and fly / Ling-ting-tong / Skinny Minnie / See you later alligator / Rock-a-beatin' boogie / Johnny B. Goode.
LP: . . . . AR 30049
MC: . . . . ORC 006
LP: . . . . SPR 8502
MC: . . . . SPC 8502
LP: . . . . AH 13
LP: . . . . MCL 1617

ROCK AROUND THE CLOCK (IMPORT) (Haley, Bill & The Comets).
Tracks: / See you later alligator / Rock-beatin' boogie / Shake, rattle and roll / Johnny B. Goode / Skinny Minnie.
MC: 511548.5

ROCK AROUND THE CLOCK (JOKER) (Haley, Bill & The Comets).
LP: . . . . SM 3869

ROCK AROUND THE CLOCK/SEE YOU LATER ALLIGATOR.
LP: . . . . BHEP 0001

ROCK AROUND THE COUNTRY (Haley, Bill & The Comets).
LP: . . . . GNPS 2097

ROCK 'N' ROLL GREATS (Haley, Bill & The Comets).
Tracks: / Shake, rattle and roll / Rock around the clock / Mambo rock / Rock-a-beatin' boogie / Don't knock the rock / Hot dog Buddy Buddy / Rock the joint / Saints rock 'n' roll / See you later alligator / Rockin' through the rye / Razzle dazzle / Rip it up / Skinny Minnie / Lean Jean / Thirteen women / Choo choo ch' boogie.
LP: . . . . MFP 5807
MC: . . . . TCMFP 5807

ROCK 'N' ROLL STAGE SHOW (Haley, Bill & The Comets).
Tracks: / Calling all Comets / Rockin' through the rye / Rocking little tune / Hide and seek / Hey then, there now / Goofin' around / Hook, line and sinker / Rudy's rock / Choo choo ch' boogie / Blue Comet blues / Hot dog Buddy Buddy / Tonight's the night.
LP: . . . . CR 30221
LP: . . . . LAT 8139

ROCK THE JOINT (Haley, Bill & The Comets).
Tracks: / Rocket 88 / Tearstains on my heart / Green tree boogie / Jukebox cannonball / Sundown boogie / Icy heart / Rock the joint / Dance with a dolly / Rockin' chair on the moon / Stop beatin' around the mulberry bush / Real rock drive / Crazy man crazy / What cha' gonna do / Pat-a-cake / Fractured / Live it up / Farewell, so long, goodbye / I'll be true / Ten little Indians / Chattanooga choo choo / Straight jacket / Yes indeed.
LP: . . . . ROLL 2009
LP: . . . . ROLL 2002

ROCKIN' ROLLIN' BILL HALEY (Haley, Bill & The Comets).
Tracks: / Rock around the clock / Thirteen women / Shake, rattle and roll / ABC boogie / Happy baby / Dim dim the lights / Birth of the boogie / Mambo rock / Two hound dogs / Razzle dazzle / R-O-C-K / Rock-a-beatin' boogie / Saints rock 'n' roll / Burn that candle / See you later alligator / Paper boy, The / Goofin' around / Rudy's rock / Hide and seek / Hey then, there now / Tonight's the night / Hook, line and sinker / Blue Comet blues / Calling all Comets / Choo choo ch' boogie / Rocking little tune / Hot dog Buddy Buddy / Rockin' through the rye / Teenager's mother / Rip it up / Don't knock the rock / Forty cups of coffee / Miss you / You hit the wrong note, billy goat / Rockin' rollin' rover / Please don't talk about me when I'm gone / You can't stop me from dreaming / I'm gonna sit right down and write myself a letter / Rock Lomond / Is it true what they say about Dixie? / Carolina in the morning / Dipsy doodle, The / Ain't misbehavin' / Beak "speaks", The / Moon over Miami / One sweet letter from you / I'll be with you in apple blossom time / Somebody else is taking my place / How many? / Move it on over / Rock the joint / Me rock a hula / Rockin' Rita / Jamaica D.J. / Piccadilly rock / Pretty alouette / Rockin' rollin' schnitzlebank / Rockin' Matilda / Vive la rock 'n' roll / It's a sin / Mary Mary-Lou / El rocko / Come rock with me / Oriental rock / Woodenshoe rock / Walkin' beat, The / Skinny Minnie / Sway with me / Lean Jean / Don't nobody move / Joey's song / Chiquita Linda / Dinah / Ida, sweet as apple cider / Whoa Mabel! / Marie / Eloise / Corina, Corina / B.B. Betty / Sweet Sue / Charmaine / Dragon rock / ABC rock / Catwalk, The / I got a woman / Fool such as I, A / By by me / Where did you stay last night? / Caldonia / Shaky / Ooh, look-a-there, ain't she pretty? / Summer souvenir / Puerto Rican peddlar / Music, music, music / Skokiaan / Drowsy waters / Two shadows / In a little Spanish town / Strictly instrumental / Mack the knife / Green door / Yeah, she's evil.
LPS: . . . . BFX 15068/5

SCRAPBOOK (Haley, Bill & The Comets).
Tracks: / Rock the joint / Rock-a-beatin' boogie / Skinny Minnie / Razzle dazzle / Rudy's rock / See you later alligator / Saints rock 'n' roll / Framed / Shake, rattle and roll / Rip it up / Crazy man crazy / Rock around the clock.
LP: 252261-1
MC: 252261-4

SEE YOU LATER ALLIGATOR (Haley, Bill & The Comets).
MC: 301372

TRIBUTE TO BILL HALEY (Haley, Bill & The Comets).
Tracks: / Shake, rattle and roll / See you later alligator / Mambo rock / Burn that candle / Birth of the boogie / Rock Lomond / Rock-a-beatin' boogie / Beat speaks, The / Hot dog buddy buddy / R-O-C-K / Dim dim the lights / Saints rock 'n' roll / Razzle dazzle / Rockin' through the rye / Rip it up / Teenager's mother / Rudy's rock / Billy goat / Rock the joint / Skinny Minnie / Forty cups of coffee / Lean Jean / Don't knock the rock / Rock around the clock.
LP: . . . . MCL 1770
MC: . . . . MCLC 1770

TWISTIN' KNIGHTS AT THE ROUND TABLE (Haley, Bill & The Comets).
Tracks: / Lullaby of Birdland twist / Twist Marie / One two three twist / Down by the riverside twist / Queen of the twisters / Caravan twist / I want a little girl / Whistlin' and walkin' twist / Florida twist / Eight more miles to Louisville.
LP: . . . . N 5012

Haley, Ed

PARKERSBURG LANDING.
LP: . . . . ROUNDER 1010

Half A Sixpence

HALF A SIXPENCE (Original London cast) (Various artists).
Tracks: / Overture: *Various artists* / All in the cause of ecomony: *Various artists* / Half a sixpence: *Various* artists / Money to burn: *Various artists* / Oak and the ash, The: *Various artists* / She's too far above me: *Various artists* / I'm not talking to you: *Various artists* / If the rain's got to fall: *Various artists*/ Old military canal, The: *Various artists* / One that's run away, The: *Various artists* / Long ago: *Various* artists / Flash, bang, wallop: *Various artists* / I know what I am: *Various artists* / I'll build a palace: *Various artists* / I only want a little house: *Various artists* / Finale: *Various artists*.
LP: . . . . TER 1041
MC: . . . . ZCTER 1041

HALF A SIXPENCE (ORIGINAL ISSUE) (London cast) (Various artists).
LP: . . . . LK 4521

Half Japanese

BAND WHO WOULD BE KING, THE.
LP: . . . . HALF 8 1
MC: . . . . HALF 8 4

CHARMED LIFE.
LP: . . . . NML 8815

HALF GENTLEMEN, NOT BEASTS.
Tracks: / No direct line from my brain to my heart / 10th Avenue freeze out / Ta sheri ta ta / My girlfriend lives like a beatnik / Her parents came home / Girls like that / No more Beatlemania / Tangled up in blue / Patti Smith / School of love / Jodi Foster / Shy around girls.
LP: . . . . ABOX 1

HORRIBLE.
LP: . . . . P 2005

LOUD.
LP: . . . . ARM 7

OUR SOLAR SYSTEM.
LP: . . . . IRID K-6

SING NO EVIL.
LP: . . . . IRID K-110

VELVET MONKEYS.
MC: . . . . KC 002

Half Man Half Biscuit

BACK AGAIN IN THE DHSS.
Tracks: / Best things in life are free, The / D'ye Ken Ted Moult / Reasons to be miserable (Part Ten) / Rod Hull is alive - Why? / Dickie Davies eyes / Bastard son of Dean Friedman, The / I was a teenage armchair supporter / Fan / Arthur's farm / All I want for Xmas is a Dukla Prague away kit / Trumpton riots.
LP: . . . . PROBE 8
MC: . . . . PROBE 8C

BACK IN THE D.H.S.S..
LP: . . . . PROBE 4

Half Moon Street

HALF MOON STREET (Film soundtrack) (Various artists).
LP: . . . . A 282
MC: . . . . C 282

Half Pint

CAN'T YOU WAIT TILL I GET YOU HOME.
LP: . . . . PHLP 014

DO IT (See under Levy, Barrington) (Half Pint & Barrington Levy).

GREETINGS.
Tracks: / Brother love / Greetings / Living is hard / Heartbreaker / Loving / Don't close the door / Sounds of reality / Jah don't love that.
LP: . . . . PHLP 21

IN FINE STYLE.
LP: . . . . Unknown

MONEY MAN SKANK.
LP: . . . . Unknown

ONE IN A MILLION.
Tracks: / One in a million / One big ghetto / You lick me first / What more can I really do / Milky way / Mr. Landlord / Roots man / Pick your choice / Puchie Lou / Tell me little girl.
LP: . . . . GREL 74
MC: . . . . GREEN 74

VICTORY.
Tracks: / Victory / Level the vibes / Come alive / Night life lady / She's mine / Desperate lover / Cost of living / When one gone / Mama / She's gone.
LP: . . . . RAS 3031
MC: . . . . RASC 3031

Halfway House

HALFWAY HOUSE ORCHESTRA 1925/8, THE.
LP: . . . . VLP 19

HALFWAY HOUSE ORCHESTRA & NEW ORLEANS OWLS - VOL.2 (Halfway House Orchestra & New Orleans Owls).
LP: . . . . VLP 22

Halfway to Eddies

FLESH, BLOOD AND LINOLEUM.
LP: . . . . PROBE 027

Halibuts

GNARLY.
LP: KIX4U 3341
LP: . . . . ROCK 3341

Hall, Adelaide

ADELAIDE HALL (Live at the Riverside Studios).
LP: . . . . MES 7080
MC: . . . . ZCVIR 8312

HALL OF MEMORIES (1927-39).
LP: . . . . CHD 169
MC: . . . . MCHD 169

THERE GOES THAT SONG AGAIN.
Tracks: / There goes that song again / How did he look? / This can't be love / My devotion / It's always you / T'aint what you do (it's the way that you do it) / Translantic lullaby / I promise you / I wanna be loved / Drummer boy / That's the moon my son / Missouri scrambler / My heart tells me / Pennsylvania polka / Infatuation / You are my sunshine / Kindergarten conga / Two pairs of shoes / You're wrong / Tzigane swing / I've got a gal in Kalamazoo / Sweetheart it's you / Victory roll rag / Our back street is Broadway / Sailor with the navy blue eyes / Singing with rig.
LP: . . . . RFL 3

Hall, Andrew

TALK OF THE TOWN (Hall, Andrew, Society Jazz Band Of New Orleans).
LP: 802

Hall, Audrey

DYNAMIC DUO, THE (Hall, Audrey & Don Evans).
LP: . . . . TRLS 229

EIGHT LITTLE NOTES.
Tracks: / Eight little notes.
LP: . . . . DG 11985

JUST YOU JUST ME.
LP: . . . . DGLP 3

Hall, Big John

CELEBRATION OF PRAISE.
LP: . . . . PC 34

IF GOD IS DEAD.
Tracks: / Something worth living for / It's in your hands / Had it not been / Reach out for Jesus / If God is dead / Thank God I'm free / He touched me / Old rugged cross made the difference, The / Whisper his name / Follow me / It doesn't matter where you come from / We are family / Look to Jesus / Healing medley / Praise medley.
LP: . . . . PC 817

LIFE IN JESUS' NAME.
LP: . . . . PC 12

Hall, Bob

JAMMIN' THE BOOGIE (see Green, George) (Hall, Bob & George Green).

ROLL AND SLIDE (Hall, Bob & Dave Peabody).
LP: . . . . AP 044

SURVIVORS (Hall, Bob & Dave Kelley).
LP: . . . . AP 001

Hall Brothers Jazzband

FIZZ WATER 25TH ANNIVERSARY.
LP: . . . . SOS 1062

WAITING AT THE END OF THE ROAD.
LP: . . . . SOS 1031

Hall, Daryl

SACRED SONGS.
Tracks: / Sacred songs / Something in 4/4 time / Babs and babs / Urban landscape / Nycny / Further away I am, The / Why was it so easy / Don't leave me alone with her / Survive / Without tears.
LP: . . . . NL 83573
LP: . . . . PL 13573

THREE HEARTS IN THE HAPPY ENDING MACHINE.
Tracks: / Dreamtime / Only a vision / I wasn't born yesterday / Someone like you / Next step / For you / Foolish pride / Right as rain / Let it out / What's gonna happen to us?.
LP: . . . . PL 87196
MC: . . . . PK 87196
LP: . . . . NL 90088
MC: . . . . NK 90088

Hall, Ed

LOVE SPOKE HERE.
Tracks: / Pay for me / Millionaire's house / Cornbull / Hearty Tom Foolery / Buddah / Sam Jackson / Ollie Ollie / Blue Poland / Turkee yell / Car talk / Go to sleep / Gilbert.
LP: . . . . TUPLP 015

Hall, Edmond

AT CLUB HANGOVER, 1954.
Tracks: / St. Louis blues / Sweet and lovely / Keeping out of mischief / Basin Street blues / Dardanella.

LP: . . . . SLP 253

COMMODORE CLASSICS (see under Ryan, Jimmy) (Hall, Edmond/Jimmy Ryan/Wilbur De Paris).

EDMOND HALL.
LP: . . . . LPJT 30

EDMOND HALL AT CLUB HANGOVER.
LP: . . . . SLP 4009

EDMOND HALL QUARTET (Hall, Edmund Quartet).
LP: . . . . SLP 190

ROMPIN' IN '44 (Hall, Edmond & His Swing Quartet).
LP: . . . . CLP 52

TAKE IT, EDMOND HALL, WITH YOUR CLARINET.
Tracks: / K.K. boogie / Ol' man river / Indiana / Royal Garden blues / I got rhythm / P-flat swing / Lady be good / It's been so long / I can't believe that you're in love with me / Big city blues / Steamin' and beamin' / At the ball / Walking the dog / Blues, The.
LP: . . . . QU 020

THIS IS JAZZ VOL.3.
LP: . . . . SLP 4069

TWO OF A KIND (Hall, Edmond Quartet & Teddy Wilson).
LP: 6.25893

Hall, Frieda

PHANTOM FINGERS OF FRIEDA HALL.
Tracks: / Zigeunerweisen Airs Bohemens / Moon river / Flight of the bumble bee / Jesu, joy of man's desiring / Famous marches / Snee waltz, The / Arrival of the Queen of Sheba, The / Amazing Grace / Stars and stripes forever / Volunteer organist, The / Auf wiedersehen.
LP: . . . . LK/LP 6255

Hall, Gary

GARAGE HEART (Hall, Gary & The Stormkeepers).
MC: . . . . RRAMC 0010
LP: . . . . RRALP 0010

WINTER TIME ALREADY (Hall, Gary & The Stormkeepers).
LP: . . . . CHOOG 001

Hall, George

GEORGE HALL, 1937.
Tracks: / It's easy to remember / Caravan / 52nd Street / Tea for two / Blue skies / I can't break the habit of you / Scattin' at the Kit Kat / Satan take a holiday / Dipsy doodle / Midnight in a madhouse / Have you got any castles, baby / Two dukes on a pier / You and me that used to be, The / Dallas blues / Snake charmer, The / It looks like rain in Cherry Blossom Lane / Gandy dancer.
LP: . . . . HSR 144

Hall, G.P.

MOVEMENTS.
Tracks: / Manifestations / Harbinger / Vanguard / Adagio manifestations / Preparation / Channel / Boundaries / Largo manifestations / Bride / Charmouth / Paradoxes, The / Inventory / Andante manifestations / Arch, The / Steps / Bottecelli hymn / Harrier / Adagio erriad / Forerunner / Affirmation / Attunement / Elemental / Denizen / Enigma / Message, The / Mirror.
LP: . . . . KNEWL 04
MC: . . . . KNEWMC 04

Hall, Henry

GOLDEN AGE OF HENRY HALL, THE.
Tracks: / Music goes round and around, The / Little man you've had a busy day / Man on the flying trapeze, The / Play to me, gypsy / Underneath the arches / I like bananas because they have no bones / Butterflies in the rain / Just an echo in the valley / Music hath charms / Wheezy Anna / Did you ever see a dream walking? / Oh Johanna / Rusty and dusty / Somewhere at sea / It's a sin to tell a lie / Here's to the next time.
LP: . . . . GX 41 2517-1

HELP YOURSELF TO HAPPINESS (Hall, Henry and The BBC Dance Orchestra).
Tracks: / Help yourself to happiness / You, just wonderful you / Moon / Singing in the moonlight / Love is the sweetest thing / Maree / Always in my heart / Nobody else but Elsie / Living in the hay / Turning of the tide / Hazel eyes / Clouds will soon roll by, The / Bahama mama / Wanderer / Marching along together / How can you say no? / My extraordinary gal / Downhearted / Same old Moon / Keep your last goodnight for me.
LP: . . . . SVL 156
MC: . . . . CSVL 156

HENRY HALL & BBC DANCE ORCHESTRA (Hall, Henry & BBC Dance Orchestra).
Tracks: / Five-fifteen / Have you ever been lonely / Goody goody / Wagon wheels / Waltz in swingtime / Mine for keeps / Sun has got his hat on / Wild ride / It's just the time for dancing / Elephant never forgets / I'm putting all my eggs in one basket / Teddy bear's picnic / Life begins when you're in love / I heard a song in a taxi / One, two, button your shoe / It's time to say goodnight / Here's to the next time.
MC: . . . . TC SH 140
LP: . . . . SH 140
LP: . . . . SH 172
LP: . . . . JOY 298

HERE'S TO THE NEXT TIME (Hall, Henry and The BBC Dance Orchestra).
Tracks: / I cover the waterfront / Did my heart beat, did I fall in love? / Making conversation / I've told every little star / Dance little lady / It's the talk of the town / You've got me crying again / Aloha-oe / Learn to croon / Maybe I love you too much / Blue cloud / Moonstruck / Moon song / Let's all sing like the birdies sing / Marching along together / Five-fifteen.
LP: . . . . JOYD 283

LOVE IS THE SWEETEST THING.
2LP: . . . . SVLD 002
MC: . . . . CSVLD 002

MY DANCE.
LP: . . . . BUR 009
MC: . . . . 4 BUR 009

SEEIN' IS BELIEVIN' (Hall, Henry & His Orchestra).
Tracks: / Seein' is believin' / My dance / Every now and then / Magic / Chasing shadows / Music goes 'round and around, The / Love is a dancing thing / Broken record, The / Life begins when you're in love / We say the sea / Got a bran' new suit / I'm putting all my eggs in one basket / Goody goody / All my life / When I'm with you / Oh my goodness / Waltz in swing time / Bye, bye baby / One, two, button your shoe / Goona goo, The.
LP: . . . . SVL 193
MC: . . . . CSVL 193

SPIN A LITTLE WEB.
Tracks: / Gold diggers of 1933 / Very thought of you, The / Got to dance my way to heaven / Red sails in the sunset / When the morning rolls around again / Experiment / They laughed / Don't let your love go wrong / Getting sentimental / Night and day.
LP: . . . . SCS D-03

THIS IS HENRY HALL (Hall, Henry & The BBC Dance Orchestra).
Tracks: / It's just the time for dancing / Five-fifteen / I cover the waterfront / Here's to the next time / Lullaby of the leaves / Leave the pretty girls alone / Keep it to yourself / Talk of the town / Making conversation / It's time to say goodbye / East wind / I was in the mood / Three of us, The / Love thy neighbour / Carolina / Sweetmeat Joe, the candyman / Olga Pullofski, the beautiful spy / Many happy returns / Just little bits and pieces / Misty island of the Highlands / When the guardsman started crooning on parade / Broken record, The / Saddle your blues to a wild mustang / Buffoon / Apple blossoms / There's a goldmine in the sky / Under the double eagle / You took the words right out of my heart / Miss Annabelle Lee / Bye bye blackbird / Hi-diddle-diddle / Silver on the sage / Highland swing / Blue skies are round the corner / One man went to blow / If ever a heart was in the right place.
2LP: . . . . SHB 48

TRIBUTE TO HENRY HALL, A (Hall, Henry & The BBC Dance Orchestra).
Tracks: / Thank you Mr. Bach / I'm feeling happy / Honey coloured moon / In my heart of hearts / There's no time like the present / Merry-go-round broke down, The / What will I tell my heart / Big ship / Song without words / Seein' is believin' / Music hath charms / Just little bits and pieces / Everything's in rhythm with my heart / Many happy returns / Say the word and it's yours / Le touquet / With my eyes wide open I'm dreaming / Moonstruck.
LP: . . . . JOYD 298

WHAT A PERFECT COMBINATION (Hall, Henry & His BBC Dance Orchestra).
Tracks: / Twenty million people / In a little second hand store / Day you came along, The / Thanks / Thats another Scottish story / Roaming / On a steamer over / I'll string along with you / Little valley in the mountains / Love in bloom / With my eyes wide open, I'm dreaming / How's chances? / What a perfect combination / In the moonlight / My darling / Just so you'll remember.
LP: . . . . SVL 178
MC: . . . . CSVL 178

Hall, Herb

FESSOR'S NIGHTHAWKS (See under Cheatham, Doc) (Cheatham, Doc/John Williams/Herb Hall).

OLD TYME MODERN (Hall, Herb Quartet).
Tracks: / Old-fashioned love / All of me / Buddy Bolden's blues / Crying my heart out for you / Swinging down Shaw's Hall / Beale Street blues / How come you do me like you do? / Willow weep for me / Do you know what it means to miss New Orleans? / Sweet Georgia Brown.
LP: 3003

Hall, Jennifer

FORTUNE AND MENS' EYES.
Tracks: / Danger men at work / Luke / February / No good / Ice cream days / Car wash / Atlas / Cat walking / Dance with me / Mastery.
LP: 925628 1
MC: 925628 4

Hall, Jim

ALL ACROSS THE CITY (Hall, Jim Quartet).
Tracks: / Beija flor / Young one (for Debra) / All across the city / Something tells me / Prelude to a kiss / How deep is the ocean / Bemsha swing / R.E.M. State / Drop shot / Big blues / Jane.
LP: . . . . CJ 384
MC: . . . . CJ 384C

CIRCLES.
LP: . . . . CJ 161

CONCIERTO.
Tracks: / Two's blues / Answer is yes / Concierto de Aranjuez / You'd be so nice to come home to.
LP: . . . . CTI 9020

FIRST EDITION (see Shearing, George) (Hall, Jim & George Shearing).

INTERMODULATION (See under Evans, Bill) (Hall, Jim/Bill Evans).

JIM HALL & RED MITCHELL (Hall, Jim & Red Mitchell).
LP: . . . . AH 5

JIM HALL'S THREE (Hall, Jim Trio).
Tracks: / Hide and seek / Skylark / Bottlenose blues / And I do / All the things you are / Poor butterfly / Three.
LP: . . . . CJ 298

LIVE AT VILLAGE WEST (see Carter, Ron).

POWER OF THREE (VIDEO) (See under Petrucciani, Michel) (Petrucciani, Michel/Wayne Shorter/Jim Hall).

TELEPHONE (see Carter, Ron).

THESE ROOMS (Hall, Jim Trio).
Tracks: / With a song in my heart / Cross court / Something tells me / Bimini / All too soon / These rooms / Darn that dream / My funny valentine / Where or when / From now on.
MC: . . . . CC 24

UNDERCURRENT (See under Evans, Bill) (Hall, Jim/Bill Evans).

Hall, Juanita

SINGS THE BLUES.
LP: . . . . FS 133

Hall, Kenny

KENNY HALL & THE SWEETS MILL STRING BAND, VOL 2 (Hall, Kenny & The Sweets Mill String Band).
LP: . . . . BAY 103

KENNY HALL & THE SWEETS MILL STRING BAND, VOL 1 (Hall, Kenny & The Sweets Mill String Band).
LP: . . . . BAY 727

Hall, Lani

BLUSH.
Tracks: / Where's your angel / In the dark / Come what may / Love me again / No strings / Ain't got nothin' for me / Wish I would've stayed / Only you / I don't you to go.
LP: . . . . AMLH 64829

COLLECTABLES.
Tracks: / Midnight lovers / Never say never again / Come what may / Send in the clowns / We could be flying / Nobody gets this close to me / Rio / Come down in time / I don't want you to go / How can I tell you.
LP: . . . . AMLX 64988

DOUBLE OR NOTHING.
Tracks: / Nobody gets this close to me / Shot in the dark / Meni devol / To the morning / Sailing without a sail / Double or nothing / Sunshine after the rain / To know / So long / Magic garden.
LP: . . . . AMLH 64760

Hall, Mike

ANOTHER OPENING, ANOTHER SHOW.
Tracks: / Birth of the blues / You're the cream in my coffee / Over the rainbow / I got rhythm / Cara mia / Sweet Georgia Brown / All of me / Peg o' my heart / I'm just wild about Harry / Sheik of Araby, The / My heart belongs to Daddy.
MC: . . . . AC 196

HALL OF MEMORIES.
Tracks: / Granada / Little things mean a lot / Britannia rag / Ivor Novello selection / Buttons and bows / Bye bye blues / That old feeling / Am I wasting my time on you / How deep is the ocean / Charleston / Baby face / When the red, red robin comes bob, bob, bobbin' along / Bye bye blackbird / More and more / Maybe / Pagan love song / So what's new / Five foot two / My blue Heaven / I'm looking over a four leaf clover (signature tune).
MC: . . . . AC 202

ONCE IN A WHILE.
Tracks: / Once in a while / Zing went the strings of my heart / You'll never know / Ponciana / Summertime / I won't send roses / Brazil / Come prima / Louisana samba / Way we were (The) / Music, music, music / Once in a lifetime.
MC: . . . . AC 174

SOUTHERN NIGHTS.
Tracks: / Southern nights / Winter wonderland / It's only a paper moon / You made me love you / Mack the knife / Crimond / Get me to the church on time / People / On Green Dolphin Street / Easter parade / Mr. Wonderful / Caravan.
MC: . . . . AC 201

Hall & Oates

20 CLASSIC TRACKS: HALL & OATES.
Tracks: / Lot of changes coming, A / In honour of a lady / Deeo river blues / Reason why, The / If that's what makes you happy / Provider, The / They needed each other / Angelina / I'll be by perkiomen / Past times behind / Everyday's a lovely day / Rose come home / Flo gene / Seventy / I'm really smokin' / Christine / Over the mountain / Lemon road / Truly good song, A.
LP: . . . . SMT 006
MC: . . . . SMTC 006

ABANDONED LUNCHEONETTE.
Tracks: / When the morning comes / Had I known you better then / Las Vegas turnaround / Stewardess song, The / She's gone / I'm just a kid (Don't make me feel like a man) / Abandoned luncheonette / Lady rain / Laughing boy / Everytime I look at you.
LP: . . . . K 40534
MC: K4 40534

ALONG THE RED LEDGE.
Tracks: / It's a laugh / Melody for a memory / Last time, The / I don't wanna lose you / Have I been away too long / Alley Katz / Don't blame it on love / Serious music / Pleasure beach / August day.
LP: . . . . INTS 5258
LP: . . . . NL 84231
MC: . . . . NK 84231

BEAUTY ON A BACK STREET.
Tracks: / Don't change / Why do lovers break each other's heart? / Winged Bill / Girl who used to be, The / Emptiness, The / Love hurts, love heals / You must be good for something / Bigger than both of us / Bad habits and infections.
LP: . . . . NL 82300
LP: . . . . PL 12300
MC: . . . . PK 12300

BIG BAM BOOM.
Tracks: / Dance on your knees / Some things are better left unsaid / Out of touch / Method of modern love / Bank on your love / Going through the motions / Cold dark and yesterday / All American girl / Possession obsession.
LP: . . . . PL 85309
MC: . . . . PK 85309

BIGGER THAN BOTH OF US.
Tracks: / Back together again / Crazy eyes / London, luck and love / You'll never learn / Room to breathe / Do what you want, be what you are / Kerry / Rich girl / Falling.
LP: . . . . INTS 5088
LP: APL1 1467
MC: . . . . PK 11740
LP: . . . . NL 83866

CHANGE OF SEASON.
Tracks: / So close / Starting all over again / Sometimes a mind changes / Change of seasons / Ain't gonna take it this time / Everywhere I look / Give it up / Don't hold back your love / Halfway there / Only love / Heavy rain / So close (Un-plugged).

LP: 210548
MC: 410548

DARYL HALL & JOHN OATES.
Tracks: / Lot of changes comin', A / In honour of a lady / Deep river blues / Reason why, The / If that's what makes you happy / Provider, The / They needed each other / Angelina / I'll be by / Perkiomen / Past times behind.
LP: .... B 90137

DARYL HALL & JOHN OATES.
Tracks: / Camellia / Alone too long / Out of me out of you / Nothing at all / Gino / It doesn't matter anymore / Ennui on the mountain / Grounds for separation / Soldering / Sara smile.
LP: .... NL 81144
MC: .... NK 81144
LP: .... INTS 5010

EARLY YEARS, THE.
Tracks: / Reason why, The / Lot of changes comin', A / In honour of a lady / Deep river blues / If that's what makes you happy / Provider, The / They needed each other / Angelina / I'll be by / Perkiomen / Past times behind.
LP: .... SHLP 134
MC: .... SHTC 134

FIRST SESSIONS.
LP: 2215012
MC: 2115012

HALL AND OATES.
Tracks: / Camellia / Sara smile / Alone too long / Out of me, out of you / Nothing at all / Gino (the manager) / (You know) it doesn't matter anymore / Ennui on the mountain / Grounds for separation / Soldering.
LP: APL1 1144
MC: .... PK 11701

HALL & OATES COLLECTION, THE.
Tracks: / Kiss on my list / It's a laugh / She's gone / Rich girl.
LP: .... STAR 104

LIVE AT THE APOLLO.
Tracks: / Get ready / Ain't too proud to beg / Way you do the things you do, The / When something is wrong with my baby / Every time you go away / I can't go for that / One by one / Possession obsession / Adult education.
LP: .... PL 87035
MC: .... PK 87035

LIVE TIME.
Tracks: / Rich girl / Emptiness / Do what you want, be what you are / I'm just a kid / Sara smile / Abandoned luncheonette / Room to breathe.
LP: .... INTS 5252
LP: .... PL 12802
MC: .... PK 12802

NO GOODBYES.
Tracks: / It's uncanny / I want to know you / For a long time / Can't stop the music / Love you like a brother / Las Vegas turnaround / She's gone / Lilly (are you happy?) / When the morning comes / Beanie G and the rose tattoo / 70's scenario.
LP: .... K 50347

OOH YEAH.
Tracks: / Downtown life / I'm in pieces / Talking all night / Rocket to God / Real love / Everything your heart desires / Missed opportunity / Rockability / Soul love / Keep on pushin' love.
LP: 208985
MC: 408985

PAST TIMES BEHIND.
Tracks: / Lot of changes comin', A / In honour of a lady / Deep river blues / Reason why, The / If that's what makes you happy / Provider, The / They needed each other / Angelina / I'll be by / Perkiomen / Past times behind.
LP: .... CHL 547

PRIVATE EYES.
Tracks: / Private Eyes / Looking for a good sign / I can't go for that / Mano a Mano / Did it in a minute / Head above water / Tell me what you want / Friday let me down / Unguarded minute / Your imagination / Some men.
LP: .... NL 90079
MC: .... NK 90079
LP: .... RCALP 6001

PROVIDER, THE.
Tracks: / Lot of changes comin', A / In honour of a lady / Deep river blues / Reason why, The / If thats what makes you happy / Provider, The / They needed each other / Angelina / I'll be by / Perkiomen.
LP: .... THBM 003
MC: .... THBMC 003

REALLY SMOKIN'.
Tracks: / Past times behind / Everyday's a lovely day / Rose come home / Flo gene / Seventy / I'm really smokin' / Christine / Over the mountain / Lemon road / Truly good song, A.
LP: .... THBL 035

ROCK 'N' SOUL PART 1.
Tracks: / Sara smile / She's gone / Rich girl / Kiss in my list / You make my dreams / Private eyes / I can't go for that / Maneater / One on one / Wait for me / Say it isn't so / Adult education.
LP: .... PL 84858
MC: .... PK 84858

VOICES.
Tracks: / How does it feel to be back / Big kids / I hear the voices / Hard to be in love with you / Kiss on my list / Gotta lotta nerve / You've lost that lovin' feeling / You make my dreams / Diddy doo wop / Everytime you go away / Africa.
LP: .... NL 90078
MC: .... NK 90078
LP: .... PL 13646

WAR BABIES.
Tracks: / Can't stop the music / He played it much too long / Is it a star / Beanie G and the rose tattoo / You're much too soon / 70's scenario / War baby son of Zorro / I'm watching you / Better watch your back / Screaming through December / Johnny Gore & the C eaters.
LP: .... K 50086

WHOLE OATS.
Tracks: / I'm sorry / All our love / Georgie / Fall in Philadelphia / Waterwheel / Lazy man / Goodnight and good morning / They needed each other / Southeast city window / Thank you for... / Lilly (are you happy).
LP: .... K 50306

X-STATIC.
Tracks: / Woman comes and goes, The / Wait for me / Portable radio / All you want is heaven / Who said the world was fair / Running from paradise / Number one / Bebop / Drop / Hallofon / Intravino.
LP: .... NTS 5152
LP: .... NL 84303
MC: .... NK 84303

Hall, Pam

PERFIDIA.
LP: .... WENLP 3032
LP: .... TRLS 239

SUPPLY AND DEMAND (Hall, Pam Mark).
LP: .... RRA R 0007
MC: .... RRA C 0007

Hall, Randy

I BELONG TO YOU.
Tracks: / I've been watching you / Real man, A / I belong to you / Gentleman, A / Older woman, younger man / Feel my eyes / Glamour boys / She's my little star / I want to touch you.
LP: .... MCF 3236
MC: .... MCFC 3236

Hall, Robin

HIGHLANDS & LOWLANDS (See McGregor, Jimmy) (Hall, Robin & Jimmy MacGregor).

TWO HEIDS ARE BETTER THAN YIN (Hall, Robin & Jimmy MacGregor).
Tracks: / Johnnie lad / Hares on the mountain / Inverary / 42nd, The / My love she's but a lassie yet / Mormond braes / Two heids are better than yin / Cuttie's waddin' / Ye banks and braes / Glasgow street song medley / Mick Maguire / Davey Fae / Recruiting sergeant, The / Wild mountain thyme / Gin I were where the gaudie rins / Ould triangle, The / Ca' the yowes / Three craws.
LP: .... BDL 1019

Hall, Roy

BOOGIE ROCKABILLY.
LP: .... R&C 1008

DIGGIN' THE BOOGIE.
Tracks: / Whole lotta shakin' goin' on / All by myself / Christine / Don't stop now / See you later alligator / Blue suede shoes / Diggin' the boogie / You ruined my blue suede shoes / Offbeat boogie / Move on / Luscious / Three alley cats / My girl & his girl.
LP: .... CR 30227

HANK 'N THE HOUND.
LP: .... R&C 1014

Hall, Tom T.

CLASSIC TOM T. HALL.
Tracks: / I washed my face in the morning dew / Ballad of forty dollars / Homecoming / Week in a country jail, A / Salute to a switchblade / Year that Clayton Delaney died, The / Me and Jesus / Old dogs, children and watermelon wine / Ravishing Ruby / I love / That song is driving me crazy / Country is / Faster horses / Your man loves you honey / Fox on the run / P.S. I love you.
LP: .... PRICE 104
MC: .... PRIMC 104

COUNTRY STORE:TOM T. HALL.
Tracks: / Shoeshine man / I like beer / Negatory romance / Senior citizen star / I wish I loved somebody else / There is a miracle in you / Jesus on the radio, Daddy on the phone / I care / Deal / It's all in the game / May the force be with you always / What have you got to lose / Old side of town, The / Son of Clayton Delaney.
LP: .... CST 48
MC: .... CSTK 48

EVERYTHING FROM JESUS TO JACK DANIELS.
LP: .... MERL 31

GREATEST HITS: TOM T. HALL.
Tracks: / Homecoming / Shoeshine man / I miss a lot of trains / Salute to a switchblade / I washed my face in the morning dew / Ballad of forty dollars / Year that Clayton Delaney died, The / That's how I got to Memphis / Week in a country jail, A / One hundred children / Me and Jesus.
LP: .... SR 61369

GREATEST HITS: TOM T. HALL VOL.2.
Tracks: / Countryside I love / Little lady preacher, The / Sneaky snake / I like beer / Ravishing Ruby / Old dogs, children and watermelon wine / Deal / Who's gonna feed them hogs / That song is driving me crazy / I care.
LP: .... SRM 11044

GREATEST HITS: TOM T. HALL VOL 3.
Tracks: / It's all in the game / Faster horses / I can't dance / Fastest rabbit dog in Carter Country today, The / Pinto the wonder horse is dead / Hang them all / Your man loves you, honey / Turn it on, turn it on, turn it on / Over the rainbow / Fox on the run / She gave her heart to Jethro.
LP: .... SRM 15008

NATURAL DREAMS.
Tracks: / Famous Missouri / My heroes have always been highways / Before Jessie died / They captured the outlaw last night / I only think about you when I'm drunk / P.S. I love you / Blackberry dreams / Brand new bartender / Whittler, The / I see.
LP: .... MERL 47
MC: .... MERLC 47

NEW TRAIN - SAME RIDER.
Tracks: / Come on back to Nashville (Ode to the Outlaws) / I'm not ready yet / Burning bridges / Dark hollow / I'd rather die young than grow old without you / May the force be with you always / Whiskey / No one feels my hurt / Mabel, you have been a friend to me / I wish I loved somebody else.
LP: .... PL 12622
MC: .... PK 12622

OL' T'S BACK IN TOWN.
Tracks: / Last country song, The / Old habits die hard / Jesus on the radio, Daddy on the phone / Old side of town / Greed kills more people than whiskey / You show me your heart / Different feeling / Girl you sure know how to say goodbye / What do you mean when you say goodbye / I left you some kisses on the door.
LP: .... PL 13495

PLACES I'VE DONE TIME.
Tracks: / What have you got to lose / I couldn't live in Southern California / Grocery truck / Man who shot himself / Son of Clayton Delaney / Mr. Bo Jangles / Three sofa story / Great East Broadway onion championship of 1978 / Hat full of feathers / Gimme peace.
LP: .... PL 13018

SOLDIER OF FORTUNE.
Tracks: / Soldier of fortune / Me and Jimmie Rodgers / We're all in this thing together / Back when gas was thirty cents a gallon / World according to Raymond / I'll go somewhere and sing my songs again / Texas never fell in love with me / Six o'clock news / People as crazy as me / Whiskey castles.
LP: .... PL 13685

STORY TELLER AND THE BANJO MAN, THE (Hall, Tom T. & Earl Scruggs).
Tracks: / Song of the south / Shackles and chains / Engineers don't wave from trains anymore, The / Don't that road look rough and rocky / Lonesome valley / Roll in my sweet baby's arms / There ain't no country music on this juke box / Lover's farewell, A / Don't give your heart to a rambler / Dim lights / Thick smoke / No expectations.
LP: .... CBS 85616
MC: 40 85616

TOM T. HALL IN CONCERT.
Tracks: / Country is / Ballad of forty dollars / Year that Clayton Delaney died, The / Foggy Mountain breakdown / I know you're married (but I love you still) / Don't tell Ruby where I'm at / Your man loves you honey / I like beer / I took a memory to lunch / Sneaky snake / I love / Old dogs, children and watermelon wine.
LP: .... NL 84749
MC: .... NK 84749

WORLD CLASS COUNTRY.
Tracks: / Who do you pray for / Say something nice about me / I expect the tears to come / Poor me, pour me another drink / Let's do this again sometime / I love / Year that Clayton Delaney died, The / Counting sorrys / Red hot memories / I can't drink / All new me.
LP: .... RANGE 7001

Hall, Tony

FIELDVOLE MUSIC.
LP: .... FRR 012

Hallberg, Bengt

A.D 1980 (See Dommerus, Arne) (Hallberg, Bengt/Arne Dommerus).

BENGT HALLBERG IN NEW YORK.
LP: .... PHONT 7550

BO OHLGREN.
LP: .... PHONT 7566

DIALOGUE IN SWING (Hallberg, Bengt & Ove Lind).
Tracks: / Cottage for sale / I guess I'll have to change my plan / Have you met Miss Jones / Blue orchids / Keepin out of mischief now / Passe / Love walked in / Dream dust / All this and heaven too / Autumn in New York / Annie Laurie / Younger than Springtime.
LP: .... PHONT 7510

DOWNTOWN MEETING (see Dommerus, Arne/Bengt Hallberg) (Hallberg, Bengt/Arne Dommerus).

EGENHANDIGT.
Tracks: / Thou swell / Cabin in the sky / Something's gotta give / Did I remember / Heaven / So rare / Some other time / What can I say / Valsette / Slumming on Park Avenue / Tea for two / Bewitched / Jeepers creepers / My guy's come back.
LP: .... PHONT 7502

EGENHANDIGT - ON HIS OWN.
LP: .... PHON 2

EVERGREENS (See Under Lind, Ove) (Hallberg, Bengt/Ove Lind/Staffan Broms).

EVERGREENS 2 (See Under Lind, Ove) (Hallberg, Bengt/Ove Lind/Staffan Broms).

GYLLENE CIRKELN 1962.
LP: .... DRLP 107

HALLBERG TOUCH, THE.
Tracks: / You do something to me / Little white lies / When lights are low / Lady be good / Coquette / Fascinating rhythm / Sometimes I'm happy / Sonny boy / In a little Spanish town / You and the night and the music / Charleston / You brought a new kind of love to me.
LP: .... PHONT 7525

HALLBERG'S HOT ACCORDION In the foreground.
Tracks: / Tiger rag / Bye bye blues / Farewell blues / St. Louis blues / Limehouse blues / Tva solroda segel / How high the moon / Sweet Sue / Blue moon / Some of these days.
LP: .... PHONT 7532

HALLBERG'S SURPRISE Not even the Old Masters are safe!.
LP: .... PHONT 7581

HALLBERG'S YELLOW BLUES.
LP: .... PHONT 7583

HALLBERT PIANO.
LP: .... PHONT 7544

POWERHOUSE-KRAFTVERK (Hallberg, Bengt/Arne Dommerus).
LP: .... PHONT 7553

TWO OF A KIND (Hallberg, Bengt/Karin Krog).
Tracks: / My man / Jeepers creepers / You must believe in spring / Touch of your lips, The / End of the day song, The / I ain't here / Like that / Hallelujah I love him so / Spring in Manhattan / Love walk right in / Dear Bix / I'm coming Virginia / Ain't nobody's business.
LP: .... FLC 5063

Halle Orchestra

INCIDENTAL MUSIC TO PEER GYNT.
MC: .... EG 7690394

SYMPHONY NO.1/NO.8 (BEETHOVEN) (see under Beethoven).

SYMPHONY NO.2/NO.4 (BEETHOVEN) (see under Beethoven).

SYMPHONY NO.3 (BEETHOVEN) (see under Beethoven).

SYMPHONY NO.5 (BEETHOVEN) (see under Beethoven).

SYMPHONY NO.6 (BEETHOVEN) (see under Beethoven).

Hallelujah Trail

HALLELUJAH TRAIL, THE (Original soundtrack) (Various artists).
LP: AUSLP 1017

Halley, David

STRAY DOG TALK.
Tracks: / Live and learn / Rain just falls / Opportunity knockin' / If ever you need me / Tonight / Darlene / When it comes to you / Further / Walk the line / Dream life.
LP: FIEND 187

Halley, Paul

NIGHTWATCH.
LP: GR 7004

Halliday, R

SEA SONGS, SHANTIES AND SAIL-TALK.
MC: 60-2305

Halliday, Toni

HEARTS AND HANDSHAKES.
Tracks: / Time turns around / Cut up / Love attraction / Make a wish / Welcome to heaven / Ode to Anna / Woman in mind / Weekday / I want more / Tales of tomorrow / Price you have to pay / Hearts and handshakes / Dull man (CD only) / Child (CD only).
LP: ZL 71680
MC: ZK 71680

Hallmark Of Harmony

YOUR ALL-TIME BARBERSHOP FAVOURITES.
Tracks: / Keep your sunny side up / My old Dutch / American trilogy / Bye bye blackbird / If you had all the world and its gold / Sweet Adeline / Red and yellow motor / It's a good day / Hello, hello, who's your lady friend / Don't dilly dally on the way / Any old iron / Call round any old time / Who were you with last night / Home town / I'm Henry the eighth I am / It's a great big shame / Maybe it's because I'm a Londoner / Toot toot tootsie goodbye / Goodbye my lady love / Zip a dee doo dah.
LP: MFP 5793
MC: TC MFP 5793

Hallom, Gerry

OLD AUSTRALIAN WAYS.
Tracks: / Where the dead men lie / Lights of Cobb & Co, The / Where the brumbies come to water / Clancy of the overflow / Old Australian ways / No more boomerang / Song of the wheat / Down the river / First surveyor, The / Northward to the sheds / Grey gulf water.
LP: FE 074
MC: FE 074C

RUN A MINUTE, A.
Tracks: / Free selector's daughter / My old man / Bond Street swell / Bright fine gold / With the cattle / General Leeds clock meeting / Black diamond / New chum shearer / How McDougal topped the score / Outside track, The.
LP: FE 036

TRAVELLIN' DOWN THE CASTLEREAGH.
Tracks: / Overlander, The / Street of Forbes / Jog along till shearing / Andy's gone with cattle / Mowing the barley / Bonnie hoose o' Airlie / Song of artesian waters / Shearing at Castlereagh / 'Ard tac / Bushman's song (travellin' down the Castlereagh), The / Gypsy.
LP: FE 026

Halloran, John

STEPHEN FOSTER SINGS (Halloran, John, Singers).
LP: TLP 2085

Hallow's Eve

DEATH AND INSANITY.
LP: RR 9676 1

MONUMENT.
LP: RR 9583

TALES OF TERROR.
LP: RR 9772

Hallyday, Johnny

NASHVILLE SESSIONS VOL.1, THE.
Tracks: / Shake the hand of a fool / Blueberry Hill / Hello Mary Lou / Feel so fine / Take good care of my baby / Bill Bailey won't you please come home / I got a woman / Be bop a lula / You're sixteen / Whole lotta shakin' goin' on / Maybelline / Diana / Tender years / Hey little girl / Caravan of lonely man / Hold back the sun / I need a whole lotta you / Hound dog / Garden of love.
LP: BFX 15316
MC: BMC 15392

NASHVILLE SESSIONS VOL.2.
Tracks: / Hey baby / Tout bas, tout bas, tout bas / Shout / Quitte moi doucement / Oui, je veux / Ce n'est pas just apres tout / Les bras en croix / C'est une fille comme toil / Qui autrait dit ca ? / Pas cette chanson.
LP: BFX 15317
MC: BMC 15393

TRIFT DIE RATTLES.
Tracks: / Mein leben fangt erst richtig an / Lass die leute doch reden (Keep searching) / Wilde boys / House of the rising sun / Ma guitare (deutsche version) / Ja der elefant (wap dou wap) / It's monkey time (English) (Monkey shine) / Vieleicht bist du fur mich noch night die / J'ai un probleme.
LP: BF 15142
MC: BMC 15391

Halo James

WITNESS.
LP: 4666761
MC: 4666764

Halo Of Flies

GARBAGEBURN.
LP: GOES ON 24

Halpin, Kieran

CRYSTAL BALL GAZING.
LP: KHLP 1
MC: KHMC 1

LIVE AND KICKING.
MC: CMC 021
LP: CM 021

MAN WHO LIVES IN BOTTLES, THE.
LP: CM 012

MISSION STREET.
Tracks: / Refugee from heaven / Foreigners / Mission street / Berlin calling / China rose / Heart and soul / Nothing to show for it all / Celtic myth / Salt into the wound / Farewell to pride / Chase the dragon / Rolling the dice / Child bearing child / Mission street.
LP: RTMLP 31
MC: RTMMC 31

PORT OF CALL (Halpin, Kieran/Tom McConville).
Tracks: / Blarney of roses / Low road, The / Doctor Gilbert / Lads of Laois / Trip through Holyhead / Hish Germany / Tailor to my trade / Hard luck stories / McGuire's / Martin Wynn's / Banks of the Bann / Port of call.
LP: RUB 041
MC: RUBC 041

STREETS OF EVERYWHERE, THE (Halpin, Kieran/Tom McConville).
Tracks: / Dear dirty Dublin / Ardee town / Freeman / Farewell, The / Blue stocking, The / I feel it in my bones / Streets of everywhere, The / Creel, The / Azalea / Willie Clancy's / Gold ring, The / Mother's delight / Farrell O' Gara / Shipyard apprentice, The.
LP: CRO 203
MC: CROC 203

Ham

BUFFALO VIRGIN.
LP: TPLP016
MC: TPC016

Hambi & The Dance

HEARTACHE.
Tracks: / Time after time / Living in a heartache / Madeleine / L'image craque / Spirits / World, The / Dancing inside you / Major major / Too late to fly the flag / Standing in the rain.
LP: V 2211
MC: TCV 2211

Hamblen, Stuart

THIS OLD HOUSE HAS GOT TO GO.
Tracks: / This old house has got to go / Tho' autumn's coming on / Green ice and mountain men / Price tag, The / Transportation / Goodnight Mrs. Jones / Walkin' my fortune / Blue bonnet for her golden hair / Pony express / Silent guest, The / Hangin' of old Zeb Hatfield, The / Dandy of the river, The.
LP: HAT 3031
MC: HATC 3031

Hambro, Lennie

NATURE OF THINGS, THE.
LP: FS 170

Hamburg ...

HAMBURG '88' (Various artists).
LP: EFA 1653

Hamburg Radio...

FESTIVAL OF STRAUSS (Hamburg Radio Symphony Orchestra).
Tracks: / Vienna blood / Wine women and song / Roses from the south / You and you from Die Fledermaus / Schatz waltz from Der Zigeunerbaron / Emperor waltz / Artist's life, An / Acceleration waltz / Blue Danube / Tales from the Vienna Woods.
LP: SPR 8534
MC: SPC 8534

Hamburg Students Choir

HARK THE HERALD ANGELS SING.
LP: GGL 0023

Hamdi, Baligh

INDO-ARABIC VARIATIONS (Hamdi, Baligh & Magid Khan).
Tracks: / Gazairia / Sahara / Achark / Lahore / Ennai / Magnouna.
LP: PS 603

Hamefarers

BREATH O' SHETLAND.
MC: CWGR 055
LP: WGR 055

Hamel, Peter Michael

LET IT PLAY 1979-83 selected pieces.
LP: LPKUCK 078
MC: MCKUCK 078

ORGANUM.
LP: LPKUCK 074
MC: MCKUCK 074

Hamid, Hmaoui Abd El

LA FLUTE DE L'ATLAS (See under El Hamid, Hmaoui Abd).

Hamill, Claire

LOVE IN THE AFTERNOON.
LP: NAGE 18
MC: NAGEC 18

OCTOBER.
Tracks: / Island / To the stars / Stay tonight / Wall to wall carpeting / Speedbreaker / I don't get any older / Warrior of the water / Artist, The / Baby what's wrong (with you) / Sidney gorgeous / Crying under the bedclothes / Peaceful.
LP: BOPA 5
MC: BOPC 5

ONE HOUSE LEFT STANDING.
Tracks: / When I was a child / Man who cannot see tomorrow's sunshine, The / Consummation / River, The / Where are your smiles at / Baseball blues / Urge for going / Flowers for grandma / Phoenix / Smile your blues away.
MC: BOPC 4
LP: BOPA 4

TOUCH PAPER.
Tracks: / Moon is a powerful lover / Denmark / Two fools in a storm / First night in New York / Come along brave lads / Jump / In the palm of my hand / Gonna be the one / Ultra-violet light / Once is not enough.
LP: CODA 8
MC: COCA 8

VOICES.
LP: NAGE 8
MC: NAGEC 8

Hamilton, Andy

SUPERCHART SAX.
Tracks: / Da ya think I'm sexy / Happy birthday / Going back to my roots / Queen of hearts / (I can't get no) satisfaction / Hold on tight / All those years ago / Night runner / Blondie medley / Being with you / Baker Street / You might need somebody / Vienna / Hungry heart / Rainy night in Georgia / Just the two of us / Imagine / One day in your life.
LP: RTL 2060
MC: 4CRTL 2060

Hamilton, Chico

EUPHORIA.
LP: CHELP 7
MC: CHEMC 7

GONGS EAST (Hamilton, Chico Quintet & Eric Dolphy).
Tracks: / Beyond the blue horizon / Long ago and far away / Far east.
LP: DS 831
MC: DSC 831

MAN FROM TWO WORLDS.
Tracks: / Child's play / Blues for O.T. / Mallet dance / Love song to a baby.
LP: JAS 48
MC: JAS C48

MAY 19TH & 20TH, 1959 (Hamilton, Chico Quintet).
Tracks: / Fat mouth / Theme for a starlet / Little lost bear / Champs Elysee / Pretty little theme / Lost in the night / Frou frou / Cawn pawn / Lullaby for dreamers / Opening / Lady E / Truth.
LP: JV 111

PASSIN' THRU (Hamilton, Chico Quintet).
Tracks: / Passin' thru / Second time around / El toro / Transfusion / Lady Gabor / Lonesome child.
LP: JAS 17
MC: JAS C17

SPECTACULAR AND MORE (see under (Pacific Jazz II collection).

THAT'S JAZZ (Hamilton, Chico & Friends).
Tracks: / Miss movement / More than you know / Newport news / Different journey, A / Vulture, The / Sun yen sen / Island blues / One Sheridan Square.
LP: K 56239

Hamilton, Colbert

COLBERT HAMILTON & THE HELL RAZORS (Hamilton, Colbert & the Hell Razors).
LP: FEARLP 1

Hamilton, David

CINEMA ORGAN ENCORES.
LP: DEROY 1373

LEICESTER SQUARE LOOKS ROUND.
MC: AC 164

SOUNDS OF CONN, VOL. 1 (Melody lingers on).
MC: KAEL 001
MC: DK 001

STATESIDE.
Tracks: / Cheek to cheek / Road to Mandalay, The / Tonight.
MC: AC 163

TOP OF THE WORLD.
Tracks: / Viva Espana / Tie a yellow ribbon / Stardust / 'S wonderful.
MC: AC 162

Hamilton, George IV

16 GREAT PERFORMANCES.
LP: ABCL 5178

20 OF THE BEST: GEORGE HAMILTON IV.
Tracks: / Three steps to the phone / To you and yours / If you don't know I ain't gonna tell you / Abilene / Fort Worth / Truck drivin' man / Walking the floor over you / Write me a picture / Steel rail blues / Early morning rain / Urge for going / Break my mind / Little world girl / Back to Denver / Canadian Pacific / Blue train / She's a little bit country / Back where it's at / Anyway / West Texas highway.
LP: NL 89371
MC: NK 89371

AMERICAN COUNTRY GOTHIC.
Tracks: / If I never see midnight again / My hometown / This is our love / Little country county fairs / Farmer's dream ploughed under / Never mind / I will be your friend / More about love / Heaven knows / Back up grinnin' again / Carolina sky / I believe in you.
MC: MCRR 304

BACK HOME AT THE OPRY.
Tracks: / Headed for the country / Streets of gold / Winterwood / Blue jeans, ice cream and Saturday shows / Follow me / Bad romancer / Crystal chandeliers / Sleeping through goodbye / It's almost tomorrow / Leaving London.
LP: PL 10192
MC: PK 10192

BEST OF GEORGE HAMILTON IV.
Tracks: / Abilene / Fort Worth / Break my mind / Rose and a baby Ruth / Before this day ends / Why don't they understand? / Early morning rain / Steel rail blues / Take my hand for a while / Urge for going / Three steps to the phone / Blue train.
LP: LSA 3005
MC: MPK 213

BEST OF GEORGE HAMILTON IV VOL 2.
Tracks: / Canadian Pacific / Dirty old man / Blue train / Suzanne / Ten degrees and getting colder / Anyway / She's a little bit country / Streets of London / Countryfied / Let's get together / West Texas highway / Second cup of coffee / Back where it's at / Country music in my soul.
LP: LFL1 7504

BLUEGRASS GOSPEL.
Tracks: / I'm using my bible for a road map / Old time religion / When it's prayer meetin' time in the hollow / I shall not be moved / Father's table grace / Will the circle be unbroken / Shake my mother's hand for me / O come angel band / Where did all the good folks go? / Build me a cabin in glory / Precious memories / Gathering flowers for the master's bouquet.
LP: LL 2012
MC: LLC 2012

CANADIAN PACIFIC.
Tracks: / Canadian Pacific / I'm gonna be a country boy again / Shake the dust / Together alone / Steel rail blues / Both sides now / Sisters of mercy / Early morning rain / My Nova Scotia home / Summer wages / Long thin dawn / Home from the forest.
LP: CDS 1220
MC: CAM 1220
LP: SF 8062
MC: PK 11622

COUNTRY CHRISTMAS, A.

MC: WST C 9707

COUNTRY STORE: GEORGE HAMILTON IV.
LP: CST 30
MC: CSTK 30

CUTTING ACROSS THE COUNTRY.
Tracks: / Williams Lake stampede / Dirty old man / Follow me / Crystal chandeliers / Fiddlers green / Abilene / Bad news / Peter Amberlay / Way of a country girl / Into the mountains / Cape Breton / Lullaby / Break my mind / Shores of P.E.I. / Canadian Pacific.
LP: PL 18106

FAMOUS COUNTRY MUSIC MAKERS-COAST TO COAST.
Tracks: / I don't believe I'll fall in love today / Big big love / Slightly used / Under your spell again / You better not do that / Keep those cards and letters coming in / Above and beyond / Long black limousine / Isle of Newfoundland / My Nova Scotia home / Prince Edward / Island is heaven to me / Take me back to old New Brunswick / Ghost of Bras D'or / Squid jigging around / Atlantic lullaby / Apple blossom time in Annapolis Valley / Thanks a lot / You nearly lose your mind / Driftwood on the river / Half a mind / I will miss you when you go / Walking the floor over you / Rainbow at midnight / Soldier's last letter / It's been so long darling / Fortunes in memories / Letters have no arms / Let's say goodbye / Farewell to Nova Scotia / Foolin' around / Excuse me (I think I've got a heartache) / Together again / Under the influence of love.
2LP: DPS 2043

FOREVER YOUNG.
LP: MCF 3016

GEORGE HAMILTON IV.
Tracks: / Abilene / Forever young / You're the best thing / Till I gain control again / Can't remember, can't forget / Early morning train / I will love you all my life / Break my mind / Good ole boys like me / Cornbread beans and sweet potato pie.
LP: MCF 3314
MC: MCFC 3314

GEORGE HAMILTON IV.
Tracks: / Till I gain control again / Can't remember, can't forget / Early morning rain / I will love you all my life / Break my mind / Good ole boys like me / Cornbread, beans and sweet potato pie / Canadian Pacific / Dirty old man / Suzanne / 10 degrees and getting colder / Anyway / She's a little bit country / Streets of London / Countryfied / Let's get together / West Texas highway / Back where it's at / Country music in my soul.
LP: MFP 5785
MC: TCMFP 5785

GIVE THANKS.
Tracks: / Little town / In the bleak mid winter / Sweet little Jesus boy / Mary what ya gonna name that pretty baby / Joseph / God rest ye merry gentlemen / Unto us a child is born / Can it be true?.
LP: WST R 9697
MC: WST C 9697

HITS OF GEORGE HAMILTON IV.
Tracks: / Travellin' light / Ten degrees and getting colder / Urge for going / Second cup of coffee / Back to Denver / Anyway / Alberta bound / Take my hand for a while / Truck driving man / Everything is beautiful / Claim on me / Carolina in my mind / She's a little bit country / Write me a picture / West Texas highway / It's my time.
LP: PL 42335
MC: PK 42335

HOMEGROWN (Hamilton, George IV & George Hege Hamilton V).
LP: LR 10225

HYMNS COUNTRY STYLE.
Tracks: / What a friend / I'd rather have Jesus / It is no secret / How great Thou art / Rock of ages / Old rugged cross, The / Blessed assurance / Abide with me / Lord's my shepherd, (The).
LP: WST 9656
MC: WC 9656

MUSIC MAN'S DREAMS.
Tracks: / It must be love / Man I used to be, The / Would you still be mine / Double or nothing / Till I gain control again / Are the good times really over / Music man's dream / Growing on me would you still be mine / Keeper of the moon / Back around to me / Water is wide / Life I love / Are the good times really over / 'Til I gain control again.
LP: RANGE 7004

ONE DAY AT A TIME.
Tracks: / One day at a time / I shall not be moved / Forever young / Shadow of the cross, The / Someone is looking for someone like you / Where did the good folks go / Some day my prince will come / You were the finger of God / Feel like a million / Old time religion / Mose rankin' / I'm using my bible for a road map.
LP: WST 9618
MC: WC 9618

REFLECTIONS.
LP: WH 5008

SING ME A SAD SONG.
LP: HAT 3124

SONGS FOR A WINTER'S NIGHT.
Tracks: / Song for a winter's night / Mull of Kintyre / When we are gone (I will love you) / When I dream / I believe in you / Castles in the air / Lucille / Bunch of thyme / Me and the elephant / England / Only love / Way old friends do, The / Waitin' for the sun to shine / Teach your children / Four strong winds / Blue eyes crying in the rain.
LP: RTL 20-82
MC: 4CRTL 2082

Hamilton, Jeff

INDIANA (Hamilton, Jeff Quintet).
Tracks: / It's you or no one / Girl talk / 2nd street samba / Jeff's express / Split season blues / Indiana / One by one / Long John.
LP: CJ 187

Hamilton, Jimmy

IT'S ABOUT TIME.
LP: 1902123

SWING LOW, SWEET CLARINET.
LP: FS 132

Hamilton, Joe E.

BEST OF JOE E. HAMILTON.
LP: HRL 218
MC: CHRL 218

COUNTRY.
LP: HRL 162
MC: CHRL 162

DO WHAT YOU DO DO WELL.
Tracks: / Do what you do do well / China doll / Love thee dearest / Silver threads among the gold / If my world should end tomorrow / Sweet sweet Judy / From the candy store on the corner / From here to there to you / She wears my ring / Golden needles / Danny boy.
LP: PHL 441
MC: CPHL 441

MOCKIN' BIRD HILL.
Tracks: / Mockin' Bird Hill / Mother of mine / Born again / Grandma's rocking chair / I love you more and more every day / Love is all / It take people like you to make people like me / American trilogy / I'll love you for ever and ever / Shame lovin' shame / Wasn't it a party? / If I had my life to live over.
LP: ARAL 1012
MC: CARAL 1012

SING ME A GOOD OLD COUNTRY SONG.
Tracks: / Back home again / Sing me a good old country song / When it's Springtime in the Rockies / Why me Lord / Garden of love / Wedding song, The / Pretty brown eyes / I am a fool / Rhinestone cowboy / Village in County Tyrone / Devil woman / Four strong winds.
LP: PHL 410
MC: CPHL 410

Hamilton, Kenny

RIGHT HERE IS WHERE YOU BELONG.
Tracks: / All strung out on you / Right here is where you belong / How could I let you get away / Right place, right time / Girl I love you / Sometime / My adorable one / Seems a million years.
LP: DK 7777
MC: DKC 7777

Hamilton Pops

DANCE PARTY.
MC: CHV 317

DISCO CHRISTMAS.
MC: CHV 323

Hamilton, Roy

UNCHAINED.
Tracks: / Don't let go / Great romance, A / I need your lovin' / Jungle fever / I'm gonna sit right down and cry / I'm on my way back home / Unchained melody / Ebb tide / Clock, The / I'll come running back to you / Since I fell for you / You're gonna need magic / Hurt / Don't come crying to me / You can have her / You'll never walk alone.
LP: CRB 1200

Hamilton Sara & David

LIVE: SARA & DAVID HAMILTON.
LP: UNKNOWN

Hamilton, Scott

APPLES AND ORANGES.
LP: CJ 165

BACK TO BACK.
LP: CJ 85

CLOSE UP.
Tracks: / All of you / I remember you / Mad about you / Robbins nest / Was I to blame for falling in love with you / Blue City / Mr. Big and Mr. Modern / Portrait of Jennie / Soft.
LP: CJ 197

CONCORD SUPER BAND.
LP: CJ 120

FIRST, A (See under Braff, Ruby).

FLIP PHILLIPS AND SCOTT HAMILTON (See Under Phillips, Flip) (Hamilton, Scott & Flip Phillips).

GRAND APPEARANCE, THE (Hamilton, Scott Quartet).
Tracks: / Crazy rhythm / I may be wrong / Body and soul / All of me / You'd be so nice to come home to / I thought about you / Out of nowhere / Cheek to cheek / New York blizzard blues.
LP: PRO 7026

LIVE AT CONCORD - 1977.
LP: CJ 51

MAJOR LEAGUE (Hamilton, Scott, Jake Hanna, Dave McKenna).
Tracks: / Swinging at the Copper Rail / Pretty girl is like a melody, A / Cocktails for two / I'm through with love / Linger awhile / September in the rain / This is all I ask / It all depends on you / April in Paris.
LP: CJ 305
MC: CJC 305

RADIO CITY.
Tracks: / Apple honey / Yesterdays / I'll be around / Touch of your lips, The / Cherokee / Tonight I shall sleep with a smile on my face / Radio city / My ideal / Wig's blues / Remember.
MC: CJ 428 C

RIGHT TIME, THE (Hamilton, Scott Quintet).
Tracks: / Just in time / If I love again / Sleep / Eventide / All through the night / Skylark / Stealing port / Dropsy.
LP: CJ 311

SCOTT HAMILTON - A GOOD WIND.
LP: CJ 42

SCOTT HAMILTON AND WARREN VACHE (Hamilton, Scott & Warren Vache).
LP: CJ 70

SCOTT HAMILTON PLAYS BALLADS.
LP: CJ 386
MC: CJ 386C

SCOTT HAMILTON QUINTET IN CONCERT, THE (Hamilton, Scott Quintet).
Tracks: / I can't believe that you're in love with me / Wrap your troubles in dreams / I've found a new baby / When I fall in love / Whispering / Sultry serenade / Stardust / One o'clock jump.
LP: CJ 233

SCOTT HAMILTON & RUBY BRAFF (See under Braff, Ruby) (Hamilton, Scott & Ruby Braff).

SCOTTS BUDDY (Hamilton, Scott & Buddy Tate).
LP: CJ 148

SECOND SET.
Tracks: / All the things you are / Time after time / Taps Miller / All too soon / How insensitive / I never knew / For all we know / Jumpin' the blues.
LP: CJ 254

SKYSCRAPERS.
LP: CJ 111

TENOR SHOES.
Tracks: / I should care / Falling in love with love / Shadow of your smile, The / Nearness of you, The / How high the moon / Our delight / My foolish heart / O.K..
LP: CJ 127

TOUR DE FORCE (see Cohn,Al/Scott Hamilton/Buddy Tate).

Hamlet

HAMLET (see under Shakespeare, William) (Jacobi, Derek & Timothy West & Barbara Jefford).

HAMLET With Richard Burton (Various artists).
LP: CBS 72259

Hamm, Stuart

RADIO FREE ALBEMUTE.
LP: GRUB 9
MC: TGRUB 9

Hammer

BLACK SHEEP.
Tracks: / Jet stream / Heavy love / Black sheep / Light of dawn / Hey girl / Waiting no more / Between the sheets of music / Manic depression / Silent one.
LP: K 53089

CONTRACT WITH HELL.
LP: EBON 29

TOO LEGIT TO QUIT.
Tracks: / This is the way we roll / Brothers hang on / Too legit to quit / Good to go / Lovehold / Living in a world like this / Tell me (why can't we live together) / Street soldiers / Releasing some pressure / Find yourself a friend / Gaining momentum / Count it off / Do not pass my by / Addams groove / Burn it up / Street soldiers.
2LP: ESTSP 26
MC: TCESTSP 26

Hammer Films

MUSIC FROM THE HAMMER FILMS (Philharmonia Orchestra).
Tracks: / Dracula suite / Dracula, Prince of Darkness suite / Hands of the Ripper suite / Taste the blood of Dracula suite / Vampire Circus suite.
LP: FILM 066
MC: FILMC 066

Hammer, Jan

EARLY YEARS, THE.
Tracks: / Seventh day, The / Plants and trees / Bambu forest / Oceans and continents / Animals, The / Your love / Night / I remember me.
LP: 4602061
MC: 4602064

ESCAPE FROM TELEVISION.
Tracks: / Crocketts theme / Theresa / Colombia / Rum cay / Trial and the search, The / Tubbs and Valerie / Forever tonight / Last flight / Rico's blues / Before the storm / Night talk / Miami Vice theme.
LP: MCF 3407
MC: MCFC 3407
MC: MCAC 10410

FIRST SEVEN DAYS, THE (Hammer, Jan Group).
Tracks: / Darkness earth in search of a sun / Light sun / Oceans and continents / Fourth day - plants and trees / Animals, The / Sixth day, The people / Seventh day.
LP: K 50184

LIKE CHILDREN (Hammer, Jan & Jerry Goodman).
Tracks: / Country and Eastern music / No fear / I remember me / Earth (still our only home) / Topeka / Steppings tones / Night / Full moon-boogie / Giving in gently / I wonder.
LP: K 50092

LIVE: JEFF BECK (See under Beck, Jeff) (Hammer, Jan & Jan Hammer Group).

OH YEAH (Hammer, Jan Group).
Tracks: / Magical dog / One to one / Evolove / Oh yeah / Bambu forest / Twenty one / Let the children grow / Red and orange.
LP: K 50276

SNAPSHOTS.
Tracks: / Eurocops / Too much to love / One way out / Skipchaser / Trance / Payback mix / Marina / Poem / Red dragon / Runner, The / Russian night.
LP: MCG 3039
MC: MCGC 6039

TIME IS FREE (see Johnson, David Earle) (Hammer, Jan & David Earle Johnson).

UNTOLD PASSION (Hammer Jan & Neil Schon).
Tracks: / Wasting time / I'm talking to you / Ride / I'm down / Arc / It's alright / Hooked on love / On the beach / Untold passion.
LP: CBS 85355

Hammet, Vic

CINEMA ORGAN ENCORES.
LP: DEROY 1345

Hammett, Dashiell

THIN MAN, THE (See also Daniel J. Travanti & Lyne Lipton).
MCSET: 2106

Hammill, Peter

AND CLOSE AS THIS.
Tracks: / Too many of my yesterdays / Faith / Empire of delight / Silver / Beside the one you love / Other old cliches / Confidente / Sleep now.
LP: V 2409
MC: TCV 2409
LP: OVED 261
MC: OVEDC 261

BLACK BOX.
Tracks: / Golden promise / Losing faith in words / Jargon king, The / Fogwalking / Spirit, The / In slow time / Wipe, The / Flight (flying blind) / Flight (white cave fandango) / Flight (control) / Flight (cockpit) / Flight (silk worm wings) /

Flight (nothing is nothing) / Flight (a black box).
LP: 6302 067
LP: .... OVED 140

ENTER K.
Tracks: / Paradox drive / Now more than ever.
LP: .... SPDP 1
MC: .... SPDC 1
LP: .... NAVL 1

FOOLS MATE.
Tracks: / Imperial zeppelin / Candle / Happy / Solitude / Vision / Re-awakening / Sunshine / Child / Summer song (in the Autumn) / Viking / Birds, The / I once wrote some poems.
LP: .... CHC 2
MC: .... CHCMC 2

FUTURE NOW, THE.
Tracks: / Pushing thirty / Second hand, The / Trappings / Mousetrap (caught in), The / Energy vampires / If I could / Future now, The / Still in the dark / Mediaevil / Motor-bike in Afrika, A / Cut, The / Palinurus (castaway).
LP: .... CHC 59

IN A FOREIGN TOWN.
Tracks: / Hemlock / Invisible ink / Sci-finance (revisited) / This book / Time to burn / Auto / Vote brand X / Play's the thing, The / Under cover names / Smile (CD & cassette only) / Time to burn (instumental) (CD & cassette only).
LP: .... ENVLP 512
MC: .... TCENV 512

IN CAMERA.
Tracks: / Ferret and featherbed / (No more) the sub-mariner / Tapeworm / Again / Faint heart and the sermon / Comet, the course, the tail, The / Gog magog (in bromine chambers).
LP: .... CHC 33
MC: .... CHCMC 33

LOVE SONGS: PETER HAMMILL.
Tracks: / Just good friends / My favourite / Been alone so long / Ophelia / Again / If I could / Vision / Don't tell me / Birds, The / (This side of) the looking glass.
LP: .... CHC 69
MC: .... CHCMC 69

MARGIN, THE (Hammill, Peter And the K Group).
Tracks: / Future now, The / Porton down / Stranger still / Sign / Jargon king, The / Second hand, The / Empress's clothes / Sphinx in the face, The / Labour of love / Sitting targets / Patient / Flight.
LP: .... FONDL 1

NADIR'S BIG CHANCE.
Tracks: / Nadir's big chance / Institute of mental health, The / Open your eyes / Nobody's business / Been alone so long / Pompeii / Shingle / Airport / People you were going to / Birthday special / Two or three spectres / Burning.
LP: .... CHC 19
MC: .... CHCMC 19

OUT OF WATER.
Tracks: / Evidently goldfish / Not the man / No moon in the water / Our oyster / Something about Ysabel's dance / Green fingers / On the surface / Way out, A.
LP: .... ENVLP 1003
LP: 773 540 1
MC: .... TCENV 1003
MC: 773 540 4

PH7.
Tracks: / My favourite / Careering / Porton down / Mirror images / Handicap / Equality / Not for Keith / Old school tie / Time for a change / Imperial walls / Mr X gets tense / Faculty X.
LP: .... CAS 1146

SILENT CORNER AND THE EMPTY STAGE, THE.
Tracks: / Modern / Wilhelmina / Lie (Bernini's Saint Theresa), The / Forsaken gardens / Red shift / Rubicon / Louse is not a home, A.
LP: .... CHC 61

SILENT CORNER & EMPTY STAGE/ CHAMELEON IN THE SHADOW.
Tracks: / German overalls / Slender threads / Rock and role / In the end / What's it worth / Easy to slip away / Dropping the torch / (In the) black room / Tower, The / Modern / Wilhelmina / Lie (Bernini's Saint Theresa), The / Forsaken gardens / Red shift / Rubicon / Louse is not a home, A.
MCSET: .... CASMC 108

SITTING TARGETS.
Tracks: / Breakthrough / My experience / Ophelia / Empress's clothes / Glue / Hesitation / Sitting targets / Stranger still / Sign / What I did for love / Central hotel.
LP: .... V 2205
LP: .... OVED 139

SKIN.
Tracks: / Skin / After the show / Painting by numbers / Shill / All said and done / Perfect date, A / Four pails / Now lover.
LP: .... FONDL 3
MC: .... FONDC 3

SPUR OF THE MOMENT (Hammill, Peter & Guy Evans).
Tracks: / Sweating it out / Surprise / Little did he know / Without a glitch / Anatol's proposal / Multiman / Deprogramming Archie / Always so polite / Imagined brother, An / Bounced / Roger and out.
MC: .... ZCRH 102

Hammond, Albert

GREATEST HITS: ALBERT HAMMOND.
Tracks: / Free electric band, The / We're running out / 99 miles from LA / Everything I want to do / I'm a train / Half a million miles from home / Peacemaker, The / It never rains in Southern California / If you gotta break another heart / Air that I breathe, The / Rebecca / Names, tags, numbers and labels / Moonlight lady / Down by the river / These are the good old days / When I need you.
LP: .... CBS 31643

YOUR WORLD AND MY WORLD.
Tracks: / Your world and my world / Memories / When I'm gone / Anyone with eyes / World of love / I want you back here with me / Experience / Take me sailing / By the night / I'm a camera.
LP: .... CBS 84824

Hammond, Beres

BERES HAMMOND.
MC: .... CRLC 1
LP: .... CRLP 1

Hammond, Clay

STREETS WILL LOVE YOU.
Tracks: / Streets will love you / License to steal / Too many irons in the fire / I know what love is / They don't makeum no more / Ask me for what you want / Part time love / Monkey.
LP: .... EJR 4014
MC: .... EJRMC 4014

TAKING HIS TIME.
Tracks: / I'll make it up to you / Take your time / Something better / I'm gonna be sweeter / You brought it all on yourself / Love made the whole world multiply / Suzy do it better than you / Good side of my girl, The / You messed up my mind / My jealous girl / Do right woman / Left me cryin' / Gonna be some changes / I got a letter this morning / My sweet baby is coming home.
LP: .... KENT 081

Hammond, Doug

ALONE.
LP: .... SC 803

Hammond, John

BEST OF JOHN HAMMOND.
Tracks: / I wish you would come back baby / They call it stormy Monday / So many roads, so many trains / Baby please don't go / Backdoor man / Travelling riverside blues / Key to the highway / Who do you love / No money down / See that grave is kept clean / 32-20 blues / I'm a man / Statesborough blues / Drop down mama / Barbecue blues.
LP: .... VNP 5314
MC: .... VNP 6314

FROGS FOR SNAKES.
Tracks: / You don't love me / Got to find my baby / Step it up and go / Fattening frogs for snakes / Gypsy woman / Key to the highway / My baby left me / Louisiana blues / Mellow down easy / Your funeral and my trial / Mellow peaches / Gone so long.
LP: .... THBL 048
LP: .... ROUNDER 3060
MC: .... ROUNDER 3060C

GEARS.
LP: .... MX 9062

HAMMONDS HITS FOR THE HIGHWAY.
MC: .... AM 54

JOHN HAMMOND LIVE.
LP: .... SPIN 105
LP: .... ROUNDER 3074
MC: .... ROUNDER 3074C

MILEAGE.
Tracks: / My babe / Standing around crying / Riding in the moonlight / Big 45 / Seventh son / Red hot kisses / Help me / It hurts me too / 32-20 blues / You'll miss me / Hot tamales / Diddley daddy.
LP: .... SNTF 835
LP: .... ROUNDER 3042

NOBODY BUT YOU.
Tracks: / Ride till I die / Sail on / Diddy daddy / Memphis town / Lost lover blues / Nobody but you / Papa wants a cookie / If I get lucky / Cuttin' out / Killing me on my feet / Mother in law blues.
LP: .... FIEND 107
LP: .... FF 502

NOBODY BUT YOU.
LP: .... FF 502

SPIRITUALS TO SWING (1938-9).
Tracks: / I got rhythm / Flying home / Memories of you / Blues with Helen / Mortgage stomp / One o'clock jump / Blues with lips / Rhythm man / Good morning blues / Way down yonder in New Orleans / I ain't got nobody / Don't be that way / Mule walk stomp / Carolina shout / Weary blues / I wish I could shimmy like my sister Kate / Stompin' at the Savoy / Honeysuckle Rose / Gospel train / I'm on my way / Four day creep / Jam session on lady be good / Mountain blues / New John Henry, The / It's all right, baby / Cavalcade of boogie / Done got wise / Louise, Louise / What more can my Jesus do? / My mother died a-shoutin' / Paging the devil.
2LP: .... VJD 550

SPOONFUL.
Tracks: / Spoonful / Coming home / I can tell / I wish you would / Brown eyed handsome man / You're so fine / I'm in the mood / My baby is sweeter / Nadine / I'm torn down / Riding in the moonlight / You'll be mine / I'm leavin' you / Crying for my baby / Smokestack lightning / Forty days and forty nights.
LP: .... ED 129

TRIUMVIRATE (see Bloomsfield, Mike) (Hammond, John/Mike Bloomfield/ Doctor John).

Hammond, Rosemary

TWO DOZEN RED ROSES See also Georgina Melville.
MC: .... PMB 013

Hammonds Sauce Works

BRASS ABLAZE (Hammonds Sauce Works Band).
Tracks: / Brass ablaze / Carnival for brass / Tzena, Tzena, Tzena / Virtuosity / Vizcaya / Inter-city / Skip to my Lou / Mission 459 / Song of the dawn / Zelda / Marching through georgia.
LP: .... PRL 005
MC: .... CPRL 005

SPECTACULAR BRASS (Hammonds Sauce Works Band).
Tracks: / Brass spectacular / None shall sleep / Tijuana holiday / Dance Hongroise / Sir duke / Caprice / Skyline / Mellow mood / Blades of Toledo / Elvira Madigan / Slavonic dance No.1.
LP: .... PRL 001
MC: .... CPRL 001

Hampshire...

HAMPSHIRE - A MUSICAL PORTRAIT (Various artists).
LP: .... FT 3014

Hampshire & Dorset

PAST AND PRESENT MUSIC (Hampshire & Dorset Band).
LP: .... MM 0590

Hampshire, Susan

SNOW WHITE (Story told by Susan Hampshire).
MC: 3604

Hampshire Youth

RHAPSODY IN BRASS (Hampshire Youth Concert Band).
LP: .... SS 060

Hampton Court Chapel

TIMES AND SEASONS AT HAMPTON COURT (Hampton Court Chapel Royal choir/John Reynolds).
Tracks: / Jubilate Deo in C / Blessed are those servants / I sing of a maiden / We've been awhile a wondering / What cheer? / From the rising of the sun / Nolo mortem peccatoris / This joyful Eastertide / O clap your hands / If He love me / Cherubim song / For I went with the multitude / My soul, there is a country / Lord, Thou hast been our refuge / Evening hymn (Balfour Gardiner).
LP: .... ACA 545

Hampton, Lionel

1937-40.
LP: .... LPJT 11

ALIVE AND JUMPING (Hampton, Lionel/Milt Buckner/All Stars).
LP: .... MPS 68 186

ALL-AMERICAN AWARD CONCERT.
Tracks: / Hamp's blues / I know that you know / Loose wig / Hamp's boogie woogie / Lady be good / Evil gal blues / Red Cross / Flying home.
LP: .... JASM 1040

AS TIME GOES BY (Hampton, Lionel/ Svend Asmussen).
Tracks: / Flying home / Midnight sun / Rose room / As time goes by / Airmail special / Avalon.
LP: .... SNTF 779
MC: .... ZCSN 779

AT NEWPORT '78 (Hampton, Lionel All Star Band).
Tracks: / Stompin' at the Savoy / Hamp's the champ / Flying home / On the sunny side of the street / Carnegie hall blues.
LP: .... SJP 142

BAD DUDE.
Tracks: / Glad Hamp / Groovin' gates / Easy living / Flying home.
LP: .... MAN 5036

BLACKOUT.
Tracks: / Blackout / After you've gone / Twelfth St. rag / Birth of the blues / Glad Hamp / I can't give you anything but love / Stompin' at The Savoy.
LP: .... GATE 7008
MC: .... CGATE 7008

BOOGIE WOOGIE ALBUM, THE.
Tracks: / Graffiti express / Rolling slow / Central Avenue breakdown / Whisky blues / Mr. Freddie blues / Sheik of Araby boogie / New York shuffle / Jivin' in Jazzland / Hamp's boogie woogie.
LP: 6.25427

CHICAGO JAZZ CONCERT.
Tracks: / Chase, The / Mark VII / Love for sale / How high the moon / Stardust / Wailin' at the moon.
LP: .... CBS 21107
MC: 40 21107

COBB'S IDEA.
Tracks: / Cobb's idea / Vibes boogie / Bongo interlude / Airmail special / Midnight sun / T.V. special / Boogie / Who cares?.
LP: .... B 90116
MC: .... MB 990116

COMPLETE 1953 PARIS SESSIONS.
Tracks: / September in the rain / Free Press oui / Always / Walking at the Trocadero / Real crazy / More and more crazy / Completely crazy / I only have eyes for you / Blue panassie.
2LP: .... VJD 532

COMPLETE 1954 PARIS SESSIONS.
2LP: 400068

COMPLETE LIONEL HAMPTON (Volume 1 & 2).
Tracks: / Rhythym, rhythym / Chinatown my Chinatown / I know that you know / Confessin' / Drum stomp / Piano stomp / I surrender dear / Object of my affection, The / Ring dem bells / Don't be that way / I'm in the mood for swing / Shoe shiner's drag / Any time at all / Muskrat ramble / Down home jump / Rock hill special / Fiddle diddle / My last affair / Jivin' the vibes / Mood that I'm in, The / Hampton stomp / Buzzin' around with the bee / Whoa babe / Stompology / On the sunny side of the street / Judy / Baby wont you please come home / Everybody loves my baby / After you've gone / I just couldn't take it baby / You're my ideal / Sun will shine tonight.
2LP: .... NL 89583
MCSET: .... NK 89583

EASY LIVING (Hampton, Lionel & His Orchestra).
Tracks: / Them changes / I'm so tired / Ain't no sunshine / California dreamin' / Eubie's boogie / Easy living / Flying home.
LP: .... MAN 5030

EUROPEAN CONCERT 1953.
LP: .... IAJRC 31

FLYING HOME.
Tracks: / Hammo's jive / On the sunny side of the street / Summertime / Blue boy / Swanee River / Flying home / Stardust / How high the moon / I only have eyes for you / Lady be good.
LP: .... F 20129

FLYING HOME (MERCURY) (Hampton, Lionel & His Quartet).
Tracks: / Always / 'S wonderful / Airmail special / Nearness of you, The / Soft winds / Stompin' at The Savoy / Love for sale / April in Paris / Just one of those things / Stardust / That old black magic / This can't be love / Willow weep for me / How high the moon / Blues for Norman / I can't get started / Moonglow / It's a blue world / High and mighty / When the saints go marching in / Flying home / Midnight sun / Tenderly / Hallelujah / Indiana / Man I love, The / Body and soul.
LPS: 8130 911

FLYING HOME (VERVE) (Hampton, Lionel & His Quartet).
LP: 837 434-1
MC: 837 434-4

GENE KRUPA, LIONEL HAMPTON & TEDDY WILSON (see Krupa, Gene)

(Hampton, Lionel/Teddy Wilson/Gene Krupa).

HAMP IN HARLEM (Hampton, Lionel/ his Giants Of Jazz).
LP: . . . . **SJP 133**

HAMP THE CHAMP (Hampton, Lionel & His Orchestra).
Tracks: / Whoa babe / On the sunny side of the street / Shine / Don't be that way / I'm in the mood for swing / Muskrat ramble / Shoe shiner's drag / Shufflin' at the Hollywood / When lights are low / Hot mallets / Flying home / Jivin' with Jarvis / Three quarter boogie.
LP: . . . . **CL 89806**
MC: . . . . **CK 89806**

HAMPS BLUES.
Tracks: / Airmail special / E.G. / Psychedelic Sally / Raunchy Rita / Fum / Ham hock blues / Ring them bells / Lion's den / Here's that rainy day / Killer joe.
MC: . . . . **MC 7973**

HAMPS BOOGIE.
LP: **2673741**
MC: **2673744**

HAMPTOLOGIA - VOL.1.
LP: **2304 527**

HAMPTOLOGIA - VOL.2.
LP: **2304 528**

HAMPTON & GETZ (See under Getz, Stan) (Hampton, Lionel/Stan Getz).

IN PARIS - 1956.
LP: . . . . **SW 8415**

IN THE BAG.
Tracks: / In the bag / Dig those vibes / Jack the fox boogie / How high the moon / Million dollar smile / Turkey hop / Double talk / Empty glass / Hamp's gumbo / Mingus fingers / Three minutes on 52nd Street / Hamp's got a Duke / Dancing on the ceiling / Blues for little 'T' / Memories of you / Silver slipper.
LP: . . . . **AFS 1017**
MC: . . . . **TCAFS 1017**

JAM BAND.
LP: . . . . **FH 54**

JAY BIRD.
Tracks: / Jay bird / Bebop / I cover the waterfront / Satchmo's blues / Hot house / Adam blew his hat / Calling Dr Mancuso / Brant Inn boogie / Good rockin' tonight / Dues in blues / Beulah's boogie.
LP: . . . . **INT 127 032**
MC: . . . . **CAS 427 032**

JAZZ AMBASSADORS, THE.
LP: **2610 022**

JAZZ TIME VOL.8.
LP: **502708**

JIVING THE BLUES - 1954 (Hampton, Lionel & His Orchestra).
Tracks: / Airmail special / Vibe boogie / Jiving the blues / Drums feature / Medium blues / How high the moon.
LP: . . . . **SWH 45**
MC: . . . . **CSWH 45**

JUMPIN' JIVE ALL STAR GROUP '37-'39, THE.
Tracks: / Jivin' the vibes / Stomp / Rhythm, rhythm (I got rhythm) / Chinatown my Chinatown / I know that you know / Drum stomp (crazy rhythm) / I surrender / After you've gone / You're my deal / Rock Hill special / High society / Sweethearts on parade / Shufflin' at the Hollywood (take 1) / Wizzin' the wizz / Memories of you / Jumpin' jive, The / When lights are low (take 2) / Haven't named it yet.
LP: . . . . **NL 82433**
MC: . . . . **NK 82433**

JUST JAZZ ALL STARS (Concert).
LP: . . . . **GNPS 15**
MC: **GNP5 15**

LEAPIN' WITH LIONEL Big band bounce & boogie (Hampton, Lionel & His Orchestra).
Tracks: / Flying home / Hamp's boogie woogie / Tempo's boogie / Beulah's boogie / Slide, hamp, slide / Hey ba ba re bop / Rockin' in rhythm / Airmail special / Cobb's idea / Hamp's walkin' boogie / Red top / Midnight sun / Beulah's sister's boogie / Rag mop.
LP: . . . . **AFS 1000**
MC: . . . . **TCAFS 1000**

LIGHT MY FIRE (Hampton, Lionel & His Orchestra).
Tracks: / Them changes / I'm so tired / Ain't no sunshine / California dreamin' / You've got a friend / I / Light my fire / Bridge over troubled water.
LP: . . . . **MAN 5004**

LIONEL HAMPTON (Compact/ Walkman jazz).
Tracks: / Flying home / Man I love, The / Je ne sais pas pourquoi / High and mighty / China boy / On the sunny side of the street / That old black magic / Moonglow / Gladyse / Airmail special.
MC: **833 287-4**

LIONEL HAMPTON (Hampton, Lionel & His Orchestra).
LP: . . . . **BO 716**

LIONEL HAMPTON 1929-1940.
MC: . . . . **ZCRP 852**

LIONEL HAMPTON AND JUST JAZZ ALL STARS, VOL.1 (Hampton, Lionel/ Just Jazz All Stars).
Tracks: / Perdido / That's my desire / Central Avenue breakdown / Kaba's blues / Hamp's boogie woogie / Flying home.
LP: . . . . **JR 102**

LIONEL HAMPTON COLLECTION (20 Golden Greats).
Tracks: / Airmail special / Hava nagila / Cool train / Lady be good / Crying / Song of the Negev / Gladysee bounce / Helpless / Railroad N.I. / I can't believe that you're in love with me / Cry of the blues / Don't feel the scene salty / Wild Bill / Hannah, Hannah / MC Ghee / Kingfish / Playboy's theme / Juice and more juice / Exodus / Kiss was just a kiss, A.
LP: . . . . **DVLP 2065**
MC: . . . . **DVMC 2065**

LIONEL HAMPTON & GENE KRUPA ORCHESTRAS (1948 & 1949) (Hampton, Lionel Orchestra & Gene Krupa Orchestra).
MC: . . . . **UMK 99008**

LIONEL HAMPTON IN CONCERT.
Tracks: / Bebop / Jay bird / Body and soul / Satchmo's blues / Adam blew his hat / Calling Dr Mancuso / Brant Inn boogie / Good rockin' tonight / Dues in blues / Hot house / Beulah's boogie.
LP: . . . . **BLJ 8015**

LIONEL HAMPTON PRESENTS GERRY MULLIGAN (Hampton, Lionel/ Gerry Mulligan).
Tracks: / Apple core / Song for Johnny Hodges / Blight of the fumble bee / Gerry meets Hamp / Blues for Gerry / Line for Lyons / Walking shoes / Limelight.
LP: . . . . **GATE 7014**
MC: . . . . **CGATE 7014**

LIONEL HAMPTON - VOL.2.
Tracks: / September in the rain / Free press oui / Always / Walking at the Trocadero.
LP: . . . . **JR 126**

LIONEL HAMPTON VOL.3.
Tracks: / Real crazy / More crazy / More and more crazy / Completely crazy / I only have eyes for you / Blue panassie.
LP: . . . . **JR 144**

LIVE AT CARNEGIE HALL (Lionel Hampton 50th anniversary concert) (Hampton, Lionel & His Orchestra).
Tracks: / Tea for two / I'm confessin' / Misty / Avalon / More than you know / Runnin' wild.
LP: . . . . **BUDLP 9000**

LIVE AT MIDEM, 1978 (see Corea, Chick) (Hampton, Lionel/Chick Corea).

LIVE AT MUZEVAL (Hampton, Lionel/ Big Band).
LP: . . . . **SJP 120**

LIVE IN PARIS - VOL.1.
LP: . . . . **SM 3543**

LIVE IN PARIS - VOL.2.
LP: . . . . **SM 3544**

MADE IN JAPAN.
Tracks: / Airmail special / Advent / Stardust / Mess is here / Interpretations, opus 5 / Minor thesis / Jodo / Valve job.
LP: . . . . **SJP 175**

MADE IN JAPAN (2) (Hampton, Lionel & His Orchestra).
Tracks: / Airmail special / Advent / Stardust - moonglow / Mess is here / Interpretations, opus 5 / Minor thesis / Jodo / Valve job / Airmail / Big bad Henry / Moment's notice / No me esqueca / Giant steps / Rodney / Round Robin / Flying home / Hamp's boogie woogie / Glad Hamp / Ol' man river / Greasy greens / Mr. P.C. / Hamp's got the blues / Ein burgermeister de Francoise.
MC: . . . . **SJP 1120**

MASTERPIECES.
LP: . . . . **LPJT 29**
MC: . . . . **MCJT 29**
LP: . . . . **LPJT 29**

MEMORABLE SESSION, A.
LP: **500 752**

MESS IS HERE, THE (Live, 1944-45) (Hampton, Lionel & His Orchestra).
LP: . . . . **AWE 18**
MC: . . . . **CAWE 18**
LP: . . . . **GOJ 1014**
LP: . . . . **SOL 502**

MOSTLY BLUES.
Tracks: / Bye bye blues / Someday my prince will come / Take the 'A' train / Blues for jazz beaux / Walkin' uptown / Honeysuckle rose / Mostly blues / Limehouse blues / Gone with the wind.
LP: . . . . **CIJD 40168L**

NEW YORK BLACKOUT.
LP: **2M 056 64824**
MC: **2M 256 64824**

NEWPORT UPROAR.
LP: . . . . **NL 89590**
MC: . . . . **NK 89590**

PLAY BRASSENS (Hampton, Lionel/ friends).
Tracks: / La premiere fille / Dans l'eau de la Claire Fontaine / Le vieux leon / Penelope / A l'ombre de coeur de ma mie / Oncle Archibald / La route aux 4 chansons / Les amoureux des bancs publics / L'orage / Le 22 Septembre / Les passantes.
LP: **8123 861**

QUARTET.
LP: **837 434-1**
MC: **837 434-4**

RIDIN' ON THE L & N.
Tracks: / Ridin' on the L & N / Pencil's broke / Doublin' with Dublin / Boogie woogie Santa Claus / Royal Family, The / There will never be another you / I've been a fool (thinking you cared) / Hawk's nest / Man I love, The / Adam blew his hat / Cherokee / Wee Albert / Moonglow / Everybody's somebody's fool / Tempo's birthday / Lavender coffin / Sky blue / I'll remember April.
LP: . . . . **AFS 1037**

RING DEM VIBES.
LP: **80706**

SOUL OF LIONEL HAMPTON, THE.
LP: . . . . **SM 3539**

STARDUST (Hampton, Lionel All Stars).
Tracks: / Man I love, The / Lady be good / One o clock jump / Stardust.
LP: . . . . **JASM 1044**

VIBES BOOGIE (Live 1955).
LP: . . . . **JJ 605**

YOU BETTER KNOW IT!!.
Tracks: / Ring dem bells / Vibraphone blues / Tempo's birthday / Sweetheart on parade / Pick a rib / Trick or treat / Cute swingle jingle / Taste of honey, A.
LP: . . . . **JAS 19**
MC: . . . . **JAS C19**

Hampton, Slide

1969 (Hampton, Slide Quartet).
LP: . . . . **PM 1552621**

DAY IN COPENHAGEN, A (see Gordon, Dexter) (Hampton, Slide/Dexter Gordon).

FLYING COLOURS (see Williams,James) (Hampton, Slide/James Williams).

ROOTS (Featuring Clifford, Jordan).
LP: . . . . **CRISS 1015**

WORLD OF TROMBONES.
LP: . . . . **BLP 60113**

Hampton Strings

QUIET NIGHTS IN.
Tracks: / Endless love / Hello again / I go to sleep / If you leave me now / Renaissance / Fly away / After the love has gone / One day I'll fly away / When he shines / Onedin line / First time ever I saw your face, The / Fantasy / Incredible hulk, Theme from / You might need somebody / Being with you / Waterfalls / You've lost that lovin' feeling / Yesterday when I was young / I can see her face / Memory / Never knew love like this before / When she was my girl / Magic / Old fashioned way, The / Sukiyaki / Riders in the sky / It's not fair / 79 Park Avenue.
2LP: . . . . **CR 079**
MCSET: . . . . **CRT 079**

Hamsters

ELECTRIC HAMSTERLAND.
LP: . . . . **FOAM 1**
MC: . . . . **FOAMC 1**

Hancock, Butch

DIAMOND HILL.
Tracks: / Golden hearted ways / You can take me for one / Neon wind / Diamond Hill / Corona Del Mar / Ghost of Give and Take Avenue, The / Some folks call it style / Her lover of the hour / Wheels of fortune.
LP: . . . . **RLT 777**

OWN AND OWN.
Tracks: / Dry land farm / Wind's dominion, The / Diamond hill / 1981: A spare odyssey / Fire water / West Texas waltz / Horseflies / If you were a bluebird / Own and own / Leo and Leona (Not available on CD) / Fools fall in love / Split and slide (Not available on CD) / Yellow rose / Like a kiss on the mouth / Ghost of Give and Take Avenue, The / Tell me what you want to know / Just a storm / Just tell me that / When will you hold me again?.
2LP: . . . . **DFIEND 150**

TWO ROADS (Hancock, Butch & Jimmie Dale Gilmour).
LP: . . . . **V 2649**
MC: . . . . **TCV 2649**

WEST TEXAS WALTZES AND DUST BLOWN TRACTOR TUNES.
Tracks: / Dry land farm / Where the West wind has blown / You've never seen me cry / I wish I was only workin' / Dirt road song / West Texas waltz.
LP: . . . . **RLT 114**

WINDS DOMINION, THE.
Tracks: / Sea's deadog catch / Capture, rapture and the rapture / Wind's dominion, The / Long road to Asia minor / Split and slide / Smokin' in the rain / Fighting for my life / Personal rendition of the blues / Dominoes / Once followed by the wind / Wild horses chase the wind / Own and own / Mario y Maria (cryin' statues) / Eternal triangles / Only born / Gift horse of mercy / Wind's dominion, The.
2LP: . . . . **RLT 1644**

YELLA ROSE (Hancock, Butch & Marce Lacouture).
Tracks: / Perfection in the mud / Yella rose / Like a kiss on the mouth / Ain't no mercy on the highway / Only makes me love ya more / So I'll run / Two roads / Sharp cutting wings / Tell me what you know.
LP: . . . . **RLP 13711**

Hancock, Herbie

BEST OF HERBIE HANCOCK.
Tracks: / Doin' it / I thought it was you / Chameleon / Hang up your hang ups / You bet your love / Tell everybody.
LP: . . . . **CBS 32526**
MC: **40 32526**

BEST OF HERBIE HANCOCK (2) (Blue Note years).
Tracks: / Watermelon man / Driftin' (CD only.) / Maiden voyage / Dolphin dance / One finger snap / Canteloupe island / Riot / Speak like a child / King cobra (CD only.).
LP: **B1 91142**

BY ALL MEANS (Hancock, Herbie & Alphonse Mouzon).
Tracks: / Do I have to? / Space invaders / Next time we love, The / Jogger, The / By all means.
LP: . . . . **MPS 68 266**

COLLECTION: HERBIE HANCOCK.
Tracks: / Chameleon / Watermelon man / Maiden voyage / I thought it was you / No means yes / Tell everybody / Rockit / Autodrive / Hard rock / Round midnight.
MC: . . . . **CCSMC 283**

COREA/ HANCOCK/ JARRET (see under Corea, Chick).

CROSSINGS.
Tracks: / Sleeping giant / Quasar / Water torture.
LP: . . . . **K 46164**

EMPYREAN ISLES.
Tracks: / One finger snap / Oliloqui valley / Canteloupe Island / Egg, The / One finger snap (alt. take) (CD only.) / Oliloqui valley (alt. take) (CD only.).
LP: . . . . **BST 84175**

EVENING WITH ..., AN (Hancock, Herbie & Chick Corea).
Tracks: / Homecoming / Ostinato / Hook / Bouquet / Maiden voyage / La fiesta.
2LP: **2672049**

EVENING WITH HERBIE HANCOCK AND CHICK COREA, AN (Hancock, Herbie & Chick Corea).
Tracks: / Someday my prince will come / Liza / Button up / February moments / Maiden voyage / La fiesta.
2LP: . . . . **CBS 88329**

FAT ALBERT ROTUNDA.
Tracks: / Wiggle waggle / Fat mama / Tell me a bedtime story / Oh! here he comes / Jessica / Fat Albert Rotunda / Li'l brother.
LP: . . . . **K 46039**

FEETS DON'T FAIL ME NOW.
Tracks: / You bet your love / Trust me / Tell everybody / Ready or not / Honey from the jar / Knee deep.
LP: . . . . **CBS 83491**

FUTURE SHOCK.
Tracks: / Rockit / Future shock / TFS / Earthbeat / Autodrive / Rough.
LP: **4506251**
MC: **4506254**
LP: . . . . **CBS 25540**
MC: **40 25540**

HANCOCK ALLEY.

Tracks: / Jammin' with Herbie / Herbie's blues / Rock your soul / Scoochie / Cycles / Witch fire.
LP: . . . . **MAN 5021**

HEADHUNTERS.
Tracks: / Chameleon / Watermelon man / Sly / Vein melter.
LP: . . . . **CBS 32008**

HERBIE HANCOCK: GREATEST HITS.
Tracks: / Doin' it / Thought it was you / Chameleon / Hang up your hang ups / You bet your love / Tell everybody.
LP: . . . . **CBS 84106**
MC: **40 84106**

HOT AND HEAVY.
Tracks: / Hot piano / Live and awake / Night walkers / Scoochie / Cycles / Witch fire (end s1) / Jammin' with Herbie / Herbie's blues / Rock your soul / Afro boogie / Far out / Hot and heavy.
LP: . . . . **SJAZZ 4**
MC: . . . . **SJAZZC 4**
LP: . . . . **CBR 1030**
MC: . . . . **KCBR 1030**
MC: . . . . **SJAZC 4**

INVENTIONS AND DIMENSIONS.
Tracks: / Succotash / Triangle / Jack rabbit / Mimosa / Jump ahead, A.
LP: **B1 84147**

JAZZ COLLECTION, A.
MC: **4679014**

LITE ME UP.
Tracks: / Lite me up / Bomb / Gettin' to the good part / Paradise / Can't hide your love / Fun tracks / Motormouth / Give it all your heart.
LP: . . . . **CBS 32474**

MAGIC WINDOWS.
Tracks: / Magic number, The / Tonight's the night / Everybody's broke / Help yourself / Satisfied with love / Twilight clone.
LP: . . . . **CBS 85144**

MAIDEN VOYAGE.
Tracks: / Maiden voyage / Eye of the hurricane / Little one / Survival of the fittest / Dolphin dance.
LP: . . . . **BST 84195**
MC: . . . . **TCBST 84195**
MC: . . . . **TCBST 841954**

MONSTER.
Tracks: / Saturday night / Stars in your eyes / Go for it / Don't hold it in / Making love / It all comes round.
LP: . . . . **CBS 84237**

MR HANDS.
Tracks: / Spiralling prism / Calypso / Just around the corner / 4 a.m. / Shifless shuffle / Textures.
MC: **40 84638**

MWANDISHI.
Tracks: / Ostinato (suite for Angela) / You'll know when you get there / Wandering spirit song.
LP: . . . . **K 46077**

MY POINT OF VIEW.
Tracks: / Blind man, blind man / Tribute to someone, A / King Cobra / Pleasure is mine / And what if I don't?.
LP: . . . . **BST 84126**

NIGHT WITH HERBIE.
Tracks: / Hot piano / Live and awake / Night walkers / Afro boogie / Far out / Hot heavy.
LP: . . . . **MAN 5027**

PERFECT MACHINE.
Tracks: / Perfect machine / Obsession / Vibe alive / Beat wise / Maiden voyage / Chemical residue.
LP: **4606791**
MC: **4606794**

PIANO, THE.
LP: . . . . **30 AP 1033**

PRISONER, THE.
Tracks: / I have a dream / Prisoner, The / Fire water / He who lives in fear / Promise of the sun.
LP: . . . . **BST 84321**

QUARTET.
Tracks: / Well you needn't / Round midnight / Clear ways / Quick sketch / Eye of the hurricane / Parade / Sorcerer, The / Pee Wee / I fall in love too easily.
LP: **22219**

SONGS FOR MY FATHER.
MC: **4BN 84195**

SOUND-SYSTEM.
Tracks: / Hardrock / Metal beat / Karabali / Junku / People are changing / Sound-system / Rockit (Extra track available on cassette only.) / Autodrive (Extra track available on cassette only.) / Future shock (Extra track available on cassette only.) / TFS (Extra track available on cassette only.) / Rough (Extra track available on cassette only.) / Chameleon (Extra track available on cassette only.).
LP: . . . . **CBS 32805**
MC: **40 32805**

SPEAK LIKE A CHILD.
Tracks: / Riot / Speak like a child / First trip / Toys / Goodbye to childhood / Sorcerer, The.
LP: . . . . **BST 84279**

SUNLIGHT.
Tracks: / I thought it was you / Come running to me / Sunlight / No means yes / Good question.
LP: . . . . **CBS 82240**
MC: **40 82240**

TAKIN' OFF.
Tracks: / Watermelon man / Three bags full / Empty pockets / Maze, The / Driftin' / Alone and I.
MC: **4BN 84109**
LP: . . . . **BST 84109**

THRUST.
LP: . . . . **CBS 80193**

VIBE ALIVE.
Tracks: / Vibe alive / Vibe alive (ext. dance remix) (Available on 12" version only.) / Vibe alive (bonus beats) (Track on 12" version only.) / Maiden voyage.
LP: . . . . **XSS 177755**

VILLAGE LIFE.
Tracks: / Moonlight / Ndan ndan nyaria / Early warning / Kanatente.
LP: . . . . **CBS 23697**

Hancock, Hunter

MIDNIGHT MATINEE Hancock, Hunter Presents Various Artists (Various artists).
Tracks: / I was born to rock: *Smilin' Smokey Lynn* / Telephone blues: *Dixon, Floyd* / I get the blues when it rains: *Crawford, Bixie* / I got loaded: *Harris, Peppermint* / Noah: *Golden Keys* / Low down dog: *Henderson, Duke* / Out of count: *Carter, Cecil "Count"* / Masquerade is over, The: *Andrews, Ernie* / What is this thing...: *Perkins, Madelyn* / Chicken...: *Dixon, Floyd* / Chicken...: *Norris, Chuck* / Elevator boogie: *Washing*, Betty Jean / Golden keys: *Bones, Dry* / We're gonna rock: *Henderson, Duke* / Deacon's hop: *McNeely, Big Jay*.
LP: . . . . **KIX 1200**

Hancock, John

MISSIPPI MOTION A legacy in river ragtime.
LP: . . . . **SOS 1025**

Hancock, Keith

MADHOUSE.
LP: . . . . **SPIV 101**
MC: . . . . **SPIV 101 C**

THIS WORLD WE LIVE IN.
LP: . . . . **GVR 237**
MC: . . . . **KJK 001**

Hancock, Larry

BORDERLINE.
LP: . . . . **CA 682**
MC: . . . . **CA 382**

TIME OUT FOR LOVE.
Tracks: / Time out for love / Universal language, A.
LP: . . . . **CA 172**

Hancock, Tony

BEST OF TONY HANCOCK.
Tracks: / Blood donor / Radio ham, The.
LP: . . . . **HMA 228**

BLOOD DONOR/RADIO HAM.
Tracks: / Blood donor / Radio ham.
LP: . . . . **PYL 22**
MC: . . . . **PYM 22**

GOLDEN HOUR OF TONY HANCOCK.
MC: . . . . **KGHMC 115**

HANCOCK.
MC: . . . . **ZCMA 872**
LP: . . . . **NPL 18068**

HANCOCK'S HALF HOUR (Various artists).
Tracks: / Americans hit town, The: *Various artists* / Poetry society: *Various artists* / Unexploded bomb, The: *Various artists* / Sid's mystery tours: *Various artists*.
MCSET: . . . . **ZBBC 1008**

HANCOCK'S HALF HOUR 3 (Various artists).
Tracks: / Hancock's war: *Various artists* / Christmas club, The: *Various artists* / Lift, The: *Various artists*/ Twelve angry men: *Various artists*.
MCSET: . . . . **ZBBC 1069**

HANCOCK'S HALF HOUR (DOUBLE).
Tracks: / Diary, The / Old school reunion, The / Hancock in the Police / East Cheam drama festival, The.
MCSET: . . . . **ZBBC 1122**

HANCOCK'S HALF HOUR, VOL. 1.
Tracks: / Poetry society, The / Sid's mystery tours.
LP: . . . . **REB 394**
MC: . . . . **ZCF 394**

HANCOCK'S HALF HOUR, VOL. 2.
Tracks: / American hit town, The / Unexploded bomb, The.
LP: . . . . **REB 423**
MC: . . . . **ZCF 423**

HANCOCK'S HALF HOUR, VOL. 3.
Tracks: / Scandal magazine, The / Last of the McHancocks.
LP: . . . . **REB 451**
MC: . . . . **ZCF 451**

HANCOCK'S HALF HOUR, VOL. 4.
Tracks: / Sleepless night / Fred's pie stall.
LP: . . . . **REB 485**
MC: . . . . **ZCF 485**

HANCOCK'S HALF HOUR, VOL. 5.
Tracks: / Hancock's war / Christmas club, The.
LP: . . . . **REB 526**
MC: . . . . **ZCF 526**

LIFT & TWELVE ANGRY MEN, THE (Soundtracks from two TV programmes).
Tracks: / Lift, The / Twelve angry men.
LP: . . . . **REB 260**
MC: . . . . **RMC 4055**

PIECES OF HANCOCK.
LP: . . . . **NPL 18054**

THIS IS HANCOCK.
LP: . . . . **NPL 18045**
LP: . . . . **GGL 0206**

UNIQUE HANCOCK.
Tracks: / Almost a gentlemen / Christmas East Cheam style / P.C. Hancock have feet will travel / Hancockelo / Doctor's dilemma, The / Like a dog's dinner / Is that your car outside / With my woogle I thee worship / Hospital or Hancock revisited, The.
LP: . . . . **REB 150**
MC: . . . . **REMC 150**

WORLD OF TONY HANCOCK, THE.
Tracks: / Missing page, The / Reunion party, The.
LP: . . . . **SPA 417**
MC: . . . . **KCPA 417**
MC: **8208954**

Hand on Heart

HAND ON HEART.
Tracks: / Fhir a bhata / Caledonia / Helen Scott of Humbry / Man's a man, A / Farewell to Sicily / Sliabh na mon / Flanders / Say will we yet / Hand me down the tackle / Cronin's / O'Rourke's / Where did you find her / Dawn / Reconciliation.
LP: . . . . **HOH 001**

HEARTS ARE BROKEN, HEADS ARE TURNED.
Tracks: / Rank and file/Crookieden / Braes of Gleniffer, The / Man of Arran/ Pigeon on the gate/High reel / I can jump puddles / Morning mist, The / Rosemary's sister / Open the door / Song for Autumn / Hearts are broken, heads are turned / Bonnie Earl O'Moray, The / St. Paul's song / One more year.
LP: . . . . **HOH 002**
MC: . . . . **HOHC 002**

Hand That Holds...

HAND THAT HOLDS THE BREAD (Various artists).
LP: . . . . **NW 267**

Hand To Mouth

HAND TO MOUTH (Various artists).
LP: . . . . **DEC 19**

Handbell Teams

RINGING CLEAR The art of handbell ringing (Various artists).
Tracks: / March (entry of the Gladiators): *Various artists* / Linden Lea: *Various artists* / Stephen Foster selection: *Various artists* / Grandfather's clock: *Various artists* / On wings of song: *Various artists* / Lord of the dance: *Various artists* / Girl with the flaxen hair, The: *Various artists* / Country gardens: *Various* artists / Ash grove, (The): *Various artists* / Ragtime dance: *Various artists* / Parade of tin soldiers: *Various* artists / Isle of Capri: *Various artists* / Lullaby: *Various artists* / Original rags: *Various artists*/ Silver threads among the gold: *Various artists* / Intermezzo from cavalleria rusticana: *Various artists* / Bells of St. Mary's: *Various artists* / O waly waly: *Various artists* / Flow gently sweet Afton: *Various artists*/ Syncopated clock: *Various artists* / O guter mond: *Various artists* / Whistling Rufus: *Various artists*.
LP: . . . . **SDL 333**
MC: . . . . **CSDL 333**

Handel (composer)

ART OF FUGUE/ HPD. SUITES (See under Bach (Gould).

CHANDOS ANTHEMS VOL 2 (16 Choir & Orchestra).
LP: . . . . **EBRD 0504**
MC: . . . . **EBTD 0504**

CONCERTI GROSSI OP.3 (HANDEL) (Northern Sinfonia of England).
MC: . . . . **ZC QS 6024**

CORONATION ANTHEMS (HANDEL) (New College Choir/King's consort).
Tracks: / Zadok the Priest / My heart is inditing / Let thy hand be strengthened / King shall rejoice, The / Musick for the royal fireworks.
MC: . . . . **KA 66350**

HANDEL (Various artists).
MC: . . . . **DLCMC 203**

HANDEL: A CELEBRATION (Various artists).
Tracks: / Arrival of the Queen of Sheba, The: *Various artists* / I know that my Redeemer liveth: *Various artists*/ Hallelujah chorus: *Various artists* / Water music (extracts): *Various artists* / Ode to St. Cecilia's Day: *Various artists*.
MC: . . . . **ZC QS 6010**

MESSIAH Highlights (Various artists).
MC: . . . . **EG 7690404**

MESSIAH HIGHLIGHTS (Winchester Cathedral Choir/London Handel Orchestra).
MC: . . . . **ZC QS 6001**

VIVALDI: THE FOUR SEASONS (Handel: Water music)(see under English Chamber Orchestra) (English Chamber Orchestra).

WATER MUSIC (Bath Festival Orchestra/Menuhin).
LP: . . . . **EMX 2047**
MC: . . . . **TCEMX 2047**

Handford, Maurice

ENCORES YOU LOVE (Handford, Maurice & Halle Orchestra).
Tracks: / Fanfare for the common man / TV athletics / Adagio (From Spartacus and Phrygia.) / Spartacus ballet / Onedin Line / Judex from Mors et vita / Land of the mountain and the flood, The / Sutherland's law (theme from) / Gymnopedie No. 1 & 3 / Last Song, The (theme from) / Suo gan / Adagio for Strings / Elephant Man / Platoon.
LP: . . . . **CFP 4543**
MC: . . . . **TCCFP 4543**

MORE ENCORES YOU LOVE.
LP: . . . . **CFP 4545**
MC: . . . . **TCCFP 4545**

Handful Of Dust

HANDFUL OF DUST (Original soundtrack) (Various artists).
Tracks: / Handful of Dust, A: *Various artists* / Cafe de Paris: *Various artists* / Talking pips: *Various* artists / Weekend episodes: *Various artists* / Moving over: *Various artists* / Memories: *Various artists*/ Fans, The: *Various artists*.
LP: . . . . **DRG 6110**
MC: . . . . **DRGC 6110**

Handful Of Keys

HANDFUL OF KEYS (13 Great Jazz Pianists) (Various artists).
Tracks: / Monday date, A: *Various artists* / I ain't got nobody: *Various artists* / Black beauty: *Various* artists / Swampy river: *Various artists* / Don't blame me: *Various artists* / Every now and then: *Various* artists / Honky tonk train blues: *Various artists* / Shout for joy: *Various artists* / How long blues: *Various* artists / Dirty dozen, the: *Various artists* / Between sets: *Various artists* / Finishing up a date: *Various* artists / Handful of keys: *Various artists* / Numb fumbling: *Various artists* / Overhand: *Various artists*/ Pearls, The: *Various artists* / Gin mill blues: *Various artists* / Onyx bringdown: *Various artists*/ In a mist: *Various artists* / In the dark: *Various artists* / Flashes: *Various artists* / Barrelhouse: *Various artists* / World is waiting for the sunrise: *Various artists* / Gone with the wind: *Various artists*/ Stormy weather: *Various artists*.
MC: . . . . **ZC AJA 5073**
LP: . . . . **AJA 5073**

Handle, Johnny

COLLIER LAD, THE.
Tracks: / Collier lad, The / Dust / Durham big meetin' day, The / Old man of the village, The / New spotlight, The / Farewell to the monty / Stottin' doon the waal / Is there owt secure / Old pubs, The / Decorating / Fearless mariner, The / Danny's.
LP: **12TS 270**

Handmaid's Tale

HANDMAID'S TALE, THE (Various artists).
LP: . . . . **GNPS 8021**
MC: . . . . **GNPS 58021**

Hands, Brian

LURE OF THE SOUTH SEAS (Hands, Brian Concert Orchestra).

Tracks: / Waitete / Haere mai / Haere ra e hine / Manarero / Paki o Matariki / Moe mai e hine / Kia ora a roha nui / Te arawae / Pokarekare / Awhi mai ra / Haki mai / Tahi nei taru kino / Blue smoke / Hine e hine / Now is the hour.
LP: SPVP 408
MC: SPVP 408C

Handsome Beasts

BEAST WITHIN, THE.
LP: HMRLP 132
MC: HMRMC 132

Handy, Capt. John

ALL ABOARD (Handy, Capt. John & His New Orleans Stompers).
LP: GHB 42

ALL ABOARD WITH JIM ROBINSON.
LP: GHB 43

ALL ABOARD WITH RIMMINGTON.
LP: GHB 41

CAPT. JOHN HANDY/GEOFF BULL/ BARRY MARTYN'S BAND (Handy, Capt. John, Geoff Bull, Barry Martyn).
LP: GHB 166

WITH THE CLAUDE HOPKINS BAND.
LP: NL 89503

Handy, John

HARD WORK.
LP: IMPL 8038

LEGENDARY HANDY SESSIONS (LONDON).
LP: GHB 251

MESSAGES (See Blakey, Art) (Handy, John & Art Blakey).

RIGHT THERE.
LP: MLP 3010

Handy, John & Mabel

JOHN & MABEL HANDY MEMORIAL ALBUM.
LP: NOLA LP 1

Hang The Dance

GHOST BLOODY COUNTRY.
LP: BMLP 001

Hangman Sampler

HANGMAN SAMPLER, A (Various artists).
Tracks: / Gonna: *Mighty Caesars* / Man with the golden gonads, The: *Tremelo* / When the sun refused to shine: *Black H* / You did him wrong: *Delmonas* / Pablo Pablo: *Mindreaders* / There's a tree: *Prisoners* / Dummy: *Aunty Vegetables* / Shead country 2001: *Three Milkshakes* / Cosmetic woman: *Various artists.*
LP: HANG 22 UP

Hangman's Beautiful

HANGMAN'S BEAUTIFUL DAUGHTERS, THE.
LP: VOXX 200049

TRASH MANTRA.
LP: BIG 5

Hank & The Midnighters

HANK & THE MIDNIGHTERS Vol. 2.
Tracks: / Open up the back door / In the doorway crying / Oh so happy / Let 'em roll / E bosta cosi / Stay by my side / Daddy's little baby / Partners for life / Is your love for real / What made you change your mind / Let me hold your hand / Early one morning.
LP: SING 581

Hanly, Michael

CELTIC FOLKWEAVE (Hanly, Michael, Michael O'Domhaill).
LP: 318 810 7

Hanly, Mick

ALL I REMEMBER.
LP: MHLP 1
MC: MHMC 1

AS I WENT OVER BLACKWATER.
LP: LUN 040
MC: CLUN 040

MY LOVE IS IN AMERICA (See under Keane, Dolores) (Hanly, Mick & Dolores Keane).

STILL NOT CURED (Hanly, Mick & Rusty Old Halo).
LP: RH 1

WARTS AND ALL.
LP: RTMLP 342
MC: RTMMC 342

Hanna, Fred

IRISH FAMILY FAVOURITES.
Tracks: / Mountains of Mourne / Forty shades of green / Holy ground / Boys from County Armagh / Danny boy / I'll take you home again Kathleen / Black velvet band / Green glens of Antrim / When Irish eyes are smiling / Old maid in a garret / If you're Irish / With my shillelagh under me arm / MacNamara's band / Homes of Donegal / Phil the fluter / Wild colonial boy.
LP: LSA 3135

Hanna, George

ON THE SHORES OF LOUGH NEAGH (Hanna, George & Sarah Anne O'Neill).
Tracks: / Brockagh brae / On yonder hill there sits a hare / Blackbird of sweet Avondale / Erin's lovely home / Young Edmund in the lowlands / Kate of Bllinamore / Rambler from Clare, The / Fair young maid in her father's garden, A / Rambler from Clare, The / John Reilly / Gosford's fair demesne / Carrickmannon lake / Fisher's cot, The.
LP: 12TS 372

Hanna, Roland

GERSHWIN, CARMICHAEL, CATS.
Tracks: / Stardust / Skylark / Memory / Nearness of you / Bess, oh where's my bess / Embraceable you.
LP: CTI 9008

GLOVE.
LP: BKH 530

INFORMAL.
LP: P 102

NEW YORK JAZZ QUARTET.
LP: BH 7013

PERUGIA.
Tracks: / Take the 'A' train / I got it bad and that ain't good / Time dust gathered / Perugia / Child is born, A / Wistful moment.
LP: FLP 41010

ROLAND HANNA AND GEORGE MRAZ (Hanna, Roland & George Mraz).
LP: BKH 527

SWING ME NO WALTZES.
LP: SLP 4018

THIS MUST BE LOVE (Hanna, Sir Roland, George Moraz, Ben Riley).
LP: AP 157

THIS TIME IT'S REAL.
LP: SLP 4145

TIME FOR THE DANCERS (Hanna, Roland Trio).
LP: PRO 7012

Hanna, Sir Roland

DUKE ELLINGTON PIANO SOLOS.
Tracks: / In my solitude / Something to live for / In a sentimental mood / Portrait of Bert Williams / Warm valley / Isfahan / Single petal of a rose / I got it bad and that ain't good / Reflections in D / Come Sunday / Caravan.
LP: 820 840-2

Hannah & Her Sisters

HANNAH AND HER SISTERS (Original soundtrack) (Various artists).
LP: IMCA 6190
MC: IMCAC 6190

HANNAH AND HER SISTERS/ SEPTEMBER (Film soundtracks) (Various artists).
LP: ENT LP 13057
MC: ENT MC 13057

Hannan, Robbie

TRADITIONAL IRISH MUSIC PLAYED ON UILLEANN PIPES.
LP: CC 53
MC: 4CC 53

Hannibal Brooks

HANNIBAL BROOKS (Original soundtrack) (Various artists).
LP: MCA 25104
MC: MCAC 25104

Hannibal Compilation

HANNIBAL COMPILATION (Collection of Vocalists on Hannibal Records) (Various artists).
LP: HNBL 8301
MC: HNBC 8301

Hanoi Rocks

ALL THOSE WASTED YEARS.
2LP: LICKDLP 5/6
MCSET: LICKCAS 5/6

BACK TO MYSTERY CITY.
Tracks: / Strange boys play weird openings / Mental beat / Until I get you / Lick summer lover / Ice cream summer / Malibu beach nightmare / Tooting Bec wreck / Sailing down the years / Beating gets faster / Back to mystery city.
LP: LICLP 1
MC: LICK 1

BANGKOK SHOCKS SAIGON SHAKES.
LP: LICLP 2
MC: LICK 2

BEST OF HANOI ROCKS.
LP: LICLP 8
MC: LICK 8

DEAD BY CHRISTMAS.
Tracks: / Oriental beat(live) / Back to Mystery city / Love's an injection / Lightning bar blues / Mental beat / Malibu beach / M.C.Baby / Vllage girl / 40 taxi driver / Tragedy / Visitor (live) / Ice cream summer / Whispers in the dark / Cheyenne / No law and order / Fallen star, A / Dead by Christmas / Lost in the city / Don't never leave me(live) / Under my wheels (live) / I feel alright (live).
LP: RAWLP 016
MC: RAWTC 016

MUSIC AND MEDIA INTERVIEW PICTURE DISCS.
LPPD: MM 1237

ORIENTAL BEAT.
LP: LICLP 3
MC: LICK 3

ROCK 'N' ROLL DIVORCE.
LP: BOOTLIC 7

SELF DESTRUCTION BLUES.
LP: LICLP 4
MC: LICK 4

TRACKS FROM A BROKEN DREAM.
Tracks: / Boulevard of broken dreams / Rebel on the run / Oil and gasoline / Shakes / Malibu calypso / Problem child / I can't get it / Do the duck / Two steps from the move / Magic carpet ride / I love you / Don't you ever leave me / Underwater world / Willing to cross the ocean / It's too late.
LP: LICLP 10
MC: LICK 10

TWO STEPS FROM THE MOVE.
Tracks: / Up around the bend / High school / I can't get it / Underwater world / Don't you ever leave me / Million miles away / Boulevard of broken dreams / Boiler, The / Futurama / Cutting corners.
LP: CBS 26066
MC: 40 26066

Hanover Band, The

BEETHOVEN ON ORIGINAL INSTRUMENTS (4 VOLUMES) (See under Beethoven for full details).

MOZART HORN CONCERTOS (See under Mozart for full details).

Hanrahan, Kip

COUP DE TETE.
LP: AMCL 10071
MC: AMCL 10074

DAYS AND NIGHTS OF BLUE LUCK INVERTED.
Tracks: / Love is like a cigarette / Poker game, A / Luck inverts itself / Four swimmers / Gender / Marriage / American clave / Model Bronx childhood, A / Ah, intruder (female) / Lisbon: blue request / My life outside of power / Road song / First and last to love me / Unobtainable days; unobtainable nights.
LP: 461158 1
MC: 461158 4
LP: AMCL 10121
MC: AMCL 10124

DESIRE DEVELOPS AN EDGE.
LP: AMCL 10081
MC: AMCL 10084

TENDERNESS.
LP: AMCL 1016 1
MC: AMCL 1016 4

VERTICAL'S CURRENCY (Hanrahan, Kip & Jack Bruce).
LP: AMCL 10101
MC: AMCL 10104

Hans Andersen (show)

HANS ANDERSEN (Original London cast featuring Tommy Steele) (Various artists).
LP: NSPL 18551

HANS ANDERSEN (London revival cast) (Various artists).
Tracks: / Overture: *Various artists* / Thumbelina: *Various artists* / Truly loved: *Various artists* / Dare to take a chance: *Various artists* / Jenny kissed me: *Various artists* / Inch worm, The: *Various artists*/ Ecclesiasticus (I can spell): *Various artists* / Wonderful Copenhagen: *Various artists* / I'm Hans Christian Andersen: *Various artists* / Don't talk to me about those happy days: *Various artists* / Have I stayed away too long: *Various artists* / Ugly duckling, The: *Various artists* / No two people: *Various artists* / Kings new clothes, The: *Various artists* / Anywhere I wander: *Various artists.*
LP: FBLP 8080
MC: ZCFBL 8080

Hans Christian

HANS CHRISTIAN ANDERSEN (FILM SOUNDTRACK) (See under Kaye, Danny) (Kaye, Danny).

Hans, Hans Raj

IK KURHI MENOON RANJION FAKIR KARGAYEE.
Tracks: / Giddhe wich melene ni / Kiddi chhetin hundian jawan kurhian / Ik kurhi menoon ranjion fakir kargayee / Tere pyar 'ch kasuti har paegi / Ve tuttie taria / Khirh khirh hasdi day / Ni toon larh farhley sohney saijjana da / Sohnian ni tere sohnay nainan / Uchi peengh na charhayin mutiare / Tere binan asin kehrhe marchale.
MC: DDP 015

Hansel & Gretel (bk)

HANSEL AND GRETEL (Unknown narrator(s)).
MC: STK 019

HANSEL AND GRETEL (well loved tales age up to 9) (Unknown narrator(s)).
MC: PLB 70

HANSEL AND GRETEL.
MC: HA 4

HANSEL & GRETEL (Various artists).
MC: STC 306A

HANSEL & GRETEL & OTHER FAIRY TALES (Brothers Grimm) (Bloom, Claire (nar)).
MC: 1274

Hanselmann, David

LET THE MUSIC CARRY ON.
LP: 145158
MC: 445158

Hansen, Finn Otto

FERSKEDRIVHUSMELONER (Hansen, Finn Otto & Jesper Thilo).
LP: SLP 230

HANSEN, FINN OTTO AND JESPER THILO (See under Thilo, Jesper).

Hansen, Kai

HEADING FOR TOMORROW.
Tracks: / Intro (welcome) / Space eater / Lust for life / Hold your ground / Heaven can wait / Money / Silence, The / Freetime / Heading for tomorrow / Look at yourself (CD only.).
LP: NUK 151
MC: ZCNUK 151

Hansen, Randy

RANDY HANSEN.
Tracks: / Champagne and cocaine / Watch what you say / Time won't stop / I want to take you higher / Millionaire / Dancin' with me / Don't pretend.
LP: EST 12119

Hanshaw, Annette

ANNETTE HANSHAW 1926 VOL 1.
Tracks: / Black bottom / Six feet of Papa / Lay me down to sleep in Carolina / Falling in love with you / Don't take that black bottom away / Cherie, I love you / Calling me home / If I'd only believed in you / My baby knows how / Do do do / Everything's made for love / Kiss your little baby goodnight / One sweet letter from you / If you can't tell the world she's a good girl / I'm all alone in a palace of stone.
LP: FV 201

ANNETTE HANSHAW 1927 VOL 2.
LP: FV 202

ANNETTE HANSHAW 1928 VOL 3.
LP: FV 205

IT WAS SO BEAUTIFUL Her last recordings 1932/34.
Tracks: / It was so beautiful / We just couldn't say goodbye / Love me tonight / Say it isn't so / I cover the waterfront / Don't blame me / Give me liberty or give me love / Let's fall in love.
LP: HDL 119
MC: CHDL 119

LOVABLE AND SWEET.
LP: SH 246

SHE'S GOT IT (1920-30'S).
LP: SH 247

SWEETHEART OF THE TWENTIES.(1926-28).
LP: HAL 5
MC: CHAL 5

Hanson & Davis

CAN'T STOP.
LP: LPRE 4

Hanson, John

DANCIN YEARS/WHITE HORSE INN.
LP: 6308 225

JOHN HANSON FAVOURITES.
Tracks: / Impossible dream, The / True love / Holy City, The / Where do I begin / Climb every mountain / Golden days / Donkey serenade, The / Somewhere my love / And I love you so / Gigi / One alone / My way.
LP: TIME 04
MC: TIMEC 04

JOHN HANSON SINGS 20 SHOWTIME GREATS.
LP: NE 1002

JOHN HANSON SINGS SONGS FROM HIS SHOWS.

Tracks: / Bachelor gay, A / Goodbye / My dearest dear / One alone / Quiet girl, A / Rose Marie / Serenade-Lilac time / Student prince, The (serenade) / Shine through my dreams / Smilin' through / Song of the vagabonds / Stout hearted men.
LP: 6382 131

SPOTLIGHT ON JOHN HANSON.
LP: 6625 032

STUDENT PRINCE/VAGABOND KING.
LP: . . . . PKL 5568

VAGABOND KING, THE.
Tracks: / Vagabond king, The / Love for sale / Song of the vagabonds / Someday / Only a rose / Tomorrow / Huguette waltz / Love me tonight / Student prince, The / Golden days / Drinking song / Deep in my heart, dear / Serenade / Come boys / Student life is as gay / Just we two! / If they knew deep in my heart, dear (reprise).
LP: . . . . FBLP 8076
MC: . . . . ZCFBL 8076

Hansson, Bo

BEST OF BO HANSSON.
Tracks: / Happy prank / Divided reality / City, The / Waltz for interbeings / Flight to the ford / Attic thoughts / Sun / Excursion with complications.
LP: 9290 425

LORD OF THE RINGS.
Tracks: / Leaving shire / Old forest, The / Tom Bombardil / Fog on the barrow / Downs / Black riders, The / Flight to the ford / At the house of Elrond / Ring goes South, The / Journey in the dark, A / Lothlorien / Horns of Rohan, The / Shadowfax / Battle of the Pelennor Fields, The / Dreams in the house of healing / Homeward bound / Scouring of the Shire, The / Grey havens, The.
LP: . . . . CAS 1059
MC: . . . . SRS 4600
LP: . . . . SR 4600

MAGICIAN'S HAT.
Tracks: / City, The / Divided reality / Elidor / Fylke / Before the rain / Findhorn's song / Playing downhill into the downs / Awakening / Wandering song / Sun, The (parallel or 90 degrees) / Excursion with complications.
LP: . . . . CHC 8
MC: . . . . CHCMC 8

MUSIC INSPIRED BY WATERSHIP DOWN.
LP: . . . . CHC 49

Hanvey, Bobbie

MUTTONBURN STREAM & WHEEN MORE (Hanvey, Bobbie & Houl Yer Whisht).
Tracks: / Mutturn burn Stream & A Wheen More / Digs in Birmingham / Scutcher / Going back to Belfast / Pride of the Springfield Road / Tailor / Ducks of Magheralin / Mickey Marley's roundabout / Garters / Ould rigadoo / Farewell to Tarwathie / Carrickmannon Lake / B for Barney / Fan a winnow / All around the lonely-o.
LP: . . . . OAS 3015
MC: . . . . COAS 3015

Hanwell Band

BLAZING BRASS.
MC: . . . . OAK C 112

Happel, Harry

INTRODUCTION.
Tracks: / Have you met Miss Jones / Wheatland / Love letters / Autumn leaves / We've only just begun / John Brown's body / If you leave me now.
LP: . . . . SJP 149

INTRODUCTION: NORTH SEA HIGH LIGHTS.
Tracks: / Jor-du / Cowboy samba / Yellow bird / Summertime / Place St. Henri / Your song / Autumn leaves / Scrapple from the apple / Love for sale / Night child / You are the sunshine of my life.
2LP: . . . . SPJ 156/157

Happy Accordion Hits

HAPPY ACCORDION HITS (Various artists).
Tracks: / Winchester Cathedral: *Various artists* / Downtown: *Various artists* / Schiwago melody: *Various artists* / Rose Marie: *Various artists* / Komm allein: *Various artists* / Ay ay ay: *Various artists*/ Maria: *Various artists* / Bleib bei mir: *Various artists* / Love is blue: *Various artists* / Dandy: *Various artists* / Oh, oh, what a kiss: *Various artists* / On the street where you live: *Various artists*/ Taste of honey, A: *Various artists* / Red roses for a blue lady: *Various artists* / Hello Dolly: *Various artists* / Annen polka: *Various artists* / Klarinettenmuckel: *Various artists.*
LP: . . . . ESP 77109
MC: . . . . ESC 77109

Happy Adventure (bk)

HAPPY ADVENTURE TALES.
MCSET: . . . . DTO 10547

Happy Anniversary...

HAPPY ANNIVERSARY CHARLIE BROWN (Tribute to the Peanuts Characters) (Various artists).
Tracks: / Linus and Lucy: *Benoit, David* / Red Baron: *Ritenour, Lee* / Joe Cool: *King, B.B.* / Christmas time is here: *Austin, Patti* / History lesson: *Grusin, Dave* / Charlie Brown theme: *Murry, Amani A.W.*/ Great pumpkin waltz, The: *Corea, Chick* / Benjamin: *Brubeck, Dave* / Little birdie: *Williams, Joe* / Breadline blues: *Kenny G.* / Rain, go away: *Mulligan, Gerry.*
LP: . . . . GRP 95961
MC: . . . . GRP 95964

Happy Days Are Here

HAPPY DAYS ARE HERE AGAIN (Various artists).
Tracks: / Happy days are here again: *Various artists* / Have you ever been lonely?: *Various artists* / Peanut vendor: *Various artists* / On the sunny side of the street: *Various artists* / Stein song, The: *Various artists*/ Everything I have is yours: *Various artists* / Nobody's sweetheart: *Various artists* / Teddy bears' picnic: *Various* artists / Me and the old folks at home: *Various artists* / Let's put out the lights: *Various artists* / Is it true what they say about Dixie: *Various artists* / Shoe shine boy: *Various artists* / On the beach at Bali Bali: *Various artists* / Everthing's in rhythm with my heart: *Various artists* / Harbour lights: *Various artists*/ Say si si: *Various artists* / Music maestro please: *Various artists* / I must see annie tonight: *Various artists* / I'm gonna lock my heart: *Various artists* / Two sleepy people: *Various artists.*
LP: . . . . EG 2606281
MC: . . . . EG 2606284

HAPPY DAYS ARE HERE AGAIN (Various artists).
LP: . . . . SH 337

Happy Daze

HAPPY DAZE VOL.1 (Various artists).
Tracks: / Real real real: *Jesus Jones* / Come home: *James* / Sherriff fatman: *Carter T.U.S.M.* / Loaded: *Primal Scream* / Progen: *Shamen* / W.F.L.: *Happy Mondays* / Circle square: *Wonder Stuff* / I'm free: *Soup Dragons* / Groovy train: *Farm* / Big: *New Fast Automatic Daffodils* / Hippy chick: *Soho*/ Only one I know, The: *Charlatans* / Velouria: *Pixies* / She comes in the fall: *Inspiral Carpets* / Taste: *Ride.*
LP: . . . . ILPTV 1
MC: . . . . ICTTV 1

HAPPY DAZE VOL.2 (Various artists).
LP: . . . . ILPTV 3
MC: . . . . ICTTV 3

Happy Drivers

INDIANS ON THE ROAD.
LP: . . . . ROCK 2228

Happy End

HAPPY END Original Broadway cast (Various artists).
LP: . . . . COS 2032

RESOLUTION.
Tracks: / Ballad of John Henry, The / Coal not dole / Pirate Jenny / It is a day / Township jazz / But I wonder / Lanagans ball / Resolution / Song of the lower classes, The / Misterioso / Singing of the socialist / Motherland.
LP: . . . . COOK 005
MC: . . . . COOKC 005

RETURN OF THE BIG SHOT.
MC: . . . . UNKNOWN

THERE'S NOTHING QUITE LIKE MONEY.
LP: . . . . RING L100

TURN THINGS UPSIDE DOWN.
Tracks: / Oakey strike evictions, The / Turn things upside down / What keeps mankind alive / Starstruck / Sailing the seas / Big rock candy mountain / Red flag, The / Nkosi Sikelelei / Afrika ANC / Rhumba for Nicaragua.
LP: . . . . COOK 033
MC: . . . . COOKC 033

Happy Ending

HAPPY ENDING (Film Soundtrack) (Various artists).
Tracks: / What are you doing the rest of your life: *Various artists* / Collage: *Various artists* / Diamonds are forever: *Various artists* / What are you doing the rest of your life: *Various artists* / Floating time: *Various* artists / Hurry up 'n' hurry down: *Various artists* / Whistle while you swing: *Various artists* / What are you doing the rest of your life: *Various artists* / Something for everyone: *Various artists* / Pause that refreshes: *Various artists* / It ought to be forever: *Various artists* / Smooth sailing: *Various artists* / What are you doing the rest of your life: *Various artists.*
LP: . . . . UAS 29084

HAPPY ENDING, THE (Original soundtrack) (Various artists).
LP: . . . . MCA 25105
MC: . . . . MCAC 25105

Happy Families

HAPPY FAMILIES (Various artists).
LP: . . . . LAP 1001
MC: . . . . CLAP 1001

HAPPY FAMILIES (Allan Ahlberg) (Jarvis, Martin (nar)).
MC: 881670

Happy Families Stories

HAPPY FAMILIES STORIES Mrs Wobble and the Waitress.
MC: . . . . TS 333

Happy Flowers

I CRUSH BOZO.
LP: . . . . HMS 106
MC: . . . . HMS 106C

OOF.
LP: . . . . HMS 136 1
MC: . . . . HMS 136 4

Happy Jazz Band

LIVE AT MEMPHIS JAZZ FESTIVAL.
LP: . . . . J 132

Happy Learning

ALPHABET, THE (Benjamin, Floella).
MC: . . . . HL 005

ANIMAL MAGIC (O'Neil, Catrine).
MC: . . . . HL 011

CALENDAR, THE (O'Neil, Catrine).
MC: . . . . HL 004

CLOCK, THE (O'Neil, Catrine).
MC: . . . . HL 002

COLOURS (O'Neil, Catrine).
MC: . . . . HL 009

COUNTING (Benjamin, Floella).
MC: . . . . HL 006

DINOSAURS (O'Neil, Catrine).
MC: . . . . HL 014

MULTIPLICATION (Benjamin, Floella).
MC: . . . . HL 001

MUSICAL SOUNDS (O'Neil, Catrine).
MC: . . . . HL 012

OPPOSITES (O'Neil, Catrine).
MC: . . . . HL 013

PRIMARY FRENCH (Pumphrey, Anne Marie).
MC: . . . . HL 008

STREETWISE (Road safety tape) (Various artists).
MC: . . . . HL 003

Happy Memories

HAPPY MEMORIES (Various artists).
LP: . . . . DTLP 6

HAPPY MEMORIES VOL 2 (Various artists).
LP: . . . . DTLP 7

Happy Mondays

BUMMED.
LP: . . . . FACT 220
MC: . . . . FACT 220C
DAT: . . . . FACT 200D

HAPPY MONDAYS-LIVE.
2LP: . . . . FACT 322
MC: . . . . FACTD 322

PILLS 'N' THRILLS AND BELLYACHES.
LP: . . . . FACT 320
MC: . . . . FACT 320C

SQUIRRELL & G MAN (24 Hour Party People Plastic Face Can't Smile At).
Tracks: / Kuff dam / Tart tart / 'Enry / Russell / Olive oil / Weekend starts here, The / Little matchstick Owen / Oasis / Desmond / Cob 20.
LP: . . . . FACT 170

UP ALL NIGHT.
LP: . . . . BAK 6019
MC: . . . . MBAK 6019

Happy Organ

20 ALL TIME FAVORITES.
LP: . . . . GNPS 2135
MC: GNP5 2135

20 CHRISTMAS FAVORITES.
LP: . . . . GNPS 2138
MC: GNP5 2138

20 POLKAS & WALTZES.
LP: . . . . GNPS 2134
MC: GNP5 2134

DANCE LITTLE BIRD (Happy Organ/ Dad & The Kids).
LP: . . . . GNPS 2149
MC: GNP5 2149

Happy Piano

HAPPY PIANO featuring Matalda (Various artists).
LP: . . . . GNPS 2141

Happy Polkateers

HAPPY POLKATEERS featuring Don Gralak (Various artists).
LP: . . . . GNPS 2143
MC: GNP5 2143

Happy Prince

CHILDREN'S OPERA, THE (Happy Prince, The).
LP: . . . . ZNF 5

HAPPY PRINCE & OTHER STORIES, THE see also under Wilde,Oscar (Wilde, Oscar (author)).
MC: . . . . TS 308

HAPPY PRINCE, THE (see Wilde, Oscar) (Unknown narrator(s)).

Happy Refugees

LAST CHANCE SALOON.
LP: . . . . HREF 002

Happy Together

HAPPY TOGETHER Various Artists (Various artists).
Tracks: / I fought the law: *Fuller, Bobby* / Tell him: *Exciters* / Birds and the bees, The: *Akens, Jewel*/ Single girl: *Posey, Sandy* / Letter, The: *Box Tops* / She'd rather be with me: *Turtles* / Double shot of my baby's love: *Swinging Medalions* / It ain't me babe: *Various artists* / Cinnamon cinder: *Various artists*/ Lightning strikes: *Christie, Lou* / New Yorks a lonely town: *Tradewinds.*
LP: . . . . TOP 145
MC: . . . . KTOP 145

Happy Yodellers

HAPPY YODELLERS (Various artists).
Tracks: / Tiroler Bravour-Jodier: *Various artists* / Dort wo die isar fliebt: *Various artists* / Immer wann der morgen kommt: *Various artists* / Heut'bin ich so jodel verliebt: *Various artists* / Der Konigs-Jodler: *Various* artists / Rob'n auf der roten wand: *Various artists* / Mei Vata is a Appenzeller: *Various artists* / Die kasermandin: *Various artists* / Am morgen wenn di sonne lacht: *Various artists* / Me liab: *Various artists* / Schatzeri machs fernsteri auf wenn ich auf hohen Bergen: *Various artists.*
LP: 825 906-1
MC: 825 906-4

Hapshash

HAPSHASH & THE COLOURED COAT (Hapshash & The Coloured Coat).
Tracks: / H-O-P-P why? / Mind blown is a mind shown, A / New messiah coming, The / Aoum / Empires of the sun.
LP: . . . . DO 2001

Haque, Fareed

VOICES RISING.
Tracks: / Paco's blues / Rain dance / Exercise one / Back bay blues / Claudia's theme / Voices rising / Yatra / Dex / Winter's tale, A / To me you are a song / War of the worlds / La rose, opus 46 no 9.
LP: 461160 1
MC: 461160 4

Harborside

HARBORSIDE (Harborside, featuring Frank Musumici).
LP: . . . . CL 2006

Harbour Crossing

HARBOUR CROSSING (Various artists).
LP: . . . . LRF 130

Harbour Kings

SUMMERCOLTS.
Tracks: / Tattoo / Grassfires / Roads to freedom / Forsyth C / Rosemary Road / Sleepers / Searchlight / Flood dream.
MLP: . . . . FIRELP 25

Harbour, Pearl

DON'T FOLLOW ME I'M LOST TOO (Harbour, Pearl & The Explosions).
Tracks: / Alone in the dark / Fujiyama mama / Everybody's boring but my baby / You're in trouble again / Do your homework / Cowboys and Indians / Losing to you / Filipino baby / Let's go upstairs / Rough kids / Out with the girls / Heaven is gonna be empty / At the dentist's.
LP: . . . . K 56885

PEARL HARBOUR AND THE EXPLOSIONS (Harbour, Pearl and the Explosions).
LP: . . . . K 56769

PEARLS GALORE.
LP: . . . . ILPS 9824

Hard As Hell

HARD AS HELL Various Artists (Various artists).
LP: MODEF 26
MC: MODEF 26C

HARD AS HELL VOL 4 (Various artists).
LP: MODEF 4
MC: MODEF 4C

HARD AS HELL VOL III (Various artists).
LP: MODEF 3

Hard Cash

HARD CASH (Various artists).
LP: SPD 1027
MC: SPDC 1027

Hard Corpuscles

DECIDE.
LP: REACTOR 13

Hard Days Night (film)

HARD DAYS NIGHT (FILM SOUNDTRACK) (See under Beatles).

Hard Luck Blues

HARD LUCK BLUES (Lissie Miles, Susie Smith & other artists) (Various artists).
LP: VLP 40

Hard Options

GENERATION TO GENERATION.
Tracks: / Generation to generation / Daylight robbery / Dark skies / World's apart / Sad / Lessons to be learned / Blind faith / Running in the night / Homeland / Who's laughing now.
2LP: MOSA 111

Hard Rock

HARD ROCK (Various artists).
LP: 6685 140
MC: 7653 140

HARD ROCK'83 (Various artists).
Tracks: / Gimme more: *Kiss* / Cold sweat: *Thin Lizzy* / Out for blood: *Ford, Lita* / Don't talk to strangers: *Dio* / Analog kid, The: *Rush* / Trashed: *Black Sabbath* / Don't say make me: *Coney Hatch* / Devil made me do it, The: *Golden Earring* / Nighthunter: *Picture* / Whipping boy: *Nazareth*.
LP: 814 462 1
MC: 814 462 4

SOFT SIDE OF HARD ROCK, THE (Various artists).
Tracks: / Silent night: *Bon Jovi* / Nobody's fool: *Cinderella (bk)* / Make time for love: *Warlock* / All the fools sailed away: *Dio*.
LP: 8166841

TEUTONIC INVASION PT.1 (Various artists).
Tracks: / Pray to the Godz of wrath: *Various artists* / Terminal breath: *Various artists* / Killer without a face: *Various artists* / Soulbursting: *Various artists* / Planed head: *Various artists* / Final fight: *Various artists* / Revelation: *Various artists* / Sphinx: *Various artists*.
LP: RR 9624

THUNDERBOLT HARD ROCK SAMPLER (Various artists).
LP: THBL 999

Hard Times

HARD TIMES.
LP: ROUNDER 4007

HARD TIMES (Various artists).
Tracks: / From my heart: *Various artists* / Say you're leavin: *Various artists* / Hard times: *Various artists*/ Bad to make a woman mad: *Various artists* / Talk fast: *Various artists* / Way I feel, The: *Various artists*/ Call my job: *Various artists* / Figure head: *Various artists* / You better stop: *Various artists* / Puppy howl: *Various artists* / Rambling woman: *Various artists* / Foot race: *Various artists* / Honky Tonk: *Various artists* / You can't love me: *Various artists* / I know better: *Various artists* / Money is the name of the game: *Various artists*.
LP: FLY 602

Hard Times (book)

HARD TIMES (see under Dickens, Charles) (Jeffrey, Peter (nar)).

HARD TIMES (see Dickens, Charles) (Thorne, Stephen).

Hard To Believe

HARD TO BELIEVE (Various artists).
LP: DAMP 121

Hard To Hold (film)

HARD TO HOLD (Film soundtrack) (See under Springfield, Rick) (Springfield, Rick).

Hardbeat Compilation

FIRST HARDBEAT COMPILATION, THE (Various artists).
LP: CK 3000

HARD BEAT/FIRST CUT (Various artists).
LP: AS 8903

Hardcastle, Paul

NO WINNERS.
LP: CDL 1549
MC: ZCDL 1549

PAUL HARDCASTLE.
Tracks: / In the beginning / 19 / King Tut / Don't waste my time / Central Park / Just for money / Moonchopper / Better / Strollin' / Rain forest.
LP: CHR 1517
MC: ZCHR 1517

ZERO ONE.
Tracks: / Forest fire / Panic / Rain forest / Sound chaser / Zero one / Ready-ready go / Drum beat / Hip hop beat.
LP: LPBR 1003

Hardcore

HARDCORE ONE (Various artists).
LP: BPLP 002

Hardcore Holocaust

HARDCORE HOLOCAUST (87-88 SESSIONS) (Various artists).
Tracks: / Heard it all before: *Stupids* / Dog log: *Stupids* / Sheep: *Electro Hippies* / Chickens: *Electro Hippies* / Mother: *Electro Hippies* / False profit: *Extreme Noise Terror* / Another nail in the coffin: *Extreme Noise Terror* / Carry on screaming: *Extreme Noise Terror* / Conned thru life: *Extreme Noise Terror* / Attack in the aftermath: *Bolt Thrower* / Pyschological warefare: *Bolt Thrower* / Skate bored: *Intense Degree*/ Intense degree: *Intense Degree* / Daydreams: *Intense Degree* / Bursting: *Intense Degree* / Voice your opinion: *Unseen Terror* / Moral crusade: *Napalm Death* / Divine death: *M.A.D.* / Control: *M.A.D.*/ Pink machine gun: *Dr. & The Crippens* / Garden centre murders, The: *Dr. & The Crippens* / Skin tight: *Dr. & The Crippens* / Exploitation: *Doom* / No religion: *Doom*.
LP: SFRLP 101
MC: SFRMC 101

Hardcore Raggamuffin

HARDCORE RAGGAMUFFIN (Various artists).
LP: GREL 151
MC: GREEN 151

Harde Tijden

HARDE TIJDEN (Various artists).
LP: SOFA 3301

Harden, Wilbur

DIAL AFRICA (See under Coltrane, John) (Harden, Wilbur & John Coltrane).

Harder They Come

HARDER THEY COME (Film soundtrack) (Various artists).
Tracks: / You can get it if you really want: *Cliff, Jimmy* / Many rivers to cross: *Cliff, Jimmy* / Harder they come, The: *Cliff, Jimmy* / Sitting in limbo: *Cliff, Jimmy* / Draw your brakes: *Scotty* / Rivers of Babylon: *Melodians* / Sweet and Dandy: *Maytals* / Pressure drop: *Maytals* / Johnny too bad: *Slickers*/ Shanty town: *Dekker, Desmond*.
LP: ILPM 9202
MC: ICM 9202
LP: ILPS 9202
MC: RRCT 11

Hardestry, Rich

INTRODUCING RICH HARDESTRY AND THE DEL-RAYS (Hardestry, Rich & The Del-Rays).
LP: SANE 4

Hardie, Ian

BREATH OF FRESH AIRS.
Tracks: / Cheviot blast / Poetic milkman, The / Bull ring, The / Omnibus, The / Junction pool, The (the timeless clock) / Duke's dyke, The / Damside hornpipe,The / Bowmont water / Pipemaj. Rev Joe Brown (border Worthie's Club) / Cleek, The / Catch-a-penny fox (the flooded goat) / Red herring,The / Old bean waltz / Hospital wood / North to England / Hoselaw chapel / Schoolroom pipers (the black hag) / Yetholm haugh / Late white swan, The (Tobermory wedding) / Leg-up,The / Tanners swee / Hen hole, The / Ambon of Torwooklee.
LP: TRAX 001
MC: CTRAX 001

Hardin, Eddie

DAWN TIL DUSK.
LP: NAGE 9
MC: NAGEC 9

MUSIC OF THE STARS - AQUARIUS.
LP: BIRTHLP 4
MC: BIRTHMC 4

SITUATIONS.
Tracks: / Red nose city / Don't thank the bank / When the going gets tough / Caribbean nights / Till summer / Friends / Situations / Just another song / Sometime never / Every night / Morning after, the.
LP: PTLS 1089
MC: PTLC 1089

SURVIVAL.
LP: NAGE 19
MC: NAGEC 19

WIND IN THE WILLOWS (Original cast) (Hardin, Eddie & Zak Starkey).
Tracks: / Wind in the willows / Good morning to you / I'd forgotten how to smile / Wild wood, The / Badger, The / I'm looking forward to tomorrow / Mr. Toad / Piper at the gates of dawn / Wayfarers all / Wind in the willows / Wild wood, The.
LP: PTLS 1078
MC: PTLC 1078

Hardin, Tim

HOMECOMING CONCERT.
Tracks: / If I were a carpenter / Hang on to a dream / Misty roses / Reason to live.
LP: KAM 004

MEMORIAL ALBUM.
LP: PD 16333

NINE.
LP: MQCLP 003
MC: MQCMC 003

THIS IS TIM HARDIN.
Tracks: / Can't slow down / Blues on the ceilin' / Stagger Lee / (I'm your) hoochie coochie man / I've been working on the railroad / House of the rising sun / Fast freight / Cocaine Bill / You got to have more than one woman / Danville dame.
LP: ED 309

Hardin & York

FOR THE WORLD.
Tracks: / Deep in my despair / Have mercy woman / For the world / Some places are better to be / Ex 345 / Cowboy / I'll be back again / Feeling seeing hearing / Natural gas / Take away today.
LP: SEE 41

Harding, John Wesley

HERE COMES THE GROOM.
Tracks: / Here comes the groom / Spaced cowgirl / When the sun comes out / Audience with you, An / Same thing twice / Nothing I'd rather do / Cathy's new clown / You're no good / Devil in me, The / Dark dark heart / Affairs of the heart / Scared of guns.
LP: 7599260871
MC: 7599260872

IT HAPPENED ONE NIGHT.
Tracks: / Headful of something / Devil in me, The / Who you really are / Famous man / July 13th 1985 / One night only / Affairs of the heart / Humankind / Night he took her to the fairground / Careers service / Biggest monument / Roy Orbison knows (the best man's song) / You and your career / Bastard son.
LP: LFIEND 137

NAME ABOVE THE TITLE, THE.
MC: 7599264814

Harding, Mike

BEST OF MIKE HARDING.
LP: RUB 046
MC: RUBC 046

BEST OF MIKE HARDING-VOLUME TWO,THE.
LP: RUB 047
MC: RUBC 047

BOMBERS' MOON.
Tracks: / January man / And the band played waltzing Matilda / Good morning morning / Factory / Bomber's moon / Thirty nights / These poor hands / Small high window / Accrington pals, The / God help the poor / Back of the back of the moon.
LP: MOO 3
MC: MOOC 3

CAPTAIN PARALYTIC AND THE BROWN ALE COWBOY.
Tracks: / Brown ale cowboys play a bit / Enter Captain Paralytic / Brum and a giant tortoise / These are my uncles / God was a golliwog / Man'nited song / Rosy cheeked girls, The / Upper echelon, The / Bloody, bloody, bloody, bloody / Old green iron lamp, The / Egremont - Gateway to oblivia / Mr. Fat Cigar / Horizontal Lil / Akroyds funeral / Captain Paralytics polka - the pishtenstein waltz / Sonny's pain / Manuel / PBI.NKD.NP.BAGA / Lochdale ploughboy / BACS play a bit more.
2LP: 6641 798

FLAT DOGS AND SHAKY PUDDEN.
Tracks: / Gropes encounters of the first kind / Mr. O'Grady / Gimme dat shaky pudden' / Flat dog, The / Somethings that the grown ups just won't tell you / Love, some thoughts / Ballad of Slack Alice, The.
LP: REH 468
MC: ZCR 468

FOO FOO SHUFFLEWICK AND HER EXOTIC BANANA.
Tracks: / Foo Foo Shufflewick and her exotic banana / I am dancing alone in the night / Dracula and the trendies / Hotel Transylvania, The / Ronald Reagan, my hero / God meets Ronnie / Son et lumiere / Sao Bras Albuferia.
LP: MOO 8
MC: MOOC 8

GOD'S OWN DRUNK.
LP: MOO 10
MC: MOOC 10

KOMIC KUTZ.
Tracks: / Is that the sun / Cameo club, The / Unluckiest man in the world, The / Can't help looking on the brightside / Jiggery pokery / Posh parties / Roggers and I / Uming face, A / Scouting for balmpots / Ladies man, The / Professional hospital visitor, The / 'Ardins theory of umour / Hole in the elephant's bottom, The.
2LP: 6625 041
MC: 7649 131

LANCASHIRE LAD, A.
LP: LER 2039

MIKE HARDING'S BACK.
Tracks: / Extra eye, The / Lobster song / Parrot, The / Whitsuntide clothes / When I drink everybody drinks / Boozing, bloody well boozing / Lord gives and the Lord takes away, The / Bide awhile.
LP: RUB 022
MC: RUBC 022

MRS.'ARDIN'S KID.
Tracks: / Joseph Anthony Capstick / Suitcase, The / Away with rum / Ballad of Cowheel Lou / Sailor courted a farmer's daughter, A / What's what / Drunken tackler, The / Strangeways Hotel, The / Man from the Pru, The / Uncle Joe's mint balls.
LP: RUB 011
MC: RUBC 011

OLD FOUR EYES IS BACK.
MC: 7108 505
LP: 6308 290

ON THE TOUCHLINE.
Tracks: / Call the night porter / For Carlo / Friends that I have known / Jinny Bobbin / Man who bangs the button / Mills of the valley / On the touchline / Sausage me a gregory / Shady Lane lady / St. George doesn't live here anymore / Wild geese.
MC: 7108193
LP: 9109230

ONE MAN SHOW.
Tracks: / Arnold my frog / Beaky knucklewart / Bogey man / Crumpsall cream cracker corned beef, The / Kamikaze cubs go to camp / Down our street / Irwell Delta blues / Jimmy Spoons / King Cotton / My dad the weatherman / Napoleon's retreat from Wigan / Polka off / Polka on / Talking Blackpool blues / Top of the Pops / Unlucky Uncle Arthur / Wedding at 18 Clegg Street, The.
LP: PRID 4
MC: PRIDC 4
MC: 7581617
LP: 6625 022

PLUTONIUM ALLEY.
LP: MOO 9
MC: MOOC 9

RED SPECS ALBUM, THE.
Tracks: / Limey in New York, A / Yank in Barnsley, A / Reagan and Thatcher apocalypse / Fall out calypso / 14 half pound budgie, The / Comrade Olga.
LP: SPELP 31
MC: SPIMC 31

ROCHDALE COWBOY RIDES AGAIN, THE (VOL 1).
Tracks: / Top of the pops / Irwell Delta Blues / Nancy / Napoleon's retreat from Wigan / My dad the weatherman / Bogey man / Unlucky uncle Arthur / Arnold my frog / King cotton / My brother Sylveste / Beaky Knucklewart / Talking Blackpool blues / Down our street / Banish misfortune / Wedding at 18 Clegg Street, The / Jimmy Spoons.
LP: RUB 015
MC: RUBC 015

ROCHDALE COWBOY RIDES AGAIN, THE (VOL 2).
LP: RUB 016
MC: RUBC 016

ROLL OVER CECIL SHARPE.
Tracks: / Buggeri, buggeri, buggeri / Just can't beat this family life / Yorkshireman in the court of King Ronnie,The / 3 legged pig,The / Roll over Cecil Sharpe / K-Tel folk song PLC, Inc..

LP: MOO 7
MC: MOOC 7

ROOTED.
Tracks: / Buckets of blue steam and square bubbles / Leroy and the foreman / When the Martians land in Huddersfield / Rooted / She'll be right mate / West Yorkshire Dobro-playin' hippy cowboy,The / Wath on dearne blues.
LP: MOO 2
MC: MOOC 2

TAKE YOUR FINGERS OFF IT.
Tracks: / Australia / Hail glorious St.Margaret / Take your fingers off it / Captain Legless meets Superdrunk / Ghost of the cafe Gungha Din, The / Crumpsall kid, The / Quasimodo meets the Virgin Mary / Viking helmet, The.
LP: MOO 1
MC: MOOC 1

Hardline

HARDLINE.
LP: SKULL 8358

Hardman, Bill

HOME.
Tracks: / Sambo do Brilho / Once I loved / My pen is hot / Rancho Cevarro / I remember love.
LP: MR 5152

Hardman, Rosie

EAGLE OVER BLUE MOUNTAIN.
Tracks: / Final analysis / When he sang Louisiana / It happens all the time / You stole the show / Poor old Rose / Eagle over blue mountain / Cry in the dark / Tongue tied / Pride of the river / Love's not part of the deal.
LP: PLR 014

FIREBIRD.
LP: LER 2075

SECOND SEASON CAME, THE.
LP: LER 3018

STOPPED IN MY TRACKS.
Tracks: / Another love song / Cleveland country / No stranger to me / Grace Darling / Reunion / Lean on me / England / This is for all the ladies / Abandoned / Dancing when the sun goes down.
LP: PLR 023

WEAKNESS OF EVE, THE.
LP: PLR 053

Hard-Ons

DICKCHEESE.
Tracks: / Made to love you / What am I supposed to do? / Oozing for pleasure / Everytime I do a fart / Get away / Pretty face / There was a time / Mickey juice / Figaro / F**k society / Yuppies suck / Something about you / All washed up / Ache to touch you / Why don't you shut up / Nerds / Got a baby / Stairway to punchbowl.
LP: SOL 10

HOT FOR YOUR LOVE BABY.
Tracks: / All set to go / Love song for Cindy / Coffs harbour blues / School days / It's cold outside / Then I kissed her (Arabic version) / By my side / I'll come again / Fifteen / Keish's new song / From my window / Rock 'n' roll all nite.
LP: SOL 8

LOVE IS A BATTLEFIELD.
Tracks: / Love is a battlefield.
LP: SOL 19

YUMMY.
LP: SOL 26
MC: SOL 26C

Hardware

HARDWARE (Film Soundtrack) (Various artists).
LP: UNKNOWN

Hardwick, Mollie

DUCHESS OF DUKE STREET.
MC: CAB 002

PARSON'S PLEASURE.
MCSET: CAB 304

Hardy, Francoise

ALL OVER THE WORLD (ALBUM).
Tracks: / Rose, The / All over the world / It's getting late / Say it now / Only you can do it / Another place / Catch a falling star / I wish it were me / You just have to say the word / This little heart / However much / Only friends / Just call and I'll be there / It's my heart / Autumn rendezvous / Find me a boy / I will change me life / So many friends.
MC: 771 041

FRANCOISE HARDY STORY VOL.4 1967-1969.
MC: 706259

GOLDEN HOUR PRESENTS THE BEST OF FRANCOISE HARDY.
Tracks: / Autumn rendezvous / La maison ou j'ai grand / This little heart / On se quit tejours / Ton meilleur ami / I wish it were me / C'est le passe / Oh, oh cheri / C'est l'amour / Au quel je pense / Je t'aime / All over the world / Et meme / Say it now / Tous les garcons et les filles / L'amour s'en Val / Le temps de l'amour / Saural je / L'amour d'un garcon / J'en attends plus personne / Je chagerais d'avis / Voila / Les petits garcons / Tout les garcons et les filles / L'amour s'en va.
LP: GH 830
MC: ZCGH 830

HIT PARADE OF FRANCOISE HARDY, THE.
LP: 509 191
MC: 707 191

IN VOGUE.
LP: 000318

Hardy, Robert (nar)

ADVENTURES OF SHERLOCK HOLMES, THE (See under Sherlock Holmes)).

BRIDGE ON THE RIVER KWAI (see under Bridge on the River Kwai).

VARIOUS SHERLOCK HOLMES STORIES (see under Sherlock Holmes).

Hardy, Thomas (aut)

FAR FROM THE MADDING CROWD (Thorne, Stephen).
MCSET: CC/003

IMAGINATIVE WOMAN, AN.
MC: TTC/TH 04

JUDE THE OBSCURE (Jeffrey, Peter (nar)).
MCSET: 418 171-4

MAYOR OF CASTERBRIDGE (Rowe, John (aut)).
MCSET: CC/028

MAYOR OF CASTERBRIDGE (Bates, Alan).
MCSET: LFP 7337

POETRY OF THOMAS HARDY, THE (Burton, Richard).
MC: 1140

RETURN OF THE NATIVE, THE (Richardson, Lee).
MC: CDL 51733

RETURN OF THE NATIVE, THE (Jeffrey, Peter (nar)).
MCSET: 414 754-4

RETURN OF THE NATIVE, THE (Rickman, Alan).
MCSET: CC/017

TESS OF THE D'URBERVILLES (Shearer, Moira (nar)).
MCSET: SAY 56
MCSET: ARGO 1187

TESS OF THE D'URBERVILLES (Thorne, Stephen).
MCSET: CC/054

THOMAS HARDY AND LOVE.
MC: THE 7622

THOMAS HARDY AND MUSIC (Unknown narrator(s)).
MC: THE 587

THREE STRANGERS.
MC: TTHC/TH0 1

WITHERED ARM, THE (Redgrave, Corin).
MCSET: COL 2017

WITHERED ARM, THE (Morant, Richard).
MC: TTCH/TH 02

Hare, Colin

MARCH HARE PLUS.
Tracks: / Get up the road / Bloodshot eyes / For where have you been / Find me / Underground girl / To my maker / Grannie, grannie / Alice / Nothing to write home about / New day / Cowboy Joe (saga) / Just like me / Charlie Brown's time / Fighting for peace.
LP: SEE 261

Hare, Phil

LIVING ON CREDIT.
Tracks: / Closed for business / All dressed up and nowhere to go / Living on credit / Fanny Power/Planxty Johnson / Ill wind / Community charge song / They've come to take our town away / Johnny don't go / All things are quite silent / Strong in the sun / Commoners ballad / Lest we forget / West wind, The.
LP: FE 077
MC: FE 077 C

Harem Scarem

LOW AND BEHOLD.
LP: CGAS 805

Haremza, Teresa

TERESA HAREMZA.
LP: LRF 161

Harewood, Al

MIDNIGHT CREEPER (see Simmons,Norman etc.).

Harewood, Dorian

LOVE WILL STOP CALLING.
MC: ZCER 1001
MC: ER 1001

Hargreaves, Jack

COUNTRY WALKING.
LP: RESM 011

KNOW YOUR DOG.
LP: RESDM 009

KNOW YOUR FISH.
LP: RESM 005
MC: ZCRM005

KNOW YOUR PONY.
LP: RESM 010

Hargreaves, Roger

VARIOUS MR. MEN RECORDINGS (See under Mr. Men) (Percival, Lance (nar)).

Hargrove, Roy

DIAMOND IN THE ROUGH.
Tracks: / Proclamation / Ruby my dear / New joy, A / Confidentially / Broski / All over again / Easy to remember / Premonition / BHG / Wee.
LP: PL 90471
MC: PK 90471

PUBLIC EYE.
Tracks: / Public eye / Spiritual companion / September in the rain / Lada / Once in awhile / Heartbreaker / End of a love affair, The / Night watch / You don't know what love is / Little Bennie / What's new (CD only).
MC: PK 83113

Haricots Rouges

LES AU JAM POTATOES 1972.
LP: PRG LP 7

Harlandic Male Voice

SINGS MAGGIE AND OTHER IRISH FAVOURITES.
Tracks: / Maggie / Star of the County Down / Off in the stilly night / Danny boy / She moved through the fair / Molly Malone-(Medley) Mick Magillian / I'll take you home again Kathleen / Trottin' to the fair / Eileen Aroon / Kathleen Mavoureen / Medley: If you're Irish - When Irish eyes are smiling / In the gloaming / If you're Irish come into the parlour / When Irish eyes are smiling.
LP: GES 1228
MC: KGEC 1228

Harle, John

HABANERA.
Tracks: / Three folksongs (from the county) / Gymnopedie no.1 / Elegy for 'Trane / Three preludes for piano / Allegro ben ritmato e diciso / Andante con moto e poco rubato / Fantasia / Deep purple / Tender is the night (theme) / Nicole's theme / Rosemary's waltz / Homage to Edith Piaf / Syrinx / Habanera / Out of the cool.
LP: HNBL 1331

Harlem

A WORLD OF JAZZ (Harlem Jazz).
LP: VG DP36

CLASSIC BIG BAND JAZZ.
Tracks: / Pay-off, The / Shout 'em Aunt Tillie / Paducah / Do you believe in love at first sight / Black and tan fantasy / Will you, won't you be my baby? / Accordion Joe / Copenhagen / Cincinnati daddy / Beedle-um-bum / Felling drowsy / Jazznocracy / Jeeps blues / Goin' to town.
LP: LA 5002
MC: LA 5002 C

HARLEM (1926-57) various artists (Various artists).
2LP: PM 43249

HARLEM COMES TO LONDON (Original Artists) (Various artists).
Tracks: / Silver rose: *Plantation Orchestra, The* / Arabella's wedding day: *Plantation Orchestra, The* / Smilin' Joe: *Plantation Orchestra, The* / For baby and me: *Plantation Orchestra, The* / Camp meeting day: *Sissle Noble* & his Orchestra / Sophisticated lady: *Ellington, Duke And His Orchestra* / Ike: *Ellington, Duke And His Orchestra*/ Dinah: *Hatch & his Harlem Stompers* / Some of these days: *Hatch & his Harlem Stompers* / I can't dance: *Various artists* / I must have that man: *Valaida* / Keep a twinkle in your eye: *Nicholas Brothers* / Your heart and mine: *Nicholas Brothers* / Dixie isn't Dixie any more: *Carter, Lavaida* / Jo Jo the cannibal kid: *Carter, Lavaida* / Breakfast in Harlem: *Buck & Bubbles* / I ain't got nobody: *Buck & Bubbles* / Sweet Georgia Brown: *Buck & Bubbles* / Harlem in my heart: *Welch, Elisabeth* / Ain't misbehavin': *Waller, Fats & his Continental Rhythm* / I can't give you anything but love: *Various artists*.
LP: SH 265
LP: SW 8444

HARLEM HEAVIES (R&B '54-62) various artists (Various artists).
LP: BLP 107

Harlem Blues

HARLEM BLUES AND JAZZ BAND 1973-80 (Harlem Jazz & Blues Band).
LP: VLP 403

Harlem Hamfats

HARLEM HAMFATS: 1936/37.
Tracks: / Weed smokers dream / I'm cuttin' out / Bad luck man / Oh red / Garbage man / Little girl / Growling dog / Move your hand.
MC: NEO 850

HARLEM HAMFATS: 1936-39.
LP: DLP 547
LP: BD 2045

HARLEM HAMFATS 1937-39 (Harlem Hamfats/Howard, Rosetta).
Tracks: / Let your linen hang low / If you're a viper / Rosetta blues / It's your turn / Let's fall in love again / Worried mind blues / It will never happen again / Trading old love for new / Stay on it / Delta bound / You got to go when the wagon comes / How long baby / Harlem jamboree / Candy man / Oh rider / Stay away from my door.
LP: BD 620
LP: OFF 3024
LP: WJS 1007

HOT CHICAGO JAZZ-BLUES & JIVE 1936-37..
LP: FL 9029

I'M SO GLAD.
LP: QUEEN 062

Harlem Hit Parade

HARLEM HIT PARADE Old town blues vol.2 (Various artists).
LP: CHD 206

Harlem Jazz

HARLEM JAZZ 1921-31 (Various artists).
LP: CJM 1

Harlem Jazz & Blues

HARLEM JAZZ AND BLUES BAND (Various artists).
LP: VLP 404

Harlem Roots

BIG BAND,THE.
LP: SLP 6000

HEADLINERS,THE.
LP: SLP 6001

JIVIN' TIME (Various artists).
LP: SLP 6003

RHYTHM IN HARMONY.
LP: SLP 6002

Harlem Shuffle

HARLEM SHUFFLE (Sixties soul classics) (Various artists).
Tracks: / Gimme little sign: *Wood, Brenton* / Dancin' holiday: *Olympics* / Love makes the world go round: *Jackson, Deon* / Spring: *Birdlegs & Pauline* / Expressway to your heart: *Soul Survivors* / Ooh wee baby: *Hughes, Fred* / Baby I'm yours: *Lewis, Barbara* / Cool jerk: *Capitols* / Get on up: *Esquires* / And get away: *Esquires* / Duck, The: *Lee, Jackie* / I know: *George, Barbara* / Snake, The: *Wilson, Al* / Harlem shuffle: *Bob & Earl* / Hello stranger: *Lewis, Barbara* / Oh how happy: *Shades Of Blue* / Oogum boogum song: *Wood, Brenton* / Bounce: *Olympics* / Backfield in motion: *Mel & Tim* / Make me your baby: *Various artists* / You can make it if you try: *Various artists*.
LP: CRB 1139
MC: TCCRB 1139

Harlem Speaks

HARLEM SPEAKS (Various artists).
Tracks: / Saratoga drag: *Various artists* / Stevedore stomp: *Various artists* / Hot bones and rice: *Various artists* / Sugarfoot stomp: *Various artists* / Cotton Club stomp: *Various artists* / Misty morning: *Various artists* / Harlem speaks: *Various artists* / Gee baby ain't I good to you: *Various artists*.
LP: LA 5013
MC: LA 5013C

Harlequin

HARLEQUIN.
Tracks: / Take this heart / Keep this fire alive / Don't waste my time / Memories / Can't turn it off / Calling / Trouble in paradise / Run for your life / Love in disguise.
LP: EPC 26263

ONE FALSE MOVE.

LP: .... HMUSA 1

Harlequin (Film)

HARLEQUIN (Film soundtrack) (Various artists).
LP: MM22002

Harley, Steve

BALLERINA.
Tracks: / Ballerina.
MC: .... STLT 14

BEST OF STEVE HARLEY & COCKNEY REBEL (Harley, Steve & Cockney Rebel).
Tracks: / Make me smile (come up and see me) / Big big deal / Psychomodo / Mr. Soft / Judy teen / Cavaliers / Sebastian / Here comes the sun / Riding the waves / Black or white / Mr. Raffles (man it was mean) / Tumbling down.
LP: .... FA 3007
MC: .... TCFA 3007
LP: .... EMC 3345

BEST YEARS OF OUR LIVES (Harley, Steve & Cockney Rebel).
Tracks: / Introducing 'The Best Years' / Mad, mad moonlight / Mr. Raffles / It wasn't me / Panorama / Make me smile (come up and see me) / Back to the farm / 49th parallel / Best years of our lives / Another journey / Sebastian (live).
LP: .... EMC 3068

CANDIDATE.
Tracks: / Audience with the man / Woodchopper / Freedom's prisoner / Love on the rocks / Who's afraid / One more time / How good it feels / From here to eternity / Young hearts.
LP: .... EMC 3311

COLLECTION: STEVE HARLEY.
LP: .... IC 028 07543

COLLECTION: STEVE HARLEY & COCKNEY REBEL (Harley, Steve & Cockney Rebel).
Tracks: / Death trip / What Ruthy said / Sebastian / Sweet dreams / Sling it / Mad mad moonlight / 49th Parallel / Red is a mean mean colour / Innocence and guilt / Love's a prima donna / Everything changes / Tumbling down / Mr. Soft / If this is love / Make me smile (come up and see me) / Roll the dice / Someone's coming / Freedom's prisoner / Irresistible / Such is life.
2LP: .... CCSLP 197
MC: .... CCSMC 197

FACE TO FACE (Harley, Steve & Cockney Rebel).
Tracks: / Here comes the sun / Mr. Soft / Make me smile (come up and see me) / Psychomode / Mirror freak / Crazy raver / Mad mad moonlight / Sweet dreams / Sebastian.
LP: .... IC 172 06421/2
MC: .... TC 172 06421/2

FACE TO FACE - A LIVE RECORDING (Harley, Steve & Cockney Rebel).
2LP: .... EMSP 320

GREATEST HITS: STEVE HARLEY & COCKNEY REBEL (Harley, Steve & Cockney Rebel).
Tracks: / Mad, mad, moonlight / Mr. Soft / Sebastian / Judy teen / Compared with you / Mr. Raffles / Riding the waves / Here comes the sun / Make me smile (come up and see me) / Best years of our lives / Psychomodo / Sling it / Freedom's prisoner / Love's a prima donna / Tumbling down.
LP: .... EMS 1291
MC: .... TCEMS 1291
LP: .... ATAK 130
MC: .... TCATAK 150

HUMAN MENAGERIE.
LP: 1C 072 05438

LOVE'S A PRIMA DONNA (Harley, Steve & Cockney Rebel).
LP: .... EMC 3156

MR. SOFT (Harley, Steve & Cockney Rebel).
Tracks: / Love's a prima donna / Another journey / What Ruthey said / Loretas tale / Compared with you / Sebastian / Mr Soft / Freedom's prisoner / Hideaway / Singular band / Panorama / Finally a card game / Psychomodo / Muriel the actor / Mirror freak / I wish it would rain / Crazy raver / Red is a mean colour / Irresistible / Big big deal / Roll the dice / Riding the waves / Bed in the corner / Sidetrack one.
2LP: .... VSOPLP 124
MC: .... VSOPMC 124

PHANTOM OF THE OPERA (see Brightman, Sarah) (Brightman, Sarah & Steve Harley).

TIMELESS FLIGHT (Harley, Steve & Cockney Rebel).
Tracks: / Red is a mean, mean colour / White, white dove / Understand / All men are hungry / Black or white / Everything changes / Nothing is sacred / Don't go, don't cry / Throw your soul down here / Mad mad moonlight (live).
LP: .... EMA 775

Harlow

HARLOW.
Tracks: / Chain reaction / Don't say we're over / When you love someone / No escape / Pictures / Silence / Empty / Cry murder / Beyond control / Edge of love.
LP: 7599258741
MC: 7599258742

Harmageddon (film)

HARMAGEDDON/CHINA FREE FALL (Film soundtrack) (See under Emerson, Keith) (Emerson, Keith/Derek Austin).

Harman, James

EXTRA NAPKINS (Harman, James Band).
LP: .... RR 505

Harmonaires

FIRST LOVE.
Tracks: / Bye bye blues / Harmonica boy / Harmonoogie / Shoe shine boy / Tribute to Stephen Foster / Lullaby of birdland / Peg o my heart / Canadian sunset / Time I get to Phoenix / Five foot two / Perfidia / 12th Street / Swedish rhapsody / Hot spud / Hello Dolly.
MC: .... PAC 105

Harmonia

DINO.
Tracks: / Watussi / Sehr kosmisch / Sonnenschein / Dino / Ohrwurm / Ahol / Veterano / Hausmusik.
LP: 0040 123

Harmonica Blues

HARMONICA BLUES 1920S & 1930S (Various artists).
LP: .... L 1053

HARMONICA BLUES 1936-40 (Various artists).
LP: .... WSE 109

SUCKIN' AND BLOWIN' (Various artists).
LP: .... CG 709-03
LP: .... SG 709-03

Harmonica Frank

HARMONICA FRANK.
LP: .... PURITAN 3003

Harmonicas...

GREAT HARMONICA PLAYERS VOL.1 (Various artists).
LP: .... RL 320

GREAT HARMONICA PLAYERS VOL.2 (Various artists).
LP: .... RL 321

HARMONICAS, WASHBOARDS, FIDDLES, JUGS (Various artists).
LP: .... RL 311

Harmonicas Unlimited

HARMONICAS UNLIMITED (Various artists).
2LP: .... DLP 503/504

Harmony

HARMONY (Various artists).
MC: .... RTE 118

Harmony Holiday

HARMONY HOLIDAY Various artists (Various artists).
Tracks: / Maybe it's because I'm a Londoner: *Various artists* / Old bull and bush, The: *Various artists* / Berkeley Square: *Various artists* / Wotcher (knocked 'em in the Old Kent Road): *Various artists* / Hey look me over: *Various artists* / Just a-wearyin' for you: *Various artists* / Cuddle up a little closer: *Various artists* / Uncle Joe: *Various artists* / Yesterday: *Various artists* / Streak, The: *Various artists* / New Ashmolian marching society: *Various artists* / Foggy day in London town: *Various artists* / Yes sir, that's my baby: *Various artists* / Something: *Various artists* / This little light of mine: *Various artists* / Riders in the sky: *Various artists* / Back in those days: *Various artists* / Auctioneer, The: *Various artists* / Goodbye my lady love: *Various artists.*
LP: .... MWM 1008

Harmony Sisters

HARMONY SISTERS.
LP: .... FF 248

SECOND HELPING.
LP: .... FF 283

Harnen, Jimmy

DON'T FORGET.
LP: 4654901
MC: 4654904

Harold, May

FLYING ON MY OWN.
Tracks: / Flying on your own / Could have been / One moment in time / Feeling single, seeing double / Can't be with you tonight / Anthem / Only he / No more the fool / Almaz / Silver threads and golden needles / Didn't we almost have it all / Heroes.
LP: .... LIDL 6029
MC: .... LIDC 6029

INTRODUCING MAY HAROLD.
Tracks: / On my own / Caravan song / Missing / Butterfly ball / Crying / Wuthering heights / Greatest love of all, The / Second time, The / Phantom of the opera, The / Only love / When will I be loved / Memory / I know him so well / Way old friends do, The / Auld lang syne.
LP: .... LIDL 6025
MC: .... LIDC 6025

Harp Attack

HARP ATTACK (Various artists).
Tracks: / Down home blues: *Various artists* / Who: *Various artists* / Keep your hand out of my pockets: *Various artists* / Little car blues: *Various artists* / My eyes keep me in trouble: *Various artists* / Broke and hungry: *Various artists* / Hit man: *Various artists* / Black night: *Various artists* / Somebody changed the lock: *Various artists* / Second hand man: *Various artists* / New kid on the block: *Various artists.*
MC: .... AC 4790

Harper, Addie

ADDIE HARPER AND THE WICK TRIO (Harper, Addie & The Wick Trio).
Tracks: / Jean's reel / Moving cloud / Jackie Coleman's reel / Covenanters, The / Sally across the sea / Song of the seashore / Craighall jig, The / Barney O'Neil / Ballycastle jig, The / Bowing the strings / Ton & Mima's golden wedding / Patrick McGovern / Manola / Teddy bears' picnic / Archie Menzies / Sally gardens / Duncan Jamieson of Carluke / Maggie's reel / PM Jim Christie of Wick / John McMillan of Barra / Addie Harper jig, The / Garstairs dream / Unshackled Lord of the hills / Hazel Villa / Tune for Sheila Hunter, A / Captain Lachlan McPhail of Tiree / Athole Highlanders, The / Forty-second Highlanders farewell to India / Acharacle midgie, The / Man's a man for a' that, A / Scots wha' hae / Auld lang syne / Donald Iain Rankine / High level, The.
LP: .... BGC 343
MC: .... KITV 343

HEAD NORTH WITH ADDIE HARPER (Harper, Addie & His Scottish Dance Band).
Tracks: / Canadian three step / Finnish waltz / Barn dance / Old English air / West Denbie reel / Waltz / Medley / Military two step / Hebridean reel / Gaelic waltz / Scottish reel / When you and I were young Maggie / Brittannia two step.
LP: .... GLN 1021

HIGHLAND SPREE.
LP: .... GLN 1006

ON THE ROAD BY THE RIVER (Harper, Addie & The Wick Band).
Tracks: / Tribute to Allan Michael ((Gay Gordon)) / Patches march ((Gay Gordon)) / McNeil's march ((Gay Gordon)) / Road by the river / Wind that blew, The ((Jig & Reel)) / John Keith Laing ((Jig & Reel)) / More than yesterday / Dumfries polka, The / Who at my door is standing / Edinburgh Caithness gathering waltz / Maid of the hill, The ((Mississippi dip, The)) / Keep your feet still Geordie Hinney ((Mississippi dip, The)) / Primrose and the daffodil, The ((Missisipi dip)) / John Gunn's anniversary ((Anniversary reel)) / Snouts and ears ((Anniversary reel)) / Geordie the boatman ((Anniversary reel)) / Wattens welcome to the Queen Mother ((Anniversary reel)) / When the gold in your hair turns to grey / Waterfall 99 / Elaine / Addie Harper of Wick / Standing stones / Caledonia march, The / Peat bog, The / Lilting fisherman, The / Boys of the town / Scotland my home / Crags of tumbledown mountain.
LP: .... ITV 374
MC: .... KITV 374

PRIDE OF THE NORTH, THE (Harper, Addie & The Wick Band).
LP: .... WGR 021
MC: .... CWGR 021
LP: .... GLN 1029

Harper, Billy

BILLY HARPER QUINTET (Harper, Billy Quintet).
LP: .... SN 1001

BLACK SAINT IN EUROPE (Harper, Billy Quintet).
LP: .... BSR 001

KNOWLEDGE OF SELF.
LP: .... YX 7801

SORAN -BUSHI B.H.
Tracks: / Trying to get ready / Loverhood / Soran-bushi, B.H..
LP: .... YX 7522

SUCH GREAT FRIENDS (See Under Cowell, Stanley) (Cowell, Stanley, Billy Harper, Reggie Workman & Billy Hart).

Harper Brothers

REMEMBERANCE.
MC: 8417234

Harper, Don

COMBO (Harper, Don - Denny Wright Duo, Trio, Quartet, Sextet).
Tracks: / It's new / Quiet one, The / Swing '77 / Little buttercup / Ragging the scale / My favourite things / Makin' whoopee / Belly dancer / Nagasaki / Out of the blue / Don't panic / Poor butterfly / Pretty trix / Mood indigo.
LP: .... OU 2202

DON HARPER.
LP: .... CLGLP 022
MC: .... ZCLG 022

LOOK UP AND LIVE (see under New Jersey Mass Choir) (Harper, Don/New Jersey Mass Choir).

SONG FOR ALICE.
LP: .... VSLP 515
MC: .... VSC 515

Harper, Roy

BORN IN CAPTIVITY.
LP: .... AWL 1001
MC: .... AWT 1001

BULLINAMINGVASE.
Tracks: / One of those days in England / These last days / Cherishing the lonesome / Naked flame / Watford gap / One of those days in England (parts 2-10).
LP: .... ATAK 101
MC: .... TCATAK 101
LP: .... EMS 1259
MC: .... TCEMS 1259
LP: .... SHSP 4060

BURN THE WORLD.
LP: .... AWL 1019
MC: .... AWT 1019

COME OUT FIGHTING.
LP: .... AWT 1035

DESCENDANTS OF SMITH.
LP: .... EMC 3524
MC: .... TCEMC 3524

FLASHES FROM THE ARCHIVES OF OBLIVION.
2LP: .... AWLD 1012
MC: .... AWTD 1012

FLAT, BAROQUE AND BERSERK.
Tracks: / Don't you grieve / I hate the white man / Feeling all the Saturday / How does it feel / Goodbye / Another day / Davey / East of the sun / Tom Tiddler's ground / Francesca / Song of the ages / Hell's angels.
LP: .... EG 2605851
MC: .... EG 2605854

FOLKJOKEOPUS.
LP: .... AWL 1003
MC: .... AWT 1003

HQ.
Tracks: / Game (parts I-V), The / Spirit lives, the / Grown ups are just silly children / Referendum / Forget me not / Hallucinating light / When an old cricketer leaves the crease.
LP: .... ATAK 68
MC: .... TCATAK 68
LP: .... SHSP 4046
MC: .... TCSHSP 4046

IN BETWEEN EVERY LINE.
Tracks: / One of those days in England / Short and sweet / Referendum / Highway blues / True story / Game, the / One man rock and roll band / Hangman.
2LP: .... EN 5004
MCSET: .... TCEN 5004

LIFEMASK.
Tracks: / Highway blues / All Ireland / Little lady / Bank of the dead / South Africa / Lord's prayer, The / Ballad of songwriter / Zaney Janey / Midspring dithering / Zenjem.
LP: .... AWL 1007
MC: .... AWT 1007

LOONY ON THE BUS.
Tracks: / No change / Playing prison / I wanna be part of the news / Burn the world / Casualty / Cora / Loony on the bus / Come up and see me / Flycatcher, The / Square boxes.
LP: .... AWL 1011
MC: .... AWT 1011

ONCE.
LP: .... AWL 1018
MC: .... AWT 1018

SOPHISTICATED BEGGAR.
Tracks: / Goldfish bowl / Sophisticated beggar / Big fat silver aeroplane / Legend / Girlie / October 12th / Black

clouds / Mr. Station Master / My friend / China girl.
LP: . . . . SDLP 051

STORMCOCK.
Tracks: / Hors d'ouvres / One man rock and roll band / Same old rock, the / Me and my woman.
LP: . . . . AWL 2001
MC: . . . . AWT 2001

UNKNOWN SOLDIER.
Tracks: / Playing games / I'm in love with you / Flycatcher / You / Old faces / Short and sweet / First thing in the morning / Unknown soldier / Ten years ago / True story.
LP: . . . . SHVL 820

VALENTINE.
LP: . . . . SHSP 4027

VALENTINE (RE-RELEASE).
Tracks: / Forbidden fruit / Male chauvinist pig blues / I'll see you again / Twelve hours of sunset / Acapulco gold / Commune / Magic woman / Che / North country / Forever / Home (studio) (on CD only) / Too many movies (on CD only) / Home (on CD only).
LP: . . . . AWL 1015
MC: . . . . AWT 1015

WHATEVER HAPPENED TO JUGULA? (Harper, Roy/Page, Jimmy).
Tracks: / Nineteen forty-eightish / Hangman / Elizabeth / Advertisement / Bad speech / Hope / Twentieth century man.
LP: . . . . BBL 60
MC: . . . . BBLC 60
LP: . . . . BEGA 60

WORK OF HEART.
LP: . . . . AWL 1002
MC: . . . . AWT 1002

Harper, Toni

CANDY STORM BLUES.
Tracks: / Candy store blues / Cinderella baby / Sam's song / You're too tall, I'm too small / Happy feet / Rock-a-bye baby / It's story time again / Dish rag, The / Get up / Muffin man, The / Dolly's lullaby / Jingle bells / Peppermint stick / Choo'n gum / Floppy / Get goin' engineer.
LP: . . . . OFF 3009

LADY LONELY.
LP: . . . . FS 46

Harpers Bizarre

BEST OF HARPER'S BIZZARE, THE.
Tracks: / 59th Street Bridge Song / Happy talk / Come to the sunshine / Simon Smith and the amazing dancing bear / Louisiana man / Me Japanese boy / Biggest night of her life / Sentimental journey / Anything goes / Chattanooga choo choo / I'll build a stairway to paradise / Milord.
LP: . . . . K 56044

Harpes Indiennes

INDIAN HARPS OF SOUTH AMERICA.
Tracks: / Perriquera / El colas / Limena / Carretaguy / Preludio / El tilingo / Crepusculo Andino / Concierto en la llanura / Llegada / Puerto Mitanda / Alma, corazon y vida / El siquisiri / La cosas del cine / Maria Chuchena / Las Virgenes del sol / Colorado.
LP: . . . . PS 807

Harpin' On It

HARPIN' ON IT (Various artists).
LP: . . . . JSP 1063

Harpo, Slim

BEST OF SLIM HARPO.
LP: . . . . LP 8010

BLUES HANGOVER (Jay Miller Sessions).
LP: . . . . FLY 520

GOT LOVE IF YOU WANT IT.
LP: . . . . FLY 558

HE KNEW THE BLUES.
LP: . . . . SNTF 769

RAININ' IN MY HEART.
LP: . . . . LP 8003

SHAKE YOUR HIPS.
Tracks: / Wonderin' blues / Baby scratch my back / I'm gonna miss you / Rainin' in my heart / We're two of a kind / I need money / Midnight blues / Harpo's blues / Buzzin' / My little queen bee / I love the life I'm livin' / Shake your hips.
LP: . . . . FLY 593

TIP ON IN.
LP: . . . . LP 8008

Harptones

HARPTONES, THE (Feat. Willie Winfield).
LP: . . . . RELIC 5001

HARPTONES VOL.2.
LP: . . . . RELIC 5003

Harrell, Bill

BALLADS AND BLUEGRASS (Harrell, Bill/Virginians).
LP: . . . . AD 2013

BLUE VIRGINIA BLUE.
Tracks: / Blue Virginia blues / Sonny boy / Fire on the North Ridge / Mary on the wild moor / God must be a cowboy at heart / God put a rainbow in the clouds / Letter at home / Kentucky is just a smile away / Bare foot Nellie / I haven't seen Mama in years / Wreck of old 97 / Muddy little shoes.
LP: . . . . REBEL 1650

DO YOU REMEMBER.
LP: . . . . REBEL 1640
MC: . . . . REBEL 1640C

SONG FOR EVERYONE, A.
LP: . . . . REBEL 1655
MC: . . . . REBEL 1655C

WALKING IN THE EARLY MORNING DEW.
LP: . . . . REBEL 1620
MC: . . . . REBEL 1620C

Harrell, Tom

MOON ALLEY (Harrell, Tom Quintet).
LP: . . . . CRISS 1018

NEW YORK JAZZ (see Cuber, Ronnie) (Harrell, Tom,Ronnie Cuber,Rein deGraff,Sam Jones,Louis Hayes).

PLAY OF LIGHT, THE.
LP: . . . . BKH 50901
MC: . . . . BKHMC 50901

THESE ROOMS (see under Hall, Jim) (Hall, Jim).

Harries, Clive

ORGAN MUSIC FROM CHRISTCHURCH PRIORY.
LP: . . . . APS 332

Harriet

WOMAN TO MAN.
LP: . . . . WX 358
MC: . . . . WX 358C

Harriott, Derrick

14 CHART BUSTER HITS.
LP: . . . . SRLP 20

GREATEST REGGAE HITS.
Tracks: / Some guys have all the luck / Brown baby / Face dog / Why do fools fall in love / Since I lost my baby.
LP: . . . . TRLS 116

MUSICAL CHARIOT.
LP: . . . . LPHB 58

SKIN TO SKIN.
LP: . . . . SRLP 22

SONGS FOR MIDNIGHT LOVERS.
Tracks: / Eighteen with a bullet / Born to love you / Message from a black man / Groovy situation / Loser, The.
LP: . . . . TRLS 198

STEP SOFTLY (Harriott, Derrick & Friends).
Tracks: / Jerk, The / Mama didn't lie / Step softly / Stop that train / Stop that man / Tang tang festival song / Lonely and blue / James Ray / Sic Him Rover / Love I / Salaam / Psychedelic train / Psychedelic train version 3 / Do your thing / Rougher than tough / Tough version.
LP: . . . . TRLS 267
MC: . . . . ZCTRL 267

Harriott, Joe

JUMP FOR ME (Harriott, Joe & The Tony Kinsey Trio).
Tracks: / Last resort, The / Best behaviour / How deep is the ocean? / Get happy / Jump for me / Can't we be friends / Raymond / Nice work if you can get it / Chirracahaua / Teddi / Song is you, The / It don't mean a thing.
LP: . . . . ESQ 326

Harris, Anita

JUST LOVING YOU (LP).
LP: . . . . SBPG 63182

Harris, Barry

BARRY HARRIS PLAYS BARRY HARRIS.
LP: . . . . X 154

FOR THE MOMENT.
LP: . . . . UP 27.20

Harris, Beaver

360 DEGREE MUSICAL EXPERIMENT.
LP: . . . . SN 1005

BEAVER IS MY NAME.
Tracks: / Ismay / My mother / African drums (medley) / Necaumong-us / It's hard to, but we do / J.C. Moses.
LP: . . . . SJP 196

Harris, Bill

ACES AT THE DEUCES (Harris, Bill & Charlie Ventura).
Tracks: / Eleven sixty / All of me / Dark eyes / Everything happens to me / Man I love, The / Aces at the Deuces.
LP: . . . . LP 14

BILL HARRIS & FRIENDS.
Tracks: / It might as well be spring / Crazy rhythm / Where are you? / Just one more chance / I surrender, dear / I'm getting sentimental over you / In a mellow tone.
LP: . . . . OJC 083

LIVE AT THE THREE DEUCES (Harris, Bill & Charlie Ventura).
Tracks: / Characteristically B.H. / Blue champagne / Mordido / High on an open mike / Body and soul / Great life, The.
LP: . . . . LP 11

PHOENIX JAZZ FIFTH ANNIVERSARY ALBUM (Harris, Bill/Dizzy Gillespie/ Eddie Costa/Coleman Hawkins).
Tracks: / Broadway / Perdido / Groovin' high / Blues / Stoned.
LP: . . . . LP 16

WORLD IS WAITING, THE (see under Powell, Mel).

Harris, Craig

BLACKOUT IN THE SQUARE ROOT OF SOUL (Harris, Craig & Tailgater's Tales).
Tracks: / Blackout in the square root of soul (phase 1 and 2) / Generations / Free 1 / Love joy / Blue dues / Dingo / Awakening ancestors.
LP: 8344151

Harris, Eddie

BLACK SAX.
2LP: . . . . GNPS 2-2073

EDDIE (Harris, Eddie, Ralph Armstrong, Sherman Ferguson).
LP: . . . . SJP 244

EXODUS TO JAZZ.
Tracks: / Exodus / Alicia / Gone home / A.T.C. / A.M. Blues / Little girl blue / Velocity / W.P..
LP: . . . . ATS 10
MC: . . . . TCATS 10

I'M TIRED OF DRIVING.
Tracks: / Two times two equals love / You are the one / Songbird / I'm tired of driving / Loneliest monk / Theme for the foxy ladies / You stole my heart / There was a time / What's wrong with the world today.
LP: . . . . PL 12942

LIVE IN BERLIN.
LP: . . . . SJP 289

STEPS UP (Harris, Eddie quartet).
LP: . . . . SCS 1151

SWISS MOVEMENT (Harris, Eddie/ Les McCann).
Tracks: / Compared to what / Cold duck time / Kathleen's theme / You got it in your soulness / Generation gap, The.
LP: . . . . K 50405

TALE OF TWO CITIES.
LP: . . . . VNLP 3
MC: . . . . VNTC 3

Harris, Emmylou

13.
Tracks: / Mystery train / You're free to go / Sweetheart of the pines / Just someone in the know / My father's house / Lacassine special / Today I started loving you again / When I was yours / I had my heart set on you / Your long journey.
LP: . . . . K 925352 1
MC: . . . . K 925352 4

BALLAD OF SALLY ROSE.
Tracks: / Ballad of Sally Rose, The / Rhythm guitar / I think I love him / You are my flower heart to heart / Woman walk the line / Bad news / Timberline / Long tall Sally Rose / White line / Diamond in my crown / Sweetheart of the Rodeo, The / K-S-O-S (Instrumental medly) / Ring of fire / Wildwood flower / Six days on the road / Sweet chariot.
LP: 925205 1
MC: 925205 4

BLUE KENTUCKY GIRL.
Tracks: / Sister's coming home / Beneath still waters / Rough and rocky / Hickory wind / Save the last dance for me / Sorrow in the wind / They'll never take his love from me / Every time you leave / Blue Kentucky girl / Even cowgirls get the blues.
LP: . . . . K 56627
MC: K4 56627

BLUEBIRD.
Tracks: / Heaven only knows / You've been on my mind / Icy blue heart / Love is / No regrets / Lonely street / Heartbreak hill / I still miss someone / River for him, A / If you were a bluebird.
LP: . . . . K 925776 1
MC: . . . . K 925776 4

BRAND NEW DANCE.
Tracks: / Wheels of love / In his world / Easy for you to stay / Better off without you / Brand new dance / Tougher than the rest / Sweet dreams of you / Rollin' and ramblin' / Never be anyone else but you / Red red rose.
LP: . . . . WX 396
MC: . . . . WX 396C

CHRISTMAS ALBUM, THE (Light of the stable).
Tracks: / Away in a manger / Golden cradles / First Noel, The / Oh little town of Bethlehem / Christmas time's a coming / Silent night / Beautiful star / Little drummer boy / Angel eyes / Light of the stable.
LP: . . . . K 56757
MC: K4 56757

CIMARRON.
Tracks: / Rose of Cimarron / Spanish is the loving tongue / If I needed you / Another lonesome morning / Last cheater's waltz, The / Born to run / Price you pay, The / Son of a rotten gambler / Tennessee waltz / Tennessee rose.
LP: . . . . K 569 55

DUETS (Harris, Emmylou & Various).
Tracks: / Price I pay, The / Love hurts / Thing about you / That lovin' feelin' again / We believe in happy endings / Star of Bethlehem / All fall down / Wild Montana skies / Green pastures / Gulf Coast highway / If I needed you / Evangeline.
LP: 7599257911
MC: 7599257914

ELITE HOTEL.
Tracks: / Amarillo / Together again / Feeling single / Seeing double / Sin city / One of these days / Till I gain control again / Here, there and everywhere / Ooh Las Vegas / Sweet dreams / Jambalaya / Satan's jewelled crown / Wheels.
LP: . . . . K 54060
MC: K4 54060
LP: . . . . ED 306

EVANGELINE.
Tracks: / Don't have to crawl / How high the moon / Spanish Johnny / Bad moon rising / Evangeline / Hot burrito / Millworker / Oh Atlanta / Mister Sandman / Ashes by now.
LP: . . . . K 56880

HER BEST SONGS.
LP: . . . . NE 1058

LAST DATE.
Tracks: / I'm movin' on / It's not love (but it's not bad) / So sad (to watch good love go bad) / Grievous angel / Restless / Racing in the streets / Long may you run / We'll sweep out the ashes in the morning / Juanita / Devil in disguise / Lost his love on our last date / Buckaroo / Love's gonna live here (medley).
LP: 9237401
MC: 9237404

LEGENDARY 'GLIDING BIRD' ALBUM, THE.
Tracks: / I'll be your baby tonight / Fugue for the fox / I saw the light / Clocks / Black gypsy / Gliding bird / Everybody's talkin' / Bobbie's gone / I'll never fall in love again / Waltz of the magic man.
LP: . . . . PKL 5577
MC: . . . . ZCPKL 5577

LUXURY LINER.
Tracks: / Luxury liner / Poncho and Lefty / Making believe / You're supposed to be feeling good / I'll be your San Antone Rose / (You never can tell) C'est la vie / When I stop dreaming / Hello stranger / She / Tulsa queen.
MC: K4 66106
LP: . . . . K 56334

PIECES IN THE SKY.
Tracks: / Bluebird wine / Too far gone / If I could only win your love / Boulder to Birmingham / Before believing / Bottle let me down, The / Sleepless nights / Coat of many colours / For no one / Queen of the silver dollar.
LP: . . . . K 54037
MC: . . . . K 454037

PROFILE: EMMYLOU HARRIS.
Tracks: / One of these days / Sweet dreams / To daddy / C'est la vie / Making believe / Easy from now on / Together again / If I could only win your love / Too far gone / Two more bottles of wine / Boulder to Birmingham / Hello stranger / You never can tell.
LP: . . . . K 56570
MC: K4 56570

QUARTER MOON IN A TEN CENT TOWN.
Tracks: / Easy from now on / Two more bottles of wine / To Daddy / My songbird / Leaving Louisiana in the broad daylight / Defying / Gravity / I ain't living long like this / One paper kid / Green rolling hills / Burn that candle.

LP: K 56443
MC: K 456 443

ROSES IN THE SNOW.
Tracks: / Roses in the snow / Wayfaring stranger / Boxer, The / Green pastures / Darkest hour is just before the dawn, The / I'll go stepping too / You're learning / Jordan / Miss the Mississippi / Gold watch and chain.
LP: K 56796

TO KNOW HIM IS TO LOVE HIM (see under Parton, Dolly) (Harris, Emmylou/ Dolly Parton/Linda Ronstadt).

TRIO (See under Parton, Dolly) (Harris, Emmylou/Dolly Parton/Linda Ronstadt).

WHITE SHOES.
Tracks: / Drivin' wheel / Pledging my love / In my dreams / White shoes / On the radio / It's only rock 'n' roll / Diamonds are a girl's best friend / Good news / Baby, better start turning 'em down / Like an old fashioned waltz.
LP: K 923961 1
MC: K 923961 4

Harris, Gene

AT LAST (Harris, Gene & Scott Hamilton Quintet).
Tracks: / You are my sunshine / It never entered my mind / After you've gone / Lamp is low, The / At last / Blues for Gene / I fall in love too easily / Some of these days / Stairway to the stars / Sittin' in the sandtrap.
MC: CJ 434 C

GENE HARRIS & THE PHILIP MORRIS SUPERBAND (Harris, Gene & The Philip Morris Superband).
Tracks: / Surrey with the fringe on top, The / Creme de menthe (on CD only) / When it's sleepy time down south / Love is here to stay / I'm just a lucky so and so / Serious grease (on CD only) / Like a lover (on CD only) / Old man river / Do you know what it means to New Orleans (on 12" only) / Porgy and Bess (medley) / You're my everything / There is no greater love / Things ain't what they used to be.
LP: CJ 397
MC: CJ 397C

GENE HARRIS TRIO PLUS ONE, THE.
Tracks: / Gene's lament / Uptown sop / Things ain't what they used to be / Yours is my heart alone / Battle hymn of the Republic.
LP: CJ 303

LISTEN HERE (Harris, Gene Quartet).
Tracks: / His masquerade / I've got a feeling I'm falling / Blues for Jezebel / Lullabye / This can't be love / Don't be that way / Listen here / Sweet and lovely / Song is ended, The / To you.
LP: CJ 385
MC: CJ 385C

TRIBUTE TO COUNT BASIE (Harris, Gene All Star Big Band).
Tracks: / Captain Bill / Night mist blues / Swingin' the blues / When did you leave Heaven? / Blue and sentimental / Riled up / Masquerade is over, The / Dejection blues.
LP: CJ 337
MC: CJC 337

WORLD TOUR 1990 (Harris, Gene & The Philip Morris Superband).
Tracks: / Airmail special / Lonely bottles / Child is born, A / Buhaina Buhaina / Don't get around much anymore / Lover (CD only.) / In the wee small hours of the morning / Tricotism (CD only.) / Centerpiece (CD only.) / Dear blues / Nica's dream / Girl talk / Battle royal / Warm valley.
MC: CJ 443C

Harris, Gerard

JOSEPH'S PAST.
LP: MVLP 17

Harris, Greg

ELECTRIC.
LP: AP 024

Harris, Hugh

WORDS FOR OUR YEARS.
Tracks: / Alice / Love kicks / Mr. Woman and Mrs. Man / Woke up laughing / Rhythm of life / Helen Highwater / Music lies bleeding / Home sweet home / Twilight session / Her engine froze.
LP: EST 2105
MC: TCEST 2105

Harris, Jack

JACK HARRIS & HIS ORCHESTRA 1937-1939 (Harris, Jack & His Orchestra).
Tracks: / Amoresque / Wake up and live / Once in a while / Toy trumpet, The / Gypsy in my soul / How many rhymes can you get / Cry baby cry / Caravan / I can't face the music / Back to back / Amazon goes a-wooing / I'm sorry for myself / It looks like rain in Cherry Blossom Lane / Snake charmer, The / Mr. Renard's nightmare.
LP: SH 219

YOU CAN'T STOP ME FROM DREAMING (Harris, Jack & His Orchestra).
Tracks: / My prayer / Says my heart / Say si si / I wanna make rhythm / Flat foot floogie / Nice work if you can get it.
LP: RD 8

Harris, Jerome

ALGORITHMS.
LP: MM 1011

Harris, Jet

ANNIVERSARY ALBUM : JET HARRIS.
LP: LPMM 1038
MC: CMM 1038

DIAMONDS (Harris, Jet & Tony Meehan).
Tracks: / Scarlett O'Hara / Besame mucho / Clap your hands (once again) / Chills and fever / Tall Texan / Rifka / Rave / Diamonds / Applejack / Man from nowhere / Hully gully / Real wild child / Footstomp / Man with the golden arm.
LP: TAB 68

REMEMBERING (Harris, Jet & Tony Meehan).
Tracks: / Diamonds / Some people / Hully gully / Big bad bass / Besame mucho / Man with the Golden Arm, Theme from / Applejack / Tall Texan, The / Song of Mexico / Man from nowhere / Footstomp / Scarlett O'Hara.
LP: REM 1
MC: KREMC 1

Harris, Jody

IT HAPPENED ONE NIGHT.
Tracks: / It happened one night / I'm after hours again / Mystic mints / Money talks / You better read before you sign / Fairly modern / My Uncle Bill / Coal black mamas.
LP: P 4001

Harris, Joey

JOEY HARRIS & THE SPEEDSTARS (Harris, Joey/Speedstars).
Tracks: / I believe in Mary / You never call / Sally / Made for each other / Stay away / Two people talking / Don't say love / Nobody's girl / Do you want to / Too young.
LP: MCF 3189
MC: MCFC 3189

Harris, Johnny

ALL TO BRING YOU MORNING.
Tracks: / Imagine / All to bring you morning / Love song / Norwegian wood / Pavane / You've lost that lovin' feeling.
LP: K 46187

MOVEMENTS.
Tracks: / Fragment of fear / Reprise / Stepping stones / Something / Give peace a chance / Footprints on the moon / Light my fire / Wichita lineman / Paint it black.
LP: K 46054

Harris, Johnny Ray

ROCKIN' IN LOUISIANA VOL.2 (Harris, Johnny Ray & Jimmy Wray).
Tracks: / Crazy kisses / Well I'm gone / Gambling / Take my love.
LP: WLP 8892

Harris, Keith

AREN'T I LUCKY? (Harris, Keith & Orville).
Tracks: / Superduck / Bein' green / Captain Cuddles / Little white bull / Dippy dragonaurus / If you believe / Colour me Cuddles / Aren't I lucky / Nappy rap / Tomorrow / Come to my party / I will / Mr. Bass man.
LP: REH 513
MC: ZCR 513

AT THE END OF THE RAINBOW.
Tracks: / Ugly duckling, The / I can sing a rainbow / Over the rainbow / Orville's song / I hate that duck / Old father time / Will you still love me in the morning / You've got a friend / If I only had a wish / If wishes were horses / Thing, The / I didn't / Nobody's told me what sort of bird I am / Where is love / Time has come, The.
LP: REH 465
MC: ZCR 465

ORVILLE & CUDDLES.
MC: 0 00 102214 8

Harris, Larnelle

CHRISTMAS (LARNELLE HARRIS).
LP: R 02474
MC: C 02474

I CAN BEGIN AGAIN.
Tracks: / Mighty Spirit.
MC: C 02506

Harris, Marion

MARION HARRIS VOL2. (1920-1921).
Tracks: / Take me to the land of jazz / Left all alone again blues / Oh! Judge he treats me mean / St.Louis blues / He done me wrong / I ain't got nobody / I'm a jazz vampire / Beale Street blues / Memphis blues / Look for the silver lining / Sweet mama.
MC: NEO 949

MARION HARRIS VOL 1. (1916-1919).
Tracks: / I ain't got nobody / I'm gonna make hay / Don't leave me daddy / My syncopated melody man / I wonder why / When I hear that jazz band play / Everybody's crazy 'bout the doggone blues / After you've gone / For Johnny and me / Good man is hard to find, A / Jazz baby / Some sweet day.
MC: NEO 947

Harris, Peppermint

I GET LOADED.
Tracks: / I get loaded.
LP: KIX 23

SHOUT AND ROCK (Harris, Peppermint & Elmore Nixon).
LP: CG 709-12
LP: SG 70912

Harris, Pete

JACK O' DIAMONDS (Harris, Pete/ Smith Casey).
LP: HERWIN 211

Harris, Phil

ALICE FAYE & PHIL HARRIS (see Faye, Alice).

BEST OF PHIL HARRIS.
Tracks: / Darktown poker club / Woodman, spare that tree / That's what I like about the South / Preacher and the bear, The / Deck of cards / Is it true what they say about Dixie? / Goofus / Thing, The / Persian kitten, The / St. James Infirmary / Muskrat ramble / Row row row.
LP: INTS 5050
MC: INTK 5050
LP: NL 89526
MC: NK 89526

PHIL HARRIS AND ORCHESTRA (1933) (Harris, Phil & Orchestra).
LP: HSR 215

THAT'S WHAT I LIKE ABOUT THE SOUTH (Harris, Phil & Orchestra).
LP: GELP 15042

Harris, R.H.

SONGS WE'LL NEVER FORGET (Harris, R.H. & The Masonic Quintet).
Tracks: / Since I met Jesus / Because He lives / Draw me nearer / That's all right / Precious memories / Tell it everywhere / Beams of heaven / Signs of the times / Golden bells / Higher ground.
LP: GCR 4033
MC: GCR 4033MC

Harris, Richard

PROPHET, THE.
Tracks: / Coming of the ship, The / On love / On marriage / On children / Trilogy (From the Prophet.) / On giving / On eating and drinking / On clothes / On work / On crime and punishment / On laws / On teaching and self knowledge / On friendship / On pleasure / Prophet, The (theme from) / On religion / On death / Farewell, The.
LP: K 50109

Harris, Rolf

CARTOON TIME FAVOURITES.
Tracks: / Heigh ho/Whistle while you work / He's a tramp / Little April showers / I wan'na be like you / Siamese cat song / Ugly bug ball, The / Zip-a-dee-doo-dah / Never smile at a crocodile / I'm late / Dream is a wish your heart makes, A / When you wish upon a star / Who's afraid of the big bad wolf / Bare necessities.
LP: REH 642
MC: ZCR 642

COOJEE BEAR AND THE MONSTER.
Tracks: / Who do think they're calling monster / Sean the shoemaker / Shoes / Siobhan / Vroom, vroom, vroom / Ghost who cannot walk through a wall, The / Stalagmites and stalactites / Animal rights.
LP: SGLP 2
MC: SGLC 2

ROLF HARRIS.
Tracks: / Two little boys / Tie me kangaroo down / Waltzing Matilda / Iko iko / Football crazy / Carra barra wirra canna / War canoe / Court of King Caractacus / My word you do look queer / I've lost my mummy / Sydney town (CD only.) / Sun arise / Nick O'Teen and Al K. Hall / Wild colonial boy (CD only.) / Jake the peg / Maximillian Mouse / Botany Bay / Click go the shears / Wild rover, The / Someone's pinched my winkles / Big dog / I'll be hanged (if they're gonna hang me) (CD only.) / Eddystone light (CD only.) / Man with the microphone, The (CD only.) / English country garden / I know a man / Six white boomers.
MC: TCIDL 103

ROLF ON SATURDAY OK.
Tracks: / It's Saturday OK / Boiled beef and carrots / Gas-man cometh, The / Turkey in the straw / Papilion / On Ilkla moor baht at / Windmill in Amsterdam / Best foot forward / Laughing policeman, The / Herrings' head / Hole in the ground / Portsmouth / Sunday by the sea / Tailor and the mouse.
LP: REH 353
MC: ZCR 353

Harris, Roy

BITTER & THE SWEET, THE.
Tracks: / Turpin hero / Bonnie green woods, The / Death of Bill Brown, The / Three butchers, The / Ullswater pack, The / Poor owd 'oss / General Ludd's triumph / Poverty knock / Streams of lovely Nancy, The / Robin Hood and the tanner / Royal oak, The / Strike the bell / McCafferty / All through the ale.
LP: 12TS 217

BY SANDBANK FIELDS (songs & ballads).
Tracks: / As I was going to Banbury / Knight and the shepherd's daughter, The / Baker of Colebrook, The / Twenty third of March, The / Go from my window / Think on this (when you smoke tobacco) / Dockyard gate / Lady of Carlisle, The / Robin Hood and Little John / Sandbank fields / Spithead sailor, The / Unhappy parting, The.
LP: 12TS 327

CHAMPIONS OF FOLLY.
Tracks: / Saucy bold robber, The / Bold lovell / Steepleford town / Captain ward / Methody parson, The / Caroline and her young sailor bold / Beggar's song, The / When I was a little boy / Dragoon's ride, The / Cropper lads / Royal charter, The / Topman and the afterguard / Jovial hunter, The / Hard times of old England.
LP: 12TS 256

RAMBLING SOLDIER, THE.
Tracks: / Balaclava / McCafferty / Muddley barracks / Rambling soldier, The / I would that the wars were all done / Young recruit, The - Or, thirteen pence a day / Scarlet and the blue, The / Lass of Swansea town / Drum major, The / Hungry army, The / Banks of the Nile / Chelsea quarters.
MC: FE 017 C
LP: FE 017

UTTER SIMPLICITY.
Tracks: / Jackie Munro / Golden glove, The / Rolling down to old Maui / Clear away the morning dew / I reckon I've served me time / Silver queen / Young Roger esq. / Budgie weed / Captain Wedderburn's courtship / Tom Brown's stormy old weather / When we raced the Robin adair / Bright fields of England.
LP: FE 044
MC: FE 044 C

Harris, Sam

SAM HARRIS.
Tracks: / Out of control / Sugar don't bite / I've heard it all before / Hearts of fire / I will not wait for you / Pretender / Don't look in my eyes / You keep me hangin' on / Inside of me / Over the rainbow.
LP: ZL 72237
MC: ZK 72237

SAM-I-AM.
Tracks: / I'll do it all again / Forever for you / Heart of the machine / Rescue, The / Suffer the innocent / Ba-doom ba-doom / Don't want to give up on love / In your eyes / Always / Bells, The / I need you / Stay with me.
LP: ZL 72415
MC: ZK 72415

Harris, Simon

BASS.
Tracks: / Bass (how low can you go) / From the vaults of good times / Sexy lady / Official voice of hip hop / Run 4 cover / Wheels of steel / (I've got your) pleasure control / London's finest / Stardate / Final frontier / We're gonna dance / Another monster jam / It is scratched / Here comes that sound (demolition album mix) / Feel.
LP: 828 153-1
MC: 828 153-4

BEATS, BREAKS AND SCRATCHES (BOX SET).
LPS: MOMIXBOX

BEATS, BREAKS AND SCRATCHES VOL.6.
LP: MOMIX 6

BEATS, BREAKS AND SCRATCHES VOL. 5.
LP: . . . . **MOMIX 5**

BEATS, BREAKS AND SCRATCHES VOL. 2.
LP: . . . . **MOMIX 2**

BEATS, BREAKS AND SCRATCHES VOL 3.
LP: . . . . **MOMIX 3**

BEATS, BREAKS AND SCRATCHES VOL 4.
Tracks: / Life beats / Dopin' drums / Groove beats / Hold tight / Funky break / Ruff loop / Samurai beats / Heavy loop / Mardi gras / Big beats / Impeach / Compton loop / Course beat / Effects and scratches.
LP: . . . . **MOMIX 4**

BEATS, BREAKS AND SCRATCHES VOL. 1.
LP: . . . . **MOMIX 1**

BEATS, BREAKS AND SCRATCHES VOL. 7.
LP: . . . . **MOMIX 7**

DISTURBING THE PEACE.
Tracks: / Theme from disturbing the peace / Time / Rock right now / Ragga house (All night long) / This is serious / Don't stop the music / Shock the house / Right here, right now / Twilight / Runaway love / Ragga house.
LP: . . . . **DISTURB 1**
MC: . . . . **DISTURB 1C**

STRETCHBEATS VOL 1.
LP: . . . . **STARMIX 2**

Harris, Sue

HAMMERS AND TONGUES.
LP: . . . . **FRR 020**

HOW TO MAKE A BAKEWELL TART.
LP: . . . . **FRR 017**

ROSE OF BRITAIN'S ISLE, THE (see Kirkpatrick, John) (Harris, Sue & John Kirkpatrick).

STOLEN GROUND (See under Kirkpatrick, John) (Kirkpatrick, John & Sue Harris).

Harris, Thurston

BE BOP WINO (Harris, Thurston & The Lamplighters).
Tracks: / You hear / Yum yum / Goody goody good things / I wanna know / Believe in me / Roll on / Love, rock and thrill / Hug a little, kiss a little / Be bop wino / Part of me / Sad and lonely / Turn me loose / Crazy times / Give me / Smootchie / I can't stand it.
LP: . . . . **OFF 6052**

LITTLE BITTY PRETTY ONE.
Tracks: / Over and over / Little bitty pretty one / Do what you did / Hey baby Leeba / You don't know / I'm asking forgiveness / hey little girl / Send me some lovin' / Only one love / Tell me so / Fine fine frame / Cross my heart / My love will last / I got loaded.
LP: . . . . **SSL 6026**
MC: . . . . **TCSSL 6026**
LP: . . . . **PM 154 665 1**

THURSTON HARRIS.
LP: . . . . **ALADDIN 3390**

Harris, W.

HEAVY HITTERS (Various artists).
LP: . . . . **HERWIN 214**

Harris, Wee Willie

GOES APE.
Tracks: / Rosie Lee / Rockin' at the 2 I's / Back to school again / Smack dab in the middle / No chemise please / Got a match / Love bug crawl / I go ape / Little bitty girl / Wild one / Trouble in mind / Riot on cell block no. 9 / Frankie and Johnny.
LP: . . . . **CHA 178**

Harris, Woody

AFTER DINNER MINTS.
LP: . . . . **KM 133**

AMERICAN GUITAR SOLOS.
LP: . . . . **ARHOOLIE 4008**

BLOOMFIELD & HARRIS (see Bloomfield, Mike) (Harris, Woody & Mike Bloomfield).

SHOW OF HANDS.
LP: . . . . **KM 159**

Harris, Wynonie

BATTLE OF THE BLUES (Harris, Wynonie & Roy Brown).
Tracks: / Mr. Blues is coming to town / Good rockin' tonight / Rock Mr. Blues / Bloodshot eyes / Just like two drops of water / Luscious woman / Lovin' machine / Keep on churnin' (till the butter comes) / Good morning judge / Quiet whiskey / Down boy down / Cadillac baby / Too much lovin' ain't no good / Hard luck blues / My gal from Kokomo / Big town / Rockabye baby / Black diamond / Ain't no rockin' no more / Fannie Brown got married / Shake 'em up baby / Good looking and foxy too.
LP: . . . . **SING 607**

BATTLE OF THE BLUES VOL. 2.
LP: . . . . **KLP 627**

BATTLE OF THE BLUES, VOL. 2 (See also Brown, Roy) (Harris, Wynonie & Roy Brown).

BATTLE OF THE BLUES VOL. 4 (See under Vinson, Eddie) (Harris, Wynonie, Eddie Vinson, Roy Brown).

GOOD ROCKIN' BLUES.
LP: . . . . **BID 8022**

GOOD ROCKING TONIGHT.
MCSET: . . . . **GD 5040**

HERE COMES THE BLUES.
Tracks: / Wynonie's blues / Here comes the blues / Straighten him out / Young man's blues / Baby look at you / She's gone with the wind / Somebody changed the lock on my door / That's the stuff you gotta watch / Mr. Blues jumped the rabbit / Whiskey and jelly roll blues / Rugged road / Come back baby / Hey-ba-ra-re-bop / Good morning Corinne / In the evenin' blues.
LP: . . . . **OFF 6024**

MR BLUES IS COMING TO TOWN.
Tracks: / Sittin' on it all the time / Drinkin' by myself / Wynonie's blues / Big city blues / Bite again bite again / Blowin' to California / Love untrue, A / Rock Mr. Blues / Mr. Blues is coming to town / Be mine my love / Keep-a-talking / Here comes the night / Christina / My playful baby's gone / Wine wine sweet wine / Fishtail blues.
LP: . . . . **KIX 3**

OH BABY.
Tracks: / Around the clock 1 - 11 / Cock-a-doodle-doo / Yonder goes my baby / Time to change your town / Hard ridin' mama / You got to get yourself a job girl / Oh babe / My baby's barrel house / Luscious woman / Bad news baby / Stormy night blues / Down boy down / Gift to gittin' baby / Don't take my whiskey away from me / I get a thrill.
LP: . . . . **KIX 20**

PLAYFUL BABY.
Tracks: / I gotta lyin' woman / Playful baby / Rebecca's blues / Take me out of the rain / Everybody's boogie / Papa tree top / Lollipop mama / Ghost of a chance / Married women - stay married / Do it again, please / Triflin' woman / Night train / Bring it back / Nearer my love to thee / Git with the grits / Good mambo tonight.
LP: . . . . **KIX 30**

ROCK MR. BLUES.
Tracks: / Good morning Judge / Down boy down / Bloodshot eyes / Lovin' machine / Mr. Blues is coming to town / I like my baby's pudding / Rock Mr. Blues / Baby shame on you / Just like two drops of water / Good rockin' tonight / Blow your brains out / Sittin' on it all the time / Luscious woman / Keep on churnin' (till the butter comes) / Quiet whiskey / I feel that old age coming on.
LP: . . . . **CRB 1097**
MC: . . . . **TCCRB 1097**

Harrison/ Blanchard

CRYSTAL STAIR.
LP: **4601641**

Harrison, Donald

NEW YORK SECOND LINE (See under Blanchard, Terence) (Harrison, Donald & Terence Blanchard).

Harrison, Elizabeth

SURGEON'S AFFAIR (see under Surgeon's Affair) (Boyd, Carole (nar)).

Harrison, George

33 1/3.
Tracks: / Woman don't you cry for me / Dear one / Beautiful girl / This song / See yourself / It's what you value / True love / Pure smokey / Crackerbox palace / Learning how to love you.
LP: . . . . **K 56319**
MC: **K4 56319**

ALL THINGS MUST PASS.
Tracks: / I'd have you anytime / My sweet Lord / Wah-wah / Isn't it a pity / What is life / If not for you / Behind that locked door / Let it down / Run of the mill / Beware of darkness / Apple scruffs / Ballad of Sir Frankie Crisp (Let it roll) / Awaiting on you all / All things must pass / I dig love / Art of dying / Isn't it a pity / Hear me Lord / Out of the blue / It's Johnny's birthday / Plug me in / I remember jeep / Thanks for the pepperoni.
LPS: . . . . **STCH 639**

BEST OF GEORGE HARRISON.
Tracks: / Something / If I needed someone / Here comes the sun / Taxman / Think for yourself / For you blue / While my guitar gently weeps / My sweet Lord / Give me love (give me peace on earth) / You / Bangladesh / Dark horse / What is life.
LP: . . . . **MFP 50523**
MC: . . . . **TCMFP 50523**

CLOUD NINE.
Tracks: / Cloud nine / That's what it takes / Fish on the sand / Just for today / This is love / When we was fab / Devil's radio / Someplace else / Wreck of the Hesperus / Breath away from heaven / Got my mind set on you.
LP: . . . . **WX 123**
MC: . . . . **WX 123 C**

DARK HORSE.
Tracks: / Hari's on tour / Simply shady / So sad / Bye bye love / May a love / Ding dong ding dong / Dark horse / Far east man / Is it he (Jai Sri Krishna).
LP: . . . . **IC 062 05774**
LP: **3C 05405774**
MC: **1057744**
LP: . . . . **MFP 50510**

DARK HORSE RECORDS 1976-89.
LP: . . . . **WX 312**
MC: . . . . **WX 312C**

EXTRA TEXTURE (READ ALL ABOUT IT).
Tracks: / You / Answer's at the end, The / This guitar (can't keep from crying) / Ooh baby (you know that I love you) / World of stone / Bit more of you, A / Can't stop thinking about you / Tired of midnight blue / Grey cloudy lies / His name is legs.
LP: . . . . **PAS 10009**

GEORGE HARRISON.
Tracks: / Love comes to everyone / Not guilty / Here comes the moon / Soft hearted Hanna / Blow away / Faster / Dark sweet lady / Your love is forever / Soft touch / If you believe'.
LP: . . . . **K 56562**
MC: **K4 56562**

GONE TROPPO.
Tracks: / Wake up my love / That's the way it goes / I really love you / Greece / Gone troppo / Mystical one / Unknown delight / Baby don't run away / Dream away / Circles.
LP: . . . . **K 923734 1**
MC: . . . . **K 923734 4**

LIVING IN THE MATERIAL WORLD.
Tracks: / Give me love (give me peace on Earth) / Sue me, sue you blues / Light that has lighted the world, The / Don't let me wait too long / Who can see it / Living in the material world / Lord loves the one (that loves the Lord) / Be here now / Try some buy some / Day the world gets 'round, The / That's all.
LP: . . . . **IC 064 05370**
LP: **3C 05405370**
MC: **1053704**
LP: . . . . **PAS 10006**

SOMEWHERE IN ENGLAND.
Tracks: / Blood from a clone / Unconsciousness rules / Life itself / All those years ago / Baltimore oriole / Teardrops / That which I have lost / Writing on the wall / Hong Kong blues / Save the world.
LP: . . . . **K 56870**
MC: **K4 56870**

WONDERWALL MUSIC.
LP: **2C 066 90490**

Harrison, Harry

OFF THE CUFF.
LP: . . . . **BRO 130**
MC: . . . . **KBRO 130**

Harrison, Jane

NEW DAY (ALBUM).
LP: . . . . **SMR 869**
MC: . . . . **SMC 869**

Harrison, Jerry

CASUAL GODS.
Tracks: / Rev it up / Song of angels / Man with a gun / Let it come down / Cherokee chief / Perfect lie, A / Are you running / Breakdown / A.K.A. love / We're always talking.
LP: . . . . **SFLP 2**
MC: . . . . **SFMC 2**

WALK ON WATER.
LP: **8463211**
MC: **8463214**

Harrison, Kevin

INSCRUTABLY OBVIOUS.
Tracks: / Inscrutably obvious.
LP: . . . . **BRED 16**

Harrison, Peter

HANDEL FLUTE SONATAS.
LP: . . . . **PLR 041**

NICE 'N' EASY.
Tracks: / Music to watch girls by / Yellow days / Little brown jug-snowbird / Desame mucho / Dream - green green grass / Innocent love / Goin' out of my head / Hawaii five-O / Parlez-moi d'amour / Melody of love / Once in a world / Canadian sunset / Bach minuet / Georgia / Softly as I leave you / You made me feel I could fly.
LP: . . . . **GRS 1083**

SALLY IN OUR ALLEY.
Tracks: / Sally in our alley with divisions / French horn jigg / Farewell ye hills and valleys / Pig in the parlour / Moggy Lawther, with early horn.
LP: . . . . **PLR 025**

Harrison, Rex

HIS FAVOURITE SONGS.
LP: . . . . **NSLP 18595**

Harrison, Stephen

I KNOW EVERYTHING.
LP: . . . . **TELQUEL 001**

Harrison, Valerie

ON MY OWN (See under Campbell, Bill) (Harrison, Valerie & Bill Campbell).

Harrison, Wilbert

LISTEN TO MY SONG.
LP: . . . . **SJL 1182**

LOVIN' OPERATOR.
Tracks: / Kansas City / Blueberry Hill / On top of Old Smokey / Why did you leave me? / Da-de-ya-da / Pretty little women / Lovin' operator / My dream / Let's stick together / Mary Ann / I really love you / Don't wreck my life / Sweet baby (cheatin' woman) / Tell on yourself / I will never trust another woman / Goodbye Kansas City.
LP: . . . . **CRB 1102**

SMALL LABELS.
Tracks: / This woman of mine / Letter edged in black / Gin and coconut milk / Nobody knows my trouble / Calypso man / Cool water / After graduation / Off to work again / Off to school again / I'm broke / Mama mama mama / New York World's fair / Baby move on / You're still my baby / Please forgive me / Poison ivy.
LP: . . . . **KK 7439**

WILBERT HARRISON.
Tracks: / My babe / Ain't that a shame / Honest I do / Going to the river / Girls on parade / When the saints go marching in / Blueberry Hill / You can make it if you try / My dream / Cold cold heart.
LP: . . . . **CHD 275**

Harrogate Male...

HARROGATE DISTRICT, THE various artists (Various artists).
MC: . . . . **AC 113**

HARROGATE MALE VOICE CHOIR (Harrogate Male Voice Choir).
LP: . . . . **LKLP 6602**

Harrold, Melanie Band

EASING UP IT IS.
Tracks: / I live in the city / Blue angel / Rudy / Careless / Beautiful and damned / Picture on the wall / Trade winds / Hard luck stories / What are friends for / Simply I love you.
LP: . . . . **DJF 20550**

WINTERFOLK 80 (see Battlefield Band).

Harrow, David

BITE THE HAND THAT FEEDS YOU (See under MacLure, Pinkie).

SUCCESSION, THE.
LP: . . . . **10 RFA 27**

Harrow, Nancy

ANYTHING GOES.
LP: . . . . **AP 142**

WILD WOMEN DON'T HAVE THE BLUES.
Tracks: / Take me back baby / All too soon / Can't we be friends / On the sunny side of the street / Wild women don't have the blues / I've got the world on a string / I don't know what kind of blues I've got / Blues for yesterday.
LP: . . . . **CS 9008**

Harry & Barton

MULCH (See under Barton & Harry).

Harry, Debbie

COMPLETE PICTURE, THE (Very best of Deborah Harry & Blondie (Harry, Deborah & Blondie).
Tracks: / Heart of glass / I want that man / Call me / Sunday girl / French kissin' in the USA / Denis / Rapture / Brite side / (I'm always touched by your) presence dear / Well, did you evah / Tide is high, The / In love with love / Hanging on the telephone / Island of lost souls / Picture this / Dreaming / Sweet and low / Union City Blue / Atomic / Rip her to shreds.
LP: . . . . **CHR 1817**
MC: . . . . **ZCHR 1817**

DEBORAH HARRY: INTERVIEW PICTURE DISC.
LPPD: . . . . **BAK 2164**

DEF, DUMB AND BLONDE.
Tracks: / I want that man / Lovelight / Kiss it better? / Bike boy / Get your way / Maybe for sure / I'll never fall in love / Calmaria / Sweet and low / He is so / Bugeye / Comic books / Forced to live / Brite side / End of the run.
LP: . . . . **CHR 1650**
MC: . . . . **ZCHR 1650**

KOO KOO.
Tracks: / Jump jump / Chrome / Under arrest / Jam was moving / Surrender / Inner city spillover / Oasis / Military rap / Backfired / Now I know you.
LP: . . . . **CHR 1347**
MC: . . . . **ZCHR 1347**

ONCE MORE INTO THE BLEACH (See under Blondie).

ROCKBIRD.
Tracks: / I want you / French kissin' in the USA / Buckle up / In love with love / You got me in trouble / Free to fall / Rockbird / Secret life / Beyond the limit.
LP: . . . . **CHR 1540**
MC: . . . . **ZCHR 1540**

Harry, Hamilton

SIR HAMILTON HARRY (Vintage collection).
LP: . . . . **REH 756**
MC: . . . . **ZCR 756**

Harry The Hipster

DIGS CHRISTMAS.
Tracks: / 'Twas the night before Christmas boogie / 'Twas the day after Christmas boogie / Only thing I want for Christmas, The / I don't want a lot for Christmas / Rudolph the red nosed reindeer / I wish my mother-in-law don't visit us / I saw mommy kissing Santa Claus / He's got the whole world in his hands / Silent night / Deck the halls / Jolly old St Nicholas / Jingle bells / White Christmas / Christmas song, The.
LP: . . . . **TOTEM 1023**

Hart, Billy

OSHUMARE.
LP: . . . . **GR 8502**

RAH.
Tracks: / Motional / Naaj / Renedap / Dreams / Reflections / Breakup / Reminder / Jungu.
LP: **1888021**
MC: **1888024**

SUCH GREAT FRIENDS (See Under Cowell, Stanley) (Cowell, Stanley, Billy Harper, Reggie Workman & Billy Hart).

Hart, Bob

I WONDER WHAT SHE'S DOING TONITE (Hart, Bob & Tommy Boyce).
LP: . . . . **RVLP 1014**

SONGS FROM SUFFOLK.
Tracks: / Cod banging / Australia / Broadside, A (the female captain) / Banks of the sweet primroses / What a funny little place to have one / Bold general wolfe / Female cabin boy, The / As I strolled out to Aylesbury / Scarlet and the blue, The / John barleycorn / Miner's dream of home, The / Young sailor cut down, The / All jolly fellows that follow the plough / Underneath her apron.
LP: **12TS 225**

Hart, Corey

BANG.
Tracks: / Little love, A / Bang (starting over) / Rain on me / Chase the sun / Diamond cowboy / Icon / Can't stand losin' you / Kisses on the train / Art of color / Slowburn / Ballad for Nien Cheng.
LP: . . . . **MTL 1055**
MC: . . . . **TCMTL 1055**

BOY IN THE BOX.
Tracks: / Boy in the box / Komrade Kiev / Never surrender / Sunny place, shady people / Eurasian eyes / Everything in my heart / Silent talking / Waiting for you / Water from the moon.
LP: . . . . **HART 1**
MC: . . . . **TC HART 1**

FIELDS OF FIRE.
Tracks: / I am by your side / Dancing with my mirror / Take my heart / Angry young man / Going home / I can't help falling in love with you / Political cry / Is it too late? / Jimmy Raeburn / Blind faith.
LP: . . . . **AML 3111**
MC: . . . . **TCAML 3111**

YOUNG MAN RUNNING.
Tracks: / Don't take me to the racetrack / In your soul / Truth will set you free / Chase the sun / So it goes / Still in love / Spot you in a coalmine / Lone wolf / No love lost / Crossroad caravan / Chippin' away.
MC: . . . . **TCMTL 1027**
LP: . . . . **MTL 1027**

Hart, Elroy

NORTH FLORIDA FIVES (Hart, Elroy & Fats Jefferson).
LP: . . . . **FLY 510**

Hart Family

HART TO HART.
Tracks: / Rocking Chantilly / Compute and turn me on / I'm a song, sing me / Georgie Porgie / My eyes adored you / I shall be released / Electric lady / Without you / You make me feel brand new / Where is the sun? / Until it's time for you to go.
LP: . . . . **SFA 066**

Hart, Freddie

MY LADY.
Tracks: / Only woman in the world / Wasn't it easy baby / Look a here / Give a little you to me / My lady loves / My lady / Hangin' on a heartstring / Guilty / More than a bedroom thing / Toe to toe.
LP: . . . . **EST 11911**

Hart, Grant

INTOLERANCE.
LP: . . . . **SST 215**
MC: . . . . **SSTC 215**

Hart, John

BLOWIN' MAN, THE (Hart, John/Cajun Twisters/Slim Notini).
Tracks: / Corina Corina / My babe / Louisiana two-step / Chante / Blowin' man / Opelousas half step / Allons a Lafayette / Back in my woman's arms again / Gunnar / I got a woman.
LP: . . . . **SNTF 844**

Hart, Lorenz

BOYS FROM SYRACUSE (See under Rodgers, Richard).

IT'S SMOOTH,IT'S SMART-IT'S RODGERS,IT'S HART (see Rodgers,Richard/Lorenz Hart) (Hart, Lorenz & Richard Rogers).

Hart, Maureen

HEY LORD, IT'S ME.
LP: . . . . **KLP 58**
MC: . . . . **ZCKLP 58**

Hart, Mickey

AT THE EDGE.
Tracks: / 4 for Garcia / Sky water / Slow sailing / Lonesome hero / Fast sailing / Cougar run / Eliminators, The / Brainstorm / Pigs in space.
MC: . . . . **RACS 0124**

Hart, Mike

ROLLING THUNDER.
Tracks: / Rolling thunder / Shoshone invocation / Fletcher carnaby / Blind John / Deep, wide and frequent / Granma's cookies / Main ten, The / Chase, The / Young man / Pump song / Hangin' on.
LP: . . . . **GDV 4009**
MC: . . . . **GDTC 4009**

SCOTTISH SOCIETY SYNCOPATORS (Hart, Mike Scottish Society Syncopators).
LP: . . . . **PR 1003**

Hart, Paul

IRISH REQUESTS.
LP: . . . . **UNKNOWN**

Hart, Robert

CRIES AND WHISPERS.
LP: . . . . **K 781 961 1**
MC: . . . . **K 781 961 4**

Hart, Tim

DRUNKEN SAILOR & OTHER KIDS SONGS.
Tracks: / What shall we do with the drunken sailor? / Froggy's courting.
LP: . . . . **MFP 5635**
MC: . . . . **TCMFP 5635**

FAVOURITE CHILDRENS SONGS (Hart, Tim & friends).
Tracks: / Grand old Duke of York, The / Sing a song of sixpence / 1-2-3-4-5, once I caught a fish alive / Hey diddle diddle / Little Jack Horner / Little Miss Muffet / Little Bo Peep / Mary, Mary, quite contrary / Old MacDonald had a farm / There was an old woman tossed up in a basket / Twinkle, twinkle little star / Boys and girls come out to play / Nick-nack paddy wack / Baa, baa, black sheep / Bobby Shaftoe / Hush-a-bye baby / Humpty Dumpty / Lavender blue / London Bridge is falling down / Oranges and lemons / Oh dear, what can the matter be? / Over the hills and far away / Fox jumped up, A / Clementine / Three jolly rogues of Lynn / Who killed Cock Robin? / What shall we do with the drunken sailor? / Riddle song, (The) / Michael Finnigan / Widdicombe Fair / Froggy's courting / Curly locks.
2LP: **41 1076 3**
MCSET: **41 1076 9**

FAVOURITE NURSERY RHYMES & OTHER CHILDREN'S SONG (Hart, Tim & friends).
Tracks: / Grand old Duke of York, The / Sing a song of sixpence / Once I caught a fish alive / Hey diddle diddle / Little Jack Horner / Little Miss Muffet / Little Bo Peep / Mary, Mary quite contrary / Old MacDonald had a farm / Twinkle, twinkle little star / Nick-nack paddy wack / Baa Baa black sheep / Bobby Shaftoe / Hush-a-bye baby / Humpty Dumpty / Lavender blue / London Bridge is falling down / Oranges and lemons / Oh dear what can the matter be / Over the hills and far away / Fox jumped up, A / Clementine / Three jolly rogues of Lynn / Who killed Cock Robin? / Cockles and mussels / Hush little baby / What shall we do with the drunken sailor? / Riddle song, The / Michael Finnigan / Froggy's courting.
MC: . . . . **HR 8173**

FOLK SONGS OF OLDE ENGLAND (Hart, Tim & Maddy Prior).
Tracks: / Lish young buy a broom / Adieu sweet lovely Nancy / Maid that's deep in love / Rambling sailor / Bruton town / Farewell Nancy / Dalesman's litany, The / Brisk butcher, The / Statley southerner, The / Who's the fool now? / Wager a wager, A / Babes in the wood / Adam and Eve.
LP: . . . . **CREST 23**
MC: . . . . **ZCEST 23**
LP: . . . . **CREST 006**
MC: . . . . **CRESTMC 006**
LP: . . . . **CREST 010**
MC: . . . . **CRESTMC**

MY VERY FAVOURITE NURSEY RHYME RECORD.
Tracks: / Grand old Duke of York, The / Once I caught a fish alive / Little Bo Peep / Mary, Mary quite contrary / Old MacDonald had a farm / There was an old woman tossed up in a basket / Twinkle twinkle little star / Boys and girls come out to play / Nick nack paddy wack / Baa baa black sheep / Bobby Shaftoe / Hush-a-bye baby / Humpty Dumpty / Lavender blue / London bridge is falling down / Oranges and lemons / Oh dear what can the matter be.
LP: . . . . **MFP 50542**
MC: . . . . **TCMFP 50542**

SING FOLK SONGS OF OLD ENGLAND VOL. 2 (Hart, Tim & Maddy Prior).
Tracks: / My son John / Earl Richard / Paddy stole the rope / Gardener, The / Bay of Biscay / Queen Eleanor's confession / Horn of the hunter / Copshawholme fair / Oatse beanse barley growa / Fiddlers green / Captain Wedderburn's courtship / Turkey rhubarb / Bold fisherman.
MC: . . . . **ZCEST 26**
LP: . . . . **CREST 26**

SUMMER SOLSTICE (Hart, Tim & Maddy Prior).
Tracks: / False knight on the road / Bring us in good ale / Of all the birds / I live not where I love / Ploughboy and the cockney, The / Westron Wynde / Sorry the day I was married / Dancing at Whitsun / Fly up my cock / Cannily cannily / Adam catched Eve / Three drunken maidens / Serving girls holiday.
MC: . . . . **ZCEST 12**
LP: . . . . **CREST 12**

TIM HART.
Tracks: / Keep on travelling / Tuesday afternoon / Hillman Avenger / Lovely lady / Come to my window / Nothing to hide / Overseas / Time after time / As I go my way.
LP: . . . . **CHR 1218**
MC: . . . . **ZCHR 1218**

Harte, Frank

AND LISTEN TO MY SONG.
LP: . . . . **SPIN 994**
MC: **4SPIN 994**

DAYBREAK AND A CANDLE END.
LP: . . . . **SPIN 995**
MC: **4SPIN 995**

DUBLIN STREET SONGS.
Tracks: / Traveller all over the world, The / Shamrock shore, The / Rag man's ball, The / Henry my son / Bold Belfast shoemaker, The / Night that Larry was stretched, The.
LP: **12T 172**

FRANK HARTE & LISTENING TO MY SONG.
LP: . . . . **LUN 025**

THROUGH DUBLIN CITY.
Tracks: / Rosemary fair / Johnny Doyle / Dunlavin green / Spanish lady / Flower of Magherally, The / James Connolly / Ship's carpenter's wife, The / Three weeks we are wed / Matt Hyland / Row in the town, The / He rolled her to the wall.
LP: **12T 218**

Harte, Jerry

PAY ANY PRICE (See under Pay Any Price).

Harter Attack

HUMAN HELL.
Tracks: / Death bells of the apocalypse / Last temptation, The / Slaves of conformity / Message from God / Nuclear attack / Human hell / Culture decay / Thugs against drugs / Symbol of hate / Let the sleeping dogs die.
LP: . . . . **CORE 1**

Hartford, John

ALL IN THE NAME OF LOVE.
Tracks: / All in the name of love / Cuckoo's nest, The / In Sara's eyes / Gentle on my mind / Boogie / Six o'clock train and a girl with green eyes / Don't cry and your tears / Ten chord blues / Dancing in the bathtub / Deck hand's waltz / Also love you for your mind.
LP: . . . . **FF 044**

ANNUAL WALTZ (Hartford, John & The Hartford String Band).
Tracks: / All in my love for you / Ohio river rag / Annual waltz / Gone gone gone / Love wrote this song / Pennington bend / Learning to smile all over again / Here's to your dreams / Short life of trouble / Living in the Mississippi valley.
MC: . . . . **MCFC 3366**
LP: . . . . **MCF 3366**

CATALOGUE.
LP: . . . . **FF 259**

CLEMENTS, HARTFORD & HOLLAND (see Clements, Vassar).

DOWN ON THE RIVER.
Tracks: / Here I am again in love / Bring your clothes back home / Wish I had our time again / All I got is gone away / Delta queen waltz / Old time river man / Men all want to be hobos / Right in the middle of falling for you / There'll never be another you / Little boy / General Jackson.
LP: . . . . **FF 514**
MC: . . . . **FF 514C**

GUM TREE CANOE.
Tracks: / I'm still here / Way down the river road / Gum tree canoe / Your long journey / Jug Harris / Piece of my heart / Take me back to Mississippi / River home / Lorena / Wrong road again / No expectations.
LP: . . . . **SDLP 030**
LP: . . . . **FF 289**

MARK TWANG.
LP: . . . . **FF 020**
MC: . . . . **FF 020C**

ME OH MY, HOW TIME DOES FLY.
LP: . . . . **FF 440**
MC: . . . . **FF 440C**

MYSTERY BELOW.
LP: . . . . **FF 063**

NOBODY KNOWS WHAT YOU DO.
LP: . . . . **FF 028**

SLEEPIN' ON THE CUMBERLAND.
LP: . . . . **FF 095**
MC: . . . . **FF 095C**

YOU AND ME AT HOME.
LP: . . . . **FF 228**

Harth, Alfred

EARTH, THE.
Tracks: / Female is the sun / Relation to the light, colour and feeling / Studying walk / Landscape / Body and mentation / Energy: blood-air / Three acts of recognition / Come Oekotopia / Waves of being / Transformate, transcend, tones and images.
LP: . . . . **ECM 1264**

Hartley, Keef

TIME IS NEAR, THE.
LP: . . . . **SML 1071**

Hartman, Dan

I CAN DREAM ABOUT YOU.
Tracks: / We are the young / I can dream about you / Shy hearts / I'm not a rolling stone / Rage to live / Name of the game / Power of a good love / Second nature / I can't get enough / Electricity.
LP: . . . . **MCF 3239**
MC: . . . . **MCFC 3239**

INSTANT REPLAY.
Tracks: / Instant replay / Countdown-this is it / Double-O-Love / Chocolate box / Love is a natural / Time and space.
MC: **40 32713**
LP: . . . . **SKY 32713**
LP: . . . . **SKY 83265**

NEW GREEN/CLEAR BLUE.
Tracks: / Sigh of relief / Romance / New green/clear blue / Swan, The / Beautiful mist / Alpha waves / Adrift in a red sky / Scaramanga / Soviet nights / Hope of no end / Home.

LP: 209 937
MC: 409 937

Hartman, Johnny

AND I THOUGHT ABOUT YOU.
LP: FS 249

FROM THE HEART.
Tracks: / Blue skies / Birth of the blues / What is there to say / Ain't misbehavin' / I fall in love too easily / We'll be together again / Down in the depths / They didn't believe me / I get a kick out of you / All of me / I'm glad there's you / When your lover has gone / I'll remember April / I see your face before me / September song / Moonlight in Vermont.
LP: AFF 189

ONCE IN EVERY LIFE.
LP: BH 7012

THIS ONE'S FOR TED.
LP: AP 181

UNFORGETTABLE SONGS.
Tracks: / Very thought of you, The / Fools rush in / Love is here to stay / Once in a while / Biddin' my time / Down in the depths / Ain't misbehavin' / Isn't it romantic / Unforgettable / More I see you, The / What do I owe her / Almost like being in love.
LP: JASM 1515

Hartman's Earth

GIVE IT TO ME DADDY Hot hillbilly rhythm from the 1930's.
Tracks: / Let me play with it / Feels good / My southern movements / Fetch it on down to my house / Grandma and Grandpa / Give it to me daddy / Please Mr. Moon don't tell on me / Oh sweet daddy / Night in Carolina, A / No huggin' or kissin'.
LP: RAMBLER 104

Harum Scarum

DOGMAN.
LP: ANDA 30

Harvey, Alex

ALEX HARVEY BAND IN CONCERT (Harvey, Alex Band).
MC: WINCMC 002

ALEX HARVEY & HIS SOUL BAND (Harvey, Alex & His Soul Band).
LP: 831 887-1
MC: 831 887-4

BEST OF THE SENSATIONAL ALEX HARVEY BAND, THE (Harvey, Alex Sensational Band).
Tracks: / Next / Framed / Faith healer / Tomahawk kid / Vambo / Man in the jar, The / Sgt. Fury / Tale of the giant stoneater, The / Action Strasse / Delilah / Weights made of lead / Boston Tea Party / Anthem / Runaway / Crazy horses / Big tree small axe / Mafia stole my guitar / Gang bang / Tomorrow belongs to me.
LP: PL 70276
MC: PK 70276
LP: RCALP 9003

BEST OF THE SENSATIONAL ALEX HARVEY BAND, THE (Sensational Alex Harvey Band).
Tracks: / Delilah (live) / Cheek to cheek (live) / Jungle rubout / Man in the jar, The / Weights made of lead / Sgt. Fury / Boston tea party / Next / Gamblin' bar room blues / Tomorrow belongs to me (live) / Snake bite / School's out / Love story / Faith healer / Framed.
MC: MCTC 001

BEST OF THE SENSATIONAL ALEX HARVEY BAND, THE (Harvey, Alex Sensational Band).
Tracks: / Delilah / Faith healer / Framed / Sgt. Fury / Jungle rub out / Love story / School's out / Boston tea party / Gamblin' bar room blues / Next / Man in the jar, The / Snake bite / Give my compliments to the chef / Cheek to cheek.
LP: NE 1368
MC: CE 2368
MC: MCTC 001

COLLECTION: ALEX HARVEY (Sensational Alex Harvey Band).
Tracks: / 25 dollars for a message / Tale of the giant stoneater, The / Action strasse / Gang bang / Next / Give my compliments to the chef / Framed / Tomorrow belongs to me / Dance to your daddy / Sgt. Fury / Sultan's choice / Delilah (Live) / Soul in chains / Faith healer / Boston tea party / Vambo / Dogs of war / There's no lights on the Christmas tree mother - they're bur / Giddy up a ding dong.
2LP: CCSLP 149
MC: CCSMC 149

COLLECTORS ITEMS (Sensational Alex Harvey Band).
Tracks: / Boston tea party / Action strasse / Give my compliments to the chef / Jungle Jenny / Vambo / Faith healer / Delilah / Sultan's choice / Dance to your daddy.
LP: TOPS 129

FOURPLAY (Harvey, Alex Band).
Tracks: / Smouldering / Chase it into the night / Shake your way to heaven / Outer boogie / Big boy / Pick it up and kick it / Love you for a lifetime / Too much American pie.
LP: SAH 113
LP: TOPC 5006

FRAMED (Sensational Alex Harvey Band).
LP: SAH 119
MC: SAH 119TC

IMPOSSIBLE DREAM, THE (Harvey, Alex Band).
MC: SAH 116TC
LP: SAH 116
LP: 6360 112

LEGEND, THE.
LP: SAH 141

LIVE: SENSATIONAL ALEX HARVEY BAND (Sensational Alex Harvey Band).
Tracks: / Compliments to the chef / Vambo / Delilah / Faith healer / Fanfare / Framed / Tomahawk kid.
LP: SAH 117
LPPD: SAH 117PD
MC: SAH 117TC
LP: FA 3161
MC: TCFA 3161

MAFIA STOLE MY GUITAR (Harvey, Alex New Band).
Tracks: / Don's delight / Back in the depot / Wait for me Mama / Mafia stole my guitar / Shakin' all over / Whalers / Oh spartacus / Just a gigolo / I ain't got nobody.
LP: PL 25257

NEXT (Sensational Alex Harvey Band).
Tracks: / Swampsnake / Gang bang / Faith healer / Giddy up a ding dong / Next / Vambo marble eye / Last of the teenage idols, The.
LPPD: SAH 114PD
LP: FA 3169
MC: TCFA 3169
LP: SAH 114
LP: 6360 103

PENTHOUSE TAPES (Sensational Alex Harvey Band).
LP: SAH 112
LP: 9102 007

PORTRAIT: SAHB (Sensational Alex Harvey Band).
LP: STFL 1
MC: STFC 1

ROCKDRILL (Harvey, Alex Band).
LP: SAH 118

SAHB STORIES.
LP: TOPS 112

SENSATIONAL ALEX HARVEY BAND (Harvey, Alex Band).
LP: SAH 115
LP: 6360 122

SOLDIER ON THE WALL, THE.
LP: AMP 2
MC: CAMP 2

TOMORROW BELONGS TO ME (Sensational Alex Harvey Band).
LP: SAH 111
LP: 9102 003

Harvey, Bobby

CEILIDH DANCES (Harvey, Bobby & His Ceilidh Band).
MC: ZCLOC 1058

GLENNEAGLES FAVOURITES (Harvey, Bobby Band).
LP: LOCLP 1042
MC: ZCLOC 1042

WELCOME TO THE PARTY.
LP: LOCLP 1046
MC: ZCLOC 1046

Harvey, Dee

JUST AS I AM.
Tracks: / Leave well enough alone / All that you want / Star / How can we be friends / Just as I am / What's next / I don't know yet / Like an echo / Nothing but emotion / Tie that binds, The.
LP: ZL 72761
MC: ZK 72761

Harvey Girls,

HARVEY GIRLS, THE (Various artists).
LP: HS 5002

Harvey, Jancis

PORTRAIT OF JANCIS HARVEY, A.
LP: WRS 107

Harvey, Jane

IT NEVER ENTERED MY MIND (Harvey, Jane with Ray Ellis & His Orchestra).
Tracks: / It never entered my mind / God bless the child / Music that makes me dance, The / I'll never go there anymore / Every time / Quess I'll hang my tears out to dry / Bye bye blues / How long has this been going on / My ship / Here's that rainy day / Glory of love / Look at that face.
LP: DS 888
MC: DSC 888

Harvey & The Wallbangers

ALLEZ BANANES.
Tracks: / Five guys named Moe / Who do you know in heaven / My baby's gone / Jailhouse rock / Shine / Your feet's too big / I'll be forever loving you / Boogie nights / Sweet talking guy / Sixteen tons / Traffic jam / Nut rocker / Right next door to an angel / Sh'boom / Blue skies.
LP: HUB LP 1
MC: ZC HUB 1

WALLBANGERS A-GOGO.
Tracks: / Make your mind up / Let's make it today / Sea cruise / Ain't nobody here but us chickens / Breakaway / Falling rain / Someday soon somehow / Needle in a haystack / Anything (you want me to do) / Sometimes Ali / Got the woo-woos / Cool dog / Every second of every minute of every hour of every day.
LP: HUB LP 2

Hashim, Michael

PEACOCKS (See Rowles, Jimmy) (Hashim, Michael & Jimmy Rowles).

Hashimoto, Ichiko

ICHIKO.
LP: NEWLP 101
MC: NEWMC101

Haskell, Gordon

HAMBLEDON HILL.
LP: WLDLP 001
MC: WLDMC 001

Haskins, Chris

CRESCENT CITY BLUES.
Tracks: / Tiger rag / Sweet Georgia Brown / Sheik of Araby, The / Poor Joe / Crescent city blues / Tenderly Hindustan / I wish I could shimmy like my sister Kate.
LP: BLM 51013

Haslam, Annie

ANNIE IN WONDERLAND.
Tracks: / Introlise / If I were made of music / I never believed in love / If I loved you / Hunioco / Rockalise / Nature boy / Inside my life / Going home.
LP: K 56453

Haslam, George

1989 AND ALL THAT (See under Rutherford, Paul) (Rutherford, Paul & George Haslam).

Hass, E.A.

INCOGNITO MOSQUITO PRIVATE INSECTIVE.
MC: 1749

Hassan, Nazia

DISO DEEWANE.
LP: PEALP 12751

HOT LINE.
LP: MUT 1043
MC: CMUT 1043

Hasselgard, Stan

JAMMIN' AT JUBILEE.
LP: DRLP 29

JAZZ CLARINET OF... STOCKHOLM/N.Y. 1945/48, THE (Hasselgard, Ake 'Stan').
LP: DRLP 25

PERMANENT STAN HASSELGARD WITH THE AMERICANS (1945-48).
LP: PHONT 8802

YOUNG CLARINET 1940-48 (Hasselgard, Ake 'Stan').
LP: DRLP 163

Hasselhoff, David

CRAZY FOR YOU (ALBUM).
Tracks: / Crazy for you / I wanna move to the beat of your heart / Passion / Was it real love / Keep the jungle alive / Let's dance tonight / One and one make three / Freedom for the world / Let's spend the night together / Lights in the darkness.
LP: 211 053
MC: 411 053

LONELY IS THE NIGHT.
Tracks: / Is everybody happy / Lonely is the night / Je t'aime means I love you / Sheltered heart / Torero - tequiero / Yesterday's love / Looking for freedom / Flying on the winds of tenderness / Lady / Song of the night / Avignon / After manana mi cielo / Amore amore (Elisabeth).
LP: 210 300
MC: 410 300

LOOKING FOR FREEDOM (ALBUM).
LP: 210050
MC: 410050

Hassell, Jon

AKA/DARBARI/JAVA (Magic realism).
LP: EGED 31

CITY: WORKS OF FICTION.
Tracks: / Voiceprint (blind from the facts) / Mombasa / In the city of red dust / Ba ya d / Out of Adedara / Pagan / Tikal / Rain / Warriors.
LP: LAND 011
MC: LANDC 011

DESERT AND HER DAUGHTERS, THE (See under Gabriel, Peter) (Hassell, Jon & Peter Gabriel's Passion Sources).

DREAM THEORY IN MALAYA.
Tracks: / Chor moire / Courage / Dream theory / Datu bintung at jelong / Malay / These times / Gift of fire.
LP: EGED 13

EARTHQUAKE ISLAND.
LP: TOM 7019

FLASH OF THE SPIRIT (Hassell, Jon/Farafina).
Tracks: / Flash of the spirit (laughter) / Night moves (fear) / Air Afrique (wind) / Out pours (kongo) / Blue (prayer) / Taboo (play) / Like warriors everywhere (courage) / Dreamworld (dance) / Tales of the near future (clairvoyance) / Vampire dances, A (symmetry) / Masque (strength).
MC: TCINTU 2
MC: 791 186 4
LP: INTU 2
LP: 791 186 1

FOURTH WORLD MUSIC (Hassell, Jon/Brian Eno).
Tracks: / Chemistry / Delta rain dream / Griot (over Contagious Magic) / Babenzele / Rising thermal 14 degrees 16N, 32 degrees 28E / Charm.
LP: EGED 1
LP: EGED 7

MEMORY OF EARTH, THE (See under Enya) (Hassell, Jon & Enya).

POWER SPOT (Hassell, Jon/Brian Eno).
Tracks: / Power spot / Passage D E / Solaire / Miracle steps / Wing melodies / Elephant and the orchid, The / Air.
LP: ECM 1327

VERNAL EQUINOX.
LP: LML 1021

VOICE PRINTS (See under 808 State) (808 State & Jon Hassell).

Hasson, Maurice

VIRTUOSO VIOLIN (Hasson, Maurice/St. Johns Smith Sq. Orchestra/Ian Brown).
Tracks: / Introduction/Rondo capriccioso (Saint-Saens) / Tzigane (Ravel) / Poeme (Chausson) / Polonaise (Weiniawski) / Scherzo Tarantelle (Weiniawski) / Cantabile (Paganini) / Caprice no.5 (Paganini) (Unaccompanied) / Caprice no.13 (Paganini) (Unaccompanied) / Sicilienne (Paradis) / Scherzo (Brahms) / Zapateado (Sarasate) / Zigeunerweisen (Sarasate).
MC: ZC QS 6034

Hastings Area..

WIND ORCHESTRA & YOUTH BIG BAND (Hastings Area Youth Wind Orchestra/Big Band).
Tracks: / Earl of Oxford's march / Trombone concertino / Moorside march / No strings attached / Shepherd's song / Traces / Peanut vendor / If I were a carpenter / Nobody knows the trouble I've seen / Ballerina girl / Tequila / That's what friends are for / Bad / Mony mony.
MC: NONE

Hastings, Count

COUNT HASTINGS PLUS DANNY TURNER, EDDIE WOODLAND 1948-50 (Hastings, Count plus Danny Turner, Eddie Woodland).
Tracks: / Diga diga doo / Sugar cane / She's funny that way / Begin the beguine / Candied jam / Patches / Baboo / Minor in the diner / Midnight moan / Jumpin' with Pio / Snap case / Danny's jump.
LP: KK 823

Hastings, Lennie

ALWAYS THE BEST (Hastings, Lennie Quintet).
LP: DC 33004

Hatari

HATARI (Film soundtrack) (Various artists).
LP: NL 43595

Hatcher, George

DRY RUN (Hatcher, George Band).
Tracks: / Sunshine / Good friend / First thing smoking / Rockin' in the morning / Find a new lover / Lucky guy / All I want to do / 4 O'clock in the morning / All night gambler.

LP: . . . . UAG 29997

TALKIN' TURKEY (Hatcher, George Band).
Tracks: / Sweet little rocker / Black moon rising / Forty ford / Cadillac, The / Ten years on / Louisiana sheriff / I can't believe it / Magic thing / I'm calling / Talkin' turkey.
LP: . . . . UAS 30090

Hatchett's Swingtette

IN THE MOOD.
Tracks: / Beat me daddy, eight to the bar / Oh lady be good / Blue skies / Watch the birdie / All the things you are / Mind, the Handel's hot / I cried for you / Wrap yourself in cotton wool / Scatter-brain / How am I to know / I got rhythm / Waiter and the porter and the upstairs maid / Ma / Sheik if Araby / Oh by jingo / I hear bluebirds / In the mood / Come, happy day.
LP: . . . . RFL 11

Hate Crew

SILENT RAGE.
Tracks: / Silent rage / American way / Screwed by a pusher / Burning hate / Negative score / Limits of pain / Benzine en idealen / Urban jungle / Stranded in Hell / Empty threats / Solitary losers / Alea iacta est.
LP: . . . . PETC 10

Hatfield & The North

AFTERS.
LP: . . . . OVED 196
LP: . . . . VR 5

HATFIELD AND THE NORTH.
Tracks: / Stubbs effect, The / Big jobs (poo poo extract) / Going up to people and tinkling / Calyx / Son of "There's no place like Homerton" / Aigrette / Rifferama / Fol de rol / Shaving is boring / Licks for the ladies / Bossa nochance / Big jobs No.2 / Lobster in cleavage probe / Gigantic land crabs in Earth takeover bid / Other Stubbs effect, The / Let's eat (real soon) (CD only) / Fitter Stoke has a bath (CD only).
LP: . . . . OVED 131

ROTTERS CLUB, THE.
Tracks: / Share it / Lounging there trying / (Big) John Wayne socks psychology on the jaw / Chaos at the greasy spoon / Yes no interlude, The / Fitter Stoke has a bath / Didn't matter anyway / Underdub / Mumps (Your Majesty is like a cream donut-quiet) / Mumps (lumps) / Mumps (prenut) / Mumps (your majesty is like a cream donut-loud) / Halfway between heaven and earth (CD only) / Oh Len's nature (CD only) / Lying and gracing (CD only).
LP: . . . . OVED 132
LP: . . . . V 2030

Hathaway, Donny

BEST OF DONNY HATHAWAY.
Tracks: / You were meant for me / Song for you, A / You've got a friend / Someday we'll all be free / Giving up / Where is the love / Ghetto, The / Valdez in the country / This Christmas.
LP: . . . . K 50525

CLOSER I GET TO YOU, THE (See under Flack, Roberta) (Hathaway, Donny & Roberta Flack).

DONNY HATHAWAY LIVE.
Tracks: / What's going on / Ghetto, The / Hey girl / You've got a friend / Little ghetto boy / We're still friends / Jealous guy / Voices inside (everything).
LP: . . . . K 40369

WHERE IS THE LOVE (see under Flack, Roberta) (Hathaway, Donny & Roberta Flack).

Hathaway, Lalah

LALAH HATHAWAY.
LP: . . . . VUSLP 24
MC: . . . . VUSMC 24

Hatrik

BEAST, THE.
LP: . . . . RR 9761

Hatshepsut

HATSHEPSUT.
MC: . . . . BIP 504

HATSHEPSUT MEETS THE HONKIES (Hatshepsut & The Honkies).
MC: . . . . BIP 202

Hattler, Hellmut

HUMANIMAL TALK (see under De Winkel, Torsten) (De Winkel, Torsten & Hellmut Hattler).

Hatton, Susie

BODY AND SOUL.
LP: 7599244151
MC: 7599244154

Hauand, Ali

VITAMINS A & D.
LP: . . . . RING 01013

Haunted

HAUNTED, THE.
LP: . . . . PSYCHO 9

Haunted Garage

POSSESSION PARK.
LP: . . . . ZORRO 27
MC: . . . . TZORRO 27

Haunted Summer

HAUNTED SUMMER (Film soundtrack) (Various artists).
Tracks: / Haunted summer: *Various artists* / Menage: *Various artists* / Villa diodati: *Various artists*/ Night was made for loving, The: *Various artists* / Polidori's potions: *Various artists* / Ariel: *Various artists* / Confreres: *Various artists* / Geneva: *Various artists* / Alby: *Various artists* / Unquiet dream, An: *Various artists* / Hauntings: *Various artists*.
LP: . . . . FILM 037
LP: . . . . C'BUS 0215

Haunter Of The Dark

HAUNTER OF THE DARK (McCallum, David).
MC: . . . . CDL 51617

Haunting Melodies

HAUNTING MELODIES Various artists (Various artists).
LP: . . . . NML 1007
MC: . . . . ZCNML 1007

Hause, Alfred

TANGO A LA CARTE.
Tracks: / Es wird in hundert jahren wieder / So ein fruhling sein / Regentropfen / Schoner gigolo, armer gigolo / La Cumparsita / Blue tango / Jalousie / Ole Guapa / Tango de sudsee / Tango Notturno / Florentinische nachte / In einer kleinen konditorei / Ich kusse ihre hand, Madame / Tango continento / Blauer Himmel.
LP: 814 035 1
MC: 814 035 4

TANGOS OF THE WORLD (TANGOS DER WELT) (Hause, Alfred/Big Tango Orchestra).
Tracks: / Adios Pampa Mia / Tango du reve (traumtango) / Tango Notturno / Blauer Himmel / Perlenfischer / Lover's tango / Tango D'Albeniz / Rio Chico / Keep on dancing / Evita / Carmen / Hey Jude / La Violetera / El amanccar / La rosita / Poema.
MC: 4.26196

Hauses Hohner...

MUSIC FOR ACCORDION ORCHESTRA NO.3 (Hauses Hohner, Das Orchestra).
Tracks: / Ballett-suite / Variati onen fur akkordeon-orchester, divertimento.
LP: . . . . HS 057

Havalinas

HAVALINAS, THE.
LP: . . . . EKT 69

Havana (film)

HAVANA (FILM SOUNDTRACK) (Grusin, Dave).
LP: . . . . GRP 20031
MC: . . . . GRP 20034

Have A Great Party...

HAVE A GREAT PARTY WITH THEM INDOORS(PARTY SINGALONG) Various artists (Various artists).
LP: . . . . IMP 2000
MC: . . . . IMPC 2000

Have A Rotten

HAVE A ROTTEN CHRISTMAS Various artists (Various artists).
LP: . . . . ASS 18

Have Gun Will Travel

HAVE GUN WILL TRAVEL Original soundtrack (Various artists).
LP: . . . . C'BUS 209

Have Moicy

HAVE MOICY (Various artists).
LP: . . . . ROUNDER 3010
MC: . . . . ROUNDER 3010C

Have Yourself..

HAVE YOURSELF A BALL various artists (Various artists).
Tracks: / My baby loves me: *Gracie, Charlie* / Head home honey: *Gracie, Charlie* / Wildwood boogie: *Gracie*, Charlie / Honey honey: *Gracie, Charlie* / Shake a hand: *Pedicin, Mike* / Mambo boogie: *Playboys*/ Everybody's going crazy: *Various artists* / Jump Figaro jump: *Various artists* / Have yourself a ball: *Haven*, Don & Hi-Fis / Everybody's going crazy: *Haven, Don & Hi-Fis* / Rockin' & Rollin': *Boyd, Bobby Jazz Bombers*/ Dilly dally: *Boyd, Bobby Jazz Bombers* / Disc jockey's boogie: *Pedicin, Mike* / Frankie and Johnny: *Gracie, Charlie*.
LP: . . . . KK 819

Havens, Bob

BOB HAVENS AND HIS NEW ORLEANS ALL-STARS.
LP: . . . . SLP 243

Havens, Richie

SIMPLE THING.
LP: . . . . RBI 400
MC: . . . . RBC 400

Havers, Nigel

LOOPHOLE, THE (See under Archer, Jeffrey (aut)).

Havoc

319.
Tracks: / 319.
LP: . . . . CPRODLP 015

Hawaii

HAWAII (Various artists).
LP: . . . . GNPS 34
MC: GNP5 34

HAWAII ISLANDS, THE guitares et ukulele (Various artists).
Tracks: / Tuamutu tamoure: *Various artists* / Last desert island, The: *Various artists* / Pacific melody: *Various* artists / Laora oahu: *Various artists* / Waikiki, waikiki: *Various artists* / Aloha Hawai: *Various artists*/ Ainahau: *Various artists* / E maruru a vah: *Various artists* / Pago pago: *Various artists* / Honolulu: *Various artists* / Eponika: *Various artists* / Aloma: *Various artists*.
LP: . . . . ARN 33707
MC: . . . . ARN 433707

HAWAIIAN STEEL GUITAR (Various artists).
MC: . . . . C 217

HAWAII'S GREATEST HITS, VOL 1 (See under New Hawaiian Band) (New Hawaiian Band).

HAWAII'S GREATEST HITS, VOL 2 (See under New Hawaiian Band) (New Hawaiian Band).

HUKILAU HULAS - HULA INSTRUCTIONS (Various artists).
LP: . . . . GNPS 35
MC: GNP5 35

HUKILAU HULAS VOL. 2 (Various artists).
LP: . . . . GNPS 2003
MC: GNP5 2003

MUSIC OF HAWAII Various artists (Various artists).
Tracks: / Sweet Leilani: *Various artists* / Song of the Islands: *Various artists* / Haole hula: *Various artists*/ Bali Ha'i: *Various artists* / Now is the hour: *Various artists* / Song of old Hawaii, A: *Various artists*/ Blue Hawaii: *Various artists* / Hawaii war chant: *Various artists* / Beyond the reef: *Various artists*/ Keep your eyes on the hands: *Various artists* / Hawaiian wedding song: *Various artists* / Aloha oe: *Various artists*.
LP: . . . . NL 89650
MC: . . . . NK 89650

NATIVES ARE RESTLESS, THE.
LP: . . . . KILLER 7018

Hawaiian Guitar...

HAWAIIAN GUITAR HOTSHOTS 1920S & 30S (Various artists).
LP: . . . . L 1055

Hawaiian Memories

HAWAIIAN MEMORIES Various artists (Various artists).
MC: . . . . AM 5

Hawaiian Paradise

HAWAIIAN PARADISE (Various artists).
LP: . . . . ADL 507
MC: . . . . ADK 507

Hawaiian Pure Gold

HAWAIIAN PURE GOLD (Various artists).
Tracks: / I'll see you in Hawaii: *Various artists* / Beyond the reef: *Various artists* / Lovely hula hands: *Various* artists / South sea island magic: *Various artists* / Hawaiian wedding song: *Various artists* / My little grass shack in Kealakekua, Hawaii: *Various artists* / Now is the hour: *Various artists* / Sweet Leilani: *Various* artists / Little brown gal: *Various artists* / Muana Loa: *Various artists* / To you sweetheart, aloha: *Various artists*.
LP: . . . . INTS 5028
MC: . . . . INTK 5028

Hawaiian Rainbow

HAWAIIAN RAINBOW (Various artists).
LP: . . . . ROUNDER 6018
MC: . . . . ROUNDER 6018C

Hawaiian Steel...

HAWAIIAN GUITAR CLASSICS VOL.2 (Various artists).
LP: . . . . FL 9027

HAWIIAN STEEL GUITAR CLASSICS 1920-1950's (Various artists).
LP: . . . . FL 9009

Hawes, Annett

LET'S DANCE.
LP: . . . . SKYLP 51

Hawes, Hampton

ALL NIGHT SESSION VOL 1.
Tracks: / Jordu / Groovin' high / Takin' care / Broadway / Hampton's pulpit.
LP: . . . . COP 027

ALL NIGHT SESSION VOL 2 (Hawes, Hampton Quartet).
Tracks: / I'll remember April / Should care, I / Woody'n you / Two bass hit / Will you still be mine / April in Paris / Blues 'n' boogie.
LP: . . . . COP 039

AN HISTORIC MEETING RECORDED IN THE EARLY HOURS (Hawes, Hampton And Pedro Iturralde Quartet).
LP: . . . . FS 229

AS LONG AS THERE'S MUSIC (see under Haden, Charlie) (Hawes, Hampton/ Charlie Haden).

CHALLENGE, THE.
LP: . . . . SLP 1013

DYNAMIC.
Tracks: / Hamp's blues / Ruhythm / Black forest / Autumn leaves / What is this thing called love / Sonora / Waltz for Debbie / My foolish heart.
LP: 5C 064 61169

EVERYBODY LIKES HAMPTON HAWES Vol 3: The trio.
Tracks: / Somebody loves me / Sermon / Embraceable you / I remember you / Night in Tunisia / Lover come back to me / Polka dots and moonbeams / Billy boy / Coolin' the blues.
LP: 1003 523

FOR REAL.
Tracks: / Hip / Wrap your troubles in dreams / Crazeology / Numbers game / for real / I love you.
LP: . . . . COP 013

FOUR.
LP: . . . . COP 022

GREENLEAVES OF SUMMER, THE.
Tracks: / Vierd blues / Green leaves of summer / Ill wind / St. Thomas / Secret love / Blue skies / More I see you, The / G.K. Blues / Fly me to the moon / Sunny / Status of Maceo, The / Suite for solo piano / First, second and third movements.
LP: 1007 614

HAMPTON HAWES.
LP: . . . . CJ 222

HAMPTON HAWES MEMORIAL ALBUM, THE.
LP: . . . . XAN 161

KEY FOR TWO.
LP: . . . . AFF 31

LITTLE COPENHAGEN NIGHT MUSIC, A.
LP: . . . . FLP 41043

LIVE AT THE JAZZ SHOWCASE CHICAGO VOL.1.
LP: . . . . ENJA 3099

LIVING LEGEND (see Pepper, Art).

SEANCE, THE.
LP: . . . . S 7621

SPANISH STEPS.
Tracks: / Blues enough / Sonora / Black forest / Dangerous / Spanish steps / My romance.
LP: . . . . BLP 30111

THIS IS HAMPTON HAWES VOL.2.
LP: 1003 515

TRIO, THE (Hampton Hawes vol.1).
Tracks: / I got rhythm / What is this thing called love / Blues the most / So in love / Feeling fine / Hamp's blues / Easy living / All the things you are / These foolish things / Carioca.
LP: . . . . COP 020

Hawk & Co

NITE LIFE (OLD GOLD) (See under Doheny, Ned/To prove my love).

Hawk The Slayer (film)

HAWK THE SLAYER (Film Soundtrack) (Robertson, Harry).
LP: . . . . CHILP 1

Hawkes, Chesney

BUDDYS SONG (See under Buddys Song).

Hawkins, Buddy Boy

BUDDY BOY HAWKINS & HIS BUDDIES 1927-34 (Hawkins, Buddy Boy & His Buddies).
LP: . . . . YAZOO 1010

Hawkins, Coleman

1933-34 (Hawkins, Coleman/Henry Allen/Horace Henderson).
LP: . . . . **GAPS 070**

ALL STAR SESSION.
LP: . . . . **JAZ 2000**
MC: . . . . **ZCJAZ 2000**

AT BAYOU CLUB (Hawkins, Coleman & Roy Eldridge).
LP: . . . . **HR 5002**

AT BAYOU CLUB, VOL. 2 (Hawkins, Coleman & Roy Eldridge).
LP: . . . . **HR 5006**

BEAN 1929-49, THE.
LP: . . . . **LPJT 51**

BEAN AND BEN (Hawkins, Coleman & Ben Webster).
Tracks: / In the hush of the night / Out to lunch / Every man for himself / Look out, Jack / On the bean / Recollections / Flyin' Hawk / Drifting on a reed / Broke but happy / Blues on the bayou / Jumpin' with Judy / Blues on the delta / Bottle's only / Save it, pretty mama / For lovers only / Peach Tree Street blues.
LP: . . . . **HQ 2004**

BEAN STALKIN' (Hawkins, Coleman & Friends).
Tracks: / Bean stalkin' / Stompin' at the savoy / Take the 'A' train / Indian Summer / Crazy rhythm / Indiana.
LP: . . . . **PAB 004**

BEAN-A-RE-BOP.
LP: . . . . **QU 038**

BEAN'S TALKING AGAIN.
LP: **500056**

BODY AND SOUL.
Tracks: / Meet Doctor Foo / Fine dinner / She's funny that way / Body and soul / When day is done / Sheik of Araby, The / My blue Heaven / Bouncing with Bean / Say it isn't so / Spotlite / April in Paris / How strange / Half step down please / Angel face / Jumping for Jane / I love you / There will never be another you / Little girl blue / Dinner for one, please James / I never knew / His very own blues / Thirty nine inches / Bean stalks again / I'm shooting high / Have you met Miss Jones? / Day you came along, The / Essence of you, The.
2LP: . . . . **NL 85658**
MC: . . . . **PK 85658**

BODY AND SOUL (WEST WIND).
LP: . . . . **WW 018**

CENTERPIECE.
Tracks: / Jellybean / Centerpiece / Disorder at the Border / If I had you / Bean and the boys / All the things you are.
LP: . . . . **PHOENIX 13**

CHOCOLATE DANDIES, LEONARD FEATHER'S ALL STARS.
LP: **624 056**

CLASSIC TENORS (Hawkins, Coleman & Lester Young).
Tracks: / Man I love, The / Sweet Lorraine / Get happy / Crazy rhythm / How deep is the ocean? / Voodte / Hello babe / Linger awhile / I got rhythm / I'm fer it too / Hawkins barrelhouse / Stumpy.
LP: . . . . **SM 3259**
LP: . . . . **ASLP 1004**
MC: . . . . **ZCAS 1004**
MC: . . . . **MC 3259**

COLEMAN HAWKINS: 1940-43.
Tracks: / Smack / I surrender, dear / I can't believe that you're in love with me / Dedication / Esquire bounce / Boff boff / My ideal / Esquire blues.
LP: **AG6 24056**

COLEMAN HAWKINS AND BEN WEBSTER (Compact/Walkman jazz) (Hawkins, Coleman & Ben Webster).
Tracks: / Blues for Yolande / It never entered my mind / Don't get around much anymore / I'll never be the same / Budd Johnson / La Rosita / De-dar like someone in love / That's all / You'd be so nice to come home to Maria.
MC: **833 296-4**

COLEMAN HAWKINS AND THE EARL HINES TRIO 1965 (Hawkins, Coleman & The Earl Hines Trio).
LP: . . . . **PUMPKIN 105**

COLEMAN HAWKINS AT THE BAYOU CLUB.
LP: **502005**

COLEMAN HAWKINS COLLECTION Retrospective.
Tracks: / Man I love, The / Lady be good / I'm in the mood for love / Back home again in Indiana / Soft winds / All the things you are.
LP: . . . . **DVLP 2125**
MC: . . . . **DVMC 2125**

COLEMAN HAWKINS IN CONCERT.
Tracks: / Bean and the boys / Yesterdays / Mop mop / Sweet Georgia Brown / Blues / I cried for you / Billie's blues / He's funny that way.
LP: . . . . **LP 8**

COLEMAN HAWKINS PLAYS THE WINDY CITY.
Tracks: / All the things you are / Centerpiece / Body and soul / Way you look tonight / Moonglow.
LP: . . . . **SPJ 137**

DESAFINADO (Hawkins, Coleman Sextet).
Tracks: / Desafinado / I'm looking over a four leaf clover / Samba para bean / I remember you / One-note samba / O pato / Un abraco no bonfa / Stumpy bossa nova.
LP: . . . . **JAS 12**
MC: . . . . **JAS C12**
LP: . . . . **AS 28**
MC: . . . . **ASC 28**

DISORDER AT THE BORDER.
Tracks: / Disorder at the Border / Blue room / Stuffy / Rifftide / I can't get started.
LP: . . . . **SPJ 121**

DUKE ELLINGTON MEETS COLEMAN HAWKINS (see Ellington, Duke) (Hawkins, Coleman & Duke Ellington).

DUTCH TREAT.
LP: . . . . **XAN 189**

ESSENTIAL COLEMAN HAWKINS, THE.
Tracks: / There's a small hotel / Sunday / Body and soul / Hanid / Picasso / How long? / In a mellow tone / Walker, The.
LP: **2304 537**

EUROPEAN CONCERT (Hawkins, Coleman & Roy Eldridge).
Tracks: / Joshua fit de battle of Jerico / Autumn leaves / If I had you / Disorder at the Border.
LP: . . . . **UJ 31**

FAVOURITES.
Tracks: / Disorder at the Border / Yesterdays / Bean and the boys / Stiffly / Body and soul / Man I love, The / Rifftide.
LP: . . . . **PHOENIX 22**

GENIUS OF, THE.
Tracks: / I'll never be the same / You're blase / I wished on the moon / How long has this been going on / Like someone in love / Melancholy baby / Ill wind / In a mellow tone / There's no you / World is waiting for the sunrise / Somebody loves me / Blues for Rene.
LP: **825 673-1**
MC: **825 673-4**

GOOD OL' BROADWAY.
LP: **1902114**

GREAT ENGLISH CONCERT, THE (Hawkins, Coleman/Stan Getz/Roy Eldridge).
LP: . . . . **JG 007**

HAWK.
Tracks: / All the things you are / Centerpiece / Body and soul / Just you, just me / One o'clock jump / Lover come back to me / How high the moon.
LP: . . . . **SS 107**

HAWK FLIES HIGH, THE.
Tracks: / Chant / Juicy fruit / Think deep / Laura / Blue lights / Sanctity.
LP: . . . . **RLP 233**

HAWK IN EUROPE, THE 1934-1937.
Tracks: / Lullaby / Lost in a fog / Lady be good / Avalon / What a difference a day made / Stardust / Meditation / Netcha's dream / Strange fact, A / Crazy rhythm / Honeysuckle rose / Out of nowhere / Sweet Georgia Brown / Mighty like the blues / Pardon me pretty baby / Somebody loves me / My buddy / Well all right then.
LP: . . . . **AJA 5054**
MC: . . . . **ZC AJA 5054**

HAWK IN GERMANY (Hawkins, Coleman & Bud Powell).
Tracks: / Shaw 'nuff / Blues in the closet / Willow, weep for me / John's abbey / Salt peanuts / All the things you are / Yesterdays / Stuffy / Just you, just me.
LP: . . . . **BLP 30125**

HAWK IN HOLLAND, THE.
Tracks: / Some of these days / After you've gone / I only have eyes for you / I wish I were twins / Chicago / Medidation / What Harlem is to me / Netcha's dream / I wanna go back to Harlem / Consolation / Strange fact, A / Original Dixieland one-step / Smiles / Something is gonna give me away.
LP: . . . . **JASM 2011**
LP: . . . . **GNPS 9002**

HAWK & ROY (Hawkins, Coleman & Roy Eldridge).
Tracks: / It's tight like that / Easy rider / Scratch my back / Save it, pretty mama / How long blues / Shake it and break it / Pretty girl is like a melody, A / Pom pom / It's my turn now / You're a lucky guy / Plucking the bass / I'm getting sentimental over you / High society / Muskrat ramble / Who told you I cared? / Does your heart beat for me?.
LP: . . . . **LP 3**

HAWK TALKS.
Tracks: / Lucky duck / I can't get started / Foolin' around / Man I love, The / Trust in me / Where is your heart? / Wishing / Carioca / If I could be with you one hour tonight / Ruby / Sin / Midnight sun / And so to sleep again / Lonely wine.
LP: . . . . **JASM 1031**
LP: . . . . **AFF 139**

HAWK & THE HUNTER, THE.
LP: **500073**
LP: . . . . **JL 73**

HAWK VARIATIONS.
LP: . . . . **ST 1004**

HAWKINS & ELDRIDGE AT THE BAYOU CLUB VOL.2 (Hawkins, Coleman & Roy Eldridge).
LP: **502009**

HAWKINS SET.
Tracks: / Yesterdays / Hawk's tune / Stuffy / Body and soul / Bean stalkin' / Riftide / Sophisticated lady / I can't get started / Time on my hands / Walker.
LP: . . . . **VRV 3**

HIGH AND MIGHTY HAWK, THE.
Tracks: / Get set / You've changed / Ooh-wee, Miss G.P.! / Vignette / My one and only love / Bird of prey blues.
LP: . . . . **AFF 163**

HIGH STANDARDS (Vol. 2) (Hawkins, Coleman & Red Allen).
LP: . . . . **JASS 11**

HOLLYWOOD STAMPEDE.
Tracks: / April in Paris / Rifftide / Stardust / Stuffy / Hollywood stampede / I'm thru with love / What is there to say? / Wrap your troubles in dreams / Too much of a good thing / Bean soup / Someone to watch over me / It's the talk of the town / Isn't it romantic? / Bean-a-re-bop / Way you look tonight, The / Phantomesque.
LP: . . . . **LP 93201**
MC: . . . . **MC 93201**

IMMORTAL COLEMAN HAWKINS, THE.
LP: . . . . **PUMPKIN 118**

IN EUROPE VOL2. (1934 to 1937).
Tracks: / Lost in a fog / Honeysuckle rose / Some of these days / Blue moon / Avalon / Star dust / Love cries / I wanna go back to Harlem.
MC: . . . . **NEO 858**

IN PARIS 1935-1946 (See under Carter, Benny).

INDISPENSABLE COLEMAN HAWKINS, THE.
Tracks: / St. Louis shuffle / Hello Lola / Hocus pocus / She's funny that way / Body and soul / My blue heaven / One o'clock jump / Say it isn't so / You were meant for me / April in Paris / Angel face / I love you / Essence of jazz.
2LP: . . . . **NL 89277**
MCSET: . . . . **NK 89277**

JAM SESSION IN SWINGVILLE (see Russell, Pee Wee) (Hawkins, Coleman & Pee Wee Russell).

JAZZ CLASSICS IN DIGITAL STEREO.
LP: . . . . **REB 698**
MC: . . . . **ZCF 698**

LESTER YOUNG/COLEMAN HAWKINS (Hawkins, Coleman & Lester Young).
LP: . . . . **SPJ 119**

LIVE FROM THE LONDON HOUSE Chicago 1963 (Hawkins, Coleman Quartet).
LP: . . . . **JASM 2521**
MC: . . . . **JASMC 2521**

LOVER MAN.
Tracks: / Stuffy / Willow weep for me / Undecided / Pleyel blues / Lover man / Caravan / Indian Summer.
LP: . . . . **FC 104**

MARCH 21 & 25, 1963 (Hawkins, Coleman & His Orchestra).
Tracks: / Peebles / Whisper to me / Traumerei / Lazy butterfly / Not quite night / Misty morning / Easy walker / Lullaby / I knew Dana / Lonely tenor / Hawk talk / All the time.
LP: . . . . **JV 103**

MASTERS OF JAZZ VOL.12.
LP: . . . . **SLP 4112**

MEMORIAL.
Tracks: / Running wild / I'll never be the same / When your lover has gone / Blue room / Breeze and I / What's new? / I'll string along with you / My own blues.
LP: . . . . **SM 3537**
LP: . . . . **AA 504**

PHOENIX JAZZ FIFTH ANNIVERSARY ALBUM (see Harris, Bill) (Hawkins, Coleman/Bill Harris/Dizzy Gillespie/ Eddie Costa).

REAL THING.
Tracks: / Soul blues / Greensleeves / Until the real thing comes along / I hadn't anyone till you / It's a blue world / I want to be loved / Red beans / While we're young / For you for me for evermore / Then I'll be tired of you / Mighty like a rose / At dawning / I'll get by / Trouble is a man / Poor butterfly.
2LP: . . . . **PR 24083**

SIRIUS.
Tracks: / Man I love, The / Don't blame me / Just a gigolo / One I love, The / Time on my hands / Sweet and lovely / Exactly like you / Street of dreams / Sugar.
LP: **2310 707**
MC: **K10 707**
LP: . . . . **PBL 211**

SOUL.
LP: . . . . **OJC 096**

STANDARDS AND WARHORSES (Hawkins, Coleman & Red Allen).
MCSET: **JASS10/11C**

SWINGVILLE 2005 (Hawkins, Coleman All Stars).
LP: . . . . **OJC 225**

TENOR TRIUMVERATE (Hawkins, Coleman/Chu Berry/Lester Young).
Tracks: / Big head / Skippy / Platinum love / There's a small hotel / Blowin' up a breeze / Monday at Minton's / Dream girl / Get lost / Six cats and a prince / I cover the waterfront / One o'clock jump / Easy does it / Tea for two.
LP: . . . . **QU 051**

TODAY AND NOW (Hawkins, Coleman Quartet).
Tracks: / Go Li'l Liza / Quintessence / Don't love me / Love song from Apache.
LP: . . . . **JAS 38**
MC: . . . . **JAS C38**

TOGETHER (Hawkins, Coleman & Lester Young).
Tracks: / Sweet Georgia Brown / I got rhythm / Lady be good.
LP: . . . . **BLJ 8037**

VERY SAXY.
LP: **1902111**

WARHORSES (Vol.1) (Hawkins, Coleman & Red Allen).
LP: . . . . **JASS 10**

WRAPPED TIGHT.
Tracks: / Wrapped tight / Intermezzo / Out of nowhere / Indian Summer / Red roses for a blue lady / Marcheta / Beautiful girl / She's fit / And I still love you / Bean's place.
LP: . . . . **JAS 50**
MC: . . . . **JAS C50**

Hawkins, Edwin

BEST OF THE EDWIN HAWKINS SINGERS (Hawkins, Edwin Singers).
Tracks: / Oh happy day / Jubilation / Someday / Every man wants to be free / Lean on me / Ooh, child / I'm coming through / Blowin' in the wind.
LP: **252 213-1**
MC: **252 213-4**

IMAGINE HEAVEN.
LP: . . . . **LN 1501**

LIVE WITH THE OAKLAND SYMPHONY ORCHESTRA.
Tracks: / Fanfare overture / Worship the Lord / Come to me / Talk / Gift of song, The / Oh happy day / Call him, he'll be there / I need to pray.
LP: . . . . **MYR 1112**
MC: . . . . **MC 1112**

Hawkins, Erskine

BIG BANDS 1940 (See under Hawkins, Coleman) (Hawkins, Erskine & Coleman Hawkins).

COMPLETE ERSKINE HAWKINS - VOL 1/2 (1938-1939).
Tracks: / Rockin' rollers jubilee / I'm madly in love with you / Let this be a warning to you / Miss Hallujah Brown / Weary blues / King Porter stomp / Strictly swing / Do you wanna jump, children? / What do you know about love? / Study in blue, A / Easy rider / Because of you / "I", the living "I" / Let the punishment fit the crime / Swing out / Raid the joint / Big wig in the wigwam / Polka dotty / No soap / Swingin' on Lenox Avenue / Hot platter / Gin mill special / Cherry / Tuxedo Junction / Weddin' blues / You can't escape from me / Rehearsal in love / Satan takes the rhumba / More than you know / Uptown

shuffle / Hadn't anyone 'til you / Baltimore bounce / Fine and mellow / Sabou.
2LP: . . . . **PM 43257**

ERSKINE HAWKINS & HIS ORCHESTRA (Hawkins, Erskine & His Orchestra).
LP: . . . . **HSR 232**

LIVE AT THE APOLLO (1944-47) (Hawkins, Erskine & His Orchestra).
LP: . . . . **EV 3003**

ONE NIGHT STAND - 1946.
LP: . . . . **JLP 1013**

ORIGINAL TUXEDO JUNCTION (Hawkins, Erskine & His Orchestra).
Tracks: / Tuxedo Junction / After hours / Tippin' in / Rockin' rollers' jubilee / Weary blues / Easy rider / Swing out / Big wig in the wigwam / Swingin' on Lenox Avenue / Gin mill special / Cherry / Dolomite / Song of the wanderer / Junction blues / Sweet Georgia Brown / Five o'clock whistle / Soft winds / Nona / Blackout / Don't cry baby / Bear mash blues.
LP: . . . . **NL 89682**
MC: . . . . **NK 89682**

SNEAKIN' OUT.
LP: . . . . **FH 30**
MC: . . . . **CFH 30**

SWINGIN' IN HARLEM.
LP: . . . . **TAX 8014**

TUXEDO JUNCTION.
MC: . . . . **NK 90363**
LP: . . . . **NL 90363**

Hawkins, Hawkshaw

16 GREATEST HITS: HAWKSHAW HAWKINS.
LP: . . . . **SLP 3013**
MC: . . . . **GT 53013**

HAWKSHAW HAWKINS Vol. 1.
Tracks: / Slow poke / Sunny side of the mountain / I'm kissing your picture counting tears / If I ever get rich mom / Rattlesnakin' daddy / I am slowly dying of a broken heart / I suppose / I can't tell my broken heart a lie / Picking sweethearts / Barbara Allen / I love the way you say goodnight / Got you on my mind / Would you like to have a broken heart / Teardrops from my eyes / Somebody lied / I hope you're crying too.
LP: . . . . **SING 587**

...SINGS.
LP: . . . . **HAT 3111**
MC: . . . . **HATC 3111**

Hawkins, P

TUBBY THE TUBA.
LP: . . . . **DQ 1287**

Hawkins, Ronnie

BEST OF RONNIE HAWKINS & THE HAWKS (Hawkins, Ronnie & The Hawks).
Tracks: / Thirty days / Forty days / Mary Lou / Wild little Willy / Oh sugar (CD only.) / One of these days / Dizzy Miss Lizzy (CD only.) / Odessa / Sick and tired / Baby Jean / Come love (CD only.) / Hey bob a lou (CD only.) / Ruby baby / Bo Diddley / Clara / I feel good / Who do you love / What'cha gonna do (when the creek runs dry).
MC: . . . . **TCROU 5009**
MC: **794 890 4**

HAWK, THE.
Tracks: / Matchbox / Dizzy Miss Lizzy / That's alright mama / Odessa / Wild little Willie / Who do you love? / Bo Diddley / Ruby baby / Johnny B. Goode / Down the line / Marylou / Forty days.
LP: . . . . **UAG 30283**
LP: . . . . **MFLP 026**
MC: . . . . **MFC 026**

HELLO AGAIN, MARY LOU (Hawkins, Ronnie & The Hawks).
LP: . . . . **PRL 70241**

ROCKIN'.
Tracks: / Forty days / Wild little Willie / Whatcha gonna do (when the creek runs dry)? / Dizzy Miss Lizzy / Odessa / My gal is red hot / One of these days / Ruby baby / Marylou / Honey don't / Bo Diddley / Sick and tired / Suzie Q / Matchbox / Baby Jean / There's a screw loose / I feel good / Kansas City / Who do you love? / Southern love.
LP: . . . . **NSPL 28238**

RONNIE HAWKINS SINGS THE SONGS OF HANK WILLIAMS.
Tracks: / Cold cold heart / Hey good lookin' / Your cheatin' heart / Weary blues from waitin' / There'll be no teardrops tonight / Nobody's lonesome for me / Ramblin' man / I'm so lonesome I could cry / You win again / I can't help it (if I'm still in love with you) / Lonesome whistle / Jambalaya.
LP: . . . . **N 5017**
MC: . . . . **ZCN 5017**

Hawkins, Roy

HIGHWAY 59.
Tracks: / Mistreatin' baby / Got my dreams under my pillow / Trouble makin' woman / You're the sweetest thing / You had a good man / Sleepless nights / Just a poor boy / Royal Hawk / Albania / You're a free little girl / Gloom and misery all around / Would you? / Highway 59 / I don't know just what to do / Real fine woman / I'm never satisfied.
LP: . . . . **CHD 103**

WHY DO EVERYTHING HAPPEN TO ME.
Tracks: / Why do everything happen to me / On my way / Where you been / Wine drinkin' woman / My temper is rising / I walk alone / Mean little girl / Blues all around me / Thrill is gone, The / Trouble makin' woman / Would you / Highway 59 / Condition I'm in, The / Doin' alright / If I had listened / Thrill hunt, The.
LP: . . . . **KIX 9**

Hawkins, Screamin' Jay

1.15.
Tracks: / Talk about me / Even though / I found my way to wine / Why did you waste my time? / No hug no kiss / Give my boots and saddle / Swing low, sweet chariot / Take me back / I is / Past, The / Armpit no.6 / Ol' man river / Darling please forgive me.
LP: . . . . **OFF 6062**

BLACK MUSIC FOR WHITE PEOPLE.
Tracks: / Is you is or is you ain't my baby / I feel alright / I put a spell on you / I hear you knocking / Heart attack and vine / Ignant and shit / Swamp gas / Voodoo priestess / Ice cream man / I want your body / Ol' man river / Strokin'.
LP: . . . . **FIEND 211**
MC: . . . . **FIENDCASS 211**

FEAST OF THE MAU MAU.
Tracks: / What that is! / Feast of the Mau-Mau / Stone crazy / I love you / Constipation blues / I'm lonely / Thing called woman / I'm your man / Ask him / Reprise / Do you really love me / Dig! / Please don't leave me / I wanta know / I need you / My Marion / Bite it / Move me / Goodnight my love / Our love is not for 3 / Ain't nobody's business / Take me back / Trying to reach my goal / So long.
2LP: . . . . **DED 252**
MC: . . . . **CED 252**

FRENZY.
Tracks: / I put a spell on you / Little demon / Alligator wine / Frenzy / I love Paris / Hong Kong / Person to person / There's something wrong with you / Orange-coloured sky / Temptation / Yellow coat / If you are but a dream / You made me love you / Deep purple.
LP: . . . . **ED 104**
MC: . . . . **CED 104**

I PUT A SPELL ON YOU.
Tracks: / Portrait of a man / Itty bitty pretty one / Don't deceive me / What's gonna happen on the 8th day / Ashes / We love / It's only make believe / Please don't leave me / I put a spell on you / I don't know / Guess who / What good is it.
LP: . . . . **CRB 1211**

LIVE: SCREAMING JAY HAWKINS (Hawkins, Screamin' Jay & The Fuzz-tones).
LP: . . . . **MIRLP 114**

REAL LIFE.
Tracks: / Deep in love / Get down France / Serving time / Feast of the Mau-Mau / Poor folks / Constipation blues / Your kind of love / All night / Alligator wine / I feel alright / Mountain jive.
LP: . . . . **CRB 1205**
MC: . . . . **TCCRB 1205**

SCREAMIN' THE BLUES.
Tracks: / Not anymore / Please try to understand / Baptise me in wine / This is all / She put the wammee on me / Well I tried / You're all of my life to me / I hear voices / Talk about me / Just don't care / Whammy, The / Poor folks / Your kind of love / All night / Monkberry moon delight / Sweet Ginny.
LP: . . . . **RL 025**

Hawkins, Ted

DOCK OF THE BAY.
LP: . . . . **BRAVE 6**
MC: . . . . **BRAVE 6C**

HAPPY HOUR.
LP: . . . . **ROUNDER 2033**
MC: . . . . **ROUNDER 2033C**
LP: . . . . **WOLP 2**
MC: . . . . **WOWC 2**

I LOVE YOU TOO.
Tracks: / Who do you love? / You've changed / Nowhere to run / Nursery rhymes / Ladder of success / Dollar tree / I ain't got nothing yet / Baby / No love / Ding dong ding.
LP: . . . . **PTLP 008**
MC: . . . . **PTLC 008**

UNDER THE BOARDWALK.
LP: . . . . **BRAVE 2**
MC: . . . . **BRAVE 2C**

WATCH YOUR STEP.
Tracks: / Watch your step ((Acoustic Version)) / Bring it home Daddy / If you love me / Don't lose your cool / Lost ones, The / Who got my natural comb? / Peace & Happiness / Sweet baby / Stop your crying / Put in a cross / Sorry you're sick / Watch your step (band version) / T.W.A. / I gave up all I had / Stay close to me / Sweet baby / Bring it home Daddy.
LP: . . . . **WOLP 1**
MC: . . . . **WOWC 1**

Hawkins, Tommy

LIVE A LITTLE (Hawkins, Tommy & His Showband).
LP: . . . . **DS 034**

Hawkins, Tramaine

FREEDOM.
LP: . . . . **REJ R 5019**
MC: . . . . **REJ C 5019**

JOY THAT FLOODS MY SOUL, THE.
LP: . . . . **SP R 1173**
MC: . . . . **SP C 1173**

SEARCH IS OVER, THE.
LP: . . . . **REJ R 5009**
MC: . . . . **REJ C 5009**

TRAMAINE.
Tracks: / Look at me / Lord I try / I'll be with him / Holy one / Call me / Highway / When you pray / Will you be there?.
LP: . . . . **LS 7054**
MC: . . . . **LC 7054**
LP: . . . . **SP 65110**

Hawkins, Walter

1927-29 (Hawkins, Walter 'Buddy Boy').
Tracks: / Shaggy dog blues / Number three blues / Jailhouse fire blues / Snatch it back blues / Workin' on the railroad / Yellow woman blues / Raggin' the blues / Awful fix blues / Rag blues / How come mama blues / Snatch it and grab it / Voice throwin' blues.
LP: . . . . **MSE 202**

JESUS CHRIST IS THE WAY (Hawkins, Walter & The Family).
Tracks: / I'm going through / I need your spirit / Strange / You're everything to me / Someday we'll meet again / God has signed my name / Jesus Christ is the way / I love Jesus more today / He brought me / Lord, give us time.
LP: . . . . **LS 7043**
MC: . . . . **LC 7043**

LOVE ALIVE (Hawkins, Walter & The Love Centre Choir).
Tracks: / Follow me / Dear Jesus, I love you / I love the Lord / Changed / I won't be satisfied / God is / I'm not the same / Goin' up yonder.
LP: . . . . **LS 7038**
MC: . . . . **LC 7038**

LOVE ALIVE 2 (Hawkins, Walter & The Love Centre Choir).
Tracks: / Come by here, good Lord / He's that kind of friend / Never alone / Until I found the Lord / Be grateful / I'm goin' away / God will open doors / Right on.
LP: . . . . **LSX 7050**
MC: . . . . **LC 7050**

LOVE ALIVE 3.
LP: . . . . **LS 7075**
MC: . . . . **LC 7075**

Hawklords

25 YEARS ON.
Tracks: / PSI power / Free fall / Automotion / 25 years / Flying doctor / Only ones, The / Only the dead dreams of the cold war kid / Age of the micro man.
LP: . . . . **CHC 10**
MC: . . . . **CHCMC 10**
LP: . . . . **CD 4014**

Hawks

RRRRACKETT TIME (see Hawkins, Ronnie) (Hawks & Ronnie Hawkins).

Hawks, Billy

MORE HEAVY SOUL.
Tracks: / O baby / Whip it on me / Heavy soul / I'll be back / That's your bag / Drown in my own tears / What more can I do / You've been a bad girl / I can make it.
LP: . . . . **PR 7556**

Hawks & Doves

HAWKS & DOVES (SVEGLIATI E UCCIDI) (Original soundtrack) (Various artists).
LP: . . . . **SP 8018**

Hawks (film)

HAWKS (Film soundtrack) (Gibb, Barry).
Tracks: / System of love / Childhood Days / My Eternal Love / Moonlight Madness / Where Tomorrow Is / Celebration de la vie (theme) / Chain Reaction / Cover You / Not in Love At All / Letting Go.
LP: . . . . **PM 156 137 1**
LP: . . . . **POLD 5234**
MC: . . . . **POLDC 5234**

HAWKS (See under Gibb, Barry) (Gibb, Barry).

Hawks, Mickey

MR.BIP BOM BOOM.
LP: . . . . **SJLP 583**

Hawkwind

ACID DAZE.
LPS: . . . . **RRBX 1**

ACID DAZE VOLUME 1.
LP: . . . . **RRLP 125**

ACID DAZE VOLUME 2.
LP: . . . . **RRLP 126**

ACID DAZE VOLUME 3.
LP: . . . . **RRLP 127**

ANGELS OF DEATH.
Tracks: / Angel voices / Nuclear drive / Rocky paths / Solitary mind games / Living on a knife edge / Fahrenheit 451 / Looking in the future / Choose your masks / Joker at the gate, The / Waiting for tomorrow / Last Messiah, The / Arrival in Utopia / Virgin of the world / Angels of death.
LP: . . . . **NL 71150**
MC: . . . . **NK 71150**

ANTHOLOGY-HAWKWIND VOL 1.
LP: . . . . **SAMR 038**
LPPD: . . . . **SAMR 038 PD**

ANTHOLOGY-HAWKWIND VOL 2.
LP: . . . . **SAMR 039**
MC: . . . . **TCSAMR 039**

ANTHOLOGY-HAWKWIND VOL 3.
MC: . . . . **SAMR 040TC**

ASTOUNDING SOUNDS, AMAZING MUSIC.
Tracks: / Reefer madness / Steppenwolf / City of Lagoons / Aubergine that ate Rangoon, The / Kerb crawler / Kadu flyer / Chronoglide skyway.
LP: . . . . **CHC 14**
MC: . . . . **CHCMC 14**
LP: . . . . **CDS 4004**

BEST OF HAWKWIND.
MC: . . . . **ARLC 1018**

BRING ME THE HEAD OF YURI GAGARIN (Live at the Empire Pool - 1973).
Tracks: / Ga-ga / Egg, The / Orgone accumulator / Wage war / Urban guerilla / Master of the universe / Welcome to the future / Sonic attack / Silver machine.
LP: . . . . **DM 002**

BRITISH TRIBAL MUSIC.
LP: . . . . **STFL 2**
MC: . . . . **STFC 2**

CHOOSE YOUR MASQUES.
Tracks: / Choose your masks / Dream worker / Arrival in Utopia / Utopia / Silver machine / Void city / Solitary mind games / Fahrenheit 451 / Scan, The / Waiting for tomorrow.
LP: . . . . **RCALP 6055**
MC: . . . . **RCAK 6055**

CHRONICLE OF THE BLACK SWORD.
Tracks: / Song of the swords / Shade gate / Sea king / Pulsing cavern / Elric the enchanter / Needle gun / Zarzinia / Demise / Sleep of a thousand tears / Chaos army / Horn of destiny.
LP: . . . . **SHARP 033**
MC: . . . . **SHARPC 033**

CHURCH OF HAWKWIND.
Tracks: / Angel voices / Nuclear drive / Star cannibal / Phenomeno of luminosity, The / Fall of Earth City / Church, The / Joker at the gate, The / Some people never die / Light specific data / Experiment with destiny / Last Messiah, The / Looking in the future.
LP: . . . . **RCALP 9004**

COLLECTION: HAWKWIND (Parts 1 & 2).
Tracks: / You shouldn't do that / We do it / Bring it on home / Silver machine / Born to go / Dealing with the devil / Urban guerilla / Masters of the universe / Who's gonna win the war / Hash cake '77 / Motorhead / Quark, strangeness and charm / Douglas in the jungle / Space is deep / Earth calling / Angels of death / Spirit of the age / Ghost dance.
MC: . . . . **CCSMC 148**
2LP: . . . . **CCSLP 148**

DOREMI FASOL LATIDO.

Tracks: / Brainstorm / Space is deep / One change / Lord of the light / Down through the night / Time we left this world today / Watcher, The.
LP: . . . . UAG 29364
MC: . . . . TCK 29364
LP: . . . . ATAK 92
MC: . . . . TCATAK 92

EARLY DAZE BEST OF.
Tracks: / Hurry on a sundown / Dreaming / Master of the universe / In the egg / Orgone accumulator / Sonic attack / Silver machine.
LP: . . . . THBL 044
MC: . . . . THBC 044

FRIENDS & RELATIONS.
Tracks: / Who's gonna win the war / Golden void / Robot / Neesh / Good girl bad girl / Valium 10 / Human beings / Time centre.
LP: . . . . SHARP 01

GOLDEN DECADE OF HAWKWIND.
MC: . . . . KNMC 10017

HALL OF THE MOUNTAIN GRILL.
Tracks: / Psychedelic warlords (disappear in smoke), The / Wind of change / D rider / Webb weaver / You'd better believe it / Hall of the mountain grill / Lost Johnny / Goat willow / Paradox.
LP: . . . . FA 41 3133 1
MC: . . . . FA 41 3133 4
LP: . . . . LBG 29672
MC: . . . . TC LBG 29672
LP: . . . . FA 3133
MC: . . . . TCFA 3133
LP: . . . . UAG 29672

HAWKWIND.
Tracks: / Hurry on sundown / Reason is, The / Be yourself / Paranoia part 1 / Paranoia part 2 / Seeing it as you really are / Mirror of illusion.
LP: . . . . LBR 1012
LP: . . . . SLS 1972 921
MC: . . . . TCSLS 1972924
LPPD: . . . . SLSP 1972 921

HAWKWIND, FRIENDS & RELATIONS
various artists (Various artists).
LP: . . . . SHARP 024

IN SEARCH OF SPACE.
Tracks: / You shouldn't do that / You know you're only dreaming / Master of the universe / We took the wrong step years ago / Adjust me / Children of the sun.
LP: . . . . ATAK 9
MC: . . . . TC-ATAK 9
LP: . . . . FA 3192
MC: . . . . TCFA 3192
LP: . . . . UAS 29202
LP: . . . . LBG 29202

IN THE BEGINNING.
Tracks: / Master of the universe / Dreaming / Shouldn't do that / Hurry on a sundown / Paranoia / See it as you really are / I do it / Came home.
LP: . . . . DM 005

INDEPENDENT DAYS - VOL.2.
LP: . . . . SHARP 036
MC: . . . . SHARP 036C

INDEPENDENTS DAY (6 TRACK).
Tracks: / Hurry on sundown / Motorway City / Motorhead / Over the top / Who's gonna win the war? / Social alliance.
LP: . . . . SHARP 019

LEVITATION.
Tracks: / Levitation / Motorway city / Psychosis / World of tiers / Prelude / Who's gonna win the war / Space chase / Second of forever / Dust of time.
LP: . . . . CLALP 129
MC: . . . . CLAMC 129
LP: . . . . BRON 530

LEVITATION / LIVE '79.
Tracks: / Levitation / Motorway city / Psychosis / World of tiers / Prelude / Who's gonna win the war? / Space chase / Fifth second of forever, The / Dust of time / Shotdown in the night / Spirit of the age / Brainstorm / Light house / Master of the universe / Silver machine (requiem).
2LP: . . . . TFOLP 17
MC: . . . . TFOMC 17

LIVE 1979.
Tracks: / Shot down in the night / Motorway city / Spirit of the age / Brainstorm / Lighthouse / Master of the universe / Silver machine.
LP: . . . . BRON 527

LIVE 70/73.
Tracks: / Sonic attack / Seven by seven / Wage war / Urban guerilla / Only dreaming / Hurry on a sundown / In the egg / Orgone accumulator (1972) / Welcome to the future / Masters of the universe.
LP: . . . . DOJOLP 11

LIVE CHRONICLES.
LP: . . . . GWSP 1

MASTERS OF THE UNIVERSE.
Tracks: / Masters of the universe / Brainstorm / Sonic attack / Orgone accumulator / It's so easy / Lost Johnny.
LP: . . . . EMS 1258
MC: . . . . TCEMS 1258
LP: . . . . FA 3008
MC: . . . . TCFA 3008
LP: . . . . ATAK 103
MC: . . . . TCATAK 103
LP: . . . . FA 3220
MC: . . . . TCFA 3220

NIGHT OF THE HAWK.
LP: . . . . POW 5502
MC: . . . . POWC 5502

OFFICIAL PICTURE LOGBOOK, THE.
LPS: . . . . HWBOX 1

OUT AND INTAKE.
Tracks: / Turning point / Waiting for tomorrow / Cajun jinx / Solitary mind games / Starflight / Ejection / Assassins of Allah / Flight to Maputo / Confrontation / 5 to 4 / Ghost dance.
LP: . . . . SHARP 040
MC: . . . . SHARP 040C

PALACE SPRINGS.
LP: . . . . GWLP 104
MC: . . . . GWTC 104

PXR5.
Tracks: / Death trap / Jack of shadows / Uncle Sam's on Mars / Infinity / Life form / Robot / High rise / P.X.R.5.
LP: . . . . CHC 25
MC: . . . . CHCMC 25
LP: . . . . CDS 4016

QUARK STRANGENESS AND CHARM.
Tracks: / Spirit of the age / Damnation alley / Fable of a failed race / Quark, strangeness and charm / Hassan I sahba / Forge of vulcan, The / Days of the underground / Iron dream, The.
LP: . . . . CHC 50
MC: . . . . CHCMC 50
LP: . . . . CDS 4008

QUARK STRANGENESS AND CHARM/PXR5.
Tracks: / Spirit of the age / Damnation alley / Fable of a failed race / Quark, strangeness and charm / Hassan I sahba / Forge of Vulcan, The / Days of the underground / Iron dream, The / Death trap / Jack of shadows / Uncle Sam's on Mars / Infinity / Life form / Robot / High rise / P.X.R.5.
MCSET: . . . . CASMC 110

REPEAT PERFORMANCE.
Tracks: / Kerb crawler / Back on the streets / Spirit of the age / Quark, strangeness and charm / Steppenwolf / 25 years / PSI power / Only ones / High rise / Uncle Sam's on Mars.
LP: . . . . BG 002

RIDICULE.
LP: . . . . OBLP 1

ROADHAWKS.
Tracks: / Hurry on Sundown / Paranoia / You shouldn't do that / Silver machine / Guerilla / Space is deep / Wind of change / Golden void.
LP: . . . . FA 413 096 1
MC: . . . . FA 413 096 4
LP: . . . . IC 038 82624
LP: . . . . UAK 29919

SONIC ATTACK.
Tracks: / Sonic attack / Rocky paths / Psychosonia / Virgin of the world / Angels of death / Living on a knife edge / Coded language / Disintegration / Streets of fear / Lost chances.
LP: . . . . RCALP 6004
MC: . . . . RCAK 6004

SPACE BANDITS.
LP: . . . . GWLP 103
MC: . . . . GWTC 103

SPACE RITUAL ALIVE.
2LP: . . . . UAD 60037/8

SPACE RITUAL VOL.2.
Tracks: / Space / Accumulator / Upside down sonic attack / Time we left / Ten seconds of forever / Brainstorm / Seven by seven / Master of the universe / Welcome to the future.
LP: . . . . APK 8
MC: . . . . APKC 8

STASIS - THE UA YEARS 1971-1975.
Tracks: / Urban guerilla / Psychedelic warlords (disappear in smoke) / Brainbox pollution / Seven by seven / Paradox / Silver machine / You'd better believe it / Lord of light / Black corridor, The / Space is deep / Earth calling (CD only.) / Born to go (CD only.) / Down through the night (CD only.) / Awakening, The (CD only.) / You shouldn't do that.
LP: . . . . NTS 300
MC: . . . . TCNTS 300

TEXT OF THE FESTIVAL, THE.
Tracks: / Master of the universe / Dreaming / Shouldn't do that / Hurry on a sundown / Paranoia / See it as you really are / I do it / Come home / Sound shouldn't / Improvise / Compromise / Reprise.
2LP: . . . . JAMS 29
2LP: . . . . THBL 2068

THIS IS HAWKWIND,DO NOT PANIC.
LP: . . . . SHARP 022

TRAVELLERS AID TRUST, THE.
2LP: . . . . SHARP 2045
MC: . . . . CSHARP 2045

UA YEARS, THE.
LP: . . . . LBG 5002
MC: . . . . TCLBG 5002

WARRIOR ON THE EDGE OF TIME.
Tracks: / Assault and battery / Golden void / Wizard blew his horn, The / Opa-loca / Demented king, The / Magno / Standing at the edge / Spiral galaxy 28948 / Warriors / Dying seas / Kings of speed.
LP: . . . . UAG 29766
MC: . . . . TCK 29766

XENON CODEX, THE.
Tracks: / War I survived, The / Wastelands of sleep / Neon skyline / Lost chronicles / Tides / Heads / Mutation zone / EMC / Sword of the East / Good evening.
LP: . . . . GWLP 26
MC: . . . . GWTC 26

ZONES.
Tracks: / Zones / Dangerous vision / Running through the back brain / Island, The / Motorway city / Utopia 84 / Social alliance / Sonic attack / Dream worker / Bainstorm.
LP: . . . . SHARP 014
MC: . . . . SHARP 014C

Haworth, Bryn

GAP, THE.
Tracks: / Gap, The / Egypt / I can do all things / New world coming / It could have been me / Power of the Holy Spirit / More of you / New Jerusalem / No time / Send down the rain.
MC: . . . . TCCLS 8004
LP: . . . . CLS 8004

GAP, THE/PASS IT ON.
MCSET: . . . . TWINC 115

KEEP THE BALL ROLLING.
Tracks: / Keep the ball rolling / First time / Let me love you / Standing on the rock / City boy / Party girl / Luxury liner / Unchained melody / Unemployment blues / Working for love.
LP: . . . . AMLH 68507

MOUNTAIN MOVER.
LP: . . . . MYR R 1204
MC: . . . . MYR C 1204

PASS IT ON.
Tracks: / Pass it on / Never give up on love / Come away / Think for yourself / Perfect love / Cure, The / Peace and understanding / Looking through different eyes / Come on over to my place / Fear God.
MC: . . . . TC CLS 8012
LP: . . . . CLS 8012
LP: . . . . CLS 8004

WINGS OF THE MORNING.
Tracks: / Give thanks / Lord I love your word / Were you there / Let us humbly worship Jesus / Make us holy / Awake O Zion / I found a love / We give thanks / More than a tent / He is Lord / Strong wall / What kind of love is this.
LP: . . . . CLS 8013
MC: . . . . TC CLS 8013

Hawthorn Scottish Band

SCOTTISH GEMS.
LP: . . . . GES 1049

Hawthorne, Nathaniel

JASON & THE GOLDEN FLEECE (Tanglewood Tales) (Nesbitt, Cathleen).
MC: 1367

Hawthorne, Nigel (nar)

ALICE'S ADVENTURES IN WONDERLAND (See under Carroll, Lewis).

INNOCENCE OF FATHER BROWN (2), THE (see under Innocence of...(bk)).

INNOCENCE OF FATHER BROWN, THE (see under Innocence of...(bk).

MORE FATHER BROWN STORIES (See under Father Brown).

MURDER IN THE MEWS (see under Murder In The...(bk).

THREE FATHER BROWN STORIES (see under Three Father Brown (bk)).

Hawthorne, Vaughan

EMANON.
LP: . . . . AUDIO 001
MC: . . . . CASSET 001

PATH, THE.
LP: . . . . AUDIO 2
MC: . . . . SPOOL 2

Hay, Colin James

LOOKING FOR JACK.
Tracks: / Hold me / Can I hold you / Looking for Jack / Master of crime / These are our finest days / Puerto Rico / Ways of the world / I don't need you anymore / Circles erratica / Fisherman's friend / Nature of the beast (Available on cassette only.).
LP: 4503551
MC: 4503554

Haycock, Pete

GUITAR AND SON.
Tracks: / Liberty / Lucienne / Spikes / Terry Anne / Doctor Brown I presume / Claymore, The / Down to bay six / Rebecca / New York stakes, The / Follow that fog.
LP: . . . . MIRF 1027
MC: . . . . MIRFC 1027

TOTAL CLIMAX (Pete Haycock's Climax).
LP: . . . . HAYLP 1
MC: . . . . ZCHAY 1

Haycox, Ernest

STARLIGHT RIDER.
MCSET: . . . . CAB 257

Haydn (composer)

DUOS FOR VIOLIN AND VIOLA (see under Mozart (composer)) (Zimmermann, Tabea/Thomas Zehetmair).

HAYDN (Various artists).
MC: . . . . DLCMC 204

HAYDN 'LONDON' TRIOS 1-3/PIANO TRIOS 15 & 16 (Nicolet, Aurele & Christiane /Rocco Filippini/Bruno Canino).
Tracks: / 'London' trio no.1 (Haydn) / 'London' trio no.2 (Haydn) / 'London' trio no.3 (Haydn) / Piano trio no.15 (Haydn) / Piano trio no.16 (Haydn).
LP: 150 047-1
MC: 150 047-4

HAYDN..'LIVE AT THE WIGMORE HALL' V3 (Lindsay String Quartet).
Tracks: / String quartet Op.20 no.5 (Haydn) / String quartet Op.33 no.4 (Haydn) / String quartet Op.71 no.2 (Haydn).
LP: . . . . DCA 674
MC: . . . . ZC DCA 674

HAYDN..'LIVE AT THE WIGMORE HALL' V1 (Lindsay String Quartet).
LP: . . . . DCA 622
MC: . . . . ZC DCA 622

HAYDN..'LIVE AT THE WIGMORE HALL' V2 (Lindsay String Quartet).
LP: . . . . DCA 637
MC: . . . . ZC DCA 637

HAYDN'S SCOTTISH SONGS (Redpath, Jean).
LP: . . . . PH 1082
MC: . . . . PH 1082C

PIANO TRIOS NOS 24-27 (Beaux Arts Trio).
MC: 422 831-4

STRING QUARTETS (Janacek Quartet).
MC: 4254224

STRING QUARTETS OP 77 & OP 103 (Salomon String Quartet).
MC: . . . . KA 66348

SYMPHONIES NOS. 93, 94 'SURPRISE' & 100 MILITARY (Berlin Philharmonic Orchestra).
MC: 4278094

SYMPHONY NOS. 103 (DRUMROLL) AND 104 (LONDON) (Vienna State Opera Orchestra).
MC: . . . . VETC 6502

THREE SYMPHONIES VOL.1 (Cantilena).
LP: . . . . ABRD 1215
MC: . . . . ABTD 1215

THREE SYMPHONIES VOL.2 (Cantilena).
LP: . . . . ABRD 1249
MC: . . . . ABTD 1249

THREE SYMPHONIES VOL.3 (Cantilena).
LP: . . . . ABRD 1355
MC: . . . . ABTD 1355

Haydock Male...

HAYDOCK SOUND, THE (Haydock Male Voice Choir).
LP: . . . . GRS 1049

Haydock, Ron

RON HAYDOCK & THE BOPPERS (Haydock, Ron & The Boppers).
LP: . . . . R&C 1001

Hayes, Cathy

IT'S ALL RIGHT WITH ME.
LP: FS 193

Hayes, Clancy

OH BY JINGO.
LP: DL 210

Hayes, Clifford

CLIFFORD HAYES DIXIELAND JUG BLOWERS (Hayes, Clifford & His Jug Blowers).
LP: L 1054

CLIFFORD HAYES, VOL 1: 1926-31.
LP: WBJ 1004

CLIFFORD HAYES, VOL 2: 1924-31.
LP: WBJ 1005

Hayes, Edgar

1937-1938 (Hayes, Edgar & His Orchestra).
LP: SWINGFAN 1003

Hayes, Isaac

BEST OF SHAFT (Film soundtrack).
Tracks: / Shaft, Theme from / Walk from Regio's / Ellie's love theme / Cafe Regio's / Early Sunday morning / Soulsville / Bumpy's blues / Do your thing / End theme, The.
LP: 1052504
LP: STAXL 5012
MC: STAXK 5012

BLACK MOSES.
2LP: 2628 004

DON'T LET GO (ALBUM).
Tracks: / Don't let go / What does it take / Few more kisses to go / Fever / Someone who will take the place of you.
LP: 2480510

FOR THE SAKE OF LOVE.
Tracks: / Just the way your are / Believe in me / If we ever needed peace / Shaft II / Zeke the freak / Don't let me be lonely tonight.
LP: 248 047 5

GOLDEN HOUR PRESENTS ISAAC HAYES.
LP: GH 844

HIS GREATEST HITS.
Tracks: / Walk on by / Joy / Never can say goodbye / Man, Theme from / By the time I get to Phoenix / Shaft, Theme from / Let's stay together / Do your thing / Ain't that lovin' you / Look of love, The / I stand accused.
LP: STX 88003

HOT BUTTERED SOUL.
Tracks: / Walk on by / Hyperbolicsyllaciscesquedalymistic / One woman / By the time I get to Phoenix.
LP: STAXL 5002
MC: STAXK 5002
LP: SXE 005
LP: SX 005

ISAAC HAYES MOVEMENT, THE.
Tracks: / I stand accused / One big unhappy family / I just don't know what to do with myself / Something.
LP: SXE 025

ISAAC'S MOODS - THE BEST OF.
Tracks: / Ike's mood / Soulsville / Joy Part 1 / If loving you is wrong I don't want to be right / Never can say goodbye / Shaft, Theme from / Ike's rap VI / Brand new me, A / Do your thing / Walk on by / I stand accused / Ike's rap I (Available on CD only) / Hyperbolicsyllabicsesquedalymistic (Available on CD only) / Ike's rap III (Available on CD only) / Ike's rap II (Available on CD only).
LP: SX 011
MC: SXC 011

LIFETIME THING.
Tracks: / I'm gonna make you love me / Three times a lady / Fugitive / Lifetime thing / Summer / I'm so proud.
LP: 231 107 4

LIGHT MY FIRE.
Tracks: / Light my fire / Feeling alright / Windows of the world / Look of love / It's too late / Rock me baby / Call it stormy Monday / Type thang / First time I ever saw your face.
LP: STM 7008

LIVE AT THE SAHARA TAHOE.
Tracks: / Shaft, Theme from / Come on, The / Light my fire / Ike's rap / Never can say goodbye / Windows of the world / Look of love, The / Ellie's love theme / Use me / Do your thing / Men, The (Theme from) / It's too late / Rock me baby / Stormy Monday blues / Type thang / First time ever I saw your face, The / Ike's rap IV / Ain't no sunshine / Feeling alright.
LP: MPS 88004
MC: MPS 588004

LOVE ATTACK.
Tracks: / Love attack / Let me be your everything / Showdown / Eye of the storm / Accused rap / I stand accussed '88 / She's got a way / Foreplay rap / Love won't let me wait.
LP: FC 40941
LP: 4625151
MC: 4625154

MAN AND A WOMAN, A (Hayes, Isaac & Dionne Warwick).
2LP: ABCD 613

ONCE AGAIN.
Tracks: / It's all in the game / Ike's rap VII / This time I'll be sweeter / I ain't never / Wherever you are / Love has been good to me.
LP: 2480538

SHAFT.
Tracks: / Shaft, Theme from / Bumpy's lament / Walk from Regio's / Ellie's love theme / Shaft's cab ride / Cafe Regio's / Early Sunday morning / Be yourself / Friend's place, A / Soulsville / No name bar / Bumpy's blues / Shaft strikes again / Do your thing / End theme, The.
2LP: SX2 021
MC: SXC2 021
LP: 2659 007

TO BE CONTINUED.
Tracks: / Monologue / Ike's rap I / Our day will come / Look of love, The.
LP: STAXL 5008
MC: STAXK 5008

U-TURN.
Tracks: / If you want my lovin' / Flash backs / You turn me on / Ike's rap VIII / Can't take my eyes off you / Thing for you / Thank God for love.
LP: 4501551

Hayes, Lesley

OXFORD MARMALADE.
MCSET: MRC 1046

Hayes, Louis

ICHI-BAN (Hayes, Louis & Junior Cook).
Tracks: / Ichi-ban / Pannonica / Brothers and sisters / Moontrane / Book's bossa.
LP: SJP 102

NEW YORK JAZZ (see Cuber, Ronnie) (Hayes, Louis,Ronnie Cuber,Tom Harrell,Rein deGraff,Sam Jones).

REAL THING, THE.
LP: MR 5125

Hayes, Lynda

YES, I KNOW.
Tracks: / Yes, I know / Big city (part 1) / Big city (part 2) / What's it to you / Jack / Atomic baby / Take me back / Don't do nothin' baby (till you hear from me) / No next time / Change of heart / Let's babalu / Why Johnny why? / You're the only one for me / Our love's forever blessed / I had a dream / You ain't movin' me / Hubba hubba.
LP: OFF 6039

Hayes, Martha

HAYES NAMED MARTHA, A.
LP: FS 259

Hayes, Tubby

1967/FOR MEMBERS ONLY (Hayes, Tubby, Quartet).
Tracks: / Dear Johnny B / This is all I ask / Dolphin dance / Mexican green / Finky minky / For members only / You know I care / Mexican green / Conversations at dawn / Nobody else but me / Dedication to Joy, A / Off the wagon / Second city steamer.
LP: MM 079

AFTER LIGHTS OUT (Hayes, Tubby Quintet).
Tracks: / Ode to Ernie / No I wouldn't / Foolin' myself / Nicole / Message to the messengers / Hall hears the blues.
LP: JASM 2015

MEXICAN GREEN (Hayes, Tubby, Quartet).
LP: MOLE 2

NEW YORK SESSIONS (Hayes, Tubby/ Clark Terry).
LP: 4663631

TUBBS (A Tribute) (Hayes, Tubby Quintet).
Tracks: / All of you / Don't fall off the bridge / Modes and blues / Blue flues.
LP: SPJ 902

TUBBS' TOURS.
LP: MOLE 4

TUBBY HAYES 1957-72 (Hayes, Tubby, Quartet).
LP: IAJRC 50

TUBBY'S GROOVE (Hayes, Tubby, Quartet).
Tracks: / Tin tin deo / Embers / Like someone in love / Surrey with the fringe on top / Sunny Monday / Blue hayes.
LP: JASM 2001

WHERE AM I GOING TO LIVE 1969.
Tracks: / Off the wagon / For heaven's sake / Where am I going / Wierd blues / Walkin'.
LP: HQ 3006

Hayford, Jack

PRIESTS AND KINGS.
LP: WST 9644
MC: WC 9644

Haymakers Band

EVERYBODY SWING West Country folk dance.
MC: 30-324

Hayman, Carole (nar)

CUCKOO SISTER, THE (See under Cuckoo Sister (bk)).

EMER'S GHOST (See under Sefton, Catherine).

Hayman, June

JUNE 1.
Tracks: / Love is the answer / Symphony of love / Over and over / L.O.V.E. / Your cheatin' heart / It's breakin' my heart / Blowin' away / Wishin' and hopin' / Love me tender / Goin' back.
LP: OKLP 3005
MC: ZCOK 3005

Haymes, Dick

AS TIME GOES BY.
LP: AP 170

BALLAD SINGER, THE.
Tracks: / Oh look at me now / On a slow boat to China / What's new / Cheek to cheek / This time the dreams on me / Very precious love, A / You're my girl / Long hot summer / So far / Moonlight becomes you / You stepped out of a dream / Sinner kissed my angel, A / My heart stood still.
MC: JAS C2525
LP: JASM 2525

BEST OF DICK HAYMES.
Tracks: / You'll never know / It can't be wrong / How blue the night / Let the rest of the world go by / More I see you / I wish I knew / My sin / Love letters / Isn't it kinda fun / It might as well be spring / That's for me / It's a grand night for singing / Oh what it seemed to be / Aren't you kind of glad we did? / For you for me for evermore / Another night like this / Stella by candlelight / Mam'selle / When I'm not near the girl I love / Little white lies.
LP: MCL 1651

CAPITOL YEARS, THE: DICK HAYMES.
Tracks: / It might as well be spring / More I see you, The / Very thought of you, The / You'll never know / If there is someone lovelier than you / How deep is the ocean / Nearness of you, The / Where or when / Little white lies / Love is here to stay / Love walked in / Come rain or come shine / If I should lose you / You don't know what love is / Imagination / Skylark / Isn't this a lovely day / What's new? / Way you look tonight, The / Then I'll be tired of you / I like the likes of you / Moonlight becomes you / Between the devil and the deep blue sea / When I fall in love.
LP: EMS 1364
MC: TCEMS 1364

CLUB 15.
LP: SR 5004

DICK HAYMES.
Tracks: / Oh, look at me now / What's new? / My heart stood still / Cheek to cheek.
LP: GLS 9006

DICK HAYMES SINGS IRVING BERLIN.
Tracks: / Girl that I marry, The / How deep is the ocean (how high is the sky) / What'll I do / Little fish in a big pond / Once upon a time today / Say it with music / Song is ended, The / Soft light and sweet music / Cheek to cheek / Say it isn't so / Girl on the magazine cover, The / All alone / Lady of the evening / Let's take an old fashioned walk / It's a lovely day today / You're just in love.
LP: MCL 1773
MC: MCLC 1773

FOR YOU, FOR ME, FOR EVERMORE.
LP: AP 130

GOLDEN GREATS: DICK HAYMES.
Tracks: / You'll never know / It can't be wrong / How blue the night / Let the rest of the world go by / More I see you, The / I wish I knew / Love letters / Isn't it kinda fun / It might as well be Spring / That's for me / It's a grand night for singing / Oh what it seemed to be / Aren't you kind of glad we did / For you, for me, for evermore / Another night like this / Stella by starlight / Mam'selle / When I'm not near the girl I love / Little white lies / My sin.
LP: MCM 5024
MC: MCMC 5024

GREAT SONG STYLISTS-VOL.1.
Tracks: / Until you fall in love / To be with you / I only wanna laugh / I'll only miss her when I think of her / Everybody has the right to be wrong / Daybreak / That's for me / Lazy / Love will find a way / My foolish heart / Just one of those things / Do-bi-do / Just another sunset / How blue the night / My favourite colour is blue / Did we dance / Ill forget you / Time for love, A.
LP: AX 4

IMAGINATION.
LP: AP 79

IT'S MAGIC (Haymes, Dick & Helen Forrest).
Tracks: / It might as well be spring / What a difference a day makes / Breeze and I / I surrender dear / It's delovely / It's magic / Best things in life are free, The / You'd be so nice to come home to / They didn't believe me / Summertime / You send me / It had to be you / Did you ever see a dream walking? / Where or when / I'll be seeing you / One I love, The / Blue skies / To each his own.
MC: PWKMC 4043

KEEP IT SIMPLE (Haymes, Dick/Loonis McGlohon Trio).
Tracks: / More I see, The / I get along without you very well / Little white lies / Almost like being in love / Stella by starlight / Very thought of you, The / I'll remember April / That's for me / It might as well be spring / Who cares / Love is here to stay / Love walked in / You'll never know / There will never be another you.
LP: AP 200

LAST GOODBYE.
Tracks: / To be with you / Far from the madding crowd / Did we dance / You are the sunshine of my life / What are you doing the rest of your life / Wave / Until you fall in love / Love will find a way / Morning after / It's nice to be with you / My favourite colour is blue / I'll remember April / I'll forget you / Where is love.
LP: DHS 7

LOVE LETTERS.
Tracks: / I could happen to you / Mam'selle / When the wind was green / What's good about goodbye / Love letters / When lights are low / Easy to love / Your home is in my arms / I'll never smile again / Lost in the stars / What'll I do / My silent love.
LP: MOIR 107
MC: CMOIR 107

MOONDREAMS.
Tracks: / If I should lose you / You don't know what love is / Imagination / Skylark / Isn't this a lovely day / What's new? / Way you look tonight / Then I'll be tired of you / I like the likes of you / Moonlight becomes you / Between the devil and the deep blue sea.
LP: 2C 068 81989

POLKA DOTS AND MOON BEAMS.
Tracks: / Too late now / Little bit independent, A / I wish I didn't love you so / Spring will be a little late this year / Count every star / Laura... / It's magic / Polka dots and moonbeams / Song is you, The / They didn't believe me / Sunday morning or always / I guess I'll have to dream the rest / How are things in Gloccamorra? / My prayer.
LP: MOIR 120
MC: CMOIR 120

POP SINGERS ON THE AIR (See under Pop Singers On The Air) (Various artists).

RAIN OR SHINE.
LP: CAPS 1019

SOMETHING TO REMEMBER YOU BY (Haymes, Dick & Helen Forrest).
Tracks: / Something to remember you by / It had to be you / In love in vain / Long ago / I'll buy that dream / You'll never know / Lost in the stars / Love letters / Little white lies / Where or when / You stole my heart / Come rain or come shine / I'm always chasing rainbows / Something old, something new / All through the day / I only have eyes for you / I'll never smile again / You'd be so nice to come home to.
2LP: CR 5141
MCSET: CRT 5141

SPECIAL MAGIC, THE.
LP: SRO 1002

V DISC YEARS, THE.
LP: SRO 1001

VIC DAMONE & DICK HAYMES (Haymes, Dick & Vic Damone).
LP: GP 702

Haymes, Joe

RAY NOBLE & JOE HAYMES 1935 (See under Noble, Ray for details) (Haymes, Joe & Ray Noble).

Haynes, Roy

DREAM (see Honda, Toshiyuki).

OUT OF THE AFTERNOON (Haynes, Roy Quartet).
Tracks: / Moon ray / Fly me to the moon / Raoul / Snap crackle / If I should lose you / Long wharf / Some other Spring.
LP: . . . . JAS 24
MC: . . . . JAS C24

QUESTION AND ANSWER (See under Metheny, Pat) (Metheny, Pat/Dave Holland/Roy Haynes).

THANK YOU, THANK YOU.
LP: . . . . GXY 5103

Haysi Fantayzee

BATTLE HYMNS FOR CHILDREN SINGING.
Tracks: / Chazoola / More money / Shoo fly love / Shiny shiny / John wayne is big leggy / I lost my dodi / Jimmy jimmy jive / Sabres of paradise / Make me a sinner / Here comes the beast.
LP: . . . . RGLP 6000

Hayward, Charles

LES BATTERIES (Hayward, Charles 'Drum Trio').
LP: . . . . AYAADT 0486

SURVIVE THE GESTURE.
LP: . . . . INK 31

Hayward, Dennis

ANOTHER HAPPY DANCING (Hayward, Dennis Organisation).
LP: . . . . SAV 138

CARRY ON DANCING (Hayward, Dennis Organisation).
LP: . . . . SAV 133

COME SEQUENCE DANCING.
LP: . . . . SAV 142

DANCE, DANCE, DANCE WITH DENNIS.
LP: . . . . SAV 146

DENNIS HAYWARD AND THE SAVOY DANCE ORCHESTRA.
LP: . . . . SAV 150

GLENN MILLER IN SEQUENCE (Hayward, Dennis & The Savoy Orchestra).
LP: . . . . SAV 127

HAPPY CHRISTMAS (Hayward, Dennis Organisation).
LP: . . . . SAV 145
MC: . . . . SAVC 145

HAPPY DANCING (Hayward, Dennis Organisation).
LP: . . . . SAV 157

HAPPY DANCING NO. 5 (Hayward, Dennis Organisation).
Tracks: / Liza Johnson / I'm going back to Himazas / Painting the clouds with sunshine / Padlin' Madelin home / Let's have a ride on your bike / That old feeling / Body and soul / Sleepytime down south / I'll string along with you / Am I wasting my time on you / Heartaches / Mighty like a rose / Outside of heaven / Why did you make me care / One day when we were young / When I grow too old to dream / Barefoot days / Boy I love is up in the gallery, The / It's a great big shame / Ragtime cowboy Joe / Don't fence me in / Back home in Tennessee / Everybody loves somebody / My foolish heart / In the chapel in the moonlight / Lazy river / Lazy bones / Ol' man river / I kiss your hand madame / Red sails in the sunset.
LP: . . . . SAV 154

HAPPY DANCING VOL.4 (Hayward, Dennis Organisation).
LP: . . . . SAV 149

HAPPY DANCING VOL 2 (Hayward, Dennis Organisation).
LP: . . . . SAV 141

HAPPY DANCING VOL 3.
LP: . . . . SAV 144
MC: . . . . SAVC 144

LET'S DANCE (Hayward, Dennis & The Savoy Orchestra).
LP: . . . . SAV 128

LONDON DANCES (Hayward, Dennis & His Orchestra).
LP: . . . . SAV 131

MAN AND HIS MUSIC.
LP: . . . . SAV 143
MC: . . . . SAVC 143

MORE HAPPY DANCING (Hayward, Dennis Organisation).
LP: . . . . SAV 132

MR. SEQUENCE.
LP: . . . . SAV 151

MUSIC FOR CELEBRATION.
LP: . . . . SAV 152
MC: . . . . SAV 152C

SEQUENCE TIME VOL.1.
LP: . . . . SAV 134

SEQUENCE TIME VOL.4.
Tracks: / It's foolish but it's fun/Who/ Yes... / It's a pity.../Over my shoulder/ One... / Three stars will tonight/Lara's theme / What a wonderful world / Into each life some rain.../I apologise / Beggar in love, A/I'll never smile again / Night and day / Beeze and I, The / Ole Gaupa / Spider of the night / Sioux City Sue/Put your shoes on Lucy / Return to sender/Waiter and the porter....
LP: . . . . SAV 153

SEQUENCE TIME, VOL 2.
LP: . . . . SAV 137

SEQUENCE TIME VOL. 3.
LP: . . . . SAV 140

SHOW STOPPERS.
LP: . . . . SAV 148
MC: . . . . SAVC 148

THIS IS ROMANCE - I REMEMBER IT WELL (Hayward, Dennis & His Orchestra).
LP: . . . . SAV 147
MC: . . . . SAVC 147

TOGETHER.
Tracks: / Together / 'A' you're adorable / When my sugar walks down the street / Red roses for a blue lady / Ramblin' rose / Estrellita / Would you? / One night of love / It's a sin to tell a lie / I found you out / Sam's song / Out of town / Lime house of blues / Ukelele lady / How wonderful to know / Marie Elena / Always / Wonderful one.
LP: . . . . SAV 155

Hayward, Justin

BLUE JAYS (Hayward, Justin & John Lodge).
Tracks: / This morning / Remember me (my friend) / My brother / You / Nights winters years / Saved by the music / I dreamed last night / Who are you now / Maybe / When you wake up.
LP: . . . . DOA 8
MC: . . . . KDOAC 8
LP: . . . . THS 12

CLASSIC BLUE.
Tracks: / Tracks of my tears, The / Blackbird / MacArthur Park / Vincent / God only knows / Bright eyes / Whiter shade of pale, A / Scarborough fair / Railway hotel / Man of the world / Forever Autumn / As long as the moon can shine / Stairway to Heaven.
LP: . . . . MODEM 1040
MC: . . . . MODEMC 1040

MOVING MOUNTAINS.
Tracks: / One again / Take your chances / Moving mountains / Silver bird / Is it just a game / Lost and found / Goodbye / Who knows / Best is yet to come, The.
LP: . . . . TOWLP 15
MC: . . . . ZCTOW 15

NIGHT FLIGHT.
Tracks: / Night flight / Maybe it's just love / Crazy lovers / Penumbra moon / Nearer to you / Face in the crowd / Suitcase / I'm sorry / It's not on / Bedtime stories.
LP: . . . . TXS 138

SONGWRITER.
Tracks: / Tightrope / Songwriter - part 1 / Songwriter - part 2 / Country girl / One lonely room / Lay it on me / Raised on love / Doin' time / Nostradamus / Marie (Only on CD) / Learning the game (Only on CD) / Stage door.
LP: . . . . SDL 15

UNEXPECTED SONGS (see under Webb, Marti) (Hayward, Justin & Marti Webb).

Hayward, Mike

MY CUP IS OVERFLOWING.
LP: . . . . IAM R 3804
MC: . . . . IAM C 3804

Hayward, Peter

ELEGANCE.
Tracks: / Under the double eagle / Do you know where you're going to (Theme from Mahogany) / Tico tico / Concierto de Aranjuez / Ain't she sweet / Dinah / Waltz for Kathy / Plink plank plunk / Hora staccato / Matchmaker / Send in the clowns / Mame / Maria / Meditation / Sally - sing as we go.
LP: . . . . GRS 1090

HAYWARD'S CHOICE.
Tracks: / Eve of the war, The / Forever Autumn / Carriage and pair / Easy winners / Sleeper's awake / Marie's little polka / Lisbon by twilight / Fiddle, faddle / Samum / Music from across the way / Feeling groovy / Strawberry fair / Pop goes the weasel / Badinerie / Solfeggieto / Consuelo's love theme / El Condor Pasa.
LP: . . . . GRS 1127

HORIZONS.
LP: . . . . GRS 1171

MIDNIGHT BLUES.
LP: . . . . GRS 1177

OVERTURE.
Tracks: / Fascinating rhythm / Scarborough Fair / Non ho l'eta / Nessun dorma / Who pays the ferryman / Beer barrel polka / Take the 'A' train / Trumpeter's lullaby, A / Manhattan skyline / Cuando sali de Cuba / 'Shillingbury tales', The theme from / Prelude in C / None but the lonely heart / Serenade for strings / Grandfather's clock / Maria Elena / Bugler's holiday / Spinning wheel.
LP: . . . . GRS 1111

RHYTHMS OF LIFE.
MC: . . . . KGRS 1173

SOUND OF MUSICALS.
Tracks: / My fair lady / Sound of music, The / South Pacific / Oklahoma.
LP: . . . . GRS 1110

Haywire

PRIVATE SPELL.
LP: 086121

Haywood, Lance

KILLING ME SOFTLY.
Tracks: / For you / Every time we say goodbye / So in love / Don't blame me / Killing me softly with her song / Till there was you / Danny Boy / Stardust / Polka dots and moonbeams / Perdido.
LP: . . . . ILPS 9904
MC: . . . . ICT 9904

Haywood, Leon

DON'T PUSH IT, DON'T FORCE IT (OLD GOLD) (See under Yarbrough & Peoples/Don't stop...).

INTIMATE.
Tracks: / Let me make it good to you / Dream dream / Strokin' / Let's get it on / Streets will love you to death / I'm your knight in shining armor / They don't make 'em no more like you / It's got to be me.
LP: . . . . CBS 81774

IT'S ME AGAIN.
Tracks: / T.V. mama / Desire / I'll always be around / Secret rendezvous / I'm out to catch / Keep it in the family / I wanta do something freaky to you / Steppin' out.
LP: 810 304-1

NATURALLY.
Tracks: / Don't push it, don't force it / Daydream / That's what time it is / Love is what we came here for / If you're looking for a night of fun / Who you been giving it up to / Lover's rap.
LP: . . . . T 613

Haywoode

ARRIVAL.
Tracks: / Roses / Getting closer / Single handed / I can't let you go / Jelly baby / You'd better not fool around / I wanna be your lover / Time like this, A / Missing you / Under fire.
LP: . . . . CBS 25704
MC: 40 25704

Hayworth, Rita

RITA HAYWORTH COLLECTION (20 Golden Greats).
Tracks: / Amado mio / Put the blame on Mame (slow version) / Put the blame on Mame (nightclub version) / My funny valentine / Zip / Trinidad lady / I've been kissed before / Blue Pacific blues / Heat is on, The / I'm old fashioned / On the gay white way / Come tell me what's your answer / Oh the pity of it all / Here you are / What does an English girl think of a Yank? / You excite me / Let's stay young forever / They can't convince me / People have more fun than anyone / Mutual admiration society.
LP: . . . . DVLP 2089
MC: . . . . DVMC 2089

SELECTIONS FROM HER FILMS.
LP: . . . . CC 100.22

Haza, Ofra

CHI.
LP: . . . . ANP 14975

DESERT WIND.
LP: . . . . WX 320
MC: . . . . WX 320 C

EARTH.
LP: . . . . ANP 15100

FIFTY GATES OF WISDOM.
LP: . . . . SHAN 64002

OFRA HAZA.
LP: . . . . WX 198
MC: . . . . WX 198 C

PLACE FOR ME, A.
LP: . . . . ANP 15018

SHADAY.
Tracks: / Im nin' alu / Da'ale, da'ale / Shaday / My aching heart / Galbi / Eshal / Face to face / Take me to paradise / Love song.
LP: . . . . WX 181
MC: . . . . WX 181 C

YEMENITE SONGS.
Tracks: / Im nin' alu / Yachilvi veyachail / A; salk / Galbi / Ode le 'eli / Lefelach / Ayelet chen.
LP: . . . . ORB 006
MC: . . . . ORBC 006

Haze

CELLAR REPLAY.
Tracks: / Night / I fear that I'll / Survive / Portrait / Firkin of mead, A / Take me home / Aardvarks anonymous / Turn around / Unto the dawn / In the light / Dig them mushrooms / Anonymous Aardvarks.
MC: . . . . GABC 2

C'EST LA VIE.
Tracks: / Rogers revenge (Written by Haze) / Don't leave me here (Karberneck) / Fallen leaves (Lyrics by Rob Heeley) / Load (Written by Haze) / Mairage (Written by Haze) / For whom (Written by Haze) / Hum, The (Written by Haze) / Gabadon (Written by Haze).
LP: . . . . GABL 1
MC: . . . . GABC 1

STOAT AND BOTTLE.
LP: . . . . GABL 6
MC: . . . . GABC 6

WARTS 'N' ALL.
Tracks: / Seven stones / In God's hands / Slight mental incapacity / What a barber does / Doal, The / Load / Exiles mega medley, The.
MC: . . . . GABC 4

Hazel & Alice

HAZEL & ALICE (See Also Under Dickens, Hazel).
Tracks: / Mining camp blues / Hello stranger / Green rolling hills of West Virginia, The / Few more years shall roll, A / Two soldiers / Sweetest gift, a mother's smile, The / Tomorrow I'll be gone / My better years / Custom made woman blues / Don't put her down, you helped put her there / You gave me a song / Pretty bird / Gallop to Kansas.
LP: . . . . ROUNDER 0027
MC: . . . . ROUNDER 0027C

HAZEL DICKENS AND ALICE GERRARD (Dickens, Hazel/Alice Gerrard).
Tracks: / When I loved you / Working girl blues / Mama's gonna stay / Montana cowboy / Mean papa blues / Nice like that / Mary Johnson / Ramblin' woman / Beaufort county jail / Banjo pickin' girl / James Alley blues / True life blues.
LP: . . . . ROUNDER 0054
MC: . . . . ROUNDER 0054C

Hazelby, Brian

HAZELBY!.
LP: . . . . GRS 1165

PLAYS THE WERSI BETA - IN THE PINK.
LP: . . . . GRS 1182

STILL TRAVELLIN'.
Tracks: / There's a coach comin' in / Birth of the blues / Angelo / Quando, quando, quando / Caravan / Tuxedo Junction / Birdie song, The.
LP: . . . . GRS 1121

TRAVELLING LIGHT.
Tracks: / Ghost riders in the sky / Summer knows, The / What are you doing the rest of your life / Nicola / Serenade for strings / Smilkino kola / Falling in love with love / Swan, The / Cuckoo, The / Certain smile, A / Never on a Sunday / Whatever Lola wants (Lola gets) / Masquerade waltz / Delicado / Once in a while / Hill billy medley / Skip to my lou / Farmer and the cowman / Turkey in the straw / Oh Susannah / London by night.
LP: . . . . GRS 1088

YASASHIKU.
Tracks: / Amor en paz / Fame / Song that I sing, The / Happy talk / Charmaine / Cuban love song / Chariots of fire / Almost like being in love / Should I / Come fly with me / Night birds / Round midnight / Pavane / Autumn in Romania / Sway / Brazilian love song / Frenesi / Anna / C jam blues.
LP: . . . . GRS 1130
MC: . . . . KGRS 1130

Hazell

HAZELL: THREE CARD TRICK (B.P. Yuill) (Venables, Terry).
MC: . . . . PTB 610

Hazell, Eddie

AT GULLIVERS, I GO FOR THAT!.
LP: . . . . AP 179

EDDIE HAZELL TRIO (Hazell, Eddie Trio).
LP: . . . . MES 7075

SUGAR, DON'T YOU KNOW.
LP: . . . . AP 137

Hazell (TV)

HAZELL (THEME FROM) (See under Bell, Maggie).

Hazzard

HAZZARD.
LP: . . . . SKULL 8371
MC: . . . . TAPE 78371

Hazzard & Barnes

HAZZARD & BARNES.
Tracks: / Journey's end / Warning lights / South west wind / Sweet green fields of England / Fox on the run / Giving out love / Home again with you / Rock and roll lady / Take to the mountains / Still in love with you.
LP: . . . . K 56233

H.D.Q.

HUNG, DRAWN & QUARTERED.
LP: . . . . EDRLP 1

SOUL FINDER.
LP: . . . . FULL 004
LP: 15572413

YOU SUCK.
LP: . . . . COX 007

He Died With His ...

HE DIED WITH HIS EYES OPEN (Original soundtrack) (Various artists).
LP: . . . . A 275

He Said

HAIL.
LP: . . . . STUMM 29
MC: . . . . CSTUMM 29

TAKE CARE.
LP: . . . . STUMM 57
MC: . . . . CSTUMM 57

Head

INTOXICATOR.
Tracks: / Walk like an angel / Stalemate / Ice cream skin / All the boyz / Party's over, The / Under the influence of books / Two or three things / Soakin' my pillow / Ships in the night / B'goode or be gone / You're so vain.
LP: . . . . V 2595
MC: . . . . TCV 2595

SNOG ON THE ROCKS,A.
Tracks: / Out of the natch / Sex cattle man / Captain, the sailor and the dirty heartbreaker / I can't stop / Crackers (fer yer knackers) / I am the king / Don't wash your hair about it / Crazy racecourse crowd / Let's snog / Me and Mrs. Jones.
LP: . . . . FIEND 95
MC: . . . . FIENDCASS 95

TALES OF ORDINARY MADNESS.
Tracks: / Sinbin / Get fishy / Machete vendetta / Cheeky little monkey / 1000 hangovers later / Time and time again / Car's outside / Jesus ain't got a daddy / 32A / Tiger tiger / This face (is a lonely place) (CD only) / Heads go up, The (Cassette only).
LP: . . . . V 2527
MC: . . . . TCV 2527

Head East

HEAD EAST LIVE.
Tracks: / Take a hand / Man I wanna be / Gettin' lucky / City of gold / Fly by night lady / Monkey shine / When I get ready / Every little bit of my heart / Get up and enjoy yourself / Since you been gone / It's for you / Never been any reason / Elijah / Prelude to 'Creek / Jefftown Creek / Love me tonight / I'm feelin' fine.
2LP: . . . . AMLM 66007

Head (Film)

HEAD (See under Monkees) (Monkees).

Head, Hands & Feet

OLD SOLDIERS NEVER DIE.
LP: . . . . K 40465

Head, Jowe

PERSONAL ORGANISER.
LP: . . . . EFA 4891
LP: . . . . HOLP 002

RAIN RAIN RAIN (see Epic Soundtracks) (Head, Jowe/Epic Soundtracks).

Head, Murray

BETWEEN US.
Tracks: / Los Angeles / How many ways / Rubberneck / Mademoise Elle / Sorry, I love you / Countryman / It's so hard, singing the blues / Good old days / Lady I could serve you well / Bye, bye, bye.
LP: 9101725
MC: 7104725

FIND THE CROWD.
Tracks: / How many ways / Old Soho / Los Angeles / Losing you / Children only play (do you remember ?) / Last days of an empire / Countryman / Never even thought / Say it ain't so Joe / Pity the poor consumer.
LP: 6313179
MC: 7200179

HOW MANY WAYS?.
LP: . . . . MLP 101

RESTLESS.
Tracks: / When your in love / Catching Eddie at it / Modern boy / Peril in Venice / Salvation (missionary madness) / Mario / African tourists / Hold me / I don't care / Maybe tomorrow.
LP: . . . . V 2305
MC: . . . . TCV 2305
LP: . . . . OVED 241
MC: . . . . OVEDC 241

SHADE.
Tracks: / Peace of mind / Corporation corridors / (All we can do is) hold on / Not your problem / Joey's on fire / Maman / Grace / Dragonfly / Shades of the prison house.
LP: . . . . V 2275
LP: . . . . OVED 236

SOONER OR LATER.
Tracks: / You are / With a passion / Love list / Love is believing / In the heart of you / Paper thin / Fear and ambition / Wanderer / Lana Turner.
LP: . . . . V 2416
MC: . . . . TCV 2416
LP: . . . . OVED 263
MC: . . . . OVEDC 263

VOICES.
Tracks: / Last days of an empire / Affair across a crowded room / Hey lady / On your own again / Time on the line / Chance encounter / Children only play (do you remember ?) / Old Soho / Tree / Going home.
LP: 6313045
MC: 7200045

Head Of David

DOGBREATH.
LP: . . . . BFFP 5

DUSTBOWL.
LP: . . . . BFFP 18

LP.
LP: . . . . BFFP 10

SHIT HITS THE FAN, THE.
LP: . . . . NOT 3

WHITE ELEPHANT.
LP: . . . . UNKNOWN
MC: . . . . UNKNOWN

Head Over Ears

HEAD OVER EARS various artists (Various artists).
Tracks: / Filthy quality: *Tot* / U.S. 80's 90's: *Fall* / Go ahead: *Railway Children* / That's not the truth: *A House* / Here comes the judge: *Prince Kool* / Dead billy (Live): *Big Black* / This is intrusion: *Twang* / House of hatchets: *Biting Tongues* / Coast to coast: *Kit* / King Steptoe & the...: *King Of The Slums* / Inch by inch: *Swival Hips.*
LP: . . . . DEC 007

Head, Roy

ROY HEAD & THE TRAITS (Head, Roy & The Traits).
LP: . . . . TNT 101

TREAT HER RIGHT.
Tracks: / Treat her right / One more time / Get back / Just a little bit / Feeling's gone, The / Operator / Get out of my life woman / Bring it to Jerome / Three o'clock blues / Who do you love? / Boogie chillun / High Sheriff.
LP: . . . . BFX 15307

Headboys

HEADBOYS.
Tracks: / Shape of things to come / Stepping stones / My favourite DJ / Kicking the kans / Changing with the times / Silver lining / Experiments / Schoolgirls / Gonna do it like this / Breakout / Ripper / Take it all down.
LP: . . . . RSS 13

Headhunters

INDUSTRIAL WARFARE.
LP: . . . . LX 004

Headless Horsemen

CAN'T HELP BUT SHAKE.
Tracks: / Can't help but shake / Bitter heart / Just yesterday / Her only friend / I see the truth / It's all away / Same old thing / Not today / Any port in a storm / She knows who / Mojo item / Cellar dwellar.
LP: . . . . R 33/8708

GOTTA BE COOL.
LP: . . . . R 33/8820

Headline Hits

HEADLINE HITS Various artists (Various artists).
LP: . . . . NE 1253
MC: . . . . CE 2253

Headon, Topper

DRUMMIN' MAN.
Tracks: / Drummin' man / Hope for Donna.
MC: . . . . ERX 194

WAKING UP.
Tracks: / Leave it to luck / I'll give you everything / Home for Donna / Got to keep on going / Dancing / Pleasure and pain / Time is tight / When you're down / Just another hit / Hanging on my back.
LP: . . . . MERH 83
MC: . . . . MERHC 83

Headpins

HEAD OVER HEELS.
Tracks: / Still the one / Death of me / Stayin' all night / Hot stuff / Chain gang / Never come down from the danger zone / Don't matter what you say / Be with you / Afraid of the dark / Burnin' at both ends.
LP: . . . . MCL 1853
MC: . . . . MCLC 1853
LP: . . . . MCF 3296

LINE OF FIRE.
LP: . . . . MCF 3196
MC: . . . . MCFC 3196

TURN IT LOUD.
Tracks: / Turn it loud / Keep walkin' away / Don't ya ever leave me / People / Don't it make you feel / Winnin' / You can't have me / Breakin' down.
LP: . . . . K 508 97

Heads On Sticks

SECOND FEEDS.
LP: . . . . DMC 023

Heads Together

FUNKY STUFF.
LP: . . . . SRTM 73345

Heads Up

SOUL BROTHER CRISIS INTERVENTION.
LP: . . . . EM 73721
MC: . . . . EM 73724

Headset

HEADSET ONE (Various artists).
MC: . . . . DMCC 001

HEADSET TWO (Various artists).
MC: . . . . DMCC 002

Healey, Jeff

HELL TO PAY (Healey, Jeff Band).
Tracks: / Full circle / I think I love you too much / I can't get my hands on you / How long can a man be strong? / Let it all go / Hell to pay / While my guitar gently weeps / Something to hold on to / How much? / Highway of dreams / Life beyond the sky.
LP: 210815
MC: 410815

SEE THE LIGHT (Healey, Jeff Band).
Tracks: / Confidence man / River of no return / Don't let your chance go by / Angel eyes / Nice problem to have / Someday, someway / I need to be loved / Blue jean blues / That's what they say / Hideaway / See the light.
LP: 209441
MC: 409441

Healy, David (nar)

FLAT STANLEY (see under Flat Stanley).

Healy-Duffy

MEMORIES OF SLIGO.
LP: 12TS 335

Heaney, Joe

IRISH TRADITIONAL SONGS IN GAELIC & ENGLISH.
LP: 12T 91

JOE HEANEY.
LP: . . . . PH 2004

SONGS IN IRISH - VOL.2.
LP: . . . . CEF 051

Heaney, Seamus

O, THE NORTHERN MUSE (Heaney, Seamus & John Montague).
LP: . . . . CCT 4

Heard, John

LONDON CONCERT, THE (see Peterson, Oscar) (Heard, John/Oscar Peterson/Louis Bellson).

Heard, Mark

ASHES & LIGHT.
LP: . . . . MYR 1185
MC: . . . . MC 1185

Hear'N'Aid

HEAR'N'AID (Various artists).
Tracks: / Up to the limit (live): *Accept* / Hungry for heaven (Live): *Dio* / Can you see me: *Hendrix, Jimi* / Heaven's on fire (Live): *Kiss* / On the road (live): *Motorhead* / Distant early warning (Live): *Rush* / Zoo (Live): *Scorpions* / Go for the throat: *Y & T.*
LP: . . . . VERH 35

Hearnshaw, Charlie

SO SLAM IT.
Tracks: / Yesterday's waltz / Fanbelt / Seventy five / Angie's mom / So slam it / Jane's little waltz / Cassocks / Once or twice.
LP: . . . . MM 080

Heart

BAD ANIMALS.
Tracks: / Who will you run to / Alone / There's the girl / I want you so bad / Wait for an answer / Bad animals / You ain't so tough / Strangers of the heart / Easy target / RSVP.
LP: . . . . ESTU 2032
MC: . . . . TCESTU 2032

BEBE LE STRANGE.
Tracks: / Bebe le strange / Down on me / Silver wheels / Break / Rockin' heaven down / Even it up / Strange night / Raised on you / Pilot / Sweet darlin'.
LP: . . . . PRT 84135

BRIGADE.
Tracks: / Wild child / All I wanna do is make love to you / Secret / Tall, dark handsome stranger / I didn't want to need you / Night, The / Fallen from grace / Under the sky / Cruel nights / Stranded / Call of the wild / I want your world to turn / I love you.
LP: . . . . ESTU 2121
LP: 791 820 1
MC: . . . . TCESTU 2121
MC: 791 820 4

DOG AND BUTTERFLY.
Tracks: / Cook with fire / High time / Hijinx / Straight on / Dog and butterfly / Lighter touch / Nada one / Mistral wind.
LP: . . . . PRT 32803
MC: 40 32803

DREAMBOAT ANNIE.
Tracks: / Magic man / Dreamboat Annie (fantasy child) / Crazy on you / Soul of the sea / Dreamboat Annie / White lightning and wine / Love me like music - I'll be your song / Sing child / How deep it goes / Dreamboat Annie (reprise).
LP: . . . . ARTY 139
MC: . . . . TCARTY 139
LP: . . . . EMS 1277
MC: . . . . TCEMS 1277
LP: . . . . ATAK 111
MC: . . . . TCATAK 111

GREATEST HITS: HEART.
LP: 4601741
MC: 4601744

GREATEST HITS LIVE : HEART.
LP: . . . . PE 236888
MC: . . . . PE 36888
CD: . . . . EGK 36888

HEART BOX SET.
LPS: . . . . HGIFT 1
MCSET: . . . . TCHGIFT 1

HEART (CAPITOL).
Tracks: / If looks could kill / What about love? / Never / These dreams / Wolf / All eyes / Nobody home / Nothin' at all / What he don't know / Shellshock.
LP: . . . . EJ 2403721
MC: . . . . EJ 2403724
LP: . . . . LOVE 1
MC: . . . . TCLOVE 1

HEART (EPIC).
Tracks: / Tell it like it is / Barracuda / Straight on / Dog and butterfly / Even it up / Bebe le strange / Sweet darlin' / I'm down/Long tall sally / Rock and roll / Unchained melody.
LP: . . . . EPC 84829
LP: 4601741
MC: 4601744

HEART: INTERVIEW PICTURE DISC.
LPPD: . . . . BAK 2080

LITTLE QUEEN.
Tracks: / Little queen / Treat me well / Say hello / Cry to me / Go on cry / Barracuda / Love alive / Sylvan song / Dream of the archer / Kick it out.
LP: . . . . PRT 82075
MC: 40 82075

MAGAZINE.
Tracks: / Heartless / Just the wine / Without you / Magazine / Here song / Mother Earth blues / I've got the music in me / Devil delight.
LP: . . . . EMS 1278
MC: . . . . TCEMS 1278
LP: . . . . ATAK 112

MC: TCATAK 112

PASSIONWORKS.
Tracks: / How can I refuse / Blue guitar / Johnny moon / Sleep alone / Together now / Allies / Jealousy / Heavy heart / Love mistake / Language of love / Ambush.
LP: PE 38800
LP: EPC 25491

PRIVATE AUDITION.
Tracks: / City's burning / Bright little girl / Perfect stranger / private audition / Angela / This man is mine / Situation, The / Hey darlin darlin / One word / Fast times / America.
LP: 4607021
MC: 460702 4
LP: EPC 85792

ROCK THE HOUSE "LIVE".
Tracks: / Wild child / Fallen from grace / Call of the wild / How can I refuse / Shell shock / Love alive / Under the sky / Night, The / Tall, dark handsome stranger / If looks could kill / Who will you run to / You're the voice / Way back machine, The / Barracuda.
LP: ESTU 2154
MC: TCESTU 2154

WITH LOVE FROM....
LPS: LOVE 2
MCSET: TC LOVE 2

Heart Beat

HEART BEAT (Film sountrack) (Various artists).
LP: FS 241

Heart Of Darkness

HEART OF DARKNESS (see under Conrad, Joseph) (Scofield, Paul (nar)).

HEART OF DARKNESS (Joseph Conrad) (Scofield, Paul (nar)).
MCSET: 414 700-4

Heart Of Oak

HEART OF OAK (And Other Songs of Britain) (Various artists).
Tracks: / Bay of Biscay: *Various artists* / Cherry ripe: *Various artists* / It was a lover and his lass: *Various* artists / Miller of Dee, The: *Various artists* / Oh, the oak and the ash: *Various artists* / Sigh no more, ladies: *Various artists* / Early one morning: *Various artists* / Bailiff's daughter of Islington: *Various* artists / Charlie is my darling: *Various artists* / A-hunting we will go: *Various artists* / Ash grove, The: *Various artists* / Heart of oak: *Various artists* / Ye banks and braes: *Various artists* / Keel row, The: *Various artists* / John Peel: *Various artists* / Where the bee sucks: *Various artists* / Vicar of Bray: *Various artists*.
LP: CFP 4556
MC: TCCFP 4556

Heart Of Rock

HEART OF ROCK (Various artists).
Tracks: / Brilliant disguise: *Springsteen, Bruce* / C'est la vie: *Nevil, Robbie* / I didn't mean to turn you on: *Palmer, Robert* / Touch of grey: *Grateful Dead* / Solitude standing: *Vega, Suzanne* / Way it is, The: *Hornsby, Bruce* / Should've known better: *Marx, Richard* / Modern woman: *Joel, Billy* / Nothing's gonna stop us now: *Starship* / Final countdown, The: *Europe*.
LP: 4630031
MC: 4630034

HEART OF ROCK'N'ROLL (Various artists).
LP: NE 1206
MC: CE 2206

Heart Of Romance

HEART OF ROMANCE, THE (Various artists).
Tracks: / Symphony No. 5 in E minor, Opus 64: *Various artists* / Serenade for strings in E minor Opus 20: *Various* artists / Piano concerto No. 21 in C, K 467 (Mozart): *Various artists* / Symphony No. 9 in E minor, Opus 95 (Dvorak): *Various artists* / Scheherazade - symphonic suite, Opus 35: *Various artists* / Piano concerto No. 5 in E flat, Opus 73: *Various artists* / Concerto for violin & orch. No. 1 in G minor: *Various artists* / Serenade No. 13 for strings in G, K.525: *Various artists* / Canon for three violins & cello (Pachelbel): *Various artists*.
LP: DUET 26

Heart & Soul

HEART AND SOUL (Various artists).
LP: EPC 32217

HEART & SOUL - 18 CLASSIC SOUL CUTS (Various artists).
Tracks: / Fine time: *Yazz* / Suddenly: *Ocean, Billy* / I heard it through the grapevine: *Gaye, Marvin* / Greatest love of all, The: *Benson, George* / One day in your life: *Jackson, Michael* / Teardrops: *Womack* & Womack / Midnight train to Georgia: *Knight, Gladys & The Pips* / Endless love: *Richie, Lionel & Diana Ross* / You're the first, the last, my everything: *White, Barry* / Your love is king: *Sade* / Let's stay together: *Green, Al* / Lovely day: *Withers, Bill* / Can't get by without you: *Real Thing* / Cherish: *Kool & The Gang* / Dreamin': *Williams, Vanessa* / You are everything: *Ross, Diana & Marvin Gaye* / Tears of a clown, The: *Robinson, Smokey & The Miracles* / Heaven help me: *Estus, Deon*.
LP: HASTV 1
MC: HASTC 1

HEART & SOUL COLLECTION VOL 1 (Various artists).
LP: KNLP 32001
MC: KNMC 32001

HEART & SOUL COLLECTION VOL 2 (Various artists).
LP: KNLP 32002
MC: KNMC 32002

HEART & SOUL : HEART BREAKERS (Various artists).
Tracks: / Candle in the wind: *John, Elton* / Teardrops: *Stevens, Shakin'* / Wonderful tonight: *Clapton, Eric* / September: *Earth, Wind & Fire* / Cry: *Godley & Creme* / Cry me a river: *Various artists*.
LP: KNLP 12011
MC: KNMC 12011

HEART & SOUL: HEART FULL OF SOUL (Various artists).
Tracks: / Jump (for my love): *Pointer Sisters* / Rockin' good way: *Shaky & Bonnie* / Don't leave me this way: *Communards* / Alone without you: *King* / Just be good to me: *S.O.S. Band* / You can do magic: *Limmie* & Family Cooking / Come back and finish what you started: *Knight, Gladys* / Don't try to stop it: *Roman Holliday* / Fantasy island: *Tight Fit* / Take that situation: *Heyward, Nick* / Fade to grey: *Visage* / How 'bout us: *Champaign* / One night in Bangkok: *Head, Murray* / Dead ringer for love: *Meatloaf*.
LP: KNLP 12018
MC: KNMC 12018

HEART & SOUL: HEART OF GOLD (Various artists).
Tracks: / Love worth waiting for, A: *Stevens, Shakin'* / Chiquitita: *Abba* / My favourite waste of time: *Paul, Owen* / Lion sleeps tonight, The: *Tight Fit* / Way we were/Try to...: *Knight, Gladys* / I'm not in love / Je t'aime...: *Birkin, Jane/ Serge Gainsbourgh* / Japanese boy: *Aneka* / My camera never lies: *Bucks Fizz* / Fame: *Cara, Irene* / Even the nights are better: *Air Supply* / Under your thumb: *Godley & Creme* / Seasons in the sun: *Jacks, Terry* / Without you: *Nilsson*.
LP: KNLP 12016
MC: KNMC 12016

HEART & SOUL: HEART SEARCHING (Various artists).
Tracks: / What do you wanna make those eyes at me for?: *Stevens, Shakin'* / What's another year: *Logan, Johnny* / Wedding bells: *Godley & Creme* / January, February: *Dickson, Barbara* / Time in a bottle: *Croce, Jim* / Breaking up is hard to do: *Sedaka, Neil* / How can I be sure: *Cassidy, David* / Lay down Sally: *Clapton, Eric* / Love & pride: *King* / Stay with me till dawn: *Tzuke, Judie* / Feels so right: *Alabama (Group)* / Amoreuse: *Dee, Kiki* / Listen to the voices: *Siffre, Labi* / You take me up: *Thompson Twins*.
LP: KNLP 12017
MC: KNMC 12017

HEART & SOUL: HEART TO HEART (Various artists).
Tracks: / Your love is king: *Sade* / Forever Autumn: *Hayward, Justin* / Taste of your tears: *King* / Lovely day: *Withers, Bill* / Longer: *Fogelberg, Dan* / Answer me: *Dickson, Barbara* / Laughter in the rain: *Sedaka, Neil* / Music: *Miles, John* / Right time of the night: *Warnes, Jennifer* / Things we do for love, The / Torn between two lovers: *MacGregor, Mary* / Uptown uptempo woman: *Edelman, Randy* / You should see how: *Manchester, Melissa* / I know him so well: *Paige, Elaine & Barbara Dickson*.
LP: KNLP 12012
MC: KNMC 12012

HEART & SOUL: HEARTBEATS (Various artists).
Tracks: / All cried out: *Moyet, Alison* / (Feels like) Heaven: *Fiction Factory* / Everyday hurts: *Sad Cafe* / Promises: *Clapton, Eric* / Stairway to Heaven: *Far Corporation* / I'll have to say I love you: *Croce, Jim* / Your song: *John, Elton* / Holding out for a hero: *Tyler, Bonnie* / Hold me now: *Thompson Twins* / Do that to me one more time: *Captain & Tennille* / Heartbeat: *Johnson, Don* / Concrete and clay: *Edelman, Randy* / I have a dream: *Abba*.
LP: KNLP 12010
MC: KNMC 12010

HEART & SOUL : SOUL BALLADS (Various artists).
Tracks: / Cherish: *Kool & The Gang* / Till my love comes home: *Vandross, Luther* / Close the door: *Pendergrass*, Teddy / Woman in love: *3 Degrees* / Girls: *Moments & Whatnauts* / Re-united: *Peaches & Herb* / How many times can we say goodbye: *Warwick, Dionne & Luther Vandross* / Caravan of love: *Isley-Jasper* / All the love in the world: *Warwick, Dionne* / Two hearts: *Mills, Stephanie & Teddy Pendergrass* / Love me: *Elliman, Yvonne* / Don't stop the music: *Yarbrough & Peoples* / Like sister and brother: *Drifters* / Too much too little too late: *Mathis, Johnny & Deniece Williams*.
LP: KNLP 12001
MC: KNMC 12001

HEART & SOUL : SOUL BALLADS VOL.2 (Various artists).
Tracks: / You'll never find another love like mine: *Rawls, Lou* / You make me feel brand new: *Stylistics* / If you don't know me by now: *Melvin, Harold & The Bluenotes* / Have you seen her: *Chi-lites* / Who'd she coo: *Ohio* Players / Hold back the night: *Trammps* / Hurt: *Manhattans* / Me & Mrs Jones: *Paul, Billy* / Best thing that ever happened to me, The: *Knight, Gladys* / Can't help falling in love: *Stylistics* / Dolly my love: *Moments (group)* / Don't give up: *Melvin, Harold & The Bluenotes* / Shine: *Bar-Kays* / Loving arms: *Jackson, Millie*.
LP: KNLP 12006
MC: KNMC 12006

HEART & SOUL : SOUL BOYS (Various artists).
Tracks: / If you were here tonight: *O'Neal, Alexander* / Do what you do: *Jackson, Jermaine* / Shake you down: *Abbott, Gregory* / I really didn't mean it: *Vandross, Luther* / Only you: *Pendergrass, Teddy* / Trying to love two: *Bell, William* / Sanctified lady: *Gaye, Marvin* / Greatest love of all, The: *Benson, George* / Hold on to my love: *Ruffin, Jimmy* / Change: *Grant, David* / Gonna make you an offer you can't refuse: *Helms, Jimmy* / Hang on in there baby: *Bristol, Johnny* / Other woman, The: *Parker, Ray Jnr.* / You're the first, the last, my everything: *White, Barry*.
LP: KNLP 12002
MC: KNMC 12002

HEART & SOUL : SOUL CLASSICS (Various artists).
Tracks: / My baby just cares for me: *Simone, Nina* / Cry like a baby: *Box Tops* / Wonderful world: *Cooke*, Sam / Natural man, A: *Rawls, Lou* / Mockingbird: *Franklin, Aretha* / It's in his kiss: *Everett, Betty* / Shout: *Isley Brothers* / It's a man's man's man's world: *Brown, James* / I can sing a rainbow: *Dells* / First cut is the deepest: *Arnold, P.P.* / Didn't I blow your mind: *Delphonics* / Only the strong survive: *Butler, Jerry* / Dance to the music: *Sly & the Family Stone* / Reet petite: *Wilson, Jackie*.
LP: KNLP 12005
MC: KNMC 12005

HEART & SOUL: SOUL DANCING (Various artists).
Tracks: / System addict: *Five Star* / When the going get tough the tough get going: *Ocean, Billy* / Living in America: *Brown, James* / My toot toot: *Lasalle, Denise* / Don't push it, don't force it: *Haywood, Leon* / Hot wild: *Jackson, Millie* / Use it up and wear it out: *Odyssey* / Ooh, la, la (let's go dancin'): *Kool* & The Gang / She's strange: *Cameo* / See the day: *Lee, Dee C* / Let's hear it for the boy: *Williams*, Deniece / Friends: *Stewart, Amii* / Signed, sealed, delivered: *Turner, Ruby* / It's a disco night (rock don't stop): *Isley Brothers*.
LP: KNLP 12015
MC: KNMC 12015

HEART & SOUL : SOUL GIRLS (Various artists).
Tracks: / Another night: *Franklin, Aretha* / (They long to be) close to you: *Guthrie, Gwen* / My simple heart: *3 Degrees* / Best of my love: *Emotions (group)* / Never knew love like this before: *Mills, Stephanie* / What a difference a day made: *Phillips, Esther* / I will survive: *Gaynor, Gloria* / Midnight train to Georgia: *Knight, Gladys* / My man's a sweet man: *Jackson, Millie* / I'll never love this way again: *Warwick, Dionne* / Right time of the night: *Warnes, Jennifer* / It's gonna take a miracle: *Williams, Deniece* / If I can't have you: *Elliman, Yvonne* / When will I see you again: *3 Degrees*.
LP: KNLP 12004
MC: KNMC 12004

HEART & SOUL : SOUL GROUPS (Various artists).
Tracks: / Native New Yorker: *Odyssey* / When you say you love somebody from the heart: *Kool & The Gang* / Summer breeze: *Isley Brothers* / Give it up: *K.C. & The Sunshine Band* / There goes my first love: *Drifters* / Just don't want to be lonely: *Main Ingredient* / When she was my girl: *Four Tops* / Going to the bank: *Commodores* / Used to be my girl: *O'Jays* / Ms. Grace: *Tymes* / Rock the boat: *Hues Corporation* / Kiss and say goodbye: *Manhattans* / You don't have to go: *Chi-lites* / Day by day: *Shakatak/Al Jarreau*.
LP: KNLP 12003
MC: KNMC 12003

HEART & SOUL: SOUL KISS (Various artists).
Tracks: / Joanna: *Kool & The Gang* / Always and forever: *Heatwave* / You're my latest, my greatest inspiration: *Pendergrass, Teddy* / Tonight I'm gonna love you all over: *Four Tops* / You're my angel: *Various artists* / When the rain begins to fall: *Jackson, Jermaine & Pia Zadora* / What a fool believes: *Franklin, Aretha* / Just the way you are: *White, Barry* / I'd rather go blind: *Turner, Ruby* / (Sittin' on) the dock of the bay: *Bolton*, Michael / Na-na is the saddest word: *Stylistics* / You're a part of me: *Carnes/ Cotton* / Lies: *Butler, Jonathan* / Suddenly: *Ocean, Billy*.
LP: KNLP 12013
MC: KNMC 12013

HEART & SOUL: SOUL LOVE (Various artists).
Tracks: / Superstar (Don't you remember): *Vandross, Luther* / Can't we try: *Pendergrass, Teddy* / Who's zoomin' who?: *Franklin, Aretha* / Single life: *Cameo* / It's gonna take a miracle: *Williams, Deniece* / Don't walk away: *Four Tops*.
LP: KNLP 12009
MC: KNMC 12009

HEART & SOUL: SOUL NIGHTS (Various artists).
Tracks: / Love come down: *King, Evelyn "Champagne"* / You said you'd gimme some more: *K.C. & The Sunshine Band* / Harvest for the world: *Isley Brothers* / Get up offa that thing: *Brown, James* / My love is waiting: *Gaye, Marvin* / Let me know (I have a right): *Gaynor, Gloria*.
LP: KNLP 12007
MC: KNMC 12007

HEART & SOUL: SOUL POWER (Various artists).
Tracks: / Caribbean Queen: *Ocean, Billy* / Baby we better try and get it together: *White, Barry* / Love train: *O'Jays* / Ain't no stoppin' us now: *McFadden & Whitehead* / What becomes of the broken hearted: *Turner, Ruby* / La la means I love you: *Delfonics* / If you're looking for: *Odyssey* / Lady Marmalade: *Labelle* / Roses: *Haywoode* / I can't help myself: *Real Thing* / Can I take you home little girl: *Drifters* / Never can say goodbye: *Gaynor, Gloria* / Runner, The: *3 Degrees* / Oops upside your head: *Gap Band*.
LP: KNLP 12014
MC: KNMC 12014

HEART & SOUL: SOUL SEEKING (Various artists).
Tracks: / Down on the beach tonight: *Drifters* / Take good care of yourself: *3 Degrees* / Zing went the strings of my heart: *Trammps* / It's in his kiss: *Lewis, Linda* / Love I lost, The: *Melvin, Harold* / Let the music play: *White, Barry*.
LP: KNLP 12008
MC: KNMC 12008

Heart To Heart

HEART TO HEART (24 love song duets) (Various artists).
Tracks: / Maria: *Various artists* / Jesamine: *Various artists* / When a man loves a woman: *Various artists* / Happy together: *Various artists* / Precious and few: *Various artists* / Everyday with you girl: *Various artists* / Cherish: *Various artists* / Baby, I'm yours: *Various artists* / Just can't help believing: *Various artists* / My special angel: *Various artists* / P.S. I love you: *Various artists* / Jean: *Various artists*.
LP: NE 1318
MC: CE 2318
LP: SPR 8523
MC: SPC 8523

Heartbeat

WINNER, THE.
Tracks: / Winner, The / One true love / Common language / Dancin' / Only ones, The / Air that I breathe, The / Tease your medium mind / Tears from heaven / People with no direction.
LP: MYRR 1249
MC: MYRC 1249
LP: PLP 2
MC: PCAS 2

Heartbeat Soucous

HEARTBEAT SOUCOUS (Top Zairean Soukous Stars) (Various artists).
Tracks: / Belle amie: *Kanda Bongo Man* / Zouke Zouke: *Kalle, Pepe & Nyboma* / Mon mari est soulard: *Loubassou, Denis* / Sauce bloque: *Mbenza, Syran* / Marie Jose: *Lokassa Ya Mbongo* / Helena: *Bopol*.
LP: . . . . **EWV 3**
MC: . . . . **TCEWV 3**

Heartbeats

HEARTBEATS (Various artists).
Tracks: / Tears are not enough: *ABC* / Really saying something: *Bananarama* / Taste of your tears: *King*/ Leaving me now: *Level 42* / You are my world: *Communards* / Cry me a river: *Wilson, Mari* (Not available on CD.) / Hold me now: *Thompson Twins* / Right time of the night: *Warnes, Jennifer* (Not available on CD.) / All out of love: *Air Supply* / Everyday hurts: *Sad Cafe* (Not available on CD.) / Caravan song: *Dickson, Barbara*(Not available on CD.) / Don't let the sun go down on me: *John, Elton* / I'm not in love: *10 CC* / Straight from the heart: *Tyler, Bonnie* (Not available on CD.) / Total eclipse of the heart: *Tyler, Bonnie* / Count on me: *Jefferson Starship* / Love somebody: *Springfield, Rick* / I can't hold back: *Survivor* / Heartbeat: *Johnson, Don*/ Spirits (having flown): *Bee Gees* / Language of love: *Fogelberg, Dan* (Not available on CD.) / Wedding bells: *Godley & Creme* / If I can't have you: *Elliman, Yvonne* (Not available on CD.) / I know there's something going on: *Frida* / Hero: *Knight, Gladys & The Pips* (Not available on CD.) / Weak in the presence of beauty: *Moyet, Alison* / Just what I always wanted: *Wilson, Mari* (Not available on CD.) / Stay with me till dawn: *Tzuke, Judie*.
2LP: . . . . **STDLP 24**
MC: . . . . **STDMC 24**

Heartbreakers

HEARTBREAKERS (Film soundtrack) (Various artists).
LP: **205.209**

HEARTBREAKERS Various artists (Various artists).
LP: . . . . **BLEND 3**
MC: . . . . **ZCEND 3**
LP: . . . . **NE 1202**
MC: . . . . **CE 2202**
MC: . . . . **AIM 110**

HEARTBREAKERS (Various artists).
2LP: **303697**
MCSET: **503697**

Heartfixers

COOL ON IT.
LP: . . . . **LM LP 1010**

LIVE AT THE MOONSHADOW.
LP: . . . . **LD 1007**

Hearthrobs (group)

CLEOPATRA GRIP.
LP: . . . . **TPLP 23**
MC: . . . . **TPLP 23C**

Heartland

HEARTLAND.
LP: **3971211**
MC: **3971214**

Heartland Consort

HEARTLAND CONSORT.
LP: . . . . **ENJA 4070**

Hearts & Flowers

NOW IS THE TIME.
Tracks: / Now is the time / Save some time / Try for the sun / Rain, rain / View from ward three / Rock 'n' roll gypsies / Reason to believe / Please / 1-2-3-rhyme in carnivour thyme / Road to nowhere / 10,000 sunsets.
LP: . . . . **KIRI 046**

Hearts Of Fire

HEARTS OF FIRE (Film soundtrack) (Various artists).
Tracks: / Hearts of fire: *Fiona* / Usual, The: *Dylan, Bob* / I'm in it for love: *Fiona* / Tainted love: *Everett, Rupert* / Hair of the dog: *Fiona* / Night after night: *Dylan, Bob* / In my heart: *Everett, Rupert* / Nights we spent on earth, The: *Fiona* / Had a dream about you, baby: *Dylan, Bob* / Let the good times roll: *Fiona*.
LP: **4600001**
MC: **4600004**

Hearts Of Love

HEARTS OF LOVE (Various artists).
Tracks: / Reilly, ace of spies - theme: *Olympic Orchestra* / Let's stay together: *Green, Al* / Making love: *Chi-lites*/ All night loving: *Imagination* / Stay with me baby: *Verity* / Save the last dance for me: *Armstrong, Herbie*/ Tracks of my tears: *Blunstone, Colin* / Best thing that ever happened to me: *Knight, Gladys & The Pips* / In your eyes: *Hill, Dan* / Falling in love: *Technos*.
LP: . . . . **PRB 5621**
MC: . . . . **ZCPRB 5621**

Heartsman, Johnny

SACRAMENTO.
LP: . . . . **CCR 1018**

Heartstones

HEARTSTONES (See under Rendell, Ruth (author)).

Heartwork

HEARTWORK (Various artists).
MC: . . . . **GVMMC 125**

Heat & Dust

HEAT & DUST (Film soundtrack) (Various artists).
LP: . . . . **TER 1032**

Heat Exchange

ONE STEP AHEAD.
Tracks: / You're gonna love this / Shake down / Love is the reason / One step ahead / Check it out / Lost on you.
LP: . . . . **EMC 3306**

Heat From The Street

HEAT FROM THE STREET Various Artists (Various artists).
LP: . . . . **CLASS 8**

Heat Is On

HEAT IS ON (Various artists).
Tracks: / Like a rose: *Various artists* / Use my body: *Various artists* / I want your stuff: *Various artists*/ Do you really want my love: *Various artists* / Too much pressure on the kid: *Various artists* / Party: *Various* artists / Just when I needed you most: *Various artists* / How can I love again: *Various artists* / I'll give you all that you ask: *Various artists* / Your love's a voodoo: *Various artists* / How do we love: *Various artists* / We all think we're right: *Various artists*.
LP: . . . . **SNTF 856**

Heat Of Soul

HEAT OF SOUL, VOLUME 1 (Various artists).
Tracks: / Stand by me: *King, Ben E.* / I heard it through the grapevine: *Reeves, Martha (1)* / Patches: *Carter, Clarence* / Rock you baby: *McCae, George* / Rescue me: *Bass, Fontella* / When a man loves a woman: *Sledge, Percy* / Soul man: *Sam & Dave* / Knock on wood: *Floyd, Eddie* / 'In' crowd, The: *Gray, Dobie* / Hold on I'm coming: *Sam & Dave*.
LP: . . . . **MASL 001**
MC: . . . . **CMASL 001**

Heath Brothers

BROTHERLY LOVE.
LP: . . . . **AN 1003**

MARCHIN' ON.
Tracks: / Warm valley / Tafadhali / Watergate blues, The / Maimouna / Smilin' Billy suite.
LP: **33790**

Heath, Eira

CHRIST IN COMPETITION.
LP: . . . . **PC 807**

Heath, Jimmy

JIMMY.
LP: . . . . **MR 5138**

TENOR TRIBUTE (See under Cobb, Arnett for details) (Heath, Jimmy/Arnett Cobb/Joe Henderson).

Heath, Ted

ALL TIME TOP TWELVE (Heath, Ted & His Music).
Tracks: / Begin the beguine / April in Paris / 'S wonderful / Tenderly / Autumn leaves / Somebody loves me / September song / Stardust / Tea for two / On the sunny side of the street / I've got the world on a string / My blue Heaven.
LP: . . . . **MOIR 126**
MC: . . . . **CMOIR 126**

AT THE LONDON PALLADIUM (Heath, Ted & His Music).
Tracks: / Champ, The / Eloquence / Do nothing till you hear from me / Pick yourself up / Blue for moderns / Fourth dimension / Retrospect / Dark eyes / Solitude / Hawk talks, The / I got it bad and that ain't good / Rhapsody for drums.
LP: . . . . **JASM 2005**

AT THE LONDON PALLADIUM, VOL 3 (Heath, Ted & His Music).
Tracks: / Flying home / Skylark / Late night final / Our love / After you've gone / And the angels sing / Crazy rhythm / Haitian ritual / Send for Henry / Lover / Sweet Georgia Brown / Concerto for Verrell.
LP: . . . . **JASM 2021**

BEGINNING, THE (Heath, Ted & His Music).
Tracks: / Caravan / Opus 1 / East of the sun / Bakerloo non-stop / My heart goes crazy / Ad lib frolic / Route 66 / Taboo / Baia / London Suite / Turn on the heath / Dark eyes / Stratford water / Sophisticated lady / That lovely weekend / Euphoria / Sweet and lovely.
2LP: . . . . **DDV 5015/6**

BIG BAND.
LP: . . . . **EJLP 06**
MC: . . . . **EJMC 06**

BIG BAND FAVOURITES (Heath, Ted & His Music).
Tracks: / Take the 'A' train / Two o'clock jump / Sentimental journey / Harlem nocturne / Jumpin' at The Woodside / Contrasts / Jersey bounce / At the woodchoppers' ball / St. James' Infirmary blues / Song of India / Fever / Tuxedo Junction / Cherokee / Intermission riff / Skyliner / Night train / St. Louis blues / Mood indigo / Blues in the night / King Porter stomp / Peanut vendor / Lullaby of Birdland / Basin Street blues / At the Jazz Band Ball / Sing, sing, sing / String of pearls / Flying home / In the mood.
MC: . . . . **KMC 25003**

BIG BAND PERCUSSION (Heath, Ted & His Music).
Tracks: / Johnny one note / Blues in the night / Peanut vendor / More than you know / Poinciana / Drum crazy / Taking a chance on love / It ain't necessarily so / Daddy / Mood indigo / Thou swell / But not for me / Tumbling tumbleweeds / Close your eyes / At last / Egyptian night / They didn't believe me / Ebb tide.
LP: . . . . **PFM 24004**

BIG BAND SOUND OF TED HEATH (Heath, Ted Orchestra).
Tracks: / Bill Bailey won't you please come home / Chapter two / Gentle winds / Hello Berlin / Roll on, roll off / Flight number one / Minor mambo / Try a little later / Stuttgart special / Long night / Skip to my lou / Sur le pont d'Avignon.
LP: . . . . **ISST 131**

DANCING TIME (Heath, Ted Orchestra).
LP: . . . . **GELP 15032**

FATS WALLER ALBUM (Heath, Ted & His Music).
Tracks: / Honeysuckle rose / Ain't misbehavin' / Blue turning grey over you / Jitterbug waltz / I've got a feeling I'm falling / Alligator crawl / London suite.
LP: . . . . **JASM 2007**

FOCUS ON TED HEATH.
2LP: . . . . **FOS 29/30**
MC: . . . . **KFOC 28082**

FROM MOIRA WITH LOVE.
Tracks: / Folks who live on the hill / Melody in F / Clair de lune / Our love / Liebestraum / Song of India / Look for the silver lining / Procession / Skylark / Retrospect (Not on CD.) / Bill / Nearness of you / Fourth dimension / Thou swell / September song / Memories of you / Birth of the blues (Not on CD.) / Sixteen going on seventeen (Not on CD.) / Hot toddy (Not on CD.) / Georgia on my mind / Harlem nocturne (Not on CD.) / Someone to watch over me (Not on CD.) / St. Louis blues (Not on CD.) / How high the moon (Not on CD.) / Tonight / Faithful Hussar / Blues for moderns (Not on CD.) / Our waltz / Obsession / Lush slide (Not on CD.) / Eloquence / Rhapsody for drums.
LP: . . . . **SIV 106**
MC: . . . . **CSIV 106**

GERSHWIN FOR MODERNS (Heath, Ted Orchestra).
Tracks: / Man I love, The / Love walked in / Nice work if you can get it / Love is here to stay / Clap yo hands / I got rhythm / But not for me / Someone to watch over me / That certain feeling / Embraceable you / Changing my tune / Soon.
LP: . . . . **TAB 76**

GOLDEN AGE OF TED HEATH VOL.1, THE.
Tracks: / Opus one / Somebody loves me (Not on CD.) / Swinging shepherd blues / My favourite things / Maria / Lullaby of Broadway / Holiday for strings / Flying home / I get a kick out of you / Jumpin' at the woodside / Man I love, The / Hawaiian war chant / At last / Cherokee / We'll git it / S'wonderful / You stepped out of a dream / Sabre dance / Blues in the night / Royal Garden blues (Not on CD.) / Moonlight in Vermont / Apple honey / Fly me to the moon / Listen to my music / Pick yourself up / Hawk talks, The / And the angels sing / Champ, The.
2LP: . . . . **SIV 102**
MC: . . . . **CSIV 102**

GOLDEN AGE OF TED HEATH VOL.2, THE.
Tracks: / 9.20 special / East of the sun / Intermission riff / Ad lib frolic / Girl talk / South Rampart St. Parade / American patrol / That lovely weekend / Swanee river / Artistry in rhythm / Nightingale sang in Berkeley Square / Bakerloo non stop / In the mood / I had the craziest dream / Soon amapola / I can't get started / Perdido / C jam blues / Sophisticated lady / First jump / Night & day / Poor little rich girl / Swing low sweet chariot.
2LP: . . . . **SIV 1121**
MC: . . . . **CSIV 1121**

GOLDEN AGE OF TED HEATH VOL.3, THE.
Tracks: / Let's dance / Chattanooga choo choo / Swinging the blues / My guy's come back / Touch of your lips, The / Chicago / Skyliner / Nightmare / Lush slide / Serenade in blue / Woodchopper's ball / Kalamazoo / On the sunny side of the street / I got it bad and that ain't good / Sidewalks of Cuba / After you've gone / Big John special / Chloe / Jersey bounce / Contrasts / Cottontail / Fascinating rhythm / Snowfall / Headin' north.
2LP: . . . . **SIV 1135**
MC: . . . . **CSIV 1135**

HITS I MISSED (Heath, Ted & His Music).
Tracks: / High noon / Ebb tide / Twelfth St. rag / Love is a many splendoured thing / Three coins in the fountain / Unchained melody / Learnin' the blues / Swedish rhapsody / Moulin Rouge / My resistance is low / My foolish heart / Secret love.
LP: . . . . **JASM 2201**

KERN FOR MODERNS (Heath, Ted & His Music).
Tracks: / Long ago and far away / They didn't believe me / Look for the silver lining / Bill / Can I forget you? / Song is you, The / Ol' man river / Folks who live on the hill, The / Dearly beloved / Make believe / I won't dance / Why was I born?.
LP: . . . . **JASM 2022**

LATINO (Heath, Ted & Edmundo Ros).
Tracks: / Cherry pink and apple blossom white / Heatwave / Mas qye nada / Malaguena / Alla en el Rancho Grande / Desafinado / La Bamba / Brazil / What a difference a day made / La paloma / Tico tico / Vaya con Dios / Tequila / La cucaracha.
LP: . . . . **TAB 64**

LISTEN TO MY MUSIC.
Tracks: / Listen to my music / Dark eyes / Bewitched / Anything goes / Don't blame me / Moonlight on the Ganges / Get happy / Show me the way to go home / Mad about the boy / If I had you / Tonight / All things you are / More than you know / Jealousy / By the sleepy lagoon / Slaughter on Tenth Avenue / Rockin' in Morocco.
LP: . . . . **TAB 39**
MC: . . . . **KTBC 39**

MY VERY GOOD FRIEND THE BANDLEADERS (Heath, Ted & His Music).
Tracks: / Sing, sing, sing / When it's sleepy time down south / Intermission riff / Duke-a train.
LP: . . . . **MOIR 214**
MC: . . . . **CMOIR 214**

OLDE ENGLYSHE (Heath, Ted & His Music).
Tracks: / Lincolnshire poacher / Greensleeves / D'ye ken John Peel? / Drink to me only with thine eyes / There's a tavern in the town / Barbara Allen / Cherry ripe / Sweet Polly Oliver / London Bridge is falling down / Early one morning / Lass of Richmond Hill / Foggy foggy dew.
LP: . . . . **JASM 2200**

PLAYS AL JOLSON CLASSICS.
Tracks: / Toot toot Tootsie / Rock a bye your baby with a dixie melody / Waiting for the Robert E. Lee / Swanee / My manny / Give my regards to Broadway / April showers.
LP: . . . . **MOIR 215**
MC: . . . . **CMOIR 215**

RODGERS FOR MODERNS (Heath, Ted & His Music).
Tracks: / Have you met Miss Jones? / There's a small hotel / Easy to remember / My heart stood still / Down by the river / Thou swell / Lady is a tramp, The / Where or when / This can't be love / I married an angel / Blue room / Dancing on the ceiling.
LP: . . . . **JASM 2925**

SENTIMENTAL JOURNEY (Heath, Ted & His Music).
Tracks: / Lullaby of Broadway / Mack the knife / Sentimental journey / Cherokee / Mood indigo / At last / Summer Place, A theme from / Fever /

Cottonfields / Blame it on the bossa nova / Norwegian wood / Canadian sunset / American patrol / Caravan.
LP: **811 004-1**
MC: **811 004-4**

SHALL WE DANCE? (Heath, Ted & His Music).
Tracks: / Dancing in the dark / I could have danced all night / Dancing with my shadow / Love dance / Shall we dance? / Let's face the music and dance / Dancing time / Ten cents a dance / Dancing with tears in my eyes / Dance, ballerina, dance / All you want to do is dance / I won't dance.
LP: . . . . **JASM 2204**

SMOOTH'N'SWINGING.
Tracks: / Lover come back to me / Summertime / How about you? / Don't get around much anymore / Smooth'n'swinging / Don't be that way / Taking a chance on love / These foolish things / Midnight sun / Fine romance, A / Night & day / You're my everything / You'd be so nice to come home to.
LP: . . . . **TAB 33**

SPOTLIGHT ON SIDESMEN (Heath, Ted & His Music).
Tracks: / Ill wind / Swinging the blues / Hey baby / Idaho / I can't get started / Love for sale / Lover man / Sidewalks of Cuba / I'll never be the same / Cottontail / Lullaby of the leaves / Witch doctor.
LP: . . . . **JASM 2026**

STRICTLY INSTRUMENTAL (Heath, Ted & His Music).
Tracks: / Jeanie with the light brown hair / I've got sixpence / Very thought of you, The / My guy's come back / Twilight time / First jump / Not so quiet please / Knocked 'em in the Old Kent Road / On Ilkley Moor baht'at / Donegal cradle song / Experiment / See me dance the polka / Nightingale sang in Berkeley Square, A / You go to my head / Touch of your lips, The / Two guitars / Move / So easy.
LP: . . . . **DVL 8**

STRIKE UP THE BAND (Heath, Ted & His Music).
Tracks: / Strike up the band / Obsession / Clair de lune / Piper's patrol / Vanessa / Hot toddy / On the bridge / Alpine boogie / You are my heart's delight / Alouette / La mer / Hawaiian war chant.
LP: . . . . **JASM 2006**

STRIKE UP THE BAND.
MCSET: . . . . **DTO 10224**

SWING IS KING.
Tracks: / Flying home / Cherokee / Begin the beguine / One o'clock jump / Song of India / At the woodchopper's ball / Elks' parade, The / In the mood / Two o'clock jump / Contrasts / Take the 'A' train / Sing, sing, sing.
LP: . . . . **DGS 6**

SWING SESSION (Heath, Ted & His Music).
Tracks: / Champ, The / Eloquence / Do nothing till you hear from me / Pick yourself up / Blues for moderns / Fourth dimension.
LP: . . . . **JASM 2205**

SWING VS. LATIN (Heath, Ted & Edmundo Ros).
LP: . . . . **MOIR 134**
MC: . . . . **CMOIR 134**

SWINGS IN HI-STEREO (Heath, Ted & His Music).
Tracks: / "C" jam blues / Three for the blues / My funny valentine / I like to recognise the tune / Love me or leave me / Ja-da / Boomsie / Big ben / Sophisticated lady / Wrap your troubles in dreams / Over the rainbow.
LP: . . . . **JAS 2202**

TED HEATH AT CARNEGIE HALL (Heath, Ted Orchestra).
Tracks: / Listen to my music / Kings Cross climax / Memories of you / R.J. boogie / Perdido / Autumn in New York / Carioca / Just one of those things / Lullaby in rhythm / Stonehenge / Procession / I remember you / Hawaiian war chant.
LP: . . . . **MOIR 132**
MC: . . . . **CMOIR 132**

TED HEATH AT THE BBC (Heath, Ted & His Music).
Tracks: / From this moment on / Buttercup / Sunday kind of love, A / Gone with the wind / Morning glory / Squattyroo / Viva Verrell / Experiment / Smooth ride / I'm beginning to see the light / Seven eleven / Cuban fantasy / Listen to my music.
LP: . . . . **REH 483**
MC: . . . . **ZCR 483**

TED HEATH RECALLS THE FABULOUS DORSEYS (Heath, Ted & His Music).
Tracks: / Opus one / I'll never smile again / Amapola / Melody in F / Oodles of noodles / Well git it / Song of India / Chloe / Green eyes / Quiet please / Marie / Liebestraum.
LP: . . . . **JASM 2027**
MC: . . . . **JASMC 2027**

TED HEATH SWINGS IN HI-STEREO (Heath, Ted & His Music).
Tracks: / C jam blues / Three for the blues / My funny Valentine / I like to recognise the tune / Love me or leave me / Ja da / Boomsie / Big Ben / Sophisticated lady / Wrap your troubles in dreams / Over the rainbow.
LP: . . . . **JASM 2202**

THANKS FOR THE MEMORY (Heath, Ted & His Music).
Tracks: / Thanks for the memory / Trumpet voluntary / Botch a me / Poor little rich girl / In a little spanish town / Early Autumn / Don't let the stars get in your eyes / Mademoiselle / Velvet glove, The / Auld lang syne / Them who has gets / Open the door Richard / Oliver Twist / Narcissus / Gone gone / Old Mother Hubbard / Leave it to love / Get out of the town before sundown / This is the time (to fall in love) / Sixty second got together.
LP: . . . . **PLE 529**
MC: . . . . **TC PLE 529**

THAT LOVELY WEEKEND (Heath, Ted & His Music).
Tracks: / Strike up the band / Smoothy / Blue skies march / Dickery dock / Rag mop / You are my heart's delight / I collect / Times a wastin' / People will say we're in love / Colonel Bogey / Harlem nocturne / Open the door Richard / Big Ben bounce / Skye boat song / Any old iron / My very good friend the milkman / That lovely weekend / Auld lang syne.
LP: . . . . **RFL 32**

YEARS OF FAME (Heath, Ted & His Music).
Tracks: / Kings Cross climax / Hot toddy / Hawk talks, The / Lullaby of Birdland / Lush slide / Send for Henry / Malaguena / Faithful Hussar / Hawaiian war chant / Walking shoes / Cool for cats / Tequila / Stardust / Champ, The / Eloquence / Sermonette / Limehouse blues / Bags' groove / Doodlin' / Beaulieu Abbey.
2LP: . . . . **DPA 3077/8**

Heathen

BREAKING THE SILENCE.
Tracks: / Death by hanging / Goblins blade / Open the grave / Pray for death / Set me free / Breaking the silence / Worlds end / Save the skull.
LP: . . . . **MFN 75**
MC: . . . . **TMFN 75**

Heather & Kirsten

BETCHA DIDN'T KNOW.
MC: . . . . **C 08717**

Heathers

HEATHERS (See under Newman, David) (Newman, David 'Fathead').

Heathrow Flyers

MUSIC FOR MOTORWAYS.
LP: . . . . **RB 006**

Heatwave

CANDLES.
Tracks: / Gangsters of the groove / Jitterbuggin' party suite / Turn around / Posin' till closin' / All I am / Dreamin' you / Goin' crazy / Where did I go wrong.
LP: . . . . **GTLP 047**

CENTRAL HEATING.
LP: . . . . **GTLP 027**
MC: . . . . **GTMC 027**

CURRENT.
Tracks: / Lettin' it loose / State to state / Look after love / Naturally / Big guns / Find it in your heart / Hold on to the one / Mind what you find.
LP: . . . . **EPC 85812**

GANGSTERS OF THE GROOVE - 90'S MIX.
Tracks: / Mind blowing decisions / Ain't no half steppin' / I surrender / Gangsters of the groove / Sweet delight / Razzle dazzle / Time out / Feel like makin' love / Groove line / Too hot to handle / Cover discover / Boogie nights / Jitterbuggin' / Always and forever.
MCSET: . . . . **STAC 2434**
LP: . . . . **STAR 2434**

GREATEST HITS: HEATWAVE.
Tracks: / Boogie nights / Always and forever / Lettin' it loose / Look after love / Groove line / Gangsters of the groove / Posin' 'til closin' / Big guns.
LP: . . . . **EPC 32503**
MC: **40 32503**

HEATWAVE (EP).
Tracks: / Boogie nights / Always and forever / Gangsters of the groove / Groove line.
MC: . . . . **EPC A 40 2631**

HOT PROPERTY.
LP: . . . . **GTLP 039**
MC: . . . . **GTMC 039**

MAXIMUM HEAT.
Tracks: / Boogie nights / Groove line / All I am / Too hot to handle / Mind-blowing decisions / Star of the story (X) / Posin' 'til closin' / Always and forever / Where did I go wrong? / Razzle dazzle / Jitterbuggin' / Gangsters of the groove.
LP: . . . . **SHM 3131**
MC: . . . . **HSC 3131**

POWER CUTS.
Tracks: / Boogie nights / Jitterbuggin' / Too hot to handle / Look after love / Big guns / Groove line / Mind blowing decisions / Always and forever / Posin' til closin' / Razzle dazzle / Lettin' it loose / Gangsters of the groove.
LP: . . . . **EPC 25199**

SOUND OF SOUL.
Tracks: / Too hot to handle / Ain't no half steppin' / Lay it on me / Boogie nights / Central heating / Mind blowing decisions / Happiness togetherness / Groove line / Put the word out / Jitterbuggin' / Where did I go wrong / Gangsters of the groove / Always and forever.
LP: . . . . **BLATLP 11**
MC: . . . . **BLATMC 11**

TOO HOT TO HANDLE.
LP: . . . . **GTLP 013**
LP: . . . . **EPC 32199**

Heaven

TWILIGHT OF MISCHIEF.
Tracks: / Fantasy / Nothing to lose / Take you higher / Tuesday morning / Storm / In the beginning / No one knows / Ballad / Get a move on / Suck City.
LP: . . . . **RCALP 3073**
MC: . . . . **RCAK 3073**

WHERE ANGELS FEAR TO TREAD.
Tracks: / Where angels fear to tread / Love child / Scream for me / Don't mean nothin' / Rock school / Madness / Hard life / She stole my heart / You / Sleeping dogs.
LP: . . . . **CBS 25783**
MC: **40 25783**

Heaven 17

DON'T STOP FOR NO-ONE (See under Eurythmics - Sexcrime (1984) (Various artists).

ENDLESS.
Tracks: / Heaven 17 megamix / We live so fast / Penthouse and pavement / Let me go / Temptation / Who'll stop the rain / (We don't need this) fascist groove thang / Let's all make a bomb (new version) / Counterforce / Crushed by the wheels of industry / And that's no lie / Sunset now / Play to win (Cassette only) / Height of the fighting (he-la-hu) (Cassette only) / I'm your money (Cassette only) / Song with no name (new version) (Cassette only).
MC: . . . . **TCV 2383**

HOW MEN ARE.
Tracks: / Five minutes to midnight / Sunset now / This is mine / Fuse, The / Shame is on the rocks / Skin I'm in, The / Flamedown / Reputation / And that's no lie.
LP: . . . . **V 2326**
MC: . . . . **TCV 2326**
LP: . . . . **OVED 182**
MC: . . . . **OVEDC 182**

LUXURY GAP.
Tracks: / Crushed by the wheels of industry / Who'll stop the rain / Let me go / Key to the world / Temptation / Come live with me / Lady Ice and Mr Hex / We live so fast / Best kept secret.
LP: . . . . **V 2253**
MC: . . . . **TCV 2253**
LP: . . . . **OVED 213**
MC: . . . . **OVEDC 213**

PENTHOUSE AND PAVEMENT.
Tracks: / (We don't need this) fascist groove thang / Penthouse and pavement / Soul warfare / Geisha boys and temple girls / Let's all make a bomb / Height of the fighting (he-la-hu) / Song with no name / Play to win / We're going to live for a very long time.
LP: . . . . **V 2208**
MC: . . . . **TCV 2208**
LP: . . . . **OVED 157**
MC: . . . . **OVEDC 157**

PLEASURE ONE.
Tracks: / Contenders / Trouble / Somebody / If I were you / Low society / Red / Look at me / Move out / Free.
LP: . . . . **V 2400**
MC: . . . . **TCV 2400**
LP: . . . . **OVED 256**
MC: . . . . **OVEDC 256**

TEDDY BEAR, DUKE AND PSYCHO.
Tracks: / Big square people / Don't stop for no-one / Snake and two people / Can you hear me / Hot blood / Ballad of Go Go Brown, The / Dangerous / I set you free / Train of love in motion / Responsibilty / Work (Available on CD only) / Giving up (Available on CD only) / Slow all over (Available on CD only) / Foolish thing to do (Available on CD & cassette only) / Last seven days, The (Available on CD & cassette only).
LP: . . . . **V 2547**
MC: . . . . **TCV 2547**
LP: . . . . **OVED 305**
MC: . . . . **OVEDC 305**

Heaven & Hell

HEAVEN AND HELL VOLUME 1 (Tribute To Velvet Underground) (Various artists).
LP: . . . . **ILLUSION 016**

HEAVEN AND HELL VOLUME 2 (Various artists).
LP: . . . . **ILLUSION 017**
MC: . . . . **ILLCASS 017**

Heavenly

HEAVENLY VS SATAN.
LP: . . . . **SARAH 603**

Heavenly Bodies (film)

HEAVENLY BODIES (Original Soundtrack) (Various artists).
LP: . . . . **EPC 70262**
MC: **40 70262**

Heavenly Bodies (group)

CELESTIAL.
Tracks: / Rains on me / Obsession / Time stands still / Con, The / Stars collide / Road to Maralinga / Shades of love / Cavatina / Senderoluminoso.
LP: . . . . **TMLP 27**

Heavenly Gospel

1935-1940.
Tracks: / Prodigal son / Lead me to the rock / Didn't it rain / Moving up the King's highway / I'm going to telephone to glory / Walk in the light / When the moon goes down / My Lord heard Jerusalem when she moaned.
LP: . . . . **HT 305**

Heavenly Tones

HEAVENLY TONES.
MC: . . . . **GVMMC 208**

Heaven's Gate

HEAVENS GATE (Film soundtrack) (Various artists).
LP: **062 83091**
MC: **1 C062 830911**
LP: . . . . **LBG 30338**
MC: . . . . **TCLBG 30338**

LIVIN' IN HYSTERIA.
LP: **0876311**
MC: **0876314**

Heavies

METAL MARATHON.
Tracks: / Go on fast mix / Hardwear mix / Slow down mix / Watch out mix.
LP: **210 531**
MC: **410 531**

Heavy

HEAVY Various groups (Various artists).
LP: . . . . **NE 1203**
MC: . . . . **CE 2203**

Heavy D

BIG TIME (Heavy D & The Boyz).
Tracks: / We got our own thang / You ain't heard nuttin yet / Somebody for me / Mood for love / EZ duz it, do it EZ / Better land, A / Gyrlz, they love me / More bounce / Big tyme / Flexin' / Here we go again y'all / Let it flow.
LP: . . . . **MCD 6057**
MC: . . . . **MCDC 6057**

LIVING LARGE (Heavy D & The Boyz).
Tracks: / Overweight lovers in the house, The / Nike / Chunky but funky / Dedicated / Here we go / On the dance floor / Money earnin Mount Vernon / I'm gonna make you love me / Overweighter, The / I'm getting paid rock the bass / Mr. Big Stuff / Don't you know.
LP: . . . . **MCA 5986**
LP: . . . . **MCF 3396**
MC: . . . . **MCFC 3396**

PEACEFUL JOURNEY, A (Heavy D & The Boyz).
LP: . . . . **MCA 10289**
MC: . . . . **MCAC 10289**

Heavy Duty

HEAVY DUTY Various artists (Various artists).
Tracks: / Fool for your loving: *Whitesnake* / Animal magnetism: *Scorpions* / Transylvania: *Iron Maiden* / I like to rock: *April Wine* / Criminal tendencies: *Wild Horses* / Speed king: *Deep Purple* / Sanctuary: *Iron Maiden* / Make it real: *Scorpions* / Roller: *April Wine* / Do you know who's looking for you: *Atomic Rooster* / Road racin': *Riot* / Medicine man: *Whitesnake*.
LP: . . . . **FA 41 3123 1**

MC: FA 41 3123 4
LP: SHSP 4115

Heavy Duty Breaks

HEAVY DUTY BREAKS Various artists (Various artists).
LP: JAMS 49
MC: JAMS 49C

Heavy Heads

CHICAGO GOLDEN YEARS.
LP: 515005

Heavy Horns

HEAVY HORNS (Various artists).
LP: 649 803 1

Heavy Jelly

TAKE ME DOWN TO THE WATER.
LP: PSYCHO 30

Heavy Metal

AT DEATH'S DOOR (A Collection of Brutal Death Metal) (Various artists).
Tracks: / Mass hypnosis: *Sepultura* / Dead by dawn: *Deicide* / Out of the body: *Pestilence* / Burnt identity: *Morgoth* / Last abide: *Sadus* / Open casket: *Death* / Decadence within: *Malevolent Creation*/ Culte des mortes: *Cerebral Fix* / Desecrator: *Exhorder* / Til death: *Obituary* / No even one: *Believer*/ Deep in your subconscious: *Atrocity*.
LP: RC 93621

AXE ATTACK (Various artists).
LP: JCI 7102
MC: JCT 7102

AXE ATTACK I (Various artists).
LP: NE 1100
MC: CE 2100

AXE ATTACK II (Various artists).
LP: NE 1120
MC: CE 2120

BEST OF BRITISH STEEL (Various artists).
Tracks: / Tales of destruction: *Dogs D'Amour* / Clerical conspiracy: *Sabbat* / (Na na) nukklear rokket: *Wrathchild*/ Seventh church of the apocalyptic lawnmower: *Lawnmower Deth* / Low life: *Trixx Federation* / Read my lips: *Tattooed* Love Boys / Goddess: *Acid Reign* / Rock and roll lady: *Dominique, Lisa* / I'm on fire: *Mantas* / Deny reality: *Re-Animator* / Surrender: *Midnight Blue* / Queen of the night: *Deathtrash* / Prey to the Lord: *Deathwish* / Living without you: *Tigertailz* / Looking for a lady: *Last Of The Teenage Idols* / Testify to me: *Virus* / Nights on fire: *Torino* / Spirit cry: *Sacrilege* / Love attack: *After Hours*/ One way ride: *Lixx* / Madman: *Metal Messiah* / So alone: *Soho Roses*.
2LP: WKFMLP 128
MC: WKFMMC 128

BEST OF HARD ROCK (Various artists).
MC: BRMC 10
LP: BRLP 10

BEST OF METAL MASSACRE (Various artists).
LP: RR 95511

BEYOND THE METAL ZONE (Various artists).
2LP: MFN 63
MC: TMFN 63

BOLT FROM THE BLACK (Various artists).
Tracks: / Runaround: *Various artists* / Little girl in yellow: *Various artists* / No way to lose: *Various* artists / Mr. Rock and Roll: *Various artists* / Cry baby cry: *Various artists* / Devil's daughter: *Various* artists / Confident but wrong: *Various artists* / Watch me grow: *Various artists* / Burn up: *Various* artists / Looked out my window: *Various artists* / What did you expect: *Various artists* / Down down: *Various artists*.
LP: THBB 001

BRITISH STEEL (Various artists).
LP: JCI 1100
MC: JCT 1100

CALIFORNIA'S BEST METAL (Various artists).
LP: GWD 90526
MC: GWC 90526

COMPLETE DEATH VOL.2 (Various artists).
LP: 722371

DEATH METAL (Various artists).
LP: NUK 006
LP: N 0006

DECLINE OF WESTERN CIVILISATION (Part II - The metal years) (Various artists).
Tracks: / Under my wheels: *Cooper, Alice* / Bathroom wall: *Faster Pussycat* / Cradle to the grave: *Motorhead*/ You can run but you can't hide: *Armored Saint* / In my darkest hour: *Megadeth* / Prophecy: *Queensryche*/ Brave, The: *Metal Church* / Foaming at the mouth: *Rigor Mortis* / Colleen: *Seduce*.
LP: EST 2065
MC: TCEST 2065

DOOMSDAY NEWS (Various artists).
Tracks: / Galactos: *Scanner* / Before the storm: *Rage* / Arrogance in uniform: *Coroner* / Total addiction: *Tankard* / Hosanna in excelsis: *Sabbat* / I'm alive: *Helloween* / And the brave man fails: *Vendetta*/ Mesmerized: *Celtic Frost* / After the attack: *Kreator* / Cockroaches: *Voi Vod*.
LP: N 0105-1
LPPD: N 0105 -1P
LP: NUK 105
LPPD: NUKPD 105

DOOMSDAY NEWS II (Various artists).
LP: NUK 130
MC: ZCNUK 130
LP: N 0130 1
MC: N 0130 4

DOOMSDAY NEWS III (Various artists).
Tracks: / Flat of hate: *Kreator* / Riot of violence: *Kreator* / Love us or hate us: *Kreator* / Alien: *Tankard* / Chemical invasion: *Tankard* / Hosanna in excelsis: *Sabbat* / I for an eye: *Sabbat*/ For those who died: *Sabbat* / DOA: *Coroner* / Absorbed: *Coroner*.
LP: NUK 155
MC: ZCNUK 155

GARAGELANDS VOL.1 (Various artists).
Tracks: / On the go: *Leather Boy* / I need love: *Third Booth* / Here to stay: *Wanted* / Gone: *Plastic* Blues Band / Soulin': *Leather Boy* / No correspondence: *Beckett Quintet* / 9 o'clock: *Peppermint Trolley* Co. / Don't blame me: *Fountain Of Youth* / Not fade away: *Corporate Image* / All I see is you: *Jokers* Wild / Two souls: *Grim Reepers* / Forest fire: *Gasoline Powered Clock* / Days of rest: *Peabody* / Don't blow your mind: *Spiders* / You make me feel good: *Gentrys* / Lay down and die: *Nazz*.
LP: STZ 5003

GREEN METAL (Various artists).
LP: METALPS 107

HEAVY METAL (Film soundtrack) (Various artists).
2LP: EPC 88558
LP: A 547
MC: ZC 547

HEAVY METAL AMERICA (Various artists).
Tracks: / Boy's night out: *Various artists* / Sing it, shout it: *Various artists* / All right now: *Various* artists / Liberty rebellion, The: *Various artists* / Don't tempt the devil: *Various artists* / Back in action: *Various artists* / Feel the fire: *Various artists* / Winter freeze: *Various artists* / Road warrior: *Various artists* / Rockin, The: *Various artists*.
LP: HMUSA 33
MC: HMAMC 33

HEAVY METAL HEROES VOL.3 (Various artists).
LP: HMRLP 153
MC: HMRMC 153

HEAVY METAL HEROES (VOL 2) (Various artists).
Tracks: / Lionheart: *Lionheart* / En cachent: *Shiva* / Arrive alive: *Pallas* / What the hell's going on: *Mendes Prey* / Ice cold swallow: *Mantle Swallow Palmer* / Out of my head: *Overkill* / Devil's triangle: *Cox, Jess* / This fire inside: *Twisted Ace* / Free country: *Witchfinder General* / Oh well: *No Faith*/ Calling for you: *Persian Risk* / Power and the key: *No Quarter*.
LP: HMRLP 7

HEAVY METAL MONSTERS (Various artists).
2LP: CR 5151
MCSET: CRT 5151

HEAVY METAL RECORDS (A TASTY TASTER) (Various artists).
LP: HMRLP 24
MC: HMRMC 24

HEAVY METAL RECORDS COMPILATION (Various artists).
LP: HMRLP 143
MC: HMRMC 143

HEAVY METAL THUNDER (Various artists).
Tracks: / Heavy metal thunder: *Saxon* / One of the boys: *Rose Tattoo* / Long way from home: *Rage* / Nightridge: *Dokken* / Total possession: *Demon* / Motorcycle man: *Saxon* / Denim and leather: *Saxon* / Assault and battery: *Rose Tattoo* / Liar: *Demon* / We're illegal: *Dokken* / Thank that woman: *Rage*.
LP: CAL 3002
MC: CAC 3002

IRON TYRANTS I (Various artists).
LP: WMR 001

IRON TYRANTS II (Various artists).
LP: WMR 002

IRON TYRANTS III (Various artists).
LP: WMR 003

KERRANG KOMPILATION (Various artists).
Tracks: / Love machine: *W.A.S.P.* / Take hold of the flame: *Queensryche* / God bless video: *Alcatrazz*/ Gimme gimme: *Helix* / Wild on the run: *Tobruk* / Aces high: *Iron Maiden* / Assassing: *Marillion*/ All men play on 10: *Manowar* / Fighting for the earth: *Warrior* / Victims of the future: *Moore, Gary*/ Don't tell mama: *Mama's Boys* / Sailor to a siren: *Meatloaf* / Ballroom blitz: *Krokus* / Can you deliver?: *Armored Saint* / Rebel yell: *Idol, Billy* / Rock you like a hurricane: *Scorpions* / Slow 'n' easy: *Whitesnake*/ Right to rock, The: *Keel* / Heaven's on fire: *Kiss* / Runaway: *Bon Jovi* / High in high school: *Madam X* / Follow your heart: *Triumph* / Break down the walls: *Stone Fury* / Heartline: *George, Robin*.
LP: KER 1
MC: TC KER 1

KIDS ARE UNITED (Various artists).
LP: MFN 4

KISS YER SKULL GOODBYE (Various artists).
Tracks: / Seven by seven: *Hawkwind* / Time we left: *Hawkwind* / Hard times: *Bernie Torme* / Beat, The: *Bernie Torme* / Take it for granted: *Atomic Rooster* / Sleepless nights: *Atomic Rooster* / Hide in the rain: *Four X* / In the fire: *Four X* / Because you lied: *McCoy, John* / Temporary threshold shift: *McCoy, John*.
LP: CFRC 509
MC: MCFRC 509

KNIGHTMARE II (Various artists).
LP: IW 1020

LAST WARRIOR, THE (Various artists).
LP: OTH 10

LEADWEIGHT (Various artists).
Tracks: / Inquisitor: *Raven* / Cheetah: *White Spirit* / Angel dust: *Venom* / S.S.Giro: *Axe*/ Inferno: *Blitzkrieg* / Noonday: *Aragorn* / Throwing in the towel: *Fist* / Messiah: *Axis* / Down the road: *Bitches Sin* / Flying high: *Warrior* / Soldiers of war: *Satan's Empire*.
MC: NEATC 1000

LIVE AND HEAVY (Various artists).
Tracks: / Smoke on the water: *Deep Purple* / Razamanaz: *Nazareth* / White line fever: *Motorhead* / Rocks off: *Def Leppard* / All night long: *Rainbow (Group)* / Roll over lay down: *Status Quo* / Ain't no love in the heart of the city: *Whitesnake* / Lights out in London: *UFO* / Unchain your brain: *Gillan* / Paranoid: *Black Sabbath*.
LP: NEL 6020

MAGNUM FORCE ROCKFILE (Various artists).
LP: MFM 006

MARQUEE METAL (Various artists).
Tracks: / We will rock you: *Queen* / Smoke on the water: *Deep Purple* / Wishing well: *Free* / Voodoo chile: *Hendrix, Jimi* / Down down: *Status Quo* / Epic: *Faith No More* / She's a little angel: *Little* Angels / Killer on the loose: *Thin Lizzy* / School's out: *Cooper, Alice* / Crazy, crazy nights: *Kiss*/ Can't get enough: *Bad Company* / Ace of spades: *Motorhead* / Paranoid: *Black Sabbath* / Walk this way: *Run D.M.C./ Aerosmith* / Is there anybody there: *Scorpions* / Wizard, The: *Uriah Heep* / Days of no trust: *Magnum* / Living after midnight: *Judas Priest* / Free 'n' easy: *Almighty*.
MC: 8454174
2LP: 8454171

MASTERS OF METAL (Various artists).
LP: NE 1295
MC: CE 2295

MEGALAMANIA (Various artists).
Tracks: / Take me I'm yours: *Various artists* / Voice on: *Di'Anno, Paul Battlezone* / Placebo: *Max & The* Broadway Metal Choir / Rock me to the limit: *Tokyo Blade* / Game, The: Game, The: *Maineeaxe* / Billy bolero: *Harvey, Alex* / Movin': *Sargent* / Damage is done: *Gillan, Pauline Band* / Lonely: *Various artists*/ Almighty S: *Max & The Broadway Metal Choir* / If heaven is hell: *Tokyo Blade* / Snow shoes: *Harvey, Alex*/ Rising: *Di'Anno, Paul Battlezone* / Set me free: *Various artists* / Fever: *Tokyo Blade*.
LP: AMP 11

MENTAL MANIAXE (Various artists).
LP: EBON 8

METAL BATTLE (Various artists).
Tracks: / Mind over metal: *Raven* / Motormount: *Anvil* / Ready to deliver: *Battleaxe* / Black funeral: *Mercyful Fate* / Laughing in the face of death: *Tank* / Leave me in hell: *Venom* / Run for your life: *Jaguar* / I'd rather go wild: *Witchfynde* / Dancin': *Hellanbach* / Hunt you down: *Satan* / Racing time: *Santers*.
LP: NEAT 1014

METAL BOX, THE (Various artists).
Tracks: / Paranoid: *Black Sabbath* / Stakk atakk: *Wrathchild* / Bounty hunter: *Molly Hatchet* / Balls to the wall: *Accept* / Somebody's out there: *Triumph* / Ace of spades: *Motorhead* / Gimme your love: *Schenker, Michael* / Sweet danger: *Angel Witch* / Stroke, The: *Squier, Billy* / Cat scratch fever: *Nugent, Ted*/ Whatever you want: *Status Quo* / Don't let me be misunderstood: *Moore, Gary* / Dead ringer for love: *Meatloaf*/ Don't take nothing: *Tygers Of Pan Tang* / Don't fear the reaper: *Blue Oyster Cult* / Start talking love: *Magnum*/ 747 (Strangers in the night): *Saxon* / Gypsy: *Uriah Heep* / Is there anybody there: *Scorpions* / Metal health: *Quiet Riot* / Up around the bend: *Hanoi Rocks* / Riding with the angels: *Samson* / Take on the world: *Judas Priest* / Born to be wild: *Steppenwolf* / Broken down angel: *Nazareth* / Freebird: *Lynyrd* Skynyrd / Ships in the night: *Be-Bop DeLuxe* / Epic: *Faith No More* / Hammer horror: *Warfare* / Blitzkrieg: *Blitzkrieg* / Black night: *Deep Purple* / Bed Of nails: *Cooper, Alice* / Satellite kid: *Dogs D'Amour*/ Moonlight: *Cheap 'n' Nasty* / Am I evil: *Diamond Head* / Rock the night: *Europe* / Planet girl: *Zodiac* Mindwarp & The Love Reaction / I want you to want me: *Cheap Trick* / Between a rock and a hard place: *UFO*/ Who do you love: *Juicy Lucy* / Please don't touch: *Headgirl* / Break the chain: *Raven* / Die hard: *Venom*/ Heavy metal love: *Helix* / Race with the Devil: *Girlschool* / Insanity addicts: *Slammer* / D Generation: *Loud*.
LPS: TMBLP 47007
MCSET: TMBMC 47007

METAL CONCUSSION (Various artists).
Tracks: / Malibu beach nightmare: *Hanoi Rocks* / Trapped under ice: *Metallica* / Black metal: *Venom*/ War pigs: *Black Sabbath* / Motorhead: *Motorhead* / Back on the streets: *Moore, Gary* / Shake your heads: *Accept* / Open fire: *Marseille* / Won't get out alive: *Waysted* / Thunder on the tundra: *Thor*/ Axe crazy: *Jaguar* / Never satisfied: *Judas Priest*.
LP: BRLP 101
MC: BRC 101

METAL EXPLOSION (Various artists).
Tracks: / Take it like a man: *Various artists* / Johnny Cool: *Various artists* / Visonary: *Various artists*/ Paper chaser: *Various artists* / Soldier: *Various artists* / Leo the jester: *Various artists* / If you believe me: *Various artists* / Extermination day: *Various artists*.
LP: REH 397
MC: ZCR 397

METAL FATIGUE (Various artists).
LP: EBON 1

METAL FOR MUTHAS (Various artists).
LP: EMC 3318
LP: BBLP 2

METAL FOR MUTHAS-VOL.2 (Various artists).
LP: EMC 3337

METAL FORCES PRESENTS DEMOLITION (Scream your brains out) (Various artists).
LP: CRE 103

METAL INFERNO (Various artists).
LP: KKLP 103
MC: KKMC 103

METAL KILLERS (Various artists).
Tracks: / White line fever: *Motorhead* / Blood guts and beer: *Tank* / Nothing to lose: *Girlschool* / Urban guerilla: *Hawkwind* / Now comes the storm: *Thor* / Not for sale: *Girlschool* / Run like hell: *Tank*/ Beer drinkers and hell raisers: *Motorhead* / Start raisin' hell: *Thor* / Last flight: *Jaguar* / Bump and grind: *O'Williams, Wendy*.
LP: RAWLP 004
MC: RAWTC 004

METAL KILLERS KOLLECTION VOL 1 (Various artists).
Tracks: / Paranoid: *Black Sabbath* / Boogie: *UFO* / Armed and ready: *Schenker, Michael* / Rocka rolla: *Judas Priest* / Ace of spades: *Motorhead* / Under the blade: *Twisted Sister* / Demolition boys: *Girlschool*/ Gypsy: *Uriah Heep* / Master of the universe (live): *Hawkwind* / Fast as a shark: *Accept* / Parisienne walkways: *Moore, Gary* / Run like hell: *Tank* / Black metal: *Venom* / Antigua: *DiAnno* / Night of the blade: *Tokyo Blade* / Twist of the knife: *Wrathchild* / Wiped out: *Raven* / Burning in the heat of love: *Lea, Jim* / Hells bells: *Hells Bells* / Bump and grind: *O'Williams, Wendy* / Start raisin' hell: *Thor* / Thanks for the angst: *Chrome Molly* / Rock

steady: *Waysted* / Am I evil: *Diamond Head*.
2LP: CCSLP 112
MC: CCSMC 112

METAL KILLERS KOLLECTION VOL 3 (Various artists).
Tracks: / Bark at the moon: *Osbourne, Ozzy* / Cat scratch fever: *Nugent, Ted* / Metal health: *Quiet Riot*/ Hit and run: *Magnum* / Don't let me be misunderstood: *Moore, Gary* / Bad or just no good: *Little Angels*/ We are the road crew: *Various artists* / All for one: *Raven* / Freewheel burning: *Judas Priest* / Burning: *Accept* / (Don't fear) the reaper: *Blue Oyster Cult* / Easy livin': *Uriah Heep* / Something special: *Chrome Molly* / Shnibob (part 1): *DRN* / Walk this way: *Aerosmith* / I'm alive: *Helloween* / I won't dance: *Celtic Frost* / Toxic trace: *Kreator* / Boots: *Megadeth* / Breaking the silence: *Heathen* / Hole in the sky: *Black Sabbath*.
2LP: CCSLP 168
MC: CCSMC 168

METAL KILLERS KOLLECTION VOL 2 (Various artists).
Tracks: / Tragedy (live): *Hanoi Rocks* / Let them eat metal: *Rods* / Rock six times: *Starz* / Hang 'em high: *Waysted* / Heat of the night: *Various artists* / Eat the rich: *Tyson Dog* / Sabbath bloody sabbath: *Black Sabbath* / Boys nite out: *Teaze* / Goin' on crazy: *Smashed Gladys* / Friends of hell: *Witchfinder* General / Destroyer: *Twisted Sister* / Burn the Kings Road: *Warfare* / Restless and wild: *Accept*/ Sorcerer, The: *Alaska* / I'll get you rockin': *Godz* / Crazy motorcycle: *Rogue Male* / Turn the hell on: *Fist* / Hot 'n' ready: *Reckless* / Break the chain: *Raven* / Heartuser: *DiAnno* / Angeline: *Sabu* / Art and illusion: *12th Night* / Ready as hell: *Jim Dandy*.
2LP: CCSLP 134
MC: CCSMC 134

METAL KILLERS VOL I (Various artists).
LP: KKLP 101
MC: KKMC 101

METAL KILLERS VOL II (Various artists).
LP: KKLP 102
MC: KKMC 102

METAL MACHINE (Various artists).
LP: RR 90841

METAL MADNESS (Various artists).
LP: NR 01
MC: NRC 01

METAL OVER AMERICA (Various artists).
LP: SKULL 8340

METAL PLATED (Various artists).
LP: EBON 14

METAL THUNDER (Various artists).
Tracks: / All wrapped up in mystery: *Arch Rival* / Digital life: *Apocalypse* / Don't feed the animals: *Sleazy* Roze / Sex shop: *Wolf Spider* / Queen of the world: *Rescue* / She goes on: *FN Guns* / Stay: *Graffiti*/ He has a grenade: *Hammer* / Suicide: *Dirty Side*.
LP: RUMLP 002

METAL TREASURES AND VINYL HEAVIES (Various artists).
LP: ARLP 105
MC: ZCAR 105

METAL WARRIOR (Various artists).
LP: OTH 9

METAL WARRIORS (Various artists).
LP: EBON 11

METALGON (Various artists).
LP: A 30

METALLERGY (Various artists).
LP: BRLP 102

METALLERGY (Various artists).
LP: JETMP 228

MOLTEN METAL (Various artists).
MC: STAC 2429
LP: STAR 2429

MONSTERS OF ROCK (Various artists).
Tracks: / Stargazer: *Rainbow (Group)* / Another piece of meat: *Scorpions* / All night long: *Rainbow (Group)*/ Don't ya know what love is: *Touch* / Loving you Sunday morning: *Scorpions* / Backs to the wall: *Saxon*/ I like to rock: *April Wine* / Road racin': *Riot*.
MC: 3199 256
LP: 2488 810
MC: 843 689 4
LP: 843 689 1

MOOSE MOLTEN METAL VOLUME 1 (Various artists).
LP: HMUSA 55

NEW WAVE OF BRITISH HEAVY METAL (1979 Revisited) (Various artists).
2LP: 8463221
MCSET: 8463224

NIGHTMARE ON CARNABY STREET (Various artists).
Tracks: / Brain dead: *Various artists* / Death by hanging: *Various artists* / Run for your life: *Various* artists / Never surrender: *Various artists* / Psychoradio: *Various artists* / Hellion: *Various artists*/ Self destruct: *Various artists* / I can't wait: *Various artists* / Pay for your love: *Various artists*/ Hollywood killer: *Various artists* / Passing, The: *Various artists* / Rock that makes me roll: *Various artists*/ Steal the away: *Various artists* / Arthur Whiteside: *Various artists* / Fall in love again: *Various artists*.
2LP: MFN 83
MC: TMFN 83

NWOBHM COMPILATION (New Wave Of British Heavy Metal) (Various artists).
LP: HMRLP 157
MC: HMRMC 157

PHENOMENA (Various artists).
Tracks: / Kiss of fire: *Various artists* / Still the night: *Various artists* / Dance with the Devil: *Various* artists / Phoenix rising: *Various artists* / Believe: *Various artists* / Who's watching you: *Various artists* / Hell on wings: *Various artists* / Twilight zone: *Various artists* / Phenomena: *Various artists*.
LP: PM 1
MC: PMC 1

PROTECT THE INNOCENT (Various artists).
Tracks: / Prime mover: *Rush* / Back on the streets: *Saxon* / Ultimate sin, The: *Osbourne, Ozzy* / Gypsy road: *Cinderella (Group)* / Paranoid: *Black Sabbath* / Don't fear the reaper: *Blue Oyster Cult* / Fireball: *Deep Purple* / Start talkin' love: *Magnum* / Ace of spades: *Motorhead* / Kiss me deadly: *Ford, Lita*/ Breakin' the law: *Judas Priest* / Fallin' in and out of love: *Femme Fatale* / Rhythm of love: *Scorpions*/ Dream evil: *Dio* / Rock seat education: *Zodiac Mindwarp* / Get it on: *Kingdom Come* / Scream dream: *Nugent, Ted* / How come it never rains: *Dogs D'Amour* / I wanna be loved: *House Of Lords (rock)* / Born to be wild: *Steppenwolf* / Na na nukklear rokket: *Wrathchild* / Rock'n'roll lady: *Dominique, Lisa* / Love overload: *Tigertailz* / Goddess: *Acid Reign* / Metal thrashing mad: *Anthrax* / Fabulous disaster: *Exodus*/ Rattlehead: *Megadeth* / Killing hand, The: *Dream Theater* / Helter skelter: *Vow Wow* / Fat man: *Mammoth*.
LP: STAR 2363
MC: STAC 2363

QUIET NIGHT IN (Various artists).
LP: BRON 537

RED HOT METAL (18 Rock Classics) (Various artists).
Tracks: / Breakthru: *Queen* / Just like paradise: *Roth, David Lee* / Wild frontier: *Moore, Gary* / Bark at the moon: *Osbourne, Ozzy* / Days of no trust: *Magnum* / Up all night: *Slaughter* / Miles away: *Winger*/ There she goes again: *Quireboys* / Your mama don't dance: *Poison* / Black velvet: *Myles, Alannah* / That's when I think of you: *1927* / All fired up: *Benatar, Pat* / Gimme some lovin': *Thunder* / I don't need no doctor: *W.A.S.P.* / Devil and daughter: *Black Sabbath* / Love is a killer: *Vixen* / Got the time: *Anthrax* / Night crawler: *Judas Priest*.
LP: ADD 21
MC: ZDD 21

SPEED KILLS VOL. 1 (Various artists).
LP: MFN 54
MC: TMFN 54

SPEED KILLS VOL. 2 (Various artists).
LP: FLAG 2
MC: TFLAG 2

SPEED KILLS VOL. 3 (Various artists).
LP: FLAG 17
MC: TFLAG 17

SPEED KILLS VOL. 4 (Speed Kills but who's Dying?) (Various artists).
MC: TFLAG 33
LP: FLAG 33

SPEED KILLS VOL. 5 (Head Crushing Metal) (Various artists).
LP: FLAG 46
MC: TFLAG 46

STAIRWAY TO HEAVEN/HIGHWAY TO HELL (Various artists).
Tracks: / My generation: *Gorky Park* / Holidays in the sun: *Skid Row* / I can't explain: *Scorpions* / Purple haze: *Osbourne, Ozzy* / Teaser: *Motley Crue* / Boys are back in town: *Bon Jovi* / Move over: *Cinderella (bk)* / Moby Dick: *Drum Madness (Torres & Bonham)* / Medley: *Various artists*.
LP: 842 093-1
MC: 842 093-4

STRICTLY FOR KONNOISEURS (Various artists).
2LP: MFN 32
MC: TMFN 32

SWEDISH METAL (Various artists).
LP: SNTF 929

TASTE OF ARMAGEDDON, A (Various artists).
Tracks: / Path of no return: *Treason* / Slayer, The: *Demont* / Death right at sunset: *Snyper* / None so blind: *First Blood* / Memories of yesterday: *Arbitrator* / Madman: *Metal Messiah* / Violence is now: *Resentment* / Dogs of war: *Wreckage* / Nothing room: *Warpspeed* / Working factory: *Purgatory*.
LP: BBSLP 003
MC: BBSMC 003

TIME TO ROCK (Various artists).
Tracks: / Jailhouse rock: *Motley Crue* / Bathroom wall: *Faster Pussycat* / Never forgive: *Raven* / Here it comes: *Ezo* / Cumin' atcha live: *Tesla* / Start the fire: *Metal Church* / Fighting for the world: *Various* artists / Breakout: *Frehley, Ace* / Shadow of your love: *Various artists* / License to kill: *Various artists* / Burnt offerings: *Testament*.
LP: WX 113
MC: WX 113C

WELCOME TO THE METAL ZONE (Various artists).
LP: MFN 49
MC: TMFN 49

WHERE TO. WHAT FOR. WITCH HUNT (Various artists).
2LP: FOAD 1

Heavy Metal Kids

ANVIL CHORUS.
LP: K 50143

CHELSEA KIDS.
Tracks: / Overture / Chelsea kids / From heaven to hell and back again / Cry for me / She's no angel / Jackie the lad / Docking in / Squalliday inn / Delirious.
LP: METALP 117

HEAVY METAL KIDS.
Tracks: / Hangin' on / Ain't it hard / It's the same old song / Runaround eyes / Always plenty of women / Nature of my game / Kind of woman / Rock 'n' roll man / We gotta go.
LP: K 50047

KITSCH.
LP: SRAK 523

Heavy Pettin'

BIG BANG.
LP: WKFMLP 130
MC: WKFMMC 130

LETTIN' LOOSE.
Tracks: / In and out of love / Broken heart / Love on the run / Love times love / Victims of the night / Rock me / Shout it out / Devil in her eyes / Hell is beautiful.
LP: HEPLP 1

ROCK AIN'T DEAD.
Tracks: / Rock ain't dead / Sole survivor / China boy / Lost in love / Northwinds / Angel / Heart attack / Dream time / Walkin' with the angels / Throw a party / Crazy (Extra track on CD only.).
LP: HEPLP 4

Heavy Rock

HEAVY ROCK (Various artists).
LP: 6498 093
MC: 7133 093

Heavy Traffic

HEAVY TRAFFIC STARRING "V" (Heavy Traffic Starring "V").
Tracks: / If you're gonna mess with me / S.O.S. (help me boy) / Jealousy / Fire is gone / Hand made love / Let's go crazy / You can't hurt me no more / Coming down with love / Promises in the dark / Deep in it.
LP: 781 682-1
MC: 781 682-4

Heavy Way

HEAVY WAY, THE (Various artists).
Tracks: / Last in line: *Dio* / Gotta let go: *Ford, Lita* / Seven seas: *New Thunder* / Between the wheels: *Rush* / Digital bitch: *Black Sabbath* / Rockin' all over the world: *Status Quo* / Breakout: *Bon Jovi*/ Eternal dark: *Picture* / Lonely is the hunter: *Kiss* / This month's messiah: *Nazareth* / Don't say make me / Rocker, The: *Thin Lizzy*.
LP: 822750 1
MC: 822750 4

Hebb, Bernard

GUITAR MUSIC.
LP: EULP 1035

Hebe

HEBE.
Tracks: / Button up your overcoat / At the balalaika / I'm a dreamer / Ukelele lady / Experiment / I apologise / Love makes the world go round / Some day I'll find you / Glad rag doll / Love, your magic spell is everywhere / Sing song girl of old Shanghai / Can't help lovin' dat man / You'd be surprised / Money song.
LP: EJ 2702841
MC: EJ 2702844

LIVE AT NELSON'S WINEBAR.
MC: CUB 3T

Hebert, Adam

BEST OF ADAM HEBERT.
LP: 6065
MC: 6065 TC

Hecke, Rudolf

GOD IS DOG SPELLED BACKWARDS.
LP: IR 003

Hect, Ben

FRONT PAGE, THE (Various artists).
MCSET: 0351

Hedda

HEDDA.
Tracks: / Good company / Rooted to the spot / Morning lovers live forever / Old bones and baggage / Gonna have another kick in life / You stood in the spotlight / Beautiful people / I have seen the light / Come closer stranger / Too long ago / You come to me / Outro.
LP: NSPL 18605

Heddix, Travis

WRONG SIDE OUT.
Tracks: / Caught in the middle / Nobody wants you when you're old / Old time music / Two heads are better than one / Wrong side out / Time to take change / Old cliche / Don't take everything away from me.
LP: ICH 1033
MC: ZCICH 1033

Hedenbratt, Sonya

ALL OF ME (Hedenbratt, Sonya & Arne Domnerus).
LP: PHONT 7573

Hedgehog Pie

GREEN LADY, THE.
MC: CROC 213

HEDGEHOG PIE.
Tracks: / Rev. Johnson & the big kerry, The / Mariners / Rosemary Lane / March of the King of Laois / Peggy / O'Rourke's flogging chair / Fishing song / Jack Orion / Spalpeen's lament, The.
LP: RUB 009
MC: RUBC 009

JUST ACT NORMAL.
Tracks: / Angels took my racehorse away, The / Lowlands of Holland, The / William Taylor / Dancing the baby / Rueben Ranzo / Peggy o'er sea with a soldier / Rambleaway / Cuckoo, The / Bold fisherman / Uncle Bulgaria.
LP: RUB 024
MC: CROC 214

Hedges, Chuck

CLARINET CLIMAX (Hedges, Chuck & Allan Vache).
LP: J 131

Hedges, Michael

AERIAL BOUNDARIES.
Tracks: / Aerial boundaries / Bensusan / Rickover's dream / Ragamuffin / After the goldrush / Hot type / Spare change / Menage a trois / Magic farmer, The.
LP: 371032-1
MC: 371032-4

LIVE ON THE DOUBLE PLANET.
Tracks: / All along the watchtower / Because it's there / Silent anticipations / Ready or not / Love bizarre, A / Breakfast in the field / Rikki's shuffle / Women of the world / Double planet, The / Funky advocado, The / Come together.
LP: 371066-1
MC: 371066-4

STRINGS OF STEEL.
Tracks: / All along the watchtower / Rickover's dream / Unexpected visitor / Ragamuffin / Silent Anticipations / Aerial boundaries / Happy couple, The / Streamlined man, The / Rikki's shuffle / Because it's there.
LP: 37 6792 1
MC: 37 6792 2

TAPROOT.
Tracks: / Naked stalk, The / Jealous tunnel, The / About face / Jade stalk, The / Nomad land / Point A / Chava's song / Ritual dance / Scenes (on the road to shrub 2) / First cutting, The / Point B / Song of the spirit farmer / Rootwitch, The / I carry your heart.
MC: WT 1093

WATCHING MY LIFE GO BY.
Tracks: / Face yourself / I'm coming home / Woman of the world / Watching my life go by / I want you / Streamlined man, The / Out on the parkway / Holiday

/ All along the watchtower / Running blind.
LP: 370303-1
MC: 370303-4

Hee Bee Gee Bees

439 GOLDEN GREATS.
Tracks: / Meaningless songs / Up the wall / Dead cicada / Quite ahead of my time / You're my son / Boring song / Ah / Too depressed to commit suicide / Simple song / Granma / Music machine / Oh me / Bird of peace.
LP: . . . . TWITS 101
MC: . . . . TWITK 101

Hee Haw

BOYS NEXT DOOR, THE.
LP: . . . . ING 008

Heera

COOL AND DEADLY.
LP: . . . . ARI 1007
MC: . . . . ARI 0107

DIAMONDS FROM HEERA.
LP: . . . . ARI 1004
MC: . . . . ARI 0104

JAGH WALA MELA.
Tracks: / Jithon de lachhi roj langdee / Mer nak wich coca paa giya / Nach lal haan diye / Dil mera lal gayee / Jagh wala mela / 'Elna de naal ayee mitro / Munda moh lila / Sadaa putt rehan vasde / Lagdee too bottle jahee / Ter akh di ishare / Sajna da chhala mordke / Tere nee nashile naina ne.
LP: . . . . DDP 1003

Heff, Klaus

STERNENTANZA.
LP: . . . . SKY 84

Heffernen, Honor

STORMY WATERS.
LP: . . . . MRLP 005
MC: . . . . MRMC 005

Hefti, Neal

BAND WITH YOUNG IDEAS, THE (Hefti, Neal & His Orchestra).
Tracks: / Coral reef / Charmaine / Waltzing on a cloud / Lake Placid / Two for a nickel, three for a dime / Why not / Sure thing / Uncle Jim / Falling in love all over again / In veradero / It's a happy holiday / Sahara's aide.
LP: . . . . JASM 1021

CLIFF BROWN QUINTET & THE NEAL HEFTI ORCHESTRA (see under Brown, Cliff) (Hefti, Neal Orchestra & Clifford Brown Quintet).

Hegamin, Lucille

BLUE FLAME.
LP: . . . . VLP 50

Hegarty, Dermot

21 YEARS.
LP: . . . . HPE 635

1990 STYLE.
LP: . . . . FRC 012

CONNEMARA BY THE LAKE.
LP: . . . . HPE 606

FAVOURITE TRADITIONAL MELODIES.
Tracks: / Danny Farrell / James Connolly / Hi for the beggarman / Town I loved so well, The.
LP: . . . . HPE 680
MC: . . . . HPC 680

HITS OF IRELAND'S DERMOT HEGARTY - VOL.3.
LP: . . . . BRL 4059

IRISH STARTIME.
LP: . . . . IST 4448
LP: . . . . ISTG 4448

WHAT IRELAND MEANS TO ME.
LP: . . . . IRB 2001

Heggarty Haggerty (bk)

ADVENTURES OF HEGGARTY HAGGERTY (See under Adventures of...) (Cole, George (nar)).

Heibel

DROPUT MELODIES.
LP: . . . . HR 012

YEAH, EVERYTHING'S GREAT.
LP: . . . . GURT 16

Heide, Florence Parry

SHRINKING OF TREEHORN, THE/ TREEHORN'S TREASURE See also Kerry Shale.
MC: 881581

Heidi (bk)

HEIDI (Unknown narrator(s)).
MCSET: . . . . DTO 10577

HEIDI (see under Spyri, Johanna) (Dench, Judi).

HEIDI (By Johanna Spyri) (Clark, Petula).
MCSET: . . . . LFP 7109

Heidt, Horace

1939: HORACE HEIDT (Heidt, Horace & His Musical Knights).
LP: . . . . HSR 194

Hein & Oss

SOLDATENLIENDER.
LP: . . . . LR 44.006

Heinlein, Robert

GREEN HILLS OF EARTH / GENTLEMEN BE SEATED (Nimoy, Leonard).
MC: 1526

Heinz

HEINZ & THE TORNADOS.
Tracks: / Just like Eddie / You were there / Summertime blues / Three steps to heaven / Country boy / Tribute to Eddie / Don't you knock at my door / Telstar / Ice cream man / Night rider / Dragonfly / Jungle fever / Robot / Globetrotter.
LP: . . . . TAB 38
MC: . . . . KTBC 38

REMEMBERING.
Tracks: / Just like Eddie / Hush-a-bye / Three steps to heaven / That lucky old sun / You were there / 20 flight rock / Country boy / Dreams do come true / Cut across shorty / Summertime blues / I ran all the way home / Tribute to Eddie.
LP: . . . . REM 7

SINGLES, THE.
LP: . . . . RGM 3267

THAT'S THE WAY IT WAS (Heinz & The Wild Boys).
Tracks: / Questions I can't answer / Beating my heart / Diggin' my potatoes / She ain't coming back / Don't think twice / Big fat spider / End of the world / You make me feel so good / Heart full of sorrow / Don't worry baby / Movin' in / I'm not a bad guy.
LP: . . . . MACH 8

Heir Apparent

GRACEFUL INHERITANCE.
LP: . . . . BD 008

ONE SMALL VOICE.
LP: . . . . RO 94721
MC: . . . . RO 94724

Helaire, Nonc

FOR KOONASSES ONLY - VOLUME 1.
LP: 7001

FOR KOONASSES ONLY - VOLUME 2.
LP: 7002

Heldon

HELDON 1.
LP: . . . . COB 37019

INTERFACE.
LP: . . . . COB 37013

STAND BY.
LP: 900578

UN REVE SANS CONSEQUENCE SPECIAL.
LP: . . . . COB 37002

Helen & The Horns

HELEN AND THE HORNS.
LP: . . . . RRR 1

Helfer, Erwin

BOOGIE PIANO - CHICAGO-STYLE.
Tracks: / Hallucinating / Rubbish boogie / Rodez stomp / Inside / Sneaky Pete / Homage to AA and PJ / Dirty dozens / Thin and thirty / Big Joe / Fat city / Four o'clock blues / Oysters.
LP: . . . . BEAR 11

Helias, Mark

CURRENT SET, THE.
Tracks: / Current set,The / No passport / Rebound / Greetings from L C / Nuclear one / Ellipsis one.
LP: . . . . ENJA 5041

Heliocentric

HELIOCENTRIC WITH JEFF PRESSING (Heliocentric & Jeff Pressing).
LP: . . . . DS 806

Helius Creed

X-RATED FAIRY TALES.
LP: . . . . SAVE 013

Helix

BACK FOR ANOTHER TASTE.
Tracks: / Storm, The / That's life / Heavy metal cowboys / Back for another taste / Midnight express / Give it to you / Runing wild in the 21st century / Breakdown / Wild in the streets / Rockin' rollercoaster / Good to the last drop / Wheels of thunder.
LP: . . . . GWLP 102
MC: . . . . GWTC 102

LONG WAY TO HEAVEN.
Tracks: / Kids are all shakin' / Deep cuts the knife / Ride the rocket / Long way to heaven / House on fire / Christine / Without you (Jasmine's song) / School of hard knocks / Don't touch the merchandise / Bangin' offa the bricks.
LP: . . . . EJ 2403481
MC: . . . . EJ 2403484

NO REST FOR THE WICKED.
Tracks: / Does a fool ever learn / Let's all do it tonight / Heavy metal love / Check out the love / No rest for the wicked / Don't get mad get even / Ain't no high like rock'n'roll / Dirty dog / Never want to lose you / White lace and black leather.
LP: . . . . EST 4001851
MC: . . . . TC EST 4001854

WALKIN' THE RAZOR'S EDGE.
Tracks: / Rock you / Young and wreckless / Animal house / Feel the fire / When the hammer falls / Gimme gimme good lovin' / My kind of rock / Anything you want / Six strings, nine lives / You keep me rockin'.
LP: . . . . EJ 2401831

WHITE LACE AND BLACK LEATHER.
Tracks: / Breaking loose / It's too late / Long-distance heartbreak / Time for a change / Hangman's tree / It's what I wanted / Mainline / Women, whisky and sin / Thoughts that bleed.
LP: . . . . MOGO 4013

WILD IN THE STREETS.
Tracks: / Wild in the streets / Kiss it goodbye / Long way to heaven / Never gonna stop the rock / Dream on / What ya bringin' to the party / High voltage kicks / Give 'em hell / Shot full of love / Love hungry eyes / She's too tough.
LP: . . . . EST 2046
MC: . . . . TC EST 2046

Hell Bastards

HEADING FOR INTERNAL DARKNESS.
Tracks: / We had evidence / Civilsed / Nazis killed / Death camp / Massacre / Heading for internal darkness / Pylons, The / Afrikkan beggar / Rise of crust.
LP: . . . . COX 008

NATURAL ORDER.
LP: . . . . MOSH 22
MC: . . . . MOSH 22 MC

Hell Can Be Heaven

HELL CAN BE HEAVEN (Original cast recording) (Various artists).
LP: . . . . TER 1068
MC: . . . . ZCTER 1068

Hell Comes To Your

HELL COMES TO YOUR HOUSE Various artists (Various artists).
Tracks: / Social distortion: *Various artists* / Legal weapon: *Various artists* / Rhino 39: *Various artists*/ Modern warfare: *Various artists* / 45 grave: *Various artists* / Christian death: *Various artists* / Super heroines: *Various artists* / Secret hate: *Various artists* / Outer circle: *Various artists.*
LP: . . . . REAGAN 1
LP: . . . . MFN 30
MC: . . . . TMFN 30

Hell Is Always Today

HELL IS ALWAYS TODAY (see Higgins, Jack) (Mackenzie, Michael).

Hell On Earth

HELL ON EARTH (Various artists).
LP: . . . . MFN 12

Hell, Richard

BLANK GENERATION (Hell, Richard & The Voidoids).
Tracks: / Love comes in spurts / Liars beware / New pleasure / Betrayal takes two / Down at the rock and roll club / Who says / Blank generation / Walking on the water / Plan, The / Another world.
LP: . . . . SR 6037
MC: 7599261374

DESTINY STREET (Hell, Richard & The Voidoids).
Tracks: / Kid with the replaceable head, The / You gotta / Going going gone / Lowest common denominator / Downtown at dawn / Time / I can only give you everything / Ignore that door / Staring in her eyes / Destiny Street.
LP: . . . . NOSE 2

R.I.P..
MC: . . . . A 134

Hellanbach

BIG...H, THE.
Tracks: / Beaten to the bone / Main man / Nobody's fool / Bandits run / S.P.G.C. / Saturday night / Panic state O.D. / Daddy dig those cats / When all is said and done / Urban paranoia.
LP: . . . . NEAT 1019

NOW HEAR THIS.
Tracks: / Dancin' / Times are getting harder / Look at me / All systems go / Maybe tomorrow / Motivated by desire / Taken by surprise / Let's get this show on the road / Kick it out / All the way / Everybody wants to be a cat.
LP: . . . . NEAT 1006

Hellborg, Jonas

AXIS.
LP: . . . . DEMLP

WORD, THE.
MC: . . . . AXCT 3009

Hellcats

CHERRY MANSIONS.
LP: . . . . ROSE 146

HELLCATS.
LP: . . . . KKR 1003

HOODOO TRAIN.
Tracks: / Where the hell is Memphis? / Crazy about you baby / Baby please don't go / I did my part / When you walk in the room / Black door slam / Wall of death / I don't need / I've been a good thing (for you) / Hoodoo train / Don't fight it / Antartica / Shine / Silly whim / Love is dying / Hard time killin' floor blues / What cha doing in the woods / Where the sirens cry.
LP: . . . . ROSE 197

Heller, Joseph

CATCH 22.
MC: 1418

Heller, Martin (nar)

CORAL ISLAND (See under Coral Island).

Hellhammer

APOCALYPTIC RAIDS.
LP: . . . . NUK 008
LP: . . . . N 0008

Hellion

BLACK BOOK, THE.
LP: . . . . MFN 108
MC: . . . . TMFN 108

HELLION.
LP: . . . . MFN 15

MINI-LP.
MLP: . . . . NRR 28
MC: . . . . NRC 28

POSTCARDS FROM THE ASYLUM.
LP: . . . . MFN 82

SCREAMS IN THE NIGHT.
Tracks: / Screams in the night / Bad attitude / Better off dead / Upside down guitar solo / Hand, The / Explode / Easy action / Put the hammer down / Stick 'em / Children of the night / Tower of air, The.
LP: . . . . MFN 73

Hello

GLAM YEARS 1971-1979, THE.
Tracks: / New York groove / Love stealer / Game's up, The / Good old USA / Round and round / You move me / C'mon / Machine-gun hustle / Oh Caroline / Shine on silver light / Tell him / Star studded sham / Let it rock / Seven rainy days / Whole lotta woman / 99 ways / Backseat talking / Dean / You shot me down / Feel this thing.
LP: . . . . BIFF 1

Hello Again

HELLO AGAIN (Original Soundtrack) (Various artists).
Tracks: / Hello again: *Various artists* / Lucy's reflection: *Various artists* / Kevin and Lucy: *Various artists*/ In the beginning: *Various artists* / Zelda visits the beyond: *Various artists* / Dinner party, The: *Various* artists / Transfiguration: *Various artists* / Jason's remorse: *Various artists* / Second thoughts: *Various artists* / Lucy despairs: *Various artists* / Kimmy pie: *Various artists* / Grand finale: *Various artists.*
MC: . . . . CDS 1003

Hello Children

HELLO CHILDREN... EVERYWHERE (Various artists).
Tracks: / Puffin Billy: *Melodi Light Orchestra* / Nellie the elephant: *Miller, Mandy* / I know an old lady: *Ives, Burl* / How much is that doggie in the window: *Roza, Lita* / Runaway train: *Dalhart, Vernon* / Swedish rhapsody: *Mantovani & His Orchestra* / Gilly gilly ossenfeffer katzenellenbogen by the sea: *Bygraves, Max* / Home on the range: *Autry, Gene* / All things bright and beautiful: *Uncle Mac/Barbara Mullen* / Little red monkey: *Nicholas, Joy/Jimmy Edwards/Dick Bentley* / Where will the baby's dimple be?: *Cogan, Alma* / King's new clothes, The: *Kaye, Danny* / You're a pink toothbrush: *Bygraves, Max* / Black hills of Dakota, The: *Day, Doris* / Bluebell polka: *Shand, Jimmy & His Band* / Three billy goats gruff, The: *Luther, Frank* / Ballad of Davy Crockett, The: *Hayes, Billy* / Mister cuckoo (sing your song): *Ross, Edmundo* / Me and my teddy bear: *Clooney, Rosemary* / Little white duck:

Kaye, Danny / Buckingham Palace: *Stephens, Anne* / Typewriter, The: *Anderson, Leroy Orchestra* / I taut I taw a puddy tat: *Blanc, Mel* / When father papered the parlour: *Williams, Billy* / Happy wanderer, The: *Obernkirchen Children's Choir* / Ugly duckling, The: *Kaye, Danny* / Laughing policeman, The: *Penrose, Charles* / Dance duet from Hansel and Gretel: *Various artists* / Little boy fishin': *Abicair, Shirley* / In the middle of the house: *Cogan, Alma* / Owl and the pussycat, The: *Hayes, Elton* / Robin Hood: *James, Dick* / Pickin' a chicken: *Boswell, Eve* / Grasshopper's dance, The: *Hylton, Jack & His Orchestra* / Deadwood stage: *Day, Doris* / Tubby the tuba: *Kaye, Danny* / Grandfather's clock: *Radio Revellers* / Big rock candy mountain: *Ives, Burl* / Twenty tiny fingers: *Cogan, Alma* / Teddy bears picnic: *Hall, Henry* / Little shoemaker, The: *Michael Twins/Frank Weir & His Band* / Bimbo: *Miller, Suzi* / Woody woodpecker: *Blanc, Mel* / Kitty in the basket: *Dekker, Diana* / Coronation scot: *Torch, Sidney & Orchestra* / There's a friend for little children: *Uncle Mac/Barbara Mullen.*
2LP: . . . . **EM 1307**
MCSET: . . . . **TCEM 1307**

HELLO CHILDREN EVERYWHERE VOL.2 (Various artists).
Tracks: / Hello my darlings: *Drake, Charlie* / Handful of songs: *Steele, Tommy* / Runaway train, The: *Holliday, Michael* / Football crazy: *Hall, Robin & Jimmy MacGregor* / I've lost my mummy: *Harris, Rolf* / Sandpaper ballet: *Anderson, Leroy* / Wonderful Copenhagen: *Kaye, Danny* / Mole in a hole, The: *Southlanders* / Looking high high high: *Johnson, Bryan* / Lady of Spain: *Rey, Monte & Geraldo's Orchestra* / Hippopotamus song, The: *Flanders* & Swann / Baby sittin' boogie: *Clifford, Buzz* / Windmill in old Amsterdam, A: *Hilton, Ronnie* / Ragtime cowboy Joe: *Chipmunks* / Nymphs and shepherds: *Manchester Childrens Choir* (Sir Hamilton Harty.) / Little blue riding hood: *Freberg, Stan* / Itsy bitsy teeny weeny yellow polka dot bikini: *Hyland, Bryan* / Last train to San Fernando: *Duncan, Johnny (1)* / Standing on the corner: *King Brothers* / Donald where's your troosers: *Stewart, Andy* / You need feet: *Bresslaw, Bernard* / Bee song: *Askey, Arthur* / Never do a tango with an eskimo: *Cogan, Alma* / Dambusters march, The: *Central Band of the RAF* / Beep beep: *Playmates* / Tulips from Amsterdam: *Bygraves*, Max / Champion the wonder horse: *Laine, Frankie* / Gypsy rover, The: *Highwaymen* / Sisters: *Beverly Sisters* / Tom Dooley: *Kingston Trio* / Post horn gallop: *Band of the Royal Marines* (K. Alford.) / Little white bull: *Steele*, Tommy / Bangers and mash: *Sellers, Peter/Sophia Loren* / Thumbelina: *Kaye, Danny* / Parade of the jelly babies: *Gollywogs* / Trains (Part 1): *Gardiner, Reginald* / Trains (Part II): *Gardiner, Reginald* / Right said Fred: *Cribbins, Bernard (nar)* / Who's afraid of the big bad wolf: *Hall, Henry Orchestra* / Seven little girls sitting in the back seat: *Avons* / Side saddle: *Conway, Russ* / Soldier won't you marry me: *Rodgers, Jimmie* (2) / Pretty little black-eyed Susie: *Mitchell, Guy* / Man from Laramie, The: *Young, Jimmy* / Tie me kangaroo down sport: *Harris, Rolf* / Never never land: *Weir, Frank /Maureen Childs/Little Tinkers* / Wiegenlied: *Schumann, Elisabeth.*
2LP: . . . . **EM 1340**
MCSET: . . . . **TCEM 1340**

HELLO CHILDREN EVERYWHERE VOL. 3 (Various artists).
Tracks: / Rawhide: *Laine, Frankie* / Run rabbit run: *Flanagan & Allen* / Fox and the goose, The: *Rodgers, Jimmie (2)* / Hey little hen: *Roy, Harry* / Poor people of Paris, The: *Atwell, Winifred* / Cab, The (Le Fiacre): *Sablon, Jean* / Pop goes the weasel: *Newley, Anthony* / Carbon the copycat: *Ritter, Tex* / Hush hush hush - here comes the bogey man: *Hall, Henry & His Orchestra* / March of the mods: *Loss, Joe & His Orchestra* / Gnu song, The: *Flanders, Michael/Donald Swann* / Close the door (they're coming in the window): *Stargazers* / Big bad John: *Dean, Jimmy* / Norman: *Deene, Carol* / Michael row the boat ashore: *Highwaymen* / I'm Henery the eighth: *Herman's Hermits* / Marching strings: *Martin, Ray & His Concert Orchestra* / Poppa Piccolino: *Clark, Petula* / Two little boys: *Harris, Rolf* / My old man's a dustman: *Donegan, Lonnie* / Little Sir Echo: *Bygraves*, Max / Scottish soldier: *Stewart, Andy* / Vespers (Christopher Robin is saying his prayers: *Stephens, Anne* / She wears red feathers: *Mitchell, Guy* / My boomerang won't come back: *Drake, Charlie* / That noise: *Newley, Anthony* / Little engine that could, The: *Ives, Burl* / Any old iron: *Sellers, Peter* / Sixteen tons: *Ford*, Tennessee Ernie / 633 squadron: *Goodwin, Ron & His Orchestra* / Where's me shirt?: *Dodd, Ken* / I can't do my bally bottom button up: *Wallace, Ian* / English country garden: *Rodgers, Jimmie (2)* / Down came the rain: *Mister* Murray / Messing about on the river: *MacRae, Josh* / Flash bang wallop: *Steele, Tommy* / Story of my life, The: *Holliday, Michael* / Frankfurter sandwiches: *Joanne & The Streamliners* / Does your chewing gum lose its flavour?: *Donegan, Lonnie* / Zambesi: *Bush, Lou & His Orchestra* / Lollipop tree, The: *Ives, Burl* / Sugartime: *Cogan, Alma* / When you come to the end of a lollipop: *Bygraves, Max* / Hand up your sticks: *Williams, Kenneth* & Lance Percival / Ballad of Bethnal Green: *Roberts, Paddy* / Hole in the ground: *Cribbins, Bernard (nar)* / Goodness gracious me: *Sellers, Peter/ Sophia Loren* / Thank U very much: *Scaffold.*
2LP: . . . . **EM 1380**
MCSET: . . . . **TCEM 1380**

Hello Dolly

HELLO DOLLY (Original cast recording) (Various artists).
Tracks: / Hello Dolly prologue: *Various artists* / I put my hand in: *Various artists* / It takes a woman: *Various* artists / Put on your Sunday clothes: *Various artists* / Ribbons down my back: *Various artists* / Motherhood: *Various artists* / Dancing: *Various artists* / Before the parade passes by: *Various artists* / Elegance: *Various artists* / Hello Dolly: *Various artists* / It only takes a moment: *Various artists* / So long dearie: *Various artists* / Hello Dolly finale: *Various artists.*
MC: . . . . **GK 83814**

HELLO DOLLY (Original Broadway Cast) (Various artists).
Tracks: / I put my hand in: *Various artists* / It takes a woman: *Various artists* / Put on your Sunday clothes: *Various artists* / Ribbons down my back: *Various artists* / Dancing: *Various artists* / Motherhood march: *Various artists* / Before the parade passes by: *Various artists* / Elegance: *Various artists* / Hello Dolly: *Various artists* / It only takes a moment: *Various artists* / So long dearie: *Various artists* / Hello Dolly finale: *Various artists.*
LP: . . . . **BL 42962**
MC: . . . . **BK 42962**

HELLO DOLLY (FIRST ISSUE) (Film soundtrack) (Various artists).
LP: . . . . **SSL 10292**

Hello Frisco Hello

HELLO FRISCO HELLO (Original soundtrack) (Various artists).
LP: . . . . **SH 2070**
MC: . . . . **CSH 2070**
LP: . . . . **HS 5005**

Hello Goodbye

HELLO GOODBYE (Film Soundtrack) (Various artists).
Tracks: / Hello goodbye: *Various artists* / Danny takes a dip: *Various artists* / No need to cry: *Various* artists / Theme 3: *Various artists* / Lazy nights: *Various artists* / Food for cats: *Various artists* / Take the plunge: *Various artists* / Harry's return: *Various artists* / Interlude: *Various artists* / Journey to Marseilles: *Various artists* / Hello goodbye: *Various artists* / No need to cry: *Various artists* / Harry remembers: *Various artists* / Bistro waltz: *Various artists* / Theme 3 (reprise): *Various artists* / Morning departure: *Various artists* / Danny's theme: *Various artists* / Destination Le Havre: *Various artists* / Together: *Various artists.*
LP: . . . . **SSL 10309**

Helloise

COSMOGONY.
Tracks: / Cosmogony / Broken hearts / Run a mile / Die hard / Ready for the night / For a moment / Gates of heaven / Hard life.
LP: **240755 1**
MC: **240755 4**

Helloween

BEST OF HELLOWEEN.
LP: . . . . **NO 1761**
MC: . . . . **NO 1764**

HELLOWEEN.
MLP: . . . . **N 0021**
MLP: . . . . **NUK 021**

JUDAS.
MLP: **88561-8128-1**

KEEPER OF THE SEVEN KEYS.
Tracks: / I'm alive / Future world / Halloween / Twilight of the gods.
LP: . . . . **N 0057**
MC: . . . . **N 0060**
LP: . . . . **NUK 057**
LPPD: . . . . **NUKPD 057**
MC: . . . . **ZCNUK 057**

KEEPER OF THE SEVEN KEYS (PART 2).
Tracks: / Eagle fly free / You always walk alone / March of time / Doctor Stein.
LP: . . . . **NUK 117**
LP: . . . . **N 01171**
MC: . . . . **ZCNUK 117**
LPPD: . . . . **NUKPD 117**
MC: . . . . **N 0117 2**

LIVE IN THE UK.
Tracks: / Little time / Doctor Stein / Future world / Rise and fall / We got the right / I want out / How many tears.
LP: . . . . **EMC 3558**
MC: . . . . **TCEMC 3558**

PINK BUBBLES GO APE.
Tracks: / Pink bubbles go ape / Kids of the century / Back on the streets / Number one / Heavy metal hamsters / Going home / Someone's crying / Mankind / I'm doin' fine - crazy man / Chance, The / Your turn.
LP: . . . . **EMC 3588**
MC: . . . . **TCEMC 3588**

WALLS OF JERICHO.
Tracks: / Ride the sky / Metal invaders / Reptile / How many tears.
LP: . . . . **N 0032**
MC: . . . . **N 0110**
MC: . . . . **ZCNUK 032**
LP: . . . . **NUK 032**

Hellraiser

HELLRAISER (Original Soundtrack) (Various artists).
Tracks: / Resurrection: *Various artists* / Hellbound heart: *Various artists* / Lament configuration, The: *Various* artists / Reunion: *Various artists* / Quick death, A: *Various artists* / Seduction and pursuit: *Various* artists / In love's name: *Various artists* / Cenobites: *Various artists* / Rat slice quartet, The: *Various* artists / Re-resurrection: *Various artists* / Uncle Frank: *Various artists* / Brought on by night: *Various artists* / Another puzzle: *Various artists.*
LP: . . . . **FILM 021**
MC: . . . . **FILMC 021**

HELLRAISER II (Hellbound: Original Soundtrack) (Various artists).
Tracks: / Hellbound: *Various artists* / Second sight seance: *Various artists* / Looking through a woman: *Various* artists / Something to think about: *Various artists* / Skin her alive: *Various artists* / Stringing the puppet: *Various artists* / Hall of mirrors: *Various artists* / Dead or living: *Various artists* / Leviathan: *Various artists* / Sketch with fire: *Various artists.*
LP: . . . . **GNPS 8015**
MC: **GNP5 8015**

Hell's Belles

HELL'S BELLES.
Tracks: / Looks like love / Overload / Desire me / Screaming for mercy / Hell's bells / Barricades / Strange love / Dirty girls / Storm break loose / Long legs.
LP: . . . . **RAWLP 015**
MC: . . . . **RAWTC 015**

Hells Bent On Rockin'

HELLS BENT ON ROCKIN' (Various artists).
LP: . . . . **NERD 017**

Hellwitch

SYZYGIAL MISCREANCY.
LP: . . . . **WRE 9021**

Helm, Levon

LEVON HELM & THE RCO ALL-STARS...PLUS (Helm, Levon & The RCO All-Stars).
Tracks: / Washer woman / Tie that binds me, The / You got me / Blues so bad / Sing, sing, sing, (Let's make a better world) / Milk cow boogie / Rain down tears / Mood I was in, A / Havana moon / That's my home / Violet eyes / Stay with me / Hurricane / Nashville wimmin.
LP: . . . . **SEE 228**

Helms, Bobby

MY SPECIAL ANGEL.
Tracks: / Apartment No.9 / Touch my heart / Expressing my love / All I need is you / Things I remember most / I can see it all / I can't promise you won't get lonely / I wouldn't take the world for you / Just between you and me / I know one / Fraulein / My special angel.
LP: . . . . **PRCV 102**

Helmut & Elisabeth

GENTLE BREEZE.
LP: . . . . **KLO 37**

Help (film)

HELP (See under Beatles).

Help Me Make It...

HELP ME MAKE IT THROUGH THE NIGHT (Various artists).
LP: **41 5708 1**
MC: **41 5708 4**

Help Yourself

HELP YOURSELF.
LP: . . . . **BGOLP 52**

Helstar

BURNING STAR.
LP: . . . . **MFN 20**

DISTANT THUNDER, A.
Tracks: / King is dead, The / Bitter end / Abandon ship / Tyrannicide / Scorcher / Genius of insanity / Whore of Babylon / Winds of love / He's a woman - she's a man.
LP: . . . . **RR 95241**

NOSFERATU.
Tracks: / Rhapsody in black / Baptized in blood / To sleep / Perchance to scream / Harker's tale (mass of death) / Perseverance and desperation / Curse has passed away, The / Benediction / Harsh reality / Surling madness / Von am lebem destro sturm / Aleliaria and Everonn.
LP: . . . . **RO 94381**

REMNANTS OF WAR.
LP: . . . . **N 0043**

Helter Skelter

CONSUME.
MC: . . . . **SIGH 4-5**
LP: . . . . **SIGH 1-5**
MC: **846 442 4**
LP: **846 442 1**

Helvette Underground

HELVETTE UNDERGROUND Various artists (Various artists).
MC: . . . . **HEND 84001**

Hemet High Jazz Band

TIME AFTER TIME.
Tracks: / Los hermanos de bop / Nobody cares but me / Lady with the pretty legs, The / Blues for Dee / Time after time / This masquerade / Baile de la mariposa / Thank you band.
LP: . . . . **AM 11**

Hemifran, Vykort

HEMIFRAN, VYKORT Various artists (Various artists).
LP: . . . . **TPLP 55**

Hemingway, Ernest

OLD MAN AND THE SEA, THE (Heston, Charlton).
MCSET: **2084**

Hemingways Adventures

HEMINGWAYS ADVENTURES OF A YOUNG MAN (Film Soundtrack) (Various artists).
LP: . . . . **LXRS 201**
LP: . . . . **ERS 6516**

Hemlock Cock & Bull

ALL BUTTONED UP.
LP: **12TS 421**

Hemphill, Jessie Mae

SHE-WOLF.
LP: **513501**

Hemphill, Julius

BUSTER BEE (Hemphill, Julius & Oliver Lake).
LP: **3018**

COON BID'NESS.
LP: . . . . **FLP 41012**

GEORGIE BLUE (Hemphill, Julius/ Jah Band).
LP: . . . . **MM 003**

LIVE IN NEW YORK.
LP: . . . . **VPA 138**

RAW MATERIALS AND RESIDUALS.
LP: . . . . **BSR 0015**

Henderson, Big Bertha

TOUGH MAMAS.
LP: . . . . **KK 7448**

Henderson, Bill

LIVE AT THE TIMES.
Tracks: / Joey / Watch what happens / Song for you, A / Skylark / Sweet pumpkin / Send in the clowns.
LP: . . . . **DS 779**

STREET OF DREAMS.
Tracks: / All the things you are / You better love me / Gentleman is a dope, The / My funny Valentine / Angel eyes / This masquerade.
LP: . . . . **DS 802**

TRIBUTE TO JOHNNY MERCER, A.
Tracks: / Something's gotta give / My shining hour / I thought about you /

Blues in the night / Out of this world / I'm an old cowhand / Hooray for Hollywood / I remember you / On the Atchison, Topeka and Santa Fe.
LP: DS 846
MC: DSC 846

Henderson, Eddie

RUNNIN' TO YOUR LOVE.
Tracks: / Runnin' to your love / Sunchaser / Hibby / This band is hot / Please your mind / Moon / Marlana.
LP: EST 11984

Henderson, Finis

FINIS.
Tracks: / Skip to my lou / Making love / Lovers / You owe it all to love / Blame it on the night / Percussion intro - call me / Vina del mar / Crush on you / I'd rather be gone / School girl.
LP: STML 12191
MC: CSTML 12191

Henderson, Fletcher

1950 (Henderson, Fletcher Sextet).
LP: SOL 517

BLUE RHYTHM 1931-32 (Henderson, Fletcher & His Orchestra).
Tracks: / Low down on the bayou / House of David blues, The / Sugar root stomp / Blue in my heart / Strangers / Milenberg joys / My sweet tooth says I wanna / Malinda's wedding day / You rascal you / Radio rhythm.
LP: VLP 64

CROWN KING OF SWING,THE.
Tracks: / After you've gone / Stardust / Tiger rag / Somebody stole my gal / You rascal you / Blue rhythm / Sugar foot stomp / Low down on the bayou / Twelfth St. rag / Milenberg joys.
LP: WL 70543
MC: WK 70543

DIXIE STOMPERS, THE (1925-26).
2LP: S 1277
2LP: SW 8445/6

DIXIE STOMPERS, THE (1927-28).
LP: S 1241

END OF AN ERA VOLUME 1,THE.
LP: ST 1008

FLETCHER HENDERSON (1937-8).
LP: VA 7995

FLETCHER HENDERSON 1923-24 VOL. 1.
MC: NEO 706

FLETCHER HENDERSON 1923-24 VOL. 2.
MC: NEO 707

FLETCHER HENDERSON 1923-24 VOL. 3.
MC: NEO 708

FLETCHER HENDERSON 1926-30.
LP: VLP 42

FLETCHER HENDERSON AND ORCHESTRA vol. 1 (Henderson, Fletcher & His Orchestra).
LP: CC 27

FLETCHER HENDERSON & HIS CONNIE'S INN ORCHESTRA (Henderson, Fletcher & His Connie's Inn Orchestra).
Tracks: / You rascal you / Blue rhythm / Sugar foot stomp / Low down on the bayou / Twelfth St. rag / Milenberg joys / After you've gone / Stardust / Tiger rag / Somebody stole my gal / Business in F / My pretty girl / Goodbye blues.
LP: SM 3077

FLETCHER HENDERSON & HIS ORCHESTRA 1923/5.
LP: FJ 112

FLETCHER HENDERSON & HIS ORCHESTRA 1931 (Henderson, Fletcher & His Orchestra).
LP: VLP 63
LP: ET 3

FLETCHER HENDERSON STORY.
LP: 66423

FLETCHER HENDERSON'S ORCHESTRA 1924/6.
LP: VLP 36

FLETCHER HENDERSON'S ORCHESTRA 1923/24.
LP: VLP 24

HENDERSON CLASSICS VOL.1 (1925-27).
MC: NEO 709

HOCUS POCUS.
Tracks: / St. Louis shuffle / Variety stomp / Sugar foot stomp / Roll on / Mississippi, roll on / Singing the blues / Strangers / Take me away from the river / Hocus pocus / Phantom fantasie / Harlem madness / Tidal wave / Moonrise on the lowlands / I'll always be in love / Jangled nerves / Grand Terrace rhythm / Riffin' / Mary had a little lamb / Shoe shine boy / Sing, sing, sing / Knock, knock, who's there / Jim Town blues.
MC: NK 90413
LP: NL 90413

INDISPENSABLE FLETCHER HENDERSON (1927-36).
Tracks: / Shufflin' Sadie / St. Louis Shuffle / Variety stomp / Sugar foot stomp / Roll on, Mississippi, roll on / Moan, you moaners / Singing the blues / Oh, it looks like rain / Sweet music / My sweet tooth says I wanna / Malinda's wedding day / Strangers / Take me away from the river / I wanna count sheep / Poor old Joe / Hocus pocus / Phantom fantasie / Harlem madness / Tidal wave / I'm a fool for loving you / Jangled nerves / Where there's you there's me / Do you or don't you love me / Grand terrace rhythm / Riffin' / Mary had a little lamb / Shoe shine boy / Sing, sing, sing / Until today / Knock, knock who's there / Jim town blues / You can depend on me.
2LP: NL 89604
MCSET: NK 89604

INDISPENSABLE FLETCHER HENDERSON (1927-1936), THE.
2LP: PM 43691

JAZZ CLASSICS IN DIGITAL STEREO (Fletcher Henderson 1925-1928).
Tracks: / Shanghai shuffle / Wang wang blues / Chinatown, my Chinatown / Clarinet marmalade / Sugarfoot stomp / Just blues / Singing the blues / New King Porter stomp / Under the Harlem moon / Big John special / Happy as the day is long / Wild party / Hotter than hell / Jangled nerves / Let 'er go.
LP: REB 720
MC: ZCF 720

JAZZ CLASSICS IN DIGITAL STEREO (Fletcher Henderson 1929-1937).
Tracks: / Shanghai shuffle / New King Porter stomp / Big John special / Jangled nerves / Just blues / Wrappin' up.
LP: REB 682
MC: ZCF 682

LOUIS ARMSTRONG & FLETCHER HENDERSON 1924/5 (See under Armstrong Louis) (Henderson, Fletcher & Louis Armstrong).

PATHE SESSIONS, THE (1923-25 - WITH HIS ORCHESTRA).
Tracks: / Old black Joe's blues / 31st Street blues / Shake your feet / Swanee river blues / It won't be long now / Warhorse mama / Chicago blues / After the storm / Driftwood / I wish I could make you cry / Say say Sadie / Tell me dreamy eyes / My Rose Marie / Don't forget you'll regret day by day / Shanghai shuffle / Poplar St. blues / Me Neenyah.
LP: S 803

RARE FLETCHER HENDERSON MASTERPIECES.
LP: VLP 10

SMACK - ORIGINATOR OF SWING ARRANGEMENT.
LP: LPJT 39

SMACK & SATCH (Henderson, Fletcher & His Orchestra).
LP: SFR 737

UNDER THE HARLEM MOON.
Tracks: / Honeysuckle Rose / New King Porter stomp / Underneath the Harlem moon / Queer notions / Night life / Nagasaki / Rhythm crazy now / Ain't cha glad? / Hocus pocus / Tidal wave / Christopher Columbus / Blue Lou / Stealin' apples / Jangled nerves / Grand Terrace rhythm / Riffin' / Shoe shine boy / Sing, sing, sing / Jimtown blues / Rhythm of the tambourine / Back in your own back yard / Chris and his gang.
LP: AJA 5067
MC: ZC AJA 5067

VERY FIRST & THE RAREST, THE.
LP: BLJ 8011

WILD PARTY (Henderson, Fletcher & His Orchestra).
LP: HEP 1009

YEAH MAN VOL. 2 (1931 - 33).
LP: HEP 1016

Henderson, Hamish

FREEDOM COME ALL YE.
LP: CCA 7

Henderson, Horace

1933-34 (see under Hawkins, Coleman) (Henderson, Horace/Coleman Hawkins/ Henry Allen).

Henderson, Joe

BARCELONA.
LP: ENJA 3037

BLACK NARCISSUS.
Tracks: / Black narcissus / Hindsight and forethought / Power to the people / Amoeba / Good morning heartache / Other side of right.
LP: M 9071

IN 'N' OUT.
Tracks: / In 'n' out / Punjab / Serenity / Short story / Brown's town.
LP: BST 84166

INNER URGE.
Tracks: / Inner urge / Isotope / El barrio / You know I care / Night and day.
LP: BST 84189

MIRROR MIRROR (Henderson, Joe & Chick Corea).
LP: MPS 69 255

MODE FOR JOE.
Tracks: / Shade of jade, A / Mode for Joe / Black / Caribbean fire dance / Granted / Freewheelin' / Black (alt. take).
LP: BST 84227

MYSTIFIED (Henderson, Joe & Tom, Rick Laird & Ron Steen).
LP: SJP 112

OUR THING.
Tracks: / Teeter totter / Pedro's time / Our thing / Black road / Escape.
LP: BST 84152

PAGE ONE.
Tracks: / Blue bossa / La mesha / Homestretch / Recorda me / Jinrikisha / Out of the night.
LP: B1 84140

RELAXIN' AT CAMARILLO.
LP: 1014 006

SOFT FOCUS (Henderson, Joe & Tom, Rick Laird & Ron Steen).
LP: SJP 104

STATE OF THE TENOR VOL. 1 (Live at the Village Vanguard).
Tracks: / Beatrice / Friday the thirteenth / Happy reunion / Loose change / Ask me now / Isotope.
LP: BT 85123

STATE OF THE TENOR VOL. 2 (Live at the Village Vanguard).
Tracks: / Boo boo's birthday / Cheryl / Y ya la quiero / Soulville / Portrait / Bead game, The / All the things you are.
LP: BT 85126

TENOR TRIBUTE (See under Cobb, Arnett for details) (Henderson, Joe/ Arnett Cobb/Jimmy Heath).

YAMA (see Farmer, Art) (Henderson, Joe/Art Farmer).

Henderson, Kelvin

HEADLITES.
Tracks: / Goodbye Marie / Scarlet woman / Dolly McGraw / Headlites / Never comin' back / Hero of the dreamers / From a jack to a king / Gotta keep movin' / Hello in there / 1643 Pennsylvania Boulevard / Truckstop lover / Hesitation blues.
LP: CRLP 1003

Henderson, Kyle

KYLE HENDERSON.
LP: KRR R 5402

Henderson, Maggie

RAGTIME (Henderson, Maggie & F.Harris).
LP: REC 182

Henderson, Michael

BEST OF MICHAEL HENDERSON.
Tracks: / Be my girl / I can't help it / In the night time / To be loved / (We are here) to geek you up / You are my starship / Make me feel better / Let me love you / You haven't made it to the top / Take me i'm yours / Do it all / Wide reciever / Valentine love / Reach out for me / Am I special?.
LP: NEXLP 117
MC: NEXMC 117

DO IT ALL.
Tracks: / Playing on the real thing / Everybody wants to now / To be loved / Do it all / In the Summertime / Wait until the rain / Riding.
LP: BDLP 4006

FICKLE.
Tracks: / Fickle / Feeling like myself once again / One step at a time / Thin walls / You wouldn't have to work at all / Assault with a friendly weapon / Love will find a way / Whip it / Fickle (instrumental version).
LP: BDLP 4070

GOIN' PLACES.
Tracks: / Whip it / Going places / Let me love you / I can't help it / I'll be understanding / At the concert / Won't you be mine.
LP: BDLH 5018

IN THE NIGHT TIME.
Tracks: / Take me I'm yours / We can go on / Happy / In the night time / Whisper in my ear / Am I special? / Yours truly, indiscreetly / One to one.
LP: BDLP 4055

WIDE RECEIVER.
Tracks: / You're my choice / Make me feel like / Reach out for me / Wide receiver / I don't need nobody else / What I'm feeling (for you) / Ask the lonely / There's no one like you / Prove it.
LP: BDLP 4065

Henderson, Scott

DOCTOR HEE.
LP: PJ 88030
MC: PJC 88030

NOMAD (Henderson, Scott & Tribal Tech).
Tracks: / Renegade / Nomad / Robot immigrants / Tunnel vision / Elegy for shoe / Bofat / No, no, no / Self defense / Rituals.
LP: LR 45022
MC: LR 65022

Hendon Band

BRASS SENTIMENTAL STYLE.
Tracks: / Mexican shuffle / Summertime / In the still of the night / Liebeslied / Cute / Ye banks and braes / So in love / Don't cry for me Argentina / Those magnificent men in their flying machines / Way you look tonight / Li'l darlin' / St. Louis blues / Waltz theme by Chopin / I know why / Moon river / Papito / Somewhere over the rainbow / What now my love.
LP: BBR 1010
MC: BBT 1010

ERIC BALL-AN EIGHTIETH BIRTHDAY TRIBUTE.
Tracks: / Main street / September fantasy / Sunset rhapsody / Softly sounds the little bell / Andaluza / Romance from 'Festival music' / English maiden, The.
LP: PRL 020
MC: CPRL 020

Hendricks, Barbara

GERSHWIN SONGS.
Tracks: / Man I love, The / They can't take that away from me / Love is here to stay / But not for me / Embraceable you / Nice work if you can get it / I got rhythm / Summertime / Has one of you seen Joe / I loves you Porgy.
LP: 9500917

MELODIES FROM FRENCH OPERAS.
Tracks: / Depuis le jour (From the opera:'Louise'by Gustave Charpentier.) / Ah, je veux vivre (From the opera:'Romeo et Juliet' by Charles Gounod) / Me voila seule dans la nuit (From the opera:'Le Pecheurs de Perles' by Georges Bizet) / Comme autrefois dans la nuit sombre (From the opera:'Le Pecheurs de Perles' by Georges Bizet) / Entre l'amour et le devoir (From the opera:'Benvenuto Cellini' by Hector Berlioz) / Adieu notre petite table (From the opera:'Manon' by Jules Massenet) / Dis-moi (From the opera:'Thais' by Jules Massenet) / Que je suis belle (From the opera:'Thais' by Jules Massenet) / Elle a fui la tourterelle (From the opera:'les Contes D'Hoffman' by Jacques Offenbach) / Dieu quel frisson (From the opera:'Romeo et Juliette' by Charles Gounod) / Je marche sur tous les chemins (From the opera:'Manon' Jules Masenet.) / Obeissons quand leur voix appelle (From the opera:'Manon' Jules Masenet.).
LP: 410446 1
MC: 410446 4

NEGRO SPIRITUALS.
Tracks: / Sometimes I feel like a motherless child / Plenty good room / Nobody knows de trouble I've seen / Git on board, li'l chilun / Oh what a beautiful city / His name so sweet / Deep river / When I lay my burden down / Swing low, sweet chariot / Talk about a child that do love Jesus / Roun' about de mountain / Hold on / Were you there / Ev'ry time I feel de spirit.
LP: ASD 1731681
MC: TCASD 1731684

Hendricks, Jon

AT NEWPORT '63 (see under Lambert) (Hendricks/Lambert).

HAVIN' A BALL AT THE VILLAGE GATE (see under Lambert) (Hendricks/ Lambert/Bavan).

LOVE (Hendricks, Jon & Co).
Tracks: / Royal Garden blues / Bright moments / Willie's tune / Good ol' lady / Li'l darlin' / I'll die happy / Love (Berkshire blues) / Tell me the truth / Swinging groove merchant(groove merchant),The / Angel eyes / In a Harlem airshaft.
LP: MR 5258
MC: MRC 5258

SWINGERS, THE (see under Lambert) (Hendricks/Lambert/Ross).

Hendriks, Gijs Quartet

CLOSE TO THE EDGE.
LP: SJP 113

DOM ROCKET.
LP: SJP 131

Hendrix, Jimi

10TH ANNIVERSARY BOX.
Tracks: / Ain't no telling / All along the watchtower / And the gods made love / Angel / Are you experienced? / Astroman / Beginnings / Belly button window / Bleeding heart / Blue suede shoes / Bold as love / Burning desire / Burning of the midnight lamp / Can you see me / Castles made of sand / Catastrophe / Changes / Come on / Coming down hard on me, baby / Crosstown traffic / Drifter's escape / Drifting / Drone blues / Easy blues / Exp / Ezy ryder / Fire / Freedom / Gypsy boy / Gypsy eyes / Have you ever been / Hear my train a comin' / Highway chile / House burning down / I don't live today / If six was nine / I'm your hoochie coochie man / In from the storm / Izabella / Jam 292 / Jimi / Jimmy jam / Johnny B. Goode / Little bears / Little Miss Lover / Little Miss Strange / Little wing / Long hot summer night / Love or confusion / Lover man / Machine gun / Manic depression / May this be love / Message of love / Midnight / Midnight lightning / Moon turn the tides / My friend / Night bird flying / Nine to the universe / 1983... / Once I had a woman / One rainy wish / Peter Gunn / Power to love / Queen, The / Rainy day dream away / Red house / Remember / Sgt. Pepper's lonely hearts club band / Stars that play with laughing Sam's dice, The / Stepping stone / Still raining, still dreaming / Straight ahead / Tax free / 3rd stone from the sun / Trashman / Up from the skies / Voodoo chile / Wait until tomorrow / We gotta live together / Who knows / Young / You've got me floating / Foxy lady.
LPS: 2625 038

16 GREAT CLASSICS.
LP: 2615251
MC: 2615254

20 GOLDEN PIECES: JIMI HENDRIX: VOL 2.
Tracks: / Good times / Voices / Suspicious / Whipper / Bessie Mae / Miracle worker / Feel that soul / Walking with Besse / Gotta find someone / Girl so fine / Soul food / Voices in the wind / Free spirit / Let me thrill your soul / Young generation / Get down / Funky / She's so fine / Let me go / Groove.
LP: BDL 2027

20 GOLDEN PIECES: JIMI HENDRIX VOL 1.
Tracks: / You got me running / Money / Let's go, let's go, let's go / You got what it takes / Sweet little angel / Walking the dog / There is something on your mind / Hard night / Hush now / Knock yourself out / Ballad of Jimi / No business / Gotta have a new dress / Don't accuse me / Flashing / Hang on, Sloopy / Twist and shout / Bo Diddley / Tutti frutti / Lucille.
LP: BDL 2010
MC: BDC 2010

ARE YOU EXPERIENCED?.
Tracks: / Foxy lady / Manic depression / Red house / Can you see me? / Love or confusion / I don't live today / May this be love / Fire / Third stone from the sun / Remember / Are you experienced? / Purple haze / Hey Joe / Wind cries Mary.
LP: SPELP 97
MC: SPEMC 97
LP: 613001
MC: 847 234 4
LP: 847 234 1
LP: 612 001

AT HIS BEST VOL. 4.
LP: SM 3535

AT HIS BEST:VOL.1.
Tracks: / She went to bed with my guitar / Free thunder / Cave man bells / Strokin' a lady on each hip / Baby chicken strut.
LP: SM 3271
MC: MC 3271

AT HIS BEST:VOL.2.
Tracks: / Feels good / Fried cola / Monday morning blues / Jimi is tender too / Madagascar.
LP: SM 3272
MC: MC 3272

AT HIS BEST:VOL.3.
Tracks: / Young Jim / Lift off / Down mean blues / Swift's wing / Spiked with heady dreams.
LP: SM 3273
MC: MC 3273

AXIS BOLD AS LOVE.
Tracks: / Experience / Up from the skies / Spanish castle magic / Wait until tomorrow / Ain't no telling / Little wing / If six was nine / You've got me floating / Castles made of sand / She's so fine / One rainy wish / Little Miss Lover / Bold as love.
LP: SPELP 3
MC: SPEMC 3
LP: 613-003
MC: 847 243 4
LP: 847 243 1

BAND OF GYPSIES.
Tracks: / Who knows? / Machine gun / Changes / Power to love / Message of love / We gotta live together / Hear my train / Foxy lady / Stop.
LP: SPELP 16
MC: SPEMC 16
LP: 2406-001
MC: 847 237 4
LP: 847 237 1

BEST OF AND THE REST OF, THE.
Tracks: / Redhouse / Bleeding heart / Tomorrow never knows / Outside woman blues / Woke up this morning and found yourself dead / Morrison's lament / Uranus rock / Sunshine of your love.
MC: ARLC 1022

CONCERTS, THE.
Tracks: / Fire / I don't live today / Red house / Stone free / Are you experienced / Little wing / Voodoo chile / Bleeding heart / Hey Joe / Wild thing / Hear my train a comin' / Foxy lady.
2LP: CCSLP 235
MC: CCSMC 235
MC: 40 22177
2LP: CBS 22177
2LP: CBS 88592

CORNERSTONES 1967-1970.
Tracks: / Hey Joe / Purple haze / Wind cries Mary, The / Foxy lady / Crosstown traffic / All along the watchtower / Voodoo chile (slight return) / Have you ever been (to Electric Ladyland) / Star spangled banner (studio version) / Stepping stone / Room full of mirrors / Ezy ryder / Freedom / Drifting / In from the storm / Angel / Fire (Available on CD and cassette format only.) / Stone free (Available on CD and cassette format only.).
LP: 847 231 1
MC: 847 231 4

COSMIC TURNAROUND.
Tracks: / No such animal (part 1) / Tomorrow / No such animal (part 2) / Come on baby / I love my baby / Down now / Louisville.
LP: AFELP 1002
MC: ZCAFS 1002

CRASH LANDING.
Tracks: / Message to love / Somewhere over the rainbow / Crash landing / Coming down hard on me, baby / Peace in Mississippi / Power of soul / Stone free again / Captain Coconut.
LP: SPELP 94
MC: SPEMC 94
LP: 2310 398
MC: 847 263 4
LP: 847 263 1

CRASH LANDING/MIDNIGHT LIGHTNING.
Tracks: / Message to love / Captain Coconut / Coming down hard on me, baby / Peace in Mississippi / Power of soul / Stone free / Somewhere over the rainbow / Trashman / Midnight lightning / Machine gun / Gypsy boy / Blue suede shoes / Hear my train a comin' / Once I had a woman / Beginnings / Crash landing.
MCSET: TWOMC 3

CRY OF LOVE.
Tracks: / Freedom / Drifting / Easy rider / Night bird flying / My friend / Straight ahead / Astro man / Angel / In from the storm / Belly button window.
LP: 2302 023
MC: 3194 025
LP: SPELP 98
MC: SPEMC 98
LP: 2408101
MC: 847 242 4
LP: 847 242 1

DORIELLA DU FONTANE (see under Lightnin' Rod) (Hendrix, Jimi & Lightnin' Rod).

ELECTRIC LADYLAND.
Tracks: / And the gods made love / Electric ladyland / Voodoo Chile / Crosstown traffic / Still raining, still dreaming / House burning down / All along the watchtower / Long hot summer night / Little Miss Strange / Come on / Gipsy eyes / Burning of the midnight lamp / Rainy day / 1983 / Moon turn the tides / Gently, gently away.
LP: SPDLP 3
MC: 350 011 2
2LP: 613-008/9
MC: 847 233 4
LP: 847 233 1

ELECTRIC LADYLAND PART 1.
Tracks: / Rainy day, dream away / 1983 / Moon, turn the tides... / Gently, gently away / Still raining / Still dreaming / House burning down / All along the watchtower / Voodoo chile (Slight return).
MC: 3100-197
LP: 2310271

ELECTRIC LADYLAND PART 2.
Tracks: / And the Gods made love / Have you ever (been to electric ladyland) / Cross town traffic / Voodoo chile / Little Miss Strange / Long hot summer night / Come on (part 1) / Gipsy eyes / Burning of the midnight lamp.
MC: 3100-198
LP: 2310 272

ESSENTIAL JIMI HENDRIX, THE.
2LP: 261 203 4
MCSET: 350 012 2

ESSENTIAL VOL.2.
Tracks: / Hey Joe / Fire / Foxy lady / Wind cries Mary, The / I don't live today / Crosstown traffic / Wild thing / Machine gun / Star spangled banner.
LP: 2311 014

EXPERIENCE.
Tracks: / Suspicious / Room full of mirrors / Purple haze / Sunshine of your love / Fire / Bleeding heart / Smashing of amps / She's so fine / Wild thing.
MC: MAMC 9201285

EXPERIENCE (1968 Film Soundtrack).
Tracks: / Sunshine of your love / Room full of mirrors / Bleeding heart / Smashing of amps.
LP: BDL 4002
MC: BDC 4002
LP: NR 5057

FREE SPIRIT.
Tracks: / Hey Leroy / Free spirit / House of the rising sun / Something you got / Let the God sing / She's a fox.
LP: PHX 1012

FREE SPIRIT (2).
Tracks: / Good times / Voices / Suspicious / Whipper / Bessie Mae / Soul food / Voice in the wind / Free spirit.
LP: THBM 006
MC: THBC 094

GANGSTER OF LOVE.
Tracks: / Gangster of love / Let me go / Voice in the wind / Two + one goes / Good times / She's so fine / Soul food / Freedom and you / Win your love / Voices.
LP: TOP 124
MC: KTOP 124

GET THAT FEELING (Hendrix, Jimi/ Curtis Knight).
LP: HA 8349

GRAFFITI COLLECTION.
MC: GRMC 13

HENDRIX 66.
LP: ENTF 1030

HENDRIX IN THE WEST.
Tracks: / Johnny B. Goode / Lover man / Blue suede shoes / Voodoo chile / Queen, The / Sgt. Pepper's lonely hearts club band / Little wing / Red house.
LP: 230 201 8

HEY JOE.
Tracks: / Hey Joe / Purple haze / Wind cries Mary, The / Burning of the midnight lamp / Crosstown traffic / Foxy lady / Stone free / Voodoo chile / Gypsy eyes / Come on.
LP: 2486 158
MC: 3186 025

IN THE BEGINNING.
Tracks: / Stand by me / Bright lights, big city / Just a little bit / Satisfaction / Sugar pie honeybunch / You got what it takes / Day tripper / Land of a thousand dances / I'm a man / Hold on to what you've got / Twist and shout / Mr. Pitiful / What I'd say / Wooly bully / Walking the dog / Hang on, Sloopy.
LP: CBR 1031
MC: KCBR 1031

INTERVIEW PICTURE DISC.
LPPD: VBAK 3008

INTROSPECTIVE: JIMI HENDRIX.
MC: MINT 5005
LP: LINT 5005

ISLE OF WIGHT/IN THE WEST.
MC: 3577 377

JIMI HENDRIX.
LP: COUNT 10
MC: ZC CNT 10

JIMI HENDRIX.
Tracks: / Voodoo chile (slight return) / Ezy ryder / Little wing / Love or confusion / House burning down / Johnny B. Goode / All along the watchtower / Little Miss Lover / Power to love / Drifters escape, The / Angel / Izabella.
LP: 2343 080

JIMI HENDRIX ALBUM, THE.
Tracks: / Coming down hard on me baby / Blue suede shoes / Jam 292 / Stars that play with laughing Sam's dice, The / Drifter's escape / Burning desire / I'm your hoochie coochie man / Have you ever been (to electric ladyland).
LP: CN 2067
MC: CN4 2067

JIMI HENDRIX CONCERTS, THE.
Tracks: / I don't live today / Stone free / Little wing / Bleeding heart / Wild thing / Red house / Are you experienced? / Voodoo chile / Hey Joe / Hear my train a comin'.
LP: MEDIA 1
MC: MEDIAC 1

JIMI HENDRIX LIVE.
Tracks: / Queen, The / Johnny B. Goode / All along the watchtower / Dolly dagger / Gloria / Wild thing / Little wing / Machine gun / Star spangled banner, The.
LP: 2302 114
MC: 3100 638

JIMI HENDRIX: PROFILE.
LP: 6.24782
MC: CL4 24782

JIMI HENDRIX VOL 2.
Tracks: / Freedom / Gypsy eyes / Remember / Castles made of sand / Stone free / Straight ahead / Red house / In from the storm / I don't live today / Crosstown traffic / Are you experienced? / Spanish castle magic / Long hot summer night / Bold as love.
LP: 2343 086

JIMI HENDRIX:VOL.1.
MC: ZCGAS 703

JIMI HENDRIX:VOL.2.
MC: ZCGAS 704

JIMI HENDRIX:VOL.3.
MC: ZCGAS 732

JIMI PLAYS MONTEREY.
Tracks: / Killing floor / Foxy lady / Like a rolling stone / Rock me baby / Hey Joe / Can you see me / Wind cries Mary, The / Purple Haze / Wild thing.
LP: 827 990-1
MC: 827 990-4
MC: 847 244 4
LP: 847 244 1

JOHNNY B.GOODE.
Tracks: / Voodoo Chile / Johnny B. Goode / All along the watchtower / Star spangled banner, The / Machine Gun.
LP: FA 3160
MC: TCFA 3160

KISS THE SKY.
Tracks: / Are you experienced / I don't live today / Voodoo Chile / Stepping stone / Castles made of sand / Killing floor / Purple haze / Red house / Crowntown traffic / All along the watchtower.
LP: 823 704-1
MC: 823 704-4
MC: 847 261 4
LP: 847 261 1

LAST EXPERIENCE, THE.
MC: MC 1627

LEGEND, THE.
LP: ADAH 430
MC: ADAHC 430

LEGENDARY JIMI HENDRIX, THE.
Tracks: / Hey Joe / Stone free / Foxy lady / Red house / I don't live today / Wind cries Mary, The / Purple haze / All along the watchtower / Burning of the midnight lamp / Gypsy eyes / Little wing / Crosstown traffic / Voodoo chile / Straight ahead.
LP: 2490 156
MC: 3100 568

LEGENDS OF ROCK.
LP: DP6 28530

LIVE AND UNRELEASED - THE RADIO SHOW.
Tracks: / Testify / Lawdy Miss Clawdy / I'm a man / Like a rolling stone / Red house / Hey Joe / Hoochie coochie man / Purple haze / Wind cries Mary, The / Foxy lady / Third stone from the wind / Wild thing / Look over yonder / Burning of the midnight lamp / Spanish castle magic / Driving south / Things that I used to do, The / All along the watchtower / Drifters escape / Cherokee mist / Voodoo chile (slight return) / 1983 / Merman I used to be, A / Voodoo chile / Come on (part 1) / Manic depression / Machine gun / Room full of mirrors / Angel / Rainy day shuffle / Valley of Neptune / Send my love to Linda / South Southern Delta / Dolly Dagger / Night bird flying.
LPS: HBLP 100
MCSET: HBMC 100

LIVE AT THE ISLE OF WIGHT.

Tracks: / Midnight lightning / Foxy lady / Lover man / Freedom / All along the watchtower / In from the storm / Intro god save the queen / Message to love / Voodoo Chile / Lover man / Machine gun / Dolly dagger / Red house / New rising sun.
MC: . . . . SPEMC 71
LP: . . . . SPELP 71
LP: 2302 016
MC: 847 236 4
LP: 847 236 1

LIVE AT WINTERLAND.
Tracks: / Prologue / Fire / Manic depression / Sunshine of your love / Spanish castle magic / Red house / Killing floor / Tax free / Foxy lady / Hey Joe / Purple haze / Wild thing / Epilogue.
LP: 833 004-1
MC: 833 004-4
MC: 847 238 4
LP: 847 238 1

MIDNIGHT LIGHTNING.
Tracks: / Trashman / Hear my train a comin' / Blue suede shoes / Once I had a woman / Midnight lightning / Gypsy boy / Machine gun / Beginnings.
LP: 2310 415
LP: 825 166-1
MC: 825 166-4

MOODS.
Tracks: / Mumblin' word / Miracle worker / From this day on / Human heart / Feel that soul / All alone / Get down / So-called friend / Girl so fine / Every little bit hurts / You say you love me.
LP: . . . . PHX 1020

MORE EXPERIENCE (Hendrix, Jimi Experience).
Tracks: / Little Ivy / Voodoo chile / Room full of mirrors / Fire / Purple haze / Wild thing / Bleeding heart.
LP: . . . . BDL 4003
MC: . . . . BDC 4003

NIGHT LIFE.
Tracks: / Good feeling / Hot trigger / Psycho / Come on baby (part 1) / Come on baby (part 2) / Night life / You got it / Woke up this morning / Lime line / Peoples people / Whoa eeh.
LP: . . . . THBL 075

RADIO ONE SESSIONS.
Tracks: / Stone free / Radio one theme / Day tripper / Killing floor / Love or confusion / Catfish blues / Drivin' South / Wait until tomorrow / Hear my train a comin' / Hound dog / Fire / Hoochie coochie man / Purple haze / Spanish castle magic / Hey Joe / Foxy lady / Burning of the midnight lamp.
2LP: . . . . RALP 00782
2LP: . . . . CCSLP 212
MC: . . . . CCSMC 212

RAINBOW BRIDGE (Film soundtrack).
Tracks: / Dolly dagger / Earth blues / Pali gap / Room full of mirrors / Star spangled banner, The / Look over yonder / Hear my train a comin' / Hey baby (new rising sun).
LP: . . . . K 44159
MC: K4 44159

RARE HENDRIX.
Tracks: / Good feeling / Voice in the wind / Go go shoes (part 1) / Good time / Bring my baby back / Suspicious / Hot trigger.
LP: . . . . ENTF 3000

RECORDINGS FROM JIMI HENDRIX 1973 (Film soundtrack).
Tracks: / Rock me baby / Wild thing / Machine gun / Interviews / Johnny B. Goode / Hey Joe / Purple haze / Like a rolling stone / Interviews II / Star spangled banner, The / Machine gun II / Hear my train a comin' / Interviews III / Red house / In the storm / Interviews IV.
LP: . . . . K 64017

RE-EXPERIENCED.
Tracks: / Hey Joe / Stone free / Wind cries Mary, The / Love or confusion / Red house / Third stone from the sun / Purple haze / Manic depression / If six was nine / Castles made of sand / All along the watchtower / Crosstown traffic / Voodoo chile / Electric ladyland / Rainy day dream away / 1983 / Moon, turn the tides / Angel / In from the storm / Stepping stone / Who knows? / Little wing.
2LP: 2679 036

REPLAY ON JIMI HENDRIX.
LP: . . . . FEDB 5032
MC: . . . . CFEDB 5032

ROOTS OF HENDRIX.
Tracks: / Wipe the sweat / Goodbye, Bessie Mae / Two in one goes / All I want / Under the table / Psycho.
LP: . . . . PHX 1026

SINGLES ALBUM: JIMI HENDRIX.
Tracks: / Hey Joe / Stone free / Purple haze / Wind cries Mary, The / 51st Anniversary / Highway Chile / Burning of the midnight lamp / Stars that play with laughing Sam's dice / All along the watchtower / Long hot summer night / Crosstown traffic / Let me light your fire / Angel / Night bird flying / Gypsy eyes / Remember / Johnny B Goode / Little wing / Foxy lady / Manic depression / 3rd stone from the sun / Gloria.
2LP: . . . . PODV 6
MCSET: . . . . PODVC 6

SMASH HITS.
Tracks: / Can you see me / 51st anniversary / Hey, Joe / Stone free / Purple haze / Fire / Wind cries Mary, The / Stars that play with laughing Sam's dice / Manic depression / Highway chile / Burning of the midnight lamp / Foxy lady.
LP: . . . . SPELP 15
MC: . . . . SPEMC 15
LP: 613-004

STONE FREE.
Tracks: / All along the watchtower / Angel / Are you experienced / Castles made of sand / Crosstown traffic / Drifter's escape / Ezy ryder / Johnny B. Goode / Little wing / Long hot summer night / Red house / Stone free.
LP: . . . . SPELP 51
MC: . . . . SPEMC 51
LP: 2343 114

STRANGE THINGS.
Tracks: / Fool for you baby / Oddball / Simon says / Come on baby (part 1) / Come on baby (part 2) / Blues blues / Lime line / Good feeling / Go go shoes (part one) / Bring my baby back / Psycho / Day tripper / Happy birthday / Don't accuse me / Welcome home / Hornets nest / Flashing / Strange things.
LP: . . . . SHLP 101
MC: . . . . SHTC 101

SUPERSTAR (MUSIC FOR THE MILLIONS).
Tracks: / Purple haze / Red house / Wind cries Mary, The / Let me light your fire / Freedom / Gypsy eyes / Voodoo chile / Angel / Who knows? / Johnny B. Goode.
LP: 823 434-1
MC: 823 434-4

TOMORROW NEVER KNOWS.
Tracks: / Red house / Wake up this morning and find yourself dead / Bleeding heart / Morrison's lament / Tomorrow never knows / Uranus rock / Outside woman blues / Sunshine of your love.
LP: . . . . B 90166
MC: . . . . MB 90166

TWO GREAT EXPERIENCES (Hendrix, Jimi & Lonnie Youngblood).
LP: . . . . SM 3536

VOODOO CHILE.
Tracks: / Voodoo chile / Are you experienced / Foxy lady / Manic depression.
LP: 2872 116
MC: 3472 116

VOODOO CHILE.
Tracks: / Voodoo chile / Power to love / Freedom / Spanish castle magic / Gypsy eyes / Love or confusion / 51st anniversary / Little miss lover / I'm your hoochie coochie man / Izabella / House burning down / Bold as love.
LP: . . . . SPELP 52
MC: . . . . SPEMC 52
LP: . . . . MA 221285
MC: . . . . MAMC 9221285
LP: 234 311 5

WAR HEROES.
Tracks: / Bleeding heart / Highway chile / Tax free / Peter Gunn / Little bears / Catastrophe / Steeping stone / Midnight / Beginning / Izabella.
LP: . . . . SPELP 4
MC: . . . . SPEMC 4
LP: 2302 020
MC: 847 262 4
LP: 847 262 1

WELL I STAND UP NEXT TO A MOUNTAIN.
LPPD: . . . . IFSIXWAS 9

WOKE UP THIS MORNING AND FOUND MYSELF DEAD.
Tracks: / Red house / Wake up this morning and find yourself dead / Bleeding heart / Morrison's lament / Tomorrow never knows / Uranus rock / Outside woman blues / Sunshine of your love.
LP: . . . . RL 015
LPPD: . . . . RLP 0048

Hendryx, Nona

ALTERNATIONS.
Tracks: / You're the only one that I ever needed / Snakes alive / Propaganda / Night ain't long enough / Bandit / Love it / King of hearts / Casanova / Alternations.
LP: . . . . SPART 1104

ART OF DEFENCE, THE.
Tracks: / I sweat (going through the motions) / Soft targets / Life, The / I want you.
LP: . . . . PL 84999
MC: . . . . PK 84999

FEMALE TROUBLE.
Tracks: / I know what you need / Big fun / Baby go go / Rhythm of change / Why should I cry / Too hot to handle / Winds of change / Female trouble / Drive me wild.
LP: . . . . AML 3120
MC: . . . . TCAML 3120

HEAT, THE.
Tracks: / Heat, The.
MC: . . . . PK 85465

HEAT, THE.
Tracks: / Revolutionary dance / Girl like that, A / Heat / I need love / If looks could kill / Rock this house / Time.
LP: . . . . PL 85465

SKINDIVER.
Tracks: / Off the coast to you / Women who fly / No emotion / Love is kind / Tears / Skindiver / 6th sense / Through the wire / Interior voices / New desire.
LP: 210 045
MC: 410 045

Henhouse Five Plus Two

IN THE MOOD (See under Stevens, Ray).

Henley, Don

BUILDING THE PERFECT BEAST.
Tracks: / Boys of Summer, The / You can't make love / Man with a mission / You're not drinking enough / Not enough love in the world / Building the perfect beast / All she wants to do is dance / Sunset grill / Drivin' with your eyes closed / Land of the living.
LP: 9240261
MC: 9240264
LP: . . . . GEF 25939
MC: . . . . GEFC 24026
LP: . . . . GEF 24026

END OF THE INNOCENCE, THE.
Tracks: / End of the innocence, The / How bad do you want it? / I will not go quietly / Last worthless evening, The / New York minute / Shangri-la / Little tin god / Gimme what you got / If dirt were dollars / Heart of the matter.
LP: . . . . WX 253
MC: . . . . WX 253C
MC: . . . . GEFC 24217
LP: . . . . GEF 24217

I CAN'T STAND STILL.
Tracks: / I can't stand still / You better hang up / Long way home / Nobody's business / Talking to the moon / Dirty laundry / Johnny can't read / Them and us / La elite / Lilah / Unclouded day, The.
LP: . . . . K 52365
MC: K4 52365

Hennessy, Frank

THOUGHTS AND MEMORIES.
LP: . . . . SAIN 1384 M

Henning, Niels

PAUL BLEY, NIELS HENNING, ORSTED PEDERSON (See Under Bley, Paul) (Henning, Niels, Paul Bley & Orsted Pederson).

PRIZE WINNERS (See Under Drew, Kenny) (Henning, Niels/ Drew/ Pedersen/ Asmussen/ Thigpen).

Henri, Adrian

BLUES IN RATS ALLEY.
MC: . . . . RTS 1833

Henriques, Basil

SOUNDS OF SUNSET.
LP: . . . . TA 1003

Henry C

I WANT TO LIVE FOR YOU, LORD.
Tracks: / His eye is on the sparrow / I want to live for your Lord / Follow your dreams / Get your house in order / Let's get married / I stand accused of loving Jesus.
LP: . . . . EJR 4015
MC: . . . . EJRMC 4015

Henry, Clarence

LEGENDARY CLARENCE 'FROGMAN' HENRY.
LP: . . . . STLP 3001
MC: . . . . STK 3001

LITTLE GREEN FROG.
Tracks: / Loving cajun style (cajun honey) / Cheatin' traces / Ain't got no home (1) / Think it over / Baby ain't that love / Heartaches by the number / Have you ever been lonely / Little green frog / You can't hide a tear / I told my pillow / I might as well / Don't take it so hard / Tore up over you / Ain't got no home / Ain't got no home (2).
LP: . . . . BFX 15278

NEW RECORDINGS.
LP: . . . . CFH 101

YOU ALWAYS HURT THE ONE YOU LOVE.
Tracks: / But I do / I want to be a movie star / Oh why / Your picture / Live it right / Never,never / Ain't got no home / You always hurt the one you love / Little Suzy / I love you,yes I do / Steady date / Just my baby and me / Oh Mickey.
LP: . . . . GCH 8121

YOU ALWAYS HURT THE ONE YOU LOVE (see under Fantastics) (Various artists).

Henry Cow

CONCERTS.
Tracks: / Beautiful as the moon / Terrible as an army with banners / Nirvana for mice / Ottawa song / Gloria gloom / Beautiful as the moon (reprise) / Bad alchemy / Little Red Riding Hood hit the road / Ruins / Oslo / Groningen / Udine / Groningen again.
LP: . . . . CAD 3002

HENRY COW LEGEND, THE.
Tracks: / Nirvana for mice / Amygdala / Teenbeat reprise / Teenbeat / Teenbeat introduction / Extract from "With the yellow half moon and blue star" / Tenth chaffinch, The / Nine funerals of Citizen King.
LP: . . . . V 2005

IN PRAISE OF LEARNING.
Tracks: / Living in the heart of the beast / War / Beginning / Long march / Beautiful as the moon / Terrible as an army with banners / Morning star.
LP: . . . . BC 3
LP: . . . . V 2027

UNREST.
Tracks: / Bitter storm over Ulm / Half asleep / Half awake / Ruins / Solemn music / Linguaphonie / Upon entering the Hotel Adlon / Arcades / Deluge.
LP: . . . . V 2011
LP: . . . . BC 4

WESTERN CULTURE.
LP: . . . . BC 1

Henry, Ernie

LAST CHORUS.
Tracks: / Autumn leaves / Beauty and the blues / All the things you are / Melba's blues / S'posin' / Ba-lue bolivar ba-lues are / Like someone in love / Cleo's chant.
LP: . . . . OJC 086

PRESENTING ERNIE HENRY.
LP: . . . . OJC 102

Henry, Haywood

GENTLE MONSTER, THE.
LP: . . . . UP 27 13

Henry IV

HENRY IV PART 1 (see under Shakespeare, William) (Various artists).

HENRY IV PART II (see under Shakespeare, William) (Various artists).

Henry & June

HENRY & JUNE (Film Soundtrack) (Various artists).
LP: . . . . VS 5294
MC: . . . . VSC 5294

Henry, Lenny

LIVE AND UNLEASHED.
Tracks: / Line up, ragamuffin style / Bad jokes / Harrassing the paying public / In clubland / International negro / Delbert Wilkins kickin' it live / I come from Dudley / Tales from Disco City / Pay attention / Everybody knows... / Men & women / Cat flaps! / Animal heaven / Blues ya'll, The / Music scene, The / Mandela day / Deakus / Theophilus P Wildebeest / I don't wanna leave.
MC: . . . . ICT 9937
LP: . . . . ILPS 9937
MC: . . . . ICM 9937

STAND UP...GET DOWN.
Tracks: / Hello everybody / Olympics / Kids' TV / School / Katanga / Blackpool / J.A. Deakus / Scratch joke / Sex and kids and growing up / Big love (it's a love thing, girl!) / Delbert / Crucial times.
LP: . . . . CHR 1484
MC: . . . . ZCHR 1484

Henry, Milton

WHO DO YOU THINK I AM.
LP: . . . . W 2450

Henry, O.

GIFT OF THE MAGI & OTHER STORIES, THE (Harris, Julie).
MC: 1273

Henry V (film)

HENRY V (Film soundtrack) (City Of Birmingham Symphony Orchestra).
Tracks: / Oh for a muse of fire / Henry V theme / Boar's head, The / Three

traitors, The / Now lords' for France / Death of Falstaff, The / Once more unto the breach / Threat to the governor of Harfleur, The / Katherine of France / March to Calais / Death of Bardolph / Upon the king / St. Crispin's day / Battle of Agincourt, The / Day is yours, The / Non nobis domine / Wooing of Katherine, The / Let this acceptance take / End title.
LP: . . . . EL 7499191
MC: . . . . EL 7499194

HENRY V (see under Shakespeare, William) (Various artists).

Henry VI

HENRY VI, PART 1 (see under Shakespeare, William) (Various artists).

HENRY VI, PART 2 (see under Shakespeare, William) (Various artists).

HENRY VI, PART 3 (see under Shakespeare, William) (Various artists).

Henry VIII

HENRY VIII (history for ages 8+) (Unknown narrator(s)).
MC: . . . . PLBH 100

KING HENRY VIII (see under Shakespeare, William) (Various artists).

Henry, Vincent

VINCENT.
LP: . . . . HIP 101
MC: . . . . HIPC 101

Henry's Bootblacks

HENRY'S BOOTBLACKS.
LP: . . . . SOS 1149

HIGH SOCIETY.
LP: . . . . CLS 332

Henry's Cat

HENRY'S CAT (Stories from the TV series) (Godfrey, Bob).
Tracks: / Disco doddle / Treasure / Hypnotists / Circus / Christmas dinner / Film, The / Diet / Competition / Fortune teller / Race, The.
LP: . . . . REC 482
MC: . . . . ZCM 482

HENRY'S CAT BECOMES PRIME MINISTER (Unknown narrator(s)).
MC: . . . . STK 009

HENRY'S CAT VOL.2.
MCSET: . . . . DTO 10582

HENRY'S CAT VOL. 1.
MCSET: . . . . DTO 10555

OUTLAWS, THE (Unknown narrator(s)).
MC: . . . . STK 010

Hensel, Carol

CAROL HENSEL'S EXERCISE AND DANCE VOL.2.
LP: . . . . CHX 1

Hensley, Ken

BEST OF KEN HENSLEY.
Tracks: / Inside the mystery / King without a throne / Black hearted lady / House on the hill, The / New routine / Through the eyes of a child / Telephone / Proud words on a dusty shelf / Winter or Summer / Cold Autumn Sunday / Last time, The / Do you feel alright (CD only.) / Take and take (CD only.) / When evening comes (CD only.) / Stargazer (CD only.).
LP: . . . . NEXLP 104

FREE SPIRIT.
Tracks: / Inside the mystery / New York / System, The / When / No more / Brown eyed boy / Do you feel alright? / Telephone / Woman / New routine.
LP: . . . . BRON 533
MC: . . . . BRONC 533

Henson, Nicky (nar)

ALAN AYCKBOURN DOUBLE BILL (See under Ayckbourn, Alan) (Aldridge, Michael/Nicky Henson).

Henson-Conant, Deborah

CAUGHT IN THE ACT.
Tracks: / Hawaii: In the afterglow / Caught in the act / Lammermuir spring / Magic string, The / Wave goodbye / Night of the roses / Anna Bella / Honeytime / Tiger dance / Greensleeves.
LP: . . . . GRP 96001
MC: . . . . GRP 96004

ON THE RISE.
LP: . . . . GR 95781
MC: . . . . C 9578

TALKING HANDS.
Tracks: / Into the night / Cali-calypso / And then he kissed me / Siana's dream: the music box / Lazy lover / My mother's Mexican hat / Day it rained forever, The / Talking hands / Farewell to arms.
LP: . . . . GRP 96361
MC: . . . . GRP 96364

Hentschel, David

EDUCATING RITA (Film music).
LP: . . . . MERL 23
MC: . . . . MERLC 23

Hentschel, Horst

GUITAR ALBUM.
LP: . . . . BF 15014

Hep Cat Hop

HEP CAT HOP (NERVOUS).
LP: . . . . NERD 003

HEP CAT HOP (ROCKHOUSE) (Various artists).
LP: . . . . LPM 8304

Hep Cats Session

HEP CATS SESSION (Various artists).
LP: . . . . CFM 511

Hepburns

MAGIC OF THE HEPBURNS.
Tracks: / I'll be back before the milkman / Five twenty five / Matchless / You're a queer one Les Mun / In pursuit of a running buffett / 1..2..3..4 / Fly boy / That's okay / Charlie Cairoli's ghost / Hat and coat / Dream car / Bed / Josephine road / Carrot top.
LP: . . . . BRED 83

Hepcat, Harry

GO CAT GO.
Tracks: / Good rockin' tonight / Go cat, go / Great balls of fire / Make out daddy / Milkcow blues / Boppin' the blues / Heartbreak hotel / Twenty flight rock / Mystery train / Everybody's trying to be my baby / Mojo man / Suprise special / Red hot / Whole lotta shakin' goin' on.
LP: . . . . DJLP 2049
LP: . . . . BB 2049

Heptones

22 GOLDEN HITS.
LP: . . . . TTLP 0043

BACK ON TOP.
LP: . . . . VSLP 4018

BETTER DAYS.
LP: 6302 037
LP: . . . . RRTG 7715

BIG AND FREE WITH 20 MASSIVE HITS.
LP: . . . . TTLP 0045

CHANGING TIME.
LP: . . . . DSR 9290

GOOD LIFE.
Tracks: / Can't hide from Jah / Repatriation is a must / Natural mystic / New York city / Everyday every night / Good life / Brother and sister / How could I leave / Ghetto living.
LP: . . . . GREL 6

HEPTONES SING GOOD VIBES, THE.
LP: . . . . CSLP 005

IN A DANCE HALL STYLE.
LP: . . . . VSLP 4031

LEGENDS FROM STUDIO 1.
LP: . . . . TTRP 0042

NIGHT FOOD.
MC: . . . . RRCT 19

NIGHTFOOD IN A PARTY TIME.
LP: . . . . TTL 0046

ON THE ROAD AGAIN.
LP: . . . . TTLP 047

ON THE RUN.
LP: . . . . SHAN 43008
MC: . . . . SHANC 43008

ORIGINAL HEPTONES, THE.
LP: . . . . TTLP 0041

PARTY TIME.
MC: . . . . RRCT 14

SWING LOW.
Tracks: / Heaven / Promise to be true / What it is / So long / I'm proud / Book of rules / Down comes the rain / Swing low / You decorated my life / Pack your things.
LP: . . . . BS 1064

Hepworth Band

MARCHING WITH HEPWORTH.
LP: . . . . LKLP 6422

Her Majesty's Guards

30 SMASH HITS OF THE WAR YEARS (Band & Chorus of Her Majesty's Guards Division).
LP: . . . . WW 5006

Herald, John

BEST OF JOHN HERALD AND THE GREENBRIAR BOYS (Herald, John & The Greenbriar Boys).
MC: . . . . MCCV 79317

JOHN HERALD AND THE JOHN HERALD BAND (Herald, John & The John Herald Band).
LP: . . . . BAY 213

Herb Dust

HERB DUST VOL 1 (Various artists).
Tracks: / Dance hall style: *Various artists* / Heart in pain: *Various artists* / Jah children: *Various artists*/ Genuine way: *Various artists* / Babylon: *Various artists* / Message: *Various artists* / Spooky: *Various artists* / Black pride: *Various artists* / Monkey fashion: *Various artists* / Give praises: *Various artists.*
LP: . . . . KVC 6001

Herb Of Death (bk)

HERB OF DEATH (Agastha Christie) (Hickson, Joan (nar)).
MCSET: . . . . LFP 7394

Herbeck, Ray

RAY HERBECK, 1942 (Herbeck, Ray & His Modern Music With Romance).
LP: . . . . CLP 78

Herbert, Christopher

TAMBU THE JOURNEY.
LP: . . . . CR 009

Herbert, Frank (aut)

BATTLE OF DUNE (See under Battle of Dune (bk)).

DUNE TRILOGY SOUNDBOOK.
MCSET: 116

HERETICS OF DUNE.
MC: 1742

WHITE PLAGUE, THE (Dillman, Bradford).
MCSET: . . . . LFP 7308
MCSET: . . . . LFP 717 308 5

Herbert, Michael

RAMPIN' CAT, THE.
LP: . . . . FRR 009

Herbert The Hedgehog

HERBERT THE HEDGEHOG Vols. 1-4.
MC: H1/H2/H3/H4

Herbert, Victor

MELACHRINO PRESENTS IMMORTAL MELODIES OF.. (Victor Herbert & Sigmund Romberg0.
2LP: . . . . DPA 3007/8

VICTOR HERBERT- SOUVENIR Various Artists (Various artists).
LP: . . . . ABQ 6529
MC: . . . . ABQC 6529

Herbman Band

HOLD TIGHT.
LP: . . . . EFA 4526

Herbolzheimer, Peter

FAT MAN BOOGIE (Herbolzheimer, Peter & his Orchestra).
LP: . . . . EWIND 713
MC: . . . . EWINDC 713

MUSIC FOR SWINGING DANCERS - VOL.1 (Herbolzheimer, Peter & his Orchestra).
MC: . . . . CT 4.25643
LP: . . . . AS 6.25643

MUSIC FOR SWINGING DANCERS - VOL 2 (Herbolzheimer, Peter & his Orchestra).
MC: . . . . CT 4.25867
LP: . . . . AS 6.25867

MUSIC FOR SWINGING DANCERS - VOL 3 (Herbolzheimer, Peter & his Orchestra).
MC: . . . . CT 4.25868
LP: . . . . AS 6.25868

Herborn, Peter

ACUTE INSIGHT.
Tracks: / Free, forward and ahead / All along the sunstream / Beauty is... / Love in tune (for B.A) / Life force / Living yet.
LP: 8344171

Herbrucken, Das

MUSIC FOR ACCORDION ORCH. NO.2.
LP: . . . . HS 056

Hercules (film)

HERCULES (Original soundtrack) (Various artists).
LP: . . . . STV 81187

HERCULES (ORIGINAL) (Original soundtrack) (Various artists).
LP: . . . . PHCAM 01

HERCULES UNCHAINED (Original soundtrack) (Various artists).
LP: . . . . PHCAM 07

Herd

PARADISE LOST.
Tracks: / From the underworld / I can fly / Impressions of Oliver / Sad / On your own / Fare thee well / Come on, believe me / Our fairy tale / On my way home / Mixed up minds / Paradise lost / Something strange / She loves me, she loves me not / Sweet William / I don't want our lovin' to die / Goodbye groovy.
LP: . . . . STL 5458
MC: 8427604
LP: 8427601

Herd, John

PRESUMED INNOCENT (See under Scott Turow).

Herdman, Priscilla

DARKNESS INTO LIGHT.
LP: . . . . FF 420

FORGOTTEN DREAMS.
LP: . . . . FF 230

SEASONS OF CHANGE.
LP: . . . . FF 309

WATER LILY, THE.
LP: . . . . PH 1014
MC: . . . . PH 1014C

Here Come The Girls

HERE COME THE GIRLS (Singers of the Sixties) (Various artists).
Tracks: / That's how it goes: *Breakaways* / We were lovers (when the party began): *Barry,Sandra* / There he goes (the boy I love): *Antoinette* / He knows I love him too much: *Macari, Glo* / As long as you're happy baby: *Shaw, Sandie* / Song without end: *Ruskin, Barbara* / Tell me what to do: *Jackson, Simone* / Put yourself in my place: *Panter, Jan* / It's hard to believe it: *Collins, Glenda* / So much in love: *Brown, Polly* / Very first day I met you: *Cannon, Judy* / How can I hide from my heart: *Darren, Maxine* / No other baby: *Davis, Billie*/ Listen people: *Lane, Sarah* / Come to me: *Grant, Julie* / Dark shadows and empty hallways: *St. John, Tammy*/ Happy faces: *Silver, Lorraine* (CD only.) / Something must be done: *Harris, Anita* (CD only.) / You'd better come home: *Clark, Petula* (CD only.) / When my baby cries: *Prenosilova, Yvonne* (CD only.) / Something I've got to tell you: *Honeycombs* (CD only.) / I want you: *Jeannie & The Big Guys* (CD only.) / I can't believe what you say: *McKenna,Val* (CD only.) / If you love me (really love me): *Trent, Jackie* (CD only.).
LP: . . . . NEXLP 111

Here Comes...

HERE COMES THE DUKE (Various artists).
LP: . . . . TILP 010

Here Comes Christmas

HERE COMES CHRISTMAS (Various artists).
LP: . . . . KIDS 6404
MC: . . . . KIDS 6424

Here Comes Garfield

HERE COMES GARFIELD (Various artists).
LP: . . . . EPC 25803

Here & Now

BEEN AND GONE.
Tracks: / Intuition / Fantasy shift / Last chance / Satellite kids / Spaces inbetween / Theatre / Room within a room / Fake it / Speed it up / Opium for the people / Glad you're here.
LP: . . . . COLDLP 002

CHARTBUSTERS.
LP: . . . . HERE 1
MC: . . . . HEREC 1

CHARTBUSTERS VOL.2.
LP: . . . . HERE 2
MC: . . . . HEREC 2

CHARTBUSTERS VOL.3.
LP: . . . . HERE 3
MC: . . . . HEREC 3

CHARTBUSTERS VOL 1 (Various artists).
Tracks: / Don't stand so close to me: *Various artists* / Shine a little love: *Various artists* / Jump to the beat: *Various artists* / Woman: *Various artists* / Carrie: *Various artists* / Lady: *Various artists*/ Tide is high: *Various artists* / Use it up, wear it out: *Various artists* / One day I'll fly away: *Various* artists / Funky town: *Various artists* / Hold me: *Various artists* / Making your mind up: *Various artists*/ De doo doo doo: *Various artists* / Everybody salsa: *Various artists* / Bette Davis eyes: *Various artists*/ Imagine: *Various artists* / No woman, no cry: *Various artists* / Woman in love: *Various artists* / Lonely together: *Various artists* / Lately: *Various artists* / O Superman: *Various artists* / Japanese boy: *Various* artists / Wired for sound: *Various artists* / Super trouper: *Various artists* / Birdie song, The: *Various artists* / Can can: *Various artists* / 9-5: *Various artists* / Feels like I'm in love: *Various artists.*
2LP: . . . . CR 1000
MCSET: . . . . CBK 1000

FANTASY SHIFT.
LP: . . . . CHRL 003

GIVE AND TAKE.

LP: .... NOW 1

THEATRE.
LP: .... QUEST 2

Here We Go

HERE WE GO (Various artists).
LP: .... SR 8

Hereford Cathedral

CAROLS FROM.....
LP: .... APS 316
MC: .... CAPS 316

Herelle, Timothey

COMPIL-COMPAS D'HAITI.
LP: .... S 1836

Here's Johnny

MERRY HELL.
Tracks: / Hellzapoppin' / Absence of malice / Torture garden / Your room / Love you to death / Idlewild / Open minded / Reckless / How do you sleep / I fall apart.
LP: .... PL 71016
MC: .... PK 71016

Here's To The Ladies

HERE'S TO THE LADIES (Various artists).
LP: .... INTS 5192
MC: .... INTK 5192

Heresy

13 ROCKING ANTHEMS.
Tracks: / Everyday madness everyday / Ghettoised / Release / Consume / Face up to it / Unity - solidarity / Open up (D.Y.S.) / Break the connection / Network ends / Genocide / Into the grey / Street enters the house / Cornered rat.
LP: .... FACE 007

FACE UP TO IT.
Tracks: / Consume / Face up to it / Too close to home / Flowers in concrete / Belief / Network of friends / When unity becomes solidarity / Acceptance / Cornered rat / Dedication from inspiration / Against the grain / Sick of the stupidity / Trapped in a scene / Believing a lie / Into the grey / Build up - knock down / Street enters the house, the / Make the connection.
LP: .... FACE 1
LP: .... K 044 109

HERESY/CONCRETE SOX (Heresy/ Concrete Sox).
LP: .... MOSH 2

Heretic

BREAKING POINT.
LP: .... RR 95341

TORTURE KNOWS NO BOUNDARY.
Tracks: / Riding with the angels / Blood will tell / Portrait of faith / Whitechapel / Torture knows no boundary.
LP: .... RR 9640

Hereticks

GODS AND GANGSTERS.
MC: .... ICT 9954
LP: .... ILPS 9954

Herge

TINTIN: THE BROKEN EAR (Sachs/ West/Morris/McAndrew/Kinnear).
MC: .... LPMC 500

TINTIN & THE PICAROS (Sachs/West/ Morris/McAndrew/Kinnear).
MC: .... LPMC 501

TINTIN & THE SEVEN CRYSTAL BALLS (Sachs/West/Morris/ McAndrew/Kinnear).
MC: .... LPMC 504

Herion, Trevor

BEAUTY LIFE.
Tracks: / Love chains / Dreamtime / Fallen angel / Kiss of no return.
LP: .... INTO 3

Heritage

CELTIC MYSTERY.
Tracks: / Julia Delaney / Ready for the night / It'll be too late / Grass roots / Love is just around the corner / Cooley's / Celtic mystery / Emigrant's tale / Sligo fair / Queen of the rushes / Tatter Jack Walsh / Chicago jig, The.
LP: .... RGLP 5
MC: .... RGMC 5

FIFE AND A' THE LANDS ABOUT IT.
Tracks: / Haughs o' Cromdale / Flooers o' Edinburgh / High road to Linton / Dainty Davie / Jocky said to Jenny / Jinglin' John / Drops of brandy / Lea rig, The / Fisherrow / Flett from Flotta / Fife and a' the lands about it / Occitan polkas / Coorie doon / Mill, mill o', The / Rowantree march / Spootiskerry / Colonel Fraser / Willafjord / Twa corbies / Jennie's black e'e / Iron man / Bottom o' the punchbowl.
MC: .... CTRAX 024

LIVING BY THE AIR.
LP: .... PLR 040

SOME RANTIN' ROVIN' FUN.
LP: .... NBLP 1

WHEN THE DANCIN' IT'S A DONE.
LP: .... NBLP 2

Heritage Hall Jazz

AT CARNEGIE HALL.
LP: .... VIKO 20011

NEW ORLEANS.
LP: .... LDM 30251
LP: .... DJA 512
MC: .... DJC 512

Heritage Of Britain

HERITAGE OF BRITAIN Various artists (Various artists).
MCSET: .... WW 6040

Heritage Of Irish Song

HERITAGE OF IRISH SONG VOL. 1 (Various artists).
Tracks: / Forty shades of green: *Various artists* / Irish rover, The: *Various artists* / Slievenamon: *Various* artists / Star of Donegal, The: *Various artists* / Eileen O'Grady: *Various artists* / Little Bridget Flynn: *Various artists* / Let him go let him tarry: *Various artists* / Lovely salthill: *Various artists* / Ballad of Christy Ring: *Various artists* / Hannigan's hooley: *Various artists* / I'll take you home again Kathleen: *Various* artists / It's heaven around Galway Bay: *Various artists* / Irish soldier boy: *Various artists* / Song of old Ireland: *Various artists* / Song of old Ireland: *Various artists* / Boys from County Armagh: *Various artists*/ Mother I left in Ireland, The: *Various artists* / Whistling gypsy: *Various artists* / Silvery sands of Tramore: *Various artists* / Eileen Oge: *Various artists* / Are you right there Michael: *Various artists*.
MC: .... IHMC 07

HERITAGE OF IRISH SONG VOL. 2 (Various artists).
Tracks: / If we only had old Ireland over here: *Various artists* / Maggie: *Various artists* / Old Claddagh ring: *Various artists* / Bantry bay: *Various artists* / Goodbye Johnny dear: *Various artists* / Moonlight on the Shannon river: *Various artists* / Glenswilly: *Various artists* / Dungarvan: *Various artists* / Teddy O'Neale: *Various artists* / Kerry dance, The: *Various artists* / Golden jubilee: *Various artists* / Darlin' girl from Clare: *Various artists* / Road by the river: *Various artists* / Three lovely lassies: *Various artists*/ Shawl of Galway grey: *Various artists* / On the road near Slievenamon: *Various artists* / Emigrant's letter: *Various artists* / Bard of Armagh, The: *Various artists* / Rose of Arranmore: *Various artists* / Next market day: *Various artists*.
MC: .... IHMC 08

Herman, Lenny

MARCHETA (Herman, Lenny & His Quintet).
LP: BH5.502

Herman, Woody

2ND HERD LIVE (1948, Vol.1).
LP: .... RARETONE 5001

40TH ANNIVERSARY CARNEGIE HALL CONCERT.
Tracks: / Introduction / Woody's theme (Blue flame & acknowledge.) / Apple honey / Sweet and lovely / Four brothers / Brotherhood of man / Early Autumn / Wrap your troubles in dreams / Everywhere / Bijou / Cousins / Blue serge / Blue Getz blues / Finale / Caldonia.
2LP: .... PL 02203

50TH ANNIVERSARY TOUR (Herman, Woody Big Band).
Tracks: / It don't mean a thing / What's new / Pools / Blues for red / Conga / Central Park West / Fried buzzard / Epistrophy.
LP: .... CJ 302
MC: .... CJC 302

1937 (Herman, Woody & His Orchestra).
Tracks: / Exactly like you / Remember me / Can't we be friends / Muskrat ramble / Jazz me blues / Old man moon / Ain't misbehavin' / Someday sweetheart / Squeeze me / Weary blues / You took the words right out of my heart / I can't be bothered now / Royal Garden blues / Apache dance / Bob White / Queen Isabella.
LP: .... HMP 5048

1944 AND 1946 (Herman, Woody & His Orchestra).
Tracks: / Perdido / Apple honey / Noah / Always / Half past jumping time / Two again / Golden wedding / Four or five times / Happiness is a thing called Joe / Blowin' up a storm / Jackson fiddles while Ralph burns / Mean to me.
LP: .... SOL 506

1945 BAND IN HI FI.
LP: .... FANFARE 22-122

1948 - 2ND HERD LIVE IN HOLLYWOOD (Herman, Woody & His Orchestra).
LP: .... Q 037

1949 - THE CALIFORNIA CONCERTS (Herman, Woody & His Orchestra).
LP: .... AR 109

1943-1946 (Herman, Woody & His Orchestra).
Tracks: / Red top / It must be jelly / Caldonia / John Hardy's wife / Apple honey / Don't worry about the mule / Dancing in the dawn / There are no wings on a foxhole / Flying home / Jones beachhead / 125th Street prophet.
LP: .... SOL 503

AMEN (1937 - 42) (Herman, Woody & His Orchestra).
LP: .... BS 7108

AT THE HOLLYWOOD PALLADIUM.
LP: .... SOL 515

AT THE WOODCHOPPERS BALL.
Tracks: / At the woodchoppers ball / On the Atchison, Topeka and Santa Fe / Wild root / Bijou / Caldonia / Put that ring on my finger / There, I've said it again / Who dat up dere? / Apple honey / Goosey gander / I'll get by / Walkin' my baby back home / Spruce juice / Kiss goodnight, A / Noah.
LP: .... DBD 09
MC: .... DBDC 09

BAND THAT PLAYS THE BLUES, THE (Big band bounce & boogie).
Tracks: / At the woodchopper's ball / Dallas blues / Blues upstairs / Blues downstairs / Casbah blues / Blue prelude / Herman at the Sherman / Golden wedding / Blue flame / Fur trapper's ball / Bishop's blues / Woodsheddin' with Woody / Blues in the night / 'Tis autumn / String of pearls / Who dat up dere?.
MC: .... TCAFS 1008
LP: .... AFS 1008

BLOWIN' UP A STORM.
Tracks: / Apple honey / Caldonia (CD only) / Goosey gander / Northwest passage / Good earth, The (CD only) / Bijou / Blowin' up a storm / Steps / Four men on a horse / Sidewalks of Cuba / Cherokee canyon / Keen and peachy / Goof and I, The / Four brothers / Summer sequence (part IV) / P.S. I love you / Mulligan tawny / Third herd, The.
LP: .... AFS 1043

BLUES GROOVE.
Tracks: / Everyday I have the blues / Trouble in mind / Smack dab in the middle / Pinetop's blues / Basin Street blues / Stormy Monday / Dupree blues / I want a little girl / Blues groove.
LP: .... EMS 1283
MC: .... TCEMS 1283
LP: 1599301

BLUES ON PARADE (1937 - 41) (Herman, Woody & His Orchestra).
LP: .... BS 7122

CALDONIA.
Tracks: / Gold and I / I got it bad and that ain't good / Red top / Good Earth, The / Northwest passage / Caldonia / Your father's mustache / Mother goose jumps / There'll be some changes made / Swing low sweet chariot / Laura / Buck dance / Skylark / Baby I need you / My pal Gonzalez / Yeah man / Goof and I, The.
LP: 20129
MC: 40131
LP: .... F 20132

CRAZY RHYTHM.
Tracks: / Woodchoppers ball / Caldonia / Midnight sun / Bijou / Northwest passage / Lullaby of Birdland / Carioca / I cover the waterfront / Blowin' up a storm / Crazy rhythm.
LP: .... F 50018
MC: .... MF 9 50018

DANCE TIME '43.
LP: .... FH 34
MC: .... CFH 34

DOUBLE EXPOSURE.
Tracks: / Flying easy / I can't get next to you / Sex machine / My cherie amour / Lancaster gate / Aquarius / Hut,The / Memphis underground / Ponteio / Impression of Strayhorn / MacArthur park / Light my fire / Here I am baby / For love of Ivy / Hard to keep my mind on you / Time for love / Blues in the night / Smiling phases / Stone called Person,A.
2LP: .... GCH 2-6029
MCSET: .... GCHK 2-6029

EARLY AUTUMN.
LP: .... PM 1804751

FAN IT - 1944-1946 (Herman, Woody & The Woodchoppers).
Tracks: / One, two, three, four, jump / Skyscraper / Heads up / Papaloma / Flip the whip / Back talk / Sargeant on a furlough / I got rhythm / Glommed / Gung ho / J.P. Vanderbilt IV / Igor / Fan it.
LP: .... SWH 19
MC: .... CSWH 19

FIRST HERD 1944 (Herman, Woody & His Orchestra).
Tracks: / Is you is or is you ain't my baby / It must be jelly / Red top / G.I. jive / Sweet Lorraine / Jones Beachhead / Four or five times / Blues on parade / 125th Street prophet / Somebody loves me / Old gold commercial / Basie's basement / Hot time in the town of Berlin / 1-2-3-4 / Apple honey.
LP: .... HMP 5058

FIRST HERD, THE.
LP: .... LP 43-143

FIRST SESSION 1937 (Herman, Woody & His Orchestra).
LP: .... CLP 95

FOUR BROTHERS AT THE ROYAL ROOST.
LP: .... BLJ 8027

FOURTH HERD, THE.
LP: 500068

GREATEST HITS:WOODY HERMAN.
Tracks: / Apple honey / Good earth, The / Woodchopper's ball / Your father's moustache / Blue flame / Northwest passage / Caldonia / Summer sequence / Bijou / Four brothers / Wild root / Keen and peachy.
LP: 525 51

HERDMAN HERD.
LP: .... BO 717

HEY, HEARD THE HERD.
LP: 2304 509

HOLLYWOOD PALLADIUM 1948.
LP: .... HEP 7

IN A MISTY MOOD.
MC: 771509

IN DISCO ORDER VOL.2.
LP: .... AJAX 109

IN ENGLAND 1959.
LP: .... JG 004

IT POURS.
LP: .... FH 43

JUKE BOX (Herman, Woody & His First Herd).
Tracks: / Red top / Put that ring on my finger / Great Northern / Walkin' my baby back home / Golden wedding / Atcheson, Topeka & the Santa Fe / Till the end of time / Perdido / It must be jelly / Superman with a horn / Day by day / Ee-ba-lee-ba / Wild root / Blue flame.
LP: .... FH 36
MC: .... CFH 36

JULY 30TH 1959.
Tracks: / Panatella / Lament for Linda / In a misty mood / Misery stay away from my door / Catty corner / Thirteenth instant / Magpie / Blues for Indian Jim / Devil and the stoker / Swing machine / Summer nights / Johnny on the spot.
LP: .... JV 104

JUMPIN' WITH WOODY HERMAN'S FIRST HERD (1939 - 1942) (Herman, Woody & His Herd).
Tracks: / Woodchoppers' ball / Blues downstairs / Blues upstairs / Casbah blues / Jumpin' blues / Blues on parade / Blue flame / Fur trappers' ball / Bishop's blues / Woodsheddin' with Woody / Hot chestnuts / Four or five times.
LP: .... SM 3059

LIVE AT CONCORD '81 (Herman, Woody Big Band).
Tracks: / Things ain't what they used to be / Dolphin, The / John Brown's other body.
LP: .... CJ 191
MC: .... CJC 191

LIVE AT MONTEREY (That's jazz (6)).
Tracks: / Four Brothers / Like some blues man / Skoobeedoobee / Monterey apple tree / Skylark / Magpie.
LP: .... ATL 50236

LIVE AT THE HOLLYWOOD PALLADIUM VOL 2 (1952).
LP: .... JS 702

LIVE AT THE HOLLYWOOD PALLADIUM VOL 1 (1951).
LP: .... JS 701

LIVE IN ANTIBES 1965.
LP: .... FC 117

LIVE IN NEW ORLEANS.
LP: .... GOJ 1022

MY BUDDY (see Clooney, Rosemary) (Herman, Woody Big Band & Rosemary Clooney).

NEW WORLD OF WOODY HERMAN.
LP: 500083

OMAHA NEBRASKA 1954.

Tracks: / Cohn's Allen / Off shore / Get out of town / Leo the lion / Stars fell on Alabama / Mambo the most / At the woodchopper's ball / Early Autumn / Lady be good / Happiness is a thing called Joe / Mulligan tawny / Apple honey.
LP: SWS 4
MC: CSWS 4

PRE-HERDS.
Tracks: / I've got you under my skin / It must be jelly / Basie's basement / Do nothing till you hear from me / As long as I live / Cherry / Ingie speaks / I ain't got nothin' but the blues / I get a kick out of you / I'll get by / Irresistible you / Cryin' sands / Noah / Perdido / Milkman, keep those bottles quiet / Going home.
LP: AFS 1027
MC: TCAFS 1027

PRE-HERDS (BULLDOG) (Herman, Woody & His Orchestra).
Tracks: / Natchel blues / Don't get around much any more / Body and soul / Ready, get set, jump / At the woodchoppers' ball / Opus de funk / Park easy / Saxy.
LP: BDL 1047

PRESENTS A CONCORD JAM, VOL 1.
Tracks: / Woodchopper's ball, The / Rose room / Just friends / Nancy (with the laughing face) / Body and soul / Someday you'll be sorry / My melancholy baby / Apple honey.
LP: CJ 142

PRESENTS FOUR OTHERS.
Tracks: / Woody's lament / Goof and I / I wanna go home / Not really the blues / Tiny's blues / Loose aberrations / Four others / Tenderly.
LP: CJ 110

RHAPSODY IN WOOD.
Tracks: / Tiny's blues / I've got the world on a string / Boomsie / I ain't getting younger / I only have eyes for you / Four brothers / Rhapsody in wood.
LP: FH 29

ROAD BAND (Herman, Woody & His Orchestra).
Tracks: / Opus de funk / Gina / I remember Duke / Sentimental journey / Cool cat on a hot tin roof / Where or when / Captain Ahab / I'll never be the same / Pimlico.
LP: EG 2604251
MC: EG 2604254

ROAD BAND 1948.
Tracks: / Lullaby in rhythm / You turned the tables on me / Happy song / Four brothers / I've got news for you / Keen and peachy / Wild root / Happiness is a thing called Joe / Tiny's blues / When you're smiling / This is new / Dance, ballerina, dance / Elevation.
LP: HEP 18

SECOND HERD LIVE IN HOLLYWOOD.
LP: QU 037

SWING GOES ON VOL 4.
LP: IC 054 52713

SWINGING HERD, THE.
LP: 500057
LP: JLA 57

THIRD HERD, THE.
Tracks: / Beau jazz / Early Autumn / Mambo the most / Mother Goose jumps / Four others / Buck dance / Sorry 'bOut the whole darned thing / Men from Mars / Wooftie.
LP: DS 845
MC: DSC 845

THIRD HERD, VOL.1, THE.
Tracks: / Stompin' at the Savoy / Moten swing / I love Paris / Moon is blue, The.
LP: DS 815
MC: DSC 815

THUNDERING HERD-LIVE.
Tracks: / Swing low sweet clarinet / I got it bad and that ain't good / Fan it / Apply honey / There'll be some changes made / Stardust / Northwest passage / Good earth, The / baby I need you / Half past jumping time.
LP: MTM 019

THUNDERING HERDS.
Tracks: / Woodchopper's ball / Apple honey / Goosey gander / Northwest passage / Good earth, The / Jug of wine, A / Your father's moustache / Bijou / Wild root / Panacea / Backtalk / Non-alcoholic / Blues are brewin' / Goof and I, The / Four brothers / Blue flame.
LP: 66378
LP: 4608251
MC: 4608254

UNCOLLECTED WOODY HERMAN AND HIS FIRST HERD.
Tracks: / It must be jelly / Sweet Lorraine / Jones beachhead / Blues on parade / Somebody loves me / There'll be a hot time in the town of Berlin / Apple honey / Red top / G.I. jive / Four or five times / 125th Street prophet / Basie's basement / 1-2-3-4 jump.
LP: HSR 134

V DISC YEARS VOL.2.
Tracks: / Don't worry 'bout that mule / 125th Street prophet / I can't put my arms / Somebody loves me / John Hardy's wife / Meshugah / Jones Beachhead / Mean to me / Caldonia / Jackson fiddles while Ralph burns / Blowin' up a storm / C jam blues and reprise.
LP: HEP 35

V-DISC YEARS VOL.1.
LP: HEP 34

WOODCHOPPERS' BALL/ AT THE FAMOUS DOOR (1940) (Herman, Woody & Will Bradley).
LP: BS 7105

WOODY AND FRIENDS.
LP: CJ 170

WOODY HERMAN, 1937.
Tracks: / Exactly like you / Remember me / Can't we be friends / Muskrat ramble / Jazz me blues / Old man moon / Ain't misbehavin' / Someday, sweetheart / Squeeze me / Weary blues / You took the words right out of my heart / I can't be bothered now / Royal Garden blues / Apache dance / Bob White / Queen Isabella.
LP: HSR 116

WOODY HERMAN 1939 VOL.4.
LP: AJAX 133

WOODY HERMAN 1939 VOL.5.
LP: AJAX 135

WOODY HERMAN 1940 VOL.6.
LP: AJAX 139

WOODY HERMAN 1940 VOL.7.
LP: AJAX 145

WOODY HERMAN 1940 VOL.8.
LP: AJAX 153

WOODY HERMAN 1938-9 VOL.3.
LP: AJAX 123

WOODY HERMAN 1913/87.
LP: 835 231 1

WOODY HERMAN 1936-37 VOL.1.
LP: AJAX 102

WOODY HERMAN 1940-41 VOL.9.
LP: AJAX 160

WOODY HERMAN AND HIS FIRST HERD 1944.
LP: HMA 5058

WOODY HERMAN AND HIS ORCHESTRA 1948.
LP: FH 21

WOODY HERMAN AND HIS ORCHESTRA 1946.
LP: FH 20

WOODY HERMAN AND HIS THIRD HERD.
LP: RARITIES 42

WOODY HERMAN AND ORCHESTRA.
LP: SM 4021

WOODY HERMAN AND THE FOUR BROTHERS LIVE.
LP: QU 005

WOODY HERMAN (BRIGHT ORANGE LABEL) (Herman, Woody (Members Of Orch.)).
LP: BO 707

WOODY HERMAN COLLECTION (Twenty Golden Greats).
Tracks: / Blue prelude / Golden wedding / Blues in the night / At the woodchoppers' ball / Herman at the Sherman / Woodsheddin' with Woody / Casbah blues / Fur trappers' ball / Blues upstairs / Who dat up dere? / Bishop's blues / Dallas blues / Blues downstairs / Northwest passage / Pancho Maximillian Hernandez / When the red, red robin comes bob, bob, bobbin' along / Lady from 29 palms / On the sunny side of the street / Up a lazy river / Four brothers.
LP: DVLP 2025
MC: DVMC 2025

WOODY HERMAN (GIANTS OF JAZZ).
LP: LPJT 5

WOODY HERMAN (JAZZ REACTIVATION).
LP: JR 151

WOODY HERMAN PRESENTS A GREAT AMERICAN EVENING,.
Tracks: / I've got the world on a string / I cover the waterfront / Leopardskin pillbox hat / Avalon / Beautiful friendship, A / Pennies from Heaven / Wave / Caldonia.
LP: CJ 220
MC: CJC 220

WOODY HERMAN PRESENTS, VOL 2.
Tracks: / Woody's lament / Goof and I, The / I wanna go home / Not really the blues / Tiny's blues / Loose abberations / Four others / Tenderly.
LP: CJ 180
MC: CJ 180 C

WOODY HERMAN (VERVE LABEL) (Compact/Walkman jazz).
Tracks: / Good earth, The / Don't get around much anymore / Bijou / Body and soul / Leo the lion / Makin' whoopee / Camel walk / Apple honey / Pee Wee blues / Preacher, The / Sidewalks of Cuba / Golden wedding / Caldonia / Blue flame.
MC: 835 319 4

WOODY'S GOLD STAR (Herman, Woody Big Band).
Tracks: / Battle royal / Woody's gold star / Mambo rockland / Round midnight / Great escape, The / Dig / Rose room / In a mellow tone / Watermelon man / Samba song.
LP: CJ 330
MC: CJC 330

WOODY'S WINNERS.
Tracks: / 23 red / My funny valentine / Northwest passage / Poor butterfly / Greasy sack blues / Woody's whistle / Red roses for a blue lady / Opus de funk.
LP: CBS 21110
MC: 40 21110

WORLD CLASS (Herman, Woody Big Band).
Tracks: / Four brothers / Rockin' chair / Claw, The / Woody's lament / Peanut vendor / Crystal silence / Greasy sack blues / Perdido.
LP: CJ 240
MC: CJC 240

Herman's Hermits

BEST OF HERMAN'S HERMITS.
Tracks: / I'm into something good / Silhouettes / Wonderful world / No milk to-day / There's a kind of hush / Sunshine girl / Something is happening / My sentimental friend / Can't you hear my heartbeat / Your hand in mine / I know why / Dream on / My lady / Take love, give love / Smile please / Museum / Man with the cigar, The / Listen people / For love / My reservations been confirmed / What is wrong - what is right / Gaslite Street / Moonshine man / Just one girl / Sleepy Joe / East West.
MC: HR 8180

BEST OF THE EMI YEARS, THE VOL. 1 (1964-1966).
Tracks: / I'm into something good / I'm Henry the Eighth I am / Silhouettes / Show me girl / Can't you hear my heartbeat / Take love, give love / Wonderful world / Mrs. Brown you've got a lovely daughter / Just a little bit better / Must to avoid, A / You won't be leaving / Listen people / Hold on / This door swings both ways / Leaning on a lamp post / All the things I do for you / Little boy sad / Dial my number / George and the dragon / East west / Dandy / No milk today.
MC: TCEMS 1415

COLLECTION: HERMANS HERMITS.
2LP: CCSLP 246
MC: CCSMC 246

EP COLLECTION, THE: HERMAN'S HERMITS.
Tracks: / Sea cruise / Mother in law / I understand / Mrs Brown you've got a lovely daughter / Show me girl / Silhouettes / Wonderful world / Can't you hear my heartbeat / I'm into something good / Must to avoid, A / I'm Henry the Eighth I am / Just a little bit better / Walkin' with my angel / Where were you when I needed you / Hold on / George and the dragon / All the things I do for you baby / Wild love / Dandy / No milk today / For love.
LP: SEE 284
MC: SEEK 284

GREATEST HITS: HERMAN'S HERMITS (IMPORT).
Tracks: / No milk today / I'm into something good / There's a kind of hush / Dandy.
LP: FUN 9053
MC: FUNC 9053

GREATEST HITS:HERMAN'S HERMITS.
LP: CRY 048 50727
LP: NE 1001
LP: 1C 148-50727

HERMAN'S HERMITS.
LP: 33SX 1727

MOST OF HERMAN'S HERMITS.
LP: MFP 5126

VERY BEST OF HERMAN'S HERMITS.
Tracks: / I'm into something good / Silhouettes / Can't you hear my heartbeat? / Wonderful world / Leaning on a lamp post / Must to avoid, A / No milk today / Years may come, years may go / I'm Henry the eighth I am / There's a kind of hush / Dandy / Sunshine girl / Something is happening / Mrs. Brown you've got a lovely daughter / My sentimental friend / Oh you pretty things.
LP: MFP 41 5685 1
MC: TCMFP 4156854

Hermine

LONELY AT THE TOP.
LP: LOM 002

WORLD ON MY PLATES, THE.
LP: CRAM 019

Hernandez, Frank

SOLO PARA ELLAS.
LP: JMVS 107

Hernandez, Patrick

BORN TO BE ALIVE.
Tracks: / Disco queen / You turn me on / Show me the way you kiss / Back to boogie / It comes so easy / Born to be alive / I give you rendez-vous.
LP: GEMLP 104

Hernandez, Wayne

TELEPATHIC.
Tracks: / Dancin' on the edge / Telepathic / Corners of the sun / Say (you want me tonight) / Someone believes in you / Livin' without your love / Let me call you angel / Why sleep alone tonight / Got the feeling / Run into your Daddy's arms.
LP: 4510551
MC: 4510554

Hernon, Marcus

TRADITIONAL MUSIC.
MC: GTDC 031

Hernon, P.J.

FIRST HOUSE IN CONNAUGHT.
MC: GTDC 075

FLOATING CROWBAR, THE.
MC: GTDC 097

Hero & The Terror

HERO AND THE TERROR (Film soundtrack) (Various artists).
Tracks: / Two can be one: *Various artists* / Obsession: *Various artists* / Workout: *Various artists*/ Terror, The: *Various artists* / Hero's seduction: *Various artists* / San Pedro bust: *Various artists*/ Ladies room, The: *Various artists* / Breakout: *Various artists* / Birthday wishes: *Various artists*/ Discovery: *Various artists* / Showtime: *Various artists* / Angela: *Various artists* / Subterranean terror: *Various artists* / Simon's lair: *Various artists* / Search, The: *Various artists* / Living nightmare: *Various artists* / Love and obsession: *Various artists*.
LP: EDL 2508.1

Heroes & Cowards

HEROES AND COWARDS (Various artists).
LP: SEWL 1000

Heroes & Villains

HEROES & VILLAINS (Various artists).
LP: OTA 1001

Herold, Helmuth

ARPA MONICA (Harmonica).
Tracks: / Acht schlichte weisen / Old Scottish air / Solo per me / Panorama Brasileiro / Pearls are for ladies / Spanish gypsy / Sol de Brasil / Mil saludos / Riding on a wave.
LP: 100012

Herold, Ted

GOODBYE SUSANN.
Tracks: / I don't know why / Bachelor boy / Don't cry Suzanne / Wild in the country / Bossa nova baby / Meet me at the twistin' place.
LP: BFX 15098

ICH BIN EIN MANN.
Tracks: / Moonlight / Dein kleiner bruder / Texas baby / Ich bin ein Mann / Carolin / Kuss mich / Isabell / Crazy boy / Down in the boondocks / Da doo ron ron / Hey Lulu / Bin schon vergeben / Mach dir den abschiedl nicht so schwer / Die gefahrlichen jahre / Der schone Johnny / Am anderen tag (Alle menschen sind freunde).
LP: BFX 15043

IDOLS.
Tracks: / Wear my ring around your neck / I got stung / Dixieland rock / Hey baby / Lover doll / Kissin' cousins / Hula rock (roll rock 'n' roll that hula hoop) / His latest flame / Good luck charm / Return to sender / One broken heart for sale / Little Linda (little sister) / Wild in the country / Bossa nova baby / Fun in Acapulco.
LP: BFX 15034

ORIGINALE.

Tracks: / Ich bin ein wanderer / 1:0 / Sunshine baby / Hey, little girl / Oh so sweet / Rock around the clock / Moonlight (original version) / Ich vertraue dem traum / Unveroffentlicht / Hula moon baby / Lonely / Ich hore deine stimme / Geh den weg mit mir / Eine kette aus roten korallen.
LP: . . . . BFX 15051

SING AND SWING MIT TED.
Tracks: / Schwarze / Das erste rendezvous / La Paloma / Maria aus bahia / Ich wered jed nacht von innen traeumen / Hay ba ba re bop / Nachts bin ich allein / Sentimental journey / Schau mich bitte nicht so an / Schlaf mein liebling / Moonlight / Sonny boy.
LP: . . . . BFX 15087

TED.
Tracks: / Kiss me Annabell / Wunderland / Angelina / Du bist viel zu schade / Sag mir niemals goodbye / Pretty Belinda / (Sittin' on) the dock of the bay / Nur sie / Ein limbo fur mich / Auch du wirst geh'n / Kleine moonlight lady / Blue night / Tausend illusionen / Du kannst ja geh'n / Das haus am Missouri.
LP: . . . . BFX 15057

Heron

BEST OF HERON.
Tracks: / Only a hobo / Lord and master / Sally Goodin / Yellow roses / Little angel / Car crash / Little boy / Goodbye / For you / John Brown / Wanderer / Great dust storm, The / Minstrel and a king / Winter harlequin / Smiling ladies (Available on CD only) / Love 13 (lone) (Available on CD only) / Big A (Available on CD only) / Miss Kiss (Available on CD only) / Upon reflection (Available on CD only).
LP: . . . . SEE 242

Heron, Mike

GLENROW TAPES, THE.
Tracks: / Maker of Islands / Blackfoot side / Tearproof days / Mexican girl / Lost in space / Lonely never win / Starship on silk / Gaugin in the South seas.
LP: . . . . MHLP 001
MC: . . . . MH 001

GLENROW TAPES VOL.2, THE.
LP: . . . . MHLP 002
MC: . . . . MH 002

GLENROW TAPES VOL.3, THE.
LP: . . . . MHLP 003
MC: . . . . MH 003

SMILING MEN WITH BAD REPUTATIONS.
MC: . . . . ICM 9146

Herring, Annie

FLYING LESSONS.
Tracks: / I'm the kinda girl / Breaking and entering / Heart of stone.
LP: . . . . OAK R 3013
MC: . . . . OAK C 3013

KIDS OF THE KINGDOM.
Tracks: / We worship and adore Thee / Twinkling of an eye / He will go before you / Jesus (He is the Son of God) / Be my Lord / I will bless Thee, O Lord / Ho, ho, ho, hosanna / I'm excited in the Lord / Be still and know that I Am God / Pure crystal rose / Hallelujah / Everybody needs to be someone / Birthday song / Kids of the Kingdom / Jesus remains the same / I start to cry / His Name is Jesus / With healing in His wings / His banner over me is love.
LP: . . . . WING 502
MC: . . . . TC WING 502

SEARCH DEEP INSIDE.
Tracks: / Search deep inside / When you come on my mind / Before you go out the door / Love comes in many shapes and colours / Killing thousands / As a matter of fact / Days gone by / Father, it's me again / Old soldier / Earthbound.
LP: . . . . BIRD 131
MC: . . . . TC BIRD 131

Herring, Vincent

EVIDENCE.
Tracks: / Mr. Wizard / Voyage / Stars fell on Alabama / Never forget / I sing a song / Evidence / Soul-Leo / Hindsight (CD only.).
LP: . . . . LLP 1527

Herriot, James

ALL CREATURES GREAT AND SMALL (Timothy, Christopher (nar)).
MCSET: . . . . LFP 7202
MCSET: . . . . LFP 4172025

ALL THINGS WISE AND WONDERFUL (Timothy, Christopher (nar)).
MCSET: . . . . LFP 7256
MCSET: . . . . TCLFP 7256

IF ONLY THEY COULD TALK / IT SHOULDN'T HAPPEN.
MCSET: . . . . LFP 7024
MCSET: . . . . TCLFP 7024
MCSET: . . . . LFP 4170245

LORD GOD MADE THEM ALL, THE (Timothy, Christopher (nar)).
MCSET: . . . . LFP 4171025

Herrmann, Bernard

BERNARD HERRMANN: OUTERSPACE SUITE (Various artists).
LP: . . . . C'BUS 208

BERNARD HERRMANN: THE WALT WHITMAN SUITE (Various artists).
LP: . . . . C'BUS 210

BERNARD HERRMANN: WESTERN SAGA (Various artists).
LP: . . . . C'BUS 207

CITIZEN KANE.
LP: ARL1 0707

CLASSIC FILM SCORES BY BERNARD HERRMANN (see under Films) (Various artists).

Hersch, Fred

HORIZONS (Hersch, Fred Trio).
Tracks: / My heart stood still / Moon and sand / Star crossed lovers / One finger snap / Surrey with the fringe on top / Miyako / Cloudless sky.
LP: . . . . CJ 267

Hertfordshire Musicale

YOUR FAVOURITE CHRISTMAS CAROL.
MC: . . . . CHV 322

Herting, Mike

WHO OWNS BRAZIL?.
Tracks: / O Sonho / Cutting of the trees, The / Amazonas burning / Rainha do mar / Algodoal / One world / Jungle voices / Festa, A / Spectre, The.
LP: . . . . VBRLP 32
MC: . . . . VBRMC 32

Hertner, Rob

BUCKY'S HEARTACHES.
LP: . . . . TEXLP 66
MC: . . . . TEXC 66

Herwig, Conrad

WITH EVERY BREATH.
LP: . . . . SB 2034

Herzog (bk)

HERZOG (Saul Bellow).
MC: 1584

He's My Girl

HE'S MY GIRL (Film soundtrack) (Various artists).
Tracks: / Rock revival: *Hallyday, David* / He's my girl: *Hallyday, David* / Kicks: *Revere, Paul & The Raiders* / I saw Mary: *Vartan, Sylvie* / Church of the poison spider: *Various artists* / One night in Hollywood: *Barrera, Micky* / She can dance: *Vartan, Sylvie* / Time has come today: *Chamber Brothers* / Mississippi queen: *Mountain* / Reggie's theme: *Bullard, Kim*.
LP: 8327641
MC: 8327644

Hesperus

CROSSING OVER.
LP: . . . . GR 0718

Hess, Nigel

SCREENS AND STAGES (Hess, Nigel/ London Film Orchestra).
Tracks: / Cyrano de Bergerac / Only game, The / Anna of the five towns / Woman of substance, A / All passion spent / Testament / Campion / London Embassy, The / Affair in mind, An / To us a child / Vidal in Venice / Summer's lease / Atlantis / Much ado about nothing / Vanity fair / Secret of Sherlock Holmes, The.
LP: . . . . FLYLP 101
MC: . . . . FLYMC 101

Hesse, Hermann

STEPPENWOLF (Jurgens, Curt).
MC: 1589

Hession, Carl

ECHOES OF IRELAND.
Tracks: / Rare ould times / Maggie / Red is the rose / Rose of Tralee, The / Slieve na mban / Fields of Athenry / Old rustic bridge / Echoes / Danny boy / Isle of Innisfree / Cliffs of Dooneen / Boulavogue / When you were sweet sixteen / Bunch of thyme / Banks of my own lovely Lee, The / I'll take you home again Kathleen / Galway bay / Forty shades of green / Cuaichin ghleann neifin / Wild colonial boy / Green glens of Antrim / Mountains of Mourne / Come back Paddy Reilly to Ballyjamesduff.
LP: . . . . RGLP 3
MC: . . . . RGMC 3

Hester, Benny

NOBODY KNOWS ME LIKE YOU.
Tracks: / Come back / No man's land / Rubber canoe / Nobody knows me like you / Step by step / One more time / Goodbye salty / Real change / You loved me.
LP: . . . . MYR 1101
MC: . . . . MC 1101

Het Reuzekoor

DANSE LA FLANDRE.
Tracks: / Mieke stout / Lief bethje / Stelten valse / Spinnewiel / Horlepiep / Streep / Ma Seurtje / Vlegard / Bonjour, bonsoir / Sala.
LP: . . . . ARN 33736

Het Zweet

HET ZWEET.
LP: . . . . ST 7539

Hewerdine, Boo

EVIDENCE (Hewerdine, Boo & Darden Smith).
Tracks: / All I want is everything / Reminds me (a little of you) / These chains / Out of this world / Evidence / Who, what where and why / Under the darkest moon / South by South West / First chill of Winter, The / Love is a strange hotel / Oil on the water / Town called blue, A.
LP: . . . . CHR 1726
MC: . . . . ZCHR 1726

Hewett, Howard

FOREVER AND EVER.
Tracks: / Strange relationship / Natural love / Once, twice, three times / You'll find another man / Forever and ever / Shakin' my emotion / Share a love / This time / Challenge / Goodbye good friend.
LP: . . . . K 9607791
MC: . . . . K 9607794

HOWARD HEWETT.
LP: 7559609041
MC: 7559609044

I COMMIT TO LOVE.
Tracks: / I'm for real / Last forever / I commit to love / In a crazy way / Love don't wanna wait / Got 2 go,I / Eye on you / Let's try it all over again / Say Amen.
LP: 9604871
MC: 9604874

Hewick, Kevin

SUCH HUNGER FOR LOVE.
Tracks: / Normandy / Spain / Gibraltar / At first sight I rap too much / Make / Door to door salesman - la swimming pool / Shells / Scapegoat in a country churchyard / Hill of leopards, The / Feathering the nest / She holds him tighter / Mothers day.
LP: . . . . BRED 48

Hewitt, Ben

GOOD TIMES AND SOME MIGHTY FINE ROCK 'N' ROLL.
Tracks: / I wanna love you tonight / Little lefen jive / Ophellia / Because I love you / Call mama (on the phone) / Somebody wants to love you baby / Shirley Vee / Good times and some mighty fine rock 'n' roll / Florida rain / Way down on my knees / Paying for love (with my heart) / Buster Brown's got the blues.
LP: . . . . BFX 15187

THEY WOULD CALL ME ELVIS.
Tracks: / For quite a while / I ain't givin' up nothing / Patricia June / You break me up / I wanna do everything for you (Previously unissued.) / My search (1st recording) (Previously unissued.) / Queen in the kingdom of my heart, The / Bundle of love (Previously unissued.) / Whirlwind blues / You got me shook (Previously unissued.) / I want a new girl / My search (2nd recording) / Slave girl / President's walk.
LP: . . . . BFX 15150

TORE UP! (Raw & raunchy feel of..).
LP: . . . . BLK 7704

Hewitt, Garth

ALIEN BRAIN.
LP: . . . . MYR R 1194
MC: . . . . MYR C 1194
LP: . . . . MYR 1194
MC: . . . . MC 1194

BEST OF GARTH HEWITT.
Tracks: / May you live to dance (on your own grave) / That's why we're here / Holy ground / I will return / Memories / Rock 'n' roll king / I've made up my mind / Get up and dance / I never knew life was in full Technicolor / Travellin' (back home to you) / Road from Eiken to Davos, The / Caretaker, The / Wooden cross rider / Friend of mine, A / Father's song, The.
LP: . . . . MYR 1093
MC: . . . . MC 1093

DID HE JUMP OR WAS HE PUSHED.
Tracks: / Not afraid to rock 'n' roll / On and on / Always on the run / Physical pain / Let's go out / Big black mamba / Did he jump or was he pushed / He's the one / World of difference / We sure do / Roll on.
MC: . . . . TC WOOF 1001
LP: . . . . WOOF 1001

IM GRATEFUL.
Tracks: / Friend of mine, A / Goodbye to all the heroes / Tropical night / How hard / Don't look / That's why were here / Memories / Holy one (has crossed the river), The / I'm grateful / All the time / May you live to dance (on your own grave).
LP: . . . . MYR 1078
MC: . . . . MC 1078

LOVE SONG FOR THE EARTH.
Tracks: / Harmonica talk / Dust of death, The / Reason and the rhyme, The / Live for now / Paint my picture / Love song for the earth / Travellin' (back home to you) / Friend of the king, A / Wooden cross rider / Holy ground / Get up and dance / I've made up my mind.
MC: . . . . MC 1051

PORTFOLIO.
LP: . . . . MYR R 1231
MC: . . . . MYR C 1231

Hewson, Richard

MUSIC OF THE STARS - SCORPIO (Songs of a Distant Chameleon).
Tracks: / Prelude / Bush music / Spanish tears / Five in the afternoon / Pipe piece / Aubade / Passacaglia / On a darkling plain / Revercussions / Secret garden.
LP: . . . . BIRTHLP 1
MC: . . . . BIRTHMC 1

Hex & Feed Your Head

HEX.
Tracks: / Diviner / Hermaphrodite / Ethereal message / Mercury towers / Out of the pink / Fire Island / In the net / Silvermine / Elizabeth Green / Arrangement, An.
LP: . . . . FIEND 156

Hexenhaus

AWAKENING.
LP: . . . . ATV 19

EDGE OF ETERNITY.
LP: . . . . ATV 13

Hexx

QUEST FOR SANITY.
LP: . . . . MFLAG 22

Hey Elastica

IN ON THE OFF BEAT.
LP: . . . . V 2273
MC: . . . . TCV 2273

Hey, Mr. Producer

HEY, MR. PRODUCER (Various artists).
2LP: . . . . ENCORE 4
MCSET: . . . . ENCOREC 4

Heydayat, Dashiel

OBSOLETE (see also Daevid Allen) (Heydayat, Dashiel & Daevid Allen).

Heyer, Georgette

PISTOL FOR TWO/HAZARD (Cazenove, Christopher).
MC: . . . . PTB 608

Heyerdahl, Thor

ACHIEVEMENT.
MC: . . . . SS 126

KON-TIKI EXPEDITION (Pigott-Smith, Tim (nar)).
MCSET: . . . . LFP 7282

Heymann & Kinnaird

HARPERS LAND, THE.
MC: . . . . CTP 012
LP: . . . . TP 012

Heyward, Nick

BEST OF NICK HEYWARD AND HAIRCUT 100.
Tracks: / Favourite shirts (boy meets girl) / Take that situation / Fantastic day / Laura / Marine boy / Blue hat for a blue day / Whistle down the wind / Love plus one / Warning sign / Baked bean / Love all day / Snow girl / Over the weekend / Nobody's fool.
MC: 410 366

I LOVE YOU AVENUE.
Tracks: / You're my world / If that's the way you feel / Traffic in Fleet Street / Lie with you / My kind of wonderful / I love you avenue / Hold on / Tell me why / Pizza tears / This is love / Change of heart / August in the morning.
LP: . . . . WX 194
MC: . . . . WX 194 C

NORTH OF A MIRACLE.
Tracks: / When it started to begin / Blue hat for a blue day / Two make it true / On a Sunday / Club boy at sea / Whistle down the wind / Take that situation / Kick of love, The / Day it rained forever, The / Atlantic Monday.
LP: . . . . NORTH 1
MC: . . . . TCNOR 1

POSTCARDS FROM HOME.
Tracks: / Over the weekend / Move it up / Goodbye yesterday / Again in my heart / We've been kissed / Pray for a miracle / Now you've gone / Come on baby run / Teach till you reach / Cry just a bit.
MC: **407205**
LP: **207205**

Heywood, Eddie

BIGGEST LITTLE BIG BAND OF THE FORTIES, THE.
Tracks: / T'aint me / Back home again in Indiana / Blue Lou / Carry me back to old Virginny / I can't believe that you're in love with me / Love me or leave me / Begin the beguine / I cover the waterfront / Save your sorrow / Just you, just me / Deed I do / Lover man.
LP: **AG6 25493**

Heywood, Heather

SOME KIND OF LOVE.
Tracks: / Sally gardens / Lord Lovat / Song for Ireland, A / Some kind of love / Let no man steal your thyme / Bonnie laddie ye gang by me / My bonnie moorhen / Cruel mother.
LP: . . . . **TRAX 010**
MC: . . . . **CTRAX 010**

Hi De Hi

HI DE HI (songs from the BBC TV series) (Various artists).
Tracks: / I've always chased rainbows: *Various artists* / Easy to love: *Various artists* / Dancing in the dark: *Various artists* / I've grown accustomed to her face: *Various artists* / Make 'em laugh: *Various artists*/ Tiptoe through the tulips: *Various artists* / Darktown poker club: *Various artists* / I don't know why: *Various* artists / Holiday rock: *Various artists* / Little white bull: *Various artists* / Chattanooga choo choo: *Various artists.*
LP: . . . . **REC 436**
MC: . . . . **ZCM 436**

Hi Five

HI FIVE.
LP: . . . . **HIP 108**
MC: . . . . **HIPC 108**

Hi Records

HI RECORDS: THE EARLY YEARS (Various artists).
Tracks: / Pipeliner: *Redell, Teddy Band* / I want to hold you: *Redell, Teddy Band* / There was a time: *Reeder, Bill* / Till I waltz again with you again: *Reeder, Bill* / Judy: *Reeder, Bill* / Secret love: *Reeder, Bill* / 7.26 miles to Juliet: *Wallace, Darlene* / Smokie part 2: *Bill's Black Combo* / Your true love: *Simmons, Gene* / Teddy bear: *Simmons, Gene* / Shape you left me in, The: *Simmons, Gene* / No other guy: *Simmons, Gene* / Tuff: *Cannon, Ace* / Jumpin': *Simmons, Gene.*
LP: . . . . **HIUKLP 434**
2LP: . . . . **DHIUKLP 434**

HI RECORDS: THE EARLY YEARS VOL.2 (Various artists).
Tracks: / My girl Josephine: *Jayes, Jerry* / Five miles from home: *Jayes, Jerry* / Middle of nowhere, The: *Jayes, Jerry* / Long black veil: *Jayes, Jerry* / Sugar bee: *Jayes, Jerry* / I'm in love again: *Jayes, Jerry*/ I washed my hands in muddy water: *Jayes, Jerry* / Shackles and chains: *Tucker, Tommy* / I'm in love with a shadow: *Tucker, Tommy* / Wild side of life: *Tucker, Tommy* / Since I met you baby: *Felts, Narvel* / Dee Dee: *Felts, Narvel* / 86 miles: *Felts, Narvel* / Little bit of soap, A: *Felts, Narvel* / Dark shaded glasses: *Eldred, Charles* / Long tall texan: *Kellum, Murray & Rhythm Four* / I gotta leave this town: *Sutton, Glenn* / Shame, shame, shame: *Tucker, Tommy* / Listen to me lie: *Simmons, Gene* / Wedding bells: *Simmons, Gene* / Invitation to the blues: *Simmons, Gene* / Time is right: *Lloyd, Jay B.* / Honey babe: *Arnold, Jerry* / Son of Smokie: *Black, Bill Combo* / Crank case: *Black, Bill Combo* / TD's boogie woogie: *Black, Bill Combo* / Deep elem blues: *Cannon, Ace/Bill Black's combo* / Sittin' tight: *Cannon, Ace.*
2LP: . . . . **DHIUKLP 442**

HI RHYTHM & BLUES (Various artists).
Tracks: / That driving beat: *Mitchell, Willie & 4 Kings* / It ain't easy: *Bryant, Don* / Sure looks good to me: *Bryant, Don* / Clear days and stormy nights: *Bryant, Don* / I will be true: *One & One* / Champion, The: *Mitchell, Willie* / Hey little girl: *West, Norm* / Love what you're doing to me: *Various artists* / Without a reason: *Janet & The Jays* / Goodest man, The: *Miller, Gene 'Bowlegs'* / Mama's boy: *Fry, James* / I've got enough: *Fry, James* / Help yourself: *Five Royales* / Roll with the punches: *Five Royales.*
LP: . . . . **HIUKLP 439**

SOUL YEARS, THE (Various artists).
Tracks: / Strong as death: *Green, Al* / Back for a taste of your love: *Johnson, Syl* / I don't do windows: *Wright, O.V.* / She's my woman: *Bobo Mr.Soul* / Teenies dream: *Mitchell, Willie* / After you: *Quiet Elegance*/ You got my mind messed up: *Quiet Elegance* / Trying to live my life without you: *Clay, Otis* / I've been there before: *Peebles, Ann* / Turning over the ground: *Mitchell, Phillip* / Wake up fool: *Masqueraders* / When the battle is over: *Joint Venture* / Let them know you care: *Jackson, George* / Aretha, sing one for me: *Jackson, George.*
LP: . . . . **HIUKLP 440**

Hi Rhythm

ON THE LOOSE.
Tracks: / On the loose / Superstar / Since you've been gone / Purple raindrops / I remember, do you / Save all my lovin' / You got me comin' / Skinny dippin'.
LP: . . . . **SHU 8506**

Hi Skool Breaks

HI SKOOL BREAKS (Various artists).
LP: . . . . **HNL 2001**

Hi Tension

HI TENSION.
LP: . . . . **ILPS 9564**

Hiatt, John

ALL OF A SUDDEN.
Tracks: / I took for love / This secret life / Overnight story / Forever yours / Some fun now / Walking dead / I could use an angel / Getting excited / Doll hospital / Something happens / Marianne / My edge of the razor.
LP: . . . . **GEF 85580**

BRING THE FAMILY.
Tracks: / Memphis in the meantime / Alone in the dark / Thing called love, A / Lipstick sunset / Have a little faith in me / Thank you girl / Tip of my tongue / Yur dad did / Stood up / Learning how to love you.
LP: . . . . **FIEND 100**
MC: . . . . **FIENDCASS 100**

RIDING WITH THE KING.
Tracks: / I don't even try / Death by misadventure / Girl on a string / Lovers will / She loves the jerk / Say it with flowers / Riding with the king / You may already be a winner / Love like blood / Love that harms / Book lovers / Falling up.
LP: . . . . **GEF 25593**
MC: . . . . **GEFC 04017**

SLOW TURNING.
Tracks: / Drive south / Trudy and Dave / Tennessee plates / Icy blue heart / Sometime other than now / Georgia Rae / Ride along / Slow turning / It'll come to you / Is anybody there? / Paper thin / Feels like rain.
LP: . . . . **AMA 5206**
MC: . . . . **AMC 5206**

SLUG LINE.
LP: . . . . **MCF 3005**

STOLEN MOMENTS.
LP: **3953101**
MC: **3953104**

TWO BIT MONSTERS.
LP: . . . . **MCF 3078**

WARMING UP THE ICE AGE.
Tracks: / Usual (The) / Crush / When we ran / She said the same things to me / Living a little, laughing a little / Zero house / Warming up the ice age / I'm a real man / Number one honest game / I got a gun.
LP: **9240551**
MC: **9240554**
MC: . . . . **GEFC 24055**

YOU'RE ALL CAUGHT.
LP: . . . . **K 9242471**
MC: . . . . **K 9242474**

Hiatus

HIATUS - THE PEACEVILLE SAMPLER (Various artists).
LP: . . . . **VILE 006**

Hiawatha

HIAWATHA Original cast (Various artists).
LP: . . . . **MMT LP 104**
MC: . . . . **MMT TC 104**

Hibbert, Jimmy

HEAVY DUTY.
Tracks: / Mr wonderful / Telephone / Out of control / Title track / Hangin' out / Tough / All wired up / Gonzo killer / Pop your cherry / Tinsel town.
LP: . . . . **LOGO 1021**

Hibbert, Ossie

ALL STARS.
Tracks: / Extra clips / Stamp out / Go for it / Monkey jungle / Eighteen and over / Your mistake / Drop out / Keep cool / What a heat / Mood of love.
LP: . . . . **WENLP 3030**

EXTRA CLIPS.
LP: . . . . **WENLP 3037**

Hibbler, Al

DEDICATED TO YOU.
MC: . . . . **SLC 61020**

GOLDEN GREATS: AL HIBBLER.
Tracks: / Unchained Melody / On a slow boat to china / Pennies from Heaven / Don't get around much anymore / I'll never smile again / All or nothing at all / You'll never know / Trees / Very thought of you, The / Stardust / Stormy weather / 11th hour medley / He / After the lights go down low / September in the rain / Stella by starlight.
LP: . . . . **MCM 5026**
MC: . . . . **MCMC 5026**

IT'S MONDAY EVERY DAY (Hibbler, Al & The Gerald Wilson Orchestra).
Tracks: / Baby, won't you please come home / Laughing on the outside (crying on the inside) / When the sun comes out / I'm a fool to want you.
LP: . . . . **DS 842**

Hicken, David

FINAL TOCATTA, THE.
Tracks: / Final toccata, The / Harbour of passion / Lost caribbean, The / Quarters / Foreign land, The / Serenity / Fantasia / Reflections of time / Rain dance / Legacy, The / English rhapsody, The.
LP: . . . . **PRCD 139**
MC: . . . . **TCPRCV 139**

Hickey, Ersel

BLUEBIRDS OVER THE MOUNTAINS.
LP: . . . . **KM 2601**

Hickman, John

B-C-H (See under Berline, Byron) (Berline, Byron & Dan Crary & John Hickman).

DON'T MEAN MAYBE.
Tracks: / Don't mean maybe / Salt river / Turkey knob / Birmingham fling / Sweet Dixie / Sally Goodin / Train 405 / Banjo signal / Ghost dance / Pike county breakdown / Goin' to town / Dixie breakdown.
LP: . . . . **ROUNDER 0101**
MC: . . . . **ROUNDER 0101C**

DOUBLE TROUBLE (See under Berline, Byron) (Berline, Byron & John Hickman).

NIGHT RUN (See under Berline, Byron) (Berline, Byron & Dan Crary & John Hickman).

NOW THERE ARE FOUR (See under Berline, Byron) (Berline, Byron & Dan Crary & John Hickman).

Hickoids

CORNTAMINATED.
Tracks: / Corntaminated / Driftwood / Vittles / Corn foo fighting / Take it easy.
LP: . . . . **HOLY 006**

WE'RE IN IT FOR THE CORN.
Tracks: / Rodeo peligroso / Williamanza / Hickoid heaven / Longest mile, The / Burnin' love / I pity the man / It's a beautiful thang / Hee haw / Animal husbandry / U kin lead a hoss to water but he still drinks on his own / Desire / O.A.F. anthem / Corntaminated / Say so long.
LP: . . . . **SAVE 052**

Hickory Dickory Dock

HICKORY DICKORY DOCK (Various artists).
MC: . . . . **BBM 105**
LP: . . . . **ONE 1290**
MC: . . . . **STC 009**

Hickory Lake

EASY COME EASY GO.
Tracks: / Wurlitzer prize / Who were you thinking of / Looking for a feeling / That's not what life's for / Easy come easy go / Amelia Earhart's last flight / Coca cola cowboy / There's no more you and me / Lucy ain't your loser looking good / I don't wanna cry.
LP: . . . . **KO 1010**
MC: . . . . **TC KO 1010**

Hickory Wind

CROSSING DEVIL'S BRIDGE.
LP: . . . . **FF 074**

FRESH PRODUCE.
LP: . . . . **FF 018**

WEDNESDAY NIGHT WALTZ, AT THE.
LP: . . . . **AD 2002**

Hicks, Bob

DARKNESS ON THE DELTA (See under Baker, Kenny) (Baker, Kenny & Bob Hicks).

TEXAS CRAPSHOOTER (Hicks, Bob & Friends).
Tracks: / Panhandle rag / Goodbye Liza Jane / Maiden's prayer / Cherokee swing / Texas crapshooter / Big beaver / Scotland / Big man / East Tennessee blue / Cheyenne / Paddy on the turnpike.
LP: . . . . **CO 772**

Hicks, Dan

DAN HICKS AND HIS HOT LICKS-ORIGINAL RECORDING (Hicks, Dan & His Hot Licks).
LP: . . . . **ED 144**

IT HAPPENED ONE BITE.
Tracks: / Cruizin' / Crazy cause he is / Garden in the rain / Boogaloo Jones / Cloud my sunny moon / Dizzy dogs / Vinnie's lookin' good / Lovers for life / Collared blues / Waiting / Reveille revisited / Mama I'm an outlaw / Boogaloo plays guitar.
LP: . . . . **ED 177**

RICH AND HAPPY IN HICKSVILLE (The very best of...) (Hicks, Dan & His Hot Licks).
Tracks: / You got to believe / Walking one and only / O'Reilly at the bar / Moody Richard (the innocent bystander) / Flight of the fly / I scare myself / Laughing song, The / Canned music / I'm an old cowhand / Woe the luck / Cowboys dream no.19 / Lonely madman / My old timey baby / Vivando / Payday blues / Sure beats me / Euphonious whale, The / It's not my time to go.
LP: . . . . **SEE 65**

Hicks, D'Atra

D'ATRA HICKS.
Tracks: / Sweet talk / You make me want to give it up / Something about you / Palm of your hand / Until forever (Theme from 'Everybody's All-American'.) / Love and happiness / Heart of gold / I wanna be loved / If my heart could lie / Wait / One touch (leads to another) / Everything I feel / Sweet talk (ext. mix) (CD only.).
LP: . . . . **EST 2104**
MC: . . . . **TCEST 2104**

Hicks, John

IN CONCERT.
LP: . . . . **TR 123**

POWER TRIO, THE (Hicks, John, Cecil McBee & Elvin Jones).
Tracks: / Cousin Mary / After the rain / 'D' Bass-IC blues / Duke's place / Chelsea Bridge / After the morning.
MC: . . . . **PK 90547**

TWO OF A KIND (Hicks, John/Ray Drummond).
Tracks: / I'll be around / Take the Coltrane / Very early / Getting sentimental over you / For Heavens sake / Come rain or come shine / Rose without a thorn, A / Without a song.
LP: . . . . **TR 128**

Hicks, Marva

MARVA HICKS.
LP: **8472091**
MC: **8472094**

Hickson, Joan (nar)

BLUE GERANIUM AND MORE STORIES (see under Blue Geranium (bk).

HERB OF DEATH (see under Herb Of Death (bk)).

THIRTEEN PROBLEMS, THE (see under Thirteen Problems (bk)).

Hidden

HIDDEN, THE (Original Soundtrack) (Various artists).
LP: . . . . **STV 81349**
MC: . . . . **CTV 81349**

Hidden Charms

HISTORY.
Tracks: / We can't stand it / Why worry 'bout tomorrow / History / Crying heart / 1986 so what blues, The / I just want to have something to do / We got it all wrong / Paradise / Moonlight night / PS waltz, The.
LP: . . . . **VOLUME 014**

Hidden Voices

HIDDEN VOICES (Various artists).
LP: . . . . **LR 123**

Hide My Eyes

HIDE MY EYES Read by Bernard Archard.
MC: . . . . **CAB 025**

Hideous Warts

20 GREAT PERFORMANCES OF AGADOO DOO DOO.
LP: . . . . **DUB 2**

Hiding In The Hangar

HIDING IN THE HANGAR (Various artists).
MC: . . . . **COCKPIT 3**

Hiding Out

HIDING OUT (Original soundtrack) (Various artists).

LP: .... V 2493
MC: .... TCV 2493

Hi-Fi

MOODS FOR MALLARDS.
Tracks: / Walk away / Blue shirt / Holding out for rain / Throw a line / Knocking on your door / Desire / Time after Time / Alcohol / When you were mine.
LP: .... HAI 102

Hi-Fi Apartment

HI-FI APARTMENT.
Tracks: / Touch of a scorpion / Hi-fi apartment / Day monk died, The / Bea's flat / Ode to Odell / Breakable / Gimme a break / Je chante miou miou / I am a lushhead / John Stone stomp / Looking at things passing by / Doubts / On a Sunday afternoon / Song for my mother / W'have the blues.
LP: .... AFF 203

Higbie, Barbara

LIVE AT MONTREUX: BARBARA HIGBIE (see under Anger, Darol) (Higbie, Barbara/Darol Anger Quintet).

TIDELINE (see under Anger, Darol) (Higbie, Barbara & Darol Anger).

Higginbotham, J.C.

HIGGY COMES HOME.
LP: .... J 28

Higginbottom, Geoff

FLOWERS TOMORROW.
LP: .... DRGN 871

Higgins, Bertie

KEY LARGO.
Tracks: / Just another day in paradise / Casablanca / Candle dancer / Key Largo / Port of call / White line fever / Heart is the hunter, The / She's gone to live on the mountains / Down at the blue moon / Tropics, The.
LP: .... EPC 85595
MC: 40 85595

PIRATES AND POETS.
Tracks: / Pirates and poets / When you fall in love (like I fell in love with you) / Leah / Under a blue moon / Tokyo Joe / Beneath the island light / Only yesterday / Marianna / Pleasure pier / Never looking back / As time goes by.
LP: .... EPC 25327
MC: 40 25327

Higgins, Billy

CEDAR WALTON PLAYS (See Under Walton, Cedar) (Higgins, Billy, Cedar Walton & Ron Carter).

EASTERN REBELLION VOL.2 (See Under Walton, Cedar) (Higgins, Billy, Cedar Walton, Sam Jones & Bob Berg).

LIVE AT THE KEYSTONE CORNER (see Montoliu, Tete) (Higgins, Billy, Tete Montoliu, Herbie Lewis).

SOLDIER, THE.
Tracks: / Sugar and spice / Midnight waltz / Just in time / If you could see me now / Peace / Sonnymoon for two.
LP: .... SJP 145

Higgins, Chuck

CHUCK HIGGINS IS A PHD.
LP: .... BRP 2009
LP: .... LP 020
LP: .... ROLL 20

PACHUKO HOP.
Tracks: / Pachuko hop / Motor head baby / Blues and mambo / Long long time / Chuck's fever / Iron pipe / Big fat Mama / Real gone hound dog / Boyle heights / Papa Charlie / Rooster, The / Duck walk, The / Stormy / Just won't treat me rite.
LP: .... CH 81

Higgins, Eddie

BY REQUEST (See under Rosengarden, Bobby).

Higgins, Jack (author)

EAGLE HAS LANDED, THE (Fox, Edward).
MCSET: .... LFP 7403

FINE NIGHT FOR DYING, A (Foster, Barry).
MCSET: .... ZC SWD 359

HELL IS ALWAYS TODAY (Mackenzie, Michael).
MCSET: .... COL 2016

IN THE HOUR BEFORE MIDNIGHT (Rea, Stephen).
MC: .... CAB 337

NIGHT JUDGEMENT AT SINOS (Talbot, Philip).
MCSET: .... COL 2027

STORM WARNING (Goring, Marius).
MCSET: .... COL 2020

TOUCH THE DEVIL (Holm, Ian (nar)).
MCSET: .... LFP 7186

MCSET: .... LFP 417 186 5

Higgins, Lizzie

PRINCESS OF THE THISTLE.
Tracks: / Wha's at the windy / Lovely Molly / Fair of Ballnafannin, The / Young Emsley / Bonnie Udny / Far over the forth / Laird of the dainty downby / Seasons, The / Davy Faa / Red roses / Young but growing / Lass o'Glenshea.
LP: 12T 185

UP & AWA' WI' THE LAVEROCK.
Tracks: / Up and awa' wi' the laverock / Lord lovat / Soo sewin' silk / Lady Mary Ann / MacDonald of Glencoe / Forester, The / Tammy toddles / Aul' roguie gray / Twa brothers, The / Cruel mother / Lassie gathering nuts, The.
LP: 12TS 260

WHAT A VOICE.
Tracks: / What a voice, what a voice / Willie's ghosst / MacPhee / Glenlogie / Tammy Toddles / Old maid in a garret, An / Tak the buckles fae your shin / MacCrimmon's lament / Cindy / Beggar, a beggar, A / Allison cross / Mankind.
LP: .... LIFL 7004
MC: .... LIFC 7004

Higgs, Joe

FAMILY.
LP: .... BMLP 021
LP: .... SHAN 43053
MC: .... SHANC 43053

TRIUMPH.
LP: .... AL 8313

UNITY IS POWER.
Tracks: / Devotion / One man kutchie / Unity is power / Gold or silver / Love can't be worng / Vineyard / Small word / Sadness is a part of my heart / Sons of Garvey.
LP: .... ILPS 9535

Higgs, Paul

FRESH BREW (Higgs, Paul & Friends).
Tracks: / Bonnie at morn / Iron bridge, The / Morpeth rant / Mrs Jamiesons favourite / Madam Bonaparte / Road to the North / Four seasons reel / Lament for Ian Dickson / Sir Sidney Smith's march / Nancy Taylor's reel / Lark in the morning, The / Wild hills o'Wannte / Golden eagle, The / Maggie Lauder / Darghah / Banjo breakdown.
MC: .... BH 8801 C

High

SOMEWHERE SOON.
Tracks: / Box set go / Take your time / This is my world / Rather be Marsanne / So I can see / Minor turn, A / Dream of dinesh / Up and down / P.W.A. / Somewhere soon.
LP: 828 224 1
MC: 828 224 4

High 5

DOWN IN THE NO-GO.
LP: .... GOLP 1
MC: .... TC-GOLP 1

High Atmosphere

HIGH ATMOSPHERE.
LP: .... ROUNDER 0028

High Commissioner (bk)

HIGH COMMISSIONER, THE (Jon Cleary) (Wheeler, Peter (nar)).
MCSET: .... SOUND 33

High Country

LAST TRAIN TO GLORY.
LP: .... PC 447

ON THE ROAD.
LP: .... SHILOH 4089

High Fashion

FEELIN' LUCKY LATELY.
Tracks: / Feeling lucky lately / You're the winner / Hold on / Next to you / Have you heard the news / When the lover strikes / I want to be your everything / Brainy children.
LP: .... EST 12214
MC: .... TCEST 12214

High Flying Irish...

HIGH FLYING IRISH SHOWBANDS (Various artists).
Tracks: / Almost persuaded: *Various artists* / Come back to Erin: *Various artists* / My elusive dreams: *Various* artists / S S Rocker: *Various artists* / Joys of love: *Various artists* / All the gold in California: *Various* artists / Funny face: *Various artists* / When: *Various artists* / Your old love letters: *Various artists*/ Yes Mr. Peters: *Various artists* / Dance, dance, dance: *Various artists* / Cuando sali de Cuba: *Various artists* / Jealous heart: *Various artists* / Candida: *Various artists.*
LP: .... SPR 8521
MC: .... SPC 8521

High Inergy

HIGH INERGY.
Tracks: / Goin' thru the motions / All of you / Heaven's just a step away / Fill the need in me / Devotion / I just wanna dance with you / Now that there's you / Don't park your loving / Soakin' wet.
LP: .... STML 12157

HOLD ON TO MY LOVE.
Tracks: / I can't help myself / Sweet man / Make me yours / Hold on to my love / If I love you tonight / Boomerang love / I'm a believer / It was you babe.
LP: .... STML 12144

SHOULDA GONE DANCIN'.
Tracks: / Shoulda gone dancin' / I've got what you need / Come and get it / Midnight music man / Let yourself go / Love of my life / Too late.
LP: .... STML 12111

SO RIGHT.
Tracks: / Journey to love / Don'tcha love it / Wrong man right touch / Wanna be your lady / First impressions / So right / Show me how / Tired of being alone / Take a chance / Match point.
LP: .... STML 12170

High Kings Of Tara

HIGH KINGS OF TARA (Various artists).
LP: .... TA 3003
MC: 4TA 3003

High Level Ranters

BONNY PIT LADDIE, THE.
Tracks: / Hewer, The / Doon the waggon way / Miner's life, A / I wish pay Friday would come / Augengeich disaster, The / Colliers' rant, The / Farewell to the Monty / Putter, The / Little chance / My gaffer's bait / Coal owner and the pitman's wife, The / Blackleg miner / Miners' lockout, The / South Medomsley strike, The / Durham lockout, The / Aa'm glad the strike's done / Colliers' pay week, The / I'll have a collier / Instrumental selection / I'll make her fain to follow me / Joyful days are coming, The / Get her bo / Stoneman's song, The / Hartley calamity / Bonnie Woodha' / Banks of the Dee, The / Bonnie pit laddie, The (instrumental) / Bonnie pit laddie, The (vocal).
2LP: 12TS 271/2

BORDER SPIRIT.
Tracks: / Billy's jig / Gan to the Kye / Border spirit / Felton lonnin / Wallington Hall / Foxhunter's, The / King's Hall / John of Carrick / Bellington show / Coilsfield house / Thom's march / Canny shepherd laddies, The / Surprise / Kielder Fells / Billy's reel.
LP: 12TS 434

FOUR IN A BAR.
Tracks: / Whinham's jig / Billy's jig / Chips and shavings / Jack's alive / Dear tobacco / Town green polka / Jenny Bell / Biddlestone hornpipe, The / Last of the twins, The / Ruby, The / Quarrelsome piper, The / Rowly Burn / Coates hornpipe / La russe / Whinshield's hornpipe, The / Jane's fancy / Da road to Houll / Blinkin' tibbie / Pear tree, The / Swalwell lasses / South Shields lasses / Moonshine polka / Quayside, The / Miss Ward's reel / Butterclout, The / Such a wife as Willy had / Willy is a bonny lad.
LP: 12TS 388

HIGH LEVEL.
LP: .... LER 2030

KEEP YOUR FEET STILL GEORDIE HINNIE.
LP: .... LER 2020

LADS OF NORTHUMBRIA, THE.
LP: .... LER 2007

MILE TO RIDE, A.
LP: .... LER 2037

NORTHUMBERLAND FOREVER.
Tracks: / Shew's the way to Wallington / Peacock followed the hen, The / Sandgate girl's lament, The / Elsie Marley / Bellingham boat / Lamb skinnet / Adam Buckham / Meggy's foot / Lads of North Tyne, The / Redesdale hornpipe / Hexhamshire lass, The / Breakdown, The / Blanchland races / Lads of Alnwick, The / Lamshaw's fancy / Byker hill / Whinham's reel / Nancy / Because he was a bonny lad / Salmon tails up the water / Sweet Hesleyside / Dance to your daddy / Billy boy / Nae guid luck aboot the house / Mi laddie sits ower late up / Keel row, The / Kafoozalum / Washing day.
LP: 12TS 186

RANTING LADS.
Tracks: / Fairly shot of her / Wife of my own, A / Dance to your daddy / Lass doon on the quar, The / Kielder hunt, The / Alston flower show / Jane of Biddlestone / Fortune turns the wheel / Fenwick of Bywell / Elsie Marley / Hoop her and grid her / Captain Bover / Here's the tender coming / Success to the fleet / Proudlocks hornpipe / Hesleyside reel / Stanley market / Marquis of Waterford, The / Bottle bank / Hawk, The.
LP: 12TS 297

High Life Stars

ONE.
LP: .... FE 004

High Noon (film)

HIGH NOON (THEME FROM) (See under Laine, Frankie) (Laine, Frankie).

High On Acid

THIS IS ACID.
LP: .... KAOS 010

High On The Hog

HIGH ON THE HOG (Various artists).
Tracks: / Polly wally doodle: *Borders Tony* / Mix and mingle: *Borders Tony* / Living high on hog: *Demon Brothers*/ Can you handle it: *Bradford, Eddie* / One minute woman: *Brandon, Bill* / Little by little: *Brandon, Bill*/ You ain't woman enough: *Edwards, June* / What kind of spell: *Borders Tony* / Nice place to visit, A: *Borders* Tony / Uh, huh: *Demon Brothers* / Full grown lovin' man: *Brandon, Bill* / Self preservation: *Brandon, Bill* / She knows what to do: *Brandon, Bill* / Close to me: *Edwards, June.*
LP: .... CRB 1222

HOGTIED.
Tracks: / Walk on by / Teardrops in my eyes / Hickory wind / Still feeling blue / Good-hearted woman / Hogtied / I wish I was in Nashville / Tex Mex lament / Breed / Still burning / Go get him, Jake / Riverboat song.
LP: .... SFA 062

High Road To China

HIGH ROAD TO CHINA (Film soundtrack) (Barry, John).
Tracks: / Main title / Charlie gets the knife / Airborne / Love theme / Waxiri Village / Attack and escape / Farewell to Struts / O'Malley and Eve / Charleston / Von Kern's attack / Flight from Katmandu / Eve finds her father / Raid on Chang's camp / High Road love theme and end title.
LP: .... FILM 001
MC: .... FILMC 001

High School

HIGH SCHOOL CONFIDENTIAL/JUKE BOX JIVE (Various artists).
Tracks: / Wanderer: *Dion* / Chain gang: *Cooke, Sam* / Happy birthday sweet sixteen: *Sedaka, Neil* / One fine day: *Chiffons* / Dance with the guitar man: *Eddy, Duane* / Keep searchin': *Shannon, Del* / Lion sleeps tonight, The: *Tokens* / End of the world: *Davis, Skeeter* / Twistin' the night away: *Cooke, Sam* / Sweet talking guy: *Chiffons* / Breaking up is hard to do: *Sedaka, Neil* / Denise: *Randy & The Rainbows* / Hats off to Larry: *Shannon, Del* / Lovers who wander: *Dion* / I can't stay mad at you: *Davis, Skeeter* / Tell Laura I love her: *Peterson, Ray* / Wonderful world: *Cooke, Sam* / I will follow him: *March, Peggy* / On the rebound: *Cramer, Floyd* / Cupid: *Cooke, Sam* / Runaway: *Shannon, Del* / He's so fine: *Chiffons*/ I wonder why: *Dion & The Belmonts* / Oh Carol: *Sedaka, Neil* / Little bit of soap, A: *Jarmels* / Boss guitar: *Eddy, Duane* / Runaround Sue: *Dion* / Out of this world: *Chiffons* / Another Saturday night: *Cooke,* Sam / Teenager in love: *Dion & The Belmonts* / Calendar girl: *Sedaka, Neil* / Swiss maid: *Shannon, Del*/ Hey Dean, hey Jean: *Dean & Jean* / Little devil: *Sedaka, Neil* / I'm on my way: *Parrish, Dean* / When the boy's happy (the girl's happy too): *Four Pennies.*
2LP: .... RCALP 1004/5
MCSET: .... RCAK 1004/5

High School Hop

HIGH SCHOOL HOP (Various artists).
Tracks: / Gotta go back to school: *Various artists* / Lucille: *Various artists* / She's walking towards me: *Various* artists / Havin' a whole lot of fun: *Various artists* / Snake, The: *Various artists* / This is Elbert operator: *Various artists* / Night train: *Various artists* / Prisoner's song: *Various artists* / Yeah yeah yeah: *Various artists* / High ride: *Various artists* / Won't somebody love me: *Various artists* / Raining in my heart: *Various artists* / Rock & roll beat: *Various artists* / Trojan walla: *Various artists.*
LP: .... FLY 616

High Skool Breaks

HIGH SKOOL BREAKS (Various artists).
LP: .... NNL 2001

High Society (Film)

HIGH SOCIETY (Film soundtrack) (Various artists).
LP: . . . . **LCT 6116**

High Society Jazzband

LASSES CANDY.
LP: . . . . **SOS 1166**

High Society (Show)

HIGH SOCIETY (Original London Cast) (Various artists).
Tracks: / High society overture: *Various artists* / How do you spell Ambassador?: *Various artists* / Give him the oo-la-la: *Various artists* / Who wants to be a millionaire?: *Various artists* / Little one: *Various artists*/ Hey good lookin': *Various artists* / I love you, Samantha: *Various artists* / Ball medley: *Various artists*/ Well, did you ever?: *Various artists* / Most gentlemen don't like love: *Various artists* / Now you has jazz: *Various artists* / In the still of the night: *Various artists* / You're sensational: *Various artists*/ True love: *Various artists* / Finale: *Various artists.*
LP: . . . . **SCX 6707**
MC: . . . . **TCSCX 6707**

HIGH SOCIETY (Broadway cast) (Various artists).
LP: . . . . **R 108**
MC: . . . . **TCR 108**

HIGH SOCIETY (SHOW) (1956 Film Soundtrack) (Various artists).
Tracks: / Overture: *Various artists* / High society calypso: *Various artists* / Little one: *Various artists*/ You're sensational: *Various artists* / I love you: *Various artists* / Samantha: *Various artists* / Now you has jazz: *Various artists* / Well did you evah: *Various artists* / Mind if I make love to you: *Various artists.*
LP: . . . . **SLCT 6116**
MC: . . . . **TC SLCT 6116**

High Spirits

HIGH SPIRITS (Original London cast) (Various artists).
Tracks: / Overture: *Various artists* / Was she prettier than I?: *Various artists* / Bicycle song: *Various* artists / You'd better love me: *Various artists* / Where is the man I married?: *Various artists* / Go into your trance: *Various artists* / Forever and a day: *Various artists* / Something tells me: *Various artists*/ I know your heart: *Various artists* / Faster than sound: *Various artists* / If I gave you: *Various artists*/ Talking to you: *Various artists* / Home sweet Heaven: *Various artists* / Something is coming to tea: *Various artists* / What in the world did you want?: *Various artists.*
LP: . . . . **FBLP 8087**
MC: . . . . **ZCFBL 8087**

HIGH SPIRITS (FILM) Film soundtrack (Various artists).
Tracks: / Overture: *Various artists* / Castle Plunkett: *Various artists* / Plunkett's lament: *Various artists*/ Ghost bus tours: *Various artists* / Ghostly reflections: *Various artists* / She is from the far land: *Various artists* / Bumps in the knight: *Various artists* / Mary appears: *Various artists.*
LP: . . . . **GNPS 8014**
MC: **GNP5 8014**

High Tide

HIGH TIDE.
Tracks: / Blankman cries again / Joke, The / Saneonymous.
LP: . . . . **PSYCHO 27**

SEA SHANTIES.
Tracks: / Futilists lament / Death warmed up / Pushed but not forgotten / Walking down their outlook / Missing out / Nowhere.
LP: . . . . **PSYCHO 26**

High Times...

HIGH TIMES ALL-STAR EXPLOSION Various artists (Various artists).
LP: . . . . **AL 8312**

High Water Blues

MISSI/LOUISIANA BLUES (1965-70).
LP: . . . . **FLY 512**

Higher & Higher

HIGHER AND HIGHER (Film soundtrack) (Various artists).
LP: . . . . **HS 411**

Highland Driving

HIGHLAND DRIVING (Various artists).
MC: . . . . **TC MMC 5013**

Highland magic

HIGHLAND MAGIC (Various artists).
Tracks: / Sir James MacDonald of the Isles lament: *Macleod, Pipe Major Donald* / An teid thu leam a mhairi: *Solley,* David / Flower of Scotland: *MacLean, Norman* / Mingulay boat song: *Drifterfolk* / Cradle song: *Gonnella,* Ron / We'd better bide a wee: *Gordon, Joe & Sally Logan* / Soraidh leis an ait': *Sound Of Mull* / Mary of Argyll: *Morrison, Peter* / Sunndach: *Run Rig* / Hebridean waltz: *Glasgow Caledonian Strathspey & Reel Society*/ Gleann baile chaoil: *Govan Gaelic Choir* / Isle of Arran: *Solley, David* / Lament for Donald of Laggan: *MacNeill, Seamas.*
MC: . . . . **LICS 5103**
LP: . . . . **LILP 5103**

Highland Strathspey

FIDDLES OF THE HIGHLAND STRATHSPEY AND REEL SOCIETY (Highland Strathspey & Reel Society).
LP: . . . . **LILP 5035**

Highlander

HIGHLANDER II - THE QUICKENING (Film soundtrack) (Various artists).
LP: . . . . **BWX 2**
MC: . . . . **BWX 2C**

Highlanders

PERFECT CRIME, A.
Tracks: / Move it up / Victim of a restless heart / Never enough / Tell me things / Children wonder why / Where did it go / Perfect crime / Look in her eyes, The / Stay with me / Follow my heart.
LP: . . . . **V 2586**
MC: . . . . **TCV 2586**

Highlights...

HIGHLIGHTS IN JAZZ (Various artists).
LP: . . . . **ST 254**

HIGHLIGHTS WEMBLEY COUNTRY MUSIC FESTIVAL (See Under Country ...) (Various artists).

Highs In The

HIGHS IN THE MID-SIXTIES (VOL 1 - LA '65) Teenage rebellion (Various artists).
LP: . . . . **AIP 1003**

HIGHS IN THE MID-SIXTIES (VOL 2 - LA '66) Riot on sunset strip (Various artists).
LP: . . . . **AIP 1004**

HIGHS IN THE MID-SIXTIES (VOL 3 - LA '67) Mondo Hollywood a go-go (Various artists).
LP: . . . . **AIP 1005**

Highs Of...

HIGHS OF THE SEVENTIES, VOL 1 (See Under 70's) (Various artists).

HIGHS OF THE SIXTIES (See Under 60's) (Various artists).

Hightower, Rosetta

EVERLASTING LOVE (see also Henry Turtle) (Hightower, Rosetta & Henry Turtle).

RIDE A WILD HORSE (see also Henry Turtle) (Hightower, Rosetta & Henry Turtle).

Hightower, Willie

FROM N.O. TO CHICA (See Jones, Richard).

Highway

HIGHWAY 1.
Tracks: / Slippin' away / Skyline / Breakdown / Don't wait too long / Winnipeg sidestep / You made a fool / Cheatin' eyes / Another night on the road / Take my heart / Steal or borrow.
LP: . . . . **EPC 83760**

Highway 101

101 SQUARED.
LP: **925742 1**
MC: **925742 4**

HIGHWAY 101.
Tracks: / Whisky, if you were a woman / Bridge across forever / Somewhere tonight / Woman walk the line / Good goodbye / Cry cry cry / Are you still mine / One step closer / Someone believed / Bed you made for me, The.
LP: . . . . **K 925608 1**
MC: . . . . **K 925608 4**

PAINT THE TOWN.
MC: . . . . **K 9259924**
LP: . . . . **K 9259921**

Highwayman

HIGHWAYMAN (Various artists).
Tracks: / Highwayman: *Various artists* / Last cowboy song, The: *Various artists* / Jim, I wore a tie today: *Various artists* / Big river: *Various artists* / Committed to Parkview: *Various artists* / Desperados waiting for the train: *Various artists* / Deportees (Plane wreck at Los Gatos): *Various artists* / Welfare line: *Various artists*/ Against the wind: *Various artists* / Twentieth century is almost over, The: *Various artists.*
LP: . . . . **CBS 26466**
MC: **40 26466**

HIGHWAYMAN 2 (Various artists).
Tracks: / Silver stallion: *Various artists* / Born and raised in black and white: *Various artists* / Two stories wide: *Various artists* / We're all in your corner: *Various artists* / American remains: *Various artists*/ Anthem '84: *Various artists* / Angels love bad men: *Various artists* / Songs that make a difference: *Various artists* / Living legend: *Various artists* / Texas: *Various artists.*
LP: **4666521**
MC: **4666524**

HIGHWAYMEN RIDE AGAIN (I Love Country) (Various artists).
Tracks: / Twentieth century is almost over, The: *Various artists* / How do you feel about foolin' around: *Various* artists / Heroes: *Various artists* / Down to her socks: *Various artists* / Blackjack country chains: *Various* artists / They're all the same to me: *Cash, Johnny* / Whiter shade of pale, A: *Various artists* / Last cowboy song, The: *Various artists* / Ballad of forty dollars: *Various artists* / Pilgrim, The: *Various artists*/ Casey's last ride: *Cash, Johnny* / Under the gun: *Various artists* / Eye of the storm: *Various artists*/ Why baby why: *Various artists.*
LP: **4504311**
MC: **4504314**

Highwaymen

MICHAEL (OLD GOLD) (see under Kingston Trio-Tom Dooley).

Highwind

HIGHWIND.
Tracks: / Late at night / Love is blind / Lies / Breakin' my heart / Devils and angels / Who's goin' to love you now / One by one / After the mystery / Everybody's in love / 1999.
MC: . . . . **TC INS 3026**
LP: . . . . **INS 3026**

Highwoods String Band

DANCE ALL NIGHT.
LP: . . . . **ROUNDER 0045**

FIRE ON THE MOUNTAIN.
LP: . . . . **ROUNDER 0023**

NO. 3 SPECIAL.
LP: . . . . **ROUNDER 0074**

Hi-Gloss

YOU'LL NEVER KNOW.
LP: . . . . **EPC 85318**
MC: **40 85318**

Higsons

ATTACK OF THE CANNIBAL ZOMBIE BUSINESS MEN, THE.
LP: . . . . **WAAP LP 1**

CURSE OF THE HIGSONS.
LP: . . . . **UPLP 6**

Hildegarde

SO RARE.
Tracks: / Darling, je vous aime beaucoup / Yours and mine / Cheek to cheek / This year's kisses / I dream too much alone / Pennies from Heaven / Ten pretty girls / It's the natural thing to do / Practising the piano / Pretty girl is like a melody / I'm feelin' like a million / I wanna go to the zoo / There's a small hotel / Eeny meeny miney mo / Will you remember? / But where are you? / Let's face the music and dance / I was lucky / Moon got in my eyes, The / All you want to do is dance / So rare.
LP: . . . . **CHD 151**
MC: . . . . **MCHD 151**

Hi-Life International

COMME CI COMME CA.
Tracks: / Comme ci comme ca.
LP: . . . . **STERNS 1206**

MUSIC TO WAKE THE DEAD.
Tracks: / All that glitters / Travel and see / Wish you were here / Abrokyire abrabo / I de tell you mama / Salaam alekum / For better for worse / Your touch is so warm.
LP: . . . . **ST 102**
LP: . . . . **ROUNDER 5014**
MC: . . . . **ROUNDER 5014C**

NA WA FOR YOU.
Tracks: / Na wa for you / Comme ci comme ca / Obrempong ahyease / Harmattan joy / Awo de me / Rice water / Seventeen / Come to Africa.
LP: . . . . **STERNS 1006**

TRAVEL AND SEE (Ghana/U.K).
Tracks: / All that glitters / Travel & See / Wish you were here / Abrokyire Abrabo / De tell you mama,I / Salaam alekum / For better for worse / Your touch is so warm.
LP: . . . . **STERNS 1002**

Hiliners

BOUND FOR GLORY.
LP: . . . . **RAZ 45**

Hill 16

HILL 16.
LP: . . . . **ML 101**

Hill, Andrew

ETERNAL SPIRIT.
Tracks: / Pinnacle / Golden sunset / Samba rasta / Tail feather / Spiritual lover45 / Bobby's tune / Pinnacle (alt. take) (CD only.) / Golden sunset (alt. take) (CD only.) / Spiritual lover (alt. take) (CD only.).
LP: **B1 92051**
LP: **792 051 1**

LIVE AT MONTREUX: ANDREW HILL.
Tracks: / Snake hip waltz / Nefertisis / Come Sunday / Relativity.
LP: . . . . **FLP 41023**

POINT OF DEPARTURE.
Tracks: / New monastery / Spectrum / Flight 19 / Dedication / Flight 19 (alt. take) (CD only.) / Dedication (alt. take) (CD only.) / Refuge.
LP: **B1 84167**

SOLO PIANO.
LP: . . . . **AH 9**

SPIRAL.
Tracks: / Tomorrow / Laverne / Message, The / Invitation / Today / Spiral / Quiet dawn.
LP: . . . . **FLP 41007**

Hill, Benny

LAUGH ALONG WITH BENNY HILL.
Tracks: / Harvest of love / Rose / Pepys' diary / Transistor radio / Lonely boy / Gather in the mushrooms / Andalucian gypsies / Wild woman / My garden of love / I'll never know / In the papers / Joe's cantina / Those days / Old fiddler, The / What a world.
MCSET: . . . . **DTO 10037**

THIS IS BENNY HILL.
Tracks: / Ernie (the fastest milkman in the west) / Anna Marie / Broken hearted lover's stew / Colleen / Rachel / Beach at San Tropez / Suzy / Ting-a-lin-a-loo / Dustbins of your mind / Fad-eyed Fal / Ted / Tour guide / Interview / Making a commercial / Birds and the bees.
LP: . . . . **THIS 27**
MC: . . . . **TC THIS 27**

WORDS AND MUSIC.
LP: . . . . **SCX 6479**

WORLD OF BENNY HILL.
LP: . . . . **SPA 116**
MC: . . . . **NEMMC 602**

Hill, Bernard (nar)

BOYS FROM THE BLACKSTUFF (see under Boys From the...).

Hill, Bertha 'Chippie'

BERTHA 'CHIPPIE' HILL.
LP: . . . . **HSLP 1005**

Hill, Blind Joe

ONE MAN BLUES.
LP: . . . . **LR 42.059**

Hill, Buck Quartet

SCOPE.
LP: . . . . **SCS 1123**

Hill, Dan

BEST OF DAN HILL.
Tracks: / Sometimes when we touch / Hold on / City madness / Let the song last forever / Frozen in the night / Phonecall / All I see is your face / Pick on me / Dark side of Atlanta / Growing up.
LP: . . . . **T 614**
MC: . . . . **C 614**

CAN WE TRY (Hill, Dan with Vonda Shepherd).
Tracks: / Can we try / Pleasure centre.
LP: **6508407**

DAN HILL.
Tracks: / Conscience / Carmelia / Blood in my veins / Can't we try / Never thought (that I could love) / Every boy's fantasy / Lose control / Perfect love / Pleasure centre / U.S.A./U.S.S.R..
LP: **4509391**
MC: **4509394**

IF DREAMS HAD WINGS.
Tracks: / Path of least resistance / I still reach for you / Ghost / Island / Perfect man / My love for you / More than just a clever game / Unloved people / You get a little harder / If dreams had wings.
LP: . . . . **EPC 84273**

LONGER FUSE.
LP: . . . . **BTH 8005**

LOVE IN THE SHADOWS.
Tracks: / Love in the shadows / Helpless / In your eyes / Just in time / You pulled me through / Where are you gonna run to / Something ain't right / Don't know where it comes from / Thru to you / Old lady song.
LP: . . . . **NFP 5500**
MC: . . . . **ZCNFP 5500**

Hill, Eric

SPOT: SPOT'S FIRST PICNIC Reader to be advised.

MC: 0 00 109027 5

SPOT: SPOT'S HOSPITAL VISIT
Reader to be advised.
MC: 0 00 109028 3

Hill, Geoffrey

POETRY AND VOICE OF GEOFFREY HILL, THE.
LP: . . . . TC 1597
MC: 1597

Hill, Jessie

Y'ALL READY NOW?.
Tracks: / Ooh poo pah doo / Why holler / Whip it on me / I got mine / Get in touch / Oogsey moo / I need your love / Pot's on strike, The / Popcorn pop pop / Scoop scoobie doobie / High head blues / Can't get enough (of that ooh poo pah do) / In my mind / Candy / Sweet jelly roll.
LP: . . . . CRB 1169
MC: . . . . TCCRB 1169

Hill, Joe Scott

ROCKIN' REBEL.
LP: . . . . REDITA 113

Hill, Lonnie

YOU GOT ME RUNNIN'.
Tracks: / Keep on dancing / Step on out / Mr. Music man / Something special to me / Galveston bay / Could it be love / My sweet love / Close to you / You got me running / Hard times.
LP: . . . . XID 13
MC: . . . . CXID 13

Hill, Noel

IG CNOC NA GRAI (See under McMahon, Tony) (Hill, Noel & Tony McMahon).

IRISH CONCERTINA, THE.
LP: . . . . CCF 21
MC: 4CCF 21

NOEL HILL AND TONY LINNANE.
LP: . . . . TA 2006

Hill, Rocky

ROCKY HILL.
Tracks: / HPD / I won't be your fool / Bad year for the blues / I'll be there / New York turn around / Take my love / Hoo doo eyes / Sam Bass / Walked from Dallas / Mississippi delta blues.
LP: . . . . V 2501
MC: . . . . TCV 2501

Hill Street Blues (tv)

HILL STREET BLUES (Music from the TV Series) (Caine, Daniel Orchestra).
LP: . . . . HSBP 2222
MC: . . . . HSBC 2222

MUSIC FROM HILL STREET BLUES (Various artists).
MC: . . . . FILMC 702

Hill, Teddy

TEDDY HILL AND CAB CALLOWAY.
LP: . . . . QU 021
LP: . . . . QUEEN 021

THAT'S ROCK'N'ROLL.
LP: 33.8010

TINY BRADSHAW 1934/TEDDY HILL 1935-36 (See under Bradshaw, Tiny).

Hill, Tiny

1943/4 (Hill, Tiny & his Orchestra).
LP: . . . . CLP 55

TINY HILL 1944.
Tracks: / Margie / Crying my heart out for you / I'm looking over a four leaf clover / Darktown strutters ball / My best girl / I want a girl / Ida / Who's sorry now (instrumental) / When you wore a tulip / If you knew Susie / Baby face / There'll be a time / My gal sal / Put on your old grey bonnet / Just because / My bonnie lies over the ocean.
LP: . . . . HSR 159

TINY HILL, VOL 2 1944.
Tracks: / Angry / Don't sweetheart me / If it's so wrong to love you / Ain't she sweet / Am I blue / Heartaches / My old Kentucky home / Shiek of Araby / Oh you beautiful doll / How many hearts have you broken / I ain't got nobody / I can't give you anything but love / Five foot two, eyes of blue / Loopin' the loop.
LP: . . . . HSR 181

Hill, Vince

20 GOLDEN FAVOURITES: VINCE HILL.
Tracks: / Edelweiss / May you always / So nice / Very thought of you, The / It might as well be spring / Sound of music / My own true love / Taste of honey / I can't make it alone / Daydream / Danny boy / Close to you / More than ever now / September song / Out of my dreams / Can't keep you out of my heart / One hand one heart / Does anybody miss me / Here, there and everywhere / Waterloo sunset.
LP: . . . . NTS 200

EDELWEISS.
LP: . . . . SCX 6141

FREEWAY SONGS.
MC: . . . . TC-MMC 5002

GREATEST HITS: VINCE HILL (An Hour of Hits).
Tracks: / Take me to your heart again / Importance of your love, The / Little bluebird / Somewhere my love / Love letters in the sand / Doesn't anybody know my name? / Here, there and everywhere / Wives and lovers / Girl talk / Merci cherie / Heartaches / Roses of Picardy / Moonlight and roses / Look around (and you'll find me there) / Love story / (They long to be) close to you / Danny boy / You're my world / Time for us, A / Spanish eyes.
MC: . . . . HR 8106
MC: . . . . HR 4181064

I WILL ALWAYS LOVE YOU.
Tracks: / I will always love you / Desperado / Love dies hard / Crying in the wind / Sweet dreams / Pray for love / When you walk through life / I want to know you / Sweet music man / Loving arms / It's not supposed to be that way / Sea of heartbreak / Always on my mind.
LP: . . . . GRALP 24
MC: . . . . GRTC 24

I'M THE SINGER.
Tracks: / Edelweiss / Touch me in the morning / Look around / Make it easy on yourself / Unchained melody / If you leave me now / Roses of Picardy / I'm the singer (end s1) / Bravo pour la musica / You've lost that lovin' feeling / Lately / Three times a lady / I can see clearly now / Where are you now, my love / Breaking up is hard to do / It's over.
LP: . . . . CBR 1033
MC: . . . . KCBR 1033

LOVE AND EMOTIONS.
MC: . . . . HSC 3049

LOVING FEELINGS.
MC: . . . . ASK 763

MIDNIGHT BLUE.
Tracks: / Midnight blue / Do you know where you're going to / When I fall in love / This time it's forever / Little bit more, A / Way we were / Arms of Mary / Hear the children sing / You'll never know / Misty blue / All by myself / Loving and free.
LP: . . . . CBS 81716

SINGS THE GREAT SONGS OF TODAY.
LP: . . . . SPR 8556
MC: . . . . SPC 8556

SINGS THE IVOR NOVELLO SONGBOOK.
Tracks: / My dearest dear / Fold your wings / Keep the home fires burning / It's a long way to Tipperary / Roses of Picardy / Keep right on to the end of the road / Nimrod / I can give you the starlight / Waltz of my heart / Shine through my dreams / My life belongs to you / Love is my reason / Some day my heart will awake / Rose of England / Music in May / Fly home little heart / Glamorous night / We'll gather lilacs.
LP: . . . . MFP 5845
MC: . . . . TC-MFP 5845

THAT LOVING FEELING.
LP: . . . . NE 1017

VERY BEST OF VINCE HILL.
Tracks: / Heartaches / Rose of Picardy / Forgotten dreams / Wives and lovers / Moonlight and roses / Look around / Where do I begin / Maybe this time / And I love you so / You are the sunshine of my life / Edelweiss / Take me to your heart again / Au revoir / No other love / Importance of your love, The / Little bluebird / Somewhere my love / Spanish eyes / Among my souvenirs / Love letters in the sand.
LP: . . . . MFP 5576

VINCE HILL.
MC: . . . . TC IDL 23

WHILE THE FEELING'S GOOD.
Tracks: / Way I am, The / Hungry years / Don't let me know / Loving arms / You don't bring me flowers / When you walk through life / Sometimes when we touch / While the feeling's good / Just when I needed you most / Country rose / Three times a lady / Ordinary people / Better than ever.
LP: . . . . CBR 1016
MC: . . . . KCBR 016
LP: . . . . ACLP 001

Hill & Wiltchinsky

ROMANTIC GUITARS.
Tracks: / When I fall in love / Gymnopedie / Way we were, The / Cavatina / Lady in red / Mona Lisa / Ave Maria / Memory / Annie's song / Romanza / Adagio Rodriguez / Music of the night, The / Barcarolle / I know him so well / Here, there and everywhere / If / Hello / Love story / Greatest love of all, The / For the love of Annie.
LP: . . . . STAR 2479
MC: . . . . STAC 2479

Hill, Z.Z.

BEST OF...Z Z HILL.
Tracks: / Next room / Down Home Blues / Please don't let our good thing end / Right arm for your love / Open house at my house / Someone else is steppin' in / Shade tree mechanic / Three into two won't go / Stop you from givin' me the blues / Friday is my day.
LP: . . . . MALP 006

BLUESMASTER.
LP: . . . . MAL 7420

DOWN HOME.
LP: . . . . MAL 7406
MC: . . . . MALC 7406

DUES PAID IN FULL.
Tracks: / Happiness is all I need / Hey little girl / I need someone (to love me) / You don't love me / If I could do it all over again / Everybody has to cry / Kind of love I want, The / That's it / What more? / Oh darling / Have mercy, someone / I found love / Set your sights higher / You got what I need.
LP: . . . . KENT 018

GREATEST HITS.
LP: . . . . MALP 7437

I'M A BLUES MAN.
LP: . . . . MAL 7415

IN MEMORIAM.
LP: . . . . MAL 7426

MAN NEEDS A WOMAN, A.
Tracks: / Blues at the opera(Communication in regards to circumstances / Act 1, Scene 1 - It Ain't no use / Act 1, Scene 2 - Ha Ha(Laughing song) / Act 2, Scene 1 - Second chance / Act 2, Scene 2 - Our love is getting better / Act 3 - Finale,Faithful and true / Chockin' kind, The / Hold back (one man at a time) / Man needs a woman, (a woman needs a man) / Early in the morning / I think I'd do it.
LP: . . . . TOP 138
MC: . . . . KTOP 138

RHYTHM AND THE BLUES.
LP: . . . . MAL 7411

WHOEVER'S THRILLING YOU (Is killing me).
Tracks: / Am I groovin' you / 'Cause I love you / Love in the street / I don't need half a love / Ain't nothing you can do / I've got to get you back / Two sides to every story / That ain't the way to make love / I keep on lovin' you / Look what you've done / Whoever's thrilling you (is killing me) / My turn.
LP: . . . . SSL 6006
MC: . . . . TCSSL 6006

Z.Z. HILL.
LP: . . . . MAL 7402
MC: . . . . MALC 7402

Hillage, Steve

FISH RISING.
Tracks: / Fish / Meditation of the snake / Sun song (Part 1 of Solar musick suite) / Canterbury sunrise (Part 2 of Solar musick suite) / Hiram Aftaglid meets the Dervish (Part 3 of Solar musick suite) / Sun song (reprise) (Part 4 of Solar musick suite) / Salmon pool (Part 1 of the Salmon song) / Solomon's Atlantis (Part 2 of the Salmon song) / Swimming with the salmon (Part 3 of the Salmon song) / King of the fishes (Part 4 of the Salmon song) / Sun Moon surfing (Part 1 of Aftaglid) / Great wave and the boat of Hermes, The (Part 2 of Aftaglid) / Silver ladder, The (Part 3 of Aftaglid) / Astral meadows (Part 4 of Aftaglid) / Lafta yoga song, The (Part 5 of Aftaglid) / Gliding (Part 6 of Aftaglid) / Golden vibe (Part 7 of Aftaglid).
LP: . . . . OVED 28
MC: . . . . OVEDC 28
LP: . . . . V 2031

FOR TO NEXT.
Tracks: / These uncharted lands / Kamikaze eyes / Alone / Anthems for the blind / Bright future / Frame by frame / Waiting / Glory.
LP: . . . . OVED 123
MC: . . . . OVEDC 123
LP: . . . . V 2244

GONNA GETCHA LOVE.
Tracks: / Gonna getcha love / At the party / Superstar / I finally found my love / I love you only / For the sake of the memories / I'm through with you / Just for your lovin'.
LP: . . . . EST 12002

GREEN.
Tracks: / Sea nature / Ether ships / Musick of the trees / Palm trees (love guitar) / Unidentified (flying being) / UFO over Paris / Leylines to Glassdom / Crystal City / Activation meditation / Glorious OM riff, The.
LP: . . . . OVED 30
LP: . . . . V 2098

"L".
Tracks: / Hurdy gurdy man / Hurdy gurdy glissando / Elecktrick Gypsies / Om nama shivaya / Lunar musick suite / It's all too much.
LP: . . . . OVED 29
MC: . . . . OVEDC 29
LP: . . . . V 2066

LIVE HERALD.
Tracks: / Salmon song / Dervish riff, The / Castle in the clouds / Light in the sky / Searching for the spark / Electric gypsies / Radiom / It's all too much / Talking to the sun / 1988 aktivator / New age synthesis (unzipping the zype) / Healing feeling / Lunar musick suite / Meditation of the dragon / Golden vibe, The.
2LP: . . . . VGD 3502

MOTIVATION RADIO.
Tracks: / Hello dawn / Motivation / Light in the sky / Radio / Wait one moment / Saucer surfing / Searching for the spark / Octave doctors and the crystal machine, The / Not fade away (glide forever).
LP: . . . . OVED 32
LP: . . . . V 2777

OPEN.
Tracks: / Day after day / Getting in tune / Open / Definite activity / Don't dither do it / Fire inside, The / Earthrise.
LP: . . . . OVED 31
LP: . . . . V 2135

RAINBOW DOME MUSIC.
Tracks: / Garden of paradise / Four ever rainbow.
LP: . . . . VR 1

Hillbilly....

HILL BILLY HOUN' DAWGS AND HONKY TONK ANGELS (Various artists).
LP: . . . . DT 33008

HILLBILLIES ON SPEED (Various artists).
LP: . . . . REDITA 116

HILLBILLY BOOGIE (Various artists).
LP: . . . . WH 2812

HILLBILLY BOOGIE & ROCK A BILLY (Various artists).
LP: . . . . RR 2009

HILLBILLY BOP-MEMPHIS STYLE (Various artists).
LP: . . . . M 5000

HILLBILLY HOP (Various artists).
Tracks: / Courtin' in the rain: *Various artists* / Flirting with you: *Various artists* / Skinny Minnie: *Various* artists / 8 more miles to Louisville: *Various artists* / Mississippi: *Various artists* / Texas vs. Alaska: *Various artists* / Steel guitar rag: *Various artists* / Four aces and a queen: *Various artists* / Lie Detector: *Various artists* / My heart, my heart: *Various artists* / Kiss me like crazy: *Various artists*/ Crawdad song: *Various artists* / All alone: *Various artists* / Happy go lucky: *Various artists* / 40th and plum: *Various artists*.
LP: . . . . CR 30251

HILLBILLY JAZZ (Various artists).
LP: . . . . FF 101

HILLBILLY ROCK (Canadian rockabilly) (Various artists).
LP: . . . . REDITA 127

HILLBILLY ROCK (Various artists).
Tracks: / Watch dog: *Various artists* / Everybody's rockin' but me: *Various artists* / Oh yeah: *Various artists*/ Roughneck blues: *Various artists* / Red hen boogie: *Various artists* / Too many: *Various artists* / Get me on your mind: *Various artists* / Hey, honey: *Various artists* / Started out a walkin' hey Mae: *Various* artists / Good deal Lucille: *Various artists* / Looking for love: *Various artists* / What's the use (I still love you): *Various artists* / I ain't gonna waste my time: *Various artists* / Billy goat boogie, The: *Various artists* / I've got a brand new baby: *Various artists* / Start all over: *Various artists* / Lonesome journey: *Various artists* / Hey you there: *Various artists* / No help wanted: *Various artists*.
LP: . . . . MFLP 034

HILLBILLY ROCK 'N' ROLL (Various artists).
LP: . . . . WLP 8939

HILLBILLY STOMP (Various artists).
Tracks: / Blue moon on the bayou: *Le Blance, Red* / Marrita: *Le Blance, Red* / Memory in my heart: *Le Blance*, Red / I love that woman (right or wrong): *Le Blance, Red* / Freed my silly heart: *Le Blance, Red* / You're laughing at me: *Le*

Blance, Red / Memory in my heart: *Hutto, Bill & His Playboys* / Wanna go steady: *Hutto, Bill & His Playboys* / Boogie woogie tout le temps: *Martin, Frenchie* / Mable's done gone: *Noble, Jerry* / Yesterday we were married: *Ferrier, Al* / I'll never do any wrong: *Ferrier, Al*.
LP: . . . . GCL 108

HILLBILLY SWEETHEART (Various artists).
LP: . . . . REDITA 128

Hillbilly Rock

HILLBILLY ROCK (Various artists).
LP: . . . . CFM 509

Hiller, Dame Wendy

JANE EYRE (see under Jane Eyre (bk)).

Hiller, Holger

AS IS.
LP: . . . . STUMM 060

BUNCH OF FOULNESS IN THE PIT, A.
Tracks: / Liebe beamtinnen und beamte / Blass schlafen rabe / Bunkarest-Budapest / Jonny, du lump / Akt mit feile / Hosen, die nicht aneinander passen / Chemische & physikalische entdeckung, mutter der fohlichkeit / Ein bundel faulnis in der grube / Das feuer / Ein hoch auf das bugelin.
LP: . . . . BRED 59

OBEN IM ECK.
LP: . . . . STUMM 38
MC: . . . . CSTUMM 38

Hilliard Ensemble

PEROTIN.
LP: . . . . ECM 1385

Hillier, Paul

PROENSA.
LP: . . . . ECM 1368

Hillman, Chris

CLEAR SAILING.
Tracks: / Nothing gets through / Fallen favourite / Quits / Hot dusty roads / Heartbreaker / Playing the fool / Lucky in love / Rollin' and tumblin' / Ain't that peculiar / Clear sailing.
LP: . . . . K 53060

DESERT ROSE.
Tracks: / Why you been gone so long / Somebody's back in town / Wall around your heart / Rough and rowdy ways / Desert rose / Running the roadblocks / I can't keep you in love with me / Treasure of love / Ashes of love / Turn your radio on.
LP: . . . . SPIN 113
LP: . . . . SDLP 060
MC: . . . . SDC 060
LP: . . . . SH 3743
MC: . . . . SH 3743C

MORNING SKY.
Tracks: / Tomorrow is a long time / Taker, The / Here today and gone tomorrow / Morning sky / Ripple / Good time Charlie's got the blues / Don't let your sweet love die / Mexico / It's happening to you / Hickory wind.
LP: . . . . SDLP 053
MC: . . . . SDC 053
LP: . . . . SH 3729
MC: . . . . SH 3279C

Hillman, McGuinn

MEAN STREETS.
Tracks: / Mean streets / Entertainment / Soul shoes / Between you and me / Angel / Love me tonight / King for a night / Secret side of you / Ain't no money / Turn your radio on.
LP: . . . . EA-ST 12108

Hillmen

HILLMEN, THE.
LP: . . . . SH 3719

Hills, Anne

WOMAN OF A CALM HEART.
LP: . . . . FF 464

Hills & Home

HILLS & HOME (Thirty years of bluegrass) (Various artists).
Tracks: / Why did you wonder?: *Monroe, Bill* / Blue ridge cabin home: *Flat, Lester, Earl Scruggs & The Foggy Mountain Boys* / Daniel prayed: *Stanley Brothers* / Love please come home: *Reno, Don & Red Smiley* / You'd better wake up: *Wiseman, Mac* / Your old standby: *Eanes, Jim* / Twenty one years: *Lonesome Pine Fiddlers* / Springhill disaster: *Clifton, Bill* / Old age: *Woolum, Dave* / Blackberry blossom: *Baker, Billy* / Hold what you've got: *Martin, Jimmy* / Diesel trains: *Jim & Jesse* / Pathway of teardrops / Hills and home: *Country Gentlemen* / Raise a ruckus tonight: *Lonesome River Boys* / Fox on the run: *Emerson & Waldron* / Body and soul: *New Grass Revival* / Dill pickle rag: *Bluegrass All Stars*.
LP: . . . . NW 225

Hills, Ian

FAR CRY.
LP: . . . . LRF 092

Hillsiders

DAY IN THE COUNTRY, A.
LP: . . . . LP 004

HILLSIDERS, THE.
Tracks: / Driver get me home on time / I'll never need you again / Yesterday's lovers / Harpin on / Sail away / I never slept a wink last night / Sleepy eyed Sam / She was my only one / Last dollar / World to him is kind, The / Hold on to me / Let me be the one.
LP: . . . . LP 005

Hi-Lo's

HI-LO'S BACK AGAIN, THE.
Tracks: / Seems like old times / When Sunny gets blue / Life is just a bowl of cherries / I remember you / My funny Valentine / Come rain or come shine / Everything must change / Misty / Then I'll be tired of you / Georgia on my mind.
LP: . . . . MOIR 106
LP: . . . . MPS 68 217

Hilt

CALL THE AMBULANCE.
LP: . . . . NET 022

Hilton Fyle Band

FRESH.
LP: . . . . NADLP 1002

Hilton, James

GOODBYE MR CHIPS (Sheddon, John).
MCSET: . . . . COL 2007

LOST HORIZON (Elder, Michael).
MCSET: . . . . COL 4002

Hilton, John Buxton

DEATH OF AN ALDERMAN (West, Timothy (nar)).
MC: . . . . CAT 4034

Hilton, Ronnie

EMI YEARS, THE: RONNIE HILTON (The best of).
Tracks: / Hey look me over / Who are we / Young and foolish / Ugly bug ball, The / Windmill in old Amsterdam, A / What do I do / Once / No other love / Happy again / One life / I've grown accustomed to her face / Ugly duckling, The / Wonder of you, The / Good, bad but beautiful / Danny the dragon / Two different worlds.
LP: . . . . EMS 1325
MC: . . . . TCEMS 1325

RONNIE HILTON.
Tracks: / I still believe / No other love / Veni vidi vici / Around the world / Magic moments / Blossom fell, A / Stars shine in your eyes / Yellow rose of Texas, The / Woman in love, A / Wonderful, wonderful / I may never pass this way again / Miracle of love, The / World outside, The / Don't let the rain come down / As I love you / One blade of grass (in a meadow) / On the street where you live / She / Marching along to the blues / Her hair was yellow / Day the rains came, The / Do I love you? / Gift, The / Beautiful bosa nova.
MC: . . . . HR 8191

VERY BEST OF RONNIE HILTON - 16 FAVOURITES OF THE 50'S.
Tracks: / I still believe / Veni vidi vici / Blossom fell, A / Stars shine in your eyes / Yellow rose of Texas / Young and foolish / No other love / Who are we? / Woman in love / Two different worlds / Around the world / Wonderful, wonderful / Magic moments / I may never pass this way again / World outside, The / Wonder of you, The.
LP: . . . . MFP 415645-1
MC: . . . . TCMFP 415645-4

Himber, Richard

1939: RICHARD HIMBER (Himber, Richard & His Orchestra).
LP: . . . . CLP 7

1940: RICHARD HIMBER (Himber, Richard & His Orchestra).
LP: . . . . CLP 91

Himmelman, Peter

GEMATRIA.
Tracks: / I feel young again / Waining moon / Burnin' shame / Salt and ashes / Fight for the world / Does it matter / Trees are testifying, the / Wrapped up in cellophane / You bought it / 1,000 years.
LP: . . . . ILPS 9892
MC: . . . . ICT 9892

Hinata, Toshifumi

ROME IMPROVISATION.
LP: . . . . IM 009

Hinchcliffe, Frank

IN SHEFFIELD PARK.
LP: 12TS 308

Hind, Nicky

HINDSIGHT.
LP: . . . . MVWC 2

Hindoustan

L'HINDOUSTAN (Various artists).
Tracks: / Purya kalyan: *Various artists* / Kalpana madhyamat sarang: *Various artists*.
LP: . . . . ARN 33332

Hinds, Justin

TRAVEL WITH LOVE.
LP: . . . . NH 309
MC: . . . . NHC 309

Hinds, Ornell

TOGETHER AGAIN (See Chandell, Tim) (Hinds, Ornell & Tim Chandell).

Hinds, Sinclair

PRODUCERS, THE.
LP: . . . . LIPS 5
MC: . . . . TCLIPS 5

Hindsight

DAYS LIKE THIS.
Tracks: / Heaven's just a breath away / Stand up / Walkin' tall / Give me your heart / Small change (the corn exchange mix) (CD & cassette only) / Lowdown / Romance / Small change / Crazy like the night / Lowdown (the highlife mix) (CD & cassette only) / Heaven's just a breath away (bliss mix) (CD & cassette only).
LP: . . . . CIRCA 3
MC: . . . . CIRC 3

Hindu Love Gods

HINDU LOVE GODS.
Tracks: / Walkin' blues / Travelin' riverside blues / Raspberry beret / Crosscut saw / Junko pardner / Mannish boy / Wang dang doodle / Battleship chains / I'm a one woman man / Vigilante man.
LP: . . . . WX 389
MC: . . . . WX 389C

Hine, Graham

BOWERY FANTASY.
LP: . . . . BG 2021

Hine, Rupert

IMMUNITY.
Tracks: / Listening is believing / I hang on to my vertigo / Immunity / Another stranger / Psycho surrender / I think a man will hang soon / Surface tension / Misplaced love / Samara / Make a wish.
MC: . . . . CAM 68519
LP: . . . . AMLH 68519

WAVING NOT DROWNING.
Tracks: / Eleven faces / Curious kind, The / Set up / Dark windows / Sniper, The / Innocents in paradise / House arrest / Outsider, The / One man's poison.
LP: . . . . AMLH 68541

WILDEST WISH TO FLY, THE.
LP: . . . . ILPS 9747
MC: . . . . ICT 9747

Hines, Earl

1965.
LP: . . . . PM 1552611

AFTER YOU'VE GONE (Hines, Earl & Muggsy Spanier All Stars).
LP: . . . . ZR 1021

ANOTHER MONDAY DATE.
Tracks: / Jitterbug waltz / Darktown strutters ball / Black and blue / Blue turning grey over you / Honeysuckle rose / Squeeze me / Ain't misbehavin' / Keepin' out of mischief now / I can't give you anything but love / I'm gonna sit right down / Lulu's back in town / Two sleepy people / Deep forest / Everything depends on you / Am I too late? / Blues for Tatum / In San Francisco / Ann / You can depend on me / When I dream of you / R. R. blues / Straight to love / Piano man / My Monday date.
2LP: . . . . P 24043

AT CLUB HANGOVER VOL.5.
LP: . . . . SLP 4063

AT HOME: EARL HINES.
LP: . . . . DS 212

BIG BAND.
LP: . . . . GELP 15059
LP: 500111

BLUE SKIES (Hines, Earl "Fatha", Et Son Orchestre).
Tracks: / Jazz is his old lady and my old man / Just squeeze me / Yellow days / Deed I do / Blue skies / Hey love / Make it easy on yourself / Feelings.
LP: 260 236 1

BLUES AND THINGS (Hines, Earl with Jimmy Rushing).
LP: . . . . S 1262
LP: 500076

BLUES FOR GARROWAY.
LP: . . . . PM 1652391
MC: . . . . PM 1652394

BOOGIE WOOGIE ON THE ST LOUIS BLUES.
Tracks: / Monday date, A / Blues in thirds / You can depend on me / Blue because of you / I can't trust myself alone / Boogie woogie on St. Louis blues.
LP: . . . . BLM 52032

BUBBLING OVER (Hines, Earl & His Orchestra).
Tracks: / That's a plenty / Fat babes / Maple leaf rag / Sweet Georgia Brown / Rosetta / Copenhagen / Angry / Wolverine blues / Rock and rye / Cavernism / Disappointed in love / Rhythm lullaby / Japanese sandman / Bubbling over / Blue / Julia.
LP: . . . . OFF 3044

CHICAGO HIGH LIFE.
Tracks: / Blues in thirds / Off time blues / Chicago high life / My Monday date / Stowaway / Chimes blues / Panther rag / Just too soon / I know that you know / Oh, sister, ain't that hot? / Blues my naughty sweetie gives to me / Glad rag doll / Everybody loves my baby / Beau-koo Jack / Down among the sheltering palms / Love me tonight.
LP: . . . . CHD 137
MC: . . . . MCHD 137

CLASSIC PIANOS (See under Garner, Erroll) (Various artists).

COLEMAN HAWKINS AND THE EARL HINES TRIO 1965 (see Hawkins, Coleman).

COMES IN HANDY.
LP: . . . . AP 112

DEEP FOREST.
Tracks: / Deep forest / Lover come back to me / I can't get started / MF blues / Just you, just me / Very thought of you, The.
LP: . . . . BLM 52002
MC: . . . . BLM 52002C
LP: . . . . HEP 1003

DINAH.
LP: . . . . NL 70577

DIXIELAND BAND.
LP: . . . . SM 3118

DOES HOAGY.
LP: . . . . AP 113

EARL 'FATHA' HINES.
LP: . . . . LPJT 46
LP: . . . . GNPS 9042

EARL 'FATHA' HINES-VOL II.
LP: . . . . GNPS 9043

EARL HINES.
LP: . . . . GNPS 9010

EARL HINES AND FRIENDS LIVE.
LP: 2MJP 1050

EARL HINES AND HIS ALL STARS (Hines, Earl & His All Stars).
LP: . . . . SLP 4071

EARL HINES ANS WALLACE DAVENPORT, VOL. 1 (Hines, Earl/ Wallace Davenport).
LP: . . . . SM 3907
MC: . . . . MC 3907

EARL HINES ANS WALLACE DAVENPORT, VOL. 2 (Hines, Earl/ Wallace Davenport).
LP: . . . . SM 3908

EARL HINES COLLECTION (20 Golden Greats).
Tracks: / Honeysuckle rose / Monday date / Darktown strutters' ball / Dark eyes / Humoresque / Hollywood hop / Web, The / Nice work if you can get it / If I had you / Relaxin' at the Touro / Ain't misbehavin' / I'm gonna sit right down and write myself a letter / Lulu's back in town / Blue turning grey over you / Squeeze me / Jumpin' something / Keepin' out of mischief now / Ugly child / Blues for Garroway / I've got the world on a string.
LP: . . . . DVLP 2057
MC: . . . . DVMC 2057

EARL HINES CONCERT (14 February 1966).
Tracks: / I've got the world on a string / I cover the waterfront / Rosetta / I know a little bit / Kiss to build a dream on, A / Do you know what it means to miss New Orleans? / St. Louis blues.
LP: . . . . SM 3074

EARL HINES FEATURING MUGGSY SPANIER.
2LP: 406501

EARL HINES IN NEW ORLEANS.
Tracks: / Bourbon Street parade / My Monday date / Song of the islands / Blues my naughty sweetie gives to me / Rosetta / Playing with fire / One I love belongs to somebody else, The / Bouncing for Panassie / Way down yonder in New Orleans.

LP: . . . . SNTF 697

EARL HINES PLAYS GEORGE GERSHWIN.
Tracks: / Rhapsody in blue / Foggy day, A / Our love is here to stay / They all laughed / Somebody loves me / Embraceable you.
LP: . . . . ORL 8582
LP: . . . . S 1339

EARL MEETS SWEETS AND JAWS (Hines, Earl/Harry Edison/Eddie (Lockjaw) Davis).
Tracks: / Lax / Bye bye blackbird / In a mellow tone / Georgia on my mind / I can't get started.
LP: 9198 205

EARL'S BACKROOM AND COZY'S CARAVAN (Hines, Earl Quartet & Cozy Cole Septet).
Tracks: / Brussels' hustle / Oooh / Backroom at the villa d'este / Caravan / Phatz' blues / Margie.
LP: . . . . AFF 167

EAST OF THE SUN.
Tracks: / If I had you / One I love belongs to somebody else, The / Just friends / Can't we talk it over? / East of the sun / I cover the waterfront.
LP: . . . . BLM 52012

EVENING WITH EARL HINES.
Tracks: / Perdido / Boogie woogie on St. Louis blues / I got it bad and that ain't good / All of me / Things ain't what they used to be / Li'l darlin' / James St. blues / Prelude to a kiss / Prisoner of love / My ship / La Rosita / Rainy day / Polka dots and moonbeams / Lester leaps in / Who / I ain't got nobody / Marie / Dinkler boogie / I wish you love.
2LP: . . . . VJD 534

FATHA JUMPS (1940 - 42) (Hines, Earl & His Orchestra).
LP: . . . . BS 7115
MC: . . . . BS 7115C

FATHA PLAYS CLASSICS.
LP: 2233012
MC: 2173012

FATHA, VOL.1.
LP: . . . . ZET 710

GIANTS, THE (see Grappelli, Stephane) (Hines, Earl & Stephane Grappelli).

HINES PLAYS HINES.
LP: . . . . S 1320

HINE'S TUNE (Paris 1965).
Tracks: / Hine's tune / One I love belongs to someone else, The / Bag's Groove / Blue turning grey over you / Don's blues / Tenderly / Boogie woogie on St. Louis blues / These foolish things / I'm a little brown bird / Que rest et il de nos amours / Little girl blue / You are the cream in my coffee / I can't get started / Petite laitue / Cherry / Sweet lorraine / I've got the world on a string / Body and soul / Clopin - clopant / Cest si bon.
LP: . . . . FC 101

IN NEW ORLEANS.
Tracks: / Someday, sweetheart / Playing with fire / Elephant stomp / Do you know what it means to miss New Orleans / Bouncing for panassie / Blues my naughty sweetie gives to me / Sugar babe / If I could be with you / Someday you'll be sorry / Moonglow.
LP: . . . . LPUP 5058
LP: . . . . MTLP 1.014

INDISPENSABLE EARL HINES VOLS.3 & 4.
Tracks: / Rosetta / Child of a disordered brain / Everything depends on you / Comin' home / Jelly jelly / Up jumped the Devil / Won't you come back? / Jersey bounce / Julia / South side / On the sunny side of the street / Melancholy baby / It had to be you / Windy City jive / Straight to love / Singin' on C / Water boy / Yellow fire / Somehow / I got it bad and that ain't good / I never dreamt / Father jumps, The / Boy with the wistful eyes / Jitney man / Earl, The / You don't know what love is / She'll always remember / Skylark / Second balcony jump / Stormy Monday blues / Scoops Carry's furlough blues.
2LP: . . . . PM 43266

INDISPENSABLE EARL HINES VOLS.5 & 6 (1944-66).
Tracks: / My fate is in your hands / I've got a feeling I'm falling / Honeysuckle rose / Squeeze me / Undecided / I've found a new baby / Fatha's blues / Sunday kind of love, A / Tosca's dance / Jim / Black coffee / You always hurt the one you love / Save it, pretty mama / Bye bye baby / Smoke rings / Shoeshine boy / Stanley steamer / Bernard's tune / Dream of you.
2LP: . . . . PM 45358

INDISPENSABLE EARL HINES VOLS.1 & 2 (1939-45).
Tracks: / Indiana / GT stomp / Ridin' and livin' / Grand Terrace shuffle / Father steps in / Piano man / Riff medley / Me and Columbus / XYZ / Gator swing / After all I've been to you / Lightly and politely / Rosetta / Boogie woogie on St. Louis blues / Deep forest / Number 19 / My heart of a disordered brain / Wait till it happens to you / Call me happy / Ann Topsy Turvy / Blue because of you / You can depend on me / Tantalizing a Cuban / Easy rhythm / In swamplands / I'm falling for you.
2LP: . . . . PM 42412

IT DON'T MEAN A THING IF IT AIN'T GOT THAT SWING (Hines, Earl & Paul Gonsalvez).
Tracks: / It don't mean a thing / Over the rainbow / What am I here for? / Moten swing / Blue sands / I got it bad and that ain't good.
LP: . . . . BLP 30153

JACK TEAGARDEN AND EARL HINES (see Teagarden, Jack & Earl Hines) (Hines, Earl & Jack Teagarden).

JAZZ TIME VOL.10.
LP: 502710

LEGENDARY LITTLE THEATRE CONCERT OF 1964 VOL.1.
Tracks: / Stealin' apples.
LP: . . . . DE 602

LIVE AT THE VILLAGE VANGUARD.
Tracks: / Lover come back to me / Cavernism / Red river remembered / Out of nowhere / Moten swing / Sometimes I'm happy / Tea for two / Breezin' along with the breeze / Rosetta.
LP: 4624011
MC: 4624014

LIVE IN ORANGE.
LP: 33305

MASTERS OF JAZZ.
LP: . . . . SLP 4102

MPS JAZZ TIME VOL 11 (Hines, Earl & Jaki Byard).
Tracks: / Toodle oo, toodle oo, A / This is always / Rosetta / I can't trust myself alone / Sweet Georgia Brown / As long as I live / Genoa to Pescara / La rosita.
LP: 5C 064 61172

MY TRIBUTE TO LOUIS.
LP: . . . . AP 111

ONCE UPON A TIME.
Tracks: / Once upon a time / Black and tan fantasy / Fantastic, that's you / Cottontail.
LP: . . . . JAS 42
MC: . . . . JAS C42
LP: . . . . AS 9108
MC: . . . . ASC 9108

PEARLS, THE.
Tracks: / I wish I knew / Indian Summer / You made me love you / Pearls, The / Wolverine blues / Mandy / Make up your mind.
LP: . . . . BLM 52022

PIANO 1938.
LP: . . . . ET 5

PIANO MAN.
Tracks: / Rosetta / Body and soul / Child of a disordered brain / On the sunny side of the street / My melancholy baby / Blues in thirds / G.T. stomp / Grand terrace shuffle / Father steps in / Piano man / Riff medley / Boogie woogie on St. Louis blues / Deep forest / Number 19 / Call me happy / Tantalizing a Cuban / Jelly jelly / Up jumped the devil / Windy city jive / Father jumps, The / Second balcony jump / Stormy Monday blues.
LP: . . . . NL 86750
MC: . . . . NK 86750

PIANO PORTRAITS OF AUSTRALIA.
LP: . . . . S 1350

PLAYS COLE PORTER.
LP: . . . . S 1345

PLAYS DUKE ELLINGTON VOL.1.
LP: . . . . S 1300

PLAYS DUKE ELLINGTON VOL.2.
LP: . . . . S 1323

PLAYS DUKE ELLINGTON VOL.3.
Tracks: / Black and tan fantasy / Don't you know I care / Caravan / I'm just a lucky so and so / Just squeeze me / Prelude to a kiss / All too soon.
LP: . . . . S 1341

PLAYS DUKE ELLINGTON VOL.4.
LP: . . . . S 1357

ROYAL GARDEN BLUES.
LP: . . . . B 2522

SAN FRANCISCO- OCT. 1957.
LP: . . . . KLJ 20006

SPONTANEOUS EXPLORATIONS.
LP: . . . . SM 3258

SWINGIN' DOWN (Hines, Earl & His Orchestra).
Tracks: / Blue drag / Sensational mood / Rosetta / Cavernism / We found romance / Blue / Swinging down.
LP: . . . . HEP 1018

SWINGIN' THE 20'S (see Carter,Benny) (Hines, Earl & Benny Carter).

TEA FOR TWO.
Tracks: / Velvet moon / Blues after midnight / Shiny stockings / Blues in thirds / When I dream of you / Sweet Lorraine.
LP: . . . . BLP 30106

TEXAS RUBY RED.
Tracks: / Cavernism / Coquette / Sometimes I'm happy / Ramona / More than you know / Texas Ruby Red / Little girl / You're mine, you.
LP: . . . . BLM 52042

TIN ROOF BLUES (see Spanier, Muggsy) (Hines, Earl & Muggsy Spanier).

TOUR DE FORCE.
Tracks: / When your lover has gone / Indian Summer / Mack the knife / I never knew (I could love anyone like I'm loving you) / Say it isn't so / Lonesome road.
LP: . . . . BLP 60140
LP: . . . . BLP 30143

VARIETIES.
LP: . . . . XAN 203

WALTZING MATILDA.
LP: . . . . S 1338

WEST SIDE STORY.
Tracks: / West Side story medley / Close to you / Why do I love you? / In my solitude / Don't get around much anymore.
LP: . . . . BLP 30170

Hines, Gregory

GREGORY HINES.
Tracks: / That girl wants to dance with me / Love don't love you anymore / You need somebody / This is what I believe / I'm gonna get to you / There's nothing better than love / Gloria my love / So much better now.
LP: 4610271
MC: 4610274

THERE'S NOTHING BETTER THAN LOVE (See under Vandross, Luther) (Vandross, Luther & Gregory Hines).

Hines, Marcia

TAKE IT FROM THE BOYS.
Tracks: / Your love still brings me to my knees / Love me like the last time / Take it from the boys / Many rivers to cross / What a bitch is love / I was free / Just this one time / Dance goes on, The / It don't take much / Taking it all in stride.
LP: . . . . LOGO 1034
MC: . . . . KLOGO 1034

Hinge & Bracket

AT ABBEY ROAD.
Tracks: / Let the people sing / This is my lovely day / No no Nanette medley / Things are seldom what they seem / So please you sir / Trot here and there / Stout hearted men / Ivor Novello medley / There's always something fishy about French / Highly respectable wife / On the road to Mandalay / Those were the days / Goodbye.
LP: . . . . NTSD 201

DEAR LADIES.
LP: . . . . REH 450
MC: . . . . ZCR 450

HINGE AND BRACKET IN CONCERT.
Tracks: / HMS Pinafore / Patience / Iolanthe / Pirates of Penzance / Yeoman of the Guard / Perchance to dream / Gondoliers / Il Trovatore.
LP: . . . . OU 2227

WE'LL GATHER LILACS (see under EMI Comedy Classics).

Hingle, Pat (nar)

DEVIL AND DANIEL WEBSTER, THE (see under Devil & Daniel... (bk)).

Hino, Terumasa

TARO'S MOOD.
LP: . . . . ENJA 2028

VIBRATIONS.
LP: . . . . ENJA 2010

HI-NRG

ENERGHIGHS (Various artists).
Tracks: / Build me a bridge: *Bertei, Adele* / They only come out at night: *Brown, Pete (Lyricist)* / Blue eyed technology: *Joli, France* / Doin' it in a haunted house: *Gage, Yvonne* / Sound of my heart: *Sleeping Lions* / Visitors, The: *Abba* / Breakdance: *Cara, Irene* / Where the boys are: *Lorna* / Why me?: *Cara, Irene.*
LP: . . . . EPC 26110
MC: 40 26110

Hinterland

KISSING THE ROOF OF HEAVEN.
MC: . . . . ICT 9949
LP: . . . . ILPS 9949
MC: 842 273 4
LP: 842 273 1

Hinton, Eddie

LETTERS FROM MISSISSIPPI.
Tracks: / My searching is over / Sad and lonesome / Everybody needs love / Letters from Mississippi / Everybody meets Mr.Blue / Uncloudy day / I want a woman / Ting a ling ling / Wet weather man / I will always love you / It's all right / I'll come running (back to you).
LP: . . . . ZN 1001

Hinton, Milt

BY REQUEST (See under Rosengarden, Bobby) (Hinton, Milt, Bobby Rosengarden & Eddie Higgins).

JUST THE TWO OF US (see under Hodes, Art) (Hinton, Milt & Art Hodes).

Hip Hop

BEST OF WEST COAST HIP HOP (Various artists).
LP: . . . . MACA 1
MC: . . . . 2C MACA

HIP HOP 17 (Various artists).
LP: . . . . ELCST 17
MC: . . . . ZCELT 17

HIP HOP 21 (Various artists).
Tracks: / Feel the horns: *Cold Crush Brothers* / You never heard of me: *Spicy Ham* / Sir vere: *Sir Fresh* & *D J Critical* / Listen to my turbo: *Raw Dope Posse* / Because I like it like that: *Jungle Brothers* / Damn I'm good: *King Tree* / Let me love you: *5 Star Motet* / Funky bass: *M.C. Rajah.*
LP: . . . . ELCST 21
MC: . . . . ZCELC 21

HIP HOP 22 (Various artists).
LP: . . . . ELCST 22

HIP HOP 23 (Various artists).
LP: . . . . ELCST 23
MC: . . . . ZCELC 23

HIP HOP AND RAPPING IN THE HOUSE (Various artists).
Tracks: / Doctorin' the house: *Cold Cut* / Rok da house: *Beatmasters, featuring The Cookie Crew* / Move the crowd: *Eric B & Rakim* / Gold: *Grandmaster Flash & The Furious Five* / Get down: *Derek B* / Cinderfella Dana Dane: *Dane, Dana* / Tramp: *Salt 'N' Pepa* / Go see the doctor: *Kool Moe Dee* / (Bang zoom) Let's go go: *Real Roxanne with Hitman Howie Tee* / Wipe out: *Fat Boys & The Beach Boys* / Beat dis: *Bomb The Bass* / It takes two: *Base, Rob & D.J. E-Z Rock* / Unity (part 1 - the third coming): *Bambaata, Afrika/James Brown* / I got da feelin': *Sweet Tee* / (Nothing serious) just buggin': *Whistle* / Show, The: *Fresh, Doug E & Get Fresh Crew* / How ya like me now: *Spyder-D/DJ Doc* / Eric B for president: *Eric B & Rakim* / Females: *Cookie Crew* / Lean on me (edit): *Club Nouveau.*
LP: . . . . SMR 852
MC: . . . . SMC 852

HIP HOP CHARTBUSTERS VOL 1 (Various artists).
Tracks: / I can't live without my radio: *L.L. Cool J* / (Nothing serious) Just buggin': *Whistle* / Amityville (house on the hill): *Lovebug Starski* / Go see the doctor: *Kool Moe Dee* / Alice, I want you just for me: *Full Force* / Show, The: *Fresh, Doug E* / Girls ain't nothing but trouble: *D.J. Jazzy Jeff & Fresh Prince* / We work hard: *U.T.F.O* / Message, The: *Grandmaster Flash & The Furious Five* / I need a beat: *Various artists* / Haunted house of rock: *Whodini.*
LP: . . . . BLATLP 4
MC: . . . . BLATMC 4

HIP HOP - THE ORIGINAL AND THE BEST (Various artists).
MC: . . . . FRESHC 1
LP: . . . . FRESH 1

HIP-HOP 18 Various artists (Various artists).
Tracks: / We'll make your body move: *Various artists* / Devastation: *Devastator* / Force desire: *Keith, Jazzy* / Take a walk: *Seville feat. Jazzy J* / Go southside: *Frick'n'Frack* / Who's on mine: *Frick'n'Frack* / You know how to reach us: *Kings of Pressure* / She's a dog: *Kay Gee the All feat.D.J.Drew* / Cotton Club, The: *Jury* / Opsta now: *Royal Ron* / We have risen: *Almighty El-Cee.*
LP: . . . . ELCST 18
MC: . . . . ZCELC 18

HIP-HOP '87 (Various artists).
LP: . . . . HHOP 87
MC: . . . . ZCHOP 87

LET THE MUSIC SCRATCH (Various artists).
Tracks: / Let the music play: *Shannon* / In the bottle: *Beat Boys* / C.O.D.: *Beat Boys* / Bebop rock: *Beat Boys* / On the up side: *Xena* / Somebody's watching me: *Mainline* / I.M.S.: *Parrsih, Man*/ Techno trax: *Parrsih, Man* / Give me tonight: *Shannon* / All arrembaggio: *Filipponi* / Let the music play (rhapsody): *Shannon*.
LP: . . . . MKLP 1

SERIOUS HIP-HOP 2 (Various artists).
Tracks: / Bridge is over, The: *D.J. Scott La Rock* / It's a demo: *D.J. Polo/Kool G Rap* / Cut it up: *2 Live Crew* / Rock and roll: *Chubb Rock/Domino* / Mega mix: *Mackintosh, Chris* / New girl in town: *Sugar Sugar*/ Saturday night: *Various artists* / Elaweazer just a skeezer: *Hard Rock Soul Movement* / Terminator, The: *Jnr Gee/A Team*.
LP: . . . . SHOP 2

STREET SOUNDS ELECTRO 1 (Various artists).
Tracks: / Return of Capt. Rock: *Various artists* / Breakdance: *Various artists* / Feel the force: *Various artists* / Jam on revenge: *Various artists* / I'm the packman: *Various artists* / Clear: *Various artists*.
LP: . . . . ELCST 1
MC: . . . . ZCELC 1

STREET SOUNDS ELECTRO 2 (Various artists).
LP: . . . . ELCST 2
MC: . . . . ZCELC 2

STREET SOUNDS ELECTRO 3 (Various artists).
LP: . . . . ELCST 3
MC: . . . . ZCELC 3

STREET SOUNDS ELECTRO 4 (Various artists).
LP: ELCST4

STREET SOUNDS ELECTRO 7 (Various artists).
Tracks: / Girls: *Various artists* / 808 beats: *Various artists* / Fresh mess: *Various artists* / Queen of rox: *Various artists* / Dedication: *Various artists* / Itchiban scratch: *Various artists* / Stick up kid: *Various artists*.
LP: . . . . ELCST 7
MC: . . . . ZCELC 7

STREET SOUNDS ELECTRO 9 (Various artists).
LP: . . . . ELCST 9
MC: . . . . ZCELCST 9

STREET SOUNDS ELECTRO 10 (Various artists).
LP: . . . . ELCST 10
MC: . . . . ZCELC 10

STREET SOUNDS ELECTRO 11 (Various artists).
LP: . . . . ELCST 11
MC: . . . . ZCELC 11

STREET SOUNDS ELECTRO 15 (Various artists).
LP: . . . . ELCST 15
MC: . . . . ZCELC 15

STREET SOUNDS HIP HOP 16 (Various artists).
Tracks: / Travelling at the speed of thought (remix): *Ultra Magnetic MC's* / New generation: *Classical Two* / Cabbage patch: *World Class Wrecking Crew* / Rap will never die (part 2): *M.C. Shy D.* / He cuts so fresh: *Marl, Marley* / Pleasure seekers: *Faze One* / Paybacks a mutha: *King Tee & DJ Kooley* / Cold gettin dumb: *Just Ice* / 2 live is what we are: *2 Live Crew*.
LP: . . . . ELCST 16
MC: . . . . ZCELC 16

STREET SOUNDS HIP-HOP ELECTRO 13 (Various artists).
LP: . . . . ELCST 13
MC: . . . . ZCELC 13

STREET SOUNDS HIP-HOP ELECTRO 12 (Various artists).
Tracks: / Fastest man alive: *Grandmaster Flash* / Square dance rap: *Sir Mix-a-Lot* / Trow the D and ghetto bass: *Ghetto Style With 2 Life Crew* / Ultimate III live: *Ultimate* / MC story: *M.C. Chill* / Girls (Rulin' the world): *Celebrity Club feat. Royal Silk* / Funky beat: *Whodini*.
LP: . . . . ELCST 12
MC: . . . . ZCELC 12

STREET SOUNDS HIP-HOP ELECTRO 14 (Various artists).
Tracks: / Monster beat: *Awesome Foursome* / Leave it to the drums (here come the drums): *Tricky Tee* / Breaking bells: *T LA Rock* / Manipulator, The: *Mixmaster Gee & The Turntable Orchestra* / Me and my possee: *Divine* Sounds / She's a skeezer: *Fresh Force* / Downbeats: *M.C. Chill featuring Beatmaster T* / Rip the cut: *Skinny Boys*.
LP: . . . . ELCST 14
MC: . . . . ZCELC 14

STREET SOUNDS N.Y. VS L.A. BEATS (Various artists).
LP: . . . . ELCST 1001

Hip House

HIP HOUSE (Various artists).
LP: . . . . NE 1430
MC: . . . . CE 2430

HIP HOUSE - 20 HIP HOUSE HITS (Various artists).
Tracks: / Get on the dancefloor: *Base, Rob* / Girl you know it's true: *Milli Vanilli* / Rollin' with kid 'n' play: *Kid 'N Play* / Faster than fast: *Jason, Jazzy* / Straight out of the jungle: *Jungle Brothers* / We call it acieed: *D Mob* / Get up on this: *She Rockers* / Getting fierce: *Shabazz, Lakim* / Black, rock and Ron: *Black Rock & Ron* / Hype: *Kid 'N Play* / Hit the rap Jack: *Debbie D* / Respect: *Adeva* / I can do this: *Love, Monie* / Respect: *Real Roxanne* / Twist and shout: *Salt 'N' Pepa* / Blow the house down: *Wee Papa Girl Rappers* / Wind me up: *Bam Bam, MC* / I'm riffin': *M.C. Duke* / Jabara: *Electra*/ Truth open our eyes: *Jefferson*.
LP: . . . . SMR 974
MC: . . . . SMC 974

Hippy Dread

HEROES (See under Beavi) (Beavi & Hippy Dread).

Hippy House...

HIPPY HOUSE & HAPPY HOP (Various artists).
LP: . . . . JAZILP 012

Hipsway

HIPSWAY.
Tracks: / Honey thief / Ask the Lord / Bad thing longing / Upon a thread / Long white car / Broken years / Tinder / Forbidden / Set this day apart.
LP: . . . . MERH 85
MC: . . . . MERHC 85

SCRATCH THE SURFACE.
LP: 838249 1
MC: 838249 4

Hirax

HATE FEAR AND POWER.
LP: . . . . R 9675

Hired Man

HIRED MAN (Various artists).
Tracks: / Song of the hired men: *Various artists* / Say farewell: *Various artists* / Work song: *Various artists*/ I wouldn't be the first: *Various artists*/ Fade away: *Various artists* / What a fool I've been: *Various* artists / If I could: *Various artists* / Hired men (reprise): *Various artists* / Black rock: *Various artists* / Men of stone(Union song): *Various artists* / When next you see that smile: *Various artists* / So tell your children (War song): *Various artists*.
LP: . . . . POLH 18
MC: . . . . POLHC 18

HIRED MAN, THE (Original London cast) (Various artists).
LP: . . . . SCENE 10
MC: . . . . SCENEC 10

Hiroshima

ANOTHER PLACE.
Tracks: / One wish / Save yourself for me / Another place / I do remember / Game, The / Undercover / Stay away / What's it to ya / Touch and go.
LP: . . . . EPC 26916
MC: 40 26916

GO.
LP: . . . . FE 40679

ODORI.
LP: . . . . SPART 1155

Hirota, Joji

RAIN FOREST DREAM.
Tracks: / Ubiquity / Purple spring / Celebration of harvest / Malaysian image / Satellite express / Rain forest dream / Demon dance / Pacific samba.
MC: . . . . CSDL 384

Hirsch, Shelly

JON ROSE AND SHELLY HIRSCH (See under Rose, Jon).

Hirst, Linda

SONGS CATHY SANG/LUCIANO BERIO:FOLK SONGS.
Tracks: / Black is the colour / I wonder as I wander / Loosin Yelav / Rossignolet du Bois / A la femminisca / La donna ideale / Ballo / Motettu de tristura / Malurous qu'o uno fenno / Lo folaire / Azerbaijan love song / Aria / Sequenza III / Phonemes pour Cathy / Stripsody.
LP: . . . . VC 7907041
MC: . . . . VC 7907044

Hirt, Al

AL HIRT.
MC: . . . . ZCGAS 724

SOLID GOLD BRASS.
MC: . . . . INTK 9007

His Land

HIS LAND (Film Soundtrack) (Various artists).
Tracks: / His land: *Richard, Cliff* / Jerusalem: *Richard, Cliff* / New 23rd: *Richard, Cliff* / His land: *Richard, Cliff* / Keep me where love is: *Richard, Cliff* / Ezekiel's vision: *Barrows, Cliff* / Hallelujah chorus: *Barrows, Cliff* / Over in Bethlehem: *Richard, Cliff/ Barrows, Cliff* / He's everything to me: *Richard, Cliff*/ Barrows, Cliff / Dry bones: *Carmichael, Ralph Orchestra & Chorus* / Hava nagila: *Carmichael, Ralph Orchestra & Chorus*.
LP: . . . . SCX 6443

His Latest Flame

LOVE'S IN THE NEIGHBOURHOOD.
Tracks: / Londonderry Road / Heart of the country / Finest hour / Big world / Cold, cold, cold / Love's in the neighbourhood / America blue / Crack me down / Sporting life / Take it in your stride / Old flame.
LP: 828 163 1
MC: 828 163 4

His Master's Metal

HIS MASTER'S METAL (Various artists).
LP: . . . . IW 1016

His Monkey Wife

HIS MONKEY WIFE (Original cast) (Various artists).
Tracks: / Emily's waltz: *Various artists* / Home and beauty and you: *Various artists* / Marriage: *Various* artists / In Boboma tonight: *Various artists* / Haverstock Hill: *Various artists* / Don't rush me: *Various* artists / Who is she?: *Various artists* / Dear human race: *Various artists* / Leave it all to Smithers: *Various* artists / Mad about your mind: *Various artists* / His monkey wife: *Various artists* / Girl like you, A: *Various* artists / Doing the chimpanzee: *Various artists* / Live like the blessed angels: *Various artists* / His monkey wife (reprise): *Various artists* / Who is she? (reprise): *Various artists*.
LP: . . . . PTLS 1051

His Name Is Alive

HOME IS IN YOUR HEAD.
LP: . . . . CAD 1013
MC: . . . . CADC 1013

LIVONIA.
LP: . . . . CAD 0008
MC: . . . . CADC 0008

His Way With The Girls

HIS WAY WITH THE GIRLS Various artists (Various artists).
LP: . . . . LPSS 111

Hiseman, Jon

ABOUT TIME TOO.
LP: . . . . TM 8
MC: . . . . ZCTM 8

Historic Gamelans

HISTORIC GAMELANS (Various artists).
LP: . . . . G 1004
MC: . . . . G 4004

History Makers

ISAAC NEWTON (History Makers 1642-1727).
MC: . . . . HM 002

History Of...

HISTORY OF ATLANTIC Various artists (Various artists).
MC: . . . . A 0048 4

HISTORY OF LATINO ROCK Various artists (Various artists).
LP: . . . . RNLP 061

HISTORY OF RHYTHM & BLUES VOCAL GROUPS (Various artists).
MC: 901 324

HISTORY OF ROCK INSTRUMENTALS VOL.2 Various artists (Various artists).
Tracks: / Tequila: *Champs* / Rebel rouser: *Eddy, Duane* / Raunchy: *Justis, Bill & His Orchestra* / Memphis: *Mack, Lonnie* / Rumble: *Wray, Link & His Raymen* / Tall cool one: *Wailers* / Twine time: *Cash, Alvin* & The Crawlers / Rawhide: *Wray, Link & His Raymen* / Wham: *Mack, Lonnie* / Ghost riders in the sky: *Ramrods*/ Because they're young: *Eddy, Duane* / Beatnik fly: *Johnny & The Hurricanes* / Topsy (pt. 2): *Cole, Cozy*/ Harlem nocturne: *Viscounts*.
LP: . . . . RNLP 70138
MC: . . . . RNC 70138

HISTORY OF ROCK INSTRUMENTALS VOL.1 Various artists (Various artists).
Tracks: / Wipe out: *Surfaris* / Let there be drums: *Nelson, Sandy* / Let's go: *Routers* / Out of limits: *Markett's* / Hawaii five-O: *Ventures* / Lonely surfer, The: *Nitzche, Jack* / Sleepwalk: *Santo & Johnny*/ Walk don't run: *Ventures* / Bongo rock: *Epps, Preston* / Hot pastrami: *Dartells* / Happy organ: *Cortez, Dave 'Baby'* / Nut rocker: *Bumble, B & The Stingers* / Red river rock: *Johnny & The Hurricanes* / Teen beat: *Nelson, Sandy*.
LP: . . . . RNLP 70137
MC: . . . . RNC 70137

HISTORY OF THE ENGLISH DERBY (History of the English Derby).
LP: . . . . REP 2

HISTORY OF THE WORLD CUP (History of the World Cup).
LP: . . . . REC 592
MC: . . . . ZCM 592

HISTORY OF THE WORLD - NEW ROSE '84 (Various artists).
LPPD: . . . . ROSE 27P

YAZOO'S HISTORY OF JAZZ (Various artists).
LP: . . . . L 1070

History Of Mr. Polly

HISTORY OF MR. POLLY, THE (see under Wells, H.G.) (Jeffrey, Peter (nar)).

History Of The World

HISTORY OF THE WORLD PART 1 (Film soundtrack) (Various artists).
LP: K56926

History Of Uptempo

HISTORY OF UPTEMPO (Various artists).
LP: . . . . TEMPOLP 10

History Reflected

HISTORY REFLECTED, ELIZABETH 1, THE ARMADA 1588 (Various artists).
MCSET: 414 712-4

WORLD WARS 1914/1939 (Various artists).
MCSET: . . . . SAY 101

Hit Action

HIT ACTION (Various artists).
LP: . . . . WW 1000
MC: . . . . WW 10004

Hit Bound

HIT BOUND (Various artists).
LP: . . . . HB 43

Hit Factory

HIT FACTORY Stock Aiken and Waterman (Various artists).
Tracks: / Never gonna give you up: *Astley, Rick* / Toy boy: *Sinitta* / I'll keep on loving you: *Princess*/ Whatever I do (wherever I go): *Dean, Hazell* / New York afternoon: *Kane, Mondo* / Let it be: *Ferry Aid*/ Respectable: *Mel & Kim* / Nothing's gonna stop me now: *Fox, Samantha* / Venus: *Bananarama* / Say I'm your number one: *Princess* / I just can't wait: *Mandy* / Roadblock: *Stock/Aitken/Waterman*.
LP: . . . . SMR 740
MC: . . . . SMC 740

HIT FACTORY VOL 2 Best of Stock Sitken Waterman Vol 2 (Various artists).
Tracks: / Nothing can divide us: *Donovan, Jason* / Harder I try, The: *Brother Beyond* / I should be so lucky: *Minogue, Kylie* / Cross my broken heart: *Sinitta* / My arms keep missing you: *Astley, Rick* / Packjammed (with the party posse): *Stock/Aitken/Waterman* / All of me: *Sabrina* / Love in the first degree: *Bananarama*/ Who's leaving who: *Dean, Hazell* / That's the way it is: *Mel & Kim*.
LP: . . . . HF 4
MC: . . . . HFC 4

HIT FACTORY VOL 3 Stock, Aitken Waterman (Various artists).
Tracks: / Take me to your heart: *Astley, Rick* / Made in heaven: *Minogue, Kylie* / Help: *Bananarama & Lananeeneenoonoo*/ He ain't no competition: *Brother Beyond* / I haven't stopped dancing yet: *Pat 'n' Mick* / Wrap my arms around you: *Donovan, Jason* / I'd rather jack: *Reynolds Girls* / Turn it into love: *Dean, Hazell* / Especially for you: *Minogue, Kylie & Jason Donovan* / I only wanna be with you: *Fox, Samantha* / S. S. Patarazi: *Stock/Aitken/Waterman*/ Ferry across the Mersey: *Various artists*.
LP: . . . . HF 8
MC: . . . . HFC 8

Hit (film)

HIT, THE (Film soundtrack) (De Lucia, Paco).
Tracks: / Hit 1 & 2, The / Willie's theme / Spanish sun/The funeral/Andalucia / John Lennon / Kidnap/Convoy / Braddock's theme / Windmills / To Madrid (Willy Parker) / Double indemnity / Wasteland/Cracking / Maggie's problem / Roncevalles / Canyon, The / Cojones / Waterfall / Moonlight / Hilltop / Maggie fights back / Very lucky girl.

LP: **822 668 1**
MC: **822 668 4**

Hit List '58

HIT LIST '58 (Various artists).
LP: . . . . **SHM 3224**
MC: . . . . **HSC 3224**

Hit Memories...

HIT MEMORIES 66-67 (Various artists).
LP: . . . . **BRLP 08**
MC: . . . . **BRMC 08**

Hit Mix

HIT MIX (Various artists).
Tracks: / Looking for a new love: *Watley, Jody* / You sexy thing: *Hot Chocolate* / Every 1's a winner: *Hot Chocolate* / Once bitten twice shy: *Williams, Vesta* / I surrender: *Fox, Samantha* / Serious mix: *Mirage*/ I wanna dance: *Houston, Whitney* / I want to be...: *Blue Mercedes* / Crush on you: *Jets (American)*/ Southern freeez: *Various artists* / Sonic boom boy: *Westworld* / La bamba: *Valens, Ritchie* / Male stripper: *Man 2 Man meets Man Parrish* / Sexy girl: *Thomas, Lillo* / Gigolo: *Damned* / Special FX: *Whispers*/ Future's so bright, The: *Timbuk 3* / Working up a sweat: *First Circle* / Let's dance: *Rea, Chris* / Miracle worker: *First Circle* / Lifetime love: *Sims, Joyce* / Alone again or: *Damned* / This brutal house: *Nitro Deluxe* / Coming around again: *Simon, Carly* / Out with her: *Blow Monkeys* / Don't stop jammin': *L.A. Mix* / Rock steady: *Whispers* / Midas touch: *Midnight Star* / Axel F: *Faltermeyer, Harold*/ Feat too tough tee....: *Dynamix II* / How soon we forget: *Abrams, Colonel* / Jack mix IV: *Mirage* / Turn me loose: *Wally 'Jump' Jnr* / Put the needle to the record: *Criminal Element Orchestra* / And the beat goes on: *Whispers* / Jimmy Lee: *Franklin, Aretha* / Jack the groove: *Raze* / Jack your body: *Hurley, Steve 'Silk'* / Jump start: *Cole, Natalie* / Let yourself go: *Sybil* / House nation: *Housemaster Boyz/Rude Boys*/ Do it properly (No way back): *Adonis* / Curiosity: *Jets (American)* / Lies: *Butler, Jonathan* / Love is forever: *Ocean, Billy* / It doesn't have to be this way: *Blow Monkeys* / French kissin' in the U.S.A.: *Harry, Debbie* / Jive talkin': *Boogie Box High* / Get that love: *Thompson Twins* / Celebrate the day (after you): *Blow Monkeys* / Radio heart: *Numan, Gary*.
2LP: . . . . **SMR 744**
MCSET: . . . . **SMC 744**

HIT MIX '86 (Various artists).
2LP: . . . . **SMR 624**
MCSET: . . . . **SMC 624**

HIT MIX '88 (Various artists).
Tracks: / I need you: *B.V.S.M.P.* / Bad young brother: *Derek B.* / I want you back '88 remix: *Jackson, Michael*/ It's like that y'all: *Sweet Tee* / I'm too scared: *Dante, Steven* / Payback mix: *Brown, James* / Bass: *Harris, Simon* / Lovers Lane: *Georgio* / I got da feelin': *Sweet Tee* / Wam bam: *N.T.Gang* / Betcha can't lose: *Magic Lady* / Walk away: *Sims, Joyce* / House arrest: *Krush* / I got da feelin': *Jackson, Michael*.
2LP: . . . . **SMR 865**
MCSET: . . . . **SMC 865**

Hit Pack

HIT PACK, THE (Various artists).
Tracks: / Groove is in the heart (peanut butter mix): *Deee-Lite* / Fantasy: *Black Box* / Mary had a little boy: *Snap* / Livin' in the light: *Wheeler, Caron* / Crazy: *Seal* / Then: *Charlatans* / Cubik (original mix): *Various artists* / Good morning Britain: *Aztec Camera & Mick Jones* / Obvious child, The (single mix): *Simon, Paul* / Are you dreaming ? (forest radio edit): *Twenty 4 Seven* / Thieves in the temple (album version): *Prince*/ Spit in the rain: *Del Amitri* / King of the road: *Proclaimers* / Show me heaven: *McKee, Maria* / Take my breath away: *Berlin* / I'll never fall in love again: *Deacon Blue* / Blue velvet: *Vinton, Bobby* / Crying in the rain (LP version): *A-Ha* / Falling (edit): *Cruise, Julee* / Tonight: *New Kids on the Block*/ Fog on the Tyne (revisited): *Gazza & Lindisfarne* / Heaven: *Chimes* ((Available on cassette format only)) / Sucker DJ: *Dimples D* ((Available on cassette format only)) / More: *Sisters Of Mercy* ((Available on cassette format only)).
MC: . . . . **COMP C1**

Hit Parade

NICK KNACK PADDY WHACK.
LP: . . . . **CATNO 7**

WITH LOVE FROM THE HIT PARADE.
Tracks: / Forever / Stop / My favourite girl / It rained on Monday afternoon / Sun shines in Gerrards cross, The / You hurt me too / Huebos Mexicana / You didn't lose me then / See you in Havana / Wipe away the tears / I get so sentimental / Sue / Sun in my eyes / Come and get me girl / You as just a memory.
LP: . . . . **JPEW 001**

Hit Singles

HIT SINGLES 1958-1977 (See Under Atlantic (Label) (Various artists).

HIT SINGLES 1980-1988 (See Under Atlantic Label) (Various artists).

Hit Songs...

HIT SONGS AND HOT SONGS Various artists (Various artists).
Tracks: / Swanee: *Various artists* / Japanese sandman: *Various artists* / Sugar foot stomp: *Various artists*/ Who: *Various artists* / Some of these days: *Various artists* / Doctor Jazz: *Various artists* / My melancholy baby: *Various artists* / Whispering: *Various artists* / Creole love call: *Various artists* / Struttin' with some barbecue: *Various artists* / Sonny boy: *Various artists* / Hard to get Gertie: *Various artists*/ Ol' man river: *Various artists* / My blue Heaven: *Various artists* / Ten cents a dance: *Various artists*/ Ain't she sweet: *Various artists*.
LP: . . . . **NOST 7604**

HIT SONGS OF THE 50'S (Various artists).
LP: . . . . **RFLD 49**
MC: . . . . **KRFLD 49**

HIT SONGS OF THE 60'S VOL 2 (Various artists).
Tracks: / Waterloo sunset: *Kinks* / Poor man's son: *Rockin' Berries* / That's the way: *Honeycombs* / Go away little girl: *Wynter, Mark* / Little bitty tear, A: *Miki & Griff* / Where are you now (my love)?: *Trent, Jackie* / Build me up buttercup: *Foundations* / My love: *Clark, Petula* / Autumn almanac: *Kinks* / Make me an island: *Dolan, Joe* / Goodbye my love: *Searchers* / (There's) always something there to remind me: *Shaw, Sandie* / Sugar and spice: *Searchers* / Don't sleep in the subway: *Clark, Petula* / Let the heartaches begin: *Baldry, Long John* / Samantha: *Ball, Kenny* / Party's over, The: *Donegan, Lonnie* / Midnight in Moscow: *Ball, Kenny & His Jazzmen* / Girl don't come: *Shaw, Sandie* / That's what love will do: *Brown, Joe* / Colours: *Donovan* / Tossing and turning: *Ivy League* / Baby now that I've found you: *Foundations*.
MCSET: . . . . **DTOL 10283**

Hit Sounds

HIT SOUNDS OF THE 70'S (Various artists).
MCSET: . . . . **DTOL 10268**

HITS SOUNDS OF THE 70'S VOL.2 (Various artists).
MCSET: . . . . **DTO 10273**

Hit The Deck

HIT THE DECK/IN THE GOOD OLD SUMMERTIME/ROYAL WEDDING (Film Soundtrack) (Various artists).
Tracks: / Sometimes I'm happy: *Powell, Jane/Vic Damone* / Keepin' myself for you: *Miller, Ann/Tony Martin & Girls*/ Kiss or two, A: *Reynolds, Debbie & Boys* / Chiribiribee (Ciribiribin): *Powell, Jane/ Vic Damone* / Lucky bird: *Powell, Jane* / Join the navy/Loo loo: *Reynolds, Debbie* / Why oh why: *Powell, Jane/Vic Damone* / I know that you know: *Powell, Jane/Vic Damone* / More than you know: *Martin, Tony* / Lady from the Bayou: *Miller, Ann* / Sometimes I'm happy: *Powell, Jane* / Hallelujah: *Martin, Tony/Vic Damone/ Russ Tamblyn/Jubilaires* / I don't care: *Garland, Judy* / Meet me tonight in dreamland: *Garland, Judy* / Play that barber shop chord: *Garland, Judy & The King's Men* / Last night when we were young: *Garland, Judy* / Put your arms around me honey: *Garland, Judy* / Merry Christmas: *Garland, Judy* / Too late now: *Powell, Jane* / Ev'ry night at seven: *Astaire, Fred* / Happiest day of my life, The: *Powell, Jane* / I left my hat in Haiti: *Astaire, Fred* / You're the world to me: *Astaire, Fred* / How could you believe me when I said I loved you when you..: *Astaire, Fred/Jane Powell*.
LP: . . . . **LPMGM 15**
LP: **794 193 1**
MC: . . . . **TCMGM 15**
MC: **794 193 4**

Hit The Floor

HIT THE FLOOR VOL 1 (Various artists).
LP: . . . . **MUT 1123**
MC: . . . . **CMUT 1123**

HIT THE FLOOR VOL 2 (Various artists).
LP: . . . . **MUT 1124**
MC: . . . . **CMUT 1124**

Hit The North

HIT THE NORTH (Various artists).
Tracks: / Lions: *New Fast Automatic Daffodils* / Girl who loved her man: *Australians* / Sunlight fades: *Rainkings*/ Soul in love with 25 people: *Bedflowers* / Soul MC: *Lavinia & Social Kaos* / No more war: *Rowetta* / All of my life: *All Of My Life* / Didn't quite make it: *Jerks* / B.R.O.: *Rig* / Don't fake mine: *Paris Angels* / My love is like a ...: *Man From Delmonte* / Here today: *Ruthless Rap Assassins* / Destroy all stereotypes: *Krispy Three* / Jesus I love you: *Revenge*.
LP: . . . . **BIP 805**
MC: . . . . **BIP 805 C**

Hitch, Curtis

INDIANA SUMMER 1923-28 (Hitch, Curtis & Hoagy Carmichael).
LP: . . . . **FJ 109**

Hitchcock, Robyn

BLACK SNAKE DIAMOND ROLE.
LP: . . . . **AFT 1**
LP: . . . . **ARM 4**

ELEMENT OF LIGHT.
LP: . . . . **MOIST 3**

EXPLODING IN SILENCE.
LPPD: . . . . **BM 80**
MC: . . . . **BMC 804**

EXPLODING IN SILENCE (Hitchcock, Robyn & The Egyptians).
LP: . . . . **EMC 8074**

FEGMANIA.
LP: . . . . **CHIME 0008**

GLOBE OF FROGS (Hitchcock, Robyn & The Egyptians).
Tracks: / Tropical flesh mandala / Vibrating / Ballroom man / Luminous rose / Sleeping with your devil mask / Unsettled / Chinese bones / Globe of frogs, A / Shapes between us, The / Turn into animals / Flesh number one / Beatle Dennis.
LP: . . . . **AMA 5182**
MC: . . . . **AMC 5182**

GOTTA LET THIS HEN OUT!.
Tracks: / Listening to the Higsons / Fly, The / Kingdom of love / Leppo and the fly / Man with the lightbulb head / Cars she used to drive, The / Sounds great when you're dead / Only the stones remain / America / Heaven / My wife and my dead wife / I often dream of trains / Surgery / Brenda's iron sledge.
LP: . . . . **CHIME 00 15 S**
MC: . . . . **CHIME 00 15 C**

GROOVY DECAY.
LP: . . . . **CHIME 00 19**
LP: . . . . **ALB 110**

I OFTEN DREAM OF TRAINS (Hitchcock, Robyn & The Egyptians).
LP: . . . . **CHIME 0005 S**

INVISIBLE HITCHCOCK (Hitchcock, Robyn & The Egyptians).
LP: . . . . **MOIST 2**

LET THIS MAN OUT.
LP: . . . . **CHIME 15**

Hitchcocks

SKINNY.
Tracks: / Fine fine / Reason sleeps / Twitch / Occasion / Hopes at home / Lover stumbles, the / There's a thing.
LP: . . . . **NISHI 204**

Hitch-hiker's Guide...

HITCH-HIKER'S 1 (Various artists).
LP: . . . . **HNBL 2301**
MC: . . . . **HNBC 2301**

HITCH-HIKER'S GUIDE TO THE GALAXY (Moore, Stephen (nar)).
MCSET: . . . . **LFP 7088**

HITCH-HIKER'S GUIDE TO THE GALAXY (Original Radio Production) (Various artists).
MCSET: . . . . **ZBBC 1035**

HITCH-HIKER'S GUIDE TO THE GALAXY (Various artists).
2LP: . . . . **ORA 042**

HITCH-HIKER'S GUIDE TO THE GALAXY VOL.2 (Various artists).
LP: . . . . **ORA 054**

Hi-Tex

HI-TEX.
Tracks: / Longview / Car tune / Rack / For you / Empathy / Take the 'A' side / Sick groove / Blue movies / New Yorker / Free fall.
LP: . . . . **ORA 105**

Hitler, Adolf

REICHSTAG SPEECH September 1, 1939.
LP: . . . . **RA LP 1003**

Hitler, Bing

BING HITLER LIVE AT THE TRON.
Tracks: / Scotland och aye / Sheep song.
LP: . . . . **JRLP 861**
MC: . . . . **JRCP 861**

Hitlist

HIT LIST (Various artists).
2LP: . . . . **ADD 13**
MC: . . . . **ZDD 13**

HIT LIST 1963 (Various artists).
Tracks: / I only want to be with you: *Springfield, Dusty* / Sugar and spice: *Searchers* / Wipe out: *Surfaris*.
MC: . . . . **HSC 3238**

Hitlist (group)

GOOD EVENING YUGOSLAVIA (Hitlist).
Tracks: / Showbiz / Party lights / Sunday is for sleeping / Mr. Mercenary / Into the fire / Good intentions / Anticipation / Nothing to lose / OK for you / Further on.
LP: . . . . **V 2379**
MC: . . . . **TCV 2379**

Hitmen

AIM FOR THE FEET.
Tracks: / OK / Private eye / She's all mine / Kid's stuff / Guess who / I still remember it / Slay me with your 45 / Eyes open / Bad timing / Hold on to her.
LP: . . . . **ZIP 84888**
MC: **40 84888**

TORN TOGETHER.
Tracks: / Bates Motel / Changing faces / What would the neighbours say / Score it blue / Picking up the pulse / Shade in fade out / Don't speak with the enemy / Hard heartbeat / Comfort me.
LP: . . . . **CBS 84902**

Hi-Tone Poppa

HI-TONE POPPA (Various artists).
Tracks: / Hot rod shotgun boogie: *Franks, Tillman* / Walking the dog: *Grimsley, Tex* / Teardrops: *Grimsley, Tex* / Beer and pinballs: *King, Claude* / 51 beers: *King, Claude* / You're just imagination: *Young, Faron* / Have I waited too long: *Young, Faron* / Hi-tone poppa: *Franks, Tillman* / Heard the juke box playing: *Faron Young/Tillman Franks* / Million mistakes, A: *King, Claude* / Why should I: *King, Claude* / Court of justice: *Wilburn, Teddy* / Call me sweetheart: *Wilburn, Teddy* / I'm a free man now: *Faron Young/Tillman Franks*.
LP: . . . . **KK 830**

Hits...

16 DYNAMIC HITS (Various artists).
LP: . . . . **TBL 191**

HITS CORRUPTION (Various artists).
Tracks: / Orgasm way: *Stump* / Touch you: *Moonsters* / Pearl and the swine ad: *Lee, C.P.* / Holy ground: *First International* / No sense at all: *Heads & Sticks* / Poetry: *Milton, Ted* / Christ was a conservative: *Jackson, Guy* / Batter matter: *3 Action* / Everything's brilliant (the poem): *Membrane, John* / Heartbreak hotel: *Thrashing Sh...* / Down the yard: *Shrubs* / Help: *Tristram Shout* / Top comedian: *Chippington, Ted* / Poetry: *Cornelius, Alan* / Interview: *Sonic Youth*.
LP: . . . . **HAC LP 001**
MC: . . . . **HAC 001**

HITS GREATEST STIFFS (Various artists).
LP: . . . . **FIST 1**
MC: . . . . **ZFIST 1**

HITS HITS HITS (Various artists).
Tracks: / Careless whisper: *Michael, George* / Jump (for my love): *Pointer Sisters* / Doctor Beat: *Miami Sound Machine* / Everybody's laughing: *Fearon, Phil & Galaxy*. / Sister of mercy: *Thompson Twins* / Time after time: *Lauper, Cyndi* / Farewell my summer love: *Jackson, Michael* / Eyes without a face: *Idol, Billy*/ Sunglasses: *Ullman, Tracy* / Whatever I do (wherever I go): *Dean, Hazell* / Love resurrection: *Moyet, Alison*/ Master & servant: *Depeche Mode* / Day before you came, The: *Blancmange* / Closest thing to heaven: *Kane Gang* / More you live, the more you love, The: *Flock of Seagulls, A* / You think you're a man: *Divine* / White lines (don't don't do it): *Various artists* / Don't do it: *Grandmaster Melle Mel* / On the wings of love: *Osborne, Jeffrey*.
LP: . . . . **STAR 2243**
MC: . . . . **STAC 2243**

HITS REVIVAL (Various artists).
Tracks: / Reet petite: *Wilson, Jackie* / Wonderful world: *Cooke, Sam* / Lean on me: *Withers, Bill* / Everything I own: *Boothe, Ken* / Loving you is sweeter than ever: *Four Tops* / You can't hurry love: *Supremes*/ It's a man's man's man's world: *Brown, James* / I heard it through the grapevine: *Gaye, Marvin* / Dancing in the street: *Reeves, Martha & The Vandellas* / What's going on: *Gaye, Marvin* / You keep me hangin' on: *Supremes*/ Whispering bells: *Del-Vikings* / Let's stay together: *Green, Al* / Harlem shuffle: *Bob & Earl* / Get up, I feel like a sex machine: *Brown, James* / I get the sweetest feeling: *Wilson, Jackie*.
LP: . . . . **NE 1363**
MC: . . . . **CE 2363**

HITS THAT MADE JOHN DENVER Various session artists (Various artists).
MC: . . . . **AM 44**

HITS THROUGH THE YEARS (Various artists).
Tracks: / When a man loves a woman: *Sledge, Percy* / My prayer: *Platters* / Girl can't help it, The: *Little* Richard / Where did our love go: *Elbert, Donnie* / Windy: *Association* / Sheila: *Roe, Tommy* / Sugar sugar: *Archies* / Kisses sweeter than wine: *Various artists* / Soul sister brown sugar: *Sam & Dave* / Rockin' Robin: *Day, Bobby* / Never my love: *Association* / Blueberry Hill: *Domino, Fats* / Ruby don't take your...: *Rogers, Kenny* / Long tall Sally: *Little Richard* / Only you (and you alone): *Platters*/ Alley oop: *Hollywood Argyles* / Warm and tender love: *Sledge, Percy* / Save the last dance for me: *Drifters*/ It's all in the game: *Edwards, Tommy* / Chapel of love: *Dixie Cups* / Down in the boondocks: *Royal, Billy Joe* / Something's burning: *Rogers, Kenny* / Just keep it up: *Clark, Dee* / Honeycomb: *Rogers, Jimmy*.
MCSET: . . . . **DTO 10271**
MCSET: . . . . **DTOL 10271**

HITS TODAY AND YESTERDAY (Various artists).
MCSET: . . . . **WW 6050**

HITS YOU MISSED VOL.1 Various artists (Various artists).
LP: . . . . **VIKLP 01**

WORLD OF HITS VOL 5 (Various artists).
LP: . . . . **SPA 177**

WORLD OF HITS VOL 7 (Various artists).
LP: . . . . **SPA 360**

Hits Album

HITS ALBUM 1 (Various artists).
Tracks: / Freedom: *Wham* / I'd like to get to know you well: *Jones, Howard* / All cried out: *Moyet, Alison*/ I'm gonna tear your playhouse down: *Young, Paul* / Big in Japan: *Alphaville* / Self control: *Branigan, Laura*/ Ghostbusters: *Parker, Ray Jnr.* / Thriller: *Jackson, Michael* / I feel for you: *Khan, Chaka* / Caribbean queen: *Ocean, Billy* / Body: *Jacksons* / Just be good to me: *S.O.S. Band* / Let's hear it for the boy: *Williams, Deniece* / Doctor beat: *Miami Sound Machine* / Lost in music: *Sister Sledge* / Purple rain: *Prince/Revolution* / Careless whisper: *Michael, George* / Drive: *Cars* / Hard habit to break: *Chicago*/ All through the night: *Lauper, Cyndi* / Sister of mercy: *Thompson Twins* / Skin deep: *Stranglers* / Each and everyone: *Everything But The Girl* / Smooth operator: *Sade* / Gimme all your lovin': *ZZ Top*/ Footloose: *Loggins, Kenny* / Apollo 9: *Ant, Adam* / Modern girl: *Meatloaf* / Some guys have all the luck: *Stewart, Rod* / Teardrops / Hole in my shoe: *Neil*.
LP: . . . . **HITS 1**
MC: . . . . **HITS C1**

HITS ALBUM 2 (Various artists).
Tracks: / You spin me round (like a record): *Dead or Alive* / Things can only get better: *Jones, Howard* / Love and pride: *King* / Wide boy: *Kershaw, Nik* / Mr. Telephone man: *New Edition* / New England, A: *MacColl, Kirsty* / Since yesterday: *Strawberry Switchblade* / 1999: *Prince* / Easy lover: *Bailey, Philip & Phil* Collins / Solid: *Ashford & Simpson* / This is my night: *Khan, Chaka* / Yah mo b there: *Ingram, James*/ Let it all blow: *Dazz Band* / Close (to the edit): *Art Of Noise* / I want to know what love is: *Foreigner*/ Everything must change: *Young, Paul* / You're the inspiration: *Chicago* / I should have known better: *Diamond,* Jim / Friends: *Stewart, Amii* / Nightshift: *Commodores* / That ole devil called love: *Moyet, Alison*/ Kiss me: *Duffy, Stephen "Tin Tin"* / Who comes to boogie: *Little Benny & The Masters* / More than I can bear: *Bianco, Matt* / This house (is where your love stands): *Big Sound Authority* / Legs: *ZZ Top* / Just another night: *Jagger, Mick* / Breaking up my heart: *Stevens, Shakin'*.
2LP: . . . . **HITS 2**
MCSET: . . . . **HITS C2**

HITS ALBUM 3 (Various artists).
Tracks: / Dress you up: *Madonna* / Take on me: *A-Ha* / Yeh yeh: *Bianco, Matt* / Lipstick, powder and paint: *Stevens, Shakin'* / Holding out for a hero: *Tyler, Bonnie* / Trapped: *Abrams, Colonel* / Sleeping bag: *ZZ Top* / Power of love, The: *Rush, Jennifer* / Raspberry beret: *Prince & The Revolution* / Every time you go away: *Young, Paul* / She sells sanctuary: *Cult* / My toot toot: *Lasalle, Denise* / Sisters are doin' it for themselves: *Eurythmics & Aretha Franklin* / Power of love, The: *Lewis, Huey & The News* / St. Elmo's fire: *Parr, John* / Drive: *Cars* / Frankie: *Sister Sledge* / Bring on the dancing horses: *Echo* & the Bunnymen / Taste of your tears: *King* / King for a day: *Thompson Twins* / Sweetest taboo, The: *Thompson* Twins / Life in a northern town: *Dream Academy* / Dancing in the dark: *Springsteen, Bruce* / Lean on me: *Red* Box / Time after time: *Lauper, Cyndi* / Loving you's a dirty job: *Tyler, Bonnie & Todd Rundgren* / Dancing in the key of life: *Arrington, Steve* / It's a man's man's man's world: *Nighttrain mix*.
2LP: . . . . **HITS 3**
MCSET: . . . . **HITS C3**

HITS ALBUM 4 (Various artists).
Tracks: / Sun always shines on TV, The: *A-Ha* / You little thief: *Sharkey, Feargal* / I'm your man: *Wham*/ Manic monday: *Bangles* / Borderline: *Madonna* / Digging your scene: *Blow Monkeys* / Imagination: *Some,* Belouis / Chain reaction: *Ross, Diana* / How will I know: *Houston, Whitney* / If you were here tonight: *O'Neal,* Alexander / System addict: *Five Star* / Don't waste my time: *Hardcastle, Paul* / (Nothing serious) just buggin': *Whistle* / Alice, I want you just for me!: *Full Force* / Eloise: *Damned* / Suspicious minds: *Fine* Young Cannibals / Rise: *Various artists* / Hit that perfect beat: *Bronski Beat* / It's alright (baby's coming back) : *Eurythmics* / West end girls: *Pet Shop Boys* / Kyrie: *Mr. Mister* / Captain of her heart, The: *Double* / Radio Africa: *Latin Quarter* / Silent running (on dangerous ground): *Mike & The Mechanics* / No one is to blame: *Jones, Howard* / Come hell or waters high: *Lee, Dee C* / Hounds of love: *Bush, Kate*/ Calling America: *E.L.O.*.
2LP: . . . . **HITS 4**
MCSET: . . . . **HITSC 4**

HITS ALBUM 5 (Various artists).
2LP: . . . . **HITS 5**
MCSET: . . . . **HITSC 5**

HITS ALBUM 6 (Various artists).
2LP: . . . . **HITS 6**
MCSET: . . . . **HITSC 6**

HITS ALBUM 7 (Various artists).
Tracks: / You win again: *Bee Gees* / Never gonna give you up: *Astley, Rick* / Wishing well: *D'Arby, Terence* Trent / Strong as steel: *Five Star* / Call me: *Spagna* / She's on it: *Beastie Boys* / I wanna be your drill instructor: *Mead, Abigail/Nigel Goulding: Full Metal Jacket* / What do you want to make those eyes at me for: *Stevens, Shakin'* / Little lies: *Fleetwood Mac* / Criticize: *O'Neal, Alexander* / U got the look: *Prince*/ Dinner with Gershwin: *Summer, Donna* / Casanova: *Levert* / Funky town: *Pseudo Echo* / Paid in full: *Eric B & Rakim* / Jack le freak: *Chic* / Living daylights, The: *A-Ha* / Bridge to your heart: *Wax*/ No memory: *Scarlet Fantastic* / Darklands: *Various artists* / This corrosion: *Sisters Of Mercy* / House nation: *Housemaster Boyz & The Rude Boy Of House* / Voyage voyage: *Desireless* / My baby just cares for me: *Simone,* Nina / Time of my life, The: *Warnes, Jennifer & Bill Medley* / Always: *Atlantic Starr* / So amazing: *Vandross,* Luther / Didn't we almost have it all: *Houston, Whitney* / I don't think that man should sleep alone: *Parker, Ray Jnr.* / I need love: *L.L. Cool J* / Songbird: *Kenny G.* / Every time you say goodbye: *Simply Red*.
2LP: . . . . **HITS 7**
MCSET: . . . . **HITS 7C**

HITS ALBUM 8 (Various artists).
Tracks: / Stay on these roads: *A-Ha* / I'm not scared: *8th Wonder* / I want you back '88: *Jackson, Michael* & The Jackson Five / Another weekend: *Five Star* / I owe you nothing: *Bros* / I saw him standing there: *Tiffany*/ Tell it to my heart: *Dayne, Taylor* / Voyage voyage: *Desireless* / Somewhere in my heart: *Aztec Camera*/ King of rock and roll: *Prefab Sprout* / Perfect: *Fairground Attraction* / Everywhere: *Fleetwood Mac*/ I found someone: *Cher* / Paradise: *Sade* / Sign your name: *D'arby, Terence Trent* / Lovers, The: *O'Neal,* Alexander / Tribute (right on): *Pasadenas* / Don't blame it on that girl: *Matt Bianco* / Love is contagious: *Sevelle, Taja* / Girlfriend: *Pebbles (Singer)* / Car wash: *Rose Royce* / Love will save the day: *Houston,* Whitney / What you see is what you get: *Goldsmith, Glen* / I gave it up (when I fell in love): *Vandross, Luther*/ You have placed a chill in my heart: *Eurythmics* / Don't turn around: *Aswad* / Theme from S.Express: *S. Express* / Shake your love: *Gibson, Debbie* / Chains of love: *Erasure* / I'm nin'alu: *Haza, Ofra*/ Crash: *Primitives* / Lucretia my reflection: *Sisters Of Mercy* / Sidewalking: *Jesus & Mary Chain*.
2LP: . . . . **HITS 8**
MCSET: . . . . **HITS 8C**

HITS ALBUM 9 (Various artists).
Tracks: / Cat among the pigeons: *Bros* / You are the one: *A-Ha* / Never trust a stranger: *Wilde, Kim*/ 1-2-3: *Estefan, Gloria/Miami Sound Machine* / Foolish beat: *Gibson, Debbie* / Enchanted lady: *Pasadenas*/ I wish U heaven: *Prince* / Orinoco flow: *Enya* / Missing you: *De Burgh, Chris* / Find my love: *Fairground* Attraction / Real gone kid: *Deacon Blue* / I don't want to talk about it: *Everything But The Girl* / Twist in my sobriety: *Tikaram, Tanita* / Somewhere down the crazy river: *Robertson, Robbie* / Stand up for your love rights: *Yazz* / Wap bam boogie: *Matt Bianco* / Can you party: *Royal House* / Spell, The: *Funky Worm*/ Party, The: *Kraze* / Love house: *Fox, Samantha* / Way you love me, The: *White, Karyn* / She wants to dance with me: *Astley, Rick* / One moment in time: *Houston, Whitney* / Lovely day: *Withers, Bill* / Fake '88: *O'Neal, Alexander* / In your room: *Bangles* / Suddenly: *Anderson, Angry* / 9 a.m. (the comfort zone): *London Beat* / Sunshine on Leith: *Proclaimers* / Driving home for Christmas: *Rea, Chris*.
2LP: . . . . **HITS 9**
MCSET: . . . . **HITSC 9**

HITS ALBUM 10 (Various artists).
Tracks: / Eternal flame: *Bangles* / This time I know it's for real: *Summer, Donna* / I beg your pardon: *Kon* Kan / People hold on: *Cold Cut* / Indestructible: *Four Tops* / Waiting for a star to fall: *Boy Meets* Girl / Requiem (hamburg edit): *London Boys* / Pink sunshine: *Fuzzbox* / If you don't know me by now: *Simply* Red / Me, myself and I: *De La Soul* / Wait: *Howard, Robert & Kym Mazelle* / That's the way love is: *Ten* City / Don't be cruel: *Brown, Bobby (1)* / You + me = love: *Funky Worm* / Make my body rock: *Jomanda*/ I haven't stopped dancing yet: *Pat 'n' Mick* / Living years, The: *Mike & The Mechanics* / Can't stay away from you: *Estefan, Gloria/Miami Sound Machine* / Come back: *Vandross, Luther* / Sleep talk: *Williams, Alyson*/ Hold me in your arms: *Astley, Rick* / That's when I think of you: *1927* / Through the storm: *Franklin, Aretha* & Elton John / Wages day: *Deacon Blue* / Sweet child o' mine: *Guns 'n' Roses* / Baby I love your way/ Freebird: *Will to Power* / I can see clearly now: *Hothouse Flowers* / Beat(en) generation, The: *The The* / Wise up sucker: *Pop Will Eat Itself* / Cuddly toy: *Roachford* / Who's in the house: *Beatmasters & Merlin* / Bring me edelweiss: *Edelweiss*.
2LP: . . . . **HITS 10**
MCSET: . . . . **HITS 10C**

Hits Collection

HITS COLLECTION, THE (Various artists).
Tracks: / Son of hickory holler's...: *Smith, O.C* / Family affair: *Sly & the Family Stone* / Samba pa ti: *Santana*/ Caravan song: *Dickson, Barbara* / I really want to do: *Byrds* / January February: *Dickson, Barbara*/ Turn turn turn: *Byrds* / Dirty ole man: *3 Degrees* / Spinning wheel: *Blood, Sweat & Tears* / Witch Queen of New Orleans: *Redbone* / Mr Tambourine man: *Byrds* / Golden age of rock and roll: *Mott The Hoople* / Rocket: *Hancock, Herbie* / And when I die: *Blood, Sweat & Tears* / Lido shuffle: *Scaggs, Boz* / Dance to the music: *Sly & the Family Stone* / I thought it was you: *Hancock, Herbie* / T.S.O.P.: *MFSB & Three Degrees*/ Gangsters of the groove: *Heatwave* / She's not there: *Santana*.
MCSET: . . . . **DTO 10277**
MCSET: . . . . **DTOL 10277**

Hits For...

HITS FOR CHILDREN (Various artists).
MC: . . . . **AM 30**

HITS FOR KIDS VOL.1 (Various artists).
Tracks: / Co co: *Various artists* / Chirpy chirpy cheep cheep: *Various artists* / Yellow submarine: *Various* artists / Ob la di ob la da: *Various artists* / Two little boys: *Various artists* / Jack in the box: *Various* artists / Beg steal or borrow: *Various artists* / Can't buy me love: *Various artists* / Knock three times: *Various artists* / Those were the days: *Various artists* / I want to hold your hand: *Various artists*/ Pushbike song: *Various artists*.
MCSET: . . . . **DTO 10035**

HITS FOR KIDS VOL.2 (Various artists).
MCSET: . . . . **DTO 10518**

HITS FOR LOVERS (Various artists).
Tracks: / Saving all my love for you: *Houston, Whitney* / See the day: *Lee, Dee C* / What's love got to do with it: *Turner, Tina* / Sexual healing: *Gaye, Marvin* / If you were here tonight: *O'Neal, Alexander* / Sweetest taboo, The: *Sade* / Who's zoomin' who?: *Franklin, Aretha* / Saturday love: *Cherrelle & Alexander O'Neal*/ Power of love, The: *Rush, Jennifer* / All cried out: *Moyet, Alison* / Missing you: *Waite, John* / When love breaks down: *Prefab Sprout* / Penny lover: *Richie, Lionel* / Still: *Commodores* / New York eyes: *Nicole with Tommy Thomas* / Every time you go away: *Young, Paul*.
LP: . . . . **EPC 10050**
MC: **40 10050**

Hits From...

FORTY HITS FROM THE 50'S AND 60'S (Various artists).
2LP: . . . . **PLD 8009**

HITS FROM HEAVEN (Various artists).
LP: . . . . **RNMA 676**

HITS FROM ROCK MUSICALS (Various artists).
Tracks: / Aquarius: *Various artists* / Day by day: *Various artists* / See me feel me: *Various artists*/ You're the one that I want: *Various artists* / Don't cry for me Argentina: *Various artists* / I don't know how to love him: *Various artists* / Acid Queen: *Various artists* / Superstar: *Various artists* / Good morning starshine: *Various artists* / Let the sun shine in: *Various artists* / Summer nights: *Various artists*/ Ain't got no....I got life: *Various artists* / Another suitcase in another hall: *Various artists* / Hopelessly devoted to you: *Various artists* / Pinball wizard: *Various artists*.
LP: . . . . **SPR 8508**
MC: . . . . **SPC 8508**

HITS FROM THE SILVER SCREEN (Various artists).
MC: . . . . **AMP 010**

HITS FROM THE SWINGING SIXTIES (Various artists).
Tracks: / How do you do it?: *Gerry & the Pacemakers* / Do you want to know a secret?: *Kramer, Billy J. & The Dakotas*/ Hippy hippy shake: *Swinging Blue Jeans* / Love to be loved: *Black, Cilla* / You were made for me: *Freddie* & The Dreamers / Searchin': *Hollies* / You're no good: *Swinging Blue Jeans* / Stay: *Hollies* / It's for you: *Black, Cilla* / Hello little girl: *Fourmost* / Little children: *Kramer, Billy J. & The Dakotas*/ You'll never walk alone: *Gerry & the Pacemakers* / Thank u very much: *Scaffold* / Hungry for love: *Kidd,* Johnny & The Pirates / On the beach / 5-4-3-2-1: *Manfred Mann* / I'll keep you satisfied: *Kramer, Billy J. & The* Dakotas / Good golly Miss Molly: *Swinging Blue Jeans* / Shindig: *Shadows* / I can't let go: *Hollies*/ Catch us if you can: *Clark, Dave Five* / I'm the one: *Gerry & the Pacemakers* / If you gotta make a fool of somebody: *Freddie & The Dreamers* / Got to get you into my life: *Bennett, Cliff & The Rebel Rousers*.
2LP: . . . . **MFP 1012**
MCSET: . . . . **TCMFP 1012**
2LP: . . . . **DL 1012**
MC: . . . . **TCDL 1012**

MORE HITS FROM RADIO 1 (Various artists).
2LP: . . . . **BEDP 015**
MC: . . . . **ZCD 015**

Hits From The Shows

HITS FROM THE SHOWS (Original Broadway Casts) (Various artists).
Tracks: / Oklahoma: *Various artists* / Getting to know you: *Various artists* / Doin' what comes naturally: *Various* artists / When the children are asleep: *Various artists* / Luck be a lady: *Various artists* / People will say we're in love: *Various artists* / Don't cry for me Argentina: *Various artists* / Surrey with the fringe on top: *Various artists* / Hello young lovers: *Various artists* / Guys and dolls: *Various artists* / You can't get a man with a gun: *Various artists* / June is bustin' out all over: *Various artists* / Another suitcase in another hall: *Various artists* / Shall we dance: *Various artists* / Oldest established craps game in New York: *Various artists*.
LP: . . . . **MFP 5842**
MC: . . . . **TCMFP 5842**

Hits & Heroes

HITS AND HEROES OF THE 80'S (Various artists).
LP: . . . . **MODEM 1044**

Hits Of...

HITS OF '83 (Various artists).
LP: . . . . **RONLP 4**
MC: . . . . **CRON 4**

HITS OF 1959 (See under An hour of the hits of 1959) (Various artists).

HITS OF CLIFF RICHARD (Various artists).
MC: . . . . **AIM 66**

HITS OF THE 50'S VOLUME 2 (Various artists).
MCSET: . . . . **DTO 10293**

HITS OF THE 60'S (Various artists).

MC: . . . . **TCIDL 15**

HITS OF THE 60S 20 original tracks (Various artists).
Tracks: / I got you babe: *Sonny & Cher* / Rhythm of the rain: *Cascades* / Save the last dance for me: *King*, Ben E. / Ruby don't take your love to town: *Rogers, Kenny & The First Edition* / Sixteen reasons: *Stevens, Connie*/ My special angel: *Vogues* / Cathy's clown: *Everly Brothers* / You're breaking my heart: *Smith, Keely*/ Click song number one, The: *Makeba, Miriam* / Let's go: *Routers* / If I had a hammer: *Lopez, Trini*/ Pata pata: *Makeba, Miriam* / Tiptoe through the tulips: *Tiny Tim* / Kookie Kookie (lend me your comb): *Byrnes*, Edward & Connie Stevens / Windmills of your mind: *Harrison, Noel* / Time for living: *Association* / Classical gas: *Williams, Mason* / 59th Street bridge song: *Harpers Bizarre* / What'cha gonna do about it: *Troy, Doris*.
MC: . . . . **X 00854**

HITS OF THE 60'S (Various artists).
LP: . . . . **SPR 8557**
MC: . . . . **SPC 8557**

HITS OF THE 70'S (Various artists).
LP: . . . . **SPR 8558**

HITS OF THE 80'S -CHART INVADERS (Various artists).
Tracks: / Super trouper: *Abba* / Carrie: *Richard, Cliff* / Funky town: *Lipps Inc.* / Lady: *Various* artists / One day I'll fly away: *Crawford, Randy* / Japanese boy: *Various artists* / Woman: *Lennon, John*/ De do do do De da da da: *Police* / Woman in love: *Streisand, Barbra* / Lately: *Wonder, Stevie* / Hold me: *Robertson, B.A. & Maggie Bell* / Feels like I'm in love: *Marie, Kelly* / Lonely together: *Various artists*/ Can can: *Bad Manners*.
LP: . . . . **CBR 1021**
MC: . . . . **KCBR 1021**

HITS OF THE FORTIES VOL.2 (Various artists).
2LP: . . . . **RFLD 14**

HITS OF THE FORTIES VOL.3 (Various artists).
2LP: . . . . **RFLD 4**

HITS OF THE FORTIES VOL.4 (Various artists).
2LP: . . . . **RFLD 39**
MC: . . . . **KRFLD 39**

HITS OF THE FORTIES-THE VOCALISTS (Various artists).
2LP: . . . . **RFLD 1886**
MC: . . . . **KRFLD 18**

HITS OF THE SCREAMING SIXTIES (Various artists).
Tracks: / I'm a believer: *Monkees* / San Francisco: *McKenzie, Scott* / Mr. Tambourine man: *Various original* artists / Sunny afternoon: *Kinks* / Ballad of Bonnie and Clyde: *Fame, Georgie* / Out of time: *Farlowe, Chris*.
2LP: . . . . **WW 5124/5**
MCSET: . . . . **WW 4 5124/5**

HITS OF THE SWINGING SIXTIES VOL.2 (Various artists).
Tracks: / Born to be wild: *Steppenwolf* / Eve of destruction: *McGuire, Barry* / Wipe out: *Surfaris* / Hey there lonely girl: *Holman, Eddy* / Moody river: *Boone, Pat*.
MCSET: . . . . **CRT 037**
2LP: . . . . **CR 037**

HITS OF THE THIRTIES (Various artists).
2LP: . . . . **RFLD 25**

HITS OF THE THIRTIES, VOL.2 (Various artists).
2LP: . . . . **RFLD 28**

HITS OF THE THIRTIES VOL.3 (Various artists).
2LP: . . . . **RFLD 45**

HITS OF WORLD WAR II (Various artists).
LPS: . . . . **ALBUM 38**
MCSET: . . . . **CASSETTE 38**

HITS OF WORLD WAR II (Various artists).
LP: . . . . **SH 343**

HITS OF WORLD WAR II VOL 2 (Various artists).
LP: . . . . **SH 349**

HOUR OF THE HITS OF 1964, AN (Various artists).
Tracks: / Hungry for love: *Kidd, Johnny & The Pirates* / Poison ivy: *Paramounts* / Little children: *Kramer*, Billy J. & The Dakotas / Anyone who had a heart: *Black, Cilla* / Just one look: *Hollies* / World without love: *Peter & Gordon* / Little loving, A: *Fourmost* / Don't let the sun catch you crying: *Gerry & the Pacemakers*/ Rise and fall of Flingel Bunt, The: *Shadows* / You're no good: *Swinging Blue Jeans* / Do wah diddy diddy: *Manfred* Mann / One way love: *Bennett, Cliff & The Rebel Rousers* / Goldfinger: *Bassey, Shirley* / We're through: *Hollies*/ Nobody I know: *Peter & Gordon* / I'm in love: *Fourmost* / I'm the one: *Gerry & the Pacemakers* / Rhythm and greens: *Shadows* / Good golly Miss Molly: *Swinging Blue Jeans* / 5-4-3-2-1: *Manfred Mann* / I'm into something good: *Herman's Hermits* / House of the rising sun, The: *Animals* / Over you: *Freddie & The Dreamers* / I understand: *Freddie & The Dreamers* / Message to Martha: *Faith, Adam*.
MC: . . . . **HR 8143**

Hits Of 40's

VOCALISTS, THE (Various artists).
2LP: . . . . **RFLD 18**

Hits Of The 90's

HITS OF THE 90'S (Various artists).
LP: . . . . **BSLP 002**

Hits Of The Brits

HITS OF THE BRITS (Various artists).
Tracks: / My kind of girl: *Monro, Matt* / There must be a way: *Vaughan, Frankie* / He was beautiful: *Williams*, Iris / Story of my life: *Holliday, Michael* / How wonderful to know: *Carr, Pearl & Teddy Johnson* / No other love: *Hilton, Ronnie* / Softly softly: *Murray, Ruby* / My foolish heart: *Conway, Steve* / Edelweiss: *Hill, Vince* / I'm confessin': *Ifield, Frank* / Alfie: *Black, Cilla* / Moon river: *Williams, Danny* / May you always: *Regan, Joan* / I pretend: *O'Connor, Des* / Little things mean a lot: *Cogan, Alma* / Please don't go: *Peers, Donald*.
LP: . . . . **MOIR 510**
MC: . . . . **CMOIR 510**

Hits of the Past

HITS OF THE PAST (Various artists).
LP: . . . . **ANGLP 0016**

Hits On 33

HITS ON 33 (Various artists).
2LP: . . . . **RTL 2057A/B**
MCSET: **4RTL 2057A/B**

Hits On Fire

HITS ON FIRE (Various artists).
Tracks: / War baby: *Various artists* / Sweet dreams (are made of this): *Eurythmics* / Temptation: *Heaven* 17 / Waiting for a train: *Flash & The Pan* / Blind vision: *Blancmange* / Run for your life: *Bucks Fizz*/ Overkill: *Men At Work* / Bring me closer: *Altered Images* / Transfer affection: *Flock Of Seagulls* / I won't hold you back: *Toto* / Love town: *Freeez* / Moonlight shadow: *Oldfield, Mike* / What kinda boy you looking for (girl): *Hot Chocolate* / Don't try to stop it: *Roman Holliday* / Na na hey hey (kiss him goodbye): *Various artists* / Looking at midnight: *Imagination* / Love lasts forever: *Kissing The Pink* / Teacher: *I-Level* / It's over: *Funkmasters*.
LP: . . . . **RTL 2095**
MC: **4CRTL 2095**

Hits & Rarities

HITS AND RARITIES (See under Fontana) (Various artists).

Hits That Missed

HITS THAT MISSED Meat & gravy from Cadillac baby vol.2 (Various artists).
Tracks: / Too late to pray: *Sunnyland Slim* / House rock: *Sunnyland Slim* / Special agent: *McMahon, Andrew*/ Lost in the jungle: *McMahon, Andrew* / Homesick Sunnyland special: *James, Homesick* / One more mile: *Cotton, Jimmy* / There must be a panic on: *Cotton, Jimmy* / Blue Monday blues: *Boyd, Eddie* / Blues is here to stay: *Boyd, Eddie* / I'm comin' home: *Boyd, Eddie* / Hootenanny blues: *Little Mac* / Hello baby: *Brown, Arelean* / I love my man: *Brown, Arelean*.
LP: . . . . **RL 020**

Hits Unlimited

NON-STOP DISCO PARTY (Various artists).
MC: . . . . **CHV 341**

WILD BOYS, THE (Various artists).
MC: . . . . **CHV 332**

Hittman

HITTMAN.
LP: **087566**

Hlungwane, M.J.

SHIVAVULA.
Tracks: / Madlayisani / Tiku ra kahle / Mafundhani / Shivavula / Atikoteni / Mudzivurisu / Yvuya hiphaxani / Sathani uhlulekile / Vuxaka bya mali / Higina xi phanga.
LP: . . . . **TUS 8006**
MC: . . . . **TUS 8006MC**

HM

HM (Various artists).
Tracks: / Black and white: *Deep Purple* / Time to burn: *Dio, Ronnie James* / Livin' on a prayer: *Bon Jovi*/ You don't remember I'll never forget: *Malmsteen, Yngwie J./Rising Force* / Angry heart: *Black Sabbath* / Love song: *Warlock* / Shake me (live): *Cinderella (bk)* / Any way you slice it: *Kiss* / Get ready: *Paganini*/ Speed demon: *Keel* / Rev it up: *Treat* / Rock on tonight: *Picture* / Talk dirty to me: *Poison*/ Way: *Stryper*.
LP: **8164931**
MC: **8164934**

HMS Pinafore

HMS PINAFORE (see under Gilbert & Sullivan).

HMS PINAFORE (Musical Operetta) (Various artists).
2LP: **TER2 1150**
MCSET: . . . . **ZCTER 1150**

Hnas

HNAS.
LP: . . . . **KK 016**

Ho Ho Kam

SEVEN DEADLY SINS.
LP: . . . . **NUMA 1006**
MC: . . . . **NUMAC 1006**

Hoagy Carmichael...

HOAGY CARMICHAEL SONGBOOK (Various artists).
Tracks: / Stardust: *Cole, Nat King* / Washboard blues: *Dorsey, Tommy* / Rockin' chair: *Armstrong, Louis*/ Little old lady: *Hutchinson, Leslie* / Lamplighter's serenade, The: *Miller, Glenn Orchestra* / Lazybones: *Carmichael, Hoagy* / Georgia on my mind: *Jones, Tom* / Skylark: *Shore, Dinah* / Old music master: *Mercer, Johnny*/ Nearness of you, The: *Fitzgerald, Ella* / Old buttermilk sky: *Four Freshmen* / I should have known you years ago: *Davis, Beryl* / One morning in May: *Monro, Matt* / Blue orchids: *Vaughan, Sarah* / I get along without you very well: *Newley, Anthony* / In the cool cool cool of the evening: *Mancini, Henry* / Doctor lawyer indian chief: *Hutton, Betty* / Judy: *Laine, Frankie* / My resistance is low: *Sarstedt, Robin* / When love goes wrong: *Whiting, Margaret/Jimmy Wakely* / Memphis in June: *Skellern, Peter* / Ivy: *Stafford, Jo* / How little we know: *Monro, Matt* / Stardust: *Shaw, Artie*.
2LP: . . . . **VSOPLP 123**
MC: . . . . **VSOPMC 123**

Hoang Mong Thuy

MUSIC OF VIETNAM (see Tran Quang Hai) (Hoang Mong Thuy/Tran Quang Hai).

Hoban, John

MUSIC FOR HOLY WEEK AND EASTER.
LP: . . . . **LPB 804**

Hoban, Russell

BARGAIN FOR FRANCES, A (Johns, Glynis (nar)).
MC: **1547**

BEDTIME FOR FRANCES.
Tracks: / Best friends for Frances / Baby sister for Frances, A / Birthday for Frances, A / Bedtime for Frances.
MC: . . . . **TS 348**

FRANCES (Johns, Glynis (nar)).
MC: **1546**

MOUSE & HIS CHILD, THE (Ustinov, Peter).
MC: **1550**

Hobbs Angel Of Death

HOBBS ANGEL OF DEATH.
LP: **087523**

Hobbs, David

NEW AND REDISCOVERED MUSICAL INSTRUMENTS (Hobbs, David/Max Eastley).
LP: . . . . **EGED 24**

Hobbs/Adams/Bryars

ENSEMBLE PIECES.
LP: . . . . **EGED 22**

Hobo Bop

HOBO BOP (Various artists).
LP: . . . . **HOBOBOP 1181**

Hobson & Lees

HAND MADE.
LP: . . . . **CALI 287**

Hockensmith, Hadley

HEART SONG.
LP: . . . . **MLR 7010**
MC: . . . . **MLC 7010**

Hockridge, Edmund

MAKE IT EASY ON YOURSELF.
Tracks: / Make it easy on yourself / You don't have to say you love me / Games that lovers play / I will warm your heart / Yesterday / Comes once in a lifetime / Sand and sea / Guantanamera / All alone am I / You can't keep me from loving you / Senza fine / Have I the right?.
LP: . . . . **PLE 516**

SINGS HITS FROM VARIOUS MUSICALS.
Tracks: / Gigi / Night they invented champagne, The / Thank Heaven for little girls / Waltz at Maxim's / Bess, you is my woman now / I got plenty o' nuttin' / Summertime / It ain't necessarily so / Seventy-six trombones / Linda Rose / Till there was you / It's you / Goodnight, my someone.
LP: . . . . **FBLP 8086**
MC: . . . . **ZCFBL 8086**

Hodes, Art

ART FOR ART'S SAKE.
LP: . . . . **J 46**

ART HODES AND MAGNOLIA JAZZ BAND VOL.2 (Hodes, Art & Magnolia Jazzband).
LP: . . . . **GHB 172**

ART HODES PLAYS BESSIE.
LP: . . . . **ESR 1213**

ART HODES RHYTHM SECTION (Hodes, Art Rhythm Section).
LP: . . . . **PARKWOOD 106**

ART HODES-VOLUME 1 Magnolia Jazz band.
LP: . . . . **GHB 171**

ART OF HODES, THE.
LP: . . . . **ESR 1207**

BLUES GROOVE (Hodes, Art Blue Six).
LP: . . . . **J 155**

BLUES IN THE NIGHT.
LP: **3039**

CLASSIC PIANOS (See under Garner, Erroll) (Various artists).

ECHOES OF CHICAGO (Hodes, Art and His Windy City Seven).
LP: . . . . **J 79**

GOSPEL ACCORDING TO ART.
LP: . . . . **JCE 93**

HOME COOKIN' (Hodes, Art Jazz Four plus 2).
LP: . . . . **J 58**

JAZZ RECORD STORY VOL 1.
LP: . . . . **J 82**

JOY TO THE WORLD.
LP: . . . . **PARKWOOD 108**

JUST THE TWO OF US (Hodes, Art & Milt Hinton).
Tracks: / Wini' / I would do 'most anything / Low down below / By and by / Down home blues / Randolph Street blues / Here comes Cow Cow / Miss Otis regrets / Milt jumps / Willow weep for me.
LP: . . . . **MR 5279**

LIVE AT HANRATTY'S, NEW YORK CITY.
Tracks: / Liza / Exactly like you / Grandpa's spells / Someone to watch over me / St. Louis blues / Georgia on my mind / Sweet Georgia Brown / Save it, pretty mama / Plain ol' blues / Washboard blues / Struttin' with some barbecue.
LP: . . . . **R 5252**

MUSIC OF LOVIE AUSTIN (Hodes, Art Blue Six).
LP: . . . . **SOS 1184**

PAGIN' MR.JELLY.
Tracks: / Grandpas spells / Mamie's blues / High society / Mr Jelly lord / Buddy Bolden's blues / Pagin' Mr Jelly / Wolverine blues / Ballin' the Jack / Pearls, The / Gone Jelly blues / Doctor jazz / Oh didn't he ramble.
LP: . . . . **CS 9037**

SELECTIONS FROM THE GUTTER.
LP: . . . . **SLP 4057**

SENSATION (Hodes, Art & John Petters Hot Three).
Tracks: / Clarinet marmalade / Lazybones / Mama's gone goodbye / Lonesome blues / Jackass blues / Cake walkin' babies from home / Sensation / Jeep's blues / Ballin' the Jack / Snowball / Dear old Southland / Wolverine blues.
MC: . . . . **CMJMC 007**

SOME LEGENDARY ART (Hodes, Art Quintet).
LP: . . . . **AP 54**

SOMETHING PERSONAL Alone with friends (Hodes, Art/Doug Dobel Memorial 10).
Tracks: / Trouble in mind / Blues keep calling / Black and blue / Forty Second Street / Atlanta blues / Organ grinder blues / Old fashioned love / Lonesome blues / Bye and bye / Aunt Hagar's blues / I'm coming Virginia / Russian ragout / Sweet Georgia Brown.
MC: . . . . **KDC 77/10**

SOUTHSIDE MEMORIES.

LP: 3032

Hodes, Bob

JAZZ OF THE ROARING 20S (Red Onion Jazzband).
LP: . . . . **MMRC 112**

Hodges Brothers

WATERMELON HANGIN.
LP: . . . . **ARHOOLIE 5001**

Hodges, Carl

BLUES ALL AROUND MY BED (See under Blues Roots vol.2).

Hodges, Johnny

2 OR 3 SHADES OF BLUE.
LP: . . . . **NL 89710**
MC: . . . . **NK 89710**

AT THE SPORTPALAST, BERLIN.
Tracks: / Take the 'A' train / In the kitchen / Mood indigo / Solitude / Satin doll / I got it bad and that ain't good / Rockin' in rhythm / Autumn leaves / Stompy Jones / C jam blues / Jeep is jumpin' / Good Queen Bess / Things ain't what they used to be / I'll get by / I let a song go out of my heart / Don't get around much anymore / Just squeeze me / Do nothing till you hear from me / Rose of the Rio Grande / All of me / On the sunny side of the street / Blue moon / Perdido.
2LP: **2620 102**
MCSET: . . . . **K 20 102**

BACK TO BACK (See under Ellington, Duke) (Hodges, Johnny & Duke Ellington).

BIG SOUND, THE (Hodges Johnny & The Ellington Men).
Tracks: / Don't call me, I'll call you / Ordinary thing / Waiting for Duke / Dust bowl / Little rabbit blues / Viscount / Johnny come lately / Bouquet of roses / Gone and crazy / Digits / Segdoh / Early morning rock.
LP: **2304 232**

DUKES IN BED.
LP: **2304 383**

EVERYBODY KNOWS.
Tracks: / Everybody knows / Jeep is jumpin' / 310 blues / Main stem.
LP: . . . . **JAS 34**

GERRY MULLIGAN MEETS JOHNNY HODGES (See under Mulligan, Gerry) (Hodges, Johnny & Gerry Mulligan).

HOMAGE TO THE DUKE (See under Christie, Keith) (Hodges, Johnny/Keith Christie/John Dankworth Etc).

IN A MELLOW TONE (Hodges, Johnny & Wild Bill Davis).
Tracks: / Just squeeze me / It's only a paper moon / Taffy / Good Queen Bess / L B blues / In a mellow tone / Rockville / I'll always love you / It don't mean a thing / Belle of Belmont.
LP: . . . . **NL 82305**
MC: . . . . **NK 82305**

INSPIRED ABANDON (see Brown, Lawrence) (Hodges, Johnny & The Lawrence Brown All-Stars).

JOHNNY HODGES AND WILD BILL DAVIS, 1965 - 1966 (Hodges, Johnny & Wild Bill Davis).
Tracks: / On the sunny side of the street / On Green Dolphin Street / Li'l darlin' / Con sould and sax / Jeep is jumpin' / I'm beginning to see the light / Sophisticated lady / Drop me off in Harlem / No one / Johnny come lately / It's only a paper moon / Taffy / Good Queen Bess / L.B. blues / In a mellow tone / Rockville / I'll always love you / It don't mean a thing / Belle of the Belmont.
2LP: . . . . **PM 42414**

JOHNNY HODGES AND WILD BILL DAVIS (Walkman jazz) (Hodges, Johnny & Wild Bill Davis).
Tracks: / Blue Hodge / Hodge podge / Knuckles / Jones / I cried for you / A&R blues / Wings and things / Peg o' my heart / Spotted dog / Blues for Madeleine / Rabbit out of the hat / Hash brown / Harmony in Harlem / Blues o' mighty.
MC: **839 288-4**

JOHNNY HODGES, VOL 1.
Tracks: / Things ain't what they used to be / In a mellow tone / Mr. Gentle and Mr. Cool / Sophisticated lady / Jeep's blues / All of me / Passion flower / On the sunny side of the street.
LP: . . . . **JR 107**

JOHNNY HODGES, VOL 2.
Tracks: / Get that geet / Perdido / That's grand / Skip it / Hop, skip and jump / Sweet Lorraine / Mix it, mix it / Jump, that's all / Mood indigo / Beau bag boogie / Time on my hands / Run about / In the shade of the old apple tree / Last legs blues.
LP: . . . . **JR 125**
LP: . . . . **AJAX 108**

JOHNNY HODGES, VOL 3.
LP: . . . . **AJAX 116**

JOHNNY HODGES, VOL 4.
LP: . . . . **AJAX 120**

LOVE IN SWINGTIME 1938-39.
LP: . . . . **TAX 8022**

MAN AND HIS MUSIC, A (Hodges, Johnny & Charlie Shavers).
LP: . . . . **SLP 4073**

MASTERS OF JAZZ VOL.9.
Tracks: / Cambridge blue / Brute's roots / Bouncing with Ben / One for the duke / Walkin' the frog / Rabbit pie / On the sunny side / Good Queen Bess / Jeep is jumpin' / Things ain't what they used to be.
LP: . . . . **SLP 4109**

MELLOW TONE.
Tracks: / Things ain't what they used to be / In a mellow tone / Mr. Gentle and Mr. Cool / Sophisticated lady / Jeeps' blues / All of me / Passion flower / On the sunny side of the street / Get that geet / Perdido / That's grand / Skip it / Hop, skip and jump / Sweet Lorraine / Nix it, mix it / Jump, that's all / Mood indigo / Beau bag boogie / Time on my hands / Run about / In the shade of the old apple tree / Last legs blues.
LP: . . . . **VJD 528**

NOT SO DUKISH.
LP: **2304 510**

RABBIT IN PARIS, THE.
LP: **500059**

RABBITS WORK VOL 5.
LP: **2304 451**

SIDE BY SIDE (see under Ellington, Duke) (Hodges, Johnny & Duke Ellington).

SMOOTH ONE, THE.
Tracks: / First class / Second klass / Straight back / Steerage / Third klass / Meet the frog / Nite life / My melancholy baby / Lotus blossom / Free for all / I told you so / Starting with you / Hare / Things you miss / Wiggle awhile / Br' rabbit / Get ready / Peaches / Hygiene.
2LP: **2632082**

TRIPLE PLAY.
Tracks: / Take 'em off (part 1) / Take 'em off (part 2) / Nearness of you, The / Monkey on a limb / Tiny bit of blues, A / For jammers only (aka Wild onions) / On the way up / Big boy blues / Very thought of you, The / Fur piece / Sir John / Figurine / C-jam blues.
LP: . . . . **NL 85903**
MC: . . . . **NK 85903**

Hodgson, Roger

HAI HAI.
Tracks: / Right place / My magazine / London / You make me love you / Hai hai / Who's afraid / Desert love / Land ho / House on the corner / Puppet dance.
LP: . . . . **AMA 5112**
MC: . . . . **AMC 5112**

IN THE EYE OF THE STORM.
Tracks: / Had a dream / In jeopardy / Lovers in the wind / Hooked on a problem / Give me love give me life / I'm not afraid / Only because of you.
LP: . . . . **AMA 5004**
MC: . . . . **AMC 5004**

Hodgson, Steve

TRILLIONS (See also Nicholas Fisk).

Hoehn, Tommy

LOSING YOU TO SLEEP.
Tracks: / Hey polarity / Losing you to sleep / Heat / She might look my way / Fresh matches / Blow yourself up / I know I love you now / Mean Nancy / Fight you.
LP: . . . . **SHU 8536**

Hoeke, Rob

JUMPIN ON THE 88.
LP: . . . . **OL 8005**

ROB HOEKE AND THE REAL BOOGIE WOOGIE.
Tracks: / Rockin' my blood away / Survival boogie / Saturday evening boogie / Sunday morning blues / Real boogie woogie / Rob's home boogie / Goodbye boogie / What's going on? / Believe me / Knocking boogie / Fine and steady / For my friend / Holland boogie / Boogie woogie me.
LP: . . . . **DS 9234**

Hoenig, Michael

DEPARTURE FROM THE NORTHERN WASTELAND.
Tracks: / Departure from the northern wasteland / Hanging garden transfer / Voices of where / Sun and moon.
LP: . . . . **LPKUCK 079**
MC: . . . . **MCKUCK 079**
LP: . . . . **K 56464**

Hoffman, E.T.A

NUTCRACKER (Plummer, Christopher).
MCSET: **128**

Hoffman, Janalea

MIND-BODY TEMPO (60 Beats a Minute Music).
MC: . . . . **C 190**

Hoffmann, Herbert M

CHRISTMAS CAROLS FOR CHURCH ORGAN.
MC: . . . . **CHV 325**

Hoffman/Tchaikovsky

STORY OF THE NUTCRACKER (Bloom, Claire (nar)).
LP: . . . . **TC 1524**
MC: . . . . **CDL 51524**

Hoffmeister

FLUTE CONCERTOS (see under Dingfelder, Ingrid) (Dingfelder, Ingrid/ English Chamber Or./Sir Charles Mackerras).

Hoffnung, Gerard

AT THE OXFORD UNION.
LP: . . . . **LF 1330**

HOFFNUNG.
2LP: . . . . **REF 157**
MCSET: . . . . **HRMC 157**

HOFFNUNG - A LAST ENCORE (Various artists).
Tracks: / Speech day: *Various artists* / My life: *Various artists* / Talking about music: *Various artists*/ Charles Richardson interviews, The: *Various artists* / Bricklayer, The: *Various artists* / Film fan, The: *Various artists* / Oxford union: *Various artists* / Hoffnung Gerard interviews, The: *Various artists.*
MCSET: . . . . **ZBBC 1062**

Hoffpauir, Sleepy

SLEEPY HOFFPAUIR FIDDLES TRADITIONAL CAJUN MUSIC.
LP: **6027**

Hoffs, Susanna

WHEN YOU'RE A BOY.
Tracks: / My side of the bed / No kind of love / Wishing on telstar / That's why girl's cry / Unconditional love / Something new / So much for love / This time / Only love / It's lonely out here / Made of stone / Boys keep swinging.
LP: **4672021**
MC: **4672024**

Hofmann, Holly

HOLLY, TAKE NOTE (Hofmann, Holly Quartet).
Tracks: / My ship / Thoughts of you / Groove merchant / Whisper not / Some other blues / But beautiful / In walked Bud / Ceora.
LP: . . . . **CAP 74011-1**

Hofmann, Peter

ROCK CLASSICS.
Tracks: / House of the rising sun / Scarborough Fair / Sun ain't gonna shine anymore, The / Long and winding road, The / MacArthur Park / Sailing / Nights in white satin / Yesterday / Say goodbye to Hollywood / Bridge over troubled water.
LP: . . . . **CBS 85965**

Hofner, Adolph

SOUTH TEXAS SWING.
LP: . . . . **ARHOOLIE 5020**

Hogan, Annie

KICKABYES.
LP: . . . . **DVR 9**

Hogan, Brendan

COME BY THE HILLS.
MC: . . . . **HSMC 047**

Hogan, Jimmy

TRIO IRISH DANCE MUSIC.
MC: **30 371**

Hogan, John

EVENING WITH JOHN HOGAN, AN.
MC: . . . . **PLAC 332**

MY FEELINGS FOR YOU.
LP: . . . . **KLP 270**
MC: . . . . **KMC 270**
MC: . . . . **OCE 2466**

TURN BACK THE YEARS.
MC: . . . . **KMC 305**

Hogan, Silas

I'M A FREE HEARTED MAN (Louisiana Blues).
Tracks: / I'm a free hearted man / Born in Texas / Let me be your hatchet / My baby walked out / Don't do that to me / Every Saturday night.
LP: . . . . **FLY 595**

TROUBLE.
LP: . . . . **LP 8019**

Hogg, Smokey

GOIN' BACK HOME.
Tracks: / Change your ways / I ain't got over it yet / Dirty mistreater / Misery blues / When I've been drinkin' / Goin' back home / You'll need my help someday / Ain't goin' t'second no more / Need my help / Keep a walking / You gotta go / My baby's gone / Penny pinching mama / Do it no more.
LP: . . . . **KK 7421**

JIVE LITTLE WOMAN - TOO LATE OLD MAN (1947-58).
LP: . . . . **IG 409**

Hoggard, Jay

LOVE SURVIVES.
Tracks: / Don't quit / Pacific vibes / Felice / Love survives / Sailing / As if in a dream / God is capable of everything.
LP: . . . . **GR 8204**

RAINFOREST.
LP: **1014 007**

Hoggins

BIG BLUE PLYMOUTH (See under Bywaters) (Hoggins/Bywaters).

Hoglund, Ola

ALLT UNDER HIMMELENS FASTE (Hoglund, Ola/Arne Domnerus).
LP: . . . . **PHONT 7565**

Hogmany In The Western

HOGMANAY IN THE WESTERN ISLES (Various artists).
LP: . . . . **HEB 3**

Hogshead

ROCKIN IN THE COUNTRY.
Tracks: / I slap the bass boogie / Big Willy and Ramona / Bright morning light / Lola's lightnin' / Plain clothes / I feed the hogs / Alligator bait / Rockabilly queen / Eastbound and down / Bop on back to Memphis.
LP: . . . . **ROLL 2003**

Hohki, Kazuko

KAZUKO HOHKI SINGS BRIDGITTE BARDOT.
LP: . . . . **OH 12**

Hohner Accordion...

ACCORDION IN CONCERT (Hohner Accordion Orchestra Augsberg).
LP: . . . . **LPO 99 027**

Hokey Cokey

HOKEY COKEY (TV Soundtrack) (Various artists).
Tracks: / Hokey cokey (instrumental): *Various artists* / Feeling good today: *Various artists* / Riverbank boatrace day: *Various artists* / Visiting song, The: *Various artists* / Doodly-doo: *Various artists* / Down at the bottom of the ocean: *Various artists* / Five tall rockets: *Various artists* / There was an old woman: *Various* artists / Moonwalking: *Various artists* / Rackaticky bleep: *Various artists* / One two three dancing: *Various* artists / Bushfright: *Various artists* / We're explorers: *Various artists* / Animal fair: *Various artists*/ Big bear growls, A: *Various artists* / Hot air balloon: *Various artists* / Blow the wind southerly: *Various artists* / Penguin strut, The: *Various artists* / Who goes there?: *Various artists* / Fox went out, The: *Various artists* / Hokey cokey (finale): *Various artists.*
LP: . . . . **REC 557**
MC: . . . . **ZCM 557**

Hokkanen, Eric

ERIC & THE OFFBEATS (Hokkanen, Eric & The Offbeats).
LP: . . . . **HLD 002**

Hokum Boys

BROONZY, WASHBOARD SAM 1935-37.
LP: . . . . **LE 300,003**

CAN'T GET ENOUGH OF THAT STUFF.
LP: . . . . **L 1051**

COMPLETE RECORDINGS 1935-37.
LP: . . . . **LE 300.003**

FAMOUS HOKUM BOYS 1930-31, THE.
LP: . . . . **MSE 1014**

HOKUM BOYS, THE.
LP: . . . . **BD 2022**

Hokum Hotshots

MAYBE IT'S THE BLUES.
LP: . . . . **CM 015**

Hokum-On-Somble

LEGACY OF GOODTIME MUSIC, A.
LP: . . . . **LRF 065**

Hold Me Strong

HOLD ME STRONG (Various artists).
Tracks: / Love me girl: *Sibbles, Leroy* / You'll never find: *Holt, John* / Moving

away: *Brown, Dennis*/ Just say who: *Wilson, Delroy* / I will never change: *Campbell, Cornell* / Let me down easy: *Harriott, Derrick*/ Rockabye woman: *McKay, Freddie*.
LP: . . . . **TRLS 271**

Hold Moses

ONE NATION UNDER GOD.
LP: . . . . **GWLP 20**

Hold Up

HOLD UP (Original soundtrack) (Various artists).
LP: **66.281**
MC: **76.281**

Holden, Ron

LOVE YOU SO (See under Fendermen).

Holder, Ace

ROCKIN' THIS JOINT TONITE (See under Thomas, Kid) (Valentine, Kid Thomas, Floyd Dixon & Ace Holder).

Holdridge, Lee

FILM MUSIC OF LEE HOLDRIDGE (see under Films) (London Symphony Orchestra).

Holdsworth, Allan

METAL FATIGUE.
Tracks: / City nights / Secrets / 54 Duncan Terrace / Joshua / Spokes / Maid Marion / Peril premonition / Endomorph.
LP: **2002 1**

SAND.
LP: **3293 1**

SECRETS.
Tracks: / City nights / 54 Duncan Terrace / Spokes / Perila premonition / Secrets / Joshua / Maid Marion / Endomorph.
LP: . . . . **ENVLP 536**
LP: . . . . **INTM 73328**
LP: **773 328 1**

Hole

OTHER TONGUES, OTHER FLESH.
Tracks: / Discordia / Breaking the circuit / Shrine / Coprolalia / War on sleep / Rising.
LP: . . . . **EYAS 017**

Holey Ha'Penny

HOLEY HA'PENNY (Various artists).
LP: **12T 283**
MC: . . . . **KTSC 283**

Holiday, Billie

16 CLASSIC TRACKS: BILLIE HOLIDAY.
Tracks: / Lover man / No more / That ole devil called love / Don't explain / You better go now / What is this thing called love? / Good morning heartache / No-good man / Big stuff / Baby I don't cry over you / I'll look around / Blues are brewin' / Guilty / Deep song / There is no greater love / Easy living.
LP: . . . . **MCL 1688**
MC: . . . . **MCLC 1688**

16 ORIGINAL HITS: BILLIE HOLIDAY.
MC: . . . . **MC 1636**

1942 - 1951 - 1954.
LP: **2C 068 86527**

ALL OF ME (HAPPY BIRD).
Tracks: / God bless the child / I cover the waterfront / Lover come back to me / All of me / Billie's blues / My man / Them there eyes / Lover man / Stormy weather / Willow weep for me / I only have eyes for you / Please don't talk about me when I'm gone.
LP: . . . . **B 90129**

ALL OF ME (PREMIER).
Tracks: / My man / Them there eyes / I cover the waterfront / Lover come back to me / You're driving me crazy / All of me (end s1) / I loves you, Porgy / Miss Brown to you / They can't take that away from me / Storyville / Blues are bluer / Road to love.
LP: . . . . **CBR 1021**
MC: . . . . **KCBR 1021**

AS TIME GOES BY.
LPPD: . . . . **AR 30071**

AT STORYVILLE.
Tracks: / I cover the waterfront / Too marvellous for words / I loves you, Porgy / Them there eyes / Willow weep for me / I only have eyes for you / You go to my head / He's funny that way / Billie's blues / Miss Brown to you / Lover come back to me / T'aint nobody's business if I do / You're driving me crazy.
LP: . . . . **INT 147 015**
LP: . . . . **BLP 60921**
LP: . . . . **BLM 51007**

BEST OF BILLIE HOLIDAY.
LP: **4670291**
MC: **4670294**

BILLIE, ELLA, LENA, SARAH (Various artists).
Tracks: / Man I love, The: *Various artists* / My melancholy baby: *Various artists* / Prisoner of love: *Various artists* / Nice work if you can get it: *Various artists* / I'll never be the same: *Various artists* / East of the sun: *Various artists* / What a little moonlight can do: *Various artists* / Ain't misbehavin': *Various* artists / Out of nowhere: *Various artists* / All my life: *Various artists* / I'm gonna lock my heart: *Various artists* / Goodnight my love: *Various artists*.
LP: . . . . **CBS 54303**

BILLIE HOLIDAY 30'S.
LP: . . . . **LOP 14 121**
MC: . . . . **LCS 14121**

BILLIE HOLIDAY 40'S.
LP: . . . . **LOP 14 122**
MC: . . . . **LCS 14122**

BILLIE HOLIDAY 50'S.
LP: . . . . **LOP 14 123**
MC: . . . . **LCS 14123**

BILLIE HOLIDAY AT MONTEREY 1958.
Tracks: / Ain't nobody's business but my own / Willow weep for me / When your lover has gone / God bless the child / I only have eyes for you / Good morning heartache / Them there eyes / Billie's blues / Oh, what a little moonlight can do / Trav'lin light / Lover come back to me.
LP: . . . . **BKH 50701**
MC: . . . . **BKHMC 50701**

BILLIE HOLIDAY AT STORYVILLE, BOSTON VOL 1.
LP: . . . . **SLP 4134**

BILLIE HOLIDAY COLLECTION (20 Golden Greats).
Tracks: / My man / Don't explain / Swing, brother, swing / Lover man / I cover the waterfront / Do you know what it means to miss New Orleans? / I'll get by / When your lover has gone / Keeps on a rainin' / Miss Brown to you / Do nothing till you hear from me / I can't get started / Fine and mellow / Yesterdays / She's funny that way / On the sunny side of the street / Strange fruit / My old flame / Lover come back to me / They can't take that away from me?.
LP: . . . . **DVLP 2018**
MC: . . . . **DVMC 2018**

BILLIE HOLIDAY (ENTERTAINERS).
LP: . . . . **ENT LP 13002**
MC: . . . . **ENT MC 13002**

BILLIE HOLIDAY & HER ORCHESTRA.
Tracks: / Lover come back to me / You go to my head / East of the sun / Blue moon / Solitude / I only have eyes for you / Autumn in New York / Tenderly / These foolish things / Remember? / I can't face the music / I cried for you / Love me or leave me / Please don't talk about me when I'm gone / It had to be you / P.S. I love you.
LP: . . . . **LPJT 98**
MC: . . . . **MCJT 98**

BILLIE HOLIDAY (JOKER).
LP: . . . . **SM 3966**

BILLIE HOLIDAY LIVE (Compact/ Walkman Jazz).
Tracks: / Body and soul / Strange fruit / Trav'lin light / He's funny that way / Man I love, The / Gee baby ain't I good to you / All of you / You better go now / You're driving me crazy / There is no greater love / I cover the waterfront / Fine and mellow / Nice work if you can get it / Willow weep for me / Lover come back to me / Lady sings the blues / What a little moonlight can do / My man / I wished on the moon / Lover man (Oh where can you be).
MC: **841 434 4**

BILLIE HOLIDAY - LIVE.
Tracks: / Introduction / My man / Don't explain / Them there eyes / Swing brother swing / Lover man / I cover the waterfront / Do nothing till you hear from me / They can't take that away from me / Lover come back to me.
LP: . . . . **PHX 1009**

BILLIE HOLIDAY - LIVE 1937/56.
Tracks: / They can't take that away from me / Lover come back to me / Stormy weather / All of me.
LP: **20809**

BILLIE HOLIDAY REVISITED (See under Jazz) (Various artists).

BILLIE HOLIDAY REVISITED (See under Billie Holiday ...) (Various artists).

BILLIE HOLIDAY SINGS THE BLUES.
MC: **833770 4**

BILLIE HOLIDAY SONGBOOK, THE.
Tracks: / Good morning heartache / My man / Billie's blues / Don't explain / Lady sings the blues / Lover man / God bless the child / Fine and mellow / Strange fruit / Stormy blues / Trav'lin' light.
LP: . . . . **VRV 7**
MC: . . . . **VRVC 7**

BILLIE HOLIDAY STORY 1.
Tracks: / Your mother's son in law / Riffin' / Scotch, The / Them there eyes / These foolish things / Did I remember / No regrets / Fine romance, A / Easy to love / Way you look tonight / Pennies from Heaven / That's life I guess / I can't give you anything but love / This year's kisses / Why was I born / Mood that I'm in, The / I'll never be the same / Without your love / Swing brother swing / They can't take that away from me / Getting some fun out of life / Travellin' all alone / When you're smiling / If dreams come true / I can't get started / Back in your own back yard / On the sentimental side / When a woman loves a man / You go to my head / Very thought of you, The / That's all I ask of you / Dream of life / Long gone blues.
2LP: . . . . **CBS 68228**

BILLIE HOLIDAY STORY 2.
2LP: . . . . **CBS 68229**

BILLIE HOLIDAY STORY 3.
2LP: . . . . **CBS 68230**

BILLIE HOLIDAY STORY, THE.
Tracks: / What a little moonlight can do / Miss Brown to you / Twenty four hours a day / These n'that n'those / Let's call a heart a heart / Let's dream in the moonlight / Night and day / What is this going to get us / Georgia on my mind / God bless the child / Until the real thing comes along / Do you know what it means to miss New Orleans / Keeps on a rainin' / He's funny that way / Fine and mellow / I cover the waterfront / Lover come back to me / Lover man / I got it bad and that ain't good / Willow weep for me / My man / Please don't talk about me when I'm gone / Don't explain / Porgy / Billie's blues.
MCSET: . . . . **DVREMC 03**

BILLIE HOLIDAY (VERVE) (Compact/ Walkman Jazz).
MC: **831 371-4**

BILLIE HOLIDAY VOL 2.
Tracks: / Solitude / Weep no more / Girls were made to take care of boys / Porgy / My man / T'aint nobody's business if I do / Baby get lost / Keeps on a rainin' / Them there eyes / Do your duty / Gimme a pigfoot and a bottle of beer / Now or never / You're my thrill / Crazy he calls me / Please tell me how / Somebody's on my mind / God bless the child / This is heaven to me.
LP: . . . . **MCL 1776**
MC: . . . . **MCLC 1776**

BILLIE HOLIDAY VOL 3.
LP: . . . . **QUEEN 067**

BILLIE HOLIDAY WITH TEDDY WILSON AND ORCHESTRA (Holiday, Billie & Teddy Wilson).
Tracks: / Nice work if you can get it / It's a sin to tell a lie / You showed me the way / Carelessly / Mood that I'm in, The / It's too hot for words / My man / Sun showers / Now you know / What a night, what a moon, what a girl / Moanin' low / How could you / If you were mine / What a little moonlight can do / They say / It's like reaching for the Moon.
LP: . . . . **LPJT 86**

BILLIE'S BLUES (BULLDOG).
Tracks: / Swing, brother, swing / Do nothing till you hear from me / You're driving me crazy / Lover man / Nobody's business / My man / They can't take that away from me / He's funny that way / Don't be late / God bless the child / Lover come back to me / Don't explain / Same old story / Detour ahead / Billie's blues / Miss Brown to you.
LP: . . . . **BDL 1007**
MC: . . . . **AJKL 1007**

BILLIE'S BLUES (CBS).
Tracks: / I'm a fool to want you / Glad to be unhappy / Sailboat in the moonlight / When a woman loves a man / I'll never be the same / Let's call the whole thing off / Summertime / Am I blue / I cover the waterfront / Billie's blues.
LP: . . . . **CBS 32733**
MC: **40 32733**
LP: . . . . **VSLP 339**
MC: . . . . **VSC 339**
LP: **20055**
MC: **40055**

BODY AND SOUL.
LP: **2304 340**

ESSENTIAL BILLIE HOLIDAY, THE.
Tracks: / Lady sings the blues / It ain't nobody's business if I do / I love my man / My man.
LP: **2304 343**

ESSENTIAL, THE.
MC: **4671494**

EVENING WITH LADY DAY.
LP: . . . . **JAZ 2003**

FINE AND DANDY (See Under Wilson, Teddy) (Wilson, Teddy/his orchestra/ Billie Holiday).

FINE AND MELLOW, 1939 & 1944.
Tracks: / Strange fruit / Yesterdays / Fine and mellow / I gotta right to sing the blues / How am I to know? / My old flame / I'll get by / I cover the waterfront.
LP: **AG6 24055**

FINE AND MELLOW (CAMBRA).
Tracks: / Ghost of a chance / God bless the child / I loves you, Porgy / All of me / My man / Them there eyes / Don't explain / Foolin' myself / Lover man / Tenderly / Easy to remember / Willow weep for me / Swing, brother, swing / He's funny that way.
2LP: . . . . **CR 139**
MCSET: . . . . **CRT 139**

GIANTS, 3 (See under Ellington, Duke) (Holiday, Billie/ Duke Ellington/ Louis Armstrong).

GOD BLESS THE CHILD.
Tracks: / God bless the child / Them there eyes / T'aint nobody's business if I do / My man / You're driving me crazy / Everything a good man needs / He's funny that way / Miss Brown to you / Detour ahead / Don't explain / Lover man.
2LP: **66 267**
2LP: . . . . **MTM 027**

GOLDEN GREATS: BILLIE HOLIDAY.
Tracks: / That ole devil called love / Don't explain / Lover man / Easy living / Good morning heartache / No more / You better go now / What is this thing called love / No good man / Big stuff / Baby I don't cry over you / I'll look around / Blues are brewin' / Guilty / Deep song / There is no greater love.
LP: . . . . **MCM 5011**
MC: . . . . **MCMC 5011**

GOLDEN YEARS 1933-41, THE.
Tracks: / Your mother's son in law / No regrets / This year's kisses / You go to my head / Body and soul / Georgia on my mind / Am I blue / Gloomy Sunday.
LPS: . . . . **CBS 66377**
MC: **40 66377**

GOLDEN YEARS OF LADY DAY.
LP: . . . . **LPJT 10**

GOLDEN YEARS, THE (Vol. 2).
LP: . . . . **QUEEN 065**

GOOD MORNING HEARTACHE.
Tracks: / Good morning heartache / What is this thing called love / God bless the child / This is heaven to me / Solitude / Don't explain / My man (mon homme) / That ole devil called love / Crazy he calls me / You're my thrill / No good man / You better go now / Weep no more / Lover man (oh where can you be).
LP: . . . . **SHM 3213**
MC: . . . . **HSC 3213**

GREATEST HITS: BILLIE HOLIDAY VOL.1.
LP: . . . . **CL 0027683**
MC: . . . . **CLMC 927683**

GREATEST HITS: BILLIE HOLIDAY VOL.2.
LP: . . . . **CL 0028683**
MC: . . . . **CLMC 0028683**
LP: . . . . **B 92683**

HOLIDAY, BILLIE: ON THE AIR.
Tracks: / Fine and mellow / All of me / Man I love, The / You've changed / I love my man / When your lover has gone / I'm just foolin' myself / Easy to remember / Moanin' low / Don't explain.
LP: . . . . **TOTEM 1037**

HOLIDAY FOR LOVERS.
Tracks: / They can't take that away from me / Don't explain / Do you know what it means to miss New Orleans / Storyville / Miss Brown to you / Them there eyes / Ain't nobody's business / My man.
LP: . . . . **MAN 5014**

I WONDER WHERE OUR LOVE HAS GONE.
LP: . . . . **GOJ 1001**
MC: . . . . **GOJC 1001**

I'LL BE SEEING YOU (1944).
Tracks: / Strange fruit / Yesterdays / Fine and mellow / I gotta right to sing the blues / How am I to know? / My old flame / I'll get by / I cover the waterfront.
LP: **AG6 24291**

IMMORTAL SESSIONS.
LP: . . . . **SLP 1000**

IMMORTAL, THE.
Tracks: / Swing brother swing / They can't take that away from me / Do nothing till you hear from me / I'll get by / I love my man / I cover the waterfront / Do you know what it means to miss New Orleans / Don't explain / Keeps on a rainin' / Lover come back to me.
LP: . . . . **SM 3131**
MC: . . . . **MC 3131**

JAZZ LEGENDS (see under Count Basie) (Holiday, Billie & Count Basie).

LADY AND THE LEGEND, VOL 1 (1949 - 1951).
Tracks: / My man / Miss Brown to you / Keeps on a rainin' / I cover the waterfront / All of me / Good morning heartache / Maybe you'll be there / You're driving me crazy / You're my thrill / He's funny that way / Billie's blues / Them there eyes.
LP: RHA 6025

LADY AND THE LEGEND, VOL 2 (1952 - 1956).
Tracks: / My man / Tenderly / God bless the child / I cover the waterfront / Lover come back to me / Billie's blues / Them there eyes / Lover man / Stormy weather / Willow weep for me / I only have eyes for you / Please don't talk about me when I'm gone.
LP: RHA 6026

LADY AND THE LEGEND, VOL 3.
Tracks: / I cover the waterfront / Lover come back to me / Ghost of a chance / Please don't talk about me when I'm gone / Nice work if you can get it / God bless the child / Don't explain / Porgy / Fine and mellow / Foolin' myself / Easy to remember / Moanin' low / When your lover has gone.
LP: RHA 6027

LADY DAY LIVE.
MC: DPC 725

LADY DAY & PREZ 1937-1941 (Holiday, Billie & Lester Young).
Tracks: / This year's kisses / Without your love / All of me / Me, myself and I (are all in love with you) / I'll get by / Mean to me / Sailboat in the moonlight / I'll never be the same / Getting some fun out of life / Man I love, The / Trav'lin' all alone / Time on my hands / Laughing at life / Back in your own back yard / Georgia on my mind / Let's do it / Foolin' myself / Easy living / Say it with a kiss / You can't be mine (and someone else's too) / I can't believe that you're in love with me / She's funny that way / Romance in the dark / I must have that man!.
LP: LPJT 45

LADY DAY/LADY IN SATIN.
Tracks: / Miss Brown to you / I wished on the moon / What a little moonlight can do / If you were mine / Summertime / Billie's blues / I must have that man / Foolin' myself / Easy living / Me, myself and I (are all in love with you) / Sailboat in the moonlight / I cried for you / I'm a fool to want you / For Heaven's sake / You don't know what love is / I get along without you very well / For all we know / Violets for your furs / You've changed / Easy to remember / But beautiful / Glad to be unhappy / I'll be around.
2LP: CBS 22189
MC: 40 22189

LADY DAY'S IMMORTAL PERFORMANCES.
LP: LPJT 40

LADY IN SATIN.
Tracks: / I'm a fool to want you / For Heaven's sake / You don't know what love is / I get along without you very well / For all we know / Violets for your furs / You've changed / Easy to remember / But beautiful / Glad to be unhappy / I'll be around / End of a love affair, The.
LP: CBS 32259
MC: 40 32259
LP: 4508831
MC: 4508834

LADY OF THE BLUES.
Tracks: / God bless the child / Them there eyes / T'aint nobody's business if I do / My man / You're driving me crazy / Billie's blues / He's funny that way / Miss Brown to you / No detour ahead / Don't explain / Lover man / All of me / Daddy he can't make no time / Tenderly.
LP: SHLP 139
MC: SHTC 139

LADY SINGS.
Tracks: / Lover man / No more / That ol' devil called love / Don't explain / You better go now / What is this thing called love? / Good morning heartache / No good man / Big stuff / Baby I don't cry over you / I'll look around / Blues are brewin' / Guilty / Deep song / There is no greater love / Easy living / Solitude / Weep no more / Girls were made to take care of boys / Porgy / My man / Ain't nobody's business / Baby get lost / Keeps on a rainin' / Them there eyes / Do your duty / Gimme a pigfoot and a bottle of beer / You can't lose a broken heart / Now or never / You're my thrill / Crazy he calls me / Please tell me now / Somebody's on my mind / God bless the child / This is heaven to me.
LPS: OFF 3017-3

LADY SINGS OF LOVE.
LP: MOIR 135
MC: CMOIR 135

LADY SINGS THE BLUES.
Tracks: / Lady sings the blues / Travelling light / I must have that man / Some other spring / Strange fruit / No-good man / God bless the child / Good morning heartache / Love me or leave me / Too marvellous for words / Willow weep for me / I thought about you.
LP: 230 412 4
LP: LPJT 50
LP: LOP 14 151
MC: LCS 14151
MC: 313 310 9

L'ART VOCAL VOLUME 1: LA SELECTION 1935-1939 (See Under L'Art Vocal).

LAST RECORDING.
LP: 2304 392

LEGEND OF BILLIE HOLIDAY.
Tracks: / That ole devil called love / Lover man (oh where can you be) / Don't explain / Good morning heartache / There is no greater love / Easy living / Solitude / Porgy / My man / Them there eyes / Now or never / Ain't nobody's business / Somebody's on my mind / Keeps on a rainin' / You're my thrill / God bless the child.
LP: BHTV 1
MC: BHTVC 1

LEGENDARY MASTERS, THE (Unissued or Rare 1939-52).
Tracks: / More than you know / Under a blue jungle moon / Night and day / What is this going to get us? / Loveless love / Georgia on my mind / Romance in the dark / God bless the child / Jim / Wherever you are / Until the real thing comes along / Do you know what it means to miss New orleans? / Keeps on a rainin' / He's funny that way / Fine and mellow.
LP: RARELP 02

LEGENDARY MASTERS, THE (Unissued or Rare 1935-38).
Tracks: / What a little moonlight can do / Miss Brown to you / Twenty four hours a day / Yankee doodle never went to town / If you were mine / These n'that n'those / Spreadin' rhythm around / Let's call a heart a heart / Please keep me in your dreams / I wish I had you / I'll never fail you / You're so desirable / You're gonna see a lot of me / Hello my darling / Let's dream in the moonlight.
LP: RARELP 01

LEGENDARY MASTERS, THE (Unissued or Rare 1952-58).
Tracks: / I cover the waterfront / Lover come back to me / Them there eyes / Lover man / I got it bad and that ain't good / Just friends / Everything happens to me / Prelude to a kiss / I must have that man / Willow weep for me / I only have eyes for you / My man / Please don't talk about me when I'm gone / Don't explain / Porgy / Ain't nobody's business / Billie's blues.
LP: RARELP 03

LEGENDARY MASTERS, THE (Unissued or rare 1935-58).
LPS: RARELP 01/02/03

LIVE, 1953.
Tracks: / Blue moon / All of me / My man / Them there eyes / I cried for you / What a little moonlight can do / I cover the waterfront / Billie's blues / Lover come back to me.
LP: RARITIES 40

LOVER MAN.
LP: ZET 706

MASTERS OF JAZZ VOL.3.
LP: SLP 4103

MISS BROWN TO YOU.
Tracks: / Good morning heartache / You're driving me crazy / Miss Brown to you / Don't explain / Man I love, The / All of me.
LP: SWH 27
MC: CATOM 6

MOST IMPORTANT RECORDINGS OF BILLIE HOLIDAY, THE.
Tracks: / Did I remember? / Fine romance, A / Easy to love / Way you look tonight, The / I've got my love to keep me warm / Why was I born? / I'll get by / Easy living / I'll never be the same / He's funny that way / Nice work if you can get it / I can't believe that you're in love with me / Now they call it swing / You go to my head / Sugar / Strange fruit / Some other Spring / Night and day / You're a lucky guy / I hear music / Let's do it / Georgia on my mind / Jim / Love me or leave me / God bless the child / I'll be seeing you / On the sunny side of the street / Don't explain / Ain't nobody's business / Lover come back to me / Stars fell on Alabama.
LPS: OFF 3048-2

NEW ORLEANS (See under Armstrong, Louis) (Holiday, Billie & Louis Armstrong).

OLD STORY, THE.
LP: CBS 68230

ON HOLIDAY.
Tracks: / My man / Them there eyes / I cover the waterfront / Lover come back to me / You've drivin' me crazy / All of me / Porgy / Miss Brown.
LP: MAN 5013

PORGY.
Tracks: / I don't stand a ghost of a chance / Please don't talk about me when I'm gone / Nice work if you can get it / God bless the child / Don't explain / I loves you, Porgy / Fine and mellow / What a little moonlight can do / Foolin' myself / Easy to remember / Moanin' low / When your lover has gone.
LP: B 90141

QUINTESSENTIAL VOL.1.
LP: 4509871
MC: 4509874

QUINTESSENTIAL VOL.3.
Tracks: / Who loves you / Pennies from Heaven / That's life I guess / I can't give you anything but love / One never knows, does one? / I've got my love to keep me warm / If my heart could only talk / Please keep me in your dreams / He ain't got rhythm / This years kisses / Why was I born / I must have that man / Mood that I'm in, The / You showed me the way / Sentimental and melancholy / My last affair.
LP: 4608201
MC: 4608204

QUINTESSENTIAL VOL.4.
LP: 4633331
MC: 4633334

QUINTESSENTIAL VOL.5.
LP: 4651901
MC: 4651904

QUINTESSENTIAL VOL. 2.
LP: 4600591
MC: 4600594

QUINTESSENTIAL VOL. 8, THE.
MC: 4679144

RADIO AND TV BROADCASTS.
LP: ESP 3003

REPLAY ON BILLIE HOLIDAY.
LP: FEDB 5018

ROCK IT FOR ME, 1937 (Holiday, Billie & Ella Fitzgerald).
LP: NOST 7663

SONGBOOK.
MC: 8232464

SONGS FOR DISTINGUISHED LOVERS.
Tracks: / Day in, day out / Foggy day, A / Stars fell on Alabama / One for my baby / Just one of those things / I didn't know what time it was.
LP: 2304 243
MC: 815 055-4

STORYVILLE.
LP: SJAZZ 3
MC: SJAZZC 3
MC: SJAZC 3

STRANGE FRUIT.
Tracks: / Strange fruit / Yesterdays / Fine and mellow / I gotta right to sing the blues / How am I to know / My old flame / I'll get by / I cover the waterfront / I'll be seeing you / I'm yours / Embraceable you / As time goes by / She's funny that way / Lover come back to me / I love my man / On the sunny side of the street.
LP: SLP 4002

SWINGING HOLIDAY.
Tracks: / Blues are bluer / Road to love / I can't pretend / Until the real thing comes along / Ain't nobody business / All of me / Porgy / Miss Brown to you.
LP: MAN 5023

TEDDY WILSON AND BILLIE HOLIDAY (see under Wilson, Teddy) (Holiday, Billie & Teddy Wilson).

TEN FABULOUS RECORDINGS OF THE FORTIES.
LP: SM 3289
MC: MC 3289

TENDERLY.
Tracks: / My man / Miss Brown to you / Keeps on a rainin' / Lover man / I cover the waterfront / All of me / You're my thrill / He's funny that way / Billie's blues / Tenderly.
LP: B 90128

THAT OLE DEVIL CALLED LOVE.
Tracks: / Them there eyes / God bless the child / Don't explain / Good morning heartache / That ole devil called love / Easy living / There is no greater love / Baby I don't cry over you / Lover man (oh where can you be) / You better go now / Deep song / Guilty / I'll look around / Blues are brewin' / What is this thing called love.
LP: PLAT 306
MC: PLAC 306

THINGS ARE LOOKING UP.
MC: CMOIR 305

TWO HOT FOR WORDS (See under Wilson, Teddy) (Holiday, Billie & Teddy Wilson).

Holiday For Strings...

HOLIDAY FOR STRINGS & BRASS (Various artists).
Tracks: / Holiday for strings: *Rose, David* / Stripper, The: *Rose, David* / Lisbon Antigua: *Riddle, Nelson* / You make me feel so young: *Riddle, Nelson* / I only have eyes for you: *Gleason, Jackie* / It could happen to you: *Gleason, Jackie* / Sophisticated lady: *Jenkins, Gordon* / Orange Blossom special: *Slatkin, Felix* / Autimn leaves: *May, Billy* / Zambesi: *Bush, Lou* / Blue tango: *Baxter, Les* / April in Portugal: *Baxter*, Les / All my loving: *Hollyridge Strings* / Moon of Manakoora: *Newman, Alfred* / Samba De Orfeu: *Anthony, Ray*.
LP: MOIR 503
MC: CMOIR 503

Holiday Hits

HOLIDAY HITS (Various artists).
Tracks: / Wake me up before you go go: *Wham* / Respectable: *Mel & Kim* / Venus: *Bananarama* / Don't leave me this way: *Communards* / Doctor Beat: *Miami Sound Machine* / Fresh: *Kool & The Gang* / Call me: *Spagna* / Hooray hooray it's a holi holiday: *Boney M* / Barbados: *Typically Tropical* / D.I.S.C.O.: *Ottowan* / Dolce vita: *Paris, Ryan* / Brother Louie: *Modern Talking* / Everybody salsa: *Modern Romance* / My toot toot: *Lasalle, Denise* / Give it up: *K.C. & The Sunshine Band* / Live is life: *Opus*.
LP: MOOD 2
MC: MOOD C2

Holiday Inn (film)

HOLIDAY INN (Original Soundtrack) (Various artists).
LP: STK 112

Holiday, Jimmy

EVERYBODY NEEDS HELP.
Tracks: / Baby boy's in love (Mono) / Yesterday died / Man ain't nothin' without a woman, A / I'm in love with you / Spread your love / Baby I love you / In the eyes of my girl / I don't want to hear it anymore / Turning point / I'm gonna help hurry my brothers home (Mono) / We forgot about love / Everybody needs help / Ready, willing and able / I've got to live while I can / I'm gonna use what I got (to get what I need) / Beauty of a girl in love, The (Mono).
LP: SSL 6010
MC: TC-SSL 6010

Holland

AMSTERDAM IN MUSIC (Various artists).
Tracks: / Geef mij maar Amsterdam: *Various artists* / By the side of the Zuyder Zee: *Various artists* / Als op het leidseplein de lichtjes: *Various artists* / Weer eens branden gaan: *Various artists* / O mooie westertoren: *Various artists* / Ik hou van jou, mooi Amsterdam: *Various artists* / Bloesem van seringen: *Various artists* / In de jordaan: *Various artists* / Pierementwals: *Various artists* / Amsterdam, dat ene Amsterdam: *Various* artists / M'n wiegie was een stijfselkissie: *Various artists* / Nou tabe dan: *Various artists* / Op de sluizen van ijmuiden: *Various artists* / Bij ons in de jordaan: *Various artists* / Het lied van het pierement: *Various artists*.
LP: 814 160 1
MC: 814 160 4

EARLY WARNING.
LP: EBON 17

HOLLAND SOUVENIR (Various artists).
LP: 824 730-1
MC: 824 730-4

Holland, Amy

AMY HOLLAND.
Tracks: / How do I survive / Strengthen my love / Here in the light / Stars / Don't kid yourself / I'm wondering / Looking for love / Holding on to you / Show me the way home / Forgetting you.
LP: EST 12071

Holland, Dave

ALL KINDS OF TIME (see Berger, Karl).

CLEMENTS, HARTFORD & HOLLAND (see Clements, Vassar).

EXTENSIONS (Holland, Dave Quartet).
Tracks: / Nemesis / Processional / Black hole / Oracle, The / 101 fahrenheit (slow meltdown) / Color of mind.
LP: ECM 1410

JUMPIN' IN (Holland, Dave Quintet).
LP: . . . . ECM 1269

LIFE CYCLE (Solo Cello).
LP: . . . . ECM 1238

QUESTION AND ANSWER (See under Metheny, Pat) (Metheny, Pat/Dave Holland/Roy Haynes).

RAZOR'S EDGE, THE (Holland, Dave Quintet).
Tracks: / Brother Ty / Vedana / Razor's edge / Blues for C.M. / Vortex / 5 four six / Wights waits for weights / Fight time.
LP: . . . . ECM 1353

SAM & DAVE- VOLUME 1 (Holland, Dave & Sam Rivers).
LP: . . . . IAI 37.38.43

SAM & DAVE-VOLUME 2 (Holland, Dave & Sam Rivers).
LP: . . . . IAI 37.38.48

SEEDS OF TIME (Holland, Dave Quintet).
Tracks: / Uhren / Homecoming / Perspicuity / Celebration / World protection blues / Grid lock / Walk-a-way / Good doctor, The / Double vision.
LP: . . . . ECM 1292

TRIPLICATE (Holland, Dave Trio).
LP: . . . . ECM 1373

Holland, Fox

FOX HOLLAND.
LP: . . . . IW 1019

Holland, Jerry

JERRY HOLLAND.
LP: . . . . ROUNDER 7008

Holland, Jools

FULL COMPLEMENT, THE.
Tracks: / Lost chord / One more time / Together again / No ones to blame / Baby let me hold your hand / Landy don't fall backwards / Cackophony / Movin' on / Me-U=loneliness / Blue guitar / Shake rattle and roll / Lady don't stings.
LP: . . . . EIRSA 1052
MC: . . . . EIRSAC 1052

JOOLS HOLLAND & HIS MILLIONAIRES (Holland, Jools & His Millionaires).
LP: . . . . ANKH 68534

WORLD OF HIS OWN.
LP: . . . . EIRSA 1018
MC: . . . . EIRSAC 1018

Holland, Lys

MAN OF HONOUR, A.
MC: . . . . SOUND 8

Holland, Maggie

SHORT CUT, A (Holland, Maggie & Jon Moore).
LP: . . . . FMST 4008

STILL PAUSE.
LP: . . . . FMSL 2002

Holland-Dozier-Holland

GREATEST SONGS WRITTEN BY HOLLAND,DOZIER,HOLLAND (See Under Motown...) (Various artists).

Holle Holle

HOLLE HOLLE.
LP: . . . . MUT 1018
MC: . . . . CMUT 1018

WICKED AND WILD.
Tracks: / Margaya margaya / Mal mal di kurti / A-A-A gale lagja / Chup kar ke / Heer saleti / Polle polle / Dil pyar karan nu karda / Haan di kuri.
LP: . . . . ARI 1006
MC: . . . . ARI 0106

Holleran, Tony

I'LL NEVER GO TO YOUR WEDDING AGAIN.
MC: . . . . GTDC 037

Hollerin'

HOLLERIN'.
LP: . . . . ROUNDER 0071

Holley, Lyin' Joe

SO COLD IN THE USA.
Tracks: / Big machine blues / So cold in the USA / Five more numbers / Drinking budweiser / Moon is rising / Dope around town / Old twister / Big legged woman / Early one morning / How long / Swanee river boogie / Monkey faced woman / Three kinds of fool / Rebate blues.
LP: . . . . JSP 1040

Holliday, Doc

DANGER ZONE.
LP: . . . . METALP 113

DOC HOLLIDAY RIDES AGAIN.
Tracks: / Last ride, The / Good boy gone bad / Don't go talkin' / Southern man / Let me be your lover / Doin' it again / Don't stop loving me / Hot rod / Lonesome guitar.
LP: . . . . AMLH 64882

SONG FOR THE OUTLAW.
LP: . . . . LOPL 504
MC: . . . . LOPC 504

Holliday, Jennifer

FEEL MY SOUL.
Tracks: / Just let me wait / I am ready now / This game of love / I am love / Shine a light / Just for a while / My sweet delight / Change is gonna come, A / This day.
LP: 9040141
MC: 9040144

GET CLOSE TO MY LOVE.
Tracks: / New at it / He ain't special / Get close to my love / Read it in my eyes / Ain't it just like love / Heart on the line / I never thought I'd fall in love again / Givin' up.
LP: 9241501
MC: 9241504

I'M ON YOUR SIDE.
Tracks: / I'm on your side / It's in there / Raise the roof / Dream with your name on it, A / Guilty / It will haunt me / Love stories / Is it love / I fall apart / More 'n' more.
LP: 211519
MC: 411519

SAY YOU LOVE ME.
Tracks: / You're the one / What kind of love is this / No frills love / Hard time for lovers / Say you love me / I rest my case / Dreams never die / Just a matter of time / He's a pretender / Come sunday.
LP: . . . . GEF 26564

Holliday, Judy

HOLLIDAY WITH MULLIGAN (Holliday, Judy and Gerry Mulligan).
Tracks: / What's the rush / Loving you / Lazy / It must be Christmas / Party's over, The / It's bad for me / Supper time / Pass that peace pipe / I've got a right to sing the blues / Summer's over / Blue prelude.
LP: . . . . SL 5191
MC: . . . . SLC 5191

Holliday, Michael

EMI YEARS, THE: MICHAEL HOLLIDAY (Best of Michael Holliday).
Tracks: / Starry eyed / Folks who live on the hill, The / Runaway train / Stairway of love / Skye boat song / Hot diggity (dog ziggity boom) / Did you ever see a dream walking / Old Cape Cod / Story of my life / Nothin' to do / Gal with the yaller shoes / Yellow rose of Texas / In love / Little boy lost / Dear heart / My last date with you.
LP: . . . . EMS 1329
MC: . . . . TCEMS 1329

EP COLLECTION, THE: MICHAEL HOLLIDAY.
LP: . . . . SEE 311
MC: . . . . SEEK 311

MIKE.
Tracks: / Strange music / In the good old summertime / Skylark / Be careful it's my heart / Love is just around the corner / Nightingale sang in Berkeley Square, A / Folks who live on the hill, The / Did you ever see a dream walking / I can't give you anything but love / Lamplighter's serenade, The / Ain't she sweet / I'll be seeing you.
LP: . . . . MOIR 208
MC: . . . . CMOIR 208

SENTIMENTAL JOURNEY, A (Holliday, Michael & Edna Savage).
Tracks: / 'S wonderful / I'll always be in love with you / May I? / Diano Marina / Be careful it's my heart / Tea for two / In the wee small hours of the morning / Skylark / I'm old fashioned / My prayer / Sunday, Monday or always / Near you / Be honest with me / Tip toe through the tulips / Moonlight becomes you / Me 'n' you 'n' the moon / I saw Esau / Nothin' to do / Please hurry home / Goodnight my love.
LP: . . . . SEE 255

TOGETHER AGAIN (Holliday, Michael & Edna Savage).
Tracks: / Story of my life, The / Arrivederci darling / Rooney / Tear fell, A / Tip toe through the tulips / Once / Girl in the yaller shoes, The / Long ago (and far away) / We'll gather lilacs / 'S wonderful / In the wee small hours of the morning / My house is your house / Let me be loved / Hot diggity (dog ziggity boom) / Tea for two / Catch me a kiss / I promise you / Me head in de barrel / I saw Esau / Never leave me / I'll be seeing you / Why why why / Nothin' to do / Goodnight my love.
MC: . . . . HR 8187

VERY BEST OF MICHAEL HOLLIDAY, THE 16 favourites of the 50's.
Tracks: / Old cape cod / Story of my life / Nothin' to love / 10,000 miles / Stairway of love / Starry eyed / Yellow rose of texas / Palace of love / Rooney / In love.
LP: . . . . MFP 415646-1
MC: . . . . TCMFP 415646-4

Holliday, Simon

RAGS, BOOGIE AND SWING.
Tracks: / Should I reveal / As long as I live / Maple leaf rag / Airmail special / Climax rag / Boogie joys / All the things you are / Way down yonder in New Orleans / Winin' boy blues / Nagasaki.
MC: . . . . CMJMC 009

TAKING IT EASY.
Tracks: / Hindustan / Mama's gone goodbye / Love me or leave me / I'm in the mood for love / Lazybones / Wild cat blues / Back to Harlem / Georgia on my mind / I want a little girl / Entertainer, The / Mood indigo / Tiger rag.
MC: . . . . CMJMC 010

Hollies

20 GOLDEN GREATS: HOLLIES.
Tracks: / Air that I breathe, The / Carrie Anne / Bus stop / Listen to me / Look through any window / I can't let go / Long cool woman in a black dress / Here I go again / I can't tell the bottom from the top / I'm alive / Yes I will / Stay / Sorry Suzanne / Gasoline Alley bred / We're through / Jennifer Eccles / Stop stop stop / On a carousel / Just one look / He ain't heavy, he's my brother.
LP: . . . . ATAK 38
MC: . . . . TCATAK 38
LP: . . . . EMTV 11
MC: . . . . TC EMTV 11

AIR THAT I BREATHE, THE (LP).
Tracks: / Sandy / I'm down / Daddy don't mind / Draggin' my heels / Air that I breathe, The / Burn out / He ain't heavy, he's my brother / Wiggle that wotsit / Love is the thing / Write on.
LP: 2384 115

ALL THE HITS AND MORE - A DEFINITIVE COLLECTION.
Tracks: / Just like me / Searchin' / Just one look / Here I go again / We're through / Yes I will / I'm alive / Look through any window / If I needed someone / I can't let go / Bus stop / Stop, stop, stop / Pay you back with interest / On a carousel / Carrie Anne / King Midas in reverse / Dear Eloise / Jennifer Eccles / Listen to me / Sorry Suzanne / He ain't heavy, he's my brother / I can't tell the bottom from the top / Gasoline Alley bred / Hey Willy / Long cool woman in a black dress / Baby, The / Day that curly Billy shot crazy Sam McGee, The / Air that I breathe, The / Sandy / I'm down / Daddy don't mind / Too young to be married / Soldiers song / If the lights go out / Take my love and run / Give me time (CD only.) / Heartbeat (CD only.) / Tell me how (CD only.) / Don't let me down (CD only.).
2LP: . . . . EM 1301
MCSET: . . . . TCEM 1301

AN HOUR OF THE HOLLIES.
Tracks: / Stop, stop, stop / Gasoline Alley bred / Searchin' / Listen to me / What kind of boy / Rockin' robin / Come on back / Memphis Tennessee / Too young to be married / Dear Eloise / He ain't heavy, he's my brother / Sweet little sixteen / Nobody (Mono) / Hey Willy / Just like me / Sorry Suzanne / Lucille / Keep off that friend of mine (Mono.) / On a carousel / Pay you back with interest / Clown / If I needed someone / Blowing in the wind.
MC: . . . . HR 8153

ANOTHER NIGHT.
Tracks: / Another night / Fourth of July, Asbury Park / Lonely hobo lullaby / Secondhand hang-ups / Time machine jive / I'm down / Look out Johnny / Give me time / You gave me life / Lucy.
LP: 2442 128

BEST OF THE HOLLIES E.P.S.
Tracks: / Here I go again / You know he did / What kind of boy / Look through any window / What kind of love / When I'm not there / Rockin' robin / Lucille / Memphis / Just one look / I'm alive / Come on back / We're through / I've got a way of my own / So lonely / To you my love / Whatcha goona do about it / Too much monkey business / Come on home / I can't let go / Baby that's all / I'm talking about you (remix version).
MC: . . . . TC NUTM 30

BEST OF THE HOLLIES, THE.
Tracks: / Here I go again / You know he did / What kind of boy / Look through any window / What kind of love / When I'm not there / Rockin' Robin / Lucille / Memphis / Just one look / I'm alive / Come on back / We're through / I've got a way of my own / So lonely / To you my love / Whatcha gonna do 'bout it / Too much monkey business / Come on home / I can't let go.
MC: 4XLL 9384
LP: . . . . NUTM 30

BUTTERFLY.
Tracks: / Dear Eloise / Maker / Would you believe / Postcard / Try it / Step inside / Away away away / Pegasus / Wish you a wish / Charlie and Fred / Elevated observations / Butterfly.
LP: . . . . BGOLP 79

CONFESSIONS OF THE MIND.
LP: . . . . PCS 7117
LP: . . . . BGOLP 96

CRAZY STEAL, A.
Tracks: / Writing on the wall / What am I gonna do / Let it pour / Burn out / Hello to romance / Amnesty / Caraccas / Boulder to Birmingham / Clown service / Feet on the ground.
LP: 2383 474

DISTANT LIGHT.
LP: . . . . BGOLP 97

EP COLLECTION, THE: HOLLIES.
Tracks: / Woodstock / Here I go again / You know he did / What kind of boy / Baby that's all / Look through any window / What kind of love / When I'm not there / Rockin' Robin / Lucille / Memphis / Just one look / I'm alive / Come on back / We're through / I've got a way of my own / So lonely / To you my love / Whatcha gonna do about it / Come on home / I can't let you go.
MC: . . . . SEEK 94
LP: . . . . SEE 94

EVOLUTION.
Tracks: / Then the heartaches begin / Water on the brain / Have you ever loved somebody / Heading for a fall / Ye olde toffee shoppe / When your lights turned on / Stop right there / Lullaby to Tim / You need love / Rain on the window / Leave me / Games we play, The.
LP: . . . . PCS 7022
LP: . . . . BGOLP 80

FIVE THREE ONE DOUBLE SEVEN O FOUR.
Tracks: / Say it ain't so / Maybe it's dawn / Song of the sun / Harlequin / When I'm yours / Something to live for / Stormy waters / Boys in the band / Satellite three / It's in every one of us.
LP: 244 216 0

FOR CERTAIN BECAUSE.
LP: . . . . BGOLP 9
MC: . . . . BGOMC 9
LP: . . . . PCS 17011

GREATEST HITS: HOLLIES.
LP: 1A 022 58056
LP: . . . . PCS 7057

HOLLIES.
LP: . . . . PMC 1261

HOLLIES (2).
LP: 2383 262

HOLLIES' LIVE HITS.
Tracks: / I can't let go / Just one look / I can't tell the bottom from the top / Bus stop / Another night / Fourth of July, Asbury Park / Star / My island / I'm down / Stop, stop, stop / Long cool woman in a black dress / Carrie Anne / Air that I breathe, The / Too young to be married / He ain't heavy, he's my brother.
LP: 2383 428

HOLLIES SING DYLAN.
Tracks: / When the ship comes in / I'll be your baby tonight / I want you / This wheel's on fire / I shall be released / Blowin' in the wind / Quit your low down ways / Just like a woman / Times they are a-changin' / All I really want to do / My back pages / Mighty Quinn.
LP: . . . . MFP 5811
MC: . . . . TCMFP 5811
LP: . . . . PCS 7078

HOLLIES, THE (IMPORT).
LP: . . . . BGOLP 25

HOLLIES, THE (MFP).
Tracks: / Here I go again / Bus stop / I can't tell the bottom from the top / Rockin' robin / Poison ivy / Jennifer Eccles / He ain't heavy, he's my brother / I can't let go / Fortune teller / Watcha gonna do 'bout it? / Zip-a-dee-doo-dah / Little bitty pretty one / On a carousel / Too much monkey business / Stop, stop, stop / We're through.
LP: . . . . MFP 41 5727-1
MC: . . . . MFP 41 5727-4

IN THE HOLLIES STYLE.
LP: . . . . BGOLP 8

LIVE: HOLLIES.
Tracks: / Just one look / Air that I breathe, The / He ain't heavy, he's my brother.
LP: 2872 110
MC: 3472 110

LONG COOL WOMAN IN A BLACK DRESS.
Tracks: / Long cool woman in a black dress / He ain't heavy he's my brother / King Midas in reverse / Blowin' in the wind / Stop, stop, stop / Mighty Quinn / I

can't let go / Carrie Anne / Dear Eloise / Hey Willy.
LP: **022 58056**
MC: **222 58056**
LP: . . . . **MFP 50450**

LOVE SONGS: HOLLIES.
Tracks: / I can't let go / Air that I breathe, The / Just one look / I can't tell the bottom from the top / Bus stop / Carrie Anne / Here I go again / Sorry Suzanne / Yes I will / To you my love / I'm a live / Come on back / Dear Eloise / Jennifer Eccles / What kind of boy / If I needed someone / You need love / King Midas in reverse / Too young to be married (CD only.) / Have you ever loved somebody (CD only.) / That's how strong my love is (CD only.) / Just like a woman (CD only.).
LP: . . . . **MFP 5883**
MC: . . . . **TCMFP 5883**

NOT THE HITS AGAIN.
Tracks: / Wings / It's in her kiss / You'll be mine / Take your time / I am a rock / Honey and wine / Very last day, The / It's only make believe / That's my desire / So lonely / Now's the time / Hard, hard year / Put yourself in my place / Please don't feel too bad / Nitty gritty-Something's got a hold on me / You better move on / I take what I want / Talkin 'bout you / Candy man / Set me free / Lawdy Miss Clawdy / Sweet little sixteen.
LP: . . . . **SEE 63**

OTHER SIDE OF THE HOLLIES.
MC: . . . . **TCPMC 7176**
LP: . . . . **SEE 302**

RARITIES.
Tracks: / Carrie Anne / Mexico gold / If it wasn't for the reason that I love you / Louisiana man / She looked my way / Eleanors' castle / Here in my dreams / Sanctuary / Relax / Tomorrow when it comes / Open up your eyes / Times they are a-changin' / Look through any window / After the fox / Non prego per me / Live every time before / Wings.
LP: . . . . **EMS 1311**
MC: . . . . **TCEMS 1311**

RUSSIAN ROULETTE.
Tracks: / Wiggle that wotsit / Forty-eight hour patrol / Thanks for the memory / My love / Lady of the night / Russian roulette / Draggin' my heels / Louise / Be with you / Daddy don't mind.
LP: **2383 421**

STAY WITH THE HOLLIES.
LP: . . . . **BGOLP 4**
LP: . . . . **PMC 1220**

STOP STOP STOP.
Tracks: / Stop stop stop.
LP: . . . . **SRS 5088**

WHAT GOES AROUND....
Tracks: / Casualty / Take my love and run / Say you'll be mine.
LP: **250139 1**
MC: **250139 4**

WOULD YOU BELIEVE.
LP: . . . . **BGOLP 24**
LP: . . . . **PMC 7008**

Hollow, Critton

GREAT DREAMS.
LP: . . . . **FF 468**

Hollow Crown

ENTERTAINMENT ON THE THEME OF THE MONARCHY, AN (Various artists).
MCSET: . . . . **SAY 34**

Hollow Men

CIRCA.
LP: **210978**
MC: **410978**

CRESTA.
Tracks: / Don't slow down / Moon's a balloon / November comes / Pantera Rosa / Tongue tied / Barefoot parade / Louder than God / Beautiful sun / Headstruck / Misunderstood.
LP: **210977**
MC: **260977**

MAN WHO WOULD BE KING, THE.
Tracks: / Drowning man, The / Gold and ivory / White train / Whisper to me / Banners and flags / Autumn Avenue / Jasmin land / Blow the man down / Juggling Joe.
LP: . . . . **DMC 025**

TALES BY THE RIVERBANK.
LP: . . . . **DMC 015**

Hollow Rock String

HOLLOW ROCK STRING BAND.
LP: . . . . **ROUNDER 0024**

Holloway, Laurie

FUNKY FLUTE (See also Ellis, Joanne) (Holloway, Laurie & Eleanor Duran).

Holloway, Red

RED HOLLOWAY AND COMPANY.
Tracks: / But not for me / Caravan / Passion flower / Blues for Q.M. / Well you needn't / What's new / Summertime / Tokyo express.
LP: . . . . **CJ 322**
MC: . . . . **CJC 322**

Holloway, Stanley

ALICE IN WONDERLAND (see under Carroll, Lewis (aut)).

BEST OF STANLEY HOLLOWAY.
Tracks: / Lion and Albert, The / Albert comes back / Albert and the 'eadsman / Jubilee sovereign / Albert evacuated / Runcorn ferry / Beefeater, The / 'Ole in the ark / Brahn boots / Pick up tha musket / Marksman Sam / One each, a piece all round / Sam's medal / Beat the retreat on thy drum / 'Alt, who goes theer? / Sam drummed out / Sam's sturgeon.
LP: . . . . **ONCM 515**
MC: . . . . **TC ONCR 515**

BRAHN BOOTS.
Tracks: / Lion and Albert / Old sam / Marksman Sam / Alberts birthday / Old Sam's party / Brahn boots / My word you do look queer / Natures made some big mistakes / Albert comes back / With her head tucked underneath her arm / Yet I don't know / Leanin'.
LP: . . . . **MOR 534**
MC: . . . . **KMORC 534**

LION AND ALBERT, THE (see under Penrose, Charles).

MANY HAPPY RETURNS.
Tracks: / Penny on the drum / Pick up tha musket / Lion and Albert, The / Join the Navy / Three ha'pence a foot / Dinder courtship, A / Old Sam's party / Albert comes back / Jubilee Sovereign / Sometimes I'm happy / Many happy returns / My old Dutch / Sam drummed out / Albert and the 'eadsman / Hand in hand.
LP: . . . . **CMS 007**
MC: . . . . **CMSC 007**

MORE MONOLOGUES AND SONGS.
Tracks: / Sam's Xmas / Old Sam's party / Sam goes to it / Recumbent posture / Three ha'pence a foot / Many happy returns / Jonah & the Grampus / Yorkshire pudding / Gunner Joe / Parson of puddle / With her head tucked underneath her arm / Careless talk / My missus / Sometimes I'm happy / Keep smiling / London pride / Comedy tonight / Burlington Bertie from Bow.
LP: . . . . **ONCM 533**

NOSTALGIC MEMORIES.
LP: . . . . **BUR 019**
LP: . . . . **LPVAG 911**
MC: . . . . **CASSVAG 911**
MC: . . . . **4 BUR 019**

STANLEY HOLLOWAY (see under EMI Comedy Classics).

WORLD OF STANLEY HOLLOWAY, THE.
LP: . . . . **SPA 199**

Hollowell, Terri

JUST YOU AND ME.
Tracks: / We've got it all together / I wrote this song for you / Was that really love that we made / Texas sunrise & me / Ain't got no time to fall in love / Hurry home cowboy / May I / It's too soon to say goodbye / One more singer in Nashville / Sharing / Big Mama Johns / Strawberry fields forever.
LP: . . . . **RKLP 5004**

Holly, Buddy

20 GOLDEN GREATS: BUDDY HOLLY (Holly, Buddy & The Crickets).
Tracks: / That'll be the day / Peggy Sue / Words of love / Everyday / Not fade away / Oh boy / Maybe baby / Listen to me / Heartbeat / Think it over / It doesn't matter anymore / It's so easy / Well all right / Rave on / Raining in my heart / True love ways / Peggy Sue got married / Bo Diddley / Brown eyed handsome man / Wishing.
LP: . . . . **MCTV 1**
MC: . . . . **MCTVC 1**

20 LOVE SONGS.
Tracks: / True love ways / Everyday / Listen to me / You've got love / Learning the game / Send me some lovin' / Love is strange / That's what they say / Because I love you / Raining in my heart / Heartbeat / Moondreams / Take your time / Dearest / Look at me / You're the one / Wishing / It doesn't matter anymore / What to do / Words of love.
LP: . . . . **MFP 5570**
MC: . . . . **TCMFP 5570**

23 ALL TIME GREATEST HITS.
LP: **20125**
MC: **40125**

BEST OF BUDDY HOLLY.
Tracks: / That'll be the day / Peggy Sue / Oh boy.
LP: . . . . **SHM 3199**
MC: . . . . **HSC 3199**

BUDDY HOLLY.
Tracks: / Early in the morning / Now we're one / It's so easy / Lonesome tears / Heartbeat / Well all right / Love's made a fool of you / Wishing / Reminiscing / It doesn't matter anymore / Come back baby / True love ways / That's my desire / Moondreams / Raining in my heart / Valley of tears / Baby let's play house / I'm gonna love you too / Peggy Sue / Look at me / Listen to me / Rave on / Valley of tears / Ready Teddy / Empty cup / Everyday / It's too late / Mailman bring me no more blues / Look at me / Words of love / Think it over / Baby I don't care / Fools paradise / Little baby.
LP: . . . . **MCL 1752**
MC: . . . . **MCLC 1752**
LP: . . . . **SSP 3070**
MC: . . . . **SSC 3070**
MCSET: . . . . **CRT 008**

BUDDY HOLLY (CAMBRA).
MCSET: . . . . **CRT 008**

BUDDY HOLLY ROCKS.
Tracks: / Gotta get you near me / Down the line / Baby let's play house / I guess I was just a fool / Rip it up / Brown eyed handsome man / Holly hop / Midnight shift / Blue days, black nights / Love me / Don't come back knockin' / I'm changing all those changes / Ting a ling / Modern Don Juan / Rock around with Ollie Vee / That'll be the day / I'm looking for someone to love / Not fade away / Oh boy / Peggy Sue / I'm gonna love you too / Rock me my baby / Tell me how / Rave on / Baby I don't care / Think it over / Love's made a fool of you / It's so easy / Early in the morning / Maybe baby / It doesn't matter anymore.
2LP: . . . . **CDX 8**

BUDDY HOLLY SHOWCASE.
LP: . . . . **LVA 9222**

BUDDY HOLLY STORY, THE (See under Buddy Holly story) (Various artists).

BUDDY HOLLY STORY, THE.
Tracks: / Gotta get you near me blues / Soft place in my heart / Door to my heart / Flower of my heart / Baby it's love / Memories / Queen of the ballroom / I gambled my heart / You and I are through? / Gone / Have you ever been lonely? / Down the line / Blue suede shoes / Shake rattle and roll / Ain't got no home / Holly bop / Baby let's play house / I'm gonna set my foot down / Baby, won't you come out tonight / Changing all those changes / Rock a bye rock / It's not my fault / I guess I was just a fool / Love me / Don't come back knockin' / Midnight shift / Blue days, black nights / Rock around with Ollie Vee / I'm changing all those changes / That'll be the day / Girl on my mind / Ting a ling / Because I love you / Modern Don Juan / You are my one desire / I'm lookin' for someone to love / Last night / Maybe baby / Words of love / Peggy Sue / Everyday / Mailman bring me no more blues / Tell me how / Send me some lovin' / Little baby / Take your time / Rave on / You've got love / Valley of tears / Rock me baby / Baby I don't care / It's too late / Empty cup / Look at me / Think it over / Fool's paradise / Early in the morning / Now we're one / Lonesome tears / Heartbeat / It's so easy / Well ... all right / Love's made a fool of you / Wishing / Reminiscing / Come back baby / That's my desire / True love ways / Moondreams / Raining in my heart / It doesn't matter anymore / Peggy Sue got married / Crying, waiting, hoping / Learning the game / That makes it tough / What to do / That's what they say / Wait 'til the sun shines, Nellie / Uum oh yeah / Smokey Joe's cafe / Slippin' and slidin' / Love is strange / Dearest / You're the one / Dearest / You're the one / Love is strange / That makes it tough / Learning the game / Real wild child / Oh you beautiful doll / Jole Blon / When sin stops / Stay close to me / Don't cha know / That'll be the day / It's so easy.
LPS: . . . . **CDMSP 807**

BUDDY HOLLY STORY - VOL. 1.
LP: . . . . **MA 191185**
MC: . . . . **MAMC 9191185**
LP: . . . . **LVA 9105**

BUDDY HOLLY STORY - VOL. 2.
LP: . . . . **MA 201185**
MC: . . . . **MAMC 9201185**
LP: . . . . **LVA 9127**

BUDDY HOLLY & THE CRICKETS (Holly, Buddy & The Crickets).
Tracks: / Raining in my heart / Baby won't you come out tonight / Modern Don Juan / Mailman bring me no more blues / Love's made a fool of you / You've got love / Girl on my mind / That'll be the day (Nashville recording) / Blue days, black nights / Midnight shift / I'm gonna love you too / Don't come back knockin' / Fool's paradise / Empty cup / Rock around the Ollie Vee (version 1) / Think it over / It's not my fault / I guess I was just a fool / I'm gonna set my foot down / Rockabye rock / Because I love you / You're the one / Ready Teddy / Send me some lovin / Lonesome tears / Rock around the Ollie Vee (version 2) / Reminiscing / Love's made a fool of you / When you ask about love / Baby my heart (Without Holly).
2LP: . . . . **CR 123**
MCSET: . . . . **CRT 123**

CHIRPING CRICKETS, THE (Holly, Buddy & The Crickets).
Tracks: / Oh boy / Not fade away / You've got love / Maybe baby / Its' too late / Tell me how / That'll be the day / I'm looking for someone to love / Empty cup / Send me some lovin' / Last night / Rock me my baby.
LP: . . . . **MCL 1753**
MC: . . . . **MCLC 1753**

COLLECTION: BUDDY HOLLY.
Tracks: / Think it over / That'll be the day / True love ways / Words of love / Rock me baby / I'm gonna love you too / Ready Teddy / Love's made a fool of you / Blue days, black nights / Maybe baby / I'm looking for someone to love / Send me some lovin' / Reminiscing / Listen to me / Well, all right / Oh boy / Wishing / Not fade away / Heartbeat / Moondreams / Raining in my heart / Don't come back knockin'... / Peggy Sue.
2LP: . . . . **CCSLP 172**
MC: . . . . **CCSMC 172**

COMPLETE BUDDY HOLLY, THE.
LPS: . . . . **CDSP 807**
MCSET: . . . . **CDSPC 807**

FOR THE FIRST TIME ANYWHERE.
Tracks: / Rockabye rock / Maybe baby / I'm gonna set my foot down / Because I love you / Changing all those changes / That's my desire / Baby won't you come out tonight? / It's not my fault / Brown eyed handsome man / Bo Diddley.
LP: . . . . **MCM 1002**
MC: . . . . **MCMC 1002**
MC: . . . . **DMCL 1712**

GIANT.
LP: . . . . **MUPS 371**
LP: . . . . **MCL 1825**

GOLDEN GREATS.
MC: . . . . **MCMC 5033**

GOLDEN GREATS: BUDDY HOLLY.
Tracks: / Peggy Sue / That'll be the day / Listen to me / Everyday / Oh boy / Not fade away / Raining in my heart / Brown eyed handsome man / Maybe baby / Rave on / Think it over / It's so easy / It doesn't matter anymore / True love ways / Peggy Sue got married / Bo Diddley.
LP: . . . . **MCM 5003**
MC: . . . . **MCMC 5003**

GREATEST HITS: BUDDY HOLLY.
Tracks: / Peggy Sue / That'll be the day / Listen to me / Everyday / Oh boy / Not fade away / Raining in my heart / Maybe baby / Rave on / Think it over / It's so easy / It doesn't matter anymore / True love ways / Peggy Sue got married.
LP: . . . . **MCL 1618**
MC: . . . . **MCLC 1618**
LP: . . . . **CP 8**
LP: . . . . **CDLM 8007**
LP: . . . . **AH 148**

GREATEST HITS: BUDDY HOLLY (IMPORT).
LP: . . . . **FUN 9043**
MC: . . . . **FUNC 9043**

GREATEST HITS/LOVE SONGS.
Tracks: / That'll be the day / Listen to me / Everyday / Oh boy / Not fade away / Raining in my heart / Maybe baby / Rave on / Think it over / It's so easy / It doesn't matter anymore / True love ways / Peggy Sue got married / You've got love / Learning the game / Send me some lovin' / Love is strange / That's what they say / Because I love you / Heartbeat / Moondreams / Take your time / Dearest / Look at me / Wishing / What to do / Words of love / You're the one.
MCSET: . . . . **MCA 2 117**

HIS UNDUBBED VERSIONS.
LP: . . . . **NORVAJAK 1-963**

HOLLY IN THE HILLS.
LP: . . . . **LVA 9227**

LEGEND (From the original master tapes).
Tracks: / That'll be the day / I'm looking for someone to love / Not fade away / Oh boy / Maybe baby / Tell me how / Think it over / It's so easy / Peggy Sue / Words of love / Everyday / I'm gonna love you too / Listen to me / Rave on / Well all right / Heartbeat / Early in the morning / Rock around with Ollie Vee / Midnight

shift / Love's made a fool of you / Wishing / Reminiscing / Baby I don't care / Brown eyed handsome man / Bo Diddley / It doesn't matter anymore / Moon dreams / True love ways / Raining in my heart / Learning the game / What to do / Peggy Sue got married / Love is strange.
2LP: . . . . **MCLD 606**
MCSET: . . . . **MCLDC 606**
2LP: . . . . **MCMD 7003**
MCSET: . . . . **MCMDC 7003**

LEGEND, THE.
Tracks: / That'll be the day / Peggy Sue / Listen to me / Because I love you / Slippin' and slidin' / Send me some lovin' / Rave on / Heartbeat / Blue days, black nights / Moondreams / Look at me / Blue suede shoes / It doesn't matter anymore / Midnight shift / You are my one desire / Girl on my mind / Empty cup / (Um oh yeah) dearest / Oh boy / Learning the game / Love is strange / Take your time / Words of love / True love ways.
2LP: . . . . **VSOPLP 114**
MC: . . . . **VSOPMC 114**

LEGENDARY BUDDY HOLLY, THE.
Tracks: / Listen to me / Words of love / You've got to love / Learning the game / Not fade away / What to do / Early in the morning / Wishing / Love's made a fool of you / Love is strange / Baby I don't care / Midnight shift / Reminiscing / Valley of tears.
LP: . . . . **SHM 3221**
MC: . . . . **HSC 3221**

MOONDREAMS.
Tracks: / Moondreams / Because I love you / I guess I was just a fool / Girl on my mind / I'm gonna love you too / You and I are through / Come back baby / You're the one / I gambled my heart / You are my one desire / Door to my heart / Crying, waiting, hoping / Now we're one / Love me / Soft place in my heart / Have you ever been lonely?.
LP: . . . . **SHM 3294**
MC: . . . . **HSC 3294**

NASHVILLE SESSIONS.
Tracks: / You are my one desire / Blue days, black nights / Modern Don Juan / Rock around with Ollie Vee / Midnight shift / Don't come back knockin / Girl on my mind / Love me / Ting a ling / That'll be the day / I'm changing all those changes.
LP: . . . . **MCL 1754**
MC: . . . . **MCLC 1754**

ONVERGETELIJKE HITS.
Tracks: / Peggy sue / Everyday / Rave on / Brown eyed handsome man / It doesn't matter anymore.
LP: **1A 222-58135**

REMINISCING.
Tracks: / Reminiscing.
LP: . . . . **MCL 1826**
MC: . . . . **MCLC 1826**
LP: . . . . **LVA 9212**

ROCK AROUND WITH BUDDY HOLLY.
Tracks: / Modern Don Juan / Midnight shift / That'll be the day / Raining in my heart / Girl on my mind / Empty cup / I guess I was just a fool / Think it over / You're the one / Ready Teddy / Lonesome tears / Baby won't you come out tonight?.
MCSET: . . . . **CRT 123**

ROCK 'N' ROLL GREATS.
Tracks: / That'll be the day / Peggy Sue / Listen to me / Oh boy / Rave on / Early in the morning / Maybe baby / Think it over / Heartbeat / Not fade away / It's so easy / Words of love / Everyday / I'm gonna love you too.
LP: . . . . **MFP 5806**
MC: . . . . **TC-MFP 5806**

ROCK ON WITH BUDDY HOLLY.
LP: . . . . **MFP 50490**

SHOWCASE.
LP: . . . . **MCL 1824**
MC: . . . . **MCLC 1824**

SOMETHING SPECIAL FROM BUDDY HOLLY.
Tracks: / Good rockin' tonight / Rip it up / Blue monday / Honky tonk / Blue suede shoes / Shake, rattle and roll / Ain't got no home / Holly hop / Brown eyed handsome man / Bo Diddley / Gone (take 1) / Gone (take 2) / Have you ever been lonely (take 1) / Have you ever been lonely (take 2) / Have you ever been lonely (take 3).
LP: . . . . **ROLL 2013**

THAT'LL BE THE DAY (LP).
LP: . . . . **AH 3**

TRUE LOVE WAYS.
Tracks: / Raining in my heart / Peggy Sue / That'll be the day / Oh boy / Everyday / True love ways / It doesn't matter anymore / Learning the game / I'm gonna love you too / Ready Teddy / Wishing / Well...alright / Midnight shift / Love's made a fool of you / Reminiscing.
LP: . . . . **PLAT 307**
MC: . . . . **PLAC 307**
LP: . . . . **STAR 2339**
MC: . . . . **STAC 2339**

UNFORGETTABLE, THE.
LPPD: . . . . **AR 30068**

Holly, Buddy Sound

BUDDY HOLLY SOUND (See under Buddy Holly Sound) (Various artists).

Holly & Hicks

ANASTASIO/HOLLY & HICKS (see under Anastasio) (Holly & Hicks/ Anastasio).

Holly, Jan

SITTIN' ON TOP OF THE WORLD.
Tracks: / Too much too soon / I can feel the leaving coming on / You're my fantasy / Woman / Sitting on top of the world / No getting over you / Lonely nights / Singing the blues again / Broke up / Wish me love / You wrote the book / Do you ever think of me and Amarillo.
LP: . . . . **YU 105**
MC: . . . . **CYU 105**

Holly & The Italians

RIGHT TO BE ITALIAN, THE.
LP: . . . . **V 2186**

Hollyday, Christopher

CHRISTOPHER HOLLYDAY.
Tracks: / Appointment in Ghana / Omega / Bloomdido / This is always / Ko-ko / Little Melonae / Embraceable you / Blues inn / Bebop.
MC: . . . . **PK 83055**
LP: . . . . **PL 83055**

ON COURSE.
Tracks: / No second quartet / Lady Street / Memories of you / West side winds / Hit and run / Skeptical spektical / In a love affair / 6th world, The.
LP: . . . . **PL 83087**
MC: . . . . **PK 83087**

Hollywood...

HOLLYWOOD (Original TV Theme) (Various artists).
LP: . . . . **DS 15006**

HOLLYWOOD HILLBILLIES (Various artists).
Tracks: / I'll take a long long time: *McDonald, Skeets* / Long time ago, A: *Young, Faron* / Gambler's love: *Maddox, Rose* / Lost John: *Thompson, Hank* / Forgive me: *James, Sonny* / My last chance with you: *Collins, Tommy* / Too busy cryin' the blues: *Reed, Jerry* / Cincinnati Lou: *Travis, Merle* / Dragging the river: *Husky, Ferlin* / I know my baby cares: *Luman, Bob* / Black cat: *Collins, Tommy* / Fallen angel: *McDonald, Skeets* / That's the way I feel: *Young, Faron* / Rockin' in the congo: *Thompson, Hank* / Looking back: *Husky, Ferlin* / You've turned into stranger: *Jackson, Wanda* / You've got that touch: *James, Sonny* / Bessie baby: *Reed, Jerry* / Move it on over: *Maddox, Rose* / Try me: *Luman, Bob*.
LP: . . . . **SEE 98**

HOLLYWOOD MUSICALS-MGM/UA (Various artists).
Tracks: / Gold diggers of 1933: *Various artists* / Go into your dance: *Various artists* / 42nd street: *Various* artists / Dames: *Various artists* / Going places: *Various artists* / Ready willing and able: *Various* artists / Hard to get: *Various artists* / Yankee doodle boy: *Various artists* / Hollywood hotel: *Various* artists / Gold diggers of 1937: *Various artists* / Rhapsody in blue: *Various artists* / Melody for two: *Various* artists / Footlight parade: *Various artist* / Broadway gondalier: *Various artists* / 20 million sweethearts: *Various artists* / Gold diggers of 1935: *Various artists*.
LP: . . . . **ACH 023**
MC: . . . . **CCH 023**

HOORAY FOR HOLLYWOOD (Various artists).
LP: . . . . **INTS 5045**

HOORAY FOR HOLLYWOOD (Various artists).
MC: . . . . **MRT 40046**

Hollywood Argyles

HOLLYWOOD ARGYLES (Featuring Gary Paxton).
LP: . . . . **REBEL 1007**

Hollywood Beyond

IF.
Tracks: / Opening scenario / Vision of love / After midnight / Save me / Crimes of passion / What's the colour of money? / No more tears / Metal on glass / Shadows I remember / Hollywood beyond.
LP: . . . . **WX 77**
MC: . . . . **WX 77C**

Hollywood Brats

GROWN UP WRONG.
LP: . . . . **LUSLP 6**

HOLLYWOOD BRATS.
Tracks: / Chez maximes / Another schoolday / Nightmare / Empty bottles / Courtesan / Then he kissed me / Tumble with me / Zurich 17 / Southern belles / Drowning sorrows / Sick on you.
LP: . . . . **ARED 6**

Hollywood Cavalcade

HOLLYWOOD CAVALCADE (Various artists).
Tracks: / Sonny boy: *Jolson, Al* / Valentine: *Chevalier, Maurice* / Parlami d'amore mariu: *De Sica, Vittorio* / When April sings: *Durbin, Deanna* / I can't be bothered now: *Astaire, Fred* / Kiss: *Monroe, Marilyn* / Ich bin von caps bis fuss auf leiber eingestel: *Dietrich, Marlene* / Captain January: *Temple, Shirley* / Over the rainbow: *Garland, Judy* / Sentimental journey: *Day, Doris* / Singin' in the rain: *Kelly, Gene* / You'll never know: *Rogers, Ginger*.
LP: . . . . **MTM 016**

Hollywood Collection

HOLLYWOOD COLLECTION (Various artists).
Tracks: / Singin' in the rain: *Kelly, Gene* / Over the rainbow: *Garland, Judy* / Entertainer, The: *Joplin*, Scott / Cheek to cheek: *Astaire, Fred* / Mammy: *Jolson, Al* / Let's face the music and dance: *Rogers*, Ginger / Couple of swells, A: *Astaire, Fred* / Diamonds are a girl's best friend: *Monroe, Marilyn* / Night and day: *Sinatra, Frank* / In the mood: *Miller, Glenn* / Trail of the lonesome pine: *Laurel & Hardy* / Ol' man river: *Robeson, Paul* / I'm in the mood for love: *Hutton, Betty* / Hello Dolly: *Armstrong, Louis* / Zip: *Hayworth, Rita* / I've got my love to keep me warm: *Bogart, Humphrey* / Gentlemen prefer blondes: *Russell*, Jane & Marilyn Monroe / Hi lili hi lo: *Caron, Leslie & Mel Ferrer* / Who's sorry now?: *De Haven, Gloria* / It had to be you: *Lamour, Dorothy*.
LP: . . . . **DVLP 2054**
MC: . . . . **DVMC 2054**

Hollywood Flames

JOHN DOLPHIN SESSIONS 1951-6.
Tracks: / Clickity clack I'm leaving / Let's talk it over / Fare thee well / I know / Wagon wheels / One night with a feel / Oooh la la / Peggy / Young girl / My love grows stronger.
LP: . . . . **JD 905**

Hollywood Hit Parade

HOLLYWOOD HIT PARADE (Various artists).
Tracks: / We're in the money: *Studio Orchestra* / I've got to sing a torch song: *Studio Orchestra* / We're in the money: *Rogers, Ginger* / She's a Latin from Manhattan: *Jolson, Al* / Shuffle off to Buffalo: *Keeler, Ruby/Clarence* Nordstrom / 42nd Street: *Keeler, Ruby/ Dick Powell* / I only have eyes for you: *Powell, Dick/Ruby Keeler* / Jeepers Creepers: *Armstrong, Louis* / Too marvellous for words: *Shaw, Winifred/ Ross Alexander/Ruby Keeler/Lee Dixson* / You must have been a beautiful baby: *Powell, Dick* / About a quarter to nine: *Jolson, Al* / Yankee doodle boy: *Cagney, James* / Hooray for Hollywood: *Goodman, Benny & His Orchestra* / With plenty of money and you: *Powell*, Dick / Let's put our heads together: *Studio Orchestra* / Life insurance song: *Studio Orchestra* / You're getting to be a habit with me: *Daniels, Bebe* / Swanee: *Jolson, Al* / September in the rain: *Melton, James* / Shanghai Lil: *Cagney, James/Ruby Keeler* / Lulu's back in town: *Powell, Dick* / By a waterfall: *Powell, Dick/Ruby Keeler* / I'll string along with you: *Powell, Dick/Ginger Rogers* / Lullaby of Broadway: *Shaw, Winifred*.
LP: . . . . **ZL 70136**
MC: . . . . **ZK 70136**

Hollywood Hotel

HOLLYWOOD HOTEL (Original soundtrack) (Various artists).
LP: . . . . **HS 5004**

Hollywood Magic

HOLLYWOOD MAGIC VOL 1 (The 1950's) (Various artists).
MC: . . . . **JST 44374**

HOLLYWOOD MAGIC VOL 2 1960's, The (Various artists).
MC: . . . . **JST 44373**

Hollywood Musicals

CUT - VOL. 1 (Out-takes from Hollywood Musicals) (Various artists).
LP: . . . . **SBL 12586**

CUT - VOL. 2 (Out-takes from Hollywood Musicals) (Various artists).
LP: . . . . **SBL 12587**

Hollywood Party

HOLLYWOOD PARTY, VOL. 1 (Various artists).
LP: . . . . **LOP 14 152**
MC: . . . . **LCS 14152**

HOLLYWOOD PARTY, VOL. 2 (Various artists).
LP: . . . . **LOP 14 153**
MC: . . . . **LCS 14153**

HOLLYWOOD PARTY, VOL. 3 (Various artists).
LP: . . . . **LOP 14 154**
MC: . . . . **LCS 14154**

Hollywood Presbyterian

CHRISTMAS (MICHAEL W. SMITH) (See under Smith, Michael W.) (Hollywood Presbyterian Choir/Michael W Smith/Hollywd Boys Ch).

Hollywood Rock'n'Roll

HOLLYWOOD ROCK'N'ROLL (Various artists).
Tracks: / Blue jeans: *Glenn, Glen* / Everybody's movin': *Glenn, Glen* / Would you: *Rock 'n' Roll* / Goofin' around: *Glenn, Glen* / I'm glad my baby's gone away: *Glenn, Glen* / One cup of coffee: *Glenn, Glen* / Don't push: *Deal, Don* / Topsy turvy: *Zeppa, Ben Joe* / Great shakin' fever: *Burnette, Dorsey* / Ezactly: *Busch, Dick* / Hollywood party: *Busch, Dick* / He will come back to me: *Leslie, Alis*.
LP: . . . . **CH 1**

Hollywood Singles

HOLLYWOOD SINGLES VOL. 1 (Various artists).
LP: . . . . **MCL 1684**

Hollywood Sings

HOLLYWOOD SINGS (Stars of the Silver Screen) (Various artists).
Tracks: / Happy feet: *Whiteman, Paul & Rhythm Boys* / Toot toot Tootsie goodbye: *Jolson, Al* / Johnny: *Dietrich, Marlene* / Day after day: *Stewart, James* / Can Broadway do without me?: *Clayton, Jackson & Durante* / If you haven't got love: *Swanson, Gloria* / Doin' the new low down: *Robinson, Bill 'Bojangles'* / Keep your sunny side up: *Gaynor, Janet* / Kashmiri love song: *Valentino, Rudolph* / Broadway melody: *King, Charles* / Puttin' on the ritz: *Richman, Harry* / How long will it last?: *Crawford, Joan* / Hooray for Captain Spaulding: *Marx, Groucho & Zeppo* / Just like a butterfly (that's caught in the rain): *Morgan, Helen* / I love Louisa: *Astaire*, Fred / Can't get along: *Rogers, Ginger* / You've got that thing: *Chevalier, Maurice* / Beyond the blue horizon: *MacDonald, Jeanette* / White dove: *Tibbett, Lawrence* / Yes yes (my baby says yes): *Cantor, Eddie*.
LP: . . . . **AJA 5011**
MC: . . . . **ZC AJA 5011**

Hollywood Studio...

18 FAMOUS FILM AND TV THEMES (Hollywood Studio Orchestra).
LP: **26018**
MC: **46018**

SWING AND SWEET (Hollywood Studio Orchestra).
LP: **26009**
MC: **46009**

WESTERN TRACKS (Hollywood Studio Orchestra).
LP: **26023**
MC: **46023**

Hollywood To Las Vegas

HOLLYWOOD TO LAS VEGAS (Various artists).
Tracks: / Cheek to cheek: *Astaire, Fred* / Let's call the whole thing off: *Astaire, Fred* / Top hat, white tie and tails: *Astaire, Fred* / Let's face the music and dance: *Astaire, Fred* / Fine romance, A: *Astaire, Fred* / World weary: *Coward, Noel* / Room with a view, A: *Coward, Noel* / Mad dogs and Englishmen: *Coward, Noel* / Let's do it: *Coward, Noel* / Party's over now, The: *Coward, Noel* / Speaking confidentially: *Faye, Alice* / I'm shooting high: *Faye, Alice* / I've got my love to keep me warm: *Faye, Alice* / Slumming on Park Avenue: *Faye*, Alice / There's a lull in my life: *Faye, Alice* / Taking a chance on love: *Dietrich, Marlene* / I couldn't sleep a wink last night: *Dietrich, Marlene* / Lili Marlene: *Dietrich, Marlene* / Miss Otis regrets: *Dietrich, Marlene* / Mean to me: *Dietrich, Marlene*.
MCSET: . . . . **DTO 10266**

Hollywood (TV)

HOLLYWOOD (TV Soundtrack) (Various artists).
Tracks: / Hollywood: *Various artists* / In the beginning: *Various artists* / Tango di Valentino: *Various* artists / Hollywood

scandal: *Various artists* (Fatty Arbuckle.) / Swashbuckler, The: *Various artists* (Douglas Fairbanks Snr.) / Kid: *Various artists* / Wagon's roll: *Various artists* / Harold Lloyd's glasses: *Various artists* / Stuntmen: *Various artists* / Stoic, The: *Various artists* (Buster Keaton's Rag.) / Garbo: *Various artists* / Great chariot race, The: *Various artists* (Ben Hur).
LP: . . . . **EMS 1308**
MC: . . . . **TCEMS 1308**
LP: . . . . **INA 1504**

Holm, Dallas

CHANGE THE WORLD (Holm, Dallas & Praise).
LP: . . . . **DAY R 4138**
MC: . . . . **DAY C 4138**

Holm, Ian (nar)

WOMAN IN WHITE, THE (see under Woman In White (bk)).

Holm, Lars

FOLKLORISTICA (On the Free Bass Accordion).
LP: . . . . **TPLP 50**

Holman, Bill

BIG BAND JAZZ IN A JAZZ ORBIT.
LP: . . . . **VSOP 25**

BILL HOLMAN BAND (Holman, Bill Band).
MC: . . . . **JC 3308**
LP: . . . . **JLP 3308**
LP: . . . . **FS 112**

BILL HOLMAN'S GREAT BAND (Holman, Bill Band).
LP: . . . . **ST 1053**

FABULOUS BILL HOLMAN ORCHESTRA.
LP: **2013**

FABULOUS BILL HOLMAN, THE.
Tracks: / Airegin / Evil eyes / You and I / Bright eyes / Come rain or come shine / Big street, The.
LP: . . . . **JASM 1009**

GROUP ACTIVITY (See under Cooper, Bob).

JIVE FOR FIVE (Holman, Eddie).
LP: . . . . **VSOP 19**

Holman, Eddie

UNITED.
Tracks: / United / Eternal love / Give it all to the Lord / I asked Jesus / Thank you for saving me / Holy ghost / Breathe on me Lord.
LP: . . . . **GNC 1001**

Holman, Libby

LEGENDARY...., THE.
LP: . . . . **MES 6501**

SOMETHING TO REMEMBER HER BY.
LP: . . . . **MES 7067**

Holmes Brothers

IN THE SPIRIT.
Tracks: / Please don't hurt me / Final round, The / When something is wrong with my baby / Hey, hey I love you / None but the righteous / Squeal like an eel / Going down slow / Ask me no questions / So fine / Baby what you want me to do / Up above my head.
LP: . . . . **ZS 103**

Holmes, Groove

CRY THE BLUES (See under Jimmy Witherspoon).

GOOD VIBRATIONS.
LP: . . . . **MR 5167**

NOBODY DOES IT BETTER.
Tracks: / Gonna fly now / Nobody does it better / Calypso holiday / Let's groove / Highway of life.
LP: . . . . **MAN 5005**

ON CONSTELLATION, 1961-62 (See under Witherspoon, Jimmy) (Holmes, Groove & Jimmy Witherspoon).

Holmes, Hoe

AFTER DAWNING (see also Len Graham) (Holmes, Hoe & Len Graham).
Tracks: / Here I am amongst you / My lone Nell / Loughinsholin / Willie Clarke's / Green grow the rushes-o / Maid of Mourne shore, The / Lovely Glenshesk / Sweet bann water, The / Girl that broke my heart, The / Gra mo chroi / Come tender hearted / Hare's lament, The / Johnnie and Molly / Dick the dasher / Parting glass, The.
LP: **12TS 401**

Holmes, Ian

IAN HOLMES & HIS SCOTTISH DANCE BAND (Holmes, Ian & Scottish Dance Band).
LP: . . . . **LILP 5086**
MC: . . . . **LICS 5086**

IDEAL HOLMES (Holmes, Ian & Scottish Dance Band).
Tracks: / Irish reels / Hesitation waltz, The / Marches in 6/8 time / Scandinavian polka / Marches in 4/4 time / Scottish reel / Pipe march / Irish jigs / Scandinavian waltz / Marches in 2/4 time / Polka / St. Bernards waltz / Swedish snoa.
LP: . . . . **LILP 5157**
MC: . . . . **LICS 5157**

LET'S DANCE IN STRICT TEMPO (Holmes, Ian & Scottish Dance Band).
Tracks: / Duke and Duchess of Edinburgh / Duke of Perth / Laird of Milton's daughter / College hornpipe, The / Balmoral strathspey / Eightsome reel / Set of Strathspeys / Set of jigs.
LP: . . . . **LILP 5097**
MC: . . . . **LICS 5097**

MORE SOUNDS SCOTTISH (Holmes, Ian & Scottish Dance Band).
Tracks: / Reels / Boston two step / Waltz / Polka / Accordion duet / Johnstone fig, The / 6/8 Marches / Military two step / March, Strathspey & reel.
LP: . . . . **BSLP 111 S**

SOUNDS SCANDINAVIAN.
Tracks: / Fasas polka.
MC: . . . . **MMCS 8701**

TO DANCE TO (Holmes, Ian & Scottish Dance Band).
Tracks: / Solway reel / Shepherd's crook / Round reel of eight / Rose of Benbecula / Bonnie Anne / Winding nith,The / Laird of Dochart's reel / MacDonald of Sleat / Bonnie Brix / Whitesands jig / MacNeil of Barra / Doon hame / Rouken Glen / Lamont of Inveryne.
LP: . . . . **SSLP 123 S**

Holmes, Joe

CHASTE MUSES, BARDS AND SAGES.
LP: . . . . **FRR 007**

Holmes, Robert

AGE OF SWING.
Tracks: / Age of swing / American lullaby / Monkey song, The / Bomb shop / Angel in the house / Free country / Stay together.
LP: . . . . **V 2568**
MC: . . . . **TCV 2568**

Holmes, Rupert

ADVENTURE.
Tracks: / Adventure / Mask, The / Black Jack / O'Brien girl, The / Crowd pleaser / You'll love me again / Cold / Morning man / I don't need you / Special thanks.
LP: . . . . **MCF 3088**

FULL CIRCLE.
Tracks: / Loved by the one you love / Full circle / You remind me of you / One of us / How do you do / Love at second sight / One born every minute / My lover's keeper / End.
LP: . . . . **K 52328**

PARTNERS IN CRIME.
Tracks: / Escape (pina colada song) / Partners in crime / Nearsighted / Lunch hour / Drop it / Him / Aswering machine / People that you never get to love, The / Get outta yourself / In you I trust.
LP: . . . . **MCL 1656**
MC: . . . . **MCLC 1656**
LP: . . . . **MCF 3051**

SONGWRITERS FOR THE STARS 1 (See under Webb, Jimmy) (Holmes, Rupert & Jimmy Webb).

Holmes, Watson

CINEMA ORGAN ENCORES.
LP: . . . . **DEROY 1326**

WURLITZER STARS VOL. 1 (see under Briggs, Noel).

Holocaust

HOLOCAUST LIVE.
LP: . . . . **PSP LP 4**

NO MAN'S LAND.
LP: . . . . **PSP LP 5**

SOUND OF SOULS, THE.
LP: . . . . **CROM 301**

Holosade

HELLHOUSE.
Tracks: / Look into the mirror / Welcome to the hellhouse / Love it to death / Madame Guillotine / Psycho / Eternal life / Bittersweet / Nightmare reality.
LP: . . . . **AMP 016**

Holsapple, Peter

MAVERICKS (Holsapple, Peter & Chris Stamey).
LP: . . . . **SPD 1042**
MC: . . . . **SPDC 1042**

Holst (composer)

EVENING WATCH, THE AND OTHER CHORAL MUSIC (Holst Singers, The & Holst Orchestra, The).
MC: . . . . **KA 66329**

PLANETS, THE (See under Solti, Sir George) (London Philharmonic Orchestra).

PLANETS, THE & OTHERS (London Philharmonic Orchestra).
MC: **4251524**

WIND MUSIC OF HOLST AND VAUGHAN WILLIAMS (see under London Wind) (London Wind Orchestra).

Holst & Elgar

HOLST & ELGAR (Various artists).
Tracks: / Planets, The: *Holst (composer)* / Enigma variations: *Various artists* / Pomp and circumstance.
MCSET: **4138524**

Holt, David

REEL AND ROCK.
LP: . . . . **FF 372**

Holt, John

16 SONGS FOR SOULFUL LOVERS.
Tracks: / I'd love you to want me / You'll never find a love like mine / Too good to be forgotten / Help me make it through the night / Winter world of love / Killing me softly with her song / If I were a carpenter / Rainy night in Georgia / I'll never fall in love again / Just the way you are / Wherever I lay my hat / Touch me in the morning / Love I can feel / Too much love / When I fall in love / I'll be there.
MC: . . . . **PLAC 16**
LP: . . . . **PLAT 16**

20 GOLDEN LOVE SONGS: JOHN HOLT.
Tracks: / Never never never / I'd love you to want me / Killing me softly with her song / You will never find another love like mine / When I fall in love / I'll take a melody / Just the way you are / Too good to be forgotten / Doctor love / Help me make it through the night / Stoned out of my life / Touch me in the morning / I'll be lonely / Too much love / Love so right / Rainy night in Georgia / If I were a Carpenter / Everybody's talkin' / Baby don't get hooked on me / Last farewell, The.
LP: . . . . **TRLS 192**
MC: . . . . **ZCTRL 192**

1000 VOLTS OF HOLT.
Tracks: / Never, never, never / Morning of my life / Stoned out of my mind / Baby I want you / Help me make it through the night / Mr. Bojangles / I'd love you to want me / Killing me softly with her song / You baby / Too much love / Girl from Ipanema / Which way you going, baby?.
LP: . . . . **TRLS 75**
MC: . . . . **ZCTRL 75**

2000 VOLTS OF HOLT.
Tracks: / Doctor Love / Yester-me, yester-you, yesterday / Touch me in the morning / Keep on moving / I will / Alfie / I'll take a melody / My guiding star / On a clear day / Peace and love / Take away my heart, Teresa / For the love of you.
LP: . . . . **TRLS 134**
MC: . . . . **ZCTRL 134**

3000 VOLTS OF HOLT.
Tracks: / Let's get it while it's hot / In the Springtime / Till I'm gone / Let's kiss and say goodbye / Winter of love / Oh what a day / Let's do it long / No place like home / Ungrateful lady / You will never find another love like man.
LP: . . . . **TRLS 143**
MC: . . . . **ZCTRL 143**

BEST OF JOHN HOLT.
MC: . . . . **ARLC 1020**

CLASSIC TRACKS (See under Boothe, Ken) (Holt, John & More/Ken Boothe).

DUSTY ROADS.
Tracks: / Tell me why / After all / I don't mind / Not so close / I'll light your fire / You'd better take time / Dusty roads / These old memories / In the middle of the night / Make this young lady mine / I won't let you forget / Same old thing.
LP: . . . . **TRLS 85**

FOR LOVERS AND DANCERS.
Tracks: / Thinking of you / In the corner / No one before you / High school dance / Stick by me / Try a thing / Your arms reaching out for me / Nobody else / Massachusetts / Stealing, stealing, stealing.
LP: . . . . **TRLS 223**
MC: . . . . **ZCTRL 223**

FROM ONE EXTREME TO ANOTHER (Holt, John & Horace Andy).
LP: . . . . **PHIL 1005**

FURTHER YOU LOOK, THE.
Tracks: / Further you look, The / I sing my song / Never let me go / Saving my love / I won't come in / Just let me know / I'm a rover / Open the door / I'll be there / Memories by the score / I'll always love you / I wanna dance.
LP: . . . . **TRLS 55**

GREATEST HITS:JOHN HOLT.
LP: . . . . **SMLP 12-170**

HELP ME MAKE IT THROUGH THE NIGHT (OLD GOLD) (See under Ken Boothe - Everything I own).

HOLT GOES DISCO.
Tracks: / I'll be lonely / Fancy make-up / Do you love me? / Rock with me baby / I'll never fall in love again / Last farewell, The.
LP: . . . . **TRLS 160**

JUST THE TWO OF US.
Tracks: / Let your love flow / I ain't gonna stand for it / Thinking / Burning sun / Bend my love / Just the two of us / Being with you / How can I / This masquerade / Vaya con dios.
LP: . . . . **CSLP 1**
MC: . . . . **ZCSLC 01**

LET IT GO ON.
Tracks: / Can I change my mind? / On the beach / Let it go on / Tide is high, The / Island in the sun / Let's start all over / Turn back the hands of time / Wear you to the ball / Strange love / When I fall in love / That's my home / Rain from the sky.
LP: . . . . **TRLS 163**

LIVE IN LONDON:JOHN HOLT.
LP: . . . . **VG 1**

LIVING LEGEND.
LP: . . . . **CLALP 401**

LOVE I CAN FEEL, A.
Tracks: / Love I can feel / Tonight / Your arms reaching out for me / Nobody else / Then you can tell me goodbye.
LP: . . . . **TRLS 225**

O.K. FRED.
Tracks: / Let's dance / My eyes / Anywhere you want to go / Sad news / OK Fred / My sweet lord / Long and winding road, The / Hollt holy / Sometimes / Silently / Don't leave be wise.
LP: . . . . **SPMP 5002**
MC: . . . . **SPMC 5002**

POLICE IN HELICOPTER.
Tracks: / Police in helicopter / Private doctor / Last train / Beach party / Reality / Fat she fat / Chanting / Sugar and spice / Can't use me / I got caught.
LP: . . . . **GREL 58**

PURE GOLD: JOHN HOLT.
LP: . . . . **VSLP 4070**

REGGAE CHRISTMAS ALBUM, THE.
LP: . . . . **TRLS 230**
MC: . . . . **ZCTR 230**

ROCK WITH ME BABY.
LP: . . . . **TRD 101**

ROOTS OF HOLT.
Tracks: / Anywhere you want to go / Everybody's talkin' / Have you ever been in love? / Why can't I touch you? / Too good to be forgotten / Love I can feel / Up park camp / Ghetto girl / Only a smile / Don't fight your brothers / My time / My brothers.
LP: . . . . **TRLS 147**

TIME IS THE MASTER.
Tracks: / Time is the master / Everybody Knows / Riding For A Fall / Looking Back / Love is gone / Stick By Me / Lost Love / It May Sound Silly / Again / Oh Girl.
LP: . . . . **CTLP 109**
LP: . . . . **HM 105**

VIBES.
LP: . . . . **Unknown**

WHY I CARE.
Tracks: / Why I care / In my life / Oh why / I've been waiting / Young lovers / Not to be blamed / Don't prepare for war / Visions.
LP: . . . . **GREL 127**

Holt, Peter

HAPPY TOGETHER.
LP: . . . . **GRS 1176**

Holt, Victoria

KING OF THE CASTLE, THE (Jameson, Susan (nar)).
MC: . . . . **CAB 310**

Holton, Gary

RUBY (DON'T TAKE YOUR LOVE TO TOWN) (see also Casino Steel) (Holton, Gary & Casino Steel).

SING IT TO ME (Holton, Gary & Mick Rossi).
LP: . . . . **RRLP 115**

Holts, Roosevelt

ROOSEVELT HOLTS AND FRIENDS.
LP: . . . . **ARHOOLIE 1057**

Holy Bible

HOLY BIBLE, THE (Various artists).
MC: . . . . **HB 1-15**

Holy Grail (film)

HOLY GRAIL, THE (see under Monty Python) (Film soundtrack).

MONTY PYTHON AND THE HOLY GRAIL (See under Monty Python).

Holy Modal Rounders

ALLEGED IN THEIR OWN TIME.
LP: . . . . ROUNDER 3004

HOLY MODAL ROUNDERS.
Tracks: / Blues in the bottle / Cuckoo, the / Long John / Hey hey baby / Mr. Bass man / Better things for you / Hop high ladies / Give the fiddler a dram / Euphoria / Hesitation blues / Reuben's train / Moving day / Same old man / Bound to lose.
LP: . . . . WIK 75

HOLY MODAL ROUNDERS 2.
Tracks: / Flop eared mule / Black eyed Susan Brown / Sail away ladies / Clinch mountain backstep / Fishin' blues / Statesboro blues / Juko partner / Mole in the ground / Hot corn, cold corn / Down the old plant road / Chevrolet 6 / Crowley waltz / Bully of the town.
LP: . . . . WIK 79

LAST ROUND.
LP: . . . . AD 1030

Holy Moses

FINISHED WITH THE DOGS.
LP: . . . . AAARRG 006

QUEEN OF SIAM.
LP: . . . . AAARRG 001

WORLD CHAOS.
LP: 085700

Holy Order

HATEFUL RAGE.
LP: . . . . CCG 009

Holy Terror

MIND WARS.
LP: . . . . FLAG 25
MC: . . . . TFLAG 25

TERROR AND SUBMISSION.
Tracks: / Black plague / Evil's rising / Blood of the saint / Mortal fear / Guardians of the Netherworld / Distant calling / Terror and submission / Tomorrow's end / Alpha omega.
LP: . . . . FLAG 10

Holy Toy

PANZER AND RABBITS.
LP: . . . . SNTF 921

PART OF FACT.
LP: . . . . TAT 001

WARSZAWA.
LP: . . . . U 010
MC: . . . . U 010 MC

WHY NOT IN CHOIR.
LP: . . . . SNTF 950

Hom Bru

OBADEEA.
LP: . . . . CM 009

Homage To Grieg

HOMAGE TO GRIEG (Various artists).
MC: TC2MOM 136

Home

HOME (Various artists).
LP: . . . . SHEER 001

HOME FROM HOME (Various artists).
Tracks: / Oriental fantasy: *Various artists* / Piecing it together: *Various artists* / Soft day: *Various artists* / Catch me if you can: *Various artists* / Winter solstice: *Various artists* / Finding speed: *Various* artists / Speedway: *Various artists* / On top of the world: *Various artists* / Zero is the hour: *Various artists.*
LP: . . . . OG 522

HOME GROWN ROCKABILLY (Various artists).
LP: . . . . ROLLS 008

HOME MADE EARLY ROCK & ROLL (Various artists).
Tracks: / Foggy river: *Holder, Jimmy* / Don't you be still: *Dixieland Drifters* / Rock away: *Sexton, Orden*/ Just rockin': *Cooper, Glen* / These blues are driving me mad: *Cooper, Glen* / Scalping party: *Tornados*/ 707: *Tornados* / I'm gonna let you go: *Rector, Hank* / Concussion: *Holydays* / Pearl River: *Holydays*/ Well, come on: *Kingsmill, Steve* / Cool, cool baby: *Smith, Bobby* / Cotton pickin': *Freeze, Sonny* / Bop a little: *Riley, Pat* / Walkin' and talkin': *Moore, Lucky.*
LP: . . . . WLP 8867

HOME NEWCASTLE (Various artists).
LP: . . . . MWM SP 2
MC: . . . . MWM CSP2

Home (band)

ALCHEMIST, THE.
LP: . . . . CBS 65550

DREAMER.
LP: . . . . CBS 67522

HOME.
LP: . . . . CBS 64752

PAUSE FOR A HOARSE HORSE.
LP: . . . . EPC 64365

Home Economics

HOME ECONOMICS (COURSE) (See under GCSE Pass Packs) (Longman/ Pickwick Pass Packs).

Home & Garden

HISTORY OF GEOGRAPHY.
LP: . . . . DMC 005

Home Movies

HOME MOVIES Original soundtrack (Various artists).
LP: . . . . STV 81139

Home Service

ALRIGHT JACK.
Tracks: / Alright Jack / Rose of Allandale / Radstock jig / Sorrow / Scarecrow / Duke of Marlborough Fanfare / Lincolnshire posy, A / Look up look up / Babylon.
LP: . . . . HCM 001
LP: . . . . SPIN 119
MC: . . . . SPIC 119

HOME SERVICE, THE.
LP: . . . . SAW 3

MYSTERIES, THE.
Tracks: / God / Creation / Serpent's dance / Cain and Abel (don't be an outlaw) / Journey to Bethlehem / Nativity, The (lay me low) / Herod / Kings, The / Entry to Jerusalem / Betrayal and denial (all in the morning part 1) / Arrest, The / Scourging (all in the morning part 2) / Trial, The (Lewk up-lewk up) / Road to Calvary, The / Crucifixion / Moon shines bright, (The) / We sing Hallelujah / Wondrous love / Death of Mary / Coronation of the Virgin / Lyke wyke dirge / Judgement (the wheel).
LP: . . . . NAT 001
MC: . . . . NATC 001

Homeboy

HOMEBOY (Film soundtrack) (Various artists).
Tracks: / I want to love you baby: *Benson, Jo* / Home boy: *Clapton, Eric* / Call me if you need me: *Magic Sam* / Final fight: *Clapton, Eric* / Travelling East: *Clapton, Eric* / Bridge: *Clapton, Eric.*
LP: . . . . V 2574
MC: . . . . TCV 2574
MC: . . . . OVEDC 364
LP: . . . . OVED 364

Homegrown Rockabilly

HOMEGROWN ROCKABILLY (Various artists).
LP: . . . . NERD 053

Homer

HOMER (Film Soundtrack) (Various artists).
Tracks: / Turn turn turn: *Byrds* / Bluebird: *Buffalo Springfield* / For what it's worth: *Buffalo Springfield*/ Nashville cats: *Lovin' Spoonful* / Rock 'n' roll woman: *Buffalo Springfield* / How many more times: *Led Zeppelin* / Brave new world: *Miller, Steve Band* / Man of music: *Scardino, Don* / Rock 'n' roll gypsies: *Various artists* / Spoonful: *Cream.*
LP: 2400 137

ILIAD, THE (Lattimore, Richard).
MC: 1196

ODYSSEY, THE (books 9-12) (Quayle, Anthony (nar)).
MC: 3001

Homer & Jethro

ASSAULT THE ROCK AND ROLL ERA.
Tracks: / Houn' dawg / Hart Brake motel / Two tone shoes / Rock boogie / At the flop / Screen door / Hernando's hideaway / Middle-aged teenager / Little arrows / She loves you / I want to hold your hand / No hair Sam / Winchester Cathedral / Ballad of Davy Crockett, The / Yaller rose of Texas, you all / Battle of Kookamonga, The.
LP: . . . . BFX 15281

BAREFOOT BALLARDS.
Tracks: / Cigarettes, whisky and wild, wild women / West Virginny Hills, The / Sweet fern / I'll go chasin' women / Frozen logger, The / Ground hog / Keep them icy cold fingers off of me / Boll weevil No.2 / High geared daddy / Dig me a grave in Missouri / Tennessee, Tennessee / Down where the watermelons grow.
LP: . . . . HAT 3068
MC: . . . . HATC 3068

Homer's Odyssey

CALYPSO CHRISTMAS PACKAGE.
LP: . . . . RR 001

Homesick James

BLUES FROM THE SOUTHSIDE.
Tracks: / Woman I'm lovin', The / Goin' down swingin' / Cloud is crying, The / She may be your woman / Homesick's shuffle / Stones in my passway / Johnny Mae / Gotta move / Lonesome road / Working with Homesick / Homesick's blues / Crawlin' / Stones in my passway.
LP: . . . . CH 257

HOME SWEET HOMESICK JAMES.
Tracks: / Highway 51 / Lonesome train / Homesick's original dust my broom / Kissing in the dark / Sweet home Chicago / Mailman / Shake your moneymaker / Dust my broom / Worried about my baby / Gotta move - can't stay here no more / Tin pan alley / Careless love.
LP: . . . . BEAR 10

HOMESICK JAMES AND SNOOKY PRYOR (Homesick James & Snooky Pryor).
Tracks: / Crossroads / Nothing but trouble / Shake your moneymaker / Cross town / Careless love / After you there won't be nobody else / Woman I love, The / I feel alright / Drivin' dog / She knows how to love me / Homesick blues again.
LP: . . . . BEAR 21

SAD AND LONESOME (Homesick James & Snooky Pryor).
LP: . . . . WOLF 120 409

SHAKE YOUR MONEYMAKER (Homesick James & Snooky Pryor).
Tracks: / Boogy fool / Crying shame / Work with me Annie / After you there won't be nobody else / Bobby's rock / I believe my time ain't long / Tin Pan Alley / Shake your moneymaker.
LP: . . . . KK 790

Homespun...

HOMESPUN COUNTRY SHOWTIME (Various artists).
Tracks: / It's hard to be humble: *Various artists* / Teddy bear: *Various artists* / Hey good lookin': *Various* artists / When it's Springtime in the Rockies: *Various artists* / Be careful of stones that you throw: *Various* artists / I have a dream: *Various artists* / Kingdom I call home: *Various artists* / I dreamed about mama last night: *Derry, Pat* / Heart you break will be your own, The: *Breen, Ann* / Angeline would you like to dance again: *Bell, Crawford* / Roses for mama: *Greer, John* / Jimmy quit the drinking: *Fitzpatrick, Gene* / You need me: *Leon* / Little Rosa: *McFarland, Billy* / Back home again: *Hamilton, J.E.* / Kentucky in the morning: *Derry, Pat.*
MC: . . . . CPHL 439

HOMESPUN FEAST OF IRISH FOLK (Various artists).
Tracks: / Dublin in the rare oul times: *Woods, Pat* / Bunch of thyme: *Clarke, Grainne* / Green fields of France: *Woods, Pat* / High reel: *Horslips* / Wind in the willows: *Brolly, Anne & Francie* / Mary from Dungloe: *Spiceland, Emmet* / Spancil hill: *Woods, Pat* / Two jigs: *Kesh & Morrisons* / And the band played waltzing Matilda: *Woods, Pat* / Nancy Spain: *Skerry Ramblers* / Four green fields: *Brolly, Anne* / Gentle Annie: *Woods, Pat* / Rambles of spring: *Skerry Ramblers* / Town I loved so well, The: *Corrib Folk.*
LP: . . . . HRL 201
MC: . . . . CHRL 201

HOMESPUN'S COUNTRY HALL OF FAME (Various artists).
Tracks: / Harper Valley PTA: *Various artists* / China doll: *Various artists* / Truck drivin' woman: *Various* artists / Church courtroom and then goodbye: *Various artists* / Door is always open, The: *Various artists*/ Mississippi: *Various artists* / Blue eyes crying in the rain: *Various artists* / Lucille: *Various artists*/ Little isle of green: *Various artists* / Union mare and confederate grey: *Various artists* / Jeannie Norman: *Various artists* / Silver threads and golden needles: *Various artists* / My son calls another man daddy: *Various* artists / What's wrong with the way that we're doing it now: *Various artists* / Once a day: *Various artists*/ Sunny side of the mountain: *Various artists* / Back home again: *Various artists* / I'll settle for old Ireland: *Various artists.*
LP: . . . . PHL 427
MC: . . . . CPHL 427

Home-T

HOLDING ON (Home T, Coco Tea & Shabba Ranks).
LP: . . . . GREL 142
MC: . . . . GREEN 142

Homi & Jarvis

FRIEND OF A FRIEND.
Tracks: / I'm in love again / Friend of a friend / I told you so / You got me fallin' / Believe in yourself / If you see him / It didn't work out that way / Love's taking over / Run that by me / Some hearts.
LP: . . . . GRPA 1005
MC: . . . . C 1005

Hommage A Duras

HOMMAGE A DURAS (Various artists).
Tracks: / Lament: *Bartok (composer)* / Lover, The: *Jobson, Richard* / Avalanche: *Jobson, Richard* / Sea wall, The: *Durutti Column/Blaine L Reininger* / Days in the tree: *Jobson, Richard* / Kiss, the dance & the death, The: *Jobson, Richard* / Square, The: *Durutti Column* / La douleur: *Durutti Column/Blaine L Reininger*/ Like the other: *Tong, Winston* / Under the rain clouds: *Jobson, Richard* / Little horse of Tarquina: *Durutti Column* / St. Michelle: *Dislocation Dance.*
LP: . . . . IM 011

Homnick

WHOOPIN' (See under Winter, Paul) (Homnick/Bill Dixon/Paul Winter).

Honda, Toshiyuki

SOMETHING COMING ON.
Tracks: / Bagus / Exoticism / A palanquin / Bells / Hello, hello / Parade / Before conclusion / Broadway.
LP: . . . . VBR 20351
MC: . . . . VBR 20354

Honduras & Nicaragua

PATRIA (Various artists).
LP: . . . . LLST 7364

Honest Sam

OUT THERE TONIGHT (Honest Sam & The Dealers).
Tracks: / Blowin' like a bandit / Still feeling blue / Restless heart / Your down home is uptown / Out here tonight / I'll change your flat tire, Merle / Nine nights (out of ten) / Sin city / Bury me / You're still on my mind / Out of my mind.
LP: . . . . BGC 477
MC: . . . . KBGC 477

Honey At The Core

HONEY AT THE CORE (Various artists).
MC: . . . . HONEY 1

Honey Boy

STRANGE THOUGHTS.
LP: . . . . TRLS 125

Honey Cone

GIRLS IT AIN'T EASY.
Tracks: / While you're out looking for sugar / Girls it ain't easy / When will it end / Feeling's gone, The / You made me come to you / Take me with you / Are you man enough, are you strong enough / Want ads / My mind's on leaving, but my heart won't let me go / We belong together / Sunday morning people / Take my love / Deaf, blind, paralyzed / Day I found myself, The.
LP: . . . . HDH LP 004

Honey Drippers

HONEY DRIPPERS - VOLUME 1.
Tracks: / I get a thrill / Sea of love / I got a woman / Young boy blues / Rockin' at midnight.
LP: 790220 1
MC: 790220 4

Honey Hush

MINI LP COLLECTION.
LP: . . . . MLP 8418

Honey Pot

HONEY POT, THE (Original Soundtrack) (Various artists).
LP: . . . . MCA 25106
MC: . . . . MCAC 25106

Honey Twins

BUR WIN KUSSCHEN.
Tracks: / Problems / Till I kissed you / Cathy's clown / Charlie Brown / Don't look now / Oh Carol / Let it be me / Banjo boy / Send a picture postcard / Hello Mary / Yes my darling.
LP: . . . . BFX 15136

Honeybus

AT THEIR BEST.
Tracks: / Story / Fresher than the sweetness in water / Ceilings No. 1 / She said yes / I can't let Maggie go / Right to choose, The / Delighted to see you / Tender are the ashes / She sold Blackpool rock / Black mourning band / He was Columbus / Under the silent tree / I remember Caroline / Julie in my heart / Do I figure in your life? / Would you believe? / How long?.
LP: . . . . SEE 264

Honeychild

INTERNATIONAL HEAVEN.
LP: . . . . V 2665
MC: . . . . TCV 2665

Honeycombs

BEST OF THE HONEYCOMBS.
LP: . . . . PYL 4009
MC: . . . . PYM 4009

MEEK AND HONEY.
Tracks: / Have I the right? / Colour slide (I got on my wall) / Once you know / Face

in the crowd / That's the way / I want to be free / Leslie Ann / Without you it is night.
LP: . . . . DOW 16
MC: . . . . ZCDOW 16

Honeycutt, Miki

SOUL DEEP.
LP: . . . . ZS 93

Honeymoon Killers

HONEYMOON KILLERS.
Tracks: / Love bandit / Hard life / I'm glad my baby's gone / Hanky panky / Smotherly love / Too much! / Sexorcist, The / Dazed'n'hazey.
LP: . . . . BORE 8901

TUERS DE LA LUNE DE MIEL, (LES).
LP: . . . . CRAM 013

Honeymoon Suite

BIG PRIZE,THE.
Tracks: / Bad attitude / Feel it again / Lost and found / What does it take (to win your love) / One by one / Wounded / Words in the wind / All along you knew / Once the feeling / Take my hand.
LP: . . . . K 252824 1
MC: . . . . K 252824 4

RACING AFTER MIDNIGHT.
Tracks: / Looking after no. 1 / Long way back / Cold look / Love fever / Other side midnight / Love changes everything / It's over now / Fast company / Tears on the page / Lethal weapon.
LP: . . . . K 955445 1
MC: . . . . K 955445 4
LP: . . . . WX 196
MC: . . . . WX 196C

Honeysuckle Rose

HONEYSUCKLE ROSE (See under Nelson, Willie) (Nelson, Willie).

Honeytree

EVERGREEN.
Tracks: / Evergreen / It's only right / Here I am (lovely Jesus) / Ruth / I am Your servant / Rattle me, shake me / Searchlight / Say you told me so / Sometimes I need You / Lullaby in Jesus' name.
LP: . . . . MYR 1039
MC: . . . . MC 1039

Honkers & Barwalkers

HONKERS AND BARWALKERS (Various artists).
LP: . . . . DL 438

Honkers & Screamers

HONKERS & SCREAMERS (Various artists).
LP: . . . . SJL 2234

Honking

HONKING INSTRUMENTALS, VOCAL GROUPS AND FEMALE VOCALISTS Various artists (Various artists).
MC: 8810

Honking Instrumentals

ROCK 'N' ROLL DANCE PARTY VOL. 1 Various artists (Various artists).
MC: 8801

Honking Tenor Saxes

HONKING TENOR SAX INSTRUMNENTALS Various artists (Various artists).
MC: 8809

Honky

HONKY !.
Tracks: / You got it / Sexy lady / I'll survive / Can't sit down / Highfalutin' / Do it / Pour it on / Give it all you got / Stretch it out / Pour it on.
LP: . . . . CRLP 513

Honky (film)

HONKY (See under Emerson, Keith) (Emerson, Keith).

Honky Tonk...

HONKY TONK DEMOS Various artists (Various artists).
LP: . . . . OVLM 5003

HONKY TONK FREEWAY (Original soundtrack) (Various artists).
Tracks: / Honky tonk freeway: *Various artists* / You're crazy but I like you: *Various artists* / Diamond trinkets: *Various artists* / Faster faster: *Various artists* / My man ain't man enough for me: *Various artists*/ Love keeps bringing me down: *Various artists* / At the diner (instrumental): *Various artists* / Years from now: *Various artists* / Ticlaw: *Various artists.*
LP: . . . . EST 12160
MC: . . . . ESTC 12160

HONKY TONK PARTY TIME (Various artists).
MC: . . . . AM 53

Honky Tonk Man

HONKY TONK MAN (Original soundtrack) (Various artists).
LP: 23739.1

Honky Tonkin'

HONKY TONKIN' (Various artists).
LP: . . . . PL 13422

Honolulu Mountain

GUITARS OF THE OCEAN.
LP: . . . . HYBLP 6

TEQUILA DEMENTIA.
Tracks: / Disturbocharger / I feel like Francis Bacon painting / Mule Brain / Collector of souls / Also Spracht Scott Thurston / Death bed bimbo / Menace in the front / Tequila dementia.
LP: . . . . ZINLP 4

Honor Role

RICTUS.
LP: . . . . HMS 102 1
MC: . . . . HMS 102 4

Honor Roll

HONOR ROLL (Various artists).
Tracks: / I've been working on the railroad: *Oliver, Sy* / Just before midnight: *Basie, Count* / Still water: *Ellington, Duke* / Heaven's full of joy: *Hackett, Bobby* / Y'know what I mean: *McPartland, Marian* / Snow in Lovers' Lane: *Shavers, Charlie* / Ain't gonna get fooled again: *Redman, Don* / Easy walker: *Hawkins, Coleman*/ Don't panic: *Winding, Kai* / Frou frou: *Hamilton, Chico* / Sunny nights: *Herman, Woody* / Burton up your lips: *Gibbs, Terry* / Why not?: *Carroll, Barbara* / Blue swing five: *Venuti, Joe* / Five o'clock rush: *Weed, Buddy.*
LP: . . . . JV 116

Honoris Causa Jazz

CHICAGO (see Marty Grosz).

Honsinger, Tristan

CONCERT... (see Bailey, Derek) (Honsinger, Tristan & Derek Bailey).

CONCERT EXTRACTS (Honsinger, Tristan & Derek Bailey).
LP: . . . . INCUS 20

Hood

COOLER THAN THOU.
Tracks: / It takes a thief / Criminal kiss / Tricks are for kids / Tough guys don't dance / Cooler than thou / Book is the law / What she keeps / Stand apart.
LP: . . . . TWI 753

Hoodlum Priest

HEART OF DARKNESS.
Tracks: / Introduction to the heart of darkness / Tyrell / Caucasian / Talk dirty / Rebel angel / Rock drill / C horse / Sex spirit / Deep dance.
LP: . . . . ZTT 4
MC: . . . . ZTT 4 C

Hoodoo Gurus

BLOW YOUR COOL.
Tracks: / Out that door / What's my scene / Good times / I was the one / Hell for leather / Where nowhere is / Middle of the land / Come on / My caravan / On my street / Party machine.
LP: . . . . CHR 1601
MC: . . . . ZCHR 1601

KINKY.
Tracks: / Head in the sand / Place in the sun, A / Castles in the air / Something's coming / Miss Freelove '69 / 1000 miles away / Desiree / I don't mind / Brainscan / Too much fun / Dressed in black.
LP: . . . . PL 90558
MC: . . . . PK 90588

MAGNUM CUM LOUDER.
Tracks: / Come anytime / Another world / Axe grinder / Shadow me / Glamourpuss / Hallucination / All the way / Baby can dance / I don't know anything / Where's that hit / Death in the afternoon.
MC: . . . . PK 90362
LP: . . . . PL 90362

MARS NEEDS GUITARS.
Tracks: / Bittersweet / Poison pen / In the wild / She / Death-defying / Like wow / Wipe out / Hayride to hell / Show some emotion / Other side of paradise / Mars needs guitars.
LP: . . . . CHR 1520
MC: . . . . ZCHR 1520

STONEAGE ROMEOS.
LP: . . . . FIEND 32

Hooghuys Organ

HOOGHUYS ORGAN.
Tracks: / Zaza / Zuider Zee / Marche des petits pierrots / Zand zand / Folksong medley / Murmures de la foret / Radetzky march / Sous les ponts de Paris / La tourterelle / Roses de France / Quand madelon / Schottische.
LP: . . . . JOYS 200

Hooka Hey

FURY IN THE SLAUGHTERHOUSE.
LP: 0888401
MC: 0888404

Hooked on...

HOOKED ON HITS (Various artists).
LP: . . . . NE 1374
MC: . . . . CE 2374

HOOKED ON NUMBER ONES (Various artists).
LP: . . . . ONE 1285
MC: . . . . OCE 2285

Hooker, Earl

CALLING ALL BLUES (Hooker, Earl & Magic Sam).
Tracks: / Rockin' wild / Blue guitar / Blues in D natural / Calling all blues / Swear to tell the truth / Rockin' with the kid galloping horses / Universal rock / My love is your love / Mr. Charlie / Square dance rock / Every night about this time / Blue light boogie / You don't have to work.
LP: . . . . CRB 1134

EARL HOOKER.
MC: . . . . C 206

FIRST AND LAST RECORDINGS.
LP: . . . . ARHOOLIE 1066

HOOKER N STEVE.
LP: . . . . ARHOOLIE 1051

LEADING BRAND, THE (Hooker Earl & Jodie Williams).
Tracks: / How long can this go on / Cotton pickin' blues / Bright sounds / Oh mama / Off the hook / You better be sure / Nothing but poison / This little voice / Leading brand, The / Nothing but good / Looking for my baby / Lonely without you / Moaning for molasses / Hide out / You may / Lucky Lou.
LP: . . . . RL 018

PLAY YOUR GUITAR, MR.HOOKER.
LP: . . . . BM 9006

THERE'S A FUNGUS AMUNG US.
Tracks: / Two bugs in a rug / Hold on / Off the hook / Dust my broom / Hot and heavy / Screw driver / Bertha / Foxtrot / End of the blues / Walkin' rag / Hooker special / Something you ate.
LP: . . . . RL 009

TWO BUGS AND A ROACH.
LP: . . . . ARHOOLIE 1044

Hooker, John Lee

1948-1949.
Tracks: / Morning blues / Boogie awhile / Tuesday evening / Miss Pearl boogie / Good business / Mercy blues / Poor Slim / We gonna make / Low down boogie / Cotton pickin' boogie / Must I make / Roll me baby / Down so long / Christmas time blues.
2LP: . . . . KK 200

BEST OF HOOKER 'N' HEAT, THE (Hooker 'N' Heat).
Tracks: / Send me your pillow / Feeling is gone, The / You talk too much / Bottle up and go / I got my eyes on you / Just you and me / Whisky and wimmen / Let's make it / Peavine / Boogie chillun No.2.
LP: . . . . SEE 234

BEST OF JOHN LEE HOOKER.
2LP: . . . . GNPS 2-10007
MCSET: GNP5 2-10007

BLACK RHYTHM 'N' BLUES.
Tracks: / Hey baby, you look good to me / I wanna dance all night / Mean woman / Why put me down? / My name is ringing / What the matter baby? / Baby don't you want to go? / Talk to your daughter / You move me / Things I tell you to do / I feel good / Baby baby / Daisy Mae / Stand by / Going home / Looking back over my day / Roll and tumble / Baby don't do me wrong / Come on baby.
2LP: . . . . ALB 186

BLUES BEFORE SUNRISE.
LP: . . . . CL 00231283
MC: . . . . CLMC 009231283
LP: 20052

BLUES BEFORE SUNRISE (BULLDOG).
Tracks: / Little wheel / I'm in the mood / Hobo blues / Crawling king snake / Blues before sunrise / Want ad blues / My first wife left me / Wednesday evening blues / Maudie / Time is marching.
LP: . . . . BDL 1011

BLUESWAY SESSIONS, THE.
Tracks: / Cry before I go / Boom boom / Backbiters and syndicators / Mr. Lucky / My own blues / I can't stand to leave you / Think twice before you go / I'm standing in line / Hot spring water (part 1) / Hot spring water (part 2) / Motor city is burning, The / Want ad blues / I don't wanna go to Vietnam / Mini skirts / Mean woman / I wanna boogaloo / Tantalizing with the blues / (Twist ain't nothin') but the old time shimmy / One room country shack / I'm just a drifter.
2LP: . . . . CDX 33

BOOGIE CHILLUN.
Tracks: / Dimples / Every night / Little wheel / You can lead me baby / I love you honey / Maudie / I'm in the mood / Boogie chillun / Hobo blues / Crawling king snake / Drive me away / Solid sender / No shoes / Want and blues / Will the circle be unbroken / I'm goin' upstairs / Boom boom / Bottle up and go / This is hip / Big legs, tight skirt / It serves me right to suffer / Your baby ain't sweet like mine.
LP: . . . . OFF 6029

BOOGIE MAN, THE.
Tracks: / Boom boom / Dirty groundhog / I'm goin' home / I love you honey / I'm in the mood / Crawling black spider / House rent boogie / Dimples / Mambo chillun / This is hip / I'm so excited / Hobo blues / Loudella / She shot me down.
LP: . . . . INS 5009
MC: . . . . TCINS 5009

BURNIN'.
Tracks: / Boom boom / Process / Lost a good girl / New leaf, A / Blues before sunrise / Let's make it / I got a letter this morning / Thelma / Drug store woman / Keep your hands to yourself / What do you say.
LP: . . . . TOP 176
MC: . . . . KTOP 176

CHESS MASTERS.
Tracks: / Walkin' the boogie / Love blues / Union station blues / It's my own fault / Leave my wife alone / Ramblin' by myself / Sugar mama / Down at the landing / Louise / Ground hog blues / High priced woman / Woman and money / Journey / I don;t want your money / Hey baby, you look good to me / Mad man blues / Bluebird / Worried life blues / Lonely boy boogie / Apologize / Please don't go / Dreamin' blues / Hey boogie / Just me and my telephone.
2LP: . . . . CXMD 4005

COLLECTION: JOHN LEE HOOKER (20 Blues Greats).
Tracks: / Dimples / I'm in the mood / Hobo blues / Boogie chillun / Boom boom / Blues before sunrise / Time is marching / Tupelo / Little wheel / Shake, holler and run / Want ad blues / Crawling king snake / Whisky and wimmen / Tease me baby / Wednesday evening blues / My first wife left me / Maudie / No shoes / I love you, honey / Rock house boogie.
LP: . . . . DVLP 2033
MC: . . . . DVMC 2033

CREAM, THE.
Tracks: / Hey hey / Rock steady / Tupelo / You know it ain't right / She's gone / T.B. sheets / Sugar mama / One room country shack / Drug store woman / I want you to roll me / Bar room drinking / Little girl / Louise / When my first wife left me (Available on double album only) / Boogie on (Available on double album only).
2LP: . . . . TOM 2 7009
MC: . . . . TCCDX 22
2LP: . . . . CDX 22

DETROIT BLUES 1950-1951.
Tracks: / House rent boogie / Wandering blues / Making a fool out of me / Questionnaire blues / Real gone gal / Squeeze me baby / Feed her all night / Gangsters blues / Where did you stay last night / My daddy was a jockey / Little boy blue / Hc·· long must I be your slave / Grieving blues / Ground hog blues / Mean old train / Catfish.
LP: . . . . KK 816

DETROIT LION, THE.
Tracks: / House rent boogie, The / I'm in the mood / Baby how can you do it / Let's talk it over / Yes, baby, baby, baby / I got the key / Four women in my life / Do my baby think of me / I'm gonna git me a woman / It hurts me so / Bluebird, bluebird, take a letter down South / Boogie chillun / Hello baby / This is 19 and 52, babe / Blues for Abraham Lincoln / Hey.
LP: . . . . FIEND 154

DO THE BOOGIE.
Tracks: / Stomp boogie / Black man blues / Helpless blues / Going mad blues / Morning blues / Rock and roll / No friend around / Low down midnight boogie / House rent boogie / Wandering blues / Landing blues / My baby's got something / Decoration day blues / Do the boogie.
LP: . . . . B 90165

ENDLESS BOOGIE.
Tracks: / (I got) a good 'un / Pots on, gas on high / Kick hit / I don't need no stream heat / We might as well call it through (I

didn't get married) / Sittin' in my dark room / Endless boogie parts 27 & 28.
LP: . . . . BGOLP 70
MC: . . . . BGOMC 70

EVERYBODY ROCKIN'.
Tracks: / Every night / Trouble blues / Road is so rough, The / I'm so excited / Your baby ain't sweet like mine / Unfriendly woman / I'm goin' upstairs / Everybody rockin' / I'm mad again / Hard headed woman / Crawlin' black spider / Little wheel / You've taken my woman / Maudie / I'm so worried baby / Want-ad blues.
LP: . . . . CRB 1014

FOLK BLUES OF JOHN LEE HOOKER, THE.
Tracks: / Black snake / How long blues / Wobblin' baby / She's long, she's tall, she weeps like a willow / Pea vine special / Tupelo blues / I'm prison bound / I rowed a little boat / Water boy / Church bell tone / Bundle up and go / Good morning little schoolgirl / Behind the plow.
LP: . . . . CH 282

FREE BEER AND CHICKEN.
LP: . . . . BGOLP 123

GREATEST HITS: JOHN LEE HOOKER.
LP: 2652211
MC: 2652214

HEALER, THE.
LP: . . . . ORELP 508
MC: . . . . OREC 508

HOOKER 'N' HEAT (see under Canned Heat) (Hooker, John Lee with Canned Heat).

HOOKER 'N' HEAT - LIVE (see under Canned Heat).

HOOKERED ON BLUES.
Tracks: / Go back to school / It serves me right to suffer / Roll your daddy right / Jesse James blues / I'll never get out of these blues alive / Boogie chillun / Dead wagon blues.
LP: . . . . JSP 1059
MC: . . . . JSP CC 1059

HOUSE OF THE BLUES.
Tracks: / Louise / High priced woman / Union station blues / Ground hog blues / Leave my wife alone / Ramblin' by myself / Walkin' the boogie / Sugar mama / Love blues / Down at the landing / It's my own fault / Women and money / Stella Mae / Peace loving' man / Let's go out tonight / I put my trust in you / One bourbon, one scotch, one beer / You know I know / I'll never trust your love again / In the mood.
LP: . . . . GCH 8042
MC: . . . . HSC 3221
LP: . . . . MAL 663
LP: 515025

I FEEL GOOD.
LP: . . . . JEWEL 5005

INFINITE BOOGIE (Hooker, John Lee & Canned Heat).
LP: . . . . RNDA 71105

INTRODUCING JOHN LEE HOOKER.
MC: . . . . MCAC 10364

IT SERVES YOU RIGHT.
Tracks: / Sugar mama / Decoration day / Money, that's what I want / It serves me right to suffer / Shake it baby / Country boy / Bottle up and go / You're wrong.
LP: . . . . JAS 74

JOHN LEE HOOKER BOX SET.
LPS: . . . . BOX 260
MCSET: . . . . TCBOX 260

JOHN LEE HOOKER LIVE.
LP: 269 602 1
MC: 269 602 4

JOHN LEE HOOKER STORY, THE.
Tracks: / Maudie / Shake, holler and run / Hobo blues / Crawling king snake / Blues before sunrise / Dimples / Want ad blues / Jesse James blues / I'm in the mood / Boom boom / Time is marching / Whisky and wimmen / Tease me baby / Boogie chillun / Cool little car / Gonna boogie / Hug and squeeze you / Ride till I die / Wednesday evening blues / Rock house boogie / No shoes / Roll your daddy right / Half a stranger / My first wife left me / I love you honey.
MCSET: . . . . DVREMC 19

JOHN LEE HOOKER VOL 1.
Tracks: / Shake, holler and run / Gonna boogie / Ride 'till I die / Hobo blues / Half a stranger / Boogie chillun / Rock house boogie / Playin' the races / Cool little car / Hug and squeeze you / Tease me baby / I'm in the mood.
LP: . . . . CH 37

LIVE AT CAFE AU GO GO.
Tracks: / I'm bad like Jesse James / She's long, she's tall / When my first wife left me / Heartaches and misery / One bourbon, one scotch and one beer / I don't want no trouble / I'll never get out of these blues alive / Seven days.
LP: . . . . BGOLP 39
MC: . . . . BGOMC 39

LIVE AT SUGARHILL VOL. 1.
Tracks: / I just can't hold on much longer / I was standing by the wayside / Run on / I like to see you walk / Driftin' and driftin' / I'm gonna keep on walking / TB is killing me / This world / It's you I love baby / You gonna miss me.
LP: . . . . CH 287

LIVE AT SUGARHILL VOL 2.
Tracks: / You're nice and kind to me Lou Della / I want to get married / Night time is the right time / You been dealin' with the devil.
LP: . . . . CH 298

MOANIN' AND STOMPIN' BLUES.
LP: . . . . BID 8021

MOANIN' & STOMPIN' THE BLUES (Hooker, John Lee/ Paul Harold/ Ralph Wills).
MCSET: . . . . GD 5032

MOANIN THE BLUES.
Tracks: / Drive me away / Wrong doin' woman / She left me one Wednesday / Nightmare / Sally Mae / Love me all the time / Moanin' blues / You're gonna miss me when I'm gone / Mama you've got a daughter / Wheel and deal / Tennessee blues / Baby Lee / Stop talking / I see you when you're weak / Little fine woman / Mambo chillun.
LP: . . . . CRB 1029

MR. LUCKY.
LP: . . . . ORELP 519
MC: . . . . OREC 519

NEVER GET OUT OF THESE BLUES ALIVE.
Tracks: / Bumble bee / Hit the road / Country boy / Booggee with the hook / If you take care of me I'll take care of you / T.B. sheets / Letter to my baby / Never get out of these blues alive / Baby I love you / Lonesome mood.
LP: . . . . SEE 89

NO FRIEND AROUND.
Tracks: / Stomp boogie / Black man blues / Helpless blues / Going mad blues / Morning blues / Rock and roll / No friend around / Low down midnight boogie / House rent boogie / Wandering blues / Landing blues / My baby's got something / Decoration day blues / Do the boogie.
LP: . . . . RL 003
LP: . . . . CR 30170

NOTHING BUT THE BLUES.
MC: . . . . BMC 070

PLAYS AND SINGS THE BLUES.
Tracks: / Journey, The / I don't want your money / Hey baby, you look good to me / Mad man blues / Bluebird / Worried life blues / Apologize / Lonely boy boogie / Please don't go / Dreamin' blues / Hey boogie / Just me and my telephone.
LP: . . . . GCH 8019
MC: . . . . GCHK 78019
LP: . . . . CH 9199

REAL FOLK BLUES.
Tracks: / Let's go out tonight / Peace lovin' man / Stella Mae / I put my trust in you / I'm in the mood / You know, I know / I'll never trust your love again / One bourbon, one scotch, one beer / Waterfront, The.
LP: 515009
LP: . . . . CH 9271

SIMPLY THE TRUTH.
Tracks: / I don't wanna go to Vietnam / I wanna boogaloo / Tantalizing with the blues / I'm just a drifter / Mini skirts / Mean mean woman / One room country shack.
LP: . . . . BGOLP 40

SITTIN' HERE THINKIN'.
Tracks: / I bought you a brand new home / I believe I'll lose my mind / Teasin' me / My cryin' days are over / Mean mistreatin' / How long? / How many more years? / C.C. rider / Sad and lonesome / Can't you see what you're doing to me?.
LP: . . . . MR 5205
LP: . . . . B 90086

SOLID SENDER.
Tracks: / You can lead me, baby / Hobo blues / No shoes / I wanna walk / Canal Street blues / Run on / I'm a stranger / Whisky and wimmen / Solid sender / Sunny land / Going to California / I can't believe / I'll know tonight / Dusty road / I left my baby / Sadie Mae.
LP: . . . . CRB 1081

TANTALIZING WITH THE BLUES.
Tracks: / It serves me right to suffer / Shake it up baby / Bottle up and go / Cry before I go / Backbiters and syndicators / Think twice before you go / I don't wanna go to Vietnam / Mini skirts / Mean, mean woman / Tantalizing with the blues / I'm just a drifter / Kick hit / I'll never get out of these blues alive.
LP: . . . . MCL 1686
MC: . . . . MCLC 1686

THAT'S MY STORY.
Tracks: / I need some money / I'm wanderin' / Democrat man / I want to talk about you / Gonna use my rod / Wednesday evenin' blues / No more doggin' / One of these days / I believe I'll go back home / You're leavin' me, baby / That's my story / Black snake / How long blues / Wobblin' baby / She's long, she's tall, she weeps like... / Pea vine special / Tupelo blues / I rowed a little boat / Water boy / Church bell tone / Bundle up and go.
LP: . . . . CH 259

THIS IS HIP.
Tracks: / Dimples / I love you, honey / I'm in the mood / Time is marching / Big legs, tight skirt / Onions / Take me as I am / Boom boom / This is hip / Boogie chillun / Crawling king snake / Blues before sunrise / Will the circle be unbroken? / House rent boogie / It serves me right to suffer / Bottle up and go.
LP: . . . . CRB 1004
MC: . . . . TCCRB 1004

URBAN BLUES.
LP: . . . . BGOLP 122

WANT-AD BLUES Vol. 3.
LP: . . . . SM 3963

Hooker, Steve

REELY GONE.
LP: . . . . LOLITA 5015

Hookfoot

COMMUNICATION.
LP: . . . . DJLPS 428

GOOD TIMES A COMIN'.
LP: . . . . DJLPS 422

HEADLINES.
Tracks: / Don't let it bring you down / Movies / SBW / Shoeshine boy / Nature changes / Bluebird (revisited) / Coombe gallows / Gimme shelter / Fire and rain / Sweet sweet funky music / Livin' in the city / If I had the words / Good times a coming / Cruisin' / Just a little communication / Nothin' changes / Tradin' riffs / Rockin' on the good / So you want to be a rock'n'roll star.
2LP: . . . . DJMD 8013

HOOKFOOT.
LP: . . . . DJLPS 413

ROARING.
LP: . . . . DJLPS 435

Hooper, Les

LOOK WHAT THEY'VE DONE (Hooper, Les Big Band).
LP: . . . . ST 3002

Hooper, Nick

PORTRAIT OF A CONCERTINA (see under Townsend, Dave) (Hooper, Nick/ Dave Townsend).

Hooper, 'Stix'

WORLD WITHIN'.
Tracks: / Brazos river breakdown / African spirit / Rum or Tequila / Passion / Cordon bleu / Jasmine breeze / Little drummer boy.
LP: . . . . MCL 1766

Hoopes, Ronnie

RESPECT FOR A GREAT TRADITION.
LP: . . . . REV 21

Hoopii, Sol

MASTER OF HAWAIIAN GUITAR, VOL 2.
LP: . . . . ROUNDER 1025
MC: . . . . ROUNDER 1025C

MASTER OF THE HAWAIIAN STEEL GUITAR.
LP: . . . . ROUNDER 1024

Hoorah For Daisy

HOORAH FOR DAISY Original London cast (Various artists).
LP: . . . . AEI 118

Hooray For Hollywood

HOORAY FOR HOLLYWOOD (Original soundtrack) (Various artists).
Tracks: / I used to be colour-blind: *Various artists* / Ich bin die fesche Lola: *Various artists* / Alone: *Various* artists / I never knew heaven could speak: *Various artists* / Got a bran' new suit: *Various artists* / All I want is just one girl: *Various artists* / Paradise: *Various artists* / When April sings: *Various artists*/ Something's gotta give: *Various artists* / I'm gonna file my claim: *Various artists* / Mary's a grand old name: *Various artists* / It's oh, so quiet: *Various artists* / That certain feeling: *Various artists* / Saga of Jenny: *Various artists* / Stardust: *Various artists* / I couldn't be more in love: *Various artists*.
MC: . . . . INTK 5045

HOORAY FOR HOLLYWOOD (See Also Under Hollywood ...) (Various artists).

Hoosier Hot Shots

ARE YOU READY, HEZZIE? 1930's NBC Radio.
LP: . . . . SH 2086

Hooters

NERVOUS NIGHTS.
Tracks: / And we danced / Day by day / All you zombies / Don't take my car out tonight / Hanging on a heartbeat / Where do the children go / South ferry road / She comes in colours / Blood from a stone.
LP: . . . . CBS 26422
MC: 40 26422

ONE WAY HOME.
Tracks: / Satellite / Karla with A K / Graveyard waltz / Fighting on the same side / One way home / Washington's day / Hard rockin' summer / Ending 999.
LP: 4508511
MC: 4508514

ZIG ZAG.
Tracks: / Brother, don't you walk away / Deliver me / 500 miles / You never know who your friends are / Heaven laughs / Don't knock it 'til you try it / Give the music back / Always a place / Mr. Big Baboon / Beat up guitar.
LP: 4650841
MC: 4650844

Hoover, Reverend

MUSIC OF REV BAYBIE HOOVER AND VIRGINIA BROWN.
LP: . . . . PH 1019

Hop Flop And Fly

HOP FLOP AND FLY (Various artists).
Tracks: / Go ahead baby: *Various artists* / Uh babe: *Various artists* / High high high: *Various artists*/ Treat me right: *Various artists* / Love crazy: *Various artists* / My baby don't rock: *Various artists*/ Greenback dollar: *Various artists* / You call everybody darlin': *Various artists* / Look at that moon: *Various* artists / Get it off your mind: *Various artists* / Stop the world, I'll jump off: *Various artists* / Juicy fruit: *Various artists* / Money money money: *Various artists* / All night rock: *Various artists*.
LP: . . . . SUN 1025

Hop Skip & Jump

HOP SKIP AND JUMP (Various artists).
Tracks: / Hop skip and jump: *Roberts, Bobby* / R'n'roll Santa: *Farr, L. Joe* / Fifty megatons: *Russell, Sonny*/ Nicotine: *Chaplain, Paul* / Shortnin' bread: *Chaplain, Paul* / I don't need no more: *Various artists*/ Pretty baby rock: *Myers, J & T. Regan* / I ain't gonna be around: *Therien, Joe Jnr.* / Rock'n chair rock: *Cavalier*, Johnny / Knock off the rock: *Cavalier, Johnny* / Motorcycle Mike: *Day, Davey* / Run here honey: *Johnson, Glenn* / Rockin little mama: *Pasett, Tony* / Roll over Beethoven: *Paige, Joey*.
LP: . . . . RR 2007

Hope, Anthony

PRISONER OF ZENDA, THE (Jacobi, Derek (nar)).
MCSET: 414 763-4
MCSET: . . . . ARGO 1214

Hope, Bob

BING, BOB AND JUDY (See under Crosby, Bing) (Hope, Bob/Bing Crosby/ Judy Garland).

BOB HOPE COLLECTION (His Golden Greats).
Tracks: / Penthouse serenade / Thanks for the memory / Two sleepy people / Lady's in love with you, The / Road to Bali / Merry go round / Hoots mon / Chicago style / Wing ding tonight / Buttons and bows / You're the top.
LP: . . . . DVLP 2124
MC: . . . . DVMC 2124

RADIO SHOWS.
LP: . . . . MR 1153

TWO COMPLETE PROGRAMS (See under Crosby, Bing) (Hope, Bob/Bing Crosby/Judy Garland).

Hope, Elmo

ELMO HOPE TRIO With Jimmy Bond & Frank Butler (Hope, Elmo Trio).
LP: . . . . FS 145

Hope & Glory

HOPE & GLORY (Original Soundtrack) (Various artists).
MC: . . . . ZCTER 1147
LP: . . . . TER 1147

Hope, Lynn

AND HIS TENOR SAX.
LP: . . . . PM 1546661

MOROCCO 1950-1955.
Tracks: / Song of the wanderer / Tenderly / She's funny that way / More bounce to the ounce / Star dust / Free and easy / Sentimental journey / Cherry.
LP: . . . . BP 508

Hope Of Glory

HOPE OF GLORY.
LP: . . . . PC 120

Hope, Peter

DRY HIP ROTATION (Hope, Peter & Jonathan S.Podmore).
Tracks: / Kitchenette / Canal / 217 / Dry bone / Haulage / Dog eared pictures / Needleheat / Hypnosis / Knife / Scurry bug / Unknown industrial fatality, The.
LP: . . . . NTVLP 14

HOODOO TALK (See Under Kirk, Richard H) (Kirk, Richard H & Peter Hope).

Hope & The Anchor

HOPE AND THE ANCHOR, THE Festival (Various artists).
Tracks: / Doctor Feelgood: *Johnson, Wilko* / Straighten house: *Stranglers* / Styrofoam: *Tyla Gang* / Don't munchen it: *Pirates* / Speed kills: *Gibbons, Steve Band* / I'm bugged: *XTC* / I hate school: *Suburban Studs* / Bill: *Pleasers* / Science friction: *XTC* / Eastbound train: *Dire Straits* / Bizz fizz: *Burlesque*/ Let's submerge: *X-Ray Spex* / Crazy: *999* / Demolition girl: *Saints* / Quite disappointing: *999*/ Creatures of doom: *Only Ones* / Gibson Martin fender: *Pirates* / Sound check: *Steel Pulse* / Zero hero: *Roogalator* / Underground romance: *Rambow, Philip* / Rock and roll radio: *Pleasers* / On the street: *Tyla Gang* / Johnny cool: *Gibbons, Steve Band* / Twenty years behind: *Johnson, Wilko* / Hanging around: *Stranglers*.
2LP: . . . . K 66077

Hopkin, Mary

POSTCARD.
Tracks: / Those were the days / Lord of the reedy river / Happiness runs (pebble and the man) / Love is the sweetest thing / Y blodyn gwyn / Honeymoon song, The / Puppy song, The / Inchworm / Voyage of the moon / Lullaby of the leaves / Young love / Someone to watch over me / Prince en avignon / Game, The / There's no business like show business / Turn turn turn (to everything there is a) / Those were the days (quelli erano giorni) / Those were the days (en aquellos dias).
LP: . . . . SAPCOR 5
MC: . . . . TCSAPCOR 5

SPIRIT.
LP: . . . . MODEM 1045
MC: . . . . MODEMC 1045

TOO MUCH MAGIC (See under Elfland Ensemble) (Hopkin, Mary/Elfland Ensemble).

WELSH WORLD OF MARY HOPKIN.
Tracks: / Pleserau serch / Blodyn Gwyn / Aderyn llwyd / Tyrd yn ol / Tamy / Drw dros y moroedd / Yfori / Gwrandewch ar y moroedd / Tro tro tro / Yn y bore.
LP: . . . . SPA 546

Hopkins, Anthony

JOHN & THE MAGIC MUSIC MAN.
LP: . . . . RHS 360

Hopkins, Claude

CLAUDE HOPKINS.
LP: . . . . JA 27

HARLEM 1934 (Hopkins, Claude & His Orchestra).
LP: . . . . ET 2

SOLILOQUY.
LP: 3004

Hopkins, Gerald

POETRY OF GERALD MANLEY HOPKINS (Cusack, Cyril (nar)).
MC: 1111

Hopkins, Lightnin'

AT HIS NATURAL BEST.
Tracks: / I don't need you woman / I wish I was a baby / Little boy blue / Crazy song / Lightnin's love / That man from New York City / Take it if you want it.
LP: . . . . RHAP 8

BAD BOOGIE.
LP: . . . . DD 4308

BALL AND CHAIN (See Thornton, Big Mama) (Hopkins, Lightnin'/Willie Mae Thornton).

BIG BOY CRUDUP AND LIGHTNIN' HOPKINS (See under Crudup, Arthur).
LP: . . . . JEWEL 5000

BLUES IN MY BOTTLE.
Tracks: / Buddy Brown's blues / Wine spodee-o-dee / Sail on little girl, sail on / DC-7 / Death bells / Goin' to Dallas to see my pony run / Jailhouse blues / Blues in the bottle / Beans beans beans / Catfish blues / My grandpa is old too.
LP: . . . . OBC 506
LP: 512504
LP: . . . . CH 290

BLUES, THE.
Tracks: / Mojo hand / Little wail / Cotton / Take me back, baby / Really nothin' but the blues / Hurricane Betsy / Guitar lightnin' / Woke up this morning / Shake yourself.
MC: . . . . MC 3071
LP: . . . . SM 3071

BLUES UNDERGROUND.
LP: . . . . D 8000

COLLECTION: LIGHTNIN' HOPKINS (20 blues greats).
Tracks: / Change your ways / Feel so bad / War news blues / House upon the hill / Honey babe / Let me play with your poodle / Black cat / Needed time / Ticket agent / Morning blues / Sis boogie / Everyday I have the blues / Bad luck and trouble / I can't stay here in your town / Appetite blues / Short-haired woman / My California / Some day baby / Mistreated blues / I just don't care.
LP: . . . . DVLP 2115
MC: . . . . DVMC 2115

DIRTY BLUES.
LP: . . . . MSL 1001

EARLY RECORDINGS.
LP: . . . . ARHOOLIE 2007

EARLY RECORDINGS VOL 2 From Gold Star label, late 1940's. (Hopkins, Lightnin' & Big Boy Crudup).
LP: . . . . ARHOOLIE 2010

ELECTRIC LIGHTNIN'.
Tracks: / In my mother's arms / It's mighty crazy / How have you been / I don't need you woman / Fore day creep / You're gonna miss me / This time we're gonna try / Christmas time blues / Aeroplane blues.
LP: . . . . JSP 1067
MC: . . . . JSP CC 1067

FLASH LIGHTNIN'.
LP: . . . . DD 4307

FREE FORM PATTERNS.
Tracks: / Mr. Charlie / Give me time to think / Fox chase, The / Mr. Ditta's grocery store / Open up your door / Baby child / Cooking done / Got her letter this morning / Rain falling / Mini skirt.
LP: . . . . CRB 1190
MC: . . . . TCCRB 1190

GOIN' AWAY.
LP: . . . . OBC 522

GREAT ELECTRIC SHOW AND DANCE, THE.
LP: . . . . JEWEL 5002

GREAT SONGS OF.
LP: 20087

HERALD MATERIAL, 1954.
LP: . . . . COL 5121

HOUSTON'S KING OF BLUES Historic recordings 1952/53.
LP: . . . . BC 30

IN BERKELEY.
LP: . . . . ARHOOLIE 1063

JOEL AND LIGHTNIN' HOPKINS 1959 (Hopkins, Lightnin' & Joel).
LP: . . . . C 5530

KING OF DOWLING STREET.
LP: . . . . BGOLP 103

LEGACY OF THE BLUES VOL. 12 (See under Legacy of the Blues).

LIGHTNIN.
LP: . . . . TOM 2 7004

LIGHTNIN' HOPKINS.
MC: . . . . C 201

LIGHTNIN' HOPKINS 1949-61.
LP: . . . . DLP 577

LIGHTNIN HOPKINS AND HIS GUITAR.
LP: . . . . ARHOOLIE 1011

LIGHTNIN HOPKINS WITH HIS BROTHERS AND BARBARA D.
LP: . . . . ARHOOLIE 1022

LIGHTNIN' IN NEW YORK.
Tracks: / Take it easy / Mighty crazy / Your own fault, baby, to treat me the way you do / I've had my fun if I don't get well no more / Trouble blues / Lightnin's piano boogie / Wonder why / Mister Charlie.
LP: . . . . CS 9010

LIGHTNIN STRIKES BACK.
Tracks: / Introduction / Big car blues / Coffee house blues / Stool pigeon blues / Ball of twine / Mary Lou / Want to come home / Rolling and rolling / Devil is watching you / Please don't quit me / Coon is hard to catch / Heavy snow / Walking round in circles / War is starting again / Got me a Louisiana woman.
LP: . . . . CRB 1031

LIGHTNING HOPKINS 1946-60.
LP: . . . . BD 2066

LIVE AT THE BIRD LOUNGE (BULLDOG).
Tracks: / I heard my children crying / Leave Jike Mary alone / You treat po' Lightnin' wrong / I'm gonna meet my baby somewhere / Don't treat that man the way you treat me / There's good rockin' tonight.
LP: . . . . BDL 1010

LIVE AT THE BIRD LOUNGE, HOUSTON (ASTAN).
LP: 20053
MC: 40053

MAD BLUES.
Tracks: / Moonrise blues / Have to let you go / Shining moon / Mercy / Lightnin' blues / No mail blues / Baby please don't go / Another fool in town / Bold-headed blues / Mad blues / Crazy 'bout my baby / Long way from Texas / Whiskey, whiskey / Getting out of the bushes tap dance / Suicide blues / Look out / Seffegast / Here me and my partner come.
LP: . . . . OFF 6054

MOVE ON OUT.
Tracks: / Fishing clothes / Wig wearing woman / Vietnam blues - parts 1 & 2 / Play with your poodle / Back door friend / Gamblers blues / Move on out - part 1 / Breakfast time / Mr. Charlie - parts 1 & 2 / Long way from home / Move on out - part 2 / Moaning blues / Found my baby crying / Ride in your automobile.
LP: . . . . CRB 1147

PO' LIGHTNIN'.
LP: . . . . ARHOOLIE 1087

SHAKE IT BABY.
LP: 500 891

SINGS THE BLUES.
LP: 2C 068 83075

STRUMS THE BLUES.
LP: 2C 068 83076

TALKING SOME SENSE.
LP: . . . . JEWEL 5001

TEXAS BLUES MAN.
LP: . . . . ARHOOLIE 1034

WALKIN' THIS ROAD BY MYSELF.
Tracks: / Walkin' this road by myself / Black gal / How many more years I got to let... / Baby don't you tear my clothes / Worried life blues / Happy blues for John Glenn / Good morning little schoolgirl / Devil jumped the black man, The / Coffee blues / Black Cadillac.
LP: . . . . CH 256

Hopkins, Linda

HOW BLUE CAN YOU GET.
MC: . . . . PAC 8034
LP: . . . . PA 8034

SHIVER AND SHAKE.
Tracks: / Shiver and shake / Rock and roll blues / My loving baby / I can't / It took a long long time baby / Empty bed blues / Trouble in mind / Willow weep for me / Come back baby / Mama needs your loving baby / I'm going to cry right out of my mind / Danny boy / Is this goodbye? / Get off my wagon / Three time loser / Tears of joy.
LP: . . . . OFF 6032

Hopper & Dean

ROGUE ELEMENT.
LP: . . . . OG 527

Hopper, Hugh

1984.
LP: . . . . IRI 5010

MONSTER BAND.
Tracks: / Golden section / Sliding dogs / Churchy Lily Kong / 12-8 theme / Lily Kong / Nozzles / Tecalemit / Get together.
LP: . . . . IRI 5003

Hopper, Kev

STOLEN JEWELS.
LP: . . . . GHETT 4
MC: . . . . GHETTC 4

Horan, Eddie

LOVE THE WAY YOU LOVE ME.
Tracks: / Love the way you love me / When I fly with you / Concert by the sea / Man without his woman / Love so easy / Turn my world back around / Can't do without you / Dancer.
LP: . . . . SHU 8533

Horde Of Torment

PRODUCT OF A SICK MIND.
Tracks: / Product of a sick mind.
LP: . . . . CCG 005

Horden, Sir Michael

MANY PADDINGTON RECORDINGS (See under Paddington Bear).

Horea, Crishan

MAGIC OF THE PAN PIPES, THE.
Tracks: / Le magique / Bird of passage / Nights on elba / Spring, The / Sunset / Panolito / Skyglider / Visions / Chariots of fire / Mirage / La rosa / Whiter shade of pale, A.
LP: 2372 161
MC: 3151 161

Horizon

NEG MAWON.
LP: . . . . HDD 2479

Horizon Quintet

GUMBO.
LP: . . . . AMLP 851

Horizons

HORIZONS (16 innovative instrumentals) (Various artists).
Tracks: / Crockett's theme: *Hammer, Jan* / Equinoxe part 5: *Jarre, Jean Michel* / Don't give up: *Shadows*/ Going home: *Butler, Jonathan* / Shepherd's song: *James, Bob* / Harry's game, Theme from: *Clannad* / When the war cry comes: *Lost Belongings* / Josie's tune: *Rea, Chris* / Songbird: *Kenny G (See Under G, Kenny)*/ As on earth as it is.....: *Mission* / Mammagamma: *Parsons, Alan* / Spring high: *Lewis, Ramsey* / Morning dance: *Spyro Gyra*.
LP: . . . . NE 1360
MC: . . . . CE 2360

Horizontal Rock Stars

QUESTION MARK.
Tracks: / Sleet mother / Missing you / Question mark / Sometimes / Late at night / Ticket to right / I had a dream / New direction / Without love / Alabama / Late in the morning / Give us a break.
LP: . . . . RACU 1

Horn

HORN, THE (The Tenor Sax in Jazz) (Various artists).
Tracks: / Bird of Prey blues: *Hawkins, Coleman* / Newport news: *Freeman, Bud* (Not on CD.) / Prelude to a kiss: *Webster, Ben* / Neenah (Not on CD.) / No dues: *Cobb, Arnett* / You are too beautiful: *Davis, Eddie Lockjaw*/ Hey there: *Gray, Wardell* / Darn that dream: *Gordon, Dexter* / Going South: *Ammons, Gene* (Not on CD.) / Jive at five: *Various artists* / Chase is on, The: *Rouse/Quinchette* / Way you look tonight, The: *Stitt/ Holloway*/ A la carte: *Various artists* / I didn't know what time it was: *Shorter, Wayne* / I want to talk about you: *Coltrane, John* / Big George: *Coleman, George* (Not on CD.).
2LP: . . . . ATSD 14
MCSET: . . . . TCATSD 14

Horn, Jim

NEON NIGHTS.
LP: 925728 1
MC: 925728 4

Horn, Paul

CHINA.
LP: . . . . LPKUCK 080
MC: . . . . MCKUCK 080

INSIDE THE CATHEDRAL.
Tracks: / Song for friendship / Song for peace / Moscow blues / Song for love / Syrinx / Song for understanding / Song for Eugene / Song for Edward / Song for Marina / Song for Riya / Oche cherrnouiye / Song for Rimsky / Song for Trane.
LP: . . . . LPKUCK 075
MC: . . . . MCKUCK 075

INSIDE THE GREAT PYRAMID.
Tracks: / Prologue / Inside / Mantra I / Meditation / Mutaz Mahal / Unity / Agra vibrations / Akasha / Jumma / Shah Jahan / Mantra II / Duality / Ustad Isa / Mantra III.
2LP: . . . . LPKUCK 060/061
MCSET: . . . . MCKUCK 060/061

INSIDE THE TAJ MAHAL.
LP: . . . . LPKUCK 062
MC: . . . . MCKUCK 062
LP: . . . . LPKUCK 11062
MC: . . . . MCKUCK 11062

MIDEM - LIVE,'80 (see Getz, Stan) (Horn, Paul/Mike Carson/Stan Getz).

PEACE ALBUM.
LP: . . . . LPKUCK 11083-1
MC: . . . . MCKUCK 11083-4

SOMETHING BLUE.
LP: . . . . FS 144

Horn, Shirley

CLOSE ENOUGH FOR LOVE.
Tracks: / This can't be love / I got lost in his arms.
LP: 837 933 1

MC: 837 933 4

YOU WON'T FORGET ME.
MC: 8474824

Horne, David (nar)

APACHE MOON (See under Apache Moon).

Horne, Jimmy 'Bo'

BEST OF JIMMY BO HORNE.
Tracks: / Dance across the floor / You get me hot / Gimme some / Going home for love / Let me / Spank / Get happy / I get lifted / Without you / Is it in.
LP: . . . . TKR 83391

Horne, Lena

20 GOLDEN MEMORIES.
LP: 2536012
MC: 2636014

20 GOLDEN PIECES: LENA HORNE.
Tracks: / Love / I wish I was back in my baby's arms / Why was I born? / Good for nothin' Joe / Love me or leave me / I got it bad and that ain't good / Stormy weather / Poppa don't preach to me / Honeysuckle Rose / Lady is a tramp, The / Lover man / Can't help lovin' dat man / From this moment on / Take me / Night and day / Old devil moon / More / My blue Heaven / Cuckoo in the clock / Meditation.
LP: . . . . BDL 2000
MC: . . . . BDC 2000

...AT THE WALDORF ASTORIA.
Tracks: / Today I love everybody / Let me love you / Come running / How's your romance / After you / Love of my life / It's alright with me / Mood indigo / I'm beginning to see the light / How d'you say it / Honeysuckle rose / Day in, day out / New fangled tango / I love to love / From this moment on.
LP: . . . . INTS 5053
MC: . . . . INTK 5053

FABULOUS...., THE.
Tracks: / Stormy weather / I'm through with love / From this moment on / One for my baby / Love me or leave me / Man I love, The / I've found a new baby / What is this thing called love / I got rhythm / I gotta right to sing the blues / I wanna be loved / Day in, day out / It might as well be spring / Love / Bewitched / I'll be around / Honey in the honeycombe / Summer time / I'm confessin' / Like someone in love.
2LP: . . . . CR 047
MCSET: . . . . CRT 047

GIVE THE LADY WHAT SHE WANTS.
Tracks: / Diamonds are a girl's best friend / People will say we're in love / Just in time / Honey in the honeycombe / You better know it / Get out of town / Baubles, bangles and beads / Bewitched / At long last love / Speak low / Love / Let's put out the lights.
LP: . . . . NL 89459
MC: . . . . NK 89459

JAZZ MASTERS.
Tracks: / Stormy weather / Can't help lovin' dat man / Lady is a tramp, The.
LP: . . . . MRS 501
MC: . . . . MRSC 501

LADY AND HER MUSIC.
Tracks: / From this moment on / I got a name / I'm glad there is you / I want to be happy / Cotton Club revue / Where or when / Can't help lovin' dat man / Just one of those things / Stormy weather / Love / Push de button / Lady is a tramp, The / Yesterday, when I was young / Deed I do / Life goes on / Watch what happens / Surrey with the fringe on top / Fly / Bewitched / Lady must live, A / That's what miracles are all about / I'm gonna sit right down and write myself a letter / If you believe.
2LP: . . . . K 66108

LENA.
MC: . . . . ZPREC 790

LENA, A NEW ALBUM.
Tracks: / I've grown accustomed to his face / Someone to watch over me / My funny Valentine / Some day my prince will come / I've got the world on a string / Softly as I leave you / I have dreamed / Flower is a lovesome thing, A / I've got to have you / My ship.
LP: . . . . RS 1089

LENA & GABOR (With Gabor Szabo).
Tracks: / Watch what happens / Something / Everybody's talkin' / Fool on the hill, The / Yesterday when I was young / Rocky raccoon / My mood is you / Message to Michael, A / Nightwind / In my life.
LP: . . . . RHAP 1

LENA GOES LATIN.
Tracks: / From this moment on / Old devil moon / Falling in love with love.
LP: . . . . MRS 510
MC: . . . . MRSC 510

LENA HORNE (Great Performers Series).
LP: . . . . GP 704
MC: . . . . ZCGAS 739

LENA HORNE & FRANK SINATRA (See under Sinatra, Frank) (Horne, Lena & Frank Sinatra).

LENA HORNE & PEARL BAILEY.
LP: . . . . GP 706

LENA.... LIVE AND LOVELY.
Tracks: / I concentrate on you / I get the blues when it rains / I've grown accustomed to his face / I got rhythm / I'm confessin' / I want to be happy / I surrender dear / I've found a new baby / I understand / I let a song go out of my heart / I ain't got nobody / I only have eyes for you.
LP: . . . . NL 90038
MC: . . . . NK 90038

PORTRAIT OF A SONG STYLIST.
MC: . . . . HARMC 111

STORMY WEATHER.
Tracks: / You're my thrill / Good for nothin' Joe / Love me a little little / Don't take your love from me / Stormy weather / What is this thing called love? / Ill wind / Man I love, The / Where or when / I gotta right to sing the blues / Moanin' low / I didn't know about you / One for my baby (and one more for the road) / As long as I live / I ain't got nothin' but the blues / How long has this been goin' on / It's love / Let me love you / It's alright with me / People will say we're in love / Just in time / Get out of town.
LP: . . . . NL 90441
MC: . . . . NK 90441

Horne, Marilyn

BEAUTIFUL DREAMER.
Tracks: / Jeanie with the light brown hair / Beautiful dreamer / If you've only got a moustache / Camptown races / Sometimes I feel like a motherless child / I've just come from the mountain / Lord's prayer, The / Shenandoah / Billy boy / Go way from my window / Simple gifts / Ching-a-ring-chaw / Long time ago, A / I bought me a cat / At the river / You're a grand old flag / When Johnny comes marching home / God bless America / I didn't raise my boy to be a soldier / Battle hymn of the republic.
LP: 4172421

Horner, Yvette

CLASSICS OF MUSETTE VOL.7.
LP: . . . . CBS 25896
MC: 40 25896

GRANDS SUCCES MUSETTE,VOL.8.
Tracks: / La petite valse Francaise / Mi jaca / Adios pampa mia / Joli peroquet / Canari samba / Bluesette / Carrelita / Beer barrel polka / Esmerelda / Les oiseaux de Prague / Brasil / Reve de ballerine.
LP: 4504091
MC: 4504094

LES PLUS GRANDES VALSES MUSETTES.
Tracks: / Reine de musette / En glissant / Gigolette / Tonnerre de musette / Geraldine / Les halles / La valse de as / Folie musette / Joli peroquet / Tristan des fauvourgs / Ronce des nieges / Ballade sur les touches.
LP: 1A 022 158375 1
MC: 1A 222 15 8375 4

TANGOS.
LP: 2M 046 12371
MC: . . . . PM 1123714

Hornsby, Bruce

NIGHT ON THE TOWN, A (Hornsby, Bruce & The Range).
Tracks: / Night on the town, A / Fire on the cross / Across the river / Stander on the mountain / Another day / These arms of mine / Carry the water / Barren ground / Stranded on Easy Street / Lost soul / Special night.
MC: . . . . PK 82041
LP: . . . . PL 82041

SCENES FROM THE SOUTH SIDE (Hornsby, Bruce & The Range).
Tracks: / Look out any window / Valley Road / I will walk with you / Road not taken, The / Show goes on, The / Old playground, The / Defenders of the flag / Jacob's ladder / Till the dreaming's done.
LP: . . . . PL 86686
MC: . . . . PK 86686
LP: . . . . NL 90492
MC: . . . . NK 90492

WAY IT IS, THE (Hornsby, Bruce & The Range).
Tracks: / On the Western skyline / Every little kiss / Mandolin rain / Long race, The / Way it is, The / Down the road tonight / Wild frontier / River runs low, The / Red plains, The.
LP: . . . . PL 89901
MC: . . . . PK 89901

Hornung, E.W.

RAFFLES - BLACK MASK VOL 1 (Elder, Michael).
MCSET: . . . . COL 2025

RAFFLES - BLACK MASK VOL 2 (Elder, Michael).
MCSET: . . . . COL 2026

RAFFLES VOL.1 (Elder, Michael).
MCSET: . . . . COL 2002

RAFFLES VOL.2 (Elder, Michael).
MCSET: . . . . COL 2012

Hornweb Sax Quartet

KINESIS.
LP: . . . . SGC 1014

Horny Genius

BURN YOUR SISTER.
Tracks: / Cha cha with Hal / Needlethreading / Trilobite / Going down to Mexico / Montanar stomp / Faults / Case of 3, A / Mother Horta / Hairball / Cancel my order / Long way to rewind, A / Slap the wall / Crossed wires.
LP: . . . . COMM 39021

Horovitz (composer)

ALICE IN WONDERLAND.
LP: . . . . MSCE 1

Horovitz, Wayne

DINNER AT EIGHT.
LP: . . . . ST 7514

PRESIDENT, THE.
Tracks: / Goes round and round / Please take that train from my door / From town to town / One bright day / Cadillac ranch / Gravity fails / Bean, The / Donna song, The / Short of breath / Early risers.
LP: . . . . ST 7528

THIS NEW GENERATION.
Tracks: / Dinner at eight / This new generation / 3 questions / Extra extra / Conjunction for C.B. / Please take that train from my door / In fields they lay / Second line / These hard times / Danced all night / Reprise for C.B. / Gravity fails.
LP: . . . . K 9607591
MC: . . . . K 9607594

Horowitz, Vladimir

VLADIMIR HOROWITZ PLAYS SCHUMANN.
LP: . . . . GD 86680
MC: . . . . GK 86680

VLADIMIR HOROWITZ PLAYS SCRIABIN.
MC: . . . . GK 86215

Horrorcomic

I'M ALL HUNG UP ON PIERREPOINT.
LP: . . . . BCS 7

Horse

SAME SKY, THE.
Tracks: / And she smiled / Speed of the beat of my heart / Never not going to / You are / Breathe in me / You could be forgiven / Don't call me / Sweet thing / Stay / Careful.
LP: . . . . EST 2123
LP: 748 966 1
MC: . . . . TCEST 2123
MC: 748 966 4

Horse Latitudes

HORSE LATITUDES.
Tracks: / Oh Caroline / What is more than life / Baby don't go / Harvest days / Thrown away / Building mansions / Northern country lie / I can't stop loving you / Younger generation (On CD only) / Someone (On CD only) / There I go again (On CD only).
LP: . . . . BRED 90

Horse (London)

HORSE.
LP: . . . . WWDP 001

Horseflies

GRAVITY DANCE.
LP: . . . . MCA 10435
MC: . . . . MCAC 10435

HUMAN FLY.
Tracks: / Human fly / Hush little baby / Jenny on the railroad / Rub alcohol blues / Cornbread / Who throwed lye on my dog / I live where it's gray / Link of chain / Blueman's daughter / Hush little baby.
LP: . . . . COOK 013
MC: . . . . COOKC 013
LP: . . . . ROUNDER 0239
MC: . . . . ROUNDER 0239C

Horseguards London

BEATING THE RETREAT.
LP: . . . . HD 51
MC: . . . . CH 51

Horslips

ALIENS.
Tracks: / Before the storm / Wrath of the rain, The / Speed the plough / Sure the boy was green / Come Summer / Stowaway / New York wakes / Exiles / Second Avenue / Ghosts / Lifetime to pay, A.
LP: . . . . DJM 22107
MC: . . . . DJM 42107
LP: 22107

BELFAST GIG.
Tracks: / Trouble with a capital 'T' / Man who built America, The / Warm sweet breath of love / Power and the glory / Blindman / Shakin' all over / Kings of the fairies / Guests of the nation / Dearg doom.
LP: . . . . MOO 20
MC: . . . . MOOMC 20

BEST OF HORSLIPS Traditional Irish rock music.
Tracks: / My Lagan love (downtown) / Dearg doom / Green gravel / Oisin's tune / Bim Istigh ag ol / Johnny's wedding / Daybreak (opening the station) / More than you can chew / King of the fairies, The / Musical far East / High reel / Flower among them all.
LP: . . . . OASMOO 21
MC: . . . . COASMOO 21

BOOK OF INVASIONS, THE.
Tracks: / Daybreak / March into trouble / Trouble (with a capital T) / Power and the glory / Rocks remain, The / Dusk / Sword of light / Warm sweet breath of love / Fantasia (my lagan love) / King of morning, Queen of day / Sideways to the sun / Drive the cold winter away / Ride to hell / Dark, The.
LP: . . . . DJM 22106
MC: . . . . DJM 42106
LP: . . . . DJF 20498
MC: . . . . MOOMC 12

DANCEHALL SWEETHEARTS.
Tracks: / Nightown boy / Blind can't lead the blind, The / Stars / We bring the Summer with us / Sunburst / Mad Pat / Blind man / King of the fairies, The / Lonely hearts / Best years of my life, The.
LP: APL1 0709

DRIVE THE COLD WINTER AWAY.
LP: . . . . MOO 9

FOLK COLLECTION.
LP: . . . . STILP 1001
MC: . . . . STILC 1001

HAPPY TO MEET, SORRY TO PART..
Tracks: / Happy to meet / Hall of mirrors / Clergy's lamentation,The / An bratach ban / Shamrock shore, The / Flower among them all / Bim istigh ag ol / Furniture / Ace and deuce of pipering, The / Dance to your daddy / High reel / Scalloway rip off / Musical priest, The / Sorry to part.
MC: . . . . DJH 40544

HORSLIPS HISTORY.
LP: . . . . OAT LP 2

HORSLIPS LIVE.
2LP: . . . . MOO 10

HORSLIPS STORY - STRAIGHT FROM THE HORSE'S MOUTH.
Tracks: / High reel / Night town boy / Flower among them all / Dearg doom / Faster than the hounds / Best years of my life, The / Man who built America, The / Guests of the nation / Daybreak / Everything will be alright / Power and the glory / Sword of light / Warm sweet breath of love / Speed the plough / Trouble (with a capital 'T') / Shamrock shore, The / King of the fairies, The / High volume love / An bratach ban / Silver spear, The.
LP: . . . . DHLP 802
MC: . . . . DHMC 802

MAN WHO BUILT AMERICA.
Tracks: / Man who built America, The / Tonight / I'll be waiting / If it takes all night / Green star liner / Lonliness / Homesick / Long weekend / Letters from home / Long time ago, A.
MC: . . . . COASMOO 17
MC: . . . . DJM 42108
LP: . . . . DJM 22108
LP: 22108
LP: . . . . DJF 20546

SHORT STORIES/TALL TALES.
LP: 9100 070

TAIN, THE.
Tracks: / Sentanta / Meave's court / Charolais / March, The (part 1) / You can't fool the beast / Dearg doom / Ferdia's song / Gae bolga / Cu chulainn's lament / Faster than the hounds / Silver spear / More than you can chew / Morrigan's dream, The / Time to kill / March, The (part 2).
LP: . . . . DJM 20544
MC: . . . . DJH 40544
LP: . . . . MOO 5
MC: . . . . MOOMC 5

UNFORTUNATE CUP OF TEA.
LP: . . . . MOO 8

Horsthuis, Maurice

CHANTENAY 80 (Horsthuis, Maurice, Lol Coxhill, Raymond Boni).
LP: NATO 10

Horta, Toninho

TONINHO HORTA (POLYDOR).
MC: 839 734 4

Horton, Johnny

EARLY YEARS, THE.
Tracks: / Smokey Joe's barbecue / Devilish love light / Candy Jones / Bawlin' Baby / It's a long rocky road / Plaid and calico / Done rovin' / On the banks of the beautiful Nile / Mean, mean son of gun / Happy millionaire / My home in Shelby County / Coal smoke, valve oil and steam / Talk gobbler, talk / Rhythm in my baby's walk / Birds 'n' butterflies / Shadows on the old bayou / Go and wash those dirty feet / Words / Betty Lorraine / Somebody's rockin' my broken heart / Honky tonk Jelly Roll blues / Love and tell / I wish heartaches were strangers / Confusion / Two eyed Sunday pants / Down that river road / Egg money / Confusion (2) / First train headin' South / Somebody rockin' my broken heart (solo) / Honk tonk Jelly Roll blues (demo recordings 1) / Won't you love me, love, love me / Why did it happen to me / You, you, you / Broken hearted gypsy / All for the love of a girl / My heart stopped, trembled and died / I'm a fishin' man / Where do you think you would stand / Devil made a masterpiece, The / Because I'm a jealous man / I'm the one that breaks in two / Train with the rhumba beat, The / Cause you're the one for me / None of you but all of me / Dark haired beauty from Cuba / Tennessee Jive / S.S. Lureline / I won't get dreamy eyed / Two red lips and warm red wine / I won't forget / First train headin' South / Mansion you stole, The / Rest of your life, The / (I wished for an angel but) the devil sent me you / Shadows on the old bayou (demo recordings 1) / Somebody's rockin' my broken heart(demo rec 1) / Talk gobbler talk (demo recordings 1) / Smokey Joe's barbeque (demo recordings 1) / This won't be the first time / Child's side of life / Another women wears my wedding ring / Move down the line / Hey, sweet sweet thing / No true love / Big wheels rollin' / Journey with no end / There'll never be another Mary / Devil made a masterpeice, The (mercury rec.) / Back to my back street / You don't move me baby, anymore / Ha ha and moonface / Ridin' the sunshine special / Where are you / The train with the rhumba beat (mercury rec.) / Broken hearted gypsy (mercury recordings) / Meant so little to you / You cry in the door of your mansion / Plaid and calico / Coal smoke, valve oil and steam (dot overdubs) / Devlish lovelight / Done rovin' / Mean, mean son of gun (dot overdubs) / Talk gobbler talk (dot overdubs) / Shadows on the old bayou (dot overdubs) / In my home in Shelby County (dot overdubs) / Go and wash those dirty feet (dot overdubs) / Smokey Joe's barbeque (dot overdubs) / It's a long rocky road / Words / Done rovin (briar overdubs) / It's a long rocky road (briar overdubs) / Smokey Joe's barbeque (brair overdubs) / Mean, mean, sun of gun (briar overdubs) / Devilish lovelight / Coal smoke, valve oil & steam (briar overdubs) / Words (briar overdubs) / Shadows on the old bayou (briar overdubs) / On the banks of the beautiful Nile (briar) / In my home in Shelby County (briar overdubs) / Go and wash those dirty feet (briar overdubs) / Talk, gobbler talk (briar overdubs) / You, you, you (mecury recordings) / All for the love of a girl(merucry recordings).
LPS: BFX 15289

JOHNNY HORTON.
MC: ZCGAS 754

MORE SPECIALS.
Tracks: / Plaid to Calico / Coal, smoke, valveoil and steam / Devilish love light / Done rovin' / Mean, mean, mean son of a gun / Gobbler, the houn' dog / Shadows on the old Bayou / In my home in Shelby county / Go and wash your dirty feet / Smokey Joe's barbeque / Long rocky road / Words.
LP: HAT 3030
MC: HATC 3030

ROCKIN' ROLLIN' JOHNNY HORTON.
Tracks: / Sal's got a sugar lip (rock'n'roll version) ((Previously unissued)) / Honky tonk hardwood floor / Honky tonk man / I'm coming home / Tell my baby I love her / Woman I need, The (Honky tonk mind) / First train heading South, The / Lover's rock / All grown up / Electrified donkey, The / Sugar coated baby / Let's take the long way home / Ole slew - foot / Sleepy eyed John / Wild one / I'm ready if you're willing.
LP: BFX 15069

ROCKIN' ROLLIN' VOL.2.
Tracks: / Tennessee jive / SS Lureline / First train headin' South / No true love / You, you, you / I won't forget / Move down the line / You don't move me baby / Hey sweet sweet thing / Devil made a masterpiece / Ridin' the sunshine special / Train with the rhumba beat.
LP: BFX 15248

Horton, Pug

DON'T GO AWAY With Bob Wilber,Roland Hanna,Milt Hinton.
Tracks: / By myself / Sweetheart o'mine / I'll string along / Don't go away / Tipperary / Miss my lovin' time / If / Breezin' along / I can dream / Melancholy / Send a little love my way / I found a new baby.
LP: BW 102

Horton, Stephen Wayne

STEPHEN WAYNE HORTON.
Tracks: / Roll over / Tennessee plates / Oh Susan / Got a lot of livin' to do / Only crying / Moonlighting / Endless sleep / That woman / Nothin' shakin' / Gone gone gone.
LP: C1 91983
MC: C4 91983

Horton, Walter

60'S GREATEST HITS (Horton, Walter & Carey Bell).
Tracks: / Have a good time / Christine / Lovin' my baby / Little boy blue / Can't hold out much longer / Under the sun / Tell me baby / Have mercy / That ain't it / Temptation blues / Trouble in mind.
LP: SNTF 677

CAN'T KEEP LOVIN' YOU.
LP: BP-1484

DEEP BLUES HARMONICA OF WALTER HORTON, THE.
Tracks: / Hard hearted woman / Sick & tired / Walter's jump / Leaving in the morning / Walter and Carey / Walking by myself / My eyes keep me in trouble.
LP: JSP 1071

FINE CUTS.
Tracks: / Everybody's fishin' / Don't get around much anymore / Relaxin' / We gonna move to Kansas City / Walter's swing / Hobo blues / La cucaracha / Worried life / Put the kettle on.
LP: BP-006
LP: BMLP 069

HARMONICA BLUES KINGS (Horton, Walter & Alfred Harris).
LP: PL 12

LITTLE BOY BLUE.
MC: JSP CC 1019
LP: JSP 1019

MOUTH HARP MAESTRO.
Tracks: / Jumpin' blues / Hard hearted woman / Cotton patch hot foot / I'm in love with you baby / What's the matter with you / Black gal / Go long woman / Little boy blues / Blues in the morning.
LP: CHD 252

OFFER YOU CAN'T REFUSE, AN (See under Butterfield, Paul) (Horton, Walter & Paul Butterfield).

SOUL OF BLUES HARMONICA, THE.
Tracks: / Groove walk / Wee baby blues / It's alright / Wrinkles / Hard hearted woman / John Henry / Good moanin' blues / Friday night stomp / Gonna bring it on home / La Cucaracha.
LP: GCH 8034
MC: GCHK 78034
LP: 515028

WALTER HORTON.
LP: BM 9010

Horvitz, Morris &

TRIOS.
LP: ST 7518

Hosanna

ALL HAIL KING JESUS.
MC: HMC 507

ARISE AND SING.
MC: HMC 504

FOREVER GRATEFUL (Hosanna/Dave Fellingham).
Tracks: / Shine down / Oh Lord, our Lord / Forever grateful / Faithful and just / I hear angels / Lord of my heart.
LP: HMR 517
MC: HMC 517

GIVE THANKS.
LP: HMR 501
MC: HMC 501

GLORIFY THY NAME.
MC: HMC 502

GLORY TO THE KING.
MC: HMC 509

HIS WORD.
MC: HMC 514

HOSANNA.
Tracks: / Fairest Lord Jesus / There is a fountain / At the Cross / Great is Thy faithfulness / Love of God, The / Amazing grace / Take my life, and let it be / Higher ground.
LP: MM 0052
MC: TC MM 0052

I EXALT THEE.
MC: HMC 510

I WILL REJOICE.
MC: HMC 503

IN HIS PRESENCE.
MC: HMC 513

JOY INSTRUMENTAL.
MC: HMC 602

LAMB OF GOD (Hosanna/Graham Kendrick).
Tracks: / Great is the Lord / Rejoice / Let praise arise / Sing for joy in the Lord / His love endures forever / Lord have mercy / Lamb of God / My heart overflows / Think about His love / Lord thy God, The / Steadfast love of the Lord, The / Thou art worthy / Song for the nations.
LP: HMR 505
MC: HMC 505

MIGHTY WARRIOR.
MC: HMC 506

PEACE INSTRUMENTAL.
MC: HMC 601

PRAISE AND HONOUR.
MC: HMC 516

SOLID ROCK, THE.
MC: HMC 518

STEADFAST LOVE.
MC: HMC 512

TO HIM WHO SITS UPON THE THRONE.
MC: HMC 508

YOU ARE MY GOD.
MC: HMC 511

Hosier, Brent

SECRET THAT LIES, THE.
LP: ROSE 131

Hosken, John

MORTAR FIRE (NORMANDY TO GERMANY 1944-45) (See also Paul Francia).

Hosszu, Janos

LE CYMBALUM HONGROIS.
Tracks: / Danse horgroise de Brahms no. 5 / Csardas / Maros vize folyik csendesen / Ochy chornia / Doina et Hora / Felszallot a pava / Kurucnota / Doina et Hora / Verbunkos / Marika / Ritka buza / Marche de Rakoczi.
LP: ARN 33718
MC: ARN 433718

Host

TRYAL.
LP: AUL 728
MC: CAS 001

Hot...

HOT AS I AM (Various artists).
LP: RAMBLER 105

HOT CHILLS AND COLD THRILLS (Various artists).
Tracks: / Something's got a hold on me: *Various artists* / What you're puttin' me through: *Newby, Dianne* / And the band played on: *Spindles* / If that ain't loving you: *Charles, Lee* / Angel baby: *Green, Garland*/ How to succeed in love: *Love, Martha Jean* / It's the little things: *Patti & The Emblems* / Something for my people: *Greatest Little Soul Band In The Land* / These kinds of blues: *Parker, Junior* / I've only got myself to blame: *Williams, Bobby* / Gonna have to show you: *Trends* / Someone's gonna cry: *Austin, Patti* / One more chance: *Lawson, Shirley* / Tell it like it is: *Marriots* / Hot thrills and cold chills: *Blue Notes*/ Right to cry, The: *Welch, Lenny*.
LP: KENT 023

HOT HITS VOLUME 1. (Various artists).
LP: WORK 3

HOT JUMPIN ROCK'N'ROLL (Various artists).
Tracks: / Mad house jump: *Daylighters* / Slow down baby: *Gaddy, Bob* / Kansas City dog: *Cameron, Little*/ Fool mule: *Terry, Dossie* / Skinny Ginny: *Terry, Dossie* / Humdinger: *Allen, L. Marie* / Fugitive, The: *Morris, Lamar* / R'n'roll call: *Four Tunes* / Horse, The: *Harison, Wilbert* / Teen town hop: *Philharmonics*/ Good golly Miss Molly: *Walients* / Frieda Frieda: *Walients* / Atlanta boogie: *Brown, Tommy* / House near the track, The: *Brown, Tommy*.
LP: RR 2005

HOT LADIES OF ROCK (Various artists).
LP: SHM 3120
MC: HSC 3120

HOT LINE (Various artists).
LP: NE 1207

HOT ROCKIN' PICKS (Various artists).
Tracks: / Ain't goin' home: *Gilley, Mickey* / Slop and stroll jolie blonde: *Dean, Gabe* / No mail today: *Terry, Gene* / Cindy Lou: *Terry, Gene* / Baby you're fine-fine: *Terry, Gene* / Teardrops in my eyes: *Terry, Gene*/ Was it me: *Hart, Larry* / Little bitty pretty one: *Teen Hearts* / Worried all the time: *Lafleur, Anita*/ Ready ready baby: *Victor, Jivin' Joe* / Rock me baby: *Jano, Johnny* / Orelia: *Teen Hearts* / Able Miss Cable: *Page, Charles* / Cat walk: *Page, Charles*.
LP: GCL 118

HOT SHOE SHOW (Various artists).
LP: REB 476

HOT SHOTS (Various artists).
2LP: SSD 8031
MCSET: SSDC 8031

HOT SHOWER (Various artists).
LP: HOT 5001
MC: HOTK 5001

HOT SOUTHERN BOPPERS (Various artists).
Tracks: / Chains of love: *Summons,Gene* / Bop bop baby: *Moore,Wade & Dick Penner* / Don't need your lovin' baby: *Penner, Dick* / Take me to that place: *Earls, Jack* / My gal Mary Ann: *Earls, Jack* / She's my baby: *Riley, Billy Lee* / Come on little mama: *Harris, Ray* / Trying to get to you: *Orbison, Roy* / Take and give: *Rhodes, Slim* / She's gone away: *Barton, Ernie* / Do what I do: *Rhodes, Slim* / Red cadillac and a black moustache: *Smith, Warren* / Eight wheel: *Bruce, Edwin* / Rock boppin' baby: *Bruce, Edwin*.
LP: SUN 1024

HOT YOU'RE HOT (Various artists).
MC: ICT 4002

Hot Antic Jazz Band

HOT ANTIC JAZZ BAND VOLUME 4.
LP: SOS 1154

HOT ANTIC JAZZ BAND-VOLUME 2.
LP: SOS 1058

HOT ANTIC JAZZ BAND-VOLUME 3'.
LP: SOS 1099

I GOT THE STINGER.
LP: SOS 1044

Hot Boogie Woogie

HOT BOOGIE WOOGIE Obscure piano blues & boogie woogie from L.A. 1945-55 (Various artists).
LP: OL 2832

Hot Boppin' Cats

HOT BOPPIN' CATS (Various artists).
LP: RR 2024

HOT BOPPIN' CATS, VOLUME 1 (Various artists).
LP: RR 2011

HOT BOPPIN' CATS, VOLUME 2 (Various artists).
LP: RR 2017

Hot Boppin' Girls

HOT BOPPIN' GIRLS, VOL 1 (Various artists).
LP: LPVF 1169

HOT BOPPIN' GIRLS, VOL 2 (Various artists).
LP: LPVF 1170

HOT BOPPIN' GIRLS, VOL 3 (Various artists).
LP: LPVF 1171

HOT BOPPIN' GIRLS, VOL 4 (Various artists).
LP: LPVF 1172

HOT BOPPIN' GIRLS, VOL 5 (Various artists).
LP: LPVF 1173

Hot Bubblegum

HOT BUBBLEGUM (Film Soundtrack) (Various artists).
LP: NE 1131
MC: CE 2131

Hot Chocolate

CICERO PARK.
LP: SRAK 507

CLASS.
Tracks: / Love me to sleep / Losing you / Gotta give up your love / Walking on the moon / Green shirt / Children of spacemen / Brand new Christmas / Are you getting enough happiness.
LP: FA 41 3111 1
MC: FA 41 3111 4
LP: SRAK 543

EVERY 1'S A WINNER.
LP: SRAK 531

GOING THROUGH THE MOTIONS.
Tracks: / Going through the motions / I just love what you're doin' / Dreaming of you / Dance / Mindless boogie / Night ride / Congas man.
LP: . . . . SRAK 536

GREATEST HITS:HOT CHOCOLATE.
Tracks: / Love is life / You could've been a lady / I believe (in love) / You'll always be a friend / Brother Louie / Rumours / Emma / Cheri babe / Disco queen / Child's prayer, A / You sexy thing / Don't stop it now / Man to man / Heaven is in the back seat of my cadillac.
LP: . . . . ATAK 50
MC: . . . . TCATAK 50
LP: . . . . MFP 5801
MC: . . . . TCMFP 5801
LP: . . . . SRAK 524

HEART AND SOUL OF HOT CHOCOLATE.
Tracks: / Love is life / Rumours / Disco queen / Cheri babe / You'll never be so wrong / You could of been a lady.
MC: . . . . KNMC 12056

HOT CHOCOLATE.
LP: . . . . SRAK 516

LOVE SHOT.
Tracks: / Sexy Caribbean girl / Let's try again / Secret hideaway / Tears on the telephone / Jeannie / I'm sorry / Friend of mine / Touch the night / Love is a good thing / I gave you my heart (didn't I).
LP: . . . . SRAK 1653831

MAN TO MAN.
LP: . . . . SRAK 522
MC: . . . . TC SRAK 522

MYSTERY.
Tracks: / Girl crazy / Mystery / Are you getting enough happiness / No tears / Chances / It started with a kiss / You'll never be so wrong / No doubt about it / One night's not enough.
LP: . . . . EMTV 42
LP: . . . . SRAK 549

TWENTY HOTTEST HITS.
Tracks: / So you win again / You sexy thing / Put your love in me / Love is life / You'll always be a friend / Rumours / I believe / Child's prayer, A / Don't stop it now / I'll put you together again / Emma / Brother Louie / Man to man / Cheri babe / Mindless boogie / You could've been a lady / Going through the motions / Heaven is in the back seat of my Cadillac / Disco queen / Every 1's a winner.
LP: . . . . EMTV 22
MC: . . . . TC EMTV 22
LP: . . . . ATAK 134
MC: . . . . TCATAK 134

VERY BEST OF HOT CHOCOLATE, THE.
Tracks: / It started with a kiss / So you win again / I gave you my heart (Didn't I) / No doubt about it / Brother Louie / Tears on the telephone / Chances / You could've been a lady / Every 1's a winner / Girl crazy / You sexy thing / I'll put you together again / Are you getting enough happiness / Emma / What kinda boy you looking for (girl) / Heaven is in the back seat of my cadillac.
LP: . . . . EMTV 42
MC: . . . . TCEMTV 42

Hot City Nights

HOT CITY NIGHTS 16 Classic rock tracks (Various artists).
Tracks: / I want to break free: *Queen* / Alone: *Heart* / New sensation: *INXS* / Crazy crazy nights: *Kiss*/ Summer of 69: *Adams, Bryan* / Big log: *Plant, Robert* / I want to know what love is: *Foreigner* / Wonderful tonight: *Clapton, Eric* / Livin' on a prayer: *Bon Jovi* / Hot in the city: *Idol, Billy* / Start talking love: *Magnum* / Here I go again: *Whitesnake* / Lavender: *Marillion* / We belong: *Benatar, Pat*/ Look away: *Big Country (group)* / Spirit of radio: *Rush*.
LP: . . . . PROTV 15
MC: . . . . PROMC 15

Hot Club

I GOT RHYTHM (see also Stephane Grappelli) (Hot Club & Stephane Grappelli).
LP: 2683 047

Hot Cookies

HOT COOKIES (A cooking vinyl collection) (Various artists).
Tracks: / Human fly, The: *Horseflies The* / L and N don't stop here anymore, The: *Shocked, Michelle* / Hal-an-tow: *Oyster Band, The* / Chile your waters run red through Soweto: *Sweet Honey in the Rock* / Koneh Peleawoe: *Rogie, S.E.* / Robin Hood: *Mekons, The* / Dawn Run: *Edward II & The Red Hot Polkas* / When my ship comes in: *Gregson & Collister* / Oxford girl, The: *Oyster Band, The* / Black Widow: *Shocked, Michelle* / Ballad of John Henry, The: *Happy End* / Stephen Baldwin's 3 hand dub: *Edward II & The Red Hot Polkas* / Wende zako: *Real Sounds*/ Prince of darkness: *Mekons* / Lannigan's ball: *Happy End* (CD only.) / Time in my life, A: *Rogie, S.E.*(CD only.).
LP: . . . . GRILL 002
MC: . . . . GRILLC 002

Hot Cotton Jazz Band

STOMPIN' ROOM ONLY - VOLUME 1..
LP: . . . . GHB 168

STOMPIN' ROOM ONLY - VOLUME 2.
LP: . . . . GHB 169

TAKE YOUR TOMORROW.
LP: . . . . GHB 188

Hot Dots

HOT DOTS 1 (Various artists).
LP: . . . . HD 784

HOT DOTS 2 (Various artists).
LP: . . . . HD 785

HOT DOTS 3 (TAP DANCING).
LP: . . . . HD 786

Hot Frogs

FROGGY DAY.
LP: . . . . KS 2058

Hot Gossip

GEISHA BOYS & TEMPLE GIRLS.
LP: . . . . DID 13

Hot Hot Reggae

HOT HOT REGGAE, VOLUME 1 (Various artists).
MC: 840604

HOT HOT REGGAE, VOLUME 2 (Various artists).
MC: 840614

Hot House

MOVERS AND SHAKERS.
Tracks: / Responsible / Taking you home / Never, never fall / Waiting for that train to come / Losing the feeling / Crawl to me / All my own / Everything you said / Twenty six hours / All comes down.
LP: . . . . PL 74660
MC: . . . . PK 74660

SOUTH.
Tracks: / Way that we walk, The / Don't come to stay / Hard as I try / Home boy / Jealous kind, The / Same place, same time / Me and you / Crazy / Catch before we fall / Evening with the blues / That's when I'll stop loving you (CD/cassette only) / My boy's arms (CD/cassette only).
LP: . . . . PL 71855
MC: . . . . PK 71855

Hot Jazz

HOT JAZZ RARITIES 1926-28 (Various artists).
LP: . . . . HERWIN 110

Hot Lips Page

HOT LIPS PAGE, 1951 (Various artists).
LP: . . . . AA 513

Hot Melt

HOT MELT ACID (Various artists).
LP: . . . . ACAC 12
MC: . . . . ACAC 1 C

HOT MELT HOUSE DANCE 1 (Various artists).
LP: . . . . TCHDC 1
MC: . . . . TCHDC 1 C

Hot Mud Family

LIVE: AS WE KNOW IT.
LP: . . . . FF 087

Hot Music...

HOT MUSIC IN THE GAMBIA 1984 (Various artists).
Tracks: / Allah l'aa ke: *Various artists* / Koruntu kelefa: *Various artists* / Na fcule: *Various artists*/ Koreang musa: *Various artists* / Alemame samori: *Various artists* / Djarabi: *Various artists.*
LP: . . . . HQ 2060

Hot Nights In The City

HOT NIGHTS IN THE CITY (Various artists).
LP: . . . . WKFMLP 134
MC: . . . . WKFMMC 134

Hot Rain

STAY TRUE.
LP: . . . . STAY 002

Hot Rize

BLASTS FROM THE PAST (Red Knuckles Trailblazers).
LP: . . . . SH 3767
MC: . . . . SH 3767C

IN CONCERT: HOT RIZE.
LP: . . . . FF 315

PRESENTS RED KNUCKLES TRAILBLAZERS (Red Knuckles Trailblazers).
Tracks: / Travellin' blues / Honky tonk man / Slade's theme / Dixie cannonball / I know my baby loves me / Trailblazer theme / Always late / Honky tonk song / Kansas City song / Waldo's discount donuts / Boot heel drag / Window up above, The / You're gonna change or I'm gonna leave / Long gone John from Bowling Green.
LP: . . . . FF 279

RADIO BOOGIE.
LP: . . . . FF 231

TAKE IT HOME.
LP: . . . . SH 3784
MC: . . . . SH 3784C

TRADITIONAL TIES.
LP: . . . . SH 3748

UNTOLD STORIES.
Tracks: / Are you tired of me, darling / Untold stories / Just like you / Country blues / Bluegrass / Won't you come and sing for me / Life's too short / You don't have to move the mountain / Shadows in my room / Don't make me believe / Wild ride / Late in the day.
LP: . . . . SH 3756
MC: . . . . SH 3756C

Hot Rod Gang

THESE STRINGS WERE MADE FOR ROCKIN'.
LP: . . . . F 3012

Hot Rod Rumble

HOT ROD RUMBLE (Original Soundtrack) (Various artists).
LP: . . . . LRP 3048

Hot Sax Band

RED HOT SAX.
LP: . . . . ADL 523
MC: . . . . ADK 523

Hot Screamin' Saxes

BACK BAY BOOGIE Hot screamin' saxes from New York 1941-51. (Various artists).
LP: . . . . OL 8013

SCREAMIN' BOOGIE Hot screamin' saxes from Chicago 1947-51. (Various artists).
LP: . . . . OL 8014

TORNADO Hot screamin' saxes from Los Angeles 1945-47 (Various artists).
LP: . . . . OL 8012

Hot Shots

SNOOPY V THE RED BARON.
LP: . . . . CREST 3

Hot Soul Music

HOT SOUL MUSIC VOL.2 (Various artists).
LP: 377 261

Hot Spot

HOT SPOT (FILM) (Film Soundtrack) (Various artists).
LP: . . . . AN 8755
LP: 846 813 1
MC: . . . . ANC 8755
MC: 846 813 4

Hot Stuff

HOT STUFF (Various artists).
MC: . . . . BBM 142

KNOCK ON WOOD.
Tracks: / Bring back the feeling / Dance / Funkytown / Knock on wood / Bad girls / Don't leave me this way / I love the nightlife.
LP: . . . . CCS 5010

Hot Stuff (2)

HOT STUFF (Various artists).
LP: 60501
MC: 60504

Hot Summer Nights

HOT SUMMER NIGHTS (Various artists).
LP: . . . . SMR 980
MC: . . . . SMC 980

Hot Swing Fiddle...

HOT SWING FIDDLE CLASSICS (Various artists).
LP: . . . . FL 9025

Hot Trumpets

JAZZ IN CHICAGO (1928-30).
LP: . . . . S 1284

Hot Tuna

BURGERS.
Tracks: / True religion / Highway song / 99 blues / Sea child / Keep on truckin' / Water song, The / Ode for Billy Dean / Let us get together right down here / Sunny day strut.
2LP: . . . . NL 37729 (2)

DOUBLE DOSE.
Tracks: / Winin' boy blues / Keep your lamp trimmed and burning / Embryonic journey / Killing time in the Crystal City / I wish you would / Genesis / Extrication love song / Talking about you / Funky No. 7 / Serpent of dreams / Bowlegged woman, knock kneed man / I see the light / Watch the north wind rise / Sunrise dance with the Devil / I can't be satisfied.
LP: . . . . FL 02545
MC: . . . . FK 02545

FINAL VINYL.
Tracks: / Hesitation blues / Candy man / Ja da / Water song / Day to day out the window blues / Easy now / Funky No. 7 / Hot jelly roll blues / Song from the stainless cymbal / I wish you would.
LP: . . . . FL 13357

HOPPKORU.
Tracks: / Santa Claus retreat / Watch the north wind rise / It's so easy / Bowlegged woman, knock kneed man / Drivin' around / I wish you would / I can't be satisfied / I'm talking about you / Extrication love song / Song from the stainless cymbal.
LP: 26 21826
LP: . . . . FTR 2006

Hot Vultures

UP THE LINE.
Tracks: / Preacher's blues / Pontchartrain / Black dog blues / Mistreated mama / Spring of 65, The / Going across the mountains / Corina Corina / T B blues / South coast bound / Bonnie light horseman, The / Black snake moan, The / Chattanooga papa / Write me a few of your lines.
LP: . . . . PLR 018

VULTURAMA-HOT VULTURES 20 BEST.
MC: . . . . BFMSC 3005

Hotel

HOTEL.
LP: . . . . MCF 3036

Hotel Bands

HOTEL BANDS (Various artists).
LP: . . . . GELP 15064

Hotel Complex

FROZEN CHICKEN LIVES,A.
LP: . . . . GYM 4

Hotel Edison

BREAKAWAY (Hotel Edison Roof Orchestra).
LP: . . . . SOS 1169

Hotel New Hampshire

HOTEL NEW HAMPSHIRE (Original Motion Picture Soundtrack) (Various artists).
LP: . . . . EJ 2401691
MC: . . . . EJ 2401694

Hotels, Motels...

HOTELS, MOTELS AND ROADSHOWS Various original artists (Various artists).
LP: 2429 182

Hotfoot

HOTFOOT.
LP: . . . . MRLP 002
MC: . . . . MRMC 002
LP: . . . . HWLP 8504
MC: . . . . CSHW 8504

Hothouse Flowers

HOME.
Tracks: / Hardstone city / Give it up / Christchurch bells / Sweet Marie / Giving it all away / Shut up and listen / I can see clearly now / Movies / Eyes wide open / Water / Home / Trying to get through (Only on CD.) / Dance to the storm (Only on CD.) / Seoladh na ngamhna.
MC: 828 197 4
LP: 828 197 1

HOTHOUSE FLOWERS - INTERVIEW PICTURE DISC.
LPPD: . . . . BAK 2139

PEOPLE.
Tracks: / I'm sorry / Don't go / Forgiven / It'll be easier in the morning / Hallelujah Jordan / If you go / Older we get / Yes I was / Love don't work this way / Ballad of Katie / Feet on the ground / Lonely lane (Available on CD only) / Saved (Available on CD only).
LP: . . . . LONLP 58
MC: . . . . LONC 58

Hotlegs

NEANDERTHAL MAN (OLD GOLD) (See under Herd - I Don't Want Our Lovin To Die).

Hotmund Family

MEAT AND POTATOES AND STUFF.
LP: . . . . FF 251

Hotrod Weekend

HOTROD WEEKEND (Various artists).
LP: . . . . WLP 8940

Hotstyle

PARTNERS IN CRIME.
LP: . . . . MAD 1

Hottest Hits

HOTTEST HITS VOL 1 Various artists (Various artists).
LP: TISLE 1

HOTTEST HITS VOL 2 Various artists (Various artists).
LP: TISLE 2

HOTTEST HITS VOL 3 Various artists (Various artists).
LP: TISLE 3

Hotvills

AROUND THE WORLD.
Tracks: / Orange blossom special / O bayuro do mar / Sambatina / Hora staccato / Le retour des hirondelles / Danse des sabres / Tarentelle / Yiddish mame / Yosel yossel / El manisero / Nocturnal ballade / 12th Street rag.
LP: 742044

DIXIELAND ALBUM,THE.
Tracks: / Tiger rag / How high the moon / Muskrat ramble / Caravan / When the saints go marching in / Hotvill's boogie / Down by the riverside / Margie / Alexander's ragtime band / Sweet Georgia Brown / Dans les rues d'antibes.
LP: 742063

HOTVILLS.
Tracks: / Reminiscene / Reballade cha cha / Camboudery orage / Nuit de camargue / Soleil / Canaveille / Canonnade / Musette / Campagnon mon ami / Chanson non engagee / Ceux qui s'aiment.
LP: 42066

Houdini, Wilmouth

TRINIDAD CALYPSOS FROM THE 30'S.
LP: FL 9040

Houdusse, Patrick.

PATRICK HOUDUSSE.
Tracks: / Les triolets / I love samba / Quand vient le soir / I feel blue / Bolero de Patrick / March de radio-may enne / La grande valse / Un Francais a Madrid / Tango bleu, blanc, rouge / Morena de la plaza / Coupe de pouce / Accordeon en fete.
LP: ILD 42027

Houghton Band

DANCE AND ENJOY THE PRIDE OF LANCASHIRE.
Tracks: / White coppice / Barn dance / Monday night / Drapers gardens / Sprigs of laurel / Farmer's quadrille / Three hand star / Pat Shaw's tradition / Dallas route / Lancashire reel / Veleta, The / Sicilian circle / Bridge of Athlone / Trip to Bavaria.
LP: FE 028

EVENING WITH HOUGHTON BAND.
Tracks: / Les longways / Circle waltz / Chinese breakdown / Alabama jubilee / Fairfield fancy / Ranch house / Pins and needles / Mariannes waltz / Yorkshire square / Nonsuch / East meets West / Long odds / Reprise.
LP: FE 022

PLAYS YOUR REQUESTS.
Tracks: / Yellow rose of Texas / Waves of Tory, The / Gone for a burton / Blaydon races / Wiltshire temptress / Postie's jig / Cottagers / Dressed ship / Vermont / Streets of Laredo / Levi Jackson's rag / Circassian circle.
LP: FE 040

Houghton Weavers

ALIVE AND KICKING.
Tracks: / All for me grog / Her Father didn't like me anyway / Any dream will do / Coal hole cavalry, The / Leaf, The / We want work / Home boys home / Bread and fishes / Mountains of Mourne / Annie's song / Kilgarry mountain.
LP: HW 1002
MC: TCHW 1002

CLATTER O' CLOGS.
Tracks: / Clatter o' clogs / Blackleg miner / Call on me / Art comin't wakes / John North / Horn of the hunter / Blue nose / Band in the park / Pulling-in song, The / Tek me on t' fair / October winds, The / Work of the weavers, The / Rape of Glencoe / Alterations / Bread and fishes / D-Day dodgers.
LP: FHR 111
MC: CFHR 111

HOUGHTON WEAVERS IN CONCERT.
Tracks: / Man like thee, A / Gypsy Rover, The / Today / Rawtenstall annual fair / Lady is a tramp, The / Band in the park / Come landlord fill the flowing bowl / Lizzey Lindsey / Mountain dew, The / Back on the bus / Tribute to the Muppets, A / Grand old Duke of York, The.
LP: FHR 117
MC: CFHR 117

HOUGHTON WEAVERS, THE.
Tracks: / Ballad of Wigan pier / Where do you fo from here? / Mingulay boat song / Our Gracie / Success to the Weavers / I'll be up your way next week / Blackpool belle / Yellow card song,The (CD only.) / Blue and yellow morning (CD only.) / Mist over the Mersey / Martians have landed in Wigan, The / Old lamplighter, The / Old miner, The / When you were sweet sixteen / Lancashire leads the way / Limerick, you're a lady (CD only.) / Coal hole cavalry, The / Rose of Tralee / All for me grog / Bread and fishes / We want work / Home boys home (CD only.).
MC: TCIDL 110

HOWFEN WAKES.
Tracks: / Howfen wakes / John North / Tek me on t' fair / Her father didn't like me anyway / Horn of the hunter / Minstrel, The / Pulling-in song, The / Butcher boy / Awterations / Glencoe / Calico printer's clerk / Pretoria pit disaster, The.
LP: FHR 084
MC: CFHR 084

IN THE RARE OLD TIMES.
Tracks: / Old miner, The / Old lamplighter / When you were sweet sixteen / On the banks of the roses / Limerick, you're a lady / Maggie / God must love the poor / That stranger is a friend / Rose of Tralee, The / H.R.H. / Dublin in the rare oul times / Jock Stewart / Will ye go lassie go? / Lancashire leads the way.
LP: HW 1003
MC: TC HW 1003

IT'S GOOD TO SEE YOU.
LP: FHR 129
MC: CFHR 129

KEEP FOLK SMILING.
LP: FHR 128
MC: CFHR 128

SIT THI DEAWN.
Tracks: / Sit thi deawn / Lancashire fusilier, The / Let no man steal your thyme / Manchester rambler, The / Calton weaver, The / Howfen wakes / My brother Sylvester / Poverty knock / Farewell she / Matchstalk men and matchstalk cats and dogs / Seth Davey (whiskey on a Sunday) / Lord of the dance / All around my hat / Minstrel, The.
LP: FHR 106
MC: CFHR 106

UP YOUR WAY.
Tracks: / Ballad of Wigan pier / Where do you go from here / Room in the sky / Mingulay boat song / Our Gracie / Success to the Weavers interpolating / That man from Firwood / I'll be up your way next week / Blackpool belle / Evacueed / Yellow card song, The / Blue and yellow morning / Dutchman, The / Mist over the Mersey / Martians have landed in Wigan, The.
LP: HW 1001
MC: TC HW 1001

Houl Yer Whist

ON BOYNE'S RED SHORE.
LP: OAS 3005
MC: OASMC 3005

Houliston, Max

MAX HOULISTON'S SCOTTISH BAND SHOW.
Tracks: / Mountain tay,The / Waiting for Sheila / Amazing Grace / Boys from County Armagh.
MC: ZCSMPS 8930

SOUND OF MAX HOULISTON AND HIS SCOTTISH BAND.
LP: GLN 1003

Houmark, Karsten

SOME OTHER TIME (Houmark, Karsten Trio).
Tracks: / I've never been in love before / Days of wine and roses, The / Nardis / Time remembered / May dance / Some other time / Groove, The / Alice in Wonderland / Beautiful friendship, A / Stella by starlight.
LP: SLP 4161

Hound Dog

GREATEST EVER JUNIOR PARTY MEGAMIX (Hound Dog & The Megamixers).
Tracks: / Great balls of fire / Don't be cruel / See you later, alligator / Let's twist again / Rock around the clock / Hound dog reprise / When the going gets tough / Agadoo / Doo doo / Too many broken hearts / Simple Simon / Itsy bitsy teeny weeny yellow polka dot bikini / Bat dance / Baggy trousers / Star trekin / Ghostbusters reprise / Doin' the do / Holiday / Right stuff, The / Chicken song, The / Lambada / Got to get / Birdie song, The / Hound dog / Look, The / Ocps upside your head / Ghostbusters / Turtle power / Brown girl in the ring / Angel face / Ain't nothing but a house party / Locomotion / Hand on your heart / Happening all over again / All shook up.
LP: PAT LP 201
MC: PAT MC 201

Hound of the... (bk)

HOUND OF THE BASKERVILLES, THE (see under Sherlock Holmes).

Houndgod

AUTOGRAPH MY CIA ASSASSINATION MANUAL.
LP: SUK 5

Hour Glass

SOUL OF TIME.
Tracks: / Out of the night / Nothing but tears / Love makes the world go round / Cast off all my fears / I've been trying / Heartbeat / So much love / Silently / Got to get away / Power of love, The / I can't stand alone / Down in Texas / I still want your love / Home for the summer / I'm hanging up my heart for you / Going nowhere / Norwegian wood / Now is the time.
LP: C5-524

Hour Of ...

HOUR OF FAIRY STORIES, AN (Various artists).
Tracks: / Cinderella: *Newman, Nanette (nar)* / Goldilocks and the three bears: *Norman, Richard* / Little Red Riding Hood (story): *Newman, Nanette (nar)* / Jack & the beanstalk: *Dench, Judi* / Rumpelstiltskin: *Craig, Wendy (nar)* / Sleeping beauty: *Craig, Wendy (nar).*
MC: HR 8169

HOUR OF MUSIC, MUSIC, MUSIC, AN (Various artists).
Tracks: / Moon river: *Williams, Danny* / Don't treat me like a child: *Shapiro, Helen* / Gonna build a mountain: *Monro, Matt* / Roses of Picardy: *Hill, Vince* / Alfie: *Black, Cilla* / Careless hands: *O'Connor, Des* / You'll never know: *Bassey, Shirley* / Gal with the yaller shoes: *Holliday, Michael* / Still: *Dodd, Ken* / If we only have love: *Newton-John, Olivia* / No other love: *Hilton, Ronnie* / Up, up and away: *Mann, Johnny Singers* / Till there was you: *Lee, Peggy* / Don't blame you: *Ifield, Frank* / Too close for comfort: *Kitt, Eartha* / There must be a way: *Vaughan, Frankie* / Arrivederci darling: *Shelton, Anne* / More than ever: *Vaughan, Malcolm* / You are my first love: *Murray, Ruby* / Out of town: *Bygraves, Max* / Why do fools fall in love: *Cogan, Alma* / World of our own, A: *Seekers* / She wears my ring: *King, Solomon* / He was beautiful: *Williams, Iris* / Somewhere my love: *Sammes, Mike Singers.*
MC: HR 8179

HOUR OF THE HITS OF 1958, AN (Various artists).
Tracks: / Summertime blues: *Cochran, Eddie* / Sugartime: *Cogan, Alma* / Book of love: *Mudlarks* / Witch doctor: *Lang, Don* / Big beat, The: *Domino, Fats* / Story of my life: *Holliday, Michael* / Poor little fool: *Nelson, Rick(y)* / Mandy: *Calvert, Eddie* / Crazy dreams: *Dale, Jim* / To be loved: *Vaughan, Malcolm* / Mad passionate love: *Bresslaw, Bernard* / Magic moments: *Hilton, Ronnie* / Army Game (signature tune): *Medwin/ Michael/Bernard Bresslaw/Alfie Bass/ Cesce Fyfson* / Lollipop: *Mudlarks* / Music, music, music: *Conway, Russ* / If you were the only girl in the world: *Conway, Russ* / I'm nobody's sweetheart now: *Conway, Russ/* Yes sir that's my baby: *Conway, Russ* / You send me: *Cooke, Sam* / Fever: *Lee, Peggy* / Big man: *Four Preps* / Stairway of love: *Holliday, Michael* / Someday you'll want me to want you: *Various artists* / Splish splash: *Drake, Charlie* / Put a light in the window: *King Brothers* / More than ever: *Vaughan, Malcolm/* Real love: *Murray, Ruby* / Bye bye baby: *Otis, Johnny Show* / Return to me: *Martin, Dean.*
MC: HR 8175

HOUR OF THE HITS OF 1966, AN (Various artists).
Tracks: / Michelle: *David & Jonathan* / Don't make me over: *Swinging Blue Jeans* / Supergirl: *Bonney, Graham/* Love's just a broken heart: *Black, Cilla* / Pretty flamingo: *Manfred Mann* / Stop, stop, stop: *Hollies/* I met a girl: *Shadows* / Woman: *Peter & Gordon* / This door swings both ways: *Herman's Hermits* / Time drags by: *Richard, Cliff* / Morningtown ride: *Seekers* / Promises: *Dodd, Ken* / High time: *Jones, Paul* / It's too late now: *Swinging Blue Jeans* / Alfie: *Black, Cilla* / Oh no, not my baby: *Manfred Mann/* Bus stop: *Hollies* / Place in the sun, A: *Shadows* / Got to get you into my life: *Bennett, Cliff* / Lady Godiva: *Peter & Gordon* / No milk today: *Herman's Hermits* / Blue turns to grey: *Richard, Cliff/* Some day one day: *Seekers* / River, The: *Dodd, Ken* / Let's talk about love: *Shapiro, Helen.*
MC: HR 8160

HOUR OF THE HITS OF 1967, AN (Various artists).
Tracks: / On a carousel: *Hollies* / All my love: *Richard, Cliff* / Kites: *Dupree, Simon & The Big Sound/* Love loves to love love: *Lulu* / Excerpt from a teenage opera: *West, Keith* / Thinkin' ain't for me: *Jones, Paul* / Roses of Picardy: *Hill, Vince* / Hi ho silver lining: *Beck, Jeff* / When will: *Seekers* / Careless hands: *O'Connor, Des* / With a little help from my friends: *Young Idea* / Day I met Marie, The: *Richard, Cliff* / There's a kind of hush: *Herman's Hermits* / Let's pretend: *Lulu* / Sam: *West, Keith* / King Midas in reverse: *Hollies* / Edelweiss: *Hill, Vince* / Thank you very much: *Scaffold* / Georgy girl: *Seekers/* Seven drunken nights: *Dubliners* / Somewhere my love: *Sammes, Mike Singers* / There must be a way: *Vaughan, Frankie.*
MC: HR 8163

HOUR OF THE HITS OF 1968, AN (Various artists).
Tracks: / Darlin': *Beach Boys* / Jennifer Juniper: *Donovan* / Weight, The: *Band* / Sunshine girl: *Herman's Hermits* / On the road again: *Canned Heat* / Jennifer Eccles: *Hollies* / She wears my ring: *King, Solomon/* Mr. Second Class: *Davis, Spencer Group* / Honey: *Goldsboro, Bobby* / Rudi's in love: *Locomotive* / Do it again: *Beach Boys* / Hurdy gurdy man: *Donovan* / I pretend: *O'Connor, Des* / Sleepy Joe: *Herman's Hermits* / For whom the bell tolls: *Dupree, Simon & The Big Sound* / Listen to me: *Hollies* / When we were young: *King, Solomon* / Me the peaceful heart: *Lulu* / Importance of your love, The: *Hill, Vince* / Step inside love: *Black, Cilla* / Lily the pink: *Scaffold.*
MC: HR 8174

Houria

T'ES CHIANT COMME MEC.
LP: F 102

House...

ACID IN THE HOUSE (Various artists).
LP: ZYX 20132

CASA LATINA - HOUSE SOUND OF EUROPE VOL.5 (Various artists).
Tracks: / Stories: *Izit* / Actions: *Horn & Art* / Split: *X-Tended* / Welcome: *Latino, Gino/* Vision: *Albert One* / Esta amour: *E., Evo* / Autumn love: *Electra* / Black water gold: *Blue Funk/* Long train runnin': *Tracks* / New York: *Secci, Chicco* / Love can do: *Blue Tattoo* / On the mix: *All* The Mix / You got me running: *Sima* / Shout in the night: *In-Side* / Pacific state: *Go-Nogo* / Right on time: *Hudson, Melvin* / I'm going to go: *Jago* / Satisfy your dream: *Paradise Orchestra.*
LP: 828 176 1
MC: 828 176 4

CHICAGO HOUSE MUSIC, VOL 2.
LP: CCLP 500

GREATEST HITS OF HOUSE (Various artists).
Tracks: / Stand up for your love rights (she's crazy remix): *Yazz* / Burn it up (acid mix): *Beatmasters* / Theme from S.Express: *S. Express* / Check this out: *L.A. Mix* / Don't make me wait (12" version): *Bomb The Bass/* Jack to the sound of the underground: *Hithouse* / Work me track: *Coldcut & God* / Humanoid: *Stakker Humanoid/* Ride the rhythm: *This Ain't Chicago* / Bust this house down (John Shaft's radio mix): *Penthouse 4* / Bass (how low can you go): *Harris, Simon* / My mind's made up: *Ambassadors Of Funk* / Barry's house: *Gotham City/* East West: *Strongman, Jay* / Hustle (to the music) (radio 1): *Various artists* / House of love (12" version): *Cool Notes* / I'll house you: *Jungle Brothers* / Move your body: *Jefferson, Marshall* / Love can't turn around: *Farley "Jackmaster" Funk* / Do it properly (fierce club mix): *Two Puerto Ricans, A Black Man And A Dominican/* Poke, The: *Adonis* / Bango (to the batmobile): *Terry, Todd* / Jack the groove: *Raze* / Godfather of house: *Chip E & House People* / This brutal house: *Nitro Deluxe* / Do it properly (no way back): *Adonis/* Houseplan: *Terrajacks* / House nation: *Housemaster Boyz & The Rude Boy Of House* / Deep space: *Nebula/* Acid thunder: *Fast Eddie* / Runaway: *Sterling Void* / I love you: *Drum & Bass.*
2LP: SMR 867
MCSET: SMC 867

HISTORY OF THE HOUSE SOUND OF CHICAGO (Various artists).
Tracks: / Trapped: *Abrams, Colonel* / Heat you up (melt you down): *Shirley Lites* / Jingo: *Candido* / We got the funk: *Positive Force* / Let no man put asunder:

First Choice / Spank: *Horne, Jimmy 'Bo'* / Que tal America: *2 Man Sound* / Can you handle it: *Redd, Sharon* / Can't fake the feeling: *Hunt, Geraldine*/ Let's go dancing: *Sparque* / You're the one for me: *D-Train* / Do it to the music: *Raw Silk* / Beat goes on: *Ripple* / Dirty talk: *Klein & Mbo* / Disco circus: *Martin Circus* / Act like you know: *Fat Larry's Band* / At midnight: *T-Connection* / Keep on: *D-Train* / Moskow diskow: *Telex* / I got my mind made up: *Instant Funk* / Music is the key: *Silk, J.M.* / Crazy: *Arrogance* / It, The: *Donnie*/ People of all nations: *Shawn Christopher* / Like this: *E. Chip* / Move: *Farm Boy* / Shadows of your love: *Silk, J.M.* / J'adore danser: *Imperial, Mark* / Never give up: *White Knight* / Apath: *Fingers Inc.* / What you make me feel: *Torres, Liz* / Everybody do it: *House Rockers* / Godfather of house: *House People* / It's you: *ESP* / I fear the night: *Tyree* / It's over: *Fingers Inc.* / Amour puerto riqueno: *Raz* / Mystery of love: *Fingers Inc.* / Jack your body: *Hurley, Steve 'Silk'* / Work your body rap: *Professor* Funk / Whatever turns you on: *Reyes, Mario* / It's U: *Farley "Jackmaster" Funk* / Time to jack: *E. Chip*/ Jack the house: *Femme Fion* / Used by D.J.: *Mk II* / Can U dance: *Jason, Kenny "Jammin" & "Fast" Eddie Smith*/ Wild about your love: *Dymond* / If you only knew: *E. Chip* / Jack me till I scream: *Perez, Julian Jumping*/ No way back: *Adonis* / Ride the rhythm: *On The House* / Funking with the drums again: *Farley "Jackmaster" Funk* / Jackin' me around: *Farm Boy* / Hey Rocky: *Badenuff, Boris* / Move your body (the house music anthem): *Jefferson, Marshall* / House beat box: *Moore, Sampson 'Butch'* / Thank ya: *D. Sweet* / Children of the night: *Irving, Kevin* / Acid tracks: *Phuture* / Love can't turn around: *Farley "Jackmaster" Funk & Daryl Pandy*/ Imnxtc: *Motto, Denise* / You used to hold me: *Rosario, Ralphi & Xavia Gold* / I like it: *Libra Libra*/ Can't get enough: *Torres, Liz* / House nation: *Housemaster Boyz & The Rude Boy Of House* / Pleasure control: *On The House* / It's OK, it's OK: *Force* / Seven ways: *Hercules* / Jackin' national anthem: *Ramos*/ Whatcha gonna do: *Blaze* / Showing out: *Mel & Kim* / Barah: *Cleavage* / Ain't nothing but a house party: *Fearon, Phil* / Set it off: *Harlequin Four's* / Jack that house built, The: *Jack 'n' Chill* / Jack the groove: *Raze* / Certain things are likely: *Kissing The Pink* / Ma foom Bay: *Cultural Vibe* / Jack mix II: *Mirage* / This brutal house: *Nitro Deluxe* / Opera house, The: *Makossa, Jack E* / Time (time to party): *Gary L* / Respectable: *Mel & Kim* / To the beat of the rhythm: *Wired* / Do it properly: *Two Puerto Ricans, A Black Man And A Dominican* / Everything bamboo: *D. Lenny & Tommy Musto* / Turn me loose: *Jump, Wally Jnr.*& The Criminal Element / Movement, The: *Movement* / Jackin': *Home Wreckers* / 122 house: *Risque Rhythm*/ Way to my heart: *Warren, Matt* / What does it take: *Mink* / Nude photo: *Rhythm is Rhythm* / Love can't turn around: *Philly Cream* / Mind games: *Quest* / Triangle of love: *Kreem* / Electric baile: *Masterplan*/ Nobody's business: *Billie* / Can't stop the horse: *Thompson & Lenoir* / Jack le freak: *Chic* / Hit and run '88 gotta be number one: *Holloway, Lolletta* / Rock steady: *Dalis* / Supernature '88: *Cerrone* / Jack in the bush: *Adams, Patrick* / IOU: *Freeez* / Don't make me jack: *Grey, Paris* / I want it to be real: *Rocca, John* / Let's begin: *Turntable Terror Trax* / U ain't really house: *Farley "Jackmaster" Funk* / Put the needle to the record: *Criminal Element Orchestra* / Real thing, The: *Jellybean featuring Steven Dante*/ You're no good for me: *Various artists* / Don't stop (jammin'): *L.A. Mix* / Strings: *Rhythm is Rhythm*/ Pump up the volume: *M/A/R/R/S* / Communicate: *Full House* / We came to jack: *Secret Secret* / Carino: *T-Coy* / Rok da house: *Beatmasters, featuring The Cookie Crew* / Beat dis: *Bomb The Bass* / Theme from S Express: *S. Express* / Doctorin' the house: *Cold Cut* / House arrest: *Krush* / Only way is up, The: *Yazz & The Plastic Population* / Spy in the house of love: *Was Not Was* / Tired of getting pushed around: *Two Men & A Drum Machine* / Bust this house down: *Penthouse 4* / Put that record back on: *Cut To Shock* / Pop goes the house: *Pop Stars* / We call it acieed: *D Mob* / Acid thunder: *Fast Eddie* / Let the music use you: *Nightwriters* / In the name of love: *Swan Lake (Group)* / Acid over: *Tyree* / Acid man: *Jolly Roger*/ Oochy koochy: *Baby Ford* / Can you party: *Royal House* / Give it to me: *Bam Bam* / Poke, The: *Adonis*/ Big fun: *Inner City* / Reachin': *Phase 2* / Get off that wall: *Bighouse* / I'll house you: *Jungle Brothers* / Get real: *Rutherford, Paul* / Party, The: *Kraze* / Can you feel it: *Fingers Inc.* / Baby wants to ride: *Principle, Jamie* / Where's your child: *Bam Bam* / Just wanna dance: *Terry, Todd*.
LPS: .... **BC 39138**

HITS OF HOUSE ARE HERE, THE (Various artists).
Tracks: / Theme from S.Express: *S. Express* / Keep this frequency clear: *DTI* / House nation: *Housemaster* Boyz & The Rude Boy Of House / Let's get brutal: *Nitro Deluxe* / Beat dis: *Bomb The Bass* / Put the needle to the record: *Criminal Element Orchestra* / House Doctors (gotta get down): *House Doctors* / We'll be right back: *Steinski & Mass Media* / Paid in full (seven minutes of madness: the cold cut re-mix): *Eric B & Rakim* / House train: *Risse* / Let's pick up the pieces: *Twin Beat* / Rock da house: *Beatmasters, featuring The Cookie Crew*/ Shake (how about a sampling, Gene?): *Gene & Jim Are Into Shakes* / Faith: *Wee Papa Girl Rappers* / Females (get on up): *Cookie Crew*.
2LP: .... **NE 1419**
MCSET: .... **CE 2419**

HOUSE House story so far (Various artists).
LPS: .... **HOBX 1**

HOUSE HALLUCINATES-PUMP UP LONDON VOLUME 1 (Various artists).
Tracks: / I've lost control: *Sleazy D* / Acid tracks: *Phuture* / Time marches on: *S. William* / Never let you go: *S. William* / Jack the bass: *Jack Master Funk* / This is acid: *Maurice* / Pump up London: *Mr. Lee* / Groove: *Townsell, Lidell*.
2LP: .... **HSEA 9002**
MC: .... **HSEC 9002**

HOUSE MUSIC VOL 1 (Various artists).
LP: .... **GERE 1**

HOUSE OF HITS (Various artists).
2LP: .... **HOH 188**
MCSET: .... **ZCHI 88**

HOUSE OF HITS (History of House Music) (Various artists).
Tracks: / Fantasy: *Z Factory* / I'm scared: *Le Noiz* / M.B. dance: *Chip E & House People* / Undercover: *Various artists* / Farley know house: *Farley "Jackmaster" Funk* / On and on: *Saunders, Jesse* / Are U hot enough: *Virgo* / Dub love: *Master C & J* / We'er rockin' the house: *Adonis* / It's you: *ESP*/ Jungle: *Jungle Wonz* / No way back: *Adonis* / Jack the house: *Fast Eddie* / DSTM: *MJ 11* / Blow: *Willie Wonka* / Move my body: *Two House People* / House master: *Baldwin, Terry* / Hold these nuts: *Pleasure Zone* / Mysteries of love: *Fingers Inc.* / Essence of a dream: *Risque 111* / Can U feel it: *Mr. Fingers* / Jacking zone, The: *Risque Rhythm* / You're mind: *Fingers Inc.* / Freedom: *Children* / Baby wants to ride: *Principle, Jamie* / Can you still dance: *Fast Eddie* / Groove that won't stop, The: *Saunders*/ Dance, The: *Rhythm is Rhythm* / Afro acid: *PW&L* / Confusion: *Armando* / Personal problems: *Dunn, Mike*.
LPS: .... **HOUSBX 1**
MCSET: .... **ZCHOUS 1**

HOUSE SOUND OF CHICAGO (Various artists).
Tracks: / Jack your body: *Hurley, Steve 'Silk'* / Mystery of love: *Fingers Inc.* / Shadows of your love: *Silk, Jim* / Love can't turn around: *Farley "Jackmaster" Funk* / Music is the key: *Silk, Jim* / Move your body: *House Music* / Anthem: *Jefferson, Marshall*.
LP: .... **LONLP 22**
MC: .... **LONC 22**

HOUSE SOUND OF CHICAGO (VOL.2) (Various artists).
Tracks: / Pleasure control: *On The House* / No way back: *Adonis* / Work the box: *Santos* / J.B. piano traxx: *Duane & Co* / House music anthem, The: *Jefferson, Marshall* / What's up Rocky: *Betanoff, Boris*/ Thank ya: *Sweet D* / Can you feel it: *Mr. Fingers* / R U hot enough: *Virgo* / 7 ways to jack: *Hercules*/ Ride the rhythm: *On The House* / Washing machine: *Mr. Fingers* / Give yourself to me: *Rude Boy Farley Keith*, The / When you hold me: *Master C & J* / House beat box: *Moore, Sampson 'Butch'* / We're rocking down the house: *Adonis* / Dum dum: *Fresh* / What is house?: *Wonka, Willie* / Jungle: *Jungle Wonz*.
2LP: .... **LONDP 32**
MCSET: .... **LONDC 32**

HOUSE SOUND OF CHICAGO VOL.III (Acid tracks) (Various artists).
Tracks: / Baby wants to ride: *Principle, Jamie* / Only the strong survive: *Knuckles, Frankie* / Girl U need a change of mind: *Paris* / Acid over: *Tyree* / Freeman: *Pandy, Darryl & Farley Jackmaster Funk* / All dis music: *Romance* / My house: *Funk, Farley Jackmaster* / It's all right: *Sterling Void*.
LP: .... **FFRLP 1**
MC: .... **FFRMC 1**

HOUSE SOUND OF LONDON VOL IV Jackin' zone, The (Various artists).
Tracks: / Living in a world of fantasy: *J & M Connection* / Going home to see my baby: *Bang The Party* / Salsa house: *Rich, Ritchie* / One for the burglar: *D.S. Building Contractors* / Come together: *House Addicts*/ We call it acieed: *D Mob* / FM (FFRR remix): *Silicon Chip* / Depth charge: *D.S. Building Contractors*/ Rebels: *Principle, Jamie* / Back to the beat: *Reese & Santonio* / I have a dream: *Speech* / Mix it up: *Acid Fingers* / Remote control: *Robot, D.J.s* / Underwater: *Thumann, Harry* / Rock to the beat: *Reese & Santonio* / Acid over: *Tyree*.
2LP: .... **FFRDP 4**
MC: .... **FFRDC 4**

MAD ON HOUSE (Various artists).
Tracks: / Poke, The: *Adonis & The Endless Poker* / Bedroom scene, The: *Triple XXX* / Give it to me: *Bam Bam*/ House this house: *Mr. Lee* / Take it the house: *Jine* / Morning after, The: *Fallout* / Don't lead me: *House Master* / Paris grey: *Baldwin artists* / Jackin' James: *Jack Factory*.
LP: .... **MADD 1**
MC: .... **ZCDD 1**

TRAX HOUSE MASTERS (Various artists).
Tracks: / Let's get busy: *On The House* / House nation (remix): *Pleasure Zone* / Rock steady: *Dalis*/ House this house: *Mr. Lee* / Baby wants to ride: *Knuckles, Frankie* / Funkin' with the drums again (Farley (oh my god) mix): *Funk, Farley Jackmaster* / Your only friend (Jones, Nathaniel P): *Phuture* / Do it properly (Adonis mix): *Adonis* / Just for you: *Irving, Kevin* / Get the bug: *Phuture Fantasy Club*.
LP: .... **BLATLP 7**
MC: .... **BLATMC 7**
LP: .... **KL 1**
MC: .... **KLC 1**

ULTIMATE HOUSE (See under Ultimate House) (Various artists).

URBAN HOUSE (Various artists).
Tracks: / I feel fine: *Pizitiv Noize* / Get on board: *Phoenix* / Where's the party: *Freeland & Morriso*/ Don't believe the hype: *Mista E* / Hydrochloric: *Funacidic* / Something special: *Rochefort, Damon* / It's all in your mind: *Pozitiv Noize*.
LP: **837 885-1**
MC: **837 885-4**

House At Pooh Corner

HOUSE AT POOH CORNER (see under Milne, A.A.) (Shelley, Norman).

House Band

HOUSE BAND, THE.
LP: **12TS 439**

PACIFIC.
Tracks: / Pacific / Diamantina drover, The / Joy after sorrow / In at the deep end / Ol' man river / Pit stands idle, The / Going places / For the sake of example / Blazing ruse.
LP: **12TS 445**

WORD OF MOUTH.
LP: **12TS 451**
MC: .... **KTSC 451**

House Beats

HOUSE BEATS (Various artists).
Tracks: / Jackin' James: *Groove lab* / Find the key: *Sisters 'D', The* / Lets all dance the house: *New chapter*/ Sucker for...: *Brotherhood of house, The* / Power house: *Dimension* / Dancing and music: *Groove* / You're not changing: *Rockin' force* / Pump house: *Love explosion* / Wiggle and waggle: *D.J. Muhammad Allah* / Jackin' confusion: *Caucasian kid*.
LP: .... **WRLP 001**

House, Bill

BILL HOUSE.
Tracks: / Dancing with a smile / Better than I ever thought I'd be / Heaven stay in my arms / Sundown / This disco sure gets lonely / You can make it big / I found you / I don't wanna grow up / Feels like Friday night / Good winners and good friends.
LP: .... **TXSR 136**

House Factor

HOUSE FACTOR (Various artists).
LP: .... **BPLP 3**

House (film)

HOUSE/HOUSE II (Film Soundtracks) (Various artists).
LP: .... **STV 81324**

House, George

GEORDIERAMA (House, George & Mike Neville).
LP: .... **MWM 1005**
MC: .... **MWMC 105**

LARN YERSEL GEORDIE (House, George & Mike Neville).
LP: .... **MWM 1001**
MC: .... **MWMC 1001**

NEW IMPROVED GEORDIERAMA (House, George & Mike Neville).
Tracks: / Introduction / Sweet waters of Tyne / Ye'll have to settle down / No-one else for me / Here is the news / Keep your feet still / Bill Charlton's fancy / Hexham races / Caddam Woods / Salmon tails up the water / True story of the venerable Bede, The / Battle hymn of the Republic / If the Lord be willing / Is that you George / Finale / Playing hard to get.
LP: .... **MWM 1016**

RADIO JARRA SLAX (See Neville, Mike) (House, George & Mike Neville).

House Hustlers

8 WONDERS OF THE WORLD (Various artists).
LP: .... **HHA 001**

House, James

JAMES HOUSE.
LP: .... **MCA 42279**
MC: .... **MCAC 42279**
LP: .... **MCG 6077**
MC: .... **MCGC 6077**

House of Cards (bk)

HOUSE OF CARDS Jilly Cooper (Gordon, Hannah (nar)).
MC: .... **PTB 602**

House Of Flowers

HOUSE OF FLOWERS (Original Broadway Cast) (Various artists).
LP: .... **COS 2320**

House Of Freaks

MONKEY ON A CHAIN GANG.
Tracks: / 40 years / Cactus land / Lonesome graveyard / Black cat bone / Bottom of the ocean / Monkey's paw / Yellow dog / Long black train / My backyard / Give me a sign / Dark & light in New Mexico / You can never go home.
LP: .... **FIEND 116**

TANTILLA.
Tracks: / When the hammer came down / Righteous will fall, The / White folk's blood / Birds of prey / King of kings / Family tree / Sun gone down / Kill the mockingbird / Broken bones / I want answers / Big houses / World of tomorrow, The.
LP: .... **VGC 13**
MC: .... **TCVGC 13**

House Of Lords (rock)

HOUSE OF LORDS, THE.
Tracks: / Pleasure palace / Edge of your love / Love don't lie / Hearts of the world / Call my name / I wanna be loved / Looking for strange / Slip of the tongue / Under blue skies / Jealous heart.
LP: .... **85301 R**
LP: .... **PL 88530**
MC: .... **PK 88530**

SAHARA.
Tracks: / Shoot / Chains of love / Can't find my way home / Heart on the line / Laydown staydown / Sahara / It ain't my love / Remember my name / American Babylon / Kiss of fire.
LP: .... **PL 82170**
MC: .... **PK 82170**

House Of Love

HOUSE OF LOVE.
Tracks: / Shine on / Love / Real animal / Hedonist, The / Flow / Plastic.
LP: .... **CRELP 034**
LP: .... **CRE 963**
MC: **885 618 2454**
LP: **8422931**
MC: **8422934**

SPY IN THE HOUSE OF LOVE, A.
LP: **8469781**
MC: **8469784**

House Of The...

HOUSE OF THE SEVEN FLIES (Read by Valentine Dyall).
MC: .... **CAB 027**

House Party

HOUSE PARTY (Various artists).
Tracks: / Why you get funky on me: *Today* / What a feeling: *Arts & Crafts* / Jive time sucker: *Force M.D.'s*/ House party: *Full Force Family featuring Lisa Lisa & Cult Jam* / U.T.F.O.: *Riley, Cheryl Pepsii* / Doctor Ice: *Ex-Girlfriend and E-Crof* / I can't do nothing for you man!: *Flavor Flav* / Fun house: *Kid 'N Play* / To da break of dawh: *L.L. Cool J* / Kid vs Play (the battle): *Kid 'N Play* / Surely: *Arts & Crafts* / This is love: *Vaughan, Kenny & The Art Of Love*.
LP: .... **ZL 72699**
MC: .... **ZK 72699**

HOUSE PARTY (Film Soundtrack) (Various artists).

LP: TER 002
MC: ZCTER 002

HOUSE PARTY (Various artists).
Tracks: / Wake me up before you go go: *Wham* / Come on Eileen: *Dexy's Midnight Runners & Emerald Express* / Dancing queen: *Abba* / It's my party: *Gore, Lesley* / Hi ho silver lining: *Beck, Jeff* / Tarzan boy: *Modern* Romance / Pass the dutchie: *Musical Youth* / Lets twist again: *Checker, Chubby* / Mony mony: *James, Tommy* & The Shondells / Agadoo: *Mardigra* / Knock on wood: *Stewart, Amii* / Celebration: *Kool & The Gang*/ Ain't no stoppin' us now: *McFadden & Whitehead* / Club tropicana: *Wham* / Dancing in the street: *Reeves*, Martha / Can can: *Bad Manners* / This ole house / Boy from New York City: *Various artists* / Black is black: *Los Bravos* / You'll never walk alone: *Gerry & the Pacemakers*.
LP: CTV 2

House Rockers

BEWARE OF THE DOG (see under Taylor, Hound Dog) (House Rockers/ Hound Dog Taylor).

House, Son

1941-42.
LP: RSE 1

BLIND LEMON JEFFERSON/SON HOUSE (See under Jefferson, Blind Lemon).

DEATH LETTER.
Tracks: / Death letter / Pearline / Louise McGhee / John the revelator / Empire state express / Preachin' blues / Grinning in your face / Sundown / Levee camp moan.
LP: ED 167

LIBRARY OF CONGRESS SESSIONS.
Tracks: / Levee camp blues / Government fleet blues / Walking blues / Special rider blues / Low down dirty dog blues / Walkin' blues / Depot blues / Camp hollars.
LP: FL 9002

SON HOUSE IN CONCERT.
Tracks: / It's so hard / Judgement day / New York central / True friend is hard to find, A / Preachin' the blues / Change your mind.
LP: BMLP 1020

House Sound

HOUSE SOUND OF EUROPE V.
LP: 828 176

House Trax

HOUSE TRAX (Various artists).
LP: JACKLP 1
MC: ZCJACK 1

HOUSETRAX 2 (Various artists).
Tracks: / Can you party: *Royal House* / Day in the life, A: *Black Riot* / Don't turn your love: *Park Avenue*/ And the break goes on: *Break Boys* / Jealousy and lies: *Jonah, Julian* / Number nine: *Dereck* / Magic: *Kahn, Bon*.
LP: HTRAX 2
MC: ZCTRAX 2

House With The

HOUSE WITH THE GREEN SHUTTERS (see Douglas, George) (Watson, Tom).

House X Ter C

HOUSE X TER C (Various artists).
Tracks: / I have a dream: *Housemaster Baldwin* / When we used to play: *Baxter, Blake* / OK Coral: *Model 500*/ Rock this place: *Mr. Lee* / I got a big dick: *Joshua, Maurice* / Dim dae: *Trible House* / Bango acid: *Wilson, Mike 'Hitman'* / Break goes on: *Break On* / Dance with the devil: *Project Club* / Spank spank: *Phuture Fantasy Club*.
LP: XTER 1
MC: ZCTER 1

Houseboat

HOUSEBOAT (Film soundtrack) (Various artists).
LP: LAALP 003

Household Cavalry

BEATING THE RETREAT.
LP: HD 51

Househunters

FEEDING FRENZY.
LP: HOLP 001

Housekeeping

HOUSEKEEPING (Original Soundtrack) (Various artists).
LP: STV 81338
MC: CTV 81338

Housemartins

HOUSEMARTINS: INTERVIEW PICTURE DISC.
LPPD: BAK 2078

LONDON 0 HULL 4.
Tracks: / Happy hour / Get up off our knees / Flag day / Anxious / Reverend's revenge / Sitting on a fence / Sheep / Over there / Think for a minute / We're not deep / Lean on me / Freedom / I'll be your shelter (just like a shelter) (Extra track on cassette version only.).
LP: AGOLP 7
MC: ZGOLP 7

NOW THAT'S WHAT I CALL QUITE GOOD.
Tracks: / I smell winter / Bow down / Think for a minute / There is always something there to remind me / Mighty ship, The / Sheep / I'll be your shelter (just like a shelter) / Five get over excited / Everybody's the same / Build / Step outside / Flag day / Happy hour / You've got a friend / He ain't heavy, he's my brother / Freedom / People who grinned themselves to death, The / Caravan of love / Light is always green, The / We're not deep / Me and the farmer / Lean on me.
2LP: AGOLP 11
MC: ZGOLP 11

PEOPLE WHO GRINNED THEMESELVES TO DEATH, THE.
LP: AGOLP 9

Housemasters

BEST OF DJ FAST EDDIE.
LP: MASTER 1
MC: XCMSTER 1

HOUSEMASTERS (Various artists).
LP: BLUEHSLP 1

HOUSEMASTERS VOL.2 (Various artists).
LP: KL 2
MC: KLC 2

Houston

HOUSTON SHUFFLE 1955-66 (Various artists).
LP: KK 7425

Houston, Bee

BEE HOUSTON,HIS GUITAR AND BAND.
LP: ARHOOLIE 1050

Houston, Cissy

MAMA'S COOKIN'.
Tracks: / Midnight train to Georgia / Nothing can stop me / Making love / It's not easy / Any guy / Long and winding road, The / Don't wonder why / I just don't know what to do with myself / This empty place / Only time you say you love me, The / I love you / Will you love me tomorrow / I'll be there / Be my baby / I believe / Down in the boondocks.
LP: CRB 1158
MC: TCCRB 1158

STEP ASIDE FOR A LADY.
Tracks: / Break it to me gently / You're the fire / It doesn't only happen at night / Just one man / Step aside for a lady / What I miss / Gonna take the easy way out.
LP: EMC 3327

Houston, Clint

INSIDE THE PLAIN OF THE ELLIPTIC.
LP: SJP 132

NEW TRUE ILLUSION (see Brackeen, Joanne) (Houston, Clint & Joanne Brackeen).

Houston, David

BEST OF DAVID HOUSTON.
LP: LWLP 101

Houston, Joe

EARTHQUAKE.
LP: PM 156 138 1

ROCKIN' AT THE DRIVE-IN.
Tracks: / Chicano hop / Joe's hot house / Rockin' at the drive-in / Bean hop / Shuckin' 'n' a-jivin' / Houston shuffle / Strollin' / All night long / Lucky 30 / Chili / Drag race / Baby don't go / We're gonna rock 'n' roll.
LP: CH 120

ROCKIN' 'N' BOPPIN'.
LP: BP 1302

Houston Jump

HOUSTON JUMP 1946-51 (Various artists).
LP: KK 7407

Houston, Penelope

BIRD BOYS.
Tracks: / Harry Dean / Talking with you / Voices / Living dolls / Out of my life / Waiting room / Bed of lies / Wild mountain thyme / Putting me in the ground / Full of wonder / Summers of war / Stoli / Rock'n'roll show / All that crimson.
LP: RTMLP 15
MC: RTMMC 15

Houston Person

WE OWE IT ALL TO LOVE.
LP: BASLP 001

Houston Post Now

HOUSTON POST NOW SOUND GROOVE IN, THE (Various artists).
LP: MMLP 66001

Houston Stackhouse

HOUSTON STACKHOUSE 1910-1980 (Various artists).
LP: WOLF 120 779

Houston, Steve

POWER AND THE PREACHER, THE.
LP: MYR 1193
MC: MC 1193

Houston, Thelma

ANY WAY YOU LIKE IT.
Tracks: / Anyway you like it / Don't leave me this way / Don't know why I love you / Come to me / Don't make me pay (for another girl's mistake) / Sharing something perfect between ourselves / If it's the last thing I do / Differently.
LP: STMS 5067
MC: CSTMS 5067
LP: STML 12049

BREAKWATER CAT.
Tracks: / Suspicious minds / Down the backstairs of my life / Understand your man / Lost and found / Something we may never know / Breakwater cat / Long lasting love / Before there could be me / Gone / What was that song.
MC: FK 13500
LP: PL 13500

I'VE GOT THE MUSIC IN ME (Houston, Thelma & Pressure Cooker).
LP: ST 200

NEVER GONNA BE ANOTHER ONE.
Tracks: / Never give you up / Too many teardrops / Ninety-six tears / There's no runnin' away from love / Never gonna be another one / If you feel it / Don't make me over / Hollywood.
LP: RCALP 5035
MC: RCAK 5035

QUALIFYING HEATS.
LP: MCF 3243

RIDE TO THE RAINBOW.
Tracks: / Saturday night, Sunday morning / I wanna be back in love again / Love machine / Imaginary paradise / Just a little piece of you / Ride to the rainbow / Paying for it with my heart / Give it to me.
LP: STML 12117

SUNSHOWER.
Tracks: / Sunshower / Everybody gets to go to the moon / To make it easier on you / Didn't we? / Crazy mixed-up girl / Someone is standing outside / Jumpin' Jack Flash / This is where I came in / Pocketful of keys / This is your life / Cheap lovin' / If this was the last song.
LP: STMS 5030
MC: CSTMS 5030

THELMA HOUSTON.
LP: MCF 3165

Houston, Whitney

I'M YOUR BABY TONIGHT.
Tracks: / I'm your baby tonight / My name is not Susan / All the man that I need / Lover for life / Anymore / Miracle / I belong to you / Who do you love / We didn't know / After we make love / I'm knockin'.
LP: 211039
MC: 411039

IT ISN'T, IT WASN'T, IT AIN'T NEVER GONNA BE (See under Franklin, Aretha) (Houston, Whitney & Aretha Franklin).

WHITNEY.
Tracks: / I wanna dance with somebody / Just the lonely talking again / Love will save the day / Didn't we almost have it all / So emotional / Where you are / Love is a contact sport / You're still my man / For the love of you / Where do broken hearts go / I know him so well.
LP: 208141
MC: 408141

WHITNEY HOUSTON.
Tracks: / How will I know? / Take good care of my heart (Duet with Jermaine Jackson.) / Greatest love of all, The / Hold me (Duet with Teddy Pendergrass.) / You give good love / Thinking about you / Someone for me / Saving all my love for you / Nobody loves me like you do (Duet with Jarmaine Jackson.) / All at once.
LP: 206978
MC: 406978

Hovhaness, Alan

SHALIMAR.
LP: LPFOR 17062-1
MC: MCFOR 17062-4

Hovington, Frank

LONESOME ROAD BLUES.
LP: ROUNDER 2017
LP: FLY 522

How Blue Can You Get

HOW BLUE CAN YOU GET (Great Blues Vocals in Jazz Tradition) (Various artists).
Tracks: / Good morning blues: *Leadbelly* / Back o' town blues: *Armstrong, Louis & His Allstars* / St. Louis blues: *Teagarden, Jack Big Eight* / That ain't right: *Bailey, Mildred* / Crowing rooster blues: *Johnson, Lonnie*/ Evil man's blues: *Bunn, Teddy/Hot Lips Page Trio* / Why don't you do right: *Green, Lil* / Corina Corina: *Manone, Wingy* Orchestra / Bessie Bessie Bessie: *Waller, Fats & His Rhythm* / St. Louis blues: *Sullivan, Maxine* / How blue can you get: *Moore's,Johnny Three Blazers/Charles Brown* / Stormy Monday blues: *Eckstine, Billy* / Taxi blues: *Little Richard* / Port wine blues: *Smith, Ruby & Gene Sedric* / Brand new wagon: *Rushing, Jimmy/Count* Basie & His Orchestra / Tiny boogie, The: *Davies, Tiny* / Rocks in my bed: *Williams, Joe & Jimmy Jones* / I sing the blues: *Humes, Helen & Red Norvo Orch* / Just another woman: *Hot Lips Page Trio*.
LP: NL 86758
MC: NK 86758

How Can You Buy..?

HOW CAN YOU BUY KILLARNEY ? (Various artists).
Tracks: / If you're Irish with my Shillelegh: *Various artists* / Forty shades of green: *Various artists* / Spinning wheel: *Various artists* / Rose of Tralee, The: *Various artists* / Old refrain, The: *Various artists* / How can you buy Killarney?: *Various artists* / Boys from County Armagh: *Various artists* / Holy ground: *Various* artists / Wild Rover: *Various artists* / I'll tell me ma: *Various artists* / If you're Irish: *Various* artists / Mother's love's a blessing, A: *Various artists* / Galway Bay: *Various artists* / Mother Machree: *Various artists* / How are things in Gloccamorra ?: *Various artists* / Baird of Armagh: *Various artists*/ Mary of Dungloe: *Various artists* / By the light of the silvery moon: *Various artists* / When Irish eyes are smiling: *Various artists* / Patsy Fagan: *Various artists*.
LP: GES 1233
MC: KGEC 1233

How Fear Came

HOW FEAR CAME (See under Kipling, Rudyard).

How Many Beans Make 5?

HOW MANY BEANS MAKE FIVE.
LP: LA DI DA 005

How Much...

HOW MUCH IS THAT DOGGIE (Various artists).
MC: STC 004
MC: STC 307B

How The West Was Won

HOW THE WEST WAS WON (Film Soundtrack) (Various artists).
Tracks: / Overture: *Various artists* / How the west was won: *Various artists* / Bereavement and fulfilment: *Various* artists / River pirates, The: *Various artists* / Home in the meadow: *Various artists* / Cleve and the mule: *Various artists* / Raise a ruckus tonight: *Various artists* / Come share my life: *Various artists* / Marriage proposal, The: *Various artists* / Entr'acte: *Various artists* / Cheyennes: *Various artists* / He's Linus' boy: *Various artists* / Climb a higher hill: *Various artists* / What was your name in the states: *Various artists* / No, goodbye: *Various artists* / Finale: *Various artists*.
LP: CBS 70284
MC: 40 70284
LP: MCA 39043
MC: MCAC 39043
LP: 2353 029

How Tiger Got His..

HOW TIGER GOT HIS STRIPES (Various artists).
Tracks: / How tiger got his stripes: *Various artists* / Postman snake: *Various artists* / Candlefly and Mancrow: *Various artists* / Perfect little gentleman, The: *Various artists* / Mancrow's corn: *Various artists*/ Rubber man: *Various artists* / Wives in the sky: *Various artists*.
MC: ANV 668

How To...

HOW TO CHANGE IDEAS (De Bono, Ted).
MC: SS 106

HOW TO GIVE YOURSELF A STEREO CHECKOUT Narrated by Jack De Manio & Elizabeth Knight.

LP: . . . . SKL 4861

HOW TO PICK A WINNER Seahorns soul farm vol.2 (Various artists).
Tracks: / Lovely woman: *Holmes, Edward* / How to pick a winner: *Toussaint, A.* / Fairchild: *Toussaint, A.*/ Just like a woman: *Lee, W.* / I love you still: *Toussaint, A.* / Man of the street: *Moore, S./V.Toussaint*/ Here comes that hurt again: *Toussaint, A.* / You got to love me: *Doe, E.K.* / Natural soul brother: *Greer, Dan* / Goodbye: *Moore, J.* / Cheatin' woman: *Holmes, Edward* / Don't set me back: *Toussaint, A.* / Did you have fun: *West, W/D.Lee/ L.Delcambre* / All I want is you: *Toussaint, A.* / Sadie Mae: *Sixon, L/ J.Haywood/L.Winnifred*/ You lie so much: *Doe, E.K.*.
LP: . . . . CRB 1124
MC: . . . . TCCRB 1124

How To Get Ahead ...

HOW TO GET AHEAD IN ADVERTISING/WITHNAIL AND I (Various artists).
Tracks: / Boilbusters: *Various artists* / Barbara Simmons: *Various artists* / It looks just like me: *Various* artists / Julia: *Various artists* / Sit down: *Various artists* / After the dinner party: *Various artists*/ Boil in a bag: *Various artists* / Bandages come off, The: *Various artists* / Get out of the bloody bath: *Various artists* / Range rover: *Various artists* / Going for the briefcase: *Various artists*.
LP: . . . . FILM 091
MC: . . . . FILMC 091

How To Make Love With

HOW TO MAKE LOVE WITH A BLACK MAN WITHOUT BEING (Original soundtrack) (Various artists).
LP: . . . . A 513
MC: . . . . AC 513

How To Steal A

HOW TO STEAL A DIAMOND IN FOUR UNEASY LESSONS (Film Soundtrack) (Various artists).
Tracks: / Listen to the melody: *Various artists* / Main title: *Various artists* / Talking drums: *Various* artists / Seldom seen Sam: *Various artists* / Parole party: *Various artists* / When you believe: *Various* artists / Hot rock theme: *Various artists* / Miasmo: *Various artists* / Sahara stone: *Various artists*/ Slam city: *Various artists* / Listen to the melody: *Various artists* / End title: *Various artists*.
LP: . . . . K 40371

How to Succeed...

HOW TO SUCCEED IN BUSINESS WITHOUT REALLY TRYING (Original Broadway Cast) (Various artists).
Tracks: / How to succeed (overture): *Various artists* / How to succeed in business without really trying: *Various* artists / Happy to keep his dinner warm: *Various artists* / Coffee break: *Various artists* / Company way, The: *Various artists* / Company, The (reprise): *Various artists* / Secretary is not a toy, A: *Various artists*/ Been a long day: *Various artists* / Grand old ivy: *Various artists* / Paris original: *Various artists*/ Rosemary: *Various artists* / Finaletto act one: *Various artists* / Cinderella, darling: *Various artists*/ Love from a heart of gold: *Various artists* / I believe in you: *Various artists* / Brotherhood of man: *Various artists* / How to succeed...Finale: *Various artists*.
MC: . . . . GK 60352

How We Live

DRY LAND.
Tracks: / Working girl / All the time in the world / Dry land / Games in Germany / India / Rainbow room, The / Lost at sea / In the city / Working town / Beat in the heart, A.
LP: 450618 1
MC: 450618 4

Howard, Bob

CHRONOLOGICAL STUDY VOL 1.
LP: . . . . RARITIES 48

CHRONOLOGICAL STUDY VOL 2.
LP: . . . . RARITIES 49

CHRONOLOGICAL STUDY VOL 3.
LP: . . . . RARITIES 57

CHRONOLOGICAL STUDY VOL 4.
LP: . . . . RARITIES 58

CHRONOLOGICAL STUDY VOL 5 Final volume.
LP: . . . . unknown

Howard, Camille

BROWN GAL 1946-1950 (Howard, Camille, Dorothy Donegan, Lil Armstrong).
Tracks: / R.M blues / Groovy blues / When I grow too old to dream / Sometimes I'm happy / Mr. Fine / If I had you / Milton's lodge / Rock it / Piano player's blues / Joogie boogie / Baby daddy.
LP: . . . . KK 808

Howard, Clint

BALLAD OF FINLEY PRESTON (Howard, Clint & Fred Price).
LP: . . . . ROUNDER 0009

Howard, Eddy

1949: EDDY HOWARD (Howard, Eddy & His Orchestra).
LP: . . . . CLP 29

1949-1953 (Howard, Eddy & His Orchestra).
LP: . . . . CLP 79

EDDY HOWARD, 1946-51.
Tracks: / Careless / To each his own / You must have been a beautiful baby / Dreamers holiday / Rose room / These foolish things / Lazy river / Toot toot tootsie, goodbye / (It's no) Sin / Our love is here to stay / Sweet Lorraine / When my dreamboat comes home / Don't take your love from me / I'll remember April / Dinner for one please, James / Ballin' the Jack / So long for now.
LP: . . . . HSR 119

EDDY HOWARD, VOL 2, 1945-48.
Tracks: / Careless (opening theme) / Thou swell / Homesick, that's all / Everything but you, oh brother, so in love / Old fashioned love / Put that ring on my finger / Words of love / Sleepy time gal / Cuddle up a little closer / Ragtime cowboy Joe / I'm gonna sit right down and write myself ... / So long for now / Little bit independent, A / Singing in the rain / You're getting to be a habit with me / Is it true what they say about Dixie / Love is here to stay / Nice work if you can get it / Caravan / Ballin' the jack / Cherokee.
LP: . . . . HSR 156

HIS TOP HITS.
MC: . . . . MC 822

PLAY 22 ORIGINAL BIG BAND RECORDINGS (Howard, Eddy & His Orchestra).
LP: . . . . HSR 405

TO EACH HIS OWN (1946 - 56) (Howard, Eddy & His Orchestra).
LP: . . . . BS 7140
MC: . . . . BS 7140C

Howard, George

ASPHALT GARDENS.
LP: . . . . PA 8035
MC: . . . . PAC 8035

DANCING IN THE SUN.
Tracks: / Love will find a way / Dancing in the sun / Quiet as it's kept / In love / Telephone / Stay with me / Moods.
MC: . . . . GRC 9626

LOVE AND UNDERSTANDING.
Tracks: / Hopscotch / Only here for a minute / Baby, come to me / Interlude / Love and understanding / Everything I miss at home / Love struck / Talk to the drum / Red, black and blue / Broad Street.
LP: . . . . GR 9629
MC: . . . . GRC 9629

NICE PLACE TO BE, A.
Tracks: / No no / Jade's world / Sweetest taboo, The / Nice place to be, A / Let's live in harmony / Pretty face / Spenser for hire / Stanley's groove.
LP: . . . . IMCA 5855
MC: . . . . IMCAC 5855
LP: . . . . MCF 3330
MC: . . . . MCFC 3330

PERSONAL.
Tracks: / I want you for myself / Shower you with love / Uptown / You and me / I'm in effect / You only come out at night / Personally / Fakin' feeling / Got it goin' on / Piano in the dark.
LP: . . . . MCA 6335

STEPPIN' OUT.
LP: . . . . PA 201
MC: . . . . PAC 201

Howard, Harlan

SINGS HARLAN HOWARD.
LP: . . . . HAT 3130
MC: . . . . HATC 3130

SONGS OF HARLAN HOWARD, THE (Various artists).
Tracks: / Blizzard: *Reeves, Jim* / She's a little bit country: *Hamilton, George IV* / Deepening snow, The: *Smith, Connie* / She called me baby: *Loudermilk, John D.* / I've got a tiger by the tail: *Jean, Norma* / Yours love: *Nelson, Willie* / Chokin' kind, The: *Davis, Skeeter* / Streets of Baltimore: *Bare, Bobby* / Thing called sadness, A: *Gibson, Don* / Too many rivers: *Colter, Jessi* / Watermelon time in Georgia: *Oxford, Vernon*/ Heartaches by the number: *Cramer, Floyd* / Lonely people: *Arnold, Eddy* / It's raining all over the world: *Locklin, Hank* / Mary Ann regrets: *Snow, Hank* / Old podner: *Harlan, Howard*.
LP: . . . . PL 42012

Howard, Jan

JAN HOWARD-THE DOT SERIES.
Tracks: / When we tried / Ozark mountain jubilee / There's no way / I don't think I've got another love / Wind beneath my wings / Evil on your mind / When I see love / Dixie road / I spent all my love on you / Money don't make a man a lover.
LP: . . . . IMCA 39030
MC: . . . . IMCAC 39030

Howard, Jim

NO COMPROMISE (Howard, Jim & Pat Sullivan Jazz Orchestra).
LP: . . . . SB 2005

STAIRWAY DOWN TO THE STARS (Howard, Jim & Pat Sullivan Jazz Orchestra).
LP: . . . . SBWRCI 2536
LP: WRC1 2536

Howard, Johnny

IRVING BERLIN HIT PARADE (Howard, Johnny Orchestra & Singers).
LP: . . . . DS 010

PLAY COLE PORTER (Howard, Johnny & His Orchestra).
LP: . . . . DS 006

PLAYS COLE PORTER.
MC: . . . . TDS 006

Howard, Kid

HEART AND BOWELS OF JAZZ (Howard, Kid and Olympia Band).
LP: . . . . JCE 18

KID HOWARD AND LA VIDA JAZZBAND (Howard, Kid and La Vida Jazzband).
LP: . . . . JCE 14

Howard, Leslie

LISTEN BEYOND TODAY.
LP: . . . . TRX 143
MC: . . . . TRCX 143

Howard, Miki

COME SHARE MY LOVE.
Tracks: / Come share my love / Love will find a way / Imagination / Come back to me lover / I can't wait (to see you alone) / I surrender / Mr. Friend / You better be ready to love me / Do you want my love.
LP: . . . . K 781 688-1
MC: . . . . K 781 688-4

LOVE CONFESSIONS.
Tracks: / Baby, be mine / You've changed / That's what love is / In too deep / Crazy / Bitter love / I wanna be there / Reasons / Love confession.
LP: . . . . K 781 810 1
MC: . . . . K 781 810 4

MIKI HOWARD.
LP: 782024 1
MC: 782024 4

Howard, Noah

TRAFFIC.
LP: . . . . RF 2005

Howard, Paul

FADED PIC BLUES (Howard, Paul & Ralph Willis).
LP: . . . . BID 8024

Howard, Peter

MIDNIGHT BLUE On Hohner piano.
MC: . . . . KGRS 1177

Howard, Roland

KISS YOU KIDNAPPED CHARABANC (See Under Sudden, Nikki) (Howard, Roland & Nikki Sudden).

Howard the Duck

HOWARD THE DUCK (Original soundtrack) (Various artists).
Tracks: / Hunger city: *Dolby's Cube* / Howard the duck: *Dolby's Cube* / It don't come cheap: *Dolby's Cube*/ Don't turn away: *Dolby's Cube* / I'm on my way: *Dolby's Cube* / Lullaby of duckland: *Various artists*/ Journey to Earth: *Various artists* / You're the duckiest: *Various artists* / Ultralight flight: *Various artists* / Beddy-bye for Howard: *Various artists* / Dark overlord: *Various artists*.
LP: . . . . MCF 3342
MC: . . . . MCFC 3342

Howard, Tom

ONE BY ONE.
LP: . . . . AS 0921
MC: . . . . TC AS 0921

SOLO PIANO.
Tracks: / First snow of winter / Road less travelled, The / Open our eyes / Heavens tell the glory, The / Hear, O Lord / Lullaby / Now thank we all our God / Metanoia - Part I: The call / Metanoia - Part II: The turning / Bells of Charlestown / Celeste (from a dream).
LP: . . . . MM R 0167
MC: . . . . MM C 0167

Howard's, Kid

N.O.-THE LEGENDS LIVE (Howard's, Kid New Orleans Band).
LP: . . . . JCE 32

Howatch, Susan

CALL IN THE NIGHT (see under Call in the Night (bk)).

Howe, Catherine

DRAGONFLY DAYS.
Tracks: / Turn the corner singing / Move on over / Mark my word / Too far gone / Don't say it / Quietly and softly / Don't make a promise / It isn't really loneliness / Daylight / God help the ones / Over and over again / Dragonfly days.
LP: . . . . ARL 5013

Howe, Deborah & James

BUNNICULA A rabbit-tale of mystery (Jacobi, Lou).
MC: . . . . CP 1700

Howe, Greg

GREG HOWE.
LP: . . . . RR 9531 1

Howe II

HIGH GEAR.
Tracks: / High gear / Carry the touch / Strat o various / Disorderly conduct / Thinking of you / Standing on the line / Ferocious / Don't let the sloe gin (order the wine) / Party favours / Social fever.
LP: . . . . RR 94671
MC: . . . . RR 94674

NOW HEAR THIS.
LP: . . . . RR 92881
MC: . . . . RR 92884

Howe, James

HOWLIDAY INN (Various artists).
MC: 1748

Howe Of Fife Dance

HOWE OF FIFE DANCE BAND.
Tracks: / Orange and blue / New high level / Davy's brae / Lochanside / Rona's voe / Laird of Drumblair, The / My love she's but a lassie yet / Corn rigs / Bluebell polka / Farewell to the Tay / My love is like a red red rose / 6.20, The / Drunken piper / I love a lassie / Davy nick nack.
MC: . . . . SPRC 501

Howe, Steve

BEGINNINGS.
Tracks: / Doors of sleep / Australia / Nature of the sea, The / Lost symphony / Beginnings / Willo the wisp / Ram / Pleasure stole the night / Breakaway from it all.
LP: . . . . K 50151

EARLY YEARS, THE (Howe, Steve with Bodast).
Tracks: / Do you remember / Beyond winter / Once in a lifetime / Black leather gloves / I want you / Tired towers / Mr. Jones / 1,000 years / Nether Street / Nothing to cry for.
LP: C5-528

STEVE HOWE ALBUM.
Tracks: / Pennants / Cactus boogie / All's a chord / Diary of a man who's disappeared / Look over your shoulder / Meadow rag / Continental, The / Surface tension / Double rondo / Concerto in D 2nd movement.
LP: . . . . K 50621
MC: K4 50621

Howell, Eddie

EDDIE HOWELL GRAMOPHONE RECORD, THE.
Tracks: / Happy affair / First day in exile / Miss Amerika / If I knew / Young lady / These walls / Chicago kid / Can't get over you / Waiting in the wings / Little crocodile / You'll never know / Enough for me / Don't say you love me.
LP: . . . . K 56154

Howell, Peg Leg

PEG LEG HOWELL-VOL.1 1926-27.
Tracks: / Sadie Lee blues / Too tight blues / Moanin' and groanin' blues / Hobo blues / Peg Leg stomp / Doin' wrong / Skin game blues / Coal man blues / Tashomingo blues / New prison blues / Fo'day blues / New jelly roll blues / Beaver slide rag / Papa stobb blues.
LP: . . . . MSE 221

PEG LEG HOWELL-VOL.2 1928-29.
Tracks: / Please ma'am / Rock and gravel blues / Low down rounder blues / Fairy blues / Banjo blues / Turkey buzzard blues / Turtle dove blues / Walkin' blues / Broke and hungry / Rolling Mill blues / Ball and chain blues / Monkey man blues / Chittlin supper / Away from home.
LP: . . . . MSE 205

Howell, Peter

LEGEND.
MC: . . . . C 148

Howes, Robert

RESCUE (Howes, Robert & Rod Argent).
Tracks: / Into the sun / Highland elegy / Travelling choppers / Journey / Seven times serenade / Sea king song / Pale horizon / Return to base (avalanche) / Avalanche search / Flying showman / Ocean flight / Requiem / Tomorrow's child.
LP: . . . . HONEYL 14
MC: . . . . HONEYC 14

Howie, Simon

SIMON HOWIE AND HIS SCOTTISH DANCE BAND (Howie, Simon & His Scottish Dance Band).
LP: . . . . LAP 125
MC: . . . . LAP 125 C

Howland, Chris

FRAULEIN.
Tracks: / Fraulein / Blonder stern / Venus / Kleines madchen aus Berlin / Das hab'ich in Paris gerlent / Patricia / Verboten / Mama / Susie darlin' / Rain falls on ev'rybody / Ja ja wunderbar / Yes, okay alright / Hundert schone frau'n / Die mutter ist immer dabei / Hammerchen polka.
LP: . . . . BFX 15116

Howlin' Wilf

BLUE MEN SING THE WHITES (Howlin' Wilf & The Vee Jays).
Tracks: / Look out baby / If I could / Letter to my girlfriend / Don't have to take no more / Black night / Tell me baby.
LP: . . . . WF 036

CRY WILF.
Tracks: / Got a thing for you / Ya ya / Same old nuthin' / I got my eyes on you / Hello stranger / Get it over baby / Boom boom / Summertime / Mellow down easy / Don't let it be in vain / Farther up the road / Can't stand it no more / Shake it.
LP: . . . . WIK 51

HOWLIN' WILF & THE VEEJAYS (Howlin' Wilf & The Vee Jays).
LP: . . . . BRAVE 8

POINT OF NO RETURN (Howlin' Wilf & The Vee Jays).
LP: . . . . BUTMLP 004

Howlin' Wolf

ALL NIGHT BOOGIE.
Tracks: / Cause of it all, The / Killing floor / Little red rooster / Built for comfort / Commit a crime / Do the do / Highway 49 / Worried about my baby / Poor boy / Wang dang doodle.
LP: . . . . CL 0022983
MC: . . . . CLMC 922983
LP: . . . . BMLP 1019

BACK DOOR MAN.
Tracks: / Howlin' for my baby / Chocolate drop / Everybody's in the mood / Decoration day / Dorothy Mae / Highway man / Oh red / Smokestack lightning / Sitting on top of the world / Wang dang doodle / Back door man / Spoonful / Built for comfort / Killing floor.
LP: . . . . INS 5020
MC: . . . . TCINS 5020

BACK DOOR WOLF,THE.
Tracks: / Moving / Coon on the moon / Speak now woman / Trying to forget you / Stop using me / Leave here walking / Back door wolf, The / You turn slick on me / Watergate blues / Can't stay here.
LP: . . . . GCH 8110
MC: . . . . GCHK 8110
LP: 515013

CADILLAC DADDY Memphis recordings.
LP: . . . . SS 28

CAN'T PUT ME OUT.
LP: 2002

CHESS MASTERS.
LP: . . . . CHXL 102
MC: . . . . CHXT 102

CHESS MASTERS 1.
Tracks: / Fourty four / Evil / Smokestack lightning / Somebody in my home / How many more years / I'm leaving you / All night long / Moanin' for my baby / Baby how long / No place to go / I asked for water / Moanin' at midnight / Shake for me / Red rooster / You'll be mine / Who's been talking / Wang dang doodle / Little baby / Spoonful / Going down slow / Down in the bottom / Back door man / Howlin' for my baby / Tell me.
2LP: . . . . CXMD 4004

CHESS MASTERS 2.
Tracks: / Killing floor / Louise / Poor boy / Sittin' on top of the world / Nature / My country sugar mama / Tail dragger / 300lbs of joy / Natchez burnin' / Built for comfort / Ooh baby hold me / Just my kind / I got a woman / Work for your money / I'll be around / You can't be beat / You gonna wreck my life / I love my baby / Neighbours / I'm the wolf / Rocking daddy / Who will be next / I have a little girl.
2LP: . . . . CXMD 4007

CHESS MASTERS 3.
Tracks: / Mr. Airplane man / Love me darling / Change my way / I walked from Dallas / I better go now / New crawlin' king snakes / Just like I treat you / I've been abused / Don't laugh at me / I ain't superstitious / Howlin' blues / My mind is ramblin' / Do the do / Hidden charms / Come to me baby / Don't mess with me baby / So glad / Break of day / My people's gone / Long green stuff / Joy to my soul / Tell me what I've done / Dust my broom.
2LP: . . . . CXMD 4014

COLLECTION: HOWLIN' WOLF (20 Blues Greats).
Tracks: / Little red rooster / My baby walked off / Killing floor / My country sugar mama / My life / Going back home / Louise / Highway 49 / Hold on to your money / Built for comfort / Ain't superstitious / My last affair / Dorothy Mae / Commit a crime / Moanin' at midnight / Wang dang doodle / Ridin' in the moonlight / Everybody's in the mood / Wolf is at your door, The / I better go now.
LP: . . . . DVLP 2032
MC: . . . . DVMC 2032

GOIN' BACK HOME.
Tracks: / Saddle my pony / Worried all the time / Howlin' Wolf boogie / Wolf is at your door, The / Oh red / My last affair / Mr. Highwayman / Gettin' old and grey / Come to me baby / Don't mess with me baby / So glad / My life / Going back home / I don't know / Howlin' blues / I better go now.
LP: . . . . SC 003

GOLDEN CLASSICS: HOWLIN' WOLF.
LP: 20019
MC: 40019

HIS GREATEST HITS VOL.1.
Tracks: / Down in the bottom / No place to go / Sitting on top of the world / Smokestack Lightnin' / Red rooster,The / Spoonful / Evil / Killing floor / Do the do / I ain't superstitious / Who's been talkin / Three hundred pounds of joy / Back door man / Wang dang doodle.
LP: . . . . GCH 8009
MC: . . . . GCHK 78009

HOWLIN' WOLF.
LPS: . . . . BOX 258
MCSET: . . . . TCBOX 258

I AM THE WOLF.
LP: . . . . CL 32683
MC: . . . . CLMC 932683

LEGENDARY SUN PERFORMERS.
Tracks: / My baby walked off / Smile at me / Bluebird / Everybody's in the mood / Chocolate drop / Come back home / Dorothy Mae / Highway man / Oh Red / My lasy affair / Howlin' for my baby / Sweet woman / C.V. wine blues / Look-a-here baby / Decoration day / Well that's alright.
LP: . . . . CR 30134

LIVE IN 1975 - CHICAGO.
LP: . . . . WOLF 120 000

LIVE IN EUROPE - 1964.
LP: . . . . CG 709-07

LONDON HOWLIN' WOLF SESSIONS, THE.
Tracks: / Rockin' daddy / I ain't superstitious / Sitting on top of the world / Worries about my baby / Built for comfort / Who's been talkin' / Red rooster (rehearsal), The / Red rooster, The / Do the do / Highway 49 / Wang dang doodle.
LP: 6 24723
LP: 515004
LP: . . . . COC 49101
LP: . . . . CXMP 2008
LP: . . . . BRP 2004
LP: . . . . DET 208
MC: . . . . DETK 7208
LP: . . . . CH 9297

MOANIN' IN THE MOONLIGHT.
Tracks: / Moanin' in the moonlight / How many more years / Smokestack lightning / Baby how long / No place to go / Evil / I'm leading you / Moanin' for my baby / I ask for water / Forty four / Somebody in my home.
LP: . . . . GCH 8023
MC: . . . . GCHK 78023

MORE REAL FOLK BLUES.
LP: 515017

REAL FOLK BLUES.
Tracks: / Killing floor / Louise / Poor boy / Sittin' on the top of the world / Nature / My country sugar mama (aka Sugar Mama) / Tail dragger / Three hundred pounds of joy / Natchez burning / Built for comfort / Ooh baby, hold me / Tell me what I've done.
LP: 515011
LP: . . . . CH 9273

RED ROOSTER.
LP: . . . . SM 3990
MC: . . . . MC 3990

RIDIN' IN THE MOONLIGHT.
Tracks: / Riding in the moonlight / Crying at daybreak / Passing by blues / Driving this highway / Sun is rising, The / Stealing my clothes / I'm the wolf / Worried about my baby / House rockin' boogie / Brown skinned woman / Keep what you got / Dog me around / Moaning at midnight / I want your picture / My baby stole off.
LP: . . . . CH 52

ROCKING CHAIR ALBUM, THE (CHESS) Off the record.
Tracks: / Little red rooster / Wang dang doodle / Spoonful / Who's been talking / Going down slow.
LP: . . . . GCH 8012
MC: . . . . GCHK 78012

SAM'S BLUES (see Little Milton) (Howlin' Wolf & Little Milton).

SHAKE FOR ME - THE RED ROOSTER.
LP: 515026

SMOKESTACK LIGHTNIN'.
2LP: 427016

WE THREE KINGS (Howlin' Wolf, Little Walter & Muddy Waters).
LP: . . . . SC 005

WOLF, THE.
Tracks: / Ain't superstitious / Going down slow / Somebody walkin' in my house / Commit a crime / My mind is ramblin' / I walked from Dallas / My country sugar mama / Louise / Hold on to your money / Streamline woman / Ridin' in the moonlight / Crying at daybreak / Passing by blues / Driving this highway / Sun is rising, The / Stealing my clothes / I'm the wolf / Worried about you baby / House rockin' boogie / Chocolate drop / Keep what you got / Dog me around / Morning at midnight / I want your picture / My baby stole off.
LP: . . . . BMLP 1009

Howling (film)

HOWLING II,THE (Original Soundtrack) (Various artists).
LP: . . . . HOWL 01
MC: . . . . HOWC 01

HOWLING, THE (Original soundtrack) (Parsons & Babel Steve).
LP: . . . . STV 81150

Howling On Dowling

HOWLING ON DOWLING R & B from Houston Texas 1947-51 (Various artists).
LP: . . . . KK 7444

Howling Sleepers

SOFT DRINKS AND SNACKS.
Tracks: / Does a man / Feeling sorry / All my troubles / Love love / Take what you want / Cosmic mates / Miserable as sin / Not a happy man / That's changed now / Idle gossip / Peace of mind.
LP: . . . . POPDY 102

Hoy, Lawrence

BEYOND THE SEAS.
Tracks: / Henry Taylor's song / Nanny Hallam / Ten thousand miles / Beyond the seas / Write to me / Lady Penrhyn / Van Diemans land / Do your worst / Twelve good men and true / Ribbands / Bound for Botany Bay / Fields of Athenry / Jim Jones / Golden pennies.
LP: . . . . GATEWAY 004
MC: . . . . GATEWAYC 004

Hoy, Steve

POSSESSION.
LP: . . . . MBELP 001

Hoyland, George

TWO GRENODIDE SWORD DANCE MUSICIANS.
MC: 60-212

Hoyt, Angel

IN THE MOOD (See under Stewart, Tinga) (Hoyt, Angel & Tinga Stewart).

Hoyte, Janice

I AM A DO RIGHT GIRL.
LP: . . . . SRTZ 77384

HP Lovecraft

AT THE MOUNTAINS OF MADNESS.
Tracks: / Any way that you want me / It's all over for you / Wayfaring stranger / Let's get together / I've been wrong before / Drifter, The / That's the bag I'm in / White ship / Country boy and Bleeker Street / Time machine / That's how much I love you baby / Gloria Patria / Spin, spin, spin / It's about time / Blue jack of diamonds / Electrallentando / At the mountains of madness / Mobius trip / High flying bird / Nothing's boy / Keeper of the key.
2LP: . . . . DED 256

HR

CHARGE.
Tracks: / Rasta / Just because I'm poor / Dancing souls / Selassie fee / Let luv lead the way / Shame in dem game / While you were sleeping / Charge / Saddest day / It's reggae.
LP: . . . . SST 256
MC: . . . . SSTC 256

H.R. TAPES, THE.
MC: . . . . SST 171C

HUMAN RIGHTS.
LP: . . . . SST 117
MC: . . . . SSTC 117

SINGIN' IN THE HEART.
Tracks: / Fools gold / Rasta time / Singin' in the heart / Treat street / Youthman sufferer / Fools gold (dub) / Don't trust no (shadows) / Youthman sufferer (dub).
LP: . . . . SST 224
MC: . . . . SSTC 224

H.R.H. Prince

OLD MAN OF LOCHNAGAR (H.R.H. The Prince of Wales) (Ustinov, Peter).
LP: . . . . MMT LP 109
MC: . . . . MMT TC 109

Huang Chung

HUANG CHUNG.
Tracks: / Ti na na / Hold back the tears / I never want to love you in a half hearted way / Straight from my heart / Dancing / Chinese girls / Why do you laugh / China / I can't sleep / Rising in the east.
LP: . . . . SPART 1174

Huband, John

JOHN HUBAND AND THE TAYSIDE SOUND.
LP: . . . . WGR 029
MC: . . . . CWGR 029

Hubback, Steve

BE ALRIGHT WHEN I'M DEAD.
Tracks: / Living with the lama / Psychic / Be alright / When I'm dead / Magic / 2-boxes / Strange Is / This world.
LP: . . . . ST 7525

Hubbard, Bruce

FOR YOU, FOR ME (Hubbard, Bruce/ Orchestra Of St. Luke's).
Tracks: / Old American songs (suite) / Bess, you is my woman now / Woman is a sometime thing, A / Bidin' my time / For you, for me, for evermore / Home blues / Hymn and song from Mass / Everybody says don't (anyone can whistle) / In praise of women / All through the day / Way you look tonight, The / All the things you are / Always / Shenandoah.
MC: . . . . EL 7499284

Hubbard, Freddie

ALTERNATE BLUES (See under Clark, Terry) (Hubbard, Freddie/Clark Terry/ Dizzy Gillespie/Oscar Peterson).

ARTISTRY OF FREDDIE HUBBARD, THE.
Tracks: / Caravan / Bob's place / Happy times / Summertime / Seventh day.
LP: . . . . JAS 71

BACKLASH.
Tracks: / Backlash / Return of the prodigal, The / Son / Little sunflower, The / On the que tee / Up jumped spring / Echoes of blue.
LP: . . . . K 50303

BEST OF FREDDIE HUBBARD.
Tracks: / Red clay / One of a kind / Born to be blue / Joy spring / Summer knows, The.
LP: 23 10 884

BEST OF FREDDIE HUBBARD (BLUE NOTE).
Tracks: / Outer forces / Cry me not / Hub-tones / D minor mint (CD only.) / Mirrors (CD only.) / Birdlike / Open sesame / Sandu / Down under (CD only.).
LP: B1 93202
LP: 793 202 1

BORN TO BE BLUE.
Tracks: / Gibraltar / True colors / Born to be blue / Joy spring / Up jumped spring.
LP: . . . . D 2312 134
MC: . . . . K 12134

DOUBLE TAKE (Hubbard, Freddie/ Woody Shaw).
Tracks: / Sandu / Boperation / Lament for Booker / Hub-tones / Desert moonlight / Just a ballad for Woody / Lotus blossom.
LP: . . . . BT 85121

ETERNAL TRIANGLE, THE (Hubbard, Freddie/Woody Shaw).
Tracks: / Down under / Eternal triangle, The / Moontrane, The / Calling Miss Khadija / Nostrand and Fulton / Tomorrow's destiny / Sao Paulo / Reets and I.
LP: **B1 48017**

FEEL THE WIND (see under Blakey, Art) (Hubbard, Freddie/Art Blakey).

HERE TO STAY.
Tracks: / Philly mignon / Father and son / Body and soul / Nostrand and Fulton / Full moon and empty arms / Assunta.
LP: . . . . **BST 84135**
MC: **4BN 84135**

HUB CAP.
Tracks: / Hub cap / Cry me not / Luan / Osie mae / Plexus / Earmon Jr. / Plexus (alt. take) (CD only.).
LP: . . . . **BST 84073**

HUB-TONES.
Tracks: / You're my everything / Phrophet / Hub-tones / Lament for Booker / For Spee's sake / Phrophet Jennings.
LP: . . . . **BST 84115**

INTERPLAY (see Evans,Bill) (Hubbard, Freddie & Bill Evans).

LIFE FLIGHT.
Tracks: / Battlescar Galorica / Saint's homecoming song, A / Melting pot / Life flight.
LP: . . . . **BT 85139**

LIVE, THE HAGUE, 1980.
Tracks: / First light / One of another kind / One of a kind / Summer knows, The / Impressions / Happiness is now / Red clay.
2LP: **2620 113**
MCSET: . . . . **K 20 113**

LOVE CONNECTION,THE.
Tracks: / Brigitte / Love connection, The / This dream / Little sunflower, The / Lazy afternoon.
LP: . . . . **CBS 83660**

MINOR MISHAP.
LP: . . . . **BLP 60122**

OPEN SESAME.
Tracks: / Open sesame / Open sesame (alt. take) (CD only.) / But beautiful / Gypsy blue / Gypsy blue (alt. take) (CD only.) / All or nothing at all / One mint julep / Hub's nub.
LP: **B1 84040**

OUTPOST.
LP: . . . . **ENJA 3095**

RED CLAY.
LP: . . . . **CTI 9018**

SING ME A SONG OF SONGMY (Hubbard, Freddie & Ilhan Mimaroglu).
Tracks: / Sing me a song of Songmy (part 1) / Threnody for Sharon Tate / This is combat I know / Crowd, The / What a good time for a Kent state / Sing me a song of Songmy (part II) / Monodrama / Black soldier / Interlude / Interlude II / And yet, there could be love / Postlude.
LP: . . . . **K 50235**

SPLASH.
Tracks: / Splash / Mystic lady / I'm yours / Touchdown / You're gonna lose me / Sister Stine / Jarri.
LP: . . . . **F 9610**

TIMES ARE CHANGIN'.
Tracks: / Spanish rose / Back to lovin' again / Was she really there? / Corason amplio (A song for Bert) / Times 'r changin' / Sabrosa / Fragile.
LP: **B1 90905**

Hubbard, John

TAYSIDE BLEND (Hubbard, John & Tayside Sound).
LP: . . . . **SM 001**

Hubbard's Cubbard

HUBBARD'S CUBBARD.
Tracks: / Alligator stomp / Relaxin' somewhere else / 3! News real / 4, dolphy dancin' / Makaha sunset / Songs from the heart of a boy.
LP: . . . . **CODA 5**

SHRINK RAP.
Tracks: / Reflexion / Can't find the time / Shrink rap / Nip it in the bud / Auspicious romance / Drivin' the porcelain bus / Emotional jungle / That's all it takes / Sleep walker / Tell me / Reach for it / New dog / Nerja / Talking city, The / Tinsel Town.
LP: . . . . **CODA 16**
MC: . . . . **COCA 16**

Hubert The Tree

WAAAAARGH WOOO WOOOO WOOO YEAH BABY.
LP: . . . . **ODD 1**

Hubner, Abbi

LOW DOWN WIZZARDS.
LP: . . . . **SOS 1093**

Huckleberry Hound

HUCKLEBERRY HOUND (TV soundtracks) (Various artists).
LP: . . . . **GGL 0004**

Hucklebuckers

SPIDER SENT ME (See under Williams, Paul).

Hucknall, Mick

EARLY YEARS, THE.
LP: . . . . **KNOB 2**

Hucko, Peanuts

JAM WITH PEANUTS (Hucko, Peanuts & His All Stars).
Tracks: / Sweet Georgia Brown / Song is ended, The / Peanut butter / Stolen Peanuts / I must have that man / Cow bell serenade / I may be wrong / Someday, sweetheart / Stand still, Stanley.
LP: . . . . **SWH 33**

PEANUTS HUCKO WITH HIS PIED PIPER QUINTET (Hucko, Peanuts & His Pied Piper Quintet).
Tracks: / Riverboat shuffle / Sweet one / Lonesome / Sweet spirit / Avalon / Raggedy Ann / Memories of you / East of the sun / Peter's blues / When you're smiling.
LP: . . . . **WJLPS 15**

PEANUTS HUCKO WITH HIS QUARTET & ORCHESTRA (Hucko, Peanuts & His Quartet & Orchestra).
MC: . . . . **HM 01**

SOUNDS OF THE JAZZ GREATS, THE.
LP: . . . . **ZR 1014**

STEALIN' APPLES (Hucko, Peanuts & His All Stars).
Tracks: / Stealin' apples / First Friday / St. Louis blues / Summer's love, A / Cute / Just a closer walk with thee / Who's sorry now? / A bientot / Tremont Place / Sweet home rag.
LP: . . . . **ZR 1020**

TRIBUTE TO ARMSTRONG & GOODMAN.
Tracks: / Swing that music / Baby won't you please come home / Muskrat ramble / Summertime / Royal Garden blues / I'm confessin' / All of me / Sheik of Araby, The / Rose room / Rockin' chair / If I had you / After you've gone / Moonglow / Seven come eleven / He is funny that way / Goodnight / Sweetheart.
2LP: . . . . **TTD 541-2**

TRIBUTE TO BENNY GOODMAN (Hucko, Peanuts/Butterfield/Erstrand).
2LP: . . . . **TTD 512/13**

Hucksters

SEVENTH SENSE.
LP: . . . . **HUCS 103**

Hudd, Bryan

BASICALLY COUNTRY.
LP: . . . . **BSS 360**

Hudd, Rita

WOODEN LEG ALBUM, THE (Hudd, Rita & Tony).
LP: . . . . **BURL 022**

Hudd, Roy

GREATEST HITS OF FLANAGAN & ALLEN (See under Smith, Bryan) (Hudd, Roy/ Bryan Smith & Monty Pierce).

ROY HUDD'S VERY OWN MUSIC HALL.
Tracks: / Spaniard that blighted my life / Nice quiet day / I live in Trafalgar Square / 'Arry 'Arry / Polly Perkins / End of my old cigar / My old dutch / Where did you get that hat? / While London sleeps / It's a great big shame / Future Mrs 'Awkins, The / Our neighbourhood / Two lovely black eyes / Hole in the elephant's bottom / When father papered the parlour.
LP: . . . . **FBLP 8079**
MC: . . . . **ZCFBL 8079**

Huddersfield...

CAROLS ALBUM, THE (Huddersfield Choral Society).
Tracks: / O come all ye faithful / Unto us is born a son / I saw three ships / Joy to the world / Away in a manger / God rest ye merry gentlemen / It came upon a midnight clear / Shepherds' farewell, The / Good Christian men rejoice / Good King Wenceslas / Once in Royal David's City / We three kings of Orient Are / In the bleak mid winter / O come, o come Emmanuel / While shepherds watched their flocks by night / First Noel, The / Silent night (still the night) / Angels, from the realms of glory / As with gladness men of old / Hark the herald angels sing / See, amid the winter's snow (CD only.).
LP: . . . . **EMTV 43**
MC: . . . . **TCEMTV 43**
LP: . . . . **MFP 5831**
MC: . . . . **TCMFP 5831**

CHRISTMAS IF FOREVER (Huddersfield Choir).
LP: . . . . **HDY 1923**
MC: . . . . **ZCHDY 1923**

HYMNS ALBUM, THE (Huddersfield Choral Society).
Tracks: / O worship the King / Praise, my soul, the King of Heaven / Lord's my Shepherd, The / O sacred head, sore wounded / When I survey the wondrous Cross / Christ the Lord is risen today / Immortal, invisible, God only wise / Abide with me / Crown Him with many crowns / Christians awake / City of God / Hallelujah, sing to Jesus / God so loved the world / There is a green hill far away / Jesu, lover of my soul / Guide me o thou great Jehovah / Eternal Father, strong to save / Day thou gavest, Lord is ended, The.
LP: . . . . **EMTV 40**
MC: . . . . **TCEMTV 40**
MC: . . . . **TCMFP 5861**
LP: . . . . **MFP 5861**

Hudik Big Band

LIVE AT MONTREUX: HUDIK BIG BAND.
LP: . . . . **DRLP 59**

Hudson, Al

HAPPY FEET.
LP: . . . . **MCF 3015**

IX.
Tracks: / Don't think about it / Who does she think she is / You better quit / Starry eyes / Whammy, The / Set it out / Stole my heart / I can't help myself / Oh girl.
LP: . . . . **MCF 3343**
MC: . . . . **MCFC 3343**

LOVE IS ONE WAY.
Tracks: / Love is / My lady / All over again / Get it over / Push / I didn't mean to break your heart / Be serious / Wait until tomorrow.
LP: . . . . **MCF 3094**

NEW BEGINNING, A (Hudson, Al & One Way).
Tracks: / Driving me crazy / Weekend lover / Let's talk / Get up off it / Say you will / Love at the count of 3 / Pleasure seekers / U, me & the other guy / You're not my problem / Must'a been crazee.
LP: . . . . **EST 2074**
MC: . . . . **TCEST 2074**

ONE WAY.
Tracks: / Music.
LP: . . . . **MCF 3043**

WHO'S FOOLING WHO?.
Tracks: / Who's foolong who / Sweet lady / Cutie pie.
LP: . . . . **MCF 3130**
MC: . . . . **MCFC 3130**

WRAP YOUR BODY.
LP: . . . . **MCF 3263**
MC: . . . . **MCFC 3263**

Hudson, Bob

PARTY PIECES.
LP: . . . . **LRF 058**

Hudson Country Players

INSTRUMENTAL COUNTRY.
Tracks: / Me and Bobby McGee / She called me baby / Blue bayou / Woman to woman / I'm having your baby / Ruby don't take your love to town / She's got you / Together again / Everytime you touch me I get high / Four walls / Happiest girl in the whole USA / Almost persuaded / Loving her was easier / Jolene / Desperado / Jamestown ferry / My love.
LP: . . . . **SHLP 147**
MC: . . . . **SHTC 147**

Hudson, Dave

NIGHT AND DAY.
Tracks: / You make me feel / Now that love has gone / Love and happiness / Translover / Let's get back together / Thin line / Love in the fast lane / Just a feeling / That's what dreams are made of / Night and day.
LP: . . . . **TRPL 125**
MC: . . . . **WAY 269507-4**

Hudson, Dean

1944-48 (Hudson, Dean & His Orchestra).
LP: . . . . **CLP 13**

DEAN HUDSON AND ORCHESTRA 1943-44 (Hudson, Dean & His Orchestra).
LP: . . . . **CLP 136**

MORE 1941 AND 1948 (Hudson, Dean & His Orchestra).
LP: . . . . **CLP 86**

NOW 1982 (Hudson, Dean & His Orchestra).
LP: . . . . **CLP 40**

SOPHISTICATED SWING (1936 - 38) (Hudson/ Delange Orchestra).
Tracks: / Sophisticated swing / On the Alamo / I never knew / Definition of swing / If we never meet again / On again, off again / How was I to know? / What the heart believes / Goin' haywire / Mr. Sweeney's learned to swing / Popcorn man / At your beck and call.
LP: . . . . **BS 7135**

Hudson, Elaine

LOVE TEARS HEARTACHE.
Tracks: / On a long and winding road / No more the fool / Feeling free / Chain of fools / Just like a woman / Bow wow wow / Oh what a life / Roses are red / Love and tears / Let it roll / Good God.
MC: . . . . **PK 74594**
LP: . . . . **PL 74594**

Hudson, Jack

SUNDAY MORNING COMING DOWN.
Tracks: / Annie's going to sing her song / Teach your children / Fire and rain / Sunday morning, coming down / Four and twenty / Mr. Bojangles / Carolina in my mind / Sweet baby James / Child's song / Yellow cat / Damn you world for turning / Me and Bobby McGee.
LP: . . . . **FHR 017 S**

Hudson, Keith

BLACK MORPHOLOGIST OF REGGAE, THE.
LP: . . . . **STLP 001**

FLESH OF MY SKIN, BLOOD OF MY BLOOD.
LP: . . . . **ATRA 1005**

RASTA COMMUNICATION.
Tracks: / Rasta communication / Felt we felt the strain / Bloody eyes / Rasta country / I broke the comb / I'm not satisfied / I'm no fool / Jonah / Musicology / I won't compromise.
LP: . . . . **GREL 5**

STEAMING JUNGLE.
LP: . . . . **KH 100**
MC: . . . . **KHC 100**

STUDIO KINDA CLOUDS (Hudson, Keith & Friends).
LP: . . . . **TRLS 258**

Hudson, Lavine

INTERVENTION.
Tracks: / Intervention / Flesh of my flesh / Create in me a clean heart / Can't see you / Material world / Learning how to love / Prodigal boy / Home / Does Jesus care / Celebrate.
LP: . . . . **V 2529**
MC: . . . . **TCV 2529**

Hudson, Leroy

PARADISE.
LP: . . . . **E 160411**
LP: **601411**

Hudson, Little

JOHN BRIM & LITTLE HUDSON (see Brim, John).

Hudson, Will

EASY ROCKER.
LP: . . . . **SOSLP 120**

Hudson, William H.

GREEN MANSIONS (Quayle, Anthony (nar)).
MC: **1241**

Hue & Cry

BITTER SUITE (LIVE).
Tracks: / Mother Glasgow / Man with the child in his eyes, The / Shipbuilding / Rolling home / Peaceful face / Widescreen / O God head hid / Looking for Linda / Remote / It was a very good year / Round midnight / Truth.
LP: . . . . **DATE 1**
MC: . . . . **DDATE 1**

ORDINARY ANGEL.
Tracks: / Ordinary angel / Looking for Linda / Guy on the wall / Violently / Dollar William / Under neon (CD & cassette only) / Only thing (more powerful than the boss), The / Where we wish to remain / Sweet invisibility / Three foot blasts of fire / Remote / Family of eyes (CD & cassette only).
MC: . . . . **CIRC 6**
LP: . . . . **CIRCA 6**

REMOTE.
Tracks: / Ordinary angel / Looking for Linda / Guy on the wall / Violently (your words hit me) / Dollar William / Under neon (Only on MC and CD.) / Only thing more powerful than the boss, The / Where we wish to remain / Sweet invisibility / Three foot blasts of fire / Remote / Family of eyes (Only on MC and CD.).
LP: . . . . **CIRCA 6**

REMOTE AND BITTER SUITE (Limited edition).

Tracks: / Mother Glasgow (live) / Man with the child in his eyes, The (live) / Shipbuilding (live) / Rolling home (live) / Peaceful face (live) / Widescreen (live) / O God head hid (live) / Looking for Linda (live) / Remote (live) / It was a very good year (live) / Round midnight (live) / Truth (live) / Ordinary angel / Looking for Linda / Guy on the wall / Violently (your words hit me) / Dollar William / Only thing more powerful than the boss, The / Where we wish to remain / Sweet invisibility / Three foot blasts of fire / Remote.
2LP: . . . . HUE 6
MCSET: . . . . TCHUE 6

SEDUCED AND ABANDONED.
Tracks: / Strength to strength / History city / Goodbye to me / Human touch / Labour of love / I refuse / Something warmer (CD only) / Alligator man / Love is the master / Just one word / Truth.
LP: . . . . CIRCA 2
MC: . . . . CIRC 2
LP: . . . . OVED 336
MC: . . . . OVEDC 336

STARS CRASH DOWN.
LP: . . . . CIRC 15
MC: . . . . CIRCA 15

Huff, Leon

HERE TO CREATE MUSIC.
Tracks: / Your body won't move if you can't feel... / I ain't jivin', I'm jammin' / No greater love / Tight money / Tasty / Low down hard time blues / This one's for us / Latin spirit.
LP: . . . . PIR 84530

Hug, Armand

1968 PIANO SOLOS.
LP: . . . . NOLA LP 19

ARMAND HUG OF NEW ORLEANS: 1971.
LP: . . . . S 1296

ARMAND HUG OF NEW ORLEANS: 1974.
LP: . . . . S 1349

ARMAND HUG PLAYS JELLY ROLL MORTON.
Tracks: / Winin' boy blues / Buddy Bolden's blues / Chicago breakdown / Sweet lips (big lip blues) / Why? / Grandpa's spells / Jelly Roll blues / My home is a Southern town / Frog-I-More rag / If you knew how I love you / Black bottom stomp / Sweet substitute.
LP: . . . . S 1365

HIS PIANO IN NEW ORLEANS.
LP: . . . . SLP 244

HUGGIN' THE KEYS.
LP: . . . . S 1361

NEW ORLEANS DIXIELANDERS AND RHYTHM PALS (Hug, Armand & Eddie Miller).
LP: . . . . SLP 221
LP: . . . . GHB 121

NEW ORLEANS ON SUNDAY AFTERNOON.
LP: . . . . S 1419

NEW ORLEANS PIANO.
LP: . . . . S 1281
LP: . . . . SLP 244

Huggy Boys's

HUGGY BOYS'S FAVOURITE OLDIES FROM CADDY RECORDS Various artists (Various artists).
Tracks: / Blacksmith blues: *Various artists* / All night long: *Various artists* / Johnny: *Various artists*/ Eternally: *Various artists* / I don't care: *Various artists* / My girl: *Various artists* / No one to talk to (but the blues): *Various artists* / Flip top box: *Various artists* / El corrida: *Various artists*/ I wish (I could meet her): *Various artists* / Is it a dream: *Various artists* / I lost you: *Various artists*/ Tom and Jerry: *Various artists* / I confess: *Various artists* / I believe: *Various artists* / Way you look tonight: *Various artists* / Moonflight: *Various artists.*
LP: . . . . CH 80

Hugh, Grayson

HOW 'BOUT US? (See also Wright, Betty) (Hugh, Grayson & Betty Wright).

Hughes, Clifford

ABIDE WITH ME.
Tracks: / God be in my head / Day thou gavest, Lord is ended, The / O love that wilt not let me go / Rock of ages / King of love my shepherd is, The / What a friend we have in Jesus / All this night / Abide with me / Child in a manger / When I survey the wondrous cross / Saw ye my Saviour? / Come Holy Ghost / Lord's my shepherd, The.
LP: . . . . LILP 5062

SONG FOR YOU, A.
Tracks: / Amazing grace / Corn rigs / Welcome home royal Charlie / Wi' a hundred pipers / Farewell thou fair day / Rattlin' roarin' Willie / Dark island / My pretty Jane / Skyline of Skye / Oft in the stilly night / When the kye come home / Lea rig, The / Lord's my shepherd, The.
LP: . . . . LILP 5018

Hughes, David

WORLD OF GREAT CLASSIC SONGS OF LOVE.
LP: . . . . SPA 287

Hughes, Dick

LAST TRAIN FOR CASABLANCA..., THE.
LP: . . . . LRF 176

Hughes, Finola

LIKE AN IMAGE PASSING BY (See under Paige, Elaine) (Hughes, Finola/ Elaine Paige).

Hughes, Gary

SACRED CITIES.
LP: . . . . SYN 102
MC: . . . . SYNC 102

Hughes, Gipsy Carolyne

BLACKDOG AND SHEEPCROOK.
Tracks: / Blackdog and sheepcrook / Blind beetles / Jew's garden, The / Lord Thomas and fair Ellen / Bird in the bush, The / Paddies lay down / Billy boy / Draggle-tail gypsies / Tuning up for step dancing / Flash-girls and airy-o / As I was-a walking / Jealous thoughts / Drowsy sleeper, the / Georgie / Soldier and the lady, The / I am a Romany / Adieu to old England, adieu / Servant-man, The / London murder / Blacksmith courted me, A / Sprig of thyme / Little boy / Brake of briars, the / Henry, my son.
MC: 60-043

Hughes, Glen

PLAY ME OUT (CONNOISSEUR COLLECTION).
Tracks: / I got it covered / Space high / It's about time / L.A. cut off / Well / Solution / Your love is like a fire / Destiny / I found a woman / Smile / There goes my baby / Gypsy woman / Any day now / Glimmer Twins medley.
LP: . . . . VSOPLP 153
MC: . . . . VSOPMC 153

PLAY ME OUT (SAFARI).
Tracks: / I got it covered / Space high / It's about time / L.A. cut off / Well / Soulution / Your love is like a fire / Destiny / I found a woman.
LP: . . . . LONG 2
MC: . . . . LONGC 2

Hughes, Jimmy

SOUL NEIGHBOURS (Hughes, Jimmy & Joe Simon).
Tracks: / Shot of rhythm and blues, A / Neighbour, neighbour / There is something on your mind / I tried to tell you / Stormy Monday blues / I'm getting better / Try me / Steal away / Say (that your love is true) / My adorable one / When your near / Whoopee, The / When I'm gone / I keep remembering / Bring it on home to me / Let's do it over.
LP: . . . . CRB 1086

Hughes, Joe

CRAFTSMAN.
LP: . . . . DT 3019

TEXAS GUITAR MASTER-CRAFTSMAN.
MC: . . . . TX 3012
LP: . . . . DT 3012
LP: . . . . DTTX 3019

Hughes, Peter

JUST FOR YOU.
LP: . . . . MTS 4

Hughes, Richard

HIGH WIND IN JAMAICA (Quayle, Anthony (nar)).
LP: . . . . TC 1563
MC: . . . . CDL 51563

Hughes, Sam

14 SONGS OF IRELAND.
Tracks: / Old house / Rose of Tralee, The / Blue hiss of Antrim.
LP: . . . . HRL 133
MC: . . . . CHRL 133

SCOTLAND THE BRAVE.
Tracks: / Scotland the brave / Gordon for me, A / My love is like a red red rose / Scottish soldier, A / Haste ye back.
LP: . . . . HRL 155
MC: . . . . CHRL 155

Hughes, Shirley (auth)

HERE COMES CHARLIE MOON.
MC: 2CCA 3059

IT'S TOO FRIGHTENING FOR ME! (Bennett, John (narr)).
MC: 881573

Hughes, Spike

1930 VOLUME 2 (Hughes, Spike & His Dance Orchestra & His Three Blind Mice).
LP: . . . . FG 409

SPIKE HUGHES (Hughes, Spike & His All-American Orchestra).
Tracks: / Nocturne / Somebody stole Gabriel's horn / Pastoral / Bugle call rag / Arabesque / Fanfare / Sweet sorrow blues / Music at midnight / Sweet Sue / Air in D flat / Donegal cradle song / Firebird / Music at sunrise / How can you do me like you do.
LP: . . . . JASM 2012

SPIKE HUGHES AND HIS DANCE ORCHESTRA VOL.3 (Hughes, Spike & His Dance Orchestra & His Three Blind Mice).
Tracks: / Moanin' low / Moon love / Some of these days / Button up your overcoat / Harlem symphony, A / Darktown strutters' ball / Witness / St James infirmary blues / Devil is afraid of music, The.
LP: . . . . FG 413

SPIKE HUGHES & DECCA-DENTS Vol. 1 (Hughes, Spike & Decca-Dents).
Tracks: / It's unamimous now / Body and soul / Miss is as good as a mile / Crazy feet / Boop boop a doopa doo trot / Man from the south / What wouldn't I do for that man / Fascinating devil / Zonky / Mouchi / Bottoms up / Bigger and better than ever / Ship without a sail / St. james infirmary / Crying out for the Carolines / My man is on the make.
LP: . . . . FG 407

Hughes, Ted

CROW.
2LP: . . . . CCT 9/10

IRON MAN, THE (Cribbins, Bernard (nar)).
MCSET: . . . . SAY 32

POETRY & VOICE OF TED HUGHES.
MC: . . . . CDL 51535

SELECTIONS FROM CROW AND WODWO.
MC: 1628

Hughes, Thomas

TOM BROWN'S SCHOOLDAYS (Atkinson, Rowan).
MCSET: . . . . LFP 7376

TOM BROWN'S SCHOOLDAYS (Derby, Brown).
MCSET: . . . . COL 3006

Hughes & Thrall

HUGHES AND THRALL.
Tracks: / I got your number / Look in your eyes / Beg, borrow or steal / Where did the time go / Muscle and blood / Hold out your life / Who will you run to / Coast to coast / First step of love.
LP: . . . . EPC 25052

Hughes, Tom

TOM HUGHES AND HIS BORDER FIDDLE (Hughes, Tom & His Border Fiddle).
Tracks: / Braes o Mar / Tam's old love song / Banks of Kale Water / Marquis of Lorne's hornpipe / Henry Hughes' favourite / Sidlaw Hills / Wife she brewed it, The / Faudenside polka / Auld Robin Gray / Flouers o Edinburgh / East neuk of Fife / Lady Mary Ramsay / Orange and blue / Millicent's favourite / Tam's untitled hornpipe / Farewell to whiskey / Roxburgh castle / Kelso hiring fair / Old rustic bridge / Morpeth rant / Auld garden Kirn.
LP: . . . . SPR 1005
MC: . . . . SPRC 1005

Hughes, Tony

C'EST LA VIE.
Tracks: / C'est la vie / It's raining in my heart / Old greyhound, The / Pilgrim chapter 33 / I'm a little bit lonesome / Sweet surrender / Love or something like it / I guess it doesn't matter anymore / Living on Tulsa time / Mexican girl / Sunday morning coming down / It's a heartache.
LP: . . . . FHR 109

Hugill, Stan

ABOARD THE CUTTY SARK.
Tracks: / Blow the man down / Boston Town, ho / New York girls / Ratcliffe highway / Lowlands / Shenandoah / Santa Ana / Leave her Johnny.
2LP: . . . . GVRX 207

REMINISCES.
Tracks: / Larry Mar / Roll bullies roll / Bounty was a packet ship / Strike the bell / Fire down below / Long time ago, A / Hilo come down below / John Cherokee / Shiny o / John Kanaka / Sacramento / Rolling down to old maui.
LP: . . . . GVR 217

SHANTIES OF THE SEVEN SEAS.
Tracks: / Ratcliffe highway / Oh aye Rio / Stormalong / Noah's ark ship / Ranzo ray / Whisky Johnny / John Kanaka / Paddy lay back / Jamboree / Liverpool packet, The / Essequibo river / Dixie / Swansea town / Alabama / Ebeneezer, The / Fire down below / Campanero / Laddy marr / Row bullies row.
MC: 60-035

Hugo Largo

DRUM.
Tracks: / Grow wild / Eskimo song / Fancy / Harpers / Scream tall / Country / Eureka / Second skin / My favourite people.
LP: 88561-8167-1
LP: . . . . LAND 002
MC: . . . . LANDC 002

METTLE.
LP: . . . . LAND 005
MC: . . . . LANDC 005

Hugo, Victor

LES MISERABLES (Jarvis, Martin (nar)).
MCSET: . . . . LFP 7463

Hula

CUT FROM INSIDE.
LP: . . . . REDLP 35

CUT FROM INSIDE/MURMUR.
MC: . . . . REDC 85

MURMUR.
LP: . . . . REDLP 53

ONE THOUSAND HOURS.
LP: . . . . REDLP 63

SHADOW LAND.
LP: . . . . REDLP 071

THRESHOLD.
LP: . . . . REDLP 083
MC: . . . . REDC 083

VOICE.
Tracks: / Give me money / See you tomorrow / Cut me loose / Bush mark 2 / Cold stare / Clear water / Torn silk / Seven sleepers / Poison.
LP: . . . . REDLP 75
MC: . . . . REDC 75

Hula Blues

VINTAGE HAWAIIAN CLASSICS.
LP: . . . . ROUNDER 1012
MC: . . . . ROUNDER 1012C

Hull, Alan

ANOTHER LITTLE ADVENTURE.
LP: . . . . CRO 219

ON THE OTHER SIDE.
LP: . . . . CRO 206
MC: . . . . CROC 206

PHANTOMS.
Tracks: / Anywhere is everywhere / Corporation rock / Dancin' / I whish you well / Love is the alibi / Love is the answer / Madmen and loonies / Make me want to stay / Somewhere out there / Walk in the sea.
LP: . . . . TRAIN 6

PIPEDREAM.
Tracks: / Breakfast / Just another sad song / Money game / United states of mind / Country gentleman's wife / Numbers (travelling band) / For the bairns / Drug song / Song for a windmill / Blue murder / I hate to see you cry.
LP: . . . . CHC 16
MC: . . . . CHCMC 16
LP: . . . . CAS 1069

SQUIRE.
Tracks: / Squire / Dan the plan / Picture (a little girl) / Nothin' shakin' / One more bottle of wine / Golden oldies / I'm Dorry Squire / Waiting / Bad side of town / Mr. Inbetween / End, The.
LP: . . . . K 56121

Hull, Dakota Dave

HULL'S VICTORY.
LP: . . . . FF 294

RIVER OF SWING (Hull, Dakota Dave & Sean Blackburn).
LP: . . . . FF 236

Hull, Rod & Emu

BIG BLOW FOR ROD, A.
MC: . . . . VCA 618

CHANGED PLACES.
MC: . . . . VCA 617

GROTBAGS MOVING DAY.
MC: . . . . VCA 615

LITTLE LOST DOG, THE.
MC: . . . . VCA 613

SUPER EMU.
MC: . . . . VCA 616

WINDY DAY, A.
MC: . . . . VCA 614

Hum

HUM (Various artists).
MC: . . . . **TCS 444476**

Human Arts Ensemble

HUMAN ARTS ENSEMBLE VOLUME 1.
LP: . . . . **RK 23578/9**

HUMAN ARTS ENSEMBLE VOLUME 2.
LP: . . . . **RK 23578/12**

Human Beinz

EVOLUTIONS.
Tracks: / Face, the / My animal / Everytime woman / Close your eyes / If you don't mind Mrs.Applebee / Cement / Two of a kind / April 15th.
LP: . . . . **LIK 5**

Human Chains

CASHIN' IN.
Tracks: / Cashin' in / Underfelt / Lucky / Hermana guapa / Bumpa bumpa / Jaytee / Eightyfree / Mug offer extended / Freely / Rocker / Potato picker / I can't get started either.
LP: . . . . **EGED 57**
MC: . . . . **EGEDC 57**

HUMAN CHAINS.
Tracks: / Freely / My Girl / Antonia / Elderberries / La la la / Grinding to the miller men / Hollyhocks / Golden slumbers / Further away / Suguxhama / Jolobe / Ikebana / Bon / Nancy D / Death.
LP: . . . . **LTLP 002**

Human League

CRASH.
Tracks: / Money / Swang / Human / Jam / Are you ever coming back? / I need your lovin' / Party / Love on the run / Real thing, The / Love is all that matters.
LP: . . . . **V 2391**
MC: . . . . **TCV 2391**
LP: . . . . **OVED 253**
MC: . . . . **OVEDC 253**

DARE.
Tracks: / Things that dreams are made of / Open your heart / Sound of the crowd, The / Darkness / Do or die / Get Carter / I am the law / Seconds / Love action (I believe in love) / Don't you want me.
LP: . . . . **V 2192**
MC: . . . . **TCV 2192**
LP: . . . . **OVED 333**
MC: . . . . **OVEDC 333**

FASCINATION (see under (Keep feeling) fascination.

GREATEST HITS: HUMAN LEAGUE.
Tracks: / Mirror man / (Keep feeling) fascination / Sound of the crowd, The / Lebanon, The / Human / Together in electric dreams / Don't you want me? / Being boiled / Love action (I believe in love) / Louise / Open your heart / Love is all that matters / Life on your own.
LP: . . . . **HLTV 1**
MC: . . . . **HLMC 1**

HYSTERIA.
Tracks: / I'm coming back / I love you too much / Rock me again & again & again..... / Louise / Lebanon, The / Betrayed / Sign, The / So hurt / Life on your own / Don't you know I want you.
LP: . . . . **V 2315**
MC: . . . . **TCV 2315**
LP: . . . . **OVED 177**
MC: . . . . **OVEDC 177**

REPRODUCTION.
Tracks: / Almost medieval / Circus of death / Path of least resistance / Blind youth / Word before last, The / Empire state human / Morale...You've lost that loving feeling / Austerity/Girl one (medley) / Zero as a limit.
LP: . . . . **OVED 114**
MC: . . . . **OVEDC 114**
LP: . . . . **V 2133**

ROMANTIC?.
LP: . . . . **V 2624**
MC: . . . . **TCV 2624**

TRAVELOGUE.
Tracks: / Black hit of space, The / Only after dark / Life kills / Dreams of leaving / Toyota city / Crow and a baby / Touchables, The / Gordon's gin / Being boiled / WXJL tonight.
LP: . . . . **OVED 115**
MC: . . . . **OVEDC 115**
LP: . . . . **V 2160**

Human Music

HUMAN MUSIC (Various artists).
LP: . . . . **HMS 100**
MC: . . . . **HMS 100 C**

Human Orchestra

HUMAN ORCHESTRA, THE (Various rhythm quartets) (Various artists).
Tracks: / Mr. Ghost goes to...: *Various artists* / Dixie rhythm: *Various artists* / Kickin'...: *Various artists*/ Wah dee-dah: *Various artists* / Let the party go on: *Various artists* / Hambone am...: *Various artists*/ My walking stick: *Various artists* / At the cotton...: *Various artists* / Jungle fever: *Various artists*/ Moonglow: *Various artists* / Pickin' a rib: *Various artists.*
LP: . . . . **CL 144-003**

Human Sexual Response

FIGURE 14.
Tracks: / Guardian angel / Dick and Jane / Jackie Onassis / Cool jerk / Dolls / What does sex mean to me? / Marone moan / Unba unba / Anne Franke story.
LP: . . . . **X 1**

IN A ROMAN MOOD.
Tracks: / Andy fell / Marone offering / Pound / Public alley 909 / 1,2,3,4,5,6,7,8,9,10 / Question of temperature, A / Keep a southern exposure / Blow up / House of Atreus / Land of the glass pinecomes / Bodyguard.
LP: . . . . **X 11**

Human Switchboard

COFFEE BREAK.
MC: . . . . **A 110**

Human Voice (bk)

HUMAN VOICE, THE (Jean Cocteau) (Bergman, Ingrid (nar)).
MC: **1118**

Humana, Vox

CHAMPION (see under Berlin, Jeff).

Humanoid

GLOBAL.
LP: . . . . **HUMAN 1989**
MC: . . . . **ZCHUM 1989**

Humanoids From ...

HUMANOIDS FROM THE DEEP (Original Soundtrack) (Various artists).
LP: . . . . **C'BUS 203**

Humara, Walter Salas

LARGARTIJA.
LP: . . . . **ROUGH 144**

Humble Pie

AS SAFE AS YESTERDAY IS.
LP: . . . . **IMSP 025**

BACK HOME AGAIN.
LP: . . . . **IML 1005**

COLLECTION: HUMBLE PIE.
Tracks: / Bang / Natural born boogie / I'll go alone / Buttermilk boy / Desperation / Nifty little number like you / Wrist job / Stick shift / Growing closer / As safe as yesterday / Heartbeat / Down home again / Take me back / Only you can see / Silver tongue / Every mother's son / Sad bag of shaky Jake / Cold lady / Home and away / Light of love.
2LP: . . . . **CCSLP 104**
MC: . . . . **CCSMC 104**

EAT IT.
Tracks: / Get down to it / Good booze and bad women / It is for love / Drug store cowboy / Black coffee / I believe to my soul / Shut up and don't interrupt me / Strong my love is / Say no more / Oh Bella Sleeve / Honky tonk women / Road runner.
2LP: . . . . **AMLS 6004**

NATURAL BORN BOOGIE (See under Atomic Rooster/Tomorrow night).

ON TO VICTORY.
LP: . . . . **JETLP 231**

PERFORMANCE - ROCKIN' THE FILMORE.
Tracks: / Four-day creep / I'm ready / Stone cold fever / I walk on gilded splinters / Rolling stone / Hallelujah, I love her so / I don't need no doctor.
LP: . . . . **AMLH 63506**
MCSET: . . . . **CDM 63506**

ROCKING AT THE FILLMORE.
LP: . . . . **AMLH 63506**

SMOKIN'.
LP: . . . . **AMLS 64342**

Humblebums

HUMBLEBUMS.
Tracks: / Look over the hill and far away / Saturday round about Sunday / Patrick everybody knows / Rick rack / Her didn't like me anyway / Please sing a song for us / Joe Dempsey / Blood and glory / Coconut tree / Dilk pyjamas / Good-bye-ee.
LP: . . . . **TRS 107**
MC: . . . . **KTRS 107**
MCSET: . . . . **CRT 134**
LP: . . . . **MTRA 2006**

Hume, Irene

PRELUDE.
LP: . . . . **MODEM 1002**
MC: . . . . **MODEMC 1002**

Humes, Helen

BE BABA LEBA.
LP: . . . . **KM 701**

E-BABA-LE-BA: THE R&B YEARS.
Tracks: / I would if I could / Keep your mind on me / Fortune tellin' man / Suspicious blues / Sad feeling / Rock me to sleep / This love of mine / He may be yours / E-BaBa-Le-Ba / If I could be with you / Ain't gonna quit you baby / Helen's advice / Knockin' myself out / Airplane blues.
LP: . . . . **WL 70824**
MC: . . . . **WK 70824**

HELEN.
Tracks: / There'll be some changes made / Easy living / You brought a new kind of love to me / Evil gal blues / Why try to change me now? / Draggin' my heart around.
LP: . . . . **MR 5233**

HELEN HUMES AND THE MUSE ALL STARS.
LP: . . . . **MR 5217**

HELEN HUMES WITH THE CONNIE BERRY TRIO (Humes, Helen & The Connie Berry Trio).
LP: . . . . **AP 107**

LET THE GOOD TIMES ROLL.
LP: **33711**

NEW MILLION DOLLAR SECRET.
Tracks: / Be baba leba / Fortune tellin' man / Every now and then / Central Avenue boogie / He don't love me anymore / Voo it / Pleasing man blues / It's better to give than to receive / They raided the joint / Airplane blues / I hear a rhapsody / Loud talkin' woman / You played on my piano / Helen's advice / All night long / If I could be with you one hour tonight.
LP: . . . . **KM 707**

ON THE SUNNY SIDE OF THE STREET.
Tracks: / Alright, okay, you win / If I could be with you one hour tonight / Ain't nobody's business / Kansas City / I'm satisfied / Blue because of you / On the sunny side of the street / I got it bad and that ain't good.
LP: . . . . **BLP 30167**

SWING WITH HELEN HUMES AND WYNTON KELLY (Humes, Helen & Wynton Kelly).
Tracks: / When day is done / Home / There'll be some changes made / Some day my prince will come / I'm confessin' / S'posin' / Pennies from Heaven / Very thought of you, The / Baby won't you please come home? / Solitude / I surrender, dear / My blue Heaven.
LP: **1007 598**

T'AIN'T NOBODY'S BIZ-NESS IF I DO.
Tracks: / You can depend on me / Trouble in mind / Among my souvenirs / Ain't misbehavin' / Stardust / Bill Bailey won't you please come home / When I grow too old to dream / Good man is hard to find, A / Bill / T'aint nobody's business if I do / I got it bad and that ain't good / When the saints go marching in.
LP: . . . . **COP 037**
LP: **1007 571**

Hummel (composer)

TRUMPET CONCERTOS AND FANFARES (See under Trumpet Music - Classical) (Philharmonia Orchestra).

Hummel, Mark

HIGH STEPPIN' (Hummel, Mark & The Blues Survivors).
LP: . . . . **DT 3018**

Hummingbird

HUMMINGBIRD.
LP: . . . . **AMLS 68292**

Hummingbirds

LOVEBUZZ.
Tracks: / Blush / She knows / Hollow inside / Tuesday / Word gets around / House taken over / Get on down / Alimony / Everything you said / Barbarian / Three in the morning / Michelle as well / If you leave / Miles to go.
LP: **828 679 1**
MC: **828 679 4**

Humperdinck, Engelbert

16 GREATEST LOVE SONGS.
Tracks: / Man without love, A / What now my love / I wish you love / There goes my everything / Dommage, dommage / Yours until tomorrow / Gentle on my mind / Am I that easy to forget / Shadow of your smile, The / Love letters / Way it used to be, The / Can't take my eyes off you / What a wonderful world / Misty blue / I'm a better man (for having loved you) / This is my song.
LP: . . . . **CN 2070**
MC: **CN4 2070**

AFTER THE LOVIN'.
Tracks: / After the lovin' / Can't smile without you / Let's remember the good times / I love making love to you / This I find is beautiful / This is what you mean to me / World without music, A / Let me happen to you / I can't live a dream / Hungry years.
LP: . . . . **EMC 3165**

ANOTHER TIME, ANOTHER PLACE.
LP: . . . . **SKL 5097**

DON'T YOU LOVE ME ANYMORE.
Tracks: / Don't you love me anymore / Stay away / When the night ends / I don't break easily / Say goodnight / Maybe this time / Baby me baby / Heart don't fail me now / Come spend the morning / Till I get it right.
LP: . . . . **EPC 84973**

ENGELBERT.
LP: . . . . **SKL 4985**

ENGELBERT - HEART OF GOLD.
Tracks: / I'm gonna dream our dreams for you / Take away the sorrow / Always on my mind / Sorry seems to be the hardest word / Tell it like it is / Our love is forever / You are so beautiful / Fashion magazine / Heart of gold / California blue / I wish I could be there / Someone to love / Something's gotten hold of my heart / I am in love again / Here we are / Let's fall in love again.
MC: **411382**

ENGELBERT HUMPERDINCK.
Tracks: / I'm a better man for having loved you / Gentle on my mind / Love letters / Time for us, A / Didn't we / I wish you love / Aquarius / All you've got to do is ask / Signs of love, The / Cafe / Let's kiss tomorrow goodbye / Winter world of love / Those were the days / Can't take my eyes off you / Love was here before the stars / Stardust.
LP: . . . . **SKL 5030**

ENGELBERT HUMPERDINCK COLLECTION ,THE.
LP: . . . . **STAR 2294**
MC: . . . . **STAC 2294**

ENGELBERT HUMPERDINCK SINGS THE HITS.
Tracks: / I can't live a dream / Baby, I'm a want you / You are the sunshine of my life / My cherie amour / First time ever I saw your face, The / And I love you so / Leaving on a jet plane / I'm stone in love with you / Raindrops keep fallin' on my head / Close to you / Can't smile without you / Help me make it through the night / Something / My love / Killing me softly with her song / Most beautiful girl / Wandrin' star / Without you / Words / Just the way you are.
LP: . . . . **SCX 6614**

ENGELBERT HUMPERDINCK'S GREATEST HITS.
Tracks: / Release me / Man without love, A / Way it used to be, The / Quando, quando, quando / Everybody knows we're through / There's a kind of hush / There goes my everything / Les bicyclettes de Belsize / I'm a better man for having loved you / Winter world of love / My world / Ten guitars / Am I that easy to forget / Last waltz, The.
LP: . . . . **TAB 8**
MC: . . . . **KTBC 8**
LP: . . . . **SKL 5198**

EYES OF LOVE.
Tracks: / Way it used to be, The / Can't take my eyes off you / Gentle on my mind / Everybody knows / Call on me / Nature boy / Love was there before the stars / Les bicyclettes de Belsize / Last waltz, The / This is my song / Spanish eyes / Place in the sun, A / Man without love, A / Quiet nights / How near is love / Through the eyes of love.
MC: . . . . **PWKMC 4026**

GETTING SENTIMENTAL.
Tracks: / As time goes by / Red sails in the sunset / In the still of the night / I don't want to walk without you / More I see you, The / You belong to my heart / Very thought of you, The / Moonlight becomes you / Lovely way to spend an evening, A / Stardust / You'll never know / Embraceable you / I'll walk alone / Harbour lights / Far away places / Getting sentimental over you.
LP: . . . . **STAR 2254**
MC: . . . . **STAC 2254**

IN LOVE.
Tracks: / This time tomorrow / Alone in the night / Love you back to sleep / Radio dancing / Aba heidschi bumbeidshi / Second time, The / I can never let you go / One and one made three / Natural love / Tokyo tears / One world.
LP: **209545**
MC: **409545**

LAST WALTZ, THE.

Tracks: / Last waltz, The / Dance with me / Two different worlds / If it comes to that / Walk hand in hand / Place in the sun, A / Long gone / All this world and the seven sea / Miss Elaine E.S. Jones / Everybody knows (we're through) / To the ends of the earth / That promise / Three little words / Those were the days / What now my love.
LP: SKL 4901

LIVE AT THE RIVIERA LAS VEGAS.
LP: TXS 105

LONG AGO AND FAR AWAY.
Tracks: / Long ago and far away / Stardust / They say it's wonderful / Harbour lights / I'll be around / But beautiful / Moonlight becomes you / Getting sentimental over you / In the still of the night / More I see you, The / Yours / I'll be seeing you.
LP: OR 0060

LOVE LETTERS (See under Jones, Tom) (Humperdinck, Engelbert/Tom Jones).

LOVE SONGS.
Tracks: / Raindrops keep falling on my head / Help me make it through the night / My love / I'm stone in love / Most beautiful girl / And I love you so / Leaving on a jet plane / Something / Baby, I'm a want you / (They long to be) close to you / Another time another place / First time ever I saw your face, The / Killing me softly with her song / I believe in miracles / Unforgettable (live) / Without you / Just the way you are / Love me tender / My cherie amour / For the good times / Spanish eyes (live) / There goes my everything (live) / If you love me (I won't care) (live) / Can't smile without you.
LP: VSOPLP 111
MC: VSOPMC 111

LOVELY WAY TO SPEND AN EVENING, A.
Tracks: / Lovely way to spend an evening, A / Far away places / I'll walk alone / My foolish heart / Very thought of you, The / You belong to my heart / Red sails in the sunset / You'll never know / I wish I knew / Embraceable you / I don't want to walk without you / As time goes by.
LP: OR 0059

LOVING YOU, LOSING YOU.
Tracks: / You light up my life / Close to you / I love you so / Love me with all your heart / Just the way you are / My love / Forever and ever / Sweetheart / Can't help falling in love / Last waltz, The / Release me / There goes my everything / Without you / Most beautiful girl, The / Am I that easy to forget / Loving you, losing you / Help me make it through the night / After the lovin' / Man without love, A / Killing me softly with her song.
LP: EPC 10024

MAN WITHOUT LOVE, A.
Tracks: / Man without love, A / Can't take my eyes off you / From here to eternity / Spanish eyes / Man and a woman, A / Quando, quando, quando / Up, up and away / Wonderland by night / What a wonderful world / Call on me / By the time I get to Phoenix / Shadow of your smile / Stardust / Pretty ribbon / Dommage dommage (too bad too bad) / When I say goodnight / Funny, familiar forgotten feelings / There goes my everything.
LP: SKL 4939

MERRY CHRISTMAS WITH ENGELBERT, A.
Tracks: / O come all ye faithful / Have yourself a merry little Christmas / Blue Christmas / Away in a manger / O little town of Bethlehem / We three kings of Orient are / First Noel, The / Silent night, holy night / Winter wonderland / Mary's boy child / God rest ye merry gentlemen / Lord's prayer, The.
LP: 4604651
MC: 4604654
MC: PWKMC 4033

MISTY BLUE.
Tracks: / Spanish eyes / Misty blue / Yours until tomorrow / Didn't we / I wish you love / Can't take my eyes off you / This is my song / Let me into your life / Shadow of your smile / From here to eternity / By the time I get to Phoenix / Funny familiar forgotten feelings / Love letters / What a wonderful world.
LP: TAB 40

MUSIC FOR THE MILLIONS.
Tracks: / Release me / Do I love you? / Let's kiss tomorrow goodbye / Call on me / Killing me softly with his song / Ten guitars / You are the sunshine of my life / Didn't we / Take my heart / Love is all.
LP: 6495105
MC: 7195105

RELEASE ME.
Tracks: / Last waltz, The / Spanish eyes / This is my song / Nature boy / There's a kind of hush / Everybody knows / How new is love / Walk hand in hand / Quiet nights / Man and a woman, A.
LP: CN 2034
MC: CN4 2304
LP: SKL 4868

REMEMBER I LOVE YOU.
Tracks: / Our time / Love is the reason (With Gloria Gaynor.) / Just for the love of you / How do I stop loving you? / After you / You made a believer out of me / I bid you goodbye / We'll meet again / Nothing's gonna change my love for you / Are you lonesome tonight? / Love is all.
LP: PL 71571
MC: PK 71571

STAR COLLECTION.
Tracks: / Release me / What a wonderful world / Am I that easy to forget? / Way it used to be, The / Place in the sun, A / There's a kind of hush / There goes my everything / I'm a better man (for having loved you) / Last waltz, The / Man and a woman, A / Quando, quando, quando / Man without love, A / Aquarius / Let the sun shine in / Les bicyclettes de Belsize / Winter world of love.
LP: 8201461
MC: 8201464

THIS IS MY LIFE.
Tracks: / Release me / Man without love, A / Way it used to be, The / Nature boy / Everybody knows we're through / There's a kind of hush / Last waltz, The / Two different worlds / Walk hand in hand / All this world and the seven seas / To the ends of the earth / Three little words / There goes my everything / Les bicyclettes de belsize / What now my love / This is my song / Misty blue / Take my heart / Winter world of love / I'm a better man (for having loved you) / Ten guitars / My world (il mondo) / Walk through this world / Am I that easy to forget.
2LP: 8207771
MCSET: 8207774

THIS MOMENT IN TIME.
Tracks: / This moment in time / First time in my life / You're something special / Maybe tomorrow / Can't help falling in love / Lovin' you too long / Much, much greater love / I believe in you / You know me / Travellin' boy.
LP: SCX 6611

VERY BEST OF ENGELBERT HUMPERDINCK.
Tracks: / Another time another place / Something / Day after day / Quando quando quando / Morning / Leaving on a jet plane / Forever and ever / Put you hand in the hand / Too beautiful too last / Help me make it through the night / Raindrops keep falling on my head / Eternally / Free as the wind / And I love you so / You are the sunshine of my life / Love me with all your heart / Most beautiful girl / Wandrin' star.
LP: MFP 50458
MC: KDKC 28063

WE MADE IT HAPPEN.
LP: SKL 5054

WORLD OF.....,THE.
LP: ADAH 439
MC: ADAHC 439

Humphrey, Paul

PAUL HUMPHREY SEXTET (Humphrey, Paul Sextet).
LP: DS 850

Humphrey, Percy

NEW ORLEANS PORTRAITS VOL 1 (Humphrey, Percy & His Crescent City Joymakers).
LP: SLP 231

PERCY HUMPHREY AND HIS CRESCENT CITY JOYMAKERS (Humphrey, Percy & His Crescent City Joymakers).
LP: GHB 85
LP: JCE 26

PERCY HUMPHREY'S HOT SIX.
LP: CLPS 1016

Humphrey, Willie

NEW ORLEANS JAZZ.
LP: GHB 248

Humphries, Barry

HOUSEWIFE SUPERSTAR.
Tracks: / Les Patterson cultural attache / Dame Edna Everage (at least you can say you (Parts 1 & 2) / Dame Edna Everage.
LP: CHC 18
MC: CHCMC 18
MC: HSC 3255

SOUND OF EDNA,THE.
LP: CHC 60

Humphries, Bobby

CITY BEAT.
LP: MJ 1502
MC: MJC 1502

Humpty Dumpty

HUMPTY DUMPTY (Various artists).
MC: STC 002

Hundredth

100TH ANNIVERSARY COLLECTION (See under Berlin, Irving) (Various artists).

Hungarian State...

SICILIAN, THE (See under Sicilian, The) (Hungarian State Symphony Orchestra).

Hungary

HUNGARIAN CHRISTMAS FOLK SONGS (Sebestyen, Marta).
LP: SLPM 17888

NORTH HUNGARIAN PEASANT SONGS & DANCES (Various artists).
Tracks: / Kaleidoscope: *Various artists* / Flute sonata: *Various artists* / Violin sonata: *Various artists.*
LP: CN 6001

SIXTH HUNGARIAN DANCE HOUSE FESTIVAL (Various artists).
LP: SLPX 12144

Hunger

STRICTLY FROM HUNGER.
LP: PSYCHO 14

Hunger (film)

HUNGER, THE (Original soundtrack) (Various artists).
LP: ACH 005

HUNGER, THE/YEAR OF LIVING DANGEROUSLY (Original Soundtrack) (Various artists).
LP: STV 81184
MC: CTV 81184

Hungerford, Bruce

MOONLIGHT PIANO SONATAS (see under Beethoven).

Hungry Chuck

SOUTH IN NEW ORLEANS.
Tracks: / Hats off, America / Cruisin' / Old Thomas Jefferson / Play that country music / Find the enemy / People do / Watch the trucks go by / Dixie highway / You better watch it Ben / Someday you're gonna run out of gas / Hoona, spoona / All bowed down / Doin' the funky lunch box.
LP: SEE 220

Hungry For Hits

HUNGRY FOR HITS various artists (Various artists).
LP: NE 1272
MC: CE 2272

Hunniford, Gloria

TASTE OF HUNNI, A.
LP: RITZLP 0002
MC: RITZC 0002

Hunningale, Peter

IN THIS TIME.
MC: SVC 001

Huns

GENE VINCENT'S 115TH DREAM.
LP: FUKU 6

Hunt, Declan

26 IRISH REPUBLICAN SONGS.
Tracks: / 3rd West Cork Brigade / James Connolly / Maurice O'Neill / Rising of the moon / Grave of wolfe tone / Signal fires / Sean Tracy / Arbour hill / Foggy dew, The / Follow me up to Carlow / Boy called Williams, A / Hurrah for the volunteers / Old howth gun / Broad black brimmer / Kevin Barry / Fergal O'Hanlon / Connolly was there / Lay him away on the hillside / Irish volunteers / Rebel heart / Boys of Killmichael / Soldiers of '22 / Valley of Knockanure / Old Fenian gun / God save Ireland / West awake.
MC: CKOL 604

REBEL SONGS OF THE 1798.
MC: CT 119

Hunt, Donald

THERE IS SWEET MUSIC (Hunt, Donald Singers of Worcester).
Tracks: / There is sweet music / Deep in my soul / O wild west wing / Owls / Shepherd, what's love, I pray? / Blows the wind to-day? / Merry miller / Dark forest, The / Song of the plough (Rhoades, James: translator. (Original doubtless in Latin.)) / Songs of springtime (Track consists of seven songs as following:) / Under the greenwood tree / River-god's song, The / Spring the sweet spring / iv! Love is a sickness / Sigh no more, ladies / Good wine / To daffodils / Bluebird, The.
LP: ACA 553

Hunt, Irvine

TALES OF MANLAFF AND TOEWOMAN.
Tracks: / Humorous poems of a pair of Stoneage people / Wild haired but somewhat timid gentleman / Travelling warily through a blistered landscape....
LP: SFA 036

Hunt, Marsha

WALK ON GUILDED SPLINTERS.
Tracks: / Walk on guilded splinters / Let the sun shine in / Hot rod pappa / Stacey Grove / No face, no name, no number / My world is empty without you / Moan, you moaners / Keep the customer satisfied / Long black veil / You ain't goin' nowhere / Woman child / Desdemona / Wild thing / Hippy Gumbo.
LP: SEE 209

Hunt, Tommy

YOUR MAN.
Tracks: / Lover / This and only this / I am a witness / Human / Your man / Don't make me over / She'll hurt you too / Didn't I tell you / It's all a bad dream / Make the night a little longer / Oh Lord what are you doing to me / Parade of broken hearts, The / I might like it / You made a man out of me / Just a little taste of your sweet lovin' / Promised land.
LP: KENT 059

Hunter

DREAMS OF ORDINARY MEN.
LP: 831 760-1
MC: 831 760-4

Hunter, Alastair

ALASTAIR HUNTER & THE LORNE SCOTTISH DANCE BAND (Hunter, Alastair & The Scottish Dance Band).
Tracks: / Baldovan reel / Moray reel / Silver tassie, The / Jimmy Shankland's reel / Diamond jubilee, The / Irish rover, The / Blooms o bon accord, The / Jimmy's fancy / Welcome to Dufftown / Black mountain reel / Haughs o' Cromdale / Rory O'More.
MC: CWGR 131

SCOTTISH RAMBLE, A (Hunter, Alastair & The Scottish Dance Band).
LP: OU 2208

Hunter, Alberta

BLUES WE TAUGHT YOUR MOTHER (Hunter, Alberta/Victoria Spivey/Lucille Hegamin).
LP: OBC 520

CHICAGO-THE LIVING LEGENDS (Hunter, Alberta & Lovie Austin).
Tracks: / St. Louis blues / Moanin' low / Downhearted blues / Now I'm satisfied / Sweet Georgia Brown / You better change / C-jam blues / Streets paved with gold / Gallion stomp / I will always be in love with you.
LP: OBC 510

CLASSIC ALBERTA HUNTER.
Tracks: / You can't tell the difference after dark / Secondhand man / Send me a man / Chirpin' the blues / Downhearted blues / I'll see you go / Fine and mellow / Yelpin' the blues / Someday, sweetheart / Love I have for you, The / Castle's rockin', The / Boogie woogie swing, The / I won't let you down / Take your big hands off / He's got a punch like Joe Louis.
LP: ST 115

GLORY OF, THE.
LP: 856 06

LEGENDARY, THE.
LP: SL 5195
MC: SLC 5195

TWENTIES, THE.
LP: ST 123

Hunter, Andy

KING FAREWEEL.
Tracks: / Ye heilan chiels / My son David / Battle of Harlaw, The / Kilbowie hill / Laird O' drum, The / Johnnie Armstrang / Twa corbies / Auld shoes, The / Up and awa' wi' the Laverock / King Fareweel.
LP: LIFL 7002
MC: LIFC 7002

Hunter, Chris

EARLY DAYS.
Tracks: / Elephants' tales / Too high / July '79 / Vocal fanfare / Waltz for Eric / Forty two / Prelude to a kiss / Happy endings.
LP: ORA 104

Hunter, Ian

ALL AMERICAN ALIEN BOY.
LP: CBS 81310

ALL THE GOOD ONES ARE TAKEN.
Tracks: / All the good ones are taken / Every step of the way / Fun / Speechless / Death 'n' glory boys / That girl is rock 'n' roll / Somethin's going on / Captain void 'n' video jets / Seeing double.

LP: . . . . CBS 25379
MC: 40 25379

AMERICAN MUSIC (See under Hunter-Ronson) (Hunter, Ian & Mick Ronson).

COLLECTION: IAN HUNTER.
MC: . . . . CCSMC 290

IAN HUNTER.
LP: . . . . CBS 80710

SHORT BACK AND SIDES.
Tracks: / Central Park N'West / Lisa likes rock 'n' roll / I need your love / Old records never die / Noises / Rain / Gun control / Theatre of the absurd / Leave me alone / Keep on burning.
LP: . . . . CHR 1326
MC: . . . . ZCHR 1326

VERY BEST OF IAN HUNTER, THE.
LP: 4675081
MC: 4675084

WELCOME TO THE CLUB.
Tracks: / F.B.I. / Once bitten twice shy / Angeline / Laugh at me / All the way from Memphis / I wish I was your mother / Irene Wilde / Just another night / Cleveland rocks / Standin' in my light / Bastard / Walkin' with a mountain / All the young dudes / Slaughter on Tenth Avenue / We gotta get out of here / Silver needles / Man 'o' war / Sons and daughters.
2LP: . . . . CJT 6
MC: . . . . ZCJT 6

YOU'RE NEVER ALONE WITH A SCHIZOPHRENIC.
Tracks: / Just another night / Wild east / Cleveland rocks / Ships / When the daylight comes / Life after death / Standin' in my light / Bastard / Outsider, The.
LP: . . . . CHR 1214
MC: . . . . ZCHR 1214

Hunter, Ivory Joe

7TH STREET BOOGIE.
Tracks: / 7th Street boogie / Boogin' in the basement / High cost low pay blues / Siesta with sonny / I quit my pretty mama / Don't fall in love with me / I got your water on / Leave her alone / Blues at sunrise / Reconversion blues / Giving blues / Send me pretty mama / Woo wee blues / What did you do to me / S P Blues / Don't you believe her.
LP: . . . . KIX 4

ARTISTRY OF IVORY JOE HUNTER, THE.
Tracks: / If you want my love / In memories / If you were my love / Lonesome cold blooded woman / How about me / I'm cuttin' out / I need you so / My baby's gone / I'm lost without you.
LP: . . . . BDL 1016

HITS, THE.
Tracks: / Blues at sunrise / Pretty mama blues / Don't fall in love with me / Waiting in vain / Guess who / Landlord blues / Jealous heart / I almost lost my mind / I quit my pretty mama / S.P. blues / I need you so / It's a sin / Since I met you baby / Empty arms / Love's a hurting game / City lights.
LP: . . . . OFF 6040

I HAD A GIRL.
Tracks: / Boogin' in the rain / I love my man / Mean woman blues / False friend blues / I like it / Stop rocking that train / Please don't cry any more / I had a girl / Let me dream / Gimme a pound o' ground / Where shall I go / It's a sin / I'm yours until eternity / U name it.
LP: . . . . KIX 25

IVORY JOE HUNTER SINGS 16 OF HIS GREATEST HITS.
Tracks: / Jealous heart / I quit my pretty mama / Waiting in vain / No money / No luck blues / Too late / I like it / I have no reason to complain / Lying woman / Guess who / In time / Code song, The / Please don't cry anymore / Don't fall in love with me / False friend blues / It's you just you / Changing blues.
LP: . . . . KLP 605
LP: . . . . SING 605

JUMPING AT THE DEWDROP.
Tracks: / Jumping at the dew drop / Blues at midnight / Are your hep / You're always looking for / She's a killer / We're gonna boogie / Old gal and new gal blues / Old man's boogie / If you see my baby / You lied.
LP: . . . . KIX 15

SINCE I MET YOU BABY.
LP: 830 897-1

THIS IS IVORY JOE.
Tracks: / Welcome home / City lights / Stolen moments / Cottage for sale / Guess who / Old fashioned love / Pretty mama blues / Can I forget you / I love you so much / Darling I need you / Did you mean it / My search was ended.
LP: . . . . CH 97

Hunter, Karen

YOUNG TRADITIONALIST.
Tracks: / Hunter, The / Summer sea / Country folks / Gossips / Hello sailor / Day in the life of a village / Sign of spring / Reminiscing / Cops 'n' robbers / Clockwork(er) / Autumn-fail / Good old days / Night on the town / Typist.
LP: . . . . LILP 5122
MC: . . . . LICS 5122

Hunter, Long John

TEXAS BORDER TOWN BLUES.
LP: . . . . DT 3011

Hunter, Robert

BOX OF RAIN.
Tracks: / Box of rain / Scarlet begonias / Franklin's tower / Jack Straw / Brown eyed women / Reuben and Cerise / Space / Deal / Promontory rider / Ripple / Boys in the bar room / Stella blue.
MC: . . . . RACS 0214

LIBERTY.
LP: . . . . RRLP 2029

TALES OF THE GREAT RUM RUNNERS.
Tracks: / Lady Simplicity / Dry dust road / Rum runners / Maybe she's a bluebird / It must have been the roses / Standing at your door / Keys to the rain / That train / I heard you singing / Children's lament / Boys in the barrooom / Arizona lightning / Mad.
LP: . . . . GDV 4013
MC: . . . . GDTC 4013

TIGER ROSE.
Tracks: / Tiger rose / Rose of Sharon / Dance a hole / Over the hills / Yellow moon / One thing to try / Wild Bill / Cruel white water / Last flash / Ariel.
LP: . . . . GDV 4010
MC: . . . . GDTC 4010

Hunter, Sonya

FAVOURITE SHORT STORIES.
MC: . . . . HEY 010CS

Hunter, Steve

DEACON, THE.
Tracks: / Idler, The / Black cat moan / Glidepath / Hidden portrait / Old man in the boat, The / Ghost riders / Koza / Road to Jakarta / Pig jam (Op. 2 in E Major) / Surge, The.
LP: . . . . ILP 031

SWEPT AWAY.
Tracks: / Eight miles high / Eldorado street / Going down / Rubber man / Of all times to leave / Jasper St Viaduct guitar rag / Sail on sailor / Swept away / Sea sonata / Deep blue.
LP: . . . . K 50357

Hunter, Willie

WILLIE HUNTER 1982.
LP: . . . . CM 010

Hunter-Ronson

YUI ORTA.
Tracks: / American music / Loner, The / Womens intuition / Cool / Big time / Livin' in a heart / Sons 'n' lovers / Beg a little love / Tell it like it is / Sweet dreamer.
LP: 838 973 1
MC: 838 973 4

Hunters

HITS FROM THE HUNTERS.
LP: 33.8023

Hunters Club

BURNT ALIVE.
LP: . . . . PIG 003

TOO FAR GONE TO TURN AROUND.
Tracks: / Play the game again / Lightning strikes / Sure feels good / Ain't seen nothing yet / Hit the street / Island of lies.
MLP: . . . . THC LP 1

Hunters & Collectors

COLLECTIVE WORKS.
Tracks: / Faraway man / Throw your arms around me / Inside a fireball / Dog / Everythings on fire / Do you see what I see / Around the flame / Give me a reason / Wishing well / Talking to a stranger / Say goodbye / January rain / Back on the breadline / Is there anybody in there / Still hanging 'round / Breakneck road.
MC: . . . . EIRSAC 1032

FATE.
Tracks: / Back on the breadline, The / Wishing Well / You can have it all / Do You See What I See? / Around the flame / Faraway man / Under The Sun / What are you waiting for? / So Long Ago? / Real World / Something to believe in.
LP: . . . . MIRF 1037
MC: . . . . MIRFC 1037

GHOST NATION.
LP: . . . . WX 348
MC: . . . . WX 348C

HUMAN FRALITY.
LP: . . . . IRS 5801

HUNTERS AND COLLECTORS.
Tracks: / Tow truck / Droptank / Mouthtrap / Lumps of lead / Talking to a stranger / Scream who / Run run run.
LP: . . . . OVED 92
MC: . . . . OVEDC 92
LP: V2260

JAWS OF LIFE.
Tracks: / 42 wheels / Holding down a.d. / Way to go out / I couldn't give it to you / It's early days yet / I believe / Betty's worry or the slab / Hayley's doorstep / Red lane / Carry me / Little chalkie.
LP: . . . . EPC 26310
MC: 40 26130

Hunting Lodge

NOMAD LODGE.
LP: . . . . SER 04

Hunting Of The Snark

HUNTING OF THE SNARK (Various artists).
Tracks: / Introduction: *Batt, Mike* / Children of the sky: *Batt, Mike* / Bellman's speech, The: *Batt, Mike* / Escapade: *Batt, Mike* / Midnight smoke: *Batt, Mike* / Snooker song, The: *Batt, Mike* / Pig must die, The: *Batt, Mike* / Beaver's lesson, The: *Batt, Mike* / Delicate combination, A: *Batt, Mike* / As long as the moon can shine: *Batt, Mike* / Dancing towards disaster: *Batt, Mike* / Vanishing, The: *Batt, Mike*.
LP: . . . . SNARK 1
MC: . . . . SNARKK 1
LP: . . . . MODEM 1007
MC: . . . . MODEMC 1007

HUNTING OF THE SNARK, THE (Various artists).
Tracks: / Hunting of the snark: *Various artists* / Two old bachelors, The: *Various artists* / Jumblies, The: *Various artists* / Mr. & Mrs. Discobbolos: *Various artists* / Jackdaw of Rheims: *Various artists*.
MC: . . . . ANV 627

Hunting The Bismarck

HUNTING THE BISMARCK Forester, C.S (Andrew , Harry).
MC: . . . . LFP 4171565

Huntsmen

ROUTE 66.
LP: . . . . RC 512

Hurby's Machine

HURBY'S MACHINE (The house that rap built) (Various artists).
Tracks: / Hit 'em with this: *Antoinette* / Keep 'em steppin': *None-Stop* / Fabulous: *Fabulous 2* / Contact sport: *Mau-Mau Clan Overlords* / I am down: *Salt 'N' Pepa* / Push it (remix): *Salt 'N' Pepa* / I got an attitude: *Antoinette* / House that rap built, The: *Mau-Mau Clan Overlords* / Let the drummer get ill: *Super Lovers* / Just go: *Future Shock*.
LP: . . . . FFRLP 2
MC: . . . . FFRMC 2

Hurdle, Les

SECRET MELODY, THE (Hurdle, Les & Thor Baldursson).
MC: . . . . C 103

Hurdy Gurdy

MUSIC OF THE HURDY-GURDY, THE (Various artists).
Tracks: / Il Pastor Fido (Vivaldi): *Various artists* / Les Amusements d'une heure (Baton): *Various artists* / Crocodile bourree, The: *Various artists* / Lady Diamond/New Jig: *Various artists* / Satins blanc: *Various artists* / Malashevska: *Various artists* / Laride: *Various artists* / Queen Adelaide: *Various artists*.
MC: . . . . CSDL 374

Hurley, Bill

DOUBLE AGENT.
Tracks: / Reconsider me / Double agent / My whole world ended / Midnight / You left the water running / Gimme gimme good lovin' / Where'd he get that idea / Let's start all over again / What is this / Party party / Alright on the night.
LP: . . . . FIEND 49

Hurley, Michael

LONG JOURNEY.
LP: . . . . ROUNDER 3011

SNOCKGRASS.
LP: . . . . ROUNDER 3043

WATER TOWER, THE.
Tracks: / Revenant, The / I paint a design / Lush green grass / Keep rockin' / You'll never go to heaven / Ma's dream blues / I still could not forget you then / Indian chiefs 'n' hula girls / Broadcasting the blues / Uncle Bob's corner / Moon song.
LP: . . . . SAVE 051

Hurley, Red

HIT SINGLES.
LP: . . . . PLAY 1010

IRISH STARTIME.
LP: . . . . IST 4443

SINCERELY.
LP: . . . . HPE 626
MC: . . . . HPC 626

Hurley, Steve 'Silk'

SILK.
LP: 7820031
MC: 7820034

WORK IT OUT.
LP: . . . . WX 296
MC: . . . . WX 296C
LP: 782 003-1

Hurrah

BEAUTIFUL, THE.
Tracks: / Big sky / Troubled brow / Wisdom waits / Diana Diana / Velveteen / Let it be her / Call for me / Sad but true / Girls of Jaina / She said.
LP: . . . . KWLP 10
MC: . . . . KWC 10
LP: 209258
MC: 409258

BOXED.
LP: . . . . SKINT 1

TELL GOD I'M HERE.
Tracks: / I would if I could / Better times / Sweet sanity / Celtic / Walk in the park, A / How many rivers? / If love could kill / Miss this kiss / How high the moon / Mr. Sorrowful.
LP: 208 201
MC: 408 201

WAY AHEAD.
LP: . . . . PACE 2

Hurray For Hollywood

HURRAY FOR HOLLYWOOD various artists (Various artists).
LP: 20106
MC: 40106

Hurricane

SLAVE TO THE THRILL.
Tracks: / Reign of love / Next to you / Young man / Dance little sister / Don't wanna dream / Temptations / Ten thousand years / In the fire / Let it slide / Lock me up / Smiles like a child.
LP: . . . . ENVLP 1004
MC: . . . . TCENV 1004

TAKE WHAT YOU WANT.
LP: . . . . RR 9723

Hurricane Zouk

HURRICANE ZOUK (World Beat from Martinique and Guadaloupe) (Various artists).
Tracks: / Guetho a liso: *Zouk Time featuring Kanda Bongo Man* / Anti-Mako: *Vincent, Frankie* / Dance bonne pa dance: *Hubert, Gerard* / Mikolasie/ Misik a negre: *Come Back des Vikings Guadaloupe* / Pina colada: *Vincent, Frankie* / Leve zouke: *Hubert, Gerard* / Tension la ka monte: *Vikin* / New York ameliore (edited): *Soukoue Ko Ou*.
LP: . . . . EWV 2
MC: . . . . TCEWV 2

Hurricanes

OVER THE EDGE.
LP: . . . . ENVLP 511
MC: . . . . TCENV 511

Hurstpierpoint College

HURSTPIERPOINT COLLEGE CHOIR (Hurstpierpoint College Choir).
Tracks: / Of the Father's heart begotten (Hymn) / Matin responsory, The / Come, Thou Redeemer of the earth (Hymn) / 'Twas in the year that King Uzziah died (Carol) / Bright the vision that delighted (Hymn) / Advent prose, The (orate caeli) / Hark, a herald voice is calling (Hymn) / This is the record of John (Anthem) / Lo, He comes with clouds descending (Hymn) / Adam lay ybounden (Carol) / Hymn to the Virgin, A (Carol) / Spotless Rose, A (Carol) / Come, Thou long-expected Jesus (Hymn) / Holly and the ivy, The (Carol) / Ding dong, merrily on high (Carol) / People that in darkness sat, The (Hymn) / Allelujah, a new work is come on hand (Carol) / O come all ye faithful (Hymn) / Closing versicles and responses / O come, o come Emmanuel (Hymn).
LP: . . . . APS 354

Hurt, Mississippi John

AVALON BLUES.
Tracks: / Stackolee / Coffee blues / Slidin' delta / Corina Corina / Nobody's dirty business / Monday morning blues.
LP: . . . . HT 301

BEST OF JOHN 'MISSISSIPPI' HURT.
2LP: . . . . VSD 19-20

BEST OF JOHN MISSISSIPPI HURT.

LP: VMLP 5304
MC: VMTC 6304

LAST SESSIONS.
MCSET: MCCV 79327

MISSISSIPPI JOHN HURT IN 1928.
LP: L 1065

MONDAY MORNING BLUES Library of Congress recordings vol. 1.
LP: FLY 553

SACRED AND SECULAR 1963 (Volume 3 of the Library of Congress sides).
Tracks: / Pallet on your floor / Stackolee / I'm satisfied / Ain't nobody but you babe / See see rider / Waiting for a train / Funky butt / Shortnin' bread / Mary don't you weep / Farther along / Do Lord remember me / Over in the gloryland / Glory halleluja / What a friend we have in Jesus / Where shall I be / Weeping and wailing.
LP: HT 320

SHAKE THAT THING.
Tracks: / Candy man / My creole belle / Make me a pallet on the floor / Shake that thing / I'm satisfied / Salty dog / Nobody's business but mine / Angels laid him away The / Casey Jones - talkin' Casey / Baby what's wrong with you / Lonesome blues.
LP: BMLP 1030

Hurt Of The ...

BIG CITY SOUL VOL.2 (Various artists).
Tracks: / I'm stepping out of the picture: *Maestro, Johnny & The Crests* / (There goes) the forgotten man: *Radcliffe, Jimmy* / Givin' up: *Lewis, Junior Trio* / Who's gonna mention my name: *Sattin, Lonnie* / Is he all right: *St. Clair, Sylvia* / Love of my man, The: *Kilgore, Theola* / Losing my touch: *Brown, Maxine* / What'cha gonna say tomorrow: *Jackson, Chuck* / I just don't know what to do with myself: *Hunt, Tommy* / Haunted house: *Wilson, Jackie* / Lonely people do foolish things: *Clay, James* / Try to get you out of my heart: *Toys* / Come the night: *Knight, Marie* / Nobody cares (about me): *Washington, Jeanette* / Remember me: *Shirelles* / How do you feel now: *Big Maybelle*.
LP: KENT 087

Hurt, Peter

LOST FOR WORDS (Hurt, Peter Orchestra).
Tracks: / Overture / Yesterdays / Lost for words / Perilous twilight / Twenty / Secret life of plants / Resolution.
LP: SPJ 525

Hurtt, Phil

PH FACTOR.
Tracks: / Boogie city / PH Factor / I've got the power / I think it's about time / Don't let this moment get away / I'm in love again / Let it flow.
LP: FT 561

Husby, Per

DEDICATIONS (Husby, Per Orchestra).
Tracks: / Accentuate the bass / I'm never happy anymore / Take a chance on spring / Prima Vera-Lasse / Good bait / Song you'll never sing / Chan's sorta Mingus blues / That's the way it goes.
LP: AFF 136

Hush

AMERICAN GIRL.
Tracks: / Callin' you / Midnight train / Take it while you can / Don't say goodbye / You really should be swingin' / Winter love / Radio station / Son of an old rock and roller / Alright on the night / Singing the blues / American girl / I do love you.
LP: USH 1

Husker Du

CANDY APPLE GREY.
Tracks: / Crystal / Don't want to know if you are lonely / I don't know for sure / Sorry somehow / Too far down / Hardly getting over it / Dead set on destruction / Eiffel Tower high / No promise have I made / All this I've done for you.
LP: WX 40
MC: WX 40 C

EVERYTHING FALLS APART.
LP: REFLEX D

FLIP YOUR WIG.
MC: SST 055 C
LP: SST 055

LAND SPEED RECORD.
LP: SST 195
MC: SSTC 195

NEW DAY RISING.
LP: SST 031

WAREHOUSE SONGS AND STORIES.
Tracks: / These important years / Charity, charity, prudence and hope / Standing in the rain / Back from somewhere / Ice cold ice / You're a soldier / Could you be the one / Too much spice / Friend, you've got to fall / She floated away / Bed of nails / Tell you why tomorrow / It's not peculiar / Actual condition / No reservations / Turn it around / She's a woman / Up in the air / You can live at home.
2LP: 925544 1

ZAN ARCADE.
LP: SST 027

Husky, Ferlin

BOP CAT BOP.
LP: DEMAND 0040

FAVOURITES OF....
LP: SLP 3018
MC: GT 53018

FERLIN HUSKY-THE DOT SERIES.
Tracks: / Sugar moon / Snap your fingers / When love comes home tonight / Once in a blue moon / There ain't enough whiskey in Tennessee / Gone / Wings of a dove / Sweet misery / Waltz you saved for me, The / Backyard, The.
LP: IMCA 39077
MC: IMCAC 39077

GREATEST HITS OF FERLIN HUSKY.
MC: 4XL 9385

SONGS OF THE HEART AND HOME.
LP: HAT 3115
MC: HATC 3115

WALKIN' AND HUMMIN'.
Tracks: / Walkin' & hummin' / I'm so lonesome I could cry / I could never be ashamed of you / I can't help it / Undesired / May you never be alone / My shadow / I lost my love today / Alone and forsaken / There'll be no teardrops tonight / Living in a trance / Why should we try anymore.
LP: HAT 3053
MC: HATC 3053

Husky, Tommy

DOUBLE EDGE BLADE.
LP: NEVLP 153

Hussain, Zakir

MAKING MUSIC (Hussain, Zakir & John McLaughlin).
Tracks: / Making music / Zakir / Water girl / Toni / Anisa / Sunjog / You and me / Sabah.
LP: ECM 1349

ZAKIR HUSSAIN & THE RHYTHM EXPERIENCE (Hussain, Zakir & The Rhythm Experience).
Tracks: / Balinese fantasy / Nines over easy / Lineage / Def and drum / Triveni / Rapanagutan / Ryupak / Rhythm sonata in E major.
LP: APN 307

Hussars

BAND OF BROTHERS (King Hussars & Gurkhas Pipes & Drums).
MC: ZC BND 1053

Hussey, Winston

GHETTO MAN PROBLEM.
LP: LLLP 17

Hustle Z

SHOW ME YOURS AND I'LL SHOW YOU MINE (Hustle Z & M.C. Cool P).
Tracks: / No more Mr. Nice Guy / Why James Brown / In the search / Now that's love / OK girl (let me in your world) / My def girl / Girl, I'm so in love with you / Face / Ayo.
LP: SDE 4010
MC: SDE 4010MC

Hustlers Convention

1989 HUSTLERS CONVENTION LIVE Music of life - live (Various artists).
LP: SPOCK 1

Huston, Cecillia

MODERATION (see Rush, Barbara) (Huston, Cecillia & Barbara Rush).

RIGHT TIME (see Rush, Barbara) (Huston, Cecillia & Barbara Rush).

'Hutch'

GOLDEN AGE OF HUTCH (THE).
Tracks: / Okay baby / Don't blame me / Murder in the moonlight / May I have the next romance with you / Remember me / Foggy day, A / Sing my heart / Goodnight my love / It's de-lovely / I won't tell a soul / I'll remember / There goes my dream / Imagination / Nearness of you, The / Best things in life are free, The / Room 504.
LP: GX 41 2550
MC: TCGX 2550

HUTCH AT THE PIANO.
2LP: WRCSHB 28

MAGIC OF HUTCH, THE.
Tracks: / Violins and violets / Imaginez / How soon will I be seeing you? / Where or when / It might have been a different story / You were never lovelier / Let's fall in love / Intermezzo (souvenir de Vienne) / Take care of my heart / What's new? / Old apple tree / Among my souvenirs / Either it's love or it isn't / Why did it have to end so? / People will say we're in love / That's the beginning of the end.
LP: JOY 269
MC: TC JOY'D 269

MOONLIGHT COCKTAIL.
Tracks: / All the things you are / Mist on the river / Maria Elena / You stepped out of a dream / Sand in my shoes / Flamingo / Stardust / Jealousy / Moonlight cocktail / Kiss me / Sophisticated lady / Till the stars forget to shine / I'll be seeing you / Spring will be a little late this year / I'll remember April / Don't you know I care / I'm confessin' / All through the day / You keep coming back like a song / La mer.
LP: EG 2604561
MC: EG 2604564

SINGING FOR YOU EVERYBODY.
Tracks: / Singing for you / These foolish things / Once in a while / September in the rain / Girl in the Alice blue gown / Moon at sea / Carelessly / No regrets / Tomorrow is another day / Your heart and mine / Night and day / Red sails in the sunset / Morning after, The / There's rain in my eyes / Love is like a cigarette / My heart is haunted by the ghost of your smile.
LP: CHD 155
MC: MCHD 155

SO MANY MEMORIES.
MCSET: DTO 10298

THAT OLD FEELING.
Tracks: / Where are you / September in the rain / Tomorrow is another day / In the chapel in the moonlight / Moon or no moon / Afterglow / In an old cathedral town / That old feeling / Paris is not the same / Singing for you / Stardust on the moon / They can't take that away from me / Way you look tonight / Carelessly / Whispers in the dark / Greatest mistake of my life / Just remember / Goodnight to you all.
LP: BUR 011
MC: 4 BUR 011

WITH A SONG IN MY HEART.
Tracks: / With a song in my heart / What would happen to me if something happened / Happy-go-lucky you and broken-hearted me / You are too beautiful / No thrill at all / Whistling in the dark / Let's call it a day / Lover / From out of nowhere / I've got a feeling I'm falling / Always your humble slave / I may be wrong / Wind's in the west / It's best to forget / Blue without you / Shadows on the window / One tiny tear / Goodbye to love.
LP: RFL 38

Hutch, Billy

CHANGE OF TIME.
LP: FLP 250

Hutch, Willie

IN & OUT.
Tracks: / In and out / Slick / Brother's gonna work it out / Sunshine lady / Get ready for the get down / You sure know how to love your man / Them of Foxy Brown / Love power / Tell me why has our love turned cold / Shake it / Party down / If you ain't got no money (you can't get no honey) / We gonna party tonight / What you gonna do after the party.
LP: STMR 9019
MC: CSTMR 9019

IN TUNE.
Tracks: / All hell broke loose / Paradise / All American funkathon / Anything is possible if you believe in love / Come on and dance with me / Easy does it / Hip shakin' sexy lady / Nothing lasts forever.
LP: K 56559

MAKING A GAME OUT OF LOVE.
LP: ZL 72378
MC: ZK 72378

Hutcherson, Bobby

AMBOS MUNDOS (BOTH WORLDS).
Tracks: / Pomponio / Tin tin deo / Both worlds / Street song / Beep d' bop / Poema para ravel / Yelapa / Besame mucho.
LP: LLP 1522

COLOUR SCHEMES.
Tracks: / Recorda me / Bemsha swing / Rosemary, Rosemary / Second-hand brown / Whisper not / Colour scheme, The / Remember / Never let me go.
LP: LLP 1508
MC: LLP 51508

CRUISIN' THE BIRD.
LP: LLP 1517

DIALOGUE.
Tracks: / Catta / Idle while / Les noirs marchant / Dialogue / Ghetto lights / Jasper.
LP: BLJ 84198

FAREWELL KEYSTONE.
Tracks: / Crescent Moon / Short stuff / Prism / Starting over / Rubber man / Mapenzi.
LP: TR 124

FOUR SEASONS (Hutcherson, Bobby/ George Cables).
Tracks: / I mean you / All of you / Spring is here / Star eyes / If I were a bell / Summertime / Autumn leaves.
LP: SJP 210

GOOD BAIT.
Tracks: / Love samba / Good bait / Highway one / Montgomery / Spring is here / Israel.
LP: LLP 501
MC: LLP 5501

TOTAL ECLIPSE.
Tracks: / Herzog / Total eclipse / Matrix / Shame, shame / Pompeian.
LP: BST 84291

Hutchings, Ashley

ALBION JOURNEY, AN.
2LP: HNBL 4802
MCSET: HNBC 4802

AS YOU LIKE IT (Hutchings, Ashley All Stars).
LP: SPIN 135

BY GLOUCESTER DOCKS I SAT DOWN AND WEPT.
Tracks: / Prologue / Ring on her finger / Dancing under the rose again / Under the rose / Keep you warm / Flower arranging / We walked in God's country / Small town romance.
LP: PAT 1
MC: PATC 1

COMPLEAT DANCING MASTER, THE (Hutchings, Ashley. Et Al).
Tracks: / Beginning of the world, The / Stantipes / Trotto / Nonesuch / Cuckholds all awry / Dashing white sergeant / Devil among the tailors / Beatrice / Haste to the wedding / Triumph, the / Off she goes / Long odds / Mr. Cosgill's delight / Bonnie breast knot / Double lead through / Barley break / Cussion dance / Arbeau and capriol / Hare's maggot, The.
LP: HNBL 4416
MC: HNBC 4416

MORRIS ON (Hutchings, Ashley/ Thompson/Nicol).
Tracks: / Bean setting / Shooting / I'll go and enlist for a sailor / Princess Royal / Cuckoo's nest, The / Morris off / Morris call / Greensleeves / Nutting girl, The / Old woman tossed up in a blanket / Shepherd's hey / Trunkles / Staines morris / Lads a bunchum / Young Collins / Vandals of Hammerwich / Willow tree.
LP: HNBL 4406
LP: IRSP 6
MC: HNBC 4406

Hutchinson, Leslie

YOU AND THE NIGHT AND THE MUSIC.
Tracks: / Out of nowhere / Close your eyes / Life is just a bowl of cherries / Maybe I love you too much / My wishing song / Did you ever see a dream walking? / That's love / I travel alone / I saw stars / As I sit here / June in january / I only have eyes for you / Blue moon / You and the night and the music / Love is everywhere / Wake / Two tired eyes / Kiss me goodnight.
LP: SVL 183
MC: CSVL 183

Hutchison, Frank

TRAIN THAT CARRIED MY GIRL....
LP: ROUNDER 1007

Hutson, Leroy

LEROY HUTSON.
Tracks: / All because of you / I bless the day it's different / Cool out / Lucky fellow / Can't stay away / So much love.
LP: K 56139

THERE'S MORE WHERE THIS CAME FROM.
Tracks: / Love the feeling / So nice / More where that came from / Never know what you can do (give it a try) / Lover's holiday / Get to this (you'll get to me) / Ghetto '74, The / After the fight / Heaven right here (on earth) / When you smile.
LP: CUR 2004
MC: ZCCUR 2004

UNFORGETTABLE.
Tracks: / Unforgettable / Funk in my life / Right or wrong / So nice / Lonely without you / More where that came from.
LP: RSS 15

Hutto, J.B.

BLUES FOR FONESSA.
LP: AMLP 823

BLUESMASTER.

LP: . . . . JSP 1096

HAWK SQUAT.
LP: . . . . DS 617
LP: . . . . DL 617

J.B. HUTTO LIVE: VOL 1.
LP: . . . . CR 30182

LIVE AT SANDY'S JAZZ REVIVAL (Hutto, J.B. & The Housebreakers).
LP: . . . . BARON LP 101

SLIDESLINGER (Hutto, J.B. & The New Hawks).
LP: . . . . VR 003
MC: . . . . VR 003C

SLIDEWINDER.
LP: . . . . DS 636

SLIPPIN' & SLIDIN' (Hutto, J.B. & The New Hawks).
Tracks: / Pretty baby / Why do things happen to me / New hawks walk / Eighteen year old girl / Black's ball / Soul over / Somebody loan me a dime / Jealous hearted woman / Little girl dressed in blue / I'm leaving you.
LP: . . . . FIEND 17
MC: . . . . VR 006C
LP: . . . . VR 006

Hutton, Betty

SONGS FROM HER FILMS.
LP: . . . . AEI 2120

Hutton, Joe

HARTHOPE BURN.
MC: . . . . MWMC 1031

JOE HUTTON OF COQUETDALE.
Tracks: / Swindon / Joe Huttons march / Foxglove, The / Wade hampton's / Stack of wheat, The / Memories / Nancy / Cameron Highlanders, The / Archie's fancy / Old drove road, The / Anniversary / Father Fielding's favourite / Hawk, The / Cheviot rant / Crawley dene / Powburn lads / Brackenrigg / Remember me / Liddell's hornpipe / Elsey's waltz / Andrews march / Bonnie cragside / Coquetdale, The / Bewshaugh / Pres. Garfield's / Cheviot hills, The.
LP: . . . . MWM 1024
MC: . . . . MWMC 1024

NORTHUMBRIAN SMALL PIPES.
Tracks: / Loch ruan / Farwell to the dene / Nancy / Major MacKay / Ann Frazer MacKenzie / Dumfries house / Nancy Taylor's reel / Pearl wedding / Tich's reel / Kelso accordian and fiddle club / Linda McFarlane / Lady's well / Idle bairn / Morpeth rant / Jock Wilson O'Fenton / Cheviot rant / Capt. Norman Orr-Wigg / Redford cottage / Mrs. Ann Jamieson's favourite / Bielbie's hornpipe / Silver wings / John Spencer of Uyea sound / Far frae hame / Lads of North Tyne, The / Minstrels fancy.
LP: . . . . MWM 1031

Hutton, June

AFTERGLOW (Hutton, June & The Boys Next Door).
Tracks: / Never in a million years / Gone with the wind / Until the real thing comes along / I should care / It's the talk of the town / You're getting to be a habit with me / Day by day / East of the sun (and west of the moon) / Taking a chance on love / I hadn't anyone till you / My baby just cares for me / Dream a little dream of me.
LP: . . . . EMS 1184
MC: . . . . TCEMS 1184

Huxtable

WALLFLOWERS (Huxtable/Christensen/Hood).
LP: . . . . PH 1053
MC: . . . . PH 1053C

Huygen, Michel

BARCELONA 992.
Tracks: / Carvalho / Impossible love / Chase, The / Meeting at the hilton / Loneliness / Barcelona 1992 / Tonight.
LP: . . . . THBL 056
LP: . . . . CBTD 056

CAPTURING HOLOGRAMS.
LP: . . . . HIP 20
MC: . . . . HIPC 20

Hyacinth Girls

HAPPY NOW.
LP: . . . . RED 002

Hybrid Kids

CLAWS.
Tracks: / We three kings of Orient are / O come all ye faithful / Deck the halls / Coventry / Holly and the ivy, The / No St. Bernard / Listen the snow is falling / Dead ducks / Good king Wenceslas / Happy Xmas (war is over).
LP: . . . . BRED 11

HYBRID KIDS Collection of classic mutants (Various artists).
Tracks: / McArthur Park: *Burtons* / God save the lean: *Punky & Porky* / Pretty bacon: *Punky & Porky* / Wuthering Heights: *Wurzel, Jah* / Catch a falling star: *Rififi* / Fever: *Galaxy, Malcolm* / Save your kisses for me: *Kapital Punishment* / D'ya think I'm sexy?: *British Standard Unit* / Enlightenment: *Combo Satori* / Get back: *US Nurds* / Something better change: *Incestors* / You've lost that lovin' feeling: *Atom, R. W.* / Take me I'm yours: *Various artists.*
LP: . . . . ARED 5

Hyde, Alex

ALEX HYDE VOL 1 - 1924 (Jazz/hot dance & doo wacka-doo from Germany vol. 1.
LP: . . . . HQ 2033

ALEX HYDE VOL 2 - 1925 (Jazz and hot dance from Germany vol.2).
Tracks: / Shine / San / Pleasure mad / No-one knows what it's all about / How I love that girl / Counting the hours / Sioux City Sue / Oh Peter / Alabamy bound / Farewell blues / Copenjagen / Glorida / Craving / Tessie / Ukulele lady / Happy four.
LP: . . . . HQ 2034

Hyde Park After Dark

HYDE PARK AFTER DARK Various artists (Various artists).
LP: . . . . BH 7014

Hydra Vein

AFTER THE DREAM.
LP: . . . . CMO 193

RATHER DEATH THAN FALSE OF FAITH.
LP: . . . . OTH 12
MC: . . . . OTH 12C

Hydravian

HYDRAVION.
LP: . . . . COB 37012

Hykes, David

CURRENT CIRCULATION (Hykes, David & The Harmonic Choir).
LP: . . . . LPCEL 010

HARMONIC MEETINGS (Hykes, David & The Harmonic Choir).
2LP: . . . . LPCEL 013/14
MCSET: . . . . MCCEL 013/14

Hyland, Brian

GINNY O GINNY.
Tracks: / Ginny o ginny / Ginny come lately / I should be getting better / Warmed over kisses / Walk a lonely mile / Summer job / Sealed with a kiss / I may not live to see tomorrow / It ain't that way at all.
LP: . . . . BFX 15335

GOLDEN DECADE 1960-70.
Tracks: / Sealed with a kiss / Warmed over kisses / If Mary's there / I'm afraid to go home / Tragedy / Million to one, A / Stay and love me all summer / Ginny come lately / Lonely teardrops / Gypsy woman / I may not live to see tomorrow / I'll never stop wanting you / Let me belong to you / Itsy bitsy teeny weeny yellow polka dot bikini.
LP: . . . . CR 30267

Hyland, Paddy

GREEN FIELDS OF FRANCE.
LP: . . . . DOLM 5036

ROSE OF MOONCOIN.
Tracks: / Rose of Mooncoin / Sligo maid, The / Colonel Rodney / Farewell to Carlingford / Summertime rolls by / Paddy lie back / Three sea captains / Rocky coast of Clare, The / Lord of the dance / Band played waltzing Matilda, The / King of the fairies, The / Leaving Nancy.
LP: . . . . DOLS 2014
MC: . . . . DOCS 2014

Hylton, Jack

BAND THAT JACK BUILT.
LP: . . . . SH 190

BANDS THAT MATTER.
LP: . . . . ECM 2046

BREAKAWAY (Hylton, Jack & His Orchestra).
Tracks: / Breakaway / On her doorstep last night / Just as we used to do / Springtime reminds me of you / That's where the South begins / Maggie's cold / Ro' ro' rollin' along / Dance of the raindrops / Steppin' out / Around the corner / Harmonica Harry / Great day / Punch and Judy show, The / Speaking of Kentucky days / Nobody's using it now / Little white lies.
LP: . . . . JOYD 267
MC: . . . . TCJOY D 267
LP: . . . . JOY 267

GOLDEN AGE OF JACK HYLTON, THE.
Tracks: / Music, maestro please / Now it can be told / One, two, button your shoe / Don't let that moon get away / Sing, baby, sing / Have you met Miss Jones / Why doesn't somebody tell me these things / Chinatown my Chinatown / She shall have music / You turned the tables on me / Get out of town / Swing is in the air / Free (why does my heart go boom) / Blue skies are round the corner.
LP: . . . . GX 41 2519-1
MC: . . . . GX 41 2519-4

GOOD NEWS (Hylton, Jack & His Orchestra).
LP: . . . . SH 218

HITS FROM BERLIN 1927-31 (Hylton, Jack & His Orchestra).
Tracks: / When day is done / Heut war ich bei der freida / Wir wollen tun, als ob wir freunde waren / Ja, da, die frau'n sind meine schwache Seite / Passen sie mal auf / I kiss your hand madame / When the white lilacs bloom again / O maiden, my maiden / Four words / Handsome gigolo / Thine is my whole heart / Falling in love again / Oh Donna Clara / White Horse Inn selection / Mausie / Today i feel so happy.
LP: . . . . SH 308

I'M IN A DANCING MOOD (Hylton, Jack & His Orchestra).
Tracks: / I'll never say "never again" again / She's a latin from Manhattan / About a quarter to nine / Rose room / I'm in a dancing mood / At the balalaika / Boo-hoo / September in the rain / Love live and rule my heart / Girls were made to love and kiss / Nice people / You must have been a beautiful baby / Jeepers creepers / Beer barrel polka / My prayer / Day in, day out / So deep is the night / Roadhouse revels / Rosita / Let the people sing.
LP: . . . . SH 505
MC: . . . . TC SH 505

JACK HYLTON.
LP: . . . . SH 127

JACK HYLTON AND HIS ORCHESTRA (Hylton, Jack & His Orchestra).
Tracks: / Gold diggers' song / Stormy weather / St. Louis blues / Black and tan fantasy / Mood indigo / It don't mean a thing / Bugle call rag / Happy-go-lucky you and broken-hearted me / Black and blue rhythm / Hylton stomp / 42nd Street / Young and healthy / You're getting to be a habit with me / Shuffle off to Buffalo / Nevertheless / Some of these days / You've got me crying again / Heartaches / Dinah.
LP: . . . . JASM 2018
LP: . . . . ACL 1205

JACK HYLTON AND HIS ORCHESTRA (FLAPPER LABEL) (Hylton, Jack & His Orchestra).
Tracks: / Just a little lady / Fleurs d'amour / Hylton medley / Lady be good (sel'n) / Desert song waltz / Kid Boots / Rising sun / Harlequin's millions / In sunny Havana / Laughing marionette / Diane / By the tamarisk / Mercenary Mary.
LP: . . . . PAST 702

JACK HYLTON AND HIS ORCHESTRA VOL.1 (Hylton, Jack & His Orchestra).
LP: . . . . MES 7033

JACK HYLTON AND HIS ORCHESTRA VOL.2 (Hylton, Jack & His Orchestra).
LP: . . . . MES 7055

JACK HYLTON & HIS ORCHESTRA (2).
LP: . . . . GNPS 9017

JACK HYLTON & HIS ORCHESTRA 1935-40 (Deep purple) (Hylton, Jack & His Orchestra).
Tracks: / I won't dance / Anything goes / There isn't any limit to my love / Did I remember / Rockin' chair / Are you having any fun? / Our love / Over the rainbow / It's a lovely day tomorrow.
LP: . . . . RD 4

JACK'S BACK (Hylton, Jack & His Orchestra).
Tracks: / Happy days are here again / Speaking of Kentucky days / My bundle of love / I'm looking over a four leaf clover / World's greatest sweetheart is you, The / Harmonica Harry / Gentlemen prefer blondes / Broadway melody / Happy feet / I wanna go places and do things / Guy that wrote 'The stein' song, The / Meadow lark / Choo choo / Life is just a bowl of cherries / Da da da / Under the ukelele tree / Hang on to me / When day is done.
LP: . . . . AJA 5018
MC: . . . . ZC AJA 5018

JACK'S BACK (GNP LABEL) (Hylton, Jack & His Orchestra).
LP: . . . . GNPS 9018

LOVABLE & SWEET.
LP: . . . . OLD 1

OH LISTEN TO THE BAND (In concert 1937-8).
Tracks: / Little old lady / Medley / Tiger rag / Love bug will bite you, The / Ich steh im regen / It looks like rain in Cherry Blossom Lane / My Gal Sal / You're my desire / Wake up and live / Night is young and you're so beautiful, The / Swing me a lullaby / Anne Laurie / Moon at sea.
LP: . . . . RD 7

PLYS DE SYLVA, BROWN & HENDERSON.
LP: . . . . WRCSH 218

SONG OF HAPPINESS 1931-33.
Tracks: / Song of happiness / I apologize / Mona Lisa / Faded summer love, A / By the sycamore tree / Now's the time to fall in love / Goopy Geer (he plays piano and he plays by ear / Who's your little who-zis? / With love in my heart / Rain on the roof / With all my love and kisses / How long will it last? / Just humming along / Lawd, you made the night too long / Dream sweetheart / You're taking a chance with me / After tonight we say goodbye / Can't we meet again / You're mine, you / Did my heart beat, did I fall in love?.
LP: . . . . SVL 187
MC: . . . . CSVL 187

SWING (Hylton, Jack & His Orchestra).
Tracks: / Good morning / I'll never say never again again / Unbelievable / Change partners / Melody maker / Midnight blue / Do the runaround / Lovely to look at / I believe in miracles / Zing went the strings of my heart / Organ grinders swing / Lovely Liza Lee / Moanin' Minnie / If the moon turns green / September in the rain / So red the rose / Hypnotised / Drop in the next time you're passing / Give a little whistle.
LP: . . . . SVL 158

TALK OF THE TOWN (Hylton, Jack & His Orchestra).
Tracks: / By a waterfall / Honeymoon Hotel / After you, who? / It's the talk of the town / You've got me crying again / Stormy weather / Hold me / Stay on the right side of the road / Fit as a fiddle / Happy as the day is long / I'm playing with fire / You're a smoothie / You are too beautiful / Don't blame me.
MC: . . . . CSVL 164
LP: . . . . SVL 164

THIS'LL MAKE YOU WHISTLE.
Tracks: / Chasing shadows / Nothing lives longer than love / South American Joe / About a quarter to nine / She's a latin from Manhattan / Drop in the next time you're passing / Put on an old pair of shoes / Life begins at Oxford Circus / She wore a little jacket of blue / Did I remember / There isn't any limit to my love / I believe in miracles / This'll make you whistle / In the middle of a kiss / Kiss me goodnight / Can't we meet again / Did my heart beat / You've got me crying again.
LP: . . . . BUR 005
MC: . . . . 4 BUR 005

Hylton, Sheila

SHE SHALL HAVE MUSIC (1935-6).
Tracks: / In a little gypsy tearoom / I'll never say never again / I'm singing a song of love / Gosh, I've got a broken heart / I'm in the mood of love / You are my lucky star / She shall have music / You never can tell / Shoe shine boy / Take my heart.
LP: . . . . RD 2

Hyman, Dick

AMERICA THE BEAUTIFUL (see Braff, Ruby).

CHARLESTON See under J.P.Johnson (Hyman, Dick/J.P.Johnson).
Tracks: / Charleston / If I could be with you one hour tonight / Just before daybreak / Caprice rag / Steeplechase rag / Eccentricity / Carolina Balmoral / Snowy morning blues / Jingles / Carolina shout / You've got to be modernistic.
LP: 4508641
MC: 4508644

DICK HYMAN & HIS TRIO (Hyman, Dick & His Trio).
LP: . . . . GVR 3309

DICK HYMAN PIANO SOLOS.
LP: . . . . MES 7065

DICK HYMAN PLAYS FATS WALLER.
LP: . . . . RR 33

GULF COAST BLUES (THE MUSIC OF CLARENCE WILLIAMS).
LP: . . . . SOS 1141

MUSIC FROM SOUTH PACIFIC (see under Braff, Ruby) (Braff, Ruby & Dick Hyman).

MUSIC OF 1937 - VOL 3 (Maybeck Recital Hall Series).
Tracks: / Where or when / Foggy day (in London town), A / Bob White / Some day my prince will come / Folks who live on the hill, The (Only on CD.) / Bei mir bist

du schon / Loch Lomond (Only on CD.) / Thanks for the memory / In the still of the night / My funny valentine / Caravan.
MC: . . . . **CJ 415 C**

SAY IT WITH MUSIC (Hyman, Dick & The Perfect Jazz Repertory Company).
Tracks: / Mandy / How deep is the ocean / Cheek to cheek / Lazy / Say it with music / Blue skies / All alone / Puttin' on the ritz / Marie / Soft lights and sweet music.
LP: . . . . **WJLPS 16**

STRIDE MONSTER Duo pianos (Hyman, Dick/Dick Wellstood).
LP: . . . . **DDA 1006**

Hyman, Phyllis

BEST OF PHYLLIS HYMAN.
Tracks: / You know how to love me / Love too good to last / We should be lovers / Answer is you / Be careful / Under your spell / Don't tell me tell her / Living inside your love / Why did you turn me on / Gonna make changes.
LP: **207830**
MC: **407830**

BEST OF PHYLLIS HYMAN (2) (Buddah years).
Tracks: / Loving you - losing you / No one can love you more / One thing on my mind / I don't want to lose you / Deliver the love / Night bird gets the love, The / Beautiful man of mine / Children of the world / Living inside your love / Sweet music / Answer is you / Love is free / Sing a song / Soon come again / Be careful (how you treat my love).
LP: . . . . **NEXLP 138**

CAN'T WE FALL IN LOVE AGAIN.
Tracks: / You sure look good to me / Don't tell me / Tell her / I ain't asking / Can't we fall in love again / Love too good to last, The / Tonight you and me / Sunshine in my life, The / Just another face in the crowd.
LP: . . . . **SPART 1154**

GODDESS OF LOVE.
Tracks: / Ridin' the tiger / Goddess of love / Why did you turn me on / Your move, my heart / Let someone love you / Falling star / We should be lovers / Just me and you / Just 25 miles to anywhere.
LP: **205543**
MC: **405543**

LIVING ALL ALONE.
Tracks: / Living all alone / First time together / If you want me / Slow dancin' / Old friend / You just don't know / Ain't you had enough love / Screaming at the moon / What you won't do for love.
LP: . . . . **PHIL 4001**
MC: . . . . **TCPHIL 4001**

SING A SONG.
Tracks: / Living inside your love / Sweet music / Answer is you / Love is free / Sing a song / Gonna make changes / Soon come again / Be careful / Here's that rainy day.
LP: . . . . **BDLP 4058**

UNDER HER SPELL.
Tracks: / Loving you, losing you / Can't we fall in love again / Why did you turn me on / You sure look good to me / Let someone love you / Just another face in the crowd / You know how to love me / Under your spell / Don't tell me, tell her / Betcha by golly wow / Love too good to last, The / Complete me / Your move, my heart / Kiss you all over.
LP: **210620**
MC: **410620**

YOU KNOW HOW TO LOVE ME (LP).
LP: . . . . **SPART 1114**

Hymns...

100 FAVOURITE HYMNS (Various artists).
MC: . . . . **MFP 4156724**

FAVOURITE HYMNS (Various artists).
Tracks: / Onward Christian soldiers: *Honley, Gledholt & Skelmanthorpe Male Voice Choirs* / I will sing the wondrous story: *Wallace, Ian* / What a friend we have in Jesus: *Monese, Valerie* / In the bleak mid winter: *Brighouse & Rastrick* Band / Tell me the old, old story: *Wallace, Ian* / Lord of all hopefulness: *Monese, Valerie* / Lord's my shepherd, The: *Honley, Gledholt & Skelmanthorpe Male Voice Choirs* / Abide with me: *Monese, Valerie* / In the sweet bye and bye: *Wallace, Ian* / Holy City, The: *Monese, Valerie* / Praise my soul: *Honley, Gledholt & Skelmanthorpe Male* Voice Choirs / Steal away: *Wallace, Ian* / My Jesus I love thee: *Monese, Valerie* / O come all ye faithful: *Brighouse & Rastrick Band* / Who is He in yonder stall: *Honley, Gledholt & Skelmanthorpe Male Voice Choirs* / Just a closer walk with thee: *Wallace, Ian* / Faith can move mountains: *Wallace, Ian/Master Singers* / Sweet hour of prayer: *Monese, Valerie* / Behold me standing at the door: *Wallace, Ian* / Old rugged cross, The: *Monese, Valerie.*
MC: . . . . **HR 8148**

HOW GREAT THOU ART (Railway Street, Lisburn, Presbyterian Choir).
Tracks: / Thine be the glory / Lord's my shepherd / Praise my soul / How great thou art / Balm in Gilead / Jesus joy of man's desiring / God so loved the world / Guide me, o thou great Jehovah / Lord's prayer / All people that on earth do dwell / Dear Lord and Father of mankind / Come let us to the Lord our God.
LP: . . . . **POL 828**

HYMNS AND SONGS FOR CHILDREN (Various artists).
MCSET: . . . . **DTO 10305**

HYMNS FOR LITTLE CHILDREN (Various artists).
Tracks: / Lord Jesus Christ: *Various artists* / Tell me the stories of Jesus: *Various artists* / Lord of the dance: *Various artists* / All things bright and beautiful: *Various artists* / All creatures of our God and King: *Various artists* / Lord of all hopefulness: *Various artists* / Seek ye first: *Various artists* / Gentle Jesus: *Various* artists / Jesus bids us shine: *Various artists* / Morning has broken: *Various artists* / Holy, holy, holy: *Various artists* / There's a friend for little children: *Various artists* / At the name of Jesus: *Various* artists / Kumbaya: *Various artists* / Go tell it on the mountain: *Various artists* / O Jesus I have promised: *Various artists* / Put your hand in the hand: *Various artists* / All glory, laud and honour: *Various artists.*
LP: . . . . **MFP 5837**
MC: . . . . **TCMFP 5837**

HYMNS OF PRAISE STRINGS Various artists (Various artists).
LP: . . . . **MM 0085**
MC: . . . . **TC MM 0085**

INTERNATIONAL HYMNS (Various artists).
LP: . . . . **SM 3604**
MC: . . . . **MC 3604**

KIDS' SING A LONG HYMNS (Various artists).
LP: . . . . **MM R 0220**
MC: . . . . **MM C 0220**

OUR HYMNS (Various artists).
Tracks: / O God, our help in ages past: *Keaggy, Phil* / Holy holy holy: *Smith, Michael W* / 'Tis so sweet to trust in Jesus: *Grant, Amy* / Saviour is waiting, The: *Take Six.*
MC: . . . . **WST C 9107**

TOP TWENTY HYMNS (See under Top Twenty Hymns) (Various artists).

YOUR 40 FAVOURITE HYMNS (Various artists).
Tracks: / Let all the world in every corner sing: *Various artists* / O worship the King: *Brighouse & Rastrick Band*/ Praise my soul: *Honley, Gledholt & Skelmanthorpe Male Voice Choirs* / Lord of the dance: *Carousel Children* / Jesus keep me near the cross: *Brighouse & Rastrick Band* / All people that on earth do dwell: *Honley, Gledholt & Skelmanthorpe* Male Voice Choirs / And can it be?: *Honley, Gledholt & Skelmanthorpe Male Voice Choirs* / I need thee every hour: *Brighouse &* Rastrick Band / Fight the good fight: *Honley, Gledholt & Skelmanthorpe Male Voice Choirs* / Lord's my shepherd, The: *Honley, Gledholt & Skelmanthorpe Male Voice Choirs* / Soldiers of Christ arise: *Honley, Gledholt & Skelmanthorpe Male* Voice Choirs / How sweet the name of Jesus sounds: *Brighouse & Rastrick Band* / Just as I am: *Carousel Children*/ Come ye thankful people come: *Brighouse & Rastrick Band* / Praise to the Lord: *Honley, Gledholt & Skelmanthorpe Male* Voice Choirs / Lead us heavenly Father, lead us: *Brighouse & Rastrick Band* / Love devine: *Brighouse & Rastrick* Band / Jesus shall reign: *Honley, Gledholt & Skelmanthorpe Male Voice Choirs* / Sun of my soul: *Brighouse & Rastrick* Band / All in the April evening: *Honley, Gledholt & Skelmanthorpe Male Voice Choirs* / Onward christian soldiers: *Honley,* Gledholt & Skelmanthorpe Male Voice Choirs / Crown Him with many crowns: *Brighouse & Rastrick Band* / He lives: *Honley,* Gledholt & Skelmanthorpe Male Voice Choirs / Rock of ages: *Honley, Gledholt & Skelmanthorpe Male Voice Choirs* / O love that wilt not let me go: *Brighouse & Rastrick Band* / All hail the power of Jesus name: *Honley, Gledholt & Skelmanthorpe* Male Voice Choirs / O Jesus I have promised: *Carousel Children* / All creatures of our God and King: *Brighouse* & Rastrick Band / There is a green hill far away: *Honley, Gledholt & Skelmanthorpe Male Voice Choirs* / O god our help in ages past: *Brighouse & Rastrick Band* / All glory laud and honour: *Various artists* / Guide me o thou great Jehovah: *Honley, Gledholt & Skelmanthorpe Male Voice Choirs* / In the bleak mid winter: *Brighouse & Rastrick Band*/ Who is he?: *Honley, Gledholt & Skelmanthorpe Male Voice Choirs* / Now thank we all our God: *Brighouse & Rastrick* Band / To God be the glory: *Honley, Gledholt & Skelmanthorpe Male Voice Choirs* / Who is on the Lord's side?: *Honley,* Gledholt & Skelmanthorpe Male Voice Choirs / Rejoice, the Lord is King: *Brighouse & Rastrick Band* / O for a thousand tongues to sing: *Honley, Gledholt & Skelmanthorpe Male Voice Choirs* / Now the day is over: *Honley, Gledholt & Skelmanthorpe Male Voice Choirs.*
2LP: . . . . **DL 1143**
MC: . . . . **TCDL 1143**

YOUR 50 BEST LOVED HYMNS (Various artists).
Tracks: / Let all the world in every corner sing: *Various artists* / For all the Saints: *Various artists* / How sweet the name of Jesus sounds: *Various artists* / I am so glad that Jesus loves me: *Various artists* / All in the April evening: *Various artists* / O worship the King: *Various artists* / Lord of the dance: *Various artists*/ Praise to the Lord: *Various artists* / Onward Christian soldiers: *Various artists* / All creatures of our God and King: *Various artists* / How great thou art: *Various artists* / To God be the glory: *Various artists*/ Lord Jesus Christ: *Various artists* / O love that wilt not let me go: *Various artists* / In Heavenly love abiding: *Various artists* / Jesus shall reign: *Various artists* / All hail the power of Jesus' name: *Various artists*/ Love divine: *Various artists* / There's a friend for little children: *Various artists* / Soldiers of Christ arise: *Various artists* / He hideth my soul: *Various artists* / O for a thousand tongues to sing: *Various artists*/ Crown him with many crowns: *Various artists* / Who is on the Lord's side: *Various artists* / Now thank we all our God: *Various artists* / Jesus wants me for a sunbeam: *Various artists* / All people that on Earth do dwell: *Various artists* / All glory laud and honour: *Various artists* / Holy, holy, holy: *Various artists* / And can it be: *Various artists* / When I survey the wondrous cross: *Various artists* / Lord's my shepherd, The: *Various artists* / Rejoice, the Lord is King: *Various artists* / Praise my soul: *Various artists* / Lead us heavenly Father, lead us: *Various artists* / Rock of ages: *Various artists* / O Jesus I have promised: *Various* artists / Come ye thankful people come: *Various artists* / Guide me o thou great Jehovah: *Various artists*/ Sun of my soul: *Various artists* / Bless this house: *Various artists* / He lives: *Various artists* / Fight the good fight: *Various artists* / Just as I am: *Various artists* / There is a green hill far away: *Various* artists / Jesus keep me near the cross: *Various artists* / Day thou gavest, Lord is ended, The: *Various artists*/ Lord, is ended: *Various artists* / O God our help in ages past: *Various artists* / Now the day is over: *Various artists* / God be with you till we meet again: *Various artists.*
MCSET: . . . . **TR 1560**
MCSET: . . . . **TR 4115605**

YOUR 100 FAVOURITE HYMNS VOL.2 (Various artists).
LP: . . . . **MFP 5621**
MC: . . . . **TCMFP 5621**

YOUR HUNDRED FAVOURITE HYMNS VOL.3 (Various artists).
LP: . . . . **MFP 5625**
MC: . . . . **TCMFP 5625**

YOUR HUNDRED FAVOURITE HYMNS VOL.1 (Various artists).
LP: . . . . **MFP 5572**
MC: . . . . **TC MFP 5572**

YOUR HUNDRED FAVOURITE HYMNS VOL.4 (Various artists).
LP: . . . . **MFP 41 5659 1**
MC: . . . . **MFP 41 5659 4**

YOUR HUNDRED FAVOURITE HYMNS VOL.5 (Various artists).
LP: . . . . **MFP 41 5672 1**
MC: . . . . **MFP 41 5672 4**

YOUR SONGS OF PRAISE CHOICE (Various artists).
Tracks: / All people that on Earth do dwell: *Various artists* / New Year carol, A: *Various artists* / Jesu, Thou joy of loving hearts: *Various artists* / Alleluia, sing to Jesus: *Various artists* / Lord's my shepherd, The: *Various artists* / Love divine: *Various artists* / Make me a channel of thy peace: *Various artists* / Hark, hark my soul: *Various artists* / Rock of ages: *Various artists* / Thou whose almighty word: *Various artists* / Guide me o thou great Redeemer: *Various artists* / Holy Virgin, by God's decree: *Various artists* / King of love my shepherd is, The: *Various artists* / Bird of heaven: *Various artists* / What is this wonderful light: *Various* artists / O Christ who holds the open gate: *Various artists* / Eternal father, strong to save: *Various artists*/ O valiant hearts: *Various artists* / Day thou gavest, Lord is ended, The: *Various artists* / O God our help in ages past: *Various artists* / Complete signature tune: *Various artists.*
LP: . . . . **REC 469**
MC: . . . . **ZCM 469**

Hynde, Chrissie

BREAKFAST IN BED (See under UB40) (UB40/Chrissie Hynde).

Hynes, Dessie

MUSIC FOR IRISH DANCING.
Tracks: / Miss McCloud's reel / Sally gardens / Humours of Bandon / Rocky road to Dublin / Off she goes / Queen of the fair / Sunshine hornpipe / St. Patrick's day / Blackbird (The) / Job of journeywork / Garden of daisies, The.
LP: . . . . **IRB 2002**
MC: . . . . **Unknown**

MUSIC FOR IRISH DANCING (ADVANCED), VOL.2.
MC: . . . . **IRBC 2003**

RAMBLIN' ROBIN.
LP: . . . . **FRC 009**

Hype

BURNED.
LP: . . . . **WEBITE 26**

LIFE IS HARD.
LP: . . . . **WEBITE 9**

Hyperactive

HYPERACTIVE 12" Dance album (Various artists).
Tracks: / Never gonna give you up: *Astley, Rick* / I want you back '88: *Jackson Five* / Dreamin': *Goldsmith,* Glen / Tell it to my heart: *Dayne, Taylor* / Get outta my dreams, get into my car: *Ocean, Billy* / I should be so lucky: *Minogue, Kylie* / Walk away: *Sims, Joyce* / Boys: *Sabrina* / Dance little sister: *D'arby,* Terence Trent / Criticize: *O'Neal, Alexander* / Give me the reason: *Vandross, Luther* / Say it again: *Stewart,* Jermaine / Push it: *Salt 'N' Pepa* / Roses are red: *Mac Band* / Payback mix: *Brown, James* / Love supreme, A: *Downing, Will* / Cross my broken heart: *Sinitta.*
2LP: . . . . **STAR 2328**
MCSET: . . . . **STAC 2328**

Hypnodance

HYPNODANCE.
LP: . . . . **CONTE 129**

Hypnosis

HYPNOSIS TAPES - SELECTION (see under 'Sutphen, Dick').

Hypnotone

HYPNOTONE.
LP: . . . . **CRELP 067**
MC: . . . . **CREMC 067**

Hypocrite Inna...

HYPOCRITE INNA DANCE HALL STYLE Various artists (Various artists).
LP: . . . . **JJ 192**

Hypothetical Prophets

AROUND THE WORLD WITH THE PROPHETS.
Tracks: / Person to person / Fast food / White zone, The / On the edge / Wallenberg / Back to the burner.
LP: . . . . **EPC 25116**
MC: **40 25116**
MC: . . . . **ZUG LP 1**

Hysterical Years

HYSTERICAL YEARS 1986-1990 (Various artists).
LP: . . . . **ACHE 020**
MC: . . . . **ACHEMC 020**

Hysterics

HYSTERICS.
LP: . . . . **KALP 001**
MC: . . . . **KALC 001**

I Ain't Lonely...

I AIN'T LONELY NO MORE (Various artists).
LP: F 3005

I & Albert

I AND ALBERT (Original London cast) (Various artists).
Tracks: / Draw the blinds: *Various artists* / I and Albert: *Various artists* / Leave it alone: *Various artists*/ I've 'eard the bloody 'indoos: *Various artists*.
LP: TERS 1004

I Am

CELEBRATION OF PRAISE, A.
LP: MM 0100
MC: TC MM 0100

CELEBRATION OF PRAISE, A VOL. 2.
LP: MM 0125
MC: TC MM 0125

I Am Siam

I AM SIAM.
Tracks: / Prologue / In the common tongue / She went pop / Te amore / I am siam / Talk to me / Stimulation / Running in place / Step into the light / Reprise.
LP: CBS 26183
MC: 40 26183

I Benjahman

FRACTION OF JAH ACTION.
LP: LKLP 001

I Can Crawl

DESERT.
LP: HYBLP 9

I Can Get It For You

I CAN GET IT FOR YOU WHOLESALE (Original Broadway cast) (Various artists).
LP: AKOS 2180
MC: BT 2180
LP: CBS 32265

I Claudius

I, CLAUDIUS (see under Graves, Robert) (Jacobi, Derek (nar)).

I Jahman

HAILE I HYMN.
Tracks: / Jah heavy load / Jah is no secret / Zion hut / I'm a levi.
LP: ILPS 9521
MC: ZCI 9521
MC: RRCT 35

I Lombardi

I LOMBARDI (See under Verdi).

I Love Melvin

I LOVE MELVIN/EVERYTHING I HAVE IS YOURS Original soundtracks (Various artists).
LP: MCA 39081
MC: MCAC 39081

I Love My Car

I LOVE MY CAR various artists (Various artists).
LP: F 3002

I Love You

I LOVE YOU.
LP: GEF 24371
MC: GEFC 24371

LIVE.
LP: MD 2437-1

I Ludicrous

I LUDICROUS.
LP: KSLP 008

IT'S LIKE EVERYTHING ELSE.
LP: KSLP 004

LIGHT AND BITTER.
LP: RODNEY 006

I Married An Angel

I MARRIED AN ANGEL Original cast recording (Various artists).
LP: AEI 1150

I Put A Spell On You

I PUT A SPELL ON YOU (See under Hawkins, Screamin' Jay) (Hawkins, Screamin' Jay).

I Refuse It

MIND THE GAP (I Refuse It/Ultima Thule).
LP: IC 1

I Remember Mama

I REMEMBER MAMA (Studio Cast recordings) (Various artists).
Tracks: / I remember mama: *Various artists* / Little bit more, A: *Various artists* / Writer writes at night, A: *Various artists* / Ev'ry day (comes something beautiful): *Various artists* / You could not please me more: *Various artists* / Most disagreeable man, A/Uncle Chris: *Various artists* / Lullaby: *Various artists* / Easy come, easy go: *Various artists* / It is not the end of the world: *Various artists* / Entr'acte: *Various artists*/ Mama always makes it better: *Various artists* / When: *Various artists* / Fair trade: *Various artists*/ I write, you read (fair trade): *Various artists* / It's going to be good to be gone: *Various artists* / Time: *Various artists* / I remember mama finale: *Various artists*.
LP: TER 1102
MC: ZCTER 1102

I Start Counting

FUSED.
LP: STUMM 50

MY TRANSLUCENT HANDS.
Tracks: / Introduction / My translucent hands / Catch that look / You and I / Lose him / Keep the sun away / Cranley Gardens / Which way is home / Letters to a friend / Still smiling / Small consolation / (There is always the) unexpected.
LP: STUMM 30

I Threes

BEGINNING.
LP: DSR 5911

CALLING OUT AROUND THE WORLD.
LP: RM 62985

I Walk The Line (film)

I WALK THE LINE (Film soundtrack) (Various artists).
Tracks: / Flesh and blood: *Various artists* / I walk the line: *Various artists* / Hungry: *Various artists*/ This town: *Various artists* / This side of the law: *Various artists* / Flesh and blood (instrumental): *Various artists* / Cause I love you: *Various artists* / Cause I love you (string instrumental): *Various artists* / World's gonna fall on you: *Various artists* / Face of despair: *Various artists* / Standing on the promise: *Various artists* / Amazing grace: *Various artists*.
LP: 700 83

I Was A Teenage Zombie

I WAS A TEENAGE ZOMBIE (Original soundtrack) (Various artists).
LP: 3296-1

Ian, Janis

AFTERTONES.
Tracks: / Aftertones / I would like to dance / Love is blind / Roses / Belle of the blues / Goodbye to morning / Boy I really tried one on / This must be wrong / Don't cry / Old man / Hymn.
LP: CBS 32018
MC: 40 32018

BEST OF JANIS IAN.
Tracks: / At seventeen / Have mercy love / Aftertones / When the party's over / In the Winter / Stars fly too high / Other side of the sun, The / Without you / Here comes the night / Jesse / Bridge, The / Between the lines / Miracle row / Maria.
LP: CBS 84711
MC: 40 84711

BETWEEN THE LINES.
Tracks: / When the party's over / At seventeen / From me to you / Bright lights and promises / In the Winter / Water colors / Between the lines / Come on, The / Light a tight / Tea & sympathy / Lover's lullaby.
LP: BS 80635
MC: 40 80635

JANIS IAN.
Tracks: / Grand illusion / Some people / Tonight will last forever / Hotels and one night stands / Do you wanna dance / Silly habits / Bridge, The / My mama's house / Streetlife serenaders / I need to live alone again / Hopper painting.
LP: CBS 82700
MC: 40 82700

JANIS IAN [VERVE].
Tracks: / Society's child / Too old to go way little girl / Hair of spun gold / Tangles of my mind, The / I'll give you a stone if you'll throw it / Pro-girl / Younger generation blues / New Christ cardiac hero / Lover be kindly / Mrs. McKenzie.
LP: 2482 572
MC: 3192 671

MIRACLE ROW.
Tracks: / Party lights / I want to make you love me / Sunset of your life / Take to the sky / Candlelight / Let me be lonely / Slow dance romance / Will you dance / I'll cry tonight / Miracle row / Maria.
LP: CBS 81879
MC: 40 81879

NIGHT RAINS.
Tracks: / Other side of the sun, The / Fly too high / Memories / Photographs / Here comes the night / Day by day / Have mercy love / Lay low / Night rains / Jenny.
LP: CBS 32298
MC: 40 32298
LP: CBS 83802

RESTLESS EYES.
Tracks: / Under the covers / I remember yesterday / I believe I'm myself again / Restless eyes / Get ready to roll / Passion play / Down and away / Bigger than real / Dear Billy / Sugar mountain.
LP: CBS 85040
MC: 40 85040

STARS.
Tracks: / Stars / Man you are in me, The / Sweet sympathy / Page nine / Thank yous / Dance with me / Without you / You've got me on a string / Applause.
LP: CBS 32049
MC: 40 32049

STARS/NIGHT RAINS.
Tracks: / Stars / Man you are in me, The / Sweet sympathy / Page nine / Thank yous / Dance with me / Without you / You've got me on a string / Applause.
MC: 40 22158

Ian & Margaret

THAT'S LIFE.
LP: JS 5005

Ian & Sylvia

GREATEST HITS.
Tracks: / Early morning rain / Tomorrow is a long time / Little beggar man / Mighty Quinn, The / Nancy Whisky / Catfish blues / Come in stranger / French girl, The / Renegade, The / Mary Anne / You were on my mind / Four strong winds / Short grass / Southern comfort / Someday soon / Ella Speed / Circle game / 90 x 90 / Cutty Wren, The / Un Canadien errant / Lonely girls / Spanish is a loving tongue / This wheel's on fire.
LP: VNP 5401
MC: VNP 6401
LP: VSD 5
MC: VCV 5

Ian & The Muscletones

HUMAN SACRIFICE.
LP: AP 009

Ibanez, Paco

LOS UNOS POR LOS OTROS.
LP: 2385 004

PACO IBANEZ' POETRY AND MUSIC.
LP: 2467 016

Ibrahim, Abdullah

AFRICAN RIVER (Ibrahim, Abdullah & Ekaya).
LP: 6018-1
MC: 6018-4

EKAYA.
LP: BKH 50205

MEMORIES.
LP: WW 2029

MOUNTAIN, THE (Ibrahim, Abdullah & Ekaya).
Tracks: / Mountain, The / Bra timing from Phomolong / Ekaya / Sotho blue / Tuang Guru / Ntyilo ntyilo / Nelson Mandela / Wedding, The / Mannenberg (revisited) / Cape Town.
LP: KAZLP 7
MC: KAZMC 7

WATER FROM AN ANCIENT WALL.
Tracks: / Mandela / Song for Fathima / Manenberg revisited / Tuang Guru / Water from an ancient well / Wedding / Mountain / Sameeda.
LP: BKH 50207
MC: BKHMC 50207

Ibsen, Henrik (author)

DOLL'S HOUSE, A (Bloom, Claire (nar)).
LP: TRS 343
MC: CDL 5343

ENEMY OF THE PEOPLE, AN (Various artists).
LP: TRS 349
MC: CDL 5349

HEDDA GABLER (Plowright, Joan).
LPS: TRS 322
MCSET: CDL 5322

MASTER BUILDER, THE (Various artists).
LP: TRS 307
MC: 307

Icarus

STATE OF MIND.
LP: RURO 03

Ice Castles

ICE CASTLES (Original soundtrack) (Various artists).
LP: ALB 6 8317
MC: ACB 6 8317
LP: ARTY 168
MC: TC ARTY 168

Ice Cube

AMERIKKKA'S MOST WANTED.
MC: BRCA 551
LP: BRLP 551

KILL AT WILL.
LP: EVF 7230
LP: BRLM 572
MC: BRCM 572

Ice Dance Orchestra

ICE DANCE.
2LP: ADL 524
MCSET: ADK 524

Ice Station Zebra

ICE STATION ZEBRA Original soundtrack (Various artists).
LP: MCA 25017
MC: MCAC 25017

Iceage

LIFE'S A BITCH.
LP: HMILP 154
MC: HMIMC 154

Icebreakers...

PLANET MARS DUB (Icebreakers with the Diamonds).
Tracks: / Dub with Garvey / Sweet answer / Work out / Who cares / Run away / Grand rock / Two brothers / Fingers out / Ital rock / Planet Mars.
LP: FL 1010

Iced Earth

ICED EARTH.
LP: 0897141

Icehouse

GREAT SOUTHERN LAND.
Tracks: / Crazy / Cross the border / Street cafe / Don't believe anymore / No promises (dance mix) / Touch the fire / Jimmy Dean / Hey little girl / Great southern land / Electric blue.
LP: CHR 1746
MC: ZCHR 1746

ICEHOUSE.
Tracks: / Icehouse / I can't help myself / Sister / Walls / Sons / We can get together / Boulevard / Fat man / Skin / Not my kind.
LP: CHR 1350
MC: ZCHR 1350

LOVE IN MOTION.
Tracks: / Uniform / Street cafe / Hey little girl / Glam / Trojan blue / Great southern land / Love in motion / Mysterious thing / One by one / Goodnight Mr. Mathews.
LP: CHR 1390
MC: ZCHR 1390

MAN OF COLOURS, A.
Tracks: / Crazy / Electric blue / My obsession / Man of colours / Heartbreak kid / Kingdom, The / Nothing too serious / Girl in the moon / Anybody's war / Sunrise.
LP: CHR 1592
MC: ZCHR 1592

MEASURE FOR MEASURE.
Tracks: / No promises / Cross the border / Spanish gold / Paradise / Flame / Regular boys / Mr. Big.

LP: . . . . CHR 1527
MC: . . . . ZCHR 1527

SIDEWALK.
Tracks: / Take the town / This time / Someone like you / Stay close / Tonight / Don't believe any more.
LP: . . . . CHR 1458
MC: . . . . ZCHR 1458

Iceland

FOLK SONGS OF ICELAND (Various artists).
LP: . . . . LLST 7335

Iceman

ICEMAN (Original soundtrack) (Various artists).
LP: . . . . SCRS 1006

Iceni Childrens...

NURSERY RHYME TIME (Iceni Childrens Choir).
LP: . . . . LJLI 5047 79

Ice-T

ICEBERG, THE.
LP: . . . . WX 316
MC: . . . . WX 316C

O.G..
LP: . . . . EX 412
MC: . . . . WX 412 C

POWER.
Tracks: / Intro / Power / Drama / Heartbeat / I'm your pusher / L.G.B.N.A.F. / Syndicate, The / Radio suckers / Soul on ice / Outro / High rollers / Personal.
LP: 925765 1
MC: 925765 4

RHYME PAYS.
Tracks: / Intro - Rhyme pays / 6'n the mornin' / Make it funky / Somebody gotta do it / 409 / I love ladies / Sex / Pain / Squeeze the trigger.
LP: 925602 1
MC: 925602 4
LP: . . . . K 925602 1
MC: . . . . K 925602 4

Icicle Works

BLIND.
Tracks: / Intro / Shit creek / Little Girl Lost / Starry blue eyed wonder / One true love / Blind / Two two three / What do you want me to do / Stood before Saint Peter / Here comes trouble / Kiss off, The / Walk a while with me.
LP: . . . . IWA 2
MC: . . . . IWC 2

ICICLE WORKS, THE.
Tracks: / Chop the tree / Love is a wonderful colour / As the dragonfly flies / Lover's day / In the cauldron of love / Out of season / Factory in the desert / Birds fly / Nirvana / Reaping the rich harvest.
LP: . . . . BBL 50
MC: . . . . BBLC 50
LP: . . . . BEGA 50

IF YOU WANT TO DEFEAT THE ENEMY SING HIS SONG.
Tracks: / Hope springs eternal / Travelling chest / Sweet Thursday / Up here in the North of England / Who do you want for your love / When you were mine / Evangeline / Truck driver's lament / Understanding Jane / Walking with a mountain / Please don't let it rain on my parade (Extra track on CD and cassette only.) / Everybody loves to play the fool (* Extra track on CD and cassette only.) / I never saw my hometown 'till I went around the world (* Extra track on CD only.) / Into the mystic (* Extra track on CD only.).
LP: . . . . BEGA 78
MC: . . . . BEGC 78
LP: . . . . BBL 78
MC: . . . . BBLC 78

MELANIE STILL HURTS.
Tracks: / Melanie still hurts / When the crying's done / Mickey's blue (Not on 7" single.) / I dreamt I was a beautiful woman (Not on 7" single.).
MC: . . . . WORKSM 101

PERMANENT DAMAGE.
Tracks: / I still want you / Motorcycle rider / Melanie still hurts / Hope street / Rag / I think I'm gonna be OK / Baby don't burn / What she did to my mind / One good eye / Permanent damage / Woman on my mind / Looks like rain / Dumb angel.
LP: 4668001
MC: 4668004

SEVEN SINGLES DEEP.
Tracks: / Hollow horse / Love is a wonderful colour / Birds fly / All the daughters / When it all comes down / Seven horses / Rapids.
LP: . . . . BEGA 71
MC: . . . . BEGC 71
LP: . . . . BBL 71
MC: . . . . BBLC 71

SMALL PRICE OF A BICYCLE, THE.
Tracks: / Hollow horse / Perambulator / Seven horses / Rapids / Windfall / Assumed sundowns / Saint's sojourn / All the daughters / Book of reason / Conscience of Kings.
LP: . . . . BBL 61
MC: . . . . BBLC 61
LP: . . . . BEGA 61

Icon

RIGHT BETWEEN THE EYES.
Tracks: / Right between the eyes / Two for the road / Take my breath away / Far cry / In your eyes / Forever young / Running under fire / Peace and love.
LP: . . . . K 820101
MC: . . . . K 820104

Icons

ART IN THE DARK.
Tracks: / Number / Lots of money / Trouble in Havana / Nothin' left to save / Try / Tonight - there's a sign / Girl is mine, The / Chains / Privilege and easy / Privilege and easy (Extra track available on cassette only.).
LP: . . . . P 4008
MC: . . . . P 4408

Icons of Filth

ONWARD CHRISTIAN SOLDIERS.
LP: . . . . MORT 5

Ideal

DER ERNST DES LEBENS.
LP: . . . . K 58471

SERIOUSNESS OF LIFE, THE.
Tracks: / Siberia / Schwein / Sex in the desert / Herrscher / Feuerzeug / Immer frei / Erschiessen / Monotony / Ich kann nicht schlafen / Spannung / Spion.
LP: . . . . K 58400

Ideal Band

MEASURE OF FREEDOM, A.
Tracks: / Dominic McGowan / Train journey north, The / Barbara's jig / Alan MacPherson of Mosspark (4.39) / Wars o' Germany. (The) (4.01) / Cumbrian girl (4.22) / Two Swedish waltzes (3.40) / Two Breton dance tunes (2.51) / Miss Ailie / McHugh's other foot (5.41) / Sturdy tinker, The (4.09) / Itinerant worker, The (2.39) / Horseguards blue (3.29) / Song for Glasgow (2.30) / Tam bain's lum / Tir aluinn / Black Watch polka (3.45).
LP: . . . . LIFP 7003
MC: . . . . LIFC 7003

Identity

SMILES ALL ROUND.
LP: . . . . YUBB LP 6

Idiot

STATIONS OF LIFE.
Tracks: / Hirnloser Schlager / Doisen of society / Der Saufer / Tagen tagus dasselbe / She's in the garden / Deadly panic / Der Idiot / Fleish / Party girl / Stations of life.
LP: 081292

WHERE IS THE LOGIC.
LP: . . . . DOPR 6

Idiots

CRIES OF THE INSANE.
Tracks: / Death brains / Freundschaft ohne ende / Nuclear war / Se lbstmord / Loser, The / Tage ohne alkohol / Insane / Revolution / Edeka / Destroy my body.
LP: . . . . WEBITE 20

Idle Race

BIRTHDAY PARTY, THE.
Tracks: / Skeleton and the roundabout / Happy birthday / Birthday, The / I like my toys / Morning sunshine / Follow me follow / Sitting in my tree / On with the show / Lucky man / Mrs. Ward / Pie in the sky / Lady who said she could fly, The / End of the road.
LP: C5-536

LIGHT AT THE END OF THE ROAD (Best of the Idle Race).
Tracks: / End of the road / Morning sunshine / Lady who said she could fly, The / Happy birthday-the birthday / Girl at the window / Big chief wooly bosher / Here we go round the lemon tree / My father's son / Skeleton and the roundabout / Come with me / Going home / Mr. Crow and Sir Norman / Please no more sad songs / Follow me, follow / On with the show / Lucky man / Imposters of life's magazine / Days of the broken arrows.
LP: . . . . SEE 60

Idle Strand

CUT AND RUN.
LP: 400243

Idles

AGROCULTURE.
Tracks: / Great white snake(s) / Matt finish / Mushead / Agroculture / Christmas day / No, no, no / Door, The / Love song / Ray's complaint / C.D.B.D.I.S..
LP: . . . . UPLP 9

Idol, Billy

BILLY IDOL.
Tracks: / Come, come on / White wedding (parts 1 & 2) / Hot in the city / Dead on arrival / Nobody's business / Love calling / Hole in the wall / Shooting star / It's so cruel / Congo man.
LP: . . . . CHR 1377
MC: . . . . ZCHR 1377

BILLY IDOL: INTERVIEW PICTURE DISC.
LPPD: . . . . BAK 2103

CHARMED LIFE.
Tracks: / Loveless, The / Pimping on steel / Prodigal blues / LA woman / Trouble with the sweet stuff / Cradle of love / Mark of Caine / Endless sleep / Love unchained / Right way, The / License to thrill.
LP: . . . . CHR 1735
MC: . . . . ZCHR 1735

IDOL SONGS (11 of the Best).
Tracks: / Rebel yell / Hot in the city / White wedding / Eyes without a face / Catch my fall / Mony mony / To be a lover / Sweet sixteen / Flesh for fantasy / Don't need a gun / Dancing with myself.
LP: . . . . BIL TV 1
MC: . . . . ZBIL TV 1
LP: . . . . BILTVD 1

INTERVIEW BY KRIS NEEDS.
LP: . . . . LSMO 2

MUSIC AND MEDIA INTERVIEW PICTURE DISC.
LPPD: . . . . IDOL 1001

REBEL YELL.
Tracks: / Rebel yell / Daytime drama / Eyes without a face / Blue highway / Flesh for fantasy / Catch my fall / Crank call / Stand in the shadows / Dead next door, The / Do not stand.
LP: . . . . CHR 1450
MC: . . . . ZCHR 1450

VITAL IDOL.
Tracks: / Dancing with myself / White wedding (parts 1 & 2) / Flesh for fantasy / Catch my fall / Mony mony / Love calling (dub) / Hot in the city.
LP: . . . . CUX 1502
MC: . . . . ZCUX 1502

WHIPLASH SMILE.
Tracks: / World's forgotten boy / Don't need a gun / Beyond belief / Fatal charm / All summer single / One night, one chance / To be a lover / Soul standing by / Sweet sixteen / Man for all seasons.
LP: . . . . CDL 1514
MC: . . . . ZCDL 1514

Idol Eyes

DIVINE PRINCIPLE IS HOPE, THE.
LP: . . . . UNKNOWN

If?

TEA BREAK OVER-BACK ON YOUR HEADS.
LP: . . . . GULP 1007

If Six Was Nine

IF SIX WAS NINE (A tribute to the late great Jimi Hendrix) (Various artists).
LP: . . . . ILLUSION 007

If They Could See ...

IF THEY COULD SEE ME NOW (Original London cast) (Various artists).
Tracks: / If they could see.. (introduction): *Sherrin, Ned/Ian Ogilvy/ Margaret* / I remember it well: *Courtney, Margaret/Joss* Acklan / I wish I was in love again: *Soper, Gay/James Warwick* / Why him: *Robertson, Liz/Alan Jay Lerner* / My gift: *March, Elspeth* / Overhead: *Morley, Sheridan* / That is the end of the news: *Douglas, Angela/David* Kernan / Ladies who lunch, The: *Karlin, Miriam* / Physician, The: *Brook, Faith* / Oldest established, The: *Pringle, Bryan/ George Sewell* / Send in the clowns: *Kennedy, Cheryl/Robert Meadmore* / Sonny boy: *Finlay,* Frank/Simon Callow / Why must the show go on?: *Matthews, Francis (nar)* / Opening second half: *Dallas, Lorna* / Introduction: *Frost, David/Alan Jay Lerner* / Typically English: *McKenna, Virginia & Louise* / Boy from...., The: *Phillips, Sian* / Oh how to be lovely: *Tindall, Hilary/Victoria Burgoyne* / Introduction: *Nimmo, Derek/* 42nd Street: *Marsh, Jean/Eileen Atkins* / You remind me of you: *Lapotaire, Jane/ Tim Curry* / Ed Sullivan stories: *Frost, David* / Introduction: *McGowan, Alec* / I'll never been jealous again: *Hordern, Michael/Joan Plowright/* Happy birthday sweet sixteen/Sixteen candles: *Reeve, Christopher* / Standing on the corner: *Various artists/* Finale: *Various artists.*
LP: . . . . TERX 1087

If You Feel Like ...

IF YOU FEEL LIKE SINGING (Film Soundtrack) (Various artists).
Tracks: / (Howdy neighbour) Happy harvest: *Various artists* / You wonderful you: *Various artists* / Friendly star: *Various artists* / If you feel like singing, sing: *Various artists* / Get happy: *Various artists* / Dig dig dig dig for your dinner: *Various artists.*
LP: 2353 038

If You Just Tuned in

IF YOU JUST TUNED IN (Live 'Mean Fiddler' acoustic room compilation) (Various artists).
Tracks: / Dollar tree: *Hawkins, Ted* / When we were young: *Orchard, Pat* / Love your shoes: *Cunningham, Andrew/* Rover: *Sons Of The Desert* / Down the wine garden: *Little Big Band* / It's not that bad anymore: *Barely* Works / White cloud: *To Hell With Burgundy* / Spitting: *And All Because The Lady Loves* / Three legged men: *Harding, John Wesley* / Tree to breathe: *Dinner Ladies* / Partisans: *Keineg, Katell* / I ain't got nothin' yet: *Hawkins, Ted.*
LP: . . . . AWL 1017
LP: . . . . AWT 1017

Ifield, Frank

20 GOLDEN GREATS: FRANK IFIELD.
Tracks: / I remember you / Confessin' (that I love you) / Don't blame me / You came along (from out of nowhere) / Nobody's darlin' but mine / Call her your sweetheart / I should care / Lucky devil / Summer is over / Please / Lovesick blues / Wayward wind / Mule train / Wolverton mountain / Gonna find me a bluebird / Paradise / She taught me how to yodel / Angry at the big oak tree / No one will ever know / Waltzing Matilda.
LP: . . . . PLAT 12
MC: . . . . PLAC 12
LP: . . . . NE 1136
MC: . . . . CE 2136

BEST OF THE EMI YEARS: FRANK IFIELD.
Tracks: / Lucky devil / I remember you / She taught me how to yodel / Lovesick blues / Confessin' (that I love you) / Just one more chance / Nobody's darlin' but mine / Wayward wind, The / My blue heaven / Say it isn't so / Don't blame me / You came a long way from St. Louis / Summer is over / Once a jolly swagman (From film: Up Jumped A Swagman) / Botany Bay (From film: Up Jumped A Swagman) / Paradise / Wild rover (From film: Up Jumped A Swagman) / Call her your sweetheart / No one will ever know / Give me your word.
MC: . . . . TCEMS 1402

BLUE SKIES.
LP: 55SX 1588

BORN FREE.
LP: 33SX 1462

EP COLLECTION, THE: FRANK IFIELD.
LP: . . . . SEE 312
MC: . . . . SEEK 312

GOLDEN HITS: FRANK IFIELD.
2LP: . . . . MFP 1017
MCSET: . . . . TCMFP 1017

GREATEST HITS: FRANK IFIELD.
LP: 33SX 1633

HIS GREATEST HITS.
Tracks: / I remember you / Gotta get a date / She taught me how to yodel / Go tell it on the mountain / I'm confessin' / Mule train / Wolverton mountain / Angry at the big oak tree / Wayward wind / Funny how time slips away / Riders in the sky / Scarlet ribbons / Lovesick blues / Nobody's darlin' but mine / Lucky devil / Summer is over / I should care / Call her your sweetheart / Paradise / No one will ever know / Happy go lucky me / Waltzing Matilda / Young love / Cool water / Don't blame me.
MC: . . . . HR 8117
MC: . . . . HR 4181174

I REMEMBER YOU.
MC: . . . . VCA 067
LP: 1A 220 1583224

I'LL REMEMBER YOU.
LP: 33SX 1467

PORTRAIT OF FRANK IFIELD.
Tracks: / Crawling back / Let's take the long way round the world / She cheats on me / Touch the morning / Crowd, The / Crystal (I can see through you) / (After sweet memories) Play born to lose again / Why don't we leave together / So sad (To watch good love go bad) / Yesterday just passed my way again.
LP: . . . . N 146
MC: . . . . ZCN 146

SOMEONE TO GIVE MY LOVE TO.
LP: . . . . SRLP 111

Iggie's House (bk)

IGGIE'S HOUSE (Judy Blume) (Fellows, Susannah (nar)).
MCSET: 086 222 0415

Iggy & The Stooges

DEATH TRIP.
LPPD: MIG 6P

FUN HOUSE.
LP: 4205579

METALLIC 2 X K.O..
Tracks: / Raw power / Head on the curb / Gimme danger / Search and destiny / Heavy liquid / I wanna be your dog / Recital / Open up and bleed / I got nothing / Rich bitch / Cock in my pocket / Louie Louie.
2LP: 622321

RAW STOOGES VOL.1.
LP: 190069

RAW STOOGES VOL.2.
LP: 190070

STOOGES, THE.
LP: K 42032

Iglesias, Julio

24 GREATEST SONGS, THE.
2LP: CBS 88469

1100 BEL AIR PLACE.
Tracks: / All of you (with Diana Ross) / Two lovers / Bambou medley / Air that I breathe, The / Last time, The / Moonlight lady / When I fall in love / Me va, me va / If / To all the girls I've loved before (with Willie Nelson).
LP: CBS 86308
MC: 40 86308

A FLOR DE PIEL.
LP: CBS 82849

A MEXICO.
LP: CBS 82853

A MIS 33 ANOS.
LP: CBS 82712

A VOUS LES FEMMES.
LP: CBS 83704

ALL OF YOU (see under Ross, Diana) (Iglesias, Julio/Diana Ross).

AMERICA.
Tracks: / Ay ay ay / Alma llanera / Caminito / Recuerdos de ipacarai / Historia de un amor / Obsesion / Sombras / Cancion de orfeo / Guantanamera / Vaya con dios / Moliendo cafe.
LP: CBS 82846

AMOR.
Tracks: / So close to me / Momentos / a paloma / Las cosas que tiene la vida / Nathalie / Quijote / L'amour fragile / No me vuelvo a enamorar / Con la misma piedra / Esa mujer / Si el amor llama a tu puerta / Amor.
LP: CBS 25103

BEGIN THE BEGUINE.
Tracks: / Begin the beguine / Quiereme / Me olvide de vivir / Por un poco de tu amour / Grande, grande, grande / Como tu / Guantanamera / Quiereme mucho / Hey / Un dia ty, un dia yo / Soy un truhan, soy un senor / Candilejas / El amor / 33 anos / Isla en el sol.
LP: CBS 85462
MC: 40 85462

DE NINA A MUJER.
Tracks: / De nina a mujer / Volver a empezar / Despues de ti / Que nadei sepa mi sufrir / Isal en el sol / O me quieres o me dejas / Y pensar..si madam / Grande, grande, grande / Come tu.
LP: CBS 85063

EL AMOR.
LP: CBS 82868

EMOCIONES.
Tracks: / Me olvide de vivir / Voy a perder la Cabeza por tu amor / Spanish girl / Pobre diablo / Quiereme mucho / Un dia tu, un dia yo.
LP: 83703

EN CONCIERTO.
Tracks: / Obertura medley / Volver a empezar / Pensami / Vivir a Dos / Grande, grande, grande / Cantando a Francia / Momentos / As time goes by / Cantando A Latinomerica / Homenaje a Cole Porter / Feelings / Hey, Nathalie / La Guerra de los mundos / Quijote / Fidele / De Nina a mujer / Ou est Passee ma Boheme / Quireme Mucho / Cantando A Latinomerica II / Samba Da Minha Terra / Un canto a galicia / Quand tu n'est pas la Caminito / Un sentimental / Cantando a Mejico / Me olvide de vivir / La paloma.
2LP: CBS 88631
MC: 40 88631

HEY.
Tracks: / For Elle / Amantes / Morrinas / Viejas tradiciones / Ron y coco cola / Hey! / Sentimental / Paloma blanca / La Nave del Olvido / Pajaro chogui.
LP: CBS 84304

JULIO.
Tracks: / Begin the beguine / Forever and ever / Yours / La paloma / Pensami / D'abord..et puis / Never, never, never / Nathalie / Feelings / Hey, amor / Limelight / Rum and coca cola / Sono lo / Je nais pas change / So close to me.
MC: 40 10038
LP: 4510771
MC: 4510774
LP: CBS 10038

LIBRA.
LP: CBS 26623

MES CHANSONS EN FRANCAIS.
LPS: CBS 66359

MOMENTOS.
Tracks: / Nathalie / Momentos / La paloma / Las cosas que tiene la vida / Quijote / No me vuelvo a enamorar / Con la misma piedra / Esa mujer / Smor / Si el amor llama a tu puerta.
MC: 4687854

NON STOP.
Tracks: / Love is on our side again / I know it's over / Never, never, never / AE, AO / Words and music / My love (featuring Stevie Wonder) / Everytime we fall in love / Too many women / If I ever needed you (I need you now).
LP: 4609901
MC: 4609904

RAICES.
Tracks: / Latino - intro latino / Tres palabras / Perfidia / Amapola / Noche de ronda / Quizas quizas quizas / Adios / El Manisero / Caballo viejo / Bamboleo / Solo 1 / Solo 2 / Italia - Intro Italia / Torna a surriento / Quando m'innamora / T'ho voluto bene (non dimenticar) / O sole mio / Quando, quando, quando / Francia - Intro Francia / Ne me quitte pas / Que c'est trist venise / Et maintenant / La vie en rose.
LP: 4653161
MC: 4653164

SENTIMENTAL.
Tracks: / C'est la vie / Un nuit de carnaval / Ma chance et ma chanson / Sentimental / Un perdant / J'ai besoin d'un peu d'amour / Je chante / Elle / Quand tu n'est pas la Caminito / Il faut toujours / Jolie.
LP: 4600291
MC: 4600294

STARRY STARRY NIGHTS.
Tracks: / Can't help falling in love / And I love her / Mona Lisa / Cryin' time / Yesterday when I was young / When I need you / 99 miles from L.A. / Vincent (starry starry night) / If you go away / Love has been a friend to me.
LP: 4672841
MC: 4672844

TO ALL THE GIRLS I'VE LOVED BEFORE (See under Nelson, Willie) (Iglesias, Julio & Willie Nelson).

UN HOMBRE SOLO.
Tracks: / Lo mejor de tu vida / O que fazer? / Il miele in corpo / Todo el amor que te hace falta / Que no se rompa la noche / Un hombre solo / Un padre come me / America / Se mi dai una mano tu / Alguien / El mar que llevo dentro.
LP: 4600081
MC: 4600084

Ignacio

IGNACIO (See under Vangelis) (Vangelis).

Ignatzek, Klaus

MONK'S VISIT (Ignatzek, Klaus Group).
LP: HEP 2036

Ignition

MACHINATION.
LP: DISCHORD 31
MC: DISCHORD 31C

SINKER.
LP: IG 3

Ignorance

CONFIDENT RAT, THE.
LP: ZORRO 17
MC: TZORRO 17

Igoe, Sonny

JERSEY SWING CONCERTS, THE (see under Meldonian, Dick).

Igus Orchestra

SCOTLAND FOR ME.
LP: KLP 59
MC: ZCKLP 59

TASTE OF SCOTLAND.
LP: KLP 60
MC: ZCKLP 60

Iheka-Chama

MANDINGO TRIBE.
LP: CLPS 1987

Ikettes

FINE, FINE, FINE.
Tracks: / Fine fine fine / Can't sit down / Don't feel sorry for me / Camel walk / Blue on blue / I'm so thankful / You're trying to make me lose my mind / Sally go round the roses / Peaches and cream / Never more will I be lonely for you / Not that I recall / You're love is me / Biggest players, The / How come / Nobody loves me / It's been so long.
LP: KENT 063

TINA TURNER & IKE TURNER & THE IKETTES.
LP: ENT 13004

Ikhwani Safaa Musical

TAARAB MUSIC OF ZANZIBAR VOL 2.
Tracks: / Usiji gambe / Nna zama / Pendo la wasikitisha / Nipe pee / Kanilemaza / Uki chungua / Waridi lisilo miba / Hidaya.
LP: ORBD 033

Il Brigante

IL BRIGANTE (Original Soundtrack) (Various artists).
LP: S'BUS 204

Ile Axe

BRAZILIAN PERCUSSION.
MC: KP 95059

I-Level

I LEVEL.
Tracks: / Minefield / Treacle / Heart aglow / Stone heart / Woman / Give me / No. 4 / Teacher / Music / Face again.
LP: 2270
LP: OVED 127
MC: OVEDC 127
LP: V 2270

SHAKE.
Tracks: / New day / In the river / Into another world / Keep me running / In the sand / Our song / Had enough / Drums / Cat amongst the pigeons.
LP: V 2320
MC: TCV 2320
LP: OVED 179

Iley, Ras

MR ENERGY.
LP: RRTG 2231

I'll Get By

I'LL GET BY (Various).
Tracks: / You'll never know / My devotion / I'll be seeing you / Don't sit under the apple tree / Send me your love for Christmas / Keep an eye on your heart / I'll get by / When you're a long long way from home / Silver wings in the moonlight.
MC: K 1007

Illapu

ILLAPU, VOL 2: RAZA BRAVA.
Tracks: / Amigo / Zamba de Lozano / Raza brava / Agonia de carnaval / Amilia rosa / Paisaje de la puna / Cacharpaya del carnaval / Atacamenos / Chango pastor / Paloma ausente / Cantos ceremoniales / El Cascabel.
LP: MFS 811
MC: 51 811

Illsley, John

GLASS.
Tracks: / High stakes / I want to see the moon / Papermen / All I want is you / World is full of glass, The / Red turns to blue / Let's dance / She wants everything / Star for now.
LP: VERH 56
MC: VERHC 56

NEVER TOLD A SOUL.
Tracks: / Boy with chinese eyes / Night cafe / Never told a soul / Jimmy on the central line / Northern land / Another Alidi / Let the river flow.
LP: VERL 15
MC: VERLC 15

Illusion

I LIKE IT LOUD.
Tracks: / I like it loud / Heartbeat (the call) / Call in the law / Heart attack / I can't wait / Call me up / Shake / Red light / Get to you / Lifetime.
LP: 9241081
MC: 9241084

OUT OF THE MIST.
LP: ILPS 9489

Illusions (bk)

ILLUSIONS (Adventures of a Reluctant Messiah).
MC: 1585

Illustrated Man

ILLUSTRATED MAN.
Tracks: / Head over heels / Dangerous kind / Just enough / Days without end / Songs for the heart / Moving forward / Time of your life / Sometimes in the night / An emotional away / Fall from grace.
LP: EMC 2400971

Illustrated Man (bk)

ILLUSTRATED MAN, THE (Ray Bradbury) (Nimoy, Leonard).
MC: 1479

I'm Coming From ...

I'M COMING FROM SECLUSION (Various artists).
LP: CI 005

I'm Getting My Act...

I'M GETTING MY ACT TOGETHER AND TAKING IT ON THE (Original London cast) (Various artists).
Tracks: / Natural high: *Various artists* / Smile: *Various artists* / In a simple way: *Various artists*/ Miss Africa: *Various artists* / Strong woman number: *Various artists* / Dear Tom: *Various artists* / Old friend: *Various artists* / Put in a package and sold: *Various artists* / If only things were different: *Various artists* / Feel the love: *Various artists* / Lonely lady: *Various artists* / Happy birthday: *Various artists*.
LP: TER 1006
MC: ZCTER 1006

I'm So Hollow

EMOTION SOUND EMOTION.
LP: JAMS 5

I'm Sorry I'll Read...

I'M SORRY I'LL READ THAT AGAIN (Various artists).
LP: REH 342
MC: ZCR 342

Images (group)

MARA.
LP: PLR 070

Imagination

BODY TALK.
Tracks: / Tell me do you want my love / Flashback / I'll always love you (but don't look back) / In and out of love / Body talk / So good, so right / Burning up.
MC: ZCRB 1001
MC: NK 74322

CLOSER.
Tracks: / I know what love is / Hold me in your arms / Paranoia / Where are you now? / Last time, The / For members only / Instinctual / Who (tell me who) / Over / Hot nights / Skin time / Closer / Operator (On cassette/compact disc only.) / Touch (part 1) (On compact disc only.).
LP: PL 71508
MC: PK 71508

IMAGINATION GOLD.
Tracks: / Flashback / Music and lights / Body talk / Changes / Looking at midnight / Just an illusion / Burning up / In and out of love / New dimension / In the heat of the night.
LP: RBLP 1006
MC: ZCRB 1006

IN THE HEAT OF THE NIGHT.
Tracks: / In the heat of the night / Heart 'n' soul / Music and lights / All night loving / Just an illusion / All I want to know / One more love / Changes.
LP: RBLP 1002
MC: ZCRB 1002

LIKE IT IS.
LP: SMR 985
MC: SMC 985

LOVE SONGS, THE.
Tracks: / Body talk / Heart 'n' soul / Changes / In and out of love / One more love / Hold me in your arms / In the heat of the night / Sunshine / So good so right / Looking at midnight / Closer / Thank you my love.
MC: NK 74483
LP: NL 74483

NIGHT DUBBING.
Tracks: / Flashback / Just an illusion / Music and lights / So good, so right / Body talk / Heart 'n' soul / Changes / Burning up.
LP: RBDUB 1
MC: ZCDUB 1

SCANDALOUS.
Tracks: / New dimension / State of love / Point of no return / When I see the fire / Shoo be doo da dabba doobee / Wrong in love / Looking at midnight / Need to be free.
LP: RBLP 1004
MC: ZCRP 1004

Imaginations

IMAGINATIONS - FURTHER REFLECTIONS (see under Reflections) (Various artists).

Imaginative Woman (bk)

IMAGINATIVE WOMAN, AN (See under Hardy, Thomas) (Morant, Richard).

Imanol

OROITUZ.
LP: ELKAR 93

Imitation Life

ICE CUBES AND SUGAR.
LP: ROSE 97

SCORING CORRECTLY AT HOME.
LP: ROSE 156

Imitation Of Life

IMITATION OF LIFE Original soundtrack (Various artists).
LP: 254532.1

Imlach, Hamish

HAMISH IMLACH & IAIN MACKINTOSH (Imlach, Hamish & Iain Mackintosh).
LP: ALLP 215

MURDERED BALLADS.
LP: XTRA 1131

ODD RARITY.
LP: XTRA 1121

SCOTTISH SABBATH.
LP: ALLP 209

SONNY'S DREAM.
Tracks: / Cod liver oil and orange juice / Ballad of William Brown / Mary Anne / Reprobate's lament / Salonika / Kisses sweeter than wine / Smoker's song / Sonny's dream / If it wasn't for the union / Parcel o' rogues / I didn't raise my boy to be a soldier / Goodbye booze / D-day dodgers / Seven men of Knoydart.
LP: LIFL 7006
MC: LIFC 7006

Immaculate Conception

IMMACULATE CONCEPTION (Various artists).
LP: PLAYD 1 LP

Immaculate Fools

ANOTHER MAN'S WORLD.
Tracks: / Another man's world / Sad / Prince, The / Bad seed / Falling apart together / Come on Jayne / Got me by the heart / Stop now.
LP: 4665371
MC: 4665374

DUMB POET.
Tracks: / Never give less than everything / Tragic comedy / One minute / Dumb poet / So much here / Wish you were here / Don't drive the hope from my heart / Pretty prize now / Stay away.
LP: AMA 5151
MC: AMC 5151

HEARTS OF FORTUNE.
Tracks: / Searching for sparks / Nothing means nothing / Save it / Hearts of fortune / Immaculate fools / What about me? / I fell / Counting on you / Day by day / Waiting.
LP: AMA 5030
MC: AMC 5030

Immediate Singles

IMMEDIATE SINGLES COLLECTION (Various artists).
Tracks: / Little Miss Understood: *Stewart, Rod* / Much to say: *Stewart, Rod* / I'm not saying: *Nico* / Last mile, The: *Nico* / Someone's gonna get their head kicked in tonite: *Vince, Earl & The Valients* / Man of the world: *Fleetwood Mac* / Out of time: *Farlowe, Chris* / Sitting on a fence: *Twice As Much* / I'm your witch doctor: *Mayall, John* / Itchycoo park: *Small Faces* / Lazy Sunday: *Small Faces* / Hang on Sloopy: *McCoys, The* / Natural born boogie: *Humble Pie* / Angel of the morning: *Arnold, P.P.* / First cut is the deepest: *Arnold, P.P.* / America: *Nice* / Second amendment: *Nice* / Ars longa vita brevis: *Nice* / Acceptance brandenburger: *Nice* / If paradise is half as nice: *Amen Corner* / Bend me, shape me: *Amen Corner*.
2LP: CCSLP 102
MC: CCSMC 102

Immolation

DAWN OF POSSESSION.
LP: RC 93101
MC: RC 93104

Impact

ULTIMATE PARTY FORMULA, THE.
LP: GS 2308

Impact Allstars

JAVA JAVA DUB.
LP: UNKNOWN

Impellitteri

STAND IN LINE.
Tracks: / Stand in line / Since you've been gone / Secret love / Somewhere over the rainbow / Tonight I'll fry / White and perfect / Goodnight and goodnight / Playing with fire / Leviathan.
LP: MFN 87
MC: TMFN 87

Imperial Metals

CHECKMATE.
LP: TT 003

Imperial Pompadours

ERSATZ.
LP: POMP 1

Imperial Rockabillies

IMPERIAL ROCKABILLIES, VOL 1 (Various artists).
LP: 2C 068 83098

Imperial Venus

IMPERIAL VENUS (VENERE IMPERIALE) Original soundtrack (Various artists).
LP: RP 013

Imperials

FOLLOW MAN WITH MUSIC.
LP: KL 025

LET THE WIND BLOW.
LP: MYRR 1196
MC: MYRC 1196

ONE MORE SONG FOR YOU.
Tracks: / What can I do for you / I'm forgiven / All my life / Livin' without your love / Closer than ever / One more song for you / Higher power / More like you.
LP: DAY 4004
MC: TC DAY 4004

PRIORITY.
Tracks: / Trumpet of Jesus, The / Come back and finish what you started / I'd rather believe in you / Any good time at all / Be still my soul / There's no time till you take it / Pieces / Into my life / Seek ye first.
LP: DAY 4005
MC: TC DAY 4005

TIME TO GET IT TOGETHER.
LP: KLO 12

Impetigo

ULTIMO MONDO CANNIBALE.
LP: WRE 9041

Impett, Jonathan

TRUMPET COLLECTION (Impett, Jonathan & Ensemble).
MC: CSAR 30

TRUMPET COLLECTION - BAROQUE TO PRESENT DAY (See also under Clarion Ensemble).

Implosion

IMPLOSION Hayward, John (Foster, Barry).
LP: JP 502

Importance Of Being...

IMPORTANCE OF BEING EARNEST (see also under Wilde,Oscar) (Gielgud, John & Dame Edith Evans).

Impossible Years

SCENES WE'D LIKE TO SEE.
LP: DREAM 1

Impressions (group)

16 GREATEST HITS: IMPRESSIONS.
LP: AB 727

BEST OF THE IMPRESSIONS.
LP: AB 654

FAN THE FIRE.
Tracks: / Fan the fire / I don't wanna lose your love / Love love love / You're mine / I surrender / Take everything / I don't mind / For your precious love.
LP: T 624
MC: C 624

FINALLY GOT MYSELF TOGETHER.
LP: BDLP 4003

FIRST IMPRESSIONS.
Tracks: / Sooner or later / Same thing it took / Old before my time / First impressions / Groove / I'm so glad / How high is high / Why must a love song be a sad song.
LP: RSS 9

IMPRESSIONS, THE.
Tracks: / It's all right / Gypsy woman / Grow closer together / Little young lover / You've come home / Never let me go / Minstrel and Queen / I need your love / I'm the one who loves you / Sad sad girl and boy / As long as you love me / Twist and limbo.
LP: KENT 005

KEEP ON PUSHING.
Tracks: / Keep on pushing / I've been trying / I ain't supposed to / Dedicate my song to you / Long long winter / Somebody help me / Amen / I thank heaven / Talking about my baby / Don't let it hide / I love you (yeah) / I made a mistake.
LP: KENT 009

LASTING IMPRESSIONS.
Tracks: / Sooner or later / Same thing it took / Old before my time / First impressions / Loving power / Sunshine / I can't wait to see you / If you have to ask.
LP: CUR 2006
MC: CURMC 2006

LOVING POWER.
Tracks: / Loving power / Sunshine / I can't wait to see you / If you have to ask / You can't be wrong / I wish I'd stayed in bed / Keep on trying.
LP: RSS 10

NEVER ENDING IMPRESSIONS, THE.
Tracks: / Sister love / Little boy blue / Satin doll / Girl don't you know me / I gotta keep on moving / You always hurt the one you love / That's what love will do / I'm so proud / September song / Lemon Tree / Ten to one / Woman who loves me, A.
LP: KENT 008

ORIGINALS.
2LP: ABSD 303

PEOPLE GET READY.
Tracks: / Woman's got soul / Emotions / Sometimes I wonder / We're in love / Just another dance / Can't work no longer / People get ready / I've found that I've lost / Hard to believe / See the real me / Get up and move / You must believe me.
LP: KENT 012

RIGHT ON TIME.
Tracks: / It's alright / Gypsy woman / Right on time / Talking about my baby / Never let me go / I've been trying / Emotions / People get ready / Ridin' high / Can't work no longer / You've come home / You must believe me / Man's temptation / Nothing can stop me / Don't cry my love / It's all over.
LP: CRB 1063

WE'RE A WINNER.
LP: AB 635

YOUR PRECIOUS LOVE.
Tracks: / Sweet was the wind / For your precious love / Lovers Lane / Don't drive me away / Gift of love / At the county fair / Come back my love / Love me / Little young lover / Lonely one, The / Long time ago, A / Senorita, I love you / Say that you love me / New love (I found a love).
LP: TOP 179
MC: KTOP 179

Improvisation

IAI FESTIVAL (Various artists).
LP: IAI 373859

MUSIC IMPROVISATION COMPANY 1968-1971 (Various artists).
LP: INCUS 17

Impulse Manslaughter

HE WHO LAUGHS LAST LAUGHS ALONE.
LP: NB 011
LP: NB 003

LOGICAL END.
LP: NB 013
LP: 082959

Imrie, Jim

I'LL TAKE YOU HOME AGAIN, KATHLEEN.
Tracks: / If I had my way / I'll take you home again, Kathleen / Let bygones be bygones / Amazing grace / I wonder who's kissing her now / Let me call you sweetheart / Try a little tenderness / Memories / Old rugged cross, The / Just loving you / One day at a time / Let the rest of the world go by / We'll meet again / When I grow too old to dream.
MC: KITV 395

YOURS IN SONG.
Tracks: / Marching through the heather / When the heather gleams like stardust / Lassie come and dance with me / When you and I were young, Maggie / Silver threads among the gold / Legend of Scotland / Rowan tree / Lass o'leven vale, The / Gallant forty twa / Lochnagar / Geordie Munro / Sunshine of your smile, The / Black Watch, The / Lonely Scapa Flow / Star o' Rabbie Burns, The.
LP: BGC 368
MC: KBGC 368

Imruh-Asha, Rass

TRIBUTE TO SELASSIE 1.
LP: HA 1LP

In A Colts Shadow

IN A COLTS SHADOW/RINGO THE TEXAN Original soundtrack (Various artists).
LP: SP 8014

In A Shallow Grave

IN A SHALLOW GRAVE (Original soundtrack) (Various artists).
LP: STV 81359

In Crowd (group)

HIS MAJESTY IS COMING.
LP: CTLP 125

MAN FROM NEW GUINEA.
Tracks: / Man from New Guinea / Natural rock / We play reggae / Marcus Garvey's back in town / His Majesty is coming / Reggae groove / Back a yard / Little dread / Time is running out.
MC: ZCI 9577
LP: ILPS 9577

In Embrace

PASSION FRUIT PASTELS.
LP: GLALP 001

SONGS ABOUT SNOGGIN.
Tracks: / Mirror mirror / Perfect stranger / What's got into me / You can laugh / Bedtime / Room upstairs, A / Shipwrecks / Somebodys / Stay here / Wallpaper, bathwater, perfume & god / Lovelorn.
LP: GLALP 022

TOO.
LP: GLALP 004

In Excelsis

PREY.
LP: FREUD 08

In Harmony

IN HARMONY 2 (Various artists).
Tracks: / Nobody knows but me: *Various artists* / Sunny skies: *Various artists* / Owl and the pussycat, The: *Various artists* / Reach out and touch (somebody's hand): *Various artists* / Ginny the flying girl: *Various artists* / Here comes the rainbow: *Various artists* / Splish splash: *Various artists* / Some kitties don't care: *Various artists* / Maryanne: *Various artists* / Santa Claus is coming to town: *Various artists*.
LP: CBS 85451
MC: 40 85451

In Love...

IN LOVE WITH THESE TIMES (Various artists).
LP: FNE 28

In Motion

IN MOTION (Various artists).
MC: ALL 387

In & Out Of Town

IN AND OUT OF TOWN Various Artists (Various artists).
LP: HOOT LP 1

In Praise Of God

IN PRAISE OF GOD (Various artists).
LP: DCA 573
MC: ZC DCA 573

In Sotto Voce

TRACKS.
LP: ANT 117

In The Beginning

IN THE BEGINNING (Various artists).
LP: LEN 001

IN THE BEGINNING: EARLY RECORDINGS OF THE SUPERS (Various artists).
Tracks: / Shake: *Stewart, Rod* / Pity the fool: *Manish Boys* / You've got a habit of leaving: *Jones, Davy* & The Lower Third / Skeleton and the roundabout: *Idle Race* / River to another day: *Love Sculpture* / Up above my head: *Baldry, Long John* / You better run: *In Betweens* / I can see her face: *Kippington Lodge* / Different drum: *Stone Poneys* / Night after day: *Hassels* / Wanted dead or alive: *Zevon, Warren* / Some of Shelly's blues: *Stone Poneys* / Night life: *Nelson, Willie* / I can stand alone: *Hourglass* / Living in the USA: *Miller, Steve Band* / Big town 2061: *Paris*.
LP: EG 2605711
MC: EG 2605714

IN THE BEGINNING TOMMY STEELE (Various artists).
Tracks: / Moon is a dandy: *Dionysus, Jean-Paul* / Only acrobats can: *Hunt Barbara* / Lonely star, A: *Cunningham, Andrew* / Smarties: *London, Johnny* / Rupert: *French, Les* / Familiar unfamiliar, The: *Miro* / Devil and The Lord, The: *Miro* / Blue: *Taz* / Save the lion: *Tylor* / Rupert man: *Slade, Rupert* / Where was Jack?: *Clawson, Trevor* / Buildings: *Khan, Brenda* / Engines ignite, The: *Browse, Paul* / Mr DJ: *London, Johnny*.
LP: SH 1008

In The Dark

IN THE DARK (Various artists).
LP: VJM 2014

In The Good Old

IN THE GOOD OLD SUMMERTIME/ GOOD NEWS/2 WEEKS (Original cast recordings) (Various artists).
LP: 4502301
MC: 4502304

In The House Of

IN THE HOUSE OF DARK MUSIC (see Lynch, Francis) (Boland, Arthur).

In The Key Of E...

IN THE KEY OF E (Various artists).
LP: . . . . LUVLP 1
MC: . . . . LUVMC 1

In The Mood

IN THE MOOD (Various artists).
LP: . . . . VS 3401

In The Nursery

COUNTERPOINT.
LP: . . . . SAX 042

KODA.
LP: . . . . SAX 034/5

L'ESPRIT.
LP: . . . . TMLP 48

PRELUDE.
LP: . . . . NORMAL 74

SENSE.
LP: . . . . TM 92711

STORY HORSE, THE.
LP: . . . . SAX 021
MC: . . . . SAXC 021

TWINS.
LP: . . . . SAX 014

WHEN CHERISHED DREAMS COME TRUE.
LP: . . . . VIRTUE 2

In Touch

IN TOUCH (Various artists).
2LP: . . . . STD 9
MCSET: . . . . STDK 9

In Tua Nua

LONG ACRE, THE.
Tracks: / Woman on fire / All I wanted / Wheel of evil / Meeting of the waters / Innocent and the honest ones, The / World wired up / Some things never change / Don't fear me now (kiss you once more) / Emotional barrier / Long acre, The / Sweet lost soul.
LP: . . . . V 2526
MC: . . . . TCV 2526

VAUDEVILLE.
Tracks: / Seven into the sea / Right road to heaven / Love / No solution / Valuable lessons / Heaven can wait / Voice of America / Rain / Pearl of dreams / Walking on glass.
LP: . . . . V 2421
MC: . . . . TCV 2421

In Vitro

IN VITRO.
Tracks: / Man and woman / I choose you / Some little something / Left me the night / I suffer / Erase the moon / Secretary / Agony of sophistication / Lightning in the dark / Not my friend / So tight.
LP: . . . . MTL 1016
MC: . . . . TCMTL 1016

In With The Old

IN WITH THE OLD BBC Radio 2 cast (Various artists).
Tracks: / In with the old: prelude: *Various artists* / Music goes round and around, The: *Various artists* / I want to be happy: *Various artists* / Did you ever see a dream walking: *Various artists* / Stompin' at the Savoy: *Various artists* / I'm putting all my eggs in one basket: *Various artists* / Only a glass of champagne: *Various* artists / Ten cents a dance: *Various artists* / Goody goody: *Various artists* / Zing went the strings of my heart: *Various artists* / Lulu's back in town: *Various artists* / Pretty baby: *Various artists* / Where are the songs we've sung: *Various artists* / Storm: *Various artists* / And her mother came too: *Various artists*/ With plenty of money and you: *Various artists* / Playout: *Various artists.*
LP: . . . . TER 1122
MC: . . . . ZCTER 1122

Inbred

KISSIN' COUSINS.
LP: . . . . K 001/118

Inca Babies

EVIL HOUR.
Tracks: / Evil hour / Long uphill trek / 9 Partisan's river / Madman's demise, A / Bad hombre / Artillery switchback / Two rails to nowhere / Volts / Burning town / Young blood.
LP: . . . . SUK 2
LP: . . . . INC 013

OPIUM DEN.
LP: . . . . INCMLP 12

RUMBLE.
LP: . . . . INCLP 005

THIS TRAIN.
LP: . . . . INC 001

Inca Gold

INCA GOLD (Various artists).
2LP: . . . . MS 102

Incantation

BEST OF INCANTATION.
MC: . . . . COCA 19
LP: . . . . CODA 19

DANCE OF THE FLAMES.
Tracks: / Dance of the flames / Cutimuy / Man from Humahuaca, The / Carnarios / Atahuallpa / Pueneno / Waynu / Festival of yotala / Boquita colorada.
LP: . . . . BEGA 49
MC: . . . . BEGC 49

MEETING, THE.
LP: . . . . HIAM 94
MC: . . . . HIAMC 94

ON THE WING OF A CONDOR.
Tracks: / On the wing of a condor / Sonccuiman / Sikuriadas / High flying bird / Dolencias / Winds on the mountain / Amores hallaras / El pajaro madrugador / Papel de plata / Condor dance / Cacharpaya / Friends of the Andes.
LP: . . . . BEGA 39

PANPIPES OF THE ANDES.
Tracks: / Amores hallaras / Cacharpaya / Papel de plata / Friends of the Andes / El pajaro madrugador / Condor dance / Sonccuiman / Dolencias / Winds on the mountain / On the wing of a condor / Sikuriadas / High flying bird.
LP: . . . . NAGE 15
MC: . . . . NAGEC 15

VIRGINS OF THE SUN.
Tracks: / Brass band / Virgins of the sun / Solo harpist / Sacsaywoman / Adios, pueblo de mi waycho / Chupizinatay yacu (Recorded live by Incantation in the Temple of the Sun, Maccu Piccu) / Noches de luna / Festival in Laja (Bolivian Independance day) / Indian street musician / Aguita de Putina / Choferito (Live at Chincero Market.) / Los senors de Potasi.
LP: . . . . CODA 13
MC: . . . . COCA 13

Incest

INCEST Various artists.
MC: . . . . CXC 003

Inchon

INCHON (Original soundtrack) (Various artists).
LP: . . . . RI 9502

Incognito

INSIDE LIFE.
LP: 8485461
MC: 8485464

INSIDE LIFE.
LP: 848546-1
MC: 848546-4

JAZZ FUNK.
Tracks: / Shine on / Wake up the city / Why don't you believe / Chase the clouds away / Interference / Incognito / Sunburn / Smile of a child, The / Walking on wheels.
LP: . . . . ENVY 504
MC: . . . . ENCAS 504

Incorporated Thang

LIFESTYLES OF THE ROACH AND FAMOUS.
Tracks: / Body Jacklin / Storyteller / Androgynous view / Jack of all trades / I'd do anything for you / What if the girls says yes?.
LP: 925617 1
MC: 925617 4

Incredible Casuals

THAT'S THAT.
Tracks: / Crazy girl / Think about me / I got to move / Wait it out / Long as you have somebody else / Discretion / Let her dance / Don't tell me / In the darkness / Dream house / Still mine / Records go round / Please don't.
LP: . . . . FIEND 77
LP: . . . . ROUNDER 9015
MC: . . . . ROUNDER 9015C

Incredible Hulk

INCREDIBLE HULK IN A GAME OF MONSTERS AND KINGS various artists (Various artists).
MC: 41 57174

Incredible Journey

INCREDIBLE JOURNEY, THE Burnford, Sheila (Cribbins, Bernard (nar)).
MC: . . . . PTB 626

Incredible Power Of

INCREDIBLE POWER OF DARKNESS (Various artists).
LP: . . . . FALL 005

Incredible String Band

5000 SPIRITS.
Tracks: / Chinese white / No sleep blues / Painting box / Mad hatter's song, The / Little cloud / Eyes of fate, The / Blues for the muse / Hedgehog's song, The / First girl I loved / You know that you could be / My name is death / Gently tender / Way back in the 1960's.
LP: . . . . K 42001
LP: . . . . EUKS 257

BIG HUGE, THE.
Tracks: / Maya / Greatest friend / Son of Noah's brother, The / Lordly nightshade / Mountain of God, The / Cousin caterpillar / Iron stone, The / Douglas Traherne Harding / Circle is unbroken, The.
LP: . . . . K 42022

CHANGING HORSES.
LP: . . . . EKS 74057

EARTHSPAN.
LP: . . . . ILPS 9211

HANGMAN'S BEAUTIFUL DAUGHTER.
Tracks: / Koee / Addi there / Minotaur's song, The / Witches hat / Very cellular song, A / Mercy I cry city / Waltz of the new moon / Water song, The / Three is a green crown / Swift as the wind / Nightfall.
LP: . . . . K 42002
LP: . . . . EUKS 258
LP: . . . . CGLP 4421

HARD ROPE AND SILKEN TWINE.
LP: . . . . ILPS 9270

I LOOKED UP.
LP: 2469 002

INCREDIBLE STRING BAND.
LP: . . . . EKL 254

LIQUID ACROBAT AS REGARDS AIR.
LP: . . . . ILPS 9172
MC: . . . . ICM 9172

NO RUINOUS FEUD.
LP: . . . . ILPS 9229

U.
LP: 2665 001

WEE TAM.
Tracks: / Job's tears / Puppies / Beyond the sea / Yellow snake, The / Log cabin in the sky / You get brighter / Half remarkable question, The / Air / Ducks on a pond.
LP: . . . . K 42021

Incredibles

HEART AND SOUL.
LP: . . . . CLP 512

Incubus

BEYOND THE UNKNOWN.
LP: . . . . NB 039

SERPENT TEMPTATION.
LP: . . . . VOV 674

TO THE DEVIL A DAUGHTER.
LP: . . . . GRC 2165

Ind Coope...

GLASS OF BRASS, A (Ind Coope Burton Brewery Brass Band).
LP: . . . . BNB 2004
MC: . . . . ZC BNB 2004

Ind, Peter

AT THE DEN (Ind, Peter & Sal Mosca).
LP: . . . . WAVE LP 2

CONTRA BACH (see Cash, Bernie) (Ind, Peter & Bernie Cash).

IMPROVISATIONS.
LP: . . . . WAVE LP 3

JAZZ BAROQUE.
LP: . . . . WAVE LP 11

LOOKING OUT.
LP: . . . . WAVE LP 1

PETER IND SEXTET (Ind, Peter Sextet).
LP: . . . . WAVE LP 13

SOME HEFTY CATS (See under Wellstood, Dick) (Ind, Peter & Dick Wellstood).

TIME FOR IMPROVISATIONS.
LP: . . . . WAVE LP 4

TRIPLE LIBRA (See under Taylor, Martin) (Ind, Peter & Martin Taylor).

Indecent Obsession

INDECENT OBSESSION.
LP: . . . . MCG 6091
MC: . . . . MCGC 6091

Indeep

INDEEP.
Tracks: / Buffalo Bill / Love is like a gun / Last night a DJ saved my life / Slow down / Lipstick politics / When boys talk / There it is.
LP: . . . . SNYLP 1001

PYJAMA PARTY TIME.
Tracks: / Girls got soul / Night the boy learned how to dance / Ten reasons why I can't be free / If you want it / You got to rock it / I got my rights / Record keeps spinning / Pyjama party time.
LP: . . . . BKLP 5681
MC: . . . . ZCBK 5681

Independents

FIRST TIME WE MET (The Greatest Hits).
Tracks: / I found love on a rainy day / First time we met / I just want to be there / Leaving me / It's all over / Let this be a lesson to you / No wind no rain / Just as long as you need me (Parts 1&2) / Sara Lee / Baby I've been missing you / Couldn't hear nobody say (I love you like I do).
LP: . . . . CRB 1146

PARKSIDE SHIVERS (Various artists).
LP: . . . . LILLP 001

PARKSIDE STEELWORKS (Various artists).
LP: . . . . LIL/LP 2

PARTY AT HANGING ROCK (Various artists).
LP: . . . . DREW 2
MC: . . . . CDREW 2
LP: . . . . NIXON 5

PEEL SESSIONS SAMPLER, THE (Various artists).
Tracks: / New rose: *Damned* / What do I get: *Buzzcocks* / Mess of my: *Fall* / Here comes summer: *Undertones*/ Big Jesus trash can: *Birthday Party* / Lion rock: *Culture* / 5-8-6: *New Order* / New England, A: *Bragg*, Billy / Good and gone: *Screaming Blue Messiahs* / V-2: *That Petrol Emotion* / This boy can wait: *Wedding Present* / Mother: *Electro Hippies* / Take no chances: *Intense Degree.*
LP: . . . . SFRLP 100
MC: . . . . SFRMC 100

PENSIONERS ON ECSTACY (Various artists).
LP: . . . . CRELP 082

PEOPLE UNITE IN PROGRESS (Various artists).
LP: . . . . PU 104

PERSPECTIVES AND DISTORTION (Various artists).
LP: . . . . BRED 15

Indestroy

INDESTROY.
LP: . . . . NRR 10
MC: . . . . NRC 10

Indestructible

INDESTRUCTIBLE (Various artists).
LP: . . . . RRLP 107

India

AU PAYS DES MAHARAJAS musique du rajasthan (Various artists).
Tracks: / Danse rajpoute: *Various artists* / Solos de double flute: *Various artists* / Chant traditionnel du Marwar: *Various artists* / Sole de double flute: *Various artists* / Musiciens du Fort de Jodhpur: *Various artists*/ Danse traditionnelle de Jaisalmer: *Various artists* / Chant traditionnel de Khuri: *Various artists* / Chant traditionnel Manghaniyar: *Various artists.*
LP: . . . . ARN 33763

CHANT THE NAMES OF GOD: FOLK MUSIC FROM INDIA (Various artists).
LP: . . . . ROUNDER 5008

CLASSICAL MUSIC OF INDIA Master of the Sarangi (Various artists).
LP: . . . . H 72062

DAMAL KRISHNA PATTAMAL le chant de raga (Various artists).
Tracks: / Kriti: Raga kalyani (cycle de 4 temps): *Various artists* / Kriti: Raga Gambhira Natai (cycle de 16 temps): *Various* artists / Varnary: raga kedava gowla (cycle de 8 temps): *Various artists* / Kriti: Raga kamas (cycle de 3 temps): *Various artists.*
LP: . . . . ARN 33425

EVENING RAGAS FROM BENARES (Various artists).
Tracks: / Raga puriya kalyan: *Various artists* / Raga pilu: *Various artists* / Raga darbari: *Various artists.*
LP: . . . . ALM 4002

FOLK MUSIC OF INDIA-UTTAR PRADESH (Various artists).
LP: . . . . LLST 7271

FOLK SONGS OF KASHMIR (Various artists).
LP: . . . . LLST 7260

FOLK SONGS OF NEPAL (Various artists).
LP: . . . . LLST 7330

INCANTATIONS (Various artists).
Tracks: / Raga - Amrit Varshni: *Various artists* / Raga - Jai jai vanti: *Various artists.*
LP: . . . . ARN 33745

INDIAN FOLK MUSIC Orissa (Various artists).
LP: . . . . LLST 7183

INSTRUMENTAL DANCES OF INDIA various artists (Various artists).
LP: . . . . H 72022

L'INDE DU NORD Le cachemire et la vallee du gange (Various artists).
Tracks: / Raga du soir: *Various artists* / Cornemuse indienne: *Various artists* / Azli Kajli: *Various artists*/ Musique religieuse au Temple de Laksminaravan: *Various artists* / Mendiant a Godhgaya: *Various artists* / La flute de krishna: *Various artists* / Raga nan: *Various artists* / Chant du Cachemire: *Various artists*/ Charmeur de serpents: *Various artists* / Bhajan au bord du Gange a Benares: *Various artists* / Chant de devotion au Temple de Laksminarayan: *Various artists* / En shikara: *Various artists.*
LP: . . . . ARN 33401
MC: . . . . ARN 433401

LOWER CASTE RELIGIOUS MUSIC IN INDIA (Various artists).
LP: . . . . LLST 7324
MC: . . . . LLCT 7324

MAGIC OF THE INDIAN FLUTE (See under Magic Of...) (Various artists).

MAGIC OF THE INDIAN FLUTE (Various artists).
LP: . . . . EULP 1090
MC: . . . . EUMC 1090

MIDDLE CASTE RELIGIOUS MUSIC FROM INDIA (Various artists).
LP: . . . . LLST 7323

MUSIC FROM THE SHRINES OF AJMAR & MUNDRA (Various artists).
LP: . . . . LLST 7236

MUSIC OF INDIA Balachander & Sivaraman (Various artists).
LP: . . . . H 72003

MUSIC OF INDIA VOL 1 (Various artists).
LP: . . . . ECSD 42001
MC: . . . . TC 7206

MUSIC OF INDIA VOL 2 (Various artists).
LP: . . . . ECSD 42002
MC: . . . . TC 7207

NORTH INDIA Music from the shrines of Ajmer & Mundra (Various artists).
LP: . . . . TGM 105

PLAIN TALES FROM THE RAJ (Various artists).
MCSET: . . . . ZBBC 1017

SOUTH INDIA Art of the vina (Various artists).
MC: . . . . PS 65015

YUGAL BANDI (see Shiv & Hari) (Shiv & Hari).

Indian Flutes Of...

INDIAN FLUTES OF SOUTH AMERICA (Various artists).
MC: . . . . KP 95060

Indian Givers

LOVE IS A LIE.
Tracks: / Hatcheck girl / Fake I.D. / Unthinking you / Under the rose / Head happy / Some kind of mover (Only on CD.) / It's a wonderful life (Only on CD.) / Love come down / Not my line / Capreice / Love is a lie / Never too late.
LP: . . . . V 2593
MC: . . . . TCV 2593

Indian Summer

INDIAN SUMMER.
Tracks: / Recado bossa nova / As long as I live / Sophisticated lady / S wonderful / Deed I do / Indian Summer / All my life / Just my luck / Long ago and far away.
LP: . . . . CJ 224

Indiana Jones

INDIANA JONES AND THE LAST CRUSADE (Original Soundtrack) (Various artists).
LP: . . . . K 925883 1
MC: . . . . K 925883 4

INDIANA JONES AND THE TEMPLE OF DOOM (Film Soundtrack) (Various artists).
Tracks: / Anything goes: *Various artists* / Fast streets of Shanghai: *Various artists* / Nocturnal activities: *Various artists* / Shortround's theme: *Various artists* / Children in chains: *Various artists* / Slalom on mountain: *Various artists* / Humol: *Various artists* / Temple of doom, The: *Various artists* / Bug tunnel and death trap: *Various artists* / Slave children's crusade: *Various artists* / Mine car chase, The: *Various artists* / Finale: *Various artists.*
LP: . . . . POLH 8
MC: . . . . POLHC 8
LP: . . . . REH 543
LP: 8215921
MC: 8215924
MC: . . . . ZCR 543

Indianapolis Jump

INDIANAPOLIS JUMP (Various artists).
LP: . . . . FLY 523

Indians

DANCE ON.
LP: . . . . HALPX 170
MC: . . . . HACS 7070

INDIAN COUNTRY.
LP: . . . . HALPX 101

INDIAN RESERVATION.
LP: . . . . HALPX 109

MAGNIFICENT SEVEN.
LP: . . . . HALPX 141

WE'RE JUST INDIANS.
LP: . . . . HALPX 154

Indians In Moscow

INDIANS IN MOSCOW.
Tracks: / Big wheel / Meeting place / Witches & heroes / Howard's at lunch / Puppet dance / Square dance in the republic / Love song / I wish I had / Singing to French / Naughty Miranda / Jack Pelter and his sex-change chicken.
LP: . . . . KLNK 1
MC: . . . . KCNK 1

Indie

11 GO MAD IN LEWISHAM (On yer bike album, The) (Various artists).
Tracks: / Golden lady: *Solid Ground* / Pray for the fallen angels: *Barflies* / Breaking up my heart: *Brother* to Brother / Hillbilly jump: *Forest Hillbillies* / Got some love: *Jerry & Unit 2* / America: *McDonnel, Phil* / 24 hours: *Jivin Instructors* / Ain't gonna trap: *Various artists* / Fish song: *Another Fine Myth*/ Lets move: *Thorn, George* / Party: *Dzata.*
LP: . . . . BIRD 001

14 SONGS FROM THE NORTH WEST (Various artists).
Tracks: / Sound of things growing: *Various artists* / Deep down: *Various artists* / Vanessa: *Various artists*/ Darkness: *Various artists* / Wednesday's child: *Various artists* / Hold tite: *Various artists* / My heart is where my home is: *Various artists* / Locked in heaven: *Various artists* / This is how I feel: *Various* artists / Dispossession dance: *Various artists* / Let go: *Various artists* / Moss one: *Various artists*/ Whirlpool of love: *Various artists* / Nervous smile: *Various artists.*
LP: . . . . ESS LP 133
MC: . . . . ESS MC 133

101 CLUB - CLUB SANDWICH (Various artists).
LP: 2478145

101 CLUB - VOLUME 4 (Various artists).
Tracks: / You've taken everything: *Huang Chung* / Don't believe a word: *Huang Chung* / Journeys without maps: *Huang Chung* / Works: *Endgames* / Visons of: *Endgames* / Stare: *Endgames* / Acrobat: *Fix*/ Soho alley: *Fix* / Eye for design: *Fix* / Why don't you: *Ray, Fay* / Dreams of heat: *Ray, Fay*/ Modern lovers: *Ray, Fay.*
LP: 2478 141

0222 (Compilation of Cardiff bands) (Various artists).
Tracks: / Sugar daddy boogie: *Snatch It Back* / Strike: *Bomb And Dagger* / Maen ok: *Cwrw Bach* / This house: *Papa's New Faith* / Strollin' with bones: *Red Hot Pokers* / Gwair gwair (ni ywr Crumblowers): *Crumblowers*/ All in the game: *Watermelons* / That's changed now: *Howling Sleepers* / Gad I'r afonydd: *Geraint Jarman* A'r Cynganeddwyr / I can't turn you loose: *Madassa* / Walk without your wings: *Pier* / Tren: *U Thant*/ When it's all gone: *Vipers.*
LP: . . . . POPDY 101

BEFORE THE FALL (Various artists).
2LP: . . . . SFRLP 203
MC: . . . . SFRMC 203

BEST OF INDIE TOP 20 (Various artists).
MC: . . . . BOTT 1MC
LP: . . . . BOTT 1

BEST OF THE RADIO 1 SESSIONS VOL. 1 (Evening Show, The) (Various artists).
LP: . . . . LPNT 100
MC: . . . . MCNT 100

BEYOND THE FENCE BEGINS THE SKY (Various artists).
Tracks: / Land of milk and honey: *Beat & The Devil* / Run silent, run deep: *Complaints* / Return of the prodigals: *Beyond The Blue* / Maybe it's because: *Shaffron, Carolyn* / Will you still wait?: *In Berlin* / Modern etiquette: *2 Sweet To Suck* / Channels crossing: *One Hand Clapping* / Never come back: *Jeremiahs* / Your trade for mine: *Thin Line, The* / Very peculiar Julia: *Rachel & Nicki* / Red: *Home and Abroad* / Spring comes early: *Enamel Animals* / Same old song: *Butch Minds The Baby.*
LP: . . . . PLASLP 008

BIG NOISE FROM NORTHWOOD (Various artists).
LP: . . . . NWLP 1002

BIRTH OF THE Y (Various artists).
LP: . . . . Y 33

BITES AND STABS (NORTHERN BANDS) (Various artists).
LP: . . . . TOR 1

BUNCH OF STIFFS, A (Various artists).
LP: . . . . SEEZ 2

BUSINESS UNUSUAL (Various artists).
Tracks: / C.I.D: *UK Subs* / 19 and mad: *Leyton Buzzards* / Just another teenage rebel: *Outcasts* / Justifiable homicide: *Goodman, Dave & Friends* / Consequences: *Outsiders* / M.O.R.: *Record Players* / 01-01-212: *Vice* Creems / Private plane: *Leer, Thomas* / A.C.C.: *Rental, Robert* / United: *Throbbing Gristle* / Do the Mussolini: *Cabaret Voltaire.*
LP: . . . . ARED 2

CD '88 (Various artists).
2LP: . . . . CD 88LP
MC: . . . . CD 88MC

CLASS OF '81 (Various artists).
Tracks: / Pop love: *Void* / Accident: *Exeros* / Love you: *Troopers* / Girl: *Emil & the Detectives*/ Dream (for my sake): *Bino* / Given up trying: *Picasso's Optician* / New day: *Fringe* / Instant magnet: *Emil & the Detectives* / Chita: *Exeros* / Starship 22: *Innocent Vicars.*
LP: . . . . CHIN 1

CLASSIFICATION OF FISHES AND GOATS (Various artists).
MC: . . . . EBS 7

CLASSIFICATION OF VEGETABLES (Various artists).
MC: . . . . EBS 4

COAL HEART FOREVER (Various artists).
LP: . . . . SUB 33011-16

COLLECTION OF DEADBEATS, A (Various artists).
LP: . . . . DMC 001

COLOURS OF THE BASTARD ART (Various artists).
LP: . . . . LM LP 005

COMPILATION OF US ARTISTS (Various artists).
LP: . . . . USOP 1

COULD YOU WALK ON THE WATERS (Various artists).
LP: . . . . TMLP 9

CRAP STOPS HERE, THE (Various artists).
LP: . . . . LAST 1

CUTTING EDGE (Various artists).
LP: . . . . RAZS 16

CUTTING EDGE (Contemporary British roots music) (Various artists).
Tracks: / Hal-an-Tow: *Oyster Band* / Can't find my money: *Mekons* / Death of the wild colonial boy: *We Free Kings* / Sea never dry: *God's Little Monkeys* / Walls of Butlins, The: *Edward II & The Red Hot Polkas* / We're not over yet: *Gregson, Clive* / Banshees dance: *McLeod, Rory* / Green brooms: *Mark T and the Brickbats*/ Tippin' it up to Nancy: *Gone To Earth* / Flanders: *Press Gang* / Forked deer: *Deighton, Dave* / Hopping down in Kent: *Black Spot Champions* / Debatable land, A: *Cronshaw, Andrew.*
LP: . . . . GRILL 001
MC: . . . . GRILLC 001

DC ROX (Various artists).
LP: . . . . WETLP 003

DE LENINE A LENNON (Various artists).
LP: . . . . ROSE 187
MC: . . . . ROSE 187C

DEAD TECH (Various artists).
LP: . . . . ST 7512

DEAD TECH II (Various artists).
Tracks: / Dead car, sun crash: *Various artists* / Russian asshole: *Leningrad Blues Machine* / Junk boogie: *Junk* Schizo / Ancient wind: *Marble Sheep & The Rundown Sun's Children* / Archiviste: *Zatopek Soccer* / Sex dick: *Off Mask Oo* / Hate and war: *Gerogerigegege* / Hawaiian disco with my bollocks: *Boredoms* / Marble sheen & the rundown: *Various artists.*
LP: . . . . ST 7541

DECLARATION OF INDEPENDENTS (Various artists).
Tracks: / Heart of stone: *Various artists* / Pushin' too hard: *Various artists* / Driving guitars: *Various* artists / Cool: *Various artists* / You can run: *Various artists* / Nadine: *Various artists* / Father be blind: *Various artists* / Green hearts: *Various artists* / Bring on the night: *Various artists* / It's all different now: *Various artists* / Feeling right tonight: *Various artists* / Meltdown: *Various artists*/ Love all over the place: *Various artists.*
LP: . . . . YANK 2

DEFINITIV (Various artists).
2LP: . . . . DEF 001

DEMOLITION BLUES (Various artists).
LP: . . . . INSANELP 1

DESPERATION (Various artists).
LP: . . . . AVA 002

DEUTSCHLAND STRIKEBACK (Various artists).
LP: . . . . SBR 024 LP

DEVASTATE TO LIBERATE (Various artists).
LP: . . . . TANGKI 1

DIAMOND HIDDEN IN THE MOUTH OF A CORPSE, A (Various artists).
LP: . . . . GPS 035
MC: . . . . GPS 035 S

DICE ARE ROLLING, THE (Various artists).
LP: . . . . BIAS 044

DIFFERENT FOR DOMEHEADS (Various artists).
LP: . . . . CRELP 005

DIFFERENT KIND OF TENSION (Various artists).
Tracks: / Like an angel: *Mighty Lemon Drops* / I know everything: *Soup Dragons* / Like one thousand violins: *1000* Violins / Cut the cake: *Wolfhounds* / Every conversation: *June Brides* / Hundred words, A: *Beloved*/ Romance is over, The: *Vee VV* / Kitchen table: *Stump* / Once more: *Wedding Present, The* / Happy days: *Shamen.*
LP: . . . . PR LP 1

DIG THIS (A tribute to the great strike) (Various artists).
LP: . . . . FORWARD 002

DIMENSIONS OF SOUND (Various artists).
LP: . . . . MS 1001

DISCREET CAMPAIGNS (Various artists).
LP: . . . . ROR 1

DISPARATE COGSCIENTI (Various artists).
LP: . . . . COG 2

DISTANT VOICES, STILL LIVES (Various artists).
LP: . . . . ROUGH 129

DIVING FOR PEARLS (Various artists).
LP: . . . . INDIE 1
MC: . . . . INDC 1

DO YOU BELIEVE IN LOVE (Various artists).
LP: . . . . CRELP 063

DORKCRUSHER (Various artists).
LP: . . . . TUPEP 031
MC: . . . . TUPEPMC 031

DOSSIERS (Various).
LP: . . . . ST 7523

DRIVING ME BACKWARDS (Various artists).
2LP: . . . . CURVE 001

EARTHLY DELIGHTS (Various artists).
LP: . . . . SR 13

EDGE OF THE ROAD (Various artists).
Tracks: / Storm, The: *Raw Herbs* / At my funeral: *Raw Herbs* / Bold: *Waltones* / British disease, The: *Waltones* / Mouthful of brains: *Corn Dollies* / What do I ever: *Corn Dollies* / Seven red apples: *Rain*/ Dry the rain: *Rain.*
LP: . . . . MC 010

EDWARD NOT EDWARD (Various artists).
LP: . . . . WPPD 007

ELECTRONIC SYLVIA PLATH (Various artists).
MC: .... **BST 013**

ELEPHANT TABLE ALBUM (Various artists).
LP: .... **XX 001**

ELEPHANT TABLE SYMPHONY (Various artists).
LP: .... **TEC 1**

EXALTED COMPANION, AN (Various artists).
LP: .... **UTA 7**

FAST AND BULBOUS (Tribute to Captain Beefheart) (Various artists).
Tracks: / Zig zag wanderer: *Various artists* / Ella Guru: *Various artists* / Clear spot: *Various artists*/ Ice cream for crow: *Various artists* / Long necked bottles: *Various artists* / Sun zoom spark: *Various artists*/ Hot head: *Various artists* / Chain pig: *Various artists* / Electricity: *Various artists* / Frying pan: *Various artists* / Big eyed beans from Venus: *Various artists.*
LP: .... **ILLUSION 002**

FEAR, POWER, GOD (Various artists).
LP: .... **PLAY LP 6**
LP: .... **CFV 004**

FEATURE MIST (Includes New Order, Simple Minds, Flesh) (Various artists).
MC: .... **T 1**

FIGHT (Various artists).
Tracks: / Work corp: *In The Nursery* / T.V. mind (it's in): *Revolting Cocks* / Corpse, The: *Pink Industry*/ Le mur: *Soviet France* / Amputate: *Project GK* / Bribery and winning ways: *Hula* / Irrtum boys: *Young Gods* / Thumbs of the: *Shock Headed Peters* / Quf harpy: *Click Click* / Pilgrims progress: *Clair Obscur*/ Dana of Framin: *Tio Koala.*
LP: .... **CRL 14**

FIGHT IS ON, THE (Various artists).
Tracks: / Music for the piano: *Haigh, Robert* / Invocation of Shiva: *Lustmord* / Stick that: *Nurse With Wound*/ Talon veil: *Organum* / Sicktone: *Coil* / Visit to dogland: *Current 93.*
LP: .... **LAY 010**

FUNKY ALTERNATIVES (Various artists).
LP: .... **A 197**

FUNKY ALTERNATIVES VOL. 6 (Various artists).
LP: .... **CPRODLP 016**

GET THIS! (Various artists).
LP: .... **OUT A1**

GHOSTS OF THE CIVIL DEAD (Various artists).
LP: .... **IONIC 3**
MC: .... **CIONIC 3**

GLAS ORCHID (Various artists).
LP: .... **KIRI 096**

GLASS ARCADE (Various artists).
LP: .... **SARAH 501**
MC: .... **SARAH 501MC**

GOD SAVE US FROM THE USA (Various artists).
Tracks: / Noo yawk squawk: *Toczek, Nick* / Sheer funk: *Toczek, Nick* / Catching flies: *Culture Shock*/ Nefoedd Un, Uffern Llall: *Anhrefn* / Best of families: *Dan* / Never hold your tongue: *Neurotics* / Demystification: *Zounds* / Libyan students: *Attila The Stockbroker* / Let them eat Somozas: *Kama Sutra* / God bless America: *Some weird sin* / Eye to eye: *Instigators* / Flowers in concrete: *Heresy* / Inner space: *Apostles.*
LP: .... **KTLP 001**

GOD'S FAVOURITE DOG (Various artists).
LP: .... **TGLP 11**

GONNA PARTY TONIGHT (Various artists).
LP: .... **BLACKOUT 1901**

GOOD FEELING (Various artists).
LP: .... **AGAS 003**

GOOD MORNING MR PRESLEY (Various artists).
LP: .... **GGAGG 1**

GOODBYE TO ALL THAT (Various artists).
LP: .... **RF 45**

GREAT FIRE OF LONDON, THE (Various artists).
LP: .... **FIRELP 8**

GREATEST HITS: ONE LITTLE INDIAN (Various artists).
LP: .... **TPLP 7**

GREATEST HITS:- ONE LITTLE INDIAN VOL 2 (Various artists).
LP: .... **TP LP 17**
MC: .... **TP C 17**

GREENBELT FRINGE '84 (Various artists).
Tracks: / Finally bought it: *Three Point Turn* / Divided, The: *Intransit* / Dark alley: *Mouse* / Highway to life: *Lifewind* / Suffer, little children: *Wheeler, Steve* / Broken hearts: *Loose Talk* / Child of the light: *Zero Option* / Keep on: *Catley, Marc* / Vicious circles: *Filament* / Man across the road: *Solid Air.*
MC: .... **PCN 110**

GREETINGS (Various artists).
Tracks: / Japanese dream: *Reininger, Blaine* / Bismallah: *Reininger, Blaine* / Party line: *Stockholm Monsters*/ Militia: *Stockholm Monsters* / Dumbstruck: *Stockholm Monsters* / Florence sunset: *Durutti Column* / All that love and maths can do: *Durutti Column* / San Giovanni dawn: *Durutti Column* / For friends in Italy: *Durutti Column.*
LP: .... **GREETINGS 1**

GRITO SUBURBANO (Various artists).
LP: .... **POGAR X1**

GRUESOME STAINS (Various artists).
LP: .... **PLAY LP 3**

GUERILLA GROOVE.
LP: .... **GRLP 001**
MC: .... **GRMC 001**

HANG ELEVEN (MUTANT SURF PUNKS) (Various artists).
Tracks: / I want my woody back: *Barracudas* / Who stole the summer: *Surfin' Lungs* / 308: *Malibooz* / Herman's new woody: *Palominos* / Fun at the beach: *B Girls* / Gas money: *Lloyd, Bobby And The Windfall Prophets*/ Pipeline: *Agent Orange* / Tuff little surfer boy: *Truth & Beauty* / Girls cars girls sun girls surf girls fun girls: *Corvettes* / Automobile: *Stickshifts* / Day they raised the Thames barrier, The: *Beach Bums* / Shotgun: *Beach Coma* / Surfin' CIA: *Buzz & The B-Days* / Mighty morris ten: *Episode Six* / Depth charge: *Jon & The Nightriders.*
LP: .... **GRAM 23**

HELLFIRE VOL.1 (Various artists).
2LP: .... **PS 1003**

HOOTENANNY (Various artists).
Tracks: / Raining: *Ancient Beatbox* / Just as the ...: *Edward II & The Red Hot Polkas* / Valentine's: *Tabor, June & The Oyster Band* / Wind and the ...: *Wedding Party's Everything* / Vimbayi: *Four Brothers* / Frontera del ensueno: *Rey De Copas* / See how I miss you: *Cockburn, Bruce* / Liberty: *Barely Works* / Polka girl: *Colorblind James Experience* / Gastown: *God's Little Monkeys* / Travelling circus: *White, Andy* / Pigeon on the gate: *Spillane, Davy* / Tape decks all over hell: *Boiled In Lead* / Rhumba for Nicaragua: *Happy End*/ Collectorman: *McLeod, Rory* / Back to back: *Jolly Boys.*
LP: .... **GRILL 003**
MC: .... **GRILLC 003**

IDEAL GUEST HOUSE (Various artists).
MC: .... **SHELTER 1**

IF YOU CAN'T PLEASE YOURSELF YOU CAN'T PLEASE YO (Various artists).
Tracks: / Only good Christian is a dead Christian, The: *Scraping Foetus Off The Wheel* / Product patrol: *Cabaret Voltaire*/ Total nervous phenomonom: *Test Department* / Love amongst the ruined: *Almond, Marc* / Twisted: *Psychic TV*/ Flesh and bones: *The The* / Wheel, The: *Coil* / Roxy cut, The: *Yello* / Waiting to fail: *Astley, Virginia* / Wardrobe: *Einsturzende Neubauten.*
LP: .... **TAPE 1**
MC: .... **TAPED 1**
LP: .... **EJ 26 0663 1**

IF YOU CAN'T PLEASE YOURSELF YOU CAN'T PLEASE YO (Various artists).
LP: .... **SBZ LP 1**

IMMINENT EPISODE ONE: ENGLAND-THE SUMMER OF 1985 (Various artists).
LP: .... **BITE 1**

IMMINENT VOL.2 (Various artists).
LP: .... **BITE 2**

IMMINENT VOL.3 (Various artists).
LP: .... **BITE 3**

IMMINENT VOL.4 (Various artists).
LP: .... **BITE 4**

IMMINENT VOL.5 (Various artists).
Tracks: / Wreckers of engines: *Rubies, The* / Snake charmer: *Shamen* / Minotaur: *Horsehunters* / Here today: *Enormous Room* / Standing into danger: *Blyth Power* / Cornwall: *Kilgore Trout* / 14 more: *Wigs*/ Probably this winter: *Yeah Jazz* / Last laugh: *Great Outdoors* / Tell you this: *Jackals* / Shadow: *Primitives*/ Shadow: *Phony American Accent* / Carousel: *BMX Bandits* / No defence in innocence: *Raw-Ho* / Big mess: *Stitched Back Foot Airman* / Candle man: *1000 Violins* / Just...: *Scatman PX/Those Howling Horrors.*
LP: .... **BITE 5**

IN FRACTURED SILENCE (Various artists).
LP: .... **UD 015**

INDIE SCENE '78 (Various artists).
LP: .... **IBMLP 78**
MC: .... **IBMMC 78**

INDIE SCENE 1977 (Various artists).
LP: .... **IBMLP 77**
MC: .... **IBMMC 77**

INDIE TOP 20 (VOL.1) (Various artists).
Tracks: / Mickey way: *A Certain Ratio* / Dickie Davies eyes: *Half Man Half Biscuit* / Sometimes: *Erasure*/ Hang-ten!: *Soup Dragons* / Please don't: *1000 Violins* / Loan shark: *Guana Batz* / Oh grebo I think I love you: *Pop Will Eat Itself* / You should...: *Various artists* / Lover & confidante: *Blue Aeroplanes*/ Transmission: *Joy Division* / Grip of love: *Ghost Dance* / Velveteen: *Rose Of Avalanche* / Into the groovy: *Ciccone Youth* / Completely and utterly: *Chesterfields* / Sorry to embarass you: *Razorcuts* / I could be in Heaven: *Flatmates* / Beatnik boy: *Talulah Gosh* / Throwaway: *Mighty Mighty* / Day before tomorrow, The: *BMX Bandits.*
LP: .... **TT 01**

INDIE TOP 20 (VOL.2) (Various artists).
LP: .... **TT 02**

INDIE TOP 20 (VOL.3) (Various artists).
LP: .... **TT 03**
MC: .... **TT 03MC**

INDIE TOP 20 (VOL.4) (Various artists).
Tracks: / William, it was really nothing: *Smiths, The* / You make me feel: *Woodentops* / Teenage: *Brilliant Corners* / Kidney bongos: *Wire* / Is this the life: *Cardiacs* / Blue Water: *Fields Of The Nephilim*/ Nobody's twisting your arm: *Wedding Present, The* / Shimmer: *Flatmates* / Stop killing me: *Primitives*/ Knature of a girl: *Shamen* / There is no love between us anymore: *Pop Will Eat Itself.*
LP: .... **TT 041**
MC: .... **TT 041 MC**

INDIE TOP 20 VOL.4 (PART 2) (Indie house) (Various artists).
Tracks: / Theme from S.Express: *S. Express* / Let's pick up the pieces: *Twin Beat* / Shake!: *Gene & Jim Are Into Shakes* / Sound of Europe, The: *Coco Steel & Lovebomb* / People of all nations: *2 The Max* / Submit to the beat: *Groove* / Dark dark house, The: *Smith & Mighty* / Housedoctors (...): *Housedoctors.*
LP: .... **TT 042**
MC: .... **TT 042MC**

INDIE TOP 20 (VOL.5) (Various artists).
LP: .... **TT 05**
MC: .... **TT 05 MC**

INDIE TOP 20 (VOL.6) (Pride of independents) (Various artists).
LP: .... **TT 06**
MC: .... **TT 06 MC**

INDIE TOP 20 (VOL.7) (Various artists).
2LP: .... **TT 07**
MCSET: .... **TT 07MC**

INDIE TOP 20 (VOL.8) (Various artists).
LP: .... **TT 008**
MC: .... **TT 008MC**

INDIE TOP 20 (VOL.9) (Various artists).
LP: .... **TT 009**
MC: .... **TT 009 MC**

INDIE TOP 20 (VOL.10) (Various artists).
LP: .... **TT 010**

INDIE TOP 20 VOL. 12 (Various artists).
2LP: .... **TT 012**

INDIPOP COMPILATION ALBUM (Various artists).
LP: .... **VM 5**
MC: .... **VMC 5**

INDUSTRIAL RECORDS STORY (Various artists).
LP: .... **JAMS 39**

IT'S A CRAMMED, CRAMMED, CRAMMED WORLD (Various artists).
LP: .... **CRAM 033**
LP: .... **CRAM 053**

JAMES DEAN OF THE DOLE QUEUE (Various artists).
LP: .... **NWLP 1006**
LP: .... **NOSE 012**

JAMMING (Various artists).
LP: .... **SITU 11**
MC: .... **SITC 11**

JOURNEY WITHOUT MAPS (Various artists).
2LP: .... **WREK 101**

JUST A MISH MASH (Various artists).
Tracks: / China doll: *Weeds* / Track eating baby: *Janitors* / 14 days: *Waterfront Dandy, The* / Spaceships: *Membranes* / I jury: *Heart Throbs* / Crimplene seed lifestyle: *Yeah Yeah Noh* / Vigilante: *Zor Gabor*/ Wanna cocktail hate tail, The: *Creepers (film)* / Horses tail,The: *Whip Crackaway* / On the rock: *June Brides*/ Resident rat: *Implied Consent* / These animals are dangerous: *Rote Kapelle* / Mull of timperley: *Sidebottom, Frank* / T.V.cabbage: *Gaye Bykers On Acid.*
LP: .... **IT 047**

L.A. FREEWAY (Various artists).
LP: .... **DINTV 25**
MC: .... **DINMC 25**

LABELS UNLIMITED (THE SECOND RECORD COLLECTION) (Various artists).
Tracks: / Big time: *Rudi* / Take it all away: *Girlschool* / Iggy Pop's jacket: *Those Naughty Lumps* / Cold city: *Spizz oil* / N.C.B.: *Ffyrning, Illygod* / Hypocrite: *Newtown Neurotics* / Holocaust: *Crisis*/ I don't want to work for British Airways: *Scissor Fits* / Wot's for lunch Mum?: *Shapes, The* / Jilly: *Piranhas*/ Pleasant valley Sunday: *Staa Marx* / Who killed Bruce Lee?: *Glaxo Babies* / Closed shop: *Poison Girls*/ Red box: *Ijog & The Tracksuits* / After all love: *Ak Process* / Metal sheet: *Second Layer.*
LP: .... **ARED 4**

LAST SUPPER (Various artists).
MC: .... **ARR 007**

LET THEM EAT JELLYBEANS (Various artists).
LP: .... **ROSE 5**

LET'S TRY ANOTHER IDEAL GUEST HOUSE (Various artists).
Tracks: / Fag lane maurice wind / Difficult, The: *Passmore Sisters* / Househunting, The: *Househunters* / Fine sense of humour, The: *Dragsters* / Miracles take longer: *TV Personalities* / She'd cave in: *Laugh* / Like a dolphin: *14 Iced Bears* / Make my money: *AC Temple* / Something you're above: *Pleasureheads* / My boy says: *Tallulah Gosh* / Block of wood, The: *Batz* / Beautiful shirt: *1000 Violins* / All about you: *Stars Of Heaven* / It happened, The: *McTells* / If only I had the guts: *3-Action* / Surfin' Vietnam, The: *Hermit Crabs* / Heaven is blue, The: *Flatmates* / Let's make some plans: *Close Lobsters.*
LP: .... **SHELTER 2**

LIFE AT THE TOP (Various artists).
Tracks: / Perversion: *Primary Industry* / Disinformation: *Porno Sect* / Lifesucker, The: *Legendary Pink Dots*/ Last refuge, The: *Attrition* / Diet of nitro glycerine, A: *Loved One* / Extract from beyond the great: *Bushido*/ Homage to sewage: *Coil* / Prayer clock, The: *Stress* / Muslin: *Nagamatzu* / Dissidents: *Muslimgauze*/ Performance parts 1-3: *Possession.*
LP: .... **TMLP 7**

LIFE IS A JOKE VOLUME 2 (Various artists).
LP: .... **WS 022**

LIFES A JOKE VOL.3 (Various artists).
LP: .... **WS 028**

LIVE AT THE BRAIN VOL. 2 (Various artists).
LP: .... **BRAINKLP 17**

LONDON PAVILION (Various artists).
Tracks: / Curtain: *Marden hill* ((Susan Daniels)) / Valleri: *King Of Luxembourg* ((Boyce & Hart)) / Ruling class, The: *Various artists* ((Bid)) / Love: *Bid* ((Bid)) / Fire: *Underneath, The* ((Brown#crane)) / Paper wraps rock: *Momus* ((Nick currie)) / Dreams of living: *Always* ((Wright)) / Never underestimate the ignorance of the rich: *Klaxon 5* ((Maclean#O'Sullivan#Maclean)) / If you're missing someone: *Louis Phillipe* ((Philippe Auclair)) / Libera me: *Cagliostra* ((McDonough-Jones#Keeffe)) / Montague Terrace (in blue): *Mayfair Charm School* ((Scott Engel)) / At the end of the corridor: *Various artists* ((Robert)) / How blue sky was: *Turner, Simon* (From the Derek Jarman film Caravaggio.).
LP: .... **UNKNOWN**

LONDON PAVILION VOL. 2 (Various artists).
Tracks: / Masque: *Marden Hill* / Curry crazy: *Bad Dream Fancy Dress* / Trial of Doctor Fancy: *King Of Luxembourg*/ You Mary you: *Philippe, Louis* / Garden of Eden: *Adverse, Anthony* / Amateur detection: *Always* / Hanging gardens of Reigate: *Would-Be-Goods* / Pop up man, The: *Ambassador 277* / Whoops what a palaver: *Raj Quartet*/ 13th day of Christmas, The: *Caprice* / Lose that long face: *Florentines* / Jude X: *Great Chefs Of Europe.*
LP: .... **ACME 10**

LONDON PAVILLION (El in 1986) (Various artists).
LP: . . . . ACME 7
MC: . . . . ACME 7 C

LONDON PAVILLION, 3 (Various artists).
Tracks: / Guess I'm dumb: *Various artists* / Camera loves me, The: *Various artists* / Flirt: *Various artists*/ Red shoes waltz, The: *Various artists* / My honeymoon hell: *Various artists* / Leigh-On-Sea: *Various artists*/ It's love: *Various artists* / Mating game, The: *Various artists* / Cavaliere servente: *Various artists*/ Supremes, The: *Various artists* / Sorry: *Various artists* / Satellite: *Various artists.*
LP: . . . . ACME 21

LONELY IS AN EYESORE (Various artists).
Tracks: / Hot doggie: *Colourbox* / Acid bitter and sad: *This Mortal Coil* / Cut the tree: *Wolfgang Press*/ Fish: *Throwing Muses* / Frontier: *Dead Can Dance* / Crushed: *Cocteau Twins* / No motion: *Dif Juz*/ Muscoviet musquito: *Clan of xymox* / Protagonist, The: *Dead Can Dance.*
LP: . . . . CAD 703
MC: . . . . CADC 703
LP: . . . . CADD 703

LUXURY CONDOS COMING TO YOUR NEIGHBOURHOOD SOON (Various artists).
LP: . . . . ROUGH 103

LYDON & O'DONNEL FAMILY ALBUM (Various artists).
LP: . . . . JOCK LP 5

MADE TO MEASURE VOL 1 (Various artists).
LP: . . . . MTM 1

MADE TO MEASURE VOLUME 1 (Various artists).
Tracks: / Pieces for nothing: *Various artists* ("Made To Measure" for a Ballet by Pierre Droulers.) / A la recherche: *Lew, Benjamin* ("Made To Measure" as an aural backdrop for a fashion show.) / Un chien: *Maboul, Aksak* ("Made To Measure" for "Un merite une morte de chien" a play by Michel Gh) / Scratch holiday: *Maboul, Aksak* ("Made To Measure" for the Honeymoon Killers' private movie "Pan dans les) / Verdun: *Tuxedo Moon* (Three tracks from the musical score 'Made To Measure' for "Het veld Van).
LP: . . . . CRAM 029

MAGNETIC NORTH (includes: Residents,Cabaret Voltaire) (Various artists).
MC: . . . . T 5

MAGNIFICENT SEVEN, THE (Various artists).
Tracks: / Loan shark: *Various artists* / King rat: *Various artists* / Piledriver boogie: *Various artists*/ PVC chair: *Various artists* / Pervy in the park: *Various artists* / Militant tendency: *Stingrays* / June rhyme: *Various artists* / Gimme the drugs: *Various artists* / Whip it up: *Various artists* / Blue sunshine: *Various artists* / Axe attack: *Various artists* / Johnny remember me: *Various artists* / I see red: *Various artists* / Mexican radio (Frenzy): *Various artists* / Girl invisible, The: *Various artists*/ Vanish without a trace: *Various artists* / After midnight (restless): *Various artists.*
LP: . . . . ABCLP 9

MAKE READY FOR THE REVELATION... BITEBACK SAMPLE (Various artists).
LP: . . . . BB 001

MANCHESTER - NORTH OF ENGLAND (Various artists).
MC: . . . . BCT 001
LP: . . . . BCV 001

MARTIN HANNET - MEMORIAL ALBUM (Various artists).
LP: . . . . FACT 325
MC: . . . . FACT 325C

MELTDOWN ON MEDIA BURN (Various artists).
LP: . . . . MB 8

MINDLESS SLAUGHTER (Various artists).
LP: . . . . ANHREFN 010

MOVING SOUNDTRACKS (Various artists).
LP: . . . . TWI 112 Z

MUSIC FROM THE DEAD ZONE (Various artists).
LP: . . . . DMCDZ 001

MUSIC, NOISE, SOUND & BEAT (Various artists).
MC: . . . . MFM 37

NEW SEASON, A (Various artists).
2LP: . . . . SFRLP 205
MC: . . . . SFRMC 205

NEXT UP (Various artists).
Tracks: / Love me: *Deja* / Red man: *Weazel Creek* / Going back to nature: *Fault* / Circus: *Ricoche*/ Candlestick park: *Average Bear* / No denial: *Northwide* / Crazy nights: *Stitch* / We move: *Garden Of Eden* / Start again: *Ginger Melon* / Broken promises: *New Spinal Chord.*
MC: . . . . BOMB 004

NIGHTLANDS (Various artists).
Tracks: / Green is the colour of the prophet: *Muslimgauze* / Do this: *Pump* / Half deepmen: *Biting Tongues*/ New York, 1940: *Gush* / Lullaby: *Bourbonese Qualk* / That Marilyn walk: *Avery, John* / Moors, The: *Story, Tim* / Zone: *Mute Calm* / First soundtrack: *Human Flesh.*
LP: . . . . FIB 005

NME C86 (Various artists).
MC: . . . . ROUGHC 100

NO RULES (Various artists).
Tracks: / Time bomb city: *Various artists* / Cold love: *Cult Maniax* / City brave: *Cult Maniax* / Poison pen letters: *Cult Maniax* / Shout and scream: *Sex Gang Children* / Time of our lives: *Various artists*/ Duty unto death: *Various artists* / Khmer Rouge: *Destructors* / Religion: *Destructors* / Electronic church: *Destructors* / No compromise: *Blitzkrieg* / Conscience prayer: *Blitzkrieg* / No rules: *Leather Nun* / Slow death: *Leather Nun.*
LP: . . . . CFRC 508

NOISE NEW YORK (Various artists).
Tracks: / Motor city: *Honeymoon Killers* / Hazed and dazed: *Honeymoon Killers* / Mind the gap: *Prong*/ Daily dose: *Prong* / I don't know: *Jad Fair* / Diamonds: *Jad Fair* / Father: *Of Cabbage & Kings*/ European son: *Moore, Thurston* / How do you spell relief ?: *Bank Of Sodom* / Rear view mirror: *Black Snakes*/ I'm cheap: *Black Snakes* / I ride a white horse: *Krackhouse* / Against UFO's: *Krackhouse* / Rock 'n' roll lifestyle: *Krackhouse* / Hell cat II: *Phantom Tollbooth* / Poly ratmatazz: *Phantom Tollbooth* / Cut you loose: *Royal Trax* / Luminous dolphin: *Royal Trax* / Spider and the fly, The: *Needlenose* / At home: *Needlenose.*
MC: . . . . A 156

NOTHING SHORT OF TOTAL WAR (Various artists).
Tracks: / Come and smash me said the boy with the magic penis: *Sonic Youth* / Bugged: *Head Of David* / Fire in Philly: *UT* / He's on fire: *Sonic Youth* / Kerosene: *Big Black* / Magic wand: *Sonic Youth* / Dutch courage: *Rapeman* / Bulbs of passion: *Ranaldo, Lee* / Scratchy heart: *Ciccone Youth* / Evangelist: *UT* / Snake domain: *Head Of David* / He's a whore: *Big Black* / Devils jukebox: *Big Stick* / 108: *Head Of David* / Sheikh: *AC Temple* / Just got payed today: *Rapeman* / Throne of blood: *Band Of Susans* / Little Hitlers: *Arsenal* / Jimi: *Butthole Surfers.*
LP: . . . . BFFP 013
MC: . . . . BFFP 013C

OBSCURE IND CLASSICS, VOL.IV (Various artists).
LP: . . . . ERICAT 25

OBSCURE INDEPENDENT CLASSICS Volume 5 (Various artists).
LP: . . . . HAM 22

OFF THE CUFF (Various artists).
Tracks: / Bop natives: *Bop Natives* / Light your fire: *Bop Natives* / Ain't it grand?: *Bop Natives* / Keep it in the family: *Rank Amateurs* / You call my love: *Rank Amateurs* / Just another lonely heart: *Rank Amateurs* / Pages of my love: *Andrew, Barry's Restaurant for Dogs* / Fruit: *Andrew, Barry's Restaurant for Dogs*/ Mice: *Andrew, Barry's Restaurant for Dogs* / Waiting for the A-bomb: *Victims Of Pleasure* / Disconnect: *Victims Of Pleasure* / Red moon: *Victims Of Pleasure.*
LP: 2478 151

OFF THE DOTTED LINE (Various artists).
Tracks: / What you have: *Voice Of The Beehive* / Again and again: *Episode Four* / Roger: *Vakeros, The*/ Falling over December: *North of Cornwallis* / I bet she's gonna go: *Brilliant Corners* / Gunning the works: *Blue Aeroplanes* / Chime: *Discipline* / Beat box baby: *Howard, Dave Singers* / Same old game: *Fun Patrol*/ Wish away, A / E-lollipop: *Hands Of A Virgin* / Area brothers: *Head Of David* / Snake eyes: *Crazyhead*/ Confusion reigns: *Giant* / Stoned and bruised: *Crows, The.*
LP: . . . . EE 3531
MC: . . . . TCEE 3531

ON THE DOTTED LINE (Various artists).
Tracks: / Redbury joy town: *Wonder Stuff* / Round and round: *Crows* / Motorcycle rain: *We Free Kings*/ Sorrow floats: *Voice of the Beehive* / In our song: *Favourites* / Murder of your smile: *Howard, Dave Singers*/ Plastic horse: *Howard, Dave Singers* / Crazyhead: *Rub the Buddha* / Parallax avenue: *Slab!* / Tolerance: *Blue Aeroplanes* / Everything I ever wanted: *Brilliant Corners* / Hunger, The: *Aslan* / Dallas blues: *Jack Rubies.*
LP: . . . . EE 3530
MC: . . . . TC EE 3530

ONE GIANT LEAP (Various artists).
LP: . . . . INTEL 5

ONE LITTLE INDIAN TAKES ON THE COWBOYS (Various artists).
LP: . . . . TPLP 6
MC: . . . . TPC 6

OPERATION TWILIGHT (Various artists).
Tracks: / Contempt: *Reininger, Blaine* / Duet: *Duritti Column & Blaine Reininger* / Ball, The: *Brown, Steven*/ Walking Home, Theme from: *French Impressionists* / Love in adversity: *Rankine, Alan* / Close cover: *Mertens, Wim* / Music no.2: *Reininger, Blaine/ Steven Brown* / Sea wall, The: *Durutti Column* / Rue Traversiere: *Rankine, Alan/Rumours Of War* / Sunny Lee: *Rankine, Alan/Rumours Of War* / A proposito de Napoli: *Marine* / History of rock and roll: *Montiana, Kid.*
LP: . . . . IM 005

PAPER BOATS IN PUDDLES (Brighton Compilation) (Various artists).
LP: . . . . WIZZ 001

PARANOIA YOU CAN DANCE TO (Various artists).
LP: . . . . WS 018

PAROXYSN (Various artists).
LP: . . . . MKT 001
MC: . . . . MKTMC 001

PILLOWS AND PRAYERS (A Cherry Red compilation 1982-3) (Various artists).
Tracks: / Portrait: *Five Or Six* / Eine symphonie des grauens: *Monochrome Set* / All about you: *Leer, Thomas*/ Plain sailing: *Thorn, Tracey* / Some things don't matter: *Watt, Ben* / Love in your heart: *Pillows & Prayers*/ Modi 2: *Milesi, Pierro* / Compulsion: *Crow, Joe* / Lazy ways: *Marine Girls* / My face is on fire: *Felt*/ No noise: *Eyeless in Gaza* / Xoyo: *Passage* / On my mind: *Everything But The Girl* / Bang and a wimpey, A: *Attila The Stockbroker* / I unseen: *Misunderstood* / Don't blink: *Nightingales* / Stop the music for a minute: *Crisp, Quentin.*
LP: . . . . ZRED 41
LPPD: . . . . PZ RED 41

POEMS (Various artists).
LP: . . . . CRELP 055

POX UPON THE POLL TAX (Various artists).
LP: . . . . REVOLT 001

PURVEYORS OF TASTE Creation compilation, A (Various artists).
LP: . . . . CRELP 010

QUICK NEAT JOB, A (Various artists).
LP: . . . . TWI 643
MC: . . . . TWIC 643

RAVE ON (Various artists).
LP: 1951197127

RECOMMENDED SAMPLER (Various artists).
2LP: . . . . RR 8/9

RECORD SHACK PRESENTS...VOL.1 (Various artists).
LP: . . . . RSTV 1
MC: . . . . RSTVK 1

ROOART PRESENTS (Various artists).
Tracks: / Get on down: *Hummingbirds* / Old beach road: *Martha's Vineyard* / Minibar of oblivion: *Trilobites*/ Tinytown: *Tall Tales & True* / Whatever it takes: *Crash Politics* / Thank you goodnight: *Kelly, Sean.*
LP: 838 924 1
MC: 838 924 4

ROUGH WITH THE SMOOTH (Various artists).
LP: . . . . TWI 651

SECOND AFTER EPIPHANY (Various artists).
LP: . . . . ZRON 37

SEEDS I: POP (Various artists).
Tracks: / World weary: *Go-Betweens* / Everybody thinks everybody else is dead bad: *Skodas* / Another reason: *Five Or Six* / Shoot to kill: *Dragees* / Jack: *Bone Orchard* / Every conversation: *June Brides* / Heavens above: *Pastels* / Stop the rain: *Suede Crocodiles* / Tough Times: *Vital Disorders* / Don't ring me up: *Protex* / Sun shines here, The: *Hurrah* / Fast boyfriends: *Girls At Our Best* / Three wishes: *TV Personalities* / Happy feeling: *Sinatras* / Mark my word: *Saint Johns Alliance* / Don't come back: *Marine girls* / Things have changed: *Wild Flowers* / Patrick: *Big Table* / Time goes by so slow: *Distractions.*
LP: . . . . BRED 74

SEEDS II : ART (Various artists).
Tracks: / Puppet life: *Punishment of luxury* / Life in reverse: *Marine* / F.T.N.: *Club Tango* / Urban ospreys: *Nightingales* / Hearts in exile: *Homosexuals* / Trendy: *Patrik Fitzgerald* / Conspiracy: *Higsons*/ My mother was a friend of the enemy of the people: *Blurt* / So many others: *Past seven days.*
LP: . . . . BRED 76
MC: . . . . CBRED 76

SEEDS III: ROCK (Various artists).
Tracks: / Big time: *Rudi* / Roger Wilson said: *New York New York* / Dance stance: *Dexy's Midnight Runners*/ Standing up: *Colenso Parade* / Europeans: *Europeans* / Favourite sister: *Riley, Marc* / She's fallen in love with a monster man: *Revillos* / Cast a long shadow: *Monochrome Set* / Terminal Tokyo: *Garage Class*/ King mob: *Rote Kapelle* / Christine Keeler: *Glaxo Babies* / So long: *Fischer-Z* / I'll remember you: *Wasted Youth* / Drunken uncle John: *Deville, Cruella.*
LP: . . . . BRED 78

SEEDS IV: PUNK (Various artists).
Tracks: / Holiday in Cambodia: *Dead Kennedys* / Run like hell: *Peter & The Test Tube Babies* / Love you more: *Buzzcocks* / Mucky pup: *Puncture* / I like drugs: *Simpletones* / Someone's gonna die: *Blitz (group)*/ Hangover: *Serious Drinking* / Cops are comin', The: *Outcasts* / Love and a molotov cocktail: *Flys, The*/ I'm in love with Margaret Thatcher: *Notsensibles* / Escalator heater: *Raped* / Murder: *Panik* / Army song: *Abrasive Wheels* / Lipstick on your collar: *Saints.*
LP: . . . . BRED 80
MC: . . . . CBRED 80

SEEDS V: ELECTRIC (Various artists).
Tracks: / Running away: *Various artists* / More than a dream: *Various artists* / Fred Vom Jupiter: *Various* artists / Letter from America: *Various artists* / Slipping into life: *Various artists* / Digital days: *Various* artists / Red pullover, The: *Various artists* / Europa and the Pirate Twins: *Various artists* / Kodak ghosts run amok: *Various artists* / Saturday night special: *Various artists* / Attention Stockholm: *Various artists*/ Never never comes: *Various artists* / Xoyo: *Various artists* / Falling from another high building: *Various artists.*
LP: . . . . BRED 84

SENT FROM COVENTRY (Various artists).
Tracks: / We're only monsters: *Wild Boys* / Mothers never know: *Clique* / Panic in the night: *End* / With you: *Mix* / Character change: *Machine* / Nuclear terrorist: *Urge* / Protection: *Protege*/ Solid action: *Solid Action* / Lorraine: *Wild Boys* / Flasher, The: *Squad* / Armageddon: *Homicide*/ Sirens: *Riot Act* / Donna Blitzen: *V. Babies.*
LP: . . . . KATH 1

SERIOUS ONE (Various artists).
LP: . . . . SOU 1
MC: . . . . ZCOU 1

SHADOW FACTORY (Various artists).
Tracks: / I'm in love: *Another Sunny Day* / Sure to see: *14 Iced Bears* / Are we gonna be alright: *Springfields*/ Tiny words: *Orchids* / Last letter, The: *Field Mice* / Please rain fall: *Sea Urchins* / Give me some: *Orchids* / Pistine Christine: *Sea Urchins* / Come get me: *14 Iced Bears* / My secret world: *Golden Dawn.*
LP: . . . . SARAH 587

SHAPE OF FINNS TO COME (Various artists).
Tracks: / Old timer: *Various artists* / John Fogarty: *Various artists* / Live your life: *Various artists*/ Suitcase: *Various artists* / Rooting for beer: *Various artists* / Secret of my success: *Various artists*/ I want you: *Various artists* / Njet njet: *Various artists* / Better say nothing: *Various artists* / Boredom's the word: *Various artists* / Car park drama: *Various artists* / London: *Various artists* / Sina umija: *Various artists.*
LP: . . . . ARED 8

SIGNATURE TUNES (Various artists).
Tracks: / Christ via wires: *Orchestra Arcana* / Bounds of reason, bonds of love: *Takahashi, Yukihiro* / Belle dux on the beach: *Various artists* / Ieyasu: *Jobson-Nelson* / Portrait of Jan with moon and stars: *Nelson, Bill* / West deep: *Nelson, Bill* / Feels like winter again: *Fiat Lux* / This illness: *Fiat Lux* / Highway 2000: *Revoc Cadets* / Airfields:

To Heaven A Jet / Certain bridge, A: *Last Man In Europe* / Telecommunication: *Flock Of Seagulls*.
LP: . . . . JC 13
MC: . . . . TCJC 13

SMALL HITS FROM NEAR MISSES (Various artists).
Tracks: / I'm falling: *Dead or Alive* / Culture won't wait: *Freeze Frame* / Precious is the pearl: *Box Of Toys* / Burning arrows: *Venusadore* / Seven minutes to midnight: *Wah!* / Jimmy's grin: *Margox* / Daytime assassins: *Builders* / Freedom fighters: *Dalek I Love You* / Flowers: *Dead or Alive* / African and white: *China Crisis*.
LP: . . . . INEVLP 1
MC: . . . . INEVLK 1
LP: . . . . ZL 70370

SMASHING TIME (A countdown compilation) (Various artists).
LP: . . . . NIXON 1

SO MUCH TO ANSWER FOR (Manchester compilation) (Various artists).
LP: . . . . SFRLP 202

SOLO ALBUM Various artists (Various artists).
LP: . . . . FRY 3

SOME BIZZARE ALBUM (Various artists).
LP: . . . . BZLP 1

SOME FASCINATING THINGS Various Artists (Various artists).
LP: . . . . TWI 082

SONGS ABOUT SPORT (Various artists).
LP: . . . . PROP 4

STATE OF THE UNION (Various artists).
LP: . . . . DISCHORD 32
MC: . . . . DISCHORD 32C

STATIK COMPILATION 1 (Various artists).
LP: 825 983-1

STATIK COMPILATION 2 (Various artists).
LP: 825 984-1

STONES OF CALLANISH, THE (A folk opera) (Various artists).
2LP: . . . . DOG 005/6
MCSET: . . . . DOG 005/6 C

STREET CAR NAMED DESIRE, A (Various artists).
MC: . . . . VENUE 1

TACKY SOUVENIR OF PRE-REVOLUTIONARY MANCHESTER (Various artists).
LP: . . . . BIP 501
MC: . . . . BIP 501C

TAKE THE SUBWAY TO YOUR SUBURB (Various artists).
LP: . . . . SUBORG 001

TECHNO ROSE OF BLIGHTY (Various artists).
LP: . . . . CRELP 072
MC: . . . . CREC 072

TEMPLE CLOUD (Various artists).
Tracks: / Yawn: *Orchids* / Carbrain: *Wake* / All of a tremble: *St. Christopher* / Darkest blue: *Gentle Despite* / You should all ...: *Another Sunny Day* / If you need someone: *Field Mice* / You deserve more: *St. Christopher* / Can't you tell: *Another Sunny Day* / Sensitive: *Field Mice* / I don't think it matters: *Brighter*/ Green: *Another Sunny Day* / George Hamilton's dead: *Golden Dawn* / Inside out: *Brighter* / These things happen: *Action Painting* / Song 6: *Field Mice* / Noah's ark: *Brighter*.
LP: . . . . SARAH 376

THERE'S A METHOD TO OUR MADNESS (Various artists).
LP: . . . . WEBITE 14

THEY SHALL NOT PASS (Various artists).
Tracks: / Lean on me: *Redskins* / Unionize: *Redskins* / Adrenochrome: *Sisters Of Mercy* / Body electric: *Sisters Of Mercy* / Mindless violence: *Newtown Neurotics* / Kick out the tories: *Newtown Neurotics* / Pink headed bug: *Three Johns* / Men like monkeys: *Three Johns*.
LP: . . . . AABT 400
MC: . . . . AABTC 400

'TIL THINGS ARE BRIGHTER (Various artists).
LP: . . . . REDLP 88

TIME BETWEEN - A TRIBUTE TO THE BYRDS (Various artists).
LP: . . . . ILLUSION 004
MC: . . . . ILLC 004

TIMEBOX (Various artists).
Tracks: / Probably won't be easy: *Blyth Power* / Persuasion: *Sin baby* / Sunday night: *Menticide* / Got you covered: *Thatcher on Acid* / Black day: *Children held hostage* / Waiting: *We Are Going To Eat You*/ Love is miles...: *Saviours of pop music* / Dirty..., The: *Stitched Back Foot Airman* / Time stood still: *Fifteenth*/ On another day: *Strange desire. A* / We wish you: *Resistance* / Lord of the dance: *Only Connect* / Let the light: *Laughing mothers, The* / Rocking on a Saturday...: *Brad Is Sex*.
LP: . . . . TIME 001

TIP OF THE ICEBERG (Various artists).
Tracks: / Gulf of your love, The: *Waldron, Michael* / Damage is done: *Harlequin* / Jerusalem: *Fabulous Salamander*/ All alone: *Circus Renz* / I think I'm losing all my hair: *Toad, Stoan* / High tonight: *Watch With Mother*/ Feel alright: *Dance Reaction* / It's over: *D Lux* / No smoke: *Pink Luxury* / No power on earth: *Where's The Fire*.
MC: . . . . Unknown

TOTALBEATFACTOR (Various artists).
Tracks: / Danger zone: *Portion Control* / Radioactive flood: *Poesie Noir* / Escape via Cessnock: *Scattered Order* / Sour pork loin: *Smersh* / Nine and a half times: *Frontline Assembly* / 10,000 visiones del Dr.Castro Viejo: *Uvegraf*.
LP: . . . . BNIA THREE

TOUCH TRAVEL includes:Andrew Poppy,Jah Wobble,1000 Mexicans (Various artists).
MC: . . . . T 4

TURN IT UP OR TURN IT OFF (Various artists).
Tracks: / Hammer on honey: *Kill Ugly Pop* / Quirky town: *Catwax Axe Co* / Beach rattle: *Gastrattle* / Love machine: *My Bloody Valentine* / Mulch: *Barton and Harry* / No place to go: *My Bloody Valentine* / Scratch: *Catwax Axe Co* / Crushing fingers: *Gastrattle* / Legendary Big Foot, The: *Kill Ugly Pop* / Ned: *Barton and Harry*.
LP: . . . . FEV 007

USUAL SUSPECTS, THE (Various artists).
LP: . . . . WF 101

USUAL SUSPECTS VOL.1 (Various artists).
LP: . . . . WF 010

USUAL SUSPECTS VOL.2 (It's all music) (Various artists).
LP: . . . . WF 014

USUAL SUSPECTS VOL.3 (Above suspicion) (Various artists).
LP: . . . . WFS 015

VILE PEACE, A (Various artists).
Tracks: / Better off without you: *Creeping Pumpkins* / Wrong side of your mind: *Three Fourvigen* / I love you: *Liquid Generation* / Every time: *Dusters* / Legend of the headless surfer: *Skeptics, The* / Hammer of love: *Subterraneans* / Bells are ringing: *Real Gone, The* / Harvest time: *Mutant Drone* / Walk without me: *Scattered Limbs* / Restless soul: *No Kings* / Egypto-tek: *Turnups, The*.
LP: . . . . VILE 001

VILE VIBES (Various artists).
LP: . . . . VILE 15
MC: . . . . VILE 15MC

WHAT A GODDAMN GROOVY WAY TO TURN 17 (Various artists).
LP: 1707

WILD PARTY SOUNDS (Various artists).
Tracks: / Woodpecker sound: *Jah Woosh Machine Gun* / Bedbound saga: *Hogg & Co* / Quante jubila: *Prince Fari*, Creation Rebel / Quit the body: *Chicken Rebel, The* / Parasitic machine: *Pellay, Alan* / Dreams are better: *London Underground* / Asian rebel: *Suns Of Arqa* / Demonic forces: *Pellay, Alan* / Afghani dub: *Mothmen*/ Things that made U.S.: *Loy, Jeb & The Oilwell* / Yippee-I-ay: *New Age Steppers* / Dice: *Nylon, Judy*.
LP: . . . . BRED 24

WINTERS OF DISCONTENT (Various artists).
2LP: . . . . SFRLP 204

WNW6 MOONLIGHT RADIO (Various artists).
LP: . . . . MOON 1

WONDERFUL WORLD OF GLASS, VOL.2 (Various artists).
LP: . . . . GLALP 007

WORDS WORTH SHOUTING (Various artists).
LP: . . . . RCLP 004

WORLD DOMINATION OF DEATH (Various artists).
LP: . . . . PLAYLP 012

WORONZOID (Various artists).
LP: W010

YOU BET WE'VE GOT SOMETHING AGAINST YOU (Various artists).
LP: . . . . PS 014

ZOO, THE (Various artists).
LP: . . . . DLP 001
MC: . . . . DMC 001

Indiens Yaquis

INDIENS YAQUIS - MUSIQUE ET DANSES RITUELLES (Various artists).
Tracks: / Mescalito: *Various artists* / Appel a l'inconnu: *Various artists* / L'atteinte: *Various artists*/ Perception de l'inconnu: *Various artists* / Triomphe de mescalito: *Various artists* / Fete de l'etre: *Various artists*.
LP: . . . . ARN 33435

Indigo Girls

INDIGO GIRLS.
Tracks: / Closer to fine / Secure yourself / Kid fears / Prince of darkness / Blood and fire / Tried to be true / Love's recovery / Land of Canaan / Center stage / History of us.
LP: 4634911
MC: 4634914

NOMADS, INDIANS, SAINTS.
Tracks: / Hammer and a nail / Welcome me / World falls / Southland in the Springtime / 1 2 3 / Keeper of my heart / Watershed / Hand me downs / You and me of the 10, 000 wars / Pushing the needle too far / Girl with the weight of the world in her hands.
LP: 4673081
MC: 4673084

Indiscretion In

INDISCRETION IN SESSION (Various artists).
LP: . . . . LEN 1

Industrial Espionage

INDUSTRIAL ESPIONAGE (See under UNESCO reports).

Industrial Workers ...

INDUSTRIAL WORKERS OF THE WORLD REBEL Voices (Various artists).
LP: . . . . FF 484

Industrials

CLONES OF RADIOLAND.
Tracks: / Clones of radioland / Voodoo / Creation / Women alone in cars / Idiot dancers / At countdown / Rings of Saturn / Headlights / Life without Mozart / Every night is Hallowe'en / In a mind garage / When the war is over.
LP: . . . . CBS 84399

Infa Riot

STILL OUT OF ORDER.
Tracks: / Emergency / You ain't seen nothing yet / Five minute fashion / Each dawn I die / Drug squad, The / Still out of order / Catch 22 / Power / Boot boys / Winner, The / Friday oh Friday / Catalogue kids / In for a riot.
LP: . . . . SEC 7
MC: . . . . TSEC 7

Infant God

PUBERTY.
LP: . . . . ILLUSION 020

Infante, Anne

FOUR DRAGONS, THE.
LP: . . . . LRF 074

Infas

SOUND AND FURY.
LP: . . . . PANLP 501
MC: . . . . PANCA 501

Infatuation

INFATUATION (See under Robins, Denise) (Latimer, Sheila).

Infectious Grooves

PLAGUE THAT MAKES YOUR BOOTY MOVE, THE (It's the Infectious Grooves).
Tracks: / Punk it up / Therapy / I look funny? / Stop funk'n with my head / I'm gonna be my King / Closed session / Infectious grooves / Infectious blues / Monster skank / Back to the people / Turn your head / You lie...and yo breath stank / Do the sinister / Mandatory love song / Infecto groovalistic / Thanx but no thanx.
LP: 4687291
MC: 4687294

Infernal Majesty

NONE SHALL DEFY.
LP: . . . . RR 9609
MC: . . . . RR 49609

Inferno & Execute

SPLIT.
LP: 0012-06

Inferno (film)

INFERNO (See under Emerson, Keith) (Emerson, Keith).

Inferno Party

INFERNO PARTY (Various artists).
LP: 1001

Infernos

1980S DOO-WOP ALBUM, THE (see Autumns) (Infernos & Autumns).

Influx One

INFLUX ONE (Various artists).
Tracks: / Radio Moscow: *Various artists* / Scratchers: *Various artists* / Stranger: *Various artists*/ Another room: *Various artists* / Jimmy Nipper five: *Various artists* / First aid: *Various artists* / Good blokes: *Various artists* / Grandma Moses: *Various artists* / Indicators: *Various artists* / Carl Lewis: *Various artists* / Kevin Salinger: *Various artists* / Perfect people: *Various artists*.
LP: . . . . ZYGOLP 1

Information Society

HACK.
Tracks: / Seek 200 / How long / Think / Wenn wellen schwingen / Knife and a fork, A / R.I.P. / Now that I have you / Fire tonight / Can't slow down / T.V. addicts / Hard currency / Move out / CP drill KKL / Mirrorshades / We don't take / Hack 1 / Charlie X / If only / Come with me / Slipping away / Here is Kazmeyer / Chemistry.
LP: 4677771
MC: 4677774

INFORMATION SOCIETY.
LP: 828126-1
MC: 828126-4

Inge, William

BUS STOP / COME BACK LITTLE SHEBA.
MC: 1771

Ingenbold, Ulrich

WINTEREISE (See under Weber, Hajo) (Ingenbold, Ulrich & Hajo Weber).

Ingman, Nick

HOME (Ingman, Nick & Friends).
Tracks: / Home / Homeward bound / Now and then / Just be close / Making tracks / Staying in / Help me make it through the night / Missing you again / Welcome home / By your side / Late night talking / Woman / Sunday morning / Home is where the heart is / On the road / Green green grass of home / When day is done / Cosy / Safe and sound / Here where you are.
MC: . . . . BATMC 10.01

Ingram

NIGHT STALKERS.
Tracks: / Night stalkers / With you / Drivin' me crazy / When you're hot you're hot / Just for you / I like it / Fantasy / Hot body.
LP: . . . . OELP 1

Ingram, James

IT'S REAL.
Tracks: / It's real / Call on me / Love come down / Love one day at a time / Someday we'll all be free / I wanna come back / So fine / (You make me feel like a) natural man / I don't have the heart / When was the last time music made.
LP: . . . . K 925924 1
MC: . . . . K 925924 4
LP: . . . . WX 280

IT'S YOUR NIGHT.
Tracks: / Party animal / Yah mo B there / She loves me (the best that I can be) / Try your love again / Whatever we imagine / One more rhythm / There's no easy way / It's your night / How do you keep the music playing?.
LP: 923970 1
MC: 923970 4

NEVER FELT SO GOOD.
Tracks: / Always / Never felt so good / Red hot lover / Lately / Wings of my heart / Trust me / Tuff / Say hey / Love's been here and gone / Right back.
LP: . . . . WX 44
MC: . . . . WX 44 C

Ingram Kingdom

FUNK IS IN OUR MUSIC.
Tracks: / Ingram kingdom / Tried it and liked it / What else can I say / He's mine / Music is our message / Funk is our music / Someone's on my side / She's all alone / Put your troubles behind.
LP: . . . . CLP 543

Ingram, Richard

SOMEWHERE OUT THERE (See under Ronstadt, Linda) (Ingram, Richard/ Rondstadt, Linda).

Inhuman Conditions

DESERVE NO RESPECT.
LP: 082931

Ink Spots

16 GOLDEN CLASSICS.
Tracks: / Whispering grass / Swing high swing low / Stompin' at the savoy / I don't want to set the world on fire / Maybe / You were only fooling / Sometime / White christmas / To each his own / You're breaking my heart / I'll get by / When the swallows come back to capist... / Street of dreams / We'll meet again / Coquette / Just for a thrill / Thoughtless / I cover the waterfront / Someone's rocking my dreamboat.
LP: . . . . **UNLP 026**
MC: . . . . **UNMC 026**

18 ORIGINAL GREATEST HITS-INKSPOTS.
LP: . . . . **K 5001**

20 GREATEST HITS: INK SPOTS.
LP: . . . . **N 22016**
MC: **42016**

BEST OF THE INK SPOTS.
Tracks: / If I didn't care / We three / My prayer / Whispering grass / It's funny to everyone but me / I don't want to set the world on fire / To each his own / Do I worry / Address unknown / Someone's rocking my dreamboat / Street of dreams / Don't get around much anymore / Gypsy, The / Maybe / When the swallows come back to Capistrane / Please take a letter, Miss Brown / Until the real thing comes along / Time out for tears / I cover the waterfront / We'll meet again / Java jive / No orchids for my lady / I'll never smile again / It is no secret.
MC: **16 6**
2LP: . . . . **MCLD 607**
MCSET: . . . . **MCLDC 607**

BEST OF THE INK SPOTS (MFP).
Tracks: / If I didn't care / Bless you for being an angel / When the swallows come back to Capistrano / Whispering grass / Maybe / Java jive / Do I worry / I don't want to set the world on fire / Every night about this time / Don't get around much anymore / To each his own / Ring, telephone, ring / I'd climb the highest mountain / Puttin' and takin' / Cow cow boogie / Into each life some rain must fall / Your feets too big / I'll never smile again / It's a sin to tell a lie / Someone's rocking my dreamboat.
LP: . . . . **MFP 50529**
MC: . . . . **TCMFP 50529**

FABULOUS INK SPOTS SING THEIR FAVOURITES.
MC: . . . . **DPC 726**

GOLDEN GREATS: INK SPOTS.
Tracks: / If I didn't care / When swallows come / Back to Capistrano / Whispering grass / Java jive / Do I worry / I don't want to set the world on fire / Don't get around much anymore / To each his own / I'll never smile again / Someone's rocking my dreamboat / We three / My prayer / Until the real thing comes along / No orchids for my lady / Gypsy, The / I'll get by / Maybe / You were only fooling / We'll meet again / It's a sin to tell a lie.
LP: . . . . **MCM 5029**
MC: . . . . **MCMC 5029**

GOLDEN HOUR OF THE INKSPOTS.
MC: . . . . **KGHMC 119**

GREATEST HITS: INK SPOTS.
MC: . . . . **GM 0206**

INK SPOTS COLLECTION (16 Golden Greats).
Tracks: / Stranger in Paradise / Don't laugh at me / Keep it moving / When you come to the end of the day / Melody of love / Here in my lonely room / Changing partners / Am I too late? / Ebb tide / Flowers, Mr. Florist, please / Someone's rocking my dreamboat / I'd walk a country mile / Yesterdays / If you should say goodbye / There is something missing / Command me.
LP: . . . . **DVLP 2107**
MC: . . . . **DVMC 2107**

INK SPOTS: ON THE AIR.
Tracks: / Swinging on the string / Did you ever see a dream walking? / Old spinning wheel / Baby brown / Pork chops and gravy / Do I worry / No wonder / It's so funny to everyone but me / Tiger rag / If I didn't care / Java jive / Lovely way to spend an evening, A.
LP: . . . . **TOTEM 1020**

INK SPOTS, THE.
Tracks: / It's the talk of the town / There goes my heart / Someone's rocking my dreamboat / Paper doll / Lazy river / In a shanty in old Shantytown / I'm confessin' / We three / Just in case you change your mind / Whispering grass.
LP: . . . . **RHAS 9011**
LP: . . . . **BID 8001**

INKSPOTS & THE PLATTERS (Ink Spots/Platters).
MCSET: . . . . **WW 6047**

JUST LIKE OLD TIMES.
Tracks: / Into each life some rain must fall / For sentimental reasons / Once in a while / On the sunny side of the street / Till then / It had to be you / Old fashioned way / I'll get by / Honeysuckle rose / Autumn leaves / Just for a thrill / Seems like old times.
LP: . . . . **CBS 54876**
MC: **40 54876**

SWING HIGH, SWING LOW.
Tracks: / Keep away from my doorstep / Alabama barbecue / T'ain't nobody's bizz-ness if I do / That cat is high / Swing, gate, swing / Slap that bass / Christopher Columbus / Ye suh / Your feet's too big / When the sun goes down / Swingin' on the strings / Stompin' at the Savoy / With plenty of money and you / Let's call the whole thing off / Don't let old age creep up on you / Mama don't allow it / Oh Red / Old Joe's hittin' the jug / Whoa babe / Swing high, swing low.
LP: . . . . **CHD 143**
MC: . . . . **MCHD 143**

VERY BEST OF THE INKSPOTS (HALLMARK).
LP: . . . . **SHM 3194**
MC: . . . . **HSC 3194**

Inmates

FAST FORWARD.
LP: . . . . **SNTF 1016**

FIRST OFFENCE.
Tracks: / Dirty water / Love got me / Mr. Unreliable / Walk, The / I can't sleep / Jealousy / Three time loser / You're the one that done it / Midnightto six man / Jeannie, Jeannie, Jeannie / If time could turn backwards / Back in history / I can't stop.
LP: . . . . **RAD 25**

FIVE.
LP: . . . . **LOLITA 5028**

SHOT IN THE DARK.
Tracks: / Tell talk / Tell me what's wrong / So much in love / Stop it baby / Waiting game, The / Crime don't pay / Feeling good / I thought I heard a heartbeat / Why when the love has gone / Sweet rain / I can't make up my mind / Show you my way / Some kinda wonderful.
LP: . . . . **RAD 28**
MC: . . . . **RAC 28**

Inner Circle

BLAME IT ON THE SUN.
Tracks: / Natty dread / Can you handle it / I shot the sheriff / When will I see you again / Road block / Irey feeling / Forward jah jah children / Judgement / Burial / Blame it on the sun / Your kiss is sweet.
LP: . . . . **TRLS 114**

EVERYTHING IS GREAT.
Tracks: / Music machine / Mary Mary / Stop breaking my heart / Roots rock symphony / Everything is great / Playing it / We 'A' rockers / I've learned my lesson.
LP: . . . . **ILPS 9558**

NEW AGE MUSIC.
Tracks: / We come to rock you / Summer in the city / Call it love / Discipline child / Carry that weight / If I can't have you / New age music / Chips and bruises.
LP: . . . . **ILPS 9608**
MC: . . . . **ZCI 9608**

ONE WAY.
Tracks: / One way / Front and centre / Champion / Keep the faith / Love one another / Massive / Bad boys / Life / Stay with me.
LP: . . . . **RAS 3030**
MC: . . . . **RASC 3030**

SOMETHING SO GOOD.
Tracks: / Something so good / Summer struttin' / World 2000 / When a man loves a woman / Telephone line / Fools of love / Ticket to heaven / Hot love / Changes.
LP: . . . . **CAL 143**

Inner City

FIRE.
LP: . . . . **DIX 99**
MC: . . . . **CDIX 99**

PARADISE.
Tracks: / Inner city theme / Ain't nobody better / Big fun / Good life / And I do / Paradise / Power of passion / Do you love what you feel / Set your body free / Secrets of the mind.
LP: . . . . **DIX 81**
MC: . . . . **CDIX 81**
LP: . . . . **OVED 341**
MC: . . . . **OVEDC 341**

PARADISE REMIXED.
Tracks: / Big fun (Juan's magic remix) / Good life (Steve Silk Hurley remix) / Ain't nobody better (groove corporation remix) / Do you love what you feel (magic Juan's smokin / What'cha gonna do with my lovin' (def mix) / House fever (Duane Bradley remix) / Paradise megamix, The (Only on MC and CD.).
LP: . . . . **XID 81**
MC: . . . . **CXID 81**
LP: . . . . **OVED 342**
MC: . . . . **OVEDC 342**

Inner City Unit

MAXIMUM EFFECT, THE.
LP: . . . . **AALP 5004**
MC: . . . . **ZCAA 5004**

NEW ANATOMY.
Tracks: / Young girls / Beyond the stars / Help sharks / Birdland / Lonesome train / Forbidden planet / Stop in the city / Doctor Strange / Wild hunt / Hectic electric.
LP: . . . . **DM 001**

PRESIDENT'S TAPES, THE.
LP: . . . . **SHARP 031**

PUNKADELIC.
Tracks: / Watching the grass grow / Space invaders / Polythene / Cars eat with autoface / God disco / Disco tango / Gas money / Alright on the flight / Blue rinse haggard robot / Bildeborg.
LP: . . . . **SHARP 103**

Inner Force

EVERLASTING LOVE (See under Deloris) (Deloris & Inner Force).

Inner Sense Percussion

INNER SENSE PERCUSSION (Bring on the Spoons).
MC: . . . . **BIP 303**

SAMBA RAT POSSE.
MC: . . . . **UNKNOWN**

Innerspace

INNERSPACE (Original Soundtrack) (Various artists).
Tracks: / Twistin' the night away: *Stewart, Rod* / Hypnotize me: *Wang Chung* / Is it really love: *Walden*, Narada Michael / Will I ever understand you: *Berlin* / Cupid: *Cooke, Sam* / Let's get small: *Various* artists / Environmental adjust: *Various artists* / Space is a flop: *Various artists* / Gut reaction: *Various artists* / Air supply: *Various artists*.
LP: **4602231**
MC: **4602234**

Innes, Hammond

BLUE ICE, THE See also Stephen Thorne.
MC: . . . . **CAB 342**

LEVKAS MAN.
MCSET: . . . . **CAB 292**

Innes, Michael

LORD MULLION'S SECRET.
MCSET: . . . . **CAT 4029**

Innes, Neil

GO GO, A.
Tracks: / Prologue / Momma bee / Immortal, invisible, God only wise / Topless a go go / Feel no shame / How sweet to be an idiot / Dream / L'amour perdu / Song for Yvonne / This love of ours / Singing a song is easy.
LP: . . . . **LBR 1018**

HOW SWEET TO BE AN IDIOT.
Tracks: / Prologue / Momma B / Immortal invisible, God only wise / Topless-a-go-go / Feel no shame / How sweet to be an idiot / Dream / L'amour Perdu / Song for Yvonne / This love of ours / Singing a song is easy.
LP: . . . . **UAS 29492**

INNES BOOK OF RECORDS.
Tracks: / Here we go again / Montana cafe / All in the name of love / Kenny and Lisa / Ameoba boogie / Theme / Human race / Spontaneous / Love is getting deeper / Etcetera.
LP: **2383556**

OFF THE RECORD.
Tracks: / Libido / City of the angels / One thing on your mind / Woman and the angel, The / Stoned on rock / Knicker elastic / Spaghetti western / Godfrey Daniel / Fortune teller / Them / Time to kill / Rock of ages / Not getting any younger / Take away / Happy ending / Mr. Eurovision / Ungawa / Mother / Burlesque / Down that road.
LP: . . . . **MMC 001**

Innocence

BELIEF.
Tracks: / Silent voice / Let's push it / Reflections / Natural thing / Matter of fact, The / Higher ground / Remember the day / Moving upwards / Come together / Reprise.
LP: . . . . **CTLP 20**
MC: . . . . **ZCTLP 20**

Innocence Mission

INNOCENCE MISSION.
LP: . . . . **AMA 5274**
MC: . . . . **AMC 5274**

UMBRELLA.
LP: **3953621**
MC: **3953624**

Innocence of...(bk)

INNOCENCE OF FATHER BROWN (2), THE (G.K Chesterton) (Hawthorne, Nigel (nar)).
Tracks: / Three tools of death, The / Queer feet, The / Wrong shape, The.
MCSET: **418 057-4**

INNOCENCE OF FATHER BROWN, THE (G.K. Chesterton) (Hawthorne, Nigel (nar)).
Tracks: / Blue cross, The / Flying stars, The / Secret garden.
MCSET: **418 054-4**

Innocent

INNOCENT, THE (Film soundtrack) (Various artists).
LP: . . . . **CIA 5023**
MC: . . . . **CIAK 75023**

Insane Picnic

FOUR DAYS IN APRIL.
MC: . . . . **EBS 3**

Insanity

INSANITY 360 degree music experience (Various artists).
2LP: . . . . **BSR 0067**

Insect

WE CAN TRUST THE INSECT.
LP: . . . . **KK 36**

Insect Trust

INSECT TRUST, THE.
Tracks: / Skin games / Miss fun city / World war 1 song / Special rider blues / Foggy river bridge fly / Been here and gone so soon / Declaration of independence / Walking on nails / Brighter than day / Mountain song / Going home.
LP: . . . . **ED 290**

Inside Movies

INSIDE MOVIES (Film soundtracks) (Various artists).
Tracks: / Just be free: *Various artists* / Outside: *Various artists* / Something's missing in my life: *Various* artists / Beautiful dreamer: *Various artists* / You make it so hard to say no: *Various artists* / Inside moves theme: *Various artists* / Love theme: *Various artists* / It's your move: *Various artists* / I can't tell you why: *Various artists* / What've you got to lose: *Various artists*.
LP: . . . . **K 56901**

Inside Treatment

ISOLATED SUBURBAN PSYCHO KILLERS IN COMA.
LP: **081118**

Insight

INSIGHT.
LP: . . . . **COX 028**

Insignificance

INSIGNIFICANCE (Film soundtrack) (Various artists).
Tracks: / Wild hearts(time): *Orbison, Roy* / When your heart runs out of time: *Gregory, Glen and Claudia Brucken*/ Life goes on: *Russell, Theresa* / Dog of a night, A: *Myers, Stanley* / Relativity 1,2 & 3: *Myers, Stanley*/ Forever(what the hell): *Myers, Stanley* / Remember, remember: *Zimmer, Hans* / B29 (shape of the universe): *Zimmer, Hans* / World of theory: *Zimmer, Hans*.
LP: . . . . **ZTTIQ 4**
MC: . . . . **ZCIQ 4**

Inspector Clouseau

INSPECTOR CLOUSEAU Original soundtrack (Various artists).
LP: . . . . **MCA 25107**
MC: . . . . **MCAC 25107**

Inspector Morse

INSPECTOR MORSE (Music From the TV Series) (Various artists).
LP: . . . . **VTLP 2**
MC: . . . . **VTMC 2**

Inspector Wexford

INSPECTOR WEXFORD - MEANS OF EVIL (Baker, George).
MCSET: . . . . **LFP 7526**

INSPECTOR WEXFORD ON HOLIDAY (see under Rendell, Ruth) (Baker, George).

Inspiral Carpets

BEAST INSIDE, THE.
Tracks: / Caravan / Please be cruel / Born yesterday / Sleep well tonight / Grip / Beast inside / Niagara / Mermaid / Further away / Dreams are all we have.
LP: . . . . **DUNG 14**
MC: . . . . **DUNG 14C**

LIFE.
LP: . . . . **DUNG 008**
MC: . . . . **DUNG 008C**

Inspirational Choir...

HIGHER AND HIGHER.
LP: 4502401
MC: 450240 4

SWEET INSPIRATION.
Tracks: / Sweet inspiration / People get ready / Up where we belong / One love / Jesus dropped the charges / I've got a feeling / You light up my life / Morning has broken / Amazing grace / What a friend we have in Jesus / When He comes / God is / Abide with me.
LP: PRT 10048
MC: 40 10048

Instant Disco

INSTANT DISCO Various artists (Various artists).
LP: NSPL 28216

Instant Funk

FUNK IS ON, THE.
Tracks: / It's cool / Funk is on, The / Funk 'n' roll / You want my love / What can I do for you? / Everybody / Can you see where I'm coming from? / You're not getting older.
LP: SALP 4

GOT MY MIND MADE UP.
Tracks: / Got my mind made up / Crying / Never let it go away / Don't you wanna party / Wide world of sports / Darth Vader / You say you want me to stay / I'll be doggone.
LP: SSLP 1511

INSTANT FUNK.
Tracks: / Blazin' / Who took away the funk? / No stoppin' that rockin' / Smack dab in the middle / You're gonna get yours / Hard day's night, A / Easy come, easy go / I'll be good to you.
LP: XL 13227

Instant Party

JUST ADD WATER.
LP: SNTF 876

Instant Sunshine

INSTANT SUNSHINE LP, THE (Song for Struggling Supergroups).
Tracks: / Worms / When I was in Bombay / Top dogs / Some dancing / Herts is trumps / Doctops / My lawn / Ruthless roues / Lily gliding / Little bit of burgling on the side / Heathrow holiday / Allotment / Kiddie's olympics / Now I'm an adolescent / Tittle tattle rag / Who mowed the lawns of Eden / Bird seed.
LP: NTS 215
MC: TCNTS 215

Insted

WHAT WE BELIEVE.
LP: E 864081

Instigators

IT HAS TO BE SPOTTED.
MC: 96 13

LIVE.
LP: COX 004

LIVE AND LOUD.
LPS: BOXLP 3

NEW OLD NOW.
LP: VILE 14

NOBODY LISTENS ANYMORE.
LP: FISH 11

PHOENIX.
Tracks: / Blind eye / Watch and wait / Hedonism / Computer age / Eye to eye / Rules / American dream / Doomsday plus one / Summer / Dark and lonely.
LP: FISH 13

RECOVERY SESSION.
LP: FC 001

SHOCKGUN.
LP: POS 004

Instrumental...

20 INSTRUMENTAL FAVOURITES (Various artists).
LP: MFP 50546
MC: TCMFP 50546

50 INSTRUMENTAL GREATS (Various artists).
2LP: PDX 1
MCSET: PDXC 1

50 PIANO FAVOURITES (Various artists).
MCSET: MFP 411 539 5
MCSET: TR 1539
MCSET: TR 41153935

DECADE OF INSTRUMENTALS, 1959-1967 (Various artists).
Tracks: / Entry of the gladiators: *Nero & The Gladiators* / Bongo rock: *Jetstreams* / Chariot: *Stoller, Rhet*/ Taboo: *Sounds Incorporated* / Eclipse: *Greenslade, Arthur & The Gee-men* / Paella: *Sunspots* / Grumbling guitar: *Other Two* / Surfside: *Revell, Digger & The Denver Men* / Saturday jump: *Midnight Shift* / Stand up and say that: *Nashville Five* / Night train: *Fifty Fingers Give Guitars* / Stand and deliver: *Snobs*/ Bogey man: *Moontreckers* / I didn't know the gun was loaded: *Cannons* / Fugitive, The: *Thunderbolts*/ Song of Mexico: *Various artists* / Treck to Rome: *Nero & The Gladiators* / More like Nashville: *Nashville Five* / Savage, part 2: *Sneaky Petes* / Pop the whip: *Dynamic Sounds* / Mind reader: *Howard, Johnny, Group*/ Curly: *Bluesbreakers.*
LP: SEE 204

GOLDEN SIXTIES - INSTRUMENTALS ON PARADE (Various artists).
Tracks: / Days of Pearly Spencer: *Various artists* / Friday on my mind: *Various artists* / San Francisco: *Various artists* / You are my world: *Various artists* / Happy together: *Various artists* / Locomotion, The: *Various* artists / Good vibrations: *Various artists* / California dreamin': *Various artists* / I started a joke: *Various artists* / I'll be there: *Various artists* / Massachussettes: *Various artists* / Eloise: *Various artists.*
LP: 625642

GREAT INSTRUMENTALS (Various artists).
LP: ADL 511
MC: ADK 511

IMPRESSIONS (Various artists).
Tracks: / Oxygene (Part IV): *Jarre, Jean Michel* / La serenissima: *Veneziano, Rondo* (Venice in peril.) / Toccata: *Sky* / Chi mai: *Morricone, Ennio* / St. Elsewhere: *Grusin, Dave* / Parisienne walkways: *Moore, Gary*/ Travelling man: *Brown, Duncan & Sebastian Graham-Jones* / Road, The: *Knopfler, Mark* / Howard's way: *May, Simon* / Gentle touch, The: *Webb, Roger* / Robin (the hooded man): *Clannad* / Shadows: *Scott, Tom*/ Black tower, The: *Harvey, Richard* / Merry Christmas Mr. Lawrence: *Various artists* / Axel F.: *Faltermeyer, Harold.*
LP: NE 1346
MC: CE 2346

INSTRUMENTAL COLLECTION (Various artists).
LPS: RML 105
MCSET: RML 4C 105

INSTRUMENTAL COUNTRY, VOL II (Various artists).
LP: CBS 31861

INSTRUMENTAL EXPLOSION (Various artists).
LP: DMLP 401

INSTRUMENTAL GEMS 1959-1970 (Various artists).
LP: NUTM 22

INSTRUMENTAL GOLD (Various artists).
LPS: EGS4 5008
MCSET: EC EGS4 5008

INSTRUMENTAL GREATS (Various artists).
LP: STAR 2341
MC: STAC 2341

INSTRUMENTAL GREATS OF THE 60'S (Various artists).
Tracks: / Walk don't run: *Ventures* / Hawaii five o: *Ventures* / Perfidia: *Ventures* / Breeze and I: *Fentones* / Cruel sea, The: *Dakotas* / Oyeh: *Dakotas* / Let there be drums: *Nelson, Sandy* / Bush fire: *Cannons* / Saturday night at the duckpond: *Cougars* / Summer place, Theme from: *Paramor, Norrie*/ Gypsy beat: *Packabeats* / McDonald's cave: *Piltdown Men* / Nut rocker: *B. Bumble & The Stingers* / Hall of mirrors: *Nu-Notes* / Fury: *Nu-Notes* / Man of mystery: *Shadows* / Scotch on the rocks: *Shadows*/ Hit or miss: *Barry, John Seven* / James Bond theme: *Barry, John Seven* / African waltz: *Dankworth, John*/ Boot Hill: *Federals* / Scorpio: *Scorpions* / Danger man theme: *Red Price Combo, The* / Mad goose: *Beachcombers*/ Bleakhouse: *Gladiators* / Swingin' low: *Outlaws (Group)* / Ambush: *Outlaws (Group)* / Topaz: *Staccato's*/ Magic carpet: *Dakotas* (Available on CD only.) / Mexican: *Fentones* (Available on CD only.) / Big man: *Packabeats*/ Tomorrow's cancelled: *Shadows* (Available on CD only.).
MC: HR 8193

INSTRUMENTAL HITS (VOL.1) (Various artists).
2LP: CR 077
MCSET: CRT 077

INSTRUMENTAL MAGIC (Various artists).
LP: SON 034

INSTRUMENTAL MAGIC VOLS 1&2 (Various artists).
2LP: STAR 2227
MCSET: STAC 2227

INSTRUMENTAL RARITIES (Various artists).
Tracks: / Danger man theme: *Red Price Combo, The* / Bush fire: *Cannons* / Big man: *Packabeats* / Bubble drum: *Thunder Company* / Nola: *Proctor, Judd* / Bat, The: *Krew Kats* / Scorpio: *Scorpions* / Our man in Siberia: *Cougars* / Oyeh: *Dakotas* / Mad goose: *Beachcombers* / Work out: *Flinstones*/ Slippery Jim De Girze: *Bennett, Brian* / Bleakhouse: *Gladiators* / Topaz, The: *Staccato* / Take five: *Fentones* / Boot Hill: *Federals* / Fury: *Nu-Notes* / Rockin' at the Phil: *Scorpions* / Black jackets: *Weedon, Bert* / Peak hour: *Krew Kats.*
LP: SEE 37

INSTRUMENTAL ROCK 1957-65 (Various artists).
Tracks: / Reveille rock: *Johnny & The Hurricanes* / McDonalds cave: *Piltdown Men* / Let there be drums: *Nelson,* Sandy / Perfidia: *Ventures* / You can't sit down (pt.2): *Upchurch, Phil Combo* / Memphis: *Mack, Lonnie*/ Topsy (pt.2): *Cole, Cozy* / Bumble boogie: *Bumble, B & The Stingers* / Raunchy: *Justis, Bill & His Orchestra*/ Bust out: *Busters* / F.B.I.: *Shadows* / Walk don't run: *Barry, John Seven* / Guitar boogie shuffle: *Weedon, Bert* / Mexican: *Fentones* / Saturday nite at the duckpond: *Cougars* / Gypsy beat: *Packabeats*/ Cruel sea: *Dakotas* / Trambone: *Krew Kats* / Swingin' low: *Outlaws (Group)* / Beat girl: *Barry, John Seven & Orchestra.*
LP: MFP 41 5750 1
MC: MFP 41 5750 4

JUKE BOX COLLECTION - SLEEPY SHORES (Instrumental classics) (Various artists).
Tracks: / Il silenzio: *Rosso, Nini* / Aria: *Bilk, Acker* / Cast your fate to the wind: *Sounds Orchestral*/ Cavatina: *Williams, John (Guitarist)* / Eye level: *Park, Simon Orchestra* / Floral dance, The: *Various artists*/ Petite Fleur: *Barber, Chris* / Midnight in Moscow: *Ball, Kenny* / Trudie: *Henderson, Joe* / Z Cars, Theme from: *Keating, Johnny* / Sleepy shores: *Pearson, Johnny* / Zorba's dance: *Minerbi, Marcello.*
MC: OG 2703
LP: OG 1703

JUKE BOX COLLECTION - STRANGER ON THE SHORE (Juke box instrumentals Vol. 2) (Various artists).
Tracks: / Harry Lime theme: *Karas, Anton* / Ebb tide: *Chacksfield, Frank* / Stranger on the shore: *Bilk, Acker* / March of the Siamese children: *Ball, Kenny & His Jazzmen* / Never on a Sunday: *Chaquito* / Desafinado: *Getz, Stan & Charlie Byrd* / Love is blue: *Mauriat, Paul* / Walk in the Black Forest, A: *Jankowski, Horst*/ Maria Elena: *Los Indios Tabajaros* / Sucu sucu: *Johnson, Laurie* / How soon: *Mancini, Henry* / Bye bye blues: *Kaempfert, Bert* / Entertainer, The: *Hamlisch, Marvin* / Galloping home: *London String Chorale.*
LP: OG 1721
MC: OG 2721

LET'S RIDE TO MUSIC (Music for dressage, canters, trots & walks) (Various artists).
Tracks: / Canters medley: *Various artists* / Boots and saddles: *Various artists* / Tanjier horse: *Various artists* / Birdcage walk: *Various artists* / Radetzky march: *Various artists* / Officer of the day: *Various* artists / Musical joke, A: *Various artists* / Flying horse, The: *Various artists* / Children of the regiment: *Various artists* / Poet's march, The: *Various artists* / Trots medley: *Various artists* / Czech polka: *Various artists* / Guildhall: *Various artists* / Ob-la-di Ob-la-da: *Various artists* / Knot's Landing: *Various artists* / Heyken's serenade: *Various artists* / Fehrbelliner reitermarsch: *Various artists* / Agrppa: *Various artists* / Standard of St.George: *Various artists* / Regimental slow march of the Life Guards, The: *Various artists* / March- The Pirates of Penzance: *Various artists.*
MC: ZC BND 7001

LOVE THEMES (Various artists).
MC: AIM 63
MC: AM 63

MAKING TRAX - GREAT INSTRUMENTALS (Various artists).
LP: ZL 72187
MC: ZK 72187

NON STOP TIJUANA 100 Party hits from the man with the golden horn (Various artists).
2LP: RTD 2097
MCSET: 4CRTD 2097

NOVELTY GUITAR INSTRUMENTALS (Various artists).
LP: SNTF 117

PRECIOUS MOMENTS (Various artists).
LP: LPIMP 3
MC: TCIMP 3

PRECIOUS MOMENTS (2) Classic instrumental love songs (Various artists).
Tracks: / Careless whisper: *Various artists* / Smooth operator: *Various artists* / Unconditional love: *Various* artists (Not available on CD.) / No more lonely nights: *Various artists* / Power of love, The: *Various artists*/ Greatest love of all, The: *Various artists* (Not available on CD.) / Easy lover: *Various artists* (Not available on CD.) / To all the girls I've loved before: *Various artists* (Not available on CD.) / Suddenly: *Various artists*(Not available on CD.) / Saving all my love for you: *Various artists* / That's what friends are for: *Various artists*(Not available on CD.) / We are the world: *Various artists* / Girls just want to have fun: *Various artists* (Not available on CD.) / Nikita: *Various artists* / Say you, say me: *Various artists* / Against all odds: *Various* artists / Drive: *Various artists* (Not available on CD.) / I want to know what love is: *Various artists* / I am what I am: *Various artists* (Not available on CD.) / Tonight I celebrate my love: *Various artists* (Not available on CD.) / I just called to say I love you: *Various artists* / Hello: *Various artists* / How will I know: *Various* artists (Not available on CD.) / All night long: *Various artists* / Islands in the stream: *Various artists*/ Every breath you take: *Various artists* (Not available on CD.) / Up where we belong: *Various artists* (Not available on CD.) / Sad songs: *Various artists.*
2LP: STDLP 28
MC: STDMC 28

RHYTHM PIANISTS (Various artists).
Tracks: / Peanut cackle, The: *Herbin, Frank* / Coaxing the piano: *Herbin, Frank* / Scale it down: *O'Neill,* Walker / Dusting the keys: *O'Neill, Walker* / Classicanna: *Siegel, Al* / Whippin' the ivories: *Siegel,* Al / Raie de costa: *Siegel, Al* / Under my umbrella: *Siegel, Al* / Girl in the little green hat: *Siegel,* Al / This is romance: *Green, John W.* / Love locked out: *Green, John W.* / Rhythm of the rain: *Renara*/ I was lucky: *Renara* / Syncopating the classics: *Bradbury, Stan.*
LP: SH 335

ROCKIN' GUITAR INSTRUMENTALS, VOL 2 (Various artists).
LP: 403836

ROIS DE LA GUITARE A DOUZE CORDES, LES (Various artists).
Tracks: / Blues wail: *Various artists* / My little Maggie: *Various artists* / Honey miss me when I'm gone: *Various* artists / Color him folky: *Various artists* / Six by twelve: *Various artists* / Cottonfields: *Various* artists / Nashville: *Various artists* / Twelve string guitar rag: *Various artists* / Bull Durem: *Various artists* / Saint's soul song: *Various artists.*
LP: ARN 33723
MC: ARN 433723

ROMANTIC PIANO MUSIC (Various artists).
LP: ADL 508
MC: ADK 508

SENTIMENTAL GUITAR (Various artists).
MC: BRC 2521

SHADOWS GUITAR GREATS (Various artists).
MC: AM 50

SINGALONG BANJO PARTY (Various artists).
Tracks: / Baby face: *Various artists* / Toot toot tootsie: *Various artists* / Let's all go down The Strand: *Various* artists / You are my sunshine: *Various artists* / Pennies from Heaven: *Various artists* / Any old iron: *Various* artists / Bye bye blackbird: *Various artists* / Mammy: *Various artists* / Underneath the arches: *Various* artists / Shine on harvest moon: *Various artists* / On Mother Kelly's doorstep: *Various artists* / Birdie song, The: *Various artists.*
2LP: PLAT 01
MCSET: PLAC 01

STEEL GUITAR CLASSICS (Various artists).
LP: OT 113

SYNTHESIZER ALBUM (Various artists).
MC: STAC 2371
LP: STAR 2371

TEN LONG FINGERS (Various artists).
LP: KEY 1590

TENNESSEE STRINGS (Various artists).
LP: ROUNDER 1033

THEMES - SPECTACULAR (Various artists).
LP: ADL 510
MC: ADK 510

TRUMPET ALBUM (Various artists).
LP: . . . . SJL 2237

TRUMPET KINGS (Various artists).
LP: 231 0754
MC: K10 754

TUTTI'S TROMBONES (inc. Joe Howard) (Various artists).
LP: . . . . BVS 2003

TUTTI'S TRUMPETS (inc.Peter Candoli) (Various artists).
LP: . . . . BVS 2002

WINNERS' PIECES (9th Annual synthesizer tape contest) (Various artists).
Tracks: / Ribesurito: *Morimoto, Kiyoto* / Sign of four: *Godsall, Stephen* / Demon's forest: *Maruyama, Tetsuji*/ Die Alpen: *Zimmerma, Friedrich.E* / War and dawn: *Iwamoto, Hirotaka* / Alla hornpipe: *Synthesiser Orchestra* of the Tado Junior High-School / Fugitive, The: *Post, Peter* / Toys dance: *Sato, Masayuki* / Lion's dance: *Kato, Takashi* / Theme: *Terada, Soichi* / Motivation: *Tani, Risa* / Waltzing cat: *Hoshide, Takashi*/ I know I've known you before: *Cook, Perry R* / Honey tears: *Francis, Rimbert*.
MC: . . . . STC 8591

WINNERS' PIECES (8th Annual synthesizer tape contest) (Various artists).
Tracks: / Brainstorming: *Various artists* / Poland: *Various artists* / Din a mix: *Various artists* / Synthetic sequences from River Amazon: *Various artists* / Landscape I: *Various artists* / Greece '84: *Various* artists / Golden ratio, The: *Various artists* / Callisto IV: *Various artists* / Kattingu (etude): *Various* artists / Airport: *Various artists* / Jinjiro jinjiro: *Various artists* / Reality in a fantasy ... and I: *Various artists* / Walk in the great city, The: *Various artists* / Alone in a bathtub: *Various artists*/ Mindscape III: *Various artists* / Animal farm: *Various artists*.
MC: . . . . STC 8261
MC: . . . . STC 8371
MC: . . . . STC 8481

WIPE OUT (Classic Instrumentals) (Various artists).
Tracks: / Wipe out: *Surfaris* / Rebel rouser: *Eddy, Duane* / Nut rocker: *Bumble, B & The Stingers* / Memphis: *Mack, Lonnie* / Sleepwalk: *Santo & Johnny* / Rinky dink: *Cortez, Dave 'Baby'* / Let there be drums: *Nelson, Sandy* / Telstar: *Tornados* / Tuff: *Cannon, Ace* / Pipeline: *Chantays* / Because they're young: *Eddy, Duane* / Teen beat: *Nelson, Sandy* / Red river rock: *Johnny & The Hurricanes* / Raunchy: *Justis, Bill* / Beatnik fly: *Johnny & The Hurricanes*.
LP: . . . . OCN 2005 WL
MC: . . . . OCN 2005 WK

WIPEOUT (Various artists).
LP: . . . . LPIMP 5

WIPEOUT - 20 INSTRUMENTAL GREATS (Various artists).
Tracks: / Tequila: *Champs* / Apache: *Shadows* / Walk don't run: *Ventures* / On the rebound: *Cramer, Floyd* / Let there be drums: *Nelson, Sandy* / Telstar: *Tornados* / Dance with the guitar man: *Eddy, Duane*/ Wipe out: *Surfaris* / Diamonds: *Harris, Jet & Tony Meehan* / Have naguila: *Various artists* / Time is tight: *Booker T & The MGs* / Red river rock: *Johnny & The Hurricanes* / Hit and miss: *Barry, John Seven*/ Nut rocker: *B. Bumble & The Stingers* / Pipeline: *Chantays* / Cruel sea: *Dakotas* / Albatross: *Fleetwood* Mac / Sabre dance: *Love Sculpture* / Shaft, Theme from: *Hayes, Isaac* / Groovin' with Mr Bloe: *Bloe, Mr*.
LP: . . . . LPIMP 2
MC: . . . . TCIMP 2

Instrumentally Yours

INSTRUMENTALLY YOURS (Various artists).
2LP: . . . . CBD 2003
MCSET: . . . . ZCCBD 2003

Insurrection

INSURRECTION.
LP: . . . . VILE 009

Integrity

INTEGRITY COLLECTION, THE (Various artists).
LP: . . . . IR 013
MC: . . . . IR 013MC

Intelligent Hoodlum

INTELLIGENT HOODLUM, THE.
LP: 3953111 1
MC: 3953111 4

Intence

TRIADE.
LP: . . . . SKY 100

Intense Degree

WAR IN MY HEAD.
LP: . . . . MOSH 9

Intense Heat

HOT.
LP: . . . . GS 2288

Intercommunal Music

INTERCOMMUNAL MUSIC Various artists (Various artists).
LP: . . . . SR 10010

Inter-Faith...

TRY HIM (Inter-Faith Community Choir).
Tracks: / Try Him / Crown for you, A / For all these blessings / Victory shall be mine / Near the cross / Thy will be done / I'm not ashamed / God will see you through / There's not a friend / Only God.
LP: . . . . MIR 5023
MC: . . . . MIR 5023MC

Intergalactic Touring

INTERGALACTIC TOURING BAND.
LP: . . . . CDS 4009

Interiors

INTERIORS.
Tracks: / Interiors.
LP: . . . . TAC 1047

International Beat

HITTING LINE, THE.
Tracks: / Headmans plans / Rocksteady / Making plans / One more chance / Danny boy / Silver bullet / Taking the pills / Stand and be counted / Are you ready / Hard world.
LP: . . . . BBSLP 009
MC: . . . . BBSMC 009

International Blue Duo

INTRODUCING.
Tracks: / Blues for real / Stanley T / Saxophone sermon / Night train / New town / Summertime / Hot cha / Please send me someone to love / 426 West Briar.
LP: . . . . CCR 1007

International

F.... BASTARDS (International Breakdown Kommando).
LP: . . . . UNKNOWN

International Hostage

EVERYBODY'S GOTTA LEARN SOMETIME.
LP: . . . . WKFMLP 155
MC: . . . . WKFMMC 155

International Jazz

INTERNATIONAL JAZZ BAND VOL. 1.
LP: . . . . GHB 20

INTERNATIONAL JAZZ BAND VOL. 2.
LP: . . . . GHB 21

International Jazz

IN NEW YORK 1956/57.
LP: . . . . SW 8416

IN PARIS 1956.
LP: . . . . SW 8407

International Pop

AT LAST 27 NON-STOP CLASSICS (International Pop Orchestra).
LP: 2870 387

International Pop All

PERCUSSION AROUND THE WORLD (International Pop All Stars).
LP: . . . . PFS 34009

International Rescue

LEATHER JACKET.
LP: . . . . CR 001

International

SIX WINDS, THE (Elephants Can Dance).
LP: 3041

International

SAFE AT HOME (See Parsons, Gram) (Parsons, Gram International Submarine Band).

International Velvet

INTERNATIONAL VELVET Original soundtrack (Various artists).
LP: 2315 400

Interns

DETOUR.
LP: . . . . BR 1003

Interplanetary Sound

CLOSE ENCOUNTERS (Interplanetary Sound Orchestra).
LP: . . . . SHM 949
MC: . . . . DMTK 2002

Interview

BIG OCEANS.
LP: . . . . V 2123

SNAKES AND LOVERS.
Tracks: / Gift / Hide and seek / It's over now / Conqueror, The / Yes man / Style on Seaview / Adventurers / I hope it's me / Crossing borders / Until I hold her / Union men.
LP: . . . . V 2157

Intervista

INTERVISTA (Film Soundtrack) (Various artists).
Tracks: / Prologo: *Various artists* / Cincetta ore nova: *Various artists* / Ritornello dell intervista: *Various* artists / Clowns: *Various artists* / Slow dell intervista: *Various artists* / Il tranvetto azzurro: *Various* artists / Swing dell intervista: *Various artists* / Il bidone: *Various artists* / La marcetta di nino rota: *Various artists* / Lo sceicco bianco: *Various artists* / Cerco la titinia: *Various artists* / La cioria di cinecitta: *Various artists* / Rock mimesis: *Various artists* / Anita e marchello: *Various artists*/ La dolce vita: *Various artists* / Dia salgariana: *Various artists* / El mercato persiano: *Various artists*/ Il tango dell capinere: *Various artists* / Imperial: *Various artists* / Tea for two: *Various artists*/ Rock mimesis: *Various artists* / Tuttie al trucco: *Various artists* / Oh akariu: *Various artists* / Dove sta zaza: *Various artists* / Toro seduto: *Various artists* / Smack smack smacchiatut: *Various artists*/ Il bidone: *Various artists* / Epilogo: *Various artists*.
LP: . . . . V 2443
MC: . . . . TCV 2443

Intifida

INTIFIDA (Various artists).
LP: . . . . K 031 116

Inti-Illimani

A VOS TE H'AI PESAR (See under Guamary).

CHILE.
LP: . . . . XTRA 1152

IMAGINATION.
LP: . . . . RR 8505

PALIMPSESTO.
LP: . . . . RR 3400

RETURN OF THE CONDOR.
LP: . . . . REH 515
MC: . . . . ZCR 515

Intimate Moments

INTIMATE MOMENTS (see under "Peg" - cat.no. TER 1024) (Various artists).

Intimate Obsessions

EREBUS TO HADES.
LP: . . . . TMLP 11

Intimate Strangers

CHARM.
Tracks: / Let go / In the wilderness / Flame on / Deliverance / Child of the dust / Struck by lightning / My brilliant career / Raise the dragon / Blue hour / What are we waiting for.
LP: . . . . MIRF 1007
MC: . . . . MIRFC 1007

Into A Circle

ASSASSINS.
Tracks: / Beneath Michail / Over and over / Swinging tree,the / Elim / Forever / Allah Akhbar / Tender skin / Evergreen / Assassins / Seraphin Town.
LP: . . . . ABT 018

Into Paradise

CHURCHTOWN.
Tracks: / Rain comes down / Burns my skin / Yesterday's men / I'm still waiting / Winter / Bring me up / All down from here / Angel / Dreaming / Dive / Tears in your eyes / Gently falls.
LP: . . . . CHEN 18
MC: . . . . ZCHEN 18

UNDER THE WATER.
Tracks: / Bring me closer / Here with you / Red light / Pleasure is you, The / Circus came to town, The / Bring me closer (version) / World won't stop, The / Hearts and flowers / Blue moon express / Say goodnight / Beautiful day / Going home.
LP: . . . . SETLP 1

Into The Night

INTO THE NIGHT (Film soundtrack) (Various artists).
Tracks: / Into the night: *Various artists* / My Lucille: *Various artists* / In the midnight hour: *Various* artists / Enter Shaheen: *Various artists* / Century city chase: *Various artists* / Don't make me sorry: *Labelle, Patti* / Keep it light: *Houston, Thelma* / Let's get it on: *Gaye, Marvin* / I can't help myself: *Four Tops*.
LP: . . . . MCF 3269
MC: . . . . MCFC 3269
LP: . . . . MCL 1828
MC: . . . . MCLC 1828

INTO THE NIGHT, THEME FROM (See under King, B.B.) (King, B.B.).

Into The Woods

INTO THE WOODS (Original Broadway Cast) (Various artists).
Tracks: / Act 1 prologue: *Various artists* / Into the woods: *Various artists* / Cinderella at the grave: *Various* artists / Hello little girl: *Various artists* / I guess this is goodbye: *Various artists* / Maybe they're magic: *Various artists* / I know things now: *Various artists* / Very nice prince, A: *Various artists*/ First midnight: *Various artists* / Giants in the sky: *Various artists* / Agony: *Various artists* / It takes two: *Various artists* / Stay with me: *Various artists* / On the steps of the palace: *Various artists*/ Ever after: *Various artists* / Act 2 prologue: *Various artists* / So happy: *Various artists* / Lament: *Various artists* / Any moment: *Various artists* / Moments in the woods: *Various artists* / Your fault: *Various artists* / Last midnight: *Various artists* / No more: *Various artists* / No one is alone: *Various artists* / Finale: *Various artists*.
LP: . . . . BL 86796
MC: . . . . BK 86796

INTO THE WOODS (Original London Cast) (Various artists).
Tracks: / Once upon a time: *Various artists* / Into the woods: *Various artists* / Fly bird, back to the sky: *Various* artists / Witch's entrance: *Various artists* / Jack, Jack Jack, head in the sack: *Various artists* / You wish to have the curse reversed?: *Various artists* / Ladies, our carriage waits: *Various artists* / Curse is on my house, The: *Various artists* / Into the woods (2): *Various artists* / Cinderella at the grave: *Various artists*/ Hello, little girl: *Various artists* / I guess this is goodbye: *Various artists* / Maybe they're magic: *Various* artists / Our little world: *Various artists* / I know things now: *Various artists* / Very nice prince, A: *Various artists* / First midnight: *Various artists* / Giants in the sky: *Various artists* / Agony: *Various artists* / It takes two: *Various artists* / Stay with me: *Various artists* / On the steps of the palace: *Various* artists / Ever after: *Various artists* / So happy: *Various artists* / Agony: *Various artists* / Lament: *Various artists* / Any moment: *Various artists* / Moments in the woods: *Various artists* / Your fault: *Various artists* / Last midnight: *Various artists* / No more: *Various artists* / No one is alone: *Various artists* / Children will listen: *Various artists*.
MC: . . . . RK 60752

Intolerance Tape

INTOLERANCE TAPE (Various artists).
MC: . . . . BLUURG 069

Intransit

OUT OF THE DARK.
Tracks: / Divided, The / Visions of blue / I want / News, not history / In transit.
MC: . . . . PCN 108

Intrinsic

INTRINSIC.
LP: 8856182431

Introspection

INTROSPECTION various artists (Various artists).
Tracks: / Body and soul: *Various artists* / Louise: *Various artists* / Introspection: *Various artists*/ We speak: *Various artists* / Strength and sanity: *Various artists* / 'S wonderful: *Various artists*/ Into the orbit: *Various artists* / Race for space: *Various artists* / II.V.I: *Various artists*.
LP: . . . . NW 275

Intruder

HIGHER FORM OF KILLING, A.
Tracks: / Time of trouble / Martyr, The / Genetic genocide / Second chance / (I'm not your) stepping stone / Killing winds / Sentence is death, The / Agents of the dark (MIB) / Antipathy.
LP: . . . . RO 94521

INTRUDER.
LPPD: . . . . IW 1024

LIVE TO DIE.
LP: . . . . IW 1023

PSYCHO SAVANT.
LP: . . . . ZORRO 25
MC: . . . . TZORRO 25

Intruders

WHO DO YOU LOVE (See under Rae, Fonda - Touch Me) (Rae, Fonda & Intruders).

Inuit Games & Songs

INUIT GAMES AND SONGS (Various artists).
LP: . . . . G 1036
MC: . . . . G 4036

Invader

WALK AND WINE.
Tracks: / Walk and wine.
LP: . . . . **SOT 022**

Invaders

TESTCARD.
Tracks: / Magic mirror / Searching / Japanese dream / Personality profile / Only a man / Backstreet romeo / Young mistake / Spirit on the ground / Second choice / Intermission / Rock methodology / Wheels of fortune.
LP: **2383 589**

Invaders Of The Heart

WITHOUT JUDGEMENT.
LP: . . . . **KKUK 001**

Invaders Steelband

DISTANT HORSES.
LP: **6.22846**

GIMME DAT.
LP: **6.23422**

Invasion U.S.A

INVASION U.S.A (Film soundtrack) (Various artists).
LP: . . . . **A 285**
MC: . . . . **C 285**

Investigation Of A...

INVESTIGATION OF A CITIZEN ABOVE SUSPICION (Film soundtrack) (Various artists).
LP: **803036**

Investigators

FIRST CASE.
LP: . . . . **LP 101**

Invisible Limits

CONSCIOUS STATE, A.
Tracks: / Golden dreams / Love will tear us apart / No doubts / I want you / Natalie's / No tears / In a dream / Kill me dearly / Power to survive.
LP: . . . . **FUNFACL 3920**
MC: . . . . **FUNFACMC 3920**

Invisible Man (bk)

INVISIBLE MAN By H.G.Wells (Harper, Gerald).
MC: . . . . **PTB 624**

Invisible Man's Band

INVISIBLE MAN'S BAND.
Tracks: / Full moon / All night thing / X country / 9 x's out of ten / Rent strike / Love can't come/love has come.
LP: . . . . **ILPS 9537**

Invitation To The ...

INVITATION TO THE DANCE Original soundtrack (Various artists).
LP: . . . . **MCA 25037**
MC: . . . . **MCAC 25037**

INXS

INXS.
LP: **8387761**
MC: **8387764**
LP: **838 925 1**
MC: **838 925 4**

INXS BOX SET.
LPS: **838 607 1**
MCSET: **838 607 4**

INXS: INTERVIEW PICTURE DISC.
LPPD: . . . . **BAK 2093**

INXS TALK (Interview Album).
LPPD: . . . . **BAK 6002**

INXSIVE.
Tracks: / Learn to smile / Wishy washy / Simple Simon / Loved one / Just keep walking.
LP: . . . . **SP 245**
MC: . . . . **SPK 245**

KICKS.
Tracks: / Guns in the sky / New sensation / Devil inside / Need you tonight / Mediate / Loved one / Wild life / Never tear us apart / Mystify / Kicks / Calling all nations / Tiny daggers.
LP: . . . . **MERH 114**
MC: . . . . **MERHC 114**
LPPD: **255080 6**
LPPD: . . . . **MERHP 114**

LISTEN LIKE THIEVES.
Tracks: / What you need / Listen like thieves / Kiss the dirt / Shine like it does / Good and bad times / Biting bullets / This time / Three sisters / Same direction / One x one / Red red sun.
LP: . . . . **MERH 82**
MC: . . . . **MERHC 82**

LOW DOWN UNDER.
LP: . . . . **POW 004**

SHABOOH SHOOBAH.
LP: **8210841**
LP: . . . . **PRICE 94**
MC: . . . . **PRIMC 94**

SWING, THE.
Tracks: / Original sin / Melting in the sun / Send a message / Dancing on the jetty / Swing, The / Johnson's aeroplane / Love is (what I say) / Face the change / Burn for you / All the voices.
LP: . . . . **MERL 39**
MC: . . . . **MERLC 39**

UNDERNEATH THE COLOURS.
Tracks: / Stay young / Horizon / Big go go / Underneath the colours / Fair weather ahead / Night of rebellion / Follow / Barbarian / What would you do? / Just to learn again.
LP: . . . . **RCALP 3058**
LP: **8387771**
MC: **8387774**

X.
Tracks: / Suicide blonde / Disappear / Stairs, The / Faith in each other / By my side / Lately / Who pays the price / Know the difference / Bitter tears / On my way / Hear that sound.
LP: **8466681**
MC: **8466684**

Inyimbo

SONGS OF THE BEMBA PEOPLE OF ZAMBIA.
LP: . . . . **ER 1203**

Iona

IONA.
LP: . . . . **CM 001**

Iona & Andy

ACROSS THE MOUNTAIN.
Tracks: / Everything but love / Part of your world / Remembering / Going gone / Even now / I'm a country girl / Across the mountain / Back on my mind again / Eyes of a child / You can take the wings off me / Heading West / Daddy's hands.
LP: . . . . **BGE LP 1003**
MC: . . . . **BGE C 1003**

Ionatos, Angelique

SAPPHO DE MYTILENE.
Tracks: / Sappho de mytilene.
MC: . . . . **AUA 53011**

Ipetty Sipetty

IPETTY SIPETTY.
MC: **45 181**

Ipi Tombi

IPI TOMBI Original South African stage (Various artists).
LP: . . . . **BAR 90026**

IPI TOMBI (ORIGINAL STAGE PRODUCTION EXTRACTS) (Various artists).
LP: . . . . **GALD 26000**
MC: . . . . **GALDTR 26000**

IPI TOMBI (STAGE CAST RECORDING) (Various artists).
LP: . . . . **BELD 23009**
MC: . . . . **BELD 423009**

Ippu Do

LUNATIC MENU.
Tracks: / Morning menu / Electric doll / Sumire / September love / Mysterious night / I love you / German road / Radio cosmos / Time of the season / Moonlight love call / Radio fantasy / Lunatic guitar.
LP: . . . . **EPC 25139**

RADIO FANTASY.
Tracks: / Radio cosmos / Time of the season / Radio fantasy / Yomotolawaiya / China step / Radio Japan / Chinese reggae / Morning menu / Magic box / Mission impossible / Dublin radio / Listen to me / I need you.
LP: . . . . **EPC 85395**

I.Q.

ARE YOU SITTING COMFORTABLY?.
Tracks: / War heroes / Drive on / Nostalgia / Falling apart at the seams / Sold on you / Through my fingers / Wurensh / Nothing at all.
LP: **836 429 1**
MC: **836 429 4**

LIVING PROOF.
LP: . . . . **SAMR 045**

NOMZAMO.
Tracks: / No love lost / Promises (as the years go by) / Nomzamo / Still life / Passing strangers / Human nature / Screaming / Common ground.
LP: . . . . **VERH 43**
MC: . . . . **VERHC 43**

TALES FROM THE LUSH ATTIC.
LP: . . . . **MAJ 1001**

WAKE, THE.
LP: . . . . **SAH 136**
MC: . . . . **SAH 136C**

IQ6

IQ6.
LP: . . . . **IQ 6**
MC: . . . . **IQC 6**

Irakere

CATALINA.
Tracks: / Aguanile bonko / Juana 1600 / El tata / Preludio a catalina / Rucu rucu a santa clara.
LP: **1115955**

CULPA DEL GUAO.
Tracks: / Homenaje / Bacalao con pan / Baila mi ritmo / Por culpa del guao / Santtaguero.
LP: **1019577**
LP: **15957**

IN LONDON.
Tracks: / Bilando Asi / Johanna / Estela va a estallar / Lo que va a paser / Duke, The.
LP: . . . . **JHR 005**

LA CHEMIN DE LA COLLINE.
LP: . . . . **EGR 6103**

LEGENDARY IRAKERE LIVE IN LONDON VOL 2, THE.
LP: . . . . **JHR 009**

MISA NEGRA (AFRICAN MASS).
LP: **15971**

TIERRA EN TRANCE.
LP: . . . . **EGR 6111**

Iran

FOLK MUSIC OF IRAN (Various artists).
LP: . . . . **LLST 7261**

LIVING TRADITION-MUSIC FROM IRAN (Various artists).
LP: . . . . **ZFB 51**

PERSIAN HERITAGE, A (Classical music of Iran) (Various artists).
LP: . . . . **H 72060**

SANTUR RECITAL VOL. 1 Mahur, Bayat-e, Esfehan, Homayun Shustari (Various artists).
LP: . . . . **LLST 7135**
MC: . . . . **LLCT 7135**

SANTUR RECITAL VOL. 2 Afshari, Dashti, Segab, Chahargah (Various artists).
LP: . . . . **LLST 7165**

SANTUR RECITAL VOL. 3 Dashti, Shue, Abu-Ata Afshari (Various artists).
LP: . . . . **LLST 7166**

Irby, Joyce

MAXIMUM THRUST (Irby, Joyce Fenderella).
Tracks: / Mr. D.J. I'm available / She's not my lover / I love you / Let's do it / Maximum thrust / Guardian angel / I'll be there / Go go girl.
LP: . . . . **ZL 72662**
MC: . . . . **ZK 72662**

Ireland

9 IRISH TRADITIONAL MUSIC CHAMPIONS PLAY 16 OF THEIR BEST (Various artists).
LP: . . . . **SOLP 1023**
MC: . . . . **COX 1023**

12 OF THE BEST IRISH REBEL SONGS (Various artists).
LP: . . . . **CSDBL 515**

16 REBEL SONGS VOL.1 (Various artists).
MC: . . . . **DOCB 7030**

16 REBEL SONGS VOL.2 (Various artists).
MC: . . . . **DOCB 7031**

16 SONGS OF ROMANCE (Various artists).
MC: . . . . **RITZSC 399**
LP: . . . . **SPC 399**

18 IRISH PUB SONGS (Various artists).
MC: . . . . **CHRL 178**

18 IRISH REBEL SONGS (Various artists).
LP: . . . . **CSDBL 510**

18 IRISH REBEL SONGS (Various artists).
LP: . . . . **SDBL 510**

18 MORE IRISH REBEL SONGS (Various artists).
LP: . . . . **CSDBL 521**

20 GREAT IRISH DRINKING SONGS (Various artists).
MC: . . . . **DOCM 5027**

20 IRISH HITS Various artists (Various artists).
LP: . . . . **HPE 632**

20 IRISH REQUESTS (Various artists).
MCSET: . . . . **DBXC 006**

20 MORE IRISH DRINKING SONGS (Various artists).
MC: . . . . **DOCM 5028**

20 REQUESTED BALLADS OF IRELAND VOL2 (Various artists).
Tracks: / Boston Burglar: *Various artists* / Enniskillen: *Various artists* / Mursheen durkin: *Various artists*.
LP: . . . . **STOL 132**

20 REQUESTED BALLADS OF IRELAND VOL 2 (Various artists).
MC: . . . . **CT 132**

20 REQUESTED BALLADS OF IRELAND - VOL.4 (Various artists).
Tracks: / If we only had old Ireland over here: *Various artists* / Mountains of Mourne: *Various artists* / Slievenamon: *Various artists* / Dublin in the rare oul times: *Various artists* / Cottage by the Lee: *Various artists*/ Hills of Glenswilly: *Various artists* / Moonshinner: *Various artists* / Mulroy Bay: *Various artists*/ When you and I were young Maggie: *Various artists* / Bunch of thyme: *Various artists* / Eileen: *Various* artists / Boys from County Mayo: *Various artists* / Gallant John Joe: *Various artists* / Emigrant's letter: *Various artists* / Galway Bay: *Various artists* / Claddagh ring: *Various artists* / Goodbye Johnny dear: *Various artists* / Westmeath bachelor: *Various artists* / Gentle mother: *Various artists* / I'll take you home again Kathleen: *Various artists*.
LP: . . . . **HRL 193**
MC: . . . . **CHRL 193**

20 REQUESTED BALLADS OF IRELAND VOL.1 (Various artists).
MC: . . . . **CT 123**

25 IRISH REPUBLICAN SONGS (Various artists).
Tracks: / Ireland's 32: *Various artists* / Gra mo chroi: *Various artists* / Take me home to Mayo: *Various artists* / Lonely woods of Upton: *Various artists* / They were soldiers everyone: *Various artists* / Four green fields: *Various artists* / Fields of Athenry: *Various artists* / Dying rebel: *Various artists* / Lid of me granny's bin: *Various artists* / I.R.E.L.A.N.D.: *Various artists* / Sean South: *Various artists* / Ireland united: *Various artists* / West awake: *Various artists* / Shall my soul pass through old Ireland: *Various* artists / Boys of the old brigade: *Various artists* / Off to Dublin in the green: *Various artists* / Lough Sheelin eviction, The: *Various artists* / Little armalite: *Various artists* / James Connolly: *Various artists*/ Broad black brimmer: *Various artists* / Kevin Barry: *Various artists* / Sniper's promise: *Various artists*/ Patriot game: *Various artists* / Only our rivers run free: *Various artists* / Nation once again, A: *Various artists*.
MC: . . . . **CKOL 602**

ANOTHER FEAST OF IRISH FOLK (See under Folk) (Various artists).

BEST IRISH BALLADS (Various artists).
MCSET: . . . . **DBXC 003**

BEST OF DOLPHIN: FAV. IRISH BALLADS (see under Dolphin (label) (Various artists).

BIT OF BLARNEY, A (20 Irish favourites) (Various artists).
Tracks: / Old Claddagh Ring: *Various artists* / Rose of Arranmore: *Various artists* / If we only had old Ireland over here: *Various artists* / Bunch of thyme: *Various artists* / Galway shawl: *Various artists* / Old bog road: *Various artists* / Three leaf shamrock: *Various artists* / Rare ould times: *Various artists*/ Rocks of Bawn: *Various artists* / Nora: *Various artists* / Rose of Tralee, The: *Various artists* / Slaney Valley: *Various artists* / Where the blarney roses grow: *Various artists* / Forty shades of green: *Various* artists / My Lagan love: *Various artists* / Rose of Mooncoin: *Various artists* / Hills of Kerry: *Various* artists / In Dublin's fair city: *Various artists* / Come back Paddy Reilly to Ballyjamesduff: *Various artists*/ Danny boy: *Various artists*.
LP: . . . . **DOLS 2004**
MC: . . . . **DOCS 2004**

BLUEBELL AND THE SHAMROCK (Various artists).
LP: . . . . **WGR 027**
MC: . . . . **CWGR 027**

BRASS FIDDLE (Various artists).
Tracks: / Muilleann Na Maidi: *Various artists* / Vincent Campbell's mazurkas: *Various artists* / Marine, The: *Various artists* / Drowsy Maggie: *Various artists* / Doodley doodley dank: *Various artists* / Frost is all over, The: *Various artists* / Low Highland, The: *Various artists* / Mary o' The Wisp: *Various artists*/ King George IV: *Various artists* / Bagpipe March: *Various artists* / Wild Irishman, The: *Various artists*/ Johnny Boyle's Jig: *Various artists* / Biddy of Muckross: *Various artists* / Jackson's bean a'ti ar lar: *Various* artists / Lancers: *Various artists* / Johnny Ward's Paddy Bartley's: *Various artists* / La Marseillaise: *Various* artists / Miss Drummond of Perth: *Various artists* / Rakish Paddy: *Various artists* / Cat that kittled in Jamie's wig, The: *Various artists* / Kilcar Mazurka, The: *Various artists* / On the road from glen to carrick: *Various artists* / Old

wheel of fortune, The: *Various artists* / James Byrne's mazurka: *Various artists*/ Seamas O'Beirn's Highland: *Various artists* / Ri Mhim Na Salach: *Various artists* / Curly haired boy, The: *Various artists.*
LP: CC 44
MC: 4CC 44

BREEZE FROM ERIN (Irish folk music on wind instruments) (Various artists).
LP: 12T 184

CEILIDH TIME IN IRELAND (Various artists).
Tracks: / St.Patrick's day: *Various artists* / Drops of brandy: *Various artists* / High cauled cap, The: *Various artists* / Siamasa beirte: *Various artists* / Sweets of May: *Various artists* / Kane's march: *Various artists* / Siege of Ennis: *Various artists* / Rocks of Cashel: *Various artists* / Farewell to whiskey: *Various artists* / Slip jigs: *Various artists* / Two steps: *Various artists.*
LP: G 009

CEILIDH TIME IN IRELAND (Various artists).
MCSET: DBXC 005
LP: STAL 8002

CELEBRATION OF DUBLIN, A (24 Street Ballads From the Fair City) (Various artists).
2LP: DOLD 1988
MCSET: DOLDC 1988

CLADDAGH'S CHOICE (Anthology of traditional Irish music) (Various artists).
LP: CC 40
MC: 4CC 40

CLASSIC COLLEENS (Various artists).
Tracks: / Bunch of violets blue: *Breen, Ann* / Dublin in my tears: *McCann, Susan* / In the gloaming: *Hunniford,* Gloria / Softly softly: *Dana* / Die for love: *Keane, Dolores* / Live not where I love: *Danann, De*/ Way old friends do, The: *Begley, Philomena* / Morning has broken: *O'Hara, Mary* / Boys from County Armagh: *Gallagher,* Bridie / Love someone like me: *Duff, Mary* / Girl from Donegal: *Margo* / Pal of my cradle days: *Gloria*/ Last waltz, The: *Rose Marie* / When I grow too old to dream: *Durkin, Kathy.*
LP: KNLP 14003
MC: KNMC 14003

CLASSIC IRISH BALLADS (Various artists).
Tracks: / Grace: *McCann, Jim* / My Donegal shore: *O'Donnell, Daniel* / I'll take you home again Kathleen: *Fureys &* Davey Arthur / Mountains of Mourne: *Irish Mist* / Rose of Allendale: *Foster & Allen* / Those endearing young charms: *Murray, Bryan* / Molly Malone: *Lynch, Joe* / Tara Hill: *Fureys & Davey Arthur* / Old rustic bridge: *Morriseys* / Song for Mira: *Grace, Brendan* / Limerick you're a lady: *Allen, Dennis* / Sometimes when we touch: *Dolan, Joe* / Galway Bay: *Lynch, Lee* / From Clare to here: *McTell, Ralph.*
LP: KNLP 14002
MC: KNMC 14002

CLASSIC IRISH COUNTRY (Various artists).
Tracks: / Summertime in Ireland: *O'Donnell, Daniel* / Blanket on the ground: *Begley, Philomena* / Rose of my heart: *Flavin, Mick* / Close all the honky tonks: *McCann, Susan* / I'm going to hire a wino: *Dallas, T.R.* / Old rugged cross, The: *Irish Mist* / Red river valley: *Foster & Allen* / Back in love by Monday: *Lynam, Ray*/ She's got you: *Duff, Mary* / Thank God I'm a country boy: *Hogan, John* / Heartaches by the number: *Cunningham,* Larry / One day at a time: *Gloria* / Hills around Clonmell, The: *Coll, Brian* / Simply divine: *Begley, Philomena & Ray Lynam.*
LP: KNLP 14004
MC: KNMC 14004

CLASSIC IRISH FOLK (Various artists).
Tracks: / Raglan Road: *McCann, Jim* / Little grey home in the West: *Reilly, Paddy* / Flight of earls: *Dublin City* Ramblers / Wild rover: *Dubliners* / Mouth music: *Keane, Dolores* / Red is the rose: *Makem, Tommy* & Liam Clancy / Green fields of France: *Fureys & Davey Arthur* / McAlpine's fusiliers: *Dubliners* / Maggie: *Fureys & Davey Arthur* / Sweet forget me not: *Morriseys* / Dublin in the rare ol' times: *Grace, Brendan*/ Fields of Athenry: *Daniels, Roly* / Setting, The: *McTell, Ralph* / Song for Ireland, A: *Danann, De.*
LP: KNLP 14005
MC: KNMC 14005

CLASSIC IRISH LOVE SONGS (Various artists).
Tracks: / When you were sweet sixteen: *Fureys & Davey Arthur* / Danny boy: *O'Donnell, Daniel* / Rose of Mooncoin: *Foster & Allen* / She moved through the fair: *Durkin, Kathy* / Ringsend Rose: *Grace, Brendan* / Village of Astee, The: *Stevens, Tony* / My Lagan love: *McCann, Jim* / I will love you all my life: *Foster & Allen*/ Cliffs of Dooneen: *Dana* / Secret love: *Dolan, Joe* / Brown eyes: *Hogan, John* / Tears on the telephone: *Curtin, Glen* / Gentle Annie: *Makem, Tommy & Liam Clancy* / I will love you (ev'ry time when we are gone): *Fureys & Davey Arthur.*
LP: KNLP 14001
MC: KNMC 14001

COUNTRY 'N' IRISH (see under Country 'n' Irish) (Various artists).

DEAR OLD DONEGAL (Various artists).
LP: HPE 676
MC: HPC 676

DREAMS OF IRELAND (Various artists).
Tracks: / When I dream: *Foster & Allen* / Silver threads: *Fureys & Davey Arthur* / What a friend we have in Jesus: *Breen, Ann* / My lovely rose of Clare: *Reilly, Paddy* / I need you: *O'Donnell, Daniel* / Now is the hour: *Fureys & Davey Arthur* / Come back Paddy Reilly to Ballyjamesduff: *Reilly, Paddy* / I'll never stop wanting you: *Rock, Dickie* / Two's company: *O' Donnell, Margo & Daniel* / Famous Shamus: *Lynch, Lee* / Don't let me: *Cunningham, Larry* / Your friendly: *O'Donnell, Daniel* / Galway Bay: *Begley, Philomena* / Spinning wheel: *Breen, Ann* / Old rustic bridge by the mill: *Big Tom* / Mountains of Mourne: *Foster & Allen.*
LP: MODEM 1035
MC: MODEMC 1035

DUBLIN SONGS (Various artists).
LP: ONE 1407
MC: OCE 2407
MC: MCTC 042

EASYRIDING: A FEAST OF IRISH FOLK (Various artists).
Tracks: / Snowy breasted pearl, The: *Wolfetones* / Green fields of France: *Furey Brothers & Davey Arthur* / Boys of Fairhill: *Crowley, Jimmy* / Seven drunken nights: *Various artists* / Pretty Peg / Craig's pipes: *Bothy* Band / Shipyard slips: *Furey Brothers & Davey Arthur* / Johnny Cope: *Planxty* / Weila weila waile: *Various artists* / Rare ould times: *Doyle, Danny* / Do you want yer oul lobby washed down?: *Crowley, Jimmy & Stokers Lodge*/ Glenbeigh hornpipe: *De Danann* / Mountain lark: *De Danann* / Musical priest, The: *De Danann* / Tipping it up to Nancy: *Moore, Christy* / Kid on the mountain, The: *Planxty* (Slip jigs.) / Boys of Killybegs: *Makem, Tommy* / Thios chios na tra domh: *Clannad* / Lannigan's ball: *Bards.*
MC: KNMC 11009
LP: KNLP 11009

EMERALD CLASSICS (Various artists).
LP: SRTV 1
MC: SCRTV 1

EMERALD CLASSICS VOL.1 (Various artists).
LP: SPWM 1
MC: SCWM 1

EMERALD CLASSICS VOL.2 (Various artists).
LP: LPWM 100
MC: LCWM 100

FAMILY FAVOURITES - VOLUME 1 (Various artists).
Tracks: / Who were you thinking of: *Various artists* / Blacksmith: *Various artists* / Pal of my cradle days: *Various* artists / Behind the footlights: *Various artists* / Could I have this dance: *Various artists* / My Jones: *Various artists* / Tears on the telephone: *Various artists* / Last cheater's waltz, The: *Various artists*/ I wanna hold your dreams tonight: *Various artists* / Crying time: *Various artists* / I'll get over you: *Various artists* / I'll take you home again Kathleen: *Various artists.*
LP: GES 1223
MC: KGEC 1223

FAMILY FAVOURITES - VOLUME 2 (Various artists).
Tracks: / I will love you all my life: *Various artists* / Sweet dreams: *Various artists* / Baby blue: *Various* artists / Birdie song, The: *Various artists* / When I grow too old to dream: *Various artists* / You ought to be in pictures: *Various artists* / Way old friends do, The: *Various artists* / Like strangers: *Various* artists / Hey: *Various artists* / Tyrolean vagabond: *Various artists* / Maggie: *Various artists*/ It didn't have to be a diamond: *Various artists* / My Lagan softly flowing: *Various artists* / We will make love: *Various artists.*
LP: GES 1227
MC: KGEC SP 1227

FEAST OF IRISH BALLADS, VOL.1 (Folklore).
MC: HSMC 1001

FEAST OF IRISH BALLADS, VOL.2 (Various artists).
MC: HSMC 1002

FEAST OF IRISH BALLADS, VOL.3 (Various artists).
MC: HSMC 1003

FEAST OF TRADITIONAL MUSIC & SONG, VOL.1 (Various artists).
MC: GTDC 033

FIGHTIN' SIDE OF THINGS (Various artists).
LP: SOLP 1007

FORGOTTEN IRELAND, THE (Various artists).
Tracks: / Goolin and rosin dub: *Various artists* / First time ever I saw your face, The: *Various artists* / My gentle harp: *Various artists* / Cortnamona: *Various artists* / Galway Bay: *Various artists.*
LP: LLST 7349

GALWAY BAY (10 original hits from home) (Various artists).
MC: CHR 06

GOLDEN COLLECTION OF IRISH MUSIC (Various artists).
MCSET: DCP 3

GOLDEN HOUR - IRISH BALLADS, VOL.2 (Various artists).
LP: GH 576

GOLDEN HOUR - IRISH BALLADS, VOL.1 (Various artists).
LP: GH 532

GOLDEN HOUR OF IRISH BALLADS (Various artists).
MC: KGHMC 114

GOLDEN SOUNDS OF IRISH FOLK (Various artists).
Tracks: / Song for Ireland, A: *Various artists* / Isle of Innisfree: *Various artists* / Men of Worth: *Various artists* / Raglan Road: *Various artists* / Bunch of thyme: *Various artists* / David's theme: *Various artists*/ Let it be: *Various artists* / Fields of Athenry: *Various artists* / Cavan girl: *Various artists* / Water is wide, The: *Various artists* / Sailing home: *Various artists* / Red is the rose: *Various artists* / Slieve na mon: *Various artists* / Parting glass, The: *Various artists.*
LP: DOLZ 8001
MC: DOCZ 8001

GRAND AIRS OF CONNEMARA (Various Traditional Irish Songs) (Various artists).
Tracks: / Mainistir na buille: *MacDonnachadha, Sean* / An Caisdeach ban: *O'Cathain, Padraic* / Piopa Andy mhoir: *O'Neachtain, Tomas* / Una bhan: *O'Connluain, Feichin* / Bean on fhir rua: *O'Cathain, Padraic* / Stor mo chroi: *MacDonnachadha, Sean* / Noirin mo mhian: *MacDonnachadha, Sean* / Cailin schoth na luachra: *O'Cathain,* Padraic / Peigi Misteal: *O'Neachtain, Tomas* / An goirtin eornan: *O'Connluain, Feichin* / Cuaichin Ghleann Neifin: *O'Cathain, Padraic* / An spailpin fanach: *MacDonnachadha, Sean.*
LP: 12T 177

GREAT BANDS OF ULSTER: VOL 1 (Various artists).
LP: GB 1000

GREAT IRISH BALLADS BY PETE ST JOHN (Various artists).
MC: DOCS 2016

GREEN FIELDS OF HOME (Various artists).
2LP: HM 004D
MCSET: HMC 004D

GREEN VELVET (Various artists).
Tracks: / Maggie: *Various artists* / When you were sweet sixteen: *Various artists* / Danny boy: *Various artists*/ Mountains of Mourne: *Various artists* / My love is like a red red rose: *Various artists* / Bunch of thyme: *Various* artists / I'll take you home again Kathleen: *Various artists* / Steal away: *Various artists* / Old rugged cross, The: *Various artists* / Silver threads among the gold: *Various artists.*
LP: PLAT 10
MC: PLAC 10
LPS: STAR 2252
MCSET: STAC 2252

GUINNESS RECORD OF IRISH BALLADS (Various artists).
Tracks: / Nation once again, A: *Various artists* / Muirsheen Durkin: *Various artists* / Banks of the Ohio: *Various* artists / Black velvet band: *Various artists* / Come to the bower: *Various artists* / Kevin Barry: *Various* artists / Kelly the boy from Killane: *Various artists* / Old maid in a garret: *Various artists* / Never wed an old man: *Various artists* / Mary from Dungloe: *Various artists* / I know my love: *Various artists*/ Shores of Amerikay, The: *Various artists* / Rising of the moon: *Various artists* / Waxies dargle: *Various artists.*
LP: DOLB 7010
MC: DOCB 7010

GUINNESS RECORD OF IRISH BALLADS, VOL 4 (Various artists).
Tracks: / Whiskey in the jar: *Various artists* / Irish soldier laddie: *Various artists* / Four green fields: *Various* artists / Slievenamon: *Various artists* / Finnegan's wake: *Various artists* / Town I loved so well, The: *Various* artists / Wild rover: *Various artists* / Irish rover, The: *Various artists* / Wind in the willows: *Various* artists / Sea around us, The: *Various artists* / Cliffs of Dooneen: *Various artists* / Spancil Hill: *Various artists* / Hills of Kerry: *Various artists.*
LP: DOLB 7022
MC: DOCB 7022

GUINNESS RECORD OF IRISH BALLADS VOL.2 (Various artists).
MC: DOCB 7017

GUINNESS RECORD OF IRISH BALLADS VOL.3 (Various artists).
MC: DOCB 7019

IF YOU'RE IRISH (Various artists).
LP: HRL 209

IF YOU'RE IRISH VOL.1 (Various artists).
Tracks: / Eileen O'Grady: *Various artists* / These are my mountains: *Various artists* / Village in County Tyrone: *Various artists* / Give an Irish girl to me: *Various artists* / Moonshiner: *Various artists* / Where the 3 countries meet: *Various artists* / Girl from Donegal: *Various artists* / Blacksmith: *Various artists*/ Sunset years of life, The: *Various artists* / Coastline of Mayo: *Various artists* / If you're Irish: *Various* artists / Gentle mother: *Various artists* / Pretty little girl from Omagh: *Various artists* / Goodbye Johnny dear: *Various artists* / Irish rover, The: *Various artists* / Donaree: *Various artists* / Irish eyes: *Various artists* / Little country town in Ireland: *Various artists* / Asthoreen Bawn: *Various artists*/ Catch me if you can: *Various artists.*
MC: CHRL 209

IF YOU'RE IRISH VOL.2 (Various artists).
Tracks: / McCarthy's party: *Various artists* / Boys from County Armagh: *Various artists* / Old Claddagh ring: *Various artists* / Three leaf shamrock: *Various artists* / Miltown Malbay: *Various artists* / Rose of Mooncoin: *Various artists* / Cottage by the Lee: *Various artists* / Green hills of Kerry: *Various artists*/ Lovely derry on the banks of the Foyle: *Various artists* / Ireland mother Ireland: *Various artists* / Village where I went to school: *Various artists* / Kellys, The: *Various artists* / Boys from County Mayo: *Various* artists / Typical Irishman: *Various artists* / Homes of Donegal: *Various artists* / Stone outside Dan Murphy's door, The: *Various artists* / My lagan love: *Various artists* / Abbeyshrule: *Various artists* / Christmas time in Ireland: *Various artists* / If we only had old Ireland over here: *Various artists.*
MC: CHRL 210

IF YOU'RE IRISH VOL.3 (Various artists).
Tracks: / I'll take you home again Kathleen: *Various artists* / Come back Paddy Reilly to Ballyjamesduff: *Various* artists / Mulroy bay: *Various artists* / Castle of Dromore: *Various artists* / Noreen Bawn: *Various artists*/ My wild Irish rose: *Various artists* / Old rustic bridge: *Various artists* / Carrickfergus: *Various artists*/ Cottage on the Old Dungannon Road: *Various artists* / Do you want yer oul lobby washed down: *Various artists*/ Travelling people: *Various artists* / Lough Sheelin: *Various artists* / Home town on the Foyle: *Various* artists / Slaney valley: *Various artists* / Faughan side: *Various artists* / Spinning wheel: *Various* artists / Mountains of Mourne: *Various artists* / Dingle Bay: *Various artists* / Take me back to Castlebar: *Various artists.*
MC: CHRL 213

IRELAND UNITED GAELIC AND FREE (Various artists).
LP: CSDBL 503

IRELAND'S BEST (Various artists).
Tracks: / Bunch of violets blue: *Various artists* / Boys from the County Mayo: *Various artists* / Bride's bouquet: *Various artists* / Old Arboe: *Various artists* / 500 miles from home: *Various artists* / Lovely Derry on the banks of the Foyle: *Various artists* / Three leaf shamrock: *Various artists* / One day at a time: *Various* artists / Whisper your mother's name: *Various artists* / 21 years: *Various artists* / I'll be glad: *Various artists* / Medals for mothers: *Various artists.*
LP: HRL 175

MC: . . . . CHRL 175

IRELAND'S BEST ON RELEASE (Various artists).
LP: . . . . BRL 4003

IRELAND'S BEST ON RELEASE VOL.2 (Various artists).
LP: . . . . BRL 4010

IRELAND'S BEST ON RELEASE VOL.3 (Various artists).
LP: . . . . BRL 4015

IRELAND'S BEST ON RELEASE VOL.4 (Various artists).
LP: . . . . BRL 4019

IRELANDS BEST ON RELEASE VOL.5 (Various artists).
LP: . . . . BRL 4029

IRELAND'S BEST VOL 2 (Various artists).
Tracks: / Dear God: *Various artists* / Galway shawl: *Various artists* / Dermot O'Brien: *Various artists*/ Roly Daniels: *Various artists*.
LP: . . . . HRL 180
MC: . . . . CHRL 180

IRELAND'S COUNTRY AND WESTERN CARNIVAL VOL 1 (Various artists).
Tracks: / Country roads: *Various artists* / Little rose: *Various artists* / There goes my everything: *Various artists*.
LP: . . . . HRL 103
MC: . . . . CHRL 103

IRELAND'S COUNTRY FESTIVAL (Various artists).
Tracks: / Someday you'll call my name: *Various artists* / Sing me back home: *Various artists* / Shenandoah: *Various artists*.
LP: . . . . HRL 146

IRELAND'S COUNTRY GIRLS (Various artists).
Tracks: / Any Tipperary town: *Margo* / Where the river Shannon flows: *McCann, Susan* / Bunch of violets blue: *Breen, Ann* / Three leaf shamrock: *Margo* / Moonlight in Mayo: *Quinn, Philomena* / Travellin' people: *McCann, Susan* / West of the old river shannon: *Margo* / Boys from County Armagh: *Margo* / Love is teasin': *Breen, Ann* / Forty shades of green: *Quinn, Philomena* / Boys from County Mayo: *Margo* / Gentle mother: *Breen, Ann* / If we only had old Ireland over here: *Quinn, Philomena* / Isle of Innisfree: *McCann, Susan*.
MC: . . . . CPHL 501

IRELAND'S COUNTRY QUEENS Ann Breen, Leon, Margo, Philomena Begley (Various artists).
Tracks: / Who's sorry now: *Various artists* / Lonely hearts club: *Various artists* / You never were mine: *Various artists* / Mississippi: *Various artists* / Will you love me tomorrow: *Various artists* / Never again will I knock on your door: *Various artists* / Teddy bear: *Various artists* / Hello darlin': *Various artists*/ One day at a time: *Various artists* / Old arboe: *Various artists* / Family bible: *Various artists* / River road: *Various artists*.
LP: . . . . PHL 456
MC: . . . . CPHL 456

IRELAND'S COUNTRY & WESTERN CARNIVAL VOL. 2 (Various artists).
Tracks: / Old Shep: *Various artists* / Your cheatin' heart: *Various artists* / It keeps right on a-hurtin': *Various artists*.
LP: . . . . HRL 111
MC: . . . . CHRL 111

IRELAND'S COUNTRY & WESTERN CARNIVAL VOL 3 (Various artists).
Tracks: / 21 years: *Various artists* / I can't stop loving you: *Various artists*.
LP: . . . . HRL 121

IRELAND'S FAVOURITE SINGERS (Various artists).
LP: . . . . HRL 160
MC: . . . . CHRL 160

IRELAND'S GREATEST HITS (Various artists).
LP: . . . . STAR 2305
MC: . . . . STAC 2305

IRELAND'S OWN (Various artists).
Tracks: / Boys from County Armagh: *Margo* / Cottage by the lee: *Breen, Ann* / Heaven around Galway Bay: *McCann, Susan* / Come my little son: *Begley, Philomena* / Dear old Killarney: *Margo* / Rose of Clare: *McCann, Susan* / Old Claddagh Ring: *Margo* / Spinning wheel: *Breen, Ann* / Rose of Tralee, The: *McCann, Susan*/ Danny boy: *Margo* / Village in County Tyrone: *Begley, Philomena* / Girl from Donegal: *Margo* / Isle of Innisfree: *McCann, Susan* / Any Tipperary town: *Margo* / Old cross of Arboe: *Begley, Philomena* / Too-ra-loo-ra-loo-ra: *Breen, Ann*.
MC: . . . . CPHL 491

IRISH CHRISTMAS PARTY (Various artists).
Tracks: / White christmas: *Various artists* / Santa look a lot like Daddy: *Various artists* / How great thou art: *Various artists* / Puppy dog for christmas: *Various artists* / Christmas time in Innisfree: *Various artists*/ Visit to Santa: *Various artists* / First Noel: *Various artists* / Silver bells: *Various artists* / Silent night: *Various artists* / Winter wonderland: *Various artists* / Santa and the kids: *Various artists* / Snowflake: *Various artists* / Wish my baby happy christmas: *Various artists* / Memory of an old christmas card: *Various artists* / Christmas time in Ireland: *Various artists* / Rudolph the red nosed reindeer: *Various artists*/ Jingle bells: *Various artists*.
LP: . . . . PHL 4080
MC: . . . . CPHL 4080

IRISH COLLECTION, THE (Various artists).
LP: . . . . KLP 265

IRISH COLLECTION, THE (Various artists).
LP: . . . . IRISHLP 1
MC: . . . . IRISHMC 1

IRISH COLLECTION VOL.1 (Various artists).
Tracks: / Tom Billy's jigs: *Cassaidigh, Na* / Brian Boru's march: *Clannad* / Dogs among the bushes, The: *Various artists* / Jenny's wedding: *Planxty* / Mrs. MacDermott: *Clannad* / Munster buttermilk: *Various artists*/ Wind that shakes the barley, The: *Ferida* / Morning on a distant shore: *Furey Brothers & Davey Arthur* / Cathleen Henir's: *De Danann* / Old torn petticoat: *Various artists* / Dublin reel: *Various artists* / Wind that shakes the barley, The: *Planxty* / Belfast hornpipe: *Ferida* / Ask me father: *Various artists* / Finbar dwyers: *Various artists* / Oak tree, The: *Various artists* / Lark on the strand, The: *Furey Brothers & Davey Arthur* / Michael Murphy's hornpipes: *Casaidigh, Na* / Tripping up the stairs (a trip to Athlone): *De Danann*.
MC: 3188112

IRISH COLLECTION VOL.2 (Various artists).
Tracks: / Gypsy savey: *Fureys & Davey Arthur* / Home by bearna: *Moore, Christy* / Siobhan ni dhuibhir: *Clannad*/ Lakes of coolfin: *Ferida* / Wexford fishing song: *MacMurrough* / Cunla: *Plaxty* / An bothan a ghaig fionnghuala: *Munroe* / Boys of Mullabawn: *Moore, Christy* / Life is just that way: *Fureys & Davey Arthur*/ Eighteen years old: *De Danann* / Nil se ina la: *Clannad* / Cold blow and rainy night: *Planxty*.
MC: 3188113

IRISH COUNTRY FLAVOUR (Various artists).
Tracks: / Old log cabin: *Big Tom & The Mainliners* / Blue Kentucky girl: *Durkin, Kathy* / Love's gonna live here: *Flavin, Mick* / We'll sweep out: *Cassidy, Noel* / Five little fingers: *McBride, Frankie* / He'll have to go: *Allen, Tony* / Hanging tree, The: *Coll, Brian* / New moon over my shoulder: *Flynn, Joe* / I love you because: *Foster & Allen* / Sea of heartbreak: *Coll, Brian* / My thanks to you: *Flynn, Joe* / Devil woman: *O'Brien, Paddy* / I fall to pieces: *McCann, Susan* / Tenessee waltz: *Morrissey, Louise* / Food on the table: *Cassidy, Noel* / I heard the bluebirds sing: *Flavin, Mick*.
LP: . . . . HM 054

IRISH COUNTRY VOL.1 (Various artists).
MC: . . . . FACS 009

IRISH EYES ARE SMILING (10 original hits from home) (Various artists).
MC: . . . . CHR 09

IRISH FOLK (Various artists).
Tracks: / Shannon waltz: *Various artists* / Sweet sixteen: *Various artists* / Pet of the pipers: *Various* artists / Father O'Flynn: *Various artists* / Irish washerwoman, The: *Various artists* / Shandon bells: *Various* artists / River Maine, The: *Various artists* / Waters of Erin: *Various artists* / Doherty's hornpipe: *Various* artists / Village where I went to school: *Various artists* / Thugamar fein an samradh linn: *Various artists*/ Peter Street: *Various artists* / Paddy on the railway: *Various artists* / Breakdown, (The): *Various artists*/ Cliffs of Dooneen: *Various artists* / Sweet-hearts: *Various artists* / In spring: *Various artists* / Sliabh geal gcua: *Various artists*.
LP: . . . . TRAAD 05 L

IRISH FOLK COLLECTION, THE (Various artists).
LP: . . . . TA 2014

IRISH FOLK FAVOURITES (Various artists).
LP: . . . . HPE 653
MC: . . . . HPC 653
MC: . . . . DOCB 7035

IRISH FOLK HITS (Various artists).
Tracks: / Old maid in a garret: *Sweeneys, The* / Curragh of Killen Dragoons, The: *Johnstons, The* / Rising of the moon: *Tinkers, the* / Enniskillen dragoons: *Ludlows, the* / Nightingale, the: *Kelly, Johnny* / Sgt. Bailey: *Mulvany, Maeeve* / Bold O'Donaghue: *Draggons* / Come to the bower: *Dunphy, Sean* / Jolly tinker: *Dolan, Joe* / Irish soldier, The: *Lynch, Pat*.
MC: . . . . ZMAL 735

IRISH FOLK PUB SING-A-LONG (Various artists).
Tracks: / Where three countries meet: *Barnbrack* / My Eileen is waiting for me: *Barnbrack* / Homes of Donegal: *Barnbrack* / Wild colonial boy: *Malachy Doris* / Rose of Mooncoin: *Malachy Doris* / Astoreen Bawn: *Malachy* Doris / Star of the County Down: *Malachy Doris* / Boys from County Armagh: *Malachy Doris* / Glenswilly: *Malachy* Doris / Blacksmith: *Woods, Pat* / Mother's love's a blessing, A: *Barnbrack* / Goodbye Johnny dear: *Barnbrack*/ Gentle mother: *Barnbrack* / Holy ground: *Malachy Doris* / I'll tell me ma: *Malachy Doris* / Boston burglar: *Barnbrack* / Moonshiner: *Barnbrack* / Hills of Connemara: *Barnbrack* / Old Claddagh ring: *Malachy* Doris / Galway shawl: *Malachy Doris* / Spancil hill: *Malachy Doris* / Do you want yer oul lobby washed down: *Malachy Doris* / Boul thady quill: *Malachy Doris* / Biddy Mulligan the pride of Coombe: *Malachy Doris*/ Rose of Allendale: *Woods, Pat* / Nancy Spain: *Barnbrack* / Leaving of Liverpool: *Barnbrack* / Mursheen Durkin: *Barnbrack* / If you're Irish come into the parlour: *Malachy Doris* / With me shillelagh under me arm: *Malachy Doris* / Westmeath bachelor: *Malachy Doris*.
MC: . . . . CPHL 505

IRISH FOLK PUB SING-A-LONG (Various artists).
Tracks: / Home boys home: *Barnbrack* / Coortin' in the kitchen: *Barnbrack* / As I roved out: *Barnbrack*/ Boul O'Donohue: *Malachy Doris* / Holy ground: *Malachy Doris* / Ireland boys hurrah: *Malachy Doris* / Humour is on me now, The: *Malachy Doris* / Barney Brannigan: *Malachy Doris*/ Phil the fluters ball: *Barnbrack* / Come back Paddy Reilly to Ballyjamesduff: *Barnbrack* / Slattery's mounted fut: *Barnbrack* / Mursheen Durkin: *Malachy Doris* / Irish rover, The: *Malachy Doris* / Hello, Patsy Fagan: *Malachy Doris* / Waves of Tory, The: *Malachy Doris* / If we only had old Ireland over here: *Margo* / Westmeath bachelor: *Barnbrack* / If you're Irish: *Barnbrack* / Dear oul Donegal: *Barnbrack* / Kelly the boy from Killane: *Malachy Doris* / Dawning of the day: *Malachy Doris* / Roddy McCorley: *Malachy Doris* / O'Brien has no place to go: *Malachy Doris* / Do you want yer oul lobby washed down: *Malachy Doris* / Catch me if you can: *Malachy Doris* / Irish rover, The: *Barnbrack* / Goodbye Mick, goodbye Pat: *Barnbrack* / Banana song: *Barnbrack*/ Gentle mother: *Malachy Doris* / Old rustic bridge: *Malachy Doris* / Bunch of violets blue: *Malachy Doris*.
MC: . . . . CPHL 504

IRISH REBEL SONGS (Various artists).
LP: . . . . CO 7001

IRISH SHOWBAND REQUESTS VOL 1 (Various artists).
Tracks: / Little Isle of Green: *Various artists* / Ring your mother wore: *Various artists* / If those lips could only speak: *Various artists*.
LP: . . . . HRL 151
MC: . . . . CHRL 151

IRISH SHOWBAND YEARS - 40 SONGS (Various artists).
Tracks: / Sunny side of the mountain: *Glenn, John & Mainliners* / Alice is in wonderland: *Kirwan, Dominic & Las Vegas*/ Gallant John Joe: *Corrigan, Ian* / I left my heart in San Francisco: *Rock, Dickie & Miami* / Any Tipperary town: *Margo & The Country Folk* / Hello darlin': *Daniels, Roly* / Twenty one years: *Hegarty, Dermot* / Sweet dreams: *Lou, Mary & Harvest* / These are my mountains: *Coll, Brian & The Buckaroos* / Gold watch and chain: *Cotton* Mill Boys / If those lips could only speak: *McCann, Susan/Storytellers* / Gypsy Joe and me: *Lynam, Ray & The Hillbillies*/ My best friend: *Quinn, Brendan & The Bluebirds* / Here today and gone tomorrow: *Begley, Philomena/Ramblin' Men*/ Happy anniversary: *Tony & Ventures* / Don't let me cross over: *Cunningham, Larry & Margo* / Dear God: *Duncan,* Hugo & The Tallmen / Silver threads and golden needles: *King, Eileen & Country Flavour* / Shores of Lough Bran, The: *Ely, Pat & The Rocky Tops* / Back home again: *Shelly & The Marines* / Door is always open, The: *Lynam, Ray* & The Hillbillies / Slaney Valley: *Cunningham, Larry* / When the sun says goodbye to the mountain: *McCann, Susan/Storytellers*/ Three leaf shamrock: *Duncan, Hugo & The Tallmen* / Black rose: *Addinell, Roy* / You'll never miss the water: *King, Eileen & The Kingsmen* / Four in the morning: *Quinn, Brendan* & The Bluebirds / China doll: *Coll, Brian* & The Buckaroos / How great thou art: *Kelley & Nevada* / Little country town in Ireland: *Glenn, John & Mainliners*/ Every step of the way: *Rock, Dickie & Miami* / Old cross of Arboe: *Begley, Philomena/Ramblin' Men* / You can't judge a book by the cover: *Corrigan, Ian* / Galway shawl: *O'Brien, Dermot & The Clubmen* / Rockin' alone in an old rockin' chair: *Margo & The Country Folk* / Combine harvester: *Dan The Farmer* / Newry town: *Exiles*/ My Eileen: *McCaffrey, Frank* / Little isle of green: *Colm & Sundowners* / Bunch of violets blue: *Shine, Brendan*.
MCSET: C2DHX 803

IRISH SONGS OF FREEDOM, VOL 1 (Various artists).
Tracks: / Come out ye black and tans: *Various artists* / James Connolly: *Various artists* / Take me home to Mayo: *Various artists* / Dying rebel: *Various artists* / Men behind the wire: *Various artists* / Rebel, The: *Various artists* / Boys of the old brigade: *Various artists* / Lonely woods of Upton: *Various artists*/ Follow me up to Carlow: *Various artists* / Banna Strand: *Various artists* / British army, The: *Various artists*/ Irish soldier laddie: *Various artists* / Michael Collins: *Various artists* / On the one road: *Various artists*/ Kevin Barry: *Various artists* / Nation once again, A: *Various artists*.
LP: . . . . DOLS 2002
MC: . . . . DOCS 2002

IRISH SONGS OF FREEDOM, VOL 2 (Various artists).
Tracks: / Four green fields: *Various artists* / Galtee mountain boy: *Various artists* / God save Ireland: *Various* artists / Wild colonial boy: *Various artists* / Tri coloured ribbon: *Various artists* / Only our rivers: *Various* artists / Shall my soul pass through old Ireland: *Various artists* / Boulavogue: *Various artists* / Irish soldier boy: *Various artists* / Bold Robert Emmett: *Various artists* / Three flowers: *Various artists*/ Man from Mullingar, The: *Various artists* / Foggy dew, The: *Various artists* / Avondale: *Various artists*/ Glen of Alerlow: *Various artists* / Fields of Athenry: *Various artists*.
LP: . . . . DOLS 2008
MC: . . . . DOCS 2008

IRISH SONGS OF FREEDOM, VOL 3 (Various artists).
LP: . . . . CO 7013

IRISH TRAD INSTRUMENTAL MUSIC FROM E. AMERICA Vol. 1 (Various artists).
LP: . . . . ROUNDER 6005

IRISH TRAD INSTRUMENTAL MUSIC FROM CHICAGO Vol. 2 (Various artists).
LP: . . . . ROUNDER 6006

IRISH TRADITIONAL CONCERTINA STYLES (Various artists).
LP: 12TS 506

IRISH TRADITIONAL MUSIC (Various artists).
MC: . . . . COX 1013

IRISH TRADITIONAL MUSIC & BALLADS (Various artists).
Tracks: / Brian Boru's march: *Clannad* / Shores of Lough Bran, The: *De Danann* / O'Carolan tribute: *Furey* Brothers & Davey Arthur / Nancy Spain: *Moore, Christy* / Danny boy: *Patterson, Frank* / Leaving Nancy: *Furey* Brothers & Davey Arthur / Gill Aodain: *Casaidigh, Na* / Paddy's green shamrock shore: *Brady, Paul* / Gipsy Dave: *Furey Brothers & Davey Arthur* / Glenbeigh hornpipe: *De Danann* / Old rustic bridge: *Patterson, Frank*/ Nil se ina la: *Clannad* / Gill Chais: *Casaidigh, Na* / Fanny Power: *Bards* / Banks of Claudy, The: *Hanly, Michael, Michael O'Domhaill*.
MC: . . . . ALPC 1

IRISH TRADITIONAL MUSIC MEET THE CHAMPIONS (Various artists).
MC: . . . . COX 1026

IRLANDE ETERNELLE harpe irlandaise - pub music (Various artists).
Tracks: / Nora Chrionna: *Various artists* / Harvest home: *Various artists* / Window smasher jig: *Various artists* / Maurice O'Connor: *Various artists* /

Sligo fancy: *Various artists* / I'm sleepy, don't awake me: *Various artists* / Reels: *Various artists* / Lament: *Various artists* / Jig: *Various artists*/ Jug of punch: *Various artists* / Teatotaler, The: *Various artists* / Dingle regatta: *Various artists*/ Spancil hill: *Various artists* / Banjo melody: *Various artists* / Kid on the mountain, The: *Various artists*/ National anthem: *Various artists*.
LP: . . . . **ARN 33196**
MC: . . . . **ARN 433196**

ITS HEROES & SONGS (Various artists).
MC: . . . . **DOCM 5026**

KERRY FIDDLES (Various artists).
LP: **12T 309**

KILMAINHAM JAIL SONGS (Various artists).
LP: . . . . **DOLM 5026**

LARK IN THE MORNING (Various artists).
LP: . . . . **TLP 1004**

LE CHANT PROFOND DE L'IRLANDE (Various artists).
Tracks: / Country song: *Various artists* / Kilfenora jig: *Various artists* / Whiskey in the jar: *Various* artists / Gravel walk: *Various artists* / Dan Malone: *Various artists* / Peter's song: *Various artists*/ Celtic lament: *Various artists* / Two corbies, The: *Various artists* / Pinch of snuff: *Various artists*/ All the little children: *Various artists* / Bucks of Oranmore, The: *Various artists* / Lullaby: *Various artists* / Denis Murphy's: *Various artists* / O'Keefe's slide: *Various artists*.
LP: . . . . **ARN 33339**
MC: . . . . **ARN 433339**

LIGHT THROUGH THE LEAVES wind instruments (Various artists).
LP: . . . . **ROUNDER 6014**
MC: . . . . **ROUNDER 6014C**

MEDALS FOR MOTHERS (Various artists).
Tracks: / Medals for mothers: *Leon* / Picture of your mother: *Stuart, Gene* / Roses for mama: *Greer, John*/ Mother like mine, A: *Big Ivan* / No charge: *Wells, Tracy* / I dreamed about mama last night: *Derry, Pat*/ Pal of my cradle days: *Breen, Ann* / Gentle mother: *Greer, John* / Mama, let me shelter in your sweet loving arms: *Leon* / Mother's love's a blessing, A: *Countrymen* / Mama sang a song: *Bell, Crawford* / Rockin' alone in an old rocking chair: *Margo*.
LP: . . . . **PHL 440**
MC: . . . . **CPHL 440**

MEMORIES OF DUBLIN (Various artists).
LP: . . . . **STAL 8005**

MORE BEST IRISH BALLADS (Various artists).
MC: . . . . **DBXC 008**

MORE CEILIDH TIME (Various artists).
MCSET: . . . . **DBXC 009**

MORE GRAND AIRS FROM CONNEMARA (Various artists).
LP: **12T 202**

MORE GREEN VELVET (IRISH SONGS) (Various artists).
LP: . . . . **STAR 2267**
MC: . . . . **STAC 2267**

MORE REBEL SONGS (Various artists).
MCSET: . . . . **DBXC 007**

MOTHER JUST FOR YOU (Various artists).
Tracks: / Gentle mother: *Breen, Ann* / My mother's home: *Woods, Pat* / Nobody's child: *Big Jim* / Come my little son: *Begley, Philomena* / Ring your mother wore: *Dan The Farmer* / Boy of mine: *Breen, Ann*/ What a friend we have in mother: *Breen, Ann* / Two loves: *Duncan, Hugo* / Nobody's darlin' but mine: *Teamwork*/ Noreen Bawn: *Glenn, John* / My mother's birthday: *Duncan, Hugo* / Coat of many colours: *Margo*.
LP: . . . . **PHL 471**
MC: . . . . **CPHL 471**

MUSICAL VIEW OF IRELAND (Various artists).
LP: . . . . **PICKTV 1**
MC: . . . . **CPICK 1**

NOSTALGIA CELEBRATION (Various artists).
Tracks: / Hucklebuck, The: *Bowyer, Brendan* / Gentle mother: *Big Tom & The Mainliners* / I gave my wedding dress away: *Reid, Eileen* / Little arrows: *O'Brien, Brendan* / Whiskey on a Sunday: *Doyle, Danny* / House with the white ....: *Dolan, Joe* / Five little fingers: *McBride, Frankie* / Simon says: *Rock, Dickie & Miami*/ Sea around us: *Ludlows, the* / Leaving of Liverpool: *Lynch, Pat* / Old man trouble: *Carroll, Doc* / Boston burglar: *McEvoy, Johnny* / Liverpool Lou: *Behan, Dominic* / Papa oom mow mow: *Freshmen* / Walking in the streets: *Moore, Butch* / If I didn't have a dime: *Dunphy, Tom* / Travelling people: *Johnstons* / Black velvet band: *Kelly, John* / If I could choose: *Dunphy, Sean* / Streets of Baltimore: *Kelly, Des*.
LP: . . . . **HM 053**

OFF TO CALIFORNIA (Traditional Irish music in San Francisco) (Various artists).
LP: . . . . **ADVENT 3501**

REBEL SONGS OF IRELAND (Various artists).
MCSET: . . . . **DBXC 002**

REBEL SONGS OF IRELAND (Various artists).
LP: . . . . **HARP 17**

REBEL SONGS OF IRELAND, VOLUME 1 (Various artists).
LP: . . . . **CBRL 4013**

REBEL SONGS OF IRELAND, VOLUME 2 (Various artists).
LP: . . . . **CBRL 4055**

REQUESTED BALLADS OF IRELAND VOL 1 (Various artists).
Tracks: / Kelly's, The: *Various artists* / Mary from Dungloe: *Various artists* / Butcher boy: *Various artists*.
LP: . . . . **TOL 123**

REQUESTED BALLADS OF IRELAND VOL 3 (Various artists).
Tracks: / Give an Irish girl to me: *Various artists* / Real old mountain dew: *Various artists* / I'll remember you love in my prayers: *Various artists*.
LP: . . . . **G 004**
MC: . . . . **GC 004**

RIADA SA GAIETY (Various artists).
LP: . . . . **CEF 027**

RITZ RADIO FAVOURITES (VOLUME 3 - IRISH FOLK) (Various artists).
LP: . . . . **RITZSP 413**
MC: . . . . **RITZSC 413**

ROSE OF MOONCOIN (10 original hits from home) (Various artists).
MC: . . . . **CHR 04**

ROSE OF TRALEE (1) (10 original hits from home) (Various artists).
MC: . . . . **CHR 01**

SALUTE TO THE SOUTH (Various artists).
LP: . . . . **STAL 8003**

SHAMROCKS AND SHILLELAGHS (20 more of your favourites) (Various artists).
Tracks: / Nightingale, The: *Various artists* / Slievenamon: *Various artists* / Paddy's green shamrock shore: *Various artists* / Maggie: *Various artists* / McMahon's reel: *Various artists* / Connemara reel: *Various artists* / Rose of Moray: *Various artists* / My Irish Molly: *Various artists* / God be with you, Kerry: *Various artists* / Old rustic bridge: *Various artists* / Kelly the boy from Killane: *Various artists* / Carnlough Bay: *Various artists* / My wild Irish Rose: *Various artists* / Come by the hills: *Various artists* / When Irish eyes are smiling: *Various artists*.
LP: . . . . **DOLS 2010**
MC: . . . . **DOCS 2010**

SHOWBAND FAVOURITES (Various artists).
LP: . . . . **STAL 8001**

SHOWCASE OF STARS (Various artists).
Tracks: / Who's sorry now: *Various artists* / Love is all: *Various artists* / Can't stop loving you: *Various artists* / Golden ring: *Various artists* / Can I have this dance: *Various artists* / Blacksmith (when the hammer strikes the anvil), The: *Various artists* / Let the rest of the world go by: *Various artists* / River road: *Various artists* / How great thou art: *Various artists* / Still the one: *Various artists* / My Lagan love: *Various artists* / Among my souvenirs: *Various artists*.
LP: . . . . **PHL 1983**
MC: . . . . **CPHL 1983**

SING A SONG OF IRISH FREEDOM (Various artists).
Tracks: / Shall my soul pass through old Ireland: *Various artists* / Drying rebel: *Various artists* / Johnston's motor car: *Various artists* / James Connolly: *Various artists* / Four green fields: *Various artists* / Nation once again: *Various artists* / Father Murphy: *Various artists* / Kevin Barry: *Various artists*/ Three flowers: *Various artists* / Patriot game: *Various artists* / Gradh mo chroidhe: *Various artists*/ Off to Dublin: *Various artists*.
LP: . . . . **SDBL 515**

SING AN IRISH SONG VOL 1 (Cottage by the Lee) (Various artists).
Tracks: / Turfman from Ardee: *Kerr, John* / Old Arboe: *Begley, Philomena* / Where is my Nora: *Stuart, Gene*/ Shores of Lough Bran, The: *Ely, Pat* / Four country roads: *Watt, John* / Cottage on the old Dungannon Road: *Duncan*, Hugo / Boys from County Mayo: *Margo* / Cottage by the Lee: *Cunningham, Larry* / Lough sheelin: *McCaffrey, Frank* / Marta the flower of sweet Strabane: *Brolly, Anne & Francie*.
MC: . . . . **CHR 1**

SING AN IRISH SONG VOL 2 (Mountains of Mourne) (Various artists).
Tracks: / If only we had old Ireland over here: *Margo* / Mountains of Mourne: *Woods, Pat* / Slievenamon: *Margo*/ When you and I were young Maggie: *Foley, Connie* / Cottage by the Lee: *Margo* / Hills of Glenswilly: *Foley*, Connie / Moonshiner: *Donaghy, Eileen* / Mulroy Bay: *Kerr, John* / Dublin in the rare oul times: *Woods, Pat* / Bunch of thyme: *Various artists*.
MC: . . . . **CHR 2**

SING AN IRISH SONG VOL 3 (I'll take you home again Kathleen) (Various artists).
Tracks: / I'll take you home again Kathleen: *Duncan, Hugo* / Come back Paddy Reilly to Ballyjamesduff: *Woods, Pat*/ Mulroy Bay: *Margo* / Castle of Dromore: *McCaffrey, Leo* / Noreen Bawn: *Various artists* / My wild Irish rose: *McCaffrey, Frank* / Old rustic bridge: *Breen, Ann* / Carrickfergus: *Woods, Pat* / Cottage on the old Dungannon Road: *McCann, Susan* / Do you want yer oul lobby washed down: *Duncan, Hugo*.
MC: . . . . **CHR 3**

SING AN IRISH SONG VOL 4 (Rose of Mooncoin) (Various artists).
Tracks: / Rose of Arranmore: *Donaghy, Eileen* / Spancil Hill: *Tinkerman, Jolly* / Old mud cabin on the hill: *Big Ivan* / Mother's love's a blessing, A: *Teamwork* / Rose of Mooncoin: *Woods, Pat* / Old rustic bridge: *Breen*, Ann / Boys from County Armagh: *Glenn, John* / Typical Irishman: *McCaffrey, Leo* / Any Tipperary town: *Margo*/ Sweet Mary: *Coll, Brian*.
MC: . . . . **CHR 4**

SING AN IRISH SONG VOL 5 (spinning wheel) (Various artists).
Tracks: / Travelling people: *McCann, Susan* / Spinning wheel: *Margo* / Home town on the Foyle: *King, Eileen*/ Slaney valley: *Cunningham, Larry* / Stone outside Dan Murphy's door, The: *Hunniford, Gloria* / Faughan side: *McCaffrey, Leo* / Lough Sheelin: *McCaffrey, Frank* / Mountains of Mourne, The: *Woods, Pat* / Dingle Bay: *McCaffrey, Leo* / Take me back to Castlebar: *Duncan, Hugo*.
MC: . . . . **CHR 5**

SING AN IRISH SONG VOL 6 (Galway Bay) (Various artists).
Tracks: / My Eileen: *McCaffrey, Frank* / Boys from County Mayo: *Margo* / Gallant John Joe: *Corrigan, Ian*/ Emigrant's letter: *Margo* / Galway Bay: *Foley, Connie* / Old Claddagh ring: *Margo* / Goodbye Johnny dear: *Foley, Connie* / Westmeath bachelor: *Curran, Noel* / Gentle mother: *Donaghy, Eileen* / I'll take you home again Kathleen: *Foley, Connie*.
MC: . . . . **CHR 6**

SING AN IRISH SONG VOL 7 (rose of Tralee) (Various artists).
Tracks: / Donaree: *Foley, Connie* / Boys from County Armagh: *Foley, Connie* / Let Mr. Maguire sit down: *Donaghy*, Eileen / Eileen O'Grady: *Countrymen* / I'll remember you love in my prayers: *Ely, Pat* / Where the three counties meet: *Kerr, John* / Paddy's green shamrock shore: *Dynes, Sean* / Come back Paddy Reilly to Ballyjamesduff: *Duffy, Teresa* / My wild Irish rose: *Magee, Harry* / Rose of Tralee, The: *Hughes, Sam*.
MC: . . . . **CHR 7**

SING AN IRISH SONG VOL 8 (village where I went to school) (Various artists).
Tracks: / Village where I went to school: *Kerr, John* / Kellys, The: *Hunniford, Gloria* / Boys from County Mayo: *Foley, Connie* / If we only had old Ireland over here: *Duncan, Hugo* / Homes of Donegal: *Foley, Connie*/ Stone outside Dan Murphy's door, The: *Duncan, Hugo* / My Lagan love: *McCaffrey, Leo* / Abbeyshrule: *Woods, Pat* / Typical Irishman: *McCaffrey, Leo* / Christmas time in Ireland: *Various artists*.
MC: . . . . **CHR 8**

SING AN IRISH SONG VOL 9 (Irish eyes) (Various artists).
Tracks: / Irish eyes: *Locklin, Hank* / Gentle mother: *Breen, Ann* / Pretty little girl from Omagh: *Ely, Pat*/ Irish rover, The: *Margo* / If you're Irish: *Craftsmen* / Doonaree: *Cunningham, Larry* / Little country town in Ireland: *Greer, John* / Asthoreen bawn: *Hamilton, Joe* / Catch me if you can: *Duncan, Hugo*.
MC: . . . . **CHR 9**

SING AN IRISH SONG VOL 10 (girl from Donegal) (Various artists).
Tracks: / Girl from Donegal: *Margo* / These are my mountains: *Coll, Brian* / Village in County Tyrone: *Begley*, Philomena / Give an Irish girl to me: *Watt, John* / Moonshiner: *Donaghy, Eileen* / Where the three counties meet: *Kerr, John* / Eileen O'Grady: *Duncan, Hugh* / Blacksmith: *Woods, Pat* / Sunset years of life, The: *Teamwork* / Coastline of Mayo: *McCaffrey, Frank*.
MC: . . . . **CHR 10**

SING AN IRISH SONG VOL 11 (town I love so well) (Various artists).
Tracks: / Ould Lammas fair: *Donaghy, Eileen* / Spancil Hill: *O'Neill, Sean (Corrib Folk)* / Shores of Lough Neagh, The: *Duffy, Teresa* / Dear old Donegal: *Kelly, Breege* / Town I loved so well, The: *Brolly, Anne* / Boys of Killybegs: *Kerr, John* / My Eileen is waiting for me: *Foley, Connie* / Give an Irish girl to me: *Watt, John* / My Kathleen: *Countrymen* / Real old mountain dew: *Hamilton, Dermot*.
MC: . . . . **CHR 11**

SING AN IRISH SONG VOL 12 (three leaf shamrock) (Various artists).
Tracks: / Ireland mother Ireland: *McCaffrey, Leo* / Boys from County Armagh: *Foley, Connie* / Old Claddagh ring: *Margo* / Three leaf shamrock: *Duncan, Hugo* / Miltown Malbay: *McCaffrey, Leo* / Rose of Mooncoin: *McClean, Hugh* / Cottage by the Lee: *Margo* / Green hills of Kerry: *Dynes, Sean* / Lovely derry on the banks of the Foyle: *Cunningham, Larry* / McCarthy's party: *Donaghy, Eileen*.
MC: . . . . **CHR 12**

SING AN IRISH SONG VOL 13 (fields of Athenry) (Various artists).
Tracks: / Fields of Athenry: *Woods, Pat* / Spancil hill: *Dynes, Sean* / Rose of Mooncoin: *O'Neill, Sean*/ My beautiful limerick: *Dynes, Sean* / Slievenamon: *Duncan, Hugo* / Four green fields: *Duncan, Hugo*/ Galway shawl: *O'Brien, Dermot* / Hills of Kerry: *Dynes, Sean* / Blacksmith: *Woods, Pat* / Catch me if you can: *O'Neill, Sean*.
MC: . . . . **CHR 13**

SING AN IRISH SONG VOL 14 (St Patrick's Day) (Various artists).
Tracks: / Three tunes, The: *Various artists* / High cauled cap, The: *Various artists* (Original tune) / Soldiers joy: *Various artists* / Girl I left behind me, The: *Various artists* / Sweets of May: *Various artists*/ Siege of Ennis: *Various artists* (Original tune) / Rocks of Cashel: *Various artists* / Farewell to whiskey: *Various* artists / Humours of Bandon: *Various artists* / Bonnie Kate: *Various artists* (Reel) / Sligo maid, The: *Various* artists (Reel) / Miss Monaghan's: *Various artists* (Reel) / St. Patrick's Day: *Various artists* (Set dance) / Drops of brandy: *Various artists* (Set dance) / Kelly the boy from Killane: *Various artists* (March) / Dawning of the day: *Various artists* (March) / Roddy McCorley: *Various artists* (March) / If you're Irish: *Various* artists (Military two step) / Come into the parlour: *Various artists* (Military two step) / With my shillelagh under me arm: *Various artists* (Military two step) / Westmeath bachelor: *Various artists* (Military two step) / Piper through the meadow straying: *Various artists* (Military two step).
MC: . . . . **CHR 14**

SING AN IRISH SONG VOL 15 (a nation once again) (Various artists).
Tracks: / Ireland's 32: *Foley, Connie* / Take me home to Mayo: *McAreavey, Ray* / Four green fields: *Freedom* Sons / Fields of Athenry: *Woods, Pat* / Sean South: *Freedom Sons* / West awake: *Freedom Sons* / Shall my soul pass through old Ireland: *McCaffrey, Frank* / Boys of the old brigade: *McAreavey, Ray* / James Connolly: *Freedom Sons* / Nation once again (A): *Freedom Sons*.
MC: . . . . **CHR 15**

SING AN IRISH SONG VOL 16 (Old Bog Road) (Various artists).
Tracks: / Old bog road: *Donnelly, Seamus* / Noreen Bawn: *Donnelly, Seamus* / Life to go: *Higgins, Sean*/ Road by the river: *Donnelly, Seamus* / Connemara cradle song: *Donnelly, Seamus* / Hills of Connemara: *Donnelly*, Seamus / My lovely Irish rose: *McAleese, Ivan* / 40 shades of green: *Donnelly, Seamus* / Wreck of the number nine, The: *Higgins, Sean*.
MC: . . . . **CHR 16**

SING AN IRISH SONG VOL 17 (Carrickfergus) (Various artists).

Tracks: / Carrickfergus: Various artists / Wild rover: Various artists / McCafferty: Various artists/ Follow me up to Carlow: Various artists / Connemara cradle song: Various artists / Mursheen Durkin: Various artists / Banks of the Ohio: Various artists / McAlpines Fusiliers: Various artists / Butcher boy: Various artists / Santiano: Various artists.
MC: . . . . **CHR 17**

SING AN IRISH SONG VOL 18 (Galway shawl) (Various artists).
Tracks: / Rose of Castlerea: Duncan, Hugo / Galway shawl: O'Brien, Dermot / Stone outside Dan Murphy's door, The: Duncan, Hugo / Abbeyshrule: Woods, Pat / Take me back to Castlebar: Duncan, Hugo / Catch me if you can: Duncan, Hugo / Village where I went to school: Duncan, Hugo / Any Tipperary town: Duncan, Hugo/ Do you want yer oul lobby washed down: Duncan, Hugo / Old bog road: Duncan, Hugo.
MC: . . . . **CHR 18**

SING AN IRISH SONG VOL 19 (where the River Shannon flows) (Various artists).
Tracks: / Home town on the Foyle: King, Eileen / 40 shades of green: Ely, Pat / Mulroy Bay: Sharon/ Any Tipperary town: Ely, Pat / Where the River Shannon flows: Sharon / Slaney valley: Sharon / Mother's love's a blessing, A: Harron, Olly / Old cross of Arboe: Lynch, Ann / Shores of Lough Bran, The: Ely, Pat/ Cliffs of Dooneen: Lou, Mary.
MC: . . . . **CHR 19**

SING AN IRISH SONG VOL 20 (Kevin Barry) (Various artists).
Tracks: / God save Ireland: Freedom Sons / Dying rebel: Margo / Lonely woods of Upton: McAreavey, Ray/ Kevin Barry: Freedom Sons / Blood stained bandage: McAreavey, Ray / Bold Fenian men: Freedom Sons/ Fields of Athenry: Woods, Pat / Father Murphy: Freedom Sons / Irish soldier boy: Margo / Who fears to speak of '98: Freedom Sons.
MC: . . . . **CHR 20**

SING AN IRISH SONG VOL 21 (mass rock in the Glen) (Various artists).
Tracks: / Mass rock in the Glen: Margo / Irish soldier boy: Margo / Moonshiner: Donaghy, Eileen / Here's a toast to you Claddagh: Margo / Slattery's mounted fut: Donaghy, Eileen / 50 years of golden jubilee: Margo / Goodbye Mick, goodbye Pat: Donaghy, Eileen / West of the old River Shannon: Margo / Castle of Dromore: Donaghy, Eileen / Hills of Glenswilly: Margo.
MC: . . . . **CHR 21**

SING AN IRISH SONG VOL 22 (old Claddagh ring) (Various artists).
Tracks: / Sing Irishmen sing: Corrib Folk / As I roved out: Blackthorn / Rocks of Bawn: Various artists/ She moved through the fair: Blackthorn / Rattlin' roarin' Willie: Blackthorn / Peggy Gordon: Blackthorn/ Doffin mistress: Corrib Folk / High Germany: Blackthorn / Sam Hall: Corrib Folk / Old Claddagh ring: Corrib Folk.
MC: . . . . **CHR 22**

SING AN IRISH SONG VOL 23 (Ireland mother Ireland) (Various artists).
Tracks: / Ireland mother Ireland: McCaffrey, Leo / Three lovely lassies: Donaghy, Eileen / Town of Galway: McCaffrey, Leo / If I were a blackbird: Donaghy, Eileen / Dingle Bay: McCaffrey, Leo / Molly Bawn boating on Lough Rhee: McCaffrey, Leo / Do you remember the good old days: Donaghy, Eileen / Miltown Malbay: McCaffrey, Leo/ Blarney roses: Donaghy, Eileen / Typical Irishman: McCaffrey, Leo.
MC: . . . . **CHR 23**

SING AN IRISH SONG VOL 24 (Galway races) (Various artists).
Tracks: / Spanish lady: Corrib Folk / Lough Erin's lovely shore: Dynes, Sean / Galway races: Dynes, Sean / Rocking the cradle: Dynes, Sean / Singing bird: Corrib Folk / Big strong man: Dynes, Sean / Ramblin' Irishman: Corrib Folk / Bunclody: Dynes, Sean / Spancil Hill: Corrib Folk / Kitty from Baltimore: Dynes, Sean.
MC: . . . . **CHR 24**

SING THE REBEL SONGS (Various artists).
Tracks: / On the one road: Various artists / Rising of the moon: Various artists / Banna Strand: Various artists / Four green fields: Various artists / Irish soldier boy: Various artists / West's awake: Various artists / Off to Dublin in the green: Various artists / Patriot game: Various artists / Irish soldier laddie: Various artists / Foggy dew, The: Various artists / Sea around us, The: Various artists / Twenty men from Dublin town: Various artists / Nation once again, A: Various artists / Bold Fenian men: Various artists/ Memory of the dead: Various artists / Boolavogue: Various artists / Sean south from Garyowen: Various artists / God save Ireland: Various artists / Kevin Barry: Various artists / Three flowers: Various artists / James Connolly: Various artists / Ireland boys' hurrah: Various artists / Johnston's motor car: Various artists / Dying rebel: Various artists.
MC: . . . . **CDOUBLE 100**

SMASH INTERNMENT AND INJUSTICE Live from Long Kesh (Various artists).
LP: . . . . **CROL 3002**

SONGS OF BELFAST (I'LL TELL ME MA) (Various artists).
LP: . . . . **PHL 495**

SONGS OF CO. DERRY & CO. DONEGAL (Various artists).
Tracks: / Danny boy: Various artists / Town I loved so well, The: Various artists.
LP: . . . . **HRL 156**
MC: . . . . **CHRL 156**

SONGS OF CO. KERRY, CO. GALWAY, CO. MAYO (Various artists).
Tracks: / Boys from County Mayo: Various artists / Galway Bay: Various artists / Rose of Tralee, The: Various artists.
LP: . . . . **HRL 168**
MC: . . . . **CHRL 168**

SONGS OF DONEGAL (Various artists).
LP: . . . . **UNKNOWN**

SONGS OF IRELAND (Various artists).
Tracks: / I'll tell my ma: Cream of Irish Bands, The / Kevin Barry: Cream of Irish Bands, The / Bold O'Donaghue: Cream of Irish Bands, The / Jolly tinker: Cream of Irish Bands, The / Danny boy: Cream of Irish Bands, The/ Wild colonial boy: Cream of Irish Bands, The / Katy Daly: Cream of Irish Bands, The / March hare: Cream of Irish Bands, The / Forty shades of green: Cream of Irish Bands, The / Mountain hue: Cream of Irish Bands, The / Galway bay: Cream of Irish Bands, The / Wild Irish rover, The: Cream of Irish Bands, The / Songs of Innesfree: Cream of Irish Bands, The / Holy grail, The: Cream of Irish Bands, The.
LP: . . . . **UNKNOWN**

SONGS OF IRELAND (Various artists).
Tracks: / Fields of Athenry: Reilly, Paddy / Song for Ireland, A: Barleycorn / Men of worth: Black, Mary/ I'll take you home again Kathleen: Fureys & Davey Arthur / Raglan Road: Fair Isle Folk / Isle of Innisfree: Dublin City Ramblers / Let it be: De Danann / When you were sweet sixteen: Fureys & Davey Arthur / Cavan girl: Barleycorn / Water is wide, The: Fair Isle Folk / Red is the rose: Makem, Tommy & Liam Clancy/ Sailing home: Dublin City Ramblers / Parting glass, The: Byrne, Bryan / Bunch of thyme: Reilly, Paddy.
LP: . . . . **SPMP 107**
MC: . . . . **SPMC 107**

SONGS OF IRELAND (2) (Various artists).
LP: . . . . **ETLP 192**
MC: . . . . **ETMC 192**

SONGS OF OLD IRELAND VOL.1 (Various artists).
MCSET: . . . . **DTO 10284**

SONGS OF OLD IRELAND VOL.2 (Various artists).
Tracks: / Irish rover, The: Various artists / Ducks of Magheralin: Various artists / Four strong winds: Various artists / Finnegan's wake: Various artists / Trip to Rathlin: Various artists / Golden jubilee: Various artists / Old maid in a garret: Various artists / Ballinderry: Various artists / Carrickfergus: Various artists / Castle of Dromore, The: Various artists / Reilly's daughter: Various artists / Gem of the roe, The: Various artists / Whisky, you're the devil: Various artists / Green fields of France: Various artists/ Doffer's song: Various artists / Roisin dubh: Various artists / Leaving of Liverpool: Various artists.
LP: . . . . **GES 1232**
MC: . . . . **KGEC 1232**
MCSET: . . . . **DTO 10290**
MCSET: . . . . **DTO 10285**

SONGS OF PERCY FRENCH (Various artists).
LP: . . . . **HRL 219**

SONGS OF THE EMERALD ISLE (Various artists).
Tracks: / Galway Bay: Locke, Josef (Track 1) / Spinning wheel: Murphy, Delia (Track 2) / Star of the County Down: McCormack, John (Track 3) / Ballyhoe: McGoldrick,Anna (Track 4) / Old bog road: Drennan, Tommy(Track 5) / Coortin' in the kitchen: Murphy, Delia (Track 6) / Mother Machree: MacEwan,Sydney (Track 7) / Trottin' to the fair: Murray, Ruby (Track 8) / Banks of my own lovely Lee, The: O'Se, Sean (Track 9) / When Irish eyes are smiling: Jones, Sandie (Track 10) / Pretty Irish girl, A: O'Dowda, Brendan & Ruby Murray (Track 11) / Mountains of Mourne: O'Dowda, Brendan (Track 12) / Castlebar Fair: Gallagher, Bridie (Track 13) / Eileen Oge: Feis Eireann Singers (Track 14) / Rose of Tralee, The: O'Dowda, Brendan / Eileen O'Grady: Gallagher, Bridie / Danny boy: O'Se, Sean / Connemara: O'Dowda, Brendan & Ruby Murray / Doonaree: Murray, Ruby / Sweet Marie: O'Dowda, Brendan / Flower of sweet Strabane: Gallagher, Bridie / Whiskey in the jar: Dubliners/ Three drunken maidens: Planxty / Dan Malone: Hasson, Gemma / Liffey barges: Owens, Jesse / Galway races: Dubliners / Kitty of Coleraine: Bunratty Singers / Bantry Bay: O'Se, Sean.
2LP: . . . . **DL 1104**
MC: . . . . **TCDL 1104**

SONGS OF THE ULSTER PROTESTANT (Various artists).
Tracks: / Union cruiser: Carson, S. / Aghalee heroes: Gilligan, F / Green grassy slopes: Muirhead, R./ Derry's walls: Patterson, S / Protestant boys: Patterson, S / Orange and blue: Williams, K. / Blackman's dream: Patterson, S / Battle of Garvagh: Hill, G. / Lily O: Patterson, S / Boyne water: Patterson, S / Sash, The: Patterson, S / Sprigs of Kilrea: Hunter, G. / Auld orange flute: Williamson / No surrender: Patterson, S.
LP: . . . . **DULP 10**
MC: . . . . **CDULP 10**

SONGS OUR FATHER LOVED VOL. 1 (Various artists).
Tracks: / When irish eyes are smiling: Various artists / Cottage by the Lee: Various artists / Conemara cradle song: Various artists / Minstrel boy: Various artists / Hills of Donegal: Various artists / Shamrock time in Donegal: Various artists / Eileen MacManus: Various artists / Ireland I love you: Various artists/ Carraigdoon: Various artists / Lake near Killaloe: Various artists / Ballad of J.F.K.: Various artists/ Tipperary so far away: Various artists / Whistling Phil McHugh: Various artists / Castle of Dromore: Various artists / Danny Boy: Various artists / Slattery's mounted fut: Various artists / Meeting of the waters: Various artists / Garden where the praties grow: Various artists / Noreen Bawn: Various artists / Lark in the clear air: Various artists.
MC: . . . . **IHMC 1**

SONGS OUR FATHER LOVED VOL. 2 (Various artists).
Tracks: / Green glens of Antrim: Various artists / If you're Irish: Various artists / Silver threads among the gold: Various artists / Galway Bay: Various artists / Mother's love's a blessing, A: Various artists/ It's a great day for the Irish: Various artists / Lovely Derry on the banks of the Foyle: Various artists / Doonaree: Various artists / Dun Laoghaire: Various artists / I'll tell my Ma: Various artists / Rose of Rosecommon: Various artists / Moonlight: Various artists / Homes of Donegal: Various artists / Boys from County Mayo: Various artists / Sweet Innismore: Various artists / My lagan love: Various artists/ Liffey valley: Various artists / Emerald Isle express: Various artists / Old Irish blessing, An: Various artists / Beautiful Bundoran: Various artists.
MC: . . . . **IHMC 2**

SOUND OF IRISH FOLK Various artists (Various artists).
Tracks: / Fields of Athenry: Various artists / Rose of Allendale: Various artists / Ferryman, The: Various artists / Rare ould times: Various artists / Where my Eileen is waiting: Various artists / I'm a rover: Various artists / Tripping up the stairs (a trip to Athlone): Various artists / Man you don't meet every day, A: Various artists / John O'Dreams: Various artists / Spancil Hill: Various artists / Town I loved so well, The: Various artists / Inner city song, The: Various artists / Bogie's bonnie belle: Various artists/ Her father didn't like me anyway: Various artists / Easy and slow: Various artists / I live not where I love: Various artists.
LP: . . . . **DOLT 3001**
MC: . . . . **DOCT 3001**

SOUNDS OF IRELAND (Various artists).
Tracks: / Kellys, The: Murray, Ruby / Mountains of Mourne: O'Dowda, Brendan / Eavesdropper: Ardellis Ceili Band / Donnybrook boy: Ardellis Ceili Band / Visit to Ireland, A: Ardellis Ceili Band / Where the river Shannon flows: Gallagher, Bridie / Galway races: Dubliners / It's a great day for the Irish: Murray, Ruby/ Galway Bay: Irish Guards Band / With my shillelagh under me arm: Irish Guards Band / Dear old Donegal: Irish Guards Band / Dear little shamrock (live): O'Dowda, Brendan / Whiskey in the jar: Dubliners / Donnybrook fair: Irish National Orchestra / Tates tantrums: Irish National Orchestra / Rakes of Kildare, The: Irish National Orchestra / Too-ra-loo-ra-loo-ra: Shannonside Ceili Band / Mother Machree: MacEwan,Sydney / Flower of sweet Strabane: Gallagher, Bridie / Danny boy: Murray, Ruby / Rose of Killarney: MacEwan,Sydney/ Queen of Connemara: Ardellis Ceili Band / Galway bay: Murray, Ruby / Paddy on the railroad: Gallowglass Ceili Band / Miss McLeod: Gallowglass Ceili Band / Typically Irish: O'Dowda, Brendan / Kelly the boy from Killane: Dubliners / Finnegan's wake: Irish National Orchestra / Connemara: O'Dowda, Brendan & Ruby Murray/ Ireland my home: MacEwan,Sydney / Slievenamon: Gallagher, Bridie / When Irish eyes are smiling: Murray, Ruby / Fairmoye lasses and sporting Paddy: Dubliners / Pretty Irish girl, A: O'Dowda, Brendan & Ruby Murray/ Come back Paddy Reilly to Ballyjamesduff: Feis Eireann Singers.
2LP: . . . . **DL 1125**
MC: . . . . **TCDL 1125**

SOUVENIR OF IRELAND (Various artists).
LP: . . . . **STAL 1040**

STARS OF IRELAND (Various artists).
Tracks: / Hello darlin': Various artists / Slaney Valley: Various artists.
LP: . . . . **HRL 181**

SWEET 16 SONGS OF IRELAND (Various artists).
MC: . . . . **OCE 2469**

THREE LEAF SHAMROCK (10 original hits from home) (Various artists).
MC: . . . . **CHR 12**

TOP OF THE MORNING (Various artists).
LP: . . . . **HPE 607**
MC: . . . . **HPC 607**

TRADITIONAL IRISH FAVOURITES Various artists (Various artists).
LP: . . . . **HPE 639**

TRADITIONAL IRISH SONGS OF FREEDOM (Various artists).
LP: . . . . **STAL 8004**

TRAVELLING PEOPLE OF IRELAND (Irish tinker music) (Various artists).
LP: . . . . **LLST 7178**

TRIBUTE TO GALWAY (Various artists).
Tracks: / Connemara by the lake: Various artists / Dear old Galway town: Various artists / Old Claddagh ring: Various artists / Connemara cradle song: Various artists / Farewell to Galway: Various artists.
LP: . . . . **HPE 677**
MC: . . . . **HPC 677**

TRIBUTE TO PRESIDENT KENNEDY (Various artists).
LP: . . . . **HARP 7**

TRIP ROUND THE NORTH (Various artists).
LP: . . . . **HPE 675**
MC: . . . . **HPC 675**

ULSTER HERITAGE (Various artists).
Tracks: / Lambeg drum: Various artists ((intro)) / Derry's walls: Houl Yer Whist / Ould orange flute: Wallace, Hugh & Tillie / Protestant boys: Patterson, Sam / Shepherd's boy: Wallace, Hugh / Green grassy slopes: District Singers / Enniskillen Dragoons: District Singers / South Down militia: District Singers / Orange and blue: Houl Yer Whist / Orange tree, The: Various artists / Blackman's dream: Patterson, Sam / Sprigs of Kilrea: Patterson, Sam / Ducks of Magheralin: District Singers / Sash, The: District Singers / Aughalee heroes: District Singers.
MC: . . . . **CDULP 15**

ULSTER ON THE MARCH FOR GOD & ULSTER (Various artists).
Tracks: / What a friend we have in Jesus: Star of Tyrone Accordian Band / Onward Christian soldiers: Star of Tyrone Accordian Band / Battle of the Somme: Armstrong, Robert Memorial Band / Archie McKinlay: Armstrong, Robert Memorial Band / Amazing grace: Bailles Mills Accordian Band / Old rugged cross, The: Bailles Mills Accordian Band/ Church in the wildwood, The: Vow Accordian Band / Nearer my God to thee: Murley Silver Band / When the roll is called up yonder: Baillies Mills Accordion Band / Mine eyes have seen the glory: Baillies Mills Accordion Band/ Along the river: Vow Accordian Band / Battle of Garvagh: Vow Accordian Band / Tartan soldier:

Millrow Loyalist Flute Band / Aghalee Heroes: *Millrow Loyalist Flute Band* / Blackman's dream: *Millrow Loyalist Flute* Band / Ramblin' Ulsterman: *Millrow Loyalist Flute Band* / Aurella: *Ballykeigle Accordion Band* / Abide with me: *Ballykeigle Accordion Band* / Onward Christian soldiers: *Baillies Mills Accordion Band* / Stand up for Jesus: *Baillies Mills Accordion Band* / Keep right on to the end of the road: *Star of Tyrone Accordian Band* / Land of hope and glory: *Star of Tyrone Accordian Band* / No surrender: *Albertbridge Accordian Band.*
MC: . . . . **CDULP 16**

ULSTER SAYS NO (Various artists).
Tracks: / No surrender: *Various artists* / Lily O: *Various artists* / Boyne water: *Various artists* / Sash, The: *Various artists* / Sprigs of Kilrea: *Various artists* / Orange and blue: *Various artists* / Battle of Garvagh: *Various artists* / Union cruiser: *Various artists* / Aghalee heroes: *Various artists*/ Green grassy slopes: *Various artists* / Derry's walls: *Various artists* / Protestant boys: *Various artists*/ Auld orange flute: *Various artists* / Blackman's dream: *Various artists.*
MC: . . . . **CDULP 14**

ULSTER WILL ALWAYS SAY NO (Various artists).
Tracks: / In the defence of the orange and blue: *Various artists* / Bold Orange heroes of Comber: *Various artists*/ Aughalee heroes: *Various artists* / Waringford rising star: *Various artists* / Biddy McDowal: *Various artists*/ Battle of Garvagh: *Various artists* / Sash, The: *Various artists* / Rifles, The: *Various artists* / Protestant boys: *Various artists* / Derry's walls: *Various artists* / Paisley: *Various artists* / Dolly's Brae: *Various artists* / Crimson banner: *Various artists* / God be with you till we meet again: *Various artists.*
MC: . . . . **CDULP 17**

UP TYRONE (Various artists).
LP: . . . . **UNKNOWN**

VERY BEST OF IRISH COUNTRY (Various artists).
LP: . . . . **FALP 009**

VERY BEST OF IRISH COUNTRY, VOLUME 2 (Various artists).
MC: . . . . **FACS 014**

WELCOME TO IRELAND (Various artists).
Tracks: / Forty shades of green: *Various artists* / Boys from County Armagh: *Various artists* / I'll take you home again Kathleen: *Various artists* / My Lagan softly flowing: *Various artists* / Mountains of Mourne: *Various* artists / Jarvey was a leprechaun (The): *Various artists* / When Irish eyes are smiling: *Various artists*/ Spinning wheel: *Various artists* / Isle of Innisfree: *Various artists* / Peter Byrnes' fancy: *Various artists*/ Ballybunion by the sea: *Various artists* / Castle of Dromore: *Various artists* / Creeping docken: *Various artists.*
LP: . . . . **GES 1221**
MC: . . . . **KGEC 1221**

WELCOME TO NORTHERN IRELAND (Various artists).
Tracks: / Forty shades of green: *Various artists* / Mountains of Mourne: *Various artists* / Faughan side: *Various artists* / Village in County Tyrone: *Various artists* / Ould Lammas Fair: *Various artists* / Inniskilling dragoons: *Various artists* / Ceili: *Various artists* / Boys from the County Armagh: *Various artists* / Lovely Derry on the banks of the Foyle: *Various artists* / Green glens of Antrim: *Various artists* / Lovely Lough Erne: *Various* artists / Old cross of Arboe: *Various artists* / Star of County Down: *Various artists* / Shores of Lough Neagh: *Various artists.*
LP: . . . . **HRL 185**

WHERE THE BLARNEY ROSES GROW (Various artists).
LP: . . . . **HPE 647**

WISH YOU WERE HERE 14 beautiful songs from Co.Donegal (Various artists).
Tracks: / Beautiful Bundoran: *Various artists* / Homes of Donegal: *Various artists* / Mulroy bay: *Various* artists / Donegal Danny: *Various artists* / Rose of Aranmore: *Various artists* / Trasna na d'Tonnta: *Various* artists / Girl from Donegal: *Various artists* / Mary from Dunloe: *Various artists* / Hills of Donegal: *Various* artists / Letterkenny Town: *Various artists* / Hills of Glenswilly: *Various artists* / Boys of Killybegs: *Various artists* / Three leaf shamrock from Glenore: *Various artists* / Star of Donegal: *Various artists.*
LP: . . . . **HRL 200**

WORLD OF IRELAND (Various artists).
LP: . . . . **SPA 53**
MC: . . . . **KCSP 53**

Ireland's Own

IRELAND'S OWN (ROSE OF TRALEE) (Various artists).
LP: . . . . **PHL 491**

Iremonger, Valentin

BY SANDYMOUNT STRAND.
LP: . . . . **CCT 12**

Irene

IRENE Original cast recording of 1920 London Production (Various artists).
LP: . . . . **MES 7057**

Irie, Clement

FOLLOW ME (LP).
LP: . . . . **HPD 15LP**
LP: . . . . **BMLP 028**

GO SIT DOWN (See also Flourgon) (Irie, Clement & Flourgon).

Irie, Derek

ME WANT A LADY.
Tracks: / Get up and run / Girl wha' you get out a man / Me want lady / Girl you mash up / Nuff loving in me / Cry for the girl / Came we go so / Got to have something / We want money / She gone.
LP: . . . . **WENLP 3036**

Irie, Tippa

AH-ME-DIS.
LP: . . . . **GTLP 3**

DRIFTING AWAY (See under Kenton, Janet) (Irie, Tippa & Janet Kenton).

IS IT REALLY HAPPENING TO ME.
Tracks: / Unlucky burglar / It's good to have the feeling you're the best / You're the best (86 remix) / Telephone, The / Heatbeat / Robotic reggae / Married life / Football hooligan / Complain neighbour / Hello darling / Is it really happening to me.
LP: . . . . **TIPLP 1**
MC: . . . . **TIPC 1**

NEW DECADE, A.
MC: . . . . **MCT 1087**
LP: . . . . **MLPS 1087**

ORIGINAL RAGAMUFFIN.
LP: . . . . **MLPS 1041**
MC: . . . . **MCT 1041**
LP: **846 501 1**
MC: **846 501 4**

RAGAMUFFIN GIRL (See under Hunningale, Peter) (Irie, Tippa & Peter Hunningale).

TWO SIDES OF TIPPA IRIE.
Tracks: / Sentimental lover / Turn you on / Plumpy baby / Auf wiedersehen / Pressure / Chain smoker / Crack / Mad / Hip hip / Say, The / Leave the rastaman.
LP: . . . . **GTLP 1**
MC: . . . . **GTC 1**

Irie, Welton

GHETTOMAN CORNER.
LP: . . . . **JGMLP 01344**

Iris, Donnie

FORTUNE 410.
LP: . . . . **MCF 3173**

KING COOL.
Tracks: / Love is like a rock / Agnes.
LP: . . . . **MCF 3127**

Irish...

BEST OF COUNTRY IRISH (Various artists).
LP: . . . . **KLP 255**

BEST OF IRISH BALLADS (Various artists).
MC: **4TA 9003**

BEST OF IRISH BALLADS, VOL 1 (Various artists).
Tracks: / Galway races: *Various artists* / Come to the bower: *Various artists* / Sam Hall: *Various artists*/ Cliffs of Dooneen: *Various artists* / Donegal Danny: *Various artists* / Annachie Gordon: *Various artists*/ Mary from Dungloe: *Various artists* / Whiskey in the jar: *Various artists* / Salonika: *Various artists*/ Spanish lady: *Various artists* / I live not where I love: *Various artists* / Band played waltzing Matilda, The: *Various artists* / Arthur McBride: *Various artists* / Four strong winds: *Various artists* / Fiddlers green: *Various artists* / Rare ould times: *Various artists.*
LP: . . . . **DOLS 2003**
MC: . . . . **DOCS 2003**

BEST OF IRISH BALLADS, VOL 2 (Various artists).
Tracks: / Farewell to the Rhonda: *Various artists* / Nancy Spain: *Various artists* / Lakes of Coolfin: *Various* artists / Three score and ten: *Various artists* / Deportees: *Various artists* / Recruiting sergeant, The: *Various artists* / Clare to here: *Various artists* / Town is not their own, The: *Various artists* / Town of Ballybay, The: *Various artists* / Crack was ninety in the Isle of Man, The: *Various artists* / Boston burglar: *Various artists* / Banks of the roses: *Various artists* / Lark in the morning, The: *Various artists* / Derroll in the rain: *Various artists* / Sun is burning, The: *Various artists* / Farewell to Nova Scotia: *Various artists.*
LP: . . . . **DOLS 2009**
MC: . . . . **DOCS 2009**

BEST OF IRISH CEILE, VOLUME 1 (Various artists).
LP: . . . . **DOLB 7023**

BEST OF IRISH CEILE, VOLUME 2 (Various artists).
LP: . . . . **DOLB 7024**

BEST OF IRISH CEILE, VOLUME 3 (Various artists).
LP: . . . . **DOLB 7025**

BEST OF IRISH CEILE, VOLUME 4 (Various artists).
LP: . . . . **DOLB 7026**

BEST OF IRISH FOLK (Various artists).
MC: . . . . **ASK 764**
2LP: . . . . **CR 5165**
MCSET: . . . . **CRT 5165**

BEST OF IRISH FOLK (CASTLE) (Various artists).
Tracks: / Rocky road to Dublin: *Dubliners* / Curragh of Kildare, The: *Furey, Finbar & Eddie* / Glenside polka: *Glenside Ceilidh Band* / Henry joy: *Grehan Sisters* / Handsome cabin boy, The: *Sweeney's Men* / Frog's wedding: *Johnstons* / Exiles' jig: *Sweeney's Men* / Lambs on the green hills: *Johnstons* / Spanish cloak, The: *Furey, Finbar & Eddie* / Golden jubilee: *Glenside Ceilidh Band* / Cook in the kitchen, The: *Dubliners*/ Orange and the green, The: *Grehan Sisters* / St. Patrick's breastplate: *Wood, Royston & Heather* / Inis dhun ramha: *Na Fili* / Foggy dew, The: *Imlach, Hamish* / Three pieces by O'Carolan: *Renbourn, John* / Madame Bonaparte: *Furey, Finbar* / Rakish Paddy: *Furey, Finbar* / Roisin dubh: *Dubliners* / Chanter's tune: *Na Fili* / Spanish lady: *Johnstons* / Killarney boys of pleasure: *Swarbrick, Dave.*
2LP: . . . . **CCSLP 221**
MC: . . . . **CCSMC 221**

BEST OF IRISH FOLK GROUPS (Various artists).
Tracks: / Bunclody: *Various artists* / Sullivan's John: *Various artists* / Slieve Gallion Braes: *Various artists.*
LP: . . . . **HRL 134**
MC: . . . . **CHRL 134**

BEST OF IRISH FOLK (HARMAC LABEL) (Various artists).
MC: . . . . **HMC 064**

BEST OF IRISH FOLK MUSIC (Various artists).
MC: . . . . **TC STAL 1047**

BEST OF IRISH JIGS AND REELS VOL.2, THE (Various artists).
MC: **4TA 9002**

BEST OF IRISH JIGS AND REELS VOL.1, THE (Various artists).
MC: **4TA 9001**

BEST OF IRISH JIGS, REELS & BALLADS (Various artists).
MC: . . . . **UNIMC 5003**

BEST OF IRISH REBEL SONGS, THE (Various artists).
Tracks: / Four green fields: *Various artists* / Sea around us: *Various artists* / Rising of the moon: *Various* artists / Black and tan gun: *Various artists* / Three flowers: *Various artists* / 20 men from Dublin town: *Various artists* / West's awake: *Various artists* / Bold Robert Emmett: *Various artists* / God save Ireland: *Various artists* / Down by the Glenside: *Various artists* / Michael Gaughan: *Various artists* / Boys of the Old Brigade: *Various artists.*
LP: . . . . **CSDBL 518**

BEST OF IRISH SHOWBANDS (Various artists).
Tracks: / Ireland swings: *Various artists* / Pub with no beer, A: *Various artists* / Chance of a lifetime: *Various artists* / Gentle mother: *Various artists* / Remember me, I'm the one who loves you: *Various artists* / Johnny: *Various artists* / Way you wrinkle your nose, The: *Various artists* / Cottage in Donegal: *Various artists*/ I need you: *Various artists* / Most beautiful girl, The: *Various artists* / Nobody's child: *Various artists*/ Answer your phone: *Various artists* / Harbour lights: *Various artists* / My elusive dreams: *Various artists*/ If: *Various artists.*
MC: . . . . **4 HOM 003**

BEST OF IRISH TRADITIONAL MUSIC (Various artists).
MC: . . . . **COX 1002**

BEST OF IRISH TRADITIONAL MUSIC & BALLADS (Various artists).
Tracks: / Shores of Lough Bran, The: *Various artists* / O'Carolan tribute: *Various artists* / Nancy Spain: *Various* artists / Brian Boru's march: *Various artists* / Danny boy: *Various artists* / Leaving Nancy: *Various* artists / Cill aodain: *Various artists* / Paddy's green shamrock shore: *Various artists* / Gipsy Dave: *Various* artists / Glenbeigh hornpipe: *Various artists* / Mountain lark: *Various artists* / Musical priest: *Various* artists / Old rustic bridge: *Various artists* / Nil se ina la: *Various artists* / Cill chais: *Various artists* / Fanny Power: *Various artists* / Banks of Claudy, The: *Various artists.*
MC: . . . . **ALPC 1**

FEAST OF IRISH MUSIC (Various artists).
LP: . . . . **HMKC 063**

FESTIVAL OF IRISH FOLK MUSIC (Various artists).
LP: . . . . **EULP 1156**
MC: . . . . **EUMC 1156**

FESTIVAL OF IRISH FOLK MUSIC (Various artists).
MCSET: **CHC3 1013**

FESTIVAL OF IRISH FOLK MUSIC (DOLPHIN LABEL) (Various artists).
MCSET: . . . . **CHBX 3 1013**

FESTIVAL OF IRISH FOLK MUSIC, VOL.2 (Various artists).
MCSET: . . . . **CHC 1035**

GOLDEN HOUR OF IRISH SHOWBAND HITS (Various artists).
MC: . . . . **KGHMC 128**

GOLDEN HOUR PRESENTS IRISH SHOWBAND HITS (Various artists).
LP: . . . . **GH 598**

GREAT IRISH FOLK FESTIVAL, THE (Various artists).
MC: . . . . **HSMC 026**

IRISH ALBUM, THE (Various artists).
LP: . . . . **GL 90459**
MC: . . . . **GK 90459**

IRISH CEILIDH DANCE TIME (Various artists).
LP: . . . . **HPE 678**
MC: . . . . **HPC 678**

IRISH CHRISTMAS FAVOURITES (Various artists).
MC: . . . . **LNMC 7014**

IRISH DANCING (Ceoltoiri ros na ri) (Various artists).
LP: . . . . **STOL 129**

IRISH ECHOES (Various artists).
LP: . . . . **HM 042**

IRISH EXPLOSION (Various artists).
LP: . . . . **SE 8006**

IRISH FAVOURITES (Various artists).
MC: . . . . **SMAC 9014**

IRISH FESTIVAL (Various artists).
LP: . . . . **LUN 042**
MC: . . . . **CLUN 042**

IRISH PARTY REQUESTS (Various artists).
LP: . . . . **HRL 152**
MC: . . . . **CHRL 152**

IRISH PIPE MUSIC (Various artists).
LP: . . . . **H 72059**

IRISH PUB DRINKING SONGS (Various artists).
LP: . . . . **CGLEN 008**

IRISH PUB SINGALONG/IRISH REBEL SONGS (Various artists).
LP: . . . . **CSDBL 524**

IRISH PUB SONG TIME (Various artists).
Tracks: / Cottage on the old Dungannon road, The: *Duncan, Hugo* / Old arboe: *Begley, Philomena* / Where is my Nora?: *Stuart, Gene* / Shore of Loch Brann: *Ely, Pat* / Four country roads: *Watt, John* / Turfman from Ardee: *Kerr, John* / Boys from County Mayo: *Margo* / Cottage by the Lee: *Cunningham, Larry* / Lough Sheelin: *McCarrfey, Frank* / Marta, the flower of sweet Strabane: *Brolly, Anne & Francie* / Rose of Arranmore: *Donaghy, Eileen* / Spancil hill: *Dynes, Sean* / Old mud cabin on the hill: *Big Ivan* / Mother's love, A: *Teamwork*/ Rose of Mooncoin: *Woods, Pat* / Old rustic bridge: *Breen, Ann* / Boys from County Armagh: *Glenn, John*/ Typical Irishman: *McCaffrey, Leo* / Any Tipperary town: *Margo* / Sweet Mary: *Coll, Brian.*
LP: . . . . **HRL 205**
MC: . . . . **CHRL 205**

IRISH REBEL SONGS (Various artists).
LP: . . . . **ACL 1136**

IRISH REELS FOR GUITAR (Anthology) (Various artists).
LP: . . . . **KM 157**

IRISH REVOLUTIONARY SONGS VOL. 1 (Various artists).

LP: . . . . CDUB 8001

IRISH REVOLUTIONARY SONGS VOL. 2 (Various artists).
LP: . . . . CDUB 8002

IRISH SING RUGBY SONGS (Various artists).
LP: . . . . ILP 1083

IRISH STARTIME TRADITIONAL (Various artists).
LP: . . . . IST 4444

PADDY AND THE BIDDIES (Various artists).
MC: . . . . SMAC 9016

REBEL SONGS OF IRELAND 2 (Various artists).
LP: . . . . BRL 4055

SLIGO CEILI (Various artists).
MC: . . . . COX 1022

TRADITIONAL MUSIC AND SONG FROM GALWAY (Various artists).
MC: . . . . GTDC 012

WALTZING IN IRELAND (Various artists).
MC: . . . . DOCB 7034

Irish Country Four

SONGS, BALLADS & INSTRUMENTAL TUNES FROM ULSTER.
LP: 12TS 209

Irish Gaelic

SONGS IN IRISH GAELIC (& OTHERS) (See under O'Donnell, Conal for details) (O'Donnell, Conal).

Irish Guards Band

CHANGING OF THE GUARD.
Tracks: / Wellington / San Lorenzo / Kerry march / Sons of the brave / Pique dame / Cockles and mussels / Farandole / Bunch of thyme / Quis separabit / Let Erin remember / Cormac of Tara / Changing of the guard / Star of St.Patrick, The / St.Patrick's day / HRH The Duke of Cambridge / Irish tune from County Derry.
LP: . . . . BND 1002
MC: . . . . ZC BND 1002

DRUMS AND PIPES OF THE 1ST. BATTALION.
LP: . . . . MM 0576

MARCHES FROM THE CLASSICS.
Tracks: / Radetzky march / Anvil chorus / Imperial march / In the hall of the mountain king / Procession of the nobles / March of the toreadors / Wedding march / Marche militaire / Wedding march from a Midsummer Nights Dream / French military march / March and cortege from The Queen Of Sheba / Bridal march from Lohengrin / March from the Pathetique symphony / Let Erin remember.
LP: . . . . BND 1018
MC: . . . . ZC BND 1018

MUSIC FOR REMEMBRANCE.
Tracks: / National anthem / March of the Royal British Legion / Heart of oak / Life on the ocean wave, A / Red, white & blue / Lass who loved a sailor, The / Great little army / W.R.A.C. march / Grey and scarlet / Old comrades / Ulster defence regiment march / Royal Air Force march past / Holyrood / Princess Royals red cross march / Boys of the old brigade / Sunset / Cwn Rhondda / Abide with me / Last post / Reveille / Eternal father strong to save / Rule Britannia / Heart of oak / Minstrel boy, The / Men of Harlech / Isle of beauty / David of the white rock / Oft in the stilly night / Nimrod / Laid in earth / Solemn melody / Funeral march / O God our help in ages past / March melody / It's a long way to Tipperary / Pack up your troubles / There'll always be an England / Keep the home fires burning / Madamoiselle from Armentieres / Take me back to dear old blighty / Run rabbit run / Kiss me goodnight Sargeant Major / Hang out the washing on the Siegfried line / Wish me good luck as you wave goodbye / Beer barrel polka / Lili Marlene / Walting Mathilda / Maple leaf forever / Maori battalion marching song.
2LP: . . . . BNC 3004
MCSET: . . . . ZC BND 3004

Irish Knights

MANTLE OF GREEN.
MC: . . . . GTDC 039

Irish Pipe Band

IRISH PIPE BAND (see under Queensland Irish).

Irish R.M.

IRISH RM, THE (TV soundtrack) (Various artists).
Tracks: / Major Yeates' fancy: *Various artists* / Teetotaller, The: *Various artists* / Sally's lament: *Various* artists / Mrs Cadogan's waltz: *Various artists* / Sheehy's runaway foal: *Various artists* / Fire at the Aussolas: *Various artists* / Phillipa's dance: *Various artists* / Sultan wins the race: *Various artists* / Lady Knox and Mrs Knox: *Various artists.*
LP: . . . . RITZLP 0011
MC: . . . . RITZLC 0011

Irish Rovers

HAVE ANOTHER PARTY.
Tracks: / Whisky, you're the devil / Rollin' river / One Sunday morning / Unicorn / Boys are going drinking tonight, The / New York girls / Swallows tail / Frail thou' my spirit may be / Orange and the green, The / Another little drink / Down in devils den / Bonnie Kellswater / Here's to the horse / Bottle of wine.
LP: . . . . ITV 469
MC: . . . . KITV 469

TALL SHIPS & SALTY DOGS.
MC: . . . . KITV 508

WASN'T THAT A PARTY.
Tracks: / Pheasant plucker's son / Does your chewing gum lose it's flavour / Black velvet band / Instrumental / Jigs / Maggie / What's a nice guy like me... / Dublin O'shea / Whiskey on a Sunday / Dig a little deeper in the well / Years may come.
LP: . . . . ITV 438
MC: . . . . KITV 438

Irish Tradition

CORNER HOUSE, THE.
LP: . . . . SIF 1016
MC: . . . . CSIF 1016

TIMES WE'VE HAD, THE.
LP: . . . . SIF 1063
MC: . . . . CSIF 1063

Irish-American...

IRISH-AMERICAN SONGS AND DANCE MUSIC Late 20s (Various artists).
LP: . . . . FL 9010

Irma La Douce

IRMA LA DOUCE (Film soundtrack) (Various artists).
Tracks: / Dis-donc, dis-donc: *Various artists* / Meet Irma: *Various artists* / Irma la douce: *Various artists*/ Nestor the honest policeman: *Various artists* / Our language of love: *Various artists* / Market/our language of love, The: *Various artists* / Easy living the hard way/our language of love: *Various artists* / Escape: *Various* artists / Return of Lord, The: *Various artists* / In the tub with fieldglasses: *Various artists* / Goodbye Lord: *Various artists* / I'm sorry Irma: *Various artists* / But that's another story: *Various artists.*
LP: 4502251
MC: 4502254

IRMA LA DOUCE (Original Broadway Cast) (Various artists).
LP: . . . . AOS 2029

Iron Angels

HELLISH CROSSFIRE.
LP: 081 853

WINGS OF WAR.
LP: . . . . SH 0047

Iron Brew

IRON BREW.
LP: . . . . LLM 132

Iron Butterfly

IN-A-GADDA-DA-VIDA.
Tracks: / Most anything you want / My mirage / Termination / Are you happy / In a gadda-da-vida / Flowers and beads.
LP: . . . . K 40022

TWO ORIGINALS OF IRON BUTTERFLY (Ball and Metamorphosis).
Tracks: / In the time of our lives / Soul experience / Lonely boy / Real fright / In the crowds / It must be love / Her favourite style / Filled with fear / Belda bear / Free flight / New day / Shady lady / Best years of our lives / Slower than guns / Stone believer / Soldier in our town / Easy rider (let the wind pay the way) / Butterfly bleu.
LP: . . . . K 80003

Iron City Houserockers

LOVE'S SO TOUGH.
LP: . . . . MCF 3031

Iron Eagle

IRON EAGLE (Film soundtrack) (Various artists).
Tracks: / One vision: *Queen* / Iron eagle (never say die): *King Kobra* / These are the good times: *Martin, Eric* / Maniac house: *Katrina & The Waves* / Intense: *Clinton, George* / Hide in the rainbow: *Dio*/ It's too late: *Helix* / Love can make you cry: *Urgent* / This ragin' fire: *Axis, Jon Butcher* / Road of the gypsy: *Adrenalin.*
LP: . . . . EST 2013
MC: . . . . TCEST 2013

Iron Fist

HOOKED ON ROCK.
LP: . . . . NL 70710
MC: . . . . NK 70710

Iron Horse

EVERYTHING IS GREY.
LP: . . . . K 50730

IRON HORSE.
Tracks: / One and only / Sweet Lui-Louise / Jump back in the light / You gotta let go / Tumbleweed / State line blues / Watch me fly / Old fashioned / She's got it / There ain't no cure.
LP: . . . . K 50598

Iron Maiden

ACES HIGH.
Tracks: / Aces high / Rainbow's gold / Cross-eyed Mary / Number of the beast, The.
LP: . . . . EMS 50148

IRON MAIDEN.
Tracks: / Prowler / Remember tomorrow / Running free / Phantom of the opera / Transylvania / Strange world / Charlotte the harlot / Iron Maiden.
LP: . . . . FA 41 3121 1
MC: . . . . FA 41 3121 4
LP: . . . . EMC 3330
LP: . . . . FA 3121
MC: . . . . TCFA 3121

IRON MAIDEN: INTERVIEW PICTURE DISC.
LPPD: . . . . BAK 2037

KILLERS.
Tracks: / Ides of March / Wrathchild / Murders in the Rue Morgue / Another life / Genghis Khan / Innocent exile / Killers / Prodigal son / Purgatory / Drifter.
LP: . . . . FA 3122
MC: . . . . TCFA 3122
LP: . . . . EMC 3357

LIVE AFTER DEATH (World Slavery Tour).
Tracks: / Aces high / Two minutes to midnight / Trooper, The / Revelations / Flight of Icarus / Rime of the ancient mariner, The / Powerslave / Number of the beast, The / Hallowed be thy name / Iron Maiden / Run to the hills / Running free / Wrathchild / Twenty two Acacia Avenue / Children of the damned / Die with your boots on / Phantom of the opera.
2LP: . . . . RIP 1
MCSET: . . . . TC RIP 1
2LP: . . . . ATAK 99
2LP: . . . . ES 240 426 3
MCSET: . . . . ES 240 426 5
MCSET: . . . . TCATAK 99
2LP: . . . . ATAK 141
MCSET: . . . . TCATAK 141
2LP: . . . . FAD 3248
MCSET: . . . . TCFAD 3248

MAIDEN JAPAN.
Tracks: / Running free / Remember tomorrow / Wrathchild / Killers / Innocent exile.
LP: . . . . MLP 15000
MC: 4LP 15000

MAIDENMANIA.
LPS: . . . . MAIDEN 1

NO PRAYER FOR THE DYING.
Tracks: / Tailgunner / Holy smoke / No prayer for the dying / Public enema number one / Fates warning / Assassin, The / Run silent run deep / Hooks in you / Bring your daughter...to the slaughter / Mother Russia.
LP: . . . . EMD 1017
MC: . . . . TCEMD 1017
LPPD: . . . . EMDPD 1017

NUMBER OF THE BEAST.
Tracks: / Invaders, The / Children of the damned / Prisoner, The / 22, Acacia Avenue / Number of the beast, The / Run to the hills / Gangland / Hallowed be thy name.
LP: . . . . FA 3178
MC: . . . . TCFA 3178
LP: . . . . EMC 3400
MC: . . . . TCEMC 3400

PIECE OF MIND.
Tracks: / Where eagles dare, Theme from / Revelations / Flight of Icarus / Die with your boots on / Trooper, The / Still life / Quest for fire / Sun and steel / To tame a land.
LP: . . . . EMA 800
MC: . . . . TCEMA 800
LP: . . . . ATAK 97
MC: . . . . TCATAK 97
LP: . . . . ATAK 139
MC: . . . . TCATAK 139
LP: . . . . FA 3245
MC: . . . . TCFA 3245

POWERSLAVE.
Tracks: / Aces high / 2 Minutes to midnight / Losfer words (big 'Orra) / Flash of the blade / Duellists, The / Black in the village / Powerslave / Rime of the ancient mariner, The.
LP: . . . . POWER 1
MC: . . . . TC POWER 1
LPPD: . . . . POWERP 1
LP: . . . . ATAK 96
LP: . . . . EJ 2402001
MC: . . . . EJ 2402004
MC: . . . . TCATAK 96
LP: . . . . ATAK 140
MC: . . . . TCATAK 140
LP: . . . . FA 3244
MC: . . . . TCFA 3244

SEVENTH SON OF A SEVENTH SON.
Tracks: / Moonchild / Infinite dreams / Can I play with madness / Evil that men do, The / Seventh son of a seventh son / Prophecy, The / Clairvoyant, The / Only the good die young.
LP: . . . . EMD 1006
MC: . . . . TCEMD 1006
LPPD: . . . . EMDP 1006
LP: . . . . ATAK 143
MC: . . . . TCATAK 143
LP: . . . . FA 3247
MC: . . . . TCFA 3247

SOMEWHERE IN TIME.
Tracks: / Caught somewhere in time / Wasted years / Sea of madness / Heaven can wait / Loneliness of the long distance runner, The / Stranger in a strange land / Deja-vu / Alexander the great.
LP: . . . . ZONE 1
MC: . . . . TC ZONE 1
LP: . . . . EMC 3512
MC: . . . . TCEMC 3512
LP: . . . . ATAK 119
MC: . . . . TCATAK 119
LP: . . . . ATAK 142
MC: . . . . TCATAK 142
LP: . . . . FA 3246
MC: . . . . TCFA 3246

Iron Man

IRON MAN, THE (see under Hughes, Ted (auth)) (Cribbins, Bernard (nar)).

Iron Muse

PORTRAIT OF INDUSTRIAL FOLK MUSIC, A.
LP: 12T 86

Iron Pirate

IRON PIRATE, THE (See under Reeman, Douglas (auth)) (Massey, Daniel (nar)).

Irons, Jeremy (nar)

EMPIRE OF THE SUN (See under Empire of the Sun (bk)).

I-Roy

AFRICAN HERBSMAN.
LP: . . . . JGML 6045

CLASSIC I-ROY.
LP: . . . . UNKNOWN

CRUCIAL CUTS.
Tracks: / Firestick / Dog war / Tiddle le bop / Package deal / Stronger strong / Jordan River / Everybody bawling / Musical shark attack / Hill and gully / World on fire / Fire in a wire.
LP: . . . . VX 1011

DREAD LOCKS IN JAMAICA.
LP: . . . . LALP 05

GENERAL.
Tracks: / African continent / Reggae rockers / Bad boy corner / Quarter pound of ishens / To the bump / General / Fire in a Vatican / Hill and guilty / Kilimanjaro / Fire in a wire.
LP: . . . . FLD 6002

GODFATHER, THE.
LP: . . . . TWS 930

MANY MOODS OF I-ROY.
LP: . . . . TRLS 91

OUTER LIMITS.
LP: . . . . INLP 4
MC: . . . . INC 4

PRESENTING I-ROY.
Tracks: / Red gold and green / Pusher man / Blackman time / Smile like an angel / Peace Coxsone affair / Screw face / First cut is the deepest / Melinda / Tourism is my business / Tripe girl / Cow town skank.
LP: . . . . TRLS 63

WE CHAT YOU ROC (See under Woosh, Jah & I. Roy).

Irsol

FIRST CONTACT.
MC: . . . . ARR 006

HALF LIVE.
MC: . . . . ARR 008

Irvine, Andy

ANDY IRVINE & PAUL BRADY (Irvine, Andy & Paul Brady).
LP: . . . . LUN 008
MC: . . . . CLUN 008

PATRICK STREET (Irvine, Andy, Jackie Daly, Kevin Burke, Arty McGlynn).
LP: SIF 1071
MC: CSIF 1071

RAINY SUNDAYS, WINDY DREAMS.
LP: TA 3002
MC: 4TA 3002

Irvine, Bill & Boggie

AT THE ROYAL ALBERT HALL (Irvine, Bill & Boggie/Bryan Smith Orchestra).
LP: DS 001
MC: TDS 001

Irvine, Weldon

IN HARMONY.
LP: SES 19749

Irving, Robert

NIGHTS AT THE BALLET.
LP: SXLP 30087

Irving, Washington

LEGEND OF SLEEPY HOLLOW / ICHABOD CRANE (Begley, Ed).
MC: 1242

Isaacs, David

PLACE IN THE SUN (Isaacs, David/ Delroy Wilson).
Tracks: / Place in the sun, A / Memories by the score / Stealing stealing / Let them say / Winter world of love / Hard road to travel / Kiss, kiss and say goodbye / Breaking up / What you gonna do? / Till I can't take it.
LP: VSLP 5003

Isaacs, Gregory

ALL I HAVE IS LOVE.
Tracks: / Give a hand / Since the other day / All I have is love / Sinner man / Help us get over / Hold me tight / Promised land / Way of life / Coming home / Lonely lover / Hard road to travel.
LP: TRLS 121
MC: ZCTRL 121
MC: TRDCT 15586
LP: TRDLP 15586

AT THE MIXING LAB.
LP: MLLP 005
MC: MLC 005

BEST OF GREGORY ISAACS.
LP: GGO 30

BEST OF GREGORY ISAACS VOL.2.
LP: GG 0025

CALL ME COLLECT.
LP: RAS 3067
MC: RASC 3067

COME ALONG.
Tracks: / Take a look / You're Like An Angel / Do your own thing / Kinky lady / Sip of Wine / Curfew / First class lover / Give her a try / Bits and Pieces / No good girl.
LP: LALP 22
MC: LALC 22

COOL RULER - SOON FORWARD - SELECTION.
Tracks: / Native woman / John Public / Party in the slum / Uncle Joe / Word of the farmer / One more time / Let's dance / Created by the father / Raving tonight / Don't pity me.
LP: FL 1020
MC: FLC 9012

CRUCIAL CUTS.
Tracks: / Universal tribulation / John Public / Mr. Brown / Uncle Joe / Raving tonight / One more time / Let's dance / Lonely girl / Slave market / Soon forward.
LP: VX 1010
MC: TCVX 1010

DANCING FLOOR.
Tracks: / Dancing floor / Crown and anchor / Give it all up / Private lesson / Nobody knows / Dealing / Shower me with love / Opel ride / Chips is down / Rock me.
LP: MR 148

DOUBLE DOSE (Isaacs, Gregory & Sugar Minott).
Tracks: / Worries and problems / Love we have, The / Rough and ready / Jah will work it out / More on more / Just be nice / Losing weight / General penitentiary.
LP: BTLP 004

EARLY YEARS, THE.
Tracks: / Rock away / Sweeter the victory / Sinner man / Lonely lover / Loving pauper / Promised land / Love is overdue / Bad da / Way of life / Financial endorsement / Give a hand / All I have is love.
LP: TRLS 196
MC: ZCTRL 196

ENCORE.
Tracks: / Out Deh / Tune in / Top ten / Private secretary / My only lover / All I have is love / Love is overdue / Can't give my love / Cool down the pace / Oh what a feeling / Addicted to you / Night nurse.
LP: KVL 9030
MC: CKVL 9030

EXPERIENCE VS. COMMON SENSE.
LP: EXO 0010

EXTRA CLASSIC.
Tracks: / Mr. Cop / My religion / Something nice.
MC: MICCAN 0011
LP: COLP 2002
LP: STL 1003
LP: STLP 1003
MC: VSMC 006

FOR EVERYONE.
LP: SRLLP 012 81

GILBERT (Isaacs, Gregory & Friends).
LP: RRI 1200
MC: KRRI 1200

GREGORY IN RED.
LP: TZ 20

GREGORY MEETS THEM ALL.
LP: STLP 1

GUILTY OF LOVING YOU.
LP: JMLP 005

HEARTBREAKER.
MC: RRTGC 7788

IN PERSON.
Tracks: / Sweeter the victory / Love is overdue / Financial endorsement / Be careful / Another heartache / If you're in love / Dreams come true / Way she walks, The / Far beyond the valley / Happiness come / No forgiveness / Love disguise.
LP: TRLS 102

I.O.U.
LP: GREL 136
MC: GREEN 136

JUDGE NOT (see under Brown, Dennis) (Isaacs, Gregory & Dennis Brown).

JUST INFATUATION (Shaka, Jah).
LP: SHAKA 847

LIVE 84.
Tracks: / My number one / My only lover / All I ask is love / Love over you / Storm / Mr. Brown / Slave master / Border / Soon forward / Oh what a feeling / Sunday morning / Addicted to you / Front door.
LP: ROUGH 74

LIVE AT REGGAE SUNSPLASH: GREGORY ISSACS.
LP: VSLP 8900

LIVE AT THE ACADEMY.
Tracks: / My number one / All I ask is love / My only lover / Love overdue / Storm / Mr. Brown / Slave master / Oh what a feeling / Soon forward / Sunday morning / Addicted to you / Front door / Border / Can't give my love (CD only.) / Cool down the pace (CD only.).
LP: KVL 9027

LONELY LOVER.
Tracks: / Happy anniversary / Gi me / Tribute to Waddy / Poor and clean / Poor natty / I am sorry / Few words, A / Protection / Hard time / Tune in.
LP: PREX 1
MC: PREXC 1

LOVERS ROCK.
Tracks: / Happy anniversary / Gimme / Tribute to Waddy / Poor and clean / Poor natty / I am sorry / Few words, A / Protection / Hard time / Tune in / Confirm reservation / Front door / Permanent lover / Hush darling / My only lover / If I don't have you / Substitute / Poor millionaire / Fugitive, The / Once ago.
LP: PRED 10
MC: PREDC 10

MORE GREGORY.
Tracks: / Confirm reservation / Front door / Permanent lover / Hush darling / My only lover / If I don't have you / Substitute / Poor millionaire / Fugitive, The / Once ago.
LP: PREX 9
MC: PREXC 9

MR. ISAACS.
LP: STLP 1014
LP: SHAN 43006
MC: SHANC 43006
MC: MICCAN 009

MY NUMBER ONE.
LP: HB 61

NEW DANCE.
LP: BG 1005 LP

NIGHT NURSE.
Tracks: / Material man / Not the way / Sad to know you're leaving / Hot stepper / Cool down the pace / Night nurse / Stranger in town / Objection overruled.
LP: ILPS 9721
MC: ICT 9721
MC: RRCT 9

NO INTENTIONS.
LP: RF 001
MC: VPCT 1133

ONCE AGO.
MC: FLC 9004

OUT DEH.
Tracks: / Good morning / Private secretary / Yes I do / Sheila / Out deh / Star / Dieting / Love me with feeling.
LP: ILPS 9748
MC: ICT 9748

PRIVATE BEACH PARTY.
Tracks: / Wish you were mine / Feeling irie / Bits and pieces / Let off supm / No rushings / Private beach party / Better plant some loving / Got to be in tune / Special to me / Promise is a comfort.
LP: GREL 85
MC: GREEN 85

RED ROSE FOR GREGORY.
LP: GREL 118
MC: GREEN 118

REGGAE GREATS: GREGORY ISAACS LIVE.
Tracks: / Number one / Tune in / Substitute / Soon forward / Mr. Brown / Sunday morning / Oh what a feeling / Love is overdue / Top 10 / Front door / Border, The.
LP: IRG 2
MC: IRGC 2

REGGAE, IT'S FRESH.
LP: TRDLP 1187
MC: TRDCT 1187

RESERVED FOR GREGORY.
MC: EXC 1
LP: EXLP 1

ROCK ON.
LP: OBS 999

SENSATIONAL GREGORY ISAACS.
LP: VS 4001

SENSATIONAL, THE.
Tracks: / Lonely man / Too late / Mr. Know it all.
LP: VSLP 4001
MC: VSMC 4001
LP: VS 4001

SLUM DUB.
LP: BS 1051

SLY & ROBBIE PRESENT GREGORY ISAACS.
LP: RAS 3206

SOON FORWARD.
Tracks: / Universal tribulation / Mr. Brown / Down the line / Lonely girl / Bumping and boring / My relationship / Slave market / Black liberation struggle / Jah music / Soon forward.
LP: FL 1044
MC: FLC 1044

TALK DON'T BOTHER ME.
LP: SKELP 007

TWO BAD SUPERSTARS (Isaacs, Gregory & Dennis Brown).
LP: BS 1057
MC: BSC 1057

UNFORGETTABLE.
LP: RRTG 7736
MC: RRTGC 7736

WARNING.
Tracks: / Long sentence / Warning / Welcome home / Rudi / This little lady / Greedy girl / I do / Let me be the one / Once a man / Badness.
LP: SSBLP 00003

WATCHMAN OF THE CITY.
MC: RIFWLC 9300
LP: RIFWL 93000

YOU GIVE ME HICCUPS (See under Tiger) (Isaacs, Gregory & Tiger).

Isaacs, Ike

LATIN GUITARS OF IKE ISAACS.
LP: DS 004

Isaacs, Mary

SO GOOD, SO RIGHT.
LP: AQGDLP 001

Isaak, Chris

CHRIS ISAAK.
Tracks: / You owe me some kind of love / Heart full of soul / Blue hotel / Lie to me / Fade away / Wild love / This love will last / You took my heart / Crying / Lover's game / Waiting for the rain to fall.
LP: WX 138
MC: WX 138 C
LP: K 925536 1
MC: K 925536 4

HEART SHAPED WORLD.
LP: WX 264
MC: WX 264C

SILVERTONE.
Tracks: / Dancin' / Talk to me / Living for your lover / Back on your side / Voodoo / Funeral in the rain / Lonely one, The / Unhappiness / Tears / Gone ridin' / Pretty girls don't cry / Western stars.
LP: 925156 1

WICKED GAME.
Tracks: / Wicked game / You owe me some kind of love / Blue Spanish sky / Heart shaped world / Heart full of soul / Funeral in the rain / Blue Hotel / Dancin' / Nothings changed / Voodoo / Lie to me / Wicked game (instrumental).
LP: WX 406
MC: WX 406 C

Isabel's A Jezebel

ISABEL'S A JEZEBEL (Original London Cast) (Various artists).
Tracks: / More than earth: *Various artists* / More than air: *Various artists* / Down by the ocean: *Various* artists / All fish in the sea: *Various artists* / On the sand by the sea: *Various artists* / Isabel's a Jezebel: *Various artists* / In another life: *Various artists* / Nothing: *Various artists* / Sand: *Various* artists / Oh mummy darling: *Various artists* / God, it matters now: *Various artists* / Saddest moon: *Various* artists / Mama don't want no baby: *Various artists* / These are the things: *Various artists* / Stanley Irritability: *Various artists* / Use your name: *Various artists* / Moon should be rising soon/ Weeds in the wind: *Various* artists / My God when I think: *Various artists* / Hah: *Various artists* / Love knows no season: *Various artists* / So ends our night: *Various artists*.
LP: UAG 29148

Isan Slete

FLOWER OF ISAN, THE.
Tracks: / Lai lam toei sam jangwa / Hua ngawk yawk sao / Sutsanaen-noeng mode / Lam phloen / Lai pu pa lan / Toei khong / Lam doeng dong / Lai-yai mode / Lam toei thammada / Lai ngua khuen phu / Lam kio / Lai phu thai / Sutsanaen mode / Kawn lawng la / Lai an nang-sue / Imae, imae.
LP: ORBD 051

Isbin, Gilbert

BLUE SOUNDS AND TOUCHES.
Tracks: / Quite blue / Sueno / Tell me / In balance / Leon / Mosca Espagnola / Mar arbierto / Full moon and little bastion / Nenia / Blue 2 / Camino verde / Come into my door / A nice advance / Blue in blue / Ballad in a cave / HWYL.
LP: HWYL 4
MC: HWYLCA 4

CLEAR PERCEPTION OF PROVENANCE WITHIN, THE.
Tracks: / Paneice / Mr. Silence / Persian tale / Never mind / Don't disturb the slumber / Filmzone / Castle tune / Leviathan / Open mind / Rough draft / Brindle.
LP: HWYL 002

Isbin, Sharon

BRAZIL, WITH LOVE (See under Lima, Carlos Barbosa) (Isbin, Sharon & Carlos Barbosa Lima).

FAVOURITE GUITAR PIECES (See under Kikuchi, Machiko) (Isbin, Sharon/ Kikuchi, Machiko).

LATIN ROMANCES FOR GUITAR.
MC: VC7911284

RHAPSODY IN BLUE/WEST SIDE STORY (see under Barbosa-Lima, Carlos) (Isbin, Sharon & Carlos Barbosa Lima).

Ish

ON THIS CORNER.
Tracks: / You're my only lover / I could love you / You're my favourite thing to do / On this corner / Holy night / More than I can bear / It ain't necessarily so / Chase the lace / Femininity.
LP: GEF 26967
MC: 4026967

Isham, Mark

CASTALIA.
Tracks: / Grand parade, The / My wife with champagne shoulders / Meeting with the parabolist, A / Tales from the maiden / Dream of three acrobats, A / Gracious core, the / In the warmth of your night (CD & cassette only).
LP: V 2513
MC: TCV 2513

EMPEROR'S NEW CLOTHES, THE (See under Emperor's New Clothes) (Gielgud, Sir John & Mark Isham).

EVERYBODY WINS (See under Everybody Wins).

MARK ISHAM.
LP: VUSLP 26
MC: VUSMC 26

MODERNS, THE (See under Moderns (film).

NEVER CRY WOLF (See under Never Cry Wolf).

SONGS MY CHILDREN TAUGHT ME.
Tracks: / Steadfast tin soldier, The / Emperor and the nightingale, The / Thumbelina / Emperor's new clothes, The.
LP: . . . . **WT 1101**

VAPOR DRAWINGS.
Tracks: / Many Chinas / Sympathy and acknowledgement / On the threshold of liberty / When things dream / Raffles in Rio / Something nice for my dog / Men before the mirror / Mr. Moto's penguin (Who'd be an Eskimo's wife) / In the blue distance.
LP: **371027-1**
MC: **371027-4**
LP: . . . . **WHA 1027**

WE BEGIN (Isham, Mark & Art Lande).
Tracks: / Melancholy of departure, The / Ceremony in starlight / We begin / Lord Ananea / Surface and symbol / Sweet circle / Fanfare.
LP: . . . . **ECM 1338**

Isherwood, Christopher

GOODBYE TO BERLIN.
MC: **1752**

Ishmael & Andy

READY SALTED.
LP: . . . . **MYR 100579**

Isis

REBEL SOUL.
LP: . . . . **BRLP 571**
MC: . . . . **BRCA 571**

Islam

MUSIC OF THE WORLD OF ISLAM (Vol 6 - Drums & rhythms) (Various artists).
MC: . . . . **TGSMC 136**
LP: . . . . **TGS 136**

MUSIC OF THE WORLD OF ISLAM (Vol. 1 - The human voice) (Various artists).
LP: . . . . **TGS 131**
MC: . . . . **TGSMC 131**

MUSIC OF THE WORLD OF ISLAM (Vol 4 - Flutes & trumpets) (Various artists).
MC: . . . . **TGSMC 134**
LP: . . . . **TGS 134**

MUSIC OF THE WORLD OF ISLAM (Vol. 3 - Strings) (Various artists).
LP: . . . . **TGS 133**
MC: . . . . **TGSMC 133**

MUSIC OF THE WORLD OF ISLAM (Vol 5 - reeds & bagpipes) (Various artists).
MC: . . . . **TGSMC 135**
LP: . . . . **TGS 135**

MUSIC OF THE WORLD OF ISLAM (Vol. 2 - Lutes) (Various artists).
LP: . . . . **TGS 132**
MC: . . . . **TGSMC 132**

Island Adventure

ISLAND ADVENTURE (See under Barbie (bk)).

Island At The Top ...

ISLAND AT THE TOP OF THE WORLD (Ravenscroft, Thurl).
LP: . . . . **ST 3814 79**

Island (Film)

ISLAND, THE (Film soundtrack) (Various artists).
LP: . . . . **STV 81147**

Islands In Between

ISLANDS IN BETWEEN (Various).
MC: . . . . **TOUCH 33 2**

Isle Of Man ...

ISLE OF MAN TT RACES, 1967 (Various artists).
2LP: . . . . **SSD 577 578**
MC: . . . . **CSS 577 578**

Isley Brothers

3 AND 3.
LP: . . . . **EPC 32039**
MC: **40 32039**

6 TRACK HITS: ISLEY BROTHERS.
Tracks: / Listen to the music / Brown eyed girl / Harvest for the world / Under the influence of love / You still feel the need / Don't let me be lonely tonight.
MC: **7SC 5026**

20 GOLDEN PIECES: ISLEY BROTHERS.
Tracks: / Drag, The / I need love / Don't be jealous / Rockin' McDonald / This is the end / Don't you feel / Hold on baby / I say love / I'm laughing to keep from crying / Let's twist again / Never leave me baby / Nobody but me / Right now / Rubberleg twist / Spanish twist / Snake, The / Time after time / Twist and shout / Twistin' with Linda / You better come home.
LP: . . . . **BDL 2032**
MC: . . . . **AJKL 2032**

BETWEEN THE SHEETS.
Tracks: / Choosy lover / Touch me / I need your body / Between the sheets / Let's make love tonight / Ballad for the fallen soldier / Slow down children / Way out love / Gettin' over / Rock you good.
LP: . . . . **EPC 25419**
MC: **40 25419**

COMPLETE VICTOR SESSIONS, THE.
Tracks: / Rock around the clock / He's got the whole world in his hands / Turn to me / Respectable / Open your heart / St. Louis blues (Track on CD only.) / Ring a ling a ling / I'm gonna knock on your door / That lucky old sun / Not one minute more / When the saints go marchin' in / Tell me who / How deep is the ocean / Gypsy love song (Track on CD only.) / Yes indeed / Say you love me too / Without a song / Shout (part 1 & 2).
MC: . . . . **NK 90540**

FOREVER GOLD.
Tracks: / That lady / Live it up / Hello it's me / You are love / Highways of my life / Harvest for the world / Summer breeze.
LP: . . . . **EPC 32238**
MC: **40 32238**

GO ALL THE WAY.
Tracks: / Go all the way / Say you will / Pass it on / Here we go again / Don't say goodnight / It's time for love / Belly dancer.
LP: . . . . **EPC 86110**
MC: **40 86110**

GO FOR YOUR GUNS.
LP: . . . . **EPC 86027**

GRAND SLAM.
Tracks: / Tonight is the night / I once had your love (and I can't let go) / Hurry up and wait / Young girls / Party night / Don't let go / Who said.
LP: . . . . **EPC 84914**
MC: **40 84914**

GREATEST HITS: ISLEY BROTHERS (Volume 1).
Tracks: / That lady / Groove with you / For the love of you / Footsteps in the dark / Between the sheets / It's your thing / Fight the power / Live it up.
LP: . . . . **EPC 32443**
MC: **40 32443**

GREATEST HITS: ISLEY BROTHERS.
Tracks: / This old heart of mine / That lady / Summer breeze / Listen to the music / Behind a painted smile / For the love of you / Highways of my life / It's a disco night (rock don't stop) / Dancin' around the world / I guess I'll always love you / It's your thing / Between the sheets / Caravan of love.
LP: . . . . **STAR 2306**
MC: . . . . **STAC 2306**

GREATEST MOTOWN HITS.
Tracks: / This old heart of mine / Just ain't enough love / Put yourself in my place / I guess I'll always love you / There's no love left / It's out of the question / Take some time out for love / Whispers / Nowhere to run / Who could ever doubt my love / Behind a painted smile / That's the way love is / Tell me it's just a rumour baby / Take me in your arms / Got to have you back / Little Miss Sweetness / My love is your love (forever) / Why when the love has gone / All because I love you / I hear a symphony.
LP: . . . . **WL 72516**
MC: . . . . **WK 72516**

HARVEST FOR THE WORLD.
Tracks: / Harvest for the world / Prelude / People of today / Who loves you better / You are love / Let me down easy / So you wanna stay down / You still feel the need.
LP: . . . . **EPC 32652**
MC: **40 32652**
LP: . . . . **EPC 81268**

HEAT IS ON, THE.
LP: **69139**

INSIDE YOU.
Tracks: / Inside you / Baby hold on / Don't hold back you love / First love / Love merry go round / Welcome into my heart / Love zone.
LP: . . . . **EPC 85252**

LET'S GO.
Tracks: / Surf and shout / Please please please / She's the one / Tango / Whatcha gonna do / Staggerlee / You'll never leave him / Let's go, let's go, lets go / She's gone / Shake it with me baby / Long tall Sally / Do the twist / Who's that lady / My little girl / Love is a wonderful thing / Open up your eyes.
LP: . . . . **SSL 6001**
MC: . . . . **TCSSL 6001**

LIVE IT UP.
LP: . . . . **EPC 80317**

MASTERPIECE.
Tracks: / May I / My best was good enough / If leaving me is easy / You never know when you;re gonna fall in love / Stay gold / Colder are my nights / Come to me / Release your love / Most beautiful girl, The.
LP: **925347 1**
MC: **925347 4**
LP: **825347 1**

REAL DEAL.
Tracks: / Real deal / Are you with me? / Stone cold lover / It's alright with me / All in my lover's eye / I'll do it all for you / Under the influence.
LP: . . . . **EPC 85790**

SHOWDOWN.
LP: . . . . **EPC 86039**

SMOOTH SAILIN'.
Tracks: / Everything is alright / Dish it out / It takes a good woman / Send a message / Smooth sailin' tonight / Somebody I used to know / Come my way / I wish.
LP: . . . . **K 925586 1**
MC: . . . . **K 925586 4**

SOUND OF SOUL, THE.
Tracks: / You walk your way / Don't let me be lonely tonight / Heat is on, The / Go for your guns / Brown eyed girl / Harvest for the world / Put a little love in your heart / I say you will / Live it up / Summer breeze / That lady / If you were here tonight.
LP: . . . . **BLATLP 10**
MC: . . . . **BLATMC 10**

SPEND THE NIGHT.
Tracks: / Spend the night (ce soir) / You'll never walk alone / One of a kind / Real woman / Come together / If you ever need somebody / Baby come back home / One of a kind (reprise).
LP: . . . . **K 9259401**
MC: . . . . **K 9259404**

SUPER HITS.
Tracks: / This old heart of mine / Just ain't enough love / Put yourself in my place / I guess I'll always love you / There's no love left / It's out of the question / Take some time out for love / I hear a symphony / Behind the painted smile / That's the way love is / Tell me it's just a rumour baby / Take me in your arms / Got to have you back / Little Miss Sweetness / All because I love you / When love is gone.
LP: . . . . **UNKNOWN**
MC: . . . . **UNKNOWN**

THIS OLD HEART OF MINE.
Tracks: / Nowhere to run / Stop in the name of love / This old heart of mine / Take some time out for love / I guess I'll always love you / Baby don't you do it / Who could ever doubt my love / There's no love left / Seek and you shall find.
LP: . . . . **STMS 5026**
MC: . . . . **CSTMS 5026**
LP: . . . . **WL 72078**
LP: . . . . **STML 11034**

TIMELESS.
Tracks: / It's your thing / Love the one you're with / I know who you've been socking it to / Get into something / I need you / Work to do / Brother, brother / Keep on doin' / I turned you on / Put a little love in your heart / Pop that thang / Lay, lady, lay / Spill the wine / Fire and rain / Freedom / Ohio / Machine gun / Nothing to do but today / Lay away.
2LP: . . . . **EPC 88327**

TWIST AND SHOUT.
Tracks: / Twistin' with Linda / Time after time / Never leave me baby / Let's twist again / Snake / Twist and shout / Nobody but me / You better come home / I say love / Rubberleg twist.
MC: . . . . **ORC 009**

VOYAGE TO ATLANTIS (OLD GOLD) (See under Isley Jasper Isley/Caravan of love).

WINNER TAKES ALL.
Tracks: / I wanna be with you / Liquid love / Winner takes all / Life in the city / It's a disco night (rock don't stop) / What you do to me / Let's fall in love / How lucky I am / You're the key to my heart / You're beside me / Let me into your life / Love comes and goes / Go for what you know / Mind over matter.
2LP: . . . . **EPC 88460**
MCSET: **40 88460**

Isley-Jasper

BROADWAY'S CLOSER TO SUNSET BLVD.
Tracks: / Sex drive / Serve you right / I can't get over losing you / Kiss and tell / Love is gonna last forever / Broadway's closer to Sunset Boulevard / Look the other way / Break this chain.
LP: **4503591**
MC: **4503594**
LP: . . . . **EPC 26307**

CARAVAN OF LOVE.
Tracks: / Dancin' around the world / Insatiable woman / I can hardly wait / Liberation / Caravan of love / If you believe in love / High heel syndrome.
LP: . . . . **EPC 26656**
MC: **40 26656**

DIFFERENT DRUMMER.
Tracks: / Different drummer / 8th wonder of the world / Blue rose / Do it right / Givin' you back the love / Once in a lifetime lady / For the sake of love / Brother to brother / I wanna be yours.
LP: **4501431**
MC: **4501434**

ISM

CONSTANTINOPLE.
LP: . . . . **UNKNOWN**

Isotope

BEST OF ISOTOPE, THE (Featuring Gary Boyle).
Tracks: / Honkey donkey / Windmills and waterfalls / Do the business / Spanish sun / Marin country girl / Temper tantrum / Black sand / Deep end.
LP: . . . . **GULP 1024**
MC: . . . . **ZCGUL 1024**

DEEP END.
Tracks: / Mr. M's picture / Crunch cake / Another side / Black sand / Pipe dream / Attila / Fone-bone / Deep end.
LP: . . . . **GULP 1017**
MC: . . . . **ZCGUL 1017**

ILLUSION.
Tracks: / Illusion / Rangoon creeper / Spanish sun / Edorian / Frog / Sliding dogs / Lion sandwich / Golden section / Marin country girl / Lily Kong / Temper tantrum.
LP: . . . . **GULP 1006**
MC: . . . . **ZCGUL 006**

ISOTOPE.
Tracks: / Then there were four / Do the business / Oh little fat man / Sunshine part / Bite on this / Upward curve / Retracing my steps / Windmills and waterfalls / Honkey donkey.
LP: . . . . **GULP 1002**
MC: . . . . **ZCGUL 1002**

Israel

FLUTE MUSIC FROM ISRAEL Lehakat ha Nodomin (Various artists).
Tracks: / Zum gali gali: *Israel* / Donna, Donna: *Israel* / Hava nagila: *Israel* / Minuit: *Israel*/ Hinnei ma tov 1: *Israel* / Hinnei ma tov 2: *Israel* / Reter Zemer attik: *Israel* / Emek: *Israel.*
LP: . . . . **ARN 33237**
MC: . . . . **ARN 433237**

ISRAEL (Songs & Music Celebrated by Robert Bahr).
LP: . . . . **FLD 637**

ISRAELI FOLK DANCES (Various artists).
LP: . . . . **LP 5/6**

SOUL OF ISRAEL (Various artists).
LP: . . . . **ADL 502**
MC: . . . . **ADK 502**

Israel Philharmonic...

PIANO CONCERTO NO. 5 IN E MAJOR OP 73, 'EMPEROR' (See under Beethoven (composer)) (Israel Philharmonic Orchestra).

Israel Vibration

BEST OF ISRAEL VIBRATION, THE.
LP: . . . . **DSR 6623**

FOREVER.
LP: . . . . **RAS 3080**
MC: . . . . **RASC 3080**

PRAISES.
LP: . . . . **RAS 3054**
MC: . . . . **RASC 3054**

SAME SONG, THE.
Tracks: / Same song / Weep and mourn / Walk the streets of glory / Ball of fire / I'll go through / Why worry? / Lift up your conscience / Prophet has arisen / Jah time has come / Licks and kicks.
LP: . . . . **DSR 6727**
LP: . . . . **SHSP 4099**

STRENGTH OF MY LIFE.
LP: . . . . **RAS 3037**

UNCONQUERED PEOPLE.
LP: . . . . **GREL 148**
MC: . . . . **GREEN 148**

Israel's Hope

INTRODUCING....
Tracks: / If you're happy and you know it / Butterfly song, The / O be careful little eyes / Heaven is a wonderful place / When I get to Heaven / Today / Joy, joy down in my heart / Birdies in the treetops, The / Love him in the morning / It's a happy day / Make a joyful noise / Zaccheus was a wee little man / First John 4: 7 & 8 / Climb, climb up sunshine mountain / This little light of mine / Give me oil in my lamp / Jesus loves the little children / Ha la la la / B-I-B-L-E, The /

Love is the greatest gift of all / Jesus loves even me / Behold, what manner of love / Deep and wide / If you can sing a song / Tell me the stories of Jesus / Rejoice in the Lord always / Wise man built his house, The / Sandyland / Special specialities / Arky, arky / Jesus love me / Amen, praise the Lord / Clap de hands / I will make you fishers of men.
LP: . . . . MM R 0184
MC: . . . . MM C 0184

It

ON TOP OF THE WORLD.
LP: . . . . BCKLP 1
MC: . . . . BCKMC 1

It Bites

BIG LAD IN THE WINDMILL.
Tracks: / I got you eating out of my hand / All in red / Whole new world / Screaming on the beaches / Turn me loose / Cold, tired and hungry / Calling all the heroes / You'll never go to heaven / Big lad in the windmill / Wanna shout.
LP: . . . . V 2378
MC: . . . . TCV 2378
LP: . . . . OVED 295
MC: . . . . OVEDC 295

EAT ME IN ST LOUIS.
Tracks: / Positively animal / Underneath your pillow / Let us all go / Still too young to remember / Murder of the planet earth / People of America / Sister Sarah / Leaving without you / Till the end of time (Only on MC and CD.) / Ice melts into water, The (Only on MC and CD.) / Charlie (Only on CD.) / Having a good day (Only on Limited edition.) / Reprise (Only on Limited edition.) / Bullet in the barrel (Only on Limited edition.).
LP: . . . . V 2591
MC: . . . . TCV 2591
MC: . . . . OVEDC 377

ONCE AROUND THE WORLD.
Tracks: / Midnight / Kiss like Judas / Yellow Christian / Rose Marie / Old man and the angel, The / Hunting the whale (CD only) / Plastic dreamer / Once around the world / Black December.
LP: . . . . V 2456
MC: . . . . TCV 2456
MC: . . . . OVEDC 376

It Had To...

IT HAD TO BE YOU (Various artists).
LP: . . . . NW 298

It Happened In

IT HAPPENED IN BROOKLYN (Film soundtrack) (Various artists).
LP: . . . . HS 5006

It Started In Naples

IT STARTED IN NAPLES (Film soundtrack) (Various artists).
LP: . . . . STV 81122

It Was Ten Years Ago

IT WAS TEN YEARS AGO TODAY Various artists (Various artists).
LP: . . . . KOMA 788019

Ita, Volcumba

REVOLUTIONARY SONGS OF EL SALVADOR.
LP: . . . . FF 276

Italian Operatic...

ITALIAN OPERATIC FAVOURITES (Various artists).
MC: TC2MOM 120

Itals

BRUTAL OUT DEH.
LP: . . . . NH 303
MC: . . . . NHC 303

GIVE ME POWER.
LP: . . . . NH 307
MC: . . . . NHC 307

RASTA PHILOSOPHY.
LP: . . . . NHM 7491
MC: . . . . NHC 7491

Italy

CARA ITALIA (Various artists).
LP: 8432641
MC: 8432644

CHANTS DE TOSCANE (Various artists).
Tracks: / Quell'uccellino che vien dal mare: *Various artists* / Diana fa l'bucato: *Various artists* / Lasciateci passare, siamo Toscani: *Various artists* / Bella al ballo: *Various artists* / Bella, belina, voi veni alla vigna?: *Various artists* / Mamma mia, mi sento male: *Various artists* / Son l'undici di notte, l'aria e scura: *Various artists* / La malmarita: *Various artists* / La montagnola: *Various artists* / Mamma voglio marito: *Various artists* / Il buon vecchio se marito: *Various artists* / Vola, columba, vola: *Various artists* / Maggiolata: *Various artists.*
LP: . . . . ARN 33773
MC: . . . . ARN 433773

CHESTA EL A VOCI CA CANUSCITE (Various artists).
LP: . . . . GVM 675

ITALIE ETERNELLE - CHANTS ET DANSES (Various artists).
Tracks: / Zumba bimba: *Various artists* / Sulfatara: *Various artists* / Lena et Urra: *Various artists* / Balletto: *Various artists* / Alla campagnola: *Various artists* / Serenata: *Various artists* / Strinna: *Various artists* / Que-li: *Various artists* / Stornelli: *Various artists* / Ninna Nanna: *Various* artists / Chant des pressureurs d'olives: *Various artists* / Tarentella di Pagani: *Various artists* / Alla fiera di Lanciano: *Various artists* / Il saltarello: *Various artists* / Stornelli: *Various artists* / Plessat po' Roseachin: *Various artists* / Villanella: *Various artists* / Donna, Donna: *Various artists* / Tralaleri: *Various artists* / Ballo tondo: *Various artists.*
LP: . . . . ARN 33688
MC: . . . . ARN 433688

MAGIC OF ITALY (Various artists).
MC: . . . . TCNTS 211

MAGIC OF ITALY (Various artists).
LP: . . . . NTS 211

MANDOLINES NAPOLITAINES (Various artists).
Tracks: / Tarentella della felicita: *Various artists* / Per Luciana: *Various artists* / Il valzer degli amici: *Various artists* / Serenata per Guilietta: *Various artists* / Ciao Sicilia mia: *Various artists* / Malinconico bolero: *Various artists* / Il zio dell' America: *Various artists* / Bravo polka: *Various artists* / Barcarola Veneziana: *Various artists* / Tarentella issena: *Various artists* / Carnavale Veneziano: *Various artists* / Tarentella della sposa: *Various artists* / Gli amanti di Roma: *Various artists* / Vendemie tarantella: *Various artists.*
LP: . . . . ARN 33302
MC: . . . . ARN 433302

SOUVENIR D'ITALIA Various artists (Various artists).
MC: . . . . MMC 4002

SWITCHED ON IN ITALY (Various artists).
LP: . . . . KMLP 400
MC: . . . . ZCMLP 400

Itchy Fingers

QUARK.
Tracks: / 7.50 / Yuppieville rodeo / Folly / Quark / Dakhut / Fruit machine / It's lovely once you're in / This morning / Headmaster's daughter, The / Hiatus / Banshee.
MC: . . . . TCV 2438
LP: . . . . V 2438

TERANGA.
Tracks: / Now and then / Building / Storm / Teranga / Drover's road, The / Woe / Transylvania / Wal's / Farewell forest / Devil's pulpit, The / Some day my cheque will come / Regine (CD only).
LP: . . . . VE 28
MC: . . . . TCVE 28

It's A Beautiful Day

IT'S A BEAUTIFUL DAY.
Tracks: / White bird / Hot summer day / Wasted union blues / Girl nothing eyes / Bombay calling / Bulgaria / Time is.
LP: . . . . CBS 83797
LP: . . . . CBS 63722

MARRYING MAIDEN.
LP: . . . . CBS 32132

THOUSAND AND ONE NIGHTS, A.
LP: . . . . CBS 32133
MC: 40 32133

It's A Children's...

IT'S A CHILDREN'S WORLD (Folk Tales) (It's A Childrens World).
LP: . . . . PRCC 100

It's A Mad Mad Mad

IT'S A MAD MAD MAD WORLD Original soundtrack (Various artists).
LP: . . . . MCA 39076
MC: . . . . MCAC 39076

It's Always Fair ...

IT'S ALWAYS FAIR WEATHER (Film soundtrack) (Various artists).
LP: 2353 036
LP: . . . . MCA 25018
MC: . . . . MCAC 25018

It's Immaterial

LIFE'S HARD AND THEN YOU DIE.
Tracks: / Happy talk / Driving away from home (Jim's tune) / Rope / Better idea, The / Space / Sweet life / Festival time / Ed's funky diner / Hang on sleepy town / Lullaby.
MC: . . . . SRNMC 4
LP: . . . . SRNLP 4
LP: . . . . OVED 289
MC: . . . . OVEDC 289

SONG.
Tracks: / New Brighton / Endless holiday / Ordinary life, An / Heaven knows / In the neighbourhood / Missing / Homecoming / Summer winds / Life on the hill / Your voice.
LP: . . . . SRNLP 27
MC: . . . . SRNMC 27

It's Just A Groove

IT'S JUST A GROOVE (Various artists).
LP: . . . . BLUERBLP 1

It's Party Time

IT'S PARTY TIME Various artists (Various artists).
Tracks: / Anniversary waltz: *Lynn, Vera* / Anniversary waltz: *Mann, Roberto* / My old dutch: *Dunn, Clive* / Always: *Mann, Roberto* / Congratulations: *Mortier Dance Organ* / Consider yourself: *Bygraves, Max* / Dashing white sergeant: *Bowman, Sidney* / Hokey cokey: *Cotton, Billy* / Knees up, Mother Brown: *Cotton, Billy* / Boomps a daisy: *Cotton, Billy* / Hatkvah: *Grenadier Guards* / Have naguila: *Black, Stanley* / Can can 62: *Jay, Peter* / I came, I saw, I conga'd: *Ros, Edmundo* / You'll never walk alone: *Bachelors* / I'll never fall in love again: *Jones, Tom* / Maybe it's because I'm a Londoner: *Cotton, Billy* / Now is the hour: *Fields*, Gracie / Last waltz, The: *Humperdinck, Engelbert* / Auld lang syne: *Lombardo, Guy* / God save the Queen: *Grenadier Guards.*
LP: . . . . DVL 3
MC: . . . . KDVC 3

IT'S PARTY TIME AGAIN (Various artists).
Tracks: / Alice blue gown: *Mann, Roberto* / Destiny: *Hermann, Jurgen* / Three o'clock in the morning: *Mann,* Roberto / Dance in the old-fashioned way: *New Big Band* / Anniversary song: *Shelton, Anne* / Auf wiederseh'n sweetheart: *Lynn, Vera* / We'll meet again: *Lynn, Vera* / My Yiddishe momma: *Jones, Tom* / Good luck, good health, God bless you: *Cotton, Billy* / It's my mother's birthday today: *Tracy, Arthur* / Fings ain't wot they used t'be: *Various artists* / Flash, bang, wallop: *Steele, Tommy* / Happy days and lonely nights: *Bygraves,* Max / Wish me luck as you wave me goodbye: *Fields, Gracie* / Hi ho silver lining: *Attack* / Hoots mon: *Lord Rockingham's XI.*
LP: . . . . DVL 5
MC: . . . . KDVC 5

It's Rollin' Rock

IT'S ROLLIN' ROCK (Various artists).
LP: . . . . ABOUT 1010

It's Too

IT'S TOO FRIGHTENING FOR ME! (See also Shirley Hughes) (Bennett, John (narr)).

It's Trad Dad

IT'S TRAD DAD (Film soundtrack) (Various artists).
LP: 33SX 1412

Itturia, Manuel

SUPERB CHA-CHA.
LP: . . . . BAR 920483

Ivan The Terrible

IVAN THE TERRIBLE (Film Soundtrack) (Various artists).
MC: . . . . EG 7695844

IVAN THE TERRIBLE (VIDEO) (see under Rimsky Korsakiv (composer)) (Bolshoi Ballet).

Ivanhoe (bk)

IVANHOE (Scott, Sir Walter (auth)) (Fairbanks, Douglas Jnr (nar)).
2LP: . . . . TC 2076
MCSET: . . . . CDL 52076

IVANHOE (see under Scott, Sir Walter (auth)) (Pigott-Smith, Tim (nar)).

IVANHOE/ ROSE OF PERSIA (Various artists).
LP: . . . . SHE 509

Ivery, Marchel

BLUE GREENS & BEANS (See under Newman, David 'Fathead').

Ives, Burl

ANIMAL FOLK.
LP: . . . . DQ 1191

BEST, THE.
LP: . . . . ENT 13020

BRAND NEW ALBUM.
LP: 2382094

BRIGHT AND BEAUTIFUL.
Tracks: / Brighten the corner where you are / Sailing home / Sailing home / Throw out the life line / Showers of blessing / Amazing grace / Rescue the perishing / Softly and tenderly / Power in the blood / All of my burdens rolling away / Stand up stand up for Jesus / Count your blessings / All things bright and beautiful / Lillie of the valley / What a friend we have in Jesus / Bringing in the sheaves / When we all get to Heaven / Shall we gather at the river? / In the sweet bye and bye / Praise God from whom all blessing flow / God be with you till we meet again.
LP: . . . . TWE 6001
MC: . . . . TC TWE 6001

BURL IVES.
LP: . . . . ENT LP 13020
MC: . . . . ENT MC 13020

CHIM CHIM CHEREE.
LP: . . . . DQ 1200

CHRISTMAS AT THE WHITE HOUSE.
LP: . . . . TC 1415

FAITH AND JOY.
LP: . . . . SAC 5069

JUNIOR CHOICE.
Tracks: / I know an old lady / Molly Malone / Horace the horse / Whistling rabbit / Polly wolly doodle / Davy Crockett / What kind of animal are you / Blue tail fly / Three jolly huntsmen / Squirrel / Riddle song / Mr. Froggie / Monkey and the elephant / Man on the flying trapeze, The.
LP: . . . . MFP 50446

LITTLE WHITE DUCK.
LP: . . . . CBS 31525

LOVE AND JOY.
Tracks: / King's business, The / Jesus loves the little children / Will there be any stars in my crown / Love lifted me / King Herod and the cock / Friendly beasts, The / Cradle hymn / In the temple / Old rugged cross, The / I can, I will, I do believe / How I love Jesus / When Jesus was a boy / Joy unspeakable / Who made this world / We thank thee / Our helpers / Oh be careful / Life's railway to heaven / Unclouded day, The / Haven of rest.
LP: . . . . TWE 6006
MC: . . . . TC TWE 6006

RETURN OF THE WAYFARING STRANGER.
Tracks: / John Henry / Billy the kid / Fare thee wall / O honey / May Lindy Lou / Mule train / Worried man blues, The / Green country bachelor / Lilly Munroe / Old blue / Ballanderie / Lord Randall / Riders in the sky / Wayfaring stranger / Woolie boogie bee.
LP: . . . . BPG 62080

SHALL WE GATHER AT THE RIVER.
LP: . . . . SAC 5073

SONGS I SANG IN SUNDAY SCHOOL.
LP: . . . . SAC 5072

STEPPING IN THE LIGHT.
LP: . . . . TWE 6017
MC: . . . . TC TWE 6017

TALENTED MAN, THE.
Tracks: / Comin' after Jenny / Galisteo / Snowbird / Real roses / Roll up some inspiration / Another day, another year / Raindrops keep falling on my head / One more time Billy Brown / Tied down here at home.
LP: . . . . BDL 1027

TIMES THEY ARE A CHANGIN'.
Tracks: / I'll be your baby tonight / By the time I get to Phoenix / Gentle on my mind / Little green apples / Don't think twice, it's all right / One too many mornings / Maria / If I were a carpenter / Homeward bound / Folk singer / Times they are a changin'.
LP: . . . . CBS 31717

Ivor Novello

MUSIC OF IVOR NOVELLO (Various artists).
Tracks: / When the gypsy played: *Various artists* / Shine through my dreams: *Various artists* / Fold your wings: *Various artists* / Primrose: *Various artists* / My life belongs to you: *Various artists* / I can give you the starlight: *Various artists* / Waltz of my heart: *Various artists* / My dearest dear: *Various artists* / We'll gather lilacs: *Various artists* / Love is my reason: *Various artists* / Manchuko, The: *Various artists* / Music in May: *Various artists* / Bridge of lovers: *Various artists* / Some day my heart will awake: *Various artists* / Fly home, little heart: *Various artists* / Violin began to play: *Various artists* / Glamorous night: *Various artists* / Perchance to dream: *Various artists* / Careless rapture: *Various artists* / If this were love: *Various artists.*
MC: . . . . HR 8161

Ivor The Engine

IVOR THE ENGINE (Stories from the BBC TV childrens series) (Various artists).
Tracks: / Railway, The: *Various artists* / Egg, The: *Various artists* / Proper container, The: *Various artists* / Alarm, The: *Various artists* / Retreat, The:

Various artists / Unidentified objects: *Various artists*/ Gold?: *Various artists* / Mrs. Porty: *Various artists* / Cold: *Various artists* / Endowment, The: *Various artists*.
LP: . . . . **REC 517**
MC: . . . . **ZCM 517**

Ivy Green

ALL ON THE BEAT.
LP: . . . . **CR 8503**

MOONRAISED.
LP: . . . . **CALCLP 019**

WHATEVER THEY HYPE.
LP: . . . . **CR 8506**
LP: . . . . **REV LP 87**

Ivy League

BEST OF THE IVY LEAGUE, THE.
LP: . . . . **PYL 4010**
MC: . . . . **PYM 4010**

Iwamoto, Yoshikazu

WHEN THE BRIGHTNESS COMES.....
LP: . . . . **OR 1**

Iwan, Dafydd

BOD YN RHYDD.
LP: . . . . **SAIN 1150**

GWINLLAN A RODDWYD.
LP: . . . . **SAIN 1385**

RHWNG HWYL A THAITH (Iwan, Dafydd & Ar Log).
LP: . . . . **SAIN 1252**

J

J, David

CROCODILE TEARS AND THE VELVET COSH.
Tracks: / And the velvet cosh / Crocodile tears / Too clever by half / First incision, The / Imitation pearls / Light & shade / Rene / Stop this city / Justine / Ballad of Cain, The / Vandal & the saint / Boats / Slip the rope / Greener.
LP: . . . . **GLALP 010**

DAVID J ON GLASS.
MC: . . . . **GLAMC 017**
LP: . . . . **GLALP 017**

ETIQUETTE OF VIOLENCE.
LP: . . . . **SITU 8**
LP: . . . . **SITL 8**
MC: . . . . **SITL 8C**

SONGS FROM ANOTHER SEASON.
LP: . . . . **BEGA 112**
MC: . . . . **BEGC 112**

J' Etais Au Bal

J' ETAIS AU BAL (Various artists).
LP: **6020**
MC: . . . . **6020 TC**

J., Johnnie

NUCLEAR HAYRIDE (J., Johnnie & The Hitmen).
LP: **11018**
MC: . . . . **11018 TC**

J T & The Big Family

J T & THE BIG FAMILY.
LP: . . . . **CHAMP 1023**
MC: . . . . **CHAMPK 1023**

Jabara, Paul

THIRD ALBUM.
Tracks: / Disco wedding / Honeymoon in Puerto Rico / Disco divorce / Foggy day / Never lose your sense of humour / Just you and me.
LP: . . . . **CAL 2056**

Jack Frost

JACK FROST.
Tracks: / Every hour God sends / Birdowner / Civil war lament / Geneva 4 a.m. / Trapeze boy / Providence / Thought I was over you / Threshold / Number eleven / Didn't know where I was / Ramble / Everything takes forever / Even as we speak (Track on CD only.).
LP: **211354**
MC: **411354**

Jack In The Box

JACK IN THE BOX (Various artists).
MC: . . . . **STC 001**

Jack Officers

DIGITAL DUMP.
LP: . . . . **NBX 3**
MC: . . . . **NBXC 3**

Jack, Ronnie

GOING FOR THE BIG ONE.
LP: . . . . **RITZLP 0005**

Jack Rubies

WITCH HUNT IN LOTUS LAND.
Tracks: / Witch hunt in lotus land.
LP: . . . . **CRIMLP 136**

Jack Star

ROCK THE AMERICAN WAY.
LP: . . . . **KILLER 7019**

Jack & The Beanstalk

JACK AND THE BEANSTALK (Various artists).
MC: . . . . **STC 303A**

JACK & THE BEANSTALK (well loved tales age up to 9) (Unknown narrator(s)).
Tracks: / Jack & the beanstalk / Spindle, the shuttle and the needle, The / Stork Caliph, The / Fisherman and his wife, The / Ninepence and the norka / Jack-me-hedgehog.
MC: . . . . **ANV 652**
MC: . . . . **PLB 60**

JACK & THE BEANSTALK (Unknown narrator(s)).
MC: . . . . **STK 020**

Jack The Bear

BEARFOOTIN'.
Tracks: / Put down your pistol / Cadillac / Fool to myself / (You're makin' me wanna make) whoopee / Carshunting / You make me feel so hard / Pennies from Heaven / Man from laramie, The / Skin and bone / Sex drive / Promised land / Sweet companion / Dirty linen / Taxis / Excuses, excuses.
LP: . . . . **NCHLP 13**

Jack the Giant Killer

JACK THE GIANT KILLER (Palin, Michael).
MC: . . . . **LP 204**

Jack The Tab

JACK THE TAB (Various artists).
Tracks: / Psyche out: *King Tubby* / Rapid bliss: *Pearl Necklace* / Aquarius rising: *Loaded Angels* / Last night: *Wolves Of The Sun* / Blue heart: *Essence* / Oxygen: *Grielda* / Youth: *Vernon Castle*/ Only human: *Nobody Uninc* / Balkan red alert: *Alligator Shear* / Meet every situation head on: *Mesh.*
LP: . . . . **ACID 001**
LPPD: . . . . **ACID 001P**

Jack Trax

JACK TRAX THE FIFTH ALBUM (Various artists).
LP: . . . . **JTRAX 5**

JACK TRAX VOL.1 (Various artists).
Tracks: / Jackin' national anthem: *Ramos* / You used to hold me: *Roasario, Ralph* / Jack up work your body: *Raze*/ Magic wand: *Ulysses* / White knight jacks: *White Knight* / Off the wall: *Scott, Paul* / Visions: *Prof.Funk/Chicago House Auth* / Just a tease: *MG 2.*
LP: . . . . **JTRAX 1**
MC: . . . . **CJTRAX 1**

Jack Walk Blues

JACK WALK BLUES (Various artists).
LP: . . . . **ST 110**

Jackanory

JACKANORY:STORIES FROM LITTLENOSE (Grant, John).
LP: . . . . **REB 229**

Jackels

PROWLIN'.
LP: . . . . **NERD 038**

Jackie & Roy

GLORY OF LOVE.
Tracks: / You inspire me / Best thing for you / I love you real / Could you use me / Miz' Margaret / Love is sweeping the country / Glory of love / Looking at you / Where did the gentleman go / Let's get away from it all / T'ain't no use / Winter of discontent.
LP: . . . . **JASM 1033**

HIGH STANDARDS.
Tracks: / I got rhythm / Stardust / Loving you / I watch you sleep / Too marvellous for words / Am I blue? / Bidin' my time / Joy spring / Mine / Nobody's heart belongs to me.
LP: . . . . **CJ 186**

SPRING CAN REALLY HANG YOU UP THE MOST.
LP: . . . . **BLP 60904**

Jack-Knife

I WISH YOU WOULD.
Tracks: / I wish you would / Good morning little schoolgirl / You can't judge a book by the cover / Confessions / Eyesight to the blind / Walk on heaven's ground / Dimples / Mustang momma / Adoration.
LP: . . . . **POLS 1010**

Jackmaster

JACKMASTER PHUTURE TRAX (Various artists).
Tracks: / Hardcore hip house: *Various artists* / Reign: *Various artists* / Do the do: *Various artists*/ Dog dance: *Various artists* / Oh yeah: *Various artists* / Jammin' piano: *Various artists* / House express: *Various artists* / How far can I go: *Various artists* / My melody: *Various artists* / No reason: *Various artists* / Different world: *Various artists* / Give a little more: *Various artists* / Halloween house: *Various artists* / Take me there: *Various artists* / I can dance: *Various artists.*
LP: . . . . **HAPYLP 1**
MC: . . . . **ZCHAPY 1**

JACKMASTER VOL.1 (Various artists).
LP: . . . . **JACKLP 501**
MC: . . . . **ZCJACK 501**

JACKMASTER VOL.2 (Various).
LP: . . . . **JACKLP 502**

JACKMASTER VOL.4 (Various artists).
Tracks: / Magic love: *Full Love* / Body and spirit: *Alexander, Christian* / Love injection: *Dillard, Ricky*/ You can't hide: *Jump, Holly* / Serve it up: *Void, Sterling* / Over you: *Knuckles, Frankie* / Learn to love: *Paris* / How far I go: *Black, Peter* / Stand by me: *Perez, Julian Jumping* / Can't U see: *Pandy, Darryl* / Breathless: *McAllister, Jerry* / I try: *Smooth, Joe.*
2LP: . . . . **JACKLP 504**
MC: . . . . **ACJACK 504**

JACKMASTER VOL 5 (Various artists).
LP: . . . . **JACKLP 505**
MC: . . . . **ZC JACKLP 505**

Jacks

JACKS ARE WILD.
LP: . . . . **ROUNDER 9016**

Jackson

JACKSON (Original Soundtrack) (Various artists).
LP: . . . . **K 790 886 1**
MC: . . . . **K 790 886 4**

Jackson, Alan

HERE IN THE REAL WORLD.
Tracks: / Ace of hearts / Blue blooded woman / Chasin' that neon rainbow / I'd love you all over again / Home / Here in the real world / Wanted / She don't get the blues / Dog river blues / Short sweet ride.
LP: **210817**
MC: **410817**

Jackson, Aunt Molly

LIBRARY OF CONGRESS RECS..
LP: . . . . **ROUNDER 1002**

Jackson, Banton, Evans

GENTLEMEN PREFER BLUES.
LP: . . . . **DMLP 1011**

Jackson, Billy

MISTY MOUNTAIN (Jackson, Billy & Billy Ross).
LP: . . . . **IR 005**
MC: . . . . **IRC 005**

WELLPARK SUITE, THE (Jackson, Billy & Ossian & Friends).
LP: . . . . **MR 001**
LP: . . . . **IR 008**
MC: . . . . **IRC 008**
MC: . . . . **MRC 001**

Jackson, Bo Weavil

1926 (Sam Butler).
Tracks: / Devil and my brown blues / Poor boy blues / Jefferson County blues / You can't keep no brown / Christians fight on, your time ain't long / Heaven is my view / Pistol blues / Some scream high yellow / When the saints come marching home / I'm on my way to the Kingdom Land / Why do you moan?.
LP: . . . . **MSE 203**

Jackson, Brian

1980 (see under Scott-Heron, Gil) (Jackson, Brian & Gil Scott-Heron).

Jackson, Bull Moose

BIG FAT MAMAS ARE BACK IN STYLE.
LP: . . . . **KIX 14**

MOOSE ON THE LOOSE.
LP: . . . . **BP 506**

Jackson, Carl

BANJO HITS.
LP: . . . . **SH 3737**

BANJO MAN: TRIBUTE TO EARL SCUGGS.
Tracks: / Earl's breakdown / John Henry / Grey eagle / You are my flower / Home sweet home / Careless love / Keep on the sunny side / Little darling pal of mine / Reuben / Ground speed / Banjo man.
LP: . . . . **SH 3715**
MC: . . . . **SH 3715C**

SONG OF THE SOUTH.
Tracks: / Love and wealth / Jerusalem ridge / Lay down my old guitar / Baby you're all mine tonight / Erase the miles / Jesse and me / Lonesome river, The / Stoney creek / Song of the South.
LP: . . . . **SH 3728**
MC: . . . . **SH 3728C**

Jackson, Chubby

CHOICE CUTS.
LP: . . . . **ESQ 323**

Jackson, Chuck

GREAT CHUCK JACKSON, THE.
Tracks: / Hula lua / I'm yours / Ooh, baby / Judy's eyes / Judy's eyes (instrumental) / Come on, squeeze me (my darling) / This is it / Let's push Mr. Pride aside / Let's push Mr. Pride aside (instrumental - slow) / Let's push Mr. Pride aside (instrumental - fast).
LP: . . . . **BDL 1015**

MR EMOTION.
Tracks: / I keep forgettin' / Tell him I'm not home / Any other way / I need you / I'm your man / Make the night a little longer / Getting ready for the heartbreak / I just don't know what to do with myself / Hand it over / Good things come to those who wait / Chains of love / Two stupid feet / Any day now / Look over your shoulder / I forgot to tell her / Since I don't have you.
LP: . . . . **KENT 033**

POWERFUL SOUL, A.
Tracks: / Millionaire / Beg me / Breaking point, The / Who's gonna pick up the pieces / If I didn't love you / I wake up crying / Forget about me / Prophet, The / Little by little / I've got to be strong / I don't want to cry / This broken heart / Don't believe him, Donna / They don't give medals / Love of my girl, The / I can't stand to see you cry.
LP: . . . . **KENT 073**

Jackson, Cliff

B&W MASTERS (Jackson, Cliff/Lil Armstrong).
LP: . . . . **SLP 806**

CAROLINA SHOUT.
Tracks: / Honeysuckle rose / Ain't misbehavin' / 'S wonderful / Tin roof blues / You took advantage of me / Carolina shout / I'm coming, Virginia / Crazy rhythm / Beale Street blues / Someday, sweetheart / Who's sorry now?.
LP: . . . . **BLP 30136**

CLIFF JACKSON & HIS CRAZY CATS.
LP: . . . . **FJ 119**

HOT PIANO.
LP: . . . . **RD 5**

Jackson, David

LONG HELLO VOL 3.
LP: . . . . **NOTT 005**

Jackson, Deon

HIS GREATEST.
LP: . . . . **SS 8020**

Jackson Five

20 GOLDEN GREATS: JACKSON 5.
Tracks: / I want you back / Lookin' through the windows / Skywriter / Ain't no sunshine / Doctor my eyes / Love you save, The / I'll be there / Rockin' robin / Never can say goodbye / Forever came today / Ben / Got to be there / Dancing machine / Boogie man, The / ABC / Little bitty pretty one / Hallelujah day / Mama's pearl / Get it together / I am love.
LP: . . . . **STML 12121**
MC: . . . . **CSTML 12121**
LP: . . . . **ZL 72031**
MC: . . . . **ZK 72031**

ABC.
Tracks: / Love you save, The / One more chance / ABC / 2-4-6-8 / I'm the one you need / Don't know why I love you / Never had a dream come true / True love can be beautiful / La la means I love you / I'll bet you / I found that girl / Young folks, The.
LP: . . . . **STMS 5068**
MC: . . . . **CSTMS 5068**

ANTHOLOGY - JACKSON FIVE (Volumes 1 & 2).
Tracks: / I hear a symphony / Dancing machine / Body language / Got to be there / Rockin' robin / Ben / Daddy's home / ABC / I want you back / I'll be there / Sugar daddy / Maybe tomorrow / Mamas pearl / I am love / Teenage symphony / Skywriter / Hallelujah day / Bogie man / Let's get serious / Let me tickle your fancy / You're supposed to keep your love for me / Love don't want to leave / That's how love goes / Just a little bit of you / We're almost there / I wanna be where you are / Forever came today / All I do is think of you / I was made to love her / Whatever you got I want / Get it together.

2LP: . . . . TMSP 6004
MCSET: . . . . CTMSP 6004

BEGINNING YEARS 65-67.
Tracks: / Monologue / You've changed / Michael the lover / My girl / Under the boardwalk / Tracks of my tears / Stormy Monday / We don't have to be over 21 / Big boy / Jam session / Soul jerk / Saturday nite at the movies / Lonely heart.
MC: . . . . SDEMC 4018
LP: . . . . SDE 4018

CHRISTMAS ALBUM.
Tracks: / Have yourself a merry little Christmas / Santa Claus is coming to town / Christmas song, The / Up on the house top / Frosty the snowman / Little drummer boy / Rudolph the red nosed reindeer / Christmas won't be the same this year / Give love on Christmas Day / Some day at Christmas / I saw mommy kissing Santa Claus.
LP: . . . . STMS 5083
MC: . . . . CSTMS 5083
LP: . . . . WL 72112
MC: . . . . WK 72112

DIANA ROSS PRESENTS THE JACKSON 5.
Tracks: / Zip-a-dee-doo-dah / Nobody / I want you back / Can you remember / Standing in the shadows of love / You've changed / My cherie amour / Who's lovin' you / Chained / I'm losing you / Stand / Born to love you.
LP: . . . . STMS 5006
MC: . . . . CSTMS 5006

GREAT LOVE SONGS OF THE JACKSON 5.
Tracks: / I'll be there / Maybe tomorrow / I found that girl / La la means I love you / All I do is think of you / To know / It all begins and ends with love / Ain't nothing like the real thing / One more chance / Never can say goodbye / Touch / Don't know why i love you.
LP: . . . . WL 72290
MC: . . . . WK 72290

GREATEST HITS: JACKSON 5.
Tracks: / I want you back / ABC / Never can say goodbye / Sugar daddy / I'll be there / Maybe tomorrow / Love you save, The / Who's loving you? / Mama's pearl / Goin' back to Indiana / I found that girl.
LP: . . . . STMS 5038
MC: . . . . CSTMS 5038
LP: . . . . WL 72087
MC: . . . . WK 72087
LP: . . . . STML 11212

JACKSON 5, THE.
Tracks: / Love you save, The / Ain't nothing like the real thing / Little bitty pretty one / Doctor my eyes / My cherie amour / Lookin' through the windows / Don't let your baby catch you / E-ne-me-ne-mi-ne-moe / Zip a dee doo dah / If I have to move a mountain / Children of the light / I can only give you love / Ready or not, here I come / Don't want to see tomorrow.
LP: . . . . TMS 3503
MC: . . . . TMC 3503

LEGEND (See under Jackson, Michael) (Jackson Five/ Michael Jackson).

LOOKIN' THROUGH THE WINDOWS.
Tracks: / Ain't nothing like the real thing / Lookin' through the windows / Don't let your baby catch you / To know / Doctor my eyes / Little bitty pretty one / E-ne-me-ne-mi-ne-moe / If I have to move a mountain / Don't want to see tomorrow / Children of the light / I can only give you love.
LP: . . . . STMS 5089
MC: . . . . CSTMS 5089
LP: . . . . STML 11214

SKYWRITER.
Tracks: / Skywriter / Hallelujah day / Boogie man / Touch / Corner of the sky / I can't quit your love / Uppermost / World of sunshine / Ooh, I'd love to be with you / You made me what I am.
LP: . . . . WL 72292
MC: . . . . WK 72292

THIRD ALBUM.
Tracks: / I'll be there / Ready or not here I come / Oh how happy / Bridge over troubled water / Can I see you in the morning / Goin' back to Indiana / How funky is your chicken / Mama's pearl / Reach in / Love I saw in you was just a mirage, The / Darling dear.
LP: . . . . STMS 5037
MC: . . . . CSTMS 5037

ZIP-A-DEE-DOO-DAH.
LP: . . . . MFP 50418

Jackson, Francis

YORK MINSTER ORGAN.
LP: . . . . LPB 794

Jackson, Franz

LET'S HAVE A PARTY.
LP: . . . . PLP 110

Jackson, Freddie

DO ME AGAIN.
Tracks: / Don't it feel good / Love me down / Main course / It takes two / I'll be waiting for you / Don't say you love me / Do me again / Live for the moment / Second time for love / I can't take it / All over you (Not on album.).
LP: . . . . EST 2134
LP: 792 217 1
MC: . . . . TCEST 2134
MC: 792 217 4

DON'T LET LOVE SLIP AWAY.
Tracks: / Nice 'n' slow / Hey lover / Don't let love slip away / Crazy (for me) / One heart too many / If you don't know me by now / You and I got a thang / Special lady / Yes, I need you / It's gonna take a long, long time.
LP: . . . . EST 2067
MC: . . . . TCEST 2067
LP: . . . . ATAK 171
MC: . . . . TCATAK 171

JUST LIKE THE FIRST TIME.
Tracks: / You are my love / Tasty love / Have you ever loved somebody / Look around / Jam tonight / Just like the first time / I can't let you go / I don't want to lose your love / Still waiting / Janay.
LP: . . . . EST 2023
MC: . . . . TCEST 2023
LP: . . . . ATAK 117
MC: . . . . TCATAK 117

ROCK ME TONIGHT.
Tracks: / He'll never love you (like I do) / Love is just a touch away / I wanna say I love you / You are my lady / Rock me tonight (for old times sake) / Sing a song of love / Calling / Good morning heartache.
LP: . . . . EJ 2403161
MC: . . . . EJ 2403164
LP: . . . . FRED 1
MC: . . . . TCFRED 1
LP: . . . . ATAK 160
MC: . . . . TCATAK 160

Jackson, George

CAIRITIONA (Jackson, George & Maggie McInnes).
LP: . . . . IR 006
MC: . . . . IRC 006

Jackson, Glenda

LITTLE WOMEN (See under Little Women).

READS FROM HER OWN STORYBOOK.
MCSET: . . . . SAY 52

STORYBOOK.
MC: . . . . ARGO 1274

Jackson, Jack

MAKE THOSE PEOPLE SWAY (Jackson, Jack & His Orchestra).
Tracks: / Make those people sway / I'm playing with fire / Long may we love / I travel alone / Come on, be happy / Miss Otis regrets / I'm getting sentimental over you / Two cigarettes in the dark / Dixie lee / Two little flies on a lump of sugar / Sittin' in the dark / What a little moonlight can do / Stars fell on alabama / Blue river, roll on / Be still, my heart / Let bygones be bygones.
LP: . . . . SH 210

THINGS ARE LOOKING UP (Jackson, Jack & His Orchestra).
Tracks: / Things are looking up / Faint harmony / Soon / You turned your head / Kiss me, dear / Ache in my heart / Now that we're sweethearts again / Have a little dream on me / Don't you cry when we say goodbye / Lonely feet / I'm on a see-saw / Dancing with a ghost / Play to me gypsy / Lonely singing fool, A / What's good for the goose / Because it's love / Ole faithful / What shall I do? / I think I can / Goodnight, lovely little lady.
LP: . . . . SVL 173
MC: . . . . CSVL 173

Jackson, Janet

CONTROL.
Tracks: / Control / What have you done for me lately / You can be mine / Pleasure principle, The / When I think of you / He doesn't know I'm alive / Let's wait awhile / Funny how time flies / Nasty.
LP: . . . . AMA 5106
MC: . . . . AMC 5106

CONTROL - THE REMIXES.
Tracks: / Control (video mix) / When I think of you (dance remix) / Pleasure principle, The (the long vocal mix) / Pleasure principle, The (the shep pettibone mix) / What have you done for me lately (extended mix) / Nasty (cool summer mix part two) / Let's wait awhile (remix).
LP: . . . . MIX LP 1
MC: . . . . MIX MC 1

DREAM STREET.
Tracks: / Don't stand another chance / Two to the power / Pretty boy / Dream Street / Communication / Fast girls / Hold back the tears / All my love to you / If it takes all night.
LP: . . . . AMA 4962
MC: . . . . AMC 4962

JANET JACKSON.
Tracks: / Say you do / You'll never find (a love like mine) / Young love / Love and my best friend / Don't mess up a good thing / Forever yours / Magic is working, The / Come give your love to me.
LP: . . . . AMLH 64907
MC: . . . . CAM 64907

RHYTHM NATION 1814.
Tracks: / Pledge / State of the world / Knowledge, The / Miss you much / Love will never do (without you) / Livin' in a world (they didn't make) / Alright / Escapade / Black cat / Lonely / Come back to me / Someday is tonight / Livin'... in complete darkness.
LP: . . . . AMA 3920
MC: . . . . AMC 3920

RHYTHM NATION 1814 (SPECIAL EDITION).
Tracks: / Miss you much (Sheps house mix) (On 1814 Bonus beats only. (previously unreleased)) / You need me (On 1814 Bonus beats only.) / Skin games (On 1814 Bonus beats only. (previously unreleased)) / Come back to me (inst.) (On 1814 Bonus beats only. (previously unreleased)) / 1814 megamix. The (On 1814 Bonus beats only.).
LPPD: . . . . AMAP 3920
MCSET: . . . . AMAC 3920

TWO TO THE POWER (see under Richard, Cliff) (Jackson, Janet & Cliff Richard).

Jackson, Jermaine

DON'T TAKE IT PERSONAL.
Tracks: / Climb out / Don't take it personal / Make it easy on love / So right / I'd like to get to know you / Two ships (in the night) / Rise to the occasion / (C'mon) feel the need / Next to you / Don't make me wait.
LP: 210230
MC: 410230

DYNAMITE.
Tracks: / Dynamite / Sweetest sweetest / Tell me I'm not dreaming / Escape from the planet of the ant men / Come to me (one way or another) / Do what you do / Some things are private / Oh Mother.
MC: 406317

I LIKE YOUR STYLE.
Tracks: / I gotta have you / I'm just too shy / You're givin' me the run around / Paradise in your eyes / Is it always gonna be like this / Signed, sealed, delivered (I'm yours) / Maybe next time / I can't take no more / It's still undone / I'm my brother's keeper.
LP: . . . . STML 12160
MC: . . . . CSTML 12160

JERMAINE.
Tracks: / Pieces fit, The / You like me don't you / Little girl don't you worry / All because of you / You've changed / First you laugh then you cry / I miss you so / Can I change my mind / Beautiful morning.
LP: . . . . STML 12147
MC: . . . . CSTML 12147

LET ME TICKLE YOUR FANCY.
Tracks: / Let me tickle your fancy / Very special part / Uh, uh, I didn't do it / You belong to me / You moved a mountain / Running / Messing around / This time / There's a better way / I like your style.
LP: . . . . STML 12174

LET'S GET SERIOUS.
Tracks: / Let's get serious / Where are you now / You got to hurry girl / We can put it back together / Burnin' hot / You're supposed to keep your love for me / Feeling free.
LP: . . . . STML 12127
MC: . . . . CSTML 12127
LP: . . . . WL 72258
MC: . . . . WK 72258

PRECIOUS MOMENTS.
Tracks: / Do you remember me? / Lonely won't leave me alone / Give a little love / Precious moments / I think it's love / Our love story / I hear heartbeat / If you say my eyes are beautiful (With Whitney Houston.) / Voices in the dark / Words into action.
LP: 207087
MC: 407087
LP: 209062
MC: 409062

Jackson, Jim

BEST OF JIM JACKSON - 1928-1930.
LP: . . . . BD 613

JIM JACKSON 1927-29.
LP: . . . . BD 2037

KANSAS CITY BLUES.
LP: . . . . AB 2004

Jackson, J.J.

GREAT J.J. JACKSON, THE.
Tracks: / But it's alright / Try me / That ain't right / You've got me dizzy / Change is gonna come, A / I dig girls / Come and see me (I'm your man) / Stones that I throw, The / Give me back the love / Ain't too proud to beg / Love is a hurting thing / Boogaloo baby / Let it out.
LP: . . . . SEE 281

Jackson, Joe

BEAT CRAZY.
Tracks: / Beat crazy / One to one / In every dream home / Evil eye / Mad at you / Crime don't pay / Someone up there / Battleground / Biology / Pretty boys / Fit.
LP: . . . . AMLH 64837
MC: . . . . CAM 64837

BIG WORLD.
Tracks: / Wild West / Right and wrong / (It's a) big world / Precious time / Tonight and forever / Shanghai sky / Fifty dollar love affair / We can't live together / Forty years / Soul kiss / Jet set, The / Tango Alantico / Home town / Man in the street.
LP: . . . . JWA 3
MC: . . . . JWC 3

BLAZE OF GLORY.
Tracks: / Tomorrow's world / Me and you (against the world) / Down to London / Sentimental thing / Acropolis now / Blaze of glory / Rant and rave / Nineteen forever / Best I can do, The / Evil empire / Discipline / Human torch.
LP: . . . . AMA 5249
MC: . . . . AMC 5249

BODY AND SOUL.
Tracks: / Verdict / Cha cha loco / Not here, not now / You can't get what you want / Go for it / Loisaida / Happy ending / Be my number two / Heart of ice.
LP: . . . . AMLX 65000
MC: . . . . CXM 65000

I'M THE MAN.
Tracks: / On your radio / Geraldine and John / Kinda kute / It's different for girls / I'm the man / Band wore blue shirts, The / Don't wanna' be like that / Amateur hour / Get that girl / Friday.
LP: . . . . AMLH 64794
MC: . . . . CAM 64794

JUMPIN' JIVE.
Tracks: / Jumpin' with symphony Sid / Jack you're dead / Is you is or is you ain't my baby / We the cats shall hep ya / San Francisco fan / Five guys named Moe / Jumpin' jive / You run your mouth I'll run my business / What's the use of getting sober / You're my meat / Tuxedo Junction / How long must I wait for you.
LP: . . . . AMLH 68530
MC: . . . . CAM 68530

LAUGHTER AND LUST.
LP: . . . . VUSLP 34
MC: . . . . VUSMC 34

LIVE 1980 - 1986.
Tracks: / One to one / I'm the man / Beat crazy / Is she really going out with him / Don't wanna be like that / Got the time / On your radio / Fools in love / Cancer / Is she really going out with him (acapella version) / Look sharp.
2LP: . . . . AMA 6706
MCSET: . . . . AMC 6706

LOOK SHARP.
Tracks: / One more time / Sunday papers / Is she really going out with him / Happy loving couples / Throw it away / Baby stick around / Look sharp / Fools in love / Do the instant mash / Pretty girls / Got the time.
LP: . . . . SHM 3154
MC: . . . . HSC 3154
MC: . . . . AMC 3187
LP: . . . . AMA 3187
LP: . . . . AMLH 64743
LP: . . . . AMID 120

MIKE'S MURDER.
Tracks: / Cosmopolitan / Laundromat Monday / Memphis / Zemio / 1-3-3 go / Moonlight / Breakdown / Moonlight theme.
LP: . . . . AMLX 64931

NIGHT AND DAY.
Tracks: / Another world / Chinatown / T.V. age / Target / Steppin' out / Breaking us in two / Cancer / Real men / Slow song.
LP: . . . . AMLH 64906
MC: . . . . CAM 64906

STEPPIN' OUT (Very best of Joe Jackson).
LP: 3970521
MC: 3970524

TUCKER (Film soundtrack).
Tracks: / Captain of industry (overture) / Car of tomorrow - today / No chance blues / (He's a shape) In a drape / Factory / Vera / It pays to advertise / Tiger rag / Showtime in Chicago / Lone bank loan blues / Speedway / Marilee / Hangin' in Howard Hughes' hangar / Toast of the town, The / Abe's blues / Trial, The / Freedom swing / Rhythm delivery.
LP: AMA 3917
MC: AMC 3917

WILLPOWER.
Tracks: / No pasaran / Solitude / Will power / Nocturne / Symphony in one movement.
LP: AMA 3908
MC: AMC 3908

Jackson, John

BLUES AND COUNTRY DANCE FROM VIRGINIA.
LP: F 1025
LP: ARHOOLIE 1025

DEEP IN THE BOTTOM.
LP: ROUNDER 2032
MC: ROUNDER 2032C

IN EUROPE.
LP: ARHOOLIE 1047

JOHN JACKSON VOL.2 (More blues & country dance tunes from Virginia).
LP: ARHOOLIE 1035

STEP IT UP AND GO.
LP: ROUNDER 2019

Jackson, Jump

CHICAGO ROCK (Jackson, Jump & Friends).
LP: REDITA 108

Jackson, Latoya

HEART DON'T LIE.
Tracks: / Think twice / Heart don't lie / Bet'cha gonna need my lovin' / Private joy / Hot potato / I like everything you're doin' / Frustration / Without you.
LP: EPC 25992

LATOYA.
Tracks: / You're gonna get rocked / You blew / Such a wicked love / Not giving up on love / If I could get to you / Turn on the radio / Just say no / Does it really matter / (Tell me) he really means nothing to you at all / (Ain't nobody loves you) like I do.
LP: PL 88502
MC: PK 88502

Jackson, Lil 'Son

BLUES COME TO TEXAS.
LP: ARHOOLIE 1004

ROCKIN' AN' ROLLIN'.
LP: PM 1546671

Jackson, Mahalia

20 GREATEST HITS: MAHALIA JACKSON.
LP: U 50041
MC: D 950041
LP: 20120
MC: 40120

GOSPEL.
Tracks: / Tell it, sing it, shout it / Somebody touched me / Only hope we have / There is power in the blood / I asked the Lord / Hold me / Give me that old time religion / Leaning on the everlasting arms / He's sweet I know / Somebody bigger than you and I / Only believe / To me it's so wonderful / I'll never turn back no more / Highway up to Heaven / Trust in God / Lord search my heart / Where he leads me / Hallelujah 'tis done / Thank you, Jesus / Never look down / You can't hurry God / It's my desire / He knows how much we can bear / My Lord.
2LP: VJD 537

I'VE DONE MY WORK.
Tracks: / He's got the whole world in his hands / Every time I feel the Spirit / Upper room, The / We shall overcome / House I live in (that's America to me) / Go tell it on the mountain / Down by the riverside / Joshua fit de battle of Jerico / When the saints go marching in / Keep your hands on the plough / Nobody knows the trouble I've seen / Deep river / Holy City, The / Crying in the chapel / You'll never walk alone.
LP: WST 9630
MC: WC 9630

JAZZ TIME VOL.16.
LP: 502716

JESUS IS WITH ME.
LP: 20081
MC: 40081

LIVE IN ANTIBES 1968.
LP: FC 122

MAHALIA JACKSON.
LP: EMB 31383
MC: 40.31383

MAHALIA JACKSON COLLECTION (20 golden greats).
Tracks: / Nobody knows the trouble I've seen / Go tell it on the mountain / Come to Jesus / My story / I believe / In the upper room / Run all the way / Shall I meet you over yonder? / Beautiful tomorrow / Last mile on the way, The / Walkin' to Jerusalem / Bless this house / I'm on my way to Canaan / Lord's Prayer, The / He's my light / Even me / It is no secret / Hand of God / Jesus is with me / Get away Jordan.
LP: DVLP 2006
MC: DVMC 2006

MAHALIA JACKSON STORY, THE.
Tracks: / Get away Jordan / Go tell it on the mountain / Lord's prayer, The / He's got the whole world in his hands / Shall I meet you over yonder / Evening prayer, An / I'm going to live the life I sing about / City called heaven / It don't cost very much / Nobody knows the trouble I've seen / Didn't it rain / He's my light / Joshua fit de battle of Jerico / I believe / Come to Jesus / My story / My God is real / Beautiful tomorrow / Last mile on the way, The / Even me / Hands of God / Walk over God's heaven / I'm on my way / Jesus is with me / Walkin' to Jerusalem.
MCSET: DVREMC 23

MAHALIA JACKSON, VOL 1.
Tracks: / Tell it, sing it, shout it / Somebody touched me / Only hope we have / There is power in the blood / I asked the Lord / Hold me / Give me that old time religion / Leaning on the everlasting arms / He's sweet, I know / Somebody bigger than you / Only believe / To me it's so wonderful.
LP: JR 115

MAHALIA JACKSON, VOL 2.
Tracks: / I'll never turn back no more / Highway up to Heaven / Lord search my soul / I trust in God / Where he leads me / Hallelujah / 'Tis done / Thank you, Jesus / Never look down / You can't hurry God / It's my desire / He knows how much we can bear / My Lord.
LP: JR 134

MEMORIAL.
2LP: 400010

MY STORY.
LP: 20080
MC: 40080

MY TASK.
Tracks: / My task / Amazing grace / God is so good / Walk in Jerusalem / Satisfied mind, A / Whither thou goest / It is no secret / Then the answer came / My friend / Bible tells me so, The / Somebody bigger than you and I / He calmed the ocean / For my good fortune / I've done my work / How I got over / That's what he's done for me.
LP: WRD 3011
MC: TCWR 3011

QUEEN OF GOSPEL.
LP: ENT LP 13029

SILENT NIGHT.
Tracks: / Silent night / Go tell it on the mountain / Bless this house.
LP: 6.24480

WARM AND TENDER SOUL OF MAHALIA JACKSON.
Tracks: / In the upper room / City called Heaven / Run all the way / Go tell it on the mountain / I'm on my way to Canaan / I bow on my knees / Shall I meet you over yonder? / Beautiful tomorrow / It is no secret / Hands of God / Jesus is with me / Nobody knows the trouble I've seen / Even me / Get away Jordan / Last mile on the way, The / Bless this house / Walkin' to Jerusalem / My story / I believe / Dig a little deeper / Lord's prayer, The / Come to Jesus / He's my light.
2LP: SM 3763/2

WARM AND TENDER SOUL OF MAHALIA JACKSON VOL.2.
LP: SM 3610

WARM AND TENDER SOUL OF MAHALIA JACKSON VOL.1.
LP: SM 3609
MC: MC 3609

WHEN THE SAINTS GO MARCHING IN.
Tracks: / I'm going to live the life I sing about in my song / When I wake up in glory / Jesus met the woman at the well / Oh Lord is it? / I will move on up a little higher / When the saints go marching in / Jesus out of the depths / Walk over God's heaven / Keep your hands on the plough / Didn't it rain.
LP: 4508691
MC: 4508694

Jackson, Marvin

OZARK ROCKABILLY.
Tracks: / Fifty-six V8 Ford / When you rock 'n' roll / Down the rolley rink / He's just a cool man, cool / Keep a shakin' / Jay bird / Debbie Gail / My baby likes to go / Rainstorm / Rock 'n' roll baby / Always-late Johnny / I only know my baby's gone / Rockin' and rollin' / Pretty, pretty Loretta / Alone and so blue / Peek-a-boo / Gee whiz Liz.
LP: WLP 8883

Jackson, Michael

12" TAPE: MICHAEL JACKSON.
Tracks: / Billie Jean / Beat it / Wanna be startin' something / Thriller / P.Y.T. (pretty young thing).
MC: 4501274

18 GREATEST HITS: MICHAEL JACKSON (Jackson, Michael & Jackson Five).
Tracks: / One day in your life / Lookin' through the windows / Got to be there / Doctor my eyes / Ben / ABC / We're almost there / Skywriter / Rockin' robin / Happy / Ain't no sunshine / I'll be there / I want you back / Love you save, The / We've got a good thing going / Mama's pearl / Hallelujah day / Never can say goodbye.
LP: STAR 2232
MC: STAC 2232
LP: WL 72629
MC: WK 72629

AIN'T NO SUNSHINE.
Tracks: / Rockin' robin / Johnny Raven / Shoo-be-doo-be-doo-da-day / Happy / Too young / Up again / With a child's heart / Ain't no sunshine / Euphoria / Morning glow / Music and me / All the things you are / Cinderella stay awhile / We've got forever.
LP: TMS 3511
MC: TMC 3511
LP: 20038
MC: 40038

BAD.
Tracks: / Bad / Way you make me feel, The / Speed demon / Liberian girl / Just good friends / Another part of me / Man in the mirror / I just can't stop loving you / Dirty Diana / Smooth criminal.
LP: 4502901
MC: 4502904
LPPD: 4502900
MC: 4502908
LP: EPC 450291 1

BEN.
Tracks: / Ben / Greatest show on earth / People make the world go round / We've got a good thing going / Everybody's fool / My girl / What goes around comes around / In our small way / Shee be doo be doo a day / You can cry on my shoulder.
LP: STMS 5008
MC: CSTMS 5008
LP: WL 72069
MC: WK 72069
LP: STML 11220

BEST OF MICHAEL JACKSON.
Tracks: / Got to be there / Ain't no sunshine / My girl / Ben / Greatest show on earth / I wanna be where you are / Happy / Rockin' robin / Just a little bit of you / One day in your life / Music and me / In our small way / We're almost there / Morning glow.
LP: STMR 9009
MC: CSTMR 9009
LP: WL 72063
MC: WK 72063

E.T. THE EXTRA TERRESTRIAL.
LP: MCA 70000
MC: MCAC 70000

FAREWELL MY SUMMER LOVE.
Tracks: / Don't let it get you down / You've really got a hold on me / Melodie / Touch the one you love / Girl you're so together / Farewell my summer love / Call on me / Here I am / To make my father proud.
LP: ZL 72227
MC: ZK 72227
LP: WL 72630
MC: WK 72630

FOREVER MICHAEL.
Tracks: / We're almost there / Take me back / One day in your life / Cinderella, stay awhile / We've got forever / Just a little bit of you / You are there / Dapper Dan / Dear Michael / I'll come home to you.
LP: STMS 5095
MC: CSTMS 5095
LP: WL 72121
MC: WK 72121

GIRL IS MINE, THE (See under McCartney, Paul) (Jackson, Michael & Paul McCartney).

GOT TO BE THERE.
Tracks: / Ain't no sunshine / I wanna be where you are / Girl don't take your love from me / In our small way / Got to be there / Rockin' robin / Wings of my love / Maria (you were the only one) / Love is here and now you're gone / You've got a friend.
LP: STMS 5007
MC: CSTMS 5007
LP: WL 72068
LP: STML 11205

GREAT LOVE SONGS OF MICHAEL JACKSON.
Tracks: / Got to be there / I wanna be where you are / In our small way / Girl don't take your love from me / Maria / Love is here and now you're gone / Happy / I'll come home to you / You are there / One day in your life.
LP: WL 72289
MC: WK 72289

GREATEST HITS: MICHAEL JACKSON (See under Jackson Five for details) (Jackson, Michael & Jackson Five).

LOOKING BACK TO YESTERDAY.
Tracks: / When I come of age / Teenage symphony / I hear a symphony / Give me half a chance / Loves gone bad / Lonely teardrops / You're good for me / That's what love is made of / I like the way you are (don't change your love on me) / She's lookin' for a lover / If I was God.
LP: WL 72424
MC: WK 72424

LOVE SONGS: MICHAEL JACKSON & DIANA ROSS (Jackson, Michael & Diana Ross).
Tracks: / I'm still waiting / Got to be there / Touch me in the morning / Ain't no sunshine / All of my life / Farewell my summer love / Love hangover / Ben / One day in your life / Ain't no mountain high enough / I'll be there / Endless love / Never can say goodbye / Reach out and touch somebody's hand / Girl you're so together / Do you know where you're going to?.
LP: WL 72691
MC: WK 72691

MICHAEL JACKSON.
MC: EPC A 40 2906

MICHAEL JACKSON AND THE JACKSON 5 LIVE (Jackson, Michael & The Jackson Five).
Tracks: / Introduction / We're gonna have a good time / Lookin' through the windows / Got to be there / I want you back / ABC / Love you save, The / Daddy's home / Superstition / Ben / Papa was a rollin' stone / That's how love goes / Never can say goodbye / Ain't that peculiar / I wanna be where you are.
LP: WL 72641
MC: WK 72641

MICHAEL JACKSON MIX, THE.
Tracks: / Ben / Ain't no sunshine / Never can say goodbye / Got to be there / Happy (Love theme from lady sings) / I'll be there / We're almost there / People make the world go round / Who's loving you? / I was made to love her / You've got a friend / Girl don't take your love from me / We've got a good thing going / I'll come home to you / ABC / I want you back / Get it together / Boogie man, The / Just a little bit of you / Love you save, The / Farewell my summer love / Love is here and now you're gone / Hallelujah day / Skywriter / Lookin' through the windows / Sugar daddy / Don't let it get you down / Girl you're so together / Mama's pearl / My girl / Dancing machine / Shoo-be-doo-be-doo-da-day / Doctor my eyes / Rockin' robin / Little bitty pretty one.
2LP: SMR 745
MCSET: SMC 745

MUSIC AND ME.
Tracks: / With a child's heart / Up again / All the things you are / Happy / Too young / Doggin' around / Johnny Raven / Euphoria / Morning glow / Music and me.
LP: WL 72291
MC: WK 72291

OFF THE WALL.
Tracks: / Don't stop til you get enough / Rock with you / Working day and night / Get on the floor / Off the wall / Girlfriend / She's out of my life / I can't help it / It's the falling in love / Burn this disco out.
LP: 4500861
MC: 4500864
LP: EPC 83468

ONE DAY IN YOUR LIFE.
Tracks: / One day in your life / We're almost there / You're my best friend, my love / Don't say goodbye again / Take me back / It's too late to change the time / We've got a good thing going / You are there / Doggin' around / Dear Michael /

Girl, don't take your love from me / I'll come home to you.
LP: . . . . STML 12158
MC: . . . . CSTML 12158

ORIGINAL SOUL OF MICHAEL JACKSON.
Tracks: / Twenty five miles / Dancing machine / It's too late to change the time / Ain't no sunshine / Melodie / Got to be there / Doggin' around / Rockin' robin / If I don't love you this way / You've got a friend / Forever came today.
LP: . . . . ZL 72622
MC: . . . . ZK 72622

THRILLER.
Tracks: / Wanna be startin' something / Baby be mine / Girl is mine, The / Thriller / Beat it / Billie Jean / Human nature / P.Y.T. (pretty young thing) / Lady in my life, The.
LP: . . . . EPC 85930
MC: 40 85930
LPPD: . . . . EPC 11 85930

Jackson, Mick

MICK JACKSON.
Tracks: / 54th Street / Sammy / Passport to paradise / Weekend / You're a dream / Blame it on the boogie / Milwaukee walking / Married men.
LP: . . . . K 50605

Jackson, Mike

PATCHWORK (Jackson, Mike & Michelle).
LP: . . . . LRF 052

ROARING DAYS, THE (Jackson, Mike & Michelle).
LP: . . . . LRF 101

Jackson, Millie

ACT OF WAR (see under John, Elton) (Jackson, Millie/Elton John).

AN IMITATION OF LOVE.
Tracks: / Hot, wild, unrestricted, crazy love / Wanna be your lover / Love is a dangerous game / Cover me (wall to wall) / Mind over matter / It's a thing / I need to be by myself / I fell in love.
LP: . . . . HIP 43
MC: . . . . HIPC 43

BACK TO THE SH.T.
LP: . . . . HIP 77
MC: . . . . HIPC 77

BEST OF MILLIE JACKSON.
Tracks: / It hurts so good / How do you feel the morning after? / My man, a sweet man / Get your love right / There you are / I still love you / If loving you is wrong I don't want to be right / Breakaway / Summer / Child of God / Loving arms.
MC: 3177 247
LP: 2391 247

CAUGHT UP.
Tracks: / If loving you is wrong I don't want to be right / Rap, The / All I want is a fighting chance / I'm tired of hiding / It's all over but the shouting / It's easy going / I'm trying to prove my love to you / Summer.
LP: 2391 147
LP: . . . . TANLP 2
MC: . . . . ZCTAN 2
LP: . . . . SEW 003
MC: . . . . SEWC 003

E.S.P (Extra sexual persuasion).
Tracks: / Sexercise, Parts 1 & 2 / This girl could be dangerous / Slow tongue (working your way down) / Why me? / I feel like walking in the rain / Too easy being easy.
LP: . . . . K 250382 1
MC: . . . . K 250382 4

FEELIN' BITCHY.
Tracks: / All the way lover / Lovin' your good thing away / Angel in your arms / Little taste of outside love / You created a monster / Cheatin' is / If you're not back in love by Monday / Feeling like a woman.
LP: 2391 301
MC: 3177 301

FOR MEN ONLY.
Tracks: / This is where I came in / This is it / If that don't turn you on / I wish that I could hurt that way again / Fool's affair / You must have known I needed love / Despair / Not on your life / Ain't no coming back.
LP: 2391 460
MC: 3177 460

FREE AND IN LOVE.
Tracks: / House for sale, A / I'm free / Tonight I'll shoot the moon / There you are / Do what makes the world go round / Bad risk / I feel like making love / Solitary love affair / I'm in love again.
LP: 2391 215
MC: 3177 215
LP: . . . . SEW 032
MC: . . . . SEWC 032

GET IT OUT CHA SYSTEM.
MC: 3177 356

HARD TIMES.
Tracks: / Blufunkes / Special occasion / I don't want to cry / We're gonna make it / Hard times / Blues don't get tired of me / Mess on your hands / Finger rap / Mess on your hands (reprise) / Finger rap (reprise) / Feel love comin' on.
LP: 2391 555
MC: 3177 555

I GOT TO TRY IT ONE TIME.
Tracks: / How do you feel the morning after / Get your love right / My love is so fly / Letter full of tears / Watch the one who brings you the news / I got to try it one time / Gospel truth / One night stand / I gotta do something about myself / In the wash.
LP: . . . . SEW 023
MC: . . . . SEWC 023

I HAD TO SAY IT.
MC: 3177 495

IT HURTS SO GOOD.
Tracks: / I cry / Hypocrisy / Two-faced world / It hurts so good / Don't send nobody else / Hypocrisy (reprise) / Good to the very last drop / Help yourself / Love doctor / Now that you got it / Close my eyes / Breakaway (reprise).
LP: . . . . SEW 019
MC: . . . . SEWC 019

LIVE AND OUTRAGEOUS.
Tracks: / Passion / Horse or a mule / Lover & girlfriends / Don't you ever stop / I had to say it / Still / Ugly man / This is it.
LP: 2391 540

LIVE AND UNCENSORED.
Tracks: / Keep the home fires burning / Logs and thangs / Put something down on it / Da ya think I'm sexy? / Just when I needed you most / What am I waiting for / I still love you / All the way lover / Soaps / Hold the line / Be a sweetheart / Didn't I blow your mind / Give it up / Moment's pleasure / If loving you is wrong I don't want to be right / Rap, The / Never change lovers / Sweet music man / It hurts so good.
2LP: 2683 073
MC: 3571 011
LP: . . . . TANLP 1

LIVE AND UNCENSORED/LIVE AND OUTRAGEOUS.
2LP: SEW2 038
MCSET: SEWC2 038

LOVINGLY YOURS.
Tracks: / You can't turn me off / Something 'bout cha / I'll continue to love you / I can't say goodbye / Love of your own, A / I'll live my love for you / Body movements / From her arms to mine / Help me finish my song / I'll be rolling.
LP: 2391 252

MILLIE JACKSON.
Tracks: / If this is love / I ain't giving up / I miss you baby / Child of God / Ask me what you want / My man, a sweet man / You're the joy of my life / I gotta get away from my own self / I just can't stand it / Strange things.
LP: . . . . SEW 009
MC: . . . . SEWC 009

MOMENT'S PLEASURE, A.
Tracks: / Never change lovers in the middle of the night / Seeing you again / Kiss you all over / Momen'ts pleasure / What went wrong last night / Rising cost of love / We got to hit it off / Once you've had it.
MC: 3177 395
LP: 2391395

ROYAL RAPPIN'S (Jackson, Millie & Isaac Hayes).
Tracks: / Sweet music, soft lights and you / Feels like the first time / You never cross my mind / Love changes / I changed my mind / Do you wanna make love / If I had my way / If you had your way / You needed me.
LP: 2480516

STILL CAUGHT UP.
Tracks: / Loving arms / Making the best of a bad situation / Memory of a wife, The / Tell her it's over / Do what makes you satisfied / You can't stand the thought / Leftovers / I still love you.
LP: 2391 183
LP: . . . . TANLP 3
MC: . . . . ZCTAN 3
LP: . . . . SEW 027
MC: . . . . SEWC 027

TIDE IS TURNING, THE.
Tracks: / Tide is turning, The / Are you that someone / You knocked the love (right outta...) / Let me show you / Something you can feel / In my dreams / Cover me (wall to wall) / I almost believed you.
LP: . . . . HIP 65
MC: . . . . HIPC 65

Jackson, Milt

AIN'T BUT A FEW OF US LEFT (Jackson, Milt/ Oscar Peterson/ Grady Tate/ Ray Brown).
Tracks: / Ain't but a few of us left / Time for love, A / If I should lose you / Stuffy / Body and soul / What am I here for?.
LP: 2310 873
MC: K10 873

AT THE MONTREUX JAZZ FESTIVAL, 1975 (Jackson, Milt Big Four).
Tracks: / Fungii mama / Everything must change / Speed ball / Nature boy / Stella by starlight / Like someone in love / Night mist blues / Mack the knife.
MC: K10 753
LP: 2310 753

BAGS AND 'TRANE (see Coltrane, John) (Jackson, Milt & John Coltrane).

BAGS' BAG.
Tracks: / Blues for Roberta / Groovin' / How are you? / Slow boat to China / I cover the waterfront / Rev, The / Tour angel / Blues for Tomi-Oka.
LP: 2310 842
MC: K10 842

BAGS MEETS WES (Jackson, Milt & Wes Montgomery).
LP: . . . . OJC 234

BAGS' OPUS.
Tracks: / Ill wind / Blues for Diahann / Afternoon in Paris / I remember Clifford / Thinking of you / Whisper not.
LP: . . . . BNZ 279

BALLADS AND BLUES.
Tracks: / So in love / These foolish things / Solitude / Song is ended, The / They didn't believe me / How high the moon / Gerry's blues / Hello / Bright blues.
LP: . . . . K 50727

BEBOP.
Tracks: / Au privave / Good bait / Woody 'n' you / Now's the time / Ornithology / Groovin' high / Birks works / Salt peanuts.
LP: 790991 1
MC: 790991 4

BEST OF MILT JACKSON.
Tracks: / Once I loved / If you went away / Yes sir, that's my baby / Three thousand miles ago / Ain't misbehavin' / My kind of trouble is you / Soul fusion / Blues for Edith.
LP: 231 0849
MC: K10 849

BIG BAND, VOL 1 (Jackson, Milt & Count Basie).
Tracks: / 9.20 special / Moonlight becomes you / Shiny stockings / Blues for me / Every tub / Easy does it / Lena and Lenny / Sunny side of the street / Back to the apple / I'll always be in love with you / Comeback / Basie / Corner pocket / Lady in lace / Blues for Joe Turner / Good time blues / Li'l darlin' / Big stuff / Blue and sentimental.
LP: 231 0822
MC: K10 822

BIG BAND, VOL 2 (Jackson, Milt & Count Basie).
Tracks: / 9/20 special / Moonlight becomes you / Shiny stockings / Blues for me / Every tub / Easy does it / Lena and Lenny / Sunny side of the street / Back to the apple / I'll always be in love with you.
LP: 231 0823
MC: K10 823

BIG MOUTH.
Tracks: / Big mouth / Look of love, The / Bag's Groove / I love you / Days of wine and roses / Yusef / Getting sentimental over you / I owes ya.
LP: 2310 867
MC: K10 867

BIG THREE, THE (Jackson, Milt/ Joe Pass/ Ray Brown).
Tracks: / Pink panther / Nuages / Blue bossa / Come Sunday / Wave / Moonglow / You stepped out of a dream / Blues for Sammy.
LP: 231 0757
MC: K10 757

BROTHER JIM.
Tracks: / Brother Jim / Ill wind / Rhythm-a-ning / Sudden death / How high the moon / Back to Bologna / Sleeves / Lullaby of the leaves / Weasel, The.
LP: 231 0916
MC: K10 916

COMPLETE MILT JACKSON (With Horace Silver) (Jackson, Milt & Horace Silver).
LP: 1902118

DATE IN NEW YORK, A VOL.1 (Jackson, Milt & Jay Jay Johnson).
LP: 500080
LP: . . . . JL 80

FEELINGS.
Tracks: / Feelings / Come to me / Trouble is a man / Moody blue / Day it rained, The / My kind of troubles is you / If you went away / Tears / Blues for Edith / You don't know what love is.
LP: 2310 774
MC: K10 774

FROM OPUS DE JAZZ TO JAZZ SKYLINE.
Tracks: / Opus de funk / You leave me breathless / Opus and interlude / Opus pocus / Lover / Can't help lovin' dat man / Lady is a tramp, The / Angel face / Sometimes I'm happy / What's new?.
LP: . . . . WL 70821
LP: . . . . WL 70501

INVITATION.
LP: . . . . OJC 260

IT DON'T MEAN A THING IF YOU CAN'T TAP YOUR FOOT TO IT (Jackson, Milt Quartet).
Tracks: / Midnight waltz / Ain't that nuthin'? / Stress and strain / Used to be Jackson / It don't mean a thing / If I were a bell / Close enough for blood.
LP: 2310909
MC: K10 909

JAZZ 'N' SAMBA.
Tracks: / Blues for Juanita / I got it bad and that ain't good / Big George / Gingerbread boy.
LP: . . . . JAS 32
MC: . . . . JAS C32

LOOSE WALK (Jackson, Milt & Sonny Stitt).
Tracks: / Loose walk / Parking lot blues / SKJ / Scrapple from the apple / Lover man / Star eyes.
LP: . . . . PAL 15009

MILT JACKSON.
Tracks: / Lillie / Tahiti / What's new / On the scene / Willow weep for me / Criss cross / Eronel / Misterioso / Evidence / Lillie (2) / Four in one / What's new (alt. take) (Not on LP.) / Don't get around much anymore (Not on LP.) / Don't get around much anymore (alt.) (Not on LP.) / Misterioso (alt.) (Not on LP.) / Epistrophy (Not on LP.) / I mean you (Not on LP.) / All the things you are (Not on LP.) / I should care (alt.) (Not on LP.) / I should care (Not on LP.).
LP: . . . . BLJ 81509

MILT JACKSON (2).
LP: . . . . GNPS 9007

MILT JACKSON AND COMPANY.
Tracks: / Jaybone / Lament / Our delight / Bag's groove / Watch what happens / My one and only love / Jumpin' blues.
LP: 2310 897

MILT JACKSON AND RAY BROWN JAM (Jackson, Milt & Ray Brown).
Tracks: / Slippery / Beautiful friendship, A / Mean to me / You are my sunshine / CMJ.
LP: 2308 205
MC: . . . . K 08 205

MILT JACKSON WITH THE THELONIUS MONK QUARTET.
Tracks: / Lillie / Tahiti / What's new / Bag's groove / On the scene / Willow weep for me / Criss cross / Eronel / Four in one / Mysterioso / Evidence.
LP: . . . . BLP 1509

NIGHT MIST.
Tracks: / Blues in my heart / Double B / Blues for Clyde / Matter of adjustment / Night mist blues / Other bag blues / D.B. blues.
LP: 231 2124
MC: . . . . K 12 124

OPUS DE FUNK.
Tracks: / Opus de funk / Buhaina / I've lost your love / Soma / Wonder why / My funny valentine / Stonewall / I should care / Nearness of you / Moon ray / Ruby my dear / Sealer / None shall wander / Ruby / Invitation / Stella by starlight / Too close for comfort / Poom a loom.
2LP: . . . . PR 24048

PLENTY PLENTY SOUL.
Tracks: / Plenty plenty soul / Boogity boogity / Heartstrings / Sermonette / Spirit feel, The / Ignunt oil / Blues at twilight.
LP: . . . . K 50299

REUNION BLUES (see Peterson, Oscar) (Jackson, Milt & Oscar Peterson).

SECOND NATURE, THE SAVOY SESSIONS.
Tracks: / Now's the time / In a sentimental mood / Mood indigo / Azure / Fred's mood / Flamingo / Minor conception / What's new / Sometimes I'm happy / Soul in 3/4 / Lover / Can't help lovin' / That man / Lady is a tramp, The / They can't take that away from me / Wild man / Come rain or come shine / Angel face / Soulful.
LP: . . . . SJL 2204

SOUL BELIEVER.
Tracks: / Ain't misbehavin' / Don't worry 'bout me / I've got the blues / Heartstrings / Roll 'em Pete / Yes sir, that's my baby / I've grown accustomed to her face / I got it bad and that ain't good / Someone I love / Parking lot blues.
LP: **231 0832**
MC: **K10 832**

SOUL FUSION (Jackson, Milt & Monty Alexander).
Tracks: / Parking lot blues / Three thousand miles ago / Isn't she lovely? / Soul fusion / Compassion / Once I loved / Yano / Bossa nova do marilla.
LP: **231 0804**
MC: **K10 804**

SOUL MEETING (see Charles, Ray & Milt Jackson) (Jackson, Milt/Ray Charles).

SOUL ROUTE (Jackson, Milt Quartet).
Tracks: / Sittin' in the sandtrap / Blues for Gene / How long has this been going on? / Dejection blues / Soul route / Afterglow / In a mellow tone / My romance / Chloe.
MC: **K10 900**
LP: **231 0900**

STATEMENT (Jackson, Milt Quintet).
Tracks: / Statement / Slowly / Thrill from the blues / Put off / Sonnymoon for two / Bad and the beautiful.
LP: . . . . **JAS 77**

TWO OF THE FEW (Jackson, Milt & Oscar Peterson).
LP: **2310 881**
MC: **K10 881**

VERY TALL (Jackson, Milt & Oscar Peterson).
Tracks: / On Green Dolphin Street / Work song / Heartstrings / John Browns body / Wonderful guy / Reunion blues.
LP: **827 821-1**
MC: **827 821-4**

Jackson, Papa Charlie

BLIND BLAKE & PAPA CHARLIE JACKSON (See under Blind Blake).

FAT MOUTH 1924-27.
LP: . . . . **L 1029**

MOSTLY NEW TO LP (1924-29).
Tracks: / Salt Lake City blues / Mama don't allow it / I'm tired of fooling around with you / Bad luck woman blues / Corn liquor blues.
LP: . . . . **MSE 1007**

PAPA CHARLIE JACKSON 1924-34.
LP: . . . . **BD 2036**

Jackson, Paul

YOU MADE ME A WINNER.
LP: . . . . **OLP 29**

Jackson, Ray

IN THE NIGHT.
Tracks: / Everything will turn out fine / Make it last / In the night / Another lonely day / Stick around joe / Waiting for the time / Little town flirt / Tread on a good thing / You send me / Easy love / Solo again / In the midnight hour.
LP: **9109 831**

Jackson, Rebbie

CENTIPEDE.
Tracks: / Centipede / Come alive, it's saturday night / Hey boy / Open up my love / Play me i'm a jukebox / I feel for you / Fork in the road / Ready for love.
LP: . . . . **CBS 25926**

REACTION.
Tracks: / Reaction / Ain't no way to love / Ticket to love / You don't know what you're missing / You send the rain away / If you don't call (you don't care) / Always wanting something / Tonight I'm yours / Lessons (in the fine art of love).
LP: . . . . **CBS 26961**
MC: **40 26961**

Jackson, R.G.

TRODDIN OUT OF BABYLON (see under Campbell, Cornell).

Jackson, Ronald

BARBEQUE DOG.
Tracks: / Barbeque dog / Trials of an honest man / Yugo boy / Say what you will / Mystery at dawn / Got it / When cherry trees bloom in winter / You can smell the summer / Harlem opera.
LP: . . . . **AN 1015**

DECODE YOURSELF.
Tracks: / Bepop / Decoding / Thieves market / Behind plastic faces / Software shuffle / Snake alley / Undressing / Love words for a queen / Tricky Vic.
LP: . . . . **ILPS 9827**

RED WARRIOR.
MC: . . . . **AXCT 3008**

Jackson, R.Zee

HIT AFTER HIT - VOLUME 4.
Tracks: / Straw dog / Same one, The / Chain gang / Heaven just knows.
LP: . . . . **STL 1005**
MC: . . . . **VSMC 005**

Jackson, Shannon

WHEN COLOURS PLAY.
Tracks: / When colours play / Sweet orange / Good omens / March of the pink wallflowers / Blue midnight / Green here, to go.
LP: . . . . **CDP 85009**

Jackson Southernairs

HYMNS.
LP: . . . . **MAL 04378**

LORD, WE NEED YOUR BLESSING.
LP: . . . . **MAL 04406**

MADE IN MISSISSIPPI.
LP: . . . . **MAL 04392**

ON THE THIRD DAY.
LP: . . . . **MALP 4435**

Jackson, Stonewall

MY FAVOURITE SIN.
Tracks: / My favourite sin / I can't sing a love song / Point of no return, The / Have your next affair with me / Spirit of St Louis / Alcohol of fame / Things that lovers do / We're the kind of people (that make the jukebox play) / Don't you say nothin' at all / Jesus took the outlaw out of me.
LP: . . . . **PRCV 101**

STONEWALL JACKSON.
MC: . . . . **ZCGAS 752**

UP AGAINST THE WALL.
Tracks: / Old chunk of coal / Let the sun shine on the people / Mary don't you weep / Help stamp out loneliness / Promises and hearts / Life to go / BJ the DJ / Wound time can't erase, A / Ole show - boat / Muddy water.
LP: . . . . **ALEB 2300**
MC: . . . . **ZCALB 2300**

WATERLOO (OLD GOLD) (See Under Battle Of New Orleans (Old Gold)) (Various artists).

Jackson, Tony

YOU'RE MY NUMBER ONE.
LP: . . . . **STZ 5005**

Jackson, Walter

FEELING GOOD.
Tracks: / Too shy to say / Play in the band / Welcome home / Please pardon me / Love is lovelier / Love woke me up this morning / Feelings / Words / I've got it bad feelin' good / Someone saved my life today.
LP: . . . . **UAS 30019**

PORTRAIT OF WALTER JACKSON, A.
LP: . . . . **BRLP 1001**

Jackson, Wanda

2 SIDES OF WANDA.
LP: **2C 068 86305**

BEST OF WANDA JACKSON.
LP: **1A 022 58072**
MC: **1A 222 58072**

CAPITOL COUNTRY CLASSICS.
Tracks: / Right or wrong / In the middle of a heartache / If I cried every time you hurt me / Violet and the rose / Box it came in / Because it's you / Tears will be the chaser for your wine / Both sides of the line / Girl don't have to drink to have fun / My baby walked out on me / My big iron skillet / Two separate bar stools / Woman lives for love / Fancy satin pillows / Back then / I already know.
LP: . . . . **CAPS 1033**

CLOSER TO JESUS.
Tracks: / Where I'm going / World didn't give it to me, The / Carpenter's son / Grandma sang off key / He was there all the time / Closer to Jesus / Learning to lean / I came to praise the Lord / I just feel that something good is about to happen / Get all excited / Walkin' in the spirit / He's been through it too.
LP: . . . . **WST 9580**
MC: . . . . **WC 9580**

COUNTRY GOSPEL.
Tracks: / I love you, Jesus / I saw the light / Jesus cares for me / Turn your radio on / I'd rather have Jesus / All in all / I know / Why me, Lord? / Special kind of man, A / Farther along / Let go...let Jesus.
LP: . . . . **WST 9515**
MC: . . . . **WC 9515**

EARLY WANDA JACKSON.
Tracks: / If you don't somebody else will / You don't have my love / I'd rather have a broken heart / You'd be the first one to know / If you knew what I know / Lovin' country style / Heart you could have had, The / Right to love, The / It's the same old world (wherever you go) / Tears at the Grand Ole Opry / Don't do the things he'd do / Nobody's darlin' but mine / I cried again / Wasted / You won't forget about me.
LP: . . . . **BFX 15109**

HER GREATEST COUNTRY HITS.
Tracks: / Stand by your man / Leave my baby alone / Wrong kind of girl / My big iron skillet / Hello darlin' / Break my mind / Two separate bar stools / Please help me, I'm falling / Your good girl's gonna go bad / Right or wrong / One minute past eternity / Silver threads and golden needles / Tuck away my lonesome blues / Jealous heart / Blue model No 6 / Try a little kindness / Love of the common people / Walk through this world with me / Oh lonesome me / Today I started loving you again / Reuben James / Great speckled bird, The / It's such a pretty world today / Both sides of the line / Tips of my fingers, The / More you see me less, The / I'm a believer / Wabash cannonball.
2LP: **5C 134 53025/26**

LET'S HAVE A PARTY.
Tracks: / Let's have a party / Rock your baby / Mean mean man / There's a party going on / Fujiyama mama / Honey bop / Rip it up / Man we had a party / Hot dog that made him mad / You bug me bad / Who shot Sam / Tongue tied / Sparklin' brown eyes / Lost weekend / Brown eyed handsome man / Honey don't / It doesn't matter anymore / Whole lotta shakin' goin' on / Long tall Sally / Money honey / Searchin' / Hard headed woman / Slippin' and slidin' / Riot in cell block 9 / I gotta know / Baby loves him / Let me explain / Savin' my love / Just a queen for a day / Cool love / Bye bye baby / Right or wrong.
2LP: . . . . **CDX 11**
MC: . . . . **TCCDX 11**

LOVIN' COUNTRY STYLE.
LP: . . . . **HAT 3021**
MC: . . . . **HATC 3021**

MY KIND OF GOSPEL.
Tracks: / If Jesus changed your heart / Glory train / Jesus is the best thing that ever.... / Help, help me Jesus / Life's journey / Jesus loves cowgirls / I've never been this homesick before / Jesus gave it to me / Thank you lord for loving me / It's your decision.
LP: . . . . **SDLP 026**
MC: . . . . **SDC 026**

MY TESTIMONY.
Tracks: / Show me the way to Calvary / Holy Ghost baptiser / Walking on the water / I go to the rock / He's still working on me / Hey devil / Come morning / Let me touch Him / Jesus, I believe what You said / My testimony.
LP: . . . . **WST 9619**
MC: . . . . **WC 9619**

NOW I HAVE EVERYTHING.
Tracks: / Don't ever let go of my hand / Let this be my attitude / Heaven's gonna be a blast / When the saints go marching in / Oh how I love Jesus / Jesus put a yodel in my heart / Now I have everything / Pick me up, Lord / Jesus, I love you / Some call him Jesus / Let's just praise the Lord / Pass me not, O gentle Saviour.
LP: . . . . **MYR 1021**
MC: . . . . **MC 1021**

RAVE ON.
Tracks: / Let's have a party / Breathless / Right or wrong / Stupid cupid / What in the world's come over you / I fall to pieces / Raining in my heart / Sweet dreams / Sweet nothin's / Oh boy / Rave on.
LP: . . . . **TOP 166**
MC: . . . . **KTOP 166**

RIGHT OR WRONG.
LP: **2C 068 85314**

ROCKABILLY FEVER.
Tracks: / Rockabilly fever / Stupid cupid / Rock 'n' roll away your blues / Sweet nothins / It's only make believe / Oh boy / Rockabilly hound dog / Breathless / Sad love songs / Rave on / Meet me in Stockholm / Ain't it the gospel.
LP: . . . . **MFLP 037**
MC: . . . . **MFC 037**

ROCKIN' WITH WANDA.
Tracks: / Hot dog / That made him mad / Baby loves him / Mean, mean man / You've turned to a stranger / Don'a wan'a / I gotta know / Yakety yak / Let's have a party / Rock your baby / Fujiyama Mama / You're the one for me / Did you miss me? / Cool love / Honey boy / Whole lotta shakin' goin' on / Savin' my love.
LP: . . . . **CAPS 1007**
MC: **2C 068 82098**

THERE'S A PARTY.
LP: **2C 068 85315**

WANDA JACKSON.
LP: **2C 068 85111**

WONDERFUL WANDA.
Tracks: / In the middle of a heartache / Seven lonely boys / If I cried every time you hurt me / Is it wrong / Don't asky me why / Let my love walk in / Little bitty tear, A / I need you now / I don't wanta go / We could / You don't know baby / I'd be ashamed.
LP: . . . . **JAS 304**
MC: . . . . **JAS C304**

Jackson, William

CELTIC SUITE FOR GLASGOW.
Tracks: / Bird, The / Tree, The / Bell, The / Fish, The.
MC: . . . . **CTRAX 041**

HEART MUSIC.
LP: . . . . **IR 010**
MC: . . . . **IRC 010**

Jackson, Willis

COOL GATOR.
LP: . . . . **OJC 220**

GATOR HORN, THE.
LP: . . . . **MR 5146**

GATOR'S GROOVE.
Tracks: / Soul grabber / Brother Elijah / Pool shark / Que sara sweetie / Good to the damned / Sportin' / Shuckin' / Penny serenade.
LP: . . . . **BGP 1021**

LOCKIN' HORNS.
Tracks: / Pow / Man I love, The / Troubled times / Summertime / Shadow of your smile / Willis and Von.
LP: . . . . **MR 5200**

NOTHING BUTT.
Tracks: / Just the way you are / Nuages / Nothing butt / Hittin' and missin' / Autumn leaves / Move.
LP: . . . . **MR 5294**

ON MY OWN.
Tracks: / Later for the gator / Call of the gators, The / On my own / Dance of the lady bug / More blues at midnight / Good gliding / Wine-o-wine / Street scene / Harlem nocturne / Back door / Howling at midnight / We'll be together again / Crackerjack / Try a little tenderness / Estrellita.
LP: . . . . **KM 705**

SINGLE ACTION.
Tracks: / Evergreen / Bolita / Makin' whoopee / You are the sunshine of my life / Hittin' the numbers / Single action.
LP: . . . . **MR 5179**

YA UNDERSTAND ME.
LP: . . . . **MR 5316**

Jackson, Yvonne

I'M TROUBLE.
Tracks: / I'm trouble / Sweet memories / Woman in me, The / She set you free / No deposit, no return / What I'd do to get your love back / Common, ordinary housewife gone bad / Whatcha gonna do about it / If tears are only water / I'm walking out.
LP: . . . . **ICH 1105**
MC: . . . . **ICH 1105 MC**

Jacksons

2300 JACKSON STREET.
Tracks: / Art of madness / Nothin' (that compares 2 U) / Maria / Private affair / 2300 Jackson Street / Harley / She / Alright with me / Play it up / Midnight rendezvous / If you'd only believe.
LP: **4633521**
MC: **4633524**

DESTINY.
Tracks: / Blame it on the boogie / Push me away / Things I do for you / Shake your body / Destiny / Bless his soul / All night dancin' / That's what you get.
LP: . . . . **EPC 32365**
MC: **40 32365**
LP: . . . . **EPC 83200**

GOIN' PLACES.
LP: . . . . **EPC 86035**

JACKSONS, THE.
Tracks: / Can you feel it / Things I do for you / Off the wall / Ben / Heartbreak hotel / She's out of my life / I want you back / Never can say goodbye / Got to be there / Love you save, The / I'll be there / Rock with you / Lovely one / Working day and night / Don't stop 'til you get enough / Shake your body.
LP: . . . . **CBS 32101**
LP: . . . . **EPC 86009**
LP: . . . . **EPC 88562**
LP: . . . . **EPC 32101**

STATE OF SHOCK (see also Mick Jagger).

TRIUMPH.
Tracks: / Can you feel it / Lovely one / Your ways / Everybody / This place hotel / Time waits for no one / Walk right now / Give it up / Wondering who.
LP: . . . . **EPC 32366**

MC: 40 32366
LP: .... EPC 86112

VICTORY.
Tracks: / Torture / Wait / One more chance / Be not always / State of shock / We can change the world / Hurt, The / Body.
LP: 4504501
MC: 4504504
LP: .... EPC 86303

Jacobi, Derek (nar)

CLAUDIUS THE GOD (see under Claudius The God (bk)).

Jacobites

FORTUNE OF FAME.
LP: .... GLALP 029

JACOBITES, THE.
Tracks: / Norwind winds / Rose of Allandale / Skye boat song / Santiano / Bunch of thyme / Mermaid, The / Broom o'the Cowdenknowes / Wild mountain thyme / Twa racruiting sergeants / Lochnagar / Thumb at the nose / Doon in the wee room.
MC: .... 001 C

ROBESPIERRE'S VELVET BASEMENT.
Tracks: / Big store snow white / Fortune of fame / Where the rivers end / Silken sheets / Ambulance station / Son of a French nobleman / Cheapside / Hearts are like flowers / It'll all end in tears / She never believes / All the dark rags / One more string of pearls / I am just a broken heart / Only children sleeping.
LP: .... GLALP 012

YE JACOBITES BY NAME.
Tracks: / Ye Jacobites by name / John Anderson, my Jo / Sound the pibroch / Island spinning song / Loch Lomond / Beautiful Highlands of home / All around my hat / Trooper and the maid, The / Kinloch Rannoch lullabye / Lads o' the fair, The / Bonnie Glenshee / Silver darlings / Mapherson's rant.
LP: .... LILP 5136
MC: .... LICS 5136

Jacobs, Dale

COBRA.
Tracks: / Cobra / Computer samba / Loose connection / Scouting party / On the wings of a song / Taiwan on / Freedom / Patch day / Almost home.
LP: .... EPC 83761

Jacobs, Debbie

UNDERCOVER LOVER.
LP: .... MCF 3019

Jacob's Ladder (film)

JACOB'S LADDER (See under Jarre, Maurice) (Jarre, Maurice).

Jacobs, Lawrence

ALL THE WAY .... LOVE.
LP: .... MCF 3012

Jacobs, Little Walter

BLUE AND LONESOME.
LP: 33 2007

SOUTHERN FEELING.
LP: 33 2012

Jacques Brel

JACQUES BREL IS ALIVE & WELL & LIVING IN PARIS (Film soundtrack) (Various artists).
2LP: .... SD 1000
MC: .... CS 1000

Jacques, Peter Band

FIRE NIGHT DANCE.
Tracks: / Walking on music / Devil's run / Fire night dance / Fly with the wind.
LP: .... ARL 5027

WELCOME BACK.
Tracks: / Counting on love / One two three / Welcome back / Louder it is, The / Exotical / Mighty fine.
LP: .... PL 25331

Jacquet, Georgie

NI JALOUISIE DANS L'AIR (Jacquet, Georgie & Sylvie Suter).
LP: 50918

Jacquet, Illinois

BIRTHDAY PARTY.
LP: .... JRC 11434

BLUES AND SENTIMENTAL.
LP: .... JAZ 2002
MC: .... ZCJAZ 2002

BLUES FROM LOUISIANA.
LP: .... JRC 11433

BOTTOMS UP.
LP: 333710

FABULOUS APOLLO SESSIONS, THE.
LP: 500 858

GENIUS AT WORK.
Tracks: / King, The / Easy living / C jam blues / Take the 'A' train / I wanna blow now.
LP: .... BLP 30118

GROOVIN'.
LP: 2304 511

ILLINOIS FLIES AGAIN.
Tracks: / On a clear day / Illinois Jacquet flies again / Robin's nest / Watermelon man / I want a little girl / Pamela's blues / Jan / Message, The / Bassoon blues / On Broadway / Like young / Turnpike / Bonita.
2LP: .... ARCD 503
LP: 500062

ILLINOIS JACQUET (Jacquet, Illinois & Wild Bill Davis).
LP: .... JR 154

KID AND THE BRUTE, THE (Jacquet, Illinois & Ben Webster).
Tracks: / Saph / Mambocito mio / September song / Jacquet's dilemma / Kid and The Brute, The / I wrote this for The Kid.
LP: 2304 565

SWINGS THE THING.
LP: 2304 434

Jacquet, Russell

RUSS IN NICE.
LP: .... JATH 11435

Jacqui & Birdie

HELLO FRIEND.
LP: .... NEVLP 102
MC: .... NEVC 102

TIS A GIFT TO BE SIMPLE.
LP: .... NEVLP 111

Jad Fair

EVERYONE KNEW BUT ME.
Tracks: / I can't believe it's over / I do.
LP: .... P 4005

GREAT EXPECTATIONS.
2LP: .... BAAL 2

ROLL OUT THE BARREL (Jad Fair & Kramer).
LP: .... SHIMMY 012

Jad W10

CONTACT.
LP: 360137

Jade

IF YOU'RE MAN ENOUGH.
LP: .... RR 9755

MR JOY.
Tracks: / Mr. Joy / Don't love / Let me / Sweet love (Instrumental) / Freak / Sweet love.
LP: .... TRPL 119

Jade 4 U

JADES'S DREAM.
LP: .... IR 001

Jade Warrior

HORIZON.
Tracks: / Images of dune / Prescient dawn / Endless desert / Endless lives / Maker, The / Freman, The / People of the sand / Spice ritual / Sietch tabre / Jurney on a dream / Giant beneath the sand / Prophet, The / Riding the maker / Caribbean wave / Horizon / East wind / Grey lake / Long wait at mount Li.
LP: .... PULSE 005

KITES.
Tracks: / Songs of the forest / Wind song / Emperor kite, The / Wind borne / Kite song / Land of the warrior / Quietly by the river bank / Arrival of the emperor / What does the venerable sir do? / Teh ch'eng - do you understand this? / Arrival of Chai Shan: discourse and liberation / Towards the mountains / Last question, The.
LP: .... ILPS 9392

REFLECTIONS.
Tracks: / English morning / Lady of the lake / Borne on the solar wind / Morning hymn / Bride of the summer / Soldiers song / Winters tale, A / Yellow eyes / Dark river / House of dreams.
LP: .... BUTT 001

WAVES.
Tracks: / Waves (part 1) / Waves (part 2).
LP: .... ILPS 9318

WAY OF THE SUN.
Tracks: / Sun ra / Sun child / Moontears / Heaven stone / Way of the sun / River song / Carnival / Dance of the sun / Death of Ra.
LP: .... AN 7068

Jaderlund

KEJSARENSNYAKLADER.
LP: .... DRLP 49

Jaffa, Max

GRAND HOTEL MEMORIES.
Tracks: / Tik tak polka / Intermezzo from Cavalleria Rusticana / Where my caravan has rested / Roses of Picardy / Czardas / Old english airs / Heykens serenade / Dearly beloved / Lark in the clear air / Romance in A minor / My dearest dear / Old folks at home / Andantino (moonlight and roses) / Old violin, An.
LP: .... VAL 8058
MC: .... VAL 68058

MAX JAFFA WITH THE PALM COURT ORCHESTRA (Jaffa, Max, Palm Court Orchestra & His Concert Orchestra).
Tracks: / Roses from the South / Great waltz selection, The / Countess Maritza / O for the wings of a dove / Hungarian dance No. 1 / Grinzing / Enough sadness and tears / Black eyes / Xzardas / Waltzing in the clouds / Souvenir D'Ukraine / Dobra dobra / Srenta / Vagabond king selection,The / Doina voda / Estrellita / Beautiful dreamer (Featuring Reginald Kilbey.) / Hejre Kate / Forgotten dreams (Featuring Jack Byfield.) / Melodies from the gypsy princess / Hungarian dance No. 5 / Roses from the South.
MC: .... TCEMS 1383

MUSIC FOR A GRAND HOTEL (Jaffa, Max Orchestra).
Tracks: / Roses from the South / Gypsy carnival / Great waltz / Canto amoroso / Fascination / Scarborough fair / Some day I'll find you / Dobra dobra / Gentle maiden, The / I dream of Jeannie with the light brown hair / Memories of Richard Tauber / Adoration / Annen polka / Victor Herbert medley / Ave Maria.
LP: .... VAL 8057
MC: .... VAL 68057

PRELUDE TO ROMANCE (Jaffa, Max His Violin & Orchestra).
Tracks: / Prlude to romance / Touch of your lips / Don't blame me / Where or when / Try a little tenserness / You made me love you / Poet & I / Easy to love / I'm getting sentimental over you / Lullaby of Birdland / More than you know / I'll see you in my dreams.
LP: .... VAL 8051
MC: .... VAL 68051

RELAX WITH THE MUSIC OF MAX JAFFA.
Tracks: / Vagabond king selection / Waltzing in the clouds / Lark in the clear air / Enough sadness and tears / Beautiful dreamer / Dobra dobra / Great waltz selection, The / Forgotten dreams / Countess Maritza / Last rose of summer / Ave Maria / Hungarian dance no. 1 / Roses from the south / Melodies of Britain (Includes: D'ye ken John Peel/ Drink to me/Only with thine eyes/Sir Roger) / Jeanie with the light brown hair / Fascination / I love the moon / Desert song (from "The desert song") / Violin song from "Tina" / Gypsy carnival / Serenade / Black eyes / Doina voda / Souvenir D'Ukraine / Softly awakes my heart / Jeanie with the light brown hair.
MC: .... TCDL 1106
2LP: .... DL 1106

WAY YOU LOOK TONIGHT, THE.
MCSET: .... WW 6036

Jaffe, Andy

MANHATTAN PROJECTIONS (Jaffe, Andy Sextet).
LP: .... ST 247

Jag Panzer

AMPLE DESTRUCTION.
Tracks: / Licensed to kill / Warfare / Symphony of terror / Harder than steel / Generally hostile / Watching, The / Reign of tyrants / Cardiac arrest / Crucifix, The.
LP: .... IW 1001

Jagged Edge

FUEL FOR YOUR SOUL.
Tracks: / Liar / You don't love me / Smooth operator / Fuel for your soul / Loving you too long / Money talking / Out in the gold / Hell ain't a long way / Sweet Lorraine / Law of the land / Burning up / All through the night.
LP: 847 201 1
MC: 847 108 4
LP: 847 108 1

TROUBLE.
Tracks: / Trouble / You don't love me / Wolf, The / Rosie Rosie / Crash and burn / Good golly Miss Molly.
MC: 841 983 4
MLP: 841 983 1

Jagged Edge (Film)

JAGGED EDGE (Film Soundtrack) (Various artists).
LP: .... TER 1107
MC: .... CTV 81252
MC: .... ZCTER 1107

Jagger, Mick

DANCING IN THE STREET (see under Bowie, David) (Jagger, Mick & David Bowie).

MICK JAGGER: INTERVIEW PICTURE DISC.
LPPD: .... BAK 2068

PERFORMANCE (Film Soundtrack) (Jagger, Mick & James Fox).
Tracks: / Gone dead train / Performance / Get away / Powis Square / Rolls Royce / Dyed, dead, red / Harry Flowers / Memo from Turner / Hashishin, The / Wake up, niggers / Poor white hound dog / Natural magic / Turner's murder.
LP: .... K 46075

PRIMITIVE COOL.
Tracks: / Throwaway / Let's work / Radio control / Say you will / Primitive cool / Kowtow / Shoot off your mouth / Peace for the wicked / Party doll / War baby.
LP: 4601231
MC: 4601234

SHE'S THE BOSS.
Tracks: / Lonely at the top / Half a loaf / Running out of luck / Turn the girl loose / Hard woman / Just another night / Lucky love / Secrets / She's the boss.
MC: 40 86310

STATE OF SHOCK (See under Jacksons) (Jagger, Mick & the Jacksons).

Jagger & Richards...

JAGGER AND RICHARDS SONGBOOK (Various artists).
MC: .... VSOPMC 159

Jags

EVENING STANDARDS.
Tracks: / Desert island discs / Women's world / She's so considerate / Little boy lost / Single vision / BWM / Evening standards / Party games / Tune into heaven / Last picture show / Tourist, The.
LP: .... ILPS 9603

Jaguar

ARGUMENT.
LP: .... W 2395

POWER GAMES.
Tracks: / Dutch connection / Out of luck / Fox, The / Master game / No lies / Run for your life / Prisoner, The / Ain't no fantasy / Raw deal / Cold heart.
LP: .... NEAT 1007

THIS TIME.
LP: .... RR 9851

Jaguars

WAY YOU LOOK TONIGHT, THE.
LP: .... JD 904

Jah Life

SMASHING SUPERSTARS.
LP: .... STLP 1015

Jah Lion

IN ACTION WITH THE REVOLUTIONARY BAND.
LP: .... STLP 1011

Jah Lloyd

SHAKE AND FLICKER.
LP: .... SHEET 4

Jah Mel

RUFF FOR YEARS (Jah Mel & The Rhythm Factory).
LP: .... JMRF 3303

Jah Shaka All Stars

MESSAGE FROM AFRICA.
LP: .... SHAKA 848 LP

Jah Warriors

NO ILLUSIONS.
LP: .... ARCLP 100

POOR MANS STORY.
LP: .... VSLP 4058

Jahson, David

COME AGAIN.
Tracks: / True believer / Believing dub / Tell me darling / Whispering dub / Live like a man / Up right dub / Ruff neck soldier / Raggamuffin dub / Rude boy gone a jail / Jailhouse dub / Back way / Move yah dub.
LP: .... SPY LPO

PAST AND PRESENT.
LP: .... LP 100

REALLY WANT TO KNOW (see under Hotta Clapps Band "Knowing it all").

Jailcell Recipes

ENERGY IN AN EMPTY TANK.
LP: .... FST 003

TWO YEARS OF TOOTHACHE.
LP: .... FST 12

Jakata

LIGHT THE NIGHT.
Tracks: / Living like there's no tomorrow / Hell is on the run / Golden girl / Can't take your games anymore / Tell him you're leaving / Racing for the dawn / Light at the end of the tunnel / Jean such a scene / Don't ever let go / Shadows of the night.
LP: . . . . . ZL 72284
MC: . . . . . ZK 72284

Jake Speed

JAKE SPEED (Film soundtrack) (Various artists).
LP: . . . . . STV 81285
MC: . . . . . CTV 81285

Jakie Jazz 'Em 'Up

JAKIE JAZZ 'EM 'UP Old time Klezmer music 1912-26 (Various artists).
MC: . . . . . GVMMC 101

Jalihouse Rock

JALIHOUSE ROCK (Various artists).
MC: . . . . . FMSC 5019

Jam

ALL MOD CONS.
Tracks: / All mod cons / To be someone / Mr. Clean / David Watts / English rose / In the crowd / Billy Hunt / It's too bad / Fly / Place I love / Bomb in Wardour Street, A / Down in the tube station at midnight.
LP: . . . . . POLD 5008
MC: . . . . . POLDC 5008

ALL MOD CONS/SETTING SONS.
Tracks: / All mod cons / To be someone / Mr. Clean / David Watts / English rose / In the crowd / Billy Hunt / It's too bad / Fly / Place I love / Bomb in wardour street, A / Down in the tube station at midnight / Girl on the phone / Thick as thieves / Private hell / Little boy soldiers / Wasteland / Burning sky / Smithers-Jones / Saturday's kids / Eton rifles / Heatwave.
MC: 1574 098

DIG THE NEW BREED.
Tracks: / In the city / All mod cons / To be someone / It's too bad / Start / Big bird / Set the house ablaze / Ghosts / Standards / In the crowd / Going underground / Dreams of children / That's entertainment / Private hell.
LP: . . . . . SPELP 107
MC: . . . . . SPEMC 107
LP: . . . . . POLD 5075
LP: 8100411
MC: 8100414

GIFT, THE.
Tracks: / Happy together / Ghosts / Precious / Just who is the five o'clock hero / Trans-Global express / Running on the spot / Circus / Planner's dream goes wrong, The / Carnation / Town called Malice / Gift, The.
LP: . . . . . POLD 5055
MC: . . . . . POLDC 5055
LP: 8232851
MC: 8232854

GREATEST HITS: JAM.
Tracks: / In the city / All around the world / News of the world / Modern world, The / David Watts / Down in the tube station at midnight / Strange town / When you're young / Eton rifles, The / Going underground / Start / That's entertainment / Funeral pyre / Absolute beginners / Town called malice / Precious / Just who is the five o'clock hero / Bitterest pill (I ever had to swallow) The / Beat surrender.
LP: 849554-1
MC: 849554-4

IN THE CITY.
Tracks: / Art school / I've changed my address / Slow down / I got by in time / Away from the numbers / Batman / In the city / Sounds from the street / Non stop dancing / Time for truth / Takin' my love / Bricks and mortar.
LP: . . . . . SPELP 27
MC: . . . . . SPEMC 27
LP: 2383 447
LP: 8171241
MC: 8171244

IN THE CITY/ THIS IS THE MODERN WORLD.
MC: 8477304

SETTING SONS.
Tracks: / Burning sky / Eton rifles / Girl on the phone / Heatwave / Little boy soldiers / Private hell / Saturdays kids / Smithers-Jones / Thick as thieves / Wasteland.
LP: . . . . . POLD 5028
MC: . . . . . POLDC 5028
MC: 831314 4

SNAP.
Tracks: / In the city / Away from the numbers / All around the world / Modern world, The / News of the world / Billy Hunt / English rose / Mr. Clean / David Watts / Bomb in Wardour Street, A / Down in the tube station at midnight / Strange town / Butterfly collector, The / When you're young / Smithers-Jones / Thick as thieves / Eton rifles / Going underground / Dreams of children / That's entertainment / Start / Man in the corner shop / Funeral pyre / Absolute beginners / Tales from the riverbank / Town called Malice / Precious / Bitterest pill (I ever had to swallow), The / Beat surrender.
2LP: . . . . . SNAP 1
MCSET: . . . . . SNAPC 1
2LP: 8155371
MCSET: 8155374

SOUND AFFECTS.
Tracks: / Pretty green / Monday / But I'm different now / Set the house ablaze / Start / That's entertainment / Dreamtime / Man in the corner shop / Music for the last couple / Boy about town / Scrape away.
LP: . . . . . POLD 5035
MC: . . . . . POLDC 5035
MC: 823 284 4
LP: 823 284 1

SOUND AFFECTS/THE GIFT.
MCSET: . . . . . TWOMC 1

THIS IS THE MODERN WORLD.
Tracks: / Modern world, The / London traffic / Standards / Life from a window / Combine, The / Don't tell them you're sane / In the street / Today / London express / I need you / Here comes the weekend / Tonight at noon / In the midnight hour.
LP: . . . . . SPELP 66
MC: . . . . . SPEMC 66
LP: 2383 475
LP: 8232811
MC: 8232814

Jam '86

WE'VE GOT THE LOVE.
LP: . . . . . UNKNOWN

Jam Afrika

FEET UP.
LP: . . . . . B 2 ST 001

Jam Session (film)

JAM SESSION / REVEILLE WITH BEVERLY (Original soundtrack) (Various artists).
LP: . . . . . HS 5014

Jamaaladen, Tacuma

JUKEBOX.
Tracks: / Meta-morphosis / Rhythm of your mind / In the mood for mood / Naima / Time a place, A / Jam-all / Jukebox / Zam Zam was such a wonderful.. / Solar system blues.
LP: 1888031
MC: 1888034

Jamaica

JAMAICA (Original Broadway cast) (Various artists).
LP: . . . . . LOC 1036

Jamaica Boys

JAMAICA BOYS, THE.
Tracks: / Palm of your hand / Let me hold you closer / Romeo / Home / People make the world go round / Spend some time with me / Sunshine (South Africa) / (It's that) lovin' / Feeling / I want to be there.
LP: . . . . . K 255990-1
MC: . . . . . K 255990-4

Jamaica Go Go

JAMAICA GO GO (Film soundtrack) (Various artists).
LP: . . . . . MLPS 1064
LP: 846 980 1
MC: . . . . . MCT 1064
MC: 846 980 4

Jamal, Ahmad

AHMAD JAMAL IN CONCERT (Jamal, Ahmad & Gary Burton).
Tracks: / Morning of the carnival / One / Bogata / Tones for Joan's bones / Autumn leaves.
LP: . . . . . GATE 7006
MC: . . . . . CGATE 7006

AHMAD'S BLUES.
MC: 771507

AHMED JAMAL.
Tracks: / I'll take romance / Like someone in love / Falling in love with love / Best thing for you / April in Paris / Second time around / We live in two different worlds / Night misty blues.
LP: . . . . . JR 153

ALHAMBRA.
LP: 515019

AT THE PERSHING.
Tracks: / But not for me / Surrey with a fringe on top / Moonlight in Vermont / Music, music, music / No greater love / Poinciana / Woody'n you / Whats new.
LP: . . . . . GCH 8032
MC: . . . . . GCHK 8032

AT THE TOP POINCIANA REVISITED.
Tracks: / Have you met Miss Jones / Poinciana / Call me / Valley of the dolls, Theme from / Frank's tune.
LP: . . . . . JAS 15
MC: . . . . . JAS C15

AWAKENING, THE (Jamal, Ahmad Trio).
Tracks: / Awakening, The / I love music / Patterns / Dolphin dance / You're my everything / Stolen moments / Wave.
LP: . . . . . JAS 44
MC: . . . . . JAS C44
MC: . . . . . ASC 9194
LP: . . . . . AS 9194

BEST OF AHMAD JAMAL.
Tracks: / Black cow / Don't ask my neighbours / Swahililand / Soul girl / Dynamo / Prelude to a kiss / Genetic walk.
LP: . . . . . T 631
MC: . . . . . C 631

CHICAGO GOLDEN YEARS.
LP: 515002

DIGITAL WORKS.
Tracks: / Poinciana / But not for me / Midnight sun / Footprints / Once upon a time / One / La Costa / Misty / M.A.S.H., Theme from / Biencavo / Time for love, A / Wave.
LP: 781 258-1
MC: 781 258-4

GOODBYE MR EVANS.
Tracks: / Lament for a dying boy / Somewhere along the Nile / Close enough for love / Firefly / Mellowdrama / Goodbye Mr. Evans / Polka dots and moonbeams.
LP: . . . . . BLM 52006

LIVE AT BUBBA'S.
Tracks: / Waltz for Debbie / House on the hill / People / Biea / It's the good life / Autumn in New York / I have never been in love before.
LP: . . . . . GATE 7002
MC: . . . . . CGATE 7002

NIGHT SONG.
Tracks: / When you wish upon a star / Deja vu / Need to smile / Bad times / Touch me in the morning / Night song / M.A.S.H., Theme from / Something's missing in my life.
LP: . . . . . STML 12145

ONE.
Tracks: / One / Just the way you are / Jet / Black cow / Dynamo / Sumayah / Festival 20th century.
LP: . . . . . T 555

Jamal, Khan

INFINITY.
LP: . . . . . ST 278

THINKING OF YOU.
LP: . . . . . SLP 4138

Jambalaya

BUGGY FULL OF CAJUN MUSIC.
LP: 6035

LE NOUVEL ESPRIT DE LA MUSIQUE CADIEN.
LP: 6075
MC: . . . . . 6075 TC

Jamboree

THESE ARE MY MOUNTAINS.
MC: . . . . . GTDC 052

Jamboree (Film)

JAMBOREE (Various session artists) (Various artists).
MC: . . . . . AIM 74

James

GOLD MOTHER (1ST VERSION).
Tracks: / Come home / Government walls / God only knows / How much suffering / Crescento / How was it for you / Hang one / Walking the ghost / Gold mother / Top of the world / Lose control / Sit down.
LP: 8485951
MC: 8485954

GOLD MOTHER (2ND VERSION).
Tracks: / Come home (flood mix) / Lose control / Government walls / God only knows / How much suffering / How was it for you? / Sit down / Walking the ghost / Gold Mother / Top of the world.
LP: 8487311
MC: 8487314

ONE MAN CLAPPING.
LP: . . . . . ONEMAN 001
MC: . . . . . ONEMAN 001C

PUT A LITTLE LOVE AWAY (James & Marshall).
LP: . . . . . BSS 230

STRIP MINE.
Tracks: / What for / Charlie dance / Fairground / Are you ready / Medieval / Not there / Ya ho / Riders / Vulture, The / Strip mining.
LP: . . . . . JIMLP 2
MC: . . . . . JIMC 2

STUTTER.
Tracks: / Skullduggery / Scarecrow / So many ways / Just hipper / John Yen / Summer songs / Really hard / Billy's shirts / Why so close / Withdrawn / Black hole.
LP: . . . . . JIMLP 1
MC: . . . . . JIMC 1

James, Bob

12.
Tracks: / No play no play / Courtship, The / Moonbop / I need more of you / Ruby, Ruby, Ruby / Midnight / Legacy.
LP: . . . . . CBS 26314

ALL AROUND THE TOWN LIVE.
Tracks: / Touchdown / Stompin' / At the Savoy / Angela (theme from "Taxi") / We're all alone / Farandole / Westchester lady / Golden apple, The / Kari.
LP: 88509
MC: 40 88509

BOB JAMES.
MC: 40 84238

DOUBLE VISION (James, Bob & Sanborn, David).
Tracks: / Maputo / More than friends / Moontune / Since I fell for you / It's you / Never enough / You don't know me.
LP: 925393 1
MC: 925393 4

FOUR.
Tracks: / Pure imagination / Where the wind blows free / Tappan zee / Nights are forever without you / Treasure Island / El verano.
LP: . . . . . CBS 84823

FOXIE.
Tracks: / Ludwig calaban / Fireball / Zebra man / Miranda / Marco polo.
LP: . . . . . CBS 25546

GENIE.
Tracks: / Brookly heights boogie / Genie / Last chance / Ballade / Groove for Julie / Hello Nardo / Marilu / New York mellow / Night moods / Angela.
LP: . . . . . CBS 25446

GRAND PIANO CANYON.
LP: 7599262561
MC: 7599262564

H.
Tracks: / Snowbird fantasy / Shepherds song / Brighton by the sea / Walkman / Thoroughbred / Reunited.
LP: . . . . . CBS 84238

HANDS DOWN.
Tracks: / Spunky / Macumba / Shamboozie / Janus / Roberta / It's only me.
LP: . . . . . CBS 85848
MC: 40 85848

IVORY COAST.
Tracks: / Ashanti / Rosalie / Yogi's dream / Adult situations / Orpheus / Moodstar.
LP: 925 757-1
MC: 925 757-4

LUCKY SEVEN.
Tracks: / Rush hour / Blue lick / Look alike / Big stone city / Friends / Fly away.
LP: . . . . . CBS 83729
MC: 40 83729

ONE.
Tracks: / Valley of the shadows / In the garden / Soulero / Night on bald mountain / Feel like makin' love / Nautilus.
LP: . . . . . CBS 84820

ONE ON ONE (James, Bob & Earl Klugh).
Tracks: / Kari / After glow / Love lips / Mallorca / I'll never see you smile again / Winding river.
LP: . . . . . CBS 83931

SIGN OF THE TIMES.
Tracks: / Hypnotique / Steamin' feelin' / Enchanted forest / Unicorn / Sign of the times / Love power.
LP: . . . . . CBS 85226

SWAN, THE.
LP: 26099

THREE.
Tracks: / One mint julep / Women of Ireland / Westchester lady / Storm king / Jamaica farewell.
LP: . . . . . CBS 84822

TOUCHDOWN.
Tracks: / Angela (Theme from "Taxi") / Touchdown / I want to thank you (very much) / Sun runner / Caribbean nights.
LP: . . . . . CBS 83175

TWO.
Tracks: / Take me to the Mardis Gras / I feel a song / Golden apple, The /

Farandole / You're as right as rain / Dream journey.
LP: CBS 84821

TWO OF A KIND (see under Klugh, Earl) (James, Bob & Earl Klugh).

James Bond

JAMES BOND SINGLES ALBUM (Original soundtrack recordings) (Various artists).
Tracks: / James Bond theme: *Various artists* / From Russia with love: *Various artists* / You only live twice: *Various artists* / Goldfinger: *Various artists* / Thunderball: *Various artists* / We have all the time in the world: *Various artists* / Diamonds are forever: *Various artists* / Live and let die: *Various artists*/ Man with the golden gun: *Various artists* / Nobody does it better: *Various artists* / Bond 77: *Various artists* / Moonraker: *Various artists*.
LP: BOND 007
MC: TCBOND 007

James Brothers

WHEN.
Tracks: / When / Endless sleep / Oh my goodness / Cowboy Billy / Blue river / Rosemarie cherie / OK Oh Veronika.
LP: BFX 15066

James, Clive

CHARLES CHARMING'S CHALLENGES ON THE PATHWAY TO (Original cast) (James, Clive with Pamela Stephenson & Russell Davies).
LP: DLART 3
MC: TLART 3

CLIVE JAMES/PETE ATKIN SONGBOOK, THE (1967-74) (James, Clive & Pete Atkin).
Tracks: / Pearl-driller, The / Sessionman's blues / Perfect moments / Between us there is nothing / No dice / Thirty year man / Sunlight gate / King at nightfall, A / Flowers and the wine, The / Girl on the train / Master of the revels / Senior citizens / Payday evening / I see the joker / Faded mansion on the hill, The / Hypertension kid, The / Beware of the beautiful stranger / You can't expect to be remembered / Touch has a memory.
MC: PK 74833

FALLING TOWARDS ENGLAND.
MCSET: LFP 7364

UNRELIABLE MEMOIRS.
MCSET: LFP 7304

James, Colin

COLIN JAMES.
Tracks: / Five long years / Voodoo thing / Down in the bottom / Chicks 'n' cars / Why'd you lie / Hidden charms / Bad girl / Dream of satin / Three sheets to the wind / Lone wolf.
LP: V 2542
MC: TCV 2542
MC: OVEDC 356
LPPD: OVED 356

SUDDEN STOP.
LP: VUSLP 20
MC: VUSMC 20

James, Dave

CALCULATED RISK.
Tracks: / Mr. James / Circles / I've been gone / Wheels go round / Will she ever / Big wave King / Running walking / You're so blind / Ballad of Billy and Sal, The / All I want.
LP: RB 120

James, Ellen

RELUCTANTLY WE (James, Ellen Society).
LP: DR 01
MC: DR 01MC

James, Elmore

BEST OF ELMORE JAMES.
Tracks: / Dust my blues / I was a fool / Dark and dreary / Late hours at midnight / Blue before sunrise / Goodbye baby / Standing at the crossroads / Sunnyland / Mean and evil / Happy home / No love in my heart / Wild about you baby.
LP: CH 31

CHICAGO GOLDEN YEARS (James, Elmore & John Brim).
LP: 515006

COLLECTION: ELMORE JAMES (20 blues greats).
Tracks: / Dust my broom / I believe / Hand in hand / Blues before sunrise / Coming home / Strange kinda feeling / I was a fool / Baby what's wrong? / Sky is crying, The / Late hours at midnight / Standing at the crossroads / Early in the morning / Rock my baby tonight / Rollin' and tumblin' / Can't stop lovin' my baby / Look on yonder wall / Dark and dreary / 1839 blues / Sinful woman / I done somebody wrong.
LP: DVLP 2035
MC: DVMC 2035

COME GO WITH ME.
Tracks: / Baby please set a date / So unkind / Sunnyland train / Twelve year old boy / My kind of woman / Hand in hand / My baby's gone / Make my dreams come true / Anna Lee / Bobby's rock / Find my kinda woman / Stranger blues / Mean mistreatin' mama / I can't stop loving you / She moved / I'm worried.
LP: CRB 1212

DUST MY BROOM.
Tracks: / Coming home / Dust my broom / Hand and hand / I believe / Done somebody wrong / It hurts me too / Pickin' the blues / Look on yonder wall / Mean mistreatin' mama / Rollin' and tumblin' / Standing at the crossroads / Sky is crying, The.
LP: TOP 120
MC: KTOP 120

DUST MY BROOM (INSTANT).
Tracks: / Dust my broom / Look on yonder wall / Done somebody wrong / It hurts me too / I'm worried / One way out / Fine little mama / Rollin' and tumblin' / Shake your moneymaker / Sky is crying, The / Stranger blues / I can't stop loving you / Coming home / My bleeding heart / Standing at the crossroads / Make my dreams come true.
MC: TCINS 5030

ELMORE JAMES STORY, THE.
Tracks: / Dust my broom / Sunnyland / Hand in hand / Sho' nuff I do / Where can my baby be / Look on yonder wall / I was a fool / Wild about you baby / Sky is crying, The / Strange kinda feeling / 1839 blues / Dark and dreary / Standing at the crossroads / Coming home / Mean mistreatin' mama / My best friend / Long tall woman / My best friend - reprise / Blues before sunrise / I done somebody wrong / Make a little love / Mean and evil / Sinful woman / So mean to me / Happy home.
MCSET: DVREMC 24

GOT TO MOVE.
LP: CRB 1017

GREATEST HITS: ELMORE JAMES (BLUE CITY).
LP: 2652711
MC: 2652714

GREATEST HITS: ELMORE JAMES (MASTERS).
LP: CL 271283
MC: CLMC 9271283
MC: CLMC 009271283

KING OF THE BOTTLENECK BLUES.
Tracks: / Wild about you baby / Mean and evil / My best friend / Dark and dreary / Hawaiian boogie / Blues before sunrise / Strange kinda feeling / Sho 'nuff I do / I was a fool / Long tall woman / One more drink / Wild about you.
LP: GEM 003
MC: GEMC 003

KING OF THE SLIDE GUITAR.
Tracks: / Lost woman blues / One more drink / Strange kinda feeling / Sho nuff I do / Wild about you / Sweet little woman / Long tall woman / Where can my baby be / My baby's gone / I may be wrong / Elmo's shuffle / Please find my baby / My best friend / So mean to me / Wild about you baby / Dark and dreary.
LP: CH 68

LET'S CUT IT.
Tracks: / Dust my blues / Blues before sunrise / No love in my heart / Sho' nuff I do / Standing at the crossroads / I was a fool / Sunnyland / Canton Mississippi breakdown / Happy home / Wild about you baby / Long tall woman / So mean to me / Hawaiian boogie / Mean and evil / Dark and dreary / My best friend / I believe / Goodbye baby.
MC: CHC 192
LP: CH 192

ONE WAY OUT.
Tracks: / Talk to me baby / Shake your moneymaker / Can't stop lovin' my baby / It hurts me too / Sky is crying, The / Cry for me baby / Something inside of me / Standing at the crossroads / Coming home / Rollin' and tumblin' / Take me where you go / I need you / Person to person / One way out / Twelve year old boy, The / Dust my broom.
LP: CRB 1008
MC: TCCRB 1008

ORIGINAL METEOR & FLAIR SIDES (James, Elmore & his Broom Dusters).
Tracks: / I believe / I held my baby last night / Baby what's wrong / Sinful woman / Early in the morning / Can't stop lovin' my baby / Hawaiian boogie / Hand in hand / Blues / Make a little love / Strange kinda feeling / Sho nuff I do / Make my dreams come true / Rock my baby tonight.
LP: CH 112

PICKIN' THE BLUES.
Tracks: / Dust my broom / Look on yonder wall / It hurts me too / Coming home / Sky is crying, The / Standing at the crossroads / Hand in hand / Mean mistreatin' mama / I done somebody wrong / Pickin' the blues / I believe.
LP: SHLP 140
MC: SHTC 140

RED HOT BLUES.
Tracks: / Dust my broom / Look on yonder wall / It hurts me too / Coming home / Sky is crying, The / Standing at the crossroads / Hand in hand / Rollin' and tumblin' / Mean mistreatin' Mama / I done somebody wrong / Pickin' the blues / I believe.
LP: BMLP 008

TO KNOW A MAN.
LP: OLLP 8018

WHO'S MUDDY SHOES? (James, Elmore & John Brim).
Tracks: / Ice cream man / Whose muddy shoes / Madison blues / I see my baby / You got me / My best friend / Sun is shining,The / Talk to me baby / Rattlesnake / Be careful / Dust my broom / Tool bag boogie / Tough times / Stormy monday.
LP: CXMP 2007
LP: BRP 2016
LP: GCH8097
MC: GCHK78097

James, Ethan

EPONYMOUS (See under Kenney, Erin) (Kenney, Erin & Ethan James).

James, Etta

AT LAST.
Tracks: / Anything to say you're mine / My dearest darling / Trust in me / Sunday kind of love / Tough Mary / I just want to make love to you / At last / All I could do was cry / Stormy weather / Girl of my dreams.
LP: GCH 8036
MC: GCHK 78036
LP: CH 9266

BLUES IN THE NIGHT (James, Etta & Eddie 'Cleanhead' Vinson).
Tracks: / Kidney stew / Railroad porter blues / Something's got a hold on me / Medley: at last / Trust in me / Sunday kind of love / I just wanna make love to you / Please send me someone to love / Love man / Misty.
LP: F 9647
MC: 5F 9647

CHESS MASTERS.
LP: CXMP 2000

CHESS MASTERS.
Tracks: / Tell Mama / I'd rather go blind / Watchdog / Love of my man, The / I'm gonna take what he's got / Some rope / Security / Steal away / My mother in law / Don't lose your good thing / It hurts me so much / Just a little bit / Something's got a hold on me / Baby what you want me to do / What'd I say / Money / Seven day fool / Sweet little angel / Ooh poo pah doo / Woke up this morning.
2LP: CXMD 4017

CHICAGO GOLDEN YEARS.
2LP: 427014

COME A LITTLE CLOSER.
Tracks: / Out on the street again / Mama told me / You give me what I want / Come a little closer / Let's burn down the cornfield / Powerplay / Feeling uneasy / St.Louis blues / Gonna have some fun tonight / Sooki sooki.
LP: GCH 8047
MC: GCHK 78047

DEEP IN THE NIGHT.
Tracks: / Laying beside you / Piece of my heart / Only women bleed / Take it to the limit / Lovesick blues / Strange man / Sugar on the floor / Sweet touch of love / I'd rather go blind.
LP: K 56492

GOOD ROCKIN' MAMA.
Tracks: / Dance with me Henry / Do something crazy / Woman / I hope you're satisfied / Strange things happening / Good rockin' daddy / Hey Henry / That's all / I'm a fool.
LP: 10 CH 33

GOOD ROCKIN' MAMA/TUFF LOVER.
Tracks: / Good rockin' mama / Dance with me Henry / Do something crazy / Woman / I hope you're satisfied / Strange things happening / Good rockin' daddy / Hey Henry / I'm a fool / That's all / Tough lover / Pick-up / By the light of the silvery moon / Fools we mortals be / Come what may / Good lookin' / Tears of joy / Shortnin' bread rock / Baby every night / Then I'll care / Market place.
MCSET: CHC 803

HER GREATEST SIDES VOL.1.
Tracks: / Tell mama / Something's got a hold on me / Pushover / Only time will tell / Stop the wedding / Security / I'd rather go blind / Trust in me / Sunday kind of love / My dearest darling / At last / Waiting for Charlie to come home / All I could do was cry / Fool that I am.
LP: GCH 8015
MC: GCHK 78015

JUICY PEACHES.
Tracks: / Next door to the blues / Pay back / Two sides to every story / Loving you more every day / That's all I want from you / It must be your love / Don't pick me for your fool / Do right woman / I worship the ground you walk on / You got it / Almost persuaded / Tighten up your own thing / Losers weepers / I found a love.
LP: GCH 8116

R & B DYNAMITE.
Tracks: / W.O.M.A.N. / Number one / I'm a fool / Strange things happening / Hey Henry / I hope you're satisfied / Good rockin' daddy / Sunshine of love / That's all / How big a fool / Market place / Tough lover / Do something crazy / Be my lovey dovey / Nobody loves you (like me) / Hickory dickory dock / You know what I mean / Wallflower, The / Baby, baby, every night / We're in love / Tears of joy (Available on CD and cassette only) / Pick-up, The (Available on CD and cassette only).
LP: CH 210
MC: CHC 210

R & B QUEEN.
Tracks: / My one and only / Pick-up / I'm a fool / By the light of the silvery moon / Come what may / That's all / Tough lover / Dance with me Henry / Tears of joy / Baby baby every night / Do something crazy / Market place.
LP: GEM 005
MC: GEMC 005

ROCKS THE HOUSE.
Tracks: / Somethings got a hold on me / Baby what you want me to do / What I say / Money / Seven day fool / Sweet little angel / Ooh poo pah doo / Woke up this morning.
LP: GCH 8030
MC: GCHK 78030

SEVEN YEAR ITCH.
Tracks: / I got the will / Jump into the fire / Shakey ground / Come to mama / Damn your eyes / Breakin' up somebody's home / Jealous kind, The / How strong is a woman / It ain't always what you do / One night.
MC: ICT 9923
LP: ILPS 9923

STICKIN' TO MY GUNS.
MC: ICT 9955
LP: ILPS 9955

TUFF LOVER.
Tracks: / Tough lover / Pick-up / By the light of the silvery moon / Fools we mortals be / Come what may / Dance with me Henry / Good lookin' / Tears of joy / Shortnin' bread rock / Baby every night / Then I'll care / Market place.
LP: CH 73

James, Frank

FRANK JAMES SPRINGBACK 1934-37.
LP: DLP 538

James, Freddie

GET UP AND BOOGIE.
Tracks: / Get up and boogie / Crazy disco music / Hollywood / Dance little blue boy.
LP: K 56735

James Gang

BANG.
LP: K 50028

BEST OF THE JAMES GANG, THE.
Tracks: / Funk 48 / Walk away / Midnight man / Take a look around / Funk 49 / Woman / Bomber / Ashes, the rain and I / Yadig / Stop.
LP: ABCL 5027
LP: MCL 1615

LIVE IN CONCERT.
LP: PROBE 1045

PASSING THROUGH.
LP: PROBE 1065

STRAIGHT SHOOTER.
LP: PROBE 1056

THIRDS.
LP: UNKNOWN

TRUE STORY OF, THE.
Tracks: / Take a look around bluebird / Collage / Wrap city in English / Yadig woman / Ashes, the rain and I / It's all the same / Things I could be / Live my life again / I'll tell you why / Run run run / Midnight man.
LP: SEE 88

YER ALBUM.

Tracks: / Take a look around / Bluebird / Stone rap / I don't have the time / Fred / Funk / Lost woman / Collage / Wrapcity in English / Stop.
LP: . . . . BGOLP 60

James, Geraldine (nar)

OUT OF AFRICA (see under Out Of Africa (bk)).

James, Harry

20 GOLDEN GREATS: HARRY JAMES (Live) (James, Harry & His Music Makers).
Tracks: / Easy / My beloved is rugged / Rose room / King Porter stomp / Your red wagon / Lady be good / Shiny stockings / Block party / Ultra / Jumping at the woodside / Flatbush Flanagan / Carnival / Dancing in the dark / Love & weather / Rockin' in rhythm / Deep purple / Trumpet blues and cantabile / Lover come back to me / Man I love, The.
MC: . . . . CAWM 2

20 GOLDEN PIECES: HARRY JAMES (James, Harry Orchestra).
Tracks: / Around the world in 80 days / Music makers / I don't want to walk without you / King Porter stomp / Back beat boogie / I'm beginning to see the light / Opus one / I've heard that song before / I had the craziest dream / More / Blue skies / One o'clock jump / You'll never know / My heart cries for you / Anytime / Three coins in the fountain / Taste of honey, A / You go to my head / I'll be seeing you / As long as he needs me.
LP: . . . . BDL 2023
MC: . . . . BDC 2023

1954: HARRY JAMES (James, Harry & His Orchestra).
LP: . . . . CLP 39

1943-46 (James, Harry & His Orchestra).
Tracks: / Charmaine / Harpie's bazaar / My old flame / Blue turning grey over you / All of me / I cover the waterfront / G flat special / Blue Lou / I've found this a new baby / Ain't she sweet / I'll be around / Exactly like you / I've had this feeling before / Cinderella / How high the moon / Old folks at home.
LP: . . . . HMP 5052

1946-66.
LP: . . . . LPJT 68

1948-49 (James, Harry & His Orchestra).
Tracks: / How high the moon / Lazy river / Better have four / New York blues / Sabre dance / You turned the tables on me / Rank Frank / Forgotten / I may be wrong / Proclamation.
LP: . . . . HMP 5060

ARRANGEMENTS OF JIMMY MUNDY & ANDY GIBSON (James, Harry & Andy Gibson).
LP: . . . . JOYCE 2025

ARRANGEMENTS OF RAINS, HOLMES, BILLY MAY.
LP: . . . . JOYCE 2026

BEST OF BIG BANDS.
LP: 4669554

BIG BAND.
LP: . . . . SM 3872

BIG JOHN SPECIAL.
Tracks: / Big John special / Cherry / Don'cha go 'way mad / Stardust / I may be wrong / Bluebeard blues / Sweet Jenny Lou / Back beat boogie / Six two and even / Slap happy / Forgotten / Body and soul / Cheek to cheek / Rank Frank / Ultra.
LP: . . . . HEP 24

CIRIBIRIBIN.
LP: . . . . PM 1551923

COMIN' FROM GOOD PLACE (James, Harry & His Band).
LP: . . . . LAB 6

DOUBLE FEATURE.
Tracks: / Ciribiribin / King-size blues / Shiny stockings / Lover come back to me / Harry's delight / Two o'clock jump / Jumping at the Woodside / One on the house / Rockin' in rhythm / Don't get around much anymore / Tweet tweet / Moonchild.
LP: . . . . FH 48
MC: . . . . CFH 48

FLASH HARRY, 1943-44.
Tracks: / Between the devil and the deep blue sea / Cherry / Flash / It's been so long / Lovely way to spend an evening, A / Jalousie Chelsea bridge / Shorty George.
LP: . . . . HEP 37

FROM HOLLYWOOD.
LP: . . . . FH 39

GLENN MILLER & HARRY JAMES BANDS (see Miller, Glenn) (James, Harry & Glenn Miller).

HARRY JAMES.
Tracks: / Ciribiribin / Perdido / Blues in the night / Honeysuckle rose / Moonlight fiesta / Two o'clock jump / Stardust / Roll 'em / Don't be that way / Cherry / Love is just around the corner / Somebody loves me / Taboo / Tenderly / Great lie, The.
LP: . . . . T 1010

HARRY JAMES (Compact/Walkman jazz).
Tracks: / Get off the stand / Moanin' low / My Monday date / I'm in the market for you / Harry, not Jesse / Lush life / Squeeze me / Sleepy time gal / Hot pink / Spring can really hang you up the most / Jazz connoisseur / Confessin' / Harry's delight / Weather bird rag / I cover the waterfront / Rockin' in the rhythm.
MC: 833 285-4

HARRY JAMES 1937-8.
LP: . . . . TAX 8015

HARRY JAMES, 1943-46.
Tracks: / If that's the way you want it baby / Indiana / Body and soul / I'm satisfied / I couldn't sleep a wink last night / Rose room / All of me / Shorty George / On the sunny side of the street / Between the devil and the deep blue sea / Stardust / It's been so long / My baby just cares for me / Girl of my dreams / You go to my head / Shady ladybird.
LP: . . . . HSR 102

HARRY JAMES AND HIS ORCHESTRA 1948-1949 (James, Harry & His Orchestra).
Tracks: / There they go / 'Cept February which has 28 / Raffles / Snooty fruity / You turned the tables on me / Six two and even / Cottontail / Lover / Big boy / Bells.
LP: . . . . SOL 501

HARRY JAMES AND HIS ORCHESTRA 1944-1945 (James, Harry & His Orchestra).
Tracks: / King Porter stomp / Joe Blow / Airmail special / Six two and even / Caravan / Talk of the town / Sad sack, The / Roll 'em / Loveless love / Eightbarriff / I may be wrong.
LP: . . . . SOL 504

HARRY JAMES AND HIS ORCHESTRA, 1947-49 (James, Harry & His Orchestra).
Tracks: / Who's got the ball / Lover come back to me / Pagan love song / Poppin' off / When it's sleepy down south / Dream a little dream of me / You came a long way from St Louis / Ooh, look-a-there, ain't she pretty / Lover / Queer Street / Tuxedo junction / Forgotten / Things ain't what they used to be / Lullaby of the leaves / One I used to love, The.
LP: . . . . HSR 150

HARRY JAMES COLLECTION (20 golden greats).
Tracks: / Ciribiribin / Remember / On the sunny side of the street / These foolish things / Stardust / With a song in my heart / Between the Devil and the deep blue sea / All of me / Always / Body and soul / Laura / Honeysuckle rose / It's been so long / Indiana / Embraceable you / Nice work if you can get it / Easy Street / I'm satisfied / Sentimental journey / Shady ladybird.
LP: . . . . DVLP 2086
MC: . . . . DVMC 2086

HARRY JAMES & HIS MUSIC MAKERS (1942-7).
LP: . . . . FH 14

HARRY JAMES & HIS ORCHESTRA 1948-9 (James, Harry & His Orchestra).
LP: . . . . HMA 5050

HARRY JAMES & HIS ORCHESTRA 1943-46, VOL 2 (James, Harry & His Orchestra).
Tracks: / Joe Blow / Sweet and lovely / Easy Street / Honeysuckle Rose / It can't be wrong / Nice work if you can get it / Sentimental journey / It must be jelly / I've had my moments / Do nothin' 'till you hear from me / Always / Just a sittin' a rockin' / Remember / Peg o'my heart / More than you know / Mr. Coed.
LP: . . . . HMA 5067

HARRY JAMES & HIS ORCHESTRA (ENTERTAINERS LABEL) (James, Harry & His Orchestra).
LP: . . . . ENT LP 13017
MC: . . . . ENT MC 13017

HARRY JAMES & HIS ORCHESTRA (JASMINE).
Tracks: / Theme - Introduction / Shorty George / To You / King Porter stomp / From the bottom of my heart / Beer barrel Polka / White sails / Well alright / Two o'clock jump / Theme - close.
LP: . . . . JASM 2514
MC: . . . . JASMC 2514

HARRY JAMES IN HI-FI.
Tracks: / You made me love you / I've heard that song before / I'm beginning to see the light / My silent love / Cherry / Trumpet blues and cantabile / Music makers / Sleepy lagoon / Velvet moon / Jealousy / I cried for you / It's been a long, long time / Two o'clock jump / James session.
LP: 1A 0381857531

HARRY JAMES -- LIVE IN LONDON.
LP: . . . . SG 8002

HARRY JAMES ON THE AIR VOL.2 (James, Harry & His Orchestra).
Tracks: / Just you, just me / Night and day / By the Shalimar / Oh brother / By the light of the silvery moon / St Louis blues / I don't want to walk without you / One dozen roses / Two O'Clock jump / Moon over Manakoora / King Porter stomp / I walk my post (in a military manner) / Pagan love song.
LP: . . . . AIRCHECK 33

HARRY JAMES VOL.1 (James, Harry (Members of Orchestra)).
LP: . . . . BO 710

HARRY JAMES, VOL. 2, 1943-46.
Tracks: / Charmaine / Harpie's bazaar / My old flame / Blue turning grey over you / I cover the waterfront / G-flat special / Blue Lou / All of me / I've found a new baby / Ain't she sweet / I'll be around / Exactly like you / I've had this feeling before / Cinderella / How high the moon / Old folks at home.
LP: . . . . HSR 123
LP: . . . . BO 715

HARRY JAMES, VOL. 4, 1943-46.
Tracks: / Sweet and lovely / Easy street / Honeysuckle rose / It can't be wrong / Nice work if you can get it / Sentimental journey / It must be jelly / I've had my moments / Do nothing till you hear from me / Always / Just a sittin' and a rockin' / Remember / Peg O' my heart / More than you know / Mr. Coed.
LP: . . . . HSR 141

HARRY JAMES, VOL. 5, 1943-53.
Tracks: / If I had you / Autumn in New York / Somebody loves me / Come rain or come shine / What is this thing called love / I don't know why / Blue skies / Opus one / Tree grows into Burbank, A / Moonlight bay / People's choice / My old flame / Piccadilly / Man I love, The / Sugar blues / Don't get around much anymore.
LP: . . . . HSR 142

HARRY JAMES WITH DICK HAYMES (James, Harry & Dick Haymes).
Tracks: / Tuxedo junction / Boog it / Four or five times / Hodge podge / Exactly like you / Come and get it / Swanee river / Sheik of araby / It's the last time / Orchids for rememberance / Moon won't talk / Maybe / Alice blue gown / Million dreams ago / You've got me / How high the moon.
LP: . . . . HQ 2008

HARRY'S CHOICE.
Tracks: / You're my thrill / Willow weep for me / Blues for sale / I want a little girl / Moten swing / Do you know what it means to miss New Orleans? / Just for fun / New two o'clock jump.
LP: 2C 068 54575
MC: . . . . PM 154575

JAMES AND HAYMES (With Dick Haymes) (James, Harry & His Orchestra).
LP: . . . . CLP 5

KING JAMES VERSION,THE (James, Harry & His Band).
LP: . . . . LAB 3

KING PORTER STOMP.
LP: . . . . HEP 31

LIVE FROM CLEARWATER CANYON, FLORIDA VOL.2 (James, Harry & His Music Makers).
LP: . . . . FH 57
MC: . . . . CFH 57

LIVE FROM CLEARWATER CANYON, FLORIDA VOL.3 (James, Harry & His Music Makers).
LP: . . . . FH 58
MC: . . . . CFH 58

LIVE FROM CLEARWATER CANYON, FLORIDA VOL.1 (James, Harry & His Music Makers).
LP: . . . . FH 56
MC: . . . . CFH 56

LIVE IN CONCERT (James, Harry & The Music Makers).
Tracks: / Opener, The / King size blues / Shiny stockings / Harry's delight / Two o'clock jump / Jumpin' at the woodside / One on the house / Rockin' in rhythm / Don't get around much anymore / Tweet tweet.
LP: . . . . DBD 03
MC: . . . . DBDC 03

LIVE IN LONDON.
Tracks: / Don't be that way shiney stockings / Moonglow / Opus £1 / That's all / Charade / HJ blues / Apples / Two o'clock jump / Hits medley.
LP: . . . . JASM 2533
MC: . . . . JASMC 2533

LIVE IN THE 1940'S VOL.2.
LP: . . . . EB 410

LIVE IN THE 1970'S Volume 1.
Tracks: / Meditation / Cherokee / Blues, The / Taste of honey, A / Satin doll / Koo koo / Sweet Georgia Brown / String of pearls / Music to watch girls by / Tie a yellow ribbon (vocal by Jeannie Stone).
LP: . . . . EB 403

MEMORIAL.
Tracks: / Harry James reminisces / Back beat boogie / Close to you / Dancing in the dark / King Porter stomp / Carnival / Man I love, The / Flatbush Flanagan / Deep purple / Arrival / Harry's blues / Dear old Southland / Trumpet blues and cantabile.
LP: . . . . FH 51
MC: . . . . CFH 51

MORE HARRY JAMES IN HI-FI (James, Harry & His Orchestra).
Tracks: / Mole / Autumn serenade / Sleepy time gal / Crazy rhythm / Melancholy rhapsody September song / Carnival / Strictly instrumental / Blue again / Don cha go way mad / These foolish things / Somebody loves me / Street scene.
LP: . . . . EMS 1148

MUSICMAKING.
Tracks: / Back beat boogie / Between the Devil and the deep blue sea / G Flat special / My beloved is rugged / Rose room / Talk of the town / Opus one / I'm beginning to see the light / Lady be good / Temptation / Easy / St. Louis blues.
LP: . . . . FH 25
MC: . . . . CFH 25

ON THE AIR (James, Harry & His Orchestra).
Tracks: / Ciribiribin / Perdido / Wouldn't it be nice? / Rose room / And then you kissed me / St Louis blues / Amor / Don't blame me / Peg O' my heart / Maybe / Concerto for trumpet / Too romantic / Feet draggin' blues / Man I love, The / I can't begin to tell you / I'm in love with two sweethearts / Blue skies.
LP: . . . . AIRCHECK 18

ONE NIGHT STAND WITH HARRY JAMES.
LP: . . . . SH 2004

PLAY 22 ORIGINAL BIG BAND RECORDINGS (James, Harry Orchestra).
LP: . . . . HSR 406

POST WAR PERIOD, THE (James, Harry & His Band).
Tracks: / All of me / I can't begin to tell you (with Ginnie Powell) / I'm in love with two sweethearts (with Buddy DiVito) / Moonglow / Opus 1 (part only) / I still get jealous (with Buddy DiVito) / Cottontail (small group) / Night special / Forgiving you (with Buddy DiVito) / I want to be loved (with Marion Morgan) / Blue turning grey over you / Six, two and even / Nearness of you, The (with Buddy Rich) / Back beat boogie.
LP: . . . . JRC 1207

REMEMBER (James, Harry & His Music Makers).
MC: . . . . CAWE 12

SATURDAY NIGHT SWING.
LP: . . . . GOJ 1016

SEPTEMBER SONG.
Tracks: / Floozie / Manhattan / Your cheatin' heart / Charmaine / Jazz me blues / Two o'clock jump / In a mellow tone / Sultry serenade / Getting sentimental over you / Pennies from Heaven / September song / If I could be with you / Cupper, The / Prince Charming / Nina / Cynthia.
LP: . . . . F 20133
MC: 40133

SOUNDS FAMILIAR (Live in California-1946) (James, Harry & His Orchestra).
Tracks: / Flash / Moten swing / Five minutes more / I'd be lost without you / Blue skies / Man I love, The / Perdido / Oh but I do / Jealousy / Seems like old times / Lover come back to me / Why does it get so late so early? / Rose room / What more can I ask for? / Keb-lah / Embraceable you / Man with the horn, The / Shine / Two o'clock jump.
LP: . . . . SVL 151
MC: . . . . CSVL 151

SPOTLIGHT ON HARRY JAMES.
LP: . . . . AWE 21

STILL HARRY AFTER ALL THESE YEARS.
LP: . . . . LAB 11

SWING GOES ON, VOL 9.
Tracks: / Moten swing / Crazy rhythm / I've heard that song before / Trumpet blues and cantabile / Sleepy lagoon / Music makers / Sleepy time gal / Ciribiribin / Two o'clock jump / Strictly instrumental / Mole, The / I'm beginning to see the light / You're my thrill / You made me love you / Just lucky.
LP: . . . . **IC 054 52718**

SWINGIN' 'N' SWEET (James, Harry Octet).
Tracks: / Ciribiribin / Perdido / Blues in the night / Honeysuckle rose / Moonlight fiesta / Two o'clock jump / Stardust / Roll 'em / Don't be that way / Cherry / Love is just around the corner / Somebody loves me / Taboo / Tenderly / Great lie, The.
LP: . . . . **GOJ 1009**

TEXAS CHATTER.
LP: . . . . **SM 3058**

TRUMPET BLUES.
LP: . . . . **FH 41**
MC: . . . . **CFH 41**

TRUMPET TOAST (James, Harry & His Orchestra).
LP: . . . . **MCL 1774**
MC: . . . . **MCLC 1774**

TWO O'CLOCK JUMP (ASTAN) (James, Harry Orchestra).
Tracks: / Music makers / Things I love, The / Flight of the bumble bee / Here comes the night / Two o'clock jump / Spring will be so sad / Maria elena / Flying home / All or nothing at all / Carnival of Venice / Cherry / Sharp as a track.
LP: **20107**
MC: **40107**
LP: . . . . **MTM 010**

TWO O'CLOCK JUMP (BANDSTAND) (1944) (James, Harry & His Orchestra).
Tracks: / Two o'clock jump / It could happen to you / It had to be you / I'll get by / Cherry / Just you, just me / I'm beginning to see the light / I'm confessin' / I cover the waterfront / Take it easy / Love I long for, The / Back beat boogie / Jiggers / Theme - close.
LP: . . . . **BS 7131**
MC: . . . . **BS 7131C**

UNCOLLECTED HARRY JAMES & HIS ORCHESTRA,THE.
Tracks: / How high the moon / Better have four / Sabre dance / Shine / You turned the tables on me / Forgotten / I may be wrong / Lazy river / New York blues / Blue and sentimental / Rank, Frank / Proclamation.
LP: . . . . **HSR 135**

UNCOLLECTED, THE.
LP: . . . . **HUK 150**

WILD ABOUT HARRY.
Tracks: / Kinda like the blues / Blues for lovers only / Countin' / Cotton pickin' / Ring for porter / Barn 12 / What am I here for / Blues for Harry's sake / Bee gee / Blues on a count.
LP: . . . . **EMS 1284**
MC: . . . . **TCEMS 1284**

James, Henry

TURN OF THE SCREW, THE (Various artists).
MCSET: . . . . **SAY 112**
MC: . . . . **TC LFP 7076**
MCSET: . . . . **ARGO 1061**

James, Hilary

MUSICAL MYSTERY TOUR (James, Hilary & Simon Mayor).
MC: . . . . **ACS 002**

James, Jimmy

DANCIN TILL DAWN.
Tracks: / I can't stop my feet from dancin' / Be what you, wanna be / If you think funk is junk you're drunk / Till I can't take it anymore / Girl, I really love you / Now that you've gone / You made love again / Tell the world.
MC: . . . . **ZNC 101**
LP: . . . . **N 101**

GOLDEN HOUR OF JIMMY JAMES (James, Jimmy & The Vagabonds).
Tracks: / Now is the time / Disco fever / Red red wine / Suspicious love / Stay with me / I want you so much / Whatever happened to the love we knew / You don't stand a chance / I'll go where your music takes me / Dancing to the music of love / Till I can't take anymore / Let's have fun / I know you don't love me but you got me anyway / Never had this dream before / Your love keeps haunting me / Come lay some lovin' on me / Chains of love.
LP: . . . . **GH 679**

James, John

ACOUSTIC ELECTICA.
Tracks: / Tiroler / Travelator / Dance of the pedestrians / Penny in my pocket / Kicking up the dust / Coda / Dangling / Blues for you / Rain on the window / Castles made of sand / Aeith dai I strata.
LP: . . . . **STOP 101**

GUITAR JUMP.
Tracks: / Trio / New nothynge / Rumble / First meeting / Hannah's skipping song / From the bridge / Of days gone by / Guitar jump / Feet on the ground / Bumpass stomp / Gazing high / You and I across the water / When I was young and easy.
LP: . . . . **SNKF 128**

GUITAR MUSIC.
LP: . . . . **STOP 102**

I GOT RHYTHM (James John & Sam Mitchell).
LP: . . . . **SNKF 1215**

LIVE IN CONCERT.
LP: . . . . **SNKF 136**

James, John

LIVE: JOHN JAMES (James, John).
LP: . . . . **KM 108**

James, Joni

AWARD WINNING ALBUM.
Tracks: / Have you heard / Almost always / Purple shades / Your cheatin' heart / Why don't you believe me / Is it any wonder / Wishing ring / My love, my love / How important can it be / You are my love / My believing heart / When we come of age.
LP: . . . . **OFF 12006**

MORE HITS.
Tracks: / There goes my heart / Little things mean a lot / There must be a way / Be my love / I still get a thrill / We know / They really don't know you / Are you sorry / My prayer of love / I laughed at love / Perhaps / I still get jealous.
LP: . . . . **OFF 12012**

James, Keith

ON THE REBOUND.
LP: . . . . **PAROLP 1**

SWALLOW,THE.
LP: . . . . **KJ 8**

James, Laurence

LATE NIGHT EXTRA (WURLITZER ORGAN BUCKINGHAM PALACE).
Tracks: / I know that you know / It's the talk of the town / Goody goody / Kiss in the dark / Late night extra / Lazy river / Glenn Miller selection / I won't dance / All the things you are / Alley cat / Love's last word is spoken / Walkin' my baby back home / Burt Bacharach selection / After you've gone.
LP: . . . . **SDL 317**
MC: . . . . **CSDL 317**

James, M.R. (author)

GHOST STORIES (Horden, Sir Michael).
Tracks: / Ash tree, The / School story, A / Haunted dolls' house, The / Diary of Mr Poynter, The.
MCSET: . . . . **SAY 62**
MCSET: . . . . **ARGO 1145**

MORE GHOST STORIES (Horden, Sir Michael).
Tracks: / There was a man dwelt by a churchyard / Lost hearts / Oh, whistle and I'll come to you, my lad / Mezzotint, The / Casting the runes.
MCSET: . . . . **SAY 113**

NUMBER 13 AND OTHER GHOST STORIES (Horden, Sir Michael).
MCSET: . . . . **ARGO 1247**

OTHER GHOST STORIES (Horden, Sir Michael).
Tracks: / Stories I have tried to write / Uncommon prayer-book, The / Warning to the curious, A / Neighbours Landmark, A / Rose garden, The.
MCSET: **418 045-4**

James, P.D.

DEATH OF AN EXPERT WITNESS (See also Michael Jayston).
MC: . . . . **CAB 311**

SKULL BENEATH THE SKIN, THE (Various artists).
MCSET: . . . . **ZBBC 1083**

James, Phil

TWO OF US, THE.
LP: . . . . **PH 005**

James, Rick

BUSTIN' OUT OF L SEVEN.
Tracks: / Bustin' out / High on your love suite / One more shot of your love / Love interlude / Spacey love / Cop 'n' blow / Jefferson ball / Fool on the street.
LP: . . . . **STML 12104**

COLD BLOODED.
Tracks: / Doin' it / U bring the freak out / 123 (U, her and me) / Cold blooded / New York town / Pimp the simp / Ebony eyes / Tell me what you want.
LP: . . . . **STMA 8038**

COME GET IT.
Tracks: / Stone city band / Hi / You and I / Sexy lady / Dream maker / Be my lady / Mary Jane / Hollywood / Stone city band.
LP: . . . . **STMS 5078**
MC: . . . . **CSTMS 5078**

FIRE IT UP.
Tracks: / Fire it up / Love gun / Lovin you is a pleasure / Love in the night / Come into my life / Stormy love / When love is gone.
LP: . . . . **STML 12128**

FLAG, THE.
Tracks: / Freak flag / Forever and a day / Sweet and sexy thing / Free to be me / Save it for me / R U experienced / Funk in America / Slow and easy / Oma raga / Painted pictures / Silly little man.
LP: . . . . **ZL 72443**
MC: . . . . **ZK 72443**

GARDEN OF LOVE.
Tracks: / Big time / Don't give up on love / Island lady / Gettin' it on / Summer love / Mary go round / Gettin' it on (Reprise).
LP: . . . . **STML 12141**

GLOW.
LP: . . . . **ZL 72362**
MC: . . . . **ZK 72362**

GREATEST HITS: RICK JAMES.
Tracks: / Super freak / You turn me on / You and I / Mary Jane / Ebony eyes / Give it to me baby / Dance wit me / Cold blooded / 17.
LP: . . . . **WL 72427**
MC: . . . . **WK 72427**

REFLECTIONS OF RICK.
Tracks: / 17 / Oh what a night / You turn me on / Fire and desire / Bustin' out / You & I / Mary Jane / Dance wit' me / Give it to me baby / Super freak.
LP: . . . . **ZL 72174**
MC: . . . . **ZK 72174**

STREET SONGS.
Tracks: / Give it to me baby / Ghetto life / Make love to me / Mr. Policeman / Super freak / Fire and desire / Call me up / Below the funk.
LP: . . . . **STML 12153**
MC: . . . . **CSTML 12153**
LP: . . . . **ZL 72036**
MC: . . . . **ZK 72036**

THROWIN DOWN.
Tracks: / Dance wit' me / Money talks / Teardrops / Throwdown / Standing on the top / Hard to get / Happy / 69 times / My love.
LP: . . . . **STML 12167**
MC: . . . . **CSTML 12167**

WONDERFUL.
Tracks: / Wonderful / Judy / Loosey's rap / So tight / Sexual luv affair / Love's fire / I believe in you / In the girls room / Hypnotize / Sherry baby.
LP: . . . . **WX 156**
MC: . . . . **WX 156 C**

James, Sally

CHILDREN'S TALES FROM AROUND THE WORLD (see under Children's...).

CHILDREN'S TALES FROM AROUND THE WORLD (See under Children's).

ONCE UPON A TIME STORIES.
LP: . . . . **STMP 9012**
MC: **STMP4 9012**

James, Shirley

HOW 'BOUT US? (See Ray, Danny) (James, Shirley & Danny Ray).

James, Skip

1931.
Tracks: / Devil got my woman / Cypress Grove blues / Cherry ball blues / Illinois blues / Four o'clock blues / Hard luck child / Hard time killin' floor blues / Yola my blues away / Jesus is a mighty good leader / Be ready when he comes / Drunken spree / I'm so glad / Special rider blues / How long buck / Little cow and calf is gonna die blues / What am I to do blues / 22-20 blues / If you haven't any hay get on down the road.
LP: . . . . **MSE 207**

COMPLETE 1931 SESSIONS.
LP: . . . . **L 1072**

I'M SO GLAD.
2LP: . . . . **VPD 20001**

LIVE AT 2ND. FRET, PHILADELPHIA 1966.
LP: . . . . **DLP 523**

TODAY.
LP: . . . . **VMLP 5310**
MC: . . . . **VMTC 6310**

James, Sonny

ALWAYS DANCING.
Tracks: / Me and my girl / Pennsylvania 6 5000 / You forgot to remember / Always (I'll be loving you) / I'll get by / Story of a starry night / My kind of girl / Swingin' safari, A / Dream / Just the way you look tonight / I know him so well / Air that I breathe, The / Music to cha-cha by / Stripper, The / Secret love / Star trek.
LP: . . . . **SUS 509**

DANCE TO MY MUSIC.
Tracks: / Dance to my music / Crazy rhythm / Why do I love you / I'll never love this way again / Old funky rolls / Sentimental journey / Let's twist again / Five foot two, eyes of blue / Manana / Diamonds are a girl's best friend / Mambo jambo / Make it soon / Every breath you take / I could be so good for you / Oh lady be good / High noon / I will survive.
LP: . . . . **SUD 2000**

SONNY.
Tracks: / Near you / Fool such as I, A / Heartaches / Ages and ages ago / I'll never get over you / Secret love / Beg your pardon / Just out of reach / How's the world treating you / I forgot more than you'll ever know / Almost.
LP: . . . . **HAT 3070**
MC: . . . . **HATC 3070**

SONNY JAMES COLLECTION, THE.
Tracks: / It's just a matter of time / Since I met you baby / World of our own, A / Endlessly / Only the lonely / That's why I love you like I do / Running bear / Take good care of her / Born to be with you / Here comes my honey again / Bright lights big city / Don't keep me hanging on / My love / Empty arms.
MC: . . . . **KNMC 13057**

James & The Giant

JAMES & THE GIANT PEACH (see under Dahl, Roald) (Dahl, Roald (aut)).

James, Tommy

ANTHOLOGY: TOMMY JAMES & THE SHONDELLS (James, Tommy & The Shondells).
Tracks: / Hanky panky / Say I am (what I am) / It's only love / I think we're alone now / Baby baby I can't take it no more / Mirage / I like the way / Run, run, baby, run (CD only.) / Gettin' together / Real girl (CD only.) / Love's closin' in on me (CD only.) / Out of the blue / Get out now / I'm taken (CD only.) / 1-2-3 and I fell / Mony mony / Somebody cares / Do something to me / Crimson and clover / Sugar on Sunday / Crystal blue persuasion / Sweet cherry wine / Loved one (CD only.) / Ball of fire / She / Gotta get back to you (CD only.) / Draggin' the line.
LP: . . . . **ROU 5004**
LP: **793 635 1**
MC: . . . . **TCROU 5004**
MC: **793 635 4**

I THINK WE'RE ALONE NOW (REISSUE) (James, Tommy & The Shondells).
LP: . . . . **XELLP 113**
MC: . . . . **XELMC 113**

SHORT SHARP SHOTS (James, Tommy & The Shondells).
Tracks: / Mony mony / Hanky panky / Sweet cherry wine / It's only love / I think we're alone now / Crystal blue persuasion / Crimson and clover / Mirage.
LP: . . . . **DOW 6**
MC: . . . . **ZCDOW 6**

James, Tony

MEMORIES OF THE FABULOUS FOX (see under Nourse,Everett/Tony James) (James, Tony/Everett Nourse).

MEMORIES OF THE FABULOUS FOX VOL.2 (see under Nourse,Everett/Tony James) (James, Tony/Everett Nourse).

Jameson, Claudia

MELTING HEART, THE (See also Georgina Melville).
MC: . . . . **PMB 010**

Jameson, Derek

JAMESON COLLECTION, THE (Various artists).
2LP: . . . . **REF 719**
MCSET: . . . . **ZCF 719**

Jameson, Nick

ALREADY FREE.
Tracks: / Sweet heat / Already free / In the blue / I ain't searching / When the blues / Come calling / I know what it is / Long way round, The.
LP: . . . . **K 55519**

Jamila

SONGS FROM A SOMALI CITY.
LP: . . . . **OMA 107**
MC: . . . . **OMA 107C**

Jamm

JAMM.
LP: . . . . **FE 44261**

JAMMS

1987 WHAT THE FUCK'S GOING ON.
LP: . . . . JAMSLP 1

SHAG TIMES.
Tracks: / All you need is love Jams / Downtown / Burn the b...... / Don't take five / Doctorin' the tardis / S... times.
2LP: JAMSLP3D

Jammy Music Library

JAMMY MUSIC LIBRARY VOL.1 (Various artists).
LP: . . . . JRML 001

JAMMY MUSIC LIBRARY VOL.2 - CHRISTMAS (Various artists).
LP: . . . . JRML 002

JAMMY MUSIC LIBRARY VOL.3 - REALLY USEFUL ALBUM (Various artists).
LP: . . . . JRML 003

JAMMY MUSIC LIBRARY VOL.4 - MADE TO MEASURE (Various artists).
LP: . . . . JRML 004

JAMMY MUSIC LIBRARY VOL.5 - HEAVY METAL (Various artists).
LP: . . . . JRML 005

JAMMY MUSIC LIBRARY VOL.6 - IRISH & SCOTS (Various artists).
LP: . . . . JRML 006

JAMMY MUSIC LIBRARY VOL.7 - COUNTRY JAMMY BLUES (Various artists).
LP: . . . . JRML 007

JAMMY MUSIC LIBRARY VOL.8 - 1937 (Various artists).
LP: . . . . JRML 008

Jammy's Angels

JAMMY'S ANGELS (Various artists).
LP: . . . . SPLP 08

Jan & Dean

15 GREATEST HITS, THE (See under Beach Boys) (Jan & Dean & The Beach Boys).

20 ROCK'N'ROLL HITS: JAN & DEAN.
Tracks: / Dead man's curve / Who put the bomp / Jennie Lee / Barbara Ann / Palisades Park / Surf city / Memphis, Tennessee / Tallahassee Lassie / Kansas City / Drag strip girl / Little old lady from Pasadena / Walk right in / Drag City / Little deuce coupe / My mighty G T O / Rockin' little roadster / Bucket T / New girl in school / You really know how to hurt a guy / Side walk surfin'.
LP: . . . . IC 064 82756
LP: 1A 062 82756

DEADMAN'S CURVE.
Tracks: / Deadman's curve / 3 window coupe / Bucket 'T' / Rockin' little roadster / 'B' gas rickshaw / Mighty GTO / New girl in school, The / Linda / Barons west LA / School days / It's as easy as 1,2,3 / Hey little freshman.
LP: C5-550

DRAG CITY.
Tracks: / Drag city / Drag strip girl / Dead man's curve / Popsicle / Sting Ray / Hot stocker / I gotta drive / Surfin' hearse / Shlock rod (part 2) / Surf route 101 / Little deuce coupe.
LP: C5-560

FUN FUN FUN.
Tracks: / Ride the wild surf / Dead man's curve / Help me Rhonda / I get around / Drag city / Baby talk / Clementine / Surf city / Sidewalk surfin' / Little deuce coupe / Little old lady from Pasadena / Fun fun fun.
LP: . . . . TOP 148
MC: . . . . KTOP 148

GREATEST HITS:JAN & DEAN.
Tracks: / Little old lady from Pasadena / Help me Rhonda / Don't fly away / Gee / Sidewalk surfin' / Little deuce coupe / Judy / I get around / Cindy / Deadman's curve / We go together / Ride the wild stuff / Drag City / Baby talk / Fun, fun, fun / Be bop a lula / Lotta lovin' / Ruby, Ruby / Ain't that too much / Bird doggin' / Love is a bird / Lonely street / Hurtin' for you baby / Poor man's prison / Born to be a rolling stone / Hi lili hi lo / I'm a lonesome fugitive / I've got my eyes on you / Say Mama / Rocky road blues / Pistol packin' mama.
LP: . . . . FUN 9027
MC: . . . . FUNC 9027

JAN & DEAN.
Tracks: / Jan and Dean.
MC: 801

JAN & DEAN MEET BATMAN.
Tracks: / Batman / Robin the boy wonder / Batman / Flight of the batmobile / Mr. Freeze / Joker is wild, The / Surprise Bat-tacular.
LP: . . . . KIRI 068

JAN & DEAN SOUND, THE.
LP: . . . . DORE 101

JAN & DEAN STORY, THE.
Tracks: / Surf city / Dead man's curve / Ride the wild surf / Help me Rhonda / Little deuce coupe / Fun fun fun / I get around / Sidewalk surfin' / Drag City / Little old lady from Pasadena / Baby talk / Gee / We go together / There's a girl / Cindy / My heart sings / Judy / You're on my mind / Clementine / Heart and soul.
LP: . . . . PAST 1
LP: . . . . NE 1084
MC: . . . . CE 2084

RIDE THE WILD SURF.
Tracks: / Surf city / Summer means fun / Surfin' / Down at Malibu Beach / Honolulu / Surfin' wild / Tell 'em I'm surfin' / Sidewalk surfin' / Ride the wild surf / Dead man's curve / Drag city / Shlock rod / I gotta drive / Bucket T / New girl in school / Linda / Little old lady from Pasadena / Anaheim, Azusa & Cucamonga sewing circle / When surfers rule.
MC: . . . . TC GO 2011
LP: . . . . GO 2011
LP: C5-562

SURF CITY (Best of Jan & Dean).
Tracks: / Sunday kind of love, A / Tennessee / Fiddle around / My favorite dream / Linda / Surf city / She's my summer girl / Honolulu / Someday you'll go walking by / Drag city / Popsicle / Dead man's curve / New girl in school, The / Little old lady from Pasadena, The / Ride the wild surf / Anaheim, Azusa & Cucamonga sewing circle,... (...book review and timing association, The) / Sidewalk surfin' / Here they come from all over the world / Freeway flyer / You really know how to hurt a guy / I found a girl / Batman.
MC: . . . . TCEMS 1384
2LP: . . . . MTLP 011

Janaway, Bruce & Roger

HOSPITAL BLUES (Psycho-neurotic fusions).
Tracks: / With sister blues / Last scene of trouble, the / Horned moon / Never leave him be / 7 stars lament.
MC: 60-038

Jane

GERMANIA.
Tracks: / Germania / Rock and roll / Revolution / Got no shadows / Cool and collected / Get back to you / No future / I'm so down / Driving me crazy / When I went to the scene / Southern line.
LP: 0060 519
MC: 0660 519
LP: 0660 061

JANE.
Tracks: / On my way / New man in town / Stay with me / Stop the clock / Rockin' around / Intro / Easy going / Love your life / Dynamite / Cadillac rider.
LP: 0060 354

SING NO.9.
LP: 0060 218

Jane & Barton

JANE & BARTON.
Tracks: / There is a man / It's a fine day / You are over there (Part 1) / I want to be with you / You are over there (Part 2) / Ha bloody ha.
LP: . . . . BRED 53

Jane Eyre (bk)

JANE EYRE (Charlotte Bronte) (O'Brien, Maureen (nar)).
MCSET: CC/008

JANE EYRE (Charlotte Bronte) (Bloom, Claire (nar)).
MCSET: 3003

JANE EYRE (Charlotte Bronte) (Hiller, Dame Wendy (nar)).
MCSET: . . . . LFP 7160
MCSET: . . . . LFP 4171605

Jane Eyre (film)

JANE EYRE (Film soundtrack) (Various artists).
Tracks: / Jane Eyre: *Various artists* / Overture (main title): *Various artists* / Lowood: *Various artists*/ To Thornfield: *Various artists* / String quartet - Festivity at Thornfield: *Various artists* / Grace Poole and Mason's arrival: *Various artists* / Trrio - The meeting: *Various artists* / Thwarted wedding: *Various artists*/ Across the Moors: *Various artists* / Restoration: *Various artists* / Reunion: *Various artists*.
LP: . . . . EST 749
LP: . . . . TER 1022

Jane Pow

STATE.
LP: . . . . PGT 001

Jane's Addiction

JANE'S ADDICTION.
Tracks: / Trip away / Rock 'n' roll / I would for you / Jane says / Pigs in zen / My time / Whores / Sympathy / Chip away / 1%.
LP: XXX1004
LP: 510041

NOTHING'S SHOCKING.
Tracks: / Up the beach / Had a dad / Standing in the shower / Jane Says / Thank you boys / Mountain song / Summertime rolls / Ted, just admit it.
LP: . . . . WX 216
MC: . . . . WX 216 C
LP: 925727 1
MC: 925727 4

RITUAL DE LO HABITUAL.
LP: . . . . WX 306
MC: . . . . WX 306 C

Janes, Roland

GUITARVILLE.
Tracks: / Guitarville (1) / Patriotic guitar / Rolando (take 2) / Roland's groove / Guitarville (2) / Patriotic guitar (2) / Rolando (take 1) / Red sails in the sunset / Impact / Sincerely yours / Roland slidin' home / My kind of people / Story of my downfall, The / Don't push me around / It's no sin.
LP: . . . . BFX 15340

Janitors

THUNDERHEAD.
Tracks: / Thunderhead.
MLP: . . . . IT 028

Jankel, Chas

CHASANOVA.
LP: . . . . AMLH 68533

CHAZ JANKEL.
Tracks: / Ai no corrida (Only on 12" single.) / Peace, at last / Just a thought / Lenta latina / Fuse / Am I honest with myself really / Reverie.
LP: . . . . AMLH 68518
MC: . . . . CAM 68518

CHAZABLANCA.
Tracks: / Theme to chazablanca / Without you / I can get over it / Tell me / Pretty thing / Whisper / All i wanna do is dance / Davis / Thankyou very much.
LP: . . . . AMLH 64917

KILLING DAD (Film Soundtrack).
Tracks: / By the sea / Morning mail / Latenight in Southend / Dead cat / Let's rock / Rockabilly party / Bonfire / Train journey / Seafront chase / Luisa's dance / Juan Martin / Body in carpet / One shoe / Emotions / That's what I'm dreamin' of.
MC: . . . . TCV 2603
LP: . . . . V 2603

LOOKING AT YOU.
Tracks: / Hard music / Tonight's our night / Rhythm in our life / Little eva / Eastern light / No 1 / Tell me tell me / Looking at you / Boy on the bridge / Love rhythms.
LP: . . . . AMA 5035

Jankowski, Horst

MEET MR. BLACK FOREST.
Tracks: / Meet Mr. Black Forest / Merry woodchoppers / Rhine river boat / Follow me to happyland / Come again / Madelein / Chance to love / Planet of love / For a lonely girl / Sambaville / Golden rain, The / Bird in the sun / Touch of Sweden.
LP: . . . . ISST 101

MEET MR BLACK FOREST, VOL. 2.
LP: . . . . ISST 128

PIANO INTERLUDE.
LP: . . . . ISST 105

RELAX AND ENJOY THE PIANO OF HORST JANKOWSKI (Jankowski, Horst/Rias Rhythm Section).
LP: . . . . ISST 192

Jano, Johnny

KING OF LOUISIANA ROCKABILLY.
LP: . . . . FLY 531

Janot, Johnny

EXPOSE YOURSELF TO CAJUN MUSIC.
LP: 6050
MC: . . . . 6050 TC

Janowski, Horst

SO MANY WAYS.
LP: . . . . ISST 197

Jansch, Bert

AVOCET.
Tracks: / Avocet / Bittern / Kingfisher / Kittiwake / Lapwing / Osprey.
LP: . . . . CLASS 6

BERT JANSCH.
Tracks: / Strolling down the highway / Smoky river / Oh how your love is strong / I have no time / Finches / Rambling's going to be the death of me / Veronica / Needle of death / Do you hear me now? / Alice's wonderland / Running, running from home / Courting blues / Casbah / Dreams of love / Angie.
LP: . . . . TRANDEM 1

FROM THE OUTSIDE.
LP: . . . . KOMA 788008

HEARTBREAK.
Tracks: / Is it real? / Up to the stars / Give me the time / If I were a carpenter / Wild mountain thyme / Heartbreak hotel / Sit down beside me / No rhyme nor reason / Blackwater side / And not a word was said.
LP: . . . . LOGO 1035
LP: . . . . HNBL 1312

JOHN RENBOURN & BERT JANSCH (See under Renbourn, John) (Jansch, Bert/John Renbourn).

LEATHER LAUNDERETTE (Jansch, Bert/Rod Clements).
Tracks: / Strolling down the highway / Sweet Rose / Brafferton / Ain't no more cane / Why me? / Sundown station / Knight's move / Brownsville / Bogie's bonnie belle / Leather launderette / Been on the road so long.
LP: . . . . CRO 218
MC: . . . . CROC 218

ORNAMENT TREE, THE.
LP: . . . . RRA 0012
MC: . . . . RRAMC 0012

THIRTEEN DOWN.
Tracks: / Una linea di dolcezza / Let me sing and I'm happy / Down river / Nightfall / If I had a lover / Time and time again / In my mind / Sovay / Where did my life go / Single rose / Ask your daddy / Sweet mother earth / Bridge.
LP: . . . . SNKF 162

Jansen, Steve

STAY CLOSE (See under Takahashi, Yukihiro) (Jansen, Steve & Yukihiro Takahashi).

WORLDS IN A SMALL ROOM.
LP: . . . . NEWLP 105
MC: . . . . NEWMC 105

Jansens, Huub

AMAZING JAZZBAND.
LP: . . . . TTD 536

Janson, Claes

SOUL TRAIN (Janson, Claes/Gustavo Bergalli).
LP: . . . . CAP 1335

Jansson, Lena

PAY SOME ATTENTION TO ME (Jansson, Lena & Nils Lindberg Combo).
LP: . . . . BELL 177

Jansson, Tove

TALES FROM MOOMIN VALLEY.
Tracks: / Last dragon on the world, The / Invisible child, The / Cedric.
MC: . . . . TS 344

Jap, Philip

PHILIP JAP.
Tracks: / Save us / Sand / Venue / Jump crew / Jap / Brain dance / Red dogs / Brave lights / Glass house / Death in a tin junk / Total erasure.
LP: . . . . AMLH 68557

Japan

ADOLESCENT SEX.
Tracks: / Transmission / Unconventional, The / Wish you were black / Performance / Lovers on main street / Don't rain on my parade / Suburban love / Adolescent sex / Communist China / Television.
LP: . . . . AHAL 8004
MC: . . . . FA 41 3108 4

ADOLESCENT SEX/ OBSCURE ALTERNATIVES.
Tracks: / Transmission / Unconventional, The / Wish you were black / Performance / Lovers on main street / Don't rain on my parade / Suburban love / Adolescent sex / Communist China / Television / Automatic gun / Rhodesia / Love is infectious / Sometimes I feel so low / Obscure alternatives / Deviation / Suburban Berlin / Tenant, The.
MC: . . . . XTWO 24

ASSEMBLAGE.
Tracks: / Adolescent sex / State line / Communist China / Rhodesia / Suburban Berlin / Life in Tokyo / European son / All tomorrow's parties / Quiet life / I second that emotion.
LP: . . . . HANLP 1
MC: . . . . ZCHAN 001
LP: . . . . FA 41 3136 1
MC: . . . . FA 41 3136 4
LP: . . . . FA 3136
MC: . . . . TCFA 3136

EXORCISING GHOSTS.
Tracks: / Methods of dance / Swing / Gentlemen take polaroids / Quiet life / Foreign place, A / Night porter / My new career / Other side of life, The / Visions of China / Sons of pioneers / Talking drum / Art of parties, The / Taking islands in Africa / Voices raised in

welcome, hands held in prayer / Life without buildings / Ghosts.
2LP: . . . . **VGD 3510**
MC: . . . . **VGDC 3510**

GENTLEMEN TAKE POLAROIDS.
Tracks: / Gentlemen take polaroids / Swing / Burning bridges / My new career / Methods of dance / Ain't that peculiar / Nightporter / Taking islands in Africa.
MC: . . . . **OVEDC 138**
LP: . . . . **V 2180**
LP: . . . . **OVED 138**

JAPANESE MASTERPIECES FOR THE SHAKUHACHI (Japanese Music).
LP: . . . . **LLST 7176**
MC: . . . . **LLCT 7176**

JAPNESE KABUTI NAGUATA-SCENES FROM 'DOJOJI' & 'K (Japanese Music).
LP: . . . . **LLST 7134**

JAPON ETERNEL (Japanese Traditional Orchestra).
Tracks: / Le Chemin vers Izumo / Le soleil se couche sur le temple de Kyoto / La fete / Les rayons du soleil sur le lac / L'oiseau pluvier / Rokoudan, Themes de / Image pur instruments Japonais / Capriccio pour trois kotos.
LP: . . . . **ARN 33234**
MC: . . . . **ARN 433234**

OBSCURE ALTERNATIVES.
Tracks: / Automatic gun / Rhodesia / Love is infectious / Sometimes I feel so low / Obscure alternatives / Deviation / Suburban Berlin / Tenant, The.
LP: . . . . **FA 4130981**
MC: . . . . **FA 4130984**
MC: . . . . **TCFA 3098**
LP: . . . . **AAL 8007**

OIL ON CANVAS.
Tracks: / Sons of pioneers / Cantonese boy / Visions of China / Ghosts / Voices raised in welcome, hands held in prayer / Nightporter / Still life in mobile homes / Methods of dance / Quiet life / Art of parties, The / Temple of dawn / Oil on canvas / Gentlemen take polaroids / Canton.
LP: . . . . **VD 2513**
MC: . . . . **TCVD 2513**

QUIET LIFE.
Tracks: / Quiet life / Fall in love with me / In vogue / Halloween / All tomorrows parties / Alien / Other side of life, The.
LP: . . . . **FA 3037**
MC: . . . . **TCFA 3037**
LP: . . . . **AHAL 8011**

SOUVENIR FROM JAPAN, A.
Tracks: / I second that emotion / Life in Tokyo / Deviation / Surburban Berlin / Adolescent sex / European son / All tomorrow's parties / Communist China / State line / Rhodesia / Obscure alternatives / Quiet life.
MC: **410.360**

TIN DRUM.
Tracks: / Visions of China / Art of parties, The / Talking drum / Cantonese boy / Canton / Ghosts / Still life in mobile homes / Sons of pioneers.
LP: . . . . **OVED 158**
MC: . . . . **OVEDC 158**
LP: . . . . **V 2209**
MC: . . . . **TCV 2209**

Japan (country)

TOKYO MOBILE MUSIC 1 (Various artists).
Tracks: / New tribe: *Various artists* / Hikashu: *Various artists* / Akiko yano: *Various artists* / Earthling: *Various artists* / Yukiro Takahashi: *Various artists* / Shoukichi Kina: *Various artists* / Sa ka na: *Various artists* / Lizard: *Various artists* / Salon music: *Various artists.*
LP: . . . . **SUIT 1**
MC: . . . . **SUITC 1**

Japanese Music

HIROSHIMA MASSES,THE (Various artists).
LP: . . . . **LLST 7180**

BUDDIST CHANT (Various artists).
LP: . . . . **LLST 7118**

IMPERIAL COURT MUSIC OF JAPAN,THE (Various artists).
LP: . . . . **LLST 7126**

JAPANESE FOLK MUSIC (Various artists).
LP: . . . . **LLST 7163**

JAPANESE KOTO CONSORT (Various artists).
LP: . . . . **LLST 7205**
LP: . . . . **LLST 7131**

JAPANESE KOTO ORCHESTRA (Various artists).
LP: . . . . **LLST 7167**

JAPANESE MASTERPIECES FOR THE KOTO (Various artists).
LP: . . . . **LLST 7219**

JAPANESE NOH MUSIC (Various artists).
LP: . . . . **LLST 7137**

JAPANESE SHAMISEN (Various artists).
LP: . . . . **LLST 7209**

JAPANESE TEMPLE MUSIC (Various artists).
LP: . . . . **LLST 7117**

JAPANESE TREASURERS (Various artists).
LP: . . . . **LLST 7228**

JORURI-MUSIC OF THE JAPANESE BUNRAKU PUPPET THEA (Various artists).
LP: . . . . **LLST 7197**

KOTO KUMUITA Classical song cycles by the great master compos (Various artists).
LP: . . . . **LLST 7304**

SONGS FROM JAPAN (Various artists).
MC: . . . . **RK 25253**

SOUL OF THE KOTO,THE (Various artists).
LP: . . . . **LLST 7218**

SPIRITS OF SAMURAI (Various artists).
LP: . . . . **LLST 7346**

ZEN,GOEIKA AND SHOMYO CHANTS (Various artists).
LP: . . . . **LLST 7116**

Jara, Victor

MANIFESTO.
Tracks: / Te recuerdo Amanda / Canto Libre / Aquime quedo / Angelita huenuman / Ni chicha ni limona / La plegaria a un labrador / Cuando voy al trabajo / El derecho de vivir en paz / Vientos del pueblo / Manifesto / La partida / Chile stadium (Production Master: Riverside Recordings Co-ordination: Laurence Aston).
LP: . . . . **CFRC 529**

UNFINISHED SONG, AN.
MC: . . . . **RR 3300**

VICTOR JARA.
Tracks: / El Arado / El cigaritto / La flor que anda de mano en mano / Deja la vida volar / La luna siempre es muy Linda / Oj itos verdes / La concinerita / Paloma quiero contarte / Que saco rogar al cielo / No pueoes volver atras / El carretero / Ja jai.
LP: . . . . **HIFLY 31**

Jaramillo, Pepe

EVENING WITH....
Tracks: / Just for you / Love is in the air / Solitaire / Entertainer, The / It's impossible / How deep is your love / Breeze and I / That's when the music takes me / Don't stay away too long / Up, up and away / I only have eyes for you / Sing baby sing / Way we were, The (Full title: The way we were (From the columbia film 'The way we were')) / Maria (Full title: Maria (From 'West side story')) / What a difference a day made / Tonight (Full title: Tonight (From 'West side story')) / Never on sunday (Full title: Never on sunday (From film of the same name)) / Laughter in the rain / Strangers in the night / She / Bimbo / My love / Old fashioned way, The / Rivers of Babylon / Distant horizon / Fool on the hill, The.
2LP: . . . . **DL 1090**
MC: . . . . **TCDL 1090**

JUST FOR YOU.
Tracks: / Just for you / Love is in the air / My love / Touch of your lips / How deep is your love / Distant horizon / That's when the music takes me / Walk in love / I only have eyes for you / A-ba-ni-bi / It must be him / Rivers of Babylon.
LP: . . . . **OU 2224**

..WITH HIS LATIN AMERICAN RHYTHMS.
Tracks: / I talk to the trees / Bali Ha'i / I could write a book / Hernando's hideaway / I could have danced all night / Bewitched / Surrey with the fringe on top / People will say we're in love / Hey there / Tonight / Get me to the church on time / Maria / June is bustin' out all over / Party's over, The / Green eyes / Cachita / Breeze and I / Amor / Siboney / Sway / South of the border / El choclo / Stairway to the sea / Torero / Capullito de aleli / Man who plays the mandolino, The.
2LP: . . . . **MFP 1008**
MCSET: . . . . **TCMFP 1008**

Jarmels

COMPLETE JARMELS,THE.
Tracks: / Little bit of soap, A / She loves to dance / One by one / Keep your mind on me / Come on girl (it's time to smile again) / Why am I a fool for you / Way you look tonight / Little lonely one / Gee oh gosh / Red sails in the sunset / Loneliness / I'll follow you / You don't believe a word I say / Little bug.
LP: . . . . **CH 174**

Jarratt, Jeff

MASTERWORKS (Jarratt, Jeff & Don Reedman).
LP: . . . . **ONE 1093**

Jarre, Jean Michel

CONCERTS IN CHINA.
Tracks: / Overture / Arpegiator / Equinoxe part 4 / Fishing junks at sunset / Band in the rain / Equinoxe part 7 / Orient Express / Magnetic fields III / Magnetic fields IV / Laser harp / Night in Shanghai / Last rumba, The / Magnetic fields II / Souvenir of China.
2LP: . . . . **PODV 3**
MCSET: . . . . **PODVC 3**

EQUINOXE.
LP: . . . . **POLD 5007**
MC: . . . . **POLDC 5007**

ESSENTIAL, THE.
Tracks: / Oxygene 2, 4, & 6 / Magnetic fields 1, 2, 4 & 5 / Orient express / Fishing junks at sunset / Overture.
LP: . . . . **PROLP 3**

IN CONCERT LYON/HOUSTON.
Tracks: / Oxygene V / Ethnicolour / Magnetic fields I / Souvenir (Of China) / Equinoxe part 5 / Rendezvous III / Rendezvous II / Ron's place / Rendezvous IV.
LP: . . . . **POLH 36**
MC: . . . . **POLHC 36**

LIVE: JEAN-MICHEL JARRE.
MC: **841 258 4**
LP: **841 258 1**

MAGNETIC FIELDS.
Tracks: / Parts 1-5 / Last rumba, The.
LP: . . . . **POLS 1033**
MC: . . . . **POLSC 1033**

MUSIK AUS ZEIT UND RAUM.
LP: **815 686-1**

OXYGENE.
LP: **231 055 5**
MC: **310 039 8**

RENDEZVOUS.
LP: . . . . **POLH 27**
MC: . . . . **POLHC 27**

REVOLUTIONS.
LP: . . . . **POLH 45**
MC: . . . . **POLHC 45**

WAITING FOR COUSTEAU.
MC: **843 614 4**
LP: **843 614 1**

ZOOLOOK.
Tracks: / Ethnicolour / Diva / Zoolook / Wooloomooloo / Zoolookologie / Blah-blah / Ethnicolour.
LP: . . . . **POLH 15**
MC: . . . . **POLHC 15**

Jarre, Maurice

JARRE BY JARRE (Royal Philharmonic Orchestra).
Tracks: / Lawrence of Arabia / Ryan's daughter: Rosy's theme / Doctor Zhivago: Prelude / Doctor Zhivago: Lara's theme / Passage to India, A: Adela's theme / Witness: Building the barn / Is Paris burning? / Damned, The / Mad Max: Beyond the Thunderdome: Fanfare / Thunderdome music / Villa Rides (main title).
LP: . . . . **FM 42307**
MC: . . . . **FMT 42307**

Jarreau, Al

AIN'T NO SUNSHINE.
Tracks: / Ain't no sunshine / Lean on me / Use me / Kissing my love / Grandma's hands / You / Lonely town / Lonely street / Same love that made me laugh, The.
LP: . . . . **BMLP 1011**
LP: **226 2233**
MC: **216 2233**

AL JARREAU.
LP: . . . . **AZ 2467**
MC: . . . . **C 467**

ALL FLY HOME.
Tracks: / Thinkin' about it too / I'm home / Brite 'n' sunny babe / I do / Fly / Wait a little while / She's leaving home / All / Dock of the bay, The.
LP: . . . . **K 56546**

ALL FLY HOME/THIS TIME.
MCSET: **923948 4**

BREAKIN' AWAY.
Tracks: / Closer to your love / My old friend / We're in this love together / Easy / Our love / Breakin' away / Roof garden / Blue rondo a la turk / Teach me tonight.
LP: . . . . **K 56917**
MC: **K4 56917**

DAY BY DAY (see under Shakatak) (Jarreau, Al/Shakatak).

GLOW.
Tracks: / Rainbow in your eyes / Your song / Agua de beber / Have you seen the child / Hold on me / Fire and rain / Somebody's watching you / Milwaukee glow.
LP: . . . . **K 54073**

HEARTS HORIZON.
Tracks: / All or nothing at all / So good / All of my love / Pleasure over pain / Yo jeans / Way to your heart / One way / 10 K HI / I must have been a fool / More love / Killer love / Heart's horizon.
LP: . . . . **WX 230**
MC: . . . . **WX 230 C**

HIGH CRIME.
Tracks: / Raging waters / Imagination / Murphy's law / Tell me / After all / High crime / Let's pretend / Sticky wicket / Love speaks louder than words / Falling.
LP: **250807 1**
MC: **250807 4**

IN LONDON.
Tracks: / Raging waters / Black and blue / I will be here for you / Let's pretend / High crime / Roof garden / Teach me tonight / We're in this love together.
LP: **252369 1**
MC: **252369 4**

JARREAU.
Tracks: / Mornin' / Boogie down / I will be here for you / Save me / Step by step / Black and blue / Trouble in paradise / Not like this / Love is waiting.
LP: . . . . **U 0070**
MC: . . . . **U 00704**

JAZZ SINGER, THE.
LP: . . . . **MA 18128**
MC: . . . . **MAMC 9181285**

L IS FOR LOVER.
Tracks: / Tell me what I gotta do / Says / Pleasure / Golden girl / Across the midnight sky / No ordinary romance / L is for lover / Real tight.
LP: **253080 1**
MC: **253080 4**

LOOK TO THE RAINBOW (LIVE).
Tracks: / Letter perfect / Rainbow in your eyes / One good turn / Could you believe / Burst in with the dawn / Better than anything / So long girl / Look to the rainbow / You don't see me / Take five / Loving you / We got by.
2LP: . . . . **K 66059**

MANIFESTO.
LP: . . . . **MA 181285**
MC: . . . . **MAMC 9181285**

MASQUERADE IS OVER, THE.
Tracks: / My favourite things / Stockholm sweetnin' / Sleeping bee / Masquerade is over, The / Sophisticated lady / Joey / Come rain or come shine / One note samba.
LP: . . . . **B 90136**
MC: . . . . **MB 990136**
LP: . . . . **BMLP 079**

MUSIC OF GOODBYE, THE (see under Manchester, Melissa).

REPLAY OF AL JARREAU.
LP: . . . . **FEDB 5003**
MC: . . . . **CFEDB 5003**

SINGS BILL WITHERS.
Tracks: / Ain't no sunshine / Lean on me / Use me / Missing my love / Grandma's hands / You / Lonely town, lonely street / That same love that made me laugh.
LP: . . . . **TOP 173**
MC: . . . . **KTOP 173**

SPIRITS AND FEELINGS.
Tracks: / Ain't no sunshine / Lean on me / Use me / Kissing my love / Grandma's hands / You / Lonely town, lonely street / Same love that made me laugh, The.
LP: . . . . **B 90168**

THIS TIME.
Tracks: / Never givin' up / Gimme what you got / This time / Your sweet love / Alonzo / Spain / Distracted / Love is real / Change your mind.
LP: . . . . **K 56804**

WE GOT BY.
Tracks: / Spirit / We got by / Susan's song / You don't see me / Lock all the gates / Raggedy Ann / Letter perfect / Sweet potato pie / Aladdin's lamp.
LP: . . . . **K 54045**

YOU.
LP: . . . . **PLP 19**
MC: . . . . **PMC 19**

Jarrell, Randall

GINGERBREAD RABBIT, THE.
MC: **1381**

RANDALL JARRELL READS POEMS AGAINST WAR.
MC: **1363**

Jarrell, Tommy

RAINBOW SIGN.
Tracks: / Say darling say / Old Molly Hare / God save Noah the rainbow sign / Little Sadie / Old time backstep Cindy / Temple / Fire on the mountain / Granny will your dog bite / Ida Red / Little

Maggie / Chapel Hill serenade / Old time Sally Ann / Poor Ellen Smith / Sugar foot rag.
LP: . . . . **SAVE 038**

Jarrett, Keith

ARBOUR ZENA.
Tracks: / Dunes / Solara march / Mirrors.
LP: . . . . **ECM 1070**

BACKHAND.
LP: . . . . **JAS 67**

BELONGING.
Tracks: / Spiral dance / Blossom / Long as you know you're living yours / Belonging / Windup, The / Solstice.
MC: **3101050**
LP: . . . . **ECM 1050**

BEST OF KEITH JARRETT.
Tracks: / Blackberry winter / Introduction / Yaqui Indian folk song / Roads travelled, roads veiled / Fantasm / Byablue / Treasure island / De drums / Silence.
LP: . . . . **IMPL 8054**

BOOK OF WAYS.
2LP: . . . . **ECM 1344**

BOP-BE.
Tracks: / Mushi mushi / Silence / Pyramids moving / Gotta get some sleep / Pocket full of cherry / Blackberry winter / Bop be.
LP: . . . . **JAS 29**
MC: . . . . **JAS C29**

CELESTIAL HAWK.
MC: **7200 188**
LP: . . . . **ECM 1175**

CHANGELESS (Jarrett, Keith Trio).
Tracks: / Dancing / Endless / Lifeline / Ecstacy.
LP: . . . . **ECM 1392**
MC: **8396184**

CHANGES.
Tracks: / Flying / Prism (In digital stereo).
LP: . . . . **ECM 1276**

CONCERTS (BREGENZ).
LP: . . . . **ECM 1227**

CONCERTS (MUNCHEN/BREGENZ).
2LP: . . . . **ECM 1227/29**

COREA/ HANCOCK/ JARRET (See under Corea, Chick).

DARK INTERVALS.
Tracks: / Opening / Hymn / Americana / Entrance / Parallels / Fire dance / Ritual prayer / Recitative.
LP: . . . . **ECM 1379**

EXPECTATIONS.
MC: **4679024**

EYES OF THE HEART.
Tracks: / Eyes of the heart (part one) / Eyes of the heart (part two) / Encore (A-B-C).
2LP: . . . . **ECM 1150**

FACING YOU.
Tracks: / In front / Ritooria / Lalene / My lady: my child / Landscape for future earth / Starbright / Vapallia / Semblence.
LP: . . . . **ECM 1017**

FORT YAWUH.
Tracks: / If the misfits wear it / Fort Yawuh / De drums / Still life, still life.
LP: . . . . **JAS 23**
MC: . . . . **JAS C23**

HYMNS / SPHERES.
2LP: . . . . **ECM 1086**

IN THE LIGHT.
2LP: . . . . **ECM 1033**

INVOCATIONS: THE MOTH AND THE FLAME.
Tracks: / Invocations (1st to 7th) / Moth and the flame part 1-v, The.
2LP: . . . . **ECM 1201**

JUDGEMENT, THE.
Tracks: / Gypsy moth / Toll road / Pardon my rags / Pre judgement atmosphere / El juicio / Piece for Ornette (lv) / Piece for Ornette (sv).
LP: . . . . **K 50154**

KOLN CONCERT, THE.
MC: **3541064**
2LP: . . . . **ECM 1064**

LUMINESSENCE (Jarrett, Keith/Jan Garbarek).
LP: . . . . **ECM 1049**

MY SONG.
Tracks: / Questar / My song / Tabarka / Mandela / Journey home, The.
MC: **3101115**
LP: . . . . **ECM 1115**

NUDE ANTS.
Tracks: / Chant of the soil / Innocence / Processional / Oasis / New dance / Sunshine song.
2LP: . . . . **ECM 1171**

PARIS CONCERT (SOLO PIANO).
Tracks: / October 17, 1988 / Wind, The / Blues.
LP: . . . . **ECM 1401**
MC: **8391734**

PERSONAL MOUNTAINS (Jarrett, Keith & Belonging).
Tracks: / Personal mountains / Oasis / Prism / Innocence.
LP: . . . . **ECM 1382**
MC: **837 361-4**

RUTA AND DAITYA.
LP: . . . . **ECM 1021**

SACRED HYMNS OF G.I. GURDJIEFF.
Tracks: / Reading of sacred books / Prayer & despair / Religious ceremony / Hymn / Orthodox hymn from Asia minor / Hymn for Good Friday / Hymn for Easter Thursday / Hymn to the endless creator / Hymn from a great temple / Story of the resurrection of Christ, The / Holy affirming, holy denying, holy reconciling / Easter night procession / Meditation.
LP: . . . . **ECM 1174**

SOLO CONCERTS - BREMEN/ LAUSANNE.
LPS: . . . . **ECM 1035**

SPHERES.
Tracks: / Spheres - 1st Movement / Spheres - 4th Movement / Spheres - 7th Movement / Spheres - 9th Movement.
LP: . . . . **ECM 1302**

SPIRITS (Volumes 1 & 2).
2LP: . . . . **ECM 1333**

STAIRCASE.
Tracks: / Staircase (part 1) / Staircase (part 2) / Staircase (part 3) / Hourglass (part 1) / Hourglass (part 2) / Sundial (part 1) / Sundial (part 2) / Sundial (part 3) / Sand (part 1) / Sand (part 2) / Sand (part 3).
2LP: . . . . **ECM 1090**

STANDARDS LIVE.
Tracks: / Stella by starlight / Wrong blues, The / Falling in love with love / Too young to go steady / Way you look tonight / Old country, The.
LP: . . . . **ECM 1317**

STANDARDS, VOL 1.
Tracks: / Meaning of the blues / All the things you are / It never entered my mind / Masquerade is over, The / God bless the child.
LP: . . . . **ECM 1255**
MC: **8119664**
MC: . . . . **TCBT 85130**
MC: **3101255**

STANDARDS, VOL 2.
Tracks: / So tender / Moon and sand / In love in vain / Never let me go / If I should lose you / I fall in love too easily.
LP: . . . . **ECM 1289**

STILL LIVE (Jarrett, Keith Trio).
Tracks: / My funny valentine / Autumn leaves / When I fall in love / Song is you, The / Come rain or come shine / Late lament / You and the night and the music / Some day my prince will come / I remember Clifford.
2LP: . . . . **ECM 1360**

SUN BEAR CONCERTS.
Tracks: / Osaka (part 1 and 2) / Nagoya (part 1 and 2) / Tokyo (part 1 and 2) / Sapporo (part 1 and 2).
LPS: . . . . **ECM 1100**

SURVIVOR'S SUITE.
MC: **7104651**
LP: . . . . **ECM 1085**

TALES OF ANOTHER (see under Peacock, Gary) (Jarrett, Kieth, J. DeJohnette & G. Peacock).

TREASURE ISLAND.
LP: . . . . **MCA 39106**

TRIBUTE (Jarrett, Keith Trio).
Tracks: / Lover man / I hear a rhapsody / Little girl blue / Solar / Sun prayer / Just in time / Smoke gets in you eyes / All of you / Ballad of the sad young man / All the things you are / It easy to remember.
2LP: . . . . **ECM 1420**
MC: **8471354**

WELL TEMPERED CLAVIER BOOK, THE.
2LP: . . . . **ECM 1362**
MC: **8352464**

WORKS: KEITH JARRETT.
Tracks: / Belonging / Journey home, The / As long as you know you are living yours / Wind up / Country / My song / Solstice / Spiral dance.
MC: **3100 388**

WORKS: KEITH JARRETT.
Tracks: / Country / Riootria / Journey, The / Staircase (part II) / String quartet (2nd Movement) / Invocations / Nagoya (part 2b)(encore).
LP: **8254251**

Jarrett, Wayne

CHIP IN.
Tracks: / Chip in / Saturday night jamboree.
LP: . . . . **GREL 28**

INNER CIRCLE.
LP: . . . . **A 108**

NICE AND EASY (see under Dread, Sammy & Lui Lepke).

Jarrett, Winston

ROCKING VIBRATION.
LP: . . . . **VSLP 5008**

WISE MAN.
LP: . . . . **TWLP 1001**

Jarrow 86

JARROW 86 (Various artists).
LP: . . . . **HHH 86**

Jarvis, John

SO FA' SO GOOD.
Tracks: / Some kind of sunrise / Month of seasons, A / Best of both worlds / Scrumpy cider / Audrey / Can't turn my heart away / Framed in a still picture / Amber / Homecoming / Long awaited / Never delivered / Blue moon of Kentucky.
LP: . . . . **IMCA 5690**
MC: . . . . **IMCAC 5690**

SOMETHING CONSTRUCTIVE.
Tracks: / Wide open spaces / Waiting / Solving a dream / Two moods / View from above, A / Southern hospitality / Something constructive / Long distances / Dancing by candlelight.
LP: . . . . **IMCA 5963**
MC: . . . . **IMCAC 5963**

Jarvis, Martin (nar)

AMAZING MONSTERS (See under Amazing Monsters).

HAPPY FAMILIES (See under Happy Families).

MATTER OF HONOUR, A (See under Archer, Jeffrey (aut)).

MY GIRL IN SKIN TIGHT JEANS (See Under My Girl In...) (Boyd, William (aut)).

PERFECT MURDER, A (See under Archer, Jeffrey (aut)) (Jarvis, Martin & Rosalind Ayres).

QUIVER FULL OF ARROWS, A VOL. 1 (See under Archer, Jeffrey (aut)).

RIDDLE OF THE SANDS, THE (2) (see under Riddle Of The...(bk).

RUNNING BLIND (See under Running Blind).

Jasani, Viram

RAGS, MALKAUNS AND MEGH (see under India) (Jasani,Viram # Gurdev Singh # Ustad Latif Ahmed Khan).

RAGS, MALKAUNS AND MEGH (Jasani,Viram # Gurdev Singh # Ustad Latif Ahmed Khan).
Tracks: / Rag Malkauns (A late-evening rag.) / Rag Megh (A romantic evening rag associated with the rainy season in India.).
MC: . . . . **CSDL 377**

Jasmine Minks

1-2-3-4-5-6-7, ALL GOOD PREACHERS GO TO HEAVEN.
LP: . . . . **CRELP 003**

ANOTHER AGE.
LP: . . . . **CRELP 025**

JASMINE MINKS.
LP: . . . . **CRELP 007**

SCRATCH THE SURFACE.
LP: . . . . **CRELP 044**

SUNSET.
LP: . . . . **CRELP 013**

Jason, David

CREATIVE RAGTIME VOL 6 (Jason,David and Neville Dickie).
LP: . . . . **ESR 1206**

Jason & The Scorchers

FERVOR.
Tracks: / Absolutely sweet Marie / Help there's a fire / I can't help myself / Hot nights in Georgia / Pray for me ma (I'm a gypsy now) / Harvest moon / Both sides of the line.
LP: . . . . **EE 2400801**

LOST AND FOUND.
Tracks: / Last time around, The / White lies / If money talks / I really don't want to know / Blanket of sorrow / Shop it around / Lost highway / Still tied / Broken whiskey glass / Far behind / Change the tune.
LP: . . . . **JS 1**
MC: . . . . **TCJS 1**
LP: . . . . **EJ 2402801**

STILL STANDING.
Tracks: / Ghost town / Take me to your promised land / Golden ball and chain / Crashin' down / Shotgun blues / Good things come to those who wait / My heart still stands with you / 19th nervous breakdown / Ocean of doubt.
LP: . . . . **AML 3110**
MC: . . . . **TCAML 3110**

THUNDER AND FIRE.
Tracks: / When the angels cry / Now that you're mine / You gotta way with me / My kingdom for a car / Close up the road / Lights out / Find you / Bible and a gun / Six feet underground / No turning back / Away from you.
LP: . . . . **AMA 5264**
MC: . . . . **AMC 5264**

Jaspar, Bobby

AT RONNIE SCOTT'S, 1962 (Jaspar, Bobby Quartet).
Tracks: / Be like Bud / Our delight / Darn that dream / Pent-up house / Oleo / Sonnymoon for two (on CD only) / Like someone in love (on CD only) / Stella by starlight (on CD only).
LP: . . . . **MOLE 11**

BOBBY JASPAR.
LP: . . . . **FS 158**

BOBBY JASPAR QUINTET.
LP: . . . . **FS 169**

NEW YORK 1956.
LP: . . . . **SW 8413**

Jasper, Chris

SUPERBAD.
Tracks: / Superbad / Givin' my all / One time love / Earthquake / Like I do / Dance for the dollar / Son of man / My soul train.
LP: **4607061**
MC: **4607064**

TIME BOMB.
Tracks: / First time / Hit on you / In your face / Margie / It's workin' / Time bomb / Sanctified you.
LP: **4654601**
MC: **4654604**

Jaubert, Maurice

MAURICE JAUBERT 1900-1940.
LP: . . . . **A 274**

MUSIC FROM THE FILMS OF FRANCOIS TRUFFAUT VOL 2.
LP: . . . . **A 293**
MC: . . . . **C 293**

Jaume, Andre

INCONTRU (Jaume, Andre Quartet/ Tavagna).
Tracks: / Qualcosa di te / Que so voce muntagnole / U primu viaghju / U pinu tunisianu / Memoria / Paghella: Stamane e tre culombe / Paghella; Pecure cume le meie / Paghella: Veju nantu / Malamorte / Terzetti / Madrigale : Ecco bella / Ventu / Paghella u 26 di lugliu / Dopu ava.
LP: . . . . **NATO 194**

Java

JAVANESE MUSIC FROM SURINAM (Various artists).
LP: . . . . **LLST 7317**

MUSIC OF MYSTICAL ENCHANTMENT (Various artists).
LP: . . . . **LLST 7301**
MC: . . . . **LLCT 7301**

STREET MUSIC OF CENTRAL JAVA (Various artists).
LP: . . . . **LLST 7310**

Javaroo

OUT.
Tracks: / Bring out the woman / Change it up / Breakin' in / Love is running through me / Problem child / Buzz / Javaroo / Behind my eyes / Bedroom secrets / Leave you wantin' more.
LP: . . . . **EST 12052**

Javier

HARD WAY, THE (Javier & The Str8jackers).
Tracks: / Intro / Shoot out / F. I. U. Jay / Other guy, The / Hammer break / Real deal / Talking shit / Plain ole gangster / Pass me da 40 ounce / Talkin' shit again / Jones, The / Never heard rappin' / Baddest M. F. out da ATL / Chillin' at da crib / Candy / Players dialogue / Player style / Str8jackin' / Wildest fantasy / Outtro.
LP: . . . . **ICH 1109**
MC: . . . . **ICH 1109MC**

Jawara, Jali Musa

DIRECT FROM WEST AFRICA.
Tracks: / Fote Mogoban / Haidari / Ye ke ye ke / Yasimika.
LP: . . . . **GGLP 1**
MC: . . . . **GGMC 1**

FOTE MOGOBAN.
LP: . . . . **OVLP 511**

SOUBINDOOR.
LP: . . . . **WCB 008**

MC: . . . . WCC 008

YASIMIKA.
LP: . . . . HNBL 1355
MC: . . . . HNBC 1355

Jaws

JAWS (Film soundtrack) (Various artists).
LP: . . . . MCA 1660
MC: . . . . MCAC 1660
LP: . . . . MCF 2716

JAWS 3-D (Film Soundtrack Music) (Various artists).
LP: . . . . MCF 3194

JAWS II (Film soundtrack) (Various artists).
LP: . . . . MCA 2045

Jaxon, Frankie

CAN'T WAIT TILL YOU GET HOME (Jaxon, Frankie 'Half Pint').
LP: . . . . CI 014

FRANKIE HALF PINT JAXON 1927-40 (Jaxon, Frankie 'Half Pint').
LP: . . . . BD 2049

FRANKIE HALF PINT JAXON 1937-39 (Jaxon, Frankie 'Half Pint').
LP: . . . . DLP 560

SATURDAY NIGHT SCRONTCH (Jaxon, Frankie 'Half Pint').
LP: . . . . CI 013

Jay, David

ARMOUR (See Hackett, Rene) (Jay, David & Rene Halkett).

Jay Jay B

OVER SEAS.
Tracks: / Flying sea / Stream of energy / Dolphin's thoughts / Sea of illusion / Source, The / Sea of secrets / Over seas.
LP: . . . . IC 80 077

Jay & the Americans

JAY AND THE AMERICANS.
MC: 809

VERY BEST OF JAY & THE AMERICANS.
Tracks: / Cara mia / Let's lock the door and throw away the key / Come a little bit closer / She cried / Only in America / This magic moment / Sunday and me.
LP: . . . . LBR 1000

Jayaraman, Lalguidi

SOUTH MEETS NORTH (Jayaraman,Lalguidi and Amjad Ali Khan).
LP: . . . . ECSD 2932
MC: 6TCS 7114

Jaye, Miles

IRRESISTIBLE.
Tracks: / Irresistible / Objective / Next time / Slo-dance / Message / Neither one of us / Interlude / I'll be there / Heaven / Love in the night.
MC: . . . . BRCA 531
LP: . . . . BRLP 531

MILES.
Tracks: / Let's start over / Lazy love / Special thing / I've been a fool for you / I cry for you / Come home / Happy 2 have U / Desiree.
LP: . . . . BRLP 515
MC: . . . . ICM 2031
MC: 842 816 4
MC: . . . . BRCA 515

STRONG.
MC: . . . . BRCA 573
LP: . . . . BRLP 573

Jaymen

DRIVE IT HOME (See Protrudi, Link) (Jaymen & Link Protrudi).

Jayston, Michael

DEATH OF AN EXPERT WITNESS (See under P.D. James).

Jaywalkers

CAN CAN '62 (see under Jay, Peter) (Jaywalkers with Peter Jay).

Jazz

20 GREAT BIG BAND HITS (Various artists).
MC: 40190

25 GEANTS DU PIANO JAZZ (Various artists).
2LP: 400064

27 CLASSIC JAZZ MASTERS (Various artists).
LP: 4651921
MC: 4651924

100 MINUTES OF TRAD JAZZ (Various artists).
MC: . . . . ZCTON 8172

ACID JAZZ JAZZ (Various artists).
LP: . . . . JAZIDLP 038

ALL STAR JAZZ SHOW (Mahogany Hall Stomp) (Various artists).
Tracks: / Apple honey: *Various artists* / Mahogany hall stomp: *Various artists* / Blueberry hill: *Various* artists / Foggy day: *Various artists* / I want to be happy: *Various artists* / Preacher, The: *Various artists.*
LP: . . . . JASM 2530
MC: . . . . JASMC 2530

ALL STAR JAZZ SHOW (Rockin' In Rhythm) (Various artists).
LP: . . . . SG 8017

ALL STAR JAZZ SHOW (Various artists).
LP: . . . . SG 8005

ALL STAR JAZZ SHOW, NO 3 (I Love Jazz) (Various artists).
LP: . . . . SG 8011

ALL STAR SAX SPECTACULAR (Various artists).
LP: . . . . PRO 7019

ALL STAR SWING (Various artists).
2LP: . . . . WL 70533

ALL STAR TROMBONE SPECTACULAR (Various artists).
LP: . . . . PRO 7018

ALL STAR TRUMPET SPECTACULAR (Various artists).
LP: . . . . PRO 7015

ALL STAR'S AT NEWPORT (Various artists).
LP: 2304 369

ALL STARS EUROPEAN CONCERT (Various artists).
LP: . . . . UJ 28

ALL STAR'S VOL 1 (Various artists).
MC: . . . . GL 1961
LP: . . . . BSLP 8803

ALL STAR'S VOL 2 (Various artists).
MC: . . . . GL 1962

ALL THAT TRAD (Various artists).
MCSET: . . . . DTO 10050

ALL THAT'S JAZZ/JUBILEE JAZZ (Various artists).
MC: . . . . BARX-SAM 001

AMERICAN JAZZ SERIES 11 (Various artists).
MC: 043

AMERICAN JAZZ SERIES 12 (Various artists).
MC: 048

AMERICAN JAZZ SERIES 13 (Various artists).
MC: 050

AMERICANS IN EUROPE VOL.1 (Various artists).
Tracks: / No smokin': *Kenny Clarke Trio* / Low life: *Idries Sulieman Quartet* / I can't get started: *Various artists* / Freeway: *Smith, Bill Quintet* / Pyramid: *Powell, Bud Trio* / Round midnight: *Various artists.*
LP: . . . . JAS 64

AMERICANS IN EUROPE VOL.2 (Various artists).
Tracks: / My buddy run rabbits: *Various artists* / My daughter how are you: *Various artists* / Rose room: *Various* artists / Wine, whiskey and gin head woman: *Various artists* / Lots of talk for you: *Various artists* / All things you are: *Various artists* / I remember Clifford: *Various artists.*
LP: . . . . JAS 65
LP: . . . . TAX 8035

ARRANGERS, THE - RCA VICTOR JAZZ WORKSHOP (Various artists).
Tracks: / Blues for Pablo: *McKusick, Hal* / Jambangle: *McKusick, Hal* / Miss Clara: *McKusick, Hal* / Day John Brown was hanged, The: *McKusick, Hal* / Lydian lullaby: *McKusick, Hal* / Honeysuckle rose: *Carisi, John* / Springsville: *Carisi, John* / Israel: *Carisi, John* / Lestorian mode: *Carisi, John* / Barry's tune: *Carisi, John* / How about you: *Carisi, John* / Hip's: *Carisi, John* / Vera Cruz: *Levitt, Rod* Orchestra / Holler no.3: *Levitt, Rod Orchestra* / Morning in Montevideo: *Levitt, Rod Orchestra* / Green up: *Levitt, Rod Orchestra* / Mr. Barrelhouse: *Levitt, Rod Orchestra.*
LP: . . . . NL 86471
MC: . . . . NK 86471

AT PEPPER'S LOUNGE, CHICAGO VOL.2 (Various artists).
Tracks: / Off the wall: *Various artists* / Pepper's other thing: *Various artists* / You're so fine: *Various* artists / Rocker: *Various artists* / Pepper's boogie woogie: *Various artists* / How long can this thing go on?: *Various artists* / These ole cotton pickin' blues: *Various artists* / Left me alone: *Various artists/* Everyday I have the blues: *Various artists* / Dynamite: *Various artists.*
LP: . . . . RARITIES 28

AT THE JAZZ BAND BALL-CHICAGO/ NEW YORK DIXIELAND (Various artists).
Tracks: / I'm gonna stomp Mr Henry Lee: *Condon, Eddie* / That's serious thing: *Condon, Eddie* / Big butter and egg man: *Spanier, Muggsy & His Ragtime Band* / Someday, sweetheart: *Spanier, Muggsy & His Ragtime Band* / Eccentric (that eccentric rag): *Spanier, Muggsy & His Ragtime Band* / That da da strain: *Spanier, Muggsy & His Ragtime Band/* At the Jazz Band Ball: *Spanier, Muggsy & His Ragtimers* / I wish I could shimmy like my sister Kate: *Spanier, Muggsy* & His Ragtime Band / Dippermouth blues: *Spanier, Muggsy & His Ragtime Band* / Livery stable blues: *Spanier, Muggsy* & His Ragtime Band / Riverboat shuffle: *Spanier, Muggsy & His Ragtime Band* / Relaxin' at the Touro: *Spanier,* Muggsy & His Ragtime Band / At sundown: *Spanier, Muggsy & His Ragtime Band* / Blu'in the blues: *Spanier, Muggsy* & His Ragtime Band / Lonesome road: *Spanier, Muggsy & His Ragtime Band* / Dinah: *Spanier, Muggsy & His Ragtime* Band / (What did I do to be so) black and blue: *Spanier, Muggsy & His Ragtime Band* / Mandy, make up your mind: *Spanier,* Muggsy & His Ragtime Band / I've found a new baby: *Freeman, Bud* / Easy to get: *Freeman, Bud* / China boy: *Freeman, Bud* / Eel, The: *Freeman, Bud.*
LP: . . . . NL 86752
MC: . . . . NK 86752

AT THE SWING SHOP (Various artists).
Tracks: / My guy's come back: *Loss, Joe & His Orchestra* / Fan it: *Loss, Joe & His Orchestra* / In Pinetop's footsteps: *Loss, Joe & His Orchestra* / Southern fried: *Loss, Joe & His Orchestra* / Oasis: *Loss, Joe & His Orchestra/* Painted rhythm: *Rabin, Oscar & His Band* / Hamp's boogie woogie: *Rabin, Oscar & His Band* / Shine: *Rabin,* Oscar & His Band / Basin Street blues march: *Rabin, Oscar & His Band* / Leave us leap: *Rabin, Oscar & His Band/* Rotten row: *Rabin, Oscar & His Band* / Washington whirligig: *Rabin, Oscar & His Band* / Eager beaver: *Geraldo* & His Orchestra / Box one five five: *Geraldo & His Orchestra* / Taps Miller: *Geraldo & His Orchestra* / Deed I do: *Geraldo & His Orchestra* / Boston bounce: *Leader, Harry & His Orchestra* / Southpaw special: *Leader,* Harry & His Orchestra / Neighbours complain, The: *Skyrockets Orchestra* / Boogie in C: *Skyrockets Orchestra/* Bayswater bustle: *Skyrockets Orchestra* / Overnight hop: *Roy, Harry & His Band* / Bobby sock bounce: *Roy,* Harry & His Band / tuxedo junction: *Gonella, Nat & His New Georgians* / At the woodchopper's ball: *Gonella, Nat* & His New Georgians / In the mood: *Gonella, Nat & His New Georgians* / Two moods: *Mairants, Ivor/ Geraldo & His Swing Orchestra* / In Charlies footsteps: *Mairants, Ivor/ Geraldo & His Swing Orchestra.*
2LP: . . . . DL 1188
MC: . . . . TCDL 1188

ATLANTIC JAZZ RECORDINGS (See under Atlantic (label)) (Various artists).

BEST OF BGP (Various artists).
LP: . . . . BGP 1030

BEST OF BIG BANDS (Various artists).
LP: 33013
MC: 63013

BEST OF BLUE NOTE VOL 1 (Various artists).
Tracks: / Un poco loco: *Powell, Bud* / Tin tin deo: *Moody, James* / Criss cross: *Monk, Thelonious* / Bag's Groove: *Various artists* / Cherokee: *Brown, Clifford* / Tempus fugit: *Davis, Miles* / Blue train: *Coltrane, John* / Maiden voyage: *Hancock, Herbie* / Cristo redentor: *Byrd, Donald* / Moanin': *Blakey,* Art / Blues walk: *Donaldson, Lou* / Song for my father: *Silver, Horace* / Back to the chicken shack: *Smith, Jimmy (USA)* / Chitlins con carne: *Burrell, Kenny* / Sidewinder, The: *Morgan, Lee.*
2LP: BST2 84429
MC: . . . . TCBST 844291

BEST OF BLUE NOTE VOL 2 (Various artists).
Tracks: / Blue Harlem: *Quebec, Ike* / Our delight: *Dameron, Tadd* / Round midnight: *Monk, Thelonious/* Gears, The: *Melle, Gil* / Collard greens and black-eyed peas: *Powell, Bud* / Senor blues: *Silver, Horace/* Brownie speaks: *Brown, Clifford* / Three o'clock in the morning: *Gordon, Dexter* / Lou's blues: *Donaldson,* Lou / Blues march: *Blakey, Art* / Wadin': *Parlan, Horace* / Rumproller, The: *Morgan, Lee* / Something else: *Adderley, Julian Cannonball & Nat Adderley* / Blues bossa: *Henderson, Joe* / Watermelon man: *Hancock, Herbie* / Decision: *Rollins, Sonny.*
2LP: BST2 84433
MC: . . . . TCBST 844292

BEST OF BRITISH (3) (Featuring Stone Fox, Noble etc) (Various artists).
LP: . . . . OLM 1

BEST OF BRITISH JAZZ (Various artists).
Tracks: / Moanin' at Minden: *Various artists* / Strutting with some barbeque: *Various artists* / Mean to me: *Various* artists / Sonny boy: *Various artists* / Exactly like you: *Various artists* / Pretty girl is like a melody: *Various artists* / Maybe it's because I'm a Londoner: *Various artists* / It don't mean a thing: *Various artists.*
LP: . . . . ALM 4001

BEST OF DANCE BAND DAYS VOL. 1 (Various artists).
Tracks: / Moonlight serenade: *Various artists* / Clarinade: *Various artists* / Jumpin' at the woodside: *Various* artists / Sweet Georgia Brown: *Various artists* / Stars fell on Alabama: *Various artists* / Angry: *Various* artists / Stardust: *Various artists* / Song of India: *Various artists* / Caldonia: *Various artists/* Airmail stomp: *Various artists* / Rockin' in rhythm: *Various artists* / Bei mir bist du schon: *Various artists/* Little brown jug: *Various artists* / Don't be that way: *Various artists* / Tweet tweet: *Various artists/* Button up your overcoat: *Various artists* / Some people: *Various artists* / 'S wonderful: *Various artists/* Opus one: *Various artists* / At the woodchoppers ball: *Various artists* / Blue moon: *Various artists/* I got a girl named Netty: *Various artists.*
LP: . . . . DBD 20
MC: . . . . DBDC 20

BEST OF DANCE BAND DAYS VOL. 2 (Various artists).
Tracks: / Symphony: *Various artists* / King Porter stomp: *Various artists* / Rockin' in rhythm: *Various artists/* I'll be seeing you: *Various artists* / Down the road apiece: *Various artists* / Man with a horn: *Various* artists / Begin the beguine: *Various artists* / Cheek to cheek: *Various artists* / There, I've said it again: *Various artists* / Everybody eats when they come to my house: *Various artists* / Newport up: *Various artists/* Lullaby of Broadway: *Various artists* / Seven-o-five: *Various artists* / All the cats join in: *Various artists/* King size blues: *Various artists* / Fare thee well to Harlem: *Various artists* / Bedford drive: *Various* artists / Blue skies: *Various artists* / Goosey gander: *Various artists* / Cruisin' with cab: *Various artists* / St. Louis blues: *Various artists* / Rum and coca cola: *Various artists.*
LP: . . . . DBD 21
MC: . . . . DBDC 21

BEST OF DIXIELAND (Various artists).
Tracks: / Rockin' chair: *Armstrong, Louis & His Orchestra* / Tiger rag: *Murphy, Turk & His San Francisco Jazz Band/* I wish I could shimmy like my sister Kate: *Spanier, Muggsy & His Ragtime Band* / High society: *Bourbon Street All Stars* / St. James infirmary: *Allen, Henry 'Red'* / When the saints go marching in: *Johnson, Bunk & His New Orleans* Jazz Band / Tin roof blues: *Dukes Of Dixieland* / Mississippi mud: *Scobey, Bob's Frisco Jazz Band* / Oh didn't he ramble: *Kelly, Pete & His Big Seven* / South Rampart Street parade: *McPartland & His Dixielanders* / Milenberg joys: *Almerico, Tony Allstars* / Livery stable blues: *Original Dixieland Jazz Band.*
LP: 26.21745
LP: . . . . NL 81431
MC: . . . . NK 81431

BEST OF DIXIELAND (Compact/ Walkman Jazz) (Various artists).
Tracks: / Loveless love: *Ory, Kid & His Creole Jazz Band* / Beale Street blues: *Lewis, George & His Jazzband/* Someday you'll be sorry: *Armstrong, Louis/Allstars* / Canal Street blues: *Allen, Henry 'Red' & his Orchestra/* Eccentric rag: *Kaminsky, Max & His All Star Dixieland Band* / St. Louis blues: *Condon, Eddie & His Band* / Basin Street blues: *Teagarden, Jack & His Orchestra* / Eh-la-bas: *Original Tuxedo Jazz Orchestra* / Over in the glory hand: *Dejan's Olympia Brass Band* / Ballin' the jack: *Colyer, Ken* / Hindustan: *Welsh, Alex & His Jazz Band/* Saturday night function: *Sunshine, Monty Jazz Band* / Perdido Street blues: *Bilk, Acker & His Paramount Jazz Band/* Savoy blues: *Lightfoot, Terry* / Stevedore stomp: *Barber, Chris Jazzband* / Christoper Columbus: *Lyttelton, Humphrey & His Band.*
MC: 831 375 4

BEST OF DIXIELAND VOL 2 (Various artists).

Tracks: / China boy: *Various artists* / Over in the gloryland: *Various artists* / Solitairess: *Various artists*/ Shimme-sha-wabble: *Various artists* / Albatross: *Various artists* / Ballin' the jack: *Various artists*/ Yama yama man: *Various artists* / Sunshine of your blues, The: *Various artists* / Blues my naughty sweetie gives to me: *Various artists* / Oh didn't he ramble: *Various artists* / Ole miss rag: *Various artists* / St Louis blues: *Various artists* / Riverboat shuffle: *Various artists* / Come back sweet papa: *Various artists*/ Lead me saviour: *Various artists* / Ida, sweet as apple cider: *Various artists* / Big Bill blues: *Various artists* / World is waiting for the sunrise, The: *Various artists.*
MC: **838 347-4**

BEST OF I LOVE JAZZ (Various artists).
LP: . . . . **CBS 21120**
MC: **40 21120**

BEST OF JAZZ MUSIC TODAY (Various artists).
Tracks: / Love phases of dimensions: *Various artists* / In the year of the dragon: *Various artists* / Comin' home: *Various artists* / At risk: *Various artists* / Josy: *Various artists* / I'll wind: *Various artists*/ Perpetual groove: *Various artists* / Now then: *Various artists* / Enchantment: *Various artists* / Just ideas: *Various artists* / I didn't know what time it was: *Various artists.*
LP: **8344381**
MC: **8344384**

BEST OF JAZZ ORGANS (Various artists).
MC: . . . . **MC 9006**

BEST OF JAZZ PIANOS (Various artists).
Tracks: / Autumn leaves: *Various artists* / Time remembered: *Various artists* / No problem: *Various artists*/ Miguel's party: *Various artists* / St. Louis blues: *Various artists* / Three little words: *Various artists*/ Light blue: *Various artists* / Sundance: *Various artists.*
MC: . . . . **MC 8519**

BEST OF JAZZ SAXOPHONES (Various artists).
Tracks: / All God's chillun got rhythm: *Various artists* / Dear old Stockholm: *Various artists* / Jeru: *Various artists* / Rose room: *Various artists* / Sommerset: *Various artists* / Honeysuckle Rose: *Various artists*/ Outside, looking in: *Various artists* / Leapin' on Lenox: *Various artists* / My little suede shoes: *Various artists* / Back home again in Indiana: *Various artists.*
MC: **MC-8520**

BEST OF JAZZ SAXOPHONES VOL.3 (Various artists).
MC: . . . . **MC 9009**

BEST OF JAZZ SINGERS (Various artists).
Tracks: / Lover come back to me: *Various artists* / Angel eyes: *Various artists* / I'm beginning to see the light: *Various artists* / My heart belongs to Daddy: *Various artists* / Just one of those things: *Various artists*/ I can't give you anything but love, baby: *Various artists* / Sophisticated lady: *Various artists* / Good enough to keep: *Various artists* / Embraceable you: *Various artists* / Scat blues: *Various artists* / Inside a silent tear: *Various artists* / Imagination: *Various artists* / Exactly like you: *Various artists* / Fine brown frame: *Various artists* / Country man: *Various artists*/ Cry me a river: *Various artists.*
MC: **MC-8517**

BEST OF JAZZ SINGERS VOLUME 2 (Various artists).
MC: . . . . **MC 9008**

BEST OF JAZZ TRUMPETS (Various artists).
Tracks: / Milestones: *Various artists* / More on the same: *Various artists* / Kush: *Various artists*/ Theme: *Various artists* / Blues for Duane: *Various artists* / Blueberry Hill: *Various artists* / When it's sleepy time down South: *Various artists* / St. James infirmary: *Various artists* / Got the spirit: *Various artists.*
MC: **MC-8516**

BEST OF ONYX (Various artists).
LP: . . . . **RELIC 5005**

BEST OF THE BIG BANDS (Various artists).
Tracks: / Stealin' apples: *Goodman, Benny* / April in Paris: *Basie, Count* / Drum boogie: *Krupa, Gene*/ Midnight sun, The: *Hampton, Lionel* / Two o'clock jump: *James, Harry* / Claxton Hall swing: *Bellson, Louis*/ Caldonia: *Herman, Woody.*
MC: **833 281-4**

BEST OF THE BIG BANDS (Various artists).
Tracks: / Swing that music: *Various artists* / Woodchoppers ball: *Herman, Woody & His Orchestra* / I'm getting sentimental over you: *Dorsey, Tommy* / One o'clock jump: *Basie, Count* / Dorsey dervish: *Dorsey, Jimmy*/ I get a kick out of you: *Shaw, Artie* / East St. Louis toodle-oo: *Ellington, Duke* / Black and tan fantasy: *Ellington, Duke* / Stompin' at the Savoy: *Goodman, Benny (duplicate)* / Flying home: *Hampton, Lionel* / Moonlight Bay: *Miller, Glenn* / Fidgety feet: *Henderson, Fletcher* / Rosetta: *Hines, Earl* / Blues in the night: *Lunceford, Jimmie* / Tisket a tasket, A: *Webb, Chick* / Undecided: *Webb, Chick.*
LP: . . . . **MCL 1861**
MC: . . . . **MCLC 1861**

BEST OF THE BIG BANDS (Various artists).
Tracks: / Let's dance: *Various artists* / King Porter stomp: *Various artists* / Don't be that way: *Various artists* / Jumpin' at the Woodside: *Various artists* / Way out Basie: *Various artists* / Whirly bird: *Various* artists / Three day sucker: *Various artists* / At the woodchoppers ball: *Various artists* / Northwest Passage: *Various artists* / Flyin' home: *Various artists* / Take the 'A' train: *Various artists* / Rockin' in rhythm: *Various artists* / Hawk talks, The: *Various artists* / Killer Joe: *Various artists* / Cotton Club stomp: *Ellington, Duke and Ella Fitzgerald.*
MC: . . . . **MC 8518**

BEST OF THE BIG DANCE BANDS (Various artists).
MC: . . . . **MC 9010**

BEST OF THE SWEET BANDS (Various artists).
LP: . . . . **HUK 312**

BIG BAND BEAT (Various artists).
Tracks: / Hawk talks, The: *Parnell, Jack & his Orchestra* / Fanfare boogie: *Parnell, Jack & his Orchestra* / Skin deep: *Parnell, Jack & his Orchestra* / Trip to Mars: *Parnell, Jack & his Orchestra* / Sky blue shirt and a rainbow tie: *Parnell, Jack & his Orchestra* / Champ, The: *Parnell, Jack & his Orchestra* / Bedtime for drums: *Ainsworth,* Alyn Orchestra / If I had you: *Ainsworth, Alyn Orchestra* / Cobblers song, The: *Ainsworth, Alyn Orchestra*/ Buckingham brownies: *Ainsworth, Alyn Orchestra* / Hells bells: *Ainsworth, Alyn/Rock-A-Fellas* / 18th century rock: *Ainsworth, Alyn/Rock-A-Fellas* / Moon was yellow, The: *Watt, Tommy & Orchestra* / Five foot two, eyes of blue: *Watt, Tommy & Orchestra* / Poor little rich girl: *Watt, Tommy & Orchestra* / Won't you come home Bill Bailey: *Watt, Tommy & Orchestra* / I'll string along with you: *Watt, Tommy & Orchestra* / Creep, The: *Mackintosh,* Ken & His Orchestra / Monster, The: *Mackintosh, Ken & His Orchestra* / Air express: *Mackintosh, Ken & His Orchestra*/ Glow worm: *Mackintosh, Ken & His Orchestra* / Berkeley hunt, The: *Mackintosh, Ken & His Orchestra* / Creeping Tom: *Mackintosh, Ken & His Orchestra* / Policeman's holiday, The: *Mackintosh, Ken & His Orchestra.*
2LP: . . . . **DL 1161**
MC: . . . . **TCDL 1161**

BIG BAND BONANZA (Various artists).
MCSET: . . . . **DTO 10221**

BIG BAND BOOGIE, 1938 - 42 (Various artists).
LP: . . . . **BS 7107**
MC: . . . . **BS 7107C**

BIG BAND CLASSICS (1940s-60s) (Various artists).
LP: . . . . **MOIR 508**
MC: . . . . **CMOIR 508**

BIG BAND CLASSICS (Various artists).
Tracks: / In the mood: *Miller, Glenn* / Little brown jug: *Miller, Glenn* / American patrol: *Miller, Glenn*/ Moonlight serenade: *Miller, Glenn* / Tuxedo junction: *Miller, Glenn* / Pennsylvania 6-5000: *Miller, Glenn*/ String of pearls: *Miller, Glenn* / Take the 'A' train: *Ellington, Duke* / Perdido: *Ellington, Duke*/ Creole love call: *Ellington, Duke* / Black and tan fantasy: *Ellington, Duke* / Mood indigo: *Ellington, Duke*/ Caravan: *Ellington, Duke* / Solitude: *Ellington, Duke* / Stompin' at the Savoy: *Goodman, Benny* / Avalon: *Goodman, Benny* / King Porter stomp: *Goodman, Benny* / Moonglow: *Goodman, Benny* / One o' clock jump: *Goodman, Benny* / And the angels sing: *Goodman, Benny* / Sing sing sing: *Goodman, Benny* / Pinetop boogie: *Dorsey, Tommy* / Night and day: *Dorsey, Tommy* / After you've gone: *Dorsey, Tommy* / Song of India: *Dorsey,* Tommy / Blue skies: *Dorsey, Tommy* / I'm getting sentimental over you: *Dorsey, Tommy* / Marie: *Dorsey, Tommy.*
2LP: . . . . **KAZLP 106**
MC: . . . . **KAZMC 106**

BIG BAND CLASSICS (Various artists).
LP: . . . . **STAR 2004**
MC: . . . . **STAC 2004**

BIG BAND CLASSICS 1957-58 (Various artists).
2LP: . . . . **DRLP 139/40**

BIG BAND JAZZ (Various artists).
LP: . . . . **GAPS 160**

BIG BAND JAZZ VOL.1 (Various artists).
Tracks: / How deep is your love: *Various artists* / Eubie's boogie: *Various artists* / All stops: *Various* artists / Lovely day: *Various artists* / Easy living: *Various artists* / How's this for choosers: *Various artists.*
LP: . . . . **MAN 5011**

BIG BAND VOL. 1 (Various artists).
LP: . . . . **VDL 1001**

BIG BAND VOL. 2 (Various artists).
LP: . . . . **VDL 1002**

BIG BAND VOL. 5 (Various artists).
LP: . . . . **SM 3951**

BIG BANDS ARE BACK VOL.2 (Various artists).
Tracks: / American patrol: *Miller, Glenn* / Kid from red band: *Basie Big Band* / East of the sun: *Teagarden, Jack* / Song of India: *Dorsey* / Tuning up: *Krupa, Gene* / Deep Purple: *Ellington, Duke.*
MC: . . . . **CONE 7**

BIG BANDS COLLECTOR'S SERIES (Various artists).
MC: . . . . **G 9010**

BIG BANDS FROM THE SWING ERA (Various artists).
Tracks: / Pigeon talk: *Beneke, Tex Orchestra* / Carioca: *Beneke, Tex Orchestra* / Lover's leap: *Beneke, Tex* Orchestra / By heck: *Webb, Chick* / I've got a right to sing the blues: *Teagarden, Jack Orchestra* / Pagan love call: *Crosby, Bob & His Bobcats* / Blue moon: *Crosby, Bob Orchestra* / Loveless love: *Hopkins, Claude* Orchestra / Old Kentucky home: *Rhythm Makers* / In the bottom: *Rhythm Makers* / Stompin' at The Savoy: *Brooks,* Randy & His Orchestra / Moonglow: *Brooks, Randy & His Orchestra* / Jimmy Cricket: *Savitte, Jan Orchestra*/ Margie: *Savitte, Jan Orchestra.*
LP: . . . . **BLJ 8009**

BIG BANDS MEET BOOGIE WOOGIE (Various artists).
LP: . . . . **SM 4086**

BIG BANDS OF THE 40'S (Various artists).
2LP: . . . . **RFLD 42**

BIG BANDS ON THE AIR, 1938-46 (Various artists).
Tracks: / There'll be some changes made: *Goodman, Benny* / Gotta be this or that: *Gray, Glen* / Together: *Dorsey,* Jimmy / Cotton pickers' congregation: *Morgan, Russ* / Tiger rag: *Miller, Glenn* / In an 18th century drawing room: *Rey, Alvino* / Kickapoo joy juice jolt: *Rey, Alvino* / Stompin' at the Savoy: *Henderson, Fletcher*/ You're a lucky guy: *Kemp, Hal* / Just an angel in disguise: *Ayres, Mitchell* / Boogie woogie lullaby: *Fio Rito, Ted.*
LP: . . . . **SOL 505**

BIRD'S NIGHT: A CELEBRATION OF THE MUSIC OF CHAR (Various artists).
LP: . . . . **SJL 2257**

BIRD'S NIGHT: A CELEBRATION OF THE MUSIC OF CHARLIE PARKER (see under Parker, Charlie) (Various artists).

BIX LIVES (See under Beiderbecke, Bix) (Various artists).

BLACK CALIFORNIA (Various artists).
Tracks: / Backbreaker: *Various artists* / Laguna: *Various artists* / Boogin' at Berg's: *Various artists*/ Dunkin' bagel: *Various artists* / Pete's beat: *Various artists* / Sippin' with cisco: *Various artists*/ This is you: *Various artists* / Gassin' the wig: *Various artists* / Phantom moon: *Various artists* / Howard's idea: *Various artists* / Love is laughing at me: *Various artists* / Little wig: *Various artists*/ Helen's advice: *Various artists* / Airplane blues: *Various artists* / Knockin' myself out: *Various artists*/ Ain't gonna quit you baby: *Various artists* / Outlandish: *Various artists* / Swingin' on Savoy: *Various* artists / San Diego bounce: *Various artists* / I'll remember April: *Various artists* / Brown gold: *Various* artists / These foolish things: *Various artists* / Surf ride: *Various artists* / Holiday flight: *Various* artists / Jumpin' Jacque: *Various artists* / Don't get around much anymore: *Various artists* / It's you or no one: *Various artists* / Thou swell: *Various artists.*
LP: . . . . **SJL 2215**

BLUE BOP (Various artists).
Tracks: / Dem tambourines: *Wilkerson, Don* / True blue: *Brooks, Tina* / Jeannie: *Byrd, Donald* / So tired: *Blakey, Art* / Nica's dream: *Silver, Horace* / Happy Johnny: *Wilkerson, Don.*
LP: . . . . **BNSLP 2**
MC: . . . . **TCBNSLP 2**

BLUE BOSSA (Latin for Beginners) (Various artists).
Tracks: / Congalegre: *Parlan, Horace* / Latona: *Patton, Big John* / Back down to the tropics: *Rouse, Charlie*/ Sandalia dela: *Pearson, Duke* / Afrodisia: *Dorham, Kenny* (MONO track) / Mambo Inn: *Green, Grant* / Cape Verdean blues, The: *Silver, Horace* / You're everything: *McRae, Carmen.*
LP: . . . . **BNSLP 1**
MC: . . . . **TCBNSLP 1**

BLUE BOSSA (2) (Cool Cuts from the Tropics) (Various artists).
Tracks: / Congalegre: *Parlan, Horace* / Back down to the Tropics: *Rouse, Charlie* / Latona: *Patton, Big John*/ Sandalia dela: *Pearson, Duke* / Loie: *Quebec, Ike* / Sambop: *Adderley, Cannonball* / Afrodisia: *Dorham,* Kenny / Mambo Inn: *Green, Grant* / Cape Verdean blues, The: *Silver, Horace* / Waters of march agua de beber: *Elias, Eliane* / Mira: *Hill, Andrew* / Recado bossa nova: *Mobley, Hank* / South of the border: *Donaldson, Lou* / Ghana: *Byrd, Donald.*
MC: **B4 95590**

BLUE BOSSA II (Various artists).
Tracks: / Recado bossa nova: *Mobley, Hank* / Samba de Orfeu: *Rouse, Charlie* / Mira: *Hill, Andrew* / Stormy: *Pearson, Duke* / South of the border: *Donaldson, Lou* / Brazil: *Green, Grant* / Ghana: *Byrd, Donald* / Old devil moon: *Johnson, J J.*
LP: . . . . **BNSLP 4**
MC: . . . . **TC-BNSLP 4**

BLUE NOTE 50TH ANNIVERSARY SET (Various artists).
LPS: **B1 92547**

BLUE NOTE '86 (Various artists).
LP: . . . . **BQ 85127**

BLUE NOTE SAMPLER VOL.2 (Various artists).
Tracks: / Better days: *Reeves, Dianne* / Timothee: *Lagrene, Bireli* / Ally the wallygator: *Smith, Tommy*/ Eleanor Rigby: *Jordan, Stanley* / Thinkin' about your body: *McFerrin, Bobby* / Two's and fews: *Ammons, Albert* & Meade Lux Lewis / Donna: *Davis, Miles* / Glass enclosure: *Powell, Bud* / Alligator boogaloo: *Donaldson, Lou* / Song for my father: *Silver, Horace.*
LP: . . . . **BNX 2**
MC: . . . . **TCBNX 2**

BLUE NOTE SAMPLER VOL.3 (Various artists).
LP: . . . . **BLP 0021**

BLUE NOTE SAMPLER VOL. 1 (Various artists).
Tracks: / Blowin' the blues away: *Silver, Horace* / Blue riff: *Turrentine, Stanley* / Sermon: *Smith, Jimmy* (USA) / Minor's holiday: *Jazz Messengers* / I guess I'll hang my tears out to dry: *Gordon, Dexter* / Round midnight: *Various artists* / Callin' all cats: *Donaldson, Lou* / Eye of the hurricane: *Various artists*/ Love for sale: *Adderley, Cannonball* / Dig dis: *Burrell, Kenny* / Midnight blue: *Burrell, Kenny* / Sidewinder, The: *Morgan, Lee* / Blowin' the blues away: *Silver, Horace* / Sermon, The: *Smith, Jimmy (USA)* / I guess I'll hang my tears out to dry: *Gordon, Dexter* / Round midnight: *Monk, Thelonious.*
LP: . . . . **BNX 1**
MC: . . . . **TCBNX 1**

BOP CITY: EVIDENCE (Various artists).
LP: . . . . **BOPM 12**

BOP CITY: MIDNIGHT (Various artists).
LP: . . . . **BOPM 9**

BOP CITY: STRAIGHT AHEAD (Various artists).
LP: . . . . **BOPM 10**

BOP CITY: THINGS ARE GETTING BETTER (Various artists).
LP: . . . . **BOPM 11**

BOP FATHERS IN PARIS (Various artists).
LP: . . . . **LOP 14 072**

BOP STOP ROCK (Various artists).
LP: . . . . **GCL 107**

BREAD & ROSES (Various artists).
Tracks: / I'm taking chances: *Various artists* / Devil: *Various artists* / Driving wheel: *Various artists*/ Tore up over you: *Various artists* / When will I be loved: *Various artists* / Basin Street blues: *Various* artists / Just an eagle stirs her nest: *Various artists* / Just a song before I go: *Various artists* / Military madness:

Various artists / Power: *Various artists* / Leeshore: *Various artists* / Lonesome house: *Various* artists / Blessing in disguise: *Various artists* / Married men: *Various artists* / Losing myself to you: *Various* artists / Bread and roses: *Various artists* / Acres of clams: *Various artists* / Lonesome valley: *Various artists* / This land is your land: *Various artists*.
2LP: F 79011
2LP: FTSP 57

BRITAIN'S GREATEST JAZZBAND (Various).
LP: IS RT 105

BRITISH BIG BAND ERA (1932-1937) (Various artists).
MC: NEO 948

BRITISH JAZZ AWARDS 1987 (Lyttelton, Williams, King, Morrissey, Green, Ta (Various artists).
LP: BEAR 27
MC: BEARMC 27

BRITISH TRADITIONAL JAZZ COLLECTIONS VOL.2 (See under Jazz ...) (Various artists).

BROTHERS & OTHER MOTHERS (Various artists).
Tracks: / Stan gets along: *Various artists* / Stan's mood: *Various artists* / Slow fast groovin' with Gus: *Various* artists / Infinity: *Various artists* / Let's get away from it all: *Various artists* / Pumpernickel: *Various* artists / Gabardine and Serge: *Various artists* / Bar a second, A: *Various artists* / Blue brew brew blue: *Various artists* / More brew: *Various artists* / No more brew: *Various artists* / Rampage: *Various* artists / Vot's dot: *Various artists* / Booby hatch: *Various artists* / Symphony Sid's idea: *Various* artists / All night all frantic: *Various* artists / Donald Jay: *Various artists* / Meeskite: *Various artists* / And that's for sure: *Various artists*.
LP: SJL 2210

BRUNSWICK HOT DANCE 1921-1925 (Various artists).
MC: NEO 952

CALLE STRADA STRAUSSE (Various artists).
MC: GVMMC 402

CATALYST (Various).
LP: MR 5170

CELEBRATION OF DUKE (Various artists).
Tracks: / Caravan: *Quadrant* / Happy-go-lucky local: *Terry, Clark* / Tonight I shall sleep: *Sims, Zoot*/ I ain't got nothin' but the blues: *Vaughan, Sarah* / Come Sunday: *Terry, Clark* / Everything but you: *Vaughan*, Sarah / Take the 'A' train: *Quadrant* / Rockin' in rhythm: *Sims, Zoot* / Echoes of Harlem: *Terry, Clark*/ Main stem: *Quadrant*.
LP: 2312 119
MC: K 12 119

CHANGING FACE OF HARLEM (Various artists).
Tracks: / I got what it takes: *Various artists* / Good for stompin': *Various artists* / I'll always love you just the same: *Various artists* / Romance without finance: *Various artists* / Bye bye: *Various artists* / My lucky day: *Various artists* / Groovin' the blues: *Various artists* / Smack that mess: *Various artists*/ Dee Dee's dance: *Various artists* / Little Bennie: *Various artists* / Shoot the arrow to me cupid: *Various artists*.
LP: SJL 2208

CHANGING FACE OF HARLEM VOL.2 (Various artists).
LP: SJL 2224

CHESKY JAZZ SAMPLER (See under Chesky (label)) (Various artists).

CHICAGO (Various artists).
2LP: PM 43267

CHICAGO AND ALL THAT JAZZ (Various artists).
LP: SG 8007

CHICAGO ERA, THE (Various artists).
2LP: 400035

CHICAGO JAZZ 1928-33 (Various artists).
Tracks: / There'll be some changes made: *Chicago Rhythm Kings* / I've found a new baby: *Chicago Rhythm Kings*/ Baby won't you please come home?: *Chicago Rhythm Kings* / Jazz me blues: *Various artists* / Trying to stop me crying: *Manone, Joe 'Wingy' & Club Royal Orchestra* / Isn't there a little love?: *Manone, Joe 'Wingy' & Club Royal* Orchestra / Eel, The: *Condon, Eddie & His Orchestra* / Copenhagen: *Schoebel, Elmer & Friars Society Orchestra*/ Prince of wails: *Schoebel, Elmer & Friars Society Orchestra* / Milenberg joys: *O'Hare, Husk & Wolverines* / My daddy rocks me: *O'Hare, Husk & Wolverines* / Wailing blues takes A & B: *Cellar Boys* / Barrel house stomp ABC: *Cellar Boys*.
LP: S 809

CHICAGO JAZZ VOL.2 (Russell's Hot Six) (Various artists).
LP: CJM 40

CHICAGO JUMP (Various artists).
LP: JSP 1004

CLANDESTINE RECORDINGS OF THE... (...Frankfurt Hot Club 1941-1944) (Various artists).
Tracks: / Bugle call rag: *Various artists* / Stomp: *Various artists* / Blues: *Various artists* / Margie: *Various artists* / Sheik of Araby, The: *Various artists* / Honeysuckle rose: *Various artists* / I can't give you...: *Various artists* / Undecided: *Various artists* / I've found a new baby: *Various artists*/ On the sunny side of the street: *Various artists* / My blue Heaven: *Various artists* / Sweet Sue: *Various artists* / Lady be good: *Various artists*.
LP: HQ 2051

CLARINET JAZZ GIANTS (Golden hour) (Various artists).
LP: GH 649

CLARINET JAZZ GIANTS (SET) (Various artists).
MCSET: DTO 10227

CLARINET PLAYING LEADERS (Various artists).
LP: GELP 15078

CLARINET SUMMIT LIVE (You better fly away) (Various artists).
LP: MPS 68 251

CLASSIC JAZZ PIANO (1927-1957) (Various artists).
Tracks: / Mr. Jelly Lord: *Morton, Jelly Roll* / Glad rag doll: *Hines, Earl* / State Street special: *Yancey, Jimmy* / Honky tonk train blues: *Lewis, Meade Lux* / Thou swell: *Johnson, James P.* / Rompin': *Johnson*, James P. / Smashing thirds: *Waller, Fats* / Contrary motions: *Smith, Willie the Lion* / Out of nowhere: *Tatum*, Art / Where or when: *Wilson, Teddy* / Daybreak serenade: *Stacy, Jess* / Rosetta: *Hines, Earl* / Honeysuckle rose: *Waller, Fats* / Solitude: *Ellington, Duke* / Tonk: *Ellington, Duke & Billy Strayhorn* / Shine on, harvest moon: *Basie, Count* / All God's chillun got rhythm: *Williams, Mary Lou* / Erroll's bounce: *Garner*, Erroll / Poor butterfly: *Peterson, Oscar* / I don't stand a ghost of a chance with you: *Tristano, Lennie*/ Shaw 'nuff: *Powell, Bud* / Concerto for Billy the Kid: *Evans, Bill*.
LP: NL 86754
MC: NK 86754

CLASSIC JAZZ TO SWING (Various artists).
Tracks: / That's my home: *Armstrong, Louis* / West end blues: *Oliver, King* / Snag it: *Johnson, Bunk*/ Everybody loves my baby: *Ladnier, Tommy* / Tip easy blues: *Collins, Lee* / Feeling drowsy: *Allen, Henry 'Red'* / Nobody knows the way I feel this morning: *De Paris, Sidney* / 'Sippi: *Smith, Jabbo* / Lonely melody: *Beiderbecke, Bix* / Davenport blues: *Nichols, Red* / Blues: *Berigan, Bunny* / (What did I do to be so) black and blue: *Spanier, Muggsy* / Jumpy nerves: *Manone, Wingy* / Shimme-sha-wabble: *Kaminsky, Max* / Peckin': *James, Harry* / Bublitchki: *Elman, Ziggy* / Concerto for Cootie (Do nothin' till you hear from me): *Williams, Cootie* / Subtle slough: *Stewart, Rex* / Little jazz: *Eldridge, Roy* / Skull duggery: *Page, Hot Lips*/ Blues my baby gave to me, The: *Newton, Frankie* / Buckin' the blues: *Clayton, Buck* / Mahogany hall stomp: *Armstrong, Louis*.
LP: NL 86753
MC: NK 86753

CLASSIC PIANOS (See under Garner, Erroll) (Various artists).

CLASSIC PIANOS (Various artists).
Tracks: / Blueberry rhyme: *Various artists* / Blues for Fats: *Various artists* / Honeysuckle rose: *Various* artists / Squeeze me: *Various artists* / My fate is in your hands: *Various artists* / I've got a feeling I'm falling: *Various artists* / I've found a new baby: *Various artists* / Four or five times: *Various artists*/ Yesterdays: *Various artists* / Loot to boot: *Various artists* / Gaslight, The: *Various artists*.
MC: ZCAS 802
LP: ASLP 802

CLASSIC RAGS AND NOSTALGIA (VOLUME 16) (Various artists).
LP: ESR 1216

CLASSIC SMALL GROUPS VOL.1 (Various artists).
LP: MERITT 6

CLASSIC TENORS VOLUME 2 (Various artists).
Tracks: / Lover come back to me: *Various artists* / Blues changes: *Various artists* / Hello babe (alternate take): *Various artists* / I'm for it too (alternate take): *Various artists* / Creamin': *Various artists* / My silent love: *Various artists* / Long moan: *Various artists* / Goin' along: *Various artists* / Lockjaw: *Various artists* / Afternoon in a doghouse: *Various artists* / Surgery: *Various artists* / Athlete's foot: *Various artists*.
LP: ASLP 808

COLLECTORS JACKPOT (Various artists).
LP: JA 21

COLLECTORS JACKPOT 2 (Various artists).
LP: JA 40

COMPLEAT KLEZMER - 78 EXCERPTS & MUSICAL INST. (Various artists).
MC: GVMMC SC 02

CONCERT AT CARNEGIE HALL (Various artists).
Tracks: / Tattooed bride, The: *Ellington, Duke* / I'm beginning to see the light: *Ellington, Duke* / Night in Tunisia, A: *Parker, Charlie & Dizzy Gillespie* / Strike up the band: *Getz, Stan* / Just friends: *Parker, Charlie*(With Charlie Parker.) / Easy to love: *Parker, Charlie* / Repetition: *Parker, Charlie* / 52nd Street theme: *Parker*, Charlie & Dizzy Gillespie / Body and soul: *Ellington, Duke* / Lover come back to me: *Holiday, Billie* / There will never be another you: *Getz, Stan*.
2LP: ATSD 2
MCSET: KATSD 2

CONCORD JAZZ GUITAR COLLECTION VOL 1 & 2 (Various artists).
Tracks: / La petite mambo: *Various artists* / Isn't this a lovely place: *Various artists* / Dolphin dance: *Various* artists / Zigeuner: *Various artists* / Prelude to a kiss: *Various artists* / I'm on my way: *Various artists*/ I can't get started: *Various artists* / Side track: *Various artists* / Georgia on my mind: *Various artists*/ You don't know what love is: *Various artists* / Claire de Lune samba: *Various artists* / Seven come eleven: *Various* artists / When sunny gets blue: *Various artists* / Orange, brown and green: *Various artists* / Don't cry for me Argentina: *Various artists*.
LP: CJ 160

CONCORD SOUND, THE (Various artists).
LP: CJ 278

CONTEMPORARY JAZZ MASTERPIECES (Various artists).
MC: 4670864

COOL CALIFORNIA (Various artists).
LP: WL 70511
LP: SJL 2254

COPULATIN' RHYTHM (Blues and jazz rarities) (Various artists).
LP: JASS 3

COPULATIN' RHYTHM VOL.2 (Various artists).
LP: JASS 5

CORNELIA ST-THE SONGWRITERS (Various artists).
LP: ST 301

COTTON CLUB LEGEND (Various artists).
LP: NL 89506
MC: NK 89506

COTTON CLUB STARS (Various artists).
2LP: ST 124

COTTON CLUB, THE (Various artists).
Tracks: / Cotton Club stomp: *Ellington, Duke and his Cotton Club Orchestra* / Just a crazy song: *Robinson, Bill 'Bojangles'* / Am I blue?: *Waters, Ethel* / Heebie jeebies: *Webb, Chick/his orchestra* / I must have that man: *Hall, Adelaide*/ Stormy weather: *Arlen, Harold* / When you're smiling: *Armstrong, Louis & His Orchestra* / Lazybones: *Williams, Midge* / Old yazoo: *Calloway, Cab & His Orchestra* / Honey just for you: *Kirk, Andy/his Twelve Clouds of Joy*/ Between the Devil and the deep blue sea: *Armstrong, Louis & His Orchestra* / Sweet rhythm: *Lunceford, Jimmie/his Chickasaw Syncopators* / Blues I love to sing: *Hall, Adelaide* / Kicking the gong around: *Calloway, Cab & His Orchestra*/ Serenade to a wealthy widow: *Foresythe, Reginald* / Jubilee stomp: *Ellington, Duke and his Cotton Club Orchestra*/ I can't give you anything but love: *Waters, Ethel* / Doin' the new low down: *Mills, Irving*.
LP: AJA 5031
MC: ZC AJA 5031

CRAZY RHYTHM (Based upon the Quintette Du Hot Club De France) (Various artists).
LP: KS 2065

CREATIV (Various artists).
LP: LR 124

CYLINDER JAZZ (Various artists).
Tracks: / Hungarian rag: *Various artists* / Clarinet squawk: *Louisiana Five* / Dardanella: *Raderman, Harry's Jazz Orchestra* / Meadow lark: *Yellman, Duke/his orchestra* / Where's my sweetie hiding?: *Merry Sparklers*/ Blue-eyed Sally: *Various artists* / Ain't she sweet: *Various artists* / She's a cornfed Indiana gal: *Oliver*, Earl's Jazz Babies / Make that trombone laugh: *Raderman, Harry's Jazz Orchestra* / Night time in Little Italy: *Frisco* Jazz Band / I'm going to park myself in your arms: *Yellman, Duke/his orchestra* / That certain feeling: *Tennessee Happy Boys* / Do it again: *Various artists* (Intro, drifting along with the tide.) / Louisville Lou: *Various artists*.
LP: SDL 334
MC: CSDL 334

DANCING ON THE FLOOR - THE 80'S REVISITED (Various artists).
Tracks: / Dancing on the floor (hooked on love): *Third World* / Rockit: *Hancock, Herbie* / Roses: *Haywoode*/ Taste of bitter love: *Knight, Gladys & The Pips* / Juicy fruit: *Mtume* / Autodrive: *Hancock, Herbie*/ See the day: *Lee, Dee C* / How 'bout us: *Champaign* / It's raining men: *Weather Girls* / I wonder if i take you home: *Lisa Lisa/Cult Jam with Full Force* / Let's hear it for the boy: *Williams, Deniece* / Give it up: *K.C. & The Sunshine Band* / Break my stride: *Wilder, Matthew* / My favourite waste of time: *Paul, Owen*/ Bourgie Bourgie: *Knight, Gladys & The Pips* / Hold me tighter in the rain: *Griffin, Billy* / Amityville (the house on the hill): *Lovebug Starski* / Alice, i want you just for me: *Full Force*.
MC: PWKMC 4059

DANCING THE NIGHT AWAY (Various artists).
Tracks: / On the sunny side of the street: *Harris, Jack & His Orchestra* / I was true: *Hall, Henry & His Gleneagles* Hotel Band (Vocalist:Tommy Whitefoot) / Ya got love: *Fox, Roy & His Band featuring Al Bowlly* / There's a ring around the Moon: *Merrin, Billy & His Commanders* (Vocalist:Billy Merrin) / Lazybones: *Kyte, Sydney & his Piccadilly Hotel Band* / In a little rocky valley: *Loss, Joe & his band* (Vocalist:Jimmy Messene) / What more can I ask?: *Winnick*, Maurice and his Orchestra / Dancing time: *Rabin, Oscar & his Strict Tempo Band* / I never had a chance: *Joyce*, Teddy & his Dance Music (Vocalist:Jimmy Messene) / Stardust: *Kinsman, Tom & his Dance Band* / You're looking for romance, I'm looking for love: *Lawrence, Brian & his Lansdowne Orchestra* (Vocalist:Brian Lawrence) / Supposing: *Lipton, Sydney* & his Orchestra / Moon over Miami: *Collins, Al & his Orchestra* (Vocalist:Barry Leary) / You're telling me: *Fox*, Roy & His Band (Vocalist:Sid Buckman) / My heart's to let: *Stone, Lew & The Monseigneur Band* (Vocalist:Al Bowlly) / La di da di da: *Barnstormers* / Old man of the mountain, The: *Starita, Ray & His Ambassadors* / Crying my heart out for you: *Kunz, Charlie & The Casani Club Orchestra* (Vocalist:Vera Lynn) / I'm keeping company: *Winnick, Maurice* & His Band (Vocalist:Harry Bentley) / Ridin' high: *Phillips, Sid Quintet* (Vocals:The Greene Sisters) / Beat me daddy, eight to the bar: *Hatchett's Swingtette* (Vocalist:Dorothy Carless) / Waves of the ocean are whisp'ring goodnight: *Martin*, Bram & His Band (Vocalist:Al Bowlly) / Will you remember: *Geraldo & His Orchestra* (Vocalist:Cyril Grantham) / One meat ball: *Gonella, Nat/his Georgians* (Vocalists:Helen Mack & Nat Gonella) / Rehearsing a lullaby (Vocalist:Elsie Carlisle) / Snakehips swing: *Johnson, Ken 'Snakehips' & his West Indian Orchestra* / New swing alphabet, The: *Jackson, Jack* & His Band (Vocalist:Jack Cooper) / I'll buy that dream: *Stone, Lew & his Novatones* (Vocalists:Helen Mack & Ronnie O'Dell) / Sweetheart of all my dreams: *Ferrie, Miff & his Ferrymen* / Sambina: *Roy, Harry & His Orchestra* / I got rhythm: *Peachey, Roland & his Royal Hawaiians* / All through the day: *Weir, Frank & his Orchestra* (Vocalist:Vivien Paget) / Gnat jump: *Gonella, Nat/his Georgians* / Nattering around: *Temple, Nat & his Club Royal Orchestra* / I'll dance at your wedding: *White, Jack & his Orchestra* / Darktown strutters' ball: *Roy, Harry & His Orchestra* (Vocalists:Harry Roy & The Keynotes) / Get happy: *Stone, Lew & his Stonecrackers* / My wubba dolly: *Rabin, Oscar & His Band* (Vocalists:Beryl Davis

& Billy Nicholls) / What do I have to do (to make you love me): *King, Felix - His Piano & Orchestra* / Quien no llora no mama: *Ros, Edmundo & his Rumba Band* (Vocalist:Edmundo Ros).
2LP: . . . . **RECDL 16**
MCSET: . . . . **RECDC 16**

DECADE OF JAZZ VOL.1 (Various artists).
2LP: . . . . **LCSP 101**

DECADE OF JAZZ VOL.2 (Various artists).
2LP: . . . . **LCSP 102**

DECADE OF JAZZ VOL.3 (Various artists).
2LP: . . . . **LCSP 103**

DECEMBER BAND VOL. 1 (Various artists).
LP: . . . . **GHB 197**

DECEMBER BAND - VOL 2 (Various artists).
LP: . . . . **GHB 198**

DISCOVERIES (Various artists).
Tracks: / Chili pepper: *Various artists* / Susie the poodle: *Various artists* / Everything happens to me: *Various* artists / Tickle toe: *Various artists* / Nutmeg: *Various artists* / Cinnamon: *Various artists* / What's new: *Various artists* / Thyme time: *Various artists* / Straight life: *Various artists* / Art's oregano: *Various artists* / Way you look tonight: *Various artists*.
LP: . . . . **WL 70507**

DIXIE FIVE (Various artists).
LP: . . . . **J 147**

DIXIE PARTY (Various artists).
Tracks: / Wild cat blues: *Various artists* / When the saints go marching in: *Various artists* / Jazz lips: *Various* artists / Toot toot, tootsie goodbye: *Various artists* / Ory's Creole trombone: *Various artists* / Jazz me blues: *Various artists* / Down by the riverside: *Various artists* / Down home rag: *Various artists* / Original Charleston strut: *Various artists* / River stay 'way from my door: *Various artists* / Bill Bailey won't you please come home: *Various artists* / Tiger rag: *Various artists* / Maple leaf rag: *Various artists*.
LP: . . . . **F 90062**
MC: . . . . **MF 90062**
LP: . . . . **INT 150 047**

DIXIELAND COLLECTION (Various artists).
Tracks: / Tiger rag: *Original Dixieland Jazz Band* / Tin roof blues: *New Orleans Rhythm Kings* / She's crying...: *New Orleans Rhythm Kings* / Royal Garden blues: *Beiderbecke, Bix* / Fidgety feet: *Wolverine Orchestra*/ Clementine: *Goldkette, Jean & His Orchestra* / Way down yonder in New Orleans: *Trumbauer, Frankie* / That's no bargain: *Nichols, Red* / Moanin' low: *Mole, Miff* / Nobody's sweetheart: *McKenzie* / Strut Miss Lizzie: *Hotsy Totsy Gang* / There'll be some changes made: *Chicago Rhythm Kings* / Basin Street blues: *Charleston Chasers* / Eel, The: *Condon, Eddie & His Orchestra* / After you've gone: *Venuti, Joe & Eddie Lang* / Spider crawl: *Banks, Billy & His Orchestra* / Rockin' chair: *Carmichael, Hoagy* / Thinking of you: *Rhythm Cats*/ Relaxin' at the Touro: *Spanier, Muggsy*.
LP: . . . . **DVLP 2119**
MC: . . . . **DVMC 2119**

DIXIELAND DOWN SOUTH (Various artists).
LP: . . . . **SLP 220**

DIXIELAND JAZZ CLASSICS (Various artists).
LP: . . . . **HERWIN 116**

DIXIELAND JUBILEE (Various artists).
2LP: . . . . **BLP 30401/2**
2LP: . . . . **INT 155 002**
MCSET: . . . . **CAS 455 002**
2LP: **80011**
MCSET: **850111/2**

DIXIELAND JUBILEE VOL 2 (Various artists).
Tracks: / Black and blue: *Lyttelton, Humphrey* / Barefoot days: *Welsh, Alex* / Jazz me blues: *Dutch Swing* College Band / Tiger rag: *Greene, Brian* / Makin' whoopee: *Barber, Chris* / St. Philip Street breakdown: *Sunshine*, Monty / I'm crazy 'bout my baby: *Collie, Max* / Careless love: *Sunshine, Monty* / Chelsea cakewalk: *Bilk*, Acker / Buddy Bolden's blues: *Various artists* / West End blues: *Bryden, Beryl & The Rod Mason Band* / All of me: *Barber, Chris* / Honeysuckle rose: *Bilk, Acker* / Tishomingo blues: *Lyttelton, Humphrey* / Just a closer walk with thee: *Sunshine, Monty* / Bill Bailey won't you please come home: *Dutch Swing College Band* / Tie a yellow ribbon: *Welsh, Alex* / You made me love you: *Dutch Swing College Band* / High society: *Barber*, Chris / St. Louis blues: *Bryden, Beryl & The Rod Mason Band* / Carry me back to old Virginny: *Various artists*/ Ice cream: *Greene, Brian* / C jam blues: *Sunshine, Monty* / Travellin' on: *Bilk, Acker* / Wild man blues: *Various artists*.
2LP: . . . . **BLP 30403/4**
2LP: . . . . **INT 155 005**
MCSET: . . . . **CAS 455 005**

DIXIELAND JUBILEE VOL 3 (Various artists).
Tracks: / High Society: *Various artists* / Savoy blues: *Various artists* / Carolina shuffle: *Various artists*/ Memphis blues: *Various artists* / Loch Lomond: *Various artists* / When the saints go marching in: *Various* artists / Theo, wir fahr'n nach lodz: *Various artists* / Lazy river: *Various artists* / Nobody knows the trouble I've seen: *Various artists* / Creole love call: *Various artists* / Saturday night function: *Various artists*/ Over in the gloryland: *Various artists* / Meet me tonight in dreamland: *Various artists* / Little brown jug: *Various artists* / Lonesome Road: *Various artists* / Makin' whoopee: *Various artists* / Smokey mokes: *Various artists* / Just a little while to stay here: *Various artists* / New Orleans function: *Various artists*/ Oh didn't he ramble: *Various artists* / Margie: *Various artists* / King of the Zulus, The: *Various artists*/ Swanee River: *Various artists* / Mood indigo: *Various artists* / Tie a yellow ribbon: *Various artists*.
2LP: . . . . **INT 155 013**
MCSET: . . . . **CAS 455 013**

DIXIELAND JUBILEE VOL 4 (Various artists).
Tracks: / Panama rag: *Various artists* / I'm going home: *Various artists* / Chinatown: *Various artists*/ Davenport blues: *Various artists* / Darktown strutters' ball: *Various artists* / Back home again in Indiana: *Various artists* / Original Charleston strut: *Various artists* / Gisela: *Various artists* / Cheek to cheek: *Various artists* / Hello Dolly: *Various artists* / Carry me back: *Various artists* / I can't give you anything but love: *Various artists* / Rovin', A: *Various artists* / Does your chewing gum lose its flavour?: *Various* artists / Dear old Southland: *Various artists* / Dippermouth blues: *Various artists* / Isle of Capri: *Various* artists / I'm crazy 'bout my baby: *Various artists* / New Orleans stomp: *Various artists* / Sweethearts on parade: *Various artists* / Go tell it on the mountain: *Various artists* / Avalon: *Various artists* / Mack the knife: *Various artists* / Wochenend und sonnenschein: *Various artists*.
2LP: . . . . **INT 155 024**
MCSET: . . . . **CAS 455 024**

DIXIELAND JUBILEE VOL 5 (Various artists).
Tracks: / Wolverine blues: *Various artists* / Sugar foot stomp: *Various artists* / Jenny's ball: *Various* artists / Georgia on my mind: *Various artists* / Kassiam: *Various artists* / Careless love: *Various artists*/ Struttin' with some barbecue: *Various artists* / Higher ground: *Various artists* / Ole miss: *Various artists*/ 'S wonderful: *Various artists* / Terrible blues: *Various artists* / When it's sleepy time down South: *Various* artists / My blue Heaven: *Various artists* / Black and blue: *Various artists* / Dardanella: *Various artists*/ Old rugged cross, The: *Various artists* / Blue and sentimental: *Various artists* / Big Bill: *Various artists*/ My bucket's got a hole in it: *Various artists* / Egyptian fantasy: *Various artists* / When you wore a tulip: *Various artists* / Whistling Rufus: *Various artists* / Light from the lighthouse: *Various artists* / Clarinet marmalade: *Various artists*.
2LP: . . . . **INT 155 032**
MCSET: . . . . **CAS 455 032**

DIXIELAND JUBILEE VOLS 1 & 2 (Various artists).
2LP: **80029**
MCSET: **850291/2**

DIXIELAND STORY, THE (Various artists).
Tracks: / Tiger bag: *Various artists* / Look at 'em doing it now: *Various artists* / Copenhagen: *Various* artists / Careless love: *Various artists* / She's crying for me: *Various artists* / That's no bargain: *Various* artists / Way down yonder in New Orleans: *Various artists* / I'm more than satisfied: *Various artists* / Royal Garden blues: *Various artists* / Nobody's sweetheart: *Various artists* / Coquette: *Various artists* / I found a new baby: *Various artists* / There'll be some changes made: *Various artists* / Shake your can: *Various* artists / Moanin' low: *Various artists* / Strut Miss Lizzie: *Various artists* / Georgia on my mind: *Various* artists / Georgia grind: *Various artists* / After you've gone: *Various artists* / Spider crawl: *Various artists* / Eel, The: *Various artists* / When the saints go marching in: *Various artists* / At the jazz band ball: *Various artists* / Relaxin' at the Touro: *Various artists* / Muskrat ramble: *Various artists*.
MCSET: . . . . **DVREMC 20**

DOWN IN THE ALLEY 1934-1938 (Various artists).
LP: . . . . **TM 8812**

DREAMING ON THE RIVER TO NEW ORLEANS (Various artists).
LP: . . . . **SLP 238**

DRIVIN BIG BAND (Various artists).
MC: . . . . **JHC 62**

'EAPS MORE OF THE COWSHED CLEANERS (Various artists).
LP: . . . . **LKLP 6362**

EARLY BLACK SWING (Various artists).
Tracks: / Louis shuffle: *Henderson, Fletcher & His Orchestra* / Sugar foot stomp: *Henderson, Fletcher & His Orchestra*/ Jimtown blues: *Henderson, Fletcher & His Orchestra* / Diga diga doo: *Ellington, Duke and his Cotton Club Orchestra*/ Saratoga swing: *Ellington, Duke and his Cotton Club Orchestra* / Blue feeling: *Ellington, Duke and his Cotton Club* Orchestra / South: *Moten, Bennie Kansas City Orchestra* / Moten swing: *Moten, Bennie Kansas City Orchestra*/ Milenberg joys: *McKinney's Cotton Pickers* / Plain dirt: *McKinney's Cotton Pickers* / Grand piano blues: *Hines*, Earl & His Orchestra / Everybody loves my baby: *Hines, Earl & His Orchestra* / Hot tempered blues: *Johnson, Charlie* Paradise Ten / Boy in the boat: *Johnson, Charlie Paradise Ten* / Market Street stomp: *Missourians* / Prohibition blues: *Missourians*.
LP: . . . . **NL 89583**
MC: . . . . **NK 89583**
MC: . . . . **NK 90365**
LP: . . . . **NL 90365**

EARLY GLENN MILLER (VARIOUS ARTISTS) (See under Early Glenn Miller) (Various artists).

EARLY NEGRO VOCAL QUARTETS 1902-28 VOL.1 (Various artists).
LP: . . . . **DLP 583**

EARLY VIPER JIVE (Rare scat vocals) (Various artists).
LP: . . . . **ST 105**

ECHOES OF AN ERA (Various artists).
Tracks: / Them there eyes: *Various artists* / All of me: *Various artists* / I mean you: *Various artists*/ I love you Porgy: *Various artists* / Take the 'A' train: *Various artists* / I hear music: *Various artists*/ High wire, the Aerialist: *Various artists* / Spring can really hang you up the most: *Various artists*.
LP: . . . . **K 52348**

ECHOES OF AN ERA, VOLUME 2 (Various artists).
Tracks: / I want to be happy: *Various artists* / I get a kick out of you: *Various artists* / 'Round midnight: *Various artists* / Rhythm-a-ning: *Various artists* / 500 miles high: *Various artists* / But not for me: *Various artists* / My one and only love: *Various artists* / Them there eyes: *Various artists*.
LP: . . . . **K 52414**

ECHOES OF NEW ORLEANS (Various artists).
LP: . . . . **GHB 139**

EDDIE CONDON ALL STARS (Various artists).
LP: . . . . **PUMPKIN 111**

ENTERTAINER, THE (Various artists).
Tracks: / Entertainer, The: *McLennan, Jim* / Magnetic rag: *Van Bergeyk, Ton* / Paragon rag: *Nicolai, Tim*/ Heliotrope bouquet: *McLennan, Jim* / Pig leaf rag (medley): *Evans, Bob* / Pethena - a concert waltz (medley): *Evans, Bob* / Maple leaf rag (medley): *Evans, Bob* / Sycamore - a concert waltz: *Wijnkamp, L.* / Kismet rag: *Fegy, Dick* / Wall Street rag: *Laibman, D.*
LP: . . . . **SNKF 115**
LP: . . . . **KM 122**

ENTERTAINERS OF THE JAZZ AGE (Series 5) (Various artists).
MC: **046**

ESQUIRE ALL AMERICAN HOT JAZZ SESSIONS, THE (Various artists).
Tracks: / Long long journey: *Esquire All American ...* / Snafu: *Esquire All American ...* / One that got away: *Esquire All American ...* / Gone with the wind: *Esquire All American ...* / Indiana winter: *Esquire All American ...* / Indian Summer: *Various artists* / Blow me down: *Various artists* / Buckin' the blues: *Various artists*/ Blues after hours: *Teagarden, Jack Big Eight* / Low flame: *52nd Street All Stars* / Allen's alley: *52nd* Street All Stars / Just one more chance: *Thompson, Lucky & Lucky Seven* / From Dixieland to Be-bop: *Thompson, Lucky* & Lucky Seven / Boulevard bounce: *Thompson, Lucky & Lucky Seven* / Boppin' the blues: *Thompson, Lucky &* Lucky Seven / Ain't misbehavin': *Tatum, Art* / Cherokee: *Tatum, Art* / Erroll's bounce: *Garner, Erroll*/ Erroll's blues: *Garner, Erroll* / I don't wanna miss Mississippi: *Bailey, Mildred*.
LP: . . . . **NL 86757**
MC: . . . . **NK 86757**

ESSENTIAL JAZZ (See under Jazz) (Various artists).

ESSENTIAL JAZZ (Various artists).
MC: **2643**

ESSENTIAL JAZZ VOCALISTS, THE (Various artists).
MC: **4671474**

EVENING WITH WINDHAM HILL-LIVE (Various artists).
LP: **371026-1**
MC: **371026-4**

FAMOUS BLACKBIRDS REVUES (Various artists).
Tracks: / Silver rose: *Plantation Orchestra, The* / Arabella's wedding day: *Plantation Orchestra, The* / Smiling Joe: *Plantation Orchestra, The* / For baby and me: *Plantation Orchestra, The* / Bandana babies: *Leslie, Lew* Blackbirds Orchest / Magnolia's wedding day: *Leslie, Lew Blackbirds Orchest* / You're lucky to me: *Ellington*, Duke And His Orchestra / Memories of you: *Ellington, Duke And His Orchestra* / I can't give you anything but love: *Mills Brothers* / Diga diga doo: *Mills Brothers/ Duke Ellington* / St. Louis blues: *Waters, Ethel/Cecil Mack* Choir / Doin' the new lowdown: *Robinson, Bill 'Bojangles'* / I must have that man: *Hall, Adelaide with Duke Ellington* & His Orchestra / Baby: *Hall, Adelaide with Duke Ellington & His Orchestra* / Shuffle your feet-Banadana babies: *Mills, Harry & Donald*.
LP: . . . . **SVL 195**
MC: . . . . **CSVL 195**

FAMOUS COLLECTION VOL.3 (Various artists).
LP: . . . . **VDL 1012**

FEMO JAZZ, LIVE '89 (Various artists).
LP: . . . . **ML 108**

FESTA NEW ORLEANS MUSIC ASCONA (Various artists).
LP: . . . . **LP 30**

FOR THE FIRST TIME (Various artists).
LP: . . . . **IAJRC 5**

FORTY YEARS OF WOMEN IN JAZZ (Various artists).
LPS: . . . . **STB 001**

FROM BOOGIE TO BOP 1939-1956 (Blue Note 50th anniversary collection vol. 1) (Various artists).
Tracks: / Two's and fews: *Ammons, Albert & Meade Lux Lewis* / Summertime: *Bechet, Sidney* / Profoundly blue: *Hall*, Edmond / Blue harlem: *Quebec, Ike* / 'Round midnight: *Monk, Thelonious* / Criss cross: *Monk, Thelonious*/ Ladybird: *Dameron, Tadd & Fats Navarro* / Tin tin deo: *Moody, James* / Un poco loco: *Powell, Bud* / Glass enclosure: *Powell, Bud* / Bag's groove: *Jackson, Milt* / Tempus fugit: *Davis, Miles* / Easy living: *Brown, Clifford* / Preacher, The: *Silver, Horace* / Avila and tequila: *Mobley, Hank* / Decision: *Rollins, Sonny* / Champ, The: *Smith, Jimmy (USA)*.
2LP: **BST2 92465**
MC: **TCBST2 92465**

GENIUS JAZZ (Various artists).
MCSET: . . . . **WW 6037**

GEORGIA STOMP (1925-35) (Various artists).
LP: . . . . **HQ 2031**

GEORGIA STRING BANDS 1928-30 (Various artists).
LP: . . . . **BD 2002**

GET WISE (Various artists).
Tracks: / Mission impossible: *Team Ten* / Long remembered thunder: *Expresso 7* / Yellow hill: *Loose Tubes*/ Childhood meditations: *Williamson, Steve* / Others (No pearls...no passion): *Various artists* / Throw it away: *Quinn, David* / Samba ingles: *Jazz Defektors* / Vanessa: *Bent, Phillip* / King of the fools: *Danger Zone* / Get wise: *Man Called Adam* / We'll be back: *Pine, Courtney* / That's why it isn't love: *Jerome*(Extra track on cassette) / So coole: *Atkins, Dominique* (Extra track on cassette).
LP: . . . . **PRT 57122**

GIANTS OF JAZZ (Various artists).
LP: . . . . **GW 2004**

GIANTS OF JAZZ AND BLUES (Various artists).
LP: . . . . **MA 28 1285**

MC: MAMC 281285

GIANTS OF JAZZ VOL.1 (Various artists).
Tracks: / Brown eyed woman: *Various artists* / Bottles empty: *Various artists* / Groovin' gates: *Various* artists / Ma cherie amour: *Various artists* / Save it pretty mama: *Various artists* / Bad dude: *Various artists*.
LP: MAN 5006

GIANTS OF JAZZ VOL.2 (Various artists).
Tracks: / Empanada: *Various artists* / Gee but it's good: *Various artists* / Yesterme, yesteryou, yesterday: *Various* artists / Nighttime in the switching yard: *Various artists* / Too bad: *Various artists* / Wedding bell blues: *Various artists*.
LP: MAN 5009

GIANTS OF JAZZ VOL.3 (Various artists).
Tracks: / Wave: *Giants of Jazz* / Boogie nights: *Giants of Jazz* / Crying blind: *Giants of Jazz* / Shake it well: *Giants of Jazz* / Big legged woman: *Giants of Jazz* / Nightime in the switching yard: *Giants of Jazz*.
LP: MAN 5012

GIANTS OF JAZZ VOL.4 (Various artists).
Tracks: / After you've gone: *Various artists* / Close to you: *Various artists* / Out to lunch: *Various artists*/ Willow weep for me: *Various artists* / In the hush of the night: *Various artists* / Nobody: *Various artists*.
LP: MAN 5015

GIANTS OF JAZZ VOL.5 (Various artists).
Tracks: / Misty: *Holmes, Groove* / Dancing in the sun: *Holmes, Groove* / Jimmy Reed blues: *Reed, Jimmy*/ Over the hump: *Reed, Jimmy* / Sweet Ginny: *Hawkins, Jay* / I put a spell on you: *Hawkins, Jay*.
LP: MAN 5018

GIANTS OF JAZZ: VOLUME 1 (Various artists).
Tracks: / Ain't misbehavin': *Various artists* / Sleepy time down south: *Various artists* / Hamp rich dido blues: *Various artists* / Limelight: *Various artists* / Buddy's rock: *Various artists* / My funny valentine: *Various artists* / Walking shoes: *Various artists*.
LP: GATE 7015
MC: CGATE 7015

GIANTS OF TRADITIONAL JAZZ (Various artists).
LP: WL 70513
2LP: SJL 2251

GIRL TALK (Various artists).
Tracks: / Lullaby of Birdland: *Connor, Chris* / Easy to love: *McRae, Carmen* / Foggy day, A: *London, Julie*/ He's got the whole world in his hands: *Simone, Nina* / You're driving me crazy: *Moore, Marilyn* / Take the 'A' train: *Roche, Betty* / I hear music: *Connor, Chris* / For all we know: *Simone, Nina* / Route 66: *Roche, Betty* / Is you is or is you ain't my baby: *Moore, Marilyn* / Out of this world: *Connor, Chris* / Old devil moon: *McRae, Carmen* / You're blase: *London, Julie* / Tiptoe gently: *McRae, Carmen* / From this moment on: *Connor, Chris* (* Extra track on CD only) / Misery: *McRae, Carmen* (Extra track on CD only) / Don't worry 'bout me: *London, Julie* (Extra track on CD only) / Sometimes I feel like a motherless child: *London, Julie* (* Extra track on CD only) / African mailman: *Simone, Nina* (* Extra track on CD only) / September in the rain: *Roche, Betty*(* Extra track on CD only).
LP: ATS 13
MC: TCATS 13

GIRL ZONE (Various artists).
Tracks: / Happy New Year: *Beverly* / Some things just stick in your mind: *Vashti* / Backstreet girl: *Posta, Adrienne* / He doesn't love me: *Posta, Adrienne* / Two lovers: *Cordet, Louise* / You: *Child, Lorraine*/ Sha la la song, The: *Faithfull, Marianne* / I'm into something good: *Lady Lee* / Mr Scrooge: *Orchids*/ Jenny let him go: *Antoinette* / Can't hear you no more: *Lulu* / He's my guy: *Parr, Catherine* / Big man: *Kirby, Kathy* / Only you can do it: *Vernon Girls* / Don't make me (fall in love with you): *Blue, Babbity*/ Save the last dance for me: *Martin, Jean*.
LP: ACT 008

GLENN MILLER STORY (Film Soundtrack) (Various artists).
Tracks: / Moonlight serenade: *Various artists* / Tuxedo Junction: *Various artists* / Little brown jug: *Various* artists / St. Louis blues: *Various artists* / In the mood: *Various artists* / String of pearls: *Various* artists / Pennsylvania 6 5000: *Various artists* / American patrol: *Various artists* / Basin street blues: *Various artists* / Otchi-tchor-hi-ya: *Various artists*.
LP: MCL 1665
MC: MCLC 1665
LP: MCF 3273

GLENN MILLER STORY (ACE OF HEARTS) (Film soundtrack) (Various artists).
LP: AH 12

GLENN MILLER TRIBUTE (Various artists).
LP: SG 8009

GOING TO CALIFORNIA (Various artists).
LP: JSP 1075

GOING TO NEW ORLEANS (Various artists).
LP: FLY 601

GOLDEN AGE OF JAZZ OF THE 30'S (Various artists).
Tracks: / Pink elephants: *Venuti, Joe* / Hiawatha's lullaby: *Venuti, Joe* / Charlie's home: *Rollini, Adrian*/ Gin mill blues: *Sullivan, Joe* / Sweet Lorraine: *Venuti, Joe* / I got a right to sing the blues: *Goodman*, Benny / Ain't ya glad?: *Goodman, Benny* / Texas tea party: *Goodman, Benny* / Hell's bells and hallelujah: *Venuti, Joe* / Barrelhouse: *Stacy, Jess* / Buzzard, The: *Freeman, Bud* / Last round-up, The: *Various artists* / Chicken and waffles: *Berigan, Bunny* / Blues of Israel: *Krupa, Gene*.
LP: GX 2509
MC: TCGX 2509

GOLDEN AGE, THE (Big Bands) (Various artists).
MC: 16-17

GOLDEN DAYS OF JAZZ (Various artists).
LP: 26.21001

GOLDEN ERA OF DIXIELAND (Various artists).
LP: SLP 805

GOLDEN HOUR OF CLARINET JAZZ GIANTS (Various artists).
Tracks: / Petite fleur: *Sunshine, Monty* / Boodle am shake: *Lightfoot, Terry, Acker Bilk & Sandy Brown* / Satin doll: *Coe, Tony* / A'rowing: *Bilk, Acker* / That old feeling: *Brown, Sandy & Archie Semple* / Wild cat blues: *Sunshine, Monty* / Here today: *Fawkes, Wally* / My journey to the sky: *Bilk, Acker & Terry Lightfoot*/ Love for sale: *Brown, Sandy* / Hiawatha: *Bilk, Acker & Terry Lightfoot* / Last western, The: *Brown, Sandy*/ Sweet Georgia Brown: *Coe, Tony* / Hush-a-bye: *Sunshine, Monty* / Louise: *Brown, Sandy & Archie Semple*/ Elephant stomp: *Lightfoot, Terry* / I'm in the market for you: *Semple, Archie* / Times a wastin': *Coe, Tony*/ Slab's blues: *Brown, Sandy & Acker Bilk*.
LP: GH 649
MC: ZCGH 649

GOLDEN HOUR OF TRAD JAZZ VOL. 2 (Various artists).
Tracks: / South Rampart Street Parade: *Bilk, Acker & His Paramount Jazz Band* / Grandpa's spells: *Lightfoot, Terry &* His Band / C.C. Rider: *Ball, Kenny & His Jazzmen* / Downhearted blues: *Melly, George & John Chilton's Feetwarmers* / Oh Mr. Jelly: *Harris, Max & The New Red Hot Peppers* / Mood indigo: *Ball, Kenny & His Jazzmen* / Chelsea cakewalk: *Bilk, Acker & His Paramount Jazz Band* / Lonesome (si tu vois ma mere): *Lightfoot, Terry & His Band* / You've got the right key but the wrong keyhole: *Melly, George & John Chilton's Feetwarmers* / Shreveport stomp: *Harris, Max &* The New Red Hot Peppers / Milenburg joye: *Ball, Kenny & His Jazzmen* / Someday sweetheart: *Melly, George & John* Chilton's Feetwarmers / Black bottom stomp: *Harris, Max & The New Red Hot Peppers* / 'Taint what you do: *Lightfoot*, Terry & His Band / Burgundy Street blues: *Bilk, Acker & His Paramount Jazz Band* / Ragsy: *Ball, Kenny & His Jazzmen*/ As time goes by: *Lightfoot, Terry & His Band* / Wolverine blues: *Bilk, Acker & His Paramount Jazz Band* / I got what it takes: *Melly, George & John Chilton's Feetwarmers* / Doctor Jazz: *Harris, Max & The New Red Hot Peppers*.
MC: KGHMC 134

GOLDEN HOUR OF TRAD JAZZ VOL. 2 (See Under Jazz...) (Various artists).

GOLDEN HOUR OF TRADITIONAL JAZZ (Various artists).
MC: ZCGH 526

GOLDEN HOUR OF TRADITIONAL JAZZ VOL.4 (Various artists).
MC: ZCGH 669

GOLDEN HOUR OF TRADITIONAL JAZZ, A (Various artists).
Tracks: / Marching through Georgia: *Bilk, Acker* / Tishomingo blues: *Lightfoot, Terry* / Sur le pont d'avignon: *Wallis, Bob* / One sweet letter: *Lightfoot, Terry* / Travelling blues: *Wallis, Bob* / Easter parade: *Bilk, Acker*.
MC: KGHMC 103

GOLDEN JUBILEES, THE (Various artists).
MC: GVMMC 21

GOT TO DANCE (Various artists).
LP: SVL 205
MC: CSVL 205

GRAB THIS AND DANCE (Various artists).
LP: GDLP 001

GRANDS SUCCES DU JAZZ (Various artists).
LP: 509172

GREAT JAM SESSIONS, VOL.1 (Various artists).
Tracks: / Just the blues: *Various artists* / China boy: *Various artists* / St. Louis blues: *Various artists*/ Someday, sweetheart: *Various artists* / Basin Street blues: *Various artists* / Honeysuckle rose: *Various artists* / Boogie woogie blues: *Various artists*.
LP: SM 3114

GREAT JAZZ LADIES VOL.1 (Various artists).
LP: KLJ 20036

GREAT JAZZ PIANOS (1926-1940) (Various artists).
LP: SM 3121

GREAT JAZZ SOLOS REVISITED (Various artists).
LP: WAVE LP 18

GREAT JAZZ TRUMPETS (1924-1937) (Various artists).
Tracks: / Deep down south: *Bix Beiderbecke Orchestra* / I'm more than satisfied: *Chicago Loopers* / Clorinda: *Various artists* / Three blind mice (takes 1 & 2): *Various artists* / I need some pettin': *Wolverines, The*/ Out where the blues begin: *Mills, Irving & His Hotsy Totsy Gang* / New twister, The: *Original Wolverines, The*/ Shimme-sha-wabble: *Various artists* / Good man is hard to find, A: *Various artists* / Swanee river: *Berigan's, Bunny Rhythm Makers* / San Francisco: *Various artists*.
LP: SM 3122

GREAT JAZZ VOCALISTS (Singin' the blues vol. 1) (Various artists).
MC: SLC 61127

GREAT MOMENTS IN JAZZ (Various artists).
Tracks: / Martians go home: *Rogers, Shorty* / Train and the river, The: *Giuffre, Jimmy* / Golden striker, The: *Modern Jazz Quartet* / Spirit feel, The: *Jackson, Milt* / Wednesday night prayer meeting: *Mingus, Charles*/ Memphis underground: *Mann, Herbie* / Comin' home baby: *Torme, Mel* / Just a little lovin': *McRae, Carmen*/ Bright moments song: *Kirk, Roland* / Compared to what: *Macann, Les & Eddie Harris* / Up jumped Spring: *Hubbard, Freddie* / Stratus: *Cobham, Billy* / In walked bud: *Blakey, Art/Thelonious Monk* / My favourite things: *Coltrane, John* / Ramblin': *Coleman, Ornette* / Hard times: *Newman, David 'Fathead'* / Whispering grass: *Crawford*, Hank / Your mind is on vacation: *Various artists* / Listen here: *Harris, Eddie* / Live humble: *Lateef, Yusef* / Cosmic messenger: *Ponty, Jean-Luc* / Birdland: *Manhattan Transfer* / Rockport: *Passport*/ Softly at sunrise: *Albright, Gerald* / Perigia: *Jamal, Ahmad*.
LPS: K 781 907 1
MCSET: K 781 907 4

GREAT PIANISTS, THE (Various artists).
LP: SFR DP 695

GREAT SINGERS OF THE 30'S (Various artists).
LP: LP 40-140

GREAT SINGERS OF THE FIFTIES (Various artists).
LP: GP 703

GREAT SOLOISTS VOL.1 (Various artists).
LP: VDL 1007

GREAT SOLOISTS VOL.2 (Various artists).
LP: VDL 1008

GREAT SOLOISTS VOL.3 (Various artists).
LP: VDL 1014

GREAT SONGSTERS 1927-29 (Various artists).
LP: BD 2007

GREAT SWING SAX (Various artists).
Tracks: / One hour (if I could be with you one hour): *Mound City Blowers* / Hello Lola: *Mound City Blowers* / Wherever there's a will baby: *McKinney's Cotton Pickers* / Hocus pocus: *Henderson, Fletcher & His Orchestra* / Dinah: *Hampton, Lionel & His Orchestra* / Body and soul: *Hawkins, Coleman & His Orchestra* / Lafayette: *Moten*, Bennie Kansas City Orchestra / Voice of Old Man River: *Bryant, Willie & His Orch* / Cottontail: *Ellington, Duke* And His Orchestra / All too soon: *Ellington, Duke And His Orchestra* / Cadillac Slim: *Carter, Benny & His Orchestra*/ I'd love it: *McKinney's Cotton Pickers* / Apologies: *Mezzrow, Mezz & His Orchestra* / I'm in the mood for swing: *Hampton, Lionel & His Orchestra* / Cocktails for two: *Carter, Benny & His Orchestra* / Ill wind: *Carter, Benny & His Orchestra*.
LP: NL 90405
MC: NK 90405

GREAT TRUMPET LEGENDS (Various artists).
LP: 2673711
MC: 2673714

GREAT VOCALISTS (Various artists).
Tracks: / Whispering: *Sinatra, Frank & Tommy Dorsey* / Dedicated to you: *Fitzgerald, Ella & Mills Brothers* / Take another guess: *Chick Webb, Ella W.* / Basin Street blues: *Crosby, Bing & J. Trotter Orch.* / Swing brother swing: *Holiday, Billie & Count Basie* / What is this thing called swing: *Armstrong, Louis & His Orchestra* / Flat foot floogie: *Armstrong & The Mills Brothers* / St. Louis blues: *Crosby, Bing & P.Whiteman* / I'm coming Virginia: *Crosby, Bing & P.Whiteman* / Yesterdays: *Holiday, Billie* / Baby won't you please come home: *Hall, Juanita & Coleman Hawkins* / St. Louis blues: *Witherspoon, Jimmy & Gerry Mulligan*.
LP: SM 3278

GREATEST ESQUIRE SWING SESSIONS (Jazz of World War II) (Various artists).
Tracks: / Mop mop: *Esquire All Stars* / I've got a feeling I'm falling: *Esquire All Stars* / Flyin' home: *Esquire* All Stars / My ideal: *Esquire All Stars* / Blues: *Esquire All Stars* / I can't give you anything but love: *Esquire All Stars* / Downhearted blues: *Bailey, Mildred & Ensemble* / World is waiting for the sunrise, The: *Goodman*, Benny Quintet / Airmail special: *Goodman, Benny Quintet* / Rachel's dream: *Goodman, Benny Quintet* / Tea for two: *Various artists*.
LP: SM 3132

GREATEST JAZZ CONCERT EVER, THE (Various artists).
Tracks: / Perdido: *Various artists* / Salt peanuts: *Various artists* / All the things you are: *Various artists*/ Wee: *Various artists* / Hot house: *Various artists* / Night in Tunisia, A: *Various artists* / Embraceable you: *Various artists* / Sure thing: *Various artists* / My devotion: *Various artists* / Polka dots and moonbeams: *Various artists* / Cherokee: *Various artists* / Jubilee: *Various artists* / I've got you under my skin: *Various artists* / My heart stood still: *Various artists* / I want to be happy: *Various artists*/ Lullaby of Birdland: *Various artists*.
2LP: PR 24024

GREATEST JAZZ CONCERT IN THE WORLD (Various artists).
Tracks: / Smedley: *Peterson, Oscar Trio* / Some day my prince will come: *Peterson, Oscar Trio* / Daytrain: *Peterson*, Oscar Trio / Now's the time: *Peterson, Oscar Trio* / Memories of you: *Peterson, Oscar Trio* / Misty: *Peterson*, Oscar Trio / I can't get started: *Peterson, Oscar Trio* / Moonglow: *Hawkins, Coleman & Oscar Peterson Trio*/ Sweet Georgia Brown: *Hawkins, Coleman & Oscar Peterson Trio* / C-jam blues: *Hawkins, Coleman & Oscar Peterson Trio*/ Woman you must be crazy: *Walker, T-Bone* / Stormy Monday: *Walker, T-Bone* / Swamp goo: *Ellington, Duke And* His Orchestra / Hurdle gurdle: *Ellington, Duke And His Orchestra* / Night flock: *Ellington, Duke And His Orchestra*/ Rue bleu: *Ellington, Duke And His Orchestra* / Salome: *Ellington, Duke And His Orchestra* / Chromatic love affair: *Ellington, Duke And His Orchestra* / Mount Harissa: *Ellington, Duke And His Orchestra* / Blood count: *Ellington*, Duke And His Orchestra / Rockin' in rhythm: *Ellington, Duke And His Orchestra* / Very tenor: *Ellington, Duke And* His Orchestra / Onions: *Ellington, Duke And His Orchestra* / Take the 'A' train: *Ellington, Duke And His Orchestra*/ Satin doll: *Ellington, Duke And His Orchestra* / Tutti for cootie: *Ellington, Duke And His Orchestra* / Up jump: *Ellington, Duke And His Orchestra* / Prelude to a kiss: *Ellington, Duke And His Orchestra* / Mood indigo: *Ellington*, Duke And His Orchestra / I got it bad and that ain't good: *Ellington, Duke And His Orchestra*

/ Things ain't what they used to be: *Ellington, Duke And His Orchestra* / Don't be that way: *Fitzgerald, Ella/Jimmy Jones/Duke Ellington*/ You've changed: *Fitzgerald, Ella/Jimmy Jones/Duke Ellington* / Let's do it: *Fitzgerald, Ella/ Jimmy Jones/Duke Ellington*/ On the sunny side of the street: *Fitzgerald, Ella/ Jimmy Jones/Duke Ellington* / It's only a paper moon: *Fitzgerald*, Ella & Jimmy Jones Trio / Daydream: *Fitzgerald, Ella & Jimmy Jones Trio* / If I could be with you: *Fitzgerald*, Ella & Jimmy Jones Trio / Between the devil and the deep blue sea: *Fitzgerald, Ella & Jimmy Jones Trio* / Cottontail: *Fitzgerald, Ella/Jimmy Jones/ Duke Ellington* (Featuring Paul Gonsalves.).
2LP: **262 5704**

GRIFFITH PARK COLLECTION 2 (Various artists).
LP: **9602621**

GROOVEY (Various artists).
LP: .... **FLC 5060**

GRP CHRISTMAS COLLECTION, A (Various artists).
Tracks: / Little drummer boy: *Stuermer, Daryl* / Have yourself a merry little Christmas: *Scott, Tom* / Carol of the bells: *Benoit, David* / Christmas song, The: *Schuur, Diane* / God rest ye merry gentlemen: *Corea, Chick* Elektric Band / White Christmas: *Ritenour, Lee* / Santa Claus is coming to town: *Valentin, Dave* / This Christmas: *Yutaka* / Sleigh ride: *Daniels, Eddie* / It came upon a midnight clear: *Szakcsi* / What child is this: *Egan, Mark* / O'Tannenbaum: *Burton, Gary* / Silent night: *Special EFX* / Silver Bells: *Eubanks, Kevin*/ Some children see him: *Grusin, Dave*.
LP: .... **GRP 95741**
MC: .... **GRP 95744**

GRP LIVE IN SESSION (Various artists).
Tracks: / Rio funk: *Various artists* / St. Elsewhere: *Various artists* / Mountain dance: *Various artists*/ Oasis: *Various artists* / Rit variations: *Various artists* / Reverend Lee: *Various artists* / Dolphin dreams: *Various artists*.
LP: .... **GRP 91023**
MC: .... **GRPM 91023**
DAT: .... **GRT 9532**

GRP ROADTRACKS (Various artists).
Tracks: / Power wave: *Grusin, Dave* / Essence: *Eubanks, Kevin* / Elektrik city: *Corea, Chick* / I can't believe that you're in love with me: *Shuur, Diane* / Uptown east: *Special EFX* / Rio funk: *Ritenour, Lee*/ Circle dance: *Daniels, Eddie* / Times of my life: *Cobham, Billy* / Can't change my heart: *Valentine, Dave* / Bofill, Angela / Can't change my heart: *Bofill, Angela/Valentine,Dave* / Shuffle city: *Grusin, Dave* / Harlequin: *Desconhencido,Arlequin/Grusin,Dave/ Ritenour,Lee* / Harlequin: *Grusin, Dave, Lee Ritenour, Arlequin Desconhencido*.
MC: .... **GRPM 91000**

GRP SUPER LIVE IN CONCERT (Various artists).
Tracks: / Deedle's blues: *Various artists* / Love dance: *Various artists* / Early AM attitude: *Various artists*/ Sauce, The: *Various artists* / Water from the moon: *Various artists* / Earth run: *Various artists* / Target: *Various artists* / Actor's life, An: *Various artists* / Light years: *Various artists* / Rumble: *Various artists* / Time track: *Various artists* / No zone: *Various artists* / Overture: *Various artists*.
2LP: .... **GRP 291650**
MC: .... **GRC 291650**

GUITAR GREATS (Various artists).
MC: .... **ZODIAC 1099C**

GUITAR WORKSHOP IN L.A. (Various artists).
Tracks: / Take it all: *Various artists* / Bawls: *Various artists* / Donna: *Various artists* / Bull funk: *Various artists* / Blues for Ronnie: *Various artists* / Skunk blues: *Various artists* / Hyper stork: *Various artists* / Vicky's song: *Various artists* / Beverly Hill: *Various artists* / Roppongi: *Various artists*.
MC: .... **JC 3314**

GYPSY VIOLIN SUMMIT (Various artists).
LP: .... **MPS 68 240**

HOLIDAY IN DIXIELAND (Various artists).
LP: .... **ISST 116**

HOT VIOLINS (Classic years in digital stereo) (Various artists).
Tracks: / Wild cat: *Various artists* / Mama Mockingbird: *Various artists* / Boodle am shake: *Various artists*/ My syncopated melody man: *Various artists* / Manhattan rag: *Various artists* / Nagasaki: *Various artists*/ Ain't misbehavin: *Various artists* / Limehouse blues: *Various artists* / Calling all keys: *Various artists*/ Nothing but notes: *Various artists* / I got rhythm: *Various artists* / Onyx club spree: *Various artists*/ Bill street blues: *Various artists* / Serenade for a wealthy widow: *Various artists* / Honeysuckle rose: *Various artists* / Fiddle blues: *Various artists*.
LP: .... **REB 680**
MC: .... **ZCF 680**

I MAESTRI DI TROMBONE (Various artists).
LP: **2MJP 1054**

I REMEMBER BEBOP (Various artists).
Tracks: / Night in Tunisia: *Various artists* / Con Alma: *Various artists* / Bebop: *Various artists*/ Salt peanuts: *Various artists* / Ladybird: *Various artists* / Casbah: *Various artists* / Afternoon in Paris: *Various artists* / Django: *Various artists* / Sacha's march: *Various artists* / Mirjana of my heart and soul: *Various artists* / Yardbird suite: *Various artists* / My little suede shoes: *Various artists*/ Now's the time: *Various artists* / Star eyes: *Various artists* / Au privave: *Various artists* / Ornithology: *Various artists* / Epistrophy: *Various artists* / In walked Bud: *Various artists* / 52nd Street theme: *Various artists* / Ruby my dear: *Various artists* / Strictly confidential: *Various artists* / Dance of the infidels: *Various artists* / Bouncing with Bud: *Various artists* / I'll keep loving you: *Various artists*/ Jeru: *Various artists* / Venus de Milo: *Various artists* / Godchild: *Various artists*.
2LP: .... **CBS 88530**

I'LL DANCE TILL DE SUN BREAKS THROUGH (Various artists).
Tracks: / Moaning saxophones rag, That: *Various artists* / Florida rag: *Various artists* / Bacchanal rag: *Various artists* / Alabama skedaddle: *Various artists* / Castle walk: *Various artists* / From soup to nuts: *Various* artists / Smokey mokes: *Various artists* / Eli Green's cake walk: *Various artists* / Cake walk, The: *Various* artists / I'll dance till de sun breaks through: *Various artists* / T'aint nobody's business if I do: *Various* artists / Whistling Rufus: *Various artists* / Wild cherries rag: *Various artists* / Bill Bailey won't you please come home: *Various artists* / Stomp dance: *Various artists* / Calico rag: *Various artists* / Smiles & chuckles: *Various artists* / On the Levee: *Various artists* / Trombone sneeze: *Various artists* / Two key rag: *Various artists*.
LP: .... **SDL 336**
MC: .... **CSDL 336**

IMPULSE JAZZ - A 30 YEAR CELEBRATION (See Impulse (Label) (Various artists).

IMPULSIVE - JAZZ DANCE 5 (Various artists).
Tracks: / Spellbinder: *Szabo, Gabor* / Hanky panky: *McFarland, Gary* / Critics choice: *Nelson, Oliver*/ Cloudburst: *Pointer Sisters* / Oo oo bossa nova, The: *Jackson, Milt* / Alfie's theme: *Rollins, Sonny*/ Mas que nada: *Gillespie, Dizzy* / Got my mojo working: *Hamilton, Chico* / Hard work: *Various artists*/ Caravan: *Tyner, McCoy* / See you later: *McCoy/ Hamilton* / Soul sauce: *Scott, Shirley*.
2LP: .... **AFFD 190**
MCSET: .... **TCAFFD 190**

IMPULSIVELY (Various artists).
2LP: .... **AS 9266**

IN THE GLENN MILLER MOOD (Various artists).
MC: .... **AM 28**

INVITATION TO DENON (Various artists).
LP: .... **ST 6008**

INVITATION TO WINDHAM HILL, AN (Various artists).
Tracks: / Thanksgiving: *Various artists* / Western: *Various artists* / Love theme: *Various artists* / Visiting: *Various artists* / In the blue distance: *Various artists*.
LP: .... **WHA 1**
MC: .... **WHC 1**

ISKRA JAZZ IN SWEDEN (Various artists).
2LP: .... **CAP 200679**

IT SOUNDS LIKE BIX (Various artists).
LP: .... **BWY 104**

JACK TEAGARDEN CLASSICS (Various artists).
LP: .... **SFR DP 649**

JACK TEAGARDEN, EDDI CONDON ALL STARS (Various artists).
LP: .... **PUMPKIN 115**

JAM SESSION (1944-46) (Various artists).
Tracks: / Roy meets horn: *Eldridge, Roy* / Old Rob Roy: *Eldridge, Roy* / Cocktails for two: *Tatum, Art*/ Liza: *Tatum, Art* / Lester leaps in: *Young, Lester* / Rose room: *James, Harry* / Lady be good: *Basie*, Count All Stars / Jammin' on A: *Various artists* / Blues: *Shavers, Charlie* / Stompin at the Savoy: *Shavers, Charlie* / Seven come eleven: *Shavers, Charlie* / Rose room: *Shavers, Charlie*.
LP: .... **SM 3119**

JAM SESSIONS (Various artists).
Tracks: / Perdido: *Various artists* / Bye bye blues: *Various artists* / Mack the knife: *Various artists*/ Milt Jackson: *Various artists* / Red top: *Brown, Ray* / That's the way it is: *Various artists* / Here 'tis: *Gillespie, Dizzy* / Freeport jump: *Basie, Count* / Sweethearts on parade: *Pablo All Stars* / Donna Lee: *Various artists*.
LP: **262 0105**
MCSET: .... **K 20 105**

JAMMIN' FOR THE JACKPOT (Various artists).
Tracks: / Caravan: *Hayes, Edgar & His Orchestra* / Casa Loma stomp: *Casa Loma Orchestra* / Dallas blues: *Kirk*, Andy/his Twelve Clouds of Joy / Mad house: *Hines, Earl 'Fatha' & His Orchestra* / Heebie jeebies: *Various artists*/ Pickin' the cabbage: *Calloway, Cab* / Ebony silhouette: *Calloway, Cab & His Orchestra* / Jammin' for the jackpot: *Mills Blue Rhythm Band* / Toby: *Moten, Bennie Kansas City Orchestra* / Blues of Avalon: *Boots & His Buddies*/ Sensational mood: *Hunter, Lloyd Serenaders* / Original dixieland one-step: *Moor, Grant & His Black Devils* / Atlanta low down: *Montgomery, J.Neal & His Orchestra* / Auburn Avenue stomp: *Montgomery, J.Neal & His Orchestra*/ West end blues: *Whyte, Zach & Chocolate Beau Brummels* / Good feelin' blues: *Whyte, Zach & Chocolate Beau Brummels*.
LP: .... **NW 217**

JAZZ '80 (Various artists).
Tracks: / Modus operandi: *Terry, Clark* / In a mellow tone: *Basie, Count* / Rockin' in rhythm: *Barber, Chris*/ Eros Hotel: *Fame, Georgie* / Interfusion: *Scott, Ronnie* / It's a sin to tell a lie: *Melly, George*/ Manteca: *Gillespie, Dizzy* / Everyday: *Williams, Joe* / Dykes on bikes: *National Youth Jazz Orchestra*/ Milenberg joys: *Ball, Kenny* / Pata pata: *Osibisa* / I heard you've been around: *Bilk, Acker* / Baby won't you please come home?: *McRae, Carmen* / Moten swing: *Basie, Count*.
2LP: .... **VJD 571**
MCSET: .... **ZC VJD 571**

JAZZ ALBUM, THE (Tribute to the Jazz Age) (Various artists).
Tracks: / Sweet Sue: *Various artists* / Makin' whoopee: *Various artists* / My blue Heaven: *Various artists*.
LP: .... **EL 747 991 1**
MC: .... **EL 747 991 4**

JAZZ AND CINEMA (Various artists).
LP: **21109**
MC: **4021109**

JAZZ AND HOT DANCE IN CHILE - 1926-1959 (Various artists).
LP: .... **HQ 2083**

JAZZ AT THE RICHMOND JAZZ FESTIVAL (Various artists).
LP: .... **WAVE LP 5**

JAZZ BAND BALL (Various artists).
Tracks: / Alexander's ragtime band: *Phillips, Sid And His Band* / Sensation rag: *Randell, Freddy And His Band*/ Crazy rhythm: *Daniel's, Joe Jazz Band* / Farewell blues: *Randall, Freddy & His Band* / Chicago: *Daniels*, Joe Jazz Group / Mama don't allow it: *Phillips, Sid And His Band* / Won't you come home Bill Bailey: *Randell*, Freddy And His Band / On Sunday I go sailing: *Richford's, Doug London Jazzmen With Nat Gonella* / Who walks in when I walk out?: *Saints Jazz Band* / Heatwave: *Lyttelton, Humphrey & His Band* / Tiger rag: *Phillips, Sid* & His Band / St. Louis blues: *Daniel's, Joe Jazz Band* / Clarinet marmalade: *Phillips, Sid And His Band* / Bad penny blues: *Lyttelton, Humphrey* / Yip-I-addy-I-ay: *Richford's, Doug London Jazzmen With Nat Gonella* / Sunday: *Randell*, Freddy And His Band / Marie: *Daniel's, Joe Jazz Band* / P.T.Q. rag: *Lyttelton, Humphrey & His Band* / Pete Kelly's blues: *Phillips, Sid And His Band* / Lily of the valley: *Crane River Jazz Band* / I wish I could shimmy like my sister Kate: *Daniel's, Joe Jazz Band* / Muskrat ramble: *Phillips, Sid & His Band* / Someday, sweetheart: *Randell, Freddy And His Band* / Susie: *Daniels, Joe Jazz Group* / Little brown jug: *Daniels, Joe Jazz Group*/ Pasadena: *Phillips, Sid & His Band* / Avalon: *Daniel's, Joe Jazz Band* / Hey lawdy papa: *Saints Jazz Band*.
2LP: .... **DL 1137**
MC: .... **TCDL 1137**

JAZZ CASSETTE SAMPLER (Various artists).
MC: .... **CC 20**

JAZZ CLASSICS IN DIGITAL STEREO (Chicago) (Various artists).
LP: .... **REB 589**
MC: .... **ZCF 589**

JAZZ CLASSICS IN DIGITAL STEREO (Kansas City) (Various artists).
LP: .... **REB 691**
MC: .... **ZCF 691**

JAZZ CLASSICS IN DIGITAL STEREO (New York) (Various artists).
LP: .... **REB 590**
MC: .... **ZCF 590**

JAZZ CLASSICS IN DIGITAL STEREO (New Orleans) (Various artists).
LP: .... **REB 588**
MC: .... **ZCF 588**

JAZZ CLASSICS IN DIGITAL STEREO (Hot town) (Various artists).
LP: .... **REB 647**
MC: .... **ZCF 647**

JAZZ CLASSICS IN DIGITAL STEREO (The Blues 1923-1933) (Various artists).
Tracks: / Give me a break blues: *Cox, Ida (with Jesse Crump)* / Nothin' but the blues: *Gibson, Cleo (with her Hot* Three) / Barrel house blues: *Henderson, Scott* / Midnight mama: *Hereford, Frances (with the Levee Serenaders)*/ Kansas City blues: *Memphis Jug Band* / Prove it on me blues: *Rainey, Ma (with her Tub Jug Washboard Band)* / Be on your merry way: *Ringgold, Issie* / Blue yodel no. 9 (Standing on the corner): *Rodgers, Jimmie (with Louis and* Lil Armstrong) / Nobody knows you (when you're down and out): *Smith, Bessie* / Jenny's ball: *Smith, Mamie*/ Moaning the blues: *Spivey, Victoria* / I got what it takes: *Webster, Margaret (with Clarence William's Washboard* Band) / That thing's done been put on me: *Whitmire, Margaret (with Arnold Wiley)* / He used to be your man: *Wilson, Lena (with the Nubian Five)*.
LP: .... **REB 683**
MC: .... **ZCF 683**

JAZZ CLUB MAINSTREAM - ALTO SAX, CLARINET AND FLUTE (Various artists).
LP: **8451451**
MC: **8451454**

JAZZ CLUB MAINSTREAM - BIG BANDS (Various artists).
LP: **8451531**
MC: **8451534**

JAZZ CLUB MAINSTREAM - DIXIELAND (Various artists).
LP: **8451491**
MC: **8451494**

JAZZ CLUB MAINSTREAM - DRUMS (Various artists).
LP: **8451481**
MC: **8451484**

JAZZ CLUB MAINSTREAM - GUITAR AND BASS (Various artists).
LP: **8451501**
MC: **8451504**

JAZZ CLUB MAINSTREAM - PIANO (Various artists).
LP: **8451471**
MC: **8451474**

JAZZ CLUB MAINSTREAM - TENOR AND BARITONE SAX (Various artists).
LP: **8451461**
MC: **8451464**

JAZZ CLUB MAINSTREAM - TROMBONE (Various artists).
LP: **8451441**
MC: **8451444**

JAZZ CLUB MAINSTREAM - TRUMPET (Various artists).
LP: **8451511**
MC: **8451514**

JAZZ CLUB MAINSTREAM - VOCAL (Various artists).
LP: **8451521**
MC: **8451524**

JAZZ COLLECTION VOL. 1 (Various artists).
LP: .... **IAJRC 1**

JAZZ COLLECTION VOL. 2 (Various artists).
LP: .... **IAJRC 2**

JAZZ FOR ABSOLUTE BEGINNERS (Various artists).
Tracks: / Moanin': *Blakey, Art* / St. Thomas: *Rollins, Sonny* / Intimacy of the blues, The: *Ellington, Duke*/ Oblivion: *Powell, Bud* / I get along without you very well (except): *Simone, Nina* / I've grown accustomed to her face: *Desmond, Paul* / Yeh yeh: *Lambert/ Hendricks/Bavan* / Straight up: *Vick, Harold* / General Mojo's well laid plan: *Burton, Gary* / Let me miss you baby: *Allen, Henry 'Red'* / Tijuana gift shop:

Mingus, Charles/ Double clutch: *Brown, Boots.*
LP: . . . . **NL 89874**
MC: . . . . **NK 89874**

JAZZ FOR YOU - HOT, HEAVY & BLUE (Various artists).
Tracks: / Bird song: *Parker, Charlie* / Blue lament: *Parker, Charlie* / It's a sin to tell a lie: *Parker, Charlie* / Cool bird: *Parker, Charlie* / All of me: *Holiday, Billie* / My man: *Holiday, Billie* / They can't take that away from me: *Holiday, Billie* / Lover come back to me: *Holiday, Billie* / Jammin' with Herbie: *Hancock, Herbie* / Hot and heavy: *Hancock, Herbie* / Cycles: *Hancock, Herbie* / Hot piano: *Hancock, Herbie* / Lover's theme: *Davis, Miles* / Cool blues: *Davis, Miles* / Love for sale: *Benson, George*/ Masquerade is over, The: *Benson, George* / There will never be another you: *Benson, George.*
2LP: . . . . **CR 5144**
MCSET: . . . . **CRT 5144**

JAZZ FROM THE GOLDEN ERA (Various artists).
LP: . . . . **VLP 52**

JAZZ GIANTS PLAY LOVE SONGS (Various artists).
2LP: . . . . **CR 027**
MCSET: . . . . **CRT 027**

JAZZ GUITAR (Various artists).
LPS: . . . . **C 76/6 BOX 6**
2LP: . . . . **NXTMC 174**

JAZZ GUITAR ALBUM Burrell, Christian, Montgomery & other artists (Various artists).
2LP: **2683 065**

JAZZ IN HARLEM (1926-31) (Various artists).
LP: . . . . **ARCADIA 2008**

JAZZ IN REVOLUTION (Big Bands in the 1940's, The) (Various artists).
Tracks: / A-la-bridges: *Leonard, Harlan and His Rockets* / Dameron stomp: *Leonard, Harlan and His Rockets* / Saint, The: *Wilson, Gerald and His Orchestra* / Elevation: *Lawrence, Elliot and His Orchestra* / Five o'clock shadow: *Lawrence, Elliot and His Orchestra* / Good jelly blues: *Eckstine, Billy & His Orchestra* / Mingus fingers: *Hampton, Lionel & His Orchestra* / Donna Lee: *Thornhill, Claude & His Orchestra* / Perdido: *Webster, Ben Quartet* / Zonky: *Six Men & A Girl* / Tea for two: *Mooney, Joe Quartet* / I can't get up the nerve: *Mooney, Joe Quartet*/ Mellow mood: *Marmarosa, Dodo Trio* / Royal roost: *Clarke, Kenny & His 52nd Street Boys* / Chase, The: *Gorden, Dexter,Wardell Gray Quintet.*
LP: . . . . **NW 284**

JAZZ IN THE THIRTIES (Various artists).
2LP: . . . . **SW 8457/8**

JAZZ IN THE THIRTIES (1933-35) (Various artists).
2LP: . . . . **SHB 39**

JAZZ - IT'S A WONDERFUL SOUND (Various artists).
Tracks: / It's a wonderful world: *Various artists* / Smoke rings: *Various artists* / Undecided: *Various artists*/ Rose of Washington Square: *Various artists* / Sweet Lorraine: *Various artists* / Rose room: *Various artists.*
LP: . . . . **QSR 0478**

JAZZ LEGENDS (Various artists).
MCSET: . . . . **M 10194**

JAZZ LIFE (Various artists).
Tracks: / R & R: *Various artists* / Black cat: *Various artists* / Lord, Lord, am I ever gonna know?: *Various artists* / Vassarlean: *Various artists* / Oh yeah, oh yeah: *Various artists.*
LP: . . . . **CS 9019**

JAZZ LIVE & RARE VOL. 1-5 (Various artists).
LPS: . . . . **JAZZLINE 95 810-14**

JAZZ MASTERS (Various artists).
2LP: **416039**

JAZZ MASTERS - 27 CLASSIC PERFORMANCES (Various artists).
LP: **4651921**
MC: **4651924**

JAZZ ME BLUES - THE CHICAGO CONNECTION (Various artists).
Tracks: / Jazz me blues: *Various artists* (Composer (Tom Delaney)) / There'll be some changes made: *Various artists*(Composer (W. Benton Overstreet/Billy Higgins) / Copenhagen: *Various artists* (Composer (Charles Davis/Frank Melrose)) / Trying to stop me crying: *Various artists* (Composer (Ray Biondi/C.J. Miskelly/Jack Lazier) / Bugle call rag: *Various* artists (Composer (Jack Pettis/Elmer Schoebel/Billy Meyers) / Downright disgusted: *Various artists* (Composer (Terry Shand/Joe Mammone) / Milenberg joys: *Various artists* (Composer (Naces/Jelly Roll Morton/ Walter Melrose)) / Wailin' blues: *Various artists* (Composer (Ted Lewis/Lester Melrose)) / Baby won't you please come home?: *Various artists* (Composer (Clarence Williams/Charles Warfield)) / Tillie's downtown now: *Various artists* (Composer (Bud Freeman)) / Fare thee well: *Various artists* (Composer (Peck Kelly/Ray Mayer/Joe Mannone)) / My daddy rocks me (with one steady rock): *Various* artists / Prince of wails: *Various artists* (Composer (Elmer Schoebel)) / I've found a new baby: *Various artists*(Composer (Spencer Williams/ Jack Palmer)) / Oh Susannah, dust off that old pianna: *Various artists* (Composer (Caeser/Lerner/Marks)) / Isn't there a little love?: *Various artists* (Composer (Joe Mannone)) / Barrel house stomp: *Various artists*(Composer (Frank Melrose)) / I've found a new baby: *Various artists* (Composer (Spencer Williams/Jack Palmer)).
LP: . . . . **AFS 1026**

JAZZ MEETING (Various artists).
LP: . . . . **FLC 5019**

JAZZ MEETING IN HOLLAND (Various artists).
LP: . . . . **CLP 10**

JAZZ MESSAGE 1956-1965 (Blue Note anniversary collection Vol. 2) (Various artists).
Tracks: / Blue train: *Coltrane, John* / Appointment in Ghana: *McLean, Jackie* / Autumn leaves: *Adderley, Cannonball* & Miles Davis / Cheesecake: *Gordon, Dexter* / Mosaic: *Blakey, Art/Jazz Messengers* / Speak no evil: *Shorter, Wayne* / Maiden voyage: *Hancock, Herbie* / Little B's poem: *Hutcherson, Bobby* / Moontrane, The: *Young, Larry.*
2LP: **BST2 92468**
MC: **TCBST2 92468**

JAZZ MONTEREY (1958-1980) (Various artists).
2LP: . . . . **PA 8080-2**

JAZZ OFF THE AIR, VOL. 1 (Various artists).
Tracks: / Ornithology: *Various artists* / Hot house: *Various artists* / Allen's alley: *Various artists*/ Lover: *Various artists* / High on an open mike: *Various artists* / Sweet Georgia Brown: *Various artists.*
LP: . . . . **SPJ 144**

JAZZ ON VERVE VOL.1 (Various artists).
Tracks: / Nobody knows: *Various artists* / Honeysuckle rose: *Various artists* / Perdido: *Hodges, Johnny* & Earl Hinds / Airmail special: *Hampton, Lionel* / Summertime: *Fitzgerald, Ella* / Sing, sing, sing: *Krupa, Gene* / Top hat, white tie and tails: *Astaire, Fred* / Cottontail: *Webster, Ben* / April in paris: *Basie, Count.*
LP: **8337794**

JAZZ ON VERVE VOL.2 (Various artists).
LP: **8337801**

JAZZ PANORAMA OF THE TWENTIES - VOL.2 (The Charleston era) (Various artists).
LP: . . . . **SM 3126**

JAZZ PIANO 2 (Various artists).
LPS: . . . . **NL 89272**

JAZZ PIANO ANTHOLOGY (Various artists).
Tracks: / Sounds of Africa: *Various artists* / Keep out of the grass: *Various artists* / Muscle shoals blues: *Various artists* / Bear trap blues: *Various artists* / In a mist: *Various artists* / Honeysuckle rose: *Various artists* / 57 Varieties: *Various artists* / World is waiting for the sunrise, The: *Various artists*/ Tiger rag: *Various artists* / Liza: *Various artists* / Boogie woogie prayer: *Various artists* / Little joe from chicago: *Various artists* / I didn't know what time it was: *Various artists* / For Miss Black: *Various artists* / Way back blues: *Various artists* / Yearning for love: *Various artists* / Round midnight: *Various* artists / Thelonious: *Various artists* / Back home again: *Various artists* / Polka Dots and Moonbeams: *Various* artists / In your own sweet way: *Various artists* / Silver: *Various artists* / Silver blue: *Various artists*/ Billy boy: *Various artists* / Pawn ticket: *Various artists* / Splendid splinter: *Various artists* / Port of call: *Various artists.*
2LP: . . . . **S 2VL 1006**

JAZZ POTPOURRI 2 (20 collector items 1925-1933) (Various artists).
Tracks: / Find me at the Greasy Spoon: *Grant, Coot/Kid Wesley Wilson* / Tack Annie: *Oliver, King Dixie Syncopators*/ Rhythmic dream, A: *Henderson, Fletcher* / Endurance stomp: *Cobb, Junie C.* / I can't give you anything but love: *Ellington, Duke* / West End blues: *Oliver, King & his Orchestra* / My good man Sam: *Oliver, King & his Orchestra*/ After you've gone: *Nichols, Red/his Five Pennies* / Is that religion: *Calloway, Cab* / Honeysuckle rose: *Trumbauer, Frank* & His Orchestra / Strange as it seems: *Hall, Adelaide* / I'll never be the same: *Hall, Adelaide* / You gave me everything but love: *Hall, Adelaide* / This time it's love: *Hall, Adelaide* / Just so you'll remember: *Wiley, Lee* / Trust me for a hamburger: *Washboard Rhythm Boys* / Mama don't allow it: *Jaxon, Frankie 'Half Pint'* / Spank it: *Jaxon, Frankie 'Half Pint'* / Mortgage blues part I: *Jaxon, Frankie 'Half Pint'* / Mortgage blues part II: *Jaxon, Frankie 'Half Pint'.*
LP: . . . . **MERITT 24**

JAZZ POTPOURRI 3 (20 collector items 1933-1947) (Various artists).
Tracks: / Everybody shuffle: *Venuti, Joe & Orchestra* / You gave me everything but love: *Chittison, Herman* / Sheik of Araby, The: *Three Peppers* / Margie: *Kyle, Billy* / Did anyone ever tell you: *Gotham Stompers*/ If dreams come true: *Johnson, James P.* / Shuffleberg shuffle: *Carter, Benny* / Shuffleberg shuffle (3rd try): *Carter, Benny* / Vagabond dreams: *Carter, Benny* / Love's got me down: *Carter, Benny* / More than you know: *Carter, Benny* / More than you know (2nd try): *Carter, Benny* / Relaxin' at the Touro: *Spanier, Muggsy* & His Ragtime Band / Untitled instrumental: *Fitzgerald, Ella & Her Orchestra* / Secrets in the moonlight: *James, Harry & His Orchestra* / It's the same old story: *Holiday, Billie & Her Orchestra* / Am I blue?: *Holiday, Billie*/ Cattin' at the Keynote: *Hawkins, Coleman Quartet* / Buddy Bolden: *Bechet, Sidney Quartet* / Song of songs: *Bechet, Sidney Quartet.*
LP: . . . . **MERITT 25**

JAZZ REACTIVATION (Various artists).
Tracks: / Confirmation: *Parker, Charlie & Dizzy Gillespie* / Kaba's blues: *Hampton, Lionel* / Boptura: *Ventura, Charlie* / Things ain't what they used to be: *Hodges, Johnny* / I got rhythm: *Wilson, Teddy (dup)* / It don't mean a thing: *Armstrong, Louis/Duke Ellington* / I cover the waterfront: *Brown, Clifford* / How high the moon: *Reinhardt, Django* / On Green Dolphin Street: *Powell, Bud* / Rat race: *Basie, Count* / Petite Fleur: *Bechet*, Sidney / Viva Gordo (long live Fats): *Richards, Johnny* / New blues up and down: *Ammons, Gene & Sonny Stitt*/ Keep on keepin' on: *Herman, Woody* / Soft winds: *Burrell, Kenny* / Mission to Moscow: *Goodman, Benny*/ 55th and state: *Sims, Zoot* / Shaw 'nuff: *Red Rodney (see under Rodney, Red)* / Off minor: *Monk, Thelonious*/ Lester leaps in: *Jacquet, Illinois.*
2LP: . . . . **JRSD 6901**
MCSET: . . . . **ZCJRS 6901**

JAZZ SAMPLER (Compact/Walkman jazz) (Various artists).
MC: **831 376 4**

JAZZ SAMPLER VOL.1 (Various artists).
Tracks: / Bye bye blackbird: *Davis, Miles Quintet* / Teach me tonight: *Garner, Erroll* / All of one: *Ellington, Duke* / What a little moonlight can do: *Holiday, Billie* / Bluebirds in the moonlight: *Goodman, Benny* / Monk's dream: *Monk, Thelonious* / Buzzard song: *Davis, Miles* / How long blues: *Basie, Count* / Fables of Faubus: *Mingus, Charles* / Newport up: *Ellington, Duke* / Gone with the wind: *Brubeck, Dave Quartet.*
LP: **4509791**
MC: **4509794**

JAZZ SAMPLER VOL.2 (Various artists).
LP: **4600631**
MC: **4600634**

JAZZ SAMPLER VOL.5 (Various artists).
LP: **4633351**
MC: **4633354**

JAZZ SAMPLER VOL. 3 (Various artists).
Tracks: / Doctor Jekyll: *Davis, Miles* / Lester Leaps In: *Basie, Count* / My Heart Stood Still: *Garner, Erroll*/ Clarinet a La King: *Goodman, Benny* / Echoes of Harlem: *Williams, Cootie* / Wholly cats: *Christian, Charlie*/ How Long: *Webster, Ben/Edison* / Mooche, The: *Ellington, Duke.*
LP: **4606101**
MC: **4606104**

JAZZ SAMPLER VOL 4 (Various artists).
Tracks: / C jam blues: *Ellington, Duke* / Ligia: *Getz, Stan* / Two bass hit: *Davis, Miles & John Coltrane*/ One never knows...: *Holiday, Billie* / Good bait: *Gillespie, Dizzy* / Old yazoo: *Boswell Sisters* / Cornet chop suey: *Armstrong, Louis* / Take the 'A' train: *Roche/ Ellington* / Thelonious: *Monk, Thelonious*/ Things ain't what they used to be: *Various artists.*
LP: **4608261**
MC: **4608264**

JAZZ SINGER (ORIGINAL) (Film soundtrack) (Various artists).
2LP: . . . . **ST 102**
2LP: . . . . **STK 102**

JAZZ SINGERS (Various artists).
2LP: . . . . **P 24113**

JAZZ SOUNDS OF THE TWENTIES (Dixieland bands) (Various artists).
LP: . . . . **S 1254**

JAZZ SOUNDS OF THE TWENTIES Blues singers (Various artists).
LP: . . . . **S 1240**

JAZZ SPECTACULAR (Various artists).
LP: . . . . **CBS 32413**
MC: **40 32413**

JAZZ STUDIO 1 (Various artists).
LP: . . . . **JASM 1022**

JAZZ STUDIO 2 (Various artists).
Tracks: / Laura: *Jazz Studio Two* / Here come the lions: *Jazz Studio Two* / Paicheck: *Jazz Studio Two*/ Graas point: *Jazz Studio Two* / Darn that dream: *Jazz Studio Two* / Do it again: *Jazz Studio Two.*
LP: . . . . **JASM 1029**

JAZZ TODAY VOL.1 (Various artists).
Tracks: / Sunday in New York: *Cole, Richie* / O.T.V.O.G.: *Rollins, Sonny* / Scrapple from the apple: *Morgan*, Frank Quartet / If dreams come true: *White, Carla* / Movin' on: *McGriff, Jimmy* / Vicki: *Crawford, Hank*/ Underground express: *Campbell, Kerry* / Samba for Isabelle: *Habian, Cliff* / Toc de bola: *Azymuth* / Jacaranda: *Roditi, Claudio.*
LP: . . . . **BGP 1026**

JAZZ WOMEN (A feminist retrospective) (Various artists).
2LP: . . . . **ST 109**

JAZZMEN (see under Capitol (label)) (Various artists).

JIVE AT FIVE (Various artists).
Tracks: / Every tub: *Basie, Count & Orchestra* / Melancholy: *Dodds, Johnny* / What is this thing: *Johnson*, James P. / What is this thing: *Becket, Sidney* / Pardon me pretty baby: *Carter, Benny* / I know that you know: *Noone, Jimmie* / I've found a new baby: *Goodman Sextet, Benny* / Body and soul: *Hawkins, Coleman* / I double dare you: *Various artists* / Passion flower: *Hodges, Johnny* / Three blind mice: *Chicago Loopers*/ Love me tonight: *Hines, Earl "Fatha"* / Bugle call rag: *Chocolate Dandies* / Wolverine blues: *Baby Dodds Trio* / Slippin' around: *Red & Miffs Stompers* / Pitter panther patter: *Ellington, Duke/ Jimmy Blanton* / Jive at five: *Basie, Count & Orchestra.*
LP: . . . . **NW 274**

KANSAS CITY MEMORIES (Various artists).
LP: . . . . **IAJRC 44**

KICKS (Jazz dance 4) (Various artists).
Tracks: / Mr. Kicks: *Brown, Oscar Jnr* / Green onions: *Santamaria, Mongo* / Hot fudge: *Doggett, Bill*/ Capricious: *Mulligan, Gerry* / Caravan: *Lambert, Hendricks & Annie Ross* / So what: *Davis, Miles* / Eso beso: *Ames, Nancy* / Fever: *Greco, Buddy* / Latin America: *Walton, Cedar* / Down Santiago way: *Various* artists / Signifying monkey, The: *Brown, Oscar Jnr* / Comin' home baby: *Torme, Mel* / Watermelon man: *Mann, Herbie* / Why not: *Pike, Dave* / Get out of town: *Mulligan, Gerry* / Take five: *Brubeck, Dave* / La Bamba: *Santamaria, Mongo.*
2LP: . . . . **AFFD 180**

KING OF DRUMS (Various artists).
LP: . . . . **CBS 21113**
MC: **40-21113**

KINGS OF DIXIELAND (See under Kings of...) (Various artists).

KINGS OF DIXIELAND: VOL 1 (Various artists).
LP: . . . . **BO 726**

KINGS OF DIXIELAND: VOL 2 (Various artists).
LP: . . . . **BO 727**

KINGS OF DIXIELAND: VOL 3 (Various artists).
LP: . . . . **BO 728**

KINGS OF DIXIELAND: VOL 4 (Various artists).
LP: . . . . **BO 729**

KINGS OF DIXIELAND: VOL 5 (Various artists).
LP: . . . . **BO 730**

KINGS OF DIXIELAND: VOL 6 (Various artists).

LP: BO 731

KINGS OF SWING (Various artists).
Tracks: / I've heard that song before: *James, Harry Orchestra* / Willow weep for me: *Goodman, Benny* / Ultra: *James, Harry* / Oh lady be good: *Goodman, Benny* / All or nothing at all: *James, Harry* / Intermission riff: *Kenton, Stan* / Peanut vendor: *Kenton, Stan* / You make me love you: *James, Harry* / Take the 'A' train: *Kenton, Stan* / Satin doll: *James, Harry* / Don't be that way: *Goodman, Benny* / Two o'clock jump: *James, Harry.*
LP: TAB 35

LADIES OF SWING, THE (Various artists).
Tracks: / Beyond the blue horizon: *Tilton, Martha* / Hundred from today, A: *Christie, June* / You and I passing by: *Lee, Peggy* / Maybe you'll be there: *Holiday, Billie* / I get along without you very well: *Clooney, Rosemary.*
MC: CONE 1

L'AIR DE COTE (Various artists).
LP: DRLP 145

LEADING LADIES OF JAZZ (Various artists).
LP: 32004
MC: 62004

LEGENDARY NFJO CONCERT, THE (Various artists).
LP: DM 10

LEGENDS OF BRITISH TRADITION (Various artists).
MC: CMJMC 014

LEGENDS OF JAZZ (Various artists).
LP: CJP 2

LEGENDS OF JAZZ, THE (Various artists).
LP: BB 1001

LIGHTING THE FUSE 1970 -1989 (Blue Note anniversary collection vol. 5) (Various artists).
Tracks: / Windjammer: *Green, Grant* / Angelina: *Klugh, Earl* / Living for the city: *Pointer, Noel* / Black Byrd: *Byrd, Donald* / Harlem river drive: *Humphrey, Bobbi* / Always there: *Laws, Ronnie* / Lady in my life, The: *Jordan, Stanley* / Boogie on reggae woman: *Turrentine, Stanley* / All night dance: *Wallace, Bennie* / Thinkin' about your body: *McFerrin, Bobby* / Better days: *Reeves, Dianne* / Never said: *Reeves, Dianne* / Timothee: *Lagrene, Bireli.*
2LP: BST2 92477
MC: TCBST2 92477

LITTLE BIT THIS, A LITTLE BIT THAT (Various artists).
Tracks: / Lying in the hay: *Stone, Lew & His Band* / Just a crazy song: *Lally, Arthur And The Millionaires* / Limehouse blues: *Hughes, Spike And His Dance Orchestra* / When you're smiling: *Gonella, Nat* / Let's put out the lights: *Stone, Lew & His Band* / Chinese laundry blues: *Hylton, Jack & His Orchestra* / Wicked Mr. Punch: *Lally, Arthur And His Orchestra* / Life's desire: *Lally, Arthur And The Millionaires* / Time alone will tell: *Philips, Sid And His Melodians* / Evening in Caroline, An: *Fillis, Len And His Hawaiian Orchestra* / Queen was in her parlour, The: *Lally, Arthur And The Millionaires* / Do de o do: *Hylton, Jack & His Orchestra* / Tell me (you love me): *Philips, Sid And His Melodians* / I can't believe that you're in love with me: *Gonella, Nat* / Brighter than the sun: *Stone, Lew & His Orchestra* / I heard: *Gonella, Nat.*
LP: JOY 274
MC: TC JOY'D 24

LITTLE CLUB JAZZ (Various artists).
Tracks: / My honey's loving arms: *Venuti's, Joe -Blue Four* / Rocky mountain blues: *Harlem Footwarmers* / Herje Kati: *South, Eddie & His International Orchestra* / Sister Kate (I wish that I could shimmy like my): *Allen, Henry* / Hawkins, Coleman and Their Orchestras / China boy: *Candy and Coco* / Square face: *Gifford, Gene & His Orchestra*/ I got rhythm: *Norvo, Red & His Swing Sextet* / Chasing shadows: *Dandridge, Putney & His Orchestra* / Knock, knock: *Smith, Stuff & His Onyx Club Orchestra* / In a little gypsy tearoom: *Prima, Louis & His New Orleans Gang* / Bugle call rag: *Roly's Tap-Room Gang* / Jungle love: *Wilson, Teddy/his orchestra* / What's the use?: *Emilio Caceres Trio* / Clarinet marmalade: *Marala, Joe Chicagoans* / Beale Street Mama: *Howard, Bob & His Orchestra* / Tapioca: *Bigard, Barney & His Jazzopaters* / Blues in my condition: *Williams, Cootie and His Orchestra* / Buglers dilemma: *Kirby, John & His Orchestra.*
LP: NW 250

LIVE AT SWEET BASIL, VOL. 2 (Eric Dolphy and Booker Little Remembered) (Various artists).
LP: K 28P 6476

LIVE AT THE HAIG, LOS ANGELES 1952 (Various artists).
LP: JAMM SESSION 101
LP: JAMM SESSION 102

LIVE AT THE TRADEWINDS, INGLEWOOD 1952 (Various artists).
LP: JAMM SESSION 103

LIVE: BIG BANDS (Various artists).
LP: LP 45-145

LIVE: BIG BANDS AT THE WALDORF (1938-40) (Various artists).
LP: LP 41-141

LIVE EUROPEAN CONCERT (Various artists).
Tracks: / Bauhaus: *Various artists* / Tenderly: *Various artists* / Makin' whoopee: *Various artists* / C jam blues: *Various artists* / Yardbird suite: *Various artists* / Sunday: *Various artists* / Willow weep for me: *Various artists* / This can't be love: *Various artists.*
LP: UJ 25

LIVE - ON THE SUNNY SIDE OF THE STREET (Various artists).
Tracks: / On the sunny side of the street: *Town Hall Jazz Festival* / What's going on?: *Town Hall Jazz Festival*/ Mighty fine wine: *Town Hall Jazz Festival* / For Heaven's sake: *Town Hall Jazz Festival* / Cecil the Great: *Town Hall Jazz Festival* / Mulligan stew: *Town Hall Jazz Festival* / Ebb tide: *Town Hall Jazz Festival.*
LP: JATH 11436

LIVING NEW ORLEANS JAZZ 1973 (Various artists).
LP: SMOKEY MARY 1973T

LIVING NEW ORLEANS JAZZ 1974 (Various artists).
LP: SMOKEY MARY 1974P

LOVE ME BLUE (The Music of Lennon & McCartney) (Various artists).
Tracks: / Can't buy me love: *Turrentine, Stanley* / Eleanor Rigby: *Jordan, Stanley* / I want to hold your hand: *Green, Grant* / Yesterday: *Morgan, Lee* / From me to you: *McFerrin, Bobby* / Hey Jude: *Turrentine, Stanley* / In my life: *Goldstein, Gil* / Get back: *Three Sounds* / Eleanor Rigby: *Smith, Lonnie* / Hey Jude: *Jazz Crusaders.*
MC: B4 94861

LUCKY DAY (Top American Bands of The 1920's) (Various artists).
Tracks: / Sweet Georgia Brown: *California Ramblers* / I'm gonna Charleston back to Charleston: *Coon-Sanders Original* Nighthawk Orchestra / Ukelele Lady: *Rester, Harry Syncopators* / I love my baby (my baby loves me): *Waring's Pennsylvanians*/ Bye bye blackbird: *Reisman, Leo Orch.* / So is your old lady: *Warner's Seven Aces* / Birth of the blues: *Reisman, Leo* Orch. / Lucky day: *Lanin, Howard & His Orchestra* / Who: *Ipana Troubadors* / It all depends on you: *Rich, Fred/Hotel* Astor Orchestra / Hallelujah: *Shilkret, Nat & His Orchestra* / My blue Heaven: *Voorhees, Don & His* Orchestra / South wind: *Davison, Walter Louisville Loons* / Good news: *Olsen, George & His Music* / I'm looking over a four leafed clover: *Goldkette, Jean & His Orchestra* / She's got it: *Weems, Ted & His Orchestra* / Sometimes I'm happy: *Kahn, Roger Wolfe & His Orchestra* / My melancholy baby: *Charleston Chasers* / Singin' in the rain: *Rich, Freddie & His Orchestra* / Turn on the heat: *Heidt, Horace & His Californians.*
LP: SVL 175
MC: CSVL 175

MADE IN CHICAGO (Various artists).
LP: SOS 1164

MADE IN DENMARK (Various artists).
LP: ML 111

MANASSAS JAZZ FESTIVAL (Various artists).
LP: J 17

MASTER JAZZ PIANO 1928-30 (Various artists).
LP: S 1298

MASTER JAZZ PIANO VOL.3 (Various).
LP: S 1337

MASTER JAZZ PIANO VOL.4 (Various).
LP: S 1363

MASTER JAZZ PIANO VOL.6 (Various).
LP: S 1387

MASTERS OF THE TENOR SAXOPHONE (Various artists).
LPS: BOX 252
MCSET: TCBOX 252

MELLOW MAYHEM (Various artists).
Tracks: / Dewey's tune: *Jones, Ed Quartet* / Mbatanga blues: *Africa, Mervi* / Woza: *Deppa, Claude Trio*/ Sunrise: *Sheppard, Andy* / When will: *O'Higgins, Mal* / Phil's blues: *Bent, Phillip Band.*
LP: JCR 902
MC: JCRMC 902

MEMPHIS JAZZ FESTIVAL 1982 (Various artists).
LP: J 134

METROPOLITAN OPERA HOUSE (Various artists).
LP: FDC 1001

MIDNIGHT ON BOURBON STREET (Various artists).
Tracks: / Sheik of Araby, The: *Various artists* / Temptation rag: *Various artists* / Eh la bas: *Various artists*/ She's crying for me: *Various artists* / Li'l Liza Jane: *Various artists* / Corina Corina: *Various artists*/ San: *Various artists* / Jazz it blues: *Various artists* / That's a plenty: *Various artists* / Won't you come home Bill Bailey: *Various artists* / On the sunny side of the street: *Various artists* / Mama don't allow it: *Various artists* / Pizza pie boogie: *Various artists.*
LP: RHA 6035

MILLS BLUE RHYTHM BAND, 1931 Mills Music Masters, Blue Rhythm Boys, Blue Ribb (Various artists).
LP: CJM 23

MODERN ART OF JAZZ BY MAT MATHEWS (Various artists).
LP: FS 245

MODERN JAZZ (Various artists).
LP: 509171

MODERN JAZZ PIANO ALBUM (Various artists).
2LP: WL 70510

MONTREUX 79 (Various artists).
LP: RHAP 9

MONTREUX SUMMIT 2 (Various artists).
2LP: CBS 88286

MONTREUX SUMMIT, VOL 1 (Various artists).
Tracks: / Montreux summit: *Various artists* / Infant eyes: *Various artists* / Blues march: *Various artists*/ Bahama mama: *Various artists* / Fried bananas: *Various artists* / Andromeda: *Various artists.*
2LP: CBS 88277

MOONLIGHT SERENADE (Various artists).
MC: 40190
LP: 20190

MORE SOUNDS OF THE SWING YEARS (Various artists).
LP: SG 8003

MUSIC BEYOND THE HORIZON (Various artists).
Tracks: / Talkin' 'bout you: *Schuur, Diane* / Night rhythms: *Ritenour, Lee* / Key to you, The: *Benoit, David*/ Flashpoint: *Scott, Tom* / Sailing at night: *Grusin, Dave & Don* / I don't wanna know: *Stuermer, Daryl*/ Times like these: *Burton, Gary* / Same ole love: *Cobham, Billy* / Columbus Avenue: *Valentin, Dave* / Touch of light, A: *Egan, Mark* / Passage: *Corea, Chick Elektric Band* / Special EFX: *Jamaica, Jamaica.*
LP: A 9576
MC: C 9576

MUSIC FROM THE COTTON CLUB (Various artists).
LP: 20186
MC: 40186

MUSIC ON THE MOVE (20 Big Band & Jazz Greats) (Various artists).
MC: INTK 9003
MC: NK 89330

MUSIC WITHOUT FRONTIERS VOL.1 (Selections from the Venture label) (Various artists).
Tracks: / 7.50: *Itchy Fingers* / Vibe waltz: *Bowie, Lester, Brass Fantasy* / For Vic: *Niebla, Eduardo/Antonio Forcione* / Fox chase, The: *O'Suilleabhain, Michael* / Myoho: *De Havilland, Peter* / Pursuit of pleasure: *Way,Daryl/Opus20*/ Dancer's song, The: *Webb, Cassell* / Nebuchadnezzar's dream: *Schulze, Klaus/Andreas Grosser* / Pas du deux: *Roedelius, Hans Joachim.*
LP: VE 9
MC: TCVE 9

MUSIC WITHOUT FRONTIERS VOL.2 (Selections from the Venture label) (Various artists).
Tracks: / Kosasa: *Gibbs, Mike Orchestra* / Teranga: *Itchy Fingers* / Big G: *McGregor, Chris/Brotherhood Of Breath* / Llano: *Webb, Cassell* / Sayonara: *McKenna, Mae* / A Esperanca: *Purim, Flora* / Snow: *Electric Circus* / Assassin: *Laswell, Bill* / Voodoo bolero: *Nocenzi, Gianni* / Green Chinese table, The: *Ono, Seigen* / An mhaighdean cheansa (The gentle maiden): *O'Suilleabhain, Michael* / Ricercare per pianoforte: *Morricone, Ennio* / Wedding tango: *Nyman, Michael* / Viennese waltz.
2LP: VESD 30
MC: TVESD 30

MUSICAL MADNESS, 1938 - 59 (Various artists).
LP: BS 7118

NEW MAGIC SAMPLER (Various artists).
DAT: GRT 9549

NEW MUSIC: SECOND WAVE (Various artists).
LP: SJL 2235

NEW ORLEANS 1924-1925 (Various artists).
Tracks: / Panama: *Droit, Johnny De & His New Orleans Jazz Orchestra* / Nobody knows blues: *Droit, Johnny De & His* New Orleans Jazz Orchestra / Southern woman blues: *Bolden, Lela* / Seawall special blues: *Bolden, Lela* / Swing, The: *Droit, Johnny De & His New Orleans Jazz Orchestra* / Frankie and Johnny: *Fate Marable Society Syncopators*/ Pianoflage: *Fate Marable Society Syncopators* / Black but sweet oh God: *Mack, Billy & Mary* / My heartbreakin' gal: *Mack, Billy & Mary* / Cross word mama: *Papalia,Russ & His Orchestra* / I never knew what a gal could do: *New* Orleans Rhythm Kings / Original Tuxedo rag: *Original Tuxedo Jazz Orchestra* / Careless love: *Original Tuxedo Jazz Orchestra* / Black rag: *Original Tuxedo Jazz Orchestra.*
LP: RHA 6033

NEW ORLEANS BANDS 1924-28 Various artists (Various artists).
MC: NEO 769

NEW ORLEANS DAYS (Various artists).
2LP: 400034

NEW ORLEANS DIXIELAND EXPRESS (Various artists).
LP: GHB 133

NEW ORLEANS HORNS (Various artists).
2LP: DLP 501/502

NEW ORLEANS IN THE TWENTIES (Various artists).
LP: VLP 46

NEW ORLEANS JAZZ FESTIVAL Various artists (Various artists).
Tracks: / Caledonia: *Various artists* / Brown skin gal: *Various artists* / Ice cream freezer: *Various artists*/ Baby what you want me to do: *Various artists* / Breaks, The: *Various artists* / Paul Barbarin's second line: *Various artists* / Rock me mama: *Various artists* / Joie blonde: *Various artists* / Charleston rag: *Various artists* / Darktown strutters ball: *Various artists* / Themes from a movie: *Various artists* / Doxology: *Various artists.*
LP: SNTF 812

NEW ORLEANS JAZZ FROM JIMMY RYAN'S (Various artists).
LP: 502004

NEW ORLEANS JAZZ & HERITAGE FESTIVAL Tenth anniversary (Various artists).
LP: FF 099

NEW ORLEANS JAZZ, NOVEMBER 1988 Live at Leatherhead (Various artists).
MC: KCT 1C

NEW ORLEANS JAZZ PARTY (Various artists).
Tracks: / Basin Street blues: *Various artists* / When the saints go marching in: *Various artists* / Buddy Bolden's blues: *Various artists* / Careless love: *Various artists* / Bucket's got a hole in it: *Various artists*/ Blues: *Various artists* / High society: *Various artists* / Milenberg joys: *Various artists* / 2.19 blues: *Various artists* / Grandpa's spells: *Various artists* / Wolverine blues: *Various artists* / Armand hug interview: *Various artists* / Buzzards parade: *Various artists* / Bill Bailey won't you please come home: *Various* artists / Fidgety feet: *Various artists* / Closer walk with thee, A: *Various artists* / Saints, The: *Various artists.*
LP: RARITIES 62

NEW ORLEANS JAZZ REVIVAL, VOL.1 (Various artists).
LP: S 855

NEW ORLEANS JAZZ REVIVAL, VOL.2 (Various artists).
LP: S 856

NEW ORLEANS JAZZ VOL.1 (Various artists).
LP: WJS 1001

NEW ORLEANS JAZZ VOL.2 (Various artists).
LP: . . . . **WJS 1002**

NEW ORLEANS LEGENDS Kid Ory, Joe Darensbourg, Singleton Palmer (Various artists).
Tracks: / Didn't he ramble: *All Star Marching band* / Bourbon Street: *All Star Marching band* / Hindustan: *All Star* Marching band / Savoy blues: *Ory, Kid* / That's a plenty: *Ory, Kid* / Sugar foot: *Ory, Kid*/ Tin roof blues: *Palmer, Singleton* / Sweet Georgia Brown: *Palmer, Singleton* / Careless love: *Palmer, Singleton*/ Ballin' the Jack: *Palmer, Singleton* / Just a closer walk with thee: *Buckner, Teddy* / Chinatown: *Buckner*, Teddy / Yellow dog blues: *Darensbourg, Joe* / That da da strain: *Darensbourg, Joe* / Copenhagen: *Darensbourg, Joe* / Bogalusa Street: *New Orleans Heritage* / Fidgety feet: *New Orleans Heritage*.
LP: **429006**
MC: **829006**

NEW ORLEANS MASTERS VOL.1 (Various artists).
LP: . . . . **SWH 42**
MC: . . . . **CSWH 42**

NEW ORLEANS RHYTHM KINGS 1922-23 Vol. 1 (Various).
LP: . . . . **S 829**

NEW ORLEANS RHYTHM KINGS 1923 Vol. 2 (Various).
LP: . . . . **S 830**

NEW ORLEANS RHYTHM KINGS 1934-35 (Various).
LP: . . . . **S 826**

NEW ORLEANS STOMP (Various artists).
LP: . . . . **VLP 35**

NEW ORLEANS, VOL 2 1924-25 (Various artists).
LP: . . . . **RHA 6038**

NEWPORT ALL STARS (Various artists).
Tracks: / Take the 'A' train: *Various artists* / These foolish things: *Various artists* / My Monday date: *Various* artists / Body and soul: *Various artists* / Mean to me: *Various artists* / I surrender, dear: *Various artists* / Please don't talk about me when I'm gone: *Various artists* / Pan Am blues: *Various artists*.
LP: . . . . **BLP 30115**

NEWPORT JAZZ FESTIVAL (Various artists).
2LP: **88605**

NEWPORT JAZZ FESTIVAL (Various artists).
LP: . . . . **BVL 011**

NEWPORT JAZZ FESTIVAL ALL STARS (Various artists).
Tracks: / Exactly like you: *Various artists* / Centennial blues: *Various artists* / I didn't know about you: *Various* artists / Nobody knows you (when you're down and out): *Various artists* / Rosetta: *Various artists* / Smiles: *Various artists* / Jeep is jumpin': *Various artists* / Mooche, The: *Various artists* / Body and soul: *Various artists* / Man I love, The: *Various artists* / What's new?: *Various artists* / Struttin' with some barbecue: *Various artists* / Moten swing: *Various artists*.
LP: . . . . **CJ 260**

NIGHT AT THE SAVOY (Various artists).
LP: . . . . **TAX 8006**

NOVUS SAMPLER (Various artists).
LP: . . . . **NL 90466**
MC: . . . . **NK 90466**

NOW: CREATIVE ARTS JAZZ ENSEMBLE (Various artists).
LP: . . . . **ARHOOLIE 8002**

OLD TIME CHAMPIONSHIP DANCES (Various artists).
2LP: . . . . **DTL 3000/3001**

OLD TIME JAZZ FOREVER (Various artists).
LP: . . . . **WAM/S No.455123**

OLYMPIC ROCK (Don Radar, Jack Earls, Leon James & others) (Various artists).
LP: . . . . **DIAL LP 004**

ON THE CUTTING EDGE (Various artists).
MC: . . . . **GRP 95904**

ONE NIGHT WITH BLUE NOTE VOL 4 (Various artists).
Tracks: / Blessing: *Various artists* / Tone poem: *Various artists* / Lady lay: *Various artists* / El encanto: *Various artists* / How long: *Various artists* / Jumpin' jack: *Various artists* / When you wish upon a star: *Various artists*.
LP: . . . . **BT 85116**

ONE NIGHT WITH BLUE NOTE VOL 3 (Various artists).
Tracks: / Moanin: *Various artists* / Child is born, A: *Various artists* / Jumpin blues: *Various artists*/ Summertime: *Various artists* / I'm glad there is you: *Various artists* / Blues walk: *Various artists*/ Getting sentimental over you: *Various artists*.
LP: . . . . **BT 85115**

ONE NIGHT WITH BLUE NOTE VOL 1 (Various artists).
Tracks: / Canteloupe island: *Various artists* / Recorda me: *Various artists* / Little b's poem: *Various artists*/ Bouquet: *Various artists* / Hat and beard: *Various artists*.
LP: . . . . **BT 85113**

ONE NIGHT WITH BLUE NOTE VOL 2 (Various artists).
Tracks: / Sweet and lovely: *Various artists* / Appointment in ghana: *Various artists* / Passion dance: *Various* artists / Blues on the corner: *Various artists* / Pontos cantados: *Various artists* / Broadside: *Various artists*.
LP: . . . . **BT 85114**

ORGAN BOOGIE WOOGIE (Various artists).
LP: . . . . **CBS 21079**
MC: **40 21079**

OTHER SIDE OF THE SINGING DETECTIVE (Various artists).
Tracks: / Umbrella man: *Kaye, Sammy Orchestra* / Copenhagen: *Various artists* / I'll just close my eyes: *Shelton*, Anne / Old Moses put Pharoah in his place: *Waring, Fred & His Pennsylvanians* / Stop crying / Three caballeros: *Crosby*, Bing & Andrews Sisters / That's for me: *Haymes, Dick* / I'll be around: *Mills Brothers* / Sing nightingale sing: *Anderson, Lale* / There's something wrong with the weather: *Stone, Lew & His Band* / Java jive: *Ink* Spots / There's a fellow waiting in Poughkeepsie: *Crosby, Bing & Andrews Sisters* / Till then: *Mills Brothers*/ Chinatown, my Chinatown: *Jolson, Al* / Let the people sing: *Payne, Jack Orchestra* / I'm making believe: *Inkspots* with Ella Fitzgerald / Little Dutch mill: *Noble, Ray & His Orchestra & Al Bowlly* / Hush, hush, hush, here comes the bogeyman: *Hall, Henry Orchestra* / Later on: *Lynn, Vera* / Bird songs at eventide: *Ronalde, Ronnie with Robert Farnon & Orchestra*.
LP: . . . . **REN 708**
MC: . . . . **ZCN 708**

OUT OF THE BLUE VOL.1 (Various artists).
LP: . . . . **LPBR 1**
MC: . . . . **LPBRC 1**

OUTSIDE IN 1964-1989 Blue Note 50th anniversary collection vol. 4 (Various artists).
Tracks: / Out to lunch: *Dolphy, Eric* / Black fire: *Hill, Andrew* / Broad way blues: *Coleman, Ornette*/ Passion dance: *Tyner, McCoy* / OTB / Life of the party: *Williams, Tony* / Calling Miss Khadija: *Hubbard, Freddie/Woody Shaw* / Song from the old country: *Pullen, Don & Adams, George Quartet* / Beatrice: *Henderson, Joe*/ She did it again: *Petrucciani, Michel*.
2LP: **BST2 92474**
MC: **TCBST2 92474**

PACIFIC JAZZ COLLECTION (Various artists).
Tracks: / St. Louis blues: *Evans, Gil* / King Porter stomp: *Evans, Gil* / Willow tree: *Evans, Gil* / Struttin' with some barbecue: *Evans, Gil* / Lester leaps in: *Evans, Gil* / Round midnight: *Evans, Gil*/ Manteca: *Evans, Gil* / Bird feathers: *Evans, Gil* / Davenport blues: *Evans, Gil* / Straight no chaser: *Evans, Gil* / Ballad of the sad young man: *Evans, Gil* / Joy Spring: *Evans, Gil* / Django: *Evans, Gil* / Chant of the weed: *Evans, Gil* / La Nevada: *Evans, Gil* / Love me or leave me: *Lewis, John/Bill* Perkins / I can't get started: *Lewis, John/Bill Perkins* / Easy living: *Lewis, John/Bill Perkins* / 2 degrees East - 3 degrees West: *Lewis, John/Bill Perkins* / Skylark: *Lewis, John/ Bill Perkins* / Almost like being in love: *Lewis, John/Bill Perkins* / Stompin' at the Savoy: *Hall, Jim* / Things ain't what they used to be: *Hall, Jim*/ Thanks for the memory: *Hall, Jim* / Tangerine: *Hall, Jim* / Stella by starlight: *Hall, Jim* / 9.20 special: *Hall, Jim* / Deep in a dream: *Hall, Jim* / Look for the silver lining: *Hall, Jim* / Seven come eleven: *Hall, Jim* / Thing's ain't what they used to be (alt. take): *Hall, Jim* / Too close for comfort: *Hall, Jim*/ To Mickey's memory: *Baker, Chet* / Slightly above moderate: *Baker, Chet* / Halema: *Baker, Chet* / Revelation: *Baker, Chet* / Something for Liza: *Baker, Chet* / Lucius Lu: *Baker, Chet* / Worrying the life out of me: *Baker, Chet* / Medium rock: *Baker, Chet* / I can't believe that you're in love with me: *Konitz, Lee & Gerry* Mulligan / Broadway: *Konitz, Lee & Gerry Mulligan* / Almost like being in love: *Konitz, Lee & Gerry Mulligan*/ Sextet I: *Konitz, Lee & Gerry Mulligan* / Lady be good: *Konitz, Lee & Gerry Mulligan* / Too marvellous for words: *Konitz, Lee & Gerry Mulligan* / Lover man: *Konitz, Lee & Gerry Mulligan* / I'll remember April: *Konitz, Lee* & Gerry Mulligan / These foolish things: *Konitz, Lee & Gerry Mulligan* / All the things you are: *Konitz, Lee &* Gerry Mulligan / Bernies tune: *Konitz, Lee & Gerry Mulligan* (CD only.) / Lady be good (alt. take): *Konitz, Lee & Gerry Mulligan* (CD only.).
LPS: . . . . **WPX 1**

PACIFIC JAZZ II COLLECTION (Various artists).
Tracks: / Four and one more: *Mulligan, Gerry* / Crazy day: *Mulligan, Gerry* / Turnstile: *Mulligan, Gerry*/ Sextet: *Mulligan, Gerry* / Disc jockey jump: *Mulligan, Gerry* / Venus de Milo: *Mulligan, Gerry* / Revelation: *Mulligan, Gerry* / I may be wrong: *Mulligan, Gerry & Chet Baker* / Aren't you glad you're you: *Mulligan, Gerry* & Chet Baker / I'm beginning to see the light: *Mulligan, Gerry & Chet Baker* / Nearness of you, The: *Mulligan*, Gerry & Chet Baker / Makin' whoopee: *Mulligan, Gerry & Chet Baker* / Tea for two: *Mulligan, Gerry & Chet Baker*/ Frenesi: *Mulligan, Gerry & Chet Baker* / Nights at the turntable: *Mulligan, Gerry & Chet Baker* / Lullaby of the leaves: *Mulligan, Gerry & Chet Baker* / Jeru: *Mulligan, Gerry & Chet Baker* / Cherry: *Mulligan, Gerry* & Chet Baker / Swing house: *Mulligan, Gerry & Chet Baker* / Bernie's tune: *Mulligan, Gerry & Chet Baker* / Freeway: *Mulligan, Gerry & Chet Baker* / Soft shoe: *Mulligan, Gerry & Chet Baker* / Walking shoes: *Mulligan*, Gerry & Chet Baker / Motel: *Mulligan, Gerry & Chet Baker* / Carson City stage: *Mulligan, Gerry & Chet Baker*/ Festive minor: *Mulligan, Gerry & Chet Baker* / I never knew: *Shank, Bud* / All the things you are: *Shank*, Bud / Body and soul: *Shank, Bud* / Blue Lou: *Shank, Bud* / Thou swell: *Shank, Bud* / Tenderly: *Shank*, Bud / Over the rainbow: *Shank, Bud* / Long ago and far away: *Shank, Bud* / Arrowhead: *Brookmeyer, Bob*/ Streetswingers: *Brookmeyer, Bob* / Hot buttered noodling: *Brookmeyer, Bob* / Musicale du jour: *Brookmeyer, Bob* / Rainy day: *Brookmeyer, Bob* / Jupiter: *Brookmeyer, Bob* / Crutch for the crab, A: *Twardzik, Richard* Trio / Albuquerque social swim: *Twardzik, Richard Trio* / Bess, you is my woman now: *Twardzik, Richard Trio*/ Round midnight: *Twardzik, Richard Trio* / I'll remember April: *Twardzik, Richard Trio* / Yellow tango: *Twardzik*, Richard Trio / Just one of those things: *Twardzik, Richard Trio* / You stepped out of a dream: *Freeman, Russ Trio*/ Don't worry 'bout me: *Freeman, Russ Trio* / Rock's tops: *Freeman, Russ Trio* / Yesterdays Gardenias: *Freeman*, Russ Trio / At last: *Freeman, Russ Trio* / Backfield in motion: *Freeman, Russ Trio* / Eye opener, The: *Freeman*, Russ Trio / Laugh cry: *Freeman, Russ Trio* / Nice day: *Hamilton, Chico* / Funny valentine: *Hamilton*, Chico / Blue sands: *Hamilton, Chico* / I want to be happy: *Hamilton, Chico* / Spectacular: *Hamilton*, Chico / Walking Carson blues: *Hamilton, Chico* / Buddy Boo: *Hamilton, Chico* / Jonalah: *Hamilton, Chico*/ Chrissie: *Hamilton, Chico* / Ghost, The: *Hamilton, Chico* / Santa Monica: *Hamilton, Chico* / Taking a chance on love: *Hamilton, Chico* / Squimp, The: *Hamilton, Chico* / Topsy: *Hamilton, Chico* / Drums West: *Hamilton, Chico* / Sleep: *Hamilton, Chico*.
LPS: . . . . **WPX 2**
MCSET: . . . . **TCWPX 2**

PERSIAN RUG (Unusual patterns in jazz) (Various artists).
Tracks: / Willow Tree: *Louisiana Sugar Babes* / Sippi: *Louisiana Sugar Babes* / Thou Swell: *Louisiana Sugar* Babes / Persian rug: *Louisiana Sugar Babes* / Mediterranean Blues: *Devillers-Novelty Instrumental Quintet*/ Hallelujah: *Devillers-Novelty Instrumental Quintet* / Zulu Wail: *Devillers-Novelty Instrumental Quintet* / You don't like it, not much: *Devillers-Novelty Instrumental Quintet* / Junk Man: *Teagarden, Jack & His Orchestra* / Your guess is as good as mine: *Teagarden, Jack & His Orchestra* / Hula girl: *Aiona, Andrew Novelty Four* / Keka: *Aiona, Andrew Novelty Four* / That lovin Hula: *Aiona, Andrew Novelty Four* / Baby, oh where can you be: *Johnson*, Merle Saxophone Quartet / Do Something: *Johnson, Merle Saxophone Quartet* / Always in all ways: *Johnson, Merle* Saxophone Quartet / It's a great life: *Johnson, Merle Saxophone Quartet* / My Silent Love: *Washboard Rhythm Kings*/ Hummin' to myself: *Washboard Rhythm Kings*.

LP: . . . . **VLP 59**

PHOENIX JAZZ FIFTH ANNIVERSARY ALBUM (Various artists).
LP: . . . . **PHOENIX 16**

PHONT MUSIC (Various artists).
LP: . . . . **PHONT 7541**

PIANO JAZZ (Boogie Woogie Pianists 1928-30) (Various artists).
LP: . . . . **S 1326**

PIANO LEGENDS (Various artists).
LP: **2673051**
MC: **2673054**

PIANO PORTRAITS VOL.3 Swingin' for joy (Various artists).
Tracks: / Swingin' for joy: *Various artists* / Mississippi moan: *Various artists* / Rosetta: *Various artists*/ Boogie woogie Maxine: *Various artists* / Yancey special: *Various artists* / Jingles: *Various artists*/ When a woman loves a man: *Various artists* / Three litle words: *Various artists* / Sheik of Araby, The: *Various* artists / Twinklin': *Various artists* / Just you, just me: *Various artists* / Oh Red: *Various artists*/ Boogie woogie cocktail: *Various artists* / (I don' stand a) ghost of a chance (with you): *Various artists* / If I were a bell: *Various artists* / Blues for Django: *Various artists*.
LP: . . . . **AFS 1035**

PIANO PORTRAITS, VOLUME 1 (Various artists).
Tracks: / You've got to be modernistic: *Various artists* / Pearls, The: *Various artists* / Early morning blues: *Various artists* / Kacyee feeling: *Various artists* / Time square blues: *Various artists* / Passionette: *Various artists* / Nobody knows you (when you're down and out): *Various artists* / Beautiful love: *Various* artists / I've got my love to keep me warm: *Various artists* / I'm sober now: *Various artists* / King Porter stomp: *Various artists* / What is this thing called love: *Various artists* / Hot and bothered: *Various artists*/ Mr. Freddie blues: *Various artists* / Morning air: *Various artists* / Dive bomber: *Various artists*.
LP: . . . . **AFS 1022**

PIANO PORTRAITS VOLUME 2 (Rockin' in Rhythm) (Various artists).
LP: . . . . **AFS 1028**

PIONEERS OF FRENCH JAZZ 1906-31 (Various artists).
LP: . . . . **PM 1552551**

PIONEERS OF THE JAZZ GUITAR (Various artists).
LP: . . . . **L 1057**

PIPE, SPOON, POT & JUG 14 jazz vocals (Various artists).
LP: . . . . **ST 102**

PIZZA EXPRESS (Various artists).
LP: . . . . **PE 5505**

PIZZA EXPRESS ALL STAR JAZZ BAND (Various artists).
LP: . . . . **PE 5506**

PLAYERS (Various artists).
LP: . . . . **PJ 88014**
MC: . . . . **PJC 88014**

PRESTIGE JAZZ SAMPLER (Various artists).
MC: . . . . **RIVMC 002**
LP: . . . . **RIVM 002**

PRIME TIME (Various artists).
LP: . . . . **SLP 4078**

PROGRESSIVE RECORDS ALL STAR TRUMPET SPECTACULAR (Various artists).
LP: . . . . **PRO 7017**

PURE JAZZ SAMPLER (Various artists).
MC: . . . . **CGATE 1001**

RAGTIME RAZZMATAZZ VOL. 1 (Various artists).
LP: . . . . **W 808**

RAGTIME RAZZMATAZZ VOL. 2 (Various artists).
LP: . . . . **W 8212**

RAGTIME RAZZMATAZZ VOL. 3 (Various artists).
LP: . . . . **W 8417**

RARE HOT MUSIC IN BRITAIN 1927-31 (Various artists).
MC: . . . . **NEO 756**

RARE JAZZ AND BLUES PIANO 1935-37 (Various artists).
LP: . . . . **BD 2070**

RARE PERFORMANCES (Various artists).
Tracks: / Swingin' at the Cotton Club: *Three Peppers* / I found a new baby: *Preer, Andy & The Cotton Club Orchestra*/ Cotton Club stomp: *Ellington, Duke and his Cotton Club Orchestra* / Misty morning: *Ellington, Duke and his Cotton* Club Orchestra / Freeze and melt: *Ellington, Duke and his Cotton Club*

Orchestra / Ozark Mountain blues: *Missourians*/ Ain't misbehavin': *Robinson, Bill 'Bojangles'* / Happy feet: *Calloway, Cab & His Orchestra* / Go Harlem: *Johnson, Jimmy & His Orchestra* / Baby: *Hall, Adelaide with Duke Ellington & His Orchestra* / King Porter stomp: *Calloway, Cab & His Orchestra* / Minnie the moocher's wedding day: *Banks, Billy & His Blue Rhythm Boys* / Stormy weather: *Ellington, Duke and his Cotton Club Orchestra* / Happy as the day is long: *Arlen, Harold* / Minor mania: *Hopkins, Claude & His Orchestra* / Breakfast in Harlem: *Buck & Bubbles* / It must be love: *Three Peppers* / Edgar steps out: *Hayes, Edgar & His Orchestra* / I'll get along somehow: *Waters, Ethel* / Jammin' for the jackpot: *Millinder, Lucky* & The Mills Blue Rhythm Band / Wrap your cares in rhythm and dance: *Nicholas Brothers* / They say he ought to dance: *Nicholas Brothers* / Say it with a kiss: *Sullivan, Maxine* / Moon ray: *Fitzgerald, Ella/her Famous* Orchestra / Give, baby, give: *Calloway, Cab & His Orchestra* / Liza: *Long, Avon* / Ain't gonna study war no more: *Dandridge Sisters with Jimmy Lunceford & His Orchestra* / How long has this been going on?: *Horne, Lena with* The Phil Moore Four / Hip hip hooray: *Kirk, Andy/ his Twelve Clouds of Joy* / Rock Daniel: *Millinder, Lucky & His Orchestra with Sister Rosetta Tharpe* / Song is ended, The: *Armstrong, Louis/Mills Brothers*.
LP: . . . . **A 252**
MC: . . . . **LC 8126**

REAL SOUND OF JAZZ, THE (Various artists).
LP: . . . . **PUMPKIN 116**

REEFER SONGS (23 Original Jazz and Blues Vocals) (Various artists).
MC: . . . . **STAC 100**
LP: . . . . **ST 100**

REFLECTIONS (Various artists).
LP: . . . . **RR 18**

REFLEXIONEN (Various artists).
LP: . . . . **SFP 199**

RELIGIOUS RECORDINGS FROM BLACK NEW ORLEANS (Various artists).
LP: **504LP20**

RETURN OF JAZZ FOR ABSOLUTE BEGINNERS (Various artists).
Tracks: / Your feet's too big: *Waller, Fats & His Rhythm* / Boogie woogie man: *Ammons, Albert & Pete Johnson*/ Conga brava: *Ellington, Duke* / Pick-a-rib (part 1): *Goodman, Benny Quintet* / Subtle slough: *Stewart, Rex*/ Whoa babe: *Hampton, Lionel* / I got it bad (and that ain't good): *Ellington, Duke* (Featuring Ivy Anderson.) / Scat song, The: *Calloway, Cab/his Cotton Club Orchestra* / Rock it for me: *Page, Hot Lips* / Bach goes to town: *Goodman, Benny & His Orchestra* / Crawl, The: *Allen, Henry 'Red'* / Riffin' at the 24th Street: *Jacquet, Illinois*/ Night in Tunisia: *Gillespie, Dizzy* / Solitude: *Various artists*.
LP: . . . . **NL 89964**
MC: . . . . **NK 89964**

RHYTHMAKERS 1932 (Various artists).
Tracks: / Bugle call rag: *Various artists* / Oh Peter: *Various artists* / Margie: *Various artists* / Spider crawl: *Various artists* / Who's sorry now?: *Various artists* / Take it slow and easy: *Various artists*/ Bald headed mama: *Various artists* / I would do anything for you: *Various artists* / Mean old bed bug blues: *Various artists* / Yellow dog blues: *Various artists* / Yes suh: *Various artists* / Who stole the lock?: *Various artists* / Shine on your shoes: *Various artists* / It's gonna be you: *Various artists* / Somebody stole Gabriel's horn: *Various artists*.
LP: . . . . **VLP 53**

RIVERBOAT SHUFFLE (Various artists).
Tracks: / Ice cream: *Various artists* / Yellow dog blues: *Various artists* / Chicago strut: *Various artists*/ Lazy river: *Various artists* / Carolina shuffle: *Various artists* / River stay 'way from my door: *Various* artists / Frankie and Johnny: *Various artists* / Nobody knows the trouble I've seen: *Various artists* / Stork room stomp: *Various artists* / St. James' Infirmary: *Various artists* / Lord, Lord you've sure been good to me: *Various artists* / Lonesome road: *Various artists* / Memphis blues: *Various artists* / Loch Lomond: *Various artists* / When the saints go marching in: *Various artists* / Tiger rag: *Various artists* / New Orleans shimmy: *Various artists* / Down by the riverside: *Various artists* / Davenport blues: *Various artists* / Dippermouth blues: *Various artists*.
2LP: . . . . **INT 157 003**

RIVERBOAT SHUFFLE (Various artists).
LP: . . . . **INT 155 003**

RIVERSIDE JAZZ SAMPLER (Various artists).
Tracks: / Scramble: *Gaylor, Bean & Norris* / Stix' trix: *Various artists* / Last time I saw Paris, The: *Various artists* / Centaur and the Phoenix, The: *Various artists* / Carol: *Various artists* / Nearness of you, the: *Various artists* / Work song: *Various artists* / Think deep: *Various artists* / Wild rice: *Various* artists / We'll be together: *Various artists* / Groovin' high: *Various artists* / Why do I love you: *Various artists*.
LP: . . . . **RIVM 001**
MC: . . . . **RIVMC 001**

ROARING 20'S, THE (Various artists).
Tracks: / If you knew Susie: *Shilkret, Jack & His Orchestra* / Sheik of Araby, The: *Pianola Roll* / I'm tellin' the birds, tellin' the bees: *Smith, Jack ('Whispering')* / That's my weakness now: *Pianola Roll* / Canadian capers: *Biese, Paul Trio* / Rose Marie: *Pianola Roll* / Colette: *Whiteman, Paul & His Orchestra* / Where the lazy daisies grow: *Pianola Roll* / Ain't misbehavin': *Hylton, Jack & His Orchestra & Sam Browne* / My inspiration is you: *Pianola Roll* / Wedding of the painted doll, The: *Pianola Roll* / Don't bring Lulu: *Garber, Jan & His* Orchestra / Always: *Pianola Roll* / Where, oh where do I live?: *Douglas, Fred/orchestra* / Birth of the blues: *Pianola Roll* / I miss my Swiss: *Golden Gate Orchestra* / Ain't she sweet?: *Pianola Roll* / Hello, Swanee, hello: *Syncopated Four* / Ramona: *Pianola Roll* / Charleston: *Various artists*.
LP: . . . . **SDL 344**
MC: . . . . **CSDL 344**

ROARING TWENTIES, THE (Classic Years in Digital Stereo) (Various artists).
Tracks: / Tiger rag: *Various artists* / Jazz me blues: *Various artists* / Doo wacka doo: *Various artists*/ I'm gonna charleston back to Charleston: *Various artists* / Ukelele lady: *Various artists* / Hi-diddle-diddle: *Various artists* / When the red red robin comes bob, bob, bobbin': *Various artists* / There's a rainbow 'round my shoulder: *Various artists* / H'lo baby: *Various artists* / Changes: *Various artists* / Varsity drag, The: *Various artists* / Plenty of sunshine: *Various artists* / That's my weakness now: *Various artists*/ Makin' whoopee: *Various artists* / Singin' in the rain: *Various artists* / Happy days are here again: *Various artists* / Sunny side up: *Various artists* / Red hot Chicago: *Various artists*.
LP: . . . . **REB 704**
MC: . . . . **ZCF 704**

RONNIE SCOTT'S 20TH ANNIVERSARY ALBUM (Various artists).
Tracks: / Lazy afternoon: *Scott, Ronnie Quintet* / Thou swell: *Getz, Stan* / Come rain or come shine: *Stitt*, Sonny / We free kings / You and me: *Various artists* / Li'l darlin': *Basie, Count & His Orchestra* / Now hear my meanin': *Boland, Clarke Big Band* / Sweet and lovely: *Herman, Woody & His Orchestra* / Two brass: *Rich, Buddy Band*.
LP: . . . . **ND 5001**

ROOTS OF ROCK 'N' ROLL (Various artists).
LP: . . . . **SJL 2221**

RUNNIN' WILD (Original Sounds of the Jazz Age) (Various artists).
Tracks: / Runnin' wild: *Ellington, Duke* / Loveable and sweet: *Hanshaw, Annette* / There's a rainbow round my shoulder: *Jolson, Al* / My song: *Vallee, Rudy* / Heebie jeebies: *Boswell Sisters* / Loveless love: *Waller*, Fats / Magnolia: *California Ramblers* / Any old time: *Rodgers, Jimmie (1)* / Egyptian Ella: *Lewis, Ted*/ How many times?: *Lucas, Nick* / She's got 'It': *Weems, Ted* / Makin' whoopee: *Whiteman, Paul* / California here I come: *Edwards, Cliff* / Mel: *Etting, Ruth* / Four or five times: *McKinney's Cotton Pickers* / Without that gal: *Austin, Gene* / Home again blues: *Original Dixieland Jazz Band* / Lindy: *Original Dixieland Jazz* Band / Oh, you have no idea: *Tucker, Sophie* / You brought a new kind of love to me: *Chevalier, Maurice* / St. James Infirmary: *Bloom, Rube* / Three little words: *Crumit, Frank* / Painting the clouds with sunshine: *Hylton, Jack*.
LP: . . . . **AJA 5017**
MC: . . . . **ZCAJA 5017**

SAMPLER 84 (Various artists).
LP: **371035-1**
MC: **371035-4**

SAMPLER 86 (MCA Master series) (Various artists).
Tracks: / Scrumpy cider: *Jarvis, John* / Month of seasons, A: *Jarvis, John* / Smiles and smiles to go: *Carlton*, Larry / Perfect peace: *Carlton, Larry* / Coco loco: *Greenidge, Robert & Michael Utley* / Seventeenth summer: *Lee, Albert* / Grant's corner: *Douglas, Jerry* / Time gone by: *Douglas, Jerry* / Cycles: *Meyer, Edgar*/ Unfolding: *Meyer, Edgar*.
LP: . . . . **IMCA 5692**
MC: . . . . **IMCAC 5692**

SAMPLER 89 (Various artists).
Tracks: / Rameau's nephew: *Various artists* / Sojourner: *Various artists* / Floyds ghost: *Various artists*/ Usually: *Various artists* / Always: *Various artists* / Credo of Ballymacoda: *Various artists* / Walking through walls: *Various artists* / Manhattan underground: *Various artists* / Hugh: *Various artists* / Through the woods: *Various artists* / Visiting card, A: *Various artists*.
LP: **371 082-1**
MC: **371 082-4**

SAX LEGENDS (Various artists).
LP: **2673041**
MC: **2673044**

SCREAMING SAXOPHONES VOLUME 1 (Various artists).
LP: . . . . **ST 1002**

SCREWBALLS OF SWINGTIME (Various artists).
LP: . . . . **BS 7106**

SCREWBALLS OF SWINGTIME, 1934 - 55 Various artists (Various artists).
LP: . . . . **BS 7106**

SENSATION '49 (Various artists).
Tracks: / When the saints go marching in: *Various artists* / Southern sunset: *Various artists* / On the sunny side of the street: *Various artists* / Laura: *Various artists* / St. Louis blues: *Various artists* / Blues in the air: *Various artists* / I ain't gonna give nobody none of my jelly roll: *Various artists* / All the things you are: *Various artists* / I surrender, dear: *Various artists* / Tea for two: *Various artists* / Indiana: *Various artists* / Squirrel, The: *Various artists* / Out of nowhere: *Various artists*.
LP: . . . . **NOST 7602**

SHAPE OF THE LAND, THE (Various artists).
LP: **371055-1**
MC: **371055-4**

SHOOTING HIGH Solo recordings by British Dance Band Vocalists (Various artists).
Tracks: / Breakaway: *Elwin, Maurice* / Lovely lady: *Plant, Jack* / What are you thinkin' about baby?: *Robins*, Phyllis / Star gazing: *Rosing, Val* / Whisper sweet: *Carlisle, Elsie* / In a blue and pensive mood: *Bowlly*, Al / Please believe me: *Browne, Sam* / Heart to heart: *Lynn, Vera* / Red sails in the sunset: *Bowlly*, Al / When did you leave heaven?: *Allen, Lee* / Farewell to arms: *Browne, Sam* / Just two hearts and a waltz refrain: *Plant, Jack* / That's what I like about you: *Robins, Phyllis* / Don't blame me: *Rosing, Val*/ Deep water: *Carlisle, Elsie* / Cheek to cheek: *Scott, Billy* / When the poppies bloom again: *Lynn, Vera*/ Don't kiss me goodnight: *Allen, Lee* / Little white gardenia, A: *Bowlly, Al* / I'm shooting high: *Browne, Sam & The Rhythm Sisters*.
LP: . . . . **SVL 186**
MC: . . . . **CSVL 186**

SHOUTERS (Various artists).
LP: . . . . **SJL 2244**

SINGING DETECTIVE, THE (Music from the T.V. series) (Various artists).
Tracks: / Peg o' my heart: *Various artists* / Limehouse blues: *Various artists* / Blues in the night: *Various* artists / Dry bones: *Various artists* / Rockin' in rhythm: *Various artists* / Cruising down the river: *Various* artists / Don't fence me in: *Various artists* / Accentuate the positive: *Various artists* / It might as well be spring: *Various artists* / Paper doll: *Various artists* / You always hurt the one you love: *Various artists*/ Lili Marlene: *Various artists* / I get along without you very well: *Various artists* / Do I worry: *Various* artists / After you've gone: *Various artists* / It's a lovely day tomorrow: *Various artists* / Into each life some rain must fall: *Various artists* / Very thought of you, The: *Various artists* / Teddy bears picnic, The: *Various artists* / We'll meet again: *Various artists*.
LP: . . . . **REN 608**
MC: . . . . **ZCN 608**

SMALL LABEL GEMS OF THE FORTIES VOL.2 (Various artists).
LP: . . . . **SOL 513**

SMALL LABEL GEMS OF THE FORTIES VOL.1 (Various artists).
LP: . . . . **SOL 512**

SMALL LABEL GEMS OF THE FORTIES VOL.3 (Various artists).
LP: . . . . **SOL 514**

SMALL LABELS 1927-1935, THE Various artists (Various artists).
LP: . . . . **CI 010**

SO BLUE SO FUNKY (Heroes of the Hammond) (Various artists).
Tracks: / All about my girl: *McGriff, Jimmy* / Silver metre, The: *Patton, Big John* / I'm movin' on: *Smith, Jimmy* (USA) / Wine, wine, wine: *Roach, Freddie* (Not on cassette) / Brown sugar: *Roach, Freddie* / Hootin' 'n' tootin': *Jackson, Fred* / Face to face: *Willette, Baby Face* / Fat Judy: *Patton, Big John* / Plaza De Toros: *Young, Larry* / Boop bop bing bash: *Braith, George* / Everything I do gonh be funky: *Donaldson*, Lou / Hot rod: *Wilson, Reuben* (Not on cassette) / Butter for yo' popcorn: *McDuff, Brother Jack* / Ain't it funky now: *Green, Grant*.
2LP: **B1 96563**
MC: **B4 96563**

SOLID GOLD SWING (Various artists).
Tracks: / Marie: *Dorsey, Tommy* / Boogie woogie: *Dorsey, Tommy* / There are such things: *Dorsey, Tommy*/ On the sunny side of the street: *Dorsey, Tommy* / Opus one: *Dorsey, Tommy* / Nightmare: *Shaw, Artie*/ Back bay shuffle: *Shaw, Artie* / Begin the beguine: *Shaw, Artie* / Traffic jam: *Shaw, Artie* / Frenesi: *Shaw, Artie* / Stardust: *Shaw, Artie* / Dancing in the dark: *Shaw, Artie* / Little brown jug: *Miller*, Glenn / In the mood: *Miller, Glenn* / St. Louis blues: *Miller, Glenn* / American patrol: *Miller, Glenn*/ Pennsylvania 6 5000: *Miller, Glenn* / Boulder buff: *Miller, Glenn* / King Porter stomp: *Miller, Glenn*/ String of pearls: *Miller, Glenn*.
MC: . . . . **NK 89425**

SON OF JAZZ FOR ABSOLUTE BEGINNERS (Various artists).
Tracks: / Doctor Jazz: *Morton, Jelly Roll* / St. Louis shuffle: *Henderson, Fletcher & His Orchestra* / Ain't misbehavin': *Bechet, Sidney* / Handful of keys: *Waller, Fats* / Flaming youth: *Ellington, Duke* / Blue washboard stomp: *Dodds, Johnny Washboard Band* / I got a right to sing the blues: *Armstrong, Louis & His Orchestra* / Maple leaf rag: *New Orleans Feetwarmers* / Hyena stomp: *Morton, Jelly Roll* / Texas stomp: *Big Maceo* / I'm gonna stomp: *Eddie's Hot Shots* / It should be you: *Allen, Henry 'Red' & his Orchestra* / Oh didn't he ramble?: *Morton, Jelly Roll* / Mr. Henry Lee: *Eddie's Hot Shots* / Edna: *Various artists*.
LP: . . . . **NL 89963**
MC: . . . . **NK 89963**

SOUL JAZZ VOL.1 (Various artists).
Tracks: / Honky tonk: *Butler, Billy* / Return of the prodigal son: *Green, Byrdie* / I've got the blues: *Moody*, James / Mom and dad: *Earland, Charles* / 322 wow: *Lytle, Johnny* / Up to date: *Smith, Johnny 'Hammond'*/ Dat dere: *Cannonball Adderley Quartet* / Light, The: *Ammons, Gene*.
LP: . . . . **BGP 1028**

SOUND OF HARLEM (Various artists).
LP: . . . . **VA 7999**

SOUNDS OF HARLEM, VOLUME 2 (Various artists).
LP: . . . . **VA 7994**

SOUNDS OF NEW ORLEANS VOL 1 (Various artists).
LP: . . . . **SLP 6008**

SOUNDS OF NEW ORLEANS VOL 2 (Various artists).
LP: . . . . **SLP 6009**

SOUNDS OF NEW ORLEANS VOL 3 (Various artists).
LP: . . . . **SLP 6010**

SOUNDS OF NEW ORLEANS VOL 4 (Various artists).
LP: . . . . **SLP 6011**

SOUNDS OF NEW ORLEANS VOL 5 (Various artists).
LP: . . . . **SPLP 6012**

SOUNDS OF NEW ORLEANS VOL 6 (Various artists).
LP: . . . . **SLP 6013**

SOUNDS OF NEW ORLEANS VOL 7 (Various artists).
LP: . . . . **SLP 6014**

SOUNDS OF NEW ORLEANS VOL 8 (Various artists).
LP: . . . . **SLP 6015**

SOUNDS OF NEW ORLEANS VOL 9 (Various artists).
LP: . . . . **SLP 6016**

SOUNDS OF NEW ORLEANS VOL 10 (Various artists).
LP: . . . . **SLP 6017**

SOUNDS OF THE SWING YEARS (Various artists).

LP: . . . . SG 8001

SOUTHERN BLUES Various artists (Various artists).
2LP: . . . . SJL 2255

SPIRIT OF JAZZ, THE (Various artists).
Tracks: / You don't know what love is: *Hargrove, Roy* / Little Bennie: *Hargrove, Roy* / Hit and run: *Hollyday*, Christopher / Cousin Mary: *Power Trio* / Blues shifting: *Coleman, Steve* / Mooche, The: *Lacy, Steve* & Mal Waldron / Jungle blues: *Roberts, Marcus* / Shout 'em Aunt Tillie: *Roberts, Marcus* / Man, that was a dream: *McRae, Carmen* / Best is yet to come, The: *McRae, Carmen* / Doin' it right: *Ruiz, Hilton* / Mutt 'n' Jeff: *Moody, James*.
MC: . . . . PK 83114

ST. LOUIS BLUES (see under Smith, Bessie) (Various artists).

STARS OF MODERN JAZZ CONCERT (Carnegie Hall 1949) (Various artists).
LP: . . . . IAJRC 20

STARS OF SWING (1935-37) (Various artists).
Tracks: / China boy: *Gardner, Freddy* / Swing me sweetly: *Davis, Lew* / When you're smiling: *Gonella, Nat* / Japanese sandman: *Gardner, Freddy* / Hummin' to myself: *Whyte, Duncan* / Keep goin': *Firman, Bert* / Ain't misbehavin': *Young, Arthur* / Swing as it comes: *Firman, Bert* / Baby won't you please come home: *Gardner*, Freddy / Tiger rag: *Gonella, Nat* / Ida, sweet as apple cider: *Miranda, Jack* / Blue strings: *Firman*, Bert / I never knew: *Davis, Lew* / Entr'acte: *Black hand gang* / Bread and jam: *Miranda, Jack* / Blind man's buff: *Young, Arthur*.
LP: . . . . HQ 3015

START TO JUMP BECAUSE IT'S JUBILEE (Various artists).
LP: . . . . ST 10009

STASH SAMPLER (See under Stash (label)) (Various artists).

STOCKHOLM 1961 (Various artists).
Tracks: / Jackie-ing: *Various artists* / I'm getting sentimental over you: *Various artists* / Crepuscule with Nellie: *Various artists* / Ba-lue bolivar ba-lues-are: *Various artists* / Rhythm a ning: *Various artists* / Epistrophy: *Various artists* / Just a gigolo: *Various artists* / Well, you needn't: *Various artists* / 'Round midnight: *Various artists* / Bemsha swing: *Various artists* / Blue Monk: *Various artists* / Epistrophy: *Various artists* / Body and soul: *Various artists*.
2LP: . . . . DRLP 151/52

STOMPIN' AT THE SAVOY (Various artists).
Tracks: / Stompin' at the Savoy: *Various artists* / T'aint what you do (it's the way that you do it): *Various artists* / My brown frame baby: *Various artists* / Midnight rambler: *Various artists* / Milkshake stand, The: *Various* artists / Howling wind: *Various artists* / Brown gold: *Various artists* / Romance without finance: *Various* artists / Cupid's boogie: *Various artists* / I ain't mad pretty baby: *Various artists* / All nite long: *Various artists* / Spinal: *Various artists* / Ornithology: *Various artists* / Birdland story, The: *Various artists* / Another hair-do: *Various artists* / Jam man, The: *Various artists* / Sweet man: *Various artists* / Rock me to sleep: *Various artists* / Write me a letter: *Various artists* / Rib joint: *Various artists*.
LP: . . . . STOMP 1
MC: . . . . STOMC 1

STORMY WEATHER, 1933 (Various artists).
LP: . . . . NOST 7647

SUNSHINE SPECIAL (Various artists).
LP: . . . . VLP 39

SUPER HORNS (Various artists).
Tracks: / Byrd house: *Byrd, Donald* / Curros: *Byrd, Donald* / Shaw 'nuff: *Terry, Clark* / Stop and listen: *Terry, Clark* / Chantized: *Hubbard, Freddie* / Court, The: *Hubbard, Freddie* / Yardbird Suite: *Davis, Miles* / Cool Blues: *Davis, Miles*.
LP: . . . . XELLP 100
MC: . . . . XELMC 100

SUPER SAX (Various artists).
Tracks: / Flutie: *Lateef, Yusef* / Big foot: *Lateef, Yusef* / Lester leaps in: *Young, Lester* / D B blues: *Young, Lester* / Happy bird blues: *Parker, Charlie All Stars* / Cool blues: *Parker, Charlie* / Breeze and I: *Pepper, Art* / Long ago & far away: *Pepper, Art* / Love for sale: *Sims, Zoot* / Strike up the band: *Sims, Zoot*.
LP: . . . . XELLP 101
MC: . . . . XELMC 101

SWEDISH SMALL BAND SWING 1936/37 features Gosta Torner/Thore Ehrling/Thore Jederb (Various artists).
LP: . . . . VA 7993

SWEET AND LOW BLUES (Various artists).
Tracks: / Static strut: *Tate, Erskine Vendome Orchestra* / Symphonic raps: *Dickerson, Carroll & His Orchestra* / Boy in the boat: *Johnson, Charlie & His Paradise Orchestra* / That's how I feel today: *Chocolate Dandies* / Sweet and low blues: *Smith, Jabbo & His Rhythm Aces* / Till times get better: *Smith, Jabbo & His Rhythm Aces* / Willow tree: *Louisiana Sugar Babes* / What is this thing called love: *Reisman, Leo Orch.* / Starvation blues: *Stone*, Jess Blue Serenaders / Blue devil blues: *Page, Walter Blue Devils* / There's a squabblin': *Page, Walter Blue Devils* / Dreamland blues: *Floyd, Troy & His Plaza Hotel Orchestra* / Dreamland blues II: *Floyd, Troy & His Plaza Hotel Orchestra* / Ruff scuffling: *Lee, George E & His Kansas Orchestra* / Black and blue rhapsody: *Trent, Alphonso & His Orchestra* / After you've gone: *Trent, Alphonso & His Orchestra* / I've found a new baby: *Trent, Alphonso & His Orchestra*.
LP: . . . . NW 256

SWING - BIG BANDS 1929-1936 (Classic Years in Digital Stereo) (Various artists).
Tracks: / King Porter stomp: *Various artists* / Blazin': *Various artists* / Hot and anxious: *Various artists* / Old man Harlem: *Various artists* / Copenhagen: *Various artists* / Don't be that way: *Various artists* / Congo caravan: *Various artists* / Farewell blues: *Various artists* / Corky jada: *Various artists* / Royal Garden blues: *Various artists* / Exposition swing: *Various artists* / Dippermouth blues: *Various artists* / Woman on my weary mind: *Various artists* / Skeleton in the closet, The: *Various artists* / Harlem shout: *Various artists*.
LP: . . . . REB 655
MC: . . . . ZCF 655

SWING COLLECTION (Various artists).
Tracks: / In the mood: *Miller, Glenn* / Moonlight serenade: *Miller, Glenn* / Chattanooga choo choo: *Miller*, Glenn / Pennsylvania 6-5000: *Miller, Glenn* / American patrol: *Miller, Glenn* / Begin the beguine: *Shaw*, Artie / Indian love call: *Shaw, Artie* / Temptation: *Shaw, Artie* / Stardust: *Shaw, Artie* / Accentuate the positive: *Shaw, Artie* / Song of India: *Dorsey, Tommy* / Sleepy lagoon: *Dorsey, Tommy* / I'm getting sentimental over you: *Dorsey, Tommy* / Hawaiian war chant: *Dorsey, Tommy* / Boogie woogie: *Dorsey, Tommy* / Let's dance (medley): *Goodman, Benny* / St. Louis blues: *Goodman, Benny* / Stompin' at the Savoy: *Goodman, Benny* / One o'clock jump: *Goodman, Benny* / Three little words: *Goodman, Benny*.
LP: . . . . DVLP 2029
MC: . . . . DVMC 2029

SWING COLLECTION (Various artists).
LP: . . . . DVLP 7029

SWING ERA (Various artists).
Tracks: / Jumpin' at The Woodside: *Basie, Count* / Lady be good: *Basie, Count* / My daddy rocks me: *Mezzrow, Mezz* / Tempo and swing: *Hampton, Lionel* / How high the moon: *Ellington, Duke* / Cottontail: *Ellington*, Duke / That's a plenty: *Webb, Chick* / Yesterdays: *Hawkins, Coleman* / St. Louis blues: *Bechet, Sidney* / Flying home: *Hampton, Lionel* / Exactly like you: *Hines, Earl* / Lazy river: *Various artists*.
LP: . . . . SM 3113

SWING IS HERE (Various artists).
LP: . . . . NL 82180
MC: . . . . NK 82180

SWING JACKPOT (Various artists).
LP: . . . . JA 50

SWING PARTY (Various artists).
LP: . . . . LOP 14 102

SWING PIANO (Various artists).
LP: . . . . SLP 829

SWING - SMALL GROUPS 1931-1936 (Classic years in digital stereo) (Various artists).
Tracks: / My melancholy baby: *Various artists* / Beale street blues: *Various artists* / Fan it: *Various artists* / Never had no livin': *Various artists* / Tomboy: *Various artists* / Toledo shuffle: *Various artists* / Buzzard, The: *Various artists* / Muskrat ramble: *Various artists* / Swing is here: *Various artists* / Blues jumped a rabbit, The: *Various artists* / Mutiny in the parlour: *Various artists* / Frolic Sam: *Various* artists / Warmin' up: *Various artists* / Rhythm saved the world: *Various artists* / Paswonky: *Various artists* / Shoe shine boy: *Various artists*.
LP: . . . . REB 666
MC: . . . . ZCF 666

SWING SOUNDS (Various artists).
LP: . . . . BLJ 8016

SWING STREET VOL 1 (Various artists).
LP: . . . . TAX 8028

SWING STREET VOL. 2 (1931-41) (Various artists).
LP: . . . . M 8030

SWING STREET VOL 3 (Various artists).
LP: . . . . TAX 8034

SWING THAT MUSIC (Various artists).
2LP: 80006
MCSET: 850061/2

SWING YEARS (Various artists).
LP: . . . . SB 8001

SWINGING BIG BANDS (Various artists).
LPS: . . . . C 68/4 BOX 4

SWINGING DIXIELAND (Various artists).
LP: . . . . PHON 9

SWINGING FLICKS, VOL 1 (1936 - 52) (Various artists).
Tracks: / Let me off uptown: *Various artists* / Semper fidelis: *Various artists* / When the saints go marching in: *Various artists* / Mood indigo: *Various artists* / Boardwalk boogie: *Various artists* / Until today: *Various artists* / Jazznocracy: *Various artists* / You: *Various artists* / Wait till the sun shines Nellie: *Various artists* / Four or five times: *Various artists* / Mooche, The: *Various artists* / Feed the kitty: *Various artists* / Mr. X blues: *Various artists* / Take everything: *Various artists* / Hot chocolate: *Various artists*.
LP: . . . . BS 7129

SWINGING FLICKS, VOL 2 (1939 - 51) (Various artists).
Tracks: / Dipsy doodle: *Various artists* / Lonesome road: *Various artists* / Basin Street boogie: *Various* artists / Reed rapture: *Various artists* / Time takes care of everything: *Various artists* / Ride, ride, ride: *Various artists* / Calloway boogie: *Various artists* / Anvil chorus: *Various artists* / Whatcha know, Joe?: *Various artists* / Margie: *Various artists* / Take the 'A' train: *Various artists* / Barnyard bounce: *Various artists* / La Rosita: *Various artists* / Solid jive: *Various artists*.
LP: . . . . BS 7130

SWING'S THE THING (Various artists).
LP: . . . . JSP 1078

SWINGSHOW (Various artists).
Tracks: / And the angels sing: *Various artists* / By the sleepy lagoon: *Various artists* / Little jazz: *Various* artists / Rainbow rhapsody: *Various artists* / Cielito lindo: *Various artists* / In a persian market: *Various* artists / Don't be that way: *Various artists* / Too-ra-loo-ra-loo-ra: *Various artists* / After our stuff: *Various artists* / This is romance: *Various artists* / Boulder buff: *Various artists* / Summer time: *Various artists*.
LP: 104 4191
MC: 710.4191

SWINGTIME JIVE (Various artists).
Tracks: / Rockin' chair theme: *Various artists* / There'll be some changes made: *Various artists* / It all comes back to me now: *Various artists* / Give me some skin: *Various artists* / Georgie: *Various artists* / Bugle boogie: *Various artists* / There eyes: *Various artists* / Airmail special: *Various artists* / Ah now: *Various artists* / Tip on the numbers: *Various artists* / Slim slam boogie: *Various artists* / Bassology: *Various artists* / Stop that dancin' up there: *Various artists* / Put a nickle in the slot: *Various artists* / You can say that again: *Various artists* / Zoot Gibson strides again: *Various artists*.
LP: . . . . ST 108

TANGOS POR AFICIANADOS, VOL 1 (The 30's) (Various artists).
LP: . . . . PHONT 7578

TENOR SAX ALBUM (Various artists).
Tracks: / Girl of my dreams: *Quebec, Ike Quintet* / I.Q. blues: *Quebec, Ike Quintet* / Scuffin': *Quebec*, Ike Quintet / Jim dawg: *Quebec, Ike Quintet* / Honeysuckle rose: *Webster, Ben Quartet* / I surrender, dear: *Webster, Ben Quartet* / Blue skies: *Webster, Ben Quartet* / Kat's fur: *Webster, Ben Quartet* / Body and soul: *Webster, Ben Quartet* / Lunatic: *Hardee, John Quintet* / Can't help lovin' dat man: *Hardee, John Quintet* / Bad man's bounce: *Hardee, John Quintet* / Baby watch that stuff: *Hardee, John Quintet* / Misty morning blues: *Taylor, Billy Quintet* / Take the 'A' train: *Taylor, Billy Quintet* / Don't blame me: *Jacquet, Illinois Sextet* / Savoy blip: *Berry, Emmett Sextet* / Jacquet in the box: *Jacquet, Illinois Sextet* / Doggin' with doggett: *Berry, Emmett Sextet* / Minor romp: *Berry, Emmett Sextet* / Berry's blues: *Berry, Emmett Sextet* / Last stop: *Hawkins, Coleman Combo* / Should I: *Hawkins, Coleman Combo* / Flight eleven: *Hawkins, Coleman Combo* / Modern fantasy: *Hawkins, Coleman Combo* / Confessin': *Hawkins, Coleman Combo* / September song: *Hawkins, Coleman Combo* / They can't take that away from me: *Hawkins, Coleman Combo*.
2LP: . . . . SJL 2220
LP: . . . . WL 70812
MC: . . . . WK 70812

TERRITORIAL BANDS (Various artists).
LP: . . . . IAJRC 6

TERRITORY BANDS,THE (Various artists).
LP: . . . . CAH 3005
LP: . . . . CJM 10
LP: . . . . M 8009

THANKS FOR THE MEMORY (Various artists).
Tracks: / Seventh Avenue: *Oliver, Sy* / Out of nowhere: *Tilton, Martha* / Beyond the blue horizon: *Tilton*, Martha / Sleepy time gal: *Leonard, Jack* / It's a long way to Tipperary: *Crosby, Bob* / Tea for two: *Eldridge, Roy* / When I grow too old to dream: *Crosby, Bob* / Thanks for the memory: *Leonard, Jack & Martha Tilton*.
LP: . . . . SWH 34

THAT NEWPORT JAZZ (Various artists).
Tracks: / Undecided: *Various artists* / These foolish things: *Various artists* / Sweet Georgia Brown: *Various artists* / Stardust: *Various artists* / Chasin' at Newport: *Various artists*.
LP: . . . . CBS 21139
MC: 40 21139

THAT TODDLIN' TOWN - CHICAGO 1926-28 (Various artists).
LP: . . . . S 1256

THAT'S THE WAY I FEEL NOW (A tribute to Thelonious Monk) (Various artists).
Tracks: / Thelonious: *Various artists* / Little rootie tootie: *Various artists* / Reflections: *Various artists* / Blue Monk: *Various artists* / Misterioso: *Various artists* / Pannonica: *Various artists* / Ba-lue bolivar ba-lues are: *Various artists* / Brilliant corners: *Various artists* / Ask me now: *Various artists* / Monk's mood: *Various artists* / Four in one: *Various artists* / Functional: *Various artists* / Evidence: *Various* artists / Shuffle boil: *Various artists* / In walked Bud: *Various artists* / Criss cross: *Various artists* / Jackie-ing: *Various artists* / Round midnight: *Various artists* / Friday the 13th: *Various artists* / Work: *Various artists* / Gallop's gallop: *Various artists*.
2LP: . . . . AMLM 66600
MCSET: . . . . CLM 66600

THEME SONGS OF THE BIG BANDS (Various artists).
LP: . . . . GE 15026

THEY ALL PLAY RAGTIME (Various artists).
LP: . . . . JCE 52

THEY ALL PLAYED MAPLE LEAF RAG (Various artists).
LP: . . . . HERWIN 401

THIS IS DIXIELAND (Various artists).
LP: 6424 061

THIS IS JAZZ (Radio series live 1947) (Various artists).
LP: 20800

THIS IS JAZZ BROADCASTS VOL.1 (Various artists).
Tracks: / High society: *Various artists* / Tiger rag: *Various artists* / Basin street blues: *Miller, Punch* / Dippermouth blues: *Various artists* / Sister Kate: *Miller, Punch* / Ain't misbehavin': *Various artists* / That's a plenty: *Various artists* / Baby won't you please come home: *Various artists* / I know that you know: *Various artists* / Caprice rag: *Various artists* / Charleston: *Various artists* / Way down yonder in New Orleans: *Various artists* / Blues: *Various artists*.
LP: . . . . RHA 6036

THIS IS JAZZ BROADCASTS VOL.2 (Various artists).
Tracks: / Sensation rag: *Various artists* / You're some pretty doll: *Various artists* / Twelfth St. rag: *Various* artists / Buddy Bolden's blues: *Various artists* / Black and blue: *Various artists* / Summertime: *Various* artists / Farewell blues: *Various artists* / Maple leaf rag: *Various artists* / Basin street blues: *Various artists* / Polka dot stomp: *Various artists* / Kansas City man blues: *Various artists* / Jazz me blues: *Various artists* / Carolina shout: *Various artists* / Panama march (rag): *Various artists* / Way down yonder in New Orleans: *Various artists*.
LP: . . . . RHA 6037

THIS IS JAZZ VOL.1 (Broadcasts) (Various artists).
LP: . . . . RARITIES 33

THIS IS JAZZ VOL.2 (Various artists).
LP: . . . . RARITIES 35

THREE WAY MIRROR (Various artists).
LP: . . . . RR 24

TIGER RAG, 1931 (Various artists).
LP: . . . . NOST 7619

TRAD JAZZ (Various artists).
Tracks: / Royal garden blues: *Various artists* / April showers: *Various artists* / Winin' boy blues: *Various* artists / Alexander's ragtime band: *Various artists* / Snag it: *Various artists* / Pananma rag: *Various* artists / Saved by the blues: *Various artists* / Sister Kate: *Various artists* / We shall march through the streets of the city: *Various artists* / Bei mir bist du schon: *Various artists* / Hot time in the old town tonight: *Various artists* / Louisiana: *Various artists* / Gettysburg march: *Various artists* / T'aint no sin: *Various* artists / Go Ghana: *Various artists* / There'll be some changes made: *Various artists* / Ostrich walk: *Various* artists / Beale Street blues: *Various artists* / Stop, look and listen: *Various artists* / When the Saints go marching in: *Various artists*.
LP: . . . . GH 669

TRAD JAZZ (Various artists).
MC: . . . . C 907

TRAD JAZZ FESTIVAL (Various artists).
Tracks: / Marching through Georgia: *Various artists* / American patrol: *Various artists* / Tishomingo blues: *Various* artists / Whistling Rufus: *Various artists* / Sur le pont d'Avignon: *Various artists* / Delia's gone: *Various* artists / One sweet letter from you: *Various artists* / Dinah: *Various artists* / Travelling blues: *Various artists* / Petite Fleur: *Various artists* / Easter parade: *Various artists*.
MCSET: . . . . DTO 10019

TRADITIONAL JAZZ (Various artists).
2LP: 416038

TRADITIONAL JAZZ IN RURAL CHURCHES (Various artists).
LP: . . . . TLP 1001

TRIBUTE TO BLACKWELL (Various artists).
LP: 1201131

TRIBUTE TO DUKE (Various artists).
LP: . . . . CJ 50

TRIBUTE TO MONK AND BIRD, A (Various artists).
Tracks: / Air conditioning: *Various artists* / Au privave: *Various artists* / Ba-lue bolivar ba-lues are: *Various artists* / Straight no chaser: *Various artists* / Misterioso: *Various artists* / Perhaps: *Various artists*.
2LP: . . . . AFFD 187

TRIBUTE TO TOMMY DORSEY (Various artists).
LP: . . . . SG 8014

TROMBONE ALBUM, THE (Various artists).
2LP: . . . . WL 70523

TRUMPET BLUES 1925/29 (Various artists).
LP: . . . . HLP 27

TRUMPET TIME (Various artists).
LP: . . . . AA 511

TWIN CITIES SHUFFLE 1927-30 (Various artists).
LP: . . . . ARCADIA 2016

UNE HISTOIRE DES GEANTS DU JAZZ (Various artists).
2LP: 400342

URBAN JAZZ (The Original Illicit Grooves) (Various artists).
Tracks: / Soul sauce: *Tjader, Cal* / Cantaloupe woman: *Green, Grant* / Eight counts for Rita: *Smith, Jimmy* (USA) / In the middle: *Brown, James* / You're starting too fast: *Pate, Johnny* / Betty Boop: *Earland, Charles* / Spinning wheel: *New Jersey Kings* / That ain't too cool: *Pate, Johnny*.
LP: 837 930-1
MC: 837 930-4

VAUDEVILLE BLUES (Various artists).
LP: . . . . VLP 30

V-DISC STOMP Hackett/Tatum/Strayhorn/Ellington (Various artists).
LP: . . . . IAJRC 51

VERVE JAZZ BEST VOL.3 (Various artists).
Tracks: / Organ grinder's swing: *Smith, Jimmy (USA)* / Cheek to cheek: *Fitzgerald, Ella & Louis Armstrong* / Samba triste: *Getz, Stan & Charlie Byrd* / Aqua de beber: *Gilberto, Astrud* / You'd be so nice to come home to: *Hawkins, Coleman & Ben Webster* / Too close for comfort: *Torme, Mel* / Caravan: *Montgomery, Wes* / I can't give you anything but love: *Fitzgerald, Ella* / Moonglow: *Hampton, Lionel/Teddy Wilson/Gene Krupa* / Just a sittin and a rockin: *Harper, Toni* / East of the sun (and west of the moon): *Various artists* / Moonlight in Vermont: *Holiday, Billie* / You look good to me: *Oscar Peterson Trio*.
LP: 827 542-1
MC: 827 542-4

VERY BEST OF BRITISH JAZZ, THE (Various artists).
Tracks: / Hi ya: *Various artists* / Watch what happens: *Various artists* / Time's a wastin': *Various artists*/ Sweet Sue: *Various artists* / Stompin' at the Savoy: *Various artists* / Misty: *Various artists* / Preacher, The: *Various artists* / Honeysuckle Rose: *Various artists* / Rosetta: *Various artists*.
LP: . . . . PRJ 501
MC: . . . . CPRJ 501

VOCAL GROUP ALBUM (Various artists).
2LP: . . . . SJL 2241

VOYAGE A LA NOUVELLE ORLEANS (Various artists).
2LP: 400664

WALK ON THE JAZZ SIDE (Various artists).
Tracks: / Stormy Weather: *Benson, George* / I thought it was you: *Hancock, Herbie* / Who can I turn to: *Marsalis, Wynton* / Captain Marvel: *Corea, Chick* / East River: *Brecker Brothers* / Bottle, The: *Scott-Heron, Gil*/ Sweet baby: *Clarke, Stanley* / Desafinado: *Getz, Stan* / Time after time: *Davis, Miles* / Birdland: *Weather Report* / Girl from Ipanema: *Gilberto, Astrud* / Brazilian love affair: *Duke, George* / Take Five: *Brubeck, Dave* / Funkin' for Jamaica: *Browne, Tom* / Blight of the fumble bee: *Desmond, Paul* / Walk on the wild side: *Smith, Jimmy (USA)*.
MC: . . . . STDMC 30

WE LOVE ELLINGTON (Various artists).
Tracks: / Johnny come lately: *Various artists* / Solitude: *Various artists* / Me and you: *Various artists*/ Just a sittin and a rockin: *Various artists* / It don't mean a thing: *Various artists* / Mood indigo: *Various* artists / Do nothing till you hear from me: *Various artists* / I got it bad and that ain't good: *Various artists*/ Caravan: *Various artists* / C jam blues: *Various artists*.
LP: . . . . PHONT 7520

WEST COAST HOT (Various artists).
Tracks: / Call to the festival: *Carter, John & Bobby Bradford* / Second set, The: *Carter, John & Bobby Bradford*/ Woman: *Carter, John & Bobby Bradford* / Abstractions for three lovers: *Carter, John & Bobby Bradford* / Giant is awakened, The: *Tapscott, Horace Quintet* / For Fats: *Tapscott, Horace Quintet* / Dark tree, The: *Tapscott, Horace Quintet* / Niger's theme: *Tapscott, Horace Quintet*.
MC: . . . . NK 83107

WEST COAST JAM SESSIONS, 1952 (Various artists).
LPS: . . . . SC 802/1-3

WEST COAST JAZZ VOLUME 1 1922-31 (Various artists).
LP: . . . . ARCADIA 2001

WEST COAST JAZZ VOLUME 2 1925-31 (Various artists).
LP: . . . . ARCADIA 2002

WEST COAST SCENE (Various artists).
MCSET: . . . . ZCVJD 536

WEST COAST SCENE VOL 2 (Various artists).
Tracks: / Bernie's tune: *Various artists* / My old flame: *Various artists* / I'll remember April: *Various* artists / Neil's blues: *Various artists* / Champ, The: *Various artists* / Chooch: *Various artists*/ Nearness of you, (The): *Various artists* / Whippet: *Various artists* / Milt's tune: *Various artists*/ Get happy: *Various artists* / Lost in a fugue: *Various artists* / Tone poem: *Various artists* / I only have eyes for you: *Various artists* / Frantastic: *Various artists* / Frankly speaking: *Various artists*/ Illusion: *Various artists* / Caleta: *Various artists* / Crazy quilt: *Various artists* / Varsity drag: *Various artists* / Swing house: *Various artists* / Love me or leave me: *Various artists* / Half Nelson: *Various artists* / Speak now: *Various artists* / Ladybird: *Various artists*.
2LP: . . . . VJD 570
MCSET: . . . . ZC VJD 570

WEST COAST SCENE VOL 3 (Various artists).
Tracks: / Jazz wave: *Flory, Med & His Orchestra* / Davy Jones: *Flory, Med & His Orchestra* / Occasional man, An: *Flory, Med & His Orchestra* / I cover the waterfront: *Flory, Med & His Orchestra* / Between the Devil and the deep blue sea: *Flory, Med & His Orchestra* / Nightmare: *Geller, Herb Quintet* / Cool day, A: *Geller, Herb Quintet*/ Princess, The: *Geller, Herb Quintet* / Little girl: *Levy, Lou Trio* / I'll never smile again: *Levy, Lou* Trio / Undecided: *Levy, Lou Trio* / Lover man: *Levy, Lou Trio* / Gypsy, The: *Levy, Lou Trio* / Sunday kind of love, A: *Levy, Lou Trio* / S'Pacific view: *Geller, Herb Sextet* / Jitterbug waltz: *Geller, Herb Sextet*/ Fruit, The: *Geller, Herb Sextet*.
2LP: . . . . VJD 578

WHEN MALINDY SINGS (JAZZ VOCALISTS 1938-1961) (Various artists).
Tracks: / Can't get started: *Holiday, Billie & Her Orchestra* / I left my baby: *Rushing, Jimmy/Count Basie & His Orchestra*/ Piney Brown blues: *Turner, Joe & His Flying Cats* / Careless love: *Turner, Joe*/ *Willie the lion Smith* / Ja da: *Watson, Leo & His Orchestra* / It's the tune that counts: *Watson, Leo & His Orchestra* / Robbins nest: *Thompson,* Sir Charles / Illinois Jacquet / Blowtop blues: *Washington, Dinah*/ *Lionel Hampton & His Septet* / Key largo: *Vaughan, Sarah* / Moonlight in Vermont: *Carter, Better* / Thou swell: *Carter, Better* / Can't we be friends: *Carter,* Better / Misty: *Connor, Chris* / Love: *Connor, Chris* / When Malindy sings: *Lincoln, Abbey* / End of the love affair, The: *Holiday, Billie & Ray Ellis & His Orchestra*.
LP: . . . . NW 295

WHITE HOT JAZZ VOL.1 (Various artists).
LP: . . . . BR 115

WILDFLOWERS (NEW YORK LOFT JAZZ SESSIONS 1976) V (Various artists).
LP: . . . . NBLP 7049

WILDFLOWERS (NEW YORK LOFT JAZZ SESSIONS 1976) V (Various artists).
LP: . . . . NBLP 7048

WILDFLOWERS (NEW YORK LOFT JAZZ SESSIONS 1976) V (Various artists).
LP: . . . . NBLP 7046

WILDFLOWERS (NEW YORK LOFT JAZZ SESSIONS 1976)VO (Various artists).
LP: . . . . NBLP 7045

WILDFLOWERS (NEW YORK LOFT JAZZ SESSIONS 1976) (Various artists).
LP: . . . . NBLP 7047

WINDHAM HILL SAMPLER '82 (Various artists).
LP: . . . . C 1024

WINDHAM HILL SAMPLER '86 (Various artists).
LP: 371048-1
MC: 371048-4

WINDHAM HILL SAMPLER '88 (Various artists).
Tracks: / Wishing well: *Schonertz & Scott* / Unseen rain: *Mathieu, W.A.* / Road to Hanna: *Shadowfax*/ Angel steps: *Cossu, Scott* / Toys not ties: *Nightnoise* / Because it's there: *Hedges, Michael* / To be: *Montreux* / Indian woman: *Rubaja & Hernandez* / Close cover: *Mertens, Wim* / Climbing in geometry: *Ackerman, Will* / Woman at the well: *Story, Tim*.
LP: 37 1065-1
MC: 37 1065-4

WINTER SOLSTICE, A (Various artists).
LP: . . . . TAC 1045

WOMEN IN JAZZ: ALL WOMEN GROUPS (Various artists).
LP: . . . . ST 111

WOMEN IN JAZZ: PIANISTS (Various artists).
LP: . . . . ST 112

WOMEN IN JAZZ: SWINGTIME TO MODERN (Various artists).
LP: . . . . ST 113

WQCD SAMPLER (Various artists).
MC: . . . . C 8804

XANADU AT MONTREUX (Various artists).
LP: . . . . XAN 163

YONDER COMES THE BLUES (Jazz classics) (Various artists).
LP: . . . . SOS 1061

Jazz '81

JAZZ '81 (Various artists).
Tracks: / Boogie on, reggae woman: *Rollercoaster* / T'aint what you do (it's the way that you do it): *Melly, George*/ Invitation: *Scott, Ronnie Quintet* / That's what friends are for: *Fame, Georgie* / Happy katz: *N.Y.J.O.*/ Spacin' home: *Bellson, Louis* / Moody magic: *Terry, Clark* / Passing strangers: *Vaughan, Sarah* / Tyrone: *Coryell, Larry* / Little pony: *Basie, Count* / Twenty four: *Edison, Harry* / Wolafunt's lament: *Newman, Joe* / I only have eyes for you: *Hampton, Lionel* / Emanon: *Gillespie, Dizzy* / Too late: *Wilson, Teddy* (dup) / Stop and listen: *Payne, Cecil* / Roll 'em Pete: *Witherspoon, Jimmy* / Mannish boy: *Waters, Muddy*/ Hoochie coochie man: *Waters, Muddy* / I just want to make love to you: *Waters, Muddy* / Promised land: *Berry, Chuck* / Let it rock: *Berry, Chuck* / Rock and roll music: *Berry, Chuck*.
2LP: . . . . VJD 575
MCSET: . . . . ZC VJD 575

Jazz A Rise

MIDLIFE HEALTH PROGRAM, A - EXPLAINED AND ILLUSTRATED.
LP: . . . . ST 401

Jazz Adoption Agency

MORE BIRDS, LESS FEATHERS (See under Berk, Dick).

Jazz And Reg

JAZZ AND REG (Various artists).
MCSET: . . . . WW 6034

Jazz Artists Guild

JAZZ LIFE, THE.
LP: . . . . CS 9019

Jazz at the ...

EXCITING BATTLE, STOCKHOLM, '55 (Various artists).
Tracks: / Little David: *Various artists* / Ow: *Various artists* / Sticks: *Various artists* / Man I love, The: *Various artists* / I'll never be the same: *Various artists* / Skylark: *Various artists* / My old flame: *Various artists*.
LP: 231 0713
MC: K10 713

JAZZ AT THE MONTREUX JAZZ FESTIVAL, 1975 (Various artists).
Tracks: / For you / Autumn leaves: *Various artists* / If I had you / I never knew.
LP: 231 0748
MC: K10 748

JAZZ AT THE OPERA HOUSE (Various artists).
LP: . . . . CBS 88622
MC: 40 88622

JAZZ AT THE PHILHARMONIC (Happy reunion) (Various artists).
2LP: 2620 117

JAZZ AT THE PHILHARMONIC 1983 (Various artists).
Tracks: / Lucky so and so: *Various artists* / I may be wrong: *Various artists* / Smoke gets in your eyes: *Various* artists / Stompin' at The Savoy: *Various artists* / Time after time: *Various artists* / Secret love: *Various artists* / It could happen to you: *Various artists* / Slow drag: *Various artists*.
LP: 2310 882

JAZZ AT THE PHILHARMONIC: HARTFORD 1953 (Various artists).
Tracks: / Cottontail: *Various artists* / Airmail special: *Various artists* / Swinging on a star: *Various* artists / Man I love, The: *Various artists* / Seven come eleven: *Various artists* / D.B. blues: *Various artists* / I cover the waterfront: *Various artists* / Up-'n'-Adam: *Various artists*.
LP: 230 8240
MC: . . . . K 08240

JAZZ AT THE SANTA MONICA CIVIC (Various artists).
Tracks: / Basie power: *Basie, Count & His Orchestra* / Meetin', The: *Basie, Count & His Orchestra* / Blues in Hoss's flat: *Basie, Count & His Orchestra* / Good time blues: *Basie, Count & His Orchestra* / In a mellow tone: *Jazz at the Philharmonic Allstars* / Loose walk: *Jazz at the Philharmonic Allstars* / Makin' whoopee: *Jazz* at the Philharmonic Allstars / If I had you: *Jazz at the Philharmonic Allstars* / She's funny that way: *Jazz* at the Philharmonic Allstars / Blue and sentimental: *Jazz at the Philharmonic Allstars* / I surrender, dear: *Jazz* at the Philharmonic Allstars / 5400 north: *Jazz at the Philharmonic Allstars* / You are my sunshine: *Peterson, Oscar &* Ray Brown / Shiny stockings: *Fitzgerald, Ella/Count Basie Orchestra/Tommy Flanagan Trio* / You've got a friend: *Fitzgerald, Ella/Count Basie Orchestra/ Tommy Flanagan Trio* / What's going

on?: *Fitzgerald, Ella/Count Basie Orchestra/Tommy Flanagan Trio* / Spring can really hang you up the most: *Fitzgerald, Ella/Count Basie Orchestra/ Tommy Flanagan Trio*/ Madalena: *Fitzgerald, Ella/Count Basie Orchestra/ Tommy Flanagan Trio* / Too darn hot: *Fitzgerald, Ella/Count Basie* Orchestra/ Tommy Flanagan Trio / It's alright with me: *Fitzgerald, Ella/Count Basie Orchestra/Tommy Flanagan Trio* / Sandford and Son theme: *Fitzgerald, Ella/Count Basie Orchestra/Tommy Flanagan Trio* / I can't stop loving you: *Fitzgerald, Ella/Count Basie Orchestra/ Tommy Flanagan Trio* / Finale: *Fitzgerald, Ella/Count Basie/JATP All Stars.*
LPS: **2625 701**

LIVE AT THE NICHIGEKI THEATRE, TOKYO (Various artists).
Tracks: / Tokyo blues: *Various artists* / Up: *Various artists* / Someone to watch over me: *Various artists*/ Flamingo: *Various artists* / I surrender dear: *Various artists* / Sweet and lovely: *Various artists*/ Stardust: *Various artists* / Embraceable you: *Various artists* / That old black magic: *Various artists*/ Sushi blues: *Various artists* / Swingin' 'til the girls come home: *Various artists* / Indiana: *Various artists*/ Cocktails for two: *Various artists* / Don't be that way: *Various artists* / Stompin': *Various artists*/ At the Savoy: *Various artists* / On the sunny side of the street: *Various artists* / Body and soul: *Various* artists / Why don't you do right: *Various artists* / Lady be good: *Various artists* / I got it bad and that ain't good: *Various artists* / How high the moon: *Various artists* / My funny valentine: *Various artists*/ Smooth sailing: *Various artists* / Frim fram sauce: *Various artists* / Perdido: *Various artists.*
2LP: **262 0104**
MCSET: . . . . **K 20 104**

Jazz Band Ball

JAZZ BAND BALL VOL 2 (Various artists).
LP: . . . . **S 1398**

Jazz Best

JAZZ BEST (Various artists).
Tracks: / Girl from Ipanema: *Gilberto, Astrud & Stan Getz* / St. Louis blues: *Ellington, Duke* / Sweet Lorraine: *Various artists* / Born to be blue: *Montgomery, Wes* / Georgia on my mind: *Peterson, Oscar Trio* / Summertime: *Fitzgerald, Ella & Louis Armstrong* / Desafinado: *Getz, Stan* / People: *Peterson, Oscar Trio* / Misty: *Fitzgerald, Ella* / Basin Street blues: *Smith, Jimmy (USA)* / My funny valentine: *Webster, Ben* / Lady sings the blues: *Holiday, Billie.*
LP: **2367 406**
LP: **33012**
MC: **63012**

JAZZ BEST, VOL 2 (Various artists).
Tracks: / Shadow of your mind: *Gilberto, Astrud* / Honeysuckle rose: *Wilson, Teddy (dup)* / Insensatez: *Jobim,* Antonio Carlos / In a mellow tone: *Various artists* / Foggy day, A: *Fitzgerald, Ella & Louis Armstrong* / Line for Lyons: *Desmond, Paul* / Mr. Paganini: *Fitzgerald, Ella* / Walk on by: *Getz, Stan* / Tequila: *Montgomery, Wes* / Way down yonder in New Orleans: *Crosby, Bing & Louis Armstrong* / Makin' whoopee: *Webster, Ben* / Stormy weather: *Holiday, Billie.*
LP: **2367 416**
MC: **3115 125**

Jazz Butcher

BATH OF BACON.
Tracks: / Gloop jiving / Party time / Bigfoot motel / Zombie love / Grey flannellette / La mer / Poisoned by food / Jazz butcher theme.
LP: . . . . **GLALP 002**

BIG PLANET.
LP: . . . . **CRELP 49**
MC: . . . . **CRELPC 49**

CULT OF THE BASEMENT.
Tracks: / Basement, The / Pineapple Tuesday / Daycare nation / Mr. Odd / Panic in room 109 / Turtle bait / She's on drugs / Onion field, The / My Zeppelin / After the euphrates / Girl go / Sister death.
LP: . . . . **CRE LP 62**
MC: . . . . **CCBE 62**

DISTRESSED GENTLEFOLK.
LP: . . . . **GLALP 020**
MC: . . . . **GLAMC 020**

FISHCOTHEQUE.
Tracks: / Next move sideways / Out of touch / Get it wrong / Living in a village / Swell / Looking for lot / Best way, The / Chickentown / Susie / Keeping the curtains closed.
LP: . . . . **CRELP 027**

LIVE AT ONCKEL P8'S.
LP: **081443**

LIVE IN HAMBURG.
LP: . . . . **RE 0016**

Jazz City Presents

JAZZ CITY PRESENTS (Various artists).
LP: . . . . **FS 205**

Jazz Classics...

JAZZ CLASSICS (Various artists).
Tracks: / It's a sin to tell a lie: *Various artists* / Potato head blues: *Various artists* / Ostrich walk: *Various* artists / Riverboat shuffle: *Various artists* / Georgia on my mind: *Various artists* / Struttin' with some bar-b-q: *Various artists* / Creole jazz: *Various artists* / I'm gonna sit right down and write myself a letter: *Various artists* / Bourbon Street parade: *Various artists* / Snag it: *Various artists* / Sweet Georgia Brown: *Various artists* / Sophisticated lady: *Various artists* / This can't be love: *Various artists*/ I can't get started with you: *Various artists* / After you've gone: *Various artists* / Old grey bonnet: *Various* artists / Old rugged cross, The: *Various artists* / There will never be another you: *Various artists* / Ain't misbehavin': *Various artists* / Woodchoppers ball: *Various artists.*
2LP: . . . . **KAZLP 11**
MCSET: . . . . **KAZMC 11**

JAZZ CLASSICS OF NEW ORLEANS (Various artists).
2LP: **400439**

JAZZ CLASSICS, VOL.1 (Various artists).
LP: . . . . **BNS 40001**

JAZZ CLASSICS, VOL.2 (Various artists).
LP: . . . . **BNS 40002**

Jazz Club

JAZZ CLUB (Various artists).
Tracks: / Take the 'A' train: *Fitzgerald, Ella* / No more blues: *Gillespie, Dizzy* / Long, long summer: *Gillespie, Dizzy* / Buh's bossa: *Blakey, Art* / Moanin': *Blakey, Art* / G'won train: *Smith, Jimmy (USA)* / Southern suite: *Hayes, Tubby* / Manha de carnaval: *Getz, Stan* / Lullaby of Birdland: *Vaughan, Sarah.*
LP: . . . . **JABB 3**
MC: . . . . **JABBC 3**

JAZZ CLUB 2 (Various artists).
Tracks: / Mack the knife: *Fitzgerald, Ella* / Tribute to Brownie: *Adderley, Cannonball* / 'Bout to wail: *Gillespie, Dizzy* / All of me: *Washington, Dinah* / Yeh yeh: *Hendricks, Jon* / Shulie a bop: *Vaughan, Sarah*/ Jordu: *Brown, Clifford* / Sackful of soul / T.V. is the thing: *Washington, Dinah* / Pint of bitter: *Hayes, Tubby.*
LP: . . . . **JABB 7**
MC: . . . . **JABBC 7**

JAZZ CLUB - ALTO SAX (Various artists).
Tracks: / Now's the time: *Parker, Charlie* / Sleepin' bee, A: *Pepper, Art* / Porky: *Adderley, Cannonball*/ C-Jam blues: *Mariano, Charlie* / Blues greasy: *Stitt, Sonny* / Blues for bird: *Konitz, Lee* / Kicks wings: *Shank, Bud* / Yesterdays: *Woods, Phil* / Funky blues: *Parker/ Hodges/Carter* / Standstill: *Desmond, Paul* / Confirmation: *McLean, Jackie* / Futurity: *Gryce, Gigi.*
LP: **840 036 1**
MC: **840 036 4**

JAZZ CLUB - BASS (Various artists).
Tracks: / Blue horizon, The (take 1): *Wayne, Chuck* / Prayer for passive: *Mingus, Charles* / Blues in the closet: *Pettiford, Oscar* / How high the moon: *Safranski, Eddie* / If I were a bell: *Mitchell, Red* / Stompin' at the Savoy: *Carter, Ron* / Muses for Richard Davis: *Davis, Richard* / Northwest passage: *Jackson, Chubby*/ Solo for unaccompanied bass: *Brown, Ray* / Golden striker, The: *Heath, Percy* / Little beaver: *Chambers,* Paul / Tribute to Brownie: *Jones, Sam* / Younger: *Hiels-Henning-Orsted-Pedersen* / Foreign fun: *Pastorius, Jaco.*
LP: **840 037 1**
MC: **840 037 4**

JAZZ CLUB - BIG BANDS (Various artists).
LP: **840 030 1**
MC: **840 030 4**

JAZZ CLUB - DRUMS (Various artists).
LP: **840 033 1**
MC: **840 033 4**

JAZZ CLUB - GUITAR (Various artists).
Tracks: / Conception: *Wayne, Chuck* / Patti cake: *Ellis, Herb* / Nobody else but me: *Raney, Jimmy* / Downstairs: *Burrell, Kenny* / Samba triste: *Powell, Baden* / O Pato: *Byrd, Charlie* / Blues for Django: *Coryell, Larry & Philip Catherine* / Interlude, Take 1: *Bauer, Billy* / Heat wave: *Kessel, Barney* / You came along: *Farlow, Tal* / Li'l darlin': *Pass, Joe* / Song for my father: *Benson, George* / Extrapolation: *McLaughlin, John.*
LP: **840 035 1**
MC: **840 035 4**

JAZZ CLUB MAINSTREAM - ALTO SAX, CLARINET AND FLUTE (See Under Jazz...) (Various artists).

JAZZ CLUB MAINSTREAM - BIG BANDS (See Under Jazz...) (Various artists).

JAZZ CLUB MAINSTREAM - DIXIELAND (See Under Jazz...) (Various artists).

JAZZ CLUB MAINSTREAM - DRUMS (See Under Jazz...) (Various artists).

JAZZ CLUB MAINSTREAM - GUITAR AND BASS (See Under Jazz...) (Various artists).

JAZZ CLUB MAINSTREAM - PIANO (See Under Jazz...) (Various artists).

JAZZ CLUB MAINSTREAM - TENOR AND BARITONE SAX (See Under Jazz...) (Various artists).

JAZZ CLUB MAINSTREAM - TROMBONE (See Under Jazz...) (Various artists).

JAZZ CLUB MAINSTREAM - TRUMPET (See Under Jazz...) (Various artists).

JAZZ CLUB MAINSTREAM - VOCAL (See Under Jazz...) (Various artists).

JAZZ CLUB - PIANO (Various artists).
LP: **840 032 1**
MC: **840 032 4**

JAZZ CLUB - TENOR SAX (Various artists).
LP: **840 031 1**
MC: **840 031 4**

JAZZ CLUB - TROMBONE (Various artists).
Tracks: / Bill, not Phil: *Harris, Bill* / How are things in Glocca Morra: *Winding, Kai* / Adam's in the apple: *Knepper, Jimmy* / Cat meets Chick: *Green, Urbie* / Blues melba: *Liston/Green/Grey/Powell* / Song is you, The: *Rosolino, Frank* / Trombone suite: *Maangelsdorff/ Hampton* / Yesterday / Christmas eve: *Liston/Cleveland/Rehak*/ He ain't got rhythm: *Brookmeyer, Bob* / Our love is here: *Cleveland, Jimmy* / Chang, chang, chang: *Fuller, Curtis* / Tonk: *Moncur, Grachan III.*
LP: **840 040 1**
MC: **840 040 4**

JAZZ CLUB - TRUMPET (Various artists).
LP: **840 038 1**
MC: **840 038 4**

JAZZ CLUB - VIBRAPHONE (Various artists).
LP: **840 034 1**
MC: **840 034 4**

JAZZ CLUB - VIOLIN (Various artists).
LP: **840 039 1**
MC: **840 039 4**

JAZZ CLUB - VOCAL (Various artists).
LP: **840 029 1**
MC: **840 029 4**

Jazz Collection

JAZZ COLLECTION (Various artists).
Tracks: / When the saints go marching in: *Various artists* / At the woodchoppers' ball: *Herman, Woody* / Take the 'A' train: *Ellington, Duke* / Stardust: *Dorsey, Tommy & Frank Sinatra* / In the mood: *Various artists*/ Begin the beguine: *Shaw, Artie* / Stompin' at the Savoy: *Goodman, Benny* / Laura: *James, Harry* / Monday date: *Hines, Earl* / Ain't misbehavin': *Waller, Fats* / Swanee: *Jolson, Al* / Minnie the moocher: *Calloway,* Cab / Lover man: *Holiday, Billie* / Sophisticated lady: *Fitzgerald, Ella* / Embraceable you: *Vaughan,* Sarah / Misty: *Garner, Erroll* / Take five: *Brubeck, Dave* / Autumn leaves: *Evans, Bill* / Blue Monk: *Monk, Thelonious* / Theme: *Davis, Miles.*
LP: . . . . **DVLP 2052**
MC: . . . . **DVMC 2052**

Jazz Composer's...

COMMUNICATIONS (Jazz Composer's Orchestra).
2LP: . . . . **JCOA 1001**

Jazz & Country...

JAZZ AND COUNTRY IN THE MOVIES (Film soundtrack) (Various artists).
Tracks: / Pourin' whiskey blues: *Labelle, Patti* / Low down dirty shame: *Labelle, Patti & Larry Riles* / Cotton-eyed Joe: *Watson, Doc & Merle* / Ida Red: *Barnes, Roosevelt* / Faded love: *Barnes, Roosevelt* / Lovesick blues: *Barnes, Roosevelt* / Down home blues: *Barnes, Roosevelt* / Every time she goes by: *Oxford Community Choir*/ I want to go home: *Oxford Community Choir* / Liberty: *Oxford Community Choir.*
LP: . . . . **ACH 030**
MC: . . . . **CCH 030**

Jazz Couriers

LAST WORD.
Tracks: / If this isn't love / Easy to love / Whisper not / Autumn leaves / Too close for comfort / Yesterdays / Love walked in.
LP: . . . . **JASM 2024**

THEME, THE.
Tracks: / Through the night roared the overland express / On a misty night / Plebus / Reunion / Oh my / Foggy day, A / Royal Ascot / Cheek to cheek.
LP: . . . . **JASM 2004**

Jazz Crusaders

YOUNG RABBITS.
2LP: . . . . **BND 4028**

Jazz Dance

JAM FOR BOPPERS (JAZZ DANCE 3) (Various artists).
Tracks: / Please don't leave me: *Shibab, Sahib* / Spanish grease: *Lewis, Ramsey Trio* / Barefoot sunday blues: *Lewis, Ramsey Trio* / Vera: *Evans,Richard Trio* / Boss Tina: *Grey, Al* / Watermelon man: *Jacquet, Illinois* / Jam for boppers: *Ammons, Gene & Sonny Stitt* / Mellow yellow: *Brown,Odell & The Organizers* / Huffin'n'puffin': *Donaldson, Lou.*
LP: . . . . **ARC 505**
MC: . . . . **ARCK 7505**

JAZZ DANCE (Various artists).
Tracks: / It's only a paper moon: *Various artists* / Jumpin' at the woodside: *Various artists* / Sweet and lovely: *Various artists* / Waltz I blew for you, The: *Various artists* / Sing, sing, sing: *Various artists* / Bundle o'funk: *Various artists* / Nature boy: *Various artists* / World is waiting for the sunrise, The: *Various artists* / Jitterbug waltz: *Various artists* / Take the 'A' train: *Various artists.*
LP: **231 0890**

JAZZ DANCE 1 (CD) (Various artists).
Tracks: / Triple threat: *Kirk, Roland* / Hold it: *Doggett, Bill* / Love me or leave me: *Simone, Nina*/ Another one: *Pettiford, Oscar* / My baby just cares for me: *Simone, Nina* / Fever: *John, Little Willie*/ Kidney stew: *Vinson, Eddie* / Tippin: *Various artists* / Boom boom: *Various artists* / Kinda Dukish: *Various artists* / Roof garden: *Various artists* / Terrible T: *Morgan, Lee* / Right down front: *Blakey, Art.*
LP: . . . . **ATS 8**
MC: . . . . **TCATS 8**

JAZZ DANCE 2 (Do it like you feel it) (Various artists).
Tracks: / Do it like you feel it: *Green, Bunky* / Back talk: *Donaldson, Lou* / Hot Bossa: *Burrell, Kenny*/ Wade in the water: *Lewis, Ramsey* / Summertime: *Moody, James* / Mas que nada: *Brown,Odell & The Organizers*/ On Broadway: *Jacquet, Illinois* / Blackfoot: *Jacquet, Illinois* / Night in Tunisia: *Clark,Buck Sound*/ Song for my father: *Bryant, Ray.*
LP: . . . . **ARC 504**
MC: . . . . **ARCK 7504**

Jazz Defektors

JAZZ DEFEKTORS.
MC: . . . . **FACT 205C**

Jazz Devils

HARD ROADS.
Tracks: / Small affair / What in the world / Young boy blues / Voices / Hard road / London / TV preacher man / Georgia on my mind / Nobody's man / Walking with the night / Clockwork nation (Only on MC and CD.).
LP: . . . . **V 2629**
MC: . . . . **TCV 2629**

OUT OF THE DARK.
Tracks: / Out of the dark / Back in town / Take it if you really want / Postman song, The / Raid, The / It's a crime / Chase the blues / Censored feelings / That girl.
LP: . . . . **V 2560**
MC: . . . . **TCV 2560**

Jazz Doctors

DOCTOR JAZZ.
LP: . . . . **SLP 409**

INTENSIVE CARE.
LP: . . . . **SGC 1011**

Jazz & Drops

PERSUASIVA.
LP: . . . . **LP 018**

Jazz Erotica

JAZZ EROTICA.
LP: .... **FS 96**

Jazz Et Cinema

JAZZ ET CINEMA (Various artists).
Tracks: / Singin' in the rain: *Various artists* / All that jazz: *Various artists* / Laura: *Various artists*/ On Green Dolphin Street: *Various artists* / Girl talk: *Various artists* / Cheek to Cheek: *Various artists*/ Somewhere: *Various artists* / Trolley song, The: *Various artists* / Way you look tonight: *Various artists*/ Whistle while you work: *Various artists* / People: *Various artists* / Autumn leaves: *Various artists*/ Stormy weather: *Various artists* / Who's afraid of the big bad wolf: *Various artists*.
LP: .... **CBS 21109**
MC: **40 21109**

Jazz Festival

JAZZ FESTIVAL (Various artists).
LP: .... **QUEEN 044**

Jazz Fiddlers

BRAG.
LP: .... **WAM/O No.6**

Jazz From...

JAZZ FROM NEW YORK (1928-29) (Various).
LP: .... **S 1299**

JAZZ FROM ST LOUIS, 1924-1926 (Various artists).
Tracks: / Pleasure mad: *Creath, Chas Jazz O Maniacs* / Market Street blues: *Creath, Chas Jazz O Maniacs* / I woke up cold in hand: *Creath, Chas Jazz O Maniacs* / King Porter stomp: *Creath, Chas Jazz O Maniacs* / Every man that wears bell bottom britches: *Creath, Chas Jazz O Maniacs* / My daddy rocks me: *Creath, Chas Jazz O Maniacs* / Market Street stomp: *Creath, Chas Jazz O Maniacs* / Won't don't blues: *Creath, Chas Jazz O Maniacs* / Grandpa's spells: *Creath, Chas Jazz O Maniacs* / Frankie and Johnny: *Marable, Fate Society Syncopaters* / Pianoflage: *Marable, Fate Society Syncopaters* / Compton Avenue blues: *Washington, Benny Six Aces* / Soap suds: *St. Louis Levee Band*.
LP: .... **S 810**

Jazz Funk

BEST OF BRITISH JAZZ FUNK VOL.2 (Various artists).
Tracks: / I'm for real: *Gee, Roy & Energee* / Body shake: *Curtis, T.C* / One to one: *Various artists*/ You and me just started: *Taylor, Linda* / Magic: *Side On* / Somebody help me out: *Beggar & Co* / Play the game: *Cool Runners* / Love train: *Light Of The World* / Come and get me: *Mullen Morrissey* / Don't be mistaken: *First Light* / You're lying: *Linx* / North London boy: *Various artists* / Tarantula walk: *Carless, Ray* / Time's running out: *Direct Drive*.
LP: .... **BEGA 41**

CERTAIN KIND OF FREEDOM, A (Various artists).
Tracks: / That guy called Pumpkin: *Talbot, Mick* / Certain kind of ...: *Morris/ White/Carr* / Thank you: *Garland, Scott & Steve White* / Liquidator: *Carr Quartet, The* / Waltz for Lucia: *McMillan Quartet* / To the top: *Backbone*/ Going away: *Peterson, Lenny* / In the mould: *Enjiem* / Road less travelled, A: *Gould, Paul* / There will never be another ...: *Husband, Gary*.
MC: **841 923 4**
LP: **841 923 1**

CLASSIC JAZZ-FUNK (Various artists).
2LP: .... **CUTSLP 2**
MC: .... **CUTSMC 2**

COOL HEAT (Various artists).
Tracks: / Garden party: *Mezzoforte* / Space Princess: *Liston Smith, Lonnie* / Brazilian love affair: *Duke*, George / Jazz carnival: *Azymuth* / Funkin' for Jamaica: *Brown, Tom* / Invitations: *Shakatak* / Let's stay together: *M, Bobby* / I thought it was you: *Hancock, Herbie* / Stuff like that: *Jones, Quincy* / Birdland: *Weather Report* / Morning dance: *Spyro Gyra* / Sign of the times: *James, Bob* / Groove: *Franklin*, Rodney / Together again: *Clarke, Stanley* / Chinese way, The: *Level 42* / Stomp: *Brothers Johnson*/ What's going on?: *Mason, Harvey* / Rockall: *Mezzoforte*.
LP: .... **NE 1231**
MC: .... **CE 2231**

SLIPSTREAM - THE BEST OF BRITISH JAZZ FUNK (Various artists).
Tracks: / London Town: *Light Of The World* / Girl: *Various artists* / Feels like the right time: *Shakatak*/ Southern Freeez: *Freeez* / Turn it on: *Level 42* / Locomoto: *Inversions* / You know you can do it: *Central* Line / Slipstream: *Morrissey Mullen* / Shaping up: *Hipnosis* / W.T.L.D.L.T.W.: *Multivision* / Roberto Who: *Cayenne* / Incognito: *Incognito*.
LP: .... **BEGA 31**
MC: .... **BEGC 31**

Jazz Gala '80

JAZZ GALA '80 (Various artists).
Tracks: / Sonny's blues: *Various artists* / Five hundred miles high: *Various artists* / Here's that rainy day: *Various artists* / Time after time: *Various artists* / Christmas song, The: *Various artists* / I'm here for you: *Various artists* / Magic spell: *Various artists* / Rhapsody in blue: *Various artists* / Hits medley: *Various artists* / Lady Day: *Various artists* / Autumn leaves: *Various artists* / Billie's bounce: *Various artists*.
2LP: .... **GATE 7009-10**

Jazz Gold

JAZZ GOLD (Various artists).
LPS: .... **EGS 4 5006**
MCSET: .... **EC/EGS 4 5006**

Jazz Group Arkhangelsk

PILGRIMS.
2LP: .... **LR 412/413**

Jazz Guitar Anthology

JAZZ GUITAR ANTHOLOGY, VOL.1 (Various artists).
LP: .... **SM 4023**
MC: .... **MC 4023**

JAZZ GUITAR ANTHOLOGY, VOL.2 (Various artists).
LP: .... **SM 4024**
MC: .... **MC 4024**

JAZZ GUITAR ANTHOLOGY, VOL.3 (Various artists).
LP: .... **SM 4025**
MC: .... **MC 4025**

JAZZ GUITAR ANTHOLOGY VOL.4 (Various artists).
LP: .... **SM 4026**

JAZZ GUITAR ANTHOLOGY, VOL.5 (Various artists).
LP: .... **SM 4027**

JAZZ GUITAR ANTHOLOGY, VOL.6 (Various artists).
LP: .... **SM 4028**

Jazz Hall of Fame

JAZZ HALL OF FAME (Various artists).
LP: .... **TAB 43**

Jazz Highlights

JAZZ HIGHLIGHTS OF THE 1920'S - 1930'S (Various artists).
LP: .... **BS 7127**
MC: .... **BS 7127C**

JAZZ HIGHLIGHTS OF THE 1930'S - 1940'S (Various artists).
Tracks: / Prisoner's song: *Various artists* / Non-stop flight: *Various artists* / In a mist: *Various artists*/ T'aint what you do (it's the way that you do it): *Various artists* / High society: *Various artists* / Rehearsal: *Various artists* / Let's stop the clock: *Various artists* / Pussy willow: *Various artists* / Losers weepers: *Various artists* / Southpaw serenade: *Various artists* / Jumpin' Jehosaphat: *Various artists* / It's sand, man!: *Various artists*.
LP: .... **BS 7128**
MC: .... **BS 7128C**

Jazz Hot & Blue

JAZZ HOT AND BLUE (Blue Note Plays the Music of Cole Porter) (Various artists).
Tracks: / Love for sale: *Adderley, Cannonball* / It's alright with me: *Griffin, Johnny* / At long last love: *Green*, Grant / Easy to love: *Mobley, Hank* / You'd be so nice to come home to: *Chambers, Paul* / I love you: *McLean*, Jackie / Just one of those things: *Morgan, Lee* / Night and day: *Henderson, Joe* / It's alright with me: *Quebec, Ike* / Love for sale: *Gordon, Dexter*.
MC: **B4 95591**

Jazz & Hot Dance In...

JAZZ AND HOT DANCE IN ARGENTINA (Various artists).
LP: .... **HQ 2010**

JAZZ AND HOT DANCE IN AUSTRALIA 1925-50 (Jazz & hot dance Vol.12) (Various artists).
LP: .... **HQ 2021**

JAZZ AND HOT DANCE IN AUSTRIA 1926-44 (Jazz & hot dance Vol.5) (Various artists).
LP: .... **HQ 2014**

JAZZ AND HOT DANCE IN BELGIUM 1910-52 (Various artists).
LP: .... **HQ 2027**

JAZZ AND HOT DANCE IN CANADA 1916-1949 (Jazz & hot dance Vol.14) (Various artists).
LP: .... **HQ 2023**

JAZZ AND HOT DANCE IN CUBA 1909-1953 (Jazz & hot dance Vol.16) (Various artists).
LP: .... **HQ 2025**

JAZZ AND HOT DANCE IN CZECHOSLOVAKIA 1910-1946 (Jazz & hot dance Vol.10) (Various artists).
LP: .... **HQ 2019**

JAZZ AND HOT DANCE IN DENMARK 1909-1953 (Jazz & hot dance Vol.15) (Various artists).
LP: .... **HQ 2024**

JAZZ AND HOT DANCE IN FINLAND 1929-1950 (Jazz & hot dance Vol.8) (Various artists).
Tracks: / Finnish rhapsody: *Various artists* / I'll remember you: *Various artists* / My baby: *Various artists*/ Jungle song: *Various artists* / You can't stop me: *Various artists* / Jeeper's creepers: *Various artists*/ As long as I live: *Various artists* / Sweet Sue: *Various artists* / Full scale of swing: *Various artists*/ 100 swing: *Various artists* / St. Louis blues: *Various artists* / Nain nain: *Various artists* / Is you is or is you ain't my baby: *Various artists* / My serenade: *Various artists* / Blue: *Various artists*/ Star dust: *Various artists*.
LP: .... **HQ 2017**

JAZZ AND HOT DANCE IN HAWAII (Various artists).
Tracks: / Andrew Aiona: *Various artists* / Brown cats of rhythm: *Various artists* / Black devils, The: *Various artists* / Wailana grass shack boys: *Various artists* / Tau Moe's tropical stars: *Various artists*.
LP: .... **HQ 2070**

JAZZ AND HOT DANCE IN HUNGARY 1912-49 (Jazz & hot dance Vol.6) (Various artists).
LP: .... **HQ 2015**

JAZZ AND HOT DANCE IN INDIA 1926-44 (Jazz & hot dance Vol.4) (Various artists).
LP: .... **HQ 2013**

JAZZ AND HOT DANCE IN MARTINIQUE 1929-1950 (Jazz & hot dance Vol.9) (Various artists).
LP: .... **HQ 2018**

JAZZ AND HOT DANCE IN NORWAY 1920-46 (Jazz & hot dance Vol.20) (Various artists).
Tracks: / Chatterbox: *Orpheum Duo* / New peasant jazz: *Oslo Jazzband* / Just let y'rself go: *Hauger, Kristian*/ Little bit of humour: *Vieth, Willie* / Caravan: *Hauger, Kristian* / Cocktail: *Funny Boys* / Nobody's sweetheart: *Valier, Freddie* / Nagasaki: *Aagard, Cecil* / Oslo jump: *Sonstevold, Gunnar* / I'm coming Virginia: *Oslo Swingklubb* / Rhythm is our business: *String Swing* / St. Louis blues: *Ork, Rowlands* / Mester Jacob: *Ottersen, Frank* / Rythm fever: *Syversen, Rolf* / Bob's lullaby: *Muntre, Syv* / Gotta be this or that: *Various artists*.
LP: .... **HQ 2029**

JAZZ AND HOT DANCE IN RUSSIA 1910-1950' (Jazz & hot dance Vol.3) (Various artists).
LP: .... **HQ 2012**

JAZZ AND HOT DANCE IN SOUTH AFRICA (Jazz & hot dance Vol.11) (Various artists).
LP: .... **HQ 2020**

JAZZ AND HOT DANCE IN SPAIN 1915-1947 (Jazz and hot dance vol.17) (Various artists).
Tracks: / Alabama jubilee: *Fusly, Nic* / Demons charleston: *Demons Jazz* / Blake's blues: *Chocolate Kiddies*/ Es una dama de...: *Demon Tetto De Hot* / Ritz hotel: *Bernard Hilda* / Loca por el hot: *Katia Morlands Hot* 5 / Eres la mas guapa: *Katia Morlands Hot 5* / Hello ma baby: *Martin De La Rosa* / Tuxedo Junction: *Orch* Gran Casino / Kuky: *Adolfo Araco* / Bum bam bum: *Ribera, Sigfredo* / Estoy contenta: *Katia Morlands Hot* 5 / Rhythm at the club: *Vives, Ramon* / Red bank boogie: *Ribalta, Jose* / Parece mentira: *Quinteto Saratoga*/ Byas jump: *Don Byas All Stars*.
LP: .... **HQ 2026**

JAZZ AND HOT DANCE IN SWITZERLAND (Jazz & hotdance Vol.2) (Various artists).
LP: .... **HQ 2011**

JAZZ AND HOT DANCE IN THAILAND 1956-67 (Jazz & hot dance Vol.19) (Various artists).
LP: .... **HQ 2028**

JAZZ AND HOT DANCE IN THE NETHERLANDS (Jazz & hot dance Vol.13) (Various artists).
LP: .... **HQ 2022**

JAZZ AND HOT DANCE IN TRINIDAD 1912-3 (Various artists).
LP: .... **HQ 2016**

JAZZ & HOT DANCE IN ITALY 1919-1948 (Various artists).
Tracks: / At the jazz band ball: *Various artists* / Don't hurry: *Various artists* / Okay baby: *Various artists*/ I'm gonna clap my hands: *Various artists* / Dear friend: *Various artists* / Rhythm of the bells: *Various artists* / Blue orchids: *Various artists* / Exactly like you: *Various artists* / Chinatown my chinatown: *Various artists* / Tiger rag: *Various artists*.
LP: .... **HQ 2078**

Jazz in July

KINGDOM OF SWING (Republic of Oop Bop Sh'bam).
Tracks: / Lester leaps in / Joshua fit the battle of Jericho.
LP: .... **CIJD 40200F**

Jazz Incorporated

WALKIN' ON.
Tracks: / Walkin' on / Poinciana / Milestones / Lazy bird / Painter's blues / Day the stranger felt at home, The / Nica's tempo / Rebus.
LP: .... **DRLP 37**

Jazz Members Big Band

LIVE AT FITZGERALDS (With Gloria Morgan).
LP: .... **SB 2028**

Jazz Messengers

HORACE SILVER & THE JAZZ MESSENGERS (See Silver, Horace) (Jazz Messengers & Horace Silver).

NIGHT IN TUNISIA, A (see Blakey, Art) (Jazz Messengers/Art Blakey).

Jazz Nouville Orleans

JAZZ TIME VOL.15.
LP: **502715**

Jazz O'Maniacs

HAVE YOU EVER FELT THAT WAY?.
LP: .... **SOS 1046**

JAZZ O'MANIACS-VOLUME 2.
LP: .... **SOS 1071**

Jazz Piano

JAZZ PIANO QUARTET (Jazz Piano Quartet).
LP: .... **NL 89368**

Jazz Police

LONG NIGHT COMING, A.
MC: .... **ZPREC 798**

Jazz Renegades

FREEDOM SAMBA.
LP: **839 651 1**
MC: **839 651 4**

PLAYING FOR REAL.
LP: .... **JAZID 006**

SUMMER TO REMEMBER, A.
LP: .... **KENNEDY 2**

Jazz Singer (film)

JAZZ SINGER (1980 VERSION) (See under Diamond, Neil) (Various artists).

Jazz Sluts

MAKING WAVES.
Tracks: / Marching dust / Morning after, The / Roger Roger / Astral jogging / Riffers paradise / Seven sisters / Snake dance / H.H boogie / Madagascar.
LP: .... **CODA 17**
MC: .... **COCA 18**

Jazz Trio

S'WONDERFUL JAZZ.
LP: .... **W 8418**

Jazz Warriors

OUT OF MANY ONE PEOPLE.
Tracks: / Warriors / In reference to our forefathers fathers dreams / Minor groove / St. Maurice (of Aragon) / Many pauses.
LP: .... **AN 8712**
MC: .... **ANC 8712**
MC: .... **ICM 2035**
LP: .... **ILPM 2035**

Jazzateers

JAZZATEERS.
LP: .... **ROUGH 46**

Jazzvaerk Vestre

JAZZ IN DENMARK.
LP: .... **SLP 437**

LIVE I KRIDHUSET.
LP: .... **SLP 441**

PLAY IT AGAIN.
LP: .... **SLP 442**

Jazzy Jeff

IN THIS CORNER.
LP: .... **HIP 84**
MC: .... **HIPC 84**

J.B. Horns

PEE WEE, FRED AND MACEO.
Tracks: / Sweet and tangy / Bumpin' / Step on you're watch (part II) / Mother's kitchen / Everywhere is out of town / Strut / We're rollin' / Let's play house / Blues a la L.S. / Frontal system / Slipstream.
LP: . . . . **GV 794621**
MC: . . . . **GV 794624**

J.C.M.B

ACNE GEL AND BRYLCREAM.
Tracks: / Dusty amplifiers / Crazy yo-yo song / Anyone seen my fuzzbox? / Extracts from Mit's special radio show / Up the tree house / Butlins at bognor / Why am I alone / Cassette 50 is crap / I slept in a haystack / Got chucked out of Roy's caravan / Gods worst experiment.
LP: . . . . **JCMB 1**
MC: . . . . **JCMBC 1**

J.D. & Dallas

KEEP IT COUNTRY.
Tracks: / Queen of the silver dollar / Just out of reach / I fall to pieces / Blanket on the ground / Why me Lord / Blackboard of my heart / Please help me I'm fallin' / Cheating heart / This song' just for you / Tiny bubbles / Crystal chandeliers / Wild side of life / Deadwood stage / Black hills of Dakota, The / Secert love / I wasn't there / Tonight I'll throw a party / Let the rest of the world go by / Texas / American trilogy.
LP: . . . . **KLP 29**

Jean De Florette

JEAN DE FLORETTE (Film soundtrack) (Various artists).
LP: . . . . **A 235**
MC: . . . . **C 235**

JEAN DE FLORETTE/MANON DE SOURCES (Film soundtrack) (Various artists).
LP: . . . . **A 378**
MC: . . . . **C 378**

Jeanette

HUM.
LP: . . . . **PREM 1**

PREFAB IN THE SUN.
Tracks: / Prefab in the sun / Woman's love.
LP: . . . . **SURLP 011**
MC: . . . . **SURC 11**
LP: . . . . **EJLP 2**
MC: . . . . **EJMC 2**

SCALE 0-100.
LP: . . . . **SURLP 12**

Jeanmaire, Zizi

ZIZI JEANMAIRE.
LP: . . . . **AZ 2445**

Jeanneke Organ

SOUND OF JEANNEKE.
Tracks: / Release me / Delilah / Last waltz, The / Lady of Spain / Delicado / Blue tango / Il silenzio / Savoy English medley / Play a simple melody / America / Spanish flea / If I had a hammer / In a Persian market / Blue Danube.
LP: . . . . **JOYS 231**

Jeannie

DIAMOND IN THE ROUGH.
LP: . . . . **ZR 1027**
LP: . . . . **LJ 2100**

Jedson, Jon

JON JEDSON JOURNEY,THE.
Tracks: / Ruby / For the good times / Detroit city / Snowbird / Sweet Georgia Brown / Jeannie, Jeannie, Jeannie / Welcome to my world / King of the road / Sunny afternoon / Travelling light / Little angel.
LP: . . . . **PRX 10**

LET'S MAKE THE BEST OF TODAY.
Tracks: / Let's make the best of today / Cracklin Rosie / When a child is born / I wanna be like you / San Antonio rose / Streets of London / City girl / Can't help falling in love / Walk on by / Sweet Caroline / Take me home country roads / When the clock chimes thirteen.
LP: . . . . **PRX 12**

MORE THAN EASY COUNTRY.
MC: . . . . **CHV 315**

Jeeves

JEEVES - A GENTLEMAN'S PERSONAL GENTLEMAN (see under Parkinson, C. Northcote) (Various artists).

JEEVES STORIES (Various artists).
MC: . . . . **PTB 620**

Jefferson Airhead

JEFFERSON AIRHEAD.
LP: . . . . **KODE 16**
MC: . . . . **CODE 16**

Jefferson Airplane

2400 FULTON STREET.
Tracks: / It is no secret / Come up the years / My best friend / Somebody to love / Comin' back to me / Embryonic journey / She has funny cars / Plastic fantastic lover / Wild tyme / Ballad of you and me and Pooneil / Small package of value will come to you shortly(Psychedelia) / White rabbit / Won't you try Saturday afternoon / Lather / We can be together / Crown of creation / Mexico / Wooden ships / Rejoyce / Volunteers / Pretty as you feel / Martha / Today / Third week in the Chelsea / Let's get together (Track on CD only.) / Blues from an airplane (Track on CD only.) / J.P.P. MC step B. blues (Track on CD only.) / Fat angel (Track on CD only.) / Last wall of the castle, The (Track on CD only.) / Greasy heart (Track on CD only.) / Have you seen the saucers (Track on CD only.) / Eat starch mom (Track on CD only.) / Good shepherd (Track on CD only.) / Eskimo blue day (Track on CD only.) / Levi commercials, The (Track on CD only.).
LP: . . . . **NL 90036**
MC: . . . . **NK 90036**

AFTER BATHING AT BAXTERS.
Tracks: / Streetmasse: The ballad of you & me & Pooneil / Streetmasse: A small package of value will com / Streetmasse: Young girl sunday blues / War is over / Hymn to an older generation:The last wall of t / Hymn to an older generation: Rejoice / How suite is it: Watch her ride / How suite is it: Spare chaynge / Shizo Forest love suite: Two heads / Shizo Forest love suite: Won't you try / Shizo Forest love suite: Saturday afternoon.
LP: **26 21071**
LP: . . . . **SF 7926**

BARK.
Tracks: / When the earth moves again / Feel so good / Crazy Miranda / Pretty as you feel / Wild turkey / Law man / Rock and roll Island / Third week in the chelsea / Never argue with a German if you're tired / Thunk / War movie.
LP: . . . . **NL 84386**
LP: . . . . **FTR 1001**

BATHING AT BAXTERS.
LP: . . . . **NL 84718**
MC: . . . . **NK 84718**

BEST OF JEFFERSON AIRPLANE.
Tracks: / Blues from an airplane / White rabbit / Somebody to love / Ballad of you and me and Pooneil / Crown of creation / Plastic fantastic lover / Volunteers / When the earth moves again / Aerie (gang of eagles) / Milk train / Mexico.
LP: . . . . **CL 42727**
LP: . . . . **NL 89186**
MC: . . . . **NK 89186**
LP: . . . . **INTS 5030**

BLESS ITS POINTED LITTLE HEAD.
Tracks: / Chergy / 3/5 of a mile in 10 seconds / Somebody to love / Fat angel / Rock me baby / Other side of this life / It's no secret / Plastic fantastic lover / Turn out the lights / Bear melt (live).
LP: **26 28004**
LP: . . . . **SF 8019**

COLLECTION: JEFFERSON AIRPLANE.
Tracks: / Blues from an airplane / Don't slip away / Somebody to love / 3/5 of a mile in 10 seconds / My best friend / White rabbit / Last wall of the castle, The / Watch her ride / Lather / Crown of creation / Greasy heart / Other side of this life / Plastic fantastic lover / It is no secret / We can be together / Farm, The / Wooden ships / Volunteers / When the earth moves again / Law man / Rock 'n' roll island / Alexander the medium / Have you seen the saucers / Meadowlands.
2LP: . . . . **CCSLP 200**
MC: . . . . **CCSMC 200**

CROWN OF CREATION.
Tracks: / Lather / In time / Star track / Share a little joke / Chushingura / If you feel / Crown of creation / Ice cream Phoenix / Greasy heart / House at Pooneil corner, The.
LP: **26 21048**
LP: . . . . **NL 83797**
MC: . . . . **NK 83797**
LP: . . . . **SF 7976**

EARLY FLIGHT.
Tracks: / High flyin' bird / Runnin'round this world / It's alright / In the morning / J.P.P. MC step B. blues / Go to her / Up or down / Mexico / Have you seen the saucers.
LP: **26 21353**

EARTH.
Tracks: / Love too good / Count on me / Take your time / Crazy feelin' / Skateboard / Fire / Show yourself / Runaway / All nite long.
LP: . . . . **FL 12515**

FLIGHT LOG (1966-76).
Tracks: / Come up the years / White rabbit / Comin' back to me / Won't you try Saturday afternoon / Greasy heart / If you feel / Somebody to love (live) / Wooden ships / Volunteers / Hesitation blues / Have you seen the stars tonite / Silver spoon / Feel so good / Pretty as you feel / Milk train / Ja da / Come again toucan / Sketches of China / Genesis / Ride the tiger / Please come back (live).
2LP: **CYL2 1255**

JEFFERSON AIRPLANE.
Tracks: / Planes / Solidarity / Summer of love / Wheel, The / True love / Now is the time / Panda / Freedom / Ice age / Madeleine Street / Common market madrigal / Upfront blues / Too many years.
LP: **465 659 1**
MC: **465 659 4**

LIVE AT THE MONTEREY FESTIVAL.
Tracks: / Somebody to love / Other side of this life / White rabbit / High flying bird / Today / She has funny cars / Young girl with Sunday blues / Ballad of you and me and Pooneil, The.
LP: . . . . **THBL 074**

LONG JOHN SILVER.
Tracks: / Long John Silver / Aerie (Gang of eagles) / Twilight double leader / Milk train / Son of Jesus, The / Easter? / Trial by fire / Alexander the medium / Eat starch mom.
LP: **26 21175**
LP: . . . . **FTR 1007**

ROCK GALAXY.
Tracks: / We can be together / Good shepherd / Farm, The / Hey Frederick / Turn my life down / Wood ships / Eskimo blue day / Song for all seasons, A / Meadowlands / Volunteers / Phoenix / Greasy heart / House at Pooneil corner, The / Clergy / Three fifths of a mile in 10 seconds / Somebody to love / Fat angel / Rock me, baby / Other side of this life / It is no secret / Plastic fantastic lover / Turn out the lights / Lather / In time / Triad / Star track / Share a little joke / Chushingura / If you feel like China breaking / Crown of creation / Ice cream Phoenix / Greasy heart / House at Pooneil corner, The.
LP: . . . . **CL 43302**

SURREALISTIC PILLOW.
Tracks: / She has funny cars / Somebody to love / My best friend / Today / Comin' back to me / 3/5 mile in 10 seconds / D.C.B.A-25 / How do you feel / White rabbit / Plastic fantastic lover / Embryonic journey.
LP: **26 21036**
LP: . . . . **SF 7889**

TAKES OFF.
Tracks: / Blues from an airplane / Let me in / Bringing me down / It is no secret / Tobacco road / Come up the years / Runaround / Let's get together / Don't slip away / Chauffeur blues / And I like it.
LP: **26 21364**

THIRTY SECONDS OVER WINTERLAND (Volunteers).
Tracks: / We can be together / Good shepherd / Farm, The / Hey Frederick / Turn my life down / Wooden ships / Eskimo blue day / Song for all seasons, A / Meadowlands / Volunteers.
LP: **26 21349**
LP: . . . . **FTR 0147**
MC: . . . . **NK 83867**
LP: . . . . **NL 83867**
LP: . . . . **CL 13867**
LP: . . . . **SF 8076**

WORST OF JEFFERSON AIRPLANE.
Tracks: / It is no secret / Blues from an airplane / Somebody to love / Today / White rabbit / Embryonic journey / Martha / Ballad of you and me and Pooneil / Crown of creation / Cushingura / Lather / Plastic fantastic lover / We can be together / Volunteers / Good shepherd.
LP: . . . . **FA 3167**
MC: . . . . **TCFA 3167**
LP: **26 21060**
LP: . . . . **SF 8164**

Jefferson, Blind Lemon

BLACK SNAKE MOAN.
LP: . . . . **SM 3103**

BLIND LEMON JEFFERSON (1925-9).
LP: . . . . **BD 2082**

BLIND LEMON JEFFERSON VOL.1.
LP: . . . . **RL 301**

BLIND LEMON JEFFERSON VOL.2.
LP: . . . . **RL 306**

BLIND LEMON JEFFERSON VOL.3.
LP: . . . . **RL 331**

BLIND LEMON JEFFERSON/SON HOUSE (Jefferson, Blind Lemon & Son House).
Tracks: / My black mama / Preachin' the blues / Dry spell blues / Delta blues / Wartime blues / Weary dog blues / Gone dead on you blues / One dime blues / Lemon's cannonball moan / Eagle eyed mama / Dynamite blues.
LP: . . . . **BMLP 1037**

CAT MAN BLUES.
LP: . . . . **ALB 1009**
MC: . . . . **ALB 1009MC**

COLLECTION: BLIND LEMON JEFFERSON 20 blues greats.
Tracks: / Hangman's blues / Chock house blues / Prison cell blues / Jack o' diamonds / Broke and hungry / Matchbox blues / Rising high water blues / Lemon's worried blues / Mean jumper blues / Shuckin' sugar blues / Easy rider blues / Teddy bear blues / Piney Woods money mama / Lonesome house blues / Low down mojo blues / Sunshine special / Bad luck blues / Lock step blues / Bootin' me 'bout / Black horse blues.
LP: . . . . **DVLP 2073**
MC: . . . . **DVMC 2073**

KING OF COUNTRY BLUES.
2LP: . . . . **YAZOO 1069**
2LP: . . . . **L 1069**

MASTER OF THE BLUES.
Tracks: / 'Lectric chair blues / How long how long blues / D.B. blues / Maltese cat blues / Fence breakin' yellin' blues / Cat Man Blues / Booger Rooger Blues / Black snake dream blues / Where Shall I Be / Chinch bug blues / Deceitful Brownskin Woman / Rambler Blues.
LP: . . . . **BMLP 1050**

REMAINING TITLES, THE.
LP: . . . . **MSE 1001**

Jefferson, Carter

RISE OF ATLANTIS, THE.
Tracks: / Why / Rise of Atlantis, The / Wind chimes / Changing trains / Song for Gwen / Blues for wood.
LP: . . . . **SJP 126**

Jefferson, Eddie

BODY AND SOUL.
Tracks: / See if you can get to that / Body and Soul / Mercy mercy mercy / So What / There I go, There I go again / Psychedelic Sally.
LP: . . . . **PR 7619**
MC: . . . . **PRC 7619**

LIVELIEST.
LP: . . . . **MR 5127**

STILL ON THE PLANET (See Under Cole, Richie) (Jefferson, Eddie & Richie Cole).

THERE I GO AGAIN.
Tracks: / Old shoes / Strictly instrumental / Workshop / I got the blues / Disappointed / Take the 'A' train / Night in Tunisia / Parker's mood / Billie's bounce / Soft and furry / Things are getting better / Letter from home / Body and soul / Now's the time / So what? / Filthy McNasty / Mercy, mercy, mercy / There I go, there I go again / Yardbird suite / Come along with me / Baby girl / Dexter digs in.
LP: . . . . **OJCD 503**

THINGS ARE GETTING BETTER.
Tracks: / Bitches brew / Things are getting better / Freedom jazz dance / Night in Tunisia / 'Trane's blues / I just got back in town / Billie's bounce / Thank you.
LP: . . . . **MR 5043**

Jefferson Starship

DRAGON FLY.
Tracks: / Ride the tiger / That's for sure / Be young you / Caroline / Devil's den / Come to life / All fly away / Hyperdrive.
LP: **BFL1 0717**

FREEDOM AT POINT ZERO.
Tracks: / Jane / Lightning rose (carry the fire) / Things to come / Awakening / Girl with the hungry eyes / Just the same / Rock music / Fading lady light / Freedom at point zero(Climbing tiger through the Sky).
LP: . . . . **RCALP 3038**
MC: . . . . **RCAK 3038**
LP: . . . . **FL 13452**
LP: . . . . **NL 89912**

GOLD.
Tracks: / Ride the tiger / Caroline / Play on love / Miracles / Fast buck Freddie / With your love / St. Charles / Count on me / Love too good / Runaway.
LP: . . . . **FL 13247**
MC: . . . . **FK 13247**

MODERN TIMES.
Tracks: / Find your way back / Stranger / Wild eyes (angel) / Save your love / Modern times / Mary / Free / Alien / Stairway to Cleveland (we do what we want).
LP: . . . . **RCALP 3050**

MC: . . . . RCAK 3050

NUCLEAR FURNITURE.
Tracks: / Laying it on the line / No way out / Sorry me, sorry you / Shining in the moonlight / Showdown / Champion.
LP: . . . . FL 84921
MC: . . . . FK 84921

RED OCTOPUS.
Tracks: / Fast buck Freddie / Miracles / Git fiddler / Al garimasu (There is love) / Sweeter than honey / Play on love / Tumblin' / I want to see another world / Sandalphon / There will be love.
LP: . . . . FA 3156
MC: . . . . TCFA 3156
LP: . . . . PL 80999
MC: . . . . PK 80999
LP: . . . . INTS 5069
LP: . . . . FTR 2002

SPITFIRE.
Tracks: / Cruisin' / Dance with the dragon / Hot water / St. Charles / Song to the sun Ozymandias / Don't let it rain / With you love / Switchblade / Big city / Love lovely love.
LP: BFL1 1557

WINDS OF CHANGE.
Tracks: / Winds of change / Keep on dreamin' / Be my lady / I will stay / Out of control / Can't find love / Black widow / I came from the jaws of the dragon / Quit wasting time.
LP: . . . . FL 84372
MC: . . . . FK 84372
LP: . . . . RCALP 6060

Jefferson, Thomas

IF I COULD BE WITH YOU (Jefferson, Thomas & His Dixieland Band).
LP: . . . . NOLA LP 10

INTERNATIONAL NOR JB.
LP: . . . . SLP 254

NEW ORLEANS AT MIDNIGHT.
LP: . . . . GHB 129

THOMAS JEFFERSON & HIS DIXIELAND ALL STARS (Featuring Sammy Rimington).
MC: . . . . TC 010

Jeffes, Simon

MUSIC FROM THE PENGUIN CAFE.
Tracks: / Penguin cafe single / Zopf - from the colonies / In a Sidney motel / Surface tension / Milk / Coronation / Giles Farnaby's dream / Pig-the sound of someone you love who's going away.... / Hugebaby / Chartered flight.
LP: . . . . OBS 7
MCSET: . . . . EGDC 3

STILL LIFE AT THE PENGUIN CAFE (BBC Concert Orchestra).
MC: 4252184

Jeffree

JEFFREE.
Tracks: / Mr. Fix-it / I can't help it baby / Better wake up girl / One last chance / All my loving (was made for your) / Take my love / Love's gonna last.
LP: . . . . CRB 1178
MC: . . . . TCCRB 1178

Jeffrey, Marc

PLAYTIME.
LP: . . . . CON 002

Jeffrey, Peter (nar)

ANNA OF THE FIVE TOWNS (See under Anna of the Five Towns).

MOONSTONE, THE (see under Moonstone (bk)).

Jeffreys, Garland

AMERICAN BOY AND GIRL.
LP: . . . . AMLH 64778

ESCAPE ARTIST.
Tracks: / Modern lovers / Christine / Ghost of a chance / 96 tears / Innocent / True confessions / R.O.C.K / Graveyard rock / Mystery kids / Jump jump.
LP: . . . . EPC 84808

GHOST WRITER.
Tracks: / Rough and ready / I may not be your kind / New York skyline / Cool down boy / Ghost writer / Lift me up / Who-O / Wild in the streets / 35 millimeter / Dreams / Spanish town.
LP: . . . . AMLH 64629

GUTS FOR LOVE.
Tracks: / Real man / Surrender / Fidelity / Rebel love / Dance up / Guts for love / Shout / What does it take / Loneliness / El Salvador / American backslide.
LP: . . . . EPC 25014

ONE-EYED JACK.
Tracks: / She didn't lie / Keep on trying / Reelin' / Haunted house / One eyed Jack / Scream in the night / No woman to cry / Oh my soul / Desperation drive / Been there and back.
LP: . . . . AMLH 64681

ROCK 'N' ROLL ADULT.
Tracks: / Wild in the street / 96 tears / I may not be your kind / Matador / R.O.C.K. / 35 millimeter / Dreams / Bound to get ahead someday / Cool down boy.
LP: . . . . EPC 85307

Jeffries, Michael

MICHAEL JEFFRIES.
Tracks: / Not thru being with you / Jealous heart / We loved / Stop in the name of us / 99 lies / Teach me / I'm waiting / Baby don't ya go / Trade dreams / It don't get no better than this.
LP: 9259251
MC: 9259254

Jekyll & Hyde (Show)

HIGHLIGHTS FROM JEKYLL AND HYDE (Eder, Linda & Colm Wilkinson).
Tracks: / Once upon a dream / Love has come of age / This is the moment / Seduction / No one must ever know / No one knows who I am / Letting go / It's over now / Once upon a dream / Hospital board / Possessed / Transformation / Someone like you / Till you come into my life / Retribution / New life, A / We still have time.
LP: . . . . BL 74442
MC: . . . . BK 74452

Jellybean

JUST VISITING THIS PLANET.
Tracks: / Little too good to me / Who found who / Just a mirage / Am I dreaming / Real thing, The / Walking in my sleep / Hypnotized / Jingo.
LP: . . . . BFV 41569
LP: . . . . CHR 1569
MC: . . . . ZCHR 1569

ROCKS THE HOUSE (12" mixes).
Tracks: / Coming back for more / Jingo / Just a mirage / Little too good to me / Who found who / Was dog a doughnut / Mirage / Sidewalk talk / Anyway you like it / Real thing, The (Not on CD.).
2LP: . . . . CHR 1652
MC: . . . . ZCHR 1652

SPILLIN' THE BEANS.
LP: 7567821801
MC: 7567821804

WOTUPSKI.
Tracks: / Compromise / Sidewalk talk / Dancing on the fire / Was dog a doughnut / Mexican.
LP: . . . . EE 2402311
MC: . . . . EE 2402314

Jellyfish

BELLYBUTTON.
LP: . . . . CUSLP 3
MC: . . . . CUSMC 3

Jellyfish Kiss

ANIMAL RITES.
Tracks: / Sinbad / Regular folk / Dead / Overdone / Wave goodbye / Zero tolerance / Screwed up papers / Little red car / Big talk / Underground / Muttonhead.
LP: . . . . SHIMMY 038

GASOLINE JUNKIE.
LP: . . . . LPIG 001

PLANK.
Tracks: / Crazy bong / Melo / A.C. 801 A / Burn / La / Soul apart / Pre mortem / Astro Z / Off the floor.
LP: . . . . FIEND 190

Jenatsch

JENATSCH (Film Soundtrack) (Various artists).
LP: . . . . ACH 036

Jenkins, Billy

BEYOND E MAJOR.
Tracks: / Country and Western / Blues, The / Heavy metal / Rock & Roll.
LP: . . . . ALMS 1

GREENWICH (Jenkins, Billy & The Voice Of God Collective).
Tracks: / Greenwich one way system / Dreadnought seaman's hospital / Arrival of the tourists / Empty river, An / Meridian council estate / Discoboats at two o'clock (*(vandalise tourist's property not resident's)).
LP: . . . . WWR 852

IN THE NUDE.
LP: . . . . WW 010

MOTORWAY AT NIGHT.
Tracks: / Motorway at night - 1 / Motorway at night - 2.
LP: . . . . DCM 108-1

PIANO SKETCHES 1973-1984.
Tracks: / Cup of tea, A / Donkey droppings / My dead cleaning lady / Slimming advert / Helsinki waking up / Cooking oil / Ragtime / Fat people / 2nd April '78 / Snowbound / Young lovers / Laban dance school early morning / Quiet Sunday afternoon, A / Jack Loussiers beard / Unborn child, The / Unborn child of the comedian, The / Invention.
LP: . . . . WWR 841

SCRATCHES OF SPAIN.
Tracks: / Monkey men / Cuttlefish / Barcelona / Benidorm motorway services / Bilbao/St.Columbus day / Cooking oil / McDonalds.
LP: . . . . SLICE 13

SOUNDS LIKE BROMLEY (Jenkins, Billy & The Voice Of God Collective).
Tracks: / High street Saturday / Fat people / Parking meters / Sunday morning / Supermarkets / Council offices / Growing up in Bromley / Exodus from Bromley.
LP: . . . . LBB 1

UNCOMMERCIALITY.
Tracks: / Brilliant / Pharaoh Sanders / Margaret's menstrual problem / Sade's lips / Spastics dancing / Bhopal.
LP: . . . . ALMS 2

Jenkins Brothers

HE SET ME FREE.
LP: . . . . SAV 14785
MC: . . . . SC 14785

Jenkins, Carl

BOP LIKE CARL.
LP: . . . . REDITA 132

Jenkins, Florence

GLORY OF THE HUMAN VOICE, THE.
Tracks: / Queen of the night / Musical snuff box, The / Like a bird / Bell song / Charmant oiseau / Biassy / Adele's laughing song / 'Faust' in English.
LP: . . . . INTS 5220
MC: . . . . INTK 5220
LP: . . . . VL 896 78

Jenkins, Gus

COLD LOVE.
LP: . . . . DD 4309

Jenkins, John

JENKINS, JORDAN & TIMMONS (Jenkins, John & Clifford Jordan & Bobby Timmons).
LP: . . . . OJC 251

Jenkins, Leroy

GEORGE LEWIS.
LP: . . . . BSR 0016

LEGEND OF AL GLATSON, THE.
Tracks: / Al Glatson / Brax Stone / Albert Ayler / Tuesday child / What goes around comes around.
LP: . . . . BSR 0022

REVOLUTIONARY ENSEMBLE.
Tracks: / Vietnam 1 / Vietnam 2.
LP: . . . . ENJA 3003

SOLO CONCERT.
LP: . . . . IN 1028

URBAN BLUES.
Tracks: / Static in the attic / Looking for the blues / Come on home baby / Why can't I fly / O W Frederick / No banks river / Through the ages / Jehovah.
LP: . . . . BSR 0083

Jenkins, Martin

CARRY YOUR SMILE.
Tracks: / Not a day can pass / Ram jam ceilidh band / Cannot keep from crying / Unsquare dance / Ain't no sunshine / Carry your smile / Cluck old hen / Lover's ghost, The / Coming back to stay / Sally / Parting glass, The.
LP: . . . . OBL 002

Jenkins, Snuffy

CAROLINA BLUEGRASS.
LP: . . . . ARHOOLIE 5011

Jenkins, Tomi

TOMI.
LP: 9608141

Jenks, Glenn

RAGTIME ALCHEMY.
LP: . . . . SOS 1179

Jenni

JENNI (Young, Vivien).
MCSET: . . . . SOUND 12

Jennings, Bill

BILLY IN THE LIONS DEN (Jennings, Bill & Leo Parker Quintet).
Tracks: / Picadilly Circus / May 1 / Billy in the lions den / Sweet and Lovely / There will never be another you / Stuffy / Just You Just Me / Down To Earth / What'll I Do / Fine and Dandy / Get Hot / Solitude.
LP: . . . . ST 1025

STOMPIN' WITH BILL (Also featuring Ray Bryant & Tiny Grimes) (Bryant, Ray & Bill Jennings).
Tracks: / Real choice blues / I let a song go out of my heart / Temptation / Flat foot floojie / Stompin' with Bill / Lonesome traveller / Long way from St.Louis / Call of the wild / St.Louis blues.
LP: . . . . KK 838

Jennings, Frank

ME AND MY GUITAR (Jennings, Frank Syndicate).
Tracks: / Me and my guitar / Devil came between us / Bed of roses / How great thou art / When you finally realise you're on your own / Everybody needs a rainbow / Thibodeaux and his Cajun band / Here I am in Nashville / Sunshine and flowers / Southbound / Go away little girl / I believe in you.
MC: . . . . TC-SCX 6608
LP: . . . . SCX 6608

ROSE OF EL PASO.
Tracks: / Rose of El Paso / Perfect stranger / I don't want to hear another she's leaving song / Love is a two way street / Memories to burn / Colinda / When you finally realise you're on your own / Carmen / Till the water stops runnin' / Ave Maria Morales.
LP: . . . . GRALP 11
MC: . . . . GRTC 11

Jennings, Waylon

18 GOLDEN HITS (See under Nelson, Willie).

20 GOLDEN HITS: WILLIE & WAYLON (See under Nelson, Wllie) (Jennings, Waylon & Willie Nelson).

20 GOLDEN HITS: WILLIE & WAYLON (see under Nelson, Willie (Jennings, Waylon & Willie Nelson).

20 OUTLAW REUNION HITS (Jennings, Waylon & Willie Nelson).
LP: 20020
MC: 40020

ARE YOU READY FOR THE COUNTRY.
Tracks: / Are you ready for the country / Them old love songs / So good woman / Jack a diamonds / Can't you see / MacArthur Park (revisisted) / I'll go back to her / Couple more years, A / Old friend / Precious memories.
LP: . . . . RS 1067

BEST OF WAYLON JENNINGS, THE.
Tracks: / Love of the common people / Days of sand and shovels, The / MacArthur Park / Delia's gone / Walk on out of my mind / Anita, you're dreaming / Only daddy that'll walk the line / Just to satisfy you / I got you / Something's wrong in California / Ruby, don't take your love to town / Brown eyed handsome man / Singer of sad songs.
LP: . . . . LSA 3000

BLACK ON BLACK.
Tracks: / Women do you know how to carry on / Honky tonk blues / Just to satisfy you / We made it as lovers / Shine / Folsom Prison blues / Gonna write a letter / May I borrow some sugar from you / Song for the life / Get naked with me.
LP: . . . . RCALP 3072
MC: . . . . RCAK 3072

BURNING MEMORIES.
Tracks: / Sally was a good old girl / Crying / Burning memories / It's so easy / White lightning / Abilene / Dream baby / Loves gonna live here / Big Mamou / Don't think twice.
LP: . . . . SHLP 107
MC: . . . . SHTC 107

COLLECTION: WAYLON JENNINGS (VOL.2).
Tracks: / Ruby, don't take your love to town / If I were a carpenter / Lucille / Entertainer, The / Turn the page / MacArthur park / Folsom Prison blues / Angel eyes / Ladies love outlaws / Honky tonk heroes / Waltz me to Heaven / Looking for Suzanne / Conversation / Shine / America / I'm a ramblin' man / I've always been crazy / Luckenbach, Texas / Come with me / I ain't living long like this / Never been to Spain / Delta dawn / Mental revenge / It's only rock 'n' roll.
2LP: . . . . CCSLP 203
MC: . . . . CCSMC 203

COLLECTION: WAYLON JENNINGS (VOL. 1).
Tracks: / Back in the saddle again / Maria / I'm looking over a four leaf clover / Misty blue / There goes my everything / Sweet mental revenge / Do you ever think of me / Chicken reel / Does your heart beat for me / Sally was a good old girl / Crying / Burning memories / It's so easy / White lightning / Abilene / Dream baby / Love's gonna live here / Big mamou / Don't think twice.
2LP: . . . . CCSLP 110
MC: . . . . CCSMC 110

COUNTRY STORE: WAYLON JENNINGS.
LP: . . . . CST 23
MC: . . . . CSTK 23

COUNTRY STORE: WAYLON JENNINGS AND WILLIE NELSON (Jennings, Waylon & Willie Nelson).
Tracks: / Just to satisfy you / Why baby why / No love at all / Year 2003 minus 25, The / Would you lay with me (in a field of stone)? / Slow rollin' low / I can get off on you / Old friends / Why do I have to choose / Homeward bound / Mamas don't let your babies grow up to be cowboys / Blackjack country chains / Till I gain control again / Take it to the limit / Pick up the tempo / Don't cuss the fiddle / Wurlitzer prize / We had it all.
LP: . . . . **CST 42**
MC: . . . . **CSTK 42**

DON'T THINK TWICE IT'S ALRIGHT.
Tracks: / Don't think twice it's alright / Sally was a good old girl / Big mamou / Burning memories / Jole blon / Lorena / When sin stops love begins / Crying / Money / It's so easy / Whit lightning / Love's gonna live here / Abilene / Dream baby.
LP: . . . . **MFP 50517**
MC: . . . . **TCMFP 50517**

DREAMING MY DREAMS.
Tracks: / Are you sure Hank done it this way? / Waymore's blues / I recall a gypsy woman / High time (you quit your lowdown ways) / I've been a long time leaving (but I'll be) / Let's all help the cowboys (sing the blues) / Door is always open, The / Let's turn back the years / She's looking good / Dreaming my dreams with you / Bob Wills is still the king.
LP: . . . . **LSA 3247**

EAGLE, THE.
Tracks: / Workin' cheap / What bothers me most / Eagle, The / Her man / Wrong / Where corn don't grow / Reno and me / Too close to call / Waking up with you / Old church hymns and nursery rhymes.
LP: **4672601**
MC: **4672604**

EARLY YEARS.
LP: . . . . **CDL 8501**

FILES: VOL 1.
Tracks: / I wonder just where I went wrong / Another bridge to burn / Now everybody knows / Down came the world / I'm a man of constant sorrow / Dream baby / Rime will tell the story / Stop the world / Dark side of fame, The / That's the chance I'll have to take / Cindy of New Orleans / What's left of me / Look into my teardrops / Anita, you're dreaming / What makes a man wander / What makes a man wander (stereo mix).
LP: . . . . **BFX 15151**

FILES: VOL 2.
Tracks: / I don't mind / Just for you / Baby don't be looking in my mind / Time to bum again / Falling for you / If you really want me to, I'll go / That's what you get for loving me / But that's alright / Doesn't anybody know my name / Taos New Mexico / You're gonna wonder about me / Norwegian wood / I tremble for you / Leavin' town / Beautiful Annabel Lee / Woman let me sing you a song.
LP: . . . . **BFX 15152**

FILES: VOL 3.
Tracks: / In this very same room / She called me baby / Everglades, The / Sunset and Vine / She's gone gone gone / Heartaches by the number / Busted / Tiger by the tail / Heartaches for a dime / Foolin' around / Nashville bum / Tennessee / Nashville rebel / Silver ribbons / Green river / I'm a long way from home.
LP: . . . . **BFX 15153**

FILES: VOL 4.
Tracks: / Hoodlum / Lang's theme / Lang's mansion / Spanish penthouse / Rush Street blues / You beat all I ever saw / Ruby don't take your love to town / Born to love you / Money cannot make the man / Yes Virginia / If the shoe fits / Young Widow Brown / John's back in town / Down came the world / Mental revenge / Road, The.
LP: . . . . **BFX 15154**

FILES: VOL 5.
Tracks: / Woman don't you ever laugh at me / California sunshine / Love of the common people / You've got to hide your love away / Two streaks of steel / Destiny's child / Shutting out the light / Don't waste your time / Chet's tune / It's all over now / Lock, stock and teardrops / I fall in love too easily / She loves me / Let me talk to you / Long gone / Chokin' kind, The.
LP: . . . . **BFX 15155**

FILES: VOL 6.
Tracks: / Just across the way / Listen, they're playing my song / Yes Virginia / Gentle on my mind / Crowd, The / Sorrow breaks a good man down / Wave goodbye to me / Right before my eyes / Looking at a heart that needs a home / Hangin' on / Walk on out of my mind / Julie / How long have you been there / I'm doing this for you / I've been needing someone like you / Straighten my mind.
LP: . . . . **BFX 15156**

FILES: VOL 7.
Tracks: / Christina / You love the ground I walk on / All of me belongs to you / No one's gonna miss me / Rings of gold / How much rain can one man stand / Mt Ramona / New York City R.F.D. / You'll think of me / I got you / Such a waste of love / Only daddy that'll walk the line / Your love / Kentucky woman / See you around (on your way down) / Too far gone.
LP: . . . . **BFX 15157**

FILES: VOL 8.
Tracks: / Poor old ugly Gladys Jones / Weakness of a man / Folsom Prison blues / Today I started loving you again / If you were mine to lose / Six strings away / Cedartown, Georgia / I lost me / Brown eyed handsome man / Alone / Something's wrong in California / Days of sand and shovels, The / Just to satisfy you / For the kids / Farewell party / Sing the blues to daddy.
LP: . . . . **BFX 15158**

FILES: VOL 9.
Tracks: / Change of mind / Change of mind (different mix) (Previously unissued.) / Lonely weekends / Don't play the game / House song, The / Delia's gone / World of our own, A / Come stay with me / Mac Arthur Park / Long way back home / These new changing times / Cindy Oh Cindy / Mary Ann regrets / But you know I love you / Drivin' nails in the wall / Let me tell you my mind.
LP: . . . . **BFX 15159**

FILES: VOL 10.
Tracks: / Games people play / It's all over now / Thirty third of August, The / I'm gonna leave (while I still love you) / Grey eyes you know / I may never pass this way again / Lila / Willie and Laura Mae Jones / I ain't the one / Singer of sad songs / Let me stay a while / Sunday morning coming down / (I'd be a) legend in my own time / It's sure been fun (Previously unissued.) / Where love has died / Yellow haired woman.
LP: . . . . **BFX 15160**

FILES: VOL 11.
Tracks: / This time tomorrow / Life goes on / Six white horses / Pickin' white gold / Donna on my mind / Honky tonk women / Time between bottles of wine / Ragged but right / If I were a carpenter / Must you throw dirt in my face / She comes running / No regrets / Rock, salt and nails / Sick and tired / It ain't easy (Previously unissued.) / Woman, you need a man (Previously unissued.).
LP: . . . . **BFX 15161**

FILES: VOL 12.
Tracks: / Marriage on the rocks (Previously unissued.) / To beat the devil / Mississippi woman / Shadow of the gallows / Big D / Gone to Denver / Taker, The / Bridge over troubled water / What about you (Previously unissued.) / Thanks / You'll look for me / Tomorrow night in Baltimore / One of my bad habits / Suspicious minds / I knew that you'd be leavin' / Don't let the sun set on you.
LP: . . . . **BFX 15162**

FILES: VOL 13.
Tracks: / Loving her was easier / Mobile blues (Previously unissued.) / Mama, I'll sing one song for you (Previously unissued.) / Casey's last ride / Love in the hot afternoon (Previously unissued.) / I've got eyes for you / Under your spell again / Atlanta's burning (Previously unissued.) / Ghost of General Lee (Previously unissued.) / Some kind of fool (Previously unissued.) / I think it's time she learned / Same old lover man / Low down freedom / Unsatisfied / It should be easier now / Crazy arms.
LP: . . . . **BFX 15163**

FILES: VOL 14.
Tracks: / Do no good woman / Sweet dream woman / Revelation / Big big love (Previously unissued.) / Ladies love outlaws / Sure didn't take him long / Nothin' worth takin' or leavin' (Previously unissued.) / Lay it down / Sandy sends her best / Come early morning (Previously unissued.) / You can have her / My God and I (Previously unissued.) / Frisco depot / Me and Bobby McGee / Black rose.
LP: . . . . **BFX 15164**

FILES: VOL 15.
Tracks: / Pretend I never happened / Delta dawn / Never been to Spain / Laid back country picker (Previously unissued.) / Good time Charlie's got the blues / San Francisco Mabel Joy / Lonesome, on'ry and mean / Freedom to stay / Lisa's only seven (Previously unissued.) / Last one to leave Seattle, The (Previously unissued.) / About that woman (Previously unissued.).
LP: . . . . **BFX 15165**

FOLK - COUNTRY.
Tracks: / Another bridge to burn / Stop the world / Cindy of New Orleans / Look into my teardrops / Down came the world / I don't mind / Just for you / Now everybody knows / That's the chance I'll have to take / What makes a man wander / I'm a man of constant sorrow / What's left of me.
LP: . . . . **NL 90005**
MC: . . . . **NK 90005**

GREATEST HITS: WAYLON JENNINGS.
Tracks: / Lonesome, on'ry and mean / Ladies love outlaws / I've always been crazy / I'm a ramblin' man / Only daddy that'll walk the line / Amanda / Honky tonk heroes / Mamas don't let your babies grow up to be cowboys / Good hearted woman / Luckenbach, Texas / Texas / Are you sure Hank done it this way.
LP: . . . . **PL 83378**
MC: . . . . **PK 83378**
LP: . . . . **PL 13378**
LP: . . . . **NL 90304**
MC: . . . . **NK 90304**

GREATEST HITS: WAYLON JENNINGS VOL.2.
Tracks: / Looking for Suzanne / Conversation / Waltz me to Heaven / Dukes of Hazzard / Don't you think this outlaw bit's done got out of hand / I ain't living long like this / Come with me / America / Shine / Women do know how to carry on.
LP: . . . . **PL 85325**
MC: . . . . **PK 85325**

HANGIN' TOUGH.
Tracks: / Baker Street / I can't help the way I don't feel / Rose in Paradise / Crying even don't come close / Chevy van / Falling out / Deep in the west / Between fathers and sons / Crown Prince, The / Defying gravity (Executioner's song).
LP: . . . . **MCF 3360**
MC: . . . . **MCFC 3360**

HEROES (See under Cash, Johnny) (Jennings, Waylon & Johnny Cash).

HITS OF WAYLON JENNINGS, THE.
Tracks: / Are you sure Hank done it this way? / Dreaming my dreams with you / I'm a ramblin' man / We had it all / This time / You can have her / Rainy day woman / Good hearted woman / Let's all help the cowboys (sing the blues) / Sweet dream woman / You ask me to / Pretend I never happened / Bob Wills is still the king.
LP: . . . . **PL 42211**
MC: . . . . **PK 4211**

HONKY TONK HEROES.
Tracks: / Honky tonk heroes / Old five and dimers (like me) / Willy the wandering gypsy and me / Low down freedom / Omaha / You ask me to / Ride me down easy / Ain't no God in Mexico / Black rose / We had it all.
LP: **AFL1 0240**

IN THE BEGINNING.
Tracks: / Sally was a good old girl / Big mamou / Don't think twice / It's all right / It's so easy / Love's gonna live here / White lightning / Crying / Burning memories / Dream baby / Abilene / Jole blon / Money (that's what I want) / Lorena / When sin stops.
LP: . . . . **BDL 1052**
MC: . . . . **BDC 1052**

LADIES LOVE OUTLAWS.
Tracks: / Ladies love outlaws / Never been to Spain / Sure didn't take him long / Crazy arms / Revelation / Delta dawn / Frisco depot / Thanis / I think it's time she learned / Under your spell again.
LP: . . . . **LSA 3142**

LEATHER AND LACE (Jennings, Waylon & Jessi Colter).
Tracks: / You never can tell / Rainy seasons / I'll be alright / Wild side of life / Pastels and harmonies / I believe you can / What's happened to blue eyes / Storms never last / I ain't the one / You're not my same sweet baby.
LP: . . . . **RCALP 5017**

LEAVIN' TOWN.
Tracks: / Leavin' town / Time to bum again / If you really want me to I'll go / Baby, don't be looking in my mind / That's alright / Time will tell the story / You're gonna wonder about me / For lovin' me / Anita, you're dreaming / Doesn't anybody know my name / Falling for you / I wonder just where I went wrong.
LP: . . . . **NL 89469**
MC: . . . . **NK 89469**

MOST WANTED NASHVILLE REBEL.
Tracks: / I'm a ramblin' man / Amanda / Can't you see / Lucille / That's alright / My baby left me / Gold dust woman / Rainy day woman / Luckenbach, Texas / Well all right / It's so easy / Maybe baby / Peggy Sue / Never been to Spain / Lonesome / On'ry and mean / Only daddy that'll walk the line.
LP: . . . . **CL 43169**
MC: . . . . **CK 43169**

MUSIC MAN.
Tracks: / Clyde / It's alright / Dukes of Hazzard / Nashville wimmin / Do it again / Sweet music man / Storms never last / He went to Paris / What about you / Waltz across Texas.
LP: . . . . **PL 13602**

NEVER COULD TOE THE MARK.
LP: . . . . **PL 85017**
MC: . . . . **PK 85017**

NEW CLASSIC WAYLON.
LP: . . . . **MCA 42287**
MC: . . . . **MCAC 42287**

OL' WAYLON.
Tracks: / Luckenbach, Texas (back to the basics of love) / If you see me getting smaller (With Larry Keith & Steve Pippin.) / Lucille / Sweet Caroline / I think I'm gonna kill myself / Belle of the ball / That's alright / My baby left me / Till I gain control again / Brand new goodbye song / Satin sheets (With Jessi Colter & Toni Wine) / This is getting funny (But there ain't nobody laughing).
LP: . . . . **PL 12317**
MC: . . . . **MK 12317**

OLD FRIENDS (see under Nelson, Willie) (Jennings, Waylon & Willie Nelson).

OUTLAWS' REUNION (see under Nelson, Willie) (Jennings, Waylon & Willie Nelson).

OUTLAWS' REUNION, VOL.2 (see under Nelson, Willie) (Jennings, Waylon & Willie Nelson).

RAVE ON.
Tracks: / River boy / Twelfth of never / Race is on, The / Just to satisfy you / Kisses sweeter than wine / Unchained melody / I don't believe you / Four strong winds / Love denied.
LP: . . . . **BFX 15029**

REPLAY ON WAYLON JENNINGS.
LP: . . . . **FEDB 5030**
MC: . . . . **CFEDB 5030**

SINGER OF SAD SONGS.
Tracks: / Singer of sad songs / Sick and tired / Time between bottles of wine / Must you throw dirt in my face / No regrets / Ragged but right / Honky tonk women / She comes running / If I were a carpenter / Donna on my mind / Rock salt and nails.
LP: . . . . **INTS 5020**
MC: . . . . **INTK 5020**

SINGS BUDDY HOLLY (See under Davis, Skeeter for details) (Jennings, Waylon/Skeeter Davis).

TAKER, THE.
Tracks: / Anita you're dreaming / That's what you get for loving me / Too far gone / Today I started loving you again / Gentle on my mind / Tonight the bottle let me down (end s1) / Ruby, don't take your love to town / Loving her was easier / Sunday morning coming down / For the kids / Taker, (The) / (I'd be a) legend in my own time.
LP: . . . . **CBR 1038**
MC: . . . . **KCBR 1038**

THEY CALL ME THE NASHVILLE REBEL.
Tracks: / If you really want me to, I'll go / In this very same room / Nashville rebel / Born to love you / Down came the world / California sunshine / Chokin' kind, The / Hangin' on / Weakness in a man / Kentucky woman / Six strings away / Today I started loving again / Lonely weekends / Cedartown Georgia / Let me stay a while / Taker / Tomorrow night in Baltimore / Casey's last ride / I've got eyes for you / Unsatisfied.
LP: . . . . **INTS 5097**

THIS TIME.
Tracks: / This time / Louisiana woman / Pick up the tempo / Slow rollin' low / Heaven or hell / It's not supposed to be that way / Slow movin' outlaw / Mona / Walkin' / If you could touch her at all.
LP: **AFL1 0539**

TURN THE PAGE.
LP: . . . . **PL 85428**
MC: . . . . **PK 85428**

WANTED (Jennings, Waylon & Willie Nelson).
Tracks: / My heroes have always been cowboys / Honky tonk heroes / I'm looking for blue eyes / You mean to say / Suspicious minds / Good-hearted

woman / Heaven or Hell / Me and Paul / Yesterday's wine / T for Texas / Put another log on the fire.
LP: . . . . RS 1048
MC: . . . . PK 11724

WAYLON.
Tracks: / It's only rock 'n' roll / Living legends (a dyin' breed) / Breakin' down / Let her do the walkin' / Mental revenge / Lucille / Angel eyes / No middle ground / Lover's legalities.
LP: . . . . RCALP 6078
MC: . . . . RCAK 6078

WAYLON AND COMPANY.
Tracks: / Hold on I'm coming / Leave them boys alone / Spanish Johnny / Just to satisfy you / So you want to be a cowboy singer / I may be used / Sight for sore eyes / I'll find it where I can / Conversation / Mason Dixon lines.
LP: . . . . PL 84826
MC: . . . . PK 84826

WAYLON AND WILLIE (Jennings, Waylon & Willie Nelson).
Tracks: / Mamas don't let your babies grow up to be cowboys / Year 2003 minus 25,The / Pick up the tempo / If you can touch her at all / Looking for a feeling / It's not supposed to be that way / I can get off on you / Don't cuss the fiddle / Gold dust woman / Couple more years, A / Wurlitzer prize / Mr. Shuck'n'jive / Roman candles / (Sittin' on) the dock of the bay / Year that Clayton Delaney died, The / Lady in the harbour / May I borrow some sugar from you / Last cowboy song, The / Heroes / Teddy bear song / Write your own songs / Old mother's locket trick,The.
LP: . . . . NL 85134
MC: . . . . NK 85134
LP: . . . . PL 12686
MC: . . . . PK 12686

WAYLON LIVE.
Tracks: / T for Texas / Rainy day woman / Me and Paul / Last letter, The / I'm a ramblin' man / Bob Wills is still the king / Pick up th tempo / House of the rising sun / Me and Bobby McGee / This time.
LP: . . . . PL 11108
MC: . . . . PK 11108

WAYLON MUSIC.
Tracks: / I wonder just where I went wrong / Look into my teardrops / Doesn't anybody know my name / Norwegian wood / Woman / Let me sing you a song / Young widow Brown / Green river / Mental revenge / You've got to hide your love away / Destiny's child / It's all over now / Crowd, The / Julie / No one's gonna miss me / Sing the blues to daddy / Let me tell you my mind / 33rd of August, The / Lila / Life goes on / Shadow of the gallows / Don't let the sun set on you / Tulsa / Loving her was easier / It should be easier now / Sweet dream woman / Nothin' worth takin' or leavin' / Pretend I never happened / Freedom to stay / San Francisco Mabel Joy / Got a lot going for me / All around cowboy / Nadine / I never said it was easy.
2LP: . . . . PL 43166

WAYLON THE RAMBLIN' MAN.
Tracks: / I'm a ramblin' man / Rainy day woman / Cloudy days / Midnight rider / Standing in that Oklahoma sunshine / Hunger, The / I can't keep my hands off you / Memories of you and I / It'll be her / Amanda.
LP: . . . . LSA 3196

WILL THE WOLF SURVIVE.
Tracks: / Will the wolf survive / They ain't got em' all / Working without a net / Where does love go / Dog won't hunt, The / What you'll do when I'm gone / Suddenly single / Shadow of your distant friend,The / I've got me a woman / Devil's right hand.
LP: . . . . MCF 3308
MC: . . . . MCFC 3308

Jenny & James...

JENNY AND JAMES LEARN TO COUNT (Unknown narrator(s)).
MC: . . . . STK 034

JENNY AND JAMES START SCHOOL (Unknown narrator(s)).
MC: . . . . STK 035

Jenny & the Cat (bk)

JENNY AND THE CAT CLUB/JENNY'S FIRST PARTY (Esther Averill) (Grimes, Tammy (nar)).
MC: 1577

Jensen, Kris

LET'S SIT DOWN: A MILESTONE IN ROCK 'N' ROLL MUSIC, VOL 1.
Tracks: / What should I do / Spying ((Previously unissued)) / Revenge ((Previously unissued)) / Let's sit down / I went a walking / Donna, Donna / Looking for love / Poor unlucky me / Come back to me / Claudette / Little wind-up doll, The / Little Dutch village.
LP: . . . . BFX 15023

TORTURE: A MILESTONE IN ROCK 'N' ROLL MUSIC, VOL 4.
Tracks: / Wait ((Previously unissued)) / Radio and TV / Somebody's smiling (while I'm crying) / No-one really cares / Lonely island / That's a whole lot of love / Torture / Don't take her from me / Cut me down from your whipping post / You've only got Mr. to lose / In time / Big as I can.
LP: . . . . BFX 15031

Jensen, Theis

DANISH JAZZ VOL.3.
LP: . . . . SLP 412

Jenson, Rich

TWO MILLION YEARS.
MC: . . . . KC 012

Jeremiah in the...

JEREMIAH IN THE DARK WOODS (Janet & Allan Ahlberg).
MC: 881 549
MC: . . . . TS 335

Jeremy Days

CIRCUSHEAD.
LP: 8439981
MC: 8439984

JEREMY DAYS, THE.
Tracks: / Julie thru the blinds / Brand new toy / Rome wasn't built in a day / Food and coffee / Starting to pretend / End, The / Are you inventive / That's what I call love / Fantastic friend / This world / Raintree country.
LP: 837 216-1
MC: 837 216-4

Jeremy's Secret

SNOWBALL EFFECT, THE.
LP: . . . . DEEP 001

Jerico Go

JERICO GO (Various artists).
LP: . . . . DBAT 18

Jernigan, Doug

BLUEGRASS JAM (see Clements, Vassar) (Jernigan, Doug, Vassar Clements, J. McReynolds).

DOUG & BUCKY (Jernigan, Doug & Bucky Pizzarelli).
LP: . . . . FF 043

ROADSIDE RAG.
LP: . . . . FF 024

Jerome, Henry

1950/52.
LP: . . . . CLP 51

Jerome, Jerome K.

THREE MEN IN A BOAT (Nicholas, Jeremy (nar)).
MCSET: . . . . SAY 86
MCSET: . . . . ARGO 1052

THREE MEN IN A BOAT (Heller, Martin (nar)).
MCSET: . . . . COL 2001

THREE MEN IN A BOAT (Rose, George (nar)).
MC: 1711

Jerome, Jerry Trio

JERRY JEROME TRIO.
LP: . . . . LP 503

Jerome Kern Goes To

JEROME KERN GOES TO HOLLYWOOD (Original cast recording) (Various artists).
Tracks: / Song is you, The/ I've told every little star: *Various artists* / I'll be hard to handle: *Various artists*/ Smoke gets in your eyes: *Various artists* / Yesterdays: *Various artists* / I won't dance: *Various artists*/ I'm old fashioned: *Various artists* / Dearly beloved: *Various artists* / Pick yourself up: *Various artists*/ She didn't say yes: *Various artists* / Folks who live on the hill, The: *Various artists* / Long ago and far away: *Various artists* / Lovely to look at/ Just let me look at you: *Various artists* / Remind me: *Various artists*/ Last time I saw Paris, The: *Various artists* / Ol' man river: *Various artists* / Why was I born?: *Various* artists / Bill/ Can't help lovin' dat man of mine: *Various artists* / All things you are/ They don't believe me: *Various artists.*
LP: . . . . JEROME 1
MC: . . . . JEROME C 1

Jerry's Girls

JERRY'S GIRLS (Original Broadway Cast) (Various artists).
Tracks: / Jerry's girls: *Various artists* / Put on your Sunday clothes: *Various artists* / It only takes a moment: *Various artists* / Wherever he ain't: *Various artists* / We need a little Christmas: *Various artists*/ I won't send roses: *Various artists* / Tap your troubles away: *Various artists* / Two a day: *Various artists*/ Bosom buddies: *Various artists* / Man in the moon, The: *Various artists* / So long dearie: *Various artists*/ Take it all off: *Various artists* / Shalom: *Various artists* / Milk and honey: *Various artists* / Showturn: *Various artists* / If he walked into my life: *Various artists* / Hello, Dolly: *Various artists* / Nelson: *Various artists* / Just go to the movies: *Various artists* / Movies were movies: *Various artists* / Look what happened to Mabel: *Various artists* / Time heals everything: *Various artists* / It's today: *Various artists*/ Mame: *Various artists* / Kiss her now: *Various artists* / That's how young I feel: *Various artists*/ Gooch's song: *Various artists* / Before the parade passes by: *Various artists* / I don't want to know: *Various* artists / La cage aux folles: *Various artists* / Song on the sand: *Various artists* / I am what I am: *Various artists* / Best of times, The: *Various artists* / Jerry's turn: *Various artists.*
2LP: . . . . TER 1093
MC: . . . . ZCTER 1093

Jerry's Kids

IS THIS MY WORLD.
LP: . . . . FH 12-001

KILL, KILL, KILL.
LP: . . . . T 027
MC: . . . . T 027C

Jerusalem

JERUSALEM VOLUME II.
Tracks: / Wake up / Rock and roll / Love song / Gethsemane / I depend on you, Jesus / Introduction / Dialogue / Bye bye world / Flower.
LP: . . . . MYR 1097
MC: . . . . MC 1097

WARRIOR.
Tracks: / Constantly changing / Warrior / Pilgrim / Man of the world / Sodom / Ashes in our hands / Farewell.
LP: . . . . MYR 1113
MC: . . . . MC 1113

Jess & The Gingerbread

COUNTRY ROOTS.
LP: . . . . BSS 130

UNTIL IT'S TIME.
LP: . . . . BSS 180

Jesse's Gang

CENTRE OF ATTRACTION.
Tracks: / Love's no mystery / Centre of attraction / Real love / Dreams / Your way / Noiz without words / Back-up / I'm back again / Do you know / My ride / Don't you care / Fantasy.
LP: . . . . K 9241291
MC: . . . . K 9241294

Jester

KEMP'S JIG.
Tracks: / Kemp's jig / Byrne's hornpipe / Fisherman's hornpipe / March of the King of Laois / Brawl / Village dance / George Whitehead and Alman / Getting upstairs, I never did see / Estampie / Dressed ship / Tourdion / Pretty Meg Morrissey / Scholar, The / Carolan's draught / Spanish pavan / Wascha mesa / Wascha tanz / Holmes fancy / Irish polka / Rose polka / Long odds.
LP: . . . . PLR 026

Jesters Of Destiny

IN A NOSTALGIC MOOD.
LP: . . . . RR 9576

Jesus Burning Liquor

STEIFEN.
LP: . . . . EFA 15065

Jesus Christ Superstar

JESUS CHRIST SUPERSTAR (Film soundtrack) (Various artists).
LP: . . . . SML 1088

JESUS CHRIST SUPERSTAR (Original 1972 studio recording) (Various artists).
Tracks: / Overture: *Various artists* / Heaven on their minds: *Various artists* / What's the buzz?: *Various* artists / Strange thing mystifying: *Various artists* / Then we are decided: *Various artists* / Everything's alright: *Various artists* / This Jesus must die: *Various artists* / Hosanna: *Various artists* / Simon Zealotes: *Various artists* / Poor Jerusalem: *Various artists* / Pilate's dream: *Various artists* / Temple, The: *Various artists* / I don't know how to love Him: *Various artists* / Damned for all time: *Various artists*/ Blood money: *Various artists* / Last supper, The: *Various artists* / Gethsemane: *Various artists* / Arrest: *Various artists* / Peter's denial: *Various artists* / Pilate and Christ: *Various artists* / King Herod's song: *Various artists* / Could we start again please?: *Various artists* / Judas's death: *Various artists*/ Trial before Pilate: *Various artists* / Superstar: *Various artists* / John 19:41: *Various artists* / Forty one: *Various artists.*
2LP: . . . . MCX 501
MC: . . . . MCXC 501
2LP: . . . . MKPS 2011/2

JESUS CHRIST SUPERSTAR (Original London cast) (Various artists).
Tracks: / Heaven on their minds: *Various artists* / Everything's alright: *Various artists* / This Jesus must die: *Various artists* / Hosanna: *Various artists* / Simon Zealotes: *Various artists* / I don't know how to love him: *Various artists* / Gethsemane: *Various artists* / Pilate's dream: *Various artists* / King Herod's song: *Various artists* / Could we start again please: *Various artists* / Trial before Pilate: *Various artists*/ Superstar: *Various artists* / John 19:41: *Various artists.*
LP: . . . . MCF 2503
MC: . . . . MCFC 2503
LP: . . . . MDKS 8008
MC: . . . . MKPC 8008

JESUS CHRIST SUPERSTAR (Various artists).
Tracks: / Overture: *Various artists* / Heaven on their minds: *Various artists* / What's the buzz: *Various* artists / Strange thing mystifying: *Various artists* / Everything's alright: *Various artists* / This Jesus must die: *Various artists* / Hosanna: *Various artists* / Simon Zealotes: *Various artists* / Pilate's dream: *Various artists* / Temple: *Various artists* / I don't know how to love him: *Various artists* / Damned for all time/ Blood money: *Various artists* / Gethsemane (I only want to say): *Various artists* / King Herod's song: *Various artists* / Trial before Pilate: *Various artists* / Superstar: *Various artists* / Crucifixion: *Various artists* / John Nineteen: *Various artists* / Forty one: *Various artists.*
LP: . . . . SRS 5125

JESUS CHRIST SUPERSTAR (Various artists).
Tracks: / Overture: *Various artists* / Heaven on their minds: *Various artists* / What's the buzz: *Various* artists / Everything's alright: *Various artists* / Hosanna: *Various artists* / Simon Zealotes: *Various* artists / Pilate's dream: *Various artists* / I don't know how to love him: *Various artists* / Damned for all time: *Various artists* / I only want to say: *Various artists* / King Herod's song: *Various artists* / Superstar: *Various artists.*
LP: 6382 060

JESUS CHRIST SUPERSTAR (1973) (Film soundtrack) (Various artists).
Tracks: / Overture: *Various artists* / Heaven on their minds: *Various artists* / What's the buzz?: *Various* artists / Strange thing mystifying: *Various artists* / Then we decided: *Various artists* / Everything's alright: *Various artists* / This Jesus must die: *Various artists* / Hosanna: *Various artists* / Simon Zealotes: *Various artists* / Poor Jerusalem: *Various artists* / Pilate's dream: *Various artists* / Temple, The: *Various artists* / I don't know how to love him: *Various artists* / Damned for all time: *Various artists*/ Blood money: *Various artists* / Last supper, The: *Various artists* / Gethsemane (I only want to say): *Various* artists / Arrest, The: *Various artists* / Peter's denial: *Various artists* / Pilate and Christ: *Various* artists / King Herod's song: *Various artists* / Could we start again please: *Various artists* / Judas's death: *Various artists* / Trial before Pilate: *Various artists* / Superstar: *Various artists* / Crucifixion: *Various artists* / John 19:41: *Various artists.*
MC: . . . . MCXC 502
2LP: . . . . MCX 502

JESUS CHRIST SUPERSTAR / GODSPELL (Stage highlights) (Various artists).
Tracks: / Overture - Heaven on their minds: *Various artists* / Everything's alright: *Various artists* / Pilate's dream: *Various artists* / I don't know how to love him: *Various artists* / Last supper, The: *Various artists*/ Arrest: *Various artists* / Superstar: *Various artists* / Crucifixion: *Various artists* / Conclusion: *Various artists* / Prepare ye: *Various artists* / Save the people: *Various artists* / Day by day: *Various* artists / O bless the Lord my soul: *Various artists* / All for the best: *Various artists* / All good gifts: *Various artists* / Turn back o' man: *Various artists* / By my side: *Various artists* / On the willows: *Various artists* / Finale: *Various artists.*
LP: . . . . GH 551

Jesus College...

JESUS COLLEGE CHOIR, CAMBRIDGE (Jesus College choir, Cambridge).
Tracks: / Libera nos, salva nos / Aeternae laudis lilium / Dum transisset Sabbatum a 5 / Fantasy on a theme by

Tallis / Spiritus Sanctus, procedens a throno a 6 / Magnificat (Byrd) (From the Great Service.) / Nunc Dimittis (Byrd) (From the Great Service.) / Fancy for two to play, A / Almighty God, the fountain of all wisdom.
LP: ACA 546

Jesus Couldn't Drum

ER......SOMETHING ABOUT A COW.
LP: LM LP 004

GOOD MORNING MR.SQUARE.
Tracks: / Intro / Jesus couldn't drum / Caught in a dream / Mr. Square / Sunday girl / Turmoil acid / Apple pie for tea / Lidice / Alphabet song / Pyramid song / Waldo wiggins dreams / Sunshine and slumber / Paper boats in puddles / Heavy goods train / Saloon bar blues / Outro.
LP: LM LP 044

RATTLING ORANGE PEEL & BLIND LEMON PIE.
LP: LM LP 444

Jesus Jones

DOUBT.
Tracks: / Trust me / Who? Where? Why? / International bright young thing / I'm burning / Right here, right now / Nothing to hold me / Real, real, real / Welcome back Victoria / Two and two / Stripped / Blissed.
LP: FOODLP 5
MC: FOODTC 5

LIQUIDIZER.
Tracks: / Move mountains / Never enough / Real world, The / All the answers / What's going on / Song 13 / Info freako / Bring it on down / Too much to learn / What would you know / One for the money / Someone to blame.
LP: FOODLP 3
MC: FOODTC 3

Jesus Lizard

GOAT.
LP: TGLP 68
MC: TG 68C

HEAD.
LP: TGLP 54

Jesus Loves You

MARTYR MANTRAS, THE.
LP: CUMLP 1
MC: CUMTC 1

Jesus & Mary Chain

AUTOMATIC.
Tracks: / Here come Alice / Coast to coast / Blues from a gun / Between planets / UV ray / Her way of praying / Head on / Take it / Halfway to crazy / Gimme hell / Drop / Sunray.
LP: BYN 20
MC: BYNC 20

BARBED WIRE KISSES.
Tracks: / Kill surf city / Head / Rider / Hit / Don't ever change / Just out of reach / Happy place / Psycho candy / Sidewalking / Who do you love / Surfin' USA / Everything's alright when you're down / Upside down / Taste of Cindy / Swing / On the wall-f hole / Bo Diddley is Jesus (on Cassette and CD only) / Here it comes again (Only on cassette and CD) / Cracked (on Cassette and CD only) / Mushroom (on Cassette and CD only).
LP: BYN 15
MC: BYNC 15

DARKLANDS.
Tracks: / April skies / Happy when it rains / Down on me / Deep one perfect / Fall / About you / Cherry came too / On the wall / Nine million rainy days.
LP: BYN 11
MC: BYNC 11

JESUS & MARY CHAIN: INTERVIEW PICTURE DISC.
LPPD: BAK 2034

MUSIC AND MEDIA INTERVIEW PICTURE DISC.
LPPD: JM 1020

PEEL SESSIONS:JESUS & MARY CHAIN.
LP: SFPMA 210

PSYCHO CANDY.
Tracks: / Just like honey / Living end, The / Taste the floor / Hardest walk / Cut dead / In a hole / Taste of Cindy / Never understand / It's so hard / Inside me / Sowing seeds / My little underground / You trip me up / Something's wrong.
MC: BYNC 7
LP: BYN 7

Jesus Of Nazareth

JESUS OF NAZARETH (TV Film Soundtrack) (Various artists).
MC: ZCP 28504
LP: AV 4102
MC: AV 5102

Jet Red

JET RED.
LP: MFN 94

Jet Vegas

BIEN VENUE.
LP: MCF 3443
MC: MCFC 3443

Jeter, Genobia

GENOBIA.
Tracks: / Sunshine / Peace of mind / Together / Blessing in disguise / I just want what's mine / We got love / All of my love / Take a look.
LP: PL 85897
MC: PK 85897

HEAVEN.
LP: SL 14547

THINGS HAVE 'GOT' TO GET BETTER.
LP: SL 14597

Jethro Tull

A.
Tracks: / Crossfire / Fylingdale flyer / Working John, working Joe / Black Sunday / Protect and survive / Batteries not included / Uniform / 4WD (low ratio) / Pine martens jig, The / And further on.
LP: CHE 1301

AQUALUNG.
Tracks: / Aqualung / Cross-eyed Mary / Cheap day return / Mother goose / Wond'ring aloud / Up to me / My God / Hymn 43 / Slipstream / Locomotive Breath / Wind up.
LP: CHR 1044
MC: ZCHR 1044
LP: ILPS 9145

BENEFIT.
Tracks: / With you there to help me / Nothing to say / Alive and well and living in / Son for Michael Collins / Jeffrey and me / To cry you a song / Time for everything, A / Inside / Play in time / Sossity / You're a woman.
LP: CHR 1043
MC: ZCHR 1043
LP: ILPS 9123

BROADSWORD AND THE BEAST, THE.
Tracks: / Beastie / Clasp / Fallen on hard times / Flying colours / Slow marching / Broadsword / Pussy willow / Watching me watching you / Seal driver / Cheerio.
LP: CDL 1380
MC: ZCDL 1380

CATFISH RISING.
Tracks: / This is not love / Occasional demons / Rocks on the road / Thinking round corners / Still loving you tonight / Doctor to my disease / Like a tall thin girl / Sparrow on the schoolyard wall / Roll yer own / Gold-tipped boots, black jacket and tie.
LP: CHR 1886
MC: ZCHR 1886

CREST OF A KNAVE.
Tracks: / Steel monkey / Farm on the freeway / Jump start / Said she was a dancer / Budapest / Mountain men / Raising steam / Waking edge, The (Extra on cassette and CD) / Dogs in the midwinter (Extra on cassette and CD).
LP: CDL 1590
MC: ZCDL 1590

HEAVY HORSES.
Tracks: / And the mouse police never sleeps / Acres wild / No lullaby / Moths / Journey man / Rover, The / One brown mouse / Heavy horses / Weathercock.
LP: CHR 1175
MC: ZCHR 1175

LIVE AT HAMMERSMITH 1984.
LP: FRSLP 004
MC: FRSMC 004

LIVE - BURSTING OUT.
Tracks: / No lullaby / Sweet dream / Skating away on the thin ice of the new day / Jack in the green / One brown mouse / New day yesterday, A / Flute solo improvisation / God rest ye merry gentlemen / Bouree / Thick as a brick / Hunting girl / Too old to rock 'n' roll, too young to die / Conundrum / Minstrel in the gallery / One-eyed Mary / Quatrain / Aqualung / Locomotive breath / Dambusters march.
2LP: CJT 4
MCSET: ZCJT 4

LIVING IN THE PAST.
Tracks: / Witches promise / Song for Jeffrey, A / Love story / Christmas song, The / Living in the past / Driving song / Bouree / Sweet dreams / Singing all day / Witches' promise / Inside / Just trying to be / By kind permission of you / Dharma for one / Wondering again / Locomotive breath / Life is a long song / Up the 'Pool / Doctor Bogenbroom / For later / Nursie.
2LP: CJT 1
MCSET: ZCJT 1

MINSTREL IN THE GALLERY.
Tracks: / Minstrel in the gallery / Cold wind to Valhalla / Black satin dancer / Requiem / One white duck / O 10 equals nothing at all / Baker St. muse / Including pig me and the whore / Nice little tune / Crash barrier waltzer / Mother England reverie / Grace.
LP: CHR 1082
MC: ZCHR 1082

M.U. BEST OF.
Tracks: / Teacher / Aqualung / Thick as a brick / Bungle in the jungle / Locomotive breath / Fat man / Living in the past / Passion play, A / Skating away on the thin ice of the new day / Rainbow blues / Nothing is easy.
LP: CHR 1078
MC: ZCHR 1078

MU/REPEAT.
MCSET: ZCDP 105

ORIGINAL MASTERS.
Tracks: / Living in the past / Aqualung / Too old to rock 'n' roll too young to die / Locomotive breath / Skating away on the thin ice of the new day / Bungle in the jungle / Sweet dreams / Songs from the wood / Witches promise / Thick as a brick / Minstrel in the gallery / Life is a long song.
LP: JTTV 1
MC: ZJTTV 1

PASSION PLAY, A.
Tracks: / Passion play, A / Story of the hare who lost his spectacles, The.
LP: CHR 1040
MC: ZCHR 1040

REPEAT, VOL.II.
Tracks: / Minstrel in the gallery / Cross-eyed Mary / New day yesterday, A / Bouree / Thick as a brick / War child / Passion play, A / To cry you a song / Too old to rock 'n' roll, too young to die / Glory row.
LP: CHR 1135
MC: ZCHR 1135

ROCK ISLAND.
Tracks: / Kissing Willie / Rattlesnake trail, The / Ears of tin / Undressed to kill / Rock Island / Heavy water / Another Christmas song / Whaler's dues, The / Big riff and Mando / Strange avenues.
LP: CHR 1708
MC: ZCHR 1708

SONGS FROM THE WOOD.
Tracks: / Songs from the wood / Jack in the green / Cup of wonder / Hunting girl / Ring out- Solstice bells / Velvet green / Whistler, The / Pibroch (cap in hand) / Fire at midnight.
LP: CHR 1132
MC: ZCHR 1132

STAND UP.
Tracks: / New day yesterday, A / Jeffrey goes to Leicester Square / Bouree / Back to the family / Look into the sun / Nothing is easy / Fat man / We used to know / Reasons for waiting / For a thousand mothers.
LP: FA 41 30861
MC: TCFA 41 30864
LP: CHR 1042
MC: ZCHR 1042
LP: ILPS 9103

STORM WATCH.
Tracks: / North Sea oil / Orion / Home / Dark ages / Warm sporran / Something's on the move / Old ghosts / Dunringill / Flying Dutchman, The / Elegy.
LP: CDL 1238
MC: ZCDL 1238

THICK AS A BRICK.
Tracks: / Thick as a brick.
LP: CHR 1003
MC: ZCHR 1003

THIS WAS.
Tracks: / My Sunday feeling / Someday the sun won't shine / For you / Beggar's farm / Move on alone / Serenadeto a cuckoo / Dharma for one / It's breaking me / Cat's squirrel / Song for Jeffrey, A / Round.
LP: ILPS 9085
LP: CHR 1041
MC: ZCHR 1041

TOO OLD TO ROCK AND ROLL.
Tracks: / Quizz kid / Crazed institution / Salamander / Taxi grab / From a dead beat to an old greaser / Bad eyed and loveless / Big dipper / Too old to rock 'n' roll; too young to die / Pied piper / Chequered flag (dead of alive), The.
LP: CHR 1111
MC: ZCHR 1111

UNDER WRAPS.
Tracks: / Lap of luxury / Under wraps (part 1) / European legacy / Later the same evening / Saboteur / Radio free Moscow / Nobody's car / Heat / Under wraps (part 2) / Paparazzi / Apologee.
LP: CDL 1461
MC: ZCDL 1461

WAR CHILD.
Tracks: / War child / Queen and country / Ladies / Back door angels / Sea lion / Skating away on the thin ice of the new day / Bungle in the jungle / Only solitaire / Third hoorah, The / Two fingers.
LP: CHR 1067
MC: ZCHR 1067

Jets (American)

CRUSH ON YOU.
Tracks: / Curiosity / Crush on you / You got it all / Love umbrella / Private number / Heart on the line / Right before my eyes / La la means I love you / Crush on you (remix) (CD only.).
LP: MCF 3312
MC: MCFC 3312

Jets (British)

100 PER CENT COTTON.
LP: EMC 3399

ALL FIRED UP.
LP: KRYP 202

COTTON PICKIN'.
LP: KRYP 200

FIFTEEN ROCKIN' YEARS.
LP: KRYP 201

JETS.
Tracks: / My baby left me / I flipped / I seen ya / Who's that knocking / Honey hush / Hit it on / Pink and black / Crazy baby / Let's get it on / Baby take me back / Sixteen chicks / Don't push / Sweet love on my mind / Booger red.
LP: EMC 3356
MC: TCFA 3036

SESSION OUT.
LP: NERD 021

Jetset

APRIL, MAY, JUNE AND THE JETSETS.
Tracks: / Story of the world, The / Does it look like rain? / What a way to go! / You won't believe your eyes / Dreaming of Jeannie / Judy's toy box / Can you hear my heartbeat ? / Late great Frank Lewis, The / Watch yourself.
LP: LO 7

FIVE.
LP: JETSET 5

GO BANANAS.
LP: NET 4

THERE GOES THE NEIGHBOUR.
LP: WORK 1

VAUDEVILLE PARK.
LP: WORK 6

Jett, Joan

ALBUM (Jett, Joan & The Blackhearts).
Tracks: / Fake friends / Handy man / Everyday people / Hundred feet away, A / Secret love / French song / Tossin' and turnin' / Why can't we be happy / I love playin' with fire / Coney Island whitefish / Had enough.
LP: EPC 25414
MC: 40 25414

BAD REPUTATION.
LP: EPC 25045
MC: 40 25045

GLORIOUS RESULTS OF A MISPENT YOUTH (Jett, Joan & The Blackhearts).
Tracks: / Cherry bomb / Someday / I love you love me love / Frustrated / hold me / Long time / Talking about my baby / Love like mine, A / I need someone / New Orleans / Push and stomp / I got no answers.
LP: EPC 25993

GOOD MUSIC (Jett, Joan & The Blackhearts).
LP: 833 078 1
MC: 833 078 4

HIT LIST, THE.
LP: CHR 1773
MC: ZCHR 1773

I LOVE PLAYING WITH FIRE (Jett, Joan & the Runaways).
Tracks: / Saturday night special / Eight days a week / Mama weer all crazee now / I'm a million / Right now / Take over / My buddy and me / Lost little girls / Black leather / Blackmail / Don't abuse me / I love playin' with fire.
LP: LAKER 1

I LOVE ROCK 'N' ROLL (Jett, Joan & The Blackhearts).
Tracks: / I love rock 'n' roll / I'm gonna run away / Love is pain / Nag / Crimson and clover / Victim of circumstance / Bits and pieces / Be straight / You're too possessive / Oh woe is me.
LP: EPC 85686
MC: 40 85686
LPPD: EPC 11-85686

UP YOUR ALLEY (Jett, Joan & The Blackhearts).
Tracks: / I hate myself for loving you / Ridin' with James Dean / Little liar / Tulane / I wanna be your dog / I still dream about you / You want in I want out / Just like in the movies / Desire / Back it up / Play that song again.
LP: . . . . LONLP 67
MC: . . . . LONC 67

Jewel In The Crown

JEWEL IN THE CROWN (TV soundtrack) (Various artists).
Tracks: / Jewel in the crown: *Various artists* / Lakes, The: *Various artists* / Triangle: *Various artists*/ Crossing the river: *Various artists* / Imprisoned: *Various artists* / Death by fire: *Various artists*/ Chillingborough School song: *Various artists* / Butterflies caught in a web: *Various artists* / Daphne and Hari: *Various artists* / Mirat: *Various artists* / Princely state: *Various artists* / Kedara and waltz dedara: *Various artists* / Barbie leaves Rose Cottage: *Various artists* / Champagne Charlie: *Various artists*/ Guy Perrons march: *Various artists* / Pankot - the hills: *Various artists* / Jewel in the crown - end titles: *Various artists*.
LP: . . . . CDL 1465
MC: . . . . ZCDL 1465

Jewel Of The Nile

JEWEL OF THE NILE, THE (Film soundtrack) (Various artists).
Tracks: / When the going gets tough (the tough get going: *Ocean, Billy* / I'm in love: *Turner, Ruby* / African breeze: *Masekela, Hugh & Johnathan Butler* / Party: *Willesden Dodgers* / Freaks come out at night: *Whodini*/ Jewel of the Nile, The: *Wilson, Precious* / Legion: *Shreeve, Mark* / Nubian dance: *Nubians* / Love theme: *Nitzsche, Jack* / Plot thickens, The: *Nitzsche, Jack*.
LP: . . . . HIP 33
MC: . . . . HIPC 33

Jewish Party

JEWISH PARTY, DANCES & STORIES (Various artists).
LP: . . . . ZR 1015

Jewkes, Noel

LEGATO EXPRESS.
LP: . . . . REV 30

Jezebelle

BAD ATTITUDE.
LP: . . . . HMRLP 148
MC: . . . . HMRMC 148

J.F.A.

JFA.
Tracks: / Deltitnu / Tent peg / Aba / It's not right / Day Walt Disney died, The / Standin' on the verge / I love broads / Ramp song / Pipetruck / Zimbobway / Untitled / I still could not forget you.
LP: . . . . SAVE 044

VALLEY OF THE YAKES.
Tracks: / Kick you / Great equaliser / Prepple / Little big man / Johnny D / Walk don't run / Skateboard / We know you suck / Too late / Sadistic release / Axed at howards / One-ten / Guess what?.
LP: . . . . SAVE 023

JIH

SHADOW TO FALL.
LP: . . . . FREUD 13

Jim & Jesse

EPIC BLUEGRASS HITS,THE.
Tracks: / Nine pound hammer / Are you missing me / It's a long, long way to the top of the world / Cotton mill man / She left me standing on the mountain / Take my ring from your finger / Don't say goodbye if you love me / Drifting and dreaming of you / Why not confess / I wish you knew.
LP: . . . . SS 20
MC: . . . . SSC 20

HANDFUL OF GOOD SEEDS, A (Jim & Jesse & the Virginia Boys).
Tracks: / Family who prays shall never part, The / Born again / How great thou art / On the wings of a snow white dove / Truth on the mountain / Family Bible / Little white church, The / Jesus is the key to the kingdom / Two thousand years ago / River of Jordan / Walking my Lord up Calvary's hill / Matthew twenty four.
LP: . . . . CGS 8512
MC: . . . . WC 8512

IN THE TRADITION (Jim & Jesse & the Virginia Boys).
LP: . . . . ROUNDER 0234
MC: . . . . ROUNDER 0234C

JIM & JESSE STORY.
LP: . . . . CMH 9022

JIM & JESSE TODAY.
LP: . . . . CMH 6250

Jimbo

JIMBO FLIES TO FRANCE See also Peter Hawkins.
MC: 00 1034537

JIMBO FLIES TO SPAIN See also Peter Hawkins.
MC: 00 1034545

Jimenez, Flaco

ACCORDION STRIKES BACK.
LP: . . . . WF 037
MC: . . . . WF 037C

ARIBA EL NORTE.
LP: . . . . ZS 92

AT THE MILKY WAY.
MC: . . . . PF 0101

AY TE DEJO EN SAN ANTONIO.
LP: . . . . ARHOOLIE 3021
MC: . . . . C 3021

EL SONIDO DE SAN ANTONIO.
LP: . . . . ARHOOLIE 3014
MC: . . . . C 3014

ENTRE HUMO Y BOTELLAS.
LP: . . . . MUNICH 141

FLACO JIMENEZ & HIS CONJUNTO.
LP: . . . . ARHOOLIE 3007

FLACO'S AMIGOS.
Tracks: / La tumba sera el final / Did I tell you / Jennette / Te quiero mas / Mi primer amor / Free Mexican air force / Lucerito / Espero tu regreso / Poquita fe / Feria polka / Para toda la vida / I'm gonna love you like there is no tomorrow / Yo quisiera saber / Atotonilco.
LP: . . . . COOK 017
MC: . . . . COOKC 017
MC: . . . . C 3027
LP: . . . . ARHOOLIE 3027

SAN ANTONIO SATURDAY NIGHT.
LP: . . . . SNTF 933

SAN ANTONIO SOUND, THE (Jimenez, Flaco Y Su Conjunto).
LP: . . . . WF 019
MC: . . . . WF 019C

TEX MEX BREAKDOWN (Jimenez, Flaco Y Su Conjunto).
Tracks: / Open your heart / Mexican Joe / Cielito lindo / La bamba / La moiadita / El Rancho Grande / El pantalon blue / San Antonio rose / Polish polka / For the good times.
LP: . . . . SNTF 895

VIVA SEGUIN.
Tracks: / Viva sequin / La botellita / Hasta la vista / Los amores del flaco / Mi duice amor / Horalia / Arriba el norte / Polka town / La piedrera / Viajando en polka marianela / Adios muchachos.
LP: . . . . FMSL 2003

Jimenez, Santiago

EL MERO MERO (Jimenez, Santiago Jnr).
MC: . . . . C 3016
LP: . . . . ARHOOLIE 3016

SANTIAGO JIMENEZ WITH FLACO JIMENEZ.
LP: . . . . ARHOOLIE 3013
MC: . . . . C 3013

STRIKES AGAIN (Jimenez, Santiago Jnr).
LP: . . . . ARHOOLIE 3020

TRADICION Y FAMILIA (Jimenez, Santiago Jnr).
LP: . . . . SPD 1025
MC: . . . . SPDC 1025

Jimmy Jimmy

HERE IN THE LIGHT.
Tracks: / Forget your sorrow / Sarah Moon / Silence / Here in the light / Lady / Following dreams / Passing dream / I met her in Paris / Love / Kettle's boiling,The.
LP: . . . . EPC 26713
MC: 40 26713

Jimmy, Tomas

LE FICHE BLIAN ANUAS.
MC: . . . . GTDC 088

Jimmy Z

ANYTIME, ANYPLACE, ANYWHERE.
Tracks: / I know / You've got me runnin' / Bum opera / Cool breeze / Colorz (une autre place) / Where's all my money / I never said that I would / We don't seem to mind / Nothing guaranteed / Shotgun cha cha.
LP: . . . . ILP 032

Jimmy's Joys

JIMMY'S JOYS & ORCHESTRA 1923-32 (Jimmy's Joys & Orchestra).
2LP: . . . . ARCADIA 2017D

Jing Ying Soloists

EVENING SONG (Traditional Chinese music).
Tracks: / Autumn moon / Ducks quacking / Love song of the grassland / Singing the night among fishing boats / Fishing song, The / Marriage of Chan Xian-Yuen, The / Moonlight over the spring river / Happy reunion / Bamboo song from the village / Variations on Yang City tune / Meditating on the past / Moon over Guan-Shan.
MC: . . . . CSDL 368

LIKE WAVES AGAINST THE SAND.
Tracks: / Flowing streams, The / Suzhou scenery / Races, The / Love at the fair / High moon, The / Night / Chinese martial arts / Flower fair, The / Shenpadei folksong / Like waves against the sand (Available on CD only) / Bird song* / Legend*.
LP: . . . . SDL 325
MC: . . . . CSDL 325

Jingle Jangle

JINGLE JANGLE (Original Broadway cast) (Various artists).
LP: . . . . JJ 001

Jingo De Lunch

AXE TO GRIND.
Tracks: / Different world / Steamed / Flapjax / Axe to grind / Did you ever / Kick and run / Tender prey / Seen and done / Chill out / Jinxed / Trouble / Shot down.
LP: 086802

PERPETUUM MOBILE.
Tracks: / Lies / Utopia / Peace of mind / Jingo / Illusions / Perpetuum mobile / Fate / Scratchings / Scarecrow / What you see / Thirteen.
LP: . . . . WEBITE 27

Jinski

EVENTUALLY.
LP: . . . . PROJECTS 112

Jism

MIND THE GAP.
LP: . . . . GRO 3

Jitters

JITTERS, THE.
Tracks: / Closer every day / Last of the red hot fools / Go ahead 'n' love me / Mad about you / Just another fine example / Hard as nails / That's when I need you / What about me / There goes love / Almost convinced.
LP: . . . . EST 2055
MC: . . . . TCEST 2055

Jivaros Quartet

NEAR THE NOISE.
LP: . . . . L 8909201
MC: . . . . L 8909401

Jive

RAP.
LP: . . . . HIP 95
MC: . . . . HIPC 95

Jive Bombers

BAD BOY.
LP: . . . . SJL 1150

Jive Bunny

IT'S PARTY TIME (Jive Bunny & The Mastermixers).
MC: . . . . STAC 2449
LP: . . . . STAR 2449

JIVE BUNNY FINDS FAME.
MC: . . . . JBM 001

JIVE BUNNY SAVES THE DAY.
MC: . . . . JBM 002

JIVE BUNNY - THE ALBUM (Jive Bunny & The Mastermixers).
Tracks: / Swing the mood / Rock and roll party mix / Lover's mix / Do you wanna rock / That's what I like / Glenn Miller medley, The / Swing sisters swing / Hopping mad.
LP: . . . . STAR 2390
MC: . . . . STAC 2390
LPPD: . . . . PSTAR 2390
MC: . . . . STAC 2418

Jive Five

OUR TRUE STORY.
Tracks: / My true story / Do you hear wedding bells / Beggin' you please / Rain / Johnny never knew / People from another world / What time is it / When I was single / These golden rings / Girl with the wind in her hair / I don't want to be without you baby / No not again / You know what I would do / Never never / Hully gully callin' time / Hurry back.
LP: . . . . CH 76

WAY BACK.
LP: . . . . ASR 801

Jive Turkey

PERFUME EXPERIMENT.
LP: . . . . DANLP 042
MC: . . . . DANMC 042

J.J (2)

INTRO.
Tracks: / Denim and blue / If this is love / Come back baby / Going nowhere / Silver / Lovers do / Slide away / Does anybody know / Crying over you / Anyway the wind blows / Success.
LP: 4680851
MC: 4680854

JKD Band

DRAGON POWER.
Tracks: / Let your body do the talking / Dream machine / Africa / Dragon power / Everything that's part of you / Hooked on the boogie / Mellow terrain.
LP: . . . . SATL 4014

J.M.

JM VOL.8 - LONESOME SUNDOWN (Bought me a ticket).
LP: . . . . FLY 529

JM VOL.9 - KATIE WEBSTER (Whooie sweet daddy) (Webster, Katie).
LP: . . . . FLY 530

JM VOL.21 - TOO HOT TO HANDLE (Nelson, Jay/Ballou).
LP: . . . . FLY 570

Jo, Damito

I'LL SAVE THE LAST DANCE FOR YOU.
LP: 33.6.202

Jo Jo

JO JO.
LP: 209232
MC: 409232

Jo Jo Dancer...

JO JO DANCER, YOUR LIFE IS CALLING (Film soundtrack) (Various artists).
Tracks: / Baby Jo Jo: *Pryor, Richard* / My destiny: *Khan, Chaka* / For the love of money: *O'Jays* / Off the cliff: *Hancock, Herbie* / I heard it through the grapevine: *Knight, Gladys & The Pips* / White kids, black kids: *Pryor, Richard* / Heckler,The: *Pryor, Richard* / What's going on: *Gaye, Marvin* / Mighty love: *Spinners*/ In the upper room: *Jackson, Mahalia* / Theme for mother: *Hancock, Herbie* / Bass behavior: *Hancock, Herbie*/ Burn ward: *Pryor, Richard* / I'm back: *Pryor, Richard* / Shotgun: *Walker, Junior & The All Stars* / Michelle: *Hancock, Herbie*.
LP: 925485 1
MC: 925485 4

Jo Jo Gunne

JO JO GUNNE.
Tracks: / Run run run / Shake that fat / Babylon / I make love / Barstow blue eyes / 99 days / Academy award / Take it easy / Flying home.
LP: . . . . K 53034

Jo Jo Zep

SCREAMING TARGETS (Jo Jo Zep & The Falcons).
Tracks: / Hit and run / Don't wanna come down / Katschara / Only the lonely heart / So young / Close to the bone / Shape I'm in / Trials and tribulations / Thin line / Open hearted.
LP: . . . . K 99094

Joan Of Arc

JOAN OF ARC (history for ages 8+) (Unknown narrator(s)).
MC: . . . . PLBH 99

Job Satisfaction

JOB SATISFACTION (See under UNESCO reports).

Jobarteh, Malamini

JALIYA (GAMBIA) (Jobarteh, Malamini & Dembo Konte).
Tracks: / Segou tutu / Mbassi / Solo / Bamba bojang / Tutu Jara / Fode keba / Cheddo.
LP: . . . . STERNS 1010
LP: . . . . ROUNDER 5021
MC: . . . . ROUNDER 5021C

Jobarteh, S

KORA MUSIC.
MC: . . . . JENAKO

Jobim, Antonio Carlos

CERTAIN MISTER, A.
Tracks: / Off-key / Photography / Surfboard / Estrada do sol / Se todos fossem iguais a voce / Once again / Bonita / I was just one more for you / Don't ever go away / Zingaro.
MC: . . . . HSC 3032
LP: . . . . SHM 3032

CERTAIN MR. JOBIM, A.
Tracks: / Once again / I was just one more for you / Estrada do sol / Don't ever go away / Zingaro / Bonita / Se tudos fossem iguais a voce / Off key / Photograph / Surfboard.
LP: . . . . DS 848
MC: . . . . DSC 848

COMPACT JAZZ: ANTONIO CARLOS JOBIM.
MC: 8432734

GIRL FROM IPANEMA.

LP: . . . . MFP 50437

PASSARIM.
LP: 833 234 1
MC: 833 234 4

PLAYS JOBIM.
Tracks: / Girl from Ipanema / O morro / Auga de beber / Dreamer / Favela / Insensatez / Corcovado / One note samba / Meditation / Jazz samba / Chega de saudade / Des finado.
LP: 2304 502
MC: 823 011-4

WONDERFUL WORLD OF....,THE.
Tracks: / She's a carioca / Agua de Beber / Surfboard / Useless landscape / So' tinha de ser com voce / A felicidade / Bonita / Favela / Valsa de Porto das Caixas / Samba do aviao / Por toda a minha vida / Dindi.
LP: . . . . DS 898
MC: . . . . DSC 898

Joboxers

LIKE GANGBUSTERS.
Tracks: / Just got lucky / Curious George / Crime of passion / She's got sex / Fully booked / Hide nor hair / Not my night / Boxerbeat / Crosstown walk up / Johnny Friendly.
LP: . . . . BOXXLP 001
MC: . . . . BOXXK 001

SKIN & BONE.
Tracks: / Is this really the first time / Strictly business / Some kind of heart / Don't keep the ladies waiting / Cry uncle / Don't add up / Lonchaney Jr / My best friend / Dead end street / One in a million / Skin and bone.
LP: . . . . PL 70603
MC: . . . . PK 70603

Jobson, Eddie

GREEN ALBUM (Jobson, Eddie & Zinc).
Tracks: / Transporter / Resident / Easy for you to say / Prelude / Nostalgia / Walking from pastel / Turn it over / Green face / Who my friends / Colour code / Listen to reason / Through the glass / Transporter II.
LP: . . . . EST 4001831

THEME OF SECRETS.
Tracks: / Inner secrets / Spheres of influence / Sojourn, The / Ice festival / Theme of secrets / Memories of Vienna / Lakemist / Outer secrets.
LP: 209 757
MC: 409 757

Jobson, Richard

16 YEARS OF ALCOHOL.
LP: . . . . TWI 807

BAD MAN (ALBUM).
Tracks: / Bad man / This thing called love / Monkey's cry / Uptown/downtown / Boat called pride, A / Angel / Heat is on, The / Fire / Big fat city (Cassette & CD only.).
LP: . . . . PCS 7321
MC: . . . . TCPCS 7321

BALLAD OF ETIQUETTE, THE.
LP: . . . . JC 1

OTHER MAN,THE.
LP: . . . . TWI 615

Jo'burg Hawk

JO'BURG HAWK.
LP: . . . . CHC 20
MC: . . . . CHCMC 20

Jock Strapp

COMPLEAT RUGBY SONGS.
2LP: . . . . SPD 100
MCSET: . . . . TC SPD 100

RUGBY SONGS VOL 2 (Jock Strapp Ensemble).
LP: . . . . ILP 1012

RUGBY SONGS VOL 3 (Jock Strapp Ensemble).
LP: . . . . ILP 1080

Jodimars

WELL NOW DIG THIS.
Tracks: / Well now dig this / Dance the bop / Let's all rock together / (Boom boom) my bayou baby / Eat your heart out Annie / Lotsa love / Rattle my bones / Rattle shakin' daddy / Clara-Bella / Midnight / Cloud 99 / Later.
LP: . . . . BDL 1031
MC: . . . . AJKL 1031

Jody & The Creams

BIG DOG, A.
LP: . . . . ERICAT 028

Joe

JOE (Original Soundtrack) (Various artists).
Tracks: / Where are you goin'?: *Butler, Jerry* / Expiration of Frank: *Butler, Jerry* / You can fly: *Butler*, Jerry / It's a crock: *Butler, Jerry* / When in Rome: *Butler, Jerry* / Send the hippies to hell: *Butler, Jerry* / Hey Joe: *Michaels, Dean* / Compton's hanhout: *Exuma* / You don't know what's going on: *Exuma*.
LP: 6338 029

Joe 90

JOE 90 (THEME FROM) (See under Gray, Barry) (Gray, Barry).

Joe & Eddie

BEST OF JOE & EDDIE.
LP: . . . . GNPS 2032
MC: GNP5 2032

Joel, Billy

52ND STREET.
Tracks: / Big shot / Honesty / My life / Zanzibar / Stiletto / Rosalinda's eyes / Half a mile away / Until the night / 52nd Street.
LP: . . . . CBS 32693
MC: 40 32693
LP: . . . . CBS 83181

AN INNOCENT MAN/ STRANGERS, THE.
LP: . . . . BJ 241

BILLY JOEL.
Tracks: / Just the way you are / Moving out / My life / She's always a woman.
MC: 40 2619

BILLY JOEL (3 LP BOX SET).
LPS: . . . . CBS 66352

BRIDGE, THE.
Tracks: / Running on ice / This is the time / Matter of trust, A / Baby grand / Big man on Mulberry street / Temptation / Code of silence / Getting closer / Modern woman.
LP: . . . . CBS 86323
MC: 40 86323
LP: 4655611
MC: 4655614

CALIFORNIA FLASH.
Tracks: / Wonder woman / California flash / Revenge is sweet / Amplifier fire / Godzilla part 1 / Rollin' home / Tear this castle down / Brain invasion.
LP: . . . . SHLP 114
MC: . . . . SHTC 114
LP: . . . . PLP 9
MC: . . . . PMC 9

COLD SPRING HARBOUR.
LP: . . . . CBS 32400
MC: 40 32400

GLASS HOUSES.
Tracks: / You may be right / Sometimes a fantasy / Don't ask me why / It's still rock and roll to me / All for Leyna / I don't want to be alone / Sleeping with the television on / C'etait toi / Close to the borderline / Through the long night.
LP: 4500871
MC: 4500874
LP: . . . . CBS 86108

GREATEST HITS: BILLY JOEL VOL.1 & 2.
Tracks: / Piano man / Say goodbye to Hollywood / New York state of mind / Stranger, The / Just the way you are / Movin' out (Anthony's song) / Only the good die young / She's always a woman / My life / Big shot / Honesty / You may be right / It's still rock and roll to me / Pressure / Allen town / Goodnight Saigon / Tell her about it / Uptown girl / Longest time, The / You're only human (Second wind) / Night is still young, The.
MC: 40 88666
LP: . . . . CBS 88666

INNOCENT MAN, AN.
Tracks: / Easy money / Innocent man, An / Longest time, The / This night / Tell her about it / Uptown girl / Careless talk / Christie Lee / Leave a tender moment alone / Keeping the faith.
LP: . . . . CBS 25554
MC: 40 25554
LP: 4663291
MC: 4663294

KOHUEPT.
Tracks: / Odoya / Angry young man / Honesty / Goodnight Saigon / Stiletto / Big man on Mulberry Street / Baby grand / Innocent man, An / Allentown / Matter of trust, A / Only the good die young / Sometimes a fantasy / Uptown girl / Big shot / Back in the USSR / Times they are a-changin'.
LP: 4604071
MC: 4604074
LP: 4674481
MC: 4674484

NYLON CURTAIN.
Tracks: / Allentown / Laura / Pressure / Goodnight Saigon / She's right on time / Room of our own / Surprises / Scandinavian skies / Where's the orchestra.
LP: 4601861
MC: 4601864
LP: . . . . CBS 85959

PIANO MAN.
Tracks: / Travellin' prayer / Ain't no crime / You're my home / Ballad of Billy The Kid / Worst comes to worst / Stop in Nevada / If I only had the words (to tell you) / Somewhere along the line / Captain Jack.
LP: 32002
MC: 40 32002

PIANO MAN/STREETLIGHT SERENADE.
MC: 4022143

SONGS IN THE ATTIC.
Tracks: / Miami 2017 (seen the lights go out on Broadway / Summer, highland falls / Streetlife serenade / Los Angelenos / She's got a way / Everybody loves you now / Say goodbye to Hollywood / Captain Jack / You're my home / Ballad of Billy The Kid / I've loved these days.
LP: . . . . CBS 32364
MC: 40 32364
LP: . . . . CBS 85273

STORM FRONT.
Tracks: / That's not her style / We didn't start the fire / Downeaster "Alexa", The / I go to extremes / Shameless / Storm front / Leningrad / State of grace / When in Rome / And so it goes.
LP: 4656581
MC: 4656584

STRANGER, THE.
Tracks: / Movin' out / Just the way you are / Scenes from an Italian restaurant / Vienna / Stranger, The / Only the good die young / She's always a woman / Get it right the first time / Everybody has a dream.
LP: 4509141
MC: 4509144
MC: 40 82311
LP: . . . . CBS 82311

STREETLIFE SERENADE.
Tracks: / Los Angelenos / Great suburban showdown / Root beer rag / Roberta / Entertainer, The / Last of the big time spenders / Streetlife serenade / Weekend song / Souvenir / Mexican connection.
LP: 32035
MC: 40 32035

TURNSTILES.
Tracks: / I've loved these days / Miami 2017 (seen the lights go out on Broadway) / Angry young man / Say goodbye to Hollywood / James / New York State of mind / Prelude / angry young man / Summer / Highland falls / All you wanna do is dance.
LP: . . . . CBS 32057
MC: 40 32057
LP: 902197 1
MC: 902197 4

Johal, H.S.

CHHAMAK JEHI MUTIAR (Johal, H.S. & Pali Cheema).
Tracks: / Chhamek jehi mutiar / Tut gayiaan choorian / Kardhi char gaye jawani / Maye ne maye / Chitti bag babey di noo / Lai gaye kadh kay kalja / Southall ch pawara paya goriay / Putt ney nishani jagg tey / Meri laggey bharjai / Sambh jawani noo.
LP: . . . . NPJ 1

Johansen, David

HERE COMES THE NIGHT.
Tracks: / She loves strangers / Bohemian love pad / You fool you / My obsession / Marquesa De Sade / Here comes the night / Havin' so much fun / Rollin' job / Heart of gold.
LP: . . . . SKY 84504

IN STYLE.
Tracks: / Melody / She / Big city / She knew she was falling in love / Swaheto woman / Justine / In style / You touched me too / Wreckless crazy / Flamingo road.
LP: . . . . SKY 83175

SWEET REVENGE.
LP: . . . . DIX 8

Johansen, Henrik

DANISH JAZZ VOL.4.
LP: . . . . SLP 413

Johansson, Ake

ENCORE (Johansson, Ake Trio).
LP: . . . . DRLP 159

LIVE AT NEFERTITI.
Tracks: / Synkopen 1 Umea / Lamesha / My shining hour / Tribute to Bud, A / Komner / New / Waiting / Igrottan / Igen.
LP: . . . . DRLP 42

Johansson, Lasse

KING PORTER STOMP.
Tracks: / Wild man blues / Mint julep / Buddy Bolden's blues / Freakish / Seattle hunch / Cannon ball blues / Kansas City stomp / Dead man blues / Mr. Jelly Lord / Sidewalk blues / Midnight momma / King Porter stomp / Chicago breakdown / Dixie knows / Jelly roll blues / Milenburg joys / Big foot ham blues / Sweet Peter / Grandpa's spells.
LP: . . . . SNKF 169

John, Elton

21 AT 33.
Tracks: / Changing the crown / Dear God / Give me the love / Little Jeannie / Never gonna fall in love again / Sartorial eloquence / Take me back / Two rooms at the end of the world / White lady white powder.
LP: . . . . PRICE 71
MC: . . . . PRIMC 71
LP: . . . . HISPD 126

17.11.70 / HERE AND THERE.
Tracks: / Honky tonk women / Sixty years on / Can I put you on / Bad side of the moon / Burn down the mission / My baby left me / Get back / Whatever gets you through the night / I saw her standing there / Honky cat / Lucy in the sky with diamonds / Rocket man / Benny and the jets / Border song / Take me to the pilot.
MCSET: . . . . TWO 419

ALBUM, THE.
Tracks: / Goodbye yellow brick road / Burn down the mission / Sixty years on / Crocodile rock / Lucy in the sky with diamonds / Rock and roll Madonna / Country comfort / Harmony / Sweet painted lady / Pinball wizard / Skyline pigeon / Lady Samantha.
LP: . . . . SHM 3088
MC: . . . . HSC 3088

BLUE MOVES.
Tracks: / Your starter tonight / One-horse town / Chameleon / Boogie pilgrim / Cage the songbird / Crazy water / Shoulder holster / Sorry seems to be the hardest word / Out of the blue / Between 17 and 20 / Wide-eyed and laughter / Someone's final love song / Where's the shoorah? / If there's a God in Heaven (what's he waiting for?) / Idol / Non-existent TV series, A theme from / Bite your lip (get up and dance).
2LP: . . . . PRID 2
MCSET: . . . . PRIDC 2
LP: . . . . ROSP 1

BREAKING HEARTS.
Tracks: / Restless / Slow down Georgie / Who wears these shoes / Breaking hearts / Li'l refrigerator / Passengers / In neon / Burning bridges / Did he shoot her / Sad songs.
LP: . . . . HISPD 25
MC: . . . . REWND 25

CAPTAIN FANTASTIC AND THE BROWN DIRT COWBOY.
LP: . . . . DJLPX 1

CAPTAIN FANTASTIC... / ELTON JOHN.
MCSET: . . . . TWO 413

CAPTAIN FANTASTIC & THE BROWN DIRT COWBOY.
Tracks: / Captain Fantastic and the Brown Dirt Cowboy / Tower of Babel / Bitter fingers / Tell me when the whistle blows / Someone saved my life tonight / Gotta get a meal ticket / Better off dead / Writing / We all fall in love sometimes / Curtains.
LP: . . . . PRICE 108
MC: . . . . PRIMC 108
LP: . . . . DJM 22094
MC: . . . . DJM 42094

CARIBOU.
Tracks: / Bitch is back, The / Pinky Grimsby / Dixie Lily / Solar prestige / Gammon, A / Don't let the sun go down on me / Ticking.
LP: . . . . PRICE 106
MC: . . . . PRIMC 106
LP: . . . . DJM 22092
MC: . . . . DJM 42092
LP: . . . . DJLPH 439

CROCODILE ROCK.
Tracks: / Honky cat / Crocodile rock / Border song / Rock and roll / Madonna / Skyline pigeon / Benny and the Jets / Candle in the wind / Son of your father / This song has no title / Empty sky / Take me to the pilot / Scaffold, The.
LP: 2872 245
MC: 3472 245
LP: 825 745-1
MC: 825 745-4

DON'T SHOOT ME I'M ONLY THE PIANO PLAYER.
Tracks: / Daniel / Teacher I need you / Elderberry wine / Blues for my baby and me / Midnight creeper / Have mercy on the criminal / I'm going to be a teenage idol / Texan love song / Crocodile rock / High flying bird.
LP: . . . . PRICE 105
MC: . . . . PRIMC 105
LP: . . . . DJM 22091
MC: . . . . DJM 42091
LP: . . . . DJLPH 427

DON'T SHOOT ME... / TUMBLEWEED CONNECTION.
MCSET: TWO 418

ELTON JOHN.
LP: DJLPS 406

ELTON JOHN (CAMBRA).
Tracks: / Your song / Elderberry wine / Friends / Grey seal / Mona Lisas and Mad Hatters / Take me to the pilot / Skyline pigeon / Daniel / Whenever you're ready / Harmony / I think I'm gonna kill myself / Greatest discovery / Blues for my baby and me / Lady Samantha / Rocket man / Teacher I need you / Tiny dancer / Cage, The / I'm gonna be a teenage idol / Border song / Crocodile rock / Ballad of Danny Bailey / High flying bird / Burn down the mission / Love song / Goodbye yellow brick road.
MCSET: CRT 003

ELTON JOHN COLLECTION, THE.
Tracks: / Funeral for a friend / Love lies bleeding / Sweet painted lady / Elderberry wine / Come down in time / Border song / Crocodile rock / Mona Lisas and mad hatters / Greatest discovery / Country comfort / Blues for my baby and me / Ballad of a well known gun.
LP: CN 2102
MC: CN4 2102

ELTON JOHN (DJM).
Tracks: / Your song / I need you to turn to / Take me to the pilot / No shoe strings on Louise / First episode at Heinton / 60 years on / Border song / Greatest discovery / Cage, The / King must die, The.
LP: PRICE 98
MC: PRIMC 98
LP: DJM 22087
MC: DJM 42087

ELTON JOHN: INTERVIEW PICTURE DISC.
LPPD: BAK 2005

ELTON JOHN LIVE New York, November 1970.
Tracks: / Take me to the pilot / Honky tonk women / Sixty years on / Can I put you on? / Bad side of the moon / Burn down the mission / My baby left me / Get back.
MC: HSC 314

ELTON JOHN LIVE ALBUM 17-11-70, THE.
LP: DJLPS 414

ELTON JOHN LIVE COLLECTION, THE.
Tracks: / Take me to the pilot / Honky tonk women / Sixty years on / Can I put you on? / Skyline pigeon / Border song / Honky cat / Love song / Crocodile rock / Bad side of the moon / Burn down the mission / Funeral for a friend / Love lies bleeding / Rocket man / Benny and the Jets.
2LP: PDA 047
MCSET: PDC 047

EMPTY SKY.
Tracks: / Empty sky / Valhalla / Western Ford gateway / Hymn 2000 / Lady what's tomorrow / Sails / Scaffold, The / Skyline pigeon / Gulliver / Hay chewed / Reprise.
LP: PRICE 97
MC: PRIMC 97
LP: DJM 22086
MC: DJM 42086

FLAMES OF PARADISE (See under Rush, Jennifer) (John, Elton & Jennifer Rush).

FOX, THE.
Tracks: / Breaking down barriers / Heart in the right place / Just like Belgium / Fox / Nobody wins / Fascist faces / Carla etude - fanfare / Chloe / Heels of the wind / Elton's song.
LP: PRICE 72
MC: PRIMC 72
LP: TRAIN 16

GOODBYE YELLOW BRICK ROAD.
Tracks: / Funeral for a friend / Love lies bleeding / Candle in the wind / Benny and the jets / Goodbye yellow brick road / This song has no title / Grey seal / Jamaica jerk off / I've seen that movie too / Sweet painted lady / Ballad of Danny Bailey / Dirty little girl / All the girls love Alice / Your sister can't twist (but she can rock'n'ro / Saturday night's alright for fighting / Roy Rogers / Social disease / Harmony.
2LP: PRID 13
MCSET: PRIDC 13
2LP: PLP 35
MCSET: PMC 35
2LP: DJE 29001
MC: DJE 49001
2LP: DJLPO 1001
2LP: 8217471
MCSET: 8217474

GREATEST HITS: ELTON JOHN.
Tracks: / Your song / Daniel / Honky cat / Goodbye yellow brick road / Saturday night's alright / Rocket man / Candle in the wind / Don't let the sun go down on me / Border song / Crocodile rock / Bitch is back, The / Lucy in the sky with diamonds / Sorry seems to be the hardest word / Don't go breaking my heart / Someone saved my life tonight / Philadelphia freedom / Island girl / Grow some funk of your own / Benny and the jets / Pinball wizard.
2LP: DJLP 1

GREATEST HITS: ELTON JOHN VOL.2.
Tracks: / Bitch is back, The / Lucy in the sky with diamonds / Sorry seems to be the hardest word / Don't go breaking my heart / Someone saved my life tonight / Philadelphia freedom / Island girl / Grow some funk of your own / Benny and the jets / Pinball wizard.
LP: DJH 20520
MC: DJH 40520

GREATEST HITS: ELTON JOHN, VOL. 1.
Tracks: / Your song / Honky cat / Goodbye yellow brick road / Saturday night's alright for fighting / Rocket man / Candle in the wind / Don't let the sun go down on me / Border song / Crocodile rock.
LP: 1A 062 64036
LP: DJH 20442
MC: DJH 40442

GREATEST HITS, VOL. 1.
MCSET: TWO 411

GREATEST HITS VOL. 2 / EMPTY SKY.
MCSET: TWO 412

HERE AND THERE.
LP: DJLPH 473

HONKY CHATEAU.
Tracks: / Honky cat / Mellow / I think I'm gonna kill myself / Susie (dramas) / Rocket man / Salvation / Slaves / Amy / Mona Lisa and mad hatters / Hercules.
LP: PRICE 101
MC: PRIMC 101
LP: DJM 22090
MC: DJM 42090
LP: DJLPH 423

ICE ON FIRE.
Tracks: / This town / Cry to heaven / Soul glove / Nikita / Too young / Wrap her up / Satellite / Tell me what the papers say / Candy by the pound / Shoot down the moon.
LP: HISPD 26
MC: REWND 26

JUMP UP.
Tracks: / Dear John / Spiteful child / Ball and chain / Legal boys / I am your robot / Blue eyes / Empty garden / Princess / Where have all the good times gone / All quiet on the Western Front.
LP: HISPD 27
MC: REWND 27

LADY SAMANTHA.
Tracks: / Rock and roll Madonna / Whenever you're ready / Bad side of the moon / Jack rabbit / Into the old man's shoes / It's me that you need / Ho, ho, ho, who'd be a turkey at Christmas? / Screw you / Skyline pigeon / Just like strange rain / Grey seal / Honey roll / Lady Samantha / Friends.
LP: PRICE 96
MC: PRIMC 96
LP: DJM 22085
MC: DJM 42085

LEATHER JACKETS.
Tracks: / Leather jackets / Hoop of fire / Don't trust that woman / Go it alone / Gypsy heart / Slow rivers / Heartache all over the world / Angeline / Memory of love / Paris I fall apart.
LP: EJLP 1
MC: EJMC 1

LIVE IN AUSTRALIA.
Tracks: / Sixty years on / I need you to turn to / Greatest discovery / Tonight / Sorry seems to be the hardest word / King must die, The / Take me to the pilot / Tiny dancer / Have mercy on the criminal / Madman across the water / Candle in the wind / Burn down the mission / Your song / Don't let the sun go down on me.
2LP: EJBXL 1
MCSET: EJBXC 1

LONDON AND NEW YORK.
Tracks: / Rocket man / Crocodile rock / Benny and the Jets / Funeral for a friend / Take me to the pilot / Skyline pigeon / Honky cat.
LP: SHM 942
MC: HSC 333

LOVE SONGS: ELTON JOHN.
Tracks: / Blue eyes / Little Jeannie / Sartorial eloquence / Chloe / Song for Guy / Shine on through / Elton's song / Tonight / Sorry seems to be the hardest word / All quiet on the Western Front / Princess / Chameleon / Return to paradise / Someone's final love song / Strangers / Never gonna fall in love again.
LP: 814 085 1
MC: 814 085 4

MADMAN ACROSS THE WATER.
Tracks: / Levon / Razor face / Madman across the water / Indian sunset / Holiday inn / Rotten peaches / All the nasties / Goodbye / Tiny dancer.
LP: PRICE 100
MC: PRIMC 100
LP: DJM 22089
MC: DJM 42089
LP: DJLPH 420

NEW COLLECTION, THE.
Tracks: / Crocodile rock / Don't let the sun go down on me / Saturday night's alright for fighting / It's me that you need / Someone saved my life tonight / Whatever gets you through the night / Lucy in the sky with diamonds / Bitch is back, The / High flying bird / Elderberry wine / Candle in the wind / Your sister can't twist (but she can rock 'n' roll) / Daniel.
LP: CBR 1027
MC: KCBR 1027

NEW COLLECTION, THE, VOL.2.
LP: CBR 1036
MC: KCBR 1036

REG STRIKES BACK.
Tracks: / Town of plenty / Word in Spanish, A / Mona Lisas and mad hatters part II / I don't wanna go on with you like that / Goodbye Marlon Brando / Heavy traffic / Poor cow / Camera never lies, The / Since God invented girls.
LP: EJLP 3
MC: EJMC 3

ROCK OF THE WESTIES.
Tracks: / Yell help / Wednesday night / Ugly / Dan Dare (pilot of the future) / Island girl / Grow some funk of your own / I feel like a bullet (in the gun of Robert Ford) / Street kids / Hard luck story / Feed me / Billy Bones and the white bird.
LP: PRICE 107
MC: PRIMC 107
LP: DJM 22093
MC: DJM 42093
LP: DJLPH 464

SEASONS: THE EARLY LOVE SONGS.
Tracks: / Amoreena / Amy / Writing / Curtains / Mellow / Empty sky / Susie / Sails / Goodbye / Come down in time / Sweet painted lady / Candle in the wind / Funeral for a friend / It's me that you need / We all fall in love sometimes.
2LP: CR 130
MCSET: CRT 130

SINGLE MAN, A.
Tracks: / Big dipper / Georgia / I don't care / It ain't gonna be easy / Madness / Part-time love / Return to Paradise / Reverie / Shine on through / Shooting star / Song for Guy.
LP: PRICE 24
MC: PRIMC 24
LP: TRAIN 1

SLEEPING WITH THE PAST.
Tracks: / Club at the end of the street / Durban deep / Sacrifice / Blue Avenue / Healing hands / Whispers.
LP: 838 839 1
MC: 838 839 4

THROUGH THE STORM (See under Franklin, Aretha) (John, Elton/Aretha Franklin).

TO BE CONTINUED.
MCSET: 8482364

TOO LOW FOR ZERO.
Tracks: / Cold as Christmas / I'm still standing / Too low for zero / Religion / I guess that's why they call it the blues / Crystal / Kiss the bride / Whipping boy / My baby's a saint / One more arrow.
LP: HISPD 24
MC: REWND 24

TUMBLEWEED CONNECTION.
Tracks: / Ballad of a well known gun / Come down in time / Country comfort / Son of your father / My father's gun / Where to now St.Peter / Love song / Amoreena / Talking old soldiers / Burn down the mission / I'm going to be a teenage idol (Extra track on CD).
LP: PRICE 99
MC: PRIMC 99
LP: DJM 22088
MC: DJM 42088
LP: DJLPS 410

VERY BEST OF ELTON JOHN, THE.
LP: ADAH 426
MC: ADAHC 426
LP: NE 1094

VERY BEST OF ELTON JOHN, THE (2).
Tracks: / Your song / Rocket man / Honky cat / Crocodile rock / Daniel / Goodbye yellow brick road / Saturday nights alright for fighting / Candle in the wind / Don't let the sun go down on me / Lucy in the sky with diamonds / Philadelphia freedom / Someone saved my life tonight / Pinball wizard (Additional track on CD and cassette.) / Bitch is back, The (Additional track on CD and cassette.) / Don't go breaking my heart / Benny and the jets / Sorry seems to be the hardest word / Song for guy / Part time love / Blue eyes / I guess that's why they call it the blues / I'm still standing / Kiss the bride / Sad songs / Passengers / Nikita / Sacrifice / You gotta love someone / I don't wanna go on with you like that (Additional tracks on CD and cassette.) / Easier to walk away (Additional track on CD and cassette.).
2LP: 846 947 1
MCSET: 846 947 4

VERY BEST OF: ELTON JOHN, VOL.2 (IMPORT).
LP: BRLP 71
MC: BRMC 71

VERY BEST OF: ELTON JOHN(IMPORT).
LP: BRLP 14
MC: BRMC 14

VICTIM OF LOVE.
Tracks: / Johnny B. Goode / Warm love in a cold world / Born bad / Thunder in the night / Spotlight / Street boogie / Victim of love.
LP: PRICE 70
MC: PRIMC 70
LP: HISPD 125

John F. Kennedy...

JOHN F. KENNEDY MEMORIAL PIPE BAND (John F. Kennedy Memorial Pipe Band).
MC: CT 105

John, Jilted

JILTED JOHN (see under Jilted John).

John & Mary

VICTORY GARDENS.
Tracks: / Red wooden beads / Azalea festival, The / Piles of dead leaves / We have nothing / Rags of flowers / I became alone / Open window, The / July 6th / Pram / Un Canadien errant.
MC: RACS 0203

John, Michael Singers

SERENADE IN SEQUENCE SING A LONG MEDLEY.
Tracks: / Snowbird / Sing little birdie / I love Paris / Boom / Shadow waltz / Another time, another love / Two sleepy people / Thanks for the memory / I'd like to teach the world to sing / Sing / Isn't it a lovely day / Touch of your lips, The / Lovers should never say goodbye / La ronde / Round and round / Anniversary waltz / I'll be seeing you / We'll meet again.
LP: DS 016

John, Monday

EGBE - KEGBE.
LP: MRLP 001

John Paul II

JOHN PAUL II (The visit of the Pope to Ireland).
MC: CIRL 1979

John, Paul... (show)

JOHN, PAUL, GEORGE, RINGO & BERT (London cast) (Various artists).
LP: 2394 141

John, Phillipa

CARIBBEAN ENCOUNTER.
MC: 85 1002

John, Robert

BACK ON THE STREET.
Tracks: / Since I felt this way / Hey there lonely girl / Just one more try / On my own / Give up your love / Sherry / Winner take all / Hurtin' doesn't go away / Back on the street again / You could have told me.
LP: AML 3014

ROBERT JOHN.
LP: AML 3003

John The Fish

COELACANTH.
LP: SFA 014

Johnnie & Jack

TENNESSEE MOUNTAIN BOYS.
Tracks: / When my blue moon turns to gold again / Slowly / Dream when you're lonely / I never can come back to you / I wonder where you are tonight / Sweet lies / You are my sunshine / Love fever / I wonder when you said goodbye / Wedding bells / I don't mean to cry.
LP: HAT 3087
MC: HATC 3087

Johnny &...

JOHNNY & THE DISTRACTIONS (Johnny & The Distractions).
LP: . . . . . **AMLH 64884**

Johnny Be Good

JOHNNY BE GOOD (Original Soundtrack) (Various artists).
Tracks: / Johnny B. Goode: *Judas Priest* / Caviar: *Goodwin, Myles* / No ring around Rosie: *Kix* / If there's any justice: *Fiona* / Been there, done that: *Astley, John* / Perfect stranger: *Saga* / Skintight: *Nugent, Ted* / Rock still rolls me: *Frozen Ghost & Friends* / No place like home: *Various artists* / It's not the way you rock: *Dirty Looks*.
LP: . . . . . **K 781 837 1**
MC: . . . . . **K 781 837 4**

Johnny C

SOUL'D OUT.
LP: . . . . . **SH 9101**

Johnny G

G BEAT.
Tracks: / Belt and the buckle / Suzy / Rubber lover / Valerie / Night after night / All aboard / Highway shoes / I man cool / Water margin / It must be magic / In my Cadillac / I'm a ding bee / Leave me alone.
LP: . . . . . **BEGA 16**

SHARP AND NATURAL.
Tracks: / Tightrope / Like Smokey I smile / All quiet on the Western Avenue / It was great while it lasted / You can't catch every train / Saddest note / Golden years / Educated monkey / Sparrow and the cuckoo / Meet me by the clocktower / Blues / Theme from Bwana / Chinese water torture / Calling card.
LP: . . . . . **BEGA 6**

Johnny Handsome (film)

JOHNNY HANDSOME (see under Cooder, Ry) (Cooder, Ry).

Johnny Hates Jazz

JOHNNY HATES JAZZ: INTERVIEW PICTURE DISC.
LPPD: . . . . . **BAK 2094**

TALL STORIES.
Tracks: / Tall stories.
LP: . . . . . **V 2615**
MC: . . . . . **TCV 2615**

TURN BACK THE CLOCK.
Tracks: / Shattered dreams / Heart of gold / Turn back the clock / Don't say it's love / What other reason / I don't want to be a hero / Listen / Different reasons / Don't let it end this way / Foolish heart / Turn back the clock (extended mix) (CD only) / Heart of gold (extended mix) (CD only) / Shattered dreams (12" extended mix) (CD only).
LP: . . . . . **V 2475**
MC: . . . . . **TCV 2475**
LP: . . . . . **OVED 331**
MC: . . . . . **OVEDC 331**

Johnny P

EVERYONE MAKE LOVE (See under Palmer, Michael) (Johnny P & Michael Palmer).

FIRST CUT (See under Ellis, Hortense for details).

FRONTLINE.
LP: . . . . . **VPRL 1057**
MC: . . . . . **VPRC 1057**

NIGHT PRETTY (See U, Thriller) (Johnny P & Thriller U).

RUDE BOY (See Under Demon Rocka - Ugly Gal).

YOUNG AND SHE GREEN.
LP: . . . . . **WRLP 21**

Johnny & The

BEST OF JOHNNY AND THE HURRICANES.
Tracks: / Red river rock / Happy time / Buckeye / Cut out / Lazy / Walkin / Cyclone / Reveille rock / Cross fire / Storm warning / Bam-Boo / Thunderbolt / Joy ride / Cornbread / Time bomb / Bean bag.
LP: . . . . . **XELLP 105**
MC: . . . . . **XELMC 105**

BIG SOUND OF JOHNNY AND THE HURRICANES (TELDEC).
Tracks: / Red river rock / Buckeye / Crossfire / Reveille rock / Sandstorm / Cyclone / Rockin' T / Beatnik fly / Tall blonde / Strange / Hep canary, The / Time bomb / Rockin' goose / Home baby / High voltage / Kaw-liga / Come on train / You are my sunshine / Priceless possession / Sheba / San Antonio / Down yonder / Revival / Molly O.
2LP: **6.28703**

BIG SOUND OF JOHNNY AND THE HURRICANES.
LP: **121302**
LP: . . . . . **HAK 2322**

COLLECTION: JOHNNY AND THE HURRICANES.
Tracks: / Red river rock / Down yonder / Hurricane / High voltage / Rene / Walkin' / Rockin' goose / Hot fudge / Ja da / Reveille rock / Honky tonk / Rock cha cha / Beatnik fly / Sheba / Crossfire / She's gone / Thunderbolt / Bean bag / Buckeye / Cut out / Old smokey / Rockin' t / You are my sunshine / Catnip.
2LP: . . . . . **CCSLP 182**
MC: . . . . . **CCSMC 182**

COUNTDOWN.
Tracks: / Red River rock / Down yonder / Rockin' goose / Reveille rock / Ja da / Crossfire / Bomb, The / Sheba / Beatnik fly / San Antonio rose / Sheik of Araby, The / Storm warning.
MC: . . . . . **ZC CNT 5**
LP: . . . . . **COUNT 5**

JOHNNY & THE HURRICANES.
Tracks: / Crossfire / Red river rock / Lazy / Buckeye / Walkin' / Reveille rock / Time bomb / Sandstorm / Beatnik fly / Down yonder / Sheba / Rockin' goose / Revival / You are my sunshine / Ja da / Traffic jam / Old smokey / High voltage.
LP: . . . . . **TAB 32**
LP: . . . . . **PHX 1027**

LET'S ROCK.
MC: **2636074**

RED RIVER ROCK.
LP: **6 26817**

STORMSVILLE.
LP: **6 26818**
LP: . . . . . **HAI 2269**

VERY BEST OF JOHNNY & THE HURRICANES.
Tracks: / Red river rock / Buckeye / Ja da / Sheba / Walkin' / Thunderbolt / Lazy happy time / Beatnik fly / Cornbread / Mr. Lonely / Time bomb / Bamboo / Revival / Cutout / Reveille rock / Sandstorm / Down yonder / Cross fire / High voltage / Greens and beans / Storm warning / Hep canary, The / Come on train / Joyride / Traffic jam / Hungry eyes / Cha / Molly O / Rockin' goose.
LP: . . . . . **CRMD 1002**

Johnny The Priest

JOHNNY THE PRIEST (Original London cast) (Various artists).
Tracks: / Doin' the burp: *Various artists* / Little box, The: *Various artists* / Vicarage tea: *Various artists* / Be not afraid: *Various artists* / I'm your girl: *Various artists* / Beyond these narrow streets: *Various* artists / Rooftops: *Various artists* / Foggy foggy blues, The: *Various artists* / He'll let you down: *Various* artists / Ping pong: *Various artists* / Johnny earn peanuts: *Various artists* / Tanner's worth of tunes, A: *Various artists* / Charge me: *Various artists* / Boy called Johnny, A: *Various artists* / Stormy evening: *Various artists* / Finale: *Various artists*.
LP: . . . . . **TER 1044**

Johnny & The Roccos

GOOD ROCKIN' TONIGHT.
Tracks: / Good rockin' tonight / Flyin' saucers rock 'n' roll / Honey hush / I'm a little mixed up / My baby left me / Holocaust boogie / Miss bobble sox / Apron strings / Maybellene / Grasshopper rock / Saturday night at the duck pond / Rough cut / Jeannie, Jeannie, Jeannie / Red hot.
LP: . . . . . **MFLP 044**

SCOTS ON THE ROCKS.
Tracks: / Crazy baby / Cat talk / Rockabilly / My baby's crazy about Elvis / Don't wake up the kids / Sneaky Pete / Stompin' with the wildcats / Blue blue day / Cherokee boogie / Rock 'n' roll record girl / Hey little girl / Beat, The / Feelings of love / Southern guitar boogie shuffle.
LP: . . . . . **MFLP 011**

STOMPIN'.
LP: . . . . . **SJLP 575**

TEARIN' UP THE BORDER.
Tracks: / Tarzan boogie / Heartbreakin' mama / I hate the disco / I was a teenage werewolf from outer space / It was foolish / Rocker's anthem, The / Go you rebel / Gotta make it / Drip dry / Chimichanga / Mescal drunk / We got the boogie.
LP: . . . . . **WIK 43**

Johns, Bibi

ABER NACHTS IN DER BAR.
Tracks: / Aber nachts in der bar / Es dreht sich die welt (Nicht nur um das geld) / Rocky Robby / Ricky Tick / Das....(fing mit dem mondenschein an) / Wenn musik spielt / Mein herz ruft nach dir / Jacky, komm wieder / Junggesellen musst du fallen stellen / Junge, junge, das war wunderschon / Jimmy, oh Jimmy / Das kann gefahrlich sein / Ein Himmel ohne sterne / Ein morgen, ein mittag, ein abendkuss / Schenk mir was schones / Ich mocht' so gern nochmal bei dir sein.
LP: . . . . . **BFX 15237**

Johns, Capt. W.E (aut)

BIGGLES (see under Biggles (bk)) (York, Michael (nar)).

Johns Children

LEGENDARY ORGASM ALBUM, THE.
Tracks: / Smashed blocked (Studio) / Just what you want -just what you'll get / Killer Ben / Jagged time lapse / Smashed blocked (Live) / You're a nothing / Not the sort of girl / Cold on me / Leave me alone / Let me know / Just what you want -just what you'll get (Live) / Why do you lie / Strange affair / But she's mine.
LP: . . . . . **BRED 31**

MIDSUMMERS NIGHT SCENE.
Tracks: / Smashed blocked / Just what you want -just what you'll get / Desdemona / Remember Thomas A'Beckett / It's been a long time / Arthur Green / Sara crazy child / Midsummer nights scene / Jagged time lapse / Go go girl / Come and play with me in the garden / But she's mine.
LP: . . . . . **KIRI 095**

Johns, Evan

BOMBS AWAY (Johns, Evan & The H-Bombs).
LP: . . . . . **DDLP 9117**

EVAN JOHNS & THE H-BOMBS (Johns, Evan & The H-Bombs).
Tracks: / Life sentence / Storms been blowin' by / Moonlight cryin' / Gonna get a new one / Moonshine runner / If I had my way / Love is murder / Hey whew / Day go by / Teeny bit of love / Bar-B-cutie / My baby, she left me / Hear the wheels go 'round.
LP: . . . . . **ZONG 016**

ROCKIT FUEL ONLY (Johns, Evan & The H-Bombs).
Tracks: / Back in the backseat / Little scene setter / Under the willows in Dixie / Rockit fuel only / Meant for you / Prove it to each other / Boogie disease / Who you are / In the groove / Dig that boogie / Sugary action / Burnin' over what I done / You always go / Juvenile delinquent.
LP: . . . . . **RCC 10168**
MC: . . . . . **RACS 0168**

ROLLIN' THRU THE NIGHT.
LP: . . . . . **VIRUS 47**

Johns, Glynis (nar)

STORY OF PETER PAN (See under Peter Pan).

Johnson, Anthony

A YA WE DEH (Johnson, Anthony & Tonto Rey).
LP: . . . . . **J 007**

GUNSHOT.
LP: . . . . . **MRLP 002**

ONCE MORE LOVING.
LP: . . . . . **DYCBLP 001**

REGGAE FEELINGS.
LP: . . . . . **STLP 1022**

ROBERT FRENCH MEETS ANTHONY JOHNSON (see French, Robert) (Johnson, Anthony & Robert French).

Johnson, Arnold

SWINGING THE CLASSICS (Johnson, Arnold & His Orchestra).
LP: . . . . . **CLP 32**

Johnson, Bessie

BESSIE JOHNSON, 1928-29.
LP: . . . . . **HER 202**

Johnson, Blind Willie

BLIND WILLIE JOHNSON (1927-30).
LP: . . . . . **BD 607**

PRAISE GOD I'M SATISFIED.
LP: . . . . . **L 1058**

Johnson, Bob

KING OF ELFLANDS DAUGHTER, THE (Johnson, Bob & Peter Knight).
Tracks: / Request, The / Lirazel / Witch / Alveric's journey / Through Elfland / Rune of the elf king, The / Cooing of the troll, The / Just another day of searching / Too much magic / Beyond the fields / We know.
LP: . . . . . **CHR 1137**
MC: . . . . . **ZCHR 1137**

Johnson, Brother

ROCKING THE GOSPEL.
Tracks: / I must tell Jesus / Don't wait 'til the battle is over / Lord lift us up where / We belong / Oh I want to see him / Magnift the lord / We are not ashame / I'm going to miss you / I love you with all my heart / Soul is reaching out.
MC: . . . . . **A 157**

Johnson, Buddy

BLUES A LA MODE (Johnson, Buddy, His Septet & Quintet).
Tracks: / Foggy nights / Leave room in your heart for me / Destination blues / A la mode / Used blues / Blues by five.
LP: . . . . . **AFF 169**

BUDDY JOHNSON WAILS.
Tracks: / Goodbye baby here I go / They all say I'm the biggest fool / I don't care who knows / Li'l dog / You get them blues / Since I fell for you / Baby don't you cry / Minglin' / Please Mr. Johnson / I wonder where our love has gone / I cry / Stop pretending.
LP: . . . . . **OFF 6010**

COME HOME.
Tracks: / Come home / Search, The / There'll be no one / I lost track of everything / Have a little faith in me / Too many hearts / Whisperers, The / My lonely heart / Crazy afternoon, A / Keep a light in the window for me / My one desire / Muddy water.
LP: . . . . . **SING 569**

GO AHEAD AND ROCK.
Tracks: / Go ahead and rock / Real fine frame / Down yonder / Get down on the road / Sliding horns / Don't fail me baby / Walk 'em / You better change your ways / Small taste / I'm tired of crying over you / Going to New York / My humble plea.
LP: . . . . . **OFF 6011**

I'LL DEARLY LOVE YOU (Johnson, Buddy Orchestra).
Tracks: / Down yonder / Li'l dog / Stars fell on Alabama / Let's beat out some love / I done found out / Be careful / I still love you / Someone so sweet as you / Am I blue / Pullamo / That's what my baby says / Stormy weather / I'll dearly love you / Tuke no.1 / You're the one for me / Ecstacy / Last laughs on me, The.
LP: . . . . . **JB 624**

IN MEMORY OF A VERY DEAR FRIEND (Johnson, Buddy Quartet).
LP: . . . . . **DRLP 94**

OLE DUDE AND FUNDANCE KID (Johnson, Buddy/ Phil Woods).
LP: . . . . . **UP 27.19**

ROCK 'N' ROLL.
Tracks: / I don't want nobody / Doot doot dow / Bring it home to me / You got it made / Pretty girl, A / Any day now / It's obdacious / Crazy / Upside your head / Ain't but one / A-12 / I'm just your fool.
LP: . . . . . **OFF 6007**

WALKIN' (Johnson, Buddy Orchestra).
Tracks: / Rockin' time / They don't want me to rock no more / There's no one like you / Rock on / Ain't cha got me / Buddy's boogie / Oh baby don't you know / You'd better believe me / You're everything my heart desires / So good / Bittersweet / Gone walkin'.
LP: . . . . . **OFF 6008**

Johnson, Bunk

1942 (Johnson, Bunk Jazz Band).
Tracks: / Big chief battle axe / Dusty rag / Franklin Street blues / Thriller rag / Sobbin' blues / Sobbin blues No 2 / When I leave the world behind / Sometimes my burden is so hard to bear / Blues bells goodbye / Yaaka hula hickey dula / Weary blues.
LP: **AG6 24547**

BUNK JOHNSON AND HIS SUPERIOR JAZZ BAND.
Tracks: / Panama / Down by the riverside / Storyville blues / Ballin' the jack / Make me a pallet on the floor / Yes Lord I'm crippled / Weary blues / Moose march / Bunk's blues / Bunk Johnson talking.
LP: **1012 048**

BUNK JOHNSON BRASS & DANCE BAND.
LP: . . . . . **SLP 670**

BUNK JOHNSON & HIS BAND (Johnson, Bunk & His Band).
LP: . . . . . **NOLA LP 3**

BUNK JOHNSON & HIS BAND 1947 (Johnson, Bunk & His Band).
MC: . . . . . **TC 003**

BUNK JOHNSON & LU WATTERS (Johnson, Bunk & Lu Watters).
Tracks: / Georgia camp meeting / Irish black bottom / Original Jelly Roll blues / Smokey mokes / Maple leaf rag / Memphis blues / Black and white rag / Muskrat ramble / Careless love / 2.19 blues / Girls go crazy, The / When I move to the sky / Ace in the hole / Ory's Creole trombone / Nobody's fault but mine / Down by the riverside.
LP: **1012 024**

BUNK JOHNSON'S JAZZ BAND (1942).
LP: . . . . . **DC 12112**

BUNK JOHNSONS'S NEW ORLEANS JAZZBAND (Johnson, Bunk & His New Orleans Jazz Band).
LP: . . . . SGC 12112

DOWN ON THE DELTA (Johnson, Bunk Band / Kid Renas Band etc...).
Tracks: / Tiger rag / Weary blues / Make me a pallet on the floor / Careless love / When the saints go marching in / Oh, didn't he ramble / Li'l Liza Jane / High society / Panama / Gettysburg march / Milenburg joys / Lowdown blues / Clarinet marmalade / Get it right.
LP: . . . . ESQ 331

NEW ORLEANS LEGENDS (Johnson, Bunk & Kid Ory).
LP: . . . . SM 3095

NEW ORLEANS VOL.5 (1945-46).
Tracks: / I wish I could shimmy like my Sister Kate / Just a closer walk with thee / Snag it / One sweet letter from you / When the saints go marching in / High society / Darktown strutters' ball / I can't escape from you / Franklin Street blues.
LP: . . . . PM 42048

NEW YORK 1945 (Johnson, Bunk & His New Orleans Jazz Band).
LP: . . . . FL 9047

PURIST ISSUES, THE.
LP: . . . . NOLA LP 6

SPICY ADVICE (Johnson, Bunk & His Band).
LP: . . . . GHB 101

Johnson, Celia (nar)

PRIDE AND PREJUDICE (See under Austen, Jane).

Johnson, Daniel

HI, HOW ARE YOU?.
LP: . . . . FU 4
LP: . . . . HMS 117
MC: . . . . HMS 117C

Johnson, David Earle

ROUTE TWO.
LP: . . . . LD 1003

TIME IS FREE (Johnson, David Earle & Jan Hammer).
LP: . . . . VSD 79401

Johnson, Dick

SWING SHIFT (Johnson, Dick & Friends).
LP: . . . . CJ 167

Johnson, Dink

DINK'S GOOD TIME MUSIC.
LP: . . . . NOLA LP 12

PROFESSORS - VOL.1 (Johnson, Dink & S.Brunson Campbell).
LP: . . . . ESR 1201

PROFESSORS - VOL.2 (Johnson, Dink & S.Brunson Campbell).
LP: . . . . ESR 1202

Johnson, Don

HEARTBEAT.
Tracks: / Heartbeat / Voice on a hotline / Last sound love makes, The / Lost in your eyes / Coco don't / Heartache away / Love roulette / Star tonight / Gotta get away / Can't take your memory.
LP: 4501031
MC: 4501034
LP: 4609481
MC: 4609484

LET IT ROLL.
Tracks: / Other peoples lives / Your love is safe with me / When you only loved me / Lonely too long / What if it takes all night / Tell it like it is / Better place, A / Angel city / Let it roll.
LP: 4608571
MC: 4608574

Johnson, Ella

SAY ELLA.
LP: . . . . JB 604

SWING ME (Johnson, Ella & Buddy Johnson).
Tracks: / What a day / That's what you gotta do / I still love you / We'll do it / Someday / If you'd say yes / Alright, okay you win / It's 'bout to break my heart in two / Thinking it over / It used to hurt me / If you would only say you're sorry / Goodbye baby.
LP: . . . . OFF 6009

Johnson Engineering

UNLEASH.
LP: . . . . CPRODLP 004

Johnson, Eric

AH VIA MUSICOM.
Tracks: / Ah via musicom / Cliffs of Dover / Desert rose / High landrons / Steve's boogie / Trademark / Nothing can keep me from you / Song for George / Righteous / Forty mile town / East West.
MC: . . . . TCEST 2128
MC: 790 517 4
LP: . . . . EST 2128

TONES.
Tracks: / Soulful terrain / Emerald eyes / Friends / Off my mind / Desert song, The / Trail of tears / Bristol shore / Zap / Victory.
LP: 925375 1
MC: 925375 4

Johnson, Frank

DIXIELAND JAZZ With his friends 1954-56.
Tracks: / Wocka the fish / Sweet patootie / Tea garden rag / When the saints go marching in / Steal away blues / Let's get together / Got no place to go / Silver bell's march / St.Louis blues / Dill pickles rag / Down South / Tiger rag / Tickle rag, The / Over in the glory land.
LP: . . . . S 1325

FRANK JOHNSON AND HIS FABULOUS DIXIELANDERS (1950).
MC: . . . . S 1412

FRANK JOHNSON AND HIS FABULOUS DIXIELANDERS (1951-55).
LP: . . . . S 1319

FRANK JOHNSON AND HIS FABULOUS DIXIELANDERS (1949-50).
LP: . . . . S 1414

Johnson, Graham

SONGMAKERS ALMANAC (see under Murray, Anne) (Johnson, Graham & Anne Murray).

Johnson, Henry

ST LOUIS STRING BAND RARITIES-1927 (Johnson, Henry & His Boys).
LP: . . . . LE 300.004

Johnson, Herman

LOUISIANA COUNTRY BLUES.
LP: . . . . ARHOOLIE 1060

Johnson, Holly

BLAST.
Tracks: / Atomic city / Americanos / Love train / Love will come / Feel good / Heaven's here / Deep in love / Got it made / Perfume / S.U.C.C.E.S.S..
LP: . . . . MCG 6042
MC: . . . . MCGC 6042

DREAMS THAT MONEY CAN'T BUY.
LP: . . . . MCA 10278
MC: . . . . MCAC 10278

HOLLELUJAH.
Tracks: / Love train (remix) / Perfume (remix) / Atomix city (remix) / Heaven's here (remix) / Hollelujah (remix).
LP: . . . . MCL 1902
MC: . . . . MCLC 1902

Johnson, Howard

DOIN' IT MY WAY.
Tracks: / My way / Jump into the fire / Let's take time out / Missing you / Much too much / You're the one I've needed / Let this dream be real / Everywhere I go.
LP: . . . . AMLX 64961
MC: . . . . CXM 64961

KEEPIN' LOVE NEW.
Tracks: / So fine / Take me through the night / This heaven / Jam song / Keepin' love new / So glad you're my lady / Say you wanna / Forever falling in love.
LP: . . . . AMLH 64895

Johnson, J J

AT THE OPERA HOUSE (See under Getz, Stan).

CONCEPTS IN BLUE.
Tracks: / Blue nun / Nermus / Village blues / Azure / Coming home / Concepts in blue / Mohawk.
LP: 2312 123
MC: . . . . K 12 123

DATE IN NEW YORK, A (VOL.1) (See Jackson, Milt) (Johnson, Jay Jay & Milt Jackson).

EMINENT J.J. JOHNSON, THE VOL. 1.
Tracks: / Capri (alt. take) / Capri / Lover man / Turnpike / Turnpike (alt. take) / Sketch 1 / Get happy / Get happy (alt. take) / Jay / Old devil moon / It's you or no one / Too marvellous for words / Coffee pot / It could happen to you.
LP: B1 81505

EMINENT J.J. JOHNSON, THE VOL. 2.
Tracks: / Time after time / Pennies from Heaven / Viscosity / You're mine, you / "Daylie" double / Groovin' / Portrait of Jennie / Turnpike (alt. take) (LP only.) / It could happen to you (LP only.) / Capri (Alt. take) (LP only.) / Old devil moon (CD only.) / Jay (CD only.) / Too marvellous for words (CD only.) / It's you or no one (CD only.) / Coffee pot (CD only.) / Pennies from Heaven (Alt. take) (CD only.) / Viscosity (alt. take) (CD only.) / "Daylie" double (Alt. take) (CD only.).
LP: B1 81506

GREAT KAI AND J.J. (Johnson, J.J. & Kai Winding).
Tracks: / This could be the start of something big / Georgia on my mind / Blue Monk / Judy / Alone together / Side by side / I concentrate on you / Picnic, Theme from / Trixie / Going, going, gone / Just for a thrill.
LP: . . . . JAS 7
MC: . . . . JAS C7
LP: . . . . AS 1
MC: . . . . ASC 1

J.J..
Tracks: / Swing spring / Bemsha swing / El camino real / Stolen moments / Train samba / So what? / Stratusphunk / My little suede shoes / Winter's waif.
LP: . . . . PL 43530

LIVE: J.J.JOHNSON.
Tracks: / Decision / Overdrive / Jay's original / It's alright with me / Undecided / Overdrive / Angel eyes / Bag's groove.
LP: . . . . QU 046

MAD BE-BOP.
LP: . . . . SJL 2232

OVERDRIVE (Johnson, Jay Jay, Quintet).
Tracks: / Naptown USA / It might as well be spring / Tumbling tumbleweeds / Angel eyes / I should care / Solar / Overdrive / Undecided / Never let me go / Chasin' the bird cube steak.
LP: . . . . AFF 177

PINNACLES.
Tracks: / Night flight / Deak / Cannonball junction / Pinnacles / See see rider / McClean.
LP: . . . . M 9093

THINGS ARE GETTING BETTER ALL THE TIME (Johnson, J.J. & Al Grey).
Tracks: / Soft winds / Let me see / Softly as in a morning sunrise / It's only a paper moon / Boy meets horn / Things ain't what they used to be / Things are getting better all the time / Doncha hear me callin' to ya.
LP: 2312 141
MC: . . . . K 12 141

TOTAL J.J. JOHNSON, THE.
LP: . . . . NL 89367

TROMBOMANIA (see under Winding, Kai) (Johnson, Jay Jay/Frank Rosolino/ Winding Kai).

TROMBONE BY THREE (Johnson, J J, Kai Winding, Bennie Green).
Tracks: / Fox hunt / Elysee / Opus V / Hilo / Night on bop mountain, A / Broadway / Sid's bounce / Waterworks / Green junction / Flowing river / Whirl-a-licks / Pennies from Heaven.
LP: . . . . OJC 091

TROMBONE MASTER, THE.
LP: 4633401
MC: 4633404

WE'LL BE TOGETHER AGAIN (Johnson, J J & Joe Pass).
Tracks: / Wave / We'll be together again / Naked as a jaybird / Blue bossa / Limehouse blues / How long has this been going on? / Bud's blues / Nature boy / Solar / When lights are low.
LP: 231 0911
MC: K10 911

YOKOHAMA CONCERT, THE (Johnson, J.J. & Nat Adderley).
Tracks: / Horace / Cyclops / Why not? / It happens / Work song / Walkin' / Jiving / Lament / Humming / Melodee.
2LP: 262 0109
MCSET: . . . . K 20 109

Johnson, James P.

AIN'TCHA GOT MUSIC.
LP: . . . . PUMPKIN 117

CLASSIC PIANOS (See under Garner, Erroll) (Various artists).

FATHER OF THE STRIDE PIANO.
LP: . . . . SOUNDS 1204

FEELIN' BLUE.
Tracks: / All that I had is gone / Snowy morning blues / Chicago blues / Mournful tho'ts / Riffs / Feeling blue / Put your mind right on it / Fare thee honey blues / You don't understand / You've got to be modernistic / Crying for the Carolines / What is this thing called love / Jingles / Go Harlem / Just a crazy song.
LP: . . . . HDL 107
MC: . . . . CHDL 107

FROM RAGTIME TO JAZZ (Piano solos).
LP: . . . . CBS 85387

HARLEM STRIDE PIANO SOLOS.
LP: S1211

IT TAKES LOVE.
LP: . . . . KLJ 20008

JAMES P. JOHNSON 1928-31.
LP: . . . . S 849

JAMES P. JOHNSON & PERRY BRADFORD (Johnson, James P & Perry Bradford).
LP: . . . . ARCADIA 2009

WATCH ME GO.
LP: . . . . IAJRC 52

Johnson, James 'Stump'

DUCK'S YAS YAS YAS, THE.
LP: . . . . AB 2007

Johnson, Jeff

NO SHADOW OF TURNING.
LP: . . . . MLR 7005
MC: . . . . MLC 7005

Johnson, Jesse

EVERY SHADE OF LOVE.
LP: . . . . UNKNOWN

JESSE JOHNSON'S REVUE.
Tracks: / Be your man / I want my girl / She won't let go / Just too much / Let's have some fun / Can you help me? / Special love / She's a doll.
MC: . . . . AMC 5024
LP: . . . . AMA 5024

SHADES OF LOVE.
Tracks: / Lovestruck / So misunderstood / I'm the one / Color shock / Every shade of love / Everybody wants somebody to love / I'm just wanting you / Stop look listen.
LP: . . . . AMA 5188
MC: . . . . AMC 5188

SHOCKADELICA.
Tracks: / Change your mind / She / Addiction / Baby let's kiss / Better way / Tonight / Crazay / Do yourself a favour / Burn you up / Black in America.
LP: . . . . AMA 5122
MC: . . . . AMC 5122

Johnson, Jimmy

HEAP SEE.
LP: 33720

I DIDN'T GIVE A DAMN IF WHITES BOUGHT IT, VOL.2.
Tracks: / Pepper's hangout / Looking for my baby / Pretty baby / High heel sneakers / When my first wife quit me.
LP: . . . . RL 051

JOHNSON'S WHACKS.
LP: . . . . DL 644

NORTH/SOUTH (Johnson, Jimmy Band).
LP: . . . . DL 647

Johnson, Johnny

JOHNNIE B.BAD.
MC: 7559611494

Johnson, Kenny

BEST OF KENNY JOHNSON.
LP: . . . . OBMLP 1003

LET ME HAVE YOU ONCE.
LP: . . . . OBMLP 1001

Johnson, Kevin

TREE IN THE MEADOW.
Tracks: / Tree in the meadow / Cheatin' kind of woman / Livin' in the nest / Lovin' arms / Rock steady / One kiss / Oklahoma rain / New York / Losing your love / Total strangers.
LP: . . . . OBMLP 1002

Johnson, Larry

WHERE DID YOU GET THAT SOUND? (Johnson, Larry & Nat Riddles).
LP: . . . . LR 42.046

Johnson, Laurie

FILM MUSIC OF LAURIE JOHNSON.
Tracks: / First men in the moon / Hedda / Captain Kronos / Dr. Strangelove.
LP: . . . . DKP 9001

MUSIC FROM THE AVENGERS AND THE NEW AVENGERS (With the London Studio Orchestra).
Tracks: / Avengers, The / Joker / Pandora / New avengers,The / Obsession / Cat amongst the pigeons / Tale of the big why / Professionals,The / Sleuthing / On the scent / In pursuit / Interlude / Waiting and ambush / On target.
LP: . . . . KPM 9

Johnson, Lil

HOTTEST GIRL IN TOWN 1936-1937.
LP: . . . . DLP 516

LIL JOHNSON (1935-1937).
LP: . . . . BD 2083

Johnson, Linton Kwesi

BASS CULTURE.
Tracks: / Bass culture / Street 66 / Reggae fi peach / De black petty booshwah / Inglan is a bitch / Lorraine / Reggae sounds / Two sides of silence.
LP: . . . . ILPS 9605
MC: . . . . ICT 9605
MC: . . . . RRCT 26

DREAD BEAT AND BLOOD.

Tracks: / Dread beat and blood / Five nights of bleeding / Doun de road / Song of blood / It dread inna Inglun (for George Lindo) / Come wi goh dung deh / Man free (for Darcus Howe) / All wi doin' is defendin'.
LP: . . . . VX 1002
MC: . . . . TCVX 1002
MC: . . . . FLC 9009

FORCES OF VICTORY.
Tracks: / Want fi goh rave / It noh funny / Sonny's lettah (anti-sus poem) / Independent inavenshan / Fite dem back / Reality poem / Forces of vicktry / Time come.
LP: . . . . ILPM 9566
MC: . . . . ICM 9566
LP: . . . . ILPS 9566
MC: . . . . RRCT 32

IN CONCERT: LINTON KWESI JOHNSON.
LP: . . . . SHAN 43034
MC: . . . . SHANC 43034

LINTON KWESI JOHNSON LIVE.
LP: . . . . ROUGH 78

LKJ IN DUB.
Tracks: / Victorious dub / Reality dub / Peach dub / Shocking dub / Iron bar dub / Bitch dub / Cultural dub / Brain smashing dub.
LP: . . . . ILPS 9650
MC: . . . . RRCT 34

MAKING HISTORY.
Tracks: / Di eagle an' di bear / Wat about di workin' class? / Di great insohreckshan / Making history / Reggae fi radni / Reggae fi dada / New craas massahkah.
LP: . . . . ILPS 9770

REGGAE GREATS.
Tracks: / Reggae sounds / Independent intavenshan / Street 66 / Bass culture / Di great insorreckshan / It noh funny / Sonny's letter / Reggae fi radni / Fit dem back / Making history.
LP: . . . . IRG 6
MC: . . . . IRGC 6
MC: . . . . ICM 2033
MC: 842 693 4

TINGS AND TIMES.
LP: . . . . STLP 2002
MC: . . . . STC 2002

Johnson, Lonnie

1927-32 HISTORICAL RECORDINGS VOL 2.
LP: . . . . MSE 1013

BLUES BY.
Tracks: / Don't ever love / No love for sale / There's no love / I don't hurt anymore / She devil / One-sided love affair / Big legged woman / There must be a way / She's drunk again / Blues 'round my door / You don't move me / You will need me.
LP: . . . . OBC 502

BLUES FOR EVERYBODY (Johnson, Lonnie & Blind Joe Davis).
LP: . . . . OL 2819

BLUES OF LONNIE JOHNSON, THE 1937-8.
LP: . . . . S 1225

IT FEELS SO GOOD.
LP: . . . . QU 043

LONNIE JOHNSON (Johnson, Lonnie/ Victoria Spivey).
LP: . . . . OBC 518

LONNIE JOHNSON:1926-42.
LP: . . . . DLP 546

LONNIE JOHNSON: 1926-40.
LP: . . . . BD 2064

LONNIE JOHNSON VOL 1 (1926-28).
Tracks: / When I was lovin' / Changed my mind blues / Sun to sun blues / Bed of sand / Lonesome jail blues / No good blues / Newport blues / Love story blues / Woman changed my life / Lonnie's got the blues / You drove a good man away / Ball and chain blues / To do this you got to know / Superstitious blues / Cotton patch blues / Black bird blues / Unkind mama / Backwater blues / Crowing rooster blues.
LP: . . . . MSE 1006

ORIGINATOR OF MODERN GUITAR BLUES.
Tracks: / In love again / Ramblers blues / Keep what you got / Little rockin' chair / Nothin' clickin' chicken / My mother's eyes / I can't sleep any more.
LP: . . . . BB 300

STEPPIN' ON THE BLUES.
MC: 4672524

TOMORROW NIGHT.
MCSET: . . . . GD 5039
LP: . . . . BID 8019

Johnson, Lorraine

FEED THE FLAME.
Tracks: / I'm learning to dance all over again / Nobody's wrong / More I get, the more I want / Feed the flame / Who do you think you're fooling / Save me your love.
LP: . . . . EPC 83591

Johnson, Louis

PASSAGE.
Tracks: / Have you heard the word / You can't be livin' / Faith walking people / I see the light / Great flood, The / Open up your heart / Power / Love eyes / Sun will come again, The.
LP: . . . . AMLH 64851

Johnson, Luther

DOIN' THE SUGAR TOO (Johnson, Luther "Guitar Junior").
LP: . . . . R 7607

I WANT TO GROOVE WITH YOU (Johnson, Luther & Magic Rockers).
Tracks: / Red beans / Can't get along with you / I'm from Mississippi / Luther's boogie / I want to groove with you / Merry Christmas baby / Graveyard dogs / Who's that come walkin' / Young boy blues / Texas cowboy / Call me Guitar Junior / I'm leaving Chicago.
LP: . . . . BB 9506

TAKIN' A BITE OUTTA THE BLUES.
Tracks: / Little car blues / Trouble blues / Pretty thing / Cryin' and thinkin' / Rock me baby / Where can my baby be? / Big money / Hi-heel sneakers / I'm goin' upside your head / What I'd say / Hush hush.
LP: . . . . ICH 1060
MC: . . . . ICH 1060MC

Johnson, L.V.

I GOT THE TOUCH.
Tracks: / I got the touch / Take a little time to know her / Are you serious / I don't want to lose your love / What do you mean love ain't got nothing to do / I am missing you / I just can't get over you / Stroking kind (choking kind).
LP: . . . . ICH 1112
MC: . . . . ICH 1112MC

IT'S SO COLD AND MEAN.
Tracks: / Get him out of your system / It's so cold and mean (the drug scene) / One in a million you / Blues in the North / It's not my time / Make you mine / Steal away / How can I live without you.
LP: . . . . ICH 1050
MC: . . . . ZCICH 1050

Johnson, Marc

BASS DESIRES.
Tracks: / Samurai hee-haw / Resolution / Black is the colour of my true loves hair / Bass desires / Wishing doll, The / Mojo highway / Thanks again.
LP: . . . . ECM 1299

SECOND SIGHT (Johnson, Marc Bass Desires).
Tracks: / Crossing the corpus callosum / Small hands / Sweet soul / Twister / Thrill seekers / Prayer beads / 1951 / Hymn for her.
LP: . . . . ECM 1351

Johnson, Marcia

MOONLIGHT.
LP: . . . . CHILLP 4
MC: . . . . ZCCHIL 4

Johnson, Marv

EARLY CLASSICS.
Tracks: / You got what it takes / I love the way you love / Come to me.
LP: . . . . LBR 1008

Johnson, Matt

BURNING BLUE SOUL.
MC: . . . . CAD 113

Johnson, Merline

YAS YAS GIRL, THE.
LP: . . . . DLP 562

YAS YAS GIRL, THE.
LP: . . . . BOB 8
LP: . . . . WBJCD 006
LP: . . . . DLP 562

Johnson, Michael

ALBUM.
Tracks: / Sailing without a sail / Foolish / Dancin' tonight / Two in love / Ridin' in the sky / Bluer than blue / Almost like being in love / 25 words or less / Gypsy woman / When you come home.
LP: . . . . AMS 2002

DIALOGUE.
LP: . . . . AML 3006

LIFE'S A BITCH.
Tracks: / Roller coaster run / True love / Oh Rosalee / Give me wings / Jacques Cousteau / Empty heart / That's what your love does to me / Hangin' on / Life's a bitch / Crying shame / Magic time / That's that / Samson and Delilah / Moon is still over her shoulder / Gotta learn to love without you / Some people's lives.
LP: . . . . PL 90312
MC: . . . . PK 90312

THAT'S THAT.
Tracks: / Rollercoaster run (up too slow, down too fast) / I will whisper your name / Crying shame / It must be you (Duet with Juice Newton.) / That's that / Oh Rosalee / Too soon to tell / Diamond dreams / Some people's lives.
LP: . . . . PL 86715
MC: . . . . PK 86715

Johnson Mountain Boys

AT THE OLD SCHOOLHOUSE (Live Farewell Album).
Tracks: / Intro / Black mountain blues / Let the whole world talk / Long journey home / Bluest man in town / John Henry / Steel driving man, The / Weathered gray stone / Unwanted love / Ricestrow / Waltz across Texas / Five speed / Dream of a miner's child / Georgia stomp / Sweetest gift / I've found a hiding place / With body and soul / Orange blossom special / Get down on your knees and pray / Going to Georgia / Now just suppose / Don't you call my name / Do you call that religion / Daniel prayed / Wake up Susan.
LP: . . . . ROUNDER 00260
MC: . . . . ROUNDER 00260C

JOHNSON MOUNTAIN BOYS.
LP: . . . . ROUNDER 0135
MC: . . . . ROUNDER 0135C

LET THE WHOLE WORLD TALK.
Tracks: / Let the whole world talk / Maury river blues / Memories cover everything I own / He said if I be lifted up / Goodbye to the blues / Virginia waltz / Maybe you will change your mind / Memories that we shared / Sweeter love than yours, A / I'll never know / Shouting in the air / Beneath the old Southern skies.
LP: . . . . REU 1017
LP: . . . . ROUNDER 0225
MC: . . . . ROUNDER 0225C

LIVE AT THE BIRCHMERE.
LP: . . . . ROUNDER 0191
MC: . . . . ROUNDER 0191C

REQUESTS.
LP: . . . . ROUNDER 0246
MC: . . . . ROUNDER 0246C

WALLS OF TIME.
LP: . . . . ROUNDER 0160
MC: . . . . ROUNDER 0160C

WE'LL STILL SING ON.
LP: . . . . ROUNDER 0205
MC: . . . . ROUNDER 0205C

WORKING CLOSE.
Tracks: / Tomorrow I'll be gone / Misery loves company / I'm still to blame / You loved died like the rose / Call his name / Five speed / Waves on the sea, The / Don't throw your life away / Say you'll take me back / Day has passed, The / Granite hill / Are you afraid to die.
LP: . . . . ROUNDER 0185
MC: . . . . ROUNDER 0185C

Johnson, Ossie

BIT OF THE BLUES.
LP: . . . . FS 116

Johnson, Paul

PAUL JOHNSON.
Tracks: / When love comes calling / Fear of falling / New love / Every kinda people / Intimate friends / Burnin' / Heaven is 10 zillion light years away / Are we strong enough / Half a world away.
LP: 4506401
MC: 4506404

PAUL JOHNSON / PERSONAL.
Tracks: / When love comes calling / Fear of falling / New love / Every kinda people / Intimate friends / Burnin' / Heaven is 10 zillion light years away / Are we strong enough / Half a world away / Best think it over / No more tomorrows / Masquerade / In a circle / Who shot Cupid / Sweet Marinda / Not enough love in the world / You're no good / Father, Father / Me oh my.
2LP: 4661481
MCSET: 4661484

PERSONAL.
Tracks: / Best think it over / No more tomorrows / Masquerade / In a circle / Who shot cupid / Sweet Marinda / Not enough love in the world / You're no good / Father? Father / Me oh my.
LP: 4632841
MC: 4632844

Johnson, Pete

ALL STAR SWING GROUPS (See under Cole, Cozy) (Johnson, Pete & Cozy Cole).

BLOWIN' THE FAMILY JEWELS.
LP: 4704

GIANTS OF BOOGIE WOOGIE (see Ammons,Albert) (Johnson, Pete/Albert Ammons).

KING OF BOOGIE BOOGIE.
LP: . . . . LPJT 17

PETE JOHNSON 1938-47.
LP: . . . . DLP 535

PETE JOHNSON VOL.1 (Master of the blues and boogie woogie).
LP: . . . . OL 2801

PETE JOHNSON VOL 2 (Master of the blues and boogie woogie).
LP: . . . . OL 2806

PETE JOHNSON VOL 3 (Master of blues and boogie woogie).
LP: . . . . OL 2823

Johnson, Philip

YOUTH IN MOURNING.
LP: . . . . NR 3

Johnson, Plas

ROCKIN' WITH THE PLAS.
LP: 2C 068 86529

Johnson, Robb

BIG TOWN WORLD.
LP: . . . . IR 009

IN AMONGST THE RAIN.
LP: . . . . IRR 001

SKEWED, SLEWED, STEWED & AWKWARD.
LP: . . . . IRR 5

Johnson, Robert

COMPLETE RECORDINGS, THE.
MC: 4672464

DELTA BLUES - ALTERNATIVE TAKES.
LP: . . . . ALB 1003

DELTA BLUES, VOLUME 1.
LP: . . . . ALB 1001
MC: . . . . ALB 1001 MC

DELTA BLUES, VOLUME 2.
LP: . . . . ALB 1002
MC: . . . . ALB 1002 MC

KING OF THE DELTA BLUES.
Tracks: / Crossroads blues / Terraplane blues / Come to my kitchen / Walkin' blues / Last fair deal gone down / 32-20 Blues / Kind hearted woman blues / If I had possession over judgement day / Preaching blues / When you got a good friend / Rambling on my mind / Stones in my passway / Travelling riverside blues / Milkcow's calf blues / Me and the devil blues / Hellhound on my trail / Kind hearted woman blues / I believe I'll dust my broom / Sweet home chicago / Rambling on my mind / Phonograph blues / They're red hot / Dead shrimp blues / Preachin' blues / I'm a steady rollin' man from four till late / Little queen of spades / Malted milk / Drunken hearted man / Stop breakin' doen blues / Honeymoon blues / Love in vain.
LP: . . . . CBS 22190
MC: 40 22190

MEMPHIS DEMOS.
Tracks: / I'll be waiting / Claudette / Burning love / Wish upon a star / Jimmy Dean's back / Shaking it down / Better love / Deep love.
LP: . . . . ENRJ 12

ROOTS OF ROBERT JOHNSON.
LP: . . . . L 1073

Johnson, Scott

JOHN SOMEBODY.
Tracks: / Part 1 / Part 2 / Involuntary songs (part 3) / Involuntary songs (conclusion) / Reprise / No memory.
LP: . . . . K 979133 1
MC: . . . . K 979133 4

Johnson, Spencer (nar)

TALKING WITH THE ONE MINUTE MANAGER (see under Talking with the..(bk)) (Johnson, Spencer & Kenneth Blanchard).

Johnson, Syl

BRINGS OUT THE BLUES IN ME.
Tracks: / Brings out the blues in me / How you need to be loved / Last night was the night / Got my eyes on you / Liberated lady / Sock it to me / Is it because I'm black / Crazy people.
LP: . . . . FLY 569

IS IT BECAUSE I'M BLACK.
Tracks: / Come on sock it to me / Dresses too short / I can take care of business / I'll take those skinny legs / I resign / Get ready / I feel an urge / I take care of homework / Is it because I'm black / Concrete reservation / Walk a mile in my shoes / I'm talkin' 'bout freedom / Right on.
LP: . . . . CRB 1125

LOVE CHIMES, THE.
Tracks: / Back for a taste of your love / We did it / I'm yours / Don't do it / I hear

the love chimes / Anyway the wind blows / Love you left behind / I want to take you home (to see Mama) / Feeling frisky / Let yourself go / I let a good girl go / Wind, blow her back my way / You don't know me / I hate I walked away / Please don't give up on me.
LP: . . . . HIUKLP 404

MS. FINE BROWN FAME.
Tracks: / Ms. Fine Brown fame / Keep on loving me / They can't see your good side / Grooves me / Sweet thing / You don't have to go / It ain't easy.
LP: . . . . EPC 25300

STUCK IN CHICAGO.
Tracks: / Watch what you do to me / Diamond in the rough / I only have love / Bustin' up or bustin' out / Stuck in Chicago / Keeping down confusion / 'Bout to make me leave home / Take me to the river / Music to my ears / Steppin' out / Could I be falling in love / It ain't easy / That's just my luck / Star bright, star lite.
LP: . . . . HIUKLP 424

Johnson, Teddy

NO TEA PARTY (see Dawson, Dan) (Johnson, Teddy & Dan Dawson).

Johnson, Tex

COLLECTION FOR LOVERS ONLY, THE.
LP: . . . . DT LP 1

PURE BLISS.
Tracks: / Young and in love (remix) / Welcome back / Butterflies / Keep her sweet / Groove me / For the sake of love / Ask for a dance / Classically magic.
LP: . . . . DT LP 2

Johnson, Thomas

HOUSE PARTY.
Tracks: / House party / It's alright / Missing love that I never had / Ain't the river that drowns / Good thangs come to them that wait / I ain't gonna hanky panky / Snake pinto beans (instrumental).
LP: . . . . ICH 1031
MC: . . . . ZCICH 1031

Johnson, Tommy

COMPLETE RECORDINGS 1928-30.
LP: . . . . WSE 104

SLEEPY JOHN ESTES 1928-30.
LP: . . . . BT 2010

Johnson, Tony

PEACE (See under B Three) (Johnson, Tony & B Three).

Johnson, Troy

GETTING A GRIP ON LOVE.
Tracks: / You make me lose my head / If you've got the heart / Mesmerized / Just get a grip / It's my groove / It's you / Wonders of your love / Time will tell / Honest lover.
LP: . . . . ZL 72416
MC: . . . . ZK 72416

Johnson, Vernard

I'M ALIVE.
MC: 7559611504

Johnson, Wayne

GRASSHOPPER (Johnson, Wayne Trio).
Tracks: / Grasshopper / Ghree man junta / Ramble scamplin / Marina / Ojai / Pilgrimage of a thousand days.
LP: . . . . ALE 5604
MC: . . . . ZCALE 5604

Johnson, Wilko

BARBED WIRE BLUES.
LP: . . . . FREUD 26

ICE ON THE MOTORWAY.
LP: . . . . FRESH LP 4

IT'S ALL OVER NOW (See also Steve Hooker) (Johnson, Wilko & Steve Hooker).

SOLID SENDERS (Johnson, Wilko & his Solid Senders).
Tracks: / Blazing fountains / Doctor Dupree / Too bad / First thing in the morning / Everybody's carrying a gun / Signboard / Keep both eyes on the road / Shop around / Burning down / I've seen the signs.
LP: . . . . OVED 36
LP: . . . . V 2105

WATCH OUT.
LP: . . . . WF 024
MC: . . . . WF 024C

Johnson, Willie Neal

JUST REHEARSAL.
LP: . . . . MAL 04403

Johnston, Allan

NORTH OF THE BORDER (Johnston, Allan & Friends).
Tracks: / North of the border / Shore 'neath the tide / Jenny's return / Homeland / Think ahead / No longer needed / Steer the wealth down here / Rachel's wedding / Wee Fergus / Sound of Mull, The / Shower of snow, The / Scrape it off the floor / Harry's heel.
LP: . . . . ODR 001
MC: . . . . ODR 001C

Johnston, Annie

SONGS OF THE HEBRIDES.
MC: 60-191

SOUTH UNIST & ERISKAT, VOL.3.
MC: 60-193

Johnston, Brian

IT'S BEEN A LOT OF FUN.
MCSET: . . . . ZBBC 1179

VIEW FROM THE BOUNDARY.
MCSET: . . . . ZBBC 1162

Johnston, Calum

SONGS, STORIES AND PIPING FROM BARRA (Johnston, Calum & Annie).
MC: . . . . TGMMC 504

Johnston, Johnnie

JOHNNIE JOHNSTON & OSIMAN BRACEY (Johnston, Johnnie & Osiman Bracey).
LP: . . . . RL 330

LITTLE OLE WINE DRINKER ME.
Tracks: / Little ole wine drinker me / Among my souvenirs / Streets of London / Boy of mine / Dublin in the rare oul times / Please help me, I'm falling / Jealous heart / Bunch of thyme / Any dream will do / Carolina Moon / Sweet Sixteen / Story of a starry night.
LP: . . . . PHL 463
MC: . . . . CPHL 463

Johnston, Luther

DOIN' THE SUGAR TOO (Johnston, Luther JR).
LP: 33723

Johnston, Sophie

SOPHIE & PETER JOHNSTON (Johnston, Sophie & Peter).
LP: . . . . WX 127
MC: . . . . WX 127C

Johnston, Tom

EVERYTHING YOU'VE HEARD IS TRUE.
Tracks: / Man on the stage / Show me / Savannah lights / Down along the river / Reachin' out for lovin' / Small time talk / I can count on you / Outlaw.
LP: . . . . K 56632

Johnstone, Arthur

GENERATIONS OF CHANGE.
Tracks: / Beggar wench / Fairfield crane / They don't write 'em like that any more / Danny Farrell / Your daughters and your sons / Freedom come all ye / Generations of change / Ramblin' rover / Victor Jara / Boston burglar / Terror time, The / Yellow on the broom, The.
LP: . . . . LIFL 7007
MC: . . . . LIFC 7007

NORTH BY NORTH.
Tracks: / North by North / Oil beneath the sea, The / Tinkermans daughter, The / Christmas 1914 / Margaret and me / Benny Lynch / Doomsday in the afternoon / Take her in your arms / Raglan Road / Crooked Jack / It's my union / Ballad of Joe Hill / Bandiera Rosa.
LP: . . . . LAP 119
MC: . . . . LAP 119C
MC: . . . . LIFC 7020

Johnstone, Daniel

1990.
Tracks: / Devil town / Held the hand / Some things last a long time / Don't play cards with Satan / Got to get you into my life / Funeral home / Spirit world rising / Lord give me hope / Tears, stupid tears / True love will find you in the end / Careless soul.
LP: . . . . SDE 9015LP

JAD FAIR & DANIEL JOHNSTONE (See Fair, Jad) (Johnstone, Daniel & Jad Fair).

Johnstone, Ian

SOME GUYS HAVE ALL THE LUCK.
MC: . . . . CHV 318

Johnstone, Jim

COME DANCE WITH ME (Johnstone, Jim & His Band).
Tracks: / Thingummyjig polka / Lewisvale waltz / Sweet biddy daly / Shandon bellsmarches / Absent minded man, The / Hawick-Queen o' all the border / Roses o' Prince Charlie / Four hundred horsemenel / Honeysuckle, The / Man from Newry, The / Tomorrow morning / Madam Bonaparte / Original tune / Tail toddle / Linen cap / Marche aux etoiles / Heroes of Kohima / MacKenzie hay / Auld wheel, The / Triste sourire / MacNeils of Ugadale / Kenneth MacDonald's jig / Ladies' fancy / Berwickshire volunteers / Irish girl, The / Kiss me quick, my mother's coming / Highland lassie / Bill Sutherland.
LP: . . . . LILP 5059
MC: . . . . LICS 5059

DANCE TIME (Johnstone, Jim & His Band).
Tracks: / Grand march / Strathspey and reel / St. Bernards waltz / Continental polka / Highland barn dance / Jig time / Two step / Victory waltz / Palais glyde / Reel touch of blarney, A / Singalong / Gay Gordons.
LP: . . . . LILP 5128
MC: . . . . LICS 5128

FAVOURITES (Johnstone, Jim & His Band).
LP: . . . . WGR 068
MC: . . . . CWGR 068

GOVERNMENT WARNING.
LP: . . . . TP 023
MC: . . . . CTP 023

JIM JOHNSTONE & HIS BAND (Johnstone, Jim & His Band).
LP: . . . . TP 023
MC: . . . . CTP 023

SCOTTISH WELCOME, A (Johnstone, Jim & Band).
Tracks: / Reivers, The / Polka / Canadian barn dance / Cumberland reel / Morag's waltz / Heroes of Vittoria / Highland laddie / Scottish reform / Military two step / Highland wedding / Ashludie rant / Gay Gordons.
LP: . . . . LILP 5029
MC: . . . . LICS 5029

SOUND OF JIM JOHNSTONE AND HIS BAND,THE (Johnstone, Jim & His Band).
LP: . . . . LILP 5005

SOUND OF JOHNSTONE, THE (Johnstone, Jim & Band).
LP: . . . . NTS 149

Johnstones

ANTHOLOGY - JOHNSTONES.
LP: . . . . MTRA 2012

Jojo, Ngalle

NA BWA BONGO.
MC: . . . . C 1010

Jolene

JOLENE WITH PART TWO.
LP: . . . . BGC 299
LP: . . . . NA 108
MC: . . . . NC 108

TOGETHER AGAIN.
Tracks: / Daydreams about night things / Pure love / Four strong winds / Clap your hands / Together again / Love is a rose / In my hour of darkness / Silver threads and golden needles / Statues without hearts / 57 chevrolet / Keeps right on a hurtin' / Blue eyes crying in the rain / I saw the light.
LP: . . . . BGC 252
MC: . . . . KBGC 252

Joli, France

ATTITUDE.
Tracks: / Walking into a heartache / Nasty love / I want you with me / Dumb blonde / Girl in the '80s / Standing in the shadows of love / Mad about the boy / Blue eyed technology / You're not alone.
LP: . . . . EPC 25721
MC: 40 25721

Jolinder, Nils

SWEDISH POPULAR SONGS.
LP: . . . . PHONT 7506

Jolini, Kiezowa

CHANTE A BAS LA VIOLENCE.
LP: . . . . JKK 153

Jolley & Swain

BACKTRACKIN'.
Tracks: / Autumn leaves / Walk on / Amazon, The / Backtrackin' / Journey, The / Patterns / Soul street / Lost in the night.
LP: . . . . RBLP 1005
MC: . . . . ZCRB 1005

Jolliffe, Steve

JAPANESE BUTTERFLY.
Tracks: / Japanese butterfly / Nada.
LP: . . . . NP 012

JOURNEY'S OUT OF THE BODY.
LP: . . . . NP 009

Jolly Beggarmen

VERY BEST OF IRISH REBEL SONGS VOL 1.
LP: . . . . STAL 8010
LP: . . . . DOLM 5027

VERY BEST OF IRISH REBEL SONGS VOL. 2.
LP: . . . . STAL 8011
LP: . . . . DOLM 5028

Jolly Boys

POP'N'MENTO.
Tracks: / Mother and wife / Love in the cemetery / River come down / Ten dollars to two / Banana / Big bamboo / Ben Wood Dick / Touch me tomato / Shaving cream / Watermelon / back to back (belly to belly) / Nightfall.
LP: . . . . COOK 040
MC: . . . . COOKC 040

Jolly Brothers

CONSCIOUSNESS.
LP: . . . . UAG 30261

Jolly Jack

LONG TIME TRAVELLING.
Tracks: / Cold and raw / Whaleman's lament / So happy I'll be / Bantry girl's lament / Northwest passage / White / Santa Fe trail / April song / Carrigdhoun / Farewell nancy / On top of the car / Shenandoah.
LP: . . . . FE 067

ROLLING DOWN TO OLD MAUI.
Tracks: / Rolling down to old maui / Jack the jolly jack tar / Maids of Culmore / Sailor's song / London's ordinary / Danny Deever / Broken down squatter, The / Davy Lowston / Clear the track / Banks of the Lee / Bigler, The / Shallow brown.
LP: . . . . FE 035
MC: . . . . FE 035 C

Jolly, Pete

DUO, TRIO, QUARTET.
LP: . . . . FS 171

FIVE, THE.
LP: . . . . FS 5

JOLLY JUMPS IN.
Tracks: / Will you still be mine? / El yorke / Jolly jumps in / I've got you under my skin / I'm with you / Pete's meat / It might as well be spring / Why do I love you? / That's all / Jolly lodger / Before and after.
2LP: . . . . PM 43666

Jolly Postman (bk)

JOLLY POSTMAN, THE (Janet & Allan Ahlberg).
MC: 0 00 109029 1

Jolson, Al

20 GOLDEN GREATS: AL JOLSON.
Tracks: / Rockabye your baby with a Dixie melody / Let me sing and I'm happy / California here I come / Sonny boy / You made me love you / Avalon / After you've gone / April showers / For me and my gal / Swanee / Mammy / I'm sitting on top of the world / When the red, red robin comes bob, bob, bobbin' along / Oh, you beautiful doll / I only have eyes for you / Ma blushin' Rosie / There's a rainbow round my shoulder / Anniversary song / Give my regards to Broadway / Toot toot tootsie.
LP: . . . . MCTV 4
MC: . . . . CTVC 4

20 GOLDEN GREATS: AL JOLSON (VOL.2).
MC: 42010

20 GOLDEN GREATS: AL JOLSON (VOL.1).
MC: 42011

AL & BING (Jolson, Al & Bing Crosby).
MC: . . . . MRT 40034

AL JOLSON AND FRIENDS (Jolson, Al & Friends).
MC: . . . . MRT 40037

AL JOLSON COLLECTION (20 golden greats).
Tracks: / My mammy / Sonny boy / Swanee / When you were sweet sixteen / Toot toot tootsie / I'm sitting on top of the world / Give my regards to Broadway / Is it true what they say about Dixie / I only have eyes for you / April showers / Alabamy bound / Alexander's ragtime band / Carolina in the morning / Avalon / California here I come / For me and my gal / Rockabye your baby with a Dixie melody / You made me love you / There's a rainbow round my shoulder / Let me sing and I'm happy.
LP: . . . . DVLP 2020
MC: . . . . DVMC 2020

AL JOLSON COLLECTION VOL 1/2.
LP: . . . . RONLP 5
MC: . . . . CRON 5

AL JOLSON: ON THE AIR VOL.3.
Tracks: / California, here I come / Swanee / I got plenty o' nuttin' / For me and my gal / Easter parade / Toot, toot, tootsie / Yes sir thats my baby / Pretty baby / Baby face / Yoo hoo / Sonny boy.
LP: . . . . TOTEM 1019

AL JOLSON: ON THE AIR VOL.4.
Tracks: / Where the black-eyed Susans grow / Basin street blues / When I leave the world behind / Little white lies / Ma

blushin' Rosie / I'll be seeing you / You brought a new kind of love to me / April showers / Body and soul.
LP: . . . . **TOTEM 1030**

AL JOLSON: ON THE AIR VOL. 1.
Tracks: / Brother can you spare a dime? / People will say we're in love / Dames / Call of the south / For me and my gal / April showers/Ma blushin' Rosie (Medley.) / When the red, red robin comes bob, bob, bobbin' along.
LP: . . . . **TOTEM 1006**

AL JOLSON: ON THE AIR VOL. 2.
Tracks: / I live the life I love / Swanee / My mammy / California, here I come / I'm sitting on top of the world / Toot, toot, tootsie! / My gal Sal / Something for the boys / We're gonna make sure there's never another war.
LP: . . . . **TOTEM 1012**

AL JOLSON: ON THE AIR VOLUME 5.
Tracks: / Alexander's ragtime band / You made me love you / About a quarter to nine / Ciribiribin / People will say we're in love / Israel / Is it true what they say about Dixie? / Poor butterfly / All alone / When the red, red robin comes bob, bob, bobbin' along / Johnny one note / Pretty baby / When I lost you.
LP: . . . . **TOTEM 1040**

AL JOLSON STORY, THE.
Tracks: / California here I come / One I love belongs to someone else, The / I'm sitting on top of the world / Miami / Tonight's my night with baby / Golden gate / My mammy / There's a rainbow round my shoulder / Why can't you / Liza / When the little red roses / Swanee / Rockabye your baby with a Dixie melody / Sonny boy / You made me / For me and my gal / Let me sing and I'm happy / Give my regards to Broadway / Alabamy bound / When the red, red robin comes bob, bob, bobbin' along / Toot toot tootsie (goodbye) / Carolina in the morning / April showers / Ma blushin' rosie / Easter parade.
MCSET: . . . . **DVREMC 12**

BING AND AL VOLUME 1 (see Crosby, Bing) (Jolson, Al & Bing Crosby).

BING AND AL VOLUME 2 (see Crosby, Bing) (Jolson, Al & Bing Crosby).

BING AND AL VOLUME 3 (see Crosby, Bing) (Jolson, Al & Bing Crosby).

BING AND AL VOLUME 4 (see Crosby, Bing) (Jolson, Al & Bing Crosby).

BING AND AL VOLUME 5 (see Crosby, Bing) (Jolson, Al & Bing Crosby).

BING AND AL VOLUME 6 (see Crosby, Bing) (Jolson, Al & Bing Crosby).

BING CROSBY WITH AL JOLSON (see Crosby, Bing) (Jolson, Al & Bing Crosby).

BROADWAY AL.
Tracks: / On revival day / Tillie Titwillow / Angel child / On the road to Calais / I'll stand beneath your window tonight and whi / Sister Susie's sewing shirts for soldiers / I'm goin' south / Toot, toot, tootsie / I'm saving up the means to get to New Orleans / Waiting for the Robert E. Lee / Where did Robinson Crusoe go with Friday on Saturday / Avalon / I'm down in Honolulu looking them over / You ain't heard nothin' yet.
LP: . . . . **TOTEM 1010**

CALIFORNIA HERE I COME.
LP: . . . . **CMS 008**
MC: . . . . **CMSC 008**

EVENING WITH....
Tracks: / California, here I come / Sonny boy / April showers / Swanee.
LP: . . . . **ASA LP 1**

GOLDEN GREATS VOL 1.
LP: **22010**
MC: **42010**

GREAT JOLSON, THE.
LP: . . . . **SHM 3225**
MC: . . . . **HSC 3225**

GREATEST HITS: AL JOLSON.
LP: **33008**
MC: **63008**

HAVIN' FUN (Jolson, Al & Friends).
LP: . . . . **SCL 61051**

JAZZ SINGER, THE.
Tracks: / California here I come / Pasadena / I'm sitting on top of the world / Blue river / Golden gate / Back in your own back yard / My Mammy / Dirty hands, Dirty face / There's a rainbow round my shoulder / Sonny boy / I'm in seventh heaven / Little pal / Used to you / Why can't you / Liza / Let me sing and I'm happy / April showers / Rockabye your baby with a Dixie melody.
LP: . . . . **HDL 102**
MC: . . . . **CHDL 102**

LIVE IN 1935.
LP: . . . . **SH 2079**

MAN AND THE LEGEND, VOL 1.
Tracks: / Baby face / Bali Ha'i / Darktown strutters' ball / Christmas dreaming / She's a Latin from Manhattan / By a waterfall / Swanee / Confidentially / Ma blushin' Rosie / Summertime / Toot toot tootsie / People will say we're in love / About a quarter to nine / Mighty like a rose / Waiting for the Robert E. Lee / I was born in Virginia / Yes, sir, that's my baby / April showers / You made me love you / Mammy.
LP: . . . . **RHMD 1**

MAN AND THE LEGEND, VOL 2.
Tracks: / California here I come / Nature boy / When the red, red robin comes bob, bob, bobbin' along / Old-fashioned girl in a gingham gown / At sundown / Mammy / Is it true what they say about Dixie? / Anniversary song / Pretty girl is like a melody, A / April showers / Ida, sweet as apple cider / Golden gate / Remember me / More than you know / I'd find you / American boy / Smoke gets in your eyes / All my love / Liza / Sonny boy.
LP: . . . . **RHMD 2**

MAN AND THE LEGEND, VOL 3.
Tracks: / Hello ma baby / Whispering / My melancholy baby / Poor butterfly / His majesty the baby / Hooray for baby and me / Good evening, friends / When day is done / By the light of the silvery moon / Avalon / Let me sing and I'm happy / I only have eyes for you / So help me / I'm just wild about Harry / Boots and saddles / Page Miss Glory / Tomorrow is just another day / This is the life / Keep smiling at trouble / Du host a liebes punim (Darling I love you) / Little bundle from Heaven / Thank you.
LP: . . . . **RHMD 3**

MAN AND THE LEGEND VOL 4.
Tracks: / I want a girl / April showers / Keep smiling at trouble / Ma blushin' Rosie / I'd rather listen to your eyes / There's a rainbow round my shoulder / If I only had a match / My blue Heaven / Am I blue / Back in your own back yard / If I could be with you / I'm just wild about Harry / Brother can you spare a dime / Crazy for you / My mammy / In the shade of the old apple tree / Liza (all the clouds will roll away) / If you were the only girl in the world / I'm sitting on top of the world / Sonny boy.
LP: . . . . **RHMD 4**
MC: . . . . **RHMC 4**

ON THE AIR.
LP: . . . . **SH 2003**
MC: . . . . **CSH 2003**

SONNY BOY.
Tracks: / I feel a song coming on / Isn't this a lovely day / I like to take orders from you / World is waiting for the sunrise, The / I'll see you in my dreams / Smoke gets in your eyes / Sonny boy / She's a latin from Manhattan / At sundown / My blue Heaven / Night and day / Avalon / Cheek to cheek / I can't give you anything but love / Lady in red, The.
LP: . . . . **TOP 175**
MC: . . . . **KTOP 175**
LP: . . . . **SHM 3195**
MC: . . . . **HSC 3195**

SWANEE RIVER 1945 BROADCAST (Jolson, Al/Dennis Morgan).
Tracks: / Oh Susannah / De Camptown races / My old Kentucky home / Ring ring the banjo / I dream of Jeannie with the light brown hair / Old black Joe / Old folks at home / April showers.
LP: . . . . **TOTEM 1028**

TWENTY MORE GOLDEN GREATS.
Tracks: / Is it true what they say about Dixie? / I want a girl / By the light of the silvery moon / Waiting for the Robert E. Lee / Pretty baby / Carolina in the morning.
LP: . . . . **MCTV 5**
MC: . . . . **MCTVC 52**

UNFORGETTABLE: AL JOLSON (16 Golden Classics).
Tracks: / Beautiful dreamer / De camptown races / Neil and I / I only have eyes for you / Smoke gets in your eyes / Confidentially / April showers / So help me / Anniversary song / Baby face / Nature boy / California here I come / Sonny boy / Remember me / I was born in virginia / Whispering / I'm just wild about harry / More than you know / Some enchanted evening / After you've gone.
LP: . . . . **UNLP 022**
MC: . . . . **UNMC 022**

VERY BEST OF AL JOLSON (20 greatest hits).
MC: . . . . **PLAC 30**

WORLD'S GREATEST ENTERTAINER.
Tracks: / Alabamy bound / Ma blushin' Rosie / My gal Sal / Bright eyes (medley 1) / Little girl (medley 1) / I've gotta get back to New York / When you were sweet sixteen / Toot toot tootsie goodbye (medley 2) / You made me love you (I didn't want to do it) (medley 2) / One I love belongs to somebody else, The / She is my Daisy / Baby face / Hello 'Tucky / I'll be seeing you / That certain party of mine.
MC: . . . . **MCLC 1734**
LP: . . . . **MFP 5813**
MC: . . . . **TCMFP 5813**
LP: . . . . **MCL 1734**

YOU AIN'T HEARD NOTHING YET (LIVING ERA).
Tracks: / California here I come / Sonny boy / April showers / Pasadena / When the red, red robin comes bob, bob, bobbin' along / You made me love you / I'm ka-razy for you / You ain't heard nothin' yet / Swanee / When the little red roses get the blues for you / Rockabye your baby with a Dixie melody / Blue river / Used to you / Steppin' out / Spaniard that blighted my life, The / Golden gate / My Mammy.
LP: . . . . **AJA 5038**
MC: . . . . **ZC AJA 5038**

YOU AIN'T HEARD NOTHING YET (MCA).
Tracks: / I only have eyes for you / About a quarter to nine / Is it true what they say about Dixie / Anniversary song / If I only had a match / All my love / Old piano roll blues, The / Let's go west again / Some enchanted evening / Just one way to say I love you / That wonderful girl of mine / Paris wakes up and smiles / No sad songs for me / God's country.
LP: . . . . **MCL 1808**
MC: . . . . **MCLC 1808**

Jolson Revue

JOLSON REVUE (Original London cast) (Various artists).
Tracks: / Shaking the blues away: *Various artists* / Let me sing and I'm happy: *Various artists* / My mammy: *Various* artists / Alabama jubilee: *Various artists* / I only have eyes for you: *Various artists* / Can't help lovin' dat man: *Various artists* / Rock a bye your baby with a Dixie melody: *Various artists* / Sonny boy: *Various* artists / Swanee: *Various artists* / Give my regards to Broadway: *Various artists* / I'm looking over a four leaf clover: *Various artists* / Baby face: *Various artists* / Toot toot toosie goodbye: *Various artists*/ Thoroughly modern Millie: *Various artists* / Anniversary song: *Various artists* / There's a rainbow round my shoulder: *Various artists* / Pretty baby: *Various artists* / April showers: *Various artists* / American trilogy: *Various artists* / He's got the whole world in his hands: *Various artists* / Carolina in the morning: *Various artists* / You made me love you: *Various artists* / Bye bye blackbird: *Various artists* / When you're smiling: *Various artists* / California here I come: *Various artists* / When the saints go marching: *Various artists*.
LP: . . . . **SLS 50426**

Jomanda

SOMEONE TO LOVE ME.
LP: **7599244141**
MC: **7599244144**

Jon K.

ADOWA.
LP: . . . . **VILL 001**

Jon & The Nightriders

CHARGE OF THE NIGHTRIDERS.
LP: . . . . **LP 8412**

STAMPEDE.
Tracks: / Stampede / Storm dancer / Wild weekend / Road agent / Minor chaos / Beneath the reef / XL-3 / Boss / Sea 'n Sorrento / Speedway / Catalina / Breeze and I.
LP: **KIX4U 3340**
LP: . . . . **ROCK 3340**

SURF BEAT '80.
LP: . . . . **CR 30213**

Jon & Vangelis

BEST OF JON AND VANGELIS.
Tracks: / Italian song / I'll find my way home / State of independence / One more time / Play within a play / Friends of Mr. Cairo / Outside of this (inside of that) / He is sailing / I hear you now.
LP: . . . . **POLH 6**
MC: . . . . **POLHC 6**

FRIENDS OF MR.CAIRO.
Tracks: / Friends of Mr.Cairo / Back to school / Outside of this, inside of that / State of independence / Beside / Mayflower.
LP: . . . . **POLD 5039**
LP: . . . . **POLD 5053**
MC: . . . . **POLDC 5053**

PAGE OF LIFE.
MC: **411373**

PRIVATE COLLECTION.
Tracks: / And when the night comes / Deborah / He is sailing / Polonaise / Horizon / King is coming.
LP: . . . . **POLH 4**
MC: . . . . **POLHC 4**

SHORT STORIES.
Tracks: / Curious electric / Each and every day / Bird song / I hear you now / Road / Far away in Baghdad / Love is / One more time / Thunder / Play within a play.
LP: . . . . **SPELP 105**
MC: . . . . **SPEMC 105**
LP: . . . . **POLD 5030**
MC: . . . . **POLDC 5030**

SHORT STORIES/FRIENDS OF MR CAIRO.
Tracks: / Curious electric / Each and every day / Bird song / I hear you now / Road, The / Far away in Baghdad / Love is / One more time / Thunder / Play within a play / I'll find my way home / State of independence / Beside / Mayflower / Friends of Mr Cairo / Back to school / Outside of this, inside of that.
MCSET: **3574 139**

Jonas, Fernando

CLASSICAL GUITAR MASTERPIECES.
MCSET: . . . . **M 10214**

Jonathan

JONATHAN LIVINGSTONE SEAGULL (Bach, Richard (aut)).
MC: . . . . **CDL 51639**

JONATHAN LIVINGSTONE SEAGULL (See Under Diamond, Neil) (Diamond, Neil).

Jones

WIDE POINT, THE (See under Mangelsdorff) (Jones/Danielson/ Mangelsdorff).

Jones, Al

AL JONES (Jones, Al/Frank Necessary/ Spruce Mountain Boys).
LP: . . . . **ROUNDER 0050**

Jones, Aled

ALBUM OF HYMNS, AN.
MC: . . . . **STAC 2272**
LP: . . . . **STAR 2272**

ALED (Music from the TV series).
Tracks: / O worship the King / Sheep may safely graze / King of love my shepherd is, The / Alleluja (Exsultate jubilate) / O my saviour lifted / Thy hand, o God, has guided / How lovely are thy dwellings / Love divine / Bist du bei mir / All thanks to thee / Benedictus / Let there be peace on earth.
LP: . . . . **AJ 3**
MC: . . . . **CAJ 3**

ALL THROUGH THE NIGHT.
LP: . . . . **REH 569**
MC: . . . . **ZCR 569**

AVE MARIA.
LP: . . . . **1304 D**

BEST OF ALED JONES, THE.
Tracks: / Walking in the air / Scarborough fair / Sailing / All through the night (Ar hyd y nos) / Art thou troubled? / Where e'er you walk (Sung in English) / Bright eyes / Love divine / Pie Jesu / Panis angelicus (Sung in latin) / Jesu, joy of man's desiring / Ave Maria (sung in Latin) / O my saviour lifted / Laudate dominum / O for the wings of a dove.
MC: . . . . **CAJ 5**
LP: . . . . **AJ 5**

BEST OF CHRISTMAS ALBUM.
Tracks: / Holy City, The / Bridge over troubled water / Ave Maria (Version 1) / O Holy night (Version 1) / Ombra / Bless this house / O for the wings of a dove / How beautiful are the feet / Star of Bethlehem / O Holy night (Version 2) / All through the night / Where 'ere you walk / Ave Maria (Version 2) / Yesterday / Little road to Bethlehem, The.
MC: . . . . **HSC 662**

DIOLCH A CHAN.
LP: . . . . **1294 D**

PIE JESU.
Tracks: / Art thou troubled? / If I can help somebody / Zion hears the watchmen's voices (from cantata 140) / Jesu, joy of man's desiring / Lullaby (op.49 no.4) / I'll walk beside you / Crown of roses, The (legend) / I know that my redeemer liveth (From 'Messiah') / Lausanne / God so loved the world / At the end of the day / Pie Jesu / Laudate dominum.
LP: . . . . **AJ 2**
MC: . . . . **CAJ 2**
MC: . . . . **VVIPC 109**

SAILING.

Tracks: / Sailing / Scarborough fair / Reverend Eli Jenkins' prayer (Troytes chant) / Puff the magic dragon / Trees / Bugeilio'r gwenth gwyn / Sea fever / Bright eyes / To music (an die musik) / Dafydd y Garreg Wen (David of the White Rock) / Little horses, The / At the river / Simple game (Shaker song) / Christopher Robin is saying his prayers.
LP: . . . . . AJ 4
MC: . . . . . CAJ 4

VOICES FROM THE HOLY LAND (Jones, Aled & BBC Welsh Chorus).
Tracks: / Let us break bread together / Ave Maria / My Lord, what a morning / Deep river / Holy City, The / There is a green hill far away / How beautiful are the feet (From Messiah) / Ave Verum Corpus / Easter hymn / Jesu, joy of man's desiring / Little road to Bethlehem, The / Shepherds' farewell, The (From 'Childhood of Christ') / Ave Maria / O for a closer walk with God / O for the wings of a dove / Tua Bethlem dref / O Holy Night / Virgin Mary had a baby boy, The.
LP: . . . . . REC 564
MC: . . . . . ZCM 564

WHERE E'ER YOU WALK.
Tracks: / Panis angelicus / Diolch a chan / Llansteffan / Y fwyalchen dou bigfelen / Sarah / Caro mio ben / Pie Jesu / Where e'er you walk / How beautiful are the feet / Heiden roslein / Water lily / Little road to Bethlehem, The / Ave Maria.
LP: . . . . . DIX 21
MC: . . . . . CDIX 21

WITH THE BBC WELSH CHORUS.
Tracks: / Away in a manger / Come unto him (from Messiah) / Sussex carol / O little town of Bethlehem / St. Joseph's carol / Coventry carol / Christmas star / Ding dong merrily on high / Deck the hall / Holy boy, The / Jesus Christ the apple tree / Gabriel's message / Rockin' / My heart ever faithful (from church cantata no. 68) / Good King Wenceslas / Hwiangerod mair (Mary's lullaby) / Unto us is born a son.
LP: . . . . . AJ 1
MC: . . . . . CAJ 1
MC: . . . . . CXID 19
LP: . . . . . VVIP 105
MC: . . . . . VVIPC 105
LP: . . . . . XID 19

Jones, Allan

BEST OF ALLAN JONES, THE.
Tracks: / Donkey serenade, The / Gianniana mia / Night was made of love, The / Rosalie / Night or day / In the still of the night / Deep in my heart dear / Falling in love with love / I love you truly / Make believe / They say it's wonderful / So in love / Who are you / I'm falling in love with someone / Thine alone / On the trail.
LP: . . . . . NL 90065
MC: . . . . . NK 90065

Jones, Barbara

10 MILLION SELLERS IN REGGAE.
LP: . . . . . TRA 600

BEST OF BARBARA JONES.
LP: . . . . . TRLS 136

DEDICATED TO THE ONE I LOVE.
LP: . . . . . PILP 025

FOREVER (See under Taylor, Tyrone) (Jones, Barbara & Tyrone Taylor).

NEED TO BELONG.
LP: . . . . . EADLP 1004

WILL IT LAST FOREVER?.
LP: . . . . . GG 024

YOU'RE ALWAYS ON MY MIND.
LP: . . . . . DY 3446

Jones, Bessie

SO GLAD I'M HERE.
LP: . . . . . ROUNDER 2015
MC: . . . . . ROUNDER 2015C

STEP IT DOWN.
LP: . . . . . ROUNDER 8004
MC: . . . . . ROUNDER 8004C

Jones, Billy

QU'EST-CE QUE C'EST.
LP: . . . . . BJ 103

Jones, Bobby

HILL COUNTRY SUITE.
LP: . . . . . ENJA 2046

SOUL SET FREE (Jones, Bobby/New Life).
Tracks: / This little light of mine / He believes in me / Close to you / I won't give up / Movin' on / Martin / No one can match your love / Soul set free, A / Celebration.
LP: . . . . . MYR 1115
MC: . . . . . MC 1115

Jones Brothers

STOP THE SUN, STOP THE MOON.
LP: . . . . . KM 708

Jones, Bryan

BRYAN JONES BIG BAND (Jones, Bryan Big Band).
LP: . . . . . BM 51

Jones, Byron

JUST BYRON.
Tracks: / Blaze away / Carillon / If I could only make you care / When your hair has turned to silver / For ever and ever / Dream, (A) / California here I come / San Francisco / If you knew Susie / Ebb tide / Romberg selection / You can't be true / In the gloaming / Whispering / Happy days and lonely nights / Who's sorry now? / Old rugged cross, The.
LP: . . . . . GRS 1097

PLAY THE WURLITZER AT COTTON (See under Beaumont, Howard) (Jones, Byron & Howard Beaumont).

PLAYS THE CHRISTIE ORGAN, ASTRA THEATRE.
LP: . . . . . GRS 1169

PLAYS THE WERSI BETA - BEST WISHES.
MC: . . . . . KGRS 1184

Jones, Carmell

REMARKABLE CARMELL JONES, THE.
LP: . . . . . AFF 132

Jones, Casey

SOLID BLUES.
LP: . . . . . R 7612

STILL KICKIN'.
LP: . . . . . AW 38 39

Jones, Charlie L.

CHARLIE L. JONES.
Tracks: / Pretty little sexy thing / I thought I was over you / Crazy over you / Love on the beach / Troubles is troubling me / It's how love should be / Now I know how love is / Blues all over / Let's have a good time / Just a smile / Woo-baby you're so sweet.
LP: . . . . . TRPL 117

Jones, Chris

NO MORE RANGE TO ROAM.
LP: . . . . . LTRA 503

Jones, Christopher

NO LOOKING BACK.
LP: . . . . . FF 4011

Jones, Coley

COLEY JONES & THE DALLAS STRING BAND (Jones, Coley & The Dallas String Band).
Tracks: / Army mule no man's land / Travelling man / Dallas rag / Sweet mama blues / So tired / Hokum blues / Chasin' rainbows / I used to call her baby / I can't stand that / He throws that thing / Listen everybody / Easin' in / Drunkard's special / Elder's / Shine / Sugar blues / He's my man.
LP: . . . . . MSE 208

Jones & Crossland Band

TOURNAMENT FOR BRASS.
Tracks: / Fanfare from La Peri / March Wellington / Mood indigo / Tournament for brass / Kings hunting jigg, (The) / Shepherd's song / Trumpets wild / La belle Americaine / Prince Rupert's march / Girl I left behind me, The / March and canzona.
LP: . . . . . GRS 1099

Jones, Curtis

BLUES AND TROUBLE.
LP: . . . . . OL 2824

CURTIS JONES (1937-1941).
LP: . . . . . BD 2078

CURTIS JONES IN LONDON.
Tracks: / Shake it baby / Syl-vous play blues / Young generation boogie / Skid Row / Honeydripper / Lonesome bedroom blues / You got good business / Alley bound blues / Curtis Jones boogie / Dusty my broom / Red river blues / Good woman blues / Please send me someone to love / Roll me over.
LP: . . . . . SEE 53

TROUBLE BLUES.
LP: . . . . . OBC 515

Jones, David Lynn

HARD TIME ON EASY STREET.
Tracks: / Bonnie Jean / High ridin' heroes / Home of my heart / Rogue, The / No easy way out / Living in the promised land / Tonight in America / Valley of a thousand years / Hard time on Easy Street / See how far we've come.
LP: 832 518-1
MC: 832 518-4

Jones, Dill

UP JUMPED YOUR LOVE.
LP: . . . . . HEP 2025

Jones, Ed

HOMECOMING, THE (Jones, Ed Quartet).
LP: . . . . . JAZID 14

Jones, Eddie

EDDIE JONES: 20 GUITAR GREATS.
Tracks: / Guitar boogie / Walk, don't run / Look at that moon / Buddy's song / Thomahawk / Hot potato / F.B.I. / Dual man, The / Blue coat boy / Bongo rock / Maria Elena / La bamba / Polkaroonie / Perfidia / Our love / Sleepwalk / Don't tear me up / Blue sunset / Eddie's boogie / Deep in the heart of Texas.
LP: . . . . . CBR 1030
MC: . . . . . KCBR 1030

Jones, Elvin

BROTHER JOHN.
LP: . . . . . PA 8039

EARTH JONES.
LP: . . . . . PA 8016
MC: . . . . . PAC 8016

ELVIN JONES.
LP: . . . . . OJC 259

JOHN COLTRANE MEMORIAL CONCERT.
LP: . . . . . PM 004

LIVE AT THE VILLAGE VANGUARD.
LP: . . . . . ENJA 2036

MR THUNDER (Jones, Elvin Quartet).
LP: . . . . . WR 7501

ON THE MOUNTAIN.
LP: . . . . . PM 005

POLY CURRENTS.
Tracks: / Agenda / Agappe love / Mr. Jones / Yes / When.
LP: . . . . . BST 84331
LP: 784 331 1

POWER TRIO, THE (See under Hicks, John) (Hicks, John, Cecil McBee & Elvin Jones).

QUINTET REUNITED (Jones, Elvin & McCoy Tyner).
LP: . . . . . BKH 521

SKYSCRAPERS: VOL 1.
LP: . . . . . HD 6602

SKYSCRAPERS: VOL 2.
LP: . . . . . HD 6603

SKYSCRAPERS: VOL 3.
LP: . . . . . HD 6605

SUMMIT MEETING.
LP: . . . . . VSD 79390

TOGETHER (Jones, Elvin with Oregon).
Tracks: / Le vin / Lucifer's fall / Charango / Three step dance / Driven omens / Teeth / Brujo.
LP: . . . . . VSD 79377

TRIP, THE (see Pepper, Art) (Jones, Elvin/Art Pepper).

Jones, Etta

IF YOU COULD SEE ME NOW.
LP: . . . . . MR 5175

MS JONES TO YOU.
LP: . . . . . MR 5099

MY MOTHER'S EYES.
Tracks: / Way you look tonight / Don't misunderstand me / Be my love / You do something to me / My mother's eyes / This girl's in love with you / Gloomy Sunday.
LP: . . . . . MR 5145

OSCULATE ME DADDY.
Tracks: / My sleepy head / I sold my heart to the junk man / Richest guy in the graveyard, The / Ain't no hurry baby / Blues to end all blues / Among my souvenirs / Mean to me / Osculate me daddy / What every woman knows / Overwork blues / Misery is a thing called Moe / This is a fine time.
LP: . . . . . OFF 6000

SAVE YOUR LOVE FOR ME.
Tracks: / Save your love for me / One I love belongs to somebody else, The / Georgia on my mind / My man / Man that got away, The / Let's beat out some love / Stardust / East of the sun.
LP: . . . . . MR 5214

SOMETHING NICE.
LP: . . . . . OJC 221

Jones, Floyd

FLOYD JONES & EDDIE TAYLOR (Jones, Floyd & Eddie Taylor).
LP: . . . . . T 2214

JAMES/BRIM/JONES (See under James, Elmore) (Jones, Floyd, Elmore James, John Brim).

Jones, Frankie

BEST OF FRANKIE JONES.
LP: . . . . . TRLS 232

HELL IN THE DANCE (See under Anthony, Pad) (Jones, Frankie & Pad Anthony).

OLD FIRE STICK.
LP: . . . . . unknown

SETTLE FE ME (see under Itals' "What about me?").

SHOWDOWN VOL.2 (Jones, Frankie/Michael Palmer).
LP: . . . . . JJ 161

THEM NICE.
LP: . . . . . Unknown

TWO NEW SUPERSTARS (See under Andy, Patrick) (Jones, Frankie & Patrick Andy).

Jones, George

15 GOLDEN CLASSICS VOL.1.
LP: 20032
MC: 40032

15 GOLDEN CLASSICS VOL.2.
LP: 20033
MC: 40033

16 GREATEST HITS: GEORGE JONES.
LP: . . . . . SLP 3021
MC: . . . . . GT 53021

20 FAVOURITES OF GEORGE JONES.
Tracks: / She thinks I still care / Race is on, The / Little bitty tear, A / Running bear.
LP: . . . . . LBR 1009

20 GOLDEN PIECES: GEORGE JONES.
Tracks: / Good year for the roses, A / Developing my pictures / Tender tears / Say it's not you / From here to the door / If my heart had windows / Favourite lies / Accidentally on purpose / Where grass won't grow / Sweet dreams / Things have gone to pieces / White lightning / 4-0-33 / Take me / I'm a people / I'm wasting good paper / Old brush arbors / Love bug / Walk through this world with me / Race is on, The.
LP: . . . . . BDL 2035
MC: . . . . . BDC 2035

ANNIVERSARY.
Tracks: / We can make it / Loving you could never be better / Bartender blues / Picture of me / What my woman can't do / Nothing ever hurt me / Once you've had the best / Grand time / Same ol' me.
2LP: . . . . . EPC 22142

BEST OF SACRED MUSIC.
LP: . . . . . GT 0135

BLUE MOON OF KENTUCKY.
Tracks: / I get lonely in a hurry / Love's gonna live here / Holiday for love / Imitation of love / Beggar to a king / What's money / She's lonesome again / Brown to blue / We could / Making the rounds / Lovin' lies / Same sweet girl / Please be my love / Blue moon of Kentucky / Yes I know why / Precious jewel / Matthew twenty four / Beacon in the night / I heard you crying in your sleep / In the shadow of a lie.
LP: . . . . . EMS 1251
MC: . . . . . TCEMS 1251

BLUEGRASS HOOTENNANY (Jones, George/Melba Montgomery).
LP: . . . . . HAT 3096
MC: . . . . . HATC 3096

BURN THE HONKY TONK DOWN.
Tracks: / Burn the honky-tonk down / Developing my pictures / Feeling single - seeing double / Where grass won't grow / Your angel steps out of heaven / I cried myself awake / Milwaukie here I come / Beneath still waters / I'll follow you (up our cloud) / Good year for the roses, A / Small time labouring man / Selfishness man, The / Wandering soul.
LP: . . . . . SS 15

COLD COLD HEART.
Tracks: / You comb her hair / Jonesy / Once a day / World's worst loser / Old brush arbors / Yes, I know why / Jambalaya / Liberty / Cold, cold heart / Just don't like this kind of livin'.
LP: . . . . . ALEB 2304
MC: . . . . . ZCALB 2304

COLLECTION: GEORGE JONES.
MC: . . . . . KNMC 13051

COUNTRY STARS (See under Wynette, Tammy for details) (Jones, George & Tammy Wynette).

COUNTRY STORE: GEORGE JONES.
Tracks: / Yesterday's wine / Almost persuaded / Even the bad times (are good) / Burning bridges / Why baby why / Roll over Beethoven / Hallelujah, I love you so / We can make it / Bartender blues / Wine coloured roses (Only on CD.) / Who's gonna fill their shoes (Only on CD.) / Radio lover (Only on CD.) / He stopped loving her today (Only on CD.) / Size seven round (made of gold) / Proud

Mary / Shine on / She thinks I still care / Some day my day will come.
LP: CST 12
MC: CSTK 12

COUNTRY STORE: GEORGE JONES & TAMMY WYNETTE (Jones, George & Tammy Wynette).
Tracks: / We're not the jet set / Take me / Ceremony, The / Golden ring / Two storey house / We're gonna hold on / We loved it anyway / Pair of old sneakers, A / God's gonna getcha (for that) / Near you / When I stop dreaming / Crying time / Never ending song of love / We could / Did you ever / World needs a melody, The / My elusive dreams / After the fire is gone.
LP: CST 45
MC: CSTK 45

CROWN PRINCE OF COUNTRY MUSIC, THE.
Tracks: / One is a lonely number / Maybe little baby / Run boy / One woman man / Settle down / Heartbroken me / Rain, rain / Frozen heart / I've got five dollars and it's Saturday night / Cause I love you / You're in my heart / You all goodnight.
LP: OFF 9002

DOUBLE TROUBLE (Jones, George & Johnny Paycheck).
Tracks: / When you're ugly like us / Along came Jones / Proud Mary / You can have her / Smack dab in the middle / Mabellene / Roll over Beethoven / Kansas city / Tutti frutti / You better move on.
LP: EPC 84458

FRIENDS IN HIGH PLACES.
Tracks: / Few ole country boys, A / All fall down / Fiddle and guitar band / All that we've got left / Love's gonna live here / If I could bottle this up / I've been there / You can't do wrong and get by / It hurts as much in Texas (as it did in Tennessee) / Travellers prayer.
MC: 4680994

GEORGE JONES AND LADIES (I Love Country) (Jones, George & Ladies).
Tracks: / All fall down / Hallelujah, I love you so / Golden ring / All I want to do in life / We sure make good love / Daisy chain / That's good, that's bad / Here we are / Two storey house / Pair of old sneakers, A / If you can touch her at all / I've turned you to stone / Size seven round (made of gold) / Our love was ahead of its time (With Deborah Allen.) / Slow burning fire, A / Best friends.
LP: 4504231
MC: 4504234

GEORGE JONES (AUDIO FIDELITY LABEL).
MC: ZCGAS 717

GEORGE JONES (DITTO).
MCSET: DTO 10088

GEORGE JONES SALUTES HANK WILLIAMS & BOB WILLS.
Tracks: / Wedding bells / I just like this kind of living / You win again / I could never be ashamed of you / You're gonna change / House without love / Your cheatin' heart / They'll never take her love from me / Mansion on the hill / Take these chains from my heart / Bubbles in my beer / Faded love / Roly poly / Trouble in mind / Take me back to Tulsa / Warm red wine / Time changes everything / Worried mind / Silver dew on the bluegrass tonight / San Antonio rose.
LP: EMS 1169
MC: TCEMS 1169

GOLDEN HITS.
LP: GT 0080

GOLDEN MEMORIES.
LP: MA 10185
MC: MAMC 910185

GOOD OL' BOY.
Tracks: / World's worst loser / Once a day / Back in baby's arms again / You comb her hair / I can't change overnight / When I wake up from dreaming / Least of all / She's just a girl I used to know / It's funny what a fool will do / Hearts in my dreams.
LP: SDLP 1.009
MC: SDC 1.009

GOOD YEAR FOR THE ROSES, A (CASTLE).
Tracks: / Where the grass won't grow / I'm a people / 4-0-33 / Things have gone to pieces / From here to the door / My favourite lies / Take me / White lightning / Tender years / Walk through this world with me / Say it's not you / Good year for the roses, A / Race is on, The / Developing my pictures / Old brush arbors.
LP: SHLP 146
MC: SHTC 146

GOOD YEAR FOR THE ROSES, A (PREMIER).
Tracks: / Apartment No.9 / Swinging doors / Am I that easy to forget? / Okie from Muskogee / Day in the life of a fool, A / Rollin' in my sweet baby's arms / All I have to offer you is me / There goes my everything / Good year for the roses, A / She thinks I still care / Talk back tremblin' lips / Hello darlin' / Almost persuaded / I can't stop loving you / Walk through this world with me.
LP: CBR 1041
MC: KCBR 1041

GOOD YEAR FOR THE ROSES, A (TOPLINE).
Tracks: / Good year for the roses, A / If my heart had windows / I'll share my world with you / I'm wasting good paper / Say it's not you / Accidentally on purpose / Love bug / Where grass won't grow / 4033 / Things have gone to pieces / My favourite lies / From here to the door.
LP: TOP 177
MC: KTOP 177

GREAT SONGS OF LEON PAYNE.
LP: GT 0136

GREATEST HITS: GEORGE JONES.
MC: 2630224

GREATEST HITS: GEORGE JONES AND TAMMY WYNETTE (Jones, George & Tammy Wynette).
MC: 40 82035

HE STOPPED LOVING HER.
Tracks: / Grand tour, The / Door, The / We can't make it / Loving you could never be better / Picture of me / These days (I barely get by) / Battle, The / Bartender blues / He stopped loving her today / I'm not ready yet / If drinkin' don't kill me (her memory will) / Still doin' time / Nothing ever hurt (Half as bad) / Once you've had the best / Shine on / Her name is.
LP: PMP 1002
MC: PMPK 1002

HEARTACHES AND HANGOVERS.
Tracks: / I threw away the rose / Blue side of lonesome / Do what you think's best / Unfaithful one / Say it's not you / Lonely street / Things have gone to pieces / From here to the door / Heartaches and hangovers / My favourite lies / Man that you once knew.
LP: SS 17
MC: SSC 17

HOMECOMING IN HEAVEN.
LP: HAT 3104
MC: HATC 3104

I AM WHAT I AM.
Tracks: / He stopped loving her today / I've aged twenty five years in five / Brother to the blues / If drikin' don't kill me / His lovin' her is gettin' in my way / I'm not ready yet / I'm the one she missed him with today / Good hearted woman / Hard act to follow / Bone dry.
LP: EPC 84627

I LOVE COUNTRY.
Tracks: / Why baby why / Tender years / Window up above / White lightning / Race is on, The / She thinks I still care / Her name is / I'm ragged but right / He stopped loving her today / Still doin' time / Shine on (Shine all your sweet love on me) / Radio lover / I always get lucky with you / Tennessee whisky / If drinkin' don't kill me (her memory will) / She's my rock.
LP: EPC 54941
MC: 40 54941
LP: CBS 54941

JONES COUNTRY.
Tracks: / Radio lover / Dream on / Hello trouble / Burning bridges / Wino the clown / You must have walked across my mind / I'd rather die young / Girl at the end of the bar, The / One of these days / Famous last words.
LP: EPC 25733
MC: 40 25733

KING OF COUNTRY MUSIC.
Tracks: / She thinks I still care / Girl I used to know, A / Sometimes you just can't win / We must have been out of our minds / I saw me / You comb her hair / What's in our heart / Your heart turned left (and I was on the right) / Where does a little tear come from? / World's worst loser / Big fool of the year / Open pity mine / Not what I had in mind / Let's invite them over / My tears are overdue / Something I dreamed / Multiply the heartaches / Race is on, The / Least of all / Wrong number.
LP: SLS 2600 421
MC: TC SLS 2600421

KING & QUEEN OF COUNTRY MUSIC (See under Wynette, Tammy) (Jones, George & Tammy Wynette).

LADIES CHOICE.
Tracks: / She's my rock / Hallelujah i love you so / All i want to do in life / We sure make good love / Daisy chain / All fall down / Size seven round / Our love was ahead of its time / Slow burning fire / Best friends.
LP: EPC 26233
MC: 40 26233

LIVE AT DANCETOWN USA.
Tracks: / White lightning / Something I dreamed / Aching breaking heart / Window up above / Bony Moronie / She thinks I still care / Ragged but right / Poor man's riches / Jole blon / Where does a little tear come from / Big Harlan Taylor / She's lonesome again / Race is on.
LP: CH 156

LONE STAR LEGEND, THE.
Tracks: / All I want to do / Give away girl / Flame in my heart / Hearts in my dreams / Into my arms again / Cup of loneliness / Still hurtin' / Let him know / With half a heart / Someone sweet to love / I've been known to cry / Holiday for love / Vitamins l-o-v-e / Your old standby / Mr. Fool / Last town I painted, The / Don't lie to me.
LP: CH 139
MC: CHC 139

MY FAVOURITES OF HANK WILLIAMS.
LP: HAT 3136
MC: HATC 3136

MY VERY SPECIAL GUESTS.
Tracks: / Night life (With Waylon Jennings) / Bartender's blues (With James Taylor) / Here we are (With Emmylou Harris) / I've turned you to stone (With Linda Ronstadt) / It sure was good (With Tammy Wynette) / I gotta get drunk (With Willie Nelson) / Proud Mary (With Johnny Paycheck) / Stranger in the house (With Elvis Costello) / I still hold her body (but I think I've lost her mind) (With Dennis and Ray of Dr.Hook) / Will the circle be unbroken (With Pop and Mavis Staples).
LP: CBS 32773
MC: 40 32773
LP: EPC 83163

ONE WOMAN MAN.
Tracks: / I'm a one woman man / My baby's gone / Don't you ever get tired (of hurting me) / Burning bridges / Ya ba da ba do (so are you) / Radio lover / Place in the country, A / Just out of reach / Writing on the wall / Pretty little lady from Beaumont Texas.
LP: 4651861
MC: 4651864

PARTY PICKIN' (Jones, George/Melba Montgomery).
LP: GT 0134

RACE IS ON.
Tracks: / Race is on / Don't let the stars get in your eyes / I'll never let go of you / She's mine / Three's a crowd / They'll never take her love from me / Your heart turned left / Ain't it funny what a fool will do / It scares me half to death / World's worse loser / Time changes everything / Take me as I am.
LP: SLS 50428
MC: 4XLL 9031

REPLAY ON GEORGE JONES.
LP: FEDB 5017
MC: FEDC 5017

SHINE ON.
Tracks: / Shine on / She hung the moon / I'd rather have what we had / Tennessee whiskey / Almost persuaded / I always get lucky with you / Mem'ryville / I should've called / Show's almost over / Ol' George stopped drinkin' today.
LP: EPC 25400

STILL THE SAME OLE ME.
Tracks: / Still doin' time / Couldn't love have picked a better place to die? / I won't need you anymore / Together alone / Daddy come home / You can't get the hell out of Texas / Good ones and bad ones / Girl, you sure know how to say goodbye / Some day my day will come / Same ole me.
LP: EPC 84949
MC: 40 84949

STRANGERS, LOVERS AND FRIENDS.
MCSET: DTO 10265

TASTE OF YESTERDAY'S WINE, A (see Haggard, Merle) (Jones, George & Merle Haggard).

TEXAS TORNADO.
Tracks: / White lightning / You gotta be my baby / What am I worth / Don't stop the music / Play it cool man / I'm gonna burn your playhouse down / Into my arms again / Let him know / Giveaway girl / All I want to do / My fool / Vitamins l-o-v-e.
LP: GEM 006
MC: GEMC 006

TOGETHER AGAIN (Jones, George & Tammy Wynette).
Tracks: / Pair of old sneakers / Right in the wrong direction / I just started livin' today / Love in the meantime / We could / Two story house / If we don't make it, it's not my fault / We'll talk about it later / Night spell.
LP: EPC 84626
MC: 40 84626

TOO WILD TOO LONG.
Tracks: / I'm a survivor / Real McCoy, The / Too wild too long / One hell of a song / Old man no one loves, The / Bird, The / I'm a long gone daddy / New patches / Moments of brilliance / U.S.A. today, The.
LP: 4608051
MC: 4608054

WALKING THE LINE (see under Haggard, Merle) (Jones, George, Merle Haggard, Willie Nelson).

WAYS OF THE WORLD.
Tracks: / Don't you ever get tired of hurting me / Open pity mind / On the banks of the old pontchartrain / House without love is not a home, A / Ways of the world / Please don't let that woman get me / Yes I know why / Jonesy / Old brush arbors / Liberty / Jambalaya / Cold cold heart / Ragged but right / Tarnished angel / Your tender years / Wedding bells / Things have gone to pieces / World of forgotten people / From now on all of my friends are gonna be strangers / I can't escape from you.
LP: SMT 008
MC: SMTC 008

WHITE LIGHTNING.
Tracks: / White lightning / What am I worth / Taggin' along / Boogie woogie Mexican boy / You gotta be my baby / Revenooer man / Who shot Sam / Play it cool man / My sweet Imogene / How come it / I'm gonna burn your playhouse down / Don't stop the music / Rock it / Maybe little baby.
LP: 10 CH 13
LP: CH 117
MC: CHC 117

WHO'S GONNA FILL THEIR SHOES.
LP: 26696

WINE COLOURED ROSES.
Tracks: / Wine coloured roses / I turn to you / Right left hand, The / Don't leave without taking your silver / Very best of me, The / Hopelessly yours / You never looked that good when you were mine (With Patti Page.) / If only your eyes could lie / Ol' Frank / These old eyes have seen it all.
LP: EPC 57040
MC: 40 57040

YOU OUGHT TO BE HERE WITH ME.
Tracks: / Hell stays open (all night long) / You oughta be here with me / Somebody always paints the wall / I sleep just like a baby / Someone that you used to know / I want to grow old with you / Cold day in December, A / Six foot deep, six foot down / If the world don't end tomorrow / Ol' Red.
LP: 4674701
MC: 4674704

YOU'VE STILL GOT A PLACE IN MY HEART.
Tracks: / You've still got a place in my heart / From strangers, to lovers, to friends / Second time around / Come sundown / Even the bad times are good / I'm ragged but right / Courtin' in the rain / Loveshine / Your lying blue eyes / Learning to do without me.
LP: EPC 26072

Jones Girls

ARTISTS SHOWCASE: JONES GIRLS.
Tracks: / You gonna make me love somebody else / 2 win u back / At peace with woman / Knockin' / Keep it coming / Get as much love as you can / Life goes on / Nights over Egypt.
LP: MUSIC 4
MC: ZCMUS 4

GET AS MUCH LOVE AS YOU CAN.
Tracks: / That man of mine / Get as much love as you can / Nights over Egypt / Love don't ever say goodbye / ASAP / Let's be friends first / World will sing our song / You're breaking my heart.
LP: PIR 85347

JONES GIRLS.
Tracks: / This feelings killing me / You made me love you / Show love today / You gonna make me love somebody else / Life goes on / Who can I run to / We're a melody / I'm at your mercy.
LP: PIR 83831

KEEP IT COMING.

Tracks: / Keep it coming / Won't let you take it back / Why you wanna do that to me / You can't have my love / Better things to do / Love is comin' atcha / Ah ah ah ah / Right stuff.
LP: PIR 25487

ON TARGET.
Tracks: / Let's hit it (dialogue) / On target / Win U back / Baby, I'm yours / Knockin' / I can make a difference / What a fool / Curious / I'm a woman here.
LP: PL 84817
MC: PK 84817

Jones, Glenn

ALL FOR YOU.
LP: HIP 74
MC: HIPC 74

FINESSE.
Tracks: / Finesse / You're the only one I love / Show me / It hurts too much / Meet me half way there / Bring back your love / Everlasting love / On the floor.
LP: PL 88036
MC: PK 88036
LP: NL 88036
MC: NK 88036

GLENN JONES.
LP: 10621 J
LP: HIP 51
MC: HIPC 51

TAKE IT FROM ME.
Tracks: / Stay / Set the night on fire / Love will show us how / Be my lady / Giving myself to you / All work and no play / Dangerous / Take it from me.
LP: PL 85807
MC: PK 85807

Jones, Gloria

TO KNOW HIM IS TO LOVE HIM (see under Bolan, Marc) (Jones, Gloria/Marc Bolan).

WINDSTORM.
Tracks: / Bring on the love / Windstorm / If the roses don't come / Blue light microphone / Hooked on you baby / Vaya con Dios / Kiss me, kiss me, kiss me / Woman is a woman.
LP: SWK 2002
LP: EMC 3290

Jones, Grace

BULLETPROOF HEART.
Tracks: / Driving satisfaction / Kicked around / Love on top of love / Paper plan / Crack attack / Bulletproof heart / On my way / Dream (Cassette & CD only.) / Seduction surrender / Someone to love / Don't cry freedom (CD only.) / Amado mio.
LP: ESTU 2106
MC: TCESTU 2106
MC: 791 737 4

FAME.
LP: ILPS 9525

GRACE JONES: INTERVIEW PICTURE DISC.
LPPD: BAK 2007

INSIDE STORY.
Tracks: / I'm not perfect (but I'm perfect for you) / Hollywood liar / Chan hitch-hikes to Shanghai / Victor should have been a jazz musician / Party girl / Crush / Barefoot in Beverly Hills / Scary but fun / White collar crime / Inside story, The.
LP: MTL 1007
MC: TCMTL 1007

ISLAND LIFE.
Tracks: / Slave to the rhythm / Pull up to the bumper / Private life / La vie en rose / I need a man / My Jamaican guy / Walking in the rain / Libertango / Love is the drug / Do or die / I've seen that face before.
LP: GJ 1
MC: GJC 1
MC: ICM 2030
LP: ILPM 2030

LIVING MY LIFE.
Tracks: / My Jamaican guy / Nipple to the bottle / Apple stretching, The / Everybody hold still / Cry now - laugh later / Inspiration / Unlimited capacity for love.
LP: ILPM 9722
MC: ICM 9722
LP: ILPS 9722
MC: ICT 9722
MC: 842 615 4

NIGHTCLUBBIN'.
Tracks: / Feel up / Walking in the rain / Pull up to the bumper / Use me / Art groupie / Libertango / I've done it again.
LP: ILPM 9624
MC: ICM 9624
LP: ILPS 9624
MC: 842 368 4

PORTFOLIO.
Tracks: / Send in the clowns / What I did for love / Tomorrow / La vie en rose / Sorry / That's the trouble / I need a man.
LP: ILPM 9470
MC: ICM 9470
MC: 842 614 4

SLAVE TO THE RHYTHM.
Tracks: / Jones the rhythm / Fashion show, The / Frog and the princess, The / Operattack / Slave to the rhythm / Crossing (ooh the action) / Don't cry - it's only the rhythm / Ladies and gentlemen: Miss Grace Jones.
LP: GRACE 1
MC: GRACEC 1
MC: ICM 2032
MC: 842 612 4

WARM LEATHERETTE.
Tracks: / Warm leatherette / Private life / Rolling stone / Love is the drug / Hunter gets captured by the game, The / Bullshit / Breakdown / Pars.
LP: ILPM 9592
MC: ICM 9592
LP: ILPS 9592
MC: 842 611 4

Jones, Grandpa

16 GREATEST HITS: GRANDPA JONES.
LP: SLP 3008
MC: GT 53008

20 OF THE BEST: GRANDPA JONES.
Tracks: / Y'all come / High silk hat and a gold top walking cane, A / Champion / Gooseberry pie / Dear old sunny south by the sea / Closer to the bone / Old Dan Tucker / In the future / New vitamins / Old rattler / Keep on the sunnyside of life / Old blue / Standing in the depot / I'm no communist / Trader / Herd o'turtles / You ain't seen nothing yet / I'm getting grey hair / Sass-a-frass / T.V. blues.
LP: NL 89415
MC: NK 89415
LP: INTS 5198

MAN FROM KENTUCKY, THE.
Tracks: / Kitty Klyde / Are you from Dixie? / My bonnie lies over the ocean / Good ole mountain dew / Eight more miles to Louisville / She's the steppin' out kind / Uncle Eph's / New vitamin, The / Bald headed end of the broom / Bile the cabbage down.
LP: BDL 1029
MC: BDC 1029

OTHER SIDE OF..., THE.
LP: KLP 888
MC: GT 5888

Jones, Hank

ARIGATO.
LP: PRO 7004

BOP REDUX.
LP: MR 5123

GOOD LIFE (See under Stitt, Sonny) (Stitt, Sonny & Hank Jones).

GROOVIN' HIGH.
LP: MR 5169

I'M ALL SMILES (Jones, Hank & Tommy Flanagan).
Tracks: / Relaxin' at Camarillo / In a sentimental mood / Some day my prince will come / Afternoon in Paris / Au privave / I'm all smiles / Rockin' in rhythm / Con Alma.
LP: 817 863-1

JAZZ TRIO, THE.
LP: WL 70526

JUST FOR FUN.
LP: GXY 5105

LAZY AFTERNOON.
Tracks: / Speak low / Lazy afternoon / Intimidation / Comin' home baby / Sublime / Peedlum / Work song / Lament / Passing time / Arrival.
MC: CJ 391C

MOREOVER (Jones, Hank/Eddie Gomez/Al Foster).
LP: 6315 097

RELAXIN' AT CAMARILLO.
LP: WL 70504

SPIRIT OF 176, THE (Jones, Hank & George Shearing).
LP: CJ 371
MC: CJ 371C

TIPTOE TAPDANCE.
LP: GXY 5108

TWO-FER, A (see Grapelli, Stephane) (Jones, Hank & Stephane Grapelli).

Jones, Harley

VIRTUOSO ACCORDIONISTS (Jones, Harley & Maurice (NZ)).
Tracks: / Bel viso / Repasz band march / Prelude and fugue in C major / I want to hold your hand / Pearls of crystal / Harmonious blacksmith, The / Day tripper / Nola / Walk in the Black Forest, A / Accordiana / Please please me / Eine kleine nachtmusik / Return march / United Nations polka / Crocodile rock / Flight of the bumble bee / Bumble boogie.
LP: ZLP 1053

Jones, Hilary

CARVING THE DEW (Jones, Hilary & Simon Mayer).
LP: WF 017

Jones, Howard

12 INCH ALBUM, THE.
Tracks: / Always asking questions / New song (new version) / What is love? / Like to get to know you well / Pearl in the shell (extended mix) / Total conditioning.
LP: WX 14
MC: WX 14C

CROSS THAT LINE.
Tracks: / Prisoner, The / Powerhouse / Cross that line / Guardians of the breath / Wanders to you / Everlasting love / Last supper, The / Out of thin air / Fresh air waltz / Those who move clouds.
LP: WX 225
MC: WX 225C

DREAM INTO ACTION.
Tracks: / Things can only get better / Life in one day / Dream into action / No one is to blame / Look mama / Assault and battery / Automaton / Is there a difference? / Elegy / Specialty / Why look for the key? / Hunger for flesh.
LP: WX 15
MC: WX 15C

HUMAN'S LIB.
Tracks: / Conditioning / What is love? / Pearl in the shell / Hide and seek / Hunt the self / New song / Don't always look at the rain / Equality / Natural / Human's lib.
LP: WX 1
MC: WX 1C

ONE TO ONE.
Tracks: / You know I love you don't you? / Balance of love, The / All I want / Where are we going? / Don't want to fight anymore / Step into these shoes / Will you still be there? / Good luck bad luck / Give me strength / Little bit of snow.
LP: WX 68
MC: WX 68C

Jones, Ieuan

IEUAN JONES.
Tracks: / La mandoline / Song for Guy / Going home (theme from 'Local Hero') / Sonata in C minor - movements 2/3 / Night and day / Summertime / New York, New York, (theme from) / Live and let die / Adagio / Do you know where you're going to? / Arabesque No.1 / On my own / Spartacus / Gayaneh / Gymnopedies No.2 / Concerto in B flat (movement 1).
LP: 209.283
MC: 409.283

UNCOMMON HARP, THE.
Tracks: / Introduction, Cadenza and Rondo / On golden pond / Clair de Lune / Spanish romance / Hello / Chess / Rustle on Spring, Op. 32. No.3 / Chi mai / Pavane pour une infante defunte / First waltz, Op.83.
LP: REN 636
MC: ZCN 636

Jones, Isham

ISHAM JONES & HIS ORCHESTRA 1920-24.
LP: FG 404

Jones, Ivan

BLACK WHIP (Jones, Ivan "Boogaloo Joe").
Tracks: / Black whip / My love / Freak off / Daniel / Ballad of mad dogs and Englishmen, The / Crank me up.
LP: CA 671

Jones, Ivy Terrace

SHOT OF RHYTHM & BLUES, A.
LP: BS 4701

Jones, Jack

16 CLASSIC TRACKS: JACK JONES.
LP: MCL 1680

ALL TO YOURSELF.
LP: TVL 2

BREAD WINNERS.
Tracks: / Make it with you / Baby I'm a want you / Coming apart / If / Daughter / Games of magic / Everything I own / Diary / It don't matter to me / Come again.
LP: SF 8280
MC: PK 11618

DEAR HEART (And other great songs of love).
LP: MOIR 119
MC: CMOIR 119

DEJA VU.
Tracks: / My eyes adored you / Deja Vu / Don't stop now / Quiet please, there's a lady on stage / Love is a game / I've been here all the time / Love boat / Wives and lovers / This is it / I could have told you so / Just the way you are / Evergreen.
MC: 3192 685
LP: 2384 128

FIRE AND RAIN.
Tracks: / Race is on, The / Bridge over troubled water / Lyin' eyes / My life / Breaking up is hard to do / Just the two of us / We can chase the rainbows / Long and winding road, The / My fault / Summertime / You've got a friend / I got plenty o' nuttin' / Fire and rain / Bess, you is my woman now.
LP: PRCV 119
MC: TC PRCV 119

FULL LIFE, THE.
Tracks: / You make it easy / L.A. breakdown (and take me in) / You need a man / Once in a while / Send in the clowns / God only knows / Don't be scared / Yesterday's news / Try it again / Love story / Disney girls.
LP: PL 12067
MC: PK 12067

GOLDEN GREATS: JACK JONES.
Tracks: / Wives and lovers / Lollipops and roses / Dear heart / Shadow of your smile / Race is on, The / Charade / Girl talk / Impossible dream, The / Day in the life of a fool, A / If you go away / Alfie / Yesterday / Michelle / Free again / People.
LP: MCM 5007
MC: MCMC 5007

HARBOUR.
Tracks: / Here's to love / Do me wrong, but do me / It didn't come easy / All cried out / Would you say I love you / Alone too long / Fools in love / 'Til I can't take it anymore / I never had it so good / That's what friends are for / Harbour.
LP: APL1 0408

I AM A SINGER.
Tracks: / I am a singer / Love dance / Foolish heart / You've changed / Leave a tender moment alone / Wind beneath my wings / Another Rio / Other woman, The / All because of love / Lovesick / You are the love of my life / Here's that rainy day / Round midnight.
LP: C5-531
MC: C5K-531

I'VE BEEN HERE ALL THE TIME.
Tracks: / This is it / Love comes for you / Deja vu / I could have told you so / Here to love you / Don't wish too hard / Don't stop now / That's good enough for now / Love is a game / I've been here all the time.
LP: POLS 1020

JACK JONES ENTERTAINS.
Tracks: / Wives and lovers / Alfie / Lollipops and roses / You've got your troubles / More / Yesterday / What now my love / Shadow of your smile / Dear heart / If you go away / Girl talk / I believe in you / She loves me / Watch what happens / Impossible dream, The / What the world needs now is love / Our song (CD only) / Love bug (CD only) / Fly me to the moon (CD only) / Charade (CD only).
LP: MFP 5859
MC: TCMFP 5859

LOVE SONGS: JACK JONES.
Tracks: / Here's that rainy day / I've grown accustomed to her face / Fly me to the moon / Girl talk / Time after time / All the things you are / Strangers in the night / Autumn leaves / Love letters / And I love you so / She loves me / What the world needs now is love / People will say we're in love / True love / To love and be loved / Moonlight becomes you.
LP: MFP 41 5728-1
MC: MFP 41 5728-4

MAGIC MOMENTS.
Tracks: / Make it with you / Everything I own / Windmills of your mind / What are you doing the rest of your life? / Sweet gingerbread man / Love story / Send in the clowns / I'll never fall in love again / I won't last a day without you / What I did for love / After the lovin' / Without her / Homeward bound / For all we know / She / Yesterday when I was young / Where is love? / I think it's going to rain today / That's the way I've always heard it should be / Old-fashioned way, The / Baby I'm a want you / That's what friends are for / Here's to love / You're a lady / Once in a while / Home thoughts from abroad / It doesn't matter to me / We had it all / Light my fire.
MC: NK 894 04

MAGIC OF JACK JONES, THE.
2LP: SDL 005

MAKE IT WITH YOU.
Tracks: / If I could read your mind / By the time I get to Phoenix / Look of love, The / You're a lady / But I loved you / I won't last a day without you / Old-fashioned way, The / Send in the clowns / If / I'll never fall in love again / Time for us, A / Light my fire / Everything I own / Once in a while / For all we know / Baby I'm a want you / Make it with you /

Somewhere / Goin' out of my head / Windmills of your mind / It's too late / Spinning wheel / It don't matter to me.
2LP: CR 072
MCSET: CRT 072

NOBODY DOES IT BETTER.
Tracks: / Love boat / Evergreen / Silver lady / Nobody does it better / Quiet please, there's a lady on stage / Wives and lovers / I could have been a sailor / Just the way you are / My eyes adored you / Ready to take a chance again.
LP: 2383547

SONG FOR YOU, A.
Tracks: / If / If you could read my mind / It's too late / Doesn't anybody know / Love looks so good on you / Song for you, A / What have they done to the moon / Let me be the one / Pure imagination / This is your life / There's still time.
LP: SF 8228

SPECIAL COLLECTION.
Tracks: / Song for you / Windmills of your mind / If you could read my mind / It's too late / We've only just begun / Diary / What are you doing the rest of your life / Since I fell for you / For all we know / If.
MC: INTK 5007
LP: INTS 5007

TOGETHER.
Tracks: / You're a lady / Little girl / We will / Maybe / I know that one / We've only just begun / I won't last a day without you / My lonely room / Simple man / That's enough for me / That's the way I've always heard it should be.
LP: SF 8342

UNFORGETTABLE: JACK JONES.
Tracks: / Race is on / Bridge over troubled water / Lyin' eyes / My life / Breaking up is hard to do / Just the two of us / Chase the rainbows / Long and winding road, The / My fault.
LP: UNLP 021
MC: UNMC 021

VERY BEST OF JACK JONES, THE.
Tracks: / Make it with you / Everything I own / If / Windmills of your mind / What are you doing the rest of your life? / Sweet gingerbread man / Love story / Send in the clowns / I'll never fall in love again / I won't last a day without you / What I did for love / After the lovin' / Without her / Homeward bound / For all we know / She / For all we know / Yesterday when I was young / Where is love? / I think it's going to rain today / That's the way I've always heard it should be.
LP: RCALP 5041
MC: RCAK 5041

WHAT I DID FOR LOVE.
Tracks: / After the lovin' / Home thoughts from abroad / What I did for love / If that's the way you want it / Don't mention love / That's what lovin' means / You turn me around / Please just go / Empty chairs / She / Over to you now / After the lovin' (reprise).
LP: RS 1014
MC: PK 11690

WITH LOVE FROM JACK JONES.
Tracks: / Light my fire / But I loved you / And I'll go / I'll never fall in love again / Sweet child / I really want to know you / You and the night and the music / Since I fell for you / Goin' out of my head / Somewhere / Look of love, The / For all we know / If you ever leave me / I'm getting sentimental over you / Love story / Mean to me / you've changed / It's nice to be with you / Dreams are all I have of you / Without her.
2LP: DPS 2038
MC: DPTK 5008

WITH ONE MORE LOOK AT YOU.
Tracks: / With one mroe look at you / Goodbye old buddies / Traces of a long forgotten tune / Jealous kind, The / Belonging / If I only had the words (to tell you) / Dixie chicken / Perfect strangers / Cajun song / Empty hearts.
LP: PL 12361
MC: PK 12361

WRITE ME A LOVE SONG CHARLIE.
Tracks: / Write me a love song, Charlie / I love you song, The / Like roses (comme les roses) / After loving you (de t'avoir aimee) / We had it all (me voila seul) / She / Happy anniversary / Old fashioned way, The / Yesterday when I was young / Happy days, The / You've let yourself go.
LP: APL1 0773

Jones, Jackie

I WILL ALWAYS LOVE YOU (See under Batson, Whitfield).

Jones, Jacqui

LOVE TONITE (See under Collins, Dave) (Jones, Jacqui & Dave Collins).

Jones, James Earl

POEMS FROM BLACK AFRICA.
MC: 1315

Jones, Jill

JILL JONES.
Tracks: / Mia Bocca / G-spot / Violet blue / With you / All day, all night / For love / My man / Baby, you're a trip / Intro (baby you're a trip).
LP: 925575 1
MC: 925575 4
LP: WX 110
MC: WX 110 C

Jones, Jimmy (comedy)

BEST OF JIMMY JONES.
LP: KIN 3
MC: KINC 3

LIVE AT THE TALK OF EAST ANGLIA.
LP: KIN 1

Jones, Jimmy (singer)

GOOD TIMIN'.
LP: CUB 3847

LET'S TALK ABOUT JESUS.
LP: SL 14715

WHEN I GET TO HEAVEN.
LP: SL 14667

Jones, Jo

ESSENTIAL JO JONES, THE.
Tracks: / Shoeshine boy / Lover man / Georgia may / Caravan / Lincoln heights / Embraceable you / Satin doll / Little Susie / Spider Kelly's blues / Cubano chant / Splittin' / Sweet Lorraine / Bicycle for two / Ol' man river / Sometimes I'm happy.
2LP: VJD 542

INTRODUCING THE GUITAR OF JOE JONES.
Tracks: / Mindbender, The / There is a mountain / Games / Sticks and stones / Blues for Bruce / Beat goes on / Call me / Right now.
LP: PR 7557

JO JONES QUARTET (Jones, Jo Quartet & Ray Bryant).
LP: FS 323

MAIN MAN, THE.
Tracks: / Goin' to Chicago / I want to be happy / Ad lib / Dark eyes / Metrical portions / Ol' man river.
LP: 23 10799
MC: K10 799

OUR MAN PAPA JO.
Tracks: / Take the 'A' train / Stompin' at the Savoy / My last affair / Broadway / As time goes by / Wrap your troubles in dreams / Solitude / It don't mean a thing.
LP: YX 7527

Jones, John Paul

SAXY.
LP: SRL 1008

SCREAM FOR HELP (Film soundtrack).
Tracks: / Spaghetti Junction / Bad child / Take it or leave it / Chilli sauce / Silver train / Christie / Here I am / Crackback.
LP: 780 190-1
MC: 780 190-4

Jones, Johnny

JOHNNY JONES & BILLY BOY ARNOLD (Jones, Johnny & Billy Boy Arnold).
LP: SNTF 821

TAMPA RED WITH JOHNNY JONES (See under Tampa Red) (Jones, Johnny & Tampa Red).

Jones, Jonah

BUTTERFLIES IN THE RAIN (Jones, Jonah & His Swing Band).
LP: CLP 83

HARLEM JUMP AND SWING (Jones, Jonah Sextet & Pete Brown Sextet).
Tracks: / There will never be another you / I can't believe that you're in love with me / Used blues / Moonlight in Vermont / World is waiting for the sunrise, The / Tea for two / Delta blues / Beatle Street blues / Down by the riverside / European blues / You're the cream in my coffee / Wrap your troubles in dreams.
LP: AFF 96

IN PARIS 1954.
LP: SW 8408
MC: SWC 8408

JONAH JONES QUARTET/GLEN GRAY & THE CASA LOMA ORCHESTRA (Jones, Jonah & Glen Gray).
Tracks: / Baubles, bangles and beads / Echoes of Harlem / Two o'clock jump / I can't get started / Boy meets horn / Hot lips / After you've gone / West end blues / Ciribiribin / Tenderly / Sugar blues / Apollo jumps.
LP: EMS 1185
MC: TCEMS 1185

JONAH'S WAIL.
LP: 500075

JUMPING WITH A SHUFFLE.
Tracks: / Dream / You're driving me crazy / Lazy river / More than you know / Nine-twenty special / Entratter's blues / Misty / Great lie, The / On the sunny side of the street / One for my baby / Lonesome road / My Monday date.
LP: PM 154 771 1

Jones, Jonathan

MUSE DELIGHT'D, THE.
LP: PLR 037

ORGAN IN THE AGE OF REASON.
LP: PLR 059

Jones, Kim

GUESS WHO CARES.
Tracks: / Guess who cares / Anyway.
LP: OWN 1

Jones, Linda

20 GOLDEN CLASSICS.
LP: COL 5120

Jones, Little Hat

TEXAS BLUES GUITAR.
LP: BD 2010

Jones, "Little" Sonny

"LITTLE" SONNY JONES.
LP: CLPS 1017

Jones, Llinos

YR UNIG UN.
Tracks: / Yr unig un.
MC: POPDY CP1

Jones, Louise

IT AIN'T EASY.
Tracks: / Don't stop / I'm holding on / It ain't easy / You can count on me / My love for you / Heart to heart talk / Let it swing / What good is a memory / Talk some more / Love like ours, A / Taking me high / Haunted house.
MC: MCLP 1001

Jones, Luke

WEST COAST R & B 1947-52 (Jones, Luke & Red Mack).
LP: KK 7440

Jones, Martin

CAPRICES AND SCHERZI (see under Mendelssohn for full details).

PRELUDES AND FUGUES (See under Mendelssohn for full details).

SONATAS (See under Mendelssohn for full details).

SONGS WITHOUT WORDS (VOLS I AND II) (See under Mendelssohn for full details).

VARIATIONS AND FANTASIES (See under Mendelssohn for full details).

Jones, Michael

PIANOSCAPES.
LP: LP 1001
MC: CAS 1001

SEASCAPES.
LP: LP 1004
MC: CAS 1004

Jones, Mick

MICK JONES.
LP: WX 290
MC: WX 290C

Jones, Moody

SNOOKY PRYOR & MOODY JONES (See under Pryor, Snooky) (Jones, Moody & Pryor, Snooky).

Jones, Mose

BLACKBIRD.
Tracks: / Do you want somebody? / Blackbird / Ooh baby / Jump back / Something's wrong / Rub / Ain't no time like the present.
LP: PL 12793

Jones, Nic

BALLADS AND SONGS.
LP: LER 2014

FROM THE DEVIL TO A STRANGER.
LP: LTRA 507

NIC JONES.
LP: LER 2027

NOAH'S ARK TRAP.
LP: LER 2091
LP: SHAN 29003

PENGUIN EGGS.
Tracks: / Canadee-i-o / Drowned lovers / Humpback whale / Little pot stove / Courting is a pleasure / Barrack Street / Planxty Davis / Flandyke Shore / Farewell to the gold.
LP: 12TS 411
MC: 5 SH 79058

SONGS OF A CHANGING WORLD (see Raven,Jon/Nic Jones/Tony Rose) (Jones, Nic/Jon Raven/Tony Rose).

Jones, Nigel

HARVEST (see under Raven, Jon/Nigel Jones/Dave Oxley) (Jones, Nigel/Jon Raven/Dave Oxley).

SENTINEL AND THE FOOLS OF THE FINEST DEGREE (Jones, Nigel Mazlyn).
Tracks: / All in the name of love / Sentinel / Flying / Roll away / Water road / All in all / Folls / Wheels.
LP: AVA 105

Jones, Nyles

WELFARE BLUES.
LP: CW 204

Jones, Oliver

COOKIN' AT SWEET BASIL.
Tracks: / Hymn to a friend / You are too beautiful / Blue mountain / Young and foolish / Take the 'A' train / Pe gros bois blues / Fly me to the moon / Someone to watch over me.
LP: BRMLP 020

JAZZ & RIBS LIVE AT BIDDLE'S (Jones, Oliver Trio & Charles Biddle & Bernard Primeau).
LP: JUST 1

MANY MOODS OF..., THE.
LP: JUST 3

SPEAK LOW SWING HARD.
LP: BRMLP 019

Jones, Oran "Juice"

G.T.O. GANGSTERS TAKIN' OVER.
Tracks: / Cold spending my $ money / Not on the outside / You don't miss the rain / How to love again / We were friends / I just can't say goodbye / Rock the night away / Baby don't walk out on me / Your song / U bring it out.
LP: 4604061
MC: 4604064

JUICE.
Tracks: / Rain, The / You can't hide from love / Here I go again / Curiosity / Your song / Love will find a way / It's yours / 1.2.1. / Two faces.
LP: DEF 26934
MC: 4026934

RAIN ,THE.
Tracks: / Rain, The / Your song.
LP: A 7303

TO BE IMMORTAL.
Tracks: / Money, honey / Pipe dreams / Gangster attitude / Never say goodbye / To be immortal / Dollar and a dream / Sacrifices / Shaniqua / Street style / Time.
LP: 466004 1
MC: 466004 4

Jones, Paul

HITS AND BLUES.
Tracks: / High time / Sonny boy williamson / When my little girl is smiling / Not before time / Bony moronie / Thinkin' ain't bad for me / I can't hold on much longer / How sweet it is / Nosher burns / Little sadie / Along came jones / You have no idea / It's getting better / Aquarius.
LP: OU 2231

MEMPHIS SLIM & PAUL JONES AT RONNIE SCOTTS (See under Slim, Memphis).

Jones, Philip

EASY WINNERS (Jones, Philip Brass Ensemble).
MC: KZRC 895

GRAND MARCH (Jones, Philip Brass Ensemble).
Tracks: / Marche Lorraine / Old comrades / Under the double eagle / Dambusters / Lilliburlero / Colonel Bogey / Entry of the gladiators / Radetzky march / Sambre et Meuse / Marching through Georgia / Celebration.
LP: 4173291

LOLLIPOPS (Jones, Philip Brass Ensemble).
Tracks: / London minatures / Londoner in New York / Flight of the bumble bee / Variations on a Tyrolean theme.
LP: D 8503

PICTURES AT AN EXHIBITION (See under Mussorgsky (composer)) (Jones, Philip Brass Ensemble).

WORLD OF BRASS.
Tracks: / Le mourisque / Il est bel et bon / Sonata plan' e forte / Heigh ho holiday / Earl of Oxford's march / Toye, A / Air / Galliard battaglia / La Peri / Fanfare for St. Edmondsbury.
LP: SPA 464

WORLD OF THE TRUMPET.
LP: SDD 274

Jones, Philly Joe

BLUES FOR DRACULA (Jones, Philly Joe Sextet).

LP: OJC 230

DAMERONIA.
Tracks: / Philly JJ / Soultrane / Sid's delight / On a misty night / Fountainbleau / Scene is clean, The.
LP: UP 27 11

GREEN DOLPHIN STREET (see under Evans, Bill) (Jones, Philly Joe & Bill Evans).

LOOK STOP LISTEN (Jones, Philly Joe & Dameronia).
LP: UP 27 15

MEAN WHAT YOU SAY.
Tracks: / Mean what you say / You tell me / DC farewell / Jim's jewel / Gretchen / Ugetsu.
LP: SNTF 735
MC: ZCSN 735

PHILLY MIGNON.
LP: GXY 5112

'ROUND MIDNIGHT.
Tracks: / That's Earl's brother / It don't mean a thing / Round midnight / Percy.
LP: LPPS 111 15

TRAILWAY EXPRESS.
Tracks: / Mo Jo / Gone gone gone / Baubles, bangles and beads / Here's that rainy day / Ladybird.
LP: BLP 30116

WEST COAST CONFERENCE (see under Perkins,Bill) (Jones, Philly Joe/Bill Perkins/Paul Chambers).

Jones, Quincy

BACK ON THE BLOCK.
LP: WX 313
MC: WX 313C
MC: 926020 4

BEST, THE.
Tracks: / Ai no corrida / Stuff like that / I heard that / You have to do it yourself / Love, I never had it so good / Betcha wouldn't hurt me / Superstition / Razzamatazz / Dude, The / Is it love that we're missin'? / One hundred ways / I'm gonna miss you in the morning / Body heat.
LP: AMLH 68542
MC: CAM 68542

BILLY ECKSTINE AND QUINCY JONES (See under Eckstine, Billy) (Jones, Quincy & Billy Eckstine).

BOSSA NOVA.
Tracks: / Soul bossa nova / Boogie bossa nova / Desafinado / Carnival / Se e tarde me pardoa / On the street where you live / Samba de una nota so / Lalo bossa nova / Serenta / Chega de saudade.
LP: 814 225 1

DEADEND WALKING IN SPACE.
LP: PLP 1
MC: PMC 1

DUDE, THE.
Tracks: / Ai no corrida / Dude, The / Just one / Betcha wouldnt hurt me / Something special / Razzamatazz / One hundred ways / Valas / Turn on the action.
LP: AMLK 63721
MC: CKM 63721

GO WEST, MAN.
LP: JASM 1048
LP: FS 73

GREAT WIDE WORLD, THE.
Tracks: / Lester leaps in / Ghana / Caravan / Everybody's blues / Cherokee / Airmail special / They say it's wonderful / Chant of the weed / I never have seen snow.
LP: 6336 705

LISTEN UP - THE LIVES OF QUINCY JONES.
LP: 7599263221
MC: 7599263224

LOVE AND PEACE.
LP: 226 2025
MC: 216 2025

MELLOW MADNESS.
Tracks: / Is it love that we're missin' / Paranoid / Mellow madness / Beautiful black girl / Listen (what it is) / Just a little taste of me / My cherie amour / Tryin' to find out about you / Cry baby / Bluesette.
LP: AMLH 64526

MUSIC IN MY LIFE.
Tracks: / Superstition / Getaway love theme / Anderson Tapes, Theme from / Cast your fate to the wind / What's going on / Guitar blues odyssey from roots to fruits / Summer in the City / Eye of love, The / You've got it bad girl / Brown ballad / Manteca / Tribute to Afro day dreaming / First time ever I saw your face, The.
LP: SHM 3126
MC: HSC 3126

QUINCY JONES ALL STARS (Jones, Quincy All Stars).
LP: ESQ 322

QUINCY JONES AND HIS ORCHESTRA (Jones, Quincy & His Orchestra).
Tracks: / Bridge over troubled water / You've got it bad, girl / Gula matari / Ironside / Smackwater Jack / Anderson Tapes, Theme from / Oh happy day / Cast your fate to the wind.
LP: MFP 50441

QUINTESSENCE, THE.
Tracks: / Quintessence / Robot portrait / Little Karen / Straight, no chaser / For Lena and Lennie / Hard sock dance / Invitation / Twitch.
LP: JAS 79
LP: AS 11
MC: ASC 11

SMACKWATER JACK.
Tracks: / Smackwater Jack / Cast your fate to the wind / Ironside / What's going on / Anderson tapes, Theme from / Brown ballad / Hikky burr / Guitar blues odyssey from roots to fruits.
LP: AMLS 63037
MC: CAM 63037

SOUNDS...AND STUFF LIKE THAT.
Tracks: / Stuff like that / Love, I never had it so good / Superwoman / I'm gonna miss you in the morning / Love me by my name / Takin' it to the streets.
LP: AMLH 64685
MC: CAM 64685

TAKE FIVE.
Tracks: / Walk on the wild side / Bossa nova USA / Take five / Gravy waltz / Exodus / Back at the chicken shack / Watermelon man / Cast your fate to the wind.
LP: B 90115
MC: MB 990115

THIS IS HOW I FEEL.
Tracks: / Walkin' / Sleepin' bee / Sermonette / Stockholm sweetenin' / Evening in Paris / Boo's blues.
LP: JASM 1035

WALKING IN SPACE.
Tracks: / Dead end / Walking in space / Killer Joe / Love and peace / I never told you / Oh happy day.
LP: AMLH 68050

WE HAD A BALL.
Tracks: / Birth of a band / Golden boy theme / Soul serenade / Midnight sun will never set, The / Boy in the tree / Happy faces / Airmail special / Back at the chicken shack / Exodus / Everybody's blues / Eesom / I had a ball.
LP: TIME 07
MC: TIMEC 07

Jones, Rev. Jim

LAST SUPPER, THE.
LP: TOPY 013

Jones, Richard M.

FROM N.O. TO CHICA (Jones, Richard M, Willie Hightower, Frankie Franko).
LP: CI 001

Jones, Rickie Lee

FLYING COWBOYS.
LP: WX 309
MC: WX 309C

GIRL AT HER VOLCANO.
Tracks: / Lush life / Walk away Rene / Hey bub / Rainbow sleeves / My funny valentine / Under the boardwalk / So long.
LP: 923805 1
MC: 923805 4

MAGAZINE.
Tracks: / Prelude to gravity / Gravity / Jukebox fury / It must be love / Magazine / Real end, The / Deep space / Runaround Rorschachs / Theme for the Pope / Unsigned painting ,The / Wierd beast, The.
LP: 925117 1
MC: 925117 4

PIRATES.
Tracks: / We belong together / Living it up / Skeletons / Woody and Dutch on the slow train to Peking / Pirates / Lucky guy / Traces of western slopes / Returns.
LP: K 56816
MC: K4 56816

POP POP.
LP: GEF 24426
MC: GEFC 24426

RICKIE LEE JONES.
Tracks: / On Saturday afternoons in 1963 / Night train / Young blood / Easy money / Last chance Texaco / Danny's all star joint / Coolsville / Weasel and the white boy's cool / Company / After hours (12 bars past midnight) / Chuck E's in love.
LP: K 56628
MC: 923949 4
MC: K4 56628

Jones, Robin

EYE OF THE HURRICANE (Jones, Robin Quartet & Esmond Selwyn).
Tracks: / Eye of the hurricane / Lush life / Up jumped spring / Passion dance / Berimbau.
LP: SPJ 519

Jones, Rodeo

GET WISE (See under Rodeo Jones).

Jones, Rodney

ARTICULATION.
Tracks: / Articulation / 1978 / Hard New York swing / Interlude 1 / Childville / Blues for Wes / Nereda.
LP: SJP 125

MY FUNNY VALENTINE (Jones, Rodney & Tommy Flanagen Quartet).
LP: SJP 162

Jones, Sam

BASSIST, THE.
Tracks: / Rhythm-a-ning / Lillie / Seascape / Tragic magic / Hymn of Scorpio / Bittersuite.
LP: DS 861
LP: IP 7720

EASTER REBELLION (see under Walton, Cedar) (Jones, Sam, Cedar Walton, Billy Higgins, George Coleman).

EASTERN REBELLION VOL.2 (See Under Walton, Cedar) (Jones, Sam, Cedar Walton, Billy Higgins, George Coleman).

NEW YORK JAZZ (see under Cuber, Ronnie) (Jones, Sam,Ronnie Cuber,Tom Harrell,Rein deGraff,Louis Hayes).

SOMETHING IN COMMON.
Tracks: / Every man is a King / For all we know / Blue silver / Something in common / Bolivia / Seven minds.
LP: MR 5149

SOMETHING NEW.
LP: IP 7726

THIS HERE IS BOBBY TIMMONS (see under Timmons, Bobby) (Jones, Sam, Bobby Timmons, Jimmy Cobb).

TWELVE PIECE BAND - SOMETHING NEW.
LP: SB 2004

VISITATION.
LP: SCS 1097
MC: SCM 51097

Jones, Sebastian

MUSIC FROM THE TRAVELLING MAN (See under Browne,Duncan & Sebastian Graham Jones) (Browne, Duncan & Sebastian Graham Jones).

Jones, Shirley

ALWAYS IN THE MOOD.
Tracks: / Do you get enough love / Breaking up / Last night I needed somebody / She knew about me / Always in the mood / I'll do anything for you / Surrender.
LP: PHIL 4000
MC: TCPHIL 4000

Jones, Spike

BEST OF SPIKE JONES - VOL.2.
LP: 26 21113

BING CROSBY WITH SPIKE JONES & JIMMY DURANTE (see under Crosby, Bing) (Jones, Spike, Bing Crosby, Jimmy Durante).

CAN'T STOP MURDERING.
LP: 26 28001

GREATEST HITS: SPIKE JONES.
MC: 818

I WENT TO YOUR WEDDING (Jones, Spike & His City Slickers).
Tracks: / I went to your wedding / I haven't been home for three whole nights / Too young / Sheik of Araby, The / Three little fishes / Pop corn snack / Rhapsody from Hunger(y) / Clink clink another drink / Old MacDonald had a farm / I'm getting sentimental over you / Our hour / People are funnier than anybody.
LP: NL 89310
MC: NK 89310
LP: INTS 5052

KING OF CORN, THE.
Tracks: / People will say we're in love / G.I. haircut / It never rains in Sunny California / Wang wang blues / My little girl / Sound effects man, The / Ragtime cowboy Joe / Vamp, The / He broke my heart in three places / Besame mucho / I'm goin' back to where I came from / Trolly song, The / Red wing / There's a fly on my music / Row row row / I wanna girl just like the girl who married dear old dad / Jingle bells.
MC: JAS C2527
LP: JASM 2527

MURDERS THEM ALL.
Tracks: / Liebestraum / Blue Danube / Flight of the bumble bee / None but the lonely heart / Rhapsody from Hunger(y) / William Tell / Carmen murdered / Dance of the hours / Glow worm / I kiss your hand madame / Love in bloom / Hotcha cornia / Black bottom / Hawiian war chant / I went to your wedding / I'm in the mood for love / That old black magic.
2LP: NL 89044
MC: NK 89044

ON THE AIR 1943 & 1944 (Jones, Spike & His City Slickers).
LP: SH 2073

RADIO RECORDINGS (Jones, Spike & His City Slickers).
LP: SH 2073
MC: CSH 2073

SPIKE JONES 1946 (Jones, Spike & his Other Orchestra).
Tracks: / Laura / When Yuba plays the rhumba on the tuba / I'll never be the same / Minka / I've got the world on a string / Spike rocks on troc / Hardly ever amber / I only have eyes for you / Pico pick up / Young man with a French horn / E-bob-o-lee-bob / Speak speaks.
LP: HSR 185

SPIKE JONES AND HIS CITY SLICKERS (Jones, Spike & His City Slickers).
LP: JASS 2
LP: LOP 14,103

SPIKE JONES MURDERS AGAIN.
2LP: 26 28019

SPIKE JONES VOL.3 (Who killed Chloe?).
Tracks: / Blacksmith song / Moo woo woo / Don't give the chair to Buster / Big bad Bill / That's what makes the world go round / Hey Mabel / And the great big saw came nearer / Now laugh / Chloe / Trailer Annie / Mary Lou / Barstool cowboy / Row, row, row / Toot toot tootsie / Siam / No no Nora.
LP: HQ 2054

STANDARD TRANSCRIPTION DISCS 1942-44 (Spike Jones vol.1).
LP: HQ 2041

THANK YOU MUSIC LOVERS.
Tracks: / Cocktails for two / William Tell / Chloe / My old flame / Glow worm / None but the lonely heart / Laura / Man on the flying trapeze, The / You always hurt the one you love / Der Fuehrer's face / Dance of the hours / Hawaiian war chant.
LP: NL 89057
MC: NK 89057
LP: LSA 3084

UNCOLLECTED, THE (1946) (Jones, Spike & his Other Orchestra).
Tracks: / Laura / When Yuba plays the rumba on the tuba / I'll never be the same / Minka / I've got the world on a string / Spike rocks the Troc / Hardly ever amber / I only have eyes for you / Pico pick-up / Young man with a French horn / E-bob-o-lee-bob / Spike speaks (theme).
LP: HUK 185

Jones, Steve

FIRE AND GASOLINE.
LP: MCG 6067
MC: MCGC 6067

MERCY.
Tracks: / Give it up / That's enough / Raining in my heart / With or without you / Pleasure and pain / Pretty baby / Drugs suck / Through the night / Love letters / Mercy.
LP: MCF 3384
MC: MCFC 3384

Jones, Tamiko

CAN'T LIVE WITHOUT YOUR LOVE (OLD GOLD) (See under Earland, Charles - Let the music ...).

CLOUDY.
Tracks: / Cloudy / Creepin' / Feel like makin' love / Make love to your mind / Afraid of losing you / Let it flow / Boy you're growing on me / Reachin' out for your love / Woman driver / Let it flow Tamiko.
LP: CLP 602

LET IT FLOW.
Tracks: / Let it flow / Reaching out for your love / Creepin' / Feel like makin' love / Boy you're growing on me / Oh how I love you / Let me in your life / Make love to your mind / Cloudy / Afraid of losing you.
LP: CLP 537

Jones, Tammy

BEST OF TAMMY JONES.
MC: 40 31624

COUNTRY GIRL.
LP: MSBWL 1

LET ME TRY AGAIN.
LP: . . . . EPC 80853

WEEKEND LOVING.
LP: . . . . Unknown

Jones, Terry (nar)

ALADDIN AND THE WONDERFUL LAMP (See under Aladdin... (bk).

ARABIAN NIGHTS: ALADDIN (See under Aladdin... (bk)).

VOYAGES OF SINBAD (See under Sinbad the Sailor).

Jones, Thad

ECLIPSE.
LP: . . . . SLP 4089

FIRST JAZZ SUITE (Jones, Thad & Mel Lewis).
Tracks: / Brasserie / Father / Sing / Ballade / For life / Little pixie.
LP: . . . . JR 122

GREETINGS AND SALUTATIONS.
LP: . . . . FLC 5001

LIVE: THAD JONES (Live Jazzhus Slukefter, Tivoli) (Jones, Thad, Eclipse).
LP: . . . . MLP 15669

THAD JONES AND AURA RULLY.
LP: . . . . FLC 5020

THAD JONES AND MEL LEWIS (Jones, Thad & Mel Lewis).
2LP: . . . . BND 4004
MC: . . . . MC 9004

THAD JONES ECLIPSE (Jones, Thad, Eclipse).
LP: . . . . MLP 15652

Jones, Tim

POWER OF LOVE.
LP: . . . . KPM 1
MC: . . . . TCKPM 1

Jones, Tom

6 TRACK HITS.
Tracks: / Daughter of darkness / My way / What becomes of the broken hearted? / Raining in my heart / Till / Say you'll stay until tomorrow.
MC: 7SC 5004

13 SMASH HITS.
Tracks: / Don't fight it / You keep me hanging on / Hold on I'm coming / I was made to love her / Keep on running / Get ready / (It looks like) I'll never fall in love again / I know / I wake up crying / Funny how time slips away / Danny boy / It's a man's man's man's world / Yesterday.
LP: . . . . SKL 4909

16 LOVE SONGS.
Tracks: / Without you (non c'e che lei) / Love me tonight / Minute of my time / More / Nearness of you / Let there be love / I can't stop loving you / Fly me to the moon / If ever i would leave you / Hello young lovers / Laura / Once there was a time / Without you / Funny how time slips away / Without love / Endlessly / He'll have to go.
LP: . . . . CN 2065
MC: CN4 2065

20 GREATEST HITS: TOM JONES.
2LP: . . . . TJD 1/1 1/2

AFTER DARK.
LP: . . . . SMR 978
MC: . . . . SMC 978

ALONG CAME JONES.
LP: . . . . LK 6693

AT THIS MOMENT.
Tracks: / Kiss / Move closer / Who's gonna take you home tonight? / I'm counting on you / Till the end of time / What you been missing / After the tears / I can't get no satisfaction / Touch my heart.
LP: . . . . TOM TV1
MC: . . . . TOM TC1

CARRYING A TORCH (ALBUM).
Tracks: / Carrying a torch / Some peace of mind / Strange boat / I'm not feeling it anymore / Do I ever cross your mind? / Fool for rock 'n' roll / Only in America / Couldn't say goodbye / Killer on the sheets / Give me a chance / Zip it up / It must be you / Old flame blue.
LP: . . . . ADD 20
MC: . . . . ZDD 20

CLOSE UP.
LP: . . . . SKL 5132

COULDN'T SAY GOODBYE (See under Art Of Noise) (Art Of Noise & Tom Jones).

COUNTRY.
Tracks: / I don't want to be alone tonight / Woman's touch, A / If I ever had to say goodbye to you / Somebody's crying / Marie / My last goodbye / Touch me / We could be the closest of friends / It'll be me.
LP: 6337 247
MC: 7141 247

COUNTRY SIDE OF TOM JONES.
MC: CN4 2074

COUNTRY STYLE - GREEN GRASS OF HOME.
Tracks: / Ring of fire / Weeping Annaleah / Detroit City / Wish I could say no to you / Funny how time slips away / Cool water / I can't stop loving you / Riders in the sky / Green green grass of home / Little green apples / Funny familiar forgotten feelings / He'll have to go / Wichita lineman / Sixteen tons.
LP: . . . . TAB 67

DARLIN'.
Tracks: / Darlin' / But I do / Lady lay down / No guarantee / What in the world's come over you / One night / Daughter's question, A / I don't want to know you that well / Dime Queen of Nevada / Things that matter most to me ,The / Come home Rhondda boy.
LP: 2480 622
MC: 3194 622
LP: 818 898 1
MC: 818 898 4

DELILAH.
Tracks: / Delilah / Riders in the sky / To wait for love is to waste your life away / Funny, familiar forgotten feelings / Get ready / Georgia on my mind / When I fall in love / Danny boy / Begin the beguine / Help yourself / I was made to love her / Hey Jude / If you go away / Yesterday / My foolish heart / Let it be me / What's he got that I ain't got / One day soon / Weeping Annaleah / Make this heart of mine smile again / Lingering on / You can't stop love / My elusive dreams / Just out of reach / Only a fool breaks his own heart / Why can't I cry / Take me.
LP: . . . . CN 2057
MC: CN4 2057
LP: . . . . SKL 4946

DO YOU TAKE THIS MAN.
Tracks: / Do you take this man / How deep is the ocean / Out of mercy / Baby as you turn away / Go easy lady / Love is in the air / You're so good / Going through the motions / Lady put the light out / If I sing you a love song / But if you'd ever leave me / Hey love it's a feeling.
LP: . . . . SCX 6620

FROM THE HEART.
LP: . . . . LK 4814

GOLDEN HITS: TOM JONES.
Tracks: / Green green grass of home / I'm coming home / I'll never fall in love again / Not responsible / Help yourself / What's new pussycat / Love me tonight / It's not unusual.. / Funny, familiar forgotten feelings / Detroit City / With these hands / Minute of your time / Without love / Delilah.
LP: . . . . TAB 2
MC: . . . . KTBC 2
LP: 8101921

GREAT LOVE SONGS, THE.
Tracks: / I can't stop loving you / Without you / When I fall in love / With these hands / Little green apples / Once upon a time / I'm coming home / Nearness of you, The / Funny familiar forgotten feelings / Smile / I believe / Green, green grass of home / Wichita lineman / My elusive dreams / If you go away / I'll never fall in love again.
LP: . . . . CN 2086
MC: CN4 2086

GREATEST HITS: TOM JONES.
Tracks: / It's not unusual / Delilah / Help yourself / Daughter of darkness / I'll never fall in love again / Without love / With these hands / I'm coming home / Funny, familiar forgotten feelings / Green green grass of home / Detroit City / Something 'bout you baby I like / I, who have nothing / Till.
LP: . . . . STAR 2296
MC: . . . . STAC 2296
LP: . . . . SKL 5162

GREEN GREEN GRASS OF HOME.
Tracks: / Green, green grass of home / She's a lady / Funny, familiar forgotten feelings / Delilah / Not responsible / Detroit City / Help yourself / Till / Love me tonight / It's not unusual / I'll never fall in love again / Daughter of darkness / What's new pussycat? / I'm coming home / Once upon a time / This and that / Riders in the sky / He'll have to go / Funny, familiar forgotten feelings / Sixteen tons / Two brothers / My mother's eyes / Ring of fire / Field of yellow daisies / Wish I could say no to you / All I get from you is heartaches / Mohair Sam / Cool water / Detroit City.
LP: 8101691
MC: 8101694
LP: . . . . SKL 4855

HELP YOURSELF.
Tracks: / Help yourself / I can't break the news to myself / Bed, The / Isadora / Set me free / I get carried away / This house (the house song) / So afraid / If I promise / If you go away / My girl Maria / All I can say is goodbye / Ten guitars / What a party / Looking out of my window / Can't stop loving you / Let there be love / Without love.
LP: . . . . SKL 4982

I (WHO HAVE NOTHING).
LP: . . . . SKL 5072

I'M COMING HOME.
LP: . . . . WH 5001

IT'S NOT UNUSUAL.
Tracks: / It's not unusual / Delilah / Land of a thousand dances (live mix) / With these hands / Kansas City / It's magic / Promise her anything / When I fall in love / Memphis Tennessee / (Sittin' on) the dock of the bay / If you go away / Green green grass of home / What's new pussycat / It looks like I'll never fall in love again / I'm coming home / Hey Jude / Detroit City / Not responsible / My prayer.
LP: . . . . CN 2053
MC: CN4 2053

IT'S NOT UNUSUAL - HIS GREATEST HITS.
Tracks: / It's not unusual / Green green grass of home / Help yourself / I'll never fall in love again / Not responsible / Love me tonight / Without love / Delilah / What's new pussycat? / Detroit City / Once upon a time / Thunderball / Minute of your time, A / With these hands / Funny, familiar forgotten feelings / I'm coming home / You keep me hangin' on (Cassette & CD only.) / It's not unusual (Cassette & CD only.) / Land of a thousand dances.
LP: . . . . TOM 2
MC: . . . . KTOM 2

KISS (REMIX) (See under Art Of Noise) (Jones, Tom & Art Of Noise).

LIVE AT CAESAR'S PALACE.
2LP: . . . . UNKNOWN

LIVE AT THE TALK OF THE TOWN.
LP: . . . . SKL 4874

LIVE IN LAS VEGAS.
Tracks: / Turn on your lovelight / Bright lights and you girl, The / I can't stop loving you / Hard to handle / Delilah / Danny boy / (It looks like) I'll never fall in love again / Help yourself / Yesterday / Hey Jude / Love me tonight / It's not unusual / Twist and shout.
LP: . . . . SKL 5032

LOVE SONGS: TOM JONES.
LP: . . . . ADAH 438
MC: . . . . ADAHC 438

MATADOR.
Tracks: / Overture / There's no way out of here / To be a matador / I was born to be me / Only other people / Manolete, belmonte, joselito! / Boy from nowhere, A / Wake up Madrid / I'll take you out to dinner / This incredible journey / Don't be deceived / I'll dress you in white / Dance with death / Panama hat, A.
LP: 4509951
MC: 4509954

MINUTE OF YOUR TIME, A (ALBUM).
Tracks: / Minute of your time, A / Not responsible / When I fall in love / Let there be love / Without love / Wichita lineman / He'll have to go / Help yourself / My prayer / My elusive dreams / Taste of honey, A / It's magic / It takes a worried man / Mohair Sam / This house / Endlessly.
MC: . . . . PWKMC 4027P

MUSIC FOR THE MILLIONS.
Tracks: / What's new pussycat / Once upon a time / Not responsible / It's not unusual / Chills and fever / To wait for love / With these hands / Thunderball. Theme from / Ten guitars / This and that / I've got a heart / Triple cross.
LP: 6495106
MC: 7195106

NOT UNUSUAL.
MC: . . . . KTOMC 2

RESCUE ME.
Tracks: / Rescue me / Never had a lady before / Somebody out there will / Dancing endlessly / Dark storm on the horizon / What becomes of the broken hearted? / Once you hit the road / Flashback / Don't cry for me Argentina.
LP: . . . . SCX 6628

SHE'S A LADY.
LP: . . . . SKL 5089

SINGS 24 GREAT STANDARDS.
Tracks: / Green, green grass of home / Fly me to the moon / More / I'll never fall in love again / Autumn leaves / That old black magic / Spanish Harlem / My mother's eyes / My foolish heart / Begin the beguine / Georgia on my mind / I believe / Hello young lovers / Nearness of you, The / If you go away / Let it be me / With these hands / It's magic / When I fall in love / Taste of honey, A / Yesterday / Someday / My prayer / I can't stop loving you.
2LP: . . . . DKL 71/2
MCSET: . . . . KDKC 28061

SOMETHIN' 'BOUT YOU BABY I LIKE.
Tracks: / She's a lady / Proud Mary / Young new Mexican puppeteer, The / You've lost that lovin' feeling / Ain't no sunshine / Resurrection shuffle / Something 'bout you baby I like / Witch Queen of New Orleans / Rescue me / Try a little tenderness / You're my world / Letter to Lucille.
LP: . . . . SHM 3128
MC: . . . . HSC 3128

SOUL OF, THE.
LP: . . . . TAB 91

THIS IS TOM JONES.
Tracks: / Fly me to the moon / Little green apples / Wichita lineman / (Sittin' on) the dock of the bay / Dance of love / Hey Jude / Without you / That's all a man can say / That wonderful sound / Only once / I'm a fool to want you / Let it be me.
LP: . . . . SKL 5007

TOM.
LP: . . . . SKL 5045

TOM JONES ALBUM, THE.
Tracks: / Green green grass of home / I'm coming home / (It looks like) I'll never fall in love again / Not responsible / Help yourself / What's new pussycat / Love me tonight / It's not unusual / Funny, familiar forgotten feelings / Detroit City / With these hands / Minute of your time, A / Without love / Delilah.
LP: . . . . TOM 1
MC: . . . . KTOMC 1

TOM JONES SINGS THE HITS.
Tracks: / Proud Mary / Ain't no sunshine / You've lost that lovin' feelin' / If I ruled the world / Love's been good to me / Try a little tenderness / I / Till / Do you what you gotta do / Nothing rhymed / Resurrection shuffle / Ebb tide / You're my world / Witch Queen of New Orleans / If / All I ever need is you / Sugar sugar / You've got a friend / To love somebody / My way.
LP: . . . . SCX 6613

VERY BEST OF TOM JONES, THE.
Tracks: / Daughter of darkness / If / Proud Mary / Letter to Lucille / Brother can you spare a dime / If I ruled the world / My way / Try a little tenderness / Puppet man / She's a lady / Ebb tide / Ballad of Billy Joe / Nothing rhymed / Young New Mexican puppeteer / Resurrection shuffle / Impossible dream, The / Somethin' bout you baby I like.
LP: . . . . MFP 50459

Jones, Tracy

HI EVERYBODY I'M TRACY JONES.
Tracks: / Love is all / Send in the clowns / Aquarius / This is my life / Bridge over troubled water / That's where the music takes me / Ave Maria / I who have nothing / Solitaire / I love you so / Stand by your man / Until it's time for you to go / River deep, mountain high / If you go away.
LP: . . . . SRTZ 76382

Jones, Trevor

ANGEL HEART (See under Angel heart (film)) (Jones, Trevor and Courtney Pine).

Jones, Vince

COME IN SPINNER (See Under Come in Spinner) (Jones, Vince & Grace Knight).

TRUSTWORTHY LITTLE SWEETHEARTS.
Tracks: / Big city / Don't worry about a thing / Stricken by a storm / Trustworthy little sweethearts / I'm a fool to want you / Like young / My only friend / That old feeling / In an attempt to be fascinating / I didn't know what time it was / Not much / Turn around / Masquerade is over, The.
LP: . . . . INT 3046 1
MC: . . . . INT 3046 4

Jones, Vivian

BANK ROBBERY.
LP: . . . . RCLP 01

JAH WORKS.
LP: . . . . SHAKA 861 LP

JAMAICA LOVE.
LP: . . . . LMLP 101
MC: . . . . LMLC 101

MONEY WORRIES (See under President Sass) (President Sass & Vivian Jones).

Jones, Willi

WILLI JONES.
LP: 7599242921

MC: 7599242924

Jones, Winston

YOU ARE (see under Cairo).

Jones, Wizz

MAGICAL FLIGHT.
Tracks: / Pictures / Mississippi John / Old-fashioned shotgun wedding / Song to Woody / Topolino song / Magical flight / Valley, The / See how the time is flying / Canned music.
LP: . . . . PLR 009

Joneses

HARD.
LP: 756782071
MC: 756782074

Jonzun Crew

DOWN TO EARTH.
Tracks: / Tonight's the night / We're going all the way / Lovin' / You got the lovin' / Mechanism / Wizard of space / Time is running out / Ugly thing.
LP: 825 167

LOST IN SPACE.
Tracks: / Pac jam / Space is the place / We are the jonzun crew / Space cowboy / Electro boogie encounter / Ground control.
LP: . . . . POLD 5098
MC: . . . . POLDC 5098

Jonzun, Michael

MICHAEL JONZUN.
Tracks: / Burning up / Games people play / Love at first sight / That girl's so fine / World is a battlefield, The / Money isn't everything / I wanna get next to you / I'm still in love / Lovers Lane / You turned my world around.
LP: . . . . SP 5111

Joolz

HEX.
Tracks: / Protection / Cat, The / Facade / Love is (sweet romance) / Stand, The / Storm / Mummy's boy / Ambition / House of dreams / Requiem / Musket fife and drum (CD only.) / Legend (CD only.) / Mad bad and dangerous to know (CD only.).
MC: . . . . TCSCX 6711
LP: . . . . SCX 6711
LP: . . . . GRAM 44

NEVER NEVER LAND.
LP: . . . . ABT 011

Joplin, Janis

CHEAP THRILLS (Joplin, Janis & Big Brother & The Holding Company).
Tracks: / Combination of the two / I need a man to love / Summertime / Piece of my heart / Turtle blues / Oh sweet Mary / Ball and chain.
LP: 32004
MC: 40 32004

CHEAPER THRILL.
LP: . . . . FC 005

FAREWELL SONG.
Tracks: / Tell mama / Magic of love / Misery 'n' / One night stand / Harry / Raise your hand / Farewell song / Amazing grace / Hi heel sneakers / Catch me daddy.
LP: . . . . CBS 85354

GOLDEN HIGHLIGHTS OF JANIS JOPLIN.
LP: 54731
MC: 40 54731

GREATEST HITS: JANIS JOPLIN.
Tracks: / Piece of my heart / Summertime / Try (just a little bit harder) / Cry baby / Me and Bobby McGee / Down on me / Get it while you can / Bye bye baby / Move over / Ball and chain / Everybody loves you now / Why Judy why / Falling of the rain / Turn around / You look so good to me / Tomorrow is today / Nocturne / Got to begin again.
LP: . . . . CBS 32190
MC: 40 32190
LP: 32190
MC: 321902

I GOT DEM OL' COSMIC BLUES AGAIN MAMA.
Tracks: / Try (just a little bit harder) / Maybe / One good man / As good as you've been to this world / To love somebody / Cosmic blues / Little girl blue / Work me Lord.
LP: . . . . CBS 32063
MC: 40 32063

JANIS JOPLIN: ANTHOLOGY.
Tracks: / Piece of my heart / Summertime / Maybe / Try (just a little bit harder) / To love somebody / Cosmic blues / Turtle blues / Oh sweet Mary / Little girl blue / Trust me / Move over / Half moon / Cry baby / Me and Bobby McGee / Mercedes benz / Down on me / Bye bye baby / Get it while you can / Ball and chain.
2LP: . . . . CBS 22101

JANIS JOPLIN IN CONCERT.
Tracks: / Down in me / Bye bye baby / All is loneliness / Piece of my heart / Road block / Flower in the sun / Summertime / Ego rock / Half moon / Kozmic blues / Move over / Try (just a little bit harder) / Get it while you can / Ball and chain.
LP: 4601281
MC: 4601284
LP: . . . . CBS 67241

PEARL.
Tracks: / Move over / Cry baby / Woman left lonely, A / Half moon / Buried alive in the blues / Me and Bobby Mc Gee / Mercedes Benz / Get it while you can / Trust me.
LP: . . . . CBS 32064
MC: 40 32064
LP: . . . . CBS 64188

Joplin, Scott

ELITE SYNCOPATION.
Tracks: / Elite syncopations / Country club / Paragon rag / Eugenia / Cleopha / Real slow rag, A / Scott Joplin's new rag / Leola / Lily Queen / Chrysanthemum / Heliotrope bouquet / Reflection rag / Maple leaf rag (On CD only) / Ole Miss Rag (On CD only) / Magnetic rag (On CD only) / Silver swan rag, The (On CD only).
LP: . . . . MTLP 1008

ENTERTAINER, THE.
Tracks: / Elite syncopations / Chrysanthemum / Scott Joplin's new rag / Eugenia / Paragon rag / Euphonic sounds / Pineapple rag / Something doing / Original rags / Entertainer, The / Maple leaf rag / Sun flower slow drag / Stoptime rag / Reflection rag / Cleopha / Lily Queen / Heliotrope bouquet / Country club / Real slow rag, A / Leola.
LP: 22022
MC: 42022
LP: . . . . CBS 73685

ENTERTAINER, THE (METEOR).
Tracks: / Entertainer, The / Easy winners / Pineapple rag / Solace / Gladiolus rag / Ragtime dance / Sugar cane / Crush collision march, The / Bethena / Combination march / Breeze from Alabama, A.
LP: . . . . MTLP 1006

JOPLIN BANQUET, A (see under Charters, Anne).

JOPLIN RAGS.
LP: . . . . SM 3909
MC: . . . . MC 3909

KING OF RAGTIME.
LP: . . . . LPJT 28
MC: . . . . MCJT 28

RAGTIME KING (Piano roll solos, 1899 - 1914).
Tracks: / Maple leaf rag / Sunflower slow drag / Entertainer, The / Something doing / Weeping willow rag / Fig leaf rag / Pineapple rag / Euphonic sounds / Stoptime rag / Scott Joplin's new rag / Magnetic rag.
LP: . . . . SM 3097

SCOTT JOPLIN COLLECTION (20 golden greats).
Tracks: / Entertainer, The / Maple leaf rag / Favourite, The / Pineapple rag / Fig leaf rag / Cascades / Peacherine rag / Pleasant moments / Strenuous life, The / Weeping willow rag / Rose leaf rag / Combination march / Ragtime dance / Felicity rag / Country club rag / Elite syncopations / Swipesy / Magnetic rag / Nonpareil.
LP: . . . . DVLP 2060
MC: . . . . DVMC 2060

SCOTT JOPLIN STORY, THE.
Tracks: / Entertainer, The / Pineapple rag / Ragtime dance / Sugar cane / Combination march / Felicity rag / Scott Joplin's new rag / Peacherine rag / Rose leaf rag / Silver rag, The / Stoptime rag / Sycamore, The / Swipesy / Original rags / Sunflower slow drag / Maple leaf rag / Cascades / Weeping willow rag / Magnetic rag / Paragon rag / Nonpareil / Search light.
MCSET: . . . . DVREMC 10

Jordan, Charley

1932-37.
LP: . . . . DLP 518

IT AIN'T CLEAN.
LP: . . . . AB 2002

Jordan, Chris

TWILIGHT OF THE GODS.
Tracks: / Pilgrims / Evening star / Grail, The / Dance for dead lovers / Prize, The / Rhinegold / Valkyrie's dream, The / Bride's lament, The.
LP: . . . . NAGE 14
MC: . . . . NAGEC 14

Jordan, Clifford

ADVENTURER.
LP: . . . . MR 5163

BLOWING IN FROM CHICAGO (Jordan, Clifford/John Gilmore).
LP: . . . . BLP 1579

CLIFFORD JORDAN (Featuring Junior Cook) (Jordan, Clifford Quartet).
LP: . . . . CRISS 1011

I'M THE BLUES (See under Simmons, Norman) (Jordan, Clifford, Norman Simmons Quintet, Jimmy Owens).

JENKINS, JORDAN & TIMMONS (See under Jenkins, John) (Jordan, Clifford/ John Gilmore).

NIGHT AT BOOMERS, A (Jordan, Clifford/C. Walton).
LP: . . . . MR 5010

NIGHT OF THE MARK VII.
LP: . . . . MR 5076

ROYAL BALLADS (Jordan, Clifford Quartet).
LP: . . . . CRISS 1025

Jordan, Duke

BE-BOP KEYBOARD MASTERS (See Be bop Keyboard Masters).

BLUE DUKE.
LP: . . . . NL 70245

CONNECTIONS/LES LIAISONS DANGEREUSES.
2LP: . . . . VJD 513

DUKE JORDAN.
LP: . . . . JL 98

DUKE'S ARTISTRY (Jordan, Duke Quartet).
LP: . . . . SCS 1103

FLIGHT TO JORDAN.
Tracks: / Flight to Jordan / Starbrite / Squawkin' / Deacon Joe / Split quick / Si-Joya / Diamond stud / I should care.
LP: . . . . BST 84046

GREAT SESSIONS, THE (Jordan, Duke Trio).
LP: . . . . SCS 1150

JORDU.
LP: 500098

LES LIAISONS DANGEREUSES (Jordan, Duke/Rouse, Charlie).
Tracks: / No problem 1-3 / Jazz vendor / Subway Inn / Feeling of love 1 and 2.
LP: . . . . JR 106

LIVE IN JAPAN.
LP: . . . . SCS 1063/4

MIDNIGHT MOONLIGHT.
LP: . . . . SCS 1143

MURRAY HILL CAPER, THE.
Tracks: / Worthless / Lay out blues / Flight to Jordan / Lady Dingbat / Night and day / 32nd Street love / Cold Bordeaux blues / Paula / Glad I met Pat.
LP: . . . . SPJ DJ5

TIME ON MY HANDS (Jordan, Duke Trio).
LP: . . . . SCS 1232

Jordan, Fred

SHROPSHIRE LAD, THE (Country songs).
MC: 30-130

SONGS OF A SHROPSHIRE FARM WORKER.
LP: 12T 150

WHEN THE FROST IS ON THE PUMPKIN.
LP: 12TS 233

Jordan, Louis

20 GOLDEN GREATS: LOUIS JORDAN (Live).
Tracks: / Mean and evil blues / Infantry blues / How high the moon / Is you is or is you ain't my baby / Broke but happy / Drippy drippers, The / Married woman blues / Buzz me / On the sunny side of the street / Five guys named Moe / I like 'em fat like that / Daddy o / Let the good times roll / Bahama Joe / Safe, sane and single / Choo choo ch' boogie / That's why we can't agree / Texas and Pacific.
MC: . . . . CAWM 3

1944/5 (Jordan, Louis & His Tympany Five).
LP: . . . . CLP 53

BEST OF LOUIS JORDAN.
Tracks: / Choo choo ch' boogie / Five guys named Moe / Is you is or is you ain't my baby / Buzz me / G.I. blues / Saturday night fish fry / Early in the morning / What's the use of getting sober / Ain't nobody here but us chickens / Let the good times roll / Reet petite and gone / Blue light boogie / Beware brother beware / School days / Beans and cornbread / Caldonia.
LP: . . . . MCL 1631
MC: . . . . MCLC 1631

CHOO CHOO CH' BOOGIE (Jordan, Louis & Chris Barber).
Tracks: / Fifty cents / Man ain't a man, A / No chance blues / I'm going to move to the outskirts of town / Jazz lips / Don't worry / 'Bout the mule / Choo choo ch' boogie / I'm gonna shimmy like my sister Kate / Is you is or is you ain't my baby / Black and tan fantasy / Back home again in Indiana.
LP: . . . . MFP 50557
MC: . . . . TCMFP 50557
LP: . . . . BLP 30175

COLE SLAW.
Tracks: / Pettin' and pokin' / I know what I've got / Don't burn the candle at both ends / Coleslaw / Push ka pee shee pie / Baby's gonna go bye bye / Heed my warning / Hungry man / You will always have a friend / Weak minded blues / Is my pop in there? / Time marches on / Oil well Texas / Azure te / Junco partner / Jordan for President.
LP: . . . . JB 605

COLLATES.
LP: . . . . SWH 9
MC: . . . . CSWH 9

FIVE GUYS NAMED MOE (ALBUM).
LP: . . . . MCL 1718
MC: . . . . MCLC 1718

G.I. JIVE.
LP: . . . . JB 602

GO BLOW YOUR HORN.
LP: 2C 068 64793
LP: . . . . PM 1546680

GOLDEN GREATS: LOUIS JORDAN.
Tracks: / Caldonia / Choo choo ch' boogie / Is you is or is you ain't my baby? / Ain't nobody here but us chickens / Beware, brother, beware / What's the use of getting sober / Let the good times roll / Reet petite and gone / Blue light boogie / School days / Beans and cornbread / Five guys named Moe / Buzz me / G.I. Jive / Saturday night fish fry / Early in the morning.
LP: . . . . MCM 5005
MC: . . . . MCMC 5005

GOOD TIMES.
LP: . . . . SWH 14
MC: . . . . CSWH 14

GREAT RHYTHM AND BLUES VOL.1.
Tracks: / Choo choo ch' boogie / Caldonia / Let the good times roll / I got the walkin' blues / Saturday night fish fry / Ain't nobody here but us chickens / Beans and cornbread / Outskirts of town / Helping hand / I'm a good thing.
LP: . . . . BDL 1000

HOODOO MAN.
LP: . . . . ST 1011

I BELIEVE IN MUSIC.
LP: 33559

JIVIN' 1956-58 VOLUME 1.
Tracks: / Big Bess / Ain't nobody here but us chickens / Choo choo ch' boogie / Knock me a kiss / Let the good times roll / Cladonia / Is you is or is you ain't my baby / Beware brother beware / Don't let the sun catch you crying / I'm gona move to the outskirts of town / Salt pork West Virginia / Ruin Joe / Early in the morning / Cat scratchin / Morning light / Fire / Rock doc / Ella Mae / I want to know / I've found my peace of mind.
LP: . . . . BFX 15201

JIVIN' 1956-58 VOLUME 2.
Tracks: / Jamf, The / Saturday night fish fry / I never had a chance / Got my mojo working / Sunday / Sweet Lorraine / Slop, The / I hadn't anyone till you / Nearness of you, The / Because of you (previously unissued: original Mercury recording) / That's what true love can do / I don't want to set the world on fire / Day away from you, A / I cried for you / Man ain't a man, A / I've found my peace of mind / Sweet hunk of junk / I love you so / Wish I could make some money / Route 66.
LP: . . . . BFX 15207

JIVIN' WITH JORDAN (Jordan, Louis & His Tympany Five).
Tracks: / At the swing cats ball / Doug the jitterbug / Honeysuckle rose / But I'll be back / You're my meat / June tenth jamboree / What's the use of getting sober / Five guys named Moe / Is you is or is you ain't my baby / Buzz me / Salt pork West Virginia / Reconversion blues / How long must I wait for you / That's chick's too young to fry / No sale / All for the love of Lil / Texas and Pacific / Reet petite and gone / Sure had a wonderful time / Open the door, Richard / Barnyard boogie / Early in the morning / Daddy o / Onions / Psycho loco / Lemonade / Chartreuse / Fat Sam from Birmingham.
MC: . . . . TCCDX 7
2LP: . . . . CDX 7

JUMP AND JIVE.
Tracks: / Let the good times roll / Ain't nobody here but us chickens / Take the

ribbon from her hair / Hard head wife / I believe in music / St. Louis blues boogie.
LP: . . . . **JSP 1069**

JUMPIN' STUFF (Jordan, Louis/Hot Lips Page/Don Byas).
LP: . . . . **RARITIES 46**

KNOCK ME OUT.
LP: . . . . **ST 1012**

LIVE JIVE (Jordan, Louis & His Tympany Five).
Tracks: / Five guys named Moe / Buzz me / Knock me a kiss / Let the good times roll / I like em' fat like that / Choo choo ch' boogie / On the sunny side of the street / All for the love of Lil / Safe, sane and single / Broke but happy / Texas and Pacific / Drippy drippers, The / Don't let the sun catch you crying / How long must I wait for you / Daddy-o / Jumping at the Jubilee / Baby thats alright for you.
MC: . . . . **CATOM 4**

LOOK OUT (Jordan, Louis & His Tympany Five).
Tracks: / Keep a knockin' / Sam Jones done snagged his britches / You run your mouth I'll run my business / Pinetop's boogie woogie / Boogie woogie came to town / Saxa woogie / I like 'em fat like that / Raided the house / Ain't that just like a woman / Jack you're dead / Boogie woogie blue plate / Look out / Pettin' and pokin' / Junco partner / House party / I want you to see my baby.
LP: . . . . **CRB 1048**
MC: . . . . **TCCRB 1048**

LOOK OUT SISTER.
Tracks: / Jack you're dead / Caldonia / My new ten gallon hat / Don't burn the candle at both ends / Chicky Mo, Craney Crow / We can't agree / Boogie in the barnyard / You're much too fat / Roamin' blues / Early in the morning / Look out sister / Jumpin' at the jubilee / Please don't cry / Down down down / Five guys named Moe.
LP: . . . . **KK 7415**

LOUIS JORDAN & FRIENDS.
LP: . . . . **MCL 1807**
MC: . . . . **MCLC 1807**

LOUIS JORDAN & TYMPANY FIVE 1945-52 (Jordan, Louis & His Tympany Five).
LP: . . . . **SP 3001**

MORE...1944-1945 (Jordan, Louis & His Tympany Five).
LP: . . . . **CLP 97**

OUT OF PRINT (Jordan, Louis & His Tympany Five).
Tracks: / Don' worry 'bout that mule / It's so easy / Why'd you do it baby / You know it too / You didn't want me baby / Man's best friend is a bed, A / Lollypop / Hog wash / Soon a baby, The / Inflation blues / 'Fore day blues / Swinging in a coconut tree / It's a great great pleasure / Teardrops from my eyes / Garmoochie / There must be a way.
LP: . . . . **OFF 6025**

PRIME CUTS.
Tracks: / Choo choo ch' boogie / Let the good times roll / Five guys named Moe / Buzz me / All for the love of Lil / Safe, sane and single.
LP: . . . . **SWH 1**
MC: . . . . **CSWH 1**

REET PETITE AND GONE.
Tracks: / Texas and Pacific / All for the love of Lil / Wham Sam / I know what you're puttin' down / Let the good times roll / Reet petite and gone / That chick's too young to fry / Ain't that just like a woman / If it's love you want / Caldonia / Honey Chile / Tillie / Buzz me.
LP: . . . . **KK 7414**

ROCK 'N' ROLL CALL.
Tracks: / It's been said / Whatever Lola wants (Lola gets) / Slo' smooth and easy / Bananas / Baby let's do it up / Chicken back / Baby you're just too much / Were can I go / Rock 'n' roll call / Man ain't a man, A' / Texas stew / Hard head.
LP: . . . . **BFX 15257**

SOMEBODY DONE HOODOOED THE HOODOO.
LP: . . . . **JB 619**

V-DISCS, THE.
Tracks: / Is you is or is you ain't my baby? / Knock me a kiss / Outskirts of town / I've found a new baby / Five guys named Moe / Jumpin' at the Jubilee / You can't get that no more / End of my worry, The / How high am I? / Hey now, let's live / Deacon James / I like 'em fat like that / Bahama Joe / Nobody but me.
LP: . . . . **OFF 6061**

Jordan, Marc

TALKING THROUGH PICTURES.
Tracks: / This independence / Kensington Gardens / Catch the moon / I Ching / Talking through pictures / Soldier of fortune / Seek and you shall find / Inside the glass bead / Human race / I was your fool.
LP: . . . . **PL 85907**
MC: . . . . **PK 85907**

Jordan, Penny

TIGER MAN (See under Georgina Melville).
MC: . . . . **PMB 002**

Jordan, Sheila

CROSSING, THE.
LP: . . . . **BKH 50501**

OLD TIME FEELING (Jordan, Sheila/ Harvie Swartz).
LP: . . . . **PA 8038**

Jordan, Stanley

CORNUCOPIA.
Tracks: / Impressions / Willow weep for me / Autumn leaves / Still got the blues / Fundance (CD only.) / What's going on / Always know / Asteroids / Cornucopia.
LP: **B1 923 56**
LP: **792 356 1**

FLYING HOME.
Tracks: / Street talk / Tropical storm / When Julia smiles / Can't sit down / Stairway to heaven / Music's gonna change, The / Time is now / Flying home.
LP: . . . . **MTL 1034**
MC: . . . . **TCMTL 1034**

MAGIC TOUCH.
Tracks: / Eleanor Rigby / Freddie Freeloader / Round midnight / All the children / Lady in my life, The / Angel / Fundance / Return expedition / Child is born, A.
LP: . . . . **BT 85101**
MC: . . . . **TCBT 85101**

STANDARDS, VOL 1.
Tracks: / Sound of silence, The / Sunny / Georgia on my mind / Send one your love / Moon River / Guitar man / One bell less to answer / Because / My favourite things / Silent night.
LP: . . . . **BT 85130**

Jordan, Steve

EL CORRIDO DE JOHNNY EL PACHUCO.
LP: . . . . **ARHOOLIE 3023**
MC: . . . . **C 3023**

EL HURACAN.
LP: . . . . **ZS 100**

RETURN OF EL PARCHE, THE.
LP: . . . . **ROUNDER 6019**
LP: . . . . **Z 5055**
MC: . . . . **ROUNDER 6019C**

Jordinaires

SING ELVIS' GOSPEL FAVOURITES.
Tracks: / Didn't it rain / Peace in the valley / Joshua fit de battle of Jerico / Search me lord / Dig a little deeper / You better run / Let us break bread together / Wonderful time up there, A / How great thou art / I'm a rollin' / Dip your fingers in some water / Roll jordan roll / One of these mornings / Onward christian soldiers.
LP: . . . . **MFLP 033**

SING ELVIS'S FAVOURITE SPIRITUALS.
LP: . . . . **LP 8505**

Jordon, Kent

ESSENCE.
LP: . . . . **FC 40868**

Jorge, Ben

BEM-VINDA AMIZADE.
Tracks: / O dia o sol declarou o seu amor pela terra / Santa Clara clareou / Oe oe faz o carro de boi na estrada / Era uma vez um aposentado marinherio / Lorraine / Curumin chama cunchata que von eontar / Katarina, Katarina / Ela mora em matogrosso fronteira com o paraguai / Para que digladiar / Luiz Wagner quitarreio.
LP: **403 6247**

BEN JORGE SONSUL.
Tracks: / Senhora dona da casa / A rainha foi embora / Irene Cara mia / My little brother / Obsessao meu amor / Bizantina bizancia / Pelos verdes mares / Me chamando de paixao / Os cavalheiros dorei Arthur / Abenco mamae abenco papa / Hooked on samba / A terra do filho do homen.
LP: **403.6305**
MC: **740.6305**

Jorgensen, Knud

DUKE'S MELODY (see under Domnerus, Arne) (Jorgensen, Knud/ Arne Domnerus).

JAZZ TRIO.
LP: . . . . **OP 8401**

Jormin, Anders

EIGHT PIECES.
LP: . . . . **DRLP 165**

Jose, Charlie

BOSCASTLE BOW WOW.
Tracks: / Pleasant and delightful / Boscastle fair / For years and years / Paddy Doodle day / Cornwall queen of all / Old mother hen / Trousers in a twist (Spoken word) / Use of the conveyance (Spoken word) / Short of sheep (Spoken word) / Heavenly motorway (Spoken word) / I like pickled onions / You are my sunshine / I touched her on the toe / Madam will you walk / Huntsman sounds his horn / Thousands or more / Cadgwith anthem / Old grey duck / Sarah Turpin's ride to York / Nellie Dean / Mr. Blacksmith / Ploughman is a happy soul, The / Cockles and mussels / Little lamb / Farmer's boy / Buttercup Joe / Wedding that wasn't, The (Spoken word) / Dog's meeting, The (Spoken word) / Lamorna / White rose, the.
MC: **60-096**

Jose, Don

FIESTA.
Tracks: / Bamboleo / Amor / Welcome to my heart / Annabel / Ave Mario, no morro / Djobi, djobi / Lola from Barcelona / A mi manera / El porompompero / Cuando calienta el sol / Costa brava / Munira, munira, munira / Me va, me va / San Jose / Tu quieras volver / Quantanamera / Maria Isabel.
MC: . . . . **HSC 3293**

Josef K

ENDLESS SOUL.
LP: . . . . **EDIT 87.6**

ONLY FUN IN TOWN, THE.
LP: . . . . **RT 817**

Joseph & Amazing....

JOSEPH & THE AMAZING TECHNICOLOR DREAMCOAT (Various artists).
Tracks: / Jacob and sons: *Various artists* / Joseph's coat: *Various artists* / Joseph's dreams: *Various artists*/ Poor poor Joseph: *Various artists* / One more angel in heaven: *Various artists* / Potiphar: *Various artists*/ Close every door: *Various artists* / Go go go Joseph: *Various artists* / Pharaoh story: *Various artists*/ Poor, poor Pharaoh: *Various artists* / Song of the king: *Various artists* / Pharoah's dreams explained: *Various* artists / Stone the crows: *Various artists* / Those Canaan days: *Various artists* / Brothers come to Egypt, The: *Various artists* / Grovel, grovel: *Various artists* / Who's the thief?: *Various artists* / Benjamin calypso: *Various artists* / Joseph all the time: *Various artists* / Jacob in Egypt: *Various artists* / Any dream will do: *Various artists*.
LP: . . . . **MCF 2544**
MC: . . . . **MCFC 2544**

Joseph Andrews

JOSEPH ANDREWS (see under Fielding, Henry) (Massey, Daniel (nar)).

Joseph Consort

TECHNICOLOUR DREAMCOAT.
MC: . . . . **KSKC 4973**

Joseph, David

JOYS OF LIFE, THE.
Tracks: / No time to waste / Joys of life / Guiding star / Baby won't you take my love / Dreaming / Be a star / I'm so in love / Do you feel my love now baby.
LP: . . . . **ILPS 9739**
MC: . . . . **ICT 9739**

Joseph, Don

ONE OF A KIND (Joseph, Don/Al Cohn).
LP: . . . . **UP 27.23**

Joseph, Jeff

JEFF JOSEPH.
Tracks: / After all / Magie de l'amour / Big beat, The / Rendez vous / Banana sweet / Side by side / Rock my soul / One two three / Sunshine everyday / Remember gramacks (creole song).
LP: **839 114 1**
MC: **839 114 4**

Joseph, Margie

IN THE NAME OF LOVE (Best of Margie Joseph).
Tracks: / Your sweet lovin' / Same thing / Tell it like it is / Never can be / Make me believe you'll stay / Takin' all the love I can / Stop in the name of love / I'm fed up / One more chance / Didn't have to tell me / What's wrong baby / What you gonna do / Sweeter tomorrow / Strungout.
LP: . . . . **SX 015**

READY FOR THE NIGHT.
LP: **7901581**

STAY.
LP: . . . . **ICH 1027**
MC: . . . . **ZCICH 1027**

Joseph, Nerious

LOVE'S GOTTA TAKE ITS TIME.
Tracks: / Love to treasure / I will follow you / Love is a dangerous thing / Something special / Bridge of love / Won't you let me be the one / I need your lovin' / Everybody's talkin' / Dedicated to Jah / She's gone and left me.
MC: . . . . **FADC 005**
LP: . . . . **FADLP 005**

YOURS TO KEEP.
Tracks: / Yours to keep.
LP: . . . . **FADLP 013**

Josephs, Wilfred

PIANO MUSIC.
LP: . . . . **NVL 104**
MC: . . . . **NVLC 104**

Joshua

INTENSE DEFENCE.
Tracks: / Reach up / I've been waiting / Only yesterday / Crying out for love / Living on the edge / Tearing at my heart / Remembering you / Look to the sky / Don't you know / Stand alone.
LP: . . . . **PL 71905**
MC: . . . . **PK 71905**

SURRENDER.
Tracks: / Surrender love / Heart full of soul / Your love is gone / Hold on / Back to the rock / Rockin' the world / Stay alive / Loveshock / Reprise.
LP: . . . . **WKFMLP 64**
MC: . . . . **WKFMMC 64**

Josky

JOTONGO (Josky & Rigo Star).
LP: . . . . **MA 4005**

Journey...

JOURNEY The classics of film & television (Various artists).
Tracks: / Morning (from Peer Gynt) / O Fortuna (from Carmina Burana): *New Philharmonia Orchestra* / Spartacus and Phrygia / Largo (from New World symphony): *London Philharmonic Orchestra* / After the storm: *London Philharmonic Orchestra*/ Daybreak (from Daphnis & Chloe): *Philharmonia Orchestra* / Promenade/Gnome (from Pictures at an exhibitio: *Philharmonia* Orchestra / Also sprach Zarathustra: *London Philharmonic Orchestra* / Mars (from Planets suite): *Philharmonia* Orchestra / Jupiter (from Planets suite): *Philharmonia Orchestra* / At the castle gate (from Pelleas & Melisande): *Bournemouth Symphony Orchestra* / Flower duet (from Lakme): *Paris Orchestra*.
LP: . . . . **TVLP 16**
MC: . . . . **ZCTV 16**

Journey (Group)

CAPTURED.
Tracks: / Majestic / Where were you / Just the same way / Line of fire / Lights / Stay awhile / Too late / Dixie highway / Feeling that way / Anytime / Do you recall / Walks like a lady / La do da / Lovin' touchin' squeezin' / Squeezin' / Wheel in the sky / Anyway you want it / Party's over, The.
2LP: **4511321**
MC: **4511324**
2LP: . . . . **CBS 88525**

DEPARTURE.
Tracks: / Anyway you want it / Walks like a lady / Someday soon / People and places / Pecious time / Where were you / I'm cryin' / Line of fire / Departure / Good morning girl / Stay a while / Home made love.
LP: . . . . **CBS 32714**
MC: **40 32714**
LP: . . . . **CBS 84101**

DREAM AFTER DREAM (Film Soundtrack).
Tracks: / Destiny / Snow theme / Sandcastles / Few coins, A / Moon theme / When the love has gone / Festival dance / Rape, The / Little girl.
LP: **27AP 1950**

ESCAPE.
Tracks: / Don't stop believin' / Stone in love / Who's crying now / Keep on running / Still they ride / Escape / Lay it down / Dead or alive / Mother, Father / Open arms.
LP: **460185 1**
MC: **460185 4**
LP: . . . . **CBS 85138**

EVOLUTION.
Tracks: / Too late / Lovin' touchin' squeezin' / City of the angels / When you're alone it ain't easy / Sweet and simple / Lovin' you is easy / Just the same way / Do you recall? / Daydream / Lady Luck / Majestic.
LP: . . . . **CBS 32342**
MC: **40 32342**
LP: . . . . **CBS 83566**

FRONTIERS.

Tracks: / Separate ways / Send her my love / Chain reaction / After the fall / Faithfully / Edge of the blade / Troubled child / Back talk / Frontier / Rubicon.
LP: CBS 25261
MC: 40 25261

FRONTIERS/ ESCAPE.
2LP: CBS J 241

GREATEST HITS: JOURNEY.
Tracks: / Only the young / Don't stop believin' / Wheel in the sky / Faithfully / I'll be alright without you / Anyway you want it / (Ask) the lonely / Who's crying now / Separate ways / Lights / Lovin' touchin' squeezin' / Open arms / Girl can't help it, The / Send her my love / Be good to yourself.
LP: 4631491
MC: 4631494

IN THE BEGINNING.
Tracks: / Journey of a lifetime / Topaz / Kohoutek / On a Saturday night / It's all too much / In my lonely feeling / Conversations / Mystery mountain / Spaceman / People / Anyway / You're on your own / Look into the future / Nickel and dime / I'm gonna leave you.
2LP: CBS 22073

INFINITY.
Tracks: / Lights / Feeling that way / Anytime / La do da / Patiently / Wheel in the sky / Somethin' to hide / Winds of March / Can do / Open the door.
LP: 32687

JOURNEY (4 track cassette EP).
Tracks: / Don't stop believin' / Who's crying now / Open arms / Lovin', touchin', squeezin'.
MC: 40 2908

JOURNEY (ALBUM).
Tracks: / Of a lifetime / In the morning day / Kohoutek / To play some music / Topaz / In my lonely feeling / Conversations / Mystery mountain.
LP: CBS 80724

LOOK INTO THE FUTURE.
Tracks: / On a Saturday nite / It's all too much / Anyway / She makes me (feel alright) / You're on your own / Look into the future / Midnight dreamer / I'm gonna leave you.
LP: CBS 32102
LP: CBS 69203

NEXT.
Tracks: / Spaceman / People / I would find you / Here we are / Hustler / Next / Nickel and dime / Karma.
LP: CBS 81554

RAISED ON RADIO.
Tracks: / Girl can't help it, The / Positive touch, The / Suzanne / Be good to yourself / Once you love somebody / Happy to give / Raised on radio / I'll be alright without you / It could have been you / Eyes of a woman, The / Why can't this night go on forever.
LP: CBS 26902
MC: 4679924

WHO'S CRYING NOW (OLD GOLD) (See under Tyler, Bonnie/Total eclipse of...).

Journey Into Space

JOURNEY INTO SPACE (Various artists).
2LP: ADL 519
MCSET: ADK 519

JOURNEY INTO SPACE-OPERATION LUNA (6 hours of space adventure) (Various artists).
MCSET: ZBBC 4002

Journey Through The

JOURNEY THROUGH THE PAST (Original soundtrack) (Various artists).
2LP: WEA 64015

Journey To Channel One

JOURNEY TO CHANNEL 1 (Various artists).
LP: LOVLP 001

Journey To The

JOURNEY TO THE CENTRE OF THE EARTH (see under Verne, Jules).

Jowett, Les

CY LAURIE & LES JOWETT 1957 (See under Laurie, Cy) (Jowett, Les & Cy Laury).

Joy

24K (See under Band Of Joy).

JOY.
LP: SGC 1006

Joy, Benny

MORE ROCKABILLY.
Tracks: / Gossip, gossip, gossip / Button nose / I'm gonna move / Kiss me / Wild, wild lover / Nosey, nosey neighbors / Cold, cold woman / Hey bossman / Come back / You're a bundle of love / Indian giver / Stompin' / She cryed for me / Dark angel / I need a whole lotta you.
LP: WLP 8825

ROCKABILLY WITH BENNY JOY.
Tracks: / Rollin' the jukebox rock / Ittie bitty everything / Money money / Miss bobby sox / Rebel rock / Crash the party / Little red book / Hey...high school baby / Talking about it / I'm doubtful of your love / Steady with Betty / Spin the bottle.
LP: WLP 8803

Joy Division

CLOSER.
Tracks: / Heart and soul / 24 hours / Eternal / Decades / Atrocity exhibition / Isolation / Passover / Colony / Means to an end.
LP: FACT 25
MC: FACT 25 C

COMPLETE PEEL SESSIONS: JOY DIVISION.
LP: SFRLP 111
MC: SFRMC 111

EARCOM 2.
Tracks: / Auto-suggestion / From safety to where?.
MLP: FAST 9

MUSIC AND MEDIA INTERVIEW PICTURE DISC.
LPPD: JOY 1001

STILL.
Tracks: / Exercise one / Ice age / Sound of music, The / Glass / Only mistake, The / Walked in line / Kill, The / Something must break / Dead souls / Sister Ray / Shadowplay / Means to an end / Passover / New dawn fades / Transmission / Disorder / Isolation / Decades / Digital.
2LP: FACT 40
MC: FACT 40 C

SUBSTANCE (1977 - 1980).
Tracks: / She's lost control / Dead souls / Atmosphere / Love will tear us apart / Warsaw / Leaders of men / Digital / Transmission / Autosuggestion.
LP: FACT 250
MC: FACT 250C
DAT: FACT 250D

UNKNOWN PLEASURES.
Tracks: / Disorder / Day of the Lords / Candidate / Insight / New dawn fades / She's lost control / Shadow play / Wilderness / Interzone.
LP: FACT 10
MC: FACT 10 C

Joy, Jimmy

CHARLIE SPIVAK & JIMMY JOY (See under Spivak, Jimmy) (Joy, Jimmy & Charlie Spivak).

Joy, Mabel

ON THE BORDER.
LP: FHR 090

Joy Of Life

ENJOY.
LP: BADVC 62

HEAR THE CHILDREN.
LP: JOL 067

Joy of Living

DEATH TO WACKY POP (See under Apostles) (Joy of Living & Apostles).

Joy Unlimited

JOY UNLIMITED.
LP: SGC 1004

Joyce

MUSIC INSIDE.
MC: 8430124

Joyce, Gina

COUNTRY 'N' IRISH FORGET-ME-NOTS.
Tracks: / Old rustic bridge / You're as welcome as the flowers in May / Mother's love's a blessing, A / Rose of Allandale / Apple blossom county / Will the angels play their harps for me / Medals for mothers / Mother dear of mine / Sweet forget me nots / Gentle mother / Mountains of Mourne / Two little orphans / Golden jubilee / Losing you.
LP: GES 1239
MC: KGEC 1239

Joyce, James

JAMES JOYCE SOUNDBOOK.
MC: SBC 112

PORTRAIT OF THE ARTIST AS A YOUNG MAN, A (Cusack, Cyril (nar)).
MC: 1110

Joyce McKinney

JOYCE OFFSPRING.
LP: COX 009

Joyce, Rosaline

LOVERS SOUL.
LP: ROSLP 1
MC: ZCROS 1

Joyeux Vendeens

VENDEE ETERNELLE.
Tracks: / Avant-deux du bocage / Ne prenez point femme / Sept Vendeens / Le tabouret / Scottish de St-Antoine / Noel vendeen / Le quadrille du bocage / Voici le moi de mai / La guimbarde / La feuill' du labouroux / Polka piquee / Voici la Toussaint / Avant-deux du Boupere / A tanto / Avant-deux de la Mouchampaise et des oiseaux.
LP: ARN 33238

Joyner, Bruce

HOT GEORGIA NIGHTS.
LP: ROSE 129

OUTTAKES COLLECTION, 78/88.
LP: FC 045

SLAVE OF EMOTION.
LP: CLO 024

SWIMMING WITH FRIENDS (Joyner, Bruce & The Plantations).
LP: CL 069

J.P.

WILD ROSE OF THE MOUNTAIN (J.P. & Annadeene Fraley).
LP: ROUNDER 0037

JTQ (James Taylor

DO YOUR OWN THING.
Tracks: / Love the life / Killing time / Money, The / JTQ theme / Ted's asleep / Always there / Oscar / Samba for Bill and Ben / Valhalla / Fat / Peace song.
MC: 843 797 4
LP: 843 797 1

GET ORGANIZED.
LP: 839 405 1
MC: 839 405 4

MISSION IMPOSSIBLE.
Tracks: / Mission impossible.
LP: REAGAN 2

MONEY SPYDER.
LP: KENNEDY 1

WAIT A MINUTE.
Tracks: / Starsky and Hutch / Wait a minute / Indian Summer / Eleven thru seven / Jungle strut / Bailon ara / Kooks korner / Lulu / Fat boy stomp / Pocket change / Out there / Natural thing, The.
LP: 837 340-1
MC: 837 340-4

Jubilee

JUBILEE - BLACK ROOTS OF ROCK 'N' ROLL VOL 2 (Various artists).
LP: ST 1009

MAKING TRACKS (Jubilee Jazzband).
LP: FLY 210

Jubilee (film)

JUBILEE (Film soundtrack) (Various artists).
Tracks: / Deutscher girls: *Adam & The Ants* / Plastic surgery: *Adam & The Ants* / Paranoia blues: *County, Wayne & The Electric Chairs* / Right to work: *Chelsea* / Nine to five: *Maneaters* / Rule Britannia: *Pinns, Suzi* / Jerusalem: *Pinns, Suzi* / Wargasm in pornotopia: *Amilcar* / Slow water: *Eno, Brian* / Dover beach: *Eno, Brian*.
LP: EGLP 34
LP: 2302 079

Jubilee live

JUBILEE LIVE A musical tribute (Various artists).
LP: REJ R 5002
MC: REJ C 5002

Jubilees

REGGAE CARNIVAL.
LP: BRMLP 027

Judas Priest

6 TRACK HITS.
Tracks: / Sinner / Exciter / Hell bent for leather / Ripper / Hot rockin' / Green manalishi.
MC: 7SC 5018

BEST OF JUDAS PRIEST.
Tracks: / Dying to meet you / Never satisfied / Rocka rolla / Diamonds and rust / Victim of changes / Island of domination / Ripper / Deceiver.
LP: GULP 1026
MC: ZCGUL 1026

BRITISH STEEL.
Tracks: / Rapid fire / Metal gods / Breaking the law / Grinder / United / You don't have to be old to be wise / Living after midnight / Race, The / Steeler.
LP: CBS 32412
MC: 40 32412
LP: CBS 84160

COLLECTION: JUDAS PRIEST.
2LP: CCSLP 213
MC: CCSMC 213

DEFENDERS OF THE FAITH.
Tracks: / Freewheel burning / Jawbreaker / Rock hard ride free / Sentinel / Love bites / Eat me alive / Some heads are gonna roll / Night comes down / Heavy duty / Defenders of the faith.
LP: CBS 25713

HERO HERO.
2LP: GUD 2005/6
MCSET: ZCGUD 2005/6

JUDAS PRIEST.
LP: PGLP 1026

JUDAS PRIEST: INTERVIEW PICTURE DISC.
LPPD: BAK 2054

KILLING MACHINE.
LP: CBS 83135
LP: CBS 32218

PAINKILLER.
Tracks: / Painkiller / Hell patrol / All guns blazing / Leather rebel / Metal meltdown / Night crawler / Between the hammer and the anvil / Touch of evil, A / Battle hymn / One shot at glory.
LP: 4672901
MC: 4672904

POINT OF ENTRY.
Tracks: / Heading out to the highway / Don't go / Hot rockin' / Turning circles / Desert plains / Solar angels / You say yes / All the way / Troubleshooter / On the run.
MC: 40 84834
LP: CBS 84834

PRIEST...LIVE.
Tracks: / Out in the cold / Heading out to the highway / Metal gods / Breaking the law / Love bites / Some heads are gonna roll / Sentinel / Private property / Rock you all around the world / Electric eye / Turbo lover / Freewheel burning / Parental guidance / Living after midnight / You've got another thing comin..
LP: 4506391
MC: 4506394

RAM IT DOWN.
Tracks: / Ram it down / Heavy metal / Love zone / Come and get it / Hard as iron / Blood red skies / I'm a rocker / Johnny B. Goode / Love you to death / Monsters of rock.
LP: 4611081
MC: 4611084

ROCKA ROLLA.
Tracks: / One for the road / Rocka rolla / Winter / Deep freeze / Winter retreat / Cheater / Never satisfied / Run of the mill / Dying to meet you / Caviar and meths.
LP: FA 41 3137 1
MC: FA 41 3137 4
LP: GULP 1005

SAD WINGS OF DESTINY.
Tracks: / Victim of changes / Ripper / Dreamer deceiver / Deceiver / Prelude / Tyrant / Genocide / Epitaph / Island of domination.
LP: GULP 1015

SCREAMING FOR VENGEANCE.
Tracks: / Hellion / Electric eye / Riding on the wind / Bloodstone / Pain and pleasure / (Take these) chains / Screaming for vengeance / You've got another thing comin' / Fever / Devil's child.
LP: CBS 32712
LP: CBS 85941
MC: 40 32712

SIN AFTER SIN.
Tracks: / Sinner / Diamonds and rust / Starbreaker / Last rose of summer / Let us prey / Call for the priest / Raw deal / Here come the tears / Dissident aggressor.
LP: CBS 32005
LP: CBS 82008

STAINED CLASS.
LP: CBS 32075
LP: CBS 82430
MC: 40 32075

TURBO.
Tracks: / Turbo lover / Locked in / Private property / Parental guidance / Rock you all around the world / Out in the cold / Wild nights, hot and crazy days / Hot for love / Reckless.
LP: CBS 26641
MC: 40 26641
LP: 4633651
MC: 4633654

UNLEASHED IN THE EAST.
Tracks: / Exciter / Running wild / Sinner / Ripper / Green manalishi / Diamonds and rust / Victim of changes / Genocide / Tyrant.
LP: CBS 83852

Judds

CHRISTMAS TIME WITH THE JUDDS.
Tracks: / Winter wonderland / Beautiful star of Bethlehem / Who is this babe / Santa Claus is coming to town / Silver

bells / What child is this / Away in a manger / Oh holy night / Silent night.
LP: PL 86422
MC: PK 86422

GIVE A LITTLE LOVE.
Tracks: / Turn it loose / Old pictures / Cow cow boogie / Maybe your baby's got the blues / I know where I'm going / Why don't you believe me / Sweetest gift, The / Give a little love to me / Had a dream (for the heart) / John Deere tractor / Isn't he a strange one / Blue Nun Cafe / Change of heart / Don't be cruel / I'm falling in love tonight.
LP: PL 90011
MC: PK 90011

GREATEST HITS: JUDDS.
Tracks: / Why not me / Mama he's crazy / Grandpa / Don't be cruel / Rockin' with the rhythm of the rain / Give a little love / I know where I'm going.
LP: PL 90243
MC: PK 90243

LOVE CAN BUILD A BRIDGE.
Tracks: / This country's rockin' / Calling in the wind / In my dreams / Rompin' stompin' blues / Love can build a bridge / Born to be blue / One hundred and two / John Deere tractor / Talk about love / Are the roses not blooming.
LP: PL 90531
MC: PK 90531

RIVER OF TIME.
Tracks: / One man woman / Young love / Not my baby / Let me tell you about life / Sleepless night / Water of love / River of time / Cadillac red / Guardian angels / Do I dare (Only on CD.).
LP: ZL 74127
MC: ZK 74127

ROCKIN WITH THE RHYTHM.
Tracks: / Have mercy / Grandpa (tell me 'bout the good old days) / Working in a coalmine / If I were you / Rockin' with the rhythm of the rain / Tears for you / Cry myself to sleep / River roll on / I wish she wouldn't treat you that way / Dream chaser.
LP: PL 87042
MC: PK 87042

WHY NOT ME.
Tracks: / Mr. Pain / Drops of water / Sleeping heart / My baby's gone / Bye bye baby blues / Girl's night out / Love is alive / Endless sleep / Mama he's crazy.
LP: PL 85319
MC: PK 85319
LP: NL 90315
MC: NK 90315

Jude The Obscure

JUDE THE OBSCURE (see under Hardy, Thomas) (Jeffrey, Peter (nar)).

Judge Dread

40 BIG ONES.
Tracks: / Lover's rock / This little piece of dinkle / Banana throat song / Confessions of a bouncer / Y'viva suspenders / Six wives of Dread, The / Donkey dick / Fatty dread / Oh she is a big girl now / Big 7 / Dread rock / My ding a ling / Rasta chat / Big six / Come outside / One eyed lodger / Belle of Snodland Town, The / Workers lament / Big 5 / Up with the cock / Big punk / Look a pussy / Doctor Kitch / Winkle man, The / Jamaica jerk off / Grandad's flannelette nightshirt / Move over darling / Will I what / Big 1 / Rudeness train / Bring back the skins / Take off your clothes / Christmas in Dreadland / Rhyme in time, A / What kung fu dat / Big 10 / Je t'aime / Dread's law / Trenchtown Billy / Big everything.
2LP: BIG 1
2LP: BID 1

BEDTIME STORIES.
LP: CTLP 113

BEST WORST OF JUDGE DREAD, THE.
LP: CTLP 126

DREADMANIA.
Tracks: / All in the mind / Big six / Deception / Doctor Kitch / Oh she is a big girl now / Mary Ann / Big 7 / Ding a ling / Donkey dick / Biggest bean you've ever seen, The / Blue cross code, The / Dread's almanac.
LP: TRLS 60

GREATEST HITS: JUDGE DREAD.
Tracks: / Big six / Y viva suspenders / Winkle man / Je t'aime / Big 9 / Up with the cock / Dr. Kitch / Big 8 / Come outside / Big 10 / Dread rock / Big 7.
LP: EMC 3287

LAST OF THE SKINHEADS.
LP: CTLP 123

LIVE AND LEWD.
LP: SKANKLP 104

NOT GUILTY.
Tracks: / Not guilty / Relax / It's a foolish way / My name's Dick / Chinese leggae / Lost in rudeness / Merry Christmas, Mr Dread / Lincolnshire peeper, The / Blow your whistle / Ten commandments / Lost in rudeness.
LP: CRX 8
MC: CRXC 8

RUB-A DUB.
Tracks: / Rub-a-dub / Hello baby / Rudy-rude medley / Brewers droop / Will I what? / Some guys have all the luck / Dread stakes / Put a little sunshine / Amazing Dread / Disco flasher.
LP: CRX 3

TROJAN EXPLOSION VOL. 11 - BIG ONE EP (see under Trojan).

VERY BEST OF JUDGE DREAD, THE.
MC: MCTC 040

WORKING CLASS 'ERO.
LP: TRLS 100
MC: ZCTR 100

Judgement At ...

JUDGEMENT AT NUREMBURG (Film soundtrack) (Various artists).
LP: MCA 39055
MC: MCAC 39055

Juel, Therese

LEVANDE.
LP: OP 7917

Juggernaut

TROUBLE WITHIN.
LP: RR 9590

Juggernaut (bk)

JUGGERNAUT (Desmond Bagley) (Marinker, Peter (nar)).
MC: 0600560503

Juggernaut String Band

GREASY COAT.
LP: WB 004

Jugular Vein

WATERLOOK ROAD.
LP: PFLP 3001

Juice On The Loose

JUICE ON THE LOOSE.
Tracks: / Fannie Mae / Dependent on you / You'll lose a good thing / Software breakdown / You're no good / Boogie thing / Party time / Don't ever leave me / It's raining / Time is the healer / Kool daddy / Going home.
LP: JOOS 1

Juicy

IT TAKES TWO.
Tracks: / Bad boy / It takes two / Love is good enough / Slow dancing / Nobody but you / Sugar free / Stay with me / Forever and ever.
LP: EPC 26886
MC: 40 26886

SPREAD THE LOVE.
Tracks: / All work, no play / Show and tell / After loving you / Make you mine / Midnight fantasy / Serious / Spread the love / Private party.
LP: 4504801
MC: 4504804

Juicy Lucy

BEST OF JUICY LUCY.
Tracks: / Who do you love / Midnight rider / Pretty woman / That woman's got something / Jessica / Willie the pimple / Lie back and enjoy it / Changed my mind, changed my sign / Just one time / I'm a thief / Built for comfort / Mr. Skin / Mr. A. Jones / Future days (CD only.) / Chicago north western (CD only.) / Hello LA, bye bye Birmingham (CD only.) / Thinking of my life (CD only.).
LP: NEXLP 105

JUICY LUCY.
LP: VO 2

LIE BACK AND ENJOY IT.
LP: 6360 014

Ju-Ju Roots

JU JU ROOTS 1930'S-50'S (Various artists).
LP: ROUNDER 5017
MC: ROUNDER 5017C

Juke Box Collection

JUKE BOX COLLECTION - SUMMER IN THE CITY (Sound of the 60's part 7) (Various artists).
Tracks: / 1-2-3: *Barry, Len* / Monday, Monday: *Mamas & Papas* / Happy together: *Turtles* / Waterloo sunset: *Kinks* / Keep searchin': *Shannon, Del* / Lighting strikes: *Christie, Lou* / It's good news week: *Hedgehoppers* Anonymous / Judy in disguise: *Fred, John & The Playboys* / Wooly Bully: *Sam The Sham & The Pharaohs* / Louie Louie: *Kingsmen* / I fought the law: *Fuller, Bobby Four* / Evil hearted you: *Yardbirds* / Summer in the city: *Lovin' Spoonful* / Eve of destruction: *McGuire, Barry.*
LP: OG 1716
MC: OG 2716

Juke Box Hits

JUKE BOX HITS: VOL 4 (Various artists).
MC: ASK 784

JUKE BOX HITS: VOL 5 (Various artists).
MC: ASK 785

JUKE BOX HITS: VOL 6 (Various artists).
MC: ASK 786

JUKE BOX HITS:VOL 1 (Various artists).
2LP: HRLP 12
MCSET: HRMC 12

JUKE BOX HITS:VOL 2 (Various artists).
2LP: DLP 2057
MCSET: DMC 4057

JUKE BOX USA / JUKE BOX UK (Various artists).
MCSET: DTO 10097

Juke Jumpers

JUMPER CABLES.
LP: V 016
MC: V 016C

Jules & The...

FENETIKS (Jules & The Polar Bears).
Tracks: / Good reasons / I give up / Smell of home / Fate / Faded red / What do you belong to / You're so complete / Real enough to love / Brave enough / All caked up.
LP: CBS 83865

Julia

JULIA (Film soundtrack) (Various artists).
LP: DRG 9514

Julia & Julia

JULIA & JULIA (Film Soundtrack) (Various artists).
LP: STV 81327

Julian's Treatment

TIME BEFORE THIS, A.
Tracks: / First oracle / Coming of the mule, The / Phantom city / Black tower, The / Alda, dark lady of the outer worlds / Altarra, princess of the blue women / Second oracle / Twin suns of Centauri / Alkon, planet of Centauri / Terran, The / Fourth from the sun / Strange things / Time before this, A / Child of the night (1 & 2) (Available on CD only) / Stranger (Available on CD only) / Death of Alda, The (Available on CD only) / Cycles (Available on CD only) / Soldiers of time (Available on CD only).
LP: SEE 288

Julie

HOME I LEFT BEHIND, THE (Julie & Bridie).
MC: GTDC 025

Julien, Ivan

BLOW (Julien, Ivan & Eddy Louis).
LP: 80712

PORGY & BESS.
LP: 80707

Julius

JULIUS (Various artists).
LP: PHONT 7542

Julius Caesar

JULIUS CAESAR Dramatised biography by John Green (Rietty, Robert, narrator; Stephen Thorne, Caesar).
MC: HM 028

JULIUS CAESAR (history for ages 8+) (Unknown narrator(s)).
MC: PLBH 102

JULIUS CAESAR Original soundtrack (Various artists).
LP: MCA 25022
MC: MCAC 25022

JULIUS CAESAR (see under Shakespeare, William) (Various artists).

Julius, Orlando

DANCE AFRO-BEAT.
LP: SHAN 43029

Juluka

MUSA UKUNGILANDELA.
LP: CEL 6783

SCATTERLINGS OF JULUKA.
MC: SHAKAC 2

Julverne

A NEUF.
LP: CRAM 274

July

DANDELION SEEDS.
LP: KIRI 097

Juma, Issa

SIGLAME 2 (Juma, Issa & Les Wanyika).
Tracks: / Sigalame 2 / Money / Pole pole / Rafki uangu / Ateka / Sarah.
LP: AFRILP 008

Jump Blues

JUMPIN' THE BLUES (Various artists).
Tracks: / Damp rag: *Various artists* / New kind of feelin': *Various artists* / Big Bob's boogie: *Various* artists / Elephant rock: *Various artists* / Riff, The: *Various artists* / Fat man blues: *Various artists*/ There ain't enough room here to boogie: *Various artists* / Doctor Jives: *Various artists* / Cadillac boogie: *Various artists* / Tra-la-la: *Various artists* / Race horse: *Various artists* / Pelican jump: *Various artists* / Hi-Yo Silver: *Various artists* / We're gonna rock this morning: *Various artists.*
LP: CH 94

JUMPIN THE BLUES VOL. 3 (Various artists).
LP: CH 162

JUMPIN' THE BLUES,VOL.2 (Various artists).
Tracks: / Cherokee boogie: *Thomas, Joey* / Take out your false teeth Daddy: *Day, Margie* / Oooh yes: *Gordon,* Stomp / She's fit 'n' fat 'n' fine: *Valentine, Billy* / Hobo boogie: *Thomas, Joey* / My bucket's got a hole in it: *Robinson, Fatman* / Woogie: *Dickens, Doles Quintet* / My kind of rocking: *Hall, Rene Trio* / Ham hocks: *Payne, Cecil* / Block buster boogie: *Payne, Cecil* / Shot gun boogie: *Gant, Cecil* / Rock little baby: *Gant, Cecil* / They call me Mr.Blues: *Jones, Grant 'Mr.Blues'* / Sit back down: *Little Esther* / He's a no good man: *Little Esther* / Barefoot Susie: *Brown, Waymon.*
LP: CH 135

Jump Dickie Jump

JUMP DICKIE JUMP.
LP: LPL 8602

Jump Leads

STAG MUST DIE, THE.
LP: OC 001

Jump, Wally Jnr.

DON'T PUSH YOUR LUCK.
Tracks: / Tighten up (I just can't stop dancing) / Thieves / Sworn to fun / Ain't gonna pay one red cent / Jump back / Private party / Turn me loose / She's gotta have it / Don't push your luck.
LP: AMA 5194
MC: AMC 5194

Jumpin' At...

JUMPIN' AT THE PEABODY & EARLE (Various artists).
LP: ARCADIA 2015

Jumpin' Jack Flash

JUMPIN' JACK FLASH (Film Soundtrack) (Various artists).
Tracks: / Set me free: *Rene & Angela* / Trick of the night, A: *Bananarama* / Misled: *Kool & The Gang*/ Rescue me: *Various artists* / Jumpin' Jack Flash: *Rolling Stones* / You can't hurry love: *Supremes*/ Hold on: *Branigan, Laura* / Window to the world: *Face To Face* / Breaking the code: *Newman, Thomas*/ Love music: *Newman, Thomas.*
LP: 830 545-1
MC: 830 545-4

Juncosa, Sylvia

NATURE.
LP: SST 146
MC: SST 146C

ONE THING.
Tracks: / 1 in 3 / Demon / Want it bad / System, The / Under the freeway / Alhambra / Love crash / Room 3 / Friend.
LP: SAVE 77

Junction 16

TO THE SPANNER BORN.
MC: JUNK 16

June Brides

THERE ARE EIGHT MILLION STORIES.
LP: PINKY 5

Jung Analysts

WISHING BALLOONS, THE.
LP: HAM 12

Jung & Parker

OFF THE PEG.
LP: UTIL 003

Jungklas, Rob

WORK SONGS FOR A NEW MOON.
LP: 9677-1-R

Jungle Band

JUNGLE GROOVE.
Tracks: / Dancing in the street - part one / Jungle groove / You got to make it

funky / Full speed ahead / Under the control of love / South fights back, The / Marvellous (red clay mix) / Dancing in the street - part two.
LP: . . . . CRB 1197
MC: . . . . TCCRB 1197

Jungle Book

JUNGLE BOOK (Unknown narrator(s)).
MC: . . . . DIS 002

JUNGLE BOOK (Various artists).
LP: . . . . D 319
MC: . . . . D 4DC
LP: . . . . D 3948
LPPD: . . . . D 3105

JUNGLE BOOK (James, Freddie & Una Stubbs).
MC: . . . . Unknown

JUNGLE BOOK (Original Film Soundtrack) (Various artists).
Tracks: / Main title: *Various artists* / Trust in me: *Various artists* / Colonel Hathi's march: *Various artists*/ Bare necessities: *Various artists* / I wan'na be like you: *Various artists* / Colonel Hathi's march: *Various* artists / That's what friends are for: *Various artists* / My own home: *Various artists* / Bare necessities: *Various artists*.
LP: . . . . SHM 937

JUNGLE BOOK (Unknown narrator(s)).
MC: . . . . STK 025

JUNGLE BOOK (ORIGINAL ISSUE) (Film soundtrack) (Various artists).
LP: . . . . ST 3948

JUNGLE BOOK, THE (Film sound track) (Various artists).
Tracks: / Trust in me: *Various artists* / Colonel Hathi's march: *Various artists* / Bare necessities: *Various* artists / I wanna be like you: *Various artists* / That's what friends are for: *Various artists* / My own home: *Various artists*.
LP: . . . . REC 536
MC: . . . . ZCM 536

JUNGLE BOOK, THE (Original soundtrack) (Various artists).
LP: . . . . WD 019
MC: . . . . WDC 019

JUNGLE BOOK/THIEF OF BAGHDAD (Film soundtrack) (Various artists).
LP: . . . . CL 0017

MARY POPPINS/THE JUNGLE BOOK (see under Mary Poppins) (Unknown narrator(s)).

MORE JUNGLE BOOK STORIES (see under Kipling, Rudyard) (Richardson, Ian).

TALES FROM THE JUNGLE BOOK (see Kipling, Rudyard) (Unknown narrator(s)).

Jungle Book (film)

JUNGLE BOOK/THIEF OF BAGHDAD (See under Nuremburg Symphony Orchestra) (Nuremberg Symphony Orchestra).

Jungle Brothers

DONE BY THE FORCES OF NATURE.
Tracks: / Done by the forces of nature / Beads on a string / Tribe vibes / Beez comin' through / Doin' our own dang / Keep accordin'.
LP: . . . . K 9260721
MC: . . . . K 9260724
LP: . . . . WX 332
MC: . . . . WX 332C

DONE BY THE FORCES OF NATURE (REMIX).
LP: . . . . WX 362
MC: . . . . WX 362 C

STRAIGHT OUT THE JUNGLE.
Tracks: / Straight out of the jungle / What's going on / Black is black / Jimbrowski / I'm gonna do you / I'll house you / On the run / Behind the bush / Because I like it like that / Braggin' and boastin' / Sounds of the safari / Jimmy's bonus beats.
MC: . . . . GEEMC 1
LP: . . . . GEEA 1
LP: . . . . WAR 2704

Jungle Crawlers

STOMPIN' ON DOWN.
LP: . . . . SOS 1084

Jungle Fever (film)

JUNGLE FEVER (See Under Wonder, Stevie) (Wonder, Stevie).

Jungle Heat

JUNGLE HEAT (Various artists).
LP: . . . . WW 5115
MC: . . . . WW 4 5115

Junior

ACQUIRED TASTE.
Tracks: / Stone lover / Somebody / Not tonight / Oh Louise / Thing called love, A / Do you really want my love / Look what you've done to me / Come on over / Together.
LP: . . . . LONLP 14
MC: . . . . LONC 14

INSIDE LOOKIN' OUT.
Tracks: / Communication breakdown / Woman say it / Sayin' something / Baby I want you back / You're the one / Storyteller / F.B. eye / Runnin' / Tell me.
LP: . . . . MERS 20
MC: . . . . MERSC 20

JI.
Tracks: / Mama used to say / Love dies / Too late / Is this love / Let me know / Down down / I can't help it / Darling you.
LP: . . . . MERS 3

SOPHISTICATED STREET.
Tracks: / Whodunnit / Right back at the start / Yes (if you want me) / It's true what some say / That's love / Living in the right way / Say that you care / High life / I'll get over you / If ever.
LP: . . . . LONLP 53
MC: . . . . LONC 53

Junior Soul

CLASSICS.
LP: . . . . TRLS 251

STORY BOOK CHILDREN.
Tracks: / Ain't misunderstanding mellow / Keep on trying / Help me make it through the night / Girl in his mind, The / Stand by me / Storybook children / Let the children play.
LP: . . . . JSLP 8801

Juniper Green

JUNIPER GREEN.
Tracks: / More than ever / Liverpool Lou / Step in the right direction / Time after time / Loving you ain't easy / All pull together / There's a kind of hush / Lovers in love / Breaking up is hard to do / For you / Water under the bridge / If you go away.
LP: . . . . GAL 6008

Junk

CUCKOOLAND.
LP: . . . . NTVLP 11

DROP CITY SOUVENIRS.
Tracks: / Junk town slam / Me and the king / Digging for victory / Killing of this town / Honey put your gun down / Kill for you / Won't let go / Devil sent a blue moon.
LP: . . . . JUNKLP 001

Junkin, John

MR. SHIFTER & THE REMOVAL MEN (see under Cribbins, Bernard) (Junkin, John/Bernard Cribbins).

Junkyard

JUNKYARD.
Tracks: / Blooze / Shot in the dark / Life sentence / Can't hold back / Hands off / Simple man / Hollywood / Long way home / Texas.
LP: . . . . WX 266
MC: . . . . WX 266C
MC: . . . . GEFC 24227

SIXES, SEVENS AND NINES.
LP: . . . . GEF 24372
MC: . . . . GEFC 24372

Junkyard Angels

STRAIGHT SHOOT (See under Bell, Carey & Lurrie) (Junkyard Angels & Carey & Lurrie Bell).

Jupiter, Duke

LINE OF YOUR FIRE.
Tracks: / Dancing on the ice / We might fall in love / Only you / I want to love you / You're my hero / Line of your fire / Since you've been gone / Turnin' me on / Never say goodbye / Sounds like love.
LP: . . . . ZL 72411

WHITE KNUCKLE RIDE.
Tracks: / She's so hot / Rescue me / Don't turn your back / Top of the bay / Backfire / Little lady / Woman like you, A / Work it out / Me & Michelle / Little black book.
LP: . . . . ZL 72193
MC: . . . . ZK 72193

Jupiter Menace

JUPITER MENACE (See under Synergy) (Film Soundtrack) (Synergy).

Jupp, Mickey

AS THE YEARS GO BY.
LP: . . . . FOAM 2

JUPPANESE.
Tracks: / Making friends / Short list / Old rock'n'roller / School / If only mother / Down in old New Orleans / You'll never get me up in one of those / Pilot / S.P.Y. / Ballad of Billy Bonney / Partir c'est mourir un peu / Brother doctor, sister nurse / Special credits.
LP: . . . . SEEZ 10

SHAMPOO, HAIRCUT AND SHAVE.
Tracks: / Stormy Sunday lunchtime / Orlando Fla / In her chair / All change / More than fair / Boxes and tins / Don't go home / Hot love / Reading glasses / Catstye Cam / Miss America.
LP: . . . . AMLH 68559

SOME PEOPLE CAN'T DANCE.
Tracks: / Modern music / Taxi driver.
LP: . . . . AMLH 68535

X.
MC: . . . . WF 041C
LP: . . . . WF 041

Jurgens, Dick

DICK JURGENS, 1938, VOL 3.
Tracks: / There's silver on the sage tonight / I wish I was a willow / There's honey on the moon tonight / Mirror's don't tell lies / Sweet Lorraine / Eight little notes / Little kiss at twilight, A / Ride, tenderfoot, ride / Martha / Night is filled with music, The / Bambino / Lady who couldn't be kissed, The.
LP: . . . . HSR 191

DICK JURGENS, 1937-1939.
Tracks: / Day dreams come true at night / Whispers in the dark / Me, myself and I / Gone with the wind / There's a brand new picture in my picture frame / This may be the night / Sailboat in the moonlight / Swamp fire / I've got a pocketful of dreams / Don't let that moon get away / Stop you're breaking my heart / Will you remember tonight tomorrow / In a sentimental mood / Merry-Go-Round broke down, The / Harbour lights / King Porter stomp.
LP: . . . . HSR 111

DICK JURGENS AND HIS ORCHESTRA 1937/39 (Jurgens, Dick & His Orchestra).
Tracks: / Daydreams come true at night / Whispers in the dark / Me, myself and I / Gone with the wind / There's a brand new picture... / This may be the night / Sailboat in the moonlight / Swamp fire / I've got a pocketful of dreams / Don't let that moon get away / Stop / You're breaking my heart / Will you remember tonight tomorrow / In a sentimental mood / Merry go round broke down / Harbour lights / King Porter stomp.
LP: . . . . HMP 5046

DICK JURGENS, VOL. 2, 1937-38.
Tracks: / I'm gonna lock my heart / I wanna go back to Bali / I married an angel / On the bumpy road to love / Put your heart in a song / Change partners / Tisket a tasket, A / I let a song go out of my heart / Bon boyage, little dream / Daddy's boy / Music maestro please / When mother nature sings her lullaby / Saving myself for you.
LP: . . . . HSR 138

UNCOLLECTED DICK JURGENS & HIS ORCHESTRA,VOL 2, THE.
Tracks: / Love is where you find it / Beside a moonlit stream / What goes on here in my heart / I'm gonna lock my heart / I wanna go back to Bali / I married an angel / On the bumpy road to love / Put your heart in a song / Change partners / Tisket a tasket, A / I let a song go / Bon voyage.
LP: . . . . FANFARE 31-131

Jurgens, Udo

UDO 1957-60.
Tracks: / He stop das ist meine braut (Be my guest) / Doch leider ist es nicht wahr (guess things happen that way) / Susanie (just about time) / Leg die knarre weg (Don't take your guns to town) / Die insel des glucks / Das war ein shoner tag (blue blue day) / Clementine / Susie, dein zug ist weg (Susie we goofed again) / Ich kusste dich einmal (Kissin' time) / Es zieht ein speilmann durch das land (My lips are sealed) / Jolly joy hat einen boy (Round and round) / Doch abends lasst du mich allein (knee deep in the blues) / Hejo-hejo gin and rum / Der lachende vagabund (Gambler's guitar) / Swing am abend / Ich komm vom Mississippi, tweedy-Cheerio.
LP: . . . . BFX 15060

Juris, Vic

BLEECKER STREET.
LP: . . . . MR 5265

HORIZON DRIVE.
LP: . . . . MR 5206

ROADSONG.
LP: . . . . MR 5150

Just A Gigolo

JUST A GIGOLO (Film soundtrack) (Various artists).
Tracks: / Just a gigolo: *Dietrich, Marlene* / Don't let it be too long: *Rome, Sydne* / Johnny: *Manhattan* Transfer / I kiss your hand: *Manhattan Transfer* / Jealous eyes: *Manhattan Transfer* / Salome: *Pasadena* Roof Orchestra / Black bottom: *Pasadena Roof Orchestra* / Charmaine: *Pasadena Roof Orchestra* / Easy winners: *Ragtimers* / Just a gigolo: *Village People*.
LP: . . . . JAM 1
MC: . . . . ZCJAM 1

Just For Fun

JUST FOR FUN (Film soundtrack) (Various artists).
LP: . . . . LK 4524

Just For The Crack

LOVING YOU (Just For The Crack & Peter Welch).
LP: . . . . HEAT 101
MC: . . . . HEATC 101

Just Ice

DESOLATE ONE, THE.
Tracks: / Desolate one, The / Hardhead / Cold getting dumb II / Na touch da just / In the jungle / Ram dance hall session / Back to the old school / And justice for all / Welfare recipients / Latoya / It's time I release / Hijack / Going way back / Put that record back on.
LP: . . . . SBUKLP 005
MC: . . . . SBUKMC 005
LP: . . . . LPRE 82010

KOOL & DEADLY.
Tracks: / Going way back / Original gangster of hip hop, The / Freedom of speech / Moshitup / Kool & deadly / On the strength / Lyric licking / Booga bandit bitch.
LP: . . . . LPRE 5

Just Kidding

WATCH THE FIRES.
LP: . . . . PHZA 38

Just Lovers

JUST LOVERS (Various artists).
LP: . . . . FR 999

Just My Imagination

JUST MY IMAGINATION (See under Reggae) (Various artists).

Just Reality

JUST REALITY - CASHBOUND VOL 1 (Various artists).
LP: . . . . CBLP 001

Just Say Yeh

JUST SAY YEH (Various artists).
LP: . . . . TANZLP 2

Just So Stories

JUST SO STORIES (see Kipling, Rudyard) (Morris, Johnny (nar)).
MCSET: CC/005

JUST SO STORIES Kipling, Rudyard (Davis, David (nar)).
MC: . . . . P 90021

JUST SO STORIES (See under Kipling, Rudyard).

JUST SO STORIES VOL 1 (see under Kipling, Rudyard) (Various artists).

JUST SO STORIES VOL 2 (see under Kipling, Rudyard) (Various artists).

Just Something...

JUST SOMETHING MY UNCLE TOLD ME (Various artists).
LP: . . . . ROUNDER 0141

Just When You...

JUST WHEN YOU THOUGHT IT WAS QUIET (Various artists).
LP: . . . . QLP 1

Just William

JUST WILLIAM (Jarvis, Martin (nar)).
MCSET: . . . . ZBBC 1165

JUST WILLIAM 2 (Jarvis, Martin (nar)).
Tracks: / Sweet little girl in white, The / Birthday treat, A / Outlaws and triplets, The / Bit of blackmail, A / William makes a night of it / William and the lost tourist / Leopard hunter, The / New neighbour, The / William the philanthropist / William and the prize cat.
MCSET: . . . . ZBBC 1180

JUST WILLIAM STORIES (see under Crompton, Richmal) (Williams, Kenneth (nar)).

MORE WILLIAMS STORIES (see under Crompton, Richmal) (Williams, Kenneth (nar)).

Justice Is Our

JUSTICE IS OUR CONVICTION (Various artists).
LP: . . . . SIJ 1

Justice League Of ...

BLACKLIST (Justice League Of America).
LP: . . . . PLASLP 011

CUPID IN REVERSE (Justice League Of America).
LP: . . . . PLASLP 023

Justified Ancients Of

ALL RECORDINGS (see under Jamms).

Juvet, Patrick

I LOVE AMERICA.
LP: **91003**

LADY NIGHT.
Tracks: / Lady night / Swiss kiss / Viva California / Gay Paris / French pillow talk.
LP: . . . . **CAL 2049**

LAURA: MUSIC FROM THE FILM.
LP: **1960 020**

PARIS BY NIGHT.
LP: **90098**

Juvies

PLAYIN' HOOKIE.
LP: . . . . **RAGELP 106**

J.V.C.F.O.R.C.E.

TALL DARK AND HANDSOME.
LP: . . . . **BBOYD 3**

JYL

JYL.
Tracks: / Mechanic Ballerina / Universe / Computer love / Positions / Dance and death / Computer generation, The / Animation / Silicon valley / Electric lady / I'm a machine.
LP: . . . . **THBL 036**

K

K-9 Posse

CHEW IT UP.
LP: . . . . AL 8569

K-9 POSSE.
Tracks: / This beat is military / Somebody's brother / No stoppin' or standin' between the rhyme / Say who say what / No sell out / Ain't nothin' to it / It gets no deeper / Tough cookie / This is the way the quick cut goes / Turn that down.
LP: 209647
MC: 409647

Kabaka, Duabi

KENYAFRICA (VOL.3) (Duadi Kabaka & The T B Eagles).
LP: . . . . PS 33003

Kabaya, Tsuruhiko

SOUND OF AFRICA, THE (See Under Africa).

Kader, Cheb

FROM ORAN TO PARIS.
MC: . . . . SHMC 64029

Kadoudal, Bagad

BOMBARDES ET BINIOUS DE BRETAGNE VOL.4 (Kadoudal, Bagad De La Kevrenn De Rennes).
Tracks: / Suite de gavottes Pourlet / Suite vannetaise / Danses bulgares / Ha pe oen me un tamm amzer / Larides / An dour du / Suite d'airs Pourlet / Introduction des - Noces thraces / Suite de melodies Pourlet / Air et gavotte Pourlet.
LP: . . . . ARN 33710

BOMBARDES ET BINIOUS DE BRETAGNE VOL.3 (Kadoudal, Bagad De La Kevrenn De Rennes).
Tracks: / Marches et Dans-tro-Plin / Deus ganin me, plac'h yaouank / Ar jouiz, son kloareg, distro ar martolod / Melodies du Tregor / Saltarello / Suites de Marches de Baud / Ductia / Suites de Marches de Pluvigner / Pachpi / Pe oen o Foennat / Suite de danses - Fisel.
LP: . . . . ARN 33526

BOMBARDES ET BINIOUS DE BRETAGNE VOL.2 (Kadoudal, Bagad De La Kevrenn De Rennes).
Tracks: / Deuxieme marche / Gwendal / Suite de Jef Le Penven / An dro / Tuchant e arriuo en hanv / Gavotte des montagnes / Melodie de Rostrenen / Suite de Larides de Baud / Chal ha dichal / Maro eo va mestrez / Dans plin / Er voraerion / Dans Leon / Melodie de Lochrist-Inzinzac.
LP: . . . . ARN 33343

BOMBARDES ET BINIOUS DE BRETAGNE VOL.1 (Kadoudal, Bagad De La Kevrenn De Rennes).
Tracks: / Kendalc'h toniou / Soubenn al laez / Tonbale a vro-Vigouden / Disul vintin pe oen o chiboesat / Kendalc'h toniou / Bale a vro-Rouzik / Deus ganin-me, plac'h yaouank / Gavotenn a vro (Bourled) / Pennherez Keroulaz / Gavotenn a vro (Vigouden) / Kimiad ar soudard yaouank / Kendalc'h toniou / Bale a vro-Bourled / Sonerez evit ar sonerien maro.
LP: . . . . ARN 30089
MC: . . . . ARN 430089

Kaeheles, Jerry

GOOD TIME LEVEE STOMPERS (Kaeheles, Jerry & Ray Ronnei).
LP: . . . . MMRC 118

Kaempfert, Bert

BERT KAEMPFERT.
Tracks: / Strangers in the night / Perdido / World we knew, The / Something / You turned my world around / Love snowbird / Spanish eyes / One smile away / Rememeber when / Sweet Caroline / Danke schon.
LP: 2848 161
MC: 3201 243
MC: 3271 141

BERT KAEMPFERT AND HIS ORCHESTRA (Kaempfert, Bert and his Orchestra).
Tracks: / Put your hand in the hand / Kiss her once with feeling / Me and my shadow / In our time / Red sky at morning / Falling tree / Dream baby / Oh woman, oh why / Grey eyes make me blue / Bell bottoms / Proud Mary / Living easy / Cracklin' Rosie / My love / Don't go / Tea and trumpets / Friends / While the children sleep / I'll be with you in apple blossom time / Snowbird / Hi de ho / Bye bye blackbird / Orange coloured sky / Wake up and live.
2LP: 262 503 6

BERT KAEMPFERT COLLECTION.
2LP: 8437101
MCSET: 8437104

BEST OF BERT KAEMPFERT.
Tracks: / Strangers in the night / Mitternachts blues / Chanson d'amour / Oh mein papa / Blue midnight / Danke schon / Spanish eyes / Swinging safari / My way of life / That happy feeling / Games people play / Bye bye blues.
LP: 2876 042
MC: 3476 042
LP: 84 012

BEST SELLER: BERT KAEMPFERT.
LP: 583 551

BYE BYE BLUES.
Tracks: / Bye bye blues / Remember when / When you're smiling / Tahitian sunset / Once in a while / Steady does it / It makes no difference / You stepped out of a dream / Auf wiedersehen / I'm beginning to see the light / Melina / Out of nowhere.
LP: 184 046
LP: . . . . BM 84086

DANKE SCHON.
LP: 2310 486
MC: 3100 333

DROP OF CHRISTMAS SPIRIT, A.
MC: 825 143 4

FOREVER MY LOVE.
Tracks: / Moon over Miami / Reggae romp / My prayer / Cry baby cry / On the sunny side of the street / Godfather, The / Perdido / Forever my love / Pagan love song / Walkin' and shoutin' / I love you so / Soft shoulders.
LP: 2310593

GREATEST HITS: BERT KAEMPFERT (IMPORT).
LP: . . . . FUN 9021
MC: . . . . FUNC 9021

HOLD ME.
LP: 184 072

HOURS OF THE STARS.
Tracks: / Strangers in the night / Besame mucho / Island in the sun / Love me tender / Blueberry Hill / Afrikaan beat / Spanish eyes / Red rose for a blue lady / My way / Swingin' safari, A / In the mood / Danke schon.
LP: 2872 303
MC: 3472 303

IMAGES: BERT KAEMPFERT.
Tracks: / Bye bye blues / My eyes adored you / Answer me / Danke schon / This guy's in love with you / Happy trumpeter / Moon over Naples (Spanish eyes) / Raindrops keep falling on my head / Afrikaan beat / Way we were, The / Zambesi / Feelings / Island in the sun / Red roses for a blue day.
MC: . . . . KNMC 16007

KAEMPFERT SPECIAL.
LP: 236 207

MAGIC MUSIC OF BERT KAEMPFERT, THE.
LP: 8439861
MC: 8439864

MOODS.
Tracks: / Can't give you anything but my love / Sunny side of life, The / Zambesi / Opus one / Who's sorry now / Night train / Proud Mary / More I see you, The / Bye bye blues.
LP: . . . . CN 2051
MC: CN4 2051

NOW AND FOREVER (Kaempfert, Bert and his Orchestra).
Tracks: / Now and forever / Lonely is the name / One lonely night / Petula song / Bell bottoms / Wake up and live / Song for Satch / In the everglades / Reggae romp / Cry baby cry / Walkin' and shoutin' / One smile away.
LP: 2311 178
MC: 3100 657

ORANGE COLOURED SKY.
LP: 2310 091

RED ROSES FOR A BLUE LADY.
Tracks: / Red roses for a blue lady / African beat / Strangers in the night / Living it up / Mitternachts blues / World we knew ,The / Can't give you anything - but my love / Remember when / Moon over Naples / Swinging safari, A / Most beautiful girl, The / That happy feeling / L-O-V-E / Wonderland by night / Bye bye blues / Danke schon.
LP: 817877 1
MC: 817877 4
LP: 827501 1
MC: 827501 4

RELAXING SOUND OF BERT KAEMPFERT.
LP: 583 501

SAFARI SWINGS AGAIN (Kaempfert, Bert and his Orchestra).
Tracks: / Woodchopper's ball / Little brown jug / One o' clock jump / Lullaby of Birdland / Two o' clock jump / Airmail special / Apple honey / Itermission riff / Jumpin' at the woodside / Marie / It's only a paper moon / In the mood / Happy safari / Soft shoe safari / Limbo lady / Tom Hark / Angelica / Sugar bush / Baby elephant walk / Monkey shuffle / Mombasa rock / Walking with fips / Way I love you / Seven up / Pata-pata.
2LP: 2664 478

SPRINGTIME.
LP: 2311 078
MC: 3100 601

STRANGERS IN THE NIGHT.
Tracks: / Strangers in the night / Fascination / Tenderly / Stardust / I'll be with you in apple blossom time / Blue moon / Almost there / Everybody loves somebody / On the sunny side of the street / Answer me / Spanish eyes (Moon over naples) / Autumn leaves / Good life / World we knew, The / Can't take my eyes off you / Who's sorry now?.
LP: . . . . CN 2088
LP: 827 500-1
MC: 827 500-4
MC: CN4 2088
LP: . . . . LPHM 84 053

SUPER STEREO SOUNDS OF BERT KAEMPFERT.
Tracks: / Swingin' safari / Red roses for a blue lady / That happy feeling / Spanish eyes / Bandit / Bye bye blues / Midnight in Moscow / Wonderland by night / Living it up / Strangers in the night / Zambesi / World we knew / Afrikaan beat / Answer me / Twilight time / Danke schon.
LP: . . . . POLTV 10
LP: . . . . SPELP 59
MC: . . . . SPEMC 59

SWINGING SAFARI, A.
Tracks: / Afrikaan beat / Black beauty / Happy trumpeter / Market day / Similau / Skokiaan / Swingin' safari, A / Take me / That happy feeling / Tootie flutie / Wimoweh / Zambesi.
LP: . . . . LPHM 46 384

THIS IS BERT KAEMPFERT.
LP: . . . . ADAH 433
MC: . . . . ADAHC 433

WONDERLAND BY NIGHT.
Tracks: / Wonderland by night / Jumpin' at the woodside / Sugar bush / Afrikaan beat / Pata pata / Lonely nightingale / Way we were, The / Lullaby of birdland / Happy safari / In the mood / Happy trumpeter / Yellow bird / Baby elephant walk / Fly robin fly.
LP: 2486 232
MC: 3186 068
LP: 827 502-1
MC: 827 502-4

Kafka, Franz (aut)

METAMORPHOSIS, THE (Mason, James (nar)).
MC: 1594

STORIES OF FRANZ KAFKA (Lenya, Lotte).
MC: 1114

Kah, Hubert

TEN SONGS.
Tracks: / Pogo the clown / Lonesome cowboy / Drowning / Something I should know / Explain the world in a word / Love is so sensible / Get strange / That girl / Limousine / Under my skin.
LP: . . . . MCF 3354
MC: . . . . MCFC 3354

Kahamba, Shaka

NAWEYI.
LP: . . . . S 1830
MC: . . . . S 1830C

Kahn Bismillah

RGS. JAUNPURI & IMAN KALYAN.
LP: . . . . ECSD 41535

Kahn, Si

DOING MY JOB.
LP: . . . . FF 221

HOME.
LP: . . . . FF 207

I'LL BE THERE.
LP: . . . . FF 509

UNFINISHED PORTRAITS.
LP: . . . . FF 312

Kahondo Style

MY HEART'S IN MOTION.
Tracks: / Tokyo ando / Games with the lights / Barbaria / Last minute jingle / Jaws of glass / Holloway Road / Lonely teardrops / Ant by ant, leaf by leaf / Mongoose / Ghost of a flea / Programs on the air / My heart's in motion.
LP: . . . . NATO 469

Kai, Seiryu

MIWAKU NO POPULAR MEI KYOKU SU (See under Yamauchi, Kimiko) (Kai, Seiryu/ Kimiko, Yamauchi).

Kaiser, Henry

DEVIL IN THE DRAIN.
Tracks: / Sugagaki for conlon / King of the wild frontier / Dark memory / Smokestack lightning / Roadside picnic / Free to choose / Lost horizons / Devil in the drain / If this goes on....
LP: . . . . SST 118

HEARTS DESIRE.
Tracks: / Dark star / Rivers edge / Fishin' hole, The / Anyone who had a heart / Losing hand / Don't let a thief steal into your heart / Number 2 Klavierstuck III / Are you experienced? / Lover, The / Flavor bud living / Ballad of Shane Muscatel, The / King Harvest (has surely come) / Black light / Buried treasure / Never again.
LP: . . . . RECK 19

IT'S A WONDERFUL LIFE.
LP: . . . . ML 124

MARRYING FOR MONEY.
LP: . . . . MM 1010

THOSE WHO KNOW HISTORY.
LP: . . . . SST 198
MC: . . . . SST 198C

Kaiser, Kurt

FATHER LIFT ME UP.
Tracks: / Enter into His gates / Father lift me up / Lord is my strength and my song, The / O bless the Lord / Grow in grace / He careth for you / If any man thirst / Oh so wonderful / Give me thine heart / Sing it out loud / Shield about me, A / Hallowed be thy name.
LP: . . . . WST 9604
MC: . . . . WC 9604

I'M HERE, GOD'S HERE, NOW WE CAN START (see under Carmichael, Ralph) (Kaiser, Kurt & Ralph Carmichael).

Kaja

CRAZY PEOPLES RIGHT TO SPEAK.
Tracks: / Do I / Shouldn't do that / Your appetite / Rivers / Sit down and shut up / Afraid of you / Jigsaw / Fear of falling / Charm of a gun / You really take my breathe away.
LP: . . . . KAJA 2
MC: . . . . TCKAJA 2

Kajagoogoo

ISLANDS.
Tracks: / Lion's mouth, The / Big apple / Power to forgive / Melting the ice away / Turn your back on me / Islands / On a plane / Part of me is you / Loop, The.
LP: . . . . KAJA 1
LP: . . . . EMC 2401161

WHITE FEATHERS.
Tracks: / White feathers / Too shy / Lies and promises / Magician man / Kajagoogoo / Ooh to be ah / Ergonomics / Hang on now / This car is fast / Frayo.
LP: . . . . EMC 3433

Kakoulli, Harry

EVEN WHEN I'M NOT.
Tracks: / Be aware / I'm on a rocket / Easy / Do not disturb / I wanna stay / Stop me, nudge me, push me / I feel sad / Waiting / Everyday's the same.
LP: . . . . OVLP 505

Kalabash Twins

OUT OF CONTROL.
LP: . . . . SHAKA 0187

Kalahari Surfers

LIVING IN THE HEART OF THE BEAST.
LP: . . . . RRC 24

SLEEP ARMED.
Tracks: / Prologue / Houghton parents / Healthy way of life / Potential aggressor / Remember the corporals / Golden rendezvous / Leaders underground / This land / Hoe ry die boere / Mafeking road / Rademeyer's letter to his wife / Maids day off / Potential aggressor (2) / Greatest hits (tear gas) / Brighter future.
LP: . . . . RR 26

Kalamas Quartette

EARLY HAWAIIAN CLASSICS.
LP: . . . . FL 9022

Kalapreet

SHAVA SHAVA.
LP: . . . . ARI 1003
MC: . . . . ARI 0103

Kaldor, Connie

MOONLIGHT GROCERY.
LP: . . . . TALKLP 1
MC: . . . . TALKC 1

Kaleidoscope

WHEN SCOPES COLLIDE.
LP: . . . . ILPS 9462

Kaleidoscope (UK)

FAINTLY BLOWING.
Tracks: / Faintly blowing / Poem / Snapdragon / Story from Tom Bitz, A / Love song for Annie / Opinion / If you so wish... / If you so wish... / Black fjord / Feathered tiger, The / I'll kiss you once / Music.
LP: . . . . TOCK 6

TANGERINE DREAM.
Tracks: / Kaleidoscope / Please excuse my face / Dive into yesterday / Mr. Small, The watch repairer man / Flight from ashiya / Murder of Lewis Tollani, The / Further reflections in the room... / Dear nelle goodrich / Holidaymaker / Lesson perhaps, A / Sky children, The.
LP: . . . . TOCK 5

Kaleidoscope (USA)

BEACON FROM MARS (Kaleidoscope).
Tracks: / Egyptian gardens / If the night / Please / Keep your mind open / Pulsating dream / Oh death / Why try / I found out / Lie to me / Petite fleur / Banjo / Cuckoo, The / Nobody / Elevator man / Hello trouble.
LP: . . . . ED 115
LP: . . . . ED 288

INCREDIBLE.
Tracks: / Lie to me / Let the good love flow / Killing floor / Petite fleur / Banjo / Cuckoo, The / Seven ate sweet.
LP: . . . . ED 292

RAMPE' RAMPE'.
LP: . . . . ED 138

SIDE TRIPS.
Tracks: / Egyptian gardens / If the night / Please / Keep your mind open / Pulsating dream / Oh death / Come on in / Why try / Minnie the moocher.
LP: . . . . ED 284

Kaley, Gerry

DELICATE TOUCH, THE.
Tracks: / Delicate touch, The / Best of now, The / Broken doll / Golden sands / This one's on me / Big fish / Pumpkin's fancy / Talkin' money / Lads of Laois / Janice.
LP: . . . . CHAOS LP 1
MC: . . . . CHAOS MC 1

Kali

RACINES VOLUME 2.
LP: . . . . 88034 LP

Kalima

FEELING FINE.
Tracks: / Shine / Take it easy / All the way through / Groovy one, The / Unreal / Thousand signs, A / Interstella / Big fat city / Azure.
LP: . . . . FACT 249

KALIMA.
LP: . . . . FACT 206
MC: . . . . FACT 206 C

NIGHT-TIME SHADOWS.
Tracks: / Mystic rhymes / After hours / Green Dolphin Street / Blackwater / In time / Father pants / Start the melody / Token freaky / Love suspended in time.
LP: . . . . FACT 155

Kalin Twins

WHEN.
Tracks: / Sweet sweet sugar lips / Chicken chief / Oh my goodness / Jumpin' Jack / Clickety clack / Three o'clock thrill / Spider and the fly, The / No money can buy / When / Forget me not / Picture of you / Zing went the strings of my heart / Walkin' to school / Momma poppa / It's only the beginning / You mean the world to me.
LP: . . . . BFX 15122

WHEN (See under Danny & The Juniors/ At the hop).

Kalle, Pepe

GIGANTAFRIQUE.
Tracks: / Tiembe raid pa moli / Ce chale carnaval / Marche commun / Bilala lala / Pon moun paka bouge / Ndaka ya zeke.
LP: . . . . ORB 062

L'ARGENT NE FAIT LE BONHEUR.
LP: 310011

MOYIBI (Kalle, Pepe & Nyboma).
LP: . . . . SYL 8353

Kallen, Kitty

LITTLE THINGS MEAN A LOT (OLD GOLD) (See under Al Hibbler - Unchained Melody).

THREE GREAT GIRLS (see under Reese, Della) (Reese, Della/Ann Margret/Kitty Kallen).

Kallmann, Gunter

CHRISTMAS SING IN WITH THE GUNTER KALLMAN CHOIR (Kallmann, Gunter Choir).
MC: 837 452 4

ELIZABETHAN SERENADE (Kallmann, Gunter Choir).
Tracks: / Elizabethan serenade / Bei walzermusik / Annabelle / Musik zum verlieben / Glocken serenade / Der reigen / Toselli's serenade / La montanara / Glocken klingen zu densternen / Drigo's serenade / Oh mein papa / Traum melodie.
LP: . . . . MOIR 109
MC: . . . . CMOIR 109

Kalnin, Teodor

TEODOR KALNIN CHOIR (LATVIAN RADIO).
LP: . . . . C 01741-2

Kamal

DANCE (Kamal & The Brothers).
LP: . . . . ST 279

Kamen, Michael

DIE HARD 2 (See under Die Hard 2).

EDGE OF DARKNESS (See under Clapton, Eric) (Clapton, Eric & Michael Kamen).

Kamen, Nick

MOVE UNTIL WE FLY.
Tracks: / I promised myself / Looking good diving / Um um um um um um / We can make it / You are / Oh how happy / Somebody's arms to hold me / Take back my hand child / Agony and ecstasy / Move until we fly.
LP: . . . . WX 338
MC: . . . . WX 338 C

NICK KAMEN.
Tracks: / Win your love / Open the door to your heart / Nobody else / Into the night / Come softly to me / Loving you is sweeter than ever / Each time you break my heart / Man in me, The / Any day now / Help me baby.
LP: . . . . WX 84
MC: . . . . WX 84C

US.
Tracks: / Bring me your love / Wonders of you / I can't live / Guilty / Turn it up / Tell me / Count on me / This is really love / Steal love.
LP: . . . . WX 176
MC: . . . . WX 176C

Kames, Bob

MELODIES OF LOVE (Kames, Bob & Happy Organ).
LP: . . . . GNPS 2165
MC: GNP5 2165

Kames & Downey

FUN AND FITNESS OVER 50.
LP: . . . . GNPS 2159
MC: GNP5 2159

Kaminsky, Max

ART FORD'S JAZZ PARTY (July 1958).
LP: . . . . AFJP 3

JACK TEAGARDEN AND MAX KAMINSKY (See under Teagarden, Jack) (Kaminsky, Max & Jack Teagarden).

Kamoku, Duke

GOLDEN HAWAIIAN HITS.
LP: . . . . GNPS 73
MC: GNP5 73

Kamon, Karen

HEART OF YOU.
Tracks: / Loverboy / Don't just stand there / Do you wanna make something of it / It's tough to be a man / Da doo ron ron / Heart of you / Sweet little girl / Real me / When you got a woman.
LP: . . . . CBS 26017

VOICES.
Tracks: / Lovesick / Give a little love / Fool for love / Love just ain't enough / Voices / All cried out / Strangeway / Heart over mind / Bop girl / Whatever we imagine.
LP: 790 575-1
MC: 790 575-4

Kamoze, Ini

INI KAMOZE.
Tracks: / Trouble you a trouble me / World-a-music / Them thing deh / General / Wings with me / Hail mi idrin.
LP: . . . . IMA 7
MC: . . . . IMC 7

PIRATE.
Tracks: / Dream / Pirate / Betty Brown's mother / Queen of my house / R.O.U.G.H. / Gunshot / Burnin' / Pull the cork.
LP: . . . . ILPS 9845
MC: . . . . ICT 9845

SHOCKING OUT.
Tracks: / Cool it off / Clown talking / Cone now / Boss, the / We run the country / Shocking out / Revolution / Girl E / Hole in the pumpkin / Spread out.
LP: . . . . GREL 115
MC: . . . . GREEN 115

STATEMENT.
MC: . . . . ICT 9800
LP: . . . . ILPS 9800

Kampala Sound

KAMPALA SOUND (Various artists).
LP: . . . . OMA 109

Kampec Dolores

KAMPEC DOLORES.
Tracks: / My, hair, my face / Hey-ho / Strange things / I saw him on two hands / Budapest / Fire lake / To shoot across / Icons.
LP: . . . . K 036 108

Kamua, Daniel

KENYAFRICA (VOL.1) (Kamua, Daniel Orchestra).
LP: . . . . PS 33001

Kamuca, Richie

JAZZ EROTICA.
LP: . . . . FS 96

RICHIE KAMUCA QUARTET (Kamuca, Richie Quartet).
LP: . . . . VSOP 17

Kan, Isho

DREAM REGGAE MUSIC (see Asinovi, Jon & Isho Kan) (Kan, Isho/Jon Asinovi).

Kanchan

KUCHI GATDAD HAI.
LP: . . . . STEREO 021

MACHU PICCHU.
MC: . . . . TUMIC 011

Kanda Bongo Man

ISAMBE-MONIE.
LP: 320031
MC: 320034

KWASSA-KWASSA.
LP: . . . . HNBL 1343
MC: . . . . HNBC 1343

NON STOP NON STOP.
Tracks: / Iyole / Ida / Djessy / Amina / Mazina.
LP: . . . . ORB 005
MC: . . . . ORBC 005

ZING ZONG.
Tracks: / Zing zong / Isambe / Mosali / Wallow / Monie / Yonde love me / Yesu Christu / Freres soki / Kadhi.
LP: . . . . HNBL 1366
MC: . . . . HNBC 1366

Kane, D.J.

D.J. KANE & THE MILLIONAIRES (Kane, D.J. & the Millionaires).
Tracks: / That's too bad / You're never satisfied / Lately things get screwed up all the time / Lonely one, (The) / Somewhere, no place special / Couldn't we meet halfway? / Morning sickness / Meanwhile, back at the front / Not safe for the city streets / After the operation / When the shit hits the fan / Killer in Vienna, A.
LP: . . . . RAD 29

Kane Gang

BAD AND LOW DOWN WORLD OF THE KANE GANG, THE.
Tracks: / Gun law / Take this train / How much longer? / Loserville / Printers devil / Respect yourself - extended version / Closest thing to heaven / Small town creed / Crease in his hat.
LP: . . . . KWLP 2
MC: . . . . KWC 2

MIRACLE.
Tracks: / Motortown / What time is it / Looking for gold / Take me to the world / King Street rain / Don't look any further / Finer place, A / Let's get wet / Strictly love it ain't.
LP: . . . . KWLP 7
MC: . . . . KWC 7

Kane, George

PLEASE COME HOME.
LP: . . . . GIE 48
MC: . . . . GIEN 48

Kane, Raymond

MASTER OF THE SLACK KEY GUITAR.
LP: . . . . ROUNDER 6020
MC: . . . . ROUNDER 6020C

Kanga, Karl

HIPS FOR SALE.
LP: . . . . AM 64

Kanguru Dreaming

KANGURU DREAMING (Various artists).
LP: . . . . LRF 096

Kansas

AUDIO VISIONS.
Tracks: / Relentless / Anything for you / Hold on / Loner / Curtain of iron / Got to rock on / Don't open your eyes / No one together / No room for a stranger / Back door.
LP: . . . . KIR 84500

BEST OF KANSAS.
Tracks: / Carry on wayward son / Point of no return, The / Fight fire / No one together / Play the game tonight / Wall, The.
LP: . . . . EPC 26065
MC: 40 26065

DRASTIC MEASURES.
Tracks: / Fight fire with fire / Everybody's my friend / Mainstream / Andi / Going through the motions / Get rich / Don't take your love away / End of the age / Incident on a bridge.
LP: . . . . EPC 25561
MC: 40 25561

IN THE SPIRIT OF THINGS.
Tracks: / Ghosts / One big sky / Inside of me / One man, one heart / House on fire / Once in a lifetime / Stand beside me / I counted on love / Preacher, The / Rainmaker / T.O. Witcher / Bells of Saint James.
LP: . . . . MCA 6254

KANSAS.
Tracks: / Can I tell you / Bringing it back / Lonely wind / Belexes / Journey from Mariabronn / Pilgrimage, The / Apercu / Death of Mother Nature suite.
LP: . . . . EPC 80174

LEFTOVERTURE.
Tracks: / Carry on wayward son / Wall, The / What's on my mind / Miracles out of nowhere / Opus insert / Questions of my childhood / Cheyenne anthem / Magnum opus / Father Padilla meets the perfect gnat / Howling at the moon / Man overboard / Industry on parade / Release the beavers / Great attack.
LP: . . . . EPC 81728

MASQUE.
Tracks: / It takes a woman's love (to make a man) / Two cents worth / Icarus - born on the wings of steel / All the world / Child of innocence / It's you / Mysteries and mayhem / Pinnacle, The.
LP: . . . . PZ 33806

MONOLITH.
Tracks: / On the other side / People of the south wind / Angels have fallen / How my soul cries out for you / Glimpse of home / Away from you / Stay out of trouble / Reason to be.
LP: . . . . KIR 83644

POWER.
Tracks: / Silhouettes in disguise / Power / All I wanted / Secret service / We're not alone anymore / Musicatto / Taking in the view / Three pretenders / Tomb 19 / Can't cry anymore.
LP: . . . . MCG 6021
MC: . . . . MCGC 6021

SONG FOR AMERICA.
Tracks: / Down the road / Song for America / Lamplight symphony / Lonely street / Devil game, The / Incomudro - hymn to the Atman.
LP: . . . . EPC 80740

TWO FOR THE SHOW.
Tracks: / Song for America / Point of no return / Paradox / Dust in the wind / Icarus / Borne on wings of steel / Portrait / Carry on wayward son / Journey from Mariabronn.
LP: KIR 88228

VINYL CONFESSIONS.
Tracks: / Play the game tonight / Right away / Fair exchange / Chaining shadows / Diamonds and pearls / Face it / Windows / Borderline / Play on / Crossfire.
LP: KIR 85714

Kansas City

KANSAS CITY 5 & 6(1938) (Kansas City 5 & 6 with Lester Young).
Tracks: / Way down yonder in New Orleans / Countless blues / Them there eyes / I want a little girl / Paging the devil / Laughing at life / Good morning blues / I know that you know / Love me or leave me.
LP: AG6 24057

PRES & FRIENDS ('44) (Kansas City 6 with Lester Young).
LP: AG6 24292

Kansas City Red

ORIGINAL CHICAGO BLUES (see Carter, Joe).

Kansas Joe

BEST OF KANSAS JOE - VOL.1 - 1929-1935 (THE).
LP: BD 603

Kantata

ASIKO (ALBUM).
LP: OVLP 508

IT'S HIGH TIME NOW.
LP: ASR 3010

Kante, Mory

10 COLA NUTS.
Tracks: / 10 cola nuts / Kebendo / Kouma / Teri ya / Lele / Nonsense.
LP: 829 087 1
MC: 829 087 4

A PARIS.
Tracks: / Ye ke ye ke / Gnaga lemba / Wari massilani / Ca va la bas / M'balou / Soumba.
LP: 829 690 1
MC: 829 690 4

AKWABA BEACH.
Tracks: / Ye ke ye ke / Deni / Inch Allah / Tama / Africa 2000 / Dia / Nanfoulen / Akwaba beach.
LP: 833 119 1
MC: 833 119 4

TOUMA.
LP: 843702 1
MC: 843702 4

Kanter, Amy

OTHER GIRL.
Tracks: / Can you feel my heartbeat / If you leave / Hurt by love / You could have fooled me / Feels like the end / Other girl / Heart to heart / Wave / Dreaming of you / All in the name of love.
LP: 780 016-1

Kantner, Paul

BLOWS AGAINST THE EMPIRE (Kantner, Paul & Starship).
Tracks: / Mau mau / Baby tree, The / Let's go together / Child is coming, A / Sunrise / Hijack / Home / Have you see the stars tonite / S.M. starship.
LP: SF 8163

SUNFIGHTER (Kantner, Paul & Grace Slick).
Tracks: / Silver spoon / Diana / Sunfighter / Titanic, The / Look at the wood / When I was a boy / I watched the wolves / Million / China / Earth mother / Diana 2 / Universal copernican mumbles / Holding together.
LP: ESSLP 001
LP: FTR 1002

Kaoma

WORLD BEAT.
Tracks: / Lambada / Lambareggae / Dancando lambada / Lambamor / Lamba / Caribe / Melodie d'amour / Sindiang / Sopenala / Jambefinete (grille) / Salsa nuestra.
LP: 4660121
MC: 4660124

Kaoru

TANTA HASHA.
LP: HAM 23

Kaos Acid...

KAOS ACID NEW BEAT COMPILATION (2) (See Under Dance...) (Various artists).

Kapelle, Rote

NO NORTH BRITON.
LP: IT 062

Kapelye

CHICKEN.
LP: SHAN 21007

FUTURE AND PAST.
LP: FF 249

LEVINE & HIS FLYING MACHINE.
LP: SHAN 21006

Kaper, Bronislaw

BRONISLAW KAPER PLAYS HIS FILM MUSIC (See Under Film Music).

Kapoor, Mahendra

BAHBI GAL NA KARI.
Tracks: / Aj tenoom nachna pao / Bhabi gal na kari / Ik Cardi Jawani / Gorian Ghulab Jayan Gallan / Toon Toon Boley Tar / Giddh wich nachdi de / Saron De Phool Wargi / Kle Doriach Mukhra Lukakey / Saun Rabdi Mauj Lag Javey / Mein ta peenia.
LP: MUT 1028
MC: CMUT 1028

BHANGRA PARTY.
MC: CMUT 1004

DILLLAN DEE GAL.
LP: SSRLP 5106
MC: SC 5106

FROM BIRMINGHAM TO SOUTHALL.
LP: MUT 1069
MC: CMUT 1069

Karadenev, Denio

BULGARIE ETERNELLE.
Tracks: / Pravo trakiisko horo / Kales kirce / Deno, mari krotko tropaj / Svatbarska melodia & ratschenitsa / Snosti si go vidoch, Mamo, ubavoto Stojne / Marice le, licno devojce / Tanc iz varnensko / Ratschenitsa gradulka / Dali znaes mila majko / Svatbarska melodia gaida / Sinke le / Dobroudjanska tropanka / Side devojcina / Schopska ratschenitsa.
LP: ARN 33712
MC: ARN 433712

Karaindrou, Eleni

MUSIC FOR FILMS.
Tracks: / Farwell theme / Elegy for rosa / Fairytale / Parade / Return / Wandering in Alexandria / Voyage, The / Scream / Adagio / Rosa's song / Improvisation on farewell and waltz theme / Song / Waltz and farewell theme.
LP: ECM 1429

Karajova, Nadka

PAZARDJIK FOLK SONGS.
LP: FMSL 1001
MC: FMSC 1001

Karamillo, Petro

THIS IS PETRO KARAMILLO.
LP: GPR 20

Karaoke...

KARAOKE ALL STARS VOL. 1 (Various artists).
Tracks: / Sugar sugar: *Various artists* / I saw her standing there: *Various artists* / You're so vain: *Various* artists / Bye bye love: *Various artists* / Addicted to love: *Various artists* / I heard it through the grapevine: *Various artists* / I can see clearly now: *Various artists* / King of the road: *Various artists* / I will survive: *Various artists* / Surfin' USA: *Various artists* / Fame: *Various artists* / We don't talk anymore: *Various artists* / Like a virgin: *Various artists* / Peggy Sue: *Various artists* / All I have to do is dream: *Various artists* / Return to sender: *Various artists* / Unchained melody: *Various artists* / When I'm 64: *Various artists* / California dreamin': *Various artists* / Leader of the pack: *Various artists*.
LP: 847 801 1
MC: 847 801 4

KARAOKE ALL STARS VOL. 2 (Various artists).
Tracks: / Daydream believer: *Various artists* / La bamba: *Various artists* / Da doo ron ron: *Various artists*/ Living doll: *Various artists* / I wanna dance with somebody: *Various artists* / I shot the sheriff: *Various* artists / Are you lonesome tonight: *Various artists* / Daniel: *Various artists* / New York, New York: *Various* artists / Summer holiday: *Various artists* / I wanna hold your hand: *Various artists* / Summernights: *Various* artists / Banana boat song: *Various artists* / Flashdance (what a feeling): *Various artists* / Big spender: *Various artists* / Locomotion, The: *Various artists* / Bachelor boy: *Various artists* / You've lost that lovin' feeling: *Various artists* / Hey Jude: *Various artists* / It's not unusual: *Various artists*.
LP: 847 802 1
MC: 847 802 4

KARAOKE PARTY (Various artists).
Tracks: / Itsy bitsy teeny weeny yellow polka dot bikini: *Various artists* / Bachelor boy: *Various artists* / With a little help from my friends: *Various artists* / Wild thing: *Various artists* / Do wah diddy diddy: *Various* artists / I'd like to teach the world to sing: *Various artists* / I like it: *Various artists* / Those were the days: *Various artists* / All you need is love: *Various artists* / I love you love me love: *Various artists*/ Ob la di, ob la da: *Various artists* / Tainted love: *Various artists* / It's not unusual: *Various artists*/ Night fever: *Various artists* / Get it on: *Various artists* / Handy man: *Various artists* / Oh pretty woman: *Various artists* / Venus: *Various artists* / Groovy kind of love: *Various artists* / When will I be famous: *Various artists* / New York, New York: *Various artists* / Yellow submarine: *Various artists*/ He ain't heavy, he's my brother: *Various artists* / You'll never walk alone: *Various artists* / Summertime blues: *Various artists* / Pearl's a singer: *Various artists* / Good luck charm: *Various artists* / He's a rebel: *Various artists* / Cathy's clown: *Various artists* / It's only make believe: *Various artists* / Imagine: *Various artists* / Be bop a lula: *Various artists* / Fame: *Various artists* / Super trouper: *Various artists* / If I fell: *Various artists* / Blowin' in the wind: *Various artists* / Singin' the blues: *Various* artists / Wooly bully: *Various artists* / Day o (banana boat song): *Various artists* / Last waltz, The: *Various artists*.
2LP: BWTX 5
MCSET: BWTXC 5

KARAOKE PARTY VOL.2 (Various artists).
LP: TXTV 1
MC: TXTVC 1

Karas, Anton

HARRY LIME THEME (THE THIRD MAN) (An Evening With Anton Karas).
LP: 6.21295
MC: 421295

WORLD OF ANTON KARAS.
LP: SPA 118

Karate Kid

KARATE KID (Film soundtrack) (Various artists).
Tracks: / Moment of truth, The: *Survivor* / On the beach: *Flirts & Jan & Dean Bop Bop* / No shelter: *Broken* Edge / It takes two to tango: *Davis, Paul* / Tough love: *Shandi* / Rhythm man: *St. Regis* / Feel the night: *Robertson, Baxter* / Desire: *Gang Of Four* / You're the best: *Esposito, Joe*.
LP: CANH 10
MC: CANHC 10
LP: 822213.1
MC: 822213.4

KARATE KID PART II, THE (Film soundtrack) (Various artists).
Tracks: / Glory of love: *Various artists* / Rock 'n' roll over you: *Various artists* / Fish for life: *Various* artists / Rock around the clock: *Various artists* / Let me at 'em: *Various artists* / This is the time: *Various* artists / Earth angel: *Various artists* / Love theme: *Various artists* / Two looking at one: *Various artists* / Storm (The): *Various artists*.
LP: 925489 1
MC: 925489 4

KARATE KID PART III, THE (Original Soundtrack) (Various artists).
Tracks: / Listen to your heart: *Little River Band* / This could take all night: *Boy's Club* / Summer in the city: *Pointer Sisters* / 48 hours: *P.B.F.* / Karate Kid (love theme): *Conti, Bill* / Under any moon: *Medeiros, Glenn* / I can't help myself: *Medeiros, Glenn* / Out for the count: *Winger* / In a trance: *Money Talks*.
LP: MCD 6061
MC: MCDC 6061

Karbi, Ras

SEVEN SEALS,THE.
LP: Unknown

Karen

EVERYBODY'S REACHING OUT.
Tracks: / Everybody's reaching out / Loving on borrowed time / Bed of roses / Beggin' to you / Snowbird / Give me another chance / Lonesome / Bright lights and country / Apartment No.9 / I wonder where you are / Blanket on the ground.
MC: CWGR 117

JUST FOR WHAT I AM.
Tracks: / Just for what I am / Good hearted woman / Keeping up appearances / I'm gonna change everything / I walk the line / Ring around my rosie / Heartaches by the number / Almost persuaded / Your own man / Oh lonesome me / Once a day / What I've got in mind / While I was making love to you.
MC: CJW 012
MC: CWGR TV 12

Karlin, M.

TAILORS OF PENZANCE.
LP: EMPL 1005

Karloff, Boris (nar)

AESOP'S FABLES (See under Aesop...).

Karlsson, Pelle

TEACH US YOUR WAY (Karlsson, Pelle & Evie).
LP: WST 9600
MC: WC 9600

Karma

IONOSPHERES.
MC: C 111

Karma Sutra

DAYDREAMS OF A PRODUCTION LINE WORKER.
LP: PARODY 1

Karn, Mick

DREAMS OF REASON PRODUCE MONSTERS.
Tracks: / First impression / Language of ritual / Buoy / Land / Three fates, The / When love walks in / Dream of reason / Answer.
LP: V 2389
MC: TCV 2389
LP: OVED 252
MC: OVEDC 252

TITLES.
Tracks: / Tribal dawn / Lost affections in a room / Passion in moisture / Weather the windmill / Saviour are you with me / Trust me / Sensitive / Piper blue.
LP: OVED 91
MC: OVEDC 91
LP: V 2249

Karpf, Eve

SEPARATION (See under Doddington, Paula (Authoress).

Karrier

WAY BEYOND THE NIGHT.
LP: TRALP 2001

Kartoon

PRACTISING THE ART.
Tracks: / In and out of love / Practising the art / Overnight sensation / We get along / Love on the rebound / Cold sweats / Different / Walking out in style / Wall, The / What else can I say.
LP: BRON 555
MC: BRONC 555

Kas Product

BLACK AND NOIR.
LP: FC 061

BY PASS.
Tracks: / Loony-bin / Seldom, often / Smooth down / Mingled and tangled / Tina town / T.M.T. / Devil fellow / W. Infatuation / Taking shape / Tape.
LP: RCALP 6079
MC: PK 37769

TRY OUT.
Tracks: / One of the kind / Man of time / No shame / Countdown / Never come back / Underground movie / So young but so cold / Digging in a hole / Sober / Breakloose / Pussy X.
LP: PL 37603
MC: RC 250

Kashif

CONDITION OF THE HEART.
Tracks: / Stay the night / Condition of the heart / I wanna have love with you / Weakness / Say you love me / Movie song / Dancing in the dark / Botha Botha (Apartheid song).
LP: 207426
MC: 407426

I JUST GOTTA HAVE YOU (OLD GOLD) (See Reel To Reel - Love Me Like This).

KASHIF.
Tracks: / Don't stop my love / Stone love / I just gotta have you / Help yourself (to my love) / Rumors / Say something love / Mood, The / All.
LP: 205347

LOVE CHANGES.
Tracks: / Reservations for two (with Dionne Warwick) / 50 ways (to fall in love) / Who's getting serious (with Expose) / Love changes (with Melisa Morgan) / Loving you only / It all begins again / Love me all over / Midnight mood / Vacant heart.
LP: 208145
MC: 408145

SEND ME YOUR LOVE.
Tracks: / Baby don't break your baby's heart / Ohh love / Are you the woman / Love has no end / Call me tonight / Send me your love / I've been missing you / Edgartown groove / That's how it goes.
LP: 206350

Kashkashian, Kim

ELEGIES (Kashkashian, Kim & Robert Levin).
Tracks: / Lacrymae op. 48 / Romance / Elegy / Alegie op. 44 / Romance oubliee / Adagio / Elegie.
LP: . . . . ECM 1316

Kashmir

STAY CALM.
LP: . . . . DOG 003
MC: . . . . DOG 003C

Kaskad...

KASKAD: HITS AUX CARAIBES (Various artists).
LP: . . . . MAS 06901
MC: . . . . CMAS 06901

Ka-Spel, Edward

CHYEKK CHINA DOLL.
LP: . . . . TORSO 33013

EYES CHINA DOLL.
LP: . . . . FACE 13

LAUGH CHINA DOLL.
LP: . . . . PHA 6
LP: . . . . LD 894

Kaspersen, Jan

BIZARRE BALLET (Kaspersen, Jan Quintet).
LP: . . . . SLP 1023

Kassap, Sylvain

L'ARLESIENNE.
Tracks: / Un ovillo de ternuras / Smogasbord / L'ile sonnante / Resonsnces / Lucille.
LP: . . . . NATO 109

Kassav

AN-BA-CHEN'N LA.
LP: . . . . GD 027
MC: . . . . C 507

KASSAV.
LP: . . . . GD 018

MAJESTIC ZOUK.
Tracks: / Se dam bonjou (Goodmorning ladies and gentlemen.) / Djoni (Johnny.) / Wep (Hey.) / Rache tche (Sorrow.) / Ou le (Would you like.) / Dezodie (Unstable.) / Konkibin (Concubine.) / Doneys (Doneus.) / An mwe (Help.) / Apre zouk la (After zouk.).
LP: 4654941
MC: 4654944

VINI POU.
LP: 4606191
MC: 4606194

ZOUK IS THE ONLY MEDICINE WE HAVE.
Tracks: / En balate / Kaya manman / Move jou / Tire mwin la / Kavalie o dam / L'Esancyei / Pa bisouin pale / Ki won a harmenw / An ba chen 'n la / Zouk la se sel medikaman nou ni.
LP: . . . . GREL 2001
MC: . . . . GREEN 2001

Kassel, Art

ART KASSEL, 1944.
Tracks: / Knocking at your door / When you wore a tulip / How many hearts have you broken / Patricia Donahue / My little girl / I'll be around / Once too often / Time waits for no one / Somebody stole my gal / Take it easy / I'm in love with someone / Louise / Time alone will tell / Hindustan / I'll walk alone / Hells bells / Doodle doo doo.
LP: . . . . HSR 162

ART KASSEL 1945.
Tracks: / Doodle dee doo / Candy / Bell bottom trousers / Can't you read between the lines / Counting the days / I've got a locket in my pocket / Chopsticks / Yah-ta-ta, ya-ta-ta / Homesick that's all / Whatcha say / All at once / Just a blue serge suit / All I do is wantcha / Kiss goodnight, A.
LP: . . . . HSR 170

Kasseya, Souzy

PHENOMENAL, THE.
LP: . . . . ELP 2008

Kassimi, Essa

LE LUTH AFGHAN (See under 'Afghanistan' for details) (Kassimi, Essa/ Nazir Khan).

Kassnerquer, Duo

FROZEN TREES.
LP: . . . . PTLS 1106
MC: . . . . PTLC 1106

Kastrierte Philosophen

BETWEEN SHOOTINGS.
Tracks: / Privacy / I call it just / Skin and pain / Lady P / One of these days / Do you think I should / Ain't it time / Sick of sermons / I'll never be kind.
LP: . . . . SF 43

INSOMNIA.
LP: . . . . SF 20

LEIPZIG D.C.
LP: . . . . NORMAL 124

NERVES.
LP: . . . . NORMAL 94

Katakumbey

GHANA O.K. (GHANA BEYEYIE).
Tracks: / Ghana Beyeyie / Glory halleluja / Odo do me / Wobegyaa-me-Jack / Wiadze / Odo Ben ni.
LP: . . . . ADRY 3

Kater, Peter

HOMAGE.
LP: 139017-1
MC: 139017-4

Katin, Peter

MAGIC PIANO.
MCSET: . . . . DTO 10053

Katmandu

KATMANDU.
Tracks: / Way you make me feel / God part II / Love hurts / Sometime again / When the rain comes / Heart and soul / Ready for the common man / Only the good die young / Let the heartache begin / Medicine man / Pull together / Warzone.
LP: 4673231
MC: 4673234

Katon, Michael

PROUD TO BE LOUD.
LP: . . . . LOPL 503
MC: . . . . LOPC 503

Katrina & The Waves

BREAK OF HEARTS.
Tracks: / Rock 'n' roll girl / Can't tame my love / That's the way / Keep running to me / Break of hearts / I can dream about it / To have and to hold / I've got a crush on you / Love calculator / Rock myself to sleep.
LP: . . . . SBKLP 2
LP: 792 649 1
MC: . . . . SBKTC 2
MC: 792 649 4

KATRINA & THE WAVES.
Tracks: / Red wine & whisky / Do you want crying / Que te quiero / Machine gunsmith / Cry for me / Walking on sunshine / Going down to Liverpool / Mexico / Sun won't shine without you / Game of love.
LP: . . . . EJ 2403151
MC: . . . . EJ 2403154
MC: . . . . TCKTW 1
LP: . . . . FA 3204
MC: . . . . TCFA 3204
LP: . . . . KTW 1

WAVES.
Tracks: / Is that it? / Tears for me / Sun Street / Lovely Lindsey / Riding shotgun / Sleep on my pillow / Money chair / Mr. Star / Love that boy / Stop trying to prove.
LP: . . . . EST 2010
MC: . . . . TCEST 2010

Katsaris, Cyprien

MOZART FANTASIAS AND SONATAS (see under Mozart (composer)).

Katydids

KATYDIDS.
LP: 7599261461
MC: 7599261464

Katzman, Nick

PANIC WHEN THE SUN GOES DOWN (Katzman, Nick & Ruby Green).
Tracks: / Tin silver / Moon's going down / Snapping turtle / Rowdy blues / If you haven't any hay get on down the road / You gonna quit me / Homage to Gary Davies / I'm going away / Panic when the sun goes down / Careless love.
LP: . . . . SNTF 112

Kaufman, I

ADRIAN SCHUBERT & HIS SALON ORCHESTRA (See under Schubert, Adran) (Kaufman, I/Adrian Schubert).

Kaukonen, Jorma

JORMA.
Tracks: / Straight ahead / Roads and roads / Valley of tears / Song for the high mountain / Wolves and lambs / Too long out/too long in / Requiem for an angel / Vampire woman / Da-ga da-ga.
LP: . . . . PL 13446

Kaula, Edna Mason

AFRICAN VILLAGE FOLKTALES VOL.2 (Peters, Brock/Diana Sands).
MC: 1312

AFRICAN VILLAGE FOLKTALES VOL.1 (Peters, Brock/Diana Sands).
MC: 1309

AFRICAN VILLAGE FOLKTALES VOL.3 (Peters, Brock/Diana Sands).
MC: 1310

Kaunzinger, Gunther.

CHARLES-MARIE WIDOR: ORGAN SYMPHONIES NO.9/10 (see under Widor (composer)).

CHARLES-MARIE WIDOR: ORGAN SYMPHONIES NO.5/6 (see under Widor (composer)).

Kavana, Ron

COMING DAYS.
LP: . . . . WIKAD 94
MC: . . . . WIKC 94

HOME FIRE.
LP: . . . . SPD 1043
MC: . . . . SPDC 1043

ROLLIN' & COASTIN' (In search of America).
LP: . . . . AP 042

THINK LIKE A HERO.
Tracks: / Waxin' the gaza / Every man is a king (in the US of A) / Gone shopping / Soweto trembles (the Jo'burg jig) / Felice / This is the night (fair dues to "The Man") / Midnight on the water / Caoimhneadh roisin / Four horsemen / Rap 'n' reel / Tre ceather a hocht / Ochra at Killarney point to points (Available on CD and cassette only) / Reconcilliation (Available on CD and cassette only).
LP: . . . . WIK 88
MC: . . . . WIKC 88

Kavanagh, Patrick

ALMOST EVERYTHING.
LP: . . . . CCT 1

Kawaski, Ryo

TRINKETS & THINGS (see Brackeen, Joanne) (Kawaski, Ryo & Joanne Brackeen).

Kawere Boys Band

KENYAFRICA (VOL.5).
LP: . . . . PS 33005

Kay, Dave

PIANO FAVOURITES (See under Moreton, Ivor) (Kay, Dave & Ivor Moreton).

Kay, Janet

CAPRICORN WOMAN.
LP: . . . . HASLP 3
LP: . . . . SGL 103
LP: . . . . ARKLP 3
MC: . . . . ARDC 3

LOVING YOU.
LP: . . . . BS 050

SILLY GAMES.
Tracks: / Silly games / Imagine that / Feel no way / Rock the rhythm / Closer to you / Do you love me / Can't give it up / That night / Capricorn woman.
LP: . . . . CELP 1001
MC: . . . . CEC 1001

SO AMAZING.
LP: . . . . JANET 10

SWEET SURRENDER.
LP: . . . . JANET 02

Kay, Kathie

FIRESIDE GIRL, THE.
Tracks: / Suddenly there's a valley / Dreams can tell a lie / Jimmy Unknown / House with love in it, A / To be sure / Everyday is Mother's Day / Wind in the willows / There is somebody waiting for me / Bonnie Scotland / From the first hello to the last goodbye / We will make love / Away from you / Be content / Summer is a comin' in / Secret of happiness / My last love / Tomorrow is my birthday / Hillside in Scotland.
LP: . . . . PLE 517

KATHIE KAY.
Tracks: / Mother's way / Spinning wheel / Aloha-oe / Wild mountain thyme / Thinking of you / Tammy / Way old friends do, The / Old rustic bridge / Our anniversary / Hawaiian wedding song / Skyline of Skye / Now is the hour.
LP: . . . . ITV 384
MC: . . . . KITV 384

MOTHER OF MINE.
LP: . . . . BGC 305

SOMETHING FOR MUSIC.
MC: . . . . VCA 109

Kayath, Marcelo

MARCELO KAYATH.
LP: . . . . A 66203

Kaye, Danny

BEST OF DANNY KAYE.
Tracks: / Ballin' the jack / Molly Malone / Bloop bleep / Civilization / Oh by jingo, oh by gee / Candy kisses / Manic depressive parents lobby number part II / Anatole of Paris / St. Louis blues / Bread and butter woman / Woody Woodpecker / Big brass band from Brazil / Triplets / Tchaikovsky / I wonder who's kissing her now.
LP: . . . . MCL 1704
MC: . . . . MCLC 1704

HANS CHRISTIAN ANDERSEN (Film soundtrack).
Tracks: / Anywhere I wander / Ugly duckling / King's new clothes, The / Thumbelina / Wonderful Copenhagen / I'm Hans Christian Andersen / No two people / Tubby the tuba.
LP: . . . . MFP 50456
MC: . . . . TC 50456

VERY BEST OF DANNY KAYE 20 golden greats.
Tracks: / I'm Hans Christian Andersen / Inch worm, The / King's new clothes, The / Thumbelina / Ugly duckling, The / Wonderful Copenhagen / Tubby the tuba (parts 1 & 2) / Woody woodpecker song, The / Popo the puppet / I taut I taw a puddy tat / Ballin' the jack / Tchaikovsky / Civilization / Molly Malone / Oh by jingo, oh by gee / Candy kisses / St. Louis blues / Manic depressive parents lobby number part I & part II.
LP: . . . . MCL 1843
MC: . . . . MCLC 1843

Kaye, M.M.

DEATH IN THE ANDAMANS.
MCSET: . . . . CAB 293

ORDINARY PRINCESS, THE.
MC: 1774

Kaye, Sammy

ONE NIGHT STAND WITH SAMMY KAYE.
LP: . . . . JOYCE 1122

PLAY 22 ORIGINAL BIG BAND RECORDINGS (Kaye, Sammy Orchestra).
LP: . . . . HSR 402

SAMMY KAYE AND HIS ORCHESTRA, VOL. 2 1944-46 (Kaye, Sammy Orchestra).
Tracks: / Come closer to me / I'm beginning to see the light / There is no greater love / Give me the simple life / Sentimental journey / Little on the lonely side, A / Along the navajo trail / One night stand / I'll be walkin' with my honey / I can't begin to tell you / It's only a paper moon / Everybody knew but me / I promise you / Candy / I'll buy that dream / You made me love you.
LP: . . . . HSR 163

SAMMY KAYE AND HIS ORCHESTRA, VOL. 1 1940-41 (Kaye, Sammy Orchestra).
Tracks: / Kaye's melody / Daddy / I think of you / Pretty please / My buddy / Hut sut song / I guess I'll have to dream the rest / Essex hop / Oh look at me now / Wasn't it you / 10 Lullaby Lane / This is no laughing matter / This love of mine / Is that nice / Liebestraum / Swing and sway stomp.
LP: . . . . HSR 158

SAMMY KAYE AND ORCHESTRA, VOL. 3 1944-48 (Kaye, Sammy Orchestra).
LP: . . . . HSR 207

SAMMY KAYE & HIS ORCHESTRA WITH CLYDE MCCOY (Kaye, Sammy Orchestra).
LP: . . . . CLP 93

Kays, Arthur

SPARKES OF INSPIRATION, THE (Kays, Arthur Originals).
LP: . . . . LINK LP 111

Kazjurol

DANCE TARANTELLA.
LP: . . . . ATV 12

Kbayashi, Izumi

MIMI.
Tracks: / On / Kicking the wind / Days / Merlin / Home / Infant sorrow / Tiny jewellery / Rubie / One million years in archway / Promise path, A / Piano ballet.
LP: . . . . MD 7885
MC: . . . . MDC 7885

KBB (Kolne Big Band)

N.
Tracks: / Jazz up / Shuck / N (part 1) / N (part 2) / N (part 3) / D.C. / N. Losses / Scofio / Six pack / Finale.
LP: 890041
MC: 890044

KBC Band

KBC BAND, THE.
Tracks: / Mariel / It's not you, it's not me / Hold me / America / No more heartaches / Wrecking crew / When love comes / Dream motorcycle / Sayonara.
LP: 208021
MC: 408021

KBLX

KBLX SAMPLER.
MC: . . . . C 8802

K.C. & The Sunshine

ALL IN A NIGHT'S WORK.
Tracks: / You'd gimme some more / Party with your body / Give it up / Don't run / You're going out of your mind / On the one / It's too hard to say goodbye / Do it / When you dance to the music / Are you feeling like me.
LP: . . . . EPC 85847

BEST OF KC AND THE SUNSHINE BAND.
Tracks: / Sound your funky horn / Get down tonight / I'm your boogie man / (Shake, shake, shake) shake your booty / Queen of clubs / That's the way (I like it) / Keep it comin' love / Please don't go / Boogie shoes / Let's go rock and roll / Give it up / Do you wanna go party (CD only.) / I like to do it (CD only.) / Shotgun shuffle (CD only.) / Wrap your arms around me (CD only.) / All I want.
LP: . . . . ROU 5007
LP: 794 879 1
MC: . . . . TCROU 5007
MC: 794 879 4

DO YOU WANNA GO PARTY.
Tracks: / Hooked on your love / I've got the feeling / Ohh, I like it / Please don't go / I betcha didn't know that / Que pasa / Do you wanna go party.
LP: . . . . TKR 83369

GREATEST HITS: K.C.& THE SUNSHINE BAND (IMPORT).
LP: . . . . BRLP 53
MC: . . . . BRMC 53

GREATEST HITS: K.C. & THE SUNSHINE BAND.
Tracks: / Sound your funky horn / Queen of clubs / Get down tonight / Boogie shoes / That's the way I like it / Shake your booty / I'm your boogie man / Keep it comin' love / Please don't go / Let's go rock and roll / All I want
LP: . . . . EPC 25717
MC: 40 25717
LP: . . . . SVLP 6601
MC: . . . . ZCSVL 6601
LP: . . . . TKR 83385

K.C. & THE SUNSHINE BAND.
LP: . . . . JSL 9
LP: 509182

PAINTER.
Tracks: / Stand up / Don't say no / It happens every night / Go now / Painter / Sway / Summer nights / Baby I'm yours / Love me / All through the night / Something's happening.
LP: . . . . EPC 85219

TEN.
Tracks: / Are you ready? / On the top / Don't break my heart / Nobody knows / Uptight / Too high / Don't let go / In my world / Let's get together / Thank you.
LP: . . . . EPC 25894

K.C.M. INC.

DOIN' IT FUNKY SMOOTH.
Tracks: / Peachtowne party jam / Is it worth it / Love stepped / That love thang / Let me groove you / All 'n' all / It's all about lovin' you / Real love / Do you / Emotion.
LP: . . . . PEA 4110
MC: . . . . PEA 4110MC

K-Doe, Ernie

BURN, K-DOE BURN.
Tracks: / Mother in law (1989) / Mother in law / Talkin' out of my head (lonelyology) / Make you love me / Reaping what I sow / Hurry up and know it / Waiting at the station / Love you the best / Te ta te ta ta / Certain girl, A / Easier said than done / Tain't it the truth / Fight, The / There's a will, there's a way / Baby, since I met you / Wanted 10,000 dollar reward / I cried my last tear.
LP: . . . . CRB 1218

MOTHER IN LAW.
Tracks: / Mother-in-law / I cried my last tear / Certain girl, A / Te-ta-te-ta-ta / Wanted $10 000 reward / Hello my lover / Ain't it the truth / Popeye Joe / Real man / Heebie jeebies / Waiting at the station / I'm the boss / Make you love me / Rub dub dub / I got to find somebody / Hurry up and know it.
LP: . . . . SSL 6012
MC: . . . . TCSSL 6012

Keaggy, Phil

GETTING CLOSER.
LP: . . . . MYRR 1218
MC: . . . . MYR C 1218

MASTER AND THE MUSICIAN,THE.
Tracks: / Pilgrim's flight / Agora / Castle's call, The / Wedding in the country manor / Suite of reflections / Golden halls / Mouthpiece / Follow me up / Jungle pleasures / Deep calls unto deep.
LP: . . . . MYR 1079
MC: . . . . MC 1079

PHIL KEAGGY.
LP: . . . . MYRR 1251
MC: . . . . MYRC 1251

PH'LIP SIDE.
Tracks: / Child (in everyone's heart), A / Little ones / Spend my life with you / Just a moment away / I belong to you / Royal commandments, A / Sunday school / Send out your light / Pulling down.
LP: . . . . BIRD 127
MC: . . . . TC BIRD 127

PRIME CUTS.
Tracks: / Full circle (From Town To Town.) / Play thru me (From Play Thru me.) / Train to glory (From Play Thru me.) / I will be there (From 'Getting Closer'.) / Movie (From 'Getting Closer'.) / Sounds (From 'Getting Closer'.) / Wall, The (From 'Play Thru Me'.) / Care free (From 'Play Thru Me'.) / Happy (From 'Play Thru Me'.) / Let everything else go (From 'Town to Town'.).
LP: . . . . MYR R 1245
MC: . . . . MYR C 1245

TOWN TO TOWN.
Tracks: / Wished you were there / Full circle / Life love and you / Town to town / What a wonder you are / Our lives / Rise up o men of god / Let everything else go.
LP: . . . . BIRD 135
MC: . . . . TC BIRD 135

WIND AND THE WHEAT, THE.
LP: . . . . MM R 0149
MC: . . . . MM C 0149

Keane, Brian

BOLERO (see Coryell,Larry & Brian Keane) (Keane, Brian & Larry Coryell).

JUST LIKE BEING BORN (see under Coryell, Larry) (Keane, Brian & Larry Coryell).

SNOWFALLS.
LP: . . . . FF 452

Keane, Dolores

DOLORES KEANE.
MC: . . . . DKMC 1
LP: . . . . DKLP 1

FAREWELL TO EIREANN (Keane, Dolores & John Faulkner/Eamonn Curran).
LP: . . . . LUN 043

LION IN A CAGE.
Tracks: / I feel it in my bones / Lion in a cage / Room, The / Moorlough shore / Across the bridge / Walking on seashells / One golden rule / Island, The / Hold me.
LP: . . . . DKLP 2
MC: . . . . DKMC 2

SAIL OG RUA (Keane, Dolores and John Faulkner).
LP: . . . . CEF 101
MC: . . . . CEFC 101

THERE WAS A MAID.
LP: . . . . CC 23
MC: 4CC 23

Keane Family

MUINTIT CHATHAIN.
LP: . . . . CEF 107
MC: . . . . CEFC 107

Keane, James

BUTTON ACCORDION (Roll Away the Reel World).
LP: . . . . SIF 1026
MC: . . . . CSIF 1026

Keane, Sean

CONTENTMENT IS WEALTH (see under Molloy, Matt) (Keane, Sean/Matt Molloy).

FIDDLE & VIOLA.
LP: . . . . BLB 5005

GUSTY'S FROLICS.
LP: . . . . CC 17
MC: 4CC 17

JIG IT IN STYLE.
LP: . . . . CCF 25
MC: 4CCF 25

Keane Sisters

ONCE I LOVED.
LP: . . . . CC 4

Kearney, Arthur

IRELAND HER OWN (See under Tunney, Arthur).

Kearney, Kevin

FROM A JACK TO A KING.
MC: . . . . MB LP 1040

Kearney, Ramsey

TENNESSEE ROCK.
LP: . . . . SJLP 591

Kearns, Martyn

HEART OF BRAILLE.
MC: . . . . P 4406

Keating, Johnny

SWING REVISITED (Keating,Johnny and his Band).
Tracks: / Night train / Saints / Stripper, The / What'd I say / Li'l darlin' / Opus one / I've got a gal in Kalamazoo / Tuxedo Junction / Oh lonesome me / Headin' north / Hallelujah gathering / One o'clock jump.
LP: . . . . JASM 2203

THIS IS THE LONDON SYMPHONY ORCHESTRA (Keating John/London Symphony Orchestra).
Tracks: / Polovtsian dances / Spartacus theme / Four seasons theme / Sabre dance / Adagio / Panorama / Sleepy shores / Thieving magpie / Symphony No. 3 / Adagietto / Firebird suite / Symphony No. 5 (Beethoven).
LP: . . . . THIS 2

Keatons

SEVEN.
Tracks: / Seven / Triangles / Space mansions / Carbonised / Bitter eyes / Angel rising / French bench.
LP: . . . . CHEWY 002

Keats

KEATS.
Tracks: / Heaven knows / Tragedy / Fight to win / Walking on ice / How can you just walk away / Avalanche / Turn your heart around / Hollywood heart / Ask no questions / Night full of voices.
LP: . . . . EJ 2401741
MC: . . . . EJ 2401744

POETRY OF KEATS (Richardson, Sir Ralph (nar)).
MC: 1087

Kee, Piet

PLAYS BACH & BUXTEHUDE.
MC: . . . . EBTD 0501
LP: . . . . EBRD 0501

Keeble,Papa

SNAKES AND LADDERS.
LP: . . . . CARLP 2

Keedy

CHASE THE CLOUDS.
Tracks: / Save some love / Wishing on the same star / Never neverland / Sorry / Only your heart / Gettin' around / Don't turn away / Pretty boy / Mama / Lazy day.
LP: 211346
MC: 411346

Keegan, Josephine

OLD FAVOURITES.
Tracks: / Stone in the field / Flax in bloom / Pigeon on the gate / Miss Monaghan / Skylark / Colonel Rodney / Spillane's delight / Spillane's fiddle / Flowers of spring / Flower of Balltmote / Quilty fishermen / Queen of the West / Captain Rock / Snake, The / Robin's nest / John Eddies / Glen of Alerlow / Mossy banks / Tobin's favourite / Connie O'Connell's / Around Loughgill / Michael Anderson / Dead piper / McKenna's.
LP: . . . . OAS 3037

ON THE FIDDLE.
Tracks: / Casey's fiddle / Crosses of Annagh, The / Ceilidhier, The / Eleanor Kane / High hill, The / O'Leary's island / Bare haven / Spring well, The / Floating crowbar, The / Tommy Maguires / Antrim rose, The / Charlie Lennon's / Jimmy McHugh's / Kevin Loughlin's / Hearne's egg, A / Paddy Fahy's jig / Paddy Taylor's / Sean Ryan's / O'Kane's / Street player, The / Jimmy Kean's / Sean Ryan / Farewell / McKillop's fancy.
LP: . . . . SOLP 1044
MC: . . . . COX 1044

TRADITIONAL IRISH MUSIC.
LP: . . . . SOLP 1040
MC: . . . . COX 1040

Keel

FINAL FRONTIER.
Tracks: / Final frontier / Rock and roll animal / Because the night / Here today and gone tomorrow / Arm and a leg / Raised on rock / Just another girl / Tears of fire / Nightfall / No pain no gain.
LP: . . . . VERH 33
MC: . . . . VERHC 33

KEEL.
Tracks: / United nations / Somebody's waiting / Cherry Lane / Calm before the storm / King of the rock / It's a jungle out there / I said the wrong thing to the right girl / Don't say you love me / If love is a crime (I wanna be convicted) / 4th of July.
LP: . . . . MCF 3393
MC: . . . . MCFC 3393

LAY DOWN THE LAW.
LP: . . . . SH 1014

RIGHT TO ROCK, THE.
Tracks: / Right to rock, The / Back to the city / Let's spend the night together / Easier said than done / So many girls, so little time / Electric love / Speed demon / Get down / You're the victim (I'm the crime).
LP: . . . . VERL 26
MC: . . . . VERLC 26

Keel, Howard

AND I LOVE YOU SO.
MC: . . . . WW 22025
LP: . . . . WW 5137
MC: . . . . WW 4 5137

CLOSE TO MY HEART (ALBUM).
Tracks: / There's no business like show business / O what a beautiful morning / Secret love / Surrey with the fringe on top, The / If I loved you / Bless your beautiful hide / Wind beneath my wings / So in love / Make believe / Love changes everything / Bring him home / Prelude into music of the night / Colours of my life.
LP: . . . . KEEL 1
MC: . . . . TCKEEL 1

COLLECTION: HOWARD KEEL.
Tracks: / Some enchanted evening / This nearly was mine / I won't send roses / If ever I would leave you / You needed me / Love story / Come in from the rain / MacArthur Park / Send in the clowns / You were always on my mind / I've never been to me.
2LP: . . . . CCSLP 217
MC: . . . . CCSMC 217

ENCHANTED EVENING WITH HOWARD KEEL, A.
Tracks: / Oklahama medley / Some enchanted evening / This nearly was mine / I won't send roses / If ever I would leave you / La Mancha medley / You needed me / Love story / Come in from the rain / Yesterday / Something / Once upon a time / What are you doing for the rest of your life / Wave / McArthur Park / Send in the clowns / You were always on my mind / I've never been to me / Annie get your gun medley.
MC: . . . . MCTC 006

GREAT MGM STARS: HOWARD KEEL.
Tracks: / Bless your beautiful hide / Sobbin' women / When you're in love / Your land and my land / Rose Marie / Right place for a girl, The / Mounties / Make believe / Why do I love you / And this is my beloved / Lovely to look at / You're devastating / Lafayette / Pagan love song / House of singing bamboo / So in love / We open in Venice (With Ann Miller & Tommy Rall.) / Were thine that special face / Wunderbar / I've come to wive it wealthily in Padua / Where is the life that late I led? / Kiss me Kate.
LP: . . . . LPMGM 30
LP: 795 858 1
MC: . . . . TCMGM 30
MC: 795 858 4

JUST FOR YOU.
LP: . . . . STAR 2318
MC: . . . . STAC 2318

LIVE IN CONCERT.
Tracks: / Overture medley / Yesterday when I was young / Robert Frost poem / This is all I ask / Oh what a beautiful morning / Surrey with the fringe on top / People will say we're in love / Oklahoma / Tribute to my leading ladies / I won't send roses / Wunderbar / Where is the life that late I led / Some enchanted evening / Lara's theme / Send in the clowns / I've never been to me / Memory / Ol' man river / Why do I love you / Softly as I leave you.
2LP: . . . . REQ 744
MCSET: . . . . ZCQ 744
MC: . . . . HSC 860

REMINISCING.
Tracks: / Oklahoma medley / Some enchanted evening / This nearly was mine / I won't send roses / If ever I would leave you / Man of La Mancha medley / You needed me / Love story / Yesterday / Something / Once upon a time / What are you doing the rest of your life? / Wave / MacArthur Park.
LP: . . . . STAR 2259
MC: . . . . STAC 2259

Keelers & Colliers

TYNESIDE.
MC: 45-409

Keen, Robert Earl

LIVE ALBUM, THE.
Tracks: / I wanna know / Torch song, The / Goin' down in style / If I were King / Copenhagen / I would change my life / Stewball / I'll go on downtown / Bluegrass widow, The / Who'll be lookin' out for me.
LP: . . . . SH 1024
MC: . . . . ZCSH 1024

NO KINDA DANCER.

Tracks: / No kinda dancer / Front porch song, The / Between hello and goodbye / Swervin' in my lane / Christabel / Willie / Young lovers waltz / Death of tail Fitzsimmons / Rolling by / Armadillo jackal, The / Lu Ann / Coldest day of Winter, The.
LP: . . . . PH 1108
MC: . . . . PH 1108C

WEST TEXTURES.
Tracks: / Leavin' Tennessee / Maria / Sing one for sister / Road goes on forever / Sonora's death row / Don't turn out the light / Five pound bass, The / It's the little things / Jennifer Johnson and me / Mariano / Love's a word I never throw around.
LP: . . . . SPD 1032
MC: . . . . SPDC 1032

Keenan, Brendan
BRENDAN KEENAN.
LP: . . . . CEF 106
MC: . . . . CEFC 106

Keenan, Paddy
PADDY KEENAN.
LP: . . . . CEF 045

POIRT AN PHOILAIRE.
LP: . . . . CEF 099

Keene, Bob Quintet
BOB KEENE QUINTET.
LP: . . . . FS 263

Keene, Tommy
PLACES THAT ARE GONE.
Tracks: / Places that are gone / Nothing happened yesterday / Baby face / Back to zero / When the truth is found / Hey little child / Something got hold of me / Real underground, The / Scam and the flimflam man, The / Misunderstood / That you do / Mr Roland.
MC: . . . . FIENDCASS 210

SONGS FROM THE FILM.
Tracks: / Places that are gone / In our lives / Listen to me / Paper words / Godtown / Kill your sons / Call on me / As life goes on / My mother looked like Marilyn Monroe / Underworld / Astronomy / Story ends, The.
LP: 9240901
MC: 9240904

Keep It Dark
FIRST DOWN AND TEN.
LP: . . . . CAS 1172
MC: . . . . CASMC 1172

Keep it Locked
KEEP IT LOCKED - THIS IS THE BIG ONE VOLUME 2 (Various artists).
LP: . . . . BIGA 3
MC: . . . . BIGAC 3

Keeper, Jimmy
TELL HIM (Keeper, Jimmy Sextet).
LP: . . . . AFF 183

Keil Isles
KEIL ISLES, THE.
Tracks: / Boogie boy / Bull moose / Splish splash / Johnny B. Goode / Shakey / Come on and get me / Country boy / Say mama / Flip flop and fly / Poor man's riches / C'mon baby / Don't come knockin' / Sea cruise / Made to be loved.
LP: . . . . DS 9214

Keillor, Garrison
LAKE WOBEGON DAYS.
MCSET: . . . . ZBBC 1065

LEAVING HOME (More tales from Lake Wobegone) (Various artists).
MCSET: . . . . ZBBC 1066

Keine Ahnung
PLASTIK.
LP: . . . . PASSIV 001

Keirie, Reg
TAPED.
LP: . . . . BRO 136

Keisa
KEISA.
LP: . . . . PPR 1744

Keita, Salif
AMBASSADEURS FEATURING SALIF KEITA (See under Ambassadeurs) (Ambassadeurs and Salif Keita).

AMEN.
MC: . . . . MCT 1073
LP: . . . . MLPS 1073

KO-YAN.
Tracks: / Lyada / Nou pas bouger / Ko-yan / Fe-so / Primpin / Tenin / Sabou.
LP: . . . . MLPS 1002
MC: . . . . MCT 1002

SORO.
Tracks: / Wamba / Soro / Souareba / Sina / Cono / Sanni kegniba.
LP: . . . . STERNS 1020
MC: . . . . STC 1020

Keith, Bill
BANJOISTICS.
LP: . . . . ROUNDER 0148
MC: . . . . ROUNDER 0148C

BILL KEITH & JIM COLLIER (Keith, Bill & Jim Rooney).
LP: 883020

COLLECTION: BILL KEITH & JIMMY ROONEY (Keith, Bill & Jim Rooney).
Tracks: / Crazy creek / Done laid around / So lonesome I could cry / Jordu / Detour / Pickin' on the country strings / Gone girl / Tragic romance / Sugarfoot rag / I'll stay around / Darling Corey is one / Interest on the loan / Out of joint / Auld lang syne.
LP: . . . . WF 004

SOMETHING AULD, SOMETHING NEWGRASS, BORROWED ....
LP: . . . . ROUNDER 0084
MC: . . . . ROUNDER 0084C

Keith, Leslie
BLACK MOUNTAIN BLUES.
LP: . . . . SBR 4201

Keith, Lex
LEX KEITH & HIS SCOTTISH COUNTRY BAND.
MC: . . . . LICS 5105

Keith, Penelope
STORYTIME TOP TEN VOL.10 (Keith, Penelope & Richard Briers).
MC: . . . . VCA 064

STORYTIME TOP TEN VOL. 1.
MC: . . . . VCA 055

STORYTIME TOP TEN VOL. 2.
MC: . . . . VCA 056

Kelday, Paul
BEYOND THE PERIMETERS.
MC: . . . . KELDAY 26

Kellaway, Roger
FIFTY FIFTY (Kellaway, Roger/Red Mitchell).
LP: . . . . ST 271

Keller, Jerry
HERE COMES SUMMER (OLD GOLD) (See Johnny Cymbal - Mr.Bassman for details).

Kellett Rowland
STREETS OF LEEDS, THE.
MC: 60-209

Kelley, Peck
PECK KELLEY JAM - VOL 1 (Kelley, Peck & Dick Shannon Quartet).
Tracks: / Tea for two / Sweet lorraine / Once in a while / Lover / Memories of you.
LP: 6.25527
LP: AG6 25527

PECK KELLEY JAM - VOL 2 (Kelley, Peck & Dick Shannon Quartet).
LP: 6.25528
LP: AG6 25528

Kelly, Alan
GREATEST HITS VOLUME 11.
LP: . . . . FR 145

Kelly, Bev
YOU GO TO MY HEAD (Kelly, Bev/Bob Graf Quartet).
LP: . . . . VGM 0007

Kelly, Breege
IRELAND'S QUEEN OF THE ACCORDION.
MC: . . . . CT 138

Kelly, Chris
DON'T GO 'WAY NOBODY (Kelly, Chris Black & White New Orleans Jazzband).
LP: . . . . SLR 2000

MY LITTLE ANGEL (Kelly, Chris Black & White New Orleans Jazzband).
LP: . . . . SLR 2001

Kelly, Dave
DAVE KELLY BAND LIVE.
LP: . . . . AP 033

FEELS RIGHT.
LP: . . . . CKLP 001

HEART OF THE CITY (Kelly, Dave Band).
Tracks: / Staight line / Come kiss me love / Crying in the rain / Tongue tied / Foreign station / Hard to find a heart / You rocked me / Gael's blue / Glad I'm living / Ee do qua qua.
LP: . . . . THBL 059
LP: 400324

SURVIVORS (see Hall, Bob) (Kelley, Dave & Bob Hall).

WILLIN'.
LP: . . . . AP 003

Kelly, Eamon
IRISH STORYTELLER.
MC: . . . . LNMC 7009

LIVE FROM IRELAND.
MC: . . . . LNMC 7011

STORIES FROM IRELAND.
MC: . . . . LNMC 7010

Kelly, Frances
CEREMONY OF CAROLS, A (see under Britten) (Kelly, Frances/Christ Church Cathedral, Oxford Choir).

HARP COLLECTION.
MC: . . . . CSAR 36

Kelly, Frank
COMEDY COUNTDOWN.
LP: . . . . SPL 402

Kelly, Gene
A.F.I. SALUTES GENE KELLY (VIDEO) (See under A.F.I. Salutes ...) (Various artists).

BEST OF GENE KELLY -- FROM MGM FILMS.
LP: . . . . MCA 25166
MC: . . . . MCAC 25166

GENE KELLY: ON THE AIR.
Tracks: / Death went along for the ride / To find help.
LP: . . . . TOTEM 1034

GREAT MGM STARS: GENE KELLY.
Tracks: / Singin' in the rain / You were meant for me / All I do is dream of you / Moses / Broadway ballet / You are my lucky star / I like myself / Blue Danube / Almost like being in love / Heather on the hill / Les girls / Why am I so gone (about that gal) / You're just too, too! / Nina / You wonderful you / Heavenly music / I got rhythm / Love is here to stay / 'S wonderful.
LP: . . . . LPMGM 31
LP: 795 862 1
MC: . . . . TCMGM 31
MC: 795 862 4

SINGIN' IN THE RAIN.
LP: . . . . SKL 5265

SONG AND DANCE MAN.
LP: . . . . DS 15010
MC: . . . . DSC 15010

SOUNDTRACKS, VOICES & THEMES (See under Astaire, Fred) (Astaire, Fred, Kelly, Gene, Buchanan, Gene).

Kelly, George
AL VASEY & GEORGE KELLY/ FESSORS SESSION BOYS (see Vasey, Al) (Kelly, George & Al Vasey/Fessors Session Boys).

FINE & DANDY (Kelly, George, Paul Sealey Trio, Harlem Jazz & Blues Band).
LP: . . . . VLP 405

PLAYS THE MUSIC OF DON REDMAN.
LP: . . . . ST 240

Kelly, Georgia
IN A CHORD (See under Huxley, Craig) (Kelly, Georgia & Craig Huxley).

Kelly, Grace
SNOWBIRD AND THE SUNBIRD (Read by Grace Kelly).
LP: . . . . ALB 6004

TRUE LOVE (see under Crosby, Bing) (Kelly, Grace & Bing Crosby).

Kelly, Hambone
DOWN HOME JAZZBAND (Kelly, Hambone Favourites).
LP: . . . . SOS 1171

Kelly, James
SPRING IS IN THE AIR (Kelly, James & Paddy O'Brien).
LP: . . . . SHAN 29018

Kelly, Jane
PARTICULAR PEOPLE.
LP: . . . . TWI 851

Kelly, Jo Ann
JO ANN KELLY.
LP: . . . . OPEN 001

JUST RESTLESS (Jo Ann Kelly Band).
LP: . . . . AP 028

RETROSPECT 1964-72.
Tracks: / Black rat swing / Walking blues / Ain't seen no whiskey / Boyfriend blues / Try me one more time / Long black hair / Buddy Brown's eyes / New Milkcow blues / Hard time killin' floor blues / Shave 'em dry / I feel so good / When I lay my burden down / Just like I treat her / I look down the road and I wonder.
LP: . . . . CSAPLP 101
MC: . . . . CSAPMC 101

STANDING AT THE BURYING GROUND (See under McDowell, Fred) (Kelly, Jo Ann & Fred McDowell).

Kelly, John
FIDDLE & CONCERTINA PLAYER.
LP: 12FRS 504

JOHN & JAMES KELLY (Kelly, John & James).
LP: . . . . TARA 1008

Kelly, Jonathan
TWICE AROUND THE HOUSES.
Tracks: / Madeleine / Sligo fair / We're all right till then / Ballad of cursed Anna / Leave them go / We are the people / Rainy town / Train song / I used to know you / Hyde park angels / Rock you to sleep.
LP: NL70401
LP: . . . . SF 8262

Kelly, Kin
KINETICS.
LP: . . . . GIPLP 1

Kelly, Kirk
GO MAN GO.
LP: . . . . SST 223
MC: . . . . SSTC 223

Kelly, Luke
LUKE KELLY ALBUM, THE (Kelly, Luke & Dubliners).
LP: . . . . CHLP 1016

LUKE'S LEGACY (Kelly, Luke & Dubliners).
LP: . . . . CHLP 1031

Kelly, Pat
BEST OF PAT KELLY.
Tracks: / No love / Good friends / One night stand.
LP: . . . . VSLP 4011

CRY FOR YOU NO MORE.
Tracks: / Cry for you no more / What goes on in your mind / It's always Summer In Jamaica / Haunted By Your Love / I wanna lock away your heart / Island Girl / Love has a mind of it's own.
LP: . . . . BMLP 057

LONELY MAN.
LP: . . . . BSLP 1001

ONE IN A MILLION GIRL.
LP: . . . . SKYLP 47

ORDINARY MAN.
LP: . . . . PAT 01

PAT KELLY AND FRIENDS.
LP: . . . . CJ 106

SREVOL.
LP: . . . . ETH 2234

Kelly, Paul
GOSSIP (Kelly, Paul & The Coloured Girls).
2LP: . . . . L 45961 2

HANGIN' ON IN THERE.
Tracks: / Stealing in the name of the Lord / 509 / Poor but proud / Hangin' on in there / Come by here / Love me now / Don't burn me / Come lay some lovin' on me / I wanna get next to you / Let your love come down (let it fall on me) / Take it away from him (put it on me) / I'm into somethin' I can't shake loose / I believe I can / Hooked, hogtied and collared.
LP: . . . . ED 316

SO MUCH WATER SO CLOSE TO HOME (Kelly, Paul & The Messengers).
Tracks: / You can't take it with you / Sweet guy / Most wanted man in the world / I had forgotten you / She's a melody (stupid song) / South of Germany / Careless / Moon in the bed / No you / Everything's turning to white / Pigeon/Jundamurra / Cities of Texas.
LP: . . . . AMA 5266
MC: . . . . AMC 5266

UNDER THE SUN (Kelly, Paul & The Messengers).
LP: . . . . AMA 5207
MC: . . . . AMC 5207

Kelly Phil
PHIL KELLY SINGS.
LP: . . . . NEVLP 015

PHIL KELLY SINGS (VOLUME 2).
LP: . . . . NEVLP 103

Kelly, Richard
WALTZING THRO' IRELAND.
LP: . . . . KLP 225

Kelly, Richie
BEST OF IRISH ACCORDION 1.
MC: . . . . DOCB 7016

Kelly, Sandy
EVENING WITH SANDY KELLY, AN.
MC: . . . . PLAC 333

I NEED TO BE IN LOVE.
MC: . . . . OCE 2465

Kelly, Tom
PENNY WHISTLE, THE.
LP: . . . . RGLP 15

Kelly, Wynton

LIVE IN BALTIMORE (Kelly, Wynton & George Coleman).
Tracks: / Unit 7 / Surrey with the fringe on top / Mister P.C. / Here's that rainy day.
2LP: . . . . **AFFD 108**

SWING WITH HELEN HUMES AND WYNTON KELLY (See under Humes, Helen for details) (Kelly, Wynton & Helen Humes).

WRINKLES (Kelly, Wynton & Friends).
Tracks: / Wrinkles / Autumn leaves / Temperance / Make the man love me / Joe's avenue / What know / Weird lullaby / Love, I've found you / June night.
LP: . . . . **AFF 151**

WYNTON KELLY IN CONCERT (Kelly, Wynton & George Coleman).
LP: . . . . **AFF 54**

Kelly's Heroes

KELLY'S HEROES (Film Soundtrack) (Various artists).
Tracks: / Kelly's heroes: *Various artists* / All for the love of sunshine: *Various artists* / Burning bridges: *Various artists* / Tiger tank: *Various artists* / Clairmont waltz: *Various artists* / Battle hymn of the republic: *Various artists* / Burning bridges: *Various artists* / Quick draw Kelly: *Various artists* / All for the love of sunshine: *Various artists* / I've been working on the railroad: *Various artists* / Commando opus: *Various artists*.
LP: **2315 019**

Kelsall, Phil

ALL I ASK OF YOU.
Tracks: / Clarinet polka / All I ask of you (Taken from The Phantom Of The Opera.) / Waltzing in the clouds / Two hearts in waltz time / I just called to say I love you / Circus renz / Embraceable you / I got plenty o' nuttin' / Liza / Svanee / Swanee / Dizzy fingers / Music of the night / Rouge et noir / Come to Fiona's wedding / If I can help somebody / I only have eyes for you / My melancholy baby / Poor butterfly / Romeo / Don't say goodbye / Your eyes / Love is a many splendoured thing / I'm in the mood for love / I'll see you in my dreams.
LP: . . . . **GRALP 23**
MC: . . . . **GRTC 23**

AT THE WURLITZER ORGAN - BLACKPOOL (2).
Tracks: / Bring me sunshine / Sun has got his hat on, The / Gal in Calico, A / Best things in life are free, The / Semper fidelis / Goodnight Vienna / Marta / Jealousy / I left my heart in San Francisco / Breezing along with the breeze / On the sunny side of the street / Love walked in / Tiger rag / Forgotten dreams / Shaddap you face / Let's all sing like the birdies sing / Birdie song, The / St Bernard's waltz / Under the bridges of Paris / I'm forever blowing bubbles / Down at the old Bull and Bush / I yi yi yi yi (I like you very much) / Enjoy yourself (It's later than you think) / S wonderful / I got rhythm / Fascinating rhythm / Maple leaf rag / Wheels / Tea for two / Isn't this a lovely day / Telstar / Scotland the brave / We're no awa to bide awa / Cock o' the North / Those lazy hazy crazy days of summer / Powder your face with sunshine / Keep your sunny side up / Tico tico / Way you look tonight, The / All the things you are / Look for the silver lining / Stranger in paradise / My foolish heart / Opus one / Five foot two, eyes of blue / Everybody loves my baby / Rose of Tralee / I'll be your sweetheart / When you and I were young, Maggie / Post horn gallop / Can-can / With a song in my heart (CD only.) / Penny serenade (CD only.) / West Side Story selection (I feel pretty-Maria-Somewhere-Tonight. CD only.) / March of the mods (CD only.) / Hear my song, Violetta.
MC: . . . . **TCIDL 111**

AT THE WURLITZER ORGAN-BLACKPOOL.
Tracks: / Day trip to Bangor / Radetzky march / Ballade pour Adeline (Composers: P. de Senneville/O. Toussaint) / Happy together (Composers: Bonner/Gordon) / Welcome to my heart (Composers: I. Ortega/B. Barratt) / Dallas (Dallas dreams), Theme from (Composer: Jerrold Immel) / Knots Landing (Composer: Jerrold Immel) / Whats another year (Composer: Shay Healy) / I'm in the mood for dancing (Composers: Findon/Myers/Puzey) / Xanadu (Composer: Jeff Lynne) / Copacabana (Composers:Sussman/Feldman/ Manilow) / Pigalle (Composer: G. Ulmer) / Domino (Composer: L. Ferrari) / Under Paris skies (Composers: Girraud/ Gannon) / Manhattan (Composers:Rodgers/Hart) / New York, New York (Composers: F. Ebb/J. Kander) / 42nd Street (Composers: A. Dubin/H. Warren) / Give my regards to Broadway (Composer: George Cohen) / Yesterday (Composers: Lennon/ McCartney) / With a little help from my friends (Composers: Lennon/ McCartney) / Ticket to ride (Composers: Lennon/McCartney) / Sabre dance (Composer: Aram Khachaturian. Arranged by Phil Kelsall.) / Old rugged cross, The (Composer: Rev. George Bennard. Arranged by: Phil Kelsall) / Toreador's march (From 'Carmen'. Composer: Georges Bizet. Arranged by: Phil Kelsall) / To a wild rose (Composer: E. McDowell. Arranged by Phil Kelsall) / Annen polka (Composer: J Strauss Jnr. Arranged by: Phil Kelsall) / Twelfth Street rag (Bowman) / Chiquitita (Composers: B. Ulvaeus/B. Anderson) / I have a dream (Composers: B. Ulvaeus/ B. Anderson) / Winner takes it all, The (Composers: B. Ulvaeus/B. Anderson) / Play off (Composers: B. Ulvaeus/B. Anderson. Brief extract only of 'Thank you for) / Thank you for the music (Composers: B. Ulvaeus/B. Anderson) / Liberty bell (Composer: Sousa. Arranged by Phil Kelsall) / Hopelessly devoted to you (From the film "Grease". Composer: Farrar.) / Star Trek (Composer: Courage) / Happy days (Composers: Gimbel/Fox) / Thomas and Sarah (Composer: Rabinowitz) / Lillie (Composer: Horovitz) / I'm in favour of friendship (Composers: Mann/Hilliard) / Red roses for a blue lady (Composers: Tepper/Brodsky) / Oh lady be good (Composer: George Gershwin) / You're the one that I want (From the film 'Grease'. Composer: Farrer.) / Summer nights (From the film 'Grease'. Composers: Casey/Jacobs) / Strangers in the night (Composer: Kaempfert) / Night and day (Composer: Cole Porter) / Night Fever / Blackpool bounce (Composer: Ross) / Poeme (Composer: Fibich. Arranged by Phill Kelsall) / Secret love (Composer: Fain) / Love is the sweetest thing (Composer: Noble) / Love is in the air (Composers: Vanda/ Young) / Heaven can wait (Composer: Grusin) / Borsalino (Composer: Bolling) / We're all alone (Composer: Scaggs) / Raining in my heart (Composers: F. & B. Bryant) / Bright eyes (From the film 'Watership Down'. Composer: Mike Batt.) / Magic of Paris, The (Composer: Barratt) / Cielito lindo (Arranged by Phil Kelsall) / I will survive (Composers: Fekaris/Perren) / Carnival is over, The (Composer: Springfield).
2LP: . . . . **DL 1100**
MC: . . . . **TC-DL 1100**

BENEATH THE LIGHTS OF HOME (At the Wurlitzer Organ Tower Ballroom, Blackpool).
Tracks: / Folies Bergere / Wedding of the painted doll, The / Stella by starlight / Nancy with the laughing face / Laura / In a party mood / Everything I have is yours / How are things in Glocca Morra / On a clear day / Black and white rag / Pennsylvannia polka / Catari, catari / Come back to Sorrento / Santa Lucia / O Maria Mari / Funiculi funicula / Let's face the music and dance / Top hat, white tie and tails / You were never lovelier / Cheek to cheek / Wistful waltz, The / Dicky bird hop / Ave Maria / Canadian capers / Ain't we got fun / Good morning / Everything's in rhythm with my heart / Roses of Picardy / Beneath the lights of home / Whispering grass / Trolley song, The.
LP: . . . . **GRALP 34**
MC: . . . . **GRTC 34**

BLACKPOOL BOUNCE.
Tracks: / Liberty bell / Hopelessly devoted to you / Casatchok / Star trek / Happy days / Lillie / Lady be good / Summer nights / Night and day / Night fever / Poeme / Secret love / Love is in the air / Borsalino / We're all alone / Bright eyes / Devil's galop / Cielito lindo / I will survive / Carnival is over, The.
LP: . . . . **NTS 176**

BLACKPOOL DANCE PARTY (Tower Ballroom, Blackpool featuring Wurlitzer Organ).
Tracks: / Fascination / In San Francisco / Love walked in / Marta / Jealousy / Flamingo / Wheels / Tea for two / Remember me / If I had you / Arcady waltz / Wonderful one / Cock o' the North / Pi-anna rag.
LP: . . . . **NTS 236**
MC: . . . . **TCNTS 236**

FASCINATING RHYTHM.
Tracks: / Wonderful / I got rhythm / Cavalleria rusticana / Eastenders (T.V. Themes) / Crossroads (T.V. Themes) / Howards way (T.V. Themes) / Walking in the air (From (The Snowman)) / Westminster waltz / Over the waves / Donauwellen / You'll never know / My very good friend the milkman / Bei mir bist du schon / Only love (From Mistrals Daughter.) / Rilley, Ace of spies (Theme Music.) / Archill Island / Maple leaf rag / We all stand together / I just called to say I love you / Little orphan Annie.
LP: . . . . **EMS 1171**
MC: . . . . **TCEMS 1171**
LP: . . . . **SCX 6702**

IT'S JUST THE TIME FOR DANCING.
Tracks: / Bewitched (Composer: Richard Rodgers) / Love in bloom (Composers: L. Robin/R. Rainger.) / Someone to watch over me (Composer: George Gershwin.) / Here's that rainy day (Composer: James Van Heusen.) / La golondrina (Composer: Serradell. Arranged by Phil Kelsall.) / Cherry pink and apple blossom white (Composer: Louiguy) / Porfavor (Composer: Joe Sherman) / Skater's waltz (Composer: Emil Waldteufel. Arranged by Phil Kelsall.) / Spanish gypsy dance (Composer: Pascual Marquina.) / Nagasaki (Composer: Harry Warren.) / Sweet Georgia Brown (Composers: Bernie/Casey/Pinkard.) / Little red monkey (Composer: Jack Jordan.) / On the prom prom promenade (Composers: Butler/Damerell/Evans.) / Consider yourself (Composer: Lionel Bart.) / Rose of Washington Square / I'll string along with you (Composer: Harry Warren) / Destination love (Composer: Bob Barratt.) / Pink lady, The (Composer: Ivan Caryll. Arranged by Phil Kelsall/) / Wyoming lullaby (Composer: Gene Williams.) / Bless 'em all (Composers: Hughes/Lake) / And the band played on (Composer: Ward. Arranged by Phil Kelsall.) / Ash grove, The (Composer: Trad. Arranged by Phil Kelsall.) / Tip toe through the tulips (Composer: Joe Burke) / I don't know why (I just do) (Composers: R. Turk/F. Albert) / My mammy (Composers: Lewis/Young/ Donaldson) / Scotch mist (Composers: Bob Barratt/Colin Fretcher) / Garden in the rain (Composer: Carroll Gibbons.) / Girl from Ipanema (Composer: Antonio Carlos Jobim.) / Paradise (Composer: Nacio Herb Brown.) / La Cumparsita (Composer: Rodriguez.) / Little white lies (Composer: Walter Donaldson.) / Happy feel (Composers: Yellen/Ager) / It's just the time for dancing (Composer: Richard Eckersley) / Mr. Sandman (Composer: Pat Ballard.) / Avalon (Composers: A.Jolson/V.Rose.) / Crazy rhythm (Composers: J.Meyer/R.W.Kahn.) / Am I wasting my time on you? (Composers: H.Johnson/I.Bibo) / Pal of my cradle days (Composer: L.Piantadosi) / Answer me (Composers: G.Winkler/F.Rauch).
MC: . . . . **GRTC 18**
LP: . . . . **GRALP 18**

I'VE HEARD THAT SONG BEFORE.
Tracks: / March of the mods / Misty / Post horn galop / Can-can / Play a simple melody / How deep is the ocean / I've got my love to keep me warm / Melanie's minuet / Nobody's sweetheart / You're dancing on my heart / You've done something to my heart / Winds of war (Love theme) / Forgotten dreams / Tiger Rag / Telstar / Nun's chorus (from Casanova) / Tico ti / Way you look tonight / All the things you are / Look for the silver lining / Sunshine of your smile, The / I'll never smile again / You're never fully dressed without a smile (from Annie) / Eleanora / Rose of Tralee, The / I'll be your sweetheart / When you and I were young, Maggie / Annie's song / One of those songs / I've heard that song before.
LP: . . . . **NTS 1078381**
MC: . . . . **TCNTS 1078384**

LOVE CHANGES EVERYTHING.
Tracks: / Heyken's first serenade / Morgens um sieben / Happy talk / I enjoy being a girl / Hello, young lovers / Love changes everything / Roses from the South / True love / Let's do it / Wunderbar / Just one of those things / Choo choo samba / Trudie / Petite waltz, The / Plink plank plunk / Tango in D. (Abeniz) / Exactly like you / Way down yonder in New Orleans / T'aint what you do / Braes of Strathnaver / Two sleepy people / For all we know / World is waiting for the sunrise, The / Romeo (CD only.) / Don't say goodbye (CD only.) / Your eyes (CD only.) / Rouge et noir (CD only.).
LP: . . . . **GRALP 36**
MC: . . . . **GRTC 36**

MEET ME AT THE TOWER.
Tracks: / March / Brass buttons / When you were sweet sixteen / Let no man steal your thyme / Shaddup you face / Let's all sing like the birdies sing / Birdie song, The / Midnite blue / Those lazy hazy crazy days of summer / Powder your face with sunshine / Keep your sunny side up / East of the sun / Very thought of you, The / How about you / Tomorrow / Come follow the band / If my friends could see me now / Samum / Memory / Si si / Yours / Seven tears / Last of the summer wine / Juliet Bravo / Brideshead revisited / Road to the isles / All through the night / MacNamara's band / Anchors aweigh / Rule Britannia / Drunken sailor / My bonnie / Skye boat song / Fingal's cave / Crimond.
LP: . . . . **NTS 234**
MC: . . . . **TCNTS 234**

PARTY DANCE NIGHT.
Tracks: / Gal in calico, A / Kiss me again / Dream lover / Only you / Agadoo / Semper fidelis / Home / Price of erin waltz / Breakaway blues / Wedgewood blue gavotte / Crazy people / Sweet sue / Ma / Gay gordons.
LP: . . . . **EG 2402711**
MC: . . . . **EG 2402714**

PHIL KELSALL'S BLACKPOOL SING-SONG.
LP: . . . . **NTS 196**

SEQUENCE OF DANCING FAVOURITES.
LP: . . . . **GRALP 39**
MC: . . . . **GRTC 39**

THANK YOU FOR THE MUSIC.
Tracks: / Waterloo / Hasta Manana / Money, money, money / Cavatina / As time goes by / Thanks for the memory / S-H-I-N-E / God bless our love / Floral dance, The / Theme from love story / Somewhere my love / Bridge too far, A / All creatures great and small / Pass me by / Stein song, The / Hey look me over / Around the world / Kiss me again / Dream lover / Whispering / Change partners / Five foot two eyes of blue / Who pays the ferryman / Enemy at the door / Here, there and everywhere / When I'm 64 / All my loving / Sailing / Casatschok / Rasputin / Midnight in Moscow / Devil's galop / World of sport march / Out of the blue / Match of the day / Agadoo / Under the linden tree / Out of nowhere / Only you (and you alone) / When the day is done / Cha Cha Chas / In a little Spanish town / Want to be happy, I / Orange coloured sky / Home (when shadows fall) / She's funny that way / By a waterfall / Irish lullaby / How can you buy Kilarney? / Believe me if all those endearing young charms / Everything stops for tea / Underneath the arches / Ragtime cowboy Joe / Crazy people / Sweet Sue, just you / If you knew Susie / Ma (he's making eyes at me) / Scotch broth / Hundred pipers, A / Campbells are coming, The / Fernando / Dancing queen / Thank you for the music.
LP: . . . . **OU 2211**
MC: . . . . **TCDL 1206**

TICKET TO RIDE.
Tracks: / Radetzky march / Ballade pour Adeline / Day trip to Bangor / Dallas / What's another year / Copacabana / Distant hills / Pigalle / Manhattan / Yesterday / World of sport / Birds were singing / Sabre dance / Old rugged cross / Toreador's march / Twelfth Street rag / Chiquitita.
LP: . . . . **NTS 219**

UNFORGETTABLE HITS OF THE 50'S.
Tracks: / He's got the whole world in his hands / Just an old fashioned girl / Eternally / You belong to me / Transatlantic lullaby / Three coins in the fountain / Arrivederci Roma / Volare / Unforgettable / Sam's song / When I take my sugar to tea / Catch a falling star / Magic moments / Hot diggity / Pretty little black-eyed Susie / Singing the blues / Chicka boom / Twilight time / April love / Tzena, Tzena, Tzena / Liechtensteiner polka / Dambusters march / Blossom fell, A / Finger of suspicion / Venus / When I fall in love / Dreamboat / Jezebel / High noon / Pickin' a chicken / Sugar bush / Gilly gilly ossenfeffer katzenellenbogen by the sea / Tom Dooley / Story of my life / China tea / Mockin' Bird Hill / My resistance is low / On top of old smokey.
LP: . . . . **GRALP 25**
MC: . . . . **GRTC 25**

Kelson, Ran

HUNGRY FOR BLOOD.
LP: . . . . **EBON 34**

Keltia Rok

KELTIA ROK (Various artists).
LP: . . . . **SAIN 1412M**

Keltner, Jim

SHEFFIELD DRUM RECORD (Keltner, Jim & Ron Tutt).
LP: . . . . **LAB 14**

Kemp, Gene (aut)

CLOCK TOWER GHOST, THE (see under Clock Tower Ghost (bk)).

TURBULENT TERM OF TYKE TILER, THE (Cochrane, Michael).
MCSET: **CC/031**

Kemp, Hal

1934: HAL KEMP (Kemp, Hal Orchestra).
LP: . . . . CLP 25

HAL KEMP, VOL. 1, 1934.
Tracks: / When summer is gone / This is romance / Boo boo booo / I guess I'll have to change my plans / I don't care / It's only a paper moon / Doin' the uptown lowdown / Everything I have is yours / Ain't cha glad / You've got me crying again / Puddin head Jones / Boulevard of broken dreams / Nuts about mutts / Suffle off to Buffalo / Swingy little thingy, A / Too many tears / Between the devil and the deep blue sea.
LP: . . . . HSR 143
LP: . . . . HMA 5069

HAL KEMP, VOL 2 1934.
Tracks: / When summer is gone (opening theme) / Did you ever see a dream walking / Brighter than the sun / Our big love scene / Hell's bells / Last year's girl / Thanks / Pettin' in the park / Some of these days / When summer is gone / When summer is gone (closing theme) / It's Winter again / Let's fall in love / Keep on (doin' what you're doin') / Love is the sweetest thing / Limehouse blues (instrumental) / You and who else / I couldn't tell them what to do / 42nd Street / When summer is gone.
LP: . . . . HSR 161

ON THE AIR 1940 (Kemp, Hal Orchestra).
Tracks: / Indian Summer / Blue moonlight / Would you mind? / Friendship / Alone together / I've got no strings / Night and day / Little red fox, The / When summer is gone / I've got my eyes on you / Why not / Clair de lune / I concentrate on you / Believing / In Dutch with the Dutchess / Speak your heart / Vamp, The.
LP: . . . . AIRCHECK 38

Kemp, Johnny

SECRETS OF FLYING.
Tracks: / Just got paid / One thing led to another / My only want is you / Dancin' with myself / Urban times / Feeling without touching / Just like flyin'.
LP: 4609041
MC: 4609044
LP: . . . . BFC 40770

Kemp, Rick

ORIGINAL OWNERS (See under Chapman, Michael) (Kemp, Rick & Michael Chapman).

Kemp, Willie

KING O' THE CORNKISTERS.
Tracks: / McGinty's meal and ale / Fornet, The / Ye canna pit it on tae Sandy / McFarlane O' the sprots O' Burniboozie / Road and the miles to Dundee, The / Sowens Jean / It's afa' like its father / Weddin' o' McGinnis to his cross-eyed pet / Baker man, The / Bonnie lass o' Fyvie / It fair cowes the cuddy / Goat of the W.R.I. The / Drumdelgie / At the bottom O' oor stair / Muckle gauket gype.
MC: . . . . ACLMC 1

Kempion

BRUMMAGEM BALLADS (see Farriers) (Kempion/Farriers).

KEMPION.
Tracks: / Humours of whiskey / Gillian's apples / Bonnie hoose o' Airlie / Bonnie lass o' Bon Accord / Scot Skinner's compliment to Dr. MacDonald / Sir David Davidson of Cantray / Sweet Trinity / Kitty goes milking / Dan Breams / Dancing tailor / Rose among the heather / Blarney pilgrim / Death of Queen Jane, The / Elise dear / Willie MacIntosh / Broomfield hill / Another jog will do / Dillon's fancy / Ships are sailing.
LP: . . . . BRO 123
MC: . . . . KBRO 123

Kendall, Felicity

BAMBI (See under Bambi (bk)).

Kendall, Tony

CLOSER TO THE HEARTLAND.
LP: . . . . STFC 003

ROSE OF ESSEX.
LP: . . . . STFC 001

Kendall-Lane, Stephen

GHOSTHUNTER, THE.
LP: . . . . DELP 311
MC: . . . . ZCELP 311

Kendalls

BEST COUNTRY DUO 1978.
LP: . . . . GT 0001

FIRE AT FIRST SIGHT.
Tracks: / Fire at first sight / Central standard time / If you get that close / I'll take you / Party line / Too late / I'm dreaming again / He can't make your kind of love / Little doll / You can't fool love.
LP: . . . . IMCA 5724
MC: . . . . MCAC 5724

HEART OF THE MATTER.
Tracks: / You'd make an angel wanna cheat / Put it off until tomorrow / Gone away / Everlasting love / I'll be hurtin' either way / Heart of the matter / I'm already blue / I take the chance / I don't drink from the river / I don't do like that no more.
LP: . . . . OV 1446

JUST LIKE REAL PEOPLE.
Tracks: / I had a lovely time / Mandolin man / Love seeds / Falling in love / Just like real people / Love is a hurting thing / Never my love / I'm coming down lonely / If you don't want the fire / Another dream just came true.
LP: . . . . OV 1739

MOVIN' TRAIN.
Tracks: / Precious love / I'll be faithful to you / Movin' train / Dark end of the street / Say the word / Thank God for radio / I'd dance every dance with you / My baby's gone / Flaming eyes / Wildflower.
LP: 8127 791

Kendrick, Graham

KENDRICK COLLECTION, THE (see under All Souls, Langham Place) (Kendrick, Graham/All Souls' Orchestra/Choir).

LAMB OF GOD (see under Hosanna) (Kendrick, Graham/Hosanna).

MAKE WAY FOR THE CROSS.
LP: . . . . MWR 4
MC: . . . . MWC 4
LP: . . . . MWL 4

Kendricks, Eddie

LOVE KEYS.
Tracks: / Oh I need your loving / I'm in need of love / I don't need nobody else / Old home town / Bernadette / You can't stop my loving / Never alone / Hot / Looking for love / In love we're one.
LP: . . . . K 50779
MC: K4 50779

RUFFIN & KENDRICKS (See under Ruffin & Kendricks) (Kendricks, Eddie/David Ruffin).

Kenia

INITIAL THRILL.
Tracks: / Brincadera / Initial thrill / Doce doce / Sim ou nao / Sina / Don't let me be lonely tonight / Cruisin' / Captivated / Missing you.
LP: . . . . MCF 3376
MC: . . . . MCFC 3376

Kennedy, Brian

GREAT WAR OF WORDS, THE.
Tracks: / Captured / Open arms / Town / Believe it / Am I looking for you? / Is it loud enough? / Hollow / He talks like traffic / Halfway home / Keep a firm grip.
LP: . . . . PL 74475
MC: . . . . PK 74475

Kennedy, Calum

CALUM KENNEDY SHOW, THE.
Tracks: / Hiking song, The / Mairi's wedding / Barnyards of Delgaty / O bin I were a Baron's heir / Waters of Kylesku / Gypsy Rover, The / Westering home / Home to Scotland / Song of the Clyde / Donald's toosers / Top of Ben Nevis / Heres to the hills / Mouth Music / Loch Maree Islands / Dark lights of old Aberdeen / These are my mountains / Brochan lom / Mhic larla / Those brown eyes / Roolin' in the heather / Scotland the brave.
MC: . . . . ZCSMPS 8921

LEGENDS OF SCOTLAND.
Tracks: / Here's to the hills / Mouth Music / Comin' thro the rye / My Bonnie lies over the ocean / Loch Lomond / Annie Laurie / Bluebells of Scotland / Gypsy Rover, The / Laird of Drumblair, The / Calum's ceilidh / Campbeltown loch / Brochan lom / Dark Island / Bratach bana / Donald, where's yer troosers / Top of Ben Nevis / Amazing Grace / Five lovely lassies from Bannion / Muirsheen Durkin / Bonnie lass o' Fyvie / Bridal path, The / Scarborough fair / Eileen Fraoich / Caristiona / Dark Lochnagar / Ae fond kiss / Bonnie Kyleswater / Leanabh og / O bin I were a Baron's heir.
MC: . . . . ZCLLS 701

Kennedy, Douglas

DUCKS AND BETTY (Kennedy, Douglas & Helen).
Tracks: / Abbots Bromley horn dance / Old tune / Betty and her ducks / Shepherd's hey / Owd towler / Jockie to the fair / On Ilkley Moor baht'at / Winster galop / Shop talk in Berwick / Hares on the mountain / Blacksmith's hornpipe / Golden farmer / Leap frog / Oor-gude man / Hole in the wall / Jack Hall / Nutting girl, The / Landlord fill the flowing bowl / Ampleforth sword dance, the / I'll go and enlist for a sailor / Golden vanity / Princess Royal / Battle of the Nile / Queen Jane / Bacca pipes / Jolly herring / Steamboat quickstep / Lady in the boat / Isaac's maggot / Cupid's waltz / Trees they do grow high, The / Bonnie green garters / Rosin the beau / Love port and sherry.
MC: 60-041

Kennedy, Grace

DESIRE.
Tracks: / By way of love's express / Fandango dancing / Cupid's defence / Woman is free / My heart keeps breaking over you / Desire / Reachin' out for your love / Don't you ever get lonely / We did it / With one more look at you.
LP: . . . . DJF 20563
MC: . . . . DJH 40563

GRACE KENNEDY.
Tracks: / (You bring out) the best of the woman in me / For better or for worse / Say it again / Keeping my head above water / You set my dreams to music / Too many people / Could this be love / I'm so glad I got cha / You can't dress up a broken heart / Home.
LP: . . . . DJF 20534
MC: . . . . DJH 40534

I'M STARTING AGAIN.
Tracks: / I'm starting again / Heart on the line / What did I see in you / It's not me anymore / Love is a serious business / Nothing's changed / Love in the sunshine / If I'm wrong about you / I'm wrong about everything / Until you / Love me to sleep.
LP: . . . . DJF 20572
MC: . . . . DJH 40572

ONE VOICE.
Tracks: / One voice / Letter, The / As time goes by / My old piano / Feeling too good today blues / I know I'll never love this way again / Your love takes me higher and higher / I love you / Don't cry out loud / Looking up / Missing you / We dont make each other laugh any more / Stop in the name of love / My cherie amour / Touch me in the morning / Let your mama know / Bandstand boogie / Do you know where you're going to (Theme from Mahogany) / Ain't no mountain high enough / Reach out I'll be there.
LP: . . . . REB 419
MC: . . . . ZCF 419

Kennedy, Hal

BEST OF HAL KENNEDY.
Tracks: / Pity the man / Remind me dear Lord / Keep your mighty hand on me / Family bible / Don't take my cross away / Who am I? / Answer's on the way, The / Same road, The / Breaking of the day / God's old clock / Full up, no vacancy / Old rugged cross, The / Prisoner of love / It'll all be over but the shouting / Sorry, I never knew you / Pilgrims have gone, The.
LP: . . . . CGS 8511
MC: . . . . WC 8511

Kennedy, Jayne

LOVE YOUR BODY.
Tracks: / Love your body / Don't stop til you get enough / Slimline / Other woman / Take your time / Ladies night / Upside down / Work that body / One hundred ways.
LP: . . . . CLTLP 2

Kennedy, John F.

JOHN F. KENNEDY MEMORIAL PIPE BAND (See under John F Kennedy...) (John F. Kennedy Memorial Pipe Band).

Kennedy, Lena (aut)

DANDELION SEED, THE (see under Dandelion Seed (bk)) (Boyd, Carole (nar)).

Kennedy, Malcolm

SOUVENIR OF SCOTLAND (Marching and dancing).
MC: . . . . CT 116

THISTLE OF SCOTLAND, THE.
Tracks: / Song of the Clyde.
LP: . . . . HRL 105
MC: . . . . CHRL 105

WALTZING THRO' IRELAND.
Tracks: / Rose of Tralee, The / Molly Bawn.
MC: . . . . COB 4004

Kennedy, Nigel

BRUCH VIOLIN CONCERTO.
LP: . . . . EL 7496631
MC: . . . . EL 7496634

FOUR SEASONS (see under Vivaldi) (Kennedy, Nigel & English Chamber Orchestra).

LET LOOSE.
Tracks: / Let loose / Zigane / Emotion / Before it's time / Way we were, The / Killer instinct / Impro 1 / Drive / Way outside.
LP: . . . . SCX 6709
MC: . . . . TCSCX 6709

PLAYS ELLINGTON & BARTOK.
Tracks: / Sonata for solo violin (Bartok) / Mainly black.
LP: . . . . EL 2705381
MC: . . . . EL 2705384
LP: . . . . NIGEL 1
MC: . . . . TCNIGEL 1

STRAD JAZZ (Kennedy, Nigel & Peter Pettinger).
Tracks: / Body and soul / Autumn leaves / Swing '39 / Isn't she lovely / Lover man / Girl from Ipanema.
LP: . . . . LBRD 011
MC: . . . . LBTD 011

VIOLIN CONCERTO (Kennedy, Nigel/ London Philharmonic Orchestra).
LP: . . . . EMX 412 058 1
LP: . . . . EMX 2058
MC: . . . . TCEMX 2058
MC: . . . . EMX 4120584

Kennedy, Norman

SCOTS SONGS AND BALLADS.
Tracks: / Merchant's son, The / Corachree / Forester, The / Jolly beggar, The / Kismuil's galley / Guise o'tough, The / Drumdelgie / Night visiting song / Wi my rovin' eye / I wish I wish / Auld beggar man, The / Puirt a beul / Bonnie highland soldier, The / Johnny my man.
LP: 12T 178

Kennedy, Ollie

SHADES OF LOVE.
MC: . . . . RGMC 4

Kennedy Rose

HAI KU.
Tracks: / Hai ku / Only chain, The / Faithful / Western fires / Who's gonna hold you / Nightline / Love like this / After your arms / Variation on a theme in D minor / Love is the healer / Born to give my love / Leavin' line.
LP: . . . . EIRSA 1030
MC: . . . . EIRSAC 1030

Kennedy,Jimmy

GREAT BRITISH DANCE BANDS (See under Dance Bands...) (Various artists).

Kennelly, Brendan

LIVING GHOSTS (Poetry).
MC: . . . . LRCS 6

Kenner, Chris

I LIKE IT LIKE THAT.
Tracks: / I like it like that / Anybody here seen my baby / Shoo-rah / Johnny Little / Gonna getcha baby / Never reach perfection / Something you got / That's my girl / Land of a thousand dances / She can dance / Come back and see / How far / Time / All night rambler / Packin' up / (I found) peace.
LP: . . . . CRB 1163
MC: . . . . TCCRB 1163

Kenney, Beverly

COME SWING WITH ME.
LP: . . . . FS 218

SINGS FOR JOHNNY SMITH.
LP: . . . . FS 124

SINGS FOR PLAYBOYS.
LP: . . . . FS 254

Kenney, Erin

EPONYMOUS (Kenney, Erin & Ethan James).
Tracks: / Winds of change / Einstein / Confession / Kill what you don't understand / Death comes to club / Evangeline / Veil of tears / I dream / Time / 1,000 miles / Paradise of fools.
LP: . . . . SAVE 83

Kenny

SOUND OF SUPER K, THE.
LP: . . . . SRAK 518

Kenny G.

DUOTONES.
Tracks: / You make me believe / Slip of the tongue / What does it take to win your love / Don't make me wait for love / Sade / Esther / Songbird / Champagne / Midnight / Three of a kind.
LP: 207792
MC: 407792

G FORCE.
Tracks: / Hi, how ya doin? / I've been missing you / Tribeca / G force / Do me right / I wanna be yours / Sunset at noon / Help yourself to my love.
LP: 206168
MC: 406168
LP: 209059
MC: 409059

GRAVITY.
Tracks: / Love on the rise / One man's poison (another man's sweetness) / Where do we take it (from here) / One

night stand / Japan / Sax attack / Virgin island / Gravity / Last night of the year.
LP: 207120
MC: 407120

KENNY G.
Tracks: / Mercy mercy mercy / Here we are / Stop and go / I can't tell you why / Shuffle, The / Tell me / Find a way / Crystal mountain / Come close.
LP: 209337
MC: 409337

MONTAGE.
Tracks: / Songbird / I can't tell you why / Tribeca / Virgin island / I've been missing you / Uncle Al / What does it take (to win your love) / Silhouette / Midnight motion / Against doctors orders / Hi, how ya doin'? / Sade / Going home / We've saved the best till last.
LP: 210621
MC: 410621

SILHOUETTE.
Tracks: / Silhouette / We've saved the best for last / Trade winds / I'll be alright / Against doctor's orders / Pastel / All in one night / Let go / Home / Summer song.
LP: 209284
MC: 409284

Kenny, Gerard

CITY LIVING.
Tracks: / Outlaw / Only love / Michael / Red hot radio / Love words / Staying power / Run for your love / City living / Crazy Sadie / You've got to be good to get me / Old friends.
LP: .... RCALP 6009
MC: .... RCAK 6009

LIVING ON MUSIC.
Tracks: / You're the best / Fantasy / Sucker for love / Crime that pays / April's end / Buckinghamshire / Southern comfort / Maggie / Jailbait / Getting to know each other / Living on music.
LP: .... PL 25318
MC: .... PK 25318

MADE IT THROUGH THE RAIN.
Tracks: / Fit to be tied / Music and words / Son of a song and dance man / D-D-D-dancin' / Love / New York, New York / Pavement princess / Drinking / Nickels and dimes / I made it through the rain.
LP: .... PL 25218

MUSIC OF GERARD KENNY, THE.
Tracks: / World full of laughter / Fantasy / I could be so good for you / I made it through the rain.
LP: .... IMP 6
MC: .... TCIMP 6

Kenny's Window

KENNY'S WINDOW (Maurice Sendak) (Grimes, Tammy (nar)).
LP: .... TC 51548
MC: .... CDL 51548

Kent, Alexander

RICHARD BOLITHO - MIDSHIPMAN (Valentine, Anthony).
MCSET: .... LFP 7252

Kent, Cindy (nar)

ADVENTURES OF MARY MOUSE (see under Blyton, Enid (aut)).

Kent, Klark

KLARK KENT.
Tracks: / Don't care / Away from home / Rich in a ditch / Grandelinquent / Guerilla / Old school / Excesses / Kinetic ritual.
LP: .... AMLE 68511

Kent, Luther

IT'S IN THE BAG (Kent, Luther & Trick Band).
LP: .... ENJA 4066

Kent, Shirley

FOREVER A WILLOW.
Tracks: / Wicker basket weaver / Harlequin and Columbia / Like morning / In my garden / Hiding there / Let us go dancing / Comical wise / Fresh out / Dedication to Bertram George Tippling / I'm glad there is you Jimmy Dorsey.
LP: .... MAGIC 001

Kent, Tommy

SUSIE DARLIN'.
Tracks: / Susie darlin' / Corina Corina / Donna / Irgendwer / Alle nachte / Sweet baby sweet / Heute nacht im mondenschein / Denn ich lebe gefahrlich / My baby doll / Ich brauche dich dazu / Wie keine andere / Ein mann de nicht nein sagen kann / Oh mister tip top / Muss das sein / Lach nicht uber mich / Ein anderer stahl mir dein herz / Das bin ich.
LP: .... BFX 15041

Kentigern

KENTIGERN.
Tracks: / Cullen bay / Jig of slurs, The / Seagull / Corncake / Breton tunes / Greenwood side / Weary farmers, The / Pipe major Donald McLean of Lewis / Weavers of Newley, The / Kail and pudding / Loch Roag / Iron horse / Last o' the tinker, The / Rathven market / Conundrum, The / Gin I were shot o' her / Hebridean air / Braes of Tullymet / Braes of Mellinish, The / Wild roving no more / Put me in the great chest / Three peaks of South Uist / South Uist.
LP: 12TS 394

Kenton, Janet

DRIFTING AWAY (See also Irie, Tippa) (Kenton, Janet & Tippa Irie).

Kenton, Stan

7.5 ON THE RICHTER SCALE (Kenton, Stan & His Orchestra).
Tracks: / Live and let die / Body and soul / Down and dirty / Country cousin / Two thousand / Zarathustra revisited / It's not easy bein' green / Speak softly love.
LP: .... JAS 201
LP: .... ST 1070
MC: .... STC 1070

1941 (Kenton, Stan & His Orchestra).
Tracks: / Artistry in rhythm / Tempo di Joe / Night life / Marvin's mumble / I haven't got the heart / El choclo / Safari / Trumpet symphonette / Little jive is good for you, A / Prelude to nothing / Old black Joe / Flamingo / Take it from the oven / Balboa bash.
LP: .... HMP 5049

1941, VOL 2 (Kenton, Stan & His Orchestra).
Tracks: / Congo clambake / Arkansas traveller / Shuffling the chords / Take sixteen / Opus in pastels / Reed rapture / Etude for saxophone / Tribute to a flattened fifth / Underneath the stars / Quit your shovin' / Let her go / Too soon / Hold back the dawn / Low bridge / Popocatapetl / Blue flare.
LP: .... HMP 5055

1944: STAN KENTON.
LP: .... SWH 26
MC: .... CSWH 26

1951 (Kenton, Stan & His Orchestra).
LP: .... FH 1004

1962,VOL.6 (Kenton, Stan & His Orchestra).
LP: .... HSR 195

1943-44 (Kenton, Stan & His Orchestra).
Tracks: / Ol' man river / Shoo shoo baby / Eager beaver / Liza / In a little Spanish town / Paper doll / Hit that jive Jack / Goon came on, The / Begin the beguine / None but the lonely heart / I know that you know / I lost my sugar in Salt Lake City / Russian lullaby / Hour of parting / Lady in red, The / I got rhythm.
LP: .... HMP 5061

ADVENTURES IN BLUES, 1961.
Tracks: / Reuben's blues / Dragonwyck / Blue ghost / Exit stage left / Night at the gold nugget / Formula SK-32 / Aphrodisia / Fitz / Blues story, The.
LP: .... ST 1012

ADVENTURES IN JAZZ.
Tracks: / Turtle talk / Stairway to the stars / Limehouse blues / Misty / Waltz of the prophets / Body and soul.
LP: .... ST 1010

ADVENTURES IN STANDARDS, 1961.
Tracks: / Some enchanted evening / Begin the beguine / It's alright with me / Make someone happy / Old devil moon / Gigi / Come rain or come shine / Almost like being in love / Just in time / If I were a bell / Bewitched, bothered and bewildered / I've grown accustomed to her face.
LP: .... ST 1025

ARTISTRY IN BOSSA NOVA, 1963.
Tracks: / Artistry in rhythm / Opus in chartreuse / Interlude / Kentonova / Eager beaver / Concerto to end all concertos / Brasilia / Painted rhythm / Opus in pastels / Jump for Joe / Loco nova / Artistry in bossa nova.
LP: .... ST 1045

ARTISTRY IN RHYTHM.
Tracks: / Just a sittin' and a rockin' / Soothe me / Ain't no misery in me / Willow weep for me / Come back to Sorrento / Artistry in percussion / Safranski / Artistry in Bolero / Cocktails for two / Fantasy / Opus in pastels / Santa Lucia.
LP: .... ST 1043

ARTISTRY IN TANGO.
LP: .... GM 7704

ARTISTRY IN VOICES & BRASS.
Tracks: / Flame / Moon love / Painted rhythm / These wonderful things / Eager beaver / Daydreams in the night / Concerto of love / It's love / Night song.
LP: .... ST 1038

AT THE HOLLYWOOD PALLADIUM, LIVE 1951.
LP: .... EB 413

BALLAD STYLE OF STAN KENTON.
MC: .... TCEMS 1248
LP: .... EMS 1248
LP: .... ST 1068

BEST OF BRANT INN (Kenton, Stan & His Orchestra).
Tracks: / Piano theme into the waltz of the prophets / Intermission riff / Reuben's blues / Genghis Khan / Begin the beguine / Artistry in Bolero / Eager beaver..... (Medley includes:- Eager Beaver, Opus in Chartreuse, Dynaflow, Jump for J).
MC: .... CFH 45
LP: .... FH 45

BIRTHDAY IN BRITAIN (Kenton, Stan & His Orchestra).
Tracks: / Happy birthday to you / Daily dance / Street of dreams / Of space and time / For better and for Worsetter / No harmful side effects / Ambivalence / Blues between & betwixt.
LP: .... JAS 200
LP: .... ST 1065

BY REQUEST VOL. 3 1943-1951 (Kenton, Stan & His Orchestra).
LP: .... ST 1062

BY REQUEST VOL. 4 (1950-1952) (Kenton, Stan Orchestra & The Four Freshmen).
LP: .... ST 1064

BY REQUEST VOL. 5 1953-1960 (Kenton, Stan Orchestra & The Four Freshmen).
LP: .... ST 1066

BY REQUEST VOL. 6 1958-1962 (Kenton, Stan Orchestra & The Four Freshmen).
LP: .... ST 1069

CARNEGIE (Kenton, Stan & His Orchestra).
LP: .... FH 1006

CHRISTY YEARS, THE (1945-47) (Kenton, Stan & June Christy).
Tracks: / It's been a long, long time / Shoo fly pie and apple pan dowdy / Rika Jika Jack / It's a pity to say goodnight / Don't want that man around / Across the valley from the Alamo / Curio City / I told ya I love ya, now get out / He was a good man as good men go / How high the moon.
LP: .... ST 1035

CITY OF GLASS AND THIS MODERN WORLD, THE.
LP: .... ST 1006

COLLECTION: STAN KENTON (20 golden greats).
Tracks: / Artistry in rhythm / Tempo de Joe / Love turns winter to spring / Shuffling the chords / Marvin's mumble / Flamingo / Harlem folk dance / Trumpet symphonette / Arkansas traveller / Little jive is good for you, A / Underneath the stars / Take sixteen / Safari / Blue flare / Congo clambake / Artistry in boogie / There is no greater love / Salute / Dynaflow / Be easy, be tender.
LP: .... DVLP 2087
MC: .... DVMC 2087

COLLECTOR'S CHOICE.
LP: .... ST 1027

CONCEPT ERA '56',THE.
LP: .... AR 103

CONCEPT ERA VOL.2.
LP: .... AR 106

CONCERT ENCORES.
LP: .... FH 40
MC: .... CFH 40

CONCERT ENCORES/ THE SOUND OF 62.
MC: .... CTP 41

CONCERT IN PROGRESSIVE JAZZ, A.
Tracks: / Lonely woman / Come rain or come shine / Cuban carnival / Monotony lament / Theme for Alto / Impressionism / Elegy for alto / This is my theme / Fugue for rhythm section / Introduction to a latin rhythm / Thermopolae.
LP: .... ST 1037

CONTEMPORARY CONCEPTS.
Tracks: / What's new / I've got you under my skin / Cherokee / Stompin' at the Savoy / Limelight.
LP: .... ST 1003

CUBAN FIRE, 1956.
LP: .... ST 1008

DEFINITIVE KENTON,THE.
2LP: .... AR 2 102

ENCORES.
Tracks: / He's funny that way / Please be kind / Painted rhythm / Peg o' my heart / Ecuador / Capitol punishment / Lover / Chorale for brass / Piano and bongo / Abstraction / Journey to Brazil / Somnambulism.
LP: .... ST 1034

EUROPE '53 PART 1'.
Tracks: / Young blood (Theme tune) / Collaboration / Love for sale / Walking shoes / Opus in pastels / Zoot / Twenty three degrees north - eighty two degrees west / Solitaire / Intermission riff / Lover man / In a lighter vein.
MC: .... CFH 49
LP: .... FH 49

EUROPE '53 PART 1 & 2.
MC: .... UNKNOWN

EUROPE '53 PART 2'.
Tracks: / Portrait of a Count / Round Robin / Eager beaver / Frank speaking / Taboo / Taking a chance on love / I'll remember April / Great Scot / My heart belongs to only you / How high the moon / Something cool / Concerto to end all concerto's.
LP: .... FH 50
MC: .... CFH 50

EXCITING STAN KENTON (Kenton, Stan Orchestra & The Four Freshmen).
LP: .... ST 1080

FABULOUS ALUMNI OF STAN KENTON, THE.
Tracks: / I want a grown-up man / Easy Street / Adios / I get a kick out of you / Thrill, The / Cellology.
LP: .... ST 1028

FIRE, FURY AND FUN (Kenton, Stan Orchestra & The Four Freshmen).
LP: .... ST 1073
MC: .... STC 1073

HITS IN CONCERT (Kenton, Stan Orchestra & The Four Freshmen).
LP: .... ST 1074
MC: .... STC 1074

HOLLYWOOD BOWL, PART 1 (Kenton, Stan & June Christy).
LP: .... FH 52

HOLLYWOOD PALLADIUM CONCERTS 1944, THE.
Tracks: / Theme & I know that you know / Gotta be getting / Eager beaver / Wish you're waiting / Poor butterfly / Artistry in rhythm / Begin the beguine / Tico tico / Tabby the cat / Man I love, The / Taboo / In a little Spanish town / Sargeant's mess / And her tears flowed like wine / Russian lullaby.
LP: .... SJP 054

INNOVATIONS IN MODERN MUSIC, 1950.
Tracks: / Trajectories / Theme for Sunday / Conflict / Incident in jazz / Lonesome road / Mirage / Solitaire / Cuban episode.
LP: .... ST 1009

JAZZ COMPOSITIONS OF STAN KENTON (Kenton, Stan Orchestra & The Four Freshmen).
LP: .... ST 1078

JAZZ OFF THE AIR, VOL.2 (Kenton All Stars).
Tracks: / Perdido / Great lie, The / Stealin' apples / WMGM jump / Cherokee.
LP: .... SPJ 145

JOURNEY INTO CAPRICORN.
LP: .... JAS 205
LP: .... ST 1077

KENTON '76.
Tracks: / Time for a change / Send in the clowns / Tiburon / My funny valentine / Decoupage / Smith named Greg, A / Samba de haps.
LP: .... JAS 204
LP: .... ST 1076
MC: .... STC 1076

KENTON AT THE TROPICANA.
Tracks: / Artistry in rhythm / Bernie's tune / Tuxedo Junction / Street scene / Puck's blues / I concentrate on you / End of a love affair, The / You and I and George / Sentimental riff / Random riff.
LP: .... ST 1032

KENTON CONDUCTS THE JAZZ COMPOSTION OF DEE BARTON.
Tracks: / Man / Lonely boy / Singing oyster, The / Dilemma / Three thoughts / New day, A / Woman.
LP: .... ST 1022

KENTON ERA, THE (Reissued collectors set).
Tracks: / Prologue (side 1) (Spoken introduction by Stan, tracing development of his music to 1955.) / Balboa bandwagon (side 2) (The original band, at the Rendezvous Ballroom, Balboa, California, 1941.) / Growing pains (side 3) (The band develops its unique sound, 1944.) / Artistry in rhythm (From the Capitol Library, 1945/6.) / Progressive jazz (side 5) (The swinging big band of 1947/8.) / Innovations (side 6) (The Kenton Band augmented by strings and horns.) / Contemporary (Music band playing in 1952/53.) /

Epilogue (side 8) (Spoken summation of the album by Stan, plus closing theme.).
LPS: . . . . **STD 1030**

KENTON FAVOURITES.
MC: **4XL 9094**

KENTON IN CONCERT.
2LP: . . . . **AR 2 100**

KENTON IN STEREO.
Tracks: / Painted rhythm / Artistry in boogie / Minor riff / Collaboration / Intermission riff / Peanut vendor / Unison riff / Eager beaver / Lover / Artistry jumps / Concerto to end all concertos / Interlude.
LP: . . . . **ST 1004**

KENTON PRESENTS, 1950.
LP: . . . . **ST 1023**

KENTON SHOWCASE, 1953-4.
Tracks: / Bags / Hav-a-hava-na / Solo for Buddy / Opener, The / Fearless Finlay / Theme & variations / In a lighter vein / King fish / Theme of four values, A / Study for bass, A / Blues before and after / Bacante / This be / Egdon heath / Sweets / Dusk.
LP: . . . . **ST 1026**

KENTON TOUCH, 1958.
Tracks: / Lush interlude / Salute / Monotony / Elegy for alto / Theme for Sunday / Ballads for drums / Minor riff / End of the world / Opus in chartreuse / Painted rhythm / Rose for David, A.
LP: . . . . **ST 1033**

KENTON'S CHRISTMAS.
Tracks: / O come all ye faithful / Christmas medley / O Tannenbaum / Holly and the ivy, The / We three kings of Orient are / Good King Wenceslas / Twelve days of Christmas, The / Once in Royal David's city / God rest ye merry gentlemen / Angels we have heard on high / Heard on high / O holy night.
LP: . . . . **ST 1001**

KENTON/WAGNER, 1964.
Tracks: / Ride of the Valkyries / Siegfried's funeral march / Prelude to Act 1 of Lohengrin / Prelude to Act 3 of Lohengrin / Prelude to Tristan and Isolde / Wedding march from Lohengrin / Pilgrims / Chorus from Tann Haeuser.
LP: . . . . **ST 1024**

LIGHTER SIDE, THE.
Tracks: / And her tears flowed like wine / His feet too big for de bed / Down in Chihuahua / Spider and the fly, The / Tortillas and beans / Stardust boogie / And the bull walked around / Ole / A-ting-a-ling.
LP: . . . . **ST 1050**

LIVE AT BILOXY VOL. 2.
LP: . . . . **ATOM 5**
MC: . . . . **CATOM 5**

LIVE AT BRIGHAM YOUNG UNIVERSITY.
Tracks: / Malaga / Rhapsody in blue / Love story / Kaleidoscope / April fool / Step beyond, A / Hank's opener / Bogota / What are you doing the rest of your life? / Macumba suite.
LP: . . . . **ST 1039**

LIVE AT BUTLER UNIVERSITY (Kenton, Stan Orchestra & The Four Freshmen).
2LP: . . . . **STD 1058**

LIVE AT REDLANDS UNIVERSITY.
Tracks: / Here's that rainy day / MacArthur Park / Minor booze / Didn't we? / Terry talk / Tico tico / Granada / Chia-pas / More peanut vendor / Artistry in rhythm / Bon homme Richard / Tiare / Hey Jude.
2LP: . . . . **STD 1015**

LIVE AT REDLANDS UNIVERSITY (JASMINE) (Kenton, Stan & His Orchestra).
LP: . . . . **JAS 202**

LIVE AT THE RED HILL INN PENNSAUKEN (1959).
Tracks: / Take me in your arms / That old black magic / I've got a right to sing the blues / Gone with the wind / I'm glad there is you / Reubens blues / My one and only love / Time after time.
MC: . . . . **CAWE 43**

LIVE CONCERT (Kenton, Stan & His Orchestra).
LP: . . . . **FS 294**

LIVE: STAN KENTON.
LP: . . . . **QU 054**

LUSH INTERLUDE, 1958.
Tracks: / Interlude / Collaboration / Opus in pastels / Theme for my lady, A / Artistry in bolero / Concerto to end all concertos (concerti, surely!) / Machito / Theme to the west / Lush waltz / Artistry in rhythm.
LP: . . . . **ST 1005**

NATIONAL ANTHEMS OF THE WORLD (Kenton, Stan Orchestra & The Four Freshmen).
2LP: . . . . **STD 1060**

NEW CONCEPTS OF ARTISTRY IN RHYTHM (Kenton, Stan & His Orchestra).
Tracks: / Twenty three degrees north - eighty two degrees west / Portrait of a count / Invention for a guitar and trumpet / My lady / Young blood / Frank speaking / Prologue (this is an orchestra) / Improvision / Taboo (CD only.) / Lonesome train (CD only.) / Swing house (CD only.) / You go to my head (CD only.).
LP: . . . . **EG 2606031**
MC: . . . . **EG 2606034**
LP: . . . . **ST 1002**

ON THE ROAD (Kenton, Stan & His Orchestra).
LP: . . . . **AR 101**

ONE NIGHT STAND WITH STAN KENTON.
LP: . . . . **JOYCE 1120**

PAINTED RHYTHM.
Tracks: / Artistry in rhythm / Artistry Jumps / We'll Be Together / I don't want to be loved / Body and Soul / Painted Rhythm / Just sittin' & rockin' / It's Only A Paper Moon / Eager Beaver / That's the stuff gotta watch / Southern Scandal / I never thought I'd sing the blues.
LP: . . . . **GOJ 1007**
MC: . . . . **GOJC 1007**

PORTRAITS ON STANDARDS, 1951-3.
Tracks: / Street of dreams / You and the night and the music / Reverie / I've got you under my skin / Autumn in New York / Lady in red, The / April in Paris / How high the moon? / Crazy rhythm / I got it bad and that ain't good / Baia / Under a blanket of blue.
LP: . . . . **ST 1042**

PROGRESSIVE JAZZ.
LP: . . . . **SWH 18**
MC: . . . . **CSWH 18**

PROGRESSIVE JAZZ/ HOLLYWOOD BOWL.
MC: . . . . **CTP 40**

RENDEZVOUS WITH KENTON.
Tracks: / With the wind and the rain in your hair / Memories of you / These things you left me / Two shades of Autumn / They didn't believe me / Walkin' by the river / High on a windy hill / Love letters / I get along without you very well / Desiderata / This is no laughing matter / I see your face before me.
LP: . . . . **PM 1547801**
MC: . . . . **PM 154 7804**
LP: . . . . **ST 1057**

RETURN TO BILOXY (Kenton, Stan & His Orchestra).
Tracks: / Theme and variations / Opus in Chatreuse / I've never been in love before / Harlem nocturne / Ad lib blues / Tenderly / Peanut vendor, The / Don't take your love / Intermission riff / When I fall in love / Younger that springtime / Day by day / Don't get around much any more / They didn't believe me / High on a windy hill / When your lover has gone / That old feeling / On the street where you live / Stompin' at the Savoy.
LP: . . . . **AWE 35**
MC: . . . . **CAWE 35**

ROAD SHOW I & II.
2LP: . . . . **STD 1019/20**

ROAD SHOW, THE (VOL.1).
Tracks: / Artistry in rhythm / Big chase / I want to be happy / It's a most unusual day / Midnight sun.
LP: . . . . **ST 1019**

ROAD SHOW, THE (VOL.2).
Tracks: / Love for sale / Stompin at the Savoy / My old flame / Artistry in rhythm / Kissing bug / Bewitched / How high the moon / Paper doll / Them there eyes / September song / Walking shoes.
LP: . . . . **ST 1020**

ROMANTIC APPROACH, THE.
Tracks: / Your lover has gone / All the things you are / I'm glad there is you / Say it isn't so / Imagination / Sweet and lovely / Fools rush in / You're mine / You / Once in a while / Moonlight in Vermont / I understood / Oh / You crazy moon.
LP: . . . . **ST 1017**

SKETCHES ON STANDARDS, 1953-4.
Tracks: / Sophisticated lady / Begin the beguine / Lover man / Pennies from Heaven / Dark eyes / Don't take your love from me / Over the rainbow / Fascinating rhythm / There's a small hotel / Shadow waltz / More love than your love / Malaguena.
LP: . . . . **ST 1041**

SOLO.
LP: . . . . **ST 1071**

SOME WOMEN I'VE KNOWN, 1944-5.
Tracks: / Are you livin' old man? / Travellin' man / Soothe me / Four months / Three weeks / Two days / One hour blues / All about Ronnie / Jeepers creepers / All because of you / Softly / Black coffee / Don't worry 'bout me / Give me a song with a beautiful melody / Warm blue stream.
LP: . . . . **ST 1029**

SOPHISTICATED APPROACH.
Tracks: / But beautiful / Darn that dream / It might as well be spring / Moonlight becomes you / How do I look in blue / You stepped out of a dream / How long has this been going on / Memories of lady / Time after time / Easy to love / My one and only love / Like someone in love.
LP: . . . . **ST 1018**

SOUND OF 62.
Tracks: / My one and only love / Malaguena / Quizas quizas quizas / Mission train / Come on back / Twist number one / Between the Devil and the deep blue sea.
LP: . . . . **FH 46**

STAGE DOOR SWINGS (Kenton, Stan & His Orchestra).
Tracks: / Lullaby of Broadway (From 'Gold diggers of 1935'.) / Party's over, The (From 'The bells are ringing') / Baubles, bangles and beads (From 'Kismet') / Every time we say goodbye (From 'Seven lively Arts') / Whatever Lola wants (Lola gets) (From 'Damn Yankees') / Bali Ha'i (From 'South Pacific') / Hey there (From 'Pajama Game') / Younger than Springtime (From 'South Pacific') / On the street where you live (From 'My Fair Lady') / I love Paris (From 'Can-Can') / All at once you love her (From 'Pipe Dream') / I've never been in love before (From 'Guys And Dolls').
LP: . . . . **EMS 1159**
MC: . . . . **TCEMS 1159**

STAGE DOOR SWINGS, 1958.
Tracks: / Younger than Springtime / Party's over, The / On the street where you live / I love Paris / Lullaby of Broadway / Baubles, bangles and beads / Every time we say goodbye / Whatever Lola wants (Lola gets) / Bali Ha'i / Hey there / I've never been in love before / All at once you love her.
LP: . . . . **ST 1044**

STAN KENTON.
LP: . . . . **EJLP 05**
MC: . . . . **EJMC 05**

STAN KENTON.
LP: . . . . **BO 705**

STAN KENTON AND HIS ORCHESTRA, VOL. 5 1945-47 (Kenton, Stan & His Orchestra).
Tracks: / Artistry in rhythm (opening theme) / Begin the beguine / Yesterdays / On the sunny side of the street / I surrender dear / Fatal apple / Solitude / No baby, nobody but you / Loverman / Two moose in a caboose / Easy street / Scotch and water / End of the world / Artistry in rhythm (closing theme).
LP: . . . . **HSR 157**

STAN KENTON AND ORCHESTRA LIVE IN BILOXI (Kenton, Stan Orchestra & The Four Freshmen).
Tracks: / Lasuerte de los tontos / I concentrate on you / Lullaby of Broadway, The / Nearness of you, The / Kingfish / Early Autumn / Love for sale / My old flame / Yesterdays / Out of nowhere / Night we called it a day, The / Everything happens to me / There will never be another you / So in love / With the wind and the rain in your hair / Big chase.
LP: . . . . **AWE 32**
MC: . . . . **CAWE 32**

STAN KENTON CONDUCTS DEE BARTON.
Tracks: / Man / Lonely boy / Singing oyster, The / Dilemma / Three thoughts / New day, A / Woman.
LP: . . . . **ST 1021**

STAN KENTON CONDUCTS THE LOS ANGELES.
LP: . . . . **ST 1013**

STAN KENTON IN HI FI.
Tracks: / Artistry jumps / Interlude / Intermission riff / Minor riff / Collaboration / Painted rhythm / Southern scandal / Peanut vendor / Eager Beaver / Concerto to end all concertos / Artistry in boogie / lover / Unison riff.
LP: . . . . **EMS 1149**
MC: . . . . **TCEMS 1149**

STAN KENTON LIVE IN PARIS, 1953.
LP: . . . . **RJ 504**

STAN KENTON & ORCHESTRA 1941 (Kenton, Stan & His Orchestra).
Tracks: / Opening theme / Tempo de Joe / Night life / Marvin's mumble / I haven't got the heart / Elegy / Love turns winter to spring / El choclo / Safari / Trumpet symphonette / Little jive is good for you, A / Prelude to nothing / Old black Joe / Flamingo / Take it from the oven / Balboa bash / Closing theme.
LP: . . . . **HSR 118**

STAN KENTON PLAYS CHICAGO (Kenton, Stan Orchestra & The Four Freshmen).
LP: . . . . **ST 1072**

STAN KENTON, VOL. 2, 1941.
Tracks: / Quit your shovin' / Underneath the stars / Let her go / Hold back the dawn / Low bridge / Blue flare / Congo clambake / Arkansas traveller / Shuffling the chords / Suite for saxophones.
LP: . . . . **HSR 124**

STAN KENTON, VOL 2 (1953-60).
Tracks: / Creep, The / Lover man / Alone too long / Suddenly / Skoot / Opus in chartreuse / Spring is here / Opus in turquoise / Sophisticated samba / Lemon twist / Lazy afternoon / Carnival.
LP: . . . . **ST 1040**

STAN KENTON, VOL. 4, 1944-45.
Tracks: / Man I love, The / Blues / Tico tico / Tabby the cat / Sargeant's mess / Elegie / Pizzicato / Conversin' with the brain / Blow Jack / Are you livin' old man? / Baby won't you please come home / Fine fine deal / Blue skies / Got a penny, Jenny / Poor butterfly / St. Louis blues.
LP: . . . . **HSR 147**

STAN KENTON/JEAN TURNER, 1963 (Kenton, Stan & Jean Turner).
Tracks: / Lot of livin' to do, A / Oh you crazy moon / Sleepy lagoon / Love is here to stay / Piel canela / It's a big wide wonderful world / Someone to watch over me / Love walked in / Daydreams / Quizas quizas quizas / You're the top.
LP: . . . . **ST 1046**

STAN KENTON'S GREATEST HITS.
Tracks: / Artistry in rhythm / Tampico / Interlude / Eager beaver / September song / Unison riff / Lover / Painted rhythm / And her tears flowed like wine / Laura / Peanut vendor.
LP: . . . . **MFP 5607**
MC: . . . . **TCMFP 5607**

STANDARDS IN SILHOUETTE, 1959.
Tracks: / Meaning of the blues / I get along without you very well / Willow weep for me / When Sunny gets blue / Lonely woman / Django / Thrill is gone, The / Ill wind.
LP: . . . . **ST 1049**

STREET OF DREAMS (Kenton, Stan Orchestra & The Four Freshmen).
LP: . . . . **ST 1079**
MC: . . . . **STC 1079**

TOGETHER AGAIN (Kenton, Stan & June Christy).
Tracks: / It could happen to you / Carioca / Let there be love / Opus in chartreuse / Willow weep for me / One hundred years from today.
LP: . . . . **FH 42**
MC: . . . . **CFH 42**

UNCOLLECTED STAN KENTON & HIS ORCHESTRA, VOL 3 (1943-44) (Kenton, Stan & His Orchestra).
Tracks: / Ol' man river / Shoo shoo baby / Eager beaver / Liza / In a little Spanish town / Paper doll / Hit that jive, Jack / Goon came on, The / Begin the beguine / None but the lonely / I know that you know / Salt Lake City blues / Hour of parting / Russian lullaby / Lady in red, The / I got rhythm.
LP: . . . . **HSR 136**

UNCOLLECTED, THE.
LP: . . . . **HUK 195**

VIVA KENTON (Kenton, Stan Orchestra & The Four Freshmen).
LP: . . . . **ST 1063**

WEST SIDE STORY (Kenton, Stan & His Orchestra).
Tracks: / Prologue / Something's coming / Maria / America / Tonight / Cool / Gee officer Krupke / Taunting scene / Somewhere / Finale.
LP: . . . . **ST 1007**

WEST SIDE STORY (Kenton, Stan & His Orchestra).
Tracks: / Prologue / Something's coming / Maria / America / Tonight / Cool / I feel pretty / Gee officer Krupke / Taunting scene / Somewhere (finale).
LP: . . . . **EMS 1285**
MC: . . . . **TCEMS 1285**

Kentucky Colonels

1966: KENTUCKY COLONELS.
LP: . . . . **SHILOH 4084**

FEATURING CLARENCE WHITE.
LP: . . . . **ROUNDER 0098**

MC: . . . . ROUNDER 0098C

NEW SOUND OF BLUEGRASS AMERICA, THE.
LP: . . . . BRIAR M109

ON STAGE.
Tracks: / John Hardy / Used to be / Shackles and chains / Durham's bull / Mountain dew / I might take you back again / Bluegrass breakdown / Flop eared mule / I wonder how the old folks at home / Over in the gloryland / Reno ride / Ocean of diamonds / Bending the strings.
LP: . . . . ROUNDER 0199
LP: . . . . SDLP 050
MC: . . . . ROUNDER 0199C

Kentucky County

BACK HOME AGAIN.
LP: . . . . BUFF L-2004

Kentucky Headhunters

ELECTRIC BARNYARDS.
LP: 8480541
MC: 8480544

PICKIN' ON NASHVILLE.
Tracks: / Walk softly on this heart of mine / Rag top / Smooth / Oh lonesome me / Dumas walker / Rock'n'roll angel / Skip a rope / My daddy was a milkman.
LP: 838 744 1
MC: 838 744 4

Kenworthy Scofield

PIPE AND TABAR (Morris & Sword dances).
MC: 30-325

Kenya

KENYA DRY - TOWN AND COUNTRY GUITAR (1950-65) (Various artists).
LP: . . . . OMA 110

MWANA WAMBELE (Various artists).
MC: . . . . ORC 002

ROOTS, AFRICAN DRUMS (Kenya: National Dancing Team).
LP: . . . . GX 7027

TRADITIONAL MUSIC (Various artists).
MC: D58004

Kenya Partout

KENYA PARTOUT, VOL.1 (Various artists).
LP: . . . . SP 2035

KENYA PARTOUT, VOL.2 (Various artists).
LP: . . . . SP 2085

KENYA PARTOUT, VOL.3 (Various artists).
LP: . . . . SP 2088

KENYA PARTOUT, VOL.4 (Various artists).
LP: . . . . SP 2091

KENYA PARTOUT, VOL.5 (Various artists).
LP: . . . . SP 2094

Kenyatta

KENYATTA.
MC: . . . . BRCA 568
LP: . . . . BRLP 568

Kenyatta, Robert

BEGGARS AND STEALERS.
LP: . . . . MR 5095

Këo

BURNING NEED.
Tracks: / Wait (I'm coming) / I've lost you / Burning need / Don't cry / Chained down again / She's gone / Stone cold / I am not alone / Keep it close / I've been waiting.
MC: . . . . KEOTC 1

Keogh, May

BUNTAS RINCE (Keogh, May & Tommy Delaney).
LP: . . . . CEF 017

RINCE AN 3U CEIM (Keogh, May & Tommy Delaney).
LP: . . . . CEF 025

RINCE AN DARA CEIM (Keogh, May & Tommy Delaney).
LP: . . . . CEF 020

Keogh, Paul

FROM THE GUITAR MAN WITH LOVE.
Tracks: / While my guitar gently weeps / Every breath you take / Guitar man / If / Boxer, The.
LP: . . . . NML 1004
MC: . . . . ZCNML 1004

Keppard, Freddie

FREDDIE KEPPARD (Keppard, Freddie/Doc Cook/Erskine Tate).
LP: . . . . JT 1002

Kern, Jerome

ALL THE THINGS YOU ARE (Various artists).
Tracks: / All the things you are: *Various artists* / In other words, seventeen: *Various artists* / All in fun: *Various artists* / That lucky fellow: *Various artists* / Heaven in my arms: *Various artists* / In the heart of the dark: *Various artists* / Your dream: *Various artists* / You were never lovelier: *Various artists*/ I'm old fashioned: *Various artists* / Dearly beloved: *Various artists* / More and more: *Various artists*/ Cover girl: *Various artists* / Long ago: *Various artists* / Sure thing: *Various artists*.
LP: . . . . MES 6808

GOLDEN AGE OF JEROME KERN, THE (Various artists).
Tracks: / Do I do wrong: *Various artists* / Blue eyes: *Various artists* / Back to the heather: *Various artists*/ Women: *Various artists* / She didn't say yes: *Various artists* / Try to forget: *Various artists* / New love is old, A: *Various artists* / Night was made for love, The: *Various artists* / I've told every little star: *Various artists* / I'm alone: *Various artists* / Song is you, The: *Various artists* / Keep smiling: *Various artists* / Hand in hand: *Various artists* / Wild rose, The: *Various artists* / Whip-poor-will: *Various artists* / Look for the silver lining: *Various artists*.
LP: . . . . GX 41 2531 1
MC: . . . . GX 41 2531 4

JEROME KERN CENTENARY (Various artists).
Tracks: / Ol' man river: *Various artists* / Can't help lovin' dat man: *Various artists* / She didn't say 'yes': *Various artists* / Song is you, The: *Various artists* / I've told every little star: *Various artists*/ Smoke gets in your eyes: *Various artists* / Lovely to look at: *Various artists* / Why was I born: *Various* artists / Pick yourself up: *Various artists* / Way you look tonight: *Various artists* / Fine romance, A: *Various* artists / Can I forget you: *Various artists* / Folks who live on the hill, The: *Various artists* / You couldn't be cuter: *Various artists* / All the things you are: *Various artists* / Last time I saw Paris, The: *Various* artists / Dearly beloved: *Various artists* / I'm old fashioned: *Various artists* / Long ago (and far away): *Various artists* / All through the day: *Various artists*.
LP: . . . . EG 2604411
MC: . . . . EG 2604414

JEROME KERN & SILVER LINING (Various artists).
LP: . . . . ABQ 6515
MC: . . . . ABQC 6515

OVERTURES AND MUSIC FROM SWING TIME (National Philharmonic Orchestra).
Tracks: / Cat and the fiddle, The / Girl from Utah, The / Leave it to Jane / Have a heart / Sweet Adeline / O lady lady / Sitting pretty / Very warm for May / Swing time (main title) / Way you look tonight.
LP: . . . . EL 749 630 1
MC: . . . . EL 749 630 4

SONG IS...JEROME KERN, THE (Various artists).
Tracks: / Song is you, The: *BBC Dance Orchestra* / Let's begin: *Coleman, Emil & His Riviera Orchestra* / Can't help lovin' dat man: *Morgan, Helen* / Hand in hand: *Stone, Lew & His Band* / She didn't say yes: *Ambrose &* His Orchestra / I'll be hard to handle: *Coleman, Emil & His Riviera Orchestra* / I've told every little star: *Ellis, Mary* / Smoke gets in your eyes: *Whiteman, Paul & His Orchestra* / Make believe: *Whiteman, Paul/his orchestra/Bing* Crosby / Who?: *Hopkins, Claude & His Orchestra* / Sunny: *Ipana Troubadors* / Bill: *Morgan, Helen*/ Something had to happen: *Whiteman, Paul & His Orchestra* / Look for the silver lining: *Miller, Marilyn & Lawrence Gray* / They didn't believe me: *Ambrose & His Orchestra* / Ol' man river: *Robeson, Paul*.
LP: . . . . AJA 5036
MC: . . . . ZC AJA 5036

Kerr, Anita

ANITA KERR.
MC: . . . . ZCJC 836

Kerr, Bob Whoopee Band

BLUES JAZZ BOOGIE & RAGS.
Tracks: / Pinetop's boogie woogie / Blueberry Hill / Pep / Someday you'll be sorry / Maple leaf rag / Good morning blues / Kitchen man / Blue Monday / Deadman blues / Crying for the Carolines / Cascades / Bi bist du shon.
LP: . . . . WP 101

BOOTLEGGING LIVE.
Tracks: / Home in Pasedena / Cocktails for two / Your driving me crazy / Chloe / Overture to Carmen / Sweet Georgia Brown / Doctor Jazz / That certain party / I love my Chilli bon bon / Maple leaf rag / My pet / My blue Heaven.
MC: . . . . WB 111

HARD PRESSED.
Tracks: / Down of Jollity farm / I've got a feeling I'm falling / 5,000 year old rock (take 2) / Sheik of Araby, The / Nightingale sang in Berkeley Square, A / Blue room / Tap dance man / Mean to me / My sweetie went away / Little boy blue / Overture to Carmen.
LP: . . . . WP 104

MUSICAL MAYHEM.
Tracks: / You always hurt the one you love / Spread a little happiness / Jollity farm / My sweetie went away / Riley's cowshed / Hard hearted Hannah / Whispering / I love my Chilli bon bon / Sweet Goergia Brown / Room with a view / That certain party / My blue Heaven / Sunday.
MC: . . . . WB 112

THINGS THAT GO BUMP IN THE NIGHT.
Tracks: / Your nobodies sweetheart now / Ukelele lady / Riley's cowshed / My girl's pussy / Pleasant pluckin' / Cuckoo waltz / Running wild / Remember remember / Ain't she sweet / Storytime / Shine / Overture to Carmen / Tiger rag.
LP: . . . . WP 108

WHOOPEE BAND, THE.
Tracks: / Crazy / Honey pie / Whispering / Victoria and Albert / Moonbeam waltz / I want a girl / Doctor Jazz / When I think of you / Ain't she sweet / Button up your overcoat / Lady Madonna.
LP: . . . . WP 102

Kerr, George

LOVE LOVE LOVE.
LP: . . . . HB 3000

Kerr, John

GREEN HILLS OF IRELAND, THE.
LP: . . . . ZCMA 1324

JOHN KERRS ISLAND.
LP: . . . . HPE 641

MEMORIES OF IRELAND.
Tracks: / Village where I went to school / Cashelmore / Four country roads / Rathlin Island / Destination Donegal / Old rustic bridge / Rose of castlerea / Asthoreen Bawn / Toast of an Irish colleen / Fields of Athenry / Galway shawl / Misty rollin' midlands.
LP: . . . . PHL 476
MC: . . . . CPHL 476

MY 14 IRISH REQUESTS.
Tracks: / Old cross of Arboe / Home town on the Foyle / Typical Irishman.
LP: . . . . HRL 149
MC: . . . . CHRL 149

MY GREEN VALLEYS.
Tracks: / Donegal Danny / Barney Brannigan / Long before your time / Foggy old London / Tonight I'm sighing for Killarney and you / Handful of earth / Old Dungannon road / My green valleys / Hills of Glenswilly / Slievenamon / My days in old Donegal / Dark island.
MC: . . . . CHRL 164
LP: . . . . HRL 164

OLD BOG ROAD.
MC: . . . . ARANC 009

THREE LEAFED SHAMROCK.
Tracks: / Someone thinks of you tonight / Tree leaves of emerald green / Mulroy bay / Cork hornpipe / Boys from Blue Hill / Mick McGilligan's daughter / Road to Creeslough / Father O'Flynn / Three leaf shamrock / Golden jubilee / Farewell Donegal / Goodbye Mick, goodbye Pat / Moon behind the hill.
MC: . . . . ZCGL 60401
MC: . . . . CHRL 190
LP: . . . . HRL 190

WHEN I HEAR THE GREEN FIELDS CALLING.
Tracks: / When I hear the green fields calling / Flight of the earls / Wedding day song / Country I'm leaving behind / My own native land / Far away a light is burning / As years roll by / Isle of Innisfree / Green fields of Ireland / Pat Murphy's meadow / Ballywhoriskey Bay / True love never dies.
LP: . . . . UNILP 5007
MC: . . . . UNICS 5007
MC: . . . . UNIMC 5007

Kerr, Madeleine (aut)

VIRTUOUS LADY (see under Virtuous Lady) (Boyd, Carole (nar)).

Kerr, Moira

BEST OF BOTH WORLDS.
LP: . . . . WGR 014
MC: . . . . CWGR 014

MACAIN OF GLENCOE.
Tracks: / Maclain of Glencoe / Dark Island / Charles Edward Stuart / Skye boat song, The / Island of Tiree, The / Always Argyll / I once loved a lad / Ca' the ewes / Mingulay boat song, The / Farewell to Tarwathie / Loch Lomond / Sense of belonging, A.
LP: . . . . REN 734
MC: . . . . ZCN 734

Kerr, Richard

NO LOOKING BACK.
Tracks: / Free / You made it beautiful / Somewhere in the night / Dance away.
LP: . . . . AMLH 68539

WELCOME TO THE CLUB.
Tracks: / I can't afford that feeling anymore / Live my love for you / Dance your life away / I know I'll never love this way again / Magic in the air / I feel it all / Hat full of rain / This is your Captain calling / Baby, don't let go / Welcome to the club.
LP: . . . . EPC 83306

Kerr, Sandra

WE WERE THERE.
LP: . . . . YOP 8

Kerry Fiddles

MUSIC FROM SLIABAH LUCHRA VOL 1.
LP: 12TS 309

Kershaw, Doug

HOT DIGGITY DOUG.
Tracks: / Cajun baby / Louisiana / Jambalaya / I wanna hold you / Calling Baton Rouge / My toot toot / Boogie queen / Just like you / Louisiana man / Mansion in Spain / Cajun stripper / Fiddlin' man.
LP: . . . . SDLP 066

MY TOOT TOOT (See under Domino, Fats) (Kershaw, Doug & Fats Domino).

Kershaw, Liz

IT TAKES TWO (See under Brookes, Bruno) (Kershaw, Liz & Bruno Brookes).

Kershaw, Martin

SOLITUDE.
Tracks: / Golden eagle, The / Solitude / Intrigue / Falcon, The / Try not to cry / 10 minutes late / Swan, The / Dance of magpies / Summer haze / Breathless / Growing up / White horses / End of term / Neck and neck / Where have you been / Enchanted river, The / Wren, The / Falling leaves.
LP: . . . . SGLP 113
MC: . . . . SGLC 113

Kershaw, Mary

LANCASHIRE SINGS AGAIN (Kershaw, Mary & Harvey).
Tracks: / Yo're allus welcome here / Gradely folk / Song of the knocker-up, The / Fireleet fancies / Pegh fox / Boggart o' Birchenbower, The / One for the road / Parson o' Waterhead, Th' / Whiff o' moorlond air, A / Love's labour lost / Friendship club, Th' / Other folks' children / Harkenin' t' Messiah / Toddlin' whoam.
LP: 12TS 302

Kershaw, Nik

HUMAN RACING.
Tracks: / Dancing girls / Wouldn't it be good / Drum talk / Bogart / Gone to pieces / Shame on you / Cloak and dagger / Faces / I won't let the sun go down on me / Human racing.
LP: . . . . MCF 3197
MC: . . . . MCFC 3197

RADIO MUSICOLA.
LP: . . . . MCG 6016
MC: . . . . MCGC 6016

RIDDLE, THE.
Tracks: / You might / Wild horses / Easy / Riddle,The / City of angels / Roses / Wide boy / Save the whale.
LP: . . . . MCF 3245
MC: . . . . MCFC 3245

WORKS, THE.
Tracks: / Wounded knee / One step ahead / Cowboys and indians / Walk about / Elizabeth's eyes / Take my place / Lady on the phone.
LP: . . . . MCG 3438
MC: . . . . MCFC 3438

Kershaw, Rusty

CAJUN COUNTRY ROCKERS 3 (Kershaw, Rusty & Doug).
Tracks: / Sweet sweet girl / Cheated too / Cajun Joe / So lovely baby / Diggy liggy lo / Louisiana man / Mey Mae / Sweet thing tell me that you love me / It's too late / Hey sherriff / Why don't you love me.
LP: . . . . BFX 15036

JAY MILLER SESSIONS VOL. 22 (Kershaw, Rusty & Doug).
LP: . . . . FLY 571

LOUISIANA MAN (Kershaw, Rusty & Doug).
Tracks: / Louisiana man / Diggy liggy lo / Cheated too / Cajun Joe / We'll do it anyway / Jole blon / So lovely baby /

Look around / Mister love / Going down the road / Never love again / Kaw-liga.
LP: . . . . SDLP 022

MORE CAJUN COUNTRY ROCK (Kershaw, Rusty & Doug).
Tracks: / Look around (take a look at me) / Can I be dreaming / Your crazy crazy heart / I'm gonna gonna gonna see my baby (Previously unissued.) / Mister love / Hey, you there / Money / You'll see / I never had the blues / Love me to pieces / Kaw-liga / Never love again / (Our own) Jole Blon / Make me realize / I'll understand / We'll do it anyway.
LP: . . . . BFX 15143

RUSTY, DOUG, WILEY & FRIENDS (Kershaw, Rusty & Doug/Wiley Barkdull).
LP: . . . . FLY 619

Kes (bk)

KES Hines, Barry (Welland, Colin).
MC: . . . . TC LFP 7060

Kessel, Barney

AUTUMN LEAVES.
LP: . . . . BLP 60112

BLUE SOUL.
Tracks: / Shuffling / Frank Mills / On a clear day / Watch what happens / Quail bait / Blue soul / Stumblin' around / Comin' home.
LP: . . . . BLP 30161

CONTEMPORARY LEADERS (see Rollins,Sonny) (Kessel, Barney, Sonny Rollins).

EXPLORING THE SCENE (Kessel, Barney/Ray Brown/Shelly Manne).
Tracks: / Little Susie / Duke, The / So what? / Misty / Doodlin' / Golden striker, The / Li'l darlin' / Blessing, The / This here.
LP: 1007 581

GREAT GUITARS AT CHARLIE'S, GEORGETOWN (Kessel, Barney/ Charlie Byrd/ Herb Ellis).
Tracks: / Where or when / New Orleans / When the saints go marching in / Change partners / Opus one / Old folks / Get happy / Trouble in mind.
LP: . . . . CJ 209
MC: . . . . CJC 209

GREAT GUITARS AT THE WINERY (Kessel, Barney/ Charlie Byrd/ Herb Ellis).
LP: . . . . CJ 131

I REMEMBER DJANGO (see Grappelli, Stephane) (Kessel, Barney & Stephane Grappelli).

IN CONCERT.
LP: 26011
MC: 46011

JELLY BEANS (Kessel, Barney Trio).
LP: . . . . CJ 164

JUST FRIENDS.
LP: . . . . SNTF 685
MC: . . . . ZCSN 685

KESSEL PLAYS STANDARDS.
LP: . . . . COP 045

LET'S COOK.
LP: . . . . COP 028

LIMEHOUSE BLUES (Kessel, Barney & Stephane Grappelli).
Tracks: / It don't mean a thing / Out of nowhere / Tea for two / Limehouse blues / How high the moon / Willow, weep for me / Little star / Undecided.
LP: . . . . BLP 30129

SLOW BURN.
Tracks: / Slow burn / Just in time / Shadow of your smile / Recado bossa nova / Sweet baby / Who can I turn to / One mint julep.
LP: 2307 011

SOLO.
Tracks: / Brazil / What are you doing the rest of your life? / Happy little song / Everything happens to me / You are the sunshine of my life / Manha de carnaval / People / Jellybeans / Alfie.
LP: . . . . CJ 221

SUMMERTIME IN MONTREUX.
Tracks: / Laura / Yesterday / It's a blue world / Summertime / In the garden of love / Bridging the blues.
LP: . . . . BLP 30151

SWINGING EASY.
Tracks: / On a clear day / Look of love, The / Autumn leaves / You're the one for me / I will wait for you.
LP: . . . . BLP 30107

TO SWING OR NOT TO SWING.
Tracks: / Begin the blues / Louisiana / Happy feeling / Embraceable you / Wail Street / Indiana / Moten swing / Midnight sun / Contemporary blues / Don't blame me / Twelfth St. rag.
LP: 1003 513

TWO-WAY CONVERSATION (Kessel, Barney & Red Mitchell).
LP: . . . . SNTF 681

Kessinger, Clark

CLARK KESSINGER.
LP: . . . . ROUNDER 0004

Ketama

KETAMA.
Tracks: / Sueno Ipossible / Luna, Quedate commigo / Ketama / Me lilama / Slo para dos / Domo arigato / No se si vivo o sueno / Vacio / Galuchi / Cuando salga la luna / Chupendi / Canasteros.
LP: . . . . HNBL 1336
MC: . . . . HNBC 1336

Ketch, Jack

BRIMFUL OF HATE (Ketch, Jack & The Crewmen).
Tracks: / Believers, The / Mass ignorance culture / I've been wrong / Ryan factor, The / Brimful of hate / Somebody else / Love lives never quite the same / You shouldn't do that / Who could be proud / Bed of rubbish / Boredom.
LP: . . . . HANG 19 UP

Ketcham, Charles

4 ALFRED HITCHCOCK FILMS (Ketcham, Charles & Utah Symphony Orchestra).
Tracks: / Family plot end credits / Strangers on a train (suite) / Suspicion (suite) / Notorious (suite).
LP: . . . . TER 1109
MC: . . . . ZCTER 1109

Key

GOLDEN AGE, THE.
Tracks: / Key theme, The / Feeling special / Those days / Pretty sparkle / Singing a lullaby / Counting away my life / Golden age, The / Short change / Boy is blue, The / Wonderful thing.
LP: . . . . PHZA 4

PHASE III PROJECT (EP) (See under 2nd Generation).

Key, Troyce

I'VE GOTTA NEW CAR (Key, Troyce & J.J Malone & The Rhythm Rockers).
Tracks: / New car / Katie Mae / You're a good-lookin' woman / Old-fashioned blues / Crawdad hole / Sweet taters and possum meat / I know you love me / Monday woman.
LP: . . . . RL 028

YOUNGER THAN YESTERDAY (Key, Troyce & J.J Malone & The Rhythm Rockers).
Tracks: / Flip flop and fly / Annie maybe / It should have been me / Louisiana blues / Crazy little chicken / Daddy Rollin Stone / Sail on / Gimme mine now / Jaywalk / Outskirts of town / Tutti frutti.
LP: . . . . RL 043

Key West

FIRST INVASION.
MC: . . . . TAPE 78318

Key(Film)

KEY, THE (Film soundtrack) (Various artists).
LP: 206 253

Keynotes

KEYNOTES.
LP: . . . . RELIC 5072

Keypers

DAYLIGHT DIG, THE.
MC: 00 102151 6

TIME FOR TEA.
MC: 00 102152 4

Keys

KEYS.
Tracks: / Hello hello / It ain't so / One good reason / Listening in / I don't wanna cry / Saturday to Sunday night / Spit it out / If it's not too much / Run run run / Greasy money / Back to black / World ain't turning.
LP: . . . . AMLH 68526

Keys, Amy

LOVER'S INTUITION.
Tracks: / I know what's good for you / Lover's intuition / Will you respect me (in the morning) / Someone's gonna fall in love / Has it come to this / Even now / Man and a woman, A / Everytime I close my eyes / Precious / Crazy love.
LP: 4633831
MC: 4633834
LP: . . . . FE 44100

Keytones

SPEAK AFTER THE TONES.
LP: . . . . KEY 1 YR

Kgagudi, Lazarus

LAZARUS KGAGUDI.
LP: . . . . TUS 8003
MC: . . . . ZCTUS 8003

LAZARUS KGAGUDI 3.
Tracks: / Sekala / Lies are no good / Who's right, who's wrong / Dust / Gauteng / Let's share this love / Masaka / Isigenbengu.
LP: . . . . TUS 8009
MC: . . . . TUS 8009MC

Khaled, Cheb

HADA RAYKOUM.
LP: . . . . TERRA 102
MC: . . . . MCPE 1198

KUTCHE (Khaled, Cheb & Safy Boutella).
LP: . . . . STERNS 1024
MC: . . . . STC 1024

LE ROI DU RAI.
LP: . . . . CEL 611981

SOBRI SOBRI.
LP: . . . . CMI 5208

Khan, Ali Akbar

AT SAN FRANCISCO (Kahn, Ali Akbar & Ravi Shankar).
LP: . . . . ECSD 41516
MC: 6TCS 02B 6104

NEW RECORDING (SAROD).
LP: . . . . CPPSLP 5161

RG. DURGA/KHAMAJ DHUN.
LP: . . . . EASD 1310

RGS. AHIR BHAIRAV/BAIRAGI.
LP: . . . . EASD 1391
MC: . . . . TC 1154

Khan, Allauddin

GREAT MASTER, GREAT MUSIC.
LP: . . . . ECSD 2757

Khan, Amir

RGS. MARWA/DARBARI KNDA.
LP: . . . . EASD 1253
MC: . . . . TC 5090

Khan, Amjad Ali

BEST OF AMJAD ALI KHAN.
MCSET: . . . . TCS 7289/90

GULDASTA-E-RAGA.
LP: . . . . EMGE 2201

KING OF RGS. RG OF KINGS.
LP: . . . . ECSD 2824
MC: . . . . TC 1115

PRISONER OF CONSCIENCE.
LP: . . . . ECSD 2864
MC: . . . . TC 1246

RG SHREE.
LP: . . . . ECSD 2542
MC: . . . . TC 3822

Khan, Bismillah

RAGAS (SHENAI).
MC: . . . . TCS 2458

RG. MULTANI BEHAG.
MC: . . . . TC 5017

RGS. AHIR BHAIRAV/BHMPLSI.
LP: . . . . ECSD 2567

SOUL OF SHENAI.
LP: . . . . ECSD 2833

Khan, Chaka

CHAKA.
Tracks: / I'm every woman / Love has fallen on me / Roll me through the rushes / Sleep on it / Life is a dance / We got the love / Some love / Woman in a man's world / Message in the middle of the bottom / I was made to love him.
LP: . . . . K 56560
MC: K4 56560

CHAKA KHAN.
Tracks: / Tearin' it up / Best in the west / Got to be there / Twisted / So not to worry / Pass it on, a sure thing / Slow dancin' / Hot house / East of Suez / Epistrophy / Yardbird suite / Con Alma / Giant steps.
LP: 923729 1

CK.
Tracks: / Signed, sealed, delivered (I'm yours) / Soul talkin' / It's my party / Eternity / Sticky wicked / End of a love affair, The / Baby me / Make it last / Where are you tonight / I'll be around.
LP: . . . . WX 124
MC: . . . . WX 124 C

DESTINY.
Tracks: / Love a lifetime / Earth to Mickey / Watching the world / Other side of the world / My destiny / I can't be loved / It's you / So close / Tight fit / Who's it gonna be / Coltrane dreams.
LP: . . . . WX 45
MC: . . . . WX 45 C

I FEEL FOR YOU.
Tracks: / This is my night / Stronger than before / My love is alive / Eye to eye / La flamme / I feel for you / Hold her / Through the fire / Caught in the act / Chinatown.
LP: 925162 1
MC: 925162 4

LIFE IS A DANCE (The Remix Project).
Tracks: / Life is a dance / This is my night / Slow dancin' / I'm every woman / Ain't nobody / I feel for you / I know you, I live you / Eye to eye / Fate / One million kisses / Clouds / Clouds (classic trax version).
LP: . . . . WX 268
MC: . . . . WX 268 C

NAUGHTY.
Tracks: / Clouds / Get ready get set / Move me no mountain / Nothing's gonna take me away / Do naughty / Too much love / All night's alright / What you did / Papillon / Our love's in danger.
LP: . . . . K 56713
MC: K4 56713

WHAT CHA GONNA DO FOR ME.
Tracks: / We can work it out / What cha gonna do for me / I know you, I live you / Any old Sunday / We got each other / Night in Tunisia / Night moods / Heed the warning / Father he said / Fate / I know you, I live you (reprise).
LP: . . . . K 56888

Khan, Genghis

ALL RECORDS (See under Genghis Khan).

Khan, Imrat

GREAT HERITAGE, GREAT TRADITION (Khan, Imrat & Sons).
LP: . . . . EASD 1423
MC: . . . . TC 2538

Khan, Nusrat Fateh Ali

BEST OF NUSRAT FATEH ALI KHAN Volume 2.
LP: . . . . WOMAD 008

BEST OF NUSRAT FATEH ALI KHAN VOL.1.
LP: . . . . WOMAD 004

IN CONCERT IN PARIS (VOL 1).
LP: 558 675
MC: 4558 658

IN CONCERT IN PARIS (VOL 2).
LP: 558 685
MC: 4558 659

MUSTT MUSTT.
LP: . . . . RWLP 15
MC: . . . . RWMC 15

NUSRAT FATEH ALI KHAN QAWWEL AND PARTY VOLS.1&2.
MC: . . . . WOMBIPC 002

SHANEN SHAH.
Tracks: / Shamas ud doha badar ud doja / Allah Mohammed char yar / Kali kali zulfon ke phande nah dalo (Only on MC and CD.) / Meri ankhon do bakhshe hain aansoo (Only on MC and CD.) / Nit khair mansan sohnia main teri / Kehna ghalat ghalat to chuupana sahi sahi.
LP: . . . . RWLP 3
MC: . . . . RWMC 3

Khan, Shah

WORLD WILL END ON FRIDAY.
LP: . . . . SKY 015

Khan, Steve

BEST OF STEVE KHAN.
Tracks: / Some down time / Darlin' darlin' baby / City suite / City monsters / Dream city / Some punk funk / Daily bulls / Daily Valley / Daily Village.
LP: . . . . CBS 84234

EVIDENCE.
Tracks: / Infant eyes / In a silent way / Melancholee / Threesome / Peace / Thelonious Monk medley.
LP: . . . . AN 3023
LP: . . . . NL 83074
MC: . . . . NK 83074

EYEWITNESS.
LP: . . . . AN 1018

PUBLIC ACCESS.
Tracks: / Sise / Blue zone / Kamarica / Mambosa / Botero people / Dedicated to you / Mama chola / Silent screen / Butane elvin.
LP: . . . . GRP 95991
MC: . . . . GRP 95994

Khan, Ustad Latif

RAGS, MALKAUNS AND MEGH (see under India) (Jasani,Viram # Gurdev Singh # Ustad Latif Ahmed Khan).

Khan, Vilayat

AFTAB E SITAR.
LP: . . . . EMGE 42003
MC: . . . . TC 7208

BRILLIANCE OF SOUND.
LP: . . . . ECSD 2828
MC: . . . . TC 1116

GREAT HERITAGE, THE (Khan, Vilayat & Imrat Khan).
LP: . . . . EASD 1308

RG. BAGESHREE KANADA (Khan, Vilayat/L Jayaraman).
LP: . . . . ECSD 1419

MC: TC 6105

RGS. JJWANTI/RGSHREE.
LP: EASD 2460

Khanyile, Noise

ART OF NOISE, THE.
Tracks: / Igobondela / Izulu seliyaduma / Viva Scotch land / Mapantsula jive / Jika jika jive / Ugabuzela / Kwazamazama / USA special / Dlamini / Baba wami / Umamemeza / London Ave. / Marimba jive / Groovin' jive (no. 1).
LP: ORB 045

Khatchaturian, Aram

SPARTACUS (Khatchaturian, A & Vienna Philharmonic Orchestra).
LP: SXL 6000

Khayyam, Omar

RUBAIYAT OF OMAR KHAYYAM, THE (fourth translation) (Drake, Alfred).
MC: 1023

Khepa, Gour

MUSICIENS BAULS - FOUS DE DIEU - DU BENGALE (Khepa, Gour/Pavan Das/Subal Das).
Tracks: / Chants sexo-yogiques / Chants philosophiques et metaphysiques / Chants a caractere social.
LP: ARN 33728

Khodjo Aquai

NHIRA.
Tracks: / Yara sullil / New York abrabo / Aladwofay / Nayanyame / Anadywofay.
LP: AQ 1004

Khord

AT HOME IN SCOTLAND.
LP: BGC 220

Kiara

CIVILISED ROGUES.
Tracks: / You're right about that / Got my eyes on you / Take my time / In the tabloids / My girl / Party intro / Mr Deejay / Perfect one, The / Summer day interlude / Always / Every little thing / Slowburn / Always (reprise).
LP: 211043
MC: 411043

TO CHANGE AND/OR TO MAKE A DIFFERENCE.
Tracks: / Best of me, The / Wait so long / Strawberry letter 23 / Just like magic / Step by step / Every little time / Candy lips / This time / Quiet guy / Same old story.
LP: 209248
MC: 409248

Kicker Boys

KICKER BOYS.
LP: LINKLP 071

Kicklighter, Richy

IN THE NIGHT.
Tracks: / Night after night / Without you / Under another sky / Between the worlds / Lucky / Time will tell / Tamiami / Angel.
LP: ICH 1051
MC: ZCICH 1051

JUST FOR KICKS.
Tracks: / Jungle Song / In The Wind / Change love / Until Then / Wind in the curtains / After You're Gone / After You're Gone / Phantoms / Now and Then.
LP: ICH 1019
MC: ZCICH 1019

Kid Creole & The Coconuts

CRE-OLE (Best of Kid Creole & The Coconuts).
Tracks: / Lifeboat party, The / Gina Gina / Me no pop I / Off the coast of me / Don't take my coconuts / Maladie d'amour / There's something wrong in paradise / Stool pigeon / Annie, I'm not your daddy / Latin music / I'm a wonderful thing baby / Imitation / Dear Addy / Back in the field again.
LP: IMA 13
MC: IMC 13
LP: IMA 113
MC: IMC 113

DON'T TAKE MY COCONUTS.
Tracks: / Don't take my coconuts / Naughty boy / Maladie d'amour / Ticket to the tropics / Indiscreet / Kriminal tango / Did you have to love me like you did / If I only had a brain / Glory that was Eden.
LP: AML 4001801

DOPPELGANGER.
LP: ILPS 9743

FRESH FRUIT IN FOREIGN PLACES.
Tracks: / Going places / In the jungle / Animal crackers / I stand accused / Latin music / Musicana Americana / I am Schweinerei / Gina Gina / With a girl like Mimi / Table manners / Dear Addy.
LP: ILPM 7014
MC: ICM 7014
LP: ILPS 7014
MC: ICT 7014

I, TOO, HAVE SEEN THE WOODS.
Tracks: / Beginning, The / Buttermilk channel / Part of my design / Agony....ecstasy / Dancin' at the Bains Douches / El hijo / Cold wave / End, The / So far, so good / Midsummer madness / Consider me / Boxed out / Call it a day.
LP: WX 112
MC: WX 112 C

IN PRAISE OF OLDER WOMEN.
Tracks: / Endicott / Particul'y int'rested / Name it / (Darlin' you can) take me / Luv got me dancen' on my kneez / Caroline was a drop-out / He can have you / Animal cop, The / Dowopsalsaboprock / You can't keep a good man down / In praise of older women / Other crimes.
LP: WX 19
MC: WX 19C

MAMBO (See under Manilow, Barry) (Kid Creole/Barry Manilow).

PRIVATE WATERS IN THE GREAT DIVIDE.
Tracks: / I love girls / No more casual sex / Sex of it, The / Cory's song / Dr.Paradise / Takin' a holiday / Lambada / Funky Audrey & the coconut rag / When Lucy does the boomerang / He's takin' the rap / Pardon my appearance / Laughing with our backs against the wall / My love.
LP: 4662511
MC: 4662514

TROPICAL GANGSTERS.
LP: ILPS 7016
MC: ICT 7016

YOU SHOULDA TOLD ME YOU WERE... (Kid Creole & The Coconuts).
Tracks: / It's automatic / Baby Doc / My soul intention / Oh Marie / Consequently your move / (She's a) party girl / Something incomplete / Madison Avenue / How can I forget you (the benedektion).
LP: 4687321
MC: 4687324

Kid Frost

HISPANIC CAUSING PANIC.
LP: VUSLP 22
MC: VUSMC 22

Kid Millions

KID MILLIONS/ROMAN SCANDALS (Original Soundtracks) (Various artists).
LP: SH 2039

Kid Montana

TEMPERAMENTAL.
LP: TWI 752

Kid 'N Play

2 HYPE.
Tracks: / Rollin' with kid 'n' play / Brother man get hip / Gittin' funky / Damn that DJ / Last night / 2 hype / Can you dig it / Undercover / Do the kid'n'play kick step / Do this my way.
LP: SEL 21628
LP: CTLP 10
MC: ZCTCD 10

Kidd, Carol

ALL MY TOMORROWS.
Tracks: / Don't worry 'bout me / I'm all smiles / Autumn in New York / My funny valentine / Round midnight / Dat dere / Angel eyes / When I dream / I thought about you / Folks who live on the hill, The / Haven't we met / All my tomorrows.
LP: AKH 005
MC: AKC 005

CAROL KIDD.
Tracks: / Then I'll be tired of you / We'll be together / You go to my head / It isn't so good it couldn't be better / More I see you, The / I've grown accustomed to your face / Yes, I know when I've had it / Waltz for Debbie / Never let me go / Like someone in love / Trouble is a man / I'm shadowing you / Spring can really hang you up the most / I like to recognise the tune.
LP: AKH 003
MC: AKC 003

NICE WORK (If you can get it).
Tracks: / Nice work if you can get it / Havin' myself a time / Isn't it a pity / Bidin' my time / Sing for your supper / Daydream / I'll take romance / New York on Sunday / What is there to say / Mean to me / I guess I'll have to change my plan / Starting tomorrow / Confessions.
LP: AKH 006
MC: AKC 006

NIGHT WE CALLED IT A DAY, THE.
Tracks: / How little we know / Where or when / I fall in love too easily / I loved him / Night we called it a day, The / Where are you / Glory of you, The / I could have told you so / I think it's going to rain today / Gloomy Sunday.
LP: AKH 007
MC: AKHCS 007

Kidd, Christine

JANET RUSSELL AND CHRISTINE KIDD (See under Russell, Janet) (Kidd, Christine/Janet Russell).

Kidd Glove

KIDD GLOVE.
Tracks: / Good clean fun / Killer instinct / Street angel / Spirit of the night / Fade to black / Hellzarockin' / Somewhere in a song / Secrets / Susie wants to be a star.
LP: ZL 72149
MC: ZK 72149

Kidd, Johnny

BEST OF JOHNNY KIDD & THE PIRATES, THE (Kidd, Johnny & The Pirates).
Tracks: / Shot of rhythm and blues, A / Shakin' all over / Longing lips / Restless / Growl / I want that / Linda lu / You've got what it takes / Your cheatin' heart / I'll never get over you / Hungry for love / I can tell / Jealous girl / Shop around / Please don't touch / Always and ever.
LP: EMS 1120
MC: TCEMS 1120

CLASSIC AND RARE (Kidd, Johnny & The Pirates).
Tracks: / I want that / So what / Feeling / Please don't touch / Restless / Let's talk about us / Birds and the bees, The / It's got to be you / Some other guy / Shakin' all over / I'll never get over you / Send me some lovin' / Fool, The / Hungry for love / Your cheatin' heart / My babe / Castin' my spell / Big blon' baby.
LP: SEE 287

RARITIES (Kidd, Johnny & The Pirates).
Tracks: / I Know / Where are you / Little bit of soap, A / Oh boy / Steady date / More of the same / I just want to make love to you / This golden ring / Right string baby but the wrong yoyo / Can't turn you loose / Shakin' all over 65 / I hate getting up in the morning / Send for that girl / Hurry on back to love / You got what it takes / Fool, The / Ecstacy / Shop around / Weep no more / Whole lotta woman.
LP: CM 120

Kidjo, Angelique

PARA KOU.
LP: 8482191
MC: 8482194

Kidnapped

KIDNAPPED (Pertwee, Jon).
MC: P 90014

KIDNAPPED (Various artists).
MCSET: ZBBC 1060

KIDNAPPED (Story Of The TV Serial) (Various artists).
2LP: DPA 3067/2

KIDNAPPED (see Stevenson, Robert Louis) (Unknown narrator(s)).

KIDNAPPED (Film Soundtrack) (Various artists).
Tracks: / Overture: *Various artists* / Main title: *Various artists* / David and Catriona: *Various artists* / Mungo Campbell: *Various artists* / Fugitives from the redcoats: *Various artists* / Alan Breck: *Various artists* / Shipwreck: *Various artists* / Cluny's cave: *Various artists* / Edinburgh Castle: *Various artists* / Highlands and Lowlands: *Various artists* / Moors and heather: *Various artists* / For all my days: *Various artists*.
LP: 2383 102

Kids

KIDS' CHRISTMAS SING-A-LONG (Various artists).
LP: MM R 0197
MC: MM C 0197

Kids For Two Farthings

KIDS FOR TWO FARTHINGS (Kossoff, David (nar)).
MC: CAB 005

Kids From Fame

FAME (TV series).
Tracks: / Starmaker / I can do anything better than you can / I still believe in me / Life is a celebration / Step up to the mike / Hi fidelity / We got the power / It's gonna be a long night / Desdemona / Be my music.
LP: REP 447
MC: ZCH 447

FROM FAME AGAIN.
Tracks: / Mannequin / Carnival / I was only trying to help / Alone in a crowd / You're the real music / Sho sho shorofsky / Special place, A / Do the gimme that / It's sonata Mozart / Come what may / Show must go on.
LP: PL 89079
MC: PK 89079
LP: RCALP 6057

LIVE: KIDS FROM FAME (T.V. soundtrack).
Tracks: / Body language / Could we be magic like you / Friday night / We got the power / Desdemona / Starmaker / Hi fidelity / Mannequin / Life is a celebration / Fame / Special place, A / It's gonna be a long night / I still believe in me / Secret / Be my music.
LP: PL 89257
MC: PK 89257
LP: KIDLP 003

SING FOR YOU.
LP: KIDLP 005

SONGS.
Tracks: / Be your own hero / Just like you / There's a train / Could we be magic like you / Lay back and be cool / Songs / Body language / Beautiful dreamer / Dancing endlessly / Bet your life it's me.
LP: KIDLP 004
MC: KIDK 004

Kids In The Kitchen

SHINE.
Tracks: / Shine / Current stand / Change in mood / Places to go / Cynical / Something that you said / Bitter desire / My life / Not the way / How come.
LP: 925377 1
MC: 925377 4

TERRAIN.
LP: L 38775

Kidson, Frank

TRADITIONAL TUNES (A collection of ballad hits).
Tracks: / Old man in the North Country, The / My Johnny was a shoemaker / Jack the sailor lad / Bold privateer / Dowie dens of Yarrow / Brewer laddie / Young Roger of the valley / Spithead fleet / Bonnie Irish boy / Forty miles / King's delight / Young Riley the Fisherman / Grey mare / Ge ho dobbin.
MC: BH 8607

Kiener, Barry

BARRY KIENER TRIO.
LP: PHOENIX 1002

INTRODUCING THE BARRY KIENER TRIO.
LP: PHONIX 1002

Kier, Nick

WAYFARER (See under Grace, John) (Kier, Nick/John Grace).

Kiernan, Ken

ERINSAGA (Kiernan, Ken/Ger MacDonald).
LP: ERLP 1
MC: ERMC 1

Kiezmer Conservatory

JUMPIN' NIGHT IN THE GARDEN OF EDEN, A.
MC: ROUNDER 3105C
LP: ROUNDER 3105

Kihn, Greg

CITIZEN KIHN.
Tracks: / I'm in love again / Go back / Lucky / Whenever / Piracy / Free country / They rock by night / Boys won't / Imitation love / Temper, temper / Good life.
LP: EJ 2403031
MC: EJ 2403034

GREG KIHN (Kihn, Greg Band).
Tracks: / Don't expect to be right / Any other woman / Emily Davison / Try try to fall in love / Kid from Louieville / Worse or better / He will break your heart / What goes on / Satisfied / Why don't you try me.
LP: BSERK 4

GREG KIHN AGAIN.
Tracks: / Love's made a fool of you / Island / Last of me / Real big man / Politics / Hurt so bad / For you / If you be my love / Madison Avenue / Untie my hands.
LP: BSERK 8

KIHNSPIRACY.
Tracks: / Jeopardy / Fascination / Tear that city down / Talkin' to myself / Can't love them all / I fall to pieces / Someday / Curious / How long? / Love never fails.
LP: E 0224

KIHNTINUED.
Tracks: / Happy man / Every love song / Everyday / Saturday / Dedication / Tell me lies / Testify / Sound system / Seeing is believing / Higher and higher / Family.
LP: BSK 85622

NEXT OF KIHN.
Tracks: / Cold hard cash / Museum / Remember / Chinatown / Sorry / Everybody else / Understander / Secret meetings.
LP: . . . . **BSERK 13**

POWER LINES.
Tracks: / Moulin Rouge / Getting away with murder / Rendezvous / In the naked eye / Beside myself / Road runner / Another lonely Saturday night / Can't get the highs / Fallen idol.
LP: . . . . **BSERK 020**

ROCKIHNROLL (Kihn, Greg Band).
Tracks: / Valerie / Breakup song / Womankind / Can't stop hurtin' myself / Trouble in paradise / Sheila / Nothing's gonna change / Girl most likely, The / When the music starts / True confessions.
LP: . . . . **BSK 85213**

WITH THE NAKED EYE (Kihn, Greg Band).
Tracks: / Rendezvous / In the naked eye / Getting away with murder / Moulin rouge / Beside my self / Roadrunner / Another lonely Saturday night / Can't have the highs / Fallen idol.
LP: . . . . **KBSERK 20**

Kik Tracee

NO RULES.
Tracks: / Don't need rules / Mrs Robinson / You're so strange / Trash city / Hard time / Big westgern sky / Generation express / Soul shaker / Tangerine man / Lost / Velvet crush / Rattlesnake eyes (Strawberry jam) / Romeo blues (CD only.) / Fade Dunaway.
LP: . . . . **PL 82189**
MC: . . . . **PK 82189**

Kikrokos

JUNGLE D.J. AND DIRTY KATE.
Tracks: / Jungle D.J. / Jungle D.J. and Dirty Kate / Jungle is not for you / Jungle dee jay / Life is a jungle.
LP: **2393208**

Kikuchi, Teiko

TRADITIONAL MUSIC OF JAPAN (See under Japan...).

Kilbey, Reginald

ELIZABETHAN SERENADE.
Tracks: / Montmartre / My love she's but a lassie yet / Route et noire / Pinch of salt / Corniche pastiche / Gabriel John / My northern hills / Lullaby for Penelope / Nights of gladness / Portrait of a flirt / Elizabethan serenade / Dance in the twilight.
LP: . . . . **SRS 5197**

GLORIOUS MELODIES (Kilbey, Reginald & His Strings).
Tracks: / Shepherd's song / Clair de lune / Greensleeves / Air on a G string / Plaisir d'amour.
MC: . . . . **HR 8170**

MELODIES FOR YOU (Kilbey, Reginald & His Strings).
MC: **TC2MOM 110**

Kilbride, Pat

ROCK AND ROSES.
LP: . . . . **TP 004**

Kilburn & The High

HANDSOME (Kilburn & The High Roads With Ian Dury).
Tracks: / Roadette song, The / Pam's moods / Crippled with nerves / Broken skin / Upminster kid / Patience / Father / Thank you mum / Rough kids / Badger and the rabbit, The / Mumble rumble and the cocktail rock, The / Call up, The.
LP: . . . . **FBLP 8094**
MC: . . . . **ZCFBL 8094**

UPMINSTER KIDS (Kilburn & The High Roads With Ian Dury).
Tracks: / Roadette song, The / Crippled with nerves / Thank you mum / Pam's moods / Rough kids / Broken skin / Mumble rumble and the cocktail rock, The / Call up, The / Love's made a fool of you / Island / Last of me / Real big man / Politics / Hurt so bad / For you / If you be my love / Madison Avenue / Untie my hands.
LP: . . . . **DOW 17**
MC: . . . . **ZCDOW 17**

WOTABUNCH (Kilburn & The High Roads With Ian Dury).
Tracks: / Call up, The / Crippled with nerves / Patience / You're more than fair / Upminster kid / Billy Bentley / Huffety puff / Rough kids / Roadette song, The / Flunkey jive / Badger and the rabbit, The / Mumble rumble and the coctail rock, The / Pam's moods.
LP: . . . . **K 56513**

Kilfernora Ceili Band

CLARE CEILI.
LP: . . . . **STAL 1013**

KILFERNORA CEILI BAND.
Tracks: / Rattigans / Morning star / Dublin porter / Belfast Town / Reels / Mullins - the reels of Rio / Paddy Murphy's wife / Flow of Edinburgh, The / Stack, The / Austin Tierney's - reels / I'm waiting for you / Boys of Ballysadare, The / File mile chaser, The / Humours of Glendart (Double jigs) / Joys of love / Down the broom (reels) / Donegal reel, The / Peadars reels / Coming back to Miltown / McDermont's (reels) / Tierney's / Lady Montomery / Double jig / Gold ring, The / Luck penny, The / Reel of bogy, The / Kerry reel, The / Sailor on the rock, The / Lady on the island, The / Stony steps, The.
LP: . . . . **TRS 108**
MC: . . . . **KTRS 108**

Kilimambogo

SIMBA AFRICA.
LP: . . . . **PAM 03**

Kilimanjaro

KILIMANJARO (Various artists).
LP: . . . . **PH 9001**
MC: . . . . **PH 9001C**

KILIMANJARO TWO (Various artists).
LP: . . . . **PH 9005**
MC: . . . . **PH 9005C**

Kill

KILL.
LP: . . . . **CFC 004**

Kill City Dragons

KILL CITY DRAGONS.
LP: . . . . **WBRLP 002**
MC: . . . . **WBRMC 002**

Kill Or Be Killed

KILL OR BE KILLED/GOD FORGIVES - I DON'T (Original Soundtracks) (Various artists).
LP: . . . . **PHCAM 08**

Kill Ugly Pop

LEATHER FACE GETS RELIGION.
LP: . . . . **DMC 004**

Killdozer

FOR LADIES ONLY.
LP: . . . . **TGLP 39**

INTELLECTUALS ARE THE SHOESHINE BOYS OF THE ....
LP: . . . . **TGLP 47**

LITTLE BABY BUNTIN'.
LP: . . . . **TGLP 26**

SNAKEBOY.
LP: . . . . **TGLP 6**

TWELVE POINT BUCK.
LP: . . . . **TGLP 48**

Killen, Louis

ALONG THE COALY TYNE (Killen, Louis & Johnny Handle).
Tracks: / Anti gallican privateer, The / Colliers' rant, The / Up the raw / Farewell to the monty / Blackleg miner / Collier lad, The / Dollia / Waggoner, The / Derwentwater's farewell / Stottin' doon the waal / Keep your feet still / Stoneman's song, The / Aw wish pay Friday was come / Durham big meetin' day, The / Trimdon grange explosion, The / Putter, The / Sair Fyeld.
LP: **12T 189**

BALLADS AND BROADSIDES.
LP: **12T 126**

Killer

DIXIE (See under Rockabilly Raiders "Hurricane rock").

READY FOR HELL.
LP: . . . . **SKULL 8301**
MC: . . . . **TAPE 78301**

SHOCK WAVES.
LP: . . . . **SKULL 8320**
MC: . . . . **TAPE 78320**

WALL OF SOUND.
LP: . . . . **SKULL 8302**
MC: . . . . **TAPE 78302**

YOUNG BLOOD.
LP: **941310**

Killer Dwarfs

BIG DEAL.
Tracks: / Tell me please / We stand alone / Startin' to shine / Breakaway / Union of pride / Lifetime / Power / I'm alive / Burn it down / Desperados.
LP: **4608121**
MC: **4608124**

DIRTY WEAPONS.
Tracks: / Dirty weapons / Nothin' gets nothin' / All that we dream / Doesn't matter / Last laugh / Comin' through / One way out / Appeal / Not foolin' / Want it bad.
LP: **4659081**
MC: **4659084**

KILLER DWARFS.
LP: . . . . **LAT 1178**
LP: . . . . **GWLP 35**

Killing Fields

1984/MERRY CHRISTMAS MR LAWRENCE/KILLING FIELDS (See under Nineteen Eighty Four) (Various artists).

Killing Fields (film)

KILLING FIELDS, THE (see under Oldfield, Mike) (Film soundtrack) (Oldfield, Mike).

Killing Joke

BRIGHTER THAN A 1000 SUNS.
Tracks: / Adorations / Sanity / Chessboards / Twilight of the moral / Love of the masses / Southern sky, A / Winter gardens / Rubicon / Goodbye to the village (CD & cassette only) / Victory (CD & cassette only) / Exile.
LP: . . . . **EGLP 66**
MC: . . . . **EGMC 66**

EXTREMITIES, DIRT AND VARIOUS REPRESSED EMOTIONS.
Tracks: / Money is not our God / Age of greed / Beautiful dead, The / Extremities / Intravenous / Inside the termite mound / Solitude / North of the border / Slipstream / Kaliyuga / Struggle.
LP: . . . . **AGR 0541**
MC: . . . . **AGR 0542**

FIRE DANCES.
Tracks: / Gathering, The / Fun and games / Rejuvenation / Frenzy / Harlequin / Feast of blaze / Song and dance / Dominator / Let's all go (to the fire dances) / Lust almighty.
LP: . . . . **EGLP 60**
MC: . . . . **EGMC 60**
LP: . . . . **EGMD 5**
MC: . . . . **EGMDC 5**

HA - KILLING JOKE LIVE.
Tracks: / Psyche / Sun goes down / Pandys are coming / Take take take / Unspeakable / Wardance.
MLP: . . . . **EGMDT 4**
MC: . . . . **EGMDC 4**
LP: . . . . **EGMLP 3**
MC: . . . . **EGMMC 3**

KILLING JOKE.
Tracks: / Requiem / War Dance / Tomorrow's World / Bloodsport / Wait, The / Complications / S.O. 36 / Primitive.
LP: . . . . **EGLP 57**
MC: . . . . **EGMC 57**
MC: . . . . **EGMDC 545**
LP: . . . . **EGMD 545**

NIGHT TIME.
Tracks: / Night Time / Darkness before dawn / Love like blood / Kings and Queens / Tabazan / Multitudes / Europe / Eighties.
LP: . . . . **EGLP 61**
MC: . . . . **EGMC 61**

OUTSIDE THE GATE.
Tracks: / America / My love of this land / Stay one jump ahead / Unto the ends of the earth / Calling, The / Obsession / Tiahuanaco / Outside the gate / America (extended mix) (CD only) / Stay one jump ahead (extended mix) (Only on CD.).
LP: . . . . **EGLP 73**
MC: . . . . **EGMC 73**

REVELATIONS.
Tracks: / Hum, The / Empire Song / We have joy / Chop chop / Pandys are coming / Chapter 2 / Have a Nice Day / Land of Milk and Honey / Good Samaritan, The / Dregs.
LP: . . . . **EGLP 59**
MC: . . . . **EGMC 59**
LP: . . . . **EGMD 3**
MC: . . . . **EGMDC 3**

WHAT'S THIS FOR.
Tracks: / Fall of because, The / Tension / Unspeakable / Butcher / Who told you how? / Follow the leader / Madness / Exit.
LP: . . . . **EGLP 58**
MC: . . . . **EGMC 58**
LP: . . . . **EGMD 550**
MC: . . . . **EGMDC 550**

Killoran, Paddy

BACK IN TOWN.
LP: . . . . **SHAN 33003**

Killycoogan Accordian

GIVE HIM THE GLORY.
LP: . . . . **CPOL 807**

Kilmarnock Concert

SHADES OF BRASS.
Tracks: / Best foot forward / Shepherd's song / Bone idyll / Trouble maker / Cornet roundabout / Scottish fantasy, A / Cortege from Mlada / Elegy and dance / Jeanie with the light brown hair / Prelude and fugue / Dear Lord and Father of mankind / Finale from Pineapple Poll.
LP: . . . . **BBRD 1022**
MC: . . . . **BBTD 1022**

Kilslug

ANSWER THE CALL.
LP: . . . . **HOLY 008**

Kilvert's Diary (tv)

HE BEING DEAD YET SPEAKETH (Davies, Timothy (nar)).
2LP: . . . . **SDX 309**
MC: . . . . **CSDX 309**

Kilzer, John

BUSMAN'S HOLIDAY.
LP: . . . . **GEF 24322**
MC: . . . . **GEFC 24322**

MEMORY IN THE MAKING.
Tracks: / Green, yellow and red / Heart and soul / Red blue jeans / Memory in the making / Pick me up / Give me a highway / Loaded dice / Dream queen / If sidewalks talked / When fools say love / Dirty dishes / I love you.
LP: . . . . **WX 170**
MC: . . . . **WX 170C**

Kim (bk)

KIM (see under Kipling, Rudyard) (Pigott-Smith, Tim (nar)).

Kimball, Jeanette

SOPHISTICATED LADY.
LP: . . . . **NOR 7208**

Kimber, William

ART OF WILLIAM KIMBER, THE.
LP: **12T 249**

COUNTRY GARDENS.
Tracks: / Morris on / Beansetting / Constant Billy / Hunting the squirrel / Rigs o'Marlow / Rodney / Blue eyed stranger / Double set back / Getting upstairs / Haste to the wedding / Laudnum bunches / Trunkles / 29th of May, the / Willow tree / Bacca pipes / Jockie to the fair / Old Mother Oxford / Old woman tossed up in a blanket / Shepherd's hey / Fool's jig / Morris off / Bonnets o' blue / Double lead through / Four hand reel / Hilly-go filly-go / Over the hills to glory / Pop goes the weasel / Quaker's wife / Ribbon dance / Triumph / Girl with the blue dress on, The / Highland fling / Father O'Flynn / Moonlight schottische / Kitty come / Little Polly polka / Bonnie Dundee / Mayblossom waltz / Kafoozalum / Wonder hornpipe, The.
MC: **90-083**

Kimbrough, Lottie

COMPLETE RECORDINGS 1928-29 (Kimbrough, Lottie/Winston Holmes).
LP: . . . . **WSE 114**

Kimera

HITS ON OPERA.
2LP: . . . . **SMR 8505**
MCSET: . . . . **SMC 8505**

Kimmel, Tom

5 TO 1.
LP: . . . . **VERH 52**
MC: . . . . **VERHC 52**

CIRCLE BACK HOME.
LP: **8431331**
MC: **8431334**

Kimoko, Dally

TOBINA (Kimoko, Dally & Soukous Stars).
LP: . . . . **KBK 908**

Kina

CERCANDO.
LP: . . . . **GURT 13**

Kincora Ceili Band

CEOL TIRE.
LP: . . . . **CL 12**

Kind Hearts & Coronets

KIND HEARTS AND CORONETS/ ARSENIC AND OLD LACE (Powell, Robert (nar)).
MCSET: . . . . **ZBBC 1125**

Kindergarten Cop

KINDERGARTEN COP (See under Edelman, Randy) (Edelman, Randy).

Kindness Of Strangers

KINDNESS OF STRANGERS, THE (Various artists).
LP: . . . . **GEL 001**

Kindred

KINDRED, THE (Original Soundtrack) (Various artists).
LP: . . . . **STV 81308**

Kinetic Dissent

I WILL FIGHT NO MORE FOREVER.
LP: . . . . **RO 93271**
MC: . . . . **RO 93274**

King

12" TAPE: KING.
Tracks: / Love and pride / Won't you hold my hand now / Alone without you / Taste of your tears / Torture.

MC: 4501264

BITTER SWEET.
Tracks: / Alone without you / Platform one / I cringed, I died, I felt hot / Kfad wait for no one / 2 M B / These things / Taste of your tears / Torture / Sugar candy mountain / Buddahs / Mind yer toes.
LP: CBS 86320
MC: 40 86320

STEPS IN TIME.
Tracks: / Fish / Love and pride / And as for myself / Trouble / Won't you hold my hand now / Unity song / Cherry / Soul on my boots / I kissed the spikey fridge / Fish (reprise).
LP: CBS 26095
MC: 40 26095

King (2)

HELLO VENRAY.
LP: 9010

King Ahaz

JEWISH SONG CYCLE.
MC: A 001 111C

King, Al

ON MY WAY.
LP: DD 4302

King, Albert

ALBERT.
Tracks: / Guitar man / I'm ready / Ain't nothing you can do / I don't care what my baby do / Change of pace / My babe / Running out of steam / Rub my back / (Ain't it) a real good sign.
LP: CRB 1173
MC: TCCRB 1173

ALBERT LIVE.
Tracks: / Watermelon man / Don't burn down the bridge / Blues at sunrise / That's what the blues is all about / Stormy Monday / Kansas city / I'm gonna call you as soon as the sun goes down (King) / Matchbox holds my clothes / Jam in a flat / As the years go passing by / Overall junction / I'll play the blues for you.
2LP: CDX 35
MC: TCCDX 35

BEST OF ALBERT KING, THE (I'll Play the Blues For You).
Tracks: / Born under a bad sign / Answer to the laundromatt blues / You threw your love on me too strong / Crosscut saw / I'll play the blues for you (Part 1) / Angel of mercy / Heart fixing business / Killing floor / Sky is crying, The / Going back to luka / (I think I'm) drowning on dry land (Part 2) / That's what the blues is all about / Left hand woman (get right with me) / Driving wheel / Firing line (Available on CD only) / Don't burn the bridge (cause you might wanna come back... (Available on CD only) / Can't you see what you're doing to me (Available on CD only).
LP: SX 007
MC: SXC 007

BLUES AT SUNRISE.
Tracks: / Don't burn the bridge (cause you might wanna come back... / For the love of a woman / I'll play the blues for you / Roadhouse blues / I believe to my soul / Blues at sunrise / Little brother (make a way).
LP: SX 017

BORN UNDER A BAD SIGN.
LP: SD7723

DOOR TO DOOR (King, Albert/Otis Rush).
LP: 515021
LP: CH 9322

GREAT KING ALBERT.
LP: 2696031
MC: 2696034

JAMMED TOGETHER (See under Cropper, Steve) (King, Albert/ Steve Cropper/ Pop Staples).

KING ALBERT.
Tracks: / Love shock / You upset me baby / Chump chance / Let me rock you easy / Boot lace / Love mechanic / Call my job / Good time Charlie.
LP: CRB 1191
MC: TCCRB 1191

LAST SESSION, THE.
Tracks: / Won't gimme no livin' / Cold in hand, The / Stop lying / All the way down / Tell me what true love is / Down the road I go / Sun gone down.
LP: MPS 8534

LAUNDROMAT BLUES.
Tracks: / Born under a bad sign / Laundromat blues / I love Lucy / Crosscut saw / You sure drive a hard bargain / You're gonna need me / (When I lost my baby) I almost lost my mind / Overall junction / Oh pretty woman / Funk-shun / Hunter, The / Personal manager / Cold feet / Kansas city / Down don't bother me / As the years go passing by.
LP: ED 130

LIVE WIRE/BLUES POWER.
Tracks: / Watermelon man / Blues power / Night stomp / Blues at sunrise / Please love me / Lookout.
LP: SXE 022

LIVE WIRE/BLUES POWER.
LP: STX 4148

NEW ORLEANS HEAT.
Tracks: / Get out of My Life Woman / Born under a bad sign / Feeling / We all wanna boogie / Very thought of you, The / I got the blues / I get evil / Angel of Mercy / Flat tire.
LP: 203.007
LP: CRB 1066

RED HOUSE.
LP: ESSLP 147
MC: ESSMC 147

SAN FRANCISCO 83.
LP: F 9627
LP: 68535

THURSDAY NIGHT IN SAN FRANCISCO.
LP: SXE 032

TRAVELLIN' TO CALIFORNIA.
LP: BID 8016

TRUCKLOAD OF LOVIN'.
Tracks: / Cold women with warm hearts / Gonna make it somehow / Sensation, communication, together / I'm your mate / Truckload of lovin' / Hold hands with one another / Cadillac assembly line / Nobody wants a loser.
LP: CRB 1180
MC: TCCRB 1180

WEDNESDAY NIGHT IN SAN FRANCISCO.
LP: SXE 031

King Arthur

EXCALIBUR (Tales of King Arthur & his Knights) (Pyle, Howard).
MC: 1462

KING ARTHUR (Jones, Freddie).
MC: SQRL 12

KING ARTHUR (Various artists).
MC: STC 301A

KING ARTHUR (Plummer, C).
MC: CDL 51629

KING ARTHUR SOUNDBOOK Various artists (Various artists).
MC: SBC 118

STORY OF SIR GALAHAD, THE (Tales of King Arthur & his Knights) (Pyle, Howard).
MC: 1625

STORY OF SIR LANCELOT, THE Tales of King Arthur & his knights (Pyle, Howard).
MC: 1609

SWORD IN THE ANVIL, THE (Tales of King Arthur & his Knights) (Pyle, Howard).
MC: 1465

King Axe

ROCK THE WORLD.
Tracks: / Rock the world / Chain, The / Red line / Devachan / Warrior / We still remember / Great escape, The / Medusa / Dark crusade, The / Magic man.
LP: RR 9611

King, B.B.

ACROSS THE TRACKS.
Tracks: / Let's do the boogie / Bad luck / When my heart beats like a hammer / Everyday I have the blues / Dark is the night (part 1) / Dark is the night (part 2) / Why I sing the blues / Troubles troubles troubles / I got a girl who lives up on the hill / Everything I do is wrong / Woman I love, The / Jump with you baby / Be careful with a fool / Talkin' the blues / Confessin' the blues / Crying won't help you.
LP: CHD 230

AMBASSADOR OF THE BLUES.
Tracks: / Ambassador of the blues / You upset my baby / Sweet little angel / Three o'clock blues / Did you ever love a woman / B.B. blues / I can't lose / Five long years / Other night blues, The / I stay in the mood / Worst thing in my life / Pray for you.
LP: GEM 001
MC: GEMC 001

B.B. BOOGIE.
Tracks: / It's my own fault / You've done lost your good thing now / B.B. boogie / New way of driving, A / Catfish blues / Long nights / That evil child / Sweet sixteen / Paying the cost to be boss / How blue can you get / Other night blues, The / Mr. Pawnbroker / Walkin' and cryin' / Letter, The / Everyday I have the blues.
LP: BMLP 076

B.B. KING STORY VOL. 1.
LP: SM 3726
MC: MC 3726

B.B. KING STORY VOL. 2.
LP: SM 3727
MC: MC 3727

BEST OF B. B. KING/MEMPHIS MASTERS.
Tracks: / Please love me / You upset me baby / Everyday I have the blues / Bad luck / 3 o'clock blues / Blind love / Woke up this morning / You know I love you / Sweet little angel / Ten long years / Did you ever love a woman / Cryin' won't help you / Pray for you / Other night blues, The / Mistreated woman / Questionnaire blues / B.B. boogie / New way of driving, A / B.B. boogie / It's my own fault / Walkin' & cryin' / Fine looking woman / She don't love me no more / Shake it up and go.
MC: CHC 801

BEST OF B.B. KING.
Tracks: / Hummingbird / Cook County jail introduction / How blue can you get / Sweet sixteen / Ain't nobody home / Why I sing the blues / Thrill is gone, The / Nobody loves me but my mother / Caldonia.
LP: FA 3055
MC: TCFA 3055
LP: MCL 1612
MC: MCLC 1612

BEST OF B.B. KING (ACE).
Tracks: / Please love me / You upset me, baby / Everyday I have the blues / Bad luck / Three o'clock blues / Blind love / Woke up this morning / You know I love you / Sweet little angel / Ten long years / Did you ever love a woman? / Crying won't help you.
LP: CH 30

BEST OF B.B. KING VOL 1.
Tracks: / You upset me baby / Everyday / Five long years / Sweet little angel / Beautician blues / Dust my broom / Three o'clock blues / Ain't that just like a woman / I'm King / Sweet sixteen / Whole lot of love / Mean ole Frisco / Please accept my love / Going down slow / Blues for me / You don't know / Early every morning / Blues at sunrise / Please love me.
LP: CH 198
MC: CHC 198

BEST OF B.B. KING VOL 2.
Tracks: / Bad luck soul / Get out of here / Jungle / Sugar mama / Ten long years / Bad case of love / House rocker / Sneakin' around / Shut your mouth / Letter, The / I've got a right to love my baby / Woman I love, The / You done lost your good thing now / Did you ever love a woman / B.B. rock / Rock me baby / It's my own fault / You know I love you / Low rider / You're gonna miss me.
MC: CHC 199
LP: CH 199

BLUES IS KING.
Tracks: / Waitin' on you / Gambler's blues / Tired of your jive / Night life / Buzz me / Sweet sixteen part 1 / Don't answer the door / Blind love / I know what you're puttin' down / Baby get lost / Gonna keep on loving you / Sweet sixteen part 2.
LP: SEE 216

BLUES 'N' JAZZ.
Tracks: / Inflation blues / Broken heart / Sell my monkey / Heed my warning / Teardrops from my eyes / Rainbow riot / Darlin' you know I love you / Make love to me / I can't let you go.
LP: MCL 1836
MC: MCLC 1836
LP: LAT 1036
LP: MCF 3170

BLUES ON TOP OF BLUES.
Tracks: / Heartbreaker / Losing faith in you / Dance with me / That's wrong little mama / Having my say / I'm not wanted anymore / Worried dream / Paying the cost to be the boss / Until I found you / I'm gonna do what they do to me / Raining in my heart / Now that you've lost me.
LP: BGOLP 69

BLUES, THE.
LP: MA 30585
MC: MAMC 30585

COLLECTION: B.B. KING (20 Blues Greats).
Tracks: / Help the poor / Everyday I have the blues / Woke up this morning / Worry worry / Sweet little angel / How blue can you get / You upset me baby / It's my own fault / Please love me / She don't love me no more / Three o'clock blues / Fine looking woman / Blind love / You know I love you / Ten long years / Mistreated woman / Shake it up and go / Sweet sixteen / You done lost your good thing now / Outside help.
LP: DVLP 2031
MC: DVMC 2031

COMPLETELY LIVE AND WELL.
Tracks: / Don't answer the door / Just a little love / My mood / Sweet little angel / Please accept my love / I want you so bad / Friends / Get off my back woman / Lets get down to business / Why i sing the blues / So exited / No good / You're losin' me / What happened / Confessin' the blues / Key to my kingdom / Crying won't help you now / You're mean / Thrill is gone, The.
2LP: CDX 14
MC: TCCDX 14

FABULOUS B.B. KING, THE.
Tracks: / Three o'clock blues / You know I love you / Please love me / You upset me baby / Bad luck / On my word of honor / Everyday I have the blues / Woke up this morning (my baby's gone) / When my heart beats like a hammer / Sweet little angel / Ten long years / Whole lotta love.
MC: FABC 004

FRIENDS.
LP: BGOLP 124

GREATEST HITS: B B KING.
LP: LOP 14 023

GREATEST HITS: B B KING (2).
LP: 33003
MC: 63003

GUESS WHO.
LP: BGOLP 71

HIS BEST : THE ELECTRIC KING.
Tracks: / Tired of your jive / B.B. Jones, The / Paying the cost to the boss / I done got wise / Sweet sixteen / I don't want you cuttin' of / Don't answer the door / All over again / Think it over / Meet my happiness / You put it on me.
LP: BGOLP 37

IN LONDON.
LP: BGOLP 42

INCREDIBLE SOUL OF B.B. KING.
Tracks: / I got papers on you, baby / Tomorrow is another day / Fool too long, A / Come by here / Woman I love, The / My silent prayer / I love you so / Sweet thing / We can't make it / Treat me right / Time to say goodbye / I'm cracking up over you.
LP: CV 1309

INDIANOLA MISSISSIPPI SEEDS.
Tracks: / Nobody loves me but my mother / You're still my woman / Ask me no questions / Until I'm dead and cold / King's special / Ain't gonna worry my life anymore / Chains and things / Go underground / Hummingbird.
LP: CLALP 141
MC: CLAMC 141

INTRODUCING B.B.KING.
Tracks: / Into the night / Better not look down / My Lucille / Caldonia / Sell my monkey / In the midnight hour / Thrill is gone, The / Broken heart / Victim, The / Sweet sixteen / Rock me baby.
LP: MCB 8001
MC: MCBC 8001

KING OF THE BLUES.
LP: MCG 6038
MC: MCGC 6038

KING OF THE BLUES GUITAR.
Tracks: / Slidin' and glidin' / Blues with B. B. / King of guitar / Jump with B. B. / 38th Street blues / Feedin' the rock / Going South / Step it up.
LP: CH 152

LIVE AT SAN QUENTIN.
LP: MCG 6103
MC: MCGC 6103

LIVE AT THE APOLLO.
Tracks: / When love comes to town / Sweet sixteen / Thrill is gone, The / Ain't nobody's bizness / All over again / Nightlife / Since I met you baby / Guess who / Peace to the world.
LP: GR 9637
MC: GRC 9637

LIVE AT THE REGAL.
Tracks: / Everyday I have the blues / Sweet little angel / It's my own fault / How blue can you get / Please love me / You upset me baby / Worry, worry / Woke up this morning / You done lost your good thing now / Help the poor.
LP: CH 86

LIVE IN COOK COUNTY JAIL.
Tracks: / Everyday I have the blues / How blues can you get / Worry, worry / 3 o'clock blues / Darlin you know I love you / Sweet sixteen / Thrill is gone, The / Please accept my love.
LP: IMCA 27005

LIVE IN LONDON: B.B. KING.
Tracks: / Introduction / Everyday I have the blues / Night life / Love the life I'm

living / When it all comes down / I've got a right to give up livin' / Encore.
LP: . . . . MCF 3226
MC: . . . . MCFC 3226

LOVE ME TENDER.
LP: . . . . MCF 3139

LUCILLE.
LP: . . . . BGOLP 36

LUCILLE HAD A BABY.
Tracks: / You don't know / Shut your mouth / Early every morning / Ruby Lee / Don't you want a man like me / I stay in the mood / Can't we talk it over / Please remember me / Sweet little angel / Baby look at you / Lonely and blue / Trouble in mind / I want to get married / Love you baby / You upset me baby / I'm cracking up over you.
LP: . . . . CHD 271

MEMPHIS MASTERS, THE.
Tracks: / Pray for you / Other night blues, The / Mistreated woman / Questionnaire blues / B.B. blues / New way of driving, A / B.B. boogie / It's my own fault / Walkin' and cryin' / Fine looking woman / She don't move me no more / Shake it up and go.
LP: . . . . CH 50

MIDNIGHT BELIEVER.
Tracks: / When it all comes down / I just can't leave your love alone / Midnight believer / Hold on (I feel our love is changing) / Never make a move too soon / World full of strangers, A / Let me make you cry a little longer.
LP: . . . . MCL 1802
MC: . . . . MCLC 1802

MY SWEET LITTLE ANGEL.
Tracks: / My sweet little angel / Crying won't help you / Ten long years / Quit my baby / Don't look now but I've got the blues / You know I go for you / Why do everything happen to me / Worry worry / Shake yours / Please accept my love / Treat me right / Going down slow / Just like a woman / Time to say goodbye / Early every morning / You've been an angel.
LP: . . . . CHD 300
MC: . . . . CHDC 300

NOW APPEARING AT OLE MISS.
Tracks: / Caldonia / Don't answer the door / You done lost your good thing now / I need love so bad / Nobody loves me but my mother / I got some outside help (I don't really need) / Darlin' you know I love you / When I'm wrong / Thrill is gone, The / Never make a move too soon / Three o'clock in the morning / Rock me baby / Guess who / I just can't leave your love alone.
2LP: . . . . MCLD 601
MCSET: . . . . MCLDC 601

ONE NIGHTER BLUES.
Tracks: / She's dynamite / Low down dirty baby / I'm so glad / I gotta find my baby / Past day (didn't have to cry) / Bye bye baby / Highway bound / Boogie woogie woman / Please Love me / Blind love / Wake up this morning / When my heart beats like a hammer / Whole lot of love / That ain't the way to do it / Everything I do is wrong / Whole lotta meat.
LP: . . . . CHD 201

RAREST B.B. KING.
Tracks: / Miss Martha King / My baby's gone / Hard working woman / Shake it up and go / Please hurry home / Woman I love, the / Everything I love is wrong / My sometime baby / When your baby packs up and goes / She's a mean woman / Someday, somewhere / Gotta find my baby / Why did you leave me / Love you baby / I need you so bad / Sugar mama.
LP: . . . . BB 301

ROCK ME BABY.
Tracks: / Rock me, baby / Blue shadows / Worst thing in my life / Jungle / Eyesight to the blind / It's a mean world / I stay in the mood / I can hear my name / Got 'em bad / And like that.
LP: . . . . CH 119

SINGIN' THE BLUES AND THE BLUES.
MC: . . . . CHDC 320

SIX SILVER STRINGS.
LP: . . . . MCF 3281
MC: . . . . MCFC 3281

SPOTLIGHT ON LUCILLE.
Tracks: / Six silver strings / Big boss man / In the midnight hour / Into the night / My Lucille / Memory blues / My guitar sings the blues / Double trouble / Memory lane.
LP: . . . . CH 187
MC: . . . . CHC 187

STORMY MONDAY (See under Stormy Monday) (King, B.B. & Mike Figgis).

TAKE IT HOME.
Tracks: / Better not look down / Same old story / Happy birthday blues / I've always been lonely / Second hand woman / Tonight I'm gonna make you a star / Beginning of the end / Story everybody knows, A / Take it home.
LP: . . . . MCL 1784
MC: . . . . MCLC 1784
LP: . . . . MCF 3010

THERE IS ALWAYS ONE MORE TIME.
LP: . . . . MCA 10295
MC: . . . . MCAC 10295

THERE MUST BE A BETTER WORLD SOMEWHERE.
LP: . . . . MCF 3095
LP: . . . . BGOLP 125

TOGETHER AGAIN - LIVE (see Bland, Bobby) (King, B.B. & Bobby Bland).

TOGETHER FOR THE FIRST TIME - LIVE (King, B.B. & Bobby Bland).
LP: . . . . MCA 24160

TWO STEPS FROM THE BLUES (See under Bland, Bobby) (King, B.B. & Bobby Bland).

King Bee

ROYAL JELLY.
Tracks: / Back by dope demand (Funky bass mix) / Feel the flow / Tonight is the night (backbeat mix) / Rockin' down the house / Havin' a good time / Must bee the music / Gettin' down / Zzignal of hope / Cold slammin' (haunted mix) / Gettin' reckless.
LP: 4677941
MC: 4677944

King, Ben E.

BEN E KING STORY, THE.
Tracks: / Amor / Don't play that song / I (who have nothing) / How can I forget / I could have danced all night / Spanish harlem / That's when it hurts / Auf Wiedersehen my dear / Around the corner / Young boy blues / What now my love / Stand by me.
LP: . . . . K 50139

BENNY & US (See under Average White Band) (King, Ben E. & Average White Band).

DRIFTERS WITH BEN E KING (See under Drifters).

GREATEST HITS: BEN E. KING.
MC: . . . . SD 33165

GREATEST HITS: BEN E KING & DRIFTERS (FUN LABEL) (See under Drifters).

HERE COMES THE NIGHT.
Tracks: / Brace yourself / Here comes the night / On the horizon / Perfidia / Ecstacy / Yes / Jamaica / Tell Daddy / Gypsy / In the middle of the night / It's all over / Let the water run down / River of tears / Seven letters / Record, The / Goodnight my love.
LP: . . . . ED 131

LET ME LIVE IN YOUR LIFE.
Tracks: / Tippin' / Wonder woman / Let me live in your life / I see the light / Fly away / Dark storm on the horizon / Family jewels / Sweet rhapsody / Spoiled / Fifty years.
LP: . . . . K 50527

MUSIC TRANCE.
Tracks: / Music trance / And this is love / Touched by your love / You've only got one chance to be young / Hired gun / Everyday / Work that body.
LP: . . . . K 50713

SAVE THE LAST DANCE FOR ME.
Tracks: / Wheel of love / Save the last dance for me / Because of last night / Lover's question / Whatever this is (it ain't true love) / Halfway to paradise / Let a man do it for you / I cry for you / Test of time / Two lovers.
LP: . . . . MTL 1013
MC: . . . . TCMTL 1013

SPANISH HARLEM.
LP: 590 001

STAND BY ME.
LP: 34045
MC: 64045

STAND BY ME (THE ULTIMATE COLLECTION).
Tracks: / Stand by me / Save the last dance for me / I (Who have nothing) / That's when it hurts / I could have danced all night / First taste of love / Dream lover / Moon river / Spanish harlem / Amor / I count the tears / Don't play that song / This magic moment / Young boy blues / It's all in the game / Supernatural thing (part 1).
LP: . . . . WX 90
MC: . . . . WX 90 C

STREET TOUGH.
Tracks: / Street tough / Made for each other / Staying power / Stay a while with me / Why is the question / You made the difference to my life / Souvenirs of love / Something to be loved.
LP: . . . . K 50787

SUPERNATURAL THING.
Tracks: / Supernatural thing (part 1) / Supernatural thing (part 2) / You're lovin' ain't good enough / Drop my heart off (on your way out the door) / Do it in the name of love / Happiness is where you find it / Do you wanna do a thing / Imagination / What do you want me to do.
LP: . . . . K 50118

King, Bev

MARTY ROBBINS SCRAPBOOK (King, Bev & Joe Knight).
Tracks: / Castle in the sky, A / Begging to you / I'll go on alone / Love me / I couldn't keep from (crying) / Sing me something sentimental / Don't worry / At the end of a long lonely day / It's your world / Hands you're holding now, The / Singing the blues / Pretty words.
LP: . . . . BFX 15217

King, Bill

MAGNOLIA NIGHTS.
LP: 139023-1
MC: 139023-4

King Biscuit Boy

MOUTH OF STEEL.
LP: . . . . RL 049

King Biscuits

GOING INDOORS.
LP: . . . . LONELY MAN 101

King Blank

REAL DIRT, THE.
Tracks: / Howl upside down / Blind box / Real dirt, The / Big pink bang / Guilty as hell / Map of pain / Shot full of holes / Killer in the rain / Uptight / Bulletproof crucifix.
LP: . . . . SITU 21
MC: . . . . SITC 21
LP: . . . . SITL 21

King, Bob

ROCK 'N' ROLL RIOT - CANADIAN ROCK 'N' ROLL (King, Bob & Joey Prestor).
LP: . . . . REDITA 129

King, Bobby

BOBBY KING.
LP: . . . . BSK 3568

LIVE AND LET LIVE (King, Bobby & Terry Evans).
LP: . . . . ROUNDER 2089
MC: . . . . ROUNDER 2089C
LP: . . . . SPD 1016
MC: . . . . SPDC 1016

LOVE IN THE FIRE.
Tracks: / Show me your magic / Somewhere along the way / Close to me / Lovequake / Ain't never met a woman like you / Sweet love / Midnight shine / Fall in love / Love in the fire.
LP: . . . . ZL 72151
MC: . . . . ZK 72151

RHYTHM, BLUES, SOUL AND GROOVES (King, Bobby & Terry Evans).
LP: . . . . SPD 1036
MC: . . . . SPDC 1036

King Carcass

BLIND.
LP: . . . . KAR 005

King, Carole

CITY STREETS.
Tracks: / City streets / Sweet life / Down to the darkness / Lovelight / I can't stop thinking about you / Legacy / Ain't that the way / Midnight flyer / Homeless heart / Someone who believes in you.
LP: . . . . EST 2092
LP: 790885 1
MC: . . . . TCEST 2092

GOFFIN AND KING (See under Goffin/King for details) (Various artists).

HER GREATEST HITS.
Tracks: / Jazzman / So far away / Sweet seasons / I feel the earth move / Brother brother / Only love is real / It's too late / Nightingale / Smackwater Jack / Been to Caanan / Corazon / Believe in humility.
LP: . . . . EPC 32345
MC: 40 32345

MUSIC.
Tracks: / Brother brother / It's gonna take some time / Sweet seasons / Some kind of wonderful / Surely / Carry your load / Music / Song of long ago / Brighter / Growing away from me / Too much rain / Back to California.
LP: . . . . CBS 32066
MC: 40-32066
LP: . . . . AMLH 67013
LP: . . . . EPC 82319

ONE TO ONE.
Tracks: / One to one / It's a war / Lookin out for number one / Life without love / Golden man / Read between the lines / Boomerang / Goar Annie / Someone you never met before / Little prince.
LP: . . . . K 50880

PEARLS (SONGS OF GOFFIN AND KING).
Tracks: / Dancin' with tears in my eyes / One fine day / Locomotion, The / Hey girl / Snow queen / Chains / Oh no not my baby / Hi de ho / Wasn't born to follow / Goin' back.
LP: . . . . FA 3014
MC: . . . . TCFA 3014
LP: . . . . EAST 12073

RHYMES AND REASONS.
LP: . . . . ODE 77016

TAPESTRY.
Tracks: / I feel the earth move / So far away / Beautiful / You've got a friend / Where you lead / Will you love me tomorrow / Smack water Jack / Tapestry / It's too late / Home again / Way over yonder / You make me feel like a natural woman.
LP: . . . . EPC 32110
MC: 40 32110
LP: . . . . AMLS 2025
LP: . . . . EPC 82308

THOROUGHBRED.
Tracks: / So many ways / Daughter of light / High out of time / Only love is real / There's a space between us / I'd like to know you better / We all have to be alone / Ambrosia / Still here thinking of you / It's gonna work out fine.
LP: 31841
MC: 40 31841

TOUCH THE SKY.
Tracks: / Time gone by / Move lightly / Dreamlike I wander / Walk with me / Good mountain people / You still want her / Passing of the days / Crazy / Eagle / Seeing red.
LP: . . . . EA-ST 11953

WRITER.
Tracks: / Spaceship races / No easy way down / Child of mine / Goin' back / To love / What have you got to lose / Eventually / Raspberry jam / Can't you be real / I can't hear you no more / Sweet sweetheart / Up on the roof.
LP: . . . . EPC 82318

King, Charlie

MY HEART KEEPS SNEAKIN' UP ON MY HEAD.
LP: . . . . FF 349

STEPPIN' OUT.
LP: . . . . FF 492

King, Claude

CLAUDE KING'S BEST.
LP: . . . . GT 0066

King, Clive

STIG OF THE DUMP (Jarvis, Martin (nar)).
MC: 882162
MCSET: CC/006

King Cobras

KING COBRAS Feat.Sonny Boy Williamson/Shakey Horton (Various artists).
LP: . . . . FLY 567

King Creole (Film)

KING CREOLE (VIDEO) (See under Presley, Elvis) (Presley, Elvis).

King Crimson

BEAT.
Tracks: / Neal and Jack and Me / Heartbeat / Sartori in Tangier / Waiting man / Neurotica / Two Hands / Howler, The / Requiem.
LP: . . . . EGLP 51
MC: . . . . EGMC 51

COMPACT KING CRIMSON, THE.
Tracks: / Discipline / Thel hun ginjeet / Matte Kudasai / Three of a perfect pair / Frame by frame / Sleepless / Heartbeat / Elephant talk / 21st century schizoid man / I talk to the wind / Epitaph / March for no reason (part of Epitaph) / Tomorrow and tomorrow (part of Epitaph) / Red (LP & cassette only) / Cat food (LP & cassette only) / Court of the crimson king / Return of the fire witch / Dance of the puppets.
2LP: . . . . EGLP 68
MCSET: . . . . EGMC 68

DISCIPLINE.
Tracks: / Elephant talk / Frame by frame / Matte Kudasai / Indiscipline / Thel hun ginjeet / Sheltering sky, The / Discipline.
MC: . . . . EGMC 49
LP: . . . . EGLP 49

EARTHBOUND.
Tracks: / 21st century / Schizoid man / Peoria / Sailors tale / Earthbound / Groon.
LP: 2343 092

IN THE COURT OF THE CRIMSON KING.
Tracks: / 21st century schizoid man / I talk to the wind / Epitaph / Tomorrow and tomorrow (part of Epitaph) / Moonchild / Illusion, The (Part of Moonchild.) / Court of the Crimson King / Return Of The fire witch / Dance of the puppets / March for no reason (part of Epitaph) / Dream, The (part of Moonchild).
LP: EGLP 1
MC: EGMC 1
LP: ILPS 9111

IN THE WAKE OF POSEIDON.
Tracks: / Peace a beginning / Pictures of a city / Cadence and cascade / In the wake of Poseidon / Peace-A theme / Cat food / Devil's triangle / Merday Morn (part 1 of the Devil's Triangle) / Hand of Sceiron (Part 2 of the Devil's Triangle) / Garden of worm (part 3 of the Devil's triangle) / Peace-an End.
LP: EGLP 2
MC: EGMC 2
LP: ILPS 9127

ISLANDS.
Tracks: / Formentera lady / Sailor's tale / Letter, The / Ladies of the road / Prelude: song of the gulls / Islands.
LP: EGLP 5
MC: EGMC 5
LP: 2302 060
MC: 3100 360
LP: ILPS 9175

KING CRIMSON BOX SET (Court of the Crimson King / Larks Tongues in Aspic).
MCSET: EGBM 6

LARK'S TONGUES IN ASPIC, A.
Tracks: / Lark's tongues in aspic, (part 1) / Book of Saturday / Exiles / Easy Money / Talking drum / Lark's tongues in aspic, (part 2).
LP: EGLP 7
MC: EGMC 7
LP: ILPS 9230

LIZARD.
Tracks: / Cirkus / Indoor games / Happy family / Lady of the dancing water / Lizard / Prince Rupert awakes (part 1 of Lizard) / Bolero (The peacocks tale) / Battle of glass tears, The / Dawn song (part a of battle of glass tears) / Last skirmish (part b of Battle of Glass Tears) / Prince Rupert's lament (Part C of Battle of Glass Tears) / Big top.
LP: EGLP 4
MC: EGMC 4
LP: ILPS 9141

RED.
Tracks: / Red / Fallen angel / One more red nightmare / Providence / Starless.
LP: EGLP 15
MC: EGMC 15
LP: 2302 066
MC: 3100 366
LP: ILPS 9308

STARLESS AND BIBLE BLACK.
Tracks: / Great deceiver, The / Lament / We'll let you know / Night watch, The / Trio / Mincer, The / Starless and bible black / Fracture.
LP: 2302 065
MC: 3100 365
LP: EGLP 12
MC: EGMC 12
LP: ILPS 9275

THREE OF A PERFECT PAIR.
Tracks: / Model man / Sleepless / Man with an open heart / Nuages (that which passes, passes like clouds) / Dig me / No warning / Lark's tongues in aspic, (part 3) (In digital stereo) / Three of a perfect pair / Industry.
LP: EGLP 55
MC: EGMC 55

USA.
Tracks: / Lark's tongues in aspic, (part 2) / Lament / Exiles / Asbury Park (Sandy) / Easy money / 21st century / Schizoid man.
LP: 2302 067
LP: EGLP 18

YOUNG PERSON'S GUIDE TO KING CRIMSON.
Tracks: / Epitaph / Cadence and cascade / Ladies of the road / I talk to the wind / Red / Starless / Night watch, The / Book of Saturday / Peace - a theme / Cat food / Groon / Coda from lark's tongue in aspic part 2 / Moonchild / Dream, The / Illusion, The / Trio / Court of the Crimson King / Return of the fire witch / Dance of the puppets.
2LP: 2612 035
MC: 3500 123
LP: EGLP 22

King Diamond

ABIGAIL.
LP: RR 9622
LPPD: RR 69622
MC: RR 49622

CONSPIRACY.
Tracks: / At the graves / Lies / Wedding dream, The / Something weird / Let it be done / Sleepless nights / Visit from the dead, A / Amon belongs to them / Victimized / Cremation.
LP: RR 9461-1
MC: RR 9461-4
LPPD: RR 9461 6

DARK SIDES, THE.
Tracks: / Halloween / Tem / No presents for Christmas / Shrine / Lake, The / Phone call.
LP: RR 24551

EYE, THE.
LP: RR 93461
MC: RR 93464

FATAL PORTRAIT.
LP: RR 9721
MC: RR 97214

THEM.
LP: RR 95501
MC: RR 95504

King, Don

1-2 PUNCH.
LP: DVR 14

King, Dr. Alexander

WORLD AND MEN.
MC: SS 108

King, Earl

BATTLE OF THE BLUES (See Under Guitar Slim) (King, Earl & Guitar Slim).

GLAZED (King, Earl With Roomful Of Blues).
Tracks: / It all went down the drain / Your love was never there / Everybody's gotta cry sometime / Love rent / Iron cupid / Somebody's got a tail! / I met a stranger / Mardi gras in the city / Those lonely lonely nights / One step beyond love.
LP: FIEND 87
LP: BT 1035
MC: BT 1035C

LET THE GOOD TIMES ROLL.
Tracks: / Is everything alright / Those lonely lonely nights / Little girl / My love is strong / I'll take you back home / It must have been love / You can fly high / Darling honey child / Mother told me not to go / Well o well o well o baby / Those lonely lonely feelings / I'll never get tired / Weary silent night / Everybody's carried away.
LP: CH 15

NEW ORLEANS ROCK 'N' ROLL.
Tracks: / Let's make a better world / Trick bag / Do-re-mi / One and one / Time for the sun to rise / Always the first time / Baby sittin' / Mama and papa / Panic's on, The / Let the good times roll.
LP: SNTF 719

SEXUAL TELEPATHY.
Tracks: / Old Mr. Bad Luck / I'll take you back home / Weary silent night, A / Time for the sun to rise / No one more for the road / Going public / Love is the way of life / Sexual telepathy / Happy little nobody's waggy tail dog / Always a first time / Make a better world.
LP: FIEND 168

SOUL BAG The best of Earl King.
Tracks: / Trick bag / You better know / Things that I used to do / Always a first time / Mama and papa / Love me now / Mother's love / Come on (Pt.1) / Come on (Pt.2) / Don't cry my friend / Don't you lose it / We are just good friends / You're more to me than gold / Case of love, A.
LP: SSL 6027
MC: TCSSL 6027
LP: 2C 068 83299

STREET PARADE.
Tracks: / Street parade (Part 1) / You make me feel good / Some people are / Fallin' / Mother's love, A / Mama and papa / Medieval days / This is what I call living / Do the grind / Part of me, A / Love look out for me / Street parade (Part 2) / All my love / I'm gonna keep on trying / Up on her hill / Am I your dog (Part 1) / Am I your dog (Part 2) / Real McCoy, The.
LP: CRM 2021

King, Eddie

BLUES HAS GOT ME, THE.
LP: DT 3017

King, Eileen

COUNTRY FLAVOUR, THE.
Tracks: / Silver threads and golden needles / Texas in my heart / Charlie Brown / Travelling home / Johnny / Jesus hears / You'll never miss the water / Hello trouble / You're driving me out of my mind / You ain't woman enough / Connemara cradle song / What's the bottle done to my baby.
LP: PHL 408
MC: CPHL 408

COUNTRY GIFTS.
MC: TSC 100

FROM NASHVILLE.
MC: TSC 124

SONGS OF IRELAND (20 songs).
LP: UNKNOWN

King, Evelyn

BEST OF EVELYN 'CHAMPAGNE' KING, THE.
Tracks: / Shame / I'm in love / If you want my lovin' / Just for the night / Betcha she don't love you / I'm so romantic / Back to love (Only on cassette and CD.) / I don't know if it's right / Love come down / Action / High horse / Get loose / Music box / Shake down / I can't stand it / Your personal touch.
LP: NL 74538
MC: NK 74538

CHAMPAGNE.
LP: PL 84725
MC: PK 84725

FLIRT.
Tracks: / Flirt / You can turn me on / Kisses don't lie / Stop it / Hold on to what you've got / When your heart says yes / Before the date / Whenever you touch me.
LP: MTL 1022
MC: TCMTL 1022
LP: EI 46968

GET LOOSE.
Tracks: / Love come down / I can't stand it / Betcha she don't love you / Get loose / Back to love / Stop that / Get up off your love / I'm just warmin' up.
LP: RCALP 3093
MC: RCAK 3093

GIRL NEXT DOOR, THE.
Tracks: / Girl next door, The / Magnet / Day to day / Cross your mind / Footsteps in the dark / Do right / Love man / Serious / This song / Thief in the night.
LP: MTL 1050
MC: TCMTL 1050

I'M IN LOVE.
Tracks: / Your personal touch / I'm in love / If you want my lovin' / Don't hide our love / What are you waiting for / Spirit of the dancer / Other side of love, The / I can't take it / Best is yet to come, The.
LP: RCALP 5048
MC: RCAK 5048

LONG TIME COMING, A.
Tracks: / Chemistry of love / Change is gonna come, A / Spellbound / If you find the time / Slow down / If I let myself go / Your personal touch / I'm scared / High horse.
LP: PL 87015
MC: PK 87015

MUSIC BOX.
Tracks: / Steppin' out / I think my heart is telling / Let's start all over again / Music box / Make up your mind / Out there / It's OK / No time for fooling around.
LP: PL 13033

SHAME.
LP: INTS 5240
MC: NK 89420

SMOOTH TALK.
Tracks: / Smooth talk / I don't know if it's right / Till I come off the road / Dancin' dancin' dancin' / Shame / Nobody knows / We're going to a party / Show is over, The.
LP: PL 12466
MC: PK 12466

SO ROMANTIC.
Tracks: / Show me / Heartbreaker / Till midnight / Just for the night / Give me one reason / Out of control / Talking in my sleep / So in love / I'm so romantic.
LP: PL 85308
MC: PK 85308

King, Freddie

BURGLAR.
LP: 831 815-1

FREDDIE KING.
LP: BID 8012

FREDDIE KING, 1934 - 1976.
LP: 831 817-1

GIVES YOU A BONANZA OF INSTRUMENTALS.
Tracks: / Surf monkey / Low tide / Remington ride / King-a-ling / Manhole / Fish fair / Funnybone / Ploughed sailin' / Sad nite owl / Nickleplated / Freddie's midnite dream / Freeway 75 / Sidetracked / Was out / Driving sideways / Untouchable glide.
LP: CCR 1010
LP: CCX 1010

HIDEAWAY.
LP: BID 8015

LARGER THAN LIFE.
LP: 831 816-1

LIVE IN ANTIBES 1974.
Tracks: / Going down the Highway / Woman across the river / It ain't nobody's business if I do / Let the good times roll / Big legged woman / Have you ever loved a woman / Hideaway.
LP: FC 111

LIVE IN NANCY 1975 VOL.1.
LP: FC 126

ROCKIN' THE BLUES LIVE.
Tracks: / Hideaway / Big legged woman / Key to the highway / Mojo boogie / Wee baby blues / Meet me in the morning / Blues band shuffle.
LP: CCR 1005

TAKIN' CARE OF BUSINESS.
Tracks: / I'm tore down / She put the wammee on me / Sen-sa-shun / Teardrops on your letter / Side tracked / Welfare, The (turns its back on you) / Stumble, The / Some day after a while (you'll be sorry) / Have you ever loved a woman / You know that you love me (but you never tell me so) / Hide away / I love the woman / San-ho-zay / Takin' care of business / High rise / You've got to love her with a feeling.
LP: CRB 1099
MC: TCCRB 1099

TEXAS CANNONBALL LIVE.
Tracks: / Spoken introduction / Ain't gonna worry anymore / Guitar blues / Boogie on down / Your move / Hideaway / Meet me in the morning / Sweet home Chicago.
LP: MMLP 99003

King, Henry

VICTORY PARADE (See Sanders, Joe) (King, Henry/Joe Sanders).

King Henrys Consort

KING HENRYS CONSORT.
LP: EDEN LP 1

King & I

KING AND I (Original Broadway cast) (Various artists).
Tracks: / Overture: *Various artists* / I whistle a happy tune: *Various artists* / My lord and master: *Various* artists / Hello, young lovers: *Various artists* / March of the Siamese children: *Various artists* / Puzzlement, A: *Various artists* / Getting to know you: *Various artists* / We kiss in a shadow: *Various artists* / Shall I tell you what I think of you?: *Various artists* / Something wonderful: *Various artists* / I have dreamed: *Various artists* / Shall we dance?: *Various artists*.
LP: MCL 1663
MC: MCLC 1663
LP: ABL 12610
LP: CDL 8026
MC: TC CDL 8026

KING AND I (1977 Broadway Cast) (Various artists).
Tracks: / Arrival at Bangkok: *Various artists* / I whistle a happy tune: *Various artists* / My lord and master: *Various artists* / Hello, young lovers: *Various artists* / March of the Siamese children: *Various artists*/ Puzzlement, A: *Various artists* / Royal Bangkok Academy: *Various artists* / Getting to know you: *Various* artists / So big a world: *Various artists* / We kiss in a shadow: *Various artists* / Shall I tell you what I think of you?: *Various artists* / Something wonderful: *Various artists* / Western people funny: *Various* artists / Dance of Anna and Sir Edward: *Various artists* / I have dreamed: *Various artists* / Song of the king: *Various artists* / Shall we dance?: *Various artists*.
LP: BL 12610
MC: BK 12610

KING AND I (Original London Cast) (Various artists).
LP: DS 15014

King in Love (bk)

KING IN LOVE, A (Barbara Cartland) (Rodska, Christian (nar)).
MC: IAB 88103

King Is Dead

KING IS DEAD, THE (Elvis Presley tribute) (Various artists).
LP: MFLP 1015

King John

KING JOHN (see under Shakespeare, William) (Various artists).

KING'S COUNTRY.
MC: CDR 006

PORTRAIT: JOHN KING.
Tracks: / True life country music / She's a go'er / I'll leave this world loving you / Time after time / Bridge that just won't burn / Coming home to you / No one will ever know / Jesus loves cowboys the same / How sure I am / Lay down beside me / That's all that matters / Neon lights.

LP: . . . . JULEP 25

King, Jonathan

BUTTERFLY THAT STAMPED, THE.
Tracks: / Everyone's gone to the moon / Hooked on a feeling / Johnny reggae / It's a tall order for a short guy / Living in a f***in' time warp / Very, very melancholy man, A / Chicka boom / Let it all hang out / One for you, one for me / Una paloma blanca / Sugar sugar / It's the same old song / Old D.J.'s / Learning the game / Just like a woman / Rag doll / Flirt / Satisfaction / Sun has got his hat on, The / You've lost that lovin' feeling / Sickly sweet odour of rotting teeth, The / He's so fine / Wild world / When I was a star / It only takes a minute / Lazybones / I say a little prayer / I'll slap your face / Million dollar bash / Can't get it out of my head / In the mood / Loop di love.
2LP: . . . . JKDLP 001
MC: . . . . JKDMC 001

IT ONLY TAKES A MINUTE (See under One Hundred Ton & A Feather).

KING SIZE KING.
Tracks: / Una paloma blanca / Sugar sugar / Let it all hang out / One for you one for me / Loop di love / It only takes a minute / It's the same old song / In the mood / Everyone's gone to the moon / Lazybones / Flirt / Johnny reggae / Chicka boom / I can't get no satisfaction / Hooked on a feeling / Sun has got his hat on, The.
LP: . . . . NCP 1007
MC: . . . . ZCNCP 1007

LICK A SMURP FOR CHRISTMAS (ALL FALL DOWN) (See under Father Abraphart) (Father Abraphart & The Smurps).

King Kobra

KING KOBRA III.
MC: . . . . TMFN 86
LP: . . . . MFN 86

THRILL OF A LIFETIME.
Tracks: / Second time around / Dream on / Feel the heat / Thrill of a lifetime / Only the strong survive / Iron eagle (never say die) / Home street home / Overnight sensation / Raise your hands to rock / Party animals.
LP: . . . . WKFMLP 83
MC: . . . . WKFMMC 83

King Kong

BIG HEAVY LOAD.
LP: . . . . WENLP 3024

DANCE HALL SESSION.
LP: . . . . WENLP 3017

IDENTIFY ME.
Tracks: / I don't cry / Digital my digital / She's on my mind / Kill them with the rythm / Bow to Jehovah / Identify me / Rave with me / Speak the truth.
LP: . . . . BSILP 001

KING KONG (ORIGINAL ISSUE) (South Africa) (Various artists).
LP: . . . . LK 4392

MUSICAL CONFRONTATION (see Nitty Gritty).

TROUBLE AGAIN.
Tracks: / Mash it up already / Move insane / Follow me / Mix up / Sweet and tender love / Trouble again / Jungle man / I don't know / Legal / Emmanual Road.
LP: . . . . GREL 101

King Kong (Film)

KING KONG (Film Soundtrack) (National Philharmonic Orchestra).
Tracks: / Boat in the fog, A / Jungle dance / Sea at night, The / Aboriginal sacrifical dance / Entrance of Kong / Log sequence, The / Cryptic Shadow / Cave, The / Sailors waiting / Return of Kong / King Kong theatre march / Aeroplanes, Finale.
LP: . . . . FILM 013
LP: . . . . ERS 6504

KING KONG LIVES (Original soundtrack) (Various artists).
LP: . . . . MCA 6203
MC: . . . . MCAC 6203

King Kurt

BIG COCK.
LP: . . . . SEEZ 62
MC: . . . . ZSEEZ 62

DESTINATION DEMOLAND.
LP: . . . . LINKLP 133

KING KURT.
Tracks: / Zulu beat / Destination Zulu land / Bo Diddley goes East / King Kurt's hound dog / Wreck a party rock / Riders in the sky / Gather your limbs / When the saints go marching in / Rockin' Kurt / Lonesome train (on a lonesome track) / Mack the knife / Oedipus / Do the rat.
LP: . . . . SEEZ 52

LAST WILL AND TESTICLE (1981 - 1988).
Tracks: / Destination Zululand / Zulu beat / Bo Diddley goes East / Mack the knife / Wreck-a-party rock / Land of Ring Dang Doo, The / America / Goats and monkeys / Banana banana / Billy / Road to rack and ruin / Slammers.
LP: . . . . GWLP 24
MC: . . . . GWTC 24

King Lear

KING LEAR (See under Shakespeare, William) (Various artists).

King, Mark

INFLUENCES.
Tracks: / Essential, The / Clocks go forward / I feel free / Pictures on the wall / There is a dog.
LP: . . . . MKLP 1
MC: . . . . MKMC 1

King, Marva

FEELS RIGHT.
Tracks: / Feels right / Do you want to make love / Think it over / Suspicions / Who's right, who's wrong / Two lovers / Memories / Isle of castaways / Here we go again / Feeling wonderful feelings.
LP: . . . . K 52287

King Missile

FLUTING THE HUMP.
LP: . . . . SR 6987
LP: . . . . SHIMMY 003

MYSTICAL SHIT.
Tracks: / Mystical shit / Rock'n'roll will never die / No point / Gary and Melissa / Frightened and freezing / How to remember your dreams / Fish that played the ponies / Jesus was way cool / Open / Sandbox, The / Neither world, The / She didn't want / Cheesecake truck / Equivalences / Love you more / Fourthly.
LP: . . . . SDE 9016 LP

THEY.
LP: . . . . SHIMMY 015

King, Morgana

EVERYTHING MUST CHANGE.
LP: . . . . MR 5190

HIGHER GROUND.
LP: . . . . MR 5224

PORTRAITS.
Tracks: / What's going on / You go to my head / Moment of truth / Time was / Send in the clowns / Lush life / You're not the kind / If you could see me now / Save the chidern.
LP: . . . . MR 5301
MC: . . . . MRC 5301

STRETCHIN' OUT.
Tracks: / What a difference a day made / Makin; whoopee / Them there eyes / I'm glad there is you / God bless the child / Could it be magic / All in love is fair / Visions / Feelings.
LP: . . . . MR 5166

TASTE OF HONEY, A.
Tracks: / Taste of honey, A / Fascinating rhythm / Prelude to a kiss / Easy living / All blues / Bluesette / Easy to love / Night has a thousand eyes, The / Lady is a tramp, The / Try to remember / Meditation / I'll follow you / Sometimes I feel like a motherless child.
LP: . . . . MRL 5009

King, Nosmo

GOODBYE NOTHING TO SAY (see under Javells) (King, Nosmo & The Javells).

King Of Comedy

KING OF COMEDY (Original soundtrack) (Various artists).
LP: 23765.1

King Of Kings

KING OF KINGS (Film Soundtrack) (Various artists).
Tracks: / King of Kings theme: *Various artists* / Holy of holies: *Various artists* / Pontius Pilate's arrival in Jerusalem: *Various artists* / Virgin Mary: *Various artists* / Nativity: *Various artists* / Temptation of Christ: *Various artists* / John the baptist: *Various artists* / Miracles of Christ: *Various artists*/ Salome's dance: *Various artists* / Mount Galilee and the sermon on the mount: *Various artists* / Prayer of our Lord: *Various artists* / Christ's entry into Jersulem: *Various artists* / Tempest in Judea: *Various artists*/ Way of cross: *Various artists* / Scourging of Christ: *Various artists* / Mary at the sepulchre: *Various artists* / Resurrection: *Various artists* / Finale: *Various artists*.
LP: 2353 035

KING OF KINGS (Film soundtrack) (Various artists).
LP: . . . . MCA 39056
MC: . . . . MCAC 39056

KING OF KINGS/GREATEST STORY EVER TOLD (MGM Original Soundtrack Album) (Various artists).
Tracks: / King of Kings theme: *Various artists* / Holy of holies: *Various artists* / Pontius Pilate's arrival into Jerusalem: *Various artists* / Virgin Mary, The: *Various artists* / Nativity: *Various artists* / Temptation of Christ, The: *Various artists* / John the Baptist: *Various artists* / Miracles of Christ, The: *Various artists*/ Salome's dance: *Various artists* / Mount Galilee and the sermon on the mount: *Various artists* / Prayer of Our Lord: *Various artists* / Christ's entry into Jerusalem: *Various artists* / Scourging of Christ, The: *Various* artists / Way of the cross, The: *Various artists* / Mary at the Sepulcher: *Various artists* / Resurrection - finale: *Various artists* / Jesus of Nazareth: *Various artists* / Prophesy, A: *Various artists* / Voice in the wilderness, A: *Various artists* / Great journey, The: *Various artists* / Time of wonders, A: *Various* artists / There shall come a time to enter: *Various artists* / New commandment, A: *Various artists* / Hour has come, The: *Various artists* / Into thy hands: *Various artists*.
LP: . . . . LPMGM 25
LP: 794 987 1
MC: . . . . TCMGM 25
MC: 794 987 4

King Of Luxembourg

ROYAL BASTARD.
Tracks: / Picture of Dorian Gray, A / Valleri / Rubens rooms, The / Mad / Poptones / Something / Baby / Wedding of Ramona Blair / Happy together (prelude) / Liar liar.
LP: . . . . ACME 3

SIR & ROYAL BASTARD, THE.
Tracks: / Flirt / Personality parade / Walnut whirl / Sorry / Penny was a tomboy / Chateau palmier '61 / Turbab disturbance / Battle for beauty / Queen of Luxembourg, The / Her eyes are a blue million miles / Virgin on the rocks / Picture of Dorian Gray / Valleri / Ruben room, The / Mad / Poptines / Something for Sophia Loren / Baby / Wedding of Ramona Blair / Happy together (prelude) / Smash hit wonder / Happy together / Liar liar.
LP: . . . . ACME 16
MC: . . . . ACME 16C

King Of The Castle

KING OF THE CASTLE, THE (See also Victoria Holt) (Jameson, Susan (nar)).

King Of The Hill

KING OF THE HILL.
Tracks: / Party in my pocket / Freak show / I do u / If I say / Roses / Take it or leave it (Kingadahill) / Something 'bout you / Place in my heart / Big groove / Electric riot.
LP: . . . . SBKLP 15
MC: . . . . SBKTC 15

King Of The Slums

BARBAROUS ENGLISH FAIRE.
Tracks: / Simpering blonde bombshell / England's leading light / Up to the fells / Bedevilment's favourite son / Bombs away on Harpurhey / Pennine spitter / Leery bleeder / Fanciable headcase.
LP: . . . . DEC 22
LP: . . . . CHIME 109

BLOWZY WEIRDOS.
Tracks: / Gone all weirdo / Smile so big / Casin' the joint / Hot pot shebeen / Keepin' it all sweet / Clubland gangs / Joy / Rimo (F. Rimson) / Mard arse / Mood on / Blowzy luv of life.
LP: BRED93

DANDELIONS.
LP: . . . . CHIME 0104
MC: . . . . CHIME 0104C

King Oney

COUNTRY PEOPLE WE LOVE.
LP: . . . . UNKNOWN

King, Paul

JOY.
Tracks: / Follow my heart / When you smile / I know / Pass on by / So brutal / It's up to you / One too many heartaches / Slow motion / Some risks / Glory's goal.
LP: 4505291
MC: 4505294

King, Pee Wee

BALLROOM KING.
Tracks: / Catty town / Plantation boogie / I don't mind / Blue suede shoes / Steel rag guitar / Railroad boogie / Rootie tootie / Half a dozen boogie / Ballroom baby / Ten gallon boogie / Hoot scoot / Chew tobacco rag / Forty nine women / Indian giver / Bull fiddle boogie / Tweedle dee.
LP: DT33-001

BEST OF PEE WEE KING (King, Pee Wee & Redd Stewart).
LP: . . . . SLP 965
MC: . . . . GT 5965

HOG WILD TOO.
LP: . . . . Z 2017

ROMPIN', STOMPIN', SINGIN', SWINGIN'.
Tracks: / Birmingham bounce / Ghost and honest Joe, The / Say good morning, Nellie / Goin' back to L.A. (Previously unissued.) / Tennessee central number nine / Texas Toni Lee / Keep them icy cold fingers off of me / Lonesome steel guitar (Previously unissued.) / Quit honkin' that horn / New York to New Orleans / I hear you knocking / Oh Monah / Mop rag boogie / Jukebox blues / Flying home / Slow bike.
LP: . . . . BFX 15101

King, Peggy

OH WHAT A MEMORY WE MADE TONIGHT.
LP: . . . . ST 238

SINGS JEROME KERN.
LP: . . . . ST 246

King, Peter

CRUSADE.
LP: . . . . BYN 19
MC: . . . . BYNC 19

MY KIND OF COUNTRY.
LP: . . . . BSS 114

King, Peter Quartet

BROTHER BERNARD.
Tracks: / Overjoyed / But beautiful / Dalin / Brother Bernard / Chatelet / Playing in the yard.
LP: . . . . MM 076

EAST 34TH STREET.
LP: . . . . SPJ 524

HI FLY (King, Peter with Philippe Briand Trio).
LP: . . . . SPJ 527

NEW BEGINNING.
Tracks: / Blues for S.J. / Dolphin dance. / Before the dawn / Dream dancing / Fourth emergence / New beginning / Three blonde mice / Gingerbread boy / Confirmation.
LP: . . . . SPJ 520

NINETY PERCENT OF ONE PERCENT.
Tracks: / Old folks / 3/4 peace / Eye of the hurricane / Gingerhead boy.
LP: . . . . SPJ 529

King, Philip

RINCE GREAG (King, Philip & Peter Browne).
LP: . . . . CEF 090

King Pin

LETTER FROM JAIL.
LP: . . . . ARILP 059

King Pleasure

KING PLEASURE & THE BISCUIT BOYS (King Pleasure & The Biscuit Boys).
LP: . . . . BEAR 30

THIS IS IT (King Pleasure & The Biscuit Boys).
LP: . . . . BEAR 32
MC: . . . . BEARMC 32

King Pleasure (2)

KING PLEASURE AND ANNIE ROSS SING (King Pleasure & Annie Ross).
Tracks: / Red top / Sometimes I'm happy / What can I say after I say I'm sorry / Parker's mood / Twisted / Time was right, The / Jumpin' with symphony sid / This is always / Don't get scared / I'm gone / Farmer's market / Annie's lament.
LP: . . . . PR 7128
MC: . . . . PRC 7128

KING PLEASURE SINGS/ANNIE ROSS SINGS (King Pleasure & Annie Ross).
LP: . . . . OJC 217

King Richard

KING RICHARD (Various artists).
MC: . . . . STC 301C

King, Sandra

CONCERT OF VERNON DUKE, A (King, Sandra/Pat Smythe).
LP: . . . . AP 197

MAGIC WINDOW, THE (King, Sandra & Richard Rodney Bennett).
LP: . . . . AP 222

King, Saunders

FIRST KING OF THE BLUES.
Tracks: / Summertime boogie part 1 / Summertime boogie part 2 / Lazy woman / Every night about midnight / Read the good book / I'm so worried / Get yourself another fool / I had a dream last night / Drop me a line / My close

friend / Quit hanging around / Long long time / Quit hanging around (alternative version) / Going mad / Empty bedroom blues / Summertime / Saunders King blues / What's the story morning glory.
2LP: . . . . CHD 248

WHAT'S YOUR STORY MORNING GLORY.
Tracks: / Swingin' / Why was I born / Write me a letter blues / What's your story, morning glory? / What's your story, morning glory? / S.K. groove / Something's worrying me / 2.00 a.m. hop / St. James infirmary blues / Little girl / Empty bedroom blues / Imagination / Stormy night / Stormy night blues / Read the good book / Misery blues / Danny boy / Going mad.
LP: . . . . BB 303

King, Sid

GONNA SHAKE THIS SHACK TONIGHT (King, Sid & The Five Strings).
Tracks: / Good rockin' baby / Put something in the pot boy / Drinking spoli oli / When my baby left me / Gonna shake this shack tonight / It's true, I'm blue / Crazy little heart / Mama, I want you / I like it / But I don't care / Warmed over kisses ((Previously unissued)) / What have ya got to lose / I've got the blues / Ooby dooby / Booger red / Twenty one ((Previously unissued)) / Sag, drag and fall / Blue suede shoes / Let 'er roll / Purr, kitty, purr.
LP: . . . . BFX 15048

LET'S GET LOOSE.
Tracks: / House of blue lights / One more time / If you really want me to I'll go / Share what you got with me / Back door man / Boogie woogie country girl / Let's get loose / Decoy baker / Don't get above your raising / It hurts me so (To see love go) / Rockabilly music / Drinkin' wine spoil oil.
LP: . . . . LP 8701

ROCKIN' ON THE RADIO (King, Sid & The Five Strings).
Tracks: / Rock the joint / Little Willie boogie / If tears could cry / In the jailhouse now / Slowly / Who put the turtle in Myrtle's girdle / That's alright / Five string hoedown / Rock my soul / Maybellene / Wildwood flower / There she goes / Making believe / Flip flop and fly.
LP: . . . . ROLL 2006

King Sisters

KING SISTERS AND FRANK DEVOL, 1947 (King Sisters/Frank DeVol & Orchestra).
Tracks: / For you / Just squeeze me / When the swallows come back to capistrano / What's the use / Sophisticated lady / Everybody loves my baby / At sundown / Between the devil and the deep blue sea / Stardust / When my dreamboat comes home / Crazy rhythm / Miss Otis regrets / Red sails in the sunset / Man I love, The.
LP: . . . . HSR 168

King Snake Roost

FROM BARBARISM TO CHRISTIAN MANHOOD.
LP: . . . . MD 7914

GROUND INTO THE DIRT.
LP: . . . . ABE 910

King, Solomon

NON SUPPORT BLUES.
LP: . . . . DD 4303

SHE WEARS MY RING.
LP: . . . . SCX 6250

King Solomon's Mines

KING SOLOMON'S MINES (see under Haggard, H. Rider) (Anderson, Miles).

KING SOLOMON'S MINES Haggard, H. Rider (Jayston, Michael).
MC: . . . . P 90039

KING SOLOMON'S MINES (see Haggard, H Rider) (Young, John).

King Solomons Mines

KING SOLOMON'S MINES (Film Soundtrack) (Various artists).
Tracks: / Main title: *Various artists* / Upside down people: *Various artists* / Crocodiles: *Various artists*/ pot luck: *Various artists* / Forced flight: *Various artists* / Dancing shots: *Various artists* / Good morning: *Various artists* / No pain: *Various artists* / Ritual, The: *Various artists* / No diamonds -Generique fin: *Various artists*.
LP: . . . . A 259
MC: . . . . C 259

King Sounds

FROM STRENGTH TO STRENGTH.
LP: . . . . VZA 001 LP

THERE IS A REWARD (King Sounds & The Israelites).
LP: . . . . KSILP 003

King Sporty

MEET ME AT THE DISCO (LP).
LP: . . . . DF 3002

King, Stephen (aut)

I AM THE DOORWAY (Bishop, Ed (aut)).
Tracks: / I am the doorway / One for the road.
MC: . . . . PTB 615

THINNER (Sorvino, Paul).
MCSET: . . . . LFP 7254
MCSET: . . . . TCLFP 7254

King Stur-Guv Sounds

LIVE AT CLARENDON J.A..
LP: . . . . DHS 004

King Sun

RIGHTEOUS BUT RUTHLESS.
LP: . . . . FILER 299
MC: . . . . FILECT 299

XL.
Tracks: / On the club tip / Lethal weapon / All in / Fat tape / Snakes / Hey love / Do I love you / Time to go / It's a heat up / Coming soon.
LP: . . . . FILER 270
MC: . . . . FILERCT 270

King Swamp

KING SWAMP.
Tracks: / Is this love / Man behind the gun, The / Widders dump / Mirror, The / Louisiana bride / Blown away / Original man, The / Year zero / Motherlode / Sacrament.
LP: . . . . V 2577
MC: . . . . TCV 2577

WISEBLOOD.
LP: . . . . V 2647
MC: . . . . TCV 2647

King, Teddy

LOVERS AND LOSERS.
LP: . . . . AP 117

SOMEONE TO LIGHT UP YOUR LIFE.
LP: . . . . AP 150

King Tee

AT YOUR OWN RISK.
LP: C1 92359
MC: C4 92359

King Tubby

DANGEROUS DUB (King Tubby/Root Radic).
LP: . . . . COP LP 2

DUB FROM THE ROOTS.
LP: . . . . TSL 106

KING AT THE CONTROLS.
Tracks: / Taos special / Raving dub / Dub up dub.
LP: . . . . VSLP 2006

KING TUBBY MEETS THE UPSETTER AT THE GRASS ROOTS (King Tubby/ The Upsetters).
Tracks: / Blood of Africa / African roots / Rain roots / Wood roots / Luke lane rock / People from the grass roots / Crime wave / No justice for the poor / 300 years at the grass roots / King and The Upsetters at Spanish town.
LP: . . . . STLP 001

KING TUBBY THE DUBMASTER WITH THE WATERHOUSE POSSE.
Tracks: / Real dub stylee / Dub you hold.
LP: . . . . VSLP 4015

KING TUBBY'S SPECIAL: '73 - '76.
LP: . . . . TRLD 409

MAJESTIC TUB.
LP: . . . . PTPLP 1029

POETS OF DUB, THE.
LP: . . . . TSL 105

SENSI DUB VOL. 2 & 3 (see under Perry, Lee) (Perry, Lee/King Tubby).

SENSI DUB VOLUME 3 (King Tubby & Prince Jammy).
Tracks: / Black up (dub) / Sensi dub (part 3) / Free herb (dub) / Ministers (dub) / No bush (dub) / Meditation (dub) / Court house (dub) / Heavy metal (dub).
LP: . . . . OMLP 016

SHALUM DUB (King Tubby & the Aggrovators).
LP: . . . . KLP 9002

SURROUNDED BY THE DREADS AT THE NATIONAL ARENA.
LP: . . . . STLP 003

TRIBUTE.
2LP: . . . . UNKNOWN

TRIBUTE TO KING TUBBY.
LP: . . . . SSBLP 1

King, Wayne

PIANO MAGIC.
Tracks: / Cross hands boogie / Taboo / As time goes by / Mambo jambo / Cavatina / Begin the beguine / Holiday for strings / Someone to watch over me / In an 18th century drawing room / Continental / Tenderly / Chopsticks.
LP: . . . . MFP 50379

WALTZ YOU SAVED FOR ME, THE (1936-53) (King, Wayne & His Orchestra).
LP: . . . . BS 7142
MC: . . . . BS 7142C

King, Will

BACK UP AGAINST THE WALL.
LP: . . . . FL 85710
MC: . . . . FK 85710

Kingbeats

PRESENTING THE KINGBEATS.
LP: . . . . RSRLP 1013

Kingdom Come

HANDS OF TIME.
LP: 8493291
MC: 8493294

IN YOUR FACE.
Tracks: / Do you like it / Wind, The / Highway 6 / Just like a wild rose / Mean dirty Joe / Who do you love / Gotta go (can't wage a war) / Faith hope and love / In your face / Moonlight sonata / Waiting on you / Perfect 'O' / Overrated / Stargazer.
LP: 839 192 1
MC: 839 192 4

KINGDOM COME.
Tracks: / Living out of touch / Pushin' hard / What love can be / 17 / Shuffle, The / Get it on / Now 'forever after' / Hideaway / Loving you / Shout it out.
LP: . . . . KCLP 1
MC: . . . . KCMC 1

KINGDOM COME: INTERVIEW PICTURE DISC.
LPPD: . . . . BAK 2149

Kingdom Under the...

KINGDOM UNDER THE SEA, THE (Joan Aiken).
MCSET: 086 222 0407

Kinghorse

KINGHORSE.
Tracks: / Freeze / Caged / Lay down and die / Brother doubt / Greatest gift / Red / Descend / As I stand / Razor / Too far gone / Clayfist.
LP: . . . . CARLP 11
MC: . . . . CARC 11

Kings

KINGS ARE HERE.
Tracks: / This beat goes on / Switchin' to glide / It's OK / Go away / Partitis / Run shoes running / Anti hero man / Love store / Don't let me know / My habit.
LP: . . . . K 52250

Kings and Queens...

KINGS AND QUEENS OF ENGLAND 1,000 years of English monarchy.
MC: . . . . WHC 006

KINGS AND QUEENS OF ENGLAND: BOOK 1 (history for ages 8+) (Unknown narrator(s)).
MC: . . . . PLBH 108

KINGS AND QUEENS OF ENGLAND: BOOK 2 (history for ages 8+) (Unknown narrator(s)).
MC: . . . . PLBH 109

Kings College Choir

BYRD - THE GREAT SERVICE.
LP: . . . . EL 270 564 1
MC: . . . . EL 270 564 4

CAROLS FOR CHRISTMAS EVE.
LP: . . . . CSD 3774
MC: . . . . TCCSD 3774

CAROLS FROM KINGS.
LP: . . . . CSD 3661
MC: . . . . TCCSD 3661

CAROLS FROM KINGS (2).
Tracks: / Once in Royal David's City / O little town of Bethlehem / First Nowell, The / I saw three ships / Personent hodie / Myn lyking / Spotless rose, A / Away in a manger / I sing of a maiden / O come, o come, Emmanuel / While shepherds watched / Up good Christian folk / In the bleak mid Winter / Silent night / Holly and the ivy, The / It came upon a midnight clear / Three kings / On Christmas night / Child is born in Bethlehem, A / In dulci jubilo / O come, all ye faithful / Hark the herald angels sing.
MC: . . . . EG 763 179 4

CHICHESTER PSALMS.
LP: . . . . ASD 3035

CHORAL FAVOURITES FROM KINGS COLLEGE.
Tracks: / Hallelujah chorus / Jesu joy of man's desiring / Lord is my shepherd, The / Holy holy holy / Land of hope and glory.
LP: . . . . SXLP 30308
MC: . . . . TCCFP 4570

CHRISTMAS CAROLS.
Tracks: / Once in Royal David's city / O come, o come Emmanuel / In the bleak mid Winter / Silent night / Hark the herald angels sing.
LP: . . . . EG 2907011
MC: . . . . EG 2907014

CHRISTMAS MUSIC FROM KINGS.
LP: . . . . ESD 7050
MC: . . . . TCESD 7050

CHRISTMAS MUSIC: MESSIAH.
LP: . . . . CSD 3669

CORONATION (HANDEL).
LP: . . . . ASD 1434451

CORONATION ODE (ELGAR).
LP: . . . . ASD 3345

FESTIVAL OF LESSONS AND CAROLS.
Tracks: / Once in Royal David's City / Bidding prayer, The / Resonet in Laudibus / First lesson / Adam lay ybounden / Sussex carol / Second lesson / Joseph and Mary / Third lesson / Maiden most gentle, A / Fourth lesson / Stille nacht / Chester carol / Fifth lesson / Angels, from the realms of glory / Sixth lesson / Babe is born, A / Seventh lesson / Adeste fideles / Collect and blessing, The / Hark the herald angels sing / Choral prelude.
LP: . . . . CN 2041
MC: CN4 2041
LP: . . . . ASD 3778
MC: . . . . TCASD 3778
MC: . . . . EG 763 180 4

FIVE MYSTICAL SONGS.
LP: . . . . ASD 2458

KING'S CHORAL FAVOURITES.
MC: . . . . TCSXLP 30308

MESSIAH CHORUSES (HANDEL).
LP: . . . . CSD 3778

MUSIC OF BYRD.
MC: CFP4 14481 4
MC: . . . . TCCFP 4481

ONCE IN ROYAL DAVID'S CITY.
LP: . . . . CSD 3698
MC: . . . . TCCSD 3698

ORLANDO GIBBONS (Tudor Church Music).
Tracks: / Almighty and everlasting God / Voluntary - nunc dimittis (Organ) / Fantasia for double organ (Organ) / Now shall the praises of the Lord be sung / Nunc dimittis (second service) / This is the record of John / O Lord of hosts / O Thou, the Central Orb / Song of joy unto the Lord we sing, A / See, see the Word is incarnate (Verse anthem) / Come, kiss me with those lips of thine / Lift up your heads, o ye gates / Hosanna to the Son of David (Full anthem).
LP: . . . . DCA 514
MC: . . . . ZC DCA 514

PROCESSION WITH CAROLS ON ADVENT SUNDAY.
Tracks: / Matin responsory / Come, Thou redeemer of the Earth / First lesson / Rorate coeli / Second lesson, The / O come, o come Emmanuel / Third lesson, The / Twas in the year / Cherry tree carol, The / King Jesus hath a garden / On Jordan's bank / Fifth lesson / Gabriel's message / Watchet auf! / Sixth lesson, The / I wonder as I wander / My dancing day / Vesper responsory / Prayers and blessing / Lo he comes with clouds descending / Nun komm der Heiden heiland.
LP: . . . . ASD 3907
MC: . . . . TCCASD 3907
MC: . . . . EG 763 181 4

PSALMS OF DAVID, THE.
MC: . . . . TCESD 1077974

PSALMS OF DAVID, THE VOL. 1.
Tracks: / I was glad / Like as the heart (psalm 42) / Give sentence with me (psalm 43) / Praise the Lord, O my soul (psalm 104) / Hear my crying, O God (psalm 61) / Earth is the Lord's, The / I will up mine eyes (psalm 121) / Lord's my shepherd, The / God is our hope and strength (psalm 46) / O how amiable (psalm 84) / Lord who shall dwell (psalm 15) / By the waters of Babylon / O praise the Lord (psalm 147) / O praise the Lord of Heaven (psalm 148) / O sing unto the Lord (psalm 149) / O praise God in his holiness (psalm 150).
MC: . . . . EG 7631004

PSALMS OF DAVID, THE VOL. 2.
Tracks: / When the Lord turned again (psalm 126) / Thou o God art praised in Sion (psalm 65) / O be joyful in God all ye lands (psalm 66) / God be merciful unto us and bless us (psalm 67) / When Israel came out of Egypt / Not unto us, O Lord (psalm 115) / Help me Lord, for there is not one godly man left (psalm 12) / Behold how good and joyful a thing it is / Behold now praise the Lord (psalm 134) / Sing we merrily unto God our strength /

My God, my God look upon me (psalm 22) / Hear my law O my people (psalm 78).
MC: EG 7631014

PSALMS OF DAVID, THE VOL. 3.
Tracks: / Lord is King, The / O Lord God, to whom vengeance belongeth / O hear ye this, all ye people (psalm 49) / O give thanks unto the Lord (psalm 107) / My heart is inditing (psalm 45) / Fret not thyself (psalm 37) / Foolish body, The (psalm 53) / Out of the deep (psalm 130) / Lord, I am not high-minded (psalm 131).
MC: EG 7631024

REQUIEM FAYRE (1).
LP: ASD 2358
MC: TCASD 2358

REQUIEM FAYRE (2).
LP: ASD 4234
MC: TCASD 4234
MC: TCCASD 4234

SOUND OF KING'S, THE.
Tracks: / Jesus Christ the apple tree / On Christmas night / Hodie Christus natus est / For unto us a child (Messiah.) / Allegri / Miserere mei, Deus / Nunc dimittis / Funeral music for Queen Mary / Thou knowest, Lord / Dixit dominus (Psalm 109) / Nationibus / Pie Jesu (Requiem.) / Ave verum corpus (K 618) / Psalm 84 / O how amiable / No. 5 Antiphon / Gloria (Missa Brevis.) / Ceremony of carols, A (There is no rose.) / Agnus dei (Requiem Op. 9.) / In paradisum (Requiem.).
LP: LPKCC 1
LP: LZ 762 852 1
MC: TCKCC 1
MC: LZ 7628524

ST. NICOLAS.
LP: ASD 2637

WORLD OF CHRISTMAS.
LP: SPA 104

WORLD OF KING'S.
Tracks: / Zadok the priest / Miserere / Hodie beata virgo / Sante deus / Gloria / Ave verum corpus / Burial service, The / This is the record of John / O Jesu so meek / O praise the Lord with one consent.
MC: 4300924

WORLD OF KINGS.
LP: SPA 245

King's Consort

CORONATION ANTHEMS (HANDEL) (see under Handel, G.F. (composer)) (King's consort/New College Choir).

Kings Go Forth

KINGS GO FORTH Original soundtrack (Various artists).
LP: AUSLP 1004

Kings of...

KINGS OF DIXIELAND (See under Jazz...) (Various artists).

KINGS OF DIXIELAND: VOL 1 (See under Jazz...) (Various artists).

KINGS OF DIXIELAND: VOL 2 (See under Jazz...) (Various artists).

KINGS OF DIXIELAND: VOL 3 (See under Jazz...) (Various artists).

KINGS OF DIXIELAND: VOL 4 (See under Jazz...) (Various artists).

KINGS OF DIXIELAND: VOL 5 (See under Jazz...) (Various artists).

KINGS OF DIXIELAND: VOL 6 (See under Jazz...) (Various artists).

KINGS OF ROCK (Various artists).
2LP: 2C 156 78211/2

KINGS OF ROCK 'N' ROLL VOL.1 (See under Rock 'n' Roll) (Various artists).

Kings Of Oblivion

ALL THIS MADNESS.
LP: FACE 009

BIG FISH POPCORN.
Tracks: / Do the stiggy (Iggy Iggy) / This band / House that zit built, The / Big fish variations, The / It's great being a girl / Tales of Vick and Kenny / Herman's helmet / Baby smells (of sand) / Greyhound bus to margeholes, The / Automatic mind command / Helmo did not laugh / Big fish popcorn.
LP: KIRI 064

WASTER MACHINE.
LP: FACE 13

Kings Of Sun

FULL FRONTAL ATTACK.
Tracks: / Crazy / Lock me up / Drop the gun / There is danger / Hooked on it / Vampire / Rescue me / Full frontal attack / Howling wind / I get lonely / Haunt you baby / Overdrive.
LP: PL 90470
MC: PK 90470

KINGS OF THE SUN.
Tracks: / Serpentine / Get on up / Black leather / Tomboy / Hot to trott / Vicious delicious / Jealous / Bottom of my heart / Cry 4 love / Medicine man / Bad love / Wildcat (CD only).
LP: PL 86826
MC: PK 86826

Kings Of Swing

SWITCHED ON SWING.
LP: ONE 1166
MC: OCE 2166

Kings Of The Road

KINGS OF THE ROAD (See Under Country...) (Various artists).

King's Own Highlanders

TARTAN TOP TWENTY: VOL 1.
Tracks: / Amazing grace / Skye boat song / Highland cradle song / My love but she's a lassie yet / Bluebells of Scotland / Blue bonnets o'er the border / Campbeltown loch / Mairi's wedding / Black bear, The / Scotch on the rocks / Dark island / March of the Cameron men, The / Horo my nut brown maiden / Flower of Scotland / Soft lowland tongue o' the borders / These are my mountains / Road to the isles / Wi' a hundred pipers / Scotland the brave / Highland laddie.
LP: GES 1014
MC: KGBC 1014

TARTAN TOP TWENTY: VOL 2.
Tracks: / Mingulay boat song / Battle is o'er, The / Scottish soldier / Barren rocks of Aden / Let's have a ceilidh / Eriskay love lilt / Wooden heart / Lass o' Fyvie / Gallowa hills / Killiecrankie / Mull of Kintyre / Rowan tree / Muckin' o' Georgie's byre / Bonnie Dundee / Cock o' the north / Lovely Stornoway / Westering home / Man's a man, A / My love is like a red red rose / Auld lang syne.
LP: KBS 1018
MC: KGBC 1018

Kings & Queens Of

KINGS AND QUEENS OF TOWNSHIP JIVE, THE (See Under Africa) (Various artists).

King's Singers

20TH ANNIVERSARY CELEBRATION (Sampler).
Tracks: / La-bas dans le Limousin / Slow train, The / Resonet in Laudibus / Short people / Blackbird / Humpty Dumpty / Chi chilichi / Oak and the ash, The / Now is the month of Maying / Veronika / You are the new day / Time piece.
LP: LPKINGS 2
MC: TCKINGS 2
LP: KINGS 2

AMERICA (King's Singers/English Chamber Orchestra).
Tracks: / Bridge over troubled water / Sound of silence, The / America / Homeward bound / If you leave me now / Simon Smith and the amazing dancing bear / Scissors cut / It's lonely at the top / Vincent / Wichita lineman.
LP: EL 749 701 1
MC: EL 749 701 4

ATLANTIC BRIDGE.
Tracks: / Ring the banjo / Sweet chariot / Dry bones / Shenandoah / Nobody knows / Keepin the middle of the road / Beautiful dreamer / Comin' thro' the rye / Oh Sussannah / Annie Laurie / Joshua / Jeanie with the light brown hair / Standing in the need of prayer / Danny boy / Last rose of summer.
MC: TC SCX 6615
LP: SCX 6615

BEATLES CONNECTION.
Tracks: / Penny Lane / Mother nature's son / Ob la di ob la da / Help / Yesterday / Hard day's night, A / Girl / Got to get you into my life / Back in the U.S.S.R. / Eleanor Rigby / Blackbird / Lady Madonna / I'll follow the sun / Honey pie / Can't buy me love / Michelle / You've got to hide your love away / I want to hold your hand.
LP: EL 7495561
MC: EL 7495564

CAPTAIN NOAH & FLOATING ZOO.
LP: ZDA 149

CARNIVAL OF THE ANIMALS.
MC: EL 270 586 4

CHRISTMAS WITH THE KING'S SINGERS.
LP: MFP 50485
MC: TCMFP 50485

COLLECTIONS.
Tracks: / Fool on the hill, The / Windmills of your mind / Horse with no name, A / Sweet gingerbread man / It don't mean a thing / Taste of honey, A / I love you Samantha / Ob la di ob la da / Building a wall / Morning has broken / Strawberry fields forever / Java jive / Jimmy Brown song, The / My colouring book / Bye bye blues / Life on Mars.
LP: MFP 5585
MC: TCMFP 5585

CONCERT COLLECTION.
LP: CSD 3766
MC: TCCSD 3766

DECK THE HALL.
LP: HQS 1308

ENCORE.
LP: SPELP 58
MC: SPEMC 58

ENGLISH AND ITALIAN MADRIGALS.
Tracks: / Now is the month of maying / Four arms, two necks, one wreathing / Hark all ye lovely saints / Since Robin Hood / Though Philomela lost her love / O wretched man / Weep, o mine eyes / Nightgingale, the organ of delight / Come, sirrah Jack, ho / Cruel, behold my heavy ending / Fair Phyllis I saw / L'ultimo di di maggio / Un cavalier di Spagna / Vezzosi augelli / Valle, che de lamenti miei / Mentre il cucolo / Chi la gagliarda / Chichilichi / Contrappunto bestiale alla mente / Mascherata de Cacciatgori / Matona mia cara.
LP: EMX 2129
MC: TCEMX 2129

HOW EXCELLENT IS THY NAME (Lassus Sacred Music).
LP: EL 749 157 1
MC: EL 749 157 4

IN CONCERT.
LP: ESD 7103
MC: TCESD 7103

IN PERFECT HARMONY.
Tracks: / Ding a dong / Windmills of your mind / I'm a train / Fool on the hill / Java jive / Widdicombe Fair / Life on Mars / Horse with no name, A / She's leaving home / Morning has broken / Bye Bye Blues / Song and dance man / Travellin' Boy (Only on CD.) / It don't mean a thing / Waltz in A flat major / Nimrod / Sympatique / Sgt. Pepper intro / Sunshine of your love / Building a wall / There are bad times just around corner / Bring me the sun again / God bless Joanna / Romance / Strawberry fields forever / Sweet gingerbread man / After the goldrush / For the peace of all mankind / Jimmy Brown song, The / Pantomime / Taste of Honey, A.
2LP: DL 41 1082 3
MC: DL 41 1082 9
MC: TC DL 1082

JOHANN STRAUSS II.
Tracks: / Herz-schmerz polka / Der Kaiser kommt / Bring einen Strauss mit roten Rosen / Pigeons of San Marco, The / Bauhandwerker polka / Fledermauschen / Die fahrt ins blaue / Picnic in the Vienna woods / Weiner blut / Die regentropf-polka / Music der nacht / Perpetuum mobile / An der schonen blauen donau.
MC: EL 754 057 4
LP: EL 754 057 1

KIDS STUFF (Nursery Rhymes).
Tracks: / Teddy bears' picnic / Humpty dumpty / Old King Cole / Grand old Duke of York, The / Lavender blue.
LP: EJ 2704661
MC: EJ 2704664
LP: EL 2704661

KING'S SINGERS BELIEVE IN MUSIC.
Tracks: / Something's coming / You needed me / All by myself / Short people / Lost in love / Betty Grable / Because / Della and the dealer / Music / I believe in music / I've got the music in me / Thank you for the music / Goodbye yellow brick road / Do you know where you're going to (Theme from Mahogany) / Save your kisses for me / Hasta Manana / Tea for two / We'll meet again / How did we fall in love / Copacabana.
LP: SCX 6637

KING'S SINGERS, THE.
Tracks: / She's leaving home / Windmills of your mind / I love you Samantha / Morning has broken / Apres un reve / Watch me / Game, The / Building a wall / My colouring book / Ask yourself why / Orange yellow ochre / Taste of honey, A.
LP: ENTM 501
LP: OU 2118

LITTLE CHRISTMAS MUSIC, A (See Under Christmas...) (King's Singers/Kiri Te Kanawa/City of London Sinfonia).

LIVE AT FESTIVAL HALL.
2LP: EX 2909593

LOVE IS THE ANSWER.
Tracks: / Let yourself off your lead / God bless Joanna / Keep on changing / For the peace of all mankind / Love is the answer / If you don't know me by now / Life on Mars / Song & dance man / Bring me the sun again / Travellin' boy.
LP: ONCR 520

MADRIGAL HISTORY TOUR.
Tracks: / Amore vittorioso / Lirum bililirum / Il bianco e dolce cigno / La bella Franceschina / Ultimi mei sospiri / Alla cazza / Or si rallegri il cielo / Fine knacks for ladies / Who made thee, Hob, forsake the plough? / Of all the birds that I do know / Too much I once lamented / Fair Phyllis I saw / Silver swan, The / Now is the month of maying / La Guerre / La la la je ne l'ose dire / Bon jour, et puis, quelles nouvelles? / Mignonne, allons voir si la rose / Il est bel et bon / Margot labourez les vignes / Un gentil amoureux / Faulte d'argent / La tricota / Triste estaba el rey David / Cucu, cucu / Fatal la parte / Tres morillas m'enamoran / La bomba / Tanzen und Springen / Ach weh des Leiden / Vitrum nostrum gloriosum / Ach Elslein / Das g'laut zu Speyer / Herzliebstes bild.
2LP: SLS 1078393
MCSET: TCSLS 1078395

MY SPIRIT SANG ALL DAY.
Tracks: / My spirit sang all day / I have loved flowers that fade / To a lady seen from the train / Gibberish / Bring us in good ale / Matthew, Mark, Luke and John / Seeds of love, The / Rest / My tocher's the jewel / Beauty is but a painted hell / Little green lane, The / Blow away the morning dew / Deep in my soul / Bee, The / O weary hearts / Hilli-ho / Music, when soft voices die / Sweet day, so cool / There comes a new moon / When winds that move not / Spring, the sweet Spring / To daffodils / Brigg fair / Autumn leaves / Quick we have but a second.
LP: EL 7497651
MC: EL 7497654

NEW DAY.
Tracks: / You are the new day / Nouveau poor / Three times a lady / What's in a tune / You'd have to be a Rosie / Can't buy me love / Singapore girl / Rhythm of life (from 'Sweet Charity'.) / Gambler, The / It was almost like a song / Here comes the sun / Hush little baby, don't say a word / Money, money, money / Summer nights (from 'Grease'.) / Summer knows, The (from 'Summer of 42'.) / Could it be magic.
LP: SCX 6629

REQUIEM FOR FATHER MALARCHY.
LP: LRL1 5104

THIS IS THE KING'S SINGERS.
Tracks: / I'm a train / Girl talk / Windmills of your mind / I love you, Samantha / Ring de banjo / God bless Joanna / Slow train / It was almost like a song / Strawberry fields forever / Gambler, The / Didn't we / After the goldrush / Dayton, Ohio, 1903 / With you on my mind / One of these songs / Transport of delight / I'll see you again / Life on Mars.
LP: THIS 9
MC: TC THIS 9

TO ALL THINGS A SEASON (Lassus Secular Music).
LP: EL 749 158 1
MC: EL 749 158 4

TRIBUTE TO THE COMEDIAN HARMONISTS.
Tracks: / Night and day / Veronika der lenz ist da / Liebling mein herz lasst dich grussen / Mein kleiner gruer kaktus / Creole love call / Eins, zwei, drei, vier / Stormy weather / Das is die liebe der matrosen / Barber of Seville / Wenn der wind weht uder das meer / Flight of the bumble bee / Tea for two / Donkey serenade, The / Gitarren spiet auf / Du armes girl vom chor / Happy days are here again.
LP: EJ 2702471
MC: EJ 2702474

VICTORIAN COLLECTION, THE.
MC: TCASD 3865

WATCHING THE WHITE WHEAT (British Folk Songs).
Tracks: / Lamorna / Barbara Allen / Bobby Shaftoe / Early one morning / Jack the jolly jack tar / Oak and the ash / O waly waly / Raggle taggle gypsies / Dance to my daddy / She moved through the air / Star of County Down / Londonderry air / Migildi magildi / Bugeilio'r gwenth gwyn / O my love is like a red rose / There's nae luck about the house.
LP: EL 2702491
MC: EL 2702494

WIND IN THE WILLOWS AND THE RELUCTANT DRAGON (See under Baker, Richard) (King's Singers & Richard Baker).
LP: MCL 412
MC: MCK 412

King's Story...

KING'S STORY, A (Film soundtrack) (Various artists).
LP: SL 5185
MC: SLC 5185

Kings X

FAITH, HOPE, LOVE.
LP: 7567821451
MC: 7567821454

GRETCHEN GOES TO NEBRASKA.
Tracks: / Out of the silent planet / Over my head / Summerland / Everybody knows a little bit of something / Difference, The (in the garden of St. Anne's-On-The-Hill) / I'll never be the same / Mission / Fall on me / Pleiades / Don't believe it (it's easier said than done) / Send a message / Burning down, The.
LP: WX 279
MC: WX 279C

OUT OF THE SILENT PLANET.
Tracks: / In the new age / Goldilox / Power of love, The / Wonder / Sometimes / King / What is this? / Far, far, away / Shot of love / Visions.
LP: K 781825-1
MC: K 781825-4

Kingsley, Charles

WATER BABIES, THE (Greene, Sarah (nar)).
MCSET: LFP 7415

Kingsmen

BEST OF THE KINGSMEN.
LP: RNLP 126

LOUIE LOUIE - GREATEST HITS.
Tracks: / Louie Louie / Money (that's what I want) / Jolly green giant / Death of an angel / Climb, The / Get out of my life woman / Little Latin lupe lu / Killer Joe / Annie Fanny / Long green / Little Sally tease / Trouble / If I need someone.
LP: LIK 6

King-Smith, Dick

MAGNUS POWERMOUSE.
MCSET: 881 557

MOUSE BUTCHER, THE (Thorne, Stephen).
MC: 881638

SADDLEBOTTOM.
MCSET: 086 222 0512

Kingsnakes

ROUNDTRIP TICKET.
LP: ROSE 67

Kings's Row

KING'S ROW (Film Soundtrack) (Various artists).
LP: SDG 305

Kingston, Paul Miles

PIE JESU (See under Brightman, Sarah).

Kingston Trio

ASSOCIATION AND THE KINGSTON TRIO (See under Association) (Kingston Trio & Association).

BEST OF KINGSTON TRIO VOL.2.
LP: SM 16184

TOM DOOLEY.
LP: 20116
MC: 40116

WE CAME TO SING.
MC: 4XL 9026

Kingstonians

SUFFERER.
LP: ATLP 114
MC: MCAT 114

Kingsway, Pete

TWO SHADES OF PETE KINGSWAY.
LP: BSS 148

Kinks

20 GOLDEN GREATS: KINKS.
LP: RPL 2031

100 MINUTES OF THE KINKS.
MC: ZCTON 102

ARTHUR -- OR THE DECLINE AND FALL OF THE BRITISH EMPIRE.
Tracks: / Victoria / Yes Sir, no Sir / Some mother's son / Drivin' / Brainwashed / Australia / Shangri-la / Mr. Churchill says / She bought a hat like Princess Marina / Young and innocent days / Nothing to say / Arthur.
LP: PYL 6009
MC: PYM 6009

BACKTRACKIN' - THE DEFINITIVE DOUBLE.......
Tracks: / You really got me / Lola / Sunny afternoon / All day and all of the night / Dedicated follower of fashion / Dead end street / Come dancing / Waterloo sunset / Apeman / Supersonic rocket ship.
LP: TRACK 1
MC: TRACK K1

BEST OF THE KINKS 1966-67, THE.
Tracks: / Sunny afternoon / Afternoon tea / Rainy day in June / Mr. Pleasant / Most exclusive residence for sale / World keeps going round, The / Big black smoke / Dedicated follower of fashion / Dead end street / Love me till the sun shines / Autumn almanac / David Watts / Act nice and gentle / Dandy / I'm not like everybody else / Waterloo sunset.
MC: PWKMC 4075

BEST OF THE KINKS, THE.
Tracks: / You really got me / All day and all of the night / Come on now / Set me free / Till the end of the day / Where have all the good times gone / Well respected man, A / Tired of waiting for you / See my friends / It's alright / Long tall Sally / Who'll be next in line / You still want me / I've got that feeling / I gotta move / Everybody's gonna be happy.
LP: SHM 3265
MC: HSC 3265

C.90 COLLECTOR.
MC: C 901

CANDY FROM MR. DANDY.
Tracks: / Dedicated follower of fashion / Dead end street / Death of a clown / Everybody's gonna be happy / Well respected man, A / See my friends / Days / Autumn almanac.
LP: DOW 12
MC: ZCDOW 12

CELLULOID HEROES.
LP: 26.21779

COLLECTION: KINKS.
Tracks: / Things are getting better / Apeman / Dedicated follower of fashion / Autumn almanac / Lola / All day and all of the night / You really got me / Set me free / Dancing in the street / Bald headed woman / Long tall Sally / Cadillac / Louie Louie / Creepin' Jean / Wonder boy / Act nice and gentle / Sittin' on my sofa / Too much monkey business / Beautiful Delilah / Tin soldier man / Victoria / Death of a clown / Wicked Annabella / Village green preservation society.
2LP: CCSLP 113
MC: CCSMC 113

COME DANCING WITH THE KINKS (Best of The Kinks 1977-86).
LP: 302778
MC: 502778

DEAD END STREET - GREATEST HITS.
Tracks: / You really got me / All day and all of the night / Everybody's gonna be happy / Till the end of the day / Dead end street / Sunny afternoon / Dedicated follower of fashion / Victoria / Set me free / Apeman / Tired of waiting for you / See my friends / Death of a clown / Lola / Waterloo sunset / Wonder boy / Plastic man / Autumn almanac / Suzannah's still alive / Misty water / Pictures in the sand / Spotty grotty Anna / Groovy movies / Time will tell / Rosemary Rose.
2LP: KINK 1
MCSET: ZCKIN 1

EP COLLECTION, THE: KINKS.
Tracks: / See my friends / I gotta move / I've got that feeling / Don't you fret / Things are getting better / Set me free / Wait till the summer comes along / Such a shame / David Watts / Lazy old sun / Death of a clown / Funny face / All day and all of the night / Louie Louie / Well respected man, A / It's all right / I gotta go now / You really got me / Til the end of the day / Dedicated follower of fashion / Two sisters / Situation vacant / Love me till the sun shines / Suzannah's still alive.
MC: SEEK 295
LP: SEE 295

EP COLLECTION VOL. 2, THE.
LP: SEE 329
MC: SEEK 329

EVERYBODY'S IN SHOWBIZ.
Tracks: / Lola / Supersonic / Rocket ship / Celluloid heroes.
LP: 26 28008

FACE TO FACE.
Tracks: / Party line / Rosy won't you please come home / Dandy / Too much on my mind / Session man / Rainy day in June / House in the country / Holiday in Waikiki / Most exclusive residence for sale / Fancy / Little Miss Queen of Darkness / You're looking fine / Sunny afternoon / I'll remember.
MC: ZCP 18149
LP: PYL 6005
MC: PYM 6005
LP: NPL 18149

GIVE THE PEOPLE WHAT THEY WANT.
Tracks: / Around the dial / Give the people what they want / Killer's eyes / Predictable / Add it up / Destroyer / Yo yo / Back to front / Art lover / Little bit of abuse, A / Better things.
LP: SPART 1171
MC: TCART 1171

GOLDEN HOUR OF THE KINKS.
LP: GH 501

GOLDEN HOUR OF THE KINKS (2).
MC: KGHMC 148

GREATEST HITS: KINKS.
Tracks: / You really got me / All day and all of the night / Tired of waiting for you / Ev'rybody's gonna be happy / Set me free / See my friends / Till the end of the day / Dedicated follower of fashion / Sunny afternoon / Dead end street / Waterloo Sunset / Autumn almanac / Wonder boy / Days / Plastic man / Victoria / Lola / Apeman.
LP: KINK 7251
MC: ZCKIN 7251

GREATEST HITS: KINKS (IMPORT).
LP: BRLP 15
MC: BRMC 15

HIT SINGLES COLLECTION, THE.
Tracks: / You really got me / All day and all of the night / Tired of waiting for you / Ev'rybody's gonna be happy / Set me free / See my friends / Till the end of the day / Dedicated follower of fashion / Sunny afternoon / Dead end street / Waterloo sunset / Death of a clown / Autumn almanac / Suzannah's still alive / Days / Plastic man / Victoria / Lola / Apeman.
LP: PYL 4001
MC: PYM 4001

INTROSPECTIVE: KINKS.
MC: MINT 5005
LP: LINT 5005

KINDA KINKS.
Tracks: / Look for me baby / Got my feet on the ground / Nothin' in the world can stop me worryin' 'bout that girl / Something better beginning / Naggin' woman / Wonder where my baby is tonight / Tired of waiting for you / Dancing in the street / So long / Don't ever change / Come on now / You shouldn't be sad.
MC: ZCP 18112
LP: PYL 6003
MC: PYM 6003
LP: NPL 18112

KINK KONTROVERSY, THE.
Tracks: / Milk cow blues / Gotta get the first plane home / I am free / When I see that girl of mine / Till the end of the day / World keeps going round / I'm on an island / Where have all the good times gone / It's too late / What's in store for me? / You can't win.
MC: ZCP 18131
LP: PYL 6004
MC: PYM 6004
LP: NPL 18131

KINKS.
Tracks: / Beautiful Delilah / So mystifying / Just can't go to sleep / Long tall shorty / I took my baby home / I'm a lover not a fighter / You really got me / Cadillac / Bald headed woman / Revenge / Too much monkey business / I've been driving on bald mountain / Stop your sobbing / Get love if you want it.
LP: PYL 6002
MC: PYM 6002
LP: NPL 18096

KINKS ARE THE VILLAGE GREEN PRESERVATION SOCIETY.
Tracks: / Village Green Preservation Society / Do you remember Walter / Picture book / Johnny Thunder / Last of the steam powered trains, The / Big sky / Sitting by the riverside / Animal farm / Village green preservation society / Starstruck / Phenomenal cat / All of my friends were there / Monica / People take pictures of each other / Wicked Annabella.
LP: FBLP 8091
MC: ZCFBL 8091
LP: NSPL 18233
LP: PYL 6008
MC: PYM 6008

KINKS BOX SET, THE.
LPS: KINKX 7254
MCSET: CKNX 7254

KINKS COLLECTION, THE.
Tracks: / Lola / Animal farm / It's alright / I need you / Till the end of the day / Stop your sobbing / You really got me / I'm not like everybody else / Victoria / Just can't go to sleep / Tired of waiting for you / Well respected man, A / Dedicated follower of fashion / Dead end street / See my friends / Louie Louie / I'm a lover not a fighter / Set me free / All day and all of the night / Waterloo sunset / Where have all the good times gone / Sunny afternoon / Come on now.
2LP: PDA 072
MCSET: PDC 072

KINKS FILE, THE.
Tracks: / Long tall Sally / You still want me / You really got me / All day and all of the night / I've got that feeling / I gotta go now / Things are getting better / Tired of waiting for you / Everybody's gonna be happy / Set me free / See my friends / Well respected man, A / Till the end of the day / Dedicated follower of fashion / Sunny afternoon / Dead end street / Mr. Pleasant / Waterloo sunset / Death of a clown / Autumn almanac / Suzannah's still alive / Wonder boy / Lincoln county / Days / Hold my hand / Plastic man / Driving / Shangri-la / Victoria / Lola / Apeman.
2LP: FILD 001
MC: ZCFLD 001

KINKS LIVE AT THE KELVIN HALL.
Tracks: / All day and all of the night / Well respected man, A / You're looking fine / Sunny afternoon / Dandy / I'm on an island / Come on now / You really got me / Milk cow blues / Tired of waiting for you / Batman.
MC: PYM 6007

KINKS, THE.
MC: C 901

KOLLECTABLES.
Tracks: / I'm not like everybody else / This is where I belong / Rats / Act nice and gentle / You still want me / You do something to me / I took my baby home / Creepin' Jean / Hold my hand / Lincoln county / Suzannah's still alive / Pretty Polly / Sittin' on my sofa / Mindless child of motherhood.
LP: KINK 7252
MC: ZCKIN 7252

KOVERS.
Tracks: / Cadillac / Dancing in the street / Louie Louie / Long tall Sally / Naggin' woman / Too much monkey business / Milk cow blues / Beautiful Delilah / Bald headed woman / I've been driving on bald mountain / I'm a lover not a fighter / Long tall shorty / Got love if you want it.
LP: KINK 7253
MC: ZCKIN 7253

LIVE AT THE KELVIN HALL.
Tracks: / Till the end of the day / Well respected man, A / You're looking fine / Sunny afternoon / Dandy / I'm on an island / Come on now / You really got me.
LP: NSPL 18191
LP: PYL 6007

LOLA.
Tracks: / Lola / House in the country / Little Miss queen of darkness / Dandy / Rosy won't you please come home / David Watts / Afternoon tea / Love me till the sun shines / God's little children / Animals in the zoo / Apeman / Situation vacant.
MCSET: DTO 10018

LOLA, PERCY & THE APEMAN COME FACE TO FACE WITH....
Tracks: / Lola / Village green preservation society / Love me till the sun shines / Wonder boy / Little miss queen of darkness / Two sisters, The / Sitting by the riverside / Dandy / Rainy day in June / Death of a clown / Village green preservation society / Johnny Thunder / Party line / Funny face / Moments / Dreams / Do you remember Walter / All of my friends were there / People take pictures of each other / Too much on my mind / Picture book / You're looking fine / Apeman / Gods children / Harry rag / Afternoon tea / Last of the steam powered trains, The / Animals in the zoo / David Watts / Rosy won't you please come home / House in the country / Situation vacant / Holiday in Waikiki / Session man / Phenomenal cat / Most exclusive residence for sale / Lazy old sun / Tin soldier man / End of the season / No return / Wicked Annabella / Starstruck / Way love used to be, The / Big sky.
2LP: GHD 50

LOLA VS POWERMAN AND THE MONEY-GO-ROUND.
Tracks: / Contenders / Strangers / Denmark Street / Get back in line / Lola / Top of the pops / Money-go-round, The / This time tomorrow / Long way from home / Rats / Apeman / Powerman / Got to be free.
LP: PYL 6010
MC: PYM 6010

LOW BUDGET.
Tracks: / Attitude / Catch me now I'm falling / Pressure / National health / Superman / Low budget / In a space / Little bit of emotion / Gallon of gas / Misery / Moving pictures.
LP: SPART 1099

MISFITS.
Tracks: / Misfits / Hay fever / Black messiah / Rock 'n' roll fantasy / In a foreign land / Permanent waves / Live life / Out of the wardrobe / Trust your heart / Get up.
LP: SPART 1055

NIGHTRIDING: THE KINKS.

Tracks: / You really got me / Long tall Sally / Dancing in the street / David Watts / It's too late / Victoria / All day and all of the night / Tired of waiting for you / Louie Louie / Too much monkey business / Where have all the good times gone / Don't ever change / Love me till the sun shines / Lola.
MC: . . . . **KNMC 10019**

ONE FOR THE ROAD.
Tracks: / Hard way, The / Catch me now I'm falling / Where have all the good times gone? / Lola / Pressure / All day and all of the night / 20th century man / Stop your sobbing / Misfits / Prince of the punks / Low budget / Attitude / Superman / National health / Till the end of the day / Celluloid heroes / You really got me / Victoria / David Watts.
2LP: . . . . **DARTY 6**
MC: . . . . **TCDAR 6**

PERCY (Film soundtrack) (See under Percy).

ROAD, THE.
Tracks: / Road, The / Destroyer / Apeman / Come dancing / Art lover / Cliches of the world (B-movie) / Think visual / Living on a thin line / Lost and found / It (I wanted it) / Around the dial / Give the people what they want.
LP: . . . . **LONLP 49**
MC: . . . . **LONC 49**

SCHOOLBOYS IN DISGRACE.
Tracks: / Schooldays / Jack the idiot dunce / Education / First time we fall in love, The / I'm in disgrace / Headmaster / Hard way, The / Last assembly, The / No more looking back / Finale.
LP: **26.21607**
LP: . . . . **RS 1028**

SHAPE OF THINGS TO COME.
Tracks: / You really got me / All day and all of the night / Till the end of the day / Set me free / Lola / Tired of waiting / Sunny afternoon / Waterloo sunset.
LP: . . . . **DOW 4**
MC: . . . . **ZCDOW 4**

SLEEPWALKER.
Tracks: / Life on the road / Mr. Big Man / Sleepwalker / Brother / Jukebox music / Sleepless night / Stormy sky / Full moon / Life goes on.
LP: . . . . **SPART 1002**

SOAP OPERA.
LP: . . . . **CL 13750**

SOMETHING ELSE BY THE KINKS.
Tracks: / David Watts / Death of a clown / Two sisters, The / No return / Harry rag / Tin soldier man / Situation vacant / Love me till the sun shines / Lazy old sun / Afternoon tea / Funny face / End of the season / Waterloo sunset.
LP: . . . . **NSPL 18193**
LP: . . . . **PYL 6006**
MC: . . . . **PYM 6006**

SPOTLIGHT ON THE KINKS.
Tracks: / You really got me / Till the end of the day / Everybody's gonna be happy / Set me free / See my friends / All day and all of the night / Tired of waiting / Dedicated follower of fashion / David Watts / Victoria / Susannah's still alive / Mr. Pleasant / Sunny afternoon / Dead End Street / Stop your sobbing / Death of a clown / Well respected man, A / Waterloo sunset / Lola / Apeman / Wonder boy / Plastic man / Autumn almanac / Days.
2LP: . . . . **SPOT 1009**
MCSET: . . . . **ZCSPT 1009**

SPOTLIGHT ON THE KINKS VOL.2.
Tracks: / Days / So mystifying / I'm on an island / Don't you fret / Just can't go to sleep / Sittin' on my sofa / Things are getting better / Come on now / I need you / Long tall Shorty / Too much monkey business / Got love if you want it / Shangri-la / Australia / Lincoln County / Animal farm / Holiday in Waikiki / Funny face / Louie louie / Look for me baby / Wait till the summer comes along / Where have all the good times gone / You still want me / Rats.
2LP: . . . . **SPOT 1029**
MCSET: . . . . **ZCSPT 1029**

STATE OF CONFUSION.
Tracks: / Definite maybe / State of confusion / Property / Labour of love / Come dancing / Don't forget to dance / Young Conservatives / Heart of gold / Once a thief / Bernadette.
LP: **205275**
MC: **405275**

SUNNY AFTERNOON.
LP: . . . . **MAL 716**

THINK VISUAL.
Tracks: / Rock 'n' roll cities / How are you / Think visual / Natural gift / Killing time / When you where a child / Working at the factory / Lost and found / Repetition / Welcome to sleazy town / Video shop, The.
LP: . . . . **LONLP 27**
MC: . . . . **LONC 27**

UK JIVE.
Tracks: / Aggravation / How do I get close / UK jive / Now and then / What are we doing / Entertainment / War is over / Down all the days (till 1992) / Loony balloon / Dear Margaret / Bright lights (On MC and CD only) / Perfect strangers (On MC and CD only).
LP: **828165 1**
MC: **828165 4**

ULTIMATE COLLECTION, THE.
Tracks: / You really got me / All day and all of the night / Tired of waiting for you / Ev'rybody's gonna be happy / Set me free / Till the end of the day / Dedicated follower of fashion / Sunny afternoon / Dead end street / Waterloo sunset / Autumn almanac / Wonder boy / Days / Plastic man / Victoria / Lola / Apeman / David Watts / Where have all the good times gone / Well respected man / I'm not like everybody else / End of the season / Death of a clown / Suzannah's still alive.
2LP: . . . . **CTVLP 001**
MC: . . . . **CTVMC 001**

WELL RESPECTED KINKS.
LP: . . . . **MAL 612**

WELL RESPECTED MEN.
Tracks: / Long tall Sally / You still want me / You do something to me / It's all right / All day and all of the night / I gotta move / Louie Louie / I've got that feeling / I gotta go now / Things are getting better / Ev'rybodys gonna be happy / Who'll be next in line? / Set me free / I need you / See my friends / Never met a girl like you / Well respected man, A / Such a shame / Wait till the summer comes / Don't you fret / Dedicated follower of fashion / Sittin' on my sofa / I'm not like everybody else / Dead End Street / Big black smoke / Act nice and gentle / Autumn almanac / Mr. Pleasant / Wonder boy / Pretty Polly / Days / She's got everything / Plastic man / King Kong / Mindless child of motherhood / This man he weeps tonight / Berkeley Mews.
2LP: . . . . **PYL 7001**
MCSET: . . . . **PYM 7001**

WORD OF MOUTH.
Tracks: / Do it again / Word of mouth / Good day / Living on a thin line / Sold me out / Massive reduction / Guilty / Too hot / Missing persons / Summer's gone / Going solo.
LP: **206685**
MC: **406685**

YOU REALLY GOT ME (ALBUM).
Tracks: / You really got me / I need you / Till the end of the day / Come on now / Long tall Sally / Cadillac / Beautiful Delilah / Everybody's gonna be happy / Things are getting better / All day and all of the night / Stop your sobbing / Don't ever change / David Watts / You still want me / Wonder where my baby is tonight / Don't you fret / Just can't go to sleep / Well respected man / I'm not like everybody else / Tired of waiting for you.
LP: . . . . **NSPL 18615**
MC: . . . . **ZCP 18615**

Kinnaird, Alison

HARP KEY, THE.
LP: . . . . **LUN 029**
LP: . . . . **SHOO 1**
MC: . . . . **CSH 001**

HARP TUTOR.
MC: . . . . **BK 003**

HARPER'S GALLERY, THE.
LP: . . . . **TP 003**
MC: . . . . **CTP 003**

MUSIC IN TRUST (Kinnaird, Alison & The Battlefield Band).
MC: . . . . **CTP 022**
LP: . . . . **TP 022**

MUSIC IN TRUST, VOL.2 (Kinnaird, Alison & The Battlefield Band).
LP: . . . . **TP 029**
MC: . . . . **CTP 029**

Kinnear, Roy (nar)

BERTHA (see under Bertha (bk)) (Kinnear, Roy & Sheila Walker).

Kinney, Fern

FERN.
Tracks: / Let the good times roll / Let me entertain you / I want you back / Love me tonite / I've been lonely for so long / It's alright / No one but you / Tonight / Never be another night like this.
LP: . . . . **K 99144**
MC: **K4 99144**

GROOVE ME.
Tracks: / Groove me / Under fire / Angel on the ground / Pillow talk / Together we are beautiful / Sun, moon, rain / Baby let me kiss you.
LP: . . . . **K 99076**
MC: **K4 99076**

SWEET MUSIC.
LP: . . . . **MAL 7410**

Kinney, Ray

HEART OF HAWAII.
LP: . . . . **GNPS 54**
MC: **GNP5 54**

Kinsella, Thomas

FAIR ELEANOR, CHRIST THEE SAVE.
LP: . . . . **CCT 6**

Kinsey, Big Daddy

BAD SITUATION (Kinsey, Big Daddy & the Kinsey report).
LP: . . . . **R 2620**

Kinsey Report

EDGE OF THE CITY.
Tracks: / Poor man's relief / I can't let you go / Got to play someday / Answering machine / Give me what I want / Full moon on Main Street / Lucky charm / Back door man / Game of love / Come to me.
LP: . . . . **SNTF 998**

MIDNIGHT DRIVE.
LP: . . . . **AL 4775**

POWERHOUSE.
LP: . . . . **VPBLP 2**
MC: . . . . **VPBTC 2**

Kinsey, Tony

JUMP FOR ME (see Harriott, Joe) (Kinsey, Tony, Trio & Joe Harriott).

THAMES SUITE (Kinsey,Tony Big Band).
Tracks: / Sunbury seminar / Chertsey mead / Kingston reach / Henley ho / Hard times / Cockham Bridge / Beachy Head / Girl Friday.
LP: . . . . **SPJ 504**

THOU SWELL (see Deucher, Jimmy) (Kinsey, Tony/ Jimmy Deucher/ Alan Clare/ Victor Feldman).

Kintone

GOING HOME (AZANIA).
Tracks: / Going home / Freedom's song / Pennin / Looks like rain / Street market / Street market / After the storm / Song for Nella / Ode to Joe.
LP: . . . . **STERNS 1013**

Kipling, Rudyard

GUNGA DIN & OTHER POEMS (Karloff, Boris (nar)).
MC: **1193**

HOW FEAR CAME (Palin, Michael).
MC: . . . . **LP 206**
MC: . . . . **LPMC 206**

JUNGLE BOOK STORIES (Richardson, Ian).
Tracks: / Mowgli's brothers / King's ankus, The / Kaa's hunting.
MCSET: . . . . **SAY 50**
MCSET: . . . . **ARGO 1154**

JUNGLE BOOK, THE (Davies, Windsor).
MCSET: . . . . **LFP 7120**
MCSET: . . . . **LFP 4171205**

JUST SO STORIES (Davis, David (nar)).
MCSET: . . . . **ZBBC 1163**

JUST SO STORIES (Ogilvy, Ian).
MC: . . . . **LPMC 207**

JUST SO STORIES - SELECTED STORIES (Dotrice, Roy & Dorothy Tutin).
MC: **0600560910**

JUST SO STORIES VOL 1 (Johnson, Richard/Barbara Jefford/Michael Hordern).
MCSET: . . . . **SAY 30**
MCSET: . . . . **ARGO 1031**

JUST SO STORIES VOL 2 (Horden, Michael/Barbara Jefford/Richard Johnson).
MCSET: . . . . **SAY 44**

KIM.
MCSET: **418 144-4**
MCSET: . . . . **ARGO 1220**

KIM.
MCSET: . . . . **LFP 7222**
MCSET: . . . . **LFP 4172225**

MAN WHO WOULD BE KING, THE (Quayle, Anthony (nar)).
MC: **1258**

MORE JUNGLE BOOK STORIES (Richardson, Ian).
Tracks: / Tiger, tiger! / Rikki-tikki-tavi / Red dog.
MCSET: . . . . **SAY 68**

MORE JUST-SO STORIES (Davis, David (nar)).
MC: . . . . **P 90033**

PLAIN TALES FROM THE HILLS (Jarvis, Martin (nar)).
MCSET: . . . . **TTDMC 401**

RED DOG (Quayle, Anthony (nar)).
MC: **1482**

RIKKI-TIKKI-TAVI / WEE WILLIE WINKIE (Quayle, Anthony (nar)).
MC: **1257**

TALES FROM THE JUNGLE BOOK (Unknown narrator(s)).
MC: . . . . **PLBC 237**

Kipper

KIPPER (Various artists).
MC: . . . . **BBM LB 2**

Kipper Family

EVER DECREASING CIRCLES.
LP: . . . . **DAM 012**

SINCE TIME IMMORAL.
LP: . . . . **DAM 005**

Kirby

COMPOSITION.
Tracks: / Bottom line / Tread softly / Don't let me down / Love won't let you down / Darkness and light / It's a crying shame / Something to show / That's some dream.
LP: . . . . **HW 2**

Kirby, John

1941: JOHN KIRBY (Kirby, John & His Orchestra).
LP: . . . . **CLP 14**

BIGGEST LITTLE BAND IN THE LAND 1938-41, THE.
LP: . . . . **LPJT 26**

JOHN KIRBY.
Tracks: / Ida / Peanut vendor / Revolutionary etude / Blue fantasy / Same old story / Polonaise / Prelude for trumpet / Last night the nightingale woke me / I give you my word / Rustle of spring No.1 / Rehearsin' for a nervous breakdown / Echoes of Harlem.
LP: . . . . **ATS 6**
MC: . . . . **TCATS 6**

JOHN KIRBY 1939-41.
LP: . . . . **TAX 8016**

JOHN KIRBY AND ORCHESTRA (With Maxine Sullivan) (Kirby, John & His Orchestra).
LP: . . . . **CLP 47**

JOHN KIRBY & ONYX CLUB BOYS (Vol.3) (Kirby, John & Onyx Club Boys).
LP: . . . . **COL 12-10**

JOHN KIRBY & ONYX CLUB BOYS (Vol. 4) (Kirby, John & Onyx Club Boys).
LP: . . . . **COL 12-11**

JOHN KIRBY & ONYX CLUB BOYS (Vol.1) (Kirby, John & Onyx Club Boys).
LP: . . . . **CC 3**

MORE (Kirby, John & His Orchestra).
LP: . . . . **CLP 64**

Kirby, Kathy

16 HITS FROM STARS AND GARTERS.
LP: . . . . **LK 5475**

LET ME SING AND I'M HAPPY.
Tracks: / Let me sing and I'm happy / I can't give you anything but love / Someone to watch over me / I'll get by / Acapulco / Following in my father's footsteps / Waiting for the Robert E. Lee / Bill / Happy days and lonely nights / Who's sorry now / Can't help lovin' dat man / If you were the only boy in the world / Man I love, The / Miss dynamite / On the sunny side of the street / Show me the way to go home.
LP: . . . . **PLE 507**
MC: . . . . **TC-PLE 507**

Kirchner, Bill

WHAT IT IS TO BE FRANK (Kirchner, Bill Nonet).
LP: . . . . **SB 2010**

Kirk, Andy

ALL OUT FOR HICKSVILLE.
LP: . . . . **HEP 1007**

ANDY KIRK AND CLOUDS OF JOY (Kirk, Andy/Clouds of Joy/June Richmond).
LP: . . . . **HSR 227**

ANDY KIRK AT TRIANNON, CLEVELAND (Kirk, Andy/Clouds of Joy/June Richmond).
LP: . . . . **AA 503**

ANDY'S JIVE (Kirk, Andy/his orchestra).
LP: . . . . **SWH 39**

CLOUDY (Kirk, Andy/his Twelve Clouds of Joy).
LP: . . . . **HEP 1002**

WALKIN' AND SWINGIN' (Kirk, Andy/his Twelve Clouds of Joy).
Tracks: / Mary's idea / Until the real thing comes along / Walkin' and swingin' / Lady who swings the band / Floyd's guitar blues / Lotta sax appeal / Ring dem bells / Twinklin' / Little Joe from Chicago / McGhee special / Moten swing / Wednesday night hop / Cloudy /

Twelfth St. rag / Big Jim blues / 47th Street live.
LP: . . . . AFS 1011

Kirk, Rahsaan

MAN WHO CRIED FIRE, THE.
LP: . . . . VNLP 1
MC: . . . . VNTC 1

Kirk, Richard H

BLACK JESUS VOICE.
LP: . . . . ROUGH 99

HOODOO TALK (Kirk, Richard H & Peter Hope).
Tracks: / Intro / Numb skull / N.O. / Cop out / Surgeons / 50 tears / Leather hands / 50 tears (reprise).
LP: . . . . NTVLP 28

UGLY SPIRIT.
Tracks: / Emperor, The / Confession / Infantile / Frankie machine (I) / Hollywood babylon / Thai / Voodoo / Frankie machine (II).
LP: . . . . ROUGH 89

Kirk, Roland

EARLY ROOTS.
LP: . . . . AFF 121

INFLATED TEAR, THE.
Tracks: / Black and crazy blues, The / Laugh for Rory, A / Many blessings / Fingers in the wind / Inflated tear, The / Creole love call / Handful of fives, A / Fly by night / Lovelievelíloqui.
LP: . . . . K 50233

INTRODUCING ROLAND KIRK.
Tracks: / Call, The / Soul station / Our waltz / Our love is here to stay / Spirit girl / Jack the ripper.
LP: . . . . GCH 8093
MC: . . . . GCHK 78093

KIRK'S WORK.
Tracks: / Three for Dizzy / Makin' Whoopee / Funk underneath / Kirk's work / Doin' the sixty-eight / Too Late Now / Skater's Waltz.
LP: . . . . PR 7210
MC: . . . . PRC 7210

LIVE IN PARIS 1970 VOL 2.
Tracks: / Sweet fire / Make me a pallet on the floor / Charlie Parker medley / Volunteer slavery / You did it, you did it / Satin doll.
LP: . . . . FC 115

NOW PLEASE DON'T YOU CRY BEAUTIFUL EDITH.
Tracks: / Blue roll / Alfie / Why don't they know? / Silverlization / Fall out / Don't you cry, beautiful Edith / Stomping ground / It's a grand night for singing.
LP: 2304 519
LP: 837 439 1

PREPARE TO DEAL WITH A MIRACLE.
Tracks: / Salvation and reminiscing / Seasons / One mind winter summer / Ninth ghost / Celestial bliss / Saxophone miracle / Saxophone concerto / One breath beyond / Dance of revolution.
LP: . . . . K 40508

PRE-RAHSAAN.
Tracks: / Three for Dizzy / Makin' whoopee / Funk underneath / Kirk's work / Doin' the sixty-eight / Too late now / Skater's waltz / Parisian thoroughfare / Hazy Eve / Shine on me / Evidence / Memories of you / Teach me tonight.
2LP: . . . . PR 24080

VIBRATION CONTINUES,THE.
Tracks: / Inflated tear, The (Introduction and medley) / Water for Robeson and Williams / Volunteered slavery / I love you / Yes I do / Rahsaanica / Do nothin' 'til you hear from me / Ain't no sunshine / Tribute to John Coltrane, A / Three for the festival / Old rugged cross / Black and crazy blues, The / Portrait of those beautiful ladies / If I loved you / Creole love call / Seasons.
LP: . . . . K 60133

VIBRATION SOCIETY.
LP: . . . . ST 261

WE FREE KINGS.
Tracks: / Three for the festival / Moon song / Sackful of soul / Haunted melody / Blues for Alice / We free kings / You did it, you did it / Some kind of love / My delight.
LP: 6336 384

Kirkbymoorside Town...

MOORSIDE BRASS (Kirkbymoorside Town Brass Band).
LP: . . . . LKLP 6471

MOORSIDE BRASS VOL 2 (Kirkbymoorside Town Brass Band).
Tracks: / Cossack / Nightingale / Sweet & low / North-east fantasy / Epigram / Aces high / On with the motley / Marching through georgia / Aranjuez (mon amour) / Music.
LP: . . . . LKLP 7052

Kirkland

MIROSLAV VITOUS GROUP (see under Vitous) (Kirkland/Vitous/Christensen/Surman).

Kirkland, Eddie

PICK UP THE PIECES.
LP: . . . . JSP 1033

WAY IT WAS,THE.
LP: . . . . RL 041

Kirklees Junior...

YOUR 40 FAVOURITE NURSERY RHYMES (Kirklees Junior Schools).
Tracks: / London Bridge is falling down / Grand old Duke of York, The / One two three four five once I caught a fish alive / Tom, Tom the piper's son / Pussy cat, pussy cat / Ride a cock horse / Where are you going to my pretty maid / See-saw, Margery Daw / Little Jack Horner / Old Mother Hubbard / Jack and Jill / Little Miss Muffet / Hey diddle diddle / Hickory dickory dock / Here we go round the mulberry bush / Ten green bottles / Cock-a-doodle-doo / Pop goes the weasel / Sing a song of sixpence / Ding dong bell / Goosey gander / There was a crooked man / Bobby Shaftoe / Humpty dumpty / Baa, baa, black sheep / Polly put the kettle on / Three blind mice / Mary, Mary quite contrary / I had a little nut tree / Oranges and lemons / Girls and boys come out to play / Here we go gathering nuts in May / Here we go Looby Loo / Farmer's in his den, The / Ring a ring a roses / Lavender blue / Wee Willie Winkie / Rockabye baby / Twinkle twinkle little star / Simple Simon.
LP: . . . . MFP 5865
MC: . . . . TCMFP 5865

Kirkpatrick, John

AMONG THE MANY ATTRACTIONS AT THE SHOW.. (Kirkpatrick, John & Sue Harris).
Tracks: / Edgmond men's souling song, The / Artichokes and cauliflowers / Bricklayers, The / Double change sides / Cherry tree carol, The / John of the greenery Cheshire way / Shropshire lad, A / I wish I wish / Old Sir Simon the king / Adieu to old England / Blue eyed stranger / Winster morris reel, The / Jim Jones / Blacksmith's morris / Charles's hornpipe / Cold blows the wind / Wilson's favourite / Shrewsbury rakes.
LP: 12TS 295

BLUE BALLOON.
Tracks: / Noah / Blue balloon / Black against the snow / Don't shoot, I'm wearing my seat belt / Tunnel of love / Laundroloverette / Length of yarn, A / Hole in my heart / Dog's gone wild.
LP: . . . . SQZ 124

FACING THE MUSIC (Kirkpatrick, John & Sue Harris).
Tracks: / John Locke's polka / Three jolly sheepskins / Kettle drum / Trip to the cottage / Hunting the squirrel / Jack of the green / Shelter in the time of storm / We shall be happy / Millfield / Saturday night and Sunday morn / Garrick's delight / Flaxley green dance / Crocker's reel / Roast beef / All flowers in Broome / Rope waltz / Cheshire hornpipe / Black Mary's hornpipe.
LP: 12TS 408

GOING SPARE.
LP: . . . . FRR 030

PLAIN CAPERS.
LP: . . . . FRR 010

ROSE OF BRITAIN'S ISLE, THE (Kirkpatrick, John & Sue Harris).
Tracks: / Rose of Britain's Isle, The / Glorishears / Up in the north / Hunsden house / Whimbleton house / Queen of the May / Old man Jones / Not for Joe / Weyhill fair / Milkmaid's song, The / Rising sun, The / Crown, The / Sweet Swansea / White joak, The / Yellow joke, The / Lady and the soldier, The / Fireside polka / Down sides and up the middle.
LP: 12TS 247

SHEEPSKINS.
Tracks: / Last night with Archie / Three jolly black sheepskins / Mad moll - the lively jig / Over the moon / Ronnets so blue / There's no doubt about it / Beating the oak / Dick the Welshman / Todley Tome / Blue eyed stranger / Watterddy Lane / Tun dish, The / Maiden's prayer / Turn again Martha / Churning butter / Abram circle dance, The / Raddled tup, The / Hunting the squirrel / Zot for Joe / Four lane end / Cocking the chafer / Threepenny ha'penny treacle / Martha's comet or the evening star / Three hand reel / Green and yellow handkerchief dance / Prince of Wales, The / Morning star, The / Half a farthing candle / Hindley circle dance, The.
MC: . . . . SQZC 125

SHREDS AND PATCHES (Kirkpatrick, John & Sue Harris).
Tracks: / Waterman's dance / Gypsy laddie, The / Apple core / Nipper / Tailor and the louse, The / Peg Huglestone's hornpipe / Little Sir William / Game of all fours, The / Penny for them / Whitefryer's hornpipe / Shreds and patches / Johnny Sands / Oakham poachers / Bread and jam waltzer / Mister Gubbin's bicycle.
LP: 12TS 355

STOLEN GROUND (Kirkpatrick, John & Sue Harris).
LP: 12TS 453
MC: . . . . KTSC 453

THREE IN A ROW: THE ENGLISH MELODEON.
Tracks: / Queen of hearts / Dummy head / Chuntering Charlie / Round-bottomed wok, The / Wriggly-tin tattoo, The / Broken rifle, The / Blaze away / Sing a full song / Putney beach / Fulham gasworks / Fulham by gaslight / Walking up town / Siberian stomp, The / Nightingale sang in Berkeley Square / Find the lady.
LP: . . . . SQZ 123

Kirsch, Barry

IMAGES IN BLACK AND WHITE.
LP: . . . . FEDK 1010

MUSIC OF THE STARS - CAPRICORN (Kisdadee and Tango frescado) (Kirsch, Barry & Dashiell Rae).
Tracks: / Out to lunch / Easy virtue / Bear, The / Kiskadee / Undertow / Pas Seul / Drift / Points of view / Crossing, The / Hannibal's tale / Canon / Le bateau / Oriental / Tango frescado.
LP: . . . . BIRTHLP 3
MC: . . . . BIRTHMC 3

Kirst, H.H.

NIGHT OF THE GENERALS (Croft, Jon).
MCSET: . . . . COL 2014

Kirton, Lew

TALK TO ME.
Tracks: / Talk to me / I can't live without you / Don't give up your dream (hang on in there) / Always will / Just can't get enough / Hooked on you / Got to find somebody to love / Here's my love.
LP: . . . . EPC 25621
MC: 40 25621

Kirwan, Danny

HELLO THERE BIG BOY.
Tracks: / Gettin' the feelin' / Wings of a dove / End up crying / Caroline / You / Only you / California / Spaceman / Summer days and summer nights.
LP: . . . . DJF 20555

Kirwin, Dominic

GREEN FIELDS OF IRELAND.
MC: . . . . MB LP 1037

LOVE WITHOUT END.
Tracks: / Like father, like son / Almost persuaded / Love letters in the sand / Straight and narrow / Just for old times sake / Stranger things have happened / Say you'll stay until tomorrow / When the girl in your arms / Love without end, amen / There's always me / Hand that rocks the cradle, The / Fool's pardon / Life is what you make it / Noreen Bawn.
MC: . . . . RITZLC 0060

TRY A LITTLE KINDNESS.
Tracks: / Oh lonesome me / I'll leave this world loving you / Achin' breaking heart / Before the next teardrop falls / Try a little kindness / More than yesterday / My beautiful wife / Sea of heartbreak / Heaven knows / Heartaches by the number / Careless hands / Golden dreams / Paper roses / St. Theresa of the roses.
MC: . . . . LC 0050

Kismet (film)

KISMET (Film soundtrack) (Various artists).
Tracks: / Fate: *Keel, Howard* / Not since Niniveh: *Gray, Dolores* / Baubles, bangles and beads: *Blyth, Ann*/ Stranger in Paradise: *Blyth, Ann/Vic Damone* / Gesticulate: *Keel, Howard* / Night of my nights: *Damone, Vic* / Bored: *Gray, Dolores* / Olive tree: *Keel, Howard* / Rahadlakum: *Keel, Howard/Dolores Gray*/ And this is my beloved: *Keel, Howard/Anne Blyth/Vic Damone* / Sands of time: *Keel, Howard.*
LP: . . . . CBS 70287
MC: 40 70287
LP: . . . . LPMGM 22
MC: . . . . TCMGM 22
LP: 2353 057

KISMET (Studio cast) (Various artists).
Tracks: / Overture: *Various artists* / Sands of time: *Various artists* / Rhymes have I: *Various artists*/ Fate: *Various artists* / Not since Nineveh: *Various artists* / Baubles, bangles and beads: *Various artists*/ Stranger in paradise: *Various artists* / Night of my nights: *Various artists* / And this is my beloved: *Various* artists / Olive tree: *Various artists* / Zubbediya - Samaris' dance: *Various artists* / Finale: *Various artists.*
LP: . . . . SRS 5054

KISMET (Stage show) (Various artists).
Tracks: / Overture: *Various artists* / Sands of time: *Various artists* / Rhymes have I: *Various artists*/ Fate: *Various artists* / Hand of fate, The / Fate (Reprise): *Various artists* / Bazaar of the caravans: *Various* artists / Entrance of Lalume: *Various artists* / Not since Ninevah: *Various artists* / Not since Ninevah dance: *Various artists* / Exit of Lalume / Stolen oranges: *Various artists* / Baubles, bangles and beads: *Various* artists / Paradise garden: *Various artists* / Stranger in paradise: *Various artists* / He's in love: *Various* artists / Gesticulate: *Various artists* / Finale act one: *Various artists* / Entr'acte: *Various artists*/ Night of my nights: *Various artists* / Stranger in paradise (Reprise): *Various artists* / Was I Wazir?: *Various* artists / Rahadlakum: *Various artists* / Rahadlakum dance: *Various artists* / And this is my beloved: *Various* artists / Poets meet, The: *Various artists* / Olive tree, The: *Various artists* / Zubbediya: *Various artists* / Samaris' dance: *Various artists* / Finale act two: *Various artists* / Bored: *Various artists.*
MCSET: . . . . ZCTER 1170
2LP: TER2 1170

KISMET (Original Broadway cast) (Various artists).
LP: . . . . PS 32605
MC: . . . . PST 32605

KISMET (See under Mancini, Henry) (Mancini, Henry & His Orchestra).

Kiss

ACE FREHLEY SOLO ALBUM (See under Frehley, Ace).

ALIVE.
Tracks: / Deuce / Strutter / Got to choose / Hotter than hell / Firehouse / Nothin' to lose / C'mon and love me / Parasite / She / Watchin' you / 100,000 years / Black diamond / Rock bottom / Cold gin / Rock and roll all nite / Let me go rock 'n' roll.
2LP: . . . . PRID 3
MCSET: . . . . PRIDC 3
2LP: . . . . CALD 5004
2LP: 6640026

ANIMALIZE.
Tracks: / I've had enough (Into the fire) / Heaven's on fire / Burn bitch burn / Get all you can take / Lonely is the hunter / Under the gun / Thrills of the night / While the city sleeps / Murder in high heels.
LP: . . . . VERL 18
MC: . . . . VERLC 18

ASYLUM.
Tracks: / King of the mountain / Any way you slice it / Who wants to be lonely / Trial by fire / I'm alive / Love's a deadly weapon / Tears are falling / Secretly cruel / Radar for love / Uh all night.
LP: . . . . VERH 32
MC: . . . . VERHC 32

BEST OF SOLO ALBUMS.
LP: 6302 060
MC: 7144060

CRAZY CRAZY NIGHTS.
LP: . . . . VERH 49
MC: . . . . VERHC 49
LPPD: 8329031

CREATURES OF THE NIGHT.
Tracks: / Creatures of the night / Saint and sinner / Keep me comin' / Rock and roll hell / I love it loud / I still love you / Killer / War machine.
LP: . . . . CANL 4

DESTROYER.
Tracks: / Detroit rock city / King of the night time world / God of thunder / Great expectations / Flaming youth / Sweet pain / Shout it out loud / Beth / Do you love me.
LP: . . . . PRICE 41
MC: . . . . PRIMC 41
LP: . . . . CBSP 4008
LP: 6399064

DOUBLE PLATINUM.
Tracks: / Strutter 78 / Do you love me / Hard woman / Calling Dr. Love / Let me go Rock 'n' Roll / Love gun / God of thunder / Firehouse / Hotter than hell / I want you / Deuce / 100,000 Years / Detroit rock city / She / Rock and Roll all nite / Beth / Making love / C'mon and love me / Cold gin / Black diamond.
LP: . . . . PRID 8
MC: . . . . PRIDC 8
LP: 6641907

DRESSED TO KILL.
Tracks: / Room service / Two timer / Ladies in waiting / Get away / Rock bottom / C'mon and love me / Anything

for my baby / She / Love her all I can / Rock and roll all nite / Detroit rock city / King of the night time world / God of thunder / Great expectations / Flaming youth / Sweet pain / Shout it out loud / Beth / Do you love me.
LP: 6399 059
MC: 7199 059

DYNASTY.
Tracks: / I was made for lovin' you / 2,000 man / Sure know something / Dirty livin' / Charisma / Magic touch / Hard times / X-ray eyes / Save your love / Dynasty.
LP: . . . . PRICE 42
MC: . . . . PRIMC 42
LP: . . . . CALH 2051
LP: 9128024

ELDER, THE.
Tracks: / Oath, The / Fanfare / Just a boy / Dark light / Only you / Under the rose / World without heroes, A / Mr. Blackwell / Escape from the island / Odyssey / I.
LP: 6302 163
MC: 7144 163

FRAMED (Interview picture disc).
LPPD: . . . . BAK 6005
MC: . . . . MBAK 6005

GENE SIMMONS SOLO ALBUM (See under Simmons, Gene) (Simmons, Gene).

HOT IN THE SHADE.
Tracks: / Rise to it / Betrayed / Hide your heart / Prisoners of love / Read my body / Love's a slap in the face / Forever / Silver spoon / Cadillac dreams / King of hearts / St. Giveth St. Taketh Away / You love me to hate you / Somewhere between heaven and hell / Little Caesar / Boomerang.
LP: 8389131
MC: 8389134

HOTTER THAN HELL.
Tracks: / Get to choose / Parasite / Goin' blind / Hotter than hell / Let me go rock 'n' roll / All the way / Watchin' you / Mainline / Comin' home / Strangeways.
LP: 6399 058
MC: 7199 058

KILLERS.
Tracks: / I'm a legend tonight / Down on your knees / Could gin / Love gin / Shout it out loud / Sure know something / Nowhere to run / Partners in crime / Detroit rock city / God of thunder / I was made for loving you / Rock and roll all nite.
LP: . . . . CANL 1

KISS.
Tracks: / Strutter / Nothin' to lose / Firehouse / Cold gin / Let me know / Kissin' time / Deuce / Kiss love theme / 100,000 years / Black diamond.
LP: . . . . PRICE 68
MC: . . . . PRIMC 68
LP: 9128024

KISS ALIVE, 2.
Tracks: / Detroit rock city / King of the night time world / Ladies room / Making love / Love gun / Calling Dr. Love / Christine sixteen / Shock me / Hard luck woman / Tomorrow and tonight / I stole your love / Beth / God of thunder / I want you / Shout it out loud / All American men / Rockin' in the USA / Larger than life / Rocket ride / Anyway you want it.
2LP: 6685 043
MC: 7599 512
LP: . . . . CBSP 401

KISS: INTERVIEW PICTURE DISC.
LPPD: . . . . BAK 2026
LPPD: . . . . CT 1012

LICK IT UP.
LP: . . . . VERL 9
MC: . . . . VERLC 9

LOVE GUN.
Tracks: / I stole your love / Christine sixteen / Got love for sale / Shock me / Tomorrow and tonight / Love gun / Hooligan / Almost human / Plaster caster / Then she kissed me.
LP: . . . . PRICE 69
MC: . . . . PRIMC 69
LP: 6399063

MUSIC AND MEDIA INTERVIEW PICTURE DISC.
LPPD: . . . . MM 1205
LPPD: . . . . KISS 1001

PAUL STANLEY SOLO ALBUM (See under Stanley, Paul) (Stanley, Paul).

PETER CRISS SOLO ALBUM (See under Criss, Peter) (Criss, Peter).

ROCK AND ROLL OVER.
Tracks: / I want you / Take me / Calling Dr. Love / Ladies room / Baby driver / Love 'em and leave 'em / Mr. Speed / See you in your dreams / Hard luck woman / Making love.
LP: 6399 060
MC: 7199 060

SMASHES, TRASHES AND HITS.
Tracks: / Let's put the 'x' in sex / Crazy crazy nights / (You make me) rock hard / Love gun / Detroit rock city / I love it loud / Deuce / Lick it up / Heaven's on fire / Strutter / Beth (Lead vocals: Eric Carr.) / Tears are falling / I was made for lovin' you / Rock and roll all nite / Shout it out loud.
LP: 836 427-1
MC: 836 427-4

UNMASKED.
Tracks: / Is that you / Shandy / What makes the world go round / Talk to me / Naked city / Torpedo / Tomorrow / Two sides of the coin / She's no European / Easy as it seems / Tears are falling.
LP: 6302032

Kiss Kiss (bk)

KISS KISS Dahl, Roald (Gray, Charles).
MC: . . . . PTB 603

Kiss Like This

BLESSINGS IN DISGUISE.
Tracks: / What the world don't know / Faith in you / Heaven in my hands / Telephone line / Straight back down to earth / One heart / If you asked me to / Sugar to taste / Seventh sense / Kissing the mirror.
LP: . . . . CHR 1766
MC: . . . . ZCHR 1766

Kiss Me Kate

KISS ME KATE (Film Soundtrack) (Various artists).
Tracks: / Too darn hot: *Various artists* / So in love: *Various artists* / We open in Venice: *Various artists*/ Why can't you behave?: *Various artists* / Were thine that special face: *Various artists* / Tom, Dick or Harry: *Various artists* / I've come to wive it wealthily in Padua: *Various artists* / From this moment on: *Various artists* / Always true to you in my fashion: *Various artists* / I hate men: *Various artists* / Where is the life that late I led?: *Various artists* / Brush up your Shakespeare: *Various artists* / Kiss me Kate: *Various artists.*
LP: . . . . CBS 70278
MC: 3110 069
LP: 2353 062

KISS ME KATE (Original Broadway Cast) (Various artists).
MC: . . . . JST 04140
LP: . . . . PS 32609
MC: . . . . PST 32609

KISS ME KATE (Royal Shakespeare Cast) (Various artists).
LP: . . . . CAST 10
MC: . . . . CASTC 10

KISS ME KATE (Film Soundtrack).
MC: 40 70278

KISS ME KATE: REPRISE REPERTORY THEATRE (Original cast) (Various artists).
Tracks: / Another opening, another show: *Various artists* / Too darn hot: *Various artists* / I hate men: *Various artists* / Bianca: *Various artists* / Where is the life that late I led: *Various artists* / Wunderbar: *Various artists* / So in love: *Various artists* / Were thine that special face: *Various artists* / Always true to you in my fashion: *Various artists* / So in love: *Various artists* / We open in Venice: *Various artists* / Overture: *Various artists.*
LP: . . . . K 54114

KISS ME KATE/BRIGADOON (Various artists).
Tracks: / Too darn hot: *Miller, Ann* / So in love: *Keel, Howard/Kathryn Grayson* / We open in Venice: *Grayson, Kathryn/ Howard Keel/Ann Miller/Tommy Rall* / Why can't you behave: *Miller, Ann* / Were thine that special face: *Keel, Howard* / Tom, Dick or Harry: *Miller, Ann/Bobby Van/Tommy Rall/Bob Fosse* / Wunderbar: *Keel, Howard/Kathryn Grayson/* Always true to you in my fashion: *Miller, Ann/Tommy Rall* / I hate men: *Grayson, Kathryn* / I've come to wive it wealthily in Padua: *Keel, Howard* (Kiss Me Kate) / From this moment on: *Miller, Ann/Bobby Van/Tommy Rall/Bob Fosse/* Where is the life that late I led?: *Keel, Howard* / Brush up your Shakespeare: *Wynn, Keenan/James Whitmore* / Kiss me Kate: *Keel, Howard/ Kathryn Grayson* / Prologue: *Various artists* / Down on MacConnachy Square: *Various artists* / Heather on the hill: *Kelly, Gene* / Waitin' for my dearie: *Richards, Carol* / I'll go home with my bonnie Jean: *Johnson, Van/John Gustafson* / Come to me, bend to me: *Gustafson, John* / Almost like being in love: *Kelly, Gene* / Heather on the hill: *Various artists* / There but for you go I: *Various artists/* Brigadoon: *Various artists.*
LP: . . . . LPMGM 2
MC: . . . . TCMGM 2

Kiss Of The

KISS OF THE SPIDERWOMAN (Film soundtrack) (Badarou, Wally).
Tracks: / Overture / Most ravishing woman, The / Visions of the ultra-rhine / Kabaret / Je me moque de l'amour / Molina's fantasies / Lunapark / Novel das nove / Spider Island / Pavihao IV / Avocado scene, The / Theme / Call, The / Valentin's message / Blue for you / Goodbye mama / Finale.
LP: . . . . ISTA 12
MC: . . . . ICT 12

Kiss That

KISS AND TELL.
Tracks: / Join us / Play cowboy / He said no / I can't stand the rain / March out / Little King / Highest rendezvous / Love only comes twice / Mullin.
LP: . . . . CHR 1513
MC: . . . . ZCHR 1513

Kiss The Blade

STATIC WAIL.
Tracks: / Static Wail / Milkman / Somethin' else / Astounded / Holy War.
LP: . . . . KISS 223123

Kissing Bandits

SUN BANDITS, THE.
LP: . . . . ROSE 72

Kissing The Pink

CERTAIN THINGS ARE LIKELY.
Tracks: / One step / Never too late to love you / Certain things are likely / Dream dream / No-one's on the same side / I won't wait / Can you hear me / Jones / Identity card / One day.
LP: . . . . KTLP 1003
MC: . . . . ZCKTP 1003

NAKED.
Tracks: / Last film / Frightened in France / Watching their eyes / Love lasts forever / All for you / Last film (hymn version) / Big man restless / Desert song, The / Broken body / Maybe this day / In awe of industry / Mr. Blunt.
LP: . . . . KTPL 1001
MC: . . . . ZCKTPL 1001

WHAT NOISE.
LP: . . . . KTLP 1002
MC: . . . . CKTP 1002

Kissoon, Katie

SWINGING SOUL OF MAC AND KATIE KISSOON (See under Kissoon, Mac) (Kissoon, Mac & Katie).

Kissoon, Mac & Katie

6 TRACK HITS: MAC & KATIE KISSOON.
Tracks: / Sugar candy kisses.
MC: 7SC 5054

GREATEST HITS: MAC & KATIE KISSOON.
MC: . . . . ASK 788

MAC & KATIE KISSOON STORY, THE.
Tracks: / Sugar candy kisses / Hold on baby / I'm just dreaming / There's a hurricane comin' / It's a million miles from Harlem / Like a butterfly / Don't do it baby / Walking in the park, together / Two of us, The / If there's no such thing as a miracle / Where would our love be / Your love.
LP: . . . . ETMP 1

SUGAR CANDY KISSES (ALBUM).
Tracks: / Sugar candy kisses / Walking in the city / No greater love / Darling I love you / Everybody move / Hold on to me babe / If there's no such thing as a miracle / Like a butterfly / High on dreams / Beautiful day / There's a hurricane comin'.
LP: . . . . ETAT 2

SWINGING SOUL OF MAC AND KATIE KISSOON.
Tracks: / Hey you love / Pidgeon / Chirpy chirpy cheep cheep / It's a hang up world / Change it all / (I found my) freedom / True love forgives / It's all over now / Love will keep us together / Vow, The / Love grows / Bless me / Don't make me cry / Swingin' on a star / Black skinned blue eyed boys / Sing along / Love me baby / Show me / Hey diddle diddle.
LP: C5-538

TWO OF US, THE.
Tracks: / Two of us, The / I'm just dreaming / Gimme gimme your lovin' / Slave in golden chains, A / Fly away / Hold on baby / Where would our love be / Walking in the park together / I just can't seem to smile again / Million miles from Harlem / And the Lord said / Your love.
LP: . . . . ETAT 7

Kit

UNSHAKEABLE FAITH.
Tracks: / Unshakeable faith.
LP: . . . . DEC 32

Kit Kat Band

HOT DANCE MUSIC 1925-1927.
Tracks: / Can't your friend find a friend for me? / Milenberg joys / My sugar / Riverboat shuffle / If you hadn't gone away / Headin' for home / Camel walk / Piccadilly strut / Breezin' along with the breeze / I've got some lovin' to do / I wonder what's become of Joe / Sunday / Brown sugar / Ain't she sweet / Sam the old accordion man / Muddy water / Lily / From now on.
LP: . . . . SH 333

Kitaev, Andrei

FIRST TAKES.
LP: . . . . RR 6

Kitajima, Osamu

SOURCE, THE.
LP: . . . . CBS 26627
MC: 40.26627

Kitamura, Eiji

SWING EIJI.
LP: . . . . CJ 152

Kitaro

BEST OF KITARO.
Tracks: / Morning prayer / Eternal springs / Oasis / Westbound / Silver moon / Four changes / Tunhuang / Sacred journey II / Revelation / Silk road fantasy / Shimmering light / Everlasting road.
LP: . . . . LPKUCK 073
MC: . . . . MCKUCK 073

FROM THE FULL MOON STORY.
Tracks: / Krpa / Aurora / Hikari / Fuji / Full moon / Resurrection / From Astra / Heavenly illusion / New lights.
LP: 810 945-1

KOJIKI.
LP: 7599242551
MC: 7599242554
MC: . . . . GEFC 24255

LIGHT OF THE SPIRIT, THE.
Tracks: / Urbanology (Side 'D'.) / Mysterious encounter / Sundance / Field, The / Light of the spirit, The / In the beginning / Moondance / Howling thunder / Journey to a fantasy.
MC: 9241634
LP: 9241631

LIVE IN AMERICA.
LP: . . . . GEF 24323
MC: . . . . GEFC 24323

LIVE IN ASIA.
Tracks: / Earth born / Caravansary / Theme of silk road / Cosmic live / Cloud / Japanese drums / Return to Russia / Straight away to Orion / Dawn in Malaysia.
LP: 825 204-1
MC: 825 204-4

OASIS.
Tracks: / Rising sun / Moro-rism / New wave / Cosmic energy / Aqua / Moonlight / Shimmering horizon / Fragrance of nature / Innocent people / Oasis.
LP: 815 340-1
MC: 815 340-4

SAMPLER.
LP: . . . . KIT 1

SILK ROAD I.
Tracks: / Silk road theme / Bell tower / Heavenly father / Great river, The / Great wall of China / Flying celestial nymphs / Silk Road fantasy / Shimmering light / Westbound time / Bodhisattva / Everlasting road.
LP: 823 736-1
MC: 823 736-4

SILK ROAD II.
Tracks: / In the silence / Takla malikan desert / Eternal springs / Silver moon / Magical sand dance / Year 40080 / Time travel / Reincarnation / Dawning / Tienshan.
LP: 817 532-1
MC: 817 532-4

SILK ROAD SUITE (TV Soundtrack) (Kitaro & London Symphony Orchestra).
Tracks: / Silk road theme / Drifting sand / Fragrance of nature / Silk road fantasy / Time / Flying celestial nymphs / Everlasting road / Bell tower / Sunset / Westbound / Magical sand dance / Tienshan / Peace / Journey.
2LP: . . . . LPKUCK 065/066
MCSET: . . . . MCKUCK 065/066

SILVER CLOUD.
Tracks: / Earth born / Flying cloud / Dreams like yesterday / Never let you go / Noah's ark / Return to Russia / Panorama / Straight away to Orion.
LP: 817 560-1
MC: 817 560-4

TEN YEARS.

Tracks: / Dawn/Rising sun / Caravansary / Shimmering horizon / Cosmic love / Silk Road, Theme from / Lord of wind / Oasis / Clouds, The / Earth born / Aqua / Mirage / Moon star / Flight / God of thunder / Bell tower / Song for peace.
2LP: 924207 1
MC: 924207 4

TENKU.
Tracks: / Tenku / Romance / Wings / Aura / Message from the Cosmos / Time travel / Legend of the road / Milky Way.
LP: 9241121
MC: 9241124

TOWARDS THE WEST.
LP: 829 006-1
MC: 829 006-4

Kitchen, Geoff

JAZZ FOUNDATIONS.
LP: .... S 1385

Kitchen, Kevin

SPLIT PERSONALITY.
Tracks: / Nowhere to run / Tightspot / One of the hopefuls / Put my arms around you / Way out, The / Fingerprints / This couldn't happen to me / Painting the cracks / Step into my world / Split personality.
LP: .... WOL 1
MC: .... ZWOL 1

Kitchens of

LOVE IS HELL.
LP: .... TPLP 9

STRANGE FREE WORLD.
LP: .... TPLP 19
MC: .... TPC 19

Kitsyke Will

DEVIL'S RIDE.
LP: .... SHY 7020

Kitt, Eartha

AT HER VERY BEST.
Tracks: / Just an old fashioned girl / Day that the circus left town, The / Smoke gets in your eyes / If I was a boy / Tea in Chicago / Heel, The / Johnny / Lilac wine / Uska dara / Under the bridges of Paris / Let's do it / Blues, The / C'est si bon monotonous / Bal petit bal / Santa baby / Proceed with caution / Mink schmink / Easy does it.
LP: .... NL 89376
MC: .... NK 89376
LP: .... INTS 5182

BEST OF EARTHA KITT.
Tracks: / C'est si bon / April in Portugal / Apres moi / I want to be evil / If I love ya, then I need ya / Shango / My heart belongs to daddy / Uska dar / Just an old fashioned girl / Let's do it / Mack the knife / Love is a gamble / Sholem / Yellow bird / I'd rather be burnt as a witch / Santa baby.
LP: .... MCL 1702
MC: .... MCLC 1702

C'EST SI BON.
Tracks: / Sell me / I wanna be evil / Waray waray / Touch, The / How could you believe me when I said I loved you... / Zhara bee zha zha / Champagne taste / C'mon a my house / Old fashioned girl / C'est si bon / Rumania Rumania.
LP: .... A 225
LPPD: .... PD 30032

CHA CHA HEELS (See under Bronski Beat) (Kitt, Eartha & Bronski Beat).

EARTHA KITT.
LP: .... SW 8410
MC: .... SWC 8410

EARTHA KITT IN PERSON AT PLAZA.
LP: .... GNPS 2008
MC: GNP5 2008

FOLK TALES OF THE TRIBES OF AFRICA (See under Folk Tales).

I LOVE MEN.
LP: .... SOHOLP 2
MC: .... SOHOTC 2

I'M A FUNNY DAME.
Tracks: / Proceed with caution / Je cherche un homme / Honolulu rock a roll a / Fredy / There is no cure for l'amore / Take my love, take my love / Nobody taught me / I'm funny dame / Nothin' for Christmas / Put more wood on the fire / Two lovers / Waydown blues / Yomme, yomme / Sho jo ji / Toujour gai.
LP: .... OFF 12001

I'M STILL HERE.
Tracks: / Do or die / Primitive man / My discarded men / All by myself / Beautiful at forty / Cha cha heels / Hit them where it hurts / Urban fantasy / I'm still here.
LP: 210324
MC: 410324

LIVE IN LONDON.
Tracks: / Old fashioned girl / I want to be evil / Guess who I saw today / Could I leave you today? / Blues, The / St Louis blues / Where is my man? / Ne me quitte pas / C'est si bon / Charleston / Here's to love / Englishman needs time, An / All by myself / Beautiful at forty / Uska dara / My discarded men / Day that the circus left town, The / When the world was young / Hymn to love / I will survive / I'm still here.
LP: 303825
MC: 503825

LOVE FOR SALE.
Tracks: / Love for sale / Autumn leaves / Girl from Ipanema / Darling, je vous aime beaucoup / Too close for comfort / Guess who I saw today / C'est magnifique / I wish you love / My man / Moon river / Last time I saw Paris, The / Love.
LP: 2C 068 65084
MC: .... PM 165 084 4

MINK SHMINK.
Tracks: / Santa baby / Spree / Annie doesn't live here any more / Woman wouldn't be a woman, A / Somebody bad stole de wedding bell / Dinner for one please / Blues, The / This year's Santa baby / Mink Shmink / Easy does it / If I was a boy / Tea in Chicago / Sweet and gentle / Sandy's tune / Salangodou / Monotonous.
LP: .... OFF 12009

MY WAY.
Tracks: / Introduction: Ms Kitt / God bless the child / Old ship of Zion / America the beautiful / Look where God has brought us / Commentary: Ms Kitt / Old rugged cross, The / Abraham, Martin and John / My way.
LP: .... CDP 85010
MC: .... CDPT 85010

REVISITED.
LP: .... HA 2296

ROMANTIC EARTHA KITT, THE.
Tracks: / I've got you under my skin / When the world was young / Wonderful illusion / Solitude / Easy to love / September song / You'll never know / Speak low / Happiness is a thing called Joe / Mirage / Chez moi / In the still of the night.
LP: .... PM 154 772 1

SONGS.
Tracks: / Sing 'em low / Jonny, wenn du geburstag hast / Smoke gets in your eyes / Memphis blues (The) / Lullaby of birdland / Heel (The) / Apres moi / St. Louis blues / April in Portugal / I want to be evil / My heart belongs to daddy / Mambo de paree / Monotonous / C'est si bon / Let's do it / Lisbon Antigua / Do you remember? / Uska dara / Beale Street blues / Fascinating man / Looking for a boy / Just an old fashioned girl / Angelitos negros / Careless love / Under the bridges of Paris / If I can't take it with me / Day that the circus left town (The).
LP: .... NL 89477
MC: .... NK 89477
LP: .... CL 42471

ST. LOUIS BLUES.
LP: .... NL 89346
MC: .... NK 89346

THAT BAD EARTHA.
Tracks: / I want to be evil / C'est si bon / Angelitos Negros / Avril au Portugal / Let's do it / My heart belongs to daddy / Uska dara / African lullaby / Mountain high, valley low / Lilac wine / Under the bridges of Paris / Smoke gets in your eyes.
LP: .... NL 89439
MC: .... NK 89439

Kix

BLOW MY FUSE.
Tracks: / Blow my fuse / Boomerang / Dirty boys / Cold blood / Get it while it's hot / She dropped me the bomb / Piece of pie.
LP: .... K 781 877 1
MC: .... K 781 877 4

MIDNITE DYNAMITE.
Tracks: / Midnite dynamite / Red hot / Bang bang / Layin' rubber / Walking away / Scarlet fever / Cry baby / Cold shower / Lie like a rug / Sex.
LP: 781 267-1

K'Jarkas

CANTO A LA MUJER DE MI PUEBLO.
LP: .... TUMI 010
MC: .... TUMIC 010

EL AMOR Y LA LIBERTAD.
MC: .... TUMIC 013

Klaatu

ENDANGERED SPECIES.
Tracks: / I can't help it / Knee deep in love / Paranoia / Howl at the moon / Set the world on fire / Hot box city / Dog star / Sell out, sell out / All good things.
LP: .... EST 12080

Klan, Kouchie

SOONER OR LATER (see under Case, Connie) (Klan, Kouchie & Connie Case).

Klangers

RIGHT OF SUCCESION.
LP: .... COD 4

Klaxons

CLAP CLAP DANCE.
LP: .... GNPS 2192
MC: GNP5 2192

HOW DO YOU DO.
LP: .... GNPS 2180
MC: GNP5 2180

Kleeer

GET READY.
LP: .... K 7800381

I LOVE TO DANCE.
Tracks: / Tonight's the night / Keep your body working / Happy me / I love to dance / It's magic / To groove you / Amour / Kleeer sailing.
LP: .... K 50614

INTIMATE CONNECTION.
Tracks: / Next time it's for real / Break / Tonight / Do you want to / Ride it / You do it again / Go for it / Intimate connection.
LP: 780 145-1

KLEEER WINNERS.
Tracks: / Intimate connection / Take your heart away / Seeekret / Never cry again / Winners / Do kleer ting / Keep your body working / Get tough / Open your mind / Wall to wall.
LP: .... WX 42
MC: .... WX 42 C

LICENSED TO DREAM.
Tracks: / De Kleeer ting / Running back to you / Sittin' and kissin' / Hypnotised / Licensed to dream / Get tough / Say you love me / Where would I be.
LP: .... SD 19288

SEEEKRET.
Tracks: / Take your heart away / You got me rockin' / Lay ya down ez / Seeekret / Do not lie to me / Never cry again / Call my name.
LP: 781 254-1

TASTE THE MUSIC.
Tracks: / Taste the music / I've had enough / De ting continues / Wall to wall / I shall get over / Fella / Swann / Affirmative mood.
LP: K50873

Klein, Herbert

ACCORDIAN OF HERBERT KLEIN.
MC: .... AIM 106

Klein, Norma

MOM, THE WOLFMAN AND ME (Sheedy, Alexandra Elizabeth).
MC: 1517

Klein, Oscar

LOW LIGHT BLUES (see Ricks, Phil Jerry) (Klein, Oscar & Phil Jerry Ricks).

Klemmer, John

BLOWIN' GOLD.
Tracks: / Excursion £2 / My love has butterfly wings / Hey Jude / Third stone from the sun / Free soul / Children of the earth flames / Summer song / Rose petals / A mon frere africain / Gardens of Uranus / All the children cried / Here comes the child / I whisper a prayer for peace / Pulsations of a green eyed lady / Journey's end / La de dah / Soliloquy for tenor and voice.
2LP: .... GCH 2-6036

FINESSE.
Tracks: / Finesse / Man and woman / Sometimes / Greatest love of all, The / Sun, the moon and the stars , The / Beloved / But are you beautiful inside.
LP: .... E 0197

HUSH.
Tracks: / Hush / Let's make love / Taboo / Life is so beautiful / Magic / Hot / I love you madly / Hummingbird bay / Feeling free.
LP: .... K 52297

MUSIC.
LP: .... MCA 6246

Klezmer Conservatory

OY CHANUKAH.
MC: .... ROUNDER 3102C
LP: .... ROUNDER 3102

Klezmer Music

KLEZMER MUSIC First recordings 1910-27 (Various artists).
MC: .... C 9034
LP: .... FL 9034

KLEZMER MUSIC 1910-42 Vivo archives recordings (Various artists).
MC: .... GVMMC 104

Klezmer Orchestra

ANDY STATMAN KLEZMER ORCHESTRA.
LP: .... SHAN 21004

KLEZMER SUITE.
LP: .... SHAN 21005

Klezmorim

EAST SIDE WEDDING.
LP: .... ARHOOLIE 3006
MC: .... C 3006

IS GEWIJN A FOLK.
LP: .... EULP 1059
MC: .... EUMC 1059

JAZZ BABIES OF THE UKRAINE - LIVE.
LP: .... FF 465

METROPOLIS.
LP: .... FF 258

NOTES FROM UNDERGROUND.
LP: .... FF 322

SHALOM.
LP: .... EULP 1060
MC: .... EUMC 1060

STREETS OF GOLD (Improvising Yiddish musicians).
LP: .... ARHOOLIE 3011
MC: .... C 3011

K.L.F.

CHILL OUT.
LP: .... JAMSLP 5

TOWARDS THE TRANCE.
LP: .... KLFKL 001

WHAT TIME IS LOVE STORY.
LP: .... JAMSLP 4

WHITE ROOM, THE.
Tracks: / What time is love? / Make it rain / 3 A.M. eternal / Church of The K.L.F. / Last train to Trancentral / Build a fire / White room, The / No more tears / Justified and ancient.
LP: .... JAMSLP 6
MC: .... JAMSMC 6

Klingonz

BLURB.
LP: .... F 3011

MONG.
LP: .... F 3014

PSYCHOS FROM BEYOND.
LP: .... F 3007

Klinik

FACE TO FACE - FEVER.
LP: .... ANT 096

PLAGUE.
Tracks: / Positively something wild / I know you rider / Fire engine / Sally go round the roses / Tangerine.
LP: .... ANT 065

SABOTAGE AND MELTING CLOSE.
Tracks: / Decay / Hours and hours / Brain damage / Sabotage / Sick in your hand / Vietnam / Burning inside / Never get out / Melting close / Nautilus / Feel the evil.
2LP: .... ANT 056

STATES.
LP: .... AS 5052
MC: .... AS 5052MC

Klique

LOVE CYCLES.
LP: .... MCF 3258

Klobe, Martin

TRONIC (Klobe, Martin & Ralf Illenberger).
LP: TUT118

Klondike Peter

SOME OF THE FELLERS (Klondike Peter & The Huskies).
Tracks: / Bubba's song / Day of the big flood / Stomping in the mud / Double whammy / Pearl / Ballad of Klondike Pete & Huskies / Cover me with love / Crazy Richard's gonna burn your house down / True love is all you need / Don't turn your back on me / Hey engineer.
LP: .... WIK 12

Kloss, Arnold

STORY LINE.
Tracks: / Time remembered / I'm all smiles / Have you met Miss Jones / You took advantage of me / Solar / Turn out the stars / Round midnight / Off minor.
LP: D-004

Kloss, Eric

CELEBRATION.
LP: .... MR 5196

DOORS.
LP: .... MR 5291

ONE TWO FREE.
LP: .... MR 5019

Klugh, Earl

BEST OF EARL KLUGH, THE.
Tracks: / Tropical legs (Wishful thinking) / Amazon (Dream come true) / Magic in your eyes / Calypso getaway / Dr. Macumba (Finger paintings) / Long ago and far away (Finger paintings) / Angelina / Heart string / Livin' inside your love / Christina (Low ride) / Wishful thinking / I don't want to leave you alone anymore.
MC: B4 46625

CARI (See under James, Bob) (Klugh, Earl and Bob James).

COLLABORATION (See under Benson, George) (Klugh, Earl & George Benson).

CRAZY FOR YOU.
Tracks: / Dance with me / I'm ready for your love / Soft stuff (and other sweet delights) / Twinkle / Broadway ramble / Calypso getaway / Rainmaker, The / Ballad in A / Crazy for you / Livin' inside your love.
LP: LBG 30329
MC: TC LBG 30329

DELTA LADY (see Matthews, David) (Klugh, Earl & David Matthews).

DREAM COME TRUE.
Tracks: / If it's in your heart (it's in your smile) / Doc / Amazon (dream come true) / I don't want to leave you alone anymore / Spellbound / Sweet rum and starlight / Dream come true / Message to Michael.
LP: IC 064 82875

FINGER PAINTING.
Tracks: / Doctor Macumba / Long ago and far away / Cabo frio / Keep your eye on the sparrow / Catherine / Dance with me / Jolanta / Summer song / This time.
LP: UAG 20011

HEART STRING.
Tracks: / Heartstring / I'll see you again / Acoustic lady (Part 1) / Spanish night / Pretty world / Waiting for Cathy / Rayna / Heartstring (reprise) / Acoustic lady (Part 2).
LP: UAG 30233

HEART STRING/LATE NIGHT GUITAR.
Tracks: / Heart string / I'll see you again / Acoustic lady (Part 1) / Spanish night / Pretty world / Waiting for Cathy / Rayna / Heart string (reprise) / Smoke gets in your eyes / Nice to be around / Like a lover / Laura / Jamaica farewell / Tenderly / Mona Lisa / Triste / Two for the road / Mirabella / Lisbon Antigua / Time for love, A / I'll never say goodbye / Acoustic lady (Part 2).
MC: TC2X 1834139

LATE NIGHT GUITAR.
Tracks: / Smoke gets in your eyes / Nice to be around / Like a lover / Laura / Jamaica farewell / Tenderly / Mona Lisa / Triste / Two for the road / Mirabella / Lisbon Antigua / Time for love, A / I'll never say goodbye.
LP: UAG 30332
LP: IC 064 83045

LIFE STORIES.
Tracks: / Traveller, The / Just for your love / Second chances / For the love of you / Debra Anne / Santiago sunset / Sandman / Return of the rainmaker / Moon and the stars / Traveller, The (part 2).
LP: 925478 1
MC: 925478 4

LIVING INSIDE YOUR LOVE.
Tracks: / Captain caribe / I heard it through the grapevine / Felicia / Living inside your love / Another time another place / April fools, The / Kiko.
LP: UAG 20009

LIVING INSIDE YOUR LOVE/ FINGER PAINTINGS.
MC: TC 2X 1834119

LOW RIDE.
Tracks: / Back in Central Park / Be my love / Low ride / Just like yesterday / If you're still in love with me / I never thought I'd leave you / Christina / Night drive.
LP: EST 12253
MC: TCEST 12253

MAGIC IN YOUR EYES.
Tracks: / Magic in your eyes / Alicia / Julie / Lode star / Cast your fate to the wind / Rose hips / Good time Charlie's got the blues / Mayaguez / Cry a little while.
LP: UAG 30171

MAGIC IN YOUR EYES/ DREAM COME TRUE.
MC: TC 2X 1834129

NIGHT SONGS.
Tracks: / Ain't misbehavin' / Pawnbroker (Theme from) / Look of love, The / Nature boy / Stay gold (Theme from The Outsiders) / Night song / See see rider / Certain smile, A / Shadow of your smile / Picnic, Theme from.
LP: EJ 2402281
MC: EJ 2402284

SODA FOUNTAIN SHUFFLE.
Tracks: / Just pretend / Baby cakes / Soda fountain shuffle / Moonlight dancing / Incognito / One night alone with you / Some other time / Rainbow man / Close to your heart / April love.
LP: 925262 1
MC: 925262 4

SOLO GUITAR.
LP: K 9260181
MC: K 9260184

TIME FOR LOVE, A.
MC: 4XLL 9287

TWO OF A KIND (Klugh, Earl and Bob James).
Tracks: / Falcon, The / Whiplash / Sandstorm / Where I wander / Ingenue, The / Wes.
MC: TCEAST 12244
LP: EAST 12244

WISHFUL THINKING.
Tracks: / Wishful thinking / Tropical legs / All the time / Natural thing / Once again / Big band / Only one for me / Right from the start.
LP: EST 2400921
MC: TCEST 2400924

WORLD STAR.
LP: 1A 064 1547911
MC: 1A 264 1547914

Klymaxx

GIRLS IN THE BAND, THE.
LP: 9602821

GIRLS WILL BE GIRLS.
Tracks: / Girls will be girls / Wild girls / Convince me / Man in my life / Heartbreaker / All turned out / Offer I can't refuse / If you love me / Don't hide your love.
LP: 9601771

KLYMAXX.
Tracks: / Sexy / Fab attack / Divas need love too / I'd still say yes / Fashion / Danger zone / Long distance love affair / Come back / Man size love.
LP: MCF 3350
MC: MCFC 3350

MAXX IS BACK, THE.
Tracks: / Maxx is back, The / Private party / Finishing touch / Don't mess with my man / Don't run away / Good love / When you kiss me / Girls chasing boys / Shame / She's a user.
LP: MCG 6096
MC: MCGC 6096

MEETING IN THE LADIES ROOM.
Tracks: / Men all pause, The / Lock and key / I miss you / Just our luck / Meeting in the ladies room / Video kid / Ask me no questions / Love bandit / I betcha.
LP: MCF 3313
MC: MCFC 3313
LP: MCF 3247

NEVER UNDERESTIMATE THE POWER OF A WOMAN.
Tracks: / All fired up / I wish you would / I want to love you tonight / You're the greatest / Never underestimate the power of a woman / Beat of my heart / No words / Can't let love just pass me by.
LP: K 52304
MC: K4 52304

K.M.F.D.M.

DON'T BLOW YOUR TOP.
Tracks: / Don't blow your top / No meat no man / Oh look / What a race / King Kong / No news / Oh look.
LP: SAW 006

NAIVE.
LP: WAXLP 148

WHAT DO YOU KNOW DEUTSCHLAND.
LP: SAW 004

WORLD VAIOE.
LP: SBR 032

Knabel, Rudi

ZAMBER DER ZITHER.
Tracks: / Der dritte man / Wien, wien nur du allein / Wenn der herrgott net will / Hoppla-hop / Stell's meine ross 'in' stall / Wiener fiakerlied / La montanara / Mein loisachtal / Zauber der berge / Grune almen / Abendstimmung / Die kleine serenade.
LP: 829 169-1
MC: 829 169-4

Knack

BUT THE LITTLE GIRLS UNDERSTAND.
LP: EST 12045

GET THE KNACK.
Tracks: / Let me out / Your number or your name / Oh Tara / She's so selfish / Maybe tonight / Good girls don't / My Sharona / Heartbeat / Siamese twins / Lucinda / That's what little girls do.
LP: FA 3039
MC: TCFA 3039
LP: EST 11948

ROUND TRIP.
Tracks: / Radiating love / Soul kissin' / Africa / She likes the beat / Just wait and see / We are waiting / Boys go crazy / Li'l Cal's big mistake / Sweet dreams / Another lousy day in paradise / Pay the devil / Art war.
LP: EST 12168

Knack (film)

KNACK, THE (Film soundtrack) (Various artists).
LP: MCA 25109
MC: MCAC 25109

Knapp, James

FIRST AVENUE.
LP: ECM 1194

Knee, Bernie

BERNIE KNEE.
LP: AP 144

Kneller Hall R.M.S

HOME GROWN.
Tracks: / Celebration / Heroic march / Jubilee overture / Choc'late dancing / Prelude to comedy / Fantasia on the Dargason / Bond of friendship / Cavalry walk / Mad major / Royal Stuart / Prince / Royal standard / Sarafand / Silver salute.
LP: PRM 109D
MC: CPRM 109D

Knepper, Jimmy

CUNNINGBIRD.
LP: SCS 1061

DREAM DANCING (Knepper, Jimmy Quintet).
LP: CRISS 1024

IDOL OF THE FLIES.
Tracks: / Love letters / Ogling ogre / You stepped out of a dream / How high the moon / Gee baby / Ain't I good to you / Idol of the flies / Close as pages in a book / Avid admirer / Irresistible you.
LP: AFF 89

JUST FRIENDS (see under Temperley, Joe) (Knepper, Jimmy/Joe Temperley).

PRIMROSE PATH (Knepper, Jimmy & Bobby Wellins).
LP: HEP 2012

TELL ME (Knepper, Jimmy Sextet).
Tracks: / Tell me / Brewery boys blues / Nearer my God / Ecclusiastics / I thought about you / Home / Tell me.
LP: AFF 183

Knickerbocker Holiday

KNICKERBOCKER HOLIDAY Original Broadway cast (Various artists).
Tracks: / September song, The: *Various artists.*
LP: AEI 1148

Knickerbockers

FABULOUS KNICKERBOCKERS.
Tracks: / Love is a bird / I can do it better / Coming generation, The / Stick with me / Please don't fight it / Can't you see I'm trying? / I must be doing something right / Please don't love him / I believe in her / Lies / Rumours, gossip, words, untrue / Sweet green fields / What does that make you? / Just one girl / One-track mind / Your kind of lovin' / Chapel in the fields / High on love.
LP: SEE 208

Knife Wounds

PLATE II.
LP: PATH 1

Knight, Bobby

CREAM OF THE CROP.
Tracks: / Rebel rouser / Li'l bit / I got rhythm / When I fall in love / Rock bottom / Strike up the band / Here's that rainy day / Recuerdos / Life's too long / Star wars.
LP: N 5003

Knight, Brian

BLUE EYED SLIDE (Featuring Laurence Scott).
LP: LMLP 022

DARK HORSE, A.
LP: BRI 1

GOOD TIME DOWN THE ROAD (Brian Knight & J McLoughlin With Steve Bray & Ray Bailey).
LP: PYL 13
MC: PYM 13

Knight, Curtis

GET THAT FEELING (See under 'Hendrix, Jimi' for details).

LIVE IN EUROPE.
LP: 088816

Knight, Frederick

KNIGHT RAP.
Tracks: / River flowing know that / River flowing / Wrapped in your love / Staying power / I love the way you love / You make my life complete / When it ain't right with my baby / Uphill peace of mind.
LP: TRLP 110
LP: TRPL 110

KNIGHT TIME.
Tracks: / Knight time / If tomorrow never comes / Old shop, The / I'll come back to you / You're the best thing in my life / When will the love need me / Shining star / Even a fool would let go / Bundle of love.
LP: TRLP 103

Knight, Gladys

16 GREAT CLASSICS (Knight, Gladys & The Pips).
Tracks: / How do you say goodbye / Jungle love / I want that kind of love / Before now, after then / I can't stand by / What shall I do? / Every beat of my heart / Room in my heart / Guess who? / Running around / Darlin' / Letter full of tears / You broke your promise / Operator / Trust in you / Morning, noon and night.
LP: XELLP 103
MC: XELMC 103

20 GOLDEN GREATS: GLADYS KNIGHT (Knight, Gladys & The Pips).
Tracks: / Help me make it through the night / Take me in your arms and love me / Just walk in my shoes / Look of love, The / Friendship train / Nitty gritty / You need love like I do / Every beat of my heart / It should have been me / Daddy could swear, I declare / Neither one of us / I heard it through the grapevine / Everybody needs love / If I were your woman / I wish it would rain / I don't want to do wrong / Make me the woman that you come home to / Letter full of tears / Didn't you know (you'd have to cry sometime) / End of our road, The.
LP: STML 12122
MC: CSTML 12122

30 GREATEST (Knight, Gladys & The Pips).
LP: NE 1004

ABOUT LOVE (Knight, Gladys & The Pips).
Tracks: / Landlord / Taste of bitter love / Still such a thing / Get the love / Add it up / Bourgie bourgie / Friendly persuasion / We need hearts.
LP: 32543
LP: CBS 84178

ALL OUR LOVE (Knight, Gladys & The Pips).
Tracks: / Love overboard / Lovin' on next to nothin' / Thief in paradise / You / Let me be the one / Complete recovery / Say what you mean / It's gonna take all our love / Love is fire / Point of view / Overnight success.
LP: MCF 3409
MC: MCFC 3409

ALL THE GREATEST HITS (Knight, Gladys & The Pips).
Tracks: / Help me make it through the night / Take me in your arms and love me / I heard it through the grapevine / End of our road, The / Nitty gritty / Friendship train / You need love like I do / Just walk in my shoes / I don't want to do wrong / Look of love, The / Neither one of us / Daddy could swear, I declare / Make me the woman that you come home to / If I were your woman.
LP: WL 72373
MC: WK 72373

ANTHOLOGY - GLADYS KNIGHT (Volumes 1 and 2) (Knight, Gladys & The Pips).
Tracks: / Every beat of my heart / Letter full of tears / Giving up / Just walk in my shoes / Do you love me just a little, honey / You don't love me no more / Take me in your arms and love me / Everybody needs love / I heard it through the grapevine / End of our road, The / I know better / Don't let her take your love from me / It should have been me / I wish it would rain / Valley of the Dolls, Theme from / Didn't you know (you'd have to cry sometime) / Got myself a good man / All I could do was cry / Friendship train / Tracks of my tears / You need love like I do / Every little bit hurts / If I were your woman / I don't want to do wrong / One less bell to answer / Is there a place (in his heart for me) / Master of my mind / No one could love you more / Can't give it up no more / For once in my life / Make me the woman that you come home to / Help me make it through the night / Neither one of us / Daddy could swear, I declare / All I need is time / Don't tell me I'm crazy / Oh what

a love I have found / Only time you love me is when you're losing me, The / Between her goodbye and my hello.
2LP: . . . . **TMSP 1127**
MCSET: . . . . **CTMSP 1127**

BEFORE NOW AFTER THEN (Knight, Gladys & The Pips).
Tracks: / I trust in you / Linda / Happiness / Love call / Room in your heart / Love like mine, A / Darlin' / It hurts so bad / Jungle love / Queen of tears / Bless the one / What shall I do.
2LP: . . . . **CR 118**
MCSET: . . . . **CRT 118**

BEST OF GLADYS KNIGHT & THE PIPS (Knight, Gladys & The Pips).
Tracks: / Taste of bitter love / Ain't no greater love / I will fight / Save the overtime for me / when you're far away / You're number one in my book / Landlord / Hero / Friend of mine, A / My time.
LP: . . . . **BDLH 5013**
MC: . . . . **ZC BDS 5013**
LP: **4624161**
MC: **4624164**

BEST OF GLADYS KNIGHT & THE PIPS, THE (1980 - 1985) (Knight, Gladys & The Pips).
LP: **4674501**
MC: **4674504**

BLESS THIS HOUSE (Knight, Gladys & The Pips).
Tracks: / Night before Christmas, The / Do you hear what I hear / Christmas song, The / Christmas song, The / Away in a manger / Ave Maria / Silent night / Bless this house / Jesu, joy of man's desiring / Jesus is my kind of people / Jesus is alright with me.
LP: . . . . **BDLP 4050**

BROKEN PROMISES (Knight, Gladys & The Pips).
Tracks: / Operator / You broke your promise / Morning noon and night / Guess who / Love like mine, A / I really didn't mean it / One more lonely night / Come see about me / I can't stand by / I want that kind of love.
LP: . . . . **TOP 169**
MC: . . . . **KTOP 169**

COLLECTION: GLADYS KNIGHT.
Tracks: / Best thing that ever happened to me, The / I heard it through the grapevine / Heaven sent / Neither one of us / Midnight train to Georgia / Take me in your arms and love me / For once in my life / One and only / Taste of bitter love / Way we were, The / Try to remember / Help me make it through the night / We don't make each other laugh anymore / Tracks of my tears / Best thing we can do is say goodbye / Look of love, The / Baby don't change your mind / Goin' out of my head / If that will make you happy / Way it was, The / Hero.
LP: . . . . **NITE 1**
MC: . . . . **KNITE 1**

COLLECTION: GLADYS KNIGHT (BOX SET) (Knight, Gladys & The Pips).
LPS: **11PP 602**

COLLECTION: GLADYS KNIGHT & THE PIPS (Knight, Gladys & The Pips).
Tracks: / Make yours a happy home / Best thing that ever happened to me / I feel a song / Georgia on my mind / Midnight train to Georgia / On and on / Where peaceful waters flow / I've got to use my imagination / I can see clearly now / Try to remember / One and only / Come back and finish what you started / It's a better than good time / Sorry doesn't always make it right / Be yourself / So sad the song / Nobody but you / Pipe dreams / Baby don't change your mind / Part time lover / Way we were, The.
2LP: . . . . **CCSLP 206**
MC: . . . . **CCSMC 206**

COLUMBIA YEARS, THE (Knight, Gladys & The Pips).
LP: . . . . **FC 40878**

EASYRIDING: GLADYS KNIGHT (Knight, Gladys & The Pips).
Tracks: / Best thing that ever happened to me / Midnight train to Georgia / Baby don't change your mind / Come back and finish what you started / Part time lover / Where peaceful waters flow / I can see clearly now / We don't make each other laugh any more / Way it was, The / I feel a song in my heart / Home is where the heart is / I love to feel the feeling.
MC: . . . . **KNMC 11003**
LP: . . . . **KNLP 11003**

EVERY BEAT OF MY HEART.
Tracks: / Tracks of my tears / Every little bit hurts / Yesterday / It's Summer / You've lost that lovin' feeling / Look of love, The.
LP: . . . . **MS 3506**
MC: . . . . **TMC 3506**

LP: . . . . **RMB 5618**

EVERY BEAT OF MY HEART (2).
Tracks: / what shall I do / I can't stand by / Before now after then / Goodnight my love / Love me again / Running around / Room in your heart / Every beat of your heart / Trust in you / Morning noon and night.
LP: . . . . **BMM 003**

EVERYBODY NEEDS LOVE.
Tracks: / Everybody needs love / I'll be standing by / Since I've lost you / I heard it through the grapevine / You don't love me no more / Ain't no sun since you've been gone / Take me in your arms and love me / He's my kind of fellow / Yes I'm ready / My bed of thorns / Do you love me just a little honey / Just walk in my shoes.
MC: . . . . **CSTMS 5039**
LP: . . . . **STMS 5039**

FIRST SHOT.
Tracks: / Every beat of my heart / Room in your heart / Guess who / Jungle love / I want that kind of love / Before now, after then / I can't stand by / What shall I do.
LP: . . . . **MAN 5002**

FUNKY.
Tracks: / Letter full of tears / Operator / Trust in you / What shall I do / Room in your heart / Guess who / Running around / Darling.
LP: . . . . **MAN 5003**

GLADYS KNIGHT.
Tracks: / Am I too late / You bring out the best in me / I just want to be with you / If you need somebody / You don't have to say I love you / I / My world / Best thing we can do is say goodbye / It's the same old song / You loved away the pain.
LP: . . . . **CBS 83341**

GLADYS KNIGHT & THE PIPS (Knight, Gladys & The Pips).
MC: . . . . **AMP 013**

GOLDEN HOUR OF GLADYS KNIGHT AND THE PIPS (Knight, Gladys & The Pips).
MC: . . . . **KGHMC 147**

GOOD WOMAN.
LP: . . . . **MCA 10329**
MC: . . . . **MCAC 10329**

HEART AND SOUL OF GLADYS KNIGHT.
Tracks: / Try to remember/The way we were / One and only, The / I can see clearly now / I've got to use my imagination / Nobody but you / On and on / Midnight train to Georgia / Baby don't change your mind / Come back and finish what you started / So sad the song / Part time love / Where peaceful waters flow / Georgia on my mind / Best thing that ever happened to me, The.
LP: . . . . **KNLP 12050**
MC: . . . . **KNMC 12050**

HELP ME MAKE IT THROUGH THE NIGHT (Knight, Gladys & The Pips).
Tracks: / Help me make it through the night / Goin' out of my head / Didn't you know (you'd have to cry sometime) / I wish it would rain / Look of love, The / Letter full of tears / Tracks of my tears / Ain't you glad you chose love / Since I've lost you / You're my everything / Everybody needs love / Ain't no sun since you've been gone / It should have been me / I know better.
LP: . . . . **STMS 5096**
MC: . . . . **CSTMS 5096**

I FEEL A SONG (Knight, Gladys & The Pips).
LP: . . . . **BDLP 4030**

IMAGINATION (Knight, Gladys & The Pips).
Tracks: / Midnight train to Georgia / I've got to use my imagination / Storms of troubled times / Best thing that ever happened to me / Once in a lifetime thing / Where peaceful waters flow / I can see clearly now / Perfect love / Window raisin' granny.
LP: . . . . **BDLP 4005**
LP: **252 210-1**
MC: **252 210-4**

JUKE BOX GIANTS (Knight, Gladys & The Pips).
Tracks: / Letter full of tears / Linda / Love call / Bless the one / I had a dream last night / Love like mine, A / Darlin' / How do you say goodbye / Jungle love / Before now, after then / What shall I do / Queen of tears / What will become of me / To whom it may concern / Happiness is the light of love / Walkin' round in circles / It hurts so bad / Every beat of my heart / One more lonely night / Really didn't mean it.
LP: . . . . **AFEMP 1022**

LOOK OF LOVE (Knight, Gladys & The Pips).
LP: . . . . **MFP 50417**

LOOKING BACK... "THE FURY YEARS" (Knight, Gladys & The Pips).
Tracks: / Guess who / Darlin' / Letter full of tears / You broke your promise / Operator / Every beat of my heart / Come see about me / One more lonely night / Really didn't mean it / How do you say goodbye / Jungle love / Room in your heart.
LP: . . . . **BDL 1040**

MEMORIES OF THE WAY WERE.
Tracks: / I'll take a melody / With you in mind / I'm coming home again / Part time love / Nobody but you / All the time / Butterfly / One and only / So sad the song / Pipe dream / Don't say no to me tonight / Seconds / Way it was / Perfect love / Try to remember / Way we were.
2LP: . . . . **BDLD 2004**
MC: . . . . **ZCBD 2004**

MIDNIGHT TRAIN TO GEORGIA (Knight, Gladys & The Pips).
LP: . . . . **SHM 3057**
MC: . . . . **HSC 3057**

MISS GLADYS KNIGHT.
Tracks: / I'm comin' home again / Sail away / Freedom for the stallion / I'm still caught up with you / It's better than a good time / We don't make each other laugh anymore / Way it was / I'll take a melody / With you in mind / Love gives you the power.
LP: . . . . **BDLP 4056**

NEITHER ONE OF US.
Tracks: / Neither one of us / It's gotta be that way / For once in my life / This child needs it's father / Who is she (and what is she to you) / And this is love / Daddy could swear, I declare / Can't give it up no more / Don't it make you feel guilty.
LP: . . . . **STMS 5041**
MC: . . . . **CSTMS 5041**

NIGHTFUL.
Tracks: / Running around / Really didn't mean it / How do you say goodbye / What shall I do / I can't stand it / One more lonely night / Letter full of tears / Operator.
LP: . . . . **MAN 5001**

NITTY GRITTY (Knight, Gladys & The Pips).
Tracks: / Cloud nine / Runnin out / Didn't you know (you'd have to cry sometime) / (I know), I'm losing you / Nitty gritty / Ain't no sun since you've been gone / All I could do was cry / Keep an eye / Got myself a good man / It's Summer / Stranger, The / I want him to say it again.
LP: . . . . **STMS 5040**
MC: . . . . **CSTMS 5040**

ON AND ON (Knight, Gladys & The Pips).
MC: . . . . **ORC 002**

ONE AND ONLY, THE (Knight, Gladys & The Pips).
LP: . . . . **BDLP 4051**

REPLAY ON GLADYS KNIGHT (Knight, Gladys & The Pips).
LP: . . . . **FEDB 5031**
MC: . . . . **CFEDB 5031**

SINGLES ALBUM - GLADYS KNIGHT & THE PIPS (Knight, Gladys & The Pips).
Tracks: / Licence to kill / Help me make it through the night / Best thing that ever happened to me / Baby don't change your mind / Bourgie bourgie / Taste of bitter love / One and only, The / Just walk in my shoes / Midnight train to Georgia / Try to remember / Look of love, The / Part time love / Come back and finish what you started / So sad the song / Take me in your arms and love me / Love overboard / Lovin' on next to nothin' / Neither one of us.
LP: . . . . **GKTV 1**
MC: . . . . **GKTVC 1**

SPOTLIGHT ON GLADYS KNIGHT & THE PIPS.
Tracks: / Baby don't change your mind / Make yours a happy home / Little bit of love, A / I can see clearly now / It's up to you / Everybody's got to find a way / Try to remember / So sad the song / Walk softly / Don't say no to me tonight / Part time lover / I'll miss you / Best thing that ever happened to me, The / Midnight train to Georgia / Once in a lifetime thing / One and only / To be invisible / You put a new life in my body / Come back and finish what you started / Be yourself / I love to feel the feeling / Nobody but you / Home is where the heart is / It's better than a good time / Way we were, The.
2LP: . . . . **SPOT 1006**
MCSET: . . . . **ZCSPT 1006**

STILL TOGETHER (Knight, Gladys & The Pips).
LP: . . . . **BDLH 5014**

TASTE OF BITTER LOVE (Knight, Gladys & The Pips).
Tracks: / Taste of bitter love / Am I too late / Love was made for two / You loved the pain / You don't have to say I love you / Get the love / Bourgie bourgie / I just want to be with you / I who have nothing / Baby baby don't waste my time / It's the same old song / Landlord.
LP: . . . . **SHM 3132**
MC: . . . . **HSC 3132**

TEEN ANGUISH VOL.3 Early years, The (Knight, Gladys & The Pips).
Tracks: / If ever I should fall in love / Every beat of my heart / Either way I lose / It hurts so bad / Why don't you love me / Maybe, Maybe baby / Letter full of tears / Giving up / Go away, stay away / What will become of me / Queen of tears / Stop and get a hold of myself / Tell her you're mine / There will never be another love / Lovers always forgive / Who knows (I just can't trust you any more).
LP: . . . . **CRM 2017**

THAT SPECIAL TIME OF YEAR (Knight, Gladys & The Pips).
Tracks: / That special time of year / Jingle bells / What are you doing New Year's Eve / This Christmas / Santa Claus is coming to town / It's the happiest time of the year / I believe / When a child is born / Lord's prayer, The / Let there be peace on earth.
LP: **4604591**
MC: **4604594**
LP: . . . . **CBS 85896**

THEIR VERY BEST BACK TO BACK (See under Wonder, Stevie) (Knight, Gladys & Stevie Wonder).

TOUCH (Knight, Gladys & The Pips).
Tracks: / I will fight / If that'll make you happy / Baby, baby don't waste my time / Friend of mine / Love was made for two / God is / Changed / Reach high / I will survive.
LP: . . . . **CBS 84908**

TOUCH OF LOVE, A (Knight, Gladys & The Pips).
LP: . . . . **NE 1090**

VERY BEST OF GLADYS KNIGHT & THE PIPS (Knight, Gladys & The Pips).
LP: . . . . **BRLP 21**
MC: . . . . **BRMC 21**

VISIONS (Knight, Gladys & The Pips).
Tracks: / When you're far away / Just be my lover / Save the overtime (for me) / Heaven sent / Don't make me run away / Ain't no greater love / Seconds / You're number one (in my book) / Oh la de da / Hero.
LP: . . . . **CBS 25096**
MC: **40 25096**

WAY WE WERE, THE (Knight, Gladys & The Pips).
Tracks: / Midnight train to Georgia / So sad the song / Baby don't change your mind / Home is where the heart is / Nobody but you / I feel a song / Feel like makin' love / Hold on / Little bit of love, A / Try to remember/The way we were / Come back and finish what you started / Part time love / It's a better than good time / Georgia on my mind / Make yours a happy home / Best thing that ever happened to me / We don't make each other laugh any more / Sorry doesn't always make it right.
MC: . . . . **MCTC 005**

Knight, Gladys & The

LIFE.
Tracks: / Strivin' / Keep giving me love / Just let me love you / Life / Till i see you again / My time / Forever / Do you wanna have some fun / Straight up / Glitter.
LP: . . . . **CBS 26184**

TAKE ME BACK.
Tracks: / How do you say goodbye / Jungle love / I want that kind of love / before now after then / Goodnight my love / Love me again / Come see about me / One more lonely night.
LP: . . . . **MAN 5000**

Knight, Grace

COME IN SPINNER (See Under Jones, Vince) (Jones, Vince & Grace Knight).

Knight, Holly

HOLLY KNIGHT.
Tracks: / Heart don't fail me now / Every man's fear / Sexy boy / It's only me / Palace of pleasure / Why don't cha luv me (like you used to) / Baby me / Love is a battlefield / Nature of the beast / Howlin' at the moon.
LP: **4611371**
MC: **4611374**

OBSESSION (See under Des Barres, Michael) (Knight, Holly/Michael Des Barres).

Knight, Jean

MR BIG STUFF.
Tracks: / Mr Big Stuff / Little bit of something, A / Don't talk about Jody / Think it over / Take him (you can have

my man) / You city slicker / Why I keep living these memories / Call me your fool if you want to / One way ticket / You six-bit change.
LP: SXE 003
LP: SX 003

Knight, Jerry

LOVE'S ON OUR SIDE.
Tracks: / She's got to be (a dancer) / I'm down for that / Nothing can hold us back / Brand new fool / Fire / Do it all for you / Do you really mean it / Beautiful.
LP: AMLH 64877

PERFECT FIT.
Tracks: / Perfect fit / Higher / Turn it out / Interlude / Play sista' / Easier to run away / Too busy / Rainbow.
LP: AMLH 64843

Knight, Joe

MARTY ROBBINS SCRAPBOOK (See under King, Bev) (Knight, Joe & Bev King).

Knight, Pete

THAT'S ALRIGHT.
LP: BSS 334

Knight, Peter

BEST OF NOVELLO AND COWARD (Knight, Peter & His Orchestra).
Tracks: / Ziguener / I'll follow my secret heart / Music in May / Violon began to play / Highwayman love / Room with a view / Party's over, The / We'll gather lilacs.
LP: FBLP 8096
MC: ZCFBLP 8096

DAYS OF FUTURE PASSED (See under Moody Blues) (Knight, Peter, London Festival Orchestra, Moody Blues).

KING OF ELFLANDS DAUGHTER, THE (see Johnson, Bob) (Knight, Peter & Bob Johnson).

Knight, Sonny

CONFIDENTIAL.
Tracks: / But officer / Keep a walking / Confidential / Baby don't want me / Jailbird / Dedicated to you / Worthless and lowdown / Inshallah / End of a dream / Teenage party / Short walk / Lovesick blues / Madness / Barbara / Cold cold night / If you want this love / Saving my love / Coldest cat in town.
LP: RB 107

Knighton, Reggie

REGGIE KNIGHTON BAND (Knighton, Reggie Band).
Tracks: / Breakin' up inside / Rock'n'roll alien / King and I, The / Clone in love / Lear jet song / Highway patrol / UFO / Ooh girl / Magnum Sally / Behind a rock'n'roll band.
LP: EPC 82627

Knights, Don

CINEMA ORGAN ENCORES.
LP: DEROY 1338

DON KNIGHTS AT TWICKENHAM.
Tracks: / Vienna, city of my dreams / It looks like rain in Cherry Blossom Lane / Forgotten melody / Valencia / Whispering.
MC: AC 173

Knights & Emeralds

KNIGHTS AND EMERALDS (Film soundtrack) (Various artists).
Tracks: / Tell me tomorrow: *Princess* / Strollin' on: *Priest, Maxi* / Life of crime: *Arrowsmith, Eugenie* / Ready or not: *Thompson, Carroll* / Tremblin': *Smith, Mel* / We won't give in: *Slade* / I'm the one who really loves you: *Howard, Austin* / Wild wild party: *Slade* / Something special: *Duffy, Stephen & Sandii* / Modern girl: *Astley, Rick* / Bubble (We ah go bubble): *Priest, Maxi* / Stand by the word: *Joubert Singers*.
LP: XID 11
MC: CXID 11
LP: DIX 28

Knights Of The ...

KNIGHTS OF THE ROUND TABLE (Film Soundtrack) (Various artists).
LP: STV 81128

Knightsbridge Strings

STRING SWAY.
LP: BUY 017

Knitters

POOR LITTLE CRITTER ON THE ROAD.
LP: SLAP 6

Knoa

INSIDE OUT.
LP: OP 8016

SUDDEN TWISTS AND TURNS.
LP: OP 7801

Knoblauch, George

GEORGE KNOBLAUCH'S BLACK DIAMOND JAZZBAND (Knoblauch, George & Black Diamond Jazzband).
LP: MMRC 119

Knopfler, David

BEHIND THE LINES.
LP: SPRAY 102
MC: CSPRAY 102

CUT THE WIRE.
Tracks: / Freakshow / Fisherman / Hurricane / When we kiss / When grandpappa sailed / Hurting / Sentenced man, The / Dedication / Charlie and Suzy.
LP: GMILP 1
MC: GMIC 1

LIFE AGAINST THE STEEL.
LP: PARIS 4
MC: CPARIS 4

RELEASE.
LP: DAVID 1
MC: ZC DAVID 1

Knopfler, Mark

CAL (FILM) (See under Cal).

LAST EXIT TO BROOKLYN (See under Last Exit To Brooklyn).

NECK AND NECK (See under Atkins, Chet) (Knopfler, Mark/Chet Atkins).

POOR BOY BLUES (See under Atkins, Chet) (Knopfler, Mark/Chet Atkins).

PRINCESS BRIDE, THE (See under 'Princess Bride').

RELEASE PARIS.
Tracks: / Soul kissing / Come to me / Madonna's daughter / Girl and the paperboy, The / Roman times / Sideshow / Little brother / Hey Henry / Great divide, The / Night train.
LP: PARIS 1

Knotty Vision

KNOTTY VISION (Various artists).
LP: NH 306

Knowles, Pat

STANDARD SETTINGS.
Tracks: / Giafis, The / O'Connels welcome to Parliament / Bob and Joan / Is meath le nora / Spring gardens / Aire / Old noll's jig / Planxty dillon / Captain O'Kane / Mary / Slap and kiss / Daniel Wright's / Northern lass, The / Dusty Miller / French revolution / Mary Young and fair / Logan water / Rattler, The / In praise of red hair / Loch Earn / Tullymet hall / Marry me now / Love me little, love me long.
LP: FE 024

Knowles, Sonny

I'LL TAKE CARE OF YOUR CARES.
Tracks: / I'll take care of your cares / Behind the tear / Rare ould times / May i have the next dream with you / Solitaire / Can I forget you / Isadora / Roses of Picardy / Help me make it through the night / Delilah / You don't know me / Tell me / My lovely rose and you / My child.
LP: 830 711-1
MC: 830 711-4

Known 2 Be Down

KNOWN 2 BE DOWN (Various artists).
LP: PBLP 1
MC: PBLC 1

Knox

PLUTONIUM EXPRESS.
LP: RAZ 7

Knox, Buddy

BEST OF BUDDY KNOX.
Tracks: / Party doll / Rock your little baby to sleep / Teasable, pleasable you / Storm clouds / Somebody touched me / Lovey dovey / That's why I cry / Hula love / Devil woman / Ling-ting-tong / I think I'm gonna kill myself / Cause I'm in love / Swingin' daddy / C'mon baby / All for you (CD only.) / Girl with the golden hair, The (CD only.) / She's gone (CD only.) / Whenever I'm lonely (CD only.).
MC: TCROU 5008
MC: 794 885 4

BUDDY KNOX.
LP: BB 575

GREATEST HITS: BUDDY KNOX.
Tracks: / Party doll / Rock house / Maybellene / Storm clouds / Devil woman / Somebody touched me / Hula love / Rock your little baby to sleep / Lovey Dovey / Ling-ting-tong / I think I'm gonna kill myself / I washed my hands in muddy water / Travellin'.
LP: TOP 142
MC: KTOP 142
LP: LP 8501

LIBERTY TAKES.
Tracks: / Three eyed man / All by myself / Open your lovin' arms / She's gone / Now there's only me / Dear Abby / Three way love affair / Shadoroom / Tomorrow is a comin' / Hitch hike back to Georgia / Thanks a lot / Good lovin / All time loser / Lovey dovey / I got you / Ling-ting-tong.
LP: CR 30260

PARTY DOLL.
LP: NSPL 28243

PARTY DOLL AND OTHER HITS.
MC: 4XLL 9177

SWEET COUNTRY MUSIC.
LP: RSRMP 4001

TEXAS ROCKABILLY MAN.
Tracks: / Lotta lovin' / Ooby dooby / I'm looking for someone to love / Blue levi jeans / Going to Hollywood / Knock kneed Nellie from Knoxville / Hole in the ground / Bip bop boom / Little bitty baby / Ham bone / Nebraska sunrise / Honky tonk man / Back to New Orleans / Kokomo Island / Restless / Too much fun.
LP: RSRLP 1012

TRAVELLIN' LIGHT.
LP: RLP 004

Knox The Fox

KNOX THE FOX (Various artists).
MC: STC 304B

Knuckles, Frankie

FRANKIE KNUCKLES PRESENTS.
LP: TRAXLP 702
MC: ZCTRAX 702

Knudsen, Mikkelborg

HEART TO HEART.
LP: SLP 4114

Knutt, Bobby

HELLO FETTLERS.
Tracks: / Ilkley Moor bah't at / St. Quentin / John and Mary / Fellow from Rhyl / Policeman's song / Immigration song / Bulloks / Comedy routines.
LP: PKL 5580

Koc, Mehmet

TURQUIE DE MEHMET KOC (Songs and dances).
Tracks: / Gelin oy / Yar basina / Dersim / Behcelerin / Anne / Gavur dagi / Nar cocuk / Kor karanlik.
LP: ARN 33790
MC: ARN 433790

Koch, Merle

MERLE KOCH'S POLITE JAZZ QUARTET.
LP: AP 126

Kockaya, Kenan

SONGS AND DANCES FROM TURKEY (See under Turkey...).

SONGS AND DANCES FROM TURKEY.
LP: EULP 1072
MC: EUMC 1072

Kode IV

POSSESSED.
LP: KK 052

Kodo

BLESSING OF THE EARTH.
Tracks: / Zoku / Kariuta / Chonlima / Issen/oasis / Hanano / Yatai-bayashi / Ryogen-no-hi.
MC: 4666304

KODO VERSUS YOSUKE YAMASHITA IN LIVE (See under: Yamashita, Yosuke) (Yamashita, Yosuke & Kodo...).

UBU-SUNA.
Tracks: / Kokyo / Yumi-ga-hama / Tjanang Sari / Yu karak / Michi (the way) / Dyu-ha / Lunar dance.
MC: 4666294

Kofi

BLACK.. WITH SUGAR.
LP: ARILP 042

PROUD OF MANDELA (See under Macka B) (Kofi & Macka B).

Kohl, Ernest

DANCE RIGHT (See under Diebold, David) (Kohl, Ernest & David Diebold).

Koinonia

VERY BEST OF KOINONIA, THE.
LP: RMR 049
MC: RMC 049

Koklin, Tony

TIME CHASER.
Tracks: / Movie faces / Slow dancing / Claude monet / Lucky man / Death in the subway / So strange / Museums / On pop / Easy Street / Struttin' / You waste my time / Time chaser / Talkin' to myself.
LP: CWK 3017

Koko Pop

KOKO POP.
Tracks: / Baby sister / Serious side / I'm in love with you / Make you feel better / I wish it would rain / Make up your mind / Baby on the run / On the beach.
LP: ZL 72191
MC: ZK 72191

SECRETS OF LONELY BOYS.
Tracks: / Lonely girl lonely boy / Brand new beat / First impression / Sugar pop baby / Fallin' in love / Tell me that you're mine / No more secrets / He's got ulterior motives / Nasty / Foolish heart.
LP: ZL72396

Kokomo (UK)

KOKOMO.
Tracks: / Little bit further away / Part time affair / Follow (the stars will bring you home) / Nowhere to go on Tuesday night / Stuck in a groove / Ain't never heard the boogie / All through the night / Keep on dancing / Let me have it all.
LP: CBS 85604

Kokubu, Hiroko

MORE THAN YOU KNOW.
MC: JC 3312

Kol Aviv

DANSES D'ISRAEL.
Tracks: / Rikoud harabbi / Rad halaila / Artsa alainou / Ke chochana / Simh'ouna / Debka druze / Chirat hanoded / Chnei h'alilim.
LP: ARN 34404
MC: ARN 433404

SONGS AND DANCES FROM ISRAEL.
Tracks: / Et dodim kala / Rakefet / Suite yemenite / Ba hachemech / Eucalyptus / Hitrag out / Debka ouria / Hine ma tov.
LP: ARN 34296
MC: ARN 434296

Koller, Hans

EARLY RECORDINGS OF HANS KOLLER (1942-50).
Tracks: / Harlem swing / Sioux city Sue / Stop / Prisoner's song / Hallo Tommy / Pipsi boogie / Nesty boogie / Dunkle schatten / Delphi / Airmail special / Amapola / Open the door Richard / Frankies boogie / Study in F / What's this / Bei mir bist du schon / Ray's idea.
LP: HQ 2066

Kollo, Rene

HELLO MARY LOU.
Tracks: / Hello Mary Lou / Dich gibt's nur einmal / Eso beso / Du Casanova, du / Weit so weit / Davon traumen alle jungen leute / Auf der strasse meines lebens / Schone rose vom Rio Grande / Mandoline und roter wein / Sweet rosary / Sag nie goodbye / Meine grosse liebe wohnt in einer kleinen stadt / Traume weiter, sweet Sue / Peggy, Peggy / Ohne liebe is alles so traurig / Wie vom wind verweht.
LP: BFX 15236

Koloc, Bonnie

WITH YOU ON MY SIDE.
LP: FF 437

Kolstad, John

BEANS TASTE FINE (Kolstad, John/ Turk, Wildman Mike).
LP: FR 114

Koma Zozan

SONGS AND MUSIC OF KURDISTAN (See also under 'Kurdistan').

Komariah, Euis

JAIPONGAN JAVA (Komariah, Euis & Jugala Orchestra).
LP: ORB 057

SOUND OF SUNDA, THE (Komariah, Euis & Yus Wiradiredja).
Tracks: / Sorban palid / Salam sono / Asa tos tepang / Bulan sapasi / Campaka kambar / Duh leung / Ramalan asih / Pengkolan / Dalingding asih.
LP: ORB 060

Kon Kan

MOVE TO MOVE.
LP: 781 984-1
MC: 781 984-4
LP: WX 276
MC: WX 276C

Kon Tiki Man

KON TIKI MAN (TV Soundtrack) (Various artists).
Tracks: / Kon Tiki man (introduction): *Various artists* / Presentation of thor heyerdahl: *Various artists* / Approaching Fatu Hiva: *Various artists* / In the forest of Fatu Hiva: *Various artists* / War, The: *Various artists* / Kon Tiki raft, The: *Various artists* / Kon Tiki towards the reef: *Various artists* / Kon Tiki man theme: *Various* artists / Old Larvik and the Norwegian winter: *Various artists* / Beside the stream on Fatu Hiva: *Various artists* / Aspects on civilisation: *Various artists* / In Canada: *Various artists* / Fishing of the Kon Tiki crew, The: *Various artists* / Big waves: *Various artists*.

MC: . . . . ZCF 780

Konadu, Alex

ONE MAN THOUSAND LIVE IN LONDON.
LP: . . . . WCB 009

Konbit:

KONBIT: BURNING RHYTHMS OF HAITI (See under Haiti) (Various artists).

Konders, Bobby

COOL CALM AND COLLECTIVE (Konders, Bobby Project).
LP: . . . . LUVLP 9

Kondo, Toshinori

KONTON.
Tracks: / Sundown / Yami / Y.O.U. / Sandswitch / Yoyoyo / Gan.
LP: . . . . EPC 57075
MC: 40 57075

METAL POSITION.
LP: . . . . LP 4127

TAIGEN.
LP: . . . . LP 4124

Kondole

PSYCHIC.
LP: . . . . TOPY 046

Kong

MUTEPOETVOCALIZER.
LP: . . . . KTB 1

Kongos, John

KONGOS.
LP: . . . . HIFLY 7

TOKOLOSHE MAN.
Tracks: / Jubilee cloud / Gold / Lift me from the ground / Tomorrow I'll go / Can someone please direct me back to Earth / Try to touch just one / Weekend lady / I would have had a good time / Come on down Jesus / Sometimes it's not enough / He's gonna step on you again / Great white lady (Only on CD.) / Higher than God's hat (Only on CD.) / Ride the lightning (Only on CD.) / Tokoloshe man.
LP: . . . . SEE 221

Konitz, Lee

ALL TOGETHER (See Baker, Chet) (Konitz, Lee & Chet Baker).

BLEW (Konitz, Lee & Space Jazz Trio).
LP: 214W 26

CHESTNUT (see Carter, Joe) (Konitz, Lee & Joe Carter).

CHET BAKER IN CONCERT (See under Baker, Chet) (Baker, Chet & Lee Konitz).

CHICAGO 'N' ALL THAT JAZZ.
Tracks: / My own best friend / Razzle dazzle / Loopin' de loop / Funny honey / Class / Me and my baby / Roxie / Ten per cent.
MC: . . . . MC 7971

DOVE TAIL.
Tracks: / I want to be happy / Night has a thousand eyes, The / Counterpoint / Dovetail / Sweet Georgia Brown / Alone together / Cherokee / Penthouse serenade.
LP: . . . . SSC 1003

EZZTHETIC (See under Davis, Miles) (Konitz, Lee & Miles Davis).

FIGURE AND SPIRIT (Konitz Lee Quintet).
LP: . . . . PRO 7003

FOUR KEYS (Konitz Lee/Matial Solal).
LP: . . . . MPS 68 241

GLAD KONITZ (Live fron the Swedish tour 1983).
LP: . . . . DRLP 104

I CONCENTRATE ON YOU.
LP: . . . . SCS 1018

IN EUROPE (see under Tristano, Lennie) (Konitz, Lee/Lennie Tristano).

IN SWEDEN 1951/53.
LP: . . . . DRLP 18

JAZZ AT STORYVILLE.
LP: . . . . BLP 60901

LEE KONITZ AND WARNE MARSH (Konitz, Lee & Warne Marsh).
Tracks: / Topsy / There will never be another you / I can't get started / Donna Lee / Two not one / Don't squawk / Ronnie's line / Background music.
LP: . . . . K 50298

LEE KONITZ AND WARNE MARSH VOL.3 (See under Marsh, Warne) (Konitz, Lee & Warne Marsh).

LEE KONITZ IN CONCERT (see Baker, Chet & Lee Konitz) (Konitz, Lee & Chet Baker).

LEE KONITZ IN RIO.
LP: . . . . A 737-1
MC: . . . . A 737-4

LEE KONITZ IN RIO VOL.2.
LP: . . . . LPA 7391
MC: . . . . MCA 7394

LEE PLAYS THE MUSIC OF LARS GULLIN (See under Sjoesten, Lars) (Konitz, Lee & Lars Sjoesten Octet).
LP: . . . . DRLP 66

LIVE AT LAREN.
Tracks: / April / Who you / Without a song / Moon dreams / Times lie / Matrix.
LP: . . . . SN 1069

LIVE AT THE MONTMARTRE CLUB (See under Marsh, Warne) (Konitz, Lee & Warne Marsh Quartet).

LONDON CONCERT (See Marsh, Warne) (Konitz, Lee & Warne Marsh).

LONDON CONCERT 1976 (Konitz, Lee & Others).
LP: . . . . WAVE LP 16

MOTION.
Tracks: / I remember you / All of me / Foolin' myself / You don't know what love is / You'd be so nice to come home to / Out of nowhere / I'll remember April / It's you or no one.
LP: 8215531

NONET, THE.
Tracks: / If dreams come true / Pretty girl is like a melody, A / Tea for two / Matrix / Times lie / Without a song / Nefertiti.
LP: . . . . NSPL 28240

OLEO (Konitz, Lee Trio).
LP: . . . . SNTF 690
MC: . . . . ZCSN 690

PYRAMID.
LP: . . . . IAI 37 38 45

ROUND AND ROUND.
Tracks: / Round and round and round / Someday my prince will come / Luv / Nancy / Boo doo / Valse hot / Lover man / Bluesette / Giant steps.
LP: . . . . CIJD 40167T

SHADES OF KENTON (Konitz, Lee/ Jiggs Whigham).
MC: . . . . HEPTDK 002

SONGS OF THE STARS (Konitz, Lee & John Taylor).
LP: . . . . JHR 006

SPIRITS.
LP: . . . . MSP 9038

STEREOKONITZ.
LP: . . . . NL 70576

TIMESPAN.
LP: . . . . WAVE LP 14

VERY COOL.
Tracks: / Sunflower / Stairway to the stars / Movin' around / Kary's trance / Crazy she calls me / Billie's bounce.
LP: 2304 344

WILD AS SPRINGTIME.
Tracks: / She's as wild as springtime / Hairy canary / Ez-thetic / Duende / Chopin Prelude No.20 / Spinning Waltz / Silly samba / Hi, Beck / Ko.
LP: . . . . GFM LP8002

WINDOWS (See Galper, Hal & Lee Konitz) (Konitz, Lee & Hal Galper).

YES YES NONET (Konitz, Lee Nonet).
LP: . . . . SCS 1119

YOUNG LEE.
LP: 500105

Konk

YO.
LP: . . . . TWI 143

Konstruktivitis

BLACK DECEMBER.
LP: . . . . TMLP 5

GLENASCANL.
LP: . . . . SR 10

Konte, Alhagi Bai

ALHAGI BAI KONTE.
LP: . . . . ROUNDER 5001

MANDINKA MUSIC.
Tracks: / Hamma ba / Balankula / Dalua / Bantamba kuyate / Jimbasengo / Masaane siise / Tutu jara / Fa banta toure.
LP: . . . . VX 1006

Konte, Dembo

JALI ROLL (Konte, Dembo & Kausu Kuyateh).
LP: . . . . FMSL 2020
MC: . . . . FMSC 3020

SIMBOMBA (Konte, Dembo & Kausu Kuyateh).
LP: . . . . FMSL 2011
MC: . . . . FMSC 2011

TANANTE (Konte, Dembo & Kausu Kuyateh).
Tracks: / Tiramakhan / Fayinkunko / Solo / Sunkariba / Allah la kanu / Yeyengo.
LP: . . . . FMSL 2009

Konte, Lamine

AFRIQUE, MON AFRIQUE (Kora et chants du Senegal).
Tracks: / Abaraka / Yasso / M'ba / Casa di mansa / Domba / Telephonista / Afrikavalse / Diatto / Fode keba / Moussol.
LP: . . . . ARN 33701
MC: . . . . ARN 433701

CHANT DU NEGRE - CHANT DU MONDE.
Tracks: / Negritude / Femme noir / Etait-ce une nuit maghrebine / New York / Legende Baoule / Hoquet.
LP: . . . . ARN 33395

LA KORA DU SENEGAL.
Tracks: / M'Besseyla / Casamance / Mama Tamba / Moune ma ko / Diouala / Kaki lambe / Africa / Ma konon / Yobalema / Yarabi / Casa saby / Chant des pilons.
LP: . . . . ARN 33179

SENEGAL VOL.2 - LA KORA.
Tracks: / Lale kouma / Fodeba / Nagnol / Malon / Gna terra / Kotoba / Coumpo / Kairaba.
LP: . . . . ARN 33313
MC: . . . . ARN 433313

Kontikis

HAWAIIAN MEMORIES (Kontikis feat. Wout Steenhuis).
LP: 9279 552
MC: 7259 552

Kontraband

NORTH STAR.
LP: . . . . SPR 1011

Koobas

BARRICADES.
LP: . . . . KIRI 047

Kool, Bo

MONEY WE LOVE (see under "Funkmasters 'Love money'").

Kool G Rap

ROAD TO THE RICHES (Kool G Rap & DJ Polo).
Tracks: / Intro / Road to the riches / Demo / Men at work / Truly yours / Cars / Triligy of terror / She love's me, she love's me not / Cold cuts / Rhyme I express / Poison.
LP: . . . . K 925820 1
MC: . . . . K 925820 4

Kool Moe Dee

FUNKE FUNKE WISDOM.
LP: . . . . HIP 114
MC: . . . . HIPC 114

HOW YA LIKE ME NOW.
Tracks: / How ya like me now / Suckers / Stupid / I'm a player / Rock you / Get paid / Don't dance / 50 ways / Wild wild west / Way way back / No respect.
LP: . . . . HIP 53
MC: . . . . HIPC 53

KOOL MOE DEE.
Tracks: / Go see the doctor / Dumb Dick / Bad mutha / Little John / Do you know what time it is? / Rock steady / Monster crack / Best, The / I'm Kool Moe Dee.
LP: . . . . HIP 44
MC: . . . . HIPC 44

Kool Rock Jay

TALES FROM THE DOPE.
LP: . . . . HIP 94
MC: . . . . HIPC 94

Kool & The Gang

AS ONE.
Tracks: / Street kids / Big fun / As one / Hi de hi, hi de ho / Let's go dancing / Pretty baby / Think it over.
LP: . . . . DSR 3

CELEBRATE.
Tracks: / Celebration / Jones Vs Jones / Take it to the top / Morning star / Love festival / Just friends / Night people / Love affair.
LP: . . . . PRICE 53
MC: . . . . PRICM 53
LP: 6359 029

EMERGENCY.
Tracks: / Emergency / Fresh / Misled / Cherish / Surrender (12" only.) / Bad woman / You are the one.
LP: . . . . DSR 6
MC: . . . . DCR 6

GREAT AND REMIXED '91.
LP: 848 604-1
MC: 848 604-4

IN THE HEART.
Tracks: / In the heart / Joanna / Tonight / Rollin' / Place for us / Straight ahead / Home is where the heart is / You can do it / September love.
LP: . . . . DSR 4
MC: . . . . DCR 4
LP: 814 351 1
MC: 814 351 4

KOOL AND THE GANG.
LP: 0144022
MC: 0144041

KOOL KUTS.
Tracks: / Open sesame / Spirit of the boogie / Kool and the gang / Hollywood swinging / Funky stuff / More funky stuff / Jungle boogie / Caribbean festival / Love and understanding / Summer madness.
LP: . . . . MIP 19318
MC: MIP4 19318

KOOL LOVE.
MC: . . . . STAC 2435
LP: . . . . STAR 2435

LADIES NIGHT.
Tracks: / Got you into my life / Hangin' out / If you feel like dancin' / Ladies' night / Tonight's the night / Too hot.
LP: . . . . PRICE 52
MC: . . . . PRIMC 52
LP: 6372763

SINGLES COLLECTION, THE.
Tracks: / Celebration / Ladies night / Too hot / Get down on it / Joanna / Jones vs. Jones / Straight ahead / Fresh / Ooh la la la (let's go dancing) / Big fun / Cherish / In the heat / Hi de hi, hi de ho / Take it to the top / Victory / Steppin' out.
LP: . . . . KGTV 1
MC: . . . . KGTVC 1

SOMETHING SPECIAL.
Tracks: / Steppin' out / Good time tonight / Take my heart / Be my lady / Get down on it / Pass it on / Stand up and sing / No show.
LP: . . . . PRICE 81
MC: . . . . PRIMC 81
LP: . . . . DSR 001

SWEAT.
Tracks: / I sweat / This is what a love can do / Never give up / You got my heart on fire / Someday / Raindrops / In your company / I'll follow you anywhere / All she wants to do is dance / Now can I get close to you / You are the meaning of friend.
LP: 838233 1
MC: 838233 4

TWICE AS KOOL.
Tracks: / Ladies night / Big fun / Celebration / Take it to the top / Get down on it / Get down on it / Hi de hi hi de ho / Funky stuff / Hollywood swinging / Summer madness (theme from Rocky) / Open sesame / Steppin' out / Night people / Street kids / Ooh la la la, let's go dancing / Jones Vs Jones / Too hot / Take my heart / Hangin' out.
2LP: . . . . PROLP 2
MCSET: . . . . PROMC 2

VICTORY.
LP: . . . . JABH 23
MC: . . . . JABHC 23

Koolcad

LIFE COULD BE A DREAM (Koolcad & Friends).
LP: . . . . EULP 1004

Kooper, Al

ACT LIKE NOTHING IS WRONG.
Tracks: / Is we on the downbeat / This diamond ring / She don't ever loose her groove / I forgot to be your lover / Missing you / Out of left field / One more time / In my own sweet way / Turn my head towards home / Visit to the rainbow bar and grill / Hollywood vampire.
LP: . . . . UAG 30020

Koosserierse

DUO (See under De Graaff, Rein) (Koosserierse & Rein De Graaff).

Koran

KORAN, THE (Sheikh Mahamound Khalil Ah-Hosary).
MC: . . . . WOOD BOX ZP
MC: . . . . UNKNOWN

Korea

KOREA: VARIOUS TRADITIONAL ASIAN MUSIC (Various artists).
Tracks: / Sangryongsan: *Various artists* / Chongmyo chereak chongdaey op: *Various artists* / Chul Pungryu: *Various artists* / Ujo samsudaeyop: *Various artists* / Yomyangchun: *Various artists* / Pohoja: *Various artists*/ Taech'wita: *Various artists* / Kakakeum pyongchange nokumbangcho: *Various artists*.
LP: . . . . PS 33527

KOREAN COURT MUSIC (Various artists).
LP: . . . . LLST 7206

KOREAN MUSIC AND DANCES (Various artists).
Tracks: / P'iri dokjoo: *Various artists* / Tei pung moo: *Various artists* / Haegeum-sanjo: *Various artists*/ Bara moo: *Various artists* / Dei kam mori:

Various artists / Salpuri: *Various artists* / Yuldoobal sang moo: *Various artists* / Ajaeng sanjo: *Various artists* / Sung moo: *Various artists*.
LP: ARN 33463

KOREAN SOCIAL AND FOLK MUSIC (Various artists).
LP: LLST 7211

Korgis

BEST OF THE KORGIS, THE.
MC: ARLC 1015

DUMB WAITERS.
Tracks: / Everybody's got to learn sometime / Dumb waiters / Perfect hostess / If it's all right with you baby / It's no good unless you love me.
LP: TENOR 104

KORGIS, THE.
Tracks: / Young 'n' Russian / I just can't help it / Chinese girl / Art school annexe / Boots and shoes / Dirty postcards / O Maxine / Mount Everest sings the blues / Cold tea / If I had you.
LP: TENOR 101

STICKY GEORGE.
Tracks: / Sticky George / Can't we be friends now / Foolishness of love / Domestic bliss / That was my big mistake / Nowhere to run / Contraband / All the love in the world / Don't say it's over / Living on the rocks.
LP: ALTO 103
MC: ZCALT 103

Kormoran

FOLK AND ROLL.
LP: SLPM 17852

Korner, Alexis

ALEXIS 1957 (with Cyril Davies).
LP: KK 789

COLLECTION: ALEXIS KORNER.
Tracks: / Gospel ship / Captain America / Thief, The / Robert Johnson / Get off my cloud / Honky tonk women / Spoonful / Daytime song / Lend me some time / Hey pretty mama / Stump blues / I got my mojo working / Geneva / Wreck of the old '97 / Casey Jones / High heel sneakers / King BB / Juvenile delinquent.
2LP: CCSLP 192
MC: CCSMC 192

COLLECTION: ALEXIS KORNER 1961-72.
Tracks: / She fooled me / Hoochie coochie man / Oh Lord don't let them drop that atom bomb on me / I got a woman / Corina Corina / Everyday I have the blues / Operator / Rosie / Polly put the kettle on / I see it / You don't miss your water till your well runs dry / Mighty mighty spade and whitey / Lo and behold / Louisiana blues / Ooh wee baby / Rock me baby / Sweet sympathy / Country shoes.
2LP: CCSLP 150
MC: CCSMC 150

GET OFF MY CLOUD.
LP: NEXLP 134

HAMMER AND NAILS.
Tracks: / Honky tonk women / Louise / Hammer and nails / Santa Fe blues / How long blues / Roberta / Precious Lord / Honour the young man / And again / East St. Louis blues.
LP: THBL 037
MC: THBC 037

JUVENILE DELINQUENT.
Tracks: / Beirut / Mean fool / Spinx, The / Get off my cloud / King B.B. / Juvenile delinquent.
LP: CAS 1165
MC: CASMC 1165
LP: CHC 64

NEW GENERATION OF BLUES, A.
LP: BGOLP 102

PROFILE: ALEXIS KORNER.
MC: CL4 24475
LP: 6.24475

R & B FROM THE MARQUEE (Korner, Alexis & Blues Inc).
Tracks: / Gotta move / Rain is such a lonesome sound / I got my brand on you / Spooky but nice / Keep your hands off / I wanna put a tiger in your tank / I got my mojo working / Finkles cafe / Hoochie coochie man / Down town / How long, how long blues / I thought i heard that train whistle blow.
LP: ACL 1130

ROCK ME, BABY (See under Slim, Memphis) (Korner, Alexis & Memphis Slim).

TESTAMENT (Korner, Alexis & Colin Hodgkinson).
Tracks: / One scotch, one bourbon, one beer / Stump blues / Stream line train / My babe / 32-20 blues / High heel sneakers / Will the circle be unbroken / Mary open the door.
LP: THBL 2.026
MC: THBC 2.026

Korngold (composer)

CLASSIC FILM SCORES BY ERICH WOLFGANG KORNGOLD (see under Films) (Various artists).

Kornog

KORNOG.
LP: BUR 811

ON SEVEN WINDS.
LP: SIF 1062
MC: CSIF 1062

PREMIERE.
LP: SIF 1055
MC: CSIF 1055

Korova Milkbar

TALKING'S BORING.
Tracks: / Something missing / Calling me again / Breakdown / Desolate despair / Satisfy / I can't see / Killing me / Stoney ground.
LP: SUBORG 13

Korshid, Omar

BELLY DANCE FROM LEBANON (Korshid, Omar & His Magic Guitar).
MC: TC GVDL 261

Kortato

FRONTLINE COMPILATION, A.
LP: ORG 87/10

Kosek, Kenny

HASTY LONESOME (Kosek, Kenny & Matt Glaser).
LP: ROUNDER 0127

Kossoff, David (nar)

BIBLE STORIES (see under Bible Stories (bk)).
MCSET: LFP 7433

BIBLE STORIES VOL. 2.
MCSET: LFP 7475

YOU HAVE A MINUTE LORD.
Tracks: / Charity / Girlwatching / Vandals, Lord / How do you condole, Lord / Thy telly / Other fellow is wrong, The / Saying it / Must a person suffer fools, Lord / Young mind / Man of peace / Words for Paul / Late great Paul / Elegant light brown suit / All right now.
LP: REC 312
MC: ZCM 312

Kossoff, Kirke ...

KOSSOFF, KIRKE, TETSU, RABBIT (Kossoff/Kirke/Tetsu/Rabbit).
Tracks: / Bluegrass / Sammy's alright / Anna / Just for the box / Hold on / Fool's life / Yellow house / Dying fire / I'm on the run / Colours.
LP: ILPS 9188
MC: ICM 9188

Kossoff, Paul

BACK STREET CRAWLER.
Tracks: / I'm ready / Time away / Molton gold / Backstreet crawler / Tuesday morning.
LP: ILPM 9264
MC: ICM 9264

BLUE SOUL.
Tracks: / Over the green hills (Part 1) / Worry / Moonshine / Trouble on double time / Crossroads / Oh I wept / We got time / Oh how we danced / Stealer, The / Hold on / Catch a train / Come together in the morning / Molten gold / I know why the sun don't shine / Tricky Dicky rides again / I'm ready / Blue soul.
MC: PKC 100
LP: PKSP 100

CROYDON - JUNE 15TH 1975.
2LP: SDLP 1002

HUNTER, THE.
LP: STLP 001

KOSS.
Tracks: / Worm, The / Song of yesterday / Mr. Big / Time away / Hole in the head / You and me / You've taken hold of me / Molten gold / Side kick to the stars / Never take me alive / Band plays on, The / It's a long way down to the top / Train song / Hunter, The / We won / Bird dog blues.
2LP: SDLP 1001
LP: CLALP 127
MC: CLAMC 127

LEAVES IN THE WIND.
LP: STLP 002

MR BIG.
MC: STC 0012

Kostbanded

COTTON CLUB STOMP.
LP: KS 2060

Kostelanetz, Andre

BEST OF GERSHWIN.
Tracks: / Girl crazy medley / Promenade / Wintergreen for President / Man I love, The / Fascinating rhythm / Love walked in / Someone to watch over me / Porgy and Bess medley / Foggy day / Strike up the band / 'S wonderful.
LP: 61449

GRAND CANYON SUITE (Cash, Johnny).
LP: CBS 61835

PLAYS CHARLIE CHAPLIN AND DUKE ELLINGTON.
Tracks: / Solitude / I got it bad and that ain't good / Single petal of a rose / Mood indigo / Looking glass / Green lantern bag / Terry theme / Morning promenade / Love song theme / Smile.
LP: CBS 61773

SHOWSTOPPERS.
Tracks: / Kiss Me Kate / South Pacific / My fair lady / Music man / Promenade / West Side story / Showboat.
LP: CBS 61425

THAT'S ENTERTAINMENT.
Tracks: / You made me love you / That's entertainment / New York, New York / Pretty girl is like a melody / Begin the beguine / Thou swell / It's a most unusual day / Easy to love / Singin' in the rain / American in Paris, An / Rhapsody in blue / Ol' man river / Strike up the band / Make believe / Dancing in the dark / Hallelujah.
LP: CBS 60303

Kotch

KOTCH.
Tracks: / Tears / Ooo baby baby / Wonderful tonight / Two occasions / Broken hearted melody / Cruising / Best of strangers / Tracks of my tears / Tequila.
MC: MCT 1003
LP: MLPS 1003

Kotsonis, George

APHRODITE INHERITANCE, THE.
LP: REB 356
MC: ZCF 356

Kottke, Leo

6 AND 12 STRING GUITAR.
Tracks: / Driving of the year nail / Last of the Arkansas greyhound / Ojo / Crow river waltz / Sailor's grave on the prairie / Vaseline machine gun / Jack Fig / Watermelon / Jesu, joy of man's desiring / Fisherman / Tennessee toad / Busted bicycle / Brain of the purple mountain / Coolidge rising.
LP: TKMLP 6002
MC: ZCTKM 6002
LP: SNTF 629

BALANCE.
Tracks: / Tell Mary / I don't know why / Embryonic journey / Disguise / Whine / Losing everything / Drowning / Dolores / Half acre of garlic / Learning the game.
MC: ZCHR 1234
LP: CHR 1234

BEST OF LEO KOTTKE.
Tracks: / Accoustic / Cripple Creek / Bouree / When the shrimps learn to whistle / Bill Cheatham / Song of the swamp / Last steam engine train / Standing in my shoes / Bumble bee / Eight miles high / Tilt Billings and the student prince / Pamela Brown / Standing on the outside / Power failure / Electric / Bean time / Spanish entomologist / Short stories / Hole in the day / Mona Roy / Venezuela, there you go / Monkey lust / Live / Busted bicycle / June bug / Eggtooth / Stealing / Living in the country / Crow river waltz / Jesu, joy of man's desiring / Jack Fig.
2LP: ESTSP 21

BURNT LIPS.
Tracks: / Endless sleep / Cool water / Frank forgets / Sonora's death row / Quiet man / Everybody lies / I called back / Low thud, A / Orange room / Credits, The / Out takes from Terry's movie / Voluntary target / Burnt lips / Sand street / Train and the gate, The / From Terry's movie.
LP: CHR 1191

GREENHOUSE.
LP: BGOLP 50

GUITAR MUSIC.
Tracks: / Part 2 / Available space / Side one suite / Some birds sounds like / Slang / My double / Three walls and bars / Some birds (reprise) / Perforated sleep / Strange / Little shoes / Jibs hat / Tumbling tumbleweeds / Agile / Song for the night of the hunter, A / All I have to do is dream / Sleepwalk.
LP: CHR 1328
MC: ZCHR 1328

LEO KOTTKE.
Tracks: / Buckaroo / White ape, The / Haysee suede / Rio Leo / Range / Airproofing / Maroon / Waltz / Death by reputation / Up tempo / Shadowland.
LP: CHR 1106
MC: ZCHR 1106

LEO KOTTKE LIVE IN EUROPE.
Tracks: / Train and the gate / Open country joy / Airproofing / Tell Mary / Up tempo / Palms Blvd. / Shadowland / Eggtooth.
LP: CHR 1284

LEO KOTTKE WITH PETER LANG & JOHN FAHEY.
LP: SNTF 675

MUDLARK.
LP: EST 682

MY FATHER'S FACE.
Tracks: / Times twelve / Everybody lies / B.J. / Why can't you fix my car / Rick and Bob report, Theme from / My Aunt Francis / William Powell / Back in Buffalo / Mona Ray / Jack gets up / Doorbell.
LP: 209.910
MC: 409.910

REGARDS FROM CHUCK.
Tracks: / I yell at traffic / Foster's feet / Dan's tune / Skinflint / Pink Christmas / Short wave / Dog quiver / Busy signal / Doodles, Theme from / Late zone, The / Taxco steps / Ojo / Mary.
LP: 209641
MC: 409641

SHOUT TOWARDS NOON, A.
Tracks: / Little beaver / Shout toward noon, A / Little Martha / Easter again / Piece / Three quarter north / Echoing gilewitz / First to go / Air proofing two / Virtuoso is his own reward, A / Ice field, The.
LP: 209.959
MC: 409.959

THAT'S WHAT.
LP: 210883
MC: 410883

TIME STEP.
Tracks: / Running all night long / Bungle party, The / Rings / Mr. Fonebone / Julie's house / Memories are made of this / Saginaw, Michigan / I'll break out again / Wrong track, The / Starving / Here comes that rain again.
LP: CHR 1411
MC: ZCHR 1411

Kotzen, Richie

ELECTRIC JOY.
LP: RR 9290 1
MC: RR 9290 4

FEVER DREAM.
LP: RR 93671
MC: RR 93674

RICHIE KOTZEN.
Tracks: / Squeeze play / Strut it / Unsafe at any speed / Rat trap / Cryptic script / Plaid plesiosaur / Spider legs / Jocose Jenny / Noblesse oblige.
MC: RR 94684
LP: RR 9468 1

Koulsoum, Oum

AL ATLAL.
MC: MC 33103
LP: SC 22103

ALF LAYLAT WA LAYLAT.
MC: MC 33126
LP: SC 22126

AMAL HAYATI.
MC: MC 33105
LP: SC 22105

AROUH LEMIN.
MC: MC 33127
LP: SC 22127

FAKEROUNI.
MC: MC 33106
LP: SC 22106

HAGERTAK.
MC: MC 33101
LP: SC 22101

HATHA LAYALTI.
MC: MC 33125
LP: SC 22125

INTA OMRI.
MC: MC 33104
LP: SC 22104

ROUBAIYAT AL KHAYAM.
MC: MC 33107
LP: SC 22107

YA THALMANI.
MC: MC 33121
LP: SC 22121

ZAKARIYAT.
MC: MC 33123
LP: SC 22123

Kouyate, Ousmane

DOMBA (Kouyate, Ousmane Band).
Tracks: / Djougouya / Domba / Kounady / Miriya / An' fananta lele / N'nafanta / Kounady.
LP: STERNS 1030
MC: STC 1030

Kouyate, Sanougoue
BALENDALA DJIRE.
LP: MLPS 1050
MC: MCT 1050
LP: 846 328 1
MC: 846 328 4

Kouyate, Tata Bambo
JATIGUI.
Tracks: / Hommage a baba cissoko / Mama batchily / Goundo tandja / Ainana bah / Ahourou bocoum / Amadou traore.
LP: ORB 042
MC: ORBC 042

Kowalski
OVERMAN UNDERGROUND.
LP: V 2265

Koyaanisqatsi (film)
KOYAANISQATSI (See under Glass, Philip) (Glass, Philip).

Krackhouse
WHOLE TRUTH...BY KARL MARX, THE.
LP: SR 0288
LP: SHIMMY 005

Kraftwerk
AUTOBAHN.
Tracks: / Autobahn / Kometenmelodie 1 / Kometenmelodie 2 / Mitternacht / Morgenspaziergang.
LP: AUTO 1
MC: TCAUTO 1
LP: EMC 3405
MC: TCEMC 3405
LP: EJ 2400701
MC: EJ 2400704
LP: 6360 620

CLASSICAL GAS (See under Beggar's Opera) (Kraftwerk & Beggar's Opera).

COMPUTER WORLD.
Tracks: / Pocket calculator / Numbers / Computer world / Computer love / It's more fun to compute / Home computer.
LP: EMC 3370
MC: TCEMC 3370

ELECTRIC CAFE.
Tracks: / Boing boom tschak / Techno pop / Musique non stop / Telephone call, The / Sex object / Electric cafe.
LP: EMD 1001
MC: TCEMD 1001

ELEKTRO KINETIK.
Tracks: / Autobahn / Ananas symphonie / Strom / Mittemacht / Kometenmelodie 2 / Heimatklange / Tanzmusik / Spule 4.
LP: 6449 066

EXCELLER 8.
LP: 6360 629

MAN MACHINE.
Tracks: / Robots / Spacelab / Metropolis / Model, The / Neon lights / Man machine.
LP: FA 41 3118 1
MC: FA 41 3118 4
LP: FA 3118
MC: TCFA 3118
LP: EST 11728

MIX, THE.
Tracks: / Robots, The / Computer love / Pocket calculator / Dentaku / Autobahn / Radioactivity / Trans Europe express / Abzug / Metal on metal / Homecomputer / Musique non stop.
2LP: EM 1408
MC: TCEM 1408

RADIO-ACTIVITY.
Tracks: / Radioactivity / Radioland / Intermission / News / Voice of energy, The / Radio stars / Geiger counter / Airwaves / Antenna / Uranium / Transistors / Ohm sweet ohm.
LP: EMS 1256
MC: TCEMS 1256
LP: 41 3103 1
MC: 41 3103 4
LP: ATAK 104
MC: TCATAK 104
LP: 1C 064 82087

RALF AND FLORIAN.
LP: 6360 616

ROBOTS.
MC: 4XL 9445

TECHNO POP.
Tracks: / Techno pop / Sex object / Telephone call / Tour de france.
LP: EMC 3407

TRANS - EUROPE EXPRESS.
Tracks: / Europe endless / Hall of mirrors / Showroom dummies / Trans - Europe express / Metal on metal / Franz Schubert / Endless endless.
LP: FA 4131511
MC: FA 4131514
LP: ATAK 5
MC: TC ATAK 5
LP: EST 11603

VARIOUS NUMBERS.
2LP: 6641 077

Krahmer, Carlo
BUGLE CALL RAG.
LP: 10-080

CARLO KRAHMER MEMORIAL ALBUM.
LP: ESQ 306

CARLO KRAHMER'S CHICAGOANS (Krahmer, Carlo Chicagoans).
LP: ESQ 319

SAVOY BLUES.
LP: 10-210

WHO'S SORRY NOW.
LP: 10-081

Kral, Roy
WE'VE GOT IT - THE MUSIC OF CY COLEMAN (see Cain, Jackie) (Kral, Roy & Jackie Cain).

Krama, Dade
ANCESTRAL MUSIC OF AFRICA.
LP: AK 1
MC: AKC 1

Kramer, Billy J.
BEST OF BILLY J KRAMER.
Tracks: / Do you want to know a secret / Bad to me / I call your name / Little children / It's up to you / Ships that pass in the night / San Diego / Sneakin' around / I'll keep you satisfied / When you walk in the room / I'll be on my way / Trains and boats and planes / Blueberry Hill / From a window / It's a mad mad world / Sugar babe / You can't live on memories.
LP: EG 2601891
MC: EG 2601894

BEST OF THE EMI YEARS: BILLY J. KRAMER (Kramer, Billy J. & The Dakotas).
Tracks: / Do you want to know a secret / Bad to me / I call your name / I'll keep you satisfied / I know / I'll be on my way / Cruel sea / Little children / Second to none / They remind me of you / From a window / Sneakin' around / I'll be doggone / Neon city / Take my hand / Trains and boats and planes / That's the way I feel / It's gotta last forever / We're doing fine / Forgive me / Going, going, gone / You can't live on memories.
MC: TCEMS 1392

BILLY J KRAMER.
LP: 1A 052 06446

GREATEST HITS: BILLY J KRAMER (Kramer, Billy J. & The Dakotas).
MC: ASK 790

KRAMER VERSUS KRAMER.
LP: ATA 007

LISTEN (Kramer, Billy J. & The Dakotas).
Tracks: / I'll keep you satisfied / Do you want to know a secret / We're doing fine / I call your name / From a window / Second to none / Beautiful dreamer / Cruel sea / Magic carpet / I'll be on my way / Bad to me / It's up to you / Little children / Take my hand / Trains and boats and planes / Still waters run deep / Tell me girl / I know / Dance with me / Sugar babe.
LP: CM 107
MC: CMK 107
LP: BGOLP 56
LP: PMC 1209

Kramer Vs Kramer
KRAMER VS KRAMER (Film Soundtrack) (Various artists).
Tracks: / Mandolin and harpsichord concerto: *Various artists* / Scott Kuney: *Various artists* / Frederick Hand: *Various artists* / New York: *Various artists* / Trumpet sonata: *Various artists* / Gordion knot untied: *Various artists*.
LP: CBS 73945
MC: 40 73945

Kramer & Wolmer
TWENTY FINGERS.
Tracks: / Train / Munastiero'e Santa Chiara / Brilliant polka / Lady and the waltz / Caravana negra / Divertimento for the accordion / Play the accordion / Toledo adios / Bella bambina / Italian polka / Tarantella boogie / Accordion polka.
LP: CA 101

Krankies
FAN-DABI-DOZI.
LP: NL 70494
MC: NK 70494

IT'S FAN DABI DOZI.
Tracks: / Hubba dubba dooby / Tony Macaroni / Press the boogie button / We're going to Spain / Wee Jimmy Krankie / Jimmy's gang / Fan-dabi-dozi / Krankie rock / Where's me mum / Haggis song / But you love me, Daddy / Magic piper.
LP: RCALP 3052
MC: RCAK 3052

KRANKIES GO TO HOLLYWOOD, THE.
LP: LAXLP 100
MC: LAXC 100

KRANKIES VOL.1.
MC: VCA 627

KRANKIES VOL.2.
MC: VCA 628

KRANKIES VOL.3.
MC: VCA 629

TWO SIDES OF THE KRANKIES.
Tracks: / Little boy routine, The / Sonny boy / Where's me mam / Song of the Clyde / Jeannie McCall / Northern lights of old Aberdeen / Road and the miles to Dundee, The / Marching through the heather / Scottish soldier, A.
LP: MWM 1012

Kraus, Peter
CONNIE FRANCIS & PETER KRAUS - VOL.1 (see Francis, Connie) (Kraus, Peter & Connie Francis).

CONNIE FRANCIS & PETER KRAUS - VOL.2 (see Francis, Connie) (Kraus, Peter & Connie Francis).

DIE NEUE LP/LIVE.
LP: BTS 964444

PETER KRAUS UND DIE ROCKIES (SUNG IN GERMAN).
Tracks: / Treat me nice / Don't be cruel / Teddy Bear / Jailhouse rock / Tutti frutti / Susie rock / Honey baby / I like your kind of love / I love you baby / Diana / Lonely boy / Adam and Eve / You are my destiny / It's time to cry / Hula baby / Teenager's romance, A.
LP: BFX 15042

TEN O'CLOCK ROCK.
Tracks: / Ten o'clock rock / Rosmarie / Reet petite / Teenager melodie / Ich denk an dich / Die strasse der vergessenen / Sugar babys / Ninety nine days / Come on and swing / Butterfly.
LP: BFX 15044

Krause, Dagmar
ANGEBOT AND NACHFRAGE (German Version of Supply & Demand).
LP: HNBL 1317D
MC: HNBC 1317D

SUPPLY AND DEMAND.
MC: HNBC 1317
LP: HNBL 1317

TANK BATTLES: SONGS OF HANNS EISLER, THE.
Tracks: / Song of the whitewash / You have to pay / Ballad of the sack slingers / Perhaps song, The / Mankind / Song of a German mother / Bankenlied / Und endlich stirbt / Mother's hands / Genvieve: Ostern ist ball sur Seine / Trenches, The / (I read about) tank battles / Chanson allemande / Mother Beimlein / Rat men - the nightmare / Bettellied / Change the world - it needs it / Failure in loving / Ballad of (Bourgeois) welfare / Berlin 1919 / Homecoming / To a little radio.
MC: ANC 8739
LP: AN 8739

Krauss, Alison
I'VE GOT THAT OLD FEELING.
Tracks: / I've got that old feeling / Dark skies / Wish I still had you / Endless highway / Winter of a broken heart / It's over / Will you be leaving / Steel rails / Tonight I'll be lonely too / One good reason / That makes two of us / Longest highway.
LP: ROUNDER 0275
MC: ROUNDER 0275C

TOO LATE TO CRY (Krauss, Alison/ Various).
Tracks: / Too late to cry / Foolish heart / Song for life / Dusty Miller / If I give my heart / In your eyes / Don't follow me / Gentle river / On the borderline / Forgotten pictures / Sleep on.
LP: ROUNDER 0235
MC: ROUNDER 0235C

TWO HIGHWAYS (Krauss, Alison & Union Station).
Tracks: / Two highways / I'm alone again / Wild Bill Jones / Beaumont rag / Heaven's bright shore / Love you in vain / Here comes goodbye / As lovely as you / Windy City rag / Lord don't you forsake me / Teardrops will kiss the morning dew / Midnight rider.
LP: ROUNDER 0257
MC: ROUNDER 0257C

Kraut
ADJUSTMENT TO SOCIETY, AN.
LP: AGE 1

Kravitz, Lenny
LET LOVE RULE.
Tracks: / Sitting on top of the world / Let love rule / Freedom train / My precious love / I build this garden for us / Fear / Does anybody out there even care / Mr Cab Driver / Rosemary / Be / Blues for sister someone (Only on CD and MC.) / Empty hands (Only on CD and MC.) / Flower child (Only on CD and MC.).
LP: VUSLP 10
MC: VUSMC 10

MAMA SAID.
LP: VUSLP 31
MC: VUSMC 31

Kray, Reg
PROTEST, LIVE, LOVE, AND SING (Kray, Reg & Peter Gillett).
LP: BRMLP 036

Krays (film)
KRAYS (Film Soundtrack) (Various artists).
LP: PMLP 5018
MC: PMMC 5018

Krazy Kat
CHINA SEAS.
Tracks: / Thirty love / No smoke without fire / Ivor's dive / Chile wind / Alcatraz / Dundee calling / How they crossed the pole / China seas / Santa Fe.
LP: TOPC 5004

Krcek, Jaroslav
RABA.
LP: RR 23

Kreator
AFTER THE ATTACK.
LPPD: N 0072

COMA OF SOULS.
LP: NUK 158
MC: ZCNUK 158

ENDLESS PAIN.
Tracks: / Endless pain / Total death / Storm of the beast / Son of evil / Flag of hate / Cry war / Bonebreaker / Living in fear / Dying victims.
LP: N 0025
LP: N 0025C
LP: NUK 025

EXTREME AGGRESSION.
Tracks: / Extreme aggression / No reason to exist / Love us or hate us / Stream of consciousness / Some pain will last / Betrayer / Don't trust / Bringer of torture / Fatal energy.
LP: NUK 129
MC: ZCNUK 129
LPPD: NUKPD 145
LP: N 0129
MC: N 0129 4

OUT OF THE DARK, INTO THE LIGHT.
MC: N 01184C
MLP: N 01184
MLP: NUK 118

PLEASURE TO KILL.
LP: N 0037
LP: N 0037C
LP: NUK 037

TERRIBLE CERTAINTY.
Tracks: / Blind faith / Storming with menace / Terrible certainty / As the world burns / Toxic trace / No escape / One of us / Behind to mirror.
LP: NOISE 086
MC: N 0087
LP: N 0086
LP: NUK 086
MC: ZCNUK 086

Krein, Henry
ACCORDION MAGIC.
MC: AMP 014

Kremer, Gidon
EDITION LOCKENHAUS VOL 3 (Kremer, Gidon & Valery Afanassiev).
LP: ECM 1328

EDITION LOCKENHAUS VOLS 1 AND 2.
Tracks: / Quintet in F minor for piano and strings / Two songs from fiancailles pour rire / Conte fantastique d'apres une des histoires extraordinaires.. / Le masque de la mort rouge / String quartet no. 1 / Tango from the soldier's tale / Concerto en re / Two waltzes for the flute, clarinet & piano / Two pieces for string octet op.11.
2LP: ECM 1304

Krenshaw, Marshall
GOOD EVENING.
Tracks: / You should've been there / She hates to go home / Radio girl / Live it up / Whatever way the wind blows / Valerie / Someplace where love can't find me / On the run / Some hearts / Let her dance.
LP: K 925908 1
MC: K 925908 4

Kress, Carl
TWO GUITARS (Kress, Carl/George Barnes).
LP: ST 222

Krew Men

ADVENTURES OF THE KREW MEN.
LP: LM LP 008

CURSE OF THE GRAVEYARD DEMON.
LP: EVIL 27

INTO THE TOMB.
LP: LNLP 014

PLAGUE OF THE DEAD.
LP: LM LP 020

POWER.
LP: LMLP 021

Kriegal, Volker

HOUSEBOAT.
LP: MPS 68 206

LONG DISTANCE.
LP: MPS 68 243

MISSING LINK.
2LP: MPS 88 030

STAR EDITION.
2LP: MPS 88 036

Krieger, Robby

NO HABLA.
Tracks: / Wild child / Eagle's song / It's gonna work out fine / Lonely teardrops / Love it or leave it / Big hurt, The / Piggy's song / I want you, I need you, I love you / You're lost little girl.
LP: EIRSA 1013
MC: EIRSAC 1013
LP: SPEAK 009

VERSIONS.
Tracks: / Tattooed love boys / Her majesty / East end, West end / Crystal ship, The / Street fighting man / Reach out I'll be there / Gavin Legget / Underwater fall / I'm gonna tell on you / Harlem nocturne.
LP: HAI 103

Krimsky, Katrina

STELLA MALU (Krimsky, Katrina & Trevor Watts).
LP: ECM 1199

Kristina, Sonja

SONGS FROM THE ACID FOLK.
LP: FHLP 1
MC: FHMC 1

SONJA KRISTINA.
Tracks: / Street run / Man he colour / Colder than a rose in snow / Breaking out in smiles / Mr.Skin / Roller coaster / Full time woman / Comforter / St.Tropez / Fade away.
LP: CHOPE 5

Kristofferson, Kris

COUNTRY STORE: KRIS KRISTOFFERSON.
Tracks: / Loving her was easier / Why me / Kiss the world goodbye / Jody and the kid / Lover please / Out of mind, out of sight / Jesus was a capricorn / Me and Bobby McGee / Help me make it through the night / I'd rather be sorry / Who's to bless, and who's to blame / Here comes that rainbow again / Breakdown (a long way from home) (Only on CD.) / Taker, The (Only on CD.) / Pilgrim, The (chapter 33) (Only on CD.) / Nobody wins (Only on CD.).
LP: CST 5
MC: CSTK 5

EVERYTHING IS BEAUTIFUL (See under Parton, Dolly) (Kristofferson, Kris/ Dolly Parton/Willie Nelson).

FULL MOON (Kristofferson, Kris/Rita Coolidge).
LP: AMLH 64403

HELP ME MAKE IT THROUGH THE NIGHT.
Tracks: / Help me make it through the night / Year 2000 minus 25, The / If it's all the same to you / Easy come on / Stallion / Rocket to stardom / For the good times / Stranger / Who's to bless and who's to blame / Don't cuss the fiddle / Silver (the hunger).
LP: 31839
MC: 40 31839

HIGHWAYMAN (see under Highwayman) (Kristofferson, Kris/ Johnny Cash/Willie Nelson/ WaylonJennings).

LEGENDARY YEARS, THE.
Tracks: / Me and Bobby McGee / Josie / Lover please / Jesus was a Capricorn / Magdalena / Living legend / Help me make it (through the night) / Smokey put the sweat on me / Why me? / Silver tongued devil / When she's wrong / I my smoke too much / Easter Island / It's never gonna be the same again / Golden Idol, The / I'd rather be sorry / Bigger the fool, The / Shake hands with the Devil / Nobody loves anybody anymore / Broken freedom song / Here comes that rainbow again / Epitaph(black and blue).
2LP: KKVSOPLP 141
MC: KKVSOPMC 141

LEGENDARY YEARS, THE.
LP: 911 083
MC: 911 090

NATURAL ACT (Kristofferson, Kris/Rita Coolidge).
Tracks: / Blue as I do / Not everyone knows / I fought the law / Number one / You're gonna love yourself (in the morning) / Loving her was easier / Back in my baby's arms / Please don't tell me how the story ends / Hoola hoop / Love don't live here anymore / Silver mantis.
LP: AMID 118
MC: CMID 118
LP: AMLH 64690
LP: SHM 3184
MC: HSC 3184

REPOSSESSED.
Tracks: / Anthem '84 / Heart, The / This old road / Love is the way / Mean old man / Shipwrecked in the eighties / They killed him / What about me / El gavilan (The hawk) / El coyote.
LP: MERH 103
MC: MERHC 103
LP: 830 460-1
MC: 830 460-4

SHAKE HANDS WITH THE DEVIL.
Tracks: / Shake hands with the devil / Prove it to you one more time again / Whiskey whiskey / Lucky in love / Seadream / Killer barracuda / Some sundown / Michoacan / Once more with feeling / Fallen angels.
LP: MNT 83793

SONGS OF KRISTOFFERSON.
Tracks: / Silver tongued devil and I, The / Loving her was easier / Me and Bobby McGee / Help me make it through the night / For the good times / Sunday morning coming down / You show me yours and I'll show you mine / Pilgrim, The / Chapter 33 / Hang in hopper / Stranger / I got a life of my own / Why me / Who's to bless and who's to blame.
LP: MNT 32106
MC: 40 32106

THIRD WORLD WARRIOR.
Tracks: / Eagle and the bear, The / Third world warrior / Aquila del norte / Hero, The / Don't let the bastards (get you down) / Love of money / Third world war / Jesse Jackson / Mal Sacate / Sandinista.
LP: 834 629 1
MC: 834 629 4

TO THE BONE.
Tracks: / Magdalena / Star crossed / Blessing in disguise / Devil to pay / Daddy's song / Snakebite / Nobody loves anybody anymore / Maybe you heard / Last time, The / I'll take any chance I can with you.
LP: MNT 84818

WINNING HAND, THE (see under Parton, Dolly) (Kristofferson, Kris/Dolly Parton/Willie Nelson/Brenda Lee).

Krixhjalters

EVILUTION.
LP: CBR 108

Krog, Karin

I REMEMBER YOU.
Tracks: / I remember you / Trane / Lester's happy / Moody's mood for love / It's you or no one / Loverman / Speak low / That old feeling.
LP: SPJ LP 22

SOME OTHER SPRING (Krog, Karin & Dexter Gordon).
LP: SLP 4045

SONG FOR YOU, A.
Tracks: / Song for you, A / Feeling too good today blues / Stardust / I won't dance / Child is born, A / I have the feeling I've been here before / I ain't here / Blue and sentimental / Sentimental and melancholy / Scandia skies / I was doing alright / Lush life / I've got the right to sing the blues.
LP: PHONT 7512
MC: PHONT 8512

SUCH WINTERS OF MEMORY (Krog, Karin/John Surman).
LP: ECM 1254

TWO OF A KIND (See under Halberg, Bengt) (Krog, Karin/Bengt Hallberg).

Krokus

ALIVE AND SCREAMIN'.
Tracks: / Long stick goes boom / Eat the rich / Screaming in the night / Hot shot city / Midnite maniac / Bedside radio / Lay me down / Stayed awake all night / Headhunter.
LP: 208025
MC: 408025

BLITZ, THE.
Tracks: / Midnite maniac / Out of control / Boxes nite out / Our love / Out to lunch / Ballroom blitz / Rock the nations / Hot stuff / Ready to rock.
LP: 206494
MC: 406494

CHANGE OF ADDRESS.
Tracks: / Now / Hot shot city / School's out / Let this love begin / Burning up the night / Say goodbye / World on fire / Hard luck hero / Long way from home.
LP: 607.647
MC: 407.647

HARDWARE.
Tracks: / Celebration / Easy rocker / Smelly nelly / Mr. 69 / She's got everything / Burning bones / Rock city / Winning man / Mad racket.
LP: ARL 5064
MC: ZCART 5064

HEADHUNTER.
Tracks: / Headhunter / Eat the rich / Screaming in the night / Ready to burn / Night wolf / Stayed awake all night / Stand and be counted / White din / Russian Winter.
LP: 205255
MC: 405255
LP: 209080
MC: 409080

HEART ATTACK.
Tracks: / Everybody rocks / Wild love / Let it go / Winning man / Axx attack / Rock and roll / Flyin' high / Shoot down the night / Bad bad girl / Speed up.
LP: IMCA 42087
MC: UNCAC 42087

METAL RENDEZVOUS.
Tracks: / Heatstrokes / Bedside radio / Come on / Streamer / Shy kid / Tokyo nights / Lady double dealer / Fire / No way / Backseat rock 'n' roll.
LP: ARL 5056
MC: ZCARL 5056

ONE VICE AT A TIME.
Tracks: / Long stick goes boom / Bad boys / Rag dolls / Playing the outlaw / To the top / Down the drain / American woman / I'm on the run / Save me / Rock and roll.
LP: SPART 1189
MC: TCART 1189

PAY IT IN METAL.
LP: 6326 800

Kronos

KRONOS (Film Soundtrack) (Various artists).
LP: CLP 1001

Kronos Quartet

IN FORMATION.
LP: RR 9

KRONOS QUARTET.
LP: 9791111
MC: 9791114

MUSIC BY BILL EVANS.
Tracks: / Waltz for Debbie / Very early / Nardis / Re: person I knew / Time remembered / Walking up / Turn out the stars / Five / Peace piece.
LP: LLP 1510
MC: LLP 51510

WHITE MAN SLEEPS.
Tracks: / White man sleeps no 1 / White man sleeps no 3 / White man sleeps no 5 / Scherzo holding your own / Pano da costa(Cloth from the coast) (/ Lonely woman / Amazing grace.
LP: K 979163 1
MC: K 979163 4
LP: STLS 1087

WINTER WAS HARD.
Tracks: / Winter was hard / Fratres / Bella by barlight / Door is ajar, A / Half wolf dances mad in moonlight / Forbidden fruit / Quartet No 3.
LP: 979181 1
MC: 979181 4

Krouse, Dagmar

BABBLE (See under Coyne, Kevin).

Kruiz

KRUIZ.
Tracks: / Knight on the road / Brave new world / Heaviest in town / Avenger / In flames / Dream 5000 years long / Iron rock / Possessed.
LP: K 243869-1
MC: K 243869-4

Krull (film)

KRULL (Film soundtrack) (London Symphony Orchestra).
Tracks: / Riding the fire mares / Slayer's attack / Widow's web / Widows's lullaby / Destruction of the black fortress / Epilogue.
LP: FILM 005

KRULL (2) (Film Soundtrack) (London Symphony Orchestra).
LP: ADE 2108

Krumbach, Wilhelm

BACH VARIATIONS.
MC: SJP 1216

Krupa, Gene

1938-1939.
Tracks: / Grandfather's clock / I know that you know / Fare thee well, Annie Laurie / Wire brush stomp / Bolero at the Savoy / Murdy purdy / Ta-ra-ra-boom-der-e / Never felt better, never had less / Apurksody / Do you wanna jump, children / Madam, swings it, The / Dracula.
LP: SM 3236
MC: MC 3236

ACE DRUMMER MAN (1943-47).
LP: GOJ 1006

BACK TO BACK (See under Rich, Buddy) (Rich, Buddy & Gene Krupa).

BLUE MOON 1944-46.
Tracks: / Blue moon / There's no you / I got it all over again lover / Wirebrush stomp no. 2 / Chickery chick / Leave us leap / Hop skip and jump / We'll gather lilacs / These foolish things / Limehouse blues / Man I love, The / Out of nowhere.
LP: HEP 16

CHALLENGING THE CHALLENGER (Krupa, Gene Orchestra & Trio).
LP: FH 35

DRUM BATTLE (Krupa, Gene & Buddy Rich).
LP: 2317 116

DRUM BOOGIE.
Tracks: / opus one / Leave us leap / Drum boogie / Body and soul / Boogie blues / Massachusetts / How high the moon / Tuxedo Junction / Dark eyes / That's what you think / Bolero at the Savoy / Lover.
LP: VSLP 345
MC: 40178
LP: 20178

DRUMMER MAN.
LP: 827 843-1
MC: 827 843-4

DRUMMIN' MAN (2).
Tracks: / Nagasaki / Jeepers creepers / Do you wanna jump children / Symphony in riffs / Drummin' man / Drumboogie / Let me off uptown / After you've gone (CD only) / Rockin' chair / Bolero at the Savoy / Massachusetts / Leave us leap / Dark eyes / Stompin' at the Savoy (CD only) / Opus one / Lover / How high the moon / Disc jockey jump / Calling Dr. Gillespie.
LP: AFS 1042

DRUMMIN' MAN (CBS).
Tracks: / Opus one / Drum boogie / Body and soul / Boogie blues / How high the moon / Massachusetts / Drummin' man / Tuxedo Junction / Leave us leap / Bolero at the Savoy / Dark eyes / That's what you think.
LP: CBS 32262

EXCITING GENE KRUPA, THE.
LP: GOJ 1028

GENE KRUPA (Compact/Walkman jazz).
Tracks: / Drummin' man / Swedish schnapps / Paradise / Just you, just me / Gene's solo flight / Disc jockey jump / 'S wonderful / Let me off uptown hippdeebip / Imagination / Who's rhythm / Mulligan stew / Gene's blues.
MC: 833 286 4

GENE KRUPA AND BUDDY RICH (Compact/Walkman jazz) (Krupa, Gene & Buddy Rich).
Tracks: / King Porter stomp / Bernie's tune / It don't mean a thing / Evolution / Sweethearts on parade / Jumpin' at the woodside / Buddy's blues / Duet.
MC: 835 314-4

GENE KRUPA & BUDDY RICH - THE DRUM BATTLE (See under Rich, Buddy) (Krupa, Gene & Buddy Rich).

GENE KRUPA COLLECTION (20 golden greats).
Tracks: / Drum boogie / Drummin' man / How high the moon / Bolero at the Savoy / Boogie blues / Opus one / Tuxedo Junction / Leave us leap / That's what you think / Massachusetts / King Porter stomp / St. Louis blues / Stompin' at the Savoy / Alexander's ragtime band / Get happy / I've got the world on a string / Dark eyes / Caravan / I left my heart in San Francisco / Big noise from Winnetka.
LP: DVLP 2093
MC: DVMC 2093

GENE KRUPA & HIS MEN OF JAZZ.
MC: SLC 61006

GENE KRUPA, LIONEL HAMPTON & TEDDY WILSON (Krupa, Gene, Lionel Hampton & Teddy Wilson).
LP: 2304 482

GENE KRUPA ON THE AIR 1944-1946 (Krupa, Gene & His Orchestra).
Tracks: / Futurama / It had to be you / Blue moon / Dear old Southland / Swingin on a star / I'll walk alone / You never say yes / Drum boogie / Liza / Hodge podge / How high the moon / Man I love, The / Ten Rich Drive / Very thought of you, The.
LP: . . . . AIRCHECK 35

GENE KRUPA ORCHESTRA (1941) (Krupa, Gene & His Orchestra).
LP: . . . . BLJ 8002

GENE KRUPA ORCHESTRA & TRIO (Krupa, Gene Orchestra & Trio).
LP: . . . . SWH 40

GENE KRUPA - VOL.1.
LP: . . . . KLJ 20014

GENE KRUPA - VOL.1 (1935-8).
LP: . . . . AJAX 101

GENE KRUPA - VOL.2 (1938).
LP: . . . . AJAX 105

GENE KRUPA - VOL.3 (1938).
LP: . . . . AJAX 110

GENE KRUPA - VOL.4 (1939).
LP: . . . . AJAX 111

GENE KRUPA - VOL.5 (1939).
LP: . . . . AJAX 121

GENE KRUPA - VOL.6 (1939-40).
LP: . . . . AJAX 122

GENE KRUPA - VOL.7 (1940).
LP: . . . . AJAX 125

GENE KRUPA - VOL.8 (1940).
LP: . . . . AJAX 127

GENE KRUPA - VOL.9 (1940).
LP: . . . . AJAX 130

GENE KRUPA - VOL.10 (1940).
LP: . . . . AJAX 132

GENE KRUPA - VOL.11 (1940-1).
LP: . . . . AJAX 138

GENE KRUPA - VOL.12 (1941).
LP: . . . . AJAX 146

GENE KRUPA - VOL.13 (1941).
LP: . . . . AJAX 154

GENE KRUPA - VOL.14 (1941).
LP: . . . . AJAX 161

GENE'S BAND.
LP: . . . . FH 26

HISTORY OF JAZZ.
LP: . . . . SM 3230

KRUPA & RICH (Krupa, Gene & Buddy Rich).
Tracks: / Buddy's blues and Bernie's tune / Gene's blues / Sweethearts on parade / I never knew.
LP: 817 109-1

LIONEL HAMPTON & GENE KRUPA ORCHESTRAS (See under Hampton, Lionel) (Hampton, Lionel Orchestra & Gene Krupa Orchestra).

ORIGINAL DRUM BATTLE (Krupa, Gene & Buddy Rich).
LP: 2304 308

RADIO DISCS OF GENE KRUPA, THE.
LP: . . . . JLP 2008

SUPERB PERFORMANCES (1945-1949) (Krupa, Gene & His Orchestra).
LP: . . . . FH 7

SWINGIN' GENE KRUPA QUARTET.
LP: . . . . SG 1019

SWINGING BIG BANDS 1947-47, THE (Krupa, Gene & His Orchestra).
LP: . . . . SM 3616

THAT DRUMMERS BAND (Krupa, Gene & His Orchestra).
LP: . . . . LP 114

WHAT'S THIS (1946-1947) (Krupa, Gene & His Orchestra).
LP: . . . . HEP 26

WIRE BRUSH STOMP 1938 - 41 (Krupa, Gene & His Orchestra).
LP: . . . . BS 7117
MC: . . . . BS 7117C

Krupps

ENTERING THE ARENA.
LP: . . . . STAB 2

Krush Groove

KRUSH GROOVE (Film soundtrack) (Various artists).
Tracks: / Can't stop the street: *Khan, Chaka* / I can't live without my radio: *L.L. Cool J* / If I ruled the world: *Blow, Kurtis* / All you can eat: *Fat Boys* / Feel the spin: *Harry, Debbie* / Holly rock: *Sheila E* / She's on it: *Beastie Boys* / Love triangle: *Gap Band* / Tender love: *Force M.D.'s* / Krush groovin': *Fat Boys/Run DMC/ Sheila E/Kurtis Blow.*
LP: 925295 1
MC: 925295 4

Krystol

PASSION FROM A WOMAN.
Tracks: / Passion from a woman / Love attack / Precious precious / All my love / I might fall in love with you / He's so jive / Baby make your mind up / Scared single.
LP: . . . . EPC 26944
MC: 40 26944

K-Solo

TELL THE WORLD MY NAME.
LP: 7821081
MC: 7821084

Kubis, Tom

TOM KUBIS BIG BAND (Kubis, Tom Big Band).
MC: . . . . MCSB 109

Kublai Khan

ANNIHILATION.
Tracks: / Death breath / Mongrel horde / Down to the inferno / Liars dice / Passing away / Clash of the swords / Battle hymn of the Republic / Kublaikhan.
LP: . . . . HMUSA 95

Kuepper, Ed

ELECTRICAL STORM.
LP: . . . . HOT 1020

EVERYBODY'S GOT TO.
Tracks: / Everybody's got to / Too many clues / When there's this party / Standing in the cold, in the rain / Lonely paradise / Burned my fingers / Not a soul around / Nothing changes in my house / Spartan spirituals / No skin off your nose.
LP: . . . . EST 2099
LP: 790 513 1
MC: . . . . TCEST 2099
MC: 790 513 4

ROOMS OF THE MAGNIFICENT.
LP: . . . . HOT 1027

TODAY WONDER.
LP: . . . . RAT 506

Kuhn, Joachim

LIVE (See under Akkerman, Jan) (Kuhn, Joachim & Jan Akkerman).

SPRING FEVER.
Tracks: / Lady Amber / Sunshine / Two whips / Spring fever / Morning / Mushroom / Equal evil / California woman.
LP: . . . . K 50280

Kuhn, Paul

BLAUE WILDLEDER SCHUH.
Tracks: / Blue suede shoes / White sports coat / Lonesome cowboy / Handful of songs / Midnight / Butterfly / Doll / Tequila / A la salud / Living doll / Charming boy / Dark dark night / Hully gully hop / Swinging on a star / I'm never gonna tell / Talk back tremblin' lips.
LP: . . . . BFX 15129

PLAY GLENN MILLER & BENNY GOODMAN (Kuhn, Paul & His Orchestra).
LP: . . . . DS 021

Kuhn, Steve

LAST YEAR'S WALTZ (Kuhn, Steve Quartet).
LP: . . . . EMC 1213

LIFE'S MAGIC (Kuhn, Steve Trio).
LP: . . . . BKH 522

MOSTLY BALLADS.
Tracks: / Yesterdays gardenias / Tennessee waltz / Danny boy / Don't explain / Body and soul / Emily / Airegin / How high the moon.
LP: . . . . NW 351

RAINDROPS LIVE IN MY....
LP: . . . . MR 5106

Kukl

EYE, THE.
LP: 1984/1

HOLIDAYS IN EUROPE.
LP: . . . . CATNO 4

Kuleta, Pompon

FAITES ATTENTION.
LP: . . . . KP 2002

Kumar, Kishare

GREAT ARTIST, GREAT HITS.
LP: . . . . CDPMLP 5082

HITS FOREVER.
LP: . . . . CDPMLP 5352

Kumar, Pramod

LE SITAR INDIEN (Le langage du raga).
Tracks: / Rag purya kalyan / Shudh sarang / Thumree sindhi bhairavi / Dhun.
LP: . . . . ARN 34207
MC: . . . . ARN 434207

Kumpf, Hans

ON A RUSSIAN TRIP.
LP: . . . . LR 122

Kunda, Toure

PARIS - ZIGUINCHOR.
LP: . . . . CEL 6722

Kuniyoshi-Kuhn, Akemi

HANDSCAPES.
LP: . . . . LR 143

MOTION-E-MOTION.
LP: . . . . LR 155

Kunz, Charlie

AND THE CASANI CLUB BAND (Kunz, Charlie & The Casani Club Orchestra).
MCSET: . . . . DTO 10258

CHARLIE KUNZ & HIS CASANI CLUB ORCHESTRA (Kunz, Charlie & The Casani Club Orchestra).
Tracks: / You gotta know how to dance / Star fell out of heaven, A / Let's sit this one out / Did you ever see a dream walking / Learn to croon / I'm putting all my eggs in one basket / On a steamer / Love is everywhere / Robins and roses / White cliffs of Dover, The / Have you forgotten so soon / Love is a dancing thing / Life begins when you're in love / Goodnight my love / I've got a feelin' you're foolin'.
LP: . . . . RFL 24

CLAP HANDS, HERE COMES CHARLIE.
Tracks: / Between 18th and 19th on Chestnut Street / Clap hands, here comes Charlie / March winds and April showers / Heart of gold / Red sails in the sunset / All alone in Vienna / Boo hoo / Cherokee / There's a small hotel / I believe in miracles / Crying my heart out for you / On then night of June 3rd / Harbour lights / Someone to care for / I'm in the mood for love / On the good ship lollipop / Did your mother come from Ireland? / Every night at eight / Swing time medley.
LP: . . . . RFL 37

DANCE YOUR WAY THROUGH THE THIRTIES (Kunz, Charlie & The Casani Club Orchestra).
Tracks: / Unless / There was an old woman / Learn to croon / Did my heart beat did I fall in love / Let's sit this one out / Did you ever see a dream walking / She fell for a feller from "Oopasala" / Dear stranger / When you're sixty / Moonstruck / By a waterfall / Roaming / Doggone I've done it / Lazybones / Memories of hours spent with you / I raise my hat / On the good ship lollipop / There's no green grass round the old North Pole.
LP: . . . . JOY'D 286

FOCUS ON CHARLIE KUNZ.
MC: . . . . KFOC 28075

MUSIC FOR THE MILLIONS.
Tracks: / Medleys / Carousels / Show boat / Oklahoma / Rodger and heart / South american.
LP: 6495 109
MC: 7195 109

MUSIC GOES ROUND, THE.
Tracks: / When Irish eyes are smiling / Comin' thro' the rye / Oh you beautiful doll / Yip I addy I ay / On Treasure Island / Thanks a million / Music goes round and around, The / I can't give you anything but love baby / Ain't she sweet / Auf wiedersehen my dear / Lost / Glory of love / Is it true what they say about dixie? / I ain't got nobody / If I had you / Time on my hands / I'll see you again / Desert song, The / My hero / Can't we talk it over / Oh you beautiful doll / Dinah / Annie Laurie / Loch Lomond / Comin' thro' the rye / Auld lang syne / She shall have music / Alone at a table for two / Pink elephants / Merry widow waltz, The / Love will find a way / Blue Danube / Some of these days / With a song in my heart / Night and day / What'll I do / Always / When you and I were seventeen / You are my lucky star / I've got a feelin' you're foolin' / She's funny that way / Shoe shine boy / When I'm with you / Somebody stole my gal / Poor butterfly / After you've gone / Whispering / Some other time / Little bit independent, A / Goodnight sweetheart.
LP: . . . . CHD 162
MC: . . . . MCHD 162

NO ONE BUT YOU.
Tracks: / My friend / I need you now / Birth of the blues / Whatever will be will be / Here in my heart / You belong to me / Kiss of fire / All my love / Mister Sandman / Softly / Under the bridge of Paris / Stars shine in your eyes / Because you're mine / Love is a many splendoured thing / Shifting whispering sands.
LP: . . . . TAB 11
MC: . . . . KTBC 11

PRETTY GIRL IS LIKE A MELODY, A.
Tracks: / Crying my heart out for you / Until tomorrow / Would you / Pretty girl is like a melody, A / Love is a dancing thing / Cheek to cheek / Misty islands of the highlands / Look up and laugh / Boo-hoo / All alone in Vienna / When my dreamboat comes home / Learn to croon / Lazybones / Did my heart beat? Did I fall in love / Dear stranger / Life is empty without love / Moonstruck / Unless.
LP: . . . . BUR 010
MC: . . . . 4 BUR 010

WORLD OF....
MC: . . . . KCSP 15
LP: . . . . SPA 15

WORLD OF... VOL. 3.
MC: . . . . KCSP 194

Kunzel, Erich

CLASSICS OF THE SILVER SCREEN (See under Film Music).

Kupferberg, Tuli

TULI AND FRIENDS.
LP: . . . . SHIMMY 020

Kurdistan

SONGS AND MUSIC OF KURDISTAN (Koma Zozan).
Tracks: / Improvisation / Sex mehmud / Chant du promenade / Nazliye / Dotmame / Govend / Narine / Gulisan.
LP: . . . . ARN 33719

Kursaal Flyers

BEST OF THE KURSAAL FLYERS.
Tracks: / Speedway / Pocket money / Yellow sox / Cruisin' for love / Palais de Danse / Hypochondriac / Walking to school / Hit records / Little does she know / Radio romance / Questionnaire, The / Sky's falling in on our love, The / Television generation / Girlfriend kinda guy / Everything but a heartbeat / Girls that don't exist.
LP: 6.25479

FORMER TOUR DE FORCE IS FORCED TO TOUR.
MC: . . . . WF 044C
LP: . . . . WF 044

IN FOR A SPIN.
LP: . . . . ED 142

Kuryokhin, Sergey

INTRODUCTION TO POP-MECHANICS.
LP: . . . . LR 146

MAD NIGHTINGALES (Kuryokhin, Sergey & Boris Grebenshohikov).
LP: . . . . LR 167

POP MECHANICS NO. 17 Live in Novosibirsk, 1983.
LP: . . . . LR 158

POPULAR ZOOLOGICAL ELEMENTS.
LP: . . . . LR 148

SENTENCED TO SILENCE (See under Vapirov, Anatoly) (Kuryokhin, Sergey & Anatoly Vapirov).

SUBWAY CULTURE (Kuryokhin, Sergey & Boris Grebenshohikov).
2LP: . . . . LR 402/403

WAYS OF FREEDOM, THE.
LP: . . . . LR 107

Kuslap, Voldemar

FOLK SONGS.
MC: . . . . M 00295

Kustbandet

KUSTBANDET (Coast line band).
LP: . . . . KS 2051

NEW CALL OF THE FREAKS.
LP: . . . . SOS 1178

Kusworth, Dave

BOUNTY HUNTERS.
LP: . . . . SWFLP 5

JACOBITES (See under Sudden, Nikki) (Kusworth, Dave & Nikki Sudden).

WIVES, WEDDINGS AND ROSES (Kusworth, Dave & The Bounty Hunters).
LP: . . . . KSLP 006

Kuti, Fela

ARMY ARRANGEMENT.
Tracks: / Army arrangement / Cross examination / Government chicken boy.
LP: 829 683 1
MC: 829 683 4
LP: . . . . CEL 6109

BLACK PRESIDENT.
Tracks: / Sorrow / Tears and blood / Colonial mentality / I.T.T.
LP: . . . . SPART 1167

BLACK PRESIDENT/ ORIGINAL SUFFERHEAD.
Tracks: / Sorrow, tears and blood / Colonial mentality / I.T.T. / Power show / Original sufferhead.
MC: . . . . XTWO 27

CONFUSION.
MC: . . . . TCNEMI 0004

EVERYTHING SCATTER.
LP: . . . . **CRLP 509**

FELA.
LP: . . . . **CELL 6109**

FELA ANIKULARO KUTI & THE AFRICA 70.
Tracks: / Alu jon jonki jon / Chop and quench / Let's start / Black man's cry / Eko ile / Je nwi temi / Ye ye de smell / Carry me i want to die.
2LP: **EDP1547203**

GENTLEMEN.
LP: . . . . **CRLP 502**

GREATEST HITS: FELA KUTI.
LP: . . . . **NEMILP 0680**
MC: . . . . **TCNEMI 0680**

LIVE IN AMSTERDAM.
2LP: . . . . **FELA 2401293**
MC: . . . . **TC2 FELA 2401293**

MUSIC IS THE WEAPON 75-78.
MC: **160443**

MUSIC IS THE WEAPON 81-84.
MC: **160444**

MUSIC IS THE WEAPON 85-86.
MC: **160445**

NO AGREEMENT.
Tracks: / No agreement / Dog eat dog.
LP: **829 682 1**
MC: **829 682 4**
LP: . . . . **CEL 6122**

ORIGINAL SUFFERHEAD.
Tracks: / Power show / Original sufferhead.
LP: . . . . **SPART 1177**

SHUFFERING AND SHMILING.
Tracks: / Shuffering and shmiling / Perambulator.
LP: **829 710 1**
MC: **829 710 4**

SUFFERING AND SMILING.
Tracks: / Permabulator / Shuffering and schmiling.
LP: . . . . **CEL 6117**

TEACHER DON'T TEACH ME NONSENSE.
Tracks: / Teacher don't teach me nonsense (instr) / Teacher don't teach me nonsense (vocal) / Look and laugh (instr) / Look and laugh (vocal).
2LP: . . . . **LONDP 28**
MCSET: . . . . **LONDC 28**

ZOMBIE (Kuti, Fela/Africa 70).
Tracks: / Zombie / Monkey banana / Everything's scotter.
LP: **829 684 1**
MC: **829 684 4**
LP: . . . . **CRLP 511**
LP: . . . . **CEL 6116**

Kuyateh, Kausu

JALI ROLL (See under Konte, Dembo) (Konte, Dembo & Kausu Kuyateh).

SIMBOMBA (See under Konte, Dembo) (Kuyateh, Kausu/Dembo Konte).

Kwane

BOY GENIUS, THE.
Tracks: / Boy genius / Man we all know and love, The / Mic is mine, The / Push the panic button / Ugotz 2 get down / Rhythm, The / Keep on doin' / Sweet thing.
LP: . . . . **K 781 941 1**
MC: . . . . **K 781 941 4**

Kweskin, Jim

GREATEST HITS: KWESKIN, JIM & JUG BAND (Kweskin, Jim & The Jug Band).
LP: . . . . **VNP 6404**

Kyle, Billy

FINISHING UP A DATE.
LP: . . . . **CI 020**

Kynaston, Nicholas

GREAT ORGAN WORKS.
MC: . . . . **HR 8136**

Kyser, Kay

DANCE DATE (Kyser, Kay/his orchestra).
LP: . . . . **BBALP 1220**

OL' PROFESSOR, THE 1935 - 42 (Kyser, Kay & His Orchestra).
Tracks: / All God's chillun got rhythm / Mighty like a rose / Humpty Dumpty heart / Fresh as a daisy / Ish kabibble / Take your girlie to the movies / East side of Heaven / That sly old gentleman / Bad humour man, The / Zoot suite / When the roses bloom again / Egg a bread.
LP: . . . . **BS 7137**
MC: . . . . **BS 7137C**

SWINGING SIDE, THE (Kyser, Kay Orchestra).
LP: . . . . **GELP 15052**

Kyte, Sydney

1931-1932 (Kyte, Sydney & his Piccadilly Hotel Band).
Tracks: / Guilty / Close your eyes / Just once for all time / Yes, yes / Live, laugh, love / Tom Thumb's drum / Starlight serenade / There's nothing to good for my baby / "Bow Bells" selection / My bluebird's back again / Sweetheart / Let's drift away on Dreamers Bay / I'll make a happy landing / It's always goodbye / Wherever you are / I do like to see a game of football.
LP: . . . . **SH 387**

L

La Bamba

LA BAMBA (Film Soundtrack) (Various artists).
Tracks: / La Bamba: *Los Lobos* / Come on: *Los Lobos* / Ooh my head: *Los Lobos* / We belong together: *Los Lobos* / Framed: *Los Lobos* / Donna: *Los Lobos* / Lonely teardrops: *Huntsberry, Howard* / Crying, waiting, hoping: *Crenshaw, Marshall* / Summertime blues: *Setzer, Brian* / Who do you love: *Diddley, Bo* / Goodnight my love: *Various artists*.
LP: . . . . **LONLP 36**
MC: . . . . **LONC 36**

La Barbera, Pat

PASS IT ON.
LP: . . . . **PM 009**

La Beef, Sleepy

AIN'T GOT NO HOME.
LP: . . . . **LPL 8312**

BEEFY ROCKABILLY.
Tracks: / Good rockin boogie / Blue moon of Kentucky / Send me some lovin / Corina Corina / Matchbox / Party doll / Baby lets play house / Too much monkey business / Roll over Beethoven / Polk salad Annie.
LP: . . . . **CR 30145**

DOWNHOME ROCKABILLY.
Tracks: / Honky tonk hardwood floor / Tore up / Flyin' saucers rock 'n' roll / Red hot / I'm ready if you're willing / I'm a one woman man / Shot-gun boogie / Rock 'n' roll Ruby / Big boss man / Boogie woogie / Country girl / Mystery train / Something on your mind / Jack and Jill boogie / Blues stay away from me.
LP: . . . . **CR 30172**

EARLY RARE & ROCKIN' SIDES.
LP: . . . . **CR 30181**

ELECTRICITY.
LP: . . . . **ROUNDER 3070**
MC: . . . . **ROUNDER 3070C**

IT AIN'T WHAT YOU EAT.
Tracks: / I got it / Roosters are crowing, The / Lost highway / I'm ready / Satisfied / Breaking up home / Wonderful time up there, A / Shake a hand / If I ever had a good thing / Let's talk about us / I don't believe you've met my baby / Walking slowly / Tutti frutti / All the time / Lonely / I walk the line / All alone / I'm through / Bell hop blues / I'm a hobo / I can't find the doorknob / Gee whiz.
LP: . . . . **SNTF 843**
LP: . . . . **ROUNDER 3052**
MC: . . . . **ROUNDER 3052C**

NOTHIN' BUT THE TRUTH.
Tracks: / Tore up over you / How do you talk to a baby / Milk cow blues / Just pickin' / Gunslinger / Ring of fire / Boogie at the Wayside Lounge / Worried man blues / Lets talk about us / My toot toot / Jambalaya / Whole lot of shakin'.
LP: . . . . **ROUNDER 3072**
MC: . . . . **ROUNDER 3072C**

ROCKABILLY GIANT, THE.
LP: . . . . **LP 8005**

ROCKABILLY HEAVYWEIGHT.
Tracks: / Sick & tired / Mind your own business / Lonesome for a letter / Detour / Shame shame shame / Smoking cigarettes and drinking coffee / Cut across shorty / I'm feeling sorry / Honky tonk man / My sweet love ain't around / If you don't love me somebody else will / Milk cow blues / Ride, ride, ride / Are you teasing me? / La boeufs cajun boogie / Go ahead on baby.
LP: . . . . **CRL 5017**

SLEEPY LA BEEF & FRIENDS (Sleepy La Beef & Friends).
Tracks: / All the time / Lonely / I walk the line / All alone / I'm through / Bell hop blues / I'm a hobo / I can't find the doorknob / Sadie / Gee whiz.
LP: . . . . **CH 16**

La Beque, Katia

AN AMERICAN IN PARIS (La Beque, Katia & Marielle).
LP: . . . . **EJ 2701221**
MC: . . . . **EJ 2701224**

BARTOK CONCERTO (La Beque, Katia & Marielle).
LP: . . . . **EL 2704181**
MC: . . . . **EL 2704184**

BERNSTEIN (La Beque, Katia & Marielle).
LP: **45531**
MC: **40 45531**

GERSHWIN SECOND RHAPSODY (Music For Two Pianos) (La Beque, Katia & Marielle).
Tracks: / Second Rhapsody / I got rhythm / Variations / Two waltzes / Blue Monday / Two songs.
LP: . . . . **EL 7497521**
MC: . . . . **EL 7497524**

GLAD RAGS (La Beque, Katia & Marielle).
Tracks: / Rialto ripples / Honky tonk / Carolina shout / Entertainer, The / Antoinette / Magnetic rag / Maple leaf / Eite syncopations / Strenuous life / Stop time / Bethera / Entertainer, The / Maple leaf rag.
LP: . . . . **EMD 5541**
MC: . . . . **TCEMD 5541**

La Boheme

LA BOHEME (See under Puccini) (Various artists).

La Bouche

STEP TIME.
LP: . . . . **LAB 1**

La Cage Aux Folles

LA CAGE AUX FOLLES (Original Broadway Cast) (Various artists).
Tracks: / La Cage Aux Folles: Prelude: *Various artists* / We are what we are: *Various artists* / Little bit more mascara, A: *Various artists* / With Anne on my arm: *Various artists* / With you on my arm: *Various artists*/ Song on the sand (La da da da): *Various artists* / La Cage aux folles: *Various artists* / I am what I am: *Various* artists / Masculinity: *Various artists* / Look over there: *Various artists* / Cocktail counterpoint: *Various artists* / Best times, The: *Various artists* / La Cage aux folles, Finale: *Various artists*.
LP: . . . . **BL 84824**
MC: . . . . **BK 84824**

LA CAGE AUX FOLLES (Film soundtrack) (Various artists).
LP: . . . . **C'BUS 102**
LP: **803 003**

La Ciapa Rusa

FARUAJI.
LP: . . . . **RD 004**

O SENTI CHE BEL CANTA.
LP: . . . . **RD 001**

La Cosa Nostra

LA COSA NOSTRA.
LP: . . . . **CRAM 040**

La Cregunta

CHAMELEON (See under Fraise, Renzo).

L.A. Dream Team

KINGS OF THE WEST COAST.
LP: . . . . **MCF 3345**
MC: . . . . **MCFC 3345**

La Dusseldorf

LA DUSSELDORF.
Tracks: / Dusseldorf / La dusseldorf / Silver cloud / Time.
LP: . . . . **RAD 7**

VIVA.
Tracks: / Viva / White overalls / Rheinita / Vogel / Geld / Cha cha 2000.
LP: . . . . **RAD 10**

L.A. Express

SHADOW PLAY.
Tracks: / Nordic winds / Double your pleasure / Shadow play / Chariot race / Dance the night away / Velvet lady / Vortez / Mad drums and Englishmen / Silhouette.
LP: . . . . **CRB 81671**

La Fanciulla

LA FANCIULLA DEL WEST (See under Puccini) (Various artists).

La Fete Sauvage (film)

LA FETE SAUVAGE (See under Vangelis) (Vangelis).

La Fille Mal Gardee

LA FILLE MAL GARDEE (See under Royal Ballet) (Royal Ballet).

L.A. Four

EXECUTIVE SUITE.
Tracks: / Blues wellington / Amazonia / You and I / Simple invention / Entr'Acte / My funny valentine / Chega de Saudade.
LP: . . . . **CJ 215**
MC: . . . . **CJC 215**

MONTAGE.
LP: . . . . **CJ 156**

ZACA.
LP: . . . . **CJ 130**

L.A. Guns

COCKED AND LOADED.
Tracks: / Letting go / Rip and tear / Never enough / Ballad of Jane, The / Give a little / 17 crash / Wheels of fire / Slap in the face / Sleazy come easy go / Malaria / Magdalaine / I'm addicted / Showdown (riot on sunset).
LP: **838 592 1**
MC: **838 592 4**

L.A. GUNS.
Tracks: / No mercy / Sex action / One more reason / Electric gypsy / Nothing to lose / Bitch is back, The / Hollywood tease / One way ticket / Shoot for thrills / Down in the city.
LP: . . . . **VERH 55**
MC: . . . . **VERHC 55**

L.A. Jazz Quintet

LA JAZZ QUINTET.
LP: . . . . **K 28P 6440**

La La

LA LA.
Tracks: / (If you) love me just a little / I got a thing for you / I don't wanna go / We'll keep striving / Any man will do / My love is on the money / Deal with it / All work, no play / So into love.
LP: **208146**
MC: **408146**

LA LA MEANS I LOVE YOU.
MC: . . . . **ZK 72753**
LP: . . . . **ZL 72753**

La Locomotora Negra

HEY, MR LANDLORD! (La Locomotora Negra & Gene Connors).
LP: . . . . **E 30 194**

La Loora

RESEDA REVEL.
LP: . . . . **ST 7521**

La Lupe

TOO MUCH.
Tracks: / La reina / Guantanamera / Jala jala / Fever / Me vengare / La lloradora / Yesterday / Goin' out of my head / Busamba / Besitos pa' ti / Palo mayimbe / Take it easy / Bembe pata pata / Negrura / Si tu no vienes / Que bueno boogaloo.
LP: . . . . **HOT 123**
MC: . . . . **TCHOT 123**

La Maniqua

MAMBOPARA ELLAS.
LP: **8207**

L.A. Mix

COMING BACK FOR MORE.
LP: **3970891**
MC: **3970894**

ON THE SIDE.
Tracks: / Get loose / You are the one / Breathe deep / Don't turn away / Love together / Just waiting / Mellow mellow / Don't stop / Check this out.
LP: . . . . **AMA 9009**
MC: . . . . **AMC 9009**

La Muerte

DEATH RACE 2000.
Tracks: / I would die faster / Ecoute cetre priere / Shoot in your back / Burst my soul / Sacred flame / Black God, white devil / Make it easy / Death race 2000 / Killing is my business.
LP: . . . . **BIAS 134**

EVERY SOUL OPPRESSED BY SIN.
LP: . . . . **BIGNESS 1**

EXPERIMENT IN TERROR.
LP: . . . . **BIAS 70**

KUSTOM KAR KOMPETITION.
LP: . . . . **BIAS 189**

La Musique Chez...

LA MUSIQUE CHEZ MULATE'S (Various artists).
LP: **6071**
MC: . . . . **O6071 TC**

La Passion Beatrice

LA PASSION BEATRICE (Film Soundtrack) (Various artists).
LP: . . . . **A 314**

La Rock, Scott

CRIMINAL MINDED (La Rock, Scott & Blastmaster KRS 1L).
LP: . . . . **WSRLP 1**
MC: . . . . **ZCWSL 1**

MEMORY OF A MAN & HIS MUSIC (La Rock, Scott & KRS-One).
Tracks: / Memory of a man & his music.
LP: . . . . **BBOY 2**

La Rue, D.C.

FORCES OF THE NIGHT.
Tracks: / Forces of the night / Have a good time / It makes me believe in love again / Hot jungle drums and voodoo rhythm / On with the dance / Don't be afraid of the dark.
LP: . . . . **N 5001**

La Serie, Rolando

AY, SE PASO LA SERIE.
Tracks: / Ay, se paso La Serie / Don Pantaleon / El cubanito / Amalia Batista / Pa' Bailar / Questo abajo / Rio Manzanares / Mi que me importa,A.
LP: . . . . **ORB 026**

La Sonora De Baru

RITMO TROPICALE.
Tracks: / Hi ja de Susana / La estrenina / Maldad / Currucuchu / Yo soy guajiro / Maria Tulia / Llora mi guitarra / Negra Linda.
LP: . . . . **ORB 015**

L.A. Sounds

HITS HITS HITS.
MC: . . . . **CHV 331**

HITS HITS HITS VOLUME 2.
MC: . . . . **CHV 338**

WISHING YOU WERE HERE.
MC: . . . . **CHV 327**

YOU TAKE ME UP.
MC: . . . . **CHV 316**

La Souris Deglinguee

LA SOURIS DEGLINGUEE.
LP: . . . . **ROSE 6**

L.A. Star

POETESS.
Tracks: / Wonderous dream / N.P.T. posse / Do you still love me / Swing to the beat / It's like that / Fade to black (UK remix) / Fade to black / My tale / It takes a real woman / Once upon a time / If you don't wanna party / N.P.T. posse (UK remix).
LP: . . . . **FILER 290**

La Traviata

LA TRAVIATA (VIDEO) (see under Verdi (composer)) (Various artists).

La Vie Est Belle

LA VIE EST BELLE (Various artists).
LP: . . . . **STERNS 1028**

Laaz Rockit

ANNIHILATION PRINCIPLE.
Tracks: / Mirror to madness / Chasin' Charlie / Fire in the hole / Shadow company / Holiday in Cambodia / Mob justice / Bad blood.
LP: . . . . **ENVLP 521**
MC: . . . . **TCENV 521**

KNOW YOUR ENEMY.
LP: . . . . **ST 73305**
LP: . . . . **MFN 81**

NO STRANGER TO DANGER.
LP: **081866**

Labbe, Lilianne

UN CANADIEN ERRANT (Labbe, Lilianne/Don Hinkley).
LP: **C-410 69**
MC: **MC-410 69**

Labelle

LADY MARMALADE (OLD GOLD) (See under Emotions/Best of my love).

Labelle, Patti

BE YOURSELF.
Tracks: / If you asked me to / Be yourself / I can't complain / Yo mister / I got it like that / Love 89 / Still in love / I'm

still scared of you / Can't bring me down / I can fly / Need a little faith.
LP: MCG 6062
MC: MCGC 6062

BEST OF PATTI LABELLE.
Tracks: / Lady marmalade / You are my friend / Joy to have our love / Little girls / Music is my way of life / I don't go shopping / It's alright with me / Come what may.
LP: EPC 32808

IM IN LOVE AGAIN.
Tracks: / I'm in love again / Lover man (oh where can you be) / Love, need and want you / If only you knew / Body language / I'll never, never give up / Love bankrupt / When am I gonna find true love.
LP: 450621 1
MC: 450621 4
LP: PIR 25398

IT'S ALRIGHT WITH ME.
Tracks: / It's alright with me / My best was good enough / What'cha doing to me / Love is just a touch away / Love and learn / Deliver the funk / Come what may / You and me / Music is my way of life.
LP: EPC 83524

SPIRIT'S IN IT.
Tracks: / Spirit's in it / Here you come again / Love lives / I fell in love without warning / Boats against the current / Rockin' pneumonia & the boogie woogie flu / Family / Shoot him on sight / Over the rainbow.
LP: PIT 85117

WINNER IN YOU.
Tracks: / Oh people / On my own / Something special / Kiss away the pain / Twisted / You're mine tonight / Finally we're back together / Beat my heart like a drum / Sleep with me tonight / There's a winner in you (From the play "Pipes".y).
LP: MCF 3319

Laboa, Mikel

6.
LP: ELKAR 106

Labours Of Heracles,

LABOURS OF HERACLES, THE (Various artists).
Tracks: / Labours of Heracles, The: *Various artists* / Ion: *Various artists* / Phaethon: *Various artists*/ Jason and the Argonauts: *Various artists* / Opheus and Eurydice: *Various artists.*
MC: ANV 647

Labrish

LABRISH VOL.2 (Various artists).
LP: DSILP 002

LABRISH VOL.3 (Various artists).
LP: DS 1993

Labyrinth (film)

UNDERGROUND (See under Bowie, David).

Lacey, Marie

YOU'RE ENOUGH.
LP: SHARON 332

Lacey St.Blues Band

BLUES IN THE NIGHT.
LP: CP 2004

Lackey & Sweeney

JUNK STORE SONGS FOR SALE.
LP: VTS 23

Lacy, Steve

ANTHEM.
Tracks: / Number one / Prayer / J.J.'s jam / Prelude and anthem.
LP: PL 83079
MC: PK 83079

COMPANY 4 (Lacy, Steve/Derek Bailey).
LP: INCUS 26

DOOR, THE.
Tracks: / Door, The / Ugly beauty / Cliches / Forgetful / Blinks / Coming up / Breath, The / Virgin jungle.
LP: PL 83049
MC: PK 83049

HOCUS POCUS.
LP: TWI 683

HOT HOUSE (Lacy, Steve & Mal Waldron).
Tracks: / House party starting / Hot house / I'll keep loving you / Friday the 13th / Mistral breeze / Mooche, The / Petite fleur / Snake out / Retreat.
MC: PK 83098

LIVE IN BUDAPEST (Lacy, Steve & Steve Potts).
Tracks: / Prospectus / Gleam, The / Morning joy / Crust stands / Stand, The / Cliches.
LP: WW 011

MOMENTUM.
Tracks: / Bath, The / Momentum / Song, The.
LP: PL 83021

MOON.
LP: AFF 23

ONE FELL SWOOP (Lacy, Steve Quartet).
LP: SHLP 103

ONE UPMANSHIP (see under Waldron, Mal) (Lacy, Steve/Mal Waldron Quintet).

RAPS.
LP: AD 5004

STRAIGHT HORN OF STEVE LACY, THE.
LP: CS 9007

TRICKLES.
LP: BSR 008

TROUBLES (Lacy, Steve Quintet).
LP: SN 1002

Ladd, Cheryl

DANCE FOREVER.
Tracks: / Dance forever / Better days / Still awake / On the run / Teach me tonight / You're the only one I ever needed / Thunder in the distance / Missing you / Whatever would I do without you? / Rock'n'roll slave.
LP: EST 11927

Laddins

BOBBY JAY PRESENTS THE LADDINS.
LP: CENTRAL 5018

Ladd's Black Aces

LADD'S BLACK ACES 1921-2 VOLUME 1.
LP: FJ 102

LADD'S BLACK ACES 1922-3/1923-4 VOLS. 2 AND 3.
LP: FJ 111

LADD'S BLACK ACES VOL 2.
LP: FJ 106

Ladies Of Burlesque

LADIES OF BURLESQUE (Various artists).
LP: SH 2019

Ladoux, Chris

RODEO'S SINGING BRONCO RIDER.
LP: WRS 143

Lady Anne

BOSANOVA (see under Metro, Peter) (Lady Ann & Peter Metro).

Lady Be Good

LADY BE GOOD (Film soundtrack) (Various artists).
LP: HS 5010

LADY BE GOOD (Original London cast) (Various artists).
Tracks: / Fascinating rhythm: *Various artists* / Swiss maid: *Various artists* / lady be good: *Various artists*/ So am I: *Various artists* / Half of it dearie blues, The: *Various artists* / I'd rather Charleston: *Various* artists / Hang on to me: *Various artists* / After you who: *Various artists* / Night and day: *Various* artists / Puttin' on the ritz: *Various artists* / Crazy feet: *Various artists* / Flying down to Rio: *Various artists* / Music makes me: *Various artists* / Louisiana: *Various artists* / Not my girl: *Various artists.*
LP: WRCSH 124
MC: TC SH 124

Lady Flash

BEAUTIES IN THE NIGHT.
Tracks: / Thunderbolt / Street singin' / Never gonna let you get away / Green plant / Right now if you believe / Jumpin' at the woodside / Nowhere to run / Arms of Mary / Buried in the ruins of love / Upfront.
LP: 2394 171

Lady G

HALF MY AGE (See under Sanchez) (Lady G & Sanchez).

Lady Groove

MAGIC LADY.
LP: 6252 ML

Lady Hawke

LADY HAWKE (Film Soundtrack) (Various artists).
Tracks: / Main title: *Various artists* / Phillipe's escape: *Various artists* / Search for Phillipe, The: *Various* artists / Tavern fight: *Various artists* / Tavern fight (Navarre): *Various artists* / Phillipe describes Isabeau: *Various artists* / Navarre's ambush: *Various artists* / Chase, the fall and the transformation, The: *Various* artists / She was sad at first: *Various artists* / Navarre returns to Aquila: *Various artists* / Navarre's and Marquet's duel: *Various artists* / Marquet's death: *Various artists* / Bishop's death: *Various artists*/ End title: *Various artists.*
LP: 781 248-1

Lady In The Dark

LADY IN THE DARK Original cast recording (Various artists).
LP: AEI 1146

LADY IN THE DARK (Studio cast) (Various artists).
LP: COS 2390
MC: BT 2390

Lady In White

LADY IN WHITE (Film Soundtrack) (Various artists).
LP: 704.530

Lady Levi

LEGEND OF LADY LEVI, THE.
Tracks: / Looking for a dope beat / Oh Jenny / Levi's leisure / Rude boys / My lover lover / Legend of Lady Levi, The / Borrow man girl / Why do they fight / Not this generation / Reality.
LP: ZL 72752
MC: ZK 72752

Lady Sings The Blues

LADY SINGS THE BLUES (Original Stage Cast) (Various artists).
LP: BEAR 33
MC: BEARMC 33

Lady & The Tramp

LADY AND THE TRAMP.
MC: DIS 011

LADY AND THE TRAMP (Film soundtrack) (Various artists).
Tracks: / Lady: *Various artists* / What is a baby?: *Various artists* / La la lu: *Various artists* / Siamese cat song: *Various artists* / Bella notte: *Various artists* / Home sweet home: *Various artists* / He's a tramp: *Various artists* / Peace on earth: *Various artists.*
LP: REC 538
MC: ZCM 538
LP: WD 015
MC: WDC 015

LADY AND THE TRAMP (Various artists).
MLP: D 307
MC: D 22DC
LP: D 3917
LPPD: D 3103

Lady With Carnations

LADY WITH CARNATIONS (Geeson, Judy).
MC: CAB 007

Ladybirds

LADYBIRD COUNTRY.
Tracks: / Tracks of my tears / Good 'n' country / Good time Charlie's got the blues / It's a heartache / That'll be the day / Blue eyes crying in the rain / Here, there and everywhere / I'd buy you Chattanooga / Silver threads and golden needles / Don't it make my brown eyes blue / Half as much / Do you hear my heart beat.
LP: MOR 517

Ladykillers

LADYKILLERS (Various artists).
LP: GWD 90541
MC: GWC 90541

Ladysmith Black...

CLASSIC TRACKS (Ladysmith Black Mambazo).
MC: SHANC 43074

INALA (Ladysmith Black Mambazo).
Tracks: / Buya uz'ekhaya / That's why I choose you / Wahlala emnyango / Ngothandaza njalo / Kulomhlaba (thula) / Udla nge'nduku zabanye / Pauline / Isala kutshelwa / Kwashintsh's isthothobala / Uthando oluphelayo.
LP: SERLP 1
MC: SERC 1

INDUKU ZETHU (Ladysmith Black Mambazo).
Tracks: / Mangosuthu / Induku selhu / Vukani / Kubi ukungalaeli / Ithemba lakho / Isono sami sentombi / Ingwe idla ngamabla / Umzalwane / Ifa lobukhosana / Wayabimba mfana / Watatazela / Bakhuphuka izwe lanke.
LP: SERLP 3
MC: SERC 3
LP: ELP 2006

JOURNEY OF DREAMS (Ladysmith Black Mambazo).
Tracks: / Umusa kankulunkulu / Lindelani / Ukhalangami / Bhasobha / Hamba dompasi / Ungayoni into enhle / Amaphiko okundiza / Wayibambezeka / Ungakhowlwa rain / Amazing grace.
LP: WX 211
MC: WX 211 C

SHAKA ZULU (Ladysmith Black Mambazo).
Tracks: / Unomathemba / Hello my baby / At Golgotha / King of kings / Earth is never satisfied, The / How long / Home of the heroes / These are the guys / Rain, rain beautiful rain / Who were you talking to.
LP: WX 94
MC: WX 94 C

TWO WORLDS ONE HEART (Ladysmith Black Mambazo).
LP: 7599261251
MC: 7599261254

ULWANDLE OLUNCGWELE (Ladysmith Black Mambazo).
Tracks: / Izithembiso zenkosi / Limnandi izulu / Ulwandle oluncgwele / Sishuma yel'Ivangeli / Siphaum emnamlezweni / Nksoi yami ngabusinswa / Ayan qikazza amagwala / Baba no mama / Khayelihle khaya lami / Lifikile Ivangeli / Woza emthon jeni / Vukari sihambe zingelosi.
LP: SERLP 2
MC: SERC 2

UMTHOMBO WAMANZI (Ladysmith Black Mambazo).
LP: SERLP 6
MC: SERC 6
LP: SHAN 43055

Lafayette, General

IMPOSSIBLE TO DO (see under Martin, Linda).

KING OF THE BROKEN HEARTS.
LP: PZA 007A
MC: PZA 007C

LOVE IS A RHAPSODY.
Tracks: / Angel in blue / For the girl who couldn't find love / Melody for you / Florence serenade / Love is a rhapsody / Life is for loving / Lonely trumpet, The / Love you love me Aloha.
LP: PZA 001A
MC: PZA 001C

PIERROT.
LP: PZA 009A
MC: PZA 009C

Lafferty, Karen

BIRD IN A GOLDEN CAGE.
LP: HS 17

LIFE PAGES LOVE OF THE AGES.
Tracks: / Every life's a story / My life is yours / New Mexico song / Aegean / Jasmine / El Salvador / Apples of gold / Streets of Amsterdam / Timothy Tucker / Love of the ages.
LP: MM 0073
MC: TC MM 0073

SWEET COMMUNION.
LP: HS 37

Laffy, Gerry

MUSIC AND THE MAGIC.
LP: WKFMLP 152
MC: WKFMMC 152

MUSIC AND THE MAGIC (IMPORT).
LP: 106461
MC: 106464

Lafitte, George

MAINSTREAM AT MONTREUX (See under Coleman, Bill) (Lafitte, George & Bill Coleman).

Laggan

I AM THE COMMON MAN.
Tracks: / Work of the weavers / Railwayman / Old man's song / Band played waltzing Matilda, The / I am the common man / Man's a man, A / Men o'the North / Workers song / Rosa Luxembourg / Joe Hill.
LP: KLP 16

Lagoya, Alexandre

60 MINUTES OF MUSIC.
Tracks: / Asturia / Concierto de Aranjuez / Recuerdos de la alhambra / Mallorca / Canarios / Pavane / Romanesca / Etude Op.35 no.17 / Lobos prelude no.1 / Lobos prelude no.2.
MC: 4169124

Lagrene, Bireli

15.
Tracks: / Douce ambiance / Schwarze augen / Valse d'Alsace / Sweet Georgia Brown / Blues for Bireli / Mirage / Anduman / Solicarnosc / Micro / Autumn leaves / I can't give you anything but love.
LP: AN 1009
MC: ICT 1009

ACOUSTIC MOMENTS.
Tracks: / Made in France / Rhythm things / Claire Marie / All the things you are / Three views of a secret / Impressions / Stretch / Acoustic moments / Bass ballad / Metal earthquake.
LP: B1 95263
LP: 795 263 1

BIRELI SWING '81.
Tracks: / B.L. / Swing valse / Djangology / Bireli hi gogoro / Lady be good / Thundering noise / September

song / Schwarze augen / Carlos / Limehouse blues / Nuages / How high the moon.
LP: . . . . **JP 1009**

DJANGO'S MUSIC (See Peters, Mike) (Lagrene,Birelli/Mike Peters/Bob WilBerg).

DOWN IN TOWN.
Tracks: / Mitti / Berga / Melodie au Crepescule / Down in town / Paris / Reinsburgstrasse / Diminishing blackness / Rue de Pierre / Zum trotz / I can't get started.
LP: . . . . **AN 1010**
MC: . . . . **ICT 1010**

FOREIGN AFFAIRS.
Tracks: / Timothee / Josef / Rue de Pierre (part IV) (CD only.) / Jack Rabbit / Passing through the night / Rue de Pierre (part V) (CD only.) / Senegal / Rue de Pierre (part III) / St. Jean / I can't get started.
LP: **B1 90967**
MC: **TCB1 90967**

INFERNO.
Tracks: / Inferno / Rue de Pierre (part II) / Action / Rock it / Incertitude / Berga / Ballade / Hips.
LP: . . . . **BLJ 48016**
MC: . . . . **TCBLJ 48016**

ROUTES TO DJANGO.
Tracks: / Night and day / All of me / My melancholy baby.
LP: . . . . **AN 1002**

Lahiri, Bappi

SNAKE DANCE.
LP: . . . . **HYTLP 1001**
MC: . . . . **HYTMC 1001**

Lahm, David

REAL JAZZ FOR THE FOLKS WHO FEEL JAZZ.
LP: . . . . **PA 8027**

Lahost

BIG SLEEP, THE (2) (See Under Boucher, Judy).

Lai, Francis

FACE TO FACE WITH THE MIRROR (see under Simon, Carly).

FRANCIS LAI.
MC: . . . . **ZCGAS 736**

GREAT FILM THEMES.
Tracks: / Bilitis / Blue rose / Happy New Year / Seduction / Par le sang des autres / Live for life / Sur notre etoile / Les unes et les autres / Solitude / Love story (theme from) / Emotion / Love in the rain / Intimate moments / Man and a woman, A / African summer / La ronde / Smic smac smoc / Whitechapel.
LP: . . . . **PREC 5002**
MC: . . . . **ZPREC 5002**

MAN, A WOMAN, AND A LOVE STORY, A (Lai, Francis/his orchestra).
Tracks: / Man and a woman, A / Bonne annee / Emotion / Live for life / Thirteen days in France / Love in the rain / Intimate moments / La ronde / Solitude / Les unes et les autres / Love.
LP: . . . . **SPR 8532**
MC: . . . . **SPC 8532**

Laibach

BAPTISM, A.
2LP: . . . . **SUB 3300679**

LET IT BE.
Tracks: / Get back / Dig a pony / Across the universe / Dig it / I've got a feeling / Long and winding road, The / One after 909 / Maggie Mae / For you blue.
LP: . . . . **STUMM 58**
MC: . . . . **CSTUMM 58**

MACBETH.
Tracks: / Preludium / Agnus dei / Wutach schlucht / Die Zeit / Ohne geld / USA / 10.5.1941 / Expectans exprectavos / Coincidentia oppositorum / Wolf / Agnus dei.
LP: . . . . **STUMM 70**
MC: . . . . **STUMM 70 C**

NOVA AKROPOLA.
Tracks: / Four personen / Nova akropola / Krvava fruda-plodna zemja / Vojna poena / Ti ki izzivas.
LP: . . . . **BRED 67**

OCCUPIED EUROPE TOUR '85.
LP: . . . . **SER 08**

OPUS DEI.
Tracks: / Great seal, The / How the west was won / Trans-national / Opus dei / Leben-tod / F I A T / Geburt einer nation / Leben heist leben.
LP: . . . . **STUMM 44**

SYMPATHY FOR THE DEVIL (ALBUM).
LP: . . . . **STUMM 080**
MC: . . . . **CSTUMM 080**

Laibman, David

CLASSICAL RAGTIME GUITAR, THE.
LP: . . . . **ROUNDER 3040**

Laid Back

KEEP SMILING.
Tracks: / White horse / Elevator boy / Slow motion girl / So wie so / Sunshine reggae / High society / Don't be mean / Fly away / Walking in the sunshine.
LP: **925 058 1**

PLAY IT STRAIGHT.
LP: **9252881**

Laila, Runa

FROM EAST TO WEST (see D.C.S.) (Laila, Runa/D.C.S.).

SUPERUNA.
LP: . . . . **PEALP 11757**

Lain, Terry

BOW TIE BOOGIE.
LP: . . . . **LP 8807**

Laine, Cleo

BEAUTIFUL THING, A.
Tracks: / All in love is fair / Skip a long Sam / Send in the clowns / Least you can do is the best you can, The / They needed each other / I loves you Porgy / Until it's time for you to go / Life is a wheel / Summer knows, The / Beautiful thing, A.
LP: . . . . **SF 8398**

BEST FRIENDS (Laine, Cleo & John Williams).
Tracks: / Feelings / Time does fly / Killing me softly with his song / Before love went out of style / My day has started with you / Wave / Eleanor Rigby / Wake my love / If / Charms / Sleep now / He was beautiful.
LP: . . . . **RCALP 3016**
MC: . . . . **RCAK 3016**
LP: . . . . **MTA 201**
MC: . . . . **ZCMTA 201**
LP: . . . . **RS 1094**
MC: . . . . **PK 11755**

BORN ON A FRIDAY.
Tracks: / Come back to me / Colours ran, The / Sunday / Do you really want you / Birdsong (sambalaya) / Let me be the one / Living is easy / I think it's gonna rain today / Unlucky woman (born on a Friday) / Streets of London / Any place I hang my hat is home.
LP: . . . . **RS 1031**

CLEO.
2LP: . . . . **ADEP 37**

CLEO AT CARNEGIE.
Tracks: / Any place (Medley.) / I'm shadowing you / Crazy rhythm / Primrose colour blue / We are the music makers / You spotted snakes / Methuselah / When I was one and twenty / Sing me no song / Triboro' fair / You've got to do what you've got to do / He was beautiful / Turkish delight / Never let me go / I want to be happy.
2LP: . . . . **PL 71399**
MCSET: . . . . **PK 71399**
MCSET: . . . . **DARC 2C 2101**
2LP: . . . . **DARC 22101**

CLEO CLOSE UP.
Tracks: / Keep the faith / We could be flying / Loving isn't easy / I saw the light / Sun, the moon and I, The / I believe / Lookin' for another pure love / There's something sad / Wish you were here (I do miss you) / That's how heartaches are made / Wondering what to write / Show and tell.
LP: **LPL1 5026**

CLEO LAINE WITH JOHN DANKWORTH ORCHESTRA (Laine, Cleo & John Dankworth Orchestra).
LP: . . . . **MRS 502**
MC: . . . . **MRSC 502**

CLEO LIVE AT CARNEGIE.
Tracks: / I know where I'm going / Music / Wish you were here (I do miss you) / Gimme a pigfoot and a bottle of beer / You must believe in Spring / Perdido / Control yourself / Send in the clowns / Ridin' high / Bill / Big best shoes / Stop and smell the roses / Please don't talk about me when I'm gone.
2LP: . . . . **TOWDLP 18**
MC: . . . . **ZCTOWD 18**
2LP: **LPL1 5015**
MC: **LPK1 5015**
2LP: . . . . **ICSD 2002**

CLEO SINGS SONDHEIM.
Tracks: / Everybody says don't (from 'Anyone can whistle') / Losing my mind (from 'Follies') / Ah but underneath (from 'Follies') / I remember (from 'Evening primrose') / Liaisons (from 'A little night music') / You could drive a person crazy (from 'Company') / Not while I'm around (from 'Sweeney Todd') / Ladies who lunch, The (from 'Company') / Send in the clowns (from 'A little night music') / Little things you do together, The (from 'Company') / Anyone can whistle (from 'Anyone can whistle') / I'm calm (from 'A funny thing happened on the way to the Forum') / No one is alone (from 'Into the woods') / Miller's son, the (from 'A little night music') / Not a day goes by (from 'Merrily we roll along') / I'm still here (from 'Follies').
LP: . . . . **RL 87702**
MC: . . . . **RK 87702**

CLEO'S CHOICE.
LP: . . . . **GNPS 9024**

COMPACT MOMENTS (see under Warwick, Dionne) (Warwick, Dionne/ Roger Whittaker/Gilbert O'Sullivan/Cleo Lain).

EVENING WITH CLEO LAINE, AN.
2LP: . . . . **MRS 608**

FEELINGS (see under Williams, John) (Laine, Cleo & John Williams).

GONNA GET THROUGH.
Tracks: / One more night / When I need you / Just the way you are / On and on / I believe you / Gonna get through / I'll have to say I love you in a song / Wish / Let's have a quiet night in / Merchant song.
LP: . . . . **PL 12926**

HE WAS BEAUTIFUL (see under Williams, John) (Laine, Cleo & John Williams).

I AM A SONG.
Tracks: / I'm gonna sit right down and write myself ... / Early Autumn / Friendly persuasion / There is a time / Day when the world comes alive / I am a song / It might as well be Spring / Music / But not for me / Two part invention / Talk to me baby / Thieving boy / Hi-heel sneakers.
LP: . . . . **SF 8352**

IN CONCERT AT THE CARNEGIE.
2LP: . . . . **FEDD 1006**
MCSET: . . . . **CFEDD 1006**

IN RETROSPECT (Laine, Cleo & Johnny Dankworth).
Tracks: / Mood indigo / Stormy weather / My one and only love / St. Louis blues / Lady sings the blues / Mean to me / I'll get by / Love is here to stay / Early Autumn / T'aint what you do (it's the way that you do it) / Happiness is a thing called Joe / Hit the road to dreamland.
LPS: . . . . **MRS 501**

INCOMPARABLE CLEO LAINE, THE (Live at the Wavendon Festival).
Tracks: / Eleanor Rigby / Song / You spotted snakes / If we lived on top of a mountain / Papaito / Happiness is a thing called Joe / Control yourself / That certain feeling / Doctor David Mantle / To music / Go and catch a falling star / Lorelei / Perdido / It's a pity to say goodnight.
LP: . . . . **BLM 51006**

JAZZ FIRST (Laine, Cleo & Jean Luc Ponty).
MC: **813**

LET THE MUSIC TAKE YOU (see Williams, John) (Laine, Cleo & John Williams).

OFF THE RECORD WITH CLEO LAINE.
2LP: . . . . **FEDD 1003**
MCSET: . . . . **CFEDD 1003**

ONE MORE DAY.
Tracks: / Driving home / All the skinny schoolgirls / Tomboy / First love half light / Goodbye friend / Over the moon / Shall we get married? / Settling down / One more day / Move / Lovers and friends / Year is gone, The.
LP: . . . . **RSR 1009**
MC: . . . . **ZC RSR 1009**
LP: . . . . **SL 5198**
MC: . . . . **SLC 5198**

PLATINUM COLLECTION.
Tracks: / He was beautiful / If / Let's have a quiet night in / Send in the clowns / Let me be the one / Summer knows, The / Streets of London / Loving isn't easy / Killing me softly with his song / Music / All in love is fair / I believe / When I need you / Don't cry for me Argentina / I think it's going to rain today / You'll never walk alone / Feelings / Wish you were here / Eleanor Rigby / Just the way you are / Gonna get through / Sunday / Unlucky woman (is born on a Friday) / Until it's time for you to go.
MC: . . . . **ZCPLT 1007**
LP: . . . . **PLAT 1007**

PORTRAIT OF A SONG STYLIST.
Tracks: / On a clear day / I could write a book / Look of love, The / Come rain or come shine / Fascinating rhythm / I can dream, can't I / I cover the waterfront / I'm a dreamer, aren't we all / I got it bad and that ain't good / Talk about me when I'm gone / They say it's wonderful / St Louis blues / Lady sings the blues / Stormy weather.
LP: . . . . **HARLP 107**
MC: . . . . **HARMC 107**

RETURN TO CARNEGIE.
Tracks: / Blues in the night / How long / Streets of London / London pride / Direction / Company (medley) / Broadway baby / Being alive / Born on a Friday / One alone / I've got the music in me / Fascinating rhythm / Jazzman / By Strauss / I gotta right to sing the blues / It don't mean a thing / Playoff (I've got the music in me) / Be a child.
LP: . . . . **PL 12407**
MC: . . . . **PK 12407**

SHAKESPEARE AND ALL THAT JAZZ (Featuring the music of John Dankworth).
Tracks: / If music be the food of love / O mistress mine / Duet of sonnets / Winter (love's labours lost) / My love is as a fever (sonnet 1477) / It was a lover and his lass / Dunsinane blues / Take all my loves (sonnet 40) / Blow, blow thou winter wind / Shall I compare thee (sonnet 18) / Witches, fair and foul / Fear no more the heat o' the sun / Sigh no more, ladies / Complete works, The.
MC: . . . . **TCAFF 196**
LP: . . . . **AFF 196**

SMILIN' THROUGH (see Moore, Dudley/Cleo Laine) (Laine, Cleo & Dudley Moore).

SOMETIMES WHEN WE TOUCH (Laine, Cleo & James Galway).
Tracks: / Drifting dreaming / Sometimes when we touch / Play it again Sam / Skylark / How, where, when? / Fluter's ball, The / Consuelo's love theme / Keep loving me / Anyone can whistle / Still was the night / Lo, hear the gentle lark / Like a sad song.
LP: . . . . **NL 70007**
MC: . . . . **NK 70007**
LP: . . . . **PL 25296**

SOMETIMES WHEN WE TOUCH (SINGLE) (see under Galway, James) (Laine, Cleo & James Galway).

SPOTLIGHT ON CLEO LAINE.
Tracks: / I want to be happy / I think of you / I can dream can't I / I've got my love to keep me warm / I got it bad and that ain't good / I'm a dreamer, aren't we all? / Popular song / I'm just wild about Harry / On a slow boat to China / Perdido / They say it's wonderful / If we lived on top of a mountain / Peel me a grape / Song without words / Fascinating rhythm / Oh, lady be good / Little boat / I cover the waterfront / Bidin' my time / Come rain or come shine / Lines to Ralph Hodgeson, Esquire / Ridin' high / Woman talk / I could write a book / Second time around, The / On a clear day / Complete works, The / Please don't talk about me when I'm gone.
2LP: **6625 008**

THEMES.
MC: . . . . **FEDC 2000**

THIS IS CLEO LAINE.
Tracks: / Feel the warm / Make it with you / From both sides now / Somethings wrong / Traces / Can it be true? / Slow motion / Stop and smell the roses / Rainy day man / Good bad but beautiful / Day by day / Prepare ye the way of the Lord / Don't talk now.
LP: . . . . **THIS 31**

UNFORGETTABLE CLEO LAINE.
Tracks: / Something's gotta give / Unforgettable / Big best shoes / All of you / Too late now / I'll remember April / Hand-me-down love / I'm putting all my eggs in one basket / Teach me tonight / Young at heart / Jeepers creepers / He needs me / Summer is a comin' in / April in Paris / I'm beginning to see the light / They were right.
LP: . . . . **PYL 6028**
MC: . . . . **PYM 6028**

UNFORGETTABLE: CLEO LAINE (16 Golden Classics).
Tracks: / He was beautiful (With John Williams. A lyric version of 'Cavatina'.) / People / Aquarius / Somewhere / Killing me softly with his song (With John Williams.) / Send in the clowns / If (With John Williams.) / Don't cry for me Argentina / Just the way you are / Streets of London / When I need you / Let's have a quiet night in / Eleanor Rigby (With John Williams.) / I believe / You'll never walk alone / Feelings (With John Williams.).
LP: . . . . **UNLP 008**
MC: . . . . **UNMC 008**

WERELD SUCCESSEN (see under Williams, John) (Laine, Cleo & John Williams).

WOMAN TO WOMAN.
LP: . . . . **RL 87999**
MC: . . . . **RK 87999**

WORD SONGS.

Tracks: / All the world's a stage / If music be the food of love / You spotted snakes / Winter, when icicles hang by the wall / Fear no more the heat o' the sun / It was a lover and his lass / Sigh no more, ladies / Dunsinane blues / When that I was a little boy / Shall I compare thee to a summer's day / Blow, blow, thou winter wind / O mistress mine, where you are roaming / Take all my loves / My love is as a fever / Who is Sylvia / Compleat works / Our revels now are ended / Lines to Ralph Hodgeson Esquire / Goe, and catche a falling starre / Bread and butter / Dr. David Mantle / Advice to a girl / O tell me the truth about love / In Tenebris 1 / Sun and fun / song / English teeth / Viva sweet love / Mungojerrie and rumpelteazer / Thieving boy / Sing me no song.
2LP: . . . . RL 25176
MC: . . . . RK 25176

Laine, Denny

HOLLYDAYS.
Tracks: / Moondreams / Rave on / Heartbeat / I'm gonna love you too / Fool's paradise / Lonesome tears / It's so easy / Listen to me / Look at me / Take your time / I'm looking for someone to love.
LP: . . . . EMA 781

HOMETOWN GIRLS.
Tracks: / Cruisin' / Foggy morning / Mistral / Stay away / Home town girl / Red sky / Twist of fate / Street / Blue night.
LP: . . . . PTLS 1080
MC: . . . . PTLC 1080

JAPANESE TEARS.
Tracks: / Japanese tears / Dangerzone / Clock on the wall / Send me the heart / Go now / Same mistakes / Silver / Say you don't mind / Somebody ought to know the way / Lover's light / Guess I'm only fooling / Nothing to go by / I would only smile / Weep for love.
LP: . . . . SCRL 5001

LONELY ROAD.
Tracks: / Land of peace / Eyes of a child / Success / First day in London / Lonely road / True to me / Without your love / If I tried / Burnin' bridges / Money talks / What can I do without you? / Fly with the dove / Black sheep / Peace must come again.
LP: . . . . PTLS 1092

MASTER SUITE.
Tracks: / Loving touch / Blue musician, The / Rory's theme / La Manzanera / Campfire / Read the cards / Thin air, The / Mountain pass / Highlands, The / Moors and Christmas / Old man loving / Diego.
LP: . . . . THBL 058

WEEP FOR LOVE.
Tracks: / Say you don't mind / Somebody ought to know the way / Guess I'm only fooling / Nothing to go by / I would only smile / Weep for love / Go now / Send me the heart / Danger zone / Lover's light / Clock on the wall / Silver / Japanese tears.
LP: . . . . PRCV 135
MC: . . . . TCPRCV 135

WINGS ON MY FEET.
Tracks: / Wings on my feet / It's never too late / Kick the ball / Portrait / Castles in the air / Roll the dice / Lucy lullaby / No sleep / Tao Princess / It's never too late / Caribbean sun / Blushing bride / Spacetrain.
LP: . . . . PTLS 1087

Laine, Frankie

21 GREATEST HITS.
Tracks: / Woman in love, A / Jealousy / High noon / On the sunny side of the street / Cool water / Kids last fight, The / You gave me a mountain / Rawhide / Moonlight gambler / Two loves have I / Jezebel / That's my desire / Cry of the wild goose / I believe / We'll be together / That lucky old sun / Shine / Your cheatin' heart / Memories / Swamp girl / Mule train.
LP: . . . . SPWM 4
MC: . . . . CSWM 4

1947: FRANKIE LAINE (Laine, Frankie with Carl Fischer & Orch.).
LP: . . . . HSR 198
LP: . . . . HSR 216

ALL OF ME.
Tracks: / Old fashioned love / All of me / Coquette / That's my desire / Georgia on my mind / Rosetta / Hold me / Singing the blues / I wish you were jealous of me / You can depend on me.
LP: . . . . BDL 1035
MC: . . . . AJKL 1035

ALL TIME HITS.
Tracks: / High noon / I believe / Answer me / Granada / Jealousy / Rain, rain, rain / Cool water / Strange lady in town / Hummingbird / Sixteen tons / Woman in love, A / Moonlight gambler / Cry of the wild goose / Mule train / Jezebel / Wheel of fortune / Rose, Rose I love you / Rawhide / Don't fence me in (CD only) / There must be a reason (CD only).
MC: . . . . TCMFP 5907

AMERICAN LEGEND.
MC: 40 31599

AMERICAN LEGENDS VOL.1 (see under American legends) (Laine, Frankie/Guy Mitchell/Johnny Ray).

BEST OF FRANKIE LAINE.
Tracks: / I believe / Mule train / Jezebel / High noon / Answer me.
LP: 1A 222-58228
MC: 1A 022 58228
MC: 16-16

BING CROSBY WITH MAURICE CHEVALIER & FRANKIE LAINE (see Crosby, Bing) (Laine, Frankie/Bing Crosby/Maurice Chevalier).

COUNTRY STORE: FRANKIE LAINE.
Tracks: / Rawhide / Hanging tree, The / Your cheatin' heart / Cry of the wild goose / Call of the wind / Mule train / Sixteen tons / Bowie knife / On the trail / Cool water / Wanted man / 3.10 to Yuma, The / North to Alaska / Gunfight at the OK Corral / Along the Navajo trail / City boy / High noon / Tumbling tumbleweeds.
LP: . . . . CST 43
MC: . . . . CSTK 43

FRANKIE LAINE.
Tracks: / High noon / Jezebel / Answer me / Cool water / Blowing wild / That lucky old sun / That's my desire / Granada / Your cheatin' heart / Jealousy.
LP: 022 58228
MC: 222 58228
LP: . . . . SPR 8538
MC: . . . . SPC 8538

FRANKIE LAINE.
MCSET: . . . . DTO 10272

GOLDEN GREATS: FRANKIE LAINE.
Tracks: / Memories in gold / Jealousy / High noon / On the sunny side of the street / That's my desire / Cool water / Woman in love / Georgia on my mind / Moonlight gambler / Jezebel / Mule train / I believe / Your cheatin' heart / That lucky old sun / Shine / We'll be together again.
LP: 2486 263
MC: 3196 093

GOLDEN MEMORIES.
LP: 2371 472

GOLDEN YEARS, THE.
Tracks: / That's my desire / Mule train / All of me / By the river Sainte Marie / Cry of the wild goose / I'm in the mood for love / That lucky old sun / Mam'selle / Kiss me again / Georgia on my mind / On the sunny side of the street / S.H.I.N.E..
LP: . . . . TIME 12
MC: . . . . TIMEC 12

HELL BENT FOR LEATHER.
LP: . . . . BBL 7468

HIS GREATEST HITS.
Tracks: / I believe / Moonlight gambler / Jealousy / Rain, rain, rain / Sixteen tons / Cry of the wild goose / Granada / Don't fence me in / Rose, Rose I love you / Answer me / Woman in love / Wheel of fortune / Rawhide / Still runs cool water / Strange lady in town / Mule train / Hummingbird / Jezebel / There must be a reason / High noon.
LP: . . . . WW 2014
MC: . . . . WW 20144

MEMORIES IN GOLD.
Tracks: / Memories in gold / Jealousy / High noon / On the sunny side of the street / Mule train / Cool water / Kid's last fight, The / Woman in love, A / Georgia on my mind / Moonlight gambler / You gave me a mountain / Jezebel / That's my desire / Cry of the wild goose / I believe / Your cheatin' heart / Rawhide / That lucky old sun / Shine / We'll be together again.
LP: . . . . PREC 5004
MC: . . . . ZPREC 5004

MY FAVOURITES.
LP: . . . . ADAH 448
MC: . . . . ADAHC 448

PORTRAIT OF A SONG STYLIST.
Tracks: / Blue moon / Side by side / Body and soul / Too marvellous for words / Try a little tenderness / Cottage of sale, A / Answer me / I get along without you very well / I cover the waterfront / Woman in love / We just couldn't say goodbye / Lover come back to me / I'm gonna live 'til I die / September in the rain / Second honeymoon / Touch of your lips, The / On the road to Mandalay.
LP: . . . . HARLP 102
MC: . . . . HARMC 102

RAWHIDE.
Tracks: / Rawhide / Mule train / Moonlight gambler / I believe / Don't fence me in / Strange lady in town / Rose, Rose I love you / There must be a reason / Answer me / Jezebel / High noon / Jealousy / Sixteen tons / Cool water / Wheel of fortune / Rain, rain, rain / Granada / Cry of the wild goose.
LP: . . . . SHLP 148
MC: . . . . SHTC 148

SIXTEEN EVERGREENS.
LP: . . . . SM 3957
MC: . . . . MC 3957

SONGBOOK.
LPS: . . . . ALBUM 53
MCSET: . . . . CASSETTE 53

SUGARBUSH (See under Day, Doris) (Day, Doris & Frankie Laine).

UNCOLLECTED, THE.
LP: . . . . HUK 198

VERY BEST OF FRANKIE LAINE, THE.
Tracks: / Rawhide / Moonlight gambler / High noon / Mule train / Jezebel / I believe.
LP: . . . . FUN 9057
MC: . . . . FUNC 9057
LP: . . . . PR 5032

WORLD OF FRANKIE LAINE, THE.
MC: 4CRTL 2071

Laing, John Band

BRICKS AND BRASS.
Tracks: / Bishop's blaize / Every time we say goodbye / I'm beginning to see the light / I fall in love too easily / Lisa / Romance de l'amour / Tritsch tratsch polka / Snowman, The / Post horn galop / Change partners / Sophisticated lady / Satin doll / Waltzes of love medley.
LP: . . . . PRL 030D
MC: . . . . CPRL 030D

Laing, Robin

EDINBURGH SKYLINE.
Tracks: / Edinburgh skyline / Burke and hare / Love is born / Union canal, The / Leaving today / Icarus / Ulysses / Isle of Eigg / Day by day / Andrew Lammie / Spring song / Passing time.
LP: . . . . TRAX 021
MC: . . . . CTRAX 021

Laing, Shona

SOUTH.
Tracks: / Drive baby drive / Caught / Neat and tidy / Migrant and the refugee, The / Soviet snow / (Glad I'm) not a Kennedy / Your reputation / Dockyard on a river / Highway warriors / South.
LP: . . . . VOZ 2009
LP: . . . . V 2486
MC: . . . . TCV 2486

TIED TO THE TRACKS.
Tracks: / Don't tell me / Touch and go / By the night / Overboard / Whistling waltzes / Money is the measure / Timmy's goin' down / Ex-best friend / No fixed abode / Getaway.
LP: . . . . EMC 3360

Laird, Skee

LOVELY LADY WITH A LOVELY VOICE.
MC: . . . . NEVC 131

SKEE LAIRD SINGS COOL COUNTRY.
LP: . . . . NEVLP 131

Laity, Pete

RASH ADVENTURE, A.
Tracks: / Outward bound / Junction XIV / Star of the County Down / CV6 5FX / Photophobia / In flight / Autumn / Ride of the Queen / There was you / Arrival.
LP: . . . . OBL 004

TRUE, DARE, KISS OR PROMISE.
Tracks: / Over the rooftops / Moondance / Girl on a boat / For the love of a lady / Black stallion / Flights of fancy / Where will you dream tonight / Making up for lost time / Besyas an Pystrior / Lost in wonder.
LP: . . . . OBL 006

Lakatos, Sandor

MASTER OF HUNGARIAN GYPSY MUSIC.
LP: . . . . SLPD 10218

Lake

PARADISE ISLAND.
Tracks: / Into the night / Glad to be here / Crystal eyes / Paradise way / Hopeless love / One way song / Hard road / Final curtain.
LP: . . . . CBS 83480

Lake, Greg

GREG LAKE.
Tracks: / Nuclear attack / Love you too much / It hurts / Black and blue / Retribution drive / Long goodbye / Lie, The / Someone / Let me love you once before you go / For those who dare.
LP: . . . . CHR 1357
MC: . . . . ZCHR 1357

MANOEUVRES.
Tracks: / Manoeuvres / Too young to love / Paralysed / Woman like you, A / I don't wanna lose your love / Tonight / It's you, you've gotta believe / Famous last words / Slave to love / Haunted / I don't know why I still love you.
LP: . . . . CHR 1392
MC: . . . . ZCHR 1392

Lake, Oliver

CLEVONT FITZHUBERT (Lake, Oliver Quertet).
LP: . . . . BSR 0054

CONCERT A SPACE (Lake, Oliver & Joseph Bowie).
LP: 2010

HOLDING TOGETHER.
LP: . . . . BSR 009

JUMP UP.
LP: . . . . GR 8106

OTHERSIDE.
LP: 188 901 1
MC: 188901 4

PLUG IT (Lake,Oliver and Jump Up).
Tracks: / Trickle down theory / Plug it / Tone clone / Breath of life / Go for it / Be the one / Stratosphere / No more wars.
LP: . . . . GR 8206

Lake, Steve

MURDER VIOLENCE SEX DIVORCE.
LP: . . . . NSB 007

SO CRUEL.
LP: . . . . BIAS 052

Lake, Tim

SAME OLD ROADSIDE INN.
LP: . . . . ROUNDER 3028

Lakeland Love

LAKELAND LOVE, A (see under Morley, Adele) (Morley, Adele).

Lakeman, Geoff

BUSHES AND BRIARS (Lakeman, Geoff/Barry Skinner).
Tracks: / Cheerful 'arn, The / Bushes and briars / Dancers of Stanton Drew, The / Duxom lass, The / Jack in the green / Shepton Mallet hornpipe / Dorset four-hand reel / Admiral Benbow / Bread and fishes / Richard of Taunton Dene / Stone-cracker John / Sailor and the string, The / Bonapartes lamentation / Wassailing song, The.
LP: . . . . FE 011

Lakeside

FANTASTIC VOYAGE.
Tracks: / Fantastic voyage / Your love is on the one / I need you / Strung out / Say yes / Eveready man / I love everything you do.
LP: . . . . SOLA 6

KEEP ON MOVING STRAIGHT AHEAD.
Tracks: / Keep on moving straight ahead / It's you / Be my lady / It's got to be love / We want you / BAck together again / Anything for you / All for you.
LP: . . . . SOLA 11
LP: . . . . RCA 11

YOUR WISH IS MY COMMAND.
Tracks: / Your wish is my command / Songwriter / Urban man / I'll be standing by / I want to hold your hand / Something about that woman.
LP: . . . . K 52340

Lamarche, Susan

SUSAN LAMARCHE & WALDOS GUTBUCKET SYNCOPATORS (Lamarche, Susan & Waldos Gutbucket).
LP: . . . . SOS 1032

Lamb, Annabel

BRIDES.
Tracks: / Chase across the world / Different drum / Country of love / Nada (trick of the light) / Baby baby / Come to me / Sweet Jane / Don't talk about love / Simple truth, The / In the land of dreamy dreams.
LP: . . . . PL 71431
MC: . . . . PK 71431

FLAME, THE.
Tracks: / Sacraments of love / Hands of the hunter / Weapon of love / Dream boy / What the eyes sees / Things that I fear / Flame / So lucky in bed / Inside of my head / Talking to me.
LP: . . . . AMLX 68564

ONCE BITTEN.
Tracks: / Once bitten / Take me in your arms / Heartland / Hold fast / Backwards through the looking glass / Dividing the spoils of love / Red for danger / Snake pliskin / Missing / No cure.
LP: . . . . AMLH 68555

Lamb, Charlotte

SILKEN TRAP, THE (Seaward, Lesley).
MC: . . . . **PMB 020**

Lamb II

DANCING IN JERUSALEM.
MC: . . . . **MMC 0215**

Lamb, Mary

TALES FROM SHAKESPEARE (Harris, Julie).
MC: **1469**

Lamb, Natalie

NATALIE LAMB, SAMMY PRICE & THE BLUES (Lamb, Natalie, Sammy Price & The Blues).
LP: . . . . **GHB 84**

Lamb, Paul

PAUL LAMB AND THE KING SNAKES (Lamb, Paul & The King Snakes).
Tracks: / Hyping woman / Mother in law blues / Don't lose your cool / Fattening frogs for snakes / Everyday (I have the blues) / I got a girl / I don't need you / I was a fool / Bloody murder / Good rockin' tonight.
LP: . . . . **BLUH 011**
MC: . . . . **BLUHC 011**

Lambe, Jeanie

JEANIE LAMBE.
LP: . . . . **FLY 215**

JEANIE LAMBE SINGS BLUES AND ALL THAT JAZZ.
Tracks: / Aunt Hagar's blues / Rockin' chair / Doctor Jazz / Chicago / Beale Street blues / Do you know what it means to miss New Orleans? / Basin Street blues / Ding dong daddy.
LP: . . . . **ZR 1019**

MIDNIGHT SUN, THE (Lambe, Jeanie & Danny Moss Quartet).
Tracks: / Time's a wastin' / Let's do it / Every time / Body and soul / God bless the child / Owl and the pussycat, The / Don't be that way / Midnight sun / Dearly beloved / All of you / Satin doll / Willow weep for me.
LP: . . . . **ZR 1023**

MY MAN (Lambe, Jeanie & Danny Moss Quartet).
Tracks: / Blues in the night / It had to be you / I've got you under my skin / My man / You & I / If you go away / Angel eyes / Time after time / I wish I were in love again / I've got a crush on you / Lazy afternoon.
LP: . . . . **ZR 1028**

Lambert, Constant

CONSTANT LAMBERT (Various artists).
LP: . . . . **EH 2913431**
MC: . . . . **EH 2913434**

Lambert, Dave

BIRDLAND (See under Rich, Buddy) (Lambert, Dave Singers/ Rich, Buddy Quintet).

Lambert, Donald

CLASSICS IN STRIDE.
LP: . . . . **PUMPKIN 110**

HARLEM STRIDE CLASSICS 1960-62.
LP: . . . . **PUMPKIN 104**

PIANO GIANT-STRIDE.
LP: . . . . **JCE 59**

Lambert, Franz

56 HOLIDAY HITS.
2LP: **6626020**
MCSET: **7598020**

FRANZ LAMBERT.
LP: **6 25225**
MC: **425225**

GREATEST HITS: FRANZ LAMBERT.
LP: **6449 055**
MC: **7143 055**

HAPPY ORGAN.
Tracks: / Super trouper / Biscaya / Duentschuldige,i kenn'di / Alone again (naturally) / You and me / Sailing / Song for Guy / Lieber Gott / One of us / Summer roses / Guilty / Oh Julie / We kill the world / My Bonnie.
MC: **4.26633**

HELLO, AMERICA.
Tracks: / There's no business like show business / I can't stop loving you / Strangers in the night / Delilah / High noon / Moon river / Up where we belong / Rock around the clock / Red river rock / This old house / Prelude / Michael, row the boat ashore / He's got the whole world in His hand / Battle of Jericho, The / Glory halleluja / Ring of fire / Wand'rin' star / San Antonio rose / Detroit City / Jesus Christ Superstar / West Side story / Hello, Dolly / Wunderbar / Denver clan / Dallas / Deep in the heart of Texas / Too fat polka / Under the double eagle.
LP: **6.25576**
MC: **425576**

HIGHLIGHTS VOL.1.
Tracks: / Woman in love / Bilitis / Guilty / Sailing / Alone again / Supertrouper / You and me / Song for Guy / Lady / Yesterday / Morning melody / Oh what a wonderful day.
LP: **AS6 24625**
MC: **CT4 24625**

IT'S PARTY TIME.
Tracks: / Comment ca va / Vamos a la playa / Flashdance... what a feeling / Jenseits von Eden / Sunshine reggae / Azzuro / Paloma blanca / Tranen lugen nicht / Uber sieben brucken (Over seven bridges) / I'd love you to want me / One way wind / Charly / Mississippi / etc.
MC: **4.26635**

KING OF HAMMOND.
2LP: **6626 020**
MCSET: **7598 020**

LA PARRANDA PARTY.
LP: . . . . **IC 056 45401**

LATIN POP HITS.
Tracks: / Cavaguinho / Girls from Parmaribo / La flauto del Indio / Cumana / Taka takata / Jamaica farewell / La parranda / Mas que nada / Toca toca / Girl from Ipanema / Adio / At the Copa - Copacabana / La cucaracha / Adelita.
LP: . . . . **NTS 184**

LET'S HAVE A PARTY.
LP: **6 28182**

POP ORGAN HIT PARADE-40 SUPER HITS.
Tracks: / Night fever / Rivers of Babylon / I can't stand the rain / Im wagon vor mir / Quando, quando, quando / Lay love on you / One for you, one for me / If you belong to me / Love me baby / Dancing in the city / La bamba / You're the one that I want / Love is in the air / Mull of Kintyre / Smurff song / Yes sir, I can boogie / Car wash.
LP: . . . . **NTS 164**

SUPER PARTY.
LP: **6.24548**
MC: **CW4 24548**

SUPERGOLD.
2LP: . . . . **IC 134 45701/02**

SYMPHONIE D'AMOUR.
LP: **6.25500**
MC: **CW4 25500**

TOP HITS.
Tracks: / Ein bisschen Frieden / Du bist mein erster Gedanke Weil / Wem / Head over heels / Ole Espana / Eviva Jupp / Biscaya / Du entschuldige-i kenn' di / Dich zu lieben / Japanese boy / Night after night / Lieber Gott / One of us / Oh Julie / We kill the world / My Bonnie / Sharazon / Ich wunsch' dir die holle auf Erden / Summer roses / Cambodia / Flash in the night / El cigarron / Aiko aiko / Polonaise blankenese / Der papa wird's schon richten / Hale hey Louise.
LP: **AS6 25044**
MC: **CT4 25044**

TOP HITS 2.
LP: **AS6.24947**
MC: **CT4 24947**

Lambert, Hendricks...

AT NEWPORT '63 (Lambert/Hendricks/ Bavan).
LP: . . . . **PL 3531**

EVERYBODY'S BOPPIN' (Lambert, Hendricks & Annie Ross).
LP: **4651991**
MC: **4651994**

HAVIN' A BALL AT THE VILLAGE GATE (Lambert/Hendricks/Bavan).
LP: . . . . **NL 89580**

SING A SONG OF BASIE (Lambert, Hendricks & Annie Ross).
Tracks: / Everyday / It's sand man / Two for the blues / One o'clock jump / Little pony / Down for double / Fiesta in blue / Down for the Count / Blues backstage / Avenue C.
LP: . . . . **JAS 6**
MC: . . . . **JAS C6**

SWINGERS, THE (Lambert, Hendricks & Annie Ross).
Tracks: / Airegin / Babe's blues / Dark clouds / Jackie / Swingin' 'til the girls come home / Four / Little niles / Where / Now's the time / Love makes the world go round / Clap hands here comes Charlie.
LP: . . . . **AFF 131**

Lambrettas

AMBIENCE.
Tracks: / Good times / Written in neon / Total strangers / Concrete and steel / Dancing in the dark / Decent town / Ambience / Men in blue / I want to tell you / Someone talking.
LP: . . . . **TRAIN 14**

BEAT BOYS IN THE JET AGE.
Tracks: / Da-a-a-ance / Cortina Mk.II / London calling / Poison ivy / Leap before you look / Beat boys in the jet age / Page three / Living for today / Watch out I'm back / Don't push me / Runaround / Face to face.
LP: . . . . **TRAIN 10**

KICK START.
LP: . . . . **RAZ 14**

Lambs On The Green

SONGS FROM COUNTY CLARE.
LP: **12TS 369**

Lamey, Bill

BILL LAMEY.
LP: . . . . **SHAN 14002**

Lammerhirt, Werner

ROLL ON RIVER.
LP: . . . . **FF 4006**

Lamond, Don

DON LAMOND & HIS BIG BAND EXTRAORDINARY.
Tracks: / Early Autumn / Four brothers / Apple honey / Apple valley / Home folks / Dear John / What am I here for? / Here's that rainy day / Yesterday I heard the rain / Cherie Amour / Uptight.
LP: . . . . **PRO 7067**

EXTRAORDINARY (Lamond, Don & His Big Swing Band).
LP: . . . . **SLP 8071**

Lamont, Duncan

BLUES IN THE NIGHT (Lamont, Duncan Quartet).
LP: . . . . **LDC 4001**

SUMMER SOUNDS.
Tracks: / Girl from Ipanema / Quiet nights of quiet stars / Shadow of your smile / Call me / Felicidade / Destination love / Wave / My cherie amour / Mas que nada / Fool on the hill / Desafinado / Un homme et une femme / Meditation / How insensitive / Summer samba / Our day will come / Look of love, The / We've only just begun / Gentle one / Alone again.
MC: . . . . **HR 8111**
MC: . . . . **HR 4181114**

Lamour, Dorothy

DOROTHY LAMOUR COLLECTION (Her Golden Greats).
Tracks: / Lovely Hula hands / Paradise / It had to be you / Moon of Manakoora / Too romantic / Your kiss / Moon over Burma / Mexican magic / You took the words... / Thanks for the memory / Palms of Paradise / I gotta right to sing the blues / True confession / That sentimental sandwich / Sweet potato piper / Moon and the willow tree, The / This is the beginning of the end / Strange enchantment.
LP: . . . . **DVLP 2108**
MC: . . . . **DVMC 2108**

ON A TROPICAL NIGHT.
LP: . . . . **CMS 009**
MC: . . . . **CMSC 009**

L'Amourder

RITUAL.
LP: . . . . **AFTER 3**

Lan Doky, Niels

DAYBREAK.
Tracks: / All or nothing at all / Why / Final decision / Jet lag / Natural / Daybreak.
LP: . . . . **SLP 4160**

HERE OR THERE (Lan Doky, Niels Trio).
LP: . . . . **SLP 4117**

TARGET, THE (Lan Doky, Niels Trio).
LP: . . . . **SLP 4140**

TRUTH, THE (Live at Montmartre) (Lan Doky, Niels Trio).
LP: . . . . **SLP 4144**

Lanadrid

SISTER ALLEY.
Tracks: / Wanna be your drug / Watch out / Is it love / Hell rider / Sister alley.
LP: . . . . **NUK 146**

Lancashire Fayre

LANCASHIRE FAYRE.
Tracks: / Calling on / Up in the morning / Ballad of Robert Attridge, The / Owdham / Pennine magic / Old Pendle / Ballad of a working man / From the north / Misty moisty / Witching hour / Three foot seam / King, The / Reflections / Tata pie / Sir Loin, The.
LP: . . . . **FHR 113**

NOT EASILY FORGOTTEN.
Tracks: / Best of order / Windhover / Not easily forgotten / Fleetwood fishermen / Hop, hop, hop / Lancashire lad / Smuggler / Lancashire scenes / Dawn brigade / John Willie's ferret / Ellison's tenement / Weaver / Bread and fishes / Lancashire's pride.
LP: . . . . **FE 045**

Lancashire Schools

LANCASHIRE SCHOOLS SYMPHONY ORCHESTRA (Lancashire Schools Symphony Orchestra).
Tracks: / Overture: Egmont (Opus 84) / Pavane pour une infante defunte (Pavane for a dead child) / Danse macabre (Opus 40) / Prelude and air (Opus 40) / Scherzo and allegro con fuoco (From Symphony no. 4 in F minor).
LP: . . . . **APS 362**

Lance, Major

LIVE AT HINKLEY.
LP: . . . . **TORCHLP 1**

LIVE AT THE TORCH.
Tracks: / Hey hey / I wanna make up / My girl / Um, um, um, um, um, um / Beat, The / Ain't no soul / Investigate / Monkey time.
LP: . . . . **CLP 523**

MONKEY TIME.
Tracks: / Matador, The / Um, um, um, um, um, um.
LP: . . . . **ED 124**

Lancelot, James

CHORAL SHOWCASE, A (see under Winchester Cathedral) (Lancelot, James/Winchester Cathedral Choir).

Land Before Time

LAND BEFORE TIME (Film Soundtrack) (Various artists).
LP: . . . . **MCA 6266**
MC: . . . . **MCAC 6266**

Land, Harold

FOX, THE.
LP: . . . . **COP 016**

GROOVEYARD.
LP: . . . . **CLPS 7550**

HAROLD IN THE LAND OF JAZZ.
Tracks: / Speak low / Delirium / You don't know what love is / Nieta / Grooveyard / Lydia's lament / Smack up.
LP: . . . . **COP 008**

TAKE AIM.
Tracks: / As you like it / Take aim / Land of peace / Refletions / Blue Nellie / You're my thrill.
LP: . . . . **LBR 1038**

Land, Nicholas

CLASSICS, THE VOL. I.
MC: . . . . **C 137**

NIGHT ECHOES.
MC: . . . . **C 134**

SHIMMERING MOON.
MC: . . . . **C 133**

Land Of Oz

LAND OF OZ, THE (see Baum, L. Frank) (Bolger, Ray).

Land O'Heart's Desire

LAND O'HEART'S DESIRE (Various artists).
MC: . . . . **KE 77008**

Landauer/Rawicz

MAGIC PIANOS OF RAWICZ & LANDAUER (see Rawicz/Landauer).

Lande

SKYLIGHT (Lande/Samuels/ McCandless).
LP: . . . . **ECM 1208**

Lande, Vidar

RINGING STRINGS (FIDDLE MUSIC OF NORWAY) (see under Buen, Hauk) (Lande, Vidar/Hauk Buen/Tom Anderson/Knut Buen).

Landlord (Film)

LANDLORD (Film Soundtrack) (Various artists).
Tracks: / Brand new day: *Various artists* / Landlord: *Various artists* / Car commercial: *Various artists*/ Walter G's boogaloo: *Various artists* / Croquet game: *Various artists* / Let me love you: *Various artists*/ Lainie's theme: *Various artists* / Rent party: *Various artists* / Elgar's fantasy: *Various artists*/ Love theme: *Various artists* / Soul hoedown: *Various artists* / Doin' me dirty: *Various artists* / Brand new day: *Various artists* / Axe: *Various artists* / God bless the children: *Various artists.*
LP: . . . . **UAS 29120**

Landreneau, Adam

CAJUN SOLE (Landreneau, Adam & Cyp).
LP: **8001**

Landry, Art

1924-1927 (Landry, Art & His Orchestra).
MC: **049**

Land's End

LAND'S END (Various artists).
MC: **T33 4**

Landscape

FROM THE TEA ROOMS OF MARS... (To the Hell Holes of Uranus).
Tracks: / European man / Shake the West awake / Computer person / Alpine tragedy / Sisters / Face of the 80's / New religion / Einstein a go go / Norman Bates / Doll's house / From the tea rooms of Mars / Beguine / Mambo / Tango.
LP: . . . . **RCALP 5003**
MC: . . . . **RCAK 5003**

LANDSCAPE.
Tracks: / Japan / Lost in the small ads / Mechanical bride / Neddy sindrum / Kaptin Whorlix / Sonja Henie / Many's the time / Highly suspicious / Gotham City / Wandsworth plain.
LP: . . . . **RCALP 3034**
MC: . . . . **RCAK 3034**
LP: . . . . **PL 25248**

MANHATTAN BOOGIE WOOGIE.
Tracks: / One rule for the rich / Manhattan boogie woogie / Colour code / Long way home / It's not my name / Bad times / Eastern girls / When you leave your lover.
LP: . . . . **RCALP 6037**
MC: . . . . **RCAK 6037**

Landslide

BAD REPUTATION.
LP: . . . . **GILP 777**

Lane, Christy

ASK ME TO DANCE.
Tracks: / Ask me to dance / Once or twice / I will / Eyes of misty blue / I knew the reason / Sexy eyes / One day at a time / Maybe i'm thinkin' / First time in a long time / Danny boy.
LP: . . . . **UAG 30293**

SIMPLE LITTLE WORDS.
LP: . . . . **UAG 30277**

Lane, Fred

CAR RADIO JEROME (Lane, Fred & His Hittite Hotshots).
Tracks: / White woman / Dial 'o' for Bigelow / Upper lip of a nostril man / French toast man, The / Pneumatic eyes / Car radio Jerome / Dondi must die / Man with the foldback ears, The / Hitite hot shot.
LP: . . . . **SHIMMY 013**

FROM THE ONE THAT CUT YOU.
Tracks: / Fun in the findus / Danger is my beer / I talk to my haircut / From the one that cut you / Rubber room / Mystic tune / Oatmeal / Meat clamp conduit.
LP: . . . . **SHIMMY 021**
LP: . . . . **SDE 8911 LP**

Lane, Morris

TENOR SAXSATION.
Tracks: / Bobby's boogie / Ghost town / Luke the spook / Down the lane / Blue jeans / B.O. plenty's return / Midnight sun / Pale moon (an Indian love song) / Moon ray / I don't want to set the world on fire / It ain't necessarily so / Stairway to the stars / Poinciana / Blues in the night / Twilight time / Everything I have is yours.
LP: . . . . **OFF 6022**

Lane, Ronnie

ANYMORE FOR ANYMORE.
Tracks: / Careless love / Don't you cry for me / Bye and bye / Silk stockings / Poacher, The / Roll on babe / Tell everyone / Amelia Earhart's last flight / Anymore for anymore / Only a bird in a gilded cage / Chicken wired.
LP: . . . . **GML 1013**

MAHONEY'S LAST STAND (See under Wood, Ronnie) (Lane, Ronnie & Ronnie Wood).

RONNIE LANE.
LP: . . . . **MQCLP 002**
MC: . . . . **MQCMC 002**

ROUGH MIX (See under Townshend, Pete) (Lane, Ronnie & Pete Townshend).

SEE ME.
Tracks: / One step / Good ol' boys boogie / Lad's got money / She's leaving / Barcelona / Kuschty Rye / Don't tell me now / You're so right / Only you / Winning with women / Way up yonder.
LP: . . . . **GEMLP 107**

STREET IN THE CITY (See under Townshend, Pete) (Lane, Ronnie & Pete Townshend).

Lane, Steve

I'VE GOT FORD ENGINE 1969-72 (Lane, Steve/Southern Stompers).
LP: . . . . **LC 14S**

JUST IMAGINE (Lane, Steve & Red Hot Peppers).
Tracks: / I got rhythm / Jubilee line / Just imagine / Sweetie dear / You've been a good old wagon / Trouble in mind / S'Posin' / There'll come a day / Flying dutchman.
MC: . . . . **VC 38**
LP: . . . . **LC 38**

MOVIN' ON (Lane, Steve/Famous Southern Stompers).
LP: . . . . **SLC 31**

STEVE LANE & HIS FAMOUS SOUTHERN STOMPERS (Lane, Steve/Famous Southern Stompers).
LP: . . . . **SOS 1040**

STEVE LANE & RED HOT PEPPERS (Lane, Steve & Red Hot Peppers).
Tracks: / New Orleans shuffle / Was I drunk? / Barney / Lady love / Lazy / Bugle boy march / Give me a call / Heaven on earth / Alexander's ragtime band / St Philip St Breakdown / Careless love blues / Wild man blues / Sweet Georgia Brown / Sweet daddy.
LP: . . . . **LC 36**

STEVE LANE'S SOUTHERN STOMPERS WITH MICHELE (Lane, Steve/Southern Stompers/Michele).
MC: . . . . **AC 10**

TAYLOR, RUSTY & STEVE LANE'S STOMPERS (see Taylor, Rusty) (Lane, Steve/Rusty Taylor).

WEMBLEY WIGGLE (Lane, Steve/Southern Stompers).
LP: . . . . **77 EU 12/3**

Lane, William

OLD POST ROAD, THE (See under The Maid's Bell) (Various artists).

Lang, Andrew

BEAUTY & THE BEAST & OTHER STORIES (Fairbanks, Douglas Jnr (nar)).
MC: **1394**

Lang, Don

20 ROCK 'N' ROLL TWISTS (Lang, Don & The Twisters).
Tracks: / Whole lotta shakin' goin' on / Great balls of fire / Rock around the clock / I go ape / Move it / Jailhouse rock / Way down yonder in New Orleans / Wiggle wiggle / What'd I say? / Quarter to three / Hit the road, Jack / Sweet little sixteen / All shook up / Chantilly lace / Shake, rattle and roll / Yakety yak / Be bop a lula / Hound dog / Splish splash / New Orleans.
LP: **C5-509**
MC: **C5K-509**
LP: . . . . **SEE 35**

DON LANG GETS THE BUG (Lang, Don & His Frantic 5).
LP: . . . . **JAM 649**

ROCK ROCK ROCK (Lang, Don & His Frantic 5).
Tracks: / Queen of the hop / Ramshackle daddy / 6-5 hand jive / Red planet rock / Texas tambourine / School day / Rock Mr. Piper / Rock around the cookhouse / Rockabilly / Rock, rock, rock / 6-5 special / Four brothers / Come go with me / Tequila / Hey daddy / Rock and roll blues / Rock around the island / I want you to be my baby / See you Friday / They call him Cliff / Time machine / Witch doctor.
LP: . . . . **CM 119**

Lang, Eddie

EDDIE LANG & LONNIE JOHNSON VOL.1.
LP: . . . . **S 1229**

EDDIE LANG & LONNIE JOHNSON VOL.2.
LP: . . . . **S 1276**

HANDFUL OF RIFFS, A.
Tracks: / Eddie's twister / April kisses / Prelude / Melody man's dream / Perfect / Rainbow / Add a little wiggle / Jeannine / I'll never be the same / Church Street sobbin' blues / There'll be some changes made / Two tone stomp / Jet black blues / Blue blood blues / Bullfrog moan / Handful of riffs, A / Bugle call rag / Freeze and melt / Hot heels / Walking the dog / March of the hoodlums.
LP: . . . . **AJA 5061**
MC: . . . . **ZC AJA 5061**

JAZZ CLASSICS IN DIGITAL STEREO (see under Venuti, Joe) (Lang, Eddie & Joe Venuti).

JAZZ GUITAR VIRTUOSO.
LP: . . . . **L 1059**

TROUBLES, TROUBLES (Lang, Eddie/ Edgar Blanchard & The Gondoliers).
LP: . . . . **ROUNDER 2080**
MC: . . . . **ROUNDER 2080C**

Lang, K.D.

ABSOLUTE TORCH AND TWANG (Lang, K.D. & The Reclines).
Tracks: / Luck in my eyes / Trail of broken hearts / Didn't I / Full moon full of love / Big big love / Walkin' in and out of your arms / Three days / Big boned gal / Wallflower waltz / Pullin' back the reins / It's me / Nowhere to stand.
LP: . . . . **WX 259**
MC: . . . . **WX 259 C**

ANGEL WITH A LARIAT (Lang, K.D. & The Reclines).
Tracks: / Turn me around / High time for detour / Diet of strange places / Got the bull by the horns / Watch your step polka / Rose garden / Tune into my wave / Angel with a lariat.
LP: **925441 1**
MC: **925441 4**

SHADOWLAND (Lang, K.D. & The Reclines).
Tracks: / Western stars / Lock, stock and teardrops / Sugar moon / I wish I didn't love you so / Once again around the dance floor / Black coffee / Shadowland / Don't let the stars get in your eyes / Tears don't care who cry them / I'm down to my last cigarette / Too busy being blue / Honky tonk angel's medley.
LP: . . . . **WX 171**
MC: . . . . **WX 171 C**

Lang, Peter

LEO KOTTKE WITH PETER LANG & JOHN FAHEY (see Kottke, Leo with Peter Lang & John Fahey).

Lang, Thomas

LITTLE MOSCOW.
Tracks: / Fail / Longest song, The / Try / Trouble / Heaven / Promise me / Out of reach / You disturb me / Away from you / Little Moscow (from Russia with love).
LP: **4668251**
MC: **4668254**

LOST LETTER 2, THE.
MC: . . . . **DRYC 10014**

SCALLYWAG JAZZ.
Tracks: / Fingers and thumbs / Happy man / Boys prefer / Me and Mrs Jones / Scallywag jazz / Shoelaces / Strength / Sleep with me / Spirit / Injury.
LP: **4509961**
MC: **4509964**

Langa Langa Stars

LIKOMBE.
LP: . . . . **EVVI 22**

MOYEBE (Langa Langa Stars & Choc Stars).
LP: . . . . **EVVI 24**

Lange, Don

LIVE : DON LANGE.
LP: . . . . **FF 222**

NATURAL BORN HEATHEN.
LP: . . . . **FF 060**

Langer, Clive

HOPE, HONOUR AND LOVE (Langer, Clive & The Boxes).
Tracks: / Hello / Whole world / Never wanted you / Inside houses / I know / Even though / Splash / Those days / Burning money / Take you down / Lovely evening / Had a nice night.
LP: . . . . **FIEND 127**

I WANT THE WHOLE WORLD (Langer, Clive & The Boxes).
Tracks: / Whole world, The / Lovely evening / I know / Those days / Simple life.
LP: . . . . **RDR 2**

SPLASH (Langer, Clive & The Boxes).
Tracks: / Hello / Never wanted you / Ain't gonna kiss you / Hope and glory / Best dressed man / If paradise is half as nice / Splash (a tear falls) / It's all over now / Burning money / Take you down / First thing in the morning / Had a nice night.
LP: . . . . **XXLP 2**

Langford, Frances

GETTIN' SENTIMENTAL.
Tracks: / I'm in the mood for love / Once in a while / Sweet someone / Is it true what they say about Dixie / Silhouetted in the moonlight / I don't want to make history / Everything you said came true / Deep shadows / I've got you under my skin / Harbour lights / You are my lucky star / Let's call a heart a heart / So do I / Speaking confidentially / Melody from the sky, A / Can't teach my old heart new tricks / If it's the last thing I do / So many memories / Rap tap on wood / Sweet heartache / I'm gettin' sentimental over you.
LP: . . . . **CMS 002**
MC: . . . . **CMSC 002**

LET'S FACE THE MUSIC & DANCE (see under Browne, Sam) (Langford, Frances & Sam Browne).

Langholm Town Band

MELODIES FROM THE MUCKLE TOON.
LP: . . . . **C 2017**

Langland, William

EVERYMAN-VISIONS FROM PIERS PLOWMAN (Various artists).
MCSET: . . . . **SAY 107**

Langley, Gerard

SIAMESE BOYFRIENDS (Langley, Gerard & Ian Kearey).
Tracks: / Nicknames / Snow-walking / Joe Taylor's / Good weather / Dear though the night is gone / Famous aren't, The.
LP: . . . . **FIRELP 4**

Langstaff, John

AMERICAN & BRITISH FOLKSONGS.
LP: . . . . **TLP 1009**

Langton, Hugh Lloyd

LIKE AN ARROW.
LP: . . . . **GAS 4014**

Langton, Lloyd Group

OUTSIDE THE LAW.
Tracks: / Outside the law / Five to four / Talk to you / Rocky paths / Space chase / Waiting for tomorrow / Mark of gain / Psychedelic warlords.
LP: . . . . **SHARP 015**

TIME SPACE AND LLG.
LP: . . . . **GWLP 27**
MC: . . . . **GWTC 27**

Language Courses

DAILY EXPRESS LANGUAGE COURSES (see under individual language,eg.Spanish).

DUTCH FOR TRAVEL (see under Berlitz) (Berlitz).

DUTCH LANGUAGE BASICS (see under Berlitz) (Berlitz).

FRANCE TRAVEL KIT (see under Berlitz) (Berlitz).

FRENCH FOR TRAVEL (see under Berlitz) (Berlitz).

FRENCH LANGUAGE BASICS (see under Berlitz) (Berlitz).

GERMAN FOR TRAVEL (see under Berlitz) (Berlitz).

GERMAN LANGUAGE BASICS (see under Berlitz) (Berlitz).

GERMANY TRAVEL KIT (see under Berlitz) (Berlitz).

GREEK FOR TRAVEL (see under Berlitz) (Berlitz).

GREEK LANGUAGE BASICS (see under Berlitz) (Berlitz).

ITALIAN FOR TRAVEL (see under Berlitz) (Berlitz).

ITALIAN LANGUAGE BASICS (see under Berlitz) (Berlitz).

ITALY TRAVEL KIT (see under Berlitz) (Berlitz).

LANGUAGE COURSE - AFRIKAANS (Linguaphone).
LPS: . . . . **Unknown**

LANGUAGE COURSE - AN ENGLISH CHILD IN FRANCE.
MC: . . . . **AECIFC**

LANGUAGE COURSE - ARABIC (MODERN STANDARD) (Linguaphone).
LPS: . . . . **074730176 X**

LANGUAGE COURSE - BUONGIORNO ITALIA BBC Publications.
LPS: . . . . **OP 260/61/62**
MCSET: . . . . **PTT 260/61/62**

LANGUAGE COURSE - CANTONESE (Teach yourself series) (Linguaphone).
LPS: . . . . **Unknown**

LANGUAGE COURSE - CHINESE (MANDARIN) (Linguaphone).
LPS: **0747306893**

LANGUAGE COURSE - CZECH (Teach yourself series) (Linguaphone).
LPS: . . . . **Unknown**

LANGUAGE COURSE - DANISH (Linguaphone).
LPS: **0747301816**

LANGUAGE COURSE - DIGAME BBC Publications.
2LP: . . . . **OP 230/31**
LP: . . . . **OP 251**
MCSET: . . . . **PTT 230/31**
MC: . . . . **PTT 251**

LANGUAGE COURSE - DUTCH (Linguaphone).
LPS: **0747303908**

LANGUAGE COURSE - ENGLISH ('Audio active' course) (Linguaphone).
LPS: **0747301891**

LANGUAGE COURSE - ENGLISH (ADVANCED) (Linguaphone).
LPS: . . . . **Unknown**

LANGUAGE COURSE - ENGLISH (AS A FOREIGN LANGUAGE) (Linguaphone).
LPS: . . . . **Unknown**

LANGUAGE COURSE - ENGLISH (INTERMEDIATE) (Linguaphone).
LPS: . . . . **Unknown**

LANGUAGE COURSE - ENSEMBLE BBC Publications.
2LP: . . . . **OP 216/7**
MCSET: . . . . **PTT 216/7**

LANGUAGE COURSE - FINNISH (Linguaphone).
LPS: **0747303126**

LANGUAGE COURSE - FRENCH ('Audio active' course) (Linguaphone).
LPS: . . . . **Unknown**

LANGUAGE COURSE - FRENCH ('Linguavision') (Linguaphone).
LPS: . . . . **UNKNOWN**

LANGUAGE COURSE - FRENCH (Sonodisc courses) (Linguaphone).
LPS: . . . . **Unknown**

LANGUAGE COURSE - FRENCH (Linguaphone).
LPS: **07473021446**

LANGUAGE COURSE - FRENCH ('Breakthrough') (Pan).
LPS: . . . . **UNKNOWN**

LANGUAGE COURSE - FRENCH (Travel pack) (Linguaphone).
LPS: **0747305978**

LANGUAGE COURSE - FRENCH AT HOME Harraps.
LPS: . . . . **HFAHC**

LANGUAGE COURSE - FRENCH (ROAD TO) (Linguaphone).
MC: . . . . **Unknown**

LANGUAGE COURSE - GERMAN ('Audio active' course) (Linguaphone).
LPS: . . . . **Unknown**

LANGUAGE COURSE - GERMAN (Linguaphone).
LPS: **0747303649**

LANGUAGE COURSE - GERMAN (Travel pack) (Linguaphone).
LPS: **0747305986**

LANGUAGE COURSE - GERMAN ('Breakthrough') (Pan).
LPS: . . . . **UNKNOWN**

LANGUAGE COURSE - GERMAN (Sonodisc courses) (Linguaphone).
LPS: . . . . **Unknown**

LANGUAGE COURSE - GERMAN, ROAD TO (Linguaphone).
MC: . . . . **Unknown**

LANGUAGE COURSE - GET BY IN FRENCH BBC Publications.
MC: . . . . **PTT 232/3**

LANGUAGE COURSE - GET BY IN GREEK BBC Publications.
MC: . . . . **PTT 264/5**

LANGUAGE COURSE - GET BY IN ITALIAN BBC Publications.
MC: . . . . **PTT 254/5**

LANGUAGE COURSE - GET BY IN PORTUGUESE BBC Publications.
MC: . . . . **PTT 258/9**

LANGUAGE COURSE - GET BY IN SPANISH BBC Publications.
MC: . . . . **PTT 227/8**

LANGUAGE COURSE - GREEK ('Breakthrough') (Pan).
LPS: . . . . **UNKNOWN**

LANGUAGE COURSE - GREEK (MODERN) (Linguaphone).
LPS: **0747302472**

LANGUAGE COURSE - HEBREW (MODERN) (Linguaphone).
LPS: **0747302480**

LANGUAGE COURSE - HINDI (Linguaphone).
LPS: **0747302502**

LANGUAGE COURSE - ICELANDIC (Linguaphone).
LPS: **0747303231**

LANGUAGE COURSE - IMPROVE YOUR FRENCH Harraps.
LPS: . . . . **HIYFC**

LANGUAGE COURSE - IRISH (Linguaphone).
LPS: **0747302510**

LANGUAGE COURSE - ITALIAN (Linguaphone).
LPS: **0747302553**

LANGUAGE COURSE - ITALIAN (Travel pack) (Linguaphone).
LPS: **0747306001**

LANGUAGE COURSE - ITALIAN ('Breakthrough') (Pan).
LPS: . . . . **UNKNOWN**

LANGUAGE COURSE - JAPANESE (Linguaphone).
LPS: **0747303266**

LANGUAGE COURSE - JAPANESE (Teach yourself series) (Linguaphone).
LPS: . . . . **Unknown**

LANGUAGE COURSE - KEIN PROBLEM BBC Publications.
2LP: . . . . **OP 234/5**
MCSET: . . . . **PTT 234/5**

LANGUAGE COURSE - LAZY LANGUAGES.
LPS: . . . . **UNKNOWN**

LANGUAGE COURSE - L'ITALIA DAL VIVO BBC Publications.
LPS: . . . . **OP 266/8**
MCSET: . . . . **PTT 266/8**

LANGUAGE COURSE - MAKE SENTENCES IN FRENCH 2.
MC: . . . . **MSIFC 2**

LANGUAGE COURSE - MAKE SENTENCES IN FRENCH 1.
MC: . . . . **MSIFC 1**

LANGUAGE COURSE - MALAY (BAHASA MALAYSIA) (Linguaphone).
LPS: **0747303304**

LANGUAGE COURSE - NORWEGIAN (Linguaphone).
LPS: **0747303320**

LANGUAGE COURSE - PERSIAN (Teach yourself series) (Linguaphone).
LPS: . . . . **Unknown**

LANGUAGE COURSE - POLISH (Linguaphone).
LPS: **0747302634**

LANGUAGE COURSE - PORTUGUESE (Linguaphone).
LPS: **0747303371**

LANGUAGE COURSE - RUSSIAN (Linguaphone).
LPS: **0747302650**

LANGUAGE COURSE - RUSSIAN LANGUAGE & PEOPLE BBC Publications.
2LP: . . . . **OP 248/3**
MCSET: . . . . **PTT 248/3**

LANGUAGE COURSE - SERBO-CROAT (Linguaphone).
LPS: **0747302758**

LANGUAGE COURSE - SPANISH (Sonodisc course) (Linguaphone).
LPS: . . . . **Unknown**

LANGUAGE COURSE - SPANISH ('Audio active' course) (Linguaphone).
LPS: . . . . **Unknown**

LANGUAGE COURSE - SPANISH ('Breakthrough') (Pan).
LPS: . . . . **UNKNOWN**

LANGUAGE COURSE - SPANISH (Travel pack) (Linguaphone).
LPS: **0747305994**

LANGUAGE COURSE - SPANISH (CASTILIAN) (Linguaphone).
LPS: **0747302804**

LANGUAGE COURSE - SPANISH (LATIN-AMERICAN) (Linguaphone).
LPS: **0747303940**

LANGUAGE COURSE - SPANISH (ROAD TO) (Linguaphone).
MC: . . . . **Unknown**

LANGUAGE COURSE - SUR LE VIF BBC Publications.
2LP: . . . . **OP 222/3**
MCSET: . . . . **PPT 222/3**

LANGUAGE COURSE - SWAHILI (Teach yourself series) (Linguaphone).
LPS: . . . . **Unknown**

LANGUAGE COURSE - SWEDISH (Linguaphone).
LPS: **0747302898**

LANGUAGE COURSE - WELSH (Linguaphone).
LPS: **0747302936**

PORTUGUESE FOR TRAVEL (see under Berlitz) (Berlitz).

PORTUGUESE LANGUAGE BASICS (see under Berlitz) (Berlitz).

SPAIN TRAVEL KIT (see under Berlitz) (Berlitz).

SPANISH FOR TRAVEL (see under Berlitz) (Berlitz).

SPANISH LANGUAGE BASICS (see under Berlitz) (Berlitz).

TURKISH FOR TRAVEL (see under Berlitz) (Berlitz).

TURKISH LANGUAGE BASICS (see under Berlitz) (Berlitz).

Lanier & Co.

DANCING IN THE NIGHT.
Tracks: / Dancing in the night / Strange love affair / You know that I want you / Afraid of losing you / Lies / I don't know / Superlady / Sassy / Lately / Let's go for it.
LP: . . . . **SYLP 6001**
MC: . . . . **TCSYLP 6001**

Lanigiro

LANIGIRO SYNKOPATING MELODY KINGS, 1929-43.
Tracks: / Happy days and lonely nights / Ice cream / Xashariana / Birmingham breakdown / Little old lady / It's the natural thing to do / September in the rain / St. Louis blues / Fifth Avenue / Two dukes on a pier / Drummer boy / Tangerine / Sweet Georgia Brown / My melancholy baby / St. Louis blues / For me and my gal.
LP: . . . . **HQ 2061**

Lanin, Lester

LESTER LANIN: 1960-62 (Lanin, Lester & His Orchestra).
LP: . . . . **HSR 210**

Lanin, Sam

IT'S FUN TO FOX-TROT (Lanin, Sam & His Orchestra).
Tracks: / I gotta get myself somebody to love / It made you happy when you made me cry / Varsity drag / Summertime sweethearts / Everybody loves my girl / What'll you do? / There must be somebody else / What a wonderful wedding that will be / Sweet Sue, just you / Get out and get under the moon / Sorry for me / Don't keep me in the dark bright eyes / I'm crazy over you / Susianna / If I had you / Hoosier hop / When I am housekeeping for you / Mona.
LP: . . . . **SH 424**

Lankchan, Hip

HIP LANKCHAN.
LP: . . . . **JSP 1010**

Lankester Brisley,

ADVENTURES OF MILLY MOLLY MANDY (See under Adventures of...) (Rayne, Janie (nar)).

BEST OF MILLY MOLLY MANDY.
Tracks: / Milly Molly Mandy And Dum Dum / Milly Molly Mandy finds a train / Milly Molly Mandy and the gang / Milly Molly Mandy goes sledging.
MC: . . . . **TS 307**

MILLY MOLLY MANDY.
Tracks: / Milly Molly Mandy has an adventure / Milly Molly Mandy and the golden wedding / Milly Molly Mandy acts for the pictures / Milly Molly Mandy finds a parcel.
MC: . . . . **TS 310**

Lanois, Daniel

ACADIE.
LP: . . . . **K 925969 1**
MC: . . . . **K 925969 4**

Lanphere, Don

DON LOVES MIDGE.
LP: . . . . **HEP 2027**

GO AGAIN (Lanphere, Don Sextet).
Tracks: / Which / Go again / Darn that dream / Shangri la / I love you / Midges late valentine / What are you doing for the rest of your life / Maddie's dance / Music that makes me dance / Darkness on the Delta / Maestro, The.
LP: . . . . **HEP 2040**

INTO SOMEWHERE (Lanphere, Don Quintet).
LP: . . . . **HEP 2022**

OUT OF NOWHERE (Lanphere, Don Quintet).
Tracks: / What / Buddip Baw / You've changed / Noble Indian song / White / Blue orchids / Who wrote this thing? / Out of nowhere / Lord's prayer, The.
LP: . . . . **HEP 2019**

STOP.
LP: . . . . **HEP 2034**

Lanz, David

HEARTSOUNDS.
LP: . . . . **LP 1003**
MC: . . . . **CAS 1003**

Lanza, Mario

20 GOLDEN FAVOURITES: MARIO LANZA.
Tracks: / Be my love / Drinking song / Only a rose / Donkey serenade / Granada / Valencia / Night and day / Vesti la guibba / La Donna e mobile / E lucevan le stelle / Loveliest night of the year, The / I love thee / Ave Maria / Santa Lucia / Funiculi funicula / O sole mio / Arrivederci Roma / Because you're mine.
LP: . . . . **PL 89086**
MC: . . . . **PK 89086**

ART & VOICE OF MARIO LANZA.
LPS: . . . . **SER 5689/91**

BEST SONGS OF MARIO LANZA.
LP: . . . . **ENT LP 13039**
MC: . . . . **ENT MC 13039**

BROADWAY HITS.
Tracks: / On the steet where you live / You'll never walk alone / Younger than springtime / More than you know.
LP: . . . . **CL 12847**

CHRISTMAS CAROLS.
LP: . . . . **NL 82333**
MC: . . . . **NK 82333**

CHRISTMAS HYMNS AND CAROLS.
LP: . . . . **CDS 1036**
MC: . . . . **CAM 430**

COLLECTION.
2LP: . . . . **CR 029**
MCSET: . . . . **CRT 029**

COLLECTION: MARIO LANZA.
Tracks: / Be my love / I'll never love you / Because you're mine / Song angels sing / Drink, drink, drink / Serenade (Overhead the moon is beaming) / Loveliest night of the year, (The) / La Donna e mobile / Because / For you alone / Golden days / Deep in my heart / If I loved you / Yours is my heart alone / One night of love / Beloved / Beautiful love / With a song in my heart / You are my love / Call me fool / All the things you are / My song my love / Love is the sweetest thing / Will you remember? / Granada / Lolita / Serenade (Drigo) / Temptation / Lygia / Lady of Spain / This land / Lee ah loo / Tine lina / Boom biddy boom boom / Bayou lullaby, The / Lord's prayer, (The) / And here you are / Song of songs / Somewhere a voice is calling / I never knew / Ciribiribin / Wonder why / Come dance with me / O sole mio / Younger than Springtime / For the first time / Never till now / Arrivederci Roma / Celeste Aida / Flower song / Brindisi / Libiamo libiamo / Questa o quella / Vesti la giubba / Addio alla madre / If you were mine / Behold / Night to remember, A / Love in a home / Do you wonder? / Softly as in a morning sunrise / One alone.
LPS: . . . . **RL 04158**

EVENING WITH MARIO LANZA.
LP: . . . . **CDS 1170**
MC: . . . . **HSC 3056**

EXCLUSIVO.
LP: **107 5001**
MC: **771 5001**

FOREVER.
Tracks: / September song / Marachiare / Song of India / Day in, day out / Song is you, The / Beloved / La danza / Mattinata / Maria mari / Guadeamus igitur / Thrill is gone, The / My romance / Rose Marie / Long ago / Falling in love with you / I'll be seeing you / Younger than Springtime / Among my souvenirs.
LP: . . . . **NL 89822**
MC: . . . . **NK 89822**

GREAT CARUSO (Film soundtrack).
LP: . . . . **RB 16112**
MC: . . . . **GK 60049**

GREATEST HITS VOL. 1.
LP: . . . . **LSB 4000**

HIS GREATEST HITS FROM OPERETTAS AND MUSICALS Volume 1..
LP: . . . . **RL 43372**
MC: . . . . **RK 43372**

HIS GREATEST HITS FROM OPERETTAS AND MUSICALS Volume 3..
LP: . . . . **RL 43387**
MC: . . . . **RK 43387**

HIS GREATEST HITS FROM OPERETTAS AND MUSICALS Volume 2..
LP: . . . . **RL 43386**
MC: . . . . **RK 43386**

I'LL SEE YOU IN MY DREAMS.
Tracks: / With a song in my heart / Among my souvenirs / Marcheta / Memories / Ah sweet mystery of life / I'll be seeing you / Cosi cosa / Lady of Spain / La spagnola / When day is done / Best things in life are free, The / I'll see you in my dreams.
LP: . . . . **NL 89060**
MC: . . . . **NK 89060**

I'LL WALK WITH GOD.
Tracks: / I'll walk with God / Virgin's slumber song, The / Lord's prayer, The / O holy night / Guardian angels / Ave Maria / Somebody bigger than you and me / Because / Trembling of a leaf / None but the lonely heart, Op.6, No.6 / Through the years / I love thee, Op. 5, No. 3 / Trees / Cavalleria rusticana / Mamma quel vino e generoso (Addio alla madre).
LP: . . . . **RB 6507**

LEGENDARY MARIO LANZA, THE.

LP: NE 1110
MC: CE 2110

MAGIC MOMENTS WITH MARIO LANZA.
Tracks: / Be my love / Drinking song / Serenade / Donkey serenade, The / Granada / Valencia / Night and day / O sole mio / Arrivederci Roma / Rose Marie / Falling in love with love / This nearly was mine / You'll never walk alone / Come prima / With a song in my heart / Begin the beguine / Temptation / Jezebel / Memories are made of this / Fools rush in / I've got you under my skin / Younger than springtime / My destiny / Ave Maria.
MC: NK 89624

MARIO LANZA - LIVE.
Tracks: / Funiculi funicula / My song my love / Granada / Diane / Thine alone / Vesti la giubba / Vuchella, A / Toselli's serenade / Because you're mine / Loveliest night of the year, The / O paradiso / Marechiare, A / Rosary, The / Lolita / If / Mattinata / They didn't believe me / Lords prayer, The / Be my love.
MC: CATOM 2
LP: ATOM 2

PORTRAIT OF MARIO LANZA.
Tracks: / Be my love / Because you're mine / O sole mio / Donkey serenade, The / Granada / Night and day / Loveliest night of the year / Drinking song / Serenade / Arrivederci Roma / Temptation / All the things you are / Santa Lucia / I'll walk with God / Ave Maria.
LP: SMR 741
MC: SMC 741

PURE GOLD: MARIO LANZA.
Tracks: / On the street where you live / Younger than springtime / Speak low / More than you know / Falling in love with love / Why was I born / And this is my beloved / So in love / September song / My romance / This nearly was mine / You'll never walk alone.
LP: INTS 5005
MC: NK 89085
LP: NL 89085

SINGS OPERAS GREATEST HITS.
2LP: DPS 2012

STUDENT PRINCE, THE (Film soundtrack).
Tracks: / Overture / Serenade / Golden days / Drink, drink, drink / Summertime in Heidelberg / I'll walk with God / Thoughts will come back to me / Student life / Just we two / Beloved / Gaudeamus igitur / Deep in my heart.
LP: RL 43567
MC: RK 43567
MC: GK 60048

STUDENT PRINCE/GREAT CARUSO.
LP: RB 16113

WITH A SONG IN MY HEART.
Tracks: / With a song in my heart / Song angels sing / If I loved you / For you alone / Lee ah loo / Tina Lina / Look for the silver lining / Love in a home.
LP: RL 43731

YOU DO SOMETHING TO ME.
LP: CDS 1001

L.A.P.D.

WHO'S LAUGHING.
LP: TX 93151
MC: TX 93154

Lapotaire, Jane

EMMA (See under Austen, Jane).

L'Apres-Midi

L'APRES-MIDI D'UN DINOSAUR (Perkins, Laurence/ Hancock, Michael).
MC: KH 88035

Laquan

NOTES OF A NATIVE SON.
MC: BRCA 559
LP: BRLP 559

Lara, Roberto

GUITAR OF THE PAMPAS, THE (see under Argentina).

Laraaji

DAYS OF RADIANCE.
Tracks: / Dance no. 1, The / Dance no. 2, The / Dance no. 3, The / Meditation no. 1 / Meditation no. 2.
LP: EGED 19
LP: EGAMB 3

ESSENCE, UNIVERSE.
LP: SYN 310

Larcarnge, Maurice

ACCORDEON AU SOLEILNET.
Tracks: / Cane cane canebier / A petit pas / Le plus beau tango du monde / Les pescadous / Ouh sur le plancher des vaches / Le marin a casquette / Adieu Venise Provencale / Deux grands yeux noirs / Un petit cabanon / J'ai reve d'une fleur / L'accordeon de la plage / C'est ma Marseillaise.
LP: 42026

ACCORDEON TRADITIONNEL.
Tracks: / La grande valse / Ou est passee ma Boheme? / Toros El Paso / Adios muchachos / Java rigolette / Rio / La marche de L'A.C. Vitry le Francois / Vitry-le-Francois / Le temps des cerises / El picador / Le tango des souvenirs / Les prolots robots / La marche de L'A.C. Vitry le Francois / Armoricaine / Nocturnal ballade / Valse du populo.
LP: 42015

C'EST FETE A L'ACCORDEON.
Tracks: / Retour de biarritz / Seville en fete / La star musette / Valse Africaine / Le tango tango / Grisonnants / Accordeon super boogie / C'est la fete a l'accordeon / Echo montagnard / Le marin a casquette / Vichy musette / Souvenir paternel.
LP: 742064

LARCANGE PLAYS TRENET (Larcange, Maurice/Roland Shaw Orchestra).
Tracks: / La mer / Fleur bleue / Serenade (Portugaise) / La romance de Paris / I wish you love / Je chante / At last, at last / Vous qui passez sans me voir / Coin de rue / En Avril a Paris.
LP: Unknown

LARCARNGE PLAYS AZNAVOUR (Larcarnge & Roland Shaw Orchestra).
Tracks: / Old fashioned way, The / Take me with you / Yesterday / Je taime / Whole world is singing my love, The / She / You've let yourself go / What makes a man / Love is new / To die of love / La boheme.
MC: KPFC 4343

MARTELETTE.
Tracks: / Martelette / Reveil du square / Beau Merle / La paloma / OK cow-boys / Dis com tu es belle / Un Francais a Madrid / Les patineurs / Corrida musette / Douceur musette / Samba due foot / Homme bien fragile / Valse du populo.
LP: 42010

MES TITRES EN OR.
Tracks: / Accordeon rockers / Pistonette / Perles de cristal / C'est ma Marseillaise / Drole de rigolade / Reve de ballerine / Polkamarade / Capricieusette / Accordeon steeple / Retour de biarritz / Accordeon dance / Operamusette.
LP: ILD 42048

PARIS ACCORDIONS.
Tracks: / Comme ci, comme ca / La vie en rose / Pigalle / My man / Under Paris skies / La valse apache / Poor people of Paris / Domino / Mademoiselle de Paris / Under the bridges of Paris / C'est si bon / I love Paris.
MC: KDGC 2
LP: DGS 2

SALUT L'ACCORDEON.
Tracks: / Operamusette / Oh oh tango disco / Petite marquise / J'ai besoin de toi / La vie n'est pas foutue / Surprise polka / Vacances parade / Nostalgia printaniere / Ouvrir les yeux / Balapapa / Caroline / Belinda.
LP: ILD 420

Lard

LAST TEMPTATION OF REID, THE.
LP: VIRUS 84

Largo

LARGO (Various artists).
2LP: 2 LP 1635187
MCSET: 2 MC 1635187

Largs Choir

SCOTLAND IN SONG.
MC: ZCLBP 2009

Laria, A.J.

A.J. LARIA AND WYNTON MARSALIS (Laria, A.J./Wynton Marsalis).
MC: TC 026

Laritz, Jamie

JAMIE LARITZ.
Tracks: / Creativity / Possibilities / Piece of mind / Eau de funk / Lonely night's blues, A / Hot off the frets (licks from hell) / Dreaming in colour.
MC: STA 4028 MC

Larkin, Patty

I'M FINE.
LP: PH 1115
MC: PH 1115C

STEP INTO THE LIGHT.
LP: PH 1103
MC: PH 1103C
LP: PHILO 1133

Larkins, Ellis

ELLIS LARKINS WITH MAXINE SULLIVAN (see also under Sullivan, Maxine) (Larkins, Ellis & Maxine Sullivan).

SWINGING FOR HAMP (Larkins, Ellis/ Tony Middleton).
LP: CJ 134

Larkins, Percy

MUSIC OF PASSION.
LP: MVLP 3

Larks (50's)

BEST OF THE LARKS VOL. 1.
LP: RELIC 8013

BEST OF THE LARKS VOL. 2.
LP: RELIC 8014

Larner, Sam

GARLAND FOR SAM.
LP: 12T 244

LaRosa, Julius

IT'S A WRAP.
LP: AP 190

Larry & The Blue Notes

MAJOR BILL TAPES - SIXTIES PUNK VOL.1.
Tracks: / In and out / Night of the sadist / It's you alone / Love is a beautiful thing / She'll love me / What made me lose my head / Train kept a rollin / Just stay / Talk about love / Everybody needs somebody to love / Phantom.
LP: WIKM 33

Larsen, Brett

SILVER WINGS (Larsen, Brett & Country Line).
LP: BSS 322

Larsen, Grey

GATHERING, THE.
LP: SH 1133

Larsen, Morton Gunnar

PLAYS ROBERTO CLEMENTINE....
LP: SOS 1009

Larson, Claude

HIGH-TEC.
LP: ISST 127

SYNTHESIS.
LP: ISST 121

Larson, Neil

JUNGLE FEVER.
Tracks: / Sudden samba / Promenade / Windsong / Emerald city / Jungle fever / Red desert / Last tango in Paris / From a dream.
LP: AMLJ 733

SMOOTH TALK.
LP: MCA 42296
MC: MCAC 42296

Larson, Nicolette

IN THE NICK OF TIME.
Tracks: / Dancin' Jones / In the nick of time / Let me go love / Rio De Janeiro blue / Breaking too many hearts / Back in my arms again / Fallen / Daddy / Isn't it always love / Trouble.
LP: K 56750

NICOLETTE.
Tracks: / Lotta love / Rhumba girl / You send me / Can't get away from you / Mexican divorce / Baby, don't you do it / Give a little / Angels / Rejoiced / French waltz / Come early mornin' last in love.
LP: K 56569

RADIOLAND.
Tracks: / Radioland / Ooo-eee / How can we go on / When you come around / Tears, tears and more tears / Straight from the heart / Been gone too long / Fool for love / Long distance love.
LP: K 56878

SAY WHEN.
LP: MCF 3266
MC: MCFC 3266

La's

LA'S.
LP: 828202 1
MC: 828202 4

Las Cancions Del Tango

LAS CANCIONS DEL TANGO (Various artists).
LP: A 367
MC: AC 367

Las Vegas Grind

LAS VEGAS GRIND.
LP: STRIP 001

Las Vegas Nights

SHIP AHOY/LAS VEGAS NIGHTS (See under Ship Ahoy) (Various artists).

Lasalle, Denise

HITTIN' WHERE IT HURTS.
LP: MAL 7447
MC: MALC 7447

HOLDING HANDS WITH THE BLUES.
LP: MALP 013

IT'S LYING TIME AGAIN.
LP: MAL 7441
MC: MALC 7441

LADY IN THE STREET, A.
LP: MAL 7412
MC: MALC 7412

LOVE TALKIN'.
LP: MAL 7422
MC: MALC 7422

MY TOOT TOOT.
Tracks: / Talkin' in your sleep / Someone else is steppin' in / Nobody loves me like you do / Give me yo' most strongest whisky / Love is a five letter word / Lady in the street, A / Love talkin' / Get what you can get / Linger a little longer / Keeps me runnin' back / Too many lovers / My toot toot / Come to bed.
LP: EPC 26603
MC: 40 26603

ON THE LOOSE.
Tracks: / Man size job, A / What it takes to get a good woman / Harper Valley PTA / What am I doing wrong / Breaking up somebody's home / There ain't enough hate around (to make me turn around) / Your man and your best friend / Lean on me / Making a good thing better / I'm over you / I'm satisfied.
LP: SEW 005
MC: SEWC 005

RAIN AND FIRE.
Tracks: / It be's that way sometimes / I'm sho gonna mess with yo man / What's goin' on in my house / Look what can happen to you.... (Look what can happen to you (if you get caught messin' with my tu tu)) / Shame shame shame / Dip, bam, thank you maam / Learnin' how to cheat on you / Rain and fire / It takes you all night / Is he lovin' someone else tonight.
LP: MAL 7434
MC: MALC 7434

RIGHT PLACE, RIGHT TIME.
LP: MAL 7417
MC: MALC 7417

TRAPPED BY A THING CALLED LOVE.
Tracks: / Trapped by a thing called love / Now run and tell that / Heartbreaker of the year / Good goody getter / Catch me if you can / Hung up, strung out / Do me right / Deeper I go (the better it gets), The / You'll lose a good thing keep it coming / It's too late.
LP: SEW 018
MC: SEWC 018

Lasha, Prince

INSIDE STORY.
LP: ENJA 3073

JOURNEY TO ZOAR (Lasha, Prince & The Firebirds).
LP: ENJA 4008

Lashley, Barbara

SWEET & LOWDOWN (Lashley, Barbara & Ray Skjelbred).
LP: SOS 1152

Lask

LASK.
LP: ECM 1217

SUCHT + ORDNUNG (Lask 2).
Tracks: / Freie Madchen arbeiten im Hafen / Apres-ski / Mamamerika / Erfolgreich und beliebt / Wir sind ein Kulturvolk / Ordnung / None the wiser / Kleine Narkosen / Kerngesund / Sigi Sigi / Sucht.
LP: ECM 1268

Lassiter

LASSITER (Film soundtrack) (Various artists).
LP: TER 1092

Last

AWAKENING.
LP: SST 230
MC: SSTC 230

CONFESSION.
LP: SST 189
MC: SST 189C

L.A. EXPLOSION.
Tracks: / She don't know why I'm here / This kind of feeling / Bombing of London / Century city rag / Walk like me / Slavedriver / Every summer day / Rack / Objections / Fool like you / Someone's laughing / I don't wanna be in love / Be bop a lula / Looking at you.
LP: SH-Z 8540

Last American Virgin

LAST AMERICAN VIRGIN, THE (Various artists).
LP: CBS 70228

Last Butterfly

LAST BUTTERFLY, THE (Original Soundtrack) (Various artists).

LP: VS 5287
MC: VSC 5287

Last Crack

BURNING TIME.
LP: RR 93301
MC: RR 93304

SINISTER FUNKHOUSE £ 17.
Tracks: / Good morning from the funkhouse / Gush volcano crush / Blood brothers of the big black bear / Concrete slaughter dogs / Slicing steel / Saraboys cage / Last crack, The / Shelter / Terse / Thee abyas.
LP: RO 9501 1
MC: RO 9501 4

Last Days Of ...

LAST DAYS OF POMPEII (Film soundtrack) (Various artists).
LP: PHCAM 03

Last Descendants

ONE NATION UNDER GOD.
LP: AAARRG 014

Last Dragon

LAST DRAGON (Film Soundtrack) (Various artists).
Tracks: / Last dragon, The: *Dwight, David* / 7th heaven: *Vanity* / Star: *Wood, Alfie* / Fire: *Charlene*/ Glow: *Hutch, Willie* / Rhythm of the night: *DeBarge* / Upset stomach: *Wonder, Stevie* / First time on a ferris wheel: *Robinson, Smokey & Syreets* / Peeping Tom: *Rockwell* / Inside you: *Hutch, Willie & Temptations.*
LP: ZL 72363
MC: ZK 72363

Last Drive

HEATWAVE.
LP: MMLP 017

Last Embrace

LAST EMBRACE THE (Film soundtrack) (Various artists).
LP: STV 81166

Last Emperor (film)

LAST EMPEROR, THE (Film soundtrack) (Sakamoto, Ryuichi & David Byrne).
Tracks: / First coronation / Open the door / Where is Armo? / Picking up brides / Last Emperor, The (theme) (variation 1) / Picking a bride / Bed / Wind, rain and water / Paper emperor / Rain (I want a divorce) / Baby was born dead, The / Last Emperor, The (theme) (variation 2) / Last Emperor, The (theme) / Main title / Lunch / Red guard / Emperor's waltz, The / Red guard dance, The.
LP: V 2485
MC: TCV 2485

Last Exit

CASSETTE RECORDING '87.
LP: EMY 105

IRON PATH.
Tracks: / Prayer / Iron path / Black bat, The / Marked for death / Fire drum, The / Detonator / Sand dancer / Cut and run / Eye for an eye / Devil's rain.
LP: VE 38
MC: TCVE 38

KOLN.
LP: EMY 10

LAST EXIT.
LP: EMY 101

Last Exit to Brooklyn

LAST EXIT TO BROOKLYN (Film Soundtrack) (Knopfler, Mark).
LP: 838 725 1
MC: 838 725 4

Last Few Days

PURE SPIRIT AND SALIVA LIVE.
LP: DMC 002

Last, James

ALL ABOARD WITH CAP'N JAMES.
Tracks: / Take us with you captain / Sail again to Bombay / Boy at the rail, The / La Paloma / My bonnie / Kari waits for me / Banks of Sacramento, The / What shall we do with the drunken sailor? / Madagascar / Wreck of the John B., The / Yellow rose of Texas / When the ship's accordion plays / Blonde sailor / Accordion Joe / Sea journey is fun / Today we sail away / Way with every sailor, The / Aloha-oe / John Kanaka / Rollin' home / Winds are blowing / Sailing through the storm / Colour flags, The / Hey hey hey / Goodnight ladies / In my homeland / Must I go?.
LP: LAST 9
MC: LASTC 9

ANNCHEN VON THARAU BITTE ZUM TANZ.
LP: 8216111
MC: 8216144
LP: 2372 074
MC: 3151 074

AT ST. PATRICK'S CATHEDRAL, DUBLIN.
Tracks: / In the cathedral / Ave Maria / Conversation / An caoineadh / Scherzo / Away in a manger / Intermezzo of Notre Dame / Darkest midnight, The / Cavalleria rusticana / Holly and the ivy, The / Coulin / Seinn ailliu / Abide with me.
LP: POLD 5171
LP: POLD 5171

BEACH PARTY 2.
LP: 2371 211

BERLIN CONCERT, THE.
Tracks: / Fanfare for the common man / Alfie / Vienna is Vienna / Eine kleine nachtmusik / Roses from the south / Broken wings / Life at the Vienna prater / On the banks of Sacramento / Macarthur Park / That's what friends are for / Missing / Star wars.
LP: POLD 5215
MC: POLDC 5215

BEST FROM 150 GOLD, THE.
LP: 268 121 1
MC: 357 121 0

BISCAYA (James Last & His Orchestra).
Tracks: / Biscaya / Beachrunner / Diving / Rain and sun / Morning after, The / Shore life / Abends im schilf / Verlorener sommer / Calm before the storm / Weekend / Empty glass.
LP: 2372 130
MC: 3151 130

BLUEBIRD.
Tracks: / Morning at Cornwall, A / Proud as a peacock / Love bird / Sandpiper / Quiberon / Bird of paradise / Alassio / Night owl / Over valley and mountain / Bill Magee / Kingfisher / Roter Milan.
MC: POLDC 5072
LP: POLD 5072

BY REQUEST.
Tracks: / Mornings at 7 / Elvira Madigan / Air that I breathe, The / Adagio from the New World Symphony / Lonely shepherd / Roses of the south / Sabre dance / Lonely bull, The / Tulips from Amsterdam / Seduction, The / Zip a dee doo dah / Spanish eyes / Valencia / That's life.
LP: POLH 34
MC: POLHC 34

CARIBBEAN NIGHTS.
LP: 2372 035
MC: 3151 035

CHRISTMAS CLASSICS.
LP: 2371 985
MC: 3150 985

CHRISTMAS DANCING.
LP: 815 198-1
MC: 815 198-4

CHRISTMAS & JAMES LAST.
LP: 2371 405
MC: 3150 405

CHRISTMAS WITH JAMES LAST.
Tracks: / Frohliche weihnacht uberall / Suber glocke nie klingen / Schlittenfahrt zum weihnachtsmarkt / Die hirten / Ave Maria / Ofreude uber freude / In der Kathedrale / Heidsche bumbeidschi / Morgen, kinder, wird's was geben / Von himmel hoch, da domm'ich her / Stille nacht / Kirchenglocken zur weihnachtzeit.
LP: 815 199-1
MC: 815 199-4

CLASSICS BY MOONLIGHT.
Tracks: / Bolero / Romeo and Juliet / Swan lake / New World symphony / Spring from 'The four seasons' / Rhapsody in blue / Morning / Blue danube / Rhapsody on a theme of Paganini / Nabucco.
LP: 843 218 1
MC: 843 218 4

CLASSICS FOR DREAMING.
LP: POLTV 11

CLASSICS UP TO DATE.
LPS: BOX 4

CLASSICS UP TO DATE.
MC: 1914545

CLASSICS UP TO DATE - VOL 1.
Tracks: / Tales of Hoffman / Bacarole / Nabucco / Prisoner's chorus / Hungarian dance no. 5 / Waltz in A flat major / Op 39 no.15 / Toreador's dance (Carmen.) / To the spring / Habanera / Nocturne Romeo & Juliet / Theme / In a Persian market / Symphony No. 9 (Dvork) / Adagio / Violin concerto no.1.
MC: 1914 061
LP: 249 371

CLASSICS UP TO DATE - VOL 2.
Tracks: / Elvira Madigan / Presto from symphony no.7 / Romance for violin and orchestra in F / Impromptu no.2 in A flat / Air from suite No. 3 (In D) / Impromptu no.3 in G flat / Adagio from piano sonata in C minor "Pathetique" / Slavonic dance No.10 / Andante from violin concerto in E minor / Prelude no.1 in C / Andante from symphony no.5 in C minor / Polovsian dance from Prince Igor.
MC: 191 460-6
LP: 184 061

CLASSICS UP TO DATE - VOL 3.
Tracks: / La mattinata / Fantasie - impromptu in C sharp minor / Orientale / Surprise / Tristesse / Music for Royal fireworks / Traumerei / Liebestraum / Peer gynt / Solveig's song / March sieve / Cavatina / Slavonic march.
LP: 2371 538

CLASSICS UP TO DATE VOL 5 (Last, James & His Orchestra).
Tracks: / Ballade pour adeline / Adagio / Romance / Jog dig oas / Concerto in F / Zwischenspiel aus 'Notre Dame' / Nocturne / Sonata No. 3 / Chanson triste / Nocturne Opus. 37, No. 2 / Largo / Piece No. 1.
LP: 2371910

CLASSICS UP TO DATE - VOL 6.
Tracks: / Eine kleine nachtmusik / Ballade / Sonata no.V (cantible) / Emperor quintet, The / Largo / Nordic ways / Allegro / Reverie / Presto / Symphony No. 1, promenade 9, Theme from (From Pictures From An Exhibition.).
MC: POLDC 5141
LP: POLD 5141

CONCERT SUCCESSES.
Tracks: / Elvira Madigan / Die moidau / Traumerei / Fur Elise / Madame Butterfly / Intermezzo / Romance / Waltz / Violin concerto / Berceuse / Nabucco / Etude concierto / Liebestraum / Adagio / Fruhlingslied.
LP: 2475 606
MC: 3236 606

COPOCABANA (Last, James & His Orchestra).
Tracks: / Gay ranchero, A / El rancho grande / Zip a dee doo dah / Sly mongoose / Feels so good / Siesta / Caminito / Perhaps perhaps / El choclo / Avalon / La sorella / Copacabana / Chili con carne.
LP: 2371929

COUNTRY AND SQUARE DANCE PARTY.
LP: 2371 830
MC: 3150 830

DANCE DANCE DANCE.
Tracks: / You win again / Frankie / Reet petite / Love will save the day / Saving all my love for you / Power of love, The / You keep me hangin' on / Heaven is a place on earth / Respect yourself / Don't leave me this way / Everybody have fun tonight / Chain reaction / Gimme hope Joanna / Easy lover / Rhythm is gonna get you / Doctorin' the tardis / So macho / Always on my mind / Nothing's gonna stop us now / La bamba / My toot toot.
LP: JLTV 1
MC: JLTVC 1

DANCING '68 VOL 1.
LP: 249 216

DE NEDERLANDSE SUCCESSEN.
Tracks: / Hoog op de gele wagen / Door de bossen door de heide / Tulpen uit Amsterdam / Amsterdam / Oh Johnny / In Holland staat een huis.
LP: 810855 1
MC: 810855 4

DEUTSCHE VITA.
LP: 829 458 1
MC: 929 458 4

EAST TO WEST.
LP: 2630 092

EVERYTHING COMES TO AN END ONLY A SAUSAGE HAS TWO.
Tracks: / Min hit heisst / Susi Schmidt / Aerobic erotic / Jenny Jones / Keine sterne in anthem / Der Holzwurmblues / Alles hat ein ende nur die wurst hat zwei / Viva la Mexico / Ba-ba-bank ubersall / Lotti's loses lotterleben / Old MacDonald had a farm / Vampire / Mein tuut tuut.
LP: 831 529-1
MC: 831 529-4

FLUTE FIESTA (Last, James & Berdien Stenberg).
Tracks: / Ayacucho / April In Portugal / Concierto de Aranjuez / El Porompompero / Who Pays The Ferryman / Torna A Surriento / Drina March.
LP: POLD 5228
MC: POLDC 5228

GALA.
Tracks: / Rare ould times / Biscaya / I just called to say I love you / Quizas quizas quizas / Paradiso / Ballade pour Adeline / Primavera / Michelle / Paradiesvogel / Arche noah / Moonriver / Tipitipitipso / Song for Guy / Seduction, The / Scottish soldier, A / Orange blossom special.
LP: 831154 1
MC: 831154 4

GAMES THAT LOVERS PLAY.
Tracks: / Lara's theme / Man and a woman, A / Games that lovers play / This is my song / What now my love / Close your eyes / I left my heart in San Francisco / Fly me to the moon / Now I know / Elizabethan serenade / Never on Sunday / Sandy's theme.
LP: LAST 8
MC: LASTC 8

GENTLEMAN OF MUSIC, THE.
Tracks: / Liebestraum / Solvieg's song / Fur Elise / Red sarafan, The / Yearning for you / Beautiful world / On my lips every kiss is like wine / You shall be king of my heart / Say you to me / You too / We love storms / When the flags are flying / Hey hey hey / Anna of Tharau / Three brothers / Lady of Spain / March from Carmen / Oh Susanna Carmen / What can Sigismund do, he's so beautiful / Pardon me madame / I saw Ms Helen taking a bath / She's too fat for me / American patrol / Charmaine / On the street where you live / Close to you / A media luz / Rum and coca cola / Quando, quando, quando / South America take it away / Anuschka / Evening has gold to offer, The / Go old woman don't look at me like that / Isle of Capri / Buona sera / Oh Marie / Come and have a drink / La felicidad.
2LP: PODV 7
MC: PODVC 7

HAMMOND A GO GO.
Tracks: / Hello Dolly / Milord / C'est magnifique / In a little Spanish town / Benita / Wheels / Sole sole sole / Ich mocht so gern mit dir nach hause geh'n / Goody goody / True love / Moon river / Letkiss / Norske Jenka / America / If I had a hammer / Lucky lips / You, you, you / Blue moon / Makin' whoopee / Cavaquinho / Cumana / Sambarita / Melancholie / La mama / Red roses for a blue lady / Bye bye blackbird / Auf wiedersehen bei dir.
MC: LASTC 5
LP: 249 043
LP: LAST 5

HANSIMANIA.
Tracks: / Master blaster / Ai no corrida / Love on the rocks.
LP: POLTV 14
MC: POLVM 14

HAPPY CHRISTMAS WITH JAMES LAST.
Tracks: / White Christmas / Jingle bells / Tannenbaum.
LP: 1249 088
MC: 1911 101

HAPPY HEART.
Tracks: / Happy heart / Amboss polka / Happy Luxemburg / Games that lovers play / Music from across the way / Mornings at seven / Fool / I left my heart in San Francisco / Happy music / Root beer rag / Lonely shepherd, The.
LP: 839 613 1
MC: 839 613 4

HAPPY LEHAR (Last, James & His Orchestra).
Tracks: / This is the life for me / I'm off to Chez Maxim / Women, women / Vilia / You are my heart's delight / Nobody loves you as much as I do / Beautiful world / On my lips every kiss is like wine / I love you, you love me / Laughing women are beautiful / On the Pai-Ho / Song of the volga boatmen / Silent lips / My fair maiden / Smiling happiness of mine / Nechledil / Heaven blue I'll get for you / In my nest of heavenly blue / I love to kiss women / Now the clouds have rolled away / Stay with me forever / Oh maiden, oh maiden / Patiently smiling / What has given you this magic power? / You alone / He will come / Napolitana / Zorika, come back.
MC: LASTC 4
LP: LAST 4

IM ALLGAU (IN THE ALPS).
Tracks: / Polka party / Schnackl polka / Ich spiel fur mich / Der Lumpensammler / Auf dem hochsten berge / Frisch vom fass / Jodler / Wo der aurhahn baizt / De schean / Im schweinsgalopp / Schottische / Frieden in den bergen / Der lustige fritz / Fesche jugend.
LP: 8219951
MC: 8219954

IN CONCERT VOL 2.
LP: 2371 320

IN HOLLAND.
LP: 833244 1
MC: 833244 4

IN IRELAND.
LP: POLD 5197

INSTRUMENTALS FOR DANCING VOLS.1 & 2.
MCSET: 3271 137

INSTRUMENTALS IN LOVE VOLS.1 & 2.
Tracks: / Make this night last forever / Now I know / What now my love / Elizabethan serenade / I left my heart in San Francisco / Blame it on me / Games that lovers play / Man and a woman, A / Lara's theme / Never on Sunday / Fly me to the moon / This is my song / Way of love, The / It's going to take some time / Face in the crowd / Close to you / Summer knows, The / Heart of gold / Without you / Godfather love theme / Speak softly love / Wedding song (there is love) / I don't know how to love him / Love must be the reason.
MCSET: 3271 135

JAMES LAST GOES POP.
LP: 249 160

JAMES LAST IN CONCERT.
Tracks: / Prelude from l'arlesienne suite no.1 / Moonlight sonata / Ritual firedance / Fur Elise / Pastrale fron L'arlesienne suite no.2 / Italian Caprice / Triestess (Etude Op. 10 no.3) / Rondo alla turca / Toccata and fugue in D minor.
LP: . . . . LAST 2
MC: . . . . LASTC 2
LP: 2371 191

JAMES LAST IN RUSSIA.
Tracks: / Midnight in Moscow / Kalinka / Red sarafan, The / Russian folk dance / Cossack patrol / Lara's theme / Sabre dance / Evening bells / Two guitars / Not the wind / Stenka rasin / Between day and night.
LP: . . . . LAST 1
MC: . . . . LASTC 1
LP: 2371 293

JAMES LAST IN SCOTLAND.
Tracks: / Skye boat song / My love is like a red red rose / I love a lassie / Roamin' in the gloamin' / Scottish soldier, A / Will ye no come back again / I belong to Glasgow / Flower of Scotland / Auld lang syne / Ye banks and braes o bonnie doon / Days of auld lang syne / Keel row, The / Barren rocks of Aden / Loch Lomond / My bonnie Mary of Argyle / Annie laurie.
LP: . . . . POLD 5166
MC: . . . . POLDC 1566

JAMES LAST LIVE IN LONDON.
Tracks: / Intro '78 / Tiger feet / Radar love / Jesus loves you / Bridge over troubled water / I've got you under my skin / Was ich dir sagen will / Jog dig oas / Rum and coca cola / Quando, quando, quando / South America take it away / Lonely shepherd / Larry O'Gaff / Fire on the mountain / Center amigos / Schwarze estrella / Ay ay ay / Costa brava / Eso es el amor / Star wars / West Side story / Silly love songs / With one more look at you / Watch closely now / Love me tender / Rip it up / Don't be cruel / Jailhouse rock / Hound dog / Chicken reel / Turkey in the straw / Orange blossom special / Cockles and mussels / Daisy Daisy / Abide with me / Yes sir I can boogie / Sorry I'm a lady / Don't leave me this way / Don't cry for me Argentina / Games that lovers play.
2LP: 2672 046
MC: 3551 076

JAMES LAST PLAYS BACH.
LP: . . . . POLD 5218
MC: . . . . POLDC 5218

JAMES LAST PLAYS ROBERT STOLZ.
Tracks: / Two hearts in three - four time / My song of love (Theme from "The White Horse Inn") / Love Vienna mine / Mood for lovers, The / Fair or dark, I love them all / You shall be king of my heart / Say you to me / You too (From "The White Horse Inn".) / Goodbye (From "The White Horse Inn".) / Spring time in Vienna / Gypsy violin / We are young, we are full of life / Charming weather / Where is it? / Earning for you / Vienna, where wine and waltz are flowing / Your eyes (From "The White Horse Inn".) / Don't say goodbye (From "Wild Violets".) / Come into the park of Sanssouci / Salome / Before my fathers house / Last rose is blooming, The.
LP: 2371 768
MC: 3150 768
LP: . . . . LAST 6

JAMES LAST PLAYS THE GREATEST SONGS OF THE BEATLES.
Tracks: / Eleanor Rigby / Hard day's night, A / Let it be / Penny Lane / She loves you / Michelle / Ob la di ob la da / Hey Jude / Lady Madonna / All you need is love / Norwegian Wood / Yesterday.
LP: . . . . POLD 5119

JAMES LAST - TANGO (Last, James Orchestra).
Tracks: / La cumparsita / Adios, pampa mia / Flutes tango / Blue sky / A media luz / Amargura / Blue tango / Caminito / Rosita / Adios muchachos / Tango / Dancing the tango.
LP: 2372 080
MC: 3151 080
MC: . . . . POLDC 5151

KAPT'N JAMES - TAKE ME WITH YOU.
LP: 2475 563
MC: 3236 563

LAST FOR EVER.
2LP: 263 013 5
MCSET: 357 706 6

LAST FOR THE ROAD.
MC: 3150 624

LAST THE WHOLE NIGHT LONG.
LP: . . . . PTD 001
MC: . . . . PTDC 001
LP: . . . . PTD 5008

LEAVE THE BEST TO LAST.
Tracks: / Tell her about it / Karma chameleon / Wake me up before you go go / Heartbreaker / Take a chance on me / You can't hurry love / Uptown girl / Caribbean queen / That was yesterday / Ghostbusters / Hooray hooray it's a holi holiday / Agadoo / I just called to say I love you / Wanderer / Easy lover / Every breath you take / You're my heart you're my soul / Super trouper / Half a minute / Do the conga / Hello / One more night / Red red wine / Live is life / Imagine.
LP: . . . . PROLP 7
MC: . . . . PROMC 7

LOVE MUST BE THE REASON.
LP: 2371 281

LOVE THIS IS MY SONG.
LP: 583 553

MAKE THE PARTY LAST.
LP: . . . . POLD 5154
LP: 2371 612

MELODIES OF THE CENTURY (Last, James & His Orchestra).
Tracks: / La vie en rose / Spanish eyes / Lili Marlene / Importance of your love, The / On the street where you live / Reach for a star / Moon river / Arrivederci Roma / La strada / Petite fleur / Nature boy / El condor pasa.
LP: 2372 116
MC: 3151 166

MEMORIES OF RUSSIA.
LP: 2371 856

MUSIC OF JAMES LAST.
2LP: 2683 010

MY FAVOURITE CLASSICS.
Tracks: / Impromptu no. 2 in A flat / Chanson triste / Moonlight sonata / In mir klingt ein lied / Moldau / Adagio / Intermezzo from Cavalleria Rusticana / Traumerai / Elvira madigan / One fine day / Air from suite No. 3 (In D) / To the spring.
LP: 2437 988
MC: 3158 304

MY FAVOURITE FOLKSONGS.
Tracks: / Alle Vogel sind schon da / Wem gott will rechte gunst erweisen / Es blies ein jager who in sein horn / Du du Liegst mir im Herzen / Horch, was kommt von Drauben rein / Jetzt kommen die lustigen Tage / Hab'mein Wagen vollgeladen / Kommt a Vogerl geflogen / Auf der schwabsche Elsebahne.
LP: 2437 992
MC: 3158 308

MY FAVOURITE INSTRUMENTALS.
Tracks: / String of pearls / Tico tico / Granada / Brazil / St. Louis blues / Hava nagila / Petite fleur / Cherry pink and apple blossom white / You are my sunshine / La Bamba / Amor, amor, amor / Copacabana.
LP: 2437 989
MC: 3158 305

MY FAVOURITE LOVE SONGS.
Tracks: / Whiter shade of pale, A / Wedding song (there is love) / What now my love / Man and a woman, A / I don't know how to love him / Air that I breathe, The / This is my song / Games that lovers play / Speak softly love / Hey Jude / Romeo and Juliet / Tenderly.
LP: 2437 987
MC: 3158 303

MY FAVOURITE PARTY SONGS.
Tracks: / La bostella / Charleston / Black bottom / Where is your hair, augustus / What are you doing with your knee dear john / Just wait a little while / Your eyes / Don't say goodbye / Come into the park of sanssouci / Sonny boy / Handsome gigolo / Chattanooga choo choo / Rock around the clock / See you later alligator / Hound dog / Don't ha ha / Shake hands / Can't buy me love / Soley soley / Amarillo / Save your kisses for me / Schmidtchen schleicher / Fernando / Hands up / Michaela / Y viva Espana.
MC: 3158 309
LP: 243 799 3

MY FAVOURITE POLKAS.
Tracks: / Schnutzenliesel / Anneliese / Trompeten echo / Vienna i remember / Flyer's march / Anvil polka / Rosamunde / Herz-Schmerz-polka / Adelheid / Wochenend und sonnenschein / Tritsce tratsch polka / Rose of the mountain.
LP: 243 799 0

MY FAVOURITE ROMANTIC SONGS.
Tracks: / Lonely sheperd / La vie en rose / Endless journey / Moonglow/ picnic / Ave Maria / Let it be / Ballade pour Adeleine / Biscaya / South of the border / I left my heart in san fransisco / Moonlight serenade / When sweetly the moonlight sleeps on the hills.
MC: 3158 301
LP: 243 798 5

MY FAVOURITE SHANTIES.
Tracks: / Eine seefahrt / Die is lustig / Nimm uns mit Kapitan auf die reise / Alloah oe / Banks of Sacramento, The / Junge komm bald wieder / Webb das Schifferklavieran / Bord ertont / Rolling home / Hamburg ist ein schones Stadchen.
LP: 2437 991
MC: 3158 307

MY FAVOURITE WORLD HITS.
Tracks: / Somewhere my love (from Dr Zhivago) / Lili Marlene / Elizabethan serenade / Yesterday / Song from Moulin Rouge / Spanish eyes / In the mood / Song sung blue / La Paloma / Guantanamera / Plaisir d'amour / El Condor Pasa.
LP: 2437 986
MC: 3158 302

MYSTIQUE.
LP: 2372 162
MC: 3151 162

NON STOP DANCING 18 (Last, James Orchestra).
MC: 3150 723

NON STOP DANCING '69.
LP: 249 294

NON STOP DANCING '70.
LP: 2371 04

NON STOP DANCING '71.
LP: 2371 111

NON STOP DANCING '81 (Last, James & His Orchestra).
Tracks: / Fanfare for the common man / Can't stop the music / Eldorado / Xanadu / Gimme some lovin' / Everything works if you let it / Santa Maria / Sexy eyes / Coming up / Ten o'clock postman / Master blaster / You're ok / Feels like I'm in love / Take your time / Matador / Why / Seduction / Lovely one / Red light / Jump to the beat / Late in the evening / They do the samba.
LP: 2372 050

NON STOP DANCING '82.
Tracks: / Hands up / Japanese boy / Agadou / Chequered love / I've done everything for you / La, la, la, la / I've seen that face before / Super freak / In for a penny / Wem / Dich zu lieben / Can you feel it / Ai no corrida / Crazy music / She's a bad mama jama / Ghost town / Hold on tight / Green door / Hearts / Everlasting love / You drive me crazy / Urgent / Bette Davis eyes / Oh no no / Endless love.
LP: 2372101

NON STOP DANCING '83 - PARTY POWER.
Tracks: / Best years of our lives / Shadows of the night / Hard to say i'm sorry / Eye of the tiger / Africa / Abracadabra / Words / Let's go dancing / Pass the dutchie / Sexual healing / Down under / Saddle up / Don't go.
LP: . . . . POLD 5094

NON STOP DANCING '85.
Tracks: / Reach out / Jump (for my love) / Dancing with tears in my eyes / Sad songs / Such a shame / I won't let the sun go down on me / Magdalena / She bop / I just called to say I love you / Loneliness / Ghostbusters / Uauauaua / Catch me I'm falling / Oh Rosita / Wake me up before you go go / It's a hard life / Smalltown boy / Searchin' / Two tribes / When doves cry / 1,000 and 1 nights / Stuck on you / Exodus.
LP: . . . . POLD 5172
MC: . . . . POLDC 5172

NON STOP DANCING '69/2.
LP: 249 354

NON STOP DANCING SOUND.
Tracks: / My sharona / Pop musik / Don't stop 'til you get enough / Sad eyes / Knock on wood / Over & over / Good times / Rise / Lead me on / I was made for lovin' you / After the love has gone.
LP: 2371991

NON STOP DANCING SPECIAL (Last, James & His Orchestra).
Tracks: / You want to dance / Sweet Gypsy Rose / Goodbye yellow brick road / 48 crash / Feeling stronger every day / Ballroom blitz / Ooh baby / Touch me in the morning / Brother Louie / Joy to the world / Do you wanna dance / Shady lady / Air that I breathe, The / Jet / This flight tonight / Juanita / Best thing that ever happened to me / Tiger feet / Dan the banjo man.
2LP: 268 121 0

NON STOP DANCING VOL 12.
LP: 2371 141

NON STOP DANCING VOL 13.
LP: 2731 189

NON STOP DANCING VOL 14.
LP: 2371 319

NON STOP DANCING VOL 15.
LP: 2371 376

NON STOP DANCING VOL 16.
LP: 2371 444

NON STOP EVERGREEN.
Tracks: / Deep in the heart of Texas / Manana / Sugarbush / Exodus song / Who's sorry now / La Bamba / Love is a many splendoured thing / My happiness / Rum and coca cola / Quando, quando, quando / South America take it away / Goody goody / Ain't she sweet / Bei mir bist du schon / Blacksmith's blues, The / Sixteen tons / Don't fence me in / Night and day / In the mood / How high the moon / Happy days are here again / Yearning / La Bostella.
MC: 191 127-7
LP: 249 370
LP: . . . . PWKLP 4020 P
MC: . . . . PWKMC 4020 P

NON STOP PARTY.
Tracks: / Schone maid / Komm gib mir deine hand / Ja, mir san mit'n radl da / Mein orma fahrt im Huhnerstall / O, wie bist du schon / Polonaise blanenese / Schneewalzer / Das kannst du nicht ahnen / Du darfst mich lieben fur drei tolle tage / Du kannst nicht treu sein / Wir kommen alle in den Himmel.
LP: 2437 994
MC: 3158 310

NON-STOP DANCING.
Tracks: / Best years of our lives / Shadows of the night / Hard to say I'm sorry / Eye of the tiger / Africa / Abracadabra / Let's go dancing / Pass the dutchie / Sexual healing / Down under / Saddle up / Don't go.
LP: 236 203

OLE.
LP: 2371 384

PARADISE.
Tracks: / Paradise / Gulf of Catania / Spanish dreams / Breton summer / Tropical paradise / Sunny hours / Helgoland / Windjammer / Daydreams / Kite flying / Sunset at Dunmore Head / Sun in your eyes.
MC: . . . . POLDC 5163
LP: . . . . POLD 5163

PIANO A GO GO.
Tracks: / Java / My Bonnie / Maria / Lingering on / Mack the knife / Everybody loves a lover / Happy days are here again / My guy's come back / Mexico City / Poeme / Bei mir bist du schon / America.
LP: . . . . CN 2105
MC: CN4 2105

PLAYS MOZART.
LP: 839 043 1
MC: 839 043 4

PLUS (Last, James & Astrud Gilberto).
Tracks: / Samba do Soho / I'm nothing without you / Champagne and caviar / Listen to your heart / Moonrain / Caravan / Amor essom / Saci / Forgive me / With love / Agua de Beber.
LP: . . . . POLD 5207
MC: . . . . POLDC 5207

POLKA PARTY.
Tracks: / Serenade / Trumpet hop / Lisa the huntsman's lass / Tritsch tratsch polka / Untern linden / Leichtenstein polka / Too fat polka / Annen polka / Goblin's parade / Mill in the Black Forest / Flyers march / Anvil polka.
LP: 2371 190
LP: . . . . LAST 3

POP SYMPHONIES (Last, James & His Orchestra).
Tracks: / Lady in red / Nights in white satin / Power of love / Another day in love / Hotel California / Living years, The / Sorry seems to be the hardest word / Broken wings / Africa / One more night / Hard to say i'm sorry / Angelia.
MC: 849 429 4
LP: 849 429 1

REFLECTIONS.

Tracks: / Reflection (Erinnerungen) / I.R.E.L.A.N.D. / Song for guy / Unforgotten / Arioso / Daydreams / Nocturne (Op.72.no.1) / Caprice (no.18) / Reverie / Sorry Elton / No answer / Missing.
MC: . . . . POLDC 5121
LP: . . . . POLD 5121

ROMANTIC DREAMS.
Tracks: / Going home / Scarborough Fair / Amazing Grace / Es waren zwei / Konigskinder / Paintings / Abide with me / Yosaku / When Irish eyes are smiling / Careless love / Rose of Tralee, The / Country train / Cockles and mussels / Londonderry Air.
MC: 3151 018
LP: 2372018

ROSE OF TRALEE AND OTHER IRISH FAVOURITES.
Tracks: / Maggie / Irish stew / Coulin / Come back to Erin / Ril mhor bhaile an chalaidh / An eriskay love lilt / On the banks of my own lovely Lee / Summer in Dublin / When Irish eyes are smiling / Rose of Tralee, The / Londonderry air / Sweepstake / Cockles and mussels / I.R.E.L.A.N.D..
LP: . . . . POLD 5131
MC: . . . . POLDC 5131
LP: 815 984 1

ROSES FROM THE SOUTH (James Last Plays Johann Strauss).
Tracks: / Roses from the South / Leichtes blut / Tales from the Vienna Woods / Annen polka / Voices of spring / Waltz / Thunder and lightning / Emperor waltz / Eljen a magyar / Radetzky march.
LP: 2372 051
MC: 3151 051
LP: . . . . SPELP 113
MC: . . . . SPEMC 113

SCHLIESS DIE AUGEN.
LP: 2475 737
MC: 3236 737

SEDUCTION.
Tracks: / Fantasy / Dancing shadows / Vibrations / Dancing shadows / Seduction / Falling star / So excited / Night drive / Glow / Infight / It's over.
LP: 2372 023

SING MIT...8.
LP: 2372 060

SING MIT LABDIE PUPPEN'TANZEN.
LP: 2372 106
MC: 3151 106

SKY BLUE.
Tracks: / Sky blue / Old folks get together, An / Three men in a boat / First meeting / Rio / Guido's love song / Hong Kong / Kowloon / New York (from Central Park to Tiffany's) / Amsterdam / LH 903 diverted to Munich / On the beach / Journey to Greece / Finale.
LP: . . . . POLD 5181
MC: . . . . POLDC 5181

SUMMER HAPPENING.
LP: 2371 133

SUPERLAST - SUPERPARTY.
Tracks: / Juliet / Africa / Love is a stranger / Moonlight shadow / Living on video.
LP: 817 329-1
MC: 817 329-4

SWING WITH JAMES LAST.
Tracks: / Study in brown, A / Who cares? / Perdido / Barcarole / Peach, The / Nutcracker / All by myself / Heart and soul / Last but not least / Where or when / Heart of rock 'n' roll.
MC: . . . . POLDC 5194

TEN YEARS NON STOP JUBILIEE.
2LP: 266 0111

THIS IS JAMES LAST.
LP: 104 678

TRAUMSCHIFF (LOVEBOAT) (TV Theme).
Tracks: / Traumschiff thema / Brasilien / Heidelinde / Bali / Dinner-marsch / Thailand / Mexico / Love theme / Ich habe das leben gelebt / Sadness.
LP: 831 129-1
MC: 831 129-4

TRUMPET A GO GO.
Tracks: / American patrol / Wheels / Granada / Never on Sunday / La paloma / Ave Maria / Tico tico / Delicado / Cherry pink and apple blossom white / La bamba / Greensleeves / Mexican hat dance / Passion flower / Mexico city.
LP: . . . . LAST 7
MC: . . . . LASTC 7
LP: 249 239

VERY BEST OF JAMES LAST.
LP: 2371 054
MC: 3150059

VIOLINS IN LOVE.
Tracks: / Air that I breathe, The / Was ich dir sagen will / don't let the sun go down on me / Sound of silence, The / Hey Jude / Unchained melody / Let it be / You make me feel brand new / Whiter shade of pale, A / Violins in love.
LP: . . . . UNKNOWN
LP: . . . . CN 2100
MC: CN4 2100

VIVA VIVALDI.
Tracks: / Primavera (Spring) / Springtime dream, A / Sicilian wedding / Largo / La cappella di venezia / La danza di Verona / La festa degli angeli / La strada d'amore / Piazza palermo / Winter / Addio mare / La stravaganza.
LP: . . . . POLD 5185
MC: . . . . POLDC 5185

VOODOO PARTY.
LP: 2371 235

WIR WOLLEN SPAB.
LP: 2372 159
MC: 3151 159

WORLD HITS (Last, James & His Orchestra).
Tracks: / People will say we're in love / September in the rain / What is this thing called love / I only have eyes for you / Charmaine / Besame mucho / Singin' in the rain / Tenderly / Volare / I've got you under my skin.
LP: 237 189 1

YESTERDAY'S MEMORIES.
LP: 2870 117

Last Man In Europe

SONGS FROM THE ARK.
LP: . . . . SITU 5

Last Metro

LAST METRO, THE (Film soundtrack) (Various artists).
LP: . . . . SL 9504

Last Night At The

LAST NIGHT AT THE PINDAR (Aba Daba) (Various artists).
Tracks: / Daisy Bell: *Dunbar, Norma* / Oh the fairies: *Beeching, Chris* / Letter, The: *Hayes, Vincent* / Every little movement: *Coulston, Jenny* / Lion and Albert, The: *Littledale, Trevor* / And then again, it might not: *Green, Hilary* / Vicar, The: *Owen, Christopher* / Sister Sarah: *McManus, Jim* / You go to my head: *Williams, Bronwen* / Night I appeared as Macbeth, The: *Curry, Shaun* / Ain't it nice?: *Various artists* / Thanks for the memory: *Bayler, Terence* / Good man is hard to find, A: *Butler, Katy* / My old dutch: *Baker, Kent.*
MC: . . . . TT 005

Last Night Of The

LAST NIGHT OF THE PROMS (Various artists).
MC: 420 085-4

Last Of England

LAST OF ENGLAND (Film Soundtrack) (Various artists).
LP: . . . . IONIC 1

Last Of The Mohicans

LAST OF THE MOHICANS, THE (see Cooper, James Fenimore) (Mason, James (nar)).

Last Of The Teenage

SATELLITE HEAD GONE SOFT.
LP: . . . . RAZ 47

Last Option

BURNING.
LP: . . . . FACE 003

Last Party

LOVE HANDLES.
LP: . . . . HRLP 001

Last Place On Earth

LAST PLACE ON EARTH, THE (Film soundtrack) (Various artists).
LP: . . . . ISTA 8
MC: . . . . ISTC 8

Last Poets

FREEDOM EXPRESS.
LP: . . . . JAZID 8LP

OH MY PEOPLE.
LP: . . . . CELL 6108
LP: . . . . CAL 208

Last Resort

DEATH OR GLORY (See also Combat 84).

WAY OF LIFE, A (Skinhead Anthems).
LP: . . . . LR 1

Last Rites

REACTION, THE.
LP: . . . . ESSLP 01

Last, Robert

FOR DANCING.
2LP: . . . . DS 3252/12

Last Roundup

TWISTER.
LP: . . . . ROUNDER 9006
MC: . . . . ROUNDER 9006C

Last, Roy

GOODTIMES AHEAD.
LP: . . . . JP 102

Last Run

LAST RUN, THE (Film soundtrack) (Various artists).
Tracks: / Last run: *Various artists* / Last run, The (main title): *Various artists* / Border crossing: *Various artists* / Spanish coast: *Various artists* / Claudie says yes: *Various artists* / Rickard escapes: *Various artists* / Last run: *Various artists* / Double cross: *Various artists* / Yo te amo: *Various artists* / Claudie's stockings: *Various artists* / Trap: *Various artists* / End title: *Various artists.*
LP: . . . . MCA 25116
MC: . . . . MCAC 25116
LP: 2315 072

Last Stand

BOSTON CALLIN'.
LP: . . . . OIR 013

Last Starfighter

LAST STARFIGHTER, THE (Film Soundtrack) (Various artists).
Tracks: / Outer space chase: *Various artists* / Into the starscape: *Various artists* / Planet of Rylos, The: *Various artists* / Death blossom: *Various artists* / Incommunicado: *Various artists* / Never crossed my mind: *Various artists* / Return to Earth: *Various artists* / Hero's march, The: *Various artists* / Centauri dies: *Various artists.*
LP: . . . . SCRS 1007

Last Tango In Paris

LAST TANGO IN PARIS (Film Soundtrack Music) (Various artists).
Tracks: / Last tango in Paris - tango: *Various artists* / Jeanne: *Various artists* / Girl in black: *Various artists* / Last tango in Paris - ballad: *Various artists* / Fake Ophelia: *Various artists* / Picture in the rain: *Various artists* / Return - tango: *Various artists* / It's over: *Various artists* / Goodbye (un largo adios): *Various artists* / Why did she choose you: *Various artists* / Last tango in Paris - jazz waltz: *Various artists.*
LP: . . . . UAS 29440

LAST TANGO IN PARIS (Original Soundtrack) (Various artists).
LP: . . . . LN 10286
MC: L4N 10286
LP: 1828971
MC: 1828974

Last Temptation Of

LAST TEMPTATION OF CHRIST (see under Gabriel, Peter) (Gabriel, Peter).

Last Touch

LADIES OF GREY.
LP: . . . . RIEN 3
MC: . . . . RIENK 3

Last Waltz

LAST WALTZ, THE (See under Band) (Band).

Last Year When...

LAST YEAR WHEN I WAS YOUNG (Bennett, Hywel).
MC: . . . . CAB 015

Laswell, Bill

BASELINES.
LP: . . . . ROUGH 51

BEST OF BILL LASWELL (Laswell, Bill Material/Friends).
LP: . . . . CEL 6715

HEAR NO EVIL.
Tracks: / Lost roads / Bullet hole memory / Illinois central / Assassin / Stations of the cross / Kingdom come.
LP: . . . . VE 12
MC: . . . . TCVE 12

POINTS BLANK/METLABLE SNAPS (Laswell, Bill and John Zorn).
LP: . . . . NML 8604

Laszlo, Ken

DON'T CRY.
MC: . . . . PRC 002

Late Flowering Love

LATE FLOWERING LOVE (see under Betjeman, Sir John) (Betjeman, Sir John).

Late Night Band

LATE NIGHT BAND.
LP: . . . . PLR 076

Late Notes

HALLELUJAH SKA.
LP: . . . . PHZA 058

Late Phoenix (bk)

LATE PHOENIX, A (Catherine Aird) (Bailey, Robin (nar)).
MC: . . . . CAT 4031

Late Show

SNAP.
Tracks: / Bristol stomp / Only child / Wish I'd stayed home and watched T.V. / Midnight rendezvous / Chains / Funny how love can be / I wrote a book / Ain't gonna stamp on his face / She cried / My love sticks out for you.
LP: . . . . TXS 134

Lateasha

LATEASHA.
Tracks: / It just ain't easy / Good lovin' / I'll be there for you / When love strikes twice / Gonna groove you right / Wanna be mine / Crazy for you / Dance floor / It's about your lovin' / There's a ghost in my room / Only you can get me off / Your love.
LP: . . . . ZL 72751
MC: . . . . ZK 72751

Lateef, Yusef

ANGEL EYES.
2LP: . . . . SJL 2238

CENTAUR & THE PHOENIX, THE.
Tracks: / Revelation / Apathy / Ev'ry lady / Centaur & the phoenix, The / Iqbal / Summer song / Philanthropist, The.
LP: . . . . RSLP 337

CONTEMPLATION.
Tracks: / Hazing / Rip de boom / Teef / I need you / Back yard / Sassy Ann.
LP: . . . . AFF 120

GOLDEN FLUTE, THE.
Tracks: / Road runner / Straighten up and fly right / Oasis / I don't stand a ghost of a chance with you / Exactly like you / Golden flute, The / Rosetta / Head hunters / Smart set, The.
LP: . . . . JAS 63

GONG.
Tracks: / Prayer to the east / I got it bad and that ain't good / Eighty five forty (8540) / Twelfth street / Sounds of nature / Suelb / Lover man / Check blues / Gypsy arab / Night in Tunisia / Love dance / Sram / Endura / Delilah.
2LP: . . . . SJL 2226

MORNING (Savoy sessions).
Tracks: / Morning / O'blues / Ameena / Metaphor / Yusef's mood / Blues in space / G. Bouk / Polarity / Midday / Happyology / Space / Beginning, The / Beauregard.
LP: . . . . SJL 2205

SAX MASTERS.
2LP: . . . . VJD 512

YUSEF LATEEF.
Tracks: / Outside blues / Solid blues / Blues rocky / Dexterity / Trudy's delight / Introlude / Train stop / Big foot.
LP: . . . . JR 104

Latimore

EVERY WAY BUT WRONG.
LP: . . . . MALP 007

GOOD TIME MAN.
LP: . . . . MAL 7423

I'LL DO ANYTHING FOR YOU.
LP: . . . . MAL 7414

SINGING IN THE KEY OF LOVE.
LP: . . . . MAL 7409
MC: . . . . MALC 7409

SLOW DOWN.
LP: . . . . MAL 7443
MC: . . . . MALC 7443

Latin...

AN INTRODUCTION TO LATIN HIP-HOP (Various artists).
Tracks: / Let me be the one: *Sa-Fire* / Tender heart: *Leather & Lace* / I wanna break night with you: *Diva (film)* / Clave rocks: *Amoretto* / Do you wanna dance: *Bad Boy Orchestra.*
LP: . . . . LEFTLP 6
MC: LEFTC6

BAZ FE JAZZ PRESENTS ILLICIT LATIN VOL. 1 (Various artists).
Tracks: / Jammin' with Joey: *Pastrana, Joey* / Fueri e cara: *Rivera, Ismael* / Jumpy: *Colon, Johnny* / Joe Cubas madness: *Cuba, Joe* / Mama guela: *Fania Allstars* / Melao papa el sabo: *Palmieri, Charlie* / Ya llego descarca: *Rodriguez, Pete* / Jala con Joey: *Pastrana, Joey* / Rush hour in Hong Kong: *Ramirez, Louie.*
MC: . . . . TCHOT 132
LP: . . . . HOT 132

CALIENTE - HOT (Various artists).
LP: . . . . NW 244

CLUB CLASS (Various artists).
Tracks: / Cloud nine: *Pucho & His Latin Soul Brothers* / Ghetto, The: *24 Karat Black* / Selim: *Lytle, Johnny* / Got my mojo working: *Hawks, Billy* / Gumbo fillet: *Poindexter, Pony* / Can't we smile: *Smith, Johnny "Hammond"* / Talking

about J.C.: *Young, Larry* / Minority: *Gryce, Gigi*.
LP: . . . . **BGP 1032**

COOL (Various artists).
Tracks: / Yeh yeh: *Santamaria, Mongo* / Money's getting cheaper: *Witherspoon, Jimmy* / Wade in the water: *Big Soul Band, The* / Animal farm: *Smith, Johnny "Hammond"* / Soul sauce (guachi guaro): *Tjader, Cal* / I'm ready: *Spann, Otis* / Soul roach: *Saunders, Merl* / Talking 'bout my woman: *McDuff, Brother Jack* / Pool shark: *Jackson, Willis* / Eyesight to the Blind: *Allison, Mose* / Tacos: *Santamaria, Mongo* / Step out and git it: *Nomos* / My train: *Saunders, Merl* / Canteloupe island: *Pucho & His Latin Soul Brothers* / Parchman farm: *Allison, Mose* / Peas 'n' rice: *McCoy, Freddie*.
LP: . . . . **KENT 077**

DANCE JUICE VOL.1 (Various artists).
Tracks: / Jungle strut: *Ammons, Gene* / Say Jack: *Green, Benny* / Something different: *Adderley, Cannonball* Quartet / So What: *Jefferson, Eddie* / Mambo with moody: *Moody, James* / Milestones: *Murphy, Mark*/ Spiderman: *McCoy, Freddie* / Kevin Devin: *Lytle, John Quintet* / Something Frantic: *King Curtis* / La bamba: *Pike, Dave*.
LP: . . . . **BGP 1005**

DANCE JUICE VOL.2 (Various artists).
Tracks: / Wutherin' like thuther 'n': *Jackson, W* / Black whip: *Jones, Ivan "Boogaloo Joe"* / Fire down below: *Curson, Ted* / Night in Tunisia: *Metronome All Star Band* / Hold it: *Butler, Billy* / Love for sale: *Pitts, Trudy* / O baby: *Hawks, Billy* / Night train: *Bryant, Rusty*.
LP: . . . . **BGP 1016**

DANCE JUICE VOL.3 (Various artists).
Tracks: / Milestones: *Latin Jazz Quintet* / Big John Grady: *Lytle, Johnny* / Thunderbird: *Jackson, Willis*/ It's like love: *Murphy, Mark* / Raunchy Rita: *Foster, Frank* / Sister Sadie: *Andy & The Bey Sisters*/ 6.30 blues: *Jones, Ivan "Boogaloo Joe"* / Money (that's what I want): *Roach, Freddie*.
LP: . . . . **BGP 1022**

DANCE THE LAMBADA (Various artists).
MC: . . . . **FLYMC 102**

DANCE THE LATIN GROOVE VOL 1 (Various artists).
Tracks: / Boss tres bien: *Various artists* / Slip slip: *Various artists* / La bamba: *Various artists*/ Wack wack: *Various artists* / Louie Louie: *Various artists* / I'll never forget you: *Various artists*/ Mambo Inn: *Various artists* / Peanut vendor: *Various artists* / Johnny's boogaloo: *Various artists*/ Que mal es querer: *Various artists* / Baby bring it to me: *Various artists*.
LP: . . . . **HOT 101**
MC: . . . . **TCHOT 101**

DANCE THE LATIN GROOVE VOL 2 (Various artists).
Tracks: / Mi mambo conga: *Various artists* / Here comes Candi: *Candido* / Come 'an get it: *Tjader, Cal* & Eddie Palmieri / Fever: *La Lupe* / Jive samba: *Woo, Gerry & Jack Contanzo* / Hit the bongo: *Puente, Tito*/ Hey sister: *Santamaria, Monguito* / Identify yourself: *Cafe* / Cumbeyea: *Ramirez, Louie* / Manteca: *Allegre All Stars*.
MC: . . . . **TCHOT 115**
LP: . . . . **HOT 115**

DANCE THE LATIN GROOVE VOL 3 (Various artists).
Tracks: / Boogaloo mania: *Palmieri, Charlie* / Vente conmigo: *Fania Allstars* / Jumpin' with symphony Sid: *Puente*, Tito / Mambo village: *Santamaria, Monguito* / Cannomology: *Machito* / Funky shingaling: *Nando, King*/ Borin quen: *Rivera, Ismael* / Do the boogaloo: *Rodriquez, Pete* / Soul gritty: *Robles, Ralph* / Boogaloo le bron: *Le Bron Brothers*.
LP: . . . . **HOT 116**
MC: . . . . **TCHOT 116**

DANCE THE LATIN GROOVE VOL 4 (Various artists).
Tracks: / Right on: *Barretto, Ray* / El hijo de obatalo: *Barretto, Ray* / De panama a nueva york: *Blades*, Ruben & Pete Rodriquez / Shaft, Theme from: *Bataan, Joe* / Last tango in Paris: *Santamaria, Mongo* / Soul makossa: *Fania Allstars* / Mambo jazz: *Cruz, Bobby & Richardo Ray* / Joe Cuba's latin hustle: *Cuba, Joe*.
LP: . . . . **HOT 117**
MC: . . . . **TCHOT 117**

LAMBADA (Various artists).
LP: **4660551**
MC: **4660554**

LAMBADA (Various artists).
LP: . . . . **DINLP 6**
MC: . . . . **DINMC 6**

LAMBADA BRAZIL (Various artists).
Tracks: / Lambarda do remelxo: *Banda Cheiro De Amor* / Zorra: *Caldas, Luiz* / Algeria da cidade: *Menezes*, Margereth / Meia lua inteira: *Veloso, Caetano* / 'Ve estrelas: *Ramalho, Elba* / Roda baiana: *Banda Cheiro* De Amor / Dancando merengue: *Banda Tomalira* / Tenda do amor (magia): *Menezes, Margereth* / La vem o trio: *Banda Tomalira* / Lambada: *Carioca* / Doida: *Ramalho, Elba* / Ode e adao: *Caldas, Luiz* / 'Vou te pegar: *Nonato Do Cavaquinho* / Grande Gandhi: *Caldas, Luiz* / Careou: *Caldas, Luiz*.
LP: **8415801**
MC: **8415804**

LAMBADA DANCE MUSIC (Various artists).
Tracks: / Lambada: *Caravelas* / El bimbi: *Gomez, Nico* / Aquarella: *Gomez, Nico* / Lambada dance: *Caravelas*/ O barquinho: *Gomez, Nico* / Samba de una nota so: *Gomez, Nico* / Lambada dance and lambada mega club: *Caravelas*/ El ladron: *Gomez, Nico* / Desafinado: *Gomez, Nico* / Brasil: *Gomez, Nico* / Noch cubana: *Gomez, Nico* / Din din din: *Gomez, Nico*.
MC: **410463**

LAMBADA - EL RITMO DO BRASIL (17 original Brazilian lambadas) (Various artists).
Tracks: / Lambada: *La Banda* / Lambada de noche: *La Banda* / Lambada de amore: *La Banda* / Doida: *Vitoria*/ Fricote: *Vitoria* / Pinga ne mim: *Vitoria* / A roda: *Vitoria* / Xo paturi: *Banda Marrakeche*/ Sou de Bahia: *Banda Marrakeche* / Grito de Igualdade: *Banda Saliva Doce* / Coceirinha: *Banda Tiete Tips*/ O fricote de galinha: *Moraes, Paulo* / A vendor de caqui: *Moraes, Paulo* / Vem pra mim: *Moraes, Paulo*/ Doce multidao: *Brito, Marcia* / Brilho egito: *Viera Tania & Banda Press* / Lambada (power mix): *Ipanema*.
LP: . . . . **INS 5025**
MC: . . . . **TCINS 5025**

LATIN JAZZ VOL.1 (Various artists).
Tracks: / Nica's dream: *Burrell, Kenny* / Gunky: *Lytle, Johnny* / Mambo inn: *Taylor, Billy Trio* / Caravan: *Pucho & His Latin Soul Brothers* / Sambop: *Adderley, Cannonball* / Baion baby: *Stitt, Sonny* / Tin tin deo: *Forrest, Jimmy* / Montuneando: *Santamaria, Mongo*.
LP: . . . . **BGP 1023**

LATIN JAZZ VOL.2 (Various artists).
Tracks: / Ping pong: *Blakey, Art/Jazz Messengers* / Mau mau: *Farmer, Art Septet* / Manteca: *Garland, Red Trio* / Sea food wally: *Rodriguez, Willie* / Screamin': *McDuff, Brother Jack* / Fat man: *Montego Joe*/ Mambo ricci: *Dolphy, Eric & Latin Jazz* / Chop sticks: *Braith, George*.
LP: . . . . **BGP 1027**

LATIN PULSE (Various artists).
Tracks: / Sopa de pichon: *Machito & His Afro Cuban Salseros* / Pablo pueblo: *Blades, Ruben* / Ran kan kan: *Puente*, Tito / Kickapoo sky juice: *Fania Allstars* / Acuyuye: *Pacheco, Johnny* / Te conozco: *Lavoe, Hector*/ Hard hands: *Barretto, Ray* / Quimbara: *Cruz, Celia* / La verdad: *Palmieri, Eddie* / Jive samba: *Constanzo, Jack* / Me vengare: *La Lupe* / Mambo jazz: *Ray, Ricardo/Bobby Cruz*.
MC: . . . . **TCINS 5031**

LATIN SOUL VOLUME III (Various artists).
Tracks: / Cool jerk: *Ray, Ricardo* / Nitty gritty: *Ray, Ricardo* / Wipe out: *Barretto, Ray* / Young gifted and brown: *Bataan, Joe* / Sookie sookie: *Ray, Ricardo* / Work song: *Puente, Tito* / Sincerely: *Pastrana*, Joey / Yaya: *Ray, Ricardo* / Make it with you: *Pagan, Ralfi* / Lady marmalade: *Santamaria, Mongo*/ Shout: *Ray, Ricardo* / Song for my father: *Valentin, Bobby* / Grazing in the grass: *Orchestra Harlow*.
LP: . . . . **HOT 125**
MC: . . . . **TCHOT 125**

LATIN VOGUE, SEQUENCE 1 (Various artists).
Tracks: / Pete's boogaloo: *Various artists* / Green onions: *Various artists* / Ran kan kan: *Various artists*/ El chisme: *Various artists* / Alex mambo: *Various artists* / El manicero: *Various artists* / Tito on timbales: *Various artists* / Descarga: *Various artists* / Bamboleo: *Various artists* / Llora como yo: *Various artists* / New guaguanco: *Various artists* / Funky mama: *Various artists*.
LP: . . . . **HOT 131**
MC: . . . . **TCHOT 131**

LATINO CLUB! (Various artists).
Tracks: / Coro miyare: *Pacheco, Johnny* / Acid: *Barretto, Ray* / Ajiaco caliente: *D.R.* / Fania: *Bolanos*, Reinaldo / Ay mi cuba: *More, Benny* / Elpito (I'll never go back to Georgia): *Sabater, Cuba* / Vente conmigo: *Fania Allstars* / Taste of latin, A: *Merraro, R.* / Nadie se salya de la rumba: *Rodriguez, Siro* / Que sabroso: *Various artists*.
LP: . . . . **HOT 108**
MC: . . . . **TCHOT 108**

LATINO CLUB VOL.2 (Various artists).
LP: . . . . **HOT 133**
MC: . . . . **TCHOT 133**

MAMBO KINGS PLAY SONGS OF LOVE, THE (Various artists).
Tracks: / Mambo tipico: *Puente, Tito & His Orchestra* / La bochinchera: *Graciela* / La jicotea: *Ruiz, Rosendo* Jr / Sopa de pichon: *Machito & His Afro Cuban Salseros* / Mr lindo guaguanco: *Gonzales, Neno* / Mambo la libertad: *Rodriguez, Tito & His Orch* / El rey del timbal: *Puente, Tito & His Orchestra* / Mambo manila: *Rodriguez*, Tito & His Orch / Este nuevo ritmo: *Fajardo, Jose & His Orch* / Four beat mambo: *Puente, Tito & His Orchestra*/ Oyeme: *Machito & His Orchestra* / Joe Lustig mambo: *Rodriguez, Tito & His Orch* / A santa barbara: *Cruz, Celia* / Mambo rama: *Puente, Tito & His Orchestra* / Mambo suavecito: *Puente, Tito & His Orchestra* / Ay Jose: *Graciela* / Carmelina: *Valdezal, Fredito* / Mambo gallego: *Puente, Tito & His Orchestra* / Quimbombo: *Machito & His Afro Cuban Salseros* / Fumando espero: *Orquesta Super Colosal* / Ran kan kan: *Puente, Tito & His Orchestra* / La veradera: *Fajardo, Jose & His Orch*.
LP: . . . . **HOT 140**
MC: . . . . **TCHOT 140**

MUCHO CALOR (Various artists).
LP: . . . . **VSOP 47**

PERFECT COMBINATION (See under Perfect Combination) (Various artists).

RIO SAMBA (Various artists).
Tracks: / Lindo balao azul: *Various artists* / O carimbador maluco: *Various artists* / Menina veneno: *Various* artists / Bahno de espuma: *Various artists* / Galinha magricela, A: *Various artists* / Pegando fogo: *Various* artists / Mintuchura: *Various artists* / Rock da cachorra: *Various artists* / Estrelar: *Various artists*/ Baile dos passarinhos: *Various artists* / Descobridor dos sete mares: *Various artists* / Tic tic nervoso: *Various* artists / Comer comer: *Various artists* / E de chocolate: *Various artists* / Deixa eu te amar: *Various* artists / Betty Frigida: *Various artists* / Meu urshino blau blau: *Various artists* / Casanova: *Various* artists / Como eu quero: *Various artists* / Transase caretas: *Various artists* / Eva: *Various artists*/ On the rocks: *Various artists*.
LP: **445007**
MC: **845007**

RITMO CALIENTE (Salsa Greats vol.2) (Various artists).
Tracks: / Oye como va: *Puente, Tito* / Quitate la mascara: *Barretto, Ray* / Juan Pena: *Colon, Willie*/ El Malecon: *Orchestra Harlow* / El escencia del guaguanco: *Pacheco, Johnny* / Muneca: *Palmieri, Eddie*/ El pito (I'll never go back to Georgia): *Cuba, Joe* / Richies jala jala: *Ray, Ricardo* / Tu loco locoy yo traquillo: *Roena, Roberto* / Huracan: *Valentin, Bobby*.
LP: . . . . **HOT 107**
MC: . . . . **TCHOT 107**

RITMO CALIENTE BOX SET (Various artists).
LPS: . . . . **BOX 261**
MCSET: . . . . **TCBOX 261**

RITMO CALIENTE SALSA GREATS VOL.1 (Various artists).
Tracks: / Azucar: *Various artists* / Mi negra mariana: *Various artists* / Che che cole: *Various artists*/ Guaganco pa'l que sabe: *Various artists* / Pedro Navaja: *Various artists* / Arsenio: *Various artists*/ Senor serano: *Various artists* / Aguzate: *Various artists*.
MC: . . . . **TCHOT 102**
LP: . . . . **HOT 102**

THIS IS LATIN MUSIC (Various artists).
Tracks: / Batman's bugaloo: *Various artists* / Berimbau: *Various artists* / Viva tirado: *Various artists*/ Fania: *Various artists* / Pedro Navaja: *Various artists* / Richies jala jala: *Various artists* / Subway Joe: *Various artists* / Hard hands: *Various artists* / Asia minor: *Various artists* / Fat mama: *Various artists* / Wampo: *Various artists* / Me Recordoras: *Various artists*.
LP: . . . . **SHOT 1**
MC: . . . . **TCSHOT 1**

TWO NATIONS UNDER A GROOVE (Presented by Club Sandino) (Various artists).
Tracks: / Mambo chillun: *Hooker, John Lee* / Fight fire with fire: *Holiday, Shay* / No more doggin: *Gordon, Roscoe* / Hercules: *Neville, Aaron* / Scotty Boo: *Davis, Eddie* / Soul makossa: *Fania Allstars* / Pedro navaja: *Blades, Ruben* / Juan pachanga: *Fania Allstars* / Congo yambumba: *Palmieri, Eddie*.
LP: . . . . **HOT 127**

WE GOT LATIN SOUL (Various artists).
LP: . . . . **HOT 100**
MC: . . . . **TCHOT 100**

WE GOT LATIN SOUL VOL 2 (Various artists).
Tracks: / Use it before you lose it: *Valentin, Bobby* / Monkey see monkey: *Various artists* / Subway Joe: *Bataan, Joe* / Good lovin': *Various artists* / Willie baby: *Colon, Willie* / Bad breath: *Santamaria, Monguito*/ Gypsy woman: *Various artists* / Meditation: *Various artists* / Boogaloo blues: *Colon, Johnny* / Willie whopper: *Colon, Willie* / Big feet: *Various artists* / Funky blues: *Various artists*.
MC: . . . . **TCHOT 111**
LP: . . . . **HOT 111**

Latin All Stars

LATIN JAZZ FUSION.
Tracks: / Los bravos / Congo bongo / Jalin pachanga / Kickapoo sky juice / Piccadillo / Hermedad fania / Viva tirado.
LP: . . . . **HOT 110**
MC: . . . . **TCHOT 110**

Latin Alliance

LATIN ALLIANCE.
LP: . . . . **VUSLP 421**
MC: . . . . **VUSMC 421**

Latin American...

34 NON STOP SAMBAS (Various artists).
LP: . . . . **NAPLP 1**
MC: . . . . **NAPMC 1**

DANCE THE PASO DOBLE (Various artists).
Tracks: / Morena de mi copla: *Various artists* / Mi jaca: *Various artists* / En "er" mundo: *Various artists*/ Puerto del sol: *Various artists* / Coplas: *Various artists* / El gato montes: *Various artists* / Espana cani: *Various artists* / El relicario: *Various artists* / El Beso: *Various artists* / Cumana: *Various artists*.
LP: **8161671**
MC: **8161674**

DANCE THE TANGO (Various artists).
Tracks: / Akios muchachos: *Various artists* / Jalousie: *Various artists* / La paloma: *Various artists*/ Le plus beau tango du monde: *Various artists* / La cumparsita: *Various artists* / Violetta: *Various artists*/ Caminito: *Various artists* / Tomo y obligo: *Various artists* / Cueta a bajo: *Various artists* / Poema: *Various artists* / Violetta: *Various artists* / Adios pampa mia: *Various artists* / Silencio: *Various artists*.
LP: **8161681**
MC: **8161684**

FESTIVAL FOR LATIN AMERICA (Various artists).
LP: . . . . **GVR 220**

GRANDS CARNAVALS D'AMERIQUE LATINE (Various artists).
Tracks: / Rio de Janeiro: *Various artists* / Salvador de Bahia: *Various artists* / Veracruz: *Various artists*/ Oruro: *Various artists* / Barranquilla: *Various artists*.
LP: . . . . **ARN 33440**
MC: . . . . **ARN 433440**

LATIN AMERICAN MUSIC (Various artists).
MC: **301064**

LATIN FOR DANCING (Various artists).
LP: **2872 160**
MC: **3472 160**

LATIN GOLD (Various artists).
LPS: . . . . **EGS 4 5003**
MC: **EC/EGS/4/5003**

LATIN SOUND (Various artists).
2LP: **26 28021**

NIGHT OF LATIN SOUNDS (Various artists).
MC: . . . . **AM 1**

ROMANTIC TANGOS FROM BUENOS ARIES (Various artists).
LP: **26340**
MC: **40.26340**

SOUNDS LATIN (Various artists).
Tracks: / Memories are made of this: *Black, Stanley & His Piano with Latin-American Rhythm* / Meditation: *Ros, Edmundo* & His Orchestra / My Cherie amour: *Ros, Edmundo & His Orchestra* / Lover come back to me: *Various artists*/ Amor amor: *Muller, Werner & His Orchestra* / Be mine tonight: *Mantovani* / Man and a woman, A: *Ros, Edmundo* & His Orchestra / Eso es el amor: *Muller, Werner & His Orchestra* / Perhaps, perhaps perhaps: *Mantovani* / Cuban love song: *Ros, Edmundo & His Orchestra* / Love walked in: *Black*,

Stanley & His Piano with Latin-American Rhythm/ Yours: *Ros, Edmundo & His Orchestra* / Maria Elena: *Mantovani* / Felicidade: *Aldrich, Ronnie & His Two Pianos*.
LP: . . . . MOR 4

Latin Brothers

BLACK GIRL, THE.
MC: . . . . MCT 1021
LP: . . . . MLPS 1021

Latin Quarter

MICK AND CAROLINE.
Tracks: / I (together) / Remember / Freight elevator / Nomzamo / Negotiating with a loaded gun / Burn again / Love has gone / Night, The / Donovan's doorway / Men below, The.
LP: 208142
MC: 408142

MODERN TIMES.
Tracks: / Modern times / No ordinary return / Radio Africa / Toulouse / America for beginners / Eddie / No rope as long as time / Seaport September / New millionaires / Truth about John / Cora / Modern times (single) / Thin white duke / No rope as long as time.
LP: . . . . RHLP 1
MC: . . . . RHMC 1
LP: 209648
MC: 409648

SWIMMING AGAINST THE STREAM.
Tracks: / Swimming against the stream / Blameless / Wounded in action / Model son / After Marlina / Dominion / Close this account / Something isn't happening / Race me down / It makes my heart stop speaking / Slow waltz for Chile, A.
LP: . . . . PL 740 37
MC: . . . . PK 740 37

Latino Collection

LATINO COLLECTION (Various artists).
Tracks: / Always there: *Bobo, Willie* / Lucumi macumba voo doo: *Palmieri, Eddie* / Jungle fantasy: *Mann, Herbie* / Cubano chant: *Blakey, Art* / Hola muneca: *Smith, Lonnie* / Highest good: *Palmieri, Eddie*/ Manteca: *Mann, Herbie* / Teach me tonight: *Labelle, Patti*.
LP: . . . . HOT 114
MC: . . . . TCHOT 114

LaTour

LATOUR.
LP: 8493871
MC: 8493874

L'Attentat

KING OF THE NEIGHBOURHOOD.
LP: . . . . CR 8508

Lattisaw, Stacy

I'M NOT THE SAME GIRL.
Tracks: / Can't stop thinking about you / Coming alive / Now we are starting over again / He's just not you / I'm not the same girl / Toughen up / Together / I thought it took a little time.
LP: 790280 1

LET ME BE YOUR ANGEL.
Tracks: / Jump to the beat / Dynamite / You don't love me anymore / Dreaming / Let me be your angel / Don't you want to feel it / You know I like it / My love.
LP: . . . . K 50710
MC: K4 50710

PERFECT COMBINATION (Lattisaw, Stacy/Gill, Johnny).
LP: 790136 1

PERSONAL ATTENTION.
Tracks: / Personal attention / Love town / Let me take you down / Ain't no mountain high enough / He's got a hold on me / Find another lover / Changes / Every drop of your love / Call me / Electronic eyes.
LP: . . . . ZL 72620
MC: . . . . ZK 72620

TAKE ME ALL THE WAY.
Tracks: / Just jump into my life / Hard way, The / Take me all the way / Little bit of heaven, A / Long shot / Nail it to the wall / Love me like the first time / You ain't leavin / Over the top / One more night.
LP: . . . . ZL 72479
MC: . . . . ZK 72479

WHAT YOU NEED.
Tracks: / What you need / Dance for you / You touched the woman in me / R U man enuff / Guilty (lock me up) / Falling (in love again) / I don't have the heart / Where do we go from here / Tender love / That's the reason why I love you.
LP: . . . . ZL 72685
MC: . . . . ZK 72685

WITH YOU.
Tracks: / Feel my love tonight / Screamin off the top / It was so easy / Baby I love you / Love on a two way street / With you / Young girl / Spotlight / You take me to heaven.
LP: . . . . K 50798

Lauder, Sir Harry

GOLDEN AGE OF HARRY LAUDER, THE.
Tracks: / Stop your ticklin' Jock / I've something in the bottle for the morning / She is my daisy / I love a lassie / Wedding of Sandy McNab / That's the reason noo' I wear a kilt / Tobermory / Lass of Killiecrankie, The / Safest o' the family, The / We parted on the shore / Roamin' in the gloamin' / Wee Deoch an' Doris / We hoose among the heather / It's nicer to be in bed / Waggle o' the kilt, The / End of the road.
LP: . . . . GX 2505
MC: . . . . TCGX 2505

I LOVE A LASSIE.
Tracks: / I love a lassie / Roaming in the gloaming / Wedding of Sandy McNab / Waggle o' the kilt / O sing to me the auld Scotch songs / When I get back to bonnie Scotland / Keep right on to the end of the road / It's just like being at home / Bonnie Leezie Lindsay / I'm looking for a bonnie lass to love me / Love makes the world a merry go round / She is my daisy / Wee deoch an doris / I think I'll get wed in the summer / I like my old home town / I'm the boss of the hoose / I've loved her ever since she was a baby / Soosie MacLean.
LP: . . . . GEMM 169

SIR HARRY LAUDER VOL 2.
Tracks: / Stop your tickling Jock / Sound advice / It's nice to get up in the morning / Saturday night / Portobello lass / Kitty lads / Dear old cronies / Message boy / Somebody is waiting for me / He was very kind to me / O'er the hills to Ardentenny.
LP: . . . . GEMM 230

WE PARTED ON THE SHORE.
MC: . . . . SEV 13

Lauer, Martin

ICH WILL MORGEN SCHON IN TEXAS SEIN.
Tracks: / Ich will morgen schon in Texas sein / Heut' am Missouri morgen bei dir / Mississippi melodie / Smoky / Das ist die gross strasse / Heidelberg / Tabak und rum / Das alte haus von rocky docky / Lass mich gehn' Madeleine / Ich gab' mein herz / Ich kenn' die welt / Rosen und kusse / Rosen und dornen / Beat unde rote rosen / Oh serenader / Eine trane sagt mir die wahrheit.
LP: . . . . BFX 15324

TAXI NACH TEXAS.
Tracks: / Sacramento / Die letzte rose der prairie / Wenn ich ein cowboy war / Jim und Joe / Am lagerfeuer / Sein bestes pferd / Taxi nach Texas / John Brown's baby / Silver dollar / Roll 'em over / Die blauen berge / Pierde und sattel / King John / Cowboy lady / Smoky / Wenn die sonne scheint in Texas.
LP: . . . . BFX 15205

Laugh

SENSATION NUMBER ONE.
LP: . . . . AQUALP 001

Laughing Academy

SOME THINGS TAKE LONGER.
LP: . . . . SF 014

SUSPICION.
LP: . . . . BRAWALB 1

Laughing All The

LAUGHING ALL THE WAY TO THE BANKS Various artists (Various artists).
LP: . . . . ZTHLP 69

Laughing Clowns

GHOSTS OF AN EVIL WIFE.
LP: . . . . HOT 1013

HISTORY OF ROCK'N'ROLL.
LP: . . . . HOT 1010

LAUGHTER AROUND THE TABLE.
LP: . . . . RF 23

LAW OF NATURE.
LP: . . . . HOT 1004

Laughing Dogs

LAUGHING DOGS.
Tracks: / Get in outa town / Low life / No lies / Johnny contender / Reason for love / I need a million / It's alright, it's OK / I'm awake / Round and round / It's just the truth / Get outa my way.
LP: . . . . CBS 83807

Laughing Hyenas

MERRY GO ROUND.
LP: . . . . TGLP 25

Laughing In Rhythm

LAUGHING IN RHYTHM (Various artists).
LP: . . . . ST 116

Laughing Soupdish

UNDERTHROW THE OVERGROUND.
LP: . . . . VOXX 200061

WE ARE THE DISH.
LP: . . . . VOXX 200047

Launton Handbell

MODAL MELODIES.
Tracks: / Lord of the dance / Ash grove, The / Linden Lea / Waly waly / O guter Mond / Brahms' lullaby / Finlandia / Nos Gloucestershire wassail / Patapan / Little donkey / Little drummer boy / Tyrolean cradle song / Rocking / In the bleak mid winter.
LP: . . . . SDL 307
MC: . . . . CSDL 307

Lauper, Cyndi

12" TAPE: CYNDI LAUPER.
Tracks: / Girls just want to have fun / Time after time / She bop / All through the night / Money changes everything.
MC: 4501294

NIGHT TO REMEMBER, A.
Tracks: / Intro / I drove all night / Primitive / My first night without you / Like a cat / Heading West / Night to remember, A / Unconditional love / Insecurious / Dancing with a stranger / I don't want to be your friend / Kindred spirit.
LP: 4624991
MC: 4624994

SHE'S SO UNUSUAL.
Tracks: / Money changes everything / Girls just want to have fun / When you were mine / Time after time / She bop / All through the night / Witness / I'll kiss you / He's so unusual / Yeah yeah.
LP: . . . . PRT 25792
MC: 40 25792
LP: 4633621
MC: 4633624

TRUE COLORS.
Tracks: / Change of heart / Maybe he'll know / Boy blue / True colors / Calm inside the storm / What's going on / Iko iko / Faraway nearby, The / 911 / One track mind / True colors (7" single version).
LP: . . . . PRT 26948
LP: 462 493 1
MC: 462 493 4

Laurel And Hardy

WHAT A BARGAIN.
LP: . . . . UPLP 4

Laurel & Hardy

ANOTHER FINE MESS.
Tracks: / Cuckoo song / Turn on the radio / Even as you and I / Clean sweep, A / Future Mrs. Hardy / Every cloud has a silver lining / Lazy moon / When the cat's away / Danger by clockwork / Food for thought / Court again / Dual deceit / Goodbye.
MC: . . . . UP 36107

GOLDEN AGE OF HOLLYWOOD COMEDY.
LP: . . . . UAG 29676

LAUREL AND HARDY (see under EMI Comedy Classics).

LAUREL AND HARDY ON THE AIR (Rare Recordings 1932-59).
MC: . . . . CMR 1104
LP: . . . . MR 1104

LAUREL & HARDY'S MUSIC BOX (Hazelhurst, Ronnie).
Tracks: / Ku-ku / On to the show / Bells / Dash and dot / We're out for fun / Drunk / Rockin' chairs / Give us a hand / Riding along / Gangway Charlie / Here we go / Moon and you / You are the one I love / Beautiful lady / Look at him now / Funny faces / On a sunny afternoon / Sons of the Desert.
LP: . . . . MON LP 024
LP: . . . . FILM 012
MC: . . . . FILMC 012

SONGS AND DIALOGUE VOL.3.
LP: . . . . MESSLPP 3
LPPD: . . . . MESSLPP 3

SONGS AND DIALOGUE, VOL. 1.
Tracks: / Cuckoo song / At the ball / Trail of the Lonesome Pine / There's gonna be a fight / Eloping / We want to get married / All aboard / Ice cream shop / School room / Where's my clothes / Lazy moon / Higher endeavours / Four rounds tonight / Hat eating / Way down South / Dixie.
LP: . . . . MESSLP 1

SONGS AND DIALOGUE, VOL. 2 (Another Fine Mess).
Tracks: / In the good old summertime / Oh Gaston / You are the ideal of my dreams / At the hotel / Phone call / Looking for Mr. Smith / We don't sell ice cream / Annual convention / Honolulu baby / Let me call you sweetheart / Box 204J / On the quayside / Get out of town / Hard boiled eggs and nuts.
LP: . . . . MESSLP 2
LPPD: . . . . MESSLP 2P

Laurence, Paul

HAVEN'T YOU HEARD.
Tracks: / Strung out / She's not a sleaze (With Lillo Thomas & Freddie Jackson.) / You hooked me / Good and plenty / Racism / Haven't you heard / There ain't nothin' (like your lovin') / I'm sensitive.
LP: . . . . EST 2005

UNDER EXPOSED.
Tracks: / Make my baby happy / I ain't wit it / She's not an ordinary girl / Main course / Cut the crap / Sue me / She's gone / I'm a business man (kick it too).
LP: . . . . EST 2090
MC: . . . . TCEST 2090
LP: . . . . C 148304

Laurence, Zack

SING-A-LONG PIANO.
Tracks: / Beatles medley / USA medley / Italian medley / Irving Berlin medley / Jolson medley / European medley / Roaring twenties / Moonlight medley / Knees up medley / Waltz medley / Soft shoe medley / Oriental medley / Fats Waller medley / Spanish medley / Vaudeville medley / Ragtime medley / London medley / Girls medley.
MCSET: . . . . DTO 10316

Laurie Accordian

LAURIE ACCORDIAN ORCHESTRA.
MC: . . . . KITV 486

Laurie, Annie

CREOLE GAL (see Gayten, Paul & Annie Laurie) (Laurie, Annie & Paul Gayten).

IT HURTS TO BE IN LOVE.
Tracks: / It hurts to be in love / Hand in hand / Nobody's gonna hurt you / We found love / You are the only one for me / Wash someday / Out of my mind / Please honey don't go / I'm a slave to you / Not wanted / Love is a funny thing / If you're lonely.
LP: . . . . SING 1155

Laurie, Cy

CY LAURIE & LES JOWETT 1957 (Laurie, Cy & Les Jowett).
Tracks: / Beale street blues / House in Harlem for sale / Jazz me blues / Ain't gonna give nobody none of my jelly roll / Mississippi mud / In a mist / Our Monday date / Louisiana / Footstpes in the sand / Spain / Gee baby ain't I good to you / It's tight like that / Reefer drag / Gatemouth / At the jazz band ball.
LP: . . . . FLY 217

DELVING BACK WITH CY (Laurie, Cy quartet/band).
LP: . . . . ESQ 324

SHADES OF CY.
LP: S/12L/A1

Laurie, Hugh

CYRIL BONHAMY AND THE GREAT DRAIN ROBBERY (See also Gathorne-Hardy, Jonathon).

Laurie, Peter

ALL THE BEST.
Tracks: / Mardi gras / Serenade / Daddy don't you walk so fast / So deep is the night / Love is all / Catari / Come back to Sorrento / Man without love, A / You are my hearts delight / Till / Loves last word is spoken / Goodbye.
LP: . . . . SRTZ 76369

Laury, Booker T.

MEMPHIS PIANO JEWEL.
LP: . . . . WOLF 120 912

ONE OF THE LAST MEMPHIS BLUES PIANO JEWELS.
LP: . . . . WOLF 120 912

Lava

CRUISIN.
LP: 2382 120

PRIME TIME.
Tracks: / Hard times / Juliet / Empty shadows / 2.12 / Prime time / Late at night / Tea beat / Holiday.
LP: 2382 134
MC: 3187 134

Lava Hay

LAVA HAY.
Tracks: / Baby / What will you do / Fall with you / Holding on / Alley song, A / Won't matter / Waiting for an answer / My friend / Midnight sun / Weeping willow / Wild eyes.
LP: 847 382 1
MC: 847 382 4

Lavelle, Sheila

FIEND NEXT DOOR, THE.
MCSET: 086 222 0466

HOLIDAY WITH THE FIEND (Bennett, Judy (nar)).
MC: **2CCA 3060**

Laverne Trio

SEE HOW IT FEELS (see Brubeck/ Laverne Trio) (Laverne Trio/Brubeck).

Lavette, Betty

I'M IN LOVE.
Tracks: / He made a woman out of me / Do your duty / We got to slip around / Piece of my heart / Easier to say than do / My train's comin' in / At the mercy of a man / Let me down easy / Games people play / Nearer to you / Love's made a fool of me / I'm in love.
LP: . . . . **CRB 1059**

TELL ME A LIE.
Tracks: / Right in the middle / Either way we lose / Suspicions / You seen one you seen 'em all / I heard it through the grapevine / Tell me a lie / I like it like that / Before I even knew your name / I can't stop / If I were your woman.
LP: . . . . **STML 12166**

Lavilliers, Bernard

O GRINGO.
LP: **1092 038**

Lavin, Christine

ATTAINABLE LOVE.
LP: . . . . **PH 1132**
MC: . . . . **PH 1132C**

BEAU WOES AND OTHER PROBLEMS.
MC: . . . . **CPH 1107**
LP: . . . . **PH 1107**

FUTURE FOSSILS.
LP: . . . . **PH 1104**
MC: . . . . **PH 1104C**

GOOD THING HE CAN'T READ MY MIND.
LP: . . . . **PH 1121**
MC: . . . . **PH 1121C**

Lavitz, T

EXTENDED PLAY.
Tracks: / Certain people / Group therapy / Crystal / Between coming and going / Times square.
LP: . . . . **P 2011**

FROM THE WEST.
LP: . . . . **PJ 88026**
MC: . . . . **PJC 88026**

STORYTIME.
LP: . . . . **PJ 88012**
MC: . . . . **PJC 88012**

T. LAVITZ AND THE BAD HABITZ.
Tracks: / September / Hobo's lullaby / Quiet one, The / Dream come true, A / Down at the docks / Times Square / Trash park / Slideways / On the street / Holidays / Young circle.
LP: . . . . **ENVLP 525**
MC: . . . . **TCENV 525**

Law (1)

LAW, THE.
LP: **7567821951**
MC: **7567821954**

Law, Johnny

JOHNNY LAW.
LP: . . . . **ZORRO 18**
MC: . . . . **TZORRO 18**

Law, Michael

GLASS ISLE.
MC: . . . . **C 124**

Lawal, Gasper

ABIO SUNNI.
LP: . . . . **HOTCAP 1**

KADARA.
MC: . . . . **ORBC 071**

Lawlor, Teresa

MOODS.
LP: . . . . **IMLP 001**
MC: . . . . **IMMC 001**

Lawndale

SASQUATCH ROCK.
LP: . . . . **SST 125**

Lawnmower

CAT, THE.
LP: . . . . **FAT 1**

Lawnmower Deth

OOH CRIKEY IT'S...
LP: . . . . **MOSH 25**
MC: . . . . **MOSH 25 MC**

QUACK EM ALL (See under Metal Duck) (Lawnmower Deth & Metal Duck).

Lawrence, Arnie

RENEWAL.
LP: . . . . **PA 8033**

Lawrence, Brian

BRIAN LAWRENCE 1935-1937.
Tracks: / Miss Annabelle Lee / Darktown strutters' ball / I want to be happy / Way down yonder in New Orleans / Tormented / Is it true what they say about Dixie / You can't pull the wool over my eyes / If you were the only girl in the world / Everybody loves my baby / China boy / Some of these days / My sweetie went away / Alexander's ragtime band / Somebody stole my gal / I'm gonna take my mother out / Broken doll.
LP: . . . . **HQ 3021**

Lawrence, D.H.

FOX, THE (Massey, Anna (nar)).
MCSET: **418 183-4**

LADY CHATTERLEY'S LOVER (Brown, Pamela).
MC: **1116**

LADY CHATTERLEY'S LOVER (Suzman, Janet (aut)).
MCSET: . . . . **LFP 7388**

SONS & LOVERS (McKellen, Ian).
MCSET: . . . . **SAY 78**
MCSET: . . . . **ARGO 1097**

TICKETS, PLEASE & OTHER STORIES & POEMS (Various artists).
Tracks: / Goose fair: *Various artists* / Her turn: *Various artists* / Shadow in the rose garden, The: *Various artists* / Tickets, please: *Various artists*.
MCSET: **418 177-4**

VIRGIN AND THE GYPSY (See also Robert Lindsay).
MC: **0600560473**

VIRGIN AND THE GYPSY, THE (Bell, Elizabeth).
MC: . . . . **PTB 622**

Lawrence, Elliot

ELEVATION.
LP: . . . . **FH 38**

ELLIOT LAWRENCE, 1946.
Tracks: / Cross your heart / Once in a while / Laura / Indiana / More than you know / You're right, I'm wrong / Cheek to cheek / April in Paris / Just a sittin' and a rockin' / Remember me / Among my souvenirs / Heart to heart.
LP: . . . . **HSR 182**

PLAYS JOHNNY MANDEL.
LP: **1902109**

Lawrence, Gary

GARY LAWRENCE & HIS SIZZLING SYCOPATORS.
LP: . . . . **BG 2020**

Lawrence, Gertrude

GERTRUDE LAWRENCE.
LP: . . . . **MES 7043**

MASTER, THE, FEATURING GERTRUDE LAWRENCE (see Coward, Noel) (Lawrence, Gertrude & Noel Coward).

STAR PORTRAIT: GERTRUDE LAWRENCE.
LP: . . . . **AEI 2119**

Lawrence, Karen

RIP AND TEAR.
Tracks: / Rip side / Shot for the heart / Never enough / What a lovely way to go / Get it up get it right / Rip and tear / Tear side / Is this love / Wild heart / Kiss from a distance / Out of the blue.
LP: . . . . **REVLP 75**

Lawrence, Lee

FASCINATION.
Tracks: / Blue tango / Story of Tina / Marta / With these hands / Waltzing the blues / Vanity / How can you buy Killarney? / Golden haired boy from the valley / World is mine tonight, The / Fascination / Song of Capri / Crying in the chapel / To live my life with you / You alone / When you're in love / Never / My love for you.
LP: . . . . **PLE 504**
MC: . . . . **TC-PLE 504**

Lawrence of Arabia

LAWRENCE OF ARABIA (Film soundtrack) (Various artists).
Tracks: / Overture: *Jarre, Maurice* / Main title: *Jarre, Maurice* / Miracle: *Jarre, Maurice* / Nefud mirage: *Jarre, Maurice* / Rescue of Gasim: *Jarre, Maurice* / Bringing Gasim into camp: *Jarre, Maurice*/ Arrival at Auda's camp: *Jarre, Maurice* / Voice of the guns, The: *Jarre, Maurice* / Continuation of the miracle: *Jarre, Maurice* / Suns anvil: *Jarre, Maurice* / Lawrence and his body guard: *Jarre, Maurice* / That is the desert: *Jarre, Maurice* / End title: *Jarre, Maurice*.
LP: . . . . **GSGL 10389**
LP: . . . . **PYL 6040**
MC: . . . . **PYM 6040**
LP: . . . . **NPL 28023**
MC: . . . . **VSC 5263**

LAWRENCE OF ARABIA (RE-RELEASE) (Film soundtrack) (Various artists).
Tracks: / Overture: *Philharmonia Orchestra* / First entrance to the desert - night and stars: *Philharmonia Orchestra*/ Lawrence and Tafas: *Philharmonia Orchestra* / Miracle: *Philharmonia Orchestra* / That is the desert: *Philharmonia* Orchestra / Nefud mirage/ Sun's anvil, The: *Philharmonia Orchestra* / Rescue of Gasim, The/ Bringing Gasim into camp: *Philharmonia Orchestra* / Arrival at Auda's camp: *Philharmonia Orchestra* / On to Akaba/ The beach at night: *Philharmonia* Orchestra / Sinai desert: *Philharmonia Orchestra* / Voice at the guns: *Philharmonia Orchestra* / Horse stampede - Ali rescues Lawrence: *Philharmonia Orchestra* / Lawrence and his bodyguard: *Philharmonia Orchestra* / End/Playoff music: *Philharmonia Orchestra*.
LP: . . . . **FILM 036**
MC: . . . . **FILMC 036**

Lawrence, Stephanie

YOU SAVED MY LIFE (see under Mathis, Johnny).

Lawrence, Steve

ACADEMY AWARD LOSERS.
Tracks: / I've got you under my skin / You'd be so nice to come home to / They can't take that away from me / Long ago / Change partners / Love letters / I'll remember April / Chattanooga choo choo / Cheek to cheek / My foolish heart / How about you / That old feeling.
LP: **32310**

BEST OF STEVE AND EYDIE (Lawrence, Steve & Eydie Gorme).
Tracks: / I want to stay here / Go away little girl / Everybody go home / Walking proud / Can't get over (the bossa nova) / Don't be afraid, little darlin' / Yes my darling daughter / Dia das roas (I think of you) / I can't stop talkin' about you / Blame it on the bossa nova / Yet...I know (et pourtant) / I want you to meet my baby / Millions of roses / Look of love, The / Everybody knows (that I feel blue) / True love.
MC: **40 32663**
LP: . . . . **CBS 31543**
MC: **40 31543**

CHARTMAKERS.
LP: . . . . **CP 8320**

I STILL BELIEVE IN LOVE (Lawrence, Steve & Eydie Gorme).
Tracks: / She's out of my life / Send in the clowns / I'd rather leave while I'm in love / We're all alone / Since I fell for you / What'll I do? / He was good for me / Maybe this time / I still believe in love / God bless the child.
LP: . . . . **PRCV 124**
MC: . . . . **TC PRCV 124**

I WANT TO STAY HERE (see Gorme, Eydie) (Lawrence, Steve & Eydie Gorme).

OUR LOVE IS HERE TO STAY (see Gorme, Eydie) (Lawrence, Steve & Eydie Gorme).

WE GOT US (Lawrence, Steve & Eydie Gorme).
LP: . . . . **JASM 1505**

WE'RE ALL ALONE.
Tracks: / New York, New York / She's out of my life / I'd rather leave while I'm in love / You had to be there / I won't break / I take it on home / I still believe in love / We're all alone / One word / Maybe this time / Welcome to paradise.
LP: . . . . **PRCV 122**
MC: . . . . **TC PRCV 122**

Lawrence, Syd

BAND BEAT (Lawrence, Syd Orchestra).
LP: . . . . **REB 254**

BIG SOUND OF SYD LAWRENCE AND HIS ORCHESTRA.
MCSET: . . . . **DTO 10308**

HOLLAND SPECIAL.
Tracks: / Als op capri de rozentuinen bloeien / Penny serenade / Weet je nog wel die avond in de regen? / Bloesem van seringen / Veel mooier dan het mooiste schilderij / Groot Rotterdam and bouncin' in Bavaria / Als sterren flonk' rend aan de hemel staan / Diep in mijn hart / 'Twas eine zommernachtfeest / Denk jij nog aan di tijd?.
LP: **637 5485**
MC: **717 4485**

MORE MILLER AND OTHER BIG BAND MAGIC.
LP: **6642 001**

MUSIC OF GLENN MILLER, THE (Lawrence, Syd & His Orchestra).
MC: **8428274**
LP: **6641017**

REMEMBER GLENN MILLER (Lawrence, Syd Orchestra).
Tracks: / Moonlight serenade / Little brown jug / Anchors aweigh / String of pearls / At last / I've got a gal in Kalamazoo / American patrol / Perfidia / Slumber song / Slow freight / Elmer's tune / St. Louis blues / In the mood / Stardust / I dreamt I dwelt in Harlem / Serenade in blue / Pennsylvania 65000 / Caribbean clipper / Tuxedo Junction / Story of a starry night / Chattanooga choo choo / Frenesi / Falling leaves / Adios.
MCSET: . . . . **DTOL 10066**

RITUAL FIRE DANCE.
MC: . . . . **ASK 762**

SOMETHING OLD, SOMETHING NEW.
LP: **6308 090**

SWING CLASSICS (Lawrence, Syd Orchestra).
Tracks: / In the mood / Take the 'A' train / Chattanooga choo choo / American patrol / Eager beaver / Begin the beguine / Opus one / At the Woodchoppers ball / Tuxedo Junction / String of pearls / Peanut vendor / Let's dance.
LP: **6381 072**
MC: **7215 072**
LP: . . . . **TIME 03**
MC: . . . . **TIMEC 03**

SYD LAWRENCE & HIS ORCHESTRA (Lawrence, Syd Orchestra).
Tracks: / Swingin' shepherd blues / Harlem nocturne / Rose Marie / Blues on parade / Poinciana / High train / Baubles, bangles and beads / Skylark / Cherokee / You'll never know / It must be jelly / Crewcut / Slaughter on Tenth Avenue / Boo hoo / Faithful hussar, The / Chip off the old block / It's always you / Bells of St. Mary's / Ritual fire dance / Intermezzo / Don't worry 'bout me / Drumming man / Dardanella.
2LP: . . . . **CR 076**
MCSET: . . . . **CRT 076**

SYD LAWRENCE ORCHESTRA VOL 1 (Lawrence, Syd & His Orchestra).
Tracks: / Baubles, bangles and beads / Skylark / Cherokee / You'll never know / Poinciana / Crew cut / Swingin shepherd blues / Harlem nocturne / Rose Marie / Blues on parade / It must be jelly / Night train.
LP: . . . . **CBR 1020**
MC: . . . . **KCBR 1020**

SYD LAWRENCE ORCHESTRA VOL 2 (Lawrence, Syd Orchestra).
Tracks: / Ritual fire dance / Intermezzo / Boo hoo / Drummin' man / Dardanella / Slaughter on 10th Avenue / Don't worry 'bout me / Faithful Hussar / Chip off the old block / It's always you / Bells of St. Mary's.
LP: . . . . **ACLP 014**
MC: . . . . **ACK 014**

SYD LAWRENCE WITH THE GLENN MILLER SOUND.
LP: . . . . **SFL 13178**

Lawrence, Trev

SONGS, POEMS AND LEGENDS.
MC: . . . . **SENC 1079**

Laws, Debra

VERY SPECIAL.
Tracks: / On my own / Meant for you / Very special / Be yourself / Long as we're together / Your love / How long / All the things I love.
LP: . . . . **K 52281**

Laws, Eloise

ELOISE LAWS.
Tracks: / Let's find those two people again / Strength of a woman / Almost all the way to love / I'm just warmin' up / You are everything / Moment to moment / Got you into my life / If I don't watch out / Search find.
LP: . . . . **UAG 30331**

Laws, Hubert

FAMILY (IMPORT).
MC: . . . . **JCC 36396**

Laws, Ronnie

ALL DAY RHYTHM.
Tracks: / Smoke house / Dreams I dream, The / All day rhythm / Rhythm of romance / Still / Junior boy / Nite life / Distant eyes / Arrival / Home dance.
LP: **4605921**
MC: **4605924**

EVERY GENERATION.
LP: . . . . **UAG 30289**

FLAME.

Tracks: / All for you / These days / Flame / Living love / Love is here / Grace / Joy / Live your life away.
LP: . . . . **UAG 30204**

MIRROR TOWN.
Tracks: / Come to me / Misled / Tell me / Mirror town / Like a crazy man / Midnight side / Cold day / You have to be in love / Take a chance.
LP: **4500681**
MC: **4500684**

MR NICE GUY.
Tracks: / Can't save tomorrow / Mr. Nice Guy / In the groove / Third hour / You / Big stars / Rollin' / What does it take (to win your love) / Off and on again.
LP: . . . . **ATAK 67**
MC: . . . . **TCATAK 67**
LP: **EST400 1671**

SOLID GROUND.
Tracks: / Solid ground / Heavy on easy / Segue / There's a way / Stay awake / Your stuff / Just as you are / Summer fool / Good feelings.
LP: . . . . **LBG 30336**

TRUE SPIRIT.
LP: . . . . **ITMP 970053**

Lawson, Doyle

BEYOND THE SHADOWS (Lawson, Doyle & Quicksilver).
LP: . . . . **SH 3753**
MC: . . . . **SH 3753C**

DOYLE LAWSON & QUICKSILVER (Lawson, Doyle & Quicksilver).
LP: . . . . **SH 3708**
MC: . . . . **SH 3708C**

HEAVENLY TREASURES (Lawson, Doyle & Quicksilver).
LP: . . . . **SH 3735**
MC: . . . . **SH 3735C**

HEAVEN'S JOY AWAITS (Lawson, Doyle & Quicksilver).
LP: . . . . **SH 3760**
MC: . . . . **SH 3760C**

HYMN TIME IN THE COUNTRY (Lawson, Doyle & Quicksilver).
LP: . . . . **SH 3765**
MC: . . . . **SH 3765C**

I HEARD THE ANGELS SINGING (Lawson, Doyle & Quicksilver).
Tracks: / Holy city, The / Stormy weather / Little mountain church house / In the shelter of his arms / I heard the angels singing / He's my guide / Little white church, The / City where's comes no strife / Rock of ages, hide thou me / I won't have far to cross Jordan alone / That new Jerusalem / That home far away.
LP: . . . . **SH 3774**
MC: . . . . **SH 3774C**

I'LL WANDER BACK SOMEDAY (Lawson, Doyle & Quicksilver).
LP: . . . . **SH 3769**
MC: . . . . **SH 3769C**

MY HEART IS YOURS (Lawson, Doyle & Quicksilver).
Tracks: / All in my love for you / Still got a crush on you / Move to the top of the mountain / I don't care / My heart is yours / Dreaming of you / Look for me and I'll be there / Date with an angel / Now there's you / Between us / I'm satisfied with you / We were made for each other.
LP: . . . . **SH 3782**
MC: . . . . **SH 3782C**

NEWS IS OUT, THE (Lawson, Doyle & Quicksilver).
Tracks: / Sweetheart you done me wrong / This dream I'm in / I've heard these words before / Vision of Jesus, A / Up on the blue ridge / I'll be true / Grass that I'm playing is really blue, The / Have I loved you too late / Let the best man win / She's walking through my memory / Wonderful, beautiful place.
LP: . . . . **SH 3757**
MC: . . . . **SH 3757C**

ONCE AND FOR ALWAYS (Lawson, Doyle & Quicksilver).
Tracks: / Blue road, The / Once and for always / Lover of the Lord, A / Speak softly, you're talking to my heart / Old timer's waltz / Come back to me in my dreams / Carolina in my dreams / Stone cold heart / Julie Ann (come on home) / You only have to say you've changed your mind / When the sun of my life goes down.
LP: . . . . **SH 3744**
MC: . . . . **SH 3744C**

QUICKSILVER RIDES AGAIN (Lawson, Doyle & Quicksilver).
Tracks: / Misery river / Georgia girl / Till all the rivers run dry / Rocking on the waves / Yellow river / Poet with wings / Kentucky song / Calm the storm / I'll be around somewhere / Mountain girl / Lonesome river, The.
LP: . . . . **SH 3727**
MC: . . . . **SH 3727C**

ROCK MY SOUL (Lawson, Doyle & Quicksilver).
LP: . . . . **SH 3717**

TENNESSEE DREAM.
LP: . . . . **CO 766**

Lawson, Hugh

UNDERDOG, THE (See under Mauro, Turk) (Lawson, Hugh/Turk Mauro).

Lawson, Stella

GOIN' FOR IT.
LP: . . . . **ST 235**

Lawson, Yank

BEST OF JAZZ IN THE TROC (Lawson-Haggart).
Tracks: / South Rampart Street parade / Vipers drag / Tin roof blues / Wolverine blues / Just a closer walk with Thee / Savoy blues / Summertime / After you've gone.
LP: . . . . **WJLPS 14**

CENTURY PLAZA (Lawson-Haggart Jazz Band).
LP: . . . . **WJLPS 1**

EASY TO REMEMBER.
LP: . . . . **FLY 208**

LAWSON-HAGGART JAZZ BAND GO TO NEW ORLEANS (Lawson-Haggart Jazz Band).
LP: . . . . **J 153**

LIVE AT LOUISIANA JAZZCLUB 1979 (Lawson-Freeman-Davern-Sutton).
LP: . . . . **FDC 3002**

PLAYS MOSTLY BLUES.
LP: . . . . **AP 221**

WORLD'S GREATEST DIXIE BAND (We want to be happy).
Tracks: / I want to be happy / Makin' whoopee / There will never be another you / Mean to me / S'wonderful / Lotus blossom / Blue room.
LP: . . . . **JC 001**

WORLDS GREATEST JAZZ BANDS (Lawson, Yank & Bob Haggart).
LP: . . . . **TTD 533**

Lawson-Haggart

WORLD'S GREATEST DIXIE BAND Songs that lost the war (Various artists).
Tracks: / Lou-easy-an-i-a: *Various artists* / West End blues: *Various artists* / Dardanella: *Various artists* / Over the rainbow: *Various artists* / Weary blues: *Various artists* / Tuxedo rag: *Various artists* / At a Georgia camp meeting: *Various artists* / Trick or treat boogie: *Various artists* / It don't mean a thing: *Various artists*.
LP: . . . . **JC 002**

Lawtell Playboys

LA LA - LOUISIANA BLACK FRENCH MUSIC (see under Carriere Brothers) (Lawtell Playboys/Carriere Bros.).

Lawton, Jimmy

ARIZONA SUNDAY.
LP: . . . . **WRS 118**

Lax

ALL MY LOVE.
Tracks: / All my love / Possessed / Thanks but no thanks / Fight back / Like a simple song of love / Love me tonight.
LP: . . . . **EPC 84859**

Layburn, Chuck

REMEMBERS.
Tracks: / I remember you / Singing the blues / Spinning wheel / Lovesick blues / Release me / Heartaches by the number / Old Shep / Cryin' time / Swiss maid / Send me the pillow / Ten guitars / Wedding bells.
LP: . . . . **JULEP 23**

Laycock, Tim

CAPERS AND RHYMES.
Tracks: / New year song, The / La guignolee / Man who broke the bank at Monte Carlo, The / Trampwoman's tragedy, A / Light of the moon / Gavioli capers / Outlandish knight, The / How Zamel got upsides wi'camel clock / Six dukes went a hunting / Munster cloak / Morrisey and the Russian sailor / Row on.
LP: . . . . **GVR 216**

GIANT AT CERNE, THE.
LP: . . . . **DIN 320**

Laye, Evelyn

GOLDEN AGE OF EVELYN LAYE, THE.
LP: . . . . **GX 41 2537 1**
MC: . . . . **GX 41 2537 4**

Layton & Johnstone

ALABAMY BOUND.
Tracks: / Anytime, anywhere / Up with the lark / Wedding of the painted doll / Alabamy bound / New kind of girl with a new kind of love form / Weary river / Paddlin' Madeline home / Turner Layton piano medley / Birth of the blues / Coquette / Hillo, 'tucky / Don't put the blame on me / Hard hearted Hannah / It all depends on you / At dawning / Medley of Layton and Johnstone successes.
LP: . . . . **PAST 703**

AMERICAN DUETTISTS WITH PIANO.
Tracks: / This is the missus / Life is just a bowl of cherries / Sweet and lovely / Guilty / Love letters in the sand / I found a million dollar baby / Home / All of me / Prisoner of love / Was that the human thing to do / Auf wiedershen my dear / I lost my heart in Heidelberg / Lullaby of the leaves / My silent love / Say it isn't so / Night and day / Home on the range / Willow weep for me / Lying in the hay.
2LP: . . . . **SHB 57**
MC: . . . . **TC-SHB 57**

SONG IS ENDED, THE.
Tracks: / To be in love espech'll with you / Can't help lovin' dat man / I've got a feeling I'm falling / Lover come back to me / My blue Heaven / Ol' man river / I'll see you again / True blue Lou / Wedding of the painted doll, The / You were meant for me / Ain't misbehavin' / Tondeleyd / Mean to me / Broadway melody / Lucky me, lovable you.
LP: . . . . **JOYD 277**

WHEN YOU'RE SMILING.
Tracks: / Wonder where my baby is tonight / My pal Harry / Meadow lark / Ramona / Dawning / After my laughter came tears / Sunny Skies / Get out and get under the moon / Was it a dream / Bluebird sing me a song / I'll never ask for more / Deep night / If i had a talking picture of you / Ro-ro-rollin' along / Stein song, The / When you're smiling / Harmony heaven / I gotta right to sing the blues / Lazybones / I like to go back in the evening / I wonder where my baby is tonight.
LP: . . . . **SVL 180**
MC: . . . . **CSVL 180**

Layton, Lindy

PRESSURE.
Tracks: / Wait for love / Echo my heart / Do me baby / Without you / Keep it up (Cassette & CD only) / Silly games / Drop the pressure / Lines / Cruel (to be kind) / This isn't fair (CD only) / Best thing / Let me keep you here.
LP: **211361**
MC: **411361**

Lazlo, Viktor

VIKTOR LAZLO.
LP: **832 147-1**
MC: **832 147-4**

Lazy Cowgirls

TAPPING THE SOURCE.
LP: . . . . **BLP 4025**

Lazy, Doug

GETTING CRAZY.
Tracks: / Can't hold back (u no) / Ahh get it / Let the rhythm pump / Let it roll / Funky beat / Can't get enough / Doug Lazy gettin' crazy / U really wanna / Go 2 work / H.O.U.S.E..
LP: **7567820661**
MC: **7567820664**

LET IT ROLL (See under Raze) (Lazy, Doug & Raze).

Lazy Lester

HARP AND SOUL.
Tracks: / I done got over it / I'm a man / Dark end of the street / Bye bye baby / Alligator shuffle / Take me in your arms / Patrol wagon / Raining in my heart / Bloodstains on the wall / Five long years.
LP: . . . . **AL 4768**

POOR BOY BLUES (Jay Miller sessions, Volume 16).
LP: . . . . **FLY 544**

RIDES AGAIN.
Tracks: / Sugar coated love / Travelling days / Same thing could happen to you, The / Can't stand to see you go / Out on the road / Lester's shuffle / I hear you knocking / Irene / St Louis blues / Blowin' a rhumba / Nothin' but the devil / Hey Mattie.
LP: . . . . **BLUH 002**
LP: . . . . **SJLP 57**

THEY CALL ME LAZY.
LP: . . . . **FLY 526**

TRUE BLUES.
LP: . . . . **LP 8006**

Lazy Racer

FORMULA II.
Tracks: / Why / True love / Heart of hearts / Carrie Ann / This time / Beautiful loser / Young man in a hurry / Takes too long / Big bang theory / Jumpin' the gun.
LP: . . . . **AMLH 64808**

LAZY RACER.
Tracks: / Keep on running away / Alone in a lonely world / Limelight / Safe harbour / Waiting for the night / One heartache / Every other day / Good for you darlin' / Heart with your name on it / Today more than ever.
LP: . . . . **AMLH 64768**

Le Bal (film)

LE BAL (Film Soundtrack) (Various artists).
LP: **66.078**
MC: **76.078**

Le Carre, John

FLEDGLING SPY, THE (See under Fledgling Spy).

PERFECT SPY, A.
MCSET: . . . . **ZBBC 1041**

RUSSIA HOUSE, THE.
MCSET: . . . . **LFP 7430**

SPY WHO CAME IN FROM THE COLD, THE.
MCSET: . . . . **LFP 7192**
MCSET: . . . . **LFP 4171925**

SPY WHO CAME OF AGE, THE (See under Spy Who Came Of Age).

Le Disque D'or Du Rai

LE DISQUE D'OR DU RAI (Various artists).
LP: **11050**
MC: . . . . **C 11050**

Le Febvre, Gary

GARY LE FEBVRE QUARTET (Le Febvre, Gary Quartet).
Tracks: / Some other time / Milestones / Windows.
LP: . . . . **DS 849**

Le Griffe

BREAKING STRAIN.
LP: . . . . **BULP 2**

Le Guin, Ursula

FARTHEST SHORE (Hood, Morag).
MCSET: . . . . **COL 4504**

GWILAM'S HARP AND INTRACOM.
MC: **1556**

TOMBS OF ATUAN (Hood, Morag).
MCSET: . . . . **COL 4503**

WIZARD OF EARTHSEA (Hood, Morag).
MCSET: . . . . **COL 4502**

Le M' Zab

LE M'ZAB (Various artists).
Tracks: / Chant de fecondation des palmiers: *Various artists* / Enfants au Bendir, Les: *Various artists* / Soir chez Daoud, Un: *Various artists* / Mariage noir a Ghardaia: *Various artists* / La haddra des femmes: *Various artists* / Mariage a Beni-Isguen: *Various artists* / Ceremonie d'envoutement: *Various artists*.
LP: . . . . **ARN 33384**

Le Mans, Tony

TONY LE MANS.
LP: . . . . **WX 294**
MC: . . . . **WX 294C**

Le Masne, Vincent

GUITARES (Masne, Vincent Le & Bertrand Porquet).
LP: . . . . **SHAN 83516**

Le Mesurier, John

NOT MUCH CHANGE (see Dunn,Clive & John Le Mesurier) (Le Mesurier, John & Clive Dunn).

Le Mort D'Arthur

LE MORT D'ARTHUR (see under Malory, Sir Thomas) (Various artists).

Le Mystere Des Voix

CATHEDRAL CONCERT, A (Le Mystere Des Voix Bulgares).
LP: . . . . **JARO 41381**
MC: . . . . **JARO 41384**

LE MYSTERE DES VOIX BULGARES (Le Mystere Des Voix Bulgares).
MC: . . . . **CADC 603**
LP: . . . . **CAD 603**

LE MYSTERE DES VOIX BULGARES VOL.2 (Le Mystere Des Voix Bulgares).
LP: . . . . **CAD 801**
MC: . . . . **CADC 801**

LE MYSTERE DES VOIX BULGARES VOL.3 (Le Mystere Des Voix Bulgares).
LP: **8466261**
MC: **8466264**

MYSTERES (Bulgarian state female choir) (Le Mystere Des Voix Bulgares).
LP: . . . . **JARO 41531**
MC: . . . . **JARO 41534**

Le M'Zab

LE M'ZAB (See under M'Zab, Le) (Various artists).

Le Nouveau Quatuor

VIVALDI CHAMBER CONCERTOS (On Original Instruments).
MC: CSAR 47

Le Professional

LE PROFESSIONAL (Film soundtrack) (Various artists).
LP: 803 026

Le Rue

DEAL YOUR CARD.
LP: BRAVE 7
MC: BRAVE 7C

LE RUE.
LP: BRAVE 4
MC: BRAVE 4C

Le Soleil

SUN AND THE MOON.
Tracks: / Speed of life / Death of imagination / Matter of conscience, A / Peace in our time / Picture of England, A / Dolphin / House on fire / Price of grain, The / This passionate breed.
LP: 9241821
MC: 9241824

Le Testement

LE TESTEMENT D'UN POETE JUIF ASSASSINE (Film Soundtrack) (Various artists).
LP: 242 261.1

Lea, Barbara

DO IT AGAIN.
LP: AP 175

Lea, Constance

SCENT OF OLEANDER, A.
MCSET: MRC 1047

Leach, Rosemary (nar)

MURDER IS ANNOUNCED, A (see under Murder is... (bk).

REEL MURDER (See under Reel Murder).

Lead into Gold

AGE OF REASON.
LP: WAX 116

Leadbelly

ALABAMA BOUND.
Tracks: / Pick a bale of cotton / Whoa back buck / Midnight special / Alabamy bound / Good morning blues / Red Cross store blues / Alberta / You can't lose-a me cholly / Gray goose / Stewball / Can't you line 'em / Rock Island line / Easy rider / New York city / Roberta / On my last go round.
LP: NL 90321
MC: NK 90321

COLLECTION: LEADBELLY (20 Blues Greats).
Tracks: / Good morning blues / Goodnight, Irene / There is a man, going around taking names / On a Monday / Gallis pole, The / Bring a little water Silvie (medley) / Stewball / We shall be free / T B blues / John Hardy / Poor Howard (medley) / Outskirts of town / Blood done signed my name / Boll weevil / Jean Harlow / Little children's blues / National defence blues / Fiddler's dram / Keep your hands off her / Cow cow yicky yicky yeah.
LP: DVLP 2072
MC: DVMC 2072

CONGRESS BLUES.
MC: ALB 1007MC

CONVICT BLUES.
LP: ALD 1004

EARLY MORNING BLUES.
Tracks: / I ain't going down / Went back to the mountains / Whoa back / Worried blues / You can't lose me Charlie / Boll weevil / Death letter blues parts 1 & 2 / Kansas City papa / Daddy I'm coming back to you / Shorty George / Yellow jacket / TB woman blues.
LP: BMLP 1038

GOOD MORNING BLUES.
LP: BT 2011

HIS GUITAR, HIS VOICE & HIS PIANO.
LP: 2C 068 80701

LAST SESSIONS (VOLUME 1).
Tracks: / Grey goose / Red cross door blues / Ham 'n' eggs / Red river in the pines / You don't miss your water / Blind lemon / Leadbelly's dance / In the evening / Diggin' my potatoes.
LP: SMPC 5001
MC: SPMC 5001

LEADBELLY.
LP: 2C 068 80701

LEADBELLY 1935.
Tracks: / Roberta (part 1) / Roberta (part 2) / Packin' trunk blues / C.C. rider / You can't lose me Charlie / New black snake moan / Alberta / Baby don't you love me no more / Death letter blues (part 1) / Death lettter blues (part 2) / Kansas City papa / Red river blues / My friend Blind Lemon / Mister Tom Hughes' town / Matchbox blues / Bull cow.
LP: TM 810

LEADBELLY: 1934-46.
LP: DLP 544

LEGENDARY LEADBELLY.
MC: DPC 405

Leaders

MUDFOOT.
Tracks: / Miss Nancy / Elaborations / Midnite train / Freedom swing song / Song of her / Mudfoot / Cupid.
LP: BKH 52001

OUT HERE LIKE THIS.
Tracks: / Zero / Luna / Cool T / Donkey dust / Portraits / Felicite / Loves I once knew.
LP: 120 119

Leadon, Bernie

NATURAL PROGRESSIONS (Leadon, Bernie/Michael Georgiades).
LP: K 53063

Leaf, Ann

LIVE IN CONCERT - MAJESTIC PIPE ORGAN.
LP: DO 1414

MIGHTY WURLITZER, THE (Leaf, Ann & Gaylord Carter).
Tracks: / Great day ((comp. Billy Rose, Edward eliscul, vincent Youlans)) / Strike up the band ((Comp. Ira Gershwin & George Gershwin)) / You do something to me ((Comp. Cole Porter)) / Son of the Sheik, The ((arr. Ann Leaf)) / You were meant for me ((Comp. Arthur Freed & Nacio Herb Brown)) / Orphans of the storm ((Arr. Ann Leaf)) / Jeannine ((COMP. L.Wolfe gilbert & Nathaniel Shilkret)) / For Heaven's sake ((Arr. Gaylord Carter)) / My romance ((Richard Rodgers & Lorenz Hart)) / Charmaine ((Comp. Lew Pollack & Erno rapee)) / Intolerance ((Arr. Gaylord Carter)) / Phantom of the opera ((Arr. Gaylord Carter)).
LP: NW 227

League Of Nations

MUSIC FOR THE NEW DEPRESSION.
LP: GLALP 009
LP: GZLP 102

League Unlimited

LOVE AND DANCING (League Unlimited Orchestra).
Tracks: / Hard times / Love action (I believe in love) / Don't you want me / Things that dreams are made of / Do or die / Open your heart / Sound of the crowd, The / Seconds.
LP: OVED 6
MC: OVEDC 6

Leake, Lafayette

SOMEBODY'S PRAYING, LORD (see under Green, Lee) (Leake, Lafayette & Lee Green).

Leandre, Joelle

DOUZE SONS, LES.
Tracks: / Pavane / Basses profondes / Pierrot / Ballde de chien / Cadenza rare / Trio en forme de bagatelle / Grand duo concertant / Les trois dames / Instant opus 3 / Sonate breve echappee / Seriozo (pour cordes et trombone) / Soupir.
LP: NATO 82

Leandros, Vicky

COME WHAT MAY (OLD GOLD) (See under Jacky / White horses).

GREEK SONGS (Leandros, Vicky/Nana Mouskouri/Demis Roussos).
LP: 6436 063

LOVE IS ALIVE.
LP: 6435 124
MC: 7106 124

Leao, Nara

GIRL FROM IPANEMA.
Tracks: / Little boats / Girl from Ipanema / Berimbau / Desafinado / Wave / Corcovado / Waters of March / Felicidade / Morning of the carnival / Chega de Saudade / Meditation / One note Samba / Agua de Beber / You and I / Samba do aviao / Que sera.
LP: 826348 1
MC: 826348 4

Leapin' On Lennox

LEAPIN' ON LENNOX (Various artists).
LP: BLP 114

Lear, Amanda

DIAMONDS FOR BREAKFAST.
Tracks: / Rockin' rollin' / I need a man / It's a better life / Oh boy / Insomnia / Diamonds / Japan / Fabulous / Ho fatto / L'amore con me / When.
LP: ARL 5051

NEVER TRUST A PRETTY FACE.
Tracks: / Never trust a pretty face / Fashion pack / Forget it / Lili Marlene / Sphinx / Black holes / Intellectuality / Miroir / Dreamer.
LP: ARL 5020

SECRET PASSION.
LP: CAL 226
MC: CAC 226

TAM TAM.
LP: 205.895
MC: 405.895

Lear, Edward

EDWARD LEAR'S NONSENSE RHYMES.
MCSET: DTO 10581

NONSENSE POETRY (Various artists).
MCSET: 418 168-4
MCSET: ARGO 1079

SELECTED BOSH (Bennett, Alan (nar)).
MCSET: CC/043

Lear, Evelyn

SINGS BERNSTEIN & SONDHEIM.
Tracks: / Who am I ? / My house / I can cook too / Some other time / Lonely town / I remember / Green finch and linnet bird / Could i leave you / Losing my mind / Send in the clowns.
LP: SRI 75136

Learn To Drive

LEARNING TO DRIVE (Various artists).
Tracks: / Entire highway code, The: *Learn To Drive* / Rules of the road, The: *Learn To Drive* / Basic manoeuvres: *Learn To Drive* / Actual driving test explained in detail, The: *Learn To Drive.*
MC: T DO 1

Learning & Memory

LEARNING AND MEMORY (By Tony Buzan) (Maag, Peter & The London Symphony Orchestra).
MC: PT 21

Learning To Control

LEARNING TO CONTROL PAIN (Bresler, David).
MC: PT 31

Leather

SHOCK WAVES.
Tracks: / All your neon / Shock waves / Something in this life / It's still in your eyes / Catastrophic hands / Battlefield of life, The / In a dream / Diamonds are for real / No place called home.
LP: RO 9463 1
MC: RO 9643-4

Leather Nun

ALIVE.
LP: WRLP 002

FORCE OF HABIT.
LP: WRLP 008
LP: MINIMUM 1

INTERNATIONAL HEROES.
LP: WIRE LP 011

LUST GAMES.
LP: WRMLP 200

SLOW DEATH.
MLP: WRMLP 100

STEEL CONSTRUCTION.
Tracks: / Dance, dance, dance / Someone special like you / Lost and found / Ride to live / I'm just a hustler / Cool shoes / Summer's so short / Trail of pain / Godzilla is back / Let me be.
LP: WRLP 005
MC: WRTC 005

Leatherface

MUSH.
LP: NECKLP 005

Leatherwolf

ENDANGERED SPECIES.
LP: HMUSA 39
MC: HMAMC 39

LEATHERWOLF.
Tracks: / Rise or fall / Calling, the / Share a dream / Cry out / Gypsies and thieves / Bad moon rising / Princess of love / Magical eyes / Rule the night.
LP: 906601
LP: ILPS 9889
MC: ICT 9889
MC: ICM 2038
MC: 842 862 4

STREET READY.
Tracks: / Wicked ways / Hideaway / Black knight / Way I feel, The / Too much / Street ready / Take a chance / Thunder / Lonely road / Spirits in the wind.
MC: ICT 9927
LP: ILPS 9927
MC: ICM 2037
MC: 842 658 4

Leave It To...

LEAVE IT TO JANE (Original Broadway cast) (Various artists).
Tracks: / Just you watch my step: *Various artists* / Leave it to Jane: *Various artists* / Siren's song: *Various* artists / Cleopatterer: *Various artists* / Crickets are calling, The: *Various artists* / Sun shines brighter, The: *Various artists* / Sir Galahad: *Various artists* / Wait 'til tomorrow: *Various artists* / I'm going to find a girl etc.: *Various artists.*
LP: DS 15002

Leaveners

BIRD OF FREEDOM.
LP: BURL 017

Leaves

1966: LEAVES.
LP: FC 006

HEY JOE.
LP: LLP 5144

Leaving Trains

FU.**
LP: SST 114

TRANSPORTATIONAL D. VICES.
LP: SST 221
MC: SST 221 C

Leblanc, Shorty

BEST OF TWO CAJUN GREATS (see under Brown, Sidney) (Leblanc, Shorty & Sidney Brown).

Lebow, Martee

LOVE'S A LIAR.
Tracks: / Where do I stand / Another lonely heart / Love's a liar / Maybe you'll remember / Learning the hard way / Hang on (to my reckless youth) / Fallen angel / Forbidden / I must be in love / One good reason.
LP: 781 729-1
MC: 781 729-4

Lebrijano, Juan Pena

ENCUENTROS.
Tracks: / Vivir un cuento de hadas / Dame la libertad / Las mil y una noches / Desafio / El anillo (chibuli) / Pensamientos / Amigo mio, no / Esos ojos asesinos.
LP: ORB 024
MC: ORBC 024

L'Echo Desluthes

MUSIQUE DE HAUTE BRETAGNE.
LP: BUR 822

Lecuona Cuban Boys

LECUONA CUBAN BOYS 1934-44.
LP: HQ 2074

Led Zeppelin

4 SYMBOLS.
Tracks: / Black dog / Rock and roll / Battle of Evermore, The / Stairway to heaven / Misty mountain hop / Four sticks / Going to California / When the levee breaks.
LP: K 50008
MC: K4 50008
LP: 2401 012

1972 INTERVIEW.
LPPD: RAMBLE ONE

1973 INTERVIEW.
LPPD: RAMBLE 2

CHRIS TETLEY INTERVIEWS LED ZEPPELIN.
LPPD: CT 1004

CODA.
Tracks: / We're gonna groove / Poor Tom / I can't quit you baby / Walter's walk / Darlene / Ozone baby / Wearing and tearing / Bonzo's montreauz.
LP: A 0051
MC: A 0051 4

HOUSES OF THE HOLY.
Tracks: / Song remains the same, The / Rain song, The / Over the hills and far away / Crunge, The / Dancing days / Yer mak'er / No quarter / Ocean, The.
LP: K 50014
MC: K4 50014

IN THROUGH THE OUT DOOR.
Tracks: / In the evening / South bound saurez / Fool in the rain / Hot dog / Carouselambra / All my love / I'm gonna crawl.
LP: SSK 59410
MC: SK4 59410

LED ZEPPELIN.
Tracks: / Good times bad times / Babe I'm gonna leave you / You shook me / Dazed and confused / Your time is gonna come / Black mountain side / Communication breakdown / I can't quit you baby / How many more times.
LP: K 40031
MC: K4 40031
LP: 588 171

LED ZEPPELIN 2.
Tracks: / Whole lotta love / What is and what should be / Lemon song, The / Thank you / Heartbreaker / Livin' lovin'

maid / (She's a woman) / Ramble on / Moby Dick / Bring it on home.
LP: K 40037
MC: K4 40037
LP: 588 198

LED ZEPPELIN 3.
Tracks: / Immigrant song / Friends / Celebration day / Since I've been loving you / Out on the tiles / Gallows pole / Tangerine / That's the way / Bron-y-aur stomp / Hats off to (Roy) Harper.
LP: K 50002
MC: K4 50002
LP: 2401 002

LED ZEPPELIN 4 (See under 4 Symbols).

PHYSICAL GRAFFITI.
Tracks: / Houses of the holy / Trampled under foot / Kashmir / Custard pie / Rover, The / In my time of dying / In the light / Bron-y-aur stomp / Down by the seaside / Ten years gone / Night flight / Wanton song, The / Boogie with Stu / Back country woman / Sick again.
2LP: SSK 89400
MCSET: SK4 89400

PRESENCE.
Tracks: / Achilles last stand / For your life / Royal Orleans / Nobody's fault but mine / Candystore rock / Hots on for nowhere / Tea for one.
LP: SSK 59402
MC: SK4 59402

REMASTERS (1) (1969 - 1980).
Tracks: / Communication breakdown / Babe I'm gonna leave you / Good times, bad times / Dazed and confused / Whole lotta love / Heartbreaker / Ramble on / Immigrant song / Celebration day / Since I've been loving you / Black dog / Rock and roll / Battle of Evermore, The / Misty mountain hop / Stairway to heaven / Song remains the same, The / Rain song, The / D'yer mak'er / No quarter / Houses of the holy / Kashmir / Trampled underfoot / Nobody's fault but mine / Achilles last stand / All my love / In the evening.
LPS: ZEP 1
MCSET: ZEPC 1

REMASTERS (2).
Tracks: / Whole lotta love / Heartbreaker / Communication breakdown / Babe I'm gonna leave you / Dazed and confused / Ramble on / Your time is gonna come / What is and what should never be / Thank you / I can't quit you baby / Friends / Celebration day / Travelling riverside blues / Hey hey what can I do / White summer/ Black mountain side / Black dog / Over the hills and far away / Immigrant song / Battle of the Evermore / Bron-y-aur stomp / Tangerine / Going to California / Since I've been loving you / D'yer mak'er / Gallows pole / Custard pie / Misty mountain hop / Rock and roll / Rain song, The / Stairway to heaven / Kashmir / Trampled underfoot / For your life / No quarter / Dancing days / When the levee breaks / Song remains the same, The / Achilles last stand / Ten years gone / Candy store rock / Moby Dick / In my time of dying / In the evening / Ocean, The / Ozone baby / Houses of the holy / Wearing and tearing / Poor Tom / Nobody's fault but mine / Fool in the rain / In the light / Wanton song, The / I'm gonna crawl / All my love.
LPS: 7567 821 44 1
MCSET: 7567 821 44 4

RUNES (See under 4 Symbols).

SONG REMAINS THE SAME, THE.
Tracks: / Rock and roll / Celebration day / Song remains the same, The / Rain song / Dazed and confused / No quarter / Stairway to heaven / Moby dick / Whole lotta love.
2LP: SSK 89402
MCSET: SK4 89402

STORY OF THE FILM "THE SONG REMAINS THE SAME".
LPPD: BAK 6017

ZO-SO (See under 4 Symbols).

Ledernacken

1ST LP.
LP: SBR 2LP

BOOGALOO AND OTHER NATTY DANCERS.
LP: SBR 14LP

SEX METAL.
LP: SBR 16 LP

Ledford String Band

LEDFORD STRING BAND.
LP: ROUNDER 0008

Ledin, Tomas

HUMAN TOUCH.
Tracks: / I love you / I've got something / Never again / She's in love with my best friend / Listen to your heart / Loving you is like chasing a dream / Keep it up / Taken by surprise / Love me like you used to / In the middle of nowhere.
LP: EPC 25136

LeDoux, Chris

COWBOYS AIN'T EASY TO LOVE.
LP: CLD 79

HE RIDES THE WILD HORSES.
LP: CLD 84

LIFE AS A RODEO MAN.
LP: CLD 76

OLD COWBOY CLASSICS.
LP: CLD 87

OLD COWBOY HEROES.
LP: CLD 83

PAINT ME BACK HOME IN WYOMING.
LP: CLD 80

RODEO SONGS OLD AND NEW.
LP: CLD 73

SING ME A SONG MR. RODEO MAN.
LP: CLD 78

SONGBOOK OF THE AMERICAN WEST.
LP: CLD 77

SONGS OF LIVING FREE.
LP: CLD 75

SONGS OF RODEO & COUNTRY.
LP: CLD 74

SONGS OF RODEO LIFE.
LP: CLD 72

SOUNDS OF THE WESTERN COUNTRY.
LP: CLD 82

THIRTY DOLLAR COWBOY.
LP: CLD 88

WESTERN TUNESMITH.
LP: CLD 81

Ledwith Tony

IRISH MUSIC FROM THE FAVOURITE (See Powers, Jimmy) (Ledwith Tony & Jimmy powers).

Lee, Albert

ALBERT LEE.
Tracks: / Sweet little Lisa / Radio girl / Your boys / So sad to watch good love go bad / Rock 'n' roll man / Real wild child / On the boulevard / Pink bedroom / Best I can / One way rider.
LP: SPELP 29

COUNTRY GUITAR MAN.
Tracks: / Jack of all trades / Meal ticket / I won't let you down / Soft word Sunday morning / One woman / Just another ambush / Stripes / Another useless day.
LP: SDLP 037
MC: SDC 037

GAGGED BUT NOT BOUND.
Tracks: / Flowers of Edinburgh / Don't let go / Midnight special / Tiger rag / Forty miles of bad road / Fun ranch boogie / Walking after midnight / Schon Rosemarin / Country gentleman / Monte Nido.
LP: IMCA 42063
MC: IMCAC 42063

HIDING.
Tracks: / Country boy / Billy Tyler / Are you wasting my time / Now and then it's gonna rain / O a real good night / Setting me up / Ain't living long like this / Hiding / Hotel love / Come up and see me anytime.
LP: AMLH 64750
MC: CAM 64750

SPEECHLESS.
Tracks: / T-Bird to Vegas / Bullish boogie / Arkansas traveller / Romany rye / Erin / Seventeenth summer / Salt creek / Cannonball.
LP: IMCA 5693
MC: IMCAC 5693

Lee, Alvin

FREE FALL.
LP: AALP 5002

RIDE ON.
Tracks: / Too much / It's a gaz / Ride on cowboy / Sittin' here / Can't sleep at night / Ain't nothin' shakin' / Scat encounter / Hey Joe / Going home.
LP: 2310678

Lee, Arthur

ARTHUR LEE.
LP: BEGA 26

Lee, Barbara

DEVIL IS AFRAID OF MUSIC, THE.
LP: AP 119

HOAGY'S CHILDREN (Lee, Barbara/ Bob Dorough/Dick Sudhalter).
LP: AP 165

REMEMBERING, REMEMBERING LEE WILEY.
LP: AP 125

WOMAN IN LOVE, A.
LP: AP 86

Lee, Benny

WHISPERING GRASS (See under Carless, Dorothy) (Lee, Benny/Adelaide Hall/Issy Bonn/Dorothy Carless).

Lee, Brenda

16 CLASSIC TRACKS: BRENDA LEE.
Tracks: / Sweet nothin's / Speak to me pretty / Dum dum / I wonder / Losing you / Christmas will be just another lonely day / Is it true / All alone am I / Let's jump the broomstick / Here comes that feeling / As usual / It started all over again / Emotions / Sweet impossible you / Rockin' around the Christmas tree / I'm sorry.
MC: TCMFP 50548
LP: MFP 50548

25TH ANNIVERSARY.
2LP: MCLD 609

ALL ALONE AM I.
LP: LAT 8530

ALL THE WAY.
LP: LAT 8383

BEST OF BRENDA LEE.
Tracks: / Sweet nothin's / I'm sorry / Emotions / Dum dum / Fool number one / You always hurt the one you love / Will you love me tomorrow / When I fall in love / I'll be seeing you / Speak to me pretty / Here comes that feeling / It started all over again / My colouring book / Someday you'll want me to want you / End of the world / All alone am i / Losing you / I wonder / My whole world / Sweet impossible you / As usual / Is it true / Think / Love letters / Too many rivers / Make the world go away / Crying time / Sweet dreams / Yesterday / Always on my mind / For the good times / Feelings.
2LP: LETV 1

BEST OF BRENDA LEE (2).
MC: 1A 222 58249
LP: 1A 022 58249

BRENDA - THAT'S ALL.
LP: LAT 8516

BRENDA'S BEST.
LPPD: AR 30084

BYE BYE BLUES.
LP: LAT 8649

EVEN BETTER.
LP: MCF 3054

GOLDEN DECADE, THE.
Tracks: / Jambalaya / Bigelow 6200 / Some people / Your cheatin' heart / Doodlebug rag / One step at a time / Dynamite / Ain't that love? / One teenager to another / Rock a bye baby blues / Rock the bop / Ring-a-my-phone / Little Jonah / Rockin' around the Christmas tree / Let's jump the broomstick / Stroll, The / Sweet nothin's / Weep no more / I'm sorry / Wee rivers / Coming on strong.
2LP: CDX 6

L.A. SESSIONS.
Tracks: / Oklahoma superstar / Taking what I can get / I let you let me down again / Ruby's lounge / When our love began / Mary's going out of her mine / Your favourite worn-out nightmare's comin home / One more time / Saved / Lumberjacks had a lady / It's another weekend.
LP: MCF 2783

LITTLE MISS DYNAMITE.
LP: WW 5083

LOVE SONGS: BRENDA LEE.
Tracks: / No one / I'll be seeing you / My colouring book / Who can I turn to / Softly as I leave you / Crying time / Can't help falling in love / Feelings / Something / Masquerade / Killing me softly with his song / My way.
LP: MCL 1793
MC: MCLC 1793

WIEDERSEHN IST WUNDERSCHON.
Tracks: / Wiedersehn ist wunderschon / Ohne dich / Drei rote / Ich will immer auf dich warten / No my boy / Darling bye bye / Geh' nicht an gluck vorbei / Am strand von Hawaii / Kansas City / Darling was ist los mit dir / In meinen traumen / Wo und wann fangt die liebe an / Pourquoi jamais (In French) / La premier fool (In French) / Nulla di me (In Italian) / Sono Sciocca (In Italian).
LP: BFX 15186

WINNING HAND, THE (see under Parton, Dolly) (Lee, Brenda/Dolly Parton/Kris Kristofferson/Willie Nelson).

Lee, Bunny

JUMPING WITH MR LEE (Lee, Bunny & Friends).
Tracks: / Long time me no / Jumping / Bangarang / Change is gonna come, A / Jumping with Val / Tribute to King Scratch / Sounds and soul / Sir Lee's whip / Love and devotion / Hold you Jack / Little boy blue / Story of love / Girls like dirt / Somebody's baby / My conversation / Beatitude, The.
LP: PERRY 2
LP: TRLS 270

Lee, Byron

ART OF MAS (Lee, Byron & The Dragonaires).
LP: DYLS 1002

BEST OF CARNIVAL (Lee, Byron & The Dragonaires).
Tracks: / Hot hot hot / Tell she / Sugar bum bum / Hot sweet and jumpy / Don't look back / Statue / Feeling it, soft man / Gimme more tempo / Solfish / Her Majesty / King Kong.
LP: DYLP 3

CARNIVAL EXPERIENCE (Lee, Byron & The Dragonaires).
Tracks: / School days / Symphony in G / More time / Taxi driver / Gaudeloupe chic / Tell she / MacArthur Park / Rastaman be careful / One for me, one for you / Jesu joy of man's desiring.
LP: DYLP 3014

DE MUSIC HOT MAMA (Lee, Byron & The Dragonaires).
LP: DY 3459
MC: DYC 3459

JAMAICA'S GOLDEN HITS (Lee, Byron & The Dragonaires).
Tracks: / My boy lollipop / Easy snappin' / Tell me darling / Green island / Wings of a dove / Sammy dead / Oh Carolina / Oil in my lamp / Occupation / Behold / Jamaica ska.
LP: DY 3380
LP: ETMP 16

JAMAICA'S GOLDEN HITS, VOL 2 (Lee, Byron & The Dragonaires).
Tracks: / Simmer down / Dancing mood / Puppet on a string / I've got to go back home / Eastern standard time / River bank / It's you / Schooling the Duke / Pressure and slide / Satisfaction / Ride you donkey / You won't see.
LP: DYLP 2
MC: DYMC 2
LP: ETMP 17

MIGHTY SPARROW (Lee, Byron & The Dragonaires).
LP: DYLP 3002

MORE CARNIVAL (Lee, Byron & The Dragonaires).
LP: DYLP 3012

REGGAE BLAST OFF (Lee, Byron & The Dragonaires).
Tracks: / Monkey man / Elizabethan reggae / Love at first sight / Birth control.
LP: TBL 110

REGGAE INTERNATIONAL (Lee, Byron & The Dragonaires).
LP: DYLP 3008

REGGAE ROUN' THE WORLD (Lee, Byron & The Dragonaires).
LP: DR 5001

SOCA BACHANNAL (Lee, Byron & The Dragonaires).
LP: DY 3461

SOCA GIRL (Lee, Byron & The Dragonaires).
Tracks: / Soca girl (calypso version of girlie girlie) / Gimme soca.
LP: DY 3450
MC: DYC 3450

SOCA THUNDER (Lee, Byron & The Dragonaires).
LP: DY 3457

SOFT LEE VOL.3 (Lee, Byron & The Dragonaires).
LP: DY 3460

SOUL-SKA (Lee, Byron All Stars).
LP: STLP 1001

THIS IS CARNIVAL (Lee, Byron & The Dragonaires).
LP: DYLP 3006

WINE MISS TINY (Lee, Byron & The Dragonaires).
Tracks: / Calabash / Tiny Winey / Theresa / Long time / Somebody in the party / Rack me / Love up / Soucouyant / Me eh fighting / Satan coming down.
LP: DY 3449

Lee, Christopher

DRACULA (See under Dracula).

TALES OF MYSTERY & HORROR (Edgar Allen Poe).
MC: TC LFP 7108

Lee, Curtis

PRETTY LITTLE ANGEL EYES.
LP: LP 2000

Lee, Darrell

DARRELL LEE.
Tracks: / Slow dance / Just a little bit / Girl, I'm alone / Sexy / She made me / Lisa / Big city life / Lock these people up.
LP: . . . . GEM 4005
MC: . . . . ZCGEM 4005

Lee, David H.

ME.
LP: . . . . BSS 316

Lee, Dee C

SHRINE.
Tracks: / Shrine / Hey what'd ya say? / That's when something special starts / He's gone / Come hell or waters high / What about me / Still the children cry / Just my type / Hold on / See the day.
LP: . . . . CBS 26915
MC: 40 26915

Lee, Dennis (nar)

ALADDIN AND HIS LAMP (See under Aladdin... (bk)).

ALI BABA AND THE FORTY THIEVES (See under Ali Baba).

ALLIGATOR PIE AND OTHER POEMS.
MC: 1530

SINBAD THE SAILOR (See under Sinbad the Sailor).

TALE OF SCHEHEREZADE (See under Tale of Scheherezade).

Lee, Dino

DINO LEE LIVE.
LP: . . . . ROSE 172

KING OF WHITE TRASH.
LP: . . . . ROSE 63

NEW LAS VEGAN, THE.
LP: . . . . ROSE 127

Lee, Frankie

FACE IT.
Tracks: / Ladies and the babies, The / Woman don't live here no more, The / Face it / Stoned, cold and blue / Nasty stuff / Don't make me go home / My first million tears / It's cold out here.
LP: . . . . FIEND 42

Lee, Freddie 'Fingers'

FREDDIE 'FINGERS' LEE.
Tracks: / One-eyed boogie boy / I'm down / Come back, baby / It's hard to lie to you / I'm gonna move did dab boogie / I don't want your rockin' love / I'm rollin' home / I'll come back / You paid to ride / Trying to get to Memphis / Rock all night / Pondering and wondering / Rocking at my house / I'm a nut / Two boiled eggs.
LP: . . . . CR 30160
LP: . . . . LP 7812

MINI LP COLLECTION.
LP: . . . . MLP 8419

OL' ONE EYES BACK.
LP: . . . . CR 30178
LP: . . . . LP 7912

ROCKIN' WITH MY PIANO.
Tracks: / Alabamy bound / Who's gonna put down? / Joe Brown and me / Angry young man / Bop, The / Old one eye's back / I got it all for you / Same old way, The / Nice like that / You can run.
LP: . . . . MFM 007
LP: . . . . BBR 1008

Lee, George

1927-29 (Lee, George & His Novelty Singing Orchestra).
LP: . . . . FJ 125

ANANSI (Lee's Anansi, George).
LP: . . . . EBUS 1
MC: . . . . EBUC 1

RUFF SCUFFLIN' (See under Barnes, Walter) (Lee, George/Walter Barnes).

Lee, Jack

GREATEST HITS: JACK LEE.
LP: . . . . LOLITA 5019

JACK LEE.
LP: . . . . LOLITA 5044

Lee, Jimmie

IT'S ME.
LP: . . . . ROLL 19

Lee, John

DOWN AT THE DEPOT.
LP: . . . . ROUNDER 2010

PUT ON YOUR DANCING SHOES.
LP: . . . . MTS 19

Lee, Johnny

JOHNNY LEE.
MC: . . . . ZCGAS 712

JOHNNY LEE & WILLIE NELSON (See under Nelson, Willie) (Lee, Johnny & Willie Nelson).

Lee, Julia

OF LIONS AND LAMBS.
Tracks: / When Jenny does that low down dance / Don't save it too long (the money song) / Backstreet / Tell me daddy / I was wrong / When a man has two women / Away from you / Your gonna miss it / It comes in like a lion / Lotus blossom / Ain't it a crime / When your lover has gone / Chuck it in a bucket / Nobody knows you (when you're down and out) / You ain't got it no more / I got news for you.
LP: . . . . CRB 1175
MC: . . . . TCCRB 1175

PARTY TIME.
LP: 2C 068 86524

PORTER'S LOVE SONG, A (Lee, Julia / Boyfriends).
Tracks: / If it's good / When a woman loves a man / Show me Missouri blues / I'll get along somehow / Porters love song, A / Young girl's blues / Since I've been with you / Oh, Marie! / Doubtful blues / On my way out / Wise guys (you're a wise guy) / All I ever do is worry / Breeze (blow my baby back to me) / Christmas spirits / Glory of love / Charmaine.
LP: . . . . JB 614

TONIGHT'S THE NIGHT.
Tracks: / Snatch and grab it / I didn't like it the first time / Come on over to my house / That's what I like / Knock me a kiss / King-size papa / Can't get enough of that stuff / Gotta gimme whatcha got / My man stands out / Tonight's the night / Don't come too soon / All this beef and big red tomatoes / Mama don't allow / Trouble in mind / Take it or leave it / Last call for alcohol.
LP: . . . . CRB 1039
MC: . . . . TCCRB 1039

UGLY PAPA (Lee, Julia / Boyfriends).
LP: . . . . JB 603

Lee, Laura

RIP OFF, THE.
Tracks: / Wedlock is a padlock / Women's love rights / I don't want nothing old (but money) / Love and liberty / Two lonely pillows / (Don't be sorry) be careful if you can't be good / If I'm good enough to love (I'm good enough to marry) / Rip off / If you can hear me rockin' (you can have my chair) / (If you want to try love again) remember me / Workin' and lovin' together / I'll catch you when you fall / I can't hold on much longer / I need it just as bad as you.
LP: . . . . HDH LP 003

THAT'S HOW IT IS.
Tracks: / Wanted: Lover no experience necessary / Up tight good man / Another man's woman / He will break your heart / Dirty man / Hang it up / Man with some backbone, A / It ain't what you do / Meet love halfway.
LP: . . . . GCH 8103

Lee, Laurie (author)

CIDER WITH ROSIE (see under Cider With Rosie (bk)).

I CAN'T STAY LONG.
MC: . . . . IAB 88081

Lee, Lonnie

GREATEST HITS: LONNIE LEE.
LP: . . . . REBEL 1004

Lee, Michael

FIRKINS.
Tracks: / Laughing stacks / Runaway train / Deja blues / Rain in the tunnel / Sargasso sea, The / 24 Grand Avenue / Cactus cruz / Space crickets / Hula hoops.
LP: . . . . RR 93991
MC: . . . . RR 93994

Lee, Peggy

16 GREATEST HITS: PEGGY LEE.
LP: 5C 054 85001

24 PHONOGRAPHIC MEMORIES.
MC: . . . . DVREMC 57

ALL AGLOW AGAIN.
Tracks: / Fever / Where do I go from here? / Whee baby / My man / You deserve / Manana / Hallelujah, I love him so / You don't know / Louisville Lou / I'm lookin' out the window / It keeps you young / Let's call it a day.
LP: . . . . EG 2606051
MC: . . . . EG 2606054

BEAUTY AND THE BEAT (Lee, Peggy & George Shearing).
Tracks: / Do I love you? / I lost my sugar in Salt Lake City / If dreams come true / All too soon / Mambo in Miami / Isn't it romantic? / Blue prelude / You came a long way from St Louis / Always true to you in my fashion / There'll be another Spring / Get out of town / Satin doll.
LP: 2C 068 54576
MC: . . . . PM 1545764
LP: . . . . EMS 1158
MC: . . . . TCEMS 1158
LP: . . . . T 1219

BEST OF PEGGY LEE.
Tracks: / Lover / Apples, peaches and cherries / Love me or leave me / I don't know enough about you / He's a tramp / Mr. Wonderful / Black coffee / Siamese cat song / He needs me / My heart belongs to daddy / Where can I go without you? / Easy living / I didn't know what time it was / They can't take that away from me / Just one of those things / Love, you didn't do right by me.
LP: . . . . MCL 1632
MC: . . . . MCFC 1632
MC: . . . . MCLC 1632

BEST OF PEGGY LEE (MFP).
LP: . . . . MFP 5605
MC: . . . . TCMFP 5605

BEST OF PEGGY LEE VOL 2.
LP: . . . . LAT 8355

BING CROSBY WITH PEGGY LEE, JACK BENNY, GARY COOPER (See under Crosby, Bing) (Lee, Peggy/ Bing Crosby/ Jack Benny/ Gary Cooper).

BLACK COFFEE.
Tracks: / Black coffee / I've got you under my skin / Easy living / My heart belongs to daddy / It ain't necessarily so / Gee baby ain't I good to you / Woman alone with the blues / I didn't know what time it was / When the world was young / Love me or leave me / You're my thrill / There's a small hotel.
LP: . . . . JASM 1026
LP: . . . . AH 5

BLUES CROSS COUNTRY.
Tracks: / Basin Street blues / Kansas city / St. Louis blues.
LP: . . . . PM 1552941
MC: . . . . PM 1552944

CAPITOL COLLECTORS SERIES: PEGGY LEE (Vol. 1 The Early Years).
Tracks: / Waiting for the train to come in / I'm glad I waited for you (From the film Tars & Spars.) / I don't know enough about you / Linger in my arms a little longer baby / It's all over now / It's a good day / Everything's movin' too fast / Chi-baba, chi-baba / Sugar (that sugar baby o' mine) / Golden earrings (From Golden Earrings.) / I'll dance at your wedding / Manana / All dressed up with a broken heart / Talking to myself about you / Why don't you do it right (get me some money too) / Deed I do / Don't smoke in bed / Caramba it's the samba / Them there eyes / Baby, don't be mad at me / Bali Ha'i (From South Pacific.) / I'm gonna wash that man right out of my hair (From South Pacific.) / Riders in the sky (A cowboy legend.) / Old master painter, The / Show me the way to get out of this world.
MC: C4 93195

CAPITOL YEARS, THE: PEGGY LEE (Best of...).
Tracks: / Manana / Golden Earrings / It's a good day / Don't smoke in bed / Why don't you do right? / Fever / Folks who live on the hill, The / Hallelujah I love him so / I'm a woman / Doodlin' song, A / Big spender / So what's new / Shining sea, The / Alright, okay, you win / Is that all there is? / I'm gonna go fishin'.
LP: . . . . EMS 1294
MC: . . . . TC EMS 1294

CLOSE ENOUGH FOR LOVE.
MC: . . . . SLC 5190

DREAM STREET.
Tracks: / Street of dreams / What's new / Too late now / You're blase / It's alright with me / My old flame / Dancing on the ceiling / It never entered my mind / I don't know enough about you / Something I dreamed last night / Last night when we were young.
LP: . . . . JASM 1032

EASY LISTENING.
LP: . . . . ART 005
MC: . . . . CART 005

FABULOUS PEGGY LEE, THE.
Tracks: / You let my love get cold / Love you didn't do right by me / Oh no (please don't go) / Tavern, The / Wrong, wrong, wrong / Gypsy with fire in his shoes, The / Do I love you / Wrong Joe / Me / Johnny guitar / I belong to you / Autumn in Rome.
LP: . . . . OFF 12002

FEVER AND OTHER HITS.
Tracks: / Fever / I'm a woman / Alright, okay, you win / Big spender / Hallelujah / I love him so / Alley cat song / Is that all there is? / Heart / Doodlin' song, A.
MC: 4XL 9095

FEVER (OLD GOLD) (see Otis, Johnny - Ma he's making eyes at me).

GOLDEN GREATS: PEGGY LEE.
Tracks: / Lover / Mr. Wonderful / He's a tramp / Siamese cat song / He needs me / Apples, peaches and cherries / Love me or leave me / I don't know enough about you / Black coffee / My heart belongs to daddy / Where can I go without you / Easy living / I didn't know what time it was / They can't take that away from me / Just one of those things / Love you didn't do right by me.
LP: . . . . MCM 5010
MC: . . . . MCMC 5010

I LIKE MEN!.
Tracks: / Charley, my boy / Good for nothin' Joe / I love to love / When a woman loves a man / I like men! / I'm just wild about Harry / My man / Bill / So in love / Jim / It's so nice to have a man around the house / Oh Johnny, oh Johnny, oh.
LP: . . . . EMS 1287
MC: . . . . TCEMS 1287

IF I COULD BE WITH YOU.
Tracks: / If I could be with you / Too young / Clarinade / Shangai / Guy is a guy, A / Lady is a tramp, The / Dorsey medley / These foolish things / Just one more chance / Make the man love me.
LP: . . . . SR 5008
MC: . . . . JASMC 2534
LP: . . . . JASM 2534

IF YOU GO.
Tracks: / As time goes by / If you go / Oh love, hast thou forsaken me? / Say it isn't so / I wish I didn't love you so / Maybe it's because I love you too much / I'm gonna laugh you out of my life / I get along without you very well / I love your gypsy heart / When I was a child / Here's that rainy day / Smile.
LP: . . . . ED 2604121
MC: . . . . ED 2604124

I'VE HAD MY MOMENTS.
MC: . . . . SLC 61008

JUMP FOR JOY.
Tracks: / Jump for joy / Back in your own back yard / When my sugar walks down the street / I hear music / Just in time / Old devil moon / What a little moonlight can do / Four or five times / Music music music / Cheek to cheek / Glory of love.
LP: . . . . T 979

LATIN A LA LEE.
Tracks: / Heart / On the street where you live / Till there was you / I am in love / Hey there / I could have danced all night / Surrey with the fringe on top / Party's over, The / Dance only with me / Wish you were here / C'est Magnifique / I enjoy being a girl.
LP: . . . . EMS 1304
MC: . . . . TC EMS 1304
LP: . . . . T 1290

MAN I LOVE, THE.
Tracks: / Man I love, The / Please be kind / Happiness is a thing called Joe / Just one way to say I love you / That's all / Something wonderful / He's my guy / Then I'll be tired of you / My heart stood still / If I should lose you / There is no greater love / Folks who live on the hill, The.
LP: . . . . CAPS 2600051
MC: . . . . TCCAPS 2600054

MINK JAZZ.
LP: . . . . MOIR 213
MC: . . . . CMOIR 213

MISS PEGGY LEE SINGS THE BLUES.
Tracks: / See see rider / Basin Street blues / Squeeze me / You don't know / Fine and mellow / Baby please come home / Kansas City / Birmingham jail / Love me / Beale street blues / T'aint nobody's biz-ness if I do / God bless the child.
MC: . . . . CIJD 20155 K
LP: . . . . CIJD 40155 H

MISS WONDERFUL.
Tracks: / Mister wonderful / They can't take that away from me / Where flamingos fly / You've got to see mama every night / Comeback, The / Take a little time to smile / I don't know enough about you / Joey, Joey, Joey / Crazy in the heart / You oughta be mine / We laughed at love / That's alright honey.
LP: . . . . OFF 12013

PEGGY LEE & BENNY GOODMAN (Lee, Peggy & Benny Goodman).
Tracks: / How long has this been going on / That did it, Marie / Elmer's tune / I threw a kiss in the ocean / We'll meet again / That's the way it goes / All I need is you / Not a care in the world / Full moon.
LP: 32417

PEGGY LEE COLLECTION (20 golden greats).
Tracks: / I can't give you anything but love / I don't know enough about you / Stormy weather / Golden earrings / On the sunny side of the street / Somebody

loves me / It's a good day / As long as I'm dreaming / You and I passing by / While we're young / It takes a long, long train / Lady from 29 palms / Manana / Why don't you do right? / Up a lazy river / Aintcha ever comin' back? / Hold me / When the red, red robin comes bob, bob, bobbin' along / Them there eyes.
LP: . . . . **DVLP 2021**
MC: . . . . **DVMC 2021**

PETE KELLY'S BLUES (Film soundtrack) (Lee, Peggy & Ella Fitzgerald).
Tracks: / Oh, didn't he ramble? / Sugar (that sugar baby of mine) / Somebody loves me / I'm gonna meet my sweetie now / I never knew / Bye bye blackbird / What can I say, after I say I'm sorry? / Hard hearted Hannah / Ella hums the blues / He needs me / Sing a rainbow / Pete Kelly's blues.
LP: . . . . **JASM 1024**

PORTRAIT OF A SONG STYLIST.
Tracks: / Folks who live on the hill, The / That old devil moon / When a man loves a woman / Party's over, The / I enjoy being a girl / Stormy weather / Something / As time goes by / Cheek to cheek / I hear music / Till there was you / Fly me to the moon / Alright, okay you win / Is that all there is.
MC: . . . . **HARMC 116**

PRETTY EYES.
Tracks: / As you desire me / It could happen to you / Pretty eyes / Moments like this / Remind me / You fascinate me so / I wanna be loved / I'm walking through / I remember you / Too close for comfort / Fly me to the moon / Because I love him so.
LP: . . . . **EMS 1153**
MC: . . . . **TCEMS 1153**

RENDEZVOUS WITH PEGGY LEE.
Tracks: / Why don't you do right? / Them there eyes / Deed I do / I don't know enough about you / It's a good day / Golden earrings / I can't give you anything but love / Stormy weather / Don't smoke in bed / While we're young / Manana / Hold me.
LP: . . . . **PM 154 773 1**
MC: . . . . **PM 154 773 4**

SEA SHELLS.
Tracks: / Brown bird singing / I don't want to play in your yard / Maid with the flaxen hair / Wearing of the green, The / Chaconde / Chinese love poems / Riddle song / Golden wedding ring / Sea fever / Nine thorny thickets / Little old car / Greensleeves / Happy monks / White birch and the sycamore / Of such is the Kingdom of God.
LP: . . . . **JASM 1046**

THINGS ARE SWINGIN'.
Tracks: / It's a wonderful world / Things are swinging / Alright, okay, you win / Ridin' high / It's been a long long time / Lullaby in rhythm / Alone together / I'm beginning to see the light / It's a good, good night / You're getting to be a habit with me / You're mine, you / Life is for living.
LP: . . . . **EMS 1139**
MC: . . . . **TCEMS 1139**

UNFORGETTABLE: PEGGY LEE (16 Golden Classics).
Tracks: / Mr. Wonderful / Lover / He needs me / Joey Joey Joey / Siamese cat song / He's a tramp / I didn't know what time it was / Let me go lover / Bouquet of blues / Johnny guitar / Straight ahead / It must be so (with the Mills Brothers) / Black coffee / Love me or leave me / My heart belongs to daddy / I've got you under my skin / When the world was young / Easy living.
LP: . . . . **UNLP 027**
MC: . . . . **UNMC 027**

WITH THE DAVID BARBOUR AND BILLY MAY BANDS 1948.
LP: . . . . **HUK 220**

YOU CAN DEPEND ON ME.
LP: . . . . **GL 6023**

Lee, Phil

TWICE UPON A TIME (Lee, Phil & Jeff Clyne).
Tracks: / Blue serge / Eiderdown / Soiree / Everything I love / P.S. for Scott / Mar descancado / Peau douce / So tender / They say its wonderful.
MC: . . . . **KSGC 1018**

Lee, Philip John

FIVE SWORDS.
Tracks: / Alegrias / London lilacs / Bulerias 1 / Travellers lament, The / Rumba / Five swords / Fall of the leaf, The / Bulerias 2 / E Sacramonte / Lullaby for a baby toad / Verdiales.
LP: . . . . **RRA 002**

Lee, Ranee

LIVE AT THE BIJOU.
LP: . . . . **JUST 2**

Lee, Rockin' Lord

OUT AT LAST.
Tracks: / Dance in the street / Your true love / Sweet little sixteen / Blue moon of Kentucky / Teenage boogie / Yes tonight Josephine / Lotta lovin' / Donna / Pink and black / Matchbox / Diggin' the boogie / Susannah / Lord Lee's guitar boogie / Flyin' saucers rock'n'roll / Honey don't / Alabama shake.
LP: . . . . **RSRLP 1018**

Lee, Rudy

GET WISE.
LP: . . . . **TLDLP 001**

TEAM WORKS PRESENTS (Lee, Rudy & Stepper).
LP: . . . . **MOWLP 003**

Lee, Rustie

INVITATION TO PARTY.
Tracks: / Caribbean party time (Medley) / Barbados / Bend down / When a man loves a woman / Clapping song, The / My guy / Where did our love go / My toot toot / 1-2-3 / I can't help myself / Spanish Harlem / In the shelter of your arms / Go out and get some (get it out'cha system) / Caribbean party time (reprise).
2LP: . . . . **SMR 8509**
MCSET: . . . . **SMC 8509**

Lee, Tim

CAN'T GET LOST WHEN YOU'RE GONE (Lee, Tim & Matt Piucci).
LP: **2126 1**

Lee, Tippa

MURDER (see Toyan) (Lee, Tipper/ Toyan/Johnny Slaughter).

NUH TROUBLE WE (Lee, Tippa & Rappa Robert).
LP: . . . . **RMM 1715**

Lee, Tony

BRITISH JAZZ ARTISTS 1 (Lee, Tony, Trio).
LP: . . . . **LYN 3416**

BRITISH JAZZ ARTISTS 2 (Lee, Tony, Trio & Terry Smith).
LP: . . . . **LAM 002**

STREETS OF DREAMS.
Tracks: / Li'l darlin' / Loss of love / Street of dreams / Dick's mood / Love for sale / My funny valentine / Green Dolphin Street.
LP: . . . . **LAM 102**

TONY LEE TRIO AND FRIENDS (Lee, Tony, Trio).
Tracks: / Blue 'n' boogie / Body and soul / Tenderly / Leeward / If / Bluesology.
LP: . . . . **N 104**

Lee, Wilma

EARLY RECORDINGS (Lee, Wilma & Stoney Cooper).
Tracks: / West Virginia polka / All on account of you / No one now / Can you forget / Thirty pieces of silver / On the banks of the old river / Sunny side of the mountain / I cried again / Walking my lord up Calgary Hill / You tried to ruin my name / White rose, The / I'm taking my audition.
LP: . . . . **CCS 103**

Leecan & Cooksey

BLUES OF BOBBIE LEECAN AND ROBERT COOKSEY.
LP: . . . . **CC 53**

REMAINING TITLES, THE 1926-27.
Tracks: / Black cat bone blues / Dirty guitar blues / Dollar blues / Royal palm blues / Blue harmonica / Macon Georgia cut out.
LP: . . . . **MSE 1010**

Leek, Andy

SAY SOMETHING.
Tracks: / Please please / Holdin' on to you / What's the problem? / Golden doors / Say something / Entangled hearts / Attitude / Sailor's song / Carry me away.
LP: . . . . **WX 205**
MC: . . . . **WX 205 C**

Leeman, Mark

MEMORIAL ALBUM (Leeman, Mark Five).
LP: . . . . **SEE 317**

Leer, Thomas

CONTRADICTIONS.
Tracks: / Hear what I say / Mr. Nobody / Contradictions / Looks that kill / Soul gypsy / Choices / Gulf stream.
LP: . . . . **ERED 26**

SCALE OF TEN.
LP: **207208**
MC: **407208**

Lees, Gene

QUIET NIGHTS OF QUIET STARS.
LP: . . . . **ST 269**

Leeson, Robert

WHEEL OF DANGER, THE.
MCSET: **086 222 0474**

Leeway

BORN TO EXPIRE.
Tracks: / Rise and fall / On the outside / Defy you / Tools for war / Marathon / Catholic high school / Mark and the squealer / Be loud / Enforcer / Born to expire / Self defence / Unexpected.
LP: . . . . **FILER 257**
MC: . . . . **FILECT 257**

DESPERATE MEASURES.
LP: . . . . **FILER 403**
MC: . . . . **FILERCT 403**

LeFevre, Mylon

CRACK THE SKY.
LP: . . . . **MYR R 1244**
MC: . . . . **MYR C 1244**

FACE THE MUSIC.
LP: . . . . **SSR 8099**
MC: . . . . **SSC 8099**

SHEEP IN WOLVES CLOTHING (Lefevre, Mylon & Broken Hearts).
LP: . . . . **MYRR 1200**
MC: . . . . **MYRC 1200**

Lefevre, Raymond

FRENCH LOVE SONGS.
Tracks: / La mer / Et maintenant / Comme d'habitude / Hier encore / La vie en rose / She / Ne me quitte pas / Hymne a l'amour / La foule / Ma vie / Love story / Les feuilles mortes.
LP: **80 616**

RAYMOND LEFEVRE.
LP: . . . . **MMLP 4**

RAYMOND LEFEVRE VOL 2.
LP: . . . . **SMLP 13**

Left Banke

AND SUDDENLY ITS.
Tracks: / Walk away Renee / There's gonna be a storm / Desiree / Myrah / Shadows breaking over my head / Let go of you girl / Sing little bird sing / I haven't got the nerve / Goodbye Holly / Dark is the bark / I've got something on my mind / Pretty ballerina / In the morning light / She may call you up tonight / My friend tonight / Barterers and their wifes / Pedestal / Foggy waterfall.
LP: . . . . **KIRI 021**

HISTORY OF THE LEFT BANKE, THE.
LP: . . . . **RNLP 123**

VOICES CALLING.
LP: . . . . **KIRI 045**

Left Hand Frank

CHICAGO BLUES (See under Rogers, Jimmy) (Left Hand Frank & Jimmy Rogers).

Leftenant, Joyce

STORMY WEATHER.
Tracks: / You loved me all the time / Let me be your woman / I believe you / Stormy weather / Send in the clowns / It's too late / Inside of me / Everything that touches you / Tell me something I can do.
LP: . . . . **MAN 5042**

Legacy of the Blues

LEGACY OF THE BLUES VOL. 1 (White, Bukka).
Tracks: / Aberdeen Mississippi blues / Baby please don't go / New Orleans streamline / Parchman Farm blues / Poor boy / Remembrance of Charlie Patton / Shake 'em on down / I am the heavenly way / Atlanta special, The / Drunk man blues / Army blues.
LP: . . . . **SNTF 609**
LP: . . . . **GNPS 10011**
MC: . . . . **ZCSN 609**

LEGACY OF THE BLUES VOL. 2 (Eaglin, Snooks).
Tracks: / Boogie children / Who's loving you? / Lucille / Drive it home / Good news / Funky Malaguena / Pinetop's boogie woogie / That same old train / I get the blues when it rains / Young boy blues / Tomorrow night / Little girl of mine.
LP: . . . . **SNTF 625**
LP: . . . . **GNPS 10012**
MC: . . . . **ZCSN 625**

LEGACY OF THE BLUES VOL. 3 (Dupree, Champion Jack).
Tracks: / Vietnam blues / Drunk again / Found my baby gone / Anything you want / Will it be? / You're the one / Down and out / Roamin' special / Life I lead, The / Jitterbug jump.
LP: . . . . **SNTF 626**
LP: . . . . **GNPS 10013**
MC: . . . . **ZCSN 626**

LEGACY OF THE BLUES VOL. 4 (Young, Mighty Joe).
LP: . . . . **SNTF 633**
LP: . . . . **GNPS 10014**
MC: . . . . **ZCSN 633**

LEGACY OF THE BLUES VOL. 5 (Bonner, Juke Boy).
Tracks: / I'm a bluesman / Problems all round / Trying to get ahead / If you don't want to get mistreated / Lonesome ride back home / Funny money / I'm lonely too / Real good money / Come to me / Yammin' the blues / Better place to go / Tired of the greyhound blues.
LP: . . . . **SNTF 634**
LP: . . . . **GNPS 10015**
MC: . . . . **ZCSN 634**

LEGACY OF THE BLUES VOL. 6 (Williams, Big Joe).
Tracks: / I've been wrong but I'll be right / Black gal you're sure looking warm / When I first left home / Little Annie May / Levee break blues / Hang it up on the wall / Lone wolf / This heavy stuff of mine / Tell my mother / Big fat mama / Back on my feet / Jefferson and Franklin blues.
LP: . . . . **SNTF 635**
LP: . . . . **GNPS 10016**
MC: . . . . **ZCSN 635**

LEGACY OF THE BLUES VOL. 7 (Memphis Slim).
Tracks: / Everyday I have the blues / I am the blues / Long time gone / I feel like ballin' the Jack / Let's get with it / Broadway boogie / Gambler's blues / Freedom / Sassy Mae.
LP: . . . . **SNTF 647**
LP: . . . . **GNPS 10017**
MC: . . . . **ZCSN 647**

LEGACY OF THE BLUES VOL. 8 (Short, J.D.).
Tracks: / Starry crown blues / My rare dog / By the spoonful / You're tempting me / Slidin' delta / I'm just wastin' my time / Red river run, The / Help me some / East St. Louis / Make me a pallet on the floor.
LP: . . . . **SNTF 648**
LP: . . . . **GNPS 10018**
MC: . . . . **ZCSN 648**

LEGACY OF THE BLUES VOL. 9 (Williams, Robert Pete).
Tracks: / Woman you ain't no good / Come here sit down on my knee / Angola patience blues / Late night boogie / I'm going to have myself a ball / Poor girl out on the mountain / Graveyard blues / You're my all day steady and my midnight dream / Keep your bad dog off me.
LP: . . . . **SNTF 649**
LP: . . . . **GNPS 10019**
MC: . . . . **ZCSN 649**

LEGACY OF THE BLUES VOL. 10 (Boyd, Eddie).
Tracks: / I'm a fool / Kindness for weakness / Tell the truth / Cannonball / Black, brown and white / Do yourself a favour / Dedication to my baby / Zip code.
LP: . . . . **SNTF 670**
LP: . . . . **GNPS 10020**
MC: . . . . **ZCSN 670**

LEGACY OF THE BLUES VOL. 11 (Sunnyland Slim).
Tracks: / Couldn't find a mule / Gonna be my baby / Woman I ain't gonna drink no more whisky / Days of old / She got a thing goin' on / She's so mellow / Get hip to yourself / Bessie Mae / I had it so hard / She used to love me.
LP: . . . . **SNTF 671**
LP: . . . . **GNPS 10021**
MC: . . . . **ZCSN 671**

LEGACY OF THE BLUES VOL. 12 (Hopkins, Lightnin').
Tracks: / Please help poor me / Way out in Abilene / Don't you call that boogie / Swing in the backyard / Hearse is parked up to the door / That meat's a little too high / Let them little things be true / I been burnin' bad gasoline / Don't you mess with my woman / Water fallin' boogie.
LP: . . . . **SNTF 672**
LP: . . . . **GNPS 10022**
MC: **GNP5 10022**
MC: . . . . **ZCSN 672**

Legal Alien

AMERICAN COLOR (See under Colon, Willie) (Colon, Willie/Legal Alien).

TOP SECRETS (see under Colon, Willie) (Legal Alien/Willie Colon).

Legal Eagles

LEGAL EAGLES (Film Soundtrack) (Various artists).
Tracks: / Love theme: *Various artists* / Moving on: *Various artists* / Hypnotic eyes: *Various artists*/ Strange birthday: *Various artists* / Tom and Kelly: *Various artists* / Scared: *Various artists* / Fire and rescue: *Various artists* / Put out the fire: *Hannah, Daryl* / Good lovin': *Rascals* / Magic carpet ride: *Steppenwolf*.
LP: . . . . **MCF 3344**

MC: . . . . MCFC 3344

Legal Limits

COVER GIRL.
LP: . . . . WKFM 62

Legal Tender

LEGAL TENDER (Various artists).
LP: . . . . SJLP 1

Legal Weapon

TAKE OUT THE TRASH.
LP: . . . . TX 92771

Legend

LEGEND.
Tracks: / Sylvia's mother / Mississippi cotton pickin' delta town / Send me no roses / She gave her heart to Jethro / Baby's gone / Brand new Tennessee waltz / Ravishing Ruby / Oh, lonesome me / Sunday morning coming down / I'll never be sorry / Okie from Muskogee / Welcome to my world of love / Guitar polka.
LP: . . . . NA 101
MC: . . . . NC 101

LOUISIANA SATURDAY NIGHT.
LP: . . . . NA 115

RING OF FIRE.
Tracks: / Ring of fire / Fugitive, The / Idol of the band / Bony fingers / Under your spell again / She didn't come here / Rider in the rain / I don't wanna cry / Tonight the bottle / Today I started loving you again / Please stay / Back on my mind.
LP: . . . . NA 121
MC: . . . . NC 121

Legend (Film)

LEGEND (Film soundtrack) (National Philharmonic Orchestra).
Tracks: / My true love's eyes / Riddle, The / Sing the wee / Goblins, The / Dress waltz, The / Ring, The / Unicorns, The / Bumps and hollows / Forgive me / Reunited.
LP: . . . . MOMENT 100
MC: . . . . MOMENTC 100

LEGEND (Film Soundtrack) (Various artists).
LP: . . . . FILM 045
MC: . . . . FILMC 045

LEGEND (AMERICAN) (Film Soundtrack) (Tangerine Dream).
LP: . . . . MCA 6165
MC: . . . . MCAC 6165

Legend, Johnny

JOHNNY LEGEND AND HIS ROCK 'N' ROLL COMBO (Legend, Johnny & His R 'n' R Combo).
LP: . . . . BOP 502

ROCKABILLY RUMBLE (Legend, Johnny & His Skullcaps).
Tracks: / Rockabilly rumble / Naked die young, The / Wild wicked Wanda / South's gonna rise again, The / Wild wild woman / Mad dog mama / Hit that jive Jack / She's gone / Rockabilly bastard / Take some ludes and get funky / Brand new baby / Running gun / Let's get goin' / Are you hep to it.
LP: . . . . ABOUT 1002

SOAKIN' THE BONE (Legend, Johnny & His Skullcaps).
Tracks: / Soakin' the bone / No escape / Guess who ain't gettin' laid tonight / Long long lonely hours / Raunchy tonk song / Crackin' up / Holy beat, The / Justine / Instead of me / Demon on the highway / Nightbird / Rollin' the rock / Rockabilly bughouse.
LP: . . . . ABOUT 7

Legend Of Glass

LEGEND OF GLASS MOUNTAIN (See under Goodwin, Ron) (Goodwin, Ron).

Legend of Jesse James

LEGEND OF JESSE JAMES (Various artists).
Tracks: / Ride of the redlegs: *Various artists* / Quantrill's guerillas: *Various artists* / Six gun shooting: *Various artists* / Have you heard the news: *Various artists* / Heaven ain't ready for you yet: *Various artists*/ Help him Jesus: *Various artists* / Old clay county, The: *Various artists* / Riding with Jesse James: *Various* artists / Hunt them down: *Various artists* / Wish we were back in Missouri: *Various artists* / Northfield the plan: *Various artists* / Northfield the disaster: *Various artists* / High walls: *Various artists*/ Death of me: *Various artists* / Plot, The: *Various artists* / One more shot: *Various artists*.
2LP: . . . . AMLK 63718
MCSET: . . . . CKM 63718

Legend, Tobi

TIME WILL PASS YOU BY (See under Parrish, Dean).

Legendary Blues Band

KEEPING THE BLUES ALIVE.
Tracks: / I don't wanna know / Stuck in the bottom / I love my woman / Cook me / Open your eyes / Nobody knows / Without her / What's wrong / Shake it for me / Reach way back / Steady worried man.
LP: . . . . ICH 1052
MC: . . . . MCICH 1052

LIFE OF EASE.
LP: . . . . ROUNDER 2029
MC: . . . . ROUNDER 2029C

RED HOT AND BLUE.
LP: . . . . ROUNDER 2035
MC: . . . . ROUNDER 2035C

U B DA JUDGE.
Tracks: / Got love if you want it / Things could be worse / Eye to eye / In the rain / Watch your enemies / Don't say that no more / I don't trust you / Man / No one to love me / When the blues come around / Who's been talkin'.
LP: . . . . ICH 9001
MC: . . . . ICH 9001 MC

WOKE UP WITH THE BLUES.
Tracks: / Another mule / I woke up with the blues / Your daughter looks good to me / Honey bee / I need you so bad / Don't throw your love on me so strong / I'd like to have a girl like you / I've got to be with you tonight / You're looking good again tonight / Having a hard time.
LP: . . . . ICH 1039
MC: . . . . ZCICH 1039

Legendary Pink Dots

ANY DAY NOW.
Tracks: / Casting the runes / Strychnine kiss, A / Laguna beach / Gallery, The / Neon mariners / True love / Peculiar funfair, The / Waiting for the cloud / Cloud zero.
LP: . . . . BIAS 080

ASYLUM.
LP: . . . . BIAS 012

BASILISK.
LP: . . . . TMT 08

BRIGHTER NOW.
LP: . . . . IPNER 1
LP: . . . . TK 001

CRUSHED VELVET APOCALYPSE.
LP: . . . . BIAS 149

CURSE.
LP: . . . . PHA 2
LP: . . . . TK 002

FACES IN THE FIRE.
LP: . . . . BIAS 001

GOLDEN AGE, THE.
LP: . . . . BIAS 103
MC: . . . . BIAS 103 TC

ISLAND OF JEWELS.
LP: . . . . BIAS 041

LEGENDARY PINK DOTS.
LP: . . . . PHA 3

LOVERS.
LP: . . . . TKAL 1

MARIA DIMENSION, THE.
LP: . . . . BIAS 184
MC: . . . . BIASC 184

STORM CIRCLES.
Tracks: / Love puppets / Black zone / Golden dawn / Curious day / Hanging gardens, The / Fifteen flies / Our lady in darkness / Apocalyse / Gladiators version.
LP: . . . . BIAS 1001

TOWER, THE.
LP: . . . . TK 003

Legendary Stardust

LEGENDARY STARDUST COWBOY RIDES AGAIN.
LP: . . . . ROSE 184

ROCK IT TO STARDOM.
Tracks: / Paralysed / I walk a hot wind / Radar / Fly me to the moon / I took a trip (on a space shuttle) / Cast iron apron / Cactus / Peppermint piston rings / Shadow of a tiger / Who's knocking on my door / Brass rainbow / Shootout on C.B. channel / Mr. Songwriter / Dynamite / Crack of dawn / Rock it to stardom / Bathroom blues.
LP: . . . . WIK 32

Legends of the Clans

LEGENDS OF THE CLANS (Various artists).
Tracks: / Legends of the clans: *Various artists* / Seal king's daughter / Glaistig, The: *Various artists* / Raven's rock / Dunvegan banner / Sixty fools.
MC: . . . . ANV 616

Legg, Adrian

FRETMELT.
LP: . . . . SPIN 115

GUITARS AND OTHER CATHEDRALS.
Tracks: / Thump the clouds / Cajun interlude / Irish girl, The / Midwest Sunday / Guitars and other cathedrals / Montreux ramble / Tracy's big moment / Divorcee's waltz / Tune for Derrol / Nail talk / Reckless love / Pass the valium (with knobs on) / Dying embers.
LP: . . . . LPMMC 1014
MC: . . . . TCMMC 1014

LOST FOR WORDS.
LP: . . . . SPIN 127

REQUIEM FOR A HICK.
LP: . . . . WRS 125

TECHNOPICKER.
LP: . . . . SPIN 201

Legge Wade

BE-BOP KEYBOARD MASTERS (See Be Bop Keyboard Masters).

Leggio Carmen Quartet

SMILE.
Tracks: / Broadway / Japanese Sandman / Smile / Cherokee / Some day my prince will come / Who can I turn to? / Okay bug / Hinchcliffs.
LP: . . . . PRO 7010

Legion Of Parasites

PRISON OF LIFE.
LP: . . . . THRASH 001

SAWN TO DUST.
LP: . . . . STUDLP 3

Lego

EDWARD GETS THE HICCUPS (age 3+).
MC: . . . . PLBL 232

EDWARD JOINS THE BAND/CLIVE'S KITE.
MC: . . . . PLBL 250

LIONEL'S CAR/EDWARD TO THE RESCUE.
MC: . . . . PLBL 249

LIONEL'S PARTY (age 3+).
MC: . . . . PLBL 231

Legrand, Michel

AFTER THE RAIN.
Tracks: / Nobody knows / I was born in love with you / After the rain / Pieces of dreams / Martina / Orson's theme.
LP: 2312 139
MC: K12 139

COMPACT JAZZ: MICHEL LEGRAND.
MC: 8409444

CONCERT LEGRAND, THE.
Tracks: / Once upon a summer time / Saddest thing of all, The / You must believe in Spring / Wonder where I'll be tomorrow / Christine / Sweet gingerbread man / Love theme from 'Lady sings the blues' / Snowbird serenade / Fickle fingers / Petite musique d'amour / Pieces of dreams.
LP: . . . . RS 1087

MICHEL LEGRAND.
MC: . . . . ZCGAS 730

PARIS WAS MADE FOR LOVERS.
Tracks: / Windmills of your mind, The / Summer of '43, The / I still see you / Sea and sky / Concerto for cars / Street where they lived, The / Where love begins / In love in Normandy / Place in Paris, A / Old lovers never die / On the road / Do you come here often / They simply fade away / Where love ends / Pavanne for people / Paris was made for lovers.
LP: . . . . PREC 5001
MC: . . . . ZPREC 5001

PEDRO PAULO, CASTRO NEVES & MICHEL LEGRAND (See under Paulo, Pedro) (Legrand, Michel/Pedro Paulo/ Castro Neves).

SARAH VAUGHAN WITH MICHEL LEGRAND (See Under Vaughan, Sarah) (Legrand, Michel & Sarah Vaughan).

UMBRELLAS OF CHERBOURG, THE/ GO-BETWEEN, THE (Film soundtracks) (Legrand, Michel & London Symphony Orchestra).
Tracks: / Umbrellas of Cherbourg / Symphonic suite / Go-between / Variations for two pianos and orchestra.
LP: . . . . CBS 73886

Legs Diamond

LAND OF THE GUN.
MC: . . . . TMFN 59
LP: . . . . MFN 59

OUT ON BAIL.
LP: . . . . MFN 52
MC: . . . . TMFN 52

TOWN BAD GIRL.
LP: . . . . ZORRO 16
MC: . . . . TZORRO 16

Legs Diamond (Show)

LEGS DIAMOND (Original Broadway Cast) (Allen, Peter).
LP: 7983.1
MC: 7983.4

Lehar, Franz

MERRY WIDOW, THE and other music of Lehar and Strauss (Vienna State Opera Orchestra).
MC: . . . . VETC 6524

Lehmann, Lotte

LOTTE LEHMANN (Wolf, Schubert, Brahms, Duparg).
MC: . . . . GK 87809

Lehrer, Murray

MUSIQUE JUIVE POUR LES REJOUISSANCES (Lehrer, Murray & Orchestra).
Tracks: / Danse de Bessarabie / Potpourri de vielles chansons Yiddish / Potpourri de valses / Danse de Sharon / Hora staccato / Neue sher / Boublitchki.
LP: . . . . ARN 33730
MC: . . . . ARN 433730

Lehrer, Tom

AN EVENING WASTED WITH....
LP: . . . . SKL 4097
LP: . . . . RS 6199
LP: . . . . LK 4332

MORE OF TOM LEHRER.
Tracks: / Poisoning pigeons in the park / Bright college days / Christmas carol / Elements / Oedipus Rex / In old Mexico / Clementine / It makes a fellow proud to be a soldier / She's my girl / Masochism tango / We will all go together when we go.
LP: . . . . LFT 1323

SONGS BY TOM LEHRER.
Tracks: / Old dope peddler, The / Be prepared / Wild west, The / I wanna go back to Dixie / Fight fiercely / Harvard / Lobachevsky / Irish ballad, The / Hunting song / My home town / When you are old and grey / I hold your hand in mine / Wiener schnitzel waltz, The.
LP: . . . . LFT 1311
LP: . . . . LF 1311

THAT WAS THE YEAR THAT WAS.
LP: . . . . RSLP 6179

TOM LEHRER REVISITED.
LP: . . . . LK 4375

Lehrman, Paul D.

CELTIC MACINTOSH, THE.
Tracks: / Irish washerwoman, The / An seaduine doite / O'Carolan's farewell / Repeal of the Union / Music in the glen / Old storyteller, The / Hewlett / Fisherman's wife, The ((Comp. Stewart, Cunningham, Hadden)) / Chanter's song, The / Sheebeg sheemore / Gile mear.
MC: . . . . ESSP 1
LP: . . . . PDL 1

Leibman, Dave

GUIDED DREAM (Leibman, Dave & Tolvan Big Band).
LP: . . . . DRLP 120

Leich, Peter

EXHILARATION.
LP: . . . . UP 27 24

Leigh, Carol

BLAME IT ON THE BLUES (Leigh, Carol/Bob Helm/Ray Skjelbred).
LP: . . . . GHB 152

GO BACK WHERE YOU STAYED LAST NIGHT.
LP: . . . . GHB 167

IF YOU DON'T I KNOW WHO (Leigh, Carol & Jim Dapogny).
LP: . . . . SOS 1064

VOLUME 2 (Leigh, Carol & Jim Dapogny).
LP: . . . . SOS 1087

YOU'VE GOT TO GIVE ME SOME.
LP: . . . . GHB 136

Leigh, Richard

RICHARD LEIGH.
Tracks: / Right from the start / Too good to throw away / Maybe tomorrow / I've come a long way / Let's do it right / If it's so easy / That's what I get for loving you / Years from now / Our love will never die / In the arms of a pretty gal.
LP: . . . . UAG 30307

Leighton, Bernie

BERNIE LEIGHTON PLAYS DUKE ELLINGTON AT JIMMY WESTONS (Leighton, Bernie Quartet).
Tracks: / Sophisticated lady / Satin doll / I'm beginning to see the light / Mood indigo / Azure / Do not ring till you hear from me / Take the 'A' train / It don't mean a thing / In a sentimental mood /

What am I here for / Kissing bug / Black butterfly.
LP: . . . . **MES 7068**

Leimgruber, Urs

REFLEXIONEN LIVE (See under Refleionen) (Leimgruber, Urs/Don Friedman Quartet).

Leipzig Gewandhaus

SYMPHONY NO.2 (MENDELSSOHN) (see under Mendelssohn (Composer)) (Leipzig Gewandhaus Orch/Leipzig Radio Chorus/).

Leipzig Radio

SYMPHONY NO.2 (MENDELSSOHN) (see under Mendelssohn (Composer)) (Leipzig Radio Chorus/Leipzig Gewandhaus Orchestra/).

Leitch, Patricia

ADVENTURES OF ROBIN HOOD (BOOK) (Barron, Keith (nar)).
MCSET: . . . . **LFP 7246**
MCSET: . . . . **LFP 417 246 5**

Leitch, Peter

MEAN WHAT YOU SAY (Leitch, Peter Quartet).
Tracks: / I've never been in love before / Blues on the East side / Stairway to the stars / Like someone in love / Hick's time / In a sentimental mood / Mean what you say / This is new / Virgo (Only on CD.).
MC: . . . . **CJ 417 C**

ON A MISTY NIGHT.
LP: . . . . **CRISS 1026**

RED ZONE - GUITAR.
LP: . . . . **RSR 103**

Leithaug, Solveig

FIRST STEP.
LP: . . . . **DAY R 4163**
MC: . . . . **DAY C 4163**

IN THE WORLD.
LP: . . . . **DAY R 4149**
MC: . . . . **DAY C 4149**

Leitmotiv

CARESS AND CURSE.
LP: . . . . **VIRTUE 3**

LeJeune, Eddie

CAJUN SOUL.
LP: . . . . **ROUNDER 6013**
MC: . . . . **ROUNDER 6013C**
LP: . . . . **HNBL 1353**
MC: . . . . **HNBC 1353**

IT'S IN THE BLOOD.
Tracks: / Le l'ai rencontree / Duralde waltz / Boire mon whiskey / Happy hop, The / Valse criminelle / Madeleine / Les conseils j'ai ecoutes / Je seras la apres t'espere / J'ai quitte ma famille dans les miseres / Teche / Fille a 'n oncle Hilaire / Reve du saoulard / Donnez moi la / J'aimerais tu viens me chercher.
LP: . . . . **HNBL 1364**
MC: . . . . **HNBC 1364**

Lejeune, Philippe

DIALOGUE IN BOOGIE (see under Memphis Slim) (Lejeune, Philippe & Memphis Slim).

Lelo

LELO.
Tracks: / In China / Step into my rocket modern man / I'm the suicide / Mad Jack / Best friend / No saving grace / Back at zero / Film / All I want / Love in my car / Too good to be true / Roola Droola.
LP: . . . . **MAMLP 5003**

Lelouch, Claude

LIFE IS FOR LIVING/ A MAN AND A WOMAN (Lelouch, Claude & Francis Lai).
MC: **101294**

Lema, Ray

GAIA.
LP: . . . . **MLPS 1055**
MC: . . . . **MCT 1055**

KINSHASA, WASHINGTON DC, PARIS.
LP: . . . . **CEL 6658**

MEDICINE.
LP: . . . . **CEL 6756**

NANGADEF.
Tracks: / Kamulang / H.A.I. 99 / Moni mambo / Boyete / Afcoeur / Nangadef / Pongi / What we need / Orchestra of the forest.
MC: . . . . **MCT 1000**
LP: . . . . **MLPS 1000**

Lemaire, Jo

JO LEMAIRE & FLOUZE (Lemaire, Jo & Flouze).
Tracks: / Running time / So static / Tintarella di luna / Stakhanov / Strolling players / Calenders / Keep step / What are we gonna do / Fat rats / Rumours said / Follow me in the air.
LP: . . . . **TRAIN 11**

Lemaire, Phillipe

WHITE CHRISTMAS.
MC: . . . . **CHV 324**

Lemming Projekt

EXTINCTION.
LP: . . . . **NO 1681**
MC: . . . . **NO 1684**

Lemon

LEMON.
Tracks: / Freak A, A / Hot bodies / Freak on / Chance to dance / Inside my heart / Hot hands.
LP: . . . . **CBS 83623**

Lemon, Brian

OUR KIND OF MUSIC.
LP: . . . . **HEP 2029**

Lemon Kittens

BIG DENTIST, THE.
Tracks: / They are both dirty / Hospital hurts, The / Girl, The / Log and the pin, The / Nudies.
LP: . . . . **JAMS 131**

Lemon Pipers

GREEN TAMBOURINE (OLD GOLD) (See under Lovin' Spoonful 'Summer in the city').

Lemon Popsicle...

LEMON POPSICLE 5 (See under 'Baby Love') (Various artists).

LEMON POPSICLE 6 (Film soundtrack) (Various artists).
Tracks: / Sea cruise: *Ford, Frankie* / You got what it takes, it's just a matter of: *Benton, Brook* / Surf city: *Jan & Dean* / Because they're young: *Eddy, Duane* / Tutti frutti: *Little Richard* / Bama lama bama loo: *Little Richard* / Green onions: *Cortez, Dave 'Baby'* / For your love: *Yardbirds* / Still I'm sad: *Yardbirds*/ Mashed potato time: *Sharp, Dee* / Peppermint twist: *Dee, Joey & The Starlighters* / Shout: *Dee, Joey & The* Starlighters / Great balls of fire: *Lewis, Jerry Lee* / Slow twistin': *Checker, Chubby* / Coma prima: *Dallera*, Tony / Teen beat: *Nelson, Sandy* / Hippy hippy shake: *Swinging Blue Jeans* / Why don't they understand: *Hamilton, George IV*.
LP: . . . . **RBMP 8471**
MC: . . . . **ZCRBM 8471**

Lemonade Hayride

JUNE BUGGY.
LP: . . . . **NISHI 210**

Lemonheads

CREATOR.
LP: . . . . **SERV 001**

HATE YOUR FRIENDS.
LP: . . . . **SERVM 004**

LICK.
LP: . . . . **T 032**
MC: . . . . **T 032C**
LP: . . . . **SERV 007**

LOVEY.
LP: **7567821371**
MC: **7567821374**

Lemper, Ute

CRIMES OF THE HEART.
LP: **4656761**
MC: **4656764**

L'Empire Bakuba

AMOUR PROPRE.
LP: . . . . **EVVI 19**

Lems, Kristin

BORN A WOMAN.
LP: . . . . **FF 379**

Lend An Ear

LEND AN EAR (Various artists).
LP: . . . . **TRY 1**

Lending, Kenn

I'M COMING HOME (Lending, Kenn Blues Band).
LP: . . . . **HSLP 1006**

Lenihan Tom

SONGS TRADITIONAL IN WEST CLARE.
Tracks: / Paddy's panacea / Talk of music at Lenihan's / Wintry evening, A / St. James hospital / Talk of Thady Casey the dancing master / Lake of Coolfin, The / Fair days in Miltown malbay / Pat O'Brian / Pddy, the cockney and the ass / Straw boys / Holland handkerchief / Bobbed hair, The / Fair London town / Garrett Barry and hurry the jug.
LP: **12TS 363**

Lennon, Charlie

EMIGRANT SUITE, THE.
LP: . . . . **CEF 112**

Lennon, John

DOUBLE FANTASY (Lennon, John & Yoko Ono).
Tracks: / Just like starting over / Kiss kiss kiss / Clean up time / Give me something / I'm losing you / I'm movin' on / Beautiful boy (darling boy) / Watching the wheels / I'm your angel / Woman / Beautiful boy, darling boy / Dear Yoko / Every man has a woman who loves him / Hard times are over.
LP: . . . . **K 99131**
MC: **K4 99131**
LP: . . . . **EST 2083**
MC: . . . . **TCEST 2083**

I SAW HER STANDING THERE (see under John, Elton) (Lennon, John & Elton John).

IMAGINE.
Tracks: / Imagine / Crippled inside / Jealous guy / It's so hard / I don't want to be a soldier / Gimme some truth / Oh my love / How do you sleep / How? / Oh Yoko!.
LP: . . . . **PAS 10004**
MC: . . . . **TCPAS 10004**

IMAGINE - THE MOVIE (Film soundtrack) (Lennon, John/Beatles).
Tracks: / Real love / Twist and shout / Help / In my life / Strawberry fields forever / Day in the life, A / Revolution / Ballad of John and Yoko / Julia / Don't let me down / Give me a chance / How? / Imagine / God / Mother / Stand by me / Jealous guy / Woman / Beautiful boy, darling boy / Starting over / Imagine.
2LP: . . . . **PCSP 722**
MCSET: . . . . **TCPCSP 722**

JOHN AND YOKO: THE INTERVIEW (Lennon, John & Yoko Ono).
MCSET: . . . . **ZBBC 1195**

JOHN LENNON (8 Album Box Set).
LPS: . . . . **JLB 8**
MC: . . . . **TCJLB 8**

JOHN LENNON COLLECTION, THE.
Tracks: / Give peace a chance / Instant karma / Power to the people / Whatever gets you through the night / Number 9 dream / Mind games / Love / Happy Xmas (war is over) / Imagine / Jealous guy / Stand by me / Starting over / Woman / I'm losing you / Beautiful boy, darling boy / Watching the wheels / Dear Yoko / Move over Ms. L. (CD only.) / Cold turkey (CD only.).
LP: . . . . **EMTV 37**
MC: . . . . **TCEMTV 37**

JOHN LENNON/PLASTIC ONO BAND.
Tracks: / Mother / Hold on / I found out / Working class hero / Isolation / Remember / Love / Well well well / Look at me / God / My mummy's dead.
LP: **41 31021**
MC: **41 3102 4**
LP: . . . . **PCS 7124**

LAST WORD, THE.
LPPD: . . . . **BAK 2096**

LENNON TRACKS (See under Beatles).

LIVE IN NEW YORK CITY.
Tracks: / New York city / It's so hard / Woman is the nigger of the world / Well, well, well / Instant Karma / Mother / Come together / Imagine / Cold turkey (With Frank Zappa and The Mothers of Invention.) / Hound dog / Give peace a chance.
LP: . . . . **PCS 7301**
MC: . . . . **TCPCS 7301**

MENLOVE AVE.
Tracks: / Here we go again / Rock and roll people / Angel baby / My baby left me / To know her is to love her / Steel and glass / Scared / Old dirt road / Nobody loves you (when you're down and out) / Bless you.
LP: . . . . **PCS 7308**
MC: . . . . **TCPCS 7308**

MILK AND HONEY: A HEART PLAY (Lennon, John & Yoko Ono).
Tracks: / I'm stepping out / Sleepless night / Don't wanna face it / Don't be scared / Nobody told me / O sanity / Borrowed time / Your hands / Forgive me, my little flower princess / Let me count the ways / Grow old with me / You're the one.
LP: . . . . **POLH 5**
MC: . . . . **POLHC 5**
LPPD: . . . . **POLHP 5**
MC: **817 160-4**

MIND GAMES.
Tracks: / Mind games / Tight as / Aisumasen (I'm sorry) / One day (at a time) / Bring on the Lucie / Nutopian international anthem / Intuition / Out of the blue / Only people / I know (I know) / You are here / Meat city.
MC: . . . . **TC MFP 50509**
LP: **02258136**
LP: . . . . **PCS 7165**
LP: . . . . **MFP 50509**

REFLECTIONS AND POETRY.
LP: . . . . **SM 10014**

ROCK 'N' ROLL.
Tracks: / Be bop a Lula / Stand by me / Rip it up / You can't catch me / Ain't that a shame / Do you wanna dance / Sweet little sixteen / Slippin' and slidin' / Peggy Sue / Bring it on home to me / Bony Moronie / Ya ya / Just because / Ready teddy.
LP: . . . . **MFP 50522**
MC: . . . . **TCMFP 50522**
LP: . . . . **PCS 7169**

SHAVED FISH.
Tracks: / Give peace a chance / Cold turkey / Instant karma / Power to the people / Mother / Woman is the nigger of the world / Imagine / Whatever gets you thru the night / Mind games / No. 9 dream / Happy Xmas (war is over) / Give peace a chance (reprise).
LP: . . . . **PCS 7173**
MC: . . . . **TCPCS 7173**

WALLS AND BRIDGES.
Tracks: / Going down on love / Whatever gets you through the night / Old dirt road / What you got / Bless you / Scared / No. 9 dream / Surprise, surprise (sweet bird of paradox) / Steel and glass / Beef jerky / Nobody loves you (when you're down and out) / Ya ya.
LP: . . . . **ATAK 43**
MC: . . . . **TCATAK 43**
LP: . . . . **PCTC 253**

Lennon, Julian

HELP YOURSELF.
LP: **V2668**
MC: **TCV2668**

MR JORDAN.
Tracks: / Now you're in heaven / I get up / Angillette / Make it up to you / Second time, The / You're the one / Mother Mary / Open your eyes / Sunday morning / I want you to know.
LP: . . . . **JLLP 3**
MC: . . . . **JLMC 3**

SECRET VALUE OF DAYDREAMING, THE.
Tracks: / Stick around / You get what you want / Let me tell you / I've seen your face / Coward till the end ? / This is my day / You didn't have to tell me / Everyday / Always think twice / I want your body.
LP: . . . . **CHC 71**
MC: . . . . **CHCMC 71**
LP: . . . . **CAS 1171**

VALOTTE.
Tracks: / Valotte / OK for you / On the phone / Space / Well I don't know / Too late for goodbyes / Lonely / Say your wrong / Jesse / Let me be.
LP: . . . . **JLLP 1**
MC: . . . . **JLMC 1**
LP: . . . . **OVED 286**
MC: . . . . **OVEDC 286**

Lennox-Martin, Anne

DON'T DILLY DALLY (See under Stephens, Sam) (Lennox-Martin, Anne and Sam Stephens).

PRETTY PLOUGHBOY, THE (see also Sam Stephens) (Lennox-Martin, Anne and Sam Stephens).
LP: . . . . **DIN 307**

TURN THE MUSIC ON (see under Stephens, Sam) (Lennox-Martin, Anne and Sam Stephens).

Lenny D

LOONY TUNES VOL.1 (See under Frankie Bones) (Lenny D & Frankie Bones).

Lenoir, J.B.

ALABAMA BLUES.
Tracks: / Alabama blues / Mojo boogie, The / God's word / Whale has swallowed me, The / Move this rope / I feel so good / Alabama march / Talk to you daughter / Mississippi road / Good advice / Vietnam / I want to go / Down in Mississippi / If I get lucky / Born dead / Feeling good.
LP: . . . . **LR 42001**

CHESS MASTERS.
Tracks: / Natural man / Don't dog your woman / Let me die with the one I love / Carrie Lee / Mama what about your daughter / If I give my love to you / Five years / Don't tough my head / I've been down so long / What have I done / Eisenhower blues / Korea blues / Everybody wants to know / I'm in love / Mama your daughter's going to miss me / We can't go on this way / Give me one more shot / When I am drinking / J.B.'s rock / If you love me / Low down dirty shame / Man watch your woman / Mama / Sitting down thinking / Daddy talk to your son / I don't know / Good lookin' woman / Voodoo boogie.
LP: . . . . **CXMD 4054**

CHICAGO GOLDEN YEARS.
2LP: **427003**

DOWN IN MISSISSIPPI.

LP: LR 42.012

FINE BLUES.
Tracks: / Deep in debt blues / My baby told me / In the evening / Please don't go away / Fine girls / I lost my baby / Daddy talk to your son / She don't know / Back door / Lou Ella / Oh baby / Do what I say / Move to Kansas City / I been down so long / Mojo boogie / I don't care what nobody say / Oh baby.
LP: OFF 6049

MOJO BOOGIE (Job series vol.2).
LP: FLY 564

NATURAL MAN.
LP: BRP 2014
LP: CH 9323

ONE OF THESE MORNINGS (Lenoir, J.B./Willie Dixon).
LP: JSP 1105

Lent, Robin

SCARECROW'S JOURNEY.
Tracks: / Scarecrow's journey / My father was a sailor / Pushboat / Leaving since you came / Almitra (the love that became us) / Sky has called us out to dance, The / Waiting for the morning / Ocean liner woman / Sea spray / Speak softly now.
LP: SEE 270

Lenya, Lotte

SEPTEMBER SONG.
Tracks: / September song / It never was you / Saga of Jenny / Foolish heart / Speak low / Sing me not a ballad / Lonely house / Boy like you, A / Green-up time / Trouble man / Stay well / Lost in the stars.
LP: MP 39513
MC: MPT 39513

Leo, Bukky

REJOICE IN RIGHTEOUSNESS (Leo, Bukky Quintet).
LP: JAZID 7

RIVER NILE.
LP: MRIL 003

Leo, Phillip

POWER OF MUSIC.
LP: FADLP 015

Leon

BEST OF LEON.
MC: CPHL 484

COUNTRY.
Tracks: / Slow / Nobody's baby but mine / Satan's jewelled crown / Sweet baby Jane / Love is a rose / Mama, let me shelter in your sweet loving arms / You made my life complete / It's a heartache / Rose has to die, A / Daytime friends / God bless the children / It only hurts for a little while.
LP: PHL 404
MC: CPHL 404

COWGIRL AND THE DANDY.
Tracks: / World needs a melody, The / Blue bayou / Rose, The / Mandolin man / Only momma, The / You needed me / Love is a word / Cowgirl and the Dandy / Stand by me, Jesus / I have a dream / Soft-spoken man / Are you teasing me?.
LP: PHL 416
MC: CPHL 416

GREAT COUNTRY SINGER COUNTRY LOVE.
Tracks: / One day at a time / To daddy / I'm gonna be a country girl again / Sunday school to Broadway / Walking piece of Heaven / Medals for mothers / Single girl / Mississippi / Heaven's just a sin away / Lonely hearts club / When I stop dreaming / River road.
LP: PHL 401
MC: CPHL 401

JEALOUS HEART.
Tracks: / Bye bye love / Your cheatin' heart / Amazing grace / When will I be loved / Stand by your man / Daddy's little girl / Can I have this dance / Please help me, I'm falling / Doesn't matter anymore / Crazy / Golden ring / Jealous heart.
LP: PHL 443
MC: CPHL 443

Leon, Craig

THIEF OF SADNESS, THE (Leon, Craig/Cassell Webb).
Tracks: / Nailed to the wall / Saturday afternoon / Letter from Marcella / Wheel of fortune / Another time / Dancer's song, The / Thomas Edison, end of discussion / Suadade.
LP: VE 6
MC: TCVE 6

Leonard, Deke

BEFORE YOUR VERY EYES.
Tracks: / Someone is calling / Fools like me / Marlene / Oh when am I coming back / Get off the line / Hiding in the darkness / Big hunk o' love, A / I feel like a pill / World exploded in my face / What am I gonna do when the money runs out? / Bad lick.
LP: UAG 30240

ICEBERG.
Tracks: / Razor blade / I just can't win / Lisa / Nothing is happening / Looking for a man / Hard way to live / Broken ovation / Jesse / Ten thousand takers / Ghost of musket flat / Crosby / 7171 551.
LP: LBR 1042

KAMIKAZE.
LP: UAG 29544

Leonard, John

BROKEN-DOWN GENTLEMEN (Leonard, John and John Squire).
Tracks: / Whitby maid / Some tunes / McShane / Dreams of a British man o'war / Librarian, The / Down where the drunkards roll / Broken down gentlemen / Willie o' Winsbury / Some more tunes / I wish I was in England.
LP: RUB 018

Leonhart, Jay

THERE'S GONNA BE TROUBLE.
Tracks: / Summers on the river / There's gonna be trouble / Ali Privaye / Life in the middle ages / Lonely rider / Jimmy don't go away / Confirmation / Couple from Duluth, The / Smile / I got the blues / Down in the south / Patience / Blues for Donna.
LP: SSC 1006

Leoni, Paul

FLIGHTS OF FANCY.
LP: NML 1002
MC: ZCNML 1002

Leonskaja, Elisabeth

FRANZ SCHUBERT: WANDERER FANTASY (see under Schubert (composer)).

VIENNESE TALES (see under Berlin Soloists) (Leonskaja, Elisabeth/Berlin Soloists/Philip Moll).

Leopard (Film)

LEOPARD, THE (Film Soundtrack) (Various artists).
LP: STV 81190

Leotis

ON A MISSION (ALBUM).
LP: 838 188-1
MC: 838 188-4

Lepke, Louis

LABOUR WARD (see Dread, Sammy) (Lepke, Louis & Sammy Dread).

Lerner, Alan J

LYRICS BY LERNER (see under Shows) (Various artists).

Leroi Brothers

CHECK THIS ACTION.
Tracks: / Are you with me baby / I can't be satisfied / Ain't I'm a dog / Big time operator / Steady with Betty / Check this action / Chicken and honey / Rockin' Daddy / Cotton pickin' / Crazy crazy lovin' / Ballad of a juvenile delinquent / Till it's too late / Arms race / Damage / Little Miss Understanding / Straight jacket / Mad about the wrong boy / Motorworld / On the third stroke / Slow patience / La la la la la loved you / Single girl / Lonesome little town / Taste of poison / High rise housewife / Talk about me / Sad about girls / Camera camera / I feel like breaking up somebodys home / Why do I / Laughin' and clownin' / If I ever had a good thing / Scarred knees / From the heart / Your love is so doggone good / We don't see eye to eye / Roadblock / Teach me to forget.
LP: FIEND 22

FORGET ABOUT THE DANGER.
LP: VEX 4

PROTECTION FROM ENEMIES.
Tracks: / Lucky, lucky me / Elvis in the army / I don't wanna stop / Walk with me darling / Give up the ghost / Fight fire with fire / Back door / Dangerous girl / Darlene, Darlene / Little bit of sugar / Move it.
LP: FIEND 41

Leroux, Gaston

PHANTOM OF THE OPERA (Rogers, Anton).
MCSET: LFP 7284
MC: 001063618

Leroy, Baby Face

BABY FACE LEROY & FLOYD JONES (Leroy, Baby Face & Floyd Jones).
Tracks: / My head can't rest / Take a little walk / Boogy fool / Raisin' sand / Pet rabbit / Louella / Late hours at midnight / Blues is killin' me / Dark road / I lost a good woman / Skinny mama / Rising wind / On the road again / My head is turning grey / Where have you been so long / I can't feel.
LP: FLY 584

Leroy Brothers

LUCKY LUCKY ME.
LP: ROSE 58

Lertxundi, Benito

ALTABIZKAR/ITZALTZUKO BARDOA.
2LP: ELKAR 47/48

GAVEKO ELE IXILLEN BALADAK.
LP: ELKAR 81

Les 4 Guitarists...

WORLD TOUR (Les 4 Guitarists De L'Apocalypso-Bar).
LP: RE 404

Les Aborigenes

SONGS AND DANCES FROM NORTH AUSTRALIA.
MC: ARN 464056

Les Aiglons

BONM LA.
LP: HDD 2435

Les Ambassadeurs

ALL RECORDINGS (See under Ambassadeurs) (Ambassadeurs).

Les Bantous

BAKOLO M'BOKA.
LP: AP 052

Les Calamites

BRIDE ABATTUE, A.
MLP: NEW 26

COMPILATION.
LP: FC 041
MC: FC 041C

Les Calchakis

AFRICAN ROOTS.
Tracks: / Cumbria de la Ciudad / El Pilon / La Maye / Al son del Alcatraz / Cancion de Cuna / Los Caminos / Azabache / Soy pan soy agua / Luna Llena / Torito Mata / America de Cobre A. Morena / Golpea ese tambor.
LP: ARN 34774
MC: ARN 434774

CALCHAKIS AU PAYS DE LA DIABLADA.
Tracks: / Diablo bailarin / Tuntuneando / Ramon / Diablos en marcha / Tierra aymara / Selvas y valles / Mariposa morena / Recuerdo azul / Negra tuntuna / Soledades / Alfarero / Amankay.
LP: ARN 34510
MC: ARN 434510

CALCHAKIS D'AUJOURD'HUI.
Tracks: / Cantata para un hombre libre / La partida / Tarde de Octubre / Hasta siempre / Hasta siempre / Que vuele el Quetzal / Homenaje a E. Guevara / Hombre voluntad / El monumento.
LP: ARN 34680
MC: ARN 434680

CALCHAKIS ET LEURS FLUTES INDIENNES.
Tracks: / La Kimba / Carnaval del diablo / Tu mirada / Variaciones sobre un tema / El rey de los pajaros / Kuty / El carnaval / Hispartay / Sikuris / Fiesta andina / Linda companera / Sumak yurak / Cuerdita / Los cisnes / Sueno larense / Pastora, La / Viento Mochica / Poncho verde / Bailecito Calchaki / Llama del altiplano / Soplo del oriente / Lunarcito / Acuarela de sikus / Aires de Tarka / Contrabandeando / Estudio para charango / Tundiki / Quiaquenita / Mi antarita.
2LP: ARN 234017
MC: ARN 423417

CALCHAKIS SING NERUDA, GUILLEN, JARA.
Tracks: / Galopa murrieta / Guitarra nueva / Milonga de andar lejos / Versos sencillos / No se porque piensas tu / Homenaje a Victor Jara / Lo unico que tengo / Coplas en la noche / Adelante / Peoncito de estancia / Dos cuerpos / Homenaje a Violeta Parra / Y arriba quemando el sol / Triptico Ernesto Guevara.
LP: ARN 34450
MC: ARN 434450

CHANT DES POETES REVOLTES.
Tracks: / Luz de amanecer / Para un presidente muerto / Recuerdo / Vasija de barro / Soldado libre / Hommage a Pablo Neruda / Cancion con todos / Plegaria del labrador / Rostro de cobre / Destino de sombras / Cuando tenga la tierra / Chile / La Murella / Hommage a Cesar Vallejo / Masa et Clamor.
LP: ARN 34250
MC: ARN 434250

FLUTES DE L'EMPIRE INCA.
Tracks: / Lima morena / Kacharpari / Presencia lejana / Vuelta y vuelta / Campanas a M. Nunez / El canto de cuculi / Rondador / Triste tondero / Mis recuerdos / Punales / Mis Perritas / Kena y siku / Huamachuco / Despedida.
LP: ARN 34300
MC: ARN 434300

FLUTES, HARPES ET GUITARES INDIENNES.
Tracks: / Antara / Isla saca / La bocina / La rosa y la espina / Pago largo / La huerfana / El cari cari / La tropilla / Perdi mi ruta / Cuatreando / Senka tankana / Madrecita / Llama da de pastoreo / Conierto en la llanura.
LP: ARN 30057
MC: ARN 430057

FLUTES INDIENNES VOL 4 (Les mysteres des Andes).
Tracks: / Amanecer andino / Cae la noche, sopla el viento / Dos sikuris / Lejana purmamarca / Santiago de chuco / Trutruca y Kenacho / Linda cambita / Misterio de Los Andes / Uskil / El Pastor / Sol de Vilcabamba / Zumampa / Manchay / Chuquicamata.
LP: ARN 30126
MC: ARN 430126

FLUTES INDIENNES VOL 5 (Les Calchakis en scene).
Tracks: / La Pastora / Viento mochica / Poncho verde / Bailecito Calchaki / Llama del altiplano / Soplo del oriente / Lunarcito / Acuarela de sikus / Aires de Tarka / Contrabandeando / Estudio para charango / Tundiki / Quiaquenita / Mi antarita.
LP: ARN 34156
MC: ARN 434156

FLUTES INDIENNES VOL 6 (A travers les siecles).
Tracks: / Flutes precolombiennes / Cerros saltenos et Sikus del Titicaca / Instruments a cordes / Fantasia para kenas et Imanaska / Flutes a bec / Kurikinga / El centinela et anata morena / Musique metisse / Musique andine de nos jours / Despues del silencio / Santa Maria de iquique.
LP: ARN 34200
MC: ARN 434200

HIMNO AL SOL.
Tracks: / Sol caribe / Aurora de paz / Sol nocturno / Cuando canta mi pueblo / Sol de libertad / Himno al sol / Virgenes del sol / Gato en sol / Crepusculo costeno / Sol fecundo / Soles y lunas / Solsticio.
LP: ARN 34560
MC: ARN 434560

LA MARIMBA INDIENNE.
Tracks: / Palmeras / Nieve, viento y sol / El toro rabon / Sumak yurak / Bachue / Sombras / La rielera / El rascapetate / Asomate a la ventana / Mi chiriguare / Antigua serenata / Huambra amorosa / La Zandunga / Joropeando.
LP: ARN 30062
MC: ARN 430062

LE VOL DU CONDOR (Flight of the condor).
Tracks: / El vuelo del condor / Los Reyes Magos / Urpillay / Dos palomitas / Bikina, La / Amigo del condor / Naranjitallay / Los halcones / El aguilucho / Siklla / El colibri / El condor pasa.
LP: ARN 34795
MC: ARN 434795

LES FLUTES INDIENNES.
Tracks: / Peregrino soy / Charanguito / Reservista purajhei / La cocinerita / Cuculi / La esdrujula / Chuqui / La peregrinacion / Vicunita / Kapullay / Sonkoy / Jilguerito / Indios guerrilleros / Canelazo.
LP: ARN 30091
MC: ARN 430091

MISA CRIOLLA.
Tracks: / Misa criolla / Carnaval y Navidad.
LP: ARN 34309
MC: ARN 434309

MUNDO NUEVO - LES FLUTES DE PAN (Volume 9).
Tracks: / Les flutes de pan des Andes: blanco palomita / Coplas de Marzo / Requiem para un afilador / Aires de mi tierra / Tiempo de paz / Tonada tarijena / La cigarra / Mundo Nuevo: introduccion / Danzante de la piedad / Takirari de la gloria / Interludio y recitativo / Cueca del mundo nuevo / Interludio / Chaya de la Igualdad / Rasguido de la paz.
LP: ARN 34390
MC: ARN 434390

PUEBLOS DEL SUR.
Tracks: / El carretero / Sanjuanero / Gracias a la vida / Cambai / Alturas de machu pichu / Diego Ribera / Himalaya / Salida al mar / Patria adentro / La escala / Cachullapie de las brujas / Es mi pueblo del sur.
LP: ARN 34740
MC: ARN 434740

TIERRAS LEGENDARIAS (Les grands titres).
Tracks: / Recuerdo / El toro rabon / Santa Maria de Iquique / La cocinerita /

Uskil / Carta a Buenos Aires / Takirari del regreso / Anata morena / Linda Cambita / Rondador / Cuculi / Bailecito triple / Joropeando / Presencia lejana / Destino de sombras / Tiempo de paz.
LP: . . . . ARN 34610
MC: . . . . ARN 434610

TOUTE L'AMERIQUE INDIENNE (Calchakis, Les & Alfredo de Robertis).
Tracks: / Kimba, La / Carnaval del diablo / Tu mirada / Variaciones sobre un tema / El rey de los pajaros / Kuty / El carnaval / Hispartay / Sikuris / Fiesta andina / Linda companera / Sumak yurak / Cuerdita / Los cisnes / Sueno larense.
LP: . . . . ARN 30069
MC: . . . . ARN 430069

TOUTE L'ARGENTINE.
Tracks: / Geografia nortena / Bailecito triple / Lejos de mi tierra / Vallecito / Alambra de puas / Imagenes Argentinas / Chamame federal / La telesita la vieja / Nostalgia abierta / Carnaval de Humahuaca / Selvas virgenes / Carta a Buenos Aires / Norte de mi territorio / Zamba gris y gato quenero.
LP: . . . . ARN 34340
MC: . . . . ARN 434340

Les Compagnons...

LES COMPAGNONS DE LA CHANSON (Les Compagnons De La Chanson).
LP: . . . . 2 C 156 72620/1
MC: . . . . 2 C 256 72622

Les Disques Blu

LES DISQUES BLU (Various artists).
LP: . . . . ABLUBOX 1

Les Elite

PATHWAYS.
LP: . . . . PHZA 8

Les Enfants

TOUCHE.
Tracks: / Shed a tear (there you go) / Slipaway / Taking your love away / Nothing has changed / Playing with fire / Dreaming of you / Funny / Flesh and blood / When summer comes / Alone again tonight.
LP: . . . . CHR 1487
MC: . . . . ZCHR 1487

Les Enfants Terribles

ANOTHER COUNTRY.
LP: . . . . CHIME 056
MC: . . . . CHIME 056CC

Les Freres Michot

LES FRERES MICHOT (Various artists).
LP: 1014
MC: . . . . 1014 TC

Les Girls (Film)

LES GIRLS/SILK STOCKINGS (Film Soundtracks) (Various artists).
LP: . . . . MCAD 6177

Les Grandes Classiques

LES GRANDES CLASSIQUES DE L'ACCORDEON (Various artists).
LP: . . . . VG 400377

Les Maniacs

LIVE AT BUDOKAN.
LP: . . . . STOP 09

Les Miserables

5 OUTSTANDING PERFORMANCES FROM LES MISERABLE (Various artists).
Tracks: / Empty chairs at empty tables: *Various artists* / Stars: *Various artists* / One day more: *Various artists* / I dreamed a dream: *Various artists* / On my own: *Various artists.*
LP: . . . . SCOREL 17

LES MISERABLES (Original Paris cast recording) (Various artists).
Tracks: / La journee est finie: *Various artists* / J'ai reve d'une autre vie: *Various artists* / La volonte du peuple: *Various artists* / L'air de la misere: *Various artists* / La devise du cabaretier: *Various artists*/ Le coeur au bonheur: *Various artists* / Donnez donnez: *Various artists* / Mon prince est en chemin: *Various* artists / Demain: *Various artists* / La faute a voltaire: *Various artists* / Noir ou blanc: *Various artists*/ La lumiere: *Various artists.*
LP: . . . . SCENE 2
MC: . . . . SCENEC 2

LES MISERABLES Original Broadway cast (Various artists).
LP: 924151.1
MC: 924151.4

LES MISERABLES (Complete symphonic recordings) (Various artists).
LP: . . . . MIZ 1
MC: . . . . MIZC 1

OM PAH (Les Miserables Brass Band).
MC: . . . . GVMMC 403

Les Morfalous

LES MORFALOUS (Film Soundtrack) (Various artists).
LP: . . . . A 243

Les Negresses Vertes

MLAH.
Tracks: / La valse / Zobi la mouche / C'est pas la mer a boire / Voila l'ete / Orane / La faim des haricots / Les yeux de ton pere / Il / L'homme des marais / Les rablablas les roubliblis / Marcelle Ratafia / La danse des negresses vertes / Hey Maria / Le pere Magloire.
LP: . . . . LEFT 011
MC: . . . . LEFTC 011

Les Nouvelles

POLYPHONIES CORSES.
MC: 848 515 4
LP: 848 515 1

Les Rita Mitsouko

RE.
MC: . . . . TCV 2637

RE (BOX SET).
LPS: . . . . VBF 2637

Les Tetes Brulees

LES TETES BRULEES.
Tracks: / Ma musique a moi / Ca fait mal / Nauom wom / Za ayi neyi / Papa / Man fo job / Ngole likas / Tetes Brulees / Zanzi collection.
LP: . . . . STERNS 9001
MC: . . . . STC 9001

Les Thugs

STILL HUNGRY.
LP: . . . . DYL 4

Les Uns Et Les Autres

LES UNS ET LES AUTRES (Film Soundtrack) (Various artists).
2LP: . . . . BL 70713
MC: . . . . BK 70713

Lese Majesty

LESE MAJESTY.
LP: . . . . IW 1029

Leshan, Lawrence

EMOTIONS AND CANCER (See Under Emotions & Cancer).

Lesley, Chris

TURNING TABLES (Lesley, Chris & Nick Hooper).
Tracks: / After the storm / Baildora.
LP: . . . . BER 105

Lesley, Jean

JEAN LESLEY & STETSON (Lesley, Jean & Stetson).
LP: . . . . SS 061
MC: . . . . SSC 061

Lesley, Kim

STORE IT UP 'TIL MORNING (Lesley, Kim & Her All Stars).
Tracks: / 500 miles high / I'm wasting my time / Store it up 'till morning / As if I cared / Natural women / I cried for you / My dearest dear / Spring can hang you up / Better than / Love is here to stay / Fine and mellow.
LP: . . . . ZR 1016

Leslie, John

SHIP OF TIME, THE (Leslie, John & Chris).
Tracks: / Dustbin melody / Winter man / Trees they do grow high, The / Jenny Lind / Polly on the shore / Ship of time / Banks of sweet Mossom / Masons apron / New St.George, The / Adieu sweet lovely Nancy.
LP: . . . . COT 901

Lesmana, Indra

FOR EARTH AND HEAVEN.
Tracks: / Stephanie / L.A. / Corrobores / Song for ... / For earth and heaven / Morro rock / Dancin' shore / First glance.
LP: . . . . IZEB 5709
MC: . . . . IZEBC 5709

NO STANDING.
Tracks: / No standing / Sleeping beauty / Samba E.T. / First, The / Tis time to part.
LP: . . . . IZEB 5711
MC: . . . . IZEBC 5711

L'Esprit

LANGUAGE OF TOUCH.
Tracks: / Kaira / Sea of change / Ripples / Shoji / Taiga / Language of touch / Verandah.
MC: . . . . ICL 001

Less Than Zero

HAZY SHADE OF WINTER (See under Bangles).

LESS THAN ZERO (Film Soundtrack) (Various artists).
Tracks: / Rockin' pneumonia and the boogie woogie flu: *Aerosmith* / Life fades away: *Orbison, Roy* / Rock and roll all nite: *Poison* / Going back to Cali: *Various artists* / You and me (less than zero): *Danzig, Glenn* & The Power & Fury Orchestra / In a gadda-da-vida: *Slayer* / Bring the noise: *Public Enemy* / Are you my woman: *Black Flames* / She's lost you: *Jett, Joan & The Blackhearts* / How to love again: *Jones, Oran "Juice"*/ Hazy shade of winter: *Bangles.*
LP: 4604491
MC: 4604494

Lessing, Doris (aut)

ANCIENT WAYS TO NEW FREEDOM (See under Ancient Ways...).

FIFTH CHILD, THE.
MC: . . . . IAB 88112

GOLDEN NOTEBOOK, THE.
MC: 1753

Lester, Bob

ONE MORE TIME (Lester, Bob & The Moonglows).
LP: . . . . RELIC 8001

Lester, Jane

DOCTOR BRENT'S BROKEN JOURNEY (Donald, Sheila (nar)).
MCSET: . . . . CLT 1007

SISTER MARCH'S SECRET (Guthrie, Gwyneth).
MCSET: . . . . CLT 1002

Lester, Julius

TO BE A SLAVE (Various artists).
MCSET: 2066

Lesueur, James

PRINCE DE L'ACCORDEON.
Tracks: / Piccolo rag / Valse emraude / Samba sympa / Matins qui chantent / Pistolette / Accordeonarama / Surprise Polka / La belle Mexicaine / Potion magique / Sambatucada / Accordeon en fete.
LP: . . . . ILD 42037

Lesurf, Cathy

SURFACE.
LP: . . . . FUN 002

SWEET REMEMBRANCE.
MC: . . . . FUNC 001

Lethal

PROGRAMMED.
Tracks: / Fire in your skin / Programmed / Plan of peace / Another day / Arrival / What they've done / Obscure the sky / Immune / Pray for me / Killing machine.
LP: . . . . ZORRO 15

Lethal Aggression

LIFE IS HARD.
LP: . . . . FH 12006

Lethal Weapon

LETHAL WEAPON (Film Soundtrack) (Various artists).
Tracks: / Lethal weapon: *Various artists* / Amanda: *Various artists* / Meet Martin Riggs: *Various artists*/ Roger: *Various artists* / Coke deal: *Various artists* / Mr. Joshua: *Various artists* / They've got my daughter: *Various artists* / Desert, The: *Various artists* / Nightclub: *Various artists* / Weapon, The: *Various artists.*
LP: 925551 1
MC: 925551 4

LETHAL WEAPON II (Film Soundtrack) (Various artists).
LP: . . . . K 925985 1
MC: . . . . K 925985 4

Let's Active

BIG PLANS FOR EVERYBODY.
Tracks: / In little ways / Talking to myself / Writing on the book of last pages / Last chance town / Won't go wrong / Badger / Fell / Still dark out / Whispered news / Reflecting pool / Route 67.
LP: . . . . MIRF 1011
MC: . . . . MIRFC 1011

CYPRESS.
Tracks: / Easy does / Waters part / Lowdown / Gravel truck / Crows on the phone line / Ring true / Blue line / Flags for everything / Prey, The / Co-star / Grey scale.
LP: . . . . IRSA 7047

EVERY DOG HAS HIS DAY.
Tracks: / Every dog has his day / Horizon / Sweepstakes winner / Orpheus in Hades lounge / Mr. Fool / Ten layers down / Too bad / Night train / Forty years / Bad machinery / I feel funny / Terminate.
LP: . . . . EIRSA 1001
MC: . . . . EIRSAC 1001

Let's Get Harry

LET'S GET HARRY (Film soundtrack) (Various artists).
LP: . . . . STV 81301

Let's Hide Away...

LET'S HIDE AWAY AND DANCE AWAY (Various artists).
LP: . . . . KING 773

Let's Kiss

LET'S KISS (Various artists).
MC: . . . . KC 014

Let's Listen

LET'S LISTEN (Harris, Julie).
MC: 1182

Let's Make Love

LET'S MAKE LOVE (Film Soundtrack) (Various artists).
LP: . . . . ACS 8327
MC: . . . . BT 8327

Let's Play

LET'S PLAY (Childrens story book).
MC: . . . . RWM 002

Let's Sea

LET'S SEA (Various artists).
MC: . . . . KC 010

Lets Together

LETS TOGETHER (Various artists).
MC: . . . . KC 008

Letter To Brezhnev

LETTER TO BREZHNEV (Film soundtrack) (Various artists).
Tracks: / Don't ask me to choose: *Fine Young Cannibals* / Bring it down (this insane thing): *Redskins* / How long: *Carmel* / Always something there to remind me: *Shaw, Sandie* / Letter to Brezhnev: *Gill, Alan* / Hit that perfect beat: *Bronski Beat* / You can't help (sentimental Sunday): *Flesh* / Wild party: *A Certain Ratio*/ Ain't that always the way: *Quinn, Paul* / Lockets and stars: *Clarke, Marie.*
LP: . . . . LONLP 8
MC: . . . . LONC 8

Lettermen

EVERGREEN.
Tracks: / What I did for love / We're all alone / You're smiling face / Evergreen / Love so right / Cherish / Precious and few / If you leave me now / Breaking up is hard to do / Don't say goodbye / Let's pretend / I'll be back.
LP: . . . . PRCV 121
MC: . . . . TC PRCV 121

Letters From My Father

LETTERS FROM MY FATHER.
MCSET: . . . . ZBBC 1161

Lettuce Spray

LET US PRAY.
LP: . . . . COD 5

Levaillant, Denis

BARIUM CIRCUS.
Tracks: / L'entree des athletes aux chevaux noirs / La trapeziste / Le jongleur masque / Les Equilibristes / La pantomime amoureuse / Les petits chiens gris / Le magicien / Le clown blanc / La parade des augustes / Le depart des fauves.
LP: . . . . NATO 382

DIRECT.
Tracks: / Un jour sur les conseils de Paul... / Comme un duc / Lennie up / Thelonious melodius / Earl's pearls / Hi Samson / Les deux noms de bud / La derniere prise / Le rendezvous (New York city, St. Mark's Place) / Le jeune franc avec le vieux cecil / Le lendemain / Paul n'avait laisse aucune instruction pour refermer la ....
LP: . . . . NATO 140

Levashov, Valentini

FOLK SONGS.
MC: . . . . SM 00387

Level 42

EARLY TAPES, THE (JULY/AUGUST, 1980).
Tracks: / Sandstorm / Love meeting love / Theme to Margaret / Autumn (paradise is free) / Wings of love / Woman / Mr. Pink / 88.
LP: . . . . SPELP 28
MC: . . . . SPEMC 28
LP: . . . . POLS 1064

FAMILY EDITION, THE.
Tracks: / It's over (extended remix) / Running in the family (Dave 'O' Remix) / Family edition megamix / It's over (instrumental) / Freedom someday.
LP: . . . . POLM 2013
MC: . . . . POLM 42013

GUARANTEED (ALBUM).
MC: . . . . PK 75055
LP: . . . . PL 75005

LEVEL 42.
Tracks: / Turn it on / 43 / Why are you leaving / Almost there / Heathrow / Love games / Dune tune / Starchild.
LP: . . . . POLS 1036
MC: . . . . POLSC 1036

LEVEL 42: INTERVIEW PICTURE DISC.

LPPD: . . . . BAK 2043

LEVEL BEST.
Tracks: / Running in the family / Sun goes down, The / Something about you / Tracie / Starchild / It's over / Hot water / Take care of yourself / Heaven in my hands / Children say / Love games / Chinese way, The / Leaving me now / Lessons in love / Micro kid (Only on CD and cassette.) / Take a look (Only on CD and cassette.) / To be with you again (Only on CD and cassette.) / Chant has begun, The (Only on CD and cassette.).
LP: . . . . LEVTC 1
MC: . . . . LEVT 1

PHYSICAL PRESENCE, A.
Tracks: / Almost there / Turn it on / Mr. Pink / Eyes waterfalling / Kansas city milkman / Follow me / Foundation and empire / Chant has begun, The / Chinese way, The / Sun goes down (living it up), The / Hot water / Love games / 88 (Available on LP and cassette only).
LP: . . . . POLH 23
MC: . . . . POLHC 23

PURSUIT OF ACCIDENTS, THE.
Tracks: / Weave your spell / Pursuit of accidents, The / Last chance / Are you hearing (what I hear) / You can't blame Louis / Eyes waterfalling / Shapeshifter / Chinese way, The / Chinese way, The (extended version) (on CD only) / You can't blame Louis (extended version) (on CD only).
LP: . . . . POLD 5067
MC: . . . . POLDC 5067
LP: 8100151
MC: 8100154

RUNNING IN THE FAMILY.
Tracks: / Lessons in love / Children say / Running in the family / It's over / To be with you again / Two solitudes / Fashion fever / Sleepwalkers, The / Freedom someday.
LP: . . . . POLH 42
MC: . . . . POLHC 42
LP: . . . . POLHA 42

RUNNING IN THE FAMILY - PLATINUM EDITION.
Tracks: / Children say / Running in the family (Dave 'O' remix) / It's over (remix) / Freedom someday / To be with you again / Two solitudes / Fashion fever / Sleepwalkers / Something about you (Shep Pettibone remix) / World machine (Shep Pettibone remix).
MC: . . . . POLHX 42
MC: 833 689 4

STANDING IN THE LIGHT.
Tracks: / Micro-kid / Sun goes down (living it up), The / Out of sight, out of mind / Dance on heavy weather / Pharaoh's dream of endless time / Standing in the light / I want eyes / People / Machine stops.
LP: . . . . POLD 5110
MC: . . . . POLDC 5110
LP: 8138651
MC: 8138654

STARING AT THE SUN.
Tracks: / Heaven in my hands / I don't know why / Take a look / Over there / Silence / Tracie / Staring at the sun / Two hearts collide / Man / Gresham blues.
LP: . . . . POLH 50
MC: . . . . POLHC 50

STRATEGY.
LP: . . . . LEVLP 1

TRUE COLOURS.
Tracks: / Chant has begun, The / Kansas City milkman / Seven days / Hot water / Floating life, A / True believers / Kouyate / Hours by the window.
LP: . . . . POLH 10
MC: . . . . POLHC 10

WORLD MACHINE.
Tracks: / World machine / Physical presence, A / Something about you / Leaving me now / I sleep on my heart / It's not the same for us / Good man in a storm / Coup d'etat / Lying still / Dream crazy / Love games (US remix) (Extra track on limited cassette) / Hot water (12" mix) (Extra track on limited cassette) / Sun goes down (living it up) (up front mix) (Extra track on limited cassette) / Chinese way, The (US mix) (Extra track on limited cassette) / I sleep on my heart (remix) (Extra track on limited cassette) / Something about you (sisa mix).
MC: . . . . POLHX 25
LP: . . . . POLH 25

WORLD MACHINE (U.S. EDITION).
Tracks: / Something about you / World machine / Physical presence / Leaving me now / Hot water / It's not the same for us / Good man in a storm / Chant has begun, The.
LP: 827 487-1

Levellers

LEVELLING THE LAND.
LP: . . . . WOL 1022
MC: . . . . WOLMC 1022

WEAPON CALLED THE WORD, A.
LP: 105571
MC: 105574

Levellers 5

SPRINGTIME.
LP: . . . . PROBE 26

Levene, Keith

I'M LOOKING FOR SOMETHING.
LP: . . . . HOLY 009

VIOLENT OPPOSITION.
LP: . . . . EM 94151

Levert

BIG THROWDOWN, THE.
Tracks: / Casanova / Good stuff / Don't u think it's time / My forever love / Love the way U love me / Sweet sensation / In 'n' out / Temptation / Throwdown.
LP: 781 773-1
MC: 781 773-4
LP: . . . . WX 131
MC: . . . . WX 131 C

JUST COOLIN'.
Tracks: / Pull over / Just coolin' / Gotta get the money / Take your time / Join in the fun / Let's get romantic / Feel real / Smilin' / Start me up again / Loveable.
LP: 781 926-1
MC: 781 926-4

RUB A DUB STYLE.
LP: 756821641
MC: 756821644

Levey, Stan

GRAND STAN (Levey, Stan Sextet).
LP: . . . . FS 147

STANLEY THE STEAMER (Levey, Stan Sextet (featuring Dexter Gordan)).
Tracks: / Diggin' for Diz / Ruby my dear / Tune up / La chaloupee / Day in, day out / Stanley the steamer / This time the drum's on me.
LP: . . . . AFF 93

WEST COAST RHYTHM (Levey, Stan & Red Mitchell).
Tracks: / Exakatamo / Drum sticks / Lightnin' bug / West coasting / Fast clip / Happy minor / Bluesology / Once in a while / Long ago and far away / Gone with the wind / Kelly Green / Scrapple from the apple.
LP: . . . . AFF 95

Levi, Ijahman

AFRICA.
LP: . . . . JMI 400
MC: . . . . CJMI 400

ARE WE A WARRIOR.
Tracks: / Are we a warrior / Moulding / Church, The / Miss Beverly / Two sides of love.
LP: . . . . ILPS 9557
LP: . . . . JMI 200
MC: . . . . CJMI 200
MC: . . . . RRCT 25

CULTURE COUNTRY.
LP: . . . . JMI 700

FORWARD RASTAMAN.
Tracks: / Waitin' on you / Gambler's blues / Tired of your jive / Night life / Buzz me / Sweet sixteen part 1 / Don't answer the door / Blind love / I know what you're puttin' down / Baby get lost / Gonna keep on loving you / Sweet sixteen part 2.
LP: . . . . JMI 800

I DO (Levi, Ijahman & Maj).
LP: . . . . JMI 600

IJAHMAN & FRIENDS.
Tracks: / Master ideas / Mellow music / African train / Struggling dub / Extended dub / Master dub / Struggling times / Let him go / Jah is coming.
LP: . . . . JMI 900

INSIDE OUT.
LP: . . . . JMI 1100

LIVE OVER EUROPE.
LP: . . . . JMI 1000

TELL IT TO THE CHILDREN.
LP: . . . . TRLPS 266
MC: . . . . CTR 266

Levi, Papa

CODE OF PRACTICE.
LP: . . . . ARILP 060
MC: . . . . ARIMC 060

Levi & The Rockats

LOUISIANA HAYRIDE.
LP: . . . . LPM 8207

Leviathan

BALLADS AND SONGS OF THE WHALING TRADE.
LP: 12T 174

SANDY JEAN.
LP: . . . . A 15

Leviathan (Film)

LEVIATHAN (Film Soundtrack) (Various artists).
LP: . . . . VS 5226
MC: . . . . VSC 5226

Leviev, Milcho

BLUES FOR THE FISHERMAN (Leviev, Milcho, Quartet with Art Pepper).
LP: . . . . MOLE 1

BLUES FOR THE FISHERMAN/TRUE BLUES (Leviev, Milcho, Quartet with Art Pepper).
Tracks: / Ophelia / Make a list, make a wish / Straight life / G.I. blues / True blues / Sad, a little bit / Goodbye / Blues for the fisherman.
MC: . . . . MOLECAS 15

MUSIC FOR BIG BAND AND SYMPHONY ORCHESTRA.
Tracks: / Riff passacaglia / Blue adagio / Fast intermezzo / Fugue dithiramb / Waltz for Maurice / Issac's touchstone / Bulgarian boogie / Sad a little bit.
LP: . . . . TR 530

PLAYS THE MUSIC OF IRVING BERLIN.
Tracks: / What'll I do / Alexander's ragtime band / How deep is the ocean / Marie / Blue skies / Waiting at the end of the road / Soft lights and sweet music / Always / Cheek to cheek.
LP: . . . . DS 876

TRUE BLUES (Leviev, Milcho & Art Pepper).
LP: . . . . MOLE 5

Levin, Marc

SOCIAL SKETCHES.
LP: . . . . ENJA 2058

Levin, Pete

PARTY IN THE BASEMENT.
Tracks: / Bells / For a place to sleep / Party in the basement / Gone / Ragtime: Saturday night at the Last Chance / Subway / Something I said / Hunter, The / Complaint department, The / One day in the schoolyard.
LP: . . . . GV 794561

Levin, Robert

ELEGIES (See under Kashkashian, Kim) (Levin, Robert & Kim Kashkashian).

Levine, James

PLAYS SCOTT JOPLIN.
LP: . . . . RL 12243

Levine, Mark

CONCEPTS.
Tracks: / Keeper of the flame / After you / Greased / Ask me now / Black masque / Skylark / Jitterbug waltz / Up jumped spring.
LP: . . . . CJ 234

Levine, Mike

SMILEY AND ME.
LP: . . . . CJ 352

Levkas Man

LEVKAS MAN (See under Innes, Hammond) (Innes, Hammond (author)).

Levy, Barrington

BARRINGTON LEVY.
LP: . . . . LPCT 0125

BARRINGTON LEVY MEETS FRANKIE PAUL (Levy, Barrington & Frankie Paul).
LP: . . . . ARILP 011

BLACK ROSE (see under Palmer Dog's "Don't smoke the seed").

COLLECTION: BARRINGTON LEVY.
LP: . . . . TIMETORLP 06

DIVINE.
MC: . . . . MCT 1077
LP: . . . . MLPS 1077

ENGLISHMAN.
Tracks: / Englishman / If you give to me / Sister Carol / Don't fuss nor fight / Look girl / Look youthman / Send a Moses / Black heart man / Money makes friends / Bend your back.
LP: . . . . GREL 9

HERE I COME.
Tracks: / Here I come / Do the dance / Under me sensi / Vibes is right / Real thing, The / Cool and loving / Struggler / Live good / Moonlight lover / Ya we deh, A / Give me your love / Don't run away.
LP: . . . . TRLP 003
MC: . . . . TRC 003

HUNTER MAN.
Tracks: / Hunter man / Shaolin temple / Captivity / A ya we deh / Shine eye gal / Collie weed / Sweet reggae music / Revelation.
LP: . . . . BS 1050

LIFESTYLE.
LP: . . . . GGLP 0032

LOVE THE LIFE YOU LIVE.
Tracks: / Love the life you live / Girl, I like your style / Too experienced / Why you do it? / Long time friction / I've caught you / My woman / Come on little girl, come on / Two sounds / She's mine.
LP: . . . . TORLP 05

OPEN BOOK.
Tracks: / Open book.
LP: . . . . RMM 659

POOR MAN STYLE.
Tracks: / Don't give up / Sensimelea / I can't wait too long / Poor man style / Man give up / She is the best girl / True love / This little boy / I love I love you / Rob & gone.
LP: . . . . TRLS 209

PRISON OVAL ROCK.
LP: . . . . VPRL 1017

ROBIN HOOD.
Tracks: / Robin Hood / Rock and come in / Love sister Carol / Gonna tell your girlfriend / Ask me what is love / Why did you leave me / Many changes in life / Na broke no fight / When Friday come / Like how you kiss and caress me.
LP: . . . . GREL 14

Levy, Bertram

FIRST GENERATION (Levy, Bertram/ Ostroushko, Peter).
LP: . . . . FF 392

THAT OLD GUT FEELING.
LP: . . . . FF 271

Levy, Jed

GOOD PEOPLE.
LP: . . . . RSR 105

Levy, Lou

BABY GRAND JAZZ (Levy, Lou Trio).
LP: . . . . FS 130

IMPROMPTU (See under Christy, June) (Christy, June & Lou Levy Sextet).

MOST MUSICAL FELLA, A (Levy, Lou Trio).
LP: . . . . FS 181

TEMPUE FUGUE-IT.
LP: . . . . IP 7711

Levy, Louis

MUSIC FROM THE MOVIES (Levy, Louis & His Gaumont British Symphony).
LP: . . . . SH 258

Levy, Marcy

HELP ME (See under Gibb, Robin) (Levy, Marcy & Robin Gibb).

Levy, Ron

RON LEVY'S WILD KINGDOM (Levy, Ron Wild Kingdom).
Tracks: / I know you know I know / Chicken fried snake / So many roads / Why you stay out so late? / Party in Nogales / Big town playboy / My heart's in trouble / It's hot in here / Knee squeeze / Must have missed a turn somewhere.
LP: . . . . FIEND 85
LP: . . . . BT 1034
MC: . . . . BT 1034C

SAFARI TO NEW ORLEANS (Levy, Ron Wild Kingdom).
MC: . . . . BT 1040C
LP: . . . . BT 1040

Levy, Stan

STAN LEVY QUINTET (Levy, Stan Quintet).
LP: . . . . VSOP 41

WEST COASTING (See under Candoli, Conte) (Levy, Stan & Conte Candoli).

Lew, Benjamin

A PROPOS D'UN PAYSAGE (Lew, Benjamin & Steven Brown).
LP: . . . . CRAM 038

DOUZIEME JOURNEE: LE VERBE, LA PARURE, L'AMOUR (see also Steven Brown) (Lew, Benjamin & Steven Brown).
LP: . . . . CRAM 020
LP: . . . . MTM 15

LES NOUVELLES MUSIQUES (Lew, Benjamin & Controlled Bleeding).
Tracks: / Des ambres / Perspectives / Une danse / Music for earth & water.
LP: . . . . SUB 330 15

NEBKA (Lew, Benjamin & Steven Brown).
LP: . . . . MTM 17

Lewie, Jona

GATECRASHER.
Tracks: / Swan / Piggyback Sue / Rockin' yobs / Seaside shuffle / Hallelujah Europa / Cherry ring / On a Saturday night / She left I died / Papa don't go / Come away / Custer's last stand.
LP: . . . . SNTF 794

HEART SKIPS BEAT.
Tracks: / I think I'll get my hair cut / Cream Jacqueline strawberry / Stop the cavalry / Abracadabra / Louise / Seed that always dies, The / Heart skips beat / What have I done? / You go / Guessing games / Rearranging the deckchairs on the Titanic.
LP: **SEEZ 40**
MC: **ZSEEZ 40**

ON THE OTHER HAND THERE'S A FIST.
Tracks: / Kitchen at parties / Baby she's on the street / Big shot - momentarily / Bit higher / Feeling stupid / Vous et moi / God bless whoever made you / Hallelujah Europa / On the road / I'll get by in Pittsburgh.
LP: **SEEZ 8**

Lewin, Hakan

EXCURSIONS (Lewin, Hakan Quartet).
LP: **DRLP 98**

Lewington Yamaha

CENTENARY (Lewington Yamaha Brass).
Tracks: / Flourish for a birthday / Sullivan fantasy, A / One day in your life / Labour and love / Oklahoma / Autumn leaves / Rocky / Rule Britannia / Centenary march.
LP: **PRL 033D**
MC: **CPRL 033D**

Lewis, Archie

SINCERELY YOURS (Lewis, Archie featuring Geraldo & his Orchestra).
Tracks: / Hold my hand / Just a prayer away / Make her mine / While the angelus was ringing / Near you / Can I forget you / If you go / I still believe / To be or not to be / Pretending / I don't stand a ghost of a chance with you / Till all our dreams come true / Long ago / I keep forgetting to remember / If I can help somebody / Au revoir / Silent night.
LP: **RFL 16**

Lewis, C. Day (nar)

FOUR TWENTIETH CENTURY POETS (See under Four Twentieth (bk)).

LEWIS, C. DAY POETRY SELECTION.
MC: **TTC/PS 02**

REQUIEM FOR THE LIVING (Lewis, C. Day & Donald Swann).
LP: **PLR 061**

Lewis, C.J.

YOUNG, GIFTED AND BLACK (See under Leo, Philip) (Lewis, C.J. & Leo, Philip).

Lewis, C.S (aut)

CHRONICLES OF NARNIA SOUNDBOOK (Various artists).
MCSET: **701**

CHRONICLES OF NARNIA, THE.
MC: **000104270 X**

HORSE AND HIS BOY, THE (Hordern, Sir Michael).
2LP: **SWD 353**
MCSET: **ZC SWD 353**

HORSE AND HIS BOY, THE (Quayle, Anthony (nar)).
MC: **1655**

LAST BATTLE, THE (Hordern, Sir Michael).
2LP: **SWD 357**
MCSET: **ZC SWD 357**

LAST BATTLE, THE (York, Michael (nar)).
MC: **1674**

LION, THE WITCH AND THE WARDROBE, THE (Hordern, Sir Michael).
2LP: **SWD 352**
MCSET: **ZC SWD 352**

LION, THE WITCH AND THE WARDROBE, THE (Richardson, Ian).
MC: **1587**

LION, THE WITCH AND THE WARDROBE, THE (Various artists).
MCSET: **ZBBC 1110**

MAGICIAN'S NEPHEW, THE (Hordern, Sir Michael).
2LP: **SWD 351**
MCSET: **ZC SWD 351**

MAGICIAN'S NEPHEW, THE (Bloom, Claire (nar)).
MC: **1660**

PRINCE CASPIAN (Hordern, Sir Michael).
2LP: **SWD 354**
MCSET: **ZC SWD 354**

PRINCE CASPIAN (Bloom, Claire (nar)).
MC: **1603**

SILVER CHAIR, THE (Quayle, Anthony (nar)).
MC: **1631**

SILVER CHAIR, THE (Hordern, Sir Michael).
2LP: **SWD 356**
MCSET: **ZC SWD 356**

TALES OF NARNIA (Various artists).
MCSET: **ZBBC 1109**

VOYAGE OF THE DAWN TREADER (Quayle, Anthony (nar)).
MC: **1615**

VOYAGE OF THE DAWN TREADER, THE (Hordern, Sir Michael).
2LP: **SWD 355**
MCSET: **ZC SWD 355**

Lewis, Dal

HEAVEN ONLY KNOWS.
LP: **PTE 5055**
MC: **PTX 5055**

Lewis, Dave

COLLECTION OF SHORT DREAMS.
Tracks: / Stay right here forever / Late show, The / Go all out to get it / Papa boy / Whole lotta something goin' on / Lucy took a ride / Beautiful woman / Open up your heart / Woman like you.
LP: **2383522**

Lewis Family

16 GREATEST HITS: LEWIS FAMILY.
LP: **SLP 3019**
MC: **GT 53019**

Lewis, Father Al

FATHER AL LEWIS AND LARS EDEGRAN'S NOR JAZZBAND (Lewis, Father Al/Lars Edegran's NOR Jazzband).
LP: **GHB 245**

Lewis, Furry

BACK ON MY FEET AGAIN.
LP: **PRE 7810**

BEALE STREET MESSAROUND (Various artists).
LP: **ROUNDER 2006**

DONE CHANGED MY MIND.
Tracks: / Baby you don't want me / Done changed my mind / Goin' to Kansas City / Judge Boushay blues / Casey Jones / This time tomorrow / I will turn your money green / Frankie and Johnny / Longing blues / Long tall gal blues.
LP: **CH 260**

FURRY LEWIS IN HIS PRIME 1927-29.
LP: **L 1050**

LIVE AT THE GASLIGHT.
LP: **C 5525**

MEMPHIS SESSIONS 1956-61 (Lewis, Furry/Will Shade).
LP: **WOLF 120 920**

REMAINING TITLES 1927-29.
LP: **WSE 101**

Lewis, Gary

20 GOLDEN GREATS (Lewis, Gary & The Playboys).
Tracks: / This diamond ring / My heart's symphony / Everybody loves a clown.
LP: **LBR 1005**

GREATEST HITS: GARY LEWIS & THE PLAYBOYS (Lewis, Gary & The Playboys).
LP: **RNLP 163**

Lewis, George

AT CLUB HANGOVER VOL.1.
LP: **SLP 4055**

AT CLUB HANGOVER VOL.3.
LP: **SLP 4061**

AT SAN JACINTO HALL (See under Bocage, Peter).

CITY OF A MILLION DREAMS (Lewis, George/Kid Thomas).
LP: **GHB 10**

FOR DANCERS ONLY (Lewis, George & His Jazzband).
LP: **GHB 37**

FROM SAXOPHONE & TROMBONE (see also Evan Parker) (Lewis, George & Evan Parker).
LP: **INCUS 35**

GEORGE LEWIS AND DOUGLAS EWART (See under Douglas Ewart) (Lewis, George & Douglas Ewart).

GEORGE LEWIS AND HIS NEW ORLEANS BAND (Lewis, George & His New Orleans Band).
LP: **SLP 4116**

GEORGE LEWIS AT CLUB HANGOVER.
LP: **SLP 251**

GEORGE LEWIS AT CONGO SQUARE.
LP: **JCE 27**

GEORGE LEWIS AT HERBERT OTTO'S PARTY.
LP: **JCE 24**

GEORGE LEWIS AUTHENTIC NEW ORLEANS-RAGTIME JAZZ BAND.
2LP: **SLP 830/31**

GEORGE LEWIS & HIS RAGTIME BAND (Lewis, George & His Ragtime Band/Paul Barbarin & His Band).
LP: **SLP 4049**

GEORGE LEWIS & HIS RAGTIME BAND (Featuring Lizzie Miles) (Lewis, George & his Ragtime band).
LP: **DC 12008**

GEORGE LEWIS IN CONCERT (Lewis, George & his Ragtime band).
LP: **SLP 4022**

GEORGE LEWIS IN EUROPE, VOL 1: "PIED PIPER".
Tracks: / Sister Kate / Old Nellie Grey / Mahogany Hall stomp / Chinatown, my Chinatown / Old man Mose / There's "yes, yes" in your eyes / Tin roof blues / Just a little while to stay here.
LP: **RARITIES 47**

GEORGE LEWIS & PAPA BUE'S VIKING JAZZ BAND (Lewis, George & Papa Bue's Viking Jazz Band).
LP: **SLP 4119**

GEORGE LEWIS & PAPA BUES VIKING JAZZ BAND.
LP: **JU 1**
LP: **SLP 4119**

GEORGE LEWIS & THE EASY RIDERS JAZZ BAND (Lewis, George & the Easy Riders Jazz Band).
LP: **GHB 29**

HOMAGE TO CHARLES PARKER (Lewis, George & Anthony Davis).
LP: **BSR 0029**

IN JAPAN.
LP: **SLP 514**

IN JAPAN VOL.2.
LP: **GHB 15**

IN JAPAN VOL.3.
LP: **GHB 16**

IN JAPAN VOL 1.
LP: **GHB 14**

JILA (Lewis, George & Douglas Ewart).
LP: **BSR 0026**

NEW ORLEANS PARADE (Lewis, George & Eureka Brass Band).
LP: **SGC 12104**
LP: **DC 12104**

NEW ORLEANS PARADE (1951) (Lewis, George & Eureka Brass Band).
LP: **DC 12104**

NEWS FOR LULU (See under Zorn, John) (Zorn, John/Bill Frisell/George Lewis).

PERENNIAL GEORGE LEWIS, THE.
Tracks: / Ace in the hole / It's a long way to Tipperary / West end blues / Jambalaya / Mack the knife / Careless love.
LP: **2304 553**

PIED PIPER, THE.
Tracks: / Chiri cheri bin / It's a long way to Tipperary / Savoy blues / Ice cream / Panama rag / Nobody knows the way I feel this morning / Who's sorry now / High society.
LP: **RARITIES 54**

PIED PIPER VOL.2, THE.
Tracks: / South rampart street parade / Bucket's got a hole in it / At a Georgia camp meeting / West end blues / That's a plenty / Lord, lord / Nobody knows the way I feel this morning / Hindustan.
LP: **RARITIES 51**

RAGTIME BAND (Lewis, George & his Ragtime band).
Tracks: / Ice cream / Down by the riverside / Burgandy Street blues / Just a closer walk with thee / Panama / Doctor Jazz / When the Saints go marching in / Lou-easy-an-i-a.
LP: **SM 3072**

RAGTIME JAZZBAND.
LP: **GHB 108**

SPIRIT OF NEW ORLEANS (Lewis, George & his Ragtime band).
LP: **ML 132**

WHEN THE SUN GOES DOWN (Dusseldorf 1959) (Lewis, George/Ken Colyers Jazzmen).
Tracks: / Swanee River / In the evening / Willie the weeper / Redwing / St Philip Street breakdown / Bourbon Street parade / Cheek to cheek / If I ever cease to love.
LP: **KC 3**

Lewis, Herbie

LIVE AT THE KEYSTONE CORNER (See under Montoliu, Tete) (Lewis, Herbie/Billy Higgins/Tete Montoliu).

Lewis, Hopeton

COOL COLLIE (See under Dekker, Desmond).

DYNAMIC HOPETON LEWIS.
LP: **DR 5008**

Lewis, Huey

FORE! (Lewis, Huey & The News).
Tracks: / Jacob's ladder / Stuck with you / Whole lotta lovin' / Hip to be square / I know what I like / I never walk alone / Power of love, The / Naturally / Simple as that / Doin' it (all for my baby).
LP: **CDL 1534**
MC: **ZCDL 1534**

HARD AT PLAY (Lewis, Huey & The News).
Tracks: / Build me up / It hit me like a hammer / Attitude / He don't know / Couple days off / That's not me / We should be making love / Best of me, The / Do you love me, or what? / Don't look back / Time ain't money.
MC: **ZCHR 1847**
LP: **CHR 1847**

HUEY LEWIS & THE NEWS (Lewis, Huey & The News).
Tracks: / Some of my lies are true / Sooner or later / Don't make me do it / Stop trying / Now here's you / I want you / Don' / Hearts / Trouble in paradise / Who cares / If you really love me.
LP: **CHR 1292**
MC: **ZCHR 1292**

PICTURE THIS (Lewis, Huey & The News).
Tracks: / Change of heart / Tattoo (giving it all up for love) / Hope you love me like you say you do / Workin' for a livin' / Do you believe in love / It is me / Whatever happened to me / Only one, The / Buzz buzz buzz.
LP: **CHR 1340**
MC: **ZCHR 1340**

SMALL WORLD (Lewis, Huey & The News).
Tracks: / Small world / Old Antone's / Perfect world / Bobo tempo / Small world (part two) / Walking with the kid / World to me / Better be true / Give me the keys (and I'll drive you crazy) / Slammin'.
LP: **CDL 1622**
MC: **ZCDL 1622**

SPORTS (Lewis, Huey & The News).
Tracks: / Heart of rock 'n' roll / Heart and soul / Bad is bad / I want a new drug / Walking on a thin line / Finally found a home / If this is it / You crack me up / Honky tonk blues.
LP: **CHR 1412**
MC: **ZCHR 1414**

Lewis, Hugh X

GOODWILL AMBASSADOR.
Tracks: / What can I do to make you love me / Once before I die / Have your next affair with me / Ballad of baby brother / Things that lovers do / My favourite sin / One night only / I'm thinkin of you thinking of him / God is making house calls / When love is the victim / Beginning tomorrow / Love don't hide from me / Meanest mother in the world / If it wasn't for the kids.
LP: **PRCV 106**

Lewis, Jeannie

SO U WANT BLOOD (Songs from Brel to Bogie).
LP: **LRF 134**

Lewis, Jerry Lee

6 TRACK HITS.
Tracks: / Great balls of fire / Breathless / Whole lotta shakin' goin' on / High school confidential / Good golly Miss Molly / What'd I say.
MC: **7SC 5014**

20 GREATEST HITS: JERRY LEE LEWIS.
LP: **MA 71184**
MC: **MAMC 971184**
LP: **28011**
MC: **48011**

AT THE STAR CLUB, HAMBURG.
Tracks: / I got a woman / High school confidential / Money / Matchbox / What'd I say? / Great balls of fire / Good golly Miss Molly / Lewis boogie / Hound dog / Long tall Sally / Whole lotta shakin' goin' on.
LP: **9279 460**

BEST OF THE COUNTRY MUSIC HALL FAME HITS.
Tracks: / I wonder where you are tonight / I'm so lonesome I could cry / Jambalaya / Four walls / Heartaches by the number / Born to lose / Oh lonesome me / You've still got a place in my heart / I love you because / Jackson / I can't stop loving you / Fraulein / He'll have to go / Why don't you love me / It makes no difference now / Pick me up on your way

down / One has my name / I get the blues when it rains / Cold cold heart / Sweet thang.
LP: 6463 085

CLASSIC JERRY LEE LEWIS, THE.
Tracks: / Whole lotta shakin' goin' on / Great balls of fire / Ubangi stomp / Down the line / Breathless / High school confidential / Jailhouse rock / Don't be cruel / Johnny B. Goode / Little Queenie / What'd I say / Sweet little sixteen / Hang up my rock 'n' roll shoes.
LP: OCN 2021WL
MC: OCN 2021WK

COLLECTION: JERRY LEE LEWIS.
Tracks: / Be bop a lula / Dixie (instrumental) / Goodnight Irene / Great balls of fire / High school confidential / Lewis boogie / Matchbox / Money / Sixty minute man / Ubangi stomp / Whole lotta shakin' goin' on / Wine drinkin' spo-dee-o-dee / C.C. rider / Good golly Miss Molly / Good rockin' tonight / Hang up my rock 'n' roll shoes / Johnny B. Goode / Long gone lonesome blues / Mean woman blues / Pumpin' piano rock / Sweet little sixteen / What'd I say / Will the circle be unbroken / Let the good times roll.
2LP: CCSLP 143
MC: CCSMC 143

COLLECTION: JERRY LEE LEWIS (20 rock 'n' roll greats).
Tracks: / Whole lotta shakin' goin' on / Great balls of fire / It'll be me / Lovin' up a storm / High heel sneakers / Roll over, Beethoven / I got a woman / Good golly Miss Molly / I believe in you / Hound dog / Long tall Sally / Johnny B. Goode / Flip flop and fly / Maybellene / What'd I say? / Money / Lewis boogie / High school confidential / Breathless / Matchbox.
LP: DVLP 2070
MC: DVMC 2070

COLLECTION: JERRY LEE LEWIS.
2LP: PDA 007

COMPLETE LONDON SESSION VOL.1.
Tracks: / Drinkin' wine spo-dee-o-dee / Music to the man. / Baby what you want me to do? / Bad moon rising / Sea cruise / I can't get no satisfaction / Jukebox / No headstone on my grave / Big boss man / Pledging my love / Dungaree Doll / Memphis Tennessee / I can't give you anything but love Baby.
LP: BFX 15240

COMPLETE LONDON SESSION VOL.2.
Tracks: / Be bop a lula / Trouble in mind / Johnny B. Goode / High school confidential / Early morning rain / Singing the blues / Goldmine in the sky / Whole lotta shakin' goin' on / Sixty minute Man / Down the line / What'd I say / Rock and roll medley.
LP: BFX 15241

COUNTRY STORE: JERRY LEE LEWIS.
Tracks: / I'm so lonesome I could cry / Heartaches by the number / Jambalaya / Cold cold heart / Sweet thang / Oh, lonesome me / You win again / Your cheatin' heart / I love you because / Jackson / You've still got a place in my heart / Pick me up on your way down / He'll have to go / I can't stop loving you.
LP: CST 39
MC: CSTK 39

DON'T DROP IT.
LP: Z 2004

DUETS (Lewis, Jerry Lee & Friends).
Tracks: / Save the last dance for me / Sweet little sixteen / I love you / Because / C.C. rider / Am I to be the one? / Cold, cold heart / Hello Josephine / It won't happen with me / What'd I say? / Good golly Miss Molly.
LP: SUNLP 1002

EP COLLECTION, THE: JERRY LEE LEWIS.
LP: SEE 307
MC: SEEK 307

ESSENTIAL JERRY LEE LEWIS, THE (20 original Rock 'n' Roll hits).
Tracks: / Down the line / Let the good times roll / Jambalaya / High school confidential / Jailhouse rock / Lewis boogie / Hound dog / What'd I say / Lovin' up a storm / Wild one / Great balls of fire / Singing the blues / Little Queenie / Mean woman blues / Sixty minute man / Lovesick blues / Breathless / It'll be me / Whole lotta shakin' goin on / Don't be cruel.
MC: TCCRM 2001
LP: CRM 2001

ESSENTIAL ONE AND ONLY, THE.
LP: MODEM 1043
MC: MODEMC 1043

FROM LONDON TO HAMBURG.
LP: SUNSTAR 003

GOOD GOLLY MISS MOLLY.
MC: BRC 2504

GOOD ROCKIN' TONIGHT.
Tracks: / Drinkin' wine spo-dee-o-dee / I could never be ashamed of you / Pink pedal pushers / Old black Joe / Johnny B. Goode / Honey hush / Big legged woman / Good rockin' tonight / Be bop a lula / Waiting for a train / Let's talk about us / Hand me down my walking cane / Matchbox / Setting the woods on fire / Bonnie B / Deep elem blues.
LP: SUNLP 1003

GOOD ROCKIN' TONIGHT.
Tracks: / Good rockin' tonight / John Henry / Rockin' the boat of love / Big blon' baby / Big legged woman / My blue heaven / Wild one / Livin' lovin' wreck / Frankie and Johnny / Jambalaya / Cold cold heart / Sail away / C.C. rider / Hang up my rock 'n' roll shoes / All night long / I'll make it all up to you / Don't be cruel / Lovin' up a storm / Slippin' around / Crazy arms / Break up / High powered woman / Rock 'n' roll baby / Teenage letter.
MCSET: DTOL 10248

GRAFFITI COLLECTION.
MC: GRMC 15

GREAT BALLS OF FIRE.
Tracks: / Great balls of fire / Breathless / Sweet little sixteen / Big blon' baby / It'll be me / Crazy arms / Your cheatin' heart / Good golly Miss Molly / What'd I say / Whole lotta shakin' goin' on / High school confidential / Little Queenie / You win again / That lucky old sun / Frankie and Johnny / Big legged woman / Let the good times roll / Release me / Lovin' up a storm / Wild one.
LP: SHM 3296
MC: HSC 3296

GREAT BALLS OF FIRE.
Tracks: / Rock 'n' roll Ruby / Ubangi Stomp / Jambalaya / Down the line / Breathless / Lovin' up a storm / Don't be cruel / Great balls of fire / Mean woman blues / Cool cool ways.
LP: CFM 516

GREAT BALLS OF FIRE (CHARLY).
Tracks: / Whole lotta shakin' goin' on / It'll be me / Lewis boogie / Drinkin' wine spo-dee-o-dee / Rock 'n' roll Ruby / Matchbox / Ubangi stomp / Great balls of fire / You win again / Mean woman blues / Milkshake madamoiselle / Breathless / Down the line / Good rockin' tonight / Jambalaya / High school confidential / Pink pedal pushers / Don't be cruel / Johnny B. Goode / Break-up / Big blon' baby / Lovin' up a storm / Little queenie / In the mood / What'd I say / Sweet little sixteen / Good golly Miss Molly / Be bop a lula / Teenage letter / Carry me back to old Virginia.
2LP: CDX 44
MC: TCCDX 44

GREAT BALLS OF FIRE (FILM) (Film Soundtrack) (See under Films) (Various artists).

GREAT BALLS OF FIRE, THE.
Tracks: / I'm feeling sorry / You're the only star in my blue heaven / I'll keep on loving you / Cool cool ways / Milkshake Mademoiselle / Mean woman blues / Great balls of fire / Turn around / Rock 'n' roll baby / Ubangi stomp / Jambalaya / Down the line / Breathless.
LP: SUNLP 1043

GREATEST HITS: JERRY LEE LEWIS.
LP: 28012
MC: 48012

I AM WHAT I AM.
Tracks: / I am what I am / Only you (and you alone) / Get out your big roll daddy / Have I got a song for you / Careless hands / Candy kisses / I'm looking over a four leaf clover / Send me the pillow that you dream on / Honky tonk heart / That was the way it was then.
LP: MCF 3227
MC: MCFC 3227
LP: MCL 1810
MC: MCLC 1810

I AM WHAT I AM.
Tracks: / Whole lotta shakin' goin' on / Great balls of fire / Big legged woman / Breathless / High school confidential / I'm throwing rice (at the girl I love) / Crazy arms / That lucky ole sun / What'd I say / Sweet little sixteen / Johnny B. Goode / Wild one (real wild child) / Jailhouse rock / Be bop a lula.
LP: INS 5008
MC: TCINS 5008

JERRY LEE LEWIS.
LP: HMB 7002

JERRY LEE LEWIS.
LP: CR 30002

JERRY LEE LEWIS.
2LP: CR 100
MCSET: CRT 100

JERRY LEE LEWIS.
Tracks: / Great balls of fire / High school confidential / Goodnight Irene / You are my sunshine / Mean woman blues / Hound dog / Lovesick blues / Your cheatin' heart / Johnny B. Goode / Wild side of life / Save the last dance for me / My girl Josephine / Wild one / Singing the blues.
LP: 6463 042
MC: 7145 042

JERRY LEE LEWIS (2).
Tracks: / Good golly Miss Molly / Breathless / Frankie and Johnny / Let the good times roll / Move down the line / It'll be me / Sweet little sixteen / Be bop a lula / Matchbox / What'd I say / Hound dog / Jailhouse rock / Crazy arms / Mean woman blues / Little Queenie / Singin' the blues / Night train to Memphis / Money / Great balls of fire / Swiss boogie / Whole lotta shakin' goin' on / High school confidential / Pumpin' piano rock / Johnny B Goode.
MCSET: DTOL 10005
MCSET: DTO 10005

JERRY LEE LEWIS (ELEKTRA).
Tracks: / Don't let go / Rita May / Every day I have to cry / I like it like that / Number one lovin' man / Rockin' my life away / Who will the next fool be (you've got) / Personality / I wish I was eighteen / Again / Rocking little angel.
LP: K 52132

JERRY LEE LEWIS VOL.2.
LP: HA 2440

JERRY LEE'S GREATEST.
LP: CRM 2008

KEEP YOUR HANDS OFF OF IT.
LP: Z 2003

KICKIN' UP A STORM.
Tracks: / Who will buy the wine / Frankie and Johnny (Trad. arr. Jerry Lee Lewis.) / Home / Little Queenie / Friday night / Big blon' baby / Lovin' up a storm / Hillbilly fever / I could never be ashamed of you / It all depends (who will buy the wine) / I'll sail my ship alone / Bonnie B. / As long as I live / Night train to Memphis / Mexicali Rose / In the mood.
LP: SUN 1045

KILLER 1963-1968, THE.
Tracks: / Whole lotta shakin' goin' on / Crazy arms / Great balls of fire / High school confidential / I'll make it all up to you / Break up / Down the line / Hit the road Jack / End of the road / Your cheatin' heart / Wedding bells / Just because / Breathless / He took it like a man / Drinkin' wine spo-dee-o-dee / Johnny B. Goode / Hallelujah I love her so / You went back on your word / Pen & paper / Hole he said he'd dig for me. The / You win again / Fools like me / Hit the road Jack / I'm on fire / I'm on fire** / She was my baby / Bread and butter man / I bet you're gonna like it / Got you on my mind / Mathilda / Corina Corina / Sexy ways / Wild side of life / Mean woman blues (live) (Live at The Star Club,Hamburg,Germany.) / High school confidential (live) (Live at The Star Club,Hamburg,Germany.) / Money (live) (Live at The Star Club,Hamburg,Germany.) / Matchbox (live) (Live at The Star Club,Hamburg,Germany.) / What'd I say (parts 1 & 2) (live) (Live at The Star Club,Hamburg,Germany.) / Down the line (live) (Live at The Star Club,Hamburg,Germany.) / Great balls of fire (live) (Live at The Star Club,Hamburg,Germany.) / Good golly Miss Molly (live) (Live at The Star Club,Hamburg,Germany.) / Lewis' boogie (Live at The Star Club,Hamburg,Germany.) / Your cheatin' heart (live) (Live at The Star Club,Hamburg,Germany.) / Hound dog (live) (Live at The Star Club,Hamburg,Germany.) / Long tall Sally (live) (Live at The Star Club,Hamburg,Germany.) / Whole lotta shakin' goin' on (Live at The Star Club,Hamburg,Germany.) / Jenny Jenny (live) (Live in Birmingham, Alabama.) / Who will the next fool be (live) (Live in Birmingham, Alabama.) / Memphis, Tennessee (live) (Live in Birmingham, Alabama.) / Hound dog (live) (Live in Birmingham, Alabama.) / Mean woman blues (2) (live) (Live in Birmingham, Alabama.) / High heel sneakers (live) (Live in Birmingham, Alabama.) / No particular place to go (live) (Live in Birmingham, Alabama.) / Together again (live) (Live in Birmingham, Alabama.) / Long tall Sally (2) (live) (Live in Birmingham, Alabama.) / Whole lotta shakin' goin' on (2) (live) (Live in Birmingham, Alabama.) / Flip flop and fly / Don't let go / Maybellene / Roll over Beethoven / Just in time** / I believe in you / Herman, the hermit / Baby hold me close / Skid Row / This must be the place / Rockin' pneumonia and the boogie woogie flu / Seasons of my heart / Big boss man / Too young / Danny boy** / City lights / Funny how time slips away / North to Alaska / Walk right in / Wolverton Mountain / King of the road / Detroit City / Ring of fire / Baby (you've got what it takes) / Green green grass of home / Sticks and stones / What a heck of a mess / Lincoln limousine / Rockin' Jerry Lee** / Memphis beat / Urge, The / Whenever you're ready / She thinks I still care / Memphis beat (take 1) / Memphis beat (take 2)** / Twenty four hours a day** / Swinging doors** / Little Queenie (live) (Live in Fort Worth,Texas.) / How's my ex treating you (live) (Live in Fort Worth, Texas.) / Johnny B. Goode (live) (Live in Fort Worth, Texas.) / Green green grass of home (live) / What'd I say (part 2) (live) (Live in Fort Worth,Texas.) / You win again (live) (Live in Fort Worth, Texas.) / I'll sail my ship alone (live) (Live in Fort Worth, Texas.) / Crying time (live) (Live in Fort Worth, Texas.) / Roll over Beethoven (live) (Live in Fort Worth, Texas.) / Swinging doors (string mix) / If I had it all to do over / Just dropped in / It's a hang up baby / Holdin' on / Hey baby / Dream baby / Treat her right / Turn on your lovelight / Shotgun man / All the good is gone / Another place, another time / Walking the floor over you / I'm a lonesome fugitive / Break my mind / Play me a song I can cry to / Before the next teardrop falls / All night long / We live in two different worlds now / What's made Milwaukee famous / On the back row / Slippin' around / She still comes around / Today I started loving you again / Louisiana / There stands the glass / I can't have a merry Christmas, Mary (without you) / Out of my mind / I can't get over you / Listen, They're playing my song / Echoes / Release me / Let's talk about us.
LPS: BFX 15210/10

KILLER 1963-1968, VOL. 1.
LP: 836 935 1
MC: 836 935 4

KILLER 1969-1972, THE.
Tracks: / Don't let me cross over / Born to lose / You belong to me (1) / You belong to me (2) / Oh lonesome me / Sweet dreams / Cold cold heart / Fraulein / Why don't you love me / Four walls / It makes no difference now / I love you because / I'm so lonesome I could cry / Jambalaya / More and more / One has my name (the other has my heart) / Burning memories / Mom and Dad's waltz / Pick me up on your way down / Heartaches by the number / I can't stop loving you / My blue Heaven / I wonder where you are tonight / Jackson / Sweet thang / He'll have to go / You've still got a place in my heart / I get the blues when it rains / Gotta travel on / Milwaukee here I come / Crying time / Roll over Beethoven / Secret places / Don't take it out on me / Earth up above / Waiting for a train / Love of all seasons / She even woke me up to say goodbye / When the grass grows over me / Wine me up / Since I met you baby / Working man blues / In loving memories / You went out of your way (to walk on me) / My only claim to fame / Brown eyed handsome man / Gather around children / I'd be talkin' all the time / Alvin / I forgot more than you'll ever know / Bottles and barstools / Life's little ups and downs / There must be more to love than this / Sweet Georgia Brown / Home away from home / Woman woman / Reuben James / Before the snow falls / Cheater pretend / He looked beyond my fault / Old rugged cross, The / Lily of the valley / If we never meet again / I'll meet you in the morning / I'm longing for home / Black mama / She even woke me up to say goodbye (live) / Jambalaya / She still comes around / Drinkin' champagne (live) / San Antonio rose (live) / Once more with feeling (live) / When you wore a tulip (and I wore a big red rose) / Take these chains from my heart / Ballad of forty dollars / Flip flop and fly / Sweet little sixteen / Jenny Jenny / Long tall Sally (live) / Tutti frutti (Live) / C.C. rider (live) / High school confidential (live) / Down the line (live) / Whole lotta shakin' goin' on (live) / Oh lonesome me (live) / Your cheatin' heart (live) / Smoke gets in your eyes (live) / Invitation to the blues (live) / Blue suede shoes (live) / When the grass grows over me (live) / Jackson (live) / Stagger Lee / Today I started loving you again / One has my name the other has my heart (live) / Shoeshine man (live) / Great balls of fire (live) / Mean woman blues (live) / You are my sunshine (live) / Homecoming (live) / Got you on my mind again (live) / What'd I say (live) / Mexicali Rose (live) Gene Autry style / Mexicali Rose (live) Jerry Lee Lewis style / I know my Jesus will be there / My God's not dead / Foolaid / One more time / Too much to gain / Jealous heart / Last letter, The / Meeting in the air / Where he leads me / Living on

the hallelujah side / Picture from life's other side, A / Hurtin part touching home, The / Coming back for more / When my baby get's the blues / Help me make it through the night / Mother / Queen of my heart / Time changes everything / Hearts were made for beating / Looking for a city / Someone who cares for you / I'm gonna meet you in the morning / Sawdust trail peace in the valley, The / Precious memories / It will be worth it all when we see Jesus / I know that Jesus will be there / I'm in the Gloryland way / Tomorrow may mean goodbye / Amazing grace / On the Jericho road / I'll fly away / My God is real / What will the answer be / I won't have to cross Jordan alone / Keep on the firing line / When he walks on you (like you walked on me) / You helped me up (when the world let me down) / Foolish kind of man / Another handshakin' goodbye / Please don't talk about me when I'm gone / Goodbye of the year, The / Someday you'll want me to want you / No honky tonks in heaven / Big blon' baby / Lonesome fiddle man / Things that matter most to me, The / I don't know why I just do / Thirteen at the table / For the good times / Would you take another chance on me / Me and Bobby McGee / And for the first time / Think about it darlin' / No traffic out of Abilene / Chantilly lace / Lonely weekends / C.C. rider / Walk a mile in my shoes / Games people play / Don't be cruel / You can have her / I'm walking / You don't miss your water / Me and Jesus / Too many rivers / Wall around Heaven / We both know which one of us was wrong / Parting is such sweet sorrow (instrumental) / Who's gonna play that old piano / Bottom dollar / Parting is such sweet sorrow (vocal) / No more hanging around / Mercy of your letter, The / She's reaching for my mind.
LPS: . . . . **BFX 15228/11**

KILLER 1969-1972, VOL. 2.
LP: **836 938 1**
MC: **836 938 4**

KILLER 1973-1977, THE (12 unit box set).
Tracks: / Alcohol of fame, The / Tomorrow's taking my baby away / Mama's hands / What my woman can't do / Tell tale signs / Morning after baby let me down, The / I think I need to pray / I hate goodbyes / Where would I be / My cricket and me / Falling to the bottom / Gods were angry with me, The / Sometimes a memory isn't enough / Bluer words / He can't fill my shoes / I'm left you're right she's gone / Keep me from blowing away / Honky tonk wine / Room full of roses / Picture from lifes other side, A / I've forgot more about you than he'll ever know / Until the day forever ends / Boogie woogie country man / I can still hear the music / Speak a little louder to us Jesus / Honey hush / Jesus is on the main line / Remember me / Shake, rattle and roll / Love inflation / I don't want to be lonely tonight / Forever forgiving / Little peace and harmony, A / No one knows me / When I take my vacation in heaven / I'm still jealous of you / You ought to see my mind / Don't boogie woogie (when you say your prayers tonight) / Thanks for nothing / Red hot memories / I was sorta wonderin' / Jerry's place / That kind of fool / Your cheatin' heart / Crawdad song / House of blue lights / Goodnight Irene / Damn good country song, A / Lord what's left for me to do / Great balls of fire / One rose (that's left in my heart) / I'm knee deep in loving you / I can help / Slippin' and slidin' / From a Jack to a King (1 & 2) / After the fool you've made of me / Closest thing to you, The / I can't keep my hands off you / One rose (that's left in my heart) / Wedding bells / Fifties, The / Only love can get you in my door / Old country church / Harbour lights / Jerry Lee's rock'n'roll revival show / I sure miss those good old times / Let's put it all back together again / Country memories / As long as we live / Jealous heart / (You'd think by now) I'd be over you / Come on in / Who's sorry now / Let's say goodbye like we said hello / Georgia on my mind / What's so good about goodbye / Tennessee Saturday night / Ivory tears / Middle age crazy / Last letter, the / Last cheater's waltz, The / Let's live a little / I hate you / Before the night is over / Sittin' and thinkin' / Blue suede shoes / Lucille / Corina Corina / Don't let the stars get in your eyes / Life's railway to heaven / Sweet little sixteen / Ivory tears / You call everybody darling / Wild and woolly ways / I'll find it where I can / Lord I've tried everything but you / You're all too ugly tonight / Arkansas seesaw / Pee Wee's place / Drinkin' wine spo-dee-o-dee / Music man / Baby what you want me to do / Bad moon rising / Sea cruise / (I can't get no) satisfaction / Jukebox / No headstone on my grave / Big boss man / Pledging my love / Dungaree doll / Memphis Tenessee / I can't give you anything but love baby / Be bop a lula / Trouble in mind / Johnny B. Goode / High school confidential / Early morning rain / Singing the blues / Goldmine in the sky / Whole lotta shakin' goin' on / Sixty minute man / Down the line / What'd I say / Rock and roll medley / Raining in my heart / Margie / Silver threads among the gold / Cry / All over hell and half of Georgia / I sure miss those good old times / Take your time / Hold on I'm coming (fast version) / Haunted house (extended version) / Meat man / When a man loves a woman / Hold on I'm coming (slow version) / Just a little bit / Born to be a loser / Haunted house / Blueberry Hill / Revolutionary man / Big blue diamonds / That old bourbon street church / Jack Daniels (old number seven) / Why me Lord / Ride me down easy / Cold cold morning light.
LPS: . . . . **BFX 15229/12**

KILLER 1973-1977, VOL. 3.
LP: **836 941 1**
MC: **836 941 4**

KILLER COUNTRY.
Tracks: / Folsom Prison blues / I'll do it all again / Jukebox junky / Too weak to fight / Late night lovin' man / Change places with me / Let me on / Thirty nine and holding / Mama, this one's for you / Over the rainbow.
LP: . . . . **ED 250**
LP: . . . . **K 52246**

KILLER ROCKS ON, THE.
Tracks: / Don't be cruel / You can have her / Games people play / You don't miss the water / Me and Bobby McGee / Shotgun man / Chantilly lace / Walk a mile in my shoes / C.C. rider / Lonely weekends / Turn on your love light / I'm walking.
LP: **2872 119**
MC: **3472 119**

KILLER STRIKES, THE.
Tracks: / Whole lotta shakin' goin' on / You win again / Break up / I'll make it all up to you / What'd I say / Sweet little sixteen / Breathless / High school confidential / It'll be me / Milkshake mademoiselle / Lovin' up a storm / I'll sail my ship alone.
LP: . . . . **TOP 105**
MC: . . . . **KTOP 105**

KILLERS BIRTHDAY CAKE.
Tracks: / My blue heaven / Let's talk about us / Break up / You can't help it / Your cheatin' heart / Hound dog / Birthday cake (hands off it) / You win again / Goodnight Irene / Great speckled bird, The / Don't drop it / Old black Joe / You can't help it / Bonnie B / Ballad of Billy Joe.
LP: . . . . **SUNLP 1051**

KILLERS RHYTHM AND BLUES.
Tracks: / John Henry / Hang up my rock 'n' roll shoes / When my blue moon turns to gold again / Billy boy / My girl Josephine / High powered woman / Hello hello baby / Matchbox / See see rider / Good rockin' tonight / Sweet little sixteen / Feeling good / Big legged woman.
LP: . . . . **SUNLP 1053**

LIVE AT THE STAR CLUB, HAMBURG.
Tracks: / Mean woman blues / High school confidential / Money / Matchbox / What'd I say / Great balls of fire / Good golly Miss Molly / Lewis boogie / Your cheatin' heart / Hound dog / Long tall Sally / Whole lotta shakin' goin' on / Down the line.
LP: . . . . **TIME 06**
MC: . . . . **TIMEC 06**

LIVE IN BERLIN, 1977 (The Killer's 20th Anniversary Show).
LP: **20JLL 1977**

LIVE IN GEORGIA, VOL 1.
LP: . . . . **SUNSTAR 004**

LIVE IN GEORGIA, VOL 2.
LP: . . . . **SUNSTAR 005**

LIVE IN ITALY.
Tracks: / Roll in my sweet baby's arms / High school confidential / Me and Bobby McGee / Jackson / There must be more to love than this / Great balls of fire / What'd I say / Jerry Lee's rock'n'roll revival show / I am what I am / Whole lotta shakin' goin' on / You win again / Mona Lisa / One of those things we all go through / Hang up my rock 'n' roll shoes.
LP: . . . . **MFLP 071**

LIVE VIDEO: JERRY LEE LEWIS (See under Perkins, Carl).

MILESTONES.
LP: . . . . **RNDA 1449**

MOTIVE SERIES.
Tracks: / Movin' on down the line / Lonely weekends / You don't miss your water / Chantilly lace / Whole lotta shakin' goin' on / What'd I say / High school confidential / Baby what you want me to do / Bad moon rising / Sea cruise / Pledging my love / Don't be cruel.
LP: **6463 097**
MC: **7145 097**

MY FINGERS DO THE TALKING.
LP: . . . . **MCF 3162**

NUGGETS VOL 1.
Tracks: / Sweet little sixteen / Hello Josephine / I've been twistin' / It won't happen with me / Ramblin' Rose / When I get paid / Love made a fool of me / I get the blues when it rains / In the mood / Ubangi stomp / It'll be me / Put me down / I'm feelin' sorry / Ballad of Billy Joe / Baby baby bye bye.
LP: . . . . **CR 30121**

NUGGETS VOL 2.
Tracks: / Crazy arms / Hillbilly music / Turn around / Night train to Memphis / My blue Heaven / It hurt me so / I can't help it / When the saints go marching in / Whole lot o' twistin' goin' on / I'll sail my ship alone / Friday nights / Just who is to blame / I just can't trust me in your arms any more / Hello hello baby / High powered woman / Crawdad hole.
LP: . . . . **CR 30129**

ORIGINAL JERRY LEE LEWIS, THE.
Tracks: / Crazy arms / End of the road / It'll be me / Whole lotta shakin' goin' on / You win again / Great balls of fire / Down the line / Breathless / High school confidential / Fools like me / Breakup / I'll make it all up to you / Lovin' up a storm / Big blon' baby / Livin' lovin' wreck / What'd I say.
MC: . . . . **TCCR 30111**
LP: . . . . **CR 30111**

OUTTAKES.
LP: . . . . **SUNSTAR 002**

PUMPIN' PIANO CAT, THE.
Tracks: / Born to lose / My Carolina sunshine girl / Long gone lonesome blues / Crazy arms / Silver threads among the gold / You're the only star in my blue heaven / End of the road / My old pal of yesterday / Little green valley / It'll be me / All night long / Pumpin piano rock / Sixty minute man / Lewis boogie / You are my sunshine / Ole pal of yesterday / Little green valley / Hand me down my walking cane / When the saints go marching in / I'm feeling sorry / If the world keeps on turning / Shame on you / I don't love nobody.
LP: . . . . **SUN 1041**
LP: . . . . **CFM 514**

RARE JERRY LEE LEWIS, VOL 1.
LP: . . . . **CR 30006**

RARE JERRY LEE LEWIS, VOL 2.
LP: . . . . **CR 30007**

ROCKET.
Tracks: / Meat man / Jailhouse rock / House of blue lights / Rock'n'roll funeral / Don't touch me / Changing mountains / Beautiful dreamer / I'm alone because I love you / Lucille / Seventeen / Mathilda / Wake up little Susie.
LP: . . . . **INS 5023**
MC: . . . . **TCINS 5023**

ROCKIN'.
LP: . . . . **MULE 201**

ROCKIN' MY LIFE AWAY.
LP: **269661-1**
MC: **269661-4**

ROCKIN' WITH JERRY LEE LEWIS.
LP: . . . . **KILLER 7005**

SUN YEARS, THE (LP SET).
Tracks: / Born to lose / Goodnight irene / I love you because / Pumpin' piano rock / Long gone lonesome blues / Ubangi stomp / Ooby dooby / Milkshake mademoiselle / Breathless / Good rockin' tonight / Frankie and johnny / I'll see you in my dreams / Come what may / Settin' the woods on fire / It hurts me so.
LPS: . . . . **SUN BOX 102**

SURVIVORS, THE (see Cash, Johnny) (Lewis, Jerry Lee/Johnny Cash/Carl Perkins).

TRIO PLUS.
Tracks: / Be bop a lula / On my knees / Dixie fried / Gentle as a lamb / Money / Breakup / Matchbox / Good rockin' tonight / Gone gone gone / Sittin' and thinkin'.
LP: . . . . **SUN 1004**

VERY BEST OF JERRY LEE LEWIS.
LP: **HO-3**

WHEN TWO WORLDS COLLIDE.
Tracks: / Rockin' Jerry Lee / Who will buy the wine / Love game / Alabama jubilee / Goodtime charlie's got the blues / When two worlds collide / Good news travels fast / I only want a buddy not a sweetheart / Honky tonk stuff / Toot toot tootsie.
LP: . . . . **K 52213**

WHOLE LOTTA SHAKIN' GOIN' ON (CHARLY).
Tracks: / Lewis Boogie / Singing the blues / Honey hush / Whole lotta shakin' goin' on / Pink pedal pushers / Drinkin' wine spo-dee-o-dee / It'll be me / All night long / Pumping piano rock / Sixty minute man.
LP: . . . . **CFM 515**

WHOLE LOTTA SHAKIN' GOIN' ON (SUN).
Tracks: / You are my sunshine / Shame on you / I don't know anybody / Whole lotta shakin' goin' on / Drinkin' wine spo-dee-o-dee / When the saints go marching in / It'll be me / Deep elem blues no.2 / Singing the blues / Honey hush / Lewis boogie / You win again / Hand me down my walking cane / Old time religion / Crawdad song.
LP: . . . . **SUN 1042**

WILD ONE AT HIGH SCHOOL HOP THE.
Tracks: / Friday night / Big blon' baby / Put me down / Let the good times roll / High school confidential / Break up / Ooby dooby / Hound dog / Jailhouse rock / Wild one.
LP: . . . . **CFM 517**

WILD ONE, THE.
Tracks: / Don't be cruel / Good rockin' tonight / Pink pedal pushers / Ooby dooby / Hound dog / Jailhouse rock / Real wild child / I forgot to remember to forget / Break up / Put me down / Milkshake Mademoiselle / Carrying on (sexy ways) / Let the good times roll / High school confidential.
LP: . . . . **SUN 1044**

Lewis, John

BOP SESSION, THE (See under Gillespie, Dizzy) (Lewis, John/Dizzy Gillespie/Sonny Stitt/Max Roach).

BRIDGE GAME.
Tracks: / One at heart / Game demand, The / Two clubs / Little slam in diamonds, A / One spade (tears from children) / One diamond / Takeout double, The / Invitation to a slam, The / Preempt, The.
LP: **826 698-1**
MC: **826 698-4**

J S BACH PRELUDES AND FUGUES.
LP: **824 381 1**
MC: **824 381 4**

Lewis, Johnny

ALABAMA SLIDE GUITAR.
LP: . . . . **ARHOOLIE 1055**

Lewis, Laurie

LOVE CHOOSES YOU.
Tracks: / Old friend / Hills of home / Point of no return / I don't know why / I'd be lost without you / When the nightbird sings / Women of Ireland / Ryestraw / Light, The / Texas bluebonnets / Love chooses you.
LP: . . . . **FF 487**

RESTLESS RAMBLING HEART.
Tracks: / Bowling green / Cowgirl's song, The / Restless rambling heart / Cry cry darlin' / Stealin' / Chickens / Magpie's lament, The / Here we go again / Green fields / Hold to a dream / I'm gonna be the wind.
LP: . . . . **FF 406**

Lewis, Lew

SAVE THE WAIL (Lewis, Lew Reformer).
LP: . . . . **SEEZ 16**

Lewis, Linda

HACIENDA VIEW.
Tracks: / Data love / Rolling for a while / Best days of my life / 109 Jamaica highway / My aphrodisiac you / Beggars and kings / I'd be surprisingly good for you / It seemed like a good idea at the time / Save the last dance for me / Sleeping like a baby now.
LP: . . . . **ARL 5033**

NOT A LITTLE GIRL ANYMORE.
LP: . . . . **ARTY 109**

TEAR AND A SMILE, A.
Tracks: / This boy / Desination love / Close the door, take your heart / Don't let it go / I am what I am / Take me for a little while / You don't know what you're missing / Why can't I be the other woman / Sweet heartache / I can't get enough.
LP: . . . . **EPC 25478**
MC: **40 25478**

WOMAN OVERBOARD.
LP: . . . . **SPARTY 1003**

Lewis, Lou

DON'T HIDE AWAY.
Tracks: / Don't let them fool you / Father of the fatherless / Sweet Lamb / Tapestry / Wedding song, The / Come to

me / Kingdom song, The / Travelling along / High Priest / Don't hide away.
MC: ZMC 01

HEALING STREAM.
Tracks: / Healing stream / Feet on the rock / I feel lovely / Valleys / Eagle's song / I know where you're coming from / Broken heart / Knowing that I need you / Breaking up / Suddenly (joy springs up).
MC: WINC 123

WALLS.
Tracks: / Walls / I'm no hero / Don't try to hide / Expert, The / Mary's song / Winds of change / If just once in a while / Jacob's song / Hazel's song / Give it away.
MCSET: CC/1006D

Lewis, Marcus

SING ME A SONG.
Tracks: / Club, The / Every now and then / Sing me a song / Say / I can tell you / Searchin' for a good time / I've got to get away / He's too young / With my eyes.
LP: 4634891
MC: 4634894

Lewis, Meade Lux

BARRELHOUSE PIANO.
LP: SLP 208

CHICAGO PIANO BLUES VOL.3.
LP: OL 2827

GIANTS OF BOOGIE WOOGIE. (see Ammons,Albert/Pete Johnson/Meade Lux Lewis) (Lewis, Meade Lux/Albert Ammons and Pete Johnson).

HONKY TONK PIANO.
LP: 22026
MC: 42026

JAZZ PIANO THE (Lewis, Meade Lux/ Albert Ammons and Pete Johnson).
Tracks: / Dying mother blues / Roll me / Sweet patootie blues / Boogie woogie blues / Boogie woogie no.2.
LP: SM 3105

MEADE LUX LEWIS 1927-39.
LP: DLP 534

MEADE LUX LEWIS 1939-54.
LP: BD 2031

MEADE LUX LEWIS VOL 1 (Tell your story).
LP: OL 2805

MEADE LUX LEWIS VOL 2 (Tell your story).
LP: OL 2820

Lewis, Mel

20 YEARS AT THE VILLAGE VANGUARD (Lewis, Mel and the Jazz Orchestra).
Tracks: / All of me / Blue note / Butter / C-Jam blues / Dearly beloved / Interloper / Alone together / American express.
LP: 781 655 1
MC: 781 655 4

GOT' CHA (Lewis, Mel Septet).
LP: FS 63

JIVE FOR FIVE (See under Holman, Bill) (Lewis, Mel Quintet/Holman, Bill).

NATURALLY, PLAY THAD JONES (Lewis, Mel & The Jazz Orchestra).
Tracks: / Cherry juice / Two as one / My centennial / 61st and Rich'id / Que pasa bossa o / Easy living.
LP: 10044

ORCHESTRA, THE (See under Jones, Thad) (Lewis, Mel & Thad Jones).

Lewis, Michael

SEVEN DEADLY SINS (see under Rinder, Laurin) (Lewis, Michael/Laurin Rinder).

Lewis, Monica

BUT BEAUTIFUL.
LP: FS 190

Lewis, Muintir

WEEDS IN THE GARDEN.
LP: TA 2003

Lewis, Nigel

WHAT I FEEL NOW.
LP: MB 10

Lewis, Philip

RHYTHM MANIACS SESSIONS 1929 VOL.1 (Lewis, Philip Rhythm Maniacs).
LP: FG 410

RHYTHM MANIACS SESSIONS 1929 VOL.2.
LP: FG 412

Lewis, Ramsey

BEST OF RAMSEY LEWIS.
Tracks: / Sun goddess / Skippin' / Caring for you / Spring high / All the way live / Tequila mockingbird / Hot dawgit / Funky serenity / Love notes / Brazilica.
LP: 515022
LP: CBS 84911

CHANCE ENCOUNTER.
Tracks: / What's going on / Chance encounter / Up where we belong / Intimacy / Special place, A / Paradise / I can't wait / Just a little ditty.
LP: CBS 25057

CLASSIC ENCOUNTER.
LP: 4608181
MC: 4608184

ELECTRIC COLLECTION.
MC: 4679034

FANTASY.
Tracks: / This ain't no fantasy / Ram jam / It's gonna change / Les clefs de mon coeur / Victim of a broken heart / Slow dancin' / Never give up / Part of me / Quest.
LP: CBS 26688

HANG ON RAMSEY (Lewis, Ramsey Trio).
LP: CRL 4520

HIS GREATEST SIDES VOL.1.
Tracks: / High heel sneakers / Hang on sloopy / Dancing in the street / Hard day's night, A / Something you've got / In crowd, The / Wade in the water / Soul man / Since you've been gone / One two three / Les fleurs / Uptight.
LP: GCH 8003
MC: GCHK 78003
LP: CXMP 2051

IN CROWD, THE (Greatest Hits).
Tracks: / Hang on sloopy / 'In' crowd, The / Dancing in the street / Hi heel sneakers / Something you've got / Soul man / One two three / Since I fell for you / Wade in the water / Hard day's night, A / Upright / You been talking 'bout me baby / Since you've been gone / Les fleurs / Tennessee waltz / Felicidade / Love theme Spartacus / Come Sunday.
MC: 2636464

KEYS TO THE CITY.
Tracks: / Keys to the city / You're falling in love / 7-11 / Strangers / My love will lead you home / Melody of life / Shamballa / Love and understanding.
LP: 4508701
MC: 4508704

LEGACY.
Tracks: / Toccata / Adagio / Fugue / All the way love / I love to please you / Well, well, well / Moogin' on / Don't look back.
LP: CBS 82964

LES FLEURS.
Tracks: / Super woman / House is not a home, A / Essence of love / Les fleurs / Physical / With a gentle touch / Reasons.
LP: CBS 25524

LIVE AT THE SAVOY.
Tracks: / Close your eyes and remember / Sassy stew / Callin' fallin' / Baby what you want me to do / You never know / Lynn / It's just called love / Wade in the water / Hang on Sloopy / In crowd, The.
LP: CBS 85502

RAMSEY LEWIS.
Tracks: / Aquarius / Let the sun shine in / Wearin' it out / I just can't give you up / Every chance I get / Dancin' / I'll always dream about you / Intermezzo / Spanoletts / Don't cry for me Argentina.
LP: CBS 83584

REUNION.
Tracks: / In crowd, The / (Song of) Delilah / Hello cello / Hang on sloopy / Wind, The / Carmen / Horizon.
LP: CBS 25804
MC: 40 25804

ROUTES.
Tracks: / Whisper zone / High point / Tondelayo / Caribbean blue / Looking glass / Come back Jack / Colors in space / Crystals in sequence / You are the reason / Hell on wheels.
LP: CBS 84243

SOUND OF CHRISTMAS, THE (Lewis, Ramsey Trio).
Tracks: / Merry Christmas baby / Winter wonderland / Santa Claus is coming to town / Christmas blues / Here comes Santa Claus / Sound of Christmas, The / Christmas song, The / God rest ye merry gentlemen / Sleigh ride / What are you doing New Year's Eve.
LP: GCH 8016
MC: GCHK 8016

THREE PIECE SUITE.
Tracks: / Lakeshore cowboy / Romance me / Will you / Love is / Michelle / Don't ever go away / So much more / Can't wait till summer / She's out of my life / Expansions.
LP: CBS 84980

WADE IN THE WATER (OLD GOLD) (See under Barry, Lee/1-2-3(Old gold).

Lewis, Sabby

BOSTON BOUNCE (Lewis, Sabby Orchestra & Quartet).
LP: PHOENIX 9

SABBY LEWIS ORCHESTRA & QUARTET, 1946 (Lewis, Sabby Orchestra & Quartet).
Tracks: / Boston bounce / Edna / Bottoms up / Hangover / I can't give you anything but love / Minor mania / Embraceable you / Sweet Georgia Brown / I surrender, dear / Undecided.
LP: LP 9

Lewis, Shirley

PASSION IN THE HEART.
LP: AMA 5270
MC: AMC 5270

Lewis, Smiley

CALDONIA'S PARTY.
Tracks: / My baby was right / Gowing old / Lowdown / Where were you / Dirty people / Sad life / Bee's boogie / Bells are ringing / Gumbo blues / Ain't gonna do it / You're not the one / Big mamou / Caldonia's party / Oh baby / Playgirl / Blue Monday.
LP: KC 103

DOWN YONDER.
Tracks: / Down the road / Rocks, The / Real gone lover / Lost weekend / Bumpity bump / I hear you knocking / I hear you knocking / Queen of hearts / Come on / Rootin' and tootin' / One night / Shame shame shame / Please listen to me / Down yonder we go ballin' / Go on fool / Bad luck blues / Stormy Monday nights.
LP: KC 104

HOOK LINE AND SINKER.
Tracks: / Lillie Mae / Gypsy blues / My baby was right / That certain door / It's music / Jailbird / Nobodys knows / Oh red / Can't stop loving you / No no / Hook, line and sinker / If you ever used a woman / Standing on the corner / It's so peaceful / Slide me down / Don't jive me.
LP: KC 102

I HEAR YOU KNOCKING.
Tracks: / I hear you knocking / One night / Down the road / Shame shame shame / She's got me hook, line and seeker / Tee nah nah / Down yonder we go ballin' / Big Mamou / Caldonia's party / Bells are ringing / Someday / Jailbird / Real gone lover / Little Fernandez.
LP: SSL 6025
MC: TCSSL 6025

I SHALL NOT BE MOVED.
Tracks: / Shame, shame, shame / Turn on your volume baby / Here comes Smiley / Little Fernandez / Too many drivers / Baby please / By the water / Sweeter words / You are my sunshine / My love is gone / Li'l Liza Jane / I shall not be moved.
LP: OFF 6033

Lewis, Steinberg

I AM AT THE HOME.
LP: REJ R 5023
MC: REJ C 5023

Lewis, Ted

IS EVERYBODY HAPPY.
LP: HDL 109

JAZZ HOLIDAY, A (Lewis, Ted/his band).
Tracks: / Jazz holiday, A / Shimme-sha-wabble / My mama's in town / Say, Arabella / Glad rag doll / Bugle call rag / Bam bam bammy shore / Where'd you get those eyes? / Milenberg joys / She's funny that way / Camel walk / Hello Montreal / New St Louis blues, The / That certain party / Some of these days / Darktown strutters' ball.
LP: AJA 5006

RARE AND UNHEARD (1923-1933).
Tracks: / Tiger rag / Aunt Hagars' blues / Wet yo' thumb / Lewisada blues / Old playmate / In the land of jazz / There's a ring around my rainbow / Rhythm.
MC: NEO 953

TED LEWIS - 1920-1933.
Tracks: / When my baby smiles at me / She's everybody's sweetheart / Try a little tenderness / Glad rag doll / Wandering in dreamland / Frankie and Johnny / One sweet letter from you / Good night / Have you ever been so lonely.
MC: NEO 955

TED'S HIGHLIGHTS VOL. 1 (Lewis, Ted/his orchestra).
LP: GAPS 020

TEDS HIGHLIGHTS VOL. 3 (Lewis, Ted/his orchestra).
LP: GAPS 140

VINTAGE SHOW BIZ GREATS (Also see under Tucker, Sophie) (Lewis, Ted/ Sophie Tucker).
LP: RFS 603

Lewis, Vic

EMI YEARS, THE.
Tracks: / Vic's tune / Ricardo / Danielle / Last minute bossa nova / Bossa nova scotia / Rio / Two note samba / Bossa nova blues / Town talk / Bass is loaded / Sax blue / Basiec riddle (alternative take - take 2) / Basiec riddle (take 5 - issued take).
MC: TCEMS 1427

IN CONCERT 1954 (Lewis, Vic & His Orchestra).
LP: HEP 20

MULLIGAN'S MUSIC (Lewis, Vic & His Orchestra).
LP: MOLE 9

NEW YORK '38 (Lewis, Vic & his American Jazzmen).
LP: ESQ 313

PLAY BILL HOLMAN (Lewis, Vic West Coast All Stars).
Tracks: / Oleo / Yesterdays / Sizzler before lunch / When I fall in love / Easter parade / As we speak / Sizzler after lunch.
MC: MOLECAS 14

PLAYS STAN KENTON 1948-54.
Tracks: / Stan Kenton speaks / Minor riff / Balbao bash / Concerto to end all concertos / Collaboration / Harlem holiday / I told ya I love ya, now get out / Metronome riff / Interlude / Rhythm incorporated / Intermission riff / Sweets / You'd be so nice to come home to / Bill's blues / Fearless Fosdike.
LP: HQ 3014

VIC LEWIS CONDUCTS-TEABREAK.
LP: VL 3

VIC LEWIS JAM SESSIONS VOL. 5 1938-46.
Tracks: / I ain't got nobody / Shine on harvest moon / Stooge blues / Don't be angry / Blues part 1 (1943), The / Blues part 2 (1943), The / Squatty roo / Jazz me blues / Jazz me blues / NRC jump / Eager beaver / Sgt on a furlough / Honeysuckle rose.
LP: HQ 3012

VIC LEWIS JAM SESSIONS VOLUME 4.
Tracks: / Soft winds / What's new / Blues / I found a new baby / Washboard blues / Woo woo / Stardust / Cottontail / Body and soul / Sweet Georgia Brown.
LP: HQ 3011

VIC LEWIS JAM SESSIONS VOLUME 6 1946-49.
Tracks: / I like to riff / In love in vain / Smiles / You do / Makin' whoopee / Things we did last summer, The / Red top / Hep Boyd's / Body and soul / I wish I didn't love you / Pat's party / I never loved anyone / Bam bam / Don't smoke in bed / It might as well be swing.
LP: HQ 3013

VIC LEWIS JAM SESSIONS VOLUME 3 (1945-46).
Tracks: / World is waiting for the sunrise, The / Blues / I've found a new baby / I got rhythm.
LP: HQ 3010

VIC LEWIS JAM SESSIONS VOLUME 1 (The war years).
Tracks: / Yellow dog blues / Blues in E. / Johnny's idea / Wigmore jump / Wigmore blues / My blue Heaven / Someday, sweetheart / Ain't misbehavin' / Ja da / Tea for two.
LP: HQ 3008

VIC LEWIS JAM SESSIONS VOLUME 2, THE 1945.
Tracks: / Tricolour blues / It's the talk of the town / Sam's blues (fast and slow versions) / Lady be good / Johnny's blues / Rose room / Ghost of a chance / Mean to me / Sweet Lorraine / Jazz me blues / Etude in ashes / I ain't gonna give nobody none of my jelly roll / Singing the blues / Riverboat shuffle / Peg O'my heart / Copenhagen / Round about eight / Etude in red / Fidgety feet.
LP: HQ 3009

VIC LEWIS & R.P.O..
Tracks: / Don't cry for me Argentina / Theme from Mash / Serenade for strings / Coco / Always Madamoiselle / Hannie Caulder / 49th parallel / So much you loved me / Louise / Escape me never / Little Prince / My ship.
LP: PL 25403

Lewis, Webster

8 FOR THE 80'S.
Tracks: / You deserve to dance / Give me some emotion / Love you give to me / I want to blow / Fire / Go for it / Heavenly / Mild wind.
LP: EPC 84283

LET ME BE THE ONE.
MC: FEC 36878

Lewis, Willie

IN PARIS 1925-1937.
2LP: . . . . SW 8400/01

Ley, Bell & Tess

NADINA.
LP: . . . . GEN 121

Ley, Eggy

COME AND GET IT (Ley, Eggy & Fiona Duncan).
LP: . . . . VELP 001

EGGY LEY'S HOTSHOTS.
LP: . . . . WAM/N No.1
MC: . . . . WAM/R NO.20

Ley, Franco

L'EVEMENT (Ley, Franco & Tabu).
LP: . . . . GEN 103
MC: . . . . C 2002

Leyland Vehicles Brass

CHRISTMAS FANFARE, A.
Tracks: / Fanfare and carol 'O come all ye faithful' / Christmas song, The / Lullaby / Fantasy on 'Good king Wenceslas' / Jingle bells / Christmas piece / Ding dong, merrily on high / Christmas fanfare, A / Coventry carol / White Christmas / Shepherds' farewell, The / Nativity for brass / Infant king, The / Three kings, The / Little drummer boy.
LP: . . . . PRL 023D
MC: . . . . CPRL 023D

CONTRASTS IN BRASS.
Tracks: / March leviathan / Winter dreams / King Cotton / Warabe UTS / Londonderry air / H.M.S. Pinafore (overture) / Nimrod from Enigma variations / Fairies of the waters / Water margin, The / Spectrum / Royal tiger / Dover coach / Slow train / Perpetuum mobile / Coronation Scot / Titan march / Daisy bell / Sailing / Concorde march / Those magnificent men in their flying machines / Tam O'Shanter's ride.
LP: . . . . BBR 1008 (S)
MC: . . . . BBT 1008 (S)

TRAVELLING WITH LEYLAND.
Tracks: / Royal tiger / Dover coach, The / Slow train, The / J Strauss, arr Winter / Perpetuum mobile / Coronation Scot / Titan march / Daisy Bell / Sailing / Concorde march / Those magnificent men in their flying ... / Tam O'Shanter's ride / Symphonic sketch.
LP: . . . . PL 25175
MC: . . . . PK 25175

Leyton, John

BEST OF JOHN LEYTON.
Tracks: / Johnny remember me / Wild wind / Six white horses / Son this is she / Lone rider / Lonely city / I think I'm falling in love / Lonely Johnny / Oh lover / I don't care if the sun don't shine / I love you for sentimental reasons / That's how to make love / I'll cut your tail off / Land of love / Cupboard love / How will it end / It would be easy / Beautiful dreamer / Another man / Make love to me / You took my love for granted (Available on CD only) / I guess you are always on my mind (Available on CD only) / Funny man (Available on CD only) / Man is not supposed to cry, A (Available on CD only) / Girl on the floor above, The (Available on CD only) / Tell Laura I love her (Available on CD only) / On Lovers Hill (Available on CD only) / Too many late nights (Available on CD only) / Lovers lane (Available on CD only) / I'm gonna let my hair down (Available on CD only) / Don't let her go away (Available on CD only) / All I want is you (Available on CD only) / I want a love I can see (Available on CD only).
LP: . . . . SEE 201
MC: . . . . SEEK 201
LP: . . . . NUTM 24

JOHNNY LEYTON.
LP: 59.6400

RARITIES.
Tracks: / You took my love for granted / Guess you are always on my mind / That's a woman / Fabulous / Funny man / Man is not supposed to cry, A / Voodoo woman / Down on the River Nile / Girl on the floor above, The / Goodbye to teenage love / Tell Laura I love her / Walk with me my angel / Terry Brown's in love with Mary Dee / On lovers' hill / To many late nights / Lovers Lane / I want a love I can see / I'm gonna let my hair down / Don't let her go away / All I want is you.
LP: . . . . CM 127

LFO

FREQUENCIES.
LP: . . . . WARPLP 3
MC: . . . . WARPMC 3

LGT

TOO LONG.
Tracks: / I want to be there / Portoriko / Slippin' away / In other words / Too long / Surrender to the heat / Bloodshot eyes / Soul on fire / Last song, The.
LP: . . . . EMC 3430
MC: . . . . TCEMC 3430

Li He

CHINESE CLASSICAL FOLK MUSIC FEATURING THE CHINE.
LP: . . . . EULP 1155
MC: . . . . EUMC 1155

Liaisons Dangereuses

LIAISONS DANGEREUSES.
LP: . . . . RR 9982

Liar

SET THE WORLD ON FIRE.
Tracks: / Set the world on fire / Town of evil people / I'm calling / Midnight promises / Five knuckle shuffle / High life / Frustration / Who cares.
LP: . . . . K 55524

Liber, Homo

UNTITLED.
LP: . . . . LR 129

Liberace

AT THE PALLADIUM.
Tracks: / Rhapsody in blue (Medley.) / Mack the knife / Tico tico / Me and my shadow / Last time I saw Paris, The (medley) (Medley includes: The last time I saw Paris/The River Seine/Autumn leaves) / Jalousie (medley) (Medley includes: Jalousie/Boogie Woogie/You Made Me Love You (I didn't w) / I'll be seeing you / I got rhythm.
LP: . . . . MCL 1849
MC: . . . . MCLC 1849

BEST OF LIBERACE.
Tracks: / Moon river / Mack the knife / Over the rainbow / Summer place, A (theme from) / Schubert's serenade / Intermezzo / Greensleeves / Misty / As time goes by / Charade / September song / Love letters / Gigi / Love is a many splendoured thing / More / Third man, Theme from / Never on Sunday / Little things mean a lot / I'll be seeing you / Me and my shadow.
LP: . . . . MCL 1737
MC: . . . . MCLC 1737

BEST OF THE CLASSICS.
Tracks: / Warsaw concerto / Piano concerto No. 1 / Nocturne F sharp major / Concerto / Moonlight sonata / Nocturne in E flat / Sunrise concerto / 14th Hungarian rhapsody / Clair de lune / Ave Maria.
LP: . . . . AVLP 502
MC: . . . . ZCAV 502

CHRISTMAS WITH LIBERACE.
MC: . . . . FUNC 9050

COLLECTION: LIBERACE.
Tracks: / Gershwin medley / Strauss waltzes / Somewhere my love / Yesterday / Long and winding road, The / Taste of honey, A / We've only just begun / You don't send me flowers / Send in the clowns / Begin the beguine / Hello Dolly / New York, New York / As time goes by / Exodus / Entertainer, The / Raindrops keep falling on my head / Georgy girl / Godfather, The / Star is born love theme / Way we were, The / Born free / Love story theme / Ben.
2LP: . . . . CCSLP 201
MC: . . . . CCSMC 201

GRAFFITI COLLECTION.
MC: . . . . GRMC 20

GREATEST HITS: LIBERACE.
Tracks: / Born free / Strangers in the night / Somewhere my love / Yesterday / San Francisco.
LP: . . . . FUN 9049
MC: . . . . FUNC 9049

IMAGES: LIBERACE.
Tracks: / It's impossible / New York, New York, Theme from / Long and winding road / Spanish eyes / I'll be seeing you / Way we were, The / You don't bring me flowers / By the time I get to Phoenix / Chopin nocturne in E flat / Love is a many splendoured thing / Clair de Lune / Warsaw concerto.
MC: . . . . KNMC 16008

JUST FOR YOU.
LP: . . . . GH 849
MC: . . . . ZCGH 849

LIBERACE.
Tracks: / Sophisticated lady / Somebody loves me / It had to be you / El bimbo / Who / Five foot two / Charleston / Sleepy time gal / Taste of honey / Twelfth Street rag / Waltzing Matilda / When Irish eyes are smiling / Strangest dream.
LP: . . . . AVI 6065

TWAS THE NIGHT BEFORE CHRISTMAS.
LP: . . . . HDY 1938
MC: . . . . ZCHDY 1938

WONDERFUL LIBERACE.
Tracks: / Chopin fantasia / Grieg's piano concerto / Stella by starlight / Warsaw / Dream of Olwen / Spellbound concerto / Laura / Excerpt from Piano concerto no.1.
LP: . . . . SPR 8540
MC: . . . . SPC 8540

Liberation Suite

STRIDE FOR STRIDE.
Tracks: / Lay your sadness down / Stride for stride / Listen / How do I get to you / Heal the broken hearted / Somehow I'm changing / All I wanna do / You are worthy / Where my home is / Song of heaven.
LP: . . . . CLS 8002
MC: . . . . TC CLS 8002

Liberties

DISTRACTED.
Tracks: / Lonely night / Feat for a King / Strong heart / From rags to riches / So much joy / Straight down the highway / This city's in love / Clouds just burst on you, The / All my doubts / I've hurt enough / Colour of my car / Man in the moon, The.
LP: . . . . CHR 1787
MC: . . . . ZCHR 1787

Liberty

PEOPLE WHO CARE ARE ANGRY.
LP: . . . . MORT 25

Liberty Bell

J-BECK STORY VOL.2.
LP: . . . . EVA 12036

Libido Boyz

HIDING AWAY.
LP: . . . . FST 005

Licence To Kill

LICENCE TO KILL (THEME FROM) (See under Knight, Gladys) (Knight, Gladys).

Lichfield Cathedral

EVENSONG FOR THE FEAST OF SAINT CHAD.
LP: . . . . ACA 505

FROM DARKNESS INTO LIGHT (Music for Advent and Christmas).
Tracks: / I look from afar / Come Thou redeemer of the Earth / Truth sent from above, The / Adam lay ybounden / There is a flower springing / People look east / Spotless rose, A / Lo, He comes with clouds descending / On this day earth shall ring / Lullay Lord Jesus / O magnum mysterium / Shepherds' farewell, The / Ding dong merrily on high / Three kings, The / Hark the herald angels sing.
LP: . . . . ACA 503
MC: . . . . CACA 503

HEAR MY PRAYER.
LP: . . . . ACA 516

LICHFIELD CATHEDRAL CHOIR.
Tracks: / Come, faithful people / Hosanna to the Son of David / Postlude glagolitic mass / Beati quorum / Deck thyself / Ave Jesu Christe / See, Christ was wounded / Christus factus est / Kyrie Gott Heiliger Geist / Fac me tecum / Stabat mater.
LP: . . . . ACA 529

SING XMAS CAROLS.
LP: . . . . XMS 698

Lick The Tins

BLIND MAN ON A FLYING HORSE, A.
Tracks: / Can't help falling in love / In the middle of the night / Light years away / Every little detail / Hey Joe / Get me to the world on time / Ghost story / Lights out / Only a year / Here comes Kali / Road to California / Belle of Belfast city.
LP: . . . . SED 9001
MC: . . . . ZCSED 9001

Lidberg, Gunnar

GUNNAR LIDBERG.
LP: . . . . OP 7904

Lidj Incorporated

BLACK LIBERATION.
LP: . . . . YOLP 1

LIBERATION DUB.
LP: . . . . YOLP 2

Lidstrom, Jack

40 YEARS AS A BAND LEADER (Lidstrom, Jack & his Hep Cats).
LP: . . . . COOP LP 871

Lie Lie, Bunny

MIDNIGHT LOVING.
LP: . . . . RILP 004

Lie To Me

LIE TO ME (Various artists).
LP: . . . . ULP 1

LIE TO ME/ TELL ME YOU LOVE ME (Various artists).
LP: . . . . UDAT 1

Liebman, David

DOIN' IT AGAIN (Liebman, David Quartet).
Tracks: / Doin' it again / Lady Stardust / Cliff's vibes.
LP: . . . . SJP 140

DOUBLE EDGE (See under Beirach, Richie) (Liebman, David & Richie Beirach).

FORGOTTEN FANTASIES (Liebman, David & Richie Beirach).
LP: . . . . AMLJ 709

IF ONLY THEY KNEW (Liebman, David Quintet).
Tracks: / If only they knew / Capistrano / Moontide / Reunion / Autumn in New York / Move on some.
LP: . . . . SJP 151

LIGHT'N UP PLEASE.
LP: . . . . AMLJ 721

OPAL HEART, THE (Liebman, David Quartet).
LP: . . . . ENJA 3065

PENDULUM (Liebman, David Quartet).
LP: . . . . AH 8

QUEST.
LP: . . . . PA 8061
LP: . . . . OJC 082

SWEET HANDS.
LP: . . . . AMLJ 702

Liebrand, Ben

STYLES.
Tracks: / Intro styles / Pul(s)tar / Eve of the war, The / Move to the big band / Spanish jam / I wish / Love come true, A / You're no good / Overture in C Major, Opus 29 / Pump the base / Give me an answer / For the love of music.
LP: 4667181
MC: 4667184

Liebrer, Franz

FAMOUS STRAUSS WALTZES (Liebrer, Franz Josef & His Viennese Orchestra).
LP: . . . . DS 043

Liege Lord

BURN TO MY TOUCH.
Tracks: / Transgressor / Birds of prey / Cast out / Portrait of despair / Black lit knights / Manic's mask, The / Legend / Walking fire / Speed of sound.
LP: . . . . RR 9625

FREEDOM'S RISE.
LP: . . . . BD 004

MASTER CONTROL.
LP: . . . . RR 95411

WARRIOR'S FAREWELL.
LP: . . . . IW 1013

Lies Damned Lies

LIES DAMNED LIES.
Tracks: / Say you won't forget me / Can't leave you alone / Lonely together / Years ago / Keeping love alive / Give me love / Love among the ruins / You laugh / Birds of the air / Believe me.
LP: . . . . SRNLP 28
MC: . . . . SRNMC 28

Lieutenant Stitchie

GOVERNOR, THE.
LP: 7820011
MC: 7820014

GREAT AMBITION.
LP: . . . . SPLP 4

WEAR YU SIZE.
MC: . . . . DSRC 1076

Life Guards Band

BOOTS AND SADDLES.
Tracks: / Life guards slow march / Imperial life guards / Foxhunter / Agrippa / Boots and saddles / Quickest and best / Washington grays / Milanollo / Moorside march / Overture- Light cavalry / Malaguena / Toccata for band / Trumpets on top / I got rhythm.
MC: . . . . ZC BND 1022
LP: . . . . BND 1022

Life & Loves...

LIFE AND LOVES OF A SHE DEVIL (Original TV soundtrack) (Various artists).
Tracks: / Revenge: *Various artists* / Warm love variations: *Various artists* / Commercial break - vista rose: *Various artists* / For Lucille: *Various artists* / Eden Grove: *Various artists* / Devil groove: *Various artists* / Ways to say goodbye: *Various artists* / Warm love gone cold: *Various artists* / All because of you: *Various artists* / It's all just talk: *Various artists* / Cavatina: *Various artists* / Some enchanted evening: *Various artists* / Cavatina (sequenced version): *Various artists*.
LP: . . . . REB 615
MC: . . . . ZCF 615

Life & Mary Ann

LIFE AND MARY ANN (Catherine Cookson) (James, Susan).
MC: . . . . **CAB 022**

Life Sentence

LIFE SENTENCE.
LP: . . . . **WTF 1736**

Life, the Universe...

LIFE, THE UNIVERSE AND EVERYTHING (Douglas Adams) (Moore, Stephen (nar)).
MCSET: . . . . **LFP 7174**
MCSET: . . . . **LFP 4171745**

Life & Times

STRAWPLAIT AND BONELACE.
Tracks: / One man's Morris / Markyate highwayman / Brickmaking / Scots of the Davis gas stove company, The / Straw plait / Let's go to the grand / Blocker's seaside / Bonelace weaver, The / Bedfordshire ale / Easter song / Tell old Charlie Irons / Why axe ye.
LP: . . . . **FE 043**
MC: . . . . **FE 043 C**

Life & Times ...

LIFE AND TIMES OF JUDGE ROY BEAN (Original Soundtrack) (Various artists).
Tracks: / Judge Roy Bean's theme: *Various artists* / Marshall's: *Various artists* / Marias fashion show: *Various* artists / Matchmaker (yellow rose of Texas): *Various artists* / Bear: *Various artists* / Marmalade, molasses and honey: *Various artists* / On the way to the opera: *Various artists* / Old ragtime: *Various artists*/ Bad Bob: *Various artists* / Justice: *Various artists* / Miss Lillie Langtry: *Various artists.*
LP: **70118**

Lifeforce (Film)

LIFEFORCE (Film Soundtrack) (London Symphony Orchestra).
Tracks: / Lifeforce / Spacewalk / Into the alien craft / Exploration / Sleeping vampires / Evil visitations / Carson's story / Girl in the raincoat / Web of destiny (parts 1-3).
LP: . . . . **A 259**
LP: . . . . **RBMP 8472**

Lifton, Lloyd

SOLO JAZZ PIANO.
LP: . . . . **ST 229**

Liggins, Jimmy

I CAN'T STOP.
Tracks: / I can't stop it / Don't put me down / Troubles good-bye / Misery blues / That song is gone / Move out baby / Answer to teardrops blues / I want my baby for Christmas / Down and out blues / That's what's knocking / Lonely nights blues / Goin' down with the sun / Brown skin baby / Lover's prayer / Dark hour blues / I'll never let you go.
LP: . . . . **KIX 18**

Liggins, Joe

DARKTOWN STRUTTERS' BALL, THE (Liggins, Joe & His Honey Drippers).
Tracks: / Miss Betty's blues / Got your love in my heart / Caravan / I know my love is true / Got a right to cry / Walkin' / Tanya / Sugar lump / Darktown strutters' ball / Downhome blues / Breaking my heart / Sweet Georgia Brown / Blues,The / Loosiana / Spooks holiday / Daddy on my mind.
LP: . . . . **JB 601**

GREAT RHYTHM AND BLUES VOL.6.
Tracks: / Honeydripper (part 1) / Honeydripper (part 2) / Pink champagne / Boom-chick-a-boogie / Goin' back to L.A. / I've got a right to cry / Tanya / Stinky / Brown angel.
LP: . . . . **BDL 1005**

HONEYDRIPPER, THE 1945-49 (Liggins, Joe & His Honey Drippers).
LP: . . . . **JB 622**

JOE & JIMMY LIGGINS (Liggins, Joe & Jimmy).
Tracks: / Honey dripper / Pink champagne / I've got a right to cry / Rhythm in the barnyard / Little Joe's boogie / So alone / Dripper's boogie / Saturday night boogie woogie man / Drunk / Homecoming blue / Nite life boogie / Tear drop blues / Cadillac boogie / Washboard special, The.
LP: . . . . **SNTF 5020**

Light

ILLUMINATION.
Tracks: / Pride of winning / Better things to cry for / 10 million years / Old man Rome / When daylight is over / Contrasting strangers / I'm thinking of you now / Something special / Masquerade / Precious is the pearl.
LP: . . . . **ZL 709 73**
MC: . . . . **ZK 709 73**

Light A Big Fire

GUNPOWDERS.
LP: . . . . **STAB 4**

SURVEILLANCE.
Tracks: / I see people / C.I.A. / Hunger / Mr. Twilight (live in London) / Women / You can love a woman / Ship on the prairie / Charlene / Two jokes / Times we cried.
LP: . . . . **SIREN LP 6**
MC: . . . . **SIREN C 6**
MC: . . . . **CXID 29**
LP: . . . . **XID 29**

Light Blues

LIGHT BLUES SING JEROME KERN.
Tracks: / Last time I saw Paris, The / Why was I born? / Can I forget you? / Folks who live on the hill, The / All the things you are / Don't ever leave me / I won't dance / Let's begin / I've told every little star / Smoke gets in your eyes / Way you look tonight / Who / Yesterdays / They didn't believe me / Dearly beloved / Go, little boat.
LP: . . . . **A 66128**

Light Crust Doughboys

LIVE 1936.
LP: . . . . **CW 207**

Light Division

LIGHT DIVISION SOUNDS RETREAT, THE (Light Division Massed Bands).
Tracks: / Parade calls, 30 & 15 minute warning / Assembly / Advance / Jellalabad / Over the hills / Geordie / Mechanised infantry / Post horn and echo (bugle solo) / Light Infantry regimental march / Five to one / Royal green jackets / Raglan / Hark forrard / Marching through Georgia and Dixie / When the saints go marching in / London airs / Bugler in Vienna / Trumpet prelude / Day thou gavest Lord is ended, The / Sunset / National anthem, The / March off / Light Infantry regimental march / Royal green jackets / Parade call / Parade call.
LP: **LFL1 5041**

Light Factory

LIVE FACTORY/BUS STOPS.
Tracks: / Light factory / C'mon c'mon (we're down at the station) / Waiting at the bus-stop / Climb onboard our great big bus.
MC: . . . . **PCN 116**

Light Infantry

BAND OF THE 2ND BATTALION, LIGHT INFANTRY IN CONCERT (Band of the 2nd Battalion, Light Infantry).
Tracks: / Governor's guard / I write the songs / On Richmond hill baht 'at / Battle hymn and war march of the Vikings / Cavatina / Homeward / Daughter of the regiment / Farmer's boy / Boney M in concert / Cornish floral dance / Northern echoes suite / High on a hill.
LP: . . . . **MM 0587**

IN STEP WITH EUROPE (Light Infantry Bands & Bugles).
LP: . . . . **GRS 1024**

LIGHT INFANTRY BANDS & BUGLES (Light Infantry Bands & Bugles).
Tracks: / Les clarions anglais / Tambourin / Marvin hamlisch showcase / Water mill / Regimental marches / Light Infantry regimental march / Silver bugles / Vivat regina / Bugle boy / Governor's guard / Keel row, The / Royal celebration / Sunset / No more parades today.
LP: . . . . **MM 0596**
MC: . . . . **MMC 0596**

Light Music Society

MUSIC OF PERCY GRAINGER.
Tracks: / Country gardens / Molly on the shore / Irish tune from County Derry / Handel in the Strand / Mock morris / Shepherd's hey / Power of love, The / Lord Peter's stable boy / Nightingale and the two sisters / Jutish medley / Immovable 'Do' walking tune, The / Knight and the shepherd's daughter, The / Man I love, The / Love walked in / Arrival platform Humlet / Gay but wistful / Pastoral / Gum-suckers' march, The / Nell.
MC: . . . . **EG 763 520 4**

Light Of Day

LIGHT OF DAY (Film Soundtrack) (Various artists).
Tracks: / Light of day: *Barbusters* / This means war: *Barbusters* / Twist it off: *Fabulous Thunderbirds*/ Cleveland rocks: *Hunter, Ian* / Stay with me tonight: *Edmunds, Dave* / It's all coming down tonight: *Barbusters*/ Rude mood: *Barbusters* / Only lonely: *Bon Jovi* / Rabbit's got the gun: *Hunzz* / You got no place to go: *Fox, Michael J* / Elegy (instrumental): *Cox, Rick, Chas Smith, Jon C Clarke & Michael Boddicker.*
LP: **4505011**
MC: **4505014**

Light Of The World

BEST OF LIGHT OF THE WORLD.
Tracks: / London Town 85 / Visualise yourself (and your mind) / Pete's crusade / I'm so happy / The boys in blue / Swingin' / I shot the Sheriff / Time.
LP: . . . . **ENGY 1**
MC: . . . . **ENGC 1**

CHECK US OUT.
Tracks: / Check us out / Famous faces / I can't stop / Don't run / Tubbs in the caribbean / Soho / Number one girl / Everybody move / Easy things to say.
LP: . . . . **EMC 3410**

LIGHT OF THE WORLD.
Tracks: / Aspects / Dreams / Liv togevver / Midnight groovin' / Mirror of my soul / Swingin' / Who are you.
LP: . . . . **ENVY 7**

REMIXED....
LP: **6359 062**

ROUND TRIP.
Tracks: / Time / London Town / I shot the sherriff / I'm so happy / More of myself / Visualise yourself / Painted lady / I walk the streets alone / Pete's crusade / Something for nothing.
LP: . . . . **ENVY 14**

Light Princess

LIGHT PRINCESS, THE (Johns, Glynis (nar)).
MC: **1676**

Lightfoot, Gordon

BEST OF GORDON LIGHTFOOT.
Tracks: / Early morning rain / Wreck of the Edmund Fitzgerald, The / Carefree highway / Minstrel of / Rainy day people / Sundown / Summer side of life / Cold on the shoulder / Endless wire / If you could read my mind / Canadian railroad trilogy / If there's a reason / Cotton Jenny / Song for the winters night / Daylight Katy / Old Dan's records / Me and Bobby McGee / Circle is small, The.
LP: . . . . **K 56915**
MC: **K4 56915**

COLD ON THE SHOULDER.
Tracks: / Bend in the water / Rainy day / People / Cold on the shoulder / Soul is the rock / Bells of the evening / Rainbow trout / Tree to weak to stand, A / All the lovely ladies / Fine as fine can be / Cherokee bend / Now and then / Slide on over.
LP: . . . . **K 54033**

DON QUIXOTE.
Tracks: / Don Quixote / Christian Island / Alberta bound / Looking at the rain / Ordinary man / Brave mountaineers / Ode to big blue / Second cup of coffee / Beautiful / On Susan's floor / Patriot's dream, The.
LP: . . . . **K 44166**

DON QUIXOTE/SUMMER SIDE OF LIFE (Two Originals of).
Tracks: / Don Quixote / Christian island / Alberta bound / Looking at the rain / Ordinary man / Brave mountaineers / Ode to big blue / Second cup of coffee / Beautiful / On Susan's floor / Patriot's dream, The / 10 degrees and getting colder / Miguel / Go my way / Summer side of life / Cotton Jenny / Talking in your sleep / Nous vivons ensemble / Same old lover man / Redwood hill / Love and maple syrup / Cabaret.
2LP: . . . . **K 64022**

DREAM STREET ROSE.
Tracks: / Sea of tranquility / Ghosts of Cape Horn / Dream street rose / On the high seas / Whisper my name / If you need me / Hey you / Make way for the lady / Mister rock of ages / Auctioneer, The.
LP: . . . . **K 56802**
MC: **K4 56802**

EARLY MORNING RAIN.
MC: **4XLL 9041**

EAST OF MIDNIGHT.
Tracks: / Stay loose / Morning glory / East of midnight / Lesson in love / Anything for love / Let it ride / Ecstacy made easy / You just gotta be / Passing ship, A / I'll tag along.
LP: **925482 1**
MC: **925482 4**

ENDLESS WIRE.
Tracks: / Daylight Katy / Sweet Guinevere / Hangdog hotel room / If there's a reason / Endless wire / Dreamland / Songs the minstrel sang / Sometimes I don't mind / If children had wings / Circle is small, The.
LP: . . . . **K 56444**
MC: **K4 56444**

GORD'S GOLD.
Tracks: / If it should please you / Endless wire / Hangdog hotel room / I'm not supposed to care / High and dry / Wreck of the Edmund Fitzgerald, The / Pony man, The / Make way for the lady / Race among the ruins / Christian island / All the lovely ladies / Alberta bound.
LP: . . . . **K 925784 1**
MC: . . . . **K 925784 4**

GORD'S GOLD (2).
2LP: . . . . **K 64033**

IF YOU COULD READ MY MIND.
Tracks: / If you could read my mind / Sundown / Minstrel of the dawn / Me and Bobby McGee / Approaching lavender Saturday clothes / Cobweb and dust / Poor little Allison / Sit down young stranger / Baby it's alright / Your love's return / Pony man, The.
LP: . . . . **K 44091**

OLD DANS RECORDS.
Tracks: / Farewell to Annabel / That same old obsession / Old Dan's records / Lazy mornin' / You are what I am / Can't depend on love / My pony won't go / It's worth believing / Mother of a miner's child / Hi way songs.
LP: . . . . **K 44219**

SALUTE.
Tracks: / Salute / Gotta get away / Whispers of the north / Someone to believe in / Romance / Knotty pine / Biscuit city / Without you / Tattoo / Broken dreams.
LP: . . . . **UNKNOWN**

SHADOWS.
Tracks: / 14 karat gold / In my fashion / Shadows / Blackberry wine / Heaven help the devil / Thank you for the promises / Baby step back / All I'm after / Triangle / I'll do anything / She's not the same.
LP: . . . . **K 56970**
MC: **K4 56970**

SUMMER SIDE OF LIFE.
Tracks: / 10 degrees and getting colder / Miguel go my way / Summer side of life / Cotton Jenny / Talking in your sleep / Nous vivons ensemble / Same old lover man / Redwood hill / Love maple syrup / Cabaret.
LP: . . . . **K 44132**

SUMMERTIME DREAM.
Tracks: / Race among the ruins / Wreck of the Edmund Fitzgerald, The / I'm not supposed to care / I'd do it again / Never too close / Protocol / House you live in / The / Summertime dream / Spanish moss / Too many clues in this room.
MC: **K4 54067**
LP: . . . . **K 54067**

SUNDOWN.
Tracks: / Somewhere USA / High and dry / Seven Island suite / Circle of steel / Is there anyone home / Watchman's gone, The / Sundown / Carefree highway / List, The / Too late for pryin'.
LP: . . . . **K 44258**

Lightfoot, Papa George

NATCHEZ TRACE.
Tracks: / My woman is tired of my lyin' / New mean old train / Love my baby / Goin' down that muddy road / Ah come on honey / I heard somebody cryin' / Take it witcha / Night time.
LP: . . . . **CCR 1001**

Lightfoot, Terry

AS TIME GOES BY.
Tracks: / Country cousin / Satin doll / T'aint what you do (it's the way that you do it) / Lonesome / Choo choo ch' boogie / Granpa's spells / Bloodshot eyes / Bra timing from Phomolong / Naw you has jazz / Back in the high life again / As time goes by / Skyliner.
LP: . . . . **N 6564**
MC: . . . . **ZCN 6564**

AT THE JAZZBAND BALL (Lightfoot, Terry & His Band).
LP: . . . . **BRMLP 028**

CLEAR ROUND (Lightfoot, Terry & His Band).
Tracks: / Tuxedo Junction / Mack the knife / Mardi gras / Plant life boogie / Rockin' in rhythm / That da da strain / Ragtime music / Jive at five / Nobody knows you (when you're down and out) / Drum boogie.
LP: . . . . **PLJ 003**

NEW ORLEANS JAZZMEN.
LP: **838 763 1**

STARDUST.
MC: . . . . **URMC 104**

TERRY LIGHTFOOT IN CONCERT.
Tracks: / Rockin' in rhythm / West End blues / Sentimental journey / Black and tan / Sweet Georgia Brown / Summertime / Honeysuckle rose / Drum boogie / Honky tonk train blues / Tuxedo Junction / Joshua fit de battle of Jerico.
2LP: . . . . **BLPX 12143/4**

VARIED JAZZ (Lightfoot, Terry & His Band).
MC: **C5MK 566**

Lighthorsemen

LIGHTHORSEMEN/SHAME (Film soundtrack) (Various artists).
LP: SL 9521
MC: SLC 9521

Lighthouse

LIGHTHOUSE, THE/KIMONO, THE (H.E.BATES) (H.E. Bates) (Jarvis, Martin (nar)).
MC: PTB 614

Lighthouse Allstars

MILES DAVIS & THE LIGHTHOUSE ALLSTARS (see Davis, Miles) (Lighthouse Allstars/Miles Davis).

Lighthouse Keepers

TALES OF THE UNEXPECTED.
LP: HOT 1011

Lightnin' Slim

BELL RINGER.
LP: LP 8004

EARLY YEARS, THE.
LP: FLY 524

FEATURE SIDES, THE (1954).
LP: FLY 583

HIGH AND LOW DOWN.
Tracks: / Rooster blues / Rooster blues / Things I used to do, The / Bad luck blues / My babe / G.I. blues / Oh baby / That's alright / Crazy 'bout you baby / Good morning heartache / Hoodoo blues.
LP: SNTF 770

LONDON GUMBO.
Tracks: / Just a little bit / Miss Sarah's a good girl / Too much monkey business / Ain't nothing but trouble / I won't give up / Mama, talk to your daughter / Mean ole Frisco blues / Hey little girl / Sky is crying, The / Help me spend my gold / I got a little woman / Take it real easy.
LP: SNTF 757

ROOSTER BLUES.
LP: LP 8000

TRIP TO CHICAGO.
LP: FLY 533

WE GOTTA ROCK.
Tracks: / Late in the evening / It been a long long time / Long leanie mama / I hate to leave you / I love to hold my baby's hand / We gotta rock tonight / I don't know / I'm warning you baby / Wintertime done rolled by / Miss Fannie Brown / Soldier boy blues / You'd better change / You give me the blues / Bye bye pretty baby.
LP: FLY 612

Lightning Seeds

CLOUD CUCKOO LAND.
LP: GHETT 3
MC: GHETTC 3

Lightning Strike

LIGHTNING STRIKE.
Tracks: / Get ready / Pack, The / Beatbox international / City of nightmares / High tech war / Beat street / Southside blues / Going for gold / Cap it all / America's calling.
LP: PL 90239
MC: PK 90239

Lights In A Fat City

SOMEWHERE.
LP: THESE 003

Lightsey, Kirk

EVERYTHING HAPPENS TO ME (Lightsey, Kirk Trio).
MC: SJP 1176

FIRST AFFAIRS (Lightsey, Kirk Quartet).
LP: MLP 0015

ISOTOPE (Lightsey, Kirk Trio).
LP: CRISS 1003

KIRK LIGHTSEY TRIO AND CHET BAKER (See under Baker, Chet) (Baker, Chet & Kirk Lightsey Trio).

KIRK 'N' MARCUS.
Tracks: / All my love / Loves I once knew / Windmill / Marcus' mates / Golden legacy / Lower bridge level.
LP: CRISS 1030

LIGHTSEY 1.
Tracks: / Fee fi fo fum / Habiba / Trinkle tinkle / Moon ra / Fresh air / Wild flower / Never let me go.
LP: SSC 1002

LIGHTSEY 2.
LP: SSC 1005

SHORTER BY TWO (Lightsey, Kirk/ Harold Denko).
LP: SSC 1004

Ligon, Bert

DANCING BARE (Ligon, Bert/Gary Willis/Jay Fort/K. Covington).
LP: SB 3002

Ligotage

FORGIVE AND FORGET-LIVE.
LP: PIKM 005

Lijado Sisters

DOUBLE TROUBLE.
LP: SHAN 43020

HORIZON UNLIMITED.
LP: DWAPS 2089

Like A Girl...

LIKE A GIRL I WANT TO KEEP YOU (Various artists).
LP: SER 008

Like Wow

LIKE WOW (Various artists).
LP: BLK 7702

Li'l Abner

LI'L ABNER (Original Broadway Cast) (Various artists).
LP: AOL 5150
MC: BT 5150

Lil Bob

SWEET SOUL SWINGER.
LP: 1001

Lil' Ed

CHICKEN, GRAVY AND BISCUITS (Lil'ed & The Blues Imperials).
LP: AL 4772

ROUGHHOUSIN' (Lil'ed & The Blues Imperials).
LP: SNTF 966
MC: ZCSN 966

Lil Louis

FRENCH KISSES.
LP: 828 170 1
MC: 828 170 4

FROM THE MIND OF LIL LOUIS (Lil Louis and the World).
Tracks: / I called U / Blackout / Tuch me / French kiss / Wargames / 6 a.m. / Nyce and slo / Insecure / Luv u wanted, The / Brittany / Li'l Tanya.
LP: 828 179 1
MC: 828 179 4

Lilac Time

AND LOVE FOR ALL.
LP: 8461901
MC: 8461904

ASTRONAUTS.
LP: CRELP 098
MC: CCRELP 098

LILAC TIME, THE.
Tracks: / Black velvet / Rockland / Return to yesterday / You've got to love / Love becomes a savage / Together / Road to happiness, The / Too sooner late than better / Trumpets from Montparnasse.
LP: SFLP 6
MC: SFMC 6

PARADISE CIRCUS.
Tracks: / American eyes / Lost girl in the midnight sun, The / Beauty in your body, The / If the stars shine tonight / Days of the week, The / She still loves you / Paradise circus / Girl who waves at trains, The / Last to know, The / Father mother wife and child / Rollercoaster song, The / Work for the weekend / Twilight beer hall.
LP: 8386411
MC: 8386414

L'ile

L'ILE (THE ISLAND) (Original Soundtrack) (Various artists).
LP: A 340

Liliput

LILIPUT.
LP: ROUGH 43

SOME SONGS.
LP: TTD 15

Lilli Marlene

LILLIE MARLENE (Original Soundtrack) (Various artists).
LP: SL 9506

Lillian Axe

LOVE AND WAR.
LP: MCG 6060
MC: MCGC 6060

Lilly Brothers

BLUEGRASS BREAKDOWN.
LP: SS 01

COUNTRY SONGS.
LP: SS 02

Lilly, Willy

LILLY, WILLY AND THE MAIL ORDER WITCH (See under Bach, Othello) (Grimes, Tammy (nar)).

Lillywhite, Derek

BANJO REMINISCENCES.
LP: ROUNDER 0095

L.I.L.T.

FOR THE CHILDREN.
LP: ETLP 191
MC: ETMC 191

Lily Was Here

LILY WAS HERE (Film Soundtrack) (Stewart, David A & Candy Dulfer).
Tracks: / Lily was here / Pink building, The / Lily robs the bank / Toyshop robbery / Toys on the sidewalk / Good hotel, The / Second chance / Here comes the rain again / Alone in the city / Toyshop (part one) / Coffin, The / Teletype / Inside the pink building / Percussion jam / Peaches / Lily was here (reprise).
LP: ZL 74233
MC: ZK 74233

Lima, Carlos Barbosa

BRAZIL, WITH LOVE (Lima, Carlos Barbosa & Sharon Isbin).
Tracks: / Luiza / Felicidade / Chovendo na Rosiera / Garoto / Estrada Do Sol / Gabrielle / Passatempo / Vou vivendo / Pretencioso / Carinhoso / Brejeiro / Apandhi-Te, Cavaquinha / Bambino / Odeon.
LP: CJP 320
MC: CJPC 320

Limahl

COLOUR ALL MY DAYS.
Tracks: / Love in your eyes / Colour all my days / Nothing on earth (Can you keep me from you) / Tonight will be the night / Working out / Don't send for me / Shock / Outside to inside / Love will tear the soul / For my hearts sake.
LP: EMC 3510
MC: TCEMC 3510

DON'T SUPPOSE.
Tracks: / Don't suppose / That special something / Your love / Too much trouble / Never ending story / Only for love / I was a fool / Waiting game, The / Tar beach / Oh girl.
LP: PLML 1
MC: TCLML 1
LP: EJ2401561

Limbomaniacs

STINKY GROOVES.
Tracks: / Butt funkin' / Maniac / Freestyle / Porno / Shake it / That's the way / Toilet's flooded, The / Pavlov's frothing dogs.
LP: 4676141
MC: 4676144

Lime

BEST OF LIME.
Tracks: / Angel eyes / Come and get your love / Take it up / Your love / Unexpected lovers / Babe we're gonna love tonight / Guilty.
LP: 827 612-1
MC: 827 612-4

LIME 2.
Tracks: / Come and get your love / Help yourself / Man and a woman, A / Wake dream / No reply / Babe we're gonna love tonight.
LP: 2311 152

LIME 3.
Tracks: / Guilty / Angel eyes / On the grid / Give me your body / Together / Rendezvous on the dark side of the moon.
LP: 8130 661

SENSUAL SENSATION.
Tracks: / It's gonna be all right (my love) / Don't you wanna do it / Sensual sensation / Take it up / I don't wanna lose you / Extrasensory perception / Party's over, The.
LP: 823 288-1
MC: 823 288-4

UNEXPECTED LOVERS.
Tracks: / Do your time on the planet / Profile of love / Are you being untrue tonight / Alive and well / Say you love me / My lovely angel / Unexpected lovers / I'm falling in love.
LP: 825 994-1

YOUR LOVE.
Tracks: / You're my magician / Agent 406 / It's you / I'll be yours / Your love.
LP: 2374 182

Lime Spiders

BEETHOVEN'S FIST.
LP: AFTER 7

CAVE COMES ALIVE, THE.
Tracks: / My favourite room / Are you loving me more / Ignormy / N.S.U. / Just one solution / Blood from a stone / Action woman / Rock star / Jessica / Space cadet / Theory of thira / Just one solution (reprise).
LP: V 2457
MC: TCV 2457
LP: VOZ 2006
LPPD: VOZ 2006 X

HEADCLEANER.
Tracks: / Slave girl.
MC: HC 1

SLAVE GIRL.
LP: RIB 1

VOLATILE.
Tracks: / Volatile / Can't hear you anymore / Odyssey, The / Lot to answer for / Captor and the captive one, The / My main attraction / Other side of you, The / Deaf, dumb and blind / Strange kind of love / Under my umbrella / Won't fall in love / Test pattern / Jagged edge (CD only) / Can't you read my mind (CD only) / Volatile (voliation mix) (CD only).
LP: V 2534
MC: TCV 2534

Limehouse Jazzband

RHYTHM IS OUR BUSINESS.
LP: SOS 1014

Limelight

LIMELIGHT.
Tracks: / Going home / Knife in your back / Mamma (I don't wanna lose you) / Man of colours / Metal man / Walk on water / Don't look back.
LP: FER 008

Limeliters

ALIVE IN CONCERT.
LP: GNPS 2188
MC: GNP5 2188

ALIVE IN CONCERT 2ND SET.
LP: GNPS 2190
MC: GNP5 2190

THEIR 1ST HISTORIC ALBUM.
MC: 814

Limey

SILVER EAGLE.
Tracks: / Both in love with you / Daddy flew a Spitfire / Silver eagle / Going home / Toledo / Cry from the streets / Nine-to-five heroes / Woman with the honeydew eyes / Desiree / Looking for Suzanne.
LP: PL 25032

Limited Warranty

LIMITED WARRANTY.
Tracks: / Last to know, The / Hit you from behind / This is serious / Beat down the door / Yesterday's news / Victory line / One of a kind / Never enough / Domestic / You can buy.
LP: 790 513 1
MC: 790 513 4

Lincoln, Abbey

AFFAIR.
LP: LRP 3025

PEOPLE IN ME (Lincoln, Abbey & Dave Liebman).
LP: ITM 0039

SOUND AS A ROACH (See under Roach, Max) (Lincoln, Abbey & Max Roach).

STRAIGHT AHEAD.
Tracks: / Straight ahead / When Malindy sings / In the red / Blue Monk / Left alone / African lady / Retribution.
LP: CS 9015

TALKING TO THE SUN.
LP: ENJA 4060

THAT'S HIM.
Tracks: / Strong man / Happiness is a thing called Joe / My man / Tender as a rose / That's him / Porgy / When a woman loves a man / Don't explain.
LP: OJC 085

Lincoln Cathedral

MUSIC FOR ALL SEASONS (Lincoln Cathedral Choir).
Tracks: / I was glad / Here is the little door / Spotless rose, A / Sing lullaby / Give ear, O Lord / Vigilate / Contique de Jean Racine / Let the people praise thee / Great Lord of Lords / O Lord, thou hast searched me out / O nata lux / Four penitential motets / Evening hymn.
MC: YORKMC 105

Lincoln, Charley

CHARLEY LINCOLN.
Tracks: / Jealous hearted blues / Hard luck blues / Mojoe blues / My wife drove me from my door / Country breakdown / Chain gang trouble / If it looks like jelly shakes like jelly it must be gelatine / Ugly papa / Jacksonville blues / Midnight weeping blues / Depot blues / Gamblin' Charley doodle hole blues / Mama don't rush me.
LP: MSE 212

Lincoln, Prince

EXPERIENCE (Lincoln, Prince & The Royal Rasses).
LP: VSLP 300

Lind, Michael

MICHAEL LIND TUBA.
LP: . . . . **FLC 5045**

Lind, Ove

DIALOGUE IN SWING (see Hallberg, Bengt) (Lind, Ove & Bengt Hallberg).

EVERGREENS (Lind, Ove/Staffan Broms/Bengt Hallberg).
Tracks: / Night and day / Change partners / Cheek to cheek / On the sunny side of the street / They can't take that away from me / Fine romance, A / Begin the beguine / It's only a paper moon / You made me love you / I've got you under my skin / As time goes by / How about you / Deep purple / White Christmas / In the mood / All the things you are / Music music music / Come fly with me / On a slow boat to China / Yesterday / Whispering / Ain't she sweet / Star dust / Let's do it / Ain't misbehavin' / I can't give you anything but love / Tea for two / You're the cream in my coffee / Best things in life are free / Side by side.
2LP: . . . . **PHONT 7401/02**
MCSET: . . . . **PHONT 8401/02**

EVERGREENS 2 (Lind, Ove/Staffan Broms/Bengt Hallberg).
Tracks: / Button up your overcoat / Dinah / I'm looking over a four leaf clover / Five foot two eyes of blue / Makin whoopee / It all depends on you / Sheik of Araby, The / Singin in the rain / Smoke gets in your eyes / Between the devil and the deep blue sea / Ramona / Shine / Lover come back to me / I get a kick out of you / Lady is a tramp, The / Chicago / Two sleepy people / These foolish things / Three little words / Take a chance on love / Boo hoo / It's been a long long time / Jeepers creepers / Don't fence me in / Sentimental journey / Baby it's cold outside / It's alright with me / Too young / Mack the knife.
2LP: . . . . **PHONT 7403/04**
MCSET: . . . . **PHONT 8403/04**

GERSHWIN - EVERGREEN.
Tracks: / 'S wonderful / Summertime / Swanee / Embraceable you / Bidin' my time / Our love is here to stay / But not for me / Changing my tune / Of thee I sing / Somebody loves me / Someone to watch over me / Oh lady be good / Aren't you kind of glad we did / I got plenty o' nuttin' / They can't take that away from me / Strike up the band / Man I love, The / Nice work if you can get it / Who cares / Love is sweeping the country / I've got a crush on you / Love walked in / Foggy day, A / My one and only / I was doing all right / They all laughed / How long has this been going on / Let's call the whole thing off.
2LP: . . . . **PHONT 7410/11**
MCSET: . . . . **PHONT 8410/11**

ONE MORNING IN MAY (Lind, Ove Quartet).
Tracks: / Just friends / Tangerine / Sky fell down, The / So would I / Cheek to cheek / I thought about you / Down by the old mill stream / Baby won't you please / I've got a feeling I'm falling / Stay as sweet as you are / I've got my eyes on you / True / One morning in May.
LP: . . . . **PHONT 7501**

SUMMER NIGHT.
Tracks: / Summer night / You leave me breathless / Say my heart / Changing my tune / Ill wind / You're a lucky guy / Lady be good / My cabin of dreams / You're the cream in my coffee / This heart of mine / Louise / Swinging on a star.
LP: . . . . **PHONT 7503**

SWINGING DIXIELAND (Lind, Ove & The Phontastic Dixie Players).
Tracks: / Mandy make up your mind / Who's sorry now / There'll be some changes made / Wolverine blues / Muskrat ramble / St. Louis blues / At the Jazz Band ball / Phontastic swing / You took advantage of me / Sleepy time gal / Japanese sandman / Honeysuckle rose.
LP: . . . . **PHONT 7509**

WE LOVE NORWAY (Various artists).
LP: . . . . **PHON 50-13**

Lind Street Dreads

DUB OF THE SEVENTIES.
LP: . . . . **ATRA 1006**

Linda & Funky Boys

SATISFIED.
Tracks: / Baby are you satisfied / Natural high / Climbing the steps of love / Shame, shame, shame / When I get home / We got love / Hey big brother / Sold my soul for rock'n'roll / Show it / Dance with my baby / Solid funk / Singing all in harmony.
LP: . . . . **SRLP 121**

Lindberg, John

COMIN' AND GOIN'.
LP: . . . . **LR 104**

DIMENSION 5 (Lindberg, John Quintet).
LP: . . . . **BSR 0062**

HAUNT OF THE UNRESOLVED.
Tracks: / Haunt of the unresolved-Part 1 / Haunt of the unresolved-Part 2.
LP: . . . . **NATO 40**

Lindberg, Nils

DUKE ELLINGTON WITH ALICE BABS AND NILS LINDBERG (See Under Ellington, Duke) (Lindberg, Nils, Alice Babs & Duke Ellington).

FAR AWAY STAR (See Under Babs, Alice) (Lindberg, Nils, Alice Babs & Duke Ellington).

Lindenberg, Udo

NO PANIC (Lindenberg, Udo & The Panik Orchestra).
Tracks: / Conductor, The / Votan wahnwitz / Nothing but a vacuum / Daniel's time machine / It was all so new / Rudi Ratlos / Elli Pyrelli / O rhesus negative / Look at it my way / Johnny Controlletti / Jack.
LP: . . . . **TXSR 116**

UDO LINDENBERG UND DAS PANIK ORCHESTRA.
Tracks: / Hoch im nordon / Ales klar auf der andrea doria / Honky Tonk show / Johnny Controletti / Rudi ratlos / Bodo ballerman / Rock 'n' roll arena in Jena / Riki Masorati / Guten tag ich heisse schmidt / Reeperbahn / New York (New York state of mind) / Baby wenn ich down bin / Grande finale / Kann denn liebe sunde sein / Kugel im colt / Zwischen rhein und aufruhr.
LP: . . . . **ZP 8.25955**

Lindenstrand, Bo

MY SHINING HOUR (Lindenstrand,Bo Quartet).
LP: . . . . **PHONT 7557**

Lindenstrand, Sylvia

FRANZ LISZT.
LP: . . . . **PHONT 7111**

Lindgren, Astrid

STORIES FROM PIPPI LONGSTOCKING.
MC: . . . . **TS 351**

Lindh, Bjorn (J:Son)

ATLANTIS.
LP: . . . . **SNTF 904**

DAY AT THE SURFACE, A.
Tracks: / Introduction / Helicopter music / Billathi Askara / Day at the surface, A / Loch Ensslin / Ah Q / Bike voyage 11 / Hotels and drumsticks / Boathouse club / Colwyn Bay / Angela's kite.
LP: . . . . **SNTF 833**

TO BE CONTINUED.
Tracks: / From here to eternity / Cloud pump / Southern belle / Ono / Scaramacazie / Salon music / Bix gong / Norwegian feedback / Escape / To be continued.
LP: . . . . **SNTF 886**

WET WINGS.
Tracks: / Sing louder little river / Swamp etude / Esther Williams / Swamp concerto / Certain nights / Into the fog / Jason's hounds / Elastic love song / Deserter's jubilee / Wet wings.
LP: . . . . **SNTF 854**

Lindisfarne

BACK AND FOURTH.
Tracks: / Angels at eleven / Get wise / Jukebox gypsy / King X blues / Make me want to stay / Marshall Rileys army / Only alone / Run for home / Warm feeling / Woman / You and me.
LP: . . . . **PRICE 54**
MC: . . . . **PRIMC 54**
LP: **9109 609**

BEST OF LINDISFARNE.
Tracks: / Meet me on the corner / Lady Eleanor / All fall down / We can swing together / Fog on the Tyne / Road to Kingdom Come / Scarecrow song / Winter song / Clear white light / January song / Down / Walke up little sister / Together forever / Alright on the night / Go back / Don't ask me.
LP: . . . . **VVIP 103**
MC: . . . . **VVIPC 103**

C'MON EVERYBODY.
Tracks: / Let's dance / New Orleans / Splish splash / Party doll / You never can tell / Little bitty pretty one / Running bear / Mr. Bass man / Sea cruise / Let's go / Wooly bully / C'mon everybody / Do you wanna dance? / Twist and shout / Do you love me / Runaround Sue / Shake, rattle and roll / See you later alligator / It'll be me / You keep a knockin' / Love you more than I can say / Oh Donna / Keep your hands off my baby / Rhythm of the rain / Speedy Gonzales / Little darlin' / Dreamin' / La bamba / Meet me on the corner / Lady Eleanor / Fog on the Tyne / Run for home / Warm feeling / Clear white light.
2LP: . . . . **SMR 738**
MCSET: . . . . **SMC 738**

DANCE YOUR LIFE AWAY.
LP: . . . . **LINDLP 1**
MC: . . . . **LINDC 1**

DINGLY DELL.
Tracks: / All fall down / Plankton's lament / Bring down the government / Poor old Ireland / Don't ask me / Oh, no, not again / Dingle regatta / Wake up little sister / Go back / Court in the act / Mandolin king / Dingly dell / We can swing together (live version).
LP: . . . . **CAS 1057**

FINEST HOUR.
Tracks: / Lady Eleanor / Road to Kingdom come / Wake up little sister / Tonight forever / Alright on the night / Scarecrow song / We can swing together / Meet me on the corner / All fall down / Go back / Winter song / Clear white light / Don't ask me / January song / Alan in the river with flowers / Fog on the Tyne / Down.
LP: . . . . **CAS 1108**
MC: . . . . **CASMC 1108**

FOG ON THE TYNE.
Tracks: / Meet me on the corner / Alright on the night / Uncle Sam / Together forever / January song / Peter Brophy don't care / City song / Passing ghosts / Train in G major / Fog on the Tyne / Scotch mist (CD only) / No time to lose (CD only).
LP: . . . . **CHC 52**
MC: . . . . **CASMC 1050**
LP: . . . . **CAS 1050**
MC: . . . . **CHCMC 52**

FOG ON THE TYNE (See under Gazza) (Lindisfarne & Gazza).

FOG ON THE TYNE/NICELY OUT OF TUNE.
Tracks: / Lady Eleanor / Road to Kingdom come / Winter song / Uncle Sam / Turn a deaf ear / Clear white light-part 2 / We can swing together / Alan in the river with flowers / Down / Things I should have said, The / Jackhammer blues / Scarecrow song / Meet me on the corner / Alright on the night / Together forever / January song / Peter Brophy don't care / City song / Passing ghosts / Train in G major / Fog on the Tyne.
MCSET: . . . . **CASMC 104**

HAPPY DAZE.
LP: . . . . **K 56070**

KEEPIN' THE BEACON BURNIN' (Lindisfarne-Amigos).
LP: . . . . **CRO 224**

LADY ELEANOR.
LP: . . . . **SHM 919**

LINDISFARNE LIVE.
Tracks: / No time to lose / Meet me on the corner / Alright on the night / Train in G minor / Fog on the Tyne / We can swing together / Jackhammer blues.
LP: . . . . **CHC 7**
MC: . . . . **CHCMC 7**
LP: . . . . **CLASS 2**

LINDISFARNE SINGLES ALBUM.
LP: . . . . **BG 5**

LINDISFARNETASTIC LIVE.
LP: . . . . **GET 2**

LINDISFARNTASTIC VOL.2.
LP: . . . . **GET 3**
MC: . . . . **ZCGET 3**

MAGIC IN THE AIR.
2LP: **6641 877**

NEWS, THE.
Tracks: / Call of the wild / People say / 1983 / Log on your fire / Easy and free / Evenings / Miracles / When Friday comes along / Dedicated hound / This has got to end / Good to be here.
LP: **9109 626**

NICELY OUT OF TUNE.
Tracks: / Lady Eleanor / Road to Kingdom come / Winter song / Turn a deaf ear / Clear white light-part 2 / We can swing together / Alan in the river with flowers / Down / Things I should have said, The / Jackhammer blues / Scarecrow song / Knackers yard blues (CD only) / Nothing but the marvellous is beautiful (CD only).
LP: . . . . **CHC 31**
MC: . . . . **CHCMC 31**
LP: . . . . **CAS 1025**

ROLL ON RUBY.
LP: . . . . **CAS 1076**

SLEEPLESS NIGHTS.
LP: . . . . **GET 1**
MC: . . . . **ZCGET 1**

Lindley, David

EL RAYO - X.
Tracks: / She took off my Romeo's / Bye bye love / Mercury blues / Quarter of a man / Ain't no way / Twist and shout / El Rayo X / Your ol' lady / Don't look back / Petit fleur / Tuber cu laca and the sinus flu / Pay the man.
LP: . . . . **K 52283**

LIVE: DAVID LINDLEY (Lindley, David & El Rayo X).
LP: **9602351**

MR.DAVE.
LP: **252161 1**

VERY GREASY (Lindley, David & El Rayo X).
LP: **960 768 1**
MC: **960 768 4**

WIN THIS RECORD.
Tracks: / Talk to the lawyer / Look so good / Something's got a hold on me / Ram a lamb a man / Premature / Rock it with I / Brother John / Make it on / Turning point / Spodie.
LP: . . . . **K 52421**

Lindley, Simon

FAVOURITE ORGAN SOLOS.
Tracks: / Nun danket alle Gott (Opus 65 no. 59 March Trionfale.) / Organo primitivo, (L') (Humoresque - Toccatina for flute.) / Song of sunshine / Andantino in D flat / Toccata from symphony No. 5 in F opus 42) (end s1) / Te Deum laudamus (Prelude.) / Toccata and fugue in D minor / Largo, allegro, aria and two variations / Les cloches de Hinckley (Pieces de fantaisiem, opus 55.).
LP: . . . . **APS 358**
MC: . . . . **CAPS 358**

Lindsay, Arto

ENVY (Lindsay, Arto & Ambitious Lovers).
Tracks: / Cross your legs / Trouble maker / Pagode Americano / Nothings monstered / Crowning roar / Too many mansions / Let's be adult / Venus lost her shirt / My competition / Babu / Dora / Beberibe / Locus coruleus.
LP: . . . . **EGED 39**

Lindsay, Balford

CAN'T FIGHT LOVE.
LP: . . . . **RTC 007**

MEMORIES OF HER LOVE.
LP: . . . . **RTC 010**

Lindsay, Elizabeth

MOUNTAIN OF ADVENTURE (see under Blyton, Enid (aut)) (Blake, Roger (nar) & Elizabeth Lindsay (nar)).

SHIP OF ADVENTURE, THE (see under Blyton, Enid (aut)) (Blake, Roger (nar) & Elizabeth Lindsay (nar)).

Lindsay, Erica

DREAMER.
Tracks: / Day dream / First movement / Walking together / Dreamer / At the last moment / Gratitude.
LP: . . . . **CS 9040**

Lindsay, Jimmy

CHILDREN OF RASTAFARI.
Tracks: / Children of Rastafari / Weh you a defend / Rastaman / Back out neak out / It's hard / Press along / Stand up / People of the third world / Truth / If it wasn't dem want.
LP: . . . . **GEMLP 110**

WHERE IS YOUR LOVE.
Tracks: / Where is your love / Easy / Love was never mean't for me / I will love you / Reaching out / Daughters of Babylon / I'll be there / Ain't no sunshine / Step inside me / Sail away.
LP: . . . . **GEMLP 101**

Lindsay, Robert

VIRGIN AND THE GYPSY (See also D.H. Lawrence).

Lindsay String Quartet

HAYDN..'LIVE AT THE WIGMORE HALL' V3 (see under Haydn (composer)).

HAYDN..'LIVE AT THE WIGMORE HALL' V2 (see under Haydn (composer)).

HAYDN..'LIVE AT THE WIGMORE HALL' V1 (see under Haydn (composer)).

Lindsey, Jimmy

TOP SCOTCH (Lindsey, Jimmy & His Band).
Tracks: / Shetland jigs / Nan, Ann and Leslie / Gaelic waltz medley / Parkhill two step / Continental waltz / Pipe medley / Gay Gordons / Hornpipe / Hornpipe jig & hornpipe.
MC: . . . . **BBRC 169**

Lindsey, Judy

SCREAMIN' DEMON (See under Carroll, Johnny) (Lindsey, Judy & Johnny Carroll).

Lindt, Virna

PLAY/RECORD.
LP: . . . . . PACT 11

SHIVER.
Tracks: / I experienced love / Swedish modern / I beat the system.
MC: . . . . . TC COMP 4
LP: . . . . . PACT 4

Lindup, Mike

CHANGES.
MC: 843 514 4
LP: 843 514 1

Liner

LINER.
Tracks: / Keep reaching out for love / Strange fascination / You and me / So much in love again / Run to the night / Sweet music (you know that) / It's alright / Ship on the ocean / Night train / Window pane.
LP: . . . . . K 50553

Lines

THERAPY.
LP: . . . . . FRESH LP 7

Lines To London...

LINES TO LONDON ARE ENGAGED (Various artists).
Tracks: / Hungry: *Various artists* / So angry: *Various artists* / French farewell: *Various artists* / Television: *Various artists* / Absent friends: *Various artists* / Big business: *Various artists* / Short on romance: *Various artists* / French girls: *Various artists* / Feeling's mutual: *Various artists* / Sin: *Various artists* / Walk on water: *Various artists* / Me & my machine: *Various artists* / Wooden heart: *Various artists* / Snowman: *Various artists* / Rich girls: *Various artists* / Strange man in town: *Various artists* / Moving target: *Various artists.*
LP: . . . . . IRSP 14

Ling Family

SINGING TRADITIONS OF A SUFFOLK FAMILY.
LP: 12TS 292

Lingle, Paul

DANCE OF THE WITCH HAZELS AT THE JUG CLUB 1951.
LP: . . . . . ESR 1217

VINTAGE PIANO.
LP: . . . . . ESR 1023

Link (film)

LINK (Film Soundtrack) (Various artists).
LP: . . . . . STV 81294
MC: . . . . . CTV 81294

Linkchain, Hip

AIRBUSTERS.
LP: . . . . . BM 9011

Linn, Ray

CHICAGO JAZZ (Linn, Ray & The Chicago Stompers).
Tracks: / Poor butterfly / Can't we be friends / Jeepers creepers / Royal Garden blues / Keepin' out of mischief now / Ain't misbehavin'.
LP: . . . . . TR 515

EMPTY SUIT BLUES (Linn, Ray & The Chicago Stompers).
Tracks: / Memories of you / Stars fell on Alabama / What is there to say?.
LP: . . . . . DS 823

Linnard, Mick

RUSSELL SQUARE (Linnard, Mick & David Hughes).
LP: . . . . . LTRA 511

Lins, Ivan

IVAN LINS.
LP: 925850 1
MC: 925850 4

LOVE DANCE.
LP: 925 850-1
MC: 925 850-4

TOGETHER.
Tracks: / Open wings aka the smiling hour / Message / We are all the same tonight / Ant hill / New times / Starting over aka the island / Together / Dinorah, Dinorah / Holy flag procession / Believe what I say / Leave me / To despair never more / Someday.
LP: . . . . . IMS 822 672 1

Linsky, Jeff

UP LATE.
Tracks: / Armony / Besame mucho / Berimbau / Carlos / Hermosa / I didn't know what time it was / Lanikai / Monterey / Up late / Wave (Only on CD.).
LP: . . . . . CJP 363
MC: . . . . . CJP 363 C

Linx

GO AHEAD.
Tracks: / So this is romance / I don't want to learn / I wanna be with you / Urban refugee / I won't play the game / Can't help myself / All my yesterdays / Know what it is to be lonely / Tinsel Town (you don't fool me).
LP: . . . . . CHR 1358
MC: . . . . . ZCHR 1358

INTUITION.
Tracks: / Wonder what you're doing now / I Won't forget / Intuition / There's love / Rise and shine / Throw away the key / Together we can shine / Count on me / Don't get in my way.
LP: . . . . . FA 41 3088 1
MC: . . . . . TCFA 41 30884
LP: . . . . . CHR 1332
MC: . . . . . ZCHR 1332
LP: . . . . . MFP 5756

LAST LINX.
Tracks: / Together we can shine / Throw away the key / You're lying / Wonder what you're doing now / Intuition / So this is romance / Urban refugee.
LP: . . . . . CHR 1409
MC: . . . . . ZCHR 1409

Lion

DANGEROUS ATTRACTION.
LP: . . . . . BFZ 40797

FATAL ATTRACTION.
Tracks: / Armed and dangerous / Hard and heavy / Never surrender / Death on legs / Powerlove / In the name of love / After the fire / Shout it out.
LP: 834 232 1
MC: 834 232 4

TROUBLE IN ANGEL CITY.
LP: . . . . . SLAM 5

Lion Of The Desert

LION OF THE DESERT (Film Soundtrack) (Various artists).
LP: . . . . . RKLP 5005
MC: . . . . . ZCRK 100

LION OF THE DESERT (OST) (See under Jarre, Maurice) (Jarre, Maurice).

Lion Youth

LOVE COMES AND GOES.
LP: . . . . . VG LP 001

SANDRA (see under Fletcher,Lorna "Just the two of us").

Lionheart

HOT TONIGHT.
Tracks: / Wait for the night / Hot tonight / Die for love / Towers of silver / Don't look back in anger / Nightmare / Living in a dream / Another crazy dream / Dangerous game.
LP: . . . . . EPC 26214

Lionheart (Film)

LIONHEART (Film Soundtrack) (Various artists).
LP: . . . . . STV 81304
MC: . . . . . CTV 81304

LIONHEART VOL 2 (Film soundtrack) (Various artists).
LP: . . . . . STV 81311
MC: . . . . . CTV 81311

Lions Breed

DAMN THE NIGHT.
LP: . . . . . ES 4008

Lions & Ghosts

VELVET KISS, LICK OF THE LIME.
LP: . . . . . EALX 46959

Lionspride

BREAKING OUT.
LP: . . . . . SKULL 8336
MC: . . . . . TAPE 78336

Lipari, Bo

THAT OLD SONG AND DANCE (Lipari, Bo & Jim Winner).
LP: . . . . . BF 15025

Lipman, Berry

NIGHT OUT WITH THE BERRY LIPMAN SINGERS AND ORCHESTRA.
LP: . . . . . DS 022

Lipman, Maureen

HOW WAS IT FOR YOU.
MCSET: . . . . . ZBBC 1025

LITTLE PRINCESS, A (see under Little Princess (bk)).

RE-JOYCE (Show Soundtrack).
LP: . . . . . LLP 129
MC: . . . . . LLK 129

Lipps Inc.

MOUTH TO MOUTH.
Tracks: / Funkytown / All night dancing / Rock it / Power.
LP: . . . . . NBLP 7197

PUCKER UP.
Tracks: / How long / Tight pair / Always lookin' / Gossip song / There they are / Jazzy.
LP: . . . . . NBLP 7242

Lipscomb, Mance

MANCE LIPSCOMB.
MC: . . . . . C 205

MANCE LIPSCOMB VOL. 2.
LP: . . . . . C 5521

MANCE LIPSCOMB, VOL. 3.
LP: . . . . . F 1026

MANCE LIPSCOMB VOL 4.
LP: . . . . . ARHOOLIE 1033

MANCE LIPSCOMB, VOL. 5.
LP: . . . . . F 1049

MANCE LIPSCOMB, VOL. 6.
LP: . . . . . F 1069

TEXAS BLUES.
LP: . . . . . ARHOOLIE 1049

TEXAS SONGSTER.
LP: . . . . . ARHOOLIE 1001

TEXAS SONGSTER VOL 2.
LP: . . . . . ARHOOLIE 1023

TEXAS SONGSTER VOL 3.
LP: . . . . . ARHOOLIE 1026

TEXAS SONGSTER VOL 6.
LP: . . . . . ARHOOLIE 1069

YOU'LL NEVER FIND ANOTHER.
LP: . . . . . ARHOOLIE 1077

Lipton, Celia

LONDON I LOVE, THE.
LP: . . . . . YU 102
MC: . . . . . CYU 102

Lipton, Sydney

1932-3 (Lipton, Sydney & his Orchestra).
LP: . . . . . SH 257

BEAUTIFUL MELODIES FROM AROUND THE WORLD.
LP: . . . . . YU 101
MC: . . . . . CYU 101

DANCING AT THE GROSVENOR HOUSE (Lipton, Sydney & his Orchestra).
Tracks: / Elmer's tune / Tisket a tasket, A / All I do is dream of you / Goodnight my love / I saw stars / Chloe / I'm sitting on top of the world / Sunday / Candy / Cabin in the sky / That old feeling / Should I / Deep in the heart of Texas / Down yonder / Frenesi / I'm thinking of my blue eyes / Adios / Till the end of the world / Perfidia / Do I worry / Petticoats of Portugal / Lisbon Antigua / My adobe hacienda / Cherry.
LP: . . . . . PLE 519

JUST DANCE (Lipton, Sydney & His Grosvenor House Orchestra).
Tracks: / Darkness on the delta / I've got an invitation to a dance / Why am I blue / Just a catchy little song / One night in Chinatown / Oh my goodness / Dinner music for a pack of hungry cannibals / Supposin' / Madame ah la marquise ah / Trusting my luck / Amoresque / It's a long way to your heart / Harlem / When a lady meets a gentleman down south / Reckless night on board an ocean liner / Souvenir of love / Just dance.
LP: . . . . . RFL 22

Liquid Faeries

EGGSHELLS AND SNAKESKINS.
Tracks: / Venetian shadow / It's sunny / Cocktails / Black snake / Another march / Raven eyes / Carousel / Indian / Devil it's cold.
LP: . . . . . SAVE 84

Liquid Gold

LIQUID GOLD.
Tracks: / Could be tonight / Substitute / Mr. Groovy / Dance yourself dizzy / My baby's baby / Anyway you do it.
LP: . . . . . POLP 101

Liquid Jesus

POUR IN THE SKY.
LP: . . . . . MCA 10191
MC: . . . . . MCAC 10191

Liquid Sky

LIQUID SKY (Film Soundtrack) (Various artists).
LP: . . . . . STV 81181

Liquidator

LIQUIDATOR, THE (Film soundtrack) (Various artists).
LP: . . . . . MCA 25137
MC: . . . . . MCAC 25137

Liquidators

LIQUIDATORS, THE.
Tracks: / Liquidator / Phoenix city / Miss Jamaica / Pressure drop / Skinhead moonstomp / Guns of Navarone / 007 (shanty town) / Shame and scandal / Ethiopia / Johnny too bad / Train to Skaville / Monkey man / Rudy, a message / It mek / Musical store room / Return of Django / Israelites / Train to Rainbow City / Guns fever / Double barrell / Dollar in the teeth / Don't be a rude boy / 12 minutes to go / Rudy's dead.
2LP: . . . . . VSOPLP 136
MC: . . . . . VSOPMC 136

Lisa Lisa

LISA LISA & CULT JAM WITH FULL FORCE (Lisa Lisa/Cult Jam with Full Force).
Tracks: / I wonder if I take you home / You'll never change / All cried out / This is Cult Jam / Can you feel the beat / Behind my eyes / Private property / Take me home.
LP: . . . . . CBS 26593
MC: 40 26593

SPANISH FLY (Lisa Lisa/Cult Jam).
Tracks: / Everything will be fine / Head to toe / Face in the crowd / Someone to love me for me / Talking nonsense / I promise you / Fool is born everyday, A / Lost in emotion / Playing with fire.
LP: 4504631
MC: 4504634

STRAIGHT OUTTA HELL'S KITCHEN (Lisa Lisa/Cult Jam).
Tracks: / Introduction (Interlude 1) / Something 'bout love / Let the music play / Let the beat hit 'em / You and me = love / Rainstorm / Don't say goodbye / Forever / Let it go / I like it / Love will get us by / Where were you when I needed you / Do it like that / Sensuality.
LP: 4685551
MC: 4685554

STRAIGHT TO THE SKY (Lisa Lisa/Cult Jam).
Tracks: / Just git it together / Little Jackie wants to be a star / Give me some of your time / U never nu how good u had it / Kiss your tears away / Dance forever / Straight to the sky / Gotta find somebody new / I can't take no more / I love what you do to me / Talking nonsense (part 2).
LP: 4634461
MC: 4634464

Lisburn Railway...

LISBURN RAILWAY ST.PRESBYTERIAN CHURCH CHOIR (Lisburn Railway St.Presbyterian Church Choir).
MC: . . . . . CPOL 828

Listen...

LISTEN MOVE AND DANCE NO.4 (Various artists).
LP: . . . . . CLP 3531

LISTEN MOVE AND DANCE NOS.1-3 (Various artists).
LP: CLP3762

LISTEN THEY'RE PLAYING MY SONG (Various artists).
MC: . . . . . AIM 71

Lister, Grahame

LUCKY DIP.
LP: . . . . . DIP 001

Liszt (composer)

HUNGARIAN AND RUMANIAN RHAPSODIES (Vienna State Opera Orchestra).
MC: . . . . . VETC 6505

LISZT (Various artists).
MC: . . . . . DLCMC 212

TRANSCENDENTAL STUDIES (Weber, Janice).
Tracks: / Transcendental studies (1838 version) / Presto / Molto vivace / Poco adagio / Mazeppa: A capriccio / Egualmente / Largo patetico / Allegro deciso / Presto strepitoso / Andantino / Presto molto agitatio / Lento assai.
LP: . . . . . MCC 10

TRANSCENDENTAL STUDIES AND OTHER WORKS (Howard, Leslie).
MC: . . . . . KA 66357

Litter

EMERGE.
Tracks: / Journeys / Feeling / Silly people / Blue ice / For What It's Worth / On our minds / Lucky 2.11 / Little Red Book / Breakfast At Gardenson's / Future of the past / Feeling.
LP: . . . . . WIK 68

Little America

LITTLE AMERICA.
Tracks: / You were right / That's the way it stays / Walk on fire / Perfect world / Lost along the way / Lies / Walk the land / Heroes / Underground / Out of bounds / Conversations / Standin' on top.
LP: 9241131
MC: 9241134

Little Angels

DON'T PREY FOR ME.
LP: 841 254 1

MC: 841 254 4

TOO POSH TO MOSH.
LP: . . . . AMP 14

YOUNG GODS.
MC: 847 846-4
LP: 847 846-1

Little Anthony

BEST OF LITTLE ANTHONY & THE IMPERIALS (Little Anthony & The Imperials).
Tracks: / Tears on my pillow / Two people in the world / So much / Diary, The (CD only.) / It's not for me (CD only.) / Wishful thinking / Prayer and a juke box, A / I'm alright (CD only.) / Shimmy, shimmy, ko-ko-bop / My empty room / I'm taking a vacation from love / Please say you want me / Traveling stranger (CD only.) / I'm on the outside (looking in) / Goin' out of my head / Hurt so bad / Take me back / I miss you so.
LP: . . . . ROU 5002
LP: 793 468 1
MC: . . . . TCROU 5002
MC: 793 468 4

OUTSIDE LOOKIN' IN... (Little Anthony & The Imperials).
Tracks: / I'm on the outside looking in / Goin' out of my head / Hurt so bad / Take me back / I miss you so / Out of sight out of mind / Hurt / Ten commandments of love / Better use your head / Gonna fix you good (every time you're bad) / It's not the same / I'm hypnotized / You better take it easy baby / Help me find a way (to say I love you) / Yesterday has gone / World of darkness.
LP: . . . . EG 2602911
MC: . . . . EG 2602914

Little Axe

SO MANY YEARS - SPIRIT OF MEMPHIS QUARTET.
LP: . . . . RF 1403

Little Bit Of

LITTLE BIT OF LIGHT RELIEF (Various artists).
LP: . . . . ROCK 2

Little Bit Of This...

LITTLE BIT OF THIS, LITTLE BIT OF THAT (Various artists).
LP: . . . . D 274

Little Black Sambo

STORY OF LITTLE BLACK SAMBO AND OTHERS (Bannerman, Helen).
Tracks: / Story of little black Quibba, The / Story of little black Quasha, The / Story of Sambo and the twins, The / Story of little black Bobtail, The / Story of little black Mingo, The.
MC: . . . . TS 322

Little Blue

LITTLE BLUE BRONTOSAURUS (George S Irving) (Priess, Bryon & William Stout).
MC: . . . . CDL 51726

Little Bo Bitch

LITTLE BO BITCH.
Tracks: / Take it easy / Lover / Hot summer / New town / Lonely boys / I'm confused / It's only love / Annoying all the neighbours / Heartbreaker / I want your love / Slow song / Stay alive.
LP: . . . . CBR 1002

Little Bob

RENDEZVOUS IN ANGEL CITY.
Tracks: / Isn't it enough / There'll never be another you / I can't wait / True love / Gimme you / Midnight crisis / As the lights go out / Keep on running / When the night falls / Never cry about the past.
LP: 104 181
MC: 104 184

Little, Booker

OUT FRONT.
Tracks: / We speak / Strength and sanity / Quiet, please / Moods in free time / Man of words / Hazy hues / New day, A.
LP: . . . . CS 9027

VICTORY AND SORROW.
Tracks: / Victory and sorrow / Forward flight / Looking ahead / If I should lose you / Calling softly / Booker's blues / Matilde.
LP: . . . . AFF 124

Little Brother

CHAMPION THE UNDERDOG.
Tracks: / Planned obsolescence / Soapmen & lumberjacks / Don't talk to me about the weather / That's not entertainment / SS spies / Never did me any warm / Sense of achievement / Time on your hands / Ugly truth / Grow up / Settle down / Wanking from the hip / Valium / Upperhand, The / Disappointed with the children / Johnny 7 / Slumping back to godliness / Nation unto nation / Pile of images / Land of the rising.
LP: . . . . CONCORD 36

Little Caesar

LITTLE CAESAR.
LP: . . . . WX 352
MC: . . . . WX 352 C

LYING WOMAN...GOODBYE BABY.
Tracks: / Goodbye baby / Long time baby / Goin' down to the river / Move me / If I could see my baby / Atomic love / Your money ain't long enough / You can't bring me down / Here is a letter / Do right blues / Chains of love have disappeared / Tried to reason with my baby / Can't stand it all alone / What kind of fool is he / Wonder why I'm leaving.
LP: . . . . KIX 24

Little Charlie

ALL THE WAY CRAZY (Little Charlie & The Nightcats).
Tracks: / T.V. crazy / Right around the corner / Clothes line / Living hand to mouth / Suicide blues / Poor Tarzan / When girls do it / Eyes like a cat / I'll take you back / Short skirts.
LP: . . . . SNTF 986

BIG BREAK, THE (Little Charlie & The Nightcats).
LP: . . . . AL 4776

CAPTURED LIVE (Little Charlie & The Nightcats).
Tracks: / Tomorrow night / Run me down / Rain / Dump that chump / Ten years ago / Thinking with the wrong head / Wildcattin' / Crawling kingsnake / Smart like Einstein / Eyes like a cat.
MC: . . . . AC 4794

DISTURBING THE PEACE (Little Charlie & The Nightcats).
Tracks: / That's my girl / Nervous / My money's green / If this is love / I ain't lyin' / She's talking / My last meal / Booty song, The / Don't boss me / V-8 Ford / I feel so sorry / Run me down.
LP: . . . . AL 4761

Little Chief

LOOSEN UP.
LP: . . . . PHZA 43

Little Dorrit

LITTLE DORRIT (Various artists).
LP: . . . . MOMENT 117
MC: . . . . MOMENTC 117

Little Drummer Girl

LITTLE DRUMMER GIRL, THE (Le Carre, John).
MC: . . . . TCLFP 417126-5

Little Eva

LIL'LOCO-MOTION.
Tracks: / Locomotion, The / Some kind-a wonderful / I have a love / Down home / Breaking up is hard to do / Run to her / He is the boy / Will you love me tomorrow / Keep your hands off my baby / Let's turkey trot / Old smokey locomotion / Locomotion (extended version), The.
LP: . . . . TAB 44
MC: . . . . KTBC 44

SWINGING ON A STAR (see under Irwin, Big Dee).

Little Feat

AS TIME GOES BY (The Best of Little Feat).
Tracks: / Dixie chicken / Willing / Rock and roll doctor / Trouble / Sailin' shoes / Spanish moon / Feats don't fail me now / All that you dream / Long distance love / Mercenary territory / Old folks boogie / 20 million things.
LP: . . . . WX 36
MC: . . . . WX 36C

DIXIE CHICKEN.
Tracks: / Dixie Chicken / Two Trains / Roll um easy / On Your Way Down / Kiss it off / Fool yourself / Walkin' all night / Fat man in the bathtub / Juliet / Lafayette Railroad.
LP: . . . . K 46200
MC: K4 46200

DOWN ON THE FARM.
Tracks: / Down on the farm / Six feet of snow / Perfect imperfection / Kokomo / Be one now / Straight from the heart / Front page news / Wake up dreaming / Feel the groove.
LP: . . . . K 56667
MC: K4 56667

FEATS DON'T FAIL ME NOW.
Tracks: / Rock and roll doctor / Cold cold cold / Tripe face boogie / Fan / Oh Atlanta / Skin It Back / Down The Road / Spanish Moon / Feats Don't Fail Me Now.
LP: . . . . K 56030
MC: K4 56030

HOY HOY.
Tracks: / Rocket in my locket / Rock & roll doctor / Skin it back / Easy to slip / Red streamliner / Lonesome whistle / Front page news / Fan / Forty four blues / Teenage nervous breakdown / Framed / Strawberry flats / Gringo / Over the edge / Two trains / China white / All that you dream / Feats don't fail me now.
2LP: . . . . K 66100
MC: K4 66100

LAST RECORD ALBUM, THE.
Tracks: / Romance Dance / All That You Dream / Long Distance Love / Day or Night / One Love / Down below the borderline / Somebody's leavin' / Mercenary Territory.
LP: . . . . K 56156
MC: K4 56156

LET IT ROLL.
Tracks: / Hate to lose your lovin' / One clear moment / Cajun girl / Hangin' on to the good times / Listen to your heart / Let it roll / Long time 'til I get over you / Business as usual / Change in luck / Voices on the wind.
LP: . . . . WX 192
MC: . . . . WX 192 C

LITTLE FEAT.
Tracks: / Snakes on everything / Strawberry flats / Truck stop girl / Brides of Jesus / Willing / Hamburger midnight / Forty four blues / How many more years / Crack in your door / I've been the one / Takin' my time / Crazy captain Gunboat Willie.
LP: . . . . K 46072

LITTLE FEAT & DIXIE CHICKEN.
Tracks: / Snakes on everything / Strawberry flats / Truck stop girl / Brides of Jesus / Willing / Hamburger midnight / Forty four blues / Crack in your door / I've been the one / Takin' my time / Crazy captain Gunboat Willie / Dixie chicken / Two trains / Roll um easy / On your way down / Kiss it off / Fool yourself / Walkin' all night / Fat man in the bathtub / Juliet / Lafayette railroad.
2LP: . . . . K 66038

REPRESENTING THE MAMBO.
LP: 7599261631
MC: 7599261634

SAILIN' SHOES.
Tracks: / Easy to slip / Cold cold cold / Trouble / Tripe face boogie / Willing / Apolitical blues / Sailin' Shoes / Teenage nervous breakdown / Got no shadows / Cat fever / Texas Rose Cafe.
MC: K4 46156
LP: . . . . K 46156

TIME LOVES A HERO.
Tracks: / Time loves a hero / Hi roller / New Delph freight train / Old folks boogie / Red streamliner / Keeping up with the Joneses / Rocket in my pocket / Missin' you / Day at the races, A.
LP: . . . . K 56349
MC: K4 56349

WAITING FOR COLUMBUS.
Tracks: / Join the band / Fat man in the bathtub / All that you dream / Oh Atlanta / Old folks' boogie / Time loves a hero / Day or night / Mercenary territory / Spanish moon / Dixie chicken / Tripe face boogie / Rocket in my pocket / Willing / Don't Bogart that joint / Political blues, A / Sailin' shoes / Feats don't fail me now.
2LP: . . . . K 66075
MC: K4 66075

Little Fish

FOUR HERTFORDSHIRE FOLK SONGS.
Tracks: / Hitchin Mayer's song / Lady Margaret / Hitchin volunteer marches / John Rand.
LP: . . . . PLR 011

Little Gerhard

IN DEUTSCHLAND.
Tracks: / Teenager in love / Jukebox baby / That's love / Baby lover / Don't promise me / Petticoat Pat / Shake baby shake / Whole lotta shakin' goin' on / All right (that's right).
LP: . . . . BF 15093

Little Ginny

COMING ON NICELY.
LP: . . . . SRT 2L003

MY DIXIE DARLING.
Tracks: / My dixie darling / No time at all / Kiss and say goodbye / Dixie chicken / Whisky get me gone / I'm an old cowhand / Miss the Mississippi / Elvira / Too good to throw away / Crystal chandeliers / Girls in love.
LP: . . . . PFL 3003

Little Grey Rabbit...

LITTLE GREY RABBIT COLLECTION, THE (see under Uttley, Allison) (Uttley, Alison).

LITTLE GREY RABBIT STORIES (Whitfield, June).
MC: . . . . P 90003

MORE LITTLE GREY RABBIT STORIES (Whitfield, June).
MC: . . . . P 90015

Little Harry

D.J.CLASH VOL. 2 (see Boyo, Billy & Little Harry).

Little Henry & The

LITTLE HENRY & THE TIGER Various artists (Various artists).
Tracks: / Little Henry & the tiger: *Various artists* / Two sisters, The: *Various artists* / Old man and his grandson, The: *Various artists* / Five servants, The: *Various artists* / Cock, the mouse and the little red hen, The: *Various artists.*
MC: . . . . ANV 626

Little Heroes

PLAY BY NUMBERS.
Tracks: / Melbourne's just not New York / Saturday afternoon inside / Something's got to happen / Running round in circles / Ophelia / One perfect day.
LP: . . . . EMC 3424

Little John

BEST OF LITTLE JOHN.
LP: . . . . LPRM 001

BOOMBASTIC.
LP: . . . . HB 74

CLARKE'S BOOTY.
LP: . . . . LALP 003

REGGAE DANCE.
LP: . . . . MRLP 1

RIVER TO THE BANK.
LP: . . . . DSR 6171

TRUE CONFESSION.
LP: . . . . Unknown

UNITE.
LP: . . . . VSLP 4061

WARRIORS AND TROUBLE.
LP: . . . . BLSCLP 004

YOUTH OF TODAY.
LP: . . . . SKDLP 003

Little & Large

LIVE AT ABBEY ROAD.
Tracks: / I could be so good for you / Crying / It's hard to be humble / Act naturally / Rock steady / Bridlington / My brudda Sylvest / Around the old campfire.
LP: . . . . EMS 1003
MC: . . . . TC MS 1003

SOOPERSONIC 'SYD SINGS'.
LP: . . . . NEVLP 132

Little Lenny

GUN IN A BAGGY.
LP: . . . . GREL 146
MC: . . . . GREEN 146

Little, Marie

MARIE LITTLE.
LP: . . . . LER 2084

MY ELDORADO.
LP: . . . . HGN 001

Little Mary Sunshine

LITTLE MARY SUNSHINE (Original London Cast) (Various artists).
LP: . . . . AEI 1105

Little Match Girl

LITTLE MATCH GIRL AND OTHER TALES (Reginald Spink) (Karloff, Boris (nar)).
Tracks: / Swineherd, The / Top and the ball, The / Red shoes, The / Thumbelina / Little match girl, The.
MC: 1117

THUMBELINA/THE LITTLE MATCH GIRL (See under Thumbelina).

Little Me

LITTLE ME (London cast recording) (Various artists).
Tracks: / Overture: *Various artists* / Truth, The: *Various artists* / On the other side of the tracks: *Various* artists / Rich kids rag: *Various artists* / I love you: *Various artists* / Deep down inside: *Various* artists / To be a performer: *Various artists* / Le grand boom-boom: *Various artists* / I've got your number: *Various artists* / Real live girl: *Various artists* / Poor little Hollywood star: *Various artists* / Little me: *Various artists* / Goodbye: *Various artists* / Here's to us: *Various artists.*
LP: . . . . FBLP 8077
MC: . . . . ZCFBL 8077

Little Mermaid

LITTLE MERMAID, THE.
MC: . . . . TS 319

LITTLE MERMAID, THE (Well Loved Tales Age Up to 9).
MC: . . . . PLB 73

LITTLE MERMAID, THE (Childrens Story Book).
MC: . . . . DIS 020

LITTLE MERMAID, THE (Original Film Soundtrack) (Various artists).
Tracks: / Fathoms below: *Various artists* / Fanfare: *Various artists* / Daughters of Triton: *Various artists*/ Part of your world: *Various artists* / Poor unfortunate souls: *Various artists* / Les poissons: *Various* artists / Kiss the girl: *Various artists* / Firework: *Various artists* / Jig: *Various artists* / Storm, The: *Various artists* / Destruction of the grotto: *Various artists* / Flotsam and Jetsam: *Various artists*/ Tour of the kingdom: *Various artists* / Bedtime: *Various artists* / Wedding announcement: *Various artists*/ Eric to the rescue: *Various artists* / Happy ending: *Various artists*.
MC: . . . . DSTMC 451

LITTLE MERMAID, THE (see Andersen, Hans Christian) (Andersen, Hans Christian).

LITTLE MERMAID, THE (Nesbitt, Cathleen).
MC: 1230

Little Milton

BACK TO BACK.
LP: . . . . MALP 7448

CHICAGO GOLDEN YEARS.
2LP: 427013

HIS GREATEST HITS.
Tracks: / Grits ain't groceries / I play dirty / Just a little bit / Who's cheating who / Losing hand / Blind man / More and more / If walls could talk / We're gonna make it / Baby I love you / Man loves two / So mean to me / Without my sweet baby / Feel so bad.
LP: . . . . GCH 8011
MC: . . . . GCHK 78011

HIS GREATEST SIDES VOL 1.
Tracks: / Grits ain't groceries / I play dirty / Just a little bit / Who's cheating who / Losing hand / Blind man / More and more / If walls could talk / We're gonna make it / Baby I love you / Man loves two / So mean to me / Without my sweet baby / Feel so bad.
LP: . . . . CXMP 2053

HITTIN' THE BOOGIE (Memphis days 1953-54).
LP: . . . . Z 2007

I WILL SURVIVE.
LP: . . . . MAL 7427

IF WALLS COULD TALK.
Tracks: / If walls could talk / Baby I love you / Let's get together / Things I used to do / Kansas City / Poor man's song / Blues get off my shoulder / I play dirty / Good to me as I am to you / Your precious love / I don't know.
LP: 515014
LP: . . . . CH 9289

LITTLE MILTON SINGS BIG BLUES.
Tracks: / Feel so bad / Reconsider / Stormy monday / Woke up this morning / Hard luck blues / Please,please,please / Sweet sixteen / Fever / Sneakin' around / Don't decieve me / Have mercy baby / Part time love.
LP: . . . . GCH 8037
MC: . . . . GCHK 78037

MOVING TO THE COUNTRY.
LP: . . . . MAL 7445
MC: . . . . MALC 7445

PLAYING FOR KEEPS.
LP: . . . . MAL 7419

RAISE A LITTLE SAND.
Tracks: / Homesick for my baby / Somebody told me / Lonesome for my baby / If you love me / Begging my baby / Let's boogie baby / Love at first sight / Hold me tight / I'm trying / Dead love / I found me a new love / Long distance operator / That will never do / My baby pleases me / Same old blues / I'm a lonely man.
LP: . . . . RL 011

SAM'S BLUES.
LP: . . . . CR 30102

WE'RE GONNA MAKE IT (CHARLY).
Tracks: / Losing hand / Believe in me / Ain't no big deal on you / Life is like that / Blind man / Stand by me / We're gonna make it / Who's cheating who / You're welcome to the club / I'm gonna move to the outskirts of town / Can't hold back the tears / Grits ain't groceries / Just a little bit / Poor man / Baby I love you / Let's get together / Your precious love / Kansas City / Good to me as I am to you / I play dirty / Things I used to do / I don't know / Blues get off my shoulder / If walls could talk.
LP: . . . . GCH 8028
MC: . . . . GCHK 78028

Little Miss Muffet

LITTLE MISS MUFFET & OTHER NURSERY RHYMES (Unknown narrator(s)).
MC: . . . . STK 015

Little Miss Stories

LITTLE MISS STORIES Read by John Alderton and Pauline Collins (Various artists).
LP: . . . . INGL 003
MC: . . . . INGC 003

Little Nemo

SOUNDS IN THE ATTIC.
LP: . . . . ARTY 9
MC: . . . . ARTYC 9

TURQUIOSE FIELDS.
LP: . . . . ARTY 22

Little Night Music

LITTLE NIGHT MUSIC, A (Original London cast) (Various artists).
Tracks: / Overture and night waltz: *Various artists* / Now: *Various artists* / Soon: *Various artists*/ Glamorous life, The: *Various artists* / You must meet my wife: *Various artists* / In praise of women: *Various* artists / Every day a little death: *Various artists* / Weekend in the country, A: *Various artists* / Sun won't set, The: *Various artists* / I would have been wonderful: *Various artists* / Perpetual anticipation: *Various* artists / Send in the clowns: *Various artists* / Miller's son, The: *Various artists* / Finale - send in the clowns (reprise): *Various artists* / Night waltz: *Various artists*.
LP: . . . . LRL 1 5090
MC: . . . . LRK 1 5090
MC: . . . . RK 11687
MC: . . . . GK 85090

LITTLE NIGHT MUSIC, A (Original Broadway cast) (Various artists).
LP: . . . . JS 32265
MC: . . . . PST 32265

Little Old...(bk)

LITTLE OLD MRS. PEPPERPOT.
MCSET: . . . . DTO 10558

Little Oz Stories

LITTLE OZ STORIES (Frank L. Baum) (Bolger, Ray).
MC: 1716

Little Princess

LITTLE PRINCESS, A (Frances Hodges Burnett) (Lipman, Maureen).
MCSET: 418 180-4
MCSET: . . . . ARGO 1112

LITTLE PRINCESS, A (Children's Classics).
MC: . . . . PLBC 210

Little Ramblers

LITTLE RAMBLERS 1924/5 VOL 1, THE.
LP: . . . . VLP 28

LITTLE RAMBLERS 1925/6 VOL 2, THE.
LP: . . . . VLP 29

Little Red Fox...

LITTLE RED FOX BOOK AND BROWN MOUSE BOOK (see under Uttley, Alison) (Scales, Prunella (nar)).

Little Red Hen...

LITTLE RED HEN, THE (well loved tales up to age 9).
MC: . . . . PLB 91

SLY FOX & THE LITTLE RED HEN (well loved tales up to age 9).
MC: . . . . PLB 92

Little Red Riding Hood

AND OTHER FAVOURITE STORIES FOR...
MC: . . . . VCA 606

LITTLE RED RIDING HOOD (Unknown narrator(s)).
MC: . . . . STK 002

LITTLE RED RIDING HOOD.
MC: . . . . TS 305

LITTLE RED RIDING HOOD (well loved tales age up to 9) (Unknown narrator(s)).
MC: . . . . PLB 55

Little Red Schoolhouse

GROOVY.
LP: . . . . DOM 3

GRUBBY HIGHWAY COUNTRY LANE.
Tracks: / When I find you / Good morning world / Hello hello / Not the only one / Full circle / Mind contracting drug / Switch of your mind / Hot day in smalltown / Good thing / Shady pool / Made of cotton / You can make me unhappy / Miss your world / Get out of my room / Yesterday's back again.
LP: . . . . BRED 87

Little Richard

16 ROCK AND ROLL CLASSICS.
Tracks: / Lucille / Tutti frutti / Hound dog / Keep a knockin' / Rip it up / Cherry red / Goodnight Irene / Girl can't help it, The / Short fat fanny / Good golly Miss Molly / Money honey / Whole lotta shakin' goin' on / Going home tomorrow / Send me some loving / Groovy little Suzie / Slippin' and slidin'.
LP: . . . . ARA 1002
MC: . . . . ARAC 1002

20 CLASSIC CUTS.
Tracks: / Long tall Sally / Ready Teddy / Girl can't help it, The / Rip it up / Miss Ann / She's got it / Lucille / Keep a knockin' / Good golly Miss Molly / Send me some lovin' / Tutti frutti / Hey hey hey / Slippin' and slidin' / Heebie jeebies / Baby face / Jenny Jenny / By the light of the silvery moon / Ooh my soul / True fine mama / Bama lama bama loo / Can't never let you go (CD & MC only) / Can't believe you wanna leave (CD & MC only).
LP: . . . . CH 195
MC: . . . . CHC 195

20 GREATEST HITS: LITTLE RICHARD (BLACK TULIP).
LP: 28013
MC: 48013

20 GREATEST HITS: LITTLE RICHARD (MASTERS).
LP: . . . . MA 0071840
MC: . . . . MAMC 971840

20 LITTLE RICHARD ORIGINAL HITS.
Tracks: / Good golly Miss Molly / Hey hey hey / Ooh my soul / Girl can't help it, The / Rip it up / Send me some lovin' / Bamba lama bama loo / She's got it / Boo hoo hoo / Lucille / Keep a knockin / True fine mama / Can't believe you wanna leave (Available on CD and cassette only) / Poor boy Paul / All around the world / Heebie jeebies / She knows how to rock / Kansas City baby / Jenny Jenny / Whole lotta shakin' goin on / Tutti frutti / I don't know what you got / Long tall Sally / Baby face / Short fat Fanny / Hound dog / (Sittin' on) the dock of the bay / Chains of love.
LP: . . . . SNTF 5017

AT HIS WILDEST Vol. 1.
LP: . . . . SM 3881

AT HIS WILDEST Vol. 3.
LP: . . . . SM 3883

BEST OF LITTLE RICHARD.
Tracks: / Rip it up / Tutti frutti / Long tall Sally / Girl can't help it, The / Whole lotta shakin' goin' on / Good golly Miss Molly / Bring me some lovin' / Hound dog / Short fat Fanny / Money honey / Cherry red / Lucille / Baby face.
MC: 16-12

BIG HITS.
LP: . . . . GNPS 9033
MC: GNP5 9033

COLLECTION: LITTLE RICHARD.
2LP: . . . . CCSLP 227
MC: . . . . CCSMC 227

DOLLARS, DOLLARS AND MORE DOLLARS.
LP: . . . . CR 30009

EARLY STUDIO OUTTAKES.
LP: . . . . SJLP 565

FABULOUS LITTLE RICHARD, THE.
Tracks: / Shake a hand / Chicken little baby / All night long / Most I can offer / Lonesome and blue / Wonderin' / Whole lotta shakin' goin' on / She knows how to rock / Kansas City / Directly from my heart / Maybe I'm right / Early one morning / I'm just a lonely guy.
LP: . . . . CH 133
MC: . . . . FABC 001

FRIENDS FROM THE BEGINNING (Little Richard & Jimi Hendrix).
Tracks: / Whole lotta shakin' goin' on / Goodnight Irene / Keep a knockin' / Going home tomorrow / Belles stars / Tutti frutti / Lawdy Miss Clawdy / Why don't you love me / Lucille / Hound dog / Money money / Funky dish rag.
LP: . . . . EMB 3434

GEORGIA PEACH, THE.
LP: . . . . CR 30190

GET DOWN WITH IT.
Tracks: / Get down with it / Little bit of something, A / I don't want to discuss it / Land of a thousand dances / Commandments of love, The / Money / Poor dog (who can't wag his own tail) / I need love / Never gonna let you go / Don't decieve me (please don't go) / Function at the junction / Hurry sundown / Rosemary / Well.
LP: . . . . ED 114

GET DOWN WITH LITTLE RICHARD.
LP: . . . . REDITA 114

GOLDEN HIGHLIGHTS OF LITTLE RICHARD.
LP: 54732
MC: 40 54732

GRAFFITI COLLECTION.
MC: . . . . GRMC 11

GREAT LITTLE RICHARD, THE.
LP: . . . . DEMAND 0025

GREATEST HITS: LITTLE RICHARD.
Tracks: / Lucille / Good golly Miss Molly / Long, tall Sally / Tutti frutti / Keep a knockin'.
MC: 40 32185
MC: . . . . GM 0227
LP: . . . . FUN 9017
MC: . . . . FUNC 9017
LP: 32185

GREATEST HITS: LITTLE RICHARD (PICKWICK).
MC: . . . . HSC 3400

HERE'S LITTLE RICHARD (Little Richard & His Band).
Tracks: / Tutti frutti / True fine mama / Ready Teddy / Baby / Slippin' and slidin' / Long tall Sally / Miss Ann / Oh why / Rip it up / Jenny Jenny / She's got it / Can't believe you wanna leave.
LP: . . . . CH 128

HE'S GOT IT.
Tracks: / Tutti frutti / Long tall Sally / Slippin' and slidin' / Rip it up / Girl can't help it, The / Lucille / Send me some lovin' / Jenny Jenny / Keep a knockin' / Good golly Miss Molly / Ooh my soul / Baby face.
LP: . . . . TOP 101
MC: . . . . KTOP 101

HIS BIGGEST HITS.
Tracks: / Rip it up / Lucille / Jenny Jenny / All around the world / Good golly Miss Molly / Long tall Sally / Slippin' and slidin' / Send me some lovin' / Boo hoo hoo / True fine mama / Tutti frutti / Keep a knockin'.
LP: . . . . SNTF 5027

HIS GREATEST RECORDINGS.
Tracks: / Ready Teddy / Rip it up / Girl can't help it, The / I'll never let you go / Miss Ann / Good golly Miss Molly / Lucille / Keep a knockin' / Can't believe you wanna leave / Tutti frutti / Heebie jeebies / Send me some lovin' / Chicken little baby / Hey hey hey / She's got it / Long tall Sally.
LP: . . . . CHA 109
MC: . . . . CHC 109

KING OF ROCK 'N' ROLL.
LP: . . . . ENT LP 13044
MC: . . . . ENT MC 13044

LIFETIME FRIEND.
Tracks: / Great gosh a'mighty / Operator / Somebody's comin' / Lifetime friends / Destruction / I found my way / World can't do me, The / One ray of sunshine / Someone cares / Big house reunion.
LP: . . . . WX 72
MC: . . . . WX 72C

LITTLE RICHARD.
Tracks: / Whole lotta shakin' goin' on / Rip it up / Baby face / Send me some lovin' / Girl can't help it, The / Lucille / Ooh my soul / Jenny Jenny / Good golly Miss Molly / Tutti frutti / Long tall Sally / Keep a knockin' / Money honey / Hound dog / Groovy little Suzie / Dancing all around the world / Slippin' and slidin' / Lawdy Miss Clawdy / Short fat Fanny / She's got it.
LP: . . . . DVLP 2083
MC: . . . . DVMC 2083
2LP: . . . . CR 102
MCSET: . . . . CRT 102

LITTLE RICHARD - NOW.
LP: . . . . CRLP 510

LITTLE RICHARD (OCEAN).
Tracks: / Good golly Miss Molly / Ready teddy / Jenny Jenny / Miss Ann / Lucille / Send me some lovin' / By the light of the silvery moon / Baby face / She's got it / Bama lama bama loo / Keep a knockin' / Slippin' and a slidin' / Girl can't help it, The / Tutti frutti.
LP: . . . . OCN 2030WL
MC: . . . . OCN 2030WK

LITTLE RICHARD (SONET) (Little Richard & His Band).
LP: . . . . SNTF 5026

LITTLE RICHARD VOL.2.
Tracks: / Keep a knockin' / Send me some lovin' / I'll never let you go / All around the world / By the light of the silvery moon / Good golly Miss Molly / Baby face / Hey hey hey / Ooh my soul / Lucille / Girl can't help it, The.
LP: . . . . CH 131

LONG LIVE ROCK 'N' ROLL (see under Berry, Chuck) (Little Richard & Chuck Berry).

LONG TALL SALLY.

Tracks: / Whole lotta shakin' goin' on / Rip it up / Baby face / Send me some lovin' / Girl can't help it ,The / Lucille / Jenny Jenny / Good golly Miss Molly / Tutti frutti / Long tall Sally / Keep a knockin' / Money honey / Hound dog / Slippin' and slidin' / Lawdy Miss Clawdy / True fine mama / She's got it.
LP: . . . . **SHLP 150**
MC: . . . . **SHTC 150**
LP: . . . . **RMB 5646**

LUCILLE.
Tracks: / Lucille / Long tall Sally / Baby face / Good golly Miss Molly / Tutti frutti (end s1) / Whole lotta shakin' goin' on / Money, honey / Girl can't help it, The / Jenny, Jenny / Hound dog.
LP: . . . . **CBR 1020**
MC: . . . . **KCBR 1020**
MC: . . . . **BRC 2510**
LP: . . . . **SM 3885 2**

MODERN SIDES.
Tracks: / Lucille / Holy mackerel / Directly from my heart / I'm back / Jenny Jenny / Long tall Sally / Slippin' and slidin' / Good golly Miss Molly / Don't you want a man like me / Sed me some lovin' / Miss Ann.
LP: . . . . **CH 38**

OOH MA SOUL (MAGNUM FORCE).
Tracks: / Precious Lord / I know the lord will make a way for me / I'm quitting show business / Does Jesus care? / Just a closer walk with thee / Milky white way / Need him now / I'm going to tell god.
LP: . . . . **MFLP 1035**

OOH MY SOUL.
Tracks: / It ain't what you do / Lawdy Miss Clawdy / Hound dog / Slippin' and slidin' / Ooh my soul / Blueberry Hill / Cherry red / Girl can't help it, The / Talking 'bout soul / Dance what you wanna / Something moves in / My heart / Baby face / Short fat Fanny / Cross over / My wheel's been slippin' / All the way / Goodnight Irene.
LP: . . . . **CR 30216**

RARE LITTLE RICHARD.
LP: . . . . **REDITA 101**

REAL THING, THE.
Tracks: / Long tall Sally / Whole lotta shakin' goin' on / Money honey / Lucille / I don't know what you got / She's got it / Hound dog / Jenny Jenny / Good golly Miss Molly / Girl can't help it, The / Tutti frutti / Goodnight Irene.
LP: . . . . **MFM 018**

REPLAY ON LITTLE RICHARD.
LP: . . . . **FEDB 5023**
MC: . . . . **FEDC 5023**

ROCK 'N' ROLL RESURRECTION.
Tracks: / Tutti frutti / Girl can't help it, The / Lucille / Good golly Miss Molly / Long tall Sally / Rip it up / Slippin' and slidin' / Keep a knockin' / Ready Teddy / She's got it / Bama lama bama loo / Send me some lovin' / Miss Ann / Ooh my soul / True fine mama / Jenny Jenny / By the light of the silvery moon / Baby face / All round the world / Can't believe you wanna leave.
LP: . . . . **CR 30258**
MC: . . . . **TCCR 30258**

ROCKIN''N'RAVIN' (Little Richard/ Boots Brown & His Blockbusters).
Tracks: / Get rich quick / Why did you leave me / Taxi blues / Every hour / I brought it all on myself / Ain't nothing happening / Thinkin' 'bout my mother / Please have mercy on me / Blockbuster / Hip boots / Shortnin' bread / Blue fairy boogie / Breakfast ball / Double clutch / Dynamite / Oh happy day.
LP: . . . . **NL 89965**
MC: . . . . **NK 89965**

SESSIONS, THE.
LP: **551 85**

SINGS GOSPEL FAVOURITES.
Tracks: / Every time I feel the Spirit / I'm tramping / Milky white way / Does Jesus care / Coming home / I know the lord / I've just come from the mountain / God is real / Troubles of the world / Certainly Lord / Tell God my troubles.
LP: . . . . **BDL 1023**

SLIPPIN', SLIDIN' AND SHAKIN'.
Tracks: / Whole lotta shakin' goin' on / Money honey / Good golly Miss Molly / Tutti frutti / Lucille / Rip it up / She's got it / Long tall Sally / Keep a knockin' / Jenny Jenny / Send me some lovin' / Slippin' and slidin' / Girl can't help it, The / Baby face.
LP: . . . . **INS 5014**
MC: . . . . **TCINS 5014**

SPECIALITY SESSIONS, THE (Box set).
LPS: . . . . **ABOXLP 1**
MCSET: . . . . **ABOXMC 1**

TWINS (See under Bailey, Phillip) (Little Richard & Phil Bailey).

UNRELEASED LITTLE RICHARD, THE.
Tracks: / Good golly Miss Molly / Rip it up / Keep a knockin' / Tutti frutti / Ooh my soul / Send me some lovin' / Bama lama bama loo / Lucille / Girl can't help it, The / Jenny Jenny / Slippin' and slidin' / By the light of the silvery moon / Baby face / Miss Ann.
LP: **2C 068 64303**

WHOLE LOTTA SHAKIN'.
Tracks: / Whole lotta shakin' goin' on / Good golly Miss Molly / Tutti frutti / Lucille / I don't know what you got / Long tall Sally / Baby face / She's got it / Short fat Fannie / Hound dog / (Sittin' on) the dock of the bay / Chains of love.
LP: . . . . **BDL 1042**
MC: . . . . **BDC 1042**

Little River Band

BACKSTAGE PASS.
Tracks: / It's a long way there / So many paths / Statue of liberty / Fall from paradise / Light of day / Night and day / Reminiscing / Man in black / Help is on it's way / Hard life / Rumour / Mistress of mine / Too lonely too long / Red shoes / I don't worry no more / Let's dance / Man on the run / It's not a wonder / Sweet old fashioned man.
2LP: . . . . **ESTSP 12061**

BEGINNINGS.
LP: **1A 022 58115**

COLLECTION: LITTLE RIVER BAND.
LP: . . . . **IC 038 82307**

DIAMANTINA COCKTAIL.
Tracks: / Help is on it's way / Days on the road / Happy anniversary / Another runaway / Everyday of my life / Home on Monday / Inner light, The / Broke again / Take me home.
LP: . . . . **EMC 3187**

FIRST UNDER THE WIRE.
Tracks: / Lonesome loser / Rumour / By my side / Cool change / It's not a wonder / Hard life / Middle man / Man on the run / Mistress of mine.
LP: . . . . **EAST 11954**

IT'S A LONG WAY THERE.
LP: **1A 054 82516**

LITTLE RIVER BAND.
LP: . . . . **FA 4130761**
MC: . . . . **TCFA 41 30764**

SLEEPER CATCHER.
Tracks: / Fall from paradise / Lady / Red-headed wildflower / Light of day / So many paths / Reminiscing / Sanity's side / Shut down, turn off / One for the road.
LP: . . . . **IC 064 82437**
LP: . . . . **EMA 786**

TIME EXPOSURES.
Tracks: / Night owls / Man on your mind / Take it easy on me / Ballerina / Love will survive / Full circle / Just say that you love me / Suicide Boulevard / Orbit zero / Don't let the needle win / Guiding light.
LP: . . . . **EST 12163**

Little Rock Combo

RAGGED AND DIRTY.
LP: . . . . **ROCK 8903**

Little Romance

LITTLE ROMANCE, A Original soundtrack (Various artists).
LP: . . . . **STV 81109**

Little Roosters

TO WHOM IT MAY CONCERN.
LP: . . . . **E 1**

Little Roy

COLUMBUS SHIP.
LP: . . . . **COP LP 1**

Little Shop Of Horrors

LITTLE SHOP OF HORRORS (Film Soundtrack) (Various artists).
Tracks: / Prologue (little shop of horrors): *Various artists* / Da doo: *Various artists* / Grow for me: *Various artists* / Somewhere that's green: *Various artists* / Some fun now: *Various artists* / Dentist: *Various* artists / Feed me: *Various artists* / Suddenly, Seymour: *Various artists* / Suppertime: *Various artists*/ Meek shall inherit, The: *Various artists* / Mean green mother from outer space: *Various artists* / Finale: *Various artists* / Skid Row (downtown): *Various artists.*
LP: . . . . **K 9241251**
MC: . . . . **K 9241254**

LITTLE SHOP OF HORRORS (Broadway cast recording) (Various artists).
LP: . . . . **GEF 70244**

Little Sonny

NEW KING OF THE BLUES HARMONICA.
Tracks: / Baby what you want me to do / Eli's pork chop / Hey little girl / Hot potato / Don't ask me no questions / Tomorrow's blues today / Back down yonder / Sad funk / Creeper return, The.
LP: . . . . **MPS 8533**
MC: . . . . **MPS 58533**

Little Steven

FREEDOM NO COMPROMISE.
Tracks: / Freedom / Trail of broken treaties / Pretoria / Bitter fruit / No more party's / Can't you feel the fire / Native American / Sanctuary.
LP: . . . . **MTL 1010**
MC: . . . . **TCMTL 1010**
LP: . . . . **MTL 1008**
MC: . . . . **TCMTL 1008**

MEN WITHOUT WOMEN (Little Steven & The Disciples Of Soul).
LP: . . . . **ATAK 60**
MC: . . . . **TCATAK 60**
LP: . . . . **AML 3027**

REVOLUTION.
Tracks: / Where do we go from here / Education / Love and forgiveness / Sexy / Liberation theology / Revolution / Balance / Newspeak / Leonard Peltier / Discipline.
LP: . . . . **PL 83431**
MC: . . . . **PK 83431**

VOICE OF AMERICA.
Tracks: / Voice of America / Justice / Checkpoint Charlie / Solidarity / Out of the darkness / Los desaparecido (The disappeared ones) / Fear / I am not a patriot (and the river opens for the righteous) / Among the believers / Undefeated (everybody goes home).
LP: . . . . **EJ 2401511**
MC: . . . . **EJ 2401514**

Little Thief

LITTLE THIEF, THE (LA PETITE VOLEUSE) (Original soundtrack) (Various artists).
LP: . . . . **A 399**

Little Tina

MINI LP COLLECTION (Little Tina & Flight '56).
LP: . . . . **MLP 8416**

THIS LITTLE GIRL IS GONNA ROCK (Little Tina & Flight '56).
LP: . . . . **CR 30155**

Little Twitch

PRETTY PRETTY (See under Mouse, John) (Little Twitch & John Mouse).

Little Walter

BEST OF LITTLE WALTER.
Tracks: / My babe / Sad hours / You're so fine / Last night / Blues with a feeling / Can't hold out much longer / Juke / Mean old world / Off the wall / You better watch yourself / Blue light / Tell me mama.
LP: . . . . **GCH 8018**
MC: . . . . **GCHK 78018**
LP: . . . . **CH 9192**

BLUES WITH A FEELING.
Tracks: / Juke / Sad hours / Crazy legs / Off the wall / Blue lights / I got to find my baby / Rocker / Mellow down easy / I got to go / Temperature / Crazy mixed up world / Key to the highway / Can't hold out much longer / Blues with a feeling / Tell me mama / You're so fine / You better watch yourself / Quarter to twelve and lights out / Last night / My babe / One more chance with you / Confessin' the blues / Rock bottom / Toddle, The.
LP: . . . . **LP 123**

BLUES WORLD OF LITTLE WALTER.
LP: . . . . **DL 648**

CHESS MASTERS - LITTLE WALTER 1.
Tracks: / Boogie / Don't have to hunt no more / Tonight with a fool / Quarter to twelve / Last boogie / Too late / Fast boogie / Lights out / Thunderbird / I got to go / Crazy for my baby / Who / It ain't right / Flying saucer / Just a feeling / Shake dancer / Ah'w baby / Confessin' the blues / Key to the highway / Back track / Blue and lonesome / Going down slow / I don't play / Just your fool.
2LP: . . . . **CXMD 4002**
2LP: . . . . **CXMD 4011**

CHICAGO GOLDEN YEARS.
2LP: **427001**

COLLECTION: LITTLE WALTER (20 blues greats).
Tracks: / Walter's blues / Going down slow / Blue mood / Lovin' you all the time / Rock bottom / I've had my fun / Mean old Frisco / Temperature / Flying saucer / Just you fool / Snake dancer / Too late / Mellow down easy / I don't play / Ah'w baby / Me and Piney Brown / I got to go / Thunderbird / One more chance with you / It's too late, brother.
LP: . . . . **DVLP 2114**
MC: . . . . **DVMC 2114**

CONFESSIN' THE BLUES.
LP: . . . . **BRP 2025**

HERE TO SEE YOU GO.
LP: . . . . **CH 9321**

LIVE AT THE CHICAGO BLUES FESTIVAL (See under Rush, Otis).

ON THE ROAD AGAIN.
LP: . . . . **XTRA 1133**

QUARTER TO TWELVE.
Tracks: / Quarter to twelve / Mellow down easy / Lights out / I hate to see you go / My baby is sweeter / Crazy mixed up world / Rocker / Oh baby / Blue midnight / It ain't right / Who / Back track / Everything gonna be alright / Crazy legs / Crazy for my baby / Toddle, The.
LP: . . . . **RL 002**

THUNDERBIRD.
Tracks: / Too late / Thunderbird / I got to go / One more chance with you / Flying saucer / It's too late brother / Just a good feeling / Teenage beat / Shake dancer / Temperature / I've had my fun / Ah'w baby / Rock bottom / Mean old Frisco.
LP: . . . . **SC 004**

WE THREE KINGS (see under Howlin Wolf) (Howlin' Wolf, Little Walter & Muddy Waters).

WINDY CITY BLUES (Little Walter/Otis Rush).
Tracks: / It's hard for me to believe baby / May be the last time / I feel good / Otis' blues / Going down slow / Walter's blues / Lovin' you all the time / Blue mood.
LP: . . . . **BMLP 1028**

Little White Doves...

LITTLE WHITE DOVES OF LOVE (Barbara Cartland) (Sinden, Jeremy (nar)).
MC: . . . . **IAB 88073**

Little Willie John

FEVER.
Tracks: / Fever / I'm stickin' with you baby / Do something for me / Love, life and money / Suffering with the blues / Dinner date / All around the world / Need your love so bad / Young girl / Letter from my darling / I've got to go cry / My nerves.
LP: . . . . **SING 564**

FREE AT LAST.
LP: . . . . **BID 8017**
MC: . . . . **GD 5034**

GRITS AND SOUL.
Tracks: / All around the world / Need your love so bad / Fever / Do something for me / Suffering with the blues / I've been around / Person to person / Talk to me, talk to me / Let's rock while the rockin's good / Let them talk / Leave my kitten alone / Walk slow / My baby's in love with another guy / You hurt me / Big blue diamonds / Come back to me.
LP: . . . . **CRB 1098**
MC: . . . . **TCCRB 1098**

MISTER LITTLE WILLIE JOHN (John, Little Willie).
Tracks: / You're a sweetheart / Let's rock while the rockin's good / Look what you've done to me / Home at last / Are you ever coming back / Don't leave me dear / All my love belongs to you / Spasms / Will the sun shine tomorrow / You got to get up early in the morning / Little bit of lovin' / Why don't you haul off and love me.
LP: . . . . **SING 603**
MC: . . . . **ZCLG 015**
LP: . . . . **BID 8004**

TALK TO ME, TALK TO ME.
Tracks: / Talk to me, talk to me / I've been around / Drive me home / I'll carry your love wherever I go / No more in life / Uh uh baby / Person to person / Until you do / Tell it like it is / Don't be ashamed to call my name / If I thought you needed me / There is someone in this world for me.
LP: . . . . **SING 596**

Little Women

LITTLE WOMEN (Louisa May Alcott) (Jackson, Glenda).
MCSET: . . . . **SAY 99**
MCSET: . . . . **ARGO 1175**

LITTLE WOMEN (see under Alcott, Louisa May) (Jackson, Glenda).

LITTLE WOMEN (Louisa May Alcott) (Harris, Julie).
MC: **1470**

LITTLE WOMEN (Stritch, Elaine).
MC: . . . . **P 90041**

Littlefield, Little

BOOTED (See under Gordon, Roscoe) (Littlefield, Little Willie/Roscoe Gordon).

HAPPY PAY DAY.
Tracks: / Since i met you baby / Fortune cookie / Spanish harlem / Easy / Hey good lookin' / Blues for moody / Happy

pay day / I love you because / Willies boogie 85 / Friend in need / There is water in my ears / Chinatown boogie.
LP: . . . . CH 150

HOUSEPARTY.
LP: . . . . OL 8003

I'M IN THE MOOD.
LP: . . . . OL 8006

IT'S MIDNIGHT.
Tracks: / It's midnight / Farewell / Drinkin' hadacol / Merry Xmas / Frightened / Your love wasn't so / Happy pay day / Rockin' chair mama / Trouble around me / You never miss a good woman / Hit the road / Once was lucky / Life of trouble / Too late for me / Ruby. Ruby.
LP: . . . . KIX 10

JUMPIN' WITH....
Tracks: / Joint jumping Mama / How long / Willie's boogie medley / Hucklebuck, The / Willie's after hours / Willie's blues / Searching for my baby / Drinking hadacol / Tell me baby / Nights are so long / So fine and brown / I want you / Sun is shining (at your front door). The / I've been lost / Just before sunrise / Three times three.
LP: . . . . CHD 114

KC LOVING.
Tracks: / Striking on you baby / Blood is redder than wine / K.C. loving / Pleading at midnight / Midnight hour was shining / Miss KC's fine / Rockabye baby / My best wishes and regards / Jim Wilson's boogie / Sitting on the curbstone / Please don't stop / Falling tears / Goofy dust blues / Don't take my heart little girl.
LP: . . . . KC 101

LITTLE WILLIE LITTLEFIELD PLAYS BOOGIE WOOGIE (July 1987).
LP: . . . . SCH 100

LITTLE WILLIE LITTLEFIELD, VOL.1.
Tracks: / Mello cats / Life of trouble / I like it / Moon is rising / Once was lucky / Ain't a better story told / Mean mean woman / Real fine mama / Nakite stomp / Lump in my throat.
LP: . . . . CH 24

LITTLE WILLIE LITTLEFIELD VOL 2.
Tracks: / Love me tonight / Blues at sunset / I'd like to see you / Cheerful baby / Hit the road / Rockin' chair mama / Trouble all around me / Tell me baby / Long about midnight / Train whistle blowing.
LP: . . . . CH 34

Littlejohn, Johnny

CHICAGO BLUES SESSIONS 13 (Littlejohn, Johnny Blues).
LP: . . . . WOLF 120 859

CHICAGO BLUES STARS.
LP: . . . . ARHOOLIE 1043

KINGS OF THE SLIDE GUITAR (see under Taylor, Hound Dog) (Littlejohn, Johnny/Hound Dog Taylor).

SO CALLED FRIENDS.
LP: . . . . R 2621

SULTANS OF THE SLIDE GUITAR.
LP: 2003

Littleton, John

STEAL AWAY.
LP: . . . . AV 4904
MC: . . . . AV 5904

Live...

LIVE AND DIRECT - VOL.2 (Various artists).
LP: . . . . INT 5
MC: . . . . INC 5

LIVE AT THE FESTIVAL (Various artists).
LP: . . . . ENJA 2030

Live at...

LIVE AT THE GREAT AMERICAN MUSIC HALL (Various artists).
LP: . . . . FF 238

LIVE AT THE ROXY (Various artists).
Tracks: / Strange boy: *Various artists* / Smile and wave goodbye: *Various artists* / Relics from the past: *Various artists* / I live in a car: *Various artists* / Telephone numbers: *Various artists* / Get yourself killed: *Various artists* / Never wanna leave: *Various artists* / Here comes the knife: *Various artists* / T.V. drink: *Various artists* / Sniper: *Various artists* / Tough on you: *Various artists* / Fun fun fun: *Various artists*/ Vertigo: *Various artists* / Lullabies lie: *Various artists.*
LP: . . . . THBL 011

LIVE AT THE ZAP CLUB (Various artists).
LP: . . . . ZAP 001

Live At Knitting...

LIVE AT KNITTING FACTORY VOL 1 (Various artists).
LP: . . . . EMY 111

LIVE AT KNITTING FACTORY VOL 2 (Various artists).
LP: . . . . EMY 112

Live At The Rockhouse

LIVE AT THE ROCKHOUSE (Various artists).
LP: . . . . LP 8604
LP: . . . . LP 8306

Live In...

LIVE IN A SCOTCH LIVING ROOM (Various artists).
MC: . . . . MCTAPE 001

Live & Let Die

LIVE AND LET DIE (THEME FROM) (See under Wings) (Wings).

LIVE & LET DIE (Film Soundtrack) (Various artists).
Tracks: / Live and let die: *McCartney, Paul & Wings* / Just a closer walk with thee: *Various artists* / New second line: *Dejan, Harold A. "Duke" & The Olympia Brass Band* / Bond meets Solitaire: *Various artists* / Whisper who dares: *Various artists* / Snakes alive: *Various artists* / Baron Samedi's dance of death: *Various artists*/ San Monique: *Various artists* / Fillet of soul: *Various artists* / Live and let die: *Arnau, BJ* / Fillet of soul: *Various artists* / Bond drops in: *Various artists* / If he finds it, kill him: *Various artists*/ Trespassers will be eaten: *Various artists* / Solitaire gets her cards: *Various artists* / Sacrifice: *Various artists* / James Bond theme: *Various artists.*
LP: . . . . EMS 1269
MC: . . . . TCEMS 1269
LP: . . . . UAS 29475

Live Sex

EXPRESSION OF FAITH, AN.
LP: . . . . HWO 4

Live Skull

BRINGING HOME THE BAIT.
LP: . . . . HMS 022

CLOUD ONE.
LP: . . . . HMS 056

DON'T GET ANY ON YOU.
LP: . . . . HMS 083

POSITRACTION.
LP: . . . . GOES ON 29

RAISE THE MANIFESTATION.
LP: . . . . HMS 080

Live Wire

CHANGES MADE.
Tracks: / Changes made / Childs eye / Sleep / Don't look now / Running / Soundtrack / Anarchists in love / Power / Wait in the shadows / Burn.
LP: . . . . AMLH 68522

NO FRIGHT.
Tracks: / Don't bite the hand / Competition / Broken glass / Break day / Castle in ever Swiss cottage / One more show / First night every night / Tagesschau / No fright / Red light is on.
LP: . . . . AMLH 64814

PICK IT UP.
LP: . . . . AMLH 64793

Lively Body

LIVELY BODY (Various artists).
LP: . . . . Unknown

Lively, Penelope

GHOST OF THOMAS KEMPE, THE (Adams, Rosalind).
MCSET: CC/040
MC: 882154

HOUSE INSIDE OUT, A (Mitchell, Sheila).
MC: 2CCA 3064

JUDGEMENT DAY.
MC: . . . . CAB 324

UNINVITED GHOSTS.
MCSET: 086 222 0482

Liverpool...

LIVERPOOL 1963-1964 VOL.2 (Various artists).
Tracks: / I know: *Marsden, Beryl* / Peter Gunn locomotion: *Starr, Freddie & the Midnighters* / You've gotta keep her underhand: *Big Three* / Walking the dog: *Dennisons* / Everything's alright: *Mojos* / Lucy (you sure did it this time): *Dennisons* / Baby blue: *Starr, Freddie & the Midnighters* / I'm gonna knock on your door: *Best, Pete Four* / Skinny Minnie (live): *Curtis, Lee And The Allstars* / What'd I say (live): *Big Three* / I've got that feeling: *Orchids* / I know: *Graham, Chick & the Coasters* / Dance baby dance: *Graham, Chick & the Coasters*/ Little you, A: *Graham, Chick & the Coasters* / Seven daffodils: *Mojos* / If you ever change your mind: *Big Three* / Everybody loves a lover: *Marsden, Beryl* / Be my girl: *Dennisons* / Why did I ever fall in love with you: *Best, Pete Four* / Forever: *Mojos.*
LP: . . . . CM 125

Liverpool Cathedral

CHOIR OF LIVERPOOL METROPOLITAN CATHEDRAL.
LP: . . . . LPB 816

CHRISTMAS AT LIVERPOOL CATHEDRAL.
LP: . . . . MVP 785

CHRISTMAS CAROLS.
Tracks: / Hark the herald angels sing / Truth from above, The / See, amid the winter's snow / Christmas pastorale on the chorale / Echo carol / I sing of a maiden / Choral prelude / Away in a manger / Geborn ist der emmanuel / O come all ye faithful / Ding dong merrily on high / Sleep Mary's son / Holly and the ivy, The / Maiden most gentle, A / Es ist ein ros' entsprungen / Tyrley tyrlow / Song of the nuns of Chester / Child in a manger / God rest ye merry gentlemen.
LP: . . . . APS 326

CHRISTMAS MUSIC FROM....
LP: . . . . LPB 661

FESTIVAL OF PRAISE ADVENT-ASCENSION.
LP: . . . . MVP 774

SINGS.
LP: . . . . LPB 663

Liverpool Ceili Band

OFF TO DUBLIN.
Tracks: / Christmas Eve / Mountain road, The / Glenallen / Youghal harbour / Morrisons / Killimor, The / Knights of St. Patrick / Centenary / Foggy dew, The / Who fears to speak of '98 / God save Ireland / Farewell to Connaught / Dublin / Tom Ward's downfall / O'Neills / Clan na h'eireann / Boys of Wexford / Off to Dublin / In the green / Reel of Rio / Wild Irishman, The / Mulhaires / Fallon's / Kitty's wedding / Bill Hart's favourite / Jimmy Ward's favourite / Ceol A. Imala / Hare's foot / Silver spear / Gregg's pipes.
MC: 823 421-4

Liverpool Express

TRACKS.
Tracks: / Smile / Hold tight / Never the same without love / You are my love / She's a lady / Call me your love / It's a beautiful day / (I remember) Julian the hooligan / Rosemary / Doing it all again / Every man must have a dream.
LP: . . . . K 56281

Lives of Angels

ELEVATOR TO EDEN.
LP: . . . . FIRELP 2

Lives & Times

SWEET DISORDER.
Tracks: / Window on the world / Someday / Whoosh of the glass machine / Below the mark / Lie living / My house.
MC: . . . . LT 1

Living Colour

TIME'S UP.
Tracks: / Time's up / History lesson / Pride / Love rears it's ugly head / New Jack theme / Someone like you / Elvis is dead / Type / Information overload / Under cover of darkness / Ology 1 / Fight the fight / Tag team partners / Solace of you / This is the life.
LP: 4669201
MC: 4669204

VIVID.
Tracks: / Cult of personality / I want to know / Middle man / Desperate people / Open letter (to a landlord) / Funny vibe / Memories can't wait / Broken hearts / Glamour boys / What's your favourite colour / Which way to America?.
LP: 4607581
MC: 4607584

Living Daylights

ANY WAY YOU WANT.
LP: . . . . PHA 4

Living Daylights

LIVING DAYLIGHTS, THE (Film Soundtrack) (Various artists).
Tracks: / Living daylights, The: *A-Ha* / Necros attacks: *Various artists* / Sniper was a woman, The: *Various artists* / Ice chase: *Various artists* / Kara meets Bond: *Various artists* / Koskov escapes: *Various artists*/ Where has everybody gone: *Various artists* / Into Vienna: *Various artists* / Hercules takes off: *Various artists* / Mujahadin and Opium: *Various artists* / Inflight flight: *Various artists* / If there was a man: *Various artists.*
LP: . . . . WX 111
MC: . . . . WX 111 C

Living Death

BACK TO THE WEAPONS.
LP: . . . . AAARRG 002

LIVE.
LP: . . . . AAARRG 012

METAL REVOLUTION.
Tracks: / Killing machine / Grippin' a heart / Rulers must come / Screaming from a chamber / Intro / Shadow of the dawn / Panic and hysteria / Road of destiny / Deep in Hell.
LP: . . . . ES 4012

PROTECTED FROM REALITY.
LP: . . . . AAARRG 005

VENGEANCE OF HELL.
LP: . . . . SKULL 8360

WORLD NUEROSES.
LP: . . . . AAARRG 015

Living Desert...

LIVING DESERT/ VANISHING PRAIRIE (Film Soundtracks) (Various artists).
Tracks: / Main title: *Various artists* / Denizens of the desert: *Various artists* / Scorpion square dance: *Various artists* / Sidewinder crawl: *Various artists* / More desert characters: *Various artists* / Wasp and the tarantula: *Various artists* / Desert bloom: *Various artists* / End title: *Various artists* / Buffalo theme: *Various artists* / Prairie home: *Various artists* / Bird's homecoming: *Various artists* / Bird dances: *Various artists* / Buffalo: *Various artists* / Coyote and the prairie dog: *Various artists* / Stampede: *Various artists* / Prairie fire: *Various artists* / Rains: *Various artists* / Winter finale: *Various artists.*
LP: . . . . DQ 1198

Living Free

LIVING FREE (Original Soundtrack Recording) (Various artists).
Tracks: / Living free - main title: *Various artists* / Trek to the Serengeti: *Various artists* / Playing for cups: *Various artists* / Life and death in the bush, part 1: *Various artists* / Big lions go hunting: *Various artists*/ Little lions get lost: *Various artists* / Living free theme: *Various artists* / Jespah, Gopa and little Elsa: *Various artists* / Joy's theme: *Various artists* / Life and death in the bush, part 2: *Various artists*/ Enticement, frustration and hope: *Various artists* / Caress and the kill: *Various artists* / Vigil and victory: *Various artists* / Living free - end title: *Various artists.*
LP: . . . . SER 5637

Living In A Box

GATE CRASHING.
LP: . . . . CDL 1676
MC: . . . . ZCDL 1676

LIVING IN A BOX.
Tracks: / Living in a box / Love is the art / So the story goes / From beginning to end / Generate the wave / Scales of justice / Going for the big one / Human story / Can't stop the wheel / Living in a box (reprise).
LP: . . . . CDL 1547
MC: . . . . ZCDL 1547

Living In Texas

COWBOY DREAM.
Tracks: / Yellow rose of Texas / Civilised world, The / Cowboy dream / Julia's child / Lust for life / Cowboy dream instrumix.
LP: . . . . NED 15

FASTEST MEN ALIVE.
LP: . . . . ATEX 010

ITALIA LIVE '85.
LP: . . . . LATEX 5

LIVING IN TEXAS.
LP: . . . . ATEXT 1

Living Proof

LIVING PROOF.
Tracks: / Hold on to your dreams / Something I like / Stay forever / Fell in love too late / Where did I go wrong / Apple of my eye / Special invitation / I'll always know.
LP: . . . . GEM 4002
MC: . . . . ZCGEM 4002

Living Sound

LET YOUR SPIRIT SING.
Tracks: / I could never live without Jesus / Let it shine / Let your spirit sing / Jesus is now my Saviour / Peace is flowing / Joshua / Clean heart / I will lift you up / I never knew I was blind / Battle is not your own, The.
LP: . . . . LS 7044
MC: . . . . LC 7044

Livings, Henry

NORTHERN DRIFT (see under Glasgow, Alex) (Livings, Henry & Alex Glasgow).

Livingston, Carlton

100 WEIGHT OF COLLIE WEED.
Tracks: / 100 weight of collie / Making love / Fret them a fret / I'm your lover / See them a-come / Call of the rastaman /

Never see come see / Soundman clash / If this girl was mine / Let the music play.
LP: GREL 66

RUMOURS.
LP: BMLP 81

TRODDING THROUGH THE JUNGLE.
LP: DYLP 002

Livingstone, Dandy

CLASSIC TRACKS (See also Greyhound).

DANDY LIVINGSTONE.
LP: TRLS 45

GREYHOUND/DANDY LIVINGSTONE (See under Greyhound) (Greyhound/ Dandy Livingstone).

RUDY A MESSAGE TO YOU (See under Trojan Explosion vol.8).

Lixx

LOOSE ON YOU.
LP: KICKASS 1

Liz & The Sandpipers

LIZ & THE SANDPIPERS Various artists (Various artists).
MC: CDSC 3

Lizard Train

SLIPPERY.
LP: ZINLP 2

Lizzy Borden

LOVE YOU TO PIECES.
LP: RR 9771

MASTER OF DISGUISE.
Tracks: / Master of disguise / One false move / Love is a crime / Sins of the flesh / Phantoms never too young / Be one of us / Psychodrama / Waiting in the wings / Roll over and play dead / Under the rose / We got the power.
LP: RR 9454-1

MENAGE TO SOCIETY.
LP: RR 9664

MURDERESS METAL ROADSHOW, THE.
LP: RR 9702

TERROR RISING.
LP: RR 9621

VISUAL LIES.
LP: RR 9592

Ljubljana Symphony

SYMPHONY NO.5 (BEETHOVEN) (see under Beethoven) (Ljubljana Symphony Orchestra).

L.L. Cool J

BIGGER AND DEFFER.
Tracks: / I'm bad / Get down / Bristol Hotel, The / My rhyme ain't done / 357- Break it on down / Go cut creator go / Breakthrough / I need love / Ahh, let's get ill / Doo wop, The / On the ill tip.
LP: 4505151
MC: 4505154

MAMA SAID KNOCK YOU OUT.
Tracks: / Boomin' system, The / Around the way girl / Eat em up L Chill / Mr. Good Bar / Murdergram (live at Rapmania) / Cheesy rat blues / Farmers boulevard (our anthem) / Mama said knock you out / Milky cereal / Jingling baby / To da break of dawn / 6 minutes of pleasure / Illegal search / Power of God, The.
LP: 4673151
MC: 4673154

RADIO.
Tracks: / I cant live without my Radio. / You cant dance. / Dear Yvette / I can give you more / Dangerous / Rock the Bells / I need a beat / You'll rock. / I want you..
LP: DEF 26745

WALKING WITH A PANTHER.
Tracks: / Droppin' Em / Smokin', dopin' / Fast peg / Clap your hands / Nitro / You're my heart / I'm that type of guy / Why do you think they call it dope? / It gets no rougher / Big ole butt / One shot at love / 1-900 LL Cool J / Two different worlds / Jealous / Jingling baby / Def Jam in the motherland / Going back to Cali (Extra track on cassette) / Crime stories (Extra track on cassette) / Change your ways (Extra track on cassette) / Jack the ripper (Extra track on cassette).
LP: 4651121
MC: 4651124

Lloyd, A. L.

ENGLISH & SCOTTISH FOLK BALLADS (see MacColl, Ewen) (Lloyd, A. L. & Ewan MacColl).

Lloyd, Carol

CAROL LLOYD.
Tracks: / Come see about me / I just want to love you / Tonight / Mr. ladies man / Baby baby i'm yours / Oh baby baby / Score.
LP: PWLP 1004

Lloyd, Charles

DREAM WEAVER (Lloyd, Charles Quartet).
Tracks: / Autumn sequence / Autumn prelude / Autumn leaves / Meditation / Dervish dance / Bird flight / Love ship / Sombrero Sam.
LP: K 50300

FISH OUT OF WATER (Lloyd, Charles Quartet).
Tracks: / Fish out of water / Haghia Sophia / Dirge, The / Bharti / Eyes of love / Mirror.
LP: ECM 1398
MC: 8410884

NIGHT IN COPENHAGEN, A.
Tracks: / Lotus land (To Thakur & Trane) / Lady Day / El encanto / Third floor Richard / Night blooming Jasmine.
LP: BT 85104

Lloyd, Floyd

BETTER TO LAUGH THAN TO CRY.
LP: STLP 1016

Lloyd, Frank

RICHARD STRAUSS: DON JUAN (ETC) (see under Strauss, Richard (composer) (Lloyd, Frank/The Philharmonia).

Lloyd, Frank Harmonica

FRANK LLOYD HARMONICA.
LP: AD 1023

Lloyd, Jeremy

CAPTAIN BEAKY - THE WOODLAND GOSPELS AND POEMS.
MCSET: LFP 7472
MCSET: DTO 10521

Lloyd, Richard

ALCHEMY.
Tracks: / Misty eyes / In the night / Alchemy / Woman's ways / Number nine / Should've known better / Blue and grey / Summer rain / Pretend / Dying words.
LP: K 52196

FIELD OF FIRE (Richard Lloyd).
LP: MLR 048

REAL TIME.
LP: CELL 6135
MC: CELL 6135C

Lloyd, Robert

ME AND MY MOUTH.
Tracks: / Cheap as sin / Nothing matters / Something nice / Top floor to let / Not forever / Sweet Georgia Black / Funeral stomp / Of course you can't / Man oh man / Hey Roberta / Better to have / Part of the anchor, The.
LP: V 2623
MC: TCV 2623

Lloyd Webber, Andrew

70'S SHOWS (Limited Edition) (Various artists).
LP: MBOX 1

ANDREW LLOYD WEBBER'S CLASSIC MUSICALS (Royal Philharmonic Pops Orchestra).
Tracks: / Think of me (prelude)/ Phantom of the opera / Think of me / Angel of music / Phantom (reprise) / Music of the night / Masquerade / Think of me (reprise) / All I ask of you / Wishing you were somehow here again / Overture / Heaven their minds / What's the buzz / Everything's alright / I don't know how to love him / Damned for all time/Blood money / Last supper, The / Pilate and Herod / Trial before Pilate.
LP: SHM 3237
MC: HSC 3237

MAGIC OF ANDREW LLOYD WEBBER (see under Cox, Derek) (Cox, Harry).

MUSIC OF ANDREW LLOYD WEBBER (Various artists).
Tracks: / Music of the night: *Various artists* / Memory: *Various artists* / Jesus Christ superstar: *Various* artists / Take that look off your face: *Various artists* / Don't cry for me Argentina: *Various artists* / All I ask of you: *Various artists*.
LP: LLOYD 1
MC: LLOYDC 1

PERFORMANCE (See under Performance) (Various artists).

PREMIERE COLLECTION, THE - BEST OF ANDREW LLOYD (see under Premier Collection).

REQUIEM (Various artists).
LP: EL 2702421
MC: EL 2702424

VARIATIONS.
Tracks: / Theme and variations 1-23 / Introductions / Paganini caprice in A minor no.24 (Full title Theme (Paganini Caprice in A minor No 24) and variation 1 - 4) / Variations 5 and 6 / Variation 7 / Variation 8 / Variation 9 / Variation 10 / Variations 11-15 / Variation 16 / Variations 14-15 varied / Variation 17 / Variation 18 / Variations 19, 20 and 6 varied / Variations 21 and 22 / Variation 23.
LP: MCL 1816
LP: MCF 2824

VARIATIONS.
Tracks: / Introduction / Theme / Paginini caprice in A minor No. 24 / Variations.
MC: MCLC 1816

Lloyd Webber, Julian

ARRIVAL OF THE QUEEN OF SHEBA, THE (Lloyd-Webber, Julian/various).
Tracks: / Arrival of the Queen of Sheba, The / Swan, The / Morning / Air on a G string / Radetzky March.
MC: ZC QS 6005

ELGAR'S CELLO CONCERTO.
LP: 416 354 1

LLOYD WEBBER PLAYS LLOYD WEBBER.
Tracks: / Variations (song and dance) / Phantom of the opera, The / Love changes everything / Memory / I don't know how to love him / Starlight express / Music of the night / Pie Jesu / Buenos Aires / Don't cry for me Argentina / First man you remember, The / All I ask of you / Tell me on a Sunday / Close every door / John 19:41.
MC: 432 291 4
LP: 432 291 1

PIECES.
Tracks: / Nights in white satin / I know him so well / First time ever I saw your face, The / Tonight I celebrate my love / Hello / Air on a G string / From suite no 3 in D / Up where we belong / Brideshead revisited / Yellow book, Theme from / Largo from the new world symphony / Cavatina / Bright eyes.
LP: PROLP 6
MC: PROMC 6

RODRIGO CELLO CONCERTO.
LP: RL 25420
MC: RK 25420

ROMANTIC CELLO, THE (Lloyd-Webber, Julian/Yitkin Seow).
Tracks: / Swan, The / Apres un reve / Salut d'amour / Song without words.
MC: ZC QS 6014

TRAVELS WITH MY CELLO.
LP: 412 231-1
MC: 412 231-4
LP: ECM 1288

Lloyd-D-Stiff

SKIN TO SKIN.
LP: GALP 003

Lloydie & Lowbites

CENSORED!.
LP: LOW 1

Lloyd-Langton

NIGHT AIR.
LP: SHARP 026

Llwybr Llaethog

BE?.
Tracks: / What? / Money lust / Live your life (for Conn O'Neill) / World so different / Jack's holiday house / Big city / Everything on this record has been ....
LP: CPRODLP 14

DA!.
LP: SER 13

LMNOP

ELEMEN OPEE ELPEE.
LP: ROSE 109

PONY.
LP: ROSE 151

Lo, Ismael

DIAWAR.
LP: STERNS 1027
MC: STC 1027

XALAT.
LP: CEL 8717

XIFF.
LP: CEL 8725

Loafers

CITY SKANKING.
Tracks: / Laughing Loafer, The / City Girl / Ice Cream / If you know / Melancholy Sally / Liquidator / My girls not / Only Time Will Tell / Time Is Tight / Too late Rudy.
LP: SKANKLP 101

CONTAGIOUS.
LP: RUDE LP 001

SKANKIN' THE PLACE DOWN.
LP: RUDELP 003

Loake, Simon & Andrew

ROGUES MARCH.
LP: SFA 096

Lobao

VIDA BANDIDA.
LP: BR 4003
MC: BRC 4003

Lobi, Kakraba

XYLOPHONE PLAYER FROM GHANA.
LP: TGS 130

Lobl, Phyl

BROADMEADOW THISTLE.
LP: LRF 051

ON MY SELECTION.
LP: LRF 017

Lobo

COME WITH ME.
Tracks: / At first sight / One more time.
LP: PXL 014

Lobo (Holland)

CARRIBEAN DISCO SHOW, THE.
Tracks: / Caribbean disco show / Day-o / Island in the sun / Caribbean magic / Matilda, Matilda / Coconut woman / Jamaica farewell / Angelique-o / Come back Liza / Judy drowned / Angelina / Mangwene Moulele / I do love you / Calypso sound / Ballymena / Sad days / If I say.
LP: POLS 1045
MC: POLSC 1045

SOCA CALYPSO.
Tracks: / Caribbean disco show / Gospel show / Soca calypso.
LP: 6423 526
MC: 7111 526

Local Hero (Film)

LOCAL HERO (THEME FROM) (See under Knopfler, Mark) (Knopfler, Mark).

MUSIC FROM LOCAL HERO (Film soundtrack) (Knopfler, Mark).
Tracks: / Rocks and the water, The / Wild theme / Freeway flyer / Boomtown / Way it always starts, The / Rocks and the thunder, The / Ceilidh and the Northern lights, The / Mist covered mountain, The / Ceilidh, The / Louis favourite Billy tune / Whistle, Theme from / Smooching / Stargazer / Rocks and the thunder, The / Going home (theme from Local Hero) / Going Home (theme from Local Hero).
LP: VERL 4
MC: VERLC 4

Local Heroes SW9

DRIP DRY ZONE.
Tracks: / Hidden meaning / Bad acting / Stabbed in the heart again / Benzine ballet / Exploitation / Cosmetic sacrifice / Another modern romance / Drip dry zone / Bluebottle / Shelter.
LP: OVLP 504

Loch Ness Monster

INDUSTRIAL POPPIES.
LP: HAM 17

MOSAIC 44.
LP: HAM 21

Lochan

LOCHAN.
LP: CM 027

Lochies

HOME TO LEWIS.
Tracks: / Oran an t seasganaich / Mo chaileag dhonn og / Amhran a hirtaich / Mucan mara bhail ailein / Nighean donn mo ribhinn og / Gur daor gur daor a cheannaich mi / Deireadh forladh, 1940 / Oran a bhradain / Am bathadh / Murchadh tobha churraig dhuibh / Ceann loch an duin / Mo luaidh's mo ribhinn.
MC: LICS 5028
LP: LILP 5028

LEWIS FOLK.
LP: LILP 5007

NORTH BY NORTH-WEST.
LP: LILP 5057

SLAINTE MHATH (Good Health).
LP: LILP 5088
MC: LICS 5088

Lock Up

SOMETHING BITCHIN' THIS WAY COME.
LP: 7599242791
MC: 7599242794

Lock Up Your Daughters

LOCK UP YOUR DAUGHTERS (Original London cast) (Various artists).
Tracks: / All's well: *Various artists* / Proper man, A: *Various artists* / It must be true: *Various artists*/ Red wine and a wench: *Various artists* / On the side: *Various artists* / When does the ravishing begin: *Various* artists / Lovely lover: *Various artists* / Lock up your daughters: *Various artists* / There's a plot afoot: *Various artists* / Mr. Jones: *Various artists* / On a sunny Sunday

morning: *Various artists* / If I'd known you: *Various artists* / 'Tis plain to see: *Various artists* / Kind fate: *Various artists* / I'll be there: *Various artists* / Finale: *Various artists*.
LP: TER 1049
MC: ZCTER 1049

Locke, Annie

LIVING EARTH, THE.
Tracks: / In a crystal cave / Crystal moments / Crystal fairies / Crystal waters / Once upon a time there was a kingdom.
MC: IH 001

MEMORIES.
MC: IH 003

PORTRAITS.
MC: IH 002

Locke Brass Consort

CONSTRASTS IN BRASS.
LP: RHS 339

JUBILANT BRASS.
LP: RL 25081

Locke, Josef

34 GREAT SINGALONG SONGS.
MC: DOCB 7027

HEAR MY SONG.
Tracks: / Hear my song, Violetta / Soldier's dream, The / March of the Grenadiers / Blaze away / Goodbye / If I were a blackbird / I'll walk beside you / At the end of the day / Mother Machree / Love's last word is spoken / Cara Mia / O maiden, my maiden / If I could hear somebody / You are my heart's delight / Come back to Sorrento / I'll take you home again, Kathleen / March of the Grenadiers / Holy City, The / Drinking song / Santa Lucia / When you were sweet sixteen / Count your blessings / My heart and I / Goodbye (from the The White Horse Inn) / Galway Bay / Macushla / Rose of Tralee, The / Bard of Armagh, The / When it's moonlight in Mayo / How can you buy Killarney / Dear old Donegal / Mother Machree / Isle of Innisfree / Maire my girl / Shades of old blarney / Shawl of Galway grey.
2LP: MFP 1033
MCSET: TCMFP 1033
2LP: MWM 1030
MCSET: MWMC 1030
2LP: DL 1033
MCSET: TCDL 1033

IN CONCERT.
2LP: HM 005D

WORLD OF JOSEF LOCKE TODAY, THE.
Tracks: / How small we are, how little we know / Blaze away / Danny boy / Edelweiss / Try a little tenderness / Just loving you / Tear, a kiss, a smile, A / Galway Bay / Marta / How can you buy Killarney / Last waltz, The / Little altar boy.
LP: SPA 21

Lockett, Mark

SLOWER THAN MOLASSES (see Sherbourne,Janet & Mark Lockett) (Lockett, Mark/Janet Sherbourne).

Lockheart, Paul

IT AIN'T THE END OF THE WORLD.
LP: FF 213

MUSIC OF THE ANDES.
LP: FF 212

PAUL LOCKHEART WITH PETER ECKLUND & FRIENDS (Lockheart, Paul/Peter Ecklund & Friends).
LP: FF 045

VOO-IT.
LP: FF 451

Lockie, Ken

IMPOSSIBLE.
LP: V 2187

Locklin, Hank

20 OF THE BEST: HANK LOCKLIN.
Tracks: / Please help me, I'm falling / Send me the pillow that you dream on / It's a little more like Heaven / Geisha girl / One step ahead of my past / From here to there to you / You're the reason / Happy birthday to me / Happy journey / We're gonna go fishing / Flyin' south / Wooden soldier / Followed closely by my teardrops / Forty-nine, fifty-one / Girls get prettier (every day) / Country hall of fame / Love song for you / Where the blue of the night / Galway Bay / Forty shades of green.
LP: NL 89331
MC: NK 89331
LP: INTS 5209

ALL KINDS OF EVERYTHING.
LP: TSLP 112
MC: TSC 112

BEST OF HANK LOCKLIN', THE.
Tracks: / Please help me, I'm falling / I was coming home to you / Danny boy / Send me the pillow you dream on / Geisha girl / From here to there to you / It's a little more like heaven / Old bog road, The / Let me be the one.
LP: LSA 3099

COUNTRY HALL OF FAME.
MC: TSC 102

FAMOUS COUNTRY MUSIC MAKERS.
Tracks: / Please help me, I'm falling / Blue side of lonesome / Why don't you haul off and love me / Just call me darling / Night train to Memphis / Jonas P. Jones / There'll be peace in the valley (for me) / Foreign love / Country hall of fame / Geisha girl / I forgot to live today / Bless her heart ... I love her / We're gonna go fishing / Where the blue of the night / It's a little more like heaven / I like a woman / Forty shades of green / Foreign car / Sweet memories / My heart needs a friend / Flying South / Softly / Who can I count on / Jambalaya / I love you because / Bonaparte's retreat / Goodbye dear old Ryman / Only a fool / Silver dew on the blue grass tonight / I'm blue / She's as close as I can get to loving you / Behind by back.
2LP: DPS 2060

FOREIGN LOVE.
LP: HAT 3082
MC: HATC 3082

FROM HERE TO THERE TO YOU.
Tracks: / Please help me, I'm falling / Geisha girl / Happy birthday to me / Happy journey / Send me the pillow that you dream on / It's a little more like Heaven / Flyin' South / From here to there to you / I was coming home to you / We're gonna go fishing.
LP: BDL 1033
MC: BDC 1033

HANK LOCKLIN.
MCSET: DTO 10216

IRISH SONGS COUNTRY STYLE.
Tracks: / Old bog road / Too-ra-loo-ra-loo-ra / Danny dear / If we only had old Ireland over here / I'll take you home again, Kathleen / My wild Irish rose / Danny boy / When Irish eyes are smiling / Little bit of Heaven, A / Galway Bay / Kevin Barry / Forty shades of green.
LP: NL 89470
MC: NK 89470
LP: LSA 3079

MR.COUNTRY.
Tracks: / Same sweet girl / Tho' I lost / Mysteries of life, The / Empty bottle, empty heart / Stumpy Joe / No one is sweeter than you / I always lose / Rio Grande waltz / I could call you darling / Year of time, A / It's hard to say I love you / Who will it be? / Place and the time, The / Queen of Hearts.
LP: SPR 8505
MC: SPC 8505

ONCE OVER LIGHTLY.
Tracks: / Send me the pillow you dream on / Same sweet girl, The / Fraulein / Flying South / I walk the line / I don't hurt anymore / Tennessee border / Wild side of life, The / Loose talk / Before I'm over you / Geisha girl / Fool No. 1 / Please help me, I'm falling / Backstreet affair / Shame on you / My shoes keep walking back to you / I'll be there / Together again / Act naturally / From here to there to you / Let me be the one / Faith and truth / This song is just for you / No one is sweeter than you.
LP: LSA 3041

PLEASE HELP ME I'M FALLING.
Tracks: / Please help me, I'm falling / Geisha girl / Send me the pillow that you dream on / Its a little more like heaven / Let me be the one / Happy Birthday to me / Happy journey / Down on my knees / Night life queen / Day time love affair / There never was a time / Baby I need you.
LP: 20068
MC: 40068

PLEASE HELP ME I'M FALLING (2).
LP: TOP 132

Lockran, Gerry

ACROSS THE TRACKS.
LP: BML 2536

Locks, Fred

BLACK STAR LINER.
Tracks: / I've got a joy / Wolf wolf / Time to change.
LP: VSLP 4007
MC: VSMC 008

Locksmith

UNLOCK THE FUNK (OLD GOLD) (See under G.Q./Disco nights).

Lockwood, Anna

GLASS WORLD OF ANNA LOCKWOOD.
LP: TGS 104

Lockwood Band

BRASS FANFARE.
LP: LKLP 6473

Lockwood, Didier

1.2.3.4..
Tracks: / Stormy day / Have to find a way / Aquamarine / Criss cross / Cleo / Badiya / Elephant blues / Precious day / Senorita / Ending to begin / Elektroperc / Ave Maria / Music is the way / Et c'est / Pour ca / Que la terre / Est arree.
2LP: JMS 041

NEW WORLD.
LP: JMS 034
LP: MPS 68 237

Lockwood, Robert Jnr.

BLUES LIVE IN JAPAN.
LP: ADVENT 2807

DUST MY BROOM (See under Shines, Johnny).

HANGIN' ON.
LP: ROUNDER 2023

MR BLUES IS BACK TO STAY.
LP: ROUNDER 2026

STEADY ROLLIN' MAN.
LP: DS 630
LP: DL 630

Lockyer, Malcolm

CLASSICS IN THE MODERN MOOD (Lockyer, Malcolm Orchestra).
MC: ZCFPA 1016

Locomotive

WE ARE EVERYTHING YOU SEE.
LP: ZAP 5

Locomotive Latenight

CENTRE CITY SUNSET.
LP: KDYLP 3

Locomotives

BOURGEOIS WOOD.
LP: WIKM 63

FROM THE FINEST ROLLING STOCK.
LP: MB 13

Lodge

SMELL OF A FRIEND.
MC: ANC 8711
LP: AN 8711

Lodge, J.C.

I BELIEVE IN YOU.
Tracks: / I believe in you / I found love / Let me down easy / Too good to be true / Night work / Cool mover / Given up / You don't want my love / Together we will stay / Happy now sorry later.
LP: GREL 104
MC: GREEN 104

REVEALED.
LP: RAS 3010

SELFISH LOVER.
Tracks: / Love's gonna break your heart / Conversations / Way up / I am in love / Sweet dreams / Cautious / Operator / Hardcore loving / Selfish love / Telephone love / Love me baby / Lonely nights / Since you came into my life.
LP: GREL 143
MC: GREEN 143

Lodge, John

BLUE GUITAR (See under Hayward, Justin for details) (Lodge, John & Justin Hayward).

BLUE JAYS (see Hayward, Justin) (Lodge, John & Justin Hayward).

NATURAL AVENUE.
Tracks: / Intro to children of rock'n'roll / Natural Avenue / Summer breeze / Carry me / Who could change / Broken dreams, hard road / Piece of my heart / Rainbow / Say you love me / Children of rock'n'roll / Street cafe.
LP: THS 21

Lodge, June

REVEALED (Lodge, June C).
LP: WKS 002

TIME FOR LOVE (see Thomas,Ruddy/ June Lodge) (Lodge, June/Ruddy Thomas).

Lodgers

LODGERS, THE.
Tracks: / The lodgers.
LP: RUDELP 015

Loesser, Frank

WHERE'S CHARLEY (Original London cast).
LP: MES 7029

Lofgren, Bruce

MOVE INTO YOUR CAR (Lofgren, Bruce & Janis Siegel).
LP: SBPHOENIX 1001
LP: PHOENIX 10973

Lofgren, Nils

AND GRIN.
Tracks: / Soft fun / Moon tears / Open wide / White lies / Take you to the movies tonight / Sometimes / Pioneer Mary / Heavy chevy / Lost a number / Ain't love nice / Rusty gun / If I were a song / Love again / We all sung together / Like rain / End unkind.
LP: CBS 31770

CODE OF THE ROAD.
2LP: TOWDLP 17
MC: ZCTOWD 17

CRY TOUGH.
Tracks: / Cry tough / It's not a crime / Incidentally... it's over / It's over / For your love / Share a little / Mud in your eye / Can't get closer / You lit a fire / Jailbait.
LP: FA 3070
MC: TCFA 3070
LP: AMLH 64573
MC: CAM 64573

DON'T WALK ROCK (Best of Nils Lofgren).
Tracks: / Moontears (Live) / Back it up / Keith don't go / Sun hasn't set on this boy get, The / Goin' back / Cry tough / Jailbait / Can't get closer / Mud in your eye / I came to dance / To be a dreamer / No mercy / Steal away / Baltimore / Shine silently / Secrets in the street / Flip ya flip / Delivery night / Anytime at all (live).
LP: VSOPLP 152
MC: VSOPMC 152

FLIP.
LP: TOWLP 11
MC: ZCTOW 11

I CAME TO DANCE.
LP: AMLH 64682

NIGHT AFTER NIGHT.
LP: UNKNOWN

NIGHT FADES AWAY.
Tracks: / Night fades away / I go to pieces / Empty heart / Don't touch me / Dirty money / Sailor boy / Anytime at all / Ancient history / Streets again / In motion.
LP: MCL 1786
MC: MCLC 1786
LP: MCF 3121

NILS.
Tracks: / No mercy / I'll cry tomorrow / Baltimore / Shine silently / Steal away / Kool skool / Fool like me, A / I found her / You're so easy.
LP: AMLH 64756
MC: CAM 64756

NILS LOFGREN.
Tracks: / Be good tonight / Back it up / One more saturday night / If I say it, it's so / I don't want to know / Keith don't go / Can't buy a break / Duty the sun hasn't set on / This boy yet / Rock and roll crook / Two by two / Goin' back.
LP: AMLS 64509
MC: CAM 64509

NILS LOFGREN AND GRIN.
Tracks: / Soft fun & moon tears / Open wide / White lies / Take you to the movies tonight / Sometimes / Pioneer Mary / Heavy chevy / Lost a number / Ain't love nice / Rusty gun / If I were a song / Love again / We all sung together / Like rain / End unkind.
LP: CBS 32717
MC: 40 32717

RHYTHM ROMANCE, A.
Tracks: / I came to dance / Incidentally... it's over / It's not a crime / Keith don't go / If I say it, it's so / Fool like me, A / Shine silently / Steal away / Sun hasn't set on this boy yet, The / Back it up / Beggar's day / Cry tough / Goin' back / Like rain.
LP: AMLH 68543
MC: CAM 68543

SILVER LINING.
LP: ESSLP 145
MC: ESSMC 145

WONDERLAND.
Tracks: / Across the tracks / Into the night / It's all over now / I wait for you / Daddy dream / Wonderland / Room without love / Confident girl / Lonesome ranger / Everybody wants / Deadline.
LP: MCL 1851
MC: MCLC 1851
LP: MCF 3182
MC: MCFC 3182

Lofsky, Lorne

IT COULD HAPPEN TO YOU.
Tracks: / It could happen to you / Riffit blues / Body and soul / Giant steps / 3 o'clock blues / Blind love / Woke up this morning / You know I love you / Sweet little angel / Ten long years / Did you ever love a woman / Crying won't help you.
LP: 2312 122

MC: . . . . K 12 122

QUARTET (Lofsky, Lorne/Ed Bickert).
LP: . . . . DDA 1002

THIS IS NEW (See under Bickert, Ed) (Lofsky, Lorne/Ed Bickert).

Loft

ONCE AROUND THE FAIR.
LP: . . . . CRELP 047
MC: . . . . CREC 047

Loften, Cripple

CLARENCE'S BLUES (Lofton, Cripple Clarence).
LP: . . . . OL 2817

CRIPPLE CLARENCE LOFTEN & WALTER DAVIS.
LP: . . . . L 1025

Lofts, Norah

MADSELIN (Rosalind Lloyd).
MCSET: . . . . COL 2018

Logan, Johnny

HOLD ME NOW.
Tracks: / Hold me now / Living a lie / Say / Foolish love / When your woman cries / I'm not in love / Helpless heart / What's another year / Heartbroken man / Such a lady.
LP: 4510731
MC: 4510734

JOHNNY LOGAN.
Tracks: / Save me / Hollywood / God given love / Love is a small town / Till you happened to me / Louisiana rain / What's another year / Heartache is one / Slippin' away / One night stand / All fall down / Give a little bit more.
LP: . . . . EPC 84477

STRAIGHT FROM THE HEART.
Tracks: / Love letters / Ginny come lately / Goin' back / Lovin' you / Love hurts / Saturday night at the movies / Take good care of my baby / Next time / When you walk in the room / Cryin' in the rain.
LP: . . . . EPC 26500

Logan, Sally

ALL RECORDINGS (see under Gordon, Joe) (Logan, Sally & Joe Gordon).

Loggins, Kenny

ALIVE.
Tracks: / Whenever I call you friend / I believe in love / Why do people lie / Wait a little while / What a fool believes / Junkanoo holiday / I'm alright / Celebrate me home / You don't know me / Now and then / All alone tonight / Here, there and everywhere / Angelique / Love has come of age / This is it / Down 'n' dirty / Easy driver / Keep the fire.
2LP: . . . . CBS 88500

BACK TO AVALON.
Tracks: / Nobody's fool (Theme from 'Caddyshack II') / I'm gonna miss you / Tell her / One woman / Back to Avalon / She's dangerous / True confessions / Hope for the runaway / Isabella's eyes / Blue on blue / Meet me half way.
LP: 4610041
MC: 4610044

HIGH ADVENTURE.
LP: . . . . CBS 85932

KEEP THE FIRE.
Tracks: / Keep the fire / Love has come of age / Mr. Night / This is it / Junkanoo holiday / Now and then / Who's right, who's wrong / Give it half a chance / Will it last.
LP: 83869

LOVE WILL FOLLOW (OLD GOLD) (See under Messina, Jim/Do you wanna dance).

VOX HUMANA.
Tracks: / Vox humana / No lookin' back / Let there be love / I'll be there / I'm gonna do it right / Forever / At last / Lorraine / Love will follow.
LP: . . . . CBS 26221
MC: 40 26221

Loggins & Messina

BEST OF LOGGINS & MESSINA.
Tracks: / Vehevala / Danny's song / Nobody but you / Whiskey / House at Pooh Corner / Angry eyes / Golden ribbons / My music / Brighter days / Watching the river run / Keep me in mind / Peacemaker / I'm movin' on / Till the ends meet.
LP: . . . . CBS 31826

Logic, Laura

PEDIGREE CHARM.
LP: . . . . ROUGH 28

Logic System

LOGIC.
Tracks: / Intro / Unit / Domino dance / Convulsion of nature / XY? / Talk back / Clash / Person to person / Logic.
LP: . . . . EMC 3375

VENUS.
Tracks: / Venus / Morpheus / I love you / Plan / Take a chance / Automatic collect, automatic correct / Be yourself / Prophet / Metamorphism / Equivalent.
LP: . . . . EMC 3403

Lois Lane

FORTUNE FAIRY TALES.
LP: 8433411
MC: 8433414

Lokassa

ADIZA.
LP: . . . . CEL 8723

Loketo

EXTRA BALL.
LP: . . . . JIP 017
MC: . . . . JIP 017C

Lola

FAIRLY TRUE.
LP: . . . . COLP 8005

Lolita (film)

LOLITA (Film soundtrack) (Various artists).
LP: . . . . MCA 39067
MC: . . . . MCAC 39067

Lolitas

FUSEE D'AMOUR.
LP: . . . . ROSE 170
MC: . . . . ROSE 170C

LOLITAS.
LP: . . . . ROSE 119

SERIES AMERICAINES.
LP: . . . . ROSE 148

Lollipop Shoppe

JUST COLOUR.
Tracks: / You must be a witch / Underground railroad / Baby don't go / Who'll read the will / It's only a reflection / Someone I know / Don't look back / Don't close the door on me / It ain't how long / It's makin' it / It's gonna be there / You don't give me no more / Sin / Through my window.
LP: . . . . WIK 36

Lollipops &

LOLLIPOPS AND FISH FINGERS (In aid of the N.S.P.C.C.) (Various artists).
LP: . . . . MFP 41 5683 1
MC: . . . . MFP 41 5683 4

Lomas, Stephen

MUSIC FOR TREBLE VOICE (see under Blaze, Robin) (Lomas, Stephen/ Robin Blaze).

Lomax

1001 NIGHTS.
LP: . . . . ZTT 5
MC: . . . . ZTT 5C

Lomax, Alan

MURDERERS HOME AND BLUES IN THE MISSISSIPPI NIGHT.
Tracks: / Road song / No more my Lord / Katy left Memphis / Old Alabama / Black woman / Jumpin' lady / Whoa back / Prettiest train / Old dollar mamie / It makes a long time man feel bad / Rosie / Leave camp roller / Early in the morning / Tangle eyes blues / Stackerlee / Prison blues / Sometimes I wonder / Bye bye baby / Blues in the Mississippi night.
LP: . . . . VJD 515

TEXAS FOLK SONGS.
Tracks: / Rambling gambler / I'm bound to follow the longhorn cows / Lord Lovel / Rich old lady, The / Long summer days / Ain't no more cane / All the pretty little horses / Billy Barlow / Wild rippling water, The / Rattlesnake / Sam Bass / Dying cowboy, The / God almighty drag / Eradie / Black Betty / My little John Henry.
LP: . . . . ARN 33690
MC: . . . . ARN 433690

Lomax, Jackie

IS THIS WHAT YOU WANT?.
Tracks: / Speak to me / Is this what you want? / How can you say goodbye? / Sunset / Sour milk sea / I fall inside your eyes / Little yellow pills / Take my word / Eagle laughs at you, The / Baby you're a lover / You've got me thinking / I just don't know / New day / Won't you come back / Liverpool / Thumbin' a ride / How the web was woven.
LP: . . . . SAPCOR 6
MC: . . . . TCSAPCOR 6

Lombard

WINGS OF A DOVE.
Tracks: / Wings of a dove / Get lost / Snowball / Empty plate / Anatomy / Burn him / Perfect melodrama / Foreign days / Wstega M (a Polish love song).
LP: KIX4U 3336
LP: . . . . ROCK 3336

Lombardo, Guy

ALL-TIME FAVOURITES.
MC: 4XL 9030

BEST OF GUY LOMBARDO & HIS ROYAL CANADIANS 1955 (See under Meet The Band Leaders (Vol 7) (Lombardo, Guy/his Royal Canadians).

GUY LOMBARDO AND ROYAL CANADIANS - 1950 (Lombardo, Guy/ his Royal Canadians).
Tracks: / Mary Lou / Snuggled on your shoulders / Pennies from Heaven / I love you / Beale Street Blues / There'll be some changes made / This can't be love / I can't begin to tell you / Music, music, music / Nevertheless / At sundown / Embraceable you.
LP: . . . . HSR 187

UNCOLLECTED, THE.
LP: . . . . HUK 187

Lomond Cornkisters

BY BONNIE LOCH LEVEN.
LP: . . . . WGR 050
MC: . . . . CWGR 050

Lomond Folk

BLENDED SCOTCH.
LP: . . . . LILP 5043

London

DON'T CRY WOLF.
Tracks: / Drop the bomb / Set me free / Hit and run lover / Under the gun / Oh darlin' / Fast as light / Put out the fire / Killing time / We want everything / For whome the bell tolls.
LP: . . . . AXISLP 1

NON STOP ROCK.
LP: . . . . RR 9733

PLAYA DEL ROCK.
LP: . . . . NUK 143
MC: . . . . ZCNUK 143
LP: . . . . N 01431
MC: . . . . NUK 143

London Beat

IN THE BLOOD.
Tracks: / It's in the blood / Getcha ya ya / She broke my heart (in 36 places) / She said she loves me / No woman no cry / This is your life / I've been thinking about you / Better love, A / In an I love you mood / You love and learn / Crying in the rain / Step inside my shoes (Only on CD).
LP: . . . . ZL 74810
MC: . . . . ZK 74810

SPEAK.
Tracks: / There's a beat going on / Beat patrol / Failing in love again / 9 a.m. (the comfort zone) / Drop! / Nice here when it's nice / Get wet / One blink / Talent on the make / Please baby (can I have my heart back please) / Jerk (CD/cassette only) / Katey / Bribe the bride (CD only) / There's a deep house going on (CD only).
LP: . . . . ZL 71857
MC: . . . . ZK 71857

London Boys

12 COMMANDMENTS OF DANCE, THE.
Tracks: / Chinese radio / My love / I'm gonna give my heart / Dance, dance, dance / Midi dance, The / Wichitah woman / London nights / El matinero / Sandra / Requiem / Kimbaley (my ma-mama say) / Harlem desire.
LP: . . . . WX 278
MC: . . . . WX 278 C

London Brass

ROMANTIC JOURNEY.
Tracks: / Nutcracker suite (5 pieces) / Intermezzi (3) / An die musik / Introduction and allegro / Midsummer night's dream (3 pieces).
MC: 246 007-4

London Chamber Orch.

MINIMALIST (London Chamber Orchestra).
LP: . . . . VC 791 168 1
MC: . . . . VC 791 168 4

UNDER THE EYE OF HEAVEN (London Chamber Orchestra).
Tracks: / Earth / Birth / Life / Dance, The / Heaven / Enigma, The / Loss, A / Search, The / Last illusion, The / Miracle, The.
LP: . . . . LCOLP 1
MC: . . . . LCOMC 1
LP: . . . . VC 7908171
MC: . . . . VC 7908174

London Choral Society

CLASSICAL SPECTACULAR (live at the Royal Albert Hall)(see under Royal Philharmonic (London Choral Society/ Royal Philharmonic Orchestra).

London Community ...

CHRISTMAS WITH THE LONDON COMMUNITY GOSPEL CHOIR (London Community Gospel Choir).
Tracks: / O little town of Bethlehem / O come all ye faithful / Little drummer boy / We three Kings / Angels in the realms of glory / Hark the herald angels sing / Joy to the world / Once in Royal David's City / Away in a manger / God rest ye merry gentlemen / Silent night / Sleep in heavenly peace.
MC: . . . . TCMFP 5900

FEEL THE SPIRIT (London Community Gospel Choir).
Tracks: / All to Jesus / O happy day.
LP: . . . . MYR R 1221
MC: . . . . MYR C 1221

GOSPEL GREATS (London Community Gospel Choir).
Tracks: / Sing low, sweet chariot / Precious Lord, amazing grace / Nobody knows the trouble I've seen / What a friend we have in Jesus / Kumbaya / Count your blessings / Love lifted me / When the saints go marching in / There is a green hill far away / Oh happy day / Old rugged cross.
LP: . . . . MFP 5731
MC: . . . . TC MFP 5731
LP: . . . . MFP 41 5731 1
MC: . . . . MFP 41 5731 4

London Concert Artists

SWEET AND LOW.
Tracks: / Sweet and low / Paradise for two, A / Gates of paradise / Nirvana / I would that my love / Excelsior / Love's old sweet song / Ascot gavotte / Little damozel, The / Dear little cafe / Down the vale / Salut d'amour / World is but a broken toy, The / Charming weather / Rose of England.
LP: . . . . ALM 4004

London Concert

MAGIC OF STRAUSS.
Tracks: / Pizzicato polka / Pester czardas op 23 / Sperl galop op 2 / Radetzky march / Unter donner und blitz galop Opus 324 / Wiener blut waltz op 354 / Champagne polka op 211 / Kettenbrucke waltz op 354 / Lorelei / Acceleration waltz / Eljen a magyar polka op 332 / Tritsch tratsch polka.
MCSET: . . . . DTO 10064

London Conference

MEDICINE THE HUMAN ASPECT.
MC: SS/128/129

London Cowboys

LONG TIME COMING, A.
LP: . . . . HORN 001

ON STAGE.
LP: . . . . UND 2

London Early Music

ORLANDO GIBBONS (see under Kings College) (London Early Music Group/ KingsCollegeCambridgeChoir/ JohnButt).

London Emmanuel Choir

BE MY SPIRIT.
LP: . . . . PRAISE 7

BE STILL MY SOUL.
LP: . . . . JLPS 200

CAROLLING WITH THE LONDON EMMANUEL CHOIR.
LP: . . . . PRAISE 20

CHOICE IS YOURS (BBC TV Songs of Praise) (London Emmanual Choir/Toad Choir).
Tracks: / Onward Christian soldiers / In Heavenly love abiding / Eternal Father, strong to save / How sweet the name of Jesus sounds / King of love my shepherd is, The / When I survey the wondrous cross / Abide with me / Day thou gavest, Lord is ended, The / Hark how the adoring hosts above / Dear Lord and Father of mankind / Love is come again / Thine be the glory / It is a thing most wonderful / Christ is made the sure foundation / Come let us sing to the Lord our God / Ye gates lift up your heads.
LP: . . . . REC 160

CHURCH'S ONE FOUNDATION.
LP: . . . . JLPS 170

GIVE GOD THE GLORY.
LP: . . . . QLPS 16

GLORY TO THE LORD.
LP: . . . . SHARON 341

HALLELUJAH JUBILEE.
LP: . . . . WST 9576

HE IS THE WAY.
LP: . . . . JLPS 178

LET THE WHOLE WORLD KNOW.
LP: . . . . JLPS 162

PRAISE AND REJOICE.
LP: . . . . QLPS 28

SINGS 20 BEST LOVED HYMNS.
LP: . . . . Unknown

TELL THE GOOD NEWS.
LP: . . . . PRAISE 25

WHISPERING HOPE.
LP: . . . . **KLPS 49**

London Festival.....

20 GOLDEN PIECES: JOHANN STRAUSS (London Festival Orchestra).
Tracks: / Blue Danube / Vienna blood waltz / Emperor waltz / Champagne polka / Tritsch tratsch polka / Artists life waltz / Blue Danube / Vienna blood waltz / Kiss waltz, The / Egyptian march / Russian march / Perpetuum mobile / Roses from the south / Tales from the Vienna Woods / Treasure waltz / Annen polka / Pizzicato polka / Persian march / Spanish march / Morning papers waltz / Die Fledermaus waltz / Du und du.
LP: . . . . **BDL 2049**
MC: . . . . **BDC 2049**

DAYS OF FUTURE PASSED (See under Moody Blues) (London Festival Orchestra/Peter Knight(cond'r)/Moody Blues).

London Festival

DREAMS (See under Dreams (Classical)).

LIMELIGHT - A TRIBUTE TO CHARLIE CHAPLIN.
Tracks: / Modern times / Chaplin revue / City lights / Kid / Great dictator / King in New York / Limelight / Countess from Hong Kong.
MC: **4212634**

London Gabrieli Brass

SPLENDOUR OF BAROQUE BRASS, THE (London Gabrieli Brass Ensemble).
MC: . . . . **ZC QS 6013**

London Handel

MESSIAH HIGHLIGHTS (see under Handel) (London Handel Orchestra/ Winchester Cathedral Choir).

London, Jack

CALL OF THE WILD, THE (Massey, Daniel (nar)).
MCSET: . . . . **ARGO 1205**

CALL OF THE WILD, THE (Begley, Ed).
MC: **1219**

PIECE OF STEAK, A (Bryce, James).
MCSET: . . . . **COL 2005**

SEA WOLF (Quayle, Anthony (nar)).
MC: . . . . **CDL 51689**

SEA WOLF (Boland, Arthur).
MCSET: . . . . **COL 2008**

London Jazz Comp...

ODE FOR JAZZ ORCHESTRA (see Guy, Barry) (London Jazz Comp Orchestra & Barry Guy).

London Jewish Male

HEAR OUR VOICE.
MC: . . . . **L 003 161C**

London, Julie

ABOUT THE BLUES.
Tracks: / Basin Street blues / I got a right to sing the blues / Nightingale can sing the blues, A / Get set for the blues / Invitation to the blues / Bye bye blues / Meaning of the blues / About the blues / Sunday blues / Blues is all I ever had / Blues in the night / Bouquet of blues.
LP: . . . . **PM 154 774 1**
MC: . . . . **PM 154 774 4**

ALL THROUGH THE NIGHT (Songs of Cole Porter).
Tracks: / I've got you under my skin / You do something to me / Get out of town / All through the night / So in love / At long last love / Easy to love / My heart belongs to daddy / Every time we say goodbye / In the still of the night.
LP: . . . . **JAS 308**
MC: . . . . **JAS C308**

AROUND MIDNIGHT.
Tracks: / Round midnight / Lonely night in Paris / Misty / Black coffee / Lush life / In the wee small hours of the morning / Don't smoke in bed / You and the night and the music / Something cool / How about me? / But not for me / Party's over, The.
LP: . . . . **EG 2606061**
MC: . . . . **EG 2606064**

BEST OF JULIE LONDON (The Liberty Years).
Tracks: / Cry me a river / Fly me to the moon / Why don't you do right / My heart belongs to daddy / How did he look / Hard hearted Hannah / Please do it again / Take back your mink / Diamonds are a girl's best friend / End of a love affair, The / Daddy / Occasional man, An / Desafinado (slightly out of tune) / Love for sale / Always true to you in my fashion / There'll be some changes made.
LP: . . . . **EMS 1310**
MC: . . . . **TC EMS 1310**

BEST OF JULIE LONDON.
Tracks: / Cry me a river / Moments like this / Hot toddy / They can't take that away from me / June in January / Mad about the boy / Don't smoke in bed / Gee baby ain't I good to you / Cuddle up a little closer / Invitation to the blues / You'd be so nice to come home to / Nearness of you, The / Daddy.
LP: . . . . **SLS 2600041**
MC: . . . . **TCSLS 2600044**

CALENDAR GIRL.
Tracks: / June in January / February brings the rain / Melancholy March / I'll remember April / People who are born in May / Memphis in June / Sleigh ride in July / Time for August / September in the rain / This October / November twilight / Warm December / Thirteenth month, The.
LP: . . . . **ED 109**

CRY ME A RIVER.
LP: . . . . **ENT LP 13038**
MC: . . . . **ENT MC 13038**
MC: **4XLL 9097**

FEELING GOOD.
Tracks: / My kind of town / Girl talk / King of the road / I bruise easily / Feeling good / Watermelon man / She's just a quiet girl / Summertime / Hello Dolly! / Won't someone please belong to me.
LP: . . . . **EMS 1282**
MC: . . . . **TCEMS 1282**

JULIE.
Tracks: / Somebody loves me / Dream of you / Daddy / Bye bye blackbird / Free and easy / All my life / When the red, red robin comes bob, bob, bobbin' along / Midnight sun / You're getting to be a habit with me / Don'cha go 'way mad / Indiana / For you.
LP: . . . . **PM 154 775 1**
MC: . . . . **PM 154 775 4**

JULIE AT HOME.
Tracks: / You'd be so nice to come home to / Lonesome road / They didn't believe me / By myself / Thrill is gone, The / You've changed / Goodbye / Sentimental journey / Give me the simple life / You stepped out of a dream / Let there be love / Everything happens to me.
LP: . . . . **EMS 1186**
MC: . . . . **TCEMS 1186**

JULIE IS HER NAME.
Tracks: / Cry me a river / I should care / I'm in the mood for love / I'm glad there is you / Can't help lovin' dat man / I love you / Say it isn't so / It never entered my mind / Easy Street / 'S wonderful / No moon at all / Laura / Gone with the wind.
LP: . . . . **ED 108**
LP: **5C 038 62384**
LP: . . . . **MFP 41 5669-1**
MC: . . . . **MFP 41 5669 4**

JULIE IS HER NAME VOLUME II.
Tracks: / Blue moon / What is this thing called love? / How has this been going on / Too good to be true / Too good to be true / Spring is here / Goody goody / One I love belongs to somebody else, The / If i'm lucky / Hot toddy / Little white lies / I guess i'll have to change my plans / I got lost in his arms.
LP: . . . . **EMS 1140**
MC: . . . . **TCEMS 1140**

JULIE LONDON SINGS COLE PORTER (Legendary Master Series).
Tracks: / All through the night / What is this thing called love / Get out of town / My heart belongs to daddy / So in love / You'd be so nice to come home to / In the still of the night / At long last love / I love you / I've got you under my skin / Love for sale / Easy to love / Make it another old fashioned, please / You do something to me / My heart belongs to daddy (version 2) / Always true to you in my fashion / Ev'ry time we say goodbye.
MC: **E4 93455**

LONDON BY NIGHT.
Tracks: / Well, sir / That's for me / Mad about the boy / In the middle of a kiss / Just the way I am / My man's gone now / Something I dreamed last night / Pousse cafe / Nobody's heart / Exciting life, The / That old feeling / Cloudy morning.
LP: **2C 068 54577**
MC: . . . . **PM 154 577 4**

LONELY GIRL.
Tracks: / Fools rush in / What'll I do? / All alone.
LP: . . . . **PM 155 290 1**
MC: . . . . **PM 155 290 4**

MAKE LOVE TO ME.
Tracks: / Body and soul / Nearness of you, The / Lover man.
LP: . . . . **PM 155 291 1**
MC: . . . . **PM 1552914**

SOPHISTICATED LADY.
Tracks: / Sophisticated lady / Blame it on my youth / Make it another old fashioned please / You're blase / Bewitched / Spring can really hang you up the most / Remind me / When she makes music / When the world was young / If I should lose you / Where am I to go? / Absent-minded me.
LP: . . . . **ED 2604211**
MC: . . . . **ED 2604214**

SWING ME AN OLD SONG.
Tracks: / Comin' thro' the rye / Cuddle up a little closer / After the ball / Be my little baby / Bumble bee / Camptown races / Old folks at home / Darktown strutters' ball / How come you do me like you do? / Row, row, row / By the beautiful sea / Bill Bailey, won't you please come home? / Three o'clock in the morning.
LP: . . . . **PM 1547761**
MC: . . . . **PM 1547764**

YOUR NUMBER PLEASE.
Tracks: / Makin' whoopee / When i fall in love / One for my baby.
LP: . . . . **PM 155 292 1**
MC: . . . . **PM 155 292 4**

London, Laurie

HE'S GOT THE WHOLE WORLD IN HIS HANDS.
Tracks: / He's got the whole world in his hands / Gospel train / Boom ladda boom boom / Up above my head / Today's teardrops / Cradle rock / Pretty eyed baby / Bun ladda bum bum / Wild und heiss / Schritt fur schritt / Schone weisse rose / Schenk mir einen traum / Itsy bitsy teeny weeny Honolulu strand bikini / Mandolino pling plang plong / Mamatschi.
LP: . . . . **BFX 15133**

London, Lew

SWINGTIME IN SPRINGTIME.
LP: . . . . **PH 1032**

London Live

LONDON LIVE (Effects of London).
LP: . . . . **ALA 3008**
MC: . . . . **ZC ALA 3008**

London Male Welsh

SONGS OF THE VALLEYS.
LP: . . . . **NE 1117**
MC: . . . . **CE 2117**

London Oratory Junior

LAETARE JERUSALEM (London Oratory Junior Choir).
LP: . . . . **MVP 782**

London Philharmonic...

AMERICAN IN PARIS, AN (London Philharmonic Orchestra).
Tracks: / American in Paris, An (Gershwin.) / Porgy and Bess suite (Gershwin.) / El salon Mexico (Copland.).
LP: . . . . **CFP 4537**
MC: . . . . **TCCFP 4537**

CHARIOTS OF FIRE (Film Soundtrack) (London Philharmonic Orchestra).
LP: . . . . **SHM 3112**
MC: . . . . **HSC 3112**

CLASSIC CASE OF FUNK (London Philharmonic Orchestra).
LP: . . . . **WW 5130**
MC: . . . . **WW 4 5130**

CLASSICAL GOLD (London Philharmonic Orchestra).
LP: . . . . **RTD 4 2020**

CLASSICAL THEMES (London Philharmonic Orchestra).
LP: . . . . **ML 1001**
MC: . . . . **ZNML 1001**

DIAMOND SYMPHONIES (Hits of Neil Diamond) (London Philharmonic Orchestra).
LP: . . . . **RTL 2045**
MC: . . . . **4 CRTL 2045**

DONA NOBIS PACEM Composer: Bryden Thompson (London Philharmonic Orchestra).
LP: . . . . **ABRD 1297**
MC: . . . . **ABTD 1297**

DRAGON DANCE (see Batt, Mike) (London Philharmonic Orchestra/Mike Batt).

DVORAK NEW WORLD SYMPHONY (see under Dvorak (composer))(Brahms Academic Fe (London Philharmonic Orchestra).

ENIGMA VARIATIONS Composed:Elgar/Conductor: Bryden Thompson (London Philharmonic Orchestra).
LP: . . . . **ABRD 1298**
MC: . . . . **ABTD 1298**

FEELING LOVE ON THE SIDE (See under Davis, Carl) (London Philharmonic Orchestra/Carl Davis).

FILM MUSIC OF SIR WILLIAM WALTON (See under Walton, Sir William) (London Philharmonic Orchestra).

HYMNS TRIUMPHANT (London Philharmonic Orchestra).
LP: . . . . **WINX 511**
MC: . . . . **TC WINX 511**
LP: . . . . **WW 5140**
MC: . . . . **WW 45140**
LP: . . . . **WING 511**
MC: . . . . **TC WING 511**

MESSIAH, THE (London Philharmonic Choir).
LP: . . . . **GGL 0062**

OPUS ONE (London Philharmonic Orchestra).
Tracks: / Jumpin' Jack Flash / We can work it out / I can see for miles / Blowin' in the wind / All you need is love / Good vibrations / House of the rising sun / If I were a carpenter.
LP: **6308 317**

PIA AND PHIL (see under Zadora, Pia) (London Philharmonic Orchestra/Pia Zadora).

PLANETS, THE (London Philharmonic Orchestra).
LP: . . . . **ESD 7135**
MC: . . . . **EG 7690454**

POMP & CIRCUMSTANCE MARCHES 1-5 Plus Enigma variations (London Philharmonic Orchestra).
LP: . . . . **ASD 3388**
MC: . . . . **TCASD 3388**

PRAISE (18 Choral Masterpieces) (London Philharmonic Choir).
Tracks: / Pomp and circumstance / Zadok the priest / Bridal chorus, The / Londonderry air / Holy city, The / All people that on earth do dwell / Mine eyes have seen the glory / Rock of ages / Eternal father strong to save / God that madest earth and heaven / O God our help in ages past / Praise my soul the King of Heaven / Brother James' air / Abide with me / O for the wings of a dove / For unto us a child is born / Hallelujah chorus.
MC: . . . . **PATMC 301**
LP: . . . . **PATLP 301**

RAVEL'S BOLERO (London Philharmonic Orchestra).
LP: . . . . **HAV 2189**

SHOSTAKOVICH: SYMPHONY NO.10 (London Philharmonic Orchestra).
LP: . . . . **VC 790784 1**
MC: . . . . **VC 790784 4**

SOUND OF GLORY (London Philharmonic Choir).
2LP: . . . . **ADEP 25**

SYMPHONY NO.8 (DVORAK) (see under Dvorak).

SYMPHONY NO.31/NO.36 (see under Mozart) (London Philharmonic Orchestra).

TORVILL & DEAN'S FIRE AND ICE (London Philharmonic Orchestra).
Tracks: / Fire and Ice: Prelude/ Fire world / Ice world / Meeting, The / Ice court / Mask dance / Ice warriors / Skating lesson / Fire and ice(love duet) / Ambush / Lament/war dance / Melting,The/ Battle / After the war / Dance of hope.
LP: . . . . **CAST 7**
MC: . . . . **CASTC 7**

VICTORY AT SEA (London Philharmonic Orchestra).
LP: . . . . **GGL 0073**

London Philharmonic

MOZART: VIOLIN CONCERTOS NOS. 1, 2 & 4 (conducted by Christoph Eschenbach).
MC: . . . . **ZCRPO 8018**
LP: . . . . **RPO 8018**

London Piano Accordion

ACCORDION PARADE.
Tracks: / Aloha oe / Wagon wheels / Remember me / It's a sin to tell a lie / In old Vienna / Play to me, gypsy / Little drummer boy / Sidewalk waltz / Poor little Angeline / Sympathy waltz / Mexicana Flo from Mexico / Moon over Miami / Whistling gypsy waltz / Au revoir.
LP: . . . . **SH 107 824 1**
MC: . . . . **TCSH 107 824 4**

LONDON PIANO ACCORDION BAND 1934-1940.
Tracks: / Tina / Continental / La cucaracha / Goodbye Hawaii / Wheel of the wagon is broken / Whistling waltz / When the sun says 'goodnight' to the mountain / It looks like rain in cherry blossom lane / Vieni, vieni / Two lovely people / All ashore / Penny serenade / Umbrella man / Mexicali rose / Beer barrel polka / They would wind him up and he would whistle / Turn your money in your pocket / I'm nobody's baby.
LP: . . . . **SH 359**

LONDON PIANO ACCORDION BAND, THE.
Tracks: / In a little gypsy tearoom / Isle of Capri / Rain / Wanderer / Dreaming / Wagon wheels / Rose of Tralee, The / Marina waltz / Happy-go-lucky you and broken-hearted me / You were so charming / Play to me gypsy / It was a tango / Lonely little lady / Jump on the wagon / Sweet dreams pretty lady / Sleepy time in sleepy hollow / My wishing song / Little valley in the mountains.
LP: . . . . JOY'D 292

London Posse

GANGSTER CHRONICLE.
LP: . . . . MLPS 1066
LP: 846 912 1
MC: . . . . MCT 1066
MC: 846 912 4

London Pro Musica

ITALIAN RENAISSANCE MUSIC.
LP: . . . . PLR 066

London Ragtime Orch.

GRACE AND BEAUTY (London Ragtime Orchestra).
LP: . . . . GHB 199

LONDON RAGTIME ORCHESTRA (London Ragtime Orchestra).
LP: . . . . SOS 1081

London Saxophone

LONDON SAXOPHONE QUARTET IN DIGITAL.
Tracks: / Little march / Fugue in G minor / Set of four in popular style / Two dances from 'Sleeping Beauty' / Rondo / In Autumn / Suite from 'Acis and Galatea' / When the saints go marching in / Something blue / King Charles Galliard, The / Promenade / Slightly blue-Piratatella.
LP: . . . . PRCD 301
MC: . . . . CPRCD 301

London Serpent Trio

FILL YOUR GLASSES (see under Canterbury Clerkes) (London Serpent Trio/Canterbury Clerkes).

London Studio Symphony

NORTH BY NORTHWEST (Film soundtrack) (See under North By Northwest) (London Studio Symphony Orch.).

London Symphony...

007 CLASSICS (London Symphony Orchestra).
Tracks: / James Bond theme / Thunderball / Goldfinger / From Russia with love / Diamonds are forever / You only live twice / Look of love, The / On Her Majesty's Secret Service / Man with the golden gun, The.
LP: . . . . EDL 25131
MC: . . . . EDL 25134

ALIENS (see under Aliens) (London Symphony Orchestra).

BEST OF CLASSIC ROCK (London Symphony Orchestra).
Tracks: / Eye of the tiger / Whole lotta love / Baker Street / Paint it black / Get back / Rhapsody in black / Reach out I'll be there / Standing in the shadows of love / Ruby Tuesday / Bohemian rhapsody / First time ever I saw your face, The / Sailing.
LP: . . . . ONE 1080
MC: . . . . OCE 1080

CLASSIC ROCK 1 (The Original) (London Symphony Orchestra).
Tracks: / Bohemian rhapsody / Life on Mars / Whiter shade of pale, A / Whole lotta love / Paint it black / Nights in white satin / Lucy in the sky with diamonds / Without you / I'm not in love / Sailing.
LP: . . . . STAR 6001
MC: . . . . STAC 6001
LP: . . . . ONE 1009
MC: . . . . CE 2009

CLASSIC ROCK 2 (The Second Movement) (London Symphony Orchestra).
Tracks: / Eve of the war, The / Pinball wizard / Hey Joe / Day in the life, A / Question / Space oddity / God only knows / River deep, mountain high / American trilogy / Don't cry for me Argentina.
LP: . . . . STAR 6002
MC: . . . . STAC 6002
MC: . . . . CE 2039
LP: . . . . NE 1039

CLASSIC ROCK 3 (Rhapsody in black) (London Symphony Orchestra).
Tracks: / Fanfare intro-rhapsody in black / Reach out I'll be there / You keep me hangin' on / First time ever I saw your face, The / Superstition / Standing in the shadows of love / Don't leave me this way / Tears of a clown / Rasputin / I heard it through the grapevine / Ain't no mountain high enough.
LP: . . . . STAR 6003
MC: . . . . STAC 6003

CLASSIC ROCK 4 (Rock classics) (London Symphony Orchestra).
Tracks: / Get back / Layla / Stairway to heaven / Baker street / Another brick in the wall / Jet / Ruby Tuesday / I don't like Mondays / Bright eyes / Hey Jude.
LP: . . . . STAR 6004
MC: . . . . STAC 6004

CLASSIC ROCK 5 (Rock Symphonies) (London Symphony Orchestra).
Tracks: / Born to run / For your love / Chariots of fire / House of the rising sun / You really got me / MacArthur park / Eye of the tiger / Vienna / She's out of my life / Pictures of Lily / Since you've been gone / Gloria.
LP: . . . . STAR 6005
MC: . . . . STAC 6005

CLASSIC ROCK COUNTDOWN (London Symphony Orchestra).
Tracks: / Final countdown, The / Take my breath away / You can call me Al / Lady in red, The / Separate lives / We don't need another hero / It's a sin / She's not there / Don't give up / You're the voice / Abbey road medley / Golden slumbers / Carry that weight / End, The.
LP: . . . . MOOD 3
MC: . . . . MOOD C3
LP: 4604821
MC: 4604824

CLASSIC ROCK - THE LIVING YEARS (London Symphony Orchestra).
LP: . . . . MOOD 9
MC: . . . . MOODC 9
MC: 4660504

CLASSICAL CLIMAXES (London Symphony Orchestra).
Tracks: / Overture: Tannhauser (Wagner) / Picture from an exhibition (Moussorgsky-Ravel) / L'arlesienne suite No. 2 (Bizet) / Symphony No. 4 in F minor, Opus 36 / Symphony No. 7 in A, Opus 92 (Beethoven) / 1812 overture / Symphony No.2 in D, Opus 73 / Symphony No.3 in C minor, Opus 78 (Saint-Saen) / Symphonie fantastique (Berlioz) / Planets: Suite for orchestra, Opus 32 (1916) / Symphony No. 9 in E minor, Opus 95 (Dvorak) / Bolero.
LP: . . . . DUET 27

FANTASY ALBUM (London Symphony Orchestra).
2LP: . . . . REF 547
MC: . . . . ZCD 547

FILM AND T.V. CLASSICS (London Symphony Orchestra).
Tracks: / Onedin line theme / Prince Igor (Polovtsian Dance) / Romeo and Juliet (Polovtsian Dance) / Sabre Dance (Polovtsian Dance) / Symphony No.3 (3rd movement) / Casanova (Theme from TV series.) / Dance of the sugar plum fairy (From the "Nutcracker Suite".) / Firebird suite / Panorama (aujourd'hui c'est toi) (From the film "A Man & A Woman".) / Adagio / La gazza ladra (the thieving magpie) / Leaves are green, The (Theme from the T.V. series "Elizabeth R".) / Sleepy shores (Theme from the TV series "Owen M.D.") / Adagietto / Last movement suite no.4 in D / Rhapsody in blue.
MC: . . . . TCEMS 1292

FIREBIRD SUITE, THE (See under Stravinsky for full details) (London Symphony Orchestra).

LOVE CLASSICS (London Symphony Orchestra).
Tracks: / Drive / Take my breath away / God only knows / Ruby Tuesday / Another day in paradise / MacArthur park / Stairway to heaven / Lady in red, The / Purple rain / Ain't no mountain high enough / Prelude in motion/The first time / I want to know what love is / Power of love, The / Nights in white satin / First time I ever saw your face, The / Separate lives / Nothing compares 2 U / Fanfare intro-Rhapsody in black / Reach out, I'll be there / She's out of my life / Whiter shade of pale, A / Without you / Eternal flame / Living years, The.
LP: . . . . STAR 2440
MC: . . . . STAC 2440

LSO BEETHOVEN COLLECTION (London Symphony Orchestra).
MCSET: . . . . PDC 066

MARCHING AND DANCING FROM THE CLASSICS (London Symphony Orchestra).
Tracks: / Menuetto trio from Serenade No. 6 in D, K 239 / Voices of Spring, Opus 410 (Johann Strauss II) / 3rd movement: Allegro molta vivace / March from the nutcracker suite Opus 71a / Waltz of the flowers (Act III) (Tchaikovsky) / Marche au supplice (Berlioz) / Saltarello (Mendelssohn) / Pomp and circumstance (Elgar) / Pizzicato polka (Johann Strauss II) / Danse boheme (Bizet) / Marche slave (Tchaikovsky) / Sabre dance (Khachaturian) / Sarabande (Grieg) / Readetzky march, Opus 228 (Johann Strauss) / Polvtsian dances from 'Prince Igor).
LP: . . . . DUET 28

MOVIE MUSIC (London Symphony Orchestra/Stanley Black).
Tracks: / Raiders of the lost ark / Big country / Superman / Star wars / 2001 / Magnificent seven, The / Lawrence of Arabia / Deer hunter (Cavatina) / 633 squadron / James Bond medley.
MC: . . . . HSC 3408

MUSIC FOR ROYAL OCCASIONS Conducted by Sir Alexander Gibson (London Symphony Orchestra).
LP: . . . . RL 7555
MC: . . . . RLT 7555

MUSIC FROM EDWARD VII (London Symphony Orchestra).
LP: 2659 041

MUSIC YOU HAVE LOVED (London Symphony Orchestra).
LP: . . . . SPR 8517
MC: . . . . SPC 8517

MUSIC YOU HAVE LOVED (2) (London Symphony Orchestra).
MCSET: . . . . PDC 036

MUSICAL FANTASY (London Symphony Orchestra/various artists).
Tracks: / Oklahoma / My fair lady / Annie get your gun / King and I, The / Sound of music, The / Guys and dolls / West side story / Porgy and Bess / South Pacific / Carousel.
LP: . . . . FANLP 1
MC: . . . . ZCFAN 1

NEW ROCK CLASSICS (London Symphony Orchestra).
LP: 6 26186
MC: 4 26186

PETRUSHKA (London Symphony Orchestra).
MCSET: 4153364

POPULAR CLASSICS (London Symphony Orchestra).
MCSET: . . . . CRT 023

POWER OF CLASSIC ROCK (London Symphony Orchestra).
Tracks: / Two tribes, relax / I want to know what love is / Drive / Purple rain / Time after time / Born in the USA / Power of love, The / Thriller / Total eclipse of the heart / Hello / Modern Girl / Dancing in the dark.
LP: . . . . PRT 10049
MC: 40 10049
LP: 4634021
MC: 4634024

RHAPSODY IN BLACK (London Symphony Orchestra).
LP: . . . . ONE 1063

ROCK CLASSICS (London Symphony Orchestra).
LP: . . . . NE 1123
MC: . . . . CE 2123

ROCK SYMPHONIES (London Symphony Orchestra).
Tracks: / Born to run / For your love / Chariots of fire / House of the rising sun / You really got me / MacArthur Park / Vienna / She's out of my life / Pictures of Lily / Since you've been gone / High heel sneakers / Gloria.
LP: . . . . NE 1243
MC: . . . . CE 2243

ROMEO AND JULIET - SUITE (see under Prokofiev (composer)) (London Symphony Orchestra).

SAMUEL BARBER (see under Barber, Samuel) (London Symphony Orchestra/ Tedd Joselson).

SIBELIUS: THE SWAN OF TUONELA Conducted by Sir Charles Mackerras (London Symphony Orchestra).
Tracks: / Swan of Tuonela (legends Opus 22, No. 2) / Symphony No. 2 in D, Opus 43 (Sibelius).
MC: . . . . CIMPC 927

STAR WARS (ORIGINAL SOUNDTRACK) (London Symphony Orchestra).
MC: . . . . C 541

STRAUSS FAMILY (London Symphony Orchestra).
2LP: 2659 014

SYMPHONIES NO.5 & 6 (TCHAIKOVSKY) (London Symphony Orchestra).
MCSET: 4134294

SYMPHONY NO.6 (GLAZUNOV) (see under Glazunov (composer)) (London Symphony Orchestra/Royal Philharmonic Orchestra).

SYMPHONY NO. 1/SYMPHONY NO. 2 (RESURRECTION) (See under Mahler (composer)) (London Symphony Orchestra).

SYMPHONY NO. 3 (See under Mahler (composer)) (London Symphony Orchestra).

TESS (Music by Philippe Sarde) (London Symphony Orchestra).
LP: . . . . MCF 3112

TOP T.V. THEMES (London Symphony Orchestra).
LP: . . . . STWO 372

VIENNA DANCES (London Symphony Orchestra).
Tracks: / Roses from the South / Emperor waltz / Pizzicato polka / Vienna blood / Radetzky march / etc.
MC: . . . . ZC QS 6020

WALLS OF THE WORLD, THE (see under Batt, Mike) (Batt, Mike/London Symphony Orchestra).

London Symphony

TOMMY (See under 'Tommy').

London Underground

CURRENT AFFAIRS SESSION.
LP: . . . . ONULP 28

London Welsh Male...

SING THE SONGS OF OUR HOMELAND (see Welsh Guards) (London Welsh Male Voice Choir / Welsh Guards).

London Wind Orchestra

WIND MUSIC OF HOLST AND VAUGHAN WILLIAMS.
Tracks: / Suite no. 1 & 2, op.28 (Holst) / Hammersmith Parade and scherzo op.52 (Holst) / English folk song suite / Toccata marziale (Vaughan Williams).
MC: . . . . ZC QS 6021

Lone Justice

LONE JUSTICE.
Tracks: / East of Eden / After the flood / Ways to be wicked / Don't toss us away / Working late / Pass it on / Wait till we get home / Soap, soup and salvation / You are the light / Sweet, sweet baby (I'm falling).
LP: . . . . GEF 32784
MC: 4032784
LP: . . . . GEF 26288
MC: . . . . GEFC 24060
LP: . . . . GEF 24060

SHELTER.
Tracks: / I found love / Shelter / Reflected / Beacon / Wheels / Belfry / Dreams come true / Gift, The / Inspiration / Dixie storms.
LP: . . . . WX 73
MC: . . . . WX 73 C
MC: . . . . GEFC 24122
LP: . . . . GEF 24122

Lone Ranger

BARNABUS COLLINS.
LP: . . . . GG 0021

HI-YO SILVER, AWAY!.
Tracks: / Tom drunk / Rub'n'scrub / Legalise the national herb / Gunshot mek daughter drop / Living as a poor / Johnny make you bad so / Clock, The / Lone Ranger and Tonto / Solomon / Love affair problem.
LP: . . . . GREL 40

LEARN TO DRIVE.
LP: . . . . BB 096

ON THE OTHER SIDE OF DUB.
LP: . . . . SOL 5454

Lone Star

FIRING ON ALL SIX.
Tracks: / Bells of Berlin / Ballad of crafty Jack, The / Time lays down / Hypnotic mover / Lovely Lubina / Seasons in your eyes / Rivers overflowing / All of us to all of you.
LP: . . . . CBS 82213

LONE STAR.
LP: . . . . EPC 81545

Lone Wolf McQuade

LONE WOLF MCQUADE (Film soundtrack) (Various artists).
LP: . . . . TER 1071

Lonely Guy

LONELY GUY (Original Soundtrack) (Various artists).
LP: . . . . MCA 36010
MC: . . . . MCAC 36010

Lonely Moans

LONELY MOANS, THE.
Tracks: / Jiggerwhack / Shocker / Heartbeat / Slave / Walkdown / Blame / Sex boots / Elvis has left the building / Moan's theme / Lonesome town / Honkies / Prom theme / Into my eyes / Rotting.
LP: . . . . TUPLP 011

Lonely Passion Of ...

LONELY PASSION OF JUDITH HEARNE (Film Soundtrack) (Various artists).
LP: AVM 2001
MC: AVMC 2001

Lonely, Roy

ROCK 'N' ROLL DANCE PARTY.
LP: ROCK 8203

Lonesome Pine Fiddlers

14 MOUNTAIN SONGS.
LP: SLP 155
MC: GT 5155

Lonesome Strangers

LONESOME PINE.
LP: SPD 1012

LONESOME STRANGERS, THE.
Tracks: / Just can't cry no more / Don't back down / Daddy's gone gray / Just walk away / We used to fuss / Clementine / Lay down my old guitar / Goodbye lonesome / Oh my train / Don't you run away from me.
LP: SPD 1023
MC: SPDC 1023

Lonesome Sundown

LONESOME SUNDOWN (Various artists).
LP: LP 8012

Lonesome Sundown (group)

BEEN GONE TOO LONG (See also under Green, Cornelius).
Tracks: / They call me sundown / One more night / Louisiana lover man / Dealin' from the bottom / Midnight blues again / Just got to know / Black cat bone / I betcha / You don't miss your water / If ain't been to Houston.
LP: SNTF 832

FROM L.A. TO L.A. (Lonesome Sundown & Phillip Walker).
LP: ROUNDER 2037
MC: ROUNDER 2037C

IF ANYBODY ASKS YOU (MY HOME AIN'T HERE) (His best).
Tracks: / If anybody asks you (my home ain't here) / Blues for my baby / Opelousas blues / Things have changed / My home is a prison / You know I love you / I never thought / You give me all kinds of misery / Lonesome whistle / If you see my baby / Learn to treat me better / I've got a broken heart baby / I found an angel / I'll still be loving you.
LP: FLY 617

LONESOME WHISTLER.
Tracks: / Don't say a word / I stood by / California blues / Lonely lonely me / Give it up / Gonna stick to you baby / Lonesome whistle / Leave my money alone / My home is a prison / Lost without love / Mojo man / Don't go.
LP: FLY 587

Lonette

LONETTE.
LP: LPSX 8

Loney, Roy

FAST AND LOOSE.
LP: LOLITA 5017

LIVE: ROY LONEY.
LP: LOLITA 5018

OUT AFTER DARK.
LP: SS 9001

ROCK AND ROLL DANCE PARTY.
LP: LPL 8203

Long, Annette

SING AND DANCE.
LP: VA 5

STAY WITH ME.
LP: GRS 1150

Long Day Of Vengeance

LONG DAY OF VENGEANCE/ SARTANA (Original Soundtracks) (Various artists).
LP: IMGM 003

Long, Glenn

GREAT THEME TUNES (FILMS) (Long, Glenn, His Piano & Orchestra).
Tracks: / What I did for love / Summer knows, The / Mahogany, Theme from / Days of wine and roses, The / Continental, The / Route 66 / Way we were, The / Music of the night / Up where we belong / Way you look tonight / Fame / All the way / In the cool cool cool of the evening / I just called to say I love you / Wind beneath my wings, The / Arthur's theme / Shadow of your smile, The / Windmills of your mind, The / Evergreen / For all we know / Chariots of fire / Lady in red, The / Mona Lisa / Somewhere out there / Say you say me / St. Elmo's fire love theme / Swinging on a star / Greatest love of all, The.
MCSET: DTO 10330

Long Good Friday

LONG GOOD FRIDAY (Film Soundtrack) (Various artists).
Tracks: / Long good Friday, The: *Various artists* / Overture: *Various artists* / Scene is set, The: *Various* artists / At the pool: *Various artists* / Discovery: *Various artists* / Icehouse, The: *Various artists*/ Talking to the police: *Various artists* / Guitar interludes: *Various artists* / Realization: *Various artists*/ Fury: *Various artists* / Taken: *Various artists.*
LP: CES 1001
LP: FILM 020
MC: FILMC 020

LONG GOOD FRIDAY (THEME FROM) (See under Barking Light Orchestra).

Long Hello

LONG HELLO-VOLUME 1 (Various artists).
LP: NOTT 002

Long, Johnny

1941: JOHNNY LONG (Long, Johnny & His Orchestra).
LP: CLP 56

Long, Larry

IT TAKES A LOT OF PEOPLE (A Tribute To Woody Guthrie).
LP: FF 508

RUN FOR FREEDOM.
LP: FF 346

SWEET THUNDER.
LP: FF 430

Long March

LONG MARCH (THEME FROM) (See under Barking Light Orchestra).

Long Pursuit

LONG PURSUIT, THE Cleary, Jon (Dunbavan, Alan).
MCSET: SOUND 17

Long Riders

LONG RIDERS, THE (Film soundtrack) (See under Cooder, Ry) (Cooder, Ry).

Long Ryders

10-5-60.
Tracks: / Join my gang / I don't care what's right / 10-5-60 / Trip, The / And she drives / Born to believe in you.
LP: ZANE 004

NATIVE SONS.
Tracks: / I had a dream / Tell it to the judge on Sunday / Wreck of the 909 / Ivory tower / Too close to the lights / Still get by / Final wild son / (Sweet) mental revenge / Never got to meet the Mom / Fair game / Run Dusty run.
LP: ZONG 003

STATE OF OUR UNION.
Tracks: / Looking for Lewis and Clarke / Lights of downtown / WDIA / Mason-Dixon line / Here comes that train again / Years long ago / Good times tomorrow, hard times today / Two kinds of love / You just cant ride the box cars anymore / Capturing the flag / State of my union.
MC: ICT 9802
LP: ILPS 9802

TWO FISTED TALES.
Tracks: / Gunslinger man / I want you bad / Stitch in time, A / Light gets in the way / Prairie fire / Baby's in toyland / Long short story / Man of misery / Harriet Tubman's gonna carry me home / For the rest of my days / Spectacular fall.
LP: ILPS 9869
MC: ICT 9869

Long Tall Shorty

1970'S BOY.
LP: NIXON 6

ROCKIN' AT THE SAVOY.
LP: LTS 7

Long Tall Texans

FIVE BEANS.
LP: RAZZ 44

LOS ME BOLEROS.
LP: RAZ 328

SATURNALIA.
LP: RAZD 37

SINGING TO THE MOON.
LP: RAGELP 108

SODBUSTERS.
Tracks: / Poison / My babe / Get up and go / Rockin' crazy / Long tall Texan / Texas boogie / Paradise / My idea of heaven / Mad about you / Wreckin' me / Dance of the head hunters / Endless sleep.
LP: RAZ 23

Longfield Crane

LONGFIELD CRANE.
LP: ASTRAG 1

Longhorns

FEELIN' DOWN.
LP: FLATOP 001

Longhouse

LONGHOUSE.
Tracks: / She don't wanna go home tonight / Don't remember / Come back / Not in love / Green, go / Heaven / Time machine / Getaway / Blind faith / Second chance.
LP: K 925693 1

Longmire, Wilbert

CHAMPAGNE.
Tracks: / Diane's dilemma / Love's holiday / Ragtown / Pleasure island / Funshine.
LP: CBS 83257

WITH ALL MY LOVE.
Tracks: / But I love you / Hawkeye / Crystal clear / Music speaks louder than words / Take your time / Just as long as we have love / Strawberry sunset.
LP: CBS 84155

Longpig

OF LOVE AND ADDICTION.
Tracks: / Interception / Language / Boy I wanna tell ya / Why do people find each other strange / Batsong / Earthrobbers / Lizard / Pollution thing / Shadow man.
LP: GRAM 11

Longshot

LONGSHOT (Branagh, Kenneth).
MCSET: LFP 7511

Longsy D

HOUSE SOUND FOR THE WORLD.
LP: BIGA 001
MC: BIGAC 001

WIV A LIKKLE BIT OF ACID.
LP: BIGA 1
MC: BIGAC 1

Longthorne, Joe

CHRISTMAS ALBUM.
MCSET: STAC 2385
2LP: STAR 2385

ESPECIALLY FOR YOU.
LP: STAR 2365
MC: STAC 2365

JOE LONGTHORNE SONG BOOK, THE (TV Theme).
Tracks: / You're my world / My prayer / Always on my mind / My mother's eyes / Just loving you / It's only make believe / To all the girls I've loved before / End of the world / It was almost like a song / Hurt / Answer me / Danny boy / Don't laugh at me / When your old wedding ring was new.
LP: STAR 2353
MC: STAC 2353

SINGER, THE.
LP: GBR 1001
MC: GBR 1001K

Look

LOOK.
Tracks: / I'm the beat / Feeding time.
LP: MCF 3120

Look At All The

LOOK AT ALL THE CHILDREN NOW (Various artists).
LP: DM 005

Look Back In Anger

CAPRICE.
LP: CRIMLP 118

Look For Your Own

LOOK FOR YOUR OWN (Various artists).
LP: SBJOMBLER 1
LP: JOMBLER 1

Look Of Love

LOOK OF LOVE (Various artists).
LP: BM 3001

Looking For A Bluebird

LOOKING FOR A BLUEBIRD (Jones, Peter).
MCSET: ZBBC 1136

Loop

ETERNITY.
LP: CHAPLP 44

FADE OUT.
Tracks: / Black sun / This is where you end / Fever knife / Torched / Fade out / Pulse / Vision stain, A / Got to get it over / Collision / Crawling heart / Thief of fire / Thief (motherfucker) / Mother sky.
LP: CHAPLP 34
MC: CHAPC 34

GILDED ETERNITY, A.
LP: SITU 27
MC: SITC 27

HEAVEN'S END.
LP: HEAD LP 1
LP: REACTORLP 1
MC: REACTORC 01

WORLD IN YOUR EYES, THE.
LP: HEADLP 2
LP: REACTORLP 2
MC: REACTORC 2

Loophole

LOOPHOLE, THE (See under Archer, Jeffrey (aut)) (Havers, Nigel).

Loos, Anita

GENTLEMEN PREFER BLONDES (Lorelei's diary) (Channing, Carol).
MC: 1148

Loos, Charles

CHARLES LOOS AND ALI RYERSON (Loos, Charles & Ali Ryerson).
LP: EMD 89011
MC: EMD 89014

Loose Ends

LITTLE SPICE, A.
Tracks: / Tell me what you want / Feels so right now / Let's rock / Dial 999 / Music makes me higher / Choose me (rescue me) / Little spice, A / So much in love.
LP: OVED 159
MC: OVEDC 159
LP: V 2381

LOOK HOW LONG.
LP: DIX 94
MC: CDIX 94

REAL CHUCKEEBOO, THE.
Tracks: / Watching you / (There's no) gratitude / Tomorrow (part 1 of the real chuckeeboo) / Mr. Bachelor (Part 2 of The Real Chuckeeboo.) / You've just got to have it all / Life / What goes around / Easier said than done / Hungry / Is it ever too late? / Remote control / Too much (CD & cassette only) / Johnny broadhead (part 2) (CD & cassette only).
LP: V 2528
MC: TCV 2528

SO WHERE ARE YOU.
Tracks: / Magic touch / New horizon / If my lovin' makes you hot / So where are you? / Golden years / Hangin' on a string (contemplating) / Give it all you got / Sweetest pain, The / You can't stop the rain / Silent talking.
LP: V 2340
MC: TCV 2340

ZAGORA.
Tracks: / Stay a little while child / Be thankful (Mama's song) / Slow down / Ooh, you make me feel / Just a minute / Who are you? / I can't wait / Nights of pleasure / Let's get back to love / Rainbow / Take the 'A' train.
LP: V 2384
MC: TCV 2384
LP: OVED 296
MC: OVEDC 296

Loose Gravel

GRAVEL RASH.
MLP: FC 001

Loose Lips

MY PAST LIFE HAS GONE (Featuring Helen Watson).
LP: AP 007

Loose Tubes

DELIGHTFUL PRECIPICE.
Tracks: / Sad Afrika / Delightful precipice / Shelley / Sosbun Brakk / Sunny / Hermeto's giant breakfast / Would I were.
LP: LTLP 003
MC: LTMC 03

LOOSE TUBES.
Tracks: / Eden express / Rowing boat delineation egg / Descarge / Descarge occuriencia / Yellow hill / Mister Zee / Arriving.
LP: LTLP 001

OPEN LETTER.
Tracks: / Sweet Williams / Children's game / Blue / Sticklebacks / Excepting suites from strangers / Last word, The / A / Open letter to Dudu Pukwana / Shadow play (CD & cassette only) / Mo Mhutrnin Ban (CD & cassette only).
LP: EGED 55
MC: EGEDC 55

Lopez, Trini

16 GREATEST HITS: TRINI LOPEZ.
LP: FUN 9025
MC: FUNC 9025

20 GREATEST HITS: TRINI LOPEZ.
LP: MA 10685
MC: MAMC 910685

AMERICA.
MC: 260 402 4

GREATEST HITS: TRINI LOPEZ (2).
MC: GM 0225

GREATEST HITS: TRINI LOPEZ (3).
Tracks: / If I had a hammer / Kansas city / Sinner man / Are you sincere / Michael

/ La bamba / Lemon tree / I'm comin' home / Cindy / Sad tomorrow / Hall of fame / What have I got of my own / A-ME-RI-CA.
LP: K 44037

HIS TOP HITS.
MC: 812

IF I HAD A HAMMER.
Tracks: / If I had a hammer / America / Bye bye blackbird / Cielito lindo / This land is your land / What'd I say / La bamba / Granada / Gotta travel on / Down by the riverside / Marianne / When the Saints go marching in / Volare / Unchain my heart.
LP: SHM 3023

INFECTIOUS.
LP: STFL 3
MC: STFC 3

THIS LAND IS YOUR LAND.
LPPD: AR 30066

TRINI LOPEZ AT P.J.'S.
LP: R 6093

TRINI LOPEZ IN LONDON.
LP: RSLP 6238

TRINI LOPEZ LIVE.
Tracks: / America / If I had a hammer / Bye bye blackbird / Cielito Lindo / This land is your land / What'd I say / La bamba / Granada / Bye bye Blondie / Nie meir ohne (German) / Lebewohl daisy girl / Long ago / Folk medley / Unchain my heart.
LP: BFX 15344
LP: ENT LP 13013
MC: ENT MC 13013

VERY BEST OF TRINI LOPEZ.
LP: NE 1210
MC: CE 2210

Lorbass

WIE ES UNS GEFALLT.
Tracks: / Der gott de niedrigkeit / Schwabenkrieg / Der tod / Moder ick will'n ding hem / Allzeit findet man grosse sorgen / Das lied von gluck / Gronlander / Nasendreher / Die geschichte vom roten papagei / Nachgesang / Vetter Michel / Marie Weigenlied.
LP: BURL 004

WOHL BEKOMM'S.
Tracks: / Di mullerin / Nachtwachterlied / Kontratanz der schlemmer / Sandmann / Die ballade von den funf sohnen / He du der sensemann / Zweifach / Billerbecker / Hopp marjelch / Monch und nahterin.
LP: BURL 011

Lorber, Jeff

PRIVATE PASSION.
Tracks: / Facts of love / True confessions / Jamaica / Back in love / Kristen / Private passion / Sand castles / Keep on lovin' her / Midnight snack.
LP: JABH 21
MC: JABHC 21

STEP BY STEP.
Tracks: / Step by step / Best part of the night / Groovacious / Every woman needs it / On the wild side / This is the night / Pacific Coast highway / It takes a woman / When you gonna come back home.
LP: JABH 9

WATER SIGN (Lorber, Jeff Fusion).
Tracks: / Toad's place / Country / Tune 88 / Sparkle / Water sign / Rain dance / Right here / Lights out.
LP: 209338
MC: 409338

L'Orchestre De ...

FORMULE 4 (L'Orchestre De La Jeunesse).
LP: KL 035

L'Orchestre

GREATEST SYNTHESIZER HITS.
LP: MODEM 1046
MC: MODEMC 1046

SOUND WAVES.
Tracks: / Heaven and hell / Chariots of fire / Oxygene / Missing / Westway / Chung Kuo (the long march) / Magnetic fields / Equinoxe / Pulstar / Carillon / Bladerunner / Prelude to earthrise / To the unknown man / Close Encounters of the Third Kind / Star Wars.
LP: NML 1005
MC: ZCNML 1005

Lord, Bobby

EVERYBODY IS ROCKIN'.
LP: REV 3006

Lord Buckley

BAD RAPPING.
Tracks: / Bad rapping of the Marquis De Sade / H bomb / Chastity belt / Ballad of Dan McGroo / His majesty the policeman.
LP: VERB 6

BLOWING HIS MIND.
LP: VERB 3

LORD BUCKLEY IN CONCERT.
LP: VERB 4

MOST IMMACULATELY HIP ARISTOCRAT.
Tracks: / Bad rapping of the Marquis de Sade, The / King of bad cats, The / Governor Slugwell / Raven, The / Train, The / Hip Einie, The.
LP: VERB 8

Lord C.M

C.M LORD.
Tracks: / I'm happy that love has found you / Flashback / Fly by night / Real thing / Taking it slow / Don't run me away / Can't wait / Delicious / Closer by the minute.
LP: RCALP 3061

Lord Crucifier

FOCUS OF LIFE.
LP: VOV 670
MC: VOV 670C

Lord, Eric

GAUMONT THEATRE MEMORIES.
MC: AC 161

GETTIN SENTIMENTAL (ORGAN RECITAL).
LP: CF 278

RECOLLECTIONS OF THE TOWER, BLACKPOOL (see under Dixon, Reginald) (Lord, Eric/Reginald Dixon/Ernest Broadbent).

TWO SIDES OF ERIC LORD.
Tracks: / Gettin' sentimental over you / Lover / Smoke gets in your eyes / Lady is a tramp, The / Sleepy time gal / You're the cream in my coffee / Charmaine / Moon River / Exactly like you / Ain't she sweet? / Whispering / Cherokee / Darktown strutters' ball / Sweet Sue / Deed I do / Twilight time / Stardust melody / Sweet Georgia Brown / Goodnight, sweetheart / My fair lady- selection / So beats my heart.
MC: AC 166

Lord, Jon

BEFORE I FORGET.
Tracks: / Chance on a feeling / Tender babes / Hollywood rock and roll / Bach onto this / Before I forget / Say it's alright / Burntwood / Where are you.
LP: SHSP 4123

COUNTRY DIARY OF AN EDWARDIAN LADY (T.V. soundtrack).
LP: DIARY 1
MC: DIARYC 1

GEMINI SUITE, THE.
LP: LONG 10
MC: LONGC 10
LP: 1C 064 92817

MALICE IN WONDERLAND (See under Paice Ashton Lord) (Paice, Ashton, Lord).

Lord & Mary Ann

LORD AND MARY ANN (Catherine Cookson (aut)) (Jameson, Susan (nar)).
MC: CAB 011

Lord Mountdrago (bk)

COLONEL'S LADY, THE/LORD MOUNTDRAGO (see under Colonel's Lady) (Burden, Hugh (nar)).

LORD MOUNTDRAGO (Maugham, Somerset) (Burden, Hugh (nar)).
MC: TTC/WSM 2

Lord Mullion's...

LORD MULLION'S SECRET. (See under Innes, Michael) (Innes, Michael).

Lord Nelson

YESTERDAY, TODAY AND FOREVER.
LP: GS 2300
MC: GSC 2300

Lord Of The Flies

LORD OF THE FLIES (Film Soundtrack) (Various artists).
Tracks: / Lord of the flies: *Various artists* / Island, The: *Various artists* / Demons: *Various artists*/ Fire on the mountain: *Various artists* / Cry of the hunters: *Various artists* / Last hope, The: *Various* artists / Savages: *Various artists* / After the storm: *Various artists* / Bacchanalia: *Various artists*/ Lord Of The Flies - finale: *Various artists*.
MC: FILMC 067

Lord Of The Rings

LORD OF THE RINGS (Film soundtrack) (Various artists).
2LP: LOR 1
2LP: LORD 11/12

Lord Sassafrass

POCCOMANIA JUMP.
LP: SCORPIO 001

Lord Savile's Crime

LORD SAVILE'S CRIME (See also under Wilde, Oscar).

Lords Of The New

IS NOTHING SACRED.
Tracks: / Dance with me / Bad timing / Johnny too bad / Don't worry children / Night is calling, The / Black girl white girl / Going down town / Tale of two cities / Partners in crime / World without end / Live for today.
LP: SP 70039
MC: CS 70039

LIVE AT THE SPIT.
LP: ILP 021
MC: ILPC 021

METHOD TO OUR MADNESS, THE.
Tracks: / Method to my madness / I never believed / Pretty baby scream / Fresh flesh / When blood runs cold / Murder style / Seducer, The / Kiss of death / Do what thou wilt / My kingdom come.
LP: IRSA 7049

SCENE OF THE CRIME.
2LP: PB 003

Lord's Taverners

BEST OF TEST MATCH SPECIAL.
LP: HAV 1017
MC: HAVC 1017

Lore & The Legends

ONE STEP AHEAD OF THE LAW.
Tracks: / Plains of Madalene / Just across the river / El Bandito / Yankees in Houston / Taffeta memories / Saying goodbye to the West / One step ahead of the law / Silver spurs / Cowboy arms hotel / Pearly gates / Sometimes it's hard to be a cowboy / Hairtrigger colts 44.
LP: COLT 2002

Loren, Brian

BRIAN LOREN.
LP: V2322

Loria, Aj

NEW ORLEANS, NEW ORLEANS.
LP: NOLA LP 26

Lorien, Duncan

ARCHITECTS OF TIME (See under Daley, Martin) (Daley, Martin & Duncan Lorien).

ARCHITECTS OF TIME (SINGLE) (See under Daley, Martin).

Lorna Doone (bk)

LORNA DOONE (R.H Blackmore) (Gilmore, Peter (nar)).
MCSET: LFP 7244
MCSET: LFP 4172445

LORNA DOONE (Children's Classics).
MC: PLBC 207

Lorre, Peter

MYSTERY IN THE AIR.
Tracks: / Lodgers, The / Mask of Medussa, The.
LP: LP 1001

Lortie, Louis

LOUIS LORTIE PLAYS 20TH CENTURY PIANO MUSIC.
LP: ABRD 1373
MC: ABTD 1373

Los Alhama

FLAMENCO.
LP: EULP 1026
MC: EUMC 1026

Los Angeles Jazz

SHOPWORK SHUFFLE.
Tracks: / Where have you gone / Angel eyes / Goodbye pork pie hat / Mickey's revenge / Greazy rider.
LP: AM 16

Los Angeles Police

LOS ANGELES POLICE BAND.
Tracks: / Mingulay boat song / Balmoral Highlanders, The / Dorney Gerry / Lacklan ferry / Flower of Scotland / Mairi's wedding / Skye boat song / Going home / Loch Lomond / Cock o' the north / Blue bonnets o'er the border / Saints / Jesus Christ superstar / Marine corps hymn / Amazing Grace / Scotland the brave / We're no awa' tae bide awa' / Auld lang syne.
LP: LILP 5142
MC: LICS 5142

Los Angeles Zydeco

T-LOU.
LP: 1014
MC: 1014 TC

Los Campesinos

CANCIONES DE MI TIERRA (Los Campesinos De Michocan).
MC: C 3024
LP: ARHOOLIE 3024

CONJUNTO DE ARPA (Los Campesinos De Michocan).
MC: C 3022

Los Gitanillos

FLAMENCO (Los Gitanillos de Cadiz).
MC: 401 984

Los Incas

EL CONDOR PASA.
2LP: 6620 040

EL VIENTO.
LP: FLDX 517

LOS INCAS.
LP: 6886 114

MUSIC FOR THE MILLIONS.
Tracks: / Huayno de la roca / El condor pasa / Achachau / Munahuanqui / Soncociman / Chunguinada / Poussiganga / Huayta huayucha / Llamerada / Urpi / Danza wipfala / Risas de bolivia.
LP: 818 256 1

MUSIC OF THE ANDES.
2LP: ALB 10678

Los Indios Tabajaros

BEST OF LOS INDIOS TABAJARAS.
Tracks: / Maria Elena / Love is a many splendoured thing / Mama you quiero / Valse in C sharp / Pajaro campana / Marta / Always in my heart / Nao tenho lagrimos / Smoke gets in your eyes / Frenesi / Recuerdos de la Alhambra / Third man theme.
LP: INTS 5003

GUITARS ON THE GO.
Tracks: / If I were a rich man / Jalousie / My balloon / Chariots of fire / Meditation / Blue angel / Duellin' banjos / Little town ten piece band / Silver strings / Happy day / St. Louis.
LP: NL 89386

IL FLAUTO INDIANO (Los Indios).
Tracks: / El huma huaqueno / Bailecito de lela / Bolivianita / Indiecito / Tema de siku / Vasija de barro / Son cayman / Variacion de tatu / El condor pasa / Bocina / Copacabana / Le cuequita.
LP: SM 3275
MC: MC 3275

Los Kenacos

EL CONDOR PASA.
Tracks: / El condor pasa / Para una orejita de tierra cocida / Tikiminiki / Dos palomitas / La peregrinacion / Tarirari / La concinerita / Chuqui / Sonkoy / Indios guerrilleros / Pregrino soy.
LP: SM 3245

Los Lobos

AND TIME TO DANCE.
Tracks: / Let's say goodnight / Walking song, The / Anselma / Come on let's go / How much can I do / Why do you do / Ay te dejo en San Antonio.
MC: SLMC 17
LP: SLMP 17
MC: SMMC 17
LP: ROUGH 71

BY THE LIGHT OF THE MOON.
Tracks: / One time one night / Shakin' shakin' shakes / Is this all there is / Prenda del Alma / All I wanted to do was dance / Set me free (Rosa Lee) / Hardest time, The / My baby's gone / river of fools / Mess we're in, The / Tears of God.
LP: SLAP 13
MC: SMAC 13

GOODNIGHT MY LOVE (see under Huntsberry, Howard).

HOW WILL THE WOLF SURVIVE.
Tracks: / Don't worry baby / Matter of time, A / Corrida No.1 / Our last night / Breakdown, The / I got loaded / Sere nata nortena / Evangeline / I got to let you know / Li'l king of everything / Will the wolf survive?.
LP: SLMP 3
MC: SMMC 3

LA PISTOLA Y EL CORAZON.
Tracks: / La guacamaya / Las amarillas / Si yo quisiera / (Sonojas) mananitas michocanas / Estoy sentado aqui / El gusto / Que nadie sepa mi sufrir / El canelo / La pistola y el corazon.
LP: 828 121-1
MC: 828 121-4

NEIGHBORHOOD, THE.
Tracks: / Down on the riverbed / Emily / I walk alone / Angel dance / Little John of God / Deep dark hole / Georgia slop / I can't understand / Giving tree, The / Take my hand / Jenny's got a pony / Be still / Neighborhood, The.
LP: 828 190 1

MC: 828 190 4

Los Machucambos

LA BAMBA.
Tracks: / La bamba / Mas que nada / Cuando calienta el sol / Pepito / Eso es el amor / Granada / Brazil / Con amor por amor / Esperanza / Fio maravilha / Garota de Ipanema / Amor amor / Tres palabras / El condor pasa / Quiereme / Guantanamera / La cucaracha / Tristeza / Perfidia / Corcovado / La mama / Maria Elena / Tico Tico / Frenesie / El manicero.
MC: 300054

LATIN HITS.
Tracks: / La cucaracha / La palomita / Amor amor / Pajaro campana / El otorrino / Granada / Pepito / Perfidia / Cascada / Subo subo / Adios.
LP: . . . . DGS 10

Los Malaguenos

FLAMENCO, VOL.2.
LP: . . . . HM 965

Los Munequitos...

CANTAR MARAVILLOSO (Los Munequitos De Matanzas).
Tracks: / Oyelos de nuevo / Lo que dice el abakua / Fundamento dilanga / El marino / Mi arer / Cantar maravilloso / Arague / A los embales.
LP: . . . . ORB 053

Los Nemus...

HARDER THAN BEFORE (Los Nemus Del Pacifico).
LP: . . . . MLPS 1052
MC: . . . . MCT 1052
LP: 864 438 1
MC: 864 438 4

Los Pinginos Del Norte

CORRIDOS FROM TEXAS.
LP: . . . . ARHOOLIE 3002

Los Romeros

EVENING OF FLAMENCO.
LP: . . . . SRI 75073

Los Rupay

FOLKLORE DE BOLIVIA.
LP: . . . . EULP 1001

Los Three Paraguayos

FLOR DE PILAR.
LP: . . . . EULP 1048

Los Tuparmaros

SALSA Y TROPICA.
Tracks: / Permiteme / Son general / Fiestas tradicionales / Son de son / Cha cun cha / Embrujo de coral / Madrigal / En la puerta del horno / Tu ausencia / El viejito parrandero.
LP: . . . . MLPS 1049
MC: . . . . MCT 1049
LP: 846 437 1
MC: 846 437 4

Los Van Van

SONGO.
Tracks: / La titimania / Que palo es ese / Muevete / Ya tu campana no suena / Calla / Sanunguera / Recaditos no / Y que tu cres.
MC: . . . . ICT 9908
LP: . . . . ILPS 9908

Loss, Joe

50 BIG BAND FAVOURITES (Loss, Joe/Parnell, Jack).
MCSET: . . . . TR 1530

50 FABULOUS YEARS.
Tracks: / Let's dance at the make believe ballroom / Begin the beguine / At the woodchopper's ball / In the mood / Amapola / Donkey serenade / Wheels cha-cha / Maigret / Must be Maidson / March of the mods / I'm looking over a four leaf clover / When the red, red robin comes bob, bob, bobbin' along / Applause / Congratulations.
LP: . . . . NTS 217
MC: . . . . TCNTS 217

ALL TIME PARTY HITS.
LP: . . . . MFP 5227

BEGIN THE BEGUINE (Loss, Joe & His Orchestra).
Tracks: / Begin the beguine / Change partners / Maria Elena / Please be kind / Heart and soul / So rare / I know now / Cinderella (stay in my arms) / My prayer / Scene changes, The / In the chapel in the moonlight / Sweet Sue / Little Sir Echo / I never knew heaven could speak / Are you having any fun? / Wish me luck (as you wave me goodbye).
LP: . . . . SH 430

BEST OF LATIN.
Tracks: / La cumparsita / Jealousy / wheels (Cha cha) / Tea for two (Cha cha) / Quando caliente el sol / Girl from Ipanema / Soul bossa nova / Best thing for you is me,The (Bossa nova) / Tequila / Spanish gypsy dance (Paso doble) / March of the Matadors (Paso doble) / Roberta (Rumba) / La bamba / Guantanamera / Brazil / Copacabana / Banda,A / Manolet (Merengue).
LP: . . . . EG 2607591
MC: . . . . EG 2607594

BLACK & WHITE MINSTRELS & THE JOE LOSS ORCHESTRA (see Black & White Minstrels) (Loss, Joe/Black & White Minstrels).

GOLDEN AGE OF, THE.
Tracks: / Over my shoulder / Madame - ah la marquise - ah / Scene changes, The / Let's dance at the make believe ballroom / Sweet Sue / Boo hoo / So rare / Please be kind / I'm gonna lock my heart / Change partners / Latin quarter, The / Little Sir Echo / Boomps a daisy / Are you having any fun? / At the woodchopper's ball / In the mood.
LP: GX41 2529 1
MC: . . . . GX 41 2529 4

HITS OF 1940, THE.
Tracks: / Are you having any fun? / Oh Johnny, Oh Johnny / Good morning (From the film "Babes In Arms".) / Where and when (From the film "Babes In Arms".) / In the mood / It's a hap-hap-happy day / At the woodchoppers ball / Gaucho serenade / Let the people sing / When you wish upon a star (From the film "Pinocchio".) / You made me care (Vocal by Chick Henderson.) / Let the curtain come down / Woodpecker song / I've got my eyes on you (Vocal by Paula Green.) / Honky tonk train blues / I'll never smile again / Breeze and I (Vocal by Cyril Grantham..) / I'm nobody's baby (Vocal by Paula Greene.) / Six lessons from Madame Le Zonga (Vocal by Paula Greene.) / All the things that you are (Vocal by Paula Greene.).
LP: . . . . SH 517
MC: . . . . TCSH 517

HOUR OF SWING, AN (Loss, Joe & His Orchestra).
Tracks: / At the woodchopper's ball / I'm getting sentimental over you / Stompin' at the Savoy / You made me love you / One o'clock jump / Take the 'A' train / Skyliner / Solitude / Don't be that way / Song of India / Begin the beguine / Trumpet blues and cantabile / Girl from Ipanema / Desafinado / Killing me softly with his song / Sheik of Araby, The / Five foot two, eyes of blue / It had to be you / Anvil chorus / Perfidia.
MC: . . . . HR 8178

IN A ROMANTIC MOOD (Loss, Joe, Big Band & Orchestra).
Tracks: / Begin the beguine / Song from Moulin Rouge / Sugar blues / April in Portugal / Ciribiribin / Summer Place, a theme from / Oh mein papa / Stranger on the shore / Humoresque / Stardust / Everything's coming up roses / I left my heart in San Francisco / Belle of the ball / On the street where you live / Fascination / Sweetie / Wheels / Can't take my eyes off you / Swingin' samba / March of the matadors (paso doble) / A banda / Do you know the way to San Jose? / Tequila.
LP: . . . . EMS 1260
MC: . . . . TCEMS 1260

IN THE MOOD WITH JOE (Loss, Joe & His Orchestra).
Tracks: / In the mood / Daddy / That lovely weekend / Fur trapper's ball / You made me care / Five o'clock whistle / Fan it / For all that I care / Yeah man / Sweet little sweetheart / No mama no / Cornsilk / Six lessons from Madame La Zonga / Memories live longer than dreams / Cow cow boogie / If I should fall in love again / Amapola / Let the curtain come down.
LP: . . . . PLE 522
MC: . . . . TC-PLE 522

ISN'T IT HEAVENLY (Loss, Joe & his band).
Tracks: / Smoke gets in your eyes / In other words we're through / When the new moon shines / I love you truly / Let's fall in love / La cucaracha / There's a ring around the Moon / For you madonna / Stars fell on Alabama / Soon / Tina / One morning in May / Isn't it heavenly / Don't forget(1933 version) / Ending with a kiss / General's fast asleep, The / Continental, The / Under a blanket of blue.
LP: . . . . CHD 128

IT'S PARTY TIME WITH JOE LOSS AND HIS ORCHESTRA (Loss, Joe & His Orchestra).
Tracks: / March of the mods / Zorba's dance / Finnjenka dance / Hey Jude / Entertainer, The / Charleston / This guy's in love with you / Twistin' in the mood / Celebration / Lily the pink / I came I saw I conga'd / We're gonna rock around the clock / Shake, rattle and roll / Tea for two / Hokey cokey, The / This is the life / Stripper / Simon says / Ob-la-di, ob-la da / Y viva Espana / Last waltz, The.
MC: . . . . TCMFP 5904

JOE LOSS PLAYS GLENN MILLER.
Tracks: / Moonlight Serenade / American patrol / At last / I've got a gal in Kalamazoo / Pennsylvania 6-5000 / Little brown jug / In the mood / Adios / Moonlight Cocktail / Jersey bounce / Tuxedo Junction / I know why / String of pearls / Serenade in blue / St. Louis blues / Chattanooga choo choo / Bugle call rag / Frenesi / Elmer's tune / My guy's come back.
MC: . . . . HR 8116
MC: . . . . HR 4181164

JOE LOSS STORY, THE.
Tracks: / Happy endings / Over my shoulder / Red sails in the sunset / Little rendezvous in Honolulu, A / Scene changes, The - blues / Let's dance at the make-believe ballroom / Boo hoo / Toy trumpet / I double dare you / OOooo-oh boom / You must have been a beautiful baby / South of the border (down Mexico way) / Begin the beguine / My heart belongs to daddy / In the mood / I've got my eyes on you / Best things in life are free, The / Oasis / Concerto for two / Someone's rocking my dreamboat / Don't sit under the apple tree / Put your arms around me honey / In pinetop's footsteps / I'll be seeing you / Kiss in the night, A / My guy's come back / Bridal waltz, The / Isle of Innisfree / Take care of yourself / Wheels cha cha / Sucu sucu, baion / Maigret, Theme from / Must be madison / Loddy lo / March of the mods / At last / Toreando / Sunrise, sunset / Speak softly love / Listen to the rhythm / Simon says / Big Ben to Bow Bells / Dear Hunter theme from / At the woodchopper's ball.
2LP: . . . . EM 1373
MCSET: . . . . TCEM 1373

LET'S DANCE AT THE MAKE-BELIEVE BALLROOM 1934-1940 (Loss, Joe Band).
2LP: . . . . SHB 46

NEW WORLD CHAMPIONSHIP BALLROOM DANCES (Loss, Joe & His Orchestra).
Tracks: / Let's keep dancing / We make music / Woman in love / Even now / Deerhunter / Blue danube / YMCA / Chiquitita / In the navy / Summer nights / We don't talk anymore / Rivers of Babylon / Too much love / Madrid.
LP: . . . . SCX 6625

OVER MY SHOULDER.
Tracks: / I've got my love to keep me warm / Head over heels in love / Caravan / I know now / Raindrops / Ev'rything you do / Boo hoo / For you Madonna / At the balalaika / Over my shoulder / September in the rain / Toy trumpet, The / May I have the next romance with you / What will I tell my heart / When the poppies bloom again / When you've got a little springtime / Love bug will bite you, The / This years kisses.
LP: . . . . BUR 004
MC: . . . . 4 BUR 004

PARTY DANCE TIME (Loss, Joe & His Orchestra).
Tracks: / Cole porter medley / Irving Berlin medley / In a little spanish town / Irish lullaby / When you and i were seventeen / Apple blossom time / Mexicali rose / Little sir echo.
LP: . . . . SH 107 825 1
MC: . . . . TCSH 107 825 4

PLAYS YOUR ALL TIME PARTY HITS (Loss, Joe & His Orchestra).
2LP: . . . . MFP 1009
MCSET: . . . . TCMFP 1009

REMEMBER ME? (Loss, Joe & His Orchestra).
Tracks: / There's a new world / Nice cup of tea, A / With plenty of money and you / Home town / Ramona / Diane / Charmaine / Felix kept on walking / Sheik of Araby, The / My blue Heaven / Remember me? / Lullaby of Broadway / Tiptoe through the tulips / If I had a talking picture of you / I double dare you / All by yourself in the moonlight / Horsey, keep your tail up / Poor little Angeline / You're an education / Cry, baby, cry / Penny serenade / You go to my head / Chestnut tree, The / And the angels sing / Boom (Why does my heart go-) / Oh, you crazy moon / Scatterbrain / Oh Johnny, oh Johnny oh.
LP: . . . . SH 506
MC: . . . . TC-SH 506

WORLD CHAMPIONSHIP BALLROOM DANCES (Loss, Joe & His Orchestra).
Tracks: / Dream / I only have eyes for you / Jealousy / Singin' in the rain / We make music / Toreando / Fascination / Can't help falling in love / Brazil / Something tells me / Mama mia / Music to watch girls by / Cavatina / Forever and ever / Waltz is for dancing, A / Save your kisses for me / Don't it make my brown eyes blue / Till / Don't cry for me Argentina / Sunrise sunset / Mull of Kintyre / Spanish gypsy dance / Fernando / Tea for two / Copacabana / Rivers of Babylon / Guantanamera / Is this the way to Amarillo / What's happened to Broadway / I'd like to teach the world to sing / My resistance is low / How deep is your love.
MC: . . . . TCDL 1146
2LP: . . . . DL 1146

Lost At Sea

LOST AT SEA.
LP: . . . . VOW 005

Lost Boys (Film)

LOST BOYS (Film soundtrack) (Various artists).
Tracks: / To the shock of Miss Louise: *Various artists* / Good times: *Various artists* / Lost in the shadows: *Various artists* / Don't let the sun go down on me: *Various artists* / Laying down the law: *Various artists*/ People are strange: *Various artists* / Cry little sister: *Various artists* / Power play: *Various artists*/ I still believe: *Various artists* / Beauty has her way: *Various artists.*
LP: 781 767-1
MC: 781 767-4

Lost Cherries

ALL PART OF GROWING UP.
LP: . . . . FIGHT 6

Lost Empires

LOST EMPIRES (TV Soundtrack) (Various artists).
Tracks: / Lost empires theme, The: *Various artists* / Army of today's alright, The: *Various artists* / Your king and country: *Various artists* / Pure white rose, A: *Various artists* / Somewhere: *Various artists* / Oh Flo: *Various artists* / They didn't believe me: *Various artists* / Wedding glide, The: *Various artists*/ Cigar girl, The: *Various artists* / Honeysuckle and the bee, The: *Various* artists / Mother Machree: *Various* artists / Alexander's ragtime band: *Various artists* / Land of hope and glory: *Various artists* / Rule Britannia: *Various artists* / I don't want to play in your yard: *Various artists* / Yankee doodle boy: *Various artists*/ Shine on harvest moon: *Various artists* / Love's old sweet song: *Various artists* / Trombone song, The: *Various* artists / Take me on the flip flap: *Various artists* / Nobody knows, nobody cares: *Various artists* / Mr. Knick Knock: *Various artists* / Poor little Dolly: *Various artists* / Waiting for the Robert E Lee: *Various* artists / Catari catari: *Various artists* / Nightingale and the star, The: *Various artists* / Julia's theme: *Various artists.*
LP: . . . . TER 1119
MC: . . . . ZCTER 1119

Lost Entity

BRING THAT BACK.
LP: . . . . NG 046

Lost & Found

ENDLESS HIGHWAY.
LP: . . . . REBEL 1607

HYMN TIME.
Tracks: / Mount up with wings / When was the last time / I'm going to make heaven my home / Boat of love / Sing an old fashioned song / When the saints go marching in / Raging storm / Shall we gather at the river / You're drifting away / Peace in the valley / What a friend we have in Jesus / Give me flowers while I'm living.
LP: . . . . REBEL 1668

LOST AND FOUND.
Tracks: / Forever lasting plastic words / Everybody's here / There would be no doubt / Don't fall down / Zig zag blues / Let me be / Realize / Stroke blues / I'm so hip to pain / Living eyes.
LP: . . . . LIK 23

NEW DAY.
LP: . . . . REBEL 1678

SUN'S GONNA SHINE.
LP: . . . . REBEL 1638

Lost Generation

MIDNIGHT MEAT TRAIN.
MC: . . . . HMAMC 156
LP: . . . . HMUSA 156

Lost Horizon

LOST HORIZON (Film Soundtrack) (Various artists).
LP: . . . . SYBEL 8000

LOST HORIZON (see Hilton, James) (Elder, Michael).

Lost In The Stars

LOST IN THE STARS/A TRIBUTE TO KURT WEILL Various artists (Various artists).
Tracks: / Mahogany Songspiel: *Various artists* / Ballad of Mack the Knife:

Various artists / Cannon song, The: *Various artists* / Ballad of the soldier's wife: *Various artists* / Johnny Johnson medley: *Various artists*/ Alabama song: *Various artists* / Youkali tangon: *Various artists* / Little lieutenant of the loving God, The: *Various artists* / September song: *Various artists* / Lost in the stars: *Various artists* / What keeps mankind alive?: *Various artists* / Surubaya Johnny: *Various artists* / Oh heavenly salvation: *Various artists*/ Call from the grave: *Various artists* / Speak low: *Various artists* / In no man's land: *Various artists*.
LP: . . . . **AMA 5104**
MC: . . . . **AMC 5104**

Lost In The Stars

LOST IN THE STARS (Original Broadway cast) (Various artists).
LP: . . . . **MCA 1535**
MC: . . . . **MCAC 1535**

Lost Jockey

ANIMAL BEHAVIOUR.
LP: . . . . **BATLM 2**
MC: . . . . **ZCBTM 2**

Lost Loved Ones

OUTCAST.
Tracks: / Raise the flag / Lost loved ones / Outcast / Echoes of the past / Dark / Celebrate / This hopeless pride / In silence / Prospect / Freakshow.
LP: . . . . **EPC 26357**

Lost Souls

CHASING A DREAM.
LP: . . . . **NERD 054**

Lost World (bk)

LOST WORLD, THE (Sir Arthur Conan Doyle) (Mason, James (nar)).
MC: . . . . **TC LFP 7070**

LOST WORLD, THE (Children's Classics).
MC: . . . . **PLBC 81**

LOST WORLD, THE (Sir Arthur Conan Doyle) (Massey, Daniel (nar)).
MCSET: . . . . **ARGO 1226**

Lothar

THIS IS IT , MACHINES (Lothar & The Hand People).
Tracks: / Machines / Today is only yesterday's tomorrow / That's another story / Sister lonely / Sex and violence / You won't be lonely / It comes on anyhow / Wedding night for those who love / Yes, I love you / This is it / This may be goodbye / Midnight ranger / Ha (ho) / Sdrawkcab / Space hymn.
LP: . . . . **SEE 75**

Lothian & Borders ...

CENTENNIAL (1890-1990) (Lothian & Borders Police Band).
Tracks: / Lothian and Borders Police centenary march / Slow air hornpipe and jigs / March strathspey and reel / 6/8 marches / Hornpipes / Strathspeys and reels / March medley / Drum fanfare / 2/ 4 marches / Slow air and jigs / Medley / March strathspey and reel (2) / Edinburgh City Police Pipe Band march.
LP: . . . . **LILP 5188**
MC: . . . . **LICS 5188**

PIPERS SALUTE (Lothian & Borders Police Band).
LP: . . . . **GLN 1011**

Lothian Dance Band

IN STRICT TEMPO.
Tracks: / Balcomie House / Farewell to the north / Black mountain / Wee cooper o' Fife, The / Duchess tree, The / Miss C.M. Barbour / Hopetoun house / None so pretty / Johnnie Walker / Argyll's fancy / Strathglass House / Spey royal / Posties jig / Lothian lads.
LP: . . . . **LILP 5112**
MC: . . . . **LICS 5112**

PRESENTING THE LOTHIAN SCOTTISH DANCE BAND.
Tracks: / Boston two step / Galloway house / Gaelic waltz / Rakish Highlandman / Continental waltz / Canadian barn dance / Gay Gordons / Dashing white sergeant / Glayva Highland schottische / Scottish waltz / Polka / Eva step / College hornpipe, The.
LP: . . . . **REL 461**
MC: . . . . **REC 461**

Lotis, Dennis

BIDIN' MY TIME.
Tracks: / How about you / Where or when / You've done something to my heart / But not for me / That lovely weekend / Over the rainbow / I've told every little star / All of you / Heart / Hold on to love / Bidin' my time / It can't be wrong / May I / Body and soul / As time goes by / Moonlight serenade / Tammy / Once upon a time / Flamingo / Love me a little.
LP: **C5-554**
MC: **C5K-554**

Lots Of...

LOTS OF LOVIN' (Various artists).
LP: . . . . **TSM 101**

Lott, Carolyn

CHRISTMAS MOMENTS WITH THE HARP.
MC: . . . . **HSH C 0024**

Lotus Eaters

NO SENSE OF SIN.
Tracks: / German girl / Love still flows / Can you keep a secret / Out on your own / Put your touch on love / Too young / Set me apart / You fill me with need / First picture of you, The / Alone of all her sex / When you look at boys.
LP: **206 263**
MC: **406 263**

Loud

D GENERATION.
LP: . . . . **WOL 1003**
MC: . . . . **WOLMC 1003**
LP: **8471681**
MC: **8471684**

Loud Minority

MANHATTAN FEVER (see Foster, Frank) (Loud Minority/Frank Foster).

SHINY STOCKINGS (see Foster, Frank) (Loud Minority/Frank Foster).

Loudermilk, John D.

TWELVE SIDES OF LOUDERMILK.
Tracks: / All of this for Sally / Angela Jones / Big daddy / Bully of the beach, The / He's just a scientist (that's all) / Rhythm and bluesy / Tobacco Road / Everybody knows / Goggle eye / This little bird / Road hog / Oh how sad.
LP: . . . . **NL 89993**
MC: . . . . **NK 89333**

Loudness

DISSOLUTION.
LP: . . . . **MFN 22**
MC: . . . . **TMFN 22**

HURRICANE EYES.
Tracks: / S.D.I. / This lonely heart / Rock 'n' roll gypsy / In my dreams / Take me home / Strike of the sword / Rock this way / In this world beyond / Hungry hunter / So lonely.
LP: **790 619-1**
MC: **790 619-4**

LIGHTNING STRIKES.
Tracks: / Let it go / Dark desire / 1000 eyes / Face to face / Who knows / Ashes in the sky / Black star oblivion / Street life dream / Complication.
LP: **790 512-1**

SOLDIER OF FORTUNE.
Tracks: / Danger of love / You shook me / Demon disease / Soldier of fortune / 25 days from home / Faces in the fire / Red light shooter / Run for cover / Long after midnight / Lost without your love.
LP: . . . . **K 791283 1**
MC: . . . . **K 791283 4**

THUNDER IN THE EAST.
LP: . . . . **MFN 38**

Loudon, Dorothy

BROADWAY BABY.
Tracks: / Broadway baby / It all depends on you / After you / It all belongs to me / Bobo's / Pack up your sins and go to the devil / Any place I hang my hat is home / I got lost in his arms / They say it's wonderful / Do it again / He was too good to me / I had myself a true love / Ten cents a dance.
LP: . . . . **SL 5203**
MC: . . . . **SLC 5203**

Loughlin, Kevin

ALL IRELAND CHAMPION TRADITIONAL ACCORDIONIST.
LP: . . . . **SOLP 1039**
MC: . . . . **COX 1039**

FROM GLEN TO GLEN.
LP: . . . . **MYLP 5004**

PRIDE OF FERMANAGH, THE.
MC: . . . . **COX 1009**

Loughsiders

LOUGHSIDERS, THE.
Tracks: / Farrell O' Gara / Dawn / Golden eagle, The / Laird of Drumblair, The / Strand, The / Friendly visit, The / Blackthorn / Kitty's wedding / Alphine herdsman, The / Skylark / Longford collector, The / Sailor's bonnet, The / Cronan's / George Whit's fancy / Lark in the morning, The / Speed the plough / John's jigs / Return, The / Dark island.
MC: . . . . **COX 1051**

Louie Bluie

LOUIE BLUIE (Original soundtrack) (Various artists).
LP: . . . . **ARHOOLIE 1095**

Louie Louie

STATE I'M IN, THE.
Tracks: / State I'm in, The / Sittin' in the lap of luxury / I wanna get back with you / Mata Hari / Penny lady / Stop lookin' for someone else / Hurt baby / Let me divorce you / I'm sorry that it happened to you / Variety is the spice of life / Rodeo clown.
LP: **4666321**
MC: **4666324**

Louis, Arthur

KNOCKIN' ON HEAVENS DOOR.
LP: . . . . **PYL 4006**
MC: . . . . **PYM 4006**

Louis, 'Big' Joe

BIG JOE LOUIS AND HIS BLUES KINGS (Louis, 'Big' Joe & His Blues Kings).
Tracks: / What's the matter with you / Now she's gone / You can't live long / I cried last night / I think you need a shot / Bloody tears / Down home blues / Monkey motion / These young girls / Hey hey now baby / She felt too good / Mean old Frisco blues.
LP: . . . . **BLUH 008**

Louis, Eddy & Ivan

BLOW (see Julien, Ivan).

Louis, Joe Hill

ONE MAN BAND 1949-56.
LP: . . . . **MUSKADINE 101**

Louis, Serge

SURPRISE.
Tracks: / El montal bonita / Le marin a casquette / Le tango de corinne / Surprise / Par amour / Tempo grande vitesse / Reine de musette / Amigo abel / La valse du papulo / La java du camionneur / Tango d'un soir des vacances / Creneau musette.
LP: **742053**

Louisiana (Film)

LOUISIANA (Original Soundtrack) (Various artists).
LP: . . . . **CBS 71127**
MC: **40 71127**

Louisiana

BAYOU BLUEGRASS.
LP: . . . . **ARHOOLIE 5010**

Louisiana Playboys

CAJUN TOOT TOOT MUSIC.
Tracks: / Lucille / Lacassine special / I don't care / Canton two step / Zydeco et pas sale / Steel guitar rag / Sugar bee / Musicians waltz / Think about me baby / Wagonwheel special / Hathaway one step.
LP: . . . . **JSP 1098**

SATURDAY NIGHT SPECIAL.
Tracks: / Lafayette / Why don't we do it in the road / Cajun blues / Saturday night special / Maggie Thatcher, won't you give me a hand / Louisiana playboy's theme / Memphis / Jole blon / Mathilda / Te petite and te meon / Accordion waltz.
LP: . . . . **JSP 1080**

Louisiana Red

ANTI-NUCLEAR BLUES.
LP: . . . . **LR 42.045**

BACK TO THE ROOTS (September 1987).
LP: . . . . **SCH 101**

BLUES FROM FRIEDEN (see under Engbarth, Gerhard) (Louisiana Red & His Chicago Friends).

BLUES FROM THE HEART.
Tracks: / Blues for Ida B / This little letter / Nothing but the blues / I wonder why / Grease me baby / Love me true / Love me mama.
LP: . . . . **JSP 1053**

BLUES MAN.
Tracks: / Little boy / Nothing but a gypsy man / Chicken lickin' / Sittin' here looking / If I had a dollar / Sweet Elesse / Whole world / Ride on.
LP: . . . . **JSP 1073**

BOY FROM BLACK BAYOU (Louisiana Red & His Chicago Friends).
LP: . . . . **LR 42.055**

HI VOLTAGE BLUES (Louisiana Red/ Sugar Blue).
Tracks: / Death of elesse / Rockin' red / Pretty woman / Clickety clack / Steel mill blues / Lousiana boogie / Rollin' and tumblin'.
LP: . . . . **JSP 1081**

HOT SAUCE.
Tracks: / Lightnin' bug / Alabama train / You're gonna need me, baby / Trouble all my days / Ride on, red, ride on / Whose ol' funky drawers is these / Wo-ho-ho baby / 'Let these' blues / Sometimes I wonder / Gonna move on down the line.
LP: . . . . **RL 071**
MC: . . . . **CRL 0071**

LOWDOWN BACK PORCH BLUES.
LP: **522 004**

MY LIFE WITH CAREY BELL (Louisiana Red & Carey Bell).
LP: . . . . **LR 42.061**

NEW YORK BLUES.
LP: . . . . **LR 42.002**

REALITY BLUES.
LP: . . . . **LR 42.011**

RED FUNK 'N' GREEN (Louisiana Red/ Sugar Blue).
LP: . . . . **BP 1001**

Louisiana Repertory...

HOT AND SWEET SOUNDS OF LOST NEW ORLEANS (Louisiana Repertory Jazz Ensemble).
LP: . . . . **SOS 1140**

LIVE AND WELL (Louisiana Repertory Jazz Ensemble).
LP: . . . . **SOS 1029**

LOUISIANA REPERTORY JAZZ ENSEMBLE NOR (Louisiana Repertory Jazz Ensemble).
LP: . . . . **SOS 1055**

MARCHING, RAGGING AND MOURNING. (The music of New Orleans) (Louisiana Repertory Jazz Ensemble).
LP: **SOS1197**

Louisiana's Le Roux

KEEP THE FIRE BURNING.
Tracks: / Keep the fire burning / Call home the heart / When I get home / You be my vision / Fa fa fa fa fa / Feel it / Thunder 'n' lightnin' / Say it with your heart / Window eyes / Back to the Levee.
LP: . . . . **EST 11926**

Louistine

TAKE ME ON.
Tracks: / Take me on / Now and forever / Dancing / Self serve woman / Love me / Trying to win your love / I don't wanna love nobody like you.
LP: . . . . **TRPL 109**

Lounge Lizards

BIG HEART (LIVE IN TOKYO).
Tracks: / Big heart / Hair street / Fat house / It could have been very very very beautiful / They were insane / Punch and Judy tango, The / Map of bubbles.
LP: . . . . **IMA 20**
MC: . . . . **IMC 20**

LIVE 1979-1981.
MC: . . . . **A 136**
LP: . . . . **DANLP 046**

LIVE FROM THE DRUNKEN BOAT.
Tracks: / In a sentimental mood / Out to lunch / Loons.
LP: . . . . **JP 2012**

LOUNGE LIZARDS.
Tracks: / Incident on South Street / Harlem nocturne / Do the wrong thing / Au contraire arto / Well you needn't / Ballad / Wangling / Conquest of Rah / Demented / I remember Coney Island / Fatty walks / Epistrophy / You haunt me.
LP: . . . . **EGED 8**

NO PAIN FOR CAKES.
Tracks: / My trip to Ireland / No pain for cakes / My clowns on fire / Carry me out / Bob and Nico / Tango no.3 determination for Rosa Parks / Magic of Palermo, The / Cue for passion / Where were you.
LP: . . . . **AN 8714**
MC: . . . . **ANC 8714**

VOICE OF CHUNK.
Tracks: / Bob the bob / Voice of chunk / One big yes / Hanging, The / Uncle Jerry / Paper bag and the Sun, A / Tarantella / Bob the bob / Sharks / Travel.
LP: . . . . **VBRLP 25**
MC: . . . . **VBRMC 25**

Lou's Blues Revenue

COME OUT AND PLAY.
LP: . . . . **WIL 3006**
MC: . . . . **ZCWIL 3006**

Loussier, Jacques

BACH TO BACH.
LP: . . . . **STML 19**
MC: . . . . **STMC 19**

BACH TO THE FUTURE.
LP: . . . . **STL 8**
MC: . . . . **STC 8**

BASICALLY BACH.
Tracks: / Fugue and fantasy in G minor / Chromatic fantasie in C minor / Sinfonia from Cantata No.29 / Prelude No.1 / Air on a G string / Choral No.1 in B flat 'Sleepers Wake' / Sicilienne en sol mineur / Toccata.
LP: . . . . **TAB 4**

BEST OF PLAY BACH (Volume 1 and 2).

LP: STL 1/2
MC: STC 1/2

BRANDENBURG CONCERTOS.
MC: 844 058 4

FOCUS ON JACQUES LOUSSIER.
2LP: FOS R5/6

GREATEST BACH, THE.
MC: 844 059 4

IMAGES.
MC: KNMC 16015

JACQUES LOISSIER PLAYS BACH.
MC: 556602

PAGAN MOON.
Tracks: / Night riders / Furies / Moonchild / Invaders, The / Phantom lady / Nocturnal sea / Enchantress / Dawn.
LP: CBS 85850

PULSION.
Tracks: / Pulsion / Soupir / Distraction / Caffeine / Mozart / Ludwig / Murmure / Secousse.
LP: CBS 84179
LP: CBS 84994
MC: 844 060 4

REFLECTIONS OF BACH.
Tracks: / Concerto in F minor / Passacaglia in c minor / Bartita in f minor / Pastorale in c minor / Vivace / Garotte in B minor / Minnet in g major.
LP: STL 9
MC: STC 9

Louvin Brothers

BEST OF THE EARLY LOUVIN BROTHERS.
LP: REBEL 852
MC: REBEL 852C

IRA & CHARLIE.
Tracks: / Don't let your sweet love die / We could / Tennessee waltz / Are you teasing me? / Too late / Here today and gone tomorrow / I wonder where you are tonight / Have I stayed away too long / Nobody's darlin' but mine / Why not confess / Making believe / Take me back into your heart.
LP: HAT 3057
MC: HATC 3057

LIVE AT THE NEW RIVER RANCH.
Tracks: / Born again / When I stop dreaming / Comedy / In the jailhouse / Family who prays shall never part, The / Is that you Myrtle / God bless her / I don't believe you've met my baby / Childish love / Just rehearsaing / Where one stands alone / Guitar inst. / There's a hole in the bottom of the sea / Listen to the mockingbird.
LP: CCLP 0105

LOUVIN BROTHERS, THE.
LP: SS 07
MC: SSC 07

LOUVIN BROTHERS, THE.
Tracks: / When I stop dreaming / I don't believe you've met my baby / Hoping that you're hoping / You're running wild / Cash on the barrelhead / My baby's gone / Knoxville girl / I love you best of all / How's the world treating you / Must you throw dirt in my face / If I could only win your love / Blues stay away from me / Nashville blues / Brown's ferry blues / Gonna lay down my old guitar / My baby came back.
LP: SDLP 044
MC: SDC 44

MY BABY'S GONE.
LP: HAT 3028
MC: HATC 3028

MY CHRISTIAN HOME.
LP: SLP 5041
MC: GT 55041

NEARER MY GOD TO THEE.
Tracks: / Are you washed in the blood / Wait a little longer, please Jesus / I won't have to cross Jordan alone / This little light of mine / Thankful / Last chance to pray / Nearer my God to thee / I can't say no / There's no excuse / Praying / Lord, I'm coming home / I steal away and pray.
LP: HAT 3081
LP: RL 304
MC: HATC 3081

SATAN IS REAL.
LP: HAT 3117
MC: HATC 3117

SING THEIR HEARTS OUT.
Tracks: / If you love me, stay away / Curly headed baby / Nellie moved to town / Stagger, The / Ruby's song / Love is a lonely street / You're learning / Childish love / Call me / What a change / New partner waltz / It hurts me more the second time around / Broken engagement / I can't keep you / Love turned to hate / I'm glad that I'm not him / Give this message to your heart / Everytime you leave / Time goes so slow / I ain't gonna work tomorrow.

LP: SEE 250

SONGS THAT TELL A STORY.
Tracks: / Theme / Kneel at the cross / I have found the way / Weapon of prayer / I'll never go back / What a friend we have in mother / Jesus is whispering now / Family that prays, The / Robe of white / Let us travel on / Sinner you'd better get ready / Shut in at Christmas / Shut in prayer.
LP: SDLP 061
LP: ROUNDER 1030
MC: ROUNDER 1030C

TRAGIC SONGS OF LIFE.
Tracks: / Kentucky / I'll be all smiles tonight / Let her go God bless her / What is home without love / Tiny broken heart, A / In the pines / Alabama / Katy dear / My brother's will / Knoxville girl / Take the news to mother / Mary of the wild moor.
LP: HAT 3043
MC: HATC 3043
LP: SS 12
MC: CSS 12

Louvin, Charlie

CHARLIE LOUVIN.
Tracks: / Who's gonna love me now? / Store up love / Warm, warm woman / Fancy place to cry, A / She's just an old love turned memory / When love is gone / Apartment No.9 / Wherever you are / Can I have what's left? / Nobody cares.
LP: PRCV 104

I FORGOT TO CRY.
LP: HAT 3134
MC: HATC 3134

Love, Adrian

PUDSEY'S PICNIC (See under Hunniford, Gloria) (Love, Adrian/Gloria Hunniford/Graham Dalby/ Grahamophones).

Love Affair

6 TRACK HITS: LOVE AFFAIR.
MC: 7SC 5037

EVERLASTING LOVE.
Tracks: / Everlasting love / Gone are the songs of yesterday / Rainbow valley / Day without love, A / One road / Bringing on back the good times / Baby I know / Lincoln county / Hush / Tobacco road / Handbags and gladrags / New day / Gypsy / Bad girl.
LP: BTS 943406

GREATEST HITS:LOVE AFFAIR.
MC: ASK 774

Love At First Bite

LOVE AT FIRST BITE (Film soundtrack) (Various artists).
LP: RRL 2008

Love (band)

DA CAPO.
Tracks: / Stepahnie knows who / Orange skies / Que vida / Seven and seven is castle / She comes in colors / Revelation.
LP: K 42011

FOREVER CHANGES.
Tracks: / Alone again or / House is not a motel, A / And more again / Daily planet, The / Old man / Red telephone, The / Maybe the people would be the times / Live and let live / Good humour man he sees everything like this / Bummer in the summer / You set the scene.
LP: K 42015
MC: K 442015
LP: K 42015
MC: K 442015

FOUR SAIL.
Tracks: / August / Friends of mine / I'm with you / Good times / Singing cowboy / Dream / Robert Montgomery / Nothin' / Talking in my sleep / Always see your face.
LP: THBL 047

LOVE.
Tracks: / My little red book / Can't explain / Message to pretty, A / My flash on you / Softly to me / No matter what you do / Emotions / You'll be following / Gazing / Hey Joe / Signed D.C. / Coloured balls falling / Mushroom clouds / And more.
LP: ED 218

LOVE LIVE.
LP: 6 25047

MASTERS.
Tracks: / My little red book / Signed D.C. / Hey Joe / 7 and 7 is number fourteen / Stephanie knows who / Orange skies / Que vida / Castle, The / She comes in colours / Laughing stock / Your mind / And we belong together / Old man / Daily planet, The / House is not a motel, A / Andmoreagain / Alone again or.
LP: K 32002

OUT THERE.
Tracks: / I'll pray for you / Love is coming / Signed D.C. / I still wonder / Listen to my song / Doggone / Nice to be / Stand out / Everlasting first, The / Gimmi a little break / Willow willow / You are something / Love is more than words / Gather round.
LP: WIKA 69

Love Battery

BETWEEN THE EYES.
Tracks: / Between the eyes / Highway of souls / 2 and 2 / Easter / Orange / Before I crawl.
LP: TUPEP 22
MC: TUOMC 22

Love, Clayton

COME ON HOME BLUES.
Tracks: / Blues come home / Big question, The / Chains of love / Worried life blues / Just like a woman / St. Louis blues / Tore up / Key to the highway.
LP: RL 0029

CONDITION YOUR HEARTS (See also Turner, Ike (Love, Clayton/ Ike Turner/ Oliver Sain).

Love Club

LIME, TWIGS AND TREACHERY.
LP: MCG 6090
MC: MCGC 6090

Love Corporation

LOVERS.
LP: CRELP 068
MC: CRECA 068

TONES.
LP: CRELP 56
MC: CCRE 56

Love, CP

ALBUM OF RHYTHM AND BLUES, AN (Love, CP & His Bluesmates).
LP: SLP 25

Love, Darlene

LIVE: DARLENE LOVE.
LP: RNLP 855

PAINT ANOTHER PICTURE.
Tracks: / He's sure the man I love / Paint another picture / I've never been the same / Desperate lover / Everybody needs / Gypsy lover / Love must be love / We stand a chance / You'll never walk alone.
LP: 4610031
MC: 4610034

WHITE CHRISTMAS (see Phil Spector Christmas EP).

Love De Luxe

AGAIN AND AGAIN.
Tracks: / Here comes that sound again / When we're dancin' / Let me make it up to you / I got that feeling.
LP: K 50585

Love Delegation

DELEGATION.
Tracks: / Hey disco / Right now / Whatever makes you happy / Delegation time / Wrap your arms around me / Spread the word / Kicked around / What goes up / Through the night.
LP: 104901
MC: 104904

Love, Geoff

20 EXPLOSIVE TV THEMES (Love, Geoff & His Orchestra).
Tracks: / Themes from "Lillie" / Starsky and Hutch / Dick Barton / Crossroads / Muppet Show / Who pays the ferryman / Hawaii Five-O / Poldark / Charlie's Angels, Theme from / All creatures great and small / Coronation Street / Nationwide.
LP: NTS 168

50 DANCING FAVOURITES (Love, Geoff & His Orchestra).
MCSET: TR 41 15335
MCSET: TR 1533
MCSET: MFP 4115335

50 FAVOURITE LOVE SONGS (Love, Geoff Singers).
MCSET: TR 1503
MCSET: MFP 4115035

50 INSTRUMENTAL FAVOURITES (Love, Geoff & His Orchestra).
Tracks: / Big country, The / Continental, The / String of pearls / Harry Lime theme / Elvira Madigan / Summer place, A (theme from) / Zorba's dance / Impossible dream, The / Eye level / Ebb tide / March of the Siamese children / Charmaine / Exodus / Pink panther (theme from) / Tijuana taxi / From Russia with love / Legend of the Glass Mountain / Aria / Johnson rag / Moulin Rouge / In an 18th century drawing room / Canadian sunset / Magnificent seven The, Theme from / Cabaret / I could have danced all night / In the mood / Ecstasy / Walk in the Black Forest, A / Spanish Harlem / Carousel waltz, The / Man and a woman, A Theme from / Cornish rhapsody / Good, the bad and the ugly, The / Birthday cakewalk, The / Chi Mai / Misty / Chariots of fire / Clair de lune / Stranger on the shore / Delicado / Raindrops keep falling on my head / Dambusters march / Nicola / Cavatina / Dream of Olwen / Blue tango / Annie's song / Poor people of Paris, The / You stepped out of a dream / High noon.
MCSET: TR 1500
MCSET: MFP 4115005

BEST OF BRITISH (Love, Geoff Banjos).
Tracks: / I've got a lovely bunch of coconuts / Soldiers of the Queen / Ship ahoy / Stop your ticklin Jock / I love a lassie / Just a wee deoch and doris / When Irish eyes are smiling / My wild Irish rose / Too-ra-loo-ra-loo-ra / Tavern in the town / What shall we do with the drunken sailor? / We'll keep a welcome / Hello, hello who's your lady friend / I'm Henry the eighth I am / Hold your hand out you naughty boy / Waiting at the church / Danny boy / Did your mother come from ireland / Galway Bay / Underneath the arches / On mother Kelly's doorstep / Leaning on a lamp post / Cruising down the river / Eton boating song / There's a lovely lake in loveland / Land of hope and glory / Maybe it's because I'm a Londoner / Let's all go down the strand / Knocked 'em in the Old Kent Road / Rose of Tralee, The / Cockles and mussels / Mother Machree / All through the night / Men of Harlech / Roamin' in the gloamin' / Comin' thro' the rye / Loch Lomond / Land of my fathers / Who were you with last night / Sun has got his hat on, The / Any old iron / Amazing grace / Ash grove, The / Drink to me / Mountains of Mourne / All by yourself in the moonlight / Keep right on to the end of the road / Show me the way to go home / Knees up mother Brown / Auld lang syne.
2LP: DL 41 1074 3
MC: DL 41 1074 9
2LP: DL 1074
MC: TCDL 1074

BIG BAND MOVIE THEMES (Love, Geoff & His Orchestra & Singers).
LP: MFP 50227

BIG BIG MOVIE THEMES (Love, Geoff & His Orchestra & Singers).
LP: MFP 50321

BIG LOVE MOVIE THEMES.
LP: MFP 5221

BIG TV THEMES ALBUM (Love, Geoff & His Orchestra).
Tracks: / Dynasty / Onedin Line / Chi Mai / Brideshead revisited / Hill Street Blues / Coronation Street / Eye level / Reilly / Edwardians / Dallas / Winds of war / Match of the day / Pink Panther / Thorn birds, The.
LP: MFP 41 5684-1
MC: MFP 41 5684 4

BIG WAR MOVIE THEMES (Love, Geoff & His Orchestra).
Tracks: / Colonel Bogey / Lawrence of Arabia / Guns of Navarone / Battle of Britain / Longest Day, The / Where eagles dare, Theme from / 633 Squadron / Dambusters / Great escape, The / Green berets, The / Cavatina (From The Deer Hunter.) / Winds of war / Victory at sea extracts / We'll meet again / Is Paris burning? / Reach for the Sky.
MC: HR 8140
LP: MFP 5171

BIG WESTERN MOVIE THEMES.
LP: MFP 5204

BIGGEST PUB PARTY IN THE WORLD, THE.
Tracks: / Who's sorry now / South of the border / On the sunny side of the street / Leaning on a lamp post / I cried for you / Alexander's ragtime band / You made me love you / Give me the moonlight / Singin' in the rain / I'm looking over a four leaf clover / Baby face / Last waltz, The / Now is the hour.
MC: TCNTS 180
LP: NTS 180
LP: SCX 6604

CLASSIC T.V. THEMES (Love, Geoff & His Orchestra & Singers).
Tracks: / Colditz march / Edwardians,The (Upstairs, downstairs) / Galloping home / Ironside / Alias Smith & Jones / Brothers / World of sport / Cheyenne.. / Sucu Sucu (Top Secret) / Hawaii five-O / Bless this house / Sleepy shores / Crossroads / Onedin line / Match of the day / Persuaders, The / Bonanza / We'll meet again / Eye level / Pink panther / Dick Barton / Return of the Saint / Good word.
MC: HR 8104
MC: HR 4181044

CLASSIC WAR THEMES (Love Geoff & LPO).

Tracks: / 1812 overture / Mars / Churchill march / Sink the Bismarck / Warsaw concerto / 8th Army march / Victory at sea / Dambusters / Colonel Bogey / River Kwai march / Colitz / 633 Squadron.
LP: . . . . **MFP 50452**

GREAT WESTERN THEMES (Love, Geoff & His Orchestra).
Tracks: / Big country, The / Fistful of dollars / Call of the faraway hills, The (From Shane.) / How the west was won / Green leaves of summer (From The Alamo.) / Magnificent seven, The / For a few dollars more / Wild bunch, The / Ballad of Cat Ballou / Virginian, The / Maverick / Legend of Jesse James, The / Good, the bad and the ugly, The / Gunfight at the OK Corral / High noon / True grit / Once upon a time in the west / Man who shot Liberty Valance, The / Hombre / Big valley, The / Laramie / Gun law / Wagons ho (From Wagon Train.) / Rawhide.
MC: . . . . **HR 8109**
MC: . . . . **HR 4181094**

HOUR OF GEOFF LOVE GOES LATIN, AN.
Tracks: / La Bamba / Spanish Harlem / Guantanamera / Sucu sucu / Girl from Ipanema / One-note samba / South of the border / Maria Elena / Spanish eyes / Desafinado / Breeze and I / Mexican hat dance / Temptation / La Cumparsita / Blue tango / Spider of the night / Serenata / La paloma / Jealousy / Adios muchachos / Ecstasy.
MC: . . . . **HR 8157**

HOUR OF GEOFF LOVE'S PIANO PARTY, AN.
MC: . . . . **HR 8149**

IN THE MOOD - FOR LOVE (Love, Geoff & His Orchestra).
Tracks: / Cavatina (Solo Violin: William Armon.) / Annie's song / Chi Mai (From The Life & Times of David Lloyd George) / Misty / Tara's theme (From Gone With The Wind.) / Begin the beguine / Time for us, A (From Romeo & Juliet.) / We'll meet again / Summer knows, The (Theme from Summer of 42.) / Godfather love theme / Summer place, A (theme from) / Man and a woman, A / Secret love / When I fall in love / Love letters / Raindrops keep falling on my head / Falling in love with love / Where do I begin (Theme from Love Story.) / Somewhere my love (From Dr. Zhivago) / Spartacus (Love theme) (From The Onedin Line.) / Love walked in (CD only.) / I wish you love (CD only.) / True love (CD only.) / I will wait for you (From The Umbrellas of Cherbourg. CD only.).
MC: . . . . **HR 8182**

IN THE MOOD FOR WALTZING (Love, Geoff & His Orchestra).
Tracks: / Falling in love with love / Ramona / Anniversary song / Always / Beautiful dreamer / I'll see you again / Fascination / My wonderful one / Charmaine / Love's last word is spoken / Love's roundabout / Now is the hour / Desert song, The / Around the world / When I grow too old to dream / Vaya con dios / One night of love / Lover / Edelweiss / Song, The / Try to remember / Ask me why I love you / Waltz of my heart / Last waltz, The.
MC: . . . . **HR 8194**

MELODIES THAT LIVE FOREVER In concert with (Love, Geoff & His Orchestra).
Tracks: / Skaters waltz / Minute waltz / Destiny / Invitation to the dance / Morning - Peer Gynt suite no. 1 / Elizabethan serenade / Largo / Moonlight sonata / Blue Danube / Sleeping beauty / Merry widow / Tales from the Vienna Woods / Dusk / Marriage of Figaro (overture) / Enigma variations no. 9 Nimrod / Air on a G string (Not on CD.) / Clair de lune (Not on CD.) / Jesu, joy of man's desiring (Not on CD.) / Ave Maria.
MC: . . . . **TCDL 1098**
2LP: . . . . **DL 1098**

NORTH AND SOUTH OF THE BORDER (Love, Geoff Singers).
Tracks: / Blanket on the ground / Paper roses / Snowbird / Annie's song / Take me home country roads / San Antonio rose / Peacful easy feeling / Behind closed doors / Jolene / Stand by your man / South of the border / How insensitive / Tangerine / Girl from Ipanema / You belong to my heart / Maria Elena / Yours / Vaya con dios / Perfidia / Adios.
MC: . . . . **HR 8144**

OPERA WITHOUT WORDS (Love, Geoff Concert Orchestra).
Tracks: / One furtive tear (L'elisir d'amour.) / Stars were shining, The (Tosca.) / None shall sleep (Turandot.) / What is life without thee? (Orpheus and Eurydice.) / Bella figlia dell'amore (Rigoletto.) / Oh my beloved father (Cianni schicchi.) / Love duet act 1 (Tosca.) / Chorus of the Hebrew slaves (Nabucco.) / Softly awakes my heart (Samson & Delilah.) / Musetta's waltz song (La Boheme.) / One fine day (Madame Butterfly.) / Celeste Aida (aida.) / Your tiny hand is frozen (La Boheme) / Love and music (Tosca.).
LP: . . . . **EMS 1261**

SINGALONG BANJO PARTY (VOL.1).
2LP: . . . . **MFP 1016**
MCSET: . . . . **TCMFP 1016**
2LP: . . . . **DL 1016**
MC: . . . . **TCDL 1016**

SINGALONG BANJO PARTY (VOL.2).
Tracks: / Side by side / Oh you beautiful doll / Is it true what they say about Dixie / There's a rainbow round my shoulder / By the light of the silvery moon / Pretty baby / April showers / There's a blue ridge round my heart Virginia / Shine on harvest moon / Toot too Tootsie goodbye / California here I come / I'm sitting on top of the world / Back in your own back yard / Give my regards to Broadway / My mammy / Rockabye your baby / Sonny boy / Swanee / Anniversary song / When the midnight choo-choo leaves for Alabam.
LP: . . . . **MFP 5569**
MC: . . . . **TCMFP 5569**

SINGALONG BANJO PARTY (VOL.3) (Love, Geoff Banjos).
Tracks: / Side by side / Oh you beautiful doll / Is it true what they say about Dixie / There's a rainbow round my shoulder / There's a blue ridge 'round my heart, Virginia / Shine on harvest moon / Toot, toot, tootsie goodbye / Won't you come home Bill Bailey / Strollin / Waiting for the Robert E. Lee / California here I come / Back in your own back yard / Give my regards to Broadway / I'm sitting on top of the world / My mammy / Rockabye your baby with a Dixie melody / Sonny boy / Swanee / Anniversary song / When the midnight choo choo leaves for Alabam / If I had a talking picture of you / When I leave the world behind / Deep in the heart of Texas.
2LP: . . . . **MFP 1034**
MCSET: . . . . **TCMFP 1034**

SONGS THAT WON THE WAR (Love, Geoff Banjos).
Tracks: / Colonel Bogey / Sentimental journey / Lili Marlene / Good morning / You'll never know / Yours / Let the people sing / That lovely weekend / This is the army Mister Jones / Arm in arm / I'll be with you in apple blossom time / I don't want to set the world on fire.
2LP: . . . . **MFP 41 1042 3**
MC: . . . . **MFP 41 1042 9**
2LP: . . . . **DL 1042**
MC: . . . . **TCDL 1042**

STRING OF PEARLS, A (Love, Geoff & His Orchestra & Singers).
Tracks: / In the mood / Satin doll / Peanut vendor / Moonlight serenade / String of pearls / Blues in the night / American patrol / Tuxedo junction / Lullaby of birdland / Little brown jug / We'll meet again / My guys come back.
LP: . . . . **MFP 5626**
MC: . . . . **TCMFP 5626**
LP: . . . . **MFP 41 5626 1**

STRING OF PEARLS, A (2) (Love, Geoff & His Orchestra).
Tracks: / String of pearls, A / Harry Lime theme / Chi Mai / Annie's song / Chariots of fire, Theme from / Carousel waltz, The / Dambusters / Moulin Rouge / Man and a woman, A / High noon / Raindrops keep falling on my head / Cavatina / Big country, The / Spanish Harlem / Stranger on the shore / Zorba's dance / Magnificent seven, The, Theme from / From Russia with love / In the mood / Exodus / Pink panther, Theme from / March of the Siamese children / Legend of the glass mountain / Misty.
2LP: . . . . **DL 1194**
MC: . . . . **TCDL 1194**

SUPER THEMES (Love, Geoff & His Orchestra).
Tracks: / Superman / Incredible Hulk, Theme from / Bionic woman,The / Spiderman / Blake's 7 / Batman theme / Wonder woman / Six million dollar man / Doctor Who / Close Encounters of the Third Kind / Star wars / U.F.O. / Star Trek / Barbarella / Space 1999 / Thunderbird / Also sprach Zarathustra / Princess Leia's theme / Logan's run.
MC: . . . . **HR 8103**
MC: . . . . **HR 4181034**

TAP DANCIN' TIME (Love, Geoff & His Orchestra).
Tracks: / 42nd Street / Yankee doodle boy / Happy feet / Razzamatazz / I won't dance / Broadway melody / Bye bye blues / Wedding of the painted doll, The / Anchors aweigh / It don't mean a thing / Singing in the rain / Lullaby of Broadway / I got rhythm / Tap dancin' time.
LP: . . . . **MMT LP 108**
MC: . . . . **MMT TC 108**

THEMES FOR SUPER HEROES (Love, Geoff & His Orchestra).
LP: . . . . **MFP 50439**

WE'RE HAVING A PARTY (Love, Geoff & His Orchestra & Singers).
Tracks: / Black is black / Rivers of Babylon / Brown girl in the ring / Yummy, yummy, yummy / Knock three times / Satisfaction / Money money.
LP: . . . . **MFP 50444**

WHEN I FALL IN LOVE (Love, Geoff Singers).
Tracks: / Imagine / What are you doing the rest of your life? / Moon river / If / I'm stone in love with you (on CD only.) / When I fall in love / More I see you, The (CD only) / I only have eyes for you / It's impossible / Annie's song / Without you / My eyes adored you / First time ever I saw your face, The / My cherie amour / Love story (where do I begin) / Something / Don't cry for me Argentina / Vincent / Killing me softly with his song / Snowbird / Send in the clowns (Available on CD only.) / For once in my life (CD only) / Michelle / You make me feel brand new (CD only) / Just the way you are / Evergreen (From 'A Star Is Born').
2LP: . . . . **DL 1102**
MC: . . . . **TCDL 1102**

WORLD'S GREATEST LOVE SONGS VOL.1.
LP: . . . . **MFP 50473**
MC: . . . . **TCMFP 50473**

YOUR HUNDRED FAVOURITE LOVE SONGS VOL 6 (Love, Geoff Singers).
Tracks: / Way you look tonight / All the things you are / Without you / Long ago and far away / Tea for two / Somewhere my love / So deep is the night / Lovely to look at / Every time we say goodbye / Killing me softly with his song / How deep is the ocean / Our day will come.
LP: . . . . **MFP 5596**
MC: . . . . **TCMFP 5596**

YOUR HUNDRED FAVOURITE LOVE SONGS VOL 11 (Love, Geoff Singers).
Tracks: / First time ever I saw your face, The / My cherie amour / I've got you under my skin / More / Unchained melody / You are the sunshine of my life / Love story / What'll i do / All my loving / Something / True love / There i've said it again / Falling in love again / Way we were.
LP: . . . . **MFP 50502**

YOUR HUNDRED FAVOURITE LOVE SONGS VOL 3.
Tracks: / Legend of the glass mountain / Aria / Johnson rag / Moulin Rouge / In an 18th century drawing room / Canadian sunset / Magnificent Seven, The / Birthday cakewalk, The / Chi mai / Misty / Chariots of fire / Stranger on the shore / Clair de Lune / Delicado.
LP: . . . . **MFP 50545**

YOUR HUNDRED FAVOURITE LOVE SONGS VOL 4 (Love, Geoff Singers).
Tracks: / Look of love / Never on Sunday / And I love you so / Annies song / Love letters / Behind closed doors / Twelfth of never / Bridge over troubled water / You'll never know / Everything is beautiful / Fools rush in / Snowbird / Don't cry for me, Argentina / Two sleepy people.
LP: . . . . **MFP 50564**

YOUR HUNDRED FAVOURITE LOVE SONGS VOL 5 (Love, Geoff Singers).
LP: . . . . **MFP 5577**
MC: . . . . **TCMFP 5577**

YOUR HUNDRED FAVOURITE LOVE SONGS VOL 7 (Love, Geoff Singers).
LP: . . . . **MFP 5619**
MC: . . . . **TCMFP 5619**

YOUR HUNDRED INSTRUMENTAL FAVOURITES VOL 7 (Love, Geoff & His Orchestra).
LP: . . . . **MFP 5618**
MC: . . . . **TCMFP 5618**

YOUR HUNDRED INSTRUMENTAL FAVOURITES VOL.2 (Love, Geoff & His Orchestra).
LP: . . . . **MFP 50512**

YOUR HUNDRED INSTRUMENTAL FAVOURITES VOL 5 (Love, Geoff & His Orchestra).
LP: . . . . **MFP 5578**
MC: . . . . **TCMFP 5578**

YOUR HUNDRED INSTRUMENTAL FAVOURITES VOL 6 (Love, Geoff & His Orchestra).
LP: . . . . **MFP 5595**
MC: . . . . **TCMFP 5595**

YOUR HUNDRED INSTRUMENTAL FAVOURITES VOL.4.
Tracks: / Tara's theme / Love is blue / Tuxedo junction / Taste of honey / James Bond / Lullaby of Birdland / Tubular bells / 633 Squadron / Apartment / Dallas / Entertainer, The / Brideshead revisited / Sleigh ride / Moonlight serenade.
LP: . . . . **MFP 50565**
MC: . . . . **TCMFP 50565**

YOUR HUNDRED INSTRUMENTAL FAVOURITES VOL 1 (Love, Geoff & His Orchestra).
Tracks: / Big country / Continental / String of pearls / Harry Lime theme / Elvira Madigan / Summer place / Zorba's dance / In the mood / Ecstacy / Walk in the Black Forest / Spanish harlem / Carousel / Man and a woman, A / Cornish rhapsody.
MC: . . . . **TCMFP 50498**
LP: . . . . **MFP 50498**

Love Gone Wrong

ALWAYS THE BRIDEGROOM.
Tracks: / Hey Steven / Eyes have it, The / When evening comes / You will find / I was confused / Singing city, The / Better days / World upside down / Stranger's kiss / Hope takes a holiday / I want you.
LP: . . . . **MBLP 7001**
MC: . . . . **MBTC 7001**

Love Hate

BLACK OUT IN THE RED ROOM.
Tracks: / Black out in the red room / Rock queen / Tumbleweed / Why do you think they call it dope? / Fuel to run / One more round / She's an angel / Mary Jane / Straightjacket / Slutsy tipsy / Slave girl / Hell?.
LP: **4663501**
MC: **4663504**

Love In A Cold Climate

LOVE IN A COLD CLIMATE (See under Mitford, Nancy) (Mitford, Nancy).

Love Is A Funny Thing

LOVE IS A FUNNY THING (Original Soundtrack) (Various artists).
LP: . . . . **MCA 25111**
MC: . . . . **MCAC 25111**

Love Isaacs

LOVE TECHNOLOGY.
LP: . . . . **SJF 5762881**

Love Jungle

WELCOME TO THE HOUSE WHERE THE EXTRAS ARE FREE.
Tracks: / Wasn't there something / Cast adrift / That's the way / I really don't care / Am I good enough / Blue skies / Between the poles / This covenant.
LP: . . . . **FOD 4**

Love & Laughter

BEGINNING.
Tracks: / I surrender / House got it / Afrika (the remix) / 1990 / Fallin' / My love (no our love) / Nefatari / Love and laughter.
LP: . . . . **LPBEES 5**
MC: . . . . **MCBEES 5**

Love & Mary Ann

LOVE & MARY ANN (Catherine Cookson) (Jameson, Susan (nar)).
MC: . . . . **CAB 017**

Love Me Or Leave Me

LOVE ME OR LEAVE ME (Original Soundtrack) (Various artists).
LP: . . . . **ACS 8773**
MC: . . . . **BT 8773**

Love, Mike

LOOKING BACK WITH LOVE.
Tracks: / Looking back with love / On & on & on / Runnin' around the world / Over & over / Rockin' the man in the boat / Calendar girl / Be my baby / One good reason / Teach me tonight / Paradise found.
LP: . . . . **EPC 85571**

Love & Money

ALL YOU NEED IS LOVE..AND MONEY.
Tracks: / Candybar express / River of people / Twisted / Pain in gun / Love and money / Dear John / Cheeseburger / You're beautiful / Temptation time.
LP: . . . . **MERH 89**
MC: . . . . **MERHC 89**

DOGS IN THE TRAFFIC.
Tracks: / Winter / Johnny's not here / My love lies in a dead house / Cheap peals / You're not the only one / Looking for Angeline / Sometimes I want to give up / Lips like ether / Whisky dream / Pappa death.
LP: **8489931**
MC: **8489934**

STRANGE KIND OF LOVE.
Tracks: / Hallelujah man / Strange kind of love / Shape of things to come / Up escalator / Jocelyn Square /

Inflammable / Scapegoat (Extra track on CD and cassette.).
LP: . . . . **SFLP 7**
MC: . . . . **SFMC 7**

Love, Monie

DOWN TO EARTH.
Tracks: / Monie in the middle / It's a shame (my sister) / Don't funk wid the Mo / Ring my bell / R U single / Just don't give a damn / What I'm supposed 2 B / Dettrimentally stable / Down 2 earth / I do as I please / Pups lickin' bone / Read between the lines / Race against reality / Swiney swiney / I'm driving you crazy / Grandpa's party / Give it to you like this (CD only.) / I can do this (CD only.).
LP: . . . . **CTLP 14**
MC: . . . . **ZCTLP 14**

LADIES FIRST (See under Queen Latifah for details) (Love, Monie/Queen Latifah).

Love, Preston

STRICTLY CASH/OMAHA BLUES.
LP: . . . . **BP 501**

Love & Rockets

EARTH, SUN, MOON.
Tracks: / Mirror people / Light, The / Welcome tomorrow / No new tale to tell / Here on earth / Lazy / Waiting for the flood / Rainbird / Telephone is empty, The / Everybody wants to go to heaven / Sun, The / Youth.
LP: . . . . **BEGA 84**
MC: . . . . **BEGC 84**

EXPRESS.
Tracks: / It could be sunshine / Kundalini Express / All in my mind / Life in Laralay / Yin and Yang (the flower pot men) / Love me / All in my mind (acoustic version) / American dream.
LP: . . . . **BEGA 74**
MC: . . . . **BEGC 74**
LP: . . . . **BBL 74**
MC: . . . . **BBLC 74**

LOVE AND ROCKETS.
LP: . . . . **BEGA 99**
MC: . . . . **BEGC 99**

SEVENTH DREAM OF TEENAGE HEAVEN.
Tracks: / If there's a heaven above / Private future, A / Dog end of a day gone by, The / Game, The / Seventh dream of teenage heaven / Haunted when the minutes drag / Saudade.
LP: . . . . **BEGA 66**
MC: . . . . **BEGC 66**
LP: . . . . **85071 R**
LP: . . . . **BBL 66**
MC: . . . . **BBLC 66**

SO ALIVE.
Tracks: / So alive.
MC: . . . . **BEG 229 C**

Love Sculpture

BLUES HELPING.
LP: . . . . **PCS 7059**

DAVE EDMUNDS - LOVE SCULPTURE YEARS (Vol.1).
Tracks: / In the land of the few / Seagull / Nobody's talking / Why (how-now) / You can't catch me / Sabre dance / People, people / Brand new woman / River to another day / Think of love / Farandole.
LP: . . . . **EMS 1127**
MC: . . . . **TCEMS 1127**

SINGLES A'S & B'S (see Edmunds,Dave & Love Sculpture) (Love Sculpture & Dave Edmunds).

Love Song

FEEL THE LOVE.
Tracks: / Front seat, back seat / Little country church / Cossack song, The / Love song / Two hands / Let us be one / Drum solo / Feel the love / So thankful / Since I opened up the door / Freedom / Jesus puts the song in our hearts / Little pilgrim / Sometimes allelujah.
LP: . . . . **MYR 1062**
MC: . . . . **MC 1062**

LOVE SONG.
Tracks: / Love song / Changes / Two hands / Little country church / Freedom / Welcome back / Front seat, back seat / Let us be one / And the wind was low / Brand new song / Feel the love.
LP: . . . . **MYR 1012**
MC: . . . . **MC 1012**

Love Songs

20 GREAT ITALIAN LOVE SONGS (Various artists).
LP: . . . . **STAR 2230**
MC: . . . . **STAC 2230**

100 MINUTES OF LOVE SONGS (Various artists).
MC: . . . . **ZCTON 120**

ALL MY LOVING (Various artists).
Tracks: / All my loving: *Various artists* / Fool on the hill: *Various artists* / Guantanamera: *Various artists*/ More I see you, The: *Various artists* / Quando m'innamora: *Various artists* / Our day will come: *Various* artists / Mas que nada: *Various artists* / Where have all the flowers gone: *Various artists* / There will never be another you: *Various artists* / Girl from Ipanema: *Various artists* / Goin out of my head: *Various* artists / Misty roses: *Various artists* / When a man loves a woman: *Various artists* / Sunny: *Various* artists / Yesterday: *Various artists* / Don't go breaking my heart: *Various artists* / Fly me to the moon: *Various artists* / Chelsea morning: *Various artists* / What now my love: *Various artists.*
LP: . . . . **MFP 50540**
MC: . . . . **TCMFP 50540**

BEST OF THE GREATEST LOVE (Various artists).
LP: . . . . **STAR 2443**
MC: . . . . **STAC 2443**

CLASSIC LOVE SONGS (Various artists).
2LP: . . . . **STAR 2316**
MCSET: . . . . **STAC 2316**

CLASSIC YEARS IN DIGITAL STEREO (see under Classic Years...) (Various artists).

DEVOTED TO YOU (16 Songs From The Heart) (Various artists).
Tracks: / Crazy: *Cline, Patsy* / Some broken hearts never mend: *Williams, Don* / Happy anniversary: *Whitman,* Slim / Wheel of fortune: *Rose Marie* / She wears my ring: *King, Solomon* / Hurt: *Yuro, Timi* / With pen in hand: *Carr, Vikki* / Devoted to you: *Everly Brothers* / Sing me an old fashioned song: *Spears, Billie* Jo / Have I got some blues for you: *Pride, Charley* / I will love you all my life: *Foster & Allen* / Pal of my cradle days: *Breen, Ann* / When I leave the world behind: *Rose Marie* / I fall to pieces: *Cline, Patsy*/ All I'm missing is you: *Williams, Don* / So sad (to watch good love go bad): *Everly Brothers* / Ebony eyes: *Everly Brothers* / Love hurts: *Everly Brothers.*
LP: . . . . **PLAT 21**
MC: . . . . **PLAC 21**

EMOTIONS 1969-1980 (Various artists).
Tracks: / It must be love: *Siffre, Labi* / I'd love you to want me: *Lobo* / If I had you: *Korgis* / Moonlight feels right: *Starbuck* / Cats in the cradle: *Chapin, Harry* / Never let her slip away: *Gold, Andrew* / Send in the clowns: *Collins, Judy* / Emotions: *Sang, Samantha* / Sunshine after the rain: *Brooks, Elkie*/ Torn between two lovers: *McGregor, Mary* / Don't give up on us: *Soul, David* / Desiderata: *Crane, Les*/ Seasons in the sun: *Jacks, Terry* / Everybody's talkin': *Nilsson* / Time in a bottle: *Croce, Jim* / All out of love: *Air Supply* / Babe: *Styx* / Help me make it through the night: *Holt, John* / Best thing that ever happened to me: *Knight, Gladys & The Pips* / Just when I needed you most: *Vanwarmer, Randy* / We do it: *Stone, R & J* / Right thing to do, The: *Simon, Carly* / Floating in the wind: *Hudson - Ford* / Heart on my sleeve: *Gallagher & Lyle.*
MCSET: . . . . **OG 2209**

ENDLESS LOVE (Various artists).
Tracks: / Little in love, A: *Richard, Cliff* / We're all alone: *Coolidge, Rita* / Lost in love: *Air Supply*/ Will you love me tomorrow: *Dickson, Barbara* / One day in your life: *Jackson, Michael* / I wanna get next to you: *Rose Royce* / You weren't in love with me: *Field, Billy* / Angel of the morning: *Newton, Juice* / Being with you: *Robinson, Smokey* / Always on my mind: *Nelson, Willie* / Endless love: *Ross, Diana & Lionel* Richie / In the air tonight: *Collins, Phil* / One of us: *Abba* / Way I want to touch you, The: *Captain & Tennille* / I've never been to me: *Charlene* / Lady of the dawn: *Batt, Mike* / I need you: *Armatrading, Joan* / Visions: *Wyman, Bill* / Shine silently: *Lofgren, Nils* / After the goldrush: *Prelude.*
LP: . . . . **TVA 2**
MC: . . . . **TVC 2**

ETERNAL LOVE (Various artists).
Tracks: / Living years, The: *Mike & The Mechanics* / Heaven help me: *Estus, Deon* / Where does the time go now: *Fordham, Julia* / Cat among the pigeons: *Bros* / Keeping the dream alive: *Freiheit* / On the inside: *Hamilton,* Lynne / Hold me in your arms: *Astley, Rick* / Can't stay away: *Estefan, Gloria* / Through the storm: *Franklin,* Aretha & Elton John / Live like a river: *Climie Fisher* / Looking for Linda: *Hue & Cry* / Air that I breathe, The: *Hollies* / Enchanted lady: *Pasadenas.*
LP: . . . . **NE 1447**
MC: . . . . **CE 2447**

EVERY MAN NEEDS A WOMAN (Various artists).
Tracks: / Every man has a woman who loves him: *Lennon, John* / Silver horse / I'm movin' on: *Money, Eddie* / Nobody sees me like you do: *Cash, Rosanne* / Wake up: *Trio* / Dream love / Now or never: *Spirit Choir* / It's alright: *Lennon, Sean Ono* / Dogtown: *Alternating Boxes* / Goodbye sadness: *Flack, Roberta* / Walking on thin ice: *Costello, Elvis.*
LP: . . . . **POLH 13**
MC: . . . . **POLHC 13**

FEELINGS: THE GOLDEN LOVE SONGS (Various artists).
Tracks: / Feelings: *Albert, Morris* / Misty: *Mantovani* / One I love, The: *Monro, Matt* / Nearness of you, The: *Jones, Tom* / I can't stop loving you: *Mantovani* / Can't take my eyes off you: *Humperdinck, Engelbert*/ Love's theme: *Candler, Norman & The Magic Strings* / Little love and understanding, A: *Becaud, Gilbert* / As time goes by: *Crosby, Bing* / Killing me softly with his song: *Aldrich, Robbie* / Fly me to the moon: *Jones,* Tom / That old feeling: *Monro, Matt* / Sandpiper love theme: *Humperdinck, Engelbert* / Nevertheless: *Crosby, Bing.*
LP: . . . . **TAB 48**
MC: . . . . **KTBC 48**

GREATEST LOVE II (Various artists).
2LP: . . . . **STAR 2352**
MCSET: . . . . **STAC 2352**

GREATEST LOVE III (Various artists).
2LP: . . . . **STAR 2384**
MCSET: . . . . **STAC 2384**

GREATEST LOVE IV (Various artists).
Tracks: / Different corner: *Michael, George* / Cuts both ways: *Estefan, Gloria* / In your eyes: *Benson, George*/ Candle in the wind: *John, Elton* / I just died in your arms: *Cutting Crew* / Baby I love your way/Freebird: *Will* to Power / You're so vain: *Simon, Carly* / I'm still waiting: *Ross, Diana* / Don't know much: *Neville*/ Be free with your love: *Spandau Ballet* / Waiting for a star to fall: *Boy Meets Girl* / Love don't live here any more: *Rose Royce* / Tell me there's a heaven: *Rea, Chris* / My cherie amour: *Wonder, Stevie* / Have you seen her: *Chi-lites* / I still haven't found what I'm looking for: *Chimes* / China in your hand: *T'Pau*/ Broken wings: *Mr. Mister* / My one temptation: *Paris, Mica* / All around the world: *Stansfield, Lisa*/ How men are: *Aztec Camera* / I don't want to talk about it: *Everything But The Girl* / We're all alone: *Coolidge,* Rita / Always and forever: *Heatwave* / Sweet surrender: *Wet Wet Wet* / I've had the time of my life: *Warnes,* Jennifer & Bill Medley / Piano in the dark: *Russell, Brenda* / Woman in love: *3 Degrees* / If you don't know me...: *Melvin, Harold* / Just the way you are: *White, Barry.*
MCSET: . . . . **STAC 2400**
2LP: . . . . **STAR 2400**

IN LOVE WITH LOVE SONGS (Various artists).
Tracks: / All out of love: *Air Supply* / Hold me now: *Thompson Twins* / Loving you is sweeter than ever: *Dee,* Kiki & Elton John / Now those days are gone: *Bucks Fizz* / Sara: *Starship* / Sara smile: *Hall & Oates*/ All by myself: *Carmen, Eric* / Without you: *Nilsson (Harry)* / Heartbreaker: *Warwick, Dionne* / Torn between two lovers: *MacGregor, Mary* / Woman in love: *3 Degrees* / Everyday hurts: *Sad Cafe* / For the good times: *Como, Perry* / Light my fire: *Feliciano, Jose.*
MC: **410772**

IN TOUCH II (More Great Love Classics) (Various artists).
Tracks: / Heartbreaker: *Warwick, Dionne* / Didn't I blow your mind: *Delfonics* / Joanna: *Walker, Scott*/ Winner takes it all, The: *Abba* / Sunny: *Hebb, Bobby* / I'll have to say I love you in a song: *Croce, Jim*/ Torn between two lovers: *MacGregor, Mary* / Feels so right: *Alabama (Group)* / Laughter in the rain: *Sedaka,* Neil / You've lost that lovin' feeling: *Righteous Brothers* / More than in love: *Robbins, Kate* / Your song: *John, Elton* / Friends: *Bailey, Razzy* / First cut is the deepest: *Arnold, P.P.* / All of my heart: *ABC*/ Without you: *Nilsson (Harry)* / Love: *Kenny, Gerard* / Air that I breathe, The: *Hammond, Albert* / Lay lady lay: *Byrds* (Not available on CD.) / Breaking up is hard to do: *Sedaka, Neil* (Not available on CD.) / Woman in love: *3 Degrees* / Best thing that ever happened to me: *Knight, Gladys & The Pips* (Not available on CD.) / Star: *Dee, Kiki* (Not available on CD.) / Just like a woman: *Cocker, Joe* (Not available on CD.) / Land of make believe: *Bucks Fizz* (Not available on CD.) / Whiter shade of pale, A: *Procul Harum* (Not available on CD.) / January February: *Dickson, Barbara* (Not available on CD.) / I will always love you: *Parton, Dolly.*
2LP: . . . . **STDLP 23**
MC: . . . . **STDMC 23**

ITALIAN LOVE SONGS (Various artists).
MC: . . . . **AIM 119**

JUKE BOX COLLECTION - I WILL ALWAYS LOVE YOU (Various artists).
Tracks: / I will always love you: *Parton, Dolly* / Torn between two lovers: *MacGregor, Mary* / We're all alone: *Coolidge, Rita* / Don't cry out loud: *Brooks, Elkie* / When I need you: *Sayer, Leo* / Come what may: *Leandros,* Vicky / And I love you so: *Como, Perry* / If I said you had a beautiful body: *Bellamy Brothers* / Streets of London: *McTell, Ralph* / Just when I needed you most: *Vanwarmer, Randy* / They shoot horses don't they: *Racing Cars* / All out of love: *Air Supply* / Suddenly: *Ocean, Billy* / All by myself: *Carmen, Eric.*
LP: . . . . **OG 1719**
MC: . . . . **OG 2719**

JUKE BOX COLLECTION - MISTY BLUE Love songs of the Seventies (Various artists).
Tracks: / Misty blue: *Moore, Dorothy* / We do it: *Stone, R & J* / Feelings: *Albert, Morris* / Have you seen her?: *Chi-lites* / Stay with me: *Blue Mink* / I will: *Winters, Ruby* / Everything is beautiful: *Stevens,* Ray / Clair: *O'Sullivan, Gilbert* / Help me make it through the night: *Holt, John* / Sad sweet dreamer: *Sweet Sensation* / Lost in France: *Tyler, Bonnie* / It must be love: *Siffre, Labi.*
MC: . . . . **OG 2706**
LP: . . . . **OG 1706**

JUST THE TWO OF US (Various artists).
Tracks: / I've had the time of my life: *Medley, Bill & Jennifer Warnes* / Don't wanna lose you: *Estefan, Gloria*/ Up where you belong: *Cocker, Joe & Jennifer Warnes* / Too much, too little, too late: *Mathis, Johnny & Deniece Williams*/ On the wings of love: *Osborne, Jeffrey* / Through the storm: *Franklin, Aretha & Elton John* / With you I'm born again: *Preston, Billy & Syreeta* / Endless love: *Ross, Diana & Lionel Richie* / Eternal flame: *Bangles*/ I know you by heart: *Parton, Dolly & Smokey Robinson* / All the love in the world: *Warwick, Dionne* / Sometimes when we touch: *Wynette, Tammy/Mark Gray* / All I want is forever: *Taylor, James 'JT' & Regina Belle* / I knew you were waiting (for me): *Michael, George and Aretha Franklin* / Wind beneath my wings, The: *Knight, Gladys.*
LP: . . . . **MOOD 11**
MC: . . . . **MOODC 11**

LAST DANCE, THE (Various artists).
Tracks: / Three times a lady: *Commodores* / All of my life: *Ross, Diana* / I'll be there: *Jackson 5*/ What becomes of the broken hearted?: *Ruffin, Jimmy* / Abraham, Martin and John: *Gaye, Marvin* / Just my imagination (running away with me): *Temptations* / Do you know where you're going to: *Ross, Diana* / You're all I need to get by: *Gaye, Marvin & Tammi Terrell* / What does it take to win your love: *Walker, Junior & The All Stars* / Ben: *Jackson, Michael* / I'm still waiting: *Ross, Diana* / My cherie amour: *Wonder, Stevie* / Tracks of my tears: *Robinson, Smokey & The Miracles* / It's all in the game: *Four Tops* / Help me make it through the night: *Knight, Gladys & The Pips* / Farewell is a lonely sound: *Ruffin, Jimmy* / Got to be there: *Jackson, Michael*/ He's misstra know it all: *Wonder, Stevie* / You are everything: *Ross, Diana & Marvin Gaye* / Still: *Commodores.*
LP: . . . . **EMTV 20**
MC: . . . . **TCEMTV 20**
LP: . . . . **ZL 72007**
MC: . . . . **ZK 72007**

LAUGHTER AND TEARS COLLECTION (Various artists).
LP: . . . . **LTC 1**
MC: . . . . **LTC 41**

LOVE ALBUM, THE (Various artists).
Tracks: / I want to know what love is: *Foreigner* / Cherish: *Kool & The Gang* / Move closer: *Nelson, Phyllis* / You're the best thing: *Style Council* / Slave to love: *Ferry, Bryan* / Do what you do: *Jackson, Jermaine*/ Everything must change: *Young, Paul* / I should have known better: *Diamond, Jim* / I know him so well: *Paige,* Elaine & Barbara Dickson / Suddenly: *Ocean, Billy* / Your love is King: *Sade* / That ole devil called love: *Moyet, Alison* / Careless whisper: *Michael, George* / Nightshift: *Commodores* / Stuck on you: *Richie, Lionel* / Sad songs: *John, Elton.*
LP: . . . . **STAR 2268**
MC: . . . . **STAC 2268**

LOVE ALBUM, THE (Various artists).
LP: . . . . **STAR 2332**
MC: . . . . **STAC 2332**

LOVE BALLADS (Various artists).

LPS: . . . . **LVBAL 1**
MC: . . . . **ZCBAL 1**

LOVE BALLADS VOL.3 (Various artists).
LP: . . . . **LVBAL 003**
MC: . . . . **ZCLVB 003**

LOVE BALLADS VOL 1 & VOL 2 (Various artists).
LP: **01409022**
MC: **01409141**

LOVE BOX (Various artists).
LPS: . . . . **IMP 94**
MCSET: . . . . **IMPC 94**

LOVE BOX, VOL. 2 (Various artists).
LPS: . . . . **IMP 0101**
MCSET: . . . . **IMPC 0101**

LOVE COLLECTION (2) VOL.1, THE (Various artists).
Tracks: / One of us: *Abba* / Free: *Williams, Deniece* / Midnight blue: *Manchester, Melissa* / All by myself: *Carmen, Eric* / Your song: *John, Elton* / Woman in love: *3 Degrees* / Everlasting love: *Gibb*, Andy / Rock me gently: *Kim, Andy* / When I need you: *Sayer, Leo* / Without you: *Nilsson (Harry)*/ You've lost that lovin' feeling: *Righteous Brothers* / Why don't you spend the night: *Miller, Frank (nar)* / Oh no not my baby: *Stewart, Rod* / Long cool woman in a black dress: *Hollies* / No regrets: *Walker Brothers*/ Sad eyes: *John, Robert*.
LP: . . . . **MODEM 1028**
MC: . . . . **MODEMC 1028**

LOVE COLLECTION (2) VOL.2, THE (Various artists).
Tracks: / Heartbreaker: *Warwick, Dionne* / You're all I need: *Mathis, Johnny* / After the love has gone: *Earth, Wind & Fire* / We've got tonight: *Easton, Sheena* / What I did for love: *3 Degrees* / When a man loves a woman: *Sledge, Percy* / How 'bout us: *Campaign* / I'll put you together again: *Hot Chocolate* / I want to stay with you: *Gallagher & Lyle* / Little bit more, A: *Various artists* / Wake up everybody: *Melvin, Harold*/ I believe in you: *Dickson, Barbara*.
LP: . . . . **MODEM 1029**
MC: . . . . **MODEMC 1029**

LOVE COLLECTION (2) VOL.3, THE (Various artists).
Tracks: / There'll be sad songs (to make you cry): *Ocean, Billy* / See the day: *Lee, Dee C* / Because of you: *Rowland, Kevin* / Broken heart can mend, A: *O'Neal, Alexander* / Mated: *Graham, Jaki & David Grant* / Smooth operator: *Sade* / Love resurrection: *Moyet, Alison* / If I had words: *Fitzgerald, Scott* / Fantasy: *Earth, Wind & Fire* / Sexual healing: *Gaye, Marvin* / Lady: *Rogers, Kenny* / Turn off the lights: *Pendergrass, Teddy*.
LP: . . . . **MODEM 1030**
MC: . . . . **MODEMC 1030**

LOVE COLLECTION (2) VOL.4, THE (Various artists).
Tracks: / Winner takes it all, The: *Abba* / More than I can say: *Sayer, Leo* / Loving you: *Ripperton, Minnie*/ Make it easy on yourself: *Walker Brothers* / Power of love, The: *Rush, Jennifer* / Sorry seems to be the hardest word: *John, Elton* / I honestly love you: *Newton-John, Olivia* / As time goes by: *Various artists* / Can't help falling in love: *Williams, A* / I will: *Winters, Ruby*.
LP: . . . . **MODEM 1031**
MC: . . . . **MODEMC 1031**

LOVE COLLECTION (2) VOL.5, THE (Various artists).
Tracks: / All the love in the world: *Warwick, Dionne* / Save the last dance for me: *Drifters* / I know him so well: *Paige, Elaine & Barbara Dickson* / Don't leave me this way: *Melvin, Harold* / Song for Guy: *John, Elton*/ Wedding bells: *Godley & Creme* / Save the last dance for me: *King, Ben E.* / Tonight I celebrate my love: *Bryson*, Peabo & Roberta Flack / I didn't mean to turn you on: *Cherrelle* / Kayleigh: *Marillion* / I'll fly for you: *Spandau Ballet* / Kiss and say goodbye: *Manhattans* / Missing you: *Waite, John*.
LP: . . . . **MODEM 1032**
MC: . . . . **MODEMC 1032**

LOVE COLLECTION (2) VOL.6, THE (Various artists).
LP: . . . . **MODEM 1033**
MC: . . . . **MODEMC 1033**

LOVE COLLECTION, THE (MFP) (Various artists).
Tracks: / Let there be love: *Cole, Nat King* / Folks who live on the hill, The: *Lee, Peggy* / With these hands: *Monro, Matt* / True love ways: *Peter & Gordon* / Tonight: *Damone, Vic* / Where do you go to (my lovely): *Sarstedt, Peter* / Rose Marie: *Whitman, Slim* / I've got my love to keep me warm: *Martin, Dean* / What now my love: *Bassey, Shirley* / Honey: *Goldsboro, Bobby* / Tears: *Dodd, Ken* / Let me go lover: *Murray*, Ruby / Here in my heart: *Martino, Al* / Somewhere my love: *Sammes, Mike Singers* / She wears my ring: *King*, Solomon / Hymn a l'amour: *Piaf, Edith* / I pretend: *O'Connor, Des* (CD only.) / My special angel: *Vaughan*, Malcolm (CD only.) / He was beautiful: *Williams, Iris* (CD only.) / Wonder of you, The: *Hilton, Ronnie* (CD only.).
LP: . . . . **MFP 5878**
MC: . . . . **TCMFP 5878**

LOVE COLLECTION - VOL 1, THE (Various artists).
MCSET: . . . . **WW 6026**

LOVE COLLECTION - VOL 2, (Various artists).
MCSET: . . . . **WW 6027**

LOVE IS A GAME (Various artists).
LP: . . . . **CABMP 1**
MC: . . . . **ZCCBM 1**

LOVE ON MY MIND (Various artists).
Tracks: / You taught me how to speak in love: *Shaw, Marlena* / Honey: *Goldsboro, Bobby* / I've got love on my mind: *Cole, Natalie* / By the time I get to Phoenix: *Campbell, Glen* / Softly as I leave you: *Horne, Lena*/ I love you more and more every day: *Martino, Al* / Can't help falling in love: *Martino, Al* / Put a little love in your heart: *DeShannon, Jackie* / Tonight I celebrate my love: *Bryson, Peabo & Roberta Flack* / You're having my baby: *Anka, Paul* / Hurt: *Yuro, Timi* / Something: *Bassey, Shirley* / Love Letters: *Cole, Nat King* / When a woman loves a man: *Lester, Ketty* / (They long to be) close to you: *Wilson, Nancy* / Something 'bout you baby I like: *Campbell, Glen & Rita Coolidge*.
LP: . . . . **MOIR 501**
MC: . . . . **CMOIR 501**

LOVE ON THE DANCE FLOOR (100 Classic Dance Floor Love Songs) (Various artists).
Tracks: / Way we were, The: *Knight, Gladys & The Pips* / Baby, come to me: *Austin, Patti & James Ingram* / Rock me tonight: *Jackson, Freddie* / Wishing on a star: *Royce, Rose* / I still can't get over loving you: *Parker*, Ray Jr / I've got love on my mind: *Cole, Natalie* / Stay with me tonight: *Osborne, Jeffrey* / If you're ready: *Turner, Ruby* / Feel so real: *Arrington, Steve* / My forbidden lover: *Chic* / Joy and pain: *Maze*/ Yah mo b there: *Ingram, James* / Let's go all the way: *Sly Fox* / Just an illusion: *Imagination* / Fool (If you think it's over): *Rea, Chris* / Never let her slip away: *Gold, Andrew* / All out of love: *Air Supply*/ I'm not in love / All by myself: *Carmen, Eric* / I can dream about you: *Hartman, Dan* / Save the last dance for me: *King, Ben E.* / We're all alone: *Coolidge, Rita* / Angel of the morning: *Mason, Mary* / You are my lover: *Liverpool Express* / How 'bout us: *Champaign* / I'm stone in love with you: *Stylistics* / Where is the love: *Mills, Stephanie* / Without you: *Nilsson* / I want to know what love is: *Foreigner* / Keep on loving you: *REO Speedwagon* / Everyday hurts: *Sad Cafe* / Babe: *Styx* / Waiting for a girl like you: *Foreigner* / Wonderful tonight: *Clapton, Eric* / Sugar walls: *Easton, Sheena* / When I fall in love: *Cole*, Nat King / I wanna stay with you: *Gallagher & Lyle* / Miss you nights: *Richard, Cliff* / I can hear your heartbeat: *Rea, Chris* / For your eyes only: *Easton, Sheena* / Just the way you are: *White, Barry* / Emma: *Hot Chocolate* / Too much, too little, too late: *Mathis, Johnny* / One day I'll fly away: *Crawford, Randy* / Always and forever: *Heatwave* / Love don't live here any more: *Royce, Rose* / On the wings of love: *Osborne, Jeffrey*/ Tonight I celebrate my love: *Bryson, Peabo* / You're my latest, my greatest ispiration: *Pendergrass, Teddy* / I live for your love: *Cole, Natalie* / Used ta be my girl: *O'Jays* / What a fool believes: *Franklin, Aretha*/ Strange love affair: *Lanier & Co.* / Best of my love: *Emotions* / When she was my girl: *Four Tops* / Lies: *Butler, Jonathan* / It's a love thing: *Whispers* / Heaven must be missing an angel: *Tavares* / Best thing that ever happened to me: *Knight, Gladys & The Pips* / Whole town's laughing at me, The: *Pendergrass, Teddy*/ More than a woman: *Tavares* / Tonight I'm gonna love you all over: *Four Tops* / You're my angel: *Abbott*, Gregory / If I can't have you: *Elliman, Yvonne* / Reunited: *Peaches & Herb* / Just my imagination: *Turner*, Ruby / In and out of love: *Imagination* / It started with a kiss: *Hot Chocolate* / Heartbreaker: *Warwick*, Dionne / Mind blowin' decisions: *Heatwave* / I don't wanna lose you: *Kandidate* / I wanna get next to you: *Royce, Rose* / Fantasy: *Earth, Wind & Fire* / Mated: *Graham, Jaki* / Woman in love: *3 Degrees*/ Body talk: *Imagination* / Take good care of me: *Butler, Jonathan* / Personal touch: *Brown, Errol* / Joanna: *Kool & The Gang* / If you're looking for a way out: *Odyssey* / You make me feel brand new: *Stylistics*/ All the love in the world: *Warwick, Dionne* / Cherish: *Kool & The Gang* / When love comes calling: *Johnson*, Paul / Little bit more, A: *Jackson, Freddie* / Lady love: *Rawls, Lou* / I want your love: *Chic* / Twilight: *Maze* / You bet your love: *Hancock, Herbie* / I shoulda loved ya: *Walden, Narada Michael* / You sexy thing: *Hot Chocolate* / Round and around: *Graham, Jaki* / I can make you feel good: *Shalamar*/ Do what you do: *Jackson, Jermaine* / Do that to me one more time: *Captain & Tennille* / We do it: *Stone*, R & J / If you don't know me by now: *Melvin, Harold & The Bluenotes* / Baby blues: *White, Barry* / I don't want to talk about it: *Everything But The Girl* / Je t'aime...: *Birkin, Jane*.
LPS: . . . . **LOVELP 1**
MCSET: . . . . **LOVEMC 1**

LOVE SONGS (I love country) (Various artists).
Tracks: / Takin' it easy: *Dalton, Lacy J* / Love can't ever get better than this: *Skaggs, Ricky* / Natural high: *Haggard, Merle and Janie Fricke* / Let it be me: *Various artists* / You are so beautiful: *Tucker, Tanya*/ Shine on shine all your sweet love on me: *Jones, George* / Always have always will: *Fricke, Janie* / My woman my woman my wife: *Robbins, Marty* / Behind closed doors: *Rich, Charlie* / You needed me: *Wynette, Tammy*/ Nothing but your love matters: *Gatlin, Larry & The Gatlin Brothers Band* / You never gave up on me: *Gayle, Crystal*/ True love ways: *Gilley, Mickey* / I love how you love me: *Anderson, Lynn* / If I were a carpenter: *Cash, Johnny & June Carter* / Sunrise: *Atkins, Chet*.
LP: **4510101**
MC: **4510104**

LOVE SONGS (Various artists).
Tracks: / When a man loves a woman: *Sledge, Percy* / All alone am I: *Yuro, Timi* / Go away little girl: *Happenings*/ More than I can say: *Vee, Bobby* / Young girl: *Puckett, Gary* / Happy together: *Turtles* / Dedicated to the one I love: *Mamas & Papas* / Come softly to me: *Fleetwoods*.
MCSET: . . . . **DTO 10015**

LOVE SONGS (Various artists).
Tracks: / Hello: *Richie, Lionel* / She's out of my life: *Jackson, Michael* / Jealous guy: *Roxy Music*/ Time after time: *Lauper, Cyndi* / Wherever I lay my hat: *Young, Paul* / Zoom: *Fat Larry's Band* / After the love has gone: *Earth, Wind & Fire* / Touche d'amour: *Rea, Chris* / Against all odds: *Collins, Phil*/ Wonderful tonight: *Clapton, Eric* / Our love: *Brooks, Elkie* / Closest thing to heaven: *Kane Gang* / Stuck on you: *Walters, Trevor* / Will you: *O'Connor, Hazel* / Farewell my summer love: *Jackson, Michael*/ On the wings of love: *Osborne, Jeffrey*.
LP: . . . . **STAR 2246**
MC: . . . . **STAC 2246**

LOVE SONGS ALBUM (Various artists).
LP: . . . . **NE 1179**
MC: . . . . **CE 2179**

LOVE SONGS FROM THE SILVER SCREEN (Various artists).
Tracks: / Gigi: *Jourdan, Louis* (From Gigi.) / Love is here to stay: *Kelly, Gene* (From An American In Paris.) / You were meant for me: *Kelly, Gene* (From Singing In The Rain.) / All I do is dream of you: *Kelly, Gene* (From Singing In The Rain.) / Almost like being in love: *Kelly, Gene* (From Birgadoon.) / So in love: *Keel, Howard/Kathryn* Grayson (From Kiss Me Kate.) / Why do I love you: *Keel, Howard/Kathryn Grayson* (From Show Boat.) / Make believe: *Keel*, Howard/ Kathryn Grayson (From Show Boat.) / And this is my beloved: *Keel, Howard/ Anne Blyth/Vic Damone* (From Kismet.) / Indian love call: *Blyth, Ann/Fernando Lamas* (From Rose Marie.) / When you're in love: *Keel, Howard, Jane Powell*(From Seven Brides for Seven Brothers.) / Stranger in paradise: *Blyth, Ann/Vic Damone* (From Kismet.) / Can't help lovin' dat man: *Gardner, Ava* (From Show Boat. CD only.) / Love of my life: *Garland, Judy* (From The Pirate. CD only.).
LP: . . . . **MFP 5877**
MC: . . . . **TCMFP 5877**

LOVE SONGS OF THE 60'S (Various artists).
Tracks: / God only knows: *Beach Boys* / Moon river: *Williams, Danny* / I'll never fall in love again: *Gentry*, Bobbie / I remember you: *Ifield, Frank* / To know you is to love you: *Peter & Gordon* / If you gotta go, go now: *Manfred Mann* / She wears my ring: *King, Solomon* / I could easily fall in love with you: *Richard, Cliff*/ Step inside love: *Black, Cilla* / Softly as I leave you: *Monro, Matt* / When the girl in your arms is the girl in your heart: *Richard, Cliff* / Here I go again: *Hollies* / Starry eyed: *Holiday, Michael* / Portrait of my love: *Monro, Matt* / Love's just a broken heart: *Black, Cilla* / All I have to do is dream: *Campbell*, Glen & Bobbie Gentry / Michelle: *David & Jonathan* / Up on the roof: *Lynch, Kenny* / As long as he needs me: *Various artists* / There's a kind of hush: *Herman's Hermits*.
LP: . . . . **MFP 5832**
MC: . . . . **TCMFP 5832**

LOVE SONGS OF THE 70'S (Various artists).
Tracks: / If I had words: *Fitzgerald, Scott/Yvonne Keeley* / Loving you: *Riperton, Minnie* / When you're in love with a beautiful woman: *Dr. Hook* / And I love you so: *McLean, Don* / I don't wanna lose you: *Kandidate*/ Love hit me: *Nightingale, Maxine* / More than a woman: *Tavares* / Storm in a tea cup: *Fortunes* / I can't tell the bottom from the top: *Hollies* / Talking in your sleep: *Gayle, Crystal* / You'll always be a friend: *Hot Chocolate* / Softly whispering I love you: *Congregation* / Honey come back: *Campbell, Glen* / Lay your love on me: *Racey* / What I've got in mind: *Spears, Billie Jo* / Let me be the one: *Shadows* / I honestly love you: *Newton-John, Olivia* (CD only.) / Summer (the first time): *Goldsboro, Bobby* (CD only.) / Oh babe what would you say?: *Smith, Hurricane* (CD only.) / Lucille: *Rogers, Kenny* (CD only.).
MC: . . . . **TCMFP 5894**

LOVE SONGS VOL.2 (Various artists).
Tracks: / Dedicated to the one I love: *Various artists* / Blue moon: *Marcels* / Runaway: *Shannon, Del*/ Remember (walking in the sand): *Shangri-Las* / Hey Paula: *Paul & Paula* / Up on the roof: *Various artists*/ Shoop shoop song: *Everett, Betty* / Baby now that I've found you: *Foundations* / Hey there lonely girl: *Holman*, Eddie / If you don't know me by now: *Melvin, Harold & The Bluenotes* / Sweet talking guy: *Various artists*/ Will you love me tomorrow: *Shirelles* / You don't have to be a star baby: *Tempo, Nino & April Stevens* / Poetry in motion: *Tillotson, Johnny* / Look of love, The: *Harris, Anita* / Let me try again: *Jones, Tammy* / Summer of 42: *Biddu* / I can't get by without you: *Dickinson, Barbara* / Angel of the morning: *Mason, Mary*/ Just loving you: *Harris, Anita* / Don't throw it all away: *Hill, Vince* / Together: *Smith, O.C* / Something: *Bennett, Tony* / Always and forever: *Heatwave* / What's in a kiss: *O'Sullivan, Gilbert* / Love of my life: *Dooleys* / Over you: *Puckett, Gary* / I'm not in love: *Clark, Petula* / Tears on my pillow / Please tell him that I said hello: *Dana* / You've made me so very happy: *Blood, Sweat & Tears* / Arms of Mary: *Sutherland Brothers* / First time ever I saw your face, The: *Various artists* / For once in my life: *Bennett, Tony*.
MCSET: . . . . **DTO 10063**

LOVE STORY - THOSE ROMANTIC 70'S (See Under 70's) (Various artists).

LOVE STORY - THOSE ROMANTIC 70'S (Various artists).
Tracks: / Love story: *Aldrich, Ronnie, His Piano & The Festival Orchestra* / It's impossible: *Mantovani & His Orchestra*/ You make me feel brand new: *Aldrich, Ronnie, His Piano & The Festival Orchestra* / (They long to be) close to you: *Chacksfield*, Frank & His Orchestra / All by myself: *Aldrich, Ronnie His Piano and Orchestra* / Way we were, The: *Black, Stanley*, His Piano & Orchestra / Killing me softly with his song: *Aldrich, Ronnie, His Piano & The Festival Orchestra* / Summer (the first time): *Aldrich, Ronnie, His Piano & The Festival Orchestra* / And I love you so: *Mantovani & His Orchestra*/ Aubrey: *Aldrich, Ronnie, His Piano & The Festival Orchestra* / Bridge over troubled water: *Chacksfield, Frank* & His Orchestra / Without you: *Aldrich, Ronnie, His Piano & The Festival Orchestra* / Just when I needed you most: *Black*, Stanley, His Piano & Orchestra / Feelings: *Aldrich, Ronnie His Piano and Orchestra* / I'll never fall in love again: *Mantovani & His Orchestra* / Evergreen: *Aldrich, Ronnie & His Two Pianos*.
MC: **8440664**

LOVE SUPREME (Various artists).
MC: . . . . **DINMC 19**
LP: . . . . **DINTV 19**

LOVERS, THE (Various artists).
Tracks: / Lovers, The: *O'Neal, Alexander* / So amazing: *Vandross, Luther* / You are my lady: *Jackson, Freddie*/ We're in this love together: *Jarreau, Al* / 2 a.m.: *Pendergrass, Teddy* / Sexual healing: *Gaye, Marvin*/ Suddenly: *Ocean, Billy* / Sexy girl: *Thomas, Lillo* / Sign your name: *D'arby, Terence Trent* / Rock me tonight (for old time's sake): *Jackson, Freddie* / What can I say to make ...: *O'Neal, Alexander* / Joy: *Pendergrass, Teddy* / Never too

much: Vandross, Luther / Mornin': Jarreau, Al.
LP: NE 1426
MC: CE 2426

LOVIN' & DREAMIN' (Various artists).
MCSET: DTO 10047

MELODIES OF LOVE (16 million selling love songs of the 50's) (Various artists).
Tracks: / Little things mean a lot: Kallen, Kitty / Let me go lover: Brewer, Teresa / Three coins in the fountain: Four Aces / I'll be home: Boone, Pat / Undecided: Ames Brothers / It's almost tomorrow: Dream Weavers / In the chapel in the moonlight: Kallen, Kitty / Tammy: Reynolds, Debbie / April love: Boone, Pat / Lover: Lee, Peggy / Stranger in paradise: Four Aces / Friendly persuasion: Boone, Pat / Fascination: Morgan, Jane / Melody of love: Vaughn, Billy / Sincerely: McGuire Sisters / Love is a many splendoured thing: Four Aces.
LP: SHM 3226
MC: HSC 3226

MIDNIGHT HOUR (COLLECTION OF GREAT SMOOCHERS) (Various artists).
LP: NE 1157
MC: CE 2157

MIDNIGHT LOVE (Various artists).
LP: SMR 981
MC: SMC 981

MISSING YOU (Various artists).
Tracks: / It must have been love: Roxette / All around the world: Stansfield, Lisa / Miss you like crazy: Cole, Natalie / I don't wanna lose you: Turner, Tina / I'm still waiting: Ross, Diana / Wishing on a star: Rose Royce / Tracks of my tears, The: Robinson, Smokey & The Miracles / Crying: Orbison, Roy / Right here waiting: Marx, Richard / Miss you nights: Richard, Cliff / Without you: Nilsson / Missing you: Waite, John/ Fool (if you think it's over): Rea, Chris / God only knows: Beach Boys / Hard to say I'm sorry: Chicago/ Missing you: De Burgh, Chris.
LP: EMTV 53
MC: TCEMTV 53

MISSING YOU 2 (An Album of Love) (Various artists).
Tracks: / Alone: Heart / Listen to your heart: Roxette / Teardrops: Womack & Womack / Have you seen her: Chi-lites / After the love has gone: Earth, Wind & Fire / She's gone: Hall & Oates / In dreams: Orbison, Roy / Crazy: Cline, Patsy / Cryin' in the rain: Everly Brothers / When two worlds drift apart: Richard, Cliff / To love somebody: Somerville, Jimmy / You win again: Bee Gees / I guess that's why they call it the blues: John, Elton / Up where we belong: Cocker, Joe & Jennifer Warnes / Don't know much: Ronstadt, Linda & Aaron Neville / Loving you: Riperton, Minnie.
LP: EMTV 57
MC: TCEMTV 57

MOODS (Various artists).
Tracks: / Float on: Floaters / I'm your puppet: Purify, James / Gaye: Ward, Clifford T. / Oh, Lori: Alessi / This time I'll be sweeter: Lewis, Linda / Rainy night in Georgia: Benton, Brook / If you're looking for a way out: Odyssey / Hold on to love: Skellern, Peter / Runaway: Gallagher & Lyle / Parisienne walkways: Moore, Gary / Lonely girl: Holman, Eddie / Daniel: John, Elton / You make me feel brand new: Stylistics / Spanish wine: White, Chris / Here I go again: Twiggy / We do it: Stone, R & J/ Amoureuse: Dee, Kiki / What a wonderful world: Various artists / You to me are everything: Real Thing/ I get a kick out of you: Shearston, Gary / Feelings: Albert, Morris / You're such a good looking woman: Dolan, Joe / Sad songs: Alessi / All by myself: Carmen, Eric.
MCSET: CRT 016

MOVE CLOSER (Various artists).
Tracks: / I knew you were waiting for me: Franklin, Aretha & George Michael / Sometimes: Erasure / Is this love?: Moyet, Alison / Give me the reason: Vandross, Luther / Rain, The: Jones, Oran "Juice" / When love comes calling: Johnson, Paul / Shake you down: Abbott, Gregory / Caravan of love: Isley-Jasper / Take my breath away: Berlin / On my own: Labelle, Patti & Michael McDonald / No more the fool: Brooks, Elkie/ Through the barricades: Spandau Ballet / Why does a man have to be strong: Young, Paul / Holding back the years: Simply Red / Move closer: Nelson, Phyllis / Frozen heart*: FM.
LP: MOOD 1
MC: MOOD C1

NIGHT LIFE (Various artists).
2LP: STD 11
MCSET: STDK 11

NIGHT LIFE II (More Classic Soul Tracks) (Various artists).
Tracks: / Fame: Cara, Irene / When smokey sings: ABC / Caravan of love: Isley-Jasper / Finest, The: S.O.S. Band / If you were here tonight: O'Neal, Alexander / Whole town's laughing at me, The: Pendergrass, Teddy / Do what you do: Jackson, Jermaine / Rain, The: Jones, Oran "Juice" / Who's zoomin' who: Franklin, Aretha / Maniac: Sembello, Michael (Not available on CD.) / She's strange: Cameo (Not available on CD.) / Who'd she coo: Ohio Players (Not available on CD.) / Oops upside your head: Gap Band (Not available on CD.) / Living in the UK: Shakatak (Not available on CD.) / See the day: Lee, Dee C / After the love has gone: Earth, Wind & Fire (Not available on CD.) / Forever, for always, for love: Vandross, Luther / Broken heart can mend, A: O'Neal, Alexander (Not available on CD.) / Shake you down: Abbott, Gregory / Summer breeze: Isley Brothers (Not available on CD.) / Walking in the rain (with the one I love): Love Unlimited / Midnight train to Georgia: Knight, Gladys & The Pips / Sexual healing: Gaye, Marvin / Lean on me: Withers, Bill / Saturday love: Cherrelle & Alexander O'Neal / Taste of bitter love: Knight, Gladys (Not available on CD.) / Stop to love: Vandross, Luther(Not available on CD.) / Living in America: Brown, James (Not available on CD.).
2LP: STDLP 22
MC: STDMC 22

OUR TUNE (Various artists).
Tracks: / Sad songs: Ocean, Billy / Romeo and Juliet: Dire Straits / Sun ain't gonna shine anymore, The / I will survive: Gaynor, Gloria / Look of love, The: ABC / Can't give you anything but my love: Stylistics/ Slave to love: Ferry, Bryan / I'm not in love: 10 CC / Head over heels: Tears For Fears / Cherish: Kool & The Gang / You've lost that lovin' feeling: Righteous Brothers / I guess that's why they call it the blues: John, Elton / How deep is your love: Bee Gees / Nights in white satin: Various artists / Leaving me now: Level 42 / Jealous guy: Various artists.
LP: PROLP 10
MC: PROMC 10

ROMANTIC LOVE SONGS (Various artists).
2LP: BRLP 41/42
MCSET: BRMC 41/42

ROSES ARE RED (16 timeless love songs) (Various artists).
MC: IHMC 05

ROSES ARE RED, VIOLETS ARE BLUE (Timeless Love Songs) (Various artists).
2LP: IHLP 56

SEDUCTION (Various artists).
LP: NE 1451
MC: CE 2451

SLEEPY SHORES 20 Classic songs of love (Various artists).
LP: MFP 50495

SOMEBODY LOVES YOU (Various artists).
Tracks: / Somebody loves you: Gayle, Crystal / All my loving: Monro, Matt / And I love you so: Reddy, Helen/ You're nobody till somebody loves you: Martin, Dean / I'll never love this way again: Williams, Iris / One love: Damone, Vic / What now my love: Bassey, Shirley / You always hurt the one you love: O'Connor, Des/ Can't help falling in love: Cogan, Alma / Portrait of my love: Monro, Matt / Somewhere my love: Hill, Vince (Lara's theme from "Dr. Zhivago") / You don't have to say you love me: Various artists / Sing my love: Martino, Al / Love is a many splendoured thing: Bassey, Shirley / I have loved me a man: Williams, Iris / This guy's in love with you: O'Connor, Des / If you love me (really love me): Various artists / No other love: Hill, Vince / Love's just a broken heart: Black, Cilla / Love is like a violin: Dodd, Ken / I'm in the mood for love: Cogan, Alma / I can't help it (if I'm still in love with you): Campbell, Glen / Step inside love: Black, Cilla / Somewhere my love: Hill, Vince / You don't have to say you love me: Various artists.
MC: TCDL 1110
2LP: DL 1110

SPOTLIGHT ON LOVE (Various artists).
Tracks: / You to me are everything: Real Thing / Baby don't change your mind: Knight, Gladys & The Pips / Isn't she lovely: Parton, David / Summer of my life: May, Simon / Never my love: Addrissi Bros. / If it's alright with you, baby: Korgis / Everybody's got to learn sometime: Korgis / Ten to eight: Castle, David/ Clair: O'Sullivan, Gilbert / I need you: Dolan, Joe / This is my song: Clark, Petula / Where are you now, my love?: Trent, Jackie / Sad sweet dreamer: Sweet Sensation / That same old feeling: Pickettywitch/ Can't get by without you: Real Thing / Tired of being alone: Green, Al / Alone again, naturally: O'Sullivan, Gilbert / Gee baby: Shelly, Peter / Way we were, The: Knight, Gladys & The Pips / Let the heartaches begin: Baldry, Long John / Ruby Tuesday: Melanie / Funny how love can be: Ivy League / All over the world: Hardy, Francoise / Aria: Bilk, Acker.
2LP: SPOT 1007
MCSET: ZCSPT 1007

TEARJERKERS & HEARTBREAKERS (Various artists).
2LP: PDA 065
MCSET: PDC 065

THAT LOVING FEELING VOL.1 (Various artists).
LP: DINTV 5
MC: DINMC 5

THAT LOVING FEELING VOL.2 (Various artists).
Tracks: / What's going on: Gaye, Marvin / Let's stay together: Green, Al / Me and Mrs Jones: Paul, Billy/ Just my imagination: Temptations / Pillow talk: Sylvia / Hang on in there baby: Bristol, Johnny / Misty blue: Moore, Dorothy / Show you the way to go: Jacksons / I'm still waiting: Ross, Diana / With you I'm born again: Preston, Billy & Syreeta / If you don't know me by now: Melvin, Harold & The Bluenotes / Reunited: Peaches & Herb / I will: Winter, Ruby / Way we were, The: Knight, Gladys / Girls: Moments & Whatnauts / Maggie May: Stewart, Rod / I'm not in love / Candle in the wind: John, Elton / I'll have to say...: Croce, Jim / Everyday hurts: Sad Cafe / Just when I needed...: Vanwarmer, Randy / Without you: Nilsson (Harry) / Summer breeze: Isley Brothers / Samba pa ti: Santana / How deep is your love: Bee Gees / You to me are everything: Real Thing / When will I see you again: 3 Degrees / Band of gold: Payne, Freda / Sad sweet dreamer: Sweet Sensation / You're the first, the last, my everything: White, Barry.
LP: DINTV 7
MC: DINMC 7

THAT LOVING FEELING VOL.4 (Various artists).
LP: UNKNOWN
MC: UNKNOWN

THAT LOVING FEELING VOL. 3 (Various artists).
LP: DINTV 11
MC: DINMC 11

THAT LOVING FEELING VOL. 5 (Various artists).
LP: DINTV 28
MC: DINMC 28

THINKING OF YOU (Various artists).
Tracks: / Here we are: Estefan, Gloria / Fool if you think it's over: Brooks, Elkie / I'll never fall in love again: Deacon Blue / Promise me: Craven, Beverley / Two out of three ain't bad: Meatloaf / All cried out: Moyet, Alison / Everytime you go away: Young, Paul / Neither one of us: Knight, Gladys & The Pips/ If you were here tonight: O'Neal, Alexander / Sorry seems to be the hardest word: John, Elton / Ain't no sunshine (eclipse mix): Withers, Bill / Blue velvet: Vinton, Bobby / Stay with me till dawn: Tzuke, Judie / How am I supposed to live without you: Bolton, Michael / Eternal flame: Bangles / Let's stay together: Green, Al / Still: Commodores.
LP: MOOD 15
MC: MOODC 15

TOGETHER - 14 UNFORGETTABLE DUETS (Various artists).
Tracks: / Through the Storm: Franklin, Aretha & Elton John / How many times can we say goodbye: Warwick, Dionne & Luther Vandross / How about us: Hugh, Grayson & Betty Wright / Can't we fall in love again: Hyman, Phyllis & Michael Henderson / This time: Wilson, Kiara & Shanice Wilson / Lovers after all: Manchester, Melissa / Beautiful: Purely Physical / Waiting for a star to fall: Boy Meets Girl / In a lifetime: Clannad & Bono/ Both to each other: Rabbitt, Eddie/Juice Newton / Love is strange: Mickey & Sylvia / Make it easy on love: Jackson, Jermaine & Miki Howard / Love all the hurt away: Franklin, Aretha & George Michael / Loving you is sweeter than ever: Dee, Kiki & Elton John.
MC: 411856

VISIONS - 15 HIT LOVE SONGS (Various artists).
LP: SHM 3162
MC: HSC 3162

WARM AND TENDER (Various artists).
LP: SHM 3123
MC: HSC 3123

WARM FEELINGS (Various artists).
Tracks: / Land of make believe: Bucks Fizz / Why do lovers break each others heart: Hall & Oates / Little bit more, A: Various artists / Love hurts: Garner, Gigi / More than in love: Robbins, Kate / When I need you: Hammond, Albert / Warm love: Carnes, Kim / Best thing that ever happened to me: Knight, Gladys & The Pips / Love: Kenny, Gerard / First time ever I saw your face, The: Lightfoot, Gordon / Warm feelings: Williams, George / Very special love song, A: Rich, Charlie / All out of love: Air Supply / Your song: John, Elton / Seven tears: Goombay Dance Band / Just one look: Carter, Linda / Where do you go to my lovely: Sarstedt, Peter / Friends: Bailey, Razzy / I love you more than you'll ever know: Blood, Sweat & Tears / Tracks of my tears: Blunstone, Colin / When I dream: Gayle, Crystal / Woman in love: 3 Degrees / Longer: Fogelberg, Dan / Torn between two lovers: MacGregor, Mary / I honestly love you: Allen, Peter / Isn't she lovely: Parton, David / I'd rather leave while I'm in love: Coolidge, Rita / Without you: Nilsson (Harry).
2LP: STD 2
MCSET: STDK 2

WHEN A MAN LOVES A WOMAN (Various artists).
Tracks: / Young girl: Puckett, Gary & The Union Gap / I've got you under my skin: Torme, Mel / Time for love, A: Bennett, Tony / Way we were, The: Hill, Vince / Most beautiful girl, The: Rich, Charlie / Tears on my pillow / Nearness of you, The: Torme, Mel / Very special love song: Rich, Charlie / Misty blue: Hill, Vince / Together: Smith, O.C / Cupid: Various artists / (I left my heart) in: Bennett, Tony / Lady Willpower: Puckett, Gary & The Union Gap / Behind closed doors: Rich, Charlie / Folks who live on the hill: Torme, Mel / Stranger in paradise: Bennett, Tony / When I fall in love: Hill, Vince / Little green apples: Smith, O.C / Woman woman: Puckett, Gary & The Union Gap / Hold me tight: Various artists.
MCSET: DTO 10282
MCSET: DTOL 10282

WINGS OF LOVE (Various artists).
Tracks: / Get here: Adams, Oleta / Sacrifice: John, Elton / Senza una donna (Without a woman): Zucchero & Paul Young / Because I love you (The postman song): Stevie B / Let's wait awhile: Jackson, Janet / Different corner, A: Michael, George / Every breath you take: Police / Wonderful tonight: Clapton, Eric / On the wings of love: Osborne, Jeffrey / Anything for you: Estefan, Gloria / Love and affection (remix): Armatrading, Joan / Unchained melody: Righteous Brothers / I'm not in love: 10 CC / Angel eyes: Wet Wet Wet/ Fool if you think it's over: Brooks, Elkie / Goodbye to love: Carpenters.
MC: 8455064
LP: 8455061

YOU'RE THE INSPIRATION (Various artists).
Tracks: / Wind beneath my wings, The: Knight, Gladys & The Pips / Your song: John, Elton / Can't stay away from you: Estefan, Gloria / Lady: Rogers, Kenny / Softly whispering I love you: Young, Paul / Through the barricades: Spandau Ballet / You're the best thing: Style Council / That's what love is all about: Bolton, Michael / Weak in the presence of beauty: Moyet, Alison / Living years, The: Mike & The Mechanics / Yesterday once more: Carpenters / Careless whisper: Michael, George / You're the best thing that ever happened to me: Knight, Gladys & The Pips / Holding on: Craven, Beverley / I wanna wake up with you: Gardiner, Boris / Everywhere: Fleetwood Mac.
LP: MOOD 17
MC: MOODC 17

Love Songs (film)

LOVE SONGS (Original Soundtrack) (Various artists).
LP: STV 81258

Love Story

LOVE STORY (Original soundtrack) (Various artists).
Tracks: / Love story theme: Various artists / Snow frolic: Various artists / Sonata No.12 in F major: Various artists / I love you Phil: Various artists / Christmas tree: Various artists / Search for Jenny: Various artists / Bozo Barrett: Various artists / Skating in Central Park: Various artists / Long walk home, The: Various artists / Concerto No.3 in D major: Various artists / Love story finale, Theme from: Various artists.
LP: MCL 1782
MC: MCLC 1782
LP: MCA 27017
MC: MCAC 27017

LOVE STORY (ORIGINAL ISSUE) (Film Soundtrack) (Various artists).
LP: . . . . SPFL 267

Love Symphony

PENTHOUSE.
LP: . . . . MLP 3003

Love The Reason...

LOVE THE REASON (Various artists).
LP: . . . . RRL 501
MC: . . . . RRC 501

Love, Timothy

DANCE AND REMEMBER CHARLIE KUNZ.
Tracks: / Pink elephants / You're dancing on my heart / Dear hearts and gentle people / You're adorable / It's only a paper moon / Roaming in the gloaming / You are my sunshine / Ain't she sweet / I Remember you / All alone / Beautiful dreamer / Shadow of your smile / Melody in f / Tea for two / I'm in the mood for love / English country garden / Memories / Maria / My Thanks to you / It's a sin to tell a lie / Sally.
LP: . . . . SUS 514
MC: . . . . CSUS 514

DANCING WITH LOVE.
Tracks: / Run rabbit run ((Foxtrot)) / Silver threads among the gold ((Foxtrot)) / Only your love ((Waltz)) / Till we meet again ((Waltz)) / Dream of Olwen ((Rumba)) / Tango d'more ((Tango)) / Honeysuckle and the bee, The ((Two step)) / sleepy time down south / By the fireside.
LP: . . . . SUS 521

Love Tractor

THIS AIN'T NO OUTER SPACE SHIP.
Tracks: / Cartoon kiddies / Small town / Chilli part two / Night club scene / Outside with ma / Rudolf Nureyev / Beatle boots / Amusement park / Party train / We all loved each other so much.
LP: . . . . ZL 71273
MC: . . . . ZK 71273

WHEEL OF PLEASURE.
Tracks: / Neon lights / March / Jeb Pharoah's / Fun to be happy / Highland sweetheart / Spin your partner / Wheel of pleasure / Chilly damn willy / Slum dungeon / Seventeen days / Paint / Timerbland.
LP: . . . . DB 74

Love Train (group)

HUMAN FEELINGS RETURN.
Tracks: / Way of all flesh, The / Night thoughts / Torch you carry, The / Rags to riches to rags / Big Mo's battleship / Bigger fool / Old flame / Lighten up / Fields of flowers / Straight sex / Portrait of St Sezni (Only on CD.).
LP: . . . . SRNLP 23
MC: . . . . SRNMC 23

Love Unlimited

LOVE IS BACK.
Tracks: / I'm so glad that I'm a woman / High steppin', hip dressin fella... / When I'm in your arms / If you want me say it / I'm giving you a love (man is searching for) / Gotta be where you are / I'm his woman.
LP: . . . . JZ 36130
LP: . . . . JA 36130
LP: . . . . ULG 83790

LOVE UNLIMITED.
Tracks: / I should have known / Are you sure / Is it really true boy / If this world were mine / Another chance / Fragile - handle with care / I'll be yours forever more / Walking in the rain with the one I love.
LP: . . . . MCL 1877
MC: . . . . MCLC 1877

Love, Willie

SHOUT BROTHER SHOUT.
LP: . . . . OL 2825

Love You Till Tuesday

LOVE YOU TILL TUESDAY (See under Bowie, David).

Lovebug Starski

HOUSE ROCKER.
Tracks: / House rocker / Positive life / Baby tell me / Amityville (house on the hill) / Saturday night / Say what you wanna say / Eighth wonder.
LP: . . . . EPC 26878
MC: 40 26878

Loved One

LOCATE AND CEMENT.
LP: . . . . M 1

Loved Ones

MAGIC BOX.
LP: . . . . RVLP 23

Loveless

TALES FROM THE GRAVE.
MC: . . . . FC 07

Loveless, Patty

HONKY TONK ANGEL.
LP: . . . . MCA 42223
MC: . . . . MCAC 42223

IF MY HEART HAD WINDOWS.
LP: . . . . IMCA 42092
MC: . . . . IMCAC 42092

ON DOWN THE LINE.
Tracks: / Overtime / Night's too long, The / Blue memories / Some morning soon / You can't run away from your heart / On down the line / I've got to stop loving you (and start living) / Looking in the eyes of love / I'm that kind of girl / Feelings of love.
LP: . . . . MCA 6401
MC: . . . . MCAC 6401

PATTY LOVELESS.
Tracks: / Lonely days, lonely nights / I did / You are everything / Blue is not a word / Slow healing heart / After all / Wicked ways / Half over you / Some blue moons ago / Sounds of Loneliness.
LP: . . . . MCF 3359
MC: . . . . MCFC 3359

Lovelight

ACTIVATE.
LP: . . . . DAY R 4035
MC: . . . . DAY C 4035

LOVELIGHT.
LP: . . . . DAY R 4034
MC: . . . . DAY C 4034

SING PRAISES.
Tracks: / Morning noon and night / When morning gilds the skies / Heaven came down / I want to praise you Lord / Day thou gavest, Lord is ended, The.
MC: . . . . DAY C 4033

Lovely To Look At

LOVELY TO LOOK AT/SUMMER STOCK (Original Soundtrack) (Various artists).
LP: . . . . MCA 39084
MC: . . . . MCAC 39084

Lover Boy

BIG ONES.
Tracks: / Working for the weekend / For you / Kid is hot tonite, The / Lovin' every minute of it / Lucky ones / This could be the night / Hot girls in love / Turn me loose / Too hot / Ain't looking for love / Notorious / Take me to the top.
LP: 4660061
MC: 4660064

GET LUCKY.
Tracks: / Working for the weekend / When it's over / Jump / Gangs in the street / Emotional / Lucky ones / It's your life / Watch out / Take me to the top.
LP: . . . . CBS 85402
MC: 40 85402

KEEP IT UP.
LP: . . . . CBS 25436
MC: 40 25436

LOVERBOY.
Tracks: / Kid is hot tonite, The / Turn me loose / Always on my mind / Lady of the 80's / Little girl / Prissy prissy / Teenage overdose / DOA / It don't matter.
LP: . . . . CBS 84798

LOVING EVERY MINUTE OF IT.
Tracks: / Loving every minute of it / Steal the thunder / Friday night / This could be the night / Too much too soon / Lead a double life / Dangerous / Destination heartbreak / Bullet in the chamber.
LP: . . . . CBS 26573

WILDSIDE.
Tracks: / Notorious / Walkin' on fire / Break it to me gently / Love will rise again / Can't get much better / Home town hero / Don't let go / That's where my money goes / Read my lips.
LP: 4600451
MC: 4600454

Lover Speaks

LOVER SPEAKS,THE.
Tracks: / Every lover's sign / No more "I love you's" / Never to forget you / Face me and smile / Absent one / Love is: "I gave you everything" / This can't go on / Still faking this art of love / Tremble dancing / Of tears.
LP: . . . . AMA 5127
MC: . . . . AMC 5127

Lovers For Lovers

LOVERS FOR LOVERS VOL.3 (Various artists).
LP: . . . . WBRLP 903

LOVERS FOR LOVERS VOL 1.
LP: . . . . BRLP 901

Lovers in Paradise

LOVERS IN PARADISE (Barbara Cartland).
MC: . . . . IAB 88063

Lovers (various)

LOVERS (Various artists).
Tracks: / On my own: *Labelle, Patti & Michael McDonald* / Captain of her heart, The: *Double* / Your latest trick: *Dire Straits* / Holding back the years: *Simply Red* / In the midnight hour: *Roxy Music* / Every time you go away: *Young, Paul* / Power of love, The: *Rush, Jennifer* / True: *Spandau Ballet* / Nikita: *John, Elton* / Drive: *Cars* / Why can't we live together: *Sade* / Fatal hesitation: *De Burgh, Chris* / I want to wake up with you: *Gardiner, Boris* / There'll be sad songs: *Ocean, Billy* / Have you ever had it blue: *Style Council* / Greatest love of all, The: *Houston, Whitney.*
LP: . . . . STAR 2279
MC: . . . . STAC 2279

Love's Labour's Lost

LOVE'S LABOUR'S LOST (see Shakespeare, William) (Various artists).

Lovesey, Peter

ABRACADAVER - A SERGEANT CRIBB MYSTERY (See under Abracadaver... (bk).

DETECTIVE WORE SILK DRAWERS, THE (Melling, John Kennedy).
MC: . . . . CAB 338

Loveslug

SLUG 'EM ALL.
LP: . . . . EFA 4471

SNAILHOUSE ROCK.
LP: . . . . EFA 4480

Lovesmith, Michael

I CAN MAKE IT HAPPEN.
Tracks: / He only looks the part / Sorry won't get it / She's trouble / Promise is a promise / What's the bottom line / I can make it happen for you / Baby i will / Even as we speak / Just say the word / I can make it happen for you.
LP: . . . . STML 12192
MC: . . . . CSTML 12192

RHYMES OF PASSION.
Tracks: / I'm good at it / Cover girl / Break the ice / You ain't been loved yet / Love in the combat zone / Temporary insanity / Haunted heart / Ain't nothin' like it / We both will have to bend / Raider of the heart.
LP: . . . . ZL 72376
MC: . . . . ZK 72376

Lovett, Eddie

ALL FOR YOU.
LP: . . . . PKL 1985

MERRY CHRISTMAS.
LP: . . . . PKL 1984

ROCKERS FOR LOVERS.
Tracks: / Shining star / Can't you tell it's me / Do that to me one more time / Hold me tight / Sail on / Just one look / Mr. Sea / Imagination.
LP: . . . . KRLP 3001
MC: . . . . KRK 3001

TRUE EXPERIENCE, A.
Tracks: / 2 experience / Red red wine / Lover's melody / Greatest love of all, The / Soca sever / Lady in red, The / Unchained melody / Two way street.
LP: . . . . PKL 1987106

Lovett, Lyle

COWBOY MAN.
Tracks: / Cowboy man / God will / Farther down the line / This old porch / Why I don't know / If I weren't the man you wanted / You can't resist it / Waltzing fool / Acceptable level of ecstasy, An (The wedding song) / Closing time.
LP: . . . . MCF 3361
MC: . . . . MCFC 3361

LYLE LOVETT AND HIS LARGE BAND.
Tracks: / Here I am / I know you know / I married her just because she looks / Once is enough / Stand by your man / Crying shame / What do you do / Nobody knows me / Which way does that old pony run / If you were to wake up.
LP: . . . . MCG 6037
MC: . . . . MCGC 6037

PONTIAC.
Tracks: / If I had a boat / I loved you yesterday / L.A. country / M-O-N-E-Y / Simple song / She's hot to go / Give back my heart / Walk through the bottomland / She's no lady / Black and blue / Pontiac.
LP: . . . . MCF 3389
MC: . . . . MCFC 3389

Lovich, Lene

FLEX.
LP: . . . . SEEZ 19

NO MAN'S LAND.
Tracks: / It's you only you (mein schmerz) / Blue hotel / Faces / Walking low / Special star / Sister video / Maria / Savages / Rocky road.
LP: . . . . SEEZ 44
MC: . . . . ZSEEZ 44

STATELESS.
LP: . . . . SEEZ 7

Lovin' Spoonful

20 GREATEST HITS: LOVIN' SPOONFUL.
LP: 2615301
MC: 2615304

BEST IN THE WEST.
Tracks: / Daydream / Did you ever have to make up your mind / Darling be home soon / Nashville cats / Summer in the city / Rain on the roof / Do you believe in magic / You didn't have to be so nice.
LP: . . . . DOW 9
MC: . . . . ZCDOW 9

BEST OF LOVIN' SPOONFUL.
LP: 6.24713

COLLECTION: LOVIN' SPOONFUL 20 Hits.
Tracks: / Do you believe in magic / Did you ever have to make up your mind? / Younger girl / Jug band music / Didn't want to have to do it / Daydream / You're a big boy now / Wash her away / Girl beautiful girl (Barbara's theme) / Respoken / Darling be home soon / Lookin' to spy / You didn't have to be so nice / Sittin' here lovin' you / Darlin' companion / Rain on the roof / Coconut grove / Nashville cats / Summer in the city / She is still a mystery / Boredom / Six o'clock / Younger generation / Till I run with you / Never goin' back.
LP: . . . . MA 15385
MC: . . . . MAMC 915385
2LP: . . . . CCSLP 187
MC: . . . . CCSMC 187

DAYDREAM.
LP: . . . . NPL 28078
LP: . . . . CLALP 194
MC: . . . . CLAMC 194

DO YOU BELIEVE IN MAGIC/ EVERYTHING PLAYING.
2LP: . . . . TFOLP 12
MC: . . . . TFOMC 12

EP COLLECTION, THE: LOVIN' SPOONFUL.
Tracks: / Did you ever.. / Day blues / Blues in the bottle / There she is / Younger girl / Other side of this life / Sporting life / Fishin' blues / Jugband music / Loving you / Let the boy rock 'n' roll / Eyes / You baby / Butchie's tune / Wild about my... / Voodoo in my basement / It's not time now / Didn't want to have to do it / Coconut grove / Do you believe in music.
LP: . . . . SEE 229
MC: . . . . SEEK 229

GOLDEN HOUR OF THE LOVIN' SPOONFUL.
Tracks: / Do you believe in magic / Summer in the city / Rain on the roof / Wild about my lovin' / Money / Jug band music / Nashville cats / You're a big boy now / Anymore / Other side of this life / Coconut grove / Did you ever have to make up your mind / Daydream / Night owl blues / She is still a mystery / Blues in a bottle / Six o clock / Darling be home soon / Didn't want to have to do it / Never going back to Nashville / Darlin' companion / You didn't have to be so nice / Younger generation.
MC: . . . . KGHMC 109

GREATEST HITS:LOVIN' SPOONFUL.
Tracks: / Do you believe in magic / You didn't have to be so nice / Did you ever have to make up your mind / Daydream / Didn't want to have to do it / Younger girl / Summer in the city / Six O'clock / Darling be home soon / She is still a mystery / Rain on the roof / Nashville cats / You're a big boy now / Younger generation.
LP: 252 274 1
MC: 252 274 4

HUMS OF....
LP: . . . . CLALP 193
MC: . . . . CLAMC 193

JUG BAND MUSIC.
LP: . . . . ED 178

NASHVILLE CATS.
Tracks: / Nashville cats.
LP: . . . . KAS 204

VERY BEST OF LOVIN' SPOONFUL.
LP: . . . . BRLP 22
MC: . . . . BRMC 22

Lovindeer

AM A HURTING YOU HONEY.
LP: . . . . TSOJ 1948

CARIBBEAN CHRISTMAS.
LP: . . . . DSR 1054

DISCO REGGAE JAM.
LP: . . . . Unknown

GOVERNMENT BOOPS.
Tracks: / What one boops can do / Government boops / Political boops / Boopsie jam session / Babylon boops / Dear boopsie / From boopsie with love / Parson boops.
LP: . . . . TSOJ 120

KRATCHES.
LP: . . . . TSOJ 325

SOCA NIGHTS.
LP: . . . . TSOJ 121

Loving Awareness

LOVING AWARENESS.
LP: . . . . Unknown

Loving Couples

LOVING COUPLES (Original Soundtrack) (Various artists).
LP: . . . . MB 949 M1
MC: . . . . MB 949 KC

Loving Sisters

NEGRO SPIRITUALS/GOSPEL SONGS.
LP: . . . . VG 400609

Loving You

LOVING YOU (See under Presley, Elvis) (Film soundtrack) (Presley, Elvis).

Low, Bruce

SEINE SCHONSTEN LIEDER.
Tracks: / Leise rauscht es am Missouri / Fahr auf dem zigeunerwagen / Ol' man river / Beautiful dreamer / Wenn mademoiselle dich kusst / Was willst du mehr, cherie / Tennessee waltz / Der sudwind der weht / Kleiner cowboy du musst reiten / Ein zigeuner ist mein herz / Die nacht ist voller zartichkeit / Wenn der herrgott net will.
LP: . . . . V 130 004

Low, David

DANCING FEET.
MC: . . . . CJW 003

DANCING FEET VOL.2.
MC: . . . . CJW 008

Low Flying Aircraft

LOW FLYING AIRCRAFT.
Tracks: / Sybilization / Fourth dimension / Baptism by fire / Poolside / Abstract blue / Moronathon / Amnesia / Reflection / What did you do / Radically conservative.
LP: . . . . R 101

Low Max

LOW MAX.
LP: . . . . EFAML 044

Low Meato

LOW MEATO.
LP: . . . . PIG 002

Lowe, Arthur

DIARY OF A NOBODY, THE (See also G & W Grossmith).

PIGWIG PAPERS.
MC: . . . . VCA 098

Lowe, Frank

EXOTIC HEARTBREAK (Lowe, Frank Quintet).
LP: . . . . SN 1032

FLAM, THE.
LP: . . . . BSR 005

FRESH.
Tracks: / Epistrophy / Play some blues / Fresh / Mysterioso / Chu's blues.
LP: . . . . FLP 41015

Lowe, Jez

BAD PENNY.
Tracks: / Another man's wife / Small coal song, A / Midnight mail / Dandelion clocks / Land of the living / Nearer to Nettles / Father Mallory's dance / Yankee boots / New town incident, A.
LP: . . . . FE 070
MC: . . . . FE 070C

GALLOWAYS.
Tracks: / Back in Durham Gaol / Galloway lad, The / Gatineau girls / Boys of belly row, The / Northern echoes / Galloways / Old bones / Shippersea bay / Honest working way, The / Chick Henderson's march.
LP: . . . . FE 049
MC: . . . . FE 049 C

JEZ LOWE.
Tracks: / Sedgefield fair / Roxburgh castle / Pit boy / Willy's lyke wake / Dark shores, The / Johnny Seddon / Beaumont's light house / Poor old wedgebury / Fill the tankard / Kildale jig / Head of wear water, The / Pretty saro / Wheel of fortune.
LP: . . . . FE 023
MC: . . . . FE 023 C

OLD DURHAM ROAD, THE.
Tracks: / Old Durham waltz, The / Hard life / Cursed be the caller / My keel lad / Mary Martindale / Annie Munro / High part of the town / I'll never get home / Foggy banks / Black diamond / Old Durham road, The.
LP: . . . . FE 034

TWO A ROUE (Lowe, Jez & Jake Walton).
Tracks: / Patrick's song / Brockie lads / Todd's dance / Monferrina / Trees / Japs and English / Reign of the fair maid / Galecian dances / Bergen, The / Rothbury races / Morpeth lasses / Gold and silver / Ballad of Johnny Collier.
LP: . . . . FE 055
MC: . . . . FE 055C

Lowe, Jim

ROCK A CHICKS.
LP: . . . . DLP 1002

Lowe, Mundell

GUITAR MOODS.
Tracks: / Speak low / We'll be together again / Memories of you / Ill wind / You don't know what love is / I dream too much / June in January / I'll take romance / It's so peaceful in the country / Our waltz / I'm old fashioned / Goodbye.
LP: . . . . RLP 208

PORGY & BESS (Lowe, Mundell Jazzmen).
LP: . . . . PL 43552

TV ACTION JAZZ (Lowe, Mundell All Stars).
LP: . . . . FS 179

Lowe, Nick

16 ALL-TIME LOWES.
Tracks: / American squirm / Big kick plain scrap / Born fighter / Cruel to be kind / Heart of the city / I love the sound of breaking glass / Little Hitler / Marie Provost / Nutted by reality / Skin deep so it goes / Switchboard Susan / They called it rock / When I write the book / Without love.
LP: . . . . FIEND 20
MC: . . . . FIENDCASS 20

ABOMINABLE SHOWMAN.
Tracks: / Wish you were here / Paid the price / Saint beneath the paint / Time wounds all heals / Tanque-Rae / Around with love / Cool reaction / Chicken and feathers / We want action / Ragin' eyes / How do you talk to an angel / Man or a fall.
LP: . . . . XXLP 18

BASHER: THE BEST OF NICK LOWE.
Tracks: / So it goes / Heart of the city / I love the sound of breaking glass / Little Hitler / No reason / 36 inches high / Marie Provost / Nutted by reality / American squirm / Peace, love & understanding / Cracking up / Big kick, plain scrap / Born fighter / Switchboard Susan / Without love / Love so fine / Cruel to be kind / When I write the book / Heart / Stick it where the sun don't shine / Ragin' eyes / Time wounds all heels / Tanque-rae / Maureen / Half a boy and half a man / Breakaway / She don't love nobody / 7 nights to rock / Long walk back / Rose of England / I knew the bride (when she used to rock 'n' roll) / Lovers jamboree.
2LP: . . . . DFIEND 142
MC: . . . . FIENDCASS 142

I LIKE YOU I DON'T LOVE YOU (See under Gomm, Ian for details) (Lowe, Nick/Ian Gomm).

JESUS OF COOL.
Tracks: / Music for money / I love the sound of breaking glass / Little Hitler / Shake and pop / Tonight / So it goes / No reason / 36" high / Marie Provost / Nutted by reality / Heart of the city.
LP: . . . . FIEND 131
MC: . . . . FIENDCASS 131
MC: . . . . RAC 1
LP: . . . . RAD 1

LABOUR OF LUST.
Tracks: / Cruel to be kind / Cracking up / Big kick, plain scrap / Born fighter / You make me / Skin deep / Switchboard Susan / Endless grey ribbon / Without love / Dose of you / Love so fine.
LP: . . . . RAD 21

NICK LOWE AND HIS COWBOY OUTFIT.
Tracks: / Half a boy and half a man / You'll never get me up (in one of those) / Maureen / God's gift to women / Gee and the rick and the three card trick, The / Hey big mouth stand up and say that / Awesome / Breakaway / Love like a glove / Live fast love hard / L.A.F.S..
LP: . . . . ZL 79338
MC: . . . . ZK 79338

NICK THE KNIFE.
Tracks: / Burning / Heart / Stick it where the sun don't shine / Queen of Sheba / My heart hurts / Couldn't love you / Let me kiss ya / Too many teardrops / Ba doom / Raining / One's too many / Zulu kiss.
LP: . . . . XXLP 14

NICK'S NACK.
Tracks: / Ragin' eyes / Dose of you / One's too many (and a hundred ain't enough) / Now and always / Endless grey ribbon / Burning / Wish you were here / Love so fine / Mess around with love / My heart hurts / Basing Street / Raining raining / Stick it where the sun don't shine / 36 inches high / Saint beneath the paint / Let me kiss ya.
LP: . . . . FIEND 59
MC: . . . . FIENDCASS 59

PARTY OF ONE.
LP: . . . . WX 337
MC: . . . . WX 337 C

PINKER & PROUDER THAN PREVIOUS.
Tracks: / (You're my) wildest dream / Crying in my sleep / Big hair / Love gets strange / Black Lincoln Continental / Cry it out / Lover's jamboree / Geisha girl / Wishing well / Big big love.
LP: . . . . FIEND 99
MC: . . . . FIENDCASS 99

ROSE OF ENGLAND.
Tracks: / I knew the bride / Indoor fireworks / I'm right / I can be the one you love / Everyone / Bob Skaddidle daddle / Darlin' angel eyes / She don't love nobody / 7 nights to rock / Long walk back / Rose of England / Lucky dog.
LP: . . . . ZL 70765
MC: . . . . ZK 70765

ROSE OF ENGLAND (RE-ISSUE).
Tracks: / I knew the bride / Long walk back / I'm right / Bo bo skediddle / Darlin' angel eyes / She don't love nobody / Rock / Indoor fireworks / I can be the one you love.
LP: . . . . FIEND 73
MC: . . . . FIENDCASS 73

Lowell, Robert

ROBERT LOWELL: A READING.
MC: 1569

Lowery, Ian

KING BLANK TO.. (Lowery, Ian Group).
Tracks: / Need / Sick little minds / Beach fire / One last blast / Kind of loathing, A / You're gonna pay / Party, The / Driver's arrived.
LP: . . . . SITU 24
MC: . . . . SITU 24 C

Lowlife

DIMINUENDO.
LP: . . . . LOLIF 004

FROM A SCREAM TO A WHISPER.
LP: . . . . LOLIF 7

GODHEAD.
LP: . . . . LOLIF 8

PERMANENT SLEEP.
LP: . . . . LOLIF 002

RAIN.
LP: . . . . LOLIF 1

SAN ANTONIUM.
LP: . . . . LOLIF 9

Lowrell

LOWRELL.
Tracks: / Out of breath / You're playing dirty / Overdose / Mellow mellow right on / Smooth and wild.
LP: . . . . AVLP 504

Loxam, Arnold

AT HOME AT THE TOWER.
LP: . . . . GRS 1161

HAPPY CHRISTMAS FROM THE TOWER.
MC: . . . . KGRS 1199

Loy, Myrna

I PRESS MY LIPS.
LP: . . . . NORMAL 108

Loyoyo

EXTRA WEAPONS.
LP: . . . . FLOP 1

L.T.D.

DEVOTION.
Tracks: / One by one / Share my love / Stand up to L.T.D. / Say that you'll be mine / Dance 'n' sing 'n' / Sometimes / Promise you'll stay / Stranger / Feel it.
LP: . . . . AMLH 64771

LOVE TO THE WORLD.
LP: . . . . AMLH 64589

SHINE ON.
Tracks: / You gave me love / Where did we go wrong / Getaway / Will love grow / Love is what you need / Shine on / Lovers everywhere / Lady love / Don'tcha know.
LP: . . . . AMLH 64819

SOMETHING TO LOVE.
LP: . . . . AMLH 64646

TOGETHERNESS.
LP: . . . . AMLH 64705

L'Trimm

GRAB IT.
Tracks: / Grab it / Better yet l'trimm / We can rock that beat / Sexy / Cutie pie / He's a mutt / Don't come to my house / Cars with the boom.
LP: . . . . K 781 925 1
MC: . . . . K 781 925 4

Luba

ALL OR NOTHING.
Tracks: / Wild heart / On my way / Giving away a miracle / No more words / As good as it gets / Too much of a good thing / Little salvation / In trouble again / Milena / Promise me anything / Bringing it all back home.
LP: . . . . EST 2127
MC: . . . . TCEST 2127

Lubich, Warren

ON THE AVENUE.
LP: . . . . DO 1410

WURLITZER ORGAN CALIFORNIA USA.
LP: . . . . DO 1419

Lucas, Carrie

IN DANCELAND.
Tracks: / Danceland / Sometimes a love goes wrong / Are you dancing? / Dance with you / I'm gonna make you happy / Southern star.
LP: . . . . FL 13219

PORTRAIT OF CARRIE.
Tracks: / It's not what you've got / Lovin' is on my mind / Career girl / Use it or lose it / Fashion / Just a memory / Keep smiling.
LP: . . . . SOLA 5

STILL IN LOVE.
Tracks: / Show me where your coming from / Sweet love / Men / Is it a dream / Rockin' for your love / Dreamer / I just can't do without your love / Still in love.
LP: . . . . K 52400

STREET CORNER SYMPHONY.
Tracks: / Street corner symphony / Stand by me / Duke of Earl / Raindrops / Licking stick, licking stick / Dancing in the street / My girl / Way you do the things you do, The / Sherry / My guy / But my heart says no / Tic toc / Depths of my soul, The / Edge of night, The / Questions / Simpler days / Reflections.
LP: . . . . FL 12773
MC: . . . . FK 12773

Lucas, "Lazy" Bill

LAZY BILL LUCAS.
LP: . . . . PH 1007

Lucas, Matt

RIDE THAT TRAIN TONIGHT (17 tracks recorded 1959-65 and 70-75).
Tracks: / Ooby dooby / Put me down / My heavenly angel / Water mocccasin / Maybellene / Tradin' kisses / No one like you / Turn on your lovelight / I'm movin' on / Motor city twine, The / Massage parlour blues / I'm so thankful / Zoo blues / You gotta love / Newspaper man blues / Peepin' Tom blues / I need your lovin'.
LP: . . . . CR 30222

Lucas, Nick

SINGING TROUBADOUR, THE.
Tracks: / You're driving me crazy / Go fly a kite / Cup of coffee, a sandwich and you, A / Evening in Caroline, An / Man with the mandolin, The / Singin' in the rain / Oh Mabel / I might have known / Looking at the world through rose coloured glasses / Over the rainbow / Good morning / Painting the clouds with sunshine / Your mother and mine / Man and his dream, A / Siboney / Apple for teacher, An / Bye, bye blackbird / My bundle of love / I've got the girl / Goodnight sweetheart.
LP: . . . . AJA 5022
MC: . . . . ZC AJA 5022

Lucas, Robin

FAVOURITE STORIES OF JESUS.
MC: . . . . BBM 116

LITTLE GINGERBREAD MAN, THE (Lucas, Robin Childrens Theatre).
MC: . . . . BBM 118

Luce, William

CURRER BELL, ESQ. (A solo portrait of Charlotte Bronte).
MCSET: 371

Lucia, Paco De

CASTRO MARIN.
LP: 6301 025
MC: 7124 025

ENTRE DOS AGUAS.
LP: 814 106 1
MC: 814 106 4

FABULOUS GUITAR OF PACO DE LUCIA.

Tracks: / Entre dos aguas / Tico tico / Monasterio de sal / Montino / Punta del faro / Danza / Solo quiero caminar / El vito / Rio ancho / Castro marin.
LP: 818 145 1
MC: 818 145 4

HIT SOUNDTRACK, THE.
LP: 822 720-1
MC: 822 720-4

MOTIVE SERIES.
LP: 6358 085
MC: 7166 085

Lucie, Lawrence

MIXED EMOTIONS (Lucie, Lawrence (Larry)).
LP: . . . . TOY 1006

THIS IS IT (Lucie, Lawrence (Larry)).
LP: . . . . TOY 1005

Lucifer's Friend

SNEAK ME IN.
Tracks: / Goodbye girls / Sneak me in / Foxy lady / Love hymn / Stardancer / Indian Summer / Don't you know what I like / Cosmic crusader.
LP: . . . . K 52203

Luckhurst, Reg

YOUR CHEATIN' HEART.
LP: . . . . RC 511

Luckhurts, Lucky

LONDON LIFE VOL.1.
MC: 45 131

LONDON LIFE VOL.2.
MC: 60-132

LONDON MUSIC HALL.
MC: 45 405

Luckley, Stu

NOWT SO GOOD'LL PASS (See Fox, Bob) (Luckley, Stu & Bob Fox).

WISH WE NEVER HAD PARTED (See Fox, Bob) (Luckley, Stu & Bob Fox).

Lucky & Flash

EARLY MORNING BLUES (see under Washboard Doc) (Lucky & Flash/ Washboard Doc).

Lucky Grills

BEST OF AUSTRALIAN HUMOUR, VOL.1.
MC: . . . . PLAC 471

BEST OF AUSTRALIAN HUMOUR, VOL.2.
MC: . . . . PLAC 472

BEST OF AUSTRALIAN HUMOUR, VOL.3.
MC: . . . . PLAC 473

Lucky Jim (bk)

LUCKY JIM (Kingsley Amis) (Courtenay, Tom (nar)).
MC: 0600560562

Lucky Luke

LUCKY LUKE (Film Soundtrack) (Various artists).
Tracks: / I'm a poor lonesome cowboy (Lucky Luke theme): *Various artists* / Lucky Luke special: *Various artists*/ Daisy town theme: *Various artists* / Town comes to life: *Various artists* / Daisy town saloon song: *Various* artists / Way West: *Various artists* / Daisy town march: *Various artists* / Dalton theme: *Various artists*/ Stamp your feet: *Various artists* / Duel: *Various artists* / Far West choo choo: *Various artists* / City life: *Various artists* / Battle: *Various artists* / I'm a poor lonesome cowboy (Lucky Luke theme): *Various artists.*
LP: . . . . UAS 29290

Lucky Seven

GET LUCKY.
Tracks: / Rosalie / Cajun man / It's only love / Rock & roll radio / Come to me / Don't know why / Big bayou / Little too dear / Call, The / I love you so / Only a hobo.
LP: KIX4U 3339
LP: . . . . ROCK 3339

Lucky Strikers

DON'T YOU POINT THAT GUN AT ME.
LP: 082880

Lucraft, Howard

SHOWCASE FOR MODERN JAZZ.
LP: . . . . FS 230

Lucy

REALLY GOT ME GOIN'.
LP: . . . . BCS 8

Lucy Show

MANIA.
Tracks: / Land and the life / View from the outside / Sojourn's end / Sad September / Million things / Sun & moon / Shame / Melody / Part of me now / New message.
LP: . . . . ZL 71724
MC: . . . . ZK 71724

UNDONE.
Tracks: / Ephemeral / Resistance / Come back to the living / White space / Wipe out / Twister / Undone / Remain / Better on the hard side / Dream days.
LP: . . . . AMA 5088
MC: . . . . AMC 5088

Ludichrist

IMMACULATE DECEPTION.
LP: . . . . WEBITE 34
LP: 081270

POWERTRIP.
LP: . . . . WEBITE 35
LP: 88561-8246-1

Ludlum, Robert

BOURNE IDENTITY, THE.
MCSET: . . . . unknown

Ludovico's Technique

LUDOVICO'S TECHNIQUE.
LP: . . . . ROSE 54

Ludus

COMPLETEMENT NUE AU SOLEIL.
LP: . . . . IM 013

Ludwig, Gene

NOW'S THE TIME.
LP: . . . . MR 5164

Luellen, Valentina

CASTLE OF THE MIST (see under Castle of the Mist (bk)) (Boyd, Carole (nar)).

Luiser, Rene

NOUS AUTRE (See Frith, Fred) (Luiser, Rene/Fred Frith).

Lukatch, Maria

RUSSIAN POPULAR SONGS.
MC: . . . . SM 00372

Lukather, Steve

LUKATHER.
Tracks: / Twist the knife / Swear your love / Fall into velvet / Drive a crooked road / Got my way / Darkest night of the year / Lonely beat of my heart / With a second chance / Turns to stone / It looks like rain / Steppin' on top of your world.
LP: 4656571
MC: 4656574

Luke, Robin

SUSIE DARLIN'.
Tracks: / Well oh well oh (don't you know) / Everlovin' / Five minutes more / You can't stop me from dreaming / Who's gonna hold your hand / Susie darlin' / Part of a fool / Poor little rich boy / So alone / All because of you / Make me a dreamer / Walkin' in the moonlight / My girl / Chicka chicka honey / School bus love affair / Strollin' blues.
LP: . . . . BFX 15022

SUSIE DARLIN' (OLD GOLD) (See under Danny & The Juniors/At the hop).

Lul

HAIL THE FRISIANS FREE.
LP: . . . . SCH 9013

INSIDE LITTLE ORAL ANNIE.
LP: . . . . EKSAKT 036

Lull & Others

LULL & OTHERS Saki (Burden, Hugh (nar)).
MC: . . . . SA 3

Lullababy

LULLABABY SOOTHING TAPE (Various artists).
MC: . . . . ZCLUL 1

Lullaby of Broadway

LULLABY OF BROADWAY (Various artists).
Tracks: / Lullaby of Broadway: *Various artists* / I found a million dollar baby: *Various artists* / Dancing in the dark: *Various artists* / You're the cream in my coffee: *Various artists* / Body and soul: *Various artists*/ Exactly like you: *Various artists* / Broadway melody: *Various artists* / Black bottom: *Various artists*/ Sleepy time girl: *Various artists* / It had to be you: *Various artists* / I'm just wild about Harry: *Various* artists / September song: *Various artists* / Chinatown my chinatown: *Various artists* / San Francisco: *Various artists.*
LP: . . . . MTLP 1009

Lulu

DON'T TAKE LOVE FOR GRANTED.
Tracks: / Bye bye now my sweet love / Come see what love / Don't take love for granted / Fool, fool / He's so in love / I could never miss you (more than I do) / I love to boogie / Love is the sweetest mistake / Nice and slow / You are still a part of me.
LP: . . . . TRAIN 8

I'M A TIGER.
Tracks: / I'm a tiger / Day tripper / Morning dew / Me the peaceful heart / Rattler / Boy / Take me in your arms and love me / Love loves to love love / Bet ya / Look out / Boom bang a bang / Best of both worlds / Sad memories / Let's pretend / March / Dreary days and nights / To sir with love / Boat that I row, The / To love somebody (CD only.) / You and I (CD only.) / Can't go on (CD only.) / Are you ready for love (CD only.).
LP: . . . . MFP 5848
MC: . . . . TCMFP 5848

LULU.
Tracks: / I could never miss you (more than I do) / Last time, The / If I were you / Loving you / Can't hold out on love / You win, I lose / Don't take love for granted / Who's foolin' who / You are still a part of me / If you're right.
LP: . . . . ALF 85388

MAN WHO SOLD THE WORLD.
LP: . . . . CHELV 1004
MC: . . . . CHELC 1004

MOST OF LULU, THE.
LP: . . . . MFP 5215

SHOUT.
LP: . . . . TAB 70
MC: . . . . KTBC 70

TAKE ME TO YOUR HEART AGAIN.
Tracks: / I will do it for your love / Nobody needs your love more than I do / You had to be there / Go now / I don't go shopping / Let her go / You're working nights now / If you steal my heart away / How can I believe you / Take me to your heart again.
LP: . . . . ALF 85628

Luman, Bob

BOB LUMAN ROCKS.
Tracks: / Let's think about living / My baby walks all over me / Class of 59 / Buttercup / Dreamy doll / You win again / Great snowman, The / Meet Mr.Mud / Hey Joe / Louisiana man / Fool / Private eye / Why why bye bye / You've got everything.
LP: . . . . DJM 22057

CARNIVAL ROCK.
Tracks: / Try me / Everbody's talkin' / Precious / I know my baby cares / Svengali / Chain of love / Lover's prayer / Carnival rock (This is the night) / Carnival rock (instrumental) / All night long / Saving it for you / Yes dear, there's a Virginia / So happy for you / Something special / Almost persuaded / Night without end / Love stay away from me.
LP: . . . . BFX 15345

LET'S THINK ABOUT LIVING.
Tracks: / Still loving you / Oh lonesome me / Hey Joe / Bad bad day / Louisiana man / Interstate forty / I love you because / Go on home boy / Great snowman, The / Jealous heart / You win again / Let's think about living.
LP: . . . . SDLP 1013
LP: . . . . WM 4025
MC: . . . . SDC 1013

LORETTA.
Tracks: / Loretta / It's a sin / If you don't love me / Love worked a miracle / Poor boy blues / Sentimental / You're welcome / Running scared / Freedom of living / Tears from out of nowhere / It's all over / Best years of my wife, The / Bigger man than I / Too hot to dance / I like your kind of love / Hardly anymore.
LP: . . . . SDLP 068

MORE OF THAT ROCKER.
Tracks: / Let's think about living / Boom boom boom yippy yi ya ((Previously unissued)) / Envy / Hey Joe / You've got everything / Love creator ((Previously unissued)) / Louisiana man / Fool, The / My baby walks all over me / Old friends / Big river rose / Throwing kisses / Great snowman, The / Pig latin song / Oh lonesome me / Bad bad day.
LP: . . . . BFX 15039

MORE ROCK-A-BILLY ROCK (Luman, Bob & Friends).
Tracks: / That's alright / Hello baby / In the deep dark jungle / Let 'er go / Meaner than an alligator / Sorry I'll never let you go / Run run run / So wild / Lover lover / That cat / Crazy about you baby / Grinding / Big boy rock / Saturday jump.
LP: . . . . WLP 8828

ROCKER, THE.
Tracks: / Loretta ((Previously unissued)) / I love you because / Private eye / Everytime the world goes round / Buttercup / Boston rocker / Why why bye bye / Meet Mister Mud / Class of 59 / You're like a stranger in my arms ((Previously unissued)) / Dreamy doll / You've turned down the lights / You're everything / Belonging to you / I love you so much it hurts / Rocks of Reno, The.
LP: . . . . BFX 15037

STILL ROCKIN'.
Tracks: / Lonely road* (Previously unissued.) / I'm gonna write a song about you / (Empty walls) A lonely room / Freedom of living / Run on home, baby brother / Fire engine red / (I can't get you) Off my mind / Interstate forty / File, The / Old George Dickel / Go on home boy / Five miles from home / Come on and sing / You can't take the country from the boy / Jealous heart* / You win again*.
LP: . . . . BFX 15140

TRY ME.
LP: . . . . RSRLP 1015

WILD-EYED WOMAN.
Tracks: / Red cadillac and a black moustache (Over-dubbed chorus.) / Whenever you're ready / Black days, blue nights / Your love (Over-dubbed electric guitar.) / Wild-eyed woman / Red cadillac and a black moustache / Your love (1st recording) / Amarillo blues / Red hot / All night long / Your love (undubbed 2nd recording) / Make up your mind / In the deep dark jungle / That's alright / Hello baby / Stranger than fiction / You're the cause of it all / Let her go.
LP: . . . . BFX 15268

Lumba Brothers

OBI ATE MESO BO.
LP: 1964

Lumina Sampler

LUMINA SAMPLER (Various artists).
MC: . . . . LUMCA 6

Lumley, Joanna

TALES OF RUPERT BEAR.
MC: . . . . PTB 616

Luna

SPACE SWELL.
LP: . . . . ARHOOLIE 8001

Luna Twist

LUNA TWIST.
LP: . . . . STAT LP 15

Lunachicks

BABYSITTERS ON ACID.
LP: . . . . BFFP 52
MC: . . . . BFFP 52C

Lunatics Without

WELCOME TO THE ASYLUM.
LP: . . . . AAARRG 21

Lunceford, Jimmie

1940: JIMMIE LUNCEFORD (Lunceford, Jimmie & Orchestra).
LP: . . . . CLP 11

1944: JIMMIE LUNCEFORD (Lunceford, Jimmie & Orchestra).
LP: . . . . CLP 92

COMPLETE, THE.
LP: 66421

FOR DANCERS ONLY (Lunceford, Jimmie & Orchestra).
Tracks: / Close out / Margie / Sit back and relax / Jimmies, The / Four or five times / Call the police / Water faucet / Cement mixer / Them who has gets / Shut out / Jay Gee / I need a lift / Just once too often / One o'clock jump.
LP: . . . . OFF 3043

GOLDEN SWING YEARS, THE (Lunceford, Jimmie & His Orchestra).
LP: . . . . SLP 828

HARLEM SHOUT (Lunceford, Jimmie & Orchestra).
LP: . . . . HEP 1022

JIMMIE LUNCEFORD AND HIS ORCHESTRA (Lunceford, Jimmie & His Orchestra).
Tracks: / Battle axe / Moonlight and music / Morning after, The / I'm waltzing through heaven with you / Annie Laurie / I had a premonition / Blue afterglow / There I go / Like a ship at sea / State and Tioga stomp.
LP: . . . . JAZ 2013
MC: . . . . ZCJAZ 2013

JIMMIE LUNCEFORD AND HIS ORCHESTRA (1935-41) (Lunceford, Jimmie & Orchestra).
Tracks: / Impromptu / By the river Sainte Marie (Vocal:Dan Grissom) / Stratosphere / Annie Laurie / Swanee River / Yard dog Mazurka / Hell's bells / Hi spook / Margie (Vocal: Johnny Young) / Pigeon walk / My blue Heaven / Siesta at the Fiesta.
LP: . . . . JASM 1023

JIMMIE LUNCEFORD & LOUIS PRIMA 1945 (Lunceford, Jimmie/Prima, Louis).
Tracks: / Jeep rhythm / Blues in the night / What to do / Are you kidding baby? / Meditation from Thais / Honeydripper / Robin Hood / Don't ever change / Angelina / St Louis blues / I wonder / Hitsum kitsum.
LP: . . . . AIRCHECK 8

JIMMIE LUNCEFORD & ORCHESTRA 1935-45.
LP: . . . . **SWINGFAN 1009**

JIMMIE LUNCEFORD VOLUME 1.
LP: . . . . **KLJ 20016**

JIMMIE LUNCEFORD VOLUME 2 (Lunceford, Jimmie & His Orchestra).
Tracks: / Impromptu / By the river Sainte Marie / Stratosphere / Annie Laurie / Swanee river / Yard dog Mazurka / Hell's bells / Hi spook / Margie / Pigeon walk / My blue Heaven / Siesta at the fiesta.
LP: . . . . **HEP 1013**

JIMMIE LUNCEFORD-VOL.1 1934 (Lunceford, Jimmie & Orchestra).
LP: . . . . **HEP 1011**

LITTLE JOHN (1945).
LP: . . . . **FH 15**

MASTERPIECES (Lunceford, Jimmie & Orchestra).
LP: . . . . **LPJT 22**

NO TITLE ON FILE (Lunceford, Jimmie Orchestra).
LP: . . . . **BLJ 8006**

OH BOY (Lunceford, Jimmie & Orchestra).
Tracks: / Miss Otis regrets (she's unable to lunch today / Because you're you / Chillun, get up / Shake your head (from side to side) / If I had rain / Rhythm in my nursery rhymes / Since my best gal turned me down / Charmaine / Babs / I'm nuts about screw music / Best things in life are free, The / On the beach at Bali-Bali / Oh boy / Melody man, The / Muddy water (A Mississippi moan) / You take the east,.. I'll take the south.
LP: . . . . **HEP 1017**
LP: . . . . **CHD 132**
MC: . . . . **MCHD 132**

RUNNIN' A TEMPERATURE.
Tracks: / Runnin' a temperature / Bird of paradise / Mood indigo / My melancholy baby / Yard dog mazurka / Coquette / Harlem shout / Unsophisticated Sue / Knock me a kiss / Stratosphere / Hittin' the bottle / Black and tan fantasy / Love nest, The / Sleepy time gal / Runnin' wild / Sweet Sue / Avalon / Posin'.
MC: . . . . **TCAFS 1033**
LP: . . . . **AFS 1033**

STRICTLY LUNCEFORD (Big band bounce and boogie) (Lunceford, Jimmie Orchestra).
Tracks: / Strictly Lunceford / My blue Heaven / Organ grinder's swing / Rhythm is our business / Sophisticated lady / Four or five times / I'm gonna move to the outskirts of town / For dancers only / Twenty four robbers / Swanee river / Blue prelude / Blues in the night (parts 1 & 2) / Annie Laurie / Down by the old mill stream / Back door stuff (parts 1 & 2) / Margie / Siesta at the fiesta.
LP: . . . . **AFS 1003**

SWING GOES ON VOL 7.
LP: . . . . **IC 054 52716**

'TAIN'T WHAT YOU DO.
LP: . . . . **LPJT 22**
MC: . . . . **MCJT 22**

TAKIN' OFF WITH JIMMIE.
LP: . . . . **M 8003**

Lunch, Lydia

13:13.
Tracks: / Stares to nowhere / 3 X 3 / This side of nowhere / Snakepit breakdown / Dance of the dead children / Suicide ocean / Lock your door / Afraid of your company.
LP: . . . . **SITU 6**
LP: . . . . **LILP 400096**

DEATH VALLEY 69 (See under Sonic Youth) (Lunch, Lydia/Sonic Youth).

DROWNING OF LADY HAMILTON, THE.
LP: . . . . **WSP 2**

HONEYMOON IN RED.
Tracks: / Done dun / Still burning / Fields of fire / Dead in the head / Come fall / So your heart / Dead river / Three kings, The.
LP: . . . . **WSP 12**

IN LIMBO.
LP: . . . . **DVR 5**

ORAL FIXATION.
LP: . . . . **WSP 016**

QUEEN OF SIAM.
LP: . . . . **WSP 1 LP**

STINKFIST/CRUMB.
2LP: . . . . **WSP 015 C**

UNCENSORED.
MC: . . . . **WSP 1**

Lundy, Carmen

GOOD MORNING KISS.
Tracks: / Time is love / Dindi / Lamp is low, The / Perfect stranger / Goodmorning kiss / Show me that you love me / Love for sale / Quiet times.
LP: . . . . **BKH 523**
MC: . . . . **BKHMC 523**

Lundy, Emmett W.

FIDDLE TUNES FROM GRAYSON COUNTY, VIRGINIA.
Tracks: / Fisher's hornpipe / Flatwoods / Evening star waltz / Sugar hill / Highlander's farewell / Sheep shell corn by the rattle of his horn / Piney woods gal / Chapel Hill march / Forky deer / Molly put the kettle on / Waves on the ocean / Deaf woman's courtship / Duck on the millpond / Lost gal / Bonapartes retreat / Susanna gal / Wild goose chase / Cleveland's march / Belle of Lexington.
LP: . . . . **STR 802**

Lundy, Ted

LOVE SICK AND SORROW (Lundy, Ted/Bob Paisley/Southern Mountain Boys).
LP: . . . . **ROUNDER 0107**

SLIPPIN' AWAY.
LP: . . . . **ROUNDER 0055**

Lunghi, Cherie (nar)

FRIEND FROM ENGLAND, A (see Friend from England).

Lunny, Donal

DONAL LUNNY.
LP: . . . . **CEF 133**

Lunny, Manus

DUBLIN LADY (See under Stewart, Andy) (Lunny, Manus/Andy M Stewart).

Lupo, Benedetto

EIGHTH VAN CLIBURN INTERNATIONAL PIANO COMPETITI (see under Sultanov, Aleksei) (Lupo, Benedetto/Aleksei Sultanov/Jose Carlos Cocarelli).

Lupot, Georges

GL SENSATION.
LP: . . . . **SCHV 0890**

Lurie, Evan

PIECES OF BANDONEON.
LP: . . . . **TWI 871**

SELLING WATER BY THE SIDE OF THE RIVER.
LP: . . . . **AN 8754**
MC: . . . . **ANC 8754**

Lurie, John

DOWN BY LAW (1987 film soundtrack).
LP: . . . . **MTM 14**
MC: . . . . **MTM 14C**

STRANGER THAN PARADISE (Film soundtrack).
LP: . . . . **MTM 7**

Lurkers

FULHAM FALLOUT.
Tracks: / Ain't got a clue / I don't need to tell her / Total war / Hey you / Shadow / Then I kicked her / Go go go / Jenny / Time of year / Self destruct / It's quiet here / Gerald / I'm on heat / Be my prisoner.
LP: . . . . **BEGA 2**

GOD'S LONELY MEN.
Tracks: / She knows / God's lonely men / Out in the dark / Cyanide / Whatever happened to Mary / Take me back to Babylon / Room 309 / I'll be with you / Non contender / Seven o' clock someday / Sleep on diamonds / Bad times.
LP: . . . . **BEGA 8**
MC: . . . . **BEGC 8**

KING OF THE MOUNTAIN.
LP: . . . . **LINKLP 087**

LAST WILL AND TESTAMENT.
Tracks: / I'm on heat / Cyanide / Shadow / Wine drinker me / Out in the dark / Freak show / Jenny / Self destruct / Ain't got a clue / Take me back to Babylon / Total war / Love story / Then I kicked her / Just thirteen / New guitar in town / She knows.
LP: . . . . **BOPA 2**
LP: . . . . **BBL 2**
MC: . . . . **BBLC 2**

THIS DIRTY TOWN.
Tracks: / This dirty town / Frankenstein again / One man's meat / Shut out the light / Midnight hour / Drag you out / Heroin it's all over / Wolf at the door / Let's dance now / By the heart.
LP: . . . . **CLAYLP 104**

WILD TIMES AGAIN.
LP: . . . . **EFA 2433**

Lurtsema, Robert J.

CHRISTMAS STORIES.
LP: . . . . **PH 1078**
MC: . . . . **PH 1078C**

Lusardi, Linda

LINDA LUSARDI: INTERVIEW PICTURE DISC.
LPPD: . . . . **BAK 2118**

Lush

SCAR.
LP: . . . . **JAD 911**
MC: . . . . **JADC 911**

Lusher, Don

DON LUSHER BIG BAND (Lusher, Don Big Band).
Tracks: / Cavatina / Blues in the night / D.L. blues / Georgia / Gospel singers / I loves you, Porgy / Send in the clowns / Stardust / Star wars / That's living / Toreador song.
LP: . . . . **BBR 1006**
MC: . . . . **BBT 1006**

DON LUSHER COLLECTION.
LP: . . . . **OU 2129**

TRIBUTE TO THE GREAT BANDS VOL. 1 (Lusher, Don Big Band).
Tracks: / Peanut vendor / Take the 'A' train / I'll never smile again (until I smile at you) / Don't be that way / I've got my love to keep me warm / Kid from Red Bank / Opus one / Adios / I get a kick out of you / Early Autumn / Caravan / Two o'clock jump.
LP: . . . . **SIV 110**
MC: . . . . **CSIV 110**

TRIBUTE TO THE GREAT BANDS VOL. 2 (Lusher, Don Big Band).
Tracks: / Trumpet blues & cantabile / Pennsylvania 6.5000 / That lovely weekend / That's right / Westlake / D.L. blues / Sing sing sing / April in Paris / I'm getting sentimental over you / Don't get around much anymore / Concerto to end all concertos.
LP: . . . . **SIV 1114**
MC: . . . . **CSIV 1114**

TRIBUTE TO THE GREAT BANDS VOL. 3 (Lusher, Don Big Band).
Tracks: / Carnival / Benny rides again / Song of India / Cute / Wales '87 / Moonlight serenade / Woodchopper's ball / Boogie woogie / Love for sale / High and the mighty / Cottontail / Tea for two.
LP: . . . . **SIV 1125**
MC: . . . . **CSIV 1125**

Lustmord

LIVE EVIL.
MC: . . . . **SRC 006**

PARADISE DISOWNED.
LP: . . . . **SER 07**

Lutcher, Joe

JOE JOE JUMP.
Tracks: / No name boogie / Strato cruiser / Be bop blues / Mo jo jump / How fine can you be / Shuffle boogie / Sunday blues / Title track / Lucy Lindy boogie / Hit the block / Sauterne special / I know you when / Bagdad bebop / Watch it gate / Walk in to my heart / Toodle-oo.
LP: . . . . **CRB 1038**

Lutcher, Nellie

DITTO FROM ME TO YOU.
Tracks: / Ditto from me to you / I took a trip on the train / One I love belongs to somebody else, The / Humoresque / Pig-Latin song, The / Imagine you having eyes for me / Princess Poo-Poo-Ly has plenty papya / Say a little prayer for me / Baby please stop and think about me / Only you / I really couldn't love you / He sends me / That's how it goes / Mean to me / If I didn't love you like I do / St. Louis blues, The.
LP: . . . . **JB 1103**

MY NEW PAPAS GOT TO HAVE EVERYTHING.
Tracks: / Kinda' blue and low / There's another mule in your stall / Song is ended, The / Chi-chi-chi-Chicago / You better watch yourself / Reaching for the moon / Lake Charles boogie / Maid's prayer, A / My new papas got to have everything / Chicken ain't nothin' but a bird, A / I'll never get tired / Little Sally Water / Pa's not home, ma's upstairs / Whee baby! / Muchly verily / Please come back.
LP: . . . . **JB 1100**

REAL GONE GAL.
Tracks: / He's a real gone guy / Fine brown frame / My new papa's got to have everything / My mother's eyes / There's another mule in your stall / I wish I was in Walla Walla / Pa's not home, ma's upstairs / For you my love / That'll just about knock me out / Lake Charles boogie / Fine and mellow / Lake Charles boogie / Come and get it honey / Lutcher's leap / So nice to see you baby.
LP: . . . . **EG 2604791**
MC: . . . . **EG 2604794**

Lute Group

LIKE AS THE LUTE DELIGHTS.
LP: . . . . **PLR 072**

Luter, Claude

BLUE CLARINET.
LP: **502612**

JAZZ NOUVELLE ORLEANS.
LP: **509007**

JAZZ TIME VOL.2.
LP: **502702**

LE DOUBLE DISQUE D'OR.
2LP: **416011**

LOUISIANA AND ME.
LP: **502610**

PEARLS, THE.
LP: **502606**

SIDNEY BECHET JUBLIEE & CLAUDE LUTER (See Bechet, Sidney) (Luter, Claude & Sidney Bechet).

SURMALE.
LP: **502604**

SWINGING CLARINETS (Luter, Claude & Barney Bigard).
LP: **500 767**

Luton Girls Choir

BEST OF LUTON GIRLS CHOIR.
Tracks: / Dream of Olwen / Take the sun / You are my heart's delight / Barcarolle / Nun's chorus / Toselli's serenade / Trees / I leave my heart in an English garden / Music in my heart / Blue Danube / Break of day / Count your blessings / My heart and I / Some day my heart will awake / Holy city, The / Easter hymn / Bells of St. Marty's / Lift up your hearts / My lady greensleeves / Tales from the Vienna Woods.
LP: . . . . **NTSM 179**
MC: . . . . **TCNTS 179**

Luxon, Benjamin

AS TIME GOES BY.
Tracks: / As time goes by / More / My foolish heart / Laura / Spring, spring, spring / Gigi / Moon river / Love is a many splendoured thing / Green leaves of summer / Long ago and far away.
LP: . . . . **RCALP 6015**
MC: . . . . **RCAK 6015**
LP: . . . . **RL 25384**

COUNTRIE FAIRE (see under Peasants All) (Luxon, Benjamin/Peasants All).

SOME ENCHANTED EVENING.
Tracks: / Some enchanted evening / Surrey with the fringe on top / On the street where you live / Ol' man river / Maria / Seventy-six trombones / Where and when / I got plenty o' nuttin' / All the things you are / Stan' up and fight / Soliloquy.
LP: . . . . **RL 25320**

Luxuria

BEAST BOX.
LP: . . . . **BEGA 106**
MC: . . . . **BEGC 106**

UNANSWERABLE LUST.
LP: . . . . **BEGA 90**
MC: . . . . **BEGC 90**

LW 5

GET TO KNOW YOU.
LP: . . . . **V 2363**
MC: . . . . **TCV 2363**

L.W.S.

JUST CONFUSED.
LP: . . . . **WEBITE 19**

Lyin' Rampant

UP AND CUMIN'.
Tracks: / Indoor games / Promises / Breakdown / Way of destiny / Don't walk away / Fantasy girl / Say goodbye (sayonara) / Time again / Crazee / Kill them all.
LP: . . . . **VT 1**

Lyle, Bobby

IVORY DREAMS.
Tracks: / Ivory dreams / Save it for a rainy day / 88 ways / Tropical / Been so long / Locomotion, The / Nova.
LP: . . . . **K 781 938 1**
MC: . . . . **K 781 938 4**

NIGHT FIRE.
Tracks: / Stop running away from love / Da ya ance / Gettin' into love / Dream lady / Space place / Blues for Scott Joplin / For love / Rhap-so-dee / Just one of those things.
LP: . . . . **EST 11956**

Lyle McGuiness Band

ACTING ON IMPULSE.
Tracks: / Elise / Put the blame on me / Yellow kimono / Hit and run love / You're

always on my mind / Faded photographs / Moody irish eyes / Darlin' man / Hot lips / Only all the time / Acting on impulse.
LP: . . . . **CKLP 003**

Lyman, Abe

ABE LYMAN, 1941.
Tracks: / Johnson special / Blues 1 / Straight eight boogie / Lament to love / Nice dreamin' baby / Blue beats / Sunset near vine / Swing tonic / Until tomorrow / With a twist of the wrist / Horse 'n' boogie / Great oaks.
LP: . . . . **HSR 184**

ABE LYMAN'S CALIFORNIANS VOL 1.
LP: . . . . **GRANNY 03308**

Lyman, Arthur

CAST YOUR FATE.
LP: . . . . **GNPS 607**
MC: **GNP5 607**

PEARLY SHELLS.
LP: . . . . **GNPS 606**
MC: **GNP5 606**

PUKA SHELLS.
LP: . . . . **GNPS 2091**
MC: **GNP5 2091**

Lymon, Frankie

BEST OF FRANKIE LYMON AND THE TEENAGERS.
Tracks: / Why do fools fall in love / I want you to be my girl / I'm not a know it all / Who can exlain / I promise to remember / ABC's of love, The / Share / I'm not a juvenile delinquent / Baby, baby / Paper castles / Teenage love / Out in the cold again / Goody goody / Creation of love / Please be mine (CD only) / Love is a clown (CD only) / Am I fooling myself again (CD only) / Thumb thumb (CD only) / Portable on my shoulder (CD only) / Little bitty pretty one (CD only).
LP: . . . . **ROU 5001**
MC: . . . . **TCROU 5001**

FRANKIE LYMON & THE TEENAGERS (Lymon, Frankie & The Teenagers).
LPS: **000148**

WHY DO FOOLS FALL IN LOVE.
LP: . . . . **NSPL 28251**

Lymon, Lewis

MEET THE KODAKS (Lymon, Lewis & The Teen Chords).
LP: . . . . **COL 5049**

Lynam, Ray

20 SHOTS OF COUNTRY.
LP: . . . . **CBRL 4069**

BACK IN LOVE BY MONDAY.
Tracks: / Back in love by Monday / Time / Hold her in your hand / Moon is still over her shoulder, The / Speak softly / Fewer threads than these / Rose in paradise / Maybe this time / Beautiful woman.
LP: . . . . **RITZLP 0047**
MC: . . . . **RITZLC 0047**

BRAND NEW MR ME.
LP: . . . . **HPE 634**

COUNTRY FAVOURITES (Lynam, Ray & Hillbillies).
MC: . . . . **CBRL 4086**

COUNTRY STARS (see under Begley, Philomena) (Lynam, Ray & Philomena Begley).

GYPSY JOE AND ME.
LP: . . . . **HPE 602**

MONA LISA.
Tracks: / Mona Lisa lost her smile / Road to Dundee, The / Too late / From now on / Winter time / Devil inside, The / To be lovers / You put the blue in me / He stopped loving her today / Blue grass medley / I heard the bluebirds sing / Nancy Myles.
LP: . . . . **RITZLP 0033**
MC: . . . . **RITZLC 0033**

SHADES OF RAY LYNAM.
LP: . . . . **RITZSP 414**
MC: . . . . **RITZSC 414**

WE GO TOGETHER AGAIN (Lynam, Ray & Philomena Begley).
LP: . . . . **SOLP 1010**
MC: . . . . **SOCAS 1010**

Lynch, Brian

PEER PRESSURE.
Tracks: / Thomasville / Park Avenue petite / Peer pressure / Outlaw / Change of plan / Nother never.
LP: . . . . **CRISS 1029**

Lynch, Claire

BREAKIN' IT.
Tracks: / Listen to a country song / Breakin' it / Old by and by / I'll never grow tired of you / I can't get you off my mind / Somebody loves you / Once in a lifetime / All the way to Texas / Livin' in the name of love / Heart made of stone / Feelings of love.
LP: . . . . **AMB 004**

Lynch, David

TWIN PEAKS THEME (See under Falling by Julee Cruise) (Lynch, David & Angelo).

Lynch, Francis (aut)

IN THE HOUSE OF DARK MUSIC (Boland, Arthur).
MCSET: . . . . **COL 2011**

Lynch, Joe

DINNY'S FAVOURITES.
MC: . . . . **KEC 1001**

JOE LYNCH.
MC: . . . . **SMAC 9009**

SHADES OF GREEN.
MC: . . . . **SMAC 9006**

Lynch, Kenny

HALF THE DAY'S GONE AND WE HAVEN'T EARNED A PENNY.
Tracks: / Because I love you / Average man / Built to last / Locked into love / They don't know you / B.A. woman / Name your game / Another groovy Saturday night / Never give up on love / Half the day's gone and we haven't earned a penny.
LP: . . . . **SATLP 400**

SINGIN' AND SWINGIN'.
Tracks: / Turn the lights down low / Heather on the hill / Younger than springtime / Hard hearted Hannah / Come with me / Guess I'll hang my tears out to dry / Up on the roof / When in Rome / In love for the very first time / Folks who live on the hill / Do you miss them too / Could I count on you / Wives and lovers / Make it easy on yourself.
LP: . . . . **OUM 2212**

VERY BEST OF KENNY LYNCH.
Tracks: / Up on the roof / What am I to you? / One thing that keeps me happy, The / You can never stop me loving you / They're jealous of me / Steady kind / For you (there's nothing I wouldn't do) / Puff (up in smoke) / Misery / Mountain of love / I'll stay by you / Stand by me / Before I count to ten / Come on, come on / World I used to know, The / It's too late / Just wanna love you / Other side of dreamland, The / Mister Moonlight / Crazy crazes / Harlem library / Shake and scream / One thing that keeps me happy.
LP: . . . . **SEE 207**

Lynch, Lee

ISLAND MY ISLAND.
LP: . . . . **SPWM 2**
MC: . . . . **CSWM 2**

Lynch Mob

WICKED SENSATION.
LP: . . . . **EKT 81**
MC: . . . . **EKT 81 C**

Lynn

SOUNDTRACK.
Tracks: / Sarabande (main title) / Women of Ireland / Piper's maggot jig / Seamaiden, The / Tin whistle / British Grenadiers, The / Hohenfriedberger march / Lilliburlero / March from Idomeneo / Sarabande-duel / German dance no.1 in C major / Il barbiere di siviglia / Cello concerto / Concerto for two harpsichords and orchestra in / Piano trio in E flat / Sarabande (end title).
LP: . . . . **K 56189**

Lynn, Barbara

YOU DON'T HAVE TO GO.
Tracks: / You make me so hot / Misty blue / Trying to love two / You're losing me / You don't have to go / We got a good thing going / Sugar coated love / You'll lose a good thing.
LP: . . . . **ICH 1024**
MC: . . . . **ZCICH 1024**

Lynn, Cheryl

CHERYL LYNN.
Tracks: / Got to be real / All my lovin' / Star love / Come in from the rain / You saved my day / Give my love to you / Nothing you say / You're the one / Daybreak.
LP: . . . . **CBS 83145**

ENCORE (OLD GOLD) (See under Nicole/New York eyes).

IN LOVE.
Tracks: / I've got faith in you / Hide it away / Feel it / Keep it hot / I've got just what you need / Love bomb / Chances / Don't let it fade away.
LP: . . . . **CBS 83829**

INSTANT LOVE.
Tracks: / Instant love / Sleep walkin' / Day after day / Look before you leap / Say you'll be mine / I just wanna be your fantasy / Believe in me / If this world was mine.
LP: . . . . **CBS 85849**

IT'S GONNA BE RIGHT.
Tracks: / It's gonna be right / Fidelity / Fade to black / Love's been here before / Let me love you / Find somebody new / Loafin' / Slipped me a mickey / Tug o' war.
LP: . . . . **CBS 26497**
MC: **40 26497**

PREPPIE.
Tracks: / Encore / Fix it / Fool a fool / This time / Change the channel / Preppie / Love rush / No one else will do / Free / Life's too short.
MC: **40 25714**
LP: **25714**

Lynn, Ian

CELEBRATION.
Tracks: / Celebration / I remember / High forest, The / Time was / Run for home / Finale / Dream for tomorrow.
MC: . . . . **TCMMC 1011**

EARLY SNOW.
Tracks: / River, The / Earth song / Snow mountain / When winter comes / Golden days / Seven bridges / Do you see / Introduction.
LP: . . . . **MMC 008**
MC: . . . . **TCMMC 1008**

FORGOTTEN SUMMER.
Tracks: / Another good reason / Forgotten summer / Grey sky blue / Someday soon / Sun dance / Waltz / First finale.
LP: . . . . **MMC 003**
MC: . . . . **TCMMC 1003**

PARTY IN THE RAIN (Lynn,Ian/Pete Brown).
Tracks: / Broken windscreen dance / White room / Big city cowboy / Walk into the sun / Comeback / Still have the love / I read the funky times / Party in the rain.
LP: . . . . **INTLP 1**

Lynn, Jim

IRISH CEILI MUSIC (Lynn, Jim Ceili Band).
LP: . . . . **UNKNOWN**

Lynn, Loretta

BEST OF CONWAY AND LORETTA (see Twitty, Conway) (Lynn, Loretta & Conway Twitty).

COAL MINERS DAUGHTER.
LP: . . . . **IMCA 37236**

CONWAY AND LORETTA (See under Twitty, Conway) (Lynn, Loretta & Conway Twitty).

COUNTRY PARTNERS (Lynn, Loretta & Conway Twitty).
Tracks: / As soon as I hang up the phone / Don't mess up a good thing / Love's not where love should be / Two lonely people / I changed my way / Country bumpkin / Spiders and snakes / I'm getting tired of losing you / Sweet things I remember about you / It all falls down / Lifetime before, A.
LP: . . . . **IMCA 836**

COUNTRY STORE: LORETTA LYNN.
Tracks: / Coal miners daughter / Letter, The / Faded love / Don't come home a drinkin' / Other woman, The / Put your hand in the hand / Behind closed doors / While he's making love / Delta dawn / Hey Loretta / As soon as I hang up the phone / Take me home country roads / Heart don't do this to me / Woman of the world.
LP: . . . . **CST 19**
MC: . . . . **CSTK 19**

DYNAMIC DUO (Lynn, Loretta & Conway Twitty).
Tracks: / I don't love you enough / You're much too close / Hey good lookin' / We can try it one more time.
LP: . . . . **MFP 5599**
MC: . . . . **TCMFP 5599**

GOLDEN GREATS: LORETTA LYNN.
Tracks: / Before I'm over you / Wine women and song / Happy birthday / Blue Kentucky girl / You ain't woman enough / Don't come home a drinkin' / Fist city / Woman of the world / Coalminer's daughter / One's on the way / Love is the foundation / Hey Loretta / Trouble in paradise / Somebody, somewhere / She's got you / Out of my head and back in my bed.
LP: . . . . **MCM 5028**
MC: . . . . **MCMC 5028**

GREAT COUNTRY HITS.
Tracks: / Minute you're gone, The / I still miss someone / You're the only good thing (that's happened to me) / End of the world / Oh lonesome me / Send me the pillow that you dream on / I won't forget you / Race is on, The / Jealous heart / I really don't want to know / There goes my everything / Your cheatin' heart / I don't wanna play house / Satisfied mind, A / Stand by your man / Snowbird / Rose garden / Me and Bobby McGee / Help me make it through the night / Paper house / Behind closed doors / Satin sheets / I fall to pieces / Sweet dreams / Crazy / Wrong road again / Rhinestone cowboy / Another somebody done somebody wrong song.
2LP: . . . . **MCLD 615**
MCSET: . . . . **MCLDC 615**

I REMEMBER PATSY.
Tracks: / She's got you / Walking after midnight / Why can't he be here / Faded love / I fall to pieces / Crazy / Sweet dreams / Back in baby's arms / Leavin' on your mind / I remember Patsy.
LP: . . . . **IMCA 1621**

JUST A WOMAN.
Tracks: / Stop the clock / Heart don't do this to me / Wouldn't it be great / When I'm in love all alone / I can't say it on the radio / I'll think of something / Adam's rib / Take me in your arms (and hold me) / Just a woman / One man band.
LP: . . . . **IMCA 5613**

LORETTA LYNN STORY, THE.
Tracks: / Honky tonk angels / Success / One's on the way / You ain't woman enough / Your squaw is on the warpath / Fist city / Don't come home a drinkin' / You're lookin' at country / Walking after midnight / Crazy / I fall to pieces.
LP: . . . . **MFP 50518**

NEVER ENDING SONG OF LOVE (Lynn, Loretta & Conway Twitty).
LP: . . . . **MFP 50474**

SINGS.
LP: . . . . **HAT 3023**
MC: . . . . **HATC 3023**

SINGS COUNTRY.
Tracks: / Stand by your man / Snowbird / Minute you're gone, The / Rose garden / Crazy / Paper roses / You're the only good thing (That's happened to me) / Me and Bobby McGee / Send me the pillow (That you dream on) / Behind closed doors / I won't forget you / Race is on, The / (Hey won't you play) (Full title: (Hey won't you play) Another somebody done somebody wrong so) / Help me make it through the night.
LP: . . . . **MFP 41 5742 1**
MC: . . . . **MFP 41 5742 4**

VERY BEST OF CONWAY & LORETTA,THE (Lynn, Loretta & Conway Twitty).
LP: . . . . **IMCA 37237**

VERY BEST OF LORETTA LYNN.
Tracks: / Coal miner's daughter / You're looking at country / Blue Kentucky girl / Wine, women and song / She's got you / One's on the way / Happy birthday / Before I'm over you / Out of my head and back in my bed / Woman of the world / Trouble in paradise / Hey Loretta / You ain't woman enough / Fist city / Somebody, somewhere / Don't come a drinkin' (with ...).
LP: . . . . **PLAT 308**
MC: . . . . **PLAC 308**

WE'VE COME A LONG WAY, BABY.
Tracks: / We've come a long way, baby / Easy street / Lady that lived here before / Lullabies to a memory / I can't feel you anymore / True love needs to keep in touch / My conscience goes to sleep / No love left inside of me / Between the preacher and the lawyer / Standing at our bedroom door.
LP: . . . . **MCF 2881**

Lynn, Trudy

COME TO MAMA.
Tracks: / Right back in the water / When something is wrong with my baby / Come to mama / When you took your love from me / One woman man / Woman's gotta have it / Do I need you (too) / Fish girl blues / Making love to me.
LP: . . . . **ICHA 1063**
MC: . . . . **ICHA 1063 MC**

TRUDY SINGS THE BLUES.
Tracks: / Sittin' and drinkin' / Just a little bit / I can tell / Trudy sings the blues / Doctor feelgood / Do I need you / Bring the beef home to me / Ball and chain.
LP: . . . . **ICH 1043**
MC: . . . . **ZCICH 1043**

Lynn, Vera

16 GOLDEN CLASSICS.
Tracks: / Auf wiederseh'n sweetheart / Yours / White cliffs of Dover, The (There'll be Bluebirds over) / My son my son / Windsor waltz / Forget me not / Homing waltz / Who are we / Faithful hussar, The / Travsellin' home / We'll meet again / As time goes by / When I grow too old to dream / Back in your own back yard / Far away places / Goodnight my love.
LP: . . . . **UNLP 015**
MC: . . . . **UNMC 015**

20 FAMILY FAVOURITES.
Tracks: / White cliffs of Dover, The / Who's taking you home tonight / Wishing (will make it so) / Wish me luck (as you

wave me goodbye) / Nightingale sang in Berkeley Square, A / Anniversary waltz / When the lights go on again (all over the world) / I'll pray for you / We'll meet again / Mr. Wonderful / Yours / There'll always be an England / My way / Unforgettable / I'll be seeing you / Those were the days / Yesterday / You'll never know / Amazing grace / Land of hope and glory.
LP: . . . . **EMTV 28**
MC: . . . . **TC EMTV 28**

20 GOLDEN PIECES: VERA LYNN.
Tracks: / I'm gonna sit right down and write myself a letter / With these hands / Love letters / To each his own / Portrait of my love / Don't worry 'bout me / Stars fell on Alabama / I'm beginning to see the light / Red sails in the sunset / Thank heaven for little girls / Till there was you / Where have all the flowers gone / Put your hand in the hand / Whose garden was this / Birth of the blues / It's impossible / I think of you / SDRM / Here's that rainy day / Until it's time for you to go / If we only have love.
LP: . . . . **BDL 2048**
MC: . . . . **BDC 2048**

BEST OF VERA LYNN.
LP: **1A 022 58073**
MC: **1A 222 58073**

COLLECTION: VERA LYNN.
Tracks: / When swallows say goodbye / Another time, another place / There'll come another day / Have I told you lately that I love you / Morgen (one more sunrise) / Goodnight my love / I'll always be in love with you / Am I wasting my time on you / Back in your own back yard / As time goes by / I'm in the mood for love / When I grow too old to dream / London I love, The / It's a sin to tell a lie / White cliffs of Dover, The / Don't blame me / Yours / Mexicali rose / Anniversary waltz / We'll meet again / Harbour lights / Little rain must fall, A / Nightingale sang in Berkeley Square, A.
2LP: . . . . **CCSLP 119**
MC: . . . . **CCSMC 119**

FOCUS ON VERA LYNN.
2LP: . . . . **FOS 33/34**
MC: . . . . **KFOC 28074**

GOLDEN MEMORIES.
Tracks: / London pride / Besame mucho / As time goes by / It had to be you / Always in my heart / Goodnight, children everywhere / Goodnight my love / Last time I saw Paris, The / Arm in arm / Beneath the lights of home / Pair of silver wings / Silver wings in the moonlight.
LP: . . . . **NTS 189**

GREAT YEARS, THE.
MC: . . . . **KVERC 30234**

GREATEST HITS: VERA LYNN.
LPPD: . . . . **AR 30047**

GREATEST HITS: VERA LYNN VOL 1.
Tracks: / White cliffs of Dover, The / Anniversary waltz / Yours / Travellin' home / Don't cry for my love / Doonaree / When I grow too old to dream / My son, my son / It's a sin to tell a lie / Glory of love / Harbour lights / As time goes by.
LP: . . . . **CN 2033**
MC: **CN4 2033**

HITS OF THE BLITZ.
Tracks: / This is the army Mr. Jones / I left my heart at the stage door canteen / It's a lovely day tomorrow / White cliffs of Dover, The / Don't fence me in / If I had my way / Deep in the heart of Texas / Lili Marlene / That lovely weekend / Who's taking you home tonight / Wishing (will make it so) / Wish me luck (as you wave me goodbye / When the lights go on again / I'll pray for you / We'll meet again / Nightinagle sang in Berkeley Square / Bless 'em all / We're gonna hang out the washing on the Siegfried Line / Kiss me goodnight, Sergeant Major / You'll never know / I don't want to set the world on fire / Maybe / Coming home / There'll always be an England.
LP: . . . . **CSD 1457**
MC: . . . . **TCCSD 1457**

HOW LUCKY YOU ARE.
Tracks: / How lucky you are / That lovely weekend / I'll keep you in my heart / Little bit of Heaven, A / So this is love / It can't be wrong / Outside of Heaven / When your hair has turned to silver / Maybe / Goodnight children everywhere (end s1) / Welcome home / My son, my son / Trying / I lived when I met you / Show me the way / Lambeth walk / My friend the robin / Speak a word of love (I wish, I wish) / Wond'ring and wishing / Doonaree.
LP: . . . . **PLE 530**
MC: . . . . **TC-PLE 530**

IN CONCERT: GUARDS' DEPOT, CATERHAM (Lynn, Vera & The Woolf Phillips Orchestra).
Tracks: / Tonight's the night / Blossom fell, A / If you love me (I don't care) / Say si si / My son my son / Little things mean a lot / Cherry pink and apple blossom white / When I grow too old to dream.
LP: . . . . **PLE 515**
MC: . . . . **TC-PLE 515**

MAGIC OF VERA LYNN, THE.
Tracks: / Travellin' home / Windsor waltz / Gathering of the clans / Yours / Homing waltz / From the time you say goodbye / When swallows say goodbye / Forget me not / Auf wiedersehn sweetheart / Doonaree / When you hear Big Ben / We'll meet again.
LP: . . . . **GDN 1**

NURSERY RHYMES (Lynn, Vera/ Kenneth McKellar).
MC: . . . . **KCSP 485**

ONE AND ONLY VERA LYNN, THE.
Tracks: / Thank you for the music / Room 504 / Rainbow connection, The / You and me against the world / Easy to remember / Caravan song / Sunshine on my shoulder / I sing the songs / One voice / Harbour lights / Colours of my life / That old feeling / One day I'll fly away / Are you lonesome tonight? / What I did for love / Until it's time for you to go.
LP: . . . . **PYL 6032**
MC: . . . . **PYM 6032**

REMEMBERS THE WORLD AT WAR.
LP: . . . . **EMA 765**

SINGING TO THE WORLD.
Tracks: / Daybreak / You / Caravan song / Colours of my life / That old feeling / Slow dance / Rainbow connection / My friend / It's easy to remember / One voice / One day I'll fly away / Room five hundred and four.
LP: . . . . **N 139**
MC: . . . . **ZCN 139**

SPOTLIGHT ON VERA LYNN.
Tracks: / Thank you for the music / What I did for love / Are you lonesome tonight / I wonder / Harbour lights / Tomorrow / Sunshine on my shoulder / Weekend in New England / In the blue Canadian rockies / You and me against the world / Until it's time for you to go.
2LP: . . . . **SPOT 6805**
MCSET: . . . . **ZCSPT 6805**

SWEETHEART OF THE FORCES.
LP: **8202161**
MC: **8202164**

THANK YOU FOR THE MUSIC.
Tracks: / Thank you for the music / What I did for love / Are you lonesome tonight / I wonder / Harbour lights / Tomorrow / Sunshine on my shoulders / Weekend in New England / In the blue Canadian Rockies / You and me against the world / Until it's time for you to go / I sing the blues.
LP: . . . . **N 108**
MC: . . . . **ZCN 108**
LP: . . . . **SPR 8564**
MC: . . . . **SPC 8564**

THIS IS VERA LYNN.
Tracks: / White cliffs of Dover, The / Lili Marlene / Bless 'em all / I'll be seeing you / Nightingale sang in Berkeley Square / Anniversary waltz / This is the army, Mr.Jones / There'll always be an England / Yours / Stars fell on Alabama / As time goes by / Autumn leaves / You'd be so nice to come home to / I've heard that song before / To each his own / Now is the hour.
LP: . . . . **THIS 22**
MC: . . . . **TCTHIS 22**

UNFORGETTABLE VERA LYNN, THE.
Tracks: / My way / Everybody's talkin' / Taste of honey, A / Strangers in the night / Yesterday / I will wait for you / Those were the days / By the time I get to Phoenix / Everybody loves somebody / Look of love, The / What a wonderful world / Sunrise sunset / Put your hand in the hand / Unforgettable / Morning of my life / It's impossible / I think of you / Here's that rainy day / Until it's time for you to go / If we only have love.
2LP: **41 10703**
MCSET: **46 10709**

VERA LYNN.
Tracks: / There'll always be an England / As time goes by / Anniversary waltz / Until it's time for you to go / You'll never know / It had to be you / Yours / Amazing grace / White cliffs of Dover, The / Unforgettable / Morning of my life / Nightingale sang in Berkeley Square, A / I'll be seeing you / Old rugged cross, The / Lili Marlene / You'd be so nice to come home to / Rose of England / Room five-hundred and four / Bless this house.
MC: . . . . **TCIDL 2**

VERA LYNN REMEMBERS.
Tracks: / White cliffs of Dover, The / Red sails in the sunset / It's a sin to tell a lie / Roll out the barrel / You'll never know / Nightingale sang in Berkeley Square / Sailing / Harbour lights / Auf wiedersehen / Yours / From the time you say goodbye / My mothers eyes / That lovely weekend / Land of hope and glory / Coming in on a wing and a prayer / We'll meet again / Be like the kettle and sing.
LP: . . . . **SIV 1120**
MC: . . . . **CSIV 1120**

VERA LYNN SONGBOOK, THE.
LPS: . . . . **ALBUM 52**
MCSET: . . . . **CASSETTE 52**

WAR YEARS, THE.
Tracks: / Nightingale sang in Berkley Square / Yours / That lovely weekend / White cliffs of Dover / Where in the world / I'll pray for you / When they sound the last "All Clear" / Be careful it's my heart / When the lights go on again / I don't want to set the world on fire / You'll never know / There's a land of begin again / We'll meet again / Coming home.
LP: . . . . **DVL 7**
MC: . . . . **KDVC 7**

WE'LL MEET AGAIN (DECCA).
Tracks: / We'll meet again / When the lights go on again / My son my son / It's a lovely day tomorrow / Harbour lights / Auf wiederseh'n sweetheart / That lovely weekend / White cliffs of Dover, The / When you hear Big Ben / From the time you say goodbye / Homing waltz / Forget-me-not / Nightingale sang in Berkeley Square / Yours.
LP: . . . . **TAB 3**
MC: . . . . **KTBC 3**

WE'LL MEET AGAIN (TELSTAR).
LP: . . . . **STAR 2369**
MC: . . . . **STAC 2369**

Lynne, Gloria

GO! GO! GO!.
LP: . . . . **FS 198**

Lynne, Jeff

ARMCHAIR THEATRE.
Tracks: / Every little thing / Lift me up / September song / Don't say goodbye / Stormy weather / Save me now / Don't let go / Nobody home / Now you're gone / What would it take / Blown away.
LP: . . . . **WX 347**
MC: . . . . **WX 347 C**

MESSAGE FROM THE COUNTRY Jeff Lynne years '68-'73.
Tracks: / Do ya / Minister, The / Girl at the window / Roll over Beethoven / Words of Aaron / Mr. Radio / Skeleton and the roundabout / Message from the country / Come with me / Morning sunshine / 10538 overture (Full version.) / Happy birthday/The birthday / No time / Showdown / In old England town (boogie no.2) (CD only.) / Big chief wooly bosher (CD only.) / Queen of the hours (CD only.) / Follow me follow (CD only.).
LP: . . . . **SHSM 2031**
LP: **792 585 1**
MC: . . . . **TCSHSM 2031**
MC: **792 585 4**

Lynn-Jones, David

WOOD, WIND AND STONE.
LP: **8369511**
MC: **8369514**

Lynott, Phil

OUT IN THE FIELDS (see Moore, Gary) (Lynott, Phil & Gary Moore).

PHILIP LYNOTT ALBUM, THE.
Tracks: / Fatalistic attitude / Man's a fool / Old town / Cathleen / Growing up / Together / Little bit of water / Ode to liberty / Gino / Don't talk about me baby.
LP: **6359 117**
MC: **7150 117**

SOLO IN SOHO.
Tracks: / Solo in Soho / Kings call / Child lullaby, A / Tattoo / Dear Miss Lonely Hearts / Yellow pearl / Girls / Ode to a black man / Jamaican rum / Talk in 79 / So what / Turn the hands of time.
LP: . . . . **PRICE 88**
MC: . . . . **PRIMC 88**
LP: **9102 038**

Lynton, Jackie

BIT NEAR THE MARK.
Tracks: / Can't take away my love / Ricky rocket / Deep inside / Out of control / Thrown it all away / If you wanna get a band together / I gotta woman / Jamming in G / Sad song / Could this be the woman in your life / Ghost of old G / Make my break / Snow.
LP: . . . . **SCRL 5002**

Lynyrd Skynyrd

ANTHOLOGY - LYNYRD SKYNYRD.
Tracks: / I ain't the one / Poison whiskey / Don't ask me no questions / Needle and spoon / Rool gypsy roll / Honky tonk night time man / Cheatin' woman / Made in the shade / Saturday night special (live) / Sweet home Alabama / Searching / Down south jukin / White dove / Freebird (live) / What's your name / One more time / Railroad song / Ballad of Curtis Loew, The / T for Texas (live) (Blue yodel no. 1).
LP: . . . . **RAWLP 031**
MC: . . . . **RAWTC 031**

BEST OF THE REST.
MC: . . . . **MCLC 1834**

GIMME BACK MY BULLETS.
Tracks: / Gimme back my bullets / Every mother's son / Trust / Same old blues / Double trouble / Roll gypsy roll / Searching / Cry for the bad man.
LP: . . . . **MCL 1653**
MC: . . . . **MCLC 1653**
LP: . . . . **MCF 2744**

GOLD AND PLATINUM (Very best of Lynyrd Skynyrd).
Tracks: / Down south junkin' / Saturday night special / Gimme three steps / What's your name / You got that right / Gimme back my bullets / Sweet home Alabama / Freebird / That smell / On the hunt / I ain't the one / Whiskey rock and roller / Simple man / I know a little / Tuesday's gone / Comin' home.
2LP: . . . . **MCDW 456**
MCSET: . . . . **MCDC 456**
2LP: . . . . **MCSP 308**

LEGEND, A.
Tracks: / Georgia peaches / When you got good friends / Sweet little missy / Four walls of ralford / Simple man / Truck drivin' man / One in the sun / Mr. Banker / Take your time.
LP: . . . . **MCF 3405**
MC: . . . . **MCFC 3405**

NUTHIN' FANCY.
Tracks: / Made in the shade / Saturday night special / Cheatin' woman / Railroad song / I'm a country boy / On the hunt / Am I losin' / Whiskey rock a roller.
LP: . . . . **MCL 1760**
MC: . . . . **MCLC 1760**
LP: . . . . **MCF 2700**

NUTHIN' FANCY/GIVE ME BACK MY BULLETS.
Tracks: / Saturday night special / Cheatin' woman / Railroad song / I'm a country boy / On the hunt / Am I losin' / Made in the shade / Whiskey rock and roller / Gimme back my bullets / Every mother's son / Trust / (I got the) same old blues / Double trouble / Roll gypsy roll / Searching / Cry for the bad man.
MCSET: . . . . **MCA 2111**

ONE MORE FOR THE ROAD.
Tracks: / Workin' for MCA / I ain't the one / Searching / Tuesdays gone / Saturday night special / Travellin' man / Whiskey rock and roller / Sweet home Alabama / Gimme three steps / Call me the breeze / T for Texas / Needle and spoon / Crossroads / Freebird.
2LP: . . . . **MCSP 279**
MCSET: . . . . **MCSPC 279**
2LP: . . . . **MCMD 7006**
MCSET: . . . . **MCMDC 7006**

PRONOUNCED LEH-NERD SKIN-NERD.
Tracks: / I ain't the one / Tuesday's gone / Gimme three steps / Simple man / Things goin' on / Mississippi kid / Poison whiskey / Freebird.
LP: . . . . **MCL 1798**
MC: . . . . **MCLC 1798**

PRONOUNCED LEH-NERD SKIN-NERD/SECOND HELPING.
Tracks: / I ain't the one / Tuesday's gone / Gimme three steps / Simple man / Things goin' on / Mississippi Kid / Poison whiskey / Freebird / Sweet home Alabama / I need you / Don't ask me no questions / Workin' for MCA / Ballad of Curtis Loew, The / Swamp music / Needle and spoon / Call me the breeze.
MCSET: . . . . **MCA 2 107**

SECOND HELPING.
Tracks: / Sweet home Alabama / I need you / Don't ask me no questions / Workin' for MCA / Ballad of Curtis Loew, The / Swamp music / Needle and spoon / Call me the breeze.
LP: . . . . **MCL 1746**
MC: . . . . **MCLC 1746**
LP: . . . . **FA 3194**
MC: . . . . **TCFA 3194**

SKYNYRD FIRST AND LAST.
LP: . . . . **MCL 1627**
MC: . . . . **MCLC 1627**
LP: . . . . **MCG 3529**

SKYNYRDS INNYRDS.
LP: . . . . **MCG 6046**
MC: . . . . **MCGC 6046**

SOUTHERN BY THE GRACE OF GOD.
Tracks: / Swamp music / Call me the breeze / Dixie / Freebird / Workin' For MCA / That smell / I know a little / Comin' home / You got that right / What's your name / Gimme back my bullets / Sweet home Alabama.

2LP: . . . . MCMD 7004
MCSET: . . . . MCMDC 7004

STREET SURVIVORS.
Tracks: / What's your name / That smell / One more time / I know a little / You got that right / I never dreamt / Honky tonk night time man / Ain't no good life.
LP: . . . . MCL 1694
MC: . . . . MCLC 1694
LP: . . . . MCG 3525

Lyon, Steve

THERE'S NO PLACE LIKE MARS.
LP: . . . . FF 306

Lyons, Jimmy

OTHER AFTERNOONS.
LP: . . . . AFF 34

Lyons, John

MAY MORNING DEW, THE.
LP: 12TS 248

Lyons, Mary (aut)

PASSIONATE DECEPTION (see under Passionate Deception) (Boyd, Carole (nar)).

Lyons, Tim

EASTER SNOW.
LP: . . . . SIF 1014
MC: . . . . CSIF 1014

GREEN LINNET, THE.
LP: . . . . LER 3036

Lyres

BOX SET,THE.
LP: . . . . LYRES 001

LYRES.
LP: . . . . FC 016

LYRES, LYERS.
LP: . . . . ROSE 103

ON FYRE.
LP: . . . . ROSE 35

PROMISE IS A PROMISE, A.
Tracks: / Promise is a promise, A / Here's a heart on fyre / Every man for himself / Feel good / I'll try you anyway / Worried about nothing / Touch / Running through the night / She's got eyes that tell lie / Jagged time lapse / Knock my socks off / Sick and tired / Trying just to please / Witch.
LP: . . . . SAVE 059
LP: . . . . ROSE 153

Lysis, Roger Dean's

LYSIS PLUS KENNY WHEELER.
LP: . . . . GCM 791

Lytell, Jimmy

JIMMY LYTELL 1926-28.
MC: . . . . NEO 712

Lytle, Cecil

READING OF A SACRED BOOK.
2LP: . . . . LPCEL 028/29
MCSET: . . . . MCCEL 028/29

SEEKERS OF THE TRUTH.
2LP: . . . . LPCEL 020/21
MCSET: . . . . MCCEL 020/21

Lytle, Johnny

EVERYTHING MUST CHANGE.
LP: . . . . MR 5158

FAST HANDS.
Tracks: / Sister silver / Tomorrow / Brightness / Bein' green / Man / Blues to be there.
LP: . . . . MR 5185

GOOD VIBES.
Tracks: / So what / Turn the hands of time / New York, New York / Didn't we / After supper / Aaron's theme.
LP: . . . . MR 5271

VIBES.
LP: . . . . BGP 1031

VILLAGE CALLER.
LP: . . . . OJC 110

Lyttelton, Humphrey

ALL THAT JAZZ (see under Dankworth, John) (Dankworth, John & Humphrey Lyttelton).

BAD PENNY BLUES (THE BEST OF HUMPH 1949-1956).
Tracks: / Maple leaf rag / Irish black bottom / Careless love / Snake rag / Trouble in mind / Buddy's habits / Panama rag / On treasure island / Trog's blues / Hoppin' mad / Don't monkey with it / Take a note from the south / Jelly roll blues / Blue for Waterloo / Fish seller.
LP: . . . . HIFLY 39

BEANO BOOGIE (Lyttelton, Humphrey & His Band).
Tracks: / Say forward I'll march / Ficklefanny strikes again / Apple honey / Do you call that a buddy / Sixth form / Beano boogie / Little king, The / Echoes of the jungle / Gnasher and me / Strange Mr. Charles, The / Cop out.
LP: . . . . CLGLP 021
MC: . . . . ZCLG 021

BEST OF HUMPHREY LYTTELTON.
Tracks: / Oh babe, maybe someday / That's my home / Blues in bolero / Big ole' tears / Mabel's dream / Prelude to a kiss / Spreadin' joy / Kansas City woman / Panama rag / We fell out of love / Let's get out.
LP: . . . . BLM 51002
MC: . . . . BLM 51002C

DELVING BACK AND FORTH WITH HUMPH (Lyttelton, Humphrey & His Band).
Tracks: / Miss Otis regrets / Working man blues / Mahogany hall stomp / Salty dog / South / Victory house drag / High society / Melancholy blues / Farewell blues / On treasure island / Blues for an unknown gipsy/ Suffolk air / Chattanooga stomp / Low down dirty shame blues / Hopfrog / Randolph Turpin stomp / Vox humana blues / I like to go back in the evening.
LP: . . . . ESQ 310
LP: . . . . SOS 1160

DOGGIN AROUND.
LP: . . . . WAM/O No.7

ECHOES OF HARLEM.
Tracks: / Big / Echoes of Harlem / You can depend on me / Adagio for David / Scorpio swings again / Unbooted character, The / Lady of the lavender mist / Pennies from Heaven / Ce mossieu qui parle.
LP: . . . . BLM 51011

ECHOES OF THE DUKE (Lyttelton, Humphrey & His Band & Helen Shapiro).
Tracks: / Take the 'A' train / I got it bad and that ain't good / Caravan / Just squeeze me / Drop me off in Harlem / Solitude / Echoes of The Duke.
LP: . . . . CLGLP 002
MC: . . . . ZCLG 002

GIGS (Lyttelton, Humphrey & His Band).
Tracks: / Stanley steams in / Black butterfly / Ah mersey / Golden gumboot, The / Grey turning blue / Barnes bridge.
LP: . . . . CLGLP 015
MC: . . . . ZCLG 015

HOOK LINE AND SINKER.
LP: 73005

HUMPH AT THE CONWAY.
Tracks: / Texas moaner / Coal black shine / Last smile blues / Elephant stomp blues / Wally plays the blues / My bucket's got a hole in it / I double dare you / That's the old man's blues / Feline stomp / St. James infirmary / Memphis shake / Mo pas lemme cas.
LP: . . . . CLGLP 006
LP: . . . . ENC 164

HUMPH LIVE AT THE BULLS HEAD (Lyttelton, Humphrey & His Band).
Tracks: / Now that we're here, let's go / Echoes of Harlem / Doggin' around / Harbourfront hangout / Miss Matilda / High society / Do nothing till you hear from me / Toot suite / Three little words / Caribana Queen.
LP: . . . . CLGLP 005
MC: . . . . ZCLG 005

HUMPHREY LYTTELTON & HIS BAND (The best of Dixieland) (Lyttelton, Humphrey & His Band).
LP: 838 764 1

IN CANADA.
LP: 3033

INDIVIDUAL TUNES.
Tracks: / Shake it and break it / Maryland / Just once for all time / Texas moaner / Oh dad / Mainly traditional / Elephant stomp.
LP: . . . . LP 60008

IT MAKES MY LOVE COME DOWN.
LP: . . . . DL 5422

IT SEEMS LIKE YESTERDAY (Lyttelton, Humphrey & Wally Fawkes).
Tracks: / Don't monkey with it / Midnight creep / Trog's blues / Blue blow blew / Doormouse.
MC: . . . . ZCLG 001
LP: . . . . CLGLP 001

LONG TALL TENOR (See under Tate, Buddy) (Lyttelton, Humphrey & Buddy Tate).

M & B JAM SESSION,THE (Lyttelton, Humphrey/Various artists).
Tracks: / Blues my naughty sweetie gives to me / On the Alamo / Frankie & Johnny / Crazy Rhythm / Jumpin' at the Woodside / Hucklebuck, The / Honeysuckle rose.
LP: . . . . BEAR 26

MEZZROW.
LP: . . . . DX 2095

ONE DAY I MET AN AFRICAN.
Tracks: / Playboy / Ladyless and lachrymose / It's a thing / Blues in the afternoon / One day I met an African / Hop frog / Sally / Hot house / Sirrumph.
LP: . . . . BLP 12199

PARLOPHONE YEARS, THE.
Tracks: / Memphis blues / Snake rag / Bad penny blues / Lady in red, The / Lightly and politely / Blues excursion / London blues / Onions / Dallas blues / Dormouse, The.
MC: . . . . DM 21 MC

SALUTE TO SATCHMO (see Welsh, Alex) (Lyttelton, Humphrey/Alex Welsh/ Bruce Turner/George Chisholm).

SCATTERBRAINS.
LP: . . . . SOS 1111

SIR HUMPH'S DELIGHT.
Tracks: / Panama rag / Toot sweet / Buddy's habits / I'm old fashioned / Squeeze me / Sir Humph's delight / Small hour fantasy / Ficklefanny strikes again / Cake walkin' babies from home.
LP: . . . . BLP 12188

SPREADING JOY.
Tracks: / Spreadin' joy / Tishomingo blues / Mabel's dream / Hundred years from today / Ugly duckling, The / Black and blue / Blues my naughty sweetie gives to me / East St. Louis toodle-oo / When your lover has gone / Honeysuckle rose / James / If I could be with you / Fish seller.
LP: . . . . BLP 12173

TAKE IT FROM THE TOP.
LP: . . . . BLP 12134

TRIBUTE TO HUMPH, A Vol.5.
LP: . . . . DM 11

TRIBUTE TO HUMPH VOL.1 (Lyttelton, Humphrey & His Band).
LP: . . . . DM 1

TRIBUTE TO HUMPH VOL.2.
LP: . . . . DM 2

TRIBUTE TO HUMPH VOL.3.
LP: . . . . DM 3

TRIBUTE TO HUMPH VOL.4.
LP: . . . . DM 4

TRIBUTE TO HUMPH VOL.6.
Tracks: / Martiniquen song / Ain't cha got music / Just once for all time / Texas moaner / Joshua fit the battle of Jericho / East Coast trot / Breeze (blow my baby back to me) / Mainly traditional / Oh Dad / Mezz's tune / Jelly bean blues / Ace in the hole / Coffee grinder / Fish seller, The / Glory of love.
LP: . . . . DM 12

TRIBUTE TO HUMPH VOL.7.
Tracks: / Ce mossieu qui parle / C'est Filon / One sweet letter from you / Dallas blues / Blues excursion / Squeeze me / Lightly and politely / It's a thing.
LP: . . . . DM 13

TRIBUTE TO HUMPH VOL.8.
Tracks: / Slippery horn / Handful of keys / She's crying for me / Lady in red, The / Pagin' Mr Fagin / Skeleton in the cupboard / Close your eyes / Waiting for Pickard / Sugar rose / Bad penny blues / Love, love.
LP: . . . . DM 14

WEARY BLUES.
LP: 1002

WHEN THE SAINTS.
LP: . . . . HJ 3003

WORLD OF BUDDY BOLDEN, THE (Lyttelton, Humphrey & Johnny Barnes).
Tracks: / Don't go away nobody / Salty dog / Home sweet home / My buckets got a hole in it / Get out of here and get on home.
LP: . . . . CLGLP 013

Lytton, Henry

HENRY LYTTON.
LP: . . . . GEMM 197

Lytton, Paul

COLLECTIVE CALLS (See under Parker, Evan) (Lytton, Paul / Evan Parker).

RA 1+2 (Lytton, Paul with Evan Parker).
LP: . . . . RING 01016

M

M

BOOGIE WITH A SUITCASE.
Tracks: / Satisfy your lust / M Factor / Woman make man / Modern man / Pop muzik (costa del pop mix) / Moonlight and muzak / Neutron / Double talk / Love life / Dance to the ruins / Yellow magic / Eureka.
LP: . . . . FRSLP 1
MC: . . . . FRSMC 1

NEW YORK/LONDON/PARIS/ MUNICH.
Tracks: / Pop muzik / Moonlight and muzak.
LP: . . . . MCF 3046

OFFICIAL SECRETS ACT.
LP: . . . . MCF 3085

M-80

M-80.
LP: . . . . MEGATON 008
LP: . . . . RR 9802

M & M

MYSTERY WALK.
Tracks: / Black stations white stations / Cooling the medium / Come out and dance / I start to stop / Big trees / In between sleep and reason / Garden in the sky / Nation of followers / Alibi room / Rhythm of life.
LP: . . . . PL 70246
MC: . . . . PK 70246
LP: . . . . PL 84922

WORLD IS A BALL.
Tracks: / World is a ball / I watch, I wait / Watching the boys fall down / Only you / By the waters of Babylon / Song in my head / Don't jump the gun / Stuck on the grid / Someone else's shoes.
LP: . . . . PL 70841

M. Walking On The

M WALKING ON THE WATER.
Tracks: / Flowers of the gone / Stones on the beach / Tears behind laughing / Love songs for you / Skin on the Cacao / Waiting / Party in the cemetery / Water in your eyes / Melitaah / Pink pink / Hands in the big machine.
LP: . . . . FUEGOLP 1114

PLUTO.
LP: . . . . FUEGOLP 1121

Maal, Baaba

BAAYO.
MC: . . . . MCT 1061
LP: . . . . MLPS 1061

DJAM LEELII (Maal, Baaba/Mansour Seck).
LP: . . . . FMSL 2014
MC: . . . . FMSC 3014

WANGO.
Tracks: / Wango arti / Demgalam / Laam tooro / Yiiri yalia / Loodo / Sehil.
LP: . . . . SYL 8348

Maastrichts Salon...

BELLE EPOQUE (Maastricht Salon Orchestra).
Tracks: / Florentiner March / Veleta, The / Muhle im schwarzwald Die / Auf der heide bluh'n die letzten rosen / Petite tonkinoise / Serenade / Funiculi funicula / Carnaval des enfants / Susi / Grossmutterchen / Jalousie / Czardasfurstin.
LP: 824 717-1
MC: 824 717-4

SERENATA (Maastrichts Salon Orchestra).
Tracks: / Serenade von toselli / Gold und silber / Bummelpetrus / Wein, du stadt meiner trauma / Adieu tristesse / Plaisir d'amour / Weiner praterleben / Heinselmannchens wachtparade / Vilja lied / Komm zigani / Meditation.
LP: 412 322-1
MC: 412 322-4

Mabele, Aurlus

AFRICA MOUSSOS.
LP: . . . . JP 001

LAISSER TOMBER.
LP: . . . . P 01

Mabern, Harold

JOY SPRING.
LP: 2016

Mabon, Willie

BLUES ROOTS VOL 16.
Tracks: / I don't know / Beggar or bandit / You're a fool / Monday woman / Willie's blues / Someday you gotta pay / Poison ivy / I'm mad at you / Lonely blues / I'm tired / He lied / Knock on wood / Why did it happen to me / Seventh son.
LP: . . . . GCH 8099

CHESS MASTERS...WILLIE MABON.
Tracks: / I don't know / Beggar or bandit / You're a fool / Monday woman / Willie's blues / Someday you gotta pay / Poison ivy / I'm mad at you / Lonely blues / I'm tired / He lied / Knock on wood / Why did it happen to me / Seventh son.
LP: . . . . CXMP 2056

CHICAGO BLUES SESSION.
LP: . . . . LR 42.003

COMEBACK, THE.
LP: . . . . BEAR 9

I'M THE FIXER.
LP: . . . . FLY 580

SEVENTH SON, THE.
Tracks: / I don't know / I'm mad / You're a fool / I got to go / Late again / Poison ivy / Wow I feel good / Seventh son / Knock on wood / Worry blues / Night latch / Monday woman / Cruisin' / Would you baby / Say man / Come on baby / Lucinda / Got to let you go.
LP: . . . . IG 402

Maboul, Aksak

ONZE DANSES POUR COMBATTRE LA MIGRAINE.
LP: . . . . CRAM 011

UN PEU DE L'AME DES BANDITS.
LP: . . . . CRAM 002

Mabsant

CHWAR'E CHWYLDRO.
LP: . . . . SYW 448

COFEB.
LP: . . . . SAIN 1508M

TRWY'R WEIAR.
LP: . . . . SAIN 1404 M

Mabus, Joel

FAIRIES AND FOOLS.
LP: . . . . FF 296

SETTIN' THE WOODS ON FIRE.
LP: . . . . FF 235

Mabuse, Sipho

CHANT OF THE MARCHING.
Tracks: / Tika jive / Refugee / Room of horror / Kululani umandela (Mandela) / Township child / Chant / Celebration / Taxi driver / Mama.
LP: . . . . V 2582
MC: . . . . TCV 2582

SIPHO MABUSE.
Tracks: / Shikisha / Rhythm lady / In the night / Path to freedom / Ti nyanga (African doctor) / Burn out / Let's get it on / Jive Soweto / Shikisha (The UB40 mix) (CD only).
LP: . . . . V 2425
MC: . . . . TCV 2425

Mac Band

MAC BAND LP, THE.
LP: . . . . MCA 42090

MAC BAND, THE.
LP: . . . . MCG 6032
MC: . . . . MCGC 6032

Mac, Pat

TWO SIDES OF PAT MAC, THE.
MC: . . . . GTDC 006

Mac, Richie

JAH IS I LIGHT.
LP: . . . . LDLP 1

Mac the Paperman

UP TO THE BOX.
Tracks: / Morning Mac / Dirty dicks / Them french / City mob / I must of pulled a muscle / I phoned Monty / No standards / Death on the Nile / Concrete mob / Royal family, The / Africa / Spain / Sex / Coin balancing.
LP: . . . . DPROMLP 1
MC: . . . . DPROMC 1

Macabre

GRIM REALITY.
LP: . . . . SOL 18

McAlindon, Hugh

DIAMOND GREEN.
Tracks: / Diamond green / My darling blue eyed boy has kicked the pail / Three thousand miles away / Toney wine / Ship's carpenter / You lie next the wall / Miss McCann / Bonnie labouring boy, The / Ducks of Magherlin / Mourne Maggie-O / Rathfriland on the hill / Nightingale / Sarah's young man / Big Lynch the policeman.
MC: . . . . COAS 3019
LP: . . . . OAS 3019

Macalla

MACALLA 2.
LP: . . . . CEF 122

MINA NA HEIREANN.
LP: . . . . CEF 110
MC: . . . . CEFC 110

McAloon, Sean

DROPS OF BRANDY Traditional Irish (McAloon, Sean & John Rea).
Tracks: / Maid in the meadow, The / Castlebar races, The / Trip to the cottage / Mountain lark, The / Crooked road to Dublin / Jackson's drum / Jackson's mistake / Jackson's coagy / Blind Mary / Madame Bonaparte / O'Dwyer's hornpipes / Crowley's No. 1 / Crowley's No. 2 / Moloney's / Paddy O'Brien's jig / First house in Connaught, The / Copperplate, The / An buachaill caol dubh / Drops of brandy / Coil the hawser / Lord McDonald's / Alexandria's / Higgin's / Sligo maid, The / Sheephan's / Wandering minstrel / Katy is waiting / Basket of Shamrocks, The / Tim the turncoat / Quarrelsome piper, The / Old siege of Valencia, The / Lark in the morning, The.
LP: 12TS 287

MacAlpine, Tony

EDGE OF INSANITY.
LP: . . . . RR 9706
MC: . . . . RR 97064

EYES OF THE WORLD.
LP: 841 516 1
MC: 841 516 4

MAXIMUM SECURITY.
Tracks: / Autumn lords / Hundreds of thousands / Tears of Sahara / Keys to the city / Time and the test, The / Kings cup, The / Sacred wonder / Etude 4 Opus 10 / Vision, The / Dreamstate / Porcelain doll.
LP: . . . . VERH 44
MC: . . . . VERHC 44

McAnally, Mac

FINISH LINES.
Tracks: / Finish lines / Alien / Be with me / Desiree / Remote control / E = MC2 (she picked you up) / Hush money / Little blue pill / History / Everything's alright.
LP: 9241911
MC: 9241914

McAndless, Paul

NAVIGATOR.
LP: . . . . LD 1005

Macarthur

MACARTHUR (Film Soundtrack) (Various artists).
LP: 255088 1
MC: . . . . VSC 5260

MacArthur, Alex

BIGGER AND BETTER SOUND, THE (MacArthur, Alex & His Scottish Dance Band).
LP: . . . . WGR 022
MC: . . . . CWGR 022

McArthur, Helen

CHRISTMAS WITH BRASS (See under Whitburn Burgh Band).
LP: . . . . NTS 139

UPON THE MIDNIGHT CLEAR.
LP: . . . . NTS 158

Macaskill, Ishbel

BELOVED LEWIS.
Tracks: / Would that you had been / Young girl of the fair hair / High swell of the sea, The / I cannot sleep / Deer are on Uig slope, The / Beloved Lewis / Brother's killing, The / Lament for John Roy, The / Near Loch an duin / I'll make a verse / Lament for Donnie Ferguson, A.
LP: . . . . LAP 117
MC: . . . . LAP 117C

Macaulay, Willie John

FROM LEWIS TO LOCHINDAAL.
Tracks: / Iondrain na hearadh / Cuimhnich a ghillean / Ghruagach og an fhuilt bhain / Iolaire, The / Creag a fhradich / Failte do Eilean Leodhais / Mairi dhonn / Na hearadh / Soluis loch an dala / Pheigi a ghraidh / Chi mi n tir / Eilean Eisdeil.
MC: . . . . LICS 5056
LP: . . . . LILP 5056

FROM SCOTLAND FOR YOU.
Tracks: / Stornoway / Harlosh by the sea / Highlands of Scotland / Dreams of port wemyss / Green Hebrides / Lovely Easdale / Dreaming of Barra / Bonnie naver bay / Scotland rule / Eileen / Barra, My home / Drumossie moor.
MC: . . . . HPCS 2007

McAuliffe, Leon

COZY INN.
LP: . . . . ABC 394

EVERYBODY DANCE, EVERYBODY SWING.
LP: . . . . HAT 3108
MC: . . . . HATC 3108

MEMBERS 1 (McAuliffe, Leon & Bob Wills' Texas Playboys).
LP: . . . . CW 205

MEMBERS 2 (McAuliffe, Leon & Bob Wills' Texas Playboys).
LP: . . . . CW 206

McAvoy, Gerry

BASSICS.
LP: . . . . BHLP 005

McBeath, Jimmy

BOUND TO BE A ROW.
Tracks: / There's bound to be a row / Banks of Inverurie, The / Ythanside / Erin go bragh / Bogie's bonnie belle / Cow wi' the iron tail, The / Arlin's fine braes / Bonnie lass o' Fyvie / Pittenweem jo / Ye canna pit it on tae Sandy / Boston smuggler, The / Highland Rorie's wedding / Magdalen green, The / Marin fair / Roving baker, The.
LP: 12T 303

HORSEMAN'S WORD.
Tracks: / Jim the Carter lad / Farmer, the ploughboy and the dairymaid, The / Come all ye lonely lovers / Bogie's bonnie belle / Drumdelgie / Mormond braes / Auld quarry knowes / Barnyards of Delgaty.
MC: 60-059

MCBEATH, MCCAFFERY AND MCPHERSON.
Tracks: / Wind blew the bonnie lassie's plaidie awa', The / Hey, jump, and on you go / Awa' tae the scrap i' the morning / Tobacco pipes and porter / Smith's a gallant fireman / When the boat comes in / Skippin' barfit' through the heather / Van Dieman's land / McCallum the poacher / He widna want his gruel / Rich girl and robbers, The / Gallant forty twa / Eppie morrie / Devil of Portsoy / Torn a ripit, torn a goon / Trooper lad, The.
MC: 60-060

STREET SINGER AND STORYTELLER VOL. 3.
MC: 60-0060

TRAMPS AND HAWKERS.
Tracks: / Tramps and hawkers / Next pudden Ken / Moss o' Burreldale, The / Muckin' o' Geordie's byre / Dowie dens of Yarrow, The / Hawick common riding song / Day we went to Rothsay-o, The / John Anderson, my Jo / Forfar soldier, The / Down by the maudlin green.
MC: 60-058

WILD ROVER NO MORE.
Tracks: / Bold english navvy, The / Come a' ye tramps an' hawkers / Johnny McIndoe / Wind blew the bonnie lassie's plaidie awa', The / Merchant and the beggar maid, The / Nicky tams / Barnyards of Delgaty / I'm a stranger in this country / Moss o' Burreldale, The / Highlandman's ball, The / McPherson's rant / Grat for gruel / Drumdelgie / Wild rover no more.
LP: 12T 173

McBee, Cecil

ALTERNATE SPACES.
LP: . . . . IN 1043

COMPASSION (McBee, Cecil Sextet).
LP: ENJA 3041

FLYING OUT.
LP: IN 1053

MUSIC FROM THE SOURCE (McBee, Cecil Sextet).
LP: ENJA 3019

POWER TRIO, THE (See under Hicks, John) (Hicks, John, Cecil McBee & Elvin Jones).

McBee, Hamper

RAW BASH.
LP: ROUNDER 0061

McBennett, Helen

THAT'S WHEN THE MUSIC.
LP: GES 1182

Macbeth

MACBETH (see under Shakespeare, William) (Various artists).

McBride, Frankie

COULD I HAVE THIS DANCE.
Tracks: / Could I have this dance / Laura (what's he got that I ain't got) / I'm that easy to forget / Till the end / Help me / Acapulco / Just beyond the moon / Rock 'n' roll (I gave you the best years) / I'm being good / Let's build a love together / If you love me / Play another slow song.
LP: JULEP 27
MC: KJULEP 27

FIVE LITTLE FINGERS.
Tracks: / Burning bridges / Forty shades of green / I really don't want to know / If I kiss you (will you go away) / Long black limousine / Do you mind if you leave me sleeping / Wanting you / How are things in Glocca morra? / Remember me / I don't love you anymore / Five little fingers / Don't make me go.
LP: GES 1097
MC: KGEC 1097

FRANKIE MCBRIDE.
LP: SLD 28

VERY BEST OF FRANKIE MCBRIDE, THE.
Tracks: / Laura / Five little fingers / Acapulco / If I kiss you (will you go away) / Burning bridges / Teach me to dance / Forty shades of green / Could I have this dance / Four in the morning / Give a lonely heart a home / Got another mountain to climb.
MC: MCLP 1008

WHY ME LORD.
MC: MB LP 1020

McBride, Jeff

DO YOU STILL REMEMBER LOVE?.
Tracks: / You go to my head / No sweeter love / Do you still remember love / Just an American girl / Good old days / Gotta good thing / Love is gonna get you / Doesn't that mean something / I just laugh.
LP: 211008
MC: 411008

McBrides

GREAT SONGS FROM IRELAND.
LP: UNKNOWN

YOUR FAVOURITE IRISH SONGS.
LP: UNKNOWN

McBroom, Amanda

GROWING UP IN HOLLYWOOD TOWN (McBroom, Amanda & Mayorga Lincoln).
LP: LAB 13

WEST OF OZ (see Mayorga, Lincoln) (Mayorga, Lincoln & Amanda McBroom).

Macc Lads

BEER AND SEX AND CHIPS AND GRAVY.
LP: WKFMLP 56
MC: HH 1

BEER NECESSITIES, THE.
LP: HHLP 14
MC: HH 14

BITTER, FIT CRACK.
Tracks: / Barrel's round / Guess me weight / Uncle Knobby / Maid of ale / Dan's big log / Got to be Gordon's / Bitter, fit crack / Julie the schooly / Doctor doctor / Torremolinos / Al o'peesha.
LP: WKFMLP 100
MC: HH 7

FROM BEER TO ETERNITY.
Tracks: / Alton Towers / Geordie girl / No sheep 'til Buxton / All day drinking / Tab after tab / Lucy Lastic / My pub / Dead cat / Lady Muck / Gordon's revenge / Pie taster / 'Dan's round yer 'andbag / Ben Nevis / Fluffy pup / Stoppyback / Ugly women.
LP: HHLP 12
MC: HH 12

LIVE AT LEEDS (The Who?).
LP: WKFMLP 115
MC: HH 10
MC: WKFMMC 115

TURTLES HEADS.
MC: HH 17

Macca B

WE'VE HAD ENOUGH.
LP: ARILP 032

McCabe, Geoffrey

GEOFFREY MCCABE RESERACT COMPILICITY.
LP: SJP 212

Maccabees

MACCABEES (Various artists).
LP: MACLP 1

McCafferty, Dan

INTO THE RING.
LP: 8309341
MC: 8309344

McCaffey, Anne

WHITE DRAGON, THE.
LP: TC 1596

McCaffrey, Frank

I'LL TAKE YOU HOME AGAIN KATHLEEN & OTHER.....
Tracks: / I'll take you home again Kathleen / Road by the river / If we only had old Ireland over here / Gypsy, The / Little grey home in the West / Moonlight in Mayo / More than yesterday / Jody and the kid / Candlelight and wine / Ring your mother wore / Love is a game / Daisy a day.
LP: RITZLP 0037
MC: RITZLC 0037

JEALOUS HEART.
LP: BRL 4096

MY WILD IRISH ROSE.
LP: HRL 222

PLACE IN MY HOME.
Tracks: / Clock in the tower, The / Place in my heart, A / Day the world stood still, The / Drive safely darling / I'd rather be sorry / Annie's story / Blackboard of my heart / All alone in New York City / It's our anniversary / Give a lonely heart a home / Rose, The / Always Mayo.
LP: RITZLC 0049

TODAY.
MC: RITZLC 0062

McCaffrey, Leo

EVENING IN THE GLENS, AN.
Tracks: / Typical Irishman / Molly Bawn / Carraigdoon / Boys from County Mayo / Castle of Dromore / Ireland mother Ireland / Bonnie green tree, The / Town of Galway / Miltown Malbay / Cushendun / Faughan side.
LP: PHL 418
MC: CPHL 418

SOUVENIR OF IRELAND.
Tracks: / Bantry bay / On the banks of my own lovely Lee / Bold Terry Quill / Rose of Tralee, The / Limerick is beautiful / Colleen Bawn lass from the county Clare / Galway shawl / Queen of Connemara / Kitty Magee / Ballyshannon / Destination donegal / Sheephaven bay / My hills of Donegal / Lovely Derry on the banks of the Foyle / Fionola, the gem of the roe / Gentle maiden, The / My Lagan love / Rathlin Island.
MC: CHRL 207
LP: HRL 207

WEEKEND IN IRELAND.
Tracks: / Bard of Armagh, The / Star of the County Down / Mountains of Mourne / Phil the fluter's ball / Come back Paddy Reilly to Ballyjamesduff / Dear old Donegal / Rose of Tralee, The / Galway Bay / Rose of Mooncoin / Old bog road / Isle of Innisfree / My wild Irish rose / Blarney roses / When Irish eyes are smiling / Danny boy / How can you buy Killarney.
LP: GES 1021
MC: KGEC 1021

MacCaig, Norman

WAY I SAY IT, THE.
LP: CCA 4

McCain, Jerry

BLUES 'N' STUFF.
Tracks: / Messin' with me baby / Three wives / Brand new mojo / Spoiled rotten (to the bone) / Love makin' showdown / Rose for my lady, A / My baby's got it / Goin' to the dogs.
LP: ICH 1047
MC: ZCICH 1047

CHOO CHOO ROCK.
Tracks: / Cute names Judy / Geronimo's rock / It must be love / Rock 'n' roll ball / I need somebody to love / Turn your damper down / I'm a ding dong daddy / Choo choo rock / Bell in my heart / My next door neighbour / Crying like a fool.
LP: WLP 9966

LOVE DESPERADO.
Tracks: / Blues tribute / Burn the crackhouse down / I need to do something / Love desperado / World's on fire, The / Lovin' school / I used to have it / Mercy, mercy, mercy / Non-stop lovin'.
LP: ICH 9008
MC: ICH 9008MC

MIDNIGHT BEAT.
Tracks: / Honky tonk / Sugar baby / Homogenised love / Midnight beat / I don't care where I get my loving / Love ain't nothing to play with / Juicy Lucy / Somebody's been talking / Soul spasm / She's crazy 'bout entertainers / 728 Texas / Stick em up / Put it where I can get it.
LP: CRB 1148

McCall, Cash

NO MORE DOGGIN'.
LP: LR 42.058

McCall, Mary Ann

DETOUR TO THE MOON.
LP: FS 258

McCall, Toussaint

NOTHING TAKES THE PLACE OF YOU (SINGLE) (See under Giles, Eddie 'That's how strong my love is').

McCalla, Noel

NIGHT TIME EMOTION.
Tracks: / Smile / Night time emotion / Girl I realise / Ain't nothing but a house party / Night life on Venus / Loving arms / Who's fooling who? / Midnight girl / Where is our love / Groovin'.
LP: EPC 83838

McCallum, Craig

IN A DIFFERENT LIGHT (McCallum, Craig Scottish Dance Band).
MC: CTRAX 037

McCallum, William

PIPERS OF DISTINCTION.
MC: ZCMON 801

McCalmans

ANCESTRAL MANOEUVRES.
Tracks: / Ancestral manoeuvres / 10000 miles away / Avalon / Aberlady Bay / Ghoulies and ghosties / Scotland / Falkirk tryate / Da sang o'de papa man / Sidmouth folk festival blues / Rolling hills of the borders / Loves the rising sun / Goodnight sweetheart.
MC: CTRAX 023
LP: TRAX 023

AUDIENCE WITH THE MCCALMANS, AN.
Tracks: / Bonnie Dundee / Trawling trade, The / My Johnny is a shoemaker / Charles in France / Love bug will bite you, The / Burning, The / Kilgannon Mountain / Mingulay boat song / Auburn maid / All around my hat / Bread and fishes / Sweet senorita / Goodnight and joy.
LP: LSA 3179

ETTRICK SHEPHERD, THE.
Tracks: / McLean's welcome / Donald McDonald / Witch of Fife, The / Bonnie Prince Charlie / King Willie / I ha'e naebody now / Highlander's farewell, The / Sir Morgan O'Doherty's farewell to Scotland/Reply to Sir.. / Moon was a-waning / Ladies' evening song / Rise, rise lowland and highland men / Good night and joy.
LP: GVR 209
MC: CTRAX 046

FLAMES ON THE WATER.
Tracks: / Ah'm e man at muffed it / Isle of Eigg / Devolution anthem / Farewell tae the haven / Sounding / Hawks and eagles / Siege, The / Who pays the piper / Festival lights / Shian Road / Men o'worth / Curtain call.
LP: TRAX 036
MC: CTRAX 036

LISTEN TO THE HEAT-LIVE.
Tracks: / I have seen the Highlands / Town of Kiandra / Mount and go / Sister Josephine / 23rd June / Prisoner's song / Song song, The / Rambling Rover / Rory Murphy / First Christmas / Lakewood (inst) / Thriepmuir hornpipe (inst) / Royal Belfast (inst) / President's men, The / Air fa la la la lo / Sickening thank you song.
LP: TRAX 019
MC: CTRAX 019

NO STRINGS ATTACHED.
Tracks: / Women are a' gane wud, The / Weaving song, The / Carrion crow, A / Kangaroo / Rise and follow Charlie / Chiefs return from war, The / Windmills / Tailor, The / Busk busk bonnie lassie / Far fairer she / Execution of Montrose, The / Veronica.
LP: PL 25086

PEACE AND PLENTY.
Tracks: / Tullochgorum / Bells of the town, The / Song of the plough / Colliery gate, The / No you won't get me down in your mines / Black bear, The / Drover's lad, The / Top house, The / South Australia / Esikibo river / Blood red roses / Little Sally Rackett / Up and rin awa' Geordie / Mothers, daughters, wives / Highland road, The / Barratt's privateers / Men of the sea / Song for Europe / Tae the weavers gin ye gang / Leave her Johnny.
LP: TRAX 002
MC: CTRAX 002

SCOTTISH SONGS.
Tracks: / Farewell tae tarwathie / Smuggler / Mormond braes / Mingulay boat song.
LP: WGR 092
MC: CWGR 092

SONGS FROM SCOTLAND.
Tracks: / Boys that broke the ground, The / Tiree love song, The / Highland laddie / Roll the woodpile down / Hundred years ago, A / Westering home / Last session, The / All the tunes in the world / Most amazing thing of all, The / I will go / Widow MacKay / April waltz / Up and awa' wi' the Laverock / Scarce o'tatties / Lark in the morning, The / Ainster Harbour / Twa recruitin' / Sergeants / Rolling home.
MC: CTRAX 045

McCandless

SKYLIGHT (see under Lande) (McCandless/Lande/Samuels).

McCann, Hoops

HOOPS MCCANN BAND PLAYS STEELY DAN (Hoops McCann Band).
LP: MCA 42202

McCann, Jim

FROM TARA TO HERE.
LP: KLP 230

GRACE AND OTHER LOVE SONGS.
MC: LNMC 7013

JIM MCCANN.
Tracks: / Copper kettle / Blow the candle out / Rare ould times / Grey sea strand, The / Town is not their own, The / Alone / From Clare to here / Follow me up to Carlow / My old man / Weather the storm / Her father didn't like me anyway.
LP: HALP 179
MC: HACS 179
MC: HACS 7079

JIM MCCANN LIVE.
MC: RTE 68

McCann, Les

LES IS MORE.
LP: VNLP 4
MC: VNTC 4

MAN, THE.
Tracks: / Just the way you are / Flow with the feeling / Blue dot / How can you / You think you're something Mr. Man / I'm always waiting, waiting for you / Para ti, para mi.
LP: AMLH 64718

MUSIC BOX.
Tracks: / Memories of compared to what (intro.) / Elephant strut / Blue 'n' boogie / All strung out on you (instrumental) / Bat yam / Memories of compared to what (outro.).
LP: PAL 3

STORMY MONDAY (see under Rawls, Lou) (McCann, Les Limited & Lou Rawls).

SWISS MOVEMENT (See under Harris, Eddie) (McCann, Les/Eddie Harris).

McCann, Phillip

WORLD'S MOST BEAUTIFUL MELODIES, THE.
Tracks: / Songs my mother taught me / Ave Maria / Lullaby / Passing by / One fine day / Madame Butterfly / None but the lonely heart / Rusalka's song to the moon / Nessun dorma / Maids of cadiz, the / My love is like a red red rose / Du bist die ruh / Girl with the flaxen hair, The / O, my beloved father / Non sp iu / Lost chord, The.
LP: BBRD 1029
MC: BBTD 1029

McCann, Susan

18 VERY BEST.
LP: TSC 209

20 COUNTRY CLASSICS.
MC: MB LP 1034

AT HOME IN IRELAND.
Tracks: / Johnny, lovely Johnny / Eileen McManus / Curragh of Kildare, The / Once upon a time / Nightingale / Blossom will flower, The / Rose of Clare / Where the river Shannon flows / Isle of Innisfree / If those lips could only speak / Noreen Bawn / Rose of Tralee, The.
LP: DHL 706

MC: . . . . CDHL 706

BACK TO ME.
LP: . . . . KLP 180
MC: . . . . KMC 180B

BEST OF 20 HITS.
LP: . . . . KLP 105
MC: . . . . KMC 105

BEST OF SUSAN MCCANN.
Tracks: / Someone is looking for someone like you / Heaven help the working girl / Rockabilly can rock / Love is supposed to be / Coat of many colours / Even cowgirls get the blues / I want your loving arms around me / Late late show, The / Seeing is believing / While I was making love to you / Blue Kentucky girl / Nothing like a rainy night / Lie to Linda / Hi-fi to cry by / Blue ribbon beer drinking song / Down to my last broken heart / '57 Chevrolet / I feel sorry for anyone who isn't me tonight / What I've got in mind / River road.
MC: . . . . TSC 205
LP: . . . . TSLP 205
LP: . . . . NE 1205
MC: . . . . CE 2205

BEST OF THE SIXTIES.
Tracks: / Daydream believer / My boy lollipop / Downtown / Bobby's girl / Come what may / Walkin' back to happiness / Lipstick on your collar / Saturday night at the movies / Stupid Cupid / Calendar guy / Another Saturday night / Mr. Tambourine man.
MC: . . . . MCLP 1005

CHART HITS.
Tracks: / Flashback / He's a heartache / Single girl / I feel love comin' on / It's you, it's you, it's you / Song for Gloria / Tennessee mountain home / I wouldn't change you if I could / True love ways / I hope you're having better luck / Broken lady / Let me go to Texas.
MC: . . . . MC 1

COUNTRY LOVE AFFAIR.
Tracks: / Never ending love affair / Johnny lovely Johnny / Blue velvet / Forever and ever amen / Little ole wine drinker me / Travellin' light / Let the rest of the world go by / Two broken hearts / Someone is looking for someone like you / Irish eyes / Boy in your arms / Wind in the willows / Mother's love is a blessing, A / Patches in heaven / How great thou art / When the sun says goodbye to the mountain.
MC: . . . . IHMC 482

DOWN RIVER ROAD.
Tracks: / 57 Chevrolet / Mama say a prayer / Baby nothing's wrong with me / It don't take much to make me cry / That little boy of mine / Hi-fi to cry by / Down river road / Most precious than ever / Awareness of nothing / Daddy come and get me / My blue tears / Good ole country music.
MC: . . . . TSC 118

GOOD 'N' COUNTRY.
Tracks: / Other side of the morning / Take me back / Lie to Linda / Sparkling look of love / I don't want to wear diamonds / Your old handy man / Seeing is believing / I'm just not that good at goodbye / Under cover lovers / Isle of Ireland / Nickels & dimes / All the love I have I give to you.
MC: . . . . TSC 122

IN NASHVILLE.
Tracks: / Someone is looking for someone like you / Slipping around again / Someone just like you / All day sucker / He's everything I wanted you to be / Just like you / Little girl gone / Dream, The / Life turned him that way / She's out there dancing alone / Love is supposed to be / Blue Kentucky girl.
LP: . . . . SSC 501

ISLE OF IRELAND.
Tracks: / Travelling people / Village of Astee, The / Green willow / 5,000 miles from Sligo / Big Tom is still the king / Heaven around Galway Bay / Cottage on the Old Dungannon Road / Where is my Nora / Rose of Allandale / Isle of Ireland / Limerick you're a lady / Christmas time in Innisfree.
LP: . . . . TSLP 206
MC: . . . . TSC 206

MERRY CHRISTMAS.
Tracks: / It's gonna be one happy Christmas / Pretty papers / Santa looks a lot like daddy / We must be having one / Christmas time in Innisfree / White Christmas / Santa & the kids / Angel and the stranger, The / Let's celebrate this Christmas / Lonely Christmas / Please daddy / Silent night.
MC: . . . . TSC 114

PAPA'S WAGON.
Tracks: / I can feel the leaving coming on / Patches in heaven / It's a no no / If you want me / Time can't erase / Big Tom is still the king / Papa's wagon / Dreamin' my dreams / Tabernacle Tom / I don't believe you've met my baby / Gentle on my mind / Country music in my soul.
MC: . . . . TSC 94
MC: . . . . MBLP 1017

SENTIMENTAL JOURNEY.
LP: . . . . KLP 120

SINCERELY YOURS.
Tracks: / Dirty cheezy jeans / When the rain disappears / I feel sorry for anyone who isn't me tonight / Blue ribbon beer drinking song / Hard loved lady and the guitar player from Tennessee, The / Nothing like a rainy night / Down to my last broken heart / Does your mama know what you're doing / Chuck the chuck wagon (Duet with Porter Wagoner) / They won't let you rock and roll no more at the Palomino / Rainy days & stormy nights / Wishful thinking.
LP: . . . . SSC 507

SINGS COUNTRY.
Tracks: / Feeling single seeing double / Galway Bay / Adios, farewell, goodbye / I don't want to play house / Did you ever hear the robin sing / What I've got in mind / Keep on the sunny side / Wrong road again / Coat of many colours / Where is my Nora / Old fashioned song / Wild side of life.
MC: . . . . TSC 92
MC: . . . . MBLP 1016

SOMETIMES WHEN WE TOUCH (McCann, Susan & Ronan Collins).
Tracks: / Islands in the stream / Everything is beautiful / All I have to do is dream / Nobody loves me like you do / Welcome home / Little bit of love, A / Just to satisfy you / Have you ever been lonely / Sometimes when we touch / Rose of my heart / I just want to stay here and love you / Somebody done somebody wrong.
MC: . . . . MCLP 1003

SONGS JUST FOR YOU.
Tracks: / Could it be I don't belong here anymore / Have I told you lately that I love you / This song is just for you / There goes my everything / Could I have this dance / Baby blue / Paper roses / Jealous heart / Country roads / Remember you're mine / Buried treasure / Part of me.
LP: . . . . DHL 713
MC: . . . . CDHL 713

SONNY'S DREAM (McCann, Susan & Brendan Quinn).
MC: . . . . MB LP 1019

SOUND OF MUSIC, THE.
LP: . . . . MC 2

STORYBOOK COUNTRY.
Tracks: / Blue jean country queen / Last one to touch me, The / Even cowgirls get the blues / Late late show, The / Heaven help the working girl / You're driving me out of my mind / I don't blame my papa / They'll never ever take his love from me / Hands / Conscience keep an eye on me tonight / It's no wonder I'm still blue / I want you loving arms around me.
LP: . . . . SSLP 503
MC: . . . . SSC 503

TOWN I LOVE SO WELL, THE.
Tracks: / Dublin in my tears / Old Dungarvan Oak / Sarah Jane / Dan O'Hara / Town I loved so well, The / Galway races / What price is peace / If I came back home / Wild colonial boy / Lakes of Coolfin / Irish rover, The.
MC: . . . . MBMC 1032
LP: . . . . MBLP 1032

TRIBUTE TO BUCK OWENS (Live at the Grand).
Tracks: / Buckaroo / I'll love you for ever and ever / Act naturally / Foolin' around / Love's gonna live here again / Gonna roll out the red carpet / Second fiddle / Lay it on the line / Crying time / We split the blanket down the middle / Above and beyond / There never was a fool / Excuse me (I think I've got a heartache) / Together again / She don't deserve you any more / I've got a tiger by the tail / It takes people like you to make people like me / Buck's polka.
LP: . . . . HOTV 1
MC: . . . . CHOTV 1

TWENTY COUNTRY CLASSICS.
LP: . . . . HM 028

WHEN THE SUN SAYS GOODBYE TO THE MOUNTAINS.
Tracks: / Bus to L.A. / Nickels & dimes / Once a day / Down river road / They'll never take his love from me / Someone is looking for someone like you / When the sun says goodbye to the mountains / It's you, it's you, its you / Single girl / Last one to touch me, The / Sing me an old fashioned song / '57 Chevrolet.
LP: . . . . TSLP 207
MC: . . . . TSC 207

YOU GAVE ME LOVE.
LP: . . . . WST R 9699
MC: . . . . WST C 9699

McCarroll, Andy

EPITAPH FOR A REBEL.
LP: . . . . PC 116

McCarters

GIFT, THE.
Tracks: / I give you music / Timeless and true love / I know love / Quiet desperation / Flower in the desert / Where would that leave me / Loving you / Letter from home.
LP: 925737 1
MC: 925737 4

McCarthy

ENRAGED WILL INHERIT THE EARTH.
LP: . . . . CHIME 047 S
MC: . . . . CHIME 047 CC

I AM A WALLET.
LP: . . . . SEPT 2
LP: . . . . CHIME 0045 S
MC: . . . . CHIME 0045CC
LP: . . . . CHIME 45

INTERNATIONAL NARCOTICS TRAFFIC, THE.
LP: . . . . SEPT 009

THAT'S ALL VERY WELL BUT....
LP: . . . . CHIME 041
MC: . . . . CHIME 041C

McCarthy, Kevin (nar)

PSYCHO (see under Psycho (bk)).

McCarthy, Maggie

MORE NAUGHTY LITTLE SISTER STORIES (See also Dorothy Edwards).

McCarthy, Willie

THOUGHTS OF IRELAND.
LP: . . . . FALT 0112
MC: . . . . FACS 012

McCartney, Paul

ALL THE BEST.
Tracks: / Coming up / Ebony and ivory / Listen to what the man said / No more lonely nights / Silly love songs / Let 'em in / C moon / Pipes of peace / Live and let die / Another day / Maybe I'm amazed / Goodnight tonight / Once upon a long ago / Say say say / With a little luck / My love / We all stand together / Mull of Kintyre / Jet / Band on the run.
2LP: . . . . PMTV 1
MC: . . . . TCPMTV 1

CHOBA B CCCP.
Tracks: / Kansas City / Twenty flight rock / I'm in love again / Lawdy Miss Clawdy / Bring it on home to me / Lucille / Don't get around much anymore / I'm gonna be a wheel someday / That's all right mama / Summertime / Ain't that a shame / Crackin' up / Just because / Midnight special.
MC: . . . . TCPCSD 117

FLOWERS IN THE DIRT.
Tracks: / My brave face / Rough ride / You want her too / Distractions / We got married / We got there / Figure of eight / This one / Don't be careless love / That day is done / How many people / Motor of love / Ou est le soleil (Not on album.).
MC: . . . . TCPCSD 106
LP: . . . . PCSD 106
MC: 791 653 4
LP: 791 653 1

GIVE MY REGARDS TO BROAD STREET (Film Soundtrack).
Tracks: / No more lonely nights / Good day sunshine / Corridor music / Yesterday / Here, there and everywhere / Wanderlust / Ballroom dancing / Silly love songs / Silly love songs (reprise) / Not such a bad boy / So bad / No values / No more lonely nights (reprise) / For no one / Eleanor Rigby / Eleanor's dream / Long and winding road, The / No more lonely nights (play out version) / Goodnight princess.
LP: . . . . PCTC 2
MC: . . . . TCPCTC 2
LP: . . . . EL 2602781
MC: . . . . EL 2602780
LP: . . . . ATAK 165
MC: . . . . TCATAK 165

LIVERPOOL PRESS CONFERENCE 1990 INTERVIEW.
LP: . . . . FORNO 1

MCCARTNEY.
Tracks: / Lovely Linda, The / That would be something / Valentine day / Every night / Hot as sun glasses / Junk / Man we was lonely / Oo you / Momma Miss America / Teddy boy / Singalong junk / Maybe I'm amazed / Kreen-akrore.
LP: . . . . FA 4131001
MC: . . . . FA 4131004
LP: . . . . PCS 7102
MC: . . . . TCPCS 7102
LP: 746 611 1
MC: 746 611 4
LP: . . . . ATAK 152
MC: . . . . TCATAK 152

MCCARTNEY II.
Tracks: / Coming up / Temporary secretary / On the way / Waterfalls / Nobody knows / Front parlour / Summer's day song / Frozen jap / Bogey music / Dark room / One of these days / Check my machine / Secret friend.
LP: . . . . PCTC 258
MC: . . . . TCPCTC 258
LP: . . . . FA 3191
MC: . . . . TCFA 3191
MC: . . . . TCFA 41 31914

MCCARTNEY INTERVIEW.
LP: . . . . CHAT 1

PAUL MCCARTNEY: INTERVIEW PICTURE DISC.
LPPD: . . . . BAK 2003

PIPES OF PEACE.
Tracks: / Pipes of peace / Say say say / Other me, The / Keep under cover / So bad / Man / Sweetest little show / Average person / Hey hey / Tug of peace / Through our love.
LP: . . . . PCTC 1652301
MC: . . . . TCPCTC 1652304
LP: . . . . PCTC 1
MC: . . . . TCPCTC 1
LP: . . . . ATAK 164
MC: . . . . TCATAK 164

PRESS CONFERENCES MADRID / LOS ANGELES.
LPPD: . . . . TUGA 4

PRESS CONFERENCES ROME/ LONDON 1989.
LP: . . . . BANDONTHE 1

PRESS TO PLAY.
Tracks: / Strangehold / Good times coming / Talk more talk / Footprints / Only love remains / Press / Pretty little head / Move over busker / Angry / However absurd / Write away (Extra track available on CD.) / It's not true (Available on CD.) / Tough on a tightrope (Track available on CD only.) / Feel the sun.
LP: . . . . PCSD 103
MC: . . . . TCPCSD 103
LP: . . . . FA 3209
MC: . . . . TCFA 3209

RAM (McCartney, Paul & Linda).
Tracks: / Too many people / 3 legs / Ram on / Dear boy / Uncle Albert / Smile away / Heart of the country / Monkberry moon delight / Eat at home / Long haired lady / Ram on / Backseat of my car.
LP: . . . . ATAK 12
MC: . . . . TCATAK 12
LP: . . . . PAS 10003
MC: . . . . TCPAS 10003

RED ROSE SPEEDWAY (McCartney, Paul & Wings).
Tracks: / Big barn bed / My love / Get on the right thing / One more kiss / Little lamb dragonfly / Single pigeon / When the night / Loup (1st indian on the moon) / Hold me tight (Denotes part of a medley.) / Lazy dynamite (part of a medley.) / Hands of love (Denotes part of a medley.) / Power cut (part of a medley) / Mony mony (instrumental version).
LP: . . . . ATAK 16
MC: . . . . TCTAK 16
LP: . . . . FA 3193
MC: . . . . TCFA 3193
LP: . . . . PCTC 251
MC: . . . . TCFA 41 31934

SPIES LIKE US (See under Spies Like Us).

TRIPPING THE LIVE FANTASTIC.
Tracks: / Showtime / Figure of eight / Jet / Rough ride / Got to get you into my life / Band on the run / Birthday / Ebony and ivory / We got married / Inner city madness / Maybe I'm amazed / Long and winding road, The / Crackin' up / Fool on the hill / Sgt. Pepper's lonely heart club band / Can't buy me love / Matchbox / Put it there / Together / Things we said today / Eleanor Rigby / This one / My brave face / Back in the U.S.S.R. / I saw her standing there / Twenty flight rock / Coming up / Sally / Let it be / Ain't that a shame / Live and let die / If I were not upon the stage / Hey Jude / Yesterday / Get back / Golden slumbers / Don't let the sun catch you crying.
LPS: . . . . PCST 7346
LPS: 794 778 1
MCSET: . . . . TCPCST 73461
MCSET: 794 779 4

TRIPPING THE LIVE FANTASTIC - HIGHLIGHTS.
Tracks: / Got to get you into my life (Not on LP.) / Birthday / We got married (Not on LP.) / Long and winding road, The / Sgt. Peppers lonely heart club band / Can't buy me love / All my trials / Things we said today (Not on LP.) / Eleanor Rigby / My brave face / Back in the

U.S.S.R. (Not on LP.) / I saw her standing there / Coming up / Let it be / Hey Jude / Get back / Golden slumbers (Not on LP.) / Carry that weight.
LP: PCSD 114
LP: 795 379 1
MC: TCPCSD 114
MC: 795 379 4

TUG OF WAR.
Tracks: / Tug of war / Take it away / Always somebody who cares / What's that you're doing? / Here today / Ballroom dancing / Pound is sinking, The / Wanderlust / Get it / Be what you see / Dress me up as a robber / Ebony and ivory.
LP: FA 3210
MC: TCFA 3210
LP: PCTC 259

UNPLUGGED - THE OFFICIAL BOOTLEG.
Tracks: / Be bop a lula / I lost my little girl / Here, there and everywhere / Blue moon of Kentucky / We can work it out / San Francisco Bay blues / I've just seen a face / Every night / She's a woman / Hi-heel sneakers / And I love her / That would be something / Blackbird / Ain't no sunshine / Good rockin' tonight / Singing the blues / Junk.
LP: PCSD 116
MC: TCPCSD 116

WILD LIFE.
LP: PCS 7142

McCaslin, Mary

BEST OF MARY MCCASLIN.
LP: PH 1075
MC: PH 1075C

LIFE AND TIME, A.
Tracks: / Northfield / You keep me hangin' on / Tender love and care / Fair and tender ladies / Band of Jesse James, The / Some of Shelley's blues / Life and time, A / Pinto pony / Farewell Lone Ranger / Santana song.
LP: FF 203
MC: FF 203C

OLD FRIENDS.
Tracks: / Things we said today / Oklahoma hills / Wendigo / Way out there / Pinball wizard / My world is empty without you babe / Wayward wind / Blackbird / Don't fence me in / Old friends.
LP: PHILO 1046
MC: PH 1046C

PRAIRIE IN THE SKY.
Tracks: / Pass me by / Priscilla Drive / Ballad of Weaverville, The / Back to Silas / Ghost riders in the sky / Last cannonball / It's my time / Cornerstone cowboy / Prairie in the sky / Cole Younger / Dealers, The / My love.
LP: PH 1024
MC: PH 1024MC

WAY OUT WEST.
Tracks: / (Waiting) music strings / Oh Hollywood / Waiting / Let it be me / Living without you / Way out West / (Down the road) down the road / San Bernardino waltz / Circle of friends / Ballad of a wanted man / Northfield / Young Westley.
LP: PHILO 1011
MC: PH 1011C

McCaslin & Ringer

BRAMBLE AND THE ROSE.
LP: PH 1055
MC: PH 1055C

SUNNY CALIFORNIA.
LP: PH 1099
MC: PH 1099C

McCaughna, David

WINDCHILL/CHILD'S PLAY (Various artists).
MC: NF 11

McCaul, Patsy

VIOLET AND THE ROSE, THE.
MC: GTDC 044

McCauley, Johnny

OUR KIND OF COUNTRY.
MC: CMC 004

McCauley, Max

20 GOLDEN YODELS.
Tracks: / Blue velvet band / Blue yodel no. 6 / Shearer's jamboree / Swiss moonlight lullaby / Lovesick blues / Ding dong bells / Yellow rose of Texas / Sunny south by the sea / Blue eyes crying in the rain / She taught me how to yodel / Down by the singing waterfall / I'll bet you my heart I love you.
LP: GES 1203

McClain, Alton

IT MUST BE LOVE (McClain, Alton & Mahogany Rush).
Tracks: / It must be love / Crazy love / Sweet temptation / Taking my love for granted / My empty room / Power of love / Push and pull / God said 'Love ye one another'.
LP: 2391370

MORE OF YOU (McClain, Alton & Destiny).
Tracks: / Love waves / I don't want to be with nobody else / Hang on in there baby / More of you / Thank heaven for you / Stares and whispers / 99 1/2 / You bring to me my morning light.
LP: 2391 452

McClain, Arthur

TWO POOR BOYS (See under Evans, Joe).

McClain, Charly

WOMEN GET LONELY.
Tracks: / When a love ain't right / Keep on loving you / Who's cheatin' who / That's what you do to me / Make believe it's your first time / I've been alone too long / Competition / Only the lonely know / Stuck right in the middle of your love / Women get lonely / You're a part of me / Men / Lay down / Let me be your baby / Sweet and East, soft and slow / Sleeping with the radio on.
LP: EPC 85778

McClain, Janice

JANICE MCCLAIN.
Tracks: / Passion and pain / When love calls / Second chance on love / Let's spend the night / Give a little bit of love / It's gonna come back to you / Hideaway / Rhythm of our love / Last goodbye.
LP: MCF 3323
MC: MCFC 3323

McClain, Marlon

CHANGES.
Tracks: / Shake it up / Star of my life / Together in the afternoon / Close to you / Pastel / Can we still be friends / Don't run away from love / Changes / Why / Do you miss that feelin'.
LP: F 9606

McClatchy, Debby

APPLES IN WINTER.
LP: PLR 057

RADIOLAND (See under Watson, Roger) (McClatchy, Debby/Roger Watson).

McClean, Hugh

COUNTRY SONGS, VOLUME 1.
LP: UNKNOWN

IRISH FAVOURITES (THE HITCH HIKER).
LP: UNKNOWN

IRISH REQUESTS.
Tracks: / Where my Eileen is waiting for me / Gartan mothers lullaby / Harvest moon / Pretty little Galway girl / Boys from Killybegs / Leprechaun / Long before your time / Rose of Moray / Hills of Glenswilly / Rose of Mooncoin / Road to Creeslough / Letterkenny town.
LP: HRL 186

THOMAS MCCLARY.
LP: ZL 72349
MC: ZK 72349

McClean, John

GONE HOME (See under Macka B) (McClean, John & Macka B).

McClelland, Harry

HARRY MCCLELLAND.
Tracks: / Old rugged cross / Harboured in Jesus / Great is thy faithfulness / My mother's prayer / Fill my cup / Will the circle be unbroken / If that isn't love / How great Thou art / Life in the risen Lord / I cannot tell / Nearer, still nearer / One day.
LP: POL 832

JESUS IS A FRIEND OF MINE.
Tracks: / Jesus is a friend of mine / Unveil Christ / Why was he there / It is well with my soul / Carol of Christmas / Pass me not / I fell on my knees and cried holy / I know who holds tomorrow / Oh what a day / Babe in the manger, The.
MC: CPOL 834

STRANGER OF GALILEE.
Tracks: / Have thine own way (Side 1 track 1) / There was no other way (Side 2 track 6) / When I say Jesus (Side 2 track 5) / Little is much (when God is in it) (Side 2 track 4) / Let me touch Him (Side 2 track 3) / It's in my heart (Side 2 track 2) / I want to see him (Side 2 track 1) / Walking with God (Side 1 track 6) / Stranger of Galilee (Side 1 track 5) / My saviour's love / Like a river glorious (Side 1 track 3) / It is finished (Side 1 track 2).
MC: CPOL 836

TILL THE STORM PASSES BY.
Tracks: / Till the storm passes by / Way that he loves, The / Where the roses never fade / Does Jesus care / Born again / Lead me, O lead me / I'm following Jesus / How big is God / I met the master / He was there all the time / Where Jesus is - tis heaven there / He hideth my soul.
MC: CPOL 835

McClennan, Tommy

BLUEBIRD.
LP: PM 24040

TOMMY MCCLENNAN.
LP: RL 305

McClintock, Harry

HALLELUJAH I'M A BUM.
LP: ROUNDER 1009

McClintock, Lil

ATLANTA BLUES (See under Daniels, Julius) (McClintock, Lil & Julius Daniels).

McClintock, Mike

LIKE SATIN.
LP: ROSE 162

McClinton, Delbert

FEELIN' ALRIGHT.
LP: 20030
MC: 40030

JEALOUS KIND.
Tracks: / Shotgun rider / I can't quit you / Giving it up for your love / Jealous kind, The / Going back to Lousiana / Baby Ruth / Bright side of the road / Take me to the river / Shaky ground / My sweet baby.
LP: EST 12115

LIVE FROM AUSTIN.
LP: AL 4773
MC: AC 4773

McCloud, Jim

COME SCOTTISH COUNTRY DANCING.
LP: MOR 526

MacCloud, Margaret

WEST OF WEST, A NEW SOUND TO GAELIC.
MC: TC GLN 1002

McClung, Tom

MOYALLAN BROWN RED.
Tracks: / Three men went a hunting / Master McGrath / Teaching McFadden to waltz / Shepherd's boy / Farrell's hill / Moyallan brown red / Charming young widow I met on the train / Turfman from Ardee / Dobson's grove / Clover hill / Flower of sweet Strabane / Rathfriland on the hill.
LP: OAS 3027
MC: COAS 3027

McClure, Bobby

CHERRY, THE.
Tracks: / Today you started leaving him (and loving me) / Cherry pie / When the flavour's gone / I can't get enough / Do do do doop / I need a job / Please don't put me out the band / I write another love song / I brought it back / Younger man blues.
LP: SDE 4008
MC: SDE 4008MC

McCluskey, John

FITBA' CRAZY.
LP: NEVLP 001

MacColl, Calum

NGATIJIRRI SUNRISE (See Maddern, Eric) (MacColl, Calum & Eric Maddern).

MacColl, Ewan

BLACK AND WHITE (THE DEFINITIVE COLLECTION).
LP: COOK 038
MC: COOKC 038

BLOOD AND ROSES COLLECTION (see under Seeger, Peggy) (MacColl, Ewan & Peggy Seeger).

BUNDOOK BALLADS.
Tracks: / Any complaints / Fortress songs / Farewell to Sicily / Ballad of Wadi Maktilla / Dying soldier, The / Ghost army of Korea, The / Browned off / When this ruddy war is over / Join the British army / On the move tonight / Second front song, The / Seven years in the sand / Hand me down me petticoat / Young trooper cut down in his prime / Bless 'em all.
LP: 12T 130

CHORUS FROM THE GALLOWS.
Tracks: / Treadmill song, The / Turpin hero / Crafty farmer, The / McKaffery / Jimmie Wilson / Lag's song, The / Van Diemans land / Go down ye murderers.
LP: 12T 16

CLASSIC SCOTS BALLADS.
LP: TLP 1015

COLD SNAP (MacColl, Ewan & Peggy Seeger).
LP: BR 1057

ENGLISH & SCOTTISH FOLK BALLADS (MacColl, Ewan & A. L. Lloyd).
LP: 12T 103

FREEBORN MAN (MacColl, Ewan & Peggy Seeger).
LP: BR 1065
LP: ROUNDER 3080
MC: ROUNDER 3080C

HOT BLAST (MacColl, Ewan & Peggy Seeger).
LP: BR 1059

ITEMS OF NEWS (MacColl, Ewan & Peggy Seeger).
LP: BR 1067

JACOBITE REBELLIONS, THE.
Tracks: / Ye jacobites by name / Such a parcel of rogues in a nation / Will ye go to sherriffmuir / Wae's me for Prince Charlie / Charlie is my darling / Haughs o' Cromdale / Bonnie moorhen, The / Johnnie Cope / Cam ye o'er frae France / There's three brave loyal fellows / This is no my ain house / Piper o'Dundee, The / Donald MacGillavry / MacLean's welcome / Will ye no come back again.
LP: 12T 79

KILROY WAS HERE (MacColl, Ewan & Peggy Seeger).
LP: BR 1063

MANCHESTER ANGEL, THE.
Tracks: / We poor labouring men / Georgie / Barbara Allen / Sheepcrook and black dog / Bramble briar (Strawberry town) / One night as I lay on my bed / Grey cock, The / At the begging I will go / Sheep stealer, The / Manchester angel, The / Bold Richard, The / Press gang, The / Round Cape Horn / Through Moorfields / Homeward bound.
LP: 12T 147

NAMING OF NAMES (MacColl, Ewan & Peggy Seeger).
Tracks: / Economic miracle / Just the tax for me / Grocer, The / Not going to give it back / Sellafield child / Bring the Summer home / Maggie went green / Nuclear means jobs / Hose hunting blues / Dracumag / Rogue's gallery / Island, The / We remember (naming of names).
LP: COOK 036
MC: COOKC 036

SATURDAY NIGHT AT THE BULL AND MOUTH.
LP: BR 1055

STEAM WHISTLE BALLADS.
Tracks: / Wark of the weavers, The / Droylsden wakes / Four loom weaver, The / Calton weaver, The / Oh dear me / Coal owner and the pitman's wife ,The / Four pence a day / Gresford disaster, The / Will Caird / Iron horse / Poor Paddy works on the railway / Cannily cannily / Song of the iron road, The / Blantyre explosion / Collier laddie / Moses of the mail.
LP: 12T 104

STREETS OF SONG (see under Behan, D.) (MacColl, Ewan & D. Behan).

WANTON MUSE.
Tracks: / Ballad of trades / Shepherd lad, The / Wanton seed, The / Bonnie lassie's plaidie / Coachman and his whip, The / Thrashing machine, The / Maid of Australia / Cuckoo's nest, The / Gairdener chylde, The / Vintner, The / Andrew and his cutty gun / All fours / Cobbler, The / Mowdiewark, The / Furze field / Long peggin' awl / Maid gaed to the mill, The / Bird in the bush, The / She was a rum one.
LP: ZFB 67

MacColl, Kirsty

DESPERATE CHARACTER.
Tracks: / Clock goes round / See that girl / There's a guy works down the chipshop (swears he's Elvis) / Teenager in love / Mexican sofa / Until the night / Falling for faces / Just one look / Real ripper, The / Hard to believe / He thinks I still care / There's a guy works down the chip shop (country version).
LP: POLS 1035
MC: POLSC 1035

ELECTRIC LANDLADY.
LP: V 2663
MC: TCV 2663

FAIRYTALE OF NEW YORK (See also Pogues) (MacColl, Kirsty/ Pogues).

KIRSTY MACCOLL.
Tracks: / There's a guy works down the chipshop (swears he's Elvis) / See that girl / You still believe in me / Roman gardens / Man with no name / Annie / Keep your hands off my baby / Hard to believe / Berlin / Falling for faces / Clock goes round / Sleepless nights.
LP: SPELP 95
MC: SPEMC 95

KITE.
Tracks: / Innocence / Mother's ruin / No victims / Don't come the cowboy with me Sonny Jim / What do pretty girls do? / End of a perfect day, The / Free world / Days / Fifteen minutes / Tread lightly / Dancing in limbo / You and me baby.
LP: .... **KMLP 1**
MC: .... **TCKM 1**

MISS OTIS REGRETS (See under Pogues for details) (MacColl, Kirsty/ Pogues).

McComb, Carol

LOVE CAN TAKE YOU HOME AGAIN (McComb, Carol & Friends).
LP: .... **BAY 302**

TEARS INTO LAUGHTER.
Tracks: / Indaho sky / Forgive and forget / Faded dresden blue / Tears into laughter / Little more love, A / Queen of sorrow / Hazel's song / Next to my skin / Through thick and thin / Ice on the fire / Bird in the wood.
MC: .... **C 41**

McComiskey, Billy

MAKIN' THE ROUNDS.
LP: .... **SIF 1034**
MC: .... **CSIF 1034**

McConnell, Cathal

ON LOUGH ERNE'S SHORE.
LP: **12TS 377**
LP: .... **FF 058**

TRADITIONAL IRISH SONGS (McConnell, Cathal/Robin Morton).
LP: **12T 290**

McConnell, Rob

AGAIN (McConnell, Rob & The Boss Band).
LP: .... **PR 7148**

ALL IN GOOD TIME (McConnell, Rob & The Boss Band).
LP: .... **JC 0006**

BIG BAND JAZZ (McConnell, Rob & The Boss Band).
LP: .... **PR 7140**

BRASS IS BACK, THE (McConnell, Rob & The Boss Band).
Tracks: / Strollin (Only on CD) / All the things you are / Love of my life / Who asked / Slow grind (Only on CD) / Winter in Winnipeg / Days gone by / Them there eyes.
MC: .... **CJ 458C**

LIVE AT THE 1990 CONCORD JAZZ FESTIVAL (First Set) (McConnell, Rob & Al Grey & Benny Powell).
Tracks: / Cottontail / Centerpiece / But beautiful / Crawdad song / St. James Infirmary / Crazy she calls me / Undecided.
MC: .... **CJ 451C**

MEL TORME/ROB MCCONNELL & BOSS BRASS (see Torme,Mel) (McConnell, Rob & Mel Torme).

OLD FRIENDS, NEW MUSIC (McConnell, Rob Sexete).
LP: .... **DDA 1001**

McConville, Tom

STREETS OF EVERYWHERE (see Halpin, Kieran) (McConville, Tom and Kieran Halpin).

McCoo, Marilyn

MARILYN & BILLY (McCoo, Marilyn & Billy Davis Junior).
LP: .... **CBS 83158**

McCook, Tommy

HOT LAVA (McCook, Tommy & The Skatalites).
LP: .... **TWS 920**

INSTRUMENTAL.
LP: .... **JUSLP 007**

KING TUBBY AT DUB STATION (McCook, Tommy & The Aggrovators).
LP: .... **LALP 02**

TOMMY MCCOOK.
LP: .... **AT 1007**

McCorkle, Susannah

NO MORE BLUES.
LP: .... **CJ 370**
MC: .... **CJ 370C**

QUALITY OF MERCER, THE.
LP: .... **BLP 12169**

SABIA.
Tracks: / Tristeza (sadness, please go away) / Estate (Summer) / Dilemma / Vivo sanhando (Only on CD.) / Sabia (songbird) / So many stars (Only on CD.) / So danco samba / Manha de carnaval / P'ra machucar meu coracao / Travessia (Only on CD.) / A felicidade.
MC: .... **CJ 418 C**

THERE WILL NEVER BE ANOTHER YOU (The music of Harry Warren).
LP: .... **WRS 1001**

McCormack, Brian

IRISH SONGS OF FREEDOM.
MC: .... **DOCM 5401**

McCormack, John

20 GOLDEN PIECES: JOHN MCCORMACK.
Tracks: / Come into the garden, Maud / Evening song / Until / When the dew is falling / Dream, A / Funiculi funicula / Sunshine of your smile, The / When my ship comes sailing home / Turn ye to me Ben Bott / Morning / Sweet Genevieve / Down in the forest / Mavis-Eileen (hearts erin) / Trumpeter, The / When you and I were young, Maggie / Little grey home in the west / Silver threads among the gold / At dawning.
LP: .... **BDL 2019**

ART OF JOHN MCCORMACK.
2LP: .... **EX 2900563**
MCSET: .... **EX 2900565**

COUNT JOHN MCCORMACK.
LPS: .... **GEMM 155-160**

GENTLE MINSTREL, THE Complete soundtrack from Song O' My Heart.
LPS: .... **GEMM 183-88**

GOLDEN AGE OF..., THE.
Tracks: / Nation once again, A / God save Ireland / Boys of Wexford / Croppy boy, The / Dear little shamrock / Snowy breasted pearl, The / Green isle of Erin, The / Kathleen Mavoureen / Come back to Erin / Killarney / My dark Rosaleen / Terence's farewell to Kathleen / Foggy dew, The / Trottin' to the fair / Savoureen deelish / Eileen Aroon.
LP: .... **GX 41 2527 1**
MC: .... **GX 41 2527 4**

GOLDEN SONGS.
LP: .... **ISLE 3001**

GOLDEN VOICE OF JOHN MCCORMACK.
Tracks: / Oft in the stilly night / Garden where the praties grow / Love thee dearest / Oh what bitter grief is mine / Off to Philadelphia / Star of the County Down / Gentle maiden, The / Ould turf fire, The / At the mid hour of night / Silent hour of prayer / By the lakes of Killarney / Londonderry air.
LP: .... **DOLS 2015**
MC: .... **DOCS 2015**

GOLDEN VOICE OF JOHN MCCORMACK (VOLUME 1).
LP: .... **DOLB 7020**

IRISH MINSTREL.
Tracks: / Love's garden of roses / Somewhere a voice is calling / Minstrel boy, The / Has sorrow thy young days shaded / By the short cut to the roses / Ireland, Mother Ireland / Ireland, my Ireland / Rose of Tralee, The / Fairytale / Far apart / Now sleeps the crimson petal / Bird songs at eventide / Auld Scots sangs, The / Swans OP.44, NO 4 / Down in the forest / There Opus 176 No.7 / I hear you calling me / Love's secret / Bitterness of love, The / Three aspects opus 176, no. 1 / Morning.
LP: .... **RL 84997**
MC: .... **RK 84997**

JOHN MCCORMACK.
LPS: .... **ALBUM 69**
MCSET: .... **CASSETTE 69**

JOHN MCCORMACK IN IRISH SONG.
Tracks: / Irish emigrant, The / Has sorrow thy young days shaded / Kathleen Mavoureen / Killarney / Come back to Erin / Ould plaid shawl, The / Savoureen deelish / Boys of Wexford / Croppy boy, The / Snowy breasted pearl, The / Avenging and bright / God save Ireland.
LP: .... **RHA 6001**

JOHN MCCORMACK IN OPERA.
LP: .... **RHA 6015**

JOHN MCCORMACK RARITIES.
Tracks: / Nora O'Neale / Child's song / Next market day / Ballynore ballad / Just a cottage small / Sunshine of your smile, The / That tumbledown shack in Athlone / Three o'clock in the morning / When you and I were seventeen / Beautiful Isle of Somewhere / You forgot to remember / My Irish song of songs / I'm falling in love with someone / I saw from the beach / When you look in the heart of a rose.
LP: .... **DOL 1012**
MC: .... **DOC 1012**

JOHN MCCORMACK SINGS BALLADS.
Tracks: / My dark Rosaleen / I hear you calling me / O lovely night / Drink to me only with thine eyes / My Lagan love / Ah moon of my delight / Li marinari / Like stars above / Child's song / Farewell / Take O take those lips away / Wearing of the green, The / Harp that once through Tara's halls, The.
LP: .... **RHA 6005**

JOHN MCCORMACK-VOL.2.
Tracks: / When you and I were young Maggie / At dawning / Little grey home in the west / Silver threads among the gold / Sospiri miei andate ove vi mando / Somewhere a voice is calling / Serenata / Beautiful isle of somewhere / Jocelyn: Berceuse / Say au revoir but not goodbye / Tommy lad / Sweet Peggy O'Neil / Cradle song / Little woman of mine / Thank God for a garden.
LP: .... **GVC 509**

JOHN MCCORMICK-VOL.1.
Tracks: / Would God I were the tender apple blossom / Old refrain, The / There's a long long trail a-winding / Only you / Bonnie wee thing / Forgotten / Somewhere / Roses of Picardy / O cease thy singing maiden fair / Mary of Argyle / Parted / Dreams / Sing sing birds on the wind / Who knows / Love's garden of roses.
LP: .... **GVC 508**

LIGHT PATTERNS.
LP: .... **SHEET 3**

MEMORIES OF JOHN MCCORMACK.
Tracks: / Farewell / Love here is my heart / Calling me home to you / June brought the roses / I look into your garden / Sweetest call, The / Mother my dear / Faraway bells, The / When twilight comes I'm thinking of you / Lilies of Lorraine / Rose for every heart, A / Bird songs at eventide / Little silver ring, The / Beloved I am lonely / Under the spell of a rose.
LP: .... **DOLM 5023**
MC: .... **DOCM 5023**

POPULAR SONGS & IRISH BALLADS.
Tracks: / Garden where the praties grow / Believe me if all those those endearing young charms / Star of the county down / Bless this house / I'll walk beside you / Drink to me only with thine eyes / Jeanie with the light brown hair / Linden lea / Little silver ring, The / Old house.
2LP: .... **EX 2900073**
MCSET: .... **EX 2900075**

RARITIES.
MC: .... **DOCS 1012**

SACRED MUSIC.
MC: .... **GEMM 176**

...SINGS OF OLD SCOTLAND.
LP: .... **SH 306**

SONGS AND BALLADS.
LP: .... **MKER 2002**

SONGS OF JOHN MCCORMACK.
LP: .... **SKL 4150**

TURN YE TO ME.
LP: .... **STAL 1057**

McCoury Brothers

MCCOURY BROTHERS.
LP: .... **ROUNDER 0230**
MC: .... **ROUNDER 0230C**

McCoury, Del

BEST OF DEL MCCOURY.
LP: **1610**
MC: **1610C**

BLUEGRASS BAND.
LP: .... **ARHOOLIE 5006**

DEL MCCOURY.
LP: .... **ROUNDER 0245**

HIGH ON A MOUNTAIN (McCoury, Del & The Dixie Pals).
LP: .... **ROUNDER 0019**
MC: .... **ROU 0019C**

SAWMILL.
LP: **1636**
MC: **1636C**

TAKE ME TO THE MOUNTAINS.
LP: **1622**
MC: **1622C**

McCowan, Alex

DON QUIXOTE.
MC: .... **BKK 408**

PYGMALION (see Shaw, George Bernard) (McCowen, Alex & Diana Rigg).

McCoy, Charlie

1928-36 (McCoy, Charlie & Walter Vincson).
LP: .... **BD 612**

APPALACHIAN FEVER.
Tracks: / Fair and tender / Ladies / Midnight flyer / Ramblin' music man / West Virginia mountain melody / Cripple creek / Red haired boy / Drifting lovers / Ruby / In the pines / Carolina morning / Appalachian fever.
LP: .... **MNT 83516**

BOOGIE WOOGIE (Nashville Hit Man).
LP: .... **MNT 80115**

NASHVILLE SOUND.
LP: .... **MNT 81117**

YOUR VALVES NEED GRINDING 1929-36.
LP: .... **BD 602**

McCoy, Clyde

CLYDE MCCOY, 1936.
Tracks: / Sugar blues / Music goes 'round and 'round, The / Streamline strut / Black and tan fantasy / Jazz me blues / I found a new baby / Is it true what they say about Dixie / Rose room / Honeysuckle rose / Farewell blues / No regrets / You can't pull the wool over my eyes.
LP: .... **HSR 180**

McCoy, George

AT HOME WITH THE BLUES (McCoy, George & Ethel).
LP: **2106**

McCoy, John

THINK HARD.
LP: .... **SKULL 8373**
MC: .... **SKULL 78373**

McCoy, Kansas Joe

KANSAS JOE MCCOY 1934-44.
LP: .... **BOB 6**

KANSAS JOE MCCOY AND JOE WILLIAMS 1929-41 (McCoy, Kansas Joe & Joe Williams).
LP: .... **BD 2032**

McCoy, Robert

BLUES AND BOOGIE WOOGIE CLASSICS.
LP: .... **OL 2814**

ROBERT 'NIGHTHAWK' LEE MCCOY VOL. 1 (1937).
LP: .... **WSE 120**

ROBERT 'NIGHTHAWK' LEE MCCOY VOL. 2 (1938-40).
LP: .... **WSE 121**

McCoy, Van

DISCO BABY (McCoy, Van & Soul City Symphony).
LP: **9109 004**

HUSTLE TO THE BEST OF VAN MCCOY.
LP: **9109 013**

SWEET RHYTHM.
Tracks: / Change with the times / Disco baby / Hustle / Keep on hustlin' / Jet setting / Love at first sight / Night walk / Pick up the pieces / Roll with the punches / Shaky ground / Shuffle / Soul cha cha / Sweet sweet rhythm / That's my philosophy.
LP: **6467651**

McCoys

HANG ON SLOOPY.
Tracks: / Meet the McCoys / Hang on Sloopy / Fever / Sorrow / If you tell a lie / I don't mind / Stubborn kind of fellow / I can't help falling in love / All I really want to do / Papa's got a brand new bag / I can't explain it / High heel sneakers / Stormy Monday blues / You make me feel (so good) / Runaway / Up and down / Everyday I have to cry / I got to go back / Dynamite / Don't worry your son's heart is pure / Come on let's go / Koko (Only on CD.).
LP: .... **SEE 236**

McCracklin, Jimmy

BLAST 'EM DEAD.
Tracks: / She's gone / My days are limited / She felt too good / End, The / Cheater / Share and share alike / Hear my story / Every time / Pleasin' papa / We could make a go I know / Blues and trouble / I don't want no woman / Hello baby / Night and day / You look so fine - take 1 / Keep trying / Swinging thing, The.
2LP: .... **CHD 219**

BLASTING THE BLUES.
Tracks: / Story of Jimmy McCracklin / If I won't talk / I have a copyright on your love / I wanna make love to you / Mama mama / Reconsider baby / I just got to know / Hop skip and jump / You're the one.
LP: .... **JSP 1057**

BLUES AND SOUL.
Tracks: / Walk, The / Looking for a woman / That's the way it goes / Every night every day / I did wrong / I had to get with it / Just got to know / Think / Get back / R M Blues / I don't care / I'll see it through / Pretty little sweet thing / What's going on / Stinger / You ain't nothing but a devil.
LP: .... **SSL 6007**
MC: .... **TCSSL 6007**

EVERYBODY ROCK! (Best of Jimmy McCracklin).
Tracks: / Walk, The / I'm to blame / Later on / I'm through / Minnie Lee / Take care of yourself / Suffer / Get tough / Everybody rock / Hurt me / Country baby

/ Wobble, The / I'll take the blame / He knows the rules / I know / Come on.
LP: .... RED LP 10
MC: .... TCRED 10

I'M GONNA HAVE MY FUN (McCracklin, Jimmy & His blues blasters).
Tracks: / I'm gonna have my fun / True love blues / What's your phone number / Your heart ain't right / I found that woman / Cheater / Beer tavern girl / She's gone / My days are limited / I cried / End, The / Take a chance / I'm the one / Blues blasters boogie / Fare you well.
LP: .... KIX 29

JIMMY MCCRACKLIN & HIS BLUESBLASTERS (McCracklin, Jimmy & His blues blasters).
Tracks: / Reelin' & rockin' / Love when it rains / Beer drinking woman / I think my time is here / I'll get a break someday / Just won't let her go / Ragged as a mop / My life depends on you / Gonna find another woman / Up and down blues.
LP: .... 10 CH 28

ROCKIN' MAN.
Tracks: / Miss Mattie left me / Rock and bye / Miss Minnie Lee blues / Bad condition blues / Gotta cut out / Rockin' man / Looking for a woman / She felt too good / I wanna make love to you / I can't understand love / Just won't let her go / Movin' on down the line / That's life / Share and share alike / Hear my story / You're the one.
LP: .... KIX 12

ROOTS OF RHYTHM AND BLUES (see under Gayten, Paul) (McCracklin, Jimmy & Paul Gayten).

SAME LOVIN'.
Tracks: / All shucks / Games to strong / Outside help / Just gotta know / Same lovin' / Do it together / My answer / Think.
LP: .... EJR 4013
MC: .... EJRMC 4013

YOU DECEIVED ME.
Tracks: / Mean mistreated lover / Baby don't you want to go / Special for you / Highway 101 / You had your chance / You deceived me / Rock and rye part 1 / Rock and rye part 2 / Bad luck and trouble / I am tired / Railroad blues / Blues blaster shuffle / Jimmy's blues / South side road / Deceiving blues / Panics on, The.
LP: .... IG 405

McCrae, George

BEST OF GEORGE MCCRAE.
LP: .... JSB 100

GEORGE MCCRAE.
LP: .... TKR 82509
LP: .... JSL 10

ONE STEP CLOSER TO LOVE.
Tracks: / Just another fool / If it wasn't for you / Never too late / Now that I have you / One step closer (to love) / Every time I say goodbye / Fire in the night / It was always you / I'm still believing / Listen to your heart.
LP: .... PTLS 1075
MC: .... PTLC 1075

ROCK YOUR BABY.
Tracks: / Ooh baby / Rock your baby / You go my heart / Don't you feel my love / I got love / You can have it all / Let's dance / Kiss me / Look at you / I can't leave you alone.
LP: .... SHM 3050
MC: .... HSC 3050
LP: .... JSL 3

TOGETHER (McCrae, George & Gwen).
LP: .... PTLS 1070

McCray, Larry

AMBITION.
Tracks: / Ambition / Count on me for love / Me and my baby / One more lonely night / Frustrated baby / Keep on walking / Sally's got a friend in New York City / I don't mind / Nobody never hurt nobody with the blues / Country girl / Secret lover (Only on MC and CD.) / Sun rises in the East, The (Only on CD.).
LP: .... VPBLP 1
MC: .... BPBTC 1

McCroby, Ron

OTHER WHISTLER, THE.
Tracks: / Four brothers / Song from M.A.S.H. / Cherokee / My foolish heart / Blue rondo a la turk / I remember Clifford / Mayberry RFD / Take five.
LP: .... CJ 257

McCue, Bill

COUNT YOUR BLESSINGS.
Tracks: / Count your blessings / Softly and tenderly Jesus is calling / Where we'll never grow old / What a friend we have in Jesus / Lord's prayer, The / If I can help somebody / Going home / Beautiful isle of somewhere / Shall we gather at the river? / Bless this house / Whispering hope / Little drummer boy / Blessed assurance / Amazing grace.
LP: .... ITV 467
MC: .... KITV 467

DREAMS OF CALEDONIA.
LP: .... MK 1
MC: .... MKC 1

LEGENDS OF SCOTLAND - BONNIE PRINCE CHARLIE.
MC: .... MKC 104

LEGENDS OF SCOTLAND: MARY QUEEN OF SCOTS.
MC: .... MKC 101

LEGENDS OF SCOTLAND: ROBERT BURNS.
MC: .... MKC 103

LEGENDS OF SCOTLAND: ROBERT THE BRUCE.
MC: .... MKC 102

LUCKY WHITE HEATHER.
MC: .... KITV 484

TAM O'SHANTER.
LP: .... RBLP 1790

MacCuill, Finn

SINK YE SWIM YE.
Tracks: / Birnie Bouzle / Newry Town / Mary Hamilton / Friar well, The / Shearing, The / New jigs / Minstrel, The / Little drummer / Gaberlunzie man, The / Poacher, The / Dances of Ruhendorf, The.
LP: .... REL 460

McCulloch, Gordeanna

GORDEANNA MCCULLOCH.
LP: 12TS 370

McCulloch, Ian

CANDLELAND.
LP: .... WX 303
MC: .... WX 303 C

McCulloch, Keff

PURPLE REIGN - THE SYNTH PLAYS PRINCE.
Tracks: / Take me with U / Paisley Park / Arms of Orion, The / Raspberry beret / Kiss / Nothing compares 2 U / Girls and boys / 1999 / Little red corvette / I wish U heaven / I feel for you / Thieves in the temple / Trust / Sign o' the times / When doves cry / Purple rain.
MC: .... PWKMC 4055

McCullough, Andy

MUSIC OF THE ORIENT EXPRESS.
LP: .... ATXLP 03
MC: .... ZCATX 03

MYSTERY OF THE UNIVERSE Featuring Judi Dench.
Tracks: / Mystery of the universe / Hear my prayer / O little town of Bethlehem / Ding dong merrily on high / In the bleak mid winter / God rest ye merry gentlemen / O come all ye faithful / Jesus Christ is risen today / When I survey the wondrous cross / Praise my soul the king of Heaven / Readings by Judi Dench / Amazing grace.
LP: .... WHY 4
MC: .... TCWHY 4

McCullough, Henry

HELL OF A RECORD.
LP: 6 25886

McCullough, Sheila

PUDDLE LANE - FIRE IN THE GRASS.
MC: .... PLBP 241

PUDDLE LANE - ON THE WAY TO THE BLUE MOUNTAIN.
MC: .... PLBP 248

PUDDLE LANE - THE DRAGON'S EGG.
MC: .... PLBP 247

PUDDLE LANE - THE FLYING SAUCER.
MC: .... PLBP 246

PUDDLE LANE - THE GRUFFLE.
MC: .... PLBP 242

PUDDLE LANE - THE GRUFFLE IN PUDDLE LANE.
MC: .... PLBP 244

PUDDLE LANE - THE SANDALWOOD GIRL.
MC: .... PLBP 243

PUDDLE LANE - THE SILVER RIVER.
MC: .... PLBP 245

McCurdy, Ed

LAST NIGHT I HAD THE STRANGEST DREAM.
Tracks: / Last night I had the strangest dream / Mrs. McGraw / Spanish is the loving tongue / Streets of Laredo / Chisholm trail, The / Whoopie ti yi yo / Jolly old Rogers / Ballynore / Good old mountain dew / Nightingale, The / Poor boy / Venezuela / Acres of clams / Drill ye tarriers drill / Blow the candle out / Midnight special.
LP: .... BF 15009

McCutchan, Philip

CAMERON'S CONVOY.
MC: .... SOUND 11

McCutcheon, John

GONNA RISE AGAIN.
LP: .... ROUNDER 0222
MC: .... ROUNDER 0222C

HOWJADOO.
MC: .... ROUNDER 8009C
LP: .... ROUNDER 8009

SIGNS OF THE TIMES (McCutcheon, John/Si Kahn).
LP: .... ROUNDER 4017
MC: .... ROUNDER 4017C

STEP BY STEP.
LP: .... ROUNDER 0216
MC: .... ROUNDER 0216C

WATER FROM ANOTHER TIME.
LP: .... RCD 8016

WINTER SOLSTICE.
LP: .... ROUNDER 0192
MC: .... ROUNDER 0192C

McCuy, Clyde

SUGAR BLUES (McCuy, Clyde & His Orchestra).
LP: .... CLP 82

McDaniel, Maisie

MAISIA MCDANIEL COLLECTION.
MC: .... GTDC 062

McDaniels, Gene

ANOTHER TEAR FALLS.
Tracks: / Hundred pounds of clay / Spanish Harlem / Walk with a winner / Point of no return / Chip chip / Hang on (just a little bit longer) / Tear, A / Tower of strength / Another tear falls / Raindrops / Forgotten man / It's a lonely town / Spanish lace / I don't want to cry / Cry baby cry / You can have her.
LP: .... CRB 1136

McDermott, Josie

DARBY'S FAREWELL (Traditional Songs Played on Flute and Whistle).
LP: 12TS 325

McDermott, Kevin

BEDAZZLED (McDermott, Kevin Orchestra).
MC: .... KMOC 1
LP: .... KMOLP 1

MOTHER NATURE'S KITCHEN (McDermott, Kevin Orchestra).
Tracks: / Wheels of wonder / Slow boat to something better / King of nothing / Diamond / Mother nature's kitchen / Into the blue / Where we were meant to be / Statue to a stone / What comes to pass / Suffocation blues / Angel / Healing at the harbour.
MC: .... ICT 9920
LP: .... ILPS 9920

SUFFOCATION BLUES.
LP: .... NO 121

McDermott, Michael

620 W.SURF.
Tracks: / 620 W.surf.
LP: 7599244161
MC: 7599244164

McDermott, Tom

NEW RAGS.
LP: .... SOS 1024

McDermott's Two Hours

ENEMY WITHIN', THE.
LP: .... HAGLP 2

McDevitt, Chas

TAKES YA BACK DON'T IT.
Tracks: / Bloodshot eyes / Thirty days / Peggy Sue / La bamba / What a crazy world we're livin' in / Freight train / Walk right in / Cottonfields / San Francisco bay / Rock Island line / Tom Dooley / Wabash cannonball.
LP: .... JOYS 263
MC: .... TC JOY S 263

Mac'Dhonncha, Sean

AN AILL BHAIN.
LP: .... CC 9

MacDiarmid, Hugh

DRUNK MAN LOOKS AT THE THISTLE, A.
2LP: .... CCA 1/2

HUGH MACDIARMID.
LP: .... CCT 5

LEGEND AND THE MAN, THE.
LP: .... NEVLP 107

QUAR EXTREMES MEET.
LP: .... TU 1

McDonagh, Owen

SONGS OF IRISH CIVIL.
MC: .... COB 4008

McDonald, Alastair

ALASTAIR MCDONALD.
LP: 2383 404

ALASTAIR MCDONALD SINGS ROBERT BURNS.
LP: .... NEVLP 112
MC: .... NEVC 112

AT THE JAZZ BAND BALL.
Tracks: / Will the circle be unbroken / Up above my head / Your feet's too big / At the jazz band ball / Just a closer walk with thee / 'Taint no sin / Chinese laundry blues / Down by the riverside / Frankie and Johnny / My bucket's got a hole in it / Marching through Georgia / Corn bread, peas and black molasses / Ballin' the jack / Mississippi mud.
LP: .... LILP 5173
MC: .... LICS 5173

BEST OF ALASTAIR MCDONALD.
Tracks: / Piper O'Dundee, The / Get up, get out / Glencoe / Music of the highlands / Land of McLeod / Tramcar song / Gypsy laddie, The / Early morning worker / Haughs o' Cromdale / Kirsteen / Wee Kirkcudbright centipede, The / Kelvingrove / Street songs / Honest poverty.
LP: .... GES 1236
MC: .... KGEC 1236

BONNIE PRINCE CHARLIE.
MC: .... NEVC 101

COLOMBE SHALOM.
Tracks: / Colombe-shalom / White wings.
LP: .... CBN 002

GLENCOE.
Tracks: / Bonnie ship the Diamond, The / Ten wee wimmin / Silver darlings / Kismuil's galley / Hie Johnny Cope / Glencoe / Wee Kirkcudbright centipede, The / Jamie Raeburn / Abu Chuile / Baron's heir / Sing me a song (requiem).
LP: .... CBN 003

JOURNEY THROUGH SCOTLAND.
Tracks: / Welcome to Scotland / Bruce's address / Ten wee wimmin / Isle of Skye (requiem) / Lament for McCrimmon / Killiecrankie / Loch Lomond / Glencoe / De'ils awa' with the exciseman, The / Loch Tay / Cam ye by Atholl / Hie Johnny Cope / Will ye no' come back again.
MC: .... CBNC 004

JOURNEY THROUGH SCOTLAND VOL.2.
Tracks: / Gallowa' hills / Puffer, The / Lochnagar / Will ye go, Lassie, go / Kismuil's galley / Silver darlings / Twa Corbies / Rothesay O / Colombe-Shalom / White wings.
MC: .... CBNC 007

MUSIC OF THE HIGHLANDS.
Tracks: / Gypsy laddie, The / Early morning worker / Jamie Raeburn / Melville Castle / Music of the highlands / Bonnie ship the diamond, The / Get up, get out / Exile song, The / Kirsteen / Perfervidum / Rory mors lament.
LP: .... BER 005
MC: .... KBER 005

SCOTLAND FIRST.
MC: .... NEVC 108

SCOTLAND IN SONG.
Tracks: / Over the sea to Skye / Rantin' rovin' Robin / Loch Lomond / Mouth music / Barras, The / Silver darlings / Glencoe / Wee cooper o' Fife, The / Bonnie Galloway / Mary Jane.
LP: .... NEVLP 002
MC: .... NEVC 002

SCOTTISH BATTLE BALLADS.
LP: .... NEVLP 014
MC: .... NEVC 014

SING A SONG OF SCOTLAND.
Tracks: / Bonnie Dundee / Scotland yet / Peoples palace, The / Eriskay love lilt / Turn ye to me / Rothesay O / Aiken drum / Willies gane tae Melville Castle / Bonnie O'Wearie / Coulter's candy / Neil Gows' farewell to whiskey / Mairis' Wedding.
LP: .... CBN 006

SONGS OF LIFE, LIBERTY AND LAUGHTER.
Tracks: / Colombe-Shalom / Toys and brooches / Lock the door / Lariston / Caveman's Saturday night / Sheep and stag remain / Heads and tales / Jeely piece song / Tog orm mo Piob / Mary Baker city mix / No, trident, no / Some hae meat.
LP: .... CBN 010

SURGE OF THE SEA, THE.
MC: .... CWGR 088

WHITE WINGS.

Tracks: / Puffer, The / Loch Tay / Bruce's address / Shoals O'Herrin' / Over the mountain / No' comin' oot / Lament for McCrimmon / Wee jock sparra / Smile in your sleep / Cam' ye by Atholl / White wings.
LP: CBN 001

McDonald, Bobby

BOBBY MCDONALD/SAMMY RIMINGTON/LIZZIE MILES (McDonald, Bobby/Sammy Rimington/ Lizzie Miles).
MC: TC 013

McDonald, Brian Group

DESPERATE BUSINESS.
LP: BFC 40582

McDonald, Country Joe

ANIMAL TRACKS.
LP: FEEL 1

BEST OF COUNTRY JOE MCDONALD.
MC: ZCGH 865
LP: GH 865

CHILD'S PLAY.
LP: RAG 1018

COLLECTORS ITEMS (First Three EP's, The) (Country Joe & The Fish).
LP: NEW 87
LP: RAG 1000

ELECTRIC MUSIC FOR THE MIND AND BODY (Country Joe & the Fish).
Tracks: / Flying high / Not so sweet Martha Lorraine / Death sound blues / Porpoise mouth / Section 43 / Super bird / Sad and lonely times / Love / Bass strings / Masked marauder, The / Grace.
LP: VSD 79244
LP: VMLP 5301
MC: VMTC 6301

FIRST THREE EP'S (Country Joe & The Fish).
Tracks: / I feel like I'm fixin' to die rag / Super bird / Thing called love / Bass strings / Section 43 / Fire in the city / Johnny's gone to war / Kiss my ass / Tricky dicky / Free some day.
LP: LIK 8

I FEEL LIKE I'M FIXIN' TO DIE (Country Joe & The Fish).
Tracks: / Fish cheer and I feel like I'm fixin' to die rag / Who am I? / Pat's song / Rock coast blues / Magoo / Though dream / Thursday / Eastern jam / Colors for Susan.
LP: VSD 79266
LP: VMLP 5306
MC: VMTC 6306

INTO THE FRAY.
Tracks: / Kiss my ass / Quiet days in clichy / Sexist pig / Here I go again / Breakfast for two / Love is a fire / Picks and lasers / Coyote / Hold on it's coming / Entertainment is my business / Holy roller / Not so sweet Martha Lorraine / janis / Get it all together / Ring of fire.
2LP: RAG 2001

LEISURE SUITE.
Tracks: / Private parts / Take time out / Sure cure for the blues / La di da / Hard work and no play / Reaching for the stars / Bo wop oh.
LP: FT 565

LIFE AND TIMES OF HAIGHT ASHBURY TO WOODSTOCK, THE (Country Joe & The Fish).
Tracks: / I feel like I'm fixin' to die rag / Bass strings / Flying high / Porpoise mouth / Untitled protest, An / Who am I? / Superbird (tricky Dicky) / Not so sweet Martha Lorraine / Marijuana / Rock and soul music / Garage / Waltzing in the moonlight / Death sound blues / Janis / Sing, sing, sing / Crystal blues / Masked marauder, The / Love machine / "Fish" cheer, The / I feel like I'm fixin' to die rag.
LP: VSD 27

ON MY OWN.
LP: RAG 1012
LP: INT 147 406

THINKING OF WOODY GUTHRIE.
Tracks: / Pastures of plenty / Talkin' dust bowl blues / Blowing down that dusty road / So long it's been good to know yuh / Tom Joad / Sinking of Reuben James / Roll on Columbia / Pretty boy Floyd / When the curfew blows / This land is your land.
MC: MCCV 6546

MacDonald, Donald

DONNY MCDONALD WITH LOZZIE MILES.
LP: NOLA LP 13

HERE COMES DONNY.
Tracks: / An cat agus an luchag / Eilidh / Road to Ness, The / A'suathadh / Mo mhathair / Smaointean balaich / Ciaradh an fheasgair / Kyleakin ferry / Ar baile / Tigh mo sheanair / Am bodach starrag / Comhradh eadar fad ban agus cnap guail.
LP: LILP 5064
MC: LICS 5064

LARGE AS LIFE.
LP: LILP 5087
MC: LICS 5087

MacDonald, Doug

NEW YORK SESSION (MacDonald, Doug & Friends).
LP: SE 0101

McDonald, Fergie

FERGIE MCDONALD & HIS HIGHLAND DANCE BAND.
LP: SGW 5001

SWING YOUR PARTNERS.
LP: LILP 5061

THERE'S IRISH ON THE ISLANDS.
Tracks: / Irish jiggery / Country down reel / Irish bottom two step / Pride of Erin waltz / Jigtime in Dublin / Sligo reels / Jigs from Tyrone / Limerick jigs / Antrim reeltime / Irish military two step / Moonlight over Shannan waltz / Connemara jigs / Marchin' thro' Ireland / Belfast jig.
LP: LILP 5126
MC: LICS 5126
LP: RCALP 3053
MC: RCAK 3053

MacDonald, George

GOLDEN KEY, THE.
MC: 1764

PRINCESS & THE GOBLIN (McBain, Rose).
MCSET: COL 3003

SIR GIBBIE (Fleming, Tom).
MCSET: COL 2021

MacDonald, Ger

ERINSAGA (See under Kiernan, Ken) (Kiernan, Ken/Ger MacDonald).

JIM FITZPATRICK'S ERINSAGA (See under Kiernan, Ken for details) (MacDonald, Ger/Ken Kiernan).

McDonald & Giles

MCDONALD & GILES.
LP: 2302 070
LP: EGLP 3

MacDonald, Iain

BENEATH STILL WATERS.
Tracks: / Coldest night of the year / Maid of Islay / Do you think it's right / lolaire, The / Santiago stadium / No fun city/Free Nelson Mandella / Ask questions later? / All our dreams / Bed of shifting stone.
LP: TRAX 003
MC: CTRAX 003

THIS LAND WAS ONCE FREE.
Tracks: / Another package deal / Comrades in the dark / This land was once free / Was it on the fields of Flanders / Heaven is / Last mystery, The / I never wondered why / In secret gardens / That quiet peace.
LP: TRAX 025
MC: CTRAX 025

MacDonald, Jeanette

APPLE BLOSSOMS.
LP: JN 122

BITTERSWEET.
LP: JN 117

CHRISTMAS ALBUM, THE (MacDonald, Jeanette/Nelson Eddy).
LP: JN 119

DREAM LOVER.
Tracks: / March of the Grenadiers / Dream lover / Always in all ways / Beyond the blue horizon / Pardon Madame / Goodnight / One hour with you / We will always be sweethearts / Isn't it romantic / Lover / I love you so / Villa / Tonight will teach me to forget / Try to forget / Italian street song / Ah sweet mystery of life / Indian love call / Farewell to dreams / Will you remember?.
LP: CHD 133
MC: MCHD 133

EARLY YEARS, THE (MacDonald, Jeanette/Nelson Eddy).
2LP: JN 110

IRENE.
LP: JN 109

JEANETTE MACDONALD & NELSON EDDY (see also Nelson Eddy) (MacDonald, Jeanette/Nelson Eddy).
Tracks: / Tramp tramp tramp / Italian street song / Neath the southern moon / I'm falling in love with someone / Ah sweet mystery of life / Mounties, The / Rose Marie / Indian love call / Will you remember / Farewell to dreams / Who are we to say / Sweetheart / Waltz / Song of love.
LP: NL 89313
MC: NK 89313
LP: INTS 5016

MERRY WIDOW, THE.
LP: JN 120

NAUGHTY MARIETTA.
LP: JN 115

OPERATIC RECITAL VOL 3 (MacDonald, Jeanette/Nelson Eddy).
LP: JN 123

SING PATRIOTIC SONGS (MacDonald, Jeanette/Nelson Eddy).
LP: JN 118

SINGS "SAN FRANCISCO" AND OTHER SILVER SCREEN FA.
Tracks: / San Francisco / One alone / Will you remember / Ah sweet mystery of life / When you're away / Indian love call / Ciribiribin / Only a rose / Beyond the blue horizon / One night of love / Waltz / Italian street song.
LP: NL 89059
MC: NK 89059

SMILIN' THROUGH.
LP: JN 125

SONG FOR CLOTILDA, A/THE NELSON EDDY SHOW (MacDonald, Jeanette/Nelson Eddy).
LP: JN 111

SONGS OF FAITH AND INSPIRATION (MacDonald, Jeanette/Nelson Eddy).
LP: JN 127

TOGETHER AGAIN 1948 (MacDonald, Jeanette/Nelson Eddy).
LP: SH 2101

TONIGHT OR NEVER.
LP: JN 112

McDonald, John

ROVING PLOUGHBOY (McDonald, John & Ena).
Tracks: / Berryfields o'Blair, The / Roving ploughboy, The / Auchan lochan / Lodgin' hoose, the / Braes of Dunphail / Haughs o' Cromdale / Dying ploughboy, The / MacGuinnesses's cross-eyed pet / Buchan Miller / Mains o'Fogieloon, The / Farewell Tomintoul / Lucky plougboy / George Morris / Harvest home / Bonnie banks of Ross-shire, the / Motor-car, The / Reel of Tulloch, The / Bonnie lady, The / Shepherd lad o'Rhynie, The / Rakes of Kildare, The / Marlin fair, the / Hotchie potchie / Froggie song / Tenpenny bit, The / I was kissed yestreen / Pibroch O'Donald Dhy.
MC: 60-061

SINGING MOLECATCHER OF MORAYSHIRE, THE Scots Ballads, Bothy songs & Melodeon tunes.
Tracks: / Sleepytoon / Mains o'Fogieloon, The / Lord Ronald / Burns waltz, A / Dewy dens o'Yarrow, The / Bonnie hoose o' Airlie / Majuba Hill / Braes o'Balquhidder, The / Ploughin' match at duffus, The / Haughs o' Cromdale / Jacobite waltz, A / Farewell tomintoul / Bonnie lassie will ye gang / My auntie Jean / Bonnie Udny / Cairngorn barn dance, The / Wandering shepherd laddie, The / Banks of Allan, The / Ball of Kerrymuir.
LP: 12TS 263

McDonald, Kathleen

SILVER VOICE OF HIGHLANDS.
LP: GES 1045

MacDonald, Kenneth

SOUND OF KINTAIL FEATURING KENNETH MACDONALD.
Tracks: / John MacColl's march to Kilbowie cottage / Col. David Murray's welcome to Kintail / Tullock Castle / Piobaireacho, Donald Gruanach's / Gregory Blend and Roddy MacDonald / Boys of Glendale / I'm going home to Kintail.
MC: KITV 460

McDonald, Michael

IF THAT'S WHAT IT TAKES.
Tracks: / Playin' by the rules / I keep forgettin' / Love lies / Gotta try / I can let go now / That's why / If that's what it takes / No such luck / Losin' end / Believe in it.
LP: K 57018
MC: K4 57018

NO LOOKING BACK.
Tracks: / No looking back / By heart / Bad times / (I'll be your) Angel / Any foolish thing / Our love / (I hang) On your every word / Lost in the parade / Don't let me down.
LP: 925291 1
MC: 925291 4

ON MY OWN (See under Labelle, Patti).

SWEET FREEDOM: BEST OF MICHAEL MCDONALD.
Tracks: / Sweet freedom / I'll be your angel / Yah mo b there / I gotta try / I keep forgettin' / Our love / On my own / No lookin back / Any foolish thing / That's why / What a fool believes / I can let go now.
LP: WX 67
MC: WX 67C

TAKE IT TO HEART.
LP: WX 285
MC: WX 285 C

YAH MO BE THERE (see Ingram,James/Michael McDonald) (McDonald, Michael/ James Ingram).

McDonald, Pete

END OF THE LINE.
Tracks: / Little bit of lovin' / Stop, in the name of love / Hold on, baby, hold on / Lady of mine / Stay the night / Three star general / Way back when / End of the line / High life / Love undecided.
LP: CRX 7

McDonald, Ralph

COUNTERPOINT.
Tracks: / I need someone / You are in love / Tell the truth / Discolypso / Always something missing / East dry river.
LP: TKR 83373

UNIVERSAL RHYTHM.
Tracks: / In the name of love / Outcasts (another time, another place), Theme from / Universal rhythm / Trade winds / Playpen / It's the game / Park Plaza.
LP: LONLP 3
MC: LONC 3

MacDonald, Ranald

MACDONALD OF KEPPOCH SINGS.
Tracks: / Welcome clan Donald / Coll nam bo / Where the river almond flows / Highbridge rout, The / Dun eideann / Wild mountain thyme / Red lion of Scotland / Mhaireearead o / Road to the isles / Sound the Pibroch / Mingulay boat song / Lochnagar / My ain folk / Dark island.
LP: REL 456

MacDonald Sisters

SONGS OF THE ISLANDS.
Tracks: / Geallach abuchaidh an eorna / Puirt a beul / Faili oro / Puirt a beul / Hug oreann oro gur toigh leam fhein thu / Dh' theidinn leat a dh' uibhist / A bhean eudaich / An ataireachd ard / Far am bi mi fhein / Fail oro mar dh' fhag sinn.
LP: LILP 5063
MC: LICS 5063

McDonald, Skeets

DON'T LET THE STARS GET IN YOUR EYES.
Tracks: / Don't let the stars get in your eyes / Looking at the moon and wishing on a star / I am music / I've got to win your love again / I need your love / But I do / Be my life's companion / Heartbreaking one / All American boy / What a lonesome life it's been / I'll make believe / I can't hold a memory in my arms / Bless your little ol'heart (You're mine) / Big family trouble / Love that hurts me so,The / Today I'm movin' out.
LP: BFX 15195

GOING STEADY WITH THE BLUES.
LP: HAT 3138
MC: HATC 3138
LP: 2C 068 86307

ROCKIN' ROLLIN'.
Tracks: / You oughta see grandma rock / Heart breaking mama / I love you mama mia / Fingertips / Keep her off your mind / What am I doing here? / I love you ,I love you / You gotta be my baby / Look who's crying now / You better not go / Let's spend some time with me / Let me know / Smoke comes out of my chimney (just the same) / I can't stand it any longer / Echo of your footsteps, The.
LP: BFX 15191

MacDonnachadha, Sean

BRUACH NA BEIRTRT.
LP: CEF 115

MacDowell, Al

TIME PEACE.
Tracks: / Fantastic voyage / St. Alban's tango / Nina's line of no return / Somewhere / Fantasia / Maybe / Peng shui / Ode bra / View from a window / Come see tomorrow / Blue age.
LP: GV 794501

McDowell, Carrie

CARRIE MCDOWELL.
Tracks: / Uh, uh, no, no casual sex (part 1) / Secret fire / When a woman loves a man / Just dance / It's the power of your love (growing on me) / Fly (white bird fly) / Tracks of my tears / I'm here for you / Up the down side of love.
LP: ZL 72590
MC: ZK 72590

McDowell, Fred

1962.
LP: HT 302

DOSE OF DOUBLE DYNAMITE, A (McDowell, Fred & Phil Guy).
LP: . . . . RL 063

FRED MCDOWELL.
MC: . . . . C 202

FRED MCDOWELL 1959.
Tracks: / Been drinking water out of a log / Shake 'em on down / Freight train blues / Drop down mama / When you get home write me a few lines / Poor boy blues / Cool water blues / 61 highway blues / Fred McDowell's blues / Keep your lamp trimmed and burning / Soon one morning / You done tol' everybody / My mother died and left me / I wished I was in heaven.
LP: . . . . KC 107

FRED MCDOWELL AND HIS BLUES BOYS.
LP: . . . . ARHOOLIE 1046

FRED MCDOWELL & JOHNNY WOODS (McDowell, Fred/John Dudley).
LP: . . . . ROUNDER 2007

KEEP YOUR LAMP TRIMMED.
LP: . . . . ARHOOLIE 1068

MISSISSIPPI DELTA BLUES.
Tracks: / Some day baby / Milk cow blues / Train I ride, The / Over the hill / Goin' down to the river / I wished I were in heaven sittin' down / Louise.
LP: . . . . BLP 30140
LP: . . . . ARHOOLIE 1021

MISSISSIPPI DELTA BLUES VOL 2.
LP: . . . . ARHOOLIE 1027

MISSISSIPPI FRED MCDOWELL 1904-72 (McDowell, Mississippi Fred).
LP: . . . . C 5526

STANDING AT THE BURYING GROUND (see also Jo Ann Kelly).
LP: . . . . RL 053

WHEN I LAY MY BURDEN DOWN (McDowell, Fred/Furry Lewis).
Tracks: / If you see my baby / John Henry / Louise / 61 highway blues / Big fat mama / When I lay my burden down / Dankin farm / Casey Jones / Harry furry blues / Everyday in the week / Grieve my mind / Beale street blues.
LP: . . . . BMLP 1047

McDowell, Roddy

BATMAN.
MC: 38843

McDowell, Ronnie

ALL TIED UP IN LOVE.
Tracks: / All tied up / Baby me baby / I love the way you say goodnight / Let me teach you how to slow dance / Sugar baby pop / When you hurt I hurt / My heart belongs to Shirley / When God made you / Lovin' that crazy feelin' / Whooplah.
LP: . . . . IMCA 5725
MC: . . . . IMCAC 5725

McDuff, Jack

GEORGE BENSON AND JACK MCDUFF (see Benson, George) (McDuff, Jack & George Benson).

HONEYDRIPPER,THE.
LP: . . . . OJC 222

Macedonian Early ...

17 MACEDONIAN FOLK DANCES (Macedonian Early Music Band).
LP: . . . . GB 1978
MC: . . . . GB 1978C

McEldowney, Eugene

IRISH REBEL BALLADS.
MC: . . . . CT 102

McElherron, Paddy

PADDY MCELHERRON.
Tracks: / My Donegal shore / Boys from County Armagh / Cottage in Donegal / Newry town / Far from Erin's shore / Going back to Castleblaney / Green glens of Antrim / Village in County Tyrone / Lovely Derry on the banks of the Foyle / Mountains of Mourne / Gallant John Joe / My lovely Irish rose / Co. Cavan.
MC: . . . . CHRL 217

SING A SONG OF IRELAND.
LP: . . . . HRL 217

McElroy, Foster

FM SQUARED.
LP: 781 994-1
MC: 781 994-4

McEnery, Peter (nar)

WUTHERING HEIGHTS (see under Wuthering Heights (bk)).

McEntire, Reba

BEHIND THE SCENE.
Tracks: / Love isn't love / Is it really love / Reasons / Nickel dreams / One good reason / You really better love me after this / There ain't no future in this / Why do we want (what we know we can't have) / I sacrificed more than you'll ever lose / Pins and needles.
LP: 8127 811

COUNTRY STORE: REBA MCENTIRE.
Tracks: / I can see forever in your eyes / Ol' man river / Sweet dreams / Can't even get the blues / You're the first time I've thought / Only you (and you alone) / That makes two of us / Today all over again / (You lift me up) to Heaven / Poor man's roses / Who? / Gonna love ya / Tears on my pillow / I'm not that lonely yet.
LP: . . . . CST 32
MC: . . . . CSTK 32

GREATEST HITS: REBA MCENTIRE.
Tracks: / Just a little love / He broke your memory last night / How blue / Somebody should leave / Have I got a deal for you / Only in my mind / Whoever's in New England / Little rock / What am I gonna do about you / One promise too late.
LP: . . . . MCG 6026
MC: . . . . MCGC 6026

HAVE I GOT A DEAL FOR YOU.
Tracks: / I'm in love all over / She's single again / Great divide, The / Have I got a deal for you / Red roses (won't work now) / Only on my mind / She's the one loving you now / Whose heartache is this anyway / I don't need nothin'you ain't got / Don't forget your way home.
LP: . . . . IMCA 5585

JUST A LITTLE LOVE.
Tracks: / Just a little love / Poison sugar / I'm getting over you / You're always there for me / Every second someone breaks a heart / Tell me what's so good about goodbye / He broke your memory last night / If only / Congratulations / Silver eagle.
LP: . . . . IMCA 5475

LAST ONE TO KNOW, THE.
Tracks: / Last one to know, The / Girl who has everything, The / Just across the Rio Grande / I don't want to mention any names / Someone else / What you gonna do about me / I don't want to be alone / Stairs, The / Love will find it's way to you / I've still got the love we made.
LP: . . . . MCF 3401
MC: . . . . MCFC 3401

MY KIND OF COUNTRY.
Tracks: / How blue / That's what he said / I want to hear it from you / It's not over (if I'm not over you) / Somebody should leave / Everything but my heart / Don't you believe him / Before I met you / He's only everything / You've got me right where you want me.
LP: . . . . IMCA 5516

REBA.
Tracks: / So so so long / New fool at the game / Silly me / Do right by me / Wish I were only lonely / Sunday kind of love / You're the one I dream about / Respect / I know how he feels / Everytime you touch her.
LP: . . . . MCG 6040
MC: . . . . MCGC 6040

REBA NELL MCENTIRE.
Tracks: / I've never stopped dreaming of you / Hold on / I know I'll have a better day tomorrow / Don't say goodnight, say good morning / Muddy Mississippi / It's another silent night / Empty arms / Love is never easy / Waitin' for the sun to shine / Good friends.
LP: 822 455 1
MC: 822 455 4

UNLIMITED.
LP: . . . . SRM 14047

WHAT AM I GONNA DO ABOUT YOU.
Tracks: / Why not tonight / What am I gonna do about you / Lookin' for a new love story / Take me back / My mind is on you / Let the music lift you up / I heard her cryin' / No such thing / One promise too late / Till it snows in Mexico.
LP: . . . . MCF 3346
MC: . . . . MCFC 3346

WHOEVER'S IN NEW ENGLAND.
Tracks: / Can't stop now / You can take the wings off me / Whoever's in New England / I'll believe it when I feel it / I've seen better days / Little Rock / If you only knew / One thin dime / Don't touch me there / To make the same mistake again.
LP: . . . . IMCA 5691

Maceo

DOING THEIR OWN THING (Maceo & All The Kings Men).
Tracks: / Maceo / Got to getcha / Southwick / Funky women / Shake it baby / Better half / Don't waste this world away / Mag-Poo / (I remember) Mr. Banks.
LP: . . . . CRB 1176
MC: . . . . TCCRB 1176

US.
LP: . . . . URBLP 8
MC: . . . . URBMC 8

Macero, Teo

IMPRESSIONS OF CHARLES MINGUS.
LP: . . . . PA 8046

McEvoy, Gloria

GOLDEN DUETS (McEvoy, Gloria & Johnny).
LP: . . . . HPE 612

McEvoy, Johnny

20 GREATEST HITS: JOHNNY MCEVOY.
Tracks: / Mursheen Durkin / Those brown eyes / Life of the rover / Long before your time / Three score and ten / Come to the bower / Cliffs of Dooneen / Sliabh na mban / Town I loved so well, The / Daniel O'Connell and his steam engine / Boston burglar / Spancil Hill / Where my Eileen is waiting / Old bog road / Gypsy, The / Nora / Sullivan's John / Rambles of spring / Bound for Botany Bay / Carrickfergus.
LP: . . . . HALP TV 1
MC: . . . . HACS TV 1

20 IRISH REQUESTS.
Tracks: / Rose of Allendale / Old rustic bridge / Bunclody / Sam Hall / Wind in the willows / Mountains of Mourne / Bard of Armagh, The / Leaves in the wind / Three flowers / Molly darlin' / And the band played Waltzing Matilda / Ramblin' boy / Slieve Gallion braes / Cricklewood / Come up the stairs, Molly O / James Connolly / Dan O'Hara / Four strong winds / All I have to offer you is me / Carnlough Bay.
MC: . . . . HATVC 3

20 MORE HITS.
Tracks: / Spanish lady / Matt Hyland / Rose of Moray / Fiddlers green / She moved through the fair / Snowy breasted pearl, The / Mary of the curling hair / Whistling gypsy / Hills of Greymore / Avondale / Wild colonial boy / Black velvet band / Sammy's Bar / Flower of sweet Strabane / Alice Ben Bolt / Dawning of the day / Galway shawl / Danny boy / Rosaleen, sweet Rosaleen / Green hills of Kerry.
LP: . . . . HALP TV 2
MC: . . . . HACS TV 2

BEST OF JOHNNY MCEVOY.
LP: . . . . HSLP 005

CHRISTMAS DREAMS.
LP: . . . . HALP 157

COUNTRY FAVOURITES.
MCSET: . . . . DBXC 004

GOLDEN HOUR - JOHNNY MCEVOY.
LP: . . . . GH 570

GREATEST HITS: JOHNNY MCEVOY, VOLUME 1.
MC: . . . . ARANC 017

I'LL SPEND A TIME WITH YOU.
LP: . . . . HALP 174

JOHNNY MCEVOY.
LP: . . . . HALPX 112
MC: . . . . RTE 72

JOHNNY MCEVOY GOES COUNTRY.
LP: . . . . HPE 621

LEAVES IN THE WIND.
LP: . . . . HALPX 164

LONG BEFORE YOUR TIME.
LP: . . . . HALP 150

MY FAVOURITE IRISH SONGS.
LP: . . . . HPE 640

SINCE MAGGIE WENT AWAY.
LP: . . . . MCF 3274
MC: . . . . MCFC 3274

SINGS COUNTRY.
LP: . . . . HALP 115

SINGS FOR YOU.
LP: . . . . PLAY 1021
MC: . . . . CPLAY 1021

SONGS OF IRELAND.
Tracks: / Home boys home / Red is the rose / Black velvet band / Maggie / Good ship Kangaroo / Wild mountain thyme / I wish I had someone to love me / Town of ballybay, The / Molly,my Irish Molly / Rare ould times / Streets of New York,The / Travelling people / Shores of America / Bunch of thyme / Irish soldier laddie / Song for Ireland, A.
LP: . . . . MCF 3327
MC: . . . . MCFC 3327

SOUNDS LIKE MCEVOY.
LP: . . . . HALPX 117

WHERE MY EILEEN IS WAITING.
LP: . . . . HALP 143

McEwan, Billy

ORGAN POPS.
MC: . . . . KBGC 242
LP: . . . . BGC 242

MacEwan, Father Sydney

ROAD TO THE ISLES 1934-6, THE.
Tracks: / Road to the isles, The / Lark in the clear air / Macushla / Turn ye to me / Loch Lomond / Island moon / Mhnathan a'chlinne so / Bonnie Earl O'Moray, The / O men from the fields / Bonnie Mary of Argyle / Lewis bridal song / Ye banks and braes / Peat fire flame, The / Tog orm mo phiob / She moved through the fair / Annie Laurie / As I sit here / Maiden of Morven / Maighdeanan na h-airidh / Will ye no come back again.
LP: . . . . CHD 148
MC: . . . . MCHD 148

McEwan, Sydney Fr.

LET ME BRING LOVE.
LP: . . . . SKER 2001

MEMORIES.
LP: . . . . STAL 8016

McEwan, William

OLD RUGGED CROSS.
Tracks: / We will talk it o'er together / Song in my heart / I come to the garden / When they ring the golden bells / Old rugged cross, The / I'm going through, Jesus / By and by / Behold I stand / Your best friend / I heard the voice / Lead me to Calvary / Wonderful story / Softly & tenderly.
LP: . . . . MWM 1029

McFadden & Whitehead

I HEARD IT IN A LOVE SONG.
Tracks: / I heard it in a love song / That lets me know I'm love / I know what I'm gonna do / Always room for one more / Why oh why / Don't feel bad / This is my song / Love song no.690.
LP: . . . . PIR 84616
MC: 40 84616

MCFADDEN & WHITEHEAD.
Tracks: / Ain't no stoppin' us now / I've been pushed aside / Mr. Music / Just wanna love you baby / Got to change / You're my someone to love / I got the love / Do you want to dance.
LP: . . . . PIR 83613

McFarland, Billy

BEYOND THE SUNSET.
Tracks: / Each step of the way / How great thou art / Pastors on vacation.
LP: . . . . HRL 140

COUNTRY SONGS AND SAD TALES.
Tracks: / Hill above the city / House without love is not a home / She gave her heart to Jethro / Wedding bells / Brown to blue / Funeral / Jennifer Johnson / Mansion on the hill / Be careful of stones that you throw / City lights / Waltz of the angels / Deck of cards.
LP: . . . . HRL 183
MC: . . . . CHRL 183

DOWN THE TRAIL OF ACHING HEARTS.
LP: . . . . STOL 127

LITTLE ROSA (Country monologues).
Tracks: / Golden guitar / Don't forget me little darlin' / Old Doc Brown / Pappa sing me a song / Royal telephone / Boot Hill / Mother went a walkin' / 99 years / Old rugged cross / Drunken driver / Little Rosa / Mama sang a song.
MC: . . . . CHRL 189

McFarland, Tom

TRAVELLIN' WITH THE BLUES.
LP: . . . . ARHOOLIE 1079

MacFayden, Iain

CEOL MOR-CEOL BEAG.
LP: . . . . TP 018
MC: . . . . CTP 018

McFerrin, Bobby

BOBBY MCFERRIN.
Tracks: / Dance with me / Feline / You really got a hold on me / All feets can dance / Sightless bird / Peace / Jubilee / Hallucinations / Chicken.
LP: . . . . K 52387

MEDICINE MUSIC.
Tracks: / Medicine man / Baby / Yes, you / Garden, The / Common threads / Sweet in the mornin' (Featuring voicestra.) / Discipline (Featuring Robert McFerrin Sr. and voicestra.) / He ran all the way / Angry (Gima) / Train, The / Soma so de la de sase / 23rd Psalm.
LP: . . . . MTL 1059
LP: 793 048 1
MC: . . . . TCMTL 1059
MC: 792 048 4

SIMPLE PLEASURES.
Tracks: / Don't worry, be happy / All I want / Drive my car / Simple pleasures / Good lovin' / Come to me / Suzie Q / Drive / Them changes / Sunshine of your love.
LP: . . . . MTL 1018
MC: . . . . TCMTL 1018

LP: ATAK 170
MC: TCATAK 170

SPONTANEOUS INVENTIONS.
Tracks: / Thinkin' about your body / Turtle shoes / From me to you / There ya go / Cara mia / Another night in Tunisia / Opportunity / Walkin' / I hear music / Beverly Hills blues / Manana Iguana.
LP: BT 85110
MC: TCBT 85110

VOICE, THE.
Tracks: / Blackbird / El brujo / I feel good / I'm my own walkman / Music box.
LP: 960661

McGaha, Rod

HIS PERSONAL TOUCH.
LP: IAM R 3803
MC: IAM C 3803

McGann, Andy

ANDY MCGANN & PADDY REYNOLDS FIDDLE (McGann, Andy & Paddy Reynolds).
LP: SHAN 29004

IT'S A HARD ROAD TO TRAVEL.
LP: SHAN 29009

McGarity, Lou

DAVISON, OLIVER JACKSON ETC..
LP: SLP 513

IN CELEBRATION.
LP: IAJRC 36

MUGGSY SPANIER, MIFF MOLE & LOU MCGARITY (See under Spanier, Muggsy) (McGarity,Lou/ Muggsy Spanier/ Miff Mole).

SOME LIKE IT HOT & SOME LIKE IT BLUE (McGarity,Lou Big 5 and 7).
MC: HM 02

McGarrigle, Kate

DANCER WITH BRUISED KNEES (McGarrigle, Kate & Anna).
Tracks: / Dancer with bruised knees / Southern boys / Biscuit song, The / First born / Blanche comme la neige / Perrine etait servante / Be my baby / Walking song, The / Naufragee du tendre / Hommage a grungie / Kitty come home / Come a long way.
LP: K 56356
LP: ED 307
LP: CGLP 4402

HEARTBEATS ACCELERATING (McGarrigle, Kate & Anna).
Tracks: / Heartbeats accelerating / I eat dinner / Rainbow ride / Mother, mother / Love is / DJ serenade / I'm losing you / Hit and run love / Leave me be / St. James Hospital.
LP: 211.142
MC: 411.142

KATE & ANNA MCGARRIGLE (McGarrigle, Kate & Anna).
Tracks: / Entre la jeunesse et la sagesse / Complainte pour Ste. Catherine / Mais quand tu danses / Cheminant a la ville / Excursion a Venise / En filant ma quenouille / La belle est etourdie / Maufragee du tendre / Avant la guerre / A boire / Prends ton manteau.
LP: CGLP 4401
MC: CGC 4401
LP: ILPS 9654
LP: HNBL 1302
MC: HNBC 1302

KATE & ANNA MCGARRIGLE (McGarrigle, Kate & Anna).
Tracks: / Kiss and say goodbye / My town / Blues in D / Heart like a wheel / Foolish you / Talk to me of Mendocino / Complainte pour Ste. Catherine / Tell my sister / Swimming song, The / Jigsaw puzzle of Life / Go leave / Travelling on for Jesus.
LP: K 56218

LOVE OVER AND OVER (McGarrigle, Kate & Anna).
Tracks: / Move over moon / Sun son (shining on the water) / I cried for us / Love over and over / Star cab company / Tu vas m'accompagner / On my way to town / Jesus lifeline / Work song / St. Valentine's day 1978 / Midnight flight.
LP: POLS 1062
MC: POLSC 1062

PRONTO MONTO.
Tracks: / On my heart / Side of fries / Just another broken heart / NA CL / Pronto monto / Stella by artois / Bundle of sorrow, bundle of joy / Come back baby / Tryin' to get to you / Fixture in the park / Dead weight / Cover up my head.
LP: K 56561

McGee, Dennis

LA VIEILLE MUSIQUE ACADIENNE (See under Courville, Sady) (Courville, Sady/Dennis McGhee).

McGee, Sam

COUNTRY GUITAR.
LP: ARHOOLIE 5012

McGee, Seamus

COME HOME DANNY BOY.
MC: UNIMC 5008

WORLD YOU LEFT BEHIND, THE.
LP: FALP 005

McGettigan, John

JOHN MCGETTIGAN & HIS IRISH MINSTRELS (McGettigan, John & His Irish Minstrels).
Tracks: / Martha, the flower of sweet Strabane / Maid of the Moorlough shore / Highland schottische / Turfman from Ardee / Stone outside Dan Murphy's door / Medley of jigs / Erin's lovely Lee / Shoe the donkey / Rare old Irish whiskey / Rambling Irishman / Medley of polkas / McGettigan's jig medley / Lovely Molly / Medley of reels / Me husband's flannel shirt / Cutting the corn in Creeslough today / Medley of hornpipes / Star of Donegal.
LP: 12T 367

McGhee, Brownie

BEST OF BROWNIE MCGHEE.
LP: SLP 4032

BROWNIE BLUES.
LP: OBC 505

BROWNIE MCGHEE BLUES 1944-59.
LP: PY 1809

BROWNIE MCGHEE, SONNY TERRY & SVEND ERIK NORREGARD (McGhee, Brownie, Sonny Terry, Svend Erik Norregard).
LP: SLP 4007

BROWNIE MCGHEE & SONNY TERRY WITH JORDAN WEBB 1940-41 (McGhee, Brownie/Sonny Terry/Jordan Webb).
LP: DLP 541

FACTS OF LIFE.
LP: BR 104

HOMETOWN BLUES (See Under Terry, Sonny) (McGhee, Brownie & Sonny Terry).

I COULDN'T BELIEVE MY EYES (McGhee, Brownie & Sonny Terry With Earl Hooker).
Tracks: / Black cat bone / Brownie's new blues / Poor man blues / Tell me why / My baby's so fine / You just usin' me for a convenience / Hole in the wall / Long way from home / Don't wait for me / I'm in love with you baby / Parcel post blues / When I was drinking / I couldn't believe my eyes / Life is a gamble / Don't mistreat me / Rock Island line.
LP: SEE 92

LETS HAVE A BALL 1945-55 (McGhee, Brownie & his Buddies).
LP: PY 1805

WALK ON (see Sonny, Terry) (McGhee, Brownie & Sonny Terry).

YOU HEAR ME TALKIN' (see Terry, Sonny) (McGhee, Brownie & Sonny Terry).
LP: MR 5131

McGhee, Dennis

EARLY RECORDINGS (McGhee, Dennis with Fruge, Courville).
LP: MS 45002

TRADITIONAL CAJUN FIDDLING (McGhee, Dennis/S.D. Courville).
LP: 16001

McGhee, Howard

COOKIN' TIME (McGhee,Howard Orchestra).
Tracks: / Blues deundi / Round midnight / Cookin' time / Willow weep for me / On Green Dolphin Street / Highest mountain / Bless you / Summertime / Satin doll / Chronos.
LP: HEP 2001

DUSTY BLUE.
Tracks: / Dusty blue / Sound of music, The / I concentrate on you / Sleep talk / Part avenue petite / Flyin'colours / With malice / Groovin' high / Cottage for sale.
LP: AFF 156

HEAT'S ON, THE (see under Eldridge, Roy) (McGhee,Howard & Roy).

HERE COMES FREDDY (McGhee, Howard & Illinois Jacquet).
Tracks: / Here comes Freddy / Suite for Dru / Deep in the hat / All soul / Stardust / Travel / Come Sunday / Yardbird suite.
LP: SNTF 714
MC: ZCSN 714

HOME RUN (McGhee, Howard & Benny Bailey).
LP: SLP 4082

HOWARD MCGHEE JAZZ BROTHERS & CHARLIE ROUSE (McGhee, Howard Jazz Brothers & Charlie Rouse).
LP: SLP 4077

LIVE AT EMERSON'S.
LP: ZMS 2006

MAGGIE.
Tracks: / Merri-Lee / Short life / Talk of the town / Bass C Jam / Bass C Jm (master) / Down home / Sweet & lovely / Fiesta / I'm in the mood for love / Belle from Bunnycock / Lip flip / Man I love, The / Last word, The / Royal Garden blues / Mood indigo / St. Louis blues / Twelfth Street / One o'clock jump / Stormy weather / Perdido / Man with a horn / Stompin' at the Savoy / Lady be good / Stardust / How high the moon / Don't blame me / Body and soul / Harvest time.
LP: SJL 2219

MAGGIE'S BACK IN TOWN.
Tracks: / Demon chase / Softly as in a morning sunrise / Maggie's back in town / Brownie speaks / Willow weep for me / Sunset eyes / Summertime.
LP: 1007 596
LP: COP 044

SHADES OF BLUE.
Tracks: / Sharpe edge, The / Shades of blue / Cool / Day after, The / Topside / Arbee / Ill wind / My delight.
LP: BLP 30146

SHARP EDGE.
LP: BLP 60110

THAT BOP THING (McGhee, Howard Quintet).
Tracks: / Get happy / Tahitian lullaby / Lover man / Lullaby of the leaves / You're teasing me / Transpicuous / Rifftide / Oo wee but I do / Don't blame me / Tweedles / I'll remember April.
LP: AFF 94

TRUMPET AT TEMPO.
Tracks: / Trumpet at tempo / Thermodynamics / Up in Dodo's room / Dilated pupils / Midnight at Mintons / High wind in Hollywood / Night mist / Dorothy / Coolerini / Turnip blood / Surrender / Sleepwalker boogie / Stoptime blues / You.
LP: SPJ 131

WISE IN TIME (McGhee, Howard & Teddy Edwards).
LP: SLP 4081

YOUNG AT HEART (McGhee, Howard & Teddy Edwards).
Tracks: / Relaxing at Camarillo / Reflection / Blues in the closet / On a misty night / In walked Bud / Yardbird suite / Moose the Mooche.
LP: SLP 4080

McGhee, Reverend F.W

REV. F.W. MCGEE.
LP: ELE 1-200

REVEREND F.W.MCGHEE.
LP: RL 338

McGhee, Sticks

DRINKIN' WINE SPOO-DE-O-DEE.
Tracks: / I ain't gonna scald you / Wee wee hours part 1 / Wee wee hours part 2 / Oh what a face / Blues in the heart / I'm doing all this time / Wiggle waggle woo, The / Things have changed / Tee nah nah / Tennessee waltz blues / One monkey don't stop no show / Housewarming boogie / She's gone / Let's do it / Blues mixture / Drinkin' wine spo-dee-o-dee.
LP: IG 401

McGhee, Wes

AIRMAIL.
LP: TRP 8062

LANDING LIGHTS.
LP: TRP 843

LONG NIGHTS AND BANJO MUSIC.
LP: TRP 7861

NEON AND DUST.
MC: MILC 004

THANKS FOR THE CHICKEN.
LP: TRP 852

ZACATECAS.
LP: TRP 286

McGill, Alan

20 BEST LOVED GOSPEL SONGS - ALAN MCGILL.
LP: PC 322

MacGillivray, Iain

ROLLING HOME.
Tracks: / Anthony Riley / Mary & The soldier / Dowie dens of Yarrow, The / Norland wind / Rollin' home / January man / Bleacher lass o' Kelvinhaugh / Lads o' the fair, The / Maid of Bunclody / Red is the rose.
LP: FE 053
MC: FE 053C

MacGillvray, Elspeth

INHERITANCE.
MC: NOR 4

McGilp, Duncan

CEOL OR MHUILE.
Tracks: / Dawn / Love I gave when young, The / Island sheiling song / Cailin donn a' chuaiein reidh / My mother / Mull of the cool high bens / Land of hearts desire / Young Margaret / Where I was last night / Fair swan, The / I would be true.
MC: MR 1005

McGilpin, Bob

SUPERSTAR.
Tracks: / Superstar / Move in closer / Moon dancin' / Go for the money / I'll always come a runnin' / Part time baby / When you feel love / Love is gonna bring me back / I'm not alone without you / Rainy day.
LP: NRH 1002

McGinn, Matt

PORTRAIT, THE.
Tracks: / Footba' referee / Dundee cat, The / Red yo yo, The / Willie Macnamara / Skinny ma linky long legs / Dundee ghost, The / Tra la la tweet / Cor wee wean / Loch Lomond / Rob Roy MacGreegor O / Moaning / I owe you / Three nights and a Sunday / I'm looking for a job / Polly had a poodle / Manura Manya / No nay never.
LP: ITV 454
MC: KITV 454

SCREWTOPS ARE FALLING ON MY HEAD.
MC: ZCSMPS 8925
LP: PKL 5527

TWO HEADED MAN STRIKES AGAIN.
LP: GES 1120

McGlohon, Loonis

KEEP IT SIMPLE (See under Haymes, Dick) (McGlohon, Loonis Trio).

LOONIS IN LONDON.
Tracks: / Foggy day / Send in the clowns / Time for love / Where's the child I used to hold / Lazybones / Blackberry winter / Songbird / Get me to the church on time / I've grown accustomed to her face.
LP: AP 166

McGlynn, Fraser

ARGYLE CONNECTION (McGlynn, Fraser Trio).
MC: LC 006

REEL MCGLYNN, THE.
MC: NBCS 1009

McGlynn, Pat Band

PAT MCGLYNN BAND.
LPPD: GP 690

McGlynn,Arty

LEAD THE KNAVE (McGlynn,Arty/ Nollaig Casey).
LP: MCGLP 1
MC: MCGMC 1

MCGLYNN'S FANCY.
Tracks: / Carolan's draught / Floating crowbar, The / I wish my love was a red, red rose / Peter Byrne's fancy / Blackbird, The / Creeping Docken / Charles O'Connor / Arthur Darley / Hills above Drumquin, The / Sally gardens.
LP: BER 011
MC: KBER 011

McGoldrick,Anna

ANNA MCGOLDRICK (VOL.1).
LP: BONUS 101

GOLDEN HITS, VOLUME 1.
MC: MB LP 1024

GOLDEN HITS, VOLUME 2.
MC: MB LP 1025

GOLDEN HITS, VOLUME 3.
MC: MB LP 1027

VOICE OF IRELAND, THE.
Tracks: / Dear old Donegal / Forty shades of green / Paddy McGinty's goat / Danny boy / Humour is on me now, The / Spinning wheel / Let him go, let him tarry / How are things in Glocca Morra / Mick McGillan's ball / Little town in the ould County Down / Teddy O'Neale / Golden jubilee.
MC: 3170 109

McGonagall, William

TRUTH AT LAST, THE.
MCSET: SAY 57

McGonigle, Mary

SONG OF LIBERTY.
MC: UNIMC 5004

McGonigle, Tom

ROAD MAP OF IRELAND (McGonigle, Tom & Robert McGouran).
LP: OAS 3014

McGorman, Fee

SONGS OF THE IRISH REPUBLIC.
LP: CSDBL 508
LP: SDBL 508

McGough & McGear

MCGOUGH & MCGEAR.
Tracks: / So much / Little bit of heaven, A / Basement flat / Prologue from Frink... Summer with Monika / Moanin' (From Frink, a life in the day of summer with Monika.) / Anji (From Frink, a life in the day of summer with Monika.) / Epilogue from Frink (Summer with Monika) / Come close and sleep now / Yellow book / House in my head / Mr. Tickle / Living room / Do you remember / Please don't run too fast / Ex art student.
LP: . . . . PCS 7332
MC: . . . . TCPCS 7332

McGough, Roger

JELLY PIE (McGough, Roger & Brian Patten).
MCSET: CC/042

SUMMER WITH MONIKA.
LP: . . . . ILPS 9551

McGovern, Jimmy

GATHERING.... (McGovern, Jimmy & his Country Dance Orchestra).
2LP: . . . . AJP 1007/8

JIMMY MCGOVERN AND HIS SCOTTISH DANCE BAND (McGovern, Jimmy and his Scottish Dance Band).
MC: . . . . AM 25

McGovern, Maureen

ACADEMY AWARD PERFORMANCE.
LP: . . . . BT 474

MacGowran, Jack (nar)

MACGOWRAN SPEAKING BECKETT (see under Beckett, Samuel).

McGrath, John

CEILE SOUND OF JOHN MCGRATH.
MC: . . . . HSMC 045

McGreevy, Johnny

JOHN MCGREEVY & SEAMUS COOLEY (McGreevy, Johnny & Seamus Cooley).
LP: . . . . PH 2005

MONDAY FEAST.
LP: . . . . SIF 1023
MC: . . . . CSIF 1023

McGregor, Chris

BLUE NOTES FOR JOHNNY.
Tracks: / Funk dem dudu to Erica / Eyomzi / Ntyilo Ntyilo / Blues for Nick / Monks & Mbizo / Ithi Gqi.
LP: . . . . OG 532

COUNTRY COOKING (McGregor, Chris/Brotherhood Of Breath).
Tracks: / Country cookin' / Bakwetha / Sweet as honey / You and me / Big G / Maxine / Dakar / Thunder in the mountains (Cassette only).
LP: . . . . VE 17
MC: . . . . TCVE 17

IN HIS GOOD TIME.
Tracks: / Call / Raincloud / Unhome / Yikiti / Mngqusho / In his good time / Bride / Ududu nombambula.
2LP: . . . . OG 521

PROCESSION.
LP: . . . . OG 524

McGregor, Freddie

ACROSS THE BORDER.
Tracks: / Across the border / Out of the valley / Work to do today / Guantanamera / Can't get you out of my mind / Love will solve the problems / War mongers / High tension / Freedom justice equally.
LP: . . . . RAS 3009

ALL IN THE SAME BOAT.
Tracks: / All in the same boat / Hungry belly pickney / Push comes to shove / Jah a the don / I'm coming home / Glad you're here with me / I don't want to see you cry / Somewhere / Mama Mama / Peace in the valley.
LP: . . . . RAS 3014
MC: . . . . RASC 3014

BIG SHIP.
Tracks: / Big ship / Sweet lady / Peaceful man / Stop loving you / Get serious / Don't play the fool / Get united / Let me be the one / Roots man skanking / Holy Mount Zion.
LP: . . . . TS 002
LP: . . . . GREL 39
MC: . . . . GREEN 39

COME ON OVER.
Tracks: / Shirley come on over / Apple of my eye / Go away pretty woman / Stand up and fight / Shortman / Are you crazy / Reggae feeling / Rhythm so nice / Natty dread / Brother man.
LP: . . . . RAS 3002

DON'T WANT TO BE LONELY.
Tracks: / There is a time / Lady Hellen / It's bound to happen / Going home / Don't want to be lonely / Loving pauper / Searching for a love / Wise words.
LP: . . . . SOLP 7777

FREDDIE.
LP: . . . . STLP 1026

FREDDIE MCGREGOR.
Tracks: / That girl (groovy situation) / Silver lining / Just don't want to be lonely / If you want it / This is a fix / Lovin' every day / Tease my love / Look me in the eyes / Slow down / Come to me.
LP: . . . . POLD 5214
MC: . . . . POLDC 5214
LP: . . . . JALP 7000

I'M READY.
LP: . . . . SOLP 1000

LOVE AT FIRST SIGHT.
LP: . . . . VSLP 4074
LP: . . . . JGM 0019

MR.MCGREGOR.
LP: . . . . OBS 1901

NOW.
LP: . . . . VP 1163
MC: . . . . VPCT 1163

RAGGAMUFFIN' (see Brown,Dennis).

REGGAE ROCKERS.
LP: . . . . RRTG 7714
MC: . . . . RRTGC 7714

RHYTHM SO NICE.
LP: . . . . TSLP 019

MacGregor, Jimmy

HIGHLANDS AND LOWLANDS (McGregor, Jimmy & Robin Hall).
LP: . . . . NEVLP 003

KIDS STUFF (McGregor, Jimmy & Robin Hall).
LP: . . . . ECS 2161

SCOTCH AND IRISH (McGregor, Jimmy & Robin Hall).
LP: . . . . ECS 2024

SCOTLANDS BEST.
LP: . . . . SBE 181

SCOTTISH CHOICE (McGregor, Jimmy & Robin Hall).
LP: . . . . ECS 2074

TWO HEIDS ARE BETTER THAN YIN (see Hall, Robin) (McGregor, Jimmy & Robin Hall).

MacGregor, Mary

TORN BETWEEN TWO LOVERS.
LP: . . . . AAS 1504

McGriff, Jimmy

BLUES FOR MR.JIMMY.
Tracks: / Bump de bump de bump / Discotheque U.S.A / Cash box / Blues for Joe / Blues for Mr.Jimmy / Dog (you dog), The / Sho' nuff / Turn blue / Party's over, The.
LP: . . . . SSL 6005
MC: . . . . TCSSL 6005

COUNTDOWN.
Tracks: / Countdown.
LP: . . . . M 9116

FLY DUDE.
LP: . . . . PLEO 14

GEORGIA ON MY MIND.
Tracks: / Let's stay together / Shaft, Theme from / What's going on / Georgia on my mind / April in Paris / Everyday I have the blues / Yardbird suite / It's you I adore / Lonesome road / Mack the knife / There will never be another you / Canadian sunset / Mr. Lucky / Moonglow / Red sails in the sunset / Secret love.
MC: . . . . MC 8513

JIMMY MCGRIFF FEATURING HANK CRAWFORD (McGriff, Jimmy & Hank Crawford).
MC: . . . . MC 9001

LAST MINUTE, THE.
LP: . . . . ENSUE 2

SOUL BROTHERS (see under Crawford, Hank) (McGriff, Jimmy & Hank Crawford).

SOUL SURVIVORS (McGriff, Jimmy & Hank Crawford).
Tracks: / Because of you / Frim fram sauce / Peeper, The / One mint julep / Second time around / After supper.
LP: . . . . M 9142
MC: 5M 9142

STARTING FIVE, THE.
LP: . . . . MX 9148

STATE OF THE ART.
Tracks: / Headbender / Stormy weather / Cheesesteak / Don't ever doubt me / New wave blues / Slow gindin' / Hip hop be bop.
LP: . . . . M 9135

McGuigan, Paddy

MY COUNTRY, MY SONG, AND ME.
LP: . . . . DOL 5012

McGuinn, Clark

LONG, LONG TIME (McGuinn, Clark & Hillman).
Tracks: / Long, long time / Little mama / Don't you write her off / Surrender to me / Backstage pass / Stopping traffic / Feeling higher / Sad boy / Release me girl / Bye bye baby.
LP: . . . . EST 11910

McGuinn, Roger

BACK FROM RIO.
Tracks: / Someone to love / Car phone / You bowed down / Suddenly blue / Trees are all gone, The / King of the hill / Without your love / Time has come, The / Your love is a gold mine / If we never meet again.
LP: 211348
MC: 411348

ROGER MCGUINN.
Tracks: / I'm so restless / My new woman / Lost my drivin' wheel / Draggin' / Time cube / Bag full of money / Hanoi Hannah / Stone / Heave away / M'Linda / Water is wide, The.
LP: . . . . ED 281

McGuinness Flint

MCGUINNESS FLINT.
LP: . . . . EA ST 22625

McGuinness, Gerry

COUNTRY AND IRISH FAVOURITES.
LP: . . . . UNKNOWN

McGuire, Barry

BEST OF BARRY.
Tracks: / Love is peace / Peace / Anyone but Jesus / What good would it do / Happy road / Clouds / Cosmic cowboy / Communion song / Bullfrogs and butterflies / There is a peace / I love you Lord / Calling me home.
LP: . . . . BIRD 126
MC: . . . . TC BIRD 126

FINER THAN GOLD.
Tracks: / Heartbreaker / Lonely lover / Music of his band, The / Don't hurt me now / I don't believe in luck / Ashes to ashes / Shaunda music / Mossyrock music / Salvation man / I can see the light / Still calling you / Christ is coming soon.
LP: . . . . BIRD 132
MC: . . . . TC BIRD 132

INSIDE OUT.
Tracks: / C'mon along / Communion song / Moment of truth / Plowman / Bullfrogs and butterflies / Tablets of our hearts, The / Baby Huey / Knowers and believers / Jesus is comin' back to stay / Cosmic cowboy.
LP: . . . . BIRD 122
MC: . . . . TC BIRD 122

TO THE BRIDE (McGuire, Barry, The 2nd chapter of acts & the David band).
Tracks: / Intro / Come to praise the Lord / Little bitty dude / He's coming back / Sad song / Happy road / Acts intro / Which way's the light / Love, peace, joy / Layers / I wonder / Ogre / Am I seeing you / Denomination blues / Friend, A / Jimmy's song / Snow White / Prince song, The / He alone is worthy / Easter song / Anyone but Jesus / Only way, The / Sing the melody / Shock absorbers / Chosen generation / Jesus people / I walked a mile / Dolphins / Calling me home / Each other / Doesn't the bible say / Brainwashed.
2LP: . . . . MYD 1044
MCSET: MC2D 1044

McGuire, Seamus &

BUTTONS AND BOWS (see under Daly, Jackie).

CAROUSEL (McGuire, Seamus & Manus Mcguire, Daithi Sproule).
LP: . . . . CEF 105
MC: . . . . CEFC 105

McGuire, Sean

BEST OF SEAN MCGUIRE.
MC: . . . . COX 1006

CHAMPION IRISH TRADITIONAL FIDDLER.
MC: . . . . COX 1005

CHAMPION OF CHAMPIONS.
LP: . . . . OLP 1005

IRELAND'S CHAMPION FIDDLER.
LP: . . . . SOLP 1031
MC: . . . . COX 1031

IRISH TRADITIONAL MUSIC (McGuire, Sean & Roger Sherlock).
LP: . . . . OLP 1002

MAN OF ACHIEVEMENT.
MC: . . . . COX 1052

ON TWO LEVELS (McGuire, Sean and Josephine Keegan).
Tracks: / Low level / High level, The / Johnny McGoohan's / Aughamore / Coleman's jig / Paddy Cronin's / Earl's chair, The / Murphy's hornpipe / Blind Mary / Maid behind the bar, The / Spellan's inspiration / Jolly seven, The / Col. Rodney / O'Malley's jig / Flag of Dunsay, The / Thomond bridge / Negro sand dance / Planxty drury / Col. Fraser / Oliver Reilly's / Moving cloud.
LP: . . . . RUB 029
MC: . . . . RUBC 029

TWO CHAMPIONS (McGuire, Sean & Joe Burke).
MC: . . . . COX 1014

McGuire Sisters

BEST OF THE MCGUIRE SISTERS.
Tracks: / Sugartime / May you always / Something's gotta give / Goodnight my love / Weary blues / Around the world / Just for old time's sake / Moonglow and theme from Picnic / Sincerely / No more / It may sound silly / Everyday of my life / Rhythm and blues / Delilah Jones / Muskrat ramble.
LP: . . . . MCL 1682
MC: . . . . MCLC 1682

JUST FOR OLD TIME'S SAKE.
Tracks: / Just for old time's sake / Chances are / Birth of the blues / I'll be seeing you / Goody goody / Mood indigo / Pennies from Heaven / Teach me tonight / Hi lili hi lo / Wouldn't it be loverly? / Twilight time / Bye bye blackbird.
LP: . . . . JASM 1511

Mach 1

LOST FOR WORDS.
2LP: . . . . FD 100

McHaile, Tom

ALL IRELAND WHISTLING CHAMPION.
MC: . . . . COX 1001

TOM MCHAILE.
LP: . . . . OLP 1001

McHardy, Forbes

SHADES OF FORBES MCHARDY.
MC: . . . . ZCSLP 613

Machel

KATCH YAACES.
LP: . . . . GS 2297
MC: . . . . GSC 2297

Machine Gunners

MACHINE GUNNERS, THE (see Westall, Robert) (Bolam, James (nar)).

Machito

AFRO-CUBAN JAZZ MOODS (See Gillespie, Dizzy) (Machito & Dizzy Gillespie).

AFRO-CUBOP (Machito & His Orchestra).
Tracks: / Howard's blues / Indianola / How high the moon / Cubop city / Boppin' the vibes / Mambo / Lament for the Congo / Reminiscing at twilight / Tanga / Lean on me / Hip hop be bop / In the beginning / Man made / Together again / Hip hop be bop (part 2) / Six simple synthesizers / Techno trax / Street clap / Heatstroke.
LP: . . . . SPJ 138

GREATEST HITS: MACHITO & HIS AFRO CUBANS (Machito & His Afro Cuban Salseros).
Tracks: / Sopa de pichon / Sisi nono / Piniero tenia razon / Caso perdido / Noche de farra / El as de la rumba / Tibiri tabara / Quimbobo / Carambou / Adoracion / Asia Minor / La paella.
LP: . . . . HOT 106
MC: . . . . TCHOT 106

LATIN SOUL PLUS JAZZ (Machito & His Orchestra).
Tracks: / Wild jungle / Congo mulence / Kenya / Oyeme / Holiday / Cannonology / Ring-a-levio / Renzy / Blues a la machito / Conversation / Tin tin deo / Minor rama.
LP: . . . . HOT 120
MC: . . . . TCHOT 120

LIVE AT NORTH SEA 82 (Machito & His Salsa Big Band).
Tracks: / Buenas noches che che / Tibiri tabara / Oye la rumba / No seras mio / Dale jamon / Mambo Inn.
LP: . . . . SJP 168

MACHITO AT THE CRESCENDO.
LP: . . . . GNPS 58

MACHITO & HIS SALSA BIG BAND (Machito & His Salsa Big Band).
LP: . . . . SJP 183

MUCHO MACHO MACHITO (Machito & His Afro Cuban Salseros).
LP: 2625 712
MCSET: . . . . K 25 712

SALSA BIG BAND 1982 (Machito & His Salsa Big Band).
Tracks: / Elas de la rumba / Quimbobo / Piniero tenia razon / Caso perdido / Manicero / Sambia / Yerbero.

LP: . . . . SJP 161
MC: . . . . SJP 1161

WORLD'S GREATEST LATIN BAND.
LP: . . . . GNPS 72

Machtoc

ZIPPY.
LP: . . . . PHZA 074

Mchugh, Bob

SOARING... ON THE WINGS OF IVORY AND BLACK.
Tracks: / Down home / Love for sale / Do what I can / Laura / Intimite / Thoughts of Cortina / Big Bill / Porgy and Bess Medley / Ko ko clips oh / Night and day / Turnpike soiree / It's de-lovely.
MC: . . . . OUTSTANDING 46

McHugh, Jimmy

JACK THE RIPPER (Original Film Soundtrack) (McHugh, Jimmy & Pete Rugolo).
LP: . . . . FS 334

Macias, Enrico

ENRICO MACIAS.
LP: 2C 068 72187

McIlwaine, Ellen

EVERYBODY NEEDS IT.
LP: BP-1081

MacInnes, Mairi

CAUSEWAY.
Tracks: / Clachan uaine (The green village) / Mendocino / Puirt a beul (mouth music) / Eala bhan, An (The white swan) / Eilidh / Cuachag nana craobh (The tree cuckoo) / Morag's na horo gheallaidh (walking song) / Mairead og (young Margaret) / Soraidh le eilean a'cheo / Indiana / Tuireadh mhic criomain (MacCrimmon's lament) / Mo chridhe trom's duilich leam / Everlasting gun.
LP: . . . . LIDL 6026
MC: . . . . LIDC 6026

McIntire, Lani

HAWAIIAN MOONLIGHT (McIntire, Lani & his Hawaiian Orchestra).
MC: . . . . BRC 2507

McIntosh, Allan

CALLING YOU WESTWARD (McIntosh, Allan & The Heather Band).
LP: . . . . CR 022

ECHOES OF BEN CRUACHAN (McIntosh, Allan & The Heather Band).
Tracks: / Set of jigs / Vocal solo / Set of reels / Highland barn dance / Fiddle solo / Gay Gordons / Accordion solo / Gaelic waltz medley / Eva three step.
MC: 021

McIntosh, Julian

WHEN A MAN LOVES A WOMAN.
LP: . . . . GS 2289

McIntyre

PEACE AND BLESSINGS (McIntyre, Maurice, Quartet).
LP: . . . . SN 1004

McIntyre, Hal

ECSTACY.
LP: . . . . GELP 15022

HAL MCINTYRE 1943-45.
Tracks: / St. Louis blues / Two again / Available Jones / Let me love you tonight / Swinging on a grapevine / Everyday of my life / Song of the bayou / Tain't me / Twilight time / Who's got the ball / Cradle song / Apple shiner / Hour never passes, An / Sheik of Araby.
LP: . . . . HSR 172

HAL MCINTYRE & HIS ORCHESTRA.
LP: . . . . FH 13

McIntyre, Ken

INTRODUCING THE VIBRATIONS (McIntyre, Ken, Sextet).
LP: . . . . SCS 1065

LOOKING AHEAD (McIntyre, Ken & Eric Dolphy).
Tracks: / Lautir / Curtsy / Geo's tune / They all laughed / Head shakin'.
LP: . . . . OJC 252

MacIntyre, Maurice

FORCES AND FEELINGS (MacIntyre, Maurice, Kalaparusha).
LP: . . . . DS 425

HUMILITY IN LIGHT OF CREATOR.
LP: . . . . DS 419

McIvor, John

GATHERING OF THE CLANS, THE.
LP: . . . . NEVLP 115

Mack, Le Roy

HOUND DOG RAMBLE.
LP: . . . . SBR 4209

Mack, Lonnie

ATTACK OF THE KILLER V (Lonnie Mack Live).
LP: . . . . AL 4786

LONNIE MACK.
LP: . . . . ED 303

SECOND SIGHT.
Tracks: / Me and my car / Rock and roll bones / Tough on me tough on you / Camp Washington Chili / Cincinnati / Rock people / Buffalo woman / Ain't nobody / Back on the road again / Song I haven't sung, A.
LP: . . . . SNTF 968
MC: . . . . ZCSN 968

STRIKE LIKE LIGHTNING.
Tracks: / Hound dog man / Satisfy Susie / Stop / Long way from Memphis / Double whammy / Strike like lightning / Falling back in love with you / If you have to know / You ain't got me / Oreo cookie blues.
LP: . . . . SNTF 935

WHAM OF THAT MEMPHIS MAN, THE.
Tracks: / Wham / I'll keep you happy / Suzie Q / Farther on down the road / Bounce / Where there's a will there's a way / Chicken pickin' / Baby what's wrong / Down in the dumps / Down and out / Satisfied / Memphis way.
LP: . . . . ED 158

Mack & Mabel

MACK & MABEL (Original Broadway cast) (Various artists).
Tracks: / Overture: *Orchestra* / Movies were movies: *Preston, Robert* / Look what happened to Mabel: *Mack & Mabel* / Big time: *Kirk, Lisa* / I won't send roses: *Preston, Robert* / I wanna make the world laugh: *Preston*, Robert / Wherever he ain't: *Peters, Bernadette* / Hundreds of girls: *Preston, Robert & The Bathing Beauties*/ When Mabel comes in the room: *Simmonds, Stanley* / My heart leaps up: *Preston, Robert* / Time heals everything: *Peters, Bernadette* / Tap your troubles away: *Kirk, Lisa* / I promise you a happy ending: *Preston, Robert*.
LP: . . . . MCL 1728
MC: . . . . MCLC 1728

MACK & MABEL IN CONCERT (Various artists).
LP: . . . . CAST 13
MC: . . . . CASTC 13

Mack, Red

WEST COAST R & B (See under Luke Jones) (Jones, Luke & Red Mack).

Mack & The Boys

FROM THE HIP.
LP: . . . . CRAM 060

Mack The Knife (Film)

MACK THE KNIFE (Film Soundtrack) (Various artists).
LP: . . . . CBS 45630
MC: 40 45630

Mack, Warner

PRINCE OF COUNTRY BLUES.
Tracks: / Is it wrong / Dragging the river / Don't wake me, I'm dreaming / Bridge is washed out, The / Love hungry / Talking to the wall / I'll still be missing you / How long will it take / Sittin' in an all nite cafe / Drifting apart.
LP: . . . . SDLP 056

Macka B

BUPPIE CULTURE.
LP: . . . . ARILP 48

LOOKS ARE DECEIVING.
Tracks: / Looks are deceiving / Badder than John / Proud to be black / Unemployment blues / What's he done / Joker / Drink too much.
LP: . . . . ARILP 038

NATURAL SUNTAN.
Tracks: / Get rid of Maggie / Don't beat her / Natural sun tan / Blackman / Proud of Mandela / Don't judge me / Get conscious / Flush it.
LP: . . . . ARILP 058

SIGN OF THE TIMES.
LP: . . . . ARILP 028
MC: . . . . ARILPC 028

MacKay, Andy

IN SEARCH OF EDDIE RIFF.
LP: 2302 064
LP: . . . . EGLP 13

MANZANERA & MACKAY (See under Manzanera, Phil for details) (Mackay, Andy & Phil Manzanera).

RESOLVING CONTRADICTIONS.
LP: . . . . EXPLP 5
MC: . . . . EXPMC 5

McKay, Arthur

ST. LOUIS PIANO STYLES 1925-37.
LP: . . . . DLP 582

McKay, Curly

ON TOUR WITH CURLY MCKAY.
LP: . . . . SK 2009

MacKay, Dave

HANDS (MacKay, Dave & Vicky Hamilton).
LP: . . . . DS 868

LOVE WILL WIN (MacKay, Dave Trio).
Tracks: / Just friends / Midnight song for Thalia / We'll be together again / Soul eyes.
LP: . . . . DS 883

MacKay, Duncan

RUSSELL GRANTS ZODIAC ALBUM.
LP: . . . . RUSLP 1
MC: . . . . RUSMC 1

VISA.
Tracks: / South American express / Third bird / Gin sing / In the pink / Night flight / Visa / Peru tu / Fistful of keyboards / See sea.
LP: . . . . HOG 2

McKay, Freddie

TRIBAL IN A YARD.
LP: . . . . MVLP 6

McKay, Heather

HEATHER MCKAY SINGS.
LP: . . . . MOR 4015

MacKay, Iain

VOICE OF THE HEBRIDES.
Tracks: / Gu ma slan do na fearaibh / Mhorag lear shiubhlainn / Tuiginn leam a ribhinn og / Far am bi mi fhein / Cath Ghairidheach / Lag na cruchan / Feasgar a steornabhagh / An eala bhan / Holiday na caillich / Saoil an till mi chaoidh / Mor a cheannaich / Faili oro.
MC: . . . . LICS 5025
LP: . . . . LILP 5025

MacKay, Jim

HIGHLAND BARN DANCE, A (Mackay, Jim Dance Band).
MC: . . . . CM 3555

MacKay, Rhona

SINGS AND PLAYS THE MUSIC OF THE HARP.
Tracks: / Cro cheann t saile / Waly waly / Gealach nan Eilean / Jamie / Bifalbh o'n uinneig / Do dh'eirinn cha'n innis mi ah - ainm / Cearcall a chuain / Gruagach og an fhuilt bhain / Father John MacMillan's farewell to Barra / Gradh mo chroidhe / Mais an taobh tuath / Peat fire flame / Dan Cadalan Samhach / Tha mi sgith / Alasdair a gleanna garradh.
LP: . . . . LILP 5130
MC: . . . . LICS 5130

McKee, Maria

MARIA MCKEE.
LP: . . . . WX 270
MC: . . . . WX 270C
MC: . . . . GEFC 24229
LP: . . . . GEF 24229

McKee, Mary

GREATER LOVE, A.
LP: . . . . PC 445

MARY MCKEE.
LP: . . . . WST R 9691
MC: . . . . WST C 9691

MEANINGS OF MY LIFE.
LP: . . . . PC 424

McKellan, Ian

IGOR STRAVINSKY'S THE SOLDIER'S TALE (See Sting) (McKellan, Ian/ Vanessa Redgrave/ Sting).

McKellar, Kenneth

ECCO DI NAPOLI.
LP: . . . . SKL 5018

HIGHLAND JOURNEY.
Tracks: / Down in the glen / Midges / My ain folk / Those happy days of summer / Farewell my love / Misty Islands of the highlands / Crooked bawbee / Aye waukin' o / Dark island / Saturday dance / Leaving lismore.
LP: . . . . LIDL 6012
MC: . . . . LIDC 6012

HOSANNA.
Tracks: / Rejoice, the Lord is king / Morning has broken / I would beside my Lord / Little road to Bethlehem, The / Agnus dei / All creatures of our God and King / Prayer to the guardian angel / Hosanna / Virgin's slumber song / Thou visitest the earth / Brother James' air / Away in a manger / Praise my soul / Abide with me.
LP: . . . . MOR 518

I BELONG TO SCOTLAND.
LP: . . . . MOR 508

IN SCOTLAND.
Tracks: / This is Scotland / Mull of the cool bens / Eriskay love lilt / Road to the isles medley / Tartan medley / Royal mile / My love is like a red rose / Oban my home / Auld lang syne.
LP: LIDC6009

MCKELLAR IN SCOTLAND.
Tracks: / This is Scotland / Mull of the cool Bens / Eriskay love lilt / Road to the isles / Island love / Ye banks and braes / Tartan medley / West Highland way / Sing tae me the auld scots songs / Royal mile / My love is like a red red rose / Oban my home / Auld lang syne.
LP: . . . . LIDL 6009
MC: . . . . LIDC 6009

OPERATIC WORLD OF..., THE.
LP: . . . . SPA 562

ROAD TO THE ISLES, THE.
Tracks: / Scotland the brave / Skye boat song / My love is like a red red rose / Lewis bridal song / My ain folk / Song of the Clyde / Road to the isles / Wi' a hundred pipers / Westering home / Annie Laurie / An eriskay love lilt / Northern lights of old Aberdeen / Keep right on to the end of the road / Auld lang syne.
LP: . . . . TAB 83
MC: . . . . KTBC 83

SACRED SONGS OF SCOTLAND.
Tracks: / All creatures of our God and King / Lord's my shepherd, The / By cool Siloam's shady rill / Brother James' air / Morning has broken / God be in my head / Do no sinful action / Rejoice, the Lord is King / I to the hills / Great is Jehovah / Praise, my soul, the King of Heaven / O God of Bethel / There is a green hill far away / When I survey the wondrous cross / O sacred head, sore wounded / O love that wilt not let me go / All people that on Earth do dwell / Come let us sing to the Lord our God / Abide with me / Holy City, The.
LP: . . . . WRD 3004
MC: . . . . TC WRD 3004
LP: . . . . SKL 4913

SCOTLAND THE BRAVE.
Tracks: / Scotland the brave / Rowan tree / Song of the Clyde / Kismuil's galley / Highlands and lowlands / Northern lights of old Aberdeen / Loch Lomond / My love she's but a lassie yet / Bluebells of Scotland / Will ye no come back again / Roamin' in the gloamin' / Annie Laurie / Gordon for me, A / Eriskay love lilt / Lewis bridal song / Marching through the heather / My heart's in the heather / Proud peaks of Scotland / Keep right on to the end of the road / Auld Lang syne.
MCSET: . . . . DTO 10232

SINGS ROBERT BURNS.
MC: . . . . KDPC 28087

SONGS OF THE JACOBITE RISINGS.
Tracks: / Bluebells of Scotland / Piper O Dundee, The / Lewie Gordon / Cam'ye by Atholl / Farewell to Glenshalloch / Ye ja cobites by name / Blackbird, The / Braes o' Killecrankie, The / Flora MacDonald's lament / Highland muster roll, The / Skye boat song, The / Owre the water to Charlie / Wae's me for Prince Charlie (a wee bird cam') / Bonnets' o' bonnie Dundee, The / Will ye no' come back again?.
LP: . . . . LIDL 6028
MC: . . . . LIDC 6028

TO ROBERT BURNS - A TRIBUTE.
Tracks: / De'ils awa' with the exciseman,The / Bonnie lass O'Ballochmyle / There was a lad / Gae bring tae me a pint o' wine / Birks o' Aberfeldy, The / John Anderson, my Jo / Green grow the rushes-o / Man's a man, A / I'll ay ca' in by yon toun / Mary Morrison / Kenmore's up and awa' / Afton water / Scots wha' hae / My heart's in the highlands / Red red rose.
LP: . . . . LIDL 6019
MC: . . . . LIDC 6019

TODAY.
Tracks: / Island of Tiree, The / Flower of Scotland / Braes o'Balquhidder, The / Old ballad (the farmer's daughter) / Northern lights of old Aberdeen, The / Rowan tree / Glencoe (the massacre of) / Wee place in the Highlands, A / Jean / Scotland again / Thou Bonnie Wood O Craigelea / Mingulay boat song / Clyde medley / Star O Rabbie Burns, The / Mull of the cool bens (Only on CD) / Eriskay love lilt (Only on CD) / Ye banks and braes (Only on CD).
LP: . . . . LIDL 6024
MC: . . . . LIDC 6024

WORLD OF KENNETH MCKELLAR.
LP: . . . . SPA 11
MC: . . . . KCSP 11

WORLD OF KENNETH MCKELLAR VOL.2.
LP: . . . . SPA 67

McKenna, Dave

CELEBRATION OF HOAGY CARMICHAEL.
Tracks: / Stardust / Riverboat shuffle / One morning in May / Moon country / Two sleepy people / Come easy, go easy love / Nearness of you, The /

Lazybones / Sky lark / Georgia / Lazy river.
LP: .... CJ 227

DANCING IN THE DARK.
Tracks: / By myself / Shine on your shoes / I see your face before me / Alone together / Me / I guess I'll have to change my plans / You and the night and the music / Dancing in the dark / Something to remember you by / New sun in the sky / Oh but I do / Gal in calico, A.
LP: .... CJ 292
MC: .... CJC 292

DUAL PIANO JAZZ See under Overton, Hal (McKenna, Dave/Hal Overton).
Tracks: / Keeping out of mischief / Dizzy atmosphere / Ruby my dear / Hi-fly / Monks mood / Baubles, bangles and beads / Dardanella.
LP: .... FS 292

KEY MAN, THE.
Tracks: / Singing the blues / Yours is my heart, alone / Garden in the rain / Don't be blue / Golden earrings / Louisiana / London by night / I'll be your friend with pleasure / We'll meet again / Gypsy, The.
LP: .... CJ 261

LIVE AT MAYBECK RECITAL HALL VOL.2.
Tracks: / Dream dancing / Detour ahead / Exactly like you / I'm glad there is you/ I'm glad I waited for you / Knowledge medley / Teach me tonight / School days / Apple for the teacher, An / I didn't know about you / Knowledge medley (pt 2).
MC: .... CJ 410C

MY FRIEND THE PIANO.
Tracks: / Margie / Only trust your heart / Mean to me / Slowly / You're driving me crazy / Summer medley: guess I'll go back home this su / Indian Summer / Baby, baby all the time / Always medley: It's always you / Always / This is always.
LP: .... CJ 313

NO BASS HIT.
LP: .... CJ 97

NO HOLDS BARRED (McKenna Dave Swing Six).
LP: .... HL 122

NO MORE OUZO FOR PUZO (McKenna, Dave Quartet).
Tracks: / Look for the silver lining / Smile / For you, for me, for evermore / You and I / You brought a new kind of love to me / Talk of the town / Shake down the stars / Lonesome me / No more ouzo for Puzo / I keep going back to Joe's / Talk to me / Please don't talk about me when I'm gone.
LP: .... CJ 365
MC: .... CJ 365C

OIL AND VINEGAR.
LP: .... HD 6613

PIANO MOVER (McKenna Dave & Dick Johnson).
LP: .... CJ 146

McKenna, Joe

AT HOME (McKenna, Joe & Antoinette).
LP: .... SHAN 29016

FAREWELL TO FINE WEATHER (McKenna, Joe & Antoinette).
LP: .... SHAN 79043

HIS ORIGINAL RECORDINGS.
LP: .... UNKNOWN

MAGENTA MUSIC (McKenna, Joe & Antoinette).
MC: .... SHMC 79076

TRADITIONAL MUSIC OF IRELAND (McKenna, Joe & Antoinette).
LP: .... SHAN 29011

McKenna, Mae

NIGHTFALLERS.
Tracks: / Nightfallers (intro) / Karisola / Moorings / Visions of time to come / Blue / Ochone / Sayonara / My Lagan love / Fields of green / Manderley / Nightfallers.
LP: .... VE 18
MC: .... TCVE 18

McKenna, Virginia

BORN FREE (See under Born Free).

TWO FACES OF LOVE.
Tracks: / Love that I have / In the morning / Feather / Until it's time for you to go / Where did they go / I must go on living / Windmills of your mind / Send in the clowns / Le vent et la jeunesse / Dance of life / I like to hear the music / Morning has broken.
LP: .... RIM 5001

MacKenzie, Billy

TAKE ME TO THE GIRL (See under JIH & Billy McKenzie) (McKenzie, Billy/JIH).

McKenzie, Bob

GREAT WHITE NORTH (McKenzie, Bob & Doug).
LP: .... SRM 14034

MacKenzie, Carl

WELCOME TO YOUR FEET AGAIN.
LP: .... ROUNDER 7005

Mackenzie, Gisele

GISELE.
Tracks: / Stranger in paradise / Hey there / Song from Moulin Rouge / Blue tango / Half as much / Too young / Moonglow / Unchained melody / Learnin' the blues / Ebb tide / Slow poke / Answer me.
LP: .... NL 89462
MC: .... NK 89462

GISELE MACKENZIE.
Tracks: / These foolish things / You're my everything / Swingin' down the lane / On top of the world / Don't worry 'bout me / Tiptoe through the tulips / Every time we say goodbye / Do you ever think of me / Between the devil and the deep blue sea / Beyond the sea / You are my lucky star / At sundown.
LP: .... NL 90046
MC: .... NK 90046

Mackenzie, Malcolm M.

MACKENZIES PIPES AND BANJO (Mackenzie, Pipe Major Malcolm M.).
MC: .... ZCLOC 1059

MACKENZIES PIPES AND STRINGS (Mackenzie, Pipe Major Malcolm M.).
Tracks: / Maggie / Bunch of thyme / Silver threads among the gold / Canon in D / Annie Laurie / Rose of Tralee / Penhalonga piper / Way old friends do / MacKenzies tune / Danny boy / Scotland the brave / Island of Aran / Mull of Kintyre / Will ye no come back again / Amazing grace / Flower of Scotland / Bright eyes.
LP: .... LOCLP 1033

MACKENZIE'S PIPES & STRINGS VOL.2.
Tracks: / Maggie / Bunch of thyme / Silver threads among the gold / Cannon in D / Annie Laurie / Rose of Tralee, The / Penhalonga piper / Way old friends do, The / MacKenzies tune / Danny boy / Scotland the brave / Island of Arran / Mull of Kintyre / Will ye no come back again / Amazing grace / Flower of Scotland / Bright eyes.
LP: .... LOCLP 1045
MC: .... ZCLPC 1045

McKenzie, Maurice

WEE KIRKCUDBRIGHT CENTIPEDE THE.
Tracks: / Wee kirkcudbright centipede / Queen Mary / Aiken drum / Kelvingrove / Ribeanan riobhach / Tramcar / Highland lullaby / Height starvation song / Yuri gagrin / Tod / Blantyre explosion / Mockin' bird / Eskimo republic / Leave them a flower.
MC: .... KGEC 1206
LP: .... GES 1206

McKenzie, Nicolette

LITTLE GREY RABBIT, THE (See also Alison Uttley).

McKenzie, Red

CHICAGOANS (McKenzie, Red & Eddie Condon).
LP: .... J 110

McKeown, John

SPORTIN' SAILOR BOY.
Tracks: / John Magowan / Sportin' sailor boy / Slievegallion braes / Murlough shore / Bonnie Irish boy / Cootehill races / Country maids of Mourne shore / John Mitchel / Bricks and mortar / My home in sweet Donegal.
LP: .... OAS 3012

McKern Leo

TRIALS OF RUMPOLE THE.
MC: .... LFP 41 7200 5

Mackey, Percival

PERCIVAL MACKEY'S BAND 1925-31.
Tracks: / Dog on the piano / Valentine / Behind the clouds / Charleston / Shake a little shoulder / Cross your heart / Beautiful baby / Everything will happen for the best / Don't forget / Drifting and dreaming / Music of a mountain stream / Blue pipes of pan / Syncopated city / Let's be sentimental / I have no words / Smile, darn ya, smile.
LP: .... SH 356

MacKie, Neil

CAROLS FOR CULZEAN CASTLE (see under Paisley Abbey) (Mackie, Neil/ Paisley Abbey Choir).

McKillop, Jim

JIM MCKILLOP ON FIDDLE AND JOSEPHINE KEEGAN ON PIANO (McKillop, Jim & Josephine Keegan).
Tracks: / Miss Monaghan / Spey in spate / Mist in the glen / Knights of St. Patrick / Fahy's / Dawn / Nellie Murphy's / Sally gardens / Skylark / Frieze britches / Maeve's reel / Fisherman's island / Farewell to Cailroe / Lord Gordon's / McKilliop's / O'Mahony's / Strike the gay harp / Donegal reel, The / McDermott's hornpipe / Eclipse, The / Aughamore / Silver spire / Dairy maid.
MC: .... COX 1045
LP: .... SOLP 1045

JOSEPHINE KEEGAN & JIM MCKILLOP (see Keegan,Josephine&Jim McKillop) (McKillop, Jim & Josephine Keegan).

McKinley, Ray

BLUE SKIES.
LP: .... FH 32
MC: .... CFH 32

CLASS OF 49.
LP: .... HEP 4

DOWN THE ROAD APIECE (McKinley, Ray & His Orchestra).
Tracks: / I'm an old cowhand (Vocal by Ray McKinley) / You started something (Vocal by Jean Finley) / You came a long way from St. Louis (Vocal by Ray McKinley) / Stars fell on Alabama / What did I do (Vocal by Ray McKinley) / Mint julep / Blue skies (Vocal by Jean Finley & The Four Hormones) / On a slow boat to China (Vocal by Ray McKinley) / Hair of gold, eyes of blue (Vocal by Ray McKinley) / Blue moon / Richest man in the cemetary (Vocal by Ray McKinley) / Down the road apiece (Vocal by Ray McKinley) / Red silk stockings and green perfume (Vocal by Ray McKinley).
LP: .... DBD 05
MC: .... DBDC 05

GLENN MILLER STORY THE.
LP: 26 21108

HOWDY FRIENDS (McKinley, Ray & His Orchestra).
Tracks: / Jug of wine, A / Day by day / Cyclops / Nobody but you.
LP: .... LE 102

RAY MCKINLEY & HIS MAGICIANS 1946-9 (McKinley, Ray & His Orchestra).
LP: .... FH 11

WILL BRADLEY & RAY MCKINLEY, 1940-41 (see Bradley, Will) (McKinley, Ray & Will Bradley).

McKinney's Cotton

BAND DON REDMAN BUILT, THE.
Tracks: / Four or five times / Put it there / Crying and sighing / Cherry / Stop kidding / Nobody's sweatheart / Some sweet day / It's tight like that / Save it pretty mama / I've found a new baby / Will you, won't you be my babe / Do something / Plain dirt / Gee baby, ain't I good to you / I'd love it / Miss Hannah / Peggy / Wherever there's a will, baby / Zonky / Just a shade corn / I want a little girl / Rocky road.
LP: .... NL 90517
MC: .... NK 90517

MCKINNEY'S COMPLETE COTTON PICKERS VOL 1 1928-29.
Tracks: / Peggy / Whenever there's a will there's a way / I'll make fun for you / Word's can't express / If I could be with you / You one more hour tonight / Then someone's in love / Honeysuckle rose / Zonky / Trav'lin all alone / Just a shade of corn / Baby won't you please come home / Okay baby / Blues sure have got me / Hullabaloo / I want a little girl / Cotton picker's scat / Rocky road / Talk to me / Laughing a life / Never swat a fly / I want your love / Hello / After all, you're all I'm after / I miss a little miss.
2LP: .... PM 42407

MCKINNEY'S COMPLETE COTTON PICKERS VOL 2 1929-1930.
2LP: .... PM 43258

MCKINNEY'S COMPLETE COTTON PICKERS VOL 5.
LP: .... NL 89161

MacKintosh, Iain

GENTLE PERSUASION.
Tracks: / Tomorrow you're gone / Uncle Walter / Run the film backwards / My old man / It's so easy to dream / When I'm gone / January man / Farm auction, The / Wheelchair talking blues, The / Song of the pineapple rag, The / First you lose the rhyming / Waltzing around in the nude / Five ways to kill a man.
MC: .... CTRAX 014
LP: .... TRAX 014

HAMISH IMLACH & IAIN MACKINTOSH (See Imlach, Hamish) (MacKintosh, Iain & Hamish Imlach).

LIVE IN GLASGOW.
LP: .... KOP 2

RISKS AND ROSES.
Tracks: / If I had a boat / Remember when the music / I wish I was in Glasgow / Cheeky young lad / Rats are winning, The / King of Rome / Flowers are red / My home town / Roses from the wrong man / Acceptable risks / Dill pickle rag / Annie McKelvie / Kilkelly / Hug song, The.
MC: .... CTRAX 043

STANDING ROOM ONLY.
LP: .... KOP 16

MacKintosh, Ken

VERY THOUGHT OF YOU, THE (Mackintosh, Ken & His Orchestra).
Tracks: / Harlem nocturne / Sh'boom / Misty / Sittin' in the sun / Till then / That's a me 'n' my love / It worries me / I'll be hangin' around / Go go go / Creep, The / Let's jump / Skin deep / Very thought of you, The / Air express / Blues in the night / Champ, The / Slow walk / Applejack.
LP: .... PLE 523
MC: .... TC-PLE 523

McKuen, Rod

AT CARNEGIE HALL.
2LP: .... K 66001

GREATEST HITS: ROD MCKUEN.
LP: .... EMC 3007

MCKUEN.
Tracks: / Time and distance / Goodbye / We musn't say goodbye / Every loner has to go alone / (There must be something) better than this / Black eagle, The / Allelujah / One / Give me a little time / Introduction and going back to Jesus / Jaws / Hand in hand / Wind of change / Disco 77.
LP: .... DJF 20521
MC: .... DJH 40521

McKusick, Hal

EAST COAST JAZZ (McKusick, Hal Quartet).
LP: .... FS 209

JAZZ WORKSHOP.
Tracks: / Tommy Hawk / Lydian lullaby / Blues for Pablo / Just leave it alone / Miss Clara / Alto cumulus / Day John Brown was hanged, The / One score and eight horns ago / Ain't nothin' but a memory now / Jambangle / Blues train.
2LP: .... PM 43637

McLachan, Sarah

TOUCH.
Tracks: / Out of the shadows / Vox / Strange world / Trust / Touch / Steaming / Sad clown / Uphill battle / Ben's song.
LP: .... NET 007
LP: 209872
MC: 409872

McLachlan, Craig

CHECK ONE TWO (Mc Lachlan, Craig & Check One Two).
Tracks: / Mona / Rock the rock / I almost felt like crying / Amanda / What is love / Jump into the fire / Bigger than Texas / Can't take it any longer / I don't mind / Hot / 60 / It's been good.
LP: 4663471
MC: 4663474

McLachlan, Ian

KINGS OF THE BUTTON KEYED BOX (McLachlan, Ian & Fergie MacDonald).
Tracks: / From Lewis to Glencoe / Goes Irish trad / Dark island / Mouth music on button box / Jiggin' across the Minch / Iain Rhuadh's lament / Gay gordons on button box / Three jigs for three friends / Two pipe marches / Two tunes for two bonnie lasses / Gaelic waltz hebridean style / Clanranald Hotel barn da*ce / Old flame, An / Fergie's own jigs / 2/4 marches.
LP: .... LILP 5160
MC: .... LICS 5160

MacLachlan, Patricia

SARAH, PLAIN AND TALL (Close, Glenn).
MC: 1793

McLain, Charly

CHARLY MCLAIN (I Love Country).
Tracks: / Sentimental ol' you / Fly into love / Dancing your memory away / With just one look in your eyes / Women get lonely / With you / Everyday love / Radio heart / Who's cheating who / Band of gold / Some hearts get all the breaks / You are my music, you are my song / When it's down to me and you / Someone just like you / Sleepin' with the radio on / Paradise tonight.
LP: 4504251
MC: 4504254

McLain, Tommy

BEST OF TOMMY MCLAIN.
LP: .... JIN 9016
MC: .... JIN 9016 TC

SWEET DREAMS.
Tracks: / Sweet dreams / Before I grow too old / Think it over / Barefootin' / I can't take it no more / Try to find another man / When a man loves a woman / After loving you / Tribute to Fats Domino, A / Going home / Poor me / Going to the

river / Just because / I'd be a legend in my time / Together again / I thought I'd never fall in love again / So sad (to watch good love go bad) / Sticks and stones / Mu heart remembers.
LP: .... CH 285
MC: .... CHC 285

TOMMY MCLAIN.
LP: .... JIN 9009
MC: .... JIN 9009 TC

MacLaine, Shirley

SHIRLEY MACLAINE IN CONCERT.
Tracks: / If my friends could see me now / My personal property / Remember me / Big spender / Irma la douce / I'm a person too / Gypsy in my soul / It's not where you start / Every little movement / Donkey serenade, The / She's a star (la chanteuse a vingt ans) / I'm a brass band / If my friends could see me now (finale).
LP: .... CBS 32669
MC: 40 32669

McLaren, Malcolm

DUCK ROCK.
Tracks: / Obatala / Buffalo gals / Merengue / Punk it up / Legba / Jive my baby / Song for Chango / Soweto / World's famous / Duck for the oyster / Double Dutch.
MC: .... CHCMC 74
LP: .... CHC 74
LP: .... MMLP 1

FANS.
Tracks: / Madame Butterfly / Fans, The / Carmen (L'oiseau rebelle) / Boys chorus / Lauretta (O mio babbino cara) / Death of Butterfly (Tu tu piccolo).
LP: .... MMDL 2
MC: .... MMDC 2

SWAMP THING.
Tracks: / Swamp thing / Duck rock cheer / Buffalo love / Supresto / B.I. Bikki / Eiffel Tower / Boom boom baby / Duck Rockers / Promises.
LP: .... CAS 1170
LP: .... CHC 65
MC: .... CHCMC 65

WALTZ DARLING.
Tracks: / House of the blue Danube / Waltz darling / Deep in vogue / Algernon's simply awfully good at ... / Something's jumpin' in your shirt / Shall we dance? / Call a wave / I like you in velvet.
LP: 4607361
MC: 4607364

WOULD YA LIKE MORE SCRATCHIN'.
Tracks: / D'ya like scratchin'? (special version) / She's looking like a hobo / Buffalo gals (D.J. cut-special stereo mix) / World's famous (radio I.D.) / Hobo scratch / Would ya like more scratchin'? (New York City remix).
LP: .... CLAM 1
MC: .... CLAC 1

McLaren, Mel

MAGIC OF MEL MCLAREN, THE.
MC: .... ZCKBP 511

McLatchy, Debbie

LADY LUCK.
Tracks: / Vandy Vandy / Sparkling blue eyes / Ballad of blasphemous Bill / Waltz across Texas / Stella Ireland and Lady Luck / Gold rush is over, The / Bir sur mists and mountains / Dainty Davie / Upside down blackbird / Cremation of Sam McGee / Roseville Fair.
LP: .... SIF 1017
MC: .... CSIF 1017

McLaughlin, John

ADVENTURES IN RADIOLAND.
Tracks: / Wait, The / Just ideas / Jozy / Half man, half cookie / Florianopolis / Gotta dance / Wall will fall, The / Reincarnation / Mitch match / 20th century limited.
LP: .... SOS 2020
MC: .... SOSMC 2020

BELO HORIZONTE.
Tracks: / Belo Horizonte / La Baleine / Very early / One melody / Stardust on your sleeve / Waltz for Katia / Zamfir / Manitas d'oro.
LP: .... K 99185

BEST OF JOHN MCLAUGHLIN.
Tracks: / Love supreme, A / New York on my mind / Dark prince / La danse du bonheur / Friendship / Face to face / Unknown dissident, The / Lotus feet.
LP: .... CBS 84455

BETWEEN NOTHING AND ETERNITY LIVE.
LP: .... BGOLP 31

BIRDS OF FIRE (McLaughlin, John & Mahavishnu Orchestra).
Tracks: / Birds of fire / Miles beyond / Celestial terrestrial commuters / Sapphire bullets of pure love / Thousand Island park / Hope / One word / Sanctuary / Open country joy / Resolution.
LP: .... CBS 32280
MC: 40 32280
LP: .... CBS 65321

DEVOTION.
LP: .... GL 65075

ELECTRIC DREAMS.
Tracks: / Guardian angels / Miles Davis / Electric dreams / Electric sighs / Love and understanding / Desire and the comforter / Singing earth / Dark prince / Unknown dissident.
LP: .... CBS 83526

ELECTRIC GUITARIST.
MC: 4670934

EXTRAPOLATION.
LP: 2310 018

FRIDAY NIGHT IN SAN FRANCISCO (See under Dio Meola, Al) (McLaughlin, John/Al Di Meola/Paco De Lucia).

FUSE ONE (see Clarke, Stanley) (McLaughlin, John/Stanley Clarke/Larry Coryell).

GREATEST HITS: JOHN MCLAUGHLIN.
LP: 4670101
MC: 4670104

HANDFUL OF BEAUTY, A (McLaughlin, John & Shakti).
LP: .... CBS 81664

INNER MOUNTAIN FLAME (McLaughlin, Mahavishnu, John).
LP: 64 717

INNER WORLDS.
LP: 69261

LIVE AT THE ROYAL FESTIVAL HALL.
LP: 834 426 1
MC: 834 426 4

MCLAUGHLIN, JOHN (WITH SHAKTI).
LP: .... CBS 81388

MUSIC SPOKEN HERE.
Tracks: / Aspan / Blues for LW / Translators / Honky tonk haven / Viene clareando / David / Negative ions / Brise de coeur / Loro.
LP: .... WEA 99254

MY GOAL'S BEYOND (McLaughlin, Mahavishnu, John).
LP: .... DGL 69014

NATURAL ELEMENTS (McLaughlin, John & Shakti).
LP: .... CBS 82329

PASSION GRACE AND FIRE (McLaughlin, John/Al Di Meola/Paco De Lucia).
Tracks: / Aspen / Orient blues / Chiquito / Sichia / David / Passion, grace and fire.
LP: .... MERL 24
MC: .... MERLC 24

SHAKTI WITH JOHN MCLAUGHIN.
MC: 4679054

THUNDERBYRD.
LP: 81883

McLaughlin, Pat

PAT MCLAUGHLIN.
Tracks: / In the mood / Lynda / Real thing, The / Wrong number / No problem / Heartbeat from havin' fun / Is that my heart breakin' / Prisoner of your love / You done me wrong / Moment of weakness / Without a melody.
LP: .... EST 2061
MC: .... TCEST 2061

WIND IT ON UP.
LP: .... AP 021

McLaurin, Bette

MASQUERADE IS OVER, THE.
Tracks: / Petticoat baby / I am past sixteen / So will I / Grow old along with me / I'm alone because I love you / Old man river / How can I / Zip / Masquerade is over, The / Crying for you / Cottage for sale / Lover come back to me / Cry / My heart belongs to only you / I won't tell a soul I love you / Do you know why.
LP: .... OFF 6045

MacLean, Alistair

BREAKHEART PASS (see under Breakheart Pass (bk)).

MacLean, Calum

SCOTTISH ACCORDIAN HITS.
Tracks: / Looking for a partner / Bluebell polka / Caddam Woods / Dark island / Shuffling samuel / Happy hours / Bonnie lass o' Bon Accord / Primrose polka, The / High-lever hornpipe / Jacqueline waltz / Woodland flowers / Whistling rufus.
LP: .... LILP 5026
MC: .... LICS 5026

SCOTTISH ACCORDIAN HITS VOL 2.
MC: .... LICS 5075
LP: .... LILP 5075

McLean, Charlie

GOD HELPS THOSE WHO HELP THEMSELVES.
Tracks: / He's going to listen / Soldiers in God's army / Wrong too long / There's room at the Cross / Somebody's watching you / Jesus of Nazareth / God helps those who help themselves / Soon I'll be done.
LP: .... MIR 5007
MC: .... ZCMIR 5007

STRAIGHT FROM HEAVEN.
Tracks: / Sweet home / Caught up to meet him / Mother loves her children / Straight from heaven / Thank you Lord / All things work together / Centre of my joy / Prayer.
LP: .... MIR 5022
MC: .... MIR 5022MC

McLean, Don

AMERICAN PIE.
Tracks: / American pie / 'Til tomorrow / Vincent / Crossroads / Winterwood / Empty chairs / Everybody loves me / Fatima / Grave / Babylon.
LP: .... FA 3023
MC: .... TCFA 3023
MC: 4XLL 9272
LP: .... UAS 29285
LP: .... GO 2004

AND I LOVE YOU SO.
Tracks: / But she loves me / Superman's ghost / Since I don't have you / Love in my heart / Empty chairs / Castles in the air / Eventually / It doesn't matter anymore / Your cheating heart / Don't burn that bridge / Crying / He's got you / Birthday song / Everyday / Going for the gold / And I love you so / Touch of her hand, The / Mountains of Mourne.
LP: .... EMS 1346
MC: .... TCEMS 1346

BELIEVERS.
Tracks: / Castles in the air / Isn't it strange / Left for dead on the road of love / Sea man / I tune the world out / Love hurts / Jerusalem / Love letters / Crazy eyes / Sea cruise / Believers.
LP: .... EMC 3396

CHAIN LIGHTNING.
Tracks: / Words and music / Crying / It's just the sun / Lotta lovin' / Chain lightning / Your cheatin' heart / Wonderful night / It doesn't matter anymore / Since I don't have you / Genesis / It's a beautiful life.
LP: .... INS 3025

DOMINION.
Tracks: / It's just the sun / Building my body / Wonderful baby / Very thought of you, The / Fool's paradise / Baby I don't care / You have lived / Statue, The / Prime time / American pie / Left for dead / Believers / Sea man / It's a beautiful life / Chain lightning / Crazy eyes / La la I love you / Dream lover / Crying / Vincent.
2LP: .... DOM 82
MCSET: .... TCDOM 82

FOR THE MEMORIES.
Tracks: / Wonderful world / I can't help it (if I'm still in love with you) / Maybe baby / Lonely as the night is long / He's got you / White sports coat / Don't / Crazy / Travellin' man / Slow and easy / You don't know me / Sittin' in the balcony.
LP: .... MFP 5836
MC: .... TCMFP 5836

HOMELESS BROTHER.
LP: .... UAG 29646

PLAYING FAVOURITES.
LP: .... BGOLP 21
LP: .... UAG 29528

SOLO.
2LP: .... UAD 60139

TAPESTRY.
Tracks: / Castles in the air / General store / Magdalene Lane / Tapestry / Respectable / Orphans of wealth / Three flights up / I love you so / Bad girl / Circus song / No reason for your dreams.
LP: .... UAS 29350
LP: 1A 022 58104
LP: .... FA 41 3107 1

VERY BEST OF DON MCLEAN.
Tracks: / American pie / Vincent / Castles in the air / Dreidel / Winterwood / Everyday / Building my body / And I love you so / Mountains of Mourne / Fool's paradise / Wonderful baby / La la love you / Prime time / Jump / Crying / Bronco Bill's lament (CD only.) / Oh my what a shame (CD only.) / If we try (CD only.) / Babylon (CD only.) / Love in my heart (CD only.).
LP: .... UAG 30314
MC: .... TCUAG 30314

MacLean, Dougie

CRAIGIE DHU.
Tracks: / Gin I were a baron's heir / Read for the storm / It was a' for our rightful king (Patsy Seddon: clarsach.) / High flying seagull / Edmonton airbus / Craigie Dhu / Bonnie Bessie Logan / Seanair's song / It fascinates me / Tullochgorum / Caledonia.
LP: .... DUN 001
MC: .... DUNC 001

FIDDLE.
Tracks: / Osprey, The / Bob MacIntosh Atholl Arms ku-ring-gai chase / Farewell to Craigie Dhu / Tattie ball, The / When are you coming over? / Mr. & Mrs. MacLean of Snaigow / Roy Ashby's buckny burn / One summer's morning / Ferry, The / Spoutwells riechip leduckie / Centre, The / Gin I were a baron's heir.
LP: .... DUN 002
MC: .... DUNC 002

ON A WING AND A PRAYER.
LP: .... PLR 034

REAL ESTATE.
LP: .... DUN 008
MC: .... DUNC 008

SINGING LAND.
Tracks: / Singing land / Desperate man / This love will carry / Kelphope glen / Another story / Bonnie woods o' Hatton / Other side, The / Tumbling down / Guillotine release / Goodnight and joy.
LP: .... DUN 004
MC: .... DUNC 004

SNAIGOW.
Tracks: / Rollin' home / King's command / Mill brae / Lassies trust in providence / Bonnie Isle of Whalsay / Northern cowboy / Back to the island / Silently sad heiland Harry / Ye banks and braes o' bonnie Doon / John McColl's reel / Alex Campbell's reel / Loch Tay boat song.
LP: .... PLR 022

WHITEWASH.
LP: .... DUN 010
MC: .... DUNC 010

McLean, Jackie

BLUESNIK.
Tracks: / Bluesnik / Goin' 'way blues / Drew's blues / Cool green / Blues function / Torchin' / Goin' 'way blues (alt. take) (CD only.) / Torchin' (alt. take) (CD only.).
LP: .... BST 84067

CONNECTION, THE (McLean, Jackie & Freddie Redd).
Tracks: / Wigglin' / Music forever / Time to smile / Theme for Sister Salvation / Jim Dunn's dilemma / O.D. (overdose) / Who killed the cock robin.
LP: .... BOP 004
LP: .... BST 84027

CONSEQUENCE.
LP: .... LBR 1027

CONTOUR.
Tracks: / Foggy day / Kerplunk / Inding / Lights out / Up / Lorraine / Sentimental journey / Why was I borne / Contour.
2LP: .... PR 24076

FAT JAZZ.
Tracks: / Filide / Millies pad / Two sons / What good am I without you / Tune up.
LP: .... FS 307

FRICKLE SONANCE,A.
LP: .... BST 84089

IT'S ABOUT TIME (see under Tyner, McCoy) (McLean, Jackie & McCoy Tyner).

JACKIE MCLEAN & CO..
Tracks: / Minor dream / Mirage / Beau Jack / Help / Flickers.
LP: .... OJC 074

JACKIE'S BAG.
Tracks: / Quadrangle / Blues Inn / Fidel / Appointment in Ghana / Ballad for Doll, A / Isle of Java / Street singer / Melonae's dance / Medina.
LP: .... BST 84051
LP: 784 051 1

LEFT ALONE '86 (See under Waldron, Mal) (McLean, Jackie & Mal Waldron).

LET FREEDOM RING.
Tracks: / Melody for Melonae / I'll keep loving you / Rene / Omega.
LP: .... BST 84106

LONG DRINK OF THE BLUES, A.
LP: .... OJC 253

MCLEANS SCENE.
LP: .... OJC 098

MONUMENTS.
Tracks: / Gotta get a piece of your soul / They all seem to disappear / Molimo / Monuments / Doctor Jackyll and Mister Funk / Long time lover / On the slick side.
LP: .... PL 13230

NEW AND OLD GOSPEL.
Tracks: / Lifeline / Offspring / Midway / Vernzone / Inevitable end / Old gospel / Strange as it seems.

LP: .... BST 84262

NEW SOIL.
Tracks: / Hip strut / Mince apprehension / Greasy / Sweet cakes / Davis cup / Formidable (CD only.).
LP: B1 84013

NEW YORK CALLING.
LP: .... SCS 1023

ONE STEP BEYOND.
Tracks: / Frankenstein / Blue rondo a la turk / Ghost town / Saturday and Sunday / Saturday and Sunday (alternate take).
LP: .... BST 84137

SWING SWANG SWINGIN'.
Tracks: / What's new? / Let's face the music and dance / Stablemates / I remember you / I love you / I'll take romance / 116th and Lennox.
LP: .... BOP 002

TIPPIN' THE SCALES.
Tracks: / Tippin' the scales / Rainy blues / Nursery blues / Nicely / Two for one / Cabin in the sky.
LP: .... BST 84427

TRIBUTE TO CHARLIE PARKER FROM THE NEWPORT JAZZ FESTIVAL.
LP: .... PL 43560

MacLean & MacLean

TAKING THE 'O' OUT OF COUNTRY.
LP: .... DOG 1
MC: .... CORG 1

McLean, Norman

BONNIE DAYS OF SUMMER.
LP: .... LILP 5014

NORMAN MCLEAN SINGS.
LP: .... LILP 5002

McLean, Penny

LADY BUMP.
LP: .... BRL 4077

MacLean, Quentin

QUENTIN MACLEAN.
Tracks: / Ride of the Valkyries / Long ago / Butterfly / Rhapsody in blue / On the sunny side of the street / Body and soul / Watching my dreams go by / Liebestraum / This lovely rose / You got me crying again / With Eric Coates thro' London / Happy days selection / Marigold.
LP: .... SH 409

MacLean, Sorley

BARRAN AGUS ASBHUAIN.
LP: .... CCA 3

MacLean, William

PIBROCH PIPE-MAJOR WILLIAM MACLEAN.
MC: .... TGMMC 501

McLean,John

BOWLED OVER.
LP: .... ARILP 037

MacLellan, Theresa

TRIP TO MABOU RIDGE, A (MacLellan, Theresa & Marie).
LP: .... ROUNDER 7006

McLelland, Sandy

CAN WE STILL BE FRIENDS (McLelland,Sandy & Backline).
Tracks: / Bad situation / Brave new world / Can we still be friends? / Heat on the street / Hot nights in Paris / Living on borrowed time / Mediocrity / So so satisfied / Sure sounds good to me / Tell me no secrets.
LP: 9109 620

McLellan,Tommy

COTTON PATCH BLUES.
LP: .... TM 804

McLennan, G.W.

WATERSHED.
LP: .... BEGJA 118
MC: .... BEGAC 118

McLeod, Bobby

AT THE DANCIN'.
Tracks: / Gay Gordons / Price of Erin waltz / Eva three step / Modern medley / Waltz / Boston two step / Waltz country dance / Strip the willow / Tango / Scottish waltz / Farewell song.
MC: .... KGEC 1211
LP: .... GES 1211

BOBBY'S KIND OF MUSIC.
Tracks: / Gay Gordon's / Old time waltzes / Singalong section / International medley / Hornpipes / Gaelic waltzes / Road to the Isles medley / Pipe marches.
LP: .... INTS 5246
LP: .... NL 25213

GENUINE ARTICLE, THE.
Tracks: / Highland two step / Strathspeys / Waltz / Irish two step / Pride of Errin / Party pieces / Traditional selection / Traditional polka / Waltz valeta / Dunoon barn dance / Kerrera polka / Eva three step.
LP: .... LILP 5127
MC: .... LICS 5127

MAN FROM TOBERMORY.
MC: .... KGEC 1200

MUSIC OF MULL.
Tracks: / Gay Gordons / MacKenzie highlanders / Caberfeidh / Lord Lovat / Road to the Isles medley / Road to the Isles, The / Skye boat song / Peat fire flame / Cocklegatherers, The / Two-four-six-eight / Captain Carswell / Patrick Og / Forty shades of green / Irish jigs / Biddy the bowl' wife / Lannigan's ball / Five barred gate, The / Pet of the pipers / Walls of Limerick, The / Rakes of Kildare, The / Humours of Donnybrook, The / Corina, Corina / Reels for real / The flowers of Edinburgh / Teetallers, The / East neuk of Fife / Singalong selection / When you wore a tulip / Waiting for the Robert E Lee / Oh, them golden slippers / Old time waltzez / Memories / Let me call you sweetheart / In the shade of the old apple tree / Comrades / Swingalong reels / Lewis lilt / Island dance / Piper's refuge / Wild mountain thyme / Island Schottische / Brochan lom / Smith's the gallant fireman / Laddie wi' the plaidie / Claum crubach / Mrs Stewart of Grantully / Pipe marches / Leaving Glen Urquhart / Bonawe highlanders, The / Irish jiggery / Connaught man's rambles, The / Roavin' jelly / Tenpenny bit, The / Irish washerwoman, The.
LP: .... INTS 5247
LP: .... PL 25088
MC: .... PK 25088

SCOTTISH DANCE-ALONG, A.
LP: .... SBE 136

SIMPLY SOLO.
Tracks: / March, Strathspey and reel / Will Hannah's flowers / Gaelic airs waltz / Jigs for dancing / Queen Mary waltz, The / Highland wedding bells / Pipe marches / Gaelic airs / Fiddlers hornpipes / Dreams of Mull / Valse bleue.
MC: .... MR 1010

MacLeod, Donald

FAREWELL MY LOVE.
Tracks: / Duan's n t-seann nos / Nighean mo ghaoil / Twa recruiting sergeants / Guma slan do na fearaibh / Puirt a beul / Land o' the leal / Ba m'eudail ban / Thoir mo shoraidh thar ghunnaidh / Farewell my love / Stay young / Cadal cuain / Farewell to Nova Scotia / Leinabh / Orain luaidh.
LP: .... LILP 5132
MC: .... LICS 5132

NEW YORK RECORDINGS 1967, THE.
Tracks: / Caberfeidh / Cronan / Island lullaby, An / Highland brigade at Waterloo / 74th farewell to Edinburgh, The / White rock / Nameless / Donald MacLellan of Rothesay / Mrs Arthur MacKerron / 79th farewell to Gibralter / Banks of Lochiel, The / Irish washerwife, The / Pretty dirk / Cock o' the North / Invercharrow highland gathering, The / Lochaber no more / Wee highland laddie, The / Mist covered mountains, The / Cronan na callaich / Malcolm Ferguson / Devil in the kitchen / Colonel Robertson / Susan MacLeod / Donald Dugal Mackay.
2LP: .... LDDL 8004
MCSET: .... LDDC 8004

NEW YORK SESSION, THE.
LP: .... LIDL 8004
MC: .... LIDC 8004

PIPE TUNES FOR HIGHLAND DANCING.
Tracks: / Devil in the kitchen / Atholl highlanders / 79th farewell to Gibraltar / Brose and butter / Ghillie calum / Highland laddie / Blue bonnets o'er the border / Earl of Mansfield / Tenpenny bit, The / Harvest home / Whistle o'er the lav o't / Lady Madeline Sinclair / Lord Blantyre / High road to Linton / Mrs. MacLeod of Raasay.
LP: .... LILP 5072
MC: .... LICS 5072

POSITIVELY PIOBAIREACHD.
Tracks: / Old woman's lullaby, The / Duncan MacRae of Kintail's lament / Lament for Red Hector of the Battles / Clan Campbell's gathering / Flame of wrath for Patrick Caogach, A / Sir James MacDonald of the Isles lament.
LP: .... LILP 5089
MC: .... LICS 5089

McLeod, Doug

NO ROAD BACK HOME.
LP: .... SPIN 208

MacLeod, Jim

COULD I HAVE THIS DANCE (MacLeod, Jim & His Band).
LP: .... WGR 081
MC: .... CWGR 081

FAMILY FAVOURITES.
LP: .... SBE 174

JIM MACLEOD BAND WITH GUESTS.
MC: .... KSBC 193

JIM MACLEOD ENCORE MUSIC ALBUM (MacLeod, Jim & His Band).
Tracks: / Come to Fiona's wedding / Dan McDowie's reel / Winding forth, The / Lights in Lochindaal / Bunesa (child in a manger) / Mull of the cool high bens / My Glasgow / Bonnie Dundee / John a doig / Easdale house / Fare thee well Annabelle / Leaving Dundee / Captain McBrides hornpipe / Miss Claytons Hornpipe / Billy Cuthbertson / Navvy, The / (I'd be a) legend in my own time / Moragś fairy glen / Star o' Rabbie Burns, The / Irish rover, The / Lovely banchory / Mrs. Mary Prentice / Tam Bain's lum.
MC: .... KITV 202
LP: .... JDM 2

JIM MACLEOD'S ANNIVERSARY COLLECTION (MacLeod, Jim & His Band).
Tracks: / I will go / Happy birthday baby / Willie Bren'da peck O'malt / Lonely Scapa flow / Whiskey on a Sunday / If my world should end tomorrow / Welcome home.
MC: .... KITV 201

JIM MACLEOD'S CALEDONIAN CEILIDH.
MC: .... KITV 200

JIM MACLEOD'S DANCE PARTY FAVOURITES.
Tracks: / Bluebell polka / Will you save the last dance just for me / Just for old times' sake / Come by the hills / Dashing white sergeant / Dashing white sergeant (encore) / Do you think you could love me again / Amazing grace / Pittenweem Jo / Shetland reels / Cruising down the river / Loch Lomond / After all these years / Gay Gordons / Gay Gordons (encore) / Leaving Dundee / Shufflin' Sammy.
LP: .... ITV 422
MC: .... KITV 422

JIM MACLEOD'S HOGMANAY PARTY.
Tracks: / Auld lang syne / Gay Gordons / Waltz / Strip the willow / Whistle and I'll dance / Bonnie lass o' Bon Accord / St. Bernards waltz / Dashing white sergeant / My love is like a red red rose / Pipe selection / Barn dance / Crooked bawbee / Military two-step.
LP: .... ITV 444
MC: .... KITV 444

MAGIC SOUNDS OF JIM MACLEOD AND HIS BAND, THE (MacLeod, Jim & His Band).
LP: .... MFP 5614
MC: .... TCMFP 5614

NORTH OF THE BORDER (Sequence Dancing) (MacLeod, Jim & His Band).
LP: .... BTS 1005

OUR KIND OF MUSIC (MacLeod, Jim & His Band).
LP: .... MOR 513

PLAY SELECTED SCOTTISH COUNTRY DANCES (McLeod, Jim & His Band).
LP: .... ITV 491
MC: .... KITV 491

SCOTTISH DANCE WORLD, THE (MacLeod, Jim & His Band).
LP: .... SPA 154

SOUND OF SCOTLAND, THE (MacLeod, Jim & His Band).
Tracks: / Highland laddie / Black bear, The / Duster reel / Ye banks and braes / Kelvingrove / Jumpin' Geordie / Ballochmyle / Rory O More / Little pickle / Cuckoo / Leaving Stornoway / Lads of Bonnie Scotland / Davie Knick Knack.
LP: .... LBLP 2002
MC: .... ZCLBP 2002

SOUNDS SCOTTISH (MacLeod, Jim & His Band).
Tracks: / Dashing white sergeant / Pittinweem Jo / Slow air and jig / Forty shades of green / Military two step / Come to Fiona's wedding / Scottish waltz / Reel selection / Dunblane / Accordion duet / Pride of Erin waltz / If my world should end tomorrow / Gay Gordons.
MC: .... TCGLN 1022
LP: .... GLN 1022

TAKE YOUR PARTNERS IT'S JIM.
LP: .... MOR 507

WELCOME TO MY WORLD.
LP: .... ITV 461
MC: .... KITV 461

MacLeod, Margaret

WEST OF WEST.
Tracks: / Tha mi sgith / Hug oireann oro / Song for a winer's night / Oran a mhalisidh / I dall u dall / Oor ain fireside / MacCrimmon's lament / He mandu / Loving arms / Am bauchaille ban / Teddy bear song / Te bhan medley / White rose of Athens / Poca sil an t sealgair.
LP: .... GLN 1002

McLeod, Pipe Major

HIGHLAND DANCERS' DELIGHT.
MC: .... CWGR 109

MacLeod, Robert

ALL ABOARD (MacLeod, Robert & Friends).
MC: .... MR 1021

McLeod, Rory

ANGRY LOVE.
Tracks: / Farewell welfare / Shirley's her name / Stop the apartheid fascists / Pauline's song / Wind is getting stronger, The / Angry love / Walking towards each other / Passing the pain down / Criminals of hunger.
LP: .... FORWARD 004

FOOTSTEPS AND HEARTBEATS.
Tracks: / Love like a rock (in a stormy sea) / Till I don't know who I am / Collectorman / Moments shared / Wandering fool / Take me home / Singing copper / Kind of loneliness, A / Mariachis love song.
LP: .... COOK 018
MC: .... COOKC 018

KICKING THE SAWDUST.
Tracks: / Baksheesh dance / Huge sky / Rip Van Winkle / Kicking the sawdust / Dad's dance song / Sssh baby / Interrogations and confessions / Dance of measureless love / Hug you like a mountain / In the ghetto of our love / When children starve in peacetime / Strangers / Everything is provocative / Immaculate deception / Ambitious to love you / Harmonkikas dreams / Last tree / Divorcee blues / Old brigades song / Commentator cried, The / Hymn for her.
2LP: .... FORWARD 005

McLollie, Oscar

OSCAR MCLOLLIE & HIS HONEY JUMPERS (McLollie, Oscar & his Honey Jumpers).
Tracks: / Roll hot rod roll / Lolly-pop / Mama don't like it / Hot banana / Wiggle-toe / Honey jump / Hey lolly lolly / What you call 'em Joe / Love my baby.
LP: .... 10 CH 27

McLoughlin, Mark

TRADITIONAL MUSIC AND SONG.
LP: .... TOL 104

McLoughlin, Noel

20 BEST OF IRELAND.
LP: .... EULP 1079
MC: .... EUMC 1079

20 BEST OF SCOTLAND.
LP: .... EULP 1080
MC: .... EUMC 1080

MacLure, Pinkie

THIS DIRTY LIFE.
LP: .... BND 5 LP

MacMahon, Dolly

DOLLY.
LP: .... CC 3

McMahon, Gerard

NO LOOKING BACK.
Tracks: / Count on me / I wouldn't take it from you / No looking back / She's the woman / Talking 'bout girls / Wearing my heart out / No sweat / When she was mine / Nickel charm Jack / So many nights.
LP: .... U 0056

MacMahon, Niall

LAND OF HOPE.
LP: .... KSLP 005

McMahon, Paul

PAUL MCMAHON.
LP: .... N 13

MacMahon, Tony

IG CNOC NA GRAI (MacMahon Tony & Noel Hill).
LP: .... CEF 114

TONY MACMAHON.
LP: .... CEF 033

McManus, Jill

SYMBOLS OF HOPE.
Tracks: / Corn dance / Cloud blessing / Symbols of Hopi / All the earth to bloom / From the four directions / Inner spirit dance / Acoma.
LP: .... CJ 242

McMenn, El

OF SOUL AND SPIRIT.
MC: .... SHMC 97012

McMillan, Neil

OUT THE BOX (See under Coghill, Sandy) (McMillan, Neil & Sandy Coghill).

McMinn, Don

HEARTACHE HOTEL (McMinn, Don & The Memphis Blues Revue).
LP: . . . . **EXIT 33104**

McMorland, Alison

ALISON MCMORLAND & PETA WEBB.
Tracks: / Two pretty boys / What can a young lassie? / Jogging up to Claudy / In London so fair / Convict's song / Sailing's a weary life / Factory girl / May morning dew / Green banks of Yarrow, The / Dowie dens of Yarrow / Our ship is ready.
LP: **12TS 403**

BELT WI' COLOURS THREE.
LP: . . . . **TGS 125**

FUNNY FAMILY, THE.
LP: . . . . **BBX 504**
MC: . . . . **BBXMC 504**

MacMurrough

CARRIG RIVER.
Tracks: / Carrig river / Follow me up to carlow / Sean dunnan gall / O'Sullivan's retreat / Johnny Shoemaker / Tunnel tigers / Reynard the fox / She moved through the fair / Tabhair dom do lamh / Rocky road to dublin / Diobhan ni dhuibhir / Courtown fishermen.
MC: **31 8800 2**

MacNab, Jim

CRYSTAL CHANDELIERS.
LP: . . . . **KMLP 301**

MacNab, J.J.

DO YOU RIGHT TONIGHT.
LP: . . . . **BGC 268**

DON'T TURN OUT THE LIGHT.
LP: . . . . **BGC 258**
MC: . . . . **KGBC 258**

McNab, Ted

BIG BAND SWING (McNab, Ted And Company).
LP: . . . . **FS 29**

McNally, John

DANNY BOY AND OTHER FAVOURITES.
LP: . . . . **HPE 618**
MC: . . . . **HPC 618**

McNamara, Frank

MUSIC OF THE NIGHT (McNamara, Frank & David Agnew).
MC: . . . . **OCE 2467**

McNamaras Band

COME INTO THE PARLOUR.
Tracks: / McNamaras Band / Molly Malone / Galway Bay / Mursheen Durkin / Green glens of Antrim / Paddy McGinty's goat / When you were sweey sixteen / It's a great day for the irish / Believe me if all those endearing young charms / I'll take you home again Kathleen / With my shillelagh under my arm / Mother Machree / Crack was ninety in the Isle Of Man, The / How can you buy Killarney?.
LP: . . . . **LRIR 3002**
MC: . . . . **LRIC 3002**

McNaughtan, Adam

GLASGOW THAT I USED TO KNOW, THE.
Tracks: / Jelly piece song, The / School songs / Dance noo laddie / They're pullin' doon the buildin' next tae oors / Mammie songs / Old Annie Brown / Jail songs / Ludgin' wi' big Aggie / Wee drappie o't, A / Glasgow that I used to know, The / Music hall fragments / Transportation ballad, The / Football songs / Derry and Cumberland boys, The / Bonnie wee country lass / Street songs / Haddie in the pan / Now that you've gone.
MC: . . . . **CTRAX 012**

WORDS, WORDS, WORDS.
Tracks: / Glasgow that I used to know, The / Airn John / West End park serenade / Nursing fathers / Haill week o' the fair, The / Glasgow Sunday school, The / Yellow on the broom, The / Glasgow courtship, The / Robin Tamson's smiddy / Fitba' crazy / Blood upon the grass / Lion and the glove, The / We shall not have a motorway / Oor hamlet.
LP: . . . . **TRAX 013**
MC: . . . . **CTRAX 013**

MacNee, Patrick

KINKY BOOTS (see Blackman, Honor) (MacNee, Patrick & Honor Blackman).

McNeely, Big Jay

BEST OF BIG JAY MCNEELY.
LP: . . . . **BP 1300**

BIG J IN 3-D.
Tracks: / Goof, The / Ice water / Big Jay shuffle / Rock candy / Whipped cream / Hot cinders / 3-D / Hardtack / Nervous man / Mule milk / Let's work / Beachcomber.
LP: . . . . **SING 650**

BIG JAY MCNEELY MEETS THE PENGUINS (McNeely, Big Jay & The Penguins).
Tracks: / Honky tonk / Night train / Harlem nocturne / Watch out, Big Jay's loose / Money honey / Hey senorita / Love will make your mind go wild / Ooky ook / Only you (and you alone) / Saturday night at the movies / Memories of El Monte / Earth angel.
LP: . . . . **CH 101**

DEACON RIDES AGAIN.
LP: . . . . **PM 1546691**

FROM HARLEM TO CAMDEN.
Tracks: / Harlem nocturne / Camden bounce / Some kinda boogie / Just because / Jumpin' with Jay / Strollin' sax / Pembridge court / Catalina swing / Rockin' the reeds.
LP: . . . . **CH 111**

ROADHOUSE BOOGIE.
LP: . . . . **BP 505**

McNeely, Larry

POWER PLAY (McNeely, Larry Band).
LP: . . . . **FF 218**

RHAPSODY FOR BANJO.
LP: . . . . **FF 025**

MacNeice, Louis

FOUR TWENTIETH CENTURY POETS (see under Lewis, C. Day).

McNeil, Bryan

UNSUNG HERO, THE.
LP: . . . . **TP 017**

McNeil, Claudia (nar)

BLACK FAIRY TALES (see under Black Fairy Tales (bk)).

McNeil, Finlay

FONN IS FURAN.
LP: . . . . **TP 009**

McNeil, Flora

AILEIN DUINN Folksongs in Scots Gaelic.
Tracks: / Ailein Duinn / Beinn a'cheathaich / Abhean iadach / Bheir mo shoraidh thar ghunnaidh / Cairistiona / Caolas eadar mi is ian / Chan e caoud mhic shiridh / Chunnaic mise mo leannan / Co sheineas an fhideag airgid / Faca sibh raghail na ailein / Fath mo mhulaid a bhith Ann / Fhir an leadain thlath / Afleasgaich oig is ceanalta / Fliuch an oidche / Ged is grianach an latha / Amhic dhughaill'ic ruairidh / Amhic ian ic sheumais / Mile mharbhaisg air a'ghaol / Mo nighean donn nan gobhar / Ochraobh nan ubhal / Aphiuthrag's a phiuthar / Sean duine cha ghabh mi idir / Thug min oidhche ged b'fhad'i.
MC: **60-001**

CRAOBH NAN UBHAL.
LP: . . . . **TGS 124**

McNeil, John

EMBARKATION.
LP: . . . . **SCS 1099**

FAUN (McNeil, John Quintet).
LP: . . . . **SCS 1117**

THINGS WE DID LAST SUMMER.
LP: . . . . **SCS 1231**

MacNeil, Rita

FLYING ON YOUR OWN.
Tracks: / Flying on your own / Neon city / She's called Nova Scotia / Baby baby / Leave her memory / Fast train to Tokyo / Everybody / Used to you / Loser (when it comes to love) / Realised your dreams.
MC: **843 423-4**
LP: **843 423-1**

REASON TO BELIEVE.
Tracks: / Walk on through / Two steps from broken / City child / Doors of the cemetary / Reason to believe / When the loving is through / Causing the fall / Music's going round again, The / Sound your own horn / Working man / Good friends.
MC: **847106-4**

RITA.
Tracks: / Crazy love / Anna I.O.U. / I'll accept the rose / You've known love / Moonlight and clover / When love surrounded you and I / Black rock / Part of the mystery / Why do I think of you today / Other one, The / In the spirit / We'll reach the sky tonight.
MC: **847105-4**

McNeil, Roddy

RODDY MCNEIL SINGS IT.
LP: . . . . **PR 126**

McNeile, H.C. (aut)

BULLDOG DRUMMOND (see under Bulldog Drummond) (Todd, Richard (nar)).

McNeill, Brian

BACK O' THE NORTH WIND, THE (Tales of the Scots in America).
Tracks: / Back o' the North wind, The / Entail, The / Strong women rule us with their tears / Rock and the tide, The / Destitution road / Muir and the master builder / Atlantic reels, The / Best o' the barley, The / Ewen and the gold / Drive the golden spike / Lang Johnny Moir / Steel man / Bridal boat, The.
MC: . . . . **CTRAX 047**

MONKSGATE.
LP: . . . . **BUR 801**

SIDETRACKS (see Reid,Alan/Brian McNeill) (McNeill, Brian/Alan Reid).

MacNeill, Seamas

PURELY PIOBAIREACHD.
LP: . . . . **LILP 5041**

McNeillstown Pipe Band

WORLD CHAMPIONS.
Tracks: / Balmoral / Shoals of herring / Auld hoose, The / Lee rig / Killiecrankie / Green hills / Battle's o'er, The / City of Hastings / Waters of Kylesku / London's bonnie woods and braes / Orange and blue / Castle Kennedy / Cullen bay / Abide with me / Jesus lover of my soul / Work for the night is coming / 1976 police tattoo / Minnie Hynd / Old toasty / Rose among the heather / High road to Linton / Jock Wilson's ball / Schiehallion / Welcome to Dunfermline / Rowan tree / No 'awa / 10th Argyll crossing the Rhine / Sweet maid of Mull / Cock o' the North / Frank Thompson / Wings / Lady McKenzie of Fairburn / Captain Horne / Morag of Dunvegan / O for a closer walk with God / I need thee every hour.
LP: . . . . **HRL 171**
MC: . . . . **CHRL 171**

McNeir, Ronnie

LOVE SUSPECT.
Tracks: / Love suspect / Lately / Summertime medley / Sexy mama / Everybody's in a hurry / I'll be loving you / Follow your heart / Tying to keep my heart / Please come and be with me.
LP: . . . . **EXLP 1**

MacNeish, Jerry

DRIVE-IN GUITARS.
LP: . . . . **LP 8803**

McNichol, Evelyn

SACRED PIANO ARRANGEMENTS.
LP: . . . . **PC 769**

TELL THE WORLD.
LP: . . . . **SAC 5096**

McNight, Sharon

ANOTHER SIDE OF SHARON MCNIGHT.
LP: . . . . **GLS 6030**

PRESENTING SHARON MCNIGHT.
LP: . . . . **GLS 6027**

McNulty, Pat

PAT MCNULTY (UILLEANN PIPES).
LP: . . . . **PSH 103**

Macon, Albert

BLUES AND BOOGIE FROM ALABAMA (Macon, Albert & Robert Thomas).
LP: **2105**

Macon, Uncle Dave

AT HOME - IN 1950.
Tracks: / Cumberland Mountain deer race / Rabbit in the pea patch / Bully of the town / Mountain dew / Old maid's love song / Rock of ages / Keep my skillet good and greasy / Death of John Henry / That's where my money goes / Long John Green / Lady in the car / Cotton-eyed Joe / Something's sure to tickle me / Chewing gum / All in down and out blues / Hungry hash house / Who mule / No one to welcome me home / Banjo solo / Jenny put the kettle on / Kissing in the sly.
LP: . . . . **BFX 15214**

LAUGH YOUR BLUES AWAY.
LP: . . . . **ROUNDER 1028**

OVER THE MOUNTAIN (1935-38 vol. 2).
LP: . . . . **OHCS 183**

WAIT TILL THE CLOUDS.
LP: . . . . **HLP 8006**

MacOrlan, Pierre

CHANSONS DU QUAI DES BRUMES (MacOrlan, Pierre/Monique Morelli).
LP: . . . . **ARN 33474**
MC: . . . . **ARN 40-33474**

McPartland, Jimmy

ON STAGE (McPartland, Jimmy and Allstars).
LP: . . . . **J 16**

ONE NIGHT STAND.
LP: . . . . **J 137**

McPartland, Joe

BLAZE AWAY.
Tracks: / Blaze away / If I can help somebody / Soldier's dream, The / Holy city, The / My heart and I / Goodbye / Hear my song, Violetta / One little candle / When you talk about old Ireland / I'll take you home again Kathleen / Rose of Tralee, The / When you were sweet sixteen.
MC: . . . . **CWGR 134**

SONGS O' SCOTLAND.
Tracks: / Scotland the brave / Bonnie Mary of Argyle / Road to the Isles, The / I belong to Glasgow / Eriskay love lilt / Keep right on to the end of the road / Star o' Rabbie Burns, The / Roamin' in the gloamin' / Annie Laurie / Wee Deoch an' Doris / Westering home / Tunes of glory.
MC: . . . . **CWGR 129**

McPartland, Marian

ALONE TOGETHER (see Shearing, George) (McPartland, Marian & George Shearing).

AT HICKORY HOUSE.
2LP: . . . . **SJL 2248**

AT THE HICKORY HOUSE.
Tracks: / I hear music / Tickle toe / Street of dreams / How long has this been going on / Let's call the whole thing off / Lush life / Mad about the boy / Love you madly / Skylark / Ja-da / I've told every little star / Moon song.
LP: . . . . **JAS 312**
MC: . . . . **JAS C312**

ELEGANT PIANO (see Wilson, Teddy) (McPartland, Marian & Teddy Wilson).

JANUARY 6TH & 8TH 1964.
Tracks: / Y'know what I mean / Easy like / Hawk talk / Ida / Blues for Indian Jim / Don't panic / Magpie / So little time / Secret / Deep river / Warmin' up / Lonely.
LP: . . . . **JV 113**

LIVE AT MAYBECK RECITAL HALL, VOLUME 9.
Tracks: / This time the dream's on me / Fine romance, A / Willow weep for me / Twilight world / Clothed Woman / Prelude to a kiss / Duke, The (Only on CD) / Theme from piano jazz / Love you madly / Easy living / Things ain't what they used to be / I should care / My funny valentine / Turn around / It's you or no one / I'll be around.
MC: . . . . **CJ 460C**

MUSIC OF LEONARD BERNSTEIN.
LP: . . . . **BT 1013**
MC: . . . . **BT 41013**

PERSONAL CHOICE.
Tracks: / I hear a rhapsody / Meditation / In your own sweet way / Sleeping bee / I'm old fashioned / When the sun comes out / Tricotism / Melancholy mood.
LP: . . . . **CJ 202**
MC: . . . . **CJC 202**

PLAYS THE BENNY CARTER SONG BOOK.
Tracks: / When lights are low / I'm in the mood for swing / Kiss from you, A (Only on CD.) / Key largo / Another time, another place / Summer serenade / Doozy / Lonely woman / Only trust your heart / Evening star (Only on CD.) / Easy money.
MC: . . . . **CJ 412 C**

PLAYS THE MUSIC OF BILLY STRAYHORN.
Tracks: / Intimacy of the blues, The / Isfahan / Lotus blossom / Raincheck / Lush life / U.M.M.G. / Flower is a lovesome thing, A / Take the 'A' train / Daydream / After all.
LP: . . . . **CJ 326**
MC: . . . . **CJC 326**

WILLOW CREEK AND OTHER BALLADS.
Tracks: / Without you / Things we did last summer, The / All in love is fair / Willow creek / Long ago and far away / Some day I'll find you / I saw stars / Blood count / I've got a crush on you / Summer song.
MC: . . . . **CJC 272**
LP: . . . . **CJ 272**

McPeak Brothers

MCPEAK BROTHERS, THE.
LP: . . . . **SAVE 034**

McPeake Family

JUG OF PUNCH (McPeake Family Trio).
Tracks: / Maidrin rua / My singing bird / Marches / Bonnie bunch of roses, The /

Reel / An dord faine / Blackbird / Erin the tear / Lament of Aughrim / Verdant braes of Skreen / Coulin / Siuban ni ghiuibhir / Jigs / Carrick down / Se fa mo mhughrach / Road to Ballynure / Seothin seo / Wild mountain thyme.
MC: 60-071

MCPEAKE FAMILY, THE.
Tracks: / McLeod's reel / Bucket of the mountain dew / Eileen Aroon / An durd fainne / My singing bird / Lament of Aughrim / Carraigdoon / Derry hornpipe / Old piper / Slievegallion braes / Ireland boys hurrah / Cock Robin / Coolin / Verdant braes of Skreen.
LP: 12T 87

WILD MOUNTAIN THYME.
LP: TOP 22

McPeake, Frank Snr

FRANK MCPEAKE (SNR).
MC: 60-176

MacPhail, Ian

ARGYLL'S FANCY (MacPhail, Ian & His Scottish Dance Band).
Tracks: / Argyll's fancy / Accordion duet / Shiftin bobbins / Hornpipes / Elizabeth's waltz / Shepherds crook / Flowers of Edinburgh / Dram O' dalwhinnie / Pride of Erin / Joan's jig / Slow air / Tarry awhile / Dashing white sergeant.
LP: LILP 5141
MC: LICS 5141

PRIDE OF EDINBURGH (MacPhail, Ian & His Scottish Dance Band).
Tracks: / Musselburgh reel / Eva three step / Waltz and march / Accordion duet / Jig wild geese / Gaelic waltz / Scottish minuet / Reel polharrow burn / Bridgecastle reel / Jig pet o the pipers / Polka / Cullivoe two step / De'ils conundrum.
LP: GES 1213

McPhatter, Clyde

18 ORIGINAL HITS: CLYDE MCPHATTER/BILLY WARD (McPhatter, Clyde/Billy Ward).
LP: K 5006

BIP BAM.
Tracks: / Money honey / Let the boogie woogie roll / Don't dog me / Gone / Such a night / Lucille / Warm your heart / Way I feel, The / Bip bam / Honey love / Whatcha gonna do / If I didn't love you like I do / There you go / Try try baby / Everyone's laughing / Three thirty three.
LP: ED 132

CLYDE MCPHATTER.
LP: BID 8006

LOVER PLEASE.
LP: CLYDE 1000

RHYTHM 'N' SOUL.
Tracks: / I'm afraid the masquerade is over / I told myself a lie / Bless you / Where did I make my mistake / Twice as nice / Let's start all over again / How deep is the ocean / Stay as sweet as you are / Someone to love / I need you so / Trust in me / That's the glory of love / Don't take your love from me / There will never be another you / I'll never be free / Don't cry baby / Everybody needs somebody / Let's try again / This is not goodbye / When the right time comes along / One right after the other / I know the feeling / Think me a kiss / Take a step / Whisper softly / I just want to love you / You're for me / I ain't givin' up nothing / Ta ta / I need a love like yours / Who's worried now / Harbour lights / Love is a many splendoured thing / You belong to me / These foolish things / Answer me / When did you leave heaven / Put your arms around me honey / As time goes by / That's my desire / What will I tell my heart / Three coins in the fountain / How many times / For all you've done / One more chance / Let me shake the hand / Why was I the one you chose / High school social / Everything's gonna be alright / What's love to me / You're moving me / All about love not me / I wanna be the only one / Before I fall in love again / I'll stop anything I'm doing / Tomorrow is a comin' / What went wrong / Whole heap of love / I'll love you til the cows come home / Happiness / I never knew / How do I make my dreams come true / Friends / Same time, same place / Honest I do / What am I living for / Kansas city / Fever / Clock, The / Your second choice / Blues stay away from me / What'd I say / Rainin' in my heart / C.C. rider / I'm gonna be a wheel someday / Honey hush / Bells, The / Hey love / Without love / White Christmas / Name of the game / Is love / You've got everything from A to Z / Let's stop / Can I be wrong / Up to my ears in tears / Best man cried, The / Lover please / Baby you been so good / Let's forget about the past / Happy good times / Little bitty pretty one / Don't let go / Rockin' Robin / Money honey / Oh lonesome me / Everybody loves a winner / I'm movin' on / Pretty girls everywhere / Sixty minute man / Such a night / Next to me / Climb that mountain of love / Maybe / I've lost again / Walking back to Baltimore / I do believe / Just a little too late / So close being in love / Lonely people do foolish things / From one to one / Soul / Everybody's got a song but me / I found my love / Crying won't help you now / I wanna know / Deep in the heart of Harlem (overdub) / My block / Surburban town, A / Spanish harlem / Three rooms with running water / Up on the roof / Second window, second floor / Chinatown / Coney Island / Shelter of your arms, The / In my tenement / On Broadway / Baby baby (Live at The Apollo.) / Lover's question (Live at The Apollo.) / Hold my hand (Live at Apollo.) / Second window, second floor (Live at Apollo.) / Lucille (Live at Apollo.) / What's love to me (Live at Apollo.) / Deep in the heart of Harlem (Live at Apollo.) / Mercy mercy baby (Live at Apollo.) / Without love (Live at Apollo.).
LPS: BFX 15271/9

ROCK AND CRY.
Tracks: / Seven days / Treasure of love / Thirty days / Without love / Rock and cry / You'll be there / Just hold my hand / Long lonely nights / No love like her love / Come what may / Deep sea ball / Lover's question / I can't stand up alone / Lovey dovey / Since you've been gone / You went back on your word.
LP: CRB 1073
MC: TCCRB 1073

MacPhee, Catherine-Ann

CANAN NAN GAIDHEAL.
Tracks: / Hi ri rio ra ill o / A nighean nan geug taladh / Puirt a beul / Soiridh leis a' bhreacan ur / Iomair thusa, choinnich chridhe / Ca'nan nan gaidheal / S fliuch an oidhche / Onan an Iolaire / Cearcall a' chuain / A ataireach ard.
MC: CTRAX 009
LP: TRAX 009

CHI MI'N GEAMHRADH (I SEE WINTER).
Tracks: / Chi mi'n greamhradh / Chaidh mo dhunnchadh dha'n bheinn / Oh hi ri lean / Bidh clann ulaidh / Mile marbhphaisg air a' ghaol / Seathan bu deonach leam tilleadh / 'S muladach mi 's mi air m'aineol / Bothan airigh am braigh rainneach / Tha na h-uain air an tulaich / Na libh o ho I.
MC: CTRAX 038

MacPhee, Doug

CAPE BRETON PIANO.
LP: ROUNDER 7009

McPhee, George

GEORGE MCPHEE PLAYS ORGAN OF PAISLEY ABBEY.
LP: LPB 790

McPhee, Joe

VISITATION (McPhee, Joe & The Bill Smith ensamble).
LP: 3036

McPhee, John

PIECES OF LIGHT (McPhee, John & John Snyder).
LP: CJ 24

MacPherson, Alexander

RULE BRITANNIA.
Tracks: / Rule Britannia / Largo / Jesus, joy of man's desiring / Hallelujah chorus / Londonderry air / Crimond / Will ye no come back again / Auld lang syne / Onward Christian soldiers / All in the april evening / Land of hope and glory / Holy City, The / Trumpet voluntary / Ave Maria / God save the queen.
LP: NA 114

McPherson, Bunty

REEKIN' LUM, THE (AND OTHER STORIES).
Tracks: / Introduction / Ailments / Slimming / Tiny's visit to the pictures / Drink and driving / Mains o' yavel's dook / Reekin' lum, The / Johnny at school / Sonia Schnell / Clockin' hen, The / Nod and a wink, A / Prunes / Affectation / Loo, The / John and Tibby's dispute / Parson's cure / Lass o' pairts / Corn, The / Cleaning oot my handbag / R.S.V.P. / Good old days / Auld man's thoughts, An / Something gaun aboot.
MC: CWGR 132

McPherson, Charles

DAVE PIKE AND CHARLES MCPHERSON (see under Pike, Dave) (McPherson, Charles/Dave Pike).

FEELIN' GOOD (See under Bowie, Pat) (McPherson, Charles & Pat Bowie).

LIVE IN TOKYO.
LP: XAN 131

NEW HORIZONS.
LP: X 149

PROPHET, THE (McPherson, Charles Sextet).
Tracks: / Starburst / Prophet, The / Dearly beloved / Fun and games / Mantra / Prelude to a kiss / Oscar for Treadwell, An.
LP: DS 882

MacPherson, Donald

MASTER PIPER, THE.
LP: LILP 5185
MC: LICS 5185

MacPherson, Fraser

I DIDN'T KNOW ABOUT YOU (MacPherson, Fraser & Oliver Gannon).
Tracks: / This heart of mine / Do nothing till you hear from me / Everything happens to me / All by myself / More I see you, The / Mean to me / I didn't know about you / Day by day / Nightingale sang in Berkeley Square, A / You go to my head / In a mellow tone.
LP: 4009

JAZZ PROSE (MacPherson, Fraser Quintet).
Tracks: / Darn that dream / It could happen to you / Happy man / All alone / On a slow boat to China / There is no greater love / I'll never be the same / You'd be so nice to come home to.
LP: CJ 269
MC: CJC 269

MacPherson, Sandy

I'LL PLAY FOR YOU.
Tracks: / Dancing with tears in my eyes / My hero / Londonderry air / Toselli serenade / Traumerei / Melody in F / Salut d'amour / Songs my mother taught me / Merry Widow waltz / Vilia / From my postbag hit medleys / Sandy forges signatures.
LP: SH 385
MC: TC SH 385

McQuaig, Scott

SCOTT MCQUAIG.
LP: UVL 76000
MC: UVLC 76000

McRae, Carmen

ALIVE.
LP: MRD 5001

ANY OLD TIME.
Tracks: / Tulip or turnip / Old devil moon / Have you met Miss Jones / Love me tender / I hear music / This is always / Body and soul / Prelude to a kiss / Mean to me / Any old time / It could happen to you / I'm glad there is you / Billie's blues.
MC: CC 13

CARMEN MCRAE.
MC: ZCGAS 750

CARMEN SINGS MONK.
Tracks: / Get it straight / Dear Ruby / It's over now / Monkery's the blues / You know who / Little butterfly / Listen to Monk / How I wish / Man, that was a dream / Round midnight / Still we dream / Suddenly (live) / Looking back.
MC: PK 83036
LP: PL 83036

FINE AND MELLOW.
Tracks: / What can I say, after I say I'm sorry? / Fine and mellow / These foolish things / Black and blue / One more chance / Until the real thing comes along / My handy man ain't handy no more / What is this thing called love? (Bonus track on CD only.).
LP: CJ 342
MC: CJC 342

HAPPY TO MAKE YOUR ACQUAINTANCE (See under Davis, Sammy Jnr) (McRae, Carmen/Sammy Davis Jnr).

HEATWAVE (McRae, Carmen/Cal Tjader).
Tracks: / Heatwave / All in love is fair / Besame mucho / Evil ways / Do nothing till you hear from me / Love / Upside down / Visit / Speak low / Don't you worry 'bout a thing.
LP: CJ 189

I HEAR MUSIC (see Connor, Chris) (McRae, Carmen & Chris Connor).

INVITATION.
Tracks: / Passing fancy / I guess I'll dress up for the blues / Never loved him anyhow / Invitation / As I love you / Moon ray / So nice to be wrong / Go for you / Lo and behold / Come down to earth, Mr. Smith / You don't know me / It's like getting a donkey to gallop / How many stars have to shine? / Tonight he's out to break another heart / It's so much fun / Belonging to you.
LP: OFF 3027

LIVE.
Tracks: / Black magic / Superwoman / New York state of mind / Underneath the apple tree / Thou swell / Send in the clowns / I just can't wait to see you / How long has this been going on / If I were a bell / My foolish heart / Secret love / I concentrate on you (CD only.).
LP: GATE 7001
MC: CGATE 7001

RONNIE SCOTT'S PRESENTS CARMEN MCCRAE LIVE.
LP: NSPL 18543

SARAH - DEDICATED TO YOU.
Tracks: / Poor butterfly / I've got the world on a string / Misty / Wonder why / Send in the clowns / Black coffee / Tenderly / Best is yet to come, The / I will say goodbye / Lamp is low, The / It's magic / Dedicated to you / I'll be seeing you / Sarah.
MC: PK 90546

TORCHY.
Tracks: / Last night when we were young / Speak low / But beautiful / If you'd stay the way I dream about you / Midnight sun / We'll be together again / I'm a dreamer / Good morning heartache / Starry eyes / I don't stand a ghost of a chance with you.
LP: MOIR 204
MC: CMOIR 204

TWO FOR THE ROAD (see under Shearing, George) (McRae, Carmen & George Shearing).

VELVET SOUL.
Tracks: / Nice work if you can get it / It takes a whole lot of human feeling / I fall in love too easily / Hey John / Where are the words / Straighten up and fly right / Inside a silent tear / Imagination / Right to love, The / All the things you are / You're mine you / You and I / How could I settle for less / Good life / Sunshine of my life / Exactly like you / There will come a time / Masquerade.
MC: MC 7970

YOU'RE LOOKING AT ME.
Tracks: / I'm an errand girl for rhythm / Beautiful moons ago / Frim fram sauce / Come in and out of the rain / How does it feel? / If I had you / I can't see for lookin' / Sweet Lorraine / You're lookin' at me / Just you,just me.
LP: CJ 235

MacRae, Dave

FORECAST (MacRae, Dave & John Yates).
Tracks: / Red sails in the sunset / Rio De Janeiro blue / You can't take it with you / Here's that rainy day / Trade winds / Green Dolphin street / This masquerade / Come rain or come shine / This time / Raining on the moon.
LP: TRL 033
MC: TCTRL 033

MacRae, Donald

HEBRIDEAN JOURNEY.
Tracks: / 'Se mo leannan an te ur / Tuigann leam thar saile / Carlabhagh / A chaillinn a mheall mi / Tairbear na hearadh / Gruagach dhonn bhrunail / A nigheanag a ghraidh / Suaicheantas na h alba / Tuigainn leum is dean cabhag / Eilean Leodhais, tir nan gaisgeach / Domhnall magaidh / Tha mise dol dhacaidh.
LP: LILP 5074
MC: LICS 5074

MacRae, Gordon

CAPITOL YEARS, THE: GORDON MACRAE (Best of).
Tracks: / Stranger in paradise / June in January / My funny valentine / It might as well be Spring / So in love / Spring is here / I'll remember April / Where or when / That's for me / All the things you are / Begin the beguine / Indian Summer / September song / Autumn leaves / And this is my beloved / Without a song.
LP: EMS 1352
LP: 793 749 1
MC: TCEMS 1352
MC: 793 749 4

COWBOY'S LAMENT.
Tracks: / Cowboy's lament / San Antonio rose / Soothe my lonely heart / Last round-up, The / How green was my valley / Oklahoma hills / Red river valley / Tumbling tumbleweeds / Wagon wheels / Green grow the lilacs / Cowboy's serenade,The / I went to the city.
LP: HAT 3054
MC: HATC 3054

MOTION PICTURE SOUNDSTAGE.
Tracks: / Singin' in the rain / Dancing in the dark / You're a sweetheart / Cabin in the sky / Hooray for love / Love is a many splendoured thing / Jealousy / Pennies from Heaven / Laura / Easy to love / Flirtation walk / Goodnight Sweetheart.
LP: EMS 1183
MC: TCEMS 1183

OLD RUGGED CROSS (see under Stafford, Jo) (MacRae, Gordon/Jo Stafford).

YOU'LL NEVER WALK ALONE (see under Stafford, Jo) (MacRae, Gordon/Jo Stafford).

McRae, Malcolm

ART OF THE SOLO PIPER.
Tracks: / Braemar gathering, The / Jeannie Mauchline / John MacKenzie's farewell / To Strathglass / Millbank cottage / John MacDonald of Glencoe / Lament for the children.
LP: . . . . **TRL 031**
MC: . . . . **TCTRL 031**

Macrae, Shel

SHEL MACRAE.
LP: . . . . **MMC 1345**

McReynolds, J.

BLUEGRASS JAM (see Clements, Vassar) (McReynolds, J./Clements, Vassar/Doug Jernigan).

McRoby, Ron

PLAYS PUCCOLO.
Tracks: / Joy spring / If you could see me now / Line for Lyons / Puccle while you work (whistle while you work) / Daahoud / Everything happens to me / Boplicity / Along came Betty.
LP: . . . . **CJ 208**
MC: . . . . **CJC 208**

McShane, Joe

HERE IN MY HEART.
MC: . . . . **RTS 2496**

MY SIDE OF THE ROAD.
MC: . . . . **RTS 3001**

PLACES, THOUGHTS AND FEELINGS.
Tracks: / Places, thoughts and feelings.
MC: . . . . **RTS 3320**

SONGS OF HOME.
MC: . . . . **RTS 2535**

McShann, Jay

AFTER HOURS.
LP: . . . . **SLP 4024**

AIRMAIL SPECIAL.
LP: **3040**

BAND THAT JUMPS THE BLUES, THE.
Tracks: / Hot biscuits / Slow drag blues / Mr. Boogie / Buttermilk / Skid Row blues / Soft winds / No name boogie / Thinking about my baby / Geronimo / Twelve o'clock whistle / Mellodrag / Eatin' watermelon.
LP: . . . . **BLP 30144**

BEST OF FRIENDS (see Casey, Al).

BLUES AND BOOGIE (McShann, Jay & Sammy Price).
Tracks: / Hands off / Ain't nobody's business / St. Louis blues / You've been a good ol' wagon / Let the good times roll / St. James' infirmary blues / In the evening / Price is right, The / Blues for two pianos / Boogie for Jay and Sam / Everyday I have the blues.
LP: **9198 203**
MC: **7298 203**

CRAZY LEGS AND FRIDAY STRUT (McShann, Jay & Buddy Tate).
LP: **3011**

EARLY BIRD (McShann, Jay and his Orchestra).
Tracks: / I found a new baby / Body and soul / Moten swing / Coquette / Lady be good / Blues / Honeysuckle rose / Cherokee / You say forward, I'll march / Lonely boy blues / Vine Street boogie / Jump the blues away / Bottle it / Sweet Georgia Brown / Wrap your troubles in dreams.
LP: . . . . **SPJ 120**

GOING TO KANSAS CITY (McShann, Jay & The All Stars).
LP: . . . . **S 1322**
LP: . . . . **NW 358**

HOOTIE'S KC BLUES (Big Band Bounce & Boogie) (McShann, Jay and his Orchestra).
Tracks: / Hootie blues / Red river blues / Confessin' the blues / Vine Street boogie / For day rider / Sepian bounce / Hold 'em Hootie / Swingmatism / Jumpin' blues / One woman's blues / Get me on your mind / Dexter blues / Hootie's ignorant oil / Lonely boy blues / So you won't jump / (New) confessin' the blues.
LP: . . . . **AFS 1006**

JUST A LUCKY SO 'N' SO.
LP: **3035**

KANSAS CITY HUSTLE.
LP: **3021**

MAGICAL JAZZ (McShann, Jay/Burks, Martha).
LP: . . . . **JAZZ MARK 102**

MAN FROM MUSKOGEE, THE.
Tracks: / Vine Street boogie / Staggers The / Yardbird waltz / My Chile / Confessin' the blues / Moten swing / Man from Muskogee, The / Blues for old cat / I ain't mad at you / Do wah doo / Dexter blues.
LP: . . . . **AFF 147**
LP: **3005**

TRIBUTE TO FATS WALLER, A.
LP: **3019**

TUXEDO JUNCTION.
Tracks: / Tuxedo Junction / One sided love / Robbins nest / Froggy bottom / Gee baby ain't I good to you / Do nothing till you hear from me / Barrelhouse bolero.
LP: **3025**

VINE STREET BOOGIE.
Tracks: / My chile / Hootie blues / Satin doll / I'm beginning to see the light / Vine Street boogie / Confessin' the blues / Yardbird waltz / Hooties ignorant oil.
LP: . . . . **BLP 30169**

McTell, Blind Willie

BLIND WILLIE MCTELL, 1927-35.
LP: . . . . **YAZOO 1037**

BLIND WILLIE MCTELL, 1933-35.
LP: . . . . **DLP 531**
LP: . . . . **RL 324**

EARLY YEARS, THE 1927-33.
LP: . . . . **YAZOO 1005**

LAST SESSION.
LP: . . . . **OBC 517**

LEGENDARY LIBRARY OF CONGRESS RECORDINGS (1940).
Tracks: / Chainey / Murderer's home / Kill it kid rag / I got to cross the river o' Jordan / Monologue / Old time religion,amen / Willie Fox / Dying crapshooter's blues / Amazing grace / Monologue / Medley / King Edward blues / Delia / Boll weevil / I got to cross the river o' Jordan.
LP: . . . . **BMLP 1049**

LOVE CHANGIN' BLUES.
Tracks: / Love changin' blues / Savannah mama / Talkin' to you mama / East St. Louis / Wee midnight hours / Pal of mine / Down home girl / Night watchman blues / Why did I make you cry / Kid man blues / Ludella.
LP: . . . . **BMLP 1073**

REMAINING TITLES 1927-49.
LP: . . . . **WSE 102**

McTell, Ralph

AT HIS BEST.
Tracks: / Streets of London / Hesitation blues / Girl on a bicycle / Clown / Michael in the garden / Blind Blake's rag / Nanna's song / Last train and ride / England 1914 / Mermaid and the seagull, The / Daddy's here / Kew Gardens / Eight frames a second / Mrs. Adlam's angels / Kind hearted woman blues / Spiral staircase / Wait until snow / Fairground / Rizrak Iaru / Are you receiving me / Louise / Granny takes a trip / Summer come along / Sleepy time blues.
2LP: . . . . **CR 057**
MCSET: . . . . **CRT 057**

AT THE END OF A PERFECT DAY.
Tracks: / Streets of London / Scarborough fair / You've got a friend / Penny Lane / Lamplighter / Last farewell, The / Sailing / Beautiful dreamer / Homeward bound / Scarlet ribbons / I'll have to say I love you in a song / Morning has broken / Weather the storm / Those were the days / Barges / England.
LP: . . . . **STAR 2263**
MC: . . . . **STAC 2263**

BEST OF ALPHABET ZOO.
Tracks: / Zoo zoo zoo / Albert the albatross / Fergus the frog / Gordon the goat / Holly the hedgehog / Impala song / Kenny the kangaroo / Maurice the mole / Nigel the Nightingale / Ollie the otter / Peter the parrot / Sally the seal / Tammy the tortoise / Victor the vulture / X ray fish / Yuri the yak / Zoe the zebra.
LP: . . . . **MFP 4156741**
MC: . . . . **MFP 4156744**

BLUE SKIES, BLACK HEROES.
LP: . . . . **TPG 010**
MC: . . . . **TPGC 010**

BRIDGE OF SIGHS.
Tracks: / Throw out a line and dream / Girl from the hiring fair, The / Shoufleur / Something the matter with Mary / Bridge of sighs / Setting, The / Little actress / Bad girl / Holiday romance / Dreams of you / Words I couldn't say.
LP: . . . . **TPG 009**
MC: . . . . **TPGC 009**

EASY.
Tracks: / Take it easy / Maddy dances / Maginot waltz / Sweet mystery / Stuff no more / Run Johnny run / Zig zag line / Let me down easy / Would I lie to you / Summer lightning.
LP: . . . . **K 54013**

FERRYMAN, THE.
LP: . . . . **TPG 001**
MC: . . . . **TPGC 001**

GREATEST HITS: RALPH MCTELL.
Tracks: / Streets of London / Hesitation blues / Girl on a bicycle / Clown.
LP: . . . . **FUN 9032**
MC: . . . . **FUNC 9032**

LOVE GROWS.
Tracks: / Promises / One heart / London apprentice / White dress / If I don't get home / Gold in California / Love grows / Harry (don't go) / Van Nuys, cruise night / Autumn / Traces / Banjo man.
LP: . . . . **TG 004**
MC: . . . . **TGC 004**

LOVE SONGS COLLECTION.
Tracks: / First song / Promises / Tequila sunset / You make me feel good / River rising, moon high / Naomi / Affairs of the heart / Would I lie to you? / Choux fleur / Words I could'nt say / Summer lightning / Nanna's song / White dress / Seeds of heaven / Let me down easy / Traces / Terminus / Heron song / Grande affaire / If I don't get home / Love grows / Dreams of you / One heart.
2LP: . . . . **CCSLP 219**
MC: . . . . **CCSMC 219**

NOT TILL TOMORROW.
Tracks: / Zimmerman blues / First song / When I was a cowboy / Nettle wine / Sylvia / Birdman / Barges / Stand down in New York town / Another rain has fallen / This time of night / Gypsy.
LP: . . . . **K 44210**

RALPH, ALBERT AND SYDNEY.
Tracks: / First song / Grande affaire / Big tree / Michael in the garden / Dry bone rag / Zimmerman blues / Maginot waltz / Five knuckle shuffle / When I was a cowboy / Let me down easy / Naomi / Sylvia / Streets of London / Sweet mystery / Winnie's rag / Waltzing Matilda.
LP: . . . . **TG 003**
MC: . . . . **TGC 003**
LP: . . . . **K 56399**

RALPH MCTELL.
LP: . . . . **SHM 962**

RALPH MCTELL (71-72).
LP: . . . . **TG 001**

RALPH MCTELL COLLECTION.
2LP: . . . . **PDA 040**
MCSET: . . . . **PDC 040**

RIGHT SIDE UP.
Tracks: / San Diego serenade / Tequila sunset / Weather the storm / River rising / Clare to here / Chairman and the little man / Country boys / Slow burning / Companion / Nightmares / May you never.
LP: . . . . **K 56296**

SLIDE AWAY THE SCREEN.
Tracks: / Love grows / One heart / Gold in California / Van nuys, cruise night / London apprentice / Traces / Heroes and villains / Harry / Autumn / Promises / White dress / Save the last dance for me.
LP: . . . . **K 56599**
MC: **K4 56599**

SONGS FROM ALPHABET ZOO.
Tracks: / Kenny the Kangaroo / Fergus the frog / Peter the Parrot / Yuri the yak / Holly the hedgehog / Tammy the tortoise / Sally the seal / Ollie the otter / Victor the vulture / Nellie the newt / Gordon the goat / Wagstaff the Woodpecker / Quentin the quail / Unwin the unicorn.
LP: . . . . **TG 007**
MC: . . . . **TGC 007**

STEALIN' BACK.
Tracks: / I'm going to Germany / Sugar babe / Prison wall blues / Hesitation blues / Weeping willow / When you've got a good friend / Candy man / When did you leave heaven? / Stealin' / That'll do babe / Black girl / Sweet Petulie / Nobody knows you when you're down and out / Lovin' I crave / Dying crapshooter's blues / This'll bring you back.
MC: . . . . **ESSMC 137**

STREETS.
Tracks: / Streets of London / You make me feel good / Grande affaire / Seeds of Heaven / El progresso / Red apple juice (trad) / Heron song / Pity the boy / Interest on the loan / Jenny Taylor - Je n'tais la / Lunar lullaby.
LP: . . . . **K 56105**

STREETS OF LONDON (LP 2).
Tracks: / Streets of London / Hesitation blues / Mrs Adlam's angels / Girl on a bicycle / Michael in the garden / Nana's song / Rizraklaru / Summer come along / Factory girl / Mermaid and the seagull / Kew Gardens.
LP: . . . . **TRS 104**
MC: . . . . **KTRS 104**
LP: . . . . **SHM 926**

STREETS OF LONDON (RE-ISSUE).
MC: **495945**

TICKLE ON THE TUM (TV Soundtrack) (McTell, Ralph & Jacqui Redding).
MC: . . . . **TPGC 008**
LP: . . . . **TPG 008**

VERY BEST OF RALPH MCTELL.
LP: . . . . **STL 17**
MC: . . . . **STC 17**

WATER OF DREAMS.
Tracks: / Got to be with you / Please don't haunt me / I'm not a rock / Hands of Joseph / Pykey boy / Bentley and Craig / Water of dreams / Affairs of the heart / Cold on the stones / I want you / Geordie's on the road / Song for Martin.
LP: . . . . **TG 005**
MC: . . . . **TGC 005**

WEATHER THE STORM.
LP: . . . . **TG 002**
MC: . . . . **TGC 002**

McTells

EXPECTING JOE.
MC: . . . . **BI-JOOP 014**

McVay, Ray

COME DANCING (McVay, Ray Orchestra).
Tracks: / Scheherazade / Waltz in A flat / Old fashioned way, The / Chanson D'amour / That's a plenty / Something's gotta give / Noche de estralles / Born free / Gold and silver waltz / We've only just begun / For ever and ever / Sunny / Daddy cool / Under the moon of love / When / Choo choo samba / Cialito lindo / Great Abaco, The.
LP: . . . . **TRS 115**
MC: . . . . **KTRS 115**

MUSIC FROM THE HIT PARADE (McVay, Ray Orchestra).
LP: . . . . **DS 008**

TIME STEP (McVay, Ray Orchestra).
Tracks: / Under the moon of love / When / That'll be the day / Stop in the name of love / Ob la di ob la da / Black is black / I only wanna be with you / Dancing queen / Chanson d'amour / We've only just begun / Daddy cool / For ever and ever / That's the way I like it.
LP: . . . . **CFRC 517**
MC: . . . . **MCFRC 517**

WORLD DISCO DANCIN' CHAMPIONSHIP (McVay, Ray Orchestra & Singers).
Tracks: / Slaughter on Tenth Avenue / Stevie Wonder medley / Scarborough fair / Sound of silence / Cecilia / i got rhythm / Somewhere / Young girl / God only knows / Nights in white satin / Hey Jude / Yesterday / Lucy in the sky with diamonds / I / Strawberry fields forever / Hello goodbye / Something / Ob-la-di, ob-la-da.
LP: . . . . **EMC 3292**

WORLD OF LATIN DANCING (McVay, Ray Orchestra).
2LP: **6641 306**

McVea, Jack

COME BLOW YOUR HORN.
Tracks: / Tryin' to tell ya / Ube dubie / You brought me heartaches / Tequila hop / Fishman / Fiddlesticks / Don't bruise the feeling / Chop chop boom / Cha cho hop / Nobody in mind / On the sunny side of the street / That'll be joyful / I owe everybody / Oh how i miss you tonight / Hoodoo you baby / I'll get along somehow.
LP: . . . . **CH 147**

NEW DEAL (McVea, Jack Allstars).
Tracks: / My business is C.O.D. / Play it over / Rainy day blues / F minor boogie / It never should have been this way / Jack's boogie / Baby make up your mind / Butch / Two timin' baby boogie / Evening / Fish for supper / New deal.
LP: . . . . **JB 625**

NOTHIN' BUT JAZZ 1962 (McVea, Jack Quintet).
LP: . . . . **HQ 2046**

OPEN THE DOOR RICHARD (McVea, Jack Allstars).
Tracks: / Bartender boogie / Tarrant blues / O-Kay for baby / We're together again / Ooh mop / Don't blame me / Frisco blues / Don't let the sun catch you crying / Open the door Richard / Wine-o / Inflation blues / Groovin' boogie / No no you can't do dot mon / Jack Frost / Mumblin' blues / Keys in the mailbox, The.
LP: . . . . **JB 607**

TWO TIMIN' BABY (McVea, Jack & His Door Openers).
Tracks: / New worried life / Houseparty boogie / Listen baby blues / Silver symphony / Frantic boogie / Lonesome blues / Richard gets hitched / Bulgin' eyes / Jam boogie / Slowly goin' crazy blues / Groove juice / Blues with a

feeling / Swing man / Fighting mama blues.
LP: JB 612

McVeigh, Father Joe

SINGS (McVeigh, Father Joe & Friends).
LP: DRL 2011

McVicar (film)

MCVICAR (Film Soundtrack) (See under Daltrey, Roger) (Daltrey, Roger).

McVie, Christine

CHRISTINE MCVIE.
Tracks: / Love will show us how / Challenge / So excited / One in a million / Ask anybody / Got a hold on me / Who's breaming this dream / I'm the one / Keeping secrets / Smile i love for.
LP: K 925059-1

CHRISTINE MCVIE.
Tracks: / Love will show us how / Challenge / So excited / One in a million / Ask anybody / Got a hold on me / Who's dreaming this dream? / I'm the one / Keeping secrets / Smile I live for.
LP: 925059 1
MC: 925059 4

McWilliams, David

DAVID MCWILLIAMS SINGS.
LP: MMLP 2

DAVID MCWILLIAMS VOL 2.
LP: MMLP 10

DAVID MCWILLIAMS VOL 3.
LP: MMLP 11

DON'T DO IT FOR LOVE.
LP: EMC 3208

WOUNDED.
LP: CAR 1001 LP

Mad Axeman

MAD AXEMAN.
LP: SKULL 8329

Mad Daddy's

APES GO WILD.
LP: ROSE 110

MUSIC FOR MEN.
LP: ROSE 71

Mad Dog

MAD DOG.
Tracks: / Falling / Johnny cyclops / It all comes down / Fortune favours the brave / Chill out / Shanghai Joe / Five bucks in New York city / Last great wilderness, The.
LP: STUDLP 1

Mad House

8.
Tracks: / One / Two / Three / Four / Five / Six / Seven / Eight.
LP: 925545 1

16.
Tracks: / Nine / Ten / Eleven / Twelve / Thirteen / Fourteen / Fifteen / Sixteen.
LP: K 925658 1
MC: K 925658 4

Mad Lad Returns

MAD LAD RETURNS (Various artists).
LP: MLP 1984

Mad Max

NIGHT OF PASSION.
Tracks: / Burnin' the stage / Wait for the night / R I P / Drive through the slag / Wild and seventeen / Hearts of fire / Love loaded / Night of passion / Star crossed lovers / Fox on the run.
LP: RR 9666

ROLLIN' THUNDER.
LP: RR 9838

STORMCHILD.
LP: RR 9763

Mad Max (Film)

MAD MAX (Film Soundtrack) (Various artists).
LP: STV 81144

MAD MAX 2 (Film Soundtrack) (Various artists).
Tracks: / Opening titles: *Various artists* / Montage: *Various artists* / Confrontation: *Various artists*/ Marauder's massacre: *Various artists* / Max enters compound: *Various artists* / Feral boy strikes: *Various* artists / Gyro saves Max: *Various artists* / Gyro flight: *Various artists* / Breakout: *Various artists*/ Chase continues, The: *Various artists* / Finale and largo: *Various artists* / End title: *Various artists.*
LP: TER 1016

MAD MAX - BEYOND THE THUNDERDOME (Film soundtrack) (Various artists).
Tracks: / We don't need another hero: *Turner, Tina* / One of the living: *Turner, Tina* / We don't need another hero (inst): *Turner, Tina* / Batertown: *Various artists* / Children, The: *Various artists* / Coming home: *Various artists.*
LP: DOME 1
MC: TCDOME 1
LP: EJ 240380 1
MC: EJ 240380 4

Mad Professor

ADVENTURES OF A DUB SAMPLER, THE.
LP: ARILP 033

AFRICAN CONNECTION.
LP: ARILP 005

BEYOND THE REALMS OF DUB.
LP: ARILP 003

CARIBBEAN TASTE OF TECHNOLOGY.
LP: ARILP 025

DUB ME CRAZY.
LP: ARILP 001

DUB ME CRAZY PART 5.
LP: ARILP 021

DUB ME CRAZY PART 8 (Experiments of the Aural Kind).
LP: ARILP 035
MC: ARILPC 035

DUB ME CRAZY PARTY.
LP: ARILP 0333

FEAST OF YELLOW DUB, A.
MC: RAS 3069C

JAH SHAKA MEETS MAD PROFESSOR AT ARIWA SOUNDS (Mad Professor & Jah Shaka).
LP: SALP 001
LP: SALP 084

LEE PERRY MEETS MAD PROFESSOR IN DUB 1 & 2 (See under Perry, Lee) (Mad Professor & Lee Perry).

MAD PROFESSOR MEETS MAFIA & FLUXY.
LP: ARILP 051

MAD PROFESSOR RECAPTURES PATO BANTON (Mad Professor & Pato Banton).
LP: ARILP 043

NEGUS ROOTS MEETS THE MAD PROFESSOR (Mad Professor & Negus Roots).
LP: NERLP 009

PETER CHEMIST MEETS THE MAD PROFESSOR (See under Chemist, Peter for details).

PROFESSOR CAPTURES PATO BANTON (Mad Professor & Pato Banton).
LP: ARILP 023

PSYCHEDELIC DUB.
LP: ARILP 057

SCHIZOPHRENIC DUB.
LP: ARILP 030

SCIENCE & THE WITCHDOCTOR (Dub me crazy part 9).
Tracks: / Anansi skank / Blue ball fire / Cry of thee old higue / Coming of the obeahe man, The / Witche's brew / Mistaken identity / Natural fact / Jumbie umbrella / Bacoo in the bottle / Bohra seed / Holokoko dub.
LP: ARILP 045

STEPPING IN DUBWISE COUNTRY (Mad Professor & Sandra Cross).
LP: ARILP 031

SWEDISH POLKA (see under Edward II) (Mad Professor & Edward II).

Mad River

MAD RIVER.
Tracks: / Merciful monks / High all the time / Amphetamine gazelle / Eastern light / Wind chimes / War goes on / Julian Hush.
LP: ED 140

PARADISE BAR AND GRILL.
Tracks: / Harfy magnum / Paradise bar and grill / Love's not the way to treat a friend / Leave me stay / Copper plates / Equinoxe / They bought sadness / Revolution's in my pockets / Academy cemetry / Cherokee queen.
MC: CED 188
LP: ED 188

Mad Romeo

LOVE IS THE LEADER.
LP: SYRLP 3
MC: SYRMC 3

Mad Sin

AMPHIGORY.
LP: F 3019

Mad Violets

WORLD OF....
LP: LOLITA 5046

Madagascar

MADAGASIKARA 1 (Various artists).
LP: ORBD 012

MADAGASIKARA 4 (Valihala malazi/ Famous valiha) (Various artists).
Tracks: / Salama 'nareo tompoko o: *Rakotozafy* / Ramanjareo: *Rakotozafy* / O zaza ny fandeha diasa: *Rakotozafy*/ Botofetsy: *Rakotozafy* / Tonga teto lala: *Rakotozafy* / Hitako o: *Rakotozafy* / Mandrosoa lahy mahaeva: *Rakotozafy* / Isa, roa, telo: *Rakotozafy* / Rey lahy, rey lahy: *Rakotozafy* / Varavarankely: *Rakotozafy*/ Sega vaovao valiha malaza: *Rakotozafy* / Mandihiza raha manan' eratra: *Rakotozafy* / Iadiavan janako aho rafozako: *Rakotozafy* / Ny fitiavana raho vao miaraka: *Rakotozafy.*
LP: ORBD 028

MADAGASIKARA VOL.2 (Various artists).
Tracks: / Raha mania any: *Various artists* / Ento rora: *Various artists* / Madirovalo: *Various artists*/ Tsapika 2000: *Various artists* / Totoy tsara: *Various artists* / Sarotra: *Various artists* / Voromby: *Various artists* / Ny any: *Various artists* / Malaza avaratna: *Various artists* / Aza mba manary toky: *Various artists.*
LP: ORBD 013

MAHALEO.
LP: LPP 187

RAINBOW (See under Hyman, Phillis/ Under your spell).

RAINBOW (OLD GOLD) (See under Hyman, Phyllis/Under your spell).

Madagasikara

MADAGASIKARA 3 (Flutemasters) (Madagasikara 3).
Tracks: / Loha Taonan-Diavolana ny Andro / Io Ranomasina 10 / Voahangy A / Voahirana An-Drano Maria/Izy Efa-Bavy / Lalana Afakando / Tovovavy jefijefy / Am Bohimanga / Jijy Lava.
LP: ORBD 027

Madam Marcel

COUPE-CLOUE.
LP: ESP 17902

Madam X

MADAM X.
Tracks: / Madam X / Just that type of girl / I'm weak for you / I wonder / Cherries in the snow / I want your body / Madam X / Flirt / Marry me.
LP: 781 774-1
MC: 781 774-4

WE RESERVE THE RIGHT.
LP: JETLP 242
MC: JETCA 242

Madama Butterfly

MADAMA BUTTERFLY (See under Puccini) (Various artists).

Madame Butterfly

MADAME BUTTERFLY (VIDEO) (see under Puccini (composer)) (Various artists).

Madame Sousatzka

MADAME SOUSATZKA (Film Soundtrack) (Various artists).
LP: VS 5204
MC: VSC 5204

Madame Tussaud

ROCKIN' IN RHYTHM (Madame Tussaud's Dance Orchestra).
Tracks: / Rockin' in rhythm / Black eyed Susan Brown / Jazz cocktail / My bluebird's singing the blues / Mood indigo / I raise my hat / Stevedore stomp / Roll up the carpet / Lightning / You're still in my heart / Wild goose chase / Sophisticated lady / Echoes of the jungle / Old man blues / We'll all go riding on a rainbow / Old fashioned sweethearts / Who walks in when I walk out? / You're gonna lose your gal.
LP: FG 408

Madden, Ciaran (aut)

OUT OF THE RAIN (see under Out of the Rain (bk)) (Cadell, Elizabeth (nar)).

Madden, Danny

THESE ARE THE FACTS OF LIFE.
LP: WX 367
MC: WX 367 C

Madden, David

REGGAE TRUMPETAA '88', THE.
LP: DM 001

Madden, Tom

LITTLE THATCHED CABIN (Madden, Tom/Frank Warren).
LP: INC 7727

Maddern, Eric

NGATIJIRRI SUNRISE (Maddern, Eric & Calum MacColl).
LP: NGATI 84

Maddo, U.U.

TEENAGER IN LOVE.
LP: JLP 002

Maddocks, John

GOOD VIBRATIONS (Maddocks, John & Jazz Maniacs).
LP: FHR 077

JUST GONE (Maddocks, John Jazzmen).
Tracks: / Come back sweet papa / Blue turning grey over you / Just gone / St. Philips street / Breakdown / Flow gently sweet Afton / Black bottom stomp / Carry me back to old Virginny / Frog-I-more rag / Chimes blues / Norwegian wood / Blue blood blues / I can't dance.
LP: FHR 091

Maddox Bros.

FAMILY FOLKS (Maddox Bros. & Rose).
Tracks: / Tall man / I'll go stepping too / One two three four Anyplace Road / Did you ever come home (Previously unissued.) / I wonder if I can lose the blues this way / Marry me again / Burrito Joe / I'm a little red Caboose / Coquita of Laredo / On Mexico's beautiful shores / I'll make sweet love to you / Kiss me quick and go / Little Willie waltz / Let this be the last time / Wish you would / Beautiful bouquet, A / Paul Bunyan love / I gotta go get my baby / Let me love you / No more time / I've got four big brothers (to look after me) / Old black choo choo / Ugly and slouchy / Death of rock and roll, The / Stop whistlin' wolf / Love is strange / Short life of it's troubles, A / Empty mansions / Looky there over there / You won't believe this / I'll find her / No help wanted.
LP: BFX 15083

MADDOX BROS & ROSE ON THE AIR VOL.2 (Maddox Bros. & Rose).
LP: ARHOOLIE 5033

MADDOX BROS & ROSE ON THE AIR VOL.1 (1940 & 1945).
LP: ARHOOLIE 5028

MADDOX BROTHERS & ROSE VOL.1 (1946-1951) (Maddox Bros. & Rose).
LP: ARHOOLIE 5016
MC: C 209

MADDOX BROTHERS & ROSE VOL.2 (1946-1951) (Maddox Bros. & Rose).
LP: ARHOOLIE 5017
MC: C 222

ROCKIN' ROLLIN' (Maddox Bros. & Rose).
Tracks: / Paul Bunyan love / I gotta go get my baby / Let me love you / No more time / I've got four big brothers (to look after me) / My black choo choo / Ugly and slouchy / Death of rock and roll, The / Stop whistlin' wolf / Love is strange / Short life of its troubles, A (Previously unissued.) / Empty mansions / Looky there, over there / You won't believe this / I'll find her / No help wanted.
LP: BFX 15076

Maddox, Rose

BEAUTIFUL BOUQUET, A (Maddox, Rose & Vern Williams).
LP: ARHOOLIE 5030

CALIFORNIA ROSE.
Tracks: / Alone with you / Let those brown eyes smile at me / If you see me baby / Long black limousine / From a beggar to a queen / Stop the world / Curly Joe from Idaho / When the sun goes down / My life has been a pleasure / Johnny's last kiss / White lightning / Long journey home / Stand up fool / Down to the river / Somebody told me / I want to live again / Silver threads and golden needles / Bluebird let me tag along / Lonely street / Gambler's love.
LP: SEE 251

GLORYBOUND TRAIN.
Tracks: / That glorybound train / Drifting too far from the shore / Empty mansion / Smoke, fire & brimstone / Wait a little longer please Jesus / I'll reap my harvest in Heaven / This world is not my home / Great speckled bird, The / Kneel at the cross / When I take my vacation in heaven / How beautiful Heaven must be / Will the circle be unbroken.
LP: HAT 3079
MC: HATC 3079

ONE ROSE, THE.
Tracks: / Honky tonkin' / Why don't you haul off and love me / Philadelphia lawyer / Move it on over / On the banks of the old pontchartain / Whoa sailor / Sally let your bangs hang down / At the first fall of snow / Live and let live / Tramp on the street / Chocolate ice cream cone / Gathering flowers for the masters....
LP: HAT 3056
MC: HATC 3056

QUEEN OF THE WEST.
LP: VR 010
LP: V 010
MC: V 010C

ROCKABILLY REUNION (Maddox, Rose/Glenn, Glen).
Tracks: / Hey little dreamboat / I gotta go get my baby / Looky there / My little baby / Over there / Move it on over / Brown eyes / I saw the light / Will the circle be unbroken / Jim Dandy / I got a woman / I'm glad my baby's gone away / Jack and Jill boogie / Everybody's movin' / One cup of coffee.
LP: MFLP 067

ROSE MADDOX & VERN WILLIAMS BAND (Maddox, Rose & Vern Williams).
LP: ARHOOLIE 5024
MC: C 5024

SINGS BLUE GRASS.
LP: HAT 3029
MC: HATC 3029

Made In Belgium

MADE IN BELGIUM.
LP: AS 8902

Made In Britain

MADE IN BRITAIN (Various artists).
2LP: DPA 3093

Made In Heaven (film)

MADE IN HEAVEN (Film Soundtrack) (Various artists).
LP: 960729.1
MC: 960729.4

Madison

BEST IN SHOW.
Tracks: / Oh rendezvous / Carry on / Hotel party / Drama / Shine / Give it back (remixed version) / Can't take it / World wide man / Out of the bunker / Mental masturbation.
LP: SNTF 960

Madison, Art

LET IT FLOW.
LP: 7567820041
MC: 7567820044

Madness

7.
Tracks: / Cardiac arrest / Shut up / Sign of the times / Missing you / Mrs. Hutchinson / Tomorrows dream / Grey day / Pac-a-mac / Promises, promises / Benny bullfrog / When dawn arrives / Opium eaters, The / Day on the town.
LP: SEEZ 39
MC: ZSEEZ 39
LP: OVED 135
MC: OVEDC 135

ABSOLUTELY.
Tracks: / Baggy trousers / Embarrassment / E.R.N.I.E. / Close escape / Not home today / On the beat Pete / Solid gone / Take it or leave it / Shadow of fear / Disappear / Overdone / In the rain / You said / Return of the Los Palmas 7.
LP: SEEZ 29
MC: ZSEEZ 29
LP: OVED 134
MC: OVEDC 134

COMPLETE MADNESS.
Tracks: / Embarrassment / Shut up / My girl / Baggy trousers / It must be love / Prince, The / Bed and breakfast man / Night boat to Cairo / House of fun / One step beyond / Cardiac arrest / Grey day / Take it or leave it / In the city / Madness / Return of the Los Palmas 7.
LP: HITTV 1
MC: ZHITV 1

IT'S MADNESS.
Tracks: / House of fun / Don't look back / Wings of a dove / Young and the old, The / My girl / Stepping into line / Baggy trousers / Business, The / Embarrassment / One's second thoughtlessness / Grey day / Memories / It must be love / Deceives the eye / Driving in my car / Animal farm.
LP: VVIP 107
MC: VVIPC 107

KEEP MOVING.
Tracks: / Keep moving / Michael Caine / Turning blue / One better day / March of the gherkins / Waltz into mischief / Brand new beat / Victoria gardens / Samantha / Time for tea / Prospects / Give me a reason.
LP: SEEZ 53
MC: ZSEEZ 53
LPPD: PSEEZ 53
LP: OVED 191
MC: OVEDC 191

MAD NOT MAD.
Tracks: / I'll compete / Yesterday's men / Uncle Sam / White heat / Mad not mad / Sweetest girl, The / Burning the boats / Tears you can't hide / Time / Coldest day.
LP: JZLP 1
MC: JZMC 1
LP: OVED 232
MC: OVEDC 232

ONE STEP BEYOND.
Tracks: / One step beyond / My girl / Night boat to Cairo / Believe me / Land of hope and glory / Prince, The / Tarzan's nuts / In the middle of the night / Bed and breakfast man / Razor blade alley / Swan lake / Rockin' in AB / Mummy's boy / Chipmunks are go.
MC: ZSEEZ 17
LP: SEEZ 17
LP: OVED 133
MC: OVEDC 133

RISE AND FALL.
Tracks: / Rise and fall / Tomorrow's just another day / Blue skinned beast / Primose hill / Mr. Speaker gets the word / Sunday morning / Our house / Tiptoes / New Delhi / That face / Calling cards / Are you coming (with me) / Madness.
LP: OVED 190
MC: OVEDC 190
LP: SEEZ 46
MC: ZSEEZ 46

UTTER MADNESS.
Tracks: / Our house / Driving in my car / Michael Caine / Wings of a dove / Yesterday's men / Tomorrow's just another day / I'll compete / (Waiting for) the ghost train / Uncle Sam / Sun and the rain, The / Sweetest girl, The / One better day / Victoria gardens.
LP: JZLP 2
MC: JZMC 2
LP: OVED 287
MC: OVEDC 287

Madness, The

MADNESS, THE.
Tracks: / Nail down the days / What's that / I pronounce you / Oh / In wonder / Song in red / Nightmare nightmare / Thunder and lightning / Beat the bride / Gabriel's horn / 11th hour (CD only) / Be good boy (CD only) / Flashings (CD only) / 4BF (CD only).
LP: V 2507
MC: TCV 2507
MC: OVEDC 378

Madonna

BEST OF AND THE REST OF, THE.
Tracks: / Wild dancing (extended dance mix) / Cosmic climb (extended dance mix) / We are the gods / Wild dancing / Cosmic climb.
MC: ARLC 1005

COSMIC CLIMB (see under Von Wernherr).

EARLY YEARS, THE.
LP: RRLP 118
MC: RRLC 118

FIRST ALBUM, THE.
Tracks: / Lucky star / Borderline / Burning up / I know it / Holiday / Think of me / Physical attraction / Everybody.
LP: WX 22

GIVE IT TO ME.
LP: RRLP 144

I'M BREATHLESS.
LP: WX 351
MC: WX 351 C

IMMACULATE COLLECTION (Best of Madonna).
Tracks: / Holiday / Lucky star / Borderline / Like a virgin / Material girl / Crazy for you / Into the groove / Live to tell / Papa don't preach / Open your heart / La Isla Bonita / Like a prayer / Express yourself / Cherish / Vogue / Justify my love / Rescue me.
LP: WX 370
MC: WX 370C

IMMACULATE CONVERSATION, THE.
MC: MBAK 6021

IN THE BEGINNING (Madonna & Otto Van Wernherr).
LP: KNOB 1
MC: MCKNOB 1

LIKE A PRAYER.
Tracks: / Like a prayer / Love song / Promise to try / Dear Jessie / Keep it together / Act of contrition / Express yourself / Till death do us part / Cherish / Oh Father / Spanish eyes.
LP: WX 239
MC: WX 239C

LIKE A VIRGIN.
Tracks: / Material girl / Shoo-bee-doo / Pretender / Stay / Angel / Like a virgin / Over and over / Love don't live here anymore / Into the groove / Dress you up.
LP: WX 20
MC: WX 20C
LP: 925157
LPPD: WX 20P

MADONNA: INTERVIEW PICTURE DISC.
LPPD: BAK 2104
LPPD: BAK 2042

MUSIC AND MEDIA INTERVIEW PICTURE DISCS.
LPPD: MAD 1001

TIME TO DANCE.
LP: REPLAY 3007

TRUE BLUE.
Tracks: / Papa dont preach / Open your heart / Love makes the world go round / Jimmy, Jimmy / La Isla Bonita / True blue / Where's the party / Live to tell.
LP: WX 54

YOU CAN DANCE.
Tracks: / Spotlight / Holiday / Everybody / Physical attraction / Over and over / Into the groove / Where's the party / Spotlight (dub) / Holiday (dub) / Into the groove (dub) / Over and over (dub).
LP: WX 76
MC: WX 76 C

Madore, Michel

LA CHAMBRE BUPTIALE.
LP: 910007

Madselin

MADSELIN (see Lofts, Norah) (Rosalind Lloyd).

Mady, Kasse

FODE.
LP: STERNS 1025
MC: STC 1025

KELA TRADITION.
LP: STERNS 1034
MC: STC 1034

Mae, Daisy

THELMA COOPER/DAISY MAE & HER HEP CATS (see under Cooper, Thelma) (Mae, Daisy & Hepcats).

Maelen, Jimmy

BEATS WORKIN'.
LP: EPC 84211

Maelstrom

STEP ONE.
LP: EM 94071

Maestro Orchestra

PERSONAL CHOICE.
LP: MTS 14

Maetsro Fresh-Wes

SYMPHONY IN EFFECT.
Tracks: / Drop the needle / MC's my piece, The / I'm showin' you / Private symphony / Maestro, The / Fortissmo / Untouchable / Ltd's on the wheels / Let your backbone slide / Just swingin' / Tear it up.
LP: HF 12
MC: HFC 12

Maffay, Peter

LONG SHADOWS.
Tracks: / Wolfe / Hund des krieges (Dog of wars) / Wenn ketten deine antwort sind / Nie wieder sieger sein / Weit von mir / Du bist nie der kassierer (You're not the cashier) / Unter sternen / Spiel ohne ziel / Schiff in der nacht (Ship in the night) / Viel zu spat / Sperr mich nicht ein / Versuch's doch mal mit mir / Zehn stunden (Ten hours) / Ringelpietz / Kalter krieg (Cold war) / Bruder (Brother) / Lange schatten (Long shadows) / Leg nich nicht auf / Freunde (Friend) / Nochmal / Spiel um deine seele.
2LP: 6.28700
MC: 4.28700

SUN IN THE NIGHT.
Tracks: / Carambolage / Spuren einer Nacht / Wo komm ich hier, wo geh ich hin? / Tausend traume weit / Rock & roll / So bist du / Sonne in der nacht / Fur immer / Eiszeit / Mensch aus Stahl / Liebe wird verboten / etc.
MC: 4.26654

Maffia Mr Huws

DA NI'M YN RHAN.
LP: SAIN 1307A

YR OCHOR ARALL.
LP: SAIN 1286M

Mafia, Leroy

ONCE UPON A TIME (See under King Kong) (Mafia, Leroy & King Kong).

Magadini, Pete

BONES BLUES (Magadini, Pete, Quartet).
LP: 4004

THREE IS COMPANY (see Galloway, Jim) (Magadini, Pete/Jim Galloway/Dick Wellstood).

Magam

SUONANDO L'ALLEGREZZA.
LP: RD 008

Magazine

AFTER THE FACT.
Tracks: / Shot by both sides / Rhythm of cruelty / You never knew me / Back to nature / Song from under the floorboards, A / Light pours out of me, The / Motorcade / About the weather / Feed the enemy / This poison.
LP: VM 1
MC: VMC 1

CORRECT USE OF SOAP, THE.
Tracks: / Because you're frightened / Model worker / I'm a party / You never knew me / Philadelphia / I want to burn again / Thank you (falletinme be mice elf agin) / Sweetheart contract / Stuck / Song from under the floorboards, A.
LP: OVED 116
LP: V 2156
MC: OVED 116C

MAGIC, MURDER AND THE WEATHER.
Tracks: / About the weather / So lucky / Honeymoon killers, The / Vigilance / Come alive / Great man's secrets / This poison / Naked eye / Suburban Rhonda / Garden, The.
LP: V 2200
LP: OVED 141
MC: OVEDC 141

PLAY.
Tracks: / Give me everything / Song from under the floorboards, A / Permafrost / Light pours out of me, The / Model worker / Parade / Thank you (falletinme be mice elf agin) / Because you're frightened / Twenty years ago / Definitive gaze.
LP: OVED 117
LP: V 2184
MC: OVEDC 117

REAL LIFE.
Tracks: / Definitive gaze / My tulpa / Shot by both sides / Recoil / Burst / Motorcade / Great beautician in the sky, The / Light pours out of me, The / Parade.
LP: OVED 62
LP: V 2100

SECONDHAND DAYLIGHT.
Tracks: / Feed the enemy / Rhythm of cruelty / Cut-out shapes / Talk to the body / I wanted your heart / Thin air, The / Back to nature / Believe that I understand / Permafrost.
LP: OVED 84
MC: OVEDC 84
LP: V 2121

Magdalen College

ENGLISH ANTHEM, (THE) (c. 1540-1600) (Magdalen College Choir Oxford).
Tracks: / O Lord, turn Thy wrath / Teach me, O Lord / Exalt Thyself, O God / Out of the deep / Nolo mortem peccatoris / Lord's prayer, The / Hide not thou thy face / Blessed art Thou / I will exalt Thee / I call and cry to thee / Purge me, O Lord / O Lord, give thy Holy Spirit / Lord's prayer, The.
LP: ACA 543

ENGLISH ANTHEM, (THE) (c. 1900-1930) (Magdalen College Choir Oxford).
Tracks: / Blessed city, heavenly Salem / Let all mortal flesh keep silence / Give us the wings of faith / Greater love hath no man / My soul, there is a country / O Thou, the Central Orb / Hail, gladdening light / Expectans expectavi / Glorious and powerful God.
LP: ACA 547

NOW THE HOLLY (Magdalen College Choir Oxford).
LP: ABBEY 653

Magee, Len

LEN MAGEE.
LP: DOVE 2

LOVE IS THE ANSWER.
LP: PC 441

ONCE UPON A WINTER.
LP: PC 442

PRAYER SONG VOL.1.
LP: DOVE 42

PRAYER SONG VOL.2.
LP: DOVE 43

PRESENCE OF YOUR SPIRIT.
LP: DOVE 6

PRICE OF PEACE, THE.
LP: DOVE 24

Mageean, J & A.

MAGEEAN/FITZSIMMONS (Mageean, J. & A.A. Fitzsimmons).
LP: GVR 223

Mageean, Jim

CAPSTAN BAR, THE.
Tracks: / I'm bound away / Mobile Bay / Yeller gals / Essequibo River / Roll the cotton down / Cheer'ly man / Ja ja ja / Hurrah sing fare ye well / Come roll me over / Roll the woodpile down / Ranzo Ray / Capstan Bar, The / Serafina / One more day / Rolling home.
LP: DIN 303

MAKE THE RAFTERS ROAR (Mageean, Jim & Johnny Collins).

Tracks: / Randy Dandy / Rosabella / Ye mariners all / London river / So far from home / Lavender blue / Last shanty, The / All the good times / Round the corner Sally / Old Moke / Napoleon Bonaparte / Died for love / Drinking song / Miners lifeguard / New railroad / Down where the drunkards roll.
LP: . . . . SFA 103

OF SHIPS AND MEN.
Tracks: / Malarkey, The / Gay head, The / Royal Oak, The / Albutina, The / Amazon, The / Ebeneezer, The / Billy Riley / Andrew Ross / John Smith / Ben Backstay / Whailing Johnny / Yer old shipmate.
LP: . . . . GVR 203

STRONTRACE (Mageean, Jim & Johnny Collins).
LP: . . . . GVR 226

Maggie & ...

MAGGIE & TENNESSEE EXPRESS (Maggie & Tennessee Express).
Tracks: / Will you love me tomorrow / Last train to Memphis / Teddy bear song / Little peace, A / Bonnie Shetland / Rhythm of the rain / Don't forget to remember me / Born to be with you / Tennessee Express / Seasons of your love / I'll get over you / Foolin' around / Amanda / Single girl / Language of love.
MC: . . . . CMP 021

Maggie May

MAGGIE MAY (Original London cast) (Various artists).
Tracks: / Overture: *Various artists* / Ballad of the Liver bird: *Various artists* / Lullaby: *Various artists* / I love a man: *Various artists* / Casey: *Various artists* / Dey don't do dat t'day: *Various artists* / I told you so: *Various artists* / Right of way: *Various artists* / Land of promises, The: *Various artists* / Maggie May: *Various artists* / Stroll on: *Various artists* / Leave her, Johnny leave her: *Various artists* / I told you so: *Various artists* / Shine, you swine: *Various artists* / World's a lovely place, The: *Various artists* / I'm me: *Various artists* / It's yourself: *Various artists* / We don't all wear d'same size boots: *Various artists* / Finale: *Various artists.*
LP: . . . . TER 1046
MC: . . . . ZCTER 1046

Magic

MAGIC.
LP: . . . . BLP 002

Magic Bastards

TOTALLI AGENST.
LP: . . . . BAST 2
MC: . . . . BAST 2C

Magic Circle

MAGIC CIRCLE RECORD (featuring Paul Daniels) (Various artists).
LP: . . . . TECLP 002

Magic Flute

MAGIC FLUTE (Various artists).
LP: . . . . STV 81179

MAGIC FLUTE (BERGMAN) (VIDEO) (see under Mozart (composer)) (Various artists).

MAGIC FLUTE (GLYNDEBOURNE) (VIDEO) (see under Mozart (composer)) (Various artists).

MOZART,WOLGANG AMADEUS (VIDEO) (See under Mozart (Composer)) (Mozart (composer)).

Magic Lady

MAGIC LADY.
Tracks: / Betcha can't lose / Love overdrive / Misty eyed / Yes I'm ready / Hit and run / Cupid / Wait a minute / Paradise / Summer love.
LP: . . . . NL 72637
MC: . . . . NK 72637

Magic Machines

DANNY THE DUMPER TRUCK.
MC: . . . . LL 41 8030 4

MAGGIE THE MECHANICAL DIGGER.
MC: . . . . LL 41 8031 4

SIMON THE CEMENT MIXER.
MC: . . . . LL 41 8029 4

Magic Moments At..

ACIDIC DREAMS WITH SISTER JODY (Magic Moments At Twilight Time).
2LP: . . . . MMATT 23/24

EXPERIMENTAL TWILIGHT AT TRANSFORMATION TIME (Magic Moments At Twilight Time).
2LP: . . . . MMATT 25/26

WILLY THE OAK TREE'S 20TH BIRTHDAY PARTY... (Magic Moments At Twilight Time).
MCSET: . . . . MMATT 21/22

Magic Muscle

PIPE, THE ROAD, THE GRID, THE.
Tracks: / I can travel anywhere / Here and now / Long hard road / Spring green blues / Schoolgirl loves / Woodcarver man / Large transit van / You better see / Desert sands / Feel it fear it.
LP: . . . . TOCK 9

Magic Mushroom Band

BOMSHAMKAR.
Tracks: / Brain machine / Nothing sacred / Open arms / Who can say? / Satisfied / Reign on you / Invasion of the flyin' wotsit thingies / Round and round / Within U.
LP: . . . . AFT 3

Magic Mushroom Room

EYES OF THE ANGEL.
LP: . . . . AFT 6

Magic Of Brazil

MAGIC OF BRAZIL (Various artists).
LP: . . . . NTS 209

Magic of Dance

MAGIC OF DANCE Magic of Dance (Various artists).
LP: . . . . REP 363
MC: . . . . ZCH 363

Magic of Lassie

MAGIC OF LASSIE (film soundtrack) (Various artists).
Tracks: / When you're loved: *Various artists* / There'll be other Friday nights: *Various artists* / Brass rings and daydreams: *Various artists* / Nobody's property: *Various artists* / I can't say goodbye: *Various artists* / Banjo song: *Various artists* / Rose is not a rose, A: *Various artists* / Travelin' music: *Various artists* / That hometown feeling: *Various artists* / Thanksgiving prayer: *Various artists* / Nobody's property: *Various artists.*
LP: . . . . SHM 992
MC: . . . . HSC 370

Magic Of The...

MAGIC OF THE FAIRGROUND ORGAN (Ruth Fair Organ (1912)).
LP: . . . . CAL 1511

Magic Pan Flutes

MAGIC OF THE PAN FLUTE.
LP: . . . . ADL 526
MC: . . . . ADK 526

Magic Quern

MAGIC QUERN, THE (Stories from Barra in Gaelic & English).
MC: 30-463

Magic Rocking Horse..

MAGIC ROCKING HORSE Rubble 14 (Various artists).
Tracks: / If (would it turn out wrong): *Esprit de corps* / Sueno: *Truth* / Little bit of Shangri-la: *Our Plastic Dream* / I can show you: *Rupert's People* / Baby I need you: *Curiosity Shoppe* / Wind, The: *Groove* / Castle has fallen: *Ghost* / June: *Nirvana* / Magic rocking horse: *Pinkerton's Colours* / Jabberwocky: *Duveen, Boeing & the Beautiful Soup* / Dream on my mind: *Rupert's People* / Love years coming: *Strawberry* Children / You got me high: *Science Poption* / Encapsulated marigold: *Our Plastic Dream* / Grounded: *Syn* / Ma-mari-huana: *Sub.*
LP: . . . . KIRI 106

Magic Sam

BLACK MAGIC.
LP: . . . . DS 620
LP: . . . . DL 620

CALLING ALL BLUES (See under Hooker, Earl) (Magic Sam & Earl Hooker).

CHIEFLY WELLS (see Wells, Junior) (Magic Sam/Junior Wells).

EASY BABY.
Tracks: / All your love / Everything gonna be alright / Look watcha done / Easy baby / All my whole life / Love me with a feeling / Every night about this time / She belongs to me / Out of bad luck / Roll your moneymaker / Call me if you need me / Magic rocker / All night long / 21 days in jail / Love me this way / My love is your love / Mr. Charlie / Blue light boogie / You don't have to work / Square dance rock (part 1) / Square dance rock (part 2).
LP: . . . . CRB 1108

LATE GREAT MAGIC SAM, THE.
LP: . . . . LR 42.014

LEGACY, THE.
LP: . . . . DL 651

LIVE AT THE ANN ARBOR BLUES FESTIVAL & ALEX CLUB 1963 & 1969.
2LP: . . . . DL 645/646

MAGIC ROCKER Cobra 1957-8 (Magic Sam & Shaky Jake).
LP: . . . . FLY 561

MAGIC TOUCH (Magic Sam & Shaky Jake).
LP: . . . . BM 9003

WEST SIDE SOUL (Magic Sam Blues Band).
LP: . . . . DS 615
LP: . . . . DL 615

Magic Shop...

MAGIC SHOP AND THE RED ROOM, THE (See under Wells, H.G.).

Magic Slim

SON OF A GUN (Magic Slim & The Teardrops).
LP: . . . . R 2618

Magic Sounds

MAGIC SOUNDS OF THE PIPES (Various artists).
LP: . . . . MFP 5615

Magic Strings

FLOWERS.
LP: . . . . ISST 112

Magic sword

MAGIC SWORD, THE (Various artists).
Tracks: / Magic sword, The: *Various artists* / Inchling: *Various artists* / Invisible man, The: *Various artists* / Old man and the sparrow, The: *Various artists* / Urashima and the turtle: *Various artists* / Mouse's husband, The: *Various artists* / Farmer and his dog, The: *Various artists.*
MC: . . . . ANV 633

Magic Toyshop

MAGIC TOYSHOP, THE (Film soundtrack) (Various artists).
LP: . . . . TER 1138
MC: . . . . ZCTER 1138

Magic Tub

ZOMBI.
LP: . . . . PG 87105

Magical Mystery Tour

MAGICAL MYSTERY TOUR (FILM SOUNDTRACK) (See under Beatles).

Magical Strings

ABOVE THE TOWER.
LP: . . . . FF 360

ON THE BURREN.
LP: . . . . FF 416

SPRINGTIDE.
LP: . . . . FF 282

Magical Tour...

MAGICAL TOUR OF MECHANICAL MUSIC, VOL. 2.
LP: . . . . GRS 1147

MAGICAL TOUR OF MECHANICAL MUSIC, VOL.1.
LP: . . . . GRS 1146

Magician

MAGICIAN.
LP: . . . . HO 501

Magma

ATTAHK.
Tracks: / Last seven minutes, The (1970-71, phase II) / Spiritual (negro song) / Rinde (Eastern song) / Lirik necronomicus kant / Maahnt / Dondai (to an eternal love) / Nono.
LP: . . . . LIK 26
MC: . . . . TCLIK 26

MAGMA LIVE.
Tracks: / Kohntark (part 1) / Kohntark (part 2) / Kobah / Lihns / Khat / Mekanik zain.
2LP: . . . . TOM 2-7008
2LP: . . . . LIKD 31
MCSET: . . . . TCLIKD 31
2LP: . . . . JARO 4122/23

MERCI.
LP: . . . . JARO 4120

OFFERING.
2LP: . . . . JARO 4129/30

UDU WUDU.
LP: . . . . TOM 6001

UDU WUDU.
Tracks: / Udu wudu / Weidorje / Troller tanz (ghost dance) / Soleil d'ork (ork' sun) / Zombies / De futura.
LP: . . . . LIK 18
MC: . . . . TCLIK 18

Magna Carta

ONE TO ONE.
Tracks: / Tiger's eyes / Evergreen / Love on the spinning wheel / Sure don't bother me / Fooled by a promise / Rings around the Moon / Loving with a woman / Every time / Rhythm of life / Long distance / Love in our time.
LP: . . . . TMB 118
MC: . . . . TMBC 118

SEASONS.
Tracks: / Airport song / Autumn song / Elizabethan / Epilogue / Give me no goodbye / Goin' my way / Road song / Prologue / Ring of stones / Scarecrow / Spring poem / Spring song / Winter song.
LP: 6381 082
MC: 7215 082
LP: 6360 003

SPOTLIGHT ON MAGNA CARTA.
2LP: 6625 031

Magnante, Charles

ACCORDION ENCORES.
Tracks: / Minute waltz / Granada / Dance of the dwarfs / I know that you know / Beer barrel polka / Pavan & Ronda / Perpetual motion / Italian medley / Waltz allegro / Waltz in B flat / Hora staccato / In a mist / Bach goes to town / Durand waltz / Reflections / Clarinet polka.
MC: . . . . MRC 1001

CHARLES MAGNANTE, VIRTUOSO.
Tracks: / Marriage of Figaro / Piano concerto in B flat min / Blue Danube / Voices of spring / Bouree / Prelude in G minor / Capricco / Italian / Waltz in C sharp min / Prelude in E minor / Dance of the reed flutes / Song of India.
MC: . . . . MRC 1000

Magne, Michael

ELEMENT NO.1 (La terre).
LP: 900587

EMMANUELLE 4 (See under Emmanuelle (film)).

Magnetic Fields

DISTANT PLASTIC TREES.
Tracks: / Railroad boy / Smoke signals / You love to fail / Kings / Babies falling / Living in an abandoned firehouse with you / Tarheel boy / Falling in love with the wolfboy / Josephine / 100.00 fireflies / Plant white roses.
MC: . . . . RFC 3

Magnetics

ROCKABILLY FOOLS.
LP: . . . . ROLL 25

Magnificent

HIT AND RUN.
LP: . . . . LINK LP 027

SKINS 'N' PUNKS VOL 3 (See under Glory) (Magnificent/Glory).

Magnificent Obsession

MAGNIFICENT OBSESSION (Film Soundtrack) (Various artists).
LP: . . . . STV 81118

Magnificent Seven

MAGNIFICENT SEVEN / RETURN OF THE SEVEN (Film soundtrack) (Various artists).
Tracks: / Magnificent Seven, The: *Various artists* / Bandidos: *Various artists* / Return of the seven: *Various* artists / Defeat: *Various artists* / Mariachis de Mexico: *Various artists* / El toro: *Various artists* / Journey, The: *Various artists* / Council: *Various artists* / Petra's declaration: *Various artists* / In the trap: *Various artists* / Battle: *Various artists* / Finale: *Various artists.*
LP: . . . . EG 2605811
MC: . . . . EG 2605814
LP: . . . . SLS 50171

Magnificents

15 COOL JEWELS (Magnificents & The Rhythm Aces).
LP: . . . . SS 8030

Magnolia Jazz Band

MAGNOLIA JAZZ BAND.
LP: . . . . SOS 1016
LP: . . . . GHB 220

SHAKE THAT THING (Magnolia Jazz 5 & Jimmy Mazzy).
LP: . . . . SOS 1137

Magnum

ANTHOLOGY - MAGNUM.
Tracks: / In the beginning / Lords of chaos / Kingdom of madness / Bringer, The / Greta adventures / Firebird / Foolish heart / Stayin' alive / If I could live forever / Reborn (live) / Changes (live) / Walking the straight line / We all play the game / Spirit, The / Prise, The / Vicious companions / Word, The / Hit and run / So far away.
2LP: . . . . RAWLP 007
MC: . . . . RAWTC 007

CHASE THE DRAGON.
LP: . . . . JETLP 235
MC: . . . . JETCA 235
LP: . . . . WKFMLP 112
MC: . . . . WKFMMC 112
LPPD: . . . . WKFMPD 112

COLLECTION: MAGNUM.
2LP: . . . . CCSLP 272

MC: . . . . CCSMC 272

ELEVENTH HOUR, THE.
Tracks: / Prize, The / Great disaster, The / Viscious companions / One night of passion / Word, The / Road to paradise.
LP: . . . . JET LP 240
MC: . . . . JETCA 240
LP: . . . . WKFMLP 111
MC: . . . . WKFMMC 111
LPPD: . . . . WKFMPD 111

FOUNDATION.
LPS: . . . . WKFMBX 145
MCSET: . . . . WKFMBXC 145

GOODNIGHT L.A..
Tracks: / Rockin' chair / Only a memory / Matter of survival / Heartbroke and busted / No way out / Born to be king / Mama / Reckless man / What kind of love is this / Shoot / Cry for you.
LP: 8435681
MC: 8435684

INVASION-MAGNUM LIVE.
LP: . . . . RRLP 113
MC: . . . . RRLC 113

KINGDOM OF MADNESS.
LP: . . . . JETLP 210
MC: . . . . JETCA 210
LP: . . . . CLALP 126
LP: . . . . WKFMLP 118
MC: . . . . WKFMMC 118
MC: . . . . CLAMC 126
LPPD: . . . . WKFMPD 118

MAGNUM II.
Tracks: / Great adventure / Changes / Battle, The / If I could live forever / Reborn / So cold the night / Foolish heart / Stayin' alive / Firebird / All of my life / In the beginning / Baby rock me / Universe / Kingdom of madness / All that is real / Bringer, The / Invasion / Lords of Chaos / All come together.
LP: . . . . CLALP 125
LP: . . . . JETLP 222
MC: . . . . JETCA 222
LP: . . . . WKFMLP 119
MC: . . . . WKFMMC 119
MC: . . . . CLAMC 125
LPPD: . . . . WKFMPD 119

MARAUDER.
Tracks: / If I could live forever / Battle, The / Foolish heart / In the beginning / Reborn / Changes / So cold the night / Lords of chaos.
LP: . . . . CLALP 124
LP: . . . . JETLP 230
MC: . . . . JETCA 230
MC: . . . . CLAMC 124

MIRADOR.
Tracks: / Just like an arrow (Only on CD.) / Soldier of the line / Changes / Sacred hour / Great adventure / Lights burned out, The / In the beginning (Only on CD.) / How far Jerusalem (Only on CD.) / Spirit, The / Word, The / Prize, The / Kingdom of madness / If I could live forever / Lords of chaos (Only on CD.) / Storyteller's night (Only on CD.).
MC: . . . . WKFMMC 106
LP: . . . . WKFMLP 106
LPPD: . . . . WKFMPD 106

MUSIC AND MEDIA INTERVIEW PICTURE DISC.
LPPD: . . . . MM 1241

NIGHTRIDING: MAGNUM.
Tracks: / Invasion / Kingdom of madness / All of my life / Great adventure / Prize, The / Back to Earth / Firebird / Changes / Battle, The / Road to Paradise.
MC: . . . . KNMC 10009
LP: . . . . KNLP 10009

ON A STORYTELLERS NIGHT.
Tracks: / How far Jerusalem / Just like an arrow / Before first light / On a storytellers night / Les morts dansant / Endless love / Two hearts / Steal your heart / All England / Last dance.
LP: . . . . WKFMLP 34
MC: . . . . WKFMMC 34
LPPD: . . . . WKFMHP 34
LP: . . . . PACK 1
LPPD: . . . . WKFMPD 34
LP: . . . . WKFMGP 34

SPIRIT, THE (Live).
2LP: 5111691
MCSET: 5111694

VIGILANTE.
Tracks: / Lonely nights / Need a lot of love / Sometime love / Midnight (you won't be sleeping) / Red on the highway / Holy rider / When the world comes down / Vigilante / Backstreet kid.
LP: . . . . POLD 5198
MC: . . . . POLDC 5198

VINTAGE MAGNUM/THE ELEVENTH HOUR.
Tracks: / Back to earth / Hold back your love / Long days black nights / Lonesome star, The / Everybody needs / Changes (studio remix) / All of my life / Kingdom of madness / Invasion / Great adventure / Prize, The / Breakdown / Great disaster, The / Vicious companions / So far away / Hit and run / One night of passion / Word, The / Young and precious souls / Road to Paradise.
MC: . . . . TFOMC 1
2LP: . . . . TFOLP 1

WINGS OF HEAVEN.
Tracks: / C'est la vie (On Ltd edition picture disc only.).
LP: . . . . POLD 5221
MC: . . . . POLDC 5221
LPPD: . . . . POLDP 5221

Magnum Band

LA SEULE DIFFERENCE.
LP: . . . . AP 190

Magnum Force

SHARE MY LOVE.
LP: . . . . BRLP 1002
LP: . . . . LPBR 1002

Magnum Mysterium

MAGNUM MYSTERIUM (Various artists).
2LP: . . . . LP 1635188
MCSET: . . . . MC 1635188

Magnum, Oliver

OLIVER MAGNUM.
LP: 089 809

Magnus Powermouse

MAGNUS POWERMOUSE (see under King-Smith, Dick) (King-Smith, Dick).

Magnusson, Bob

REVELATION (Magnusson, Bob Quintet).
LP: . . . . DS 804

ROAD WORK AHEAD (Magnusson, Bob Quartet).
LP: . . . . DS 824

SONG FOR JANET LEE (Magnusson, Bob Quintet).
Tracks: / Song for Janet Lee / Waltz you saved, The / Poet, The / When it comes to pass / Peace of mine / Double play (a pitcher's delight).
LP: . . . . DS 912
MC: . . . . DSC 912

TWO GENERATIONS OF MUSIC (Magnusson, Bob Classical Jazz Chamber).
LP: . . . . TR 528

Magpie

IF IT AIN'T LOVE (Leonino, Terry & Greg Artzner).
LP: . . . . PH 1112
MC: . . . . PH 1112C

Maguire, Alex

STEVE NOBLE, LIVE AT OSCARS.
Tracks: / Shake, raffle & stroll / Rope shoe ladder / Ports of paul / Monastic trail / Ping pong song / Gumbo gamble partisans washingtons / Odds, The / Smell the smoke / Ironing song.
LP: . . . . INCUS 52

Maguire, John

COME DAY, GO DAY, GOD SEND SUNDAY.
LP: . . . . LEE 4062

Maguire, Sean

PORTRAID.
LP: . . . . CEF 137

Mah, Marchella

I'M YOURS MAYBE (see under Marchella Mah).

Mahabharata

MAHABHARATA (Film Soundtrack) (Various artists).
Tracks: / Nibiro ghono andare: *Various artists* / Draupadi: *Various artists* / Ontoro momo: *Various artists*/ Satvati: *Various artists* / Virata: *Various artists* / Bushi ok sudure: *Various artists* / Cities: *Various* artists / Bhima: *Various artists* / Markandeya (part 1): *Various artists* / Duryodhana: *Various artists*/ Dhire: *Various artists* / Markandeya (part 2): *Various artists* / Svetasvatara upanisad: *Various artists.*
LP: . . . . RWLP 9
MC: . . . . RWMC 9

Maharry, Wendy

WENDY MAHARRY.
LP: 3952831
MC: 3952834

Mahavishnu Orchestra

APOCALYPSE.
MC: 4670924

BEST OF THE MAHAVISHNU ORCHESTRA.
Tracks: / Birds of fire / Open country joy / Wings of Karma / Sister Andrea / Dance of Maya / Meeting of the spirits / Lila's dance / Be happy.
LP: . . . . CBS 4232

MAHAVISHNU.
Tracks: / East side west side / Radio activity / Nostalgia / Nightriders / Clarendon hills / Jazz / Unbeliever, The / When blue turns gold.
LP: 251351 1

VISIONS OF THE EMERALD BEYOND.
MC: 4679044

Maher, Ashley

HI.
Tracks: / Dreaming / So many times / Honeycomb grey / Shine, shine, shine / Tick tock / Giving / Step by step / Homecoming (Only on CD.) / Jumping mouse / Hugh child / Sage is under my feet, The.
LP: . . . . V 2611
MC: . . . . TCV 2611

Maher, Big Joe

GOOD ROCKIN' DADDY.
Tracks: / Good rockin' Daddy / Cat scratchin' / Let's go jumpin' / Hook line and sinker / No good woman blues / Okeshemokeshepop / Handclappin' / You know yeah / Don't send me flowers / Blow man blow / Dynaflow.
LP: . . . . POW 4102
MC: . . . . POW 4102 MC

Maher, Fred

BASIC (see under Quine, Robert) (Maher, Fred & Robert Quine).

Mahlathini

LION OF SOWETO.
Tracks: / Baba-ye / Bayasazi / Kudala besifuna / Kwa mfazi onge mama / Bhula mngoma / Kumnyama endlini / Kumnandi Emgababa / Amagoduka / Mahlalela / Abake ba bonana / Bayasimenmeza / Ngibuzindela.
LP: . . . . EWV 4
MC: . . . . TCEWV 4

LION ROARS, THE (Mahlathini & the Mahotella Queens).
Tracks: / Lion roars, The.
MC: . . . . SHMC 42081

MBAQANGA (Mahlathini & the Mahotella Queens).
Tracks: / Mbaqanga / Yuya / Bayeza / Umashihlalisane / Jive motella / Thonthodi / Hayi kabi / Stop crying / Bon jour / Josefa / Noluthando / Kwa makhutha.
MC: . . . . KAZ MC 901

PARIS SOWETO.
LP: 839 676 1
MC: 839 676 4

THOKOZILE (Mahlathini & the Mahotella Queens).
Tracks: / Thokozile / Lilizela Mlilzeli / Sibuyile / Nina Majuba / I wanna dance / Uyavutha umlilo / Sengikala Ngiyabaleka / Izulu liyaduduma.
LP: . . . . EWV 6
MC: . . . . TCEWV 6

Mahler (composer)

LIEDER EINEES FAHRENDEN GESELLEN (Berlin Philharmonic Orchestra).
MC: 4044935

MAHLER (Various artists).
MC: . . . . DLCMC 222

MAHLER: SYMPHONY NO.4 (see under Royal Philharmonic Orchestra) (Royal Philharmonic Orchestra).

SYMPHONY NO. 5 IN C SHARP MINOR (See under Solti, Sir George) (Chicago Symphony Orchestra).

Mahogany

MAHOGANY (Film soundtrack) (Various artists).
Tracks: / Do you know where you're going to?: *Ross, Diana* / Feeling again: *Various artists* / You don't ever have to be alone: *Various artists* / Can you hear it in my music ?: *Various artists* / Christian's theme: *Various* artists / After you: *Various artists* / My hero is a gun: *Various artists* / Cat fight: *Various artists*/ Erucu: *Various artists* / Let's go back to day one: *Various artists* / Tracy: *Various artists* / She's the ideal girl: *Various artists* / Sweets (and other things): *Various artists* / Mahogany suite: *Various artists.*
LP: . . . . STMS 5082
MC: . . . . CSTMS 5082

Mahogany Rush

DOUBLE LIVE.
2LP: 784 612

LIVE: MAHOGANY RUSH Featuring Frank Marino.
LP: . . . . CBS 82621

LIVE: MAHOGANY RUSH & FRANK MARINO (see under Marino, Frank).

MAHOGANY RUSH 4 (see under Marino Frank).

WORLD ANTHEM (see under Marino, Frank).

Mahon, Derek

DEREK MAHON READS HIS OWN POETRY.
LP: . . . . CCT 11

Mahoney, Skip

LAND OF LOVE (Mahoney, Skip & The Casuals).
Tracks: / Land of love / This is my last time / Bless my soul / It's love / Wherever you go / Running away from love / I love you / Happily ever after.
LP: . . . . CLP 539

Mahotella Queens

IZIBANI ZOMGQASHIYO.
LP: . . . . SHAN 43036
MC: . . . . SHANC 43036

LIGHTS OF THE INDESTUCTIBLE BEAT, THE.
LP: . . . . EMW 5504

MARRIAGE IS A PROBLEM.
Tracks: / Marriage is a problem.
MC: . . . . SHMC 43081

PHEZULU EQHUDENI (Mahotella Queens, Mahlathanini & Other Stars).
LP: . . . . CGLP 4415
LP: . . . . ERT 1002
MC: . . . . CGC 4415

Mahy, Margaret

GREAT PIRATICAL RUMBUSTIFICATION, THE.
MC: 881 530

Mai Tai

HISTORY.
Tracks: / History / Body and soul / Chemistry / Rhythm of the street, The / What, where, when, who / What goes on / You control me / Rules of love, The / Am I losing you forever.
LP: . . . . V 2359
MC: . . . . TCV 2359
LP: . . . . OVED 192
MC: . . . . OVEDC 192

Maid Of The Mountains

MAID OF THE MOUNTAINS (1917 Recording).
LP: . . . . SH 169

Maiden Theatre

3 LITTLE PIGS.
MC: . . . . ZCPTE 7

ALADDIN.
MC: . . . . ZCPTE 5

AUGUSTUS ANT.
LP: . . . . EME 6504

GRUMBLEY.
LP: . . . . EME 6505

SNOW WHITE.
MC: . . . . ZCPTE 6

TOAD'S ARMY Volume 1.
LP: . . . . EME 6503

Maid's Bell

MAID'S BELL, THE/THE OLD POST ROAD (Dramatised by John Douglas).
MC: . . . . NF 4

Maigret

MAIGRET (THEME) (See under Loss, Joe) (Loss, Joe).

Mailer, Norman

ANCIENT EVENINGS (See under Ancient Evenings).

NAKED AND THE DEAD.
MC: . . . . CDL 51619

Main Event (Film)

MAIN EVENT (Film Soundtrack) (Various artists).
Tracks: / Main event: *Various artists* / Fight: *Various artists* / Body shop: *Various artists* / Copeland meets the Coasters: *Various artists* / Get a job: *Various artists* / Big girls don't cry: *Various artists*/ It's your foot again: *Various artists* / Angry eyes: *Various artists* / I'd clean a fish for you: *Various artists.*
LP: . . . . NE 1046
LP: . . . . JS 36115
MC: . . . . JST 36115
LP: . . . . CBS 70171
MC: 40 70171

Main Ingredient

I JUST WANNA LOVE YOU.
MC: 841 249 4
LP: 841 249 1

Main Stream Power Band

BEST IN SWING, THE.
2LP: . . . . MWM 008#009

Main Street Piano Band

PIANO TO THE PEOPLE.
LP: . . . . ISST 132

Maineeaxe

GIMME SOME GOLD.
LP: . . . . . **AMP 5**
MC: . . . . . **CAMP 5**

HOUR OF THUNDER, THE.
LP: . . . . . **AMP 007**

SHOUT IT OUT.
LP: . . . . . **AMP 3**

Mainer, J.E.

GOOD OLE MOUNTAIN MUSIC (Mainer, J.E. & Mountaineers).
LP: . . . . . **KLP 666**
MC: . . . . . **GT 5666**

J.E. MAINER & HIS MOUNTAINEERS.
LP: . . . . . **ARHOOLIE 5002**

J.E. MAINERS MOUNTAINEERS (Mainer, J.E. & Mountaineers).
LP: . . . . . **OT 106**

J.E. MAINERS MOUNTAINEERS VOL.2 (Mainer, J.E. & Mountaineers).
LP: . . . . . **OT 107**

Maines Brothers

AMARILLO HIGHWAY.
Tracks: / Amarillo highway / Ain't nobody lonely / Honky tonk blues / Love is a gamble / Kay / Dreams of Destree / Farm Road 40 / Time for one more song / Shelley's winter love / Home in Louisiana / Dream spinner / If I don't love you / I like your music / That's alright mama.
LP: . . . . . **CRLP 1000**

Mairants, Ivor

SWING GUITAR - 1934-1954 (Mairants, Ivor & Albert Harris).
MC: . . . . . **ZR 1990**

Maire Ni Chanthasaigh

NEW STRING HARP, THE.
LP: . . . . . **TP 019**
MC: . . . . . **CTP 019**

Mairs, Julie

GIVE ME A SIGN.
LP: . . . . . **PLR 062**

Maisonettes

FOR SALE.
Tracks: / Addicted / Sticks and stones / Hot club / Lessons in love / Nightmares / Heartache Avenue / This affair / Say it again / Roni come home / Daddy don't know / Lifeboat / Last one to know.
LP: . . . . . **RSGL 1**
MC: . . . . . **RSGK 1**

Majaivana, Lovemore

AMANDLA.
LP: . . . . . **ZIM 003**

JIRI.
LP: . . . . . **TRALP 2004**

Majella

AFTER ALL THESE YEARS.
LP: . . . . . **KLP 62**
MC: . . . . . **ZCKLP 62**

EVERY BEND IN THE ROAD.
MC: . . . . . **ZCKLP 68**

ISLE OF MY DREAMS.
Tracks: / Dear God / Another year passes (Anniversary song) / Bunch of Thyme / Old maid in a garret / Spinning wheel / Isle of Innisfree / Mother's love's a blessing, A / Hannigan's hooley / Too-ra-loo-ra-loo-ra / Wild Irish rose / When Irish eyes are smiling / This song is just for you / Green glens of Antrim / Singing bird / Morning has broken.
LP: . . . . . **KLP 39**
MC: . . . . . **ZCKLP 39**

MAGIC OF MAJELLA.
LP: . . . . . **KLP 66**
MC: . . . . . **ZCKLP 66**

OLD FLAME.
LP: . . . . . **KLP 56**

REQUESTS.
MC: . . . . . **ZCKLP 70**

SPINNING WHEEL.
LP: . . . . . **SHM 699**

Majestic Praise

MAJESTIC PRAISE (Songs of Jack Hayford Acapella) (Various artists).
LP: . . . . . **MM R 0205**
MC: . . . . . **MM C 0205**

Majestic Singers

LOOK WHERE.
LP: . . . . . **MYR 1198**
MC: . . . . . **MC 1198**

Majestic Wind Ensemble

PAN FLUTE FAVOURITES.
Tracks: / Day in the life, A / Something / Michelle / Yesterday / Strawberry fields forever / MacArthur Park / Don't cry for me Argentina / Feelings / Fool on the hill, The / Whiter shade of pale, A / She's out of my life / Unchained melody / Morning has broken / Nights in white satin / El condor pasa / Tara's theme / Let it be / I'm stone in love with you.
LP: . . . . . **SHLP 155**
MC: . . . . . **SHTC 155**

Majestics

MYSTIC MIRACLE STAR (see Perry,Lee & Majestics).

Majestics (tv)

TUTTI FRUTTI (Songs from the TV series).
Tracks: / Almost grown / Rockin' through the rye / No particular place to go / Promised land / Rip it up / Bye, bye love / Great balls of fire / Tutti frutti / Love is strange / That'll be the day / You're sixteen / Love hurts / Almost grown/ Tutti frutti.
LP: . . . . . **REN 629**
MC: . . . . . **ZCN 629**

Major Accident

PNEUMATIC PNEUROSIS.
LP: . . . . . **SHARP 027**

TORTURED TUNES LIVE - THE OFFICIAL BOOTLEG.
LP: . . . . . **SYNLP 9**

Major Hardy

WOLF COUCHON.
LP: . . . . . **BEDLP 7**

Major League

MAJOR LEAGUE (Film Soundtrack) (Various artists).
Tracks: / Wild thing: *X* / Cryin' shame: *Lovett, Lyle* / Walkaway: *Snakes* / Hideaway: *Beat Farmers*/ How can the girl refuse: *Beckett* / U.S. male: *Lonesome Romeos* / Trial and error (inst. score): *Various artists* / Pennant fever (inst. score): *Various artists* / Most of all you: *Medley, Bill.*
LP: . . . . . **ZL 74277**
MC: . . . . . **ZK 74277**

Major Thinkers

MAJOR THINKERS, THE.
LP: . . . . . **SPIN 991**

Majority Of One

THINK ABOUT TOMORROW.
LP: . . . . . **FST 002**

Makaton Chat

STRANGE BEACH.
LP: . . . . . **SLP 1**

Makaya & The Tsosis

MAKAYA & THE TSOSIS.
LP: . . . . . **ENJA 2042**

Make Me An Offer

MAKE ME AN OFFER (Original London Cast) (Various artists).
LP: . . . . . **AEI 1112**

MAKE ME AN OFFER (ORIGINAL ISSUE) (London cast) (Various artists).
LP: . . . . . **CLP 1333**

Makeba, Miriam

CLICK SONG.
MC: **7/C 1029**
LP: . . . . . **ESP 155564**

COMME UNE SYMPHONIE D'AMOUR.
MC: **7/C 1027**

EVENING WITH BELAFONTE & MAKEBA, AN (see Belafonte, Harry).

EYES ON THE TOMORROW.
Tracks: / I still long for you / Eyes on tomorrow / Don't break my heart / Thina sizonqoba / We speak peace / Thulasizwe- I shall be released / Vukani / Birds / Live the future.
LP: **849313-1**
MC: **849313-4**

FORBIDDEN GAMES.
LP: **26 21247**

GRAFFITI COLLECTION.
MC: . . . . . **GRMC 16**

HARRY B & MIRIAM M (see Belafonte, Harry).

PATA PATA.
LP: . . . . . **ESP 165508**
MC: . . . . . **C 1005**

PROMISE, A.
LP: . . . . . **ESP 155506**
MC: . . . . . **C 1015**

SANGOMA.
Tracks: / Emabhaceni / Baxabene Oxamu / Ngalala Phantsi / Ihoyiya / Kulo Nyaka / Baya Jabula / Mabhongo / Ingwemabala / Mosadi Ku Rima / Angilalanga / Ungakananai / Ngiya Khuyeka / Nyankwabe / Sabumoya / Congo / Nginani Uyajabula / Nyamuthla / Icala.
LP: . . . . . **K 925673 1**
MC: . . . . . **K 925673 4**

SYMPHONIE D'AMOUR.
MC: . . . . . **ESPC 7501**

VOICE OF AFRICA, THE.
LP: **26 21228**

WELELA.
LP: **838 208-1**
MC: **838 208-4**

Makem & Clancy

DUTCHMAN, THE.
LP: . . . . . **SHAN 52005**

IN CONCERT: MAKEM & CLANCY.
LP: . . . . . **SHAN 52003**
LP: . . . . . **BLB 1002**

LIVE: MAKEM & CLANCY.
LP: . . . . . **SHAN 52006**

MAKEM & CLANCY COLLECTION.
LP: . . . . . **SHAN 52001**
LP: . . . . . **BLB 1009**

TOMMY MAKEM & LIAM CLANCY.
LP: . . . . . **EPC 82081**
LP: . . . . . **SHAN 52002**

TWO FOR THE EARLY DEW.
LP: . . . . . **SHAN 52004**
LP: . . . . . **BLB 1007**

WE'VE COME A LONG WAY.
Tracks: / We've come a long way together / Frog in the well / Roseville Fair / Drill ye tarriers drill / Coast of Malabar, The / Queen of Connemara / Highwayman / Fair & tender lady / Peg leg Jack / Parcel o' rogues / Fagfaidh mise an baile seo / Golden / Mary Ellen Carter, The.
LP: **830 533-1**
MC: **830 533-4**

WE'VE COME A LONG WAY.
LP: . . . . . **SHAN 52013**

Makem, Sarah

ULSTER BALLAD SINGER.
Tracks: / Farewell my love / Remember me / Banks of red roses, The / It was in the month of January / Robert Burns and his Highland Mary / Factory girl / Jolly thresher, The / Caroline and her young sailor bold / Wind that shakes the barley, The / I courted a wee girl / Servant maid in her father's garden, The / Barbara Allen.
LP: **12T 182**

Makem, Tommy

BEST OF TOMMY MAKEM & THE CLANCY BROTHERS (Tommy Makem & The Clancy Brothers).
LP: . . . . . **GES 1030**

COME FILL YOUR GLASS WITH US.
LP: . . . . . **TLP 1032**

EVENING WITH TOMMY MAKEM, AN.
LP: . . . . . **SHAN 52008**

LONESOME WATERS.
LP: . . . . . **SHAN 52011**

ROLLING HOME.
LP: . . . . . **SH 52021**
MC: . . . . . **SH 52021 C**

Makems

AT HOME.
Tracks: / Manchester rambler / Bold tenant farmer / Strangers / Blarney stone, The / Limerick rake / Drops of brandy / Old Ballymoe / Slievegallon brais / Madadhin ruadh / Nell Flaherty's drake / I am an ould rake / Knights of Planxty Irwin / Over the mountain / Bunch of tombstones / Si Bea si mor / Blancher's hornpipes.
LP: . . . . . **OAS 3033**

Makin' Time

NO LUMPS OF FAT OR GRISTLE GUARANTEED.
LP: . . . . . **READY 1**

RHYTHM 'N' SOUL.
LP: . . . . . **DOWN 1**
MC: . . . . . **CDOWN 1**

TIME TROUBLE AND MONEY.
LP: . . . . . **REAGAN 1**

UNCHAIN MY HEART.
LP: . . . . . **FABML 11**

Making Love To Lettuce

LETTUCE IN THE CARAVAN.
Tracks: / Summer of '86 / Triffids / Two cans of special brew / I tried to make you understand.
LP: . . . . . **MLTL 286**

Making The Grade

MAKING THE GRADE (Film soundtrack) (Various artists).
LP: . . . . . **STV 81204**

Makowicz, Adam

CLASSIC JAZZ DUETS (Makowicz, Adam & George Mraz).
LP: . . . . . **ST 216**

INTERFACE (Makowicz, Adam Trio).
LP: . . . . . **SNTF 963**

NAME IS MAKOWICZ, THE (Makowicz, Adam & Phil Woods).
LP: . . . . . **LAB 21**

SOLO.
LP: . . . . . **SNTF 964**

Makvirag

BEKESSEG (Peacefulness).
Tracks: / Dudanotak (Hungarian bagpipe tunes) / Szerelem, szerelem (Love, love (three love songs)) / Villo (Palm Sunday song from Slovakia) / Tinodi (Three variations on a song by Sebestyen L. Tinodi (c1505-1556)) / Kalotaszegi tancok (Dances from Kalotaszeg (Mid-west Romania, large Hungarian population)) / Tavasz, tavasz (Spring, spring - a lament from Moldavia.) / Szatmari dallamok (Tunes from Szatmar (Eastern Hungary)) / Punkosdolo (Whitsuntide song (3 from Rabakoz (Western Hungary))) / Az hegedusokrol (About the fiddle-players. Appeared in print 1580.) / Bethlehemes (Christmas tunes.).
LP: . . . . . **TRAX 5001**
MC: . . . . . **CTRAX 5001**

Malach, Bob

SOME PEOPLE.
LP: . . . . . **MPS 68 258**

Malachi Favors

NATURAL AND SPIRITUAL.
LP: . . . . . **AECO 003**

Malachy, Doris

33 FAVOURITE SONGS.
MC: . . . . . **CHRL 187**

BEST OF MALACHY DORIS.
Tracks: / Bold O'Donaghue / When Irish eyes are smiling / Humors of Bandon / England's motorway / O'Brien has no place to go / Waves of Tory / Town I loved so well / Come to the Ceilidah / Old Claddagh ring / High cauled cap, The / Whiskey on a Sunday / Belfast hornpipe.
LP: . . . . . **HRL 169**
MC: . . . . . **CHRL 169**

CEILI DANCE TIME (Malachy Doris Ceili Band).
LP: . . . . . **HRL 143**
MC: . . . . . **CHRL 143**

CONTINENTAL ACCORDION.
Tracks: / Y viva Espana / Aye aye aye / Under the bridges of Paris / Village band / Seine / Isle of Capri / La golondrina / Whistling Rufus / White rose of Athens / Beer barrel polka / Cuckoo waltz / April in Portugal / Come back to Sorrento / La paloma / Yellow bird / Clarinet polka.
LP: . . . . . **HRL 159**
MC: **CHRL,159**

DANCING THROUGH IRELAND'S HITS.
LP: . . . . . **HRL 132**
MC: . . . . . **CHRL 132**

IRISH DANCE TIME.
LP: . . . . . **G 006**

IRISH PARTY SING ALONG.
Tracks: / MacNamara's band / Curragh of Kildare, The / Fields of Athenry / Courtin' in the kitchen / Slattery's mounted fut / Willie McBride / Inniskilling dragoons / Cliffs of Dooneen / Will ye go lassie go / Moonlight in Mayo / Molly Malone#Galway shawl / Carrickfergus / Star of the County Down / Are you right there Michael / Dingle regatta / Rose of Tralee, The.
LP: . . . . . **DHL 710**
MC: . . . . . **CDHL 710**

IRISH PARTY SING SONG VOCALS (Malachy Doris & Brendan Clancy).
Tracks: / When Irish eyes / 40 shades of green / I'll tell me ma.
LP: . . . . . **HRL 154**
MC: . . . . . **CHRL 154**

IRISH PUB :30 SINGALONGS.
MC: . . . . . **CPHL 482**

IRISH PUB SING-ALONG.
Tracks: / Dear oul Donegal / Where three counties meet / Galway bay / Rathlin island / Rose of Castlerea / My Kathleen / Golden jubilee / It's hard to be humble / Sweet sixteen / Wild colonial boy / Drink up the cider / Green hills of Kerry.
LP: . . . . . **PHL 470**
MC: . . . . . **CPHL 470**
LP: . . . . . **PHL 482**

IRISH PUB SINGALONG (33 Favourite Songs).
Tracks: / O'Brien has no place to go / Back to Castleblaney / Isle of Innisfree / Treat my daughter kindly / Pretty little girl from Omagh / Moonshiner / Rambles of Spring / Any Tipperary town / Irish rover, The / Cottage on the borderline / Cliffs of Dooneen.
LP: . . . . . **HRL 187**

SOUVENIR OF SCOTLAND.
LP: . . . . . **HRL 137**
MC: . . . . . **CHRL 137**

WALTZING THRO' IRELAND (Malachy Doris Accordion Band).

Tracks: / Mountains of Mourne / When Irish eyes are smiling.
LP: . . . . **HRL 130**
MC: . . . . **CHRL 130**

WALTZING THRO' IRELAND VOL 3.
Tracks: / Cottage by the Lee / Long before your time / Ben Bulben / Give an Irish girl to me / Kerry dances / Terence's farewell to Kathleen / Green fields of France / Do you want your aul lobby washed down / Bridle hanging on the wall / Farewell to Galway / Star of the County Down / Three leaf shamrock.
LP: . . . . **HRL 192**
MC: . . . . **CHRL 192**

WE ALL HAVE A SONG IN OUR HEARTS (Malachy Doris Orchestra & Chorus).
Tracks: / We all have a song in our hearts / More than yesterday / Pal of my cradle days / I'll be your sweetheart / Skye boat song / Lovely Irish rose / Too-ra-loo-ra-loo-ra / Cottage by the lee / If I had my life to live over / It's a sin to tell a lie / Bunch of violets blue / Spinning wheel / Joys of love / Mother's love's a blessing, A / Goodbye Johnny dear / Gentle mother.
LP: . . . . **PHL 488**
MC: . . . . **CPHL 488**

YOU'RE AS WELCOME AS THE FLOWERS IN MAY.
Tracks: / You're as welcome as the flowers in May / Brady of Strabane / Connemara shore / Me Uncle Mike / After all these years / Belfast / Forty shades of green / Sailing away from Ireland / Come by the hills / Rose of Tralee, The / If I were a blackbird / Donegal shore / Twenty one years / Three leaf shamrock / Moonlight in Mayo / If you're Irish / Home boys home / Westmeath bachelor / Waltz of the angels, The / Irish eyes / 5,000 miles from Sligo / My home in County Down / Day I get back to Tyrone, The / Cottage on the Old Dungannon Road / Green glens of Antrim / If we only had old Ireland over here / Rose of Clare / Nightingale, The / Marino waltz / Moonshiner.
MC: . . . . **CPHL 502**

Malandraki, Lilli

EVENING IN CRETE, AN (Malandraki, Lilli & Donald Swann).
LP: . . . . **WRS 1006**

Malapet, Nino

MOKILIMBEMBE.
LP: . . . . **MP 33004**

Malaria

MALARIA REVISITED.
MC: . . . . **A 123**

Malasian Pale

NATURE'S FANTASIES.
LP: . . . . **LPFOR 17053**
MC: . . . . **MCFOR 17053**

Malaurie, Jean

INUIT.
LP: **455 9021**

Malavoi

LA FILO.
2LP: . . . . **GD 03/04**

Malcahy, Mick

MICK MULCAHY-ACCORDION.
LP: . . . . **CEF 050**

Malchak, Tim

DIFFERENT CIRCLES.
Tracks: / Not like this / Different circles / I've been there / I owe it all to you / Sweet Virginia / I wish you had a heart / I always leave my heart at home / That's no way to love / On a good night / American man.
LP: . . . . **UVL 76002**
MC: . . . . **UVLC 76002**

Malcolm

MALCOLM (see Penguin Cafe Orchestra) (Penguin Cafe Orchestra).

Malcolm & Alwyn

LIVE: MALCOLM & ALWYN.
Tracks: / Say it like it is / I love / I feel fine / Morning star / Fools wisdom / Growing old / Things are getting better / World needs Jesus, The / Tomorrow's news.
LP: . . . . **MRC 007**
MC: . . . . **TC MRC 007**

Malcolm, Johnny

MASTER PERFORMANCE VOL.4.
Tracks: / Oh happy day / It's a heartache / Greensleeves / Barcarolle / Whiter shade of pale, A / Bye, bye my love.
MC: . . . . **AIM 98**

Malcolm's Interview

BREAKFAST IN BEDLAM.
LP: . . . . **SPD 1006**
MC: . . . . **SPD 1006 C**

Maldaur, Geoff

I AIN'T DRUNK (Maldaur, Geoff & The Nite-Lites).
Tracks: / Boogie chillun / Nobody knows (the way I feel this morning) / I ain't drunk / Natural ball / Down for the count / Meanest woman blues / As long as I'm moving / Caledonia / See see rider.
LP: . . . . **HNBL 1304**

Maldore, Michel

LA CHAMBRE NUPTIALE.
LP: **900576**

Malemen

FIRST CLASS MALE.
LP: . . . . **MSS 2207**
MC: . . . . **MSSC 2207**

Malevolent Creation

TEN COMMANDMENTS, THE.
LP: . . . . **RC 93611**
MC: . . . . **RC 93614**

Malfatti, Radu

BRACKNELL BREAKDOWN (Malfatti, Radu/Harry Miller).
LP: . . . . **OG 320**

FORMU.
Tracks: / Funf leichte stucke / Formu.
LP: . . . . **NATO 175**

Mali

EPIC HISTORICAL POLITICAL AND PROPAGANDA SONGS (Various artists).
LP: . . . . **LLST 7325**

MALI MUSIC (Various artists).
LP: . . . . **STERNS 3001**

Malice

CRAZY IN THE NIGHT.
Tracks: / Captive of light / Vice versa / Crazy in the night / Death or glory.
LP: . . . . **RO 94451**

IN THE BEGINNING.
Tracks: / Rockin' with you / Into the ground / Air attack / Stellar masters / Tarot dealer / Squeeze it dry / Hellrider / No haven for the raven / Unwanted, The / Godz of thunder.
LP: **781 250-1**

LICENCED TO KILL.
LP: . . . . **K 781 714 1**
MC: . . . . **K 781 714 4**

Malicorne

FIRST.
LP: **883002**

LEGENDE: DEUXIEME EPOQUE.
Tracks: / Le Prince D'Orange / Le ballet des coqs / Compagnons qui roulez en provence / La mule la conduite / Pierre De Grenoble / Vive la lune / La dance des dames / La Chasse Gallery / La nuit des sorcieres / Dormeur / L'ecolier assassin / Beau charpentier / Quand le cypes.
LP: . . . . **HNBL 1360**
MC: . . . . **HNBC 1360**

SECOND.
LP: **883004**

Malinga, Joe Group

SOUTHERN AFRICAN FORCE.
LP: . . . . **MOR 32034**

Malinvernie, Pete

DON'T BE SHY (Malinvernie, Pete/Mel Lewis/Dennis Irwin).
LP: . . . . **SB 2037**

Malkowsky, Liselotte

DAS HERZ VON ST. PAULI.
Tracks: / Sonntag nacht auf der reeperbahn / Der alte Seemann kann nachts nicht schlafen / Fang' keine Liebe mit Matrosen an / Das rote licht an backbord / Das lied vom hafenmadchen / In deiner Koje hangt ein Bild von mir / Auf St.Pauli spielt der Jonny Mundharmonika / Warum zahlen die Matrosen nachts die Sterne? / Das wunder von der Reeperbahn / Ein kleiner Akkordeonspeiler / Matrosen brauchen Liebe / Auch dein Kap'ten war mal klein / Mein Schiff hab' gute Reise.
LP: . . . . **BFX 15353**

Mallan, Peter

LEGENDS OF SCOTLAND.
MC: . . . . **ZCCLS 713**

LONELY I WONDER.
Tracks: / Lochnagar / Annie Laurie / Peat fire flame / Ye banks and Braes / I love a lassie / Roamin in the gloamin / Keep right on to the end of the road / Rowan tree / When you and I were young Maggie / Glencoe / Bonnie Galloway / Rat tap tap / Silver threads among the gold / Down in the glen / Old rugged cross, The / Amazing grace / Old house.
LP: . . . . **KLP 36**
MC: . . . . **ZCKLP 36**

RELAX WITH PETER MALLAN.
Tracks: / Ae fond kiss / Ma belle Marguerite / These are my mountains / My lagan love / Anniversary song / My love is like a red red rose / Jean / Fishin' song / Sweet afton / Foggy foggy dew / Skye boat song / Jenny kissed me.
LP: . . . . **KLP 18**
MC: . . . . **ZCKLP 18**

THESE ARE MY MOUNTAINS.
Tracks: / These are my mountains / Jock O'Hazeldean / Piper o'Dundee / Bonnie Earl O'Moray, The / Barra fishers' song / Rothesay Bay / Scotland the brave / Thistle of Scotland / Song of the Clyde / She mov'd through the fair / Tay boat song / Come by the hills / Ae fond kiss / Scots wha' Ma'e.
LP: . . . . **GLN 1019**

Mallet Head

MALLET HEAD.
Tracks: / Spoonfed / Killer pussy / Tear down the walls / Don't lock me in / It was blasphemy, was it a blast / Fight / Die for my soul / Blinders / Duel / You and I know.
LP: . . . . **RR 94971**
LP: . . . . **FLP 1030**

Mallett, David

FOR A LIFETIME.
Tracks: / For a lifetime / Sweet Tennessee / My old man / Some peace will come / Night on the town / Hometown girls / This city life / Lost in a memory of you / Light at the end of the tunnel / Summer of my dreams.
LP: . . . . **FF 497**
MC: . . . . **FF 497C**

OPEN DOORS AND WINDOWS.
LP: . . . . **FF 291**
MC: . . . . **FF 291C**

VITAL SIGNS.
LP: . . . . **FF 373**
MC: . . . . **FF 373C**

Mallinder, Stephen

POW WOW PLUS.
LP: . . . . **DVR 16**

Malmquist, Siw

DIE GROSSEN ERFOLGE, 2.
Tracks: / Schade, schade, schade / Die wege der liebe / Mister casanova / Regen auf benguela / Kusse nie nach mitternacht / Carneval in Caracas / Das funfte rad am wagen / 1999 / Ein neues spiel / Ein neues gluck / Harlekin / Prima ballerina / Clementine.
LP: . . . . **LB 213 002**

LIEBESKUMMER LOHNT SICH NICHT.
Tracks: / Leibeskumer lohnt sich nicht / Colubus fand Amerika / Ein herz ist kein spielzeug / Mir fehit der knopf am pyjama / Der clown / Liebe wie im rosengarten (Rose Garden) / Nie und niemals / War ich auch konigin / Hier kommt ein herz fur dich / Das tagebuch der ersten liebe / Prinz eugen / Ein junggeselle weniger.
LP: . . . . **LB 213 001**

SCHOTTEN-ROCK.
Tracks: / Rhythmus 1920 / Der mann ist allright / Prego senore / Du, du, du bist kein held / September im regen / Traume sind wie der wind / Bye bye bye biddi biddi bum bum / Der eine, der bist du / Merci beaucoup / Buon giorno amore / Shotten rock / Hundertmal / So wie es damais war (My heart has a mind of its own) / Augustin / Preacher, The / Sermonette / You can't get to Heaven on rollerskates / There's never been a night / Johnny Wonderland / Red roses and little white lies.
LP: . . . . **LB 213 004**

Malmsteen, Yngwie J.

ECLIPSE.
Tracks: / Making love / Save our love / Devil in disguise / What do you want / Faultline / Eclipse / Bedroom eyes / Motherless child / Judas / Demon driver / See you in hell (don't be late).
LP: **843 361 1**
MC: **843 361 4**

MARCHING OUT (Malmsteen, Yngwie J./Rising Force).
Tracks: / Prelude / I'll see the light tonight / Don't let it end / Disciples of hell / I'm a viking / Overture 1383 / Anguish and fear / On the run again / Soldier without faith / Caught in the middle / Marching out.
LP: . . . . **POLD 5183**
MC: . . . . **POLDC 5183**

ODYSSEY (Malmsteen, Yngwie J./Rising Force).
Tracks: / Rising force / Hold on / Heaven tonight / Dreaming (tell me) / Bite the bullet / Riot in the dungeons / Deja vu / Crystal ball / Now is the time / Faster than the speed of light / Krakatau / Memories.
LP: . . . . **POLD 5224**
MC: . . . . **POLDC 5224**

RISING FORCE.
Tracks: / Black star / Far beyond the sun / Now your ships are burned / Evil eye / Icarus' dream suite / As above, so below / Little savage / Farewell.
LP: **825 324-1**

TRIAL BY FIRE (Live in Leningrad) (Malmsteen, Yngwie J./Rising Force).
Tracks: / Liar / Queen in love / Deja vu / Far beyond the sun / Heaven tonight / Dreaming (tell me) / You don't remember, I'll never forget / Guitar solo (Spasebo blues) / Black star / Spanish castle magic (edit version).
LP: **839 726 1**
MC: **839 726 4**

TRILOGY.
Tracks: / You don't remember, I'll never forget / Liar / Queen in love / Crying / Fury / Fire / Magic mirror / Dark ages / Trilogy suite, Opus 5.
LP: . . . . **POLD 5204**
MC: . . . . **POLDC 5204**

Malombo

MAN PHILY.
LP: . . . . **PAM 04**

Malone, J.J.

YOUNGER THAN YESTERDAY (see Key, Troyce) (Malone, J.J. & Troyce Key & the Rhythm Rockers).

Maloney, Bunny

ON MY MIND.
Tracks: / Always on my mind / Easy loving / Baby I've been missing you / Lady of magic / Ethiopia / Help / Julia / I've been a loser.
LP: . . . . **LDR LP 002**
LP: . . . . **HM 113**

SINGS OLD HITS IN REGGAE RUB A DUB STYLE.
Tracks: / Oh what a night / Jamaica / Stand by me / Don't go please stay / Precious love / Sincerely / Oh Donna / Tenderly / When I fall in love / Silhouette / Sweets for my sweet / Spanish harlem / Only sixteen / Mona Lisa / You're mine / Goodnight my love.
LP: . . . . **HM 117**

Maloney, Paddy

TIN WHISTLES (Maloney, Paddy & Sean Potis).
LP: . . . . **CC 15**
MC: **4CC 15**

Malopoets

LIFE IS FOR LIVING.
Tracks: / Weh nduna / Azania / Life is for living / Ingalile / End is near, The / Friday night / Shik wembu / Zuluman / Thembi / Bayeza.
LP: . . . . **V 2565**
MC: . . . . **TCV 2565**

MALOPOETS.
Tracks: / Sanibonnai / Bouyane / Madoda / Sound of the people / Lengoma / Sikelela / Xinkongolotwana / Intsizwa / Dimakatso.
MC: . . . . **EJ 2402934**
LP: **2402931**

Malory, Sir Thomas

LE MORT D'ARTHUR (Various artists).
MCSET: . . . . **SAY 46**

MORTE D'ARTHUR (McKenna, Siobhan).
MC: **1374**

Malta

HIGH PRESSURE.
MC: . . . . **JC 3303**
LP: . . . . **JLP 3303**

MY BALLADS.
MC: . . . . **JC 3315**

OBSESSION.
LP: . . . . **JLP 3310**
MC: . . . . **JC 3310**

Malta G.C.

OLIVER TWIST/MALTA G.C. (See under Oliver Twist) (Film Soundtracks) (Royal Philharmonic Orchestra).

Maltese Falcon

MALTESE FALCON, THE (Film Soundtrack) (Various artists).
LP: . . . . **MR 1091**

METAL RUSH.
LP: . . . . **RR 9824**

Mama don't allow it

MAMA DON'T ALLOW IT Various Artists (Various artists).
LP: . . . . **RAL 503**

Mama's Boys

GROWING UP THE HARD WAY.
LP: . . . . **10591 J**
LP: . . . . **HIP 49**
MC: . . . . **HIPC 49**

LIVE TONITE.
LP: . . . . **MFN 114**

MC: TMFN 114

MAMA'S BOYS.
LP: HIP 15
MC: HIPC 15

PLUG IT IN.
Tracks: / In the heat of the night / Burning up / Needle in the groove / Reach for the top / Silence is out of fashion / Straight forward / Runaway dreams / Getting out / Belfast city blues.
LP: CLALP 111
MC: CLAMC 111
LP: ULTRA 1
MC: CULTRA 1

POWER AND PASSION.
LP: HIP 24
MC: HIPC 24

TURN IT UP.
Tracks: / Face to face / Loose living / Gentleman rogues / Lonely soul / Freedom fighters.
LP: SPLP 001

Mamas & Papas

20 GOLDEN HITS: MAMAS & PAPAS.
Tracks: / California dreamin' / Dedicated to the one I love / I call your name / Twelve thirty / Creeque alley / Dancing in the street / For the love of Ivy / Go where you wanna go / My girl / Look through my window / Monday, Monday / Words of love / Twist and shout / I saw her again last night / Dream a little dream of me / People like us / You baby / Got a feelin' / Trip, stumble and fall / Straight shooter.
LP: MCLD 613
MC: MCLDC 613

20 GREATEST HITS: MAMAS & PAPAS.
Tracks: / California dreamin' / I saw her again last night / I call your name / Twist and shout / Sing for your supper / Look through my window / Do you wanna dance / Dancing in the street / You baby / Dedicated to the one I love / Monday Monday / Words of love / Glad to be unhappy / Go where you wanna go / Safe in my garden / Spanish Harlem / Trip, stumble and fall / My girl / Creeque Alley / Dream a little dream of me.
LP: MFP 50493
MC: TCMFP 50493

COLLECTION: MAMAS & PAPAS.
Tracks: / People like us / Look through my window / Monday monday / I call your name / Pacific coast highway / I wanna be a star / Dedicated to the one I love / Creeque alley / California dreamin' / Dancing in the street / Shooting star / I saw her again last night / My girl / Spanish Harlem / For the love of Ivy / Whatcha gonna do? / Mississippi / Dream a little dream of me / Words of love / Move in a little closer baby.
MC: CCSMC 173
2LP: CCSLP 173
LP: RD 7803

DELIVER.
LP: SF 7880

ELLIOTT, PHILLIPS, GILLIAM, DOCHERTY.
Tracks: / California dreamin' / Dedicated to the one I love / Even if I could / Once there was a time I thought / You baby / In crowd, The / I saw her again / Did you ever want to cry / John's music box / Too late / Go where you wanna go / Midnight voyage / Creeque alley / Strange young girls / Dancing bear / No salt on her tail / My cart stood still / Dream a little dream of me / California earthquake / Somebody groovy / Sing for your supper / Free advice / String man / I can't wait.
2LP: VSOPLP 119
MC: VSOPMC 119

GOLDEN GREATS: MAMAS & PAPAS.
Tracks: / Dedicated to the one I love / Monday Monday / Look through my window / California dreamin' / I call your name / My girl / Dream a little dream of me / Go where you wanna go / Got a feelin' / I saw her again last night / Words of love / Twelve thirty / Dancing in the street / Glad to be unhappy / Creeque alley / Midnight voyage / Spanish Harlem / You baby / Do you wanna dance / Twist and shout / Safe in my garden / California earthquake.
MC: MCMC 5001
LP: MCM 5001

GREATEST HITS: MAMAS & PAPAS.
LP: BRLP 56
MC: BRMC 56

HITS OF GOLD.
Tracks: / California dreamin' / Dedicated to the one I love / Monday, Monday / I saw her again / Creeque alley.
LP: MCL 1614
MC: MCLC 1614
LP: S 5007

MAMAS & PAPAS.
Tracks: / Go where you wanna go / Down on the bayou / Dedicated to the one I love / Straight shooter / Sunday will never be the same / I saw her again / Dream a little dream of me / Creeque alley / Monday Monday / California dreamin'.
LP: OR 0057

VERY BEST OF MAMAS & PAPAS.
Tracks: / Monday Monday / California dreamin' / Dedicated to the one I love / Creeque alley / It's getting better / Straight shooter / Spanish Harlem / Twelve thirty / Go where you wanna go / I saw her again last night / People like us / My girl / California earthquake / For the love of Ivy / Got a feelin'.
LP: PLAT 302
MC: PLAC 302
2LP: ADEP 30

VERY BEST OF THE MAMAS & PAPAS.
Tracks: / California dreamin' / Dream a little dream of me / Monday Monday / Dedicated to the one I love / Make your own kind of music / Do you wanna dance / Dancing in the street / Spanish Harlem / I call your name / Words of love / It's getting better / In crowd, The / Go where you wanna go / Creeque Alley / My heart stood still / I saw her again.
LP: SHM 3301
MC: HSC 3301

Mame

MAME (Original Broadway Cast) (Various artists)
LP: PS 3000
MC: PST 3000

Mami, Sheb

PRINCE OF RAI.
LP: TERRA 105
MC: TERRAC 105
LP: HM 014
MC: HMC 014

TEGDI LABGHATI TEGDI.
LP: AM 6043

Mammoth

MAMMOTH.
Tracks: / All the days / Can't take the hurt / Dark star / Long time coming / Home from the storm / Fat man / 30 pieces of silver / Bet you wish / Bad times.
LP: HIP 56
MC: HIPC 56

Mampi Spliff

MAMPI SPLIFF (Various artists).
LP: UJAM 0020

Mamu

TOWNSHIP BOY.
Tracks: / What a lie / Soweto - so where to? / Mpoho / We don't buy from town / Love (uthando) / Township boy / Today someone died / Prologue/monologue / Don't bother me / War is declared.
LP: KAZ LP 9
MC: KAZ MC 9

Man

BACK INTO THE FUTURE.
2LP: UAD 60053/4

BE GOOD TO YOURSELF AT LEAST ONCE A DAY.
LP: BGOLP 14

DO YOU LIKE IT HERE NOW, ARE YOU SETTLING IN?.
Tracks: / Angel easy / All good clean fun / We're only children / Many are called but few get up / Manillo / Love your life.
LP: LBR 1032

FRIDAY 13TH.
LP: PIK 001
MC: PIKC 001

GREEN FLY.
Tracks: / Rainbow eyes / Sospan fach / C'mon / Babe, I'm gonna leave you / 7171 551 / Back to the future / Ain't their fight / Keep on crinting / Intro - Kerosene / Four day Louise / California silks and satins.
2LP: D LATE 1

MAXIMUM DARKNESS.
LP: UAG 29872
LP: BGOLP 43

PERFECT TIMING (THE U.A. YEARS).
Tracks: / Daughter of the fireplace / Romain / Many are called but few get up / Manillo (Not on LP.) / All good clean fun (Not on LP.) / C'mon / Bananas / Back into the future / Thunder and lightning kid, The / Scotch corner (Not on LP.) / Hard way to die / Babe I'm gonna leave you.
LP: EMS 1403
MC: TCEMS 1403

REVELATION.
Tracks: / And in the beginning... / Sudden life / Empty room / Puella, puella (woman, woman) / Love / Erotica / Blind man / And castles rise in children's eyes / Don't just stand there (come out of the rain) / Missing pieces, The / Future hides its face, The.
LP: SEE 274

RHINOS WINOS AND LUNATICS.
LP: UAG 29631

TWO OUNCES OF PLASTIC.
Tracks: / Prelude / Storm, The / It is as it must be / Spunk box / My name is Jesus Smith / Parchment and candles / Brother Arnold's red and white striped tent.
LP: SEE 273

WELSH CONNECTION.
LP: MCF 2753

Man 2 Man

MAN TO MAN FEATURING PAUL ZONE.
LP: BOLP 1002

Man And A Woman

MAN AND A WOMAN (Film Soundtrack) (Various artists).
Tracks: / Man and a woman, A: *Various artists* / Stronger than us: *Various artists* / Today it's you: *Various* artists / 124 miles an hour: *Various artists* / Samba: *Various artists* / Today it's you (aujourd 'hui c'est toi): *Various artists* / Shadows of our love: *Various artists.*
LP: 1831841
MC: 1831844
LP: SLS 50409
LP: SULP 1155

Man Behind The Wheel

MAN BEHIND THE WHEEL, THE (Various artists).
LP: SLP 404
MC: GT 5404

Man Could Get Killed

MAN COULD GET KILLED, A (See under Short, Luke) (Clancy, Jack).

Man From Delmonte

BIG NOISE (Live from the Broadwalk).
Tracks: / Good things in life, The / Louise and I / Country, The / Bored by you / Casual friends / M.I.C.H.A.E.L. / Monday morning after / Water in my eyes / Sun serious / My girl / Big noise / Louise / Mathematically speaking / Lasha me.
MC: BIP 503

Man From Snowy River

MAN FROM SNOWY RIVER (Film Soundtrack) (Various artists).
LP: STV 81167
MC: CTV 81167

Man In Her Life

MAN IN HER LIFE, THE Ballard, Jane (Ayers, Ruby M.).
MCSET: SOUND 37

Man In Love

MAN IN LOVE, A (UN HOMME AMOUREUX) (Original Soundtrack) (Various artists).
LP: 240801.1

Man In The Wilderness

MAN IN THE WILDERNESS (Film Soundtrack) (Various artists).
Tracks: / Main title (Capt. Henry theme): *Various artists* / Zach discovers water: *Various artists* / Shadows of Reckerys: *Various artists* / Zach makes his bed: *Various artists* / Zach's music box: *Various artists*/ Zach bass theme: *Various artists* / Zach meets Redthorn: *Various artists* / Zach goes for Henry: *Various artists* / Finale (Zach bass theme): *Various artists.*
LP: K 46126

Man Jumping

JUMP OUT.
Tracks: / Belle dux on the beach / Buzz buzz buzz goes the honeybee / World service / Walk on by / Down the locale / Squeezi / Arotropics.
LP: JC 5
MC: TC 5

WORLD SERVICE.
Tracks: / Perils of tourism, The / Trouble is, The / Big swing, The / Something in the city / On the rocks / It's been fun / Wedding, The.
LP: EGED 49
MC: EGEDC 49

Man Of A Thousand

MAN OF A THOUSAND FACES (Film soundtrack) (Various artists).
LP: STV 81121

Man Of La Mancha

MAN OF LA MANCHA (Film Soundtrack) (Various artists).
Tracks: / Man of La Mancha, Overture: *Various artists* / Man of La Mancha: *Various artists* / It's all the same: *Various artists* / Dulcinea: *Various artists* / I'm only thinking of him: *Various artists* / I really like him: *Various artists* / Barber's song/ Golden helmet of Mambrino: *Various artists* / Little bird, little bird: *Various artists* / Impossible dream, The: *Various artists* / Dubbing: *Various artists* / Life as it really is: *Various artists* / Aldonza: *Various artists* / Little gossip: *Various artists* / Dulcinea/ Impossible dream (reprise): *Various artists* / Man of La Mancha (reprise): *Various artists* / Psalm: *Various artists*/ Impossible dream, The: *Various artists* (The Quest).
LP: MCL 1722
LP: UAG 29422

MAN OF LA MANCHA (Original London Cast) (Various artists).
2LP: MCA 2 10010

Man On Fire

MAN ON FIRE (Film Soundtrack) (Graunke Symphony Orchestra).
LP: STV 81343
MC: CTV 81343

Man Parrish

MAN PARRISH.
Tracks: / Hip hop be bop / In the beginning / Man made / Together again / Six simple synthesisers / Techno trax / Street clap / Heatstroke.
LP: POLD 5101
MC: POLDC 5101

Man Seezer

EACH MAN KILLS THE THING HE LOVES (See under Friday, Gavin) (Man Seezer/Gavin Friday).

Man With Golden Arm

MAN WITH THE GOLDEN ARM, THE (Original Soundtrack) (Various artists).
LP: MODEM 1013
MC: MODEMC 1013
LP: MCA 1526
MC: MCAC 1526

Man With Golden Gun

MAN WITH THE GOLDEN GUN, THE (Film Soundtrack) (Various artists).
MC: E 41 E 90619

Man With No Image

S.O.S..
LP: CLP 010

Man With The Golden

MAN WITH THE GOLDEN ARM (THEME FROM) (See under Harris, Jet) (Harris, Jet).

Manakas, Van

LOVE SONGS: VAN MANAKAS.
LP: ROUNDER 3063

Manapsara

QUEER.
LP: SUB 33017-22

Mance, Clare

ALL DRESSED UP AND LONELY (See under Gline, Bob) (Gline, Bob & Clare Mance).

FEELINGS AT CHRISTMAS (See under Gline, Bob) (Gline, Bob & Clare Mance).

Mance, Junior

DEEP (Mance, Junior Trio).
LP: JSP 1013

FOR DANCERS ONLY (Mance, Junior & Martin Rivera).
LP: 3031

TENDER TOUCH OF..., THE (Mance, Junior & Martin Rivera Duo).
LP: NQ 3405

Manchester Boys Choir

NEW KIND OF CHRISTMAS, A.
LP: ONE 1316
MC: OCE 2316

NEW SOUND OF CHRISTMAS, THE.
LP: ONE 1314

SINGING FOR YOU.
Tracks: / Waltz of my heart / Chorus of ariel spirits / Count your blessings / Streamlet, The / Mary Stuart's prayer / Break o' day / Over the waves / This little light of mine / Gruss / Happy wanderer, The / Tulerunt dominum meum / Stodola pumpa / Morgenblatter / Psalm 150.
LP: GRALP 12
MC: GRTC 12

Manchester, Melissa

MATHEMATICS.
LP: MCF 3262

TRIBUTE.
Tracks: / Over the rainbow / Gypsy in my soul / La Vie en rose / Tenderly / Walk on by / Stardust / Kind of man a woman wants, The / Lady be good / Sophisticated lady / To make you smile again.
MC: 841 273 4
LP: 841 273 1

Manchild

MANCHILD.
LP: . . . . A 65

Mancini, Henry

AT THE MOVIES.
Tracks: / Moon river / Pink panther / Peter Gunn / Good, the bad and the ugly, The / Midnight cowboy / Magnificent seven, The / How soon / Shot in the dark / Dear heart / Seventy-six trombones / Days of wine and roses / Shaft, Theme from / Raindrops keep falling on my head.
LP: . . . . MFP 5778
MC: . . . . TCMFP 5778

BEST OF HENRY MANCINI (Mancini, Henry & His Orchestra).
Tracks: / You'll never know / Stella by starlight / Love is a many splendoured thing / Charade / Mona Lisa / Moonlight serenade / Whatever will be will be / Raindrops keep falling on my head / As time goes by / Over the rainbow / Romeo and Juliet love theme / Midnight cowboy / Gigi / Peter Gunn.
LP: 107 4065
MC: 770 4065

BEST OF HENRY MANCINI & HIS ORCHESTRA VOL 3 (Mancini, Henry & His Orchestra).
Tracks: / Symphonic soul / Hangin' out / Sunflower / Mancini generation / Amazing grace / Moonlight sonata / Mystery movie / What's happening / Just you and me together love / NBC Nightly news theme / Once is not enough / Charlie's Angels, Theme from.
LP: . . . . PL 13347

BLUES AND THE BEAT, THE.
LP: . . . . FS 160

DISCO DE OURO (Mancini, Henry & His Orchestra).
Tracks: / Moon river / Charade / Days of wine and roses / Pink panther (theme from) / Peter Gunn / Girl from Ipanema / Dear heart / Romeo and Juliet love theme / Mr. Lucky / Moment to moment / Baby elephant walk / Airport (love theme) / Secret love / Rhapsody in blue.
LP: 109 4004
MC: 709 4004

HENRY MANCINI.
2LP: . . . . ADEP 24

HENRY MANCINI & THE ROYAL PHILHARMONIC POPS ORCHESTRA (Mancini, Henry & The Royal Philharmonic Pops Orchestra).
Tracks: / Thorn birds suite / Sunflower / Moon river / Charade.
LP: . . . . UNKNOWN
MC: . . . . CC 72320

HOLLYWOOD MUSICALS (See under Mathis, Johnny) (Mathis, Johnny & Henry Mancini).

IN THE PINK (see Galway, James & Henry Mancini) (Mancini, Henry & James Galway).

IT MIGHT AS WELL BE SPRING (see also Johnny Mathis) (Mancini, Henry & Johnny Mathis).

JUST YOU AND ME TOGETHER LOVE (Mancini, Henry & His Orchestra).
Tracks: / Just you and me together, love / Scent of your nearness, The / Forgetting the time / Empty glasses, crumpled sheets / Closer / That little old maid / Rhythm of wanting, The.
LP: . . . . PL 12362
MC: . . . . PK 12362

MAGIC OF HENRY MANCINI, THE.
LP: . . . . K 925090 1
MC: 925090 4

MAN AND HIS MUSIC, A.
Tracks: / Baby elephant walk / Peter Gunn / Pink panther (theme from) / Cade's County theme / M.A.S.H., Theme from / Silver streak / Charade / Moon river / It had better be tonight / Shadow of your smile / Girl from Ipanema / Borsalino / Hawaii / Dear heart / How soon? / Midnight cowboy / Lightly latin / Love theme for Laura / Shot in the dark / Days of wine and roses / Sweetheart tree, The / Misty / Charlie's Angels, Theme from / Mona Lisa.
2LP: . . . . CR 059
MCSET: . . . . CRT 059

MANCINI GOES TO THE MOVIES.
Tracks: / Midnight cowboy / Windmills of your mind / Raindrops keep falling on my head / Secret love / As time goes by / Thief who came to dinner, The / Adventures, Love theme from / Love story, Theme from / Evergreen / Shadow of your smile, The / Heaven can wait / Shot in the dark, A / Z, Theme from / Romeo and Juliet, Love theme from.
MC: . . . . NK 75067

MANCINI IN SURROUND.
Tracks: / Surround fantastique / Artic whale hunt (from The White Dawn) / Mommie dearest (theme from) / Frenzy rejected (main title) / Monster movie music suite / Monster gets Mark, The (from Creature from the Black Lagoon) / Thing strikes, The / Desert rendezvous (From It Came From Outer Spa / Terror strikes (from Tarantula) / Casey's theme (from Fear) / Little boys (From: The Man Who Lovem Woman) / Prisoner of Zenda (theme from) / Coronation waltz / Croquette / Nightwing (main title) / Without a clue (music from) / Super sleuth / Without a clue (end title) / Music from sunset / Sunset theme / Cheryl's theme / Cowboys, The.
MC: . . . . RK 60471

MANCINI ROCKS THE POPS (Mancini, Henry/RPO Pops Orchestra).
Tracks: / Walk like an Egyptian / In the air tonight / Thriller / Every breath you take / Material girl / With or without you / Sweet dreams are made of this / La bamba / On the turning away / It's a sin / Imagine / Good old rock 'n' roll / Rock around the clock / Bye bye love / Great balls of fire / Proud Mary / Bad bad Leroy Brown / Blue suede shoes / Shake, rattle and roll / Peggy Sue.
MC: . . . . CC 73078

MANCINI'S ANGELS.
Tracks: / Charlie's Angels, Theme from / Evergreen / Car wash / Inspector Clouseau theme / Silver streak / What's Happening, Theme from / Moneychangers, The / Gonna fly now / Music from Roots / Many rains ago (oluwa) / Roots, Theme from.
LP: . . . . PL 12290

MERRY MANCINI CHRISTMAS, A.
Tracks: / Little drummer boy / Jingle bells / Sleigh ride / Christmas song, The / Winter wonderland / Silver bells / Frosty the snowman / Rudolph the red nosed reindeer / White Christmas / Carol for another Christmas / Silent night / O holy night / O little town of Bethlehem / God rest ye merry gentlemen / Deck the halls / Hark the herald angels sing / We three kings of Orient are / O come all ye faithful / Joy to the world / It came upon a midnight clear / Away in a manger / First Noel, The.
LP: . . . . INTS 5123
MC: . . . . INTK 5123
LP: . . . . NL 81928
MC: . . . . NK 81928

NIGHT VISITOR (Film Soundtrack).
LP: . . . . CT 6015

PURE GOLD: HENRY MANCINI.
Tracks: / Moon river / Days of wine and roses / Charade / Moment to moment / Romeo and Juliet / Pink Panther (theme from) / Mr. Lucky / Baby elephant walk / Peter Gunn / It had better be tonight.
LP: . . . . INTS 5018
MC: . . . . INTK 5018

THEME SCENE (Mancini, Henry & His Orchestra).
Tracks: / Heaven can wait / Battlestar Galactica / Little house on the prairie / Fantasy Island / Star Trek / Three's company / Children of Sanchez / Cheap detective / NBC nightly news theme / Once is not enough.
LP: . . . . PL 13052

THIS IS HENRY MANCINI, VOL.1.
Tracks: / Peter Gunn / Days of wine and roses / Lightly latin / Midnight cowboy / Sweetheart tree, The / Pink Panther theme, The / Romeo and Juliet, Love theme from / Dear heart / Snowfall / Brothers go to mother's, The / Baby elephant walk / Moon river / My friend Andamo / Dreamsville / March of the cue balls / Mr. Lucky / Misty / Robbin's nest / My one and only love / Softly, as I leave you.
2LP: 26 28030
LP: . . . . DPS 2010

THIS IS HENRY MANCINI, VOL.2.
2LP: 26 28038

TOUCH OF EVIL, A (Original Soundtrack).
LP: . . . . FS 293

UNIQUELY MANCINI.
Tracks: / Green onions / Stairway to the stars / Night train / Lullaby of Birdland / Chelsea Bridge / Duke's place / Bonzai pipeline / Rhapsody in blue / Cheers / Lonesome / Hot canary, The / Moonlight serenade.
LP: . . . . NL 89058
MC: . . . . NK 89058

VERY BEST OF HENRY MANCINI, THE.
Tracks: / Moon river / Days of wine and roses / Latin snowfall / Two for the road / Fluter's ball, The / Raindrops keep falling on my head / Loss of love / Peter Gunn / Dreamsville / Love story theme / Pink panther (theme from) / Greatest gift / How soon? / Baby elephant walk / Brass on ivory / Dear heart / Softly as I leave you / Evergreen / Breakfast at Tiffany's.
LP: . . . . PL 89337
MC: . . . . PK 89337

Mancuso, Gus

INTRODUCING GUS MANCUSO.
LP: . . . . FSR 3233
LP: . . . . FS 109

Mandalaband

EYE OF WENDOR, THE.
Tracks: / Eye of Wendor, The / Florians song / Ride to the city / Almars tower / Like the wind / Tempest / Dawn of a new day / Departure from Carthillias Elsethea / Witch of Waldow wood / Silesandre / Aenord's lament / Funeral of the king / Coronation of Damien.
LP: . . . . CHR 1181
MC: . . . . ZCHR 1181

MANDALABAND.
Tracks: / Om mani padme hum (in four movements) / Determination / Song for a king / Roof of the world / Looking in.
LP: . . . . CHR 1095
MC: . . . . ZCHR 1095

Mandator

PERFECT PROGENY.
LP: 081 716 1

Mandel, Harvey

CRISTO REDENTOR.
Tracks: / Wade in the water / Lights out / Bradley's barn / You can't tell me / Nashville 1 am / Cristo redentor / Before six / Lark, The / Snake / Long wait.
LP: . . . . EGED 62
MC: . . . . EGEDC 62

Mandell, Mike

SKY MUSIC.
Tracks: / Pyramids / Just the way you are / Elephant and castle / Peg / As fine as you are / Jupiter finger / Another kind of spring.
LP: . . . . VSD 79409

Mandell, Robert

EASTERN EUROPEAN HURDY-GURDY MUSIC.
LP: . . . . SLPX 18083

ROBERT MANDELL COLLECTION, THE.
MC: . . . . GB 005

Mandeville, John

TRAVELS OF SIR JOHN MANDEVILLE (Various artists).
MC: . . . . ANV 629

Mandingo

NEW WORLD POWER.
LP: . . . . AXLPS 3004
MC: . . . . AXCT 3004

WATTO SITTA.
LP: . . . . CEL 6103

Mandingo (2)

SAVAGE RITE.
LP: . . . . EMC 3217

Mandingo Griot Society

MANDINGO GRIOT SOCIETY.
LP: . . . . FF 076

ONE TRACK MIND.
LP: . . . . FF 269

Mandrell, Barbara

BARBARA MANDRELL LIVE.
LP: . . . . MCF 3124

BEST OF BARBARA MANDRELL.
Tracks: / Woman to woman / Love is thin ice / Hold me / After the lovin' / Married but not to each other / Sleeping single in a double bed / That's what friends are for / Midnight angel / Standing room only / Tonight.
LP: . . . . IMCA 1493

CLEAN CUT.
LP: . . . . MCF 3218
MC: . . . . MCFC 3218

COUNTRY STORE: BARBARA MANDRELL.
LP: . . . . CST 36
MC: . . . . CSTK 36

GET TO THE HEART.
Tracks: / I'm a believer / Fast lanes and country roads / I'd fall in love tonight / Don't look in my eyes / Angel in your arms / For your love / If they grew tired of my music / You only you / Survivors / When you get to the heart.
LP: . . . . IMCA 5619

GREATEST HITS: BARBARA MANDRELL.
Tracks: / I was country when country wasn't cool / Years / Wish you were here / Best of strangers / Happy birthday dear heartache / If loving you is wrong I don't want to be right / Crackers / One of a kind pair of fools / In times like these / There's no love in Tennessee.
LP: . . . . IMCA 5566

IN BLACK AND WHITE.
LP: . . . . MCF 3140

LOOKING BACK.
LP: . . . . CBS 32127

MIDNIGHT ANGEL.
Tracks: / From Saturday night to Sunday quiet / Partners / Better off by myself / Fool's gold / It's a beautiful morning with you / Pillow pleasure / Midnight angel / I count you / I never said I love you / Slippin' around again / Married but not to each other.
LP: . . . . ABCL 5206

MOODS.
LP: . . . . MCF 3011

SURE FEELS GOOD.
Tracks: / You keep me hangin' on / Child support / Angels love bad men / One of us is always leaving / Sunshine street / I'm glad I married you / Sure feels good / Just to satisfy you / You can't get there from here / It all came true / Hangin' on / If it don't come easy / Love me like you used to / I won't take less than your love / I wonder what he's doing tonight / I'll Tennessee you in / Alien / Temporarily blue / If I didn't love you / Heartbreaker / Hope you find what you're loving for.
LP: . . . . AML 3122
MC: . . . . TCAML 3122

Mandrell, Louise

LOUISE MANDRELL.
LP: . . . . EPC 32130
MC: 40 32130

Mandrill

NEW WORLDS.
Tracks: / Too late / It's so easy lovin' you / Third world girl / Mean streets / When you smile.
LP: . . . . ARTY 162

Manetta, Fess

WHOREHOUSE PIANO.
LP: . . . . JCE 6

Manfila, Kante

TRADITION.
LP: . . . . STERNS 1021

Manfred Mann

20 YEARS OF MANFRED MANN'S EARTHBAND (Manfred Mann's Earthband).
Tracks: / Blinded by the light / Joybringer / Somewhere in Africa / You angel you / Questions / For you / California / Tribal statistics / Davy's on the road again / Runner, The / Mighty quinn, The / Angels at the gate.
LP: . . . . BOMME 1LP
MC: . . . . BOMME 1MC

ANGEL STATION (Manfred Mann's Earthband).
Tracks: / Don't kill it Carol / You angel you / Hollywood town / Belle of the earth / Platform end / Angels at the gate / You are / I am / Waiting for the rain / Resurrection.
LP: . . . . LLP 124
MC: . . . . LLK 124
LP: . . . . BRON 516
LP: . . . . COMME 4
MC: . . . . COMMEC 4

AS IS.
LP: . . . . TL 5377

BEST OF MANFRED MANN.
Tracks: / Do wah diddy diddy / 5-4-3-2-1 / One in the middle, The / If you gotta go, go now / Sha-la-la / Hi lili hi lo / Oh no, not my baby / Come tomorrow / Pretty flamingo / There's no living without your loving / With God on our side / Watermelon man / It's gonna work out fine / Don't ask me what I say / I'm your kingpin / Got my mojo working / Cock-a-hoop.
LP: 9279 307
MC: 7259 307
LP: . . . . NUT 7
LP: 1A 022 58029
MC: 1A 222 58029

BUDAPEST (Manfred Mann's Earthband).
Tracks: / Spirits in the night / Demolition man / For you / Davy's on the road again / Lies (through the 80's) / Blinded by the light / Redemption song / Mighty Quinn.
MC: . . . . BRONC 550
LP: . . . . BRON 550

CHANCE (Manfred Mann's Earthband).
Tracks: / Lies (through the 80's) / One the run / For you / Adolescent dream / Fritz the blank / Stranded / This is your heart / No guarantee / Heart on the street.
LP: . . . . CLALP 133
MC: . . . . CLAMC 133
LP: . . . . BRON 529
LP: . . . . COMME 9
MC: . . . . COMMEC 9

COLLECTION: MANFRED MANN.

2LP: CCSLP 245
MC: CCSMC 245

COLLECTION: MANFRED MANN.
LP: IC 028 07532

CRIMINAL TANGO (Manfred Mann's Earthband).
Tracks: / Going underground / Who are the mystery kids / Banquet / Killer on the loose / Do anything you wanna do / Rescue / You got me right through the heart / Hey bulldog / Crossfire.
LP: XID 17
MC: CXID 17

EP COLLECTION, THE: MANFRED MANN.
Tracks: / 5-4-3-2-1 / Cock-a-hoop / Without you / Groovin' / Do wah diddy diddy / Can't believe it / One in the middle, The / Watermelon man / What am I to do / With God on our side / There's no living without your loving / Tired trying, bored of lying, scared of dying / I can't believe what you say / That's all I ever want from you baby / It's getting late / Machines / She needs company / Tenessee waltz / When will I be loved / I got you babe.
LP: SEE 252
MC: SEEK 252

FIVE FACES OF MANFRED MANN.
LP: CLP 1731

GLORIFIED MAGNIFIED (Manfred Mann's Earthband).
Tracks: / Meat / Look around / One way glass / I'm gonna have you all / Down home / Our friend George / Ashes to the wind / Wind / It's all over now / Baby blue / Glorified magnified.
LP: BRON 257

GOOD EARTH, THE (Manfred Mann's Earthband).
Tracks: / Give me the good earth / Launching place / I'll be gone / Earth hymn (parts 1 & 2) / Sky high / Be not too hard.
LP: BRON 306

HITS 1966-69.
LP: PRICE 66
MC: PRIMC 66

LIVE IN BUDAPEST (Manfred Mann's Earthband).
Tracks: / Spirits in the night / For you / Lies (through the '80s) / Redemption song / Demolition man / Davy's on the road again / Blinded by the light / Mighty Quinn, The.
LP: COMME 10
MC: COMMEC 10

MANFRED MANN.
LP: 1A 052 05021

MANFRED MANN'S EARTHBAND (Manfred Mann's Earthband).
Tracks: / California coastline / Captain Bobby Stout / Sloth / Living without you / Tribute / Please Mrs. Henry / Jump sturdy / Prayer / Part-time man / Up and leaving.
LP: BRON 252
LP: CLALP 150
MC: CLAMC 150
LP: COMME 6
MC: COMMET 6

MANN MADE.
LP: CLP 1911

MANN MADE HITS.
LP: CLP 3559

MANN MADE/FIVE FACES OF MANFRED MANN.
Tracks: / You're for me / Look away / Bare hugg / L.S.D. / Sack o'woe / I'm your kingpin / Hoochie Coochie man / Untie me / Without you / Bring it to Jerome / Smokestack lightning / Down the road apiece.
2LP: EDP 1546363

MANNERISMS.
LP: SON 016

MASQUE (Manfred Mann's Earthband).
Tracks: / Joybringer / Billies orno bounce (including Billies bounce) / What you give is what you get (start) / Rivers run dry, The / Planets schmanets / Geronimo's cadillac / Sister Billies bounce (inc. Sister Sadie and B / Telegram to Monica / Couple of mates, A (from Mars and Jupiter) / Neptune (icebringer) / Hymn (from Jupiter) / We're going wrong.
LP: DIX 69
MC: CDIX 69

MESSIN' (Manfred Mann's Earthband).
Tracks: / Messin' / Buddah / Cloudy eyes / Get your rocks off / Sad joy / Black and blue / Mardi Gras day.
LP: BRON 261
LP: CLALP 151
MC: CLAMC 151
LP: COMME 7
MC: COMMET 7

NIGHTINGALES AND BOMBERS (Manfred Mann's Earthband).
Tracks: / Spirits in the night / Countdown / Time is right / Crossfade / Visionary mountains / Nightingales and bombers / Fat Nelly / As above so below.
LP: BRON 337
LP: CLALP 137
LP: COMME 8
MC: COMMET 8

R & B YEARS, THE.
Tracks: / Without you / Don't ask me what I say / I'm your kingpin / Got my mojo working / Down the road apiece / Hoochie coochie man / Can't believe it / Driva man / Hubble bubble (toil and trouble) / Smokestack lightning / It's gonna work out fine / Did you have to do that / Let's go get stoned / I put a spell on you / Why shouldn't we not / Bring it to Jerome / Poison ivy / Cock-a-hoop / You've got to take it.
LP: CM 105
MC: CMK 105

ROARING SILENCE, THE (Manfred Mann's Earthband).
LP: LLP 122
MC: LLK 122
LP: COMME 2
MC: COMMET 2

ROARING SILENCE, THE (Manfred Mann's Earthband).
Tracks: / Blinded by the light / Singing the dolphin through / Waiter, there's a yawn in my ear / Road to Babylon, The / This side of paradise / Starbird / Questions.
LP: BRON 357
LP: ILPS 9357
LP: LLP 122
MC: LLK 122
LP: COMME 2
MC: COMMET 2

SEMI-DETACHED SUBURBAN (20 great hits).
Tracks: / Do wah diddy diddy / 5-4-3-2-1 / Sha la la / Hubble bubble / Hi lili hi lo / One in the middle / Got my mojo working / With God on our side / Come tomorrow / If you gotta go, go now / Pretty flamingo / Semi detached suburban Mr. Jones / Mr. James / There's no loving without your loving / Just like a woman / Oh no not my baby / Ha ha said the clown / My name is Jack / Fox on the run / Ragamuffin man / Mighty Quinn.
MC: TC EMTV 19
LP: EMTV 19

SINGLES ALBUM: MANFRED MANN.
Tracks: / Why should we not / Brother Jack / Cock a hoop / Now you're needing me / 5-4-3-2-1 / Without you / Hubble bubble toil and trouble / I'm your kingpin / Do wah diddy diddy / What you gonna do / Sha-la-la / John Hardy / Come tomorrow / What did I do wrong / Oh no not my baby / What am I doing wrong / If you gotta go, go now / Stay around / Pretty flamingo / You're standing by.
LP: EMS 1121
MC: TCEMS 1121

SOLAR FIRE (Manfred Mann's Earthband).
LP: LLP 121
MC: LLK 121
LP: COMME 1
MC: COMMET 1

SOLAR FIRE (BRONZE) (Manfred Mann's Earthband).
Tracks: / Father of night / In the beginning / Pluto the dog / Solar fire / Saturn - (Mercury) / Earth the circle (parts 1 and 2).
LP: BRNA 265

SOMEWHERE IN AFRICA (Manfred Mann's Earthband).
Tracks: / Tribal statistics / Eyes of nostradamus / Third world service / Demolition man / Brothers and sisters / To Bantustan (Africa suite) / Koze kobenini (How long must we wait?) (Africa) / Lalela, redemption song (no kwazulu) / Somewhere in Africa.
LP: BRON 543
MC: BRONC 543
LP: LLP 125
MC: LLK 125
LP: COMME 3
MC: COMMET 3

SOUL OF MANFRED MANN.
Tracks: / I got you babe / Bare hugg / Spirit feel / Why should you not / L.S.D. / I can't get no satisfaction / God rest ye merry gentlemen / My generation / Mr. Anello / Still I'm sad / Tengo, tengo / Brother Jack / Abominable snowman / Sack o' woe.
LP: SEE 52
LP: CSD 3594

VERY BEST OF MANFRED MANN (1963-1966).
LP: MFP 41 5651 1
MC: MFP 41 5651 4

WATCH (Manfred Mann's Earthband).
LP: LLP 123
MC: LLK 123
LP: BRON 507
LP: COMME 3
MC: COMMET 3

Manga, Bebe

AMIE.
LP: 425001

Mangal

PUNJABI EXTRA.
MC: CMUT 1089

RAIN GADDI 2.
MC: CMUT 1088

Mangas, Yiorgos

YIORGOS MANGAS.
Tracks: / Tsifteteli rok / Roumaniko / Autoschediasmos / Ibon / Chorepste / Ta chrysa dactyla / Yia tous anthropous pou agapao / Skaros / To diko mou.
LP: ORB 021

Mangelsdorff

ETERNAL RHYTHM.
LP: MPS 68 225

LIVE IN TOKYO.
LP: ENJA 2006

SPONTANEOUS.
LP: ENJA 2064

TRILOGUE-LIVE.
LP: MPS 68 175

WIDE POINT, THE (Mangelsdorff/ Jones/Danielson).
LP: MPS 68 071

Mangeshkar, Lata

BEST OF LATA MANGESHKAR - VOLUME 4.
MC: TCS 42566

Mangione, Chuck

BEST OF CHUCK MANGIONE Compact/Walkman jazz.
MC: 830 696 4

BEST OF CHUCK MANGIONE.
Tracks: / Hill where the Lord hides / Lullaby for Nancy Carol / And in the beginning / Land of make believe / Legend of the one eyed sailor / As long as we're together / Freddie's walkin' / Friends and love theme.
2LP: 6672 019

BEST OF CHUCK MANGIONE VOL 1.
LP: 9279 150
MC: 7159 150

EVENING OF MAGIC, AN.
Tracks: / Feels so good / XIth commandment / Chase the clouds away / Hill where the Lord hides / Doin' everything with you / Love the feelin' / I get crazy / Land of make believe / Hide and seek / Day after / Children of Sanchez / B'bye.
2LP: AMLM 66701

EYE OF THE VEILED TEMPTRESS.
Tracks: / That's nice / Eyes of the veiled temptress / Do you ever think about me / Open their eyes / Long hour soulful / Sweet butterfly / Freedom song.
LP: 4611621
MC: 4611624

FEELS SO GOOD.
Tracks: / Feels so good / Maui waui / Side Street, Theme from / Hide and seek / Last dance / XIth commandment, The.
LP: AMLH 64658

JAZZ BROTHER.
Tracks: / Hey baby / Bag's groove / Night has a thousand eyes / Givin' the business / Wha's happ'nin' / Just you, just me / Old folks / Bassett sound / Recuerdo / Big foot / I had the craziest dream / Solar / Blues for Saandar / If ever I should leave you / Little prince.
2LP: M 47042

JOURNEY TO A RAINBOW.
LP: CBS 25435
MC: 40 25435

LOVE NOTES.
Tracks: / Steppin' out / No problem / Memories of Scirocco / To the 80's / Love notes.
LP: CBS 85879

SAVE TONIGHT FOR ME.
LP: 26890

TARANTELLA.
Tracks: / Tarantella / Neopolitan tarantella / XIth Commandment suite / Legend of the one eyed sailor / Bellavia / Hill where the Lord hides / Lake Placid fanfare / Things to come / Round midnight / Manteca / My one and only love / All blues.
2LP: AMLM 66703

Mangorama

SHIFTING SANDS.
LP: LRF 192

Mangrove Steel Band

FEEL FOR STEEL, A.
LP: LLP 2

Mangwana, Sam

ALADJI.
Tracks: / Trans beros / Aladji / Toyaki kobina / Kabi bi / Antonio / Soweto.
LP: SYL 8336

N'SIMBA ELI.
LP: CEL 6639

Manhattan

MANHATTAN (Film Soundtrack) (Various artists).
Tracks: / Rhapsody in blue: *Various artists* / Someone to watch over me: *Various artists* / I've got a crush on you: *Various artists* / Embraceable you: *Various artists* / Land of the gay caballero: *Various artists*/ Do do do: *Various artists* / S'wonderful: *Various artists* / Mine: *Various artists* / He loves and she loves: *Various artists* / Bronco buster's ball: *Various artists* / Lady be good: *Various artists* / Love is here to stay: *Various artists* / Sweet and low down: *Various artists* / Blue, blue, blue: *Various artists*/ But not for me: *Various artists* / Strike up the band: *Various artists* / Love is sweeping the country: *Various artists.*
LP: 73875
MC: 40 73875

Manhattan Jazz Quintet

AUTUMN LEAVES.
Tracks: / Jordu / Recado bossa nova / Confirmation / Autumn leaves / Mood piece.
LP: K 28P 6350

LIVE: MANHATTAN JAZZ QUINTET.
2LP: K 20P 6429

MANHATTAN JAZZ QUINTET.
Tracks: / Summertime / Rosario / Milestones / My favourite things / Airegin / Summer waltz.
LP: K 28P 6313

MY FAVOURITE THINGS.
LP: K 28P 6452

MY FUNNY VALENTINE.
Tracks: / Mr. P.C. / Round midnight / On a clear day / New York state of mind / U blues.
LP: K 28P 6410

PLAYS BLUE NOTE.
Tracks: / Cleopatra's dream / Cool struttin' / Sweet love of mine / Dear old Stockholm / Wolf pack / Cheesecake / For Alfred / Moanin'.
LP: K28P 6480

Manhattan Jazz Septet

MANHATTAN JAZZ SEPTET.
Tracks: / King Porter stomp / Never never land / Like listen / Since when / Love of my life / Rapid transit / Flute cocktail / At bat for K.C. / Do you know what it means to miss New Orleans / My shining hour / Thou svelt / There will never be another you.
LP: JASM 1017

Manhattan Project

MANHATTAN PROJECT, THE (Film Soundtrack) (Various artists).
Tracks: / Michel's waltz: *Various artists* / Dania: *Various artists* / Old wine, new bottles: *Various artists*/ Stella by starlight: *Various artists* / Goodbye pork pie hat: *Various artists* / Virgo rising: *Various artists*/ Nefertiti: *Various artists* / Summertime: *Various artists.*
LP: STV 81282
MC: CTV 81282
LP: B1 94204
MC: 794 204 1

Manhattan Sounds

FAX AND STEEL VOL 1.
LP: AALP 57

Manhattan Transfer

BODIES AND SOULS.
Tracks: / Spice of life / This independence / Mystery / American pop / Soldier of fortune / Code of ethics / Malaise en malaise / Down South camp meeting / Why not / Goodbye love / Night that Monk returned to heaven, The.
LP: 780 104-1
MC: 780 104-4

BOP DOO WOP.
Tracks: / Unchained melody / Route 66 / My cat fell in the well / Duke of Dubuque / How high the moon / Baby come back to me / Safronia B / Heart's desire / That't the way it goes.
LP: 781 233-1
MC: 781 233-4

BRASIL.

Tracks: / Soul food to go / Zoo blues / So you say / Capim / Metroplis / Hear the voices / Agua / Jungle pioneer, The / Notes from the underground.
LP: 781 803-1
MC: 781 803-4

COMING OUT.
Tracks: / Don't let go / Zindy Lou / Chanson d'amour / Helpless / Scotch and soda / Speak up mambo, The / Cuentame / Poinciana / S.O.S. / Popsicle toes / It wouldn't have made any difference / Thought of loving you, The.
LP: . . . . K 50291
MC: K4 50291

EXTENSIONS.
Tracks: / Birdland / Wacky dust / Nothin' you can do about it / Coo coo-u / Body and soul (Eddie and the bean) / Twilight zone (part 1) / Twilight zone (part 2) / Trickle trickle / Shaker song, The / Foreign affair.
LP: . . . . K 50674
MC: K4 50674

LIVE: MANHATTAN TRANSFER.
Tracks: / Four brothers / Rambo / (You should) meet Benny Bailey / Airegin II / To you / Sing joy Spring / Move / That's killer Joe / Duke of Dubuque,The / Gloria / On the boulevard / Shaker song, The / Ray's rockhouse.
LP: 781 723-1
MC: 781 723-4
LP: . . . . K 50540
MC: K4 50540

MANHATTAN TRANSFER.
Tracks: / Tuxedo Junction / Sweet talking guy / Operator / Candy / Gloria / Clap your hands / That cat is high / You can depend on me / Blue champagne / Occapella / Heart's desire.
LP: . . . . K 50138

MANHATTAN TRANSFER & GENE PISTILLI.
LP: . . . . MFP 50387

MECCA FOR MODERNS.
Tracks: / On the Boulevard / Boy from New York City / Smile again / Dead or alive / Spies in the night / Corner pocket / Confirmation / Kafka / Nightingale sang in Berkeley Square.
MC: K4 50789
LP: . . . . K 50789

PASTICHE.
Tracks: / Four brothers / Gal in Calico, A / Love for sale / Je voulais (te dire que je t'attends) / On a little street in Singapore / In a mellow tone / Walk in love / Who, what, when, where and why / It's not the spotlight / Pieces of dreams / Where did our love go.
LP: . . . . K 50444
MC: K4 60167

VOCALESE.
Tracks: / That's killer Joe / Rambo / Airegin / To you / (You should) meet Benny Bailey / Another night in Tunisia / Ray's rockhouse / Blee blop blues / Oh yes, I remember Clifford / Sing joyspring / Move.
LP: 781 266-1
MC: 781 266-4

Manhattans

6 TRACK HITS.
Tracks: / Kiss and say goodbye / There's no me without you / Don't take your love / Wonderful world of love / We never danced to a love song / La la la wish upon a star.
MC: 7SC 5027

AFTER MIDNIGHT.
Tracks: / Shining star / It's not the same / Girl of my dream / Cloudy, with a chance of tears / Closer you are, The / If my heart could speak / One life to love / Just as long as I have you / It couldn't hurt / Tired of the single life / I'll never run away from love again.
LP: . . . . CBS 84223

BACK TO BASICS.
Tracks: / Change of heart / Where did we go wrong / All I need / I'm through trying to prove my love to you / Mr. D.J. / Back into the night / Just like you / Maybe tomorrow / Don't look in my eyes / Neither one of us.
LP: 4500631
MC: 4500634

BEST OF THE MANHATTANS.
Tracks: / Hurt / We never danced to a love song / Reasons / Am I losing you / Fever / There's no me without you / La la la wish upon a star / Kiss & say goodbye / Don't take your love / Soul train / Summertime in the city / Tomorrow / It's you.
LP: . . . . CBS 31806
MC: 40 31806

CRAZY (OLD GOLD) (See under O'Jays - Put our heads together).

FOREVER BY YOUR SIDE.
Tracks: / Crazy / Start all over again / Forever by your side / Just the lonely talking again / Locked up in your love / Lover's paradise / Love is gonna find you / I'm ready to love you again.
LP: . . . . CBS 25353
MC: 40 25353

HEART AND SOUL OF THE MANHATTANS.
Tracks: / Kiss and say goodbye / Hurt / It's you / Shining star / Crazy / There's no me without you / Don't take your love / I kinda miss you / It feels so good to be loved so bad / We never danced to a love song / Am I losing you / You send me / Where did we go wrong? / Forever by your side.
MC: . . . . KNMC 12057

LOVE TALK.
Tracks: / After you / Love talk / Right feeling / At the wrong time / Devil in the dark / Here comes the hurt again / I just wanna be the one in your life / That's not part of the show / Way we were / Memories / We tried.
LP: . . . . CBS 83342

MANHATTANS.
LP: . . . . CBS 81513

TOO HOT TO STOP IT.
Tracks: / Don't say no / You send me / Angel of the night / When we are made as one / C'est la vie / Dreamin' / You're gonna love being loved by me / Too hot to stop it.
LP: . . . . CBS 26162

Mania

CHANGING TIMES.
Tracks: / Prelude (intro) / Expulsion, The / Turn towards the light / No way back / Be strong / To the end of the world / Vision, The / Gambler / We don't need war / Violent time.
LP: . . . . NUK 139
MC: . . . . ZCNUK 139

WIZARD OF THE LOST KINGDOM.
MLP: . . . . NUK 127
MLP: . . . . N 0127 4

Maniacs

OVERSAXED.
LP: . . . . PENT 1211

Manifesto

MANIFESTO (Various artists).
LP: . . . . MASO 33045

Manifold, Keith

DANNY BOY.
LP: . . . . WRS 096

REMEMBERING.
LP: . . . . WRS 139

TIME.
LP: . . . . FER 020

Manilla Road

MANILLA ROAD LIVE.
LP: . . . . BD 033

MYSTIFICATION.
LP: . . . . BD 024

Manilow, Barry

2.00 AM PARADISE CAFE.
Tracks: / Where have you gone / Say no more / Blue / When October goes / What am I doin' here / Goodbye my love / Big city blues / When love is gone / I've never been so low on love / Night song.
LP: 206496
MC: 406496
MC: 410961

BARRY.
Tracks: / Lonely together / Bermuda Triangle / I made it through the rain / Twenty four hours a day / Dance away / Life will go on / Only in Chicago / Last duet, The / London / We still have time.
LP: . . . . DLART 2
MC: . . . . TLART 2
MC: 411321

BARRY - LIVE IN BRITAIN.
Tracks: / It's a miracle / Old songs medley, The (Tracks include The Old Songs, Don't wanna walk without you, Let's hang o) / Stay / Beautiful music / I made it through the rain / Bermuda Triangle / Break down the door / Who's been sleeping in my bed / Copacabana / Could it be magic / Mandy / London - we'll meet again / One voice.
LP: . . . . ARTV 4
MC: . . . . ARTVC 4
MC: 411320

BARRY MANILOW 1.
LP: . . . . FA 3067
MC: . . . . TCFA 3067

BARRY MANILOW BOX SET.
Tracks: / I want to be somebody's baby / Early morning strangers / Mandy / Two of us, The / Something's comin' up / It's a miracle / Avenue C / My baby loves me / Sandra / Home again / New York City rhythm / Tryin' to get the feeling again / Why don't we live together / Bandstand boogie / You're leavin' too soon / She's a star / I write the songs / As sure as I'm standin' here / Nice boy like me, A / Lay me down / Beautiful music / This one's for you / Daybreak / You oughta be home with me / Jump shout boogie / Weekend in New England / Riders to the stars / Let me go / Looks like we made it / Say the words / All the time / Why don't you see the show again.
LPS: . . . . BM BOX 1
MCSET: . . . . TCBOX 1

BECAUSE IT'S CHRISTMAS.
Tracks: / Christmas song, The / Jingle bells / Silent night / I guess there ain't no Santa Claus / First Noel, The / When the meadow was bloomin' / For unto us a child is born / Because it's Christmas (for all children) / Baby, it's cold outside / White Christmas / Carol of the bells / Bells of Christmas / Joy to the world / Have yourself a merry little Christmas / We wish you a merry Christmas / It's just another New Years Eve.
LP: 211127
MC: 411127

EVEN NOW.
Tracks: / Copacabana / Somewhere in the night / Linda song, A / Can't smile without you / Leavin' in the morning / Where do I go from here / Even now / I was a fool (to let you go) / Losing touch / I just want to be the one in your life / Starting again / Sunrise.
LP: 201125
MC: 401125
LP: . . . . SPART 1047
MC: . . . . TCART 1047

GIFT SET.
LP: . . . . BOX 1

GREATEST HITS: BARRY MANILOW (Volume 1).
Tracks: / Ships / Some kind of friend / I made it / Through the rain / Put a quarter in the jukebox / One voice / Old songs, The / Let's hang on / Memory / You're looking hot tonight.
LP: 208552
MC: 408552

I WANNA DO IT WITH YOU.
LP: 210927
MC: 410927

IF I SHOULD FALL IN LOVE AGAIN.
LP: 210926
MC: 410926

IF I SHOULD LOVE AGAIN.
Tracks: / Old songs, The / Let's hang on / If I should love again / Don't fall in love with me / Break down the door / Somewhere down the road / No other love / Fools get lucky / I haven't changed the room / Let's take all night (to say goodbye).
LP: . . . . BMAN 1
MC: . . . . TCBM 1

LIVE ON BROADWAY.
Tracks: / Sweet life / It's a long way up / Brooklyn blues / Memory / Upfront / God bless the other 99 / Mandy / It's a miracle / Some good things never last / If you remember me / Do like I do / Best seat in the house / Gonzo hits medley, The / If I can dream.
MCSET: 503785
2LP: 303785

MANDY.
Tracks: / Mandy / Copacabana / Mandy / I want to be somebody's baby / Early morning strangers / It's a miracle / Avenue.
LP: . . . . ARTY 100
MC: . . . . TCART 100

MANILOW.
Tracks: / At the dance / If you were here with me tonight / Sweet heaven / Ain't nothing like the real thing / It's a long way up / I'm your man / It's all behind us now / In search of love / He doesn't care (but I do) / Some sweet day.
LP: . . . . PL 87044
MC: . . . . PK 87044

MANILOW LIVE.
Tracks: / Riders to the stars / Why don't we live together / Looks like we made it / New York City / Very strange medley, A / Beautiful music (part II) / Could it be magic / Mandy / It's a miracle / It's just another New Year's Eve / I write the songs / Beautiful music (part III) / Jump shout boogie (medley) / This one's for you / Beautiful music / Daybreak / Lay me down / Weekend in New England / Studio musician.
2LP: . . . . DARTY 3
MCSET: . . . . TCDAR 3

MANILOW MAGIC-THE BEST OF BARRY MANILOW.
Tracks: / Mandy / Copacabana / Could it be magic / Can't smile without you / New York city rhythm / Looks like we made it / Ready to take a chance again / Tryin' to get the feelin' again / Weekend in New England / It's a miracle / All the time / I write the songs.
LP: . . . . ARTV 2
MC: . . . . ARTCV 2

MANILOW MIRACLES.
Tracks: / Copacabana / Can't smile without you / I don't want to walk without you / Even now / One voice / Riders to the stars / Why don't we live together / Looks like we made it / New York City rhythm / Beautiful music part II / Could it be magic / Mandy / It's a miracle / It's just another New Year's Eve / I write the songs / Beautiful music (part III) / Very strange medley, A / Jump shout boogie (medley) / This one's for you / Beautiful music / Daybreak / Lay me down / Weekend in New England / Studio musician / (Why don't we try) a slow dance / Rain / Ships / You could show me / Who's been sleeping in my bed / Where are they now / Bobble Lee (what's the difference I gotta live) / When I wanted you / Sunday father / Somewhere in the night / Linda song, A / Leavin' in the morning / Were do I go from here / I was a fool / Losing touch / I just want to be the one in your life / Starting again / Sunrise.
LPS: . . . . BMBOX 2
MC: . . . . TCBOX 2

ONE VOICE.
Tracks: / One voice / (Why don't we try) a slow dance / Rain / Ships / You could show me / I don't want to walk without you / Who's been sleeping in my bed / Where are they now / Bobble Lee (what's the difference, I gotta live) / When I wanted you / Sunday Father.
LP: 201154
MC: 401154

REFLECTIONS.
Tracks: / It's a miracle / Could it be magic / Looks like we made it.
LP: . . . . CDS 1231
MC: . . . . CAM 1231

SONGS 1975-1990, THE.
Tracks: / I write the songs / One voice / Old songs, The / Don't want to walk without you / Some good things never last (live) / Somewhere down the road / When I wanted you / Stay / Even now / Read 'em and weep / Somewhere in the night / I made it through the rain / Daybreak (live) / Please don't be scared / Looks like we made it / Mandy / If I should love again (live) / All the time / Copacabana / Keep each other warm / Weekend in New England / Lonely together / Can't smile without you / Trying to get the feeling again / Could it be magic? / Brooklyn blues / Who needs to dream? / Ready to take the chance again / If I can dream.
LP: 303868
MC: 503868

SONGS TO MAKE THE WHOLE WORLD SING.
Tracks: / Please don't be scared / One that got away, The / Keep each other warm / Once and for all / When the good times come again / In another world / My moonlight memories of you / Little travelling music please, A / Some good things never last / You begin again / Anyone can do the heartbreak.
LP: 209927
MC: 409927

SWING STREET.
Tracks: / Swing Street / Big fun / Stompin' at the Savoy / Black and blue / Hey mambo / Summertime / Brooklyn blues / Stardust / Once when you were mine.
LP: 208860
MC: 408860

THIS ONE'S FOR YOU.
Tracks: / Daybreak / You oughta be home with me / Jump shout boogie / Weekend in New England / Riders to the stars / This ones for you / Let me go / Looks like we made it / Say the words / All the time / Why don't you see the show again.
LP: . . . . ARTY 137
MC: . . . . TCART 137

TOUCH MORE MAGIC, A.
Tracks: / You're looking hot tonight / Let's hang on / I wanna do it with you / I'm gonna sit right down and write myself a letter / Some kind of friend / Bermuda Triangle / Stay / Put a quarter in the jukebox / Old songs, The / I made it through the rain / Lonely together / Even now / Memory / One voice.
LP: . . . . BMAN 3
MC: . . . . TCBM 3

TRYIN' TO GET THE FEELING.
LP: . . . . FA 3050
MC: . . . . TCFA 3050

Maninnya Blade

MERCHANTS IN METAL.
Tracks: / Live life at speed / Fireborn / Bearer of the ring / Attila the hun / Raiders / Dance to evil / No pax Romana / Nosferatu / Voyage to Hades, A / Metal pride.
LP: . . . . **KILP 4005**

Manish Boys

MANISH BOYS/DAVY JONES & THE LOWER THIRD (Manish Boys/Davy Jones & Lower Third).
Tracks: / I pity the fool / Take my tip / You've got a habit of leaving / Baby loves that way.
MLP: . . . . **CYM 1**

Manitobas Wild Kingdom

AND YOU.
Tracks: / Party starts now, The / New York, New York / I want you tonite / Perfect high, The / Prototype / Haircut and attitude / DWI / Fired up / Had it coming / Speedball.
LP: . . . . **MCG 6087**
MC: . . . . **MCGC 6087**

Manklan

FLESH MACHINE.
LP: . . . . **WRLP 007**

Mann, Barry

SONGWRITERS FOR THE STARS 2 (see Foster, David) (Mann, Barry/David Foster/Cynthia Weil).

Mann, Carl

GONNA ROCK'N'ROLL TONIGHT.
Tracks: / Till I waltz again with you / Gonna rock'n'roll tonight / Why do I keep telling lies to me / Look at that moon / Paradise / I'm left you're right she's gone / No one to talk to / Red sails in the sunset / I'm coming home / South of the border / Mountain dew / Rockin' love / If I could change you / Pretend / You win again / Mona Lisa.
LP: . . . . **CRL 5008**

IN ROCKABILLY COUNTRY.
LP: . . . . **CR 30205**

LEGENDARY SUN PERFORMERS.
Tracks: / Mona Lisa / Rockin' love / Pretend / Kansas City / I'm coming home / Walkin' and thinkin' / If I ever needed love / Don't let the stars get in your eyes / Ain't got no home / Look at the moon / Baby I don't care / I'm bluer than anyone can be / Mexicala rose / Tbangi stomp / Walking the dog.
LP: . . . . **CR 30130**

LIKE MANN.
LP: . . . . **CRM 2006**

MONA LISA ROCKER, THE.
LP: **33.8022**

ROCKING MANN, THE.
Tracks: / Mona Lisa / Foolish one / Pretend / Rockin' love / Some enchanted evening / I can't forget / South of the border / I'm coming home / Baby I don't care / Vanished / Wayward wind / Born to be bad / I ain't got no home / If I could change you / Mountain dew / When I grow too old to dream / I'm bluer than anyone can be / Walkin' and thinkin' / If I ever needed love / Island of love / Stop the world / Don't let the stars get in your eyes / Look at that moon / Too young / Because of you / Ain't you got no lovin' for me? / Kansas City / Blueberry Hill / Walking the dog / Ubangi stomp / Mona Lisa (reprise).
2LP: . . . . **CDX 17**

Mann, Charles

WALK OF LIFE.
Tracks: / Walk of life / Borderline / She's about a mover / Hearts of stone / Slowdown / Mama mama / Red red wine / Don't tell me, tell my heart / My life is a lonely one / I'm just a wondering / Hey baby / She's my kind of girl / You're no longer mine.
LP: . . . . **GUMBO 002**
MC: . . . . **GUMBOC 002**

Mann, Dany

NA BABY, WEI GEHT'S.
Tracks: / Hula hoop song / Little bird told me, A / Stupid cupid / Forget me not / Love me in the daytime / Such a night.
LP: . . . . **BFX 15077**

Mann, David

GAMES.
Tracks: / Games / Illumination / Song for Amy / Under the bridge / Night version / Urban eyes / Heart of darkness / Travelling song.
LP: . . . . **AN 8702**
MC: . . . . **ANC 8702**

Mann, Doug

SINGING STREET, THE.
Tracks: / Monkey Mary / Poor Hans / Cocoanit Tam / Mister Penny / Monster legend / Balloon Bobby / Singing street, The / Claude / Summer in Seville / Dali the bashful elephant / Crows over a cornfield / Kamikaze budgie, The / Hirondelle.
LP: . . . . **OKLP 3002**
MC: . . . . **ZCOK 3002**

Mann, Herbie

BIRD IN A SILVER CAGE.
Tracks: / Bird in a silver cage / Aria / Fly, robin, fly / Birdwalk / Years of love / Piper, The.
LP: . . . . **K 50338**

LONDON UNDERGROUND.
Tracks: / Bitch / Something in the air / Layla / Spin ball / Mellow yellow / White shade of pale, A / Memphis spoon and dover sole / Paper sun / You never give me your money.
LP: . . . . **K 50032**

MEMPHIS UNDERGROUND.
Tracks: / Memphis underground / New Orleans / Hold on I'm coming / Chain of fools / Battle hymn of the republic.
LP: . . . . **K 50520**
LP: . . . . **K 40038**

NIRVANA (Mann, Herbie & Bill Evans).
Tracks: / Nirvana / Gymnopedie / I love you / Willow weep for me / Lover man / Cashmere.
LP: . . . . **K 50238**

OPALESCENCE.
LP: **139020 1**
MC: **139020 4**

TWO AMIGOS (See under Valentin, Dave) (Valentin, Dave & Herbie Mann).

Mann, John

CHRISTIE SOUND, THE.
Tracks: / Alicante / Even now / Gold and silver waltz / New Turkish patrol, The / Flanagan & Allen selection / Elephants tango, The / Macushla / H.M.S. Pinafore selection / Little red monkey / Haunting rag / Sussex by the sea.
LP: . . . . **GRS 1114**

EMINENT EXPERIENCE, AN (Eminent 2000 Grand Theatre Organ).
Tracks: / Tik tak polka / Music box dancer / Ballade pour Adeline / I don't want to walk without you / Windmill samba / Elegy / Money, money, money / Sentimental journey / Golden tango / Gymnopedie no.1 / Sleepy shores / Pierrette / Happy talk / Softly awakes my heart / Can't smile without you.
LP: . . . . **GRS 1124**

EMINENT MANN & HIS MUSIC, AN (Eminent 2000 Grand Theatre Organ).
Tracks: / Wein bleibt wein marsch / Lonely ballerina / Glad rag doll / Canary polka / Adagio / I'm gonna sit right down and write myself a letter / My very good friend the milkman / When somebody thinks you're wonderful / Eighteen carat samba / Barcarolle / Typewriter, The / I'm stone in love with you / Oh babe / King and I, The.
LP: . . . . **GRS 1085**
MC: . . . . **KGRS 1085**

EMINENT OCCASION, AN (Eminent 2000 Grand Theatre Organ).
LP: . . . . **GRS 1067**

FOREVER MELODIES.
Tracks: / Snow bells / Cara mia / Caraquinto / Jesu, joy of man's desiring / Cuckoo waltz / New York, New York / One / La uran tango Argentin / St. Louis blues / Brighton sea step / Song on the sand / Swedish rhapsody / All I ask of you / Romeo and Juliet.
MC: . . . . **KGRS 1194**
LP: . . . . **GRS 1194**

JOHN MANN ENTERTAINS.
LP: . . . . **GRS 1167**
MC: . . . . **KGRS 1167**

Mann, Johnny Singers

GREAT BAND WITH GREAT VOICES SWING.. (see Zenter, Si & His Orchestra/Johnny Mann Singers).

Mann, Ritchie

WUNDERBAR.
LP: . . . . **SKY 017**

Mann, Roberto

GREAT WALTZES.
LP: . . . . **SML 1010**

Mannan

NIGHT PATROL.
LP: . . . . **ART 001**

Manne, Shelly

AT THE BLACK HAWK VOL.2 (Manne, Shelly & His Men).
LP: **1007 578**

AT THE BLACK HAWK VOL.3 (Manne, Shelly & His Men).
LP: **1007 579**

AT THE BLACK HAWK VOL.4 (Manne, Shelly & His Men).
LP: **1007 580**

DOUBLE PIANO JAZZ QUARTET IN CONCERT AT CARMELO'S, VOL.2.
Tracks: / Midnight song for Thalia / Lament / In your own sweet way / Alone together / Along came Betty.
LP: . . . . **TR 527**

DOUBLE PIANO JAZZ QUARTET IN CONCERT AT CARMELO'S, VOL.1.
Tracks: / Sweet and lovely / Night has a thousand eyes, The / I'll take romance.
LP: . . . . **TR 526**

ESSENCE.
LP: . . . . **GXY 5101**

JAZZ QUARTET INTERPRETATIONS (Manne, Shelly Jazz Quartet).
Tracks: / Violin concerto in E major / Air from suite in D / Divertimento K. 136 / Adante.
LP: . . . . **TR 525**

LIVING LEGEND (see Pepper, Art) (Manne,Shelley/Art Pepper/Hampton Hawes).

MANNE - THAT'S GERSHWIN (Manne, Shelly Quintet & Big Band).
Tracks: / BR Strauss / My man's gone now / Love is here to stay / Summertime / Real American folk song / Man I love, The / How long has this been going on / Concerto in F, Theme from.
LP: . . . . **DS 909**

MORE SWINGING SOUNDS (Manne, Shelly & his men).
Tracks: / Moose the mooche / Wind / Pint of blues / Tommyhawk / Quartet.
LP: . . . . **COP 036**
LP: . . . . **COP 036**

MY FAIR LADY (Manne, Shelly/Andre Previn/Leroy Vinnegar).
Tracks: / Get me to the church on time / I've grown accustomed to her face / Ascot gavotte / With a little bit of luck / On the street where you live / Wouldn't it be loverly / Show me / I could have danced all night.
LP: . . . . **MFP 50527**
LP: . . . . **COP 042**
LP: . . . . **LAC 12100**
MC: . . . . **TCMFP 50527**

PLAYS RICHARD RODGERS' MUSICAL REX.
LP: . . . . **DS 783**
MC: . . . . **DSC 783**

POLL WINNERS, THE (See Kessel, Barney).

REMEMBER (Manne, Shelly Trio).
Tracks: / Speak low / Medley, A / Young and foolish / Last night when we were young / 'B' for Budwig / My romance / Dream / Hi-fly / Take the Coltrane/ Theme / Introductions / Remember.
LP: . . . . **JIR 4004**

SHELLY MANNE & HIS FRIENDS (Manne, Shelly & His Friends).
Tracks: / Tea for two / How high the moon / When we're alone / On the sunny side of the street / Time on my hands / Moonglow / Them there eyes / Sarcastic lady / Night and day / Flamingo / Steps steps up / Steps steps down.
LP: . . . . **ASLP 1002**
MC: . . . . **ZCAS 1002**

TWO THREE FOUR.
Tracks: / Take the 'A' train / Sicks of us, The / Slowly / Lean on me / Cherokee / Me and some drums.
LP: . . . . **JAS 58**
MC: . . . . **JAS C58**

WAY OUT WEST (See Rollins, Sonny) (Manne, Shelly & Sonny Rollins).

WEST COAST SOUND, THE (Manne, Shelly & his men).
Tracks: / Grasshopper / La mugura / Summer night / Afrodesia / You, the night, and the music / Gazelle / Sweets / Spring is here / Mallets / You're getting to be a habit with me / You're my thrill / Fugue.
LP: . . . . **COP 012**

Mannella, A.

CORSE ETERNELLE.
Tracks: / Tarentelle / Niolu / Lettera a Mamma / U pastore / Singhiozzi / Notte Curtinese / Polka de Giacometti / I travagliatori / U paisolu / Sirinatu in currente / A mazurka d'u Ricantu / Sole e grippa / Una sera in lumio / U candidatu.
LP: . . . . **ARN 30149**
MC: . . . . **ARN 430149**

CORSICA ETERNA.
Tracks: / U mio figliolu / Parlemu corsu / Trinchettu / Natale / I me regali / Chiami e rispondi / Suspiru / Terzetti / Paghella / Versu piuvisgianu / Lettera di u piuvanu / Sirinatu in currente / Quatru viulini / I travagliatori / Sturnelli / Canzona di a vadina / Francesca Maria.
LP: . . . . **ARN 33536**

Mannequin Beach

DON'T LAUGH, YOU'RE NEXT.
LP: . . . . **MDR 6**

Mannequin Romance

FOR THE LOVE OF A PLASTIC WOMAN
MC: . . . . **FLAP 003**

Mannheim Steamroller

CHRISTMAS (MANNHEIM STEAMROLLER).
LP: . . . . **AG 1984**
MC: . . . . **AGC 1984**

FRESH AIRE I.
LP: . . . . **AG 355**
MC: . . . . **AGC 355**

FRESH AIRE II.
LP: . . . . **AG 359**
MC: . . . . **AGC 359**

FRESH AIRE III.
LP: . . . . **AG 365**
MC: . . . . **AGC 365**

FRESH AIRE IV.
LP: . . . . **AG 370**
MC: . . . . **AGC 370**

FRESH AIRE V.
LP: . . . . **AG 385**
MC: . . . . **AGC 385**

FRESH AIRE VI.
LP: . . . . **AG 386**
MC: . . . . **AGC 386**

Manning, Barbara

ONE PERFECT GREEN BLANKET.
LP: . . . . **HEY 018LP**
MC: . . . . **HEY 018CS**

SCISSORS.
LP: . . . . **HEY 002**

Manning, Bernard

LIVE AT THE EMBASSY CLUB.
Tracks: / Life is only what you make it / True love.
LP: . . . . **PRX 1**

Manning, Roger

ROGER MANNING.
LP: . . . . **SST 203 LP**
MC: . . . . **SST 203 CA**

Manning, Sam

BARBADOS BLUES (Manning, Sam & Wilmoth Houdini).
LP: . . . . **CI 015**

Manning-Sanders, Ruth

GOBLINS AT THE BATH HOUSE / CALAMANDER CHEST, THE (Price, Vincent (nar)).
MC: **1574**

Mano Negra

KING OF BONGO.
LP: . . . . **VIR 5**
MC: . . . . **MCVIR 5**

PUTTA'S FEVER.
Tracks: / Man negra / Rock'n'roll band / King kong five / Soledad / Sidi h bibi / Rebel spell, The / Peligro / Pas assez de toi / Magic dice / Mad house / Guayaquil City / Voodoo / Patchanka / La rancon du succes / Devil's call, The / Roger Cageot / El sur / Patchuko hop.
LP: . . . . **V 2608**
MC: . . . . **CTV 2608**

Manon Lescaut

MANON LESCAUT (See under Puccini) (Various artists).

Manone, Wingy

1947: WINGY MANONE (Manone, Wingy & Sidney Bechet).
LP: . . . . **JA 29**

WINGY MANONE & PAPA BUE'S VIKING JAZZ BAND (Manone, Wingy & Papa Bue's Viking Jazzband).
Tracks: / When you're smiling / Up the country blues / Sister Kate.
LP: . . . . **SLP 4066**

WINGY MANONE & WILL BRADLEY (Manone, Wingy & Will Bradley).
Tracks: / Jingle bells / Cryin' the boogie blues / Lightnin' boogie / Sugar Hill boogie woogie / O sole mio / Snake the blues away / That glory day / Bread and gravy / That's a gasser / Mr. Boogie Man.
LP: . . . . **HQ 2001**

WINGY MANONE-VOLUME 4.
LP: . . . . **LITTLE GEM 1073**

Manowar

BATTLE HYMNS.
Tracks: / Death tone / Metal daze / Fast taker / Shell shock / Battle hymns / Dark avenger / William's tale.
LP: . . . . **LBG 30349**
MC: . . . . **TC LBG 30349**

CHRIS TETLEY INTERVIEWS MANOWAR.
LPPD: . . . . **CT 1009**

FIGHTING THE WORLD.
Tracks: / Fighting the world / Blow your speakers / Carry on / Violence and bloodshed / Defender / Drums of doom / Holy war / Blackwind, fire and steel.
LP: 790 563-1
MC: 790 563-4
LP: 781 693-1

HAIL TO ENGLAND.
LP: . . . . MFN 19
MC: . . . . TMFN 19

INTO GLORY RIDES.
LP: . . . . MFN 6
MC: . . . . TMFN 6

METAL KINGS, THE.
Tracks: / Wheels of fire / Kings of metal / Heart of steel / Sting of the bumblebee / Crown and the ring, The / Kingdom come / Hail and kill / Warriors prayer, The / Blood of the kings.
LP: . . . . K 781 930 1
MC: . . . . K 781 930 4

SIGN OF THE HAMMER.
Tracks: / All men play on 10 / Animals / Thor / Mountains / Sign of the hammer / Oath, The / Thunderpick / Guyana (cult of the damned).
LP: . . . . DIX 10
MC: . . . . CDIX 10
MC: . . . . CXID 21

SIGN OF THE HAMMER (HARDROCK BOX SET) (See under Hard Rock).

Manring, Michael

DRASTIC MEASURE.
Tracks: / Spirits in the material world / Hopefull / Red right returning / Gizmo / Oyasumi nasai / Purple haze / Deja voodoo / Watson and Crick / Wide asleep / 500 miles high / When we last spoke.
MC: . . . . WT 1102

UNUSUAL WEATHER.
Tracks: / Welcoming / Huge moon / Almost April / Unusual weather / Sung to sleep / Thunder tactics / Lonhair mobile / Homeward / Not even the summer / Sightings / Big feelings / Thunder tactics (reprise) / Manthing.
LP: 371 044-1
MC: 371 044-4

Mansell, Tony Singers

TRIBUTE TO SIMON & GARFUNKEL.
MC: . . . . OAK C 115

Mansfield, Darrell

HIGHER POWER.
Tracks: / Children don't run / Prize, The / That's alright / He has overcome / No more blues / Love conquers all / Giver of life / Every night every day / Higher power.
LP: . . . . MM 0055
MC: . . . . TC MM 0055

Mansfield, David

DESPERATE HOURS (Film Soundtrack).
Tracks: / Chase, The / Nancy slashes the jaguar / Jailbreak / Tim leaves with Zeck / Too many bad memories / Into the lake / Tim meets Bosworth / Nancy's apartment / May meets Bosworth / Tim stabbed / Tim and Nora's theme / Albert leaves / Dumping the body / I'll be back / Albert persued / Give me the Gun / Tim and Nora / Bosworth and the FBI / Stadium, The / Aftermath, The / End credits.
LP: . . . . VS 5284
MC: . . . . VSC 5284

Mansfield, Katherine

GARDEN PARTY, THE (Ashcroft, Dame Peggy (nar)).
MCSET: CC/004

Mansfield Park (bk)

MANSFIELD PARK (See under Austen, Jane) (O'Brien, Maureen (nar)).

Mantas

WINDS OF CHANGE.
Tracks: / Hurricane / Desperado / Sionara / Nowhere to hide / Deciever / Let it rock / King of the rings / Western days / Winds of change.
LP: . . . . NEAT 1042
LP: . . . . RR 95151

Mantilla, Ray

SYNERGY (Mantilla, Ray Space Station).
LP: . . . . VPA 198

Mantler, Karen

GET THE FLU (Mantler, Karen & Her Cat Arnold).
Tracks: / Flu, The / I love Christmas / Let's have a baby / My organ / Au lait / Waiting / Call a doctor / Good luck / I'm not such a bad guy / Mean to me.
LP: . . . . XTRAWATT 5

MY CAT ARNOLD.
LP: . . . . XTRAWATT 3

Mantler, Michael

ALIEN.
Tracks: / Alien (part 1) / Alien (part 2) / Alien (part 3) / Alien (part 4).
LP: . . . . WATT 15

LIVE: MICHAEL MANTLER.
Tracks: / Preview - no answer / Slow orchestra piece no.3 (Prisonniers) / For instance / Slow orchestra piece no.8 (A l'abattoir) / When I run / Remembered visit / Slow orchestra piece no.6 / Hapless child, The / Doubtful guest, The.
LP: . . . . WATT 18

MANY HAVE NO SPEECH.
LP: . . . . WATT 19

SOMETHING THERE.
LP: . . . . WATT 13

Mantovani

16 GOLDEN CLASSICS.
Tracks: / Love story theme / Lawrence of Arabia / Moon River / Smoke gets in your eyes / Good morning starshine (From 'Hair) / Sunrise sunset / Tulips from Amsterdam / Walk in the Black Forest, A / West side story / Mona Lisa / When I fall in love / Summertime / Over the rainbow / Some enchanted evening (From 'South Pacific') / Lemon tree / Taste of honey, A.
LP: . . . . UNLP 013
MC: . . . . UNMC 013

20 GOLDEN GREAT: MANTOVANI.
LP: . . . . WW 5067

AS TIME GOES BY.
LP: . . . . CN 2085
MC: CN4 2085

AT THE THEATRE.
Tracks: / C'est magnifique (Not on CD.) / I feel pretty (Not on CD.) / Hey there / Out of my dreams / I've grown accustomed to her face / Almost like being in love / Hello, Dolly / They say it's wonderful / I've never been in love before / Edelweiss / What kind of fool am I / Do-ra-me / Whatever Lola wants / Shall we dance / Stranger in Paradise / Tonight / Maria / Somewhere / As long as he needs me / Ascot gavotte (Not on CD.) / Where is love / Mr. Wonderful (Not on CD.) / 76 trombones / Wunderbar / Embraceable you (Not on CD.) / Climb every mountain / If I were a rich man (Not on CD.) / Windmills of your mind / Summertime / Sunrise sunset (Not on CD.) / You'll never walk alone / How are things in Glocca Morra / Carousel waltz, The.
2LP: . . . . SIV 1108
MC: . . . . CSIV 1108

BEAUTIFUL MUSIC.
Tracks: / Charmaine / Tie a yellow ribbon round the old oak tree / Green cockatoo, The / Entertainer, The / Blue tango / Stardust / Cara mia / Edelweiss / Three o'clock in the morning / Windmills of your mind / Jealousy / You'll never walk alone.
LP: . . . . CN 2035
MC: CN4 2035

CASCADE OF PRAISE.
Tracks: / All people that on Earth do dwell / Saviour of the world / Jesu, joy of man's desiring / Wonderful Saviour / Onward Christian soldiers / Nearer my God to thee / Exodus / Holy City, The / Climb every mountain / Little brown church in the vale / Impossible dream, The / Praise the Lord our Saviour / Abide with me / Home of the soul (home on the range) / Battle Hymn of the Republic / Blessed Assurance / Lost Chord, The / Eli Jenkins' Prayer.
LP: . . . . WRD 3012
MC: . . . . TC WRD 3012

CHRISTMAS MAGIC.
LP: . . . . HDY 1919
MC: . . . . ZCHDY 1919

COLLECTION: MANTOVANI.
Tracks: / Out of my dreams / Charmaine / Blue tango / Deep purple / Auf wiederseh'n sweetheart / Whispering / Give my regards to Broadway / It takes two to tango / Over the rainbow / Trolley song, The / Diane / Wunderbar / Cabaret / Hernando's hideaway / Three o'clock in the morning / Skaters waltz / Harlem nocturne / Forgotten dreams / Anniversary waltz / Autumn leaves / Tulips from Amsterdam / Me and my shadow / Taste of honey, A / Jealousy / Home on the Range / Jamaica farewell / April in Portugal / May each day.
2LP: . . . . CCSLP 130
MC: . . . . CCSMC 130

CONCERT SPECTACULAR.
LP: . . . . LK 4377

CONTINENTAL ENCORES.
Tracks: / More than ever (come prima) / La vie en rose / Under Paris skies / Oh mein papa / April in Portugal / Arrivederci Roma / Anema E core / La mer / I only know I love you / Autumn leaves / Answer me / Poppa Piccolino / Walk in the Black Forest, A / Happy wanderer, The / My way.
LP: . . . . LK 4298

EIN TRAUM FUR ZWEI (THE RED ALBUM).
LP: 6 24000
MC: 4 24000

EVENING WITH MANTOVANI.
MC: . . . . KSKC 5172

EVERGREEN.
LP: . . . . ADAH 431
MC: . . . . ADAHC 431

FARAWAY PLACES.
2LP: . . . . DKL 103
MCSET: . . . . KCKC 28100

FAVOURITE SCREEN THEMES (Mantovani & His Orchestra).
Tracks: / Tara's theme / Secret love / True love / Exodus (Theme from) / Days of wine and roses, The / Alfie / Wand'rin star / On a clear day you can see forever / Over the rainbow / Edelweiss / Moon river / When you wish upon a star / As long as he needs me / Gigi / Lara's theme / As time goes by.
MC: CN4 2106

FILM ENCORES.
MC: . . . . KSKC 4002

FILM FAVOURITES.
2LP: . . . . DKL 105
MCSET: . . . . KDKC 28114

FILM THEMES.
Tracks: / Moon river (Not on CD) / Love is a many splendoured thing / Never on a Sunday / Laura / Born free / Limelight / Over the shadow / Gigi (Not on CD) / On a clear day / Man and a woman, A / Hello young lovers / Que sera sera / Secret love / High and mighty / Days of wine and roses / Exodus / True love / High noon / Be my love / Hi lili hi lo / Tammy (Not on CD) / I could have danced all night / Moulin Rouge theme / This is my song / Around the world / September song / Intermezzo / When you wish upon a star (Not on CD).
2LP: . . . . SIV 105
MC: . . . . CSIV 105

FOCUS ON MANTOVANI.
2LP: . . . . FOS 3/4
MCSET: . . . . KFOC 28034

FOR LOVERS EVERYWHERE.
MC: . . . . KDKC 28099

FROM MANTOVANI WITH LOVE.
Tracks: / Try to remember / It's impossible / My prayer / If I only had time / Loss of love / Gwendolyn / Rosy's theme / Love Story theme / Little green apples / Last Summer / Where have all the flowers gone / May each day.
MC: . . . . KSKC 5092

GOLDEN AGE OF THE YOUNG MANTOVANI 1935-1939, THE.
Tracks: / I wished on the moon / Please believe me / Cuban Pete / Serenade in the night / All alone in Vienna / Where are you / Blue Hawaii / You're laughing at me / Ten pretty girls / Waltz of the gipsies / Something to sing about / In my little red book / So little time (so much to do) / There's rain in my eyes / My prayer / Spider of the night.
LP: . . . . GX 41 2545-1
MC: . . . . GX 41 2545-4
MC: . . . . TCSH 386
LP: . . . . SH 386

GOLDEN HITS: MANTOVANI.
Tracks: / Charmaine / Moon river / Moulin Rouge / Summertime in Venice / Diane / Exodus / Greensleeves / True love / La vie en rose / Around the world / Some enchanted evening / Swedish Rhapsody.
LP: . . . . SKL 4818
MC: . . . . KSKC 4818

GOLDEN VIOLINS.
Tracks: / Greensleeves / Moulin Rouge / Elizabethan serenade / Love's roundabout / Diane / Send in the clowns / Beautiful dreamer / Dear father / Charmaine / Mexicali rose / I wonder who's kissing her now / Melodia / Autumn leaves / Ich tanze mit dir in den Himmelhinein / Estrellita / Elvira Madigan.
LP: 8200161
MC: 8200164

GREAT MANTOVANI, THE.
Tracks: / Story of three lovers / Dream of Olwen / Around the world / Waltz from Swan Lake / Song of India / Moulin Rouge / Blue Danube / Stranger in Paradise / Charmaine / Lonely ballerina / Gigi / Tenderly / With these hands / Tonight.
LP: . . . . PLE 520
MC: . . . . TC-PLE 520

GREATEST GIFT IS LOVE, THE.
Tracks: / Greatest gift / Old-fashioned way, The / Go (before you break my heart) / Solitude / Sing / Cool summer evening / What are you doing the rest of your life? / Day of the locusts / Entertainer, The / Send in the clowns / Love song / Freak, The / She.
LP: . . . . SKL 5216
MC: . . . . KSKC 5216

HOLLYWOOD.
LP: . . . . SKL 4887

HOLY NIGHT.
LP: . . . . HDY 1928
MC: . . . . ZCHDY 1928
LP: . . . . AFEMP 1015

I WISH YOU LOVE.
Tracks: / I wish you love / Stardust / Almost there / Be my love / I can't stop loving you / Embraceable you / Lover / Isn't it romantic? / Love me with all your heart / Misty / Deep purple / I have dreamed / Till the end of time / Ebb tide.
LP: . . . . CN 2071
MC: CN4 2071

IMAGES: MANTOVANI.
Tracks: / It's impossible / Mona Lisa / Certain smile, A / And I love you so / True love / Blue Danube / Almost there / Exodus / Send in the clowns / September in the rain / Party's over,The / Deep purple / Embraceable you / Some enchanted evening.
MC: . . . . KNMC 16013

INCOMPARABLE, THE (DECCA).
Tracks: / I wonder who's kissing her now / As time goes by / Catch a falling star / Where are you? / I left my heart in San Francisco / I'll be seeing you / Yesterdays / Fly me to the moon / I'll get by / September in the rain / Long ago / More.
LP: . . . . SKL 4640
MC: . . . . KSKC 4640

INTERNATIONAL HITS (Mantovani & His Orchestra).
Tracks: / Amazing grace / Swedish Rhapsody / Greensleeves.
MC: . . . . HSC 3407

KISMET.
Tracks: / Overture / Sands of time / Rhymes have I / Fate / Baubles, bangles and beads / Not since Nineveh / Stranger in paradise / He's in love / Night of my nights / Gesticulate / Was I Wazir / Rahadiakum / And this is my beloved / Olive tree / Zubbediya / Samaris dance / Kismet (finale).
LP: . . . . DGS 3
MC: . . . . KDGC 3

LATIN RENDEZVOUS.
LP: . . . . SKL 4528

LIFETIME OF MUSIC, A.
Tracks: / Charmaine / Tenderly / If i loved you / Summertime / Greensleeves / People / No other love / Forgotten dreams / Swedish rhapsody / Man and a woman, A / My way / Try to remember / Almost there / Blue tango / Mexican hat dance / Around the world / Andalucia / As time goes by / So in love / Very thought of you / Way you look tonight / All the things you are / Catari, catari / Lonely ballerina / Italia mia / Elizabethan serenade / In San Fransico / On a clear day / Moulin rouge / Londonderry air.
2LP: . . . . DPA 3089
MCSET: . . . . KDPC 28123

LIVE AT THE FESTIVAL HALL VOL. 1.
Tracks: / Love is a many splendoured thing / Some enchanted evening / Summertime in Venice / Merry waltz / Cavatina / Autumn leaves / Elizabethan serenade / Big country, The.
LP: SHLP129

LOVE ALBUM - 20 ROMANTIC FAVOURITES, THE.
Tracks: / Some enchanted evening / Very thought of you, The / I can't stop loving you / April love / It's impossible / My cherie amour / Shadow of your smile / Lovely way to spend an evening, A / Love is all / Charmaine / Hello young lovers / Man and a woman, A / Dear heart / For all we know / She / I will wait for you / And I love you so / What are you doing the rest of your life / Spanish eyes / More.
LP: . . . . PLAT 14
MC: . . . . PLAC 14

LOVE LETTERS (Mantovani & His Orchestra).
Tracks: / Secret love / And I love you so / Love story theme.
LP: . . . . CN 2089
MC: CN4 2089

LOVE THEMES, THE.
Tracks: / Charmaine / Love Story theme / For once in my life / Shadow of your smile / If I loved you / Love letters / Stardust / Long ago and far away / Some enchanted evening / Embraceable you / Moon river / Tenderly / When I fall in love / Most beautiful girl, The / And I love you so / Till there was you (Not on CD.) / Way

you look tonight, The / Love me with all your heart / Nearness of you / You are beautiful (Not on CD.) / Tea for two / Lover / Till / I have dreamed / September song / I wish you love / My prayer (Not on CD.) / Very thought of you, The (Not on CD.).
2LP: . . . . **SIV 101**
MC: . . . . **CSIV 101**

MAGIC OF THE MANTOVANI ORCHESTRA (Mantovani & His Orchestra).
LP: . . . . **SHLP 129**
MC: . . . . **SHTC 129**

MANHATTAN.
Tracks: / Give my regards to Broadway / Autumn in New York / Bowery, The / Harlem nocturne / Slaughter on Tenth Avenue / Manhattan serenade / Take the 'A' train / Manhattan lullaby / Maria / Somewhere / Belle of New York / Tenement symphony.
LP: . . . . **JASM 2207**

MANTOVANI.
Tracks: / Charmaine / Greensleeves / Mexicali rose / Song from Moulin Rouge / Love's roundabout / Candlelight / Warsaw Concerto / Waltz from Serenade for Strings / Barcarolle / Wiegenlied / Ave maria.
LP: **6495110**

MANTOVANI CHRISTMAS ALBUM.
Tracks: / Deck the halls with boughs of holly / Once in Royal David's City / Jingle bells / Toy waltz / Holly and the ivy, The / O Thou that tellest good tidings / It came upon a midnight clear / Twelve days of Christmas / While shepherds watched / Christmas bells / Mary's boy child / I saw three ships.
LP: . . . . **CN 2040**
MC: **CN4 2040**
LP: . . . . **DGS 8**

MANTOVANI ... (DAKOTA).
Tracks: / Mull of Kintyre / Whiter shade of pale, A / You've got a friend / Rose, The / Just the way you are / First time ever I saw your face, The / Time for us, A / Nights in white satin / MacArthur Park / When I need you / You don't bring me flowers / Killing me softly with his song.
LP: . . . . **COUNT 4**
MC: . . . . **ZC CNT 4**

MANTOVANI FAVOURITES.
Tracks: / Londonderry air / Walk in the Black Forest, A / Dream / Black eyes / Welcome home / Party's over, The / Happy wanderer, The / Till the end of time / Trumpeter's lullaby, A / Whiffenpoof song, The / Tulips from Amsterdam / Auld lang syne.
LP: . . . . **SKL 5271**
MC: . . . . **KSKC 5271**

MANTOVANI & HIS DANCE ORCHESTRA (Mantovani & His Orchestra).
Tracks: / Our love affair / Say it / You made me care / No souvenirs / Dreaming / There goes my dream / Devil may care / You don't have to tell me / When shall we two meet again / Only forever / Until you fall in love / Remember September / When June comes / Dancing is another name for love / Tell your troubles to the breeze / Love is all / If it's only a dream / They're building another alley.
LP: . . . . **RFL 31**

MANTOVANI IN VIENNA.
Tracks: / Blue danube / O maiden, my maiden / Chocolate soldier-my hero / Tales from the Vienna Woods / Gypsy love / Gypsy princess / Die fledermaus / Morning papers / Frasquita / Village swallows / Gypsy baron / Your eyes shine in my own / Emperor waltz / Count of Luxembourg / Treasure waltz / Voices of spring / Merry widow / Roses from the south / Thousand and one nights / Wine, women and song / Countess Maritza / Play gypsies, dance gypsies / Accelerations waltz / Perpetuum mobile.
2LP: . . . . **DKL 102**
MCSET: . . . . **KDKC 28097**

MANTOVANI MAGIC 1.
Tracks: / Misty / Red roses for a blue lady / Chim chim cheree / Love me with all your heart / Goodnight sweetheart / Cara mia / I wish you love / Lover / Stardust / Mona Lisa / Most beautiful girl in the world / Auf wiederseh'n sweetheart.
LP: . . . . **DELD 302**
MC: . . . . **CELD 302**
LP: . . . . **LK 7949**

MANTOVANI MAGIC 2.
Tracks: / Love is a many splendoured thing / Charmaine / Send in the clowns / Cavatina / Elizabethan serenade / Three coins in the fountain / Summertime in Venice / Merry widow waltz / Entertainer, The / Sound of music, The / Italian fantasy / Autumn leaves / What are you doing for the rest of your life / Some enchanted evening / Big country, The / Swedish Rhapsody.
MC: . . . . **STAC 2237**
LP: . . . . **STAR 2237**

MANTOVANI ORCHESTRA (CAMBRA).
Tracks: / When I need you / Touch me in the morning / Just the way you are / Copacabana / You light up my life / Nobody does it better / You don't bring me flowers / She's out of my life / Evergreen / Annie's song / You make me feel brand new / Can't smile without you / Midnight blue / She believes in me / Tomorrow / I write the songs / September morn / Somewhere in the night / What I did for love / Don't cry out loud / I honestly love you / Let it be me / New York, New York / Way we were, The / Do you know where you're going to? (Theme from Mahogany) / I'll never love this way again / You've got a friend / Weekend in New England / You needed me / Mull of Kintyre.
2LP: . . . . **CR 014**
MCSET: . . . . **CRT 014**

MANTOVANI ORCHESTRA (PHOENIX).
Tracks: / Annie's song / Mull of Kintyre / Way we were, The / Greensleeves / I write the songs / MacArthur Park / Scarborough fair / You don't bring me flowers / Plaisir d'amour / Evergreen.
LP: . . . . **PHX 1007**

MANTOVANI PLAYS ALL-TIME ROMANTIC HITS.
Tracks: / Together / Deep purple / Very thought of you, The / Gigi / Louise / Thank Heaven for little girls / Valentine / Isn't it romantic? / Dearly beloved / You were meant for me / London pride / Some day I'll find you / Zigeuner / Mad dogs and Englishmen / I'll see you again.
MC: . . . . **KSKC 5204**

MANTOVANI, THE LEGEND (Mantovani & His Orchestra).
Tracks: / New York New York / Way we were, The / Scarborough Fair 80 / Copacabana / You don't bring me flowers / Manhattan skyline / Evergreen / Mull of Kintyre / Can't smile without you / What I did for love / Just the way you are / Annie's song / One / I'll never love this way again / Don't cry out loud / Greensleeves 80 / MacArthur Park suite / I write the songs / You make me feel brand new / Nobody does it better / Let it be me / Plaisir d'amour / Weekend in New England.
2LP: . . . . **AFESD 1001**

MANTOVANI TODAY.
LP: . . . . **SKL 5003**

MANTOVANI TOUCH, THE.
Tracks: / On a clear day / Alfie / Release me / Man and a woman, A / Almost there / What now my love / Edelweiss / Day in the life of a fool, A / My cup runneth over / Days of wine and roses / Impossible dream, The / Puppet on a string.
MC: . . . . **KSKC 4921**

MANTOVANI VOLUME I.
MC: . . . . **ZCGAS 705**

MANTOVANI VOLUME II.
MC: . . . . **ZCGAS 706**

MANTOVANI VOLUME III.
MC: . . . . **ZCGAS 733**

MANTOVANI VOLUME IV.
MC: . . . . **ZCGAS 742**

MANTOVANI'S ITALIA.
Tracks: / Italian fantasy / More / Carnival of Venice / Nessun dorma / La danza / Three coins in the fountain / Summer time in Venice / Arrivederci Roma / Catari (Cor'Ngrato) / Barber of Seville.
LP: . . . . **OR 0055**

MANTOVANI'S MAGIC TOUCH.
Tracks: / Misty / Red roses for a blue lady / Chim chim cheree / Love me with all your heart / Goodnight sweetheart / Cara Mia / I wish you love / Lover / Stardust / Mona Lisa / Most beautiful girl in the world, The / Auf wiederseh'n sweetheart / On a clear day / Alfie / Release me / Man and a woman, A / Almost there / What now my love? / Edelweiss / Day in the life of a fool, A / My cup runneth over / Days of wine and roses / Impossible dream, The / Puppet on a string.
2LP: . . . . **DDS 1**

MASTERWORKS.
LP: . . . . **STAR 2335**
MC: . . . . **STAC 2335**

MEMORIES.
Tracks: / Smoke gets in your eyes / What a wonderful world / Trolley song, The / Sweet Leilani / Try to remember / Sunrise, sunset / Anniversary waltz / In the still of the night / Once upon a time / Embraceable you / How are things in Glocca Morra? / You'll never walk alone.
MC: . . . . **KSKC 4977**

MORE MANTOVANI GOLDEN HITS.
Tracks: / Cara Mia / Stranger in Paradise / Gigi / Deep purple / Certain smile, A / Limelight / Way you look tonight / Love is a many splendoured thing / Long ago and far away / Till / Lovely way to spend an evening, A / Together / Ebb tide.
LP: . . . . **SKL 5230**
MC: . . . . **KSKC 5230**

MR. MUSIC... MANTOVANI.
LP: . . . . **LK 4809**

MUSIC FILMS.
MC: . . . . **KSKC 4014**

MUSIC FOR THE MILLIONS - SONGS OF PRAISE.
LP: **6495 127**
MC: **7195 127**

MUSIC FROM THE FILMS.
Tracks: / Warsaw concerto / Serenata d'amore / Dream of Olwen / Legend of the Glass Mountain / Story of three lovers / Cornish rhapsody.
LP: . . . . **SKL 4014**
MC: . . . . **KSKCL 4014**

MUSIC OF LOVE, THE.
Tracks: / And I love you so / Very thought of you, The / For all we know / As time goes by / More / Till / Spanish eyes / What are you doing the rest of your life ? / Whispering / Old fashioned way, The / Some enchanted evening / I will wait for you / Way you look tonight, The / Moon river.
LP: . . . . **CN 2069**
MC: **CN4 2069**

MUSICAL MOMENTS WITH MANTOVANI & HIS ORCHESTRA.
Tracks: / And I love you so / Eye level / La chanson de Maria / For all we know / Tie a yellow ribbon / It's different now / Say, has anybody seen my sweet Gypsy Rose? / Our last affair / Elizabethan serenade / Fool / Dear father.
LP: . . . . **SKL 5187**

REPLAY ON MANTOVANI.
LP: . . . . **FEDB 5025**
MC: . . . . **FEDC 5025**

ROMANTIC MOOD (Mantovani & His Orchestra).
Tracks: / I wish you love / Stardust / Be my love / Almost there / I can't stop loving you / Embraceable you / Lover / Isn't it romantic / Love me with all your heart / Misty / Deep purple / I have dreamed / Till the end of time / Ebb tide.
LP: . . . . **TAB 15**

STRAUSS WALTZES.
Tracks: / Blue Danube / Voices of spring / Roses from the south / Village swallows / Thousand and one nights / Treasure waltz (From The Gypsy Baron.) / Emperor waltz / Wine women and song / Accelerations / Tales from the Vienna woods / Morning papers / Fledermauswaltz (du und du).
LP: . . . . **SKL 4010**
MC: . . . . **KSKC 4010**

TENDERLY (Mantovani & His Orchestra).
Tracks: / Flamingo / Midnight cowboy / Mer, La / Begin the beguine / Send in the clowns / Song of Skye / Autumn leaves / Some enchanted evening / Love is a many splendoured thing / Deep purple / Swedish rhapsody / What are you doing for the rest of your life / Tenderly / Colours of my life / Three coins in the fountain / Charmaine.
MC: . . . . **HSC 3275**

THEATRE FAVOURITES.
Tracks: / C'est magnifique / I feel pretty / Hey there / Out of my dreams / I've grown accustomed to her face / Almost like being in love / Till there was you / Hello Dolly / They say it's wonderful / Maria / Somewhere / As long as he needs me / Sunrise, sunset / Where is love / Mr. Wonderful / Seventy-six trombones / Wunderbar / I've never been in love before / Gigi / Edelweiss / Hello young lovers / What kind of fool am I / Do-re-mi / Whatever Lola wants (Lola gets) / I could have danced all night / Shall we dance / Stranger in paradise / Tonight / Climb every mountain.
2LP: . . . . **DKL 106**
MCSET: . . . . **KDKC 28115**

TO LOVERS EVERYWHERE.
LP: . . . . **SKL 5112**

TREASURY OF MELODY.
LPS: . . . . **ALBUM 90**
MCSET: . . . . **CASSETTE 90**

UNFORGETTABLE SOUND OF MANTOVANI.
Tracks: / Elizabethan serenade / Cara mia / I'll never fall in love again / Spanish eyes / Vaya con dios / Big country / Valencia / I love Paris / Good life / Golden earrings / Besame mucho / Smoke gets in your eyes / Give my regards to Broadway / Tico tico / Eye level / Sweetest sounds, The / September song / Black eyes / In the still of the night / Try to remember / Sapateado / Perfidia / Till / Walk in the Black Forest, A / How are things in Glocca Morra / Days of wine and roses / Cabaret / Goodnight sweetheart.
2LP: . . . . **DPA 3095**
MCSET: . . . . **KDPC 23095**

VERY BEST OF MANTOVANI, THE.
Tracks: / Charmaine / Swedish rhapsody (Adapted by Faith.) / Lonely ballerina / Tonight / Exodus / Hello young lovers / Red roses for a blue lady / Love is a many splendoured thing / And I love you so / Send in the clowns / Moulin Rouge / Stardust / Some enchanted evening / Unchained melody / Way you look tonight / Edelweiss / Smoke gets in your eyes / More / Around the world / What a wonderful world.
LP: . . . . **WW 2005**
MC: . . . . **WW 20054**

WHISTLING UNDER THE MOON (Mantovani & His Tipica Orchestra).
Tracks: / Hej haj / For love time / When the poppies bloom again / Let's fall in love for the last time / Red sails in the sunset / Aloha marimba / Street in old Seville, A / Lady sing your gypsy song / Vienna you've stolen my heart / Whistling under the moon / Si si / I dream of San Marino / Si petite / Fold your wings / O'Balalaika / Marie Louise / Me and the moon / Please believe me.
LP: . . . . **JOYD 293**

WORLD OF MANTOVANI.
Tracks: / Some enchanted evening / Hava nagila / Cara mia / Jealousy / Fiddler on the roof / Merry widow waltz / Onward christian soldiers / More / Big country, The / Ebb tide / Perhaps, perhaps, perhaps / Catari, catari / Village swallows / Can can (From La Boutique Fatasque.).
LP: . . . . **SPA 1**
MC: . . . . **KCSP 1**

WORLD OF MANTOVANI, VOL 2.
Tracks: / Those were the days / Lara's theme / Take the 'A' train / Beautiful dreamer / Hernando's hideaway / Legend of the Glass Mountain / Tonight / Secret love / What now my love? / April in Portugal / Air on a G string / Exodus.
LP: . . . . **SPA 36**
MC: . . . . **KCSP 36**

Mantronix

BEST OF MANTRONIX, THE.
Tracks: / Ladies / Who is it (club mix) / Ladies revived / Listen to the bass of get stupid fresh (part 2) / Sing a song / Electronic energy of... / Needle to the groove / Bassline / Scream (remix) / Mantronix to the groove megamix.
LP: . . . . **DIX 91**
MC: . . . . **CDIX 91**

IN FULL EFFECT.
Tracks: / Join me please...(home boys make some noise) / Love letter (Dear Tracey) / Gangster boogie / In full effect / Get stupid (part 3) / Simple Simon (you gotta regard) / Sing a song (break it down) / Do you like...Mantronix? / Megamix '88.
LP: . . . . **DIX 74**
MC: . . . . **CDIX 74**
MC: . . . . **OVEDC 359**

INCREDIBLE SOUND MACHINE, THE.
Tracks: / Step to me (do me) / Don't go messin' with my heart / Flower child (summer of love) / Gimme' something / Put a little love on hold / Well I guess you / Step to me (do me) (12" ext. mix) (Not on album.) / If you could read my mind / Make it funky / I'm just adjustin' my mic '91 / Operation mindcrime.
LP: . . . . **EST 2139**
MC: . . . . **TCEST 2139**

MANTRONIX.
Tracks: / Bassline / Needle to the groove / Mega-mix / Hardcore hip-hop / Ladies / Get stupid ('fresh' part 1) / Fresh is the word.
LP: . . . . **DIX 37**
MC: . . . . **CDIX 37**

MUSIC MADNESS.
Tracks: / Who is it? / We control the dice / Listen to the bass of get stupid fresh (part 2) / Big band b boy / Musical madness / Electronic energy of... / Scream / Mega mix / Who is it? (freestyle club mix) / Scream (primal scream) / Needle to the groove (Live at the Town and Country Club) / Ladies (Live at the Town and Country Club) / Scream (Live at the Town and Country Club).
MC: . . . . **CDIX 50**
LP: . . . . **DIX 50**
MC: . . . . **OVEDC 360**
LP: . . . . **OVED 360**

THIS SHOULD MOVE YA.

Tracks: / This should move ya / Got to have your love / Sex-n-drugs and rock-n-roll / Tonight is right / I'm just adjustin' my mic / Stone cold roach / I get lifted / Don't you want more / I like the way (you do it) / Get stupid Part IV (get on up '90) / I'm just adjustin' my mic ('90) (Not on album.) / King of the beats lesson (Not on album.) / Take your time (Reissue only.) / Don't you want more (Reissue only.).
LP: . . . . EST 2117
MC: . . . . TCEST 2117
MC: 791 119 4
LP: . . . . ESTX 2117
LP: 794 479 1
MC: . . . . TCESTX 2117
MC: 794 479 4

Manual Scan

MANUAL SCAN.
LP: . . . . LO 5

Manuel

BLUE TANGOS (Manuel & The Music of the Mountains).
LP: . . . . NTS 113

BOLERO (Manuel & The Music of the Mountains).
Tracks: / Bolero / Granada / Bright eyes / Fiesta / Carillon / Rodrigo's guitar concerto de aranjuez / El Rancho Grande / Ramona / Hooray hooray it's a holi holiday / Summertime / Yellow bird / Albinoni's adagio in G minor / Spanish Harlem / Strangers in the night / Cavatina / Begin the beguine / Cuando calienta el sol / El condor pasa.
LP: . . . . MFP 41 5678 1
MC: . . . . MFP 41 5678 4
LP: . . . . MFP 5678
MC: . . . . TCMFP 5678

CARNIVAL (Manuel & The Music of the Mountains).
LP: . . . . TWO 337

DIGITAL SPECTACULAR (Manuel & The Music of the Mountains).
Tracks: / Bolero / Adagio / To be with you / Eclipse / Interlude / Bright eyes / Great gate of Kiev, The / Gymnopede No. 1 & 3 / Scilienne / Norwegian dance No. 2 / Sicilian vespers.
LP: . . . . THIS 30

FANTASY (Manuel & The Music of the Mountains).
Tracks: / Summertime / Fantasy / Annie's song / Little drummer boy / Carillon / Blue tango / Bolero / La campanilla / Daniella / That old black magic.
LP: . . . . TWOD 2004

FIESTA (Manuel & The Music of the Mountains).
Tracks: / Granada / In a little spanish town / Donkey serenade / Rise / Music box dancer / Mexican whistler / Title track / You belong to my heart / Behind the mask / Hooray hooray it's a holi holiday / Ramona / Tzena, tzena, tzena.
LP: . . . . TWOD 2003
MC: . . . . TC-TWOD 2003

FOR YOUR PLEASURE (Manuel & The Music of the Mountains).
LP: . . . . MFP 5598

HONEYMOON SONG.
MC: . . . . TC IDL 10

IMAGES OF (Manuel & The Music of the Mountains).
MC: . . . . KNMC 16017

LATIN HITS (Manuel & The Music of the Mountains).
Tracks: / Guantanamera / Mascrara negra / You belong to my heart / Tico-tico / Vaya con dios / Ramona / La golondrina / Cumana / Meditation / Siboney / Eso beso / El rancho grande / Besame mucho / La bamba / Estrellita / Frenesi / A banda / El condor pasa / Brazil / Adios muchachos / Begin the beguine / Blue tango.
MC: . . . . TCEMS 1300

LATIN ROMANCE (Manuel & The Music of the Mountains).
Tracks: / You are the sunshine of my life / What are you doing the rest of your life? / I talk to the trees (From 'Paint Your Wagon') / So in love (From 'Kiss Me Kate') / Song is you, The (From 'Music In The Air') / Umbrellas of Cherbourg, The (From 'I Will Wait For You') / Stranger in Paradise (From 'Kismet') / And I love you so / Yesterday once more / Spanish eyes / Shadow of your smile, The (Love theme from 'The Sandpiper') / Story of a starry night, The / Come closer to me / Love story / Man and a woman, A / Symphony / Stardust / Strangers in the night / Killing me softly with his song / Feelings / What I did for love (From 'A Chorus Line') / Cavatina.
MC: . . . . TCEMS 1393

MAGIC OF MANUEL AND THE MUSIC OF THE MOUNTAINS, THE.
Tracks: / Somewhere my love / Sunrise, sunset / Love Story theme / Shadow of your smile / Spanish Harlem / Strangers in the night / If / Bali Ha'i / El condor pasa / Cuando calienta el sol / Spartacus love theme / Moonlight serenade / Sun, the sea and the sky, The / Do you know the way to San Jose / Cavatina / Autumn leaves / Ebb tide / Moon river / Begin the beguine / Stranger on the shore / Misty / What are you doing the rest of your life / And I love you so / Killing me softly with his song.
2LP: . . . . DL 41 1086 3
MC: . . . . DL 41 1086 9
2LP: . . . . DL 1086
MC: . . . . TCDL 1086

MANUEL AND THE MUSIC OF THE MOUNTAINS.
Tracks: / Granada / Barcarolle / Old black magic, That / Yellow bird / Adagio / Don Valero, it was nice to see you / Summertime / In a little Spanish town / Annie's song / Tzena, Tzena, Tzena / Donkey serenade, The / Little drummer boy / Music box dancer / Rivers of Babylon / Hooray hooray it's a holi holiday / Our concerto / Eso es el amor / Fantasy / Ob la di ob la da / Fiesta / Mexican whistler.
LP: . . . . EMS 1262
MC: . . . . TCEMS 1262

MOUNTAIN FIESTA (Manuel & The Music of the Mountains).
Tracks: / Moonlight fiesta / Windmills of your mind, The / Stranger in Paradise / On days like these / Girl from Impanema / Bossa de Cid / Carlos' theme / Little sparrow of Paris, The / La golondrina / Wand'rin star / You and the night and the music / Time for love is anytime, A / Umbrellas of Cherbourg / Stella by starlight / Malaguena / Singer not the song, The / Carnival / Gardens in Ibiza / Al di la / Boa noite.
MC: . . . . HR 8188

MOVIE HITS (Manuel & The Music of the Mountains).
Tracks: / Cavatina / You light up my life / As time goes by / Princess Leia's theme / Way we were / Evergreen / Moon river / Love story / What are you doing the rest of your life? / Romance / Can you read my mind / Raindrops keep fallin'.
LP: . . . . NTS 172

MUSIC OF THE MOUNTAINS (Manuel & The Music of the Mountains).
LP: 33SX 1212

SPECTACULAR SOUND OF..., THE (Manuel & The Music of the Mountains).
Tracks: / Emergency / Paloma blanca / Cavatina / Spanish eyes / Sun, the sea and the sky, The / El bimbo / Spartacus love theme / Delicado / In a little Spanish town / Spanish flea / La bamba / Rodrigo's guitar concerto de Aranjuez / Honeymoon song / Aria / Y viva Espana / As time goes by / Adios muchachos / Sabara / Brazil / Way we were, The / Viva.
LP: . . . . THIS 23
MC: . . . . TCTHIS 23

SUPERNATURAL.
Tracks: / Rivers of Babylon / Adagio / Barcarolle / Our concerto / Yellow bird / Bright eyes / Ob la di, ob la da / Bolero / To be with you / Eso es el amor / Eclipse / Interlude / Don Vallero.
2LP: . . . . TWOD 2001

THIS IS DIGITAL RECORDING (Manuel & The Music of the Mountains).
Tracks: / El rancho grande / Yellow bird / Ob la di ob la da / Eso es el amor / Barcarolle / Don Valero it was nice to see you / Carmen (overture) / Tango / Ritual fire dance / Intermezzo from Cavalleria Rusticana.
LP: . . . . THIS 1
MC: . . . . TCTHIS 1

THIS IS MANUEL (Manuel & The Music of the Mountains).
LP: . . . . STWO 5

VERY BEST OF MANUEL, THE.
Tracks: / Brazil / Rodrigo's guitar concerto de Aranjuez / Eso beso / Eye level / Carioca / Lisbon Antigua / Twelfth of never / El bimbo / Beyond the mountains / Peanut vendor / Y viva Espana / Spartacus love theme / Way we were, The / Spanish flea / Island in the sun / Honeymoon song / Summer Place, A theme from / Magic fountains / Moon river / La bamba.
LP: . . . . TWOX 1051
MC: . . . . TC-TWOX 1051

Y VIVA ESPANA (Manuel & The Music of the Mountains).
Tracks: / Y viva Espana / El relicario / Anna / Cuando calienta el sol / Cachita / Breeze and I / Man of La Mancha / Recuerdos de La Alhambra / Delicado / Madrid / Malaguena / Proud matador / Viva Carmen (From Carmen) / Rodrigo's guitar concerto de Aranjeuz (Theme from 2nd movement.) / Hasta la vista / El bimbo / La paloma / Serenata / Flamingo / Carnival / Paloma blanca / Plaza de toros / Adios / El manisero (the peanut vendor).
MC: . . . . TCEMS 1369

Manuel, Ian

DALES OF CALEDONIA, THE.
Tracks: / Haughs o' Cromdale / Are ye sleeping Maggie / Young beichan / Moneymusk lads / Jamie Raeburn / Gallant forty twa / Bonnie Bessie Logan / Merchant's son and the beggar wench / MacCrimmon's lament / Sweet kumadie, The / Overgate, The / Let me in this ae night / Lothian hairst / Lass of roch royal.
LP: 12TS 301

FROSTY PLOUGHSHARE.
Tracks: / Drumdelgie / Bogie's bonnie belle / Tarves rant, The / Lowlands of Holland, The / Sleepytoon / Moss o' Burreldale, The / Bonnie lads that handle the ploo / Guise o'tough, The / Scrankly black farmer, The / Muckin' o' Geordie's byre / Braes o' Strathblane, The / Tinker's wedding, The / Toon o' Dalry, The / Erin go bragh.
LP: 12TS 220

Manufacture

TERRORVISION.
Tracks: / Slugger / Passion for the future / Little Caesar / Obsolete / Armed forces / As the end draws near / Bond Street station / Terrorvision / Ballet mechanique / American Embassy.
LP: . . . . NET 006

VOICE OF WORLD CONTROL, THE.
LP: . . . . NET 030

Manx Gaelic

SONGS IN MANX GAELIC (AND OTHERS) (See under Douglas, Mona for details) (Douglas, Mona).

Manyeruke, Machanic

MACHANIC MANYERUKE & THE PURITANS.
Tracks: / Kana vatsvene vopinda / Ndofara / Zvandaiva mutadzi zvangu / Ndiani achandiudza / Jesu unomutsa razaro / Cain na Abel / Jesu pamuchinjikwa / Zakewu / Jonah Weninivha / Mwari wakanka / Petro anoramba (CD only.) / Mwari wakanka (CD only.) / Huyai tinamate (CD only.).
LP: . . . . COOK 025
MC: . . . . COOKC 025

Manyika, Zeke

CALL AND RESPONSE.
Tracks: / House of memory / Heaven help us / Red hot / Kelvingrove / Lay them down / Call and response / Cold light of day / 17 faces / It doesn't matter to me / This lamp.
LP: ZMLP1

MASTERCRIME.
Tracks: / Mastercrime / Third World child / Love you feel / Turn it over / Bible belt / Mercenary / Runaway freedom train / Go go get ready / Bible belt (12" version) (CD only.).
LP: . . . . PCS 7330
LP: 792 999 1
MC: . . . . TCPCS 7330
MC: 792 999 4

R.F.T. (RUNAWAY FREEDOM TRAIN) (See under Runaway Freedom Train).

ZEKE MANYIKA.
LP: . . . . UNKNOWN

Manzanera, Phil

801 LIVE.
Tracks: / Lagrima / TNK (Tomorrow never knows) / East of Asteroid / Rongwrong / Sombre reptiles / Baby's on fire / Diamond head / Miss Shapiro / You really got me / Third uncle.
LP: . . . . EGLP 26
MC: . . . . EGMC 26

DIAMOND HEAD.
Tracks: / Frontera / Diamond head / Big day / Flex, The / Same time next week / Miss Shapiro / Lagrima / Alma.
LP: 2302 062
LP: . . . . ILPS 9315
LP: . . . . EGLP 19

GUITARISSIMO.
Tracks: / K-scope (part 1 of La Escena) / Frontera (part 2 of La Escena) / TNK (part 3 of La Escena) / Criollo / Diamond head / You are here / Rude awakening / Listen now / Big dome (part 2) / Caracas (part 2 of Corrida y Carnaval) / Lagrima / Europe 70-1 (part 2 of La Tristeza) / Island (part 3 of La Tristeza) / That falling feeling / Big dome (part 1) (CD & cassette only) / City of light (CD & cassette only) / Initial speed (CD & cassette only).
LP: . . . . EGLP 69
MC: . . . . EGMC 69

LISTEN NOW (Manzanera, Phil & Eight Hundred & One).
Tracks: / Listen now / Flight 19 / Island / Law and order / Que / City of light / Initial speed / Postcard love / That falling feeling.
LP: 2302 074
LP: . . . . EGLP 30

MANZANERA & MACKAY (Manzanera, Phil & Andy Mackay).
Tracks: / Black gang chine / Free yourself / Built for speed / Many are the ways / I can be tender / Dreams of the East / Sacrosanct / Every king of stone / Men with extraordinary / Safe in the arms of love / Forgotten man.
LP: . . . . EXPLP 4
MC: . . . . EXPMC 4

PRIMITIVE GUITARS.
Tracks: / Criollo / Caracas / La nueva ola / Bogota / Ritmo de Los Angeles / Europe 70-1 / Impossible guitar / Big dome / Europe 80-1.
MC: . . . . EGEDC 14
LP: . . . . EGED 14

SOUTHERN CROSS.
LP: . . . . VG 406506236
LP: . . . . EXPAL 1
MC: . . . . EXPMC 1

Manzanilla Sound

MANZANILLA SOUND.
LP: . . . . GNPS 2058

Manzarek, Ray

CARMINA BURANA.
Tracks: / Wheel of fortune / Wounds of fate / Face of Spring / Sunrise / Welcome / Dance / Sweetest boy / If the world was mine / Boiling rage / Roasted swan / In the tavern / Love flies everywhere / Young girl / Come, my beauty / Lovers.
LP: . . . . AMLX 64945

Mao, Tse-Tung

QUOTATIONS FROM THE CHAIRMAN.
LP: . . . . PRCS 111

Maono

MAONO.
LP: . . . . BSR 0025

Maori Songs

MAORI LOVE SONGS (Maori Love Songs).
LP: . . . . VP 409

MAORI SONGS AND MUSIC FROM NEW ZEALAND (Maori Songs And Music From New Zealand).
LP: . . . . EXP 53

Mapangala, Samba

VIRUNGA VOLCANO (Mapangala, Samba & Orchestre Virunga).
Tracks: / Malako / Ahmed sabit / Virunga / Yembele / Neliya (Only on CD.) / Mansita (Only on CD.).
LP: . . . . EWV 16
MC: . . . . TCEWV 16

Mapfumo, P

NDANGARIRO.
LP: . . . . CGLP 4414
MC: . . . . CGC 4414

Mapfumo, Thomas

CHAMUNORA.
MC: . . . . MCT 1075
LP: . . . . MLPS 1075

CHIMURENGA FOR JUSTICE.
LP: . . . . ROUGH 91

CHIMURENGA SINGLES, THE.
LP: . . . . ELP 2004
LP: . . . . ML 403
MC: . . . . MLC 403

CORRUPTION.
Tracks: / Moyo wangu / Vorombo kuvarombo / Shabeen / Corruption / Muchadura / Handina munyama / Kupera kwevanhu / Chigwindiri.
MC: . . . . MCT 1019
LP: . . . . MLPS 1019

MABASA.
LP: . . . . ERT 1007

MR. MUSIC.
LP: . . . . ERT 1008

SHUMBA (Vital Hits Of Zimbabwe).
LP: . . . . EMW 5506
LP: . . . . EWV 22
MC: . . . . TCEWV 22

Maphis, Joe

BOOGIE WOOGIE FLAT TOP GUITAR PICKIN' MAN.
Tracks: / Boogie woogie flat top guitar pickin' man / Fiddle pickin' / Joe Maphis blues / Devil's dream / Old fiddler Joe / Somewhere between / Don't you cry Melinda / Sweet Georgia Brown / Your sweet, sweet lips / Six by five.
LP: . . . . CMH 6239

DIM LIGHTS, THICK SMOKE.

Tracks: / Dim lights, thick smoke / Mother Maybelle / Eighteen wheels / Down at the front of the mountain / Town Hall rag / Carter county / My baby's doin' alright / Hilltop pickin' / Rocky mountain special / Yodeling bird / You ain't got the sense you were born with / Snowflakes.
LP: CMH 6224

JOE MAPHIS & ROSE LEE WITH THE BLUE RIDGE MOUNTAIN BOYS (Maphis, Joe & Joe Lee).
Tracks: / Flowers on the sunny side / Why do you weep, dear willow / There'll come a time / Maple on the hill / Teardrops falling in the snow / Put my little shoes away / Lonesome train / Little rosewood casket, The / Whisky is the devil in liquid form / Speak to me little darlin' / Little mother of the hills / Picture on the wall.
LP: HAT 3048
MC: HATC 3048

Maple Leaf Scottish...

WELCOME TO TAYSIDE (Maple Leaf Scottish Dance Band).
LP: BSLP 1175

Maple Town

LONELY EAGLE, THE (Unknown narrator(s)).
MC: STK 011

TREASURE MAP, THE (Unknown narrator(s)).
MC: STK 012

Mar Keys

LAST NIGHT (OLD GOLD) (See under Bar kays/Soul finger (Old Gold).

Mara

ON THE EDGE.
LP: SSM 025

Mara, Nat

TAHITI-VOILA (Mara, Nat & His Tahitians).
LP: VP 289

Marable Quartet,

TENORMAN.
LP: FS 111

Maranatha Singers

ABBA (Songs to the Father).
LP: MM R 0238
MC: MM C 0238

BEST OF PRAISE 2, THE.
LP: MM 0110
MC: TC MM 0110

BEST OF PRAISE, THE.
Tracks: / Seek ye first / Lord be glorified / Sing hallelujah / Spirit song / I want to praise you, Lord / Sweetest name of all, The / We have come into His house / Open our eyes / In His time / Father I adore you / I love you Lord.
LP: MM 0083
MC: TC MM 0083

CHRISTMAS CLASSICS.
Tracks: / Hark the herald angel sing / First Nowell, The / Silent night / Good Christian men rejoice / O little town of Bethlehem / Silent night / O Holy night (8 more tracks).
LP: MM R 0242
MC: MM C 0242

FEAST, THE A celebration of Communion.
LP: MM R 0157
MC: MM C 0157

HALLELUJAH.
LP: MM R 0248
MC: MM C 0248

HOSANNA (15 SONGS OF FREEDOM) (Words of Worship).
LP: MM R 0274
MC: MM C 0274

HYMNS AND CHORUSES V1.
LP: MM R 0249
MC: MM C 0249

HYMNS AND CHORUSES V2.
LP: MM R 0250
MC: MM C 0250

HYMNS AND CHORUSES V3.
LP: MM R 0258
MC: MM C 0258

IN HIS TIME.
Tracks: / I want to praise You, Lord / In His time / Micah / I will serve you (thee) / Psalm 5 / Sweetest name of all, The / Worship song (Lord, you're worthy), The / Jesus, what wonder you are (Jesus how lovely you are) / Isn't he / I love the Lord.
LP: MM 0064
MC: TC MM 0064

MOVE INTO HIS PRESENCE (Maranatha: Men's chorus).
LP: MM R 0140
MC: MM C 0140

PRAISE 3.
Tracks: / We have come into His house / Humble thyself in the sight of the Lord / Lord be glorified / Behold what manner of love / Shepherd's song / Spirit song / Behold, bless ye the Lord / John 3: 16 / Father, I believe you / Jesus, name above all names / His name is Jesus / Wait on the Lord / We must wait (on the Lord).
LP: MM 0048
MC: TC MM 0048

PRAISE 5.
Tracks: / Don't you know it's time / As we gather / Steadfast love of the Lord, The / Shield about me, A / Jesus I love you / Praise song / Call on the Lord / More I get to know you (the more I fall in love) / I believe in you / In moments like these / Glorify Thy name.
LP: MM 0076
MC: TC MM 0076

PRAISE 6.
MC: TC MM 0095

PRAISE 7.
LP: MM 0123
MC: TC MM 0123

PRAISE 8.
LP: MM R 0153
MC: MM C 0153

PRAISE 9.
Tracks: / Majesty / All hail King Jesus / Be exalted, O God / Meekness and majesty / How excellent your name / Thy word / Servant king, The / Unto thee, O Lord / We are here to praise You / May the fragrance of Jesus fill this place / He alone (deserves our praise) / I just want to praise you / Great are You, Lord / Great is Thy name / You are the Almighty King / When I look into Your holiness / Lord, have mercy on us / Change my heart, O God / Blessed by the Lord God Almighty.
LP: MM R 0190
MC: MM C 0190

PRAISE 10.
LP: MM R 0240
MC: MM C 0240

PRAISE 11.
Tracks: / Soften my heart / Battle belongs to the Lord, The / He is exalted / Great is the Lord / Rejoice.
LP: MM R 0251
MC: MM C 0251

PRAISE ALBUM, THE.
Tracks: / Heavenly Father / Father I adore you / Praise the Lord / Praise the Lord together / Thy loving kindness / Set my spirit free / Bring my body closer / Love (one another) / Seek ye first / 'Cause me to come / Holy, thou art holy / Peace give I to thee.
LP: MM 0008
MC: TC MM 0008

PRAISE STRINGS 1.
Tracks: / Praise you, Father / Sing to the Father / Father, I adore you / Praise the Lord / Unto thee, O Lord / Sing hallelujah / Open your eyes / Light our way / My peace / Seek ye first.
LP: MM 0029
MC: TC MM 0029

PRAISE STRINGS 2.
Tracks: / Jesus / Peace give I to thee / Set my spirit free / Holy, holy, holy / John (these things I have spoken unto you) / 'Cause me to come / Thy loving kindness / Love (one another) / Thank you Jesus / Psalm 5.
LP: MM 0039
MC: TC MM 0039
MC: MM 0026
MC: TC MM 0026

PRAISE STRINGS 3.
Tracks: / Humble thyself / Wait on the Lord / Behold, what manner of love / His name is Jesus / Spirit song / Jesus, name above all names / Behold, bless ye the Lord / Lord, be glorified / Father I believe you / Shepherd's song.
LP: MM 0054
MC: TC MM 0054

PRAISE STRINGS 4.
Tracks: / I want to praise you Lord / In his time / Micah / I will serve You (Thee) / Psalm 5 / Sweetest name of all, The / Worship song (Lord you're worthy), The / Jesus, what wonder you are (Jesus, how lovely / Isn't he / I love you Lord.
LP: MM 0067
MC: TC MM 0067

PRAISE STRINGS 5.
Tracks: / It's time to praise the Lord / Shield about me, A / Jesus I love you / I believe in you / Praise song / As we gather / Steadfast love of the Lord, The / More I get to know you (the more I fall in love) / Call on the Lord / In moments like these / Glorify Thy name.
LP: MM 0082
MC: TC MM 0082

PRAISE STRINGS 7.
LP: MM 0130
MC: TC MM 0130

PRAISE STRINGS 8.
LP: MM R 0162
MC: MM C 0162

PRAISE STRINGS 9.
LP: MM R 0214
MC: MM C 0214

PRAISE STRINGS 10.
LP: MM R 0243
MC: MM C 0243

PRAISE STRINGS 11.
MC: MM C 0252

PSALMS ALIVE.
MC: TC MM 0097

PSALMS ALIVE 2.
MC: TC MM 0113

PSALMS ALIVE 3.
Tracks: / Those who sow in tears / Break into songs of joy / My soul waits / Bless the Lord, my soul / Clap your hands / I take refuge in the Lord / There's a longing in my heart / To every generation / Teach me thy way / Give glory to the Lord.
LP: MM R 0150
MC: MM C 0150

SCRIPTURE IN SONG.
LP: MM R 0160
MC: MM C 0160

Marc & The Mambas

TORMENT AND TOREROS.
LP: BIZL 4
MC: BIZLC 4

UNTITLED.
Tracks: / Untitled / Empty eyes / Angels / Big Louise / Caroline says / Margaret / If you go away / Terrapin / Twilights and lowlife.
LP: BZS 13
MC: BZM 13
2LP: SOB 4

Marc V

TOO TRUE.
Tracks: / Cops and robbers / Let them stare / Paint the moonlight black / Powerful love / Can't stop lovin' you / House arrest / Something to believe in / I remember / When am I gonna learn / You can turn the lights out.
LP: K 9608111
MC: K 9608114

Marcantel, Nancy Tabb

LAGNIAPPE.
LP: 6026

MA LOUISIANA.
LP: 6022
MC: 6022 TC

SAUTE CRAPAUD.
LP: 6029
MC: 6029 TC

Marce Et Tumpak

ZOUK CHOUV.
Tracks: / Gren-n lanmou / Chien cho / Zouk chouv / Lans difou / Lese woule.
LP: ORB 035

Marcels

BEST OF THE MARCELS.
Tracks: / Blue moon / I'll be forever loving you / I wanna be the leader / That old black magic / Honestly sincere / Summertime / Crazy bells / Heartaches / Goodbye to love / Find another fool / My melancholy baby / Sweet was the wine / One last kiss / Over the rainbow / Footprints in the sand (CD only.) / Alright, okay, you win (CD only.) / Friendly loans (CD only.) / Blue heartaches (CD only.).
MC: TCROU 5006
MC: 794 555 4

BLUE MOON.
Tracks: / Blue moon.
LP: ES 12041

HEARTACHES.
LP: CP 520

RARE ITEMS.
LP: CP 521

March Hare Murders

MARCH HARE MURDERS, THE (Elizabeth Ferrars) (Bron, Eleanor (nar)).
MC: CAT 4033

March Of...

MARCH OF THE FALSETTOS (Original Broadway cast) (Various artists).
LP: SBL 12581
MC: SBLC 12581

March, Stella

BARRIER TO LOVE.
MC: SOUND 35

CARRIAGE FOR FIONA, A.
MC: SOUND 21

March Violets

NATURAL HISTORY.
LP: VRB 25

Marchan, Bobby

FIFTIES IN NEW ORLEANS, THE.
Tracks: / Just a little walk / Have mercy / You made a fool of me / Just a little ol' wine / Give a helping hand / Pity poor me / Chickee wah-wah / Don't take your love from me / I can't stop loving you / I'll never let you go / Hush your mouth / Well I'll be John Brown / You can't stop her / Rockin' behind the iron curtain / Quit my job / Havin' a good time.
LP: OFF 6034

GOLDEN CLASSICS.
LP: COL 5113

Marcos

FLAMENCO HORIZONS.
Tracks: / Flamenco horizons.
LP: STOP 100

Marcotte, Marion

CAJUN FRENCH HUMOR.
LP: 6018

FAVORITE CAJUN TALES.
LP: 6004
MC: 6004 TC

Marcovic Gut Sextet

MARCOVIC GUT SEXTET.
MC: SJP 1195

Marcus Ben

JUST A SHAGGY DOG STORY (Marcus Ben Band).
Tracks: / Angelene / Wearing thin / No one can tell you / Promise to show / You'll never know / Feeling's right, The / All I know / White room / Can't go back.
MC: CITMC 202

Mardi Gras

MARDI GRAS IN NEW ORLEANS (Various artists).
LP: MG 1001

NEW ORLEANS MARDI GRAS (Various artists).
LP: R 107
MC: RC 107

Mardones, Benny

BENNY MARDONES.
Tracks: / I never really loved you at all / For a little ride / How could you love me / Into the night / We've got to run / I'll be good to you / If you loved me / Never far away / Close to the flame / Run to you.
LP: ZL 74432
MC: ZK 74432

Marentic, James

NIMBUS.
Tracks: / Baile de las Cacharaches / Aphrodesia / Lick's for chicks kicks / Nimbus / Mr. Silver, I persume / Bronx waltz, The.
LP: DS 879

Maresca, Ernie

SHOUT SHOUT (KNOCK YOURSELF OUT).
Tracks: / Shout shout (knock yourself out) / Someday you'll change your ways / They don't know / Don't know why / Down on the beach / Crying like a baby over you / Mary Jane / What good is living / How I cry / I'm gonna make it somehow / Subway blues / Can't forget about you.
LP: SEL 3

Margin Of Sanity

MARGIN OF SANITY.
LP: SEX 11

Margitza, Rick

COLOR.
Tracks: / Widow's walk / Color scheme / Ferris wheel / Our song / Waltz / Anthem / Brace yourself / Karensong / We stand adjourned / Point of view.
LP: B1 92279

Margo

18 IRISH SONGS.
Tracks: / If we only had old Ireland over here / Old Claddagh ring / Golden jubilee / Cottage by the Lee / Road by the river / Donegal Danny / Cliffs of Dooneen / Boys of Killybegs / Gra mo chroi / Boys from County Mayo / Irish eyes / I'll settle for old Ireland / Slievenamon / Three leaf shamrock / Girl from Donegal / Shades of green / Boys from County Armagh / Any Tipperary town.
LP: ARAM 2005
MC: CARAM 2005

ALL TIME HITS.
Tracks: / Irish eyes / Gra mo chroi / Cliffs of Dooneen / Dear God / Through the eyes of a child / Galway Bay / Road by the river / Destination Donegal / Road and miles to Dundee / Shamrock from Glenore / Banks of Mulroy Bay / Girl from Donegal.

LP: . . . . ARAL 1011
MC: . . . . TC/ARAL 1011

AT HOME IN IRELAND.
Tracks: / Dear old Killarney / Irish rover, The / If we only had old Ireland over here.
LP: . . . . ARAL 1004

COUNTRY GIRL.
Tracks: / There has to be an end to it someday / Coat of many colours / To Chicago with love / You ain't woman enough / Our last night together (soldier's farewell) / Tomorrow never comes / Lovely Stornoway / I thought I heard you calling my name / Baby's back again / Yodel I love you / It rains the same in Missouri / Memories from the past.
LP: . . . . PHL 422
MC: . . . . CPHL 422

COUNTRY LOVIN'.
Tracks: / Be nice to everybody / Crazy dreams / Hello darlin'.
LP: . . . . ARAL 1002
MC: . . . . TC/ARAL 1002

COUNTRY STYLE.
Tracks: / I love you drops / Billy Christian / Ribbon of darkness / Once a day / I don't love you anymore / Family bible / Lonely hearts club / Don't read the letter / Gathering flowers for the master's bouquet / Eight more miles to Louisville / Why / Mama say a prayer.
LP: . . . . ARAL 1010
MC: . . . . TC/ARAL 1010

DESTINATION DONEGAL.
LP: . . . . ARAM 2004

FROM MARGO WITH LOVE.
Tracks: / Roving Galway Bay / San Antonio rose / Hills of Glenswilly.
LP: . . . . ARAL 1001
MC: . . . . TC/ARAL 1001

GALWAY BAY.
LP: . . . . ARAL 1009

GIRL FROM DONEGAL.
Tracks: / Donegal / Goodbye Johnny dear / Sprig of Irish heather, A / Old rustic bridge / Village in County Tyrone / Noreen Bawn / Isle of Innisfree / Tipperary, so far away / Old flames / Rose of Mooncoin / Doonaree / Green white and gold / Isle of Ireland / My gentle daddy / Green hills of Sligo.
LP: . . . . IHLP 03
MC: . . . . IHMC 03

GREATEST HITS: MARGO (Volume 1).
LP: . . . . ARAL 1005

GREATEST HITS: MARGO VOL.2.
MC: . . . . TC ARAM 2002
LP: . . . . ARAM 2002

I LONG TO SEE OLD IRELAND FREE ONCE MORE.
LP: . . . . CSDBL 519

IRELAND MUST BE HEAVEN.
LP: . . . . SMLP 9002
MC: . . . . ROLP 1001

IRISH COLLEEN.
MC: . . . . BTC 304

IRISH REQUESTS.
Tracks: / Boys from the County Armagh / Forty shades of green / Cottage by the Lee / Cutting the corn in Cresslough today / Spinning wheel / I'll settle for old Ireland / Donegal Danny / Little sweetheart / Faithful sailor boy / Slievenamon / Shores of Amerikay / Come my little son.
LP: . . . . ARAM 2003
MC: . . . . CARAM 2003

MARGO NOW.
Tracks: / Violet and the rose, The / Country music / Plains of sweet Kildare / Home is where you're happy / Signed, sealed, delivered, I'm yours / Sweethearts in Heaven / Two's company / These are the colours / Forty miles to donegal / Little more like Heaven, A / Shanagolden / You'll never miss the water.
LP: . . . . RITZLP 0045
MC: . . . . RITZLC 0045

MARGO'S FAVOURITES.
LP: . . . . HPE 622
MC: . . . . HPC 622

TOAST FROM AN IRISH COLLEEN.
Tracks: / Thank you for the roses / Bunch of thyme / Little Isle of Green / Toast from an Irish Colleen, A / James Connolly.
LP: . . . . RRL 8018
MC: . . . . CRRL 8018

TOAST TO CLADDAGH, A.
LP: . . . . ARAM 2001
MC: . . . . TC ARAM 2001

TRIP TO IRELAND.
Tracks: / Three leaf shamrock / Shanagolden / Old house / Old Claddagh ring / Cliffs of Dooneen / Mass rock in the glen / Galway Bay / If we only had old Ireland over here / Boys of Killybegs / Boys from County Mayo / West of the old River Shannon.
LP: . . . . PHL 436
MC: . . . . CPHL 436

Margolin, Bob

CHICAGO BLUES.
Tracks: / She's so pretty / She and the devil (Only on cassette and CD) / Steady rollin' man / Sugar sweet / Something inside me / Dust my broom / Wee wee baby / Rollin' and tumblin' / Mean disposition / Tribute to Howlin' Wolf / Not what you said last night / Welcome home / Telephone answering machine blues / Born in the wrong time (Only on cassette and CD) / She and the devil.
LP: . . . . POW 4105
MC: . . . . POW 4105MC

Margolyes, Miriam

COLD COMFORT FARM (see under Cold Comfort Farm (bk)).

DAYLIGHT DIG, THE (See also the Keypers).

SNOW WHITE AND THE SEVEN DWARFS Read by Miriam Margolyes.
MC: . . . . PTB 630

WORST WITCH, THE (See under Worst Witch).

Margret, Ann

THREE GREAT GIRLS (see under Reese, Della) (Reese, Della/Ann Margret/Kitty Kallen).

Maria, Fernanda

FADO... FADOS.
Tracks: / Castelo Branco / Traquitanas / Penas / Quadras soltas / A Rosa da Madragoa / Rua do Capelao / Anda ca Manel / Passou / Ronda da saudade / Esperas de gado / Viram por ai o fado? / Flor esquecida.
LP: . . . . ARN 33722
MC: . . . . ARN 433722

Maria, Tania

BRAZIL WITH MY SOUL.
LP: 90169

COME WITH ME.
Tracks: / Sangria / Embraceable you / Lost in Amazonia / Come with me / Sementes, graines and seeds / Nega / Euzinha / Its all over now.
LP: . . . . CJP 200
MC: . . . . CJPC 200

LIVE: TANIA MARIA.
Tracks: / Mr. & Mrs. Gatoamante / Pingas da vida / Seu dia vai chegar / O que e amar / Carona.
LP: . . . . ACV 13005
MC: 130 189

LOVE EXPLOSION.
Tracks: / Funky tambourine / It's all in my hands / You've got me feeling your love / Love explosion / Bela la bela / Rainbow of your love / Deep cove view / Pour toi.
LP: . . . . CJP 230
MC: . . . . CJPC 230

MADE IN NEW YORK.
Tracks: / Don't go / E carnival / My space / I do love you / Made in New York / Together / Forock / Walking in the rain.
LP: . . . . EJ 2403211
MC: . . . . EJ 2403214

PIQUANT.
LP: . . . . CJP 151

REAL TANIA MARIA-WILD, THE.
Tracks: / Yatra - ta / A cama na varanda / Vem pra roda / Come with me / Funy tamborine / 2 a.m. / Sangria.
LP: . . . . CJP 264
MC: . . . . CJPC 264

TAURUS.
LP: . . . . CJP 175
MC: . . . . CJPC 175

VIA BRAZIL (VOLUME 1).
LP: 80550

Mariachis

MEXICO.
LP: . . . . PS 801
MC: . . . . PS 9801

Mariano, Charlie

ALTO SAX-FOR YOUNG MODERNS (Mariano, Charlie, Quartet).
Tracks: / Johnny one note / Very thought of you, The / Smoke gets in your eyes / King for a day / Darn that dream / Floormat / Blues - traditional / I heard you cried last night.
LP: . . . . AFF 99

CHARLIE MARIANO AND THE KARNATAKA COLLEGE OF PERCUSSION LIVE.
MC: . . . . VBR 2034 3
LP: . . . . VBR 2034 1

CHARLIE MARIANO PLAYS.
LP: . . . . FS 260

JYOTHI.
Tracks: / Voice solo (Ramamani,R.A.-Tamboura.Mani,T.A.S.-Mridangam.Rajagopal,R.A.-ghatam,morsi) / Vandanam / Varshini / Saptarshi / Kartik / Bhajan.
LP: . . . . ECM 1256

Marie

MARIE: A TRUE STORY (Film Soundtrack) (Various artists).
LP: . . . . STV 81265

Marie, Donna

REGGAE LOVE MUSIC, VOLUME 1.
LP: . . . . LUDLP 02

Marie, Kelly

FEELS LIKE I'M IN LOVE.
Tracks: / Feel like I'm in love / Take me to paradise / I can't get enough / Get up on your feet / Make love to me / Loving just for fun / Do you like it like that / New York at night / Run to me / Fill me with your love.
LP: . . . . CABLP 1005

WHO'S THAT LADY WITH MY MAN.
LP: . . . . NSPL 18525

Marie, Teena

EMERALD CITY.
Tracks: / Emerald city / Once is not enough / Lips to find you / You so heavy / Shangri-la / Batucada suite / Love me down easy / Sunny skies.
LP: . . . . EPC 26935
MC: 40 26935

GREATEST HITS: TEENA MARIE (...and more).
Tracks: / Behind the groove / It must be magic / I'm a sucker for your love / Square biz / Why can't I get next to you / Lonely desire / Revolution / Co-pilot to pilot / I need your lovin' / 365 / Portuguese love / Love just wouldn't be right / Where's California / Don't look back / Every little bit hurts.
LP: . . . . WL 72428
MC: . . . . WK 72428

IRONS IN THE FIRE.
Tracks: / I need your lovin' / Young love / First class love / Irons in the fire / Chains / You make love like springtime / Tune in tomorrow / You make love like springtime (reprise).
LP: . . . . STML 12143
MC: . . . . CSTML 12143

IT MUST BE MAGIC.
Tracks: / It must be magic / Revolution / Where's California / 365 / Opus 111 (does anybody care) / Square biz / Ballad of Cradle Rob and me / Portuguese love / Yes indeed.
LP: . . . . STML 12154
MC: . . . . CSTML 12154

IVORY.
Tracks: / Here's looking at you / Sugar shack, The / If I were a bell / Just us two / Ivory (a tone poem) / Mr. Icecream / Cupid is a real straight shooter / How can you resist it / Since day one / Miracles need wings to fly.
LP: 4658781
MC: 4658784

LADY T.
Tracks: / Behind the groove / Now that I have you / Lonely desire / Aladdin's lamp / You're all the boogie I need / Can it be love / Young girl in love / Why did I fall in love with you / Too many colors.
LP: . . . . STML 12130

NAKED TO THE WORLD.
Tracks: / Trick bag / Call me (I got yo number) / Ooo la la la / Crocodile tears / Opus III - the second movement / Surrealistic pillow / Once and future dream, The / Work it / Ball, The / Naked to the world.
LP: 4600941
MC: 4600944

ROBBERY.
Tracks: / Robbery / Playboy / Shadow boxing / Midnight magnet / Fit it / Ask your momma / Dear lover / Stop the world / Casanova brown.
LP: . . . . EPC 25655
MC: 40 25655

STAR CHILD.
LP: . . . . EPC 26315
MC: 40 26315

WILD AND PEACEFUL.
Tracks: / I'm a sucker for your love / Turnin' me on / Don't look back / Deja vu / I'm gonna have my cake / I can't love anymore.
LP: . . . . STML 12109
MC: . . . . CSTML 12109

Marie & The

MARIE & THE WILDWOOD FLOWERS (Marie & The Wildwood Flowers).
LP: . . . . CALCLP 015

Marie Ward

MARIE WARD (Film Soundtrack) (Various artists).
LP: . . . . CST 8015
LP: . . . . STV 81268

Marienthal, Eric

CROSSROADS.
Tracks: / Sun was in my eyes, The / Spoons / Yellow roses / Upside down / Schmooze / Cross country / Hide and seek / Two bits / On the eve of tomorrow / Rain on the roof.
LP: . . . . GRP 96101
MC: . . . . GRP 96104

ROUND TRIP.
Tracks: / Round trip / I'm gonna wait on your love / Reunion / Lee Ann / I'll be home soon / Moonwalk / It's better than nothing / Afrique / Road goes on, The / Serengeti.
LP: . . . . GRP 95861
MC: . . . . GRP 95864

VOICES OF THE HEART.
Tracks: / Voices of the heart / Your eyes / Blue space / Brazilian dream / Premonition / Tippin' / Being with you / Harvest dance / Written in the wind / Walk like an emu.
LP: . . . . GRP 91052
MC: . . . . GRPM 91052

Marigold

MARIGOLD (Original London Cast) (Various artists).
LP: . . . . AEI 1120

Marillion

BRIEF ENCOUNTER.
Tracks: / Lady Nina (live) / Freaks (live) / Kayleigh (live) / Fugazi (live) / Script for a jester's tears.
LP: . . . . MLP 15023
MC: 4LP 15023

B'SIDES THEMSELVES.
Tracks: / Grendel / Charting the single / Market square heroes / Three boats down from the Candy / Cinderella search / Lady Nina / Freaks / Tux on / Margaret.
LP: . . . . EMS 1295
MC: . . . . TCEMS 1295
LP: . . . . ATAK 113
MC: . . . . TCATAK 113

CLUTCHING AT STRAWS.
Tracks: / Hotel hobbies / Warm wet circles / That time of the night / Going under / Just for the record / White Russian / Incommunicado / Torch song, The / Slainte Mhath / Sugar mice / Last straw, The.
LP: . . . . EMD 1002
MC: . . . . TCEMD 1002
LPPD: . . . . EMDP 1002
LP: . . . . EMC 3533
MC: . . . . TCEMC 3533
LP: . . . . ATAK 135
MC: . . . . TCATAK 135

FUGAZI.
Tracks: / Assassing / Punch and Judy / Jigsaw / Emerald lies / She chameleon / Incubus / Fugazi.
LP: . . . . MRL 1
MC: . . . . TC MRL 1
LPPD: . . . . MRLP 1
LP: . . . . FA 3196
MC: . . . . TCFA 3196
LP: . . . . EMC 2400851
MC: . . . . EMC 2400854

HOLIDAYS IN EDEN.
Tracks: / Splintering heart / Cover my eyes (pain and heaven) / Party, The / No one can / Holidays in Eden / Dry land / Waiting to happen / This town / Rakes's progress, The / 100 nights.
LP: . . . . EMD 1022
MC: . . . . TCEMD 1022

MARILLION: INTERVIEW PICTURE DISC.
LPPD: . . . . BAK 2021

MISPLACED CHILDHOOD.
Tracks: / Pseudo-silk kimono, The / Kayleigh / Lavender / Bittersuite / Heart of Lothian / Waterhole / Lords of the backstage / Blind curve / Childhood's end? / White feather.
LP: . . . . MRL 2
MC: . . . . TC MRL 2
LPPD: . . . . MRLP 2
LP: . . . . EJ 2403401
MC: . . . . EJ 2403404
LP: . . . . FA 3258
MC: . . . . TCFA 3258

REAL TO REEL.
Tracks: / Assassing / Incubus / Cinderella search / Emerald lies (Cassette & CD only.) / Forgotten sons / Garden party / Market Square heroes.
LP: . . . . FA 41 3142 1
MC: . . . . FA 41 3142 4
LP: . . . . FA 3142
MC: . . . . TCFA 3142
LP: . . . . EG 2603031
LP: . . . . JEST 1

MC: . . . . EG 2603030
MC: . . . . TCJEST 1
LPPD: . . . . EG 2603036

SCRIPT FOR A JESTER'S TEAR.
Tracks: / He knows, you know / Web, The / Garden party / Chelsea Monday / Forgotten sons.
LP: . . . . EMC 3429
MC: . . . . TCEMC 3429
LPPD: . . . . EMCP 3429
LP: . . . . FA 3235
MC: . . . . TCFA 3235

SEASONS END.
Tracks: / King of Sunset town / Easter / Uninvited guest, The / Seasons end / Holloway girl / Berlin / After me (Cassette & CD only.) / Hooks in you / Space, The.
LP: . . . . EMD 1011
MC: . . . . TCEMD 1011
LPPD: . . . . EMDPD 1011

THIEVING MAGPIE, THE (La gazza ladra).
Tracks: / La gazza ladra (Rossini.) / Slainte Mhath / He knows you know / Chelsea Monday / Freaks (CD only.) / Jigsaw (CD only.) / Punch and Judy (CD only.) / Sugar mice (CD only.) / Fugazi (CD only.) / Script for a jester's tear (CD only.) / Incommunicado (CD only.) / White Russian (CD only.) / Pseudo-silk kimono, The (Misplaced Childhood part one.) / Kayleigh (Misplaced Childhood part one.) / Lavender (Misplaced Childhood part one.) / Bitter suite (Misplaced Childhood part one.) / Heart of Lothian (Misplaced Childhood part one.) / Waterhole (Misplaced Childhood part two. CD only.) / Lords of the backstage (Misplaced Childhood part two. CD only.) / Blind curve (Misplaced Childhood part two. CD only.) / Childhood's end? (Misplaced Childhood part two. CD only.) / White feather (Misplaced Childhood part two. CD only.).
2LP: . . . . MARL 1
MC: . . . . TCMARL 1

Marilyn

DESPITE STRAIGHT LINES.
Tracks: / Calling your name / Mountain to the ocean / Surrender to your love / Pray for that sunshine / Third eye / Baby U left me / Wear it out / You don't love me / Give it up / Cry and be free.
LP: . . . . MERH 69

Marine Girls

BEACH PARTY.
Tracks: / In love / Fridays / Tonight / Times we used to spend / Flying over Russia / Tutti lo sanno / All dressed up / Honey / Holiday song / He got the girl / Day/night dreams / Promises / Silent red / Dishonesty / 20,000 leagues / Marine Girls.
LP: . . . . BRED 75

LAZY WAYS.
Tracks: / Place in the sun, A / Leave me with the boy / Falling again / Love to know / Different light, A / Sunshine blue / Second sight / Don't come back / That fink jazz me blues boy / Fever / Shell island / Lazy ways / Such a thing / You must be mad.
LP: . . . . BRED 44
MC: . . . . CBRED 44

Marinker, Peter (nar)

JUGGERNAUT (See under Juggernaut).

Marino

AFTER FOREVERS GONE.
Tracks: / Northern sky (part 1) / Jasmine / El Salvador / Look into the sun / After forever's gone / Fishermen (part II). The / Borderline / Ian's garden / Did I say that / Northern sky (part II) / Present light / Northern sky (part III).
LP: . . . . WKFMLP 139
MC: . . . . WKFMMC 139

BLUES FOR LOVERS.
LP: . . . . WKFMLP 167
MC: . . . . WKFMMC 167

Marino, Frank

FULL CIRCLE.
LP: . . . . GR 0951

JUGGERNAUT.
Tracks: / Strange dreams / Midnight highway / Memories of a hero / Free / Maybe it's true / Ditch queen / For your love / Juggernaut.
LP: . . . . CBS 85793

MAHOGANY RUSH 4.
LP: . . . . CBS 81417

TALES OF THE UNEXPECTED.
Tracks: / Sister change / All along the watchtower / Norwegian wood / Tales of the unexpected / Down, down, down / Door of illusion / Woman / Bottom of the barrel.
LP: . . . . CBS 83494

THERE'S NO GOOD IN GOODBYE.
LP: 82567

WHAT'S NEXT.
Tracks: / You got livin' / Finish line / Rock me baby / Something's comin' our way / Roadhouse blues / Loved by you / Rock'n'roll hall of fame / Mona.
LP: . . . . CBS 8 3897

WORLD ANTHEM.
LP: . . . . CBS 8 1978

Marino The Band

WANNA KEEP YOU SATISFIED.
LP: . . . . LRM 100

Marinos, George

RED MOON.
LP: . . . . SNTF 617

Marionette

AVA DEMENTIA.
LP: . . . . SHARP 048

BLONDE SECRETS AND DARK BOMBSHELLS.
LP: . . . . HMRLP 38
MC: . . . . HMRMC 38

Marjorie Morningstar

MARJORIE MORNINGSTAR (Film soundtrack) (Various artists).
LP: . . . . LOC 1005

Mark Almond (group)

OTHER PEOPLE'S ROOMS.
Tracks: / City / Girl on table 4 / You look just like a girl again / Other people's rooms / Lonely people / Just a friend / Then I have you / Vivaldi's song.
LP: . . . . AMLJ 730

Mark, Jan

HAIRS IN THE PALM OF THE HAND (Robinson, Tony).
MC: 2CCA 3061

Mark, Jon

STANDING STONES OF CALLANDISH.
LP: . . . . LPKUCK 11082-1
MC: . . . . MCKUCK 11082-4

Mark, Stan

STAN MARK & HIS BIG NEW BAND (Mark, Stan & band).
LP: . . . . PRO 7070

Mark T

FROM MID-EAST TO MID-WEST (Mark T and the Brickbats).
LP: . . . . WF 034

JOHNNY THERE (Mark T and the Brickbats).
Tracks: / Green brooms / Colours I know, The / Going down the road / Loop to lee / Remain in light / Avant le blond / Highway 51 / Johnny there / Sweet William / Living in the land of Cain.
LP: . . . . FE 052

ROOM, THE (Mark T & Tim Hill).
LP: . . . . WF 047

Markham, Richard

TWO PIANOS (See under Nettle, David) (Nettle, David/Richard Markham).

Markopoulos, Yannis

RIZITIKA - LE CHANT PROFOND DE LA CRETE.
Tracks: / Pote tha kani xasteria / Inda hete jirou jirou / Agrima ki agrimakia mou / Mana ki an erthoun i fili mou / Horos tou sifaka / Apo tin akri ton akipo / Kosme hrise / Se psilo vouno (o aitos) / O dighenis / Ton plousio ghiorgi ivrika / Madara.
LP: . . . . ARN 34279

WHO PAYS THE FERRYMAN.
MC: . . . . ZCF 315
LP: . . . . REB 315

WHO PAYS THE FERRYMAN (OLD GOLD) (See Ennio Morricone - Chi Mai for details).

Markowitz, Phil

RESTLESS DREAMS (See under Locke, Joe) (Markowitz Phil, Quartet and Locke, Joe).

Marks, Alan

LADY FAINTED, THE (See under Gottschalk).

Marks, Kenny

ATTITUDE.
Tracks: / Life after high school / Attitude / It doesn't hurt that much / Heroes / Friends.
LP: . . . . DAY R 4136
MC: . . . . DAY C 4136

MAKE IT RIGHT.
LP: . . . . DAY R 4151
MC: . . . . DAY C 4151

Marks, Louisa

BREAKOUT.
LP: . . . . BFMLP 101

Mark's Men

STICK 'EM UP.
MC: . . . . COB 4011

Marks, Roger

JUST THE FIVE OF US (Roger Marks Quintet).
Tracks: / Deed I do / In a mellow tone / Mona Lisa / Without a song / Games people play / Ain't misbehavin' / I can't get started / There will never be another you.
LP: 7677

SUNNY.
Tracks: / Sunny / Summertime / Stormy weather / Dindi / Rosetta / Fizz dog blues / Blues for Russ / On Green Dolphin Street / Stardust / Certain smile, A.
MC: . . . . RM 01

Markusfeld, Alain

CONTEMPORUS.
LP: 900581

PLATOCK.
LP: 900556

Marl, Marley

IN CONTROL VOLUME 1.
Tracks: / Droppin' science / We write the songs / Rebel, The / Keep your eye / Symphony, The / Live motivator / Duck alert / Simon says / Freedom / Wack it.
LP: 925 783-1
MC: 925 783-4

Marlettes

BOTH SIDES OF THE MARLETTES.
Tracks: / Daddy Frank / We can't go on / Country roads / Why don't you spend the night / There never was a time / Together / Kelty clippie / Mountain thyme / Massacre of Glencoe / Bonnie Galloway / Bonnie Scotland / Granny's heilan' hame.
LP: . . . . BGC 312
MC: . . . . KBGC 312

MASSACRE OF GLENCOE.
MC: . . . . KITV 392

MORNING IN THE COUNTRY.
Tracks: / Grandma's feather bed / Somebody loves you / Your good girl's gonna go bad / Morning / Happiest girl in the whole USA / Sing me an old fashioned song / Keep on singing / We'll get ahead someday / Let me be / I washed my face in the morning dew / Kiss an angel good morning / Race is on, The.
LP: . . . . NA 102
MC: . . . . NC 102

PURE LOVE.
Tracks: / Pure love / Some days are diamonds / Tennessee / Islands in the stream / Let it shine / I wish you joy / Liberty / Silver darlin' / Willawhit / Come by the hills / Scotland again / Loch Lomond.
LP: . . . . ITV 370
MC: . . . . KITV 370

SONGS OF SCOTLAND.
Tracks: / Fiery cross, The / Sing me a song medley / Tobermory bay / Dark island / Mull of Kintyre/Amazing grace / Nut brown maiden / Rose of Allandale / Rowan tree / Wee room underneath, The / Stair, The / Skye boat song / Old rugged cross, The / Roses of Prince Charlie / Way old friends do, The / Pride of bonnie Scotland, The / People all over the world.
MC: . . . . KITV 457

SOUVENIR SPECIAL (Marlettes, The).
MC: . . . . KITV 392

TENNESSEE MOUNTAIN HOME.
Tracks: / Tennessee mountain home / Blanket on the ground / Every road leads back to you / Silver threads and golden needles / Allentown jail / Farewell party / Sweet surrender / I wish you joy / Wolverton mountain / Did you ever / I won't go huntin' with you, Jake / I'm going to parcel up my broken heart.
LP: . . . . LILP 5068

Marley, Bob

20 GREATEST HITS: BOB MARLEY.
LP: 28014
MC: 48014

20 GREATEST HITS: BOB MARLEY & THE WAILERS (Marley, Bob & The Wailers).
Tracks: / One love / Kaya / Kinky reggae / Stir it up / Stop that train / It hurts to be alone.
MC: . . . . BT 555 014C
LP: . . . . FUN 9016
MC: . . . . FUNC 9016
LP: . . . . MA 20284
MC: . . . . MAMC 920284

25 GREATEST HITS: BOB MARLEY.
Tracks: / Lively up yourself / Small axe / Kaya / Sun is shining / Mr. Brown / Put it on / Fussing and fighting / Soul shakedown party / All in one / African herbsman / Brain washing / Do it twice / Duppy conqueror / Stand alone / Stop the train / Caution / Soul captives / Go tell it on the mountain / Soon come / Back out.
2LP: . . . . DB 80072
MC: . . . . MDB 980072

AFRICAN HERBSMAN.
Tracks: / Lively up yourself / Small axe / Keep on moving / Duppy conquerer / Trench town rock / African herbsman / Fussing and fighting / All in one / Stand alone / Don't rock the boat / Put it on / Sun is shining / Kaya / 400 years / Riding high / Brain washing.
LP: . . . . FA 41 3082 1
MC: . . . . TCFA 41 3082 4
LP: . . . . TRLS 62
MC: . . . . ZCTRL 62

ALL THE HITS.
LP: . . . . RRTG 7757
MC: . . . . RRTGC 7757

BABYLON BY BUS (Marley, Bob and The Wailers).
Tracks: / Positive vibration / Funky reggae party / Exodus / Rat race / Lively up yourself / Rebel music (three o'clock road block) / War / No more trouble / Stir it up / Concrete jungle / Kinky reggae / Is this love? / Heathen / Jamming.
2LP: . . . . ISLD 11
LP: . . . . TGDLP 1
MC: . . . . TGDMC 1

BEST OF BOB MARLEY (1968-1972).
Tracks: / Trench town rock / Don't rock the boat / Kaya / Soul shakedown party / Cheer up / Keep on moving / Try me / Lively up yourself / All in one / Soul rebel / Duppy conqueror / Keep on skanking / Caution / Mr Brown.
LP: . . . . CSAP 107
MC: . . . . CSAPMC 107

BEST RARITIES.
Tracks: / Soul rebel / Memphis / Rebel's hop / 400 years / Trench town rock / Try me / It's alright / No sympathy / My cup / Corner stone / Reaction / Don't rock my boat.
LP: . . . . B 50037
MC: MB9 50037

BIRTH OF A LEGEND, THE.
Tracks: / I made a mistake / One love / Let me go / Love and affection / Simmer down / Maga dog / I am going home / Donna / Nobody knows / Lonesome feeling.
LP: . . . . CBS 31815

BOB MARLEY: INTERVIEW PICTURE DISC.
LPPD: . . . . BAK 2065

BOB MARLEY & THE WAILERS (Marley, Bob and The Wailers).
LP: . . . . HMR 9006

BOB MARLEY & THE WAILERS WITH PETER TOSH (Marley, Bob & The Wailers).
LP: . . . . SHM 3048
MC: . . . . HSC 3048

BURNIN' (Marley, Bob & The Wailers).
Tracks: / Get up stand up / Hallelujah time / I shot the sheriff / Burnin' and lootin' / Put it on / Small axe / Pass it on / Duppy conqueror / One foundation / Rastaman chant.
LP: . . . . ILPM 9256
MC: . . . . RRCT 2
MC: 846200 4
LP: . . . . ILPS 9256
MC: . . . . ZCI 9256

CATCH A FIRE.
Tracks: / Concrete jungle / 400 years / Stop the train / Baby we got a date / Rock it baby / Kinky reggae / No more trouble / Midnight ravers.
LP: . . . . ILPM 9241
MC: . . . . ICM 9241
MC: . . . . RRCT 1
MC: 846201 4
LP: . . . . TGLLP 1
LP: . . . . ILPS 9241
MC: . . . . ZCI 9241

CHANCES ARE.
Tracks: / Reggae on Broadway / Gonna get you / Chances are / Soul rebel / Dance do the reggae / Mellow mood / Stay with me / Hurting inside.
LP: . . . . K 99183
MC: K4 99183

CLASSIC TRACKS.
LP: . . . . ARA 1010
MC: . . . . ARAC 1010

COLLECTION: BOB MARLEY.
Tracks: / Soul shakedown party / Stop the train / Caution / Soul captives / Go tell it on the mountain / Can't you see / Soon come / Cheer up / Back out / Do it twice / Try me / It's alright / Sun is shining / No sympathy / My cup / Corner stone / No water / Soul almighty / Reaction / One love / Love and affection

/ Mega dog / Donna / Lonesome feeling / It hurts to be alone / Who feels it / Dancing Shoes.
2LP: CCSLP 123
MC: CCSMC 123

CONFRONTATION.
Tracks: / Chant down Babylon / Buffalo soldier / Jump Nyabinghi / Mix up, mix up / Give thanks and praises / Blackman redemption / Trench town / I know / Stiff necked fools / Rastaman live up.
MC: ICM 9760
LP: ILPS 9760
MC: RRCT 4
MC: 846207 4
LP: TGLLP 10

EARLY MUSIC.
Tracks: / Wings of a dove / It hurts to be alone / I'm still waiting / Who feels it / Do you remember / Dancing shoes / I don't need your love / Lonesome track / Do you feel the same way too / Ten commandments of love.
LP: CBS 32089
MC: 40 32089

ESSENTIAL BOB MARLEY, THE.
LP: DELP 301
MC: ZCELP 301
LPPD: PIXLP 1

ETERNAL.
2LP: CR 5147
MCSET: CRT 5147

EXODUS (Marley, Bob and The Wailers).
Tracks: / Natural mystic / So much things to say / Guiltiness / Heathen, The / Exodus / Jamming / Waiting in vain / Turn your lights down low / Three little birds / Obe love - people get ready.
LP: ILPM 9498
MC: ICM 9498
LP: ILPS 9498
LP: TGLLP 6
MC: TGLMC 6

GREATEST HITS: BOB MARLEY.
Tracks: / Lively up yourself / Small axe / Kaya / Sun is shining / Mr. Brown / Keep on moving / All in one / African herbsman / Brain washing / Do it twice / Duppy conqueror / Stand alone.
LP: B 80015
MC: MB9 80015
LP: 266 225 1
MC: 266 225 4

IN MEMORIAM.
LPS: TALL 400
MCSET: ZCTAL 400

IN THE BEGINNING.
Tracks: / Soul shakedown party / Adam and Eve / Brand new secondhand / Cheer up / This train / Jah is mighty / Caution / Thank you Lord / Keep on skanking / Wisdom / Stop the train / Mr. Chatterbox / Turn me loose.
LP: TRSL 221
MC: ZCTRL 221

IN THE BEGINNING (Marley, Bob and The Wailers).
LP: TRLS 221

INTERVIEWS.
LP: RM 007

KAYA (Marley, Bob and The Wailers).
Tracks: / Easy skanking / Is this love / Sun is shining / Satisfy my soul / She's gone / Misty morning / Crisis / Kaya / Running away / Time will tell.
LP: ILPM 9517
MC: ICM 9517
LP: ILPS 9517
LP: TGLLP 7
MC: TGLMC 7

LEE PERRY SESSIONS THE.
LP: BITR 78802223

LEGEND (Marley, Bob and The Wailers).
Tracks: / Is this love / Jamming / No woman no cry / Stir it up / Get up and stand up / Satisfy my soul / I shot the sheriff / One love people get ready / Buffalo soldier / Exodus / Redemption song / Could you be loved / Want more.
LP: BMW 1
MC: BMWC 1
LP: BMWX 1
MC: BMWCX 1

LIVE AT THE LYCEUM.
Tracks: / Trench town rock / Burnin' and lootin' / Them belly full / Lively up yourself / No woman no cry / I shot the sheriff / Get up stand up.
LP: ILPM 9376
MC: ICM 9376

LIVE: BOB MARLEY (Marley, Bob and The Wailers).
LP: ILPS 9376
LP: TGLLP 4
MC: TGLMC 4

LIVELY UP YOURSELF.
LP: CBR 1046
MC: KCBR 1046

MELLOW MOOD.
Tracks: / There she goes again / Put it on / How many times / Mellow mood / Chances are / Hammer / Tell me / Touch me / Treat me right / Soul rebel.
LP: TOP 104
MC: KTOP 104

MUSIC AND MEDIA INTERVIEW PICTURE DISC.
LPPD: MM 1234

NATTY DREAD.
LP: ILPM 9281
MC: ICM 9281
LP: ILPS 9281
MC: RRCT 3
MC: 846204 4
LP: TGLLP 3

ONE LOVE.
Tracks: / One love / Small axe / Rebel's hop / Soul almighty / Kaya / Duppy conqueror / Trench town rock / Lord I'm comin' / 400 years / Lively up yourself / Stir it up / Soul captive / Back out / Riding high / Baby we got a date / Soul shakedown party / Slave driver / Do it twice / Stop the train.
MCSET: DTO 10203
MCSET: DTOL 10203

ONE LOVE.
Tracks: / One love / Love and affection / Mega dog / Donna / Lonesome feeling / It hurts to be alone / Who feels it / Dancing shoes / Lonesome track / Ten commandments of love (end s1) / Treat you right / Stop the train / There she goes / Mellow moods / Chances are / Soul rebel / Hammer / You can't do that to me / Touch me / How many times.
LP: CBR 1001
MC: KCBR 1001

ONE LOVE.
LP: PLP 41
MC: PMC 41

ONE LOVE/ROOTS VOL 2.
Tracks: / One love / Love and affection / Mega dog / Donna / Lonesome feeling / It hurts to be alone / Who feels it / Dancing shoes / Lonesome talk / Ten commandments of men / Soul rebel / Chances are.
LP: BMLP 1052

PUT IT ON.
Tracks: / One love / Love and affection / Mega dog / Donna / Lonesome feeling / It hurts to be alone / Who feels it / Dancing shoes / You can't do that to me / Touch me / Put it on / How many times / There she goes / Mellow moods / Treat you right / Chances are / Soul rebel / Hammer.
LP: SHLP 109
MC: SHTC 109

RASTA REVOLUTION.
Tracks: / Mr. Brown / Soul rebel / Try me / It's alright / No sympathy / My cup / Duppy conqueror / Rebels hop / Corner stone / 400 years / No water / Reaction / Soul almighty.
LP: TRLS 89
MC: ZCTRL 89
LP: 41 3127 1
MC: 41 3127 4

RASTAMAN VIBRATION (Marley, Bob and The Wailers).
Tracks: / Positive vibration / Roots rock reggae / Johnny was / Cry to me / Want more / Crazy bald head / Who the cap fits / Night shift / War / Rat race.
LP: ILPM 9383
MC: ICM 9383
LP: ILPS 9383
LP: TGLLP 5
MC: TGLMC 5

REACTION.
Tracks: / Reaction / I gotta keep on moving / Put it on.
MC: HSC 3406

REBEL MUSIC.
Tracks: / Rebel music (three o'clock roadblock) / So much trouble in the world / Them belly full / Rat race / War / Roots / Slave driver / Ride natty ride / Crazy bald head / Get up stand up / No more trouble.
LP: ILPS 9843
MC: ICT 9843
MC: RRCT 5
MC: 846206 4
LP: TGLLP 11

REGGAE GREATS (Marley, Bob & The Wailers).
Tracks: / Concrete jungle / No more trouble / Get up stand up / Rock it baby / Burnin' and lootin' / Small axe / Pass it on / Midnight ravers / Stop that train / Rastaman chant.
LP: IRG 15
MC: IRGC 15

REPLAY ON BOB MARLEY.
LP: FEDB 5000
MC: CFEDB 5000

RIDING HIGH.
Tracks: / Keep on moving / Don't rock my boat / Put it on / Fussing and fighting / Duppy conqueror / Memphis (end s1) / Riding high / Kaya / African herbsman / Stand alone / Sun is shining / Brain washing.
LP: CBR 1004
MC: KCBR 1004

ROOTS.
Tracks: / I made a mistake / Let him go / I'm going home / Nobody knows / Wings of a dove / Soul captives / Don't rock my boat / Stand alone / Soul shakedown party / Caution / Do it twice / Back out / Try me / Corner stone / No water / Soul almighty.
LP: BMLP 1032
MC: BMLC 1032

SAGA.
MC: UMK 99026

SOUL REBEL (Marley, Bob and The Wailers).
Tracks: / There she goes / Put it on / How many times? / Mellow mood / Changes are / Hammer / Tell me / Touch me / Treat you right / Soul rebel.
LP: NC 001
MC: CFK 1020
LP: BMLP 1018
MC: BMC 1.018
LP: RRLP 106
MC: RRLC 106
MC: ARLC 1013

SOUL REVOLUTION I & II (Marley, Bob and The Wailers).
Tracks: / Keep on moving / Don't rock my boat / Fussing and fighting / Put it on / Memphis / Soul rebel / Riding high / Kaya / Stand alone / African herbsman / Brain washing / Mr. Brown.
2LP: TRLD 406
MCSET: ZCTRL 406

SURVIVAL.
Tracks: / So much trouble / Africa unite / Babylon system / Ride Natty ride / One prop / Fighting against ism and skism / Top ranking / Wake up and live / Survival / Zimbabwe.
LP: ILPM 9542
MC: ICM 9542
LP: ILPS 9542
LP: TGLLP 8
MC: TGLMC 8

TALKIN' BLUES.
LP: TGLLP 12
MC: TGLMC 12

UPRISING (Marley, Bob and The Wailers).
Tracks: / Coming in from the cold / Real situation / Bad card / We and them / Work / Zion train / Pimpers paradise / Could you be loved / Forever loving Jah / Redemption song.
LP: ILPS 9596
MC: ICT 9596
LP: TGLLP 9
MC: TGLMC 9

VERY BEST OF THE EARLY YEARS (Marley, Bob & The Wailers).
MC: MCTC 033

WAILERS LIVE (Marley, Bob and The Wailers).
Tracks: / Trench town rock / Burnin' and lootin' / Them belly full / Lively up yourself / No woman no cry / I shot the sheriff / Get up, stand up.
LP: ILPS 9376

Marley, Rita

HARAMBE.
LP: 6 25597
LP: SHAN 43010
MC: SHANC 43010

RITA MARLEY.
LP: TLP 001

WE MUST CARRY ON.
Tracks: / We must carry on.
MC: SHMC 43082

WHO FEELS IT KNOWS IT.
LP: 6.24532
LP: SHAN 43003
MC: SHANC 43003

Marley, Ziggy

CONSCIOUS PARTY.
Tracks: / Conscious party / Tumblin' down / Who a say, A / Have you ever been to hell? / Lee and Molly / Tomorrow people / We propose / What's true / Dreams of home / We a guh some weh (CD only) / New love.
LP: V 2506
MC: TCV 2506
LP: OVED 339
MC: OVEDC 339

HEY WORLD (Marley, Ziggy & The Melody Makers).
Tracks: / Give a little love / Get up jah jah children / Hey world / Fight to survive / Freedom road / Say people / 666 / Police brutality / Lord we a come / Reggae revolution.
LP: AML 3112
MC: TCAML 3112
LP: RMM 299
LP: ST 17234

ONE BRIGHT DAY.
Tracks: / Black my story (not history) / One bright day / Who will be there / When the lights gone out / Problems / All love / Look who's dancing / Justice / Love is the only law / Pains of life / Urban music / Give it all you got / When the light's gone out (Jamaican style).
LP: VUSLP 5
MC: VUSMC 5
MC: OBRFV 381

TIME HAS COME - THE BEST OF (Marley, Ziggy & The Melody Makers).
Tracks: / Give a little love / Get up jah jah children / Freedom road / Children playing in the streets / Lyin' in bed / Aiding and abetting / Say people / Natty dread rampage / Naah leggo / Met her on a rainy day / Reggae revolution / Reggae is now.
LP: FA 3221
MC: TCFA 3221

Marlowe, Christopher

DOCTOR FAUSTUS (Various artists).
MC: 1033

EDWARD II (Various artists).
MCSET: SAY 82

Marlowe Dramatic

TRAGEDY OF RICHARD III, THE (See under Shakespeare, William).

Marmalade

6 TRACK HITS.
Tracks: / Ob la di ob la da / I shall be released / Summer in the city / Loving things / Wait for me / Baby make it soon.
MC: 7SC 5045

BACK ON THE ROAD.
Tracks: / Back on the road / My little one / Carolina in my mind / Sarah / Life is / Kaleidoscope / Cousin Norman / Rainbow / Lovely nights / Ride boy ride / Yours is a piece of mine / Bad weather / Radancer.
LP: TAB 19

DOING IT ALL FOR YOU.
Tracks: / Pepsey / Alright o.k. / Fat Sally / You're a lady / Doing it all for you / Space pioneer / Make it real easy / Heavens above / Colour my world / So good to have you / Sentimental value.
LP: SKYLP 1

GREATEST HITS: MARMALADE - VOL.1.
Tracks: / Ob-la-di, ob-la-da / Cousin Norman / Lovin' things / Rainbow / Baby make it soon / My little one / Wait for me Marianne / Reflections of my life / Radancer / Falling apart at the seams / Heartbreaker / Back on the road.
LP: ZOOML 1
MC: ZOOMK 1

OB LA DI OB LA DA.
MC: ASK 777

Marmarosa, Dodo

CHICAGO SESSIONS.
Tracks: / Mellow mood / Cottage for sale / April played the fiddle / Everything happens to me / On Green Dolphin Street / Why do I love you / I thought about you / Me and my shadow / Tracy's blues / You call it madness / Gone with the wind / Someday / Automation / Dodo's tune / Analysis / Only a rose.
2LP: ARCD 502

DODO'S DANCE.
Tracks: / Bopmatism (x2) / Dodo's dance (x2) / Trade winds (x2) / Dary departs / Cosmo Street / Tone paintings 1 & 2 / Deep purple / Tea for two.
LP: SPJ 128

EXPERIMENT IN BOP.
LP: FC 5020

KEYBOP (see Dameron,Tadd & Dodo Marmarosa) (Marmarosa, Dodo/Tadd Dameron).

LIVE DODO, A.
Tracks: / C jam blues / Be bop / Deep purple / Rose room / How high the moon / Perdido / Great lie, The.
MC: CSWH 10
LP: SWH 10

PIANO MAN.
LP: LP 20

Marmolejo, Cirilo

MEXICO'S MARIACHIS VOL. 1 (Earliest Recordings).
LP: FL 9051

MEXICO'S MARIACHIS VOL. 2 Cirilo Marmolejo.
LP: FL 9052

Maroc Eternel

MAROC ETERNEL (Various artists).
Tracks: / Chant d'amour: *Various artists* / Danse des Gnaouas: *Various artists* / Chant berbere: *Various* artists / Le chasseur: *Various artists* / Charmeur de serpents: *Various artists* / Chant Saharien: *Various artists* / Mort, La: *Various artists* / La fille du bled: *Various artists*.
LP: ARN 33266
MC: ARN 433266

Marocana

PORTRAITS OF PICASSO.
MC: ZPM 508

Marocco, Frank

JAZZ ACCORDION (Marocco, Frank & Ray Pizzi).
Tracks: / Night and day / Easy living / Round midnight / I love you / Giant steps / Joy Spring.
LP: DS 797

NEW COLORS (Marocco, Frank & Ray Pizzi).
Tracks: / Night has a thousand eyes, The / You don't know what love is / I'm old fashioned / Jitterbug waltz / My one and only love / Artists spoken autograph / More friends / Into somewhere.
LP: TR 516

ROAD TO MAROCCO (Marocco, Frank Quintet).
Tracks: / Spain / My Desiree / Baubles, bangles and beads / Sleeper / Ballad for Anne / Sweet gorgeous George / Brazilian waltz / Vision / Giddy girl / My ship.
LP: DS 854

TRIO, THE (Marocco, Frank & Ray Pizzi).
Tracks: / Home again / Reverie / All the things you are / One by one / Spring is here / One morning in May / La fiesta ecaroh.
LP: DS 838

Maroon Town

HIGH AND DRY.
Tracks: / Thatchers children / Woman say no / Pound to the dollar / Man in the street / Average man / Nostalgia / Fire / Welcome / Travelling light / Possee.
LP: RUDELP 004

Marotto, Peppino

SARDAIGNE - CHANTS ET MUSIQUE DE BERGERS (Marotto, Peppino & Le Choeur De Neoneli).
Tracks: / Ballu tundu Neonelesu / Per la morte di Guido Rossa / Natale / Ballo sardo / Sa ninnia / Ballo sardo / Mutos / Ballu -e trese / Gosos / Saludu a sos emigrados sardos / Ballo sardo.
LP: ARN 33529

Marques, Matan

COMBOIO (Marques, Matan/Ricardo Leo).
Tracks: / Goiania / Lua E Fogueira / Chegando Junto / Leblon / Comboio / Beer / Caminhois / Tacando a tinta / Disparada.
LP: RRPL 005

Marra, Jan

THESE CRAZY YEARS.
LP: FF 482

Marra, Michael

GAELS BLUES.
LP: SHS 2

MIDAS TOUCH.
Tracks: / Midas touch / Pity street / Hooky's little eyes / Foolish boy / Take me out drinking tonight / Glasgow / Features / Cheese for the moondog / Benny's going home / Taking the next train home.
LP: POLS 1016

Marriage of Gawain

MARRIAGE OF GAWAIN, THE (Various artists).
Tracks: / Marriage of Gawain: *Various artists* / Coming of the grail, The: *Various artists*.
MC: ANV 613

Married To The Mob

MARRIED TO THE MOB (Film Soundtrack) (Various artists).
MC: 925163 4
LP: 925163 1

Marriner, Neville

MORE AMADEUS (See under Academy of St. Martins) (Marriner, Neville & Academy of St Martin in the Field).

Marriott, Steve

30 SECONDS TO MIDNIGHT.
LP: MODEM 1037
MC: MODEMC 1037

PACKET OF THREE.
Tracks: / What'cha gonna do about it / Bad moon rising / All shook up / Fixer, The / All or nothing / Five long years / I don't need no doctor.
LP: AUL 729
MC: AUC 729

Marry Me A Little

MARRY ME A LITTLE (Original Broadway Cast) (Various artists).
Tracks: / Saturday night: *Various artists* / Two fairy tales: *Various artists* / Can that boy foxtrot: *Various* artists / All things bright and beautiful: *Various artists* / Bang: *Various artists* / All things bright and beautiful (part 2): *Various artists* / Girls of Summer, The: *Various artists* / Uptown, downtown: *Various artists* / So many people: *Various artists* / Your eyes are blue: *Various artists* / Moment with you, A: *Various* artists / Marry me a little: *Various artists* / Happily ever after: *Various artists* / Pour le sport: *Various* artists / Silly people: *Various artists* / There won't be trumpets: *Various artists* / It wasn't meant to happen: *Various artists* / Who could be blue: *Various artists* / Little white house: *Various artists*.
LP: AGL 1 7142
MC: AGK 1 7142
MC: GK 87142

Mars

78.
LP: WSP 10

PROJECT: DRIVER.
MC: RR 96324
LP: RR 9632 1

VENUS FLY TRAP.
LP: DANLP 360

Mars, Johnny

BORN UNDER A BAD SIGN.
LP: GENIELP 2
MC: GENIELC 2

JOHNNY MARS WITH MIGHTY MARS (Mars, Johnny/Mighty Mars).
LP: JSP 1023

KING OF THE BLUES HARP.
Tracks: / Horses and places / Rocket 88 / Johnny's groove / Desert island / I'll go crazy / Imagination / Mighty Mars / Cash ain't nothing / If I had a woman.
LP: JSP 1089

LIFE ON MARS.
Tracks: / Born under a bad sign / Don't start me talking / Back door man / Steal away / Standing in line / Hot lips boogie / I can't take a jealous woman / Get on up / Desert island / Keep on swinging.
LP: LSULP 2

OAKLAND BOOGIE, THE.
Tracks: / I've been down so long / Nine below zero / Rocket 88 / Call me / Love is a wonderful thing / Honey bee / Blue midnight / Cruisin' / If I had a woman / My dog can't bark.
LP: BEAR 12

Marsala, Joe

1944: JOE MARSALA (Marsala,Joe & his band).
LP: J 106

JOE MARSALA 1942 (Marsala, Joe & His Orchestra with Adele Girard).
Tracks: / I've got a gal in Kalamazoo / Lullaby of the rain / Can't get out of this mood / Blue skies / There are such things / Solid geometry for squares / Barrel roll / So nobody cares / Mr. Five by five / Lover / Be careful, it's my heart / Topsy.
LP: AIRCHECK 14

LOWER REGISTER.
LP: IAJRC 38

Marsalis, Branford

CRAZY PEOPLE MUSIC.
Tracks: / Spartacus / Dark knight, The / Wolverine / Mr. Steepee / Rose petals / Ransom abstract (diddle it) / Ballad of Chet Kincald (hikky burr), The.
LP: 4668701
MC: 4668704

RANDOM ABSTRACT.
Tracks: / Yes and no / Crescent city / Broadway fools / Lonjellis / I thought about you / Lonely woman / Steep's theme.
LP: 4610671
MC: 4610674

RENAISSANCE.
Tracks: / Just one of those things / Lament / Peacocks, The / Love stone / Citadel / Wrath, The (structured burnout) / St. Thomas.
LP: 4602291
MC: 4602294

ROYAL GARDEN BLUES.
Tracks: / Swingin at the haven / Dienda / Strike up the band / Emanon / Royal Garden blues / Shadows / Wrath of Tain, The.
LP: 4501511
MC: 4501514

SCENES IN THE CITY.
Tracks: / No backstage pass / Scenes in the city / Solstice / Waiting for Tain / No sidestepping / Parable.
LP: CBS 25952

TRIO GP.
Tracks: / Housed from Edward / Three little words / UMMG / Doxy / Stardust / Random abstract (Tain's rampage) / Nearness of you, The / Makin' whoopee / Gutbucket steepy / Makin' whoopee (reprise) / Peace.
LP: 4651341
MC: 4651344

Marsalis, Ellis

PIANO IN E - SOLO PIANO.
Tracks: / Hallucinations / Django / Jitterbug waltz / Nica's dream / So in love / Fourth autumn / Zee blues.
MC: C 2100

Marsalis, Wynton

AMERICAN HERO, AN.
Tracks: / One by one / My funny valentine / Round 'bout midnight / ETA / Time will tell / Blakey's theme.
LP: GATE 7018
MC: CGATE 7018

BLACK CODES (From the underground).
Tracks: / Black codes / For wee folks / Delfeayo's dilemma / Phryzzian march / Aural oasis / Chambers of Tain / Blues.
LP: CBS 26686
MC: 40 26686

CARNAVAL (With Eastman Wind Ensemble).
Tracks: / Variations on Le Carnaval de Venise / Grand Russian fantasia / Debutante, The / Believe me if all those endearing young charms / Moto perpetuo / 'Tis the last rose of Summer / Flight of the bumble bee / Napoli / Variations on a Neapolitan song / Fantasie brillante / Sometimes I feel like a motherless child / Valse brillante.
LP: IM 42137
MC: IMT 42137

CRESCENT CITY CHRISTMAS CARD.
Tracks: / Carol of the bells / Silent night / Hark the herald angels sing / Little drummer boy / We three kings of Orient are / Oh tannenbaum / Sleigh ride / Let it snow let it snow let it snow / God rest ye merry gentlemen / Winter wonderland / Jingle bells / O come all ye faithful / Twas the night before Christmas.
LP: 4658791
MC: 4658794

FIRST RECORDINGS WITH ART BLAKEY.
Tracks: / Angel eyes / Bitter dose / Wheel within a wheel, A / Gipsy / Jody.
LP: GATE 7013
MC: CGATE 7013

HOT HOUSE FLOWERS.
Tracks: / Stardust / Lazy afternoon / For all we know / When you wish upon a star / Django / Melancholia / Hot house flowers / Confession.
LP: CBS 26145
MC: 40 26145

J MOOD.
Tracks: / J mood / Presence that lament brings / Insane asylum / Skain's domain / Melodique / After / Much later.
MC: 40 57068

LIVE AT BLUES ALLEY.
Tracks: / Knozz-Moe-King / Just friends / Juan / Cherokee / Delfeayo's dilemma / Chambers of Tain / Au privave / Do you know what it means to miss... / Skain's domain / Much later.
LP: 4611091
MC: 4611094

MAJESTY OF THE BLUES, THE.
Tracks: / Majesty of the blues, The (Puheeman strut) / Hickory dickory dock / New Orleans function, The / Death of jazz, The / Premature autopsies (sermon) / Oh, but on the third day (happy feet blues).
MC: 4651294
LP: 4651041

MARSALIS STANDARD TIME.
Tracks: / Caravan / April in Paris / Cherokee / Goodbye / New Orleans / Soon all will know / Foggy day in London town, A / Song is you, The / Memories of you / In the afterglow / Autumn leaves.
LP: 4510391
MC: 4510394

THINK OF ONE.
Tracks: / Think of one / Knozz-Moe-King / Fuschia / My ideal / What is happening here (now) / Bell ringer / Later / Melancholia.
LP: CBS 25354
MC: 40 25354

WYNTON MARSALIS.
Tracks: / Father time / I'll be there when the time is right / RJ / Hesitation / Sister Cheryl / Who can I turn to / Twilight / Knozz-Moe-King / Just friends / Knozz-Moe-King(interlude) / Juan / Cherokee / Delfeayo's dream / Chambers of Tain / Au privave / Do you know what it means to miss New Orleans / Juan(Skip Mustaad) / Autumn leaves / Skain's domain / Much later.
LP: CBS 85404

Marsden, Bernie

ABOUT TIME TOO.
Tracks: / You're the one / Song for Fran / Love made a fool of me / Here we go again / Still the same / Sad clown / Brief encounter / Are you ready / Head the ball.
LP: PCS 7215

AND ABOUT TIME TOO.
MC: TCPCS 7215

LOOK AT ME NOW.
Tracks: / Look at me now / So far away / Who's foolin' who / Always love you so / Behind your dark eyes / Byblos shack / Thunder and lightnng / Can you do it / After all the madness.
LP: PCS 7217
MC: TCPCS 7217
LP: PCF 7217

Marsden, Gerry

LENNON & MCCARTNEY SONGBOOK BY G. MARSDEN, THE.
LP: ONE 1274
MC: OCE 2274

Marseille

TOUCH THE NIGHT.
LP: ULTRA 3

Mars-Fenwick Band

FIRE IN THE CITY.
Tracks: / Fire in the city / Raise the price / Lover not a fighter / T-Bird Ford / I lose again / Whatcha gonna do? / Poontang kid, The / Hot lips / Hard luck and trouble / There's a party going on / Date with an angel / I need love / Ash ain't nothing but trash.
LP: PTLS 1083
MC: PTLC 1083

Marsh, Alison

SILVER AND WHITE (Marsh, Alison & Rebecca).
Tracks: / Dark sphere / Mad / Silver / Red / With light / Pearls of dawn / Alone / Amber / Moonlight / White.
MC: ONKE C184

Marsh, Carl

TOO MUCH FUN.
LP: 839 292 1
MC: 839 292 4

Marsh, Hugh

BEAR WALKS, THE.
LP: VBR 20111

Marsh, Linda

HAPPY HEART.
LP: BSS 150

Marsh, Warne

ALL MUSIC.
LP: N 7

ART OF IMPROVISING VOL 1.
Tracks: / Strike up the band / It's you or no one / Sub-conscious Lee / You stepped out of a dream / Scrapple from the apple / I'll remember April / Indiana / Lunar elevation / Song for you, A / How about you / Blues / I can't believe that you're in love wtih me / Indian Summer / Half Nelson.
LP: REV 22

ART OF IMPROVISING VOL 2.
Tracks: / Sweet Georgia Brown / Out of nowhere / Fishin' around / Tangerine / Will you still be mine / What is this thing called love / You stepped out of a dream / Lennie's pennies / Yardbird.
LP: REV 27

ART PEPPER WITH WARNE MARSH (See under Pepper, Art) (Marsh,Warne/ Art Pepper).

ART PEPPER WITH WARNE MARSH (see under Pepper,Art).

BACK HOLME (Marsh, Warne Quartet & Quintet).
LP: CRISS 1023

HOW DEEP, HOW HIGH (Marsh, Warne Group).
Tracks: / Hard way, The / Note worthy / Finishing touch / How deep how high / Background music / She's funny that way.
LP: DS 863
LP: IP 7725

JAZZ FROM THE EAST VILLAGE.
LP: WAVE LP 10

LIVE AT THE MONTMARTRE CLUB (Marsh, Warne/Lee Konitz Quintet).
LP: . . . . **SLP 1020**

LIVE AT THE MONTMARTRE CLUB (2) (Marsh, Warne/Lee Konitz Quintet).
LP: . . . . **SLP 4026**

MARSH,WARNE/LEE KONITZ VOL 3 (Warne Marsh/ Lee Konitz).
LP: . . . . **SLP 4096**

MUSIC FOR PRANCING (Marsh, Warne Quartet & Quintet).
LP: . . . . **CRISS 1004**

NE PLUS ULTRA.
Tracks: / You stepped out of a dream / Lennie's pennies / 317 E. 32nd / Subconscious Lee / Touch & go.
LP: . . . . **REV 12**

POSTHUMOUS.
LP: . . . . **IP 8604**

REPORT OF THE SYMPOSIUM ON RELAXED IMPROVISATION VOLUME 1 (Marsh, Warne/Clare Fischer/Gary Foster).
Tracks: / It could happen to you / Bluesy rouge / In a mellow tone / Yesterdays.
LP: . . . . **REV 17**

TWO DAYS IN THE LIFE OF....
LP: . . . . **IP 8602**

WARNE MARSH.
LP: . . . . **WAVE LP 6**

WARNE MARSH AND SUSAN CHEN (Marsh, Warne & Susan Chen).
LP: . . . . **IP 8601**

WARNE MARSH QUINTET (Marsh, Warne Quintet).
LP: . . . . **SLP 1017**

WARNE MARSH QUINTET (2) (Marsh, Warne Quintet).
LP: . . . . **SLP 4001**

WARNE OUT.
LP: . . . . **FLY 212**
LP: . . . . **IP 7709**

Marshall, Arthur

LIFE'S RICH PAGEANT.
MCSET: . . . . **ZBBC 1024**

Marshall, Billy

SONGS OF A SKYE MAN (Marshall, Billy (Uilleam)).
Tracks: / Eilean mo chridh / Ar maduinn sabaid a' steornabhagh / Mo shoraidh thar chuain / Cha'n ol mi ri'm mhairean / Dhomhnuill, c'ait bheil do thriubahis / Moladh na rhoinn / Air m'uilean smi nam onar / Gillean uidhist / Mal Macluski / Ceuf tutus mhic dhomhnuill a chlaschu / Fagail bhornish / An uinneag bheag aig domhnuill.
LP: . . . . **LILP 5079**
MC: . . . . **LICS 5079**

Marshall, Eddie

ALMANAC (With Bennie Maupin, Cecil McBee, Mike Nock).
LP: . . . . **IAI 373835**

DANCE OF THE SUN (Hutcherson, Bobby/Eddie Marshall/Manny Boyd/ George Cables).
LP: . . . . **SJP 109**

Marshall, Evan

MANDOLIN UNLIMITED.
LP: . . . . **ROUNDER 0243**
MC: . . . . **ROUNDER 0243C**

Marshall Hain

FREE RIDE.
Tracks: / Different point / Dancing in the city / You two / Real satisfaction / Coming home / Take my number / Free ride / Mrs. The train / Back to the green.
LP: . . . . **SHSP 4087**

Marshall, Jack

LEONARD FEATHER PRESENTS "JAZZ FROM BOTH SIDES" (See Lewis, Vic).

Marshall, Jimmy

JIMMY MARSHALL.
LP: . . . . **NEVLP 109**

Marshall, Keith

KEITH MARSHALL.
LP: . . . . **SPIN 1**
MC: . . . . **ROLL 1**

TONIGHT WE DANCE (The Singles Collection).
LP: . . . . **BIFF 2**

Marshall, Larry

I ADMIRE YOU (Larry Marshall).
LP: . . . . **JRLP 001**

Marshall Law

MARSHALL LAW.
LP: . . . . **HMRLP 138**
MC: . . . . **HMRMC 138**

Marshall, Lyn

COMPLETE YOGA.
2LP: . . . . **SLD 509**
MC: . . . . **TCSLD 509**

COMPLETE YOGA VOL. 2.
MC: . . . . **TCT 50394**

EVERYDAY YOGA.
Tracks: / Complete breath / Standing stretch into the refresher / Triangle / Leg grip / Front push up / Cat / Fish / Coil / Back push up / Slow motion firming / Leg over into deep relaxation.
LP: . . . . **REH 461**
MC: . . . . **ZCR 461**

Marshall, Mike

CHIAROSCURO (See under Darol Anger) (Marshall, Mike & Darol Anger).

GATOR STRUT.
LP: . . . . **ROUNDER 0208**
MC: . . . . **ROUNDER 0208C**

Marshall, Susan

DON'T PLAY INNOCENT WITH ME.
LP: . . . . **DFG 8406**

Marshall Tucker

BEST OF THE MARSHALL TUCKER BAND (Marshall Tucker Band).
Tracks: / Can't you see / Fire on the mountain / Another cruel love / Searchin' for a rainbow / Long hard ride / 24 hours at a time / Heard it in a love song / Take the highway / Walkin' the streets alone.
LP: **2429 190**

RUNNING LIKE THE WIND (Marshall Tucker Band).
Tracks: / Running like the wind / Last of the singing cowboys / Answer to love, The / Unto these hills / Melody Ann / My best friend / Pass it on.
LP: . . . . **K 56621**

TOGETHER FOREVER (Marshall Tucker Band).
LP: **2476 139**

Marson, Stuart

NIGHT FALLS ON THE ORCHESTRA.
LP: . . . . **SFA 012**

Martell, Lena

6 TRACK HITS: LENA MARTELL.
Tracks: / One day at a time / Beautiful noise / Bridge over troubled water / I believe / If we only have love / Let me try again.
MC: **7SC 5010**

100 MINUTES OF LENA MARTELL.
MC: . . . . **ZCTON 105**

BEAUTIFUL SUNDAY.
LP: . . . . **RTL 2052**
MC: . . . . **4C RTL 2045**

BEST OF LENA MARTELL.
Tracks: / It's a beautiful night for love / Let me try again / All I ever need is you / Somewhere my love / Old fashioned way, The / Bridge over troubled water / Make the world a little younger / Goodbye tomorrow / Without you / Think about it baby / Nevertheless (I'm in love with you) / If we only have love.
LP: . . . . **NSPL 18506**
MC: . . . . **ZCP 18506**

BY REQUEST.
LP: . . . . **RTL 2046**
MC: **4CRTL 2046**

COLLECTION: LENA MARTELL.
2LP: **11PP 604**

COUNTRY STYLE.
Tracks: / Six weeks every summer / I'm gonna be a country girl again / Stay away from the apple tree / Hillbilly hoedown / Pledging my love / Danny come home / Make the world go away / Call, The / Old rugged cross, The / Call collect / Movin' on / Feelings.
LP: . . . . **NSPH 18**
MC: . . . . **ZCP 18**

FEELINGS.
Tracks: / Help me make it through the night / One day at a time / You've got a friend / Feelings / Take me home country roads / First time ever I saw your face, The / Hello misty morning / Bridge over troubled water / I can see clearly now / Old rugged cross, The / With pen in hand / You'll never walk alone.
LP: . . . . **SHM 3056**

GOLDEN HOUR OF LENA MARTELL, A.
MC: . . . . **KGHMC 125**

HELLO MISTY MORNING.
Tracks: / Hello misty morning / I know / Take me home country roads / I don't see me in your eyes anymore / If I didn't care / Hava nagila / Impossible dream, The / One day at a time / Take me / Time on my hands / Beautiful noise / I'll never fall in love again / Time to say goodbye.
LP: . . . . **NSPL 18534**
MC: . . . . **ZCP 18534**

LENA MARTELL COLLECTION, THE.
LP: . . . . **RTL 2028**

LENA MARTELL IN CONCERT, ROYAL FESTIVAL HALL.
Tracks: / Beautiful noise / I'm gonna be a country girl again / Apple tree / Take me country roads / Help me make it through the night / Las Vegas / Take me / Something 'bout you baby I like / Nevertheless (I'm in love with you) / Blue suede shoes / Teddy bear / It looks like I'll never fall in love / Last blues song / American trilogy.
LP: . . . . **NSLP 18585**
MC: . . . . **ZCP 18585**

LENA MARTELL (PICKWICK).
LP: . . . . **SSP 3072**
MC: . . . . **SSC 3072**

LENA MARTELL (PRT).
MC: . . . . **C 909**

LENA MARTELL TODAY.
Tracks: / You're my hero (wind beneath my wings) / Our anniversary / Words / When I dream / Sometimes when we touch / Love the world away / Memories / Don't cry out loud / Annie's song / But I do (I don't know why I love you) / One day at a time / Time to go / Have you ever been lonely / Nickels & dimes.
LP: . . . . **BGC 376**
MC: . . . . **KBGC 376**

LENA'S MUSIC ALBUM.
Tracks: / Can't smile without you / As time goes by / Darlin' / Come to me / Forever in blue jeans / You / One day at a time / Say maybe / You needed me / Delta dawn / We love each other / Don't remember your name / Don't cry for me Argentina.
LP: . . . . **N 123**

LET THE MUSIC PLAY.
LP: . . . . **OU 2229**

LOVE ALBUM, THE.
Tracks: / Let's put it all together / First time ever I saw your face, The / Love letters / Where do I begin / Nevertheless (I'm in love with you) / You'll never walk alone / You light up my life / If we only have love / Let it be me / Way we were, The / When I need you / Until it's time for you to go.
LP: . . . . **HMA 263**
MC: . . . . **HSCM 263**

MAGIC OF LENA MARTELL.
Tracks: / I can see clearly now / Don't take your love from me / I've been waiting for you / Send in the clowns / Proud to be a woman / After all I said and done / Help me make it through the night / Let's put it all together / Nevertheless / It's a beautiful night for love / Smile smile smile / Way we were, The.
MC: . . . . **ZCP 18466**
LP: . . . . **NSPL 18466**

PRESENTING LENA MARTELL.
Tracks: / It's too late / Put your hand in the hand / Carnival / Somewhere my love / In time / Bridge over troubled water / Better by far / You'll never walk alone / How insensitive / With pen in hand / Yesterday when I was young / Bring me sunshine.
LP: . . . . **NSPL 18378**
LP: . . . . **FBLP 8093**
MC: . . . . **ZCFBL 8093**

SOMETHING SIMPLE.
Tracks: / Something simple / Now / I'm a fool to want you / Why was I born? / Too soon / Lost in the stars / You're free / Don't remember your name / Love made a fool of me / There will never be another you / Jennie on the green / Where is love? / Masquerade is over / It's another world.
LP: . . . . **TAB 20**
MC: . . . . **KTBC 20**

SOMEWHERE IN MY LIFE TIME.
Tracks: / Rollin' with the flow / When I need you / Seeker / Windsong / You light up my life / Somewhere in my lifetime / Love is in the air / Anniversary song / Dark and lonely night / My baby's smile / Wishful thinking / One and only.
LP: . . . . **NSPL 18590**
MC: . . . . **ZCP 18590**

SONGS.
Tracks: / Songs / Peace in the valley / Something / Hasta manana / Everybody wants to be loved by someone / Without you / I want to give / In the ghetto / Last blues song / Someday, somewhere / Fools rush in / Let me try again.
LP: . . . . **NSPL 18447**

SONGS OF LIFE/ SONGS OF LOVE.
2LP: . . . . **RTL 2078AB**
MCSET: **4CRTL 2078AB**

SPOTLIGHT ON LENA MARTELL.
Tracks: / I know / If we only have love / Let me try again / Bridge over troubled water / I've gotta be me / Until it's time for you to go / One day at a time / Make the world go away / Hello misty morning / Las Vegas / Put your hand in the hand / This is my song / Somewhere my love / Better by far / Love story (where do I begin) / It's too late now / Six weeks every summer / Don't cry for me Argentina / That rugged old cross / Amazing grace / Pledging my love / I believe / With pen in hand / American trilogy.
2LP: . . . . **SPOT 1004**
MCSET: . . . . **ZCSPT 1004**

SPOTLIGHT ON LENA MARTELL VOL. 2.
LP: . . . . **SPOT 1025**
MC: . . . . **ZCSPT 1025**

THAT WONDERFUL SOUND OF LENA MARTELL.
Tracks: / That wonderful sound / Old fashioned way, The / You are my sunshine / Why did I choose you / Everyday people / When you're smiling / Make the world go away / Killing me softly with his song / So many ways / First time ever I saw your face, The / Think about it baby / I believe.
LP: . . . . **NSPL 18427**
MC: . . . . **ZCP 18427**

THIS IS LENA MARTELL.
Tracks: / Four and twenty hours / And I love you / Amazing Grace / Keep me in mind / Where do I begin / Love, this is my song / If / Try a little kindness / Till / Miracles / While we're still young / People.
LP: . . . . **NSPL 18414**
MC: . . . . **ZCP 18414**

TOUCH OF LENA MARTELL.
Tracks: / Let it be me / Love letters / Goodbye to love / Speak softly love / My man / If we only have time / You've got a friend / Until it's time for you to go / Las Vegas / All I ever need is you / Games people play / I've gotta be me.
LP: . . . . **NSPL 18385**

VERY BEST OF LENA MARTELL, THE.
Tracks: / Somewhere my love / Nevertheless / Country roads / Help me make it through the night / Ramblin' rose / Bridge over troubled water / Old rugged cross, The / Last blues song / One day at a time / Put your hand in the hand / I'm gonna be a country girl again / This is my song / I can see clearly now / Amazing grace / Smile, smile, smile / Scottish trilogy.
LP: . . . . **PYL 6033**
MC: . . . . **PYM 6033**

VERY SPECIAL LOVE FROM LENA.
Tracks: / Very special love / He called me baby / Rambling rose / My elusive dreams / Running bear / Solitaire / Times were / Easy part's over, The / Crazy arms / Lights of Cincinnati / Everybody get together / Everytime you touch me I get high.
LP: . . . . **NSPL 18513**
MC: . . . . **ZCP 18513**

Martha & The Muffins

METRO MUSIC.
Tracks: / Echo beach / Paint by number heart / Saigon / Indecision / Terminal twilight / Hide and seek / Monotone / Sinking land / Revenge (against the world) / Cheesies and gum.
LP: . . . . **OVED 54**
MC: . . . . **OVEDC 54**
LP: . . . . **DID 1**

THIS IS THE ICE AGE.
Tracks: / Swimming / Women around the world at work / Casualties of glass / Body without filters / Jets seem slower in London skies / This is the ice age / One day in Paris / You sold the cottage / Three hundred years / Chemistry.
LP: . . . . **OVED 79**

TRANCE AND DANCE.
Tracks: / Luna park / Suburban dream / Was ezo / Teddy the dink / Symptomatic love / Primal weekend / Halfway through the week / Am I on? / Motorbikin' / About insomnia / Be blase / Trance and dance.
LP: . . . . **DID 5**
MC: . . . . **DIDC 5**
LP: . . . . **OVED 78**

Martha's Vineyard

MARTHA'S VINEYARD.
Tracks: / Old beach road / Trying too hard / Unravelling / Three a.m. / Green heart / More of the same / Skin on skin / Shadow / Sweet love / What's going on / Time will fly.
LP: **8382101**
MC: **8382104**

Marthely, J P

SAINT-ELOI (Marthely, J P & Patrick).
LP: . . . . **GD 034**

TI COQ.
LP: . . . . **GD 017**

TOULOULOU.
LP: . . . . **GD 023**

Marti, Virgilio

SALUDANDO A LOS RUMBEROS.
Tracks: / Saludando a los rumberos / Mucho cante / Todos vuelven / El panuelito / Inyere / La mula / Odiame / Quimeras.
LP: ORB 016

Martian Chronicles

MARTIAN CHRONICLES, THE (Ray Bradbury) (Nimoy, Leonard).
MC: 1466

Martika

MARTIKA.
Tracks: / If you're Tarzan, I'm Jane / Cross my heart / More than you know / Toy soldiers / You got me into this / I feel the earth move / Water / It's not what you're doing / See if I care / Alibis.
LP: 4633551
MC: 4633554

MARTIKA'S KITCHEN.
Tracks: / Martika's kitchen / Spirit / Love... thy will be done / Magical place, A / Coloured kisses / Safe in the arms of love / Pride and prejudice / Take me to forever / Temptation / Don't say U love me / Broken heart / Mi tierra.
LP: 4671891
MC: 4671894

Martikorena, Erramon

OTSOBI.
LP: ELKAR 49

Martin, Asa

DOCTOR GINGER BLUE.
LP: ROUNDER 0034

Martin, Barry

SKATER'S WALTZ (See Nelson, Louis) (Martin, Barry Seranaders/Louis Nelson).

Martin, Benny

FIDDLE COLLECTION, THE.
Tracks: / Muleskinner blues / Sweet bunch of daisies / Alabama jubilee / Home sweet home / Little footprints in the snow / Georgia moon / Back up and push / Flint Hill special / Blue moon of Kentucky / Bile the cabbage down / Salty dog / Fiddler's dream / Dueling fiddles / Somewhere my love / Black mountain rag / Under the double eagle / How will I explain about you / Beautiful dream / Foggy mountain breakdown / Ragtime Annie / Fire on the mountain / Bury beneath the willow / Cotton-eyed Joe / Sunnyside of the mountain / Night train to Memphis.
2LP: CMH 9006

TENNESSEE JUBILEE.
Tracks: / Lester, Bill and Earl / Sunny side of the mountain / Windows in my mind / Will someone be lonesome too / Someone took my place with you / Six white horses / Bonaparte's retreat / Smell good on Sunday / That's a good enough reason / Pig in the pen / If I had my life to live over / Ice cold love / One drink is too many / Crag rock pass.
LP: SNTF 703
LP: FF 012

TURKEY IN THE GRASS (Martin, Benny & His Electric Turkeys).
Tracks: / Turkey in the grass / I love you a thousand ways / Freight train blues / Dixie on my mind / Wash 'n' wear conscience / Poison love / Oh baby mine / Gentle on my mind / Who's gonna hold you when I'm gone / Mocking bird hill / Always late / I can hear the hallelujahs in the air.
LP: CMH 6218

Martin, Bogan

MARTIN, BOGAN & ARMSTRONG (Martin, Bogan & Armstrong).
LP: FF 003

THAT OLD GANG OF MINE (Martin, Bogan & Armstrong).
LP: FF 056

Martin, Carl

CARL MARTIN 1930-36.
LP: WSE 123

Martin, David

EAST SIDE, WEST SIDE (see Bell, Madelaine) (Martin, David/Madeleine Bell).

I'M NOT REALLY ME WITHOUT YOU (see Bell, Madelaine) (Martin, David/ Madeleine Bell).

Martin, Dean

20 LOVE SONGS.
LP: 2236245
MC: 2136245

20 ORIGINAL HITS.
Tracks: / Everybody loves somebody / Corina Corina / Things / Houston / Lay some happiness on me / In the chapel in the moonlight / Little ole wine drinker me / Birds and the bees, The / King of the road / Send me the pillow that you dream on / I'm sitting on top of the world / You're nobody till somebody loves you / That's when I see the blues / Tie a yellow ribbon / Green green grass of home / Door is still open, The / Ramblin' rose / Amor mio / In the misty moonlight / Detroit City.
LP: K 54066

ALL I DO IS DREAM OF YOU.
MC: 4XL 8304

AT EASE WITH DEAN.
LP: RSLP 6322

BEST OF DEAN MARTIN (The Capitol Years).
Tracks: / That's amore / Kiss / Memories are made of this / Sway / Money burns a hole in my pocket / Hey brother pour the wine / Naughty lady of Shady Lane / Man who plays the mandolino, The / Mambo Italiano / Innamorata / Volare / Relax-ay-voo / All in a nights work / Return to me / Cha cha cha d'amour / Just in time.
LP: EMS 1297
MC: TC EMS 1297

BEST OF DEAN MARTIN.
LP: 1A 022 58129
MC: 1A 222 58129
LP: ST 21194

CHA CHA DE AMOR.
Tracks: / Somebody loves you / I wish you love / Let me love you tonight.
LP: PM 1553031
MC: PM 1553034

CHRISTMAS WITH NAT & DEAN (see under Cole, Nat King) (Cole, Nat King & Dean Martin).

CLASSIC DINO, THE.
Tracks: / Watching the world go by / Lucky song / Simpatico / In Napoli / I'm gonna steal you away / Giuggiola / How do you speak to an angel / What could be more beautiful / Me 'n' you 'n' the moon / If / Where can I go without you / Be an angel / Money burns a hole in my pocket / Only trust your heart / You belong to me / Good mornin' life.
LP: CAPS 1029

COLLECTION: DEAN MARTIN.
Tracks: / Everybody loves somebody / My heart cries for you / I'll hold you in my heart / In the chapel in the moonlight / Release me / Born to lose / Somewhere there's a someone / Green green grass of home / You've still got a place in my heart / You'll always be the one I love / Door is still open, The / Welcome to my world / In the misty moonlight / Room full of roses / I wonder who's kissing her now / Crying time / One I love belongs to somebody else, The / I'm so lonesome I could cry / Take these chains from my heart / I can't help it (if I'm still in love with you).
2LP: CCSLP 207
MC: CCSMC 207

DEAN MARTIN COLLECTION (18 Golden Greats).
Tracks: / If you knew Susie / Pistol-packin' mama / I've grown accustomed to her face / Somewhere there's a someone / Georgia sunshine / Don't fence me in / How deep is the ocean? / Welcome to my world / I get a kick out of you / She's a little bit country / Raindrops keep falling on my head / You are my everything / Second hand Rose / Do you believe this town? / Little green apples / Oh Marie / Walkin' my baby back home / Santa Lucia.
LP: DVLP 2129
MC: DVMC 2129

DEAN MARTIN SINGS.
Tracks: / I feel a song coming on / That's amore / Come back to sorrento.
LP: T 401

DEAN MARTIN (WORLD).
LPS: ALBUM 45
MCSET: CASSETTE 45

GENTLE ON MY MIND.
Tracks: / Not enough indians / That old time feeling / Honey / Welcome to my heart / By the time I get to Phoenix / Gentle on my mind / That's when I see the blues / Rainbows are back in style / Drowning in my tears / April again.
LP: K 44062
LP: RSLP 6330

GRAFFITI COLLECTION.
MC: GRMC 18

GREATEST HITS: DEAN MARTIN.
MC: 4XL 9389

GREATEST HITS: DEAN MARTIN VOL 2.
Tracks: / Door is still open, The / I will / Send me the pillow that you dream on / Little ole wine drinker me / You've still got a place in my heart / In the misty moonlight / Lay some happiness on me / (Open up the door) Let the good times in / Somewhere there's a someone / Glory of love / King of the road / Old yellow line.
LP: K 44060

GREATEST HITS: DEAN MARTIN VOL 1.
Tracks: / Everybody loves somebody / You're nobody till somebody loves you / In the chapel in the moonlight / Houston (remember me) / I'm the one who loves you / I can't help remembering you / Nobody's baby again / Every minute every hour / Bumming around / You'll always be the one I love / Come running back / Birds and the bees, The.
LP: K 44054
LP: RSLP 6301

MEMORIES ARE MADE OF THIS.
Tracks: / Memories are made of this / That's amore / Volare / Makin' love ukelele style / I've got my love to keep me warm / Wrap your troubles in dreams / Just in time / Dream a little dream of me / Let me go lover / I love the way you say goodnight / Two sleepy people / Just one more chance / Solitaire / Don't you remember / 100 years from today / There's no tomorrow / That lucky old sun / Innamorata / Arrivederci Roma.
LP: MFP 50531
MC: TCMFP 50531

NASHVILLE SESSIONS.
Tracks: / Old bones / Everybody's had the blues / Don't give up on me / In love up to my heart / Shoulder to shoulder / Since I met you baby / My first country song / Drinking champagne / Hangin' around / Love put a song in my heart.
LP: 923 870 1

ONCE IN A WHILE.
Tracks: / Twilight on the trail / Love thy neighbour / Without a word of warning / That old gang of mine / Day you came along / It's magic / If I had you / Only forever / I cried for you / Once in a while.
LP: K 54103

PRETTY BABY.
Tracks: / Only forever / I can't give you anything but love / Sleepy time gal / Maybe / I don't know why / Pretty baby / You've got me crying again / Once in a while / Object of my affection, The / For you / It's easy to remember / Nevertheless.
LP: PM 154 777 1
MC: PM 154 777 4

SINGS ITALIAN FAVOURITES.
Tracks: / That's amore / Return to me / Arrivaderci Roma / Volare / You're breaking my heart (Mattinata) / Just say I love her / Non dimenticar / I have but one heart / There's no tomorrow.
MC: 4XL 9098

SLEEP WARM.
Tracks: / Sleep warm / Hit the road to dreamland / Dream / Cuddle up a little closer / Sleepy time gal / Goodnight sweetheart / All I do is dream of you / Let's put out the lights / Dream a little dream of me / Wrap your troubles in dreams / Goodnight my love / Brahms' lullaby.
LP: EG 2606071
MC: EG 2606074

SUPERGOLD.
Tracks: / Volare / Buena sera / That's amore / Return to me.
2LP: 1C 134 85926-7

SWINGIN' DOWN YONDER.
Tracks: / Carolina moon / Waiting for the Robert E Lee / When it's sleepy time down South / Mississippi mud / Alabamy bound / Dinah / Carolina in the morning / Way down yonder in New Orleans / Georgia on my mind / Just a little bit south of North Carolina / Basin Street Blues / Is it true what they say about Dixie? / Hominy grits / I'm gonna paper all my walls with your love letters / Muskrat ramble / Be honest with happy feet / Darktown strutters' ball.
MC: C4 94306

THAT'S AMORE.
Tracks: / That's amore / Innamorata / Buona sera / I'm yours / One I love, The / Release me / Sway / My heart cries for you / Memories are made of this / Return to me / Volare / Write to me from Naples / Everybody loves somebody / Crying time / When you're smiling / Take these chains from my heart.
LP: ENT LP 13031
MC: ENT MC 13031

THIS TIME I'M SWINGING.
LP: T 1442

VERY BEST OF DEAN MARTIN, THE.
Tracks: / Return to me / Angel baby / Rio bravo / I've got my love to keep me warm / Baby it's cold outside / Buona sera / That's amore / Goodnight sweetheart / Volare / Write to me from Naples / Memories are made of this / June in January / Come back to Sorrento / Hey, brother pour the wine / Cha, cha, cha, d'amour / I have but one heart.
LP: MFP 41 5730-1
MC: MFP 41 5730-4
LP: GO 1815261
MC: TCGO 1815264
LP: MFP 5730
MC: TCMFP 5730

WELCOME TO MY WORLD.
Tracks: / In the chapel in the moonlight / Release me / I can't help remembering you / Turn to me / Wallpaper roses / Little ole wine drinker me / Green green grass of home / Place in the shade, The / Pride / Welcome to my world.
LP: K 44041

WHEN YOU'RE SMILING.
LP: MFP 50228

WHITE CHRISTMAS (see under Cole, Nat King) (Martin, Dean & Nat King Cole).

WINTER ROMANCE, A.
Tracks: / Let it snow, let it snow, let it snow / Baby it's cold outside / I've got my love to keep me warm / White Christmas.
LP: PM 1553021
MC: PM 1553024

YOU'RE NOBODY TILL SOMEBODY.
MC: 4XL 57005

Martin, Doug & Sarah

REELIN'.
LP: MDS 1

Martin, Eric

ERIC MARTIN.
LP: MFN 57

SUCKER FOR A PRETTY FACE.
Tracks: / Sucker for a pretty face / Don't stop / Private live / Ten feet tall / Letting it out / Young at heart / Just another pretty boy / One more time / Catch me if you can / Love me.
LP: 9602381

Martin, Freddy

FREDDY MARTIN AND HIS ORCHESTRA, VOL. 1 (1940) (Martin, Freddy & His Orchestra).
Tracks: / Blue champagne / Essential to me / I do, do you / Braggin' / Have you changed? / Smile your troubles away / Delilah / Where in the world / At the Karlstad ball / May I never love again / You and I / Here's my heart / What word is sweeter than sweetheart / So long for now / Tonight we love.
LP: HSR 151

FREDDY MARTIN AND ORCHESTRA, VOL. 2 (1944-46) (Martin, Freddy & His Orchestra).
Tracks: / Smoke gets in your eyes / Wish you were waiting for me / I get a kick out of you / I had you / Cherry / Till the end of time / Nola / Dream / Way you look tonight, The / You've got me where you want me / Sweet and lovely / Dancing in the dark / I promise you / On the sunny side of the street.
LP: HSR 169

FREDDY MARTIN AND ORCHESTRA, VOL. 4 (Martin, Freddy & His Orchestra).
LP: HSR 205

FREDDY MARTIN AND ORCHESTRA, VOL. 3 (1952) (Martin, Freddy & His Orchestra).
Tracks: / Ballin' the jack / Please mister sun / Kiss to build a dream on, A / Eternally / More than you know / Manhattan / I hear a rhapsody / Anytime / Tenderly / Be my life's companion / Until / Dreamy melody.
LP: HSR 190

Martin, George

OFF THE BEATLE TRACK (Martin, George Orchestra).
Tracks: / All my loving / Don't bother me / Can't buy me love / All I've got to do / I saw her standing there / She loves you / From me to you / There's a place / This boy / Please please me / Little child / I want to hold your hand.
LP: CM 101
MC: CMK 101
LP: C5-519
MC: C5K-519

Martin, Gregory

AUSTRALIAN SONGS & BALLADS (Martin, Gregory & Norma Williams).
LP: LRF 153

Martin, Horace

MIX UP.
LP: RRM 1655

Martin, Janis

COMPLETE RCA JANIS MARTIN.
Tracks: / Drugstore rock n roll / Bang bang / My boy Elvis / Blues keep calling / One more year to go / Will you, Willyum / Love and kisses / Billy boy my Billy boy / I'll never be free / Love me love / Just squeeze me / I don't hurt anymore /

Ooby dooby / Let's elope baby / Love me to pieces / All right baby / Half loved / Please be my love / William / Barefoot baby / Two long years / Crackerjack / Love me love / My confession.
2LP: . . . . PL 43153

ELVIS PRESLEY & JANIS MARTIN
(See under Presley, Elvis) (Martin, Janis & Elvis Presley).

THAT ROCKIN' GAL ROCKS ON.
Tracks: / Love and kisses / Love me love ((Previously unissued)) / Two long years / All right / Billy boy my Billy boy / Let's elope baby / Please be my love / One more year to go / Here today and gone tomorrow / Teen street / Hard times ahead / Cry guitar / I don't hurt anymore / Half loved / My confession / I'll never be free.
LP: . . . . BFX 15046

THAT ROCKIN' GAL SINGS MY BOY ELVIS.
Tracks: / Just squeeze me / Crackerjack / Good love drugstore rock 'n' roll / Bang bang / Will you Willyum? / Blues keep calling ((Previously unissued)) / My boy Elvis / Love me to pieces / Barefoot baby / Little bit / William ((Previously unissued)) / Love me, love ((Previously unissued)).
LP: . . . . BFX 15032

Martin, Jimmy

GREATEST BLUEGRASS HITS.
LP: . . . . GT 0003

SING.
Tracks: / Widow maker / I'll never take no for an answer / There's more pretty girls than one / My walking shoes / Ocean of diamonds / Old man's drunk again / Six days on the road / I'm thinking tonight of / Hey lonesome / Truck driving man / Truck driver's queen / In foggy old London.
LP: . . . . HAT 3062
MC: . . . . HATC 3062

WILL THE CIRCLE BE UNBROKEN.
LP: . . . . GT 0059

Martin, John

THROUGH THE MOVING.
Tracks: / Cats, The / Knights of the desert / Andean river flow / My aquarian / La Bahia / Palomino / Through the moving window / Fiesta en Sevilla / Sailing home.
LP: . . . . PL 83086
MC: . . . . PK 83086

Martin, Juan

OLE-DON JUAN FLAMENCO.
LP: . . . . NTS 126

PICASSO PORTRAITS.
Tracks: / Harlequin / Desire caught by the tail / Three musicians / Sleeping girl / Self portrait / Afcionado / Girls of Algiers / Weeping woman / Piccador.
LP: . . . . POLD 5048
LP: . . . . SPELP 70

ROMANCE.
Tracks: / Romance / Bouquet of barbed wire / Waves of majorca / Memories of majorca / Memories of summer / Serenade to summertime / Once upon a time in the west / Spanish rider / Winds of ronda / Mi favorita / Out of town / Malaguena.
MC: . . . . TC THIS 2600374

SERENADE (Martin, Juan & Royal Philharmonic Orchestra).
LP: . . . . NE 1267
MC: . . . . CE 2267

SOLO ALBUM, THE.
Tracks: / Guernica / Foreboding, The / Bombing / Lament / Miro's metronome / Leonardo's head of Christ / Velazquez's Prince Baltasar Carlos on horseback... / Sadness of the king (solea) / At the carnival / Lorca's dream / Goya's 3rd of may (sequdilla) / Danza (zapateado).
LP: . . . . WX 17
MC: . . . . WX 17C

Martin, Lou

RECENT WORK.
LP: . . . . ROUNDER 0214
MC: . . . . ROUNDER 0214C

Martin, Marilyn

MARILYN MARTIN.
Tracks: / Body and the beat / Night moves / Too much too soon / Turn it on / Thank you (Available on Album and cassette) / One step closer to you / Beauty or the beast / Move closer / Dream is always the same, The / Here is the news.
LP: . . . . WX 33
MC: . . . . WX 33 C

THIS IS SERIOUS.
Tracks: / Possessive love / This is serious / Best is yet to come, The / Quiet desperation / Lay me down / Love takes no prisoners / Try me / Wait is over, The / Homeless / Pretender.
LP: . . . . K 781 814 1
MC: . . . . K 781 814 4

Martin, Marty

GERTRUDE STEIN (Various artists).
MC: 0367

THEY CALL ME BOXCAR WILLIE.
Tracks: / Boxcar Willie / Mississippi river queen / Kind of man / Change of heart / Picture of you and me / River thru' Reno / Living, loving angel / Speed limit's thirty, The / I hope your world don't end / Was it all in fun? / You and a fool / Hey doctor man.
LP: . . . . BDL 1060

Martin, Mary

MARY MARTIN SINGS, RICHARD ROGERS PLAYS (Martin, Mary & Richard Rogers).
Tracks: / Getting to know you / You're nearer / I could write a book / Sleepy head / It might as well be spring / My funny valentine / To keep me alive / It never entered my mind / Moon of my delight / You are never away / There's a small hotel / Some enchanted evening.
LP: . . . . NL 89457
MC: . . . . NK 89457

ON BROADWAY.
LP: . . . . P 14282
MC: . . . . BT 14282

TOGETHER WITH MUSIC (See under Coward, Noel).

Martin, Mel

SHE WHO LISTENS (Mel Martin and the Listen).
LP: . . . . MVLP 15

Martin, Mike

ON THE ROAD.
LP: . . . . FLY 301

Martin, Moon

ESCAPE FROM DOMINATION.
Tracks: / I've got a reason / She made a fool of you / Dreamer / Gun shy / Hot house baby / Feeling's right / Rolene / No chance / Dangerous / Bootleg woman.
LP: . . . . EST 11933

MYSTERY TICKET.
Tracks: / X-ray vision / Witness / She's in love with my car / Paid the price / Firing line / Dangerous game / Don't you double / Aces with you / Deeper / Chain reaction.
LP: . . . . EST 12200

SHOTS FROM A COLD NIGHTMARE.
Tracks: / Hot nite in Dallas / Victim of romance / Nite thoughts / Paid killer / Cadillac walk / Bad case of lovin' you / Hands down / All I've got to do / You don't care about me / She's a pretender.
LP: . . . . EST 11787

STREET FEVER.
Tracks: / Five days of fever / Signal for help / Pushed around / Love gone bad / Stranded / Breakout tonight / Bad news / No dice / Whispers / Cross your fingers / Rolling in my rolls.
LP: . . . . EST 12099
MC: . . . . TC EST 12099

Martin, Neil

INTRODUCING NEIL MARTIN.
LP: . . . . EMC 3235

Martin, Nicholas

HEY LOOK ME OVER.
Tracks: / Hey look me over / Under the double eagle / Whistle while you work / Spread a little happiness / Happy days are here again / Far away places / My happy heart / Amarillo / I know why / In the mood / Dardanella / Dream of Olwen / Coronation Scot / Little red monkey / Bring me sunshine / Yakety sax / Save your love / You don't have to say you love me / Room 504 / On a little street in Singapore / Bridge over troubled water / E.T., Theme from / Russian rag / Temptation rag / Ol pianna rag.
LP: . . . . GRS 1134
MC: . . . . KGRS 1134

Martin, Robert

DIVINE LIGHT.
MC: . . . . C 149

GREAT PEACE.
MC: . . . . C 129

Martin, Skip

WITH THE HOLYWOOD ALL.
LP: . . . . FS 225

Martin, Steve

WILD AND CRAZY GUY.
Tracks: / Wild and crazy guy / I'm feelin' it / Philosophy/religion/college/language / Creativity in action / I'm in the mood for love / Charitable kind of guy / Expose / Cat handcuffs / You naive Americans / My real name / King Tut.
LP: . . . . K 56573

Martin, Tony

20 GOLDEN PIECES: TONY MARTIN.
Tracks: / I'll see you in my dreams / I surrender, dear / Those were the days / Canadian sunset / Aquarius / I'm always chasing rainbows / Harbour lights / Ebb tide / Red sails in the sunset / Night is young and you're so beautiful, The / Cuando calienta el sol / Imagine / This beautiful / It's all in the game / Guantanamera / Our love is here to stay / Meditation / Fools rush in / Yours / For every man there's a woman / It's magic / Circus / There's no tomorrow / Over a bottle of wine / Domino / La vie en rose / Would I love you / I get ideas / I said my pyjamas / Valencia / Kiss of fire / Dance of destiny / Stranger in paradise / Here / Walk hand in hand / It's better in the dark / Do I love you?.
LP: . . . . BDL 2047
MC: . . . . BDC 2047

BEST OF TONY MARTIN.
Tracks: / For every man there's a woman / It's magic / Circus / There's no tomorrow / Over a bottle of wine / Domino / La vie en rose / Would i love you / I get ideas / I said my pyjamas / Valencia / Kiss of fire / Dance of destiny / Stranger in paradise / Here / Walk hand in hand / It's better in the dark / Do i love you.
LP: . . . . NL 89468
MC: . . . . NK 89468

SOMETHING IN THE AIR.
Tracks: / Rainbow on the river / Star fell out of heaven, A / It's love I'm after / Where the lazy river goes by / Afraid to dream / By a wishing well / My sweetheart / That week in Paris / When did you leave heaven? / Loveliness of you, The / Sweetheart, let's grow old together / There's something in the air / Mist is over the moon, A / You're slightly terrific / Song of old Hawaii, A / This may be the night / So do I / World is mine tonight, The.
LP: . . . . CMS 004
MC: . . . . CMSC 004

TENEMENT SYMPHONY.
Tracks: / Tenement symphony / Let me love you tonight / No orchids for my lady / It was written in the stars / I don't care if the sun don't shine / Tonight / Are you just a beautiful dream / Sea of the moon, The / Music, Maestro, please / Comme ci comme ca / Goodnight sweetheart.
LP: . . . . NL 90069
MC: . . . . NK 90069

Martinez, Narciso

FATHER OF TEX MEX (Conjunto, 1948-60).
LP: . . . . FL 9055

Martinez, Nigel

BETTER THINGS TO COME.
Tracks: / Better things to come / Number one lady / Don't go / Luv the way you luv / You're mine now / Masterpiece / I'll never be leaving you / Let the feeling take you there / Caribbean lady / Hey girl.
LP: . . . . ETAT 17

Martini Ranch

HOLY COW.
Tracks: / New deal / Reach / World without ends / Fat burning formula / Richard Cory / Hot dog / Serious girl / How can the labouring man find time for self-culture / Brother take it out / Power tool.
LP: . . . . K 925674 1
MC: . . . . K 925674 4

Martino, Al

AL MARTINO.
Tracks: / Spanish eyes / Painted, tainted rose / That's the way it's got to be / Bouquet of roses / Take these chains from my heart / Are you lonesome tonight / Living a lie / Tears and roses / All my dreams / Don't cry Joe / Vaya con dios / What now my love.
LP: . . . . IC 048 81442

AL MARTINO IN CONCERT.
MC: . . . . ZPRST 841

BEST OF AL MARTINO.
LP: 1A 022 58066
LP: . . . . ST 21363
MC: 1A 222 58066

FAVOURITE ITALIAN LOVE SONGS.
MC: 4XL 9179

GREATEST HITS: AL MARTINO.
MC: 4XL 9390

HITS OF AL MARTINO, THE.
Tracks: / Here in my heart / Spanish eyes / Granada / Wanted / Story of Tina / Now (before another day goes by) / Mary in the morning / White rose of Athens, The / Man from Laramie, The / Volare / Painted tainted rose / To the door of the sun / Rachel / I won't last a day without you / Take my heart / I love you because.
LP: 41 57361
MC: 41 57364

LOVE SONGS: AL MARTINO.
Tracks: / Spanish eyes / Love is blue / My foolish heart / It's now or never / Hey mama / I love you because / Can't take my eyes off you / More I see you / Take my heart / May I have the next dream with you / Yesterday / I love you more and more every day / Speak softly love / End of the world.
LP: . . . . MFP 415642-1
MC: . . . . TCMFP 415642-2

PORTRAIT OF A SONG STYLIST.
Tracks: / Can't take my eyes off you / What now my love / Losing you / Take these chains (from my heart) / Yesterday / Sweet Caroline (good times never) / Somewhere my love (Lara's theme) / It's impossible / I won't last a day without you / Here in my heart / There must be a way / Are you lonesome tonight / I love you because / Volare (nel blue dipinto di blu).
MC: . . . . HARMC 115

REMINISCING WITH AL MARTINO.
MC: 4XL 8306

SING MY LOVE SONGS.
Tracks: / Sing my love songs / Volare / Dream of me / My thrill / More I see you, The / There's nothing greater / You belong to me / It's now or never / If there's no such thing as a miracle / May I have the next dream with you.
LP: . . . . EST 11572

SPANISH EYES.
LP: . . . . ST 2435

SUPERGOLD.
Tracks: / Spanish eyes / I'll never find another you / I love you because / Unchained melody / Painted tainted rose / Speak softly love.
2LP: 1C 134 85928-9

VERY BEST OF AL MARTINO, THE.
Tracks: / Here in my heart / Shadow of your smile / Can't take my eyes off you / Yesterday / Speak softly love / My foolish heart / I love you and you love me / It's impossible / I have but one heart / Walking in the sand / Sweet Caroline / Goin' out of my head / Living a lie / Spanish eyes / Hey mama / Granada.
LP: . . . . CAPS 2600781
MC: . . . . TCCAPS 2600784
LP: . . . . EST 23203

Martino, Pat

CONSCIOUSNESS.
Tracks: / Impressions / Consciousness / Passata on guitar / Along came Betty / On the stairs / Willow / Both sides now.
LP: . . . . MR 5039

EAST.
LP: . . . . OJC 248

EXIT.
LP: . . . . MR 5075

FOOTPRINTS.
LP: . . . . MR 5096

LIVE: PAT MARTINO.
LP: . . . . MR 5026

STRINGS.
LP: . . . . OJC 223

WE'LL BE TOGETHER AGAIN.
LP: . . . . MR 5090

Martyn, Barry

VINTAGE BARRY MARTYN.
LP: . . . . GHB 75

Martyn, John

APPRENTICE, THE.
Tracks: / Live on love / Look at that gun / Send me one line / Hold me / Apprentice, The / River, The / Income town / Deny this love / UPO / Patterns in the rain.
LP: . . . . PERMLP 1
MC: . . . . PERMMC 1

BLESS THE WEATHER.
Tracks: / Go easy / Bless the weather / Sugar lump / Walk to the water / Just now / Head and heart / Let the good things come / Back down the river / Glistening Glyndebourne / Singing in the rain.
LP: . . . . ILPS 9167
MC: . . . . ICM 9167

COOL TIDE.
LP: . . . . PERMLP 4
MC: . . . . PERMMC 4

ELECTRIC JOHN MARTYN, THE.
Tracks: / Johnny too bad / Certain surprise / Sweet little mystery / Dancing.
LP: . . . . ILPS 9715
MC: . . . . ICT 9715

FOUNDATIONS.
Tracks: / Mad dog days / Angeline / Apprentice, The / May you never / Deny this love / Send me one line / John Wayne / Johnny too bad / Over the rainbow.

LP: ILPS 9884
MC: ICT 9884

GLORIOUS FOOL.
Tracks: / Couldn't love you anymore / Amsterdam / Hold on my heart / Perfect hustler / Hearts and keys / Glorious fool / Never say never / Pascanel (get back home) / Didn't do that / Please fall in love with me / Don't you go.
LP: K 99178
MC: K4 99178

GRACE AND DANGER.
Tracks: / Some people are crazy / Grace and danger / Lookin' on / Johnny too bad / Sweet little mystery / Hurt in your heart / Baby please come home / Save some for me / Our love.
LP: ILPS 9560
MC: ICT 9560
MC: ICM 2040
MC: 846 006 4

INSIDE OUT.
Tracks: / Fine lines / Eibi gheal chiuin ni chearbhaill / Ain't no saint / Outside in / Glory of love / Look in / Beverley / Make no mistake / Ways to cry / So much in love with you.
LP: ILPS 9253

LIVE AT LEEDS.
Tracks: / Outside in / Solid air / Make no mistake / Bless the weather / Man in the station, The / I'd rather be the devil.
LP: SKELP 001

LONDON CONVERSATION.
Tracks: / Fairytale lullaby / Sandy Grey / London conversation / Ballad of an elder woman / Cocaine / Run honey run / Back to stay / Rollin' home / Who's grown up now / Golden girl / This time / Don't think twice, it's alright.
LP: ILP 952
MC: ICM 2074

ONE WORLD.
Tracks: / Dealer / One world / Smiling stranger / Big muff / Couldn't love you anymore / Certain surprise / Dancing / Small hours.
LP: ILPM 9492
MC: ICM 9492
LP: ILPS 9492
MC: 842 555 4

PHILENTROPY.
Tracks: / Make no mistake / Don't want to know / Root love / Lookin' on / Hung up / Johnnie too bad / Sunday's child / Smiling stranger.
LP: DOJOLP 26
MC: DOJOTC 26

PIECE BY PIECE.
Tracks: / Nightline / Lonely lover / Angeline / One step too far / Piece by piece / Serendipity / Who believes in angels / Love of mine / John Wayne.
LP: ILPS 9807
MC: ICT 9807

ROAD TO RUIN, THE (Martyn, John & Beverley).
Tracks: / Primrose hill / Parcels / Auntie Aviator / New day / Give us a ring / Sorry to be so long / Tree green / Say what you can / Road to ruin, The.
LP: ILPS 9133

SAPPHIRE.
Tracks: / Over the rainbow / You know / Watching her eyes / Acid rain / Sapphire / Fisherman's dream / Mad dog days / Climb the walls / Coming in on time / Rope souled.
LP: ILPS 9779
MC: ICT 9779
MC: ICM 2039
MC: 822 971 4

SO FAR SO GOOD.
Tracks: / May you never / Bless the weather / Head and heart / Over the hill / Spencer the rover / Glistening Glyndebourne / Solid air / One day without you / I'd rather be the devil.
LP: ILPS 9484

SOLID AIR.
Tracks: / Over the hill / Don't want to know / I'd rather be with the devil / Go down easy / Dreams by the sea / May you never / Man in the station, The / Easy blues / Solid air.
LP: ILPM 9226
MC: ICM 9226
MC: 842 554 4

STORMBRINGER (Martyn, John & Beverley).
Tracks: / Go out and get it / Can't get the one I want / Stormbringer / Sweet honesty / Woodstock / John the baptist / Ocean, The / Traffic light lady / Tomorrow time / Would you believe me.
LP: ILPS 9113
MC: ICM 9113

SUNDAY'S CHILD.
Tracks: / One day without you / Lay it all down / Root love / My baby girl / Sundays child / Spencer the rover / Clutches / Message, The / Satisfied mind, A / You can discover / Call me crazy.
LP: ILPS 9296

TUMBLER, THE.
Tracks: / Sing a song of summer / River, The / Goin' down to Memphis / Gardener, The / Day at the sea, A / Fishin' blues / Dusty / Holto train / Winding boy / Fly on home / Kuckledy crunch and slipledge slee song / Seven black roses.
LP: ILPS 9091

WELL KEPT SECRET.
Tracks: / Could've been me / You might need a man / Hung up / Gun money / Never let go / Love up / Changes her mind / Hiss on the tape / Back with a vengeance / Livin' alone.
LP: K 99255

Martyn, Nicky

LAUGHTER SHOW.
LP: NEVLP 199

Martyr

FOR THE UNIVERSE.
LP: MEGATON 0010

Marvelettes

ANTHOLOGY - MARVELETTES.
Tracks: / Please Mr. Postman / Locking up my heart / Too many fish in the sea / Don't mess with Bill / When you're young and in love / Reachin' for something I can't have / Breathtaking guy.
LP: STMR 9018
MC: CSTMR 9018

Marvel-Masters

MARVEL-MASTERS VOL 1 (Various artists).
LP: COWBOY CARL 100

Marvels

IN THE MIDDLE OF THE NIGHT.
LP: NORLP 1002

SH-BOOM.
LP: BP 309

Marvin, Hank

ALL ALONE WITH FRIENDS.
Tracks: / Just another heartbreak / Hawk and the dove, The / Invisible man, The / Lelia (Danny's got a song) / Where do you go when you dream / Don't answer / Stardom / Rainy day goodbye / 99 days / All alone with friends.
LP: POLD 5104
MC: POLDC 5104
MC: PWKMC 4070

GUITAR SYNDICATE.
Tracks: / New Earth / Have you never been mellow / St. Louis blues / I've got you under my skin / Syndicated / Ebb tide / Bird of beauty / Thunder thumbs and lightnin' licks / Flamingo / Silvery rain / You are everything.
LP: SEE 289

HANK MARVIN.
LP: SCX 6352

WORDS AND MUSIC.
Tracks: / Don't talk / Slow down / Bad cop / Tahlia take your time / Chinatown / Captain Zlogg / Trouble with me is you / Oh Suzie / Night nurse / Go Jimmy / Then I found love / Lifeline.
LP: SPELP 32
MC: SPEMC 32
LP: POLD 5054
MC: PWKMC 4040

WOULD YOU BELIEVE IT... PLUS.
Tracks: / Aquarius / Born free / This guy's in love with you / Tokyo guitar / Chameleon / Lara's theme / Big Country, The / Love and occasional rain / Georgia on my mind / Windmills of your mind / Sacha / High sierra / Evening comes / Wahine / Morning star / Sunday for seven days / Boogatoo / Would you believe it / Midnight cowboy / Goodnight Dick.
LP: SEE 210

Marvin, Lee

WAND'RIN STAR (OLD GOLD) (See under Deck of cards (Old Gold).

Marvin & Tige

MARVIN & TIGE (Film Soundtrack) (Various artists).
LP: EST 7123071
MC: TCEST 7123074

Marvin, Welch & Farrar

MARVIN, WELCH & FARRAR.
LP: SRZA 8502

STEP FROM THE SHADOW.
Tracks: / Marmaduke / Lady of the morning / Time to come, The / Lonesome mole / Black eyes / Brownie Kentucky / Skin deep / Faithful / You never can tell / Hard to live with / Music makes my day / Mistress fate and father time / Silvery rain / Wish you were here / Thousand conversations, A / Tiny Robin / Thank heavens I've got you / Please Mr., please.
LP: SEE 78

Marx Brothers

3 HOURS, 59 MINUTES, 51 SECONDS.
LPS: 931680

MOVIE MADNESS (Selections from their films).
LP: MR 1097
MC: CMR 1097

Marx, Groucho

ON RADIO.
MC: CMR 1072

ON THE RADIO.
LP: MR 1072

Marx, Richard

REPEAT OFFENDER.
Tracks: / Nothin' you can do about it / Satisfied / Angelia / Too late to say goodbye / Right here waiting / Heart on the line / Living in the real world / That was Lulu / Wait for the sunrise / Children of the night.
LP: MTL 1043
MC: TCMTL 1043
LP: EST 2153
MC: TCEST 2153

RICHARD MARX.
Tracks: / Should've known better / Don't mean nothing / Endless Summer nights / Lonely heart / Hold on to the nights / Have mercy / Remember Manhattan / Flame of love / Rhythm of life / Heaven only knows.
LP: MTL 1017
MC: TCMTL 1017
LP: ST 53049
LP: ATAK 166
MC: TCATAK 166
LP: EST 2152
MC: TCEST 2152

Marxer, Marcy

JUMP CHILDREN.
LP: ROUNDER 8012
MC: ROUNDER 8012C

Mary Goes Round

70 SUNS IN THE SKY.
LP: ARTY 17

SUNSET.
LP: MGR 01

Mary Jane Girls

MARY JANE GIRLS.
Tracks: / Candy man / Boys / Prove it / Jealousy / You are my heaven / On the inside / All night long / Musical love.
LP: STML 12189
MC: CSTML 12189
LP: WL 72626
MC: WK 72626
LP: ZL 72055

ONLY FOR YOU.
Tracks: / In my house / Break it up / Shadow lover / Lonely for you / Wild and crazy love / Girlfriend / I betcha / Leather queen.
LP: ZL 72341
MC: ZK 72341

Mary My Hope

MONSTER IS BIGGER THAN THE MAN.
LP: MMHLP 1
MC: MMHC 1

MUSEUM.
Tracks: / Wildman childman / Suicide king / Communion / Heads and tales / Death of me / It's about time / Untitled / I'm not singing / I'm not alone.
LP: ORELP 504
MC: OREC 504

Mary Poppins

MARY POPPINS (Film soundtrack) (Various artists).
Tracks: / Overture: *Various artists* / Perfect nanny, The: *Various artists* / Sister suffragette: *Various* artists / Life I lead, The: *Various artists* / Spoonful of sugar, The: *Various artists* / Pavement artist: *Various artists* / Jolly holiday: *Various artists* / Supercallifragilisticexpiallidocious: *Various artists*/ Stay awake: *Various artists* / I love to laugh: *Various artists* / British bank, A: *Various artists*/ Feed the birds: *Various artists* / Fidelity fiduciary bank: *Various artists* / Chim chim cheree: *Various* artists / Step in time: *Various artists* / Man has dreams, A: *Various artists* / Let's go fly a kite: *Various artists.*
MLP: D 302
MC: D 12DC
LP: D 3922
LPPD: D 3104
LP: REH 535
MC: ZCR 535

MARY POPPINS Film soundtrack (Various artists).
Tracks: / Overture: *Various artists* / Perfect nanny: *Various artists* / Sister suffragette: *Various artists*/ Life I lead, The: *Various artists* / Spoonful of sugar, A: *Various artists* / Pavement artist, The: *Various* artists / Jolly holiday: *Various artists* / Super-cali-fragil-istic-expi-ali-docious: *Various artists* / Stay awake: *Various artists* / I love to laugh: *Various artists* / British bank, A: *Various artists* / Feed the birds: *Various artists* / Fidelity fiduciary bank: *Various artists* / Chim chim cheree: *Various artists*/ Step in time: *Various artists* / Man has dreams, A: *Various artists* / Let's go fly a kite: *Various artists.*
LP: D 5005
LP: WD 100
MC: WDC 100

MARY POPPINS.
MC: DIS 015

MARY POPPINS (ORIGINAL ISSUE) (Film soundtrack) (Various artists).
LP: CLP 1794

MARY POPPINS/THE JUNGLE BOOK.
MCSET: DTO 10510

Mary Queen Of Scots

MARY QUEEN OF SCOTS (Film Soundtrack) (Various artists).
Tracks: / Mary's theme: *Various artists* / Vivre et mourir: *Various artists* / But not through my realm: *Various artists* / Journey to Scotland: *Various artists* / Black Knight: *Various artists* / Escape with Bothwell: *Various* artists / Mary's theme: *Various artists* / Journey to England: *Various artists* / Death at Kirk O'Fields: *Various artists* / March to the castle: *Various artists* / Mary at Chartley: *Various artists* / Execution: *Various artists* / Reprise - Vivre et Mourir: *Various artists* / Mary's theme: *Various artists.*
LP: 255 099.1
LP: MUPS 441

Maryland Jazzband

25 YEARS OF JAZZ.
LP: GHB 178

Mas, Carolyne

ACTION PACT.
LP: 089209

CAROLYNE MAS.
Tracks: / Baby please / Call me / Do you believe I love you / It's no secret / Never two without three / Quote goodbye quote / Sadie says / Sittin' in the dark / Snow / Still sane.
LP: 9100068

HOLD ON.
Tracks: / Stay true / You cannot play if you do not win / Running from the high life / Go ahead and cry now / Hold on / All for you / He's so cool / Remember the night / Thomas Dunson's revenge / Amsterdam.
LP: 6337105

MAS HYSTERIA.
LP: 6337 163

Mas, Jean Pierre

JEAN PIERRE MAS & CESARIUS ALVIM (Mas, Jean Pierre & Cesarius Alvim).
LP: 2392 101

Masada

MASADA (Film Soundtrack) (Various artists).
MC: VSC 5249

MASADA (THE ANTAGONISTS)/THE LONE RANGER (TV soundtrack) (Various artists).
LP: MCA 1564
MC: MCAC 1564

Masai

BOOGY MAN.
Tracks: / Boogy man / Lets go crazy / So mad so crazy.
MLP: ANT 041

CAPTURED BY CAPTAIN ROCK.
Tracks: / Captured by Captain Rock.
LP: ANT 066

Mascara

SEE YOU IN L.A.
Tracks: / Comin' home baby / Golden years / I feel so at home here / If you don't want to be in my life / It's cool / Jet plane ride / See you in L.A..
LP: ENVY 9

Masekela, Hugh

LIBERATION - THE BEST OF.
Tracks: / Don't go lose it baby / Rainmaker, the / Run no more / Lady / Joke of a life, The / Coal train / African breeze / It's raining / Grazing in the grass / Politician / Ritual dancer.
LP: HOP 222
MC: HOPC 222

MAIN EVENT (LIVE) (see under Alpert, Herb).

TECHNO-BUSH.
LP: . . . . HIP 11
MC: . . . . HIPC 11

TOMORROW (Masekela, Hugh, with Kalahari).
Tracks: / Bring him back home / Mayibuyi / Ke bale / London fog / Everybody's standing up / Bird on the wing / Something for nothing / Serengeti.
LP: 254573 1
MC: 254573 4

UPTOWNSHIP.
Tracks: / Uptownship / If you don't know me by now / Now or never / Hold on / Ooo baby baby / Egoli / No woman, no cry / Emavungweni / Naledi.
LP: . . . . PL 83070
MC: . . . . PK 83070

WAITING FOR THE RAIN.
LP: . . . . HIP 25
MC: . . . . HIPC 25

M.A.S.H.

M.A.S.H. (Film soundtrack) (Various artists).
Tracks: / Suicide is painless: *Various artists* / Duke and Hawkeye arrive at MASH: *Various artists* / Jeep ride to camp: *Various artists* / Tokyo shoe shine boy: *Various artists* / Onward christian soldiers: *Various artists* / My blue Heaven: *Various artists* / Operating theatre, The: *Various artists* / Happy days are here again: *Various* artists / Major Houlihan and Major Burns: *Various artists* / Hi lili hi lo: *Various artists* / Hail to the chief: *Various artists* / Sayonara, painless suicide, funeral and resurr: *Various artists* / Jig's up, The: *Various* artists / Tent scene, Hot Lip's shows her true colours: *Various artists* / Chattanooga choo choo: *Various artists* / Moments to remember: *Various artists* / Football game, The: *Various artists* / Washington post march: *Various artists*.
LP: 31842
MC: 40 31842

M*A*S*H* (Original Soundtrack) (Various artists).
MC: . . . . PST 32753

Mashiyane, Spokes

KING OF KWELA: PENNY WHISTLE JIVE FROM JO' BURG.
LP: . . . . TWLP 001

Masi

FIRE IN THE RAIN.
LP: . . . . RR 9616

VERTICAL INVADER.
Tracks: / Instant army / Rhythm workers / Silver memories / Dance of floda / Trapped in a warm feeling / Rock of changes / Finn (she's so pink) / Quick escape / Tribute to T.B., A / Xperimental.
LP: . . . . ZORRO 9
MC: . . . . TZORRO 9

Masi, Alex

ATTACK OF THE NEON SHARK.
Tracks: / Under fire / Average green band / Twilight passion / Toccata / Attack of the neon shark / DFWM / Cold sun / Wasted in the West / Alleys of Albion.
LP: . . . . RO 74701

DOWNTOWN DREAMER.
LP: . . . . RR 9543 1

Mask

ADVENTURES OF MASK (Various artists).
MC: 00 1041983

CAR WARS.
MC: 00 102133 8

MASK.
MC: 0 00 102212 1

MASK-A-RAID.
MC: 00 102140 0

Maslak, Keshavan

BETTER AND BETTER.
LP: . . . . LR 150

BIG TIME (Maslak, Keshavan Quartet).
Tracks: / Mr. Moffett / You'll love it / 2300 skiddoo / Big money cha, cha, cha / Big time / Big heart / You left your big shoe at my house.
LP: . . . . AFF 185

BLASTER MASTER (Maslak, Keshavan with Charles Moffett).
Tracks: / Blast yo mama / Jizz and cocktails / Blaster master / Jim jizz bo / Judy jizz bo.
LP: . . . . BSR 0079

HUMANPLEXITY.
LP: . . . . LR 101

LOVED BY MILLIONS.
LP: . . . . LR 105

Maslon, Jimmie

IT'S ME JIMMIE.
Tracks: / It's me Jimmie.
LP: . . . . LP 019

SALACIOUS ROCKABILLY CAT.
LP: 6901

YOUR WILDCAT WAYS (Maslon, Jimmie & Crazy Sounds).
Tracks: / Long gone daddy / Your wild cat ways / 1981 / Turn me all around / Please give me something / Warm and tender love / She she little Sheila / Gonna love you tonight / Hard hard man / I'm ready / Yeh I'm moving / Rockin' good way, A / Be careful.
LP: . . . . ABOUT 1003

Mason

LIVING ON THE EDGE.
Tracks: / Livin' on the edge / Pour it on / Double-x-posure / Forever yours / Crazy life / Breathless / Somethin-x-tra / Stay in love.
LP: . . . . K 960472 1
MC: . . . . K 960472 4

Mason, A.E.W. (aut)

FOUR FEATHERS (Heller, Martin (nar)).
MCSET: . . . . COL 4003

Mason, Barbara

PIECE OF MY LIFE, A.
Tracks: / Let me give you love / I'll never love the same / Oh and off / Playing with my feelings / So in love with you / Yes I'm ready / Love having you around / You know who I love / All inside of me / You did not stay last night.
LP: . . . . WMLP 5002
LP: . . . . LPBR 1004
MC: . . . . MCBR 1004

TIED UP.
LP: . . . . OEBM 1

Mason, Barry

MASTERS OF THE BAROQUE GUITAR.
Tracks: / Fandango / Espanoletas / Clarines y trompetas / Pavanas / Folia / Musette / Ricercata / Corrente (Domenico Pellegrini) / Sarabande / Battaglia Francese / Preludio / Ciaccona / Suite in D minor (Prelude #Gavotte #Minuet #Sarabande #Gigue) / Ruggiero / Corrente / Passamezzo / Aria di Firenze.
MC: . . . . CSAR 45

Mason, Dave

BEST OF DAVE MASON.
Tracks: / Let it go, let it flow / So high / Show me some affection / Will you still love me tomorrow / All along the watchtower / We just disagree / Paralyzed / Every woman / Only you and I know / Feeling alright.
LP: 84910

HEADKEEPER.
LP: . . . . ILPS 9203

OLD CREST ON A NEW WAVE.
Tracks: / Paralyzed / You're a friend of mine / I'm missing you / Talk to me / Gotta be on my way / Save me / Life is a ladder / Tryin' to get back to you / Get it right / Old crest on a new wave.
LP: . . . . CBS 83828

SHOW ME SOME AFFECTION.
Tracks: / I'm missing you / Save me / Tryin' to get back to you / Let it go let it flow / Show me some affection / Will you still love me tomorrow / Every woman / Only you know and I know / Spend your life with me / Searchin' (for a feeling) / Warm and tender love / So good to be home / Look at you, look at me / Gimme some lovin' / Take it to the limit / Sad and deep as you.
MC: . . . . ELITE 010 MC

VERY BEST OF DAVE MASON.
MC: . . . . MCLC 1639

Mason & Fenn

PROFILES.
Tracks: / Malta / Lie for a lie / Rhoda / Profiles / Israel / And the address / Mumbo jumbo / Zip code / Black ice / At the end of the day.
LP: . . . . MAF 1
MC: . . . . TCMAF 1

Mason, Harvey

M.V.P..
Tracks: / How does it feel / We can start tonight / Flesh / Universal rhyme / Spell / On and on / Going through the motions / You and me / Don't doubt my love.
LP: . . . . AB 4283

Mason, Jackie

I'M THE GREATEST COMEDIAN IN THE WORLD.
LP: 839 675 1
MC: 839 675 4

Mason, James (nar)

BALLAD OF READING GAOL (NARRATIVE) (see under Ballad of Reading Gaol).

CRIME AND PUNISHMENT (See under Dostoevsky, Fydor (Author)).

LOST WORLD, THE (see under Lost World (bk)).

MY LAST DUCHESS AND OTHER POEMS (see under My Last Duchess...).

PILGRIM'S PROGRESS, THE (see under Pilgrim's Progress (bk)).

POETRY OF BROWNING, THE (see under Browning, Robert).

POETRY OF CATULLUS (see under Poetry of Catullus).

Mason, James (reggae)

DANGEROUS TIMES.
LP: . . . . LALP 002

Mason, John

FIDDLER'S FAYRE (Mason, John & the Scottish Fiddle Orchestra).
LP: . . . . RELS 482

Mason, Moses

WHEN THE SAINTS GO MARCHING IN (Mason, Moses/Blind Willie Davis).
LP: . . . . WSE 134

Mason, Nick

FICTITIOUS SPORTS.
Tracks: / Can't you get my motor to start / I was wrong / Siam / Hot river / Boo to you too / Do ya? / Wervin' / I'm a mineralist.
LP: . . . . SHSP 4116
MC: . . . . TCSHSP 4116

Mason, Rod

AFTER HOURS (Mason, Rod/Beryl Bryden).
LP: . . . . BLP 12194

CARRY ME BACK.
LP: . . . . WAM/O No.8

COME BACK SWEET PAPA (Mason, Rod Hot Five).
Tracks: / Last time, The / Melancholy blues / Papa de da da / Wild man blues / Georgia grind / Heebie jeebies / Perdido street blues / Potato head blues / Winnin' boy / Come back sweet papa / Sweet substitute / Do what Ory say / You made me love you.
LP: . . . . BLM 51102

GOOD COMPANIONS.
LP: . . . . BLP 12145

GREAT HAVING YOU AROUND.
Tracks: / Down home rag / Great having you around / I want a big butter and egg man / Pennies from Heaven / It's only a paper moon / There'll be some changes made / Memphis blues / Professor Foxley's manipulations / Sweet Lorraine / Way down yonder in New Orleans.
LP: . . . . BLP 12180

JAZZ HOLIDAY (See under Barber, Chris).

MEET ME WHERE THEY PLAY THE BLUES.
LP: . . . . BLP 12167

PEARLS, THE (Jelly Roll Morton Interpretations) (Mason, Rod Hot Seven).
Tracks: / Pearls, The / Grandpa's spells / Don't you leave me here / King Porter stomp / Cannon ball blues / Frog-I-more rag / Kansas City stomp / Dead man blues / Wolverine blues / My home in a southern town / Frenchman's, The / Original Jelly Roll blues.
LP: . . . . BLM 51114

ROD MASON'S HOT FIVE.
LP: . . . . TTD 538

SAVANNAH ORCHESTRA AND HOT FIVE (Mason, Rod Hot Five).
2LP: . . . . TTD 551

Mason, Sylvia

SYLVIA MASON.
LP: . . . . CAL 114

Masonics

MASONICS.
LP: . . . . HANG 043UP

Masqualero

RE-ENTER.
Tracks: / Re-enter / Lill' Lisa / Heimo gardsjenta / Gaia / Little song / This is no jungle in Baltimore / Find another animal / Stykkevis og delt.
LP: . . . . ECM 1437

Mass

LABOUR OF LOVE.
LP: . . . . CAD 107

METAL FIGHTER.
Tracks: / Metal man / Fire from hell / Breakout / High heel thrills / Born to lose / Outlaw / I cut through / Night of steel / Leaders call / Born to be wild.
LP: 6.25645

RUSHING FLOOD PERFUME.
LP: . . . . ABT 090

TAKE YOU HOME.
LP: . . . . GWLP 41

VOICES IN THE NIGHT.
Tracks: / Voices in the night / Reach for the sky / Carry your heart / Staying alive / Nine tonight / Turn it all around / Call out your name / Follow me.
LP: . . . . ENVLP 522
MC: . . . . TCENV 522

Mass Production

BELIEVE.
Tracks: / Free and happy / I believe in music / Being here / We love you / Keep my heart together / Cosmic lust / Superlative / People get up.
LP: . . . . K 50400

IN A CITY GROOVE.
Tracks: / Maybe maybe / Never ever / One more chance / Should have known better / Rock / Inner city / Solid love / Weird.
LP: . . . . K 50877

IN THE PUREST FORM.
Tracks: / Firecracker / Love you / With pleasure / Our thought (purity) / Can't you see I'm fired up / Next year / Strollin'.
LP: . . . . K 50601

TURN UP THE MUSIC.
Tracks: / Our thought / Turn up the music / I can't believe you're going away / Sunshine / Bopp / Saucey / I got to have your love / Diamond chips / Clinch quencher.
LP: . . . . K 50784

WELCOME TO OUR WORLD.
Tracks: / Welcome to our world / Wine flow / Disco / I like to dance / Our thought / Magic / Galaxy / Just a song / Fun in the sun.
LP: . . . . K 50331

Massa, Bumba

BAROMETRE.
LP: . . . . MB 50564

Massacre

FINAL HOLOCAUST.
LP: . . . . SHARK 014

FROM BEYOND.
LP: . . . . MOSH 027
MC: . . . . MOSH 027 MC

SECOND COMING, THE.
LP: . . . . MOSH 27
MC: . . . . MOSH 27 MC

Massed Bands And Pipes

IN YORK MINSTER (Various artists).
Tracks: / Trumpet prelude: *Various artists* / Festive overture: *Various artists* / Irish tune from County Derry: *Various artists* / Pipe set: *Various artists* / Cortege from Mlada: *Various artists* / Nimrod: *Various* artists / Suite in E flat: *Various artists* / Ode to joy: *Various artists* / Epologue: Things to come: *Various artists*.
LP: . . . . MM 0610

Massed Bands Of..

FESTIVAL OF MUSIC (Massed Bands of The Royal Air Force).
Tracks: / National anthem / RAF march past / Flight of the bumble bee / Sounds of Glen Miller, The / Crown imperial / Dambusters march / Star wars / Hora staccato / Touch of your lips, The / 633 squadron / Rule Britannia / Pomp and circumstance march no.1.
LP: . . . . PRM 103D
MC: . . . . CPRM 103D

FESTIVAL OF MUSIC 1985 (Massed Bands of The Royal Air Force).
Tracks: / Dambusters march / Big band sounds of Duke Ellington, The / Where is the life? / March from Symphony no. 6 / T.V. sports themes / Lark in the clear air / Academic festival overture / Pomp and circumstance march no.1.
LP: . . . . PRM 106D
MC: . . . . CPRM 106D

FESTIVAL OF MUSIC 1986 (Massed Bands of The Royal Air Force).
Tracks: / Fanfare for the common man / Le carnaval Romain overture / Bless 'em all / Fireworks music (overture) / Raiders of the lost ark / My fair lady- symphonic senario / Jupiter from 'The Planets' suite.
LP: . . . . PRM 110D
MC: . . . . CPRM 110D

FESTIVAL OF MUSIC 1987 (Massed Bands of The Royal Air Force).
Tracks: / Fanfare and National Anthem / Jaguar / Marvin Hamlish showcase / Trumpet concerto-3rd movement (Hadyn) / Those magnificent men in their

flying machines / Eleanor Rigby / Overture: Prince Igor / Marching with Sousa / Pines of the Appian Way (from 'The pines of Rome').
LP: . . . . PRM 112D
MC: . . . . CPRM 112D

GRAND MILITARY CONCERT (Massed bands of British Armed Forces).
Tracks: / Fanfare / Tradition / Fugue from Musik Marziale / Pomp and circumstance march no.4 / Adjutant, The / Irish tune from County Derry ((Danny boy)) / Rakes of mallow / Irish washerwoman, The / God bless the Prince of Wales / Argyll broadswords, The / Kate Dalrymple / Kilt is my delight, The / Bonnie Dundee / Highland cathedral / Souvenir de France / Battle hymn of the republic / Grand march from Tannhauser / 1812 overture / Evening hymn and last post / March off / Berliner luft.
LP: . . . . GRALP 6
MC: . . . . GRTC 6

HORSE GUARDS PARADE (Massed Bands of The Light Division).
Tracks: / Bugle calls / Light Division assembly / Advance, The / Sambre et meuse / Les clarions anglais / Mechanised infantry / Quick silver / Slaves chorus / Silver bugles / St. Mary / Run runaway / Light Cavalry / Keel row, The / Road to the Isles / Five to one / Three to one / Bugle boy / Light Division assembly / Secunderabad / Horse Guards echoes / Great gate of Kiev, The / Fanfare Sir John Moore / Sunset / National Anthem / Light Infantry regimental march / Royal Green Jackets / No more parades today / High on a hill.
LP: . . . . BND 1041
MC: . . . . ZC BND 1041

PRESENTATION OF STANDARDS (Massed band of the Household Cavalry).
Tracks: / Boots and saddles / Golden spurs / Rule Britannia / Soldiers chorus / With sword and lance / Down the mall / Children of the regiment / Steadfast and true / Eton boating song / Royal standard / Milanollo / Aida / Auld lang syne / Standard of St.George / Trumpet voluntary / Slow march / Preobrajensky march / Life guards slow march / Blues and royals / With sword and lance / Birdcage walk.
LP: . . . . BND 1016
MC: . . . . ZC BND 1016

SCARLET AND GOLD (Massed Bands of Guards Div).
MCSET: . . . . ZC BND 3005

TRIBUTE IN MUSIC, A (Massed Bands of The Royal Air Force).
Tracks: / Festive overture / Solemn melody / March from 'Things to come' / Broadway showstoppers / RAF march past / In a sentimental mood / Tambourin / Feels so good / Suite: Pineapple roll.
LP: . . . . PRM 104D
MC: . . . . CPRM 104D

Massey, Anna (nar)

PERSUASION (See under Austen, Jane).

Massey, Cal

BLUES TO COLTRANE.
LP: . . . . CS 9029

Massey, Daniel (nar)

BIG SLEEP, THE (see under Big Sleep (bk)).

CHRISTMAS CAROL, A (see under Dickens, Charles (aut)).

LOST WORLD, THE (see under Lost World (bk)).

WUTHERING HEIGHTS (see Wuthering Heights (bk)).

Massey, Roy

MOONLIGHT AND ROSES.
LP: . . . . APS 334

Massey, Will T

WILL T. MASSEY.
LP: . . . . MCA 10305
MC: . . . . MCAC 10305

Massive Dread

MASSIVE DREAD.
LP: . . . . HM 1001

Massive (Group)

BLUE LINES.
Tracks: / Blue lines.
LP: . . . . WBRLP 1
MC: . . . . WBRMC 1

Massive Horns

MERRY MELODIES.
LP: . . . . TOPLP 002

Masso, George

DIALOGUE AT CONDON'S (Al Klink, Lou Stein, Jack Lesberg, Bobby Roseng (Masso, George Quintet).
Tracks: / This can't be love / Man I love, The / Coquette / Mean to me / Tea for two / Let's get away from it all.
LP: . . . . WJLPS 18

GENOVA JAZZBAND AND GEORGE MASSO 1986 (See under Genova Jazzband) (Masso, George/Genova Jazzband).

Massters, Joe

JAZZ MASS BY MASSTERS, THE.
LP: . . . . DS 785

Master

THEY HAVE A HIT (Master, The & The Grandmaster).
LP: . . . . KCR 138

Master Ace

TAKE A LOOK AROUND.
Tracks: / Music man / Letter to the better (remix) / Other side of town, The / Can't stop the bumrush / Brooklyn battles / Postin' high / Take a look around / I gotta / Me and the biz / Ace iz wild / Movin' on / Maybe next time / As I reminisce.
LP: 7599261791
MC: 7599261794

Master of Ballantrae

MASTER OF BALLANTRAE (see Stevenson, Robert Louis) (Watson, Tom).

Master Of Blacktower

MASTER OF BLACKTOWER, THE (see under Michaels, Barbara) (Michaels, Barbara).

Master Of The Islands

MASTER OF THE ISLANDS (Original Film Soundtrack) (Various artists).
Tracks: / Theme from Master of the islands: *Various artists* / Auntie's theme: *Various artists* / Pineapple pirates: *Various artists* / Music for a Japanese bath: *Various artists* / Quiet thoughts: *Various artists* / Fumiko: *Various artists* / Molaka: *Various artists* / Street of Chinatown: *Various artists* / Theme from Master of the islands: *Various artists* / Auntie's theme (end title): *Various artists.*
LP: . . . . UAS 29122

Master Series- Sampler

MASTER SERIES SAMPLER (Various artists).
Tracks: / My home away from home: *Various artists* / St. Anne's reel: *Various artists* / Creation: *Various* artists / Hello tomorrow: *Various artists* / Waltzing on thin ice: *Various artists* / Midnight romance: *Various artists* / Maraval: *Various artists* / Oklahoma stroke: *Various artists.*
LP: . . . . IMCA 42064
MC: . . . . IMCAC 42064

Master Singers

SPIRITUALS.
MC: . . . . WRD C 3037

Mastercraftsman

MASTERCRAFTSMAN (Various artists).
MC: . . . . NPCA 003

Masterfleet

HIGH ON THE SEA.
LP: . . . . LPSX 5

Masterpiece

MASTER PIECE (Various artists).
LP: . . . . LDRLP 10

Masters Apprentices

HANDS OF TIME.
LP: . . . . RVLP 01

Masters, Frank

1941/2 (Masters, Frank & His Orchestra).
LP: . . . . CLP 48

1946-1947 (Masters, Frank & His Orchestra).
LP: . . . . CLP 63

ACCENTUATE THE POSITIVE.
LP: . . . . GELP 15063

Masters, Mark

EARLY START (Masters, Mark Jazz Composers Orchestra).
LP: . . . . SB 2022

SILVER THREADS AMONG THE BLUES (Masters, Mark Jazz Composers Orchestra).
LP: . . . . SB 2033

Masters Of Reality

MASTERS OF REALITY.
LP: 8384741
MC: 8384744

Masters Of The Obvious

THIS CORPSE IS A WARNING.
LP: . . . . RES 339026

Masters of the... (tv)

CASTLE GRAYSKULL UNDER ATTACK (for ages 5-10).
MC: . . . . PLBM 124

HE-MAN MEETS THE BEAST (for ages 5-10).
MC: . . . . PLBM 153

HE-MAN & THE ASTEROID OF DOOM (for ages 5-10).
MC: . . . . PLBM 187

HE-MAN & THE LOST DRAGON (for ages 5-10).
MC: . . . . PLBM 188

HE-MAN & THE MASTERS OF THE UNIVERSE.
MCSET: . . . . DTO 10561

IRON MASTER, THE (for ages 5-10).
MC: . . . . PLBM 123

MASTERS OF THE UNIVERSE (Film Soundtrack) (Various artists).
LP: . . . . CST 8029

MASTERS OF THE UNIVERSE Various artists (Various artists).
LP: . . . . SPR 8552
MC: . . . . SPC 8552

MASTERS OF THE UNIVERSE (Film Soundtrack) (Various artists).
LP: . . . . STV 81333
MC: . . . . CTV 81333

SKELETOR'S ICE ATTACK (for ages 5-10).
MC: . . . . PLBM 147

TRAP FOR HE-MAN, A (for ages 5-10).
MC: . . . . PLBM 122

WINGS OF DOOM, THE (for ages 5-10).
MC: . . . . PLBM 146

Masters, Rip

ROCK THAT ROCK.
LP: . . . . ROLL 17

Masters, Sammy

ROCKIN' RED WING.
LP: . . . . BLK 7708

Masters & Slaves

WELCOME TO THE MEAT MACHINE.
LP: . . . . LLP 136
MC: . . . . LLPK 136

Master's Wife (bk)

MASTER'S WIFE (see Ramsay, Fay) (Olsson, Diana).

Masuda, Mikio

SMOKIN' NIGHT.
MC: . . . . JC 3313

Masuka, Dorothy

PATA PATA.
LP: . . . . MLPS 1074
MC: . . . . MCT 1074

Masusa Band

MASUSA.
LP: . . . . MON 004

Mata Hari

MATA HARI (Film soundtrack) (Various artists).
LP: . . . . ACH 020

Matador

MATADOR (Original Soundtrack) (Various artists).
Tracks: / Overture: *Various artists* / There's no way out of here: *Various artists* / To be a Matador: *Various* artists / I was born to me: *Various artists* / Only other people: *Various artists* / Manolete, Belmonte, Joselito.: *Various artists* / Boy from nowhere, A: *Various artists* / Wake up Madrid: *Various artists* / I'll take you out to dinner: *Various artists* / This incredible journey: *Various artists* / Don't be deceived: *Various* artists / I'll dress you in mourning: *Various artists* / Dance with death: *Various artists* / Panama hat, A: *Various artists.*
LP: . . . . VIVA 1
MC: . . . . VIVA C 1

SUN.
LP: . . . . NORMAL 121

TOUCH BEYOND CANNED LOVE, A.
Tracks: / Komm / On the boat / Abortion / Low / Release / Angel / Nite time / You made me / Seerose.
LP: . . . . SF 40

Matar, Mohamed

BELLY DANCE.
LP: . . . . VOS 10002

Matchbox

CROSSED LINE.
Tracks: / One more Saturday night / I ain't taking no prisoners / Crossed line / Mad, bad and dangerous / I want out / Rollin' on / Riding the night / Gatecrashing / Hot loving / Dreamers sometimes do / Mean 'n' evil / Ain't much fun.
LP: . . . . MAGL 5052
MC: . . . . ZCMAG 5052

FLYING COLOURS.
Tracks: / Love's made a fool of you / Heartaches by the number / Angels on Sunday / Lonestar dreamer / Bonaparte's retreat / Whiplash / Babe's in the wood / Don't let the stars get in your eyes / You're the one / 24 hours / Wish that I had never / Arabella's on her way.
LP: . . . . MAGL 5042
MC: . . . . ZCMAG 5042

GOING DOWN TOWN.
Tracks: / Get up and get out / Going down town / Stealing hearts / Nothing to do but rock'n'roll all day / She's hot / Can't get over you / Roller skating Sally / Flip flop floosie / Shooting gallery / Think you took my loving and run / Hot love / This is where I'm getting off.
LP: . . . . MFLP 038
MC: . . . . MFC 038
LP: . . . . SJLP 570

MATCHBOX.
Tracks: / Rockabilly rebel / Buzz buzz a diddle it / Seventeen / Tell me how / Hurricane / Everybody needs a little love / Rockin' at the Ritz / Hi-fly woman / Love is going out of fashion / Poor boy / Lord Mr. Ford / Black slacks.
MC: . . . . TCMAGL 5031
LP: . . . . MAG 5031

MIDNITE DYNAMOS.
Tracks: / Midnite dynamos / Shocked'n'shattered / C'mon let's go / Marie Marie / Southern boys / Back row Romeo / Green chicks / Lolita / When you ask about love / Jellyroll / We were in Boston / Stranded in Nevada.
LP: . . . . MAGL 5036
MC: . . . . ZCMAG 5036
LP: . . . . MAG 5036

RIDERS IN THE SKY.
LP: . . . . CR 30157

SETTIN' THE WOODS ON FIRE.
LP: . . . . WIK 80

THOSE ROCKBILLY REBELS.
LP: . . . . MFP 5627
MC: . . . . TCMFP 5627

Matching Mole

MATCHING MOLE.
LP: . . . . CBS 32105

Matchroom Mob

SNOOKER LOOPY (See under Chas & Dave) (Matchroom Mob with Chas & Dave).

Material

MEMORY SERVES.
LP: . . . . ILPS 9693

ONE DOWN.
LP: . . . . E 60206

SECRET LIFE (1979-81).
2LP: . . . . FREUD 011

SEVEN SOULS.
Tracks: / Ineffect / Seven souls / Soul killer / Western lands, The / Deliver / Equation / End of words, The.
LP: . . . . V 2596
MC: . . . . TCV 2596

TEMPORY MUSIC COMPILATION.
LP: . . . . CEL 6576

THIRD POWER.
MC: . . . . AXCT 3005
LP: . . . . AXLPS 3005

Material Issue

INTERNATIONAL POP OVERTHROW.
Tracks: / Valerie loves me / Diane / Renae remains the same / This letter / Our right now / Crazy / Chance of a lifetime / International pop / Very first lie / Trouble / There was a few / This far idea / Very good idea / Li'l Christine.
LP: 8481551
MC: 8481554

Matfied & The Pond

NOT QUITE 'IT'.
Tracks: / It / Magical crowd / Don't surf / Energy crisis / Jungle / Jam / Cloned / End, The / Theme from the Wyrd / En ni wun kan b / Snorkelling.
LP: . . . . DIST 003

Mathematics

MATHEMATICS (COURSE) (see under G.C.S.E. Packs) (Longman/Pickwick Pass Packs).

Mathematiquo Moderne

LES VISITEURS DU SOIR.
LP: . . . . ILPS 9690

Mather, Anne

FOR THE LOVE OF SARA (See also Georgina Melville).
MC: .... PMB 001

Matheson, Andrew

MONTEREY SHOES.
Tracks: / True romance / St. Catherine's Wheel / Debbie / Eyes of Harlem / My girls / Johnny let's run / Tender is the night / It only hurts when I cry / Can't stop the angels.
LP: .... ARL 5025

Mathews Brothers

KISS IN THE MORNING EARLY.
Tracks: / Boys of Kilkenny / Bucks of Oranmore, The / Banks of the Lea / Men from Mallow / Lover's ghost / Step it out Mary / Kiss in the morning early / Paddy Ryan's dream / Skolbereen lassies / Burragh of Kildare / West wind / Galbelly farmer / As I roved out.
LP: .... AVA 101

Mathews, Mat

DAVISON, BUTTERFIELD, TATE, WINDING (Mathews, Mat & Friends).
LP: .... AP 219

JUST LIKE THIS (Mathews, Mat(elect) & Roy Hansen (Acoustic)).
LP: .... MC 8174

Mathews, Tony

ALIEN IN MY OWN HOME.
Tracks: / Too many people in my bed / Alien in my own home / (Coming with) loving on my mind / My life ain't nothing but a blues song / You send me / Warning (big danger ahead) / One hour ago / She rides in the fast lane / Who needs it / I'll tell you, I do.
LP: .... SDE 4004
MC: .... SDE 4004MC
LP: .... SNTF 1028

CONDITION BLUE.
Tracks: / I really got the blues today / White powder / Coming home to you / Uncle Joe / Lovely Linda / Ann Marie / Laid off / Let me know when you're comin' / Changes.
LP: .... SNTF 866

Mathieson, Greg

AMERICAN FLYERS (See under Ritenour, Lee).

Mathieson, P/M Robert

EBB-TIDE (Mathieson, Pipe Major Robert).
LP: .... LILP 5192

GRACE NOTES.
Tracks: / Hornpipes / Air and jigs / March strathspey and reel / Galician dance / Irish reels and hornpipe / Mazurka / Air and jigs (2) / Dance and jig / Hornpipes (2) / Slip jig and Viennese waltz / Jigs / Airs and reels.
LP: .... LILP 5171
MC: .... LICS 5171

Mathieu, Mireille

GREATEST HITS VOL 1: MATHIEU, MIREILLE.
Tracks: / Mon credo / Le funambule / C'est soir ils vont s'aimer / Un monde avec toi / Petit papa noel / Mon bel amour d'ete / Force de rever, A / Quelle est belle / J'ai garde l'accent / Celui que j'aime / La derniere valse / Un homme et une femme / La vielle barque / Je ne suis rien sans toi / C'est a mayerling / Tous les violons de vienne / Paris en colere / Quand on revient / La premiere etoile.
LP: 666 13
MC: 766 13

LES CONTES DE CRI-CRI (Mathieu, Mireille & Placido Domingo).
LP: .... FM 41001

MIREILLE MATHIEU.
LP: .... SCX 6210

RECONTRES DE FEMME.
Tracks: / Recontres de femmes / Je veux te dire / Ma deliverance / Je suis revenue vers toi / Reve ton reve / L'enfant volant / Embrasse-moi / Comme une adolescente / Chanter au soleil / L'amour.
LP: 208480
MC: 408480

SINGS PAUL ANKA.
Tracks: / Man and a woman, A / After you / Life song / Bring the wine / Paris is something wrong / Andi / Closing doors / Leave it all to me.
LP: .... ARL 5041

TOGETHER WE ARE STRONG (see Duffy, Patrick) (Mathieu, Mireille & Patrick Duffy).

Mathilde Mouse... (bk)

MATHILDE MOUSE AND THE STORY OF SILENT NIGHT (Jacoby Coleman).
MC: .... CDL 51681
MC: .... TC 1681

Mathis, Country Johnny

COUNTRY HEARTFELT.
Tracks: / Come home to my heart / It's so lonesome in my heart / There's no more love / Expressing my love / I'm a dreamer / Take your heart and go / All I need is you / If you should come back today / My heart needs a heart / I'll cry when I call your name / Big old heart full of love.
LP: .... PRCV 107

Mathis, Edith

LIEDER (SCHUBERT) (see under Schubert).

Mathis, Johnny

99 MILES FROM LA.
Tracks: / You light up my life / When I need you / I write the songs.
LP: .... SHM 3091
MC: .... HSC 3091

ALL FOR YOU.
Tracks: / Different kinda different / With you I'm born again / I'll do it all for you / Never givin' up on you / Deep purple / Three times a lady / I will survive / Paradise / Lights of Rio / Love without words / Temptation.
LP: .... CBS 86115
MC: 40 86115

BEST DAYS OF MY LIFE.
Tracks: / Would you like to spend the night with me / As time goes by / Best days of my life / Gone gone gone / Bottom line / Last time I felt like this, The / Begin the beguine / How can I make it on my own / There you are / We're in love.
LP: .... CBS 86080
MC: 40 86080

CELEBRATION.
Tracks: / You saved my life / Misty / Evergreen / Stop, look, listen (to your heart) / When a child is born / How deep is your love / Three times a lady / When I need you / Chances are.
LP: .... CBS 10028
MC: 40 10028

CELEBRATION - THE ANNIVERSARY ALBUM.
LP: 4674521
MC: 4674524

CHANTE NOEL.
LP: 81481

CHRISTMAS EVE WITH JOHNNY MATHIS.
Tracks: / It's beginning to look like Christmas / Toyland / It's the most wonderful time of the year / Jingle bells / Christmas is for everyone / Where can I find Christmas / Christmas waltz / We need a little Christmas / Caroling, caroling - happy holiday.
LP: 4501441
MC: 4501444

FIRST TIME EVER I SAW YOUR FACE.
LP: .... CBS 64930

FRIENDS IN LOVE.
Tracks: / Got you where I want you / I remember you & me / When the lovin' goes out of the lovin' / Something's goin' on / What do you do with the love / Friends in love / What's forever for / Warm / Memory / Lately.
LP: .... CBS 85652

GREATEST HITS: JOHNNY MATHIS VOL 4.
Tracks: / When a child is born / Soleado / I'm coming home / Ninety nine miles from L A / First time ever I saw your face, The / Laughter in the rain / Feelings / I'm stone in love with you / Stardust / When will I see you again / Me and Mrs Jones / Killing me softly with her song / If we only have love.
LP: 32091
MC: 40 32091
MC: 40 86022
LP: .... CBS 86022
LP: .... CBS 32091

GREATEST ORIGINAL HITS.
MC: 40 3068

HEART OF A WOMAN, THE.
LP: .... CBS 80533

HEAVENLY.
MC: 40 31410

HOLLYWOOD MUSICALS (Mathis, Johnny & Henry Mancini).
Tracks: / You stepped out of a dream / Taking a chance on love / When you wish upon a star / True love / Whistling away the dark / Time after time / It might as well be Spring / I had the craziest dream / Long ago (and far away) / Crazy world / Moonlight becomes you / It could happen to you / But beautiful.
LP: 4502581
MC: 4502584

I ONLY HAVE EYES FOR YOU.
LP: .... CBS 81329

I'LL BUY YOU A STAR.
LP: .... TFL 5143

I'M COMING HOME.
LP: .... CBS 65690

I'M STONE IN LOVE WITH YOU.
Tracks: / Life is a song worth singing / I'm coming home / I'd rather be here with you / And I think that's what I'll do / I'm stone in love with you / Stop, look and listen to your heart / Foolish / I just want to be me / Sweet child / Baby's born, A.
LP: .... SHM 3130
MC: .... HSC 3130

IN THE STILL OF THE NIGHT.
Tracks: / In the still of the night / Since I fell for you / True love ways / Then you can tell me goodbye / All alone am I / It's all in the game / You belong to me / Since I don't have you / End of the world / For your love.
LP: 4651851
MC: 4651854

JOHNNY MATHIS COLLECTION.
2LP: .... PDA 015
MCSET: .... PDC 015
2LP: .... CBS 10003

JOHNNY MATHIS COLLECTION: VOL 2.
2LP: .... PDA 032
MCSET: .... PDC 032

JOHNNY MATHIS SINGS DUKE ELLINGTON.
Tracks: / Overture - a musical tribute to Duke Ellington / Lush life / Don't you know I care (or don't you care) / I didn't know about you / Things ain't what they used to be (inst) / In a sentimental mood / What am I here for / I got it bad and that ain't good / Something to live for / Solitude / Perdido (instrument) / Prelude to a kiss / In a mellow tone / Don't get around much anymore / Satin doll (instrumental) / Come Sunday / Do nothin' till you here from me / Caravan (piano interlude) / Day dream.
LP: 4671301
MC: 4671304

JOHNNY MATHIS SINGS OF LOVE.
LP: .... SHM 749

JOHNNY MATHIS SINGS THE MUSIC OF BACHARACH & KAEMPFERT.
Tracks: / Wonderland by night / Spanish eyes / Lady smiles, The / Danke schon / Times will change, The / Remember when (we made these memories) / Strangers in the night / Don't stay / If there's a way / Lady / L.O.V.E / Walk on by / Look of love, The / I say a little prayer / Heavenly / This guy's in love with you / I'll never fall in love again / Alfie / Odds and ends / Faithfully / Don't go breaking my heart.
2LP: 66 275

KILLING ME SOFTLY.
LP: 32014
MC: 40 32014

LIVE: JOHNNY MATHIS.
LP: .... SHM 3214
MC: .... HSC 3214

LOVE SONGS: JOHNNY MATHIS.
Tracks: / Love story (where do I begin?) / Look of love, The / Never my love / Somewhere my love / Goodbye to love / If only we have love / This guy's in love with you / Love is blue / Flame of love / Let's love / Love me tonight / I'll never fall in love again.
LP: 31538
LP: .... EMB 31393

LOVE STORY.
LP: .... CBS 64334

MAKE IT EASY ON YOURSELF.
LP: .... CBS 65161

MATHIS COLLECTION, THE.
MC: 40 88278

MATHIS MAGIC.
Tracks: / No one but the one you love / Night and day / Love / My body keeps changing my mind / New York state of mind / She believes in me / That old black magic / You saved my life / To the ends of the earth / Heart, soul, body and mind.
LP: .... CBS 86103
MC: 40 86103

MERRY CHRISTMAS.
Tracks: / Winter wonderland / Christmas song, The / Sleigh ride / Blue Christmas / I'll be home for christmas / White Christmas / O holy night / What child is this / First Noel, The / Silver bells / It came upon a midnight clear / Silent night, holy night.
LP: 4604581
MC: 4604584

MISTY.
Tracks: / What'll I do / More than you know / Strangers in the night / Baby, baby, baby / Danke schon / Stranger in paradise / Misty / By myself / Spanish eyes / There goes my heart / L-O-V-E / That's all.
LP: .... SHM 913
MC: .... HSC 286

NEW SOUND IN POPULAR SONG, A.
LP: .... FS 266

NIGHT AND DAY.
Tracks: / Night and day / Would you like to spend the night with me / Help me make it through the night / Midnight blue / Stardust / Last night I didn't get to sleep at all / Midnight cowboy / Come Saturday morning / You are the sunshine of my life / Yesterday when I was young / Those were the days / Aquarius / Let the sun shine in / Yellow days / One day in your life / Good morning heartache / On a clear day.
LP: .... CBS 32090
MC: 40 32090
LP: .... CBS 31863

ONCE IN A WHILE.
Tracks: / I'm on the outside looking in / It wouldn't have made any difference / Two strong hearts / Once in a while / Fallen / Daydreaming / From a whisper to a scream / Ain't no woman (like the one I've got) / Just like you / Love brought us here tonight.
LP: 4628751
MC: 4628754
LP: 4628750

PORTRAIT OF A SONG STYLIST.
MC: .... HARMC 118

RAINDROPS KEEP FALLING ON MY HEAD.
LP: .... CBS 63587

RHYTHMS AND BALLADS OF BROADWAY.
LP: .... SET 101

RIDE ON A RAINBOW.
LP: .... TFL 5061

RIGHT FROM THE HEART.
Tracks: / Touch by touch / Love shock / Just one touch / Hooked on goodbye / I need you / Step by step / Right from the heart / Falling in love / Here we go again / I hold on.
LP: .... CBS 26365
MC: 40 26365

SPECIAL PART OF ME, A.
Tracks: / Simple / Love won't let me wait / Best is yet to come, The / Lead me to your love / You're a special part of me / Love never felt so good / Priceless / One love / Right here and now.
LP: .... CBS 25475

SWEET SURRENDER.
LP: .... CBS 86036

SWING SOFTLY.
LP: .... TFL 5039

TEARS AND LAUGHTER.
Tracks: / Don't give up on us / Goodbye to love / Gone, gone, gone / Midnight blue / Solitaire / Hungry years / Alone again (naturally) / You are the sunshine of my life / Everything is beautiful / Most beautiful girl / Betcha by golly wow / Just the way you are / And I love you so / Song of joy / Life is a song worth singing / You light up my life.
MC: 40 10019
2LP: .... CBS 10019
MC: 4683074

THAT'S WHAT FRIENDS ARE FOR (Mathis, Johnny & Deniece Williams).
Tracks: / You're all I need to get by / Until you come back to me that's what I'm gonna / You're a special part of my life / Ready or not / Me for you, you for me / Your precious love / Just the way you are / That's what friends are for / I just can't get over you / Touching me with love.
LP: .... CBS 86068

THIS GUY'S IN LOVE WITH YOU.
LP: .... SHM 872

TOO MUCH, TOO LITTLE, TOO LATE (see under Deniece Williams) (Mathis, Johnny/Deniece Williams).

UNFORGETTABLE: A TRIBUTE TO NAT KING COLE (Mathis, Johnny & Natalie Cole).
Tracks: / Unforgettable / Sweet Lorraine / Nature boy / Orange coloured sky / Too young / Christmas song, The / To the ends of the earth / That Sunday that summer / Let there be love (Duet.) / When I fall in love / Route 66 / Red sails in the sunset / For sentimental reasons / Walkin' my baby back home / It's only a paper moon / Stardust / Straighten up and fly right / Mona Lisa / L.O.V.E. / Ballerina / Ramblin' Rose.
LP: .... CBS 10042
MC: 40 10042

WARM.
LP: .... TFL 5015

WHEN A CHILD IS BORN.

Tracks: / When a child is born / Silent night / White Christmas / Little drummer boy.
LP: SHM 3185
MC: HSC 3185
LP: CBS 83266

WHEN WILL I SEE YOU AGAIN?.
LP: CBS 80738

YOU LIGHT UP MY LIFE.
Tracks: / You light up my life / Emotions / All I ever need / Where or when / If you believe / Too much too little too late / How deep is your love / Till love touches your life / I wrote a symphony on my guitar / It was almost like a song.
LP: CBS 32521
MC: 40 32521
LP: CBS 86055

Mathis, Kathy

KAT WALK.
Tracks: / Automatic stop and go / Late night hour / Straight from the heart / Crunch / Kat walk / Baby I'm hooked / All to yourself / Now that you've gone / Olive branch, The (instrumental) / Love festival.
LP: 460092 1
MC: 460092 4

Mathisen, Leo

DANISH JAZZ VOL.2.
LP: SLP 411

Matinee Idols

LINE-UP.
Tracks: / Who'll be next in line? / Video world / Touch sense / My baby (comes from the west) / Peralandra / Big bang, The / You told me / Tilley.
LP: PTLS 1076

Matrix

HARVEST.
Tracks: / El tigre / Pony / Harvest - prayer of thanksgiving / Feast / Celebration dance / Blue black / Maestro / Balthazar.
LP: 231 2121
MC: K 12 121

Matsu, Tokyo

COUNTRY LADY FROM JAPAN.
LP: CMLF 1031

Matsubara, Masaki

BEEN.
LP: DUDLP 100
MC: DUDMC 100

Matsui, Keiko

DROP OF WATER.
LP: PJ 88024
MC: PJC 88024

NO BORDERS.
Tracks: / First four years, The / Light in the rain / White corridor, The / Mover / Wind and the wolf, The / In the mist / Three silhouettes / Kappa (water elf) / Souvenir / Believer.
LP: MCA 6380

Matt Bianco

BEST OF MATT BIANCO.
LP: WX 376
MC: WX 376 C

INDIGO.
Tracks: / Don't blame it on that girl / Nervous / Slide / Say it's not too late / Wap bam boogie / Good times / R & B / Hanging on / Jack of clubs / Indigo.
LP: WX 181
MC: WX 181C

MATT BIANCO.
Tracks: / Yeh yeh / Dancing in the street / Undercover / Fly by night / Smooth / I wonder / Just can't stand it / Summer song / Sweetest love affair / Up front.
LP: WX 35
MC: WX 35C

WHOSE SIDE ARE YOU ON ?.
Tracks: / More than I can bear / No no never / Half a minute / Matt's mood / Get out of your lazy bed / It's getting late / Sneaking out the back door / Riding with the wind / Matt's mood II / Whose side are you on / Big Rosie (Only on cassette.) / Other side, The (Only on cassette.).
LP: WX 7
MC: WX 7C

Mattea, Kathy

TIME PASSES BY.
LP: 8469751
MC: 8469754

UNTASTED HONEY.
LP: 832 793-1
MC: 832 793-4

UNTOLD STORIES (A Collection of Hits).
Tracks: / Train of memories / Eighteen wheels and a dozen roses / Goin' gone / Love at the five & dime / Come from the heart / She came from Fort Worth / Walk the way the wind blows / Where've you been / Life as we knew it / Burnin' old memories / Battle hymn of the Republic / Few good things remain, A / Untold stories.
LP: 846 877-1
MC: 846 877-4

WALK THE WAY THE WIND BLOWS.
Tracks: / Walk the way the wind blows / Train of memories / Reason to live / Evenin' / Leaving West Virginia / Love at the five and dime / You plant my fields / Back up grinnin' again / You're the power / Song for the life.
LP: MERH 104
MC: MERHC 104
LP: 830 405-1
MC: 830 405-4

WILLOW IN THE WIND.
Tracks: / Come from the heart / Burnin' old memories / True North / Willow in the wind / I'll take care of you / Here's hopin' / She came from Fort Worth / Hills of Alabama / Love chooses you / Where've you been.
LP: 836 950-1
MC: 836 950-4

Matter Babies

SKINNY DIPPING.
MLP: NISHI 212

Matter Of Choice (bk)

MATTER OF CHOICE (Churchill, Sarah).
MC: ZSW 637

Matter Of Honour (bk)

MATTER OF HONOUR, A (see Archer, Jeffrey (aut)) (Jarvis, Martin (nar)).

Matthews, David

BILLY BOY (Matthews, David Trio).
LP: K 28P 6442

DELTA LADY.
LP: 520388

DELTA LADY (Matthews, David & Earl Klugh).
Tracks: / Funky turkey / If / Gosman's gazebo / Spanish heat / Mato grosso / Rolling song / Westlake drive / Delta lady.
LP: PRT N5014
MC: PRT Z5014
LP: GNPS 2153
MC: GNP5 2153
LP: 520388

DUNE.
LP: CTI 5005

GRAND CONNECTION (Matthews, David Orchestra).
LP: GNPS 2162
MC: GNP5 2162

GRAND CROSS.
Tracks: / Grand cross / Kingston connection / Afro sax / Pipe dreams / Movin' man / For a little love baby / Sambafrique / Star island.
LP: N 5018
MC: ZCN 5018
LP: GNPS 2157
MC: GNP5 2157

ICE FUSE ONE.
Tracks: / Ice / Groovin' song / Lonely smile, A / Just funkin' around / Requiem for Marvin / Fuse it.
LP: N 6554
LP: GNPS 2174
MC: GNP5 2174

SHOOGIE WANNA BOOGIE.
Tracks: / Shoogie wanna boogie / My girl / You keep me hanging on / California dreamin' / Gotta be where you are / Just my imagination.
LP: ABCL 5206

SPEED DEMON (Matthews, David Orchestra).
LP: GNPS 2185
MC: GNP5 2185

SUPER FUNKY SAX.
LP: GNPS 2169
MC: GNP5 2169

UNKNOWN STANDARDS (Matthews, David Trio).
LP: K28P 6490

Matthews, Francis

MORE WORK FOR THE UNDERTAKER (See under More Work For The...).

Matthews, Geoffrey

JEFFY, THE BURGLAR'S CAT (See also Ursula Moray Williams).

Matthews, Iain

HIT AND RUN.
LP: CBS 81930

JOURNEYS FROM GOSPEL OAK.
Tracks: / Things you gave me / Tribute to Hank Williams / Met her on a plane / Do right woman / Knowing the game / Polly / Mobile blue / Bride 1945 / Franklin Avenue / Sing me back home.
LP: CREST 18
LP: BD 3009
LP: CREST 004
MC: CREST MC 004

PURE AND CROOKED.
LP: VGC 15
MC: TCVGC 15

SIAMESE FRIENDS.
Tracks: / You don't see me / Survival / Heatwave / Home somewhere / Crying in the night / Baby she's on the street / Hearts on the line / Anna / Lies / Runaway.
LP: ROC 107

SPOT OF INTERFERENCE.
Tracks: / I survived the 70's / She may call you up tonight / I can't fade away the hurt / Driftwood from disaster / Why am I? / No time at all / For the lonely hunter / See me / Civilization / What do I do?.
LP: SDLP 034
LP: 2383 582

WALKING A CHANGING LINE.
Tracks: / Dream sequence / Standing still / Except for a tear / Following every finger / Alive alone / On Squirrel Hill / Shadows break / This fabrication / Lovers by rote / Only a motion.
LP: 37 1070 1
MC: 37 1070 4

Matthews, Jessie

DANCING ON THE CEILING.
Tracks: / Dancing on the ceiling / When you've got a little springtime in your heart / It's love again / Gangway / Everything's in rhythm with my heart / Your heart skips a beat / One little kiss from you / When you gotta sing you gotta sing / Tony's in town / By the fireside / Head over heels in love / Lord and Lady Whoozis / One more kiss and then goodnight / Let me give my happiness to you / Tinkle tinkle tinkle / Just by your example / I'll stay with you / Three wishes / May I have the next romance with you? / Looking around corners for you / Souvenir of love / My river.
LP: AJA 5063
MC: ZC AJA 5063

GOLDEN AGE OF JESSIE MATTHEWS.
LP: GX 41 2541-1
MC: GX 41 2541

JACK WHITING AND JESSIE MATTHEWS.
LP: MES 7049

SPRINGTIME IN YOUR HEART.
Tracks: / Journey's end / By the fireside / I'll stay with you / Three wishes / Just by your example / When you've got a little springtime / Over my shoulder / Whip-poor-will / Hello young lovers / Hold my hand / One more kiss and then goodnight / One little kiss from you / Let me give my happiness to you / Dancing on the ceiling / Tinkle, tinkle, tinkle / Look for the silver lining / I was young.
LP: SH 425

TRIBUTE TO A STAR, A.
Tracks: / Gangway / I can wiggle my ears / Everything's in rhythm with my heart / Tony's in town / It's love again / Slipping through my fingers / Got to dance my way to heaven / My heart stood still / Medley / Lord and lady whoozies / Say the word and it's yours / May I have the next romance with you / Little silkworm / Looking around corners for you / Head over heels in love / There's that look in your eyes again / Just a memory.
LP: RFL 17

Matthews, Ronnie

ROOTS, BRANCHES AND DANCES.
LP: BH 7008

Matthews Southern

BEST OF MATTHEWS SOUTHERN COMFORT.
LP: MCL 1644

LATER THAT SAME YEAR.
LP: MCF 2686

MATTHEWS SOUTHERN COMFORT MEET SOUTHERN COMFORT.
Tracks: / Woodstock / Something in the way she moves / Blood red roses / And when she smiles (she makes the sun shine) / I've lost you / Once in a lifetime / Brand new Tennessee waltz / To love / I sure like your smile / Wedding song (there is love) / I need help / April lady / I wanna be your mama again / Something said / Dreadful ballad of Willie Hurricane / Belle.
LP: SEE 85
MC: TCSEE 85

SECOND SPRING.
LP: UNLS 112

WOODSTOCK (OLD GOLD) (2) (see under McGuire, Barry - Eve Of Destruction.

Matthews, Wall

RIDING HORSES.
LP: CD 709

Matthews/ Wilson/

MATTHEWS/ WILSON/ DOONAN.
Tracks: / Reels / Ramblin' sailor / Geordie / Jigs / Flash company / Maid on the shore / Binnorie-o / Bonnie light horseman, The.
LP: R 008LP

Mattson, Dave

LEAD ME HOME.
LP: MYR 1081

Matty, Marie

NATTY DREAD MEK ME WANT (Matty, Marie/Max Asher).
LP: WAR 142

Matumbi

BEST OF MATUMBI.
Tracks: / After tonight / Can't satisfy / Low of the land / Wipe them out / Brother Louie / Running in and out of life / Man in me, The / Go back home / Come back sunshine / Take it from me / Reggae stuff.
LP: TRLS 145

MATUMBI.
Tracks: / Nothing at all / Sus / Write them / Zimbabwe / Breakdown / My love / Straight to my head / Blood of Jesus / War / Malfunction.
LP: EMC 3355

POINT OF VIEW.
Tracks: / Come with me / Bookie to the bank / Daughters of Babylon / Nothing to do with you / Black civilisation / Good book / Point of view / Judy McQueen / Ordinary man / Boy oh boy / Things I do for you / Living in a dream.
LP: RDC 2001

TESTIFY.
LP: SGL 105

Matusewitch, Sergei

ACCORDION-CONCERTINA RECITAL.
Tracks: / Rhapsodies no.1 & 2 / Carnival of Venice / Ziguernerweisen / Hungarian dance no. 1 / Double concerto D minor / Meditation / Melodie / Czardas.
LP: SM 002

Mau Maus

FEAR NO EVIL.
LP: REBLP 001

LIVE AT THE MARPLES.
LP: PAX 16

MY JUDGE AND JURY.
LP: REBLP 1

RUN WITH THE PACK.
LP: PAX 20

Maugham, W. Somerset

COLONEL'S LADY, THE/LORD MOUNTDRAGO (see under Colonel's Lady) (Burden, Hugh (nar)).

FACTS OF LIFE, THE (See under Burden, Hugh) (Maugham, Somerset/ Hugh Burden).
MC: TTC/WSM 4

GIGOLO AND GIGOLETTE/ THE FACTS OF LIFE (Burden, Hugh (nar)).
MC: TTC/WSM 1

LOTUS EATER, THE (Howard, Alan).
MC: CDL 51663

MOON AND SIXPENCE, THE (Langella, Frank).
MCSET: 2096

SHORT STORIES (Burden, Hugh (nar)).
MCSET: LFP 7442

SHORT STORIES VOL. 2 (Tony Britton/ Burden, Hugh).
MCSET: LFP 7466

Maulidi & Musical

MOMBASA WEDDING SPECIAL.
Tracks: / Mkufu / Hukomi mpelelezi / Shuga dedi / Mume ni moshi wa koko / Fadhila kama kukopa / Vishindo vya mashua / Ukiondoka mpenzi / Hasidi.
LP: ORBD 058

Maupin, Bennie

ALMANAC (See also under Cecil McBee, Mike Nock, Eddie Marshall).

Mauriat, Paul

BRASIL EXCLUSIVAMENTE.
LP: 9120 233

BRAZILIAN LANDSCAPE.
LP: 6325 144

CLASSICS IN THE AIR.
Tracks: / Toccata and fugue in D minor / Canon / Symphony No. 9 / La gazza ladra (overture) / Liebestraum No. 3 /

Barber of Seville (overture) / La traviata (Prelude.) / Prelude in C / Symphony No. 40 / Moonlight sonata / Hungarian dance no. 5 / Sonata pathetique.
LP: **826 072-1**
MC: **826 072-4**

MUSIC OF PAUL MAURIAT (Mauriat, Paul & His Orchestra).
2LP: **6641 130**

TOUT POUR LA MUSIQUE.
Tracks: / Souvenirs / Tout pour la musique / Staccato / Head over heels / Night feeling / Felicita / Physical / Paris ballade / One of us / On my own / Festa do interior / Blue eyes.
LP: **6313 329**
MC: **7200 329**

WINDY (Mauriat, Paul & His Orchestra).
Tracks: / Windy / That's what friends are for / Nikita / Saving all my love for you / You are my world / Waiting / Day after day / Part time lover / Only love (l'amour en heritage) / Quoi / Sara / Say you, say me.
LP: **826 971-1**
MC: **826 971-4**
LP: . . . . **IMS 8269711**

Maurice (Film)

MAURICE (Original Soundtrack) (Various artists).
LP: . . . . **BL 86618**
MC: . . . . **BK 86618**

Maurice (NZ)

VIRTUOSO ACCORDIONISTS (see under Jones, Harley) (Maurice (NZ)/ Harley Jones).

Mauro, Turk

HEAVYWEIGHT.
Tracks: / Cottontail / Old folks / Big sound from the east, The / You're my everything / Home / Jazz guys / East 121st Street.
LP: . . . . **LP 1004**

UNDERDOG, THE (Mauro, Turk#Al Cohn#Hugh Lawson#Bob Cranshaw).
LP: . . . . **SLP 4076**

Mawer, Ryan

ENCOUNTERS.
Tracks: / God is the answer / Runaway / I love so hard to find / Take your eyes off yourself / You are my child / Face to face / God so loved the world / Don't say no / Give him your heart / Trinity song.
MC: . . . . **RM 316**

Max Q

MAX Q.
Tracks: / Sometimes / Way of the world / Ghost of the year / Everything / Zero 2-0 / Soul engine / Buckethead / Monday night by satellite / Tight / Ot-ven-rot.
LP: **838 942 1**
MC: **838 942 4**

Max & The Broadway...

AND GOD GAVE US MAX (Max & The Broadway Metal Choir).
LP: . . . . **AMP 9**

Maxie & Mitch

DOUBLE TROUBLE.
LP: . . . . **RUB 045**

Maximum Joy

STATION M.X.J.Y..
LP: . . . . **Y 28LP**

Maximum Overdrive

MAXIMUM OVERDRIVE (Film Soundtrack) (See under AC/DC - Who made).

Maxwell, Bob

LOWLANDS AWAY.
LP: **MWSL5 503**

Maxwell, Jimmy

LET'S FALL IN LOVE (Maxwell, Jimmy & His Band).
LP: . . . . **CLP 50**

Maxwell St. Klezmer

MAXWELL ST. KLEZMER DAYS.
LP: . . . . **GVM 116**

Maxwells

COUNTRY STYLE.
LP: . . . . **SRTZ 77379**

May, Bill

THAT'S DELIGHTS (May,Bill Quintet).
Tracks: / That's delights / Blues Marx / Mavrodaphnes dance / Goodbye California / S'wonderful / Goodbye.
LP: . . . . **TR 532**
MC: . . . . **TRC 532**

May, Billy

20 GOLDEN PIECES: BILLY MAY.
Tracks: / Come rain or come shine / Little green apples / It's getting baby / Baby I need your loving / Walk on by / Cherry cherry / Spanish harlem / Come back to me / Hold me / Blues in the night / Marrakesh express / Jackie / Soulful strut / Pepito / Pass me by / Soul coaxing / Stripper, The / Little games / Some of these days / Summer place, A (theme from).
LP: . . . . **BDL 2025**
MC: . . . . **AJKL 2025**

BACCHANALIA! (May, Billy & His Orchestra).
Tracks: / Top hat, white tie and tails / Cocktails for two / You and the night and the music / Pick yourself up / Show me the way to go home / Little brown jug / Makin' whoopee / Bacchanalia / Let's put out the lights / Accent on youth / It's the natural thing to do.
LP: . . . . **ED 2604201**
MC: . . . . **ED 2604204**

BEST OF BILLY MAY.
LPS: . . . . **RA 1013**
MCSET: . . . . **RA 1013C**

BEST OF BILLY MAY AND HIS ORCHESTRA (May, Billy & His Orchestra).
Tracks: / Bye bye blackbird / Fascinating rhythm / Preacher man / You're driving me crazy / Mad about the boy / In a Persian market.
LP: . . . . **MFP 5609**
MC: . . . . **TCMFP 5609**

BILLY MAY'S BIG FAT BRASS.
Tracks: / Brassmen's holiday / Autumn leaves / Love is the thing / Ping pong / Moonlight becomes you / Pawn ticket / Solving the riddle / Invitation / Continental, The / Return of the zombie / On a little street in Singapore / Joom jooms.
LP: . . . . **EMS 1155**
MC: . . . . **TCEMS 1155**

BILLY MAY'S NAUGHTY OPERETTA (May, Billy & His Orchestra).
Tracks: / Serenade from the student prince / Italian street song / Desert song, The / Rose Marie / I'll see you again / She didn't say yes / Vilia / Hugette waltz / Softly as in a morning sunrise / One kiss / March of the toys.
LP: . . . . **CAPS 2400151**
MC: . . . . **TC CAPS 2400154**

CAPITOL YEARS, THE: BILLY MAY (May, Billy & His Orchestra).
Tracks: / Cute piece of property, A (Vocal:The Encores) / Memphis in June (Vocal:Johnny Mercer) / Lemon twist / What does it take to make you take to me (Vocal:Nat King Cole) / Good gravy (Vocal:The Encores) / Christopher Columbus / Belly up to the bar, boys (With Stan Kenton & Nelson Riddle) / Dixieland band / Oklahoma / Street of dreams / Breeze and I / Mean to me (Vocal:Nellie Lutcher) / High noon / What kind of fool am I? (Vocal:Vic Damone) / Floater, The / When I take my sugar to tea (Vocal:The Maytimers) / Song is you, The / Young at heart.
LP: . . . . **EMS 1275**
MC: . . . . **TC EMS 1275**

FANCY DANCIN'.
Tracks: / It happened in monterey / Say isn't so / Star eyes / I'll never say 'never again' again / Stumbling / She reminds me of you / Songs of the wanderer / Azure / Bye bye blackbird / You turned the tables on me.
LP: . . . . **PM 1547781**
MC: . . . . **PM 1547784**

GIRLS AND BOYS ON BROADWAY, THE (May, Billy Big Band).
LP: . . . . **FS 1**

I BELIEVE IN YOU.
LP: . . . . **BT 1001**
MC: . . . . **BT 41001**

MAY BE (May, Billy & His Orchestra).
Tracks: / Conrail flyer / Blonde again / I'm back where I started from / Chloe's song / Too soon for June / Blue and all alone / These are the good old days / Once more won't hurt / Pretty plaything / Opportunity rag / Old Cayucas / I heard you the first time.
LP: . . . . **RRS 101**

SKYLINER.
LP: . . . . **GH 868**

SORTA DIXIE (May, Billy & His Orchestra).
LP: . . . . **ST 1054**

SORTA MAY (May, Billy & His Orchestra).
LP: . . . . **M 562**

SORTA MAY/ SORTA DIXIE (May, Billy & His Orchestra).
LP: . . . . **STD 1051**

SWING GOES ON VOL 8.
LP: . . . . **IC 054 52717**

VOLUMES 2 AND 3 ON CASSETTE.
MCSET: . . . . **RAC 1014/5**

YOU MAY SWING.
Tracks: / You ain't makin' it / Jornal do Brasil / Silvery cloud / I don't know where I'm going / Sunset colours / Santa Lucia / Bouncin' runners / Second chance / You may swing / Novo amor / Fingers / Sooper sloop.
LP: . . . . **ISST 118**

May Blitz

MAY BLITZ.
LP: . . . . **BGOLP 16**

May, Brian

STAR FLEET PROJECT (May, Brian & Friends).
MLP: . . . . **SFLT 1078061**
MC: . . . . **TCSFLT 1078061**

May, Cyril

GREAT AUSTRALIAN SALUTE (May, Cyril & Fabulous Jack).
LP: . . . . **LRF 088**

May Day

MAY DAY.
LP: . . . . **AMLH 64873**

May Linn

MAY LINN.
Tracks: / Soldier / Joey don't care / In the shelter of the night / Breakout / Dangerous games / Backstreet life / Fit for fight / Long way from home.
LP: . . . . **SHARK 007**

May, Phil

PHIL MAY & FALLEN ANGELS (May, Phil & Fallen Angels).
Tracks: / Fallen angels / California / 13 floor suicide / Dance again / Shine on baby / My good friend / Cold wind / I keep on / Dogs of war / Girl like you, A.
LP: . . . . **NOTT 006**

May, Raymond

UNADULTERATED ADDICT.
Tracks: / Romantic guy / True life / New emotion / You turn me on / True pretender / Living in exile / Turn your love light on / Tiger and the butterfly / Yellow ribbons / Ride 'em high.
LP: **9607961**
MC: **9607964**

May, Simon

ALWAYS THERE (see Webb, Marti).

SIMON'S WAY.
Tracks: / Howard's way / Variations on the theme of Howard's Way / Orrin New England / Frere / Abbey's theme / Tarrant set, The / Barracuda / Always there / Anyone can fall in love / Warm light of a brand new day, The / Holiday suite / Julia's theme / Eastenders.
LP: . . . . **REB 594**
MC: . . . . **ZCF 594**

THEMES (May, Simon Orchestra).
MC: **837 613-4**

May You Always

MAY YOU ALWAYS (See under Rediscover Series) (Various artists).

Mayall, John

BACK TO THE ROOTS.
LP: **2657 005**

BARE WIRES (Mayall, John & The Bluesbreakers).
Tracks: / Bare wires suite / Bare wires suite / Where did I belong / Start walking / Open a new door / Fire / I know now / Look in the mirror / I'm a stranger / No reply / Hartley quits / Killing time / She's too young / Sandy.
LP: . . . . **SKL 4945**

BEHIND THE IRON CURTAIN.
LP: . . . . **NCP 709**
MC: . . . . **ZCNCP 709**
LP: . . . . **GNPS 2184**
MC: **GNP5 2184**

BEYOND THE TURNING POINT.
LP: **2483 016**

BLUES ALONE, THE.
Tracks: / Brand new start / Please don't tell / Down the line / Sonny boy blow / Marsha's mood / No more tears / Catch that train / Cancelling out / Harp man / Brown sugar / Broken wings / Don't kick me.
LP: . . . . **SCL 1243**

BLUES FROM LAUREL CANYON.
Tracks: / Vacation / Walking on sunset / Laurel Canyon home / 2401 / Ready to ride / Medicine man / Somebody's acting like a child / Bear, The / Miss James / First time alone / Long gone midnight / Fly tomorrow.
LP: . . . . **SKL 4972**

BLUESBREAKERS (See under Clapton, Eric) (Mayall, John & Eric Clapton).

BOTTOM LINE.
Tracks: / Bottom line / Dreamboat / Desert flower / I'm gonna do it / Revival / Game of love / Celebration / Come with me.
LP: . . . . **DJF 20556**

COLLECTION: JOHN MAYALL.
Tracks: / Key to love / Hideaway / Ramblin' on my mind / All your love / They call it stormy Monday / Hoochie coochie man / Crocodile walk / Crawling up a hill / Marsha's mood / Sonny boy blow / Looking back / Hard road / Supernatural, The / You don't love me / Leaping Christine / Suspicions, part 2 / Picture on the wall / Death of J. B. Lenoir, The / Sandy / Bear, The / Walking on sunset / Fly tomorrow.
2LP: . . . . **CCSLP 137**
MC: . . . . **CCSMC 137**

CRUSADE (Mayall, John & The Bluesbreakers).
Tracks: / Oh, pretty woman / Stand back baby / My time after awhile / Snowy wood / Man of stone / Tears in my eyes / Driving sideways / Death of J. B. Lenoir, The / I can't quit you baby / Streamline / Me and my woman / Checkin' up on my baby.
LP: . . . . **SKL 4890**

DIARY OF A BAND VOL 1 (Mayall,John Bluesbreakers).
LP: . . . . **SKL 4918**

DIARY OF A BAND VOL 2 (Mayall,John Bluesbreakers).
LP: . . . . **SKL 4919**

EMPTY ROOMS.
2LP: **2683 039**
2LP: **583 580**

GREATEST HITS: JOHN MAYALL.
2LP: **2664 436**
MC: **3578 483**

HARD ROAD, A (Mayall,John Bluesbreakers).
Tracks: / Hard road / It's over / You don't love me / Stumble, The / Another kinda love / Hit the highway / Leaping Christine / Dust my blues / There's always work / Same way, The / Supernatural, The / Top of the hill / Some day after a while (you'll be sorry) / Living alone.
LP: . . . . **SKL 4853**

JAZZ BLUES FUSION.
LP: **2425 103**

JOHN MAYALL PLAYS JOHN MAYALL.
Tracks: / Crawling up a hill (version 2) / I wanna teach you everything / When I'm gone / I need your love / Hoot owl, The / R & B time / Night train / Crocodile walk (version 1) / What's the matter with you / Doreen / Runaway / Heartache / Chicago line.
LP: . . . . **LK 46800**

JOHN MAYALL STORY, THE VOL 1.
LP: . . . . **TAB 74**

JOHN MAYALL STORY, THE, VOL 2.
Tracks: / Pretty woman / My time after a while / Death of JB Lenoir / Suspicions / Picture on the wall / Open a new door / No reply / Harely quits / Sandy / Walking on sunset / Medicine man / Somebody's acting like a child.
LP: . . . . **TAB 75**

LAST EDITION.
Tracks: / Gasoline blues / Perfect peace / Going to take my time / Deep down feelings / Troubled times / Pusher man / One of the few / Love song / Little kitten / Crazy games.
LP: **2486 278**
MC: **3186 104**

LAST OF THE BRITISH BLUES,THE.
Tracks: / Tucson lady / Parchman farm / There's only now / Teaser, The / Hideaway / Bear, The / Lonely birthday / Lowdown blues / It must be there.
LP: . . . . **MCL 1643**
MC: . . . . **MCLC 1643**

LOOKING BACK (Mayall, John & The Bluesbreakers).
Tracks: / Mr. James / Blues city shake down / They call it stormy Monday / So many roads / Looking back / Sitting in the rain / It hurts me too / Double trouble / Suspicions (part 2) / Jenny / Picture on the wall.
LP: . . . . **SKL 5010**

MOVING ON.
LP: **2459 325**

NIGHTRIDING: JOHN MAYALL.
Tracks: / Law must change, The / Saw mill gulch road / I'm gonna fight for you J.B. / So hard to share / California / Thoughts about Roxanne / Room to move.
MC: . . . . **KNMC 10010**
LP: . . . . **KNLP 10010**

NO MORE INTERVIEWS.
Tracks: / Hard going up / Bigger slice of pie, A / Falling / Take me home tonight / Sweet honey bee / Stars in the night / Consideration / Gypsy lady / Wild new lover.
LP: . . . . **DJF 20564**

NOTICE TO APPEAR.

LP: . . . . ABCL 5142

POWER OF THE BLUES, THE.
Tracks: / Ridin' on the L & N / Help me / Racehorse man / All your love / I ain't got you / Wild about you / It ain't right / Room to move.
LP: . . . . LIK 62

PRIMAL SOLOS.
Tracks: / Intro - Maudie / It hurts to be in love / Have you ever loved a woman / Bye bye bird / Hoochie coochie man / Intro - look at the girl / Wish you were mine / Start walking.
LP: . . . . TAB 66
MC: . . . . KTBC 66

RAW BLUES.
LP: . . . . SCL 1220

ROADSHOW BLUES.
Tracks: / Why worry / Road show / Mama talk to your daughter / Big man / Lost and gone / Mexico City / John Lee Boogie / Reaching for a mountain / Baby what you want me to do.
LP: . . . . DJF 20570
MC: . . . . DJH 40570
LP: . . . . THBL 060

ROOM TO MOVE.
Tracks: / Room to move / Took the car / Crying / My pretty girl / Don't waste my time / Thinking of my woman / Plan your revoloution / Something new / Deep blue sea / Don't pick a flower.
LP: 2486 041

SENSE OF PLACE, A (Mayall, John & The Bluesbreakers).
Tracks: / I want to go / Send me down to Vicksburg / Sensitive kid / Let's work together / Black cat moan / All my life / Congo square / Without her / Jacksborn highway / I can't complain / Sugarcane.
MC: . . . . ICT 9958
LP: . . . . ILPS 9958

SOME OF MY BEST FRIENDS ARE BLUES.
Tracks: / All your love / It ain't right / You don't love me / Dust my blues / Oh pretty woman / My time after awhile / I can't quit you baby / Double trouble / So many roads / All my life.
LP: . . . . LIK 1

TURNING POINT.
LP: 2485 222
MC: 3201 294
LP: 583 571

USA UNION.
LP: 2425 020

WAITING FOR THE RIGHT TIME.
Tracks: / Hideaway / Steppin' out / They call it stormy Monday / Hard road / Laurel Canyon home / Ramblin' on my mind / Man of stone / Don't waste my time / Waiting for the right time / Red sky / Crying / R & B time / Another kinda love / Another man / Picture on the wall / No reply / It hurts me too / Crawling up a hill / Ready to ride.
MC: . . . . ELITE 001 PMC

WORLD OF JOHN MAYALL VOL 2.
LP: . . . . SPA 138

Mayaula - Mayoni

MIZELE.
LP: . . . . KPS 001

Maycock, George

GEORGE MAYCOCK TRIO (Maycock, George Trio).
LP: . . . . RING 01008

Mayday (dance)

RHYTHM IS RHYTHM VERSUS MAYDAY EP (See under Rhythm Is Rhythm) (Rhythm is Rhythm vs Mayday).

Mayer, John

ETUDES (Mayer, John & Indo Jazz Fusions).
LP: . . . . SNTF 603

Mayerl, Billy

KING OF SYNCOPATION.
LP: . . . . SH 189

MARIGOLD.
Tracks: / Marigold / Baby's birthday party / Sweet nothin's / Please handle with care / Here comes the bride medley / Honeysuckle / Three dances medley / Ace of clubs / Ace of hearts / Wedding of the painted doll, The / Jasmine / Hollyhock / Balloons, who'll buy my balloons? / Wake up and dream medley / Love lies medley / Mignonette / House that Jack built, The (medley) / Ace of diamonds / Ace of spades.
LP: . . . . JOYD 294

VERSATILITY OF BILLY MAYERL.
Tracks: / Golliwog / Judy / Punch / Honky tonk - A rhythmical absurdity / Sweet nothings / Wistaria / Personal course in modern syncopation / Rag doll / Sennen Cove / Wedding of the painted doll / Old fashioned girls / He loves and she loves / It don't do nothing but rain / Drink to me only / Rainbow (So long Lefty) / Chopsticks / Masculine women / Lay me down to sleep in Carolina / I ain't got nobody / Toodle-oo-sal / Hire purchase system / When lights are low in Cairo / More we are together, The.
2LP: . . . . PAST 704/5

Mayes, Pete

I'M READY.
MC: . . . . TX 3013
LP: . . . . DT 3013

Mayfield, Curtis

ALL TIME CLASSIC COLLECTION.
Tracks: / If there's a hell below / Dirty laundry / Move on up / Only you babe / Doo doo wap is strong here / She don't let nobody (but me) / So in love / Tripping out / Do be down / You are, you are / This year / Between you baby and me / Ain't no love lost / Hard times / Tomorrow night for sure / We people who are darker than blue.
2LP: . . . . CUR 22902
MC: . . . . CUR 22902MC

CURTIS.
Tracks: / If there is a hell below we're all gonna go / Other side of town, The / Wild and free / Makings of you, The / Miss Black America / Move on up / We the people who are darker than blue / Give it up.
LP: . . . . K 56252

CURTIS IN CHICAGO.
Tracks: / Superfly / For your precious love / I'm so proud for once in my life / Preacher man / If I were a child again / Duke of Earl / Love oh love / Amen.
LP: . . . . K 56250

CURTIS LIVE.
Tracks: / Mighty mighty / I plan to stay a believer / We've only just begun / People get ready / Star and stare / Check out your mind / Gypsy woman / Makings of you, The / We, the people who are darker than blue / Don't worry if there's a hell below we're all / Stone junkie.
2LP: . . . . K 66047

DAY AFTER YOU, THE (CELEBRATE) (See under Blow Monkeys).

GIVE GET TAKE AND HAVE.
LP: . . . . BDLP 4042

HEARTBEAT.
Tracks: / Tell me, tell me / What is my woman for / Between you baby and me / Victory / Over the hump / You better stop / You're so good to me / Heartbeat.
LP: . . . . RSS 4

HONESTY.
Tracks: / Hey baby, give it all to me / Still within your heart / If you need me / Dirty laundry / Nobody but you / What you gawn do / Summer hot.
LP: . . . . EPC 25317
MC: 40 25317

LIVE IN EUROPE.
Tracks: / Intro / Freddie's dead / We gotta have peace / People get ready / Move on up / Back to the world / Gypsy woman / Pusher man / We've only just begun / When seasons change / If there's a hell below.
2LP: CUR2 2901
MC: MCCUR2 2901

NEVER SAY YOU CAN'T SURVIVE.
LP: . . . . K 56352

PEOPLE GET READY (Live at Ronnie Scott's).
Tracks: / Little child runnin' wild / It's all right / People get ready / Freddie's dead / Pusherman / I'm so proud / We've gotta have peace / Billy Jack / Move on up / To be invisible.
MC: . . . . ESMMC 003

RIGHT COMBINATION (See under Clifford, Linda for details) (Mayfield, Curtis/Linda Clifford).

ROOTS.
Tracks: / Get down / Keep on moving on / Underground / We got to have peace / Beautiful brother of mine / Now you're gone / Love to keep you in mind.
LP: . . . . K 56249

SOMETHING TO BELIEVE IN.
Tracks: / Love me, love me now / Never let me go / Tripping out / People never give up / It's alright / Something to believe in / Never stop loving me.
LP: . . . . RS 13077
LP: 2394271
LP: . . . . CUR 2005
MC: . . . . CURMC 2005

SUPERFLY (Film soundtrack).
Tracks: / Little child runnin' wild / Freddie's dead / Give me your love / No thing on me / Superfly / Pusherman / Junkie chase / Eddie you should know / Think.
MC: . . . . ZCCUR 2002
LP: 2318 065
LP: . . . . CUR 2002

LP: . . . . RSS 5

TAKE IT TO THE STREET.
Tracks: / Homeless / Got to be real / Do be down / Who was that lady / On and on / He's a fly guy / Don't push / I mo git U sucka.
LP: . . . . CUR 2008
MC: . . . . MCCUR 2008

THERE'S NO PLACE LIKE AMERICA TODAY.
LP: . . . . CUR 2003
MC: . . . . ZCUR 2003

THIS YEAR.
Tracks: / This year (pt 1) / This year (pt 2).
LP: . . . . RSO 28

WE COME IN PEACE.
LP: . . . . CRC 2001
MC: . . . . CRC 2001 MC

Mayfield, Percy

HIT THE ROAD AGAIN.
LP: . . . . SJP 170

MY HEART IS ALWAYS SINGING SAD SONGS.
Tracks: / I need love so bad / It's good to see you baby / Nightmare / Hunt is on / My heart / Lonesome highway / You don't exist no more / Bachelor blues, The / Proposal / Come home / One room country shack / Ain't gonna cry no more / Does anyone care for me / I dare you baby / Wasted dream / Big question, The.
LP: . . . . CHD 153

PERCY MAYFIELD.
Tracks: / Life is suicide / Hunt is on, The / Hopeless / My heart is crying / Baby, you're rich / My blues / I dare you, baby / Memory pain / You are my future / Get way back / Advice (for men only) / Lonesome highway / Kiss tomorrow goodbye / Strange things happening / Ruthie Mae / Pease send me someone to love / Hit the road, Jack / Prayin' for your return / What a fool I was / Lost love / Nightless lover / Cry baby / Lost mind / River's invitation, The / Big question, The / Wasted dream / Louisiana / Bachelor blues, The / Loose lips / You don't exist no more / Nightmare.
LP: . . . . CHD 283

VOICE WITHIN, THE.
Tracks: / How wrong can a good man be / Leary blues / Hunt is on, The / Hopeless / Two hearts are greater than one / Lonesome highway / I dare you, baby / How deep is the well / Lonely one, The / Bachelor blues, The / Sugar mama - peachy papa / Voice within, The / My heart / Are you out there / Bluest blues / Blues blues.
LP: . . . . KIX 22

Maynard, George

RUMPSY BUMPSY.
Tracks: / Poor old weaver's daughter, The / Talks about himself (Spoken word) / Irish hop pole puller, The / Oxford City murder / Prickle thorn bush, The / Three sons o'rogues / Down by the seaside / Story / two riddles (Spoken word) / Rolling in the dew / Marble championships, Tinsley Green (Spoken word) / Banks of Claudy, The / Birds in the spring / Jones's ale / Lakes of Coolfin / Banks of the sweet primroses / Frank Taylor, tooting murder / Broomfield wager / Pretty Susan / Pride of Kildare, The.
MC: 60-080

YE SUBJECTS OF ENGLAND (Traditional songs from Sussex).
LP: 12T 286

Mayne, Lynda

MY FAVOURITE 14 COUNTRY SONGS.
Tracks: / Rose garden / Tennessee waltz / Crazy dreams / Tear fell, A / I fall to pieces / Just out of reach.
MC: . . . . CPHL 445

Mayne, Natasha

TOUCH (See under Diamond Cut) (Diamond Cut feat. Natasha Mayne).

Mayor Of Casterbridge

MAYOR OF CASTERBRIDGE (see under Hardy, Thomas) (Bates, Alan).

Mayor, Simon

MANDOLIN ALBUM, THE.
MC: . . . . ACSC 012

SECOND MANDOLIN ALBUM.
MC: . . . . ACSC 014

Mayorga, Lincoln

GROWING UP IN HOLLYWOOD TOWN (see under McBroom, Amanda) (Mayorga, Lincoln & Amanda McBroom).

LINCOLN MAYORGA AND DISTINGUISHED COLLEAGUES, VOL 3.
LP: . . . . LAB 1

WEST OF OZ (Mayorga, Lincoln & Amanda McBroom).
LP: . . . . LAB 15

Mays, Lyle

AS FALLS WICHITA, SO FALLS WICHITA FALLS (See under Metheny, Pat) (Mays, Lyle & Pat Metheny).

LYLE MAYS.
Tracks: / Highland aire / Teiko / Slink / Mirror of the heart / Alaskan suite: Northern Lights invocation ascent / Close to home.
LP: 9240971
MC: 9240974

SWEET DREAMS.
LP: 924 204-1
MC: 924 204-4

Mays, Rev. Oris L.

GOD CAN DO IT (Mays, Rev. Oris L. & The Bostonians).
Tracks: / God is able / Everybody ought to know / I need thee / Unchanging love / I've been changed / God can do it / Haven of rest.
LP: . . . . MIR 5014
MC: . . . . ZCMIR 5014

Maytals

DO THE REGGAE 1966-70.
Tracks: / Bam bam / 54-46 was my number / Struggle / Reborn / Just tell me / Do the reggae / Hold on / Don't trouble trouble / Alidina / Oh yeah / Sweet and dandy / Johnny cool man / Night and day.
LP: . . . . ATLP 103

TOOTS PRESENTS THE MAYTALS.
Tracks: / Black rose / Big splash down / Cash box / Dub a little reggae / Disco reggae / La la song / Give us a piece of the action / Virgo / Live with your brother / Mister music.
LP: . . . . ETAT 16

Maytime

MAYTIME (Radio soundtrack) (Various artists).
LP: . . . . SH 2008
MC: . . . . CSH 2008

Maytones

AFRICA WE WANT TO GO.
LP: . . . . BS 012

BEST OF THE MAYTONES.
Tracks: / Judgement a come / Boat to Zion / Do good / Music is a part of life / Zion land / Ital Queen / God bless the day / Who feels it / Don't show off / When will peace be / Madness / Contiquros.
LP: . . . . BS 1052
MC: . . . . BSC 1052

MADNESS.
LP: . . . . BS 1002

ONLY YOUR PICTURE.
LP: . . . . VSLP 4076

Mazarati

MAZARATI.
Tracks: / Players ball / Lonely girl on Bourbon Street / 100 m.p.h. / Stroke / Suzy / Strawberry lover / I guess it's all over.
LP: 925368 1
MC: 925368 4

Maze

CAN'T STOP THE LOVE (Maze featuring Frankie Beverly).
Tracks: / Back in stride / Can't stop the love / Reaching down inside / Too many games / I want to feel I'm wanted / Magic / Place in my heart, A.
LP: . . . . MAZE 1
MC: . . . . TC MAZE 1
LP: . . . . EJ 2402881
MC: . . . . EJ 2402884

GOLDEN TIME OF DAY (Maze featuring Frankie Beverly).
Tracks: / Travelling man / Song for my mother / You're not the same / Working together / Golden time of day / I wish you well / I need you.
LP: . . . . CAPS 1040
MC: TC2GO 1866849

INSPIRATION.
Tracks: / Lovely inspiration / Feel that you're feelin' / Call on me / Timin' / Welcome home / Woman is a wonder / Ain't it strange.
LP: . . . . EST 11912

JOY AND PAIN (Maze featuring Frankie Beverly).
Tracks: / Changing times / Look in your eyes / Family / Roots / Joy and pain / Southern girl / Happiness.
LP: . . . . EST 12087
MC: . . . . TCEST 12087

LIFELINES VOL. 1 (Maze featuring Frankie Beverly).
Tracks: / Joy and pain (Featuring Kurtis Blow.) / golden time of day / Happy

feelin's / Back in stride / Before I let go (Featuring Woody Wood.) / Running away / while I'm alone / Southern girl / Joy and pain (original LP version) / Before I let go (original LP version).
LP: EST 2111
LP: 792 810 1
MC: TCEST 2111
MC: 792 810 4

LIVE IN LOS ANGELES (Maze featuring Frankie Beverly).
Tracks: / Running away / Too many games / I wanna thank you / You / Happy feelin's / Feel that you're feelin' / Joy and pain / Before I let go / Back in stride / I wanna be with you / Freedom / Dee's song / When you love someone.
2LP: ESTSP 24
MCSET: TC2 ESTSP 24

LIVE IN NEW ORLEANS (Maze featuring Frankie Beverly).
Tracks: / Changing times / Joy and pain / Southern girl / Look at California / Feel that you're feelin' / Look in your eyes / Running away / Before I let go / We need love to live / Reason / You (Not on CD.) / Happy feelin's (Not on CD.).
2LP: ESTSP 22
MCSET: TC2 ESTSP 22

MAZE (Maze featuring Frankie Beverly).
Tracks: / Time is on my side / Happy feelin's / Color blind / Lady of magic / While I'm alone / You / Look at California.
LP: CAPS 1039
LP: FA 3202
MC: TCFA 3202

SILKY SOUL.
LP: WX 301
MC: WX 301 C

WE ARE ONE (Maze featuring Frankie Beverly).
Tracks: / Love is the key / Right on time / Your kind of way / I want to thank you / We are one / Never let you down / I love you so much / Metropolis.
LP: EST 12262
MC: TC EST 12262

Mazel, Judy

LIFE IN THE SLIM LANE.
Tracks: / Over the rainbow / Why? because I'm fat / I don't like me / Why can't I be like other kids / Problems of your own / Excuses, excuses / I hate being fat / Positive talkback / Best friend and lover / Mirror mirror / Insult to injury / Nothing's leaving the planet / Hymn for slim.
LP: CBS 25504
MC: 40 25504

Mazelle, Kym

BRILLIANT.
Tracks: / No one can love you more than me (Boilerhouse version) / Useless (I don't need you now) / Don't scandalise my name (U.S. remix) / Skin I'm in / Love strain / Missing you (soul to soul remix) / Never in a million years (Doc & James remix) / Crazy 'bout the man (Frankie knuckles mix) / Was that all it was (David Morales mix).
LP: PCS 7354
MC: TCPCS 7354

CRAZY.
Tracks: / Love strain / No one can love you more than me / This love will never die / Don't scandalize my name / Wait (short) / Just what it takes / Was that all it was / Don't make me over / Got to get you back / Crazy 'bout the man / Never in a million years / Useless (I don't need you now) / Can't make nobody love you.
LP: SYLP 6004
MC: TCSYLP 6004
LP: 793 382 1

WAIT (see under Howard, Robert) (Mazelle, Kym & Robert Howard).

Mazeltones

MESHUGGE FOR YOU.
MC: GVMMC 137

ODESSA, WASHINGTON.
MC: GVMMC 118

SEATTLE, ROMANIA.
MC: GVMMC 103

Mazina

MAZINA (African music by two native musicians).
LP: ASF 6001

Mazique

RADAR LOVE.
LP: RAGEX 1

Mazuhashi, Takashi

GON'S DELIGHT (Mazuhashi, Takashi & his friends).
LP: YX 7540

Mazzy, Jimmy

SHAKE IT DOWN (Mazzy, Jimmy and Eli Newberger).
LP: SOS 1109

Mazzy Starr

SHE HANGS BRIGHTLY.
LP: ROUGH 158
MC: ROUGHC 158

M'Banga, Lapiro

NO MAKE ERREUR.
LP: TSHI 003

Mbarga, Prince Nico

FREE EDUCATION.
LP: ROUNDER 5011
MC: ROUNDER 5011C

SWEET MOTHER.
LP: ROUNDER 5007
MC: ROUNDER 5007C

M'Bilia Bell

DANS KENYA ET CADANCE MUDANA (M'Bilia Bell/Tabu Ley).
LP: GEN 114

M'boom

COLLAGE.
Tracks: / Circles / It's time / Jamaican sun / Street dance / Mr. Seven / Quiet place, A.
LP: SN 1059

Mbuli, Mzwakhe

CHANGE IS PAIN.
Tracks: / Many years ago / Behind the bars / Drum beats, The / Now is the time / Change is pain / Day shall dawn, The / Ignorant / Triple M / What a shame / I have travelled / Spear has fallen, The / Last struggle, The / Ngizwa ubgina bguzwa usajako / Sisi bayasinyanyisa.
LP: PIR 3
LP: ROUNDER 4024

M.C.5

BABES IN ARMS.
MC: A 122
LP: DANLP 031

BACK IN THE USA.
Tracks: / Tutti frutti / Tonight / Teenage lust / Let me try / Looking at you / High school / Call me animal / American ruse, The / Shakin' street / Human being lawnmower, The / Back in the USA.
LP: K 50346

KICK OUT THE JAMS.
Tracks: / Ramblin' rose / Kick out the jams / Come together / Rocket reducer No.62 / Borderline / Motor city is burning / I want you right now / Starship.
LP: K 42027

M.C. 900ft Jesus

HELL WITH THE LID OFF.
Tracks: / Greater God, A / UFO's are real / I'm going straight to heaven / Talking to the spirits / Place of lonliness, A / Real black angel / Shut up / Spaceman / Too bad.
LP: NET 015

M.C. Breed

M.C. BREED & DFC (M.C. Breed & D.F.C.).
Tracks: / Underground slang / Job corp / That's life / Ain't no future in yo' frontin' / Just kickin' it / Better terms / I will excell / Get loose / Black for black / Guanja / More power.
LP: SDE 4103
MC: SDE 4103 MC

M.C. Buzz B

WORDS ESCAPE ME.
LP: 8490671
MC: 8490674

M.C. Cool P

NO MORE MR MISTER NICE GUY (See under Z, Hustle) (M.C. Cool P & Hustle Z).

SHOW ME YOURS AND I'LL SHOW YOU MINE (See under Z, Hustle) (M.C. Cool P & Hustle Z).

M.C. Duke

ORGANISED RHYME.
Tracks: / Organised rhyme / We go to work / Free / Throw your hands in the air / I'm riffin' / Miracles / For the girls / Gotta get your own / Running man / Alternative argument, The.
LP: DUKE 1
MC: DUKE 1C

M.C. Hammer

LET'S GET IT STARTED.
Tracks: / Intro: Turn this mutha out / Let's get it started / Ring 'em / Cold go M.C. Hammer / You're being served / It's gone / They put me in the mix / Son of the king / That's what I said / Feel my power / Pump it up (here's the news).
LP: EST 2108
LP: 790 924 1
MC: TCEST 2108
MC: 790 924 4

LET'S GET IT STARTED (RE-ISSUE).
Tracks: / Intro: Turn this mutha out / Let's get it started (radio edit) / Ring 'em / Cold go M.C. Hammer / You're being served / Turn this mutha out (edit) / It's gone / (Hammer, Hammer) they put me in the mix (edit) / Son of the king / That's what I said / Feel my power / Pump it up (here's the news) (radio edit).
LP: EST 2140
MC: TCEST 2140

PLEASE HAMMER DON'T HURT 'EM.
Tracks: / Here comes the Hammer / U can't touch this / Have you seen her / Yo sweetness (Not on album.) / Help the children (Incorporates Mercy Mercy, Me.) / On your face / Dancin' machine / Pray / Crime story / She's soft and wet / Black is black (Not on album.) / Let's go deeper (W) / Work this (CD only.).
LP: EST 2120
LP: 792 857 1
MC: TCEST 2120
MC: 792 857 4

YOU'VE GOT ME DANCIN' (See under Goldsmith, Glen) (Goldsmith, Glen & MC Hammer).

M.C. Lyte

LYTE AS A ROCK.
Tracks: / Lyte vs Vanna Whyte / Lyte as a rock / I am woman / M C Lyte likes swingin' / 10 dis / Paper thin / Lyte thee MC / I cram to understand U / Kickin' 4 Brooklyn / Don't cry big girls.
LP: K 790905-1
MC: K 790905-4

M.C. Mello

MINCALOR (See under Dibango, Manu) (M.C. Mello & Manu Dibango).

THOUGHTS RELEASED.
Tracks: / Our time / Let the crowd catch breath / All terrain M.C.'s / Subtraction / From the heart / Total eclipse of the art, A / Voodoo khan / Open up your mind / Acknowledge yourself.
LP: LICLP 015
MC: LICMC 015

M.C. Merlin

WHO'S IN THE HOUSE (See under Beatmasters) (M.C. Merlin/ Beatmasters).

M.C. Shan

BORN TO BE WILD.
Tracks: / I pioneered this / Back to the basics / Born to be wild / Juice crew law / They used to do it out in the park / Give me my freedom / Go for yours / She's gone / Words of freestyle / Never rock a party.
LP: 925979 1
MC: 925783 4

DOWN BY LAW.
Tracks: / Jane, stop this crazy thing! / Project ho' / Bridge, The / Kill that noise / Down by law / Left me - lonely / Another one to get jealous of / M.C. Space / Living in the world of hip hop.
LP: K 925676 1
MC: K 925676 4

PLAY IT AGAIN SHAN.
LP: 7599261551
MC: 7599261554

M.C. Trouble

GOTTA GET A GRIP.
Tracks: / (I wanna) make you mine / Push up, The / Gotta get a grip / Fly guy / Black line / Here comes trouble / Power move / Thing for you / Points proven / Well equipped / Is it live? / Body.
LP: ZL 72715
MC: ZK 72715

M.C. Tunes

NORTH AT ITS HEIGHTS, THE.
LP: ZTT 3
MC: ZTT 3 C

M'Carver, Kimberly

BREATHE THE MOONLIGHT.
Tracks: / Silver wheeled pony / Whistle down the wind / Cryin' wolf / Borrowed time / Only in my dreams / Jose's lullaby / Springtime friends / My way back home to you / Carnival man / Serious doubt / Texas home.
LP: PH 1129
MC: PH 1129C

MCD

WHO'S ROCKIN' Y'ARSE ON THE MIC?.
Tracks: / Who's rockin' y'arse on the mic / I am the law.
MC: BIP 204

MDC

BEST OF MDC 1981-7.
LP: 081 268

ELVIS IN RHEINLAND.
LP: EFA 147

METAL DEVIL COKES.
LP: EFA 1756708

MILLIONS OF DAMN CHRISTIANS.
LP: WEBITE 22

MILLIONS OF DEAD COPS.
LP: VIRUS 26

MORE DEAD COPS.
LP: WEBITE 33

SMOKE SIGNALS (Millions Of Dead Cops).
LP: MDC 4

M.D.M.A.

M.D.M.A. COMPILATION.
LP: CALCLP 073

Me & My Girl

ME AND MY GIRL (London stage cast) (Various artists).
Tracks: / Overture: *Various artists* / Weekend at Hareford, A: *Various artists* / Thinking of no one but me: *Various artists* / Family solicitor, The: *Various artists* / Me and my girl: *Various artists* / English gentleman, An: *Various artists* / You would if you could: *Various artists* / Lambeth walk: *Various artists* / Sun has got his hat on, The: *Various artists* / Once you lose your heart: *Various artists* / Take it on the chin: *Various artists* / Song of Hareford: *Various artists* / Love makes the world go round: *Various artists* / Leaning on a lamp post: *Various artists* / If only you cared for me: *Various artists* / Finale: *Various artists*.
LP: EJ 2403011
MC: EJ 2403014

ME AND MY GIRL (Original Broadway Cast) (Various artists).
LP: TER 1145
MC: ZCTER 1145

Me & The Colonel

ME & THE COLONEL (Film Soundtrack) (Various artists).
LP: LOC 1046

Me & You

ACCESS TO FILE.
LP: THTLP 001

Mead, Cheryl

LIVING IN THE LOVE (see under Turner, Ruth) (Mead, Cheryl & Ruth Turner).

Meader, Vaughn

FIRST FAMILY, THE.
LP: HAA 8048
LP: GNPS 7002
MC: GNP5 7002

Meadow

MEADOW, THE/LITTLE NUNS Film soundtrack (Various artists).
LP: C'BUS 115

Meadows, Marion

FOR LOVERS ONLY.
Tracks: / I found a new love / Forbidden love / Sleepless nights / For lovers only / Real thing, The / Personal touch / Paradise / Wonderland / Dear world / Just before dawn.
LP: PL 83097
MC: PK 83097

Meal Ticket

CODE OF THE ROAD.
LP: INS 3008

KEEPIN' THE FAITH.
LP: MACH 9

TAKE AWAY.
Tracks: / Why in the world / Down on my knees after Memphis / Lucy / Lone star motel / Shape I'm in / Blame / Simple / Bonnie Lee's dinette / At the funny farm / Get on board.
LP: LOGO 1008

THREE TIMES A DAY.
LP: INS 3010

Mean Red Spiders

DARK HOURS.
MC: GBMC 1
LP: GBLP 1

NUDE GUITARIST IN WET LETTUCE FRENZY.
LP: MRS 1

Meanstreak

ROADKILL.
Tracks: / Roadkill / Nostradamus / Lost stranger / Congregation, The / Searching forever / It seems to me / Warning, The.
LP: MFN 89
MC: TMFN 89

Mearns, John

HAME AND GUID NICHT WITH JOHN MEARNS.
LP: WGR 073
MC: CWGR 073

WAG AT THE WA, THE.
Tracks: / Wag at the wa, The / Bonnie Udny / Maggie Jardine / Farm yard gate.

The / Flat footed Jean / Oor fairm toon / Braes of Bonald / Tillietudlem Castle / Roving ploughboy, The / When I was twenty one / Lassie wi the yellow coatie / Wee drappie o't, A / Ship that never returned, The / Auld meal mill, The.
MC: . . . . **CWGR 123**

Measure For Measure

MEASURE FOR MEASURE (see under Shakespeare, William) (Various artists).

Meat Beat Manifesto

99%.
LP: . . . . **BIAS 180**

ARMED AUDIO WARFARE.
LP: . . . . **LD 9048**
MC: . . . . **LD 9048 MC**

STORM THE STUDIO.
2LP: . . . . **SDX 040**

SUCK HARD.
LP: . . . . **SAX 029**

VERSION GALORE.
LP: . . . . **BIAS 192**

Meat Puppets

HUEVOS.
LP: . . . . **SST 150**

MEAT PUPPETS.
LP: . . . . **SST 019**

MIRAGE.
LP: . . . . **SST 100**
MC: . . . . **SSTC 100**

MONSTERS.
LP: . . . . **SST 253**
MC: . . . . **SSTC 253**

OUT MY WAY.
LP: . . . . **SST 049**

UP ON THE SUN.
LP: . . . . **SST 039**

Meatballs

MEATBALLS (Film soundtrack) (Various artists).
Tracks: / Are you ready for the summer?: *Camp North Star Kids Chorus* / Makin' it: *Naughton, David* / Moondust: *Black, Terry* / Good friend: *MacGregor, Mary* / Meatballs: *Dees, Rick* / CIT song: *Various artists* / Rudy and tripper: *Various artists* / Olympiad: *Various artists* / Rudy wins the race: *Various artists*.
LP: . . . . **RSS 11**

Meatfly

MEATFLY.
LP: . . . . **FACE 10**

Meatloaf

12" TAPE: MEAT LOAF.
Tracks: / Bat out of hell / Dead ringer for love / Read 'em and weep / If you really want to / Razor's edge.
MC: **4501314**

BAD ATTITUDE.
Tracks: / Bad attitude / Modern girl / Nowhere fast / Surf's up / Piece of the action / Jumping the gun / Cheatin' in your dreams / Don't leave your mark on me / Sailor to a siren.
LP: . . . . **FA 413 150 1**
MC: . . . . **FA 413 150 4**
LP: **206619**
MC: **406619**
LP: . . . . **FA 3150**
MC: . . . . **TCFA 3150**

BAT OUT OF HELL.
Tracks: / You took the words right out of my mouth / Heaven can wait / All revved up with no place to go / Two out of three ain't bad / Bat out of hell / For cryin' out loud / Paradise by the dashboard light / Praying for the end of time / Man and woman / Dead ringer for love.
LP: . . . . **EPC 82419**
MC: **40 82419**
LP: **82419**

BAT OUT OF HELL/ HIT OUT OF HELL.
LP: . . . . **EPC ML 241**

BLIND BEFORE I STOP.
Tracks: / Execution day / Rock 'n' roll mercenaries / Getting away with murder / One more kiss (night of the soft parade) / Blind before I stop / Burning down / Standing on the outside / Masculine / Man and a woman, A / Special girl / Rock 'n' roll here.
LP: **207741**
MC: **407741**

CHRIS TETLEY INTERVIEWS MEATLOAF.
LPPD: . . . . **CT 1003**

DEAD RINGER.
Tracks: / Peel out / I'm gonna love her for both of us / More than you deserve / I'll kill you if you don't come back / Read 'em and weep / Nocturnal pleasure / Dead ringer for love / Everything is permitted.
LP: . . . . **EPC 32692**
MC: **40 32692**
LP: . . . . **EPC 83645**

DEAD RINGER FOR LOVE (OLD GOLD) (See under Tyler, Bonnie/Total eclipse of...).

HEAVEN AND HELL (See under Tyler, Bonnie for details) (Meat Loaf/Bonnie Tyler).

HITS OUT OF HELL.
Tracks: / Bat out of hell / Read 'em and weep / Midnight at the lost and found / To out of three ain't bad / Dead ringer for love / Modern girl / I'm gonna love her for both of us / You took the words right out of my mouth (Hot Summer night) / Razor's edge / Paradise by the dashboard light.
LP: . . . . **EPC 26156**
MC: **40 26156**
LP: **4504471**
MC: **4504474**

LIVE: MEAT LOAF.
Tracks: / Blind before I stop / Rock 'n' roll mercenaries / Took the words / Midnight at the lost and found / Modern girl / Paradise by the dashboard light / Two out of three ain't bad / Bat out of hell / Masculine (This track on cassette and CD only.) / Rock and roll medley (This track on cassette and CD only.).
LP: **208599**
MC: **408599**

MEAT LOAF FEATURING STONEY & MEAT LOAF.
Tracks: / Jimmy Bell / She waits by the window / It takes all kinds of people / Stone heart / Who is the leader of the people / What you see is what you get / Kiss me again / Sunshine / Jessica White / Lady be mine / Everything under the sun.
LP: . . . . **PDL 2010**
MC: . . . . **CPDL 2010**
LP: . . . . **ZL 72217**

MIDNIGHT AT THE LOST AND FOUND.
Tracks: / Razor's edge / Midnight at the Lost and found / Wolf at your door / Keep driving / Promised land / You never can be too sure about that girl / Priscilla / Don't you look at me like that / If you really want to / Fallen angel.
LP: **4503601**
MC: **4503604**
LP: . . . . **EPC 25243**

PRIMECUTS.
Tracks: / Modern girl / Getting away with murder / Bat out of hell (live) / Surfs up / Blind before I stop / Bad attitude / Jumpin' the gun / Two out of three ain't bad (live) / Paradise by the dashboard light (live) / Rock 'n' roll mercenaries.
LP: **210.363**
MC: **410.363**

Meatmen

CRIPPLED CHILDREN SUCK.
LP: . . . . **TGLP 59**
MC: . . . . **TG 59 C**

Meazza, Max

BETTER LATE THAN NEVER.
Tracks: / Better late than never.
LP: . . . . **AP 045**

PERSONAL EXILE.
LP: . . . . **AP 030**

SHARING THE CAR.
LP: . . . . **AP 018**

Mecano

DONDE EST EL PAIS DE LAS HADES.
LP: . . . . **S 25497**
MC: **40 25497**

Mechali, Francois

CONVERSATIONS (Mechali, Francois/ Beb Guerin).
Tracks: / Rappel / Grand II / Arca.
LP: . . . . **NATO 5**

LE GRANDIER VOLTIGEUR.
Tracks: / Offrande (1re partie: decocher) / Offrande (2re partie: decocher) / Arca / Duo / Ensemble (1) / Kenny Wheeler solo / Ensemble (2).
LP: . . . . **NATO 70**

Mechanical Instruments

DEVON MUSEUM OF MECHANICAL MUSIC (Various artists).
Tracks: / Rag melody: *Various artists* / Nights of gladness: *Various artists* / Victorious eagle: *Various* artists / Geisha's life, The: *Various artists* / Lady's maid: *Various artists* / Private Tommy Atkins: *Various* artists / Dinah: *Various artists* / Entertainer and the new rag, The: *Various artists* / Indiana: *Various* artists / Colonel Bogey: *Various artists* / Lady farmer's dance: *Various artists* / Liechtensteiner polka: *Various artists*.
LP: . . . . **SDLB 314**
MC: . . . . **CSDL 314**

GOLDEN AGE OF MECHANICAL MUSIC (Various artists).
LP: . . . . **SDSAM 218**

MECHANICAL INSTRUMENTS From the Paul Corin collection vol.2 (Various).
LP: . . . . **RESM 022**

MECHANICAL MUSIC HALL (Various).
Tracks: / Burlington Bertie from Bow / After the ball / Nellie Dean / Where did you get that hat? / K-K-K-Katy / Flanagan / Down at the old Bull and Bush / Lily of Laguna / If it wasn't for the 'ouses in between / Bill Bailey won't you please come home / Beside the seaside / Ask a policeman / Don't have any more, Mrs. Moore / Any old iron / My old dutch / Boiled beef and carrots / Ta-ra-ra-boom-de-ay.
MC: . . . . **CSDL 232**
LP: . . . . **SDL 232**

MUSIC FOR THE MAGIC LANTERN.
Tracks: / Rule Britannia / Pomona / Man who broke the bank at Monte Carlo / Oh oh Antonio / Whistling Rufus / Dandy Queen / Messenger boy / Goodbye-ee / Put me amongst the girls / At Trinity Church I met my doom / Colonel Bogey / Softly awakes my heart / I've got a motto / Xenia / Latter polka / Molly O Morgan / Get out and get under the moon / Roamin' in the gloamin' / Little Dolly Daydream / Charmaine / Honeysuckle and the bee, The / Bicycle barn dance polka / Soldiers of the Queen / Goodbye Dolly Gray / Let the great big world keep turning.
LP: . . . . **SDL 297**
MC: . . . . **CSDL 297**

MUSIC OF THE STREETS (Mechanical Street Entertainment) (Barrel Organ...).
Tracks: / Man who broke the bank at Monte Carlo, The / I've got a lovely bunch of coconuts / Charmaine / Oh, oh, Antonio / La Marseillaise / Pomone waltz / Rule Britannia / Honeysuckle and the bee, The / Just one girl / Bicycle barn dance polka / Bells of St. Mary's / Soldiers of the Queen / Goodbye Dolly Gray / Molly O'Morgan / Little Dolly Daydream / Roamin' in the gloamin' / He had to get out and get under / At Trinity Church / Let the great big world keep turning.
LP: . . . . **SDL 340**
MC: . . . . **CSDL 340**

REGINA SINGS OPERA (Regina music box-Bornand Collection) (Various).
Tracks: / La traviata - Drinking song / La traviata - Chorus of the matadors / Stabat mater / Toreador song / Tannhauser overture / Tannhauser grand march / Il Travatore grand march / Il Travatore Gypsies chorus / Barber of Seville / William Tell / Les Huguenots chorus / Les Huguenots Benediction of swords / Freischutz huntsmen's chorus / Freischutz overture / Cavalleria rusticana (inst) / Faust - soldiers chorus / Oberon - barcarolle / Salome (Intermezzo) / Ernani - grand march / Barber of Seville.
LP: . . . . **RCB 6**
MC: . . . . **RHCB C 6**

ROAD TO HEAVEN, THE.
Tracks: / Abide with me / Judas Maccabaeus / Lost chord, The / When I survey the wondrous cross / How sweet the name of Jesus sounds / Lead kindly light / Nearer my God to thee / All people that on Earth do dwell / Shall we meet beyond the river? / Only an armour bearer / I will sing of my Redeemer / Scatter seeds of kindness / Shall we gather at the river? / Beaulah land / Holy City, The / O worship the King / Christians awake / Awake my soul / Morning hymn / Evening hymn / Onward Christian soldiers / Rescue the perishing / What shall the harvest be? / We'll work 'til Jesus comes / Washed in the blood of the Lamb / Safe in the arms of Jesus / What a friend we have in Jesus / Glorious things of Thee are spoken / Sicilian mariners / Luther's hymn / Mount Ephraim / God save the Queen.
LP: . . . . **SDL 331**
MC: . . . . **CSDL 331**

VICTORIA SUNDAY, A (Various artists).
Tracks: / Abide with me: *Various artists* / Judas Maccabaeus: *Various artists* / Lost chord (sullivan), The: *Various* artists / When I survey the wondrous cross: *Various artists* / How sweet the name of Jesus sounds: *Various artists*/ Lead kindly light: *Various artists* / Nearer my god to thee: *Various artists* / Shall we meet beyond the river: *Various artists* / Only an armour bearer: *Various artists* / I will sing of my redeemer: *Various artists*/ Scatter seeds of kindness: *Various artists* / Shall we gather at the river: *Various artists* / Beaulah land: *Various artists* / Hold City, The: *Various artists* / Morning hymn: *Various artists* / Evening hymn: *Various* artists / Onward Christian Soldiers: *Various artists* / Rescue the perishing: *Various artists* / What shall the harvest be: *Various artists* / We'll work til Jesus comes: *Various artists* / Washed in the blood of the lamb: *Various artists* / What a friend we have in Jesus: *Various artists* / Sicilian mariners: *Various artists*/ Helmsley: *Various artists* / Luther's hymn: *Various artists* / London new: *Various artists* / Mountain Ephraim: *Various artists* / God save the Queen: *Various artists*.
MC: . . . . **CS-DL 331**

WORLD OF MECHANICAL MUSIC (Various artists).
Tracks: / Every little breeze: *Various artists* / I lift up my finger: *Various artists* / Yellow dog blues: *Various* artists / Wedding of the painted doll, The: *Various artists* / Flapperette: *Various artists* / Amarantina: *Various artists*.
MC: . . . . **CSDLB 292**

WORLD OF MECHANICAL ORGANS (Various artists).
LP: . . . . **SPA 115**
MC: . . . . **KCSP 115**

Mechanical Organs

FAIR ORGAN MELODIES.
MC: . . . . **AC 140**

GAUDIN MELODIES.
Tracks: / Alexander's ragtime band / My blue Heaven / I'll see you in my dreams / Dinah / Lady of Spain / Miss Annabelle Lee.
MC: . . . . **AC 189**

MORTIER ORGAN FAVOURITES.
Tracks: / Blue Danube / Can-can / Washington Post / Roll out the barrel / Manhattan / Skaters' waltz.
MC: . . . . **AC 190**

POPPER'S HAPPY JAZZ BAND AND THE RUTH FAIR ORGAN.
Tracks: / Silver threads among the gold / Two lovely black eyes.
MC: . . . . **CSDLB 263**

SUMMERTIME SERENADE.
MC: . . . . **AC 188**

Meco

ACROSS THE GALAXY.
Tracks: / Superman / Star wars / Can you read my mind / Star Trek medley / Black hole / Moondancer / Close Encounters of the Third Kind suite / Wizard of Oz.
LP: . . . . **FL 43242**

ENCOUNTERS OF EVERY KIND.
Tracks: / Time machine / In the beginning / Roman nights / Lady Marion / Icebound / Hot in the saddle / Crazy rhythm / Topsy / Meco's theme / 3W.57 / Close Encounters of the Third Kind suite.
LP: . . . . **XL 13050**
MC: . . . . **XK 13050**

IMPRESSIONS OF AN AMERICAN WEREWOLF IN LONDON.
Tracks: / Blue moon / You gotta hurt me / Moon dance / Bad moon rising / No more Mister nice guy / Werewolf loose in London / Werewolf serenade.
LP: **648 006 5**

MOONDANCER.
Tracks: / Moondancer / Love me love me / Dracula / Grazing in the grass / Spooky / Devil delight / Living in the night.
LP: . . . . **XL 13084**

MUSIC INSPIRED BY STAR WARS AND OTHER FILMS.
Tracks: / Imperial attack / Desert and the robot auction, The / Princess appears, The / Land of the sandpeople, The / Princess Leia's theme / Cantina band / Last battle, The / Throne room, The / Galactic funk.
LP: . . . . **XL 13043**
MC: . . . . **XK 13043**

SUPERMAN AND OTHER GALLACTIC HEROES.
Tracks: / Superman, Theme from / Boy wonder / Caped crusader, The / Lord of the jungle / Amazing Amazon.
LP: . . . . **XL 13070**

Medals

BLUE BLOOD.
MC: . . . . **PCN 128**

Medeiros, Glenn

GLENN MEDEIROS.
Tracks: / Cracked up / Best man, The / Niki / Just like rain / Boyfriend / She ain't worth it / M-U= Blue / Lovely little lady / All I'm missing is you / Doesn't matter anymore.
LP: **8464701**
MC: **8464704**

NOT ME.
Tracks: / Falling / Never get enough of you / I don't want to lose your love / No way out of love / Love always finds a reason / Some day love / Long and

lasting love, A / Heart don't change my mind / I don't wanna say goodnight / Not me / Nothing's gonna change my love for you ('88 style) / You're my woman, you're my lady (Extra track on MC & CD.).
LP: . . . . LONLP 68
MC: . . . . LONC 68

Medema, Ken

FLYING UPSIDE DOWN.
MC: . . . . DAY C 4040

KINGDOM IN THE STREETS.
Tracks: / Don't tell me / Is there a place for dreaming / Those love songs / I saw you / Kingdom in the streets / Barn builder / By the waters of luxury / Corner drugstore Jesus.
LP: . . . . WST 9615
MC: . . . . WC 9615

LOOKING BACK.
Tracks: / Mister Simon / Lead the way / Flyin' like an eagle / Jesu, lover of my soul / Fork in the road / Symphony of praise / Moses / Don't play the game / Sonshiny day.
LP: . . . . WST 9616
MC: . . . . WC 9616

Mediaeval Music

CANTIGAS OF SANTA MARIA (See under Best, Martin) (Best, Martin).

DANTE TROUBADOURS, THE (See under Best, Martin) (Best, Martin).

SONGS OF CHIVALRY (See under Best, Martin) (Best, Martin).

Medicine Head

BEST OF MEDICINE HEAD.
LP: 2485 204
MC: 3201 278

MEDICINE HEAD.
Tracks: / One and one is one / Rising sun / Slip and slide / Pictures in the sky.
MC: 843 901 4

Medieval

MEDIEVAL.
MLP: . . . . NRR 20
MC: . . . . NRC 20

Medieval Players

AL MANERE MINSTRELSYE.
LP: . . . . PLR 052

Meditations

FOR THE GOOD OF MAN.
Tracks: / Mr. Vulture man / Rootsman party / Tin sardin / Wallah up / For the good of man / Bourgeois game / Dem a fight / Man no better than woman / Woman, Woman / Rocking in America.
LP: . . . . GREL 114

GREATEST HITS: MEDITATIONS.
Tracks: / Fly your natty dread / Tricked / Rasta shall conquer / Woman is like a shadow / Standing on the corner / Wake up / Running from Jamaica / Awey mi do / Turn me loose / Ram jam session.
LP: . . . . GREL 69

MEDITATIONS & RELAXATION (Various artists).
LP: . . . . ACH 035
MC: . . . . ACH 035 C

NO MORE FRIEND.
Tracks: / No more friend / Forcing me / Jack on top / Mother love / Book of history / Carpenter rebuild / Fuss and fight / Slick chick / Talk of the town / Big city.
LP: . . . . GREL 52

WAKE UP.
LP: . . . . TWS 929

Mediterranean Melody

MEDITERRANEAN MELODY (Various artists).
MC: . . . . AMP 005

Medium Medium

GLITTER HOUSE, THE.
Tracks: / Hungry so angry / Serbian village / Glitter house / Guru Maharaji / Futher than funk dream / Mice and monsters / That Haiku.
LP: . . . . BRED 19

Medley, Bill

ALL-TIME GREATEST HITS OF BILL MEDLEY, THE.
Tracks: / I'm gonna be strong / He ain't heavy - he's my brother / I've had the time of my life / Brown eyed woman / You've lost that lovin' feeling / American rock 'n' roll / Loving on borrowed time / Little Latin Lupe Lu / I just want to make love to you / Georgia on my mind.
LP: . . . . ZL 71924
MC: . . . . ZK 71924

THEIR TOP HITS (See under Righteous Brothers) (Medley, Bill & The Righteous Brothers).

Medlocke, Rick

RICK MEDLOCKE AND BLACKFOOT (Medlocke,Rick and Blackfoot).
Tracks: / Back on the streets / Staurday night / Closest thing to heaven / Silent type / Reckless boy / Private life / liar / Steady Rockin' / My wild romance / Rock 'n' roll tonight.
LP: 781 743-1
MC: 781 743-4

Medway Poets

MEDWAY POETS, THE.
Tracks: / Muscle horse / Drone / Our future monarch / Bring it on / Mind the gap / Narcissisia / His life / Baby what... / I need lovin' / Ismail the teacher / When I was a ... / Romford / Question / War is like man / Conversation / Super cat saves the day / Octopus weeps for you / Arthur Lowe work bench / Hanna / Nicaragua / Doctor who / Messerschmit / Long legged woman dressed in black / Manager, the / Tchunka witko / Dog fight / Change and death / Glug glug car, The / Spineless creature / Dung beatle, the / Prayer to the god of... / Ghost dance / You make me die / Archbishop romero.
LP: . . . . HANG 15 UP

Medway Sound

FROM THE WATERS OF THE MEDWAY.
LP: . . . . REC 206

Meece, David

CANDLE IN THE RAIN.
LP: . . . . MYR R 1239
MC: . . . . MYR C 1239

CHRONOLOGY.
LP: . . . . MYR R 6844
MC: . . . . MYR C 6844

SEVEN.
LP: . . . . MYR R 1208
MC: . . . . MYR C 1208

Meehan, Tony

DIAMONDS (See under Harris, Jet) (Meehan, Tony & Jet Harris).

DIAMONDS AND OTHER GEMS (See under Harris, Jet) (Meehan, Tony & Jet Harris).

REMEMBERING (see Harris, Jet) (Meehan, Tony & Jet Harris).

Meek, Gary

GARY MEEK.
Tracks: / Shuffle / My song for Donna / Struck by lightning / Cats / Passage / I'll be here / Triple play / Bingo bango bongo / Tours from hell / Hey you / Fun in the D.D.R..
LP: 890031
MC: 890034

Meeks, Carl

JACKMANDORA.
LP: . . . . GREL 132
MC: . . . . GREEN 132

WEH DEM FAH.
LP: . . . . REDLP 12

Meet Me In St Louis

MEET ME IN ST LOUIS (Original Soundtrack) (Various artists).
LP: . . . . HS 5007

Meeting

MEETING, THE.
Tracks: / Groove now and then / Walk your talk / Steppin' out / And I think about it all the time / Meeting, The / African flower / Joyful noise / Cherry blossom / Lowness / Elements of mystery (Only on CD) / Virgin (Only on CD) / Tango (Only on CD).
LP: . . . . GRP 96201
MC: . . . . GRP 96204

Mega City Four

TRANZOPHOBIA.
LP: . . . . DYL 3
MC: . . . . DYC 3

WHO CARES WINS.
LP: . . . . DYL 20

Megabyte

POWERPLAY.
Tracks: / Glow energy / My father was a teacher / Skyline sculptures / Powerplay / Hello, Ralph here / Secret destination.
LP: . . . . THBL 2.049

Megadeth

KILLING IS MY BUSINESS AND BUSINESS IS GOOD.
Tracks: / Last rites / Skin beneath the skin / These boots were made for walking / Rattle head / Looking down the cross / Mechanix.
LP: . . . . MFN 46
LPPD: . . . . MFN 46P
MC: . . . . TMFN 46
2LP: . . . . MFN 46DM

PEACE SELLS....BUT WHO'S BUYING.
Tracks: / Wake up dead / Conjuring, The / Peace sells / Devil's Island / Good morning / Bad omen / I ain't superstitious / My last words / Black Friday.
LP: . . . . EST 2022
MC: . . . . TC EST 2022
LPPD: . . . . ESTP 2022
LP: . . . . FA 3242
MC: . . . . TCFA 3242

RUST IN PEACE.
Tracks: / Holy wars...the punishment due / Hangar 18 / Take no prisoners / Five magics / Poison was the cure / Lucretia / Tornado of souls / Dawn patrol / Rust in peace...Polaris.
LP: . . . . EST 2132
LP: 791 935 1
MC: . . . . TCEST 2132
MC: 791 935 4
LPPD: . . . . ESTPD 2132
LPPD: 791 935 0

SO FAR SO GOOD SO WHAT.
Tracks: / Into the lungs of hell / Set the world afire / Anarchy in the U.K. / Mary Jane / 502 / In my darkest hour / Liar / Hook in mouth.
LP: . . . . EST 2053
MC: . . . . TCEST 2053
LPPD: . . . . ESTP 2053

Meganuisance

CAMBRIDGE NUISANCE '86.
MC: . . . . UNKNOWN

Megatone

OPEN ALL HOURS.
LP: . . . . ISST 176

Mehead

ONE GOOD EYE.
Tracks: / With scissors / Thin skinned / Big breathe / P.Filth Esq / Float / Not friendly / Backwards man / Hippo / Audience is turning on the magician, The / Too much soup / Bag of blood / Interiors.
LP: . . . . MAKE TWO CD

Mehler & Nash

JAZZ PRAISE.
LP: . . . . MM 0132
MC: . . . . TC MM 0132

Mehmed My Hawk

MEHMED MY HAWK (Original Soundtrack) (Various artists).
LP: . . . . TER 1088
MC: . . . . ZCTER 1088

Mehta, Zubin

IN CONCERT (WITH CARRERAS, DOMINGO AND PAVAROTTI) (See under Carreras, Jose).

Meijer, Johnny

BLUE SKIES.
LP: . . . . H 2014

Meirelles

CAMA DE GATO (Meirelles/Senise/Maia/Pantoja).
LP: . . . . RRPL 001

Meislin, Barbara

CARVINGS IN THE CANYON.
LP: . . . . ST 302

Meisner, Randy

ONE MORE SONG.
Tracks: / One more song / Hearts on fire / Gotta get away / Come on back to me / Deep inside my heart / I need you bad / Trouble ahead / White shoes / Anyway bye bye.
LP: . . . . EPC 84531
MC: 40 84531

RANDY MEISNER.
LP: . . . . K 53079

RANDY MEISNER (2).
Tracks: / Never been in love / Darkness of the heart / Jealousy / Tonight / Playin' in the deep end / Strangers / Still runnin' / Nothing is said / Doin' it for Delilah.
LP: . . . . EPC 85913

Mejia Godoy, Luis E

YO SOY DE UN PUEBLO SENCILLO.
LP: . . . . P 88475

Mekong Delta

DANCES OF DEATH (AND OTHER WALKING SHADOWS).
LP: . . . . ARG 230341
MC: . . . . ARG 230342

FINISHED WITH THE DA.
LP: . . . . GWLP 19

MEKONG DELTA.
LP: . . . . AAARRG 004

MUSIC OF ERICH ZANN.
LP: . . . . AAARRG 011
LP: . . . . GWLP 25

PRINCIPLE OF DOUBT, THE.
LP: . . . . AAARRG 19

TOCCATA.
LP: . . . . AAARRG 017

Mekongo, President

BIKUTSI ROBA.
LP: . . . . MH 116
MC: . . . . MHK 116

Mekons

EDGE OF THE WORLD,THE.
LP: . . . . SIN 003

FEAR AND WHISKEY.
LP: . . . . SIN 001

HONKY TONKIN'.
Tracks: / I can't find my money / Hole in the ground / Sleepless nights / Keep hoppin' / Charlie cake park / If they hang you / Prince of darkness / Kidnapped / Sympathy for The Mekons / Spit / Trimdon Grange explosion, The / Please don't let me love you / Gin palace.
LP: . . . . SIN 006
MC: . . . . SINC 006

MEKONS N.Y..
Tracks: / Big zombie / Trouble down south of the border / Story of nothing, The / Flit craft / Prince of darkness / Abernant 84/87 / I can't find my money / Shape I'm in, The / Hard to be human / Beaten or broken / Not long ago / Shanty / Revenge / Sophie / Chivalry.
MC: . . . . A 154

ORIGINAL SIN.
LP: . . . . SIN 001R

QUALITY OF MERCY IS NOT STRONG, THE.
Tracks: / Like spoons no more / Join us in the countryside / Rosanne / Trevira trousers / After 6 / What are we going to do tonight / What / Watch the film / Beetroot / I saw you dance / Lonely and wet / Dan dare / Teeth (Only on CD.) / Guardian (Only on CD.) / Kill (Only on CD.) / Stay cool (Only on CD.) / Work all week (Only on CD.) / Unknown wrecks (Only on CD.).
LP: . . . . V 2143

SO GOOD IT HURTS.
Tracks: / I'm not here (1967) / Ghosts of American astronauts / Road to Florida / Johnny Miner / Dora / Poxy lips / Sometimes I feel like Fletcher Christian / Fantastic voyage / Robin Hood / Heart of stone / Maverick / Vengeance / Revenge (CD only.).
LP: . . . . SIN 008
MC: . . . . SINC 008

Mel & Kim

F.L.M.
Tracks: / F.L.M. / Showing out / Respectable / Feel a whole lot better / I'm the one who really loves you / More than words can say / System / From a whisper to a scream / Who's gonna catch you / Showing out (freehold mix) (Parlophone cassette & CD only.) / Respectable (extra beats version) (Parlophone cassette & CD only.).
LP: . . . . SU 2
MC: . . . . ZCSU 2
MC: . . . . TCPCS 7351
LP: . . . . PCS 7351

GREATEST HITS: MEL AND KIM.
Tracks: / Respectable / F.L.M. / I'm the one who really loves you / From a whisper, to a scream / Showing out / Respectable (remix).
MC: . . . . THPA 1235

Melachrino, George

BEYOND THE BLUE HORIZON (Melachrino Strings).
LP: . . . . WW 5042

GERSHWIN AND KERN GALA, A (Melachrino Strings).
LP: . . . . LC 775
MC: . . . . LC C775

MELACHRINO MAGIC (Melachrino,George & His Orchestra).
MCSET: . . . . DTO 10240

ROMANTIC SERENADE (Melachrino Strings).
LP: . . . . LC 776
MC: . . . . LC C776

STARDUST (Melachrino Strings).
Tracks: / Stardust / Misty / Temptation / Alone / Kiss me again / Smile / La vie en rose / Poor butterfly / Mam'selle / Fascination / Among my souvenirs / Chopin nocturne in E-flat.
LP: . . . . LC 773
MC: . . . . LC C773

TIME FOR LOVING, A (Melachrino Strings).
Tracks: / Love walked in / Love is here to stay / Love letters / Stairway to the stars / Fascination / Most beautiful girl in the world, The / You're nobody till somebody loves you / There goes my heart / Love is a many splendoured thing / Time for us, A / Man and a woman, A / You've lost that lovin' feeling.
MCSET: . . . . DTO 10034

Melanie

20 GREATEST HITS: MELANIE.
LP: 261 554 1
MC: 261 554 4

ARABESQUE.
Tracks: / Detroit of Buffalo / It don't matter now / Any way that you want me / Roadburn / Fooling yourself / Too late / Standing on the other side / Love you to loath me / When you're dead and gone / Imaginary heroes / Chances.
LP: RCALP 3078
MC: RCAK 3078

BALLROOM STREETS.
Tracks: / Runnin' after love / Holdin' out / Cyclone / Beautiful sadness / Do you believe / Nickel song / Any guy / What have they done to my song Ma? / I believe / Poet / Save me / Together alone / Ruby Tuesday / Buckle down / Miranda / Brand new key / Ground hog day / Friends and company.
2LP: XL 13073

BEST OF MELANIE.
Tracks: / What have they done to my song, Ma / Lay down (candles in the rain) / Good book / Beautiful people / Mr. Tambourine man / Ruby Tuesday / Nickel song / Animal crackers / Leftover wine / Peace will come.
LP: 252 212 1
MC: 252 212 4

BEST OF MELANIE, THE.
Tracks: / Ruby Tuesday / Brand new key / Animal crackers / Mr. Tambourine man / Baby day / Beautiful people / Save the night / Lay down (candles in the rain) / Close it all / What have they done to my song, Ma / Lay lady lay / Some day I'll be a farmer / Good book / Peace will come according to my plan / Gardens in the city / Nickel song / Pebbles in the sand / Tell me why.
MC: MCTC 011

BORN TO BE.
LP: BDLH 5002

CANDLES IN THE RAIN.
LP: BDLH 5003
LP: 2318 009
LP: MACHM 12
LP: TALP 2
MC: TAMC 2002

COLLECTION: MELANIE.
Tracks: / Somebody loves me / Beautiful people / In the hour / I really loved Harold / Johnny boy / Any guy / I'm back in town / What have they done to my song, Ma? / Lay down (candles in the rain) / Peace will come / Good book / Nickle song / Babe rainbow (reprise) / Carolina on my mind / Ruby Tuesday / Sign in the window / Lay lady lay / Christopher Robin / Animal crackers / I don't eat animals / Psychotherapy / Leftover wine.
2LP: CCSLP 195
MC: CCSMC 195

COWABONGA.
Tracks: / Ruby tuesday / Racing heart / Show you / To be a star / What have they done to the rain / On a lam from a cow / Another lie / Window pain / Lovin' / Prematurely gay / Chosen few / Boy next door, The.
LP: GRUB 12
MC: TGRUB 12

EASYRIDING: MELANIE.
Tracks: / Ruby Tuesday / What have they done to my song Ma? / Brand new key / Lay down (candles in the rain) / Peace will come / Good book / Beautiful people / Mr. Tambourine man / Lay lady lay / Nickel song / Animal crackers / Stop, I don't want to hear it anymore.
MC: KNMC 11007
LP: KNLP 11007

FOUR SIDES OF MELANIE.
LP: 2659 013

GARDEN IN THE CITY.
LP: 2318 054

GATHER ME.
LP: 2322 002

GOOD BOOK.
LP: 2322 001

GREATEST HITS: MELANIE.
LP: MA 10784
MC: MAMC 910784

LEFTOVER WINE.
LP: 2318 011

PHONOGENIC - NOT JUST PRETTY FACE.
Tracks: / Knock on wood / Bon apetite / Spunky / Runnin' after love / We can work it out / I'd rather leave while I'm in love / Let it be me / Yankee man / Record people / California dreamin'.
LP: XL 13056
MC: XK 13056

PROFILE: MELANIE.
LP: 6.24022
MC: CL4 24022

SEVENTH WAVE.
LP: NBL 100

SPOTLIGHT ON MELANIE.
Tracks: / Brand new key / Nickel song, The / Good book / Pebbles in the sand / Save the night / I really loved Harold / What have they done to my song Ma / Beautiful people / Some day I'll be a farmer / Peace will come / Psychotherapy / Mr. Tambourine man / Lay down (candles in the rain) / In the hour / Close to it all / Baby day / Tell me why / Babe rainbow / Ruby Tuesday / Carolina in my mind / Lay lady lay / Garden in the city / Christopher Robin / Leftover wine.
2LP: SPOT 1020
MCSET: ZCSPT 1020

VERY BEST OF MELANIE.
LP: BRLP 23
MC: BRMC 23

Melba, Nellie

NELLIE MELBA.
Tracks: / Mad scene / Hamlet / Valse / Romeo and Juliet / On m'appelle mini / Boheme / Pur dicesti / Ave Maria / Pastorale / Lo, hear the gentle lark / Sur le lac / Away on a hill / Les anges pieurent / Home sweet home.
LP: GVC 501

Meldonian, Dick

IT'S A WONDERFUL WORLD (Meldonian, Dick Trio).
LP: SLP 8076

JERSEY SWING CONCERTS, THE.
Tracks: / Jump the blues away / You gotta try / In a mellow tone / Love for sale / I'll never say "never again" again / Three little words / Jeeps' blues / When you done went / Spring is here / Chicago.
LP: PRO 7058

SOME OF THESE DAYS (Meldonian, Dick & Jersey Swingers).
LP: PRO 7033

SWING GENE ROLAND (Meldonian, Dick & Jersey Swingers).
LP: CLP 150

Melford, Mike

MANDOLIN FANTASY.
LP: FF 023

Meliah Rage

KILL TO SURVIVE.
Tracks: / Beginning of the end / Bates motel / Meliah rage / Deadly existence / Enter the darkness / Impalling doom / Pack, The.
LP: 4632571
MC: 4632574

SOLITARY SOLITUDE.
Tracks: / Solitary solitude / No mind / Decline of rule / Retaliation / Deliver me / Witching, The / Lost life / Swallow your soul / Razor ribbon.
LP: 4666751
MC: 4666754

Melick, Jack

HIS PIANO & ORCHESTRA WITH CHERI GODWIN (Melick, Jack & Cheri Godwin).
LP: CHA 2

JACK MELICK & HIS PIANO & ORCHESTRA.
LP: CHA 1

Melillo, Mike

SEPIA.
LP: VPA 170

Melis, Marcello

MARCELLO MELIS.
LP: BSR 0023

NEW VILLAGE ON THE LEFT.
LP: BSR 0012

Melle, Gil

MINDSCAPE.
Tracks: / Mindscape / Double exposure / Message from Mozambique / Bird of paradise / Blue lion, The / Anti-gravitational / Neon canyons / Swamp girl / Richest man in Bogota, The.
LP: B1 92168
LP: 792 168 1

QUADRAMA (Melle, Gil Quartet).
LP: 1902115

Mellencamp, John

AMERICAN FOOL.
Tracks: / Can you take it / Hurt so good / Jack and Diane / Hand to hold on to / Danger list / Can you fake it / Thundering hearts / China girl / Close enough / Weakest moments.
LP: PRICE 85
MC: PRIMC 85
LP: RVLP 16

BIG DADDY (Cougar, John Mellencamp).
Tracks: / Big daddy of them all / To live / Martha say / Theo and weird Henry / Jackie Brown / Pop singer / Void in my heart / Mansions in heaven / Sometimes a great notion / Country gentleman / J.M.'s question.
LP: 838 220 1
MC: 838 220 4

CHESTNUT STREET INCIDENT.
Tracks: / American dream / Oh, pretty woman / Jailhouse rock / Dream killin' town / Supergirl / Chestnut Street revisited / Good girls / Do you believe in magic / Twentieth Century Fox / Chestnut Street revisited / Sad lady.
LP: CLALP 113
MC: CLAMC 113
LP: MML 602
MC: MMK 602

COLLECTION: JOHN COUGAR MELLENCAMP.
Tracks: / American dream / Oh, pretty woman / Jailhouse rock / Dream killin' town / Supergirl / Chestnut Street revisited / Kid inside / Take what you want / Cheap shot / Side walks and street lights / R. gang / Good girls / Do you believe in magic / Twentieth Century Fox / Chestnut Street revisited / Sad lady / Gearhead / Young genocides / Too young to live / Survive.
2LP: CCSLP 124
MC: CCSMC 124

JOHN COUGAR.
Tracks: / Little night dancin', A / Miami / Do you think that's fair / Welcome to Chinatown / Pray for me / Small paradise / Great midwest / I need a lover / Sugar Marie / Taxi dancer.
LP: PRICE 119
MC: PRIMC 119
LP: RVLP 9
MC: RV 49

KID INSIDE, THE.
Tracks: / Kid inside / Take what you want / Cheap shot / Sidewalks and streetlights / R. Gang / American son / Gearhead / Young genocides / Too young to live / Survive.
LP: CLALP 112
MC: CLAMC 112

LONESOME JUBILEE, THE.
Tracks: / Paper in fire / Down and out in paradise / Check it out / Real life, The / Cherry bomb / We are the people / Empty hands / Hard times for an honest man / Hot dogs and hamburgers / Rooty toot toot.
LP: MERH 109
MC: MERHC 109

NOTHIN' MATTERS.
Tracks: / Hot night in a cold town / Ain't even done with the night / Don't misunderstand me / This time / Make me feel / To M.G. / (Wherever she may be) tonight / Wild angel / Cheapshot.
LP: RVLP 10
MC: RV 410

SCARECROW.
Tracks: / Rain on the scarecrow / Grandma's theme / Small town / Minutes to memories / Lonely ol' night / Face of the nation, The / Justice and independence '85 / Between a laugh and a tear / Rumbleseat / You've got to stand for something / R.O.C.K. in the U.S.A. / Kind of fella I am,The.
LP: RIVH 2
MC: RIVHC 2

UH-HUH.
Tracks: / Crumblin' down / Pink houses / Authority song / Hurt so good / Thundering hearts / Warmer place to sleep.
LP: RIVL 1
MC: RIVLC 1

Mellow Fellows

STREET PARTY.
Tracks: / I've got to find a way / Street party / I've got a feeling / Feels like rain / Driving wheel / We'll be friends / Don't turn your heater down / Since I fell for you / Last night / Me and my woman / Broad daylight.
MC: AC 4793

Mellow Man Ace

ESCAPE FROM HAVANA.
Tracks: / Hip hop creature / Mentirosa / Rhyme fighter / If you were mine / River Cubano / Rap guanco / Mas pingon / Gettin' stupid / Talkapella / B boy in love / En la casa / Enquentren amor.
LP: C1 91295

Mellstock Band

UNDER THE GREENWOOD TREE.
Tracks: / Triumph, The / Ashley's hornpipe / Gipsy hornpipe / One-eyed fiddler, The / Enrico / Lord Nelson's hornpipe / Tink a tink / Fairy dance, The / Morgiana / Pantaloon Quadrille, The / Kiss me my love and welcome / Drops of brandy (2 versions) / Moss roses / Droll Johnny / Flight / Off to Charlestown / Arise and hail the sacred day / Arise and hail the joyful day / Awake and join the cheerful choir / Awake, awake, behold the morning star / Hail happy morn / Rejoice, this glorious day has come / See Heaven's high portal / While shepherds watched their flocks by night / Musical lovers, The.
LP: SDL 360
MC: CSDL 360

Mellstock Quire

MELLSTOCK QUIRE.
LP: FT 3016

Melly, George

16 GOLDEN CLASSICS.
Tracks: / Mississippi mud / Hound dog / This train / Abdul Abulbul Amir / Mama don't allow it / Frankie and Johnny / Send me to the 'lectric chair / I'm a ding dong daddy / My canary has circles under his eyes / Heebie jeebies / Black bottom / Sporting life / Ma Rainey's black bottom / St. Louis blues / Spider crawl / Sent for you yesterday.
LP: UNLP 014
MC: UNMC 014

AIN'T MISBEHAVIN (Melly, George & John Chilton's Feetwarmers).
Tracks: / Ain't misbehavin / Squeeze me / I'm gonna sit right down / Awful lot my gal ain't got, An / Your feet's too big / My very good friend the milkman / Joint is jumpin' / It's a sin to tell a lie / Foolin' myself / Honeysuckle Rose / Blue, turning grey over you / Keepin' out of mischief now / I've got a feeling I'm falling.
LP: NSPL 18602
MC: ZCP 18602
LP: PYL 4
MC: PYM 4

ANYTHING GOES (Melly, George & John Chilton's Feetwarmers).
Tracks: / Route 66 / September song / Maybe not at all / It had to be you / Wrap your troubles in dreams / Chicago / I got what it takes / Then I'll be happy / Anything goes / Someday sweetheart / Life with you / Lock and key.
LP: PYL 15
MC: PYM 15
LP: LLM 3024
MC: LLMK 3024

GEORGE MELLY AND MATES.
LP: OU 2074

GOLDEN HOUR OF GEORGE MELLY.
MC: KGHMC 150

HOMETOWN (Melly, George & John Chilton's Feetwarmers).
Tracks: / Home town / I won't grow old / Sweet Georgia Brown / Boogie woogie man / I'm busy and you can't come in / It's de-lovely / My momma rocks me / Shakin' the blues away / Draggin my heart around / Don't get around much anymore / Thinking blues / Running wild.
LP: UNKNOWN

IT'S GEORGE (Melly, George & The Feetwarmers).
Tracks: / I don't mean a thing / Waiter, the porter & the upstairs maid, The / Boogie woogie man / Gee baby ain't I good to you / Give her a little drop more / Food of love / Rosetta / Hard hearted Hannah / T'ain't no sin / Trouble in mind / Lulu's back in town / All the whores go crazy.
LP: K 56087

LET'S DO IT (Melly, George & John Chilton's Feetwarmers).
Tracks: / Gonna catch you with your britches down / Let's do it / Lady wants some jazz, The / Backwater blues / Monday on, my Monday date / Fannie Brown / Downhearted blues / You're driving me crazy / Hundred years from today / Was I drunk? / T'aint what you do (it's the way that you do it) / On revival day.
LP: N 131
MC: ZCN 131
LP: PYL 5
MC: PYM 5

LIKE SHERRY WINE (Melly, George & John Chilton's Feetwarmers).
Tracks: / Wait till you see my baby do the Charleston / Baby won't you please come home? / You've got the right key but the wrong keyhole / Papa de da da / Way down yonder in New Orleans / Jerry the junker / Beale Street mama / Michigan water blues / Please don't mention your sign / I wanna hot dog for my roll / Dapper Dan / Empty bed blues.
LP: N 140
MC: ZCN 140
LP: PYL 6
MC: PYM 6

MAKIN' WHOOPEE (Melly, George & John Chilton's Feetwarmers).

Tracks: / Goody goody / Sporting life / Makin' whoopee / Shake your can / Someday you'll be sorry / Everybody loves my baby / Watch the birdie / I wish I could shimmy like my sister Kate / Yellow dog blues / I can't give you anything but love / Bye bye boogie.
LP: N 147
MC: ZCN 147
LP: PYL 7
MC: PYM 7

MANY MOODS OF MELLY, THE (Melly, George & John Chilton's Feetwarmers).
Tracks: / Masculine women, feminine men / It's the bluest kind of blues my baby sings / Nobody's sweetheart / Drunk again / Kitchen man / St. Louis blues / Do your duty / As time goes by / Black mountain blues / Give her a little drop more / Send me to the 'lectric chair / Happy feet.
LP: N 6550
MC: ZCN 6550
LP: PYL 8
MC: PYM 8

MELLY IS AT IT AGAIN.
Tracks: / Milenberg joys / Animule ball / Marie Laveau / Jeepers creepers / When my ship comes in / Barrelhouse music / Punch and Judy / Punch drunk mama / Yonder comes the blues / Pennies from Heaven.
LP: K 54084

MELLY SINGS HOAGY (Melly, George & John Chilton's Feetwarmers).
MC: ZCP 18557
LP: PYL 3
MC: PYM 3
LP: NSPL 18557

NUTS (Melly, George & The Feetwarmers).
Tracks: / Doctor Jazz / T'aint nobody's business if I do / Sugar / Sam Jones' blues / If you're a viper / There'll be some changes made / I want a little girl / Nuts / Nobody knows you / Viper mad.
LP: K 36005
MC: K4 46188

PUTTIN' ON THE RITZ.
LP: LLP 135
MC: LLPK 135

RUNNING WILD (Melly, George & John Chilton's Feetwarmers).
LP: N 6562
MC: ZCN 6562
LP: PYL 9
MC: PYM 9

SON OF NUTS.
Tracks: / Old fashioned love / I need a little sugar in my bowl / Good time George / Winnin' boy / Joint is jumpin', The / Buddy Bolden's blues / Heebie jeebies / Kitchen man / Roll 'em Pete / Young woman's blues / Show me the way to go home.
LP: K 46269
LP: K 36006

Melodeons

CLEVELAND LONG SWORD DANCE MUSIC.
MC: 30-111

Melodians

IRIE FEELING.
LP: RAS 3003

PREMEDITATION.
LP: SKYLP 18

SWEET SENSATION.
LP: IRSP 13

Melodie, Ms

DIVA.
Tracks: / Intro / Remember when / Wake up wake up / Roll on over / More / Sneaking out / Live on stage / B B B Bklyn / What do you do / To sing all night / Communication / Shaka beats.
LP: HIP 91
MC: HIPC 91

Melody

MELODY (Film Soundtrack) (Various artists).
Tracks: / In the morning: *Various artists* / In the morning (reprise): *Various artists* / Melody fair: *Various* artists / Melody fair (reprise): *Various artists* / Spicks and specks: *Various artists* / Romance: *Various* artists / Theme in F: *Various artists* / Give your best: *Various artists* / To love somebody: *Various* artists / Working on it night and day: *Various artists* / First of May: *Various artists* / First of May (reprise): *Various artists* / Seaside banjo: *Various artists* / Teachers chase: *Various artists* / Teach your children: *Various artists.*
MC: 3170 032
LP: 2383 043

Melody, Bobby

LIVESTOCK.
LP: UNKNOWN

TWO UPRISING STARS (see Singie Singie/Bobby Melody) (Melody, Bobby/ Singie Singie).

Melody, Courtney

BAD BOY.
MC: WRLC 14

I REMEMBER SHOWCASE.
LP: PICKLP 01

MAN IN LOVE.
LP: TZLP 1003
MC: TZRLC 001

MODERN GIRL.
Tracks: / Modern girl / Just my type of girl / She turns me on / African girl / Turn them back / Bad boy business / Sing it off / Down in the dance hall.
LP: BMLP 024
MC: BMC 024

NINJA MI NINJA.
LP: WELP 344
MC: SCM 1

NINJA SHOWCASE.
LP: UNKNOWN

PROTECTION (Melody, Courtney & Ninja Man).
LP: HJ 198 829 2

SUMMERTIME GIRL.
LP: SGLP 050

Melody Four

LOVE PLAYS SUCH FUNNY GAMES.
Tracks: / You've become habitual to me / You go to my head / How long has this been going on / I see your face before me / Harvest moon / I get along without you very well / My romance / I know it now / Secret love / Mister lucky / I'm sending you back your engagement ring / I feel romantic.
LP: CHABADA 06

MELODY FOUR? SI SENOR.
Tracks: / Melody Four? Si senor / Brazil / Always in my heart / Silly song / Besame Mucho / Please stop / Taboo / Bahia / Donkey serenade, The / Begin the beguine / Perfidia.
LP: CHABADA 011
LP: OH 11

TV MAIS OUI.
LP: OH 13

Melody, Lilly

GIVE IT TO ME.
LP: PH 0012

Melody Makers

PLAY THE GAME RIGHT.
LP: ABL 110070

Melody, Mikey

MONA LISA.
MC: DSC 8902

Melody Of Broadway

MELODY OF BROADWAY (Various artists).
LP: AEI 1154

Melon

DEEP CUT.
Tracks: / Quiet village / Uptown downtown / Hard core Hawaiian / Hawaiian break / Time enough for love / Somewhere far away / Faraway / Pleasure before your breakfast / Funkasia / Gate of Japanesia.
LP: 4505311
MC: 4505134

WATER MELON.
LP: LPU 006

Melos Quartet

SCHUBERT STRING QUARTETS (see under Schubert (composer)).

Mel-O-Tones

BOMB SUTRA.
LP: PROBE 3

Melrose

ANOTHER PIECE OF CAKE.
Tracks: / Sexuality / Little Queenie / Slow motion / Horse doughnut / Look out / I wanna go / Trouble bound / I can hear the devil calling.
LP: EKR 1002

MELROSE.
LP: CL 0075

Melson, Joe

BARBARA (A MILESTONE IN ROCK 'N' ROLL).
Tracks: / Barbara / Shook up / Oh yeah / Love is a dangerous thing / What's the use / Any little thing can start the flame of love / Raining in my heart / Stay away from her / Dance / Wake up little Susie / Hey, Mr. Cupid / His girl / No one really cares / Take it like a man.
LP: BFX 15027

Melt Down

MELTDOWN- THE ALBUM (Various artists).
LP: HUR 001

Melted Americans

EVIL MONKEY BOWL.
Tracks: / Do I know anything? / It's not alright / Never seen a face / Between dreams / Whats going on? / Fax requiem / Through a 100 years / She can do anything she wants to / How long (before they take me away) / Spoiled Paul.
LP: 338 293

Melton, Barry

LEVEL WITH ME (Melton, Barry (The Fish)).
Tracks: / I can't dance / Astral lover / You gave me the sunshine / Colorado town / Level with me / Dance / Remember the song / San Francisco shuffle / Money / Seventh seal.
LP: RAG 1004

Mel-tones

BACK IN TOWN (See Torme, Mel) (Mel-tones/Mel Torme).

THERE'S NO BUSINESS LIKE SHOW BUSINESS (See Torme, Mel) (Mel-tones/Mel Torme).

Melville, Georgina

NOT WANTED ON VOYAGE (See also Kay Thorpe).

TO CATCH AN EARL (See also Rosina Pyatt).

Melville, Herman

BILLY BUDD (Rose, George (nar)).
MC: CDL 51653

MOBY DICK (Heston, Charlton).
MC: 2077

MOBY DICK (Kennedy, George).
MCSET: LFP 7240

Melvin, Brian

JAZZ STREET (see under Pastorius, Jaco) (Melvin, Brian's Nightfood/ Jaco Pastorius).

Melvin, Harold

6 TRACK HITS (Melvin, Harold & The Bluenotes).
Tracks: / Love I lost, The / Wake up everybody / If you don't know me by now / Don't leave me this way / Satisfaction guaranteed / I miss you.
MC: 7SC 5028

BLUE ALBUM (Melvin, Harold & The Bluenotes).
Tracks: / Tonight's the night / Prayin' / Baby I'm back / I should be your lover / If you're looking for somebody to love / Your love is taking me on a journey.
LP: SOR 5000

GOLDEN HIGHLIGHTS OF HAROLD MELVIN.
LP: 547 35
MC: 40 54735

GREATEST HITS: HAROLD MELVIN & THE BLUE NOTES (Melvin, Harold & The Bluenotes).
Tracks: / Love I lost, The / Bad luck / If you don't know me by now / I miss you / Wake up everybody / Hope that we can be together soon / Where are all my friends / Be for real / Satisfaction guaranteed.
LP: PIR 32569

SATISFACTION GUARANTEED/THE BEST OF ... (Melvin, Harold & Teddy Pendergrass).
LP: NE 1448
MC: CE 2448

Melvins

BULLHEAD.
LP: TUPLP 26

GLUEY PORCH TREATMENTS.
LP: VM 103

OZMA.
LP: TUPLP 007

Members

AT THE CHELSEA NIGHTCLUB.
Tracks: / Electricity / Soho-a-go-go / Don't push / Solitary confinement / Frustrated, bagshot / Stand up and spit / Sound of the suburbs, The / Phone in show / Love in a lift / Chelsea nightclub / Sally.
LP: OVED 44
LP: V 2120

CHOICE IS YOURS.
LP: V 2153

GOING WEST.
LP: ALB 115

Membranes

BACK CATALOGUE.
LP: DRIPLP 1

CRACK HOUSE.
LP: CRIMLP 105

GIANT.
LP: CON 00004

GIFT OF LIFE, THE.
LP: CRELP 006

KISS ASS GODHEAD.
LP: GLALP 028

PULP BEATING 1984 AND ALL THAT.
LP: CRIMLP 130

SONGS OF LOVE AND FURY.
LP: IT 038

TO SLAY THE ROCK PIG.
LP: SUK 9

Memoirs Of A Sword

MEMOIRS OF A SWORD SWALLOWER (Dolenz, Mickey).
MCSET: ZBBC 1157

Memoirs Of Barry

MEMOIRS OF BARRY LYNDON VOL 1 (see Thackeray, W. M.) (Boland, Arthur).

Memoirs Of Sherlock...

MEMOIRS OF SHERLOCK HOLMES (see under Sherlock Holmes (bk)) (Hardy, Robert (nar)).

Memories...

MEMORIES ARE MADE (Various artists).
LP: FUN 9042
MC: FUNC 9042

Memories-15 Golden

MEMORIES-15 GOLDEN HITS (Various artists).
LP: SHM 987
MC: HSC 366

Memory Of Earth

MEMORY OF EARTH, THE (See under Enya) (Enya & Jon Hassell).

Memory Of Justice Band

MASH DOWN BABYLON.
LP: PER 1114

Memphis..

MEMPHIS-ROCK'N'ROLL CAPITAL OF THE WORLD VOL.4 (Various artists).
Tracks: / Rockin' at the Y: *Ingle, Thomas* / Bright lights and wild, wild women: *Shaw, Jim* / Boogie beat: *Shaw*, Jim / Rockin' boppin' teenager: *Shaw, Jim* / Wishing on a star: *Shaw, Jim* / Today and tomorrow: *Feathers*, Charlie / Sweet girl of mine: *Nelson, Doyle* / Rising mercury: *Sabres, Les* / Prom, The: *Runabouts*/ When I get the blues: *Runabouts* / Tennessee twist: *Arnold, Lloyd* / Sugaree: *Arnold, Lloyd* / Go go go: *Arnold, Lloyd* / Night surfing: *Rebel Rousers* / You don't know what to do: *Rebel Rousers* / Run don't walk: *Davis, Bobby.*
LP: WLP 8916

Memphis Belle

MEMPHIS BELLE (Original Soundtrack) (Various artists).
Tracks: / Londonderry air/Front titles: *Various artists* / Green eyes: *Various artists* / Flying home: *Various* artists / Steel lady, The: *Various artists* / Prepare for take-off: *Various artists* / Final mission, The: *Various artists* / With deep regret...: *Various artists* / I know why (and so do you): *Various artists*/ Bomb run, The: *Various artists* / Limping home: *Various artists* / Crippled Belle: The landing: *Various* artists / Resolution: *Various artists* / Memphis Belle end title suite: *Various artists* / Danny Boy: *Various artists.*
LP: VS 5293
MC: VSC 5293

Memphis Horns

GET UP AND DANCE.
Tracks: / Get up and dance / Just for your love / Waitin' for the flood / Love is happiness / Memphis nights / What the funk / Country soul / No go betweens / Don't abuse it / Keep on smilin'.
LP: PL 12198

Memphis Jug Band

MEMPHIS JUG BAND 1927-34.
Tracks: / Packed my suitcase started to the train / Kansas City blues / Evergreen money blues / Coal oil blues / Peaches in the springtime / Jug band waltz / Feed your friend with a long handled spoon / I whipped my woman with a single-tree / Stonewall blues / He's in the jailhouse now / Move that thing / You got me rollin' / My love is cold / Jazzbo stomp / Tear it down bed slat and all / Fishin' in the dark / Rukus juice & chittlin' / Jug band quartette.
LP: MSE 1008

MEMPHIS JUG BAND VOL.1.
LP: RL 322

MEMPHIS JUG BAND VOL.2.

LP: RL 337

MEMPHIS JUG BANDS & ASSOCIATES 1927-32.
LP: WSE 131

MEMPHIS JUG BLUES.
2LP: YAZOO 1067

Memphis Minnie

CITY BLUES.
LP: ALB 1008
MC: ALB 1008MC

HOODOO LADY 1933-37.
MC: 4678884

HOT STUFF 1936-49.
LP: PY 1806

I'M WILD ABOUT MY LOVIN'.
LP: HLP 32

IN MY GIRLISH DAYS.
Tracks: / She wouldn't give me none / Mr tango blues / I'm gonna bake my biscuits / What fault you find of me / I'm talking about you / Bumble bee / Fishin' blues / Kind treatment blues / Jailhouse trouble blues / Keep it to yourself / Dirty mother for you / Sylvester and his mule blues / You can't give it away / You wrecked my happy home.
LP: TM 803

KEEP ON GOIN' 1931-41.
LP: DLP 559

MEMPHIS & DELTA-FIFTIES (Memphis & Delta).
LP: BC 15

MEMPHIS MINNIE.
MC: C 215

MEMPHIS MINNIE 1930-41.
LP: BD 2048

MEMPHIS MINNIE & KANSAS JOE (Memphis Minnie & Kansas Joe).
LP: PL 101

MEMPHIS MINNIE & KANSAS JOE, VOL.2 (Memphis Minnie & Kansas Joe).
LP: BD 617

MEMPHIS MINNIE VOL.1 (1934-1942).
LP: BC 1

MEMPHIS MINNIE VOL.2.
LP: BC 13

MEMPHIS MINNIE, VOL. 1 (1929/38) (Memphis Minnie/Blind John Davis/Black Bob).
LP: BD 608

QUEEN OF COUNTRY BLUES (1930-41).
LP: OT 1207

TRAVELLING BLUES.
MC: ALB 1004MC

WORLD OF TROUBLE.
LP: FLY 585

Memphis Rockabilly

BETTY JEAN (Memphis Rockabilly Band).
LP: BP-2186

Memphis Slim

20 GREATEST HITS: MEMPHIS SLIM.
LP: CL 23983

ALL KINDS OF BLUES.
Tracks: / Blues is trouble / Grinder man blues / Three in one boogie / Letter home / Churnin' man blues / Two of a kind / Blacks, The / If you see Kay / Frankie and Johnny Boogie / Mother earth.
LP: OBC 507

AMBASSADOR OF THE BLUES, THE.
Tracks: / Lonesome / Cold blooded woman / One man's mad / Let the good times roll Creole / Where is the mare rack / Pigalle love / Four walls / It's been so long / Big Bertha / I'm lost without you / I'll just keep on singin' the blues / True love.
LP: OFF 6016
LP: BMLP 1061

BLUES EVERY WHICH WAY, THE (Slim, Memphis & Willie Dixon).
LP: 2304 505

BLUES IS EVERYWHERE.
LP: 512601
LP: GNPS 10002

BLUES... MY OWN WAY.
Tracks: / No mail blues / Gonna need my baby some day / Question, The / Never let me love / Train time / Blue evening / Treat me like I treat you / My country girl / Four years of torment / Back alley / Living the life I love / Comeback, The / Five o'clock blues / Call before you go home / This is my lucky day / I love my baby.
LP: OFF 6006

BOOGIE WOOGIE PIANO.
Tracks: / Panic street / Hustler / Carried away / Bluesnick / Back home / Olympia boogie / Sonophone boogie / Blue Slim / Musing / West Side trot / Hotfan's delight.
LP: CBS 21106
MC: 40 21106

CHICAGO BOOGIE.
LP: BLP 30196

COLLECTION: MEMPHIS SLIM 20 blues greats.
Tracks: / Baby please come home / Sassy Mae / Rock me, baby / Caldonia / Strollin' thru the park / Ballin' the jack / Forty years or more / Pigalle love / Ramble this highway / Gone again / Piney Brown blues / Only fools have fun / Little lonely girl / Long time baby / Careless love / Freedom / All by myself / Everyday I have the blues / I am the blues / This little woman.
LP: DVLP 2075
MC: DVMC 2075
LP: ZET 711

COMPACT JAZZ (see under Blakey, Art) (Blakey, Art/Chet Baker/Anita O'Day/Memphis Slim).

DIALOGUE IN BOOGIE.
LP: ZET 711

DIALOGUE IN BOOGIE (Slim, Memphis & Philippe Lejeune).
Tracks: / Rockin' / E.E.C. boogie / C'est normal, c'est normand / Jefferson county blues / Fourth and beale / This is the way I feel / Three, two, one boogie / Midnite tempo / Cooky boogie / C and L boogie.
LP: B 90120
MC: MB 990120

GREATEST HITS: MEMPHIS SLIM.
LP: MA 23983

I'LL JUST KEEP ON SINGIN' THE BLUES.
Tracks: / Lonesome / Cold blooded woman / One man's man / Let the good times roll creole / What is the mare rack / Pigalle love / Four walls / It's been too long / Big Bertha / I'm lost without you / I'll just keep on singin' the blues / True love.
LP: MR 5219

LEGACY OF THE BLUES VOL. 7 (See under Legacy of the Blues).

LIVE: FROM THEATRE MUNICIPAL, BAYONNE,FRANCE.
LP: SLP 4058

MEMPHIS SLIM.
LP: SM 3588

MEMPHIS SLIM.
Tracks: / I guess I'm a fool / Rock in the pad / Havin' fun / Marack / Mother earth / Really got the blues / Tia Juana / I'm crying / Reverend bounce / Slim blues / Blues for my baby.
LP: GCH 8024
MC: GCHK 78024
LP: CH 9250

MEMPHIS SLIM STORY, THE.
Tracks: / All by myself / Sassy Mae / Baby please come home (1st version) / Gone again / Rock my baby / Careless love / Gambler's blues / Broadway boogie / Ballin' the Jack / Pigalle love / Ramble this highway / Baby please come home (2nd version) / Little lonely girl / Caldonia / This little woman / Strollin' thru' the park / I am the blues / Long time baby / Freedom / Only fools have fun / Let's get with it / Forty years or more.
MCSET: DVREMC 18

MEMPHIS SLIM USA.
Tracks: / Born with the blues / Just let it be me / Red haired boogie / Blue and disgusted / New key to the highway / I'd take her to Chicago / Harlem bound / El capitan / I just landed in your own / John Henry / I believe I'll settle down / Bad luck and trouble / Late afternoon blues / Memphis Slim U.S.A.
LP: CS 9024

MESSIN' AROUND WITH THE BLUES (Slim, Memphis/Pete Guitar Lewis/Little Willie Littlefield).
MCSET: GD 5038
LP: BID 8018

REAL FOLK BLUES.
LP: 515024

ROCK ME, BABY (Slim, Memphis & Alexis Korner).
Tracks: / Pinetop's blues / Blue this evening / Caught the old coon at last / We're just two of the same old kind / Don't think you're smart / I'm going to Kansas City / Got a little old mama / Rock me, baby / In the evening.
LP: BLP 30122

ROCKIN' THE BLUES.
Tracks: / Gotta find my baby / Comeback, The / Messin' around / Sassy Mae / Lend me your love / Guitar cha cha / Stroll on little girl / Rockin' the house / Wish me well / Blue and lonesome / My gal keeps me crying / Slim's blues / Steppin' out / Mother Earth / What's the matter / This time I'm through.
LP: CRB 1030

STEADY ROLLIN' BLUES.
LP: OBC 523

STEPPIN' OUT (Live at Ronnie Scott's).
Tracks: / Health shaking / Mother earth / Rock this house tonight / If you see Kay / Feel so good / Tribute to Gaillard / Four hundred years / Steppin' out / Baby please come home / Where do I go from here / Didn't we / Christina / Animal / Beer drinking woman / What is this world coming to / Bye bye blues.
MC: ESMMC 016

TOGETHER AGAIN ONE MORE TIME (LIVE IN 85) (Slim, Memphis & Matt Murphy).
LP: AN 003

TRAVELLING WITH THE BLUES.
LP: SLP 4033
LP: SLP 118

TRIBUTE TO BIG BILL ETC..
LP: CS 9023

UNISSUED 1963 BLUES FESTIVAL, THE (Slim, Memphis/Sonny Boy Williamson/etc).
LP: RL 060

USA.
LP: PL 10

WILLIE'S BLUES (See under Dixon, Willie).

Men 2nd

ANTIBODY SONGS, THE.
MLP: ANT 079

RED TAPE.
LP: ANT 070

Men At Work

BUSINESS AS USUAL.
Tracks: / Who can it be now / I can see it in your eyes / Down under / Underground / Helpless automation / People just love to play with words / Be good Johnny / Touching the untouchables / Catch a star / Down by the sea.
LP: 4508871
MC: 4508874
LP: EPC 85669

CARGO.
Tracks: / Doctor Heckyll and Mr. Jive / Overkill / Settle down my boy / Upstairs in my house / No sign of yesterday / It's a mistake / High wire / Blue for you / I like to / No restrictions.
LP: EPC 32781
MC: 40 32781
LP: EPC 25372

TWO HEARTS.
Tracks: / Man with two hearts / Giving up / Everything I need / Sail to you / Children on parade / Maria / Stay at home / Hard luck story / Still life / Snakes and ladders.
LP: EPC 26492
MC: 40 26492

Men In War

MEN IN WAR (Original Soundtrack) (Various artists).
LP: NA 240

Men O' Brass

FIREMAN'S GALLOP (Men O' Brass Grand Massed Bands).
Tracks: / Thunderbirds march / H.M.S. Pinafore overture / Can Can / Colditz march / Match of the day / Who do you think you are kidding Mr. Hitler / Tricky trombones / 633 Squadron / Rovers return / Tango taquin / Three trumpeters / New world fantasy / Fireman's gallop.
LP: EMS 1058181
MC: TCEMS 1058184

Men Of Courage

MEN OF COURAGE.
LP: VOW 013

Men They Couldn't Hang

DOMINO CLUB, THE.
Tracks: / Lion and the unicorn, The / Family way, The / Kingdom of the blind / Industrial town / Australia / Billy Morgan / Great expectations / Handy man / Grave robbing in Gig harbour / You're the one / Dogs eyes, owl meat, man chop / On the razzle.
LP: ORELP 512
MC: OREMC 512

FIVE GLORIOUS YEARS.
LP: ORELP 509
MC: OREMC 509

HOW GREEN IS THE VALLEY.
Tracks: / Gold strike / Ghosts of Cable Street / Bells, The / Shirt of blue / Tiny soldiers / Parted from you / Gold rush / Dancing on the pier / Going back to Coventry / Rabid underdog / Parade, The.
LP: MCF 3337
MC: MCFC 3337

NIGHT OF A THOUSAND CANDLES.
Tracks: / Day after, The / Jack Dandy / Night to remember / Johnny come home / Green fields of France / Iron masters / Hush little baby / Walkin' talkin' / Kingdom come / Scarlet ribbons.
LP: FIEND 50
MC: FIENDCASS 50

SILVERTOWN.
Tracks: / Rosettes / Homefires / Lobotomy, gets 'em home / Rain, steam and speed / Hellfire and damnation / Place in the sun, A / Company town / Blackfriars bridge / Down all the days / El vaquero.
LP: ORELP 503
MC: OREC 503

WAITING FOR BONAPARTE.
Tracks: / Crest, The / Smugglers / Dover lights / Bounty hunter / Island in the rain / Colours, The / Midnight train / Father's wrong / Life of a small fry / Mary's present / Silver dagger* (*Extra track on cassette & CD only) / Restless highway* (*Extra track on cassette & CD only) / Country song* (*Extra track on cassette & CD only) / Crest, The (12" version) (Extra track on CD only).
LP: WX 183
MC: WX 183 C

WELL HUNG.
LP: AFTER 10
MC: TAFTER 10

Men & Volts

MULE, THE.
LP: SHIMMY 008

TRAMPS IN BLOOM.
LP: ROSE 49

Men Without Hats

FOLK OF THE 80'S PART 3.
LP: STAT LP 18
MC: STAT C 18

RHYTHM OF YOUTH.
Tracks: / Cocoricci / Safety dance / I've got the message / Ideas for walls / Living in China / Out of space / Freeway / Modern dancing.
LP: STAT LP 10
MC: STAT C 10

Menace

GLC - R.I.P.
LP: RAZ 18

Menage All'Italiana

MENAGE ALL'ITALIANA Film soundtrack (Various artists).
LP: SP 8013

Menard, D.L.

BACK DOOR, THE.
LP: 6038
MC: 6038 TC

CAJUN SATURDAY NIGHT.
Tracks: / Cajun Saturday night / Why should we try anymore / This little girl / Wedding bells / Judge did not believe my story, The / Green oak tree / Letters have no arms / House of gold / Bachelor's life, The / Banks of the old Pontchartrain / My son calls another man Daddy / Long gone lonesome blues.
LP: FIEND 64
LP: ROUNDER 0198
MC: ROUNDER 0198C

D.L. MENARD AND THE LOUISIANA ACES (Menard, D.L. & Louisiana Aces).
LP: ROUNDER 6003

NO MATTER WHERE YOU AT, THERE YOU ARE.
LP: ROUNDER 6021
MC: ROUNDER 6021C
LP: HNBL 1352
MC: HNBC 1352

Mendelssohn (composer)

CONCERTO FOR VIOLIN AND PIANO (Various artists).
MC: 4273384
LP: 4273381

MENDELSSOHN (Various artists).
MC: DLCMC 210

MENDELSSOHN WORKS FOR CLARINET, BASSET HORN AND PIANO (Hacker, Alan/Lesley Schatzberger/Richard Burnett).
Tracks: / Konzertstuck no.2 in D minor op.114 (Mendelssohn) (Presto-pianissimo/Andante/Allegretto grazioso-adagio-presto e con fuoco) / Rondo capriccioso op.14 (Mendelssohn) / Songs without words (Mendelssohn) (Op. 67 no.2 (F sharp minor)/op.62 no.6 (A)/op.53 no.4 (F)/op.67 no.4 (C)) / Sonata in E flat (1824) (Mendelssohn) (Adagio-allegro moderato/Andante/ Allegro moderato) / Songs without

words (Mendelssohn) (Venetian gondola song (A minor) op.62 no.5/Venetian gondola song (A)1842) / Variations serieuses (17) op. 54 (Mendelssohn) / Konzertstuck no.1 in F minor op.113 (Mendelssohn) (Allegro con fuoco/ Andante/Presto).
MC: . . . . **CSAR 38**

MIDSUMMER NIGHT'S DREAM, A (Concertgebouw Orchestra Amsterdam).
MC: **426 071-4**

PIANO CONCERTOS NOS. 1 & 2 Capriccio brilliant & Rondo brilliant (Various artists).
MC: **4255044**

SCOTTISH AND ITALIAN SYMPHONIES (MENDELSSOHN) (Scottish Chamber Orchestra).
Tracks: / Symphony no. ('Scottish')(Mendelssohn) / Symphony no. ('Italian')(Mendelssohn) / Scherzo from Octet (Mendelssohn) (Orchestral reworking by composer.).
LP: . . . . **DCA 700**
MC: . . . . **ZC DCA 700**

SYMPHONIES NOS 3 'SCOTTISH' & 4 'ITALIAN' (London Symphony Orchestra).
MC: **4278104**

SYMPHONY NO.2 (MENDELSSOHN) Hymn of praise (Lobgesang) (Leipzig Gewandhaus Orch/Leipzig Radio Chorus/).
LP: **244 178-1**
MC: **244 178-4**

SYMPHONY NO.3/NO.4 (MENDELSSOHN) (St. John's Smith Sq. Orchestra).
Tracks: / Symphony no.3 op.56 'Scottish' / Symphony no.4 op.90 'Italian'.
MC: . . . . **ZC QS 6004**

SYMPHONY NO.4 (MENDELSSOHN) Music for A Midsummer Night's Dream (Vienna State Opera Orchestra).
MC: . . . . **VETC 6506**

Mendelssohn, Felix

ALOHA (Mendelssohn, Felix & his Hawaiian Serenaders).
LP: . . . . **SH 259**

EVERGREEN HAWAIIAN STYLE (Mendelssohn, Felix & his Hawaiian Serenaders).
Tracks: / Japanese sandman / Tiger rag / Lady be good / Goodbye blues / Sheik in araby / In the mood / I got rhythm / St.louis blues / Dinah / Crazy rhythm / Nobody's sweetheart / Cherokee / Solitude / Mood indigo / Whispering / Wabash blues.
MC: . . . . **TC SH 394**
LP: . . . . **SH 394**

GOLDEN AGE OF,THE (Mendelssohn, Felix & his Hawaiian Serenaders).
Tracks: / Japanese sandman / Tiger rag / Oh lady be good / Goodbye blues / Sheik of Araby, The / In the mood / I got rhythm / St. Louis blues / Dinah / Crazy rhythm / Nobody's sweetheart / Cherokee / Solitude / Mood indigo / Whispering / Wabash blues.
LP: . . . . **GX 41 2544 1**
MC: . . . . **GX 41 2544 4**

SERENADE TO HAWAII (Mendelssohn, Felix & his Hawaiian Serenaders).
Tracks: / Bali Ha'i / Sweet hawaiian kisses / Hawaiian hospitality / Moon over miami / Hawaii sing me to sleep / Kalua lullaby / Hilo march / Sweet gardenia lei.
LP: . . . . **SH 1078261**

Mendes, Sergio

ALEGRIA.
Tracks: / Fato consumado / To voltando / Ultima batucada / Aquelas coisas todas / Adeus America / Milagre / Horizonte aberto / O mar e meu chao / Desenredo.
LP: . . . . **K 99096**

BRAZIL 86'.
Tracks: / Daylight / Take this love / What do we mean to each other / Your smile / River (o rio), The / Nonstop / It hurts a whole lot more / Flower of Bahia / No place to hide / Here where I belong.
LP: . . . . **AMA 5135**
MC: . . . . **AMC 5135**

CONFETTI.
Tracks: / Olympia / Say it with your body / Let's give a little more this time / Sound of one song / Alibis / Dance attack / Kisses / Real life / To die of love.
LP: . . . . **AMLX 64984**

SERGIO MENDES.
Tracks: / Davy / I believe / All in love is fair / Let them work it out / Here comes the sun / If I ever lose this heaven / Looking for another pure love / Someday we'll all be free / You been away too long / Trouble is hello is goodbye, The.
LP: . . . . **K 52014**

SERGIO MENDES.
Tracks: / Voo doo / Never gonna let you go / My summer love / Carnival / Rainbow's end / Love is waiting / Dream hunter / Life in the movies / Si senor.
LP: . . . . **AMHL 64937**
MC: . . . . **CAM 64937**

SERGIO MENDES & THE NEW BRAZIL 77 (Mendes,Sergio/New Brazil 77).
Tracks: / Love me tomorrow / Love city / Mozambique / If you leave me now / Peninsula / Why / Real thing, The / P-ka-boo / Life.
LP: . . . . **K 52056**
LP: . . . . **MFP 50434**

VERY BEST OF SERGIO MENDES (Mendes Sergio & Brazill 66).
LP: . . . . **SHM 3144**
MC: . . . . **HSC 3144**

Mendez, Gerd Mayer

VILLAGE SONGS.
LP: . . . . **VM 1001**

Mendoza, Lydia

FIRST RECORDINGS.
MC: . . . . **C 219**

LA GLORIA DE TEXAS.
LP: . . . . **ARHOOLIE 3012**

Mendoza Sisters

JUANITA & MARIA.
LP: . . . . **ARHOOLIE 3017**

Menezes, Margereth

ELLEGIBO.
LP: **843 556 1**
MC: **843 556 4**

Mengo,Jerry &

GET ON THE BANDWAGON.
LP: . . . . **ISST 113**

Mensah, E.T.

ALL FOR YOU.
LP: . . . . **RETRO 1**

Mental As Anything

CREATURES OF LEISURE.
Tracks: / Spirit got lost / Float away / Brain brain / Bitter to swallow / Close again / Nothing's going right today / Working for the man / Fiona / Seems alright to me / Drinking of her lips / Red to green / Let's not get sentimental / Business and pleasure.
LP: . . . . **AMLX 64946**

FUNDAMENTAL.
Tracks: / You're so strong / Big wheel / Live it up / Surf and mull and sex and fun / Good Friday / Date with destiny / Hold on / Stones of the heart / I just wanna be happy / Splashing / Bus ride.
LP: . . . . **EPC 26836**
MC: **40 26836**

IF YOU LEAVE CAN I COME TOO?.
LP: . . . . **AMLH 64921**

MENTAL AS ANYTHING.
LP: . . . . **V 2148**

MOUTH TO MOUTH.
Tracks: / He's just no good for you / Thinking out loud / Too many times / Mouth to mouth / I'm glad / Wandering through heaven / Love me tender / Don't tell me now / My door is always open to you / Stay at home girl / Put me back / If you leave me can I come too / Mad king.
LP: **4503611**
LP: **4600491**
MC: **4600494**

Mental, Ella

ELLA MENTAL.
Tracks: / Eddie's cat / No woman no cry / Is it any wonder / Seasons come seasons go / Walking in the light / Freedom jive / Song for Jenny / Africa / Seeds of tomorrow / Madman.
LP: . . . . **K 9258821**
MC: . . . . **K 9258824**

Mental Illness

MYTHS OF MENTAL ILLNESS (Szasz, Thomas S.) (Szasz, Thomas S.).
MC: . . . . **PT 24**

NEW PHYSICAL TREAMENTS DR W SARGENT.
MC: . . . . **SS 104**

Mental Stress

MENTAL STRESS & PHYSICAL FITNESS By Kenneth R.Pelletier (Pelletier, Kenneth R.).
MC: . . . . **PT 37**

Mentors

UP THE DOSE.
Tracks: / Kick it on down / Secretary hump / Couch test casting / S.F.C.C. / Up the dose / Hetrosexuals have the right to rock / Rock 'em and sock 'em / White trash women / Adultery / On the rag.
LP: . . . . **RR 9657**

YOU AXED FOR IT.
LP: . . . . **RR 9749**

Menuhin, Yehudi

FASCINATING RHYTHM (Menuhin,Yehudi & Stephane Grappelli).
LP: . . . . **EMD 5523**

FOR ALL SEASONS (Menuhin, Yehudi & Stephane Grappelli).
Tracks: / Winter set / Button up your overcoat / I've got my love to keep me warm / I'll remember April / Spring will be a little late this year / Giboules de mars / April in Paris / On the sunny side of the street / Heatwave / Automne / Autumn in New York.
LP: . . . . **EL 2701121**
MC: . . . . **EL 2701124**

GIFT OF MUSIC.
MC: . . . . **SS 116**

MENUHIN AND GRAPPELLI PLAY GERSHWIN (Menuhin, Yehudi & Stephane Grappelli).
Tracks: / Fascinating rhythm / Summertime / Nice work if you can get it / Foggy day, A / 'S wonderful / Man I love, The / I got rhythm / They all laughed / Funny face / Lady be good.
MC: . . . . **EG 769 218 4**

MENUHIN AND GRAPPELLI PLAY 'JEALOUSY' (and Other Great Standards) (Menuhin, Yehudi & Stephane Grappelli).
Tracks: / Jealousy / Tea for two / Limehouse blues / These foolish things / Continental, The / Nightingale sang in Berkeley Square, A / Sweet Sue / Skylark / Laura / Sweet Georgia Brown / I'll remember April / April in Paris / Things we did last summer, The / September in the rain / Autumn leaves / Autumn in New York / Button up your overcoat.
LP: . . . . **EMD 5504**
MC: . . . . **TCEMD 5504**
MC: . . . . **EG 769 220 4**

MENUHIN & GRAPPELLI PLAY BERLIN/KERN/PORTER (Menuhin, Yehudi & Stephane Grappelli).
Tracks: / Cheek to cheek / Isn't this a lovely day / Piccolino, The / Change partners / Top hat, white tie and tails / I've got my love to keep me warm / Heatwave / Way you look tonight / Pick yourself up / Fine romance, A / All the things you are / Why do I love you / I get a kick out of you / Night and day / Looking at you / Just one of those things / My funny valentine / Thou swell / Lady is a tramp, The / Blue room.
MC: . . . . **EG 769 219 4**

MUSIC FOR STRING ORCHESTRA (See under Bartok for full details) (Menuhin, Sir Yehudi conducting the English String Orchestra).

STRICTLY FOR THE BIRDS (Menuhin, Yehudi & Stephane Grappelli).
Tracks: / Nightingale sang in Berkeley Square, A / Lullaby of Birdland / When the red, red robin comes bob, bob, bobbin' along / Skylark / Bye bye blackbird / Coucou / Flamingo / Dinah / Rosetta / Sweet Sue / Once in love with Amy / Laura / La route du roi / Sweet Georgia Brown.
LP: . . . . **EMD 5533**
MC: . . . . **TCEMD 5533**
LP: . . . . **CFP 4549**
MC: . . . . **TCCFP 4549**

TEA FOR TWO (see Grappelli, Stephane) (Menuhin, Yehudi & Stephane Grappelli).

TOP HAT - SONGS MADE FAMOUS BY FRED ASTAIRE (Menuhin,Yehudi & Stephane Grappelli).
Tracks: / Puttin on the Ritz / Way you look tonight / He loves and she loves / Isn't this a lovely day / Piccolino, The / Alison / Change partners / Top hat, white tie and tails / They can't take that away from me / Continental, The / They all laughed / Amanda / Funny face / Carioca.
LP: . . . . **CFP 4509**
MC: . . . . **TCCFP 4509**

YEHUDI MENUHIN.
LP: . . . . **REGL 409**
MC: . . . . **ZCF 409**

Menza, Don

BALLADS (Menza, Don & Frank Strazzeri).
LP: . . . . **FS 281**

EL ENCUENTRO (See under Bingert, Hector) (Menza, Don & Hector Bingert).

HIP POCKET (LIVE AT CARMELOS).
LP: . . . . **PA 8010**

Menzies, Ian

REUNION JAZZ REVIVAL (Menzies, Ian & His Clyde Valley Stompers).
Tracks: / Maryland, my Maryland / Georgia on my mind / Pearly gates / That's my desire / Lady be good / Just a closer walk with thee / Mention my name.
LP: . . . . **BGC 307**
MC: . . . . **KBGC 307**

Mephisto

MEPHISTO (Film Soundtrack) (Various artists).
LP: . . . . **WM 8850**

Mephisto Waltz

MEPHISTO WALTZ.
LP: . . . . **SR 010R**

Mercer, Jerry

RADIO ROCKABILLIES (See under Felts, Narvel) (Mercer, Jerry & Narvel Felts).

Mercer, Johnny

AUDIO SCRAP BOOK.
Tracks: / Huggin' and chalkin' / Blue in the night / Gentle on my mind / Love is just around the corner / Java jive / Little lost dream / Slippin' around the corner / Shooby doolin' / Shake it but don't break it / Accentuate the positive / Little ol' tune / Spring spring spring / Dance of life / Them there eyes / I wanna be in love again.
LP: . . . . **AWE 5**
MC: . . . . **CAWE 5**

CAPITOL COLLECTORS SERIES: JOHNNY MERCER.
Tracks: / Strip polka / I lost my sugar in Salt Lake City / G.I. jive / Blues in the night / Accentuate the positive / Candy / I'm gonna see my baby / On the Atchison, Topeka & the Santa Fe / Surprise party / Personality / My sugar is so refined / One for my baby (and one more for the road) / Zip-a-dee-doo-dah / Gal in calico, A / Winter wonderland / Moon faced, starry eyed / Sugar blues / Save the bones for Henry Jones ('cause Henry don't eat meat) / Glow worm / Baby, it's cold outside.
MC: . . . . **C 492125**

DON'T FENCE ME IN (Mercer, Johnny & His Music Shop).
LP: . . . . **DBD 04**
MC: . . . . **DBDC 04**

JOHNNY MERCER.
Tracks: / Jeepers creepers / St. Louis blues / Hear them bells.
LP: . . . . **GLS 9005**

JOHNNY MERCER 1944.
Tracks: / By the river Sainte Marie / Sugar / Sweet Georgia Brown / When the blooms is on the sage / Margie / Sweet Lorraine / Someday sweetheart / Indiana / I can't get the one I want / Lulu's back in town / Gee, baby, ain't I good to you / Button up your overcoat / I never knew / Louisville Lou / Love is just around the corner / Crazy rhythm.
LP: . . . . **HSR 152**

JOHNNY MERCER AND FRIENDS.
Tracks: / Huggin' and a chuggin', A / Blues in the night / Gentle on my mind / Spring, Spring, Spring / Little lost dream / Slippin' around the corner / Shooby dooin / Pin apple Pete / Air minded executive, The / Susie for everybody / Wreck of the old 97 / Shake it but don't break it / Accentuate the positive / Li'l ol' tune / Love is just around the corner / Dance of life / Them there eyes / Pleasure of your company, The / Good companions / Watcha-ma-call-it, The / Java jive / I'll tell the world / St. Louis blues / Anyplace I hang my hat is home.
MC: . . . . **CMOIR 407**

MR.CROSBY AND MR.MERCER (See under Crosby, Bingo) (Mercer, Johnny/ Bing Crosby).

MUSIC SHOP.
Tracks: / Music shop theme / Conversation while dancing / Day after forever, The / Steamboat Bill / Don't fence me in / Rain / Fare thee well to Harlem / Sweet Georgia Brown / It could happen to you / Tired teddy bear / Amor / Somebody loves me / Button up your overcoat / I'll be seeing you.
LP: . . . . **ART 002**
MC: . . . . **CART 002**

TWO OF A KIND (See under Darin, Bobby) (Mercer, Johnny & Bobby Darin).

Mercer, Mabel

ECHOES OF MY LIFE.
2LP: . . . . **AP 161/2**

Merchant

POWER PLAY.
Tracks: / Soca power play / Don't you / Symphony of love / Simmer down / Private conversation / Hot line baby.

LP: HVLP 006

Merchant Ivory..

MERCHANT IVORY PRODUCTIONS (Various artists).
Tracks: / Savages: *Various artists* / Quartet: *Various artists* / Europeans: *Various artists* / Bostonians, The: *Various artists* / Room with a view, A: *Various artists* / Maurice: *Various artists* / Householder, The: *Various artists* / Shakespeare Wallah: *Various artists* / Courtesans of Bombay: *Various artists*/ Mahatma and mad boy: *Various artists* / Guru: *Various artists* / Heat and dust: *Various artists*.
MC: BK 87773
LP: BL 87773

Merchant Of Venice

MERCHANT OF VENICE, THE (see under Shakespeare, William) (Various artists).

Merciless

VOMIT NAUSEA.
LP: CCG 013

Mercury All Stars

KID ORY 1944 (Mercury All Stars Jazz Combination).
Tracks: / High society / Muskrat ramble / That - a - plenty / Panama rag / Jimmie's blues / Sugarfoot stomp / Savoy blues / Weary blues / Tiger rag / E flat blues / Didn't he ramble / Royal Garden blues.
LP: JOY 264

Mercury, Freddie

BARCELONA (Mercury, Freddie & Montserrat Caballe).
Tracks: / Barcelona / Fallen priest, The / Golden boy, The / Guide me home / Overture piccante / La japonaise / Ensueno / Guid me home / How can I go on.
LP: POLH 44
MC: POLHC 44

MR BAD GUY.
Tracks: / Let's turn it on / Made in heaven / I was born to love you / Foolin' around / Your kind of lover / Mr Bad guy / Man-made paradise / There must be more to life than this / Living on my own / My love is dangerous / Love me like there's no tomorrow.
LP: CBS 86312
MC: 40 86312

Mercy Ray

SWOOP SWOOP ROCK ROCK.
LP: CAS 1168
MC: CASMC 1168

Mercy Seat

MERCY SEAT, THE.
Tracks: / Let me ride / Soul on right / Don't forget about me / I don't need nobody else / He said / Get up / I am a pilgrim / I've got a feeling / Mother talking.
LP: SLAP 23
MC: SMAC 23

Mercyful Fate

BEGINNING, THE.
LP: RR 9603

DON'T BREAK THE OATH.
LP: MFN 28
LP: RR 9835

MELISSA.
LP: MFN 10
LP: RR 9898

MELISSA/DON'T BREAK THE OATH.
MCSET: RR 49648

Mercyland

NO FEET ON THE COWLING.
LP: TUPLP 2

Merdichian, George

ON THE BUD - ARMENIAN GUITAR DUETS.
MC: GVMMC 803

Mergener, Peter

BEAM SCAPE (Mergener, Peter & Michael Weisser).
LP: KS 80046

Merger

ARMAGEDDON TIME.
LP: ERD 010

Merino Brothers

VALLENTINO DYNAMOS.
Tracks: / De mi vida una ilusion / Acompaname a sufrir / Mal procedimiento / La democracia / Riquezas de la vida / Minutos felices / Ese soy yo / Maria Elena / Noches de desvelos / Mi padre el campesino.
LP: ORB 049

Merle & Roy

REQUESTS.
LP: RMBR 8713

UNTIL WE MEET AGAIN....
Tracks: / Let your love flow / Always on my mind / It keeps right on a-hurtin' / Somewhere my love / You keep me hangin' on / Just a closer walk with thee / Don't forget to remember / When your old wedding ring was new / Harbour lights / I can't stop loving you / Sunshine of your smile, The / Forty shades of green / In the chapel in the moonlight / Home is where you're happy / May the road rise to meet you.
LP: GRALP 31
MC: GRTC 31

Merlin

MERLIN.
LP: LEFT LP 9
MC: LEFT C 9

NEW RAP MESSIAH, THE.
LP: WX 402
MC: WX 402C

Merlin & Perceval

MERLIN & PERCEVAL (Various artists).
Tracks: / Merlin & Nimue: *Various artists* / Young Perceval, The: *Various artists*.
MC: ANV 607

Mermaids (film)

MERMAIDS, THE (Film Soundtrack) (Various artists).
Tracks: / Shoop shoop song (it's in his kiss), The: *Cher* / Big girls don't cry: *Valli, Frankie & Four Seasons*/ You've really got a hold on me: *Robinson, Smokey & The Miracles* / It's my party: *Gore, Leslie* / Johnny angel: *Fabares, Shelly* / Baby, i'm yours: *Cher* / Just one look: *Troy, Doris* / Love is strange: *Mickey & Sylvia* / Sleep walk: *Santo & Johnny* / If you wanna be happy: *Soul, Jimmy*.
LP: 4678741
MC: 4678744

Merman, Ethel

ETHEL MERMAN.
MC: MRT 40039

ETHEL WAS A LADY.
LP: MCL 1804

MERMAN SINGS MERMAN.
Tracks: / You're the top / I got rhythm / You're just in love / Alexander's ragtime band / I got lost in his arms / Eadie was a lady / There's no business like show business / They say it's wonderful / It's de-lovely / I get a kick out of you / Everything's coming up roses / Blow, Gabriel, blow.
MC: KTBC 81
LP: JASM 2209
LP: TAB 81

WORLD IS YOUR BALLOON, THE.
Tracks: / Little girl from little rock, A / Diamonds are a girl's best friend / Dearie / I said my pyjamas / It's so nice to have a man around the house / If I knew you were coming I'd've baked a cake / Calico Sal / She's shimmyin' on the beach again / Hawaii / Ukulele lady / Lake song, The / Don't believe it / Once upon a nickel / Oldies / Love is the reason / World is your balloon, The / Make the man love me / You say the nicest things / Husband, a wife / If you catch a little cold (I'll sneeze for you).
LP: MCL 1839
MC: MCLC 1839

Merrell, Ray

BIG COUNTRY.
Tracks: / Riders in the sky / One day at a time / Movin' on down to Nashville / I recall a gypsy woman / I love you because / He'll have to go / I won't forget you / Snowbird / Take me home country roads / Lucille / I believe / Make the world go away / High noon / Big John Wayne / Old rugged cross, The.
LP: PRX 18
MC: TC PRX 18

DISCO COUNTRY STYLE.
Tracks: / City girl / Freight train / Green green grass of home / Two little pieces of heaven / Red chimneys / Distant drums / My prayer / Send me the pillow that you dream on / How lucky you are / Ghost of love / Morning has broken / Jezebel.
LP: PRX 6

SEEDS OF LOVE.
Tracks: / My mother's eyes / Door is still open, The / Every step I made / Seed / Bingo cowboys / Crystal chandeliers / You're my best friend / Touch my heart / Sixteen tons / Apartment No.9 / Love me tender.
LP: PRX 20

Merrill, Buddy

25 GREAT HITS.
2LP: GNPS 2-5038

BEST OF BUDDY MERRILL.
LP: GNPS 5030
MC: GNP5 5030

BEYOND THE REEF HAWAIIAN.
LP: GNPS 5034

STEEL GUITAR COUNTRY.
LP: GNPS 5036

Merrill, Helen

RODGERS & HAMMERSTEIN ALBUM.
Tracks: / It might as well be spring / Hello young lovers / I have dreamed / People will say we're in love / Getting to know you / My lord and master / If I loved you / My favourite things / Sound of music, The.
LP: SL 5204
MC: SLC 5204

SHADE OF DIFFERENCE.
Tracks: / Never will I marry / While we're young / Lonely woman / I should care / Lady must live, A / I want a little boy / Spring can really hang you up the most / My funny valentine / Lover come back to me / Where do you go? / Where do you go?.
LP: LLP 1308
MC: LLP 51308
LP: SPJLP 12

SINGS RODGERS & HAMMERSTEIN.
LP: SL 5204
MC: SLC 5204

SOMETHING SPECIAL.
Tracks: / It don't mean a thing / You're my thrill / Here's that rainy day / Baltimore Oriole / Don't explain / What is this thing called love / Winter of my discontent / Day dream / Deep in a dream.
LP: IC 1060

S'POSIN.
LP: SLP 1014

Merrily We Roll ..

MERRILY WE ROLL ALONG (Original Broadway Cast) (Various artists).
LP: CBL 1 4197
MC: CBK 1 4197

Merrin, Billy

TROUBLES ARE LIKE BUBBLES (1932-1937) (Merrin, Billy & His Commanders).
Tracks: / Troubles are like bubbles / No more heartaches, no more tears / Gosh I must be falling in love / Red sails in the sunset / Sweet music / Dance your blues away / Nice cup of tea, A / Captivating rhythm / Set your heart on me / You / Because it's love.
LP: RD 5

Merritt, Max

KEEPING IN TOUCH.
LP: 2383 514

LITTLE EASIER, A (Merritt, Max & The Meteors).
LP: ARTY 108

OUT OF THE BLUE.
LP: ARTY 134

Merry Christmas (film)

MERRY CHRISTMAS MR. LAWRENCE (Original Soundtrack) (Sakamoto, Ryuichi & David Sylvian).
Tracks: / Batavia / Germination / Hearty breakfast, A / Before the war / Seed and the sower, The / Brief encounter, A / Ride, ride, ride / Flight / Father Christmas / Dismissed / Assembly / Beyond reason / Sowing the seed / 23rd Psalm / Last regrets / Ride, ride, ride (reprise) / Seed, The / Forbidden colours / Merry Christmas Mr. Lawrence.
LP: V 2276
MC: TCV 2276
LP: OVED 237
MC: OVEDC 237

Merry Christmas Mr.

1984/MERRY CHRISTMAS MR LAWRENCE/KILLING FIELDS (See under Nineteen Eighty Four) (Various artists).

Merry Go Round

BEST OF MERRY GO ROUND.
LP: RNLP 125

Merry Widow

MERRY WIDOW (Various artists).
LP: 6.22992
MC: CH4 22992

MERRY WIDOW (Film soundtrack) (Various artists).
Tracks: / Merry widow waltz: *Various artists* / Maxim's: *Various artists* / Vilia: *Various artists* / Girls, girls, girls.: *Various artists* / Night: *Various artists* / Gypsy music: *Various artists* / Can-can: *Various artists*.
MC: 4502314
LP: 4502311

MERRY WIDOW, THE (Highlights) (Various artists).
MC: TCCFP 4485

MERRY WIDOW, THE (Original Soundtrack) (Various artists).
LP: HS 5015

Merry Widow (opera)

MERRY WIDOW, THE (Musical Operetta 86) (New Sadler's Wells Cast).
LP: TER 1111
MC: ZCTER 1111
LP: NTS 103

Merry Wives Of Windsor

MERRY WIVES OF WINDSOR, THE (see under Shakespeare, William) (Various artists).

Merrybell Choir

TELL IT TO THE PEOPLE.
LP: MYR 1186
MC: MC 1186

Mersey...

15 MERSEY HITS (Various artists).
LP: SHM 983
MC: HSC 363

LET'S STOMP (Various artists).
Tracks: / Let's stomp: *Various artists* / I can tell: *Various artists* / Who shot Sam: *Various artists*/ Beechwood 4-5789: *Various artists* / Thumbin' a ride: *Various artists* / Do you love me: *Various artists*/ Doctor Feelgood: *Various artists* / Someday: *Various artists* / Shake sherry: *Various artists* / Beautiful dreamer: *Various artists* / You've got everything: *Various artists* / Hallelujah, I love her: *Various artists*/ All around the world: *Various artists* / See if she cares: *Various artists* / Border of the blues: *Various artists* / Fragile: *Various artists*.
LP: ED 103

LIVE AT THE CAVERN (Various artists).
Tracks: / Doctor Feelgood: *Various artists* / Keep on rolling: *Various artists* / She's sure the girl I love: *Various artists* / You've really got a hold on me: *Various artists* / Everybody loves a lover: *Various artists*/ Devoted to you: *Various artists* / You better move on: *Various artists* / Somebody to love: *Various artists*/ I got a woman: *Various artists* / Little queenie: *Various artists* / Diddley, diddley daddy: *Various artists*/ Bring it on home to me: *Various artists* / Skinny Minnie: *Various artists* / Jezebel: *Various artists*/ I'm talking about you: *Various artists* / Little Egypt: *Various artists* / What'd I say: *Various artists*/ Don't start running away: *Various artists* / Zip-a-dee-doo-dah: *Various artists* / Reelin' and rockin': *Various artists*.
LP: SEE 58

LIVERPOOL '63 -'68 (Various artists).
Tracks: / Ferry cross the Mersey: *Gerry & the Pacemakers* / Skinny Lizzie: *Gerry & the Pacemakers* / Abyssinian secret: *Black, Cilla* / For no one: *Black, Cilla* / Sandy: *Swinging Blue Jeans* / It's too late now: *Swinging Blue Jeans* / Everything in the garden: *Fourmost* / Breakaway: *Marsden, Beryl* / Que sera sera: *Royce, Earl & The Olympics* / I really do: *Royce, Earl & The Olympics* / America: *Storm, Rory & The Hurricanes* / I got a woman: *Black Knights* / Angel of love: *Black Knights* / I love her: *Kubas* / Magic potion: *Kubas*/ First cut is the deepest: *Kubas* / Why don't you love me: *Blackwells* / One way ticket: *Various artists*/ Do you do it no more: *Kramer, Billy J. & The Dakotas* / How I won the war: *Musketeer Gripweed & The Third Troup*.
LP: CM 118

MERSEY BEAT (Various artists).
Tracks: / She loves you: *Beatles* / Sweets for my sweet: *Searchers* / Hippy hippy shake: *Swinging Blue Jeans*/ Do you love me: *Faron's Flamingoes* / Some other guy: *Big Three* / I'm the one: *Gerry/ Pacemakers* / Just a little bit: *Undertakers* / Money: *Taylor, Kingsize And The Dominoes* / Let's stomp: *Curtis, Lee And* The Allstars / Love of the loved: *Black, Cilla* / Baby I need your loving: *Fourmost* / Little children: *Kramer, Billy J.* / Ferry 'cross the mersey: *Gerry/ Pacemakers* / It's love that really counts: *Merseybeats* / I know: *Marsden, Beryl* / Wild side of life: *Quickly, Tommy* / Lies: *Sandon, Johnny And The Remo Four* / Watch your step: *Preston, Earl And The T T's* / I want to hold your hand: *Beatles* / Sugar and spice: *Searchers*/ Good golly Miss Molly: *Swinging Blue Jeans* / Reelin' and rockin': *Big Three* / Bad to me: *Kramer, Billy J.* / Beechwood: *Ian And The Zodiacs* / Honey don't: *Rhytm And Blues Incorporated* / One to cry, The: *Escorts*/ Ain't nobody like me babe: *Dennisons* / Everything's alright: *Mojos* / All my loving: *Trends* / Who told you: *Star, Freddie And The Midnighters* / Thousand stars, A: *Chants* / America: *Storm, Rory & The Hurricanes*/ I'm gonna knock on your door: *Best, Pete Four* / Magic potion: *Kubas* / Please stay: *Cryin' Shames*/ Tears on my pillow: *Dimensions* / Que sera sera: *Royce, Earl & The Olympics*.
2LP: PCSP 1783293
MCSET: TC 2 PCSP 1783

MERSEY SOUNDS (Various artists).
Tracks: / Cavern stomp: *Various artists* / Why did I fall in love with you: *Various artists* / I'm late: *Various* artists / I know: *Various artists* / Baby blue: *Various artists* / Skinny Minnie: *Various artists*/ Walk right back: *Various artists* / Be my girl: *Various artists* / Don't do it anymore: *Various artists*/ Twist and shout: *Various artists* / By the way: *Various artists* / Little you, A: *Various artists* / I've got my eyes on you: *Various artists* / Sticks & stones: *Various artists* / Give your lovin' to me: *Various artists* / You: *Various artists* / I'm with you: *Various artists* / I only care about you: *Various artists*/ I'm gonna knock on your door: *Various artists* / Everybody loves a lover: *Various artists* / I've got to know now: *Various artists* / I've been watching you: *Various artists* / We know: *Various artists* / Who told you: *Various artists* / Hurt me if you will: *Various artists* / Forever: *Various artists* / Don't start running away: *Various artists* / Do you love me: *Various artists* / Dance baby dance: *Various artists*/ They say: *Various artists* / Love is going to happen to me: *Various artists* / Peter Gunn locomotion: *Various artists* / Around: *Various artists* / Let's stomp: *Various artists* / Devoted to you: *Various artists*/ Reelin' & rockin': *Various artists*.
2LP: . . . . **DPA 3091/2**

THIS IS MERSEYBEAT (Various artists).
2LP: . . . . **DED 270**

Merseybeats

BEAT AND BALLADS.
Tracks: / Fortune teller / It's love that really counts / Really mystified / I think of you / Mister moonlight / Don't turn around / I'm gonna sit right down and cry over you / Wishin' and hopin' / Milkman / See me back / Don't let it happen to us / Last night / Fools like me / He will break your heart / I love you yes I do / I stand accused.
LP: . . . . **ED 105**

GREATEST HITS: MERSEYBEATS.
Tracks: / I think of you / Wishin' and hopin' / Fortune teller / Mister moonlight / It's love that really counts / I'll be home / Sorrow / Don't turn around / I love you yes I do / You can't judge a book by the cover / American dream.
LP: . . . . **LKLP 6160**

I THINK OF YOU (OLD GOLD) (See Four Pennies - Juliet for details).

MERSEYBEATS, THE.
LP: . . . . **TL 5210**
MC: **8427614**
LP: **8427611**

Mersinary

DEAD IS DEAD.
LP: . . . . **IW 1027**

Mertens, Wim

AFTER VIRTUE.
LP: . . . . **TWI 825**

INSTRUMENTAL SONGS.
LP: . . . . **TWI 666**

MAXIMIZING THE AUDIENCE.
2LP: . . . . **MASO 33042 43**
MC: . . . . **MASO 33042 43C**

Merthyr Lewis Band

WINTER CELEBRATION, A.
LP: . . . . **TB 3108**

Merton Parkas

FACE IN THE CROWD.
MC: . . . . **BEGC 11**
LP: . . . . **BBL 11**
MC: . . . . **BBLC 11**

Mervyn, Junior

APARTHEID.
Tracks: / Apartheid / Nuclear boom / Swell-headed black man / Mr. Percy / Too much division / Jah took six days / Quick to lick / Jack Slick / Handcuff / Third world girls.
LP: . . . . **GREL 95**

Mervyn Mouse

MERVYN MOUSE (rhyming stories for the very young) (Unknown narrator(s)).
MC: . . . . **PLB 86**

MERVYN MOUSE AT THE FAIR.
MC: . . . . **LL 41 8025 4**

MERVYN MOUSE AT THE ZOO.
MC: . . . . **LL 41 8026 4**

MERVYN MOUSE GOES CAMPING.
MC: . . . . **LL 41 8027 4**

Merzy

MERZY.
LP: . . . . **MMT 3303**

Meshuggah

CONTRADICTIONS AND ....
LP: . . . . **NB 049LP**

Mesing, Ron

NO MINORS ALLOWED.
LP: . . . . **FF 067**

Message

MESSAGE PART 2 Compilation recording (Various artists).
Tracks: / I don't know if I can make it: *Smith, Dawson* / Mama's got the wagon: *Murray, Mickey* / Message, the: *Cymande* / Mr. Bump man: *Beavers, Jackie* / Check your bucket: *Bo, Eddie* / Brothers on the slide: *Cymande*/ Mr. Brown: *African Music Machine* / Fug: *Cymande* / Bra: *Cymande* / Thank you: *Maceo & All The Kings Men.*
LP: . . . . **SHAKA 857 LP**

Message (Group)

ASTRAL JOURNEY.
Tracks: / Feeling so high / Places / City of fright / All in a dream / Soldiers / Life is short / World keeps on turning / I feel glad.
LP: **0060 165**

Message In The Music

MESSAGE IN THE MUSIC (Various artists).
LP: . . . . **ABYSSLP 1**
MC: . . . . **ABYSSMC 1**

Message People

AFRICAN PEOPLE.
LP: . . . . **MESS 1001**

Messaoud, Bellemou

LE PERE DU RAI.
LP: . . . . **WCB 011**
MC: . . . . **WCC 011**

Messenjah

COOL OPERATOR.
LP: . . . . **SHAN 43056**

Messer, Michael

DIVING DUCK.
Tracks: / Write me a few short lines / Hum hum dinger from Dingersville / Milk cow blues / Secret to a long life, The / Minnetonka stomp / Wild Canadian swan / If you were the river / Hula girl / Rollin' and tumblin' / Shouldn't do that / Brownsville blues / Death letter.
LP: . . . . **PTLP 002**
MC: . . . . **PTLC 002**

SLIDEDANCE (Messer, Michael Band).
Tracks: / Lone wolf, The / Hummingbird / What life brings / Hilo / Cherry blossom Hawaiian agency / Rolling in my sweet baby's arms / Dead sea scrolls / Doghouse / Savannah le mar / Sweetheart darling / Mannish boy.
MC: . . . . **MILC 003**

Messiaen (composer)

QUARTET FOR THE END OF TIME (Various artists).
MC: **422 834-4**

Messiah

EXTREME COLD WEATHER.
Tracks: / Extreme cold weather / Enjoy yourself / Johannes Paul der Letzie / Mother Theresa / Hyperborea / Radetzky march: We hate to be in the.. / Nero / Hymn To Abramelin / Messiah / Space invaders / Trashing madness / Golden dawn / Last inferno, The / Resurrection / Ole Perverus.
LP: . . . . **CM 004**

Messiah Force

LAST DAY, THE.
Tracks: / Sequel, The / Watch out / White night / Hero's saga / Third one, The / Call from the night / Spirit killer / Silent tyrant / Last day, The.
LP: . . . . **BRMLP 022**

Messiah Prophet

MASTER OF METAL.
Tracks: / Hit and run / Master of the metal / For whom does the bell toll / Fear no evil / Heavy metal thunder / Friend, The / Battle cry / Voice that's calling.
LP: . . . . **US 9**

Messina, Jim

OASIS.
Tracks: / New and different way / Do you want to dance / Seeing you for the first time / Free to be me / Talk to me / Love is here / Waitin' on you / Lovin' you lady / Magic of love.
LP: **83803**

Messina, Russ

ACCORDION IN THE MODERN MOOD.
Tracks: / Breezin' along / Gone with the wind / Cheek to cheek / Foggy day, A / Minor detail / All the things you are / Just one of those things / Get happy / Keepin' cool / Our love is here to stay / Blue moon / This can't be love.
LP: . . . . **ALP 106**

Messner, Johnny

JOHNNY MESSNER AND HOTEL MCALPIN ORCHESTRA 1939-1940 (Messner, Johnny/Hote McAlpin Orchestra).
Tracks: / Are you having any fun? / I give you my word / I can't love you / So you're the one / What's new / Toy piano jump / Accidently on purpose / It's a hundred to one / We three / Little man who wasn't there, The / Day in, day out / Can't we be friends?.
LP: . . . . **HSR 186**

Meta

SONGS AND DANCES FROM HUNGARY.
LP: . . . . **EULP 1068**
MC: . . . . **EUMC 1068**

Metal Church

BLESSING IN DISGUISE.
Tracks: / Fake healer / Rest in pieces / Of unsound mind / Anthem to the estranged / Badlands / Spell can't be broken, The / It's a secret / Cannot tell a lie / Powers that be, The.
LP: . . . . **K 96087 1**
MC: . . . . **K 96087 4**

DARK, THE.
Tracks: / Method of your madness / Watch the children play / Over my dead body / Dark, The / Psycho / Line of death / Burial at sea / Western alliance / Ton of bricks / Start the fire.
LP: **960 493-1**
MC: **9604034**

HUMAN FACTOR, THE.
Tracks: / Human factor, The / Date with poverty / Final word, The / In mourning / In harm's way / In due time / Agent green / Flee from reality / Betrayed / Fight song, The.
LP: **4678161**
MC: **4678164**

METAL CHURCH: INTERVIEW PICTURE DISC.
LPPD: . . . . **BAK 2146**

MUSIC AND MEDIA INTERVIEW PICTURE DISCS.
LPPD: . . . . **MM 1255**

Metal Duck

AUTO DUCKO DESTRUCTO MONDO.
Tracks: / Gore littoral / Duckulla assault / Drunk and a flirt / Smell of sex / To kill again / Gate of Asgard / Twilight zone / Rod, Jane and Freddy (part two) / Mean, green and pink / Well fu(n)ked up / In death / Apollyon communique.
LP: . . . . **CMO 196**

QUACK EM ALL (Metal Duck & Lawnmower Death).
LP: . . . . **CMO 192**

Metal Massacre

METAL MASSACRE 10 (Various artists).
LP: . . . . **ZORRO 4**

Metal Messiah

HONOUR AMONG THIEVES.
Tracks: / Intro / Mad dogs of war / Madman / Kiss of Nosferatu / Honour among thieves / Metal messiah / Curse of the king / Nightwing / Awakening, The.
LP: . . . . **CMO 195**

Metal Onslaught

CEASE TO EXIST.
Tracks: / Waiting for death / Chester / Welcome to my hell / Redneck / Victims of the axe / Cease to exist / Run For Your Life / Death do us part / Buttf..k.
LP: . . . . **SHARK 003**

Metal Urbaine

L'AGE D'OR.
LP: . . . . **FC 011**

Metal Virgins

ANIMAL PEOPLE.
LP: . . . . **MV 1**

Metallica

AND JUSTICE FOR ALL.
Tracks: / Blackened / Shortest straw, The / Eye of the beholder / Shortest straw, The / Frayed ends of sanity, The / Dyes eve / And justice for all / One / Harvester of sorrow / To live is to die.
LP: . . . . **VERH 61**
MC: . . . . **VERHC 61**

CHRIS TETLEY INTERVIEWS METALLICA.
LPPD: . . . . **CT 1008**

END OF THE WORLD AS WE KNOW IT, THE (Interview picture disc).
LPPD: . . . . **BAK 6011**
MC: . . . . **MBAK 6011**

GARAGE DAYS REVISITED.
MC: **888 788 4**
LP: **888 788 1**

KILL 'EM ALL.
Tracks: / Hit the lights / Four horsemen / Motorbreath / Jump in the fire / Pulling teeth (Anesthesia) / Whiplash / Phantom lord / No remorse / Seek and destroy / Metal militia.
2LP: . . . . **MFN 7DM**
LP: . . . . **MFN 7**
LP: **8381421**
MC: **8381424**
MC: . . . . **TMFN 7**

MASTER OF PUPPETS.
Tracks: / Battery / Master of puppets / Thing that should not be, The / Welcome home (sanitarium) / Disposable heroes / Leper messiah / Orion / Damage Inc..
LP: . . . . **MFN 60**
MC: . . . . **TMFN 60**
LPPD: . . . . **MFN 60P**
2LP: . . . . **MFN 60DM**
LP: **8381411**
MC: **8381414**
MC: **8384874**
LP: **8384871**

METALLICA.
Tracks: / Creeping death / Am I evil? / Blitzkrieg / Jump in the fire / Seek and destroy (live) / Phantom Lord (live).
MC: **8422194**

METALLICA (2).
MC: **5100224**
LP: **5100221**

METALLICA: INTERVIEW PICTURE DISC VOL.2.
LPPD: . . . . **BAK 2163**

METALLICA: INTERVIEW PICTURE DISC.
LPPD: . . . . **BAK 2066**

MUSIC AND MEDIA INTERVIEW PICTURE DISC.
LPPD: . . . . **MM 1253**

RIDE THE LIGHTNING.
Tracks: / Fight fire with fire / Ride the lightning / For whom the bell tolls / Fade to black / Trapped under ice / Escape / Creeping death / Call of Ktulu, The.
LPPD: . . . . **MFN 27P**
LP: . . . . **MFN 27**
MC: . . . . **TMFN 27**
LP: **8384101**
MC: **8384104**
2LP: . . . . **MFN 27DM**

Metamorphosis

GREAT BABEL GIVES BIRTH.
LP: . . . . **FM 003**
LP: . . . . **TMPL 4**

Meteors

CURSE OF THE MUTANTS.
Tracks: / Mutant rock / Insane / Scream of the mutants / When a stranger calls / Fear of the dark / Hills have eyes, The / Wild thing / Get off my cloud / Wrecking crew / Zombie noise / Johnny remember me / Phantom of the opera / Blue sunshine / I dont worry about it / Axe attack / Rattle snake daddy.
LP: . . . . **DOJOLP 2**

DON'T TOUCH THE BANG BANG FRUIT.
Tracks: / Go buddy go / Midnight people / Low livin' daddy / Your worst nightmare / Wildkat ways / Repo man / Crack me up / Shakey snakey / Psycho kat / Let's go / Revenge of El Trio Los Bastardos / Don't touch the bang bang fruit.
LP: . . . . **GRAM 30**
MC: . . . . **CGRAM 30**
LP: **KIX4U 3343**

LIVE AND LOUD.
LP: . . . . **LINK LP 06**

LIVE: METEORS.
Tracks: / Wipe out / Maniac rockers from hell / Lonesome train / I ain't ready / Ain't gonna bring me down / Sick things / Crazy lovin' / When a stranger calls / Rawhide / I don't worry about it / Voodoo rhythm / You crack me up / Mutant rock / Graveyard stomp / Wrecking crew / Long blonde hair.
LPPD: . . . . **DOJOLP 4P**
LP: . . . . **WRECK 1**
LP: **66060**
LP: . . . . **DOJOLP 4**

LIVE OF THE SICK AND SHAMELESS.
Tracks: / Ex man boogie / Wipe out / Rattle snake daddy / Mutant rock / Maniac / Blue sunshine / Mind over matter / These boots are made for walking / Little Red Riding Hood / Hills have eyes, The / Wild thing / I go to bed with the undead / Voodoo rhythm / I ain't ready / Wreckin' crew / Lonesome train (CD only.) / Rock bop (CD only.) / Ain't gonna bring me down (CD only.) / Graveyard stomp (CD only.).
LP: . . . . **GRAM 45**
MC: . . . . **CGRAM 45**

LIVE VOL. 2.
Tracks: / Torture / Sweet love on my mind / Mutant rock / Rhythm of the bell / Big Sandy / Rock house / Michael Myers / Meat is meat / Li'l Red Riding Hood / Voodoo rhythm / Long blonde hair / Rock-bop.

LP: . . . . DOJOLP 22

METEORS.
Tracks: / Wipe out / Maniac rockers from hell / I ain't ready / Lonesome train / A int gonna bring me down / Sick things / Crazy love / When a stranger calls / Voodoo rhythm / Mutant rock / I dont worry about it / Rawhide / These boots were made for walking / Graveyard stomp / Long blonde hair / Wrecking crew.
LP: . . . . MAD 1

MONKEY BREATH.
LP: . . . . CHOP 2

MONKEYS BREATH/STAMPEDE.
Tracks: / X men boogie / Power of steel / Hoover rock / Kick boy / Eat the baby / Maybe tomorrow / Hogs and cuties / Alligator man / Rhythm of the bell / Sweet love on my mind / Meat is meat / Take a ride / Just the three of us / Jobba's snake / Night of the werewolf / Ain't gonna bring me down / Electro / Stampede / I'm just a dog / In too deep / Cecil drives a combine harvester / Michael Myers / Out of the dark / Only a fury in my heart / Do the demolition / Out of time.
2LP: . . . . DCHOP 1

MUTANT MONKEY AND THE SURFERS FROM ZORCH.
Tracks: / Swamp thing / Electro II (the revenge) / Side walk psycho / I'm invisible man / She's my baby again / Surfin' on the planet Zorch / Spine bender / Dance crazy baby / Rawhide / Oxygen dog / Yellow zone / Meet me in the morgue.
LP: . . . . GRAM 37

NIGHT OF THE WEREWOLFS.
Tracks: / X-men boogie / Rawhide / Maniac / Rock house / Just a dog / Stampede / Deep dark jungle / Hills have eyes, The / Kit boy / Domino / Shout so loud / Night of the Were-Wolf / Graveyard stomp / These boots are made for walking / It's all over now.
LP: . . . . DOJOLP 56

ONLY THE METEORS ARE PURE PSYCHOBILLY.
Tracks: / Voodoo rhythm / Graveyard stomp / Wrecking crew / Sick things / Blue sunshine / Mutant rock / Hills have eyes, The / Fire fire / Power of steel / Eat the baby / Rhythm of the bell / Sure city / Go buddy go / Somebody put something in my drink.
LP: . . . . GRAM 33
MC: . . . . CGRAM 33

SEWERTIME BLUES.
Tracks: / Ain't taking a chance / So sad / Here's Johnny / Mind over matter / Acid and psyam / Sewertime blues / Return of Ethel Merman / Deep dark jungle / Never get away / I bury the living / Vibrate / Surf city / Go Buddy go / Midnight people / Low livin' daddy / Your worst nightmare / Wildkat ways / Repo man / Don't touch the bang bang fruit / Crack me up / Shakey shakey / Psycho kat / Let's go / Revenge of the el trio los bastados.
MC: . . . . CGRAM 27
LP: . . . . GRAM 27
LP: KIX4U 3338

STAMPEDE.
Tracks: / Ex man boogie / Power of steel / Hoover rock / Kit boy / Maybe tomorrow / Electro / Stampede / Just a dog / In too deep / Cecil drives a combine harvester / Michael Myers / Only a fury in my heart / Hogs and cuties / Alligator man / Rhythm of the bell / Your out of time / Ain't gonna bring me down / Night of the werewolf / Take a ride / Just the three of us / Meat is meat / Jobba's revenge.
LP: . . . . CHOP 1
LP: KIX4U 3333

TEENAGE HEART.
Tracks: / Action / It's you, only you / Teenage heart / Wired / Orbit / Blitzkrieg / Everything I touch turns into gold / Nina / My balls ache / Berlin / Hold me tight.
LP: . . . . EMC 3315

TEENAGERS FROM OUTER SPACE.
Tracks: / Voodoo rhythm / Maniac rockers from hell / My daddy is a vampire / You can't keep a good man down / Graveyard stomp / Radioactive kid / Leave me alone / Dog eat robot / Walter Mitty blues / Just the three of us / Blue sunshine / Insight / Attack of the zorch men / Jupiter stroll / Another half hour till sunrise (Available on CD only) / Island of lost souls (Available on CD only) / Napoleon solo, The (Available on CD only) / Get me to the world on time (Available on CD only).
LP: . . . . WIKA 47

UNDEAD, UNFRIENDLY AND UNSTOPABLE.
Tracks: / Razorback / Disneyland / My kind of rockin' / Lonesome train / Johnny God / I go to bed with the undead / Out of the attic / Brains as well / Charlie Johnny Rawhead and me / Lies in wait / Surf mad pig / Please don't touch.
LP: . . . . GRAM 43
MC: . . . . CGRAM 43

WRECKIN' CREW.
Tracks: / Wrecking crew / Scream of the mutants / Hills have eyes, The / Mutant rock.
LP: . . . . NOSE 1

Meters

BEST OF THE METERS.
Tracks: / Jungle man / Hey pocky away / Can you do without / Just kissed my baby / Love slip upon you / People say / Africa / Fire on the Bayou.
LP: . . . . K 54076

GOOD OLD FUNKY MUSIC.
Tracks: / Look-ka-py-py / Seahorn's farm / Art / Ease back / Cissy strut / Message from the Meters / Thinking / Good old funky music / Live wire / Stretch your rubber band / Doodle-opp / Tippi-toes / Rigor mortis / 9 'til 5 / Sophisticated Cissy / Chicken strut / Here comes the meter man / Darling darling / Dry spell / Ride your pony.
LP: . . . . PKL 5578
LP: . . . . SPD 1039
MC: . . . . SPDC 1039

HERE COME THE METERMEN.
Tracks: / Sophisticated cissy / Here come the Metermen / Mob, The / Funky miracle / Ride your pony / Art / Dry spell / Thinking / Handclapping song / Britches / Liver splash / Joog / Same old thing / 6V6 LA / Sehorns farm / Sing a simple song.
LP: . . . . CRB 1112

NEW DIRECTIONS.
Tracks: / No more okey doke / I'm gone / Be my lady / My name up in lights / Funkify your life / Stop that train / We got the kind of love / Give it what you can.
LP: . . . . K 56378

SECOND LINE STRUT.
Tracks: / Look-ka py py / Nine til five / Cissy strut / I need more time / Pungee / Ease back / Cardova / Yeah, you're right / Tippi-toes / Chicken strut / Sassy lady / Little money maker / Rigor mortis / Live wire / Message from the Meters, A / Hey last minute.
LP: . . . . CRB 1009

Metheny, Mike

DAY IN-NIGHT OUT.
Tracks: / Like the ocean / Day in-night out / Vanity / Segment / Suadade / Olvidar / Lakeview ballad / Epilogue.
LP: . . . . IMCA 5755
MC: . . . . IMCAC 5755

Metheny, Pat

80-81.
Tracks: / Goin' ahead / Two folk songs / Bat / Turn around / Open / Pretty scattered / Everyday I thank you.
MCSET: 3541180
2LP: . . . . ECM 1180

ABSOLUTELY LIVE.
LP: . . . . PLP 17
MC: . . . . PMC 17

AMERICAN GARAGE.
Tracks: / Heartland (Cross the) / Airstream / Search, The / American garage / Epic.
LP: . . . . ECM 1155
MC: 3101155

AS FALLS WICHITA, SO FALLS WICHITA FALLS (Metheny, Pat & Lyle Mays).
Tracks: / As falls Wichita, so falls Wichita Falls / September 15th / It's for you / Estupenda graca.
LP: . . . . ECM 1190
MC: 7200189

BRIGHT SIZE LIFE.
Tracks: / Bright size life / Sirabhorn / Unity village / Missouri incompromised / Midwestern nights dream / Unquity road / Omaha celebration / Round trip-Broadway blues.
LP: . . . . ECM 1073

FIRST CIRCLE (Metheny, Pat Group).
Tracks: / Forward march / Yolanda / You learn / First circle, The / If I could / Tell it all / End of the game, The / Mas alla (beyond) / Praise.
LP: . . . . ECM 1278

LETTER FROM HOME (Metheny, Pat Group).
MC: . . . . GEFC 24245
LP: . . . . GEF 24245

LIVE IN CONCERT (Metheny, Pat, Heath Bros, Dave Brubeck Quartet, B B King).
Tracks: / Introduction / Move to the groove / Lover man / Blue rondo a la turk / Ol' Bill Basie / Thrill is gone, The / Guess who? / Pay in the cost to be the boss / Move to the groove / Lover man / Blue rondo a la turk / Ol' Bill Basie / Thrill is gone, The / Guess who / Payin' the cost to be the boss.
LP: . . . . GATE 7017
MC: . . . . CGATE 7017

NEW CHAUTAUQUA.
Tracks: / New chautauqua / Country poem / Long-ago child / Fallen star, A / Hermitage / Sueno con Mexico / Daybreak.
LP: . . . . ECM 1131

OFFRAMP.
Tracks: / Barcarolle / Are you going with me? / Au lait / Eighteen / Offramp / James / Bat, The (part 2).
LP: . . . . ECM 1216
MC: 3101216

PAT METHENY GROUP (Metheny, Pat Group).
LP: . . . . ECM 1114

QUESTION AND ANSWER (Metheny, Pat/Dave Holland/Roy Haynes).
LP: 7599242931
MC: 7599242934
MC: . . . . GEFC 24293

REJOICING.
Tracks: / Lonely woman / Tears inside / Humpty dumpty / Blues for Pat / Rejoicing / Story from a stranger / Calling, The / Waiting for an answer.
LP: . . . . ECM 1271

SONG X (See under Coleman, Ornette).

STILL LIFE (TALKING) (Metheny, Pat Group).
Tracks: / Minuano / So may it secretly begin / Last train home / It's just talk / Third wind / Distance / In her family.
LP: 9241451
MC: 9241454

TRAVELS (Metheny, Pat Group).
Tracks: / Are you going with me? / Fields, the sky, The / Goodbye / Phase dance / Straight on red / Farmer's trust / Extradition / Goin' ahead / As falls Wichita, so falls Wichita Falls / Travels / Song for Bilbao / San Lorenzo.
2LP: . . . . ECM 1252

WATERCOLOURS.
Tracks: / Watercolours / Icefire / Lakes, The / River Quay / Florida Greeting song / 11 - Legend of the fountain / Sea song.
LP: . . . . ECM 1097

WORKS II: PAT METHENY.
Tracks: / Uniquity Road / Unity village / Open / Story from a stranger / Oasis / Sirabhorn / Farmer's trust.
LP: 8372721

WORKS: PAT METHENY.
Tracks: / Sueno con Mexico / (Cross the) heartland / Travels / James / It's for you / Everyday I thank you / Goin' ahead.
LP: 8232701
MC: 3100 389

Method Actors

LITTLE FIGURES.
LP: . . . . P 4002
LP: . . . . MAD 1

LIVE IN A ROOM.
LP: . . . . P 2006

LUXURY.
Tracks: / Beating on a drum / House on fire / Detective / Luxury / You the international language / Problem / Another world / All tomorrows parties / Can't act / Planet whales / Pumkin eaters / Annoymous / M.R.K.S..
2LP: . . . . P 4004

LUXURY PLUS.
MLP: . . . . P 2012

Methods Of Silence

CAMOUFLAGE.
LP: 782 002 1
MC: 782 002 4

Metro

FUTURE IMPERFECT.
Tracks: / Going up in flames / Alone / Promise / Exterminating angels / Face / America in my head / Gemini / Middle of the night.
LP: . . . . EMC 3334
MC: . . . . TCEMC 3334

JOURNEY THROUGH THE N.Y. UNDERGROUND.
LP: . . . . LICMLP 36

NEW LOVE.
Tracks: / Cut up / Now I wanna dance / Christine / Madness is a virtue / Mystery / New love / Underworld / Woman zone.
LP: . . . . EMC 3295

Metro, Peter

DEDICATED TO YOU (Metro, Peter & Friends).
Tracks: / To you / Lord ho / Vegetable dish / Seems to me / Rock her / Want some money / Mi queen / Bossanova / Love letter / Warn them / Girl is mine, The.
LP: . . . . CSLP 12

NO PROBLEM.
Tracks: / No problem / Memories of Anadulsia.
LP: . . . . DSR 8384

SINBAD AND METRIC SYSTEM (See under Captain Sinbad) (Metro, Peter & Captain Sinbad).

WHAT KIND OF WORLD ARE WE LIVING IN? (see Campbell, Cornell) (Metro, Peter and Cornell Campbell).

YES DADDY (Metro, Peter & Jackie Statement).
Tracks: / Yes daddy.
LP: . . . . DSR 8372

Metropolis

EUROPEAN SUITE, THE.
Tracks: / Theme from liberty / London / Paris / Wien / Dublin / Athinai / Madrid.
LP: . . . . HH 1
MC: . . . . ZCHH 1

METROPOLIS.
LP: . . . . CCF 4
LP: . . . . CBS 70252

METROPOLIS Original London cast (Various artists).
Tracks: / One hundred and one point eleven: *Various artists* / Hold back the night: *Various artists* / Machines are beautiful, The: *Various artists* / He's distant from me now: *Various artists* / Elitists' dance: *Various artists* / Oh my, what a beautiful city: *Various artists* / This is the vision we're forbidden: *Various artists*/ Children of Metropolis: *Various artists* / Fifty thousand pounds of power: *Various artists* / One more morning: *Various artists* / It's only love: *Various artists* / Bring on the night: *Various artists* / Pressure chant: *Various artists* / Day after day: *Various artists* / When Maria comes: *Various artists* / You are the light: *Various artists* / Girl is a witch, The: *Various artists* / It's only love (reprise): *Various artists*/ Sun, The: *Various artists* / Almost done: *Various artists* / I don't need help from you: *Various artists*/ There's a girl down below: *Various artists* / Futura: *Various artists* / End of act one: *Various artists*/ We're the cream: *Various artists* / I've seen a nightmare: *Various artists* / This is life: *Various artists*/ Look at this girl who stands before you: *Various artists* / Futura's dance: *Various artists* / Where do you think she's gone, your precious Maria?: *Various artists* / If that was love: *Various artists* / Listen to me: *Various* artists / Learning song: *Various artists* / Old friends: *Various artists* / When Maria wakes: *Various* artists / Futura's promise: *Various artists* / Maria's insane: *Various artists* / Perfect face: *Various* artists / Haven't you finished with me?: *Various artists* / Let's watch the world go to the devil: *Various artists*/ One of those nights: *Various artists* / Requiem: *Various artists* / Metropolis: *Various artists* / Finale: *Various artists*.
2LP: TER2 1168
MCSET: ZCTER2 1168

Metropolitan Police...

METROPOLITAN POLICE BAND (Directed by Captain C. Taylor) (Metropolitan Police Band).
Tracks: / Fan-fare / Metropolitan march / Bright eyes march / Policeman's holiday / Because / Pomp and circumstance / Clarinet polka / Big beat, The / Estrellita / Come back to Sorrento / Oliver (medley).
LP: . . . . PRD 2001

ON THE BEAT WITH THE METROPOLITAN POLICE BAND (Metropolitan Police Band).
LP: 2460 270

RHAPSODY IN BLUE (Metropolitan Police Band).
LP: . . . . DR 2
MC: . . . . CR 2

Metsers, Paul

CAUTION TO THE WIND.
LP: . . . . SHY 7014

FIFTH QUARTER.
LP: . . . . SGM 479

IN THE HURRICANE'S EYE.
LP: . . . . SGM 279

MOMENTUM.
LP: . . . . SHY 7021

PACIFIC PILGRIM.
LP: . . . . SGM 379

Mexican State...

SORCERER'S APPRENTICE, THE (Mexican State Symphony Orchestra).
Tracks: / Le corsaire overture (Berlioz) / Espana (Chabrier) / Prelude to the afternoon of a faun (Debussy) / Sorcerer's apprentice, The (Dukas) / Pavane for a dead infanta (Ravel) /

Danse macabre (Saint-Saens) / Wedding cake caprice (Saint-Saens).
MC: . . . . **ZC QS 6026**

SYMPHONY NO.2/PRINCE IGOR EXCERPTS (see under Borodin) (Mexican State Symphony Orchestra).

Mexicano

ALONE AGAIN.
Tracks: / Just the way you are / First of May / Annie's song.
LP: . . . . **ICE L 1012**

GODDESS OF LOVE.
LP: . . . . **ICE L 1003**

MOVE UP STARSKY.
LP: . . . . **PION LP 1**

Mexico...

HEART OF MEXICO (Various artists).
LP: . . . . **GNPS 53**
MC: **GNP5 53**

MEXICAN MUSIC (Various artists).
LP: . . . . **RHS 365**

MEXICAN REVOLUTION (Various artists).
LPS: . . . . **FL 9041/4**
MCSET: . . . . **C 9041/4**

MEXICO'S MARIACHIS (Various artists).
MC: . . . . **C 225**

MISAS Y FIESTAS MEXICANAS (Various artists).
Tracks: / Misa panamericana (messe des mariachis): *Various artists* / Misa tepozteca: *Various artists* / La charreada: *Various artists* / Sones de michoacan: *Various artists* / El taconaso: *Various artists* / Hymne au soleil: *Various artists* / Danza de los negritos: *Various artists* / Danza de los voladores: *Various artists*/ Danza de los viejitos: *Various artists*.
LP: . . . . **ARN 34174**
MC: . . . . **ARN 434174**

MUSIC OF MEXICO (Various artists).
MC: . . . . **C 208**

MUSIC OF MEXICO VOL. 1 (Sones jarochos) (Various artists).
LP: . . . . **ARHOOLIE 3008**

MUSIC OF MEXICO VOL. 2 (Sones huastecos) (Various artists).
LP: . . . . **ARHOOLIE 3009**

PSALMS, STORIES & MUSIC OF THE TZOTZILS PEOPLE (Various artists).
LP: . . . . **SUB 33012 17**

Mexico City...

1812 OVERTURE (see under Tchaikovsky) (Mexico City Philharmonic Orchestra).

FAURE VIOLIN CONCERTO (see under Faure (composer)) (Orquesta Filarmonica de la Ciudad de Mexico).

PIANO CONCERTO NO.3 (RACHMANINOV) (see under Rachmaninov) (Mexico City Symphony Orchestra/Jorge Luis Prats).

Meyer, Edgar

DREAMS OF FLIGHT.
Tracks: / Webbed feet / Dreams of flight / Moderato (from Amalgamations for solo bass) / Expedition, The / For Dotsy / Andante (from Trio) / Moderato (from Trio) / Allegro vivace / Life in Antartica (Is cold and lonely).
MC: . . . . **IMCAC 5964**
LP: . . . . **IMCA 5964**

UNFOLDING.
Tracks: / Unfolding / Cottonwood / My pet frog / Duet / After dark / Early morning.
LP: . . . . **IMCA 5694**
MC: . . . . **IMCAC 5694**

Meyers, Augie

AUGIE'S BACK.
LP: . . . . **SNTF 955**

AUGUST IN NEW YORK.
Tracks: / Baby of mine / Before I grow too old / Don't turn away / Looking for the money / Cruisin' (on a Saturday night) / I'm not someone you want / All my life / Missing you / Sugar blue / Money / To nothing at all.
LP: . . . . **SNTF 910**

FINALLY IN LIGHTS (Meyers, Augie & Doug Shams).
Tracks: / Release me / Deep in the heart of Texas / Cryin' out loud / It's alright / My friend / Sky high / Deed to Texas / Miller's cave / Don't let me / Baby, baby.
LP: . . . . **SNTF 803**

STILL GROWING.
LP: . . . . **SNTF 883**

Meyers, Steve

LOVE'S GONNA LAST.
MC: . . . . **STEC 02**
LP: . . . . **STELP 02**

Meynell, Anthony

HITS FROM 3000 YEARS AGO (Meynell, Anthony & Squire).
LP: . . . . **LO 1**

SEPTEMBER GIRLS (Meynell, Anthony & Squire).
LP: . . . . **HIS 005**

Mezcla

FRONTERAS DE SUENOS.
Tracks: / La Guagua / Fronteras de Suenos / La mulata de Caramelo / Ikiri adda / Rio quibu / Vivir para ver / Como una campana de cristal / Muros transparentes / Ando buscando uno amor.
LP: . . . . **INT 30471**
MC: . . . . **INT 30474**

Mezzoforte

CATCHING UP WITH MEZZOFORTE.
LP: . . . . **STELP 03**
MC: . . . . **STEC 03**

MEZZOFORTE.
LP: . . . . **STE 01**

NO LIMIT.
MC: . . . . **MEZZC 08**
LP: . . . . **MEZZLP 08**

OBSERVATIONS.
Tracks: / Midnight sun / Spring fever / Summer dream / Venue, The / Rockall / Double orange juice / We're only here for the beer / Observations / Distance.
LP: . . . . **STELP 04**
MC: . . . . **STEC 04**

PLAYING FOR TIME.
Tracks: / Playing for time / Expressway / Magic / Take a breath / Prime time / Hitchiker / High season / Quick step / In a word.
LP: . . . . **PL 74056**
MC: . . . . **PK 74056**

RISING.
Tracks: / Check it in / Take off / Happy hour / Waves / Blizzard / Solid / Northern comfort / Fiona rising / Check it out.
LP: . . . . **STELP 06**
MC: . . . . **STEC 06**

SURPRISE SURPRISE.
Tracks: / Garden party / Action man / Funk suite no. 1 / Easy Jack / Fusion blues / Early party / Surprise / Gazing at the clouds / Old neighbourhood, The.
LP: . . . . **STELP 07**
MC: . . . . **NK 74131**

Mezzron

THEN CAME THE KILLING.
Tracks: / Then came the killing / Final holocaust, The / Distant death / Where death begins / Ancient terror / Frozen soul / Prevent necessary / Cross of torment, The.
LP: . . . . **ATV 11**

Mezzrow, Mezz

CLARINET MARMALADE.
LP: **500065**

IN PARIS 1955.
LP: . . . . **SW 8409**

Mezzrow-Bechet

KING JAZZ VOL.5 (Mezzrow-Bechet Quintet & Septet).
LP: . . . . **SLP 4115**

KING JAZZ VOL 1 (Mezzrow-Bechet Quintet & Septet).
LP: . . . . **SLP 6004**

KING JAZZ VOL 2 (Mezzrow-Bechet Quintet & Septet).
LP: . . . . **SLP 6005**

KING JAZZ VOL 3 (Mezzrow-Bechet Quintet & Septet).
LP: . . . . **SLP 6006**

KING JAZZ VOL 4 (Mezzrow-Bechet Quintet & Septet).
LP: . . . . **SLP 6007**

MEZZROW/BECHET QUINTET/ SEPTET (THE) (Mezzrow-Bechet Quintet & Septet).
LP: . . . . **SLP 820/1**

OUT OF THE GALLION.
LP: . . . . **SLP 837**

REALLY THE BLUES (Mezzrow Bechet Quintet).
LP: . . . . **SLP 137**

M.F.Q.

MOONLIGHT SERENADE.
Tracks: / Moonlight serenade / Laura / Look for the silver lining / Brooklyn girl / Harbour lights / Dream / Rendezvous / Stella by starlight / After you've gone / Once in a while / As time goes by / September song.
LP: . . . . **WIK 55**

MFSB

GAMBLE-HUFF ORCHESTRA, THE.
Tracks: / Dance with me tonight / To be in love / Let's party down / Wishing on a star / Use ta be my guy / Is it something I said / Redwood Beach.
LP: . . . . **PIR 83010**

MYSTERIES OF THE WORLD.
Tracks: / Manhattan skyline / Mysteries of the world / Tell me why / Metamorphosis / Fortune teller / Old San Juan / Thank you Miss Scott / In the shadow.
LP: . . . . **PIR 84521**

MG Cars Documentary

MG JUST FOR THE RECORD - VOL.1 (Various).
LP: . . . . **WES 88000**

Mgema, Mbonegeni

TIME TO UNITE.
Tracks: / Afrika / Melody maker (madlokuvu) / Mafufanye / Time to unite / Bhulukwe lokuswenka / Simelane / Brrr / Umagumede.
MC: . . . . **ICT 9912**
LP: . . . . **ILPS 9912**

MGM Musicals

THOSE MAGNIFICENT MGM MUSICALS Vol. 1 1939-1952 (Various artists).
Tracks: / Over the rainbow: *Garland, Judy* (Wizard of Oz.) / Ol' man river: *Peterson, Caleb* (Till the clouds roll by.) / Look for the silver lining: *Garland, Judy* (Till the clouds roll by.) / Leave it to Jane and Cleopatterer: *Allyson,* June (Till the clouds roll by.) / Can't help lovin' dat man: *Horne, Lena* (Till the clouds roll by.) / Who?: *Garland,* Judy (Till the clouds roll by.) / Best things in life are free, The: *Allyson, June/Peter Lawford* (Good news.) / Pass that peace pipe: *McCracken, Joan* (Good news.) / Lucky in love: *Marshall, Pat/Peter Lawford/ June Allyson* (Good news.) / Varsity drag, The: *Allyson, June/Peter Lawford* (Good news.) / Steppin' out with my baby: *Astaire, Fred*(Easter parade) / Fella with an umbrella, A: *Garland, Judy/ Peter Lawford* (Easter Parade.) / Shaking the blues: *Miller,* Ann (Easter Parade.) / Couple of swells, A: *Garland, Judy & Fred Astaire* (Easter Parade.) / Easter parade: *Garland,* Judy & Fred Astaire (Easter Parade.) / Manhattan: *Rooney, Mickey* (Words and music.) / Johnny one note: *Garland,* Judy (Words and music.) / Lady is a tramp, The: *Horne, Lena* (Words and music.) / I wish I were in love again: *Rooney,* Mickey/ Judy Garland (Words and music.) / Where or when: *Horne, Lena* (Words and music.) / Thou swell: *Allyson,* June (Words and music.) / Be a clown: *Garland, Judy/Gene Kelly* (The Pirate.) / Love of my life: *Garland, Judy*(The Pirate.) / I don't care: *Garland, Judy* (In the good old summertime.) / Meet me tonight in dreamland: *Garland,* Judy (In the good old summertime.) / Play that barber shop chord: *Garland, Judy & The King's Men* (In the good old summertime.) / Last night when we were young: *Garland, Judy* (In the good old summertime.) / Put your arms around me honey: *Garland, Judy* (In the good old summertime.) / Merry Christmas: *Various artists* (In the good old summertime.) / Pagan love song: *Keel, Howard* (Pagan love song.) / House of singing bamboo: *Keel, Howard* (Pagan love song.) / Who's sorry now?: *De Haven, Gloria* (Three little words.) / I wanna be loved by you: *Kane, Helen* (Three little words.) / Nevertherless (I'm in love with you): *Astaire, Fred/Red Skelton/Anita Ellis* (Three little words.) / I love you so much: *Dahl, Arlene* (Three little words.) / Where did you get that girl: *Astaire, Fred/Anita Ellis* (Three little words.) / Get happy: *Garland, Judy* (Summer Stock (UK: If you feel like singing)) / Howdy neighbour happy harvest: *Garland,* Judy (Summer Stock (UK: If you feel like singing)) / You wonderful you: *Kelly, Gene* (Summer Stock (UK: If you feel like singing)) / Friendly star: *Garland, Judy* (Summer Stock (UK: If you feel like singing)) / Heavenly music: *Kelly,* Gene/Phil Silvers (Summer Stock (UK: If you feel like singing)) / If you feel like singing, sing: *Garland, Judy* (Summer Stock (UK: If you feel like singing)) / Dig-dig-dig-dig for your dinner: *Kelly, Gene/Phil Silvers* (Summer Stock (UK: If you feel like singing)) / Aba daba honeymoon: *Carpenter, Carleton/Debbie Reynolds* (Two weeks with love.) / By the light of the silvery moon: *Powell, Jane* (Two weeks with love.) / Row, row, row: *Carpenter, Carleton/Debbie Reynolds*(Two weeks with love.) / My hero: *Powell, Jane* (Two weeks with love.) / Ol' man river: *Warfield, William* (Showboat.) / Make believe: *Keel, Howard/Kathryn Grayson* (Showboat.) / I might fall back on you: *Champion, Marge & Gower*(Showboat.) / Can't help lovin' dat man: *Gardner, Ava* (Showboat.) / Why do I love you: *Keel, Howard/Kathryn Grayson*(Showboat.) / Bill: *Gardner, Ava* (Showboat.) / Life upon the wicked stage: *Champion, Marge & Gower* (Showboat.) / You are love: *Keel, Howard/Kathryn Grayson* (Showboat.) / Wonder why?: *Powell, Jane* (Rich, young and pretty.) / Paris: *Lamas, Fernando* (Rich, young and pretty.) / I can see you: *Powell, Jane* (Rich, young and pretty.) / There's danger in your eyes, cherie: *Darrieux, Danielle* (Rich, young and pretty.) / Too late now: *Powell, Jane*(Royal wedding (UK: Wedding bells).) / Ev'ry night at seven: *Astaire, Fred* (Royal wedding (UK: Wedding bells).) / Happiest day of my life, The: *Powell, Jane* (Royal wedding (UK: Wedding bells).) / I left my hat in Haiti: *Astaire, Fred*(Royal wedding (UK: Wedding bells).) / You're all the world to me: *Astaire, Fred* (Royal wedding (UK: Wedding bells).) / How could you believe me when I said I love you: *Astaire, Fred/Jane Powell* (Royal wedding (UK: Wedding bells).) / 'S wonderful: *Kelly, Gene/Georges Guetary* (An American in Paris.) / Love is here to stay: *Kelly, Gene* (An American in Paris.) / I'll build a stairway to paradise: *Guetary, Georges* (An American in Paris.) / I got rhythm: *Kelly, Gene* (An American in Paris.) / Singin' in the rain: *Kelly, Gene* (Singin' in the rain.) / Fit as a fiddle: *Kelly, Gene/Donald* O'Connor (Singin' in the rain.) / You were meant for me: *Kelly, Gene* (Singin' in the rain.) / Make 'em laugh: *O'Connor,* Donald (Singin' in the rain.) / Good morning: *Kelly, Gene/Donald O'Connor* (Singin' in the rain.) / All I do is dream of you: *Kelly, Gene* (Singin' in the rain.) / Moses: *Kelly, Gene/Donald O'Connor* (Singin' in the rain.) / You are my lucky star: *Kelly, Gene/Debbie Reynolds* (Singin' in the rain.) / Oops: *Astaire, Fred* (Belle of New York.) / Naughty but nice: *Ellis, Anita* (Belle of New York.) / Seeing's believing: *Astaire, Fred* (Belle of New York.) / I wanna be a dancin' man: *Astaire, Fred* (Belle of New York.) / Everything I have is yours/Seventeen thousand telephones: *Astaire, Fred* (Everything I have is yours.) / Maxim's: *Lamas, Fernando/Richard Haydn* (Merry widow.) / Vilia: *Lamas, Fernando* (Merry widow.) / Girls, girls, girls: *Various artists* (Merry widow.) / Night: *Lamas, Fernando*(Merry widow.) / Merry widow waltz: *Lamas, Fernando/Trudy Erwin* (Merry widow.).
LPS: . . . . **MGB 1**

THOSE MAGNIFICENT MGM MUSICALS (Vol. 2 1952-1971) (Various artists).
Tracks: / Shine of your shoes, A: *Astaire, Fred* (Band Wagon.) / By myself: *Astaire, Fred* (Band Wagon.) / Triplets: *Astaire, Fred/Nanette Fabray/Jack Buchanan* (Band Wagon.) / New sun in the sky: *Adams, India* (Band Wagon.) / I guess I'll have to change my plans: *Astaire, Fred/Jack Buchanan* (Band Wagon.) / I love Louisa: *Astaire, Fred & Chorus*(Band Wagon.) / That's entertainment: *Astaire, Fred/Nanette* Fabray/Jack Buchanan (Band Wagon. With India Adams.) / Smoke gets in your eyes: *Grayson, Kathryn* (Lovely To Look At.) / I'll be hard to handle: *Miller, Ann* (Lovely To Look At.) / Yesterdays: *Grayson, Kathryn* (Lovely To Look At.) / Touch of your hand, The: *Keel, Howard/ Kathryn Grayson*(Lovely To Look At.) / Lovely to look at: *Keel, Howard/Kathryn Grayson* (Lovely To Look At.) / Hi lili hi lo: *Caron,* Leslie & Mel Ferrer (Lili.) / Too darn hot: *Miller, Ann* (Kiss me Kate.) / So in love: *Keel, Howard/Kathryn Grayson*(Kiss me Kate.) / Tom, Dick or Harry: *Miller, Ann/Bobby Van/Tommy Rall/Bob Fosse* (Kiss me Kate.) / Were thine that special face: *Keel, Howard* (Kiss me Kate.) / Why can't you behave: *Miller, Ann* (Kiss me Kate.) / Wunderbar: *Keel,* Howard/Kathryn Grayson (Kiss me Kate.) / Always true to you in my fashion: *Miller, Ann/Tommy Rall* (Kiss me Kate.) / I hate men: *Grayson, Kathryn* (Kiss me Kate.) / From this moment on: *Rall, Tommy/Ann Miller/Bobby Van/Bob Fosse*(Kiss me Kate.) / Brush up your Shakespeare: *Wynn, Keenan/James Whitmore* (Kiss me Kate.) / Spring, spring, spring: *Various* artists (Seven Brides For Seven Brothers.) / Bless your beautiful hide: *Keel, Howard* (Seven Brides For Seven Brothers.) / Wonderful, wonderful day: *Powell, Jane* (Seven Brides For Seven Brothers.) / Goin' co'tin': *Various artists*(Seven Brides For Seven Brothers.) / Sobin' women: *Keel, Howard & Brothers* (Seven Brides For Seven Brothers.) / Sometimes I'm happy: *Powell, Jane/Vic Damone* (Hit The Deck.) / Chiribiribee

(ciribiribin): *Powell, Jane/Vic Damone* (Hit The Deck.) / More than you know: *Martin, Tony* (Hit The Deck.) / I know that you know: *Powell, Jane/Vic Damone* (Hit The Deck.) / Rose Marie: *Keel, Howard* (Rose Marie) / I'm a mountie who never got his man: *Lahr, Bert* (Rose Marie) / Indian love call: *Blyth, Ann/Fernando Lamas* (Rose Marie) / Softly as in a morning sunrise: *Traubel, Helen* (Deep In My Heart.) / Serenade: *Olvis, William* (Deep In My Heart.) / Lover come bact to me: *Martin, Tony* (Deep In My Heart.) / Road to paradise: *Damone, Vic* (Deep In My Heart.) / Will you remember (sweetheart): *Damone, Vic/Powell, Jane* (Deep In My Heart.) / Once in the highlands: *Various artists* (Brigadoon.) / Brigadoon: *Various artists* (Brigadoon.) / Heather on the hill: *Kelly, Gene* (Brigadoon.) / Waitin' for my dearie: *Richards, Carol* (Brigadoon.) / I'll go home with Bonnie Jean: *Johnson, Van/ John Gustafson* (Brigadoon.) / Come to me, bend to me: *Gustafson, John* (Brigadoon.) / Fate: *Keel, Howard* (Kismet.) / Not since Nineveh: *Gray, Dolores* (Kismet.) / Baubles, bangles and beads: *Blyth, Ann* (Kismet.) / Stranger in paradise: *Blyth, Ann/Vic Damone* (Kismet.) / Gesticulate: *Keel, Howard* (Kismet.) / Night of my nights: *Damone, Vic* (Kismet.) / Bored: *Gray, Dolores* (Kismet.) / Olive tree, The: *Keel, Howard* (Kismet.) / Rahadlakum: *Keel, Howard* (Kismet.) / Rahadlakum: *Keel, Howard/ Dolores Gray* (Kismet.) / And this is my beloved: *Keel, Howard/Anne Blyth/Vic Damone* (Kismet.) / March, march: *Kelly, Gene/Dan Dailey/Michael Kidd* (It's Always Fair Weather.) / Thanks a lot, but no thanks: *Gray, Dolores* (It's Always Fair Weather.) / Blue Danube: *Kelly, Gene/Dan Dailey/Michael Kidd* (It's Always Fair Weather.) / Music is better than words: *Gray, Dolores* (It's Always Fair Weather.) / I like myself: *Kelly, Gene* (It's Always Fair Weather.) / Les girls: *Kelly, Gene/Kay Kendall* (Les Girls. With Mitzi Gaynor/Taina Elg.) / You're just too too: *Kelly, Gene/Kay Kendall* (Les Girls.) / Ca, c'est l'amour: *Elg, Tania* (Les Girls.) / Ladies in waiting: *Gaynor, Mitzi/ Kay Kendall/Taina Elg* (Les Girls.) / Why am I so gone (about the girl): *Kelly, Gene* (Les Girls.) / Thank heaven for little girls: *Chevalier, Maurice* (Gigi.) / Say a prayer for me tonight: *Caron, Leslie* (Gigi.) / I remember it well: *Chevalier, Maurice & Hermione Gingold* (Gigi.) / Gaston's soliloquy: *Jordan, Louis* (Gigi.) / I'm glad I'm not young anymore: *Chevalier, Maurice* (Gigi.) / Night they invented champagne, The: *Caron, Leslie/Louis Jordan/Hermione Gingold* (Gigi.) / Paris loves lovers: *Astaire, Fred/Cyd Charisse/Carol Richards* (Silk Stockings.) / All of you: *Astaire, Fred* (Silk Stockings.) / Fated to be mated: *Charisse, Cyd/Fred Astaire* (Silk Stockings.) / Siberia: *Various artists* (Silk Stockings.) Portrayed by Peter Lorre/ Joseph Buloff/Jules Munshin.) / Ritz roll and rock, The: *Astaire, Fred* (Silk Stockings.) / I ain't down yet: *Reynolds, Debbie* (Unsinkable Molly Brown.) / I'll never say no: *Presnell, Harve/Debbie Reynolds* (Unsinkable Molly Brown.) / Belly up to the bar, boys: *Reynolds, Debbie* (Unsinkable Molly Brown.) / London is London: *Clark, Petula & Chorus* (Goodbye Mr. Chips.) / You and I: *Clark, Petula* (Goodbye Mr. Chips.) / I could be happy with you: *Twiggy/ Christopher Gable* (The Boyfriend.) / It's never too late to fall in love: *Adrian, Max/ Georgina Hale* (The Boyfriend.) / Room in Bloomsbury, A: *Twiggy/Christopher Gable* (The Boyfriend.) / Riviera: *Various artists* (The Boyfriend.) / Boy friend finale, The: *Various artists* (The Boyfriend.).
LPS: . . . . **MGB 2**
LPS: **794 081 1**

Mhac An Saoi, Maire

OMOS DO SCOIL DHUN CHAOIN.
LP: . . . . **CCT 8**

M.I.A.

MURDER IN A FOREIGN PLACE.
LP: . . . . **VIRUS 35**

Miami Bass Machine

MIAMI BASS MACHINE (Various artists).
LP: . . . . **JAMACR 9002**

Miami Sound Machine

CAN'T STAY AWAY FROM YOU (see under Estefan, Gloria).

EYES OF INNOCENCE.
Tracks: / Doctor Beat / Prisoner of love / OK / Love me / Orange express / I need a man / Eyes of innocence / When someone comes into your life / I need your love / Do you want to dance.
LP: **4606991**
MC: **4606994**
LP: . . . . **EPC 26167**

PRIMITIVE LOVE.
Tracks: / Body to body / Primitive love / Words get in the way / Falling in love (uh-oh) / Conga / Mucho money / You made a fool of me / Movies / Surrender paradise.
LP: . . . . **EPC 26491**
MC: **40 26491**
LP: **4634001**
MC: **4634004**

Miami Vice

BEST OF MIAMI VICE (Various artists).
LP: **241 746 1**
MC: **241 746 4**

MIAMI VICE (TV Soundtrack) (Various artists).
Tracks: / Original Miami Vice theme, The (instrumental): *Hammer, Jan* / Smuggler's blues: *Frey, Glenn* / Own the night: *Khan, Chaka* / You belong to the city: *Frey, Glen* / In the air tonight: *Collins, Phil* / Miami Vice (instrumental): *Hammer, Jan* / Vice: *Hammer, Jan* / Better be good to me: *Turner, Tina* / Flashback (instrumental): *Hammer, Jan* / Chase (instrumental): *Hammer, Jan* / Evan (instrumental): *Hammer, Jan.*
LP: . . . . **MCF 3287**
MC: . . . . **MCFC 3287**
LP: . . . . **REMV 584**
MC: . . . . **ZCMV 584**

MIAMI VICE (THEME) (See under Hammer, Jan) (Hammer, Jan).

Miasma

FIRST BIG GAMBLE, THE.
Tracks: / Johnny Jarvis Part 1 / Do you really care? / Video nasty / Some reality / Rough justice / This is halloween / Taken for a ride / By still waters / Shout / Johnny Jarvis Part 2.
MC: . . . . **BILKO 1**

TILL DARKNESS FALLS.
MC: . . . . **BILKO 2**

Mice

SCOOTER.
LP: . . . . **GOESON 15**

Michael, Alan

LOST IN ASIA.
LP: . . . . **PJ 88041**

Michael & Elaine

IN LOVE.
LP: . . . . **BLP 005**

Michael, George

FAITH.
Tracks: / Faith / Father figure / I want your sex (parts 1&2) / One more try / Hard day / Hand to mouth / Look at your hands / Monkey / Kissing a fool / Last request (I want your sex, part 3) (on 12" and CD single only.).
LP: **4600001**
MC: **4600004**
LP: **631522 1**
MC: **631522 4**

I KNEW YOU WERE WAITING (FOR ME) (see under Franklin, Aretha) (Michael, George and Aretha Franklin).

LISTEN WITHOUT PREJUDICE VOLUME 1.
Tracks: / Praying for time / Freedom 90 / They won't go when I go / Something to save / Cowboys and angels / Waiting for that day / Mothers pride / Heal the pain / Soul free / Waiting (Reprise).
LP: **4672951**
MC: **4672954**

Michael, Ras

DISARMAMENT (Michael, Ras & The Sons of Negus).
Tracks: / Jah Jah power endure / International year of the child / Where is your goldmine / International children dub / Stop pay the price of sin / Unity.
LP: . . . . **TRLS 203**

MOVEMENTS (Michael, Ras & The Sons of Negus).
LP: . . . . **DSR 6165**

RASTAFARI (Michael, Ras & The Sons of Negus).
LP: . . . . **DSR 1604**
MC: . . . . **GREEN 153**
LP: . . . . **GREL 153**

REVELATION (Michael, Ras & The Sons of Negus).
Tracks: / Black vibes / Red gold and green / Black and white / Build up your house / Ethiopian people / Rastafari.
LP: . . . . **TRLS 212**

TRIBUTE TO THE EMPEROR (Michael, Ras & The Sons of Negus).
Tracks: / Gabrail a Alma / Jazzboe abub aka at large / Tennaeslyn / Fa fa fa I want you / Tribute to Rastafori / Tena in love / Keep cool Babylon / Needs understanding / Peace and love / Rasta liveth.
LP: . . . . **TRLS 132**

Michaels, Barbara

MASTER OF BLACKTOWER, THE.
MCSET: . . . . **CAB 300**

Michaels, Bobby

I HAVE A REASON.
LP: . . . . **MYR R 1207**
MC: . . . . **MYR C 1207**

TIME.
MC: . . . . **WST C 9694**

Michaels, Hilly

LUMIA.
Tracks: / Look at that face / Our love will last forever / I've go no right to love you / Assembly line, The / In the city / Reach for the vitamins / I still think about you / Russian girls / Institutional home / One.
LP: . . . . **K 56916**

Michelangeli

MICHELANGELI.
LP: . . . . **REGL 431**
MC: . . . . **ZCF 431**

Michele

LET'S PERCOLATE (Michele & Red Hot Peppers).
MC: . . . . **VJMAC 10**

MICHELE IN CONCERT (see under Lane, Steve) (Michele/Steve Lane/ Southern Stompers).

Michell, Keith

CAPTAIN BEAKY AND HIS BAND.
LP: **2383 462**

Michel'le

MICHEL'LE.
Tracks: / No more lies / If? / 100 % woman / Never been in love / Special thanks / Nicety / Keep watchin' / Silly love song / Close to me / If? (reprise).
LP: . . . . **WX 343**
MC: . . . . **WX 343C**

Michelow, Sybil

IN RECITAL (Michelow, Sybil & Malcolm Williamson).
MC: . . . . **A 002 111C**

Michener, J.

TALES OF THE SOUTH PACIFIC Spoken Word.
MC: . . . . **CDL 51648**

Michigan & Smiley

DOWNPRESSION (Michigan, Papa & General Smiley).
Tracks: / Downpression / Natty heng on in deh / Come when Jah call you / Ghetto man / Jah army / Diseases / Living in a babylon / Jah know / Arise / Come on black people.
LP: . . . . **GREL 42**

GHETTO MAN (see under Campbell, Al's "Being with you") (Michigan, Papa & General Smiley).

LIVE AT REGGAE SUNSPLASH (Michigan, Papa & Smiley).
LP: . . . . **TRLS 8906**

SUGAR DADDY.
LP: . . . . **RAS 3004**

Mickey & Sylvia

NEW SOUNDS.
LP: . . . . **LX 1102**

Microdisney

39 MINUTES.
Tracks: / Singer's Hampstead home / High and dry / Send Herman home / Ambulance for one / Soul boy / Back to the old town / United colours / Gale force wind / Herr direktor / Bluerings.
LP: . . . . **V 2505**
MC: . . . . **TCV 2505**

CLOCK CAME DOWN THE STAIRS, THE.
LP: . . . . **ROUGH 85**

CROOKED MILE.
Tracks: / Town to town / Angels / Our children / Mrs. Simpson / Hey hey Sam / Give me all of your clothes / Armadillo man / Bullwhip road / And he descended into hell / Big sleeping house / People just want to dream / Rack.
LP: . . . . **V 2415**
MC: . . . . **TCV 2415**

EVERYTHING IS FANTASTIC.
LP: . . . . **ROUGH 75**

PEEL SESSIONS: MICRODISNEY.
Tracks: / Sun / Moon / Everybody is dead / Friend with a big mouth, A / Teddy dogs / Before famine / 7 464 / Loftholdingswood / Horse overboard / Town to town / Bullwhip road / Begging bowl.
LP: . . . . **SFRLP 105**
MC: . . . . **SFRMC 105**

WE HATE YOU WHITE SOUTH AFRICAN BASTARDS.
Tracks: / Helicopter of the holy ghost / Michael Murphy / Love your enemies / Fiction land / Pink skinned man / Patrick Moore says you can't sleep here / Hell rascals.
MLP: . . . . **RTM 155**

Microgroove

HUMAN GROOVE, THE.
Tracks: / Crash the party / Walkin' / You'll never find what it is / Get hip / You know what to do to me / Get loose / My dog's an animal.
MC: . . . . **ANC 8747**
LP: . . . . **AN 8747**

Micronotz

40 FINGERS.
LP: . . . . **HMS 054**

Microscopic 7

BEAUTY BASED ON SCIENCE.
LP: . . . . **ST 276**

TAKE THE Z TRAIN.
Tracks: / Chinese twilight zone / Wishful thinking / Take the Z train / Mr. Bradley - Mr. Martin / Pack the ermines army Mary / I didn't do it / Strange thought entered my head, A.
LP: . . . . **P 4003**

Micus, Stephan

BEHIND ELEVEN DESERTS.
LP: . . . . **VBR 20421**

DARKNESS AND LIGHT.
LP: . . . . **ECM 1427**
MC: **8472724**

EAST OF THE NIGHT.
Tracks: / East of the night / For Nobuko.
LP: . . . . **JAPO 60041**
MC: **8256554**

IMPLOSIONS.
LP: . . . . **JAPO 60017**
MC: **3101017**

KOAN.
LP: . . . . **ECMSP 2305 804**

LISTEN TO THE RAIN.
Tracks: / For Abai and Togshan / Dancing with the morning / Listen to the rain / White paint on silver wood.
LP: . . . . **JAPO 60040**
MC: **3106040**
MC: **8156144**

MUSIC OF STONES, THE.
Tracks: / Resonating stone / Resonating stone, two players / Three stone chimes / Shakuhachi solo / Shakuhachi / Tin whistle / Solo for three resonating stones / Resonating stones, voice.
LP: . . . . **ECM 1384**
MC: **8377504**

OCEAN.
Tracks: / Part 1 / Part II / Part III / Part IV.
LP: . . . . **ECM 1318**
MC: **8292794**

TILL THE END OF TIME.
MC: **3101026**

TWILIGHT FIELDS.
LP: . . . . **ECM 1358**
MC: **8350854**

WINGS OVER WATER.
LP: . . . . **JAPO 60038**
MC: **3106038**

Midas Run (film)

MIDAS RUN, THE (See under Bernstein, Elmer) (Bernstein, Elmer).

Midas Touch

PRESAGE OF DESASTER.
Tracks: / Forcibly incarcerated / Sinking censorship / When the boot comes down / True believers inc. / Sepulchral ephitaph / Lost paradise / Accessory before the fact / Terminal breath / Subhumanity / New beginning.
LP: . . . . **NUK 124**
MC: . . . . **ZCNUK 124**
LP: . . . . **N 0124 1**
MC: . . . . **N 0124 3**

Middle Class

MIDDLE CLASS UPBRINGING (Various artists).
LP: . . . . **WS 030**

Middle East

MUSIC FROM AROUND THE WORLD VOLUME 2 THE NEAR EAST (Various artists).
LP: . . . . **LLST 7288**

Middleton, Ian

BRAND NEW BILLIN', A.
Tracks: / Dumplin', The / Gale warnin', The / Lifetime on the lan', A / It's a sair fecht / Lament for the mini / Lispin' leghorn, The / Neep, The / Fin the binder laid-by / Skweel sports, The / Kittly problem, A / Lang-life recipe, The / For the want of education / Hame comfort / Awkward ailment, The / Road o' the travellin' man.
MC: . . . . **CWGRTV 8**

TATTIES, MILK AND MEAL.
MC: . . . . CWGR 106

TATTIES THROU' THE BREE.
MC: . . . . CWGR 089

Middleton, Max

ANOTHER SLEEPER (Middleton, Max & Robert Ahwai).
Tracks: / Dance by the light of the moon / Snake hips / Partial eclipse / Total madness / Plane sailing / Theme for a B movie / Pacific mist / Soliloquy / Hi jinx.
LP: . . . . TXSR 135

Middleton, Velma

RARE LOUIS ARMSTRONG VOLUME 3 (see Armstrong, Louis) (Middleton, Velma/Louis Armstrong/Ann Baker).

Middleton-Pollock, M

NOBODY KNOWS YOU.
Tracks: / Ain't goin' to play no second fiddle / Vampire / Man in the moon, The / Hesitation blues / You can't stay here / Nobody knows you (when you're down and out) / Try / Wild women don't have the blues / Green fields / Lock keeper / Bring on the starlight / Bedlam boys.
LP: . . . . FE 064
MC: . . . . FE 064 C

THOSE WOMEN OF THE VAUDEVILLE BLUES.
Tracks: / Miss Jenny's blues / Aggravatin' papa / Handy man / Barrelhouse blues / It's tight like that / Moanin' the blues / Mighty tight woman / Trouble in mind / Hot time in the old town, A / Last journey blues / Wild women don't get the blues / Dark man / I got a mind to ramble / St.Louis blues / Women don't need no mens / Nobody knows you / Some of these days.
MC: . . . . LA 5018C
LP: . . . . LA 5018

YONDER COME THE BLUES.
Tracks: / Into each life / Yonder come the blues / Viper mad / Melancholy blues / Avalon / Hot time in the old town, A / Georgia camp meeting / Gulf coast blues / Ace in the hole / Texas moaner / Miss Jenny's ball / Aged and mellow / Let's get drunk and truck / San.
MC: . . . . LCA 2

Midgeley, Richard

BODIES (See under Bodies).

Midland Radio

BY REQUEST - BBC TOP TUNES 4 (Midland Radio Orchestra/Norrie Paramor).
LP: . . . . REB 326

Midland Youth Jazz...

STARBURST (Midland Youth Jazz Orchestra).
Tracks: / Decoupage / Clearway / Majella / Blue rondo a la turk / Starburst / I remember Clifford / Chiefs blues / 920 special / Soul squeeze.
LP: . . . . GRS 1092

Midler, Bette

BEACHES (Film soundtrack).
Tracks: / Under the boardwalk / I've still got my health / Otto Titsling / Glory of love / Oh industry / Wind beneath my wings / I think it's going to rain today / I know you by heart / Baby mine / Friendship theme.
LP: . . . . K 781933-1
MC: . . . . K 781933-4

BEST OF BETTE.
Tracks: / Friends / In the mood / Superstar / Say goodbye to Hollywood / Do you wanna dance / Buckets of rain / Boogie woogie bugle boy / You're moving out today / Delta dawn / Uptown / Da doo ron ron / Hello in there / Higher and higher / La vie en rose / I shall be released.
LP: . . . . K 50530
MC: K4 50530

BETTE MIDLER.
Tracks: / Skylark / Drinking again / Breaking up somebody's home / Surabaya Johnny / I shall be released / Optimistic voices / Lullaby of broadway / In the mood / Uptown / Da doo ron ron / Twisted / Higher and higher.
LP: . . . . K 40517

BROKEN BLOSSOM.
Tracks: / Empty bed blues / Dream is wish your heart makes, A / Paradise / Yellow umbrella / La vie en rose / Make yourself comfortable / You don't know me / Say goodbye to Hollywood / I never talk to strangers / Storybook children / Red.
LP: . . . . K 50432

DIVINE MADNESS (Original soundtrack).
Tracks: / Big noise from Winnetka / Paradise / Shiver me timbers / Fire down below / Stay with me / My other's eyes / Chapel of love / Boogie woogie bugle boy / E. street shuffle, The / Summer / Leader of the pack / You can't always get what you want / I shall be released.
LP: . . . . K 50760

DIVINE MISS M, THE.
Tracks: / Do you want to dance / Chapel of love / Superstar / Daytime hustler / Am I blue / Friends / Hello in there / Leader of the pack / Delta dawn / Boogie woogie bugle boy.
LP: . . . . K 40453

LIVE AT LAST.
Tracks: / Hospital: friends, The / Oh my my / Bang you're dead / Birds / Comic relief / In the mood / Hurry on down / Shiver me timbers / Vicki Eydie show around the world, The / Istanbul / Fiesta in Rio / South seas scene / Hawaiian war chant / Lullaby of Broadway / Intermission / Delta town / Long John blues / Those wonderful Sophie Tucker jokes / Story of Nanette, The / Nanette / Alabama song / Drinkin' again / Mr. Rockfeller / Ready to begin again / Do you wanna dance / Hello in there / Up the ladder to the roof / Boogie woogie bugle boy / Friends.
LP: . . . . K 60129

MUD WILL BE FLUNG TONIGHT.
Tracks: / Taking aim / Fit or fat 'fat as I am' / Marriage, movies, Madonna and Mick / Vickie Eydie 'I'm singing Broadway' / Coping / Unfettered boob, The / Otto titzling / Why bother? / Soph.
LP: 781 291-1
MC: 781 291-4

NO FRILLS.
Tracks: / Is it love / (You're my) favourite waste of time / All I need to know / Only in Miami / Heart over head / Let me drive / My eye on you / Beast of burden / Soda and a souvenir / Come back Jimmy Dean.
LP: 780 070-1
MC: 780 070-4

ROSE, THE (Film soundtrack).
Tracks: / Whose side are you on? / Midnight in Memphis / Concert monologue / When a man loves a woman / Sold my soul to rock'n'roll / Keep on rockin' / Love me with a feeling / Camellia / Homecoming monologue / Stay with me / Let me call you sweetheart / Rose, The.
MC: K4 50681
LP: . . . . K 50681

SOME PEOPLES LIVES.
LP: 8567821291
MC: 8567821294

SONGS FOR THE NEW DEPRESSION.
Tracks: / Strangers in the night / I don't want the night to end / Mr. Rockefeller / Old Cape Cod / Buckets of rain / Shiver me timbers / Samedi et vendredi / No jestering / Tragedy / Marahuana / Let me just follow behind.
LP: . . . . K 50212

THIGHS AND WHISPERS.
Tracks: / Big noise from Winnetka / Millworker / Cradle days / My knight in black leather / Hang on in there baby / Hurricane / Rain / Married men.
LP: . . . . K 50636

Midney, Boris

MUSIC FROM THE EMPIRE STRIKES BACK.
Tracks: / Yoda's theme / Imperial march / Han Solo and the princess / Star wars.
LP: 2394 268

Midnight

MIDNIGHT SERENADES (Various artists).
LP: . . . . UNKNOWN

Midnight Choir

GIDEON TURTLE & THE MIDNIGHT CHOIR (see Turtle, Gideon) (Midnight Choir/Gideon Turtle).

TRUSSED BY BUDDHA.
LP: . . . . PROBE 16
LP: . . . . PROBE M19

WORM BELLY GRIN.
LP: . . . . NTVLP 16

WORM BELLY GRUNT.
LP: . . . . NTVLP 10

Midnight Creepers

DAYTONA BLUES.
Tracks: / Ridin' the dog / Catch me when i fall / Jookin' / Big mistake / Missing you (And drinking wine) / Keeping a secret / Hard times / Beer drinking woman / Fork in the road / Two headed woman / Prove your love / Daytona blues.
LP: . . . . BEDLP 2

Midnight Express

BIEN BENIDOS.
LP: . . . . BGC 308

Midnight Express

MIDNIGHT EXPRESS (Original Soundrack) (Various artists).
Tracks: / Chase, The: *Various artists* / Love's theme: *Various artists* / Midnight express, Theme from: *Various* artists / Istanbul blues: *Various artists* / Wheel, The: *Various artists* / Istanbul opening: *Various artists* / Cacaphoney: *Various artists* / Billy's theme: *Various artists.*
LP: . . . . PRICE 91
MC: . . . . PRIMC 91
LP: 9128 018
MC: 7268 014
LP: . . . . CAL 2030
MC: . . . . ZCCAN 2030

MIDNIGHT EXPRESS, THEME FROM (See under Bennett, Chris) (Bennett, Chris).

Midnight Flyer

MIDNIGHT FLYER.
Tracks: / Hey boy / Love games / French kisses / In my eyes / Over and over / Last resort, The / Do you want my love / Sweet loving woman / Whatever I want / Midnight flyer / Rough trade.
LP: . . . . SSK 59412

Midnight Mothers

MONDO TEENAGE EXPERIENCE.
LP: . . . . PETC 018

Midnight Oil

10,9,8,7,6,5,4,3,2,1.
Tracks: / Outside world / Only the strong / Short memory / Read about it / Scream in blue / US Forces / Power & the passion / Maralinga / Tinlegs & tin mines / Somebody's trying to tell me something.
LP: . . . . CBS 25314
MC: 40 25314

BLUE SKY MINING.
Tracks: / Blue sky mining / Stars of Warburton / Bedlam Bridge / Forgotten years / Mountains of Burma / King of the mountain / River runs red / Shakers and movers / One country / Antarctica.
LP: 4656531
MC: 4656534

DIESEL AND DUST.
Tracks: / Beds are burning / Put down that weapon / Dreamworld / Arctic world / Warakuma / Dead heart, The / Woah / Bullroarer / Sell my soul / Sometimes.
LP: 4600051
MC: 4600054

HEAD INJURIES.
MC: 4509034

MIDNIGHT OIL.
LP: . . . . CJM 26
LP: 4510081

PLACE WITHOUT A POSTCARD.
LP: 4608971
MC: 4608974

RED SAILS IN THE SUNSET.
Tracks: / When the generals talk / Best of both worlds / Sleep / Minutes to midnight / Jimmy Sharman's boxers / Bakerman / Who can stand in the way / Kosiusko / Helps me help you / Harrisburg / Bells and horns in the back of beyond / Shipyards of new zealand.
LP: . . . . CBS 26355

Midnight Run

MIDNIGHT RUN (Original Soundtrack) (Various artists).
LP: . . . . MCA 6250
MC: . . . . MCAC 6250

Midnight Star

BEGINNING.
Tracks: / Two in love / Follow the path / You're the star / Searching for love / Set me on fire / Keep the spirit high / Make it last.
LP: . . . . SOLA 2

HEADLINES.
Tracks: / Searching for love / Headlines / Get dressed / Stay here by my side / Midas touch / Close encounter / Engine no.9 / Dead end / Headlines (extra extra mix) / Operator / Curious.
MC: . . . . MCFC 3322
LP: . . . . MCF 3322

MIDNIGHT STAR.
Tracks: / Don't rock my boat / Heartbeat / Snake in the grass / Love song / 90 days / I don't wanna be lonely / Request line / Pamper me.
LP: . . . . DI 72564
LP: . . . . MCG 6041
MC: . . . . MCGC 6041

NO PARKING ON THE DANCE FLOOR.
Tracks: / Electricity / Night rider / Feels so good / Wet my whistle / No parking (on the dance floor) / Freak-a-zoid / Slow jam / Play mates.
LP: . . . . MCL 1841
MC: . . . . MCLC 1841

PLANETARY INVASION.
Tracks: / Operator / Body snatchers / Can you stay with / Scientific love / Planetary invasion / Today my love / Let's celebrate / Curious.
LP: . . . . MCL 1840
MC: . . . . MCLC 1840
LP: . . . . MCF 3251

STANDING TOGETHER.
Tracks: / Standing together / Tuff / Can't give you up / Hold out / I've been watching you / I won't let you be lonely / I've got what you need / Open up to love.
LP: . . . . K 52305
MC: K4 52305

VICTORY.
Tracks: / Victory / Strike a match / Move me / Make time / Hot spot / You can't stop me / Be with you / Love is alive.
LP: . . . . K 52394

WORK IT OUT.
Tracks: / Do it (one more time) / Work it out / All I want / Money can't buy you love / Love of my life, The / Luv-u-up / Red roses / One life to live / If walls could talk / Take your shoes off.
LP: . . . . Z 75316
LP: 4660761
MC: 4660764

Midnight String

CHRISTMAS RHAPSODIES FOR YOUNG LOVERS.
LP: . . . . HDY 1905
MC: . . . . ZCHDY 1905

Midnite Follies

JUNGLE NIGHTS IN HARLEM.
Tracks: / Shakin' the African / Jungle nights in Harlem / Happy as the day is long / Mooche, The / Okay baby / Alligator crawl / Blue skies / He's the viper / Kicking the gong around / Snake hips / Sophisticated lady / Ring dem bells / Truckin' / Black beauty / Let's do it / Stomp de luxe.
LP: . . . . ALA 3002
MC: . . . . ZC ALA 3002

Midnite Ramblers

ALWAYS LEAVING.
Tracks: / I've got a yearning / Back home again / Put another log on the fire / Drift away / Crazy arms / City of New Orleans / Unmitigated gall / Good time Charlie's got the blues / Too many bridges / Someone to give my love to / Ram jig / Kentucky gambler / Always leaving.
LP: . . . . FHR 097

MIDNITE RAMBLERS, THE.
Tracks: / Love of the common people / Streets of Baltimore / Teach your children / Anne / Midnite breakdown / Send tomorrow to the moon / Ride me down easy / Ruby / Cotton Jenny / Shelly's winter love / Kentucky woman / Sundown.
LP: . . . . FHR 064

ONE NIGHT STAND.
Tracks: / Redwood hill / Little green apples / Divorce / Good old days / What's your mamma's name child / Shutters and boards / Omaha / Mrs. Jones your daughter cried all night / What made Milwaukee famous / Yakety axe / Sunday morning coming down / One night stand.
LP: . . . . FHR 076

Midniters

BEST OF THE MIDNITERS.
LP: . . . . RNLP 063

EASY MONEY.
LP: . . . . RAZ 36

SINGIN' AND SWINGIN' (See under Ballard, Hank).

WALK THE LINE.
LP: . . . . RAGELP 102

Midsummer Night's...

MIDSUMMER NIGHT'S DREAM, A (see under Shakespeare, William) (Various artists).

Midsummer night's

MIDSUMMER NIGHTS DREAM (VIDEO) (see under Mendelssohn (composer)).

Midsummer Night's

MIDSUMMER NIGHT'S SEX COMEDY (Original Soundtrack) (Various artists).
LP: . . . . CBS 73673
MC: 40 73673

Midway Special

MIDWAY SPECIAL, THE.
LP: . . . . FJ 115

Mielke, Bob

BOB MIELKE'S BEARCATS (Mielke, Bob Bearcats).
LP: . . . . ARHOOLIE 1099

Miffy & Other... (bk)

MIFFY AND OTHER STORIES (Bruna, Dick (nar)).
MC: 3S 321

Migenes, Julia

LIVE AT OLYMPIA.
LP: A503
MC: C503

Mighty Absalom

MIGHTY ABSALOM SINGS BATHROOM BALLADS.
LP: ILP 1081

Mighty Baby

EGYPTIAN TOMB.
LP: PSYCHO 31

Mighty Ballistics...

HERE COME THE BLUES (Mighty ballistics hi-power).
LP: CRIMLP 131

Mighty Caesars

ACROPOLIS NOW.
Tracks: / I've got everything indeed / When the night comes / (Miss America) got to get you outside / Ask the dust / I don't need no baby / Dictator of love / Now I know / I can judge a daughter / Li'l Red Riding Hood / Loathsome 'n' wild / Despite all this / I feel like giving in / I was led to believe.
LP: PLAT-0

BEWARE THE IDES OF MARCH.
Tracks: / It ain't no sin / You'll be sorry now / Young man afraid of his horses / All of your love / Cyclonic / Little by little / Give it to me / This man's determined / You can't judge a book by the cover / baby please / Rumble / Road runner.
LP: WIK 45

CAESARS OF TRASH, THE.
Tracks: / It's you I hate to lose / Don't say it's a lie / Devious means / Not fade away / I've been waiting / Don't break my laws / Man taken from guts / Oh yeah / All night worker / Jack the ripper / True to you / Psycho.
LP: APOLL-0

DON'T GIVE ANY DINNER TO HENRY CHINASKI.
LP: HANG 3 UP

LIVE IN ROME.
Tracks: / Wily coyote / Give it to me / When the night comes / I've got everything indeed / Comanche / Devious means / Little by little / Neat neat neat / Bay of pigs, The / Don't say it's a lie / Too much monkey business / Submission / All of my love / Baby what's wrong.
LP: WIK 60

MIGHTY CEASARS, THE.
LP: NER-0

PUNK ROCK SHOW CASE.
LP: HANG 7 UP

WISEBLOOD.
Tracks: / I can't find pleasure / Come into my life / Signals of love / I self destroy / Wiseblood, The / Bay of pigs, The / Double axe, The / Tushunka witko / Stay the same / Kinds of women / Signals of love/Slight return / Action time vision.
LP: AMBAS 2
LP: HANG 26 UP

Mighty Clouds Of Joy

BEST OF THE MIGHTY CLOUDS OF JOY.
LP: MCA 28019

CATCHIN' ON.
LP: REJ R 5013
MC: REJ C 5013

CLOUDBURST.
Tracks: / Wings of faith / Glow love / Walk around heaven all day / Praise the Lord / I ain't no ways tired / I'll always stay with God / Showing each other love / Everybody ought to praise His Name / I made a step / I'll always stay with God.
LP: MYR 1096
MC: MC 1096

MIRACLE MAN.
Tracks: / Miracle man / He'll be there / You oughta been there / You are my happiness / Home of the lord, The / Help me to be strong / This world is not my home / Any good time at all / Jesus is the rock / Son of God / Build me a cabin in glory.
LP: MYR 1118
MC: MC 1118

NIGHT SONG.
Tracks: / I can't turn back no way / All that I am / Just keep on trusting God / You'll never walk alone.
LP: REJ R 5029
MC: REJ C 5029

SING AND SHOUT.
LP: MYR 1156
MC: MC 1156

THEIR BEST.
MC: 2651014

TRUTH IS THE POWER.
Tracks: / There's love in the world / That's what friends are made of / Music is my way of life / Truth will set you free / God is not dead / I'll keep my light in my window / Listen people / Like a child.
LP: MYR 1111
MC: MC 1111

Mighty Diamonds

CHANGES.
LP: MWLP 11981
MC: MWC 11981

DEEPER ROOTS (BACK AT THE CHANNEL).
LP: FLD 6001

DUBWISE.
LP: MW 2191

FIGHT IT OUT THERE (see under Jones,Frankie "Loving arms").

GET READY.
Tracks: / Schoolmate / Another day another raid / Tonight I'm gonna take it easy / Idlers' corner / Cannot say you didn't know / Sensimillia / My baby / Get ready / Up front / Modeller.
LP: GREL 112
MC: GREEN 112

GO SEEK YOUR RIGHTS.
MC: FLC 9002

IF YOU'RE LOOKING FOR TROUBLE.
Tracks: / Peace pipe / Where is Garvey / Fight, fight, fight / Make up your mind / Accept me / That's the life / Cartoon living / African rootsman / If you looking for trouble / Love love come get me tonight.
LP: LLLP 22
MC: LLC 22

KOUCHIE VIBES.
LP: BS 1061

LIVE IN EUROPE.
Tracks: / Party time / Country living / Mr. Botha / Have mercy / I need a roof / My baby / Puttin' on the Ritz / Real enemy, The / I don't mind / Right time, The / Africa / Keep on moving / Heavy load.
LP: GREL 124
MC: GREEN 124

NEVER GET WEARY.
LP: LLLP 29

PLANET EARTH.
LP: V 2102

REAL ENEMY.
Tracks: / Real enemy, The / Gang war / Play girl / Babylon is dangerous / Dem a worry / Free Africa / Right feelin' / I say no / Mr. Botha / Chant down war.
LP: GREL 102
MC: GREEN 102

REGGAE STREET.
LP: SHAN 43004
MC: SHANC 43004

RIGHT TIME.
Tracks: / Right time, The / Why me black brother why? / Shame and pride / Gnashing of teeth / Them never love poor Marcus / I need a roof / Go seek your rights / Have mercy / Natural natty / Africa.
LP: SHAN 43014
LP: OVED 107
MC: SHANC 43014

ROOTS IS THERE, THE.
LP: SHAN 43009
MC: SHANC 43009

STAND UP TO YOUR JUDGEMENT.
LP: CHANNEL ONE

STRUGGLING.
LP: LLLP 015

VITAL SELECTION.
Tracks: / Have mercy / Right time, The / Bodyguard / Why me black brother why? / Natural natty / I need a roof / Country living / Sweet lady / Just can't figure it out / Shame and pride / One brother short / Master plan.
LP: VX 1005

Mighty Dillinger

DETENTION CAMP.
LP: BS 002

Mighty Fire

NO TIME FOR MASQUERADING.
Tracks: / Sweet fire / One good love is worth two in the bush / I could write a love song / Love fantasy / Look what you made me do / Missing you / Love attack / Love fuzz.
LP: K 52294

PORTRAITS.
LP: K 52294

Mighty Flyers

FILE UNDER ROCK.
Tracks: / Too young to have fun / Take out some insurance / Stranded in the jungle / Spin and win / Texas twister / Strange looks / Boogie woogie teenage girl / It wasn't me / Cry cry baby / Waitin' on you baby.
LP: TKMLP 6001
MC: ZCTKM 6001

FROM THE START TO THE FINISH.
Tracks: / From the start to the finish / Where was your love / 502 / Queenie was your love / Hard work boogie / P.S. I love you / Somebody / Sinister woman / Blues for honey.
LP: RL 066

UNDERCOVER.
LP: SPD 1020

Mighty Four

MUSIC FROM THE MELODY INN.
LP: JCE 36

Mighty Houserockers

FINE LOOKIN' WOMAN.
Tracks: / Down, but not out / Fine looking woman / Bluesman boogie / Party time / Talk to me, baby / Play the blues for you / Houserockin' blues / She's my baby / Alcohol please / Just because / Drinkin' and thinkin' / Can't stop lovin'.
LP: RL 0084

Mighty Lemon Drops

HAPPY HEAD.
Tracks: / Other side of you, The / My biggest thrill / All the way / Hypnotised / Like an angel / Behind your back / Pass you by / Take me up / On my mind / Something happens / Turn me round.
LP: AZLP 1
MC: ZAZLP 1

LAUGHTER.
LP: CHR 1733
MC: ZCHR 1733

SOUND.
LP: 7599265121
MC: 7599265124

WORLD WITHOUT END.
Tracks: / Inside out / One by one / In everything you do / Hear me call / No bounds / Fall down (like the rain) / Crystal clear / Hollow inside / Closer to you / Breaking down.
LP: AZLP 4
MC: ZAZLP 4

Mighty Marenghi..

AIN'T WE GOT FUN (Mighty Marenghi Fairground Organ).
Tracks: / Harry Lime theme / All my loving / Dambusters march / Get out and get under the moon / Tritsch tratsch polka / On Mother Kelly's doorstep / I'd like to teach the world to sing / Jack in the box / Wonderful guy / Blue Danube / Can can / Ain't we got fun / Get me to the church on time / Boomps a daisy / Wiener blut / We'll all go riding on a rainbow / She loves you / Mammy o'mine / In a little Spanish town / Barber of Seville overture.
LP: NTS 169

BEST OF MIGHTY MARENGHI ORGAN, THE (Mighty Marenghi Fairground Organ).
Tracks: / Entry of the gladiators / If you knew Susie / Rose Marie / March of the cobblers / 12th Street rag / Thoroughly modern Millie / Turkey in the straw / You were meant for me / I've got a lovely bunch of coconuts / National emblem / Music goes round and around, The / Lambeth walk / South rampart street parade / Spanish gypsy dance / Marching along together / Tip-toe through the tulips / I was Kaiser Bill's batman / Canadian capers / Congratulations / Shepherd of the hills / Show me the way to go home.
MC: GRTC 28

Mighty Mighty

DEVILS NIGHT OUT (Mighty Mighty Bosstones).
Tracks: / Devils night out / Howwhywuz, Howwhyyam / Drunks and children / Hope I never lose my wallet / Haji / Bartender's song, The / Patricia / Cave, The / Do something crazy / Little bit ugly, A.
LP: EM 93581

SHARKS.
LP: CHAPLP 24

Mighty Quinn

MIGHTY QUINN, THE (Original Soundtrack) (Various artists).
LP: 393 924-1
MC: 393 924-4

Mighty Sam

NOTHING BUT THE TRUTH.
Tracks: / I need a lot of lovin' / In the same old way / Nothing but the truth / I who have nothing / Sweet dreams / Talk to me, talk to me / Georgie pines / Baby come on home / Fannie mae / I'm a man / When she touches / I came to get my (baby out of jail) / Silent tears / Just like old times / Badmouthin' / Good humour man.
LP: CRB 1189
MC: TCCRB 1189

Mighty Sparrow

25TH ANNIVERSARY.
LP: JAF 001

ALL IN THE GAME.
LP: SCR 3868
MC: SCRC 3868

KING OF THE WORLD.
LP: DY 3443

ONLY A FOOL.
Tracks: / Endlessly / Let it be me / El Reloj / To love somebody / Let me try again / Save the last dance for me / Angel / I just wanna be free / Alone again naturally / Only a fool breaks his own heart.
LP: TRLS 162

PEACE AND LOVE.
Tracks: / Maria / No money no love / More and more amour / Born free / Sandra / Walk away / Peace and love / Only a fool breaks his own heart / Doctor Zhivago, Theme from / More / Make the world go away / Try a little tenderness.
LP: TRLS 159

SPARROW'S PARTY CLASSICS.
LP: SCR 7194
LP: SCR 3247

TOUCH OF CLASS, A.
LP: LP 041
MC: MC 041

Mighty Wah

WORD TO THE WISE GUY, A.
Tracks: / Yuh learn I / Weekends / Lost generation, The / Yuh learn II / Know there was something / Yuh learn III / In the bleak (body and soul) mid winter / What's happening here / Papa crack - God's lonely man / Yuh learn IV / Come back.
LP: BBL 54
MC: BBLC 54
LP: BEGA 54

Migliori, Jay

COURAGE, THE.
LP: DS 859

Mikado

MIKADO, THE (see under Gilbert & Sullivan).

Mike Sammes Singers,

SONGS FROM ONCE UPON A TIME.
LP: LBR 014
MC: LBT 014

Mike & The Mechanics

LIVING YEARS, THE.
Tracks: / Nobody's perfect / Seeing is believing / Nobody knows / Poor boy down / Blame / Don't / Black and blue / Beautiful day / Why me / Living years, The.
LP: WX 203
MC: WX 203 C

MIKE AND THE MECHANICS.
Tracks: / Silent running (on dangerous ground) / All I need is a miracle / Par avion / Hanging by a thread / I get the feeling / Take the reins / You are the one / Call to arms, A / Taken in.
LP: WX 49
MC: WX 49 C

WORD OF MOUTH (ALBUM).
Tracks: / Get up / Word of mouth / Time and place, A / Yesterday, today, tomorrow / Way you look at me, The / Everybody gets a second chance / Stop baby / My crime of passion / Let's pretend it didn't happen / Before (the next heartache falls).
LP: V 2662
MC: TCV 2662

Mikey & Glen

MEETS RHYTHM FOUNDATION IN A SOUND CLASH.
LP: RFDLP 1

Miki & Griff

AT HOME WITH MIKI AND GRIFF.
Tracks: / Born to be with you / Please Mr. Conductor / Way old friends do, The / Old rugged cross, The / My grandfather's clock / Loves old sweet song / He stopped loving her today / Nobody's child / Please help me, I'm falling / Wino the clown / Love lifted me / Who's your friend / Your cheatin' heart / Lonely in a crowd.
LP: ITV 425
MC: KITV 425

BEST OF MIKI AND GRIFF.
Tracks: / Walk through this world / You're my best friend / Country roads / These hands / I have to say I love you in a song / You lay so easy on my mind / Even the bad times are good / Baptism of Jesse Taylor, The / Streets of London

/ Shelly's winter love / Before the day is done / One day at a time / For the good times / I thought I'd drop by (and pick up the pieces) / Annie's song / When I stop dreaming / Crying time / Top of the world / Let it be me / Making believe / God was here / Tell me my lying eyes were wrong / Blowin' in the wind.
LP: . . . . COMP 8
MC: . . . . ZCCOM 8

COUNTRY.
LP: . . . . NSPL 18588

COUNTRY IS.
LP: . . . . PKL 5522

ETCHINGS.
LP: . . . . NSPL 18533

GOLDEN HOUR OF MIKI AND GRIFF.
LP: . . . . GH 573

Mikulic, Boris

HERESY.
LP: . . . . AS 5017

Mila

SKY WITHOUT END - CONCERT GUITAR.
MC: . . . . C 374

Milburn, Amos

13 UNRELEASED MASTERS.
LP: . . . . PM 1546701

CHICKEN SHACK BOOGIE.
LP: . . . . PM 1561411

GREATEST HITS: AMOS MILBURN.
Tracks: / Chicken shack boogie / Bewildered / Roomin' house boogie / Bad bad whiskey / One scotch, one bourbon, one beer / Hold me baby / In the middle of the night / Let's make Christmas merry baby / Let's rock awhile / Let me go home, whiskey / Empty arms blues / Tears, tears / It took a long, long time / Walkin' blues / Thinking and drinking / Sax shack boogie.
LP: . . . . OFF 6018

JUST ONE MORE DRINK.
Tracks: / Amos blues / I love her / Pool playing blues / Real pretty mama blues / Let's make Christmas merry baby / I'm going to tell my mama / She's gone again / Tell me how long has the train gone / Just one more drink / Why don't you do right / Love you anyway / Please Mr. Johnson / How could you hurt me so / Milk and water / That's it / One two three everybody.
LP: . . . . KIX 7

LET'S HAVE A PARTY.
LP: . . . . PM 154671-1
MC: . . . . PM 15467-4

LET'S ROCK AWHILE.
Tracks: / After midnite / Blues at sundown / My love is limited / Hold me baby / In the middle of the night / Let's rock awhile / Walkin' blues / Birmingham bounce / Anybody's blues / Everybody clap hands / Tears tears tears / Ain't nothing shakin' / Thinking and drinking / I won't be a fool anymore / Long long day / Kiss me again / Vicious vicious vodka.
LP: . . . . KIX 28

ROCK ROCK ROCK.
LP: . . . . KIX 21

VICIOUS VODKA.
LP: . . . . PM 1561401

YOU USE ME.
Tracks: / Jump and shout / Come here baby / Pledging my love / Big building / Dearest darling / Look at a fool / Gloria / You used me / How's my ex treating you / My baby / You made a boo boo / Shut up / Forever and always / Sad crying / I wanna know / Got my mojo working / Long tall Sally.
LP: . . . . RB 1000

Milder, Bjorn

SWING PIANO MY WAY.
LP: . . . . KS 2048

Milder, Joakim

LIFE IN LIFE.
LP: . . . . DRLP 166

Miles, Barry

FUSION IS.
Tracks: / Tandoori / Follow me / Country miles / Sunrise / Dreams / Routes.
LP: . . . . PL 25188

Miles, Buddy

LIVE: BUDDY MILES (Miles, Buddy & Carlos Santana).
LP: . . . . CBS 32271
MC: 40 32271

SNEAK ATTACK (Miles, Buddy Regiment).
Tracks: / Latin rock fusion / Can you hold me / Sunshine of your love / I've made up my mind / Working hard every day / Colossus / Let's make it together / Jazz fusion / Buddy Miles, live at CIM, Chino, Ca / Hold her tight / Dust in the wind / For your precious love.
LP: . . . . K 60156

Miles, Dick

CHEATING THE TIDE.
LP: . . . . GVR 227

DUNMOW FLITCH, THE (Miles, Dick & Sue).
Tracks: / Dunmow flitch, The / Primrose polka / Bald headed end of the broom / Archies fancy / Isle of Cloy / Shanty boy / Greenwood laddie / Swaffham tinker / Woodland flowers / Cuckoo the ball of yarn, The.
LP: . . . . SFA 106

ON MY LITTLE CONCERTINA.
Tracks: / Sailortown / Plains of Boyle / Coast of Peru, The / Lea Riggs / Jack the lad / Flowing tide, The / Around the harbour town / Crossed lines / Blarney pilgrim / Tam Linn / Range of the buffalo, The / Trail to Mexico, The / Sitting on top of the world / On my little concertina.
LP: . . . . BH 8812
MC: . . . . BHC 8812

PLAYING FOR TIME.
LP: . . . . GVR 238

Miles, Graeme

EAGLE AND DOVE (Songs of Point and Protest).
MC: 60-229

ENTERTAINERS (Contemporary Country Song).
MC: 45-226

HERE'S TO THE LADS (Sporting Songs).
MC: 45-227

IRONMASTER, MINERS, MOULDERS, FOUNDERS.
MC: 45-225

LYKE WAKE (Primievil Ballads of Moors).
MC: 45-230

RING OF IRON, THE.
MC: 60-228

RURAL SONGS OF CLEVELAND AND TEES-SIDE.
MC: 90-221

SMOKESTACK LANO (Industrial Ballads).
MC: 90-222

SONGS AND SHANTIES OF FISHER AND SAILORS.
MC: 45-223

SQUADDIES DREAM (Barrackroom Ballads).
MC: 45-224

WEALDEN FOLK (Ballads of Kentish Folk).
MC: 60-231

Miles, Helena

HELENA MILES.
LP: 7819561
MC: 7819564

Miles, John

MILES HIGH.
Tracks: / Turn yourself loose / Don't stop now / Foolin' / Don't want the same things / Out of the cradle / Hold on / Peaceful waters / Dancin' for joy / One step closer to paradise / Reggae man.
LP: . . . . EMC 3374

MORE MILES PER HOUR.
LP: . . . . TXS 135

MUSIC.
Tracks: / Music / Remember yesterday / Zaragon / Stand up / Can't keep a good man down / Stranger in the city / Manhattan skyline / No hard feelings / Rebel / Highfly.
LP: . . . . TAB 50
MC: . . . . KTBC 50
LP: 8209111

PLAY ON.
Tracks: / Take me to my heaven / Right to sing / Song for you / Ready to spread your wings / That's rock 'n' roll / Carrie / Heart of stone / Home / Close eyes, count to ten / It wasn't love at all / I'll never do it again.
LP: . . . . EMC 1651471

REBEL.
LP: . . . . SKL 52319
LP: . . . . SKL 5231

STRANGER IN THE CITY.
Tracks: / Stranger in the city / Slow down / Stand up (and give me a reason) / Time / Manhattan skyline / Glamour boy / Do it anyway / Remember yesterday / Music man / House on the hill / Man behind the guitar / Putting my new song together / Sweet Lorraine.
MC: . . . . KTXC 118
MC: . . . . TXS 118

TRANSITION.
Tracks: / Once in your life / Run blinded / You're the one / I need your love / Hard time / Who knows / Don't like to me / Watching over me.
LP: 790476 1
MC: 790476 4

ZARAGON.
LP: . . . . TXS 126

Miles, Lizzie

MELLOW RHYTHM (Miles, Lizzie & Melrose Stompers).
Tracks: / Mellow rhythm / He's my man / That's alright daddy / Hold me parson / Keep knockin' no. 2 / Stranger blues / Twenty grand blues / He's red hot to me / Reefer man's dream / Sweet heart of my dreams / When your love comes down / Blue baby / Breakin' 'em down tonight / Someone to take your place / Got a mind to ramble / True love.
LP: . . . . CI 022

Miles, Luke 'Long

COUNTRY BOY.
LP: . . . . CG 709-05
LP: . . . . SG 709-05

Miles, Ron

WITNESS.
MC: 740144

Miles-Kingston, Paul

MUSIC WINCHESTER CATHEDRAL.
LP: . . . . EL 2703721
MC: . . . . EL 2703724

Milestone Jazzstars

IN CONCERT.
Tracks: / Cutting edge, The / N.O. blues / Don't stop the carnival / In a sentimental mood / Alone together / Continuum / Willow weep for me / Little pianissimo.
2LP: . . . . M 55006

Milira

MILIRA.
Tracks: / Mercy mercy me (The ecology) / Go inside the rain / Waiting here for you / That man in my life / Good times are back again / I want to be to you (What you are to me) / Let me have a chance / Treat me right / Home / That four letter word (Only on CD) / Mercy mercy me(The ecology)(Vocal mix) (Only on CD).
LP: . . . . MOT 6297
LP: . . . . ZL 72714
MC: . . . . ZK 72714

Militant Barry

GREEN VALLEY.
LP: . . . . STLP 1012

Militant Mothers

DIFFERENT SOULS.
LP: 082577

Military

13TH & 18TH REGIMENTS (Royal Hussars Regiment Band).
LP: . . . . GRS 1029

23 MOST FAMOUS INTERNATIONAL MILITARY MARCHES (Various artists).
LP: 400 648
MC: 817 123

AIRBORNE SALUTE (Parachute Regiment Massed Bands).
Tracks: / Airborne salute / Red beret, The / Steadfast and true / Skye boat song / Wild geese, The / Grand march from Aida / Also sprach Zarathustra / Dark island / Sounding brass / Red devils, The / Dzerjinsky march / Ride of the Valkyries.
LP: . . . . BND 1005
MC: . . . . ZC BND 1005

AIRBORNE WARRIOR (Parachute Regiment 1st Battalion).
Tracks: / Airborne warrior / Golden lanyard / Holmegaard / Cavatina / King cotton / Chariots of fire / Snowcat / Longest day, The / Songs of world war 2 / March of the royal british legion / Prelude of the supreme sacrifice / Act of rememberance / Ride of the Valkyries.
MC: . . . . ZC BND 1025
LP: . . . . BND 1025

BAND OF THE JUNIOR LEADERS REGIMENT (Royal Armoured Corps).
Tracks: / In triumph / More of the beatles / Freckles & flowers / Star wars / Angelus / Kraken / Sparks / Chariots of fire / Sounds of James Bond.
LP: . . . . MM 0594
MC: . . . . MMC 0594

BANDS ACROSS THE SEA (Band Of The Royal Regiment Of Fusiliers).
Tracks: / Drum beatings / Cockney coctail / Mull of Kintyre / Marching songs 1939/45 / Maple leaf forever / Flower of Scotland / Farewell to Nova Scotia / Lass O'Fyveo / Now is the hour / Sunset / O Canada / God save the Queen / British grenadiers, The / Campbells are coming, The / Black bear, The / No awa to bide awa / Mon ami / Royal Fusiliers arrival at Quebec / Die normandie / Northumbrian airs.
LP: . . . . BND 1032

BANDSTAND (Royal Corps of Transport Band).
Tracks: / Wait for the wagon / Music box dancer / Spanish march / 88th Regiment / Duel for drummers / Napoleon galop / Mountain patrol / Free and easy / Carillon / Medley, Trumpton and friends / Glad chatter / Trumpet by candlelight / Ship to shore / Bourre from Terpsichore / Drumsticks for two / 89th regiment overture, Marinarella.
LP: . . . . BND 1011
MC: . . . . ZC BND 1011

BIG BAND SOUNDS (Royal Artillery Mounted Band).
Tracks: / Brass buttons / Souvenir de Montmartre / Doghouse / Regency rumba / I love you and don't you forget it / Zapateado (sarasate) / Chubby chuba / Trumpets trocadera / Serenade for a gondolier / Yes we have no bananas / Harlem nocturne / Sonatina for mandolin / Swaggy / Auchtermuchty gala march, The.
LP: . . . . NTS 131

BRITISH MILITARY BANDS ON PARADE (Various artists).
LPS: . . . . D 141D4

CALL FOR THE GUNS (Royal Artillery Band).
Tracks: / Call for the guns / Overture- The force of destiny / Nocturne / Blaze away / Lucy Long / Washington post / Festive overture / Gymnopedie no.1 / March- la pere la victoire / March- Rapier / Selections from Barnum / Regimental quick march / Regimental slow march.
LP: . . . . BND 1021
MC: . . . . ZC BND 1021

DIE GROSSEN MARSCHE (Various artists).
Tracks: / Alte kameraden: *Various artists* / Weidmannsheil: *Various artists* / Tolzer Schutzenmarsch: *Various* artists / Radetzky marsch: *Various artists* / Konig Ludwig II marsch: *Various artists* / In die weite welt: *Various artists* / Preussens Gloria: *Various artists* / Gamsgebirgsmarsch-so leb'denn wohl...: *Various artists*/ Waldlemarsch-ja, mir sab vom wald.juchhee: *Various artists* / Konig Karl marsch: *Various artists* / Gruss an Kiel: *Various artists* / Egerlander marsch: *Various artists*.
LP: 829 182-1
MC: 829 182-4

EDINBURGH MILITARY TATTOO 1975 (Various artists).
Tracks: / Sanderson's farewell: *Various artists* / Caberfeidh: *Various artists* / March of the Cameron men: *Various* artists / Oh, Luaidh: *Various artists* / Hills of Alva, The: *Various artists* / Australian ladies: *Various* artists / Aspen bank: *Various artists* / Fairy dance, The: *Various artists* / Maid of Morven, The: *Various* artists / Duchess of Atholl: *Various artists* / Friendly piper, The: *Various artists* / H.M. jollies: *Various* artists / Blaze of brass: *Various artists* / Edinburgh Castle: *Various artists* / Timpat: *Various artists*/ Life on the ocean wave, A: *Various artists* / Karangatia ra: *Various artists* / E Pari ra: *Various artists*/ Beefeater fanfare, The: *Various artists* / Slaughter on Tenth Avenue: *Various artists* / High Society: *Various* artists / Riff Interlude: *Various artists* / Bonnie lass o' Fyvie: *Various artists* / Largo: *Various* artists / Sunset: *Various artists* / Scotland the brave: *Various artists* / We're no awa' tae bide awa': *Various artists* / Black bear, The: *Various artists*.
LP: . . . . SZLP 2146

EDINBURGH MILITARY TATTOO 1977 (Various artists).
LP: . . . . SZLPA 101

EDINBURGH MILITARY TATTOO 1978 (Various artists).
Tracks: / Triple salute: *Various bands* / Coburg: *Various bands* / Glasgow week in Hamburg: *Various bands*/ 79th Farewell to Gibraltar: *Various bands* / Duncan McInnes: *Various bands* / Leaving Eriskay: *Various bands*/ Duke of Edinburgh: *Various bands* / Weary we've been: *Various bands* / Come by the hills: *Various bands*/ Burns on the march: *Various bands* / Good old bad old days, The: *Various bands* / Swing march, The: *Various* bands / Semper fidelis: *Various bands* / Lass of Richmond Hill: *Various bands* / Light Division assembly: *Various bands* / Light Infantry regimental march: *Various bands* / Geordie: *Various bands* / St. Cross: *Various bands* / Jellalabad: *Various bands* / Keel row, The: *Various bands* / Road to the Isles: *Various bands* / Huntsman's chorus, The: *Various bands* / Scotch on the rocks: *Various*

bands / Earl of Mansfield: *Various bands* / Nut Brown maiden: *Various bands* / Lion rock: *Various bands* / Happy wanderer, The: *Various bands* / Coronation march from 'La Prophete': *Various bands* (From La Prophete) / Imperial echoes: *Various bands*/ Hail smiling morn: *Various bands* / Blue bonnets o'er the border: *Various bands* / Soutard of Selkirk: *Various bands* / Lilting, The: *Various bands* / Crimond: *Various bands* / Bugle retreat: *Various bands* / Donald of Leggan: *Various bands* / Sons of the brave: *Various bands* / Garb of old Gaul: *Various bands*/ Scotland the brave: *Various bands* / Will ye no' come back again: *Various bands* / We're no awa' tae bide awa': *Various bands* / Loch Lomond: *Various bands*.
LP: . . . . **SZLP 2155**

EDINBURGH MILITARY TATTOO 1979 (Various artists).
Tracks: / Fanfare for a dignified occasion: *Various bands* / Erin far o'er the sea: *Various bands* / Anderson's welcome to Arran: *Various bands* / My native highland home: *Various bands* / Green glens of Antrim: *Various bands* / Paddy's leather breeches: *Various bands* / MacNeil's oran mor: *Various bands* / Gallowa' hills: *Various bands* / Pipe Major J.K.Cairns: *Various bands* / Kings troop call: *Various bands* / Royal Artillery regimental call: *Various bands* / Boots and saddles: *Various bands* / General parade: *Various bands* / Walk march: *Various bands* / Voice of the guns: *Various bands* / Royal Artillery salute: *Various bands* / Royal Artillery Show March: *Various bands* / Drummer's call: *Various bands* / Laridah: *Various bands* / Gfollermarsch: *Various bands* / Holzhackerblabmarsch: *Various bands* / Royal Navy display: *Various bands* / Killaloe: *Various bands* / Faugh a' ballagh: *Various bands* / Boys of the town: *Various bands* / Mairi's wedding: *Various bands* / Dumbarton's drums: *Various bands* / Parade of champions: *Various bands* / Adjo, farval for Sista Gang: *Various bands* / Clog dance: *Various bands* / Prinz Carlmarsch: *Various bands* / Caubeen trimmed with blue, The: *Various bands* / Heart of oak: *Various bands* / British Grenadiers, The: *Various bands*/ Abide with me: *Various bands* / Royal Artillery last post: *Various bands* / Lament for Red Hector of the battles: *Various bands* / Scotland the brave: *Various bands* / Zum steedt li hinaus: *Various bands* / We're no awa' tae bide awa': *Various bands* / Loch Lomond: *Various bands*.
LP: . . . . **GLN 1009**
MC: . . . . **TC GLN 1009**

EDINBURGH MILITARY TATTOO 1980 (Various artists).
MC: . . . . **TC GLN 1020**

EDINBURGH MILITARY TATTOO 1982 (Various artists).
LP: . . . . **WGR 030**
MC: . . . . **CWGR 030**

EDINBURGH MILITARY TATTOO 1983 (Various artists).
LP: . . . . **WGR 058**
MC: . . . . **CWGR 058**

ENGINEERS EVERYWHERE (Royal Engineers Band).
Tracks: / Fanfare- Phoenix / Wings / First post / Colonel Bogey / Waldmere / Ubique / Iron regiment, The / Scarlet and gold / Old comrades / Coronation march / Overture- Poet and peasant / Brazillance / Theme from the 'A' team / Dynasty, Theme from / Las castanuelas.
LP: . . . . **BND 1023**
MC: . . . . **ZC BND 1023**

FARE THEE WELL INNISKILLING (Royal Inniskilling Dragoon Guards).
Tracks: / Fanfare- Inniskilling dragoon / Der sander marsch / Regimental slow march- Soldier chorus / I know him so well / Gaelic hot pot / When you and I were young / Maggie / 'Bouree' from Terpichore / Der grossen kurfusten reitermarsch / Fare thee well Inniskilling / Rocky / I wonder / Clarinet polka / Manilow medley / Where no man has gone before.
MC: . . . . **ZC BND 1029**
LP: . . . . **BND 1029**

FIJI BRASS (Royal Fiji Military Forces Band).
LP: . . . . **VP 362**

FORWARD OF THE LINE (16th/5th Queen's Royal Lancers).
Tracks: / Fanfare- Waterloo / Forward of the line / Staffordshire knot / Victory salute / Scorpion / Thundering guns / Schoenfield march / Scarlet and green / Fanfare- Centenary / Theme from the 'A' team / Galloping home / Polly Oliver / Theme from 'Rocky' / Misty / Mardi gras / Sunset salute.
MC: . . . . **ZC BND 1026**
LP: . . . . **BND 1026**

FREEFALL (Falklands Band of Parachute Regt.).
LP: . . . . **BND 1048**
MC: . . . . **ZC BND 1048**

GET FIGHTING FIT WITH TWO PARA (Parachute Regiment, Band & Drums of 2nd Battalion).
LP: . . . . **X 0068**
MC: . . . . **X 00684**

GOLDEN HOUR OF MILITARY BANDS, A (Various artists).
MC: . . . . **KGHMC 143**

GREAT MARCHES OF THE WORLD (Various artists).
Tracks: / Radetzky march: *Band of the Grenadier Guards* / She wore a yellow ribbon: *Band of the Grenadier Guards*/ Hands across the sea: *Band of the Grenadier Guards* / When Johnny comes marching home: *Band of the Grenadier Guards*/ Colonel Bogey: *Band of Her Majesty's Royal Marines Commando Forces, The* / Nibelungen march: *Band of the Grenadier Guards* / Liberty bell: *Band of the Grenadier Guards* / Entry of the gladiators: *Band of the Royal Corps of Transport, The* / Stars and stripes: *Band of the Grenadier Guards* / Marche Militaire: *Band of the Grenadier Guards* / Berliner luft: *Band of Her Majesty's Royal Marines Commando Forces, The* / Toreadors march from 'Carmen': *Band and Corps of drums of Prince of Wales Division* / Father Rhine: *Band of the Grenadier Guards* / Anchors aweigh: *Band of the Grenadier Guards*.
LP: . . . . **TAB 14**

GREAT MILITARY BANDS (Various artists).
Tracks: / Liberty bell: *Various bands* / Drummer boy: *Various bands* / Snow queen: *Various bands* / Fairest of the fair, The: *Various bands* / Children of the regiment: *Various bands* / Radetzky march: *Various bands*/ Blaze away: *Various bands* / Men O Wales: *Various bands* / Boots and saddles: *Various bands* / Die Fledermaus march: *Various bands* / Sprig of shillelagh & G Garryown, The: *Various bands* / Toreadors march: *Various bands*/ Imperial echoes: *Various bands*.
MCSET: . . . . **DTO 10036**

GREAT TRADITIONAL MARCHES (Various artists).
2LP: . . . . **IC 178 31503/04**

HAPPY MUSIC (Royal Artillery Mounted Band).
Tracks: / Masterpiece, The / Mexican whistler, The / Here, there and everywhere / On the flipside / Gipsy blood / Who's sorry now? / French horns, country style / Happy music / Zacatecas / Mediterranean honeymoon / Clarinade / Merry matelots, The / Bossa nova.
LP: . . . . **LILP 5031**

HO' WAY THE LADS (15th/19th King's) (Royal Hussars Regiment Band).
LP: . . . . **MM 0582**

KNELLER HALL 1857-1982 (Royal Military School of Music).
Tracks: / Fanfare for heroes / H.R.H The Duke of Cambridge / Soldier, The / Introduction & dance from 'Duke of Cambridge suite' / Thundering drums / Wigan pier / Task force / Carambina / Marching sergeants / Vivat regina.
LP: . . . . **PRM 101**
MC: . . . . **CPRM 101**

KNELLER HALL IN CONCERT (Royal Military School of Music).
Tracks: / Fanfare for a festival / Advance guard, The / Watermill, The / Aberdonian, The / Year of the dragon / Fanfare for a royal occasion / Barnard castle / March from 'Suite in B flat' / Introduction and allegro / Lyric suite.
LP: . . . . **PRM 111D**
MC: . . . . **CPRM 111D**

LAND OF SUGAR (Royal Crescent Mob).
LP: . . . . **BIAS 040**

LILLY WHITES, THE (13th & 18th regiments) (Royal Hussars Regiment Band).
MC: . . . . **KGRS 1021**
LP: . . . . **GRS 1021**

MAGIC SOUNDS OF THE EDINBURGH MILITARY TATTOO (Various artists).
LP: . . . . **MFP 5616**
MC: . . . . **TCMFP 5616**

MAGNIFICENT MARCHES (Various artists).
2LP: . . . . **CR 091**
MCSET: . . . . **CRT 091**

MARCHING TO GLORY (Various artists).
MCSET: . . . . **DTO 10214**

MARCHING WITH ROYAL PAPUA NEW GUINEA ... (Various artists).
Tracks: / Convoy: *Various artists* / Flying eagle: *Various artists* / Steadfast and true: *Various artists*/ Florentina: *Various artists* / Thundercrest: *Various artists* / Wait for the wagon: *Various artists*/ Ponderoso: *Various artists* / Anchors aweigh: *Various artists* / Milanallo: *Various artists* / Colours flying: *Various artists* / Captain general, The: *Various artists* / Colonel Bogey: *Various artists* / Old comrades: *Various artists*.
LP: . . . . **VP 416**

MARCHING WITH THE GUARDS (Various artists).
MCSET: . . . . **DTO 10081**

MARCHING WITH THE GUNNERS (Royal Artillery Mounted Band).
Tracks: / Through night to light / Masterpiece, The / Adelita / Die Fledermaus march / La soiree / Zatecatecus / Boccaccio / Florian march / Who's sorry now / Petersburg march / Trumpet prelude / Hogan's heroes / Fliegermarsch / Good word.
LP: . . . . **NTS 204**

MASSED BANDS (Parachute Regiment Band).
LP: . . . . **PRD 2012**

MASSED BANDS & BUGLES OF THE LIGHT DIVISION (Various artists).
Tracks: / Duke of Cambridge march: *Various artists* / Marvin Hamilisch showcase: *Various artists* / Haydn trumpet concerto: *Various artists* / Finale: *Various artists* / Light Division assembly and advance: *Various artists*/ Silver bugles: *Various artists* / Post horn and echo: *Various artists* / Les clarions Anglais: *Various artists*/ Bohemian rhapsody: *Various artists* / St. Mary's fanfare: *Various artists* / Light infantry regimental march: *Various artists* / High on a hill: *Various artists* / Crown imperial: *Various artists* / Nightfall in camp: *Various artists* / Royal green jackets regimental march: *Various artists*.
LP: . . . . **MM 0604**

MASSED BANDS OF THE PARACHUTE REGIMENT (Parachute Regiment Massed Bands).
MC: . . . . **PRD 4 2012**

MEN OF HARLECH (Royal Regiment of Wales Regimental Band & Choir).
MC: . . . . **RRW 11882**

MILITARY BAND FAVOURITES (Various artists).
MC: . . . . **TC2 MOM 119**

MILITARY BAND FAVOURITES (Various artists).
LP: . . . . **OCN 2027WL**
MC: . . . . **OCN 2027WK**

MILITARY BAND SPECTACULAR (Various artists).
LPS: . . . . **EMSP 338**

MILITARY BANDS PLAY FAVOURITE THEMES (Various artists).
Tracks: / Musical joke, A: *Royal Corps of Transport Band* / Trumpton: *Royal Corps of Transport Band* / Mr. Benn: *Royal Corps of Transport Band* / Flumps, The: *Royal Corps of Transport Band* / Postman Pat: *Royal Corps of* Transport Band / Chi mai: *Welsh Guards Band* / Chariots of fire: *Parachute Regiment Band* / Thunderbird: *Parachute* Regiment Band / Noblimente (from Elgar's 1st symphony): *Royal Marines...* / Squadron: *Royal Air Force Germany* Band / Luftwaffe march: *Grenadier Guards Band* / Imperial echoes: *Grenadier Guards Band* / Horse Guards, Whitehall, The: *Blues & Royals Band* / Knightsbridge march: *Blues & Royals Band* / Mack and Mabel: *Royal Artillery Mounted Band*.
LP: . . . . **CFRC 503**
MC: . . . . **MCFRC 503**

MILITARY CLASSICS (Various artists).
2LP: . . . . **STAR 2009**
MCSET: . . . . **STAC 2009**

MILITARY GOLD (Various artists).
LP: **RTD4 2042**
MC: **RTD4C 2042**

MILITARY GREATS (Various artists).
Tracks: / Dambusters: *Various bands* / Aces high: *Various bands* / 633 Squadron: *Various bands* / Zeebrugge: *Various bands* / Amethyst: *Various bands* / Radetzky march: *Various bands* / Blue devils: *Various bands* / Pathfinders: *Various bands* / Anchors aweigh: *Various bands* / Hearts of oak: *Various bands*/ Soliloquy: *Various bands* / Mountbatten march: *Various bands* / Naval occasion: *Various bands*.
LPS: . . . . **RML 104**
MCSET: . . . . **RML 4C 104**
2LP: . . . . **CR 5146**
MCSET: . . . . **CRT 5146**

MILITARY MUSIC THROUGH THE AGES (Royal Military School of Music).
Tracks: / Trumpet voluntary / Concerto for two trumpets / Prince of Wales march / Overture / Grand march / Coronation march / Rakoczy march / Tannhauser grand march / Princess of Wales / Spitfire prelude and fugue / Intrada and march from "March for a festival" / Paean.
LP: . . . . **BND 1003**
MC: . . . . **ZC BND 1003**

MILITARY SPIRIT, THE (Various).
Tracks: / Let's bring new glory to old glory / Fifth army march / Roll tanks roll / That's the infantary / Bombadiers song, The / God bless America / Spirit of independence / General Pershing march / General H.H. Arnold march / General marshall march / Over there / Any bonds today?.
MC: . . . . **K 1009**

MUSIC BY THE REGIMENT BAND,BUGLES,PIPES & DRUMS (Royal Irish Rangers).
LP: . . . . **MM 0578**

MUSIC FROM THE GUARDS DEPOT (Various artists).
Tracks: / Life guards slow march: *Various artists* / Blues and royals: *Various artists* / Scipio: *Various artists* / Figaro: *Various artists* / Garb of Old Gaul: *Various artists* / Let Erin remember: *Various* artists / Men of Harlech: *Various artists* / Milanollo: *Various artists* / Aida and the royals: *Various* artists / British grenadiers, The: *Various artists* / Heilan' laddie: *Various artists* / St.Patricks day: *Various artists* / Rising of the lark, The: *Various artists* / Royal Artillery slow march: *Various artists*/ Wings: *Various artists* / Begone dull care: *Various artists* / Wait for the wagon: *Various artists*/ Village blacksmith: *Various artists* / Lilliburlero: *Various artists*.
LP: . . . . **BND 1035**
MC: . . . . **ZC BND 1035**

MUSIC FROM TIDWORTH TATTOO 1975 (Various artists).
LP: . . . . **LILP 5023**

MUSIC OF THE MILITARY (Various artists).
Tracks: / Royal Air Force march past: *Various artists* / Cavalry of the Steppes: *Various artists* / Light of foot: *Various artists* / Blaze away: *Various artists* / Amazing Grace: *Various artists* / Men of Harlech & God bless the Prince of Wales: *Various artists* / Aces high: *Various artists* / Anchors aweigh: *Various artists*/ Battle of Britain: *Various artists* / Old comrades: *Various artists* / Coronation march: *Various artists*/ Lochanside: *Various artists* / Green hills of Tyrol: *Various artists* / Dambusters: *Various artists*/ Washington post, The: *Various artists* / Sons of the brave: *Various artists* / National Emblem: *Various* artists / Battle of the Somme: *Various artists* / Dagshai hills: *Various artists* / Argyll and Sutherland Highlanders: *Various artists* / Under the double eagle: *Various artists* / Australian march: *Various artists*/ Redetzky: *Various artists* / 633 Squadron: *Various artists* / Flower of Scotland: *Various artists* / Famous British marches: *Various artists* / British Grenadiers, The: *Various artists* / Lilliburlero: *Various* artists / All through the night: *Various artists* / Highland Laddie: *Various artists* / Rule Britannia: *Various* artists / Bonnie Anne: *Various artists* / Atholl cummers, The: *Various artists* / Sheepwife, The: *Various* artists / Macleod of Mull: *Various artists* / Semper fidelis: *Various artists* / Those magnificent men in their flying machines: *Various artists*.
2LP: . . . . **DL 41 1078 3**
MC: . . . . **DL 41 1078 9**
2LP: . . . . **DL 1078**
MC: . . . . **TCDL 1078**

MUSICAL DRIVE (Royal Horse Artillery King's Troop).
LP: . . . . **LR 103**

OUT OF THE BLUE (RAF Western Band).
LP: . . . . **BND 1054**
MC: . . . . **ZC BND 1054**

PARACHUTE REGIMENT, 2ND BATTALION (Parachute Regiment, Band & Drums of 2nd Battalion).
Tracks: / Bridge too far / Major General John Frost / Drummie / Marche des Parachutistes belges / Blue devils / Pomp & circumstance no 4 / Ride of the Valkries / Bruneval raid / Ave Maria / Bohemian rhapsody / Rise / Marchalong.
LP: . . . . **MM 0588**

PEGASUS (Parachute Regiment, Band of the 3rd Battalion).
Tracks: / Ride of the Valkyries / Winged dagger / All American soldier / Marche des parachutistes Belges / Canadian airborne / Les gars de Bigeard /

Pegasus / Pomp and circumstance march £4 / Mount Longdon / Standard of St.George / Air despatch / Dakota / Thunderbirds / Great little army.
LP: BND 1014
MC: ZC BND 1014

PIPES & DRUMS OF THE ROYAL IRISH RANGERS (Royal Irish Rangers).
Tracks: / Bugle major / Tipperary / Regimental marches / Irish tune from County Derry / Killaloe / Royal Irish polka / Irish rhapsody / Steal away / Endearing young charms.
LP: LILP 5036
MC: LICS 5036
LP: MM 0609

PROUD HERITAGE (Pipes & drums & military band) (Royal Highland Fusiliers).
LP: LILP 5146
MC: LICS 5146

RIGHT OF THE LINE (Royal Scots Reg. Band & Pipes & Drums).
MC: CWGR 025

ROYAL ARTILLERY MOUNTED BAND (Royal Artillery Mounted Band).
Tracks: / Overture / Mack and Mabel / La reve passe / Battle axe company / Gunners, The / Triumph of right / Marche Lorraine / Concerto for clarinet in A / Serenade for band / Squadron / Regimental quick march / Regimental slow march / Trots and canters / Earl of Oxford's march / Russian sailors dance.
LP: BND 1013
MC: ZC BND 1013

ROYAL BRITISH LEGION BAND (Conducted by Jeremy F.Royle) (Royal British Legion Band).
LP: MM 0572

ROYAL FAMILY ALBUM (Royal Family Album).
2LP: REL 593
MC: ZCD 593

ROYAL GREEN JACKETS 2ND BATTALION BAND & BUGLES (Under the direction of bandmaster WOI C.R.Donald) (Royal Green Jackets).
Tracks: / Sgt at arms / Tijuana holiday / High on a hill / Swing march, The / Chorale and rock out / Luftwaffe march / Elizabethan tapestry / Latin lullaby / Clochmerle / Eldorado.
LP: MM 0531

ROYAL GREEN JACKETS 3RD BATTALION BAND & BUGLES (Royal Green Jackets).
LP: MM 0589
MC: MMC 0589

ROYAL HAMPSHIRE REGIMENT 1ST BATTALION (Royal Hampshire Regiment).
LP: MM 0562

ROYAL HUSSARS (13th/18th Queen Mary's Own) (Royal Hussars Regiment Band).
LP: MM 0579

ROYAL MILITARY SPECTACULAR (Various artists).
LP: DKM 6002

ROYAL REGIMENT OF FUSILIERS BAND IN CONCERT (Royal Regiment Of Fusiliers-Band Of The 1st Battalion).
LP: MM 0557

ROYAL TOURNAMENT 1978 (Various artists).
LP: SCX 6589

ROYAL TOURNAMENT 1979 (Various artists).
LP: NTS 173

ROYAL TOURNAMENT 1980 (Centenary special various bands).
LP: NTS 206

ROYAL TOURNAMENT 1982-MUSICAL HIGHLIGHTS (Various bands).
LP: POLS 1069

ROYAL TOURNAMENT 1983-MUSICAL HIGHLIGHTS (Various artists).
Tracks: / Opening sequence: *Various artists* / Cockney pops: *Various artists* / Lifeline: *Various artists*/ Pipes & drums: *Various artists* / Massed bands: *Various artists* / Nighingale sang: *Various artists*/ Glenn Miller sequence: *Various artists* / Finale: *Various artists* / March out: *Various artists.*
LP: POLD 5107
MC: POLDC 5107

ROYAL TOURNAMENT 1989 (Various artists).
Tracks: / Firebird suite: *Various bands* / I don't want to join the Air Force: *Various bands* / Bold aviator was dying, The: *Various bands* / Another thousand revs wouldn't do him any harm: *Various bands* / There were three huns sat on his tail: *Various bands* / I left the mess room early: *Various bands* / Far far away: *Various bands* / Glory flying regulations: *Various bands* / RAF march past, The: *Various bands* / Bonnie Dundee: *Various bands* / Old Towler: *Various bands* / Gary Owen: *Various bands* / Hunting the hare: *Various bands*/ Round the Marble Arch: *Various bands* / Come lasses and lads: *Various bands* / Galloping major, The: *Various* bands / Light cavalry: *Various bands* / Post horn gallop: *Various bands* / John Peel: *Various bands*/ Campbells are coming, The: *Various bands* / Royal Artillery slow march: *Various bands* / Keel row, The: *Various* bands / In the mood: *Various bands* / Little brown jug: *Various bands* / String of pearls: *Various bands*/ Moonlight serenade: *Various bands* / St. Louis blues march: *Various bands* / Bugle calls from St. Mary's church: *Various bands* / Cracow: *Various bands* / Sky eagles: *Various bands* / March march Polonia: *Various* bands / Brothers it is time to fight: *Various bands* / Uhlans have come, The: *Various bands* / War, my little war: *Various bands* / How nice it is on a little war: *Various bands* / March of the 1st brigade: *Various bands*/ Oka: *Various bands* / Victory victory: *Various bands* / General Maczek's salute: *Various bands* / General salute: *Various bands* / Fanfare - Oranges and lemons: *Various bands* / Maybe it's because I'm a Londoner: *Various* bands / Heart of oak: *Various bands* / H.M.S. Pinafore: *Various bands* / All the nice girls love a sailor: *Various bands* / Alla Marcia: *Various bands* (From Karelia March) / Glorious victory: *Various bands* / Bond of friendship: *Various bands* / Trumpet prelude: *Various bands* / Symphony no. 3 in C minor: *Various* bands (Saint Saens (excerpt)) / Last post and evening hymn: *Various bands* / Hands across the sea: *Various bands*/ National anthem: *Various bands.*
MCSET: BNT 4089

RULE BRITANNIA (Royal Anglian Regiment, 1st Battalion Band).
LP: MM 0502

SABRE AND SPURS (Royal Hussars Regiment Band).
Tracks: / Fanfare - Arrival / Princess of Wales march / Sabre and spurs / With sword and lance / Cavalry walk / Parade / March of the 18th Hussars / Golden spurs / Cavalry of the Steppes / Step lightly / New Colonial / Old Panama / Ca ira / Light of foot / Waveney namur, The / British eights / Rogues march / Lincolnshire poacher / Regimental quick and slow marches.
MC: BND 61059

SANDHURST (Royal Military Academy Band Corps).
Tracks: / Officer of the day / Old grey mare / San Lorenzo / WRAC march / Here we are again / Sussex by the sea / Flight of the bumble bee / Bolero for band / Georgia on my mind / Agnus Dei.
LP: BND 1009
MC: ZC BND 1009

SCOTS ROYAL (Royal Scots Reg. Band & Pipes & Drums).
Tracks: / Saint Andrew's cross / Heroes of Vittoria / Highland brigade at Magersfontein, The / Dream valley of Glendaruel, The / Castle dangerous / Auchmountain's bonnie glen / Highland Harry / Over the isles to America / Tenth crossing, The / Friendly piper, The / Heights of Dargai, The / Battle of the Somme / Scots royal / Greenwood side / Sweet maid of Glendaruel, The / Earl of Mansfield / Marie's wedding / Corn rigs / Drum salute / Queen Elizabeth's march / Hundred pipers, A / Steam boat, The / Bonnie Dundee / Dark island / Denholm Dempsey, The / Hammer and the anvil, The / Going home / Muir of Ord / Black bear, The / Caller herrin' / Rowan tree, The / Highland laddie / Sergeant James Murray / Banjo breakdown / Liberton polka, The.
LP: LSA 3248

SERVICES SILVER JUBILEE MUSICAL PAGEANT 1977 various bands (Various artists).
Tracks: / Royal review: *Various bands* / Heart of oak: *Various bands* / Great little army: *Various bands*/ Voice of the guns: *Various bands* / Guard of honour: *Various bands* / Royal Air Force march past: *Various* bands / Skywatch: *Various bands* / Standard of St.George, The: *Various bands* / Scotland the brave: *Various* bands / Opening fanfare: *Various bands* / All the Queen's men: *Various bands* / Preobrajensky march: *Various* bands / To your guard: *Various bands* / Pathfinders: *Various bands* / Knights of the queen: *Various bands*/ Life on the ocean wave, A: *Various bands* / When the guards are on parade: *Various bands* / Skirl o' the pipes, The: *Various bands* / Teribus: *Various bands* / Flower of Scotland: *Various bands* / Bugle horn, The: *Various bands* / Killaloe: *Various bands* / Black bear, The: *Various bands* / Crown imperial: *Various* bands / Homage to the Queen: *Various bands* / Pomp and circumstance march no.1: *Various bands* / Silver and green: *Various bands* / Light Division assembly: *Various bands* / Advance: *Various bands* / Secunderabad: *Various bands* / Bugler in Vienna: *Various bands* / Regimental march of the Royal Green Jackets: *Various bands*/ Happy and glorious: *Various bands* / Shrewbury fair: *Various bands* / Congratulations: *Various bands*/ Long live Elizabeth: *Various bands* / Coronation bells: *Various bands* / Bells across the meadow: *Various* bands / Let the bells ring: *Various bands* / Symphonic salute: *Various bands* / Mexican hat dance: *Various* bands / Cavalry walk: *Various bands* / Royal Scots polka: *Various bands* / Wembley way: *Various bands*/ Sambre et meuse: *Various bands* / Vivat regina: *Various bands* / Rule Britannia: *Various bands* / Abide with me: *Various bands* / Sunset: *Various bands* / God save the Queen: *Various bands.*
2LP: PKDX 2002

SERVICES SILVER JUBILEE MUSICAL PAGEANT (Various artists).
LP: PKDX 2002

SOLDIERS FROM THE SKIES (Parachute Regt. Regimental Band).
Tracks: / Liberty bell / Victory drums / Screaming eagles / Pentland hill / Arnhem / Flying horse / Trombones to the fore / Ride of the Valkyries / Soldiers form the skies / Thunderer, The / El capitan / Army air corps slow march / New colonial, The / Queens avenue / El abanico.
LP: BND 1020
MC: ZC BND 1020

SOUNDS OF CEREMONY (Royal Army Ordance Corps Staff Band).
LP: MM 0584

SOVEREIGNS BANNER, THE (Royal Military Band Corps).
LP: DR 7

TAKE IT EASY (Parachute Regiment, Band of the 3rd Battalion).
LP: MB 301

TRADITIONAL MARCHES VOL 1 (Various artists).
2LP: DP6 28048

TRAFALGAR (Various artists).
Tracks: / Opening fanfare: *Various artists* / Aces high: *Various artists* / Imperial echoes: *Various artists*/ Grandioso march: *Various artists* / Jesus Christ Superstar: *Various artists* / Holyrood: *Various artists*/ Per mare per terram: *Various artists* / Aranjuez mon amour: *Various artists* / Cavalry of the Steppes: *Various* artists / Corp of drums: *Various artists* / Royal salute: *Various artists* / Life on the ocean wave, A: *Various* artists / Sea shanties: *Various artists* / Sailing: *Various artists* / Hey look me over: *Various artists*/ Viterzny: *Various artists* / Nights of Moscow: *Various artists* / Lady o'Mary Gaff: *Various artists*/ Fire on the mountain: *Various artists* / Caribbean selection: *Various artists* / Hora staccato: *Various artists* / British medley: *Various artists* / Finale: *Various artists.*
LP: NTS 224

TRIBUTE TO BRAVERY (Royal Regiment of Wales Regimental Band & Choir).
LP: DR 6

TRIBUTE TO HAROLD WALTERS (Royal Army Corps Staff Band).
LP: DR 42

TRIBUTE TO R.A.F (Various artists).
MC: DY 26

TROOPING THE COLOUR, 1977 (Various artists).
LP: QBP 1

TROOPING THE COLOUR, 1978 (Various artists).
LP: QBP 2
MC: CQ 2

TROOPING THE COLOUR, 1979 (Various artists).
LP: QBP 3
MC: CQ 3

TUNES OF GLORY (Pipes/Drums/ Military Band of Scottish Div.School of Music).
LP: PRD 2014
MC: PRD 4 2014

VOICE OF GUNS (Royal Artillery Alanbrooke Band).
LP: PRD 2008
MC: PRD 42008

WORLD OF MILITARY BAND (Various artists).
LP: SPA 18
MC: KCSP 18

WORLD OF MILITARY BANDS VOL 2 (Various artists).
LP: SPA 66
MC: KCSP 66

Military Bands

DUKE OF EDINBURGH'S ROYAL REGIMENT (Duke Of Edinburgh's Royal Regiment).
LP: GRS 1056

Military Musical

MILITARY MUSICAL PAGEANT (Various military bands).
Tracks: / Trooping the colours / Bands and bugles of the Royal Green Jackets / Massed bands / Massed pipes and drums / Military pageant.
2LP: PRD 2002/3
LP: GLNA 502

MILITARY MUSICAL PAGEANT 1981 (Various military bands).
2LP: PRD 2016/7
MCSET: PRD4 2016/7

MILITARY MUSICAL PAGEANT 1983 Wembley Stadium (Various military bands).
Tracks: / Artillery salvo and opening fanfare / Music of the Queens guards / Celtic pride and pageantry / Massed bands in concert / Swift and bold / Wellington's victory at Vittoria / Grand finale- The Muster Parade.
2LP: BNC 3001
MCSET: ZC BNC 3001

Milk & Honey

MILK & HONEY WITH GALI (Milk & Honey with Gali).
Tracks: / Lonely in the night / Goodbye New York / Isn't it magic / Lady sun / For your love / World is like a roundabout / Chinatown / Grand Prix / Happiness recipe / Hallelujah.
LP: 2310690

Milk Monitors

REVENGE REVENGE.
LP: NOSE 22

Milk'N'Cookies

MILK'N'COOKIES.
LP: ILPS 9320

Milkshakes

14 RHYTHM AND BEAT GREATS.
Tracks: / Seven days / Black sails (in the moonlight) / Exactly like you / Girl called mine, A / Sad girl mambo / I want you / Cadalina / No one else / I need no one / You did her wrong / Can you tell me / Red monkey, The / Take you home tonight / Wo now.
LP: WIK 23
LP: NED 4

20 ROCK'N'ROLL HITS OF THE 50'S & 60'S.
Tracks: / Hippy hippy shake / Rip it up / I'm gonna sit right down and cry over you / Say mama / Peggy Sue / Jaguar and the thunderbirds / Commanche / I'm talking about you / Sweet little sixteen / Money (that's what I want) / Carol / Boys / Something else / Some other guy / Who do you love / Jezebel / Hidden charms / Little Queenie / Ya ya (twist) / I wanna be your man.
LP: WIKM 20

107 TAPES.
2LP: MB 9

AFTER SCHOOL SESSIONS.
Tracks: / Shimmy shake / Tell me child / I can tell / Soldiers of love / Let's stomp / Jaguar / You can only lose / Cadillac / More honey / El Salvador / Hide and scatter / That girl of mine / Little Minnie / Goodbye girl.
LP: UPLP 1
LP: HANG 24 UP

LAST NIGHT AT THE MIC CLUB, THE (Milkshakes & Prisoners).
LP: MIC 001

LIVE FROM CHATHAM.
LP: HANG 11 UP

MILKSHAKES IN GERMANY, THE.
LP: EFA 065 403

MILKSHAKES REVENGE, THE.
LP: HANG 1 UP

MILKSHAKES V PRISONERS LIVE (Milkshakes & Prisoners).
LP: MB 17

NOTHING CAN STOP THESE MEN.
Tracks: / You got me girl / Ida honey (tell me you'll be mine) / Chatham train / She's just fifteen years old / Everywhere I look / That's my revenge / Little Bettina / She's no good to me / Dull knife / Grim reaper / I'm the one for you / You've been lyin'.
LP: HARP-0

TALKING 'BOUT MILKSHAKES.
LP: MILK-0

THEY CAME THEY SAW THEY CONQUERED.
Tracks: / Bo Diddlius / Did I tell you / Little girl / I'm needing you / Quiet lives / Best things in life / This feeling inside / Wounded knee / Just like you / Shed country / Thinking 'bout that girl / Gringles and groyles / Mother I want your daughter / How can I love you / Don't destroy you.
LP: . . . . **WIK 30**

THREE KNIGHTS OF TRASH.
LP: **GARB-0**

Milky Way

MILKY WAY.
LP: . . . . **LR 45012**

Mill City Seven

MILL CITY SEVEN.
LP: . . . . **J 19**

Mill on the Floss (bk)

MILL ON THE FLOSS, THE (see Eliot, George) (Atkins, Eileen).

Millar, Gertie

OUR MISS GIBBS (And Other Gertie Millar Successes).
LP: . . . . **SH 186**

Millar, Leslie

LESLIE MILLAR.
Tracks: / Lonely / Key, The / Music of unity / Comes and goes / Eternal flame / Consumociety / There is a place / Bepop and the bomb.
LP: . . . . **DIR 2**

Millay, Edna (poet)

MILLAY READING HER POETRY.
MC: **1123**

Millenium

MILLENIUM.
LP: . . . . **GRC 2163**

Miller, Al

NEGRO STRING BAND (1927-36).
LP: . . . . **LE 300 001**

Miller, Arthur

CRUCIBLE, THE (Various artists).
MCSET: **0356**

DEATH OF A SALESMAN (Various artists).
MCSET: **0310**

Miller, Bob

BOB MILLER AND M.
LP: . . . . **NEVLP 140**

Miller, Brian

FAVOURITE DRAM, THE (Miller, Brian & Charlie Soane).
LP: . . . . **CM 006**

Miller, Chris

PIPER'S MAGGOT, THE (Miller, Chris & Ken Campbell).
Tracks: / Piper's maggot, The / Hector the hero / Left handed fiddler, The / Diggins / Cuddly Clauder / Mally Stewart / When the tide comes in / Norwegian wedding march / Hamburger polka / Adieu France / Farewell to Gartly / Danny Deever / Honourable James Ramsay / Speed the plough / Auld Bougar / Meeting of the waters / Stool of repentance / Captain Jimmy Thompson / Heilan' King o' China / Boots of Malin / Dancing feet.
LP: . . . . **12 TS 423**

Miller, Chuck

GOIN' GOIN' GONE.
LP: . . . . **REV 3002**

Miller, Dale

FINGER PICKING RAGS AND OTHER DELIGHTS.
Tracks: / Sweet Georgia Brown / Stagger Lee / God bless the child / Cheap wine / Chattanooga choo choo / Boys from Blue Hill / Inflation blues / Bicycle built for two / Sidewalks from New York / Air on a G string / Too tite rag / Amtrack shuffle / Pitchel theme / Blue / Prelude / Take it on the run / Nice work if you can get it / Son of diddle / Birth of the blues / Shelley's swing / Fleabites / Hey Jude / Little fugue.
LP: . . . . **SNKF 110**

FINGERS DON'T FAIL ME NOW.
LP: . . . . **SNKF 163**
LP: . . . . **KM 155**

GUITARISTS CHOICE.
Tracks: / All my loving / Sweet Lorraine.
LP: . . . . **SNKF 140**

Miller, Donnie

ONE OF THE BOYS.
Tracks: / One of the boys / Normal guy (I want sex) / I can't stop flying / Me and you / Devil wears lingerie, The / Man said no, The / Blind man's buff / No time for running / You can't stop emotion / Welcome home.
LP: **4658171**
MC: **4658174**

Miller, Douglas

SING UNTIL MORNING.
LP: . . . . **REJ R 5025**
MC: . . . . **REJ C 5025**

Miller, Eddie

LAZY MOOD FOR TWO (Miller, Eddie & Lou Stein).
Tracks: / I've got a crush on you / Lady be good / I got it bad and that ain't good / Dizzy fingers / Little girl blue / Coquette / Lazy mood / I'm gonna sit right down and write myself ... / Sophisticated lady / Diane / Bag balm boogie / Can't we be friends.
LP: **77S 59**

LIVE AT MICHELE'S SILVER STOPE (Miller, Eddie/Merle Koch).
LP: . . . . **AP 135**

NEW ORLEANS DIXIELANDERS AND RHYTHM PALS (See under Hug, Armand) (Miller, Eddie & Armand Hug).

PIANO BLUES 1929-34 (Miller, Eddie/ John Oscar).
LP: . . . . **BD 2060**

SWINGING TENORS (see Freeman, Bud) (Miller, Eddie & Bud Freeman).

Miller, Frank (nar)

GREAT RAILWAY BAZAAR BY TRAIN THROUGH ASIA (See also Paul Theroux).

Miller, Frankie

DANCING IN THE RAIN.
Tracks: / I'd lie to you for your love / Do it till we drop / That's how long my love is / How many tears can you hide / Dancing in the rain / Shakey ground / Boys and girls are doing it / Game of love / Gladly go blind / You're a puzzle I can't put down.
LP: . . . . **VERH 34**
MC: . . . . **VERHC 34**

DOUBLE TROUBLE.
Tracks: / Have you seen me lately Joan / Double heart trouble / Train / You'll be in my mind / Good time love / Love waves / Breakaway / Stubborn kind of fellow / Love is all around / Goodnight sweetheart.
LP: . . . . **CHR 1174**

FALLING IN LOVE.
Tracks: / When I'm away from you / Is this love / If I can love somebody / Darlin' / And it's your love / Woman to love, A / Falling in love with you / Every time a teardrop falls / Papa / Don't know / Good to see you.
LP: . . . . **CHR 1220**

FRANKIE MILLER.
LP: . . . . **IC 0647 400098**

FULL HOUSE.
Tracks: / Be good to yourself / Doodle song, The / Jealous guy / Searching / Love letters / Take good care of yourself / Down the honky tonk / This love of mine / Let the candlelight shine / I'll never live in vain.
LP: . . . . **CHR 1128**
MC: . . . . **ZCHR 1128**

HEY WHERE YA GOIN'.
Tracks: / I don't know why I love you / Day by day / It's not big thing to me / What have I ever done (Previously unissued.) / My wedding song to you / You're crying on my shoulder again / Hey where ya goin' / Paid in full / You don't show me much / Paint powder and perfume / You'll never be true / What you do from now on.
LP: . . . . **BFX 15082**

ROCK, THE.
Tracks: / Fool in love, A / Heart break, The / Rock, The / I don't know why the sun don't shine / Hard on the levee / Ain't got no money / All my love to you / I'm old enough / Bridgeton / Drunken nights in the city.
LP: . . . . **CHR 1088**

ROCKIN' ROLLIN' FRANKIE MILLER.
Tracks: / Too hot to handle / Blackland farmer / True blue / If I'd know then / Rain rain / Gotta win my baby back / Mean old greyhound bus / Baby rocked her dolly / Cat and the mouse, The / Poppin' Johnny / Picture at St. Helene, The / Fifteen acres of peanut land / Richest poor boy / Truck driving buddy / Starving for love (Previously unissued.) / True love stays (Previously unissued.) / Family man / Reunion.
LP: . . . . **BFX 15128**

STANDING ON THE EDGE.
Tracks: / Standing on the edge / Danger danger / Zap zap / To dream the dream / Don't stop / Angels with dirty faces / Firing line / Jealousy / It's all coming down tonight / Oh my way.
LP: **1C 064 400098**
LP: . . . . **EST 12206**

Miller, Gary

GARY MILLER: CELEBRATION ROAD SHOW BAND (Miller, Gary Celebration Road Show Band).
LP: . . . . **CLP 2**

Miller, Glenn

20 CLASSIC TRACKS: GLENN MILLER.
Tracks: / String of pearls / It happened in Sun Valley / Deep purple / Sun Valley jump / Red cavalry march / Tuxedo Junction / Bugle brown jug / I've got a gal in Kalamazoo / Pennsylvania 6 5000 / Little brown jug / Sunrise serenade / Serenade in blue / Moonlight serenade / Adios / American patrol / Anvil chorus / Chattanooga choo choo / Moonlight cocktail / Boomshot / In the mood.
LP: . . . . **ARA 1006**
MC: . . . . **ARAC 1006**

20 GREATEST HITS: GLENN MILLER.
LP: **20124**
MC: **40124**

21 GOLDEN GREATS LIVE.
Tracks: / Moonlight serenade / Caribbean clipper / Summertime / American patrol / Nearness of you, The / Anvil chorus / Tuxedo Junction / El capitan / Deep purple / In the mood / Anchors aweigh / I want to be happy / Snafu jump / I dream of you / Long ago and far away / St. Louis blues / My blue Heaven / Chattanooga choo choo / Rhapsody in blue / In the gloaming / Little brown jug.
MC: . . . . **CAWM 1**

40TH ANNIVERSARY ALBUM.
LP: . . . . **AWE 11**
MC: . . . . **CAWE 11**

1940: GLENN MILLER.
LP: . . . . **AWE 14**

1943 BAND IN HI-FI, THE.
LP: . . . . **LP 1015**

AMERICAN PATROL (Miller, Glenn & His Orchestra).
Tracks: / Serenade in blue / Song of the volga boatmen / Moonlight cocktail / Anvil chorus / I've got a gal in Kalamazoo / Sunrise serenade / Under the double eagle / Danny boy / Chattanooga choo choo / American Patrol / Jeep jockey jump / Sanfu jump / Keep 'em flying / Lover / Little brown jug.
MC: . . . . **SHTC 103**
LP: . . . . **SHLP 103**

AMERICAN RHAPSODY.
Tracks: / Rhapsody in blue / Symphony / El capitan / In the gloaming / Deep purple / Killarney I've got a heart filled with love / Moonlight serenade / Wabash blues / Oranges and lemons / Buckle down winsocki / Stealin apples / Red cavalry march.
LP: . . . . **SWH 11**
MC: . . . . **CSWH 11**

AMERICA'S NO. 1 DANCE BAND (Live 1940).
LP: . . . . **SG 8018**

AND THE ARMY AIR FORCE BAND.
Tracks: / Over there / Anvil chorus / Stardust / Song of the volga boatmen / Farewell blues / They are Yanks / My ideal / Mission to Moscow / Sun Valley jump / Tuxedo Junction / I'll be around / Poinciana / I hear you screaming / Jukebox Saturday night / My blue Heaven / St. Louis blues march / It must be jelly / Blues in my heart / Everybody loves my baby / Alexander's ragtime band / Stompin' at the Savoy / Deep purple / Don't be that way / I can't give you anything but love / Wang wang blues / Shoo shoo baby / Way you look tonight / Victory polka / There'll be a hot time in the town of Berlin / Flying home / Here we go again / Jeep jockey jump / Enlisted mens mess / Begin the beguine / In the mood / It's love love love / Eighteenth century drawing room / There are Yanks / Closing theme and announcements.
2LP: . . . . **PM 43172**

APRIL 3, 1940, CHESTERFIELD SHOW, CAFE ROUGE.
LP: . . . . **JASM 2520**
MC: . . . . **JASMC 2520**

ARMY AIR FORCE BAND - COMPLETE VDISC SESSIONS.
LP: . . . . **SG 8013**

ARMY AIRFORCE ORCHESTRA-JOHNNY DESMOND.
Tracks: / I hear you screaming / In the gloaming / For the first time / Stomping at the Savoy / Deep purple / Along the Santa Fe trail / Oh what a beautiful morning / Christmas medley / Airforce drama.
LP: . . . . **JASM 2532**
MC: . . . . **JASMC 2532**

AT MEADOWBROOK 1939 (Miller, Glenn Orchestra).
Tracks: / Moonlight serenade (theme) / Little brown jug / Blue rain / Oh Johnny, oh Johnny oh / In an old Dutch garden / Tiger rag / Love with a capital you / Bugle call rag / Blue moonlight / Indian Summer / Why couldn't it last last night / This changing world / I just got a letter / On a little street in Singapore / Faithful to you / Farewell blues / Moonlight serenade (theme and fadeout).
LP: . . . . **AWE 34**
MC: . . . . **CAWE 34**

AT THE GLENN ISLAND CASINO.
LP: . . . . **JASM 2517**
MC: . . . . **JASMC 2517**

AT THE STEEL PIER IN 1941.
LP: . . . . **AJAZ 316**

AUTUMN SERENADE (Miller, Glenn & His Orchestra).
LP: . . . . **AWE 9**
MC: . . . . **CAWE 9**

BBC NOVEMBER 1944.
LP: . . . . **JASM 2504**
MC: . . . . **JASMC 2504**

BEST OF GLENN MILLER (CBS) (Miller, Glenn & His Orchestra).
Tracks: / In the mood / Sunrise serenade / String of pearls / Rhapsody in blue / American patrol / Little brown jug / Alice blue gown / Tuxedo Junction / Adios / My sentiment.
LP: . . . . **CBS 32665**
MC: **40 32665**

BEST OF GLENN MILLER (CREOLE).
MC: **16-9**

BEST OF GLENN MILLER (FLASHBACK) (Miller, Glenn & His Orchestra).
MC: **64027**

BEST OF GLENN MILLER (PICKWICK) (Miller, Glenn & His Orchestra).
Tracks: / Nearness of you, The / Lamplighter's serenade, The / Nightingale sang in Berkeley Square, A / Fools rush in / Missouri waltz / Say si si / My blue Heaven / My melancholy baby / Alice blue gown / Faithful forever / Old black Joe / In the mood.
LP: . . . . **CDS 1165**
MC: . . . . **CAM 475**

BEST OF GLENN MILLER (RCA) (Miller, Glenn & His Orchestra).
Tracks: / In the mood / Along the Santa Fe trail / Johnson rag / Sunrise serenade / Chattanooga choo choo / Anvil chorus / St. Louis blues march / Don't sit under the apple tree / Tuxedo Junction / Stairway to the stars / Jukebox Saturday night / Song of the volga boatmen.
LP: . . . . **NL 83871**
MC: . . . . **NK 83871**

BEST OF GLENN MILLER VOL.2 (RCA) (Miller, Glenn & His Orchestra).
Tracks: / Moonlight serenade / Elmer's tune / String of pearls / Lamplighter's serenade, The / Who's sorry now? / I've got a gal in Kalamazoo / Moonlight cocktail / By the waters of Minnetonka / Serenade in blue / Glenn Island special / Take the 'A' train / American patrol.
LP: . . . . **NL 83809**
MC: . . . . **NK 83809**
LP: . . . . **INTS 5091**

CARNEGIE HALL CONCERT (Miller, Glenn & His Orchestra).
Tracks: / Moonlight serenade / Running wild / Sunrise serenade / Little brown jug / Stairway to the stars / To you / One o'clock jump / Londonderry air / Jumpin' jive / F.D.R. Jones / Hold tight, hold tight / In the mood / Bugle call rag.
LP: . . . . **NL 42010**

CHATANOOGA CHOO CHOO.
MC: **64026**

CHESTERFIELD SHOWS, 1941-42 (Miller, Glenn & His Orchestra).
Tracks: / Sweet Eloise / I've got a gal in Kalamazoo / People like you and me / I don't want to walk without you / V for victory hop / Jingle bells / Story of a starry night / Nobody ever wants me / Sun Valley jump / Jersey bounce.
LP: . . . . **JASM 2501**
MC: . . . . **JASMC 2501**
LP: . . . . **LP 1002**

CHESTERFIELD SHOWS-CHICAGO 1940 (Civic Theatre, Chicago) (Miller, Glenn & His Orchestra).
Tracks: / In my solitude / Rumba jumps, The / I'm stepping out with a memory tonight / Everybody loves my baby / Five o'clock whistle / Siren's song, The / Handful of stars, A / Love in bloom / Birth of the blues / Beat me daddy, eight to the bar / Slumber song / Lights out / Hold me tight / Along the Santa Fe trail / Tiger rag.
LP: . . . . **LP 1012**

CHESTERFIELD SHOWS-N.Y.C. 1940 (Radio Playhouse, NYC) (Miller, Glenn & His Orchestra).

Tracks: / Woodpecker song, The / Sweet and lovely / Sierra Sue / Very thought of you, The / Blue evening / Tiger rag / Midnight on the Nile / Shadows on the sand / Fresh as a daisy / Yesterthoughts / Solid as a stone wall, Jackson / Isn't that just like love / I dreamt I dwelt in Harlem / Slumber song.
LP: . . . . LP 1010

CHRISTMAS PROGRAMME.
LP: . . . . LP 1017

COLLECTION: GLENN MILLER.
Tracks: / Serenade in blue / Chattanooga choo choo / Little brown jug / Anvil chorus / In the mood / Elmer's tune / American patrol / Don't sit under the apple tree / Take the 'A' train / Bugle call rag / I know why / Who's sorry now / St. Louis blues march / Moonlight cocktail / (Bluebirds over) the white cliffs of Dover / Don't worry 'bout me / My prayer / Song of the volga boatmen / Sun valley jump / That old black magic / When Johnny comes marching home / Stardust / Perfidia / Nearness of you, The.
MC: . . . . CCSMC 185
2LP: . . . . CCSLP 185

COLLECTION: GLENN MILLER.
LP: . . . . NL 45169
MC: . . . . NK 45169

COLLECTION, THE.
Tracks: / Moonlight serenade / Hallelujah / In a sentimental mood / Back to back / Jumpin' jive / In the mood / Chattanooga choo choo / Happy in love / Serenade in blue / Don't sit under the apple tree / Moonlight cocktail / Pennsylvania 6 5000 / Johnson rag / St. Louis blues / My prayer / Anchors aweigh / I've got a gal in Kalamazoo / Woodpecker song, The / I know why / Medley / My melancholy baby / Moon love / Stompin' at the Savoy / Blue moon.
LP: . . . . AWE 22
LP: . . . . LPJT 12

COMPLETE SUNSET SERENADE PROG/LIVE, CAFE ROUGE.
LP: . . . . JASM 2505

EARLY GLENN MILLER VOL.1.
LP: . . . . M 8003

EARLY GLENN MILLER VOL.2.
LP: . . . . M 8004

EARLY YEARS - PARADISE RESTAURANT N.Y.C, THE.
Tracks: / Butcher boy / Don't wake up my heart / Cowboy from Brooklyn / My best wishes / I know that you know / On the sentimental side / On the Alamo / Dipsy doodle, The / Closing / Please come out of your dream / Poinciana / Running wild.
LP: . . . . LP 1014

FOREVER.
Tracks: / Take the 'A' Train / Back to back / Stairway to the stars / One I love belongs to somebody else, The / Song of the volga boatmen / Little man who wasn't there, The / Who's sorry now? / Runnin' wild / I want to be happy / Ding dong the witch is dead / Over the rainbow / You stepped out of a dream / Bugle call rag / Story of a starry night / When Johnny comes marching home / Adios / Skylark / Say si si / On a little street in Singapore / Ciri-biri-bin / Jingle bells / Baby me / Nearness of you / Blueberry Hill / Frenesi / At last / Woodpecker song, The / I'll never smile again / Keep them flying / My prayer / Yours is my heart alone.
LP: . . . . NL 89214
MC: . . . . NK 89214

GLENN MILLER (Live, April - June 1940).
LP: . . . . SG 8012

GLENN MILLER, 1937 - 1942 (Miller, Glenn & His Orchestra).
Tracks: / Wistful and blue / I got rhythm / Sunrise serenade / Moon love / Sold American / Glenn Island special / In the mood / Johnson rag / Yes, my darling daughter / Sun Valley jump / Caribbean clipper / Here we go again.
LP: . . . . SM 3060
MC: . . . . MC 3060

GLENN MILLER 1940-42.
Tracks: / Theme...intro St.Louis blues / I close my eyes / Sing and be gay / How deep is the ocean (medley) / Here after / I've got no strings / Isn't it romantic (medley) / She's funny that way / Breakfast for two / Morning after, The / I hear you screaming.
LP: . . . . JASM 2506
MC: . . . . JASMC 2506

GLENN MILLER AIR FORCE ORCHESTRA, JUNE 10, 1944 (Miller, Glenn Army Air Force Orchestra).
Tracks: / D-Day announcement / Flying home / Long ago and far away / My buddy / Now I know / Music makers / Farewell blues / Poinciana / Caribbean clipper / Songs my mother taught me / Eighteenth century drawing room / Blue orchids / There are Yanks.
LP: . . . . LP 1004
LP: . . . . EB 412

GLENN MILLER AIR FORCE ORCHESTRA, NOVEMBER 1944 (Miller, Glenn Army Air Force Orchestra).
Tracks: / In the mood / Stardust / Tuxedo Junction / Now I know / String of pearls / Poinciana / Long ago and far away / Is you is or is you ain't my baby / Great day.
LP: . . . . LP 1005

GLENN MILLER AND HIS ORCHESTRA.
LP: . . . . BLJ 8005

GLENN MILLER ARMY AIR FORCE BAND(1943-1944),THE.
Tracks: / Anvil chorus / Stormy weather / Jukebox Saturday night / Jeep jockey jump / All the things you are / Song of the volga boatmen / With my head in the clouds / I hear you screaming / Long ago and far away / Cherokee / Peggy and the pin-up girl / In the mood / Holiday for strings / String of pearls / Don't be that way.
LP: . . . . RARITIES 63

GLENN MILLER COLLECTION (20 Golden Greats).
Tracks: / In the mood / Moonlight serenade / Chattanooga choo choo / Pennsylvania 6 5000 / Danny boy / Indian Summer / American patrol / Blueberry Hill / Little brown jug / Tuxedo Junction / Don't sit under the apple tree / I've got a gal in Kalamazoo / Serenade in blue / That old black magic / String of pearls / Moonlight cocktail / Pavanne / Woodpecker song, The / Johnson rag / Sunrise serenade.
LP: . . . . DVLP 2010
MC: . . . . DVMC 2010

GLENN MILLER & HIS ARMY AIR FORCE ORCHESTRA 1944.
LP: . . . . LP 1018

GLENN MILLER & HIS ORCHESTRA.
Tracks: / Butcher Boy / Don't wake up my heart / Cowboy from Brooklyn / My best wishes / I Know that you know / On the sentimental side / On the Alamo / Dipsy Doodle, The / Meadowbrook, The / Sold American / Please come out of your dream / Poinciana / Runnin' wild / Broadcast closing.
LP: . . . . JASM 2511
MC: . . . . JASMC 2511

GLENN MILLER IN CONCERT.
Tracks: / Moonlight serenade / Perfidia / Little brown jug / Bless you / One o'clock jump / Don't sit under the apple tree / Lady be good / My devotion / String of pearls / Fresh as a daisy / Flagwaver / Make believe / Blues / Under a blanket of blue / Twenty four robbers / My melancholy baby / Moon love / Stompin' at the Savoy / Blue moon / Chattanooga choo choo / It must be jelly / Hop / I guess I'll have to change my plans / Bugle call rag / Porter stomp / Introduction to a waltz / Down the count / Farewell blues.
2LP: . . . . NL 45153
MCSET: . . . . NK 45153
2LP: . . . . NL 89216
MCSET: . . . . NK 89216

GLENN MILLER LIVE (1939).
Tracks: / Lady's in love with you, The / Wishing / Pavanne / And the angels sing / King Porter stomp / Moon is over a silver dollar, The / Sometime / Hold tight / Glenn Island special / Lamp is low, The / Jumpin' jive / My blue Heaven / Closing.
LP: . . . . JASM 2507
MC: . . . . JASMC 2507

GLENN MILLER MEETS THE DORSEY BROTHERS (See under Dorsey Brothers) (Miller, Glenn/Dorsey Brothers).

GLENN MILLER ORCHESTRA.
Tracks: / St. Louis blues / I close my eyes (June 30, 1942 - slow version with Bobby Hackett solo.) / Sing and be gay (Vocal Ray Eberle January 22, 1941.) / How deep is the ocean (Vocal Paula Kelly-May 22, 1941) / Hearafter / I've got no strings (Vocal Ray Eberie - Nov 13,1941.) / Isn't it romantic (Vocal Andrews Sisters - February 13,1940) / Shadows on the sand (Vocal Andrews Sisters - February 13,1940) / Blue prelude (Vocal Andrews Sisters - February 13,1940) / She's funny that way (Spetember 25, 1940.) / Breakfast for two (Johnny Best solo August 25, 1942.) / Morning after, The (Vocal Paully, Tex & The Modernaires-April 23,1941.) / I hear you screaming (Vocal Ray Eberie-February 20, 1941).
LP: . . . . LP 1007

GLENN MILLER ORCHESTRA, AUGUST 30, 1941 (Sunset Serenade & Chesterfield Broadcasts) (Miller, Glenn & His Orchestra).
Tracks: / Here we go again / Cowboy serenade, The / Booglie wooglie piggy, The / Georgia on my mind / It's great to be an American / Till reveille / Daddy / Things I love, The / Intermezzo / Moonlight cocktail / Jersey bounce / I left my heart at the stage door canteen / Keep 'em flying.
LP: . . . . LP 1001
LP: . . . . JASM 2500
MC: . . . . JASMC 2500

GLENN MILLER ORCHESTRA, DECEMBER 27, 1941.
Tracks: / Here we go again / White cliffs of Dover, The / Jingle bells / Introduction to a waltz / This is no laughing matter / Oh so good / Tuxedo Junction / It's great to be an American / Chattanooga choo choo / Papa Niccolini / This time the dream's on me / Dear Arabella / Elmer's tune / Keep 'em flying.
LP: . . . . LP 1006

GLENN MILLER ORCHESTRA (JOKER) (Miller, Glenn Orchestra).
LP: . . . . SM 3865

GLENN MILLER ORCHESTRA, VOL. 1 (Miller, Glenn Orchestra).
LP: . . . . EJLP 02
MC: . . . . EJMC 02

GLENN MILLER ORCHESTRA, VOL 2 (Miller, Glenn Orchestra).
LP: . . . . EJLP 10
MC: . . . . EJMC 10

GLENN MILLER PLAYS SELECTIONS (Miller, Glenn & His Orchestra).
LP: . . . . RD 27068

GLENN MILLER REUNION IN CONCERT.
LP: . . . . GNPS 76
MC: GNP5 76

GLENN MILLER SOUND, THE.
MC: . . . . VCA 019

GLENN MILLER STORY, THE.
Tracks: / Moonlight serenade / Little brown jug / Sunrise serenade / Beer barrel polka / Indian Summer / Woodpecker song, The / Pennsylvania 6-5000 / Slumber song / Chattanooga choo choo / String of pearls / Don't sit under the apple tree / My blue Heaven / In the mood / Sun valley jump / Farewell blues / Tuxedo Junction / Blues in my heart / Begin the beguine / Anvil chorus / St. Louis blues march / Everybody loves my baby / Over there / Song of the volga boatmen / Enlisted men's mess / It must be jelly.
MCSET: . . . . DVREMC 06
2LP: 20187
MCSET: 40187

GLENN MILLER STORY: VOL 1.
Tracks: / Moonlight serenade / In the mood / String of pearls / Blue skies / Little brown jug / St. Louis blues march / American patrol / Tuxedo junction / Anchors aweigh / Chattanooga choo choo / Pennsylvania 6500 / Star dust.
LP: . . . . NL 89005
MC: . . . . NK 89005
LP: 26 21415
MC: 260171

GLENN MILLER STORY: VOL 2.
Tracks: / Flyin' home / Sun valley jump / Solitude / Tisket a tasket, A / I got rhythm / Johnson rag / One o'clock jump / Here we go again / Under a blanket of blue / Rhapsody in blue / King Porter stomp / Hop, The.
LP: . . . . NL 89221
MC: . . . . NK 89221
LP: 26 21424

GLENN MILLER STORY: VOL 3.
Tracks: / I've got a gal in Kalamazoo / Sunrise serenade / Don't sit under the apple tree / Serenade in blue / My melancholy baby / Caribbean clipper / Seet Eloise / Elmer's tune / Beethoven's moonlight sonata / Yes, my darling daughter / Say it / Perfidia / My blue heaven / Cradle song.
LP: . . . . NL 89222
MC: . . . . NK 89222

GLENN MILLER STORY: VOL 4.
Tracks: / Slow freight / Booglie wooglie piggy, The / Kiss polka / Boulder buff / Sweeter than the sweetest / Moonlight cocktail / Rainbow rhapsody / It's always you / I guess I'll have to dream the rest / Chip off the old block / Lamplighter's serenade, The / I wanna hat with cherries / Everything I love.
LP: . . . . NL 89223
MC: . . . . NK 89223

GLENN MILLER & THE ARMY AIR FORCE BAND.
Tracks: / Over there / Anvil chorus / Star dust / Song of the volga boatmen / Farewell blues / They are yanks / My ideal / Mission to Moscow / Sun valley jump / Tuxedo Junction / I'll be around / Poinciana / I hear you screaming / Jukebox Saturday night / My blue Heaven / St. Louis blues march / It must be jelly / Blues in my heart / Everybody loves my baby / Alexander's ragtime band / Stompin' at the savoy / Deep purple / Don't be that way / I can't give you anything but love / Wang wang blues / Shoo shoo baby / Way you look tonight / Victory polka / There'll be a hot time in the town of Berlin / Flying home / Here we go again / Jeep jockey jump / Enlisted men's mess / Begin the Beguine / In the mood.
2LP: . . . . NL 89767
MCSET: . . . . NK 89767
2LP: . . . . M 43172

GLENN MILLER'S UPTOWN HALL GANG.
LP: . . . . ESQ 302

GLENN MILLER'S UPTOWN HALL GANG VOLUME 2 (Miller's, Glenn Uptown Hall Gang).
LP: . . . . ESQ 316

GO TO WAR (Radio Broadcasts from the 1940's) (Miller, Glenn & His Orchestra).
MC: . . . . CMR 1160

GOLDEN HOUR OF GLENN MILLER.
Tracks: / Moonlight serenade / American patrol / It happened in Sun Valley / I've got a gal in Kalamazoo / I know why and so do you / Measure for measure / In the mood / People like you and me / At last / Chattanooga choo choo / Sun Valley jump / Moonlight sonata / Boom shot / Bugle call rag / Spirit is willing, The / That's sabotage / You say the sweetest things / Serenade in blue.
LP: . . . . GH 831

GOLDEN SERENADE (Miller, Glenn & AAF Band).
LP: . . . . SWS 1
MC: . . . . CSWS 1

GRAVACIOES INEDITAS.
Tracks: / From one love to another / I know why / Rug cutters swing / Yesterday's gardenias / It happened in Sun Valley / When the roses bloom again / Stardust / You stepped out of a dream / Caribbean clipper / Song of the volga boatmen / Slumber song / Story of a starry night.
LP: 107 4042
MC: 770 4042

GREATEST HITS: GLENN MILLER.
LP: 33009
MC: 63009

GREATEST HITS: GLENN MILLER (FUN).
LP: . . . . FUN 9022
MC: . . . . FUNC 9022

HALLELUJAH.
Tracks: / Hallelujah / Now we know / Irresistible you / Alouette / Tuxedo Junction / Way you look tonight / Kingport stomp / Wham.
LP: . . . . AWE 6
MC: . . . . CAWE 6

HERE WE GO AGAIN-VOL 2 1940-41.
LP: . . . . AWE 17

HITS FROM THE GLENN MILLER STORY.
Tracks: / Moonlight serenade / American patrol / Pennsylvania 6 5000 / In the mood / I've got a gal in Kalamazoo / Boulder buff / Tuxedo Junction / St. Louis blues / String of pearls / Little brown jug / Farewell blues / King Porter stomp.
LP: . . . . LSA 3274

I SUSTAIN THE WINGS SHOWS 1941-42.
LP: . . . . JASM 2503
MC: . . . . JASMC 2503

IN 1940.
MC: . . . . CAWE 14

IN HOLLYWOOD.
LP: 826 635 1
MC: 826 635 4

IN THE DIGITAL MOOD (Miller, Glenn Orchestra).
Tracks: / In the mood / Chattanooga choo choo / American Patrol / String of pearls / Little brown jug / I've got a gal in Kalamazoo / Tuxedo Junction / St. Louis blues march / Pennsylvania 6-5000 / Moonlight serenade.
LP: . . . . GRPA 1002
MC: . . . . GRPC 1002

IN THE MOOD (ASTAN).
LP: 20103
MC: 40103

IN THE MOOD (CBS).
LP: . . . . CBS 54575
MC: 40 54575

IN THE MOOD (FLASHBACK).
MC: **64024**

IN THE MOOD (PATHE MARCONI).
LP: **2M 056 64872**
MC: **2M 256 64872**

IN THE MOOD (TOPLINE).
Tracks: / In the mood / Chattanooga choo choo / American patrol / St. Louis blues march / Pennsylvania 6-5000 / Jumpin' jive / Moonlight serenade / Don't sit under the apple tree / I've got a gal in Kalamazoo / Serenade in blue / I know why / String of pearls.
LP: **TOP 140**
MC: **KTOP 140**

JAZZ TIME VOL.12.
LP: **502712**

KEEP 'EM FLYING.
LP: **SWS 5**
MC: **CSWS 5**

LEGEND LIVES ON, THE (Miller, Glenn Orchestra).
LP: **KNO 001**
MC: **CKNO 001**

LEGEND, THE.
LP: **DBD 01**
MC: **DBDC 01**

LEGENDARY GLENN MILLER: VOL 1.
Tracks: / My reverie / By the waters of Minnetonka / King Porter stomp / Shut eye / How I'd like to be with you in Bermuda / Cuckoo in the clock / Romance runs in the family / 'Neath the chestnut tree / And the angels sing / Moonlight serenade / Lady's in love with you, The / Wishing (will make it so) / Three little fishes / Sunrise serenade / Little brown jug.
LP: **LFM1 7500**

LEGENDARY GLENN MILLER VOL 2.
Tracks: / My last goodbye / But it didn't mean a thing / Pavane / Runnin' wild / To you / Stairway to the stars / Blue evening / Lamp is low, The / Rendezvous time in Paree / We can live on love / Cinderella (stay in my arms) / Moon love / Guess I'll go back home / I'm sorry for myself / Back to back.
LP: **LFM1 7501**

LEGENDARY GLENN MILLER: VOL 3.
Tracks: / Oh you crazy moon / Ain't cha comin' out / Day we meet again, The / Wanna hat with cherries / Sold American / Pagan love song / Ding dong, the witch is dead / Over the rainbow / Little man who wasn't there, The / Man with the mandolin, The / Starlit hour / Blue orchids / Glenn Island special / Love with a capitol 'you' / Baby me.
LP: **LFM1 7502**

LEGENDARY GLENN MILLER: VOL 4.
Tracks: / In the mood / Wham, re-bop-boom-bam / Angel in a furnished room, An / Twilight interlude / I want to be happy / Farewell blues / Who's sorry now / My isle of golden dreams / My prayer / Blue moonlight / Basket weaver man / Melancholy lullaby / Last night / Out of space / So many times.
LP: **LFM1 7593**

LEGENDARY GLENN MILLER: VOL 5.
Tracks: / Blue rain / Can I help it? / I just got a letter / Bless you / Blue birds in the moonlight / Faithful forever / Speaking of heaven / (American idyll) Indian summer / It was written in the stars / Johnson rag / Ciri-biri-bin / Careless / Oh Johnny, oh Johnny / In an old Dutch garden / This changing world.
LP: **LFM1 7512**

LEGENDARY GLENN MILLER: VOL 6.
Tracks: / On a little street in Singapore / Vagabond dreams / I beg your pardon / Faithful to you / It's a blue world / Oh what you said / Gaucho serenade / Sky fell down, The / When you wish upon a star / Give a little whistle / Missouri waltz / Beautiful Ohio / What's the matter with me / Say 'si si' / Rumba jumps, The.
LP: **LFM1 7513**

LEGENDARY GLENN MILLER: VOL 7.
Tracks: / Stardust / My melancholy baby / Let's all sing together / Rug cutter's swing / Woodpecker song / Sweet potato piper / Too romantic / Tuxedo junction / Londonderry air / Imagination / Shake down the stars / I'll never smile again / Starlight and music / Polka dots and moonbeams / My my / Say it.
LP: **LFM1 7514**

LEGENDARY GLENN MILLER: VOL 8.
Tracks: / Moments in the moonlight / Hear my song Violetta / Sierra Sue / Boog it / Yours is my heart alone / I'm stepping out with a memory tonight / Alice blue gown / Wonderful one / Devil may care / April played the fiddle / Fools rush in / I haven't time to be a millionaire / Slow freight / Pennsylvania 6-5000 / Bugle call rag / Nearness of you, The.
LP: **LFM1 7515**

LEGENDARY GLENN MILLER: VOL 9.
Tracks: / Mister Meadowlark / My blue heaven / When the swallows come back to Capistrano / Million dreams ago, A / Blueberry Hill / Cabana in Havana, A / Be happy / Angel child / Call of the canyon, The / Our love affair / Cross town / What's your story Mornin' Glory / Fifth Avenue / I wouldn't take a million / Handful of stars, A / Old Black Joe.
LP: **LFM1 7516**

LEGENDARY GLENN MILLER: VOL 10.
Tracks: / Yesterthoughts / Falling leaves / Shadows on the sand / Goodbye little darling / Five o'clock whistle / Beat me daddy, eight to the bar / Ring telephone ring / Make believe ballroom time / You've got me this way / Nightingale sang in Berkeley Square, A / I'd know you anywhere / Fresh as a daisy / Isn't that just like love / Along the Santa Fe trail / Do you know why / Somewhere / Yes my darling daughter.
LP: **LSA 3237**

LEGENDARY GLENN MILLER: VOL 11.
Tracks: / Stone's throw from heaven, A / Helpless / Long time no see / You are the one / Anvil chorus / Frenesi / Mem'ry of a rose, The / I do, do you / Chapel in the valley / Prairieland lullaby / Ida, sweet as apple cider / Song of the volga boatmen / One I love, The / You stepped out of a dream / I dreamt I dwelt in Harlem / Sun Valley jump.
LP: **LSA 3238**

LEGENDARY GLENN MILLER: VOL 12.
Tracks: / When that man is dead and gone / Spirit is willing, The / Little old church in England, The / Perfidia / It's always you / Spring will be so sad / Air minded executive / Below the equator / Boulder buff / Booglie wooglie piggy, The / Chattanooga choo choo / I know why / Don't cry cherie / Cradle song / Sweeter than the sweetest.
LP: **LSA 3239**

LEGENDARY GLENN MILLER: VOL 13.
Tracks: / I guess I'll have to dream the rest / Take the 'A' train / Peekaboo to you / Angels came through, The / Under blue Canadian skies / Cowboy serenade, The / You and I / Adios / It happened in Sun Valley / I'm thrilled / Kiss polka / Delilah / From one love to another / Elmer's tune.
LP: **LSA 3240**

LEGENDARY GLENN MILLER: VOL 14.
Tracks: / Says who, says you, says I / Orange blossom lane / Dear Arabella / Man in the moon, The / Ma ma maria / This time the dream's on me / Dreamville, Ohio / Papa Niccolini / Jingle bells / This is no laughing matter / Humpty Dumpty heart / Ev'rything I love / String of pearls / Baby mine / Long tall mama / Daydreaming.
LP: **PL 42016**

LEGENDARY GLENN MILLER: VOL 15.
Tracks: / Moonlight sonata / Slumber song / White cliffs of Dover, The / We're the couple in the castle / It happened in Hawaii / Moonlight cocktail / Happy in love / Fooled / Keep them flying / Chip off the old block / Story of a starry night / President's birthday ball, The / Angels of mercy / On the old assembly line / Let's have another cup of coffee / Skylark / Dear mom.
LP: **PL 42017**

LEGENDARY GLENN MILLER: VOL 16.
Tracks: / When the roses bloom again / Always in my heart / Sh it's a military secret / Don't sit under the apple tree / She'll always remember / Lamplighter's serenade, The / When Johnny comes marching home / American patrol / Soldier let me read your letter / Sleep song / Sweet Eloise / I've got a gal in Kalamazoo / Serenade in blue / At last / Lullaby of the rain / Knit one, purl one.
LP: **PL 42018**

LEGENDARY GLENN MILLER: VOL 17.
Tracks: / That's sabotage / Conchita, Marquita, Lolita, Pepita, Rosita, Juanita, Lopez / Hummingbird / Yesterdays gardenias / Dearly beloved / Moonlight mood / Caribbean clipper / Here we go again / That old black magic / Moonlight becomes you / Jukebox Saturday night / It must be jelly / I'm old fashioned / Pink cocktail for a blue lady / Rainbow rhapsody / Sleepy town train / Rhapsody in blue.
LP: **PL 42019**

LEGENDARY PERFORMER.
Tracks: / Moonlight serenade / Talk / Sunrise serenade / Little brown jug / Londonderry air / Tuxedo junction / My melancholy baby / Pennsylvania 6500 / So you're the one / Sentimental me / Song of the Volga boatmen / Jack and Jill / Take the A train / String of pearls, A / Stardust / Ev'rything I love / Tchaikovsky's piano concerto / Elmer's tune / Jingle bells / In the mood / Chattanooga choo choo / At last / Moonlight cocktail / I've got a gal in Kalamazoo / Juke box Saturday night.
LP: **DPM 2065**
MC: **DPMK 1035**

LEGENDARY PERFORMER, VOL. 2.
Tracks: / Make believe ballroom time / Don't sit under the apple tree / Lamplighters serenade, The / I've got a gal in Kalamazoo / Serenade in blue / Beethoven's moonlight sonata / Johnson rag / Blueberry Hill / Oh, you crazy moon / Chestnut tree, The / Fools rush in (where angels fear to tread) / I guess I'll have to dream the rest.
LP: **PL 12080**
MC: **PK 12080**

LEGENDARY PERFORMER VOL 3.
Tracks: / Over there / Stardust / I've got a heart filled with love for you / Londonderry air (medley) / Way you look tonight, The / Blue Danube / Vict'ry polka / St. Louis blues march / Stormy weather / Mission to Moscow / Long ago and far away / Pistol packin' mama.
LP: **PL 12495**
MC: **PK 12495**

LEGENDARY, THE.
MC: **MRT 40050**

LIVE 1938/39 PARADISE RESTAURANT NEW YORK (Miller, Glenn Orchestra).
Tracks: / Lovelight in the starlight / How'd ya like to to love me / You leave me breathless / Please come out of your dreams / What have you got that get's me / Room with a view, A / Wait until.
MC: **CAWE 42**

LIVE AT GLENN ISLAND CASINO (Summer, 1939) (Miller, Glenn & His Orchestra).
Tracks: / Moonlight serenade (theme) / At sundown / Cinderella, stay in my arms / Slip horn jive / Ain't cha comin' out? / Lamp is low, The / My isle of golden dreams / We can live on love / By the waters of Minnetonka / Moonlove / King Porter stomp / I want my share of love / In the middle of a dream / Lady's in love with you, The / In the mood / Chestnut tree, The / Pagan love song / Moonlight serenade (theme and fadeout).
LP: **AWE 31**
MC: **CAWE 31**

LIVE AT MEADOWBROOK 1939 (Miller, Glenn Orchestra).
LP: **LP 1023**

LIVE AT THE CARNEGIE HALL 6 OCTOBER 1939 (See under Goodman, Benny) (Miller, Glenn & Benny Goodman).

LIVE FROM GLENN ISLAND CASINO (July 24, 1939).
Tracks: / I want to be happy / Bless you / Little man who wasn't there, The / Oh you crazy moon / Baby me / My isle of golden dreams / Johnson rag / Faithful to you / I just got a letter / In an old Dutch garden / Tiger rag / Closing.
LP: **LP 1009**

LIVE FROM THE CAFE ROUGE, NOVEMBER 1940 (Chesterfield show 1942) (Miller, Glenn & His Orchestra).
Tracks: / Down for the count / Blueberry Hill / Long time no see baby / Shadows on the sand / Limehouse blues / Handful of stars, A / Cross town / Tiger rag / Something to remember you by / One dozen roses / Moonlight cocktail / Oh so good.
LP: **LP 1003**
LP: **JASM 2502**
MC: **JASMC 2502**

LIVE REMOTES-1938.
LP: **LP 1022**

LOVE SONGS FROM THE FABULOUS FORTIES.
Tracks: / Fools rush in / Chattanooga choo choo / Sentimental me / My prayer / Chestnut tree, The / Everything i love / Stardust / Lamplighter's serenade, The / Don't sit under the apple tree / Moonlight cocktail / That old black magic / Serenade in blue / My melancholy baby / At last / I've got a gal in Kalamazoo / Stairway to the stars.
LP: **CDS 1223**
MC: **CAM 1223**

MAGIC MOMENTS.
Tracks: / Elmer's tune / String of pearls / Moonlight cocktail / American patrol / I've got a gal in Kalamazoo / Jukebox Saturday night / Beautiful Ohio / Missouri waltz / Adios / Oh Johnny, oh Johnny oh / Moonlight serenade / Little brown jug / In the mood / Johnson rag / Stardust / Tuxedo Junction / Pennsylvania 65000 / Song of the volga boatmen / Chattanooga choo choo / Along the Santa Fe trail / Anvil chorus / St. Louis blues march / Don't sit under the apple tree / Stairway to the stars / Lamplighter's serenade, The / Who's sorry now / By the waters of Minnetonka / Serenade in blue / Take the 'A' train.
MC: **NK 89406**

MEMORIAL, 1944-69.
Tracks: / Moonlight serenade / Sunrise serenade / Little brown jug / To you / Stairway to the stars / In the mood / My prayer / Johnson rag / Indian Summer / Stardust / Tuxedo Junction / Londonderry air / Pennsylvania 65000 / Anvil chorus / Song of the volga boatmen / Perfidia / Chattanooga choo choo / Adios / Elmer's tune / String of pearls / Moonlight cocktail / Skylark / Don't sit under the apple tree / American patrol / At last / I've got a gal in Kalamazoo / Serenade in blue / Jukebox Saturday night / That old black magic / St. Louis blues march.
LP: **NL 86019**
MC: **NK 86019**
LP: **GM 1**
MC: **DPMK 1006**

MEMORIAL FOR GLENN MILLER (Miller, Glenn Orchestra).
MC: **402302**

MILLER MAGIC (Miller, Glenn & His Orchestra).
Tracks: / In the mood / Moonlight serenade / Chattanooga choo choo / Frenesi / Pennsylvania 6-5000 / Farewell blues / Don't sit under the apple tree / I've got a gal in Kalamazoo / Stardust / My blue Heaven / Bugle call rag / American patrol / St. Louis blues / Jukebox Saturday night / Boulder buff / Who's sorry now? / I want to be happy / At last / Lamplighter's serenade, The / Tuxedo Junction / Indian Summer / Little brown jug / Perfidia / White cliffs of Dover, The / Take the 'A' train / King Porter stomp / Sunrise serenade / String of pearls.
2LP: **CR 083**
MCSET: **CRT 083**

MILLION DREAMS AGO, A (1939-41) (Miller, Glenn & His Orchestra).
Tracks: / Million dreams ago, A / Pagan love song / Blue orchids / At sundown / In a sentimental mood / Deep purple / Jumpin' jive / Hour of parting / Daisy Mae / Crosstown / Swingin' at the seance / I dreamt I dwelt in Harlem.
LP: **BS 7136**
MC: **BS 7136C**

MOONLIGHT SERENADE.
MC: **64025**

MOSTLY SWINGING.
LP: **NOST 7601**
MC: **NOST 8601**

NEARNESS OF YOU (Miller, Glenn & His Orchestra).
LP: **INTS 1019**

NIGHT AND DAY (Miller, Glenn & His Orchestra).
MC: **CAM 1230**
LP: **CDS 1230**

OH SO GOOD, 1940-42.
LP: **AWE 29**
MC: **CAWE 29**

ON THE AIR (Volumes 1-3).
Tracks: / Slumber song(opening theme) / Yes, my darling daughter / I don't want to set the world on fire / Song of the bayou / Nightingale sang in Berkerley Square, A / On the sentimental side / Mutiny in the nursery / Lamp is low, The / Don't wake up my heart / I,m not much on looks / My best wishes / Moonshine over Kentucky / Gentlemen needs a shave / Slumber song(closing theme) / Beat me daddy, eight to the bar / Eight to the bar / Handful of stars, A / I know that you know / There I go / You've got me this way / I guess I'll have to dream the rest / Back to back / Dreamsville, Ohio / Oh baby / Do you care? / When paw was courtin' maw / This time the dream's on me / Light's out / Light's out, hold me tight / Moonlight serenade / Show boat / Why do I love you / Can't help lovin' dat man / Make believe / Ol' man river / Papa Niccolini / Moon is a silver dollar / Don't worry 'boat me / Hold tight / Masquerade is over, The / Our love / Pinball Paul / Sometime / Beer barrel polka / Starlit hour.
LPS: **NL 89714**
MCSET: **NK 89714**

ON THE AIR.
LP: **QU 047**

ON THE AIR: VOLUME 1 (Miller, Glenn & His Orchestra).
Tracks: / Moonlight seranade / King Porter stomp / Please come out of your

dream / FDR Jones / One o'clock jump / Guess I'll go back home / Wishing will make it so / By the waters of Minnetonka / Lady's in love with you, The / Rendezvous time in Paree / I'm sorry for myself / Cinderella / I want to be happy / My last goodbye / Little man who wasn't there, The / Dippermouth blues.
LP: AIRCHECK 39

ON THE AIR: VOLUME 2 (Miller, Glenn & His Orchestra).
Tracks: / Moonlight seranade / Rug cutters swing / I love you too much / I wanna hat with cherries / Sweet and low / Hallelujah! / Stardust / Five O'Clock whistle / Blueberry hill / Anchors aweigh / Oh so good! / Along the Santa Fe trail / You've got me this way / Helpless / Anvil chorus / Call of the canyon, The / On brave old army team / Slumber song.
LP: AIRCHECK 40

ON THE CONTINENT.
LP: LP 1016

ORIGINAL RECORDINGS.
Tracks: / Moonlight serenade / Hallelujah / In a sentimental mood / Back to back / Jumpin' jive / In the mood / Chattanooga choo choo / Happy in love / Serenade in blue / Don't sit under the apple tree / Moonlight cocktail / Pennsylvania 6-5000.
LP: MTM 015
MC: MTMC 015

ORIGINAL RECORDINGS BY GLENN MILLER & HIS ORCHESTRA.
LP: CDS 1040
MC: CAM 1040
MC: CAM 409

ORIGINAL RECORDINGS, THE.
LP: CDS 1004

ORIGINAL SESSIONS VOL 2.
Tracks: / Rhapsody in blue / Johnson rag / St louis blues / My prayer / Caribbean clipper / Anchors aweigh / I've got a gal in Kalamazoo / Medley-my melancholy baby / Moon love / Stompin' at the savoy / Blue moon / Woodpecker song, The / Song of the volga boatmen / I know why / Lamplighter's serenade, The.
LP: MTM 017
MC: MTMC 017

ORIGINAL SOUNDS OF THE SWING ERA VOL. 5.
LP: CL 05514

POPULAR RECORDINGS 1938-1942, THE (Miller, Glenn Orchestra).
Tracks: / Moonlight serenade / King Porter stomp / And the angels sing / Lady's in love with you, The / Little brown jug / But it didn't mean a thing / Stairway to the stars / Pagan love song / Over the rainbow / We can live on love (we haven't got a pot) / Glenn island special / It's a blue world / Ain't cha comin' out? / Runnin' wild / Moon love / Farewell blues / Blue evening / Bluebirds in the moonlight / Sunrise serenade / In the mood / Indian Summer / Rhumba jumps, The / Star dust / Polka dots and moonbeams / Tuxedo junction / April played the fiddle / Danny boy / Be happy / Nearness of you, The / My blue heaven / It's always you / Bugle call rag / Nightingale sang in Berkeley Square, A / Pennsylvania 65000 / Yes, my darling daughter / Anvil chorus (parts 1 & 2) / I know why (and so do you) / You stepped out of a dream / I dreamt I dwelt in Harlem / String of pearls, A / Perfidia / Sun vally jump / Slumber song, The / Adios / Moonlight cocktail / Moonlight sonata / Chattanooga choo choo / At last / Don't sit under the apple tree / Rhapsody in blue / (I've got a gal in) Kalamazoo / Serenade in blue / Caribbean clipper / That old black magic / Juke box Saturday night / Moonlight becomes you / American patrol.
LPS: NL 90412
MCSET: NK 90412

REAL GLENN MILLER AND HIS ORCHESTRA, THE (Music from The Glenn Miller Story soundtrack) (Miller, Glenn Orchestra).
LP: INTS 1157

REMEMBER GLENN (Vol. 3).
LP: SM 4042

REMEMBER GLENN (Vol. 2).
LP: SM 4008

RETURN TO THE CAFE ROUGE.
LP: AWE 38
MC: CAWE 38

REUNION IN HI-FI (Miller, Glenn, Singers).
Tracks: / I've got a gal in Kalamazoo / Serenade in blue / Chattanooga choo choo / Wham / Nightingale sang in Berkeley Square, A / Sweet Eloise / Elmer's tune / Moonlight cocktail / Don't sit under the apple tree / Booglie wooglie piggy, The / Perfidia / I know why.
LP: JASM 1015
MC: JASMC 1015

REVIVAL ORCHESTRA.
LP: JC 11004

RHAPSODY IN BLUE.
LP: 20104
MC: 40104

SALUTE TO TRINIDAD ARMY BASE NOV.3 1941.
Tracks: / Introduction / Dear Arabella / Till reveille / Chattanooga choo choo / Song of the volga boatmen / Keep em flying / One I love, The / In the mood / Closing / Sweeter than the sweetest / High on a windy hill.
LP: LP 1011

SILVER SERENADE (Miller, Glenn & AAF Band).
Tracks: / Poinciana / Serenade in blue / Easter parade / Paper doll / White Christmas / Spirit is willing, The / Silent night / Blue rain / Chattanooga choo choo / St. Louis blues march / My buddy / Body and soul / Songs my mother taught me / I'll never mention your name / I'll be home for Christmas / Here we go again.
LP: SWS 2
MC: CSWS 2

SLOW FREIGHT (Miller, Glenn Orchestra).
Tracks: / American patrol / Slow freight / Nearness of you, The / Sanfu jump / And the Alamo / In the mood / St. Louis blues / I don't want to be loved / Devil may care / My blue heaven.
MC: CONE 4

STARDUST.
Tracks: / Down for the count / I wouldn't take a million / Be happy / Little brown jug / Sweet potato piper / On the Alamo / Say it / Stardust / Never took a lesson in my life / When the swallows come back to Capistrane / Can't yo' heah me callin' Caroline? / King Porter stomp / Story of a starry night / Sunrise serenade.
LP: AWE 25
MC: CAWE 25

STRING OF PEARLS.
Tracks: / String of pearls / Falling leaves / Caribbean clipper / Sun valley jump / My love for you / Lover / Seven-o-five / Little brown jug / Music makers / Jeep jockey jump.
LP: BDL 1055
LP: F 20126
LP: 20126
MC: 40126

SUNSET SERENADE BROADCAST 22, NOVEMBER 1941 (Miller, Glenn & His Orchestra).
LP: EB 417
MC: EBC 417

SWING AND SWEET (With Army Airforce Band).
LP: NOST 7651

SWINGING BIG BANDS, 1939-42.
2LP: SM 3766/2

SWINGING BIG BANDS, 1939-42: VOL 1.
LP: SM 3617

SWINGING BIG BANDS, 1939-42: VOL 2.
LP: SM 3618

SWINGING BIG BANDS, 1939-42: VOL 3.
LP: SM 3619

SWINGING GLENN MILLER.
Tracks: / King Porter stomp / Little brown jug / Runnin' wild / Sliphorn jive / Solid American / Pagan love song / Glenn Island special / In the mood / My blue heaven / What's your story, morning glory / I dreamed I dwelt in Harlem / Sun Valley jump / When that man is dead and gone / Spirit is willing / Take the 'A' train / String of pearls / Wham / I want to be happy / My Isle of golden dreams / Johnson rag / Rug cutter's swing / Hallelujah / Slow freight / Bugle call rag / Swing low sweet chariot / Long tall mama / Keep 'em flying / Chip off the old block / Blues in the night / Here we go again / Sleepy town train.
2LP: NL 89162
MCSET: NK 89162

SWINGING SUPERSTAR ORCHESTRA, THE.
LP: LPUP 5007

THAT OLD MILLER MAGIC.
Tracks: / In the mood / Chattanooga choo choo / St. Louis Blues / Don't sit under the apple tree / Tuxedo Junction / Little brown jug / American patrol / When Johnny comes marching home / I've got a gal in Kalamazoo / Serenade in blue / That old black magic / King Porter stomp.
LP: MFP 5776
MC: TCMFP 5776

UNCLE SAM PRESENTS (Miller Direct Aatco, Capt.Glenn).
LP: HEP 32

UNFORGETTABLE GLENN MILLER, THE.
LP: TVL 1

VERY BEST OF GLENN MILLER, THE.
Tracks: / Elmer's tune / String of pearls / Moonlight cocktail / American patrol / I've got a gal in Kalamazoo / Jukebox Saturday night / Beautiful Ohio / Missouri waltz / Adios / Oh Johnny, oh Johnny oh / Moonlight serenade / Sunrise serenade / Little brown jug / In the mood / Johnson rag / Stardust / Tuxedo Junction / Pennsylvania 65000 / Song of the volga boatmen / Chattanooga choo choo.
LP: PL 89009
MC: PK 89009
LP: RCALP 3055

Miller, Harry

CHILDREN AT PLAY.
LP: OG 200

IN CONFERENCE.
LP: OG 523

Miller, Henry

TROPIC OF CANCER (Balsam, Martin).
MCSET: LFP 7236

Miller, Herb

MEMORIES OF GLENN MILLER (Miller, Herb & His Orchestra).
Tracks: / On a clear day / Boulder buff / Little brown jug / Song that I sing, The / Danny boy / Stairway to the stars.
LP: AVI 3
MC: AVIC 3

MUSIC OF GLENN MILLER, THE (Miller, Herb & His Orchestra).
Tracks: / Adios / American patrol / At last / Little brown jug / Chattanooga choo choo / I've got a gal in Kalamazoo / Moonlight serenade / Perfidia / Pennsylvania 6-5000 / String of pearls / Serenade in blue / St. Louis blues march / Boulder buff / Tuxedo Junction / In the mood.
LP: AVI 1

REMEMBER GLENN MILLER (Miller, Herb & His Orchestra).
Tracks: / Sun Valley jump / I'm thrilled / Johnson rag / Angel divine / Bugle call rag / Quiet nights of quiet stars / Long tall mama / Slumber song / Caribbean clipper / Remember Glenn Miller / Anchors aweigh / Days of wine and roses / Here we go again / Skylark / I dreamt I dwelt in Harlem.
LP: PRST 504
MC: ZPRST 504

TRIBUTE TO SWING.
Tracks: / Rhapsody in blue / Smoke gets in your eyes / Shine on harvest moon / Limelight / Time after time / Moon river.
LP: AVI 2
MC: RIMC 510

Miller, Ina

BACK OF BEYOND.
Tracks: / Back of beyond / Leaving Nancy / No more good times / Gallant forty twa / Last thing on my mind / Green glens of Antrim / Patsy Fagan / Sweet forget me not / Ballad of William Brown / Red River Valley / Sonny's Dream / Leaving of Liverpool / Hame and Guid Night.
MC: CWGRTV 6

BONNIE MORVEN HILLS.
MC: CWGR 097

BONNIE WEE HOOSE ON THE HILLSIDE.
LP: WGR 040
MC: CWGR 040

BUNCH OF VIOLETS BLUE.
Tracks: / Bunch of violets blue / Farewell to Nova Scotia / Uist tramping song / Bonnie lass o' Fyvie / Summer road / Fionnphort ferry, The / South Georgia Whaling song / Leaving Lismore / Sweet sixteen / Farewell tae Tarwathie / Road to the Isles / Glorious North, The / Piper Donald John MacPherson / Come by the hills.
MC: CWGR 121

INA MILLER'S SONGS OF SCOTLAND.
LP: WGR 072
MC: CWGR 072

MY SCOTTISH HOMELAND.
LP: WGR 060
MC: CWGR 060

SONG OF THE MIRA.
LP: WGR 078
MC: CWGR 078

Miller, Jack

CHINA.
LP: 269 513 1
MC: 269 513 4

Miller, Jacob

GREATEST HITS: JACOB MILLER.
LP: RAS 3204
MC: RASC 3204

KILLER MILLER.
MC: RASC 3205

NATTY CHRISTMAS.
LP: RAS 3103

REGGAE GREATS.
Tracks: / Shaky girl / Tenement yard / Suzy Wong / Sinners / Healing of the nation / 80,000 careless Ethiopians / I've got the handle / Tired fe lickweed in a bush / Roman soldiers of Babylon / Standing firm / All night 'til daylight / Forward Jah Jah children.
LP: IRG 11
MC: IRGC 11

UNFINISHED SYMPHONY.
LP: CSLP 0012

Miller, Jay

JAY MILLER STUDIO BAND 1961-63.
LP: FLY 608

Miller, John

BIDING MY TIME.
LP: ROUNDER 3034

JOHN MILLER.
LP: ROUNDER 3002

SAFE SWEET HOME.
LP: ROUNDER 3016

Miller, Larry

RIGHT CHAPS.
LP: MR 010

Miller, Luella

COMPLETE RECORDINGS 1926-27 (Miller, Luella/Lonnie Johnson).
LP: WSE 125

LOTTIE BEAMAN/LUELLA MILLER (See under Beaman, Lottie) (Miller, Luella/Lottie Beaman).

Miller, Marcus

MARCUS MILLER.
LP: 925074 1

SUDDENLY.
LP: K 123806

Miller, Mary

ON THE ROAD (Miller, Mary & Saratoga Freeway).
LP: LKLP 6556

Miller, Max

ALL GOOD STUFF, MARY.
Tracks: / Mary from the dairy / Woman improver / Ophelia / Down in the valley / Old oak tree / Put it down / I never thought that she'd do that to me / Let's all have a charabanc ride / Ain't love grand / Annie the farmer's daughter / She said she wouldn't / I'm the only bit of comfort that she's got / Every Sunday afternoon / Um-ta-ra-ra / I bought a horse / Does she still remember / Everything happens to me / At the bathing parade / She'll never be the same again / No, no, no.
LP: NTS 214

CHEEKIE CHAPPIE.
LP: 6382 114

CHEEKY CHAPPIE (FLAPPER LABEL) (Holborn Empire and Finsbury Park 1936-39).
Tracks: / Max with the band / Max on stage - first house (Holborn Empire) / Max on stage - second house (Holborn Empire) / Max on stage - (Finsbury Park Empire) / Max: The farewell.
MC: PAST 714

CHEEKY CHAPPIE, THE (see under EMI Comedy Classics).

GOLDEN AGE OF MAX MILLER.
Tracks: / Mary from the dairy / Woman improver, The / Ophelia / Down in the valley / Old oak tree, The / Put it down / I never thought she'd do that to me / Let's all have a charabanc ride / Ain't love grand? / Annie the farmer's daughter / She said she wouldn't / I'm the only bit of comfort that she's got / Every sunday afternoon / Um-ta-ra-ra / I bought a horse / Does she still remember? / Everything happens to me / At the bathing parade / She'll never be the same again / No, no, no.
LP: GX 2503
MC: TCGX 2503

IN THE THEATRE.
Tracks: / Mary from the dairy / She shall have music / Cheeky Chappie tells one / Cheeky Chappie tells a few more / Cheeky Chappie tells a few more / Lulu / Hiking song, The / I thought we came here to pick some flowers / All because I rolled my eyes / Cheeky chappie concludes.
LP: OU 2075

MC: TCOU 2075

MAX AT THE MET, PLUS TWO.
Tracks: / With a little bit of luck / Influence / Max at the Met / Mother Brown story / There's always someone worse off than you.
LP: FBLP 8089
MC: ZCFBL 8089

YOU CAN'T HELP LIKING HIM.
LP: GH 675

Miller, Mulgrew

COUNTDOWN, THE.
LP: LLP 1519

FROM DAY TO DAY.
LP: LLP 1525

WINGSPAN.
LP: LLP 1515

Miller, Phil

SPLIT SECONDS.
LP: RECK 8

Miller, Punch

DELEGATES OF PLEASURE.
LP: JCE 17

Miller, Rodney

AIRPLANE.
LP: ROUNDER 0193
MC: ROUNDER 0193C

Miller, Roger

BEST OF ROGER MILLER.
LP: 6336 229

BIG INDUSTRY, THE.
Tracks: / Portrait of a mechanical dog / Boil away / Hammers / Upon this boat in this sea / Age of reason / Groping hands / Manic depression / Big industry, The / We don't know why.
LP: SAVE 054

COUNTRY COLLECTION, THE.
MC: CSTK 51

LITTLE GREEN APPLES.
LP: CN 2013

MAKING A NAME FOR MYSELF.
Tracks: / Hat / If I ever fall in love / Ringing up Rosie / Freedom / Hey would you hold it down / It's a miracle that you're mine / Pleasing the crowd / Disco man / Old friends / Opera ain't over till the fat lady sings.
LP: T 592

MOTIVE SERIES.
LP: 6463 059
MC: 7145 059

OFF THE WALL.
Tracks: / Oklahoma woman / There's nobody like you / Baby me, baby / Dark side of the woman / Stephen Foster / Some people make it / I've gotten used to the cryin' / Roll away / Ain't gonna work no more / Na-nominee.
LP: FL 12337

OLD FRIENDS (Miller Roger & Willie Nelson).
LP: CBS 32195
MC: 40 32195

ROGER MILLER.
Tracks: / River in the rain / Hand for the hog / Leavin's not the only way to go / Guv'ment / You oughta be here with me / Some hearts get all the breaks / Arkansas / Indian giver / Days of our wives / Muddy water.
LP: IMCA 5722
MC: IMCAC 5722

ROGER MILLER'S GREATEST HITS.
LP: CDS 2073
MC: CAM 2073

WHAM ON EXPRESS.
LP: SST 267
MC: SSTC 267

Miller, Shirley

I MUST GO ON.
LP: LS R 5709
MC: LS C 5709

Miller, Sima

SIMA MILLER, VOL.1.
MC: GVMMC 123

SIMA MILLER, VOL.2.
MC: GVMMC 124

SIMA MILLER, VOL.3.
MC: GVMMC 130

SIMA MILLER, VOL.4.
MC: GVMMC 131

SIMA MILLER, VOL.5.
MC: GVMMC 132

Miller, Steve

ABRACADABRA (Miller, Steve Band).
Tracks: / Keeps me wondering why / Something special / Give it up / Never say no / Things I told you / Young girl's heart / Goodbye love / Abracadabra / Cool magic / While I'm waiting.
LP: 6302 204

ANTHOLOGY - STEVE MILLER BAND (Miller, Steve Band).
2LP: IC 188 81312/3
2LP: ESTSP 12

BEST OF...1968-1973, THE (Miller, Steve Band).
Tracks: / Joker, The / Living in the USA / My dark hour / Going to the country / Shu ba da du ma ma ma / Going to Mexico / Come on into the kitchen / Evil / Song for our ancestors / Your saving grace / Quicksilver girl / Seasons / Space cowboy / Gangster of love / Kow kow calqulator / Little girl (CD only.) / Don't let nobody turn you around (CD only.) / Jackson-Kent blues / Sugar babe.
LP: EST 2133
MC: TCEST 2133
LP: EMS 1191
MC: TCEMS 1191
LP: FA 3030
MC: TCFA 3030
LP: ATAK 86
MC: TCATAK 86

BOOK OF DREAMS (Miller, Steve Band).
LP: PRICE 78
MC: PRIMC 78
LP: 9286 456

BORN 2 B BLUE.
Tracks: / Zip-a-dee-doo-dah / Ya ya / God bless the child / Filthy McNasty / Born to be blue / Mary Ann / Just a little bit / When sunny gets blue / Willow weep for me / Red top.
LP: EST 2072
MC: TCEST 2072

BRAVE NEW WORLD (Miller, Steve Band).
LP: IC 038 80117

CHILDREN OF THE FUTURE.
LP: ST 2920

CIRCLE OF LOVE (Miller, Steve Band).
Tracks: / Heart like a wheel / Get on home / Circle of love / Baby wanna dance / Macho city.
LP: 6302 061

FLY LIKE AN EAGLE (Miller, Steve Band).
Tracks: / Blue odyssey / Dance, dance, dance / Fly like an eagle / Mercury blues / Rock'n'me / Serenade / 2001 / Sweet Marie / Take the money and run / Wild mountain honey / Window / You send me.
LP: PRICE 75
MC: PRIMC 75
LP: 9286 177

GREATEST HITS: STEVE MILLER (Miller, Steve Band).
Tracks: / Dance, dance, dance / Fly like an eagle / Joker / Jet airliner / Jungle love / Rock'n'me / Serenade / Stake / Take the money and run / Swingtown / Threshold / True fire love / Winter time / Wild mountain honey.
LP: HS 9199 916

GREATEST HITS: STEVE MILLER (Decade of American Music 76-86) (Miller, Steve Band).
Tracks: / Space intro / Fly like an eagle / Bongo bongo / Rock n' me / Jet airliner / Take the money and run / Mercury blues / Swing town / Shangri-la / Abracadabra / Italian x rays / Out of the night / Who do you love / Harmony of the spheres.
LP: PRICE 86
MC: PRIMC 86
LP: MERH 105
MC: MERHC 105

ITALIAN X RAYS (Miller, Steve Band).
Tracks: / Radio 1 & 2 / Italian X Rays / Daybreak / Shangri-la / Who do you love / Harmony of the spheres / Bongo bongo / Out of the night / Golden opportunity / Hollywood dream / One in a million.
LP: MERL 50

JOKER, THE (Miller, Steve Band).
Tracks: / Sugar babe / Marylou / Shu ba da du ma ma ma / Your cash ain't nothin' but trash / Joker, The / Lovin' cup / Come on in my kitchen / Evil / Something to believe in.
LP: EAST 11235
LP: IC 062 81514
LP: FA 3250
MC: TCFA 3250

JOURNEY FROM EDEN (Miller, Steve Band).
LP: IC 062 81099

LIVING IN THE 20TH CENTURY (Miller, Steve Band).
Tracks: / Nobody but you baby / I want to make the world turn around / Slinky / Living in the 20th century / Maelstrom / I wanna be loved / My babe / Big boss man / Caress me baby.
LP: EST 2027
MC: TCEST 2027

NUMBER 5.
LP: EAST436

RECALL THE BEGINNING- A JOURNEY FROM EDEN.
LP: EAST 110 22

ROCK LOVE.
LP: ESW 748

SAILOR (Miller, Steve Band).
Tracks: / Song for our ancestors / Dear Mary / My friend / Living in the U.S.A. / Quicksilver girl / Lucky man / Gangster of love / You're so fine / Overdrive / Dime-a-dance romance.
LP: FA 41 30851
MC: TCFA 41 30854
LP: FA 3254
MC: TCFA 3254

STEVE MILLER BAND LIVE (Miller, Steve Band).
Tracks: / Gangster of love / Rock 'n' me / Living in the USA / Fly like an eagle / Jungle love / Joker, The / Mercury blues / Take the money and run / Abracadabra / Jet airliner.
LP: MERL 18
MC: MERLC 18

STORY SO FAR (Miller, Steve & Lol Coxhill).
LP: C 1507

Miller's Crossing

MILLER'S CROSSING (Original Soundtrack) (Various artists).
Tracks: / Opening titles: *Various artists* / Caspar laid out: *Various artists* / Man and his hat, A: *Various* artists / King Porter stomp: *Various artists* / Long way around, The: *Various artists* / Miller's crossing: *Various artists* / After Miller's crossing: *Various artists* / Running wild: *Various artists* / Rage of the dane: *Various artists* / All a you whores (sic): *Various artists* / Rage of the dane (2): *Various artists*/ All a you whores (sic) 2: *Various artists* / Nightmare in the trophy room: *Various artists* / He didn't like his friends: *Various artists* / Danny boy: *Various artists* / What heart?: *Various artists* / End title: *Various artists* / Goodnight sweetheart: *Various artists.*
LP: VS 5288
MC: VSC 5288

Miller's Tale (bk)

MILLER'S TALE, THE (see under Chaucer, Geoffrey (aut)).

Milli Vanilli

ALL OR NOTHING.
MC: ZCTLP 11
LP: CTLP 11

TWO X TWO.
Tracks: / Can't you feel my love / Boy in the tree / Money / Dance with the devil / I'm gonna miss you / All or nothing / Baby don't forget my number / Dreams to remember / Is it love / Ma Baker / Girl you know it's true / Blame it on the rain (Club mix long version) / More than you'll ever know / Take it as it comes / It's your thing / Dreams to remember (Remix) / All or nothing (club mix) / Baby don't forget my number (Remix) / I'm gonna miss you (Remix) / Girl you know it's true (N.Y.Subway mix).
LP: CTLPD 1724
MC: ZCTLP 1724

Millican & Nesbitt

CANADIAN SUNSET.
LP: SPL 18505

COUNTRY ROADS.
LP: NSPL 18565

EVERYBODY KNOWS MILLICAN AND NESBITT.
LP: NSPL 18446

GOLDEN HOUR OF MILLICAN AND NESBITT.
LP: GH 640

MILLICAN AND NESBITT.
LP: NSPL 18428

Milligan, Spike

ADOLPH HITLER- MY PART IN HIS DOWNFALL.
MC: TX SCX 6636
LP: SCX 6636

COLLECTION OF SPIKES, A (see under EMI Comedy Classics).

EVENING WITH SPIKE MILLIGAN.
LP: MFP 50408

HE'S INNOCENT OF WATERGATE (see Sellers, Peter) (Milligan, Spike & Peter Sellers).

MILLIGAN PRESERVED.
LP: PMC 1152

MUSSOLINI: HIS PART IN MY DOWNFALL.
MC: IAB 88091

PUCKOON (Milligan, Spike & Friends).
LP: SCX 6630

ROMMEL?GUNNER WHO/MONTY....
MC: IAB 88061

SNOW GOOSE, THE.
Tracks: / Marshland theme, The / Rhayader's theme / Snow goose theme, The / Fritha's theme / Goose walk, The / Walking by the sea / Lonely man / Goose conversations / Sailing.
LP: RS 1088
MC: PK 11765

UNSPUN SOCKS FROM A CHICKENS LAUNDRY.
LP: SPIKE L1
MC: SPIKE C1

WEEKEND STARTS HERE, THE (Milligan, Spike & The London Symphony Orchestra).
Tracks: / Marshland theme / Rhayaders theme / Snow goose, The / Fritha's theme / Goose walk, The / Walking by the sea / Lonely man / Goose conversations / Sailing.
LP: INTS 5224
MC: INTK 5224
MC: WIKC 48
LP: WIKA 48

WOLVES, WITCHES AND GIANTS.
LP: MIL 2
MC: TCMIL 2

Millinder, Lucky

APOLLO JUMP Big band bounce & boogie (Millinder, Lucky And His Orchestra).
Tracks: / Apollo jump / Ride, red ride / That's all / Shipyard social function / Hurry, hurry / Shout, sister shout / Mason flyer / Slide Mr Trombone / There's good blues tonight / Let me off uptown / Rock me / Little John special / Who threw the whiskey in the well / Trouble in mind / Big fat mama / Rock Daniel / All the time / I want a tall skinny papa.
LP: AFS 1004

LET IT ROLL AGAIN.
Tracks: / Hey huss / How big can you get little men / We're gonna have to slap the dirty ... / I can't see for lookin' / Fightin' Doug MacArthur / Spider and the fly, The / Your heart belongs to me / My little baby / Let it roll again / Blues done got me (and gone), The / Georgia rose / Teardrops from my eyes / Don't hesitate too long / Right kind of lovin', The / Bongo boogie / Mr. Trumpet man.
LP: JB 613

LUCKY MILLINDER AND HIS ORCHESTRA.
LP: HSR 233

RAM-BUNK-SHUSH.
Tracks: / Ram-bunk-shush / Oh babe / Please open your heart / Silent George / I'm waiting just for you / No one else could be / It's been a long, long time / Please be careful / Loaded with love / When I gave you my love / Heavy sugar / Old spice / I'm here love / It's a sad, sad feeling / Owl / Goody good love.
LP: SING 1163

SHORTY'S GOT TO GO.
Tracks: / Are you ready / Shorty's got to go / More more more / I know how to do it / Chew tobacco rag / I love you I love you I do / Lord knows I tried / Bacslider's ball / Darlin' / Baby, you've been wrong / Fare thee well Deacon Jones / Someday / Jumpin' Jack / Grapevine / Clap your hands / Who said Shorty wasn't coming back.
LP: JB 609

STOMPIN' AT THE SAVOY 1943 - 44 (Millinder, Lucky & His Orchestra).
Tracks: / Savoy / Down by the riverside / I'll get by / Is you is or is you ain't my baby / Chinatown, my Chinatown / After I say I'm sorry / Cherokee / Rhythm changes / Rock me / St. Louis breakdown / I want a tall skinny papa / Little John special.
LP: BS 7134
MC: BS 7134C

Million Dollar Quartet

COMPLETE MILLION DOLLAR QUARTET.
Tracks: / You belong to my heart / When God dips his love in my heart / Just a little walk with Jesus / Walk that lonesome valley / I shall not be moved / Peace in the valley / Down by the riverside / I'm in the crowd but oh so alone / Farther along / Blessed Jesus hold my hand / As we travel along the Jericho road / I just can't make it by myself / Little cabin on the hill / Summertime has passed and gone / I hear a sweet voice calling / Sweetheart you done me wrong / Keeper of the key / Crazy arms / Don't forbid me / Brown eyed handsome man / Out of sight out of mind / Brown eyed handsome man (take 2) / Don't be cruel / Don't be cruel (take 2) / Paralysed / Don't be cruel (take 3) / There's no place like home / When the

saints go marching in / Softly and tenderly / Is it so strange / That's when the heartaches begin / Brown eyed handsome man (take 3) / Rip it up / I'm gonna bid my blues goodbye / Crazy arms (take 2) / That's my desire / End of the road / Jerry's boogie / You're the only star in my blue heaven / Elvis, farewell.
2LP: . . . . CDX 20
MC: . . . . TCCDX 20

MILLION DOLLAR QUARTET.
Tracks: / Peace in the valley / Just a little walk with Jesus / Walk that lonesome valley / Down by the riverside / I shall not be moved / I'm with the in crowd but oh so alone / Farther along / Blessed Jesus hold my hand / As we travel along the Jericho road / I just can't make it by myself / Little cabin on the hill / Summertime has passed and gone / I hear a sweet voice calling / And now sweetheart / You've done me wrong / Keeper of the key / Crazy arms / Don't forbid me.
LP: . . . . SUN 1006
MC: . . . . CFK 1019

Millionaires Concert

GLENN MILLER ANNIVERSARY CONCERT.
Tracks: / Moonlight serenade / Pennsylvania 65000 / Stardust / String of pearls / Story of a starry night / My guy's come back / I'll remember April / Rosetta / I sustain the wings / Lovely way to spend an evening / Tail end Charlie / At last / In the mood / Stealin' apples / St. Louis blues march / How sweet you are / Swing low sweet chariot / Jeep jockey jump / All the things you are / Chattanooga choo choo / London bridge is falling down / Way we were / Don't be that way / Blue champagne / Oranges and lemons / Goodnight sweetheart.
2LP: . . . . DPA 30312
2LP: . . . . DL 41 1056 1
MC: . . . . TCDL 41 1056 4

Millions Like Us

MILLIONS LIKE US.
Tracks: / In love with yourself / Guaranteed for life / Beautiful enemy / Waiting for the right time / What you want is what you get / Million voices, A / Heart to heart / One world (ideal world) / Chain, The / Heaven and sky / Heartbroken man (CD only).
LP: . . . . CIRCA 1
MC: . . . . CIRC 1

Millions Of Dead Cops

MILLIONS OF DEAD COPS (See under M.D.C.).

Millman, Jack

SHADES OF THINGS TO COME (Millman, Jack All Stars).
LP: . . . . FS 20

Millns, Paul

FINALLY FALLS THE RAIN.
LP: 300 550 5

TILL THE MORNING COMES.
Tracks: / Too much between us / Down in the danger zone / Look at the madam / Out of tune and out of time / Till the morning comes / Count me out / Untidy song / Stormy Moon / Superstar blues / Sweet is the wine.
LP: . . . . TG 006
MC: . . . . TGC 006

Mills, Alan

CANADIAN FOLK SONGS.
MC: 90-905

Mills, Betty Lou

20 BEST LOVED GOSPEL SONGS - BETTY LOU MILLS.
LP: . . . . PC 320

COUNTRYSTYLE.
LP: . . . . PC 824

Mills Blue Rhythm Band

BLUE RHYTHM 1930-31.
Tracks: / They satisfy / Please don't talk about me when I'm gone / Straddle the fence / Levee down low / Moanin' / Minnie the moocher / Blue Rhythm / Blue flame / Red devil / Stardust / (Poor) Minnie the moocher / Black and tan fantasy / Sugar blues / Low down on the bayou / Futuristic jungleism.
LP: . . . . HEP 1008

DOIN' THE NEW LOW DOWN 1928/29 (Mills, Irving & His Hotsy Totsy Gang).
LP: . . . . FJ 122

HIGH AND DRY (1930-1 vol.3) (Mills, Irving & His Hotsy Totsy Gang).
LP: . . . . FJ 127

RHYTHM SPLASH.
Tracks: / Rhythm spasm / Swanee lullaby / White lightning / Wild waves / Feeling gay / Jazz Martini / Harlem after midnight / Reefer man smoke rings / Sentimental gentleman from Georgia.
LP: . . . . HEP 1021

SAVAGE RHYTHM.
Tracks: / Moanin' / Heebie jeebies / Minnie the moocher / Savage rhythm / I'm sorry I made you blue / Everytime I look at you / Snake hips / Scat song, The / Heat waves / Doin' the shake / Cabin in the cotton / Minnie the moocher's wedding day / Growl / Mighty sweet.
LP: . . . . HEP 1015

SOME FUN 1929-30.VOL.2 (Mills, Irving & His Hotsy Totsy Gang).
Tracks: / Some fun / Can't we get together / Sweet Savannah Sue / Ain't misbehavin' / Doin' the new low down / Harvey ((Two takes)) / March of the hoodlums / Stardust / Nobody's sweetheart / Manhattan rag / What kind of man is you? / My little honey and me / High and dry / Barbaric.
LP: . . . . FJ 123

Mills Brothers

20 GREATEST HITS: MILLS BROTHERS.
LP: . . . . N 22017
MC: 42017

1931-34.
Tracks: / Dinah / Chinatown, my chinatown / Shine / Diga diga do / My honey's lovin' arms / Bugle call rag / Out for no good / Nagasaki / I heard / Doin' the new low down / Nobody's sweet heart / It don't mean a thing / Life is just a bowl of cherries / Old man on the mountain, The / Rockin' chair / I can't give you anything but love.
LP: . . . . LPJT 85

BEST OF THE MILLS BROTHERS (CREOLE).
Tracks: / Paper doll / You always hurt the one you love / Mr. Sandman / Across the valley from the Alamo / Glow worm / Autumn leaves / Till then.
MC: 16 11

BEST OF THE MILLS BROTHERS (EMI) (Featuring the Ink Spots).
LP: 1A 022 1583701
MC: 1A 222 1583704

BEST OF THE MILLS BROTHERS (MFP).
Tracks: / Paper doll / I'll be around / Lindy Lou / Cherry / Goodbye blues / Lazy river / You always hurt the one you love / Put another chair at the table / I guess I'll get the papers and go home / Till then / Glow worm / Say si si / Opus one / Please don't talk about me when I'm gone / I got her off my hands / Smack dab in the middle.
LP: . . . . MFP 50560
MC: . . . . TCMFP 50560

BOARD OF DIRECTORS, THE (see under Basie, Count) (Mills Brothers & Count Basie).

CHRONOLOGICAL, VOLUME 2.
LP: . . . . JSP 1101

CHRONOLOGICAL, VOLUME 3.
LP: . . . . JSP 1109

CHRONOLOGICAL, VOLUME 4.
LP: . . . . JSP 1115

ELLA WITH (see under Fitzgerald, Ella) (Mills Brothers/EllaFitzgerald/Savoy8/ChickWebb/BennyGoodman).

FOUR BOYS AND A GUITAR.
LP: . . . . GNPS 9016
MC: GNP5 9016

FROM THE BEGINNING VOL.1.
LP: . . . . JSP 1099

GOLDEN GREATS: MILLS BROTHERS.
Tracks: / Paper doll / Glow worm / Basin street blues / Nevertheless (I'm in love with you) / Till then / Cielito lindo / You always hurt the one you love / Across the valley from the Alamo / I'll be around / Rockin' chair swing / Be my life's companion / Put another chair at the table / I guess I'll get the papers and go home / Pennies from Heaven / When you were sweet sixteen / Someday you'll want me to want you / All myself / Opus one / Please don't talk about me when I'm gone / Lazy river.
LP: . . . . MCM 5030

GOODBYE BLUES.
Tracks: / Pennies from Heaven / Limehouse blues / Lambeth walk / Lazy river.
LP: . . . . MCL 1790

GREATEST HITS: MILLS BROTHERS.
Tracks: / Paper doll / Glow worm / Basin St. Blues / Till then / Nevertheless / Cielito Lindo / Lazy river / You always hurt the one you love / Across the alley from the Alamo / I'll be around / Rockin' chair / Be my life's companion.
LP: . . . . MCL 1649

MILLS BROTHERS.
LP: . . . . LOP 14 118
MC: . . . . LCS 14118

MILLS BROTHERS AND LOUIS ARMSTRONG, THE (Mills Brothers & Louis Armstrong).
LP: . . . . LPJT 49

SWEETER THAN SUGAR.
Tracks: / Tiger rag / Old-fashioned love / Fiddlin' Joe / Smoke rings / I've found a new baby / Chinatown, my Chinatown / Lazybones / Diga diga doo / Nagasaki / Sweeter than sugar / Miss Otis regrets / Ida, sweet as apple cider / Rockin' chair / Some of these days / Sweet Georgia Brown / Nobody's sweetheart.
LP: . . . . AJA 5032
MC: . . . . ZC AJA 5032

SWING IS THE THING.
Tracks: / Swing is the thing / Lazybones / Solitude / London rhythm / Shoe shine boy / Rhythm saved the world / Old man of the mountain, The / Bugle call rag / How'm I doin' / Nagasaki / Organ grinder's song / My gal Sal / Ida sweet as apple cider / I've found a new baby / Put on your old gray bonnet / Baby won't you please come home / You rascal you / Nobody's sweetheart.
MC: . . . . KMORC 535
LP: . . . . JOY'D 297
LP: . . . . MOR 535

VOLUME 1 1931-33.
MC: . . . . NEO 918

Mills, Frank

MUSIC BOX DANCER.
Tracks: / Music box dancer / From a sidewalk cafe / Silver broom / When you smile / Love's like that / Storm warning / Poet and I / Spanish coffee / You don't love me no more / Valse classique / 401 West.
LP: . . . . EJ 2602081
LP: 2480484

SPECIAL CHRISTMAS A.
LP: . . . . EG 2603191
MC: . . . . EG 2603194

Mills, Garry

LOOK FOR A STAR (OLD GOLD) (See Mike Berry - Tribute To Buddy Holly).

Mills, Hayley

BEDTIME STORIES (See Bedtime Stories).

BLACK BEAUTY (see under Black Beauty (bk)).

Mills, Joan

JOLLY MACHINE, THE (see Raven, Michael/Joan Mills) (Mills, Joan and Michael Raven).

Mills, Mick

MUSIC.
LP: . . . . WRS 084

Mills, Mrs.

ALL TIME PARTY DANCES.
LP: . . . . ONCR 508
MC: . . . . TC ONCR 508

AN HOUR OF MRS. MILLS.
Tracks: / Put your arms around me, honey (Accompaniment directed by Geoff Love.) / I'm in the mood for love (Accompaniment directed by Geoff Love) / Yes sir, that's my baby (Accompaniment directed by Geoff Love) / Moonlight and roses (Accompaniment directed by Geoff Love) / Oh Johnny, oh Johnny oh (Accompaniment directed by Geoff Love) / Give me the moonlight, give me the girl (Accompaniment directed by Geoff Love) / Winchester Cathedral (Accompaniment directed by Geoff Love) / Green green grass of home (Accompaniment directed by Geoff Love) / I'm nobody's baby (Accompaniment directed by Geoff Love) / In the good old summertime (Accompaniment directed by Geoff Love) / Tiptoe through the tulips (Accompaniment directed by Geoff Love) / You are my sunshine (Accompaniment directed by Geoff Love) / April showers (Accompaniment directed by Geoff Love) / Down at the old Bull and Bush (Accompaniment directed by Geoff Love) / Cruising down the river (Accompaniment directed by Geoff Love) / Shine on harvest moon (Accompaniment directed by Geoff Love) / I do like to be beside the seaside (Accompaniment directed by Geoff Love) / Out of town (Accompaniment directed by Geoff Love) / Let's all sing like the birdies sing (Accompaniment directed by Geoff Love) / Good morning (Accompaniment directed by Geoff Love) / Me and my shadow (Accompaniment directed by Geoff Love) / My melancholy baby (Accompaniment directed by Geoff Love) / Second hand Rose (Accompaniment directed by Geoff Love) / There's a blue ridge 'round my heart, Virginia (Accompaniment directed by Geoff Love) / Let him go, let him tarry (Accompaniment directed by Geoff Love) / I belong to Glasgow (Accompaniment directed by Geoff Love) / Over the rainbow (Accompaniment directed by Geoff Love) / Get out and get under the moon (Accompaniment directed by Geoff Love).
MC: . . . . HR 8152

COME TO MY PARTY.
LP: . . . . PMC 7010

EP COLLECTION: MRS MILLS.
LP: . . . . SEE 332
MC: . . . . SEEK 332

EVERYBODY'S WELCOME AT MRS MILLS PARTY.
LP: . . . . SH 2600761
MC: . . . . TC SH 260 076 4

I'M MIGHTY GLAD.
LP: . . . . MFP 5225

LET'S HAVE ANOTHER PARTY.
LP: . . . . PCS 7035

MRS MILLS' PARTY PIECES.
LP: . . . . PCS 7066

MUSIC FOR ANYTIME.
LP: . . . . DTL 3011

PIANO PARTY TIME.
2LP: . . . . DL 41 1058 1
MC: . . . . TCDL 41 1058 4

PLAYS THE ROARING TWENTIES.
LP: . . . . DTL 3010

Mills, Sir John (nar)

BRIDGE ON THE RIVER KWAI (see under Bridge on the River Kwai).

Mills, Stephanie

FOR THE FIRST TIME.
Tracks: / I took my strength from you / Living on plastic / No one remembers my name / If you can learn how to cry / Loneliness remembers (what happiness forgets) / This empty place / Way I feel about you, The / I see you for the first time / All the way to Paradise / Please let go.
LP: . . . . STMS 5069
MC: . . . . CSTMS 5069

HEART AND SOUL OF STEPHANIE MILLS.
MC: . . . . KNMC 12064

HOME (IMPORT).
LP: . . . . MCA 6312
MC: . . . . MCAC 6312

IF I WERE YOUR WOMAN.
Tracks: / I feel good all over / If I were your woman / Rush on me, A (You're puttin') / Jesse / Secret lady / Touch me now / Running for your love / Can't change my ways.
LP: . . . . MCF 3385
MC: . . . . MCFC 3385

IN MY LIFE.
LP: . . . . JABB 25
MC: . . . . JABBC 25

I'VE GOT THE CURE.
Tracks: / Medicine song / Edge of the razor / In my life / Give it half a chance / You just might need a friend / Everlasting love / Rough trade / Undercover.
LP: . . . . JABL 5

MERCILESS.
Tracks: / How come you don't call me anymore? / Never get enough of you / Eternal love / His name is Michael / Here I am / My body / Do you love him? / Pilot error / Since we've been together.
LP: 811 364 1

STEPHANIE MILLS.
LP: . . . . T 700
MC: . . . . C 700

SWEET SENSATION (LP).
Tracks: / Sweet sensation / Try my love / I just wanna say / Wish that you were mine / D-a-n-c-i-n / Still mine / Never knew love like this before / Mixture of love.
LP: . . . . T 603

TANTALIZINGLY HOT.
Tracks: / Last night / Still lovin' you / Keep away girls / You can't run from my love / True love don't come easy / Ole love / Your love is always new / I can't give back the love I feel.
LP: . . . . CANS 2
MC: . . . . CANSC 2

Mills, Warren

WARREN MILLS.
Tracks: / Flame in the fire / Roxanne, Roxanne / I wonder if I take you home / Sunshine / Biochemistry / Choosy girl / You thrill me / Don't tell me about your boyfriend / It's peculiar / Tell me what you want me to do.
LP: . . . . HIP 30

MC: . . . . HIPC 30

Mills-Cockell, John

NEON ACCELERANDO.
Tracks: / Getaway / Collision / Maelstrom / Dreamstripper / Whiteface / Red slash / Sky opens / Mirage / Neon accelerando.
LP: . . . . **AUL 705**

Milltown Brothers

SLINKY.
MC: **3953464**
LP: **3953461**

Milly Molly Mandy

ADVENTURES OF MILLY MOLLY MANDY (See under Adventures of...) (Rayne, Janie (nar)).

MILLY MOLLY MANDY STORIES (Joyce Lankester Brisley) (Goddard, Liza (nar)).
MC: . . . . **TC LFP 7100**

Milly Molly Mandy (bk)

MILLY MOLLY MANDY.
MCSET: . . . . **DTO 10539**

Milne, A.A.

HOUSE AT POOH CORNER.
LP: . . . . **REC 493**
MC: . . . . **ZCM 493**

HOUSE AT POOH CORNER (Shelley, Norman).
MCSET: . . . . **SAY 96**
MCSET: . . . . **ARGO 1121**

HOUSE AT POOH CORNER (Jeffries, Lionel).
MCSET: . . . . **LFP 7079**
MCSET: . . . . **TCLFP 7079**
MCSET: . . . . **LFP 4170795**

HOUSE AT POOH CORNER (Channing, C.).
MC: . . . . **CP 1670**

HOUSE AT POOH CORNER (Anderson, Dame Judith).
MC: **1670**

HOUSE AT POOH CORNER PART 1. (Unknown narrator(s)).
MCSET: . . . . **DTO 10553**

HOUSE AT POOH CORNER PART 2. (Unknown narrator(s)).
MCSET: . . . . **DTO 10554**

NOW WE ARE SIX (Unknown narrator(s)).
MCSET: . . . . **DTO 10563**

POOH SONG BOOK (Channing, Carol).
MC: **1686**

THREE CHEERS FOR POOH (Tear, Robert & Phillip Ledger).
Tracks: / Isn't it funny / How sweet to be a cloud / Cottleston pie / Lines written by a bear of very little brain / Three cheers for Pooh / More it snows, The / What shall we do about poor little Tigger / Oh, the butterflies are flying / I lay on my chest / Here lies a tree / Christopher Robin is going / Down by the pond / Sneezles / Friend, The / Furry bear / Emperor's rhyme, The / Wind on the hill / Twice times / Forgiven / Shoes and stockings / Spring morning / Disobedience / Four friends / Bad Sir Brian Botany / Christopher Robin at Buckingham Palace / At the zoo / Christening, The.
LP: . . . . **ACM 2001**
MC: . . . . **ZC ACM 2001**

WHEN WE WERE VERY YOUNG (Shelley, Norman).
MCSET: . . . . **SAY 97**

WHEN WE WERE VERY YOUNG (Anderson, Dame Judith).
MC: **1356**

WINNIE THE POOH (Jeffries, Lionel).
MCSET: . . . . **LFP 7052**

WINNIE THE POOH (Shelley, Norman).
MCSET: . . . . **SAY 95**
MCSET: . . . . **ARGO 1055**

WINNIE THE POOH (Bennett, Alan (nar)).
LP: . . . . **REC 528**
MC: . . . . **ZCM 528**

WINNIE THE POOH (Anderson, Dame Judith).
MC: **1408**

WINNIE THE POOH AND CHRISTOPHER ROBIN (Anderson, Dame Judith).
MC: **1744**

WINNIE THE POOH AND CHRISTOPHER ROBIN.
MC: **1743**

WINNIE THE POOH AND EEYORE.
MC: **1747**

WINNIE THE POOH AND KANGA AND ROO (Anderson, Dame Judith).
MC: **1685**

WINNIE THE POOH AND THE HOUSE AT POOH CORNER (Bennett, Alan (nar)).
MCSET: . . . . **ZBBC 1001**

WINNIE THE POOH AND TIGGER.
MC: . . . . **CP 1696**
MC: **1696**

WINNIE THE POOH PART 1 (Unknown narrator(s)).
MCSET: . . . . **DTO 10548**

WINNIE THE POOH PART 2. (Unknown narrator(s)).
MCSET: . . . . **DTO 10549**

WINNIE THE POOH - SELECTED STORIES (Shelley, Norman).
MC: **0600560864**

WINNIE THE POOH SUPER SOUNDBOOK (Anderson, Dame Judith).
MCSET: **702**

WINNIE THE POOH & THE HONEY TREE (Various artists).
LP: . . . . **D 313**
MC: . . . . **D 21DC**

WINNIE THE POOH & TIGGER TOO (Various artists).
LP: . . . . **D 366**
MC: . . . . **D 10DC**

Milne, Jimmy

JIMMY AND ANGUS LIVE ON MULL (Milne, Jimmy & Angus).
MC: . . . . **MR 1002**

MY BONNIE ISLAND HOME (Milne, Jimmy & Angus).
MC: . . . . **MR 1008**

Milne, Roseleen

BORROWED PLUMES (Derby, Brown).
MCSET: . . . . **CLT 1001**

Milo

POSITIVE MOVEMENTS.
LP: . . . . **RRI 1204**
MC: . . . . **KRRI 1204**

Milsap, Ronnie

20-20 VISION.
Tracks: / 20-20 vision / Lovers, friends and strangers / Not that I care / Lovesick blues / You snap your fingers / Looking out my window through the pain / What goes on when the sun goes down / You've still got a place in my heart / I got home just in time to say goodbye / (I'm a) stand by my woman man.
LP: . . . . **LSA 3278**

GREATEST HITS: RONNIE MILSAP.
Tracks: / Smokey mountain rain / Legend in my time, A / Pure love / Stand by my woman man / I hate you / It was almost like a song / Let's take the long way round the world / Daydreams about night things / Let my love be your pillow / Please don't tell me how the story ends / Back on my mind again / What a difference you've made in my life.
LP: . . . . **PL 13772**

GREATEST HITS: RONNIE MILSAP VOL.2.
LP: . . . . **PL 85425**
MC: . . . . **PK 85425**

HITS OF RONNIE MILSAP, THE.
Tracks: / (I'd be) a legend in my time / What goes on when the sun goes down / Pure love / Daydreams about night things / Honky tonk women / Country cookin' / Please don't tell me how the story ends / (After sweet memories) Play born to lose / 20-20 vision / (I'm a) Stand by my woman man / Remember to remind me (I'm leaving) / That girl who waits on tables / Too late to worry, too blue to cry / Four walls.
LP: . . . . **PL 42429**
MC: . . . . **PK 42429**

IMAGES.
Tracks: / Nobody likes sad songs / Keep the night away / I really don't want to know / Just because it feels good / You don't look for love / Hi heel sneakers / In no time at all / Delta queen / All good things don't have to end / Get it up.
LP: . . . . **PL 13346**

INSIDE.
Tracks: / Inside / Carolina dreams / Wrong end of the rainbow / I love New Orleans music / He got you / Hate the lies, love the liar / Who's counting / You took her off my hands / It's just a room / Any day now.
LP: . . . . **RCALP 3095**
MC: . . . . **RCAK 3095**

IT WAS ALMOST LIKE A SONG.
Tracks: / What a difference you've made in my life / No one will ever know / It was almost like a song / Selfish / Long distance memory / Here in love / Future's not what it used to be, The / It don't hurt to dream / Crystal fallin' rain / Lovin' kind.
LP: . . . . **PL 12439**

KEYED UP.
Tracks: / Stranger in my house / Show her / Don't your memory ever sleep at night / Watch out for the other guy / I'm just a redneck at heart / Don't you know how much I love you / Feelings change / Like children I have known / Is it over / We're here to love.
LP: . . . . **RCALP 6077**
MC: . . . . **RCAK 6077**

LEGEND IN MY TIME, A.
Tracks: / Busiest memory in town / Too late to worry, too blue to cry / (I'd be) a legend in my time / Biggest lie, The / Country cookin' / She came here for the change / I'll leave this world loving you / I'm still not over you / I honestly love you / Clap your hands.
LP: . . . . **LSA 3209**

LOST IN THE FIFTIES TONIGHT.
Tracks: / Lost in the fifties tonight / In love / Old fashioned girl like you / I heard it through the grapevine / Don't take it tonight / How do I turn you on? / Happy, happy birthday baby / Nashville moon / I only remember the good times / Money.
LP: . . . . **PL 81794**
MC: . . . . **PK 81794**

MILSAP MAGIC.
Tracks: / Why don't you spend the night / She thinks I still care / My heart / Silent night / It's a beautiful thing / Misery loves company / I let myself believe / If you don't want me / What's one more time / Still in love with you.
LP: . . . . **PL 13563**

MR MAILMAN.
Tracks: / Nothing's as good as it used to be / Only one woman / Denver / Kentucky woman / I saw pity in the face of a friend / Ain't no soul / If you go away / When it comes to my baby.
LP: . . . . **PHX 1002**

NIGHT THINGS.
Tracks: / (After sweet memories) Play born to lose again / Who'll turn out the lights (in your world) / Daydreams about night things / I'm no good at goodbyes / Just in case / Remember to remind me (I'm leaving) / Borrowed angel / Love takes a long time to die / (Lying here with) Linda on my mind / I'll be there (if you ever want me).
LP: . . . . **LSA 3261**

ONE MORE TRY FOR LOVE.
Tracks: / One more try for love / She loves my car / Still losing you / Suburbia / Prisoner of the highway / She's always in love / I might have said / I guess I just missed you / I'll take care of you / Night by night.
LP: . . . . **PL 85016**
MC: . . . . **PK 85016**

ONLY ONE LOVE IN MY LIFE.
Tracks: / Let's take the long way around the world / Back on my mind again / Only one love in my life / I'm not trying to forget / No relief in sight / Once I get over you / Santa Barbara / Too soon to know / Yesterday's lovers never make good friends / I've got the music in me.
LP: . . . . **PL 12780**
MC: . . . . **PK 12780**

OUT WHERE THE BRIGHT LIGHTS ARE GLOWING.
Tracks: / Out where the bright lights are glowing / Four walls / Pride goes before a fall / I'm beginning to forget you / He'll have to go / I'm getting better / Am I losing you / I won't forget you / I guess I'm crazy / When two worlds collide / Missing you / Dear friend.
LP: . . . . **RCALP 5022**
MC: . . . . **RCAK 5022**

RONNIE MILSAP.
MC: . . . . **ZCGAS 756**

RONNIE MILSAP LIVE.
Tracks: / Pure love / I hate you (medley) / Welcome / I'm a stand by my woman man (medley) / Busy makin' plans / Kaw-liga / Country cookin' / I can almost see Houston from here / After sweet memories play born to lose again / Daydreams about night things (medley) / Let my love be your pillow / (I'd be) a legend in my time / Honky tonk women.
LP: . . . . **PL 12043**

SPINNING WHEEL.
Tracks: / Do what you gotta do / Didn't we / House of the rising sun / Spinning wheel / Only one woman / Let's go get stoned / I can't stop crying.
LP: . . . . **SDLP 1.041**

THERE GOES MY HEART.
MC: . . . . **ORC 010**

Milton, Billy

AT THE CHESTERFIELD.
MC: . . . . **ZODIAC 1022C**

Milton, John (aut)

PARADISE LOST (books 1-4) (Quayle, Anthony (nar)).
MC: **4004**

PARADISE LOST (Various artists).
MC: **4004**
MCSET: **414 736-4**

Milton, Roy

BIG FAT MAMA (Milton, Roy and his Solid Senders).
Tracks: / Rhythm cocktail / Big fat mama / I'll always be in love with you / Little boy blues / So tired / Thelma Lou / Someday / Roy rides / Blue turning grey over you / Believe me baby / T-Town twist / Am I wasting my time? / Don't you remember baby? / I stood by / Bird in the hand, A.
LP: . . . . **JB 616**

GRANDFATHER OF R & B.
Tracks: / Burma Road blues / Red light / It never should have been this way / Them there eyes / When I grow too old to dream / My blue Heaven / I've had my moments / Hop,skip and jump / Everything I do is wrong / Sympathetic blues / My sweetheart / Junior jives / Where there is no love / Playboy blues / Cryin' & singin' the blues / Short sweet and snappy.
LP: . . . . **JB 600**

Milton, Ted

ODE: OH TO BE SEEN THROUGH YOUR EYES.
LP: . . . . **TBL 001**

Milva

IMMER MEHR.
Tracks: / Immer mehr / So bin ich nun mal / Auch der Mensch er stand da und weinte / Menschen an der Macht / Wieder mal / Ich musste langst was tun / Ein Traum von einem Mann / Meine Freundin / Wer will das nicht.
LP: **1060 528**
MC: **1660 528**

Mimms, Garnet

ROLL WITH THE PUNCHES.
Tracks: / All about love (M.Shuman/ J.Rogovoy) / One woman man (Pomus/ Poncia/Andreoli) / Don't change your heart (Samuel Bell) / Prove it to me (E.Marshall/J.Ragovoy) / Truth hurts, The / There is something on my mind (McNeely/Warner) / Looking for you (Jerry Ragovoy) / Roll with the punches (J.Shaw) / (It won't hurt) half as much (Bert Berns) / Please send me someone to love (Percy Mayfield) / Only your love (M Shuman/J Ragovoy) / I keep wanting you (Kaye/Springer) / Until you were gone (Byers) / Anytime you want me (N.Meade/G.Mimms) / I'll make it up to you (J.Ragovoy/B.Raleigh) / Welcome home (C.Taylor).
LP: . . . . **CRB 1121**

WARM AND SOULFUL: THE BEST OF GARNET MIMMS.
Tracks: / Cry baby / For your precious love / Baby don't you weep / Tell me baby / Quiet place / One girl / Look away / Little bit of soap, A / It was easier to hurt her / That goes to show you / I'll take good care of you / More than a miracle / As long as i have you / It's just a matter of time / It's been such a long way home / My baby.
LP: . . . . **EG 2602921**
MC: . . . . **EG 2602924**

Mimran, Patrick

BACK TO EARTH.
Tracks: / Back to earth / Born again / About Eve / Crystal wind / Samovar / No sex no cross / Water and ice / Red tears / White revenge / Refuznik / Blinking shadows / Horses of Babylon / Parfums de chine / Masha and Laetitia / Fleurs.
LP: **6.26430**

Mina

HEISSER SAND.
Tracks: / Heisser sand / Capitano / Ein treuer mann / Er liebte dieses leben / Fremdes land / Manner, madchen und pistolen / Grenzenlos / Grosste schau, Die / Fiesta Brasiliana / Tabu, es scheint gefahrlich zu sein, was ich tu' / Welt der verlorenen traume / Rhapsodie / Wenn du an wunder glaubst / Meine tur steht immer offen / Eine weisse dschunke / Bis zum nachsten mal.
LP: . . . . **BFX 15226**

Mince, Johnny

MASTER COMES HOME, THE (Mince, Johnny & His All-Stars).
LP: . . . . **J 126**

Mind Of Mr... (bk)

MIND OF MR. J.G.REEDER, THE (see under Wallace, Edgar) (West, Timothy (nar)).

Mind Over 4

GODDESS, THE.
Tracks: / Prayer for the dying / Goddess, The / 12 days of wind / Post / Gemini / Ice water steam / Autumn's here / Hell's bravest song / Airplanes.

MC: CARC 9
LP: CARLP 9

OUT HERE.
LP: 51005 1

Mind Over Matter

COLOURS OF LIFE, THE.
Tracks: / La vie (the dance of life) / Bali sunrise / Ganga (The river of life) / Mountains of karma.
LP: THBL 2.062

Mind The Gap

I REFUSE IT/ULTIMA THULE.
LP: IC 001

MIND THE GAP.
Tracks: / Panama praise / Lead me on / Good news / Only this I want / Come see the beauty / Freedom / Operator / Belize boogie / Come spirit move me / Servant king / Jesu azali awa / Many and great / Be ye glad / Wake up.
LP: WHY 3
MC: TCWHY 3
LP: WHY 3
MC: TCWHY 3

Mindbenders

MINDBENDERS, THE.
LP: TL 5324

Mindfunk

MINDFUNK.
Tracks: / Sugar ain't so sweet / Ride and drive / Bring it on / Big house / Burning / Fire / Blood runs red, The / Sister Blue / Woke up this morning / Innocence / Touch you.
LP: 4677901
MC: 4677904
LPPD: 4677900

Mindreaders

BAN THE MINDREADER.
LP: SKILL 1

Mindstorm

MINDSTORM.
LP: PRL 70231

Mineo, Sal

MAKE BELIEVE BABY.
LP: 33.8029

Miner, Tim

I KNOW YOU THINK YOU KNOW.
LP: SP R 1162
MC: SP C 1162

TIM MINER.
LP: BIRD R 171
MC: BIRD C 171

TRUE STORY, A.
MC: C 9083

Miners Of Muzo

ARE YOU THERE?.
LP: COL 269519

DIG DEEP FOR THE MINERS.
LP: CALCLP 030

MAKE MY DAY.
LP: MMLP 016

Minerva Jazz Band

PILE OF LOGS AND STONE (CALLED HOME).
LP: SOS 1117

Ming, Sexton

BIRDS WITH TEETH.
LP: HANG 36 UP

MAN WHO CREATED HIMSELF, THE.
LP: WORDUP 002

OLD HORSE OF THE NATION.
Tracks: / Mind is in your town, The / I am your god / Hot rod man / Many years ago / Get the kid / Old horse of the nation / Shot of the street, A / You can't polish a turd / Lieutenent Uhura / Rumbling man / Votory of the lutus satre / Duff you / Old horse of the nation 2.
LP: HANG 6 UP

SIX MORE MILES TO THE GRAVEYARD.
Tracks: / Bad wife arising / Kick boogie / Octopus weeps for you / This world this life / 6 more miles to the graveyard / Wristwatch explosion / Bored depressed and lonely / Sanoras death row / Wife done gone / Smash your face in / Learning the game / Frank forgets / Children are scum.
LP: HANG 18 UP

Minglewood, Matt

ME AND THE BOYS.
MC: SVMC 9402

PROMISE, THE.
LP: SVLP 9207
MC: SVMC 9407

Mingus, Charles

ABSTRACTIONS (Mingus, Charles Jazz Workshop).
Tracks: / What is this thing called love / Minor intrusion / Stormy weather / Abstractions / Four hands / Thrice upon a theme / Spur of the moment.
LP: AFF 135

AH UM.
Tracks: / Better git it in your soul / Goodbye pork pie hat / Boogie stop shuffle / Self portrait in three colours / Open letter to Duke / Bird calls / Fables of Faubus / Pussy cat dues / Jelly roll.
LP: CBS 21071
MC: 40 21071

BLACK SAINT AND THE SINNER LADY, THE.
Tracks: / Solo dancer / Group and solo dancers / Single solos and group dance / Trio and group dancers / Group dancers freewoman / Duet solo dancers / Stop look and listen / Sinner Jim Whitney / Heart's beat and shades in physical embraces / Stop, look and sing songs of revolutions / Saint and sinner join in merriment on battle front / Group and solo dance of love / Pain & passioned revolt then / Farewell my beloved.
LP: JAS 13
MC: JAS C13
LP: AS 35
MC: ASC 35

BLUES AND ROOTS.
Tracks: / Wednesday night prayer meeting / Crying blues / Moanin' / Tension / My Jelly Roll soul / E's flat ah's flat too.
LP: K 50232

CHANGES ONE.
Tracks: / Remember rockefeller at Attica / Sue's changes / Devil blues / Duke Ellington's sound of love.
LP: K 50201

CHANGES TWO.
Tracks: / Free cell block F, tis Nazi USA / Orange was the colour of her dress / Then silk blue / Black bats and poles / Duke Ellington's sound of love / For Harry Carney.
LP: K 50202

COLLECTION: CHARLES MINGUS.
Tracks: / Pithecanthropus erectus / New York sketchbook / Orange was the colour of her dress / Duke Ellington medley / Duke's choice / Slippers / Nouroog / Epitaph, Part 1 / Epitaph, Part 2 / Clark in the dark / My search / Don't come back / Finale / From "Meditations on integration".
MC: DVMC 2038

CONNECTION.
Tracks: / I'll remember April / If I could be with you / Sweet and lovely / Shine on, harvest moon / Ladybird / I'm beginning to see the light / All the things you are / Yesterdays / Back home blues / I can't get started / Hamp's new blues / Summertime / Dizzy moods / Laura.
LP: VJD 562

CUMBRIA & JAZZ FUSION.
Tracks: / Cumbia and jazz fusion / Music for Todo Modo.
LP: K 50486

EAST COASTING (Mingus, Charlie Sextet).
Tracks: / Memories of you / East coasting / West Coast ghost / Celia / Conversation / Fifty First Street blues.
LP: AFF 86

EPITAPH.
Tracks: / Main score (part 1) / Percussion discussion / Main score (part 2) / Started melody / Better git it in your soul / Soul, The / Moods in mambo / Self portrait in three colours / Chill of death, The / P.O. / Please don't come back from the moon.
LP: 4666311
MC: 4666314

FABLES OF FAUBUS VOL 2.
LP: INGO 13

HIS FINAL WORK.
Tracks: / Just for laughs (part 1) / Peggy's blue skylight / Caroline Kiekki Mingus / Just for laughs (part 2) / Fables of Faubus / Duke Ellington's sound of love / Farewell farewell / So long Eric / Slop (CD only.) / It might as well be spring (CD only.).
LP: GATE 7016
MC: CGATE 7016

HOPE SO ERIC VOL 1 (Mingus, Charlie Orchestra with Eric Dolphy 1964).
LP: INGO 10

IN BERLIN 1970 (Mingus, Charlie Sextet).
LP: BEP 508

JAZZ WORKSHOP.
LP: WL 70519

LIVE: CHARLIE MINGUS.
Tracks: / Better get it in your soul / Wednesday night prayer meeting / Folk forms No. 2 / Prayer for passive resistance / What love / I'll remember April.
LP: AFF 19

LIVE IN CHATEAUVALLON 1972.
LP: FC 135

LIVE IN EUROPE (Mingus, Charlie Sextet).
LP: UJ 23

LIVE IN PARIS 1964 VOL 2.
LP: FC 110

ME MYSELF AN EYE.
Tracks: / Three worlds of drums / Devil woman / Wednesday night prayer / Meeting / Carolyn 'Keki' Mingus.
LP: K 50571

MEDITATION.
Tracks: / Peggy's blue skylight / Orange was the colour of her dress, then silk blue / Meditation for integration / Fables of Faubus.
LP: FC 102

MINGUS.
LP: CS 9021

MINGUS AH UM.
Tracks: / Better git it in your soul / Goodbye pork pie hat / Boogie stop shuffle / Self portrait in three colours / Open letter to Duke / Bird calls / Fables of Faubus / Pussy cat dues / Jelly roll.
LP: 4504361
MC: 4504364

MINGUS AND DUKE.
LP: CJZ LP 10

MINGUS AT ANTIBES.
Tracks: / Wednesday night prayer meeting / Prayer for passive resistance / What love / I'll remember April / Folk forms 1 / Better git it in your soul.
2LP: SD 23001

MINGUS AT MONTEREY.
Tracks: / Duke Ellington medley / Orange was the colour of the dress, then blue / Meditations on integration.
2LP: P 24100

MINGUS IN EUROPE VOL 1.
LP: ENJA 3049

MINGUS IN EUROPE VOL 2.
LP: ENJA 3077

MINGUS IN STUTTGART.
2LP: UJ 07/8

MINGUS IN STUTTGART VOL 2.
LP: UJ 09

MINGUS, MINGUS, MINGUS, MINGUS, MINGUS.
Tracks: / II B.S. / I x love / Celia / Mood indigo.
LP: JAS 36
MC: JAS C36
LP: MCA 39119

MINGUS OH YEAH.
Tracks: / Hog callin' blues / Devil woman / Wham bam thankyou ma'am / Ecclusiastics / Oh Lord don't let them drop that atomic bomb on me / Eat that chicken / Passions of a man.
LP: K 40387

MINGUS PLAYS PIANO.
Tracks: / Myself when I am real / I can't get started / Body and soul / Roland Kirk's message / Memories of you / She's just Miss Popular hybrid / Orange was the colour of her dress, then silk blues / Meditations for Moses / Old portrait / I'm getting sentimental over you / Compositional theme story (Medley's, Anthems and Folklore.).
LP: JAS 49
MC: JAS C49

MINGUS QUINTET MEETS CAT ANDERSON.
LP: UJ 20

MINGUS THREE.
LP: JLP 1054

MYSTERIOUS BLUES.
Tracks: / Mysterious blues / Wrap your troubles in dreams / Body and soul / Vassarlean / Re-incarnation of a love bird / Me and you blues / Melody for the drums.
LP: CS 9042

NEW TIJUANA MOODS.
Tracks: / Dizzy moods (2 takes) / Ysabel's table dance (2 takes) / Los mariachis (the street musicians) (2 takes) / Flamingo (2 takes) / Tijuana gift shop (2 takes).
LP: PL 85635
MC: PK 85635

NEWPORT REBELS (Mingus, Charles/ Eric Dolphy/Roy Eldridge/Max Roach/ Jo Jones).
Tracks: / Mysterious blues / Cliff walk / Wrap your troubles in dreams / T'aint nobody's business if I do / Me and you.
LP: CS 9022

PARKERIANA VOL 3.
LP: INGO 15

PASSIONS OF A MAN.
Tracks: / Passions of a man / Pithecantropus erectus / Profile of Jackie / Reincarnation of a love bird / Haitian fight song / Wednesday night prayer meeting / Cryin' blues / Devil woman / Duke Ellington's sound of love / Better git it in your soul / Sue's changes / Canon / Free cell block F 'tis Nazi USA / Goodbye pork pie hat / Mingus on Mingus / Wham bam thank you M'am / Passions of a woman loved / Tonight at noon.
LPS: SD3 600

PORTRAIT: CHARLES MINGUS.
Tracks: / So long eric / Playing with Eric / Meditation for a pair of wirecutters / So long Eric / She's funny that way / Embraceable you / I can't get started / Ghost of a chance / Old portrait / Cocktails for two.
2LP: PR 24092

PRE-BIRD.
Tracks: / Take the 'A' train / Prayer for passive resistance / Eclipse / Mingus fingus No.2 / Weird nightmare / Do nothing till you hear from me / Bemoanable / Half mast inhibition.
LP: 6336 321

PRESENTS CHARLES MINGUS.
LP: CS 9005

QUINTET OF THE YEAR, THE (see Gillespie, Dizzy/Parker/Powell/Mingus & Roach) (Mingus, Charlie/Powell/ Powell/Roach & Gillespie).

REINCARNATION OF A LOVEBIRD.
Tracks: / Reincarnation of a lovebird (Take 1) / Wrap your troubles in dreams (take 4) / R & R (Take 1) / Body and soul (Take 2) / Bugs (Take 3).
LP: CS 9026

REVISITED.
Tracks: / Take the 'A' train / Prayer for passive resistance / Eclipse / Mingus fingus (No.2) / Weird nightmare / Do nothing till you hear from me / Bemoanable lady / Half mast inhibition.
LP: 2478 146

RIGHT NOW: LIVE AT THE JAZZ WORKSHOP.
LP: OJC 237

SCENES IN THE CITY.
Tracks: / Scenes in the city / Nou roug / New York sketchbook / Duke's choice / Slippers.
LP: AFF 105

SHOES OF THE FISHERMANS WIFE.
Tracks: / Slop / Song with orange / Gunslinging bird / Things ain't what they used to be / Shoes of the fisherman's wife are... / Far wells, mill valley / Mood indigo.
LP: 4608221
MC: 4608224

STATEMENTS.
LP: LOP 14 066

STATEMENTS.
LP: LPPS 111 08
LP: LOP 14066

STRINGS AND KEYS.
LP: 1902110

TRIO (Mingus, Charles Trio).
LP: FS 279

WILD BASS, THE.
LP: 500081

YOUNG REBEL.
LP: ST 1010

Mingus Dynasty

LIVE AT MONTREUX: MINGUS DYNASTY.
Tracks: / Haitian fight song / Consider me Oh Lord / Fables of Faubus / Ysabel's table dance / Sketch two / Better git it in your soul.
LP: K 99145

Mingus Dynasty Band

LIVE AT THE VILLAGE VANGUARD.
LP: SLP 4124

Minh Doky, Christian

APPRECIATION.
LP: SLP 4169

Minimal Compact

DEADLY WEAPONS.
LP: CRAM 030

FIGURE ONE CUTS.
LP: CRAM 055

LOWLANDS FLIGHT.
LP: MTM 10

MINIMAL COMPACT.
LP: CRAM 015

MINIMAL COMPACT LIVE.
LP: CRAM 061

ONE PLUS ONE BY ONE.
LP: CRAM 021

RAGING SOULS.
LP: CRAM 042
MC: CRAM 042C

Minimal Man

HUNGER IS ALL SHE'S EVER KNOWN.
LP: BIAS 071

PURE.
Tracks: / Grind/cash / Grave in space, A / Daybreaking / Happiest man in Europe / Mighty thing / More graves / Songs for dead astronauts / All I want is out of here / Nobody has time / Weatherbeqten.
LP: LD 8819

SAFARI.
LP: CD 017

SEX WITH GOD.
LP: ST 7502

SLAVE LULLABY.
LP: BIAS 024

Minion, Frank

SOFT LAND OF MAKE BELIEVE, THE.
LP: FS 202

Minipops

LET'S DANCE.
Tracks: / Locomotion / Too shy / Cruel summer / I'll be there / Tears of a clown / Charlie brown / Rock this town / Let's dance / Gloria / Blue suede shoes / Friends / Give it up / Ooh la la.
LP: CBS 54681
MC: 40 54681

MINI POPS CHRISTMAS ALBUM.
LP: BUL 1
MC: ZCBUL 1

MINIPOPS.
MC: CE 2102
LP: NE 1102

MINIPOPS.
LP: MTVLP 4
MC: ZCMTV 4

ROCKET TO THE STARS.
LP: BUL 3
MC: CBUL 3

WE'RE THE MINIPOPS.
LP: NE 1187
MC: CE 2187

Minister Of Noise

HELL IN HEAVEN.
Tracks: / Hell in heaven / Siamese twins / Zone drone / You can groove / Shopping precinct / Dread my soul / Black hole / In the stink.
LP: VILE 18

Ministry

LAND OF RAPE AND HONEY.
Tracks: / Stigmata / Missing, The / Deity / Golden dawn / Destruction / Land of rape and honey, The / You know what you are / Flashback / Abortive / Hizbollah (Only on CD.) / I prefer (Only on CD.).
LP: 925799 1
MC: 925799 4

MIND IS A TERRIBLE THING, THE.
Tracks: / Thieves / Never believe / Breathe / Burning inside / Cannibal song / So what / Test / Dream song / Faith collapsing.
LP: 7599260041
MC: 7599260044

TWITCH.
Tracks: / Just like you / We believe / All day (remix) / Angel, The / Over the shoulder / My possession / Where you at now ? / Crash and burn / Twitch (version 11).
LP: 925309 1
MC: 925309 4

WORK FOR LOVE.
Tracks: / Work for love / Do the etawa / I wanted to tell her / Say you're sorry / Here we go / Effigy / Revenge / She's got a cause / Should've known better.
LP: 205306
MC: 405306

Mink Deville

CABRETTA.
Tracks: / Venus of avenue D / Little girl / One way street / Mixed up shook up girl / Gunslinger / Can't do without it / Cadillac walk / Spanish stroll / She's so tough / Party girl.
LP: RAZ 24

COUP DE GRACE.
Tracks: / Just give me one good reason / Help me to make it / Maybe tomorrow / Teardrops may fall / You better move on / So in love are we / Love and emotion / Love me like you did before / She was made in heaven / End of the line.
LP: K 50833

LE CHAT BLEU.
Tracks: / This must be the night / Savoir faire / That world outside / Slow drain / You just keep holding on / Lipstick traces / Bad boy / Mazurka / Just to walk that little girl home / Heaven stood still.
LP: EST 25390

MINK DEVILLE.
Tracks: / Venus of Avenue D / Little girl / One way street / Mixed up shook up girl / Gunslinger / Can't do without it / Cadillac walk / Spanish stroll / She's so tough / Party girl.
LP: EST 11631

RETURN TO MAGENTA.
Tracks: / Just your friends / Soul twist / 'A' train lady / Rolene / Desperate days / Guardian angel / Steady drivin' man / Easy slider / I broke that promise / Confidence to kill.
LP: EST 11780

SAVOIR FAIRE.
Tracks: / This must be the night / Train lady, A / Spanish stroll / Cadillac walk / Soul twist / Just your friends / Mixed up shook up girl / Gunslinger / One way street / Mazurka / I broke that promise / Just to walk that little girl home.
MC: TCEST 26716
LP: EST 26716
LP: 186435 1
MC: 186435 4

SPORTIN' LIFE.
Tracks: / Easy street / In the heart of the city / I must be dreaming / Italian shoes / Slip away / When you walk my way / Woman's touch, A / Easy street / Little by little / There's no living (without your loving) / Something beautiful dying.
LP: 825 776-1
MC: 825 776-4

WHERE ANGELS FEAR TO TREAD.
Tracks: / River of tears / Each word's a beat of my heart / Demasiado / Corazon / Lilly's daddy's cadillac / Around the corner / Pick up the pieces / Love's got a hold on me / Keep your monkey away / From my door / Are you lonely tonight / Moonlight let me down.
LP: 780 115-1
MC: 780 115-4

Minks, Jasmine

SOUL STATION.
LP: CRELP 112

Minnelli, Liza

LIVE AT CARNEGIE HALL.
LP: DG 15502
MC: CS 85502

LIZA WITH A 'Z'.
LP: CBS 65212
LP: 32040

RESULTS.
Tracks: / I want you now / Losing my mind / If there was love / So sorry, I said / Don't drop bombs / Twist in my sobriety / Rent / Love pains / Tonight is forever / I can't say goodnight.
LP: 4655111
MC: 4655114

SINGER.
Tracks: / I believe in music / Use me / I'd love you to want me / Oh babe / You're so vain / Where is the love / Singer / Don't let me be lonely tonight / Dancing in the moonlight / You are the sunshine of my life / Baby don't get hooked on me.
LP: CBS 32501
LP: CBS 65555

STEPPING OUT.
LP: A 628
MC: AC 628

ULTIMATE EVENT, THE (VIDEO) (see under Sinatra, Frank) (Minnelli, Liza/ Sammy Davis Jnr/Frank Sinatra).

Minnesota Rockabilly

MINNESOTA ROCKABILLY ROCK, VOL 3 (Various artists).
Tracks: / Diggin' that rock 'n' roll: *Stinton Brothers* / Lightning strikes: *D.J. & The Cats* / What's up, Doug?: *Inn Truders* / Never been blue: *Urness, Harvey* / Ad lib: *Danny & The Galaxies* / If you want to be my baby: *Danny & The Galaxies* / Oh yeah: *Blue Kats* / Volcano: *Carvairs* / Come back baby: *Carroll, Evens* / Living doll: *Eddy, Jim* / Wrong kinda lovin': *Tucker, Les* / Flip, The: *Arlington, Sue* / Lost love: *Torrells* / Blue black hair: *Jades* / Surfin' cow: *Jades.*
LP: WLP 8854

Minnypops

EIN KUS.
Tracks: / Ein kus.
MCSET: CSBT 4/5

SPARKS IN A DARK ROOM.
LP: FBN 15

Minogue, Dannii

LOVE AND KISSES.
LP: MCA 10340
MC: MCAC 10340

Minogue, Kylie

ENJOY YOURSELF.
Tracks: / Hand on your heart / Wouldn't change a thing.
LP: HF 9
MC: HFC 9

KYLIE MINOGUE: INTERVIEW PICTURE DISC (Minogue, Kylie & Jason Donovan).
LPPD: BAK 2116

KYLIE - THE ALBUM.
Tracks: / I should be so lucky / Locomotion, The / Je ne sais pas pourquoi / It is no secret / Got to be certain / Turn it into love / I miss you / I'll still be loving you / Look my way / Love at first sight.
LP: HF 3
MC: HFC 3

RHYTHM OF LOVE.
LP: HF 18
MC: HFC 18

Minor Detail

MINOR DETAIL.
Tracks: / Canvas of life / Hold on / 20th century / Why take it again / I've got a friend / Ask the kids / We are winners / Others need you / I'll always love you / Columbia.
LP: POLD 5113
MC: POLDC 5113

Minor Miracle

MINOR MIRACLE, A (Original Soundtrack) (Various artists).
LP: STV 81193

Minor Threat

MINOR THREAT.
LP: DISCHORD 12
MC: DISCHORD 12C

OUT OF STEP.
LP: DISCHORD 10
MC: DISCHORD 10C

Minott, Echo

SHOWCASE: ECHO MINOTT ALONG WITH SLY & ROBBIE (Minott, Echo/Sly & Robbie).
LP: PHLP 001

WHAT THE HELL.
LP: DSR 8765

Minott, Robert

TRUMP JACK PRESENTS ROBERT MINOTT.
LP: TJPLP 001

Minott, Sugar

AFRICAN SOLDIER (ALBUM).
LP: HB 49
MC: HBC 49

BEST OF SUGAR MINOTT VOL 1.
LP: LMLP 20283

BITTER SWEET.
LP: VSLP 4002
MC: VSMC 010

BLACK ROOTS.
Tracks: / Mankind / Hard time pressure / River Jordan / Jailhouse / I'm gonna hold on / Oppressors oppression / Two time loser / Black roots / Clean runnings / Mr. Babylon man.
LP: ILPS 9591

BOSS IS BACK, THE.
LP: RAS 3039
MC: RASC 3039

BUY OFF THE BAR.
Tracks: / Buy off the bar (bar dub) / Can't cross the border (border dub) / Frontline (line dub) / Two timer (timer dub) / Strictly sensi (sensi dub) / Dread upon your head (dread dub).
LP: UNKNOWN
LP: DSR 3351

COLLECTORS ITEM (Minott, Sugar & African Brothers).
Tracks: / All kin a people / You make me feel so good / Love we had / You tried to hurt me / Fight against Rasta / Righteous kingdom / Youths of today / Lead us heavenly Father, lead us / King son / King dub.
LP: TEMPLP 006

DANCE HALL SHOWCASE.
Tracks: / Informer, The / Genuine lover / Dance hall / Showcase & dub versions for all tracks.
LP: BRST 1002

GHETTO YOUTH DEM RISING.
LP: HB 60

GHETTO-OLOGY.
Tracks: / Man hungry / People gotto know, The / Walking through the ghetto / Dreader than dread / So many things / Never gonna give jah up / Ghetto-ology / Africa is the black man's home / Strange things / Free Jah Jah children.
LP: TRLS 173
MC: ZCTRL 173

GIVE THE PEOPLE.
Tracks: / Not for sale / Give the people / Never too young / Be careful / Right track / Can't get over / Save the children / This world.
LP: UAG 30310

GOOD THING GOING.
Tracks: / Good thing going / High up above / Never my love / House on a hill / My sister / Jasmine / Life without money / Lonely days / Walk on by / Family affair.
LP: RCALP 3051
MC: RCAK 3051
LP: HB 13
MC: HBC 13

HERBMAN HUSTLING.
LP: MLMRP 001

INNA REGGAE DANCE HALL.
LP: HB 29
MC: HBC 29

JAMMING IN THE STREET.
LP: 8027

LEADER OF THE PACK, THE.
LP: BLP 5

LOVERS ROCK INNA DANCEHALL.
Tracks: / Ready for love / Ready for love (Dub) / You ah mi lover / You ah mi lover (dub) / Jah have mercy / Jah have mercy (dub) / Love grows / Love grows (dub) / Close to you / Close to you (Dub) / Stormy days / Stormy days (Dub).
LP: YPLP 10

MAKE IT WITH YOU (see Thompson, Carroll) (Minott, Sugar/Carrol Thompson).

MORE IDEAS.
LP: JUSLP 005

ROCKERS AWARD WINNERS (Minott, Sugar/Leroy Smart).
Tracks: / Nah follow no fashion / True / Cell block one / Roots rock reggae / Girls are skanking / Mankind a failure / Give love a try / Reggae music / Love life.
LP: GREL 84

RYDIM.
Tracks: / Feel the rydim / Mass mi mass / Old King Cole / Nah go to South Africa / Jah is on my side / Bubbling / If a didn't love you / Chatty chatty mouth.
LP: GREL 82

SHOWCASE.
LP: SOL 1137

SINCE YOU CAME INTO MY LIFE (See under Lodge, J.C.) (Minott, Sugar & J.C. Lodge).

SLICE OF THE CAKE.
LP: HB 24
MC: HBC 24

SUFFERERS CHOICE.
LP: HB 21
MC: HBC 21

SUGAR AND SPICE.
LP: TAXI LP 003
LP: RAS 3017

SUGAR MINOTT AND YOUTH PROMOTION.
LP: A 28U 5

SWEET STUFF.
2LP: LMLP 003/4

SWEET STUFF VOLS. 1 AND 2.
LP: LM LP 003

TIME LONGER THAN ROPE.
Tracks: / Can't get me out / Jah you make me sing / It's happening / I'm no slave / Ease up Mr.Custom man / Time longer than rope / Rockers master.
LP: GREL 88

TOUCH OF CLASS, A.
LP: JMLP 001
MC: JMC 001

TRUE, A.
LP: ARILP 014

WICKED A GO FEEL IT.
LP: W 1718

Minox

LAZARE.
LP: LACER 009

Mint Addicts

BONES.
Tracks: / Bones.
LP: CON 00029

NAKED EYES.
LP: CON 00019

Mint Juleps

ONE TIME.
LP: JULP 1
MC: CJULP 1

Mint Sauce

MINT SAUCE (Various artists).
LP: PLAY 001

Minting Sisters

STRIKE COUNTRY.
Tracks: / Listen to a country song / Soupstone, The / Rocky top / Paper roses / Streets of London / I'll get over you / All I ever need is you / Operator / Let's get together / Ozark mountain lullaby / Somebody loves you.
LP: . . . . BGC 274
MC: . . . . KGBC 274

Minton, Phil

AMMO (Minton, Phil & Roger Turner).
LP: . . . . LR 116

FERALS RUFF, THE (Minton/Turner/Tomlinson/Davies).
LP: . . . . LR 138

VOICE (see under Tippetts, J).

Minutemen

3 WAY TIE (FOR LAST).
LP: . . . . SST 058

PROJECT MERSH.
LP: . . . . SST 034

Minutes To...

MINUTES TO GO (Various artists).
LP: . . . . IM 001

Mioritza

SONGS AND DANCES FROM ROMANIA.
LP: . . . . EULP 1070
MC: . . . . EUMC 1070

Miracle Legion

BACKYARD.
LP: . . . . SPIN 302

GLAD.
LP: . . . . ROUGHUS 034

ME AND MR RAY.
LP: . . . . ROUGH 136
MC: . . . . ROUGHC 136

SURPRISE SURPRISE SURPRISE.
Tracks: / Story teller / Truly / Little man / Miss domingo / Crooked path / Paradise / Everyone in heaven / Country boy / Wonderment / All for the best.
LP: . . . . ROUGH 112
MC: . . . . ROUGHC 112

Miracle Workers

LIVE AT THE FORUM.
LP: . . . . EFA 4488

OVERDOSE.
Tracks: / Rock 'n' revolution in the streets / Light camera action / Just can't find a better way / No use / Without her hand / When a woman calls my name.
LP: . . . . EGA 7206

Mirage

AND THE EARTH SHALL CRUMBLE.
LP: . . . . METALP 109

AVANT-GARDE AND THIRD-STREAM JAZZ.
Tracks: / Summer sequence (Ralph Burns) / Clothed woman (Duke Ellington) / Yesterdays (Jerome Kern & Otto Harbach) / Mirage (Pete Rugolo) / Eclipse (Charles Mingus) / Egdon Heath (Bill Russo) / Concerto for Billy the kid (George Russell) / Transformation (Gunther Schuller) / Piazza navona (John Lewis) / Laura (David Raksin & Johnny Mercer).
LP: . . . . NW 216

DANCE MASTERS.
Tracks: / Give me the night medley / Let's groove medley / Ain't no stoppin' medley / Into the groove medley / Get down on it medley / Good times (medley).
LP: . . . . DBLP 501

JACK MIX '88 (Best of Mirage).
LP: . . . . SMR 746
MC: . . . . SMC 746

JACK MIX 89.
LP: . . . . UNKNOWN

JACK MIX IN FULL EFFECT.
Tracks: / Beat dis / Just a mirage / Love supreme, A / Pink cadillac / Just a minute / Push beat / Let's all chant / I should be so lucky / Boogie oogie oogie / Don't turn around.
LP: . . . . SMR 856
MC: . . . . SMC 856

MIRAGE MIX '87.
LP: . . . . MIRLP 87
MC: . . . . ZCMIR 87

NOW YOU SEE IT.
LP: . . . . FID 9

ROYAL MIX '89.
2LP: . . . . SMR 871
MCSET: . . . . SMC 871

Miranda, Carmen

SOUTH AMERICAN WAY.
Tracks: / South American way / Mama eu tuero (I want my mama) / I yi yi yi yi (I like you very much) / Chica chica boom chic / Weekend in Havana, A / When I love I love / Chattanooga choo choo / Manuelo / O passo du kanguru / Bambu bambu / Cae cae / Turadas em madrid / Tic tac do meu coracao / Co co co co ro / Cuanto Lagusta / Wedding samba, The.
LP: . . . . MCL 1703
MC: . . . . MCLC 1703

Mirk

MODDAN'S BOWER (Various).
LP: . . . . MUM 1205

TAK A DRAM.
Tracks: / Why should I / Dowie dens of Yarrow, The / Lady Charlotte Durham / Bonnie wee lassie's answer / Och hey Johnnie lad / PM George Ross' farewell to the Blackwatch / Glenlogie / Cairn-o-mount / Farewell to Cape Helles / Glasgow Caithness centenary gathering / Eighth Blackwatch on Passchendale ridge / John Keith Laing / Bill Powrie (marches and reels) / Tak a dram.
LP: . . . . SPR 1009
MC: . . . . SPRC 1009

Miro

ANGEL N1.
LP: . . . . SH 2008LP
MC: . . . . SH 2008CASS

Miro, Steve

TRILEMNA.
LP: . . . . GZLP 101

Mirrlees Works Band

SNAPSHOTS.
Tracks: / Bandology / Rule Britannia / Nightingale, The / Napoleon Galop / Whitehall / Portuguese party / I don't know how to love him / Swedish rhapsody / Blaydon races / Plymouth hoe.
LP: . . . . GRS 1069

Mirror Image

MIRROR IMAGE (Various artists).
MC: 180.072/73

MIRROR IMAGE VOLS 1 & 2 (Various artists).
Tracks: / House in the storm: *Various artists* / Powerplay: *Various artists* / Strollin': *Various artists*/ Where's the walrus: *Various artists* / Island sunrise: *Various artists* / Gib mir: *Various artists*/ Sweet music for you and me: *Various artists* / Listen to the music: *Various artists* / Secrets of darkness: *Various* artists / Across the view: *Various artists* / Acton art: *Various artists* / Oceans breath: *Various artists*/ Secret garden: *Various artists* / Sade: *Various artists* / Obsession: *Various artists* / Grand finale: *Various artists* / Crockett's theme: *Various artists* / Bali sunrise: *Various artists* / Mountain peaks: *Various artists*.
2LP: 80.072/73

Mirrors

MIRRORS, THE.
LP: . . . . AUL 726

Mirrors Over Kiev

NORTHERN SONGS.
LP: . . . . RRA 014
MC: . . . . RRAMC 014

Mirwais

MIRWAIS.
LP: . . . . ROSE 235
MC: . . . . ROSK 235

Mirza, Mahmud

CLASSICAL SITAR.
Tracks: / Kalawati / Alhaia bilawal raga.
LP: . . . . CFR 121
MC: . . . . MCFR 121

RAG DARBARI/RAG KAFI.
LP: . . . . TGS 123

Mischa Elman

MISCHA ELMAN (Various artists).
LP: . . . . REH 717
MC: . . . . ZCR 717

Mi-Sex

COMPUTER GAMES (LP).
Tracks: / Computer games / Graffiti crimes / Wot do you want / Not such a bad boy / Stills / But you don't care / Loser / 21-20 / I wanna be with you / Camera kazi / Inside you.
LP: 84157

WHERE DO THEY GO.
Tracks: / Only thinking / Where do they go / Castaway / Blue day / I lose control / Falling in and out / Down the line / 5 o'clock / Stranger in you / Don't look back in anger / Computer games.
LP: . . . . CBS 25942

Misfits

BEST OF THE MISFITS.
LP: . . . . REVLP 74

EARTH AD/WOLF'S BLOOD.
LP: . . . . AG 0024

EVIL LIVE.
LP: . . . . PL 908
LP: . . . . AGO 023

WALK AMONG US.
Tracks: / All hell breaks loose / Hatebreeders.
LP: 925756 1

WOLFSBLOOD.
LP: . . . . AG 024

Misha Lobko Sextet

RITUALS.
LP: . . . . LR 141

Mishima

MISHIMA (Original Soundtrack) (Various artists).
Tracks: / Opening: *Various artists* / November 25: *Various artists* / Morning 1934: *Various artists*/ Grandmother and Kimitake: *Various artists* / Temple of the golden pavillion: *Various artists* / Osamu's theme: *Various artists* / Kyoko's house: *Various artists* / 1937: *Various artists* / Saint Sebastian: *Various* artists / Kyoko's house: *Various artists* / November 25th: *Various artists* / Ichigaya: *Various artists*/ 1957: *Various artists* / Award montage: *Various artists* / Runaway horses: *Various artists* / 1962: *Various artists* / Bodybuilding: *Various artists* / November 25: *Various artists* / Last day, The: *Various* artists / F 104: *Various artists* / Epilogue from sun and steel: *Various artists* / Closing: *Various artists*.
LP: . . . . EKT 23
MC: . . . . EKT 23 C

Misiani, Daniel Owino

BENGA BLAST (Misiani, Daniel Owino & Shirati Band).
Tracks: / Joshirati misiani / Wuoro monono / Honourable Horace Owiti Ongili / Alice atieno / Safari ya tanzania / Doctor J Abuya / Agnes Nyashirati / Okoth atari.
LP: . . . . EWV 13
MC: . . . . TCEWV 13

PINY OSE MER/THE WORLD UPSIDE DOWN (Misiani, Daniel Owino & Shirati Band).
Tracks: / Isabella Muga / Rose Akoth / Margret Odero / Piny Ose Mer / Makuru bor / Otieno anyango / Wuoth iye tek / Dora Mamy.
LP: . . . . ORB 046

Miss Behaven

NOBODY'S ANGEL.
LP: . . . . WX 334
MC: . . . . WX 334 C

Miss Daisy

PIZZA CONNECTION.
LP: . . . . GWLP 36

Miss Lou

YES M'DEAR.
LP: . . . . DSR 6168

Miss Saigon

MISS SAIGON (Various artists).
LP: . . . . WX 329
MC: . . . . WX 329C

Missing Ambassador

MISSING AMBASSADOR, THE.
MC: . . . . PLB 136

Missing Brazilians

WARZONE.
LP: . . . . ONULP 34

Missing Persons

SPRING SESSION M.
Tracks: / Noticeable one / Windows / It ain't none of your business / Destination unknown / Walking in L.A. / U.S. drag / Tears / Here and now / Words / Bad streets / Rock and roll suspension / No way out.
LP: . . . . EST 12228

Mission

CARVED IN SAND.
Tracks: / Amelia / Into the blue / Butterfly on a wheel / Sea of love / Deliverance / Grapes of wrath / Belief / Paradise (will shine like the moon) / Hungry as the hunter / Lovely.
LP: 842 251 1
MC: 842 251 4

CHILDREN.
Tracks: / Beyond the pale / Wing and a prayer / Heaven on earth / Tower of strength / Kingdom come / Breathe / Shamara Kye / Black mountain mist / Heat / Hymn (for America).
LP: . . . . MISH 2
MC: . . . . MISHC 2

FIRST CHAPTER, THE.
Tracks: / Over the hills and far away / Serpent's kiss / Crystal ocean, The / Dancing barefoot / Like a hurricane / Naked and savage / Garden of delight / Wake / Tomorrow never knows (Only on UK edition.) / Wishing well (Only on UK edition.).
LP: . . . . MISH 1
MC: . . . . MISHC 1
LP: 8327321

GOD'S OWN MEDICINE.
Tracks: / Wasteland / Bridges burning / Garden of delight / Stay with me / Let sleeping dogs die / Sacrilege / Dance on glass / And the dance goes on / Severina / Love me to death.
LP: . . . . MERH 102
MC: . . . . MERHC 102

GRAINS OF SAND.
Tracks: / Hands across the ocean / Grip of disease, The / Divided we fall / Mercenary / Mr. Pleasant / Kingdom come (forever again) / Heaven sends you / Sweet smile of mystery / Love / Bird of passage.
LP: 846 937 1
MC: 846 937 4

MISSION: INTERVIEW PICTURE DISC (2).
LPPD: . . . . BAK 2024

MUSIC AND MEDIA INTERVIEW PICTURE DISC.
LPPD: . . . . MM 1259

Mission (Film)

MISSION, THE (see under Morricone, Ennio) (Various artists).

Mission Impossible

MISSION IMPOSSIBLE (Various artists).
LP: . . . . DSR 8618

MISSION IMPOSSIBLE (Original soundtrack) (Various artists).
LP: 250674.1

Mission Of Burma

FORGET MISSION OF BURMA.
LP: . . . . TAANG 24

HORRIBLE TRUTH ABOUT BURMA, THE.
LP: . . . . ROSE 76

LET THERE BE BURMA.
LP: . . . . EM 94081

Mission USA

SEARCH.
Tracks: / Show a little love / Lena / Lover for life / Turn me up / Energy to burn / Ready to give my heart / Sensuous mood / Back on track.
LP: 4602651
MC: 4602654

Mississippi Burning

MISSISSIPPI BURNING (Original Soundtrack) (Various artists).
Tracks: / Take my hand precious Lord: *Jackson, Mahalia* / Murder in Mississippi (Part 1): *Jones, Trevor* / Some things are worth dying for: *Jones, Trevor* / Murder in Mississippi (Part 2): *Jones, Trevor* / Anderson and Mrs Pell: *Jones, Trevor* / When we all get to heaven: *Choral* / Try Jesus: *Williams, Vesta* / Abduction: *Jones*, Trevor / You live it, you breathe it, you marry it: *Jones, Trevor* / Murder in Mississippi (Part 3): *Jones, Trevor*/ Requiem for three young men: *Jones, Trevor* / Burning cross: *Jones, Trevor* / Justice in Mississippi: *Jones, Trevor* / Walk by faith (vocal): *McBride, Lannie* / Walk on by faith: *McBride, Lannie*.
MC: . . . . ANC 8745
LP: . . . . AN 8745

Mississippi Delta

FROM THE DELTA TO THE WASH.
Tracks: / Rainy day woman / Heaven is my woman's love / Something's wrong in California / Someday / Heart over mind / Your cheatin' heart / What about you / Please don't let me love you anymore / You're shaking the hand / Together again / Cannonball rag / Good hearted woman.
LP: . . . . SFA 094

Mississippi Mass Choir

LIVE.
LP: . . . . MALP 6003
MC: . . . . MALC 6003

Mississippi Sheiks

MISSISSIPPI SHEIKS VOL 1 (1930).
LP: . . . . MSE 1005

MISSISSIPPI SHEIKS VOL. 2 1930-34.
LP: . . . . MSE 1012

Missouri Breaks

MISSOURI BREAKS, THE (Original Soundtrack) (Various artists).
LP: . . . . MCA 25113
MC: . . . . MCAC 25113

Mister Guitar Man

28 GUITAR GREATS.
2LP: . . . . CR 5150
MCSET: . . . . CRT 5150

Mister Spin

DROPPIN' IT.
MC: . . . . **BIP 502**

Mistinguett

MISTINGUETT Various artists (Various artists).
2LP: **2C 178 15422/23**

Mistletoe...

GOLDEN HOUR: MISTLETOE CHILDREN'S CHOIR (Mistletoe Children's Choir).
LP: . . . . **HDY 1911**
MC: . . . . **ZCHDY 1911**

GOLDEN HOUR: MISTLETOE ORGAN AND CHIMES (Mistletoe Organ & Chimes).
LP: . . . . **HDY 1909**
MC: . . . . **ZCHDY 1909**

GOLDEN HOUR OF CHRISTMAS CAROLS, A (Mistletoe Singers).
LP: . . . . **HDY 1908**
MC: . . . . **ZCHDY 1908**

GOLDEN HOUR OF CHRISTMAS STORIES (Mistletoe Players).
LP: . . . . **HDY 1912**
MC: . . . . **ZCHDY 1912**

Mistrals Daughter

MISTRALS DAUGHTER, THE (TV soundtrack) (Various artists).
Tracks: / Only love: *Mouskouri, Nana* / Cavaillion series, The: *Various artists* / I remember Mistral: *Various* artists / Teddy's theme: *Various artists* / Flower market, The: *Various artists* / Surrealist ball, The: *Various* artists / Maggie's theme: *Various artists* / Paula's theme: *Various artists* / Model's fair, The: *Various* artists / Mistral's daughter, The: *Various artists* / La Rue Hebraique: *Various artists* / La tourello: *Various* artists / Death of Teddy, The: *Various artists* / Mistral theme: *Various artists* / War: *Various artists*/ Last Mistral, The: *Various artists* / Mistral's daughter, The (fade): *Various artists.*
LP: **66180**
LP: . . . . **CAL 221**
MC: . . . . **CAC 221**

Mistress

MISTRESS.
Tracks: / Situations / High on the ride / Mistrusted love / Dixie flyer / China lake / Whose side are you on / You got the love / Tellin' me lies / Cinnamon girl / Letter to California.
LP: . . . . **RSS 14**

Mistress Of Mellyn

MISTRESS OF MELLYN (Holt, Victoria) (Kendall, Felicity (nar)).
MC: . . . . **CAB 014**

Misty (2)

RAGGAMUFFIN DARLIN' (See under Asher D) (Misty (2) & Asher D).

Misty In Roots

EARTH.
LP: . . . . **PU 102**

FORWARD.
Tracks: / Fiesta / Midas touch, The / Hawks on the street / Save a thought / Forward / Jah see Jah know / Envy us / Look before you leap / Feelings / Sinner.
LP: . . . . **KAZ LP 900**
MC: . . . . **KAZ MC 900**

LIVE AT THE COUNTER EUROVISION.
Tracks: / Introduction / Mankind / Ghetto of the city / How long Jah / Oh wicked man / Judas Iscariote / See them ah come / Sodom and Gomorrah.
LP: . . . . **KAZLP 12**
MC: . . . . **KAZMC 12**

MUSI O TUNYA.
LP: . . . . **PU 105**

Misty Mornings

MISTY MORNINGS Various original artists (Various artists).
LP: . . . . **RTL 2066**
MC: **4CRTL 2066**

Misunderstood

BEFORE THE DREAM FADED.
Tracks: / Children of the sun / My mind / Who do you love? / Unseen / Find a hidden door / I can take you to the sun / I'm not talking / Who's been talkin' / I need your love / You don't have to go / I cried my eyes out / Like I do / Crying over love.
LP: . . . . **BRED 32**

GOLDEN GLASS.
Tracks: / Never had a girl like you before / Golden glass / I don't want to discuss it / Little red rooster / You're tuff enough / Flamingo music / Freedom / Keep on running / I'm cruising.
LP: **TSSLP1**

Mitchell, Alda Denise

OH TASTE AND SEE.
LP: . . . . **IAM R 3806**
MC: . . . . **IAM C 3806**

Mitchell, Barbara

HIGH ON LOVE.
Tracks: / Ace of my heart / High on love / Never had a love like this before / Can't help the way I feel / I need some loving / Take your time / Don't look me over.
LP: **826 887-1**
MC: **826 887-4**

Mitchell, Bill

VINTAGE PIANO VOL.3 (Mitchell, Bill/ Paul Lingle).
LP: . . . . **ESR 1203**

Mitchell, Billy

FACES.
LP: . . . . **VR 2501**

IN FOCUS.
LP: . . . . **OP 2502**

NIGHT FLIGHT TO DAKAR (see Cohn,Al/Billy Mitchell/etc.) (Mitchell/ Cohn/Coker/Vinnegar/Butler).

Mitchell, Blue

CUP BEARERS, THE.
Tracks: / Turquoise / Why do I love you? / Dingbat blues / Capers / Cup bearers / How deep is the ocean? / Tiger Lily.
LP: . . . . **RSLP 439**

GRAFFITI BLUES.
Tracks: / Graffiti blues / Yeah ya right / Express / Asso kam / Dorado / Alone again (naturally) / Where it's at / Funky walk / Blue funk.
LP: . . . . **MRL 5006**

THING TO DO, THE.
Tracks: / Fungii mama / Mona's mood / Thing to do, The / Step lightly / Chick's tune.
LP: . . . . **BST 84178**

Mitchell, Bobby

I'M GONNA BE A WHEEL SOMEDAY.
Tracks: / I'm crying / Rack 'em back / Wedding bells are ringing, The / Meant for me / One Friday morning / Baby's gone / Sister Lucy / I'm gonna be a wheel someday / Try rock and roll / 64 hours / I've got my fingers crossed / I try so hard / Wailing in circles / Well, I done got over it / I don't want to be a wheel no more.
LP: . . . . **RB 101**

Mitchell/ Coe

EXILED various artists (Various artists).
Tracks: / Lost in the stars: *Various artists* / Children of the universe: *Various artists* / Hold on to love: *Various artists* / Something inside us dying: *Various artists* / Dreaming: *Various artists* / Time dance: *Various artists* / Ships in the night: *Various artists* / Return to the stars: *Various artists.*
LP: . . . . **PL 25297**
MC: . . . . **PK 25297**

Mitchell, Eamon

IRISH TRADITIONAL MUSIC.
LP: . . . . **SOLP 1034**

IRISH TRADITIONAL MUSIC FROM SLIABH GALLION BRAE.
MC: . . . . **COX 1034**

Mitchell, Eddy

EDDY MITCHELL.
LP: . . . . **PL 70069**

Mitchell, Freddie

DERBY, THE (Mitchell, Freddie & Orchestra).
Tracks: / Pony Express / Preachin' / Louise / Jersey bounce / Summertime boogie / Long lean boogie / Hot ice / Rockin' and jumpin'.
LP: . . . . **KM 712**

ROCK 'N' ROLL.
Tracks: / Jersey bounce / Fish market boogie / Till Tom boogie / Slider / I've got your boogie / Derby, The / Wedding march / String of pearls / Hot ice / Moon dog boogie / Delicado / Later gator / I'm goin' home / Preachin' / 3 strikes you're out / Freddie's new calypso.
LP: . . . . **OFF 6021**

Mitchell, Geoffrey

JOY OF CHRISTMAS, THE Conducted by Edward Heath (Mitchell, Geoffrey Choir & English Chamber Orchestra).
Tracks: / Twelve days of Christmas / Ding dong merrily on high / In dulci jubilo / Birds, The / When the crimson sun has set / Infant holy / I saw three ships / Hark the herald angels sing / Sussex carol, The / Crown of roses, The / Good King Wenceslas / Gloucestershire wsassail / Christmas bells / Holly and the ivy, The / Unto us is born a son / We wish you a merry Christmas.
LP: . . . . **MFP 5665**
MC: . . . . **TCMFP 5665**
LP: . . . . **CSD 3784**

Mitchell, George

30 GOLDEN GREATS (Mitchell,George Minstrels With Joe Loss Orchestra).
Tracks: / Baby face / Ain't she sweet / Good ole mammy song / Nostalgia / Home town / Strollin' / Y viva Espana / Happy feet / I want to be happy / Happy days are here again / Consider yourself / Mame / Tzena-tzena-tzena / Hava Nagila / Bring me sunshine / Paloma blanca / Old-fashioned way / You are my sunshine / Laugh a happy laugh / Continental / Piccolino / When the red, red robin comes bob, bob, bobbin' along / Hopscotch / Mexican shuffle / Tijuana taxi / La bamba / Rock around the clock / Little brown jug / When the saints go marching in / Underneath the arches.
LP: . . . . **THIS 18**
MC: . . . . **TC THIS 18**
MC: . . . . **MFP 415 720 4**
MC: . . . . **TCMFP 5720**
LP: . . . . **EMTV 7**

ANOTHER BLACK AND WHITE MINSTREL SHOW (Mitchell, George Minstrels).
LP: . . . . **CLP 1460**

BLACK AND WHITE MINSTREL SHOW, THE (Mitchell, George Minstrels).
Tracks: / Weep no more / Camptown races / Little Dolly Daydream / Lily of Laguna / Shadow waltz / When I grow too old to dream / You must have been a beautiful baby / Yes sir, that's my baby / Lulu's back in town / Ramona / I'm sitting on top of the world / My mammy / Poor old Joe / Beautiful dreamer / Polly wolly doodle.
LP: . . . . **EG 2601851**
MC: . . . . **EG 2601854**
LP: . . . . **CLP 1399**

DOWN MEMORY LANE (Mitchell, George Minstrels).
Tracks: / Ring up the curtain / Ring ring the banjo / When the saints go marching in / Chicago / You made me love you / Mr. Gallagher and Mr. Shean / Put your arms around me honey / Down where the Swanee river flows / While strolling through the park one day / In the good old summertime / Sweet Rosie O'Grady / I'll be your sweetheart / Little Annie Rooney / And the band played on / Alabamy bound / Swanee / Is it true what they say about Dixie? / Carolina / Toot Toot Tootsie goodbye / Old ark's a moverin, The / Along the Navajo trail / In ol' Oklahoma / Old Dan Tucker / Country Style / Skip to my Lou / Buffalo gal / Singin' in the rain / Together / No two people / My blue Heaven / Falling in love with love / Maria from Bahia / I yi yi yi yi (I like you very much) / When I love I love / Bandit,The / Cielito lindo / Cuonto le Gusta / I'll si si ya in Bahia / Hard times come again no more / Gentle Annie / Way down upon the Swanee river / Tell me pretty maiden / Put on your tata, little girlie / Hello Hello who's your lady friend / I was a good girl until I met you / In the twi twilight / Two little girls in blue / North and south / You're in Kentucky sure as you're born / Yellow rose of Texas / Georgia on my mind / Stars fell on Alabama / I'm going back to old Nebraska / Dixieland / Carry me back to old Virginny / Lady is a tramp, The / In a shanty in old Shantytown / Ain't we got fun / I'm sittin' high on a hill top / Big rock candy mountain / Side by side / Widdicombe fair / Home on the range / Back in those old Kentucky days / I went down to Virginia / Sonny boy / Goin' to the county fair / Dicky bird hop / Cuckoo waltz / She was one of the early birds / When the red, red robin comes bob, bob, bobbin' along / Too-Whit Too-Whoo / Chee Chee oo Chee / Lets all sing like the birdies sing / Load of hay, A / One, two, button your shoe / You are my sunshine / Bei mir bist du schon / Memories are made of this / Sing a song of Sunbeams / South of the border / Where or when / Frog and the mouse, The / Long long ago / Roamin' in the gloamin' / Let me call you sweetheart / Meet me tonight in dreamland / Pack up your troubles in your old kit bag / Till we meet again / Roses of Picardy.
2LP: . . . . **DL 1096**
MC: . . . . **TCDL 1096**

FROM THE BLACK AND WHITE MINSTREL SHOW (Mitchell, George Minstrels).
Tracks: / Let's all go the music hall (medley) / All aboard the minstrel train (medley) / Spotlight on John (medley) / Around the Emerald Isle (Medley.) / In the moonlight (medley) / Comedy characters (medley) / Ole ole (medley) / Tribute to Al Jolson (medley) / Spotlight on Dai (medley) / Calypso time / In Bonnie Scotland (medley) / Songs from films (medley) / Spotlight on Tony (medley) / Spotlight on Music Hall (various artists).
MC: . . . . **TCIDL 105**
MC: **795 426 4**

HERE COMES THE MINSTRELS (Mitchell, George Minstrels).
LP: . . . . **CLP 3579**

MAGIC OF CHRISTMAS (Mitchell, George Minstrels).
LP: . . . . **SCX 6431**

MAGIC OF THE MINSTRELS (Mitchell, George Minstrels).
LP: . . . . **CLP 1917**

ON STAGE WITH THE GEORGE MITCHELL MINSTRELS (Mitchell, George Minstrels).
LP: . . . . **CLP 1599**

ON TOUR WITH THE GEORGE MITCHELL MINSTRELS (Mitchell, George Minstrels).
LP: . . . . **CLP 1667**

SHOW TIME (Mitchell, George Minstrels).
LP: . . . . **CSD 3642**

SING THE IRVING BERLIN SONGBOOK (Mitchell, George Minstrels).
LP: . . . . **SCX 6267**

SING...RODGERS & HAMMERSTEIN & RODGERS & HART (Mitchell, George Minstrels).
LP: . . . . **MFP 5579**
MC: . . . . **TCMFP 5579**

SPOTLIGHT ON THE GEORGE MITCHELL MINSTRELS (Mitchell, George Minstrels).
LP: . . . . **CLP 1803**

THIS IS THE GEORGE MITCHELL MINSTRELS (Mitchell, George Minstrels).
Tracks: / Everybody's doing it / Let's all go to the music hall / Ole-ole / All aboard the minstrel train / Michael row the boat ashore / Around the Emerald Isle / Calypso time / In bonnie Scotland.
LP: . . . . **THIS 4**

Mitchell, Graeme

CAIRNIE'S CANTER.
LP: . . . . **LAP 102**
MC: . . . . **LAP 102 C**

FINE FETTLE (Mitchell,Graeme & His Scottish Dance Band).
MC: . . . . **LAP 109C**
LP: . . . . **LAP 109**

Mitchell, Grover

TRUCKIN' WITH GROVER MITCHELL (Mitchell, Grover & His Orchestra).
LP: . . . . **ST 277**

Mitchell, Guy

20 GOLDEN PIECES: GUY MITCHELL.
Tracks: / There's a pawnshop on a corner in Pittsburgh, Pennsylvania / Feet up / Heartaches by the number / She wears red feathers / Sparrow in the tree top / Sippin' soda / Rockabilly / Cuff of my shirt / Cloud lucky seven / Chicka boom / Pretty little black-eyed Susie / Side by side / Music, music, music / Roving kind, The / My heart cries for you / My shoes keep walking back to you / Call Rosie on the 'phone / My truly, truly fair / Knee deep in the blues / Singing the blues.
LP: . . . . **BDL 2041**

ALL TIME HITS.
Tracks: / She wears red feathers / Pretty little black eyed Susie / Feet up / Chicka boom / Cloud lucky seven / Cuff of my shirt / Sippin' soda / Side by side / My heart cries for you / Singing the blues / Knee deep in the blues / Rock a billy / Call Rosie on the phone / Heartaches by the number / Pittsburgh Pennsylvania / Music, music, music / Sparrow in the tree top / My truly, truly fair / My shoes keep walking back to you (CD only.) / Roving kind, The (CD only.).
MC: . . . . **TCMFP 5908**

AMERICAN LEGENDS VOL.1 (See under American legends) (Mitchell, Guy/ Frankie Laine/Johnny Ray).

GARDEN IN THE RAIN, A.
Tracks: / My kind of girl / Garden in the rain / Georgy girl / Limehouse blues / Something / Come let me love you tonight / Yesterday / I hadn't anyone till you / Downtown / Smile / I'll see you again.
LP: . . . . **PRCV 129**
MC: . . . . **TC PRCV 129**

GREATEST HITS: GUY MITCHELL.
Tracks: / Look at that girl / Sparrow in the tree top / Chicka boom / Cuff of my shirt / Cloud lucky seven / Rockabilly / She wears red feathers / My truly, truly fair / Feet up / Dime and a dollar / Pretty little black-eyed Susie / Singing the blues.

LP: . . . . SPR 8516
MC: . . . . SPC 8516
MC: 40 32519
MCSET: . . . . WW 6038

GREATEST HITS: GUY MITCHELL.
Tracks: / Singing the blues / Sparrow in the treetop / Pittsburgh Pennsylvania / She wears red feathers / Knee deep in the blues / Christopher Columbus / My heart cries for you / Roving kind / My truly truly fair / Feet up / Belle Belle my liberty Belle / Rock a billy.
LP: . . . . CBS 32519

HIT SINGLES-1950/1960.
Tracks: / Singing the blues / Roving kind / Cuff of my shirt / In the middle of a dark dark night / Unless / Sweet stuff / Chicka boom / Belle Belle my liberty belle / Rock-a-billy / My truly truly fair / That's a why / Feet up / Look at that girl / My shoes keep walking back to you / Sparrow in the tree top / My heart cries for you / Pittsburgh, Pennsylvania / Ninety nine years / Crazy with love / Cloud lucky seven / Same old me / Dime and a dollar / Heartaches by the number / Knee deep in the blues / Pretty little black eyed Suzie / Take me back baby / Slippin' soda / Call Rosie on the phone / She wears red feathers.
2LP: . . . . CBS 22109
MC: 40 22109

PORTRAIT OF A SONG STYLIST.
Tracks: / My heart cries for you / Pennies from Heaven / Pittsburgh Pennsylvania / My dreams are getting better all the time / Heart aches by the number / Under a blanket of blue / She wears red feathers / Everybody loves a lover / Roving kind, The / Singing the blues / My truly, truly fair / I've got a pocketful of dreams / East of the sun (and west of the moon) / Zip a dee doo dah / Symphony of spring / Allegheny moon / Eastside of heaven / Was it rain.
LP: . . . . HARLP 106
MC: . . . . HARMC 106

SINGIN' UP A STORM.
LP: . . . . SLP 432

SINGING THE BLUES.
LP: . . . . SHLP 144
MC: . . . . SHTC 144

SINGING THE BLUES (DITTO).
MCSET: . . . . DTO 10263

Mitchell, Joni

BLUE.
Tracks: / All I want / My old man / Little green / Carey / Blue / California / This flight tonight / River / Case of you, A / Last time I saw Richard, The.
LP: . . . . K 44128
MC: K4 44128

CHALK MARK IN A RAINSTORM.
Tracks: / My secret place / Number one / Lakota / Tea leaf prophecy, The / Dancing clown / Cool water / Beat of black wings, The / Snakes and ladders / Reoccuring dream, The / Bird that whistle, The.
LP: . . . . K 9241721
MC: . . . . K 9241724
LP: . . . . WX 141
MC: . . . . WX 141C
MC: . . . . GEFC 24172
LP: . . . . GEF 24172

CLOUDS.
Tracks: / Tin angel / Chelsea morning / I don't know where I stand / That song about the Midway / Roses blue / Gallery, The / I think I understand / Songs to ageing children come / Fiddle and the drum, The / Both sides now.
LP: . . . . K 77070
LP: . . . . K 44070
MC: 444070

CLOUDS/ BLUE.
MC: K4 64046

COURT AND SPARK.
Tracks: / Court and spark / Help me / Free man in Paris / People's parties / Same situation / Car on a hill / Down to you / Just like this train / Raised on robbery / Trouble child / Twisted.
LP: . . . . K 53002
MC: K4 53002
LP: . . . . SYLA 8756

COURT AND SPARK/ FOR THE ROSES.
MC: 960 276-4

DOG EAT DOG.
Tracks: / Good friends / Fiction / Three great stimulants / Tax free / Smokin' / Dog eat dog / Shiny toys / Ethiopia / Impossible dreamer / Lucky girl.
LP: . . . . K 9240741
MC: 9240744
LP: . . . . GEF 26455

DON JUAN'S RECKLESS DAUGHTER.
Tracks: / Cotton Avenue / Talk to me / Jericho / Paprika plains / Otis and Marlena / Tenth world, The / Dreamland / Don Juan's reckless daughter / Off night backstreet / Silky veils of ardor.
2LP: . . . . K 63003
MCSET: K4 63003

FOR THE ROSES.
Tracks: / Banquet / Cold blue steel and sweet fire / Barangrill / Lesson in survival / Let the wind carry me / For the roses / You see sometime / Electricity / You turn me on, I'm a radio / Blonde in the bleachers / Woman of heart and mind / Judgement of the moon and stars.
LP: . . . . K 53007
MC: K4 53007

HEJIRA.
Tracks: / Coyote / Amelia / Furry sings the blues / Strange boy / Hejira / Song for Sharon / Black crow / Blue motel room / Refuge of the roads.
LP: . . . . K 53053
MC: K4 53053

HISSING OF SUMMER LAWNS, THE.
Tracks: / In France they kiss on Main Street / Jungle line / Edith and the kingpin / Don't interrupt the sorrow / Shades of scarlet conquering / Hissing of summer lawns, The / Boho dance / Harry's house / Sweet bird / Shadows and light.
LP: . . . . K 53018
MC: K4 53018
LP: . . . . SYLA 8763

JONI MITCHELL.
Tracks: / I had a King / Michael from the mountains / Night in the city / Marcie / Nathan La Franeer / Sisotowbell Lane / Dawntreader, The / Pirate of penance / Song to a seagull / Cactus tree.
LP: . . . . K 44051

LADIES OF THE CANYON.
Tracks: / Morning Morgan town / For free / Conversation / Ladies of the canyon / Willy / Arrangement, The / Rainy night house / Priest, The / Blue boy / Big yellow taxi / Woodstock / Circle game.
LP: . . . . K 44085
MC: K4 44085
LP: . . . . RSLP 6376

MILES OF AISLES.
Tracks: / You turn me on, I'm a radio / Big yellow taxi / Rainy night house / Woodstock / Cactus tree / Cold blue steel and sweet fire / Woman of heart and mind / Case of you, A / Circle game / People's parties / All I want / Real good for free / Both sides now / Carey / Last time I saw Richard, The / Jericho / Love or money.
2LP: . . . . K 63001
MCSET: K4 63001
2LP: . . . . SYSP 902

MINGUS.
Tracks: / Happy birthday / God must be a boogie man / Funeral / Chair in the sky / Wolf that lives in Lindsey, The / Is a muggin' / Dry cleaner from Des Moines / Lucky / Goodbye pork pie hat / Sweet sucker dance / Coin in the pocket.
LP: . . . . K 53091

NIGHT RIDE HOME.
LP: . . . . GEF 24302
MC: . . . . GEFC 24302

SHADOWS AND LIGHT.
Tracks: / Introduction / In France they kiss on Main Street / Edith and the kingpin / Coyote / Goodbye pork pie hat / Dry cleaner from Des Moines / Amelia / Pat's solo / Hejira / Black crow / Don's solo / Dreamland / Free man in Paris / Furry sings the blues / Why do fools fall in love? / Shadows and light / God must be a boogie man / Woodstock.
2LP: . . . . K 62030
MC: K4 62030

WILD THINGS RUN FAST.
Tracks: / Chinese cafe / Unchained melody / Wild things run fast / Ladies man / Moon at the window / Solid love / Be cool / Baby I don't care / You dream flat tires / Man to man / Underneath the streetlight / Love.
LP: 9020191
MC: 9020194
LP: . . . . GEF 25102
LP: . . . . GEF 02019
MC: . . . . GEFC 02019

Mitchell, Kevin

FREE AND EASY (Traditional songs mainly from North West Ulster).
LP: 12TS 314

Mitchell, Kim

AKIMBO ALOGO.
Tracks: / Go for soda / That's a man / All we are / Diary for rock 'n' roll man / Love ties / Feel it burn / Lager and ale / Rumour has it / Caroline / Called off.
LP: . . . . BRON 556

ROCKLAND.
Tracks: / Rockland wonderland / Lost lovers found / Rock 'n' roll duty / Tangle of love / Moodstreet / Crossroads, The / Expedition sailor / O mercy Louise / This dream / Great embrace, The.
LP: 781 963-1
MC: 781 963-4

Mitchell, Les

WHISKEY (Mitchell, Les & Country Pride).
LP: . . . . BSS 362

Mitchell, Mark

EIGHTEEN YELLOW ROSES.
Tracks: / Little ole wine drinker me / Spanish eyes / Twelfth of never / He'll have to go / Bunch of thyme / When my blue moon turns to gold again / Behind the footlights / I'm not that good at goodbye / Let's do it right / Could I have this dance? / Story of a starry night / Eighteen yellow roses.
LP: . . . . PHL 444
MC: . . . . CPHL 444

Mitchell, Pat

UILLEANN PIPES.
LP: 12TS 294

Mitchell, Prince

DEVASTATION.
Tracks: / Body shop / I taught her everything she knows / Show must go on / In her own way / This is our song / I can't get used to sleeping by myself / You're gonna come back to love / She was my lady.
LP: . . . . ICH 1004
MC: . . . . ZCICH 1004

LONER.
Tracks: / While the cat's away / Starting from scratch / Come to bed / Can't nobody love you better than me / Never let her down / Nothing hurts like love / You did what you had to do / Loner / She's a party animal.
LP: . . . . ICH 1110
MC: . . . . ICH 1110MC

Mitchell, Red

ALONE TOGETHER (See under Kellaway, Roger) (Kellaway, Roger/Red Mitchell).

BLUES FOR A CRUSHED SOUL.
LP: . . . . SNTF 762

DOGGIN' AROUND (see under "Ellis, Herb") (Mitchell, Red & Herb Ellis).

HOLIDAY.
LP: . . . . PHONT 7548

HOME COOKING (See under Flanagan, Tommy) (Mitchell, Red/Nisse Sandstrom/Tommy Flanagan).

JAM FOR YOUR BREAD.
Tracks: / Jam for your bread / Duff / You go to my head / Where or when / Ornithology / Section blues / East coast outpost / I'll never be the same / Will you still be mine.
LP: . . . . AFF 159

RED MITCHELL QUARTET (Mitchell, Red Quartet).
Tracks: / Sandu / Paul's pal / Out of the blue / Scrapple from the apple.
LP: 1007 538

Mitchell, Roscoe

CONCERT TORONTO 4/5 OCT 1975.
LP: 2009

CONGLIPTIONS.
LP: . . . . N 2

DUETS WITH ANTHONY BRAXTON.
LP: 3016

L.R.G/ THE MAZE/ S II EXAMPLES.
2LP: . . . . N 14/15

MORE CUTOUTS (Mitchell,Roscoe/ Hugh Ragin).
LP: . . . . CECMA 1003

NONAAH.
2LP: . . . . N 9/10

OLD/ QUARTET.
LP: . . . . N 5

ROSCOE MITCHELL SOLO SAXOPHONE CONCERTS.
LP: 2006

SOUND.
LP: . . . . DL 408

Mitchell, Ross

CONTINENTAL (Mitchell, Ross & His Band & Singers).
LP: . . . . DS 077

FLAMINGO.
Tracks: / I'm getting sentimental over you / Lollipops and roses / Winter dreams / Thorn Birds - love theme / Flamingo / I'm not at all in love / She was the one / Isn't this a lovely day / Le conga / Moonlighting / Always there / Spanish Gypsy dance / Bye bye love.
LP: . . . . DL 1001
MC: . . . . DLC 1001

LET'S TEACH THE WORLD TO DANCE (Mitchell, Ross - Band And Singers).
LP: . . . . DS 070

MERRY CHRISTMAS (Mitchell, Ross & His Band & Singers).
LP: . . . . DL 1006
MC: . . . . DLC 1006

RAINBOW COLLECTION, THE.
2LP: . . . . DL 1004
MCSET: . . . . DLC 1004

STAR REQUESTS (Mitchell, Ross & His Band & Singers).
Tracks: / I won't dance / Tap your troubles away / Desert song, The / Kisses in the dark / Fascination / Wish upon a star / Jealousy / Star / Tea for two / Brazil / Shall we dance? / All I ask of you / I won't send roses / Wake up little Susie.
LP: . . . . DL 1003
MC: . . . . DLC 1003

ZING.
Tracks: / Zing went the strings of my heart / Top hat / Rainbow connection / With you i'm born again / Gal in galico / Slow boat to china / Just an old fashioned girl / Chattanooga choo choo / It's cha cha / Peanut vendor / Breakin' down / Breeze and I / Moving south / Opus 1.
LP: . . . . DS 073

ZING II (Mitchell, Ross & His Band & Singers).
Tracks: / Baubles, bangles and beads / Dancing in the dark / London by night / Where is your heart (From 'Moulin Rouge') / Swingin' down the lane / One / Rain in Spain, The / Wrap your troubles in dreams / Sway / Zambesi / Quand tu chantes / If I loved you / With a song in my heart / Trickle trickle.
LP: . . . . DL 1002
MC: . . . . DLC 1002

Mitchell, Sam

BOTTLENECK AND SLIDE GUITAR.
LP: . . . . SNKF 121
LP: . . . . KM 129

FOLLOW YOU DOWN.
LP: . . . . SNKF 146

Mitchell, Sheila

JUDGEMENT DAY (See also Penelope Lively).

Mitchell, Tom

TOM MITCHELL.
LP: . . . . PH 1027

Mitchell, Warren

THOUGHTS OF CHAIRMAN ALF.
LP: . . . . K 56425

Mitchell, Whitey

WHITEY MITCHELL SEXTETTE (Mitchell, Whitey Sextette).
LP: . . . . FS 72

Mitchell, Willie

SPARKLE.
Tracks: / Sparkle / Reachin' out / Honey bear / Midnight rhapsody / Give the world more love / Sugar candy / Expressions / Happy hour.
LP: C5-517
MC: C5K-517

THAT DRIVING BEAT.
Tracks: / That driving beat / 20-75 / Percolatin' / Champion, The / Ooh baby you turn me on / Mercy / 30-60-90 / Young people / Everything is gonna be alright / Bad eye / Buster Browne / Soul serenade / At the woodchoppers ball / Up-hard / Bum daddy / Crawl, The.
LP: . . . . HIUKLP 408

Mitchenko, Edvard

RUSSIAN ACCORDEON MUSIC.
MC: . . . . M 00204

Mitchum, Robert

CALYPSO.
Tracks: / Jean and Dinah / From a logical point of view / Not me / What is this generation coming to / Tic tic tic / Beauty is only skin deep / I learn a merengue, mama / Take me down to lover's row / Mama look a boo boo / Coconut water / Matilda, Matilda / They dance all night.
LP: . . . . PM 1547791

Mitford Girls

MITFORD GIRLS (London Cast Album) (Various artists).
LP: 635 908 8

Mitford, Nancy

LOVE IN A COLD CLIMATE.
MCSET: . . . . CAB 295

Mitsouko, Rita

MARC & ROBERT.
LP: . . . . V 2572
MC: . . . . TCV 2572

NO COMPRENDO, THE.
Tracks: / Les histoires d'a / Andy / C'est comme ca / Vol de nuit / Someone to love / Marcia Baila / Stupid anyway / Un soir, un chien / Bad days / Nuit d'ivresse.
LP: V 2451
MC: TCV 2451

Mitterhof, Barry

MANDOLIN MUSIC.
LP: FF 472

Mittoo, Jackie

LET THE SUN SHINE (see under Ryvers, Debie) (Mittoo, Jackie/Ryvers, Debie).

ORIGINAL JACKIE MITTOO, THE.
LP: TDWD 5

YOU BRING THE SUN OUT (See under Kay, Janet) (Kay, Janet/Jackie Mittoo).

Mix Blood

SKAVILLE.
LP: JSLP 0022

Mix Up & Scandal

MIX UP AND SCANDAL (Various artists).
LP: CFR 8003

Mixdown...

MIXDOWN VOL.1 (See Sleeping Bag mixtown vol.1) (Various artists).

Mixing Lab

SHOWCASE, VOL. 1 (Scientific master mix) (Various artists).
LP: MLLP 001
MC: MLC 001

SHOWCASE VOL. 2 (Master mix) (Various artists).
LP: MLLP 003
MC: MLC 003

Miyano, Hiroki

HOTEL CALIFORNIA (See under Klugh, Earl) (Klugh, Earl & Hiroki Miyano).

Mizarolli, John

GIGGING FOR THE ANGELS.
LP: JABALP 1

MESSAGE FROM THE 5TH STONE.
Tracks: / No magic love / Granny did it / Ain't nobody gonna bring me down / Message from the 5th stone / Lost your love my love / Wake up and live / Is mamma the president / Menopause / Mama never told you.
LP: CAL 142

Mizell, Hank

JUNGLE ROCK.
Tracks: / Jungle rock / Burning eyes.
MC: ZCCH 5000

M.K.P.A.

WORLD WAS A GHETTO (THE WORLD ACCORDING TO).
LP: FW 880520/P

Mladen Franko..

PIANO ON THE ROAD (Mladen Franko Group).
LP: ISST 181

Mnemonists

BELLOWING ROOM.
LP: RCC 27

Mo Better Blues (film)

MO BETTER BLUES (Various artists).
Tracks: / Harlem blues: *Various artists* / Say hey: *Various artists* / Knocked out the box: *Various artists*/ Again never: *Various artists* / Pop top 40: *Various artists* / Mo' better blues: *Various artists* / Beneath the underdog: *Various artists* / Jazz thing: *Various artists*.
LP: 4671601
MC: 4671604

Moas

SPAZOUT.
LP: FN 76

Mob

LET THE TRIBE INCREASE.
LP: MAD 4

LIVE AT LMC (Mob/Apostles).
MC: CFC 015
LP: CFC 002

Mobley, Hank

ANOTHER WORKOUT.
Tracks: / Out of Joe's bag / I should care / Gettin' and jettin' / Hank's other soul / Hello young lovers / Three coins in the fountain.
LP: BST 84431
MC: 4BN 84431

BREAKTHROUGH (See Under Walton, Cedar) (Mobley, Hank & Cedar Walton).

FAR AWAY LANDS.
Tracks: / Dab of this and that / Far away lands / No argument / Hippity hop, The / Bossa for baby / Soul time.
LP: BST 84425

HIGH VOLTAGE.
Tracks: / High voltage / Two and one / No more goodbyes / Advance notice / Bossa deluxe / Flirty gerty.
LP: BST 84273

MONDAY NIGHT AT BIRDLAND.
LP: VJD 565

NO ROOM FOR SQUARES.
Tracks: / No room for squares / Three way split / Me 'n' you / Carolyn / No room for squares (alt. take) (CD only.) / Comin' back (CD only.) / Carolyn (alt. take) (CD only.) / Syrup and biscuits (CD only.) / Up a step (LP only.) / Old world, new imports (LP only.).
LP: B1 84149

PECKIN' TIME.
Tracks: / High and flighty / High and flighty (alternate take) / Speak low / Speak low (alternate take) / Peckin' time / Stretchin' out / Stretchin' out (alt. take) / Git go blues.
LP: B1 81574
LP: 781 574 1

SOUL STATION.
Tracks: / Remember / This I dig of you / Dig dis / Split feelin's / Soul station / If I should lose you.
LP: BLJ 84031

STRAIGHT NO FILTER.
Tracks: / Straight no filter / Chain reaction / Soft impression / Third time around (Not on CD.) / Hank's waltz (Not on CD.) / Feeling's good, The / Old world, new imports (CD only.) / Up a step (CD only.) / East of the village (CD only.) / Yes indeed (CD only.) / Good life (CD only.).
LP: BST 84435

TURNAROUND.
Tracks: / Pat 'n' chat / Third time around (CD only.) / Hank's waltz (CD only.) / Turn around / Straight ahead / My sin / East of the village (LP only.) / Good life (LP only.).
LP: B1 84186
LP: 784 186 1

WORKOUT.
Tracks: / Workout / Uh huh / Smokin' / Best things in life are free, The / Greasin' easy / Three coins in the fountain.
LP: BST 84080
LP: B1 84080
LP: 784 080 1

Moby Dick (bk)

MOBY DICK (see Melville, Herman) (Heston, Charlton).

Moby Grape

20 GRANITE CREEK.
Tracks: / Gypsy wedding / I'm the kind of man that baby you can't trust / About time / Goin' down to Texas / Road to the sun / Apocalypse / Chinese song / Roundhouse blues / Ode to the man at the end of the bar / Wild oats moan / Horse out in the rain.
LP: ED 176
MC: CED 176

LIVE GRAPE.
LP: 400 335

MOBY GRAPE.
Tracks: / Hey Grandma / Mr. Blues / Fall on you / 8.05 / Come in the morning / Omaha / Naked, if I want to / Someday / Ain't no use / Sitting by the window / Changes / Lazy me / Indifference.
LP: ED 137

MURDER IN MY HEART.
Tracks: / Murder in my heart for the judge / Can't be so bad / Motorcycle Irene / Three four / Rose coloured eyes / Bitter wind / I am not willing / It's a beautiful day today / If you can't learn from my mistakes / What's to choose / Seeing / Changes circles spinning / Right before my eyes.
LP: ED 171

Mock Turtles

87-90.
LP: ILLUSION 019
MC: ILLCASS 019

TURTLE SOUP.
LP: ILLUSION 012
MC: ILLCASS 012

TWO SIDES.
MC: SRNMC 31
LP: SRNLP 31

M.O.D.

GROSS MISCONDUCT.
LP: NUK 133
MC: ZCNUK 133
LP: N 0133 1
MC: N 0133 4

MODS MAYDAY 79 (Various artists).
Tracks: / Time for action: *Secret Affair* / Let your heart dance: *Secret Affair* / Don't throw your life away: *Beggar* / Hanging in the balance: *Small Hours* / Tonight's the night: *Mods* / Let me be the one: *Mods*/ B-a-b-y baby love: *Squire* / Midnight to six: *Small Hours* / Broadway show: *Beggar* / All night: *Beggar*/ Love only me: *Mods* / Walking down the King's Road: *Squire* / Live without her love: *Squire* / I'm not free: *Secret Affair* / End of the night: *Small Hours*.
LP: DOJOLP 5

SURFIN' M.O.D. (ALBUM).
LP: CAROL 1359

UPPERS ON THE SOUTH DOWN (Various artists).
LP: UPPA 1

U.S.A. FOR M.O.D..
LP: CAROL 1344
LP: N 0089
LP: NUK 089
MC: ZCNUK 089
MC: N 0090

Models

ALPHABRAVO, ETC.
Tracks: / 21 Hz / Strategic air command / Two people per sq KM / Pull the pin / Twice removed / Pate pedestrian / Kissing 'round corners / All stop / Uncontrollable boy / Young rodents / Hans stand / Happy birthday IBM.
LP: AMLH 68529

LOCAL OR GENERAL.
Tracks: / Bantam lad / Local or general.
LP: AMLH 68536

OUT OF MIND OUT OF SIGHT.
Tracks: / Out of mind out of sight / Big on love / Ringing like a bell / Stormy tonight / These blues / Cold fever / Sooner in heaven / Seeing is believing / Barbados / King of kings / Down in the garden / Seeing is (Extra track on 12"version only.).
LP: 9241001
MC: 9241004

Modern Art

DIMENSION OF NOISE.
MC: COLOR 8

STEREOLAND.
LP: COLOR 3

Modern English

AFTER THE SNOW.
Tracks: / I melt with you / Tables turning / Carry me down.
LP: CAD 206
MC: CADC 206

MESH AND LACE.
Tracks: / Sixteen days / Just a thought / Move in light / Grief / Token man, The / Viable commercial, A / Black houses / Dance of devotion (love song).
LP: CAD 105

RICOCHET DAYS.
LP: CAD 402
MC: CADC 402

STOP START.
Tracks: / Border, The / Ink and paper / Night train / I don't know the answer / Love breaks down / Breaking away / Greatest show, The / Love forever / Start stop - stop start.
LP: 925343 1
MC: 925343 4

Modern Eon

FICTION TALES.
LP: DID 11
MC: DIDC 11

Modern Girl

MODERN GIRL SHE IS MINE (Various artists).
LP: GALP 008

Modern heroes

MODERN HEROES (Various artists).
LP: TVA 1
MC: TVC 1

Modern Jazz Quartet

ART OF MODERN JAZZ QUARTET (Atlantic Years).
Tracks: / Golden striker, The / Cortege / Bags groove / Cylinder, The / England's Carol / Lonely woman / Today (home) / Django / Sketch / Bluesology / Spanish steps / Concorde / Summertime / Fun / Ralph's new blues.
LP: K 60041

AT THE MUSIC INN WITH SONNY ROLLINS.
Tracks: / Oh Bess, oh where's my Bess / Fugue for Music Inn / Two degrees East, three degrees West / Serenade / Fun / Sun dance / Man that got away, The / Morning in Paris / God rest ye merry gentlemen (variation no. 1).
LP: K 30026

AT THE OPERA HOUSE (Modern Jazz Quartet & Oscar Peterson Trio).
Tracks: / Now's the time / Round midnight / D & E blues / Should I love you? / Big fat mama / Indiana / Joy spring / Elevation.
LP: 823 092-1

BEST OF MODERN JAZZ QUARTET, THE.
Tracks: / Valeria / Le cannet / Nature boy / Watergate blues / Connie's blues / Reunion blues / Echoes.
LP: PEM 003
MC: PEMC 003

BLUES ON BACH.
Tracks: / Regret / Blues in B flat / Rise up in the morning / Blues in A minor / Precious joy / Blues in C minor / Don't stop this train blues in H / Tears from the children.
LP: K 50039

COLLECTION: MODERN JAZZ QUARTET.
Tracks: / One bass hit / Queen's fancy, The / Now's the time / Django / D & E blues / Autumn in New York / Round about midnight / Delaunay's Dilemma / But not for me / Milano / La ronde suite (piano) / La ronde suite (bass) / La ronde suite (vibes) / La ronde suite (drums).
MC: DVMC 2043

COMEDY.
Tracks: / Spanish steps / Columbine / Pulcinella / Pierrot / La cantarice / Harlequin / Piazza navona.
LP: K 50729

CONCORDE.
Tracks: / Ralph's new blues / All of you / I'll remember April / Gershwin melodies / Softly as in a morning sunrise / Concorde.
LP: PR 7005
MC: PRC 7005

ECHOES.
Tracks: / That Slavic smile / Echoes / Watergate blues / Hornpipe / Connie's blues / Sacha's march.
LP: 2312 142
MC: K12 142

FOR ELLINGTON.
Tracks: / For Ellington / Jack the bear / Prelude to a kiss / It don't mean a thing / Koko / Maestro E.K.E. / Sepia panorama / Rockin' in rhythm.
LP: 790926 1
MC: 790926 4

IN MEMORIAM.
Tracks: / In memoriam / First movement / Second movement / Jazz ostinato / Adagio from the guitar concerto / Converto de aranjuez.
LP: K 59650

LAST CONCERT, THE.
Tracks: / Softly as in a morning sunrise / Cylinder, The / Summertime / Trav'lin blues in a minor / One never knows / Bag's groove / Confirmation / Round midnight / Night in Tunisia / Golden striker, The / Skating in central park / Django / What's new.
LP: K 60098

LESTER MEETS MILES (MJQ & Jack Teagarden All Stars).
LP: UJ 14

LIVE AT DONAUSCHINGEN, 1957, AND SAN REMO, 1958.
LP: INGO 12

LONELY WOMAN.
Tracks: / Lonely woman / Animal dance / New York / Belkis / Why are you blue / Fugato / Lamb, leopard / Trieste.
LP: K 50723

LONGING FOR THE CONTINENT.
Tracks: / Animal dance / Django / England's carol / Bluesology / Bag's groove / Sketch 3 / Ambiquite / Midsummer.
MC: MC 7678

MJQ.
LP: CJZ LP 6
MC: CJZ MC 6

MODERN JAZZ QUARTET (Compact/ Walkman Jazz).
Tracks: / Golden striker, The / On Green Dolphin Street / D & E / I'll remember April / Cortege / Now's the time / J.B. blues / Reunion blues / Round midnight / Three windows.
MC: 833 290-4

MODERN JAZZ QUARTET.
Tracks: / Django / Autumn in New York / Queen's fancy, The / But not for me / One bass hit / Milano / Delaunay's dilemma / Nows the time / D & E blues / Round about midnight.
LP: LPJT 56
LP: SM 3785
MC: MC 3785

MODERN JAZZ QUARTET (PRESTIGE).
Tracks: / Concorde / Vendome / Milano / Gershwin medley / La ronde / Django / All the things you are / One bass hit / Autumn in New York / Queens fancy / I'll remember April / Softly as in a morning's sunrise / Delauney's dilemma / But not

for me / La ronde suite / All of you / Rose of the Rio Grande / Ralph's new blues.
LP: PR 24005

MORE FROM THE LAST CONCERT.
Tracks: / Really true blues / Tears from the children / Blues in H / England's carol / Jasmine tree, The / In memoriam.
LP: K 50407

SAIT ON JAMAIS.
Tracks: / Golden striker, The / One never knows / Rose true / Cortege / Venice / Three windows.
LP: K 50231

SHERIFF, THE.
Tracks: / Natural affection / Donnie's theme / In a crowd / Carnival / Bachianas Brasilieras / Mean to me / Sheriff.
LP: K 40285

THREE WINDOWS.
Tracks: / Three windows / Kansas City breaks / Encounter in Cagnes / Django / Day in Dubrovnik, A (first movement: afternoon) / Day in Dubrovnik, A (second movement: night) / Day in Dubrovnik, A (third movement: morning).
LP: 254833 1
MC: 254833 4

TOGETHER AGAIN.
LP: 230 9244
MC: K 8244

TOPSY THIS ONE'S FOR BASIE.
Tracks: / Reunion blues / Nature boy / Topsy / D and E / Valeria / Milano / Le cannet.
LP: 2310917
MC: K 10917

UNDER THE JASMINE TREE.
Tracks: / Blue necklace / Three little feelings (parts 1, 2 and 3) / Exposure / Jasmine tree, The.
LP: SAPCOR 4
MC: TCSAPCOR 4

Modern Jazz Sextet

MODERN JAZZ SEXTET.
Tracks: / Tour de force / Dizzy meets Sonny / Old folks / What's new / How deep is the ocean / Mean to me / Blues for bird.
LP: 823 091-1

Modern Jazz Society

CONCERT OF CONTEMPORARY MUSIC.
LP: 823 089-1

Modern Lovers

MODERN LOVERS LIVE.
Tracks: / I'm a little airplane / Hey there little insect / Egyptian reggae / Ice cream man / I'm a little dinosaur / My little kookenhaken / South American folk song / New England, A / Morning of our lives, The.
LP: BSERK 12
LP: BZ 0055
MC: BZCA 0055

MODERN LOVERS, THE.
Tracks: / Roadrunner / Astral plane / Old world / Pablo Picasso / I'm straight / She cracked / Hospital / Someone I care about / Girlfriend / Modern world.
LP: BZ 0050
MC: BZCA 050

ORIGINAL MODERN LOVERS.
LP: 400 310
LP: LBOM 1

ROCK 'N' ROLL WITH THE MODERN LOVERS.
Tracks: / Sweeping wind, The / Ice cream man / Rockin' rockin' leprechauns / Summer morning / Afternoon / Fly into the mystery / South American folk song / Roller coaster by the sea / Dodge Veg-O-matic / Egyptian reggae / Coomyah / Wheels on the bus, The / Angels watching over me.
LP: BSERK 9
LP: BZ 0053
MC: BZCA 0053

Modern Man

CONCRETE SCHEME.
Tracks: / Good time ideology / Wonderful world segue / Cosmetics / All the little idiots / Little white boys / Wastelands / I think you better go home / Body music / I couldn't stop / Advance / War.
LP: MAMLP 5001

Modern Rocketry

HOMOSEXUALITY.
LP: 20052

Modern Romance

ADVENTURES IN CLUBLAND.
Tracks: / Bring on the Funkateers / Nothing ever goes the way you plan / Queen of the rapping scene / Everybody salsa / Moose on the loose / Salsa rhapsody / Ay ay ay ay moosey / We've got them running / I stand alone / I can't get enough / Stand up.
LP: K 58407

MOVE ON.
Tracks: / Move on / Wasting away / Blame my jealousy / Take another look / Burn it / That's what friends are for / Keep a candle burning / That's entertainment / I'll always remember you.
LP: PL 70386
MC: PK 70386

PARTY TONIGHT.
Tracks: / Best years of our lives / Ay ay ay ay moosey / Everybody salsa / Don't stop that crazy rhythm / High life / Band of gold / Queen of the rapping scene / Nothing ever goes the way you plan / Good friday / Salsa rhapsody / Cherry pink and apple blossom white / Moose on the loose / Just my imagination / Love letters / Walking in the rain.
LP: RONLP 3
MC: CRON 3

TRICK OF THE LIGHT.
Tracks: / High life / Don't stop that crazy rhythm / Best years of our lives / Good feelings / Walking in the rain / Let's go / Cherry pink and apple blossom white / After all this time / She's so fine / Leave me on my own.
LP: WEAX 0127

Modern Talking

READY FOR ROMANCE.
Tracks: / Atlantis is calling / Cheri cheri lady / Keep love alive / Hey you / Angie's heart / Only love can break a heart / Brother Louie / Just we two / Lady Lai / Doctor for my heart / Save me, don't break me.
LP: PL 71133
MC: PK 71133

Modern Times (film)

MODERN TIMES (Film soundtrack-Charlie Chaplin) (Various artists).
LP: IC 064 82892
LP: LN 10288

Modernaires

1946-47.
LP: CLP 77

Modernique

MODERNIQUE.
Tracks: / Tossin' 'n turnin' / One hot ticket / I believe in love / Call it what you want / Linda, my love / Take a risk on love / Falling in love / From friends to lovers / You can call on me.
LP: K 925633 1
MC: K 925633 4

Moderns (film)

MODERNS, THE (Original Soundtrack) (Isham, Mark).
Tracks: / Les modernes / Cafe Selavy / Paris la nuit / Really the blues / Madame Valentin / Dada je suis / Parlez-moi d'amour / La valse moderne / Les peintres / Death of Irving Fagelman / Je ne veux pas de tes chocolats / Parlez-moi d'amour / Selavy.
LP: V 2530
MC: TCV 2530

Modesty Blaise

MODESTY BLAISE-I HAD A DATE WITH LADY JANET (Peter O' Donnell) (Thaw, John).
MC: PTB 611

Modesty Kills

MODESTY KILLS (Various artists).
LP: AVA 001

Mo-Dettes

STORY SO FAR, THE.
Tracks: / Fandango / Satisfy / Dark park creeping / Kray twins / Paint it black / White mouse disco / Bedtime stories / Masochistic opposite / Foolish girl / Norman / Sparrow / Mi Lord.
LP: SML 1120
MC: KSCM 1120

Moebius & Beerbohm

DOUBLE CUT.
LP: SKY 019

Moebius (film)

BLUE MOON (1986 film soundtrack).
LP: SKY 109

Moebius, Plank &

ZERO SET.
LP: SKY 85

Moeran (composer)

SYMPHONY IN G MINOR Overture for a masque (Ulster Orchestra).
LP: ABRD 1272
MC: ABTD 1272

THREE RHAPSODIES In the mountain country (Ulster Orchestra).
LP: ABRD 1327
MC: ABTD 1327

Moerlen, Pierre

DOWNWIND (Moerlen, Pierre Gong).
LP: PIPLP 025
MC: PIPMC 025

PIERRE MOERLENS' GONG.
Tracks: / Downwind / Mandrake / Golden dilemma / Soli / Drum solo / Esnuria / Crosscurrents.
LP: SPART 1130
LP: PIPLP 019
MC: PIPMC 019

TIME IS THE KEY.
LP: SPART 1105
LP: PIPLP 018
MC: PIPMC 018

Moev

DUSK AND DESIRE.
LP: NTL 30001

YEAH WHATEVER.
LP: NTL 30020
LP: NET 003

Moffat, Peter

ZOE'S SONG.
Tracks: / Rocinante / Destination / Big stuff / Zoe's song / Poem / Gathering, The.
LP: PL 83020

Moffat, Stuart

OCTOBER ISLAND.
LP: DAM 007

Moffatt, Hugh

LOVING YOU.
Tracks: / When you held me in your arms / Mama Rita / Old flames can't hold a candle to you / Words at twenty paces / Slow moving freight train / No stranger to the blues / Loving you / Tomorrow is a long time / Carolina star / Jack and Lucy / Roll with weather.
LP: PH 1111
MC: PH 1111C

TROUBADOUR.
Tracks: / Way love is, The / Rose of my heart / I'll leave the rest to you / Somewhere in Kansas / How could I love her so much / Roses, love and promises / Hard times come again no more / Praise the Lord and send me the money / Devil took the rest, The / Old songs, The / For Mary.
LP: BD 500
MC: BD 500MC
LP: PH 1127
MC: PH 1127C

Moffatt, Katy

CHILD BRIDE.
Tracks: / Child bride / In a moment / Lonely avenue / Look out it must be love / Playin' fool / We ran / You better move on / Anna / Settin' the woods on fire.
LP: HLD 009
MC: HLD 009C
LP: PH 1133

WALKIN' ON THE MOON.
Tracks: / Walkin' on the moon / I'm sorry darlin' / If anything comes to mind / Papacita (Mama Rita) / Mr. Banker / Borderline / Fire in your eyes / I'll take the blame / Hard time on Easy street / I know the difference now.
LP: PH 1128
MC: PH 1128C

Moffet, Billy

MUSIC FOR GIRLS (Moffet, Billy Playboy Club).
LP: 572 911 62

Moffett, Charles

BEAUTY WITHIN.
Tracks: / Love never fails / Love never fails / Angela / My little one / Beauty within / Message, The / Eastwood.
LP: B1 91650
LP: 791 650 1

BLASTER MASTER (See under Maslak, Keshavan) (Moffett, Charles & Keshavan Maslak).

NET MAN.
Tracks: / Mizzom / Swing bass / One left over / Mona Lisa / Dance, The / Nett man / Softly as in a morning sunrise / For you.
LP: BLJ 46993

Moffitt, Matt

AS LITTLE AS A LOOK.
Tracks: / Heathen kind / By as little as a look / Miss this night / Thursday / Overland / All that stuff / Save your worry / B.b's / Fever pitch / Ocean chimes / Light me up.
LP: CBS 26746
MC: 40 26746

Moffitt, Peter

RIVERDANCE.
Tracks: / Candle power / Talk talk talk talk / Birds / Al dente / When a man loves a woman / Toast / Heartweb / Rainforest (for Nina) / Riverdance / Wise and foolish virgins.
LP: PL 83059
MC: PK 83059

Moffs

LABYRINTH.
LP: CGAS 811

Mofungo

WORK.
LP: SST 240
MC: SSTC 240

Mohamed

DIWANNA EAST.
Tracks: / Ham safar / Delbar / Forget everything / Mara / Didor / Love is the answer / Ma meham / Pajam.
LP: FUNFACL 1914

Mohawk, Essra

ESSRA MOHAWK.
LP: CREST 24

Moho Pack

FLESH TO THE DREAM.
Tracks: / Let us touch / Be with me / Procession of ghosts, A / One eternal moment / New love / Sacred and scared / We are one / Reign / Mercenaries.
LP: AFTER 5

Mohyeddin, Zia

FABLES OF INDIA.
MC: 1168

Mojo Jazzin' Five

MOJO JAZZIN FIVE.
LP: SOS 1086

Mojos

WORKING.
Tracks: / Forever / They say / Everything's alright / Give your lovin' to me / Why not tonight / Don't do it anymore / Seven daffodils / Nothin' at all / I got my Mojo working / One who really loves you, The / Nobody but me / Comin' on to cry / That's the way it goes / Wait a minute / Wonder if she knows.
LP: ED 110

Mojos, Dee

IN THE SOOP.
LP: RVC 701

Mokhali, Johnny

SOUND OF FREEDOM, THE.
Tracks: / O wa mpelaetsa - I doubt you / Luki / Mafoka a bofelo - Last words / Tsa lerato - love matters / Ke na le Jesu - I've got Jesus / Setlhare ke sefe - What is the remedy / Semphete - Don't pass me / Ramatlantlane / Lerato ka mogala - Love on the telephone / Rre o kae - Where is my father / Ba tlogeleng - Leave them / Sesa feleng - That doesn't end / Go siame - It's alright / Mosala gae - You remain at home / Ngwanaka - my child / Go sa itse - Not to know.
MC: ELITE 011 MC

Moldgreen Junior Folk

LAST SONGS TOGETHER (Moldgreen Junior Folk Choir).
LP: LK/LP/6380

Mole, Miff

JAZZ CLASSICS IN DIGITAL STEREO (see under Nichols, Red) (Mole, Miff & Red Nichols).

MIFF MOLE'S MOLERS(1927).
Tracks: / Alexander's ragtime band / Some sweet day / Hurricane / Davenport blues / Hot time in the old town tonight, A / Darktown strutters' ball / After you've gone / I ain't got nobody / One sweet letter from you / Fifty million Frenchmen can't be wrong / Imagination / Feeling no pain / Original dixieland one-step / My gal Sal / Honolulu blues / New twister, The.
LP: SH 503
MC: TC SH 503
LP: S 1295

MIFF MOLE'S MOLERS(1928-30) (Mole, Miff, Molers).
LP: S 1297

MUGGSY SPANIER, MIFF MOLE & LOU MCGARITY (See under Spanier, Muggsy) (Mole, Miff/ Muggsy Spanier/ Lou McGarity).

WORLD JAM SESSION BAND (1944).
LP: J 105

Moliere

MOLIERE (Film Soundtrack) (Various artists).
LP: HM 1020

Molinari, John

ACCORDION CONCERT.
Tracks: / Rumanian rhapsody / Hungarian fantasy / Dance of the hours / Rhapsody 2 in C minor / Bacchanale / Gypsy airs / Finlandia / Poet and peasant / Semiramide overture.
LP: ALP 102

ACCORDION SOLOS NO.5.

Tracks: / Carioca / 12th Street rag / Hora staccato / Cuckoo waltz / Dizzy fingers / Flight of the bumble bee / Bumble boogie / Beer barrel polka / St. Louis blues / Canadian capers / Dark eyes / Nola / Jealousie / Brazil.
LP: . . . . ALP 105

ACCORDION VARIETY CONCERT.
Tracks: / Loco loco samba / Snow train shuffle / Waltz accordia / Siboney / La danza / Scherzo in A minor / Polka dot polka / Concert overture / Shopin valse / Mexican hat dance.
LP: . . . . ALP 104

Molineux, John

DOUCE AMERE: BITTER SWEET.
LP: . . . . CCF 1

Moll Flanders

MOLL FLANDERS (see under Defoe, Daniel) (Leigh-Hunt, Barbara).

Moll, Philip

VIENNESE TALES (see under Berlin Soloists) (Moll, Philip/Berlin Soloists/ Elisabeth Leonskaja).

Moller, Peter

RINGSIDE MAISIE (Moller, Peter/ Randy Hutton).
LP: . . . . ONARI 005

Molloy, Matt

CONTENTMENT IS WEALTH (Molloy, Matt & Sean Keane).
LP: . . . . SIF 1058
MC: . . . . CSIF 1058

HEATHERY BREEZE.
LP: 2904 018
LP: . . . . SHAN 9064

MATT MOLLOY.
LP: . . . . LUN 004

MOLLOY, BRADY, PEOPLES (See under Brady, Paul) (Molloy, Matt/ Paul Brady/ Tommy Peoples).

STONY STEPS.
Tracks: / McFadden's favourite / Boys of the town / City of Savannah / Primrose lass mullinger races / Parting of friends / Stony steps/Michael Dwyers's favourite / Mrs. Kenny's barndance / Paddy Murphy's wife / Jig of slurs, The / O Rathaille's grave / Miss Mcguiness/Reel of mullinavat / Frank Roche's favourite / Johnny 'Watt' Henry's favourite / Gravel walk / Slip jig.
MC: 4CCF 18
LP: . . . . CCF 18

Molly Hatchet

BEATIN' THE ODDS.
Tracks: / Beatin' the odds / Double talker / Rambler / Sailor / Dead and gone / Few and far between / Penthouse pauper / Get her back.
LP: . . . . EPC 84471
MC: 40 84471
LP: 32746

DEED IS DONE, THE.
Tracks: / Satisfied man / Backstabber / She does she does / Intro piece / Stone in your heart / Man on the run / Good smoke and whiskey / Heartbreak radio / I ain't got you / Straight shooter / Song for the children.
LP: . . . . EPC 26213
MC: 40 26213

DOUBLE TROUBLE LIVE.
Tracks: / Whisky man / Bounty hunter / Gator country / Flirtin with disaster / Stone in your heart / Satisfied man / Bloody reunion / Boogie no more / Freebird / Walk on the side of the angels / Walk with you / Dreams I'll never see / Edge of sundown / Fall of the peacemakers / Beatin' the odds.
2LP: . . . . EPC 88670
MCSET: 40 88670

FLIRTING WITH DISASTER.
Tracks: / Whiskey man / It's all over now / One man's pleasure / Jukin' city / Boogie no more / Flirtin' with disaster / Good rockin' / Gunsmoke / Long time / Let the good times roll.
LP: . . . . EPC 83791

MOLLY HATCHET.
Tracks: / Bounty hunter / Gator country / Big apple / Creeper / Price you pay / Dreams I'll never see / I'll be running / Cheatin' woman / Trust your old friend.
LP: . . . . EPC 83250

NO GUTS NO GLORY.
Tracks: / What does it matter / Ain't even close / Sweet dixie / Fall of the peacemakers / What's it gonna take / Kinda like love / Under the gun / On the prowl / Both sides.
LP: . . . . EPC 32718
MC: 40 32718
LP: . . . . EPC 25244
MC: 40 25244

TAKE NO PRISONERS.
Tracks: / Bloody reunion / Respect me in the morning / Long tall Sally / Loss of control / All mine / Lady luck / Power play / Don't mess around / Don't leave me lonely / Dead giveaway.
LP: . . . . EPC 85296
MC: 40 85296

Molly Maguires

BEST OF IRISH DRINKING SONGS.
LP: . . . . UNKNOWN

Molly Maguires (film)

MOLLY MAGUIRES (Film soundtrack) (Various artists).
Tracks: / Theme from the Molly Maguires: *Various artists* / Molly's strike: *Various artists* / Main title: *Various artists* / Fiddle and fife: *Various artists* / Work montage: *Various artists* / Jamie and Mary (the hills of yesterday): *Various artists* / Room and board (theme from the Molly Maguires): *Various artists* / Hills of yesterday: *Various artists* / Penny whistle jig: *Various artists* / Sandwiches and tea: *Various artists* / Trip to town: *Various artists* / Molly's strike again: *Various artists* / Brew with the boys: *Various artists*/ Suit for Grandpa: *Various artists* / End: *Various artists*.
LP: 255065.1
LP: . . . . SPFL 259

Moloney, Mick

AH-SURLEY (see Cahill, Eddie) (Moloney, Mick and Eddie Cahill).

MICK MOLONEY FEATURING....
LP: . . . . SHAN 84001

MICK MOLONEY WITH EUGENE O'DONNELL (Moloney, Mick & Eugene O'Donnell).
LP: . . . . SIF 1010
MC: . . . . CSIF 1010

STRINGS ATTACHED.
LP: . . . . SIF 1027
MC: . . . . CSIF 1027

THERE WERE ROSES.
LP: . . . . SIF 1057
MC: . . . . CSIF 1057

UNCOMMON BONDS (Moloney, Mick & Eugene O'Donnell).
LP: . . . . SIF 1053
MC: . . . . CSIF 1053

Moloney, Peter

LOAD OF MOLONEY, A.
LP: . . . . BB 00 02

Mom & Dads

20 FAVORITE WALTZES.
LP: . . . . GNPS 2173
MC: GNP5 2173

AGAIN.
LP: . . . . GNPS 2068
MC: GNP5 2068

BEST OF THE MOM & DADS.
LP: . . . . GNPS 2087
MC: GNP5 2087

BLUE CANADIAN ROCKIES.
LP: . . . . GNPS 2063
MC: GNP5 2063

BLUE HAWAII.
LP: . . . . GNPS 2130
MC: GNP5 2130

DANCE WITH THE MOM & DADS.
LP: . . . . GNPS 2078
MC: GNP5 2078

DOWN THE RIVER OF GOLDEN DREAMS.
LP: . . . . GNPS 2106
MC: GNP5 2106

DREAM.
LP: . . . . GNPS 2092
MC: GNP5 2092

GOLDEN COUNTRY.
2LP: . . . . GNPS 22123
MCSET: GNP5 22123

GOODNIGHT SWEETHEART.
LP: . . . . GNPS 2150
MC: GNP5 2150

GRATEFULLY YOURS.
LP: . . . . GNPS 2117
MC: GNP5 2117

IN THE GOOD OLD SUMMERTIME.
LP: . . . . GNPS 2102
MC: GNP5 2102

LOVE IS A BEAUTIFUL SONG.
LP: . . . . GNPS 2084
MC: GNP5 2084

LOVE LETTERS IN THE SAND.
LP: . . . . GNPS 2125
MC: GNP5 2125

MEMORIES.
LP: . . . . GNPS 2096
MC: GNP5 2096

MERRY XMAS-HAPPY NEW YEAR.
LP: . . . . GNPS 2067
MC: GNP5 2067

MOM & DADS PLAY YOUR FAVORITE HYMNS.
LP: . . . . GNPS 2082
MC: GNP5 2082

ONE DOZEN ROSES.
LP: . . . . GNPS 2110
MC: GNP5 2110

RANGERS WALTZ.
LP: . . . . GNPS 2061
MC: GNP5 2061

RED SAILS IN THE SUNSET.
LP: . . . . GNPS 2189
MC: GNP5 2189

REMINISCING.
LP: . . . . GNPS 2072
MC: GNP5 2072

SOUVENIRS.
LP: . . . . GNPS 2065
MC: GNP5 2065

TO MOM & DAD WITH LOVE.
LP: . . . . GNPS 2136
MC: GNP5 2136

VERY BEST OF MOM & DADS.
2LP: . . . . GNPS 2-2129
MCSET: GNP5 2-2129

WALTZ ACROSS TEXAS.
LP: . . . . GNPS 2139
MC: GNP5 2139

WHISPERING HOPE.
LP: . . . . GNPS 2108
MC: GNP5 2108

Moment

WORK GETS DONE, THE.
LP: . . . . RAVE 1

Moment By Moment

MOMENT BY MOMENT (Film soundtrack) (Various artists).
Tracks: / Moment to moment: *Various artists* / Lady wants to know: *Various artists* / Everybody needs love: *Various artists* / You know I love you: *Various artists* / Your heart never lies: *Various artists* / Sometimes when we touch: *Various artists* / For you and I: *Various artists* / Hollywood Boulevard: *Various artists*.
LP: . . . . RSD 5004
MC: . . . . TRSD 5004

Moments

MOMENTS Various artists (Various artists).
LP: . . . . N 5005

Moments (group)

GREATEST HITS: MOMENTS.
LP: . . . . DET 202

Momus

CIRCUS MAXIMUS.
Tracks: / Lucky like St. Sebastian / Lesson of Sodom, The / John the baptist Jones / King Solomon's song and mine / Little Lord Obedience / Day the circus came to town, The / Rape of Lucretia, The / Paper wraps rock / Rules of the game of quoits.
LP: . . . . ACME 2

HIPPOPOTAMOMUS.
LP: . . . . CRELP 097
MC: . . . . CCRE 097

HOLD BACK THE NIGHT.
LP: . . . . CRELP 52
MC: . . . . CREC 52

MONSTERS OF LOVE.
LP: . . . . CRELP 059
MC: . . . . CCRELP 059

POISON BOYFRIEND.
LP: . . . . CRELP 021

TENDER PERVERT.
LP: . . . . CRELP 036

Mon Oncle Americain

MON ONCLE AMERICAIN (Film soundtrack) (Various artists).
LP: . . . . SL 9505

Mona Lisa

MONA LISA (Film soundtrack) (Various artists).
Tracks: / When I fall in love: *Cole, Nat King* / Introduction (When I fall in love): *Various artists* / Story, The: *Kamen, Michael* / George: *Kamen, Michael* / Elevator attack and after: *Kamen, Michael* / Slap you back: *Exception* / Mona Lisa: *Cole, Nat King* / Kings Cross/ follow Anderson: *Kamen, Michael* / Pimp: *Kamen*, Michael / Simone's story: *Kamen, Michael* / Daughters of Babylon: *Lindsay, Jimmy* / Love duet from Madame Butterfly & Puccini: *Tibaldi, Renata/Carlo Bergonzi*.
LP: . . . . SCX 6705
MC: . . . . TCSCX 6705

Moncur, Grachan III

EVOLUTION.
Tracks: / Air raid / Evolution / Coaster, The / Monk in wonderland.
LP: . . . . BST 84153

NEW AFRICA.
LP: . . . . AFF 38

Mondays

FORTUNE AND GLORY.
LP: . . . . PHZA 19

Mondo Cane

MONDO CANE.
LP: KIX4U 2223
LP: . . . . PLAT 2223

Mondo, Jean-Paul

ZANGANA.
LP: . . . . BN 51025

Mondo Rock

BOOM BABY BOOM.
Tracks: / Primitive love rites / Boom baby boom / Rule of threes / Get to you / Our time / Rise and fall / Do it yourself / Roman holiday / Let it rain / Under lights.
LP: 829 829-1
MC: 829 829-4

CHEMISTRY.
Tracks: / Step up step out / Summer of '81 / Cool world / Mondo sexo / We're no angels / Chemistry / Trash / Popular view / State of the heart / Moves.
LP: K50843

Mondostereo

TINNITUS.
LP: . . . . TR 520868

Monese, Valerie

THIS IS VALERIE MONESE.
Tracks: / Summertime / Close the door / Tonnight / King's daughter / This is my beloved / Don't cry for me Argentina / Vilia / He was beautiful / Ciribiribin / Smoke gets in your eyes / Live for another day / Amazing grace.
LP: . . . . MFP 50562
MC: . . . . TCMFP 50562

Money

FIRST INVESTMENT.
Tracks: / Mari-Anna / Leo the jester / Searching / Geneva / Cosmic lullaby / Opening night / Finale / Statements and demands / Remembering (MGO) goddess.
LP: . . . . GULP 1031

TRUST ME.
LP: . . . . HMUSA 2
MC: . . . . HMUSA MC 2

Money, Curley

CURLEY MONEY.
Tracks: / Stop your knockin' / Gonna rock / Lazy man / Bojangles rock / Wire guitar / Ho bo / Hurricane baby / Many tears ago / Shortnin' bread / White lightning / Honk tonk man / Rambler.
LP: . . . . BB 2003

Money, Eddie

CAN'T HOLD BACK.
Tracks: / Take me home tonight / One love / I wanna go back / Endless nights / One chance / We should be sleeping / Bring on the rain / I can't hold back / Stranger in a strange land / Calm before the storm.
LP: . . . . CBS 57048
MC: 40 57048

GREATEST HITS: EDDIE MONEY.
Tracks: / Baby hold on / Two tickets to paradise / Peace in our time / Where's the party (live version) / I wanna go back / Walk on water / Shakin' / Take me home tonight / Think I'm in love / Looking through the eyes of a child / No control / We should be sleeping / Stop steppin' on my heart.
LP: 4659931
MC: 4659944

LIFE FOR THE TAKING.
Tracks: / Life for the taking / Can't keep a good man down / Nightmare / Gimme some water / Rock 'n' roll the place / Maybe I'm a fool / Love the way you love me / Maureen / Nobody / Call on me.
LP: . . . . CBS 83159

NO CONTROL.
Tracks: / Shakin' / Runnin' away / Think I'm in love / Hard life / No control / Take a little bit / Keep my motor runnin' / My friends, my friends / Drivin' me crazy / Passing by the graveyard / It could happen to you.
LP: . . . . CBS 85969

NOTHING TO LOSE.
LP: 4629091
MC: 4629094

PLAYING FOR KEEPS.
Tracks: / Trinidad / Running back / Wish / Get a move on / When you took my

heart / Satin angel / Let's be lovers again / Nobody knows / Million dollar girl.
LP: CBS 84731

WHERE'S THE PARTY?.
LP: CBS 25656
MC: 40 25656

Money To Burn

MONEY TO BURN (Various artists).
Tracks: / Craig song, The: *Various artists* / When the sun stops shining: *Various artists* / Loose ends: *Various artists* / Money to burn: *Various artists* / Who's counting on me: *Various artists* / Make it soon: *Various artists* / Until tomorrow (part 1): *Various artists* / Until tomorrow (part 2): *Various artists* / Until tomorrow (part 3): *Various artists* / Until tomorrow (part 4): *Various artists* / She's a woman: *Various artists*/ Swanks and swells part 1: *Various artists* / Swanks and swells part 2: *Various artists*.
LP: PTLS 1079
MC: PTLC 1079

Money, Zoot

MR. MONEY.
LP: LUNE 1

ZOOT (Money, Zoot Big Roll Band).
LP: SX 6075

ZOOT MONEY'S BIG ROLL BAND.
Tracks: / Chauffeur / One and only man, The / I've been trying / Florence of Arabia / Let the good times roll / James Brown medley / I'll go crazy / Papa's got a brand new bag / Out of sight / I feel good / Mashed potato USA / Nothing can change this love / Barefootin'.
LP: SPELP 79
MC: SPEMC 79

Monger, Eileen

ENCHANTED VALLEY, THE (Monger, Eileen/Jim Couza).
Tracks: / Jenny Lind medley / Londonderry air (medley) / High cauled cap, The / Christine's medley / Belle Katherine (Medley) / Perfect cure medley / Enchanted valley, The / Devil's dream / Nola / Take five / Norwegian wood.
LP: SDL 335
MC: CSDL 335

LILTING BANSHEE, THE.
Tracks: / King of the fairies, The / Lilting banshee, The / O South wind / Great high wind / Wild geese, The / Bonnie Portmore / Morning dew, The / Ivy leaf, The / Limerick's lamentation / Give me your hand / Neil Gow's lament / Farewell to Craigie Dhu / Fingal's cave.
LP: SDL 348
MC: CSDL 348

Mongolia

INSTRUMENTAL MUSIC.
LP: TGS 127

VOCAL MUSIC.
LP: TGS 126

Moni Bile

CHAGRIN D'AMOUR.
LP: AT 0064

MAKOSSA AMBIANCE.
LP: MB 114

Monick, Susie

MELTING POTS.
LP: AD 4107

Monk, Meredith

BOOK OF DAYS.
Tracks: / Early morning melody / Dawn / Traveller 4 / Churchyard entertainment / Afternoon melodies / Field/Clouds / Dusk / Eva's song / Evening / Travellers / Jewish storyteller/Dance/Dream / Plague / Madwoman's vision / Cave song.
LP: ECM 1399

DO YOU BE.
Tracks: / Scared song / I don't know / Window in 7's / Double fiesta / Do you be / Panda chant 1 / Memory song / Panda chant 11 / Quarry lullaby / Shadow song / Astronaut anthem / Wheel.
LP: ECM 1336

DOLMEN MUSIC.
Tracks: / Gotham lullaby / Travelling / Biography / Tale / Dolmen music.
LP: ECM 1197

TURTLE DREAMS.
LP: ECM 1240

Monk, Thelonious

1961 EUROPEAN TOUR, VOL 1.
Tracks: / I'm getting sentimental over you / Jackie-ing / Crepuscule with Nellie / Round midnight / Blue Monk.
LP: INGO 5

1961 EUROPEAN TOUR, VOL 2.
Tracks: / Sweet Georgia Brown / Rhythm-a-ning epistrophy / Well you needn't / Blue Monk.
LP: INGO 8

ALONE IN SAN FRANCISCO.
LP: OJC 231

APRIL IN SPRING-LIVE.
Tracks: / Epistrophy / April in Paris / I'm getting sentimental over you / Just a gigolo / I mean you / Jackie-ing / Off minor / Rhythm-a-ning / Hackensack / Well you needn't.
LP: OJCD 508
LP: M 47060

BEBOP LEGENDS, THE (See under Johnson, JJ).

BLUE MONK.
LP: CJZ LP 8

BLUE SPHERE.
Tracks: / Tinkle tinkle / Crepuscule with Nellie / Darn that dream / Little rootie tootie / Nice work if you can get it / Melancholy baby / Jackie-ing / Blue Sphere.
LP: BLM 51501

BUD POWELL & THELONIOUS MONK (See under Powell, Bud) (Monk, Thelonious & Bud Powell).

CLASSIC MONK.
LP: 2273252
MC: 2173252

COLLECTION: THELONIOUS MONK.
Tracks: / Blue Monk / Nutty / Evidence / Epistrophy / Hackensack / Bemsha swing / I'm getting sentimental over you / Straight, no chaser / Pannonica / Epistrophy 2.
MC: DVMC 2040

COMPLETE GENIUS.
2LP: BND 4032

COMPOSER, THE.
LP: 4633381
MC: 4633384

CRISS-CROSS.
LP: CBS 85691

EPISTROPHY.
2LP: AFFD 26

EUROPEAN TOUR (Monk, Thelonious & Max Roach).
Tracks: / Blue Monk / Light blue / Evidence / To Lady / Stop motion.
MC: MC 7683

EVIDENCE.
Tracks: / Rhythm-a-ning / Ruby my dear / Bright Mississippi / Round about midnight / Evidence / Jackie-ing / Stuffy / Blue Monk.
LP: FC 105

GENIUS OF MODERN MUSIC VOL.1.
Tracks: / Round midnight / Off minor / Ruby my dear / I mean you (Not on CD.) / April in Paris / In walked Bud / Thelonious / Epistrophy / Misterioso (Not on CD.) / Well you needn't / Introspection / Humph / Evonce (CD only.) / Evonce (alt. take) (CD only.) / Suburban eyes (alt. take) (CD only.) / Nice work if you can get it (CD only.) / Nice work if you can get it (alt. take) (CD only.) / Ruby my dear (alt. take) (CD only.) / Well you needn't (alt. take) (CD only.) / April in Paris (alt. take) (CD only.) / Monk's mood (CD only.) / Who knows (CD only.) / Who knows (alt. take) (CD only.).
MC: 4BN 81510
LP: BST 81510
LP: 781 510 1
LP: BLP 1510

GENIUS OF MODERN MUSIC VOL.2.
Tracks: / Carolina moon / Hornin' in / Skippy / Let's cool one / Suburban eyes (Not on CD.) / Evonce (Not on CD.) / Straight no chaser / Four in one / Nice work if you can get it (Not on CD.) / Monk's mood (Not on CD.) / Who knows (Not on CD.) / Ask me now / Four in one (alt. take) (CD only.) / Criss cross (alt. take) (CD only.) / Eronel (CD only.) / Ask me now (alt. take) (CD only.) / Willow weep for me (CD only.) / Skippy (alt. take) (CD only.) / Hornin' in (alt. take) (CD only.) / Sixteen (first take) (CD only.) / Sixteen (second take) (CD only.) / I'll follow you (CD only.).
LP: BST 81511
MC: 4BN 81511
LP: BLP 1511

GREATEST HITS: THELONIUS MONK.
Tracks: / Well you needn't / Misterioso / Bemsha swing / Round midnight / Epistrophy / Ruby my dear / Crepuscule with Nellie / Blue monk / Straight, no chaser.
LP: CBS 21069
MC: 40 21069

I MEAN YOU.
LP: 65610

IN ACTION (Monk, Thelonious Quartet).
LP: OJC 103

IN STOCKHOLM.
LP: D 1020

IT'S MONK'S TIME.
Tracks: / Lulu's back in town / Memories of you / Stuffy turkey / Brake's sake / Nice work if you can get it / Shuffle boil.
LP: 4508681
MC: 4508684

JAZZ MESSENGER (see Blakey, Art) (Monk, Thelonious & Art Blakey).

LIVE AT THE IT CLUB.
Tracks: / Blue Monk / Well you needn't / 'Round midnight / Rhythm-a-ning / Blues five spot / Bemsha swing.
LP: CBS 88584

LIVE IN PARIS, 1964 VOL.1.
LP: FC 132

LIVE IN PARIS, 1964 VOL.2.
LP: FC 134

LIVE IN PARIS 1967.
Tracks: / Presentation A. Francis / Ruby my dear / We see / Epistrophy / Oska T / Evidence / Blue monk / Epistrophy (reprise).
LP: FC 113

LIVE PERFORMANCES.
LP: 2MJP 1063

LONDON COLLECTION, VOLUME 1.
Tracks: / Trinkle tinkle / Crepuscule with Nellie / Darn that dream / Little rootie tootie / Meet me tonight in dreamland / Nice work if you can get it / My melancholy baby / Jackie-ing / Loverman / Blue sphere.
LP: BLP 60101

LONDON COLLECTION, VOLUME 2.
LP: BLP 60116

MAN I LOVE, THE.
Tracks: / I mean you / Man I love, The / Ruby my dear / Little rootie tootie / Misterioso / Trinkle tinkle / Crepuscule with Nellie.
LP: BLP 30141
MC: BLP 30141C

MONK.
LP: CBS 21117

MONK & BIRD (A tribute to Monk & Bird) (Monk, Thelonious & Charlie Parker).
LP: TOM 2-9002

MONK ON RIVERSIDE.
LP: RIV 40047

MONK ON TOUR IN EUROPE.
Tracks: / Oska T / Epistrophy / Evidence / Blue monk / Monk's mood / We see aka Ganese / Hackensack / Lulu's back in town / I mean you / Round midnight.
2LP: AFFD 192
MCSET: TCAFFD 192

MONK WITH COLTRANE.
Tracks: / Ruby, my dear / Trinkle tinkle / Nutty / Well, you need'nt / Off minor / Epistrophy / Crepuscule with Nellie / Abide with me / Monk's mood / Blues for tomorrow.
2LP: M 47011

MONK'S DREAM (Monk, Thelonious Quartet).
Tracks: / Monk's dream / Body and soul / Bright Mississippi / Five spot blues / Bolivar blues / Just a gigolo / Bye ya / Sweet and lonely.
LP: CBS 85682
LP: 4600651
MC: 4600654

MONK'S MUSIC.
Tracks: / Abide with me / Well you needn't / Ruby my dear / Epistrophy / Crepuscule with Nellie.
LP: OJC 084

MULLIGAN MEETS MONK (Monk, Thelonious & Gerry Mulligan).
Tracks: / Round midnight / Rhythm-a-ning / Sweet and lonely / Decidedly / Straight, no chaser / I mean you.
LP: RSLP 247

PLAYS DUKE ELLINGTON.
Tracks: / It don't mean a thing / Sophisticated lady / I got it bad and that ain't good / Black and tan fantasy / Moon indigo / I let a song go out of my heart / Solitude / Caravan.
LP: RLP 201

PORTRAIT OF AN ERMITE.
LP: 500104
LP: JL 104

RIVERSIDE TRIOS.
Tracks: / It don't mean a thing / Sophisticated lady / I got it bad and that ain't good / Black and tan fantasy / Mood indigo / I let a song go out of my heart / Solitude / Caravan / Liza / Memories of you / Honeysuckle Rose / Darn that dream / Tea for two / You are too beautiful / Just you, just me.
LP: M 47052

ROUND MIDNIGHT.
Tracks: / Round midnight / Off minor / Mysterioso / Criss cross / Hornin' in well / You needn't / Ruby my dear / Let's cool one / Straight, no chaser / Ask me now / Thelonious / Evidence / Epistrophy / Monk's dream / Little rootie tootie / Reflections / Blue monk / Let's call this / Bemesha swing / Rhythm-a-ning.
LP: LPJT 19
MC: MCJT 19

SOLO MONK.
LP: SJAZZ 8
MC: SJAZZC 8

SOMETHING IN BLUE.
LP: BLP 30119
MC: BLP 30119C

SPHERE (Monk, Thelonious Quartet).
LP: AFF 20

THELONIOUS HIMSELF.
Tracks: / April in paris / Ghost of a chance / Functional / I'm getting sentimal over you / I should care / All alone / Monk's mood / Round midnight.
LP: OJC 254

THELONIOUS MONK.
LP: JR 162
LP: KLJ 20012

THELONIOUS MONK AND HERBIE NICHOLS (Monk, Thelonious & Herbie Nichols).
Tracks: / Brake's sake / Gallop's gallop / Shuffle boil / Nica's tempo / Who's blues / 'S wonderful / 'S wonderful (alternative version) / Nichols & dimes / Nichols & dimes (alternative take) / My lady gingersnap / Good story blues.
LP: WL 70829
MC: WK 70829

THELONIOUS MONK AT TOWN HALL.
Tracks: / Thelonious / Friday The 13th / Monk's Mood / Little Rootie Tootie / Off Minor / Crepuscule with Nellie.
LP: RSLP 300

THELONIOUS MONK & JOHN COLTRANE (Monk, Thelonious & John Coltrane).
LP: CBS 85682

THELONIOUS MONK MEMORIAL ALBUM, THE.
Tracks: / 'Round midnight / I want to be happy / Bemsha swing / Black and tan fantasy / Brilliant corners / I mean you / Jackie-ing / Little rootie tootie / Epistrophy / Ruby / My dear / Nutty / Let's cool one / I'm getting sentimental over you.
LP: M 47064

THELONIOUS MONK QUARTET & OCTET IN EUROPE.
LP: UJ 12

UNDERGROUND.
LP: 4600661
MC: 4600664

Monk, T.S.

HOUSE OF MUSIC.
Tracks: / Bon bon vie / Candidate for love / Hot night in the city / Last of the wicked romancers / Can't keep my hands to myself / Stay free of his love / House of music.
LP: K 50773

MORE OF THE GOOD LIFE.
Tracks: / Everybody get on up and dance / Too much too soon / Falling in love with you / You / Oh Oh Oh speedo / First lady of love / More to love / You're asking me, I'm askin' you.
LP: K 50844

Monkees

6 TRACK HITS: MONKEES.
Tracks: / I'm a believer / Alternate title / Somebody man / Little bit me, a little bit you / Valleri / Pleasant valley Sunday.
MC: 7SC 5035

20 GOLDEN GREATS: MONKEES.
LP: RTL 2085
MC: 4CRTL 2085

BEST OF THE MONKEES.
Tracks: / Monkee's theme / Last train to Clarksville / She / Daydream believer / Listen to the band / Little bit me, a little bit you / I'm a believer / I wanna be free / Pleasant Valley Sunday / Steppin' stone / Shades of grey.
LP: MFP 50499
MC: TCMFP 50499

BIRDS, BEES & THE MONKEES.
LP: RNLP 144

HEAD (Film soundtrack).
LP: RNLP 145

HEADQUARTERS.
LP: SF 7886

HEY HEY IT'S THE MONKEES - GREATEST HITS.
Tracks: / Monkees, The / Pleasant valley Sunday / Girl I knew somewhere, The / D.W. Washburn / Last train to Clarksville / Little bit me, a little bit you / Teardrop City / Some day man / What am I doing hangin' round / Daydream

believer / I'm not your stepping stone / Alternate title / Words / I'm a believer / Listen to the band / Valleri / Tapioca tundra / That was then, this is now.
LP: . . . . NE 1432
MC: . . . . CE 2432

IDOLIZED, PLASTICISED.
LP: . . . . CIRCUSBOY 1

INSTANT REPLAY.
LP: . . . . RNLP 146

LIVE-1967.
Tracks: / Last train to Clarksville / You just may be the one / Girl I knew somewhere, The / I wanna be free / Sunny girlfriend / Your Auntie Grizelda / Forget that girl / Sweet young thing / Mary, mary / I'm a believer / Randy scouse git / I'm not your stepping stone.
LP: . . . . RNLP 70139
MC: . . . . RNC 70139

MAGIC MOMENTS WITH THE MONKEES.
Tracks: / Monkees, The (theme from the) / Last train to Clarksville / I wanna be free / Take a giant step / Sweet young thing / I'm a believer / I'm not your stepping stone / Little bit me, a little bit you / Girl I knew somewhere, The / Pleasant Valley Sunday / Words / Daydream believer / Valleri / Tapioca tundra / Alternate title / What am I doing hangin' round / She / Shades of Gray / You just may be the one / D W Washington / Porpoise song, The / Tear drop city / Listen to the band / Someday man.
MC: 407708

MISSING LINKS.
Tracks: / Apples, peaches, bananas and pears / I don't think you know me / So goes love / Teeny tiny gnome / War games / All of your toys / You have the time / Nine times blue / Party / Carlisle wheeling / Storybook of you.
LP: . . . . RNLP 70150
MC: . . . . RNC 70150

MONKEE FLIPS.
LP: . . . . RNLP 113

MONKEES' GREATEST HITS, THE.
LP: . . . . PLAT 05
MC: . . . . PLAC 05

MONKEES, THE.
Tracks: / Monkees, Theme from / Last train to Clarksville / I'm not your stepping stone / I'm a believer / I wanna be free / Papa Gene's blues / Take a giant step / Some time in the morning / Little bit me, a little bit you / Girl I knew somewhere, The / Mary Mary / She / Look out (here comes tomorrow) / You just may be the one / Alternative title (Randy scouse git) / Shades of grey / Pleasant valley Sunday / What am I doing hangin' round / For Pete's sake / Words / Daily, nightly / Vallen / Going down / Daydream believer / Tapioca tundra / D.W. Washborn / Teardrop city / Porpoise song, The / Some day man / Listen to the band.
2LP: . . . . DARTY 12
MCSET: . . . . TCDAR 12

MONKEES, THE, VOL.1 (LP).
LP: . . . . SF 7844

MORE OF THE MONKEES.
Tracks: / She / When love comes knockin' / Mary Mary / Hold on girl / Your Auntie Grizelda / Look out (here comes tomorrow) / Kind of girl I could love, The / Day we fell in love, The / Sometime in the morning / Laugh / I'm a believer.
LP: . . . . SF 7868

PISCES, AQUARIUS, CAPRICORN & JONES LTD..
LP: . . . . SF 7912

POOL IT.
Tracks: / Heart and soul / I'd go the whole wide world / Long way home / Secret heart / Gettin' in / I'll love you forever / Every step of the way / Don't bring me down / Midnight / She's movin' in with Rico / Since you went away / Counting on you.
LP: . . . . RNLP 70706
MC: . . . . RNC 70706

PRESENT.
LP: . . . . RNLP 147

TALK DOWNUNDER.
LPPD: . . . . VBAK 3005

THEN AND NOW (Best of the Monkees).
Tracks: / Then and now / Tripwire / Monkees, The (Theme from) / Last train to Clarksville / Take a giant step / I'm a believer / I'm not your stepping stone / Little bit me, a little bit you / Anytime, anyplace, anywhere / That was then, this is now / Girl I knew somewhere, The / Pleasant Valley Sunday / What am I doing hangin' round / Daydream believer / Valleri / Kicks.
LP: 207874
MC: 407874

Monkey Joe

MONKEY JOE, 1938-39.
LP: . . . . OT 1208

Monkey (tv)

MONKEY (BBC TV SERIES) (See under Godiego) (Various artists).

MONKEY (THEME FROM) (See under Godiego 'Monkey magic') (Godiego).

Monkey's Paw

MONKEY'S PAW, THE (See under Graham, John - Hands off) (Dramatised by Len Peterson).

Monkman, Francis

MIND-BODY-SPIRIT.
MC: . . . . ESSP FM1

Monks

BAD HABITS.
Tracks: / Johnny B. Rotten / Drugs in my pocket / Love in stereo / Bad habits / Spotty face / Dear Jerry / Nice legs / Inter-city Kitty / Out of musician / Ain't gettin' any / No shame / Skylab.
LP: . . . . EMC 3309

BLACK MONK TIME.
LP: . . . . KIRI 079
LP: . . . . ISR 003

Monks of Science

I'M A DOCTOR, NOT AN ESCALATOR.
LP: . . . . FACE 14

Monks Without God (bk)

MONKS WITHOUT GOD (Wild Billy Childish).
LP: . . . . WORDUP 005

Monmouthshire...

LAND OF SONG (Monmouthshire Massed Choir).
Tracks: / Counting the goats / Tydi a roddaist / Lily of the valley / Soldiers' chorus Faust / Lord's prayer / O Isis and Osiris / Speed your journey / Laudamus / Close thine eyes / Llef / Myfanwy / Jacob's ladder / Bidaros / Mae hen wlad fy nhadau.
LP: . . . . MFP 50475

Mono, Niki

CONTRADICTIONS ARE A LUXURY.
LP: . . . . ANT 112

Monochrome Set

ELIGIBLE BACHELORS.
Tracks: / Jet set junta / I'll cry instead / On the 13th day / Cloud 10 / Mating game / March of the eligible bachelors / Devil rides out / Fun for all the family / Midas touch / Ruling class, The / Great barrier riff.
LP: . . . . BRED 34

FIN! (Monochrome Set live).
Tracks: / He's Frank / Martians go home / Straits of Malacca / Sugar plum / B-I-D spells BID / Alphaville / Heaven can wait / Goodbye Joe / Strange boutique, The / Jacob's ladder / Wallflower / Apocalypso / Mr. Bizzaro / I'll cry instead / Expresso / Lines / Ein symphonies des grauens / Monchrome Set, The.
LP: . . . . ACME 1

LOST WEEKEND, THE.
Tracks: / Jacob's ladder / Sugar plum / Cargo / Take foz / Letter from Viola / Don't touch / Twitch / Wallflower / Starry nowhere / Le boom boom / Cowboy country / Yo ho ho / Andiamo.
LP: . . . . BYN 5
MC: . . . . BYNC 5

LOVE ZOMBIES.
Tracks: / Love zombies / Adeste fideles / 405 lines / B.I.D. spells bid / R.S.V.P. / Apocalypso / Karma sutra / Man with the black moustache, The / Weird, wild and wonderful world of Tony Potts, The / In love, Cancer?.
LP: . . . . OVED 56
LP: . . . . DID 8

STRANGE BOUTIQUE.
Tracks: / Monochrome set (I presume), The / Lighter side of dating, The / Expresso / Puerto Rican fence climber, The / Tomorrow will be too long / Martians go home / Love goes down the drain / Ici les enfants / Etcetera stroll, The / Goodbye Joe / Strange boutique, The.
LP: . . . . OVED 55
LP: . . . . DID 4

VOLUME, BRILLIANCE, CONTRAST.
Tracks: / Eine symphonie des grauens / Jet set junta / Love zombies / Silicon carne / Ruling class, The / Viva death row / Man with the black moustache, The / He's Frank / Fun for all the family / Lester leaps in / Ici les enfants / Fat fun / Alphaville / Avanti.
LP: . . . . BRED 47

WESTMINSTER AFFAIR.
Tracks: / Jet set junta / Cast a long shadow / Ruling class, The / Lester leaps in / Mating game, The / On the 13th day / March of the eligible bachelors / Devil rides out / Fun for all the family / Andiamo / Cowboy country / J.D.H.A.N.E.Y. / Noise / Eine symphonie des grauens / Viva death row (Extra track, available on CD only.) / Jacob's ladder (Extra track, available on CD only.) / Ici les enfants (Extra track, available on CD only.) / Avanti.
LP: . . . . ACME 17

Monocled Mutineer

MONOCLED MUTINEER (see Let the great big world keep turning) (Fenton, George).

Monopoly, Tony

GAME OF LIFE.
Tracks: / Touch me in the morning / I wish I could hurt that way again / If you've got nothing on tonight / Rose / Who gets the loving / I go to Rio / New York, New York / She's out of my life / I could have been a sailor / Stay the night / Slip away / I'm always chasing rainbows.
LP: . . . . ACLP 005

INSPIRATION.
Tracks: / I believe / Bless This House / Holy City, The / Michael Row The Boat / Abide With Me / We Shall Overcome / Battle Hymn Of The Republic / He's got the whole world in his hands / Old Rugged Cross, The / How Great Thou Art / Lord's my shepherd, The / Swing Low Sweet Chariot / Amazing Grace / Lord's prayer, The / Love Is The Answer.
LP: . . . . ITV 448
MC: . . . . KITV 448

TONY MONOPOLY.
LP: . . . . BULP 2000

Monotomy Commission

ONE HAND TURNS TO HEAVEN.
LP: . . . . CHIME 046

Monotones

BOOK OF LOVE.
LP: . . . . MAR 1000

Monro

MONRO.
Tracks: / Some boys / Here comes the night / Give me love again / It's love / Lonely people / American girls / Princess / Surrender / Open up your heart / Rock this city.
LP: . . . . SPELA 332

Monro, Matt

16 GOLDEN CLASSICS.
Tracks: / Ev'rybody falls in love with someone / Out of sight out of mind / One I love belongs to somebody else, The / That old feeling / Cried for you (now it's your turn to cry for me) / Cottage for sale / Do you ever think of me / Dancing with tears in my eyes / Gone with the wind / Memories of you / My old flame / Once in a while / You always hurt the one you love / Love me do / My house is your house (mi casa su casa) / What can I say after I say I'm sorry.
LP: . . . . UNLP 020
MC: . . . . UNMC 020

BY REQUEST.
Tracks: / I get along without you very well / I will wait for you / Time after time / Wednesday's child / Music played, The / Honey on the vine / Rain sometimes / When you wish upon a star / Over the rainbow / If I never sing another song / When you become a man / Beyond the hill / You've got possibilities / Let there be love / If she walked into my life / Apple tree, The / You're sensational / My friend, my friend / When I fall in love / Look for small pleasures.
LP: . . . . EMS 1129
MC: . . . . TCEMS 1129

CAPITOL YEARS: MATT MONRO.
Tracks: / Put on a happy face / I'm glad there's you / Laura / Real live girl / Born free / Wednesday's child / I'll take romance / If she walked into my life / Strangers in the night / In the arms of love / Here's to my lady / When Joanna loved me / You've got possibilities / People / Sunrise sunset / Man and a woman, A / And we were lovers / Georgie girl / On day's like these / Come back to me.
LP: . . . . EMS 1376
LP: 795 410 1
MC: . . . . TCEMS 1376
MC: 795 410 4

EMI YEARS, THE: MATT MONRO.
Tracks: / My kind of girl / Portrait of my love / From Russia with love / Who can I turn to / Let's face the music and dance / Jeannie / April fool / Cheek to cheek / Softly as I leave you / Here and now / Love is a many splendored thing / How little we know / Stardust / Small fry / Skylark / One morning in May / I get along without you very well / Memphis in June / Blue orchids / I have dreamed.
LP: . . . . EMS 1377
MC: . . . . TCEMS 1377

GOLDEN LOVE SONGS.
Tracks: / Diana / You light up my life / If I never sing another song / Let there be love / I can't stop loving you / You and me against the world / Answer me / Friend, lover woman wife / With these hands / I love you because / Be my love / So little time / Happy / Warsaw concerto theme.
LP: . . . . OU 2238

HEARTBREAKERS.
Tracks: / Impossible dream, The / And you smiled / Didn't we / If I never sing another song / From Russia with love / Born free / Softly / As I leave you / Walk away / Without you / My kind of girl / Somewhere / We're gonna change the world / Speak softly, love / Why not now / Yesterday / Portrait of my love / My love and devotion / For mama / When love comes along / Gonna build a mountain.
LP: . . . . EMTV 23
MC: . . . . TCEMTV 23
LP: . . . . ATAK 137
MC: . . . . TCATAK 137

HITS OF YESTERDAY.
Tracks: / Portrait of my love / Gonna build a mountain / From Russia with love / One day / For mama / Somewhere (West Side story) / My kind of girl / Unchained melody / Yesterday / Walk away (warum nur warum) / Girl I love, The / Softly as I leave you.
MC: 1A 220 1583254
LP: C5-546
MC: C5K-546

I HAVE DREAMED.
LP: . . . . PMC 1250

IF I NEVER SING ANOTHER SONG.
Tracks: / With these hands / You light up my life / Answer me / I think I'm getting over you / When a child is born / If I never sing another song / Long and winding road / May each day / Morning has broken / By her side / Mary's boy child / Last farewell, The.
LP: . . . . SCX 6605

INVITATION TO THE MOVIES.
LP: . . . . ST 2730

LATE, LATE SHOW, THE.
Tracks: / If she could come to you / When I fall in love / Maria / Time after time / This is all I ask / I've grown accustomed to her face / Days of wine and roses / Shadow of your smile / Autumn leaves / Party's over, The.
LP: . . . . MOIR 205
MC: . . . . CMOIR 205

MATT MONRO.
MC: . . . . TCIDL 11

MATT MONRO SINGS.
Tracks: / I have dreamed / Who can I turn to? / My friend, my friend / Love is a many splendoured thing / It's a breeze / Without the one you love / Once in every long and lonely while / All my loving / If this should be a dream / How soon? / Exodus / Here and now / Friendly persuasion / Start living / Stardust / Small fry / How little we know / Nearness of you, The / Georgia on my mind / Skylark / One morning in May / I get along without you very well / Memphis in June / I guess it was you all the time / Blue orchids / Rockin' chair / You're sensational (CD set only) / Love walked in (CD set only) / Yesterday (CD set only) / Yesterday (CD set only) / Alfie (CD set only) / Hello young lovers (CD set only) / Michelle (CD set only) / Softly as I leave you (CD set only) / Here, there and everywhere (CD set only) / Somewhere (CD set only) / From Russia with love (CD set only).
2LP: . . . . DL 41 1072 3
MC: . . . . DL 41 1072 9
2LP: . . . . DL 1072
MC: . . . . TC DL 1072

MATT MONRO SINGS DON BLACK.
Tracks: / On days like these / All the wishing in the world / If I never sing another song / Beyond the hill / For mama / One day soon (Mono.) / Born free / Wish now was then / All of a sudden / If there ever is a next time / Pretty Polly (Mono.) / Two people / When you come a man / Walk away.
LP: . . . . EMS 1355
MC: . . . . TCEMS 1355

MEMORIES.
Tracks: / That old feeling / One I love belongs to somebody else, The / Cottage for sale / Memories of you / What can I say, after I say I'm sorry? / Do you ever think of me? / My old flame / I cried for you / Love me do / Everybody falls in love with someone / Gone with the wind / You always hurt the one you love / Dancing with tears in my eyes / Once in a while.
LP: . . . . TAB 87
MC: . . . . KTBC 87

MORE HEARTBREAKERS.
Tracks: / On days like these / If there ever is a next time / When I fall in love / Stardust / I have dreamed / Alguien canto (the music played) / People / As long as she needs me / Long and winding road, The / When Joanna loved me / Who can I turn to? / He ain't heavy, he's my brother / I get along without you very well / Sarah's coming home / Todo pasara / One day / For all we know / You're gonna hear from me.
LP: . . . . **EG 2402321**
MC: . . . . **EG 2402324**

PORTRAIT OF A SONG SYLIST.
Tracks: / When I fall in love / People / All my loving / When Joanna loved me / Let there be love / Stardust / Without you / Friendly persuassion / Georgia on my mind / Somewhere / Michelle / Unchained melody / Didn't we / Time after time.
MC: . . . . **HARMC 113**

THIS IS MATT MONRO.
Tracks: / Portrait of my love / For all we know / Michelle / I can't stop loving you / Sunday kind of woman / I love you because / Gonna build a mountain / Softly as I leave you / From Russia with love / You and me against the world / Chattanooga choo choo / Who can I turn to / For Mama / This time / By her side / Speak softly love.
LP: . . . . **THIS 24**
MC: . . . . **TCTHIS 24**

THIS IS THE LIFE.
LP: . . . . **T 2540**

TIME FOR LOVE, A.
Tracks: / Portrait of my love / Softly as I leave you / Why not now / Can this be love / My kind of girl / When love comes along / Without you / Speak softly love (Love theme from 'The Godfather'.) / Wednesday's child / I will wait for you / Time after time / Love walked in / And we were lovers (Theme from 'The Sand Pebbles'.) / Time for love, A / With these hands / Answer me / Till then my love / Man and a woman, A / On days like these (CD only.) / Didn't we (CD only.) / Alguien Canto (The music played) (CD only.) / Be my love (CD only.) / In the arms of love (CD only.) / You light up my life (CD only.).
LP: . . . . **MFP 5868**
MC: . . . . **TCMFP 5868**

VERY BEST OF MATT MONRO, THE.
Tracks: / Born free / Softly as I leave you / From Russia with love / On days like these / Walk away / Around the world / My love and devotion / Michelle / On a clear day / Somewhere / Impossible dream, The / Gonna build a mountain / Who can I turn to? / Portrait of my love / Speak softly love / My kind of girl / For mama / Yesterday / This time / We're gonna change the world.
LP: . . . . **MFP 5568**
MC: . . . . **TCMFP 5568**

Monroe

MONROE.
Tracks: / Take the money / Jane / Love may be the answer / Loser / Who's foolin' who / Keep on movin' / You can't trust a woman / Love ya / Who needs you / Give me a little love.
LP: **2383 597**

Monroe, Bill

BEST OF BILL MONROE.
Tracks: / Gold rush / Blue moon of Kentucky / Close by / Memories of mother and dad / Is the blue moon still shining / Kentucky mandolin / I'm going back to old Kentucky / Footprints in the snow / Little girl and the dreadful snake / Highway of sorrow / Uncle Pen / Let me rest at the end of the day / Blue grass twist / It's mighty dark to travel / Roane country prison / Pretty fair maiden in the garden / First whippoorwill / I live in the past / Come back to me in my dreams / Put my little shoes away.
2LP: **IMCA2 4090**

BLUE GRASS RAMBLES (Monroe, Bill & His Blue Grass Boys).
LP: . . . . **HAT 3014**
MC: . . . . **HATC 3014**

CLASSIC BLUEGRASS INSTRUMENTALS.
LP: . . . . **REB 850**
MC: . . . . **REB 850C**

CLASSIC BLUEGRASS RECORDINGS VOL.1.
Tracks: / True life blues / Travelling this lonesome road / Kentucky waltz / I'm travelling on and on / Bluegrass special / Mother's only sleeping / Can't you hear me callin' / How will I explain about you / Old cross road, The / Goodbye old pal / Alone about daybreak / Little community church.
LP: . . . . **CCS 104**
MC: . . . . **CCS 104MC**

CLASSIC BLUEGRASS RECORDINGS VOL.2 (Monroe, Bill & Flatt & Scruggs).
LP: . . . . **CCS 105**
MC: . . . . **CCS 105MC**

COUNTRY MUSIC HALL OF FAME.
Tracks: / Mule skinner blues / Kentucky waltz / Get up John / You'll find her name written there / Blue Moon of Kentucky / Put my little shoes on / Rocky road blues / Girl in the blue velvet band / Summertime is past and gone / Footprints in the snow / Gold rush.
LP: . . . . **IMCA 140**
LP: . . . . **CDL 8505**

FATHER OF BLUE GRASS MUSIC.
Tracks: / Six white horses / Dog house blues / Tennessee blues / No letter in the mail today / Blue yodel no. 7 (Anniversary blue yodel) / Orange blossom special / Mule skinner blues / Katy Hill / I wonder if you feel the way I do / Honky tonk swing / In the pines / Back up.
LP: . . . . **NL 90008**
MC: . . . . **NK 90008**

HIGH, LONESOME SOUND OF BILL MONROE.
Tracks: / My little Georgia rose / Letter from my darling / Memories of mother and dad / Highway of sorrow / On the old Kentucky shores / On and on / My dying bed / Memories of you / Whitehouse blues / Sugar coated love / I'm blue, I'm lonesome / When the golden leaves begin to fall.
LP: . . . . **IMCA 110**

IN THE PINES.
LP: . . . . **REB 853**
MC: . . . . **REB 853C**

KNEE-DEEP IN BLUEGRASS (Monroe, Bill & His Blue Grass Boys).
Tracks: / Cry cry darlin' / Roane country prison / Goodbye old pal / Out in the cold world / Good women's love / Come back to me in my dreams / Lonesome road to travel / I'm sitting on top of the world / Sally Joe / Brand new shoes / Molly and Ten Brooks.
LP: . . . . **HAT 3002**
MC: . . . . **HATC 3002**

ORANGE BLOSSOM SPECIAL.
LP: **20018**
MC: **40018**

STARS OF THE BLUEGRASS HALL OF FAME.
Tracks: / I'm on my way back to the old home / Can't you hear me callin' / Lord, protect my soul / Golden west / Travellin' this lonesome road / I'm going back to old Kentucky / I hear a sweet voice calling / Remember the cross / True life blues / Let the gates swing wide.
LP: . . . . **IMCA 5625**

Monroe, Marilyn

BEST OF BROADWAY.
LP: **26 21566**

COLLECTION: MARILYN MONROE (20 Golden Greats).
Tracks: / Diamonds are a girl's best friend / River of no return / Heatwave / Do it again / Kiss / My heart belongs to daddy / I'm gonna file my claim / This is a fine romance / Little girl from Little Rock, A / Happy birthday Mr. President / After you get what you want you don't want it / You'd be surprised / She acts like a woman should / Lazy / When love goes wrong nothing goes right / One silver dollar / When I fall in love / Things / Bye bye duet (With Jane Russell.) / Bye bye baby.
LP: . . . . **DVLP 2001**
MC: . . . . **DVMC 2001**

COMPLETE RECORDINGS.
LP: . . . . **RARE 6**

COMPLETE RECORDINGS, THE: MARILYN MONROE.
Tracks: / Ladies of the chorus / Every baby needs a da da daddy / Anyone can see I love you / Kiss / Do it again / She acts like a woman should / Two little girls from Little Rock / Bye bye baby / Diamonds are a girl's best friend / When love goes wrong / Fine romance, A / River of no return / I'm gonna file my claim / One silver dollar / Down in the meadow / Man chases a girl, A / After you get what you want you don't want it / There's no business like show business / Heatwave / Lazy / You'd be surprised / Rachmaninov & Chopsticks / That old black magic / I found a dream / I'm through with love / I wanna be loved by you / Running wild / Some like it hot / My heart belongs to daddy / Let's make love / Incurably romantic / Specialization / When I fall in love / Happy birthday Mr. President / Thanks for the memory.
LPS: . . . . **RARELP 06/07**

FINE ROMANCE, A.
2LP: . . . . **LEGENDS 1000/1**

GOODBYE NORMA JEAN.
Tracks: / My heart belongs to daddy / Diamonds are a girl's best friend / River of no return / I'm gonna file my claim / Bye bye baby / After you get what you want you don't want it / One silver dollar / Heatwave / When I fall in love / Specialisation.
LP: . . . . **ZUMA 1**
MC: . . . . **ZUMAC 1**

GOODBYE PRIMADONNA.
LP: **6.24800**
LP: . . . . **AZ 2372**
MC: . . . . **C 372**
LP: **6 23430**
LP: . . . . **ZUMA 1001**
MC: . . . . **ZUMAK 1001**

LEGEND, THE.
LP: . . . . **LEGENDS 1000.1**

LET'S MAKE LOVE.
LPPD: . . . . **AR 30077**

MARILYN MONROE.
LP: . . . . **LOP 14 119**
MC: . . . . **LCS 14119**

MARILYN MONROE (PIC DISC).
LP: . . . . **PD 83003B**

MARILYN MONROE STORY, THE.
Tracks: / Every baby needs a da da daddy / Anyone can see I love you / Kiss / Do it again / She acts like a woman should / Two little girls from little rock / Bye bye baby / Diamonds are a girl's best friend / (This is) a fine romance / River of no return / I'm gonna file my claim / One silver dollar / Down in the meadow / After you get what you want you don't want it / Heatwave / Lazy / You'd be surprised / That old black magic / I'm through with love / I wanna be loved by you / Running wild / My heart belongs to Daddy / Incurably romantic / When I fall in love / Happy birthday Mr. President / Thanks for the memory.
MCSET: . . . . **DVREMC 01**

NEVER BEFORE AND NEVER AGAIN (Original soundtrack).
Tracks: / Gentlemen prefer blondes / Diamonds are a girl's best friend / Little girl from little rock, A / Ain't there anyone here for love? / When love goes wrong / Bye bye baby / Do it again / Kiss / You'd be surprised / Fine romance, A / She acts like a woman should / Heatwave / Happy birthday Mr. President.
LP: . . . . **DS 15005**
MC: . . . . **DSC 15005**

PORTRAIT: MARILYN MONROE.
Tracks: / I wanna be loved by you / Diamond's are a girl's best friend / Little girl from little rock, A / When love goes wrong / Bye bye baby / My heart belongs to Daddy / I'm gonna file my claim / River of no return / Do it again / Kiss / You'd be surprised / This is a fine romance / I'm through with love / Heat wave / Running wild / Lazy / Happy birthday Mr. President.
LP: . . . . **PLAT 3905**
MC: . . . . **PLAC 3905**

RARE RECORDINGS (1948-62).
Tracks: / Some like it hot / Diamonds are a girl's best friend / Like a woman should.
LP: . . . . **SH 2013**
MC: . . . . **CSH 2013**

REMEMBER MARILYN.
LP: . . . . **NSPH 28500**

SOME LIKE IT HOT (See under Some Like It Hot).

VERY BEST OF MARILYN MONROE, THE.
Tracks: / My heart belongs to Daddy / Diamonds are a girl's best friend / Specialisation.
LP: . . . . **FUN 9001**
MC: . . . . **FUNC 9001**

VOICE SONGS AND FILMS, THE.
LP: . . . . **NL 89345**
MC: . . . . **NK 89345**

Monroe, Michael

NOT FAKIN' IT.
Tracks: / Dead jail or rock'n'roll / While you were lookin' at me / She's no angel / All night with the lights on / Not fakin' it / Shakedown / Man with no eyes / Love is thicker than blood / Smokescreen / Thrill me.
LP: **838 627 1**
MC: **838 627 4**

Monroe, Vaughn

1943 (Monroe, Vaughn & Orchestra).
LP: . . . . **CLP 45**

BEST OF VAUGHN MONROE (Monroe, Vaughn & Orchestra).
Tracks: / Racing with the moon / There I go / My devotion / When the lights go on again / Trolley song, The / There, I've said it again / Let it snow, let it snow, let it snow / I wish I didn't love you so / Ballerina / You do / Cool water / Red roses for a blue lady / Riders in the sky / Someday you'll want me to want you / That lucky old sun / Mule train / Sound off (the duckworth chant) / On top of Old Smokey / They were doin' the mambo.
LP: . . . . **NL 90068**
MC: . . . . **NK 90068**

MONROE DOCTRINE, THE.
LP: . . . . **SELP 1014**

MORE 1943 (Monroe, Vaughn & Orchestra).
LP: . . . . **CLP 116**

Monroes

FACE ANOTHER DAY.
Tracks: / Jeanette / Wish you were here / Beating of a lover's heart / Lady on 5th Avenue / Cheerio / Let's go / Heaven can wait / How strong is your love? / Move in closer.
LP: . . . . **PCS 7302**
MC: . . . . **TCPCS 7302**

Monsarrat, Nicholas

CRUEL SEA, THE (Hawkins, Jack).
MC: . . . . **CDL 51604**
MC: . . . . **LFP 41 7154 5**

Monsbourgh, Lazy Ade

ADELAIDE COLLECTION - ALL STEAMED UP.
LP: . . . . **S 1417**

JAZZ PARADE, THE.
LP: . . . . **S 1420**

RECORDER IN RAGTIME.
LP: . . . . **S 1405**

VINTAGE SELECTION (1950-70).
LP: . . . . **S 1344**

WILD LIFE (1956-70).
LP: . . . . **S 1283**

Monsieur Beaucaire

MONSIEUR BEAUCAIRE (Original 1919 Cast) (Various artists).
LP: . . . . **OPAL 817**

Monsignor Quixote

MONSIGNOR QUIXOTE SUITE (TV soundtrack) (See under English Chamber) (Various artists).

Monsoon

THIRD EYE.
Tracks: / Wings of the dawn / Tomorrow never knows / Third eye & Tikka TV / Eyes / Shauti / Ever so lonely / You can't take me with you / And I you / Kashmir / Watchers of the night.
LP: . . . . **PIPLP 001**
MC: . . . . **PIPMC 001**

Monstars

MONSTARS, THE.
LP: . . . . **AQL 101**

Monster Band

MONSTER BAND.
LP: . . . . **CP 2002**

Monster Club

MONSTER CLUB, THE (Original soundtrack) (Various artists).
LP: . . . . **CHILP 2**

Monster Tracks

MONSTER TRACKS (Various artists).
LP: . . . . **HOPTV 2**
MC: . . . . **HOPMC 2**

Monster Walk

MONSTER WALK.
LP: . . . . **PAL 5020**

Montage

MONTAGE.
Tracks: / She'll call her Mary / She's alone / Grand pianist / Men are building sand / Desiree / Song is love, The / Tinsel is ivy / All audience with Miss Priscilla Grey / My love / Wake up Jimmy.
LP: . . . . **KIRI 055**

Montague, John

O, THE NORTHERN MUSE (See under Heaney, Seamus (Montague, John & Seamus Heaney).

Montana

DANCE FANTASY, A.
LP: . . . . **K 50462**

GOOD OLD COUNTRY MUSIC.
MC: . . . . **AB 001**

Montana, Lee

ON THE RUN.
LP: . . . . **SFA 060**

YOU'RE ON MY MIND (WITH TIME ON MY HANDS).
Tracks: / It's a hard life / Amanda / Big iron / That was before I met you / Thing called love, A / Just out of reach / In the shelter of your eyes / Canadian Pacific / I don't want the money / Streets of Baltimore / Partners / Time on my hands.
LP: . . . . **SFA 090**

Montana, Patsy

EARLY COUNTRY FAVOURITES.
LP: OHCS 307

ORIGINAL HITS FROM THE WEST.
Tracks: / I wanna be a cowboy's dream girl / Swing time cowgirl / My poncho pony / Back on Montana plains / I wanna be a cowboy's sweetheart / Ridin' old paint / Lone star / Old black mountain trail / Smile and drive your blues away / Goodnight soldier / Out on the lone prairie / Shy little Ann from Cheyenne / Stand / Pass it on / Game of love / M for machine / Flesh and blood / Man of the hour / Hard headed woman / Don't damage the rock / Ready willing and able.
MC: CSR 3C

Montana, Vince Jr.

CHRISTMAS IS HERE (Montana, Vince Jr. Sextet).
LP: PSWLP 004

SUBTLE VIBES.
LP: PSWLP 003

Montand, Yves

HIS GREATEST HITS - VOL.2.
LP: 54620
MC: 40 54620

IN ENGLISH.
Tracks: / Durango / Montsouris Park / Le carrosse / Brother / Dans les plaines du far west / Against my will / Totting will / Intermission / My Clementine / Hollywood odyssey / Tangerine luxious fruit / On bicycle / Autumn.
LP: 6313 489

YVES MONTAND.
Tracks: / La bicyclette / Jazz et la Java / Le chat de la voisine / La chansonnette / Est-ce ainsi que les hommes vivent? / Je t'aime / La plus belle des mers / L'amoureuse / Coucher avec elle / Le port / Me souviens (Le) / En sortant d'ecole / On frappe / Paris at night / Quelqu'un / Page d'ecriture / Le jardin / Le miroir brise / Dans ma maison / Trois petites notes de musique / Il n'y plus d'apres.
MC: 824 784 4

Monteith, Kelly

LETTUCE BE COOL.
LP: CHR 1486
MC: ZCHR 1486

Montellas

CONSCIENCE.
Tracks: / Protection / Stop talking / What you gonna take / Conscience / Flag talk / How does your garden grow / Mornings like midnight / New rules for lovers / Get Lucky / Oblivion / Mersey serenade.
LP: 208965
MC: 408965

Monten, Bennie

BENNIE MONTEN'S KANSAS CITY ORCHESTRA 1923-25 (Monten, Bennie Kansas City Orchestra).
LP: S 820

MONTEN, BENNIE K.C. ORCHESTRA 1929-31/HARRY DIAL (Monten, Bennie K.C. Orchestra/Harry Dial Sextet).
LP: IAJRC 7

Montenegro, Hugo

BEST OF BROADWAY.
LP: GH 866

BEST OF HUGO MONTENEGRO.
Tracks: / Good, the bad and the ugly, The / Valley of the dolls, Theme from / Fox, The (theme from) / Fistful of dollars / Hang 'em high / Good vibrations / Love is blue / For a few dollars more / Happy together / Classical gas.
LP: INTS 5004
MC: INTK 5004

BROADWAY MELODIES 1.
Tracks: / Lady be good / Man I love, The / Tea for two / Girl friend / Who / Thou swell / Hallelujah / I got rhythm / Of thee I sing / Song is you / Yesterdays / Night & day / Varsity drag / Make believe / Easter parade.
LP: CBR 1003
MC: KCBR 1003

MUSIC FROM THE GOOD, THE BAD & THE UGLY (Original Soundtrack).
Tracks: / Good the bad and the ugly, The / Marcia (march) with hope / Story of a soldier, The / Ecstasy of gold / Fistful of dollars, A / Square dance / Titoli - man with no name / Aces high / Vice of killing / Sixty seconds to what / For a few dollars more.
LP: SF 7994
MC: VCS 67200

PLAYS FOR LOVERS.
MC: AMP 018

Monterose, J.R.

LIVE IN ALBANY.
Tracks: / Shadow of your smile / Ruby my dear / Lu-an / Just friends.
LP: UP 27 02

Monteverdi Academy

MADRIGALS, ARIAS, CANZONAS (See under Caceres, Emilio).

Monteverdi (composer)

MADRIGALS (Various artists).
MC: 4277224

MADRIGALS AND SACRED CONCERTOS (Various artists).
MC: MC 4277224 GW

Montez, Chris

"LET'S DANCE" AND HAVE "SOME KINDA FUN".
LP: MLP 100

MORE I SEE YOU (ALBUM).
LP: MFP 50435

Montgomery, Buddy

SO WHY NOT?.
LP: LLP 1518

Montgomery Clifts

DEADWOOD CHRONICLES.
LP: NTVLP 058

Montgomery, Erick

JUST PASSING THROUGH.
Tracks: / Pablo Colorado rain forest / Call / Bhutam / Magnetic knock-knee / Just passing through / Kaibito plateau / They leave ground / Ashir view / Nagual / Spaces.
LP: HDLP 001

Montgomery, James

SEPTEMBER MORNINGS.
LP: AMB 001

Montgomery, Little...

1930-69 (Montgomery, Little Brother).
LP: RSE 3

CHICAGO - THE LIVING LEGENDS (Montgomery, Little Brother).
Tracks: / Home again blues / Up the country blues / Saturday night function / Michigan water blues / Sweet daddy (your mam's done gone mad) / Prescription for the blues / 44 Vicksburg / Trouble in mind / Riverside boogie / Oh daddy blues / Somethin' keep worryin' me.
LP: CH 263
LP: OBC 525

DEEP SOUTH PIANO (Montgomery, Little Brother).
LP: SLP 228

LITTLE BROTHER MONTGOMERY, 1960 (The Piano Blues Unissued Recordings Vol.1) (Montgomery, Little Brother).
LP: PY 4451

LITTLE BROTHER MONTGOMERY, 1960 VOL.2 (Montgomery, Little Brother).
LP: PY 4452

LITTLE BROTHER MONTGOMERY & SUNNYLAND SLIM (Montgomery, Little Brother & Sunnyland Slim).
LP: 77LA 12/21

TISHOMINGO BLUES (Montgomery, Little Brother).
LP: JSP 1015

Montgomery, L.M.

ANNE OF GREEN GABLES (Jermyn, Jane).
MC: SOUND 22

ANNE OF GREEN GABLES (Braden, Kim (nar)).
MCSET: LFP 7355

Montgomery, Maree

WOMAN OF MYSTERY.
LP: LRF 189

Montgomery, Marian

I GOTTA RIGHT TO SING.
Tracks: / In the dark / Deed I do / Love dance / People will say we're in love / That old black magic / You came a long way from St. Louis / Mean to me / Ol' man river / Georgia on my mind / Yesterday's wine / I gotta right to sing the blues / He's my guy / Lady is a tramp, The.
LP: JHR 003

MARIAN MONTGOMERY ON STAGE.
Tracks: / Way I am, The / Oh Johnny / Don't it make my brown eyes blue? / Ain't no sunshine since you've gone / Rain sometimes / If I had my way / Seventeen / What's a lady like me doing in a joint like this? / Kansas City / It never entered my mind / If you could read my mind / There'll be some changes made / He's funny that way.
LP: HIFLY 29
MC: ZCFLY 29

PUTTIN' ON THE RITZ (Montgomery, Marian & Richard Rodney Bennett).
LP: Unknown
MC: ZCFLY 40

SOMETIMES IN THE NIGHT.
Tracks: / Man I love, The / Somebody loves me / Just in time / People that you never get to love, The / My foolish heart / Maybe (if he knew me) / Tell me softly / You're the best love / I don't want to walk without you / But love (that's another game) / Very thought of you, The / You've come a long way from St Louis / Not funny / Tender trap, The / You are my lucky star / Sometimes in the night.
LP: C5-532
MC: C5K-532

SURPRISE SURPRISE (Montgomery, Marian & Richard Rodney Bennett).
MC: ZCFLY 24
LP: HIFLY 24

TOWN AND COUNTRY (Montgomery, Marian & Richard Rodney Bennett).
Tracks: / Do you know the way to San Jose? / Night owl / I'm always drunk in San Francisco / Let's go and live in the country / On Broadway / New York state of mind / Ballad of the sad young man / Any place I hang my hat is home / Summerhouse / Folks who live on the hill, The / Save the sunlight / Skylark / Eagle and me / Peaceful.
LP: HIFLY 28
MC: ZCFLY 28

Montgomery, Melba

BLUEGRASS HOOTENNANY (See under Jones, George) (Jones, George/Melba Montgomery).

DON'T LET THE GOOD TIMES FOOL YOU.
LP: Unknown

MELBA MONTGOMERY.
Tracks: / Angel of the morning / Your love sure saved me from myself / There's nothing I don't see in you / Everybody's got a special song / Before the pain comes / We've been lyin' here too long / Pinkerton's flowers, The / Leavin' me in your mind / Hope for your happiness / Never-ending love affair.
LP: UAS 30152

PARTY PICKIN' (See under Jones, George) (Jones, George/Melba Montgomery).

Montgomery, Wes

BAGS MEETS WES (See under Jackson, Milt) (Montgomery, Wes / Milt Jackson).

BOSS GUITAR.
Tracks: / Besame mucho / Dearly beloved / Days of wine and roses / Trick bag / Canadian sunset / Fried pies / Breeze and I / For heavens sake.
LP: OJC 261

COLLECTION: WES MONTGOMERY.
Tracks: / Starlight / Round midnight / Come rain or come shine / Mister Walker / Cariba / Here's that rainy day / Full house / Blue 'n' boogie / To Django / I've grown accustomed to her face / S.O.S..
MC: DVMC 2044

ENCORES.
Tracks: / Movin' along / Body and soul / Trick bag / Moanin' / Delilah / Blue Roz / If I should lose you / Tune up.
LP: OJC 3001

FULL HOUSE (Montgomery, Wes/ Johnny Griffin).
LP: OJC 106

GREATEST HITS:WES MONTGOMERY.
LP: AMLS 976

GROOVE BROTHERS.
Tracks: / D-natural blues / Lover man / June in January / Jeannine / Angel eyes / Beaux arts / Snowfall / Bock to bock / Groove yard / If I should lose you / Delirium / Just for now / Doujie / Heart strings / Remember.
2LP: M 47051

IMPRESSIONS.
Tracks: / 4 on 6 / Wes' rhythm / Impressions / To when.
LP: AFF 13

LIVE AT JORGIES AND MORE.
LP: VGM 0008

LIVE AT JORGIES JAZZ CLUB.
Tracks: / All of you / Heartstrings / Summertime / Back to Bach.
LP: VGM 0001

LIVE IN PARIS 1965.
LP: FC 108

MIDNIGHT GUITARIST.
LP: CJZ LP 9

MOVIN' ALONG.
Tracks: / Movin' along / Tune up / Ghost of a chance / Sandu / Body and soul / So do it / Says you.
LP: OJC 089

MOVIN' WES.
Tracks: / West Coast blues / Caravan / Movin' Wes / Moca flor / Matchmaker matchmaker / Senza fine / Theodora / In and out / Born to be blue / People / Movin' Wes.
LP: 810 045-1
MC: 810 045-4
LP: 2304 377

SOLITUDE.
LP: AFF 18

WES MONTGOMERY PLAYS THE BLUES Compact/Walkman jazz.
Tracks: / Bumpin' on Sunset / California dreamin' / Movin' Wes (part 1) / Golden earrings / Sunny / Shadow of your smile, The / OGD / Tequila / Caravan / Once I loved / Movin' Wes (part 2) / Here;s that rainy day / Goin' out of my head / How insensitive / What the world needs now is love.
MC: 835 318-4

WES MONTGOMERY TRIO, THE (Montgomery, Wes Trio).
Tracks: / Round midnight / Yesterdays / End of a love affair, The / Whisper not / Ecaroh / Satin doll / Missile blues / Too late now / Jingles.
LP: RSLP 310

WORK SONG (see Adderley,Nat/Wes Montgomery).

Montoliu, Tete

CATALONIAN FOLKSONGS.
Tracks: / Cigales al ven / Canco de matinada / Manuel / Me embaix apeu / Una gitarra / Ruco / Cuin plan teniu, senor / La Amelia esta malalba / Els segadors.
LP: SJP 116

CATALONIAN NIGHTS VOL.1.
LP: SCS 1148

LIVE AT THE KEYSTONE CORNER (Montoliu, Tete/Herbie Lewis/Billy Higgins).
LP: SJP 138

SECRET LOVE (Montoliu, Tete Trio).
Tracks: / Secret love / Airegin / Confirmation / Four / Stella by starlight.
LP: SJP 111

SONGS FOR LOVE.
LP: ENJA 2040

TALK ABOUT YOU.
LP: SCS 1137

TETE!.
LP: SCS 1029

TOOTIE'S TEMPO.
LP: SCS 1108

YELLOW DOLPHIN STREET.
Tracks: / Yellow Dolphin Street / Come Sunday / I hate you / You've changed / Walse for Nicolien / Where are you? / Napoleon / If you could see me now.
LP: SJP 107

Montoya, Carlos

FLAMENCO DIRECT V1.
Tracks: / Aires de genil.
LP: CCS 6004

FLAMENCO DIRECT V2.
Tracks: / Jerez / Macarena en Tango / Saeta / Solea cana Zambra / Zapateao.
LP: CCS 6005

Montreal Symphony...

ENIGMA VARIATIONS/FALSTAFF SYMPHONIC STUDY (see under Elgar (composer)) (Montreal Symphony Orchestra).

LA MER (See under Debussy (composer)) (Montreal Symphony Orchestra).

Montreux Band

LET THEM SAY.
Tracks: / Let them say / October wedding / Astronomics / Barbara's dream / Mandolin rising / Finding time / Road to Vernazza / King sod / Still mountain / Free D.
LP: 37 10841
MC: 37 10844

SIGN LANGUAGE.
Tracks: / Skywriting / Sign language / Sweet intentions / Jacob Do Bandolim / In the shadow of the blimp / To be / Grant wood / Circular birds / Just walking.
LP: 37 1058 1
MC: 37 1058 4

Montrose

JUMP ON IT.
Tracks: / Let's go / What are you waiting for / Tuft sedge / Music man / Jump on it / Rich man / Crazy for you / Merry go round.

LP: K 56291

MONTROSE.
Tracks: / Rock the nations / Bad motor scooter / Space station No 5 / I don't want it / Good rockin' tonight / Rock candy / One thing on my mind / Make it last.
LP: K 46276

PAPER MONEY.
Tracks: / Underground / Connection / Dreamer, The / Starliner / I got the fire / Spaceage sacrifice / We're going home / Paper money.
LP: K 56069

WARNER BROS PRESENT MONTROSE.
Tracks: / Matriarch / All I need / Twenty flight back / Whaler, The / Dancin' feet / O lucky man / One and a half / Clown woman / Black train.
LP: K 56170

Montrose, J.R.

AND A LITTLE PLEASURE (Montrose, J.R. & Tommy Flanagan).
LP: UP 27 06

IN ACTION.
LP: SS 100

Montrose, Ronnie

DIVA STATION, A.
Tracks: / Sorcerer / Weirding way / Choke Canyon / Stay with me / High and dry / Diva station, The / New kid in town / Little demon / Quid pro quo / Solitaire.
LP: RR 9400 1

MEAN.
LP: ENIG 32641

SPEED OF SOUND.
LP: 3323 1
LP: GWLP 53

TERRITORY.
LP: PJ 88009
MC: PJC 88009

Monty Python's Flying

ANOTHER MONTY PYTHON RECORD.
Tracks: / Trondheim hammer dance / Liberty bell / Fanfare opening / Formal presentation / Contesana padwana / Man of power / Gold lame / Southern breeze / Spam song / Man of power / Bahama parakeet / House of fashion / Circus tumble / Fanfare / Mystery drums. / Mystery place / Ode to Edward / In step with Johann / Knees up Mother Brown.
LP: CHC 79
MC: CHCMC 79
LP: CAS 1049

CONTRACTUAL OBLIGATION.
Tracks: / Henry Kissinger / Never be rude to an Arab / I like Chinese / Medical love song / Finland / I'm so worried / I bet you they won't play this song on the rad / Here comes another one / Do wot John / Muddy knees / Traffic lights / All things dull and ugly / Scottish farewell, A / Sing as we go / Polygon / Sportstrack / Decomposing composers.
LP: CAS 1152
LP: CHC 34
MC: CHCMC 34

FINAL RIP OFF, THE (Highlights Compilation album).
Tracks: / Introduction / Constitutional peasants / Fish licence / Eric the half bee / Finland song / Travel agent / Are you embarrassed easily? / Australian table wines / Argument / Henry Kissinger / Parrot (Oh not again) / I like Chinese / Spanish inquisition (parts 1/2/3) / Cheese soup / Cherry orchard / Architect's sketch / Spam / Comfy chair / Famous person quiz / You be the actor / Nudge nudge / Cannibalism / Spanish inquisition revisited / Sit on my face / Undertaker / Novel writing (Live from Wessex) / String / Bells / Traffic lights / Cocktail bar / Four Yorkshiremen / Election special / Lumberjack song / I bet you they won't play this song on the radio / Bruces / Do wot John / Rock notes / I'm so worried / Crocodile / French taunter / Marylin monroe / Swamp castle / Last word, The / Bookshop / French taunter (part 2).
LP: MPD 1
MC: MPDC 1

INSTANT RECORD COLLECTION.
Tracks: / Introductions / Alastair Cooke / Nudge nudge / Mrs. Nigger Baiter / Constitutional peasants / Fish licence / Eric the half a bee / Australian table wines / Silly noises / Novel writing / Elephantoplasty / How to do it / Gumby cherry orchard / Oscar Wilde / Introduction / Argument / French taunter / Summarized Proust competition / Cheese emporium / Funerals at Prestatyn / Camelot / Word association / Bruces / Parrot / Monty Python.
LP: CAS 1134
MC: CASMC 1134

LIFE OF BRIAN (Film soundtrack).
LP: K 56751
MC: K4 56751

LIVE AT DRURY LANE.
Tracks: / Introduction / Llamas / Gumby cherry orchard / Flower arranging / Secret service / Wrestling / Communist quiz / Idiot song / Albatross / Colonel / Nudge nudge / Cocktail bar / Travel agent / Spot the brain cell / Bruces / Argument / Four Yorkshiremen / Election special / Lumberjack song / Parrot sketch.
LP: CLASS 4
LP: VVIP 104
MC: VVIPC 104

MATCHING TIE AND HANDKERCHIEF.
LP: CHC 81
MC: CHCMC 81
LP: CAS 1080

MONTY PYTHON.
LP: CAS 1003

MONTY PYTHON AND THE HOLY GRAIL (Film soundtrack).
Tracks: / Jeunesse / Honours list / Big country / Homeward bound / God choir / Fanfare / Camelot song, The / Sunrise music / Magic finger / Sir Robin's song / In the shadows / Desperate moment / Knights of Ni / Circle of danger / Love theme / Magenta / Starlet in the starlight / Monk's chat / Promised land, The.
LP: CHC 17
MC: CHCMC 17

MONTY PYTHON'S FLYING CIRCUS.
Tracks: / Flying sheep / Television interviews / Trades descriptions act / Nudge nudge / Mouse problem / Buying a bed / Interesting people / Barber, The / Interviews / More television interviews / Children's stories / Visitors, The / Cinema / North Minehead by-election / Me, doctor / Pet shop / Self defence.
LP: REB 73
MC: REMC 73

MONTY PYTHON'S MEANING OF LIFE (Film soundtrack).
MC: 40 70239
LP: CBS 70239

PREVIOUS ALBUM.
Tracks: / Fashion parade / Alla handel / Sporting news / Money song / Dennis Moore (Robin Hood theme) / Happy movement / Eric the half a bee / Holiday time / Beethoven's 5th / Comic giggles / Beachy head / Yangtse music / Medieval fanfares / Great adventure suite / Fairytale music / Ya de bucketty / Television tensions.
LP: CHC 80
MC: CHCMC 80
LP: CAS 1063

SINGS.
Tracks: / Always look on the bright side of life / Sit on my face / Lumberjack song / Penis song (not the Noel Coward song) / Oliver Cromwell / Money song / Accountancy shanty / Finland / Medical love song / I'm so worried / Every sperm is sacred / Never be rude to an arab / I like Chinese / Eric the half a bee / Brian song / Bruce's philosophers song / Meaning of life / Knights of the Round Table / All things dull and ugly / Decomposing compers / Henry Kissinger / I've got two legs / Christmas in heaven / Galaxy song / Spam song.
LP: MONT 1
MC: MONTC 1

Monyaka

GO DEH YAKA (GO TO THE TOP) (OLD GOLD) (See under Hot streak/Body work).

Mood Six

DIFFERENCE IS..., THE.
LP: PSYCHO 33

MATTER OF..., A.
Tracks: / Contemporary scene, The / Voice of reason, The / Eternal / Back to the day / Life that Jack built, The / Matter of, A / What have you ever done? / Love of money / Far Away / When the time comes / Perfect life, The / Game show.
LP: BRED 71
MC: CBRED 71

Moodie

BACKSLATE MEET SOUL SYNDICATE.
Tracks: / Rum dub / Hold dub / Lost dub / Bearded dub / Love dub / Crazy dub / Wine dub / Expensive dub / World dub / Ms World dub.
MC: SS 95

DO THE JAM.
Tracks: / Jenny goes to Paris / Radio DJ / Radio dub / Stay alive / Stay alive dub / Mockery of democracy / Do the jam / Tease me / Chill the night / Christ is lord / Woman woman.
LP: LRM 99
MC: LRMC 99

DUBS TO TREASURE.
Tracks: / Touchable dub / Nobody dub / Somebody dub / Untouchable dub / Revolution dub / Natty dub / Dread dub / Duffus dub / Framed dub / More movie dub / Imagine.
LP: SS 106
MC: SSC 106

JUDAH DUB.
Tracks: / Whole town's dubbing / Bum dub / Hold me tight dub / Original dub / Bearded dub / Last dub / Blue dub.
MC: SS 100

LEGEND OF JUDAH CONTINUES, THE.
Tracks: / Woman woman / Petrol / I love you / Loving feeling / Be happy / I say / Organisation of African unity / I can't do without her / Living on the dole / Love me tonight hate me tomorrow night / Politics / Reggae on the moon / Smallpox alert in Birmingham / My girl Pearl / Hollywood / Blokes on coke, The / Cashflow / Trench town rock / Many moods of moodie, The / Trevor Wallace / Jesus Christ / Cash / Smallpox alert / Revolution in Rhodesia.
2LP: PTLP 1001
LP: SS 99
MC: SSC 99

LEGEND OF MOODIE.
LP: SS 102

LIVE IN GERMANY.
LP: SS 1017

LOVER'S.
Tracks: / Love is a wonderful thing / Reveal your love / Tease me / Nobody loves you / Loving feeling / Give I a love / I love you / Radio DJ / Whole town talking / Janie goes to Paris.
MC: SS 97

LOVINGLY MOODIE.
LP: SS 1011

MANY MOODS.
LP: SS 107

MOODIE.
LP: SS 103

MOODIE AND FRIENDS.
LP: SS 101

MOODIE AND THE CREW.
LP: SS 1015

MOODIE: EARLY DAYS.
Tracks: / Mafia / Nobody cares 4 u / Untouchable / Trevor Wallace / Jah live / It's a natty affair / Miss world / Drama of the day / Down in the ghetto.
LP: SS 105
MC: SSC 105

MOODIE LOVE DANCE.
LP: SS 109

MOODIE MEETS DUNKLEY (Moodie & Dunkley).
Tracks: / Whole town's talking / Hold me tight / Never let you go / I love you / Love is a wonderful thing / Sticksman / King Pharoah / Oau trench town rock / School days / Ropey.
MC: SS 102

MOODIE MEETS FERGIE.
LP: SS 1013

MOODIE SEAL.
LP: SS 1016

MORE MOODIE.
LP: SS 104

OAU-TRENCH TOWN ROCK.
Tracks: / Woman woman / Petrol / I love you / Loving feeling / Be happy / I say / Sticksman / OAU trench town rock / Can't do without her.
LP: SS 1014
MC: SSC 114
LP: SS 114

PHYSICAL ATTRACTION.
Tracks: / I love you, I think you love me too / Do the jam / Heartbeat / Physical attraction / Instrubeat / We've got the vibes / Physical dub / Vibes.
LP: LRM 133
MC: SS 96

REGGAE ON THE MOON.
Tracks: / Living on the dole / Love me tonight and hate me tomorrow night / Politics / Reggae on the moon / Small pox alert in Birmingham / My girl Pearl / Hollywood / Bloke on coke / Cashflow.
LP: SS 1017
MC: SS 98

UNIVERSITY.
Tracks: / Live your life / Emperor / University of life / Donald Duffus / Mid Summer dub / Expensive dub / Miss world dub / Female dub / Radio DJ.
LP: SS 1010
MC: UNKNOWN

UNMISTAKEDLY MOODIE.
LP: SS 1012

YOUNG LION.
LP: SS 108

Moodists

DOUBLE LIFE.
LP: RFM 44

ENGINE SHUDDER.
Tracks: / Kept spectre / Road is holy, The / Junkyard.
LP: RFM 21

THIRSTY'S CALLING.
LP: RFA 39

Moody Blues

BLUE.
Tracks: / Voices in the sky / Out and in / Candle of life / After you came / For my lady / Cities / Simple game, A / Fly me high / Steppin' in a slide zone / So deep without you / I'll be level with you / Leave this man alone / Dr Livingstone, I presume / Gimme a little somethin' / Question.
LP: PWKLP 4022 P
MC: PWKMC 4022 P

COLLECTION: MOODY BLUES.
Tracks: / Go now / Steal your heart away / Lose your money / Don't mind / Let me go / I'll go crazy / Time is on my side / It's easy child / Something you got / I've got a dream / From the bottom of my heart / Can't nobody love you / Come back / Stop / Bye bye bird / It ain't necessarily so / True story / And my baby's gone.
2LP: CCSLP 105
MC: CCSMC 105

DAYS OF FUTURE PASSED (Moody Blues/London Festival Orchestra/Peter Knight).
Tracks: / Day begins, The / Dawn - dawn is a feeling / Morning, The / Another morning / Lunch break / Peak hour / Afternoon / Forever afternoon (Tuesday?) / Time to get away / Evening / Sunset, The / Twilight time / Night, The / Nights in white satin.
LP: DOA 6
MC: KDOAC 6
LP: SML 707

EVERY GOOD BOY DESERVES FAVOURS.
Tracks: / Procession / Story in your eyes / Our guessing game / Emily's song / After you came / One more to live / Nice to be here / You can never go home / My song.
LP: THS 5
MC: KTHC 5

GO NOW (OLD GOLD) (See under Zombies/She's not there (Old Gold).

GREATEST HITS: MOODY BLUES.
LP: 840 659 1
MC: 840 659 4

IN SEARCH OF THE LOST CHORD.
Tracks: / Departure / Ride my see-saw / Doctor Livingstone, I presume / House of four doors / Legend of a mind / House of four doors (part 2) / Voices in the sky / Best way to travel, The / Visions of paradise / Actor, The / Word, The / Om.
LP: DOA 7
MC: KDOAC 7
LP: SML 711

KEYS OF THE KINGDOM.
LP: 849433-1
MC: 849433-4

LONG DISTANCE VOYAGER.
Tracks: / Voice / Talking out of turn / Gemini dream / In my world / Meanwhile / 22,000 days / Nervous / Painted smile / Reflective smile / Veteran cosmic rocker.
MC: KTXC 139
LP: TXS 139

MUSIC FOR MILLIONS.
Tracks: / I'll go crazy / Something you got / Go now / Can't nobody love you / I don't mind / I got a dream / Let me go / Thank you baby / It ain't necessarily so / True story / Bye bye bird.
LP: 64595107
MC: 7195107

OCTAVE.
Tracks: / One step into the light / Day we met again, The / Steppin' in a slide zone / Under moonshine / Had to fall in love / I'll be level with you / Driftwood / Top rank suite / I'm your man / Survival.
LP: TXS 129
MC: KTXC 129

ON THE THRESHOLD OF A DREAM.
Tracks: / In the beginning / lovely to see you / Dear diary / Send me no wine / To share our love / So deep within you / Never comes the day / Lazy day / Are you sitting comfortably / Dream, The / Have you heard (part 1) / Voyage, The / Have you heard (part 2).
LP: SML 1035
MC: KSCM 1035

OTHER SIDE OF LIFE.

LP: . . . . POLD 5190
MC: . . . . POLDC 5190

OUT OF THIS WORLD.
LP: . . . . NE 1051

PRESENT, THE.
Tracks: / Blue world / Meet me halfway / Sitting at the wheel / Going nowhere / Hole in the world / Under my feet / It's cold outside of your heart / Running water / I am / Sorry.
LP: . . . . TXS 140
MC: . . . . KTXC 140

QUESTION OF BALANCE, A.
Tracks: / Question / How is it (we are here) / And the tide rushes in / Don't you feel small / Tortoise and the hare / It's up to you / Minstrel's song / Dawning is the day / Melancholy man / Balance, The.
LP: . . . . THS 3
MC: . . . . KTHC 3

SEVENTH SOJOURN.
Tracks: / Lost in a lost world / New horizons / For my lady / Isn't life strange! / You and me / Land of make believe / When you're a free man / I'm just a singer (in a rock and roll band).
LP: . . . . THS 7
MC: . . . . KTHC 7

SUR LA MER.
Tracks: / I know you're out there somewhere / Want to be with you / River of endless love / No more lies / Here comes the weekend / Vintage wine / Breaking point / Miracle / Love is on the run / Deep.
LP: . . . . POLH 43
MC: . . . . POLHC 43

THIS IS THE MOODY BLUES.
Tracks: / Question / Actor, The / Word, The / Eyes of a child / Dear diary / Legend of a mind / In the beginning / Lovely to see you / Never comes the day / Isn't life strange / Dream, The / Have you heard / Voyage / Ride my see-saw / Tuesday afternoon / And the tide rushes in / New horizons / Simple game / Watching and waiting / I'm just a singer (in a rock and roll band) / For my lady / Story in your eyes / Melancholy man / Nights in white satin.
2LP: . . . . MB 1/2
MCSET: . . . . KMBC 1
2LP: 8200071

TO OUR CHILDREN'S, CHILDREN'S, CHILDREN.
Tracks: / Higher and higher / Eyes of a child / Floating / Eyes of a child II / I never thought I'd live to be a hundred / Beyond / Out and in / Gypsy / Eternity road / Candle of life / Sun is still shining / I never thought I'd live to be a million / Watching and waiting.
LP: . . . . THS 1
MC: . . . . KTHC 1
LP: 8203641

VOICES IN THE SKY.
Tracks: / Ride my see-saw / Talking out of question / Driftwood / Never comes the day / I'm just a singer (in a rock and roll band) / Gemini dream / Voice, The / After you came / Question / Veteran cosmic rocker / Isn't life strange / Nights in white satin.
LP: . . . . SKL 5341
MC: . . . . KSKC 5341

Moody Brothers

CARLTON MOODY & THE MOODY BROTHERS.
Tracks: / Shame on me / I tried at first not to / You turned the light on / Aunt Bea's breakdown / I'll know you're gonna cheat on me / You / You left the water running / Dreaming / Showboat gambler / Little country county fair / Start with the talking / Drive over the mountain.
LP: . . . . SDLP 042
MC: . . . . SDC 042

COTTON EYED JOE.
Tracks: / Midnight flyer / My mind's already home / Let me dance with you / Redneck girl / It's my turn to sing with ol' Willie / Southern railroad / Brown eyed girl / When she tells you goodbye / Line dancing / Our love / Cotton-eyed Joe.
LP: . . . . SDLP 032
MC: . . . . SDC 032

Moody, James

BEBOP REVISITED, VOL 4 (Moody, James & Bennie Green).
Tracks: / That's it / Mean to me / Date with Kate / Embraceable you / Big and little / 'S wonderful / Choice taste / Lesson in bopology / Loop-plu-e-du / Honeysuckle / Our very own / Lowland bounce / La vie en rose / Blues is green.
LP: . . . . XAN 197

EASY LIVING.
Tracks: / Flutin' the blues / Birdland story, The / It could happen to you / I cover the waterfront / Body and soul / Breaking the blues / Parker's mood / Easy living / Boo's tune / Richard's blues / Great day / Search, The / Let's try / One never knows / Opalesque / Blues impromptu / Malice towards none.
2LP: . . . . CXJD 6702
MCSET: . . . . ZCCJD 6702

FLUTE 'N' THE BLUES.
Tracks: / Flute'n' the blues / Birdland story, The / It could happen to you / I cover the waterfront / Body and soul / Breaking the blues / Parker's mood / Easy living / Boo's tune / Richard blues.
LP: . . . . GCH 8088
MC: . . . . GCHK 8088

GREAT DAY, THE.
Tracks: / Great day / Search,The / Let's try / One never knows / Opalesque / Blues impromptu / Malice towards none.
LP: . . . . GCH 8090
MC: . . . . GCHK 78090

HONEY.
Tracks: / Honey's tune / It might as well be spring / Mutt and Jeff / Sepia / Someone to watch over me / Look into my eyes / I can't get started / Moody's blue / When you wish upon a star.
MC: . . . . PK 83111

MOODY'S MOOD FOR LOVE.
LP: . . . . DRLP 95

MOVING FORWARD.
Tracks: / Autumn leaves / Round midnight / Summer afternoon, A / November afternoon / Giant steps / What do you do / Cupbearers / Night has a thousand eyes, The / Moody's theme.
LP: . . . . PL 83026

MPS JAZZ TIME, VOLUME 10 (see Cohn,Al & James Moody) (Moody, James & Al Cohn).

NEW SOUNDS (See under Blakey, Art) (Blakey, Art/James Moody).

SOMETHING SPECIAL.
Tracks: / Moody's mood update / I'm in the mood for love / Real feels good / Nubian fantasies / Transfer to Manhattan / More than you know / Inside lover / Shake, rattle and boogie (On compact disc only.).
LP: . . . . PL 83004

SWEET AND LOVELY.
Tracks: / My melancholy baby / Sweet and lovely / Con alma / Skippin' / Confirmation / My ideal / Get the booty / Rain (CD only.) / Get the booty (CD only.).
LP: . . . . PL 83063
MC: . . . . PK 83063

TENOR CONTRASTS (Moody, James/ Stan Getz).
Tracks: / S'cool boy / Dear old Stockholm / I only have eyes for you / I'm getting sentimental over you / Prelude to a kiss / Night and day / Don't be afraid / Flamingo / Out of nowhere / These foolish things / I'm in the mood for bop / Flight of the bopple bee / Body and soul / I'm in the mood for love / Lester leaps in / Indiana / Esquire.
LP: . . . . ESQ 309

TENOR CONTRASTS VOLUME 2 (See under Sims, Zoot) (Moody, James & Zoot Sims).

Moon, Derek

AT THE HAMMOND ORGAN VOL 3.
LP: . . . . PC 339

CHRISTMAS CELEBRATION.
LP: . . . . PC 340

DEREK MOON PLAYS FOR YOU.
LP: . . . . PC 834

DEREK MOON PLAYS FOR YOU VOL.2.
LP: . . . . PC 313

Moon In The Gutter

MOON IN THE GUTTER, THE (Original Soundtrack) (Various artists).
LP: . . . . SL 9516
MC: . . . . SLC 9516

Moon, Maggie

DEAR ANYONE.
LP: . . . . DJH 20541

I WANNA BE LOVED BY YOU.
LP: . . . . RBLP 1009
MC: . . . . ACRB 1009

THRILL OF LOVE, THE.
MC: . . . . STAC 2357
LP: . . . . STAR 2357

Moon, Mick

FOR MY FRIENDS.
LP: . . . . BSS 226

Moon Over Parador

MOON OVER PARADOR, THE (Original Soundtrack) (Various artists).
LP: . . . . MCA 6249
MC: . . . . MCAC 6249

Moon Princess

MOON PRINCESS, THE (Various artists).
Tracks: / Moon princess: *Various artists* / Luck of the sea and the luck of the mountains, The: *Various artists* / Peach boy: *Various artists* / Badger kettle, The: *Various artists*.
MC: . . . . ANV 666

Moondoc, Jemel

ATHENS CONCERT, THE (Moondoc, Jemel/Quartet Muntu).
LP: . . . . CM 107

Moondogs

TEENAGE BLUES.
LP: . . . . LP 8802

Mooney, Art

1945-46 (Mooney, Art & Orchestra).
LP: . . . . CLP 134

Mooney, Claire

ROCKING THE BOAT.
LP: . . . . BWLP 1

Mooney, Gordon

OVER THE BORDER.
LP: . . . . TP 031

Mooney, John

COMIN' YOUR WAY.
LP: BP-779

LATE LAST NIGHT.
Tracks: / Late last night / Rip / Country gal / Baby please don't go / Travelin' on / Lovin' mood / It don't matter / Out that door / Late on in the evening / Coma mama / Country boy.
LP: . . . . BB 9505

TELEPHONE KING.
Tracks: / Wibble whim she when she walk / Watcha gonna do / Telephone king / Let me go / Please baby please / Oh Louise / Rainin' down on my broken heart / Ain't done wrong / Coal stove Mama / Please please please.
LP: BP-1383
LP: . . . . POW 4101
MC: . . . . POW 4101 MC

Mooney, Ralph

CORN PICKIN' & SLICK SLIDIN' (Mooney, Ralph/ James Burton).
LP: . . . . PM 1550751

Moonglows

LOOK, IT'S THE MOONGLOWS.
Tracks: / Love is is a river / Blue velvet / This is love / When I'm with you / I'll stop wanting you / Don't say goodbye / Ten commandments of love / Kiss me baby / Penny arcade / Mean old blues / Sweeter than words / Cold feet.
LP: . . . . GCH 8045
MC: . . . . GCHK 78045

Moonlight Broadcasters

WITH KEITH NICHOLS see also under Nichols,Keith.
LP: . . . . SOS 1193

Moonlight Moods

REFLECTIONS.
Tracks: / For once in my life / More / Where or when / Stranger on the shore / On a clear day / Exodus / Softly as I leave you / Shadow of your smile / Love letters / I wish you love / Very thought of you, The / I'll be seeing you / I have dreamed / Impossible dream, The / Man and a woman, A / Long ago and far away.
MC: . . . . HSC 3271

THEMES AND DREAMS.
Tracks: / Deer Hunter (Cavatina), Theme from / Fantasy / Bright eyes / North star / Xanadu / Angel of the morning / Give us shelter / Chariots of fire / M.A.S.H, Theme from / Chi mai / Waterfalls / Bermuda triangle / I made it through the rain / Imagine / To love the Lord / Riders in the sky / For your eyes only / Sukiyaki / Sailing / Magic.
LP: . . . . SHM 3102
MC: . . . . HSC 3102

THEMES AND DREAMS.
LPS: . . . . IMP 103
MCSET: . . . . IMPC 103

THEMES AND DREAMS, VOL.2.
Tracks: / Heartbreaker / One day I'll fly away / Total eclipse of the heart.
LP: . . . . SHM 3148
MC: . . . . HSC 3148

Moonlight Serenaders

LOVE FOR SALE - THE COLE PORTER ALBUM.
Tracks: / Who wants to be a millionaire / Friendship / Anything goes / It's de-lovely / Let's do it (let's fall in love) / Love for sale / All of you / I love Paris / Every time we say goodbye / Begin the beguine / I've got you under my skin / I get a kick out of you / What is this thing called love / I concentrate on you / Easy to love / Did you ever? / Just one of those things / From this moment on.
MC: . . . . PWKMC 4060

STARDUST MEMORIES (Hits of the 30's and 40's).
Tracks: / Change partners / Night and day / Cheek to cheek / Let's face the music and dance / Way you look tonight, The / You're the top / Zing! Went the strings of my heart / Nice work if you can get it / We're in the money / I've got a gal in Kalamazoo / In the mood / Chattanooga choo choo / Moonlight serenade / Boogie woogie bugle boy / Don't sit under the apple tree / White cliffs of Dover / Easter parade / Trolley song, The.
MC: . . . . PWKMC 4038

Moonlighters

PAINS OF 17.
LP: . . . . STING 013

RUSH HOUR.
LP: . . . . FIEND 10

Moonlighting

MOONLIGHTING (Television Soundtrack Album) (Various artists).
Tracks: / Moonlighting: *Jarreau, Al* / Limbo rock: *Checker, Chubby* / This old heart of mine: *Isley Brothers* / I told ya I love Ya, now get out: *Sheperd, Cybill* / Good lovin': *Willis, Bruce* / Since I fell for you: *James, Bob & David Sanborn* / When a man loves a woman: *Sledge, Percy* / Someone to watch over me: *Ronstadt, Linda* / Stormy weather: *Holiday, Billie*.
LP: . . . . MCF 3386
MC: . . . . MCFC 3386

Moonlizards

FOOOM.
Tracks: / Mercy's on celebrities / Happy / Sexist cliche love song / August '85 / Cracked / Hippymen / Mr Volcano / Big bum / Simply hate / Up against myself / You eats you / Big ego type of thing / Consider me fan / In.
LP: . . . . SCH 9012

Moonmaids Plus One

CURTAIN CALL.
MC: . . . . MOONMAIDS 2.588

HERE - WE SING IT AGAIN.
MC: . . . . MOONMAIDS 1.886

Moonraker

MOONRAKER (Film soundtrack) (Various artists).
Tracks: / Moonraker (main title): *Bassey, Shirley* / Space laser battle: *Barry, John* / Miss Goodhead meets Bond: *Barry, John* / Cable car and snake fight: *Barry, John* / Bond lured to pyramid: *Barry, John* / Flight into space: *Barry, John* / Bond arrives in Rio & boat chase: *Barry, John* / Centrifuge and Corrine put down: *Barry, John* / Bond smells a rat: *Barry, John* / Moonraker (end title): *Barry, John*.
LP: 3C 054 82696
LP: . . . . UAG 30247
MC: 1C 064 82696
MC: . . . . TCK 30247

MOONRAKER (Original Soundtrack) (Various artists).
MC: . . . . E 41 E 90620
LP: 1826961
MC: 1826964

Moonshine Hollow Band

GEORGIA YELLOW HAMMERS, THE.
LP: . . . . ROUNDER 1032

Moonshiners

BLESS ALL MOONSHINERS.
LP: . . . . LRF 075

Moonstomp

THEY NEVER SEE.
LP: . . . . LNKLP 086

Moonstone (bk)

MOONSTONE, THE (William Wilkie Collins) (Jeffrey, Peter (nar)).
MCSET: CC/052

Moonstruck

MOONSTRUCK (Original Soundtrack) (Various artists).
Tracks: / That's amore: *Martin, Dean* / Canzone per Loretta: *Various artists* / Addio, Mulberry Street: *Various artists* / Mr. Moon: *Various artists* / It must be him: *Various artists* / Old man Mazurka: *Various artists* / Lament for Johnny's mama: *Various artists* / La boheme: *Various artists* / Che gelida manina: *Various artists* / Donde lieta usci: *Various artists* / O soave fanciulla: *Various artists* / Musettas waltz: *Various artists* / Musettas entrance: *Various artists* / Instrumental excerpts: *Various artists* / Getting ready: *Various artists* / Brooklyn heights stroll: *Various artists* / Beautiful senorita: *Various artists* / Moonglow: *Various artists* / Gioventu mia, tu non sei morta: *Various artists*.

LP: EST 2060
MC: TCEST 2060

Moonwalker

MOONWALKER (VIDEO) (See under Jackson, Michael) (Jackson, Michael).

Moore, Alex

IN EUROPE.
LP: ARHOOLIE 1048

PIANO BLUES.
LP: ARHOOLIE 1008

WIGGLE TAIL.
LP: ROUNDER 2091
MC: ROUNDER 2091C

Moore, Alice

LONESOME WOMAN BLUES.
LP: AB 2013

Moore, Barry

IN GRONINGEN (Moore, Barry & Eamon Murray).
LP: KLOET 001

TREATY STONE.
LP: LUN 022

Moore, Ben

PURIFIED.
Tracks: / I've got a winner in you / Slipping away / Got to see if I can get mommy (to come back home) / Love music / I ain't got to love nobody else / Slow dancing / Get closer / Keeping in touch / Easy as pie.
LP: DJF 20552

Moore, Bob

MEXICO.
Tracks: / Mexico / Hot spot / Cologne / Ooh la la Paloma / Fireball mail / Blue tango / Auf wiedersehen, Marlene / El picador / South of the border / Hooten trumpet / My adobe hacienda / Mexicali rose / Nuevo laredo / Mexican wedding / Vaya con dios.
LP: BFX 15288

Moore, Brew

BREW MOORE QUINTET (Moore, Brew & Lars Sjosten Trio).
LP: OJC 100

BREW'S STOCKHOLM DEW.
Tracks: / King Frederik's blues / Old folks / Ladislav / Batie / Brew's Stockholm Dew's.
LP: SNTF 624

DANISH BREW.
LP: JAZZ MARK 101

NO MORE BREW.
LP: SLP 4019

Moore, Brian

COLOUR OF BLOOD, THE.
MC: CAB 343

Moore, Charlie

ORIGINAL REBEL SOLDIER, THE.
Tracks: / Rebel soldier / Lonesome road blues / Convict and the rose, The / Best female actress of the year / Chubby's lonesome blues / Philadelphia lawyer / Six white horses / Little blossom / Cacklin' hen, The / Don't let your sweet love die / Put my little shoes away.
LP: REBEL 1662
MC: REBELMC 1662

Moore, Christy

CHRISTY MOORE.
LP: 2383 426

CHRISTY MOORE - COLLECTION 1981-91, THE.
LP: WX 434
MC: WX 434C

CHRISTY MOORE & FRIENDS (incl. Ralph McTell).
LP: RTE 59

IRON BEHIND THE VELVET.
LP: TA 2002
MC: 4TA 2002

LIVE IN DUBLIN.
LP: TA 2005
MC: 4TA 2005

NICE 'N' EASY.
Tracks: / Bunch of thyme / Nancy Spain / Galtee mountain boy / Boys of Mullabawn / Lanigans rake / Tippin' it up to Nancy / Home by bearna / Little musgrave / Ballad of Timothy Evans / Moving on song (Go.Move.Shift.) / Sacco and Vanzetti.
LP: 823 099-1
MC: 3192689

ORDINARY MAN.
Tracks: / Sweet music roll on / Delirium tremens / Ordinary man / Matty / Reel in the flickering light / Diamondtina drover / Blantyre explosion / Hard cases / Continental ceili / St. Brendan's voyage / Another song is born / Quiet desperation.
LP: FIEND 82
MC: FIENDCASS 82

LP: 2407631

PROSPEROUS.
LP: TA 2008
MC: 4TA 2008

RIDE ON.
Tracks: / Ride on.
LP: 240407 1
MC: 240407 4

SMOKE AND STRONG WHISKEY.
MC: CM 00024
LP: CM 00021

SPIRIT OF FREEDOM.
LP: IR 0840

TIME HAS COME, THE.
LP: 240150 1
MC: 240150 4

UNFINISHED REVOLUTION.
Tracks: / Biko drum / Natives / Metropolitan Avenue / Unfinished revolution / Other side, The / Messenger boy / On the bridge / Suffocate / Derby day / Doctor Vibes / Pair of brown eyes, A.
LP: WX 104
MC: WX 104 C

VOYAGE.
Tracks: / Mystic lipstick / Voyage, The / Mad lady and me, The / Deportees club, The / Night visit, The / All for the roses / Missing you / Bright blue rose / Farewell to pripchat / Muscha God help her / First time ever I saw your face, The / Middle of the island.
LP: WX 286
MC: WX 286C

WHATEVER TICKLES YOUR FANCY.
LP: 2383 344

Moore, Dorothy

DOROTHY MOORE.
Tracks: / Let the music play / I believe you / Love me / Make it soon / With pen in hand / 1-2-3 (you and me) / Loving you is just an old habit / Daddy's eyes / For old time's sake / Too blind to see.
LP: EPC 82356

DOROTHY MOORE ALBUM, THE.
Tracks: / Misty blue / I dont want to be with nobody but you / Too much love / Laugh it off / Only time you ever say you love me / I believe you / Funny how time slips away / Dark end of the street / Ain't that mother's luck / Enough woman left / It's so good / With pen in hand.
LP: CBS 31776
MC: 40 31776

FEEL THE LOVE.
LP: MAL 7455
MC: MALC 7455

MISTY BLUE (LP).
LP: MAL 6351
MC: MALC 6351

ONCE MOORE WITH FEELING.
Tracks: / Special occasion / What am I to do? / Girl overboard / Write a little prayer / Going ups and coming downs / We need more loving time / Being alone / If I could find my way back to you / He knows just where to touch me.
LP: EPC 83450

TALK TO ME.
Tracks: / Talk to me / Every beat of my heart / Crazy in love / Angel of the morning / It's all in the game / If I could feel that old feeling again / There'll never be another night like this / Something / Lonely.
LP: EPC 84255

TIME OUT FOR ME.
Tracks: / Time out for me / Endless summer nights / He may not be mine / I still get turned on / Can't get over you / Don't hold your breath / Whatever you can do / Walk through this pain.
LP: VOLT 401

Moore, Dudley

AT THE WAVENDON FESTIVAL.
Tracks: / Should care,I / Two for the road / Chimes / Amalgam / Yesterdays / You'd be so nice to come home to / Cornfield / Waltz for Suzie / And the same to you / Horizon / Morning walk.
LP: BLP 12151

CLEAN TAPES (see under Cook, Peter) (Moore, Dudley & Peter Cook).

COME AGAIN (see under 'Cook, Peter') (Moore, Dudley & Peter Cook).

DEREK & CLIVE COME AGAIN (See under Cook, Peter for details) (Moore, Dudley & Peter Cook).

DEREK & CLIVE LIVE (See under Cook, Peter for details) (Moore, Dudley & Peter Cook).

DUDLEY DOWN UNDER.
Tracks: / Love walked in / Here's that rainy day / Prelude / Georgia on my mind / Young prince and young princess / Tricotism / Autumn in New York / Song for Suzy / Lover.
LP: ICS 1003
MC: ZCICS 1003

GENUINE DUD (Moore, Dudley Trio).
LP: LK 4788

MUSIC OF DUDLEY MOORE.
Tracks: / Head first / Waltz for Suzy / Hello sailor / Rupert Street concerto / Madrigal / Mating cry / Thirty is a dangerous age, Cynthia / Italy / Bedazzled / Millionaire / Cornfield / Lillian Lust / Exactly like you / You'd be so nice to come home to / My blue Heaven / Poova nova / Sad one for George / Sooz blooz / Yesterdays / Straight life.
2LP: TOOFA 14
MCSET: ZCTOF 14

ONCE MORE WITH COOK (See under Cook, Peter for details) (Moore, Dudley & Peter Cook).

ORCHESTRA! (See under Solti, Sir George) (Moore, Dudley/Sir George Solti).

ORCHESTRA (VIDEO) VOL.1 (See under Solti, Sir George) (Moore, Dudley/ Sir George Solti).

ORCHESTRA (VIDEO) VOL.2 (See under Solti, Sir George) (Moore, Dudley/ Sir George Solti).

ORCHESTRA (VIDEO) VOL.3 (See under Solti, Sir George) (Moore, Dudley/ Sir George Solti).

OTHER SIDE OF DUDLEY MOORE.
LP: LK 4732

SMILIN' THROUGH (Moore, Dudley/ Cleo Laine).
Tracks: / Smilin' through / Love me or leave me / I don't know why / When I take my sugar to tea / I'll be around / Strictly for the birds / Before love went out of style / Brown soft shoe / I can't give you anything but love / It's easy to remember / Play it again Sam / Be a child.
LP: CBS 25137
MC: 40 25137

Moore, Freddie

GREAT FREDDIE MOORE & HOT JAZZ ORCHESTRA OF NEW YORK (Moore, Freddie & Hot Jazz Orchestra).
Tracks: / I got it bad and that ain't good / Rockin' chair / Save it pretty mama / Rag alley blues / Blue turning grey over you / Snowball.
LP: J 001

Moore, Gary

AFTER THE WAR.
Tracks: / After the war / Speak for yourself / Livin' on dreams / Led clones / Running from the storm / This thing called love / Ready for love / Blood of emeralds / Messiah will come again, The (Only on CD and MC.) / Dunluce (part 1) (Only on CD.) / Dunluce (part 2) (Only on CD.) / Dunluce (Only on MC.).
LP: V 2575
MC: TCV 2575
LP: OVED 335
MC: OVEDC 335

AND THEN THE MAN SAID TO HIS....
LPS: 100 101

ANTHOLOGY - GARY MOORE.
Tracks: / Fanatical fascists / Don't believe a word / Spirit / Run to your mama / Women in love / Rest in peace / White knuckles / Back on the streets / Don't let me be misunderstood / What would you rather bee or a wasp / Dallas warhead (live) / Hurricane / Bad news / I look at you / She's got you / Parisienne walkways.
2LP: RAWLP 023
MCSET: RAWTC 023

BACK ON THE STREETS.
Tracks: / Back on the streets / Don't believe a word / Fanatical fascists / Flight of the snow moose / Hurricane / Song for Donna / What would you rather bee or a wasp / Parisienne walkways.
LP: MCL 1622
MC: MCLC 1622
LP: MCF 2853

COLLECTION: GARY MOORE.
2LP: CCSLP 273
MC: CCSMC 273

CORRIDORS OF POWER.
Tracks: / Don't take me for a loser / Always gonna love you / Wishing well / Gonna break my heart again / Falling in love with you / End of the world / Rockin' every night / Cold hearted / I can't wait until tomorrow.
LP: OVED 210
MC: OVEDC 210
LP: V 2245

DIRTY FINGERS.
Tracks: / Hiroshima / Dirty fingers / Bad news / Don't let me be misunderstood / Run to your Mama / Nuclear attack / Kidnapped / Really gonna rock / Lonely nights / Rest in peace.
LP: JETLP 241
MC: JETCA 241
LP: CLALP 131
MC: CLAMC 131

G-FORCE/LIVE AT THE MARQUEE.
Tracks: / You / White knuckles / Rockin' and rollin' / She's got you / I look at you / Because of your love / You kissed me sweetly / Hot gossip / Woman's in love, The / Dancin' / Back on the streets / Run to your Mama / Parisienne walkways / Nuclear attack / Dallas warhead.
MC: TFOMC 2
2LP: TFOLP 2

GOLDEN DECADE OF GARY MOORE.
MC: KNMC 10014

GRINDING STONE.
LP: CBS 32699
MC: 40 32699
LP: 4674491
MC: 4674494

LIVE AT THE MARQUEE.
Tracks: / Back on the streets / Run to your mama / Dancin' / She's got you / Parisienne walkways / You / Nuclear attack / Dallas warhead.
LP: RAWLP 034
MC: RAWTC 034
LP: CLALP 211
MC: CLAMC 211

NUCLEAR ATTACK - BEST OF.
LP: 626227

PARISIENNE WALKWAYS.
Tracks: / Back on the streets / Fanatical fascists / Don't believe a word / Spanish guitar / Parisienne walkways / Put it this way / Desperado / Castles / Fighting talk / Scorch, The.
LP: MCL 1864
MC: MCLC 1864

ROCKIN' EVERY NIGHT (Live in Japan).
Tracks: / Rockin' every night / Wishing well / I can't wait until tomorrow / Nuclear attack / White knuckles / Rockin' and rollin' / Back on the streets / Sunset.
LP: XID 1
MC: CXID 1

ROCKIN' EVERY NIGHT (HARDROCK BOX SET) (See under Hard Rock).

RUN FOR COVER.
Tracks: / Out in the fields / Reach for the sky / Run for cover / Military man / Empty rooms / Nothing to lose / Once in a lifetime / All messed up / Listen to your heartbeat / Out of my system (CD only).
LP: DIX 16
MC: CDIX 16
LP: OVED 274
MC: OVEDC 274

STILL GOT THE BLUES.
Tracks: / Moving on / Oh pretty woman / Walking by myself / Still got the blues / Texas strut / All your love / Too tired / King of the blues / As the years go passing by / Midnight blues / That kind of woman / Stop messin' around.
LP: V 2612
MC: TCV 2612

VICTIMS OF THE FUTURE.
Tracks: / Murder in the skies / All I want / Hold on to love / Law of the jungle, The / Victims of the future / Teenage idol / Shape of things to come / Empty rooms.
LP: OVED 206
MC: OVEDC 206
LP: DIX 2

WE WANT MOORE.
Tracks: / Murder in the skies / Shape of things to come / Victims of the future / Cold hearted / End of the world / Back on the streets / So far away / Empty rooms / Don't take me for a loser / Rockin' and rollin'.
2LP: GMDL 1
MC: CGMDL 1

WHITE KNUCKLES.
Tracks: / Nuclear attack / White knuckles / Rockin' and rollin' / Run to your mama (live) / You / Dirty fingers / Parisienne walkways (live) / Really gonna rock tonight / Hiroshima / You kissed me sweetly / Dancin' / Hot gossip / He's got you (live).
MC: RAWTC 006
LP: RAWLP 006

WILD FRONTIER.
Tracks: / Over the hills and far away / Wild frontier / Take a little time / Loner, The / Friday on my mind / Strangers in the darkness / Thunder rising / Johnny boy / Wild frontier (12" version) (On CD only) / Over the hills and far away (12" version) (On CD only) / Crying in the shadows (On CD only).

LP: DIX 56
MC: CDIX 56
LP: OVED 285
MC: OVEDC 285

Moore, Geoff

FOUNDATIONS (Moore, Geoff/ Distance).
LP: SP R 1191
MC: SP C 1191

PLACE TO STAND, A (Moore, Geoff/ Distance).
LP: SP R 1151
MC: SP C 1151

Moore, Gerald

EVENING WITH GM & FRIENDS.
MC: TCASD 1435944

Moore, Glen

TRIOS/SOLOS (See under Towner, Ralph) (Moore, Glen & Ralph Towner).

Moore, Grace

ART OF GRACE MOORE, THE.
Tracks: / Old refrain, The / Always / Du Barry, The (From the operetta 'Du Barry'.) / I give my heart (From the operetta 'Du Barry'.) / Ciribiribin (In Italian) / You are love (From 'Showboat') / Psyche / Si mes vers avaient des ailes / Que deviennent les roses / Toi seule (Tchaikovsky: Op 57 No.6) / Phidyle / Il est doux,il est bon (From Massenet: Herodiade,act 1).
LP: NL 90040
MC: NK 90040

Moore, Hamish

BEES KNEES, THE (Moore, Hamish/ Lee, Dick).
MC: HARC 014

CAULD WIND PIPES.
Tracks: / Calanish high over Bunachton / Got to Berwick, Johnny Jocky said to .... / Old bean waltz / Thinkan and Daean (Mary's tune) / Sailor's lass Mrs Isabella Sutherland / Country dance drink the worts and....A / Euphemia Low of Garvary / Roslyn Castle / Campbeltown kiltie ball / MacCrummen's lament (MacCrummen will...) / Mill,mill,O,The.
LP: DUN 003
MC: DUNC 003

OPEN ENDED.
Tracks: / Lark in the morning, The / Moving cloud / Torment / Ellis Kelly's delight / Back man, the / Maggie Lauder / Spey, the / Galician jigs.
LP: DUN 006
MC: DUNC 006

Moore, Jackie

I'M ON MY WAY.
Tracks: / This time baby / Joe can you tell me why / Let's go somewhere and make love / I'm on my way / How's your love life baby / Wrapped up in your lovin' / Do ya got what it takes.
LP: CBS 83786

Moore, John

DISTORTION.
LP: 847 109-1
MC: 847 109-4

EXPRESSWAY RISING (Moore, John & The Expressway).
LP: 839 379 1
MC: 839 379 4

Moore, Johnny

SUNNYLAND (see under Brown,Charles) (Moore's,Johnny Three Blazers/Charles Brown).

THIS IS ONE TIME, BABY (Moore, Johnny's Three Blazers).
Tracks: / Blazer boogie / Hard tack / Melancholy Madelaine / Gugue in C major / Don't get salty baby / Pasadena / Cut off the fat / You won't let me go.
LP: JB 1105

WHY, JOHNNY, WHY (Moore, Johnny's Three Blazers).
LP: KIX 33

Moore, Johnny B.

CHICAGO BLUES SESSION 5 (Moore, Johnny B. & West Side All Stars).
LP: WOLF 120 851

Moore, Kid Prince

COMPLETE RECORDINGS 1936-38 (Moore, Kid Prince/Shorty Bob Parker).
LP: WSE 126

Moore, Marilyn

MOODY MARILYN MOORE.
Tracks: / I'm just a lucky so and so / I'll wind / If love is trouble / Is you is or is you ain't my baby / Born to blow the blues / Lover come back to me / You're driving me crazy / Trav'lin all alone / I cried for you / Leavin' town / Trouble is a man / I got rhythm.
LP: AFF 157

Moore, Mavor

BOOK OF HELL, THE (See under Ezrin, Arlene - Deadly Developments) (Various artists).

Moore, Melba

BURN.
Tracks: / Burn / Hot and tasty / If you believe in love / Night people / I don't wanna lose your love / Can't give it up / Miss thing / Need love.
LP: EPC 83788

DANCIN' WITH MELBA MOORE.
Tracks: / Standing right here / Free / Play boy scout / Promises land / Make me believe in you.
LP: BDLP 4059

I'M IN LOVE.
Tracks: / Love and kisses / I'm in love / Love always finds a way / I can't complain / I don't know no one else to turn to / I'll never find another you / Keeps me runnin' back / First love / This time / Test of time.
LP: EST 2058
MC: TCEST 2058

LITTLE BIT MORE, A (See under Jackson, Freddie).

LOT OF LOVE, A.
Tracks: / There I go falling in love again / Falling / It's been so long / I'm not gonna let you go / Love the one I'm with (A lot of love) / You trip me out / Little bit more, A / Stay / When we touch (it's like fire) / Don't go away.
LP: EST 2017
MC: TCEST 2017

MELBA.
Tracks: / There's no other like you / You stepped into my life / It's hard not to like you / Together forever / Pick me up / I'll never dance / Happy / I promise to love you / Where did you ever go.
LP: EPC 83269

NEVER SAY NEVER.
Tracks: / Love me right / Keepin my lover satisfied / Got to have your love / Living for your love / It's really love / Never say never / Lovin' touch / Lean on me.
MC: TCEST 712305 4
LP: EST 7123051

OTHER SIDE OF THE RAINBOW.
Tracks: / Love's comin' at ya / Underlove / Mind up tonight / Knack for me / How's love been treatin' you / Don't go away / I can't help myself / Other side of the rainbow.
LP: EST 12243

PICK ME UP I'LL DANCE (OLD GOLD) (See under Moore, Jackie).

PORTRAIT OF MELBA, A.
Tracks: / You are my river / Promised land / I don't know no one else to turn to / Standing right here / Just another link / Living free / Is this the end / Love and I.
LP: BDLP 4049

READ MY LIPS.
Tracks: / Love of a lifetime / I can't believe it (it's over) / Read my lips / Dreams / When you love me like this / Winner, The / King of my heart / To those who wait / Mind over matter.
LP: MEL 1
MC: TC MEL 1

SOUL EXPOSED.
Tracks: / Do you really want my love / Hold me / New love / I love being in love / Lift every voice and sing / Face to face / Crying in the night / Don't you want to be my lover / Too many lovers / Stormy weather / Lift every voice and sing (long version) (Not on LP.).
LP: EST 2122
LP: 792 355 1
MC: TCEST 2122
MC: 792 355 4

THIS IS IT (OLD GOLD) (See under True, Andrea/More more more).

WHAT A WOMAN NEEDS.
Tracks: / Let's stand together / Your sweet lovin' / What a woman needs / Take my love / Overnight sensation / Each second / Piece of the rock / Let's go back to lovin'.
LP: AML 3019

Moore, Merrill E.

20 GOLDEN PIECES: MERRILL E. MOORE.
Tracks: / Buttermilk baby / Ten, ten, a.m. / Cow cow boogie / Sweet Jenny Lee / Five foot two, eyes of blue / It's a one-way door / Down the road apiece / Gotta gimme whatcha got / Nola boogie / King Porter stomp / Yes, indeed / She's gone / Snatchin' and grabbin' / Cooing to the wrong pigeon / House of blue lights / Rock rockola / Fly right boogie / Corina Corina / Hard top race / Bartender's blues.
LP: BDL 2011

Moore, Michael

TALLEST MAN IN THE WORLD, THE.
Tracks: / I remember / Circus song / Tallest man in the world / Smiling rag / When you come home / Holland / Music man / When will I see you again / Writer, The / Solitary bird / Storm.
LP: PLR 007

Moore & Napier

BEST OF MOORE & NAPIER.
LP: SLP 963
MC: GT 5963

LONESOME TRUCK DRIVERS.
LP: KLP 936
MC: GT 5936

Moore, Nicky

SAMSON AND....
LP: STLP 008

Moore, Patrick

MUSIC OF PATRICK MOORE, THE.
Tracks: / Halley's comet march / Adriadne (from Theseus) / March of the Centaurs / Penguin parade / Triumphal march(entrance of Theseus) / King Neptune / Sunrise polka / Intermezzo (from Perseus & Andromeda) / Vienna clouds / Herald.
LP: CFRC 511
MC: MCFRC 511

Moore, R. Stevie

EVERYTHING YOU EVER WANTED TO KNOW.
LP: ROSE 31

GLAD MUSIC.
LP: ROSE 83

HAS-BEENS AND NEVER WERES.
Tracks: / Intelligence / Near tonight / Love is the way to my heart / Skin mags / You came along just in time / I'm out of my mind / Sit down / Banana jerseyjam / I will want to die / Martyrdom / Pow wow / Residents, The / What's the point? / If you see Kay / 14 months back.
LP: HLT 2

QUIET GATHERING, A.
LP: RRC 30

TEENAGE SPECTACULAR.
LP: ROSE 132

THOROUGHLY YEARS.
LP: LOGICAL FISH 2

VERVE.
LP: HAM 15

WARNING....
LP: ROSE 157

Moore, Ralph

623 C STREET (Moore, Ralph Quartet).
LP: CRISS 1028

FURTHERMORE.
LP: LLP 1526

IMAGES: RALPH MOORE.
Tracks: / Freeway / Episode from a village dance / This I dig of you / Punjab / Enigma / Morning star / Blues for John / One second please.
LP: LLP 1520

ROUND TRIP.
LP: RSR 104

Moore, Scotty

FIRST YEAR, THE (see Presley, Elvis) (Moore, Scotty/Elvis Presley/Bill Black).

GUITAR THAT CHANGED THE WORLD.
Tracks: / Hound dog / Loving you / Honey honey / My baby left me / Heartbreak hotel / That's alright / Milk cow blues / Don't / Mystery train / Don't be cruel / Love me tender / Mean woman blues.
LP: EPC 32306

Moore, Seamus

ON THE BREW.
MC: MIRBC 2007

Moore, Stephen (nar)

HITCH-HIKER'S GUIDE TO THE GALAXY (See under Hitch-hikers Guide... (bk).

LIFE, THE UNIVERSE AND EVERYTHING (See under Life, the Universe...).

RESTAURANT AT THE END OF THE UNIVERSE (See under Restaurant at... (bk)).

SO LONG, AND THANKS FOR ALL THE FISH (See under So Long & Thanks... (bk).

Moore, Tim

FOOL LIKE YOU, A.
LP: CREST 16

Moore, Tiny

TINY MOORE'S MUSIC.
LP: F 12

Moore, Vinnie

MIND'S EYE.
Tracks: / In control / Saved by a miracle / Lifeforce / Mind's eye / Journey, The / Daydream / Hero without honour / N.N.Y. / Shadows of yesterday / Journey, the.
LP: RR 9635
MC: RR 96354

TIME ODYSSEY.
LP: VERH 60
MC: VERHC 60

Mop & Smiff

MOP AND SMIFF (Various artists).
Tracks: / Two of a kind: *Various artists* / Happy birthday Mop and Smiff: *Various artists* / Special day: *Various* artists / Big top travelling show: *Various artists* / Sniffin': *Various artists* / Trackin' through the bracken: *Various artists* / Wooly friends: *Various artists* / Flower floats and beauty queens: *Various artists*/ With the May Queen: *Various artists* / Down by the lakeside: *Various artists* / Bumpity bang: *Various artists*/ Fluttering by: *Various artists* / Home for gnomes, A: *Various artists* / Mop's no Sherlock Holmes: *Various artists* / Painting song, The: *Various artists.*
LP: REC 558
MC: ZCM 558

MOP & SMIFF GO TO SCHOOL (Various artists).
MC: BBM 109

MOP & SMIFF IN SEARCH OF A PEDIGREE (Various artists).
MC: BBM 108

MOP & SMIFF ON BUNNY HILL (Various artists).
MC: BBM 106

MOP & SMIFF'S DAY SUNNYSEAS (Various artists).
MC: BBM 107

M.O.R.

MUSIC ON THE MOVE (20 LADIES & GENTLEMEN OF SONG (Various artists).
MC: INTK 9005

MUSIC WHILE YOU WORK (Various artists).
LP: MOR 537

ONE HUNDRED MINUTES OF STRINGS AND THINGS (Various artists).
MC: ZCTON 8173

PIANO FAVOURITES (Various artists).
Tracks: / Strangers in the night: *Various artists* / I'll never find another you: *Various artists* / Happiness: *Various artists* / It's not unusual: *Various artists* / Nut rocker: *Various artists* / Walk in the Black Forest, A: *Various artists* / Cast your fate to the wind: *Various artists* / On the rebound: *Various artists*/ I remember you: *Various artists* / There, I've said it again: *Various artists* / You'd be so nice to come home to: *Various artists* / There will never be another you: *Various artists* / Elusive butterfly: *Various artists*/ World of our own: *Various artists* / All my loving: *Various artists* / Spanish flea: *Various artists*/ Entertainer, The: *Various artists* / Exodus: *Various artists* / Borsalino theme: *Various artists* / In crowd, The: *Various artists* / Everyone's gone to the moon: *Various artists* / One of those songs: *Various artists* / I left my heart in San Francisco: *Various artists* / Lullaby of Broadway: *Various artists.*
MC: HR 8184

RADIO 2 FAVOURITES (Various artists).
Tracks: / It's now or never: *Presley, Elvis* / I have a dream: *Abba* / Solitaire: *Williams, Andy* / Miss you nights: *Richard, Cliff* / Your song: *John, Elton* / When you're in love with a beautiful woman: *Dr. Hook*/ Stand by your man: *Wynette, Tammy* / Behind closed doors: *Rich, Charlie* / Blanket on the ground: *Spears,* Billie Jo / I love you because: *Reeves, Jim* / Portrait of your love: *Monro, Matt* / I remember you: *Ifield,* Frank / Manhattan: *Fitzgerald, Ella* / Stardust: *Cole, Nat King* / You and the night...: *Damone, Vic*/ Light my fire: *Feliciano, Jose* / In the mood: *Miller, Glenn* / Magic moments: *Como, Perry* / Green green grass of home: *Jones, Tom* / Old rugged cross, The: *Power, Ethna* / You're a lady: *Skellern, Peter*/ Wedding, The: *Rogers, Julie* / Anniversary waltz: *Harris, Anita* / Edelweiss: *Hill, Vince.*
2LP: VSOPLP 112
MC: VSOPMC 112

SALUTE TO SINATRA (Various artists).
Tracks: / I'll never smile again: *Aldrich, Ronnie, His Piano & The Festival Orchestra* / Night and day: *Chacksfield,* Frank & His Orchestra / All or nothing at all: *James, Harry & His Orchestra* / Lovely way to spend an evening, A:

Mantovani & His Orchestra / Dream: Mantovani & His Orchestra / Stella by starlight: Aldrich, Ronnie & His Orchestra/ Some enchanted evening: Mantovani & His Orchestra / Learnin' the blues: Heath, Ted & His Music / Three coins in the fountain: Chacksfield, Frank & His Orchestra / Love and marriage: Mantovani & His Orchestra / (Love is) the tender trap: Heath, Ted & His Music / All the way: Chacksfield, Frank & His Orchestra / Lady is a tramp, The: Chacksfield, Frank & His Orchestra / Just one of those things: Chacksfield, Frank & His Orchestra / It's nice to go trav'ling: Franks, Gordon & His Orchestra / Me and my shadow: Howard, Johnny & His Orchestra / Strangers in the night: Mantovani & His Orchestra / Somethin' stupid: Aldrich, Ronnie, His Piano & The Festival Orchestra/ My way: Mantovani & His Orchestra / Send in the clowns: Mantovani & His Orchestra.

MC: **8440624**

SOPHISTICATED GENTLEMEN (Various artists).

Tracks: / Where do I begin...: Various artists / As time goes by: Damone, Vic / I left my heart: Bennett, Tony / Softly as I leave you: Monro, Matt / Dream a little dream of me: Various artists / It's impossible: Martino, Al / Night and day: Mathis, Johnny / More: Cole, Nat King / Just walking in the rain: Ray, Johnnie / Take me to your heart: Hill, Vince / Lazy river: Carmichael, Hoagy / What kind of fool am I: Goulet, Robert / Edelweiss: Hill, Vince / On a clear day: Mathis, Johnny / All I do is dream of you: Martin, Dean / My foolish heart: Martino, Al / Unforgettable: Cole, Nat King / Love for sale: Bennett, Tony/ I can't stop loving you: Monro, Matt / On the street where you live: Damone, Vic / Hey there: Ray, Johnnie/ Something stupid: Williams, Andy.

2LP: . . . . **VSOPLP 103**
MC: . . . . **VSOPMC 103**

SOPHISTICATED GENTLEMEN VOL.2 (Various artists).

Tracks: / Shadow of your smile: Como, Perry / On the street where you live: Whitfield, David / Best things in life are free, The: Lanza, Mario / Moon river: Williams, Danny / Ain't misbehavin': Armstrong, Louis/ All by myself: Darin, Bobby / Rainy night in Georgia: Benton, Brook / Mack the knife: Darin, Bobby/ Love is a many splendoured thing: Williams, Danny / Answer me: Whitfield, David / My melancholy baby: Bowly, Al / Take me: Rushing, Jimmy/Count Basie & His Orchestra / Jealousy: Various artists / Fools rush in: Benton, Brook / King Joe: Robeson, Paul / Love is the sweetest thing: Bowly, Al / How long: Rushing, Jimmy/Count Basie & His Orchestra / Honeysuckle rose: Murphy, Mark / Moonglow: Como, Perry / Blue skies: Darin, Bobby / High noon: Laine, Frankie / Memories: Lanza, Mario / Nobody knows the trouble I've seen: Robeson, Paul / I only have eyes for you: Murphy, Mark.

2LP: . . . . **VSOPLP 127**
MC: . . . . **VSOPMC 127**

SOPHISTICATED GENTLEMEN VOL.3 (Various artists).

Tracks: / Lady is a tramp, The: Greco, Buddy / Oh look at me now: Darin, Bobby / What kind of fool am I?: Vale, Jerry / Stranger in paradise: Bennett, Tony / Shadow of your smile: Monro, Matt / I'll buy you a star: Mathis, Johnny / At long last love: Greco, Buddy / Sunday in New York: Darin, Bobby / Sunrise sunset: Vale, Jerry / For once in my life: Bennett, Tony / Walking happy: Monro, Matt / Stairway to the stars: Mathis, Johnny / In the still of the night: Damone, Vic / Street of dreams: Rawls, Lou / Day in day out: Cole, Nat King / I don't know enough: Jones, Jack / Canadian sunset: Williams, Andy / Spanish eyes: Martino, Al / Change partners: Damone, Vic / Beautiful friendship, A: Rawls, Lou / To the ends of the earth: Cole, Nat King / This love of mine: Jones, Jack / Man and a woman, A: Williams, Andy / Three coins in the fountain: Martino, Al.

2LP: . . . . **VSOPLP 146**
MC: . . . . **VSOPMC 146**

SOPHISTICATED LADIES (Various artists).

Tracks: / When I fall in love: Day, Doris / I've got you: Shore, Dinah & Andre Previn / Summertime: Holiday, Billie / Younger than...: Whiting, Margaret / As time goes by: Lee, Peggy / Over the rainbow: Garland, Judy / Fever: Lee, Peggy / What is this thing: Smith, Keely / Come rain or come shine: Garland, Judy/ Too old to cut the mustard: Clooney, Rosemary / Blowin' in the wind: Dietrich, Marlene / It ain't necessarily so: Franklin, Aretha / I'll never stop loving you: Day, Doris / Moonlight in Vermont: Whiting, Margaret/ It might as well be Spring: Vaughan, Sarah / Keep on a-rainin': Smith, Bessie.

2LP: . . . . **VSOPLP 102**
MC: . . . . **VSOPMC 102**

SOPHISTICATED LADIES VOL.2 (Various artists).

Tracks: / Every time we say goodbye: Fitzgerald, Ella (Not on CD) / Girl from Ipanema: Gilberto, Astrud (Not on CD) / Killing me softly with his song: Laine, Cleo / Sweet Georgia Brown: Vaughan, Sarah (Not on CD) / Careless love: Washington, Dinah (Not on CD) / La vie en rose: Piaf, Edith / Cry me a river: Washington, Dinah(Not on CD) / I can dream, can't I: Shore, Dinah / Summertime: Staton, Dakota / Non, je regrette rien: Piaf, Edith / September song: Lenya, Lotte / Eleanor Rigby: Laine, Cleo / I'm beginning to see the light: Reese, Della / I'd love you to want me: Minnelli, Liza / Walk over God's heaven: Jackson, Mahalia / Late late show, The: Staton, Dakota / Let's do it: Kitt, Eartha / Saga of Jenny: Lenya, Lotte / Didn't it rain: Jackson, Mahalia / Manhattan: Fitzgerald, Ella (Not on CD) / Take the 'A' train: Vaughan, Sarah (Not on CD) / Old fashioned girl: Kitt, Eartha / Certain smile, A: Gilberto, Astrud (Not on CD) / You are the sunshine of my life: Minnelli, Liza / Mr. Wonderful: Martin, Millicent (CD only.) / Smoke gets in your eyes: Shelton, Anne(CD only.) / Come rain or come shine: Martin, Millicent (CD only.) / Let's face the music and dance: Shelton, Anne(CD only.).

2LP: . . . . **VSOPLP 126**
MC: . . . . **VSOPMC 126**

SOPHISTICATED LADIES VOL.3 (Various artists).

Tracks: / If I were a bell: Bassey, Shirley / So tired: Starr, Kay / This girls in love with you: Warwick, Dionne / Fascinating rhythm: Clark, Petula / I wish you love: Smith, Keely / You must have been a beautiful baby: Lee, Peggy / I thought about you: Zadora, Pia / Caravan song: Dickson, Barbara / No moon at all: Staton, Dakota / Talking in your sleep: Gayle, Crystal / Something wonderful: Whiting, Margaret / When will I see you again: 3 Degrees / Can't help lovin' dat man: Bassey, Shirley / Wheel of fortune, The: Starr, Kay / Close to you: Warwick, Dionne / Darn that dream: Clark, Petula / It's been a long long time: Smith, Keely / Man I love, The: Lee, Peggy / I had the craziest dream: Zadora, Pia / As time goes by: Dickson, Barbara / Someone to watch over me: Staton, Dakota / Don't it make your brown eyes blue: Gayle, Crystal/ A tree in the meadow: Whiting, Margaret / Take good care of yourself: 3 Degrees.

2LP: . . . . **VSOPLP 145**
MC: . . . . **VSOPMC 145**

THEY CALLED IT CROONING (Various artists).

Tracks: / Where the blue of the night: Crosby, Bing / Cheerful little earful: Ellis, Segar / My song: Bullock, Chick / She's a new kind of old-fashioned girl: Smith, Jack / Got a date with an angel: O'Malley, Pat / Living in dreams: Columbo, Russ / Orange blossom time: Edwards, Cliff / She's wonderful: Shalson, Harry/ Am I blue?: Bellew, Smith / Here lies love: Browne, Sam / Thrill is gone, The: Vallee, Rudy / Ain't misbehavin': Austin, Gene / My sweet Virginia: Bowlly, Al / Please: Rosing, Val / Little by little: Marvin, Johnny / You're a real sweetheart: Coslow, Sam / Sweet Sue: Metaxa, George / Tell your father: Richman, Harry.

LP: . . . . **AJA 5026**
MC: . . . . **ZC AJA 5026**

TRANQUILITY (Various artists).

Tracks: / Sailing: Various artists / Light my fire: Various artists / Forse: Various artists / Melissa: Various artists / Adagio: Various artists / Yesterday: Various artists / I have a dream: Various artists / Bird of paradise: Various artists / Un jour d'ete: Various artists / Feelings: Various artists/ Largo: Various artists / Barcarolle: Various artists / Autumn dream: Various artists.

2LP: . . . . **CR 069**
MCSET: . . . . **CRT 069**

UNCHAINED MELODIES (Various artists).

LP: . . . . **STAR 2480**
MC: . . . . **STAC 2480**

UNCHAINED MELODIES II (Various artists).

LP: . . . . **STAR 2515**
MC: . . . . **STAC 2515**

WE WISH YOU LOVE (Various artists).

Tracks: / I wish you love: Ryan, Marion / It's you that I love: Ryan, Marion / Somebody: Ryan, Marion/ As long as you love me: Whitfield, David / This heart of mine: Whitfield, David / Impossible: Whitfield, David / You belong in someone elses arms: Whitfield, David / Where do I go from here: Roza, Lita / Keep watch over him: Roza, Lita / What am I supposed to do: Roza, Lita / Stranger things have happened: Roza, Lita / If I had my way: Vaughan, Frankie / I walked right in (with my eyes wide open): Shapiro, Helen / Woe is me: Shapiro, Helen / Miss you: Young, Jimmy / Auf wiedersehen my dear: Howard, Les / From the time you say goodbye: Lynn, Vera / Dear heart: Holliday, Michael / My year of love: Holliday, Michael/ Blue snowfall: Squires, Dorothy / Stella by starlight: Weston, Glen / Invisible tears: Hill, Vince/ If he walked into my life: Squires, Rosemary / Say it with flowers: Squires, Dorothy/Russ Conway / Paradise: Ifield, Frank / Tennessee waltz, The: Cogan, Alma.

2LP: . . . . **DL 1170**
MC: . . . . **TCDL 1170**

WHEN HOUSEWIVES HAD THE CHOICE (Various artists).

Tracks: / In party mood: West End Celebrity Orchestra / This is my lovely day: Guetary, G & L Webb / La mer: Trenet, Charles / Cherry pink and apple blossom white: Calvert, Eddie / Finger of suspicion: Valentine, Dickie / Good luck, good health: Conway, Steve / See you all again: Elrick, George / Rock and roll waltz: Starr, Kay / Stranger in paradise: Four Aces / On the street where you live: Damone, Vic / Whatever will be will be: Day, Doris / Moon river: Mancini, Henry / When somebody thinks ...: Waller, Fats / Don't sit under the apple tree: Andrews Sisters / My truly truly fair: Mitchell, Guy / Just walking in the rain: Ray, Johnnie / Answer me: Laine, Frankie / Love letters in the sand: Boone, Pat / Stay as sweet as you are: Cole, Nat King / Softly softly: Murray, Ruby / Mr. Wonderful: Lee, Peggy / Magic moments: Como, Perry / Passing strangers: Eckstine, Billy & Sarah Vaughan / When housewives had the choice: Covington, Julie.

2LP: . . . . **REQ 730**
MCSET: . . . . **ZCQ 730**

Moraba, Kori

VICTIMS OF THE SYSTEM.

Tracks: / Victims of the system / Kgutlang / Thatohatse / Tsoang tsoang tsoang (trad. wedding song) / Oanqaka / Hope / Batho ke ho to thusana / Ke binela wena / Maditaba / O rata mang / Thsepha thapelo / Don't drive drink / Coming or going / Lenyalo ke kabelo.

MC: . . . . **ELITE 016MC**

Moral Crusade

AN ACT OF VIOLENCE.

LP: . . . . **CMFT 5**

Morality Of Strikes

MORALITY OF STRIKES (See under UNESCO reports).

Moran, Thomas

BONNY BUNCH OF ROSES-O.

Tracks: / As I roved out / Bilberry courtship / Boy in love he fears no cold, A / Blind beggar's daughter / Broken token / Captain Thunder-bolt / Drumhullogan's bottom / Frog in the well / Green bushes / Handsome Polly-o / Indian lass, The / Jack Mulroe / Chester merchant / Jolly tinker / Lovely Annie / Maid of Magheracloone / Next Monday morning / Old cow of Kinlough, the / Paisley officer / Tailor's courtship / Rigs of London / Marrow-bones.

MC: **60-076**

Moran, Tim

CITY SPIRITS (Moran, Tim & Tony Vacca).

LP: . . . . **PH 9007**
MC: . . . . **PH 9007C**

Morath, Max

PLAYS THE BEST OF SCOTT JOPLIN AND OTHER RAGS.

2LP: . . . . **VSD 39**

Moray Players

TASTE OF MORAY, A.

LP: . . . . **WGR 011**
MC: . . . . **CWGR 011**

Moraz, Patrick

COEXISTANCE (Moraz, Patrick & Syrinx).

Tracks: / Mind your body / Boonoonoonoos / Soundrise / Adagio for a hostage / Freedom to.... / Black gold / Moments of love / Chain reaction / Peace on the hills.

LP: . . . . **CAL 117**
LP: . . . . **JUNGLE 67499**
MC: . . . . **JUNGLE 70499**

FLAGS (Moraz, Patrick & Bill Bruford).

Tracks: / Temples of joy / Split seconds / Karu karu / Impromptu too / Flags / Machines programmed by genes / Drum also waltzes, The / Infra dig / Way with words, A / Everything you've heard is true.

LP: . . . . **EGLP 63**
MC: . . . . **EGMC 63**

FUTURE MEMORIES PATRICK MORAZ LIVE ON TV.

LP: . . . . **JUNGLE 67435**
MC: . . . . **JUNGLE 70435**

HUMAN INTERFACE.

Tracks: / Light elements / Beyond binary / Cin-a-maah / Stormtroops in loops / Modular symphony (1st movement) / Goto Ophioplomel / Kyushu / Stressless / Hyperwaves.

LP: . . . . **EST 2043**
MC: . . . . **TCEST 2043**

MUSIC FOR DRUMS AND PIANO (Moraz, Patrick & Bill Bruford).

Tracks: / Children's concerto / Living space / Any suggestions / Eastern sundays / Blue brains / Symmetry / Galatea / Hazy.

LP: . . . . **EGED 33**

OUT IN THE SUN.

Tracks: / Out in the sun / Rana batucada / Nervous breakdown / Silver screen / Tentacles / Kabala / Love hate sun rain you / Time for a change.

LP: . . . . **CDS 4007**

PATRICK MORAZ.

LP: . . . . **CDS 4002**
LP: . . . . **CDS 4015**

STORY OF I, THE.

Tracks: / Impact / Warmer hands / Storm, The / Cachaca / Intermezzo / Indoors / Best years of our lives / Descent / Incantation (procession) / Dancing now / Impressions (the dream) / Like a child in disguise / Rise and fall / Symphony in the space.

LP: . . . . **CHC 9**
MC: . . . . **CHCMC 9**

TIMECODE.

LP: . . . . **LMGLP 6000**
MC: . . . . **ZCLMG 6000**

Morbid Angel

ALTARS OF MADNESS.

Tracks: / Visions from the darkside / Chapel of ghouls / Maze of torment / Damnation / Bleed for the devil.

LP: . . . . **MOSH 11**
MC: . . . . **MOSH 11 MC**
LPPD: . . . . **MOSH 11 P**

BLESSED ARE THE SICK.

MC: . . . . **MOSH 31MC**
LP: . . . . **MOSH 31**

Morbid Outburst

MY EXPLOSION.

LP: . . . . **FH 12-003**

Morbid Taste For Bones

MORBID TASTE FOR BONES, A (See under Peters, Ellis) (Houston, Glyn).

Mordred

FOOLS GAME.

LP: . . . . **NUK 135**
MC: . . . . **ZCNUK 135**
LP: . . . . **N 0135 1**
MC: . . . . **N 0135 4**

IN THIS LIFE.

Tracks: / Esse quam videri / Downtown / Progress / Killing time / Larger than life / High potence / Falling away / Window / In this life / Strain, The.

LP: . . . . **NO 159-1**
MC: . . . . **NO 159-4**

More

WARHEAD.

Tracks: / Warhead / Fire / Soldier / Depression / Road rocket / Lord of twilight / Way of the world / We are the band / I have no answers.

LP: . . . . **K 50775**
MC: **K4 50775**

More, Anthony

ONLY CHOICE, THE.

Tracks: / Find one voice / Only choice, The / No parlez / Humana / Souvenirs / Industrial drums / Goodbye kisses / Your stars / Conference / O for the ocean.

LP: . . . . **MORE 1**
MC: . . . . **TCMORE 1**

WORLD SERVICE.

Tracks: / World service / Diving girls.

LP: . . . . **RIDE 7**

More Deadly Than The

MORE DEADLY THAN THE MALE (Chase, James Hadley) (Lankester, Barry).

MC: . . . . **SOUND 28**

More Disney Favourites

MORE DISNEY FAVOURITES (See under Disney) (Various artists).

More Fiends

TOAD LICKIN'.
LP: . . . . **SR 330290**

YO ASPHALT HEAD.
LP: . . . . **RAVE 003**

More From Ten... (bk)

MORE FROM TEN IN A BED (Allan Ahlberg) (Boyd, Carole (nar)).
MC: . . . . **TS 340**

More Ghost Stories

MORE GHOST STORIES (see under James, M.R.) (Horden, Sir Michael).

More Louisiana ...

MORE LOUISIANA SWAMP BLUES (See under Louisiana Swamp Blues) (Various artists).

More Railway Stories

MORE RAILWAY STORIES (1) (See under Railway Stories) (Rushton, Willie (nar)).

More Sherlock

MORE SHERLOCK HOLMES STORIES (see under Sherlock Holmes (bk)) (Hardy, Robert (nar)).

More Work For...

MORE WORK FOR THE UNDERTAKER (Margery Allingham) (Matthews, Francis (nar)).
MC: . . . . **CAB 334**

Morecambe & Wise

BBC TV SHOWS.
Tracks: / Here you are / 45 minutes of fun and laughter / Eric Morecambe, you'll do anything for a laugh / There's a lot of flu about / Diamond ring in the window, The / Ern, you have got a magnificent body / Carry on Ern / Visit from the police, A / Are you Mrs. T Potter / Welcome to the show / I'm going to be Bob Hope's chief scriptwriter / Finale.
LP: . . . . **REC 534**
MC: . . . . **ZCM 534**

IT'S MORECAMBE & WISE.
MC: . . . . **MRMC 052**

SO WHAT DO YOU THINK OF THE SHOW SO FAR.
Tracks: / Overture and beginners / Byron and Keats / Marriage with licence, A / Pilchards / Bath time for Ernie / Spy with the cold nose, The.
LP: . . . . **REB 210**
MC: . . . . **RMC 4020**

WEEKEND SOUNDS.
Tracks: / Here you are / Forty-five minutes of fun and laughter / Eric Morecambe, you'll do anything for a laugh / There's a lot of 'flu about - 'flu's a nasty thing / Diamond ring in the window, The / Ern, you have got a magnificent body / Carry on, Ern / Visit from the police, A - are you Mrs. T. Potter? / Welcome to the show / I'm going to be Bob Hope's chief scriptwriter / And finale.
LP: . . . . **REC 258**

Moreira, Airto

COLOURS OF LIFE, THE (Moreira, Airto & Flora Purim).
LP: . . . . **IORLP 001**

STRUCK BY LIGHTNING.
Tracks: / It's time for carnival / Burning money / Berimbau first cry / Sea horse / Struck by lightning / Samba louco (crazy samba) / Seven dwarfs / Samba nosso (our samba) / Skins and rattle (Only on CD.).
LP: . . . . **VE 44**
MC: . . . . **TCVE 44**

SUN IS OUT, THE (See under Purim, Flora) (Moreira, Airto & Flora Purim).

Morel, Terry

SONGS OF A WOMAN IN LOVE.
LP: . . . . **FS 291**

Moreland, Ace

SIZZLIN' HOT.
Tracks: / Sizzlin' hot / Open up your heart / You got a way with me / Devil in my soul / Nightmares in the daytime / True fine love / Blamin' me / My heart is beating lonely tonight / Watcha gonna do / Full time love / Blues for cryin' out loud.
LP: . . . . **KIN 4030**
MC: . . . . **KIN 4030 MC**

Morello, Joe

JOE MORELLO.
Tracks: / Shortnin' bread / When Johnny comes marching home / Brother Jack / Every time we say goodbye / Just in time / That's the way it goes / Shimwa / Carioca / It's easy / Summertime / Little bit of blues, A / Every time / Sounds of the loop.
LP: . . . . **NL 90406**
MC: . . . . **NK 90406**

Moren, Fredrik

TO MR. J (Moren, Fredrik Band).
Tracks: / Inner city baby / Part of / I'm hip / Damerance / Rollo's little sister / To Mr. J / No comments / Mirrors / Someone to watch over me / Master.
LP: . . . . **SNTF 1037**

Moreno, Buddy

1947: BUDDY MORENO (Moreno, Buddy & His Orchestra).
LP: . . . . **CLP 49**

Moresure

ACCELERATION PROCESS.
LP: . . . . **MAD 2014**

Moreton, Ivor

PIANO FAVOURITES (Moreton, Ivor & Dave Kay).
LP: . . . . **BUR 022**
MC: . . . . **4 BUR 022**

Moreton, Jeff

PERFECTLY ORGANIZED.
LP: . . . . **BSS 380**

Morgan, Dennis

SWANEE RIVER 1945 BROADCAST (see under Jolson, Al) (Morgan, Dennis & Al Jolson).

Morgan, Derrick

BLAZIN' FIRE.
LP: . . . . **PHZA 072**

BLAZING FIRE II.
LP: . . . . **PHZA 7Z**

CONQUEROR, THE.
LP: . . . . **VSLP 4069**

JUDGE DREAD IN COURT (See under Dekker, Desmond).

PEOPLE DECISION.
LP: . . . . **TWLP 203**

RIDE THE RHYTHM.
LP: . . . . **LALP 003**

Morgan, Edwin

DOUBLE SCOTCH, A (Morgan, Edwin & Alexander Scott).
LP: . . . . **CCA 5**

Morgan, Frank

FRANK MORGAN.
LP: . . . . **GNPS 9041**

MOOD INDIGO.
MC: . . . . **ANC 8748**
LP: . . . . **AN 8748**
MC: . . . . **ICM 2059**
LP: . . . . **ILPM 2059**

Morgan G.

TEA WITH MR. TIMOTHY (Read by Garard Green).
MC: . . . . **CAB 019**

Morgan, Geoff

AT THE EDGE.
LP: . . . . **FF 350**

FINALLY LETTING GO.
LP: . . . . **FF 277**

TALK IT OVER.
LP: . . . . **FF 436**

Morgan, George

BEST OF GEORGE MORGAN.
LP: . . . . **SLP 957**
MC: . . . . **GT 5957**

Morgan, Jack

DANCING IN THE DARK (Morgan, Jack/ Russ Morgan Orchestra).
LP: . . . . **RME 1005**

REFLECTIONS OF DAD (Morgan, Jack/ Russ Morgan Orchestra).
LP: . . . . **RME 1004**

Morgan, Jamie J

SHOTGUN.
Tracks: / Shotgun / Walk on the wild side / Could you be that girl / Third world man / I'm no angel / Rocksteady / Shame / She's on it / Mercedes blue / Blind love.
LP: **4664851**
MC: **4664854**

Morgan, Jane

DAY THE RAINS CAME, THE (OLD GOLD) (See Debbie Reynolds - Tammy for details).

Morgan, Jaye P

JUST YOU, JUST ME.
LP: . . . . **FS 276**

Morgan, Kris

FOR A WOMAN IN LOVE.
Tracks: / Woman in love / Crystal keys / Winner takes it all / Play that song again / Xanadu / Maibritt / Oh God, I wish I was home / Blues connection / Sambra a dois / Ballad for Birgid / Lonesome loser / Mull of Kintyre.
LP: . . . . **K 58264**

Morgan, Lanny

IT'S ABOUT TIME.
LP: . . . . **PA 8007**

Morgan, Laurie

LEAVE THE LIGHT ON.
Tracks: / Trainwreck of emotion / Out of your shoes / I'll take the memories / Far side of the bed / Dear me / Five minutes / He talks to me / It's too late (to love me now) / Gonna leave the light on / Eight days a week (CD only.) / If I didn't love you (CD only.).
LP: . . . . **PL 90392**
MC: . . . . **PK 90392**

SOMETHING IN RED.
Tracks: / Autumn's not that cold / We both walk / Something in red / Except for Monday / Picture of me (without you) / Tears on my pillow / In tears / Best woman wins / Hand over your heart / Faithfully.
LP: . . . . **PL 90560**
MC: . . . . **PK 90560**

Morgan, Lee

BEST OF LEE MORGAN (Blue Note Years).
Tracks: / Ceora / Speedball / Night in Tunisia / Since I fell for you / Rumproller, The / I remember Clifford (CD only.) / Mr. Kenyatta (CD only.) / Cornbread (CD only.).
LP: **B1 91138**
MC: **B4 91138**

COOKER, THE.
Tracks: / Night in Tunisia / Heavy dipper / Just one of those things / Lover man / New-ma.
LP: . . . . **BST 81578**

CORNBREAD.
Tracks: / Cornbread / Our man Higgins / Ceora / Ill wind / Most like Lee.
LP: **B1 84222**

DELIGHTFULEE MORGAN.
Tracks: / Ca-lee-so / Zambia / Yesterday / Sunrise, sunset / Nite flite / Delightful Deggie / Need I? (CD only.) / Fillet of soul (CD only.) / Zambia (big band version) (CD only.).
LP: . . . . **BST 84243**

EXPOOBIDENT.
Tracks: / Expoobident / Easy living / Triple track / Fire / Just in time / Hearing / Lost and found.
LP: . . . . **AFF 134**

GIGOLO, THE.
Tracks: / Yes I can, no you can't / Trapped / Speedball / Gigolo, The / You go to my head.
LP: . . . . **BST 84212**

HERE'S LEE MORGAN.
LP: . . . . **AFF 143**

LEE MORGAN.
2LP: . . . . **GNPS 2-2074**

MINOR STRAIN (Morgan, Lee/Thad Jones).
Tracks: / Suspended sentence / Minor strain / Bid for Sid / Subtle rebuttal / Tip toe / H and T blues / Friday the 13th.
LP: . . . . **ROU 1015**

ONE, TWO AND FOUR (Morgan, Lee & John Coltrane).
Tracks: / Essie's dance / Doxy / I talk to the trees / Yesterdays / Oleo / Angel eyes / Suspended sentence / Minor strain / Bid for Sid / Exotica / One and four / Simple life.
2LP: . . . . **VJD 560**

RAJAH, THE.
Tracks: / Pilgrim's funny farm, A / Rajah, The / Is that so / Davisamba / What now my love / Once in a lifetime.
LP: . . . . **BST 84426**
MC: **4BN 84426**

RUMPROLLER, THE.
Tracks: / Rumproller, The / Desert moonlight / Eclipso / Edda / Lady, The / Venus de mildew.
LP: . . . . **BST 84199**

SEARCH FOR THE NEW LAND.
Tracks: / Search for the new land / Joker, The / Mr. Kenyatta / Melancholee / Morgan the Pirate.
LP: . . . . **BST 84169**

SIDEWINDER.
Tracks: / Sidewinder, The / Totem pole / Gary's notebook / Boy, what a night! / Hocus pocus.
LP: . . . . **BST 84157**
MC: . . . . **TCBST 84157**

SONIC BOOM.
Tracks: / Sneaky Pete / Mercenary / Sonic boom / Fathead / I'll never be the same / Mumbo jumbo.
LP: . . . . **LBR 1020**

Morgan, Liz (nar)

MYSTERY OF TALLY-HO COTTAGE, THE (see under Blyton, Enid (aut)) (Morgan, Liz & John Baddeley (nars)).

MYSTERY OF THE BURNT COTTAGE, THE (see under Blyton, Enid (author)) (Morgan, Liz & John Baddeley (nars)).

MYSTERY OF THE STRANGE MESSAGES, THE (see under Blyton, Enid (author)) (Morgan, Liz & John Baddeley (nars)).

Morgan, Maria

ANOTHER HANDFUL OF SONGS (Morgan, Maria & Keith Field).
Tracks: / Handful of songs / High hopes / My favourite things / When I first came to this land / Changing the guard at Buckingham Palace / Inch worm, The / Horsey horsey / Coming round the mountain / Where are you going to, my pretty maid? / Singing silly songs / Ugly duckling, The / Aiken drum / Wonderful baby / Nursery rhymes medley / Skip to my lou.
LP: . . . . **PRCV 111**
MC: . . . . **TC PRCV 111**

HANDFUL OF SONGS, A (Morgan, Maria & Keith Field).
Tracks: / Handful of songs / Yellow submarine / Rupert the bear / Owl and the pussycat, The / How much is that doggie in the window / Puff the magic dragon / Nellie the elephant / Caterpillar song / Windmill in old Amsterdam, A / Froggie went a courtin' / Animals went in two by two, The / When we were two little boys / Sing a rainbow / You're a pink toothbrush / King's new clothes, The / Teddy bears' picnic.
LP: . . . . **PSP 10**

Morgan, Meli'sa

DO ME BABY.
Tracks: / Fool's paradise / Heart breaking decision / Do you still love me? / I'll give it when I want it / Do me baby / Getting to know you / Now or never / Lies.
LP: . . . . **EST 2008**
MC: . . . . **TCEST 2008**
MC: . . . . **TCATAK 118**
LP: . . . . **ATAK 118**

GOOD LOVE.
Tracks: / If you can do it I can too / Here comes the night / Just for your touch / Good love / Love changes / Think it over / Ill love no more / I still think about you / You're all I got.
LP: . . . . **EST 2051**
MC: . . . . **TCEST 2051**

LADY IN ME, THE.
Tracks: / Can you give me what I want / Stop, love and listen / You belong to me / Situations / Dancing into love / Don't you know / Wrong lane / Lady in me, The / I'm better now / So long, goodbye.
LP: . . . . **EST 2124**
MC: . . . . **TCEST 2124**
MC: **792 804 4**

Morgan, Mike

RAW AND READY (Morgan, Mike & The Crawl).
Tracks: / Pretty woman / Baby please don't lie to me / Nothing's gonna be alright / I've got a good thing / I can't take it / She made my mind / If my baby quit me / You better watch yourself / Looky there / I'm worried / Take me back / Flatfoot Sam.
LP: . . . . **FIEND 167**

Morgan, O

CHERISH THE LOVE (See under Hilton, J) (Morgan, O & J. Hilton).

Morgan, Paul

EVENSONG AT EXETER CATHEDRAL (See under Exeter Cathedral).

Morgan, Russ

BEST OF RUSS MORGAN.
LP: . . . . **GNPS 9015**
MC: **GNP5 9015**

GOLDEN FAVOURITES (Morgan, Russ & His Orchestra).
Tracks: / Does your heart beat for me / Object of my affection, The / Do you ever think of me / Cruising down the river (Medley) / Linger awhile / Dogface soldier / Wang wang blues / So tired / Josephine / You're nobody till somebody loves you / Wabash blues / Johnson rag.
LP: . . . . **MOIR 207**
MC: . . . . **CMOIR 207**

MAGIC LINGERS ON, THE.
LP: . . . . **RME 1000**

MUSIC IN THE MORGAN MANNER (Morgan, Russ & His Orchestra).
LP: . . . . **CLP 87**

ONE NIGHT STAND.
LP: . . . . **JLP 1019**

PLAY 22 ORIGINAL BIG BAND RECORDINGS (Morgan, Russ & His Orchestra).
LP: . . . . **HSR 404**

RUSS MORGAN AND ORCHESTRA 1937-38 (Morgan, Russ & His Orchestra).
Tracks: / Does your heart beat for me / You must have been a beautiful baby / Moonlight and shadows / So help me / Boo hoo / What do you know about love / You got me / Room with a view / Could be / Say it with a kiss / To you / Moonlight serenade / I must see Annie tonight / Hurry home / I go for that / Goodnight, my beautiful / So long.
LP: . . . . **HSR 145**

Morgan, Sam

GET HAPPY BAND, THE.
LP: . . . . **VLP 32**

KID HOWARD (Morgan, Sam Revisited).
LP: . . . . **JCE 20**

Morgan Sheppard

LITERACY OF LUNACY.
Tracks: / Forecast / Pain factory / See you there / Myth of Mo / Persian breath / Seven pillars of wisdom / Grove in / Water torture / State we're in, The / Preying on your weakness (Parts 1&2).
LP: . . . . **ZK 1003**

Morgoth

ETERNAL FALL.
Tracks: / Burnt identity / White gallery / Eternal sanctify / Female infanticide / Pits of utumno.
LP: **6097111**
MC: **0897114**

Mori, Toshi

ABBA - THE BIG BAND (Mori, Toshi & The Blue Coats).
Tracks: / Dancing queen / Eagle / Money money money / I do I do I do / Waterloo / Waterloo / Chiquitita / That's me / I am just a girl / Thank you for the music.
LP: . . . . **SX 7009**

Moriarty, Brendan

SONGS OF CLARE.
MC: . . . . **EI 807**

SONGS OF CORK.
MC: . . . . **EI 816**

SONGS OF DONEGAL.
MC: . . . . **EI 809**

SONGS OF KERRY.
MC: . . . . **EI 806**

SONGS OF LIMERICK.
MC: . . . . **EI 813**

SONGS OF MAYO.
MC: . . . . **EI 812**

SONGS OF WEXFORD.
MC: . . . . **EI 814**

SONGS OF WICKLOW.
MC: . . . . **EI 815**

Moriarty, Dermot

SONG FOR IRELAND.
LP: . . . . **FALP 010**

Moriyama, Takeo

GREEN RIVER.
LP: . . . . **ENJA 4080**

Morks, Jan

PORTRAIT OF JAN MORKS.
Tracks: / Weary blues / Three little words / Kansas city stomp / Meditation / African queen / It's alright with me / Buddy's habits / You don't know how much you can suffer / Some of these days / Opus / After you're gone / Mon homme / Wabash blues / Too silver.
LP: **824 160 1**
MC: **824 160 4**

Morley, Adele

LAKELAND LOVE, A.
MCSET: . . . . **MRC 1044**

Morlocks

EMERGE.
LP: . . . . **MIRLP 11**

Mormon Tabernacle

BEYOND THE BLUE HORIZON (1930's at the movies).
Tracks: / You must have been a beautiful baby / It's only a paper moon / Pick yourself up / As time goes by / Love thy neighbour / Love is just around the corner / Love walked in / I only have eyes for you / Hooray for Hollywood / It's a hap-hap-happy day / Beyond the blue horizon / Singin' in the rain / Folks who live on the hill, The / Wishing / Foggy day, A / Shadow waltz / June in January / Way you look tonight / Easy to remember / Let's face the music and dance.
LP: **61996**

LORD'S PRAYER,THE.
LP: **31509**

MEMORIES.
Tracks: / I'll see you in my dreams / Smilin' through / On the banks of the Wabash / Indiana / Smiles / Love's old sweet song / Pretty baby / You are my sunshine / Avalon / I wonder who's kissing her now / When day is done / Moonlight and roses / Beautiful Ohio / Moonlight Bay / Anniversary Song / When you were sweet sixteen / In the gloaming / Meet me tonight in dreamland / Memory lane / Memories / Let me call you sweetheart.
LP: . . . . **CBS 61897**

MORMON TABERNACLE CHOIR'S GREATEST HITS.
MC: **40 79025**

SING SONGS OF THE BRITISH ISLES.
LP: . . . . **CBS 60301**
MC: **40 60301**

WHEN YOU WISH UPON A STAR.
Tracks: / When you wish apon a star / Hi diddle dee dee / Who's afraid of the big bad wolf / Dream is a wish your heart makes / Bibbidi bobbidi boo / You can fly ? / Zip-a-dee-doo-dah / Love is a song / Whistle while you work / Heigh ho, heigh ho / Some day my prince will come / Spoonful of sugar / Chim chim cheree / Supercalifragilisticexpialidocious.
LP: . . . . **CBS 73998**
MC: **40 73998**

Morning Has Broken

MORNING HAS BROKEN (Various artists).
LP: . . . . **STAR 2337**
MC: . . . . **STAC 2337**

Morning, Noon & Night

MORNING, NOON AND NIGHT various artists (Various artists).
LPS: . . . . **RTL 2094**
MCSET: **4CRTL 2094**

Morning, Noon & Night

MORNING NOON AND NIGHT.
Tracks: / Bite your granny / Feeling strong.
LP: . . . . **UAS 30114**

Morocco (country)

MOROCCAN FOLK MUSIC (Various artists).
LP: . . . . **LLST 7229**

MOROCCAN STREET MUSIC (Various artists).
LP: . . . . **LLST 7263**

MOROCCAN SUFI MUSIC (Various artists).
LP: . . . . **LLST 7238**
MC: . . . . **LLCT 7238**

MUSIC OF MOROCCO-THE PAN ISLAMIC TRADITION (Various artists).
LP: . . . . **LLST 7240**

RWAIS MOROCCAN BERBER MUSICIANS FROM HIGH ATLAS (Various artists).
LP: . . . . **LLST 7316**

SONGS AND RHYTHMS OF MOROCCO (Various artists).
LP: . . . . **LLST 7336**

Moroder, Giorgio

FIRST ELECTRONIC LIVE TO DIGITAL ALBUM.
LP: . . . . **OSLP 507**

GOODBYE BAD TIMES (See under Oakey, Philip) (Moroder, Giorgio & Philip Oakey).

PAUL'S THEME (See under Bowie, David - Cat People).

PHIL OAKEY/GIORGIO MORODER (see under Oakey, Philip).

SOLITARY MEN (Moroder, Giorgio & Joe Esposito).
Tracks: / Solitary man / Show me the night / My girl / Too hot to touch / Diamond Lizzy / Washed in the neon light / Love affair / Nights in white satin / Lady lady / White hotel / To turn the stone.
LP: **6.25519**
MC: **CR4 25519**

TOGETHER IN ELECTRIC DREAMS (see under Oakey, Philip) (Moroder, Giorgio & Philip Oakey).

Morpeth Rant

NORTHUMBRIAN COUNTRY MUSIC.
LP: **12TS 267**
MC: . . . . **KTSC 267**

Morrice, David

LOCHNAGAR (See under Geddes, Graham) (Morrice, David & Graham Geddes).

Morricone, Ennio

CHAMBER MUSIC.
Tracks: / Sestetto / Musica per 11 violini / 3 studi / Ricercare per pianoforte / 4 pezzi per chitarra / Suoni per dino / Distanze.
LP: . . . . **VE 24**
MC: . . . . **TCVE 24**

CHI MAI.
Tracks: / Chi mai / Kontano / Fistful of dynamite / Poem of a woman / Secret / Come Maddalena / Once upon a time in the west / Good luck Jack / Here's to you / My name is nobody.
LP: . . . . **REH 414**
MC: . . . . **ZCR 414**

CINEMA ITALIANO (See Under Mancini, Henry) (Mancini, Henry & His Orchestra).

ENDLESS GAMES, THE (T.V. soundtrack).
Tracks: / Endless game, The / Alec's journey / Game goes on, The / Summer solitude / Caroline's song / From Russia / Love game, The / Anif / Silvia's game / Just a game / Chess game.
LP: . . . . **V 2602**
MC: . . . . **TCV 2602**

ENNIO MORRICONE 1 The greatest film music of (Various artists).
LP: **240576.1**
MC: **240576.4**

ENNIO MORRICONE 2 The greatest film music of (Various artists).
LP: **240577.1**
MC: **240577.4**

ENNIO MORRICONE 3 The greatest film music of (Various artists).
LP: **240077.1**
MC: **240077.4**

ENNIO MORRICONE 4 The greatest film music of (Various artists).
LP: **242049.1**
MC: **242049.4**

ENNIO MORRICONE 5 The greatest film music of (Various artists).
LP: **242052.1**
MC: **242052.4**

FILM HITS.
Tracks: / Once upon a time in the West / For a few dollars more / Moses theme / Bye bye Colonel / Fistful of dollars / Gun for Ringo / Ballad of Sacco and Vanzetti / Here's to you / Vice of killing / Paying off scores / Adventurer / What have you done to Solange / Violent city / Mertello.
LP: . . . . **NL 70091**
MC: . . . . **NK 70091**
LP: . . . . **INTS 5059**

FILM MUSIC 1966-1987.
Tracks: / Good, the bad and the ugly, The / Sicilian clan,The / Chi Mai / Investigation of a citizen above suspicion / Mosca Addio / Marche en la / Battle of Algiers, The / Infernal trio, The / Dedicace / Sacco and Vanzetti / La tragedia di un uomo ridicolo / Once upon a time in the west (Main theme.) / Mission, The (remix) / Once upon a time in America (Cokey's song.) / Gabriel's oboe / Atto di dolore / Baci dopo il tramonto / Le marginal / Estate 1943 / Falls, The / Man with the harmonica / Lontano / My name is Nobody / Peur sur la ville / Le vent, le cri / Once upon a time in America (Deborah's theme.).
2LP: . . . . **VD 2516**
MC: . . . . **TCVD 2516**

FOR A FEW DOLLARS MORE (See under For a few dollars more).

GREATEST FILM THEMES.
MC: **402224**

MASTERPIECES.
LP: . . . . **CL 31559**

MISSION, THE (Original Soundtrack) (Morricone, Ennio & The London Philharmonic Orch).
Tracks: / On earth as it is in Heaven / Mission, The / Falls, The / River / Gabriel's oboe / Ave Maria Guarani / Te Deum Guarani / Brothers / Refusal / Carlotta / Asuncion / Vita nostra / Alone / Climb / Guarani / Remorse / Sword, The / Penance / Miserere.
LP: . . . . **V 2402**
MC: . . . . **TCV 2402**

MOSES (Original Soundtrack).
LP: . . . . **NSPH 28503**

MY NAME IS NOBODY (see under My Name Is Nobody).

ONCE UPON A TIME IN THE WEST (Film soundtrack).
Tracks: / Once upon a time in the West / As a judgement / Farewell to Cheyenne / Transgression, The / First tavern, The / Second tavern, The / Man with a harmonica / Dimly lit room, A / Bad orchestra / Man / Jill's America / Death rattle / Finale.
LP: . . . . **NL 70032**
MC: . . . . **NK 70032**
LP: . . . . **PL 31387**
MC: . . . . **PK 31387**

OUT WEST WITH MORRICONE'S HIT FILM THEMES.
Tracks: / For a few dollars more / My name is Nobody / Once upon a time in the West / L'homme a l'harmonica / Good, the bad and the ugly, The / Professional gun, A / Il etait une fois la revolution / Mercenary / La liberated / Exorcist 2 theme.
MC: . . . . **BBM 57**

RAMPAGE (Film Soundtrack).
Tracks: / Rampage / Son / Findings / Over to the jury / Run, Run, Run / Since childhood / Magma / Gruesome discovery / Carillon / District attorney / Mother / Recollections.
MC: . . . . **TCV 2491**
LP: . . . . **V 2491**

STATE OF GRACE (See Under State Of Grace).

THIS IS ENNIO MORRICONE.
Tracks: / Chi mai / Come Maddalena / Good, the bad and the ugly, The / Death rides a horse / Navajo Joe / Big gundown.
LP: . . . . **THIS 33**
MC: . . . . **TCTHIS 33**

UNTOUCHABLES, THE (Original soundtrack).
Tracks: / Untouchables, The / Al Capone / Waiting at the border / Death theme / On the rooftops / Victorious / Man with the matches, The / Strength of the righteous, The (main title) / Ness and his family / False alarm / Untouchables, The / Four friends / Machine gun lullaby.
LP: **393 909-1**
MC: **393 909-4**

Morris, Audrey

BISTRO BALLADS.
LP: . . . . **FS 277**

VOICE OF AUDREY MORRIS, THE.
LP: . . . . **FS 204**

Morris, Byron

VIBRATIONS, THEMES AND SERENADES.
LP: . . . . **EPI 03**

Morris, Chris

YOUNG WOMAN (Morris, Chris & Golden Eagle Jazz Band).
LP: . . . . **SOS 1100**

Morris Concert Band

AN HOUR OF BRASS BAND MUSIC WITH....
Tracks: / Out with the hunt (track 1) / Scarborough fair (track 2) / Shepherd's song (track 3) / English country garden (track 4) / To a wild rose (track 5) / Barwick Green (track 6) / Greensleeves (track 8) / Londonderry air (track 9) / English rose (track 10) / Horse Guards, Whitehall, The (track 11) / Overture on famous English airs (track 12) / Three dale dances (track 13) / Hailstorm (track 14) / Red musketeer (track 15) / Fanfare polka (track 16) / High spirits (track 17) / Paperchase (track 18) / Padstow lifeboat (track 19).
MC: . . . . **HR 8145**

BRASS TRACKS.
LP: . . . . **A 22001**

MORRIS CONCERT BAND VOL.1.
LP: . . . . **VAR 5968**

MORRIS CONCERT BAND VOL.2.
LP: . . . . **VAR 5953**

Morris, Dr. Desmond

MANWATCHING.
MC: . . . . **PT 23**

SOCCER TRIBE, THE.
MC: . . . . **SS 130**

Morris, Gary

SECOND HAND HEART.
Tracks: / Love she found in me, The / Velvet chains / Runaway heart / Sweet red wine / Headed for a headache / West Texas highway and me / Roll back the rug and dance / Baby bye bye / Wind beneath my wings / Mama you can't give me no whippin' / Why lady why / Lasso the moon / 100% chance of rain / Second hand heart / Love she found in me, The.
LP: **925392 1**
MC: **925392 4**

Morris, James D

WHERE DOES THE NEWS COME FROM?/FUTURE FEAR.
MC: . . . . **NF 13**

Morris, Jenny

BODY AND SOUL.
Tracks: / Body and soul / You I know / Light hearted / Beating on the same drum / Rising sun / You're gonna get hurt / Animal magnetism / Tested sentences / Pass it over / Trust yourself.
MC: **781 819-4**
LP: **781 819-1**
LP: **2548971**
MC: **2548974**

SHIVER.
LP: **256462 2**

Morris, Joan

OTHER SONGS BY LIEBER AND STOLLER (Morris, Joan & William Bolcom).
LP: . . . . **H 71346**

SONGS BY IRA AND GEORGE GERSHWIN (Morris, Joan & William Bolcom).
LP: . . . . **H 71378**

Morris, Joe

LOW DOWN BABY.
Tracks: / Lowdown baby / You're my baby / I hope you're satisfied / Midnight grinder / Bald head woman / That's what makes my baby fat / Who's gonna cry for me / Crazy mixed up world / Jump everybody jump / Ghost train / Pack up all your rags / Can't stop crying / Love fever blues / I had a notion / Take your time / Going going gone.
LP: . . . . **JB 610**

Morris, Johnny (nar)

BEDTIME STORIES.
LP: . . . . **REC 264**
MC: . . . . **ZCM 264**

KING'S BREAKFAST, THE.
Tracks: / More it snows, The / Wind on the hill / Oh the butterflies are flying / Spring morning / At the zoo / Half way down the stairs / King's breakfast, The / Teddy bear / Lines and squares / Bears / If I was a bear / Isn't it funny? / Buckingham Palace / Market square / There was an old sailor / In the fashion / Cottleston pie / If I were a King / Dormouse and the doctor, The / Missing the christening.
LP: . . . . **RUB 037**
MC: . . . . **RUBC 037**

MORE BEDTIME STORIES.
LP: . . . . **REC 333**
MC: . . . . **ZCM 333**

MORE RAILWAY STORIES (2) (See under Railway Stories).

RAILWAY STORIES (See under Railway Stories).

Morris, Leon

HONKY TONK BLUEGRASS (Morris, Leon & Buzz Busby).
LP: . . . . **ROUNDER 0031**

Morris, Lynn

LYNN MORRIS BAND (Morris, Lynn Band).
Tracks: / My heart skips a beat / You'll get no more me / Adams county breakdown / Black pony / Come early morning / Help me climb that mountain / Kisses don't die / Handy man / What was I supposed to do / If lonely was the wind / Don't tell me stories / Valley of peace.
LP: . . . . **ROUNDER 0276**
MC: . . . . **ROUNDER 0276C**

Morris Motors Band

MARCHING CONTRASTS.
Tracks: / Marche militaire-la ronde / Oh, listen to the band / Ballycastle bay / Mancunian way / Queen's trumpeters, The / St. John march, The / Semper sousa / By royal command / Bugle call blues / Rover's return, The / Duke of York's patrol, The / Corner flag / European, The / Seventy-six trombones.
LP: . . . . **PRL 002**
MC: . . . . **CPRL 002**

Morris, Rex

HORNES AND MELODY.
LP: . . . . **ANG 002LP**

Morris, Richard

SONIC FIREWORKS V1 (Morris, Richard/Atlanta Brass Ensemble).
Tracks: / Fanfare for the common man / Salute / Grand choeur en dialogue / Toccata and fugue in D minor (BMV 538 'Dorian' & 565) / Let nothing ever grieve thee.
LP: . . . . **CCS 7010**

SONIC FIREWORKS V2 (Morris, Richard/Atlanta Brass Ensemble).
Tracks: / Also sprach Zarathustra / Toccata from symphony no.5 / Poeme heroique / Suite No. 1-Rondeau, Fanfares / Chaconne in D minor for organ / Voluntaries for trumpet and organ (three).
LP: . . . . **CCS 7011**

Morris, Sarah Jane

SARAH JANE MORRIS.
Tracks: / Loving a dream / I'll be your angel / She's leaving home / This ain't livin' / Alone again naturally / Hello like before / Me and Mrs Jones / Sunny / Can't get to sleep without you / This will be / Rains have failed again, The / Me and Mrs Jones (Minneapolis version).
LP: . . . . **HIP 59**
MC: . . . . **HIPC 59**

Morris, Thomas

GOIN' CRAZY WITH THE BLUES (Morris, Thomas & The Blues Singers).
LP: . . . . **FB 306**

PAST JAZZ MASTER (1923).
Tracks: / E flat blues, No 2 / Original Charleston strut / Lonesome journey blues / When the jazz band starts to play / Just blues, that's all / Bull blues / Those blues / Ceaucoupe de jazz / Achin' heart blues / Wild cat blues / Kansas City man blues / T'aint nobody's business if I do / New Orleans hop scop blues / Oh daddy blues / Old-fashioned love / House rent blues / Mean blues.
LP: . . . . **S 805**

THOMAS MORRIS AND 7 HOT BABIES (New Orleans Blue 5).
LP: . . . . **CC 49**

TOM MORRIS PAST JAZZ MASTERS & CLARENCE WILLIAMS (Morris, Tom Past Jazz Masters & Clarence Williams Blue Five).
LP: . . . . **FJ 113**

Morrish, Ken

BATH WURLITZER ORGAN, THE.
LP: . . . . **ARS 104**

Morrison, Alan

CORNET CASCADE.
Tracks: / Bride of the waves / Lost chord, The / Fee des eaux / Anna Karenina / Prelude and capriccio / Take a pair of sparkling eyes / Southern Cross / Dear Lord and Father of mankind / Carnival of Venice.
LP: . . . . **LKLP 7071**

Morrison, Dennis

DENNIS MORRISON & THE GLENMOR SCOTTISH DANCE BAND (Morrison, Dennis/Glenmor Scottish Dance Band).
Tracks: / Grand march 4/4 / Strathspey and reel / Two to one / March strathspey and reel / Irish medley / Gaelic waltz / Two hornpipes / March and reel / Clansman reel, The / Pipe medley / Continental waltz / Pipe hornpipes / Two step / Fiddle selection / Gay Gordons.
LP: . . . . **LILP 5166**
MC: . . . . **LICS 5166**

Morrison, James

JAMES MORRISON AND TOM ENNIS (See under Ennis, Tom) (Morrison, James & Tom Ennis).

POSTCARDS FROM DOWN UNDER.
Tracks: / Wednesday race, The / From this day / Saturday sailing / Wet Monday / Freshwater girls / Outback / Under the reef / Sydney by night.
LP: **2556971**
MC: **2556974**

PURE GENIUS OF JAMES MORRISON.
LP: . . . . **SHAN 33004**

SNAPPY DOO.
MC: **9031712114**

Morrison, Peter

GAELIC STORIES.
MC: . . . . **TGMMC 505**

MEMORIES.
Tracks: / Thistle of Scotland / Bonnie Galloway / Ellan Vannin / Campbeltown Loch / Lassie who loves me still / Watching the wheat / Star o' Rabbie Burns, The / Barnyards of Delgaty / Bonnie wee thing / Johnnie Cope / Lark in the clear air / Will ye no come back again.
LP: . . . . **LIDL 6005**
MC: . . . . **LIDC 6005**

SCOTLAND THE BRAVE.
Tracks: / Scotland the brave / Kelvingrove / De'ils awa' with the exciseman, The / Skye boat song / Laird of Cockpen, The / Mary of Argyll / Ae fond kiss / Lewis bridal song / O gin I were a baron's heir / I'll ay ca' in by yon toun / My love she's but a lassie yet / Annie Laurie / Killiecrankie.
LP: . . . . **LILP 5004**
MC: . . . . **LICS 5004**

SON OF THE HOMELAND.
Tracks: / Road to the isles / Lovely Stornoway / Soor milk cairt / Nicky Tams / Winter of life / Roses of Prince Charlie / Bonnie Strathyre / Tramps and hawkers / Land for all seasons, A / Muckin' o' Geordie's byre / Dark Lochnagar.
LP: . . . . **LIDL 6003**
MC: . . . . **LIDC 6003**

TOAST TO THE MUSIC OF SCOTLAND, A.
Tracks: / Toast is music / There was a lad / Roamin' in the gloamin' / Wee Deoch an' Doris / I Love a Lassie / My love is like a red red rose / Calling me home / Man's a man, A / Lass I lo'v ye dearly / Bonnie lass O'Ballochmyle / Dancing in Kyle / Of a the airts / Think on me / Hail Caledonia.
LP: . . . . **LIDL 6015**
MC: . . . . **LIDC 6015**

Morrison, Roger

PICTURES IN MY MIND.
LP: . . . . **CHILLP 8**

Morrison, Tommy

PLACE YOUR BETS.
Tracks: / Blind driver / How wrong / What you need / I come to the battle / Alone / Tangled webs / How come this weak man / Iron bird / You ain't got nothing / There is a way / Pour the wine / When this pub closes.
LP: . . . . **RAL 2**

Morrison, Van

ASTRAL WEEKS.
Tracks: / Astral weeks / Beside you / Sweet thing / Cyprus Avenue / Young lovers do / Madame George / Ballerina / Slim slow rider.
LP: . . . . **K 46024**
MC: **K4 46024**

AT RONNIE SCOTT'S (See under Baker, Chet) (Baker, Chet (with Van Morrison)).

AVALON SUNSET.
LP: **8392621**
MC: **8392624**

BEAUTIFUL VISION.
Tracks: / Celtic ray / Northern music / Dweller on the threshold / She gives me religion / Beautiful vision / Aryan mist / Across the bridge where angels dwell / Vanlose stairway / Scandinavia / Cleaning windows.
LP: . . . . **PRICE 82**
MC: . . . . **PRIMC 82**
LP: **6302 122**
LP: **839 601 1**
MC: **839 601 4**

CARRYING A TORCH (See Under Jones, Tom) (Morrison, Van & Tom Jones).

COMMON ONE.
Tracks: / Haunts of ancient peace / Summertime in England / Satisfied / When heart is open / Wild honey / Spirit.
LP: . . . . **PRICE 01**
MC: . . . . **PRIMC 1**
LP: **6302 021**
LP: **839 600 1**
MC: **839 600 4**

CUCHULAINN.
MC: . . . . **MRILC 012**

ENLIGHTENMENT.
Tracks: / Real real gone / Enlightenment / So quiet in here / Avalon of the heart / See me through / Youth of 1,000 summers / In the days before rock 'n' roll / Start all over again / She's a baby / Memories.
LP: **847 100-1**
MC: **847 100-4**

HARD NOSE THE HIGHWAY.
Tracks: / Snow in San Anselmo / Warm love / Hard nose the highway / Wild children / Great deception, The / Being green / Autumn song / Purple heather.
LP: . . . . **K 46242**
LP: **839 163-1**
MC: **839 163-4**

HIS BAND & STREET CHOIR.
Tracks: / Domino / Crazy face / Give me a kiss / I've been working / Call me up in Dreamland / I'll be your lover too / Blue money / Virgo clowns / Gypsy queen / Sweet Jannie / If I ever needed someone / Street choir.
LP: . . . . **K 46066**

HYMNS OF THE SILENCE.
LP: **8490261**
MC: **8490264**

INARTICULATE SPEECH OF THE HEART.
Tracks: / Higher than the world / Connswater / River of time / Celtic swing / Rave on, John Donne / Inarticulate speech of the heart no.1 / Irish heartbeat / Street only knew your name, The / Cry for home / Inarticulate speech of the heart no.2 / September night.
LP: . . . . **PRICE 93**
MC: . . . . **PRIMC 93**
LP: . . . . **MERL 16**
MC: . . . . **MERLC 16**
LP: **839 604 1**
MC: **839 604 4**

INTO THE MUSIC.
Tracks: / Bright side of the road / Full-force gale / And the healing has begun / Steppin' out queen / Troubadors / Rolling hills / You make me feel so free / Angelou / It's all in the game / You know what they're writing about.
LP: . . . . **PRICE 2**
MC: . . . . **PRIMC 2**
LP: **9120 852**
LP: **839 603 1**
MC: **839 603 4**

IRISH HEARTBEAT (Morrison, Van & the Chieftains).
Tracks: / Star of the County Down / Irish heartbeat / Ta mo chleamhnas deanta / Raglan Road / She moved through the fair / I'll tell me ma / Carrickfergus / Celtic ray / My lagan love / Marie's wedding.
LP: . . . . **MERH 124**
MC: . . . . **MERHC 124**

IT'S TOO LATE TO STOP NOW.
Tracks: / Ain't nothin' you can do / Warm love / Into the mystic / These dreams of you / I believe in my soul / I've been working / Help me / Wild children / Domino / I just want to make love to you / Bring it on home to me / St. Dominic's preview / Take your hand out of my pocket / Listen to the lion / Here comes the night / Gloria / Caravan / Cyprus Avenue.
2LP: . . . . **K 86007**
2LP: **839 166-1**
MCSET: **839 166-4**

LIVE AT THE GRAND OPERA HOUSE, BELFAST.
Tracks: / Into the mystic / Inarticulate speech of the heart / Dweller on the threshold / It's all in the game / You know what they're writing about / She gives me religion / Haunts of ancient peace / Full-force gale / Beautiful vision / Vanlose stairway / Rave on, John Donne / Rave on, part 2 / Northern muse / Cleaning windows.
LP: . . . . **MERL 36**
MC: . . . . **MERLC 36**
LP: **839 602 1**
MC: **839 602 4**

MOONDANCE.
Tracks: / Stoned me / Moondance / Crazy love / Caravan / Into the mystic / Come running / These dreams of you / Brand new day / Everyone / Glad tidings.
LP: . . . . **K 46040**
LP: . . . . **WS 1835**
MC: **446040 2**

MOONDANCE/HIS BAND AND STREET CHOIR.
LP: . . . . **K 46116**

NO GURU, NO METHOD, NO TEACHER.
Tracks: / Got to go back / Oh the warm feeling / Foreign window / Town called Paradise / In the garden / Tir na nog / Here comes the knight / Thanks for the information / One Irish rover / Ivory tower.
LP: . . . . **MERH 94**
MC: . . . . **MERHC 94**
LP: **8496191**
MC: **8496194**

PERIOD OF TRANSITION, A.
Tracks: / You gotta make it through the world / It fills you up / Eternal Kansas City / Joyous sound / Flamingoes fly (heavy connection) / Cold wind in August.
LP: . . . . **K 56322**
LP: **839 165-1**
MC: **839 165-4**

POETIC CHAMPIONS COMPOSE.
Tracks: / Spanish Steps / Mystery / Queen of the slipstream / I forgot that love existed / Sometimes I feel like a motherless child / Celtic excavation / Someone like you / Alan Watts Blues / Give me my rapture / Did ye get healed? / Allow me.
LP: . . . . **MERH 110**
MC: . . . . **MERHC 110**

SENSE OF WONDER, A.
Tracks: / Tore down a'la rimbaud / Ancient of days / Evening meditation / Master's eyes, The / What would I do / Sense of wonder, A / Boffyflow and Spike / If you only knew / Let the slave.
LP: . . . . **MERH 54**
MC: . . . . **MERHC 54**
MC: **843 116 4**
LP: **843 116 1**

ST. DOMINIC'S PREVIEW.
Tracks: / Jackie Wilson said / Gypsy / I will be there / Listen to the lion / St. Dominic's preview / Redwood tree / Almost Independence Day.
LP: . . . . **K 46172**
LP: **839 162-1**
MC: **839 162-4**

T.B.SHEETS.
Tracks: / He ain't give you none / Beside you / It's all right / Madame George / T.B. sheets / Who drove the red sports car / Ro Ro Rosy / Brown eyed girl.
LP: **22007014**
MC: **4678274**

THEM FEATURING VAN MORRISON.
2LP: . . . . **DPA 30012**

THIS IS WHERE I CAME IN.
LP: **6467 625**

TUPELO HONEY.
Tracks: / Wild night / Straight to your heart like a cannonball / Old old Woodstock / Starting a new life / You're my woman / Tupelo honey / I wanna roo you / When that evening sun goes down / Moonshine whisky.
LP: . . . . **K 46114**
LP: **839 161-1**
MC: **839 161-4**

TWO ORIGINALS OF VAN MORRISON.
Tracks: / Domino / Crazy face / Give me A kiss / I've been working / Call me up in dreamland / I'll be your lover, too / Blue money / Virgo clowns / Gypsy queen / Sweet Jannie / If I ever needed someone / Street choir / Wild night / (Straight to your heart) like A cannonball / Old old Woodstock / Starting A new life / You're my woman / Tupelo honey / I wanna roo you (Scottish derivative) / When that evening sun goes down / Moonshine whisky.
LP: . . . . **K 86009**

VAN - BEST OF VAN MORRISON, THE.
Tracks: / Whenever God shines his light / Jackie Wilson said / Brown eyed girl / Brown side of the road / Have I told you lately that I love you / Moondance / Here comes the night / Domino / Gloria / Baby please don't go / And it stoned me / Sweet thing / Warm love / Wild night / Cleaning windows / Did ye get healed / Dweller on the threshold (Only on CD.) / Queen of the slipstream (Only on CD.) / Wonderful remark (Only on cassette and CD.) / Full force gale (Only on cassette and CD.).
LP: **841 970 1**
MC: **841 970 4**

VEEDON FLEECE.
Tracks: / Fair play / Linden Arden stole the highlights / Who was that masked man? / Streets of Arklow / You don't pull no punches but you don't push the river / Bulbs / Cul de sac / Comfort you / Come here, my love / Country fair.
LP: . . . . **K 56068**
LP: **839 164-1**
MC: **839 164-4**

WAVELENGTH.
Tracks: / Kingdom Hall / Checkin' it out / Natalia / Venice U.S.A. / Lifetimes / Wavelength / Santa Fe: Beautiful obsession / Hungry for your love / Take it where you find it.
MC: **K4 56526**
LP: . . . . **K 56526**
LP: **839 169-1**
MC: **839 169-4**

Morrissey

BONA DRAG.
Tracks: / Piccadilly palare / Interesting drug / November spawned a monster / Will never marry / Such a little thing makes such a big difference / Last of the famous international playboys, The / Ouija board, ouija board / Hairdresser on fire / Everyday is like Sunday / He knows I'd love to see him / Yes, I am blind / Luckylisp / Suedehead / Disappointed.
LP: . . . . **CLP 3788**
LP: **794 298 1**
MC: . . . . **TCCLP 3788**
MC: **794 298 4**

KILL UNCLE.
Tracks: / Our Frank / Asian rut / Sing your life / Mute witness / King Lear / Found found found / Driving your girlfriend home / Harsh truth of the camera eye, The / (I'm) the end of the family line / There's a place in hell for me and my friends.
LP: . . . . **CSD 3789**
MC: . . . . **TCCSD 3789**

VIVA HATE.
Tracks: / Alsatian cousin / Little man, what now? / Everyday is like Sunday / Bengali in platforms / Angel, angel, down we go together / Late night, Maudlin Street / Suedehead / Break up the family / Ordinary boys, The / I don't mind if you forget me / Dial a cliche / Margaret on the guillotine.
MC: . . . . **TCCSD 3787**
LP: . . . . **RP 285611**
LP: . . . . **FA 3243**
MC: . . . . **TCFA 3243**
LP: . . . . **CSD 3787**

Morrissey, Bill

BILL MORRISSEY.
LP: . . . . **PHILO 1105**
MC: . . . . **PHILO 1105C**

NORTH.
LP: . . . . **PH 1106**
MC: . . . . **PH 1106C**

Morrissey, Dick

AFTER DARK.
Tracks: / I won't last a day without you / March on / They say it's wonderful / Pili-pili / Way we were, The / Running out of time / Lou Grant / Change partners.
LP: . . . . **CODA 2**

CAPE WRATH (Morrissey, Dick & Jim Mullen).
Tracks: / Lovely day / Cape Wrath / Bristol boogie / Return to Tooting Broadway / Soul eyes / Song for Carla / Dreams so real / Night song.
LP: . . . . **SHSP 4098**

RESURRECTION RITUAL (Morrissey, Dick Quartet).
Tracks: / Resurrection ritual / Germina / Maestro, The / Lush life / Love dance / Star trek.
LP: . . . . **MM 077**

SOULILOQUY.
Tracks: / Clouds 10, 33 / Lord Mayo / Angel / Soliloquy / East sunrise / Blue star Delhi / Red shoes.
LP: . . . . **CODA 23**
MC: . . . . **COCA 23**
LP: **8329401**
MC: **8329404**

UP (see under Mullen, Jim).

Morrissey, Louise

LOUISE.
LP: . . . . **CMLP 1034**

WHEN I WAS YOURS.
Tracks: / I couldn't leave you if I tried / He thinks I still care / Old flames / Blue eyes crying in the rain / Oh what a love / I still love you / Night Daniel O'Donnell came to town, The / When I was yours / Tipperary on my mind / Rose of Allendale / Hills of Killinaule / Green willow / Slieveenamon / Roses and violets / Amazing grace.
MC: . . . . **RITZLC 0054**

Morrissey Mullen

BADNESS.
Tracks: / Do like you / Dragonfly / Blue tears / Stay awhile / Badness / Pass the music on / Slipstream.
LP: . . . . **BEGA 27**
LP: . . . . **CODA 24**

HAPPY HOUR.
2LP: . . . . **CODA 29**
MC: . . . . **COCA 29**

IT'S ABOUT TIME.
Tracks: / Stop and look around / It's about time / Ounce of bounce / So so fine / Ol' sax and Captain Axe / Bladerunner / Why does it always happen to me? / Do I do / Above the clouds.
LP: . . . . **BEGA 44**

LIFE ON THE WIRE.
Tracks: / Life on the wire / Takin' time / Face of a child / Come and get me / Brazil nut / Ships that pass in the night / Making waves / Running out of time.
LP: . . . . **BEGA 33**

THIS MUST BE THE PLACE.
Tracks: / Tear for crystal, A / Mean time / This must be the place / With you / Southend Pier / Visions / All I want to do.
LP: . . . . **CODA 15**
MC: . . . . **COCA 15**

Morrisseys

IRELAND'S MORRISSEYS.
MC: . . . . **CMRC 1001**

LETS SING TOGETHER.
LP: . . . . **HM 024D**

OLD RUSTIC BRIDGE BY THE MILL.
LP: . . . . **CMRLP 1011**

Morriston Orpheus

AMAZING GRACE (Morriston Orpheus Male Choir).
Tracks: / Amazing Grace / Without you / Eli Jenkin's prayer / Lord's prayer, The / Speed your journey / Battle hymn of the Republic / For king and country / Memory / Kentucky babe / Little drummer boy / Shenandoah / Portrait of my love / Softly as I leave you / Walk away.
LP: . . . . **MFP 41 5753 1**
MC: . . . . **MFP 41 5753 4**
MC: . . . . **TC MFP 5753**

GOD BLESS THE PRINCE OF WALES.
Tracks: / God bless the Prince Of Wales / Gwymru'n un / Gwahoddiad / O Isis and Osiris / Lost chord / One world / Comrades in arms / Arise o sun / Martyrs of the arena / When evening's twilight / Easter hymn.
LP: . . . . **OU 2236**

GOLDEN AND NEW.
Tracks: / Y delyn aur / Gloria / Ave verum corpus / Crusaders / Farewell my love / Fantasia on famous Welsh airs / If I had words / When a child is born / Mamy blue / Mumbles train / Smile beyond the looking glass / If I could see the Rhondda one more time / If I were a rich man.
LP: . . . . **NTS 159**

HIRAETH.
Tracks: / Cydganed pawb (Let all the world in every corner sing) / Hiraeth / Credo / My bonny lass she smileth / Hyder / Jesu, who didst ever guide me / Tydi a roddaist / Kalinka / I'm gonna walk / Chorus and Laura's song from Casanova / Rock-a my soul / Rose, The / Duet from the Pearl Fishers / From far inside the shrine.
LP: . . . . **GRALP 21**
MC: . . . . **GRTC 21**

HOW GREAT THOU ART.
LP: . . . . **MFP 5592**
MC: . . . . **TCMFP 5592**

HYMNS OF GLORY.
LP: . . . . **EG 2700891**
MC: . . . . **EG 2700894**

I'LL WALK BESIDE YOU.
Tracks: / I'll walk beside you / Mary's boy child / Deep harmony / My Lord, what a morning / He / American trilogy / All I ask of you / There is nothin' like a dame / My dearest dear / You are my heart's delight / I got plenty o' nuttin' / What would I do without my music? / Going home.
LP: . . . . **GRALP 32**
MC: . . . . **GRTC 32**

LAND OF MY FATHERS.
MC: . . . . **GRTC 40**

MORRISTON ORPHEUS CHOIR & BAND OF H.M. ROYAL MARINES, THE (Morristons Orpheus Choir & Band of the Welsh Guards).
Tracks: / It's a grand night for singing (From "State Fair".) / Bloody Mary / There is nothin' like a dame / Younger than Springtime (From "South Pacific".) / You'll never walk alone (From "Carousel".) / Edelweiss (From "The Sound Of Music".) / Getting to know you (From "The King & I".) / Oklahoma / Oh what a beautiful morning (From "Oklahoma!") / Overture (Iolanthe) / March of the peers / None shall part us / When Britain really ruled the waves (Iolanthe) / He loves (Iolanthe) / Young Strephon is a kind of lout (Iolanthe) / Finale / U.S. Marine Corps hymn / I believe / Oh what a lovely war / It's a long way to Tipperary / There's a long, long trail / Keep the home fires burning / Mademoiselle from Armentiers / Over there / Roses of Picardy / Pack up your troubles in your old kit bag / If you want to know who we are (From "The Mikado".) / So please you sir, we much regret (From "The Mikado".) / Three little maids from school are we (From "The Mikado".) / Brightly dawns our wedding day (From "The Mikado".) / Sun whose rays ablaze, The (From "The Mikado".) / Flowers that bloom in the spring, The (From "The Mikado".) / Braid the raven hair (From "The Mikado".) / Tit willow (From "The Mikado".) / Threatened cloud has passed away, The (From "The Mikado".) / Army, the Navy and the Air-Force, The (From "The Mikado".) / Bless 'em all / Kiss me goodnight Sergeant Major / Lili Marlene / I'll be seeing you / Now is the hour / This is the army / Mister Jones / Washing on the siegfried line, The.
MC: . . . . **TCEMS 1264**

MYFANWY.
Tracks: / Myfanwy / With a voice of singing / Kula serenade / High on a hill / Ave verum corpus / Come back to Sorrento / Old rugged cross, The / Love, could I only tell thee / Roll Jordan roll / Scarborough fair / My little Welsh home / We'll gather lilacs / How soon / Gloria in excelsis / Amazing grace / Eli Jenkin's prayer / Speed your journey / Battle hymn of the Republic / Little drummer boy.
LP: . . . . **MFP 41 5662-1**
MC: . . . . **MFP 41 5662-4**

SAY IT WITH MUSIC (Morriston Orpheus Choir & Band of H.M. Royal Marines).
Tracks: / Say it with music / Marie / Easter parade / How deep is the ocean / Always / White Christmas / Moonlight Bay / By the light of the silvery moon / Ramona / Whiffenpoof song, The / Sweet Genevieve / On the banks of the Wabash / And the band played on / In the good old summertime / Mermaid, The / Rovin', A / Belle, belle my liberty belle / My truly, truly fair / Last farewell, The / Shenandoah / Spanish ladies / Portsmouth / She was beautiful / There's a coach comin' in / Once a year day / Deadwood stage / Get me to the church on time / Thank heaven for little girls / How to handle a woman / Camelot / Hello Dolly / Flash, bang, wallop / He's in love / Stranger in paradise / My heart and I / Pedro the fisherman / Donkey serenade, The / Indian love call / Vilja / Drinking song / White Horse Inn, The / My prayer.
LP: . . . . **MFP 41 5701 1**
MC: . . . . **MFP 41 5701 4**
MC: . . . . **TC MFP 5701**
LP: . . . . **TWOX 1080**

SING THE HITS OF ANDREW LLOYD WEBBER.
Tracks: / One more angel in Heaven / Mr. Mistoffelees / Music of the night / Starlight express / Any dream will do / Memory / Old deuteronomy / Phantom of the opera / Don't cry for me Argentina / All I ask of you / Pie Jesu.
LP: . . . . **MFP 5862**
MC: . . . . **TCMFP 5862**

SING WE MERRILY.
LP: . . . . **NTS 119**

THIS IS CHRISTMAS.
Tracks: / First Nowell, The / Away in a manger / We three kings / Once in Royal David's city / Coventry carol / While shepherds watched / Hark the herald angels sing / Silent night / Holly and the ivy, The / O little town of Bethlehem / Ding dong merrily on high / O come, all ye faithful.
LP: . . . . **THIS 14**

THIS IS WALES.
MC: . . . . **TC THIS 6**

WE'LL KEEP A WELCOME.
Tracks: / Holy city, The / Cwm Rhondda / Hiraeth / Men of Harlech / All through the night / Bless this house / Land of my fathers / Jerusalem / Ave Maria / Steal away / Myfanwy / We'll keep a welcome.
MC: . . . . **TCNTS 185**
LP: . . . . **NTS 185**

WE'LL KEEP A WELCOME - VOL.3.
LP: . . . . **SM 393**

WE'LL KEEP A WELCOME - VOL.4.
LP: . . . . **SM 394**

YOU'LL NEVER WALK ALONE.
Tracks: / Dies irae / Let it be me / Anvil chorus / Miserere / Rise up shepherd and foller / You'll never walk alone / Cymru fach / Creation's hymn / Old folks at home / Li'l Liza Jane / My hero / Martyrs of the arena.
LP: . . . . **GRALP 7**
MC: . . . . **GRTC 7**

Morrow, Buddy

BUDDY MORROW 1963-64.
Tracks: / Invitation / Candy / Preacher, The / More / Mambo / Soft talk / Exodus (Theme from) / Breakfast at Charlie's / I'll be around / You'd better love me / Time after time / What kind of fool am I? / Prelude II / Lock the door / I remember Waldo / Central Park South.
LP: . . . . **HSR 154**

Morse, Ella Mae

BARRELL HOUSE, BOOGIE AND THE BLUES.
LP: . . . . **PM 1546721**

HITS OF ELLA MAE MORSE, THE.
Tracks: / Cow cow boogie / Blacksmith's blues, The / I love you yes I do.
LP: . . . . **PM 1553041**
MC: . . . . **PM 1553044**

MORSE CODE, THE.
Tracks: / Day in, day out / My funny valentine / Accentuate the positive / When my sugar walks down the street / Dream a little dream of me / Heart and soul / Jersey bounce / I can't get started / Baby, won't you please come home / You go to my head / Music, Maestro, please.
LP: . . . . **T 898**

SENSATIONAL.
Tracks: / Mr. Memory maker / Put your arms around me honey / Livin' livin' livin' / Greyhound / Jump back / Tennessee saturday night / Sensational / Ain't that a shame / Razzle dazzle / Down in Mexico / Smake dab in the middle / I'm gone / T'aint what you do (it's the way that you do it) / Seventeen.
LP: . . . . **EMS 1145**

Morse, Lee

1925-1938.
Tracks: / Oh boy what a girl / Ain't she sweet / Mollie make up your mind / Careless love / Jersey walk / I've got five dollars / Walkin' my baby back home / Daddy's home.
LP: . . . . **HQ 2072**

LEE MORSE & HER BLUE GRASS BOYS (Morse, Lee & Her Blue Grass Boys).
LP: . . . . **TT 201**

LEE MORSE & HER BLUE GRASS BOYS 1925-32 (Morse, Lee & Her Blue Grass Boys).
MC: **044**

Morse, Steve

HIGH TENSION WIRES.
LP: . . . . **MCA 6275**
MC: . . . . **MCAC 6275**

INTRODUCTION, THE (Morse, Steve Band).
Tracks: / Cruise missile / General lee / Introduction / VHF / On the pipe / Whistle / Mountain waltz / Huron river blues.
LP: 960 369-1

SOUTHERN STEEL (Morse, Steve Band).
Tracks: / Cut to the chase / Simple Simon / Vista grande / Sleaze factor / Battle lines / Southern steel / Wolf song / Weekend overdrive / Arena rock / Point counterpoint.
MC: . . . . MCAC 10112

STAND UP (Morse, Steve Band).
Tracks: / Book of dreams / English rancher / Rockin' guitars / Distant stars / Pick your poison / Stand up / Travels of Marco Polo / Golden Quest / Unity gain.
LP: . . . . EKT 24
MC: . . . . EKT 24C

Mortal Sin

EVERY DOG HAS IT'S DAY.
LP: . . . . FLAG 61
MC: . . . . TFLAG 61

FACE OF DESPAIR.
Tracks: / Martyrs of eternity / Infantry corps, The / Robbie soles / Suspended animation / For richer for poorer / Voyage of the disturbed / Terminal reward.
LP: 8363701
MC: 8363704

MAYHEM DESTRUCTION.
LP: . . . . VERH 48
MC: . . . . VERHC 48

MAYHEMIC DESTRUCTION.
LP: . . . . AJLP 1016

Mortal Terror

L.P. (See under Generic) (Mortal Terror/ Generic).

Morter, Doug

BEEN THERE, SEEN IT AND BOUGHT THE TEE-SHIRT.
LP: . . . . FUN 004

Morticians

SHE'S LIKE HEROIN.
LP: . . . . DIST 2

Mortimer, Carole (aut)

SAVAGE INTERLUDE (see under Savage Interlude) (Boyd, Carole (nar)).

Mortimer, Harry

CAROLS AT CHRISTMAS (Mortimer, Harry & His All Stars).
LP: . . . . MFP 50483
MC: . . . . TCMFP 50483

HERITAGE (Mortimer, Harry & The London Brass Players).
Tracks: / Heritage / Honesty / Beast of the black mountain, The / Happy ending / Journey's end / Nights of gladness / Old haunted colliery, The / Jubilee hoe down / Hafod heights / Free as air / Music for a pageant / Barwick Green.
LP: . . . . ETMP 7

MAN OF BRASS.
Tracks: / Zampa / Mac and Mort / Richmond Hill / Polka brillante / Shylock / Alpine echoes / March no. 3 / Trumpet concerto / Zelda / Hailstorm / Swallows serenade / Hunting medley / Three trumpeters / Kenilworth / Jenny Wren / Shepherd's song / Lost chord / Radetzky march / To a wild rose / Blazon / Ride of the Valkyries / Barber of Seville overture / Spring / Jesu joy of man's desiring / William Tell / Galop and finale.
2LP: . . . . DUO 130

Mortimer, John

CHARADE.
MC: . . . . CAB 268

CLINGING TO THE WRECKAGE.
MCSET: . . . . ZBBC 1019

PARADISE POSTPONED (Horden, Sir Michael).
MCSET: . . . . LFP 7276

RUMPOLE (4 plays with Maurice Denham) (Various artists).
MCSET: . . . . ZBBC 1022

SUMMER'S LEASE (Fleetwood, Susan).
MCSET: . . . . ZBBC 1098

TRIALS OF RUMPOLE, THE (McKern, Leo).
MCSET: . . . . LFP 7200
MCSET: . . . . LFP 4172005

Mortimer's Cross

MORTIMER'S CROSS (Joan Aiken) (Bennett, Judy (nar)).
MC: 2CCA 3047

Morton, Craig

THEM LIVERPOOL JUDIES.
LP: . . . . PH 1002

Morton Gould Sym...

SOUSA GREAT MARCHES (Morton Gould Symphonic Band).
Tracks: / Stars and stripes forever / El Capitan / Hands across the sea / National Fencibles / Manhattan Beach / On parade / Gladiator / Washington Post / High school cadets / US field artillery march / Corcoran cadets / Thunderer / Semper fidelis / Sound off.
LP: . . . . VL 84626

Morton, Jelly Roll

1926-39.
LP: . . . . LPJT 23

BEST OF JELLY ROLL MORTON.
LP: . . . . CL 43291

BLACK BOTTOM STOMP.
LP: . . . . LPJT 23
MC: . . . . MCJT 23

CLIMAX RAG 1.
LP: 20101
MC: 40101

COMPLETE JELLY ROLL MORTON 1 & 2 1926-27.
Tracks: / Black bottom stomp / Smoke house blues / Chant / Sidewalk blues / Dead man blues / Steamboat stomp / Someday, sweetheart / Grandpa's spells / Original Jelly Roll blues / Doctor Jazz / Cannon ball blues / Hyena stomp / Billy goat stomp / Wild man blues / Jungle blues / Beale Street blues / Pearls, The / Wolverine blues / Mister jelly roll.
2LP: . . . . NL 89768
MCSET: . . . . NK 89768
2LP: . . . . PM 42405

COMPLETE JELLY ROLL MORTON 3 & 4 1927-29.
Tracks: / Georgia swing / Wild man blues / Kansas City stomp / Shoes shiner's drag / Boogaboo / Shreveport stomp (1 & 2) / Mournful serenade / Red hot pepper stomp / Deep creek / Pep / Seattle hunch (1 & 2) / Frances / Freakish (1 & 2) / Burnin' the iceberg / Courthouse bump / Pretty Lil (1 & 2) / Sweet Aneta mine / New Orleans bump (1 & 2) / Down my way / Try me out / Tank town bump (1 & 2) / Sweet Peter (1 & 2).
2LP: . . . . NL 89769
MCSET: . . . . NK 89769
2LP: . . . . PM 43170

COMPLETE JELLY ROLL MORTON 5 & 6 1929-1930.
Tracks: / Mississippi mildred / Mint julep / You oughta see my gal / Futuristic blues / Keep your business to yourself / She's got what I need / I hate a man like you / Don't tell me nothin' 'bout my man / Smilin' the blues away / Turtle twist / My little Dixie home / That's like it ought to be / Each day / If someone would only love me / That'll never do / I'm looking for a little bluebird / Little Lawrence / Harmony blues / Fussy Mabel / Ponchartrain / When they get lovin, they's gone / You done played out blues / Oil well / Load of coal / Jersey Joe.
2LP: . . . . PM 43690
2LP: . . . . NL 89757
MCSET: . . . . NK 89757

COMPLETE JELLY ROLL MORTON 7 & 8 1930-1940.
Tracks: / Crazy chords / Primrose stomp / Big time woman / I'm her pappa she's my mama / New crawley blues / She saves her sweetest smile for me / Low gravy / Strokin' away / Blue blood blues / Mushmouth / Gambling Jack / Fickle fay creep / Oh, didn't he ramble / High society / I thought I heard Buddy Bolden say / Winin' boy blues / Climax rag / Don't you leave me here / West End blues / King Porter stomp.
2LP: . . . . PM 45372
2LP: . . . . NL 89748
MCSET: . . . . NK 89748

DOC COOK DREAMLAND ORCHESTRA (See under Cook, Doc) (Morton, Jelly Roll/Doc Cook).

DOCTOR JAZZ.
Tracks: / Black bottom stomp / Chant / Sidewalk blues / Dead man blues / Original Jelly Roll blues / Doctor jazz / Wild man blues / Red hot pepper stomp / Jungle blues / Pearls / Kansas city stomp / Little Lawrence.
LP: . . . . CL 89808
MC: . . . . CK 89808

GENNET PIANO SOLOS, THE 1923-24.
Tracks: / King Porter stomp / New Orleans (Blues) / Joys (2 takes) / Grandpa's spells / Kansas City stomp / Wolverine blues / Pearls / Tia Juana / Shreveport stomp / Tom cat blues / Stratford hunch / Perfect rag.
LP: . . . . S 801

HIS RED HOT PEPPERS & TRIOS VOL.6 (Morton, Jelly Roll & His Red Hot Peppers).
LP: . . . . SM 3555

HIS RED HOT PEPPERS & TRIOS VOL.7 (Morton, Jelly Roll & His Red Hot Peppers).
LP: . . . . SM 3556

HIS RED HOT PEPPERS VOL.1 (Morton, Jelly Roll & His Red Hot Peppers).
LP: . . . . SM 3550

HIS RED HOT PEPPERS VOL.2 (Morton, Jelly Roll & His Red Hot Peppers).
LP: . . . . SM 3551

HIS RED HOT PEPPERS VOL.3 (Morton, Jelly Roll & His Red Hot Peppers).
LP: . . . . SM 3552

HIS RED HOT PEPPERS VOL.4 (Morton, Jelly Roll & His Red Hot Peppers).
LP: . . . . SM 3553

HIS RED HOT PEPPERS VOL.5 (Morton, Jelly Roll & His Red Hot Peppers).
LP: . . . . SM 3554

I'M A WINNIN' BOY.
Tracks: / Honeysuckle rose / Melancholy baby / I'd do anything for you / I ain't got nobody / Pearls, The / Tiger rag / Trees / Winnin' boy blues / King Porter stomp.
LP: . . . . JOY 265

INCOMPARABLE.
LP: 22024
MC: 42024

JAZZ CLASSICS IN DIGITAL STEREO (Jelly Roll Morton 1926-1934).
Tracks: / Black bottom stomp / Chant / Dead man blues / Grandpa's spells / Original Jelly Roll blues / Beale Street blues / Ham 'n' eggs / You need some loving / Kansas City stomp / Shoe shiner's drag / Deep creek / Pretty Lil / New Orleans bump / Ponchartrain / Blue blood blues / I'm alone without you.
MC: . . . . ZCF 604
LP: . . . . REB 604

JELLY ROLL MORTON.
LP: . . . . MERITT 1

JELLY ROLL MORTON.
LP: . . . . SM 3091

JELLY ROLL MORTON.
LP: . . . . CC 7

JELLY ROLL MORTON 1939.
LP: AG6 24062

JELLY ROLL MORTON 1923/24.
Tracks: / King Porter stomp / New Orleans joys / Grandpa's spells / Kansas city stomp / Wolverine blues / Pearls / Tia Juana / Shreveport stomp / Frog-i-more rag / Mamanita / Jelly roll blues / Big foot ham blues / My gal / Muddy water blues / Steady roll / Fish tail blues / High society / Weary blues / Tiger rag.
LP: . . . . M 47018

JELLY ROLL MORTON 1923-25.
LP: . . . . FJ 104

JELLY ROLL MORTON CENTENNIAL, THE (His Complete Victor Recordings).
Tracks: / Black bottom stomp / Smoke house blues / Chant (takes 1/3) / Sidewalk blues (takes 2/3) / Dead man blues (takes 1/2) / Steamboat stomp / Someday sweetheart (takes 2/3) / Grandpa's spells (takes 2/3) / Original Jelly Roll blues (takes 1/2) / Doctor Jazz / Cannon ball blues (takes 1/2) / Hyena stomp (takes 2/3) / Billy goat stomp (Takes 1/2) / Wild man blues (takes 1/3) / Jungle blues (takes 2/3) / Beale Street blues ((Take 1/2) / Pearls, the (takes 2/3) / Wolverine blues (takes 1/2) / My Jelly Lord / Georgia swing / Kansas City stomp / Shoeshiner's drag / Boogaboo / Shreveport (takes 1/2) / Mournful serenade / Red hot Pepper / Deep creek / Pep / Seattle hunch (takes 1/2) / Frances / Freakish (takes 1/2) / Burnin' the iceberg (Takes 1/2) / Courthouse bump (Takes 1 & 2) / Pretty Lil (takes 1/2) / Sweet Anita mine (takes 1/2) / New Orleans bump (takes 1/2) / Down my way / Try me out / Tank town bump (takes 1/2) / Sweet Peter (takes 1/2) / Jersey Joe / Mississippi Mildred (takes 1/2) / Mint julep / Smilin' the blues away / Turtle twist / My little Dixie home / That's like it ought to be / Each day (takes 1/2) / If someone would only love me / That'll never do / I'm looking for a little bluebird / Little Lawrence / Harmony blues / Fussy Mabel / Ponchatrain / Oil well (takes 1/2) / Load of coal (takes 1/2) / Crazy chords (takes 1/2) / Primrose stomp (takes 1/2) / Low gravy / Strokin' away (takes 1/2) / Blue blood blues (takes 1/2) / Mushmouth shuffle / Gambling Jack (takes 1/2) / Fickle Fay creep / Oh, didn't he ramble (takes 1/2) / High society / I thought I heard Buddy Bolden say / Winin' boy blues (takes 1/2) / Climax rag (takes 1/2) / Don't you leave me here (takes 1/2) / West End blues / Ballin' the jack.
LPS: . . . . NL 82361
MCSET: . . . . NK 82361

JELLY ROLL MORTON COLLECTION (20 Golden Greats).
Tracks: / Jelly Roll blues / King Porter stomp / London blues / New Orleans joys / Wolverine blues / Mr. Jelly Lord / Tank town bump / Wild man blues / Pep / Burnin' the iceberg / New Orleans bump / Shreveport stomp / Seattle hunch / Freakish / Red hot pepper stomp / Mississippi Mildred / My little Dixie home / Jersey Joe / Don't you leave me here / Crazy chords.
LP: . . . . DVLP 2084
MC: . . . . DVMC 2084

JELLY ROLL MORTON'S HOT SEVEN AND HOT SIX 1940.
LP: 6.24546

KING AND MISTER JELLY LORD, THE (See under Oliver, King) (Morton, Jelly Roll & King Oliver).

KING OF NEW ORLEANS JAZZ (Morton, Jelly Roll & His Red Hot Peppers).
Tracks: / Black bottom stomp / Chant / Smoke house blues / Steamboat stomp / Sidewalk blues / Dead man blues / Cannon ball blues / Grandpa's spells / Doctor Jazz / Original Jelly Roll blues / Jungle blues / Pearls, The / Beale Street blues / Kansas city stomp / Shoe shiner's drag / Georgia swing.
LP: . . . . NL 89015
MC: . . . . NK 89015
LP: . . . . INTS 5092

LAST BAND DATES 1940.
Tracks: / Sweet substitute / Panama / Good old New York / Big lips blues / Why / Get the bucket / If you knew / Shake it / Dirty dirty dirty / Swinging the elks / Mama's got a baby / My home is in a southern town.
LP: AG6 24546

LIBRARY OF CONGRESS RECORDINGS VOL.1.
LP: . . . . S 1311

LIBRARY OF CONGRESS RECORDINGS VOL. 7.
LP: . . . . S 1317
LP: . . . . CJM 8

LIBRARY OF CONGRESS RECORDINGS VOL.3.
LP: . . . . CJM 4
LP: . . . . S 1313

LIBRARY OF CONGRESS RECORDINGS VOL. 5.
LP: . . . . S 1315
LP: . . . . CJM 6

LIBRARY OF CONGRESS RECORDINGS VOL. 6.
LP: . . . . S 1316
LP: . . . . CJM 7

LIBRARY OF CONGRESS RECORDINGS VOL.4.
LP: . . . . CJM 5
LP: . . . . S 1314

LIBRARY OF CONGRESS RECORDINGS VOL.2.
LP: . . . . CJM 3
LP: . . . . S 1312

LIBRARY OF CONGRESS RECORDINGS VOL. 8.
LP: . . . . S 1318
LP: . . . . CJM 9

MISTER JELLY LORD (Morton, Jelly Roll & His New Orleans Rhythm Kings).
Tracks: / Sobbin blues / Marguerite / Angry angry / Clarinet marmalade / Mister Jelly Lord / London blues / Milenberg joys / Mad.
LP: . . . . RHA 6022

NEW ORLEANS JAZZ.
LP: 22027
MC: 42027

NEW ORLEANS MEMORIES.
Tracks: / Sporting / House rag / Original rags / Crave, The / Naked dance / Mister Joe / King Porter stomp / Winin' boy blues / Don't you leave me here / Mamie's blues / Michigan water blues.
LP: AG6 24062

RARITIES VOL.1.
Tracks: / Big fat ham big fat ham / Muddy water blues / Mr. Jelly Roll / Mr. Jelly Roll (take 2) / Steady roll / Steady roll (take 2) / Fish tail blues / High Society / Weary blues / Tiger rag / King Porter stomp / Tom cat / My gal / Wolverine blues / Mr. Jelly Lord.
LP: . . . . RHA 6021

RARITIES VOL.2.
Tracks: / Someday sweetheart / London blues / Soap suds / Sergeant Dunn's bugle call blues / Ham 'n' eggs / Buffalo blues / You need some lovin' / Never had

no lovin' / I'm alone without you / Pearls, The / Sweetheart o'mine / Fat meat and greens / King Porter stomp / Georgia grind / Dead man blues / Midnight mama / Mr Jelly Lord.
LP: . . . . RHA 6030

SOLO PIANO SESSION 1924-1938.
Tracks: / Honky tonk music (2 takes) / Finger buster / Creepy feeling / Winnin' boy blues / Pep / Seattle hunch / Frances / Freakish / Pearls, The / Sweetheart o mine / Fat meat and greens / King Porter stomp / Thirty fifth street blues / Mamanita / Froggie Moore / London blues.
LP: . . . . S 816

WEST END BLUES.
Tracks: / Oh didn't he ramble / Strokin' away / Blue blood blues / Mushmouth shuffle / Fickle fay creep / High society / Thought I heard Buddy Bolden say / Winnin' boy blues / Climax rag (take 1) / Don't you leave me here / West end blues / Ballin' the jack.
LP: . . . . MTM 005

Morton, Mandy Band

SEA OF STORMS.
LP: 238 210-1

Morton, Mike

UNFORGETTABLE CHRISTMAS (Morton, Mike Orchestra).
LP: . . . . MHLP 203

UNFORGETTABLE GREATS (Morton, Mike Orchestra).
LP: . . . . MHLP 202
MC: . . . . ZCMH 202

UNFORGETTABLE SWING TIME (Morton, Mike Orchestra).
LP: . . . . MHLP 201
MC: . . . . ZCMH 201

Morton, Pete

FRIVOLOUS LOVE.
Tracks: / Sloth and the greed, The / Mother's day / Last god of England, The / Time / Tamyin / Babe of the world / Without thinkng love / Backward king, The / Frivolous love / Rachel / Just like John Barley.
LP: . . . . HAR 001
MC: . . . . HARC 001

FRIVOLOUS LOVE.
LP: . . . . PH 1122
MC: . . . . PH 1122C

ONE BIG JOKE.
LP: . . . . HAR 004
MC: . . . . HAR 004C

Morton, Robin

TRADITIONAL IRISH SONGS (see McConnell, Cathal) (Morton, Robin & Cathal McConnell).

Morton, Ronnie

RONNIE & JOHNNY (Morton, Ronnie & John Pugh).
LP: . . . . WF 013

Morton, Tom

REVENGER'S COMEDY, THE.
Tracks: / If only for a moment / Before the night comes / Wealeness / Search & destroy / Ships in the night / Angels train / I don't sleep / Man who nearly signed the Beatles, The / Which school do you go to / Gin or champagne / Party / Dancing in a mine field.
LP: . . . . VOE 001

Morty

LOVE BLIND.
Tracks: / Are you big enough / Honeymoon in Babylon / Love blind / Hot day in June / Between love / Take it to the heart / You / You put yourself in my place / Tear your playhouse down / Little Miss World.
LP: . . . . BPLP 001

Morwells

BEST OF THE MORWELLS.
LP: . . . . NH 302

Morwells Unlimited

AL DUB.
LP: . . . . TRLS 193

Mosalini

LA BORDONA (See under Beytelman) (Mosalini;Beytelman;Caratini).

Mosca, Sal

AT THE DEN (See under Ind, Peter) (Mosca, Sal & Peter Ind).

SAL MOSCA MUSIC.
LP: . . . . IP 7712

Mosch, Ernst

BLEIB IM HERZEN JUNG (Stay young at heart) (Mosch, Ernst & The Original Street Musicians).
Tracks: / Bleib im Herzen jung (Stay young at heart) / Als der Herrgott durch bohmen ging / Auf der ponyfarm / Seefest-walzer (Sea-festival waltz) / Eine frau wie du / Los geht's / Musikantenball (Musicians' ball) / Beim Vinzenzifest (At (St.) Vincent's feast) / Ein ganzes leben lang / Wir sind die freunde vom sportverein / etc.
LP: 6.26418
MC: 4.26418

DIE ERNST MOSCH SUPER HIT PARADE (Mosch, Ernst & his Original Egerland Musicians).
Tracks: / Fuchsgraben / Bohmischer wind / Loffelpolka / Rauschende birken / Egerlander musikanten marsch / Bis bald auf wiederseh'n / Egerland heimatland / Dort tief im Bohmerwald / Wir sind kinder von der Eger / Mondschein an der Eger / Dompfaff / Pfeffer und salz.
LP: 6.26741
MC: 4.26741

GERMAN OOM-PAH MUSIC.
LP: 6 25541
MC: 425541

GOLDEN CHRISTMAS (Goldene Weihnacht) (Mosch, Ernst & his Original Egerland Musicians).
Tracks: / Herbei, o ihr glaubigon / Ihr kinderlein kommet / Kommet ihr hirten / Morgen kommt der Weihnachtsmann / White Christmas / Stille nacht / O, du frohliche / Jingle bells / Aber heidschi bumbeidschi / Von himmel hoch, da domm'ich her / Kling, glockchen, klingelingeling / Alle jahre weider.
LP: 6.26890
MC: 4.26890

GOLDEN MARCH ALBUM, THE (Das goldene marschalbum).
Tracks: / Salve imperator / Die alte garde / Parade-defilier-marsch / Castaldo-marsch / Washington post, the / Junges leben / Fest und treu / Unter der admiralsflagge / Elbetal-gruss / Im tempo unsrer zeit / Andulka-marsch / Astronauten marsch.
LP: 6.26488
MC: 4.26488

MIT FREUNDLICHE GRUSSEN (With friendly greetings) (Mosch, Ernst & his Original Egerland Musicians).
Tracks: / Astronauten marsch / Schone Pragerin (Beautiful Prague girl) / Liebe und musik (Love and music) / Gruss mir mein heimatland (Greetings from my homeland) / Salve imperator (Hail Emperor) / Mama / Musikantentraum (Musicians' dream) / Elbetal-gruss.
MC: 4.26645

ORIGINAL EGERLANDER.
Tracks: / Kleine etelka / Heut aben lad' ich mire die Liebe ein / Am manznares / Ein paar tranen werd ich weinem um dich / Ein waltzer zu zwei'n / Florentinische nachte / Sagt die eine schone frau / Vielleicht heimatland / Im steh'im regen / Ich muss was wunderbares sein / Einmal dommt der Tag / Ich lade sie ein Fraulein / Ach Luise.
LP: 6.25583
MC: CR4 25583

Mose, Deacon

PREACHING THE GOSPEL 1927-31.
LP: . . . . WSE 139

Moseley & Johnson

MOSELEY AND JOHNSON.
LP: . . . . MS 2203

PREMIUM.
LP: . . . . MSS 2205
MC: . . . . MSSC 2205

Moses

MOSES (See under Morricone, Ennio) (Morricone, Ennio).

Moses, Bob

EAST SIDE (Moses, Bob & Billy Martin).
LP: . . . . ITM 0015

STORY OF MOSES.
2LP: 188703-1
MC: 188703-4

VISIT WITH THE GREAT SPIRIT.
Tracks: / Fan man / Deepest blues / Machupicchu / Visit with the great spirit / Monktional / Carinhoso / Suite Bahia.
LP: . . . . GR 8307
MC: . . . . GRC 8307

WHEN ELEPHANTS DREAM OF MUSIC.
Tracks: / Trevor / Picolo and Lulu / Everybody knows when you're up and in / Lava flow / Happy to be here today / For miles / Black orchid / Disappearing blues / Blame it on the egg / River, The.
LP: . . . . GR 8203

Moses, Pablo

IN THE FUTURE.
Tracks: / In the future / Ready, aim, fire / Who? / Reggae warrior / I & I now bow / Subway rider / Slayer / What is it? / Rhythm track / Silly Willy.
LP: 814 392 1
MC: 814 392 4

LIVE TO LOVE.
LP: . . . . BM 114

SONG, A.
Tracks: / Song / Dubbing is a must / Revolutionary step / Music is my desire / Each is I servant / One people / Let's face it / Protect I.
LP: . . . . ILPS 9541

TENSION.
Tracks: / Tension / Watch out / Don't force me / Outlaw / Open / Bomb the nation / Play, play, play / In the streets / Cuttin' out / Work, work, work.
LP: 824 281 1

WE REFUSE.
LP: . . . . FILER 295
MC: . . . . FILECT 295

Mosher, Jimmy

CHICK FROM CHELSEA, A (Mosher, Jimmy Quartet).
Tracks: / Quasimodo / You know I care / Blue walls / Gramp's prance / Miss Krissy / Chick from Chelsea.
LP: . . . . DS 860

Mosley, Snub

LIVE AT PIZZA EXPRESS.
Tracks: / Exactly like you / Out of nowhere / Stormy Monday / Juice head Willie / Jitters / Basin Street blues / Duck's yas, The / Kansas City / Indiana.
LP: . . . . PIZZA 5502

MAN WITH THE FUNNY LITTLE HORN (Mosley, Snub & His Band).
LP: . . . . KM 709

Mosquito Coast

MOSQUITO COAST (Film Soundtrack) (Various artists).
Tracks: / Mosquito Coast: *Jarre, Maurice* / Goodbye America: *Jarre, Maurice* / Gimme soca: *Lee, Byron & The Dragonaires* / Up the river: *Jarre, Maurice* / Jeronimo: *Jarre, Maurice* / Fat boy: *Jarre, Maurice*/ Destruction: *Jarre, Maurice* / Storm, The: *Jarre, Maurice* / Allie's theme: *Jarre, Maurice*.
LP: . . . . LONLP 30
MC: . . . . LONC 30
LP: FSP21005
MC: FSPC21005

Mosquito Story

MOSQUITO STORY, THE.
LP: . . . . RL 7050

Moss, Anne Marie

DON'T YOU KNOW ME?.
LP: . . . . ST 211

Moss, Buddy

BUDDY MOSS 1933-35.
LP: . . . . DLP 528

GEORGIA BLUES (1930-1935).
Tracks: / I'm on my way / Diddle da diddle / She looks so good / She's coming back / Bye bye mama / Cold country blues / Prowling woman / When I'm dead and gone / Jealous hearted man / It must have been her / Joker man / Back to my used to be / Broke down engine no.2 / Some lonesome day / My baby won't pay for me.
LP: . . . . TM 800

RED RIVER BLUES.
Tracks: / Red river blues / Prowlin' gambler blues / Tampa strut / Who stole de lock / When the hearse rolls me / Insane blues / Dough rollin' papa / Some lonesome day / Jinx man blues / Evil hearted woman / Worrysome woman / Mistreated boy / You need a woman / Joy rag / I'm sittin' here / Unfinished business.
LP: . . . . TM 802

Moss, Danny

DANNY MOSS & GEOFF SIMPKINS VOL.2 (Moss, Danny & Geoff Simpkins).
LP: . . . . FLY 218

MIDNIGHT SUN, THE (see Lambe, Jeanie) (Moss, Danny Quartet & Jeanie Lambe).

Moss, David

BERLIN TANGO (See under Sachse, Joe for details) (Moss, David/Joe Sachse).

Moss, George

PIBROCH-GEORGE MOSS.
MC: . . . . TGMMC 506

Moss Poles

SHORN.
Tracks: / Things you say, The / Don't worry / All in your eyes / Don't you know / More & more / You came up and smiled / What can I do / Take it or leave it / Amanda's dreams / I hear you scream / Underground / Sweetest girl, the / Little Prince / To kiss you.
LP: . . . . IDEALP 002

Moss, W. Stanley

ILL MET BY MOONLIGHT.
MC: . . . . SOUND 18

Mosse, Sandy

RELAXIN' WITH ... (Mosse, Sandy Quintet).
LP: . . . . FS 66

Most Happy Fella

MOST HAPPY FELLA (Original Broadway cast) (Various artists).
LP: . . . . ACS 2330

MOST HAPPY FELLA (ORIGINAL ISSUE) (Broadway cast) (Various artists).
LP: . . . . BBL 7374

MOST HAPPY FELLA (ORIGINAL ISSUE) (London cast) (Various artists).
LP: . . . . CLP 1365

Most, Sam

FLUTE FLIGHT.
LP: . . . . XAN 141

FLUTE TALK (Most, Sam & Joe Farrell).
LP: . . . . XAN 173

MOSTLY FLUTE.
LP: . . . . XAN 133

PLAYS BIRD, MONK & MILES.
LP: . . . . FS 305

RAY BROWN THREE, A (See under Brown, Ray).

Mote, Danny

ROCKIN' IT OUT.
Tracks: / Paralized / Oh baby / Roll over beethoven / Love's gonna live here again / Lonesome / Twistin' dog / I took her home / Since I met you baby / Ditch digger / Done you wrong / Josephine / Shakey's theme / I feel so bad / I've got swinging doors.
LP: . . . . WLP 8911

Motels

ALL FOUR ONE.
Tracks: / Mission of mercy / Take the L / Only the lonely / Art fails / Change my mind / So L.A. / Tragic surf / Apocalypso / He hit me (and it felt like a kiss) / Forever mine.
LP: . . . . EST 12177
MC: . . . . TC EST 12177

CAREFUL.
Tracks: / Danger / Envy / Careful / Bonjour baby / Party professionals / Days are OK / Cry baby / Whose problem? / People, places and things / Slow town.
LP: . . . . EST 12070

LITTLE ROBBERS.
Tracks: / Where do we go from here / Suddenly last summer / Isle of you / Trust me / Monday shut down / Remember the nights / Little robbers / Into the heartland / Tables turned / Footsteps.
LP: . . . . EST 7122881

MOTELS.
Tracks: / Anticipating / Kix / Total control / Love don't help / Closets and bullets / Atomic cafe / Celia / Porn reggae / Dressing up / Counting.
LP: . . . . EST 11996

Moten, Bennie

BASIC BEGINNINGS.
Tracks: / Jones law blues, The / Small black / Rit dit ray / New Vine Street blues / Oh Eddie / That too, do blues / Count, The / Liza Lee / Somebody stole my gal / Now that I need you / Toby / Moten swing / Blue room / New Orleans / Lafayette / Prince of Wales.
LP: . . . . NL 90403
MC: . . . . NK 90403

BENNIE MOTEN'S KANSAS CITY ORCH. 1923-25 (Moten, Bennie Kansas City Orchestra).
Tracks: / Ill natured blues / Chattanooga blues / Evil mama blues / Elephant's wobble / Crawdad blues / Selma 'bama blues / Break o'day blues / Waco Texas blues / South / Vine Street blues / Tulsa blues / Goofy dust / Baby dear / She's sweeter than sugar / South Street blues / Sister honky tonk / As I like it / Things seem so blue to me / 18th Street strut / Kater Street rag.
LP: . . . . FJ 120
MC: . . . . CFJ 120

COMPLETE BENNIE MOTEN-1/2-1926-1928.
Tracks: / Thick lip stomp / Harmony City shuffle / Yazoo / White lightnin' blues / Muscle shoals blues / Missouri wobble / Sugar / Dear heart / New Tulsa blues / Baby dear / Twelfth St. rag / Pass out lightly / Ding dong blues / Moten stomp / Justrite / Slow motion / Tough breaks / It's hard to laugh or smile / Sad man blues / Kansas City breakdown / Trouble

in mind / Hot water blues / Get low down blues.
2LP: . . . . PM 42410

COMPLETE BENNIE MOTEN-3/4-1928-1930.
Tracks: / She's no trouble / South / Terrific stomp / Let's get it / Kansas City squabble / Rite tite / Moten blues / That's what I'm talking about / That certain motion / It won't be long / When life seems so blue / Loose like a goose / Just say it's me / New goofy dust rag / Rumba negro / Jones law blues / Band box / Everyday blues / Boot it / Mary Lee / Rit-dit-ray / New Vine Street blues / Sweetheart of yesterday / Won't you be my baby.
2LP: . . . . PM 43693

MOTEN STOMP.
Tracks: / Thick lip stomp (track 1) / Harmony blues (track 2) / Kansas City shuffle (track 3) / Yazoo blues (track 4) / White lightnin' blues (track 5) / Muscle shoals blues (track 6) / Midnight mama (track 7) / Missouri wobble (track 8) / Sugar (track 9) / Dear heart (track 10) / New Tulsa blues (track 11) / Baby dear (track 12) / 12th Street rag (track 13) / Pass out lightly (track 14) / Ding-dong blues (track 15) / Moten stomp (track 16).
LP: . . . . HDL 108
MC: . . . . CHDL 108

Mother Gong

OWL AND THE TREE, THE.
LP: . . . . DMLP 1019

ROBOT WOMAN.
LP: . . . . BUTT 003

ROBOT WOMAN 2.
LP: . . . . HAI 100

ROBOT WOMAN 3.
Tracks: / It's you and me baby / Faces of woman / Desire / War / Children's song / Lady's song / Woman of streams / I'm sorry / Men cry / Solutions / Magenta part one.
LP: . . . . HAI 109

Mother Liza

MOTHER LIZA MEETS PAPPA TOLLO (Mother Liza/Pappa Tollo).
LP: . . . . VSLP 4017

Mother Love Bone

APPLE.
Tracks: / This is shangrila / Holy roller / Come bite the apple / Heartshine / Man of golden words / Gentle groove / Crown of thorns / Stardog champion / Bone China / Stargazer / Captain hi-top / Capricorn sister / Mr. Danny Boy.
LP: 843 191 1
MC: 843 191 4

Mother Nature

BREATH OF FRESH AIR, A.
LP: . . . . ARILP 017

Mother Tongue

OPEN IN OBSCURITY (Various artists).
LP: . . . . T 10

Mother Wore Tights

MOTHER WORE TIGHTS/THE SHOCKING MISS PILGRIM (Film soundtrack) (Various artists).
LP: . . . . CIF 3008

Mothers

FIRST BORN.
LP: . . . . EKT 84
MC: . . . . EKT 84C

OVER NITE SENSATION.
Tracks: / Camarillo brillo / I'm the slime / Dirty love / Fifty fifty / Zomby woof / Dinah moe humm / Montana.
LP: . . . . K 41000

Mothers Finest

FIRE.
Tracks: / Give you all the love / Niggizz can't sing rock'n'roll / My baby / Fly with me / Dontcha wanna love me / Rain.
LP: . . . . EPC 81595

IRON AGE.
Tracks: / Movin' on / Luv drug / Rock'n'roll 2 nite / U turn me on / All the way / Evolution / Illusion / Time / Gone with the rain / Earthling.
LP: . . . . EPC 84924

LOOKS COULD KILL.
Tracks: / For your love / I'm 'n danger / Legs and lipstick / Dream come true / Still over each other / I'll never be the same / Brave and strong / Your wish is my command / Cherish your lover / Heartbreaker / Call me Mister (CD only.) / Too serious (CD only.).
LP: . . . . EST 2114
MC: . . . . TCEST 2114

MOTHER FACTOR.
Tracks: / Can't fight the feelin' / Tell me / Watch my stylin' / Love changes / Don't wanna come back / Give it up / Mr. Goodbar / I can't believe / More and more.
LP: . . . . EPC 83011

ONE MOTHER TO ANOTHER.
Tracks: / Secret service / What kind of fool / Victory / Love me too / Everybody needs somebody / Big shot Romeo / What you do to me / In my baby's arms / Some kind of madness / Take me to the middle (of your luv).
LP: . . . . EPC 25363
MC: 40 25363
LP: . . . . EPC 25263

Mothers of Invention

JUST ANOTHER BAND FROM L.A.
Tracks: / Billy the mountain / Call any vegetable / Eddie, are you kidding? / Magdalena / Dog breath.
LP: . . . . K 44179

LIVE - FILLMORE EAST JUNE 1971.
Tracks: / Little house I used to live in / Mud shark, The / What kind of girl do you think we are? / Bwana dik / Latex solar beef / Willie the pimp part one / Willie the pimp part two / Do you like my new car? / Happy together / Lonesome electric turkey / Peaches en regalia / Tears begin to fall.
LP: . . . . K 44150

WE'RE ONLY IN IT FOR THE MONEY.
LP: . . . . SVLP 9199

Mothers Ruin

ROAD TO RUIN.
LP: . . . . SPA 1

Mothmen

ONE BLACK DOT.
Tracks: / Wa da da / Temptation / One more weapon / Let's talk about it / No rest / One black dot / Weekend / House and car / Home sweet home / Thank you I like it.
LP: . . . . RIDE 9

Moths

SUMMER SNOW.
Tracks: / Pimlico (the peoples show) / Maggie says / Stay / Memories / Wooden horse / Sexual suicide / Plastic christians / World turned upside down, the / Out in the rain / Years away.
LP: . . . . MOTH 1

WALKING ON A WIRE.
Tracks: / Walking on a wire / There's always something / Dance your life away.
LP: . . . . DIST 1

Motian, Paul

IN THE YEAR OF THE DRAGON (See Under Allen, Geri) (Motian, Paul/ Charlie Haden/ Geri Allen).

IT SHOULD'VE HAPPENED A LONG TIME AGO (Motian, Paul Trio).
LP: . . . . ECM 1283

MONK IN MOTIAN (Motian, Paul/Joe Lovano/Bill Frisell).
LP: 834421-1

PAUL MOTIAN ON BROADWAY VOL 2.
Tracks: / Good morning heartache / You and the night and the music / Moonlight becomes you / But not for me / Bess, oh where's my Bess? / I got rhythm / All the things you are / Nice work if you can get it / It might as well be spring / Look to the rainbow.
LP: 834 440 1
MC: 834 440 4

PAUL MOTIAN PLAYS BILL EVANS.
Tracks: / Show-type tune / Turn out the stars / Walkin' up / Very early / Five / Time remembered / 34 skidoo / Re: person I knew / Children's play song.
LP: 8344451

PSALM (Motian, Paul Band).
LP: . . . . ECM 1222

Motion

MOTION.
Tracks: / Walk on by / Rainbow / No man is an island / Basshoven / I'm coming home / Love uprising / Let go / Crazy beat / You love me only / Hawaiian hi.
LP: . . . . DDLP 4
LP: . . . . LPBR 1005

Motley Crue

DOCTOR FEELGOOD.
Tracks: / Same old situation / Slice of your pie / Rattlesnake shake / Kick start my heart / Without you / Don't go away mad / She goes down / Sticky sweet / Time for a change / TNT / Dr. Feelgood / Terror in tinseltown.
LP: . . . . EKT 59
MC: . . . . EKT 59 C

GIRLS, GIRLS, GIRLS..
Tracks: / Wild side / Girls, girls, girls. / Dancin' on glass / Bad boy boogie / Nona / Five years dead / All in the name of rock / Somethin' for nuthin' / All I need / Jailhouse rock (live).
LP: . . . . EKT 39
MC: . . . . EKT 39 C

MOTLEY CRUE: INTERVIEW PICTURE DISC.
LPPD: . . . . BAK 2051

RAW TRACKS.
Tracks: / Live wire / Piece of your action / Too young to fall in love (remix) / Knock 'em dead kid / Home sweet home (remix).
MLP: . . . . P 6261

SHOUT AT THE DEVIL.
Tracks: / In the beginning / Shout at the devil / Looks that kill / Bastard / Knock 'em dead kid / Danger / Too young to fall in love / Helter skelter / Red hot / Ten seconds 'til love / God bless the children of the beast.
LP: 9602891
MC: 9602894

THEATRE OF PAIN.
Tracks: / City boy blues / Fight for your rights / Use it or lose it / Smokin' in the boys room / Louder than hell / Keep your eye on the money / Home sweet home / Tonight (we need a lover) / Save our souls / Raise your hands to rock.
LP: . . . . EKT 8
MC: . . . . EKT 8C

TOO FAST FOR LOVE.
Tracks: / Live wire / Come on and dance / Public enemy No. 1 / Merry go round / Take me to the top / Piece of your action / Starry eyes / Too fast for love / On with the show.
LP: . . . . K 52425

Motley, Frank

FRANK MOTLEY 1951 - 1952.
Tracks: / Movin' man (Unreleased title.) / Herbert's jump / That's alright / Hurricane lover / Diggin' (Unreleased title.) / Fat man's scat (Unreleased title.) / Early in the morning (Alternative take.) / Nothin' (Unreleased title.) / Frank's jump (Unreleased title.) / Fat man (Unreleased title.) / Dual trumpet blues (Alternative take.) / Bow wow wow (Alternative take.).
LP: . . . . KK 805

Motor Boys Motor

MOTOR BOYS MOTOR.
Tracks: / Drive friendly / Here comes the Flintstones / Sacred pie / Freeze up the truth.
LP: . . . . ALB 111

Motor City Eight

MOTOR CITY EIGHT various artists (Various artists).
LP: . . . . ZYKLP 01

Motor City Madness

MOTOR CITY MADNESS (Various artists).
LP: . . . . GR 0033
LP: . . . . EFA 4467

Motor Cycle Boy

SCARLET.
LP: . . . . CHR 1689
MC: . . . . ZCHR 1689

Motorcycles...

CLASSIC MOTORCYCLES (Various artists).
MC: . . . . AC 145

Motorhead

1916.
Tracks: / One to sing the blues, The / I'm so bad (baby I don't care) / No voices in the sky / Going to Brazil / Nightmare/The dreamtime / Love me forever / Angel city / Make my day / Ramones / Shut you down / 1916.
LP: 4674811
MC: 4674814
LPPD: 4674810

ACE OF SPADES.
Tracks: / Ace of spades / Bite the bullet / Chase is better than the catch, The / Dance / Fast and loose / Fire fire / Hammer, The / Jailbait / Live to win / Love me like a reptile / Road crew, The / Shoot you in the back.
LP: . . . . BRON 531
MC: . . . . BRONC 531

ANOTHER PERFECT DAY.
Tracks: / Back at the funny farm / Shine / Dancing on your grave / Rock it / One track mind / Another perfect day / Marching off to war / I got mine / Tales of glory / Die you bastard.
LP: . . . . BRON 546
MC: . . . . BRONC 546
MC: . . . . CLAMC 225
LP: . . . . CLALP 225

ANOTHER PERFECT DAY/OVERKILL.
Tracks: / Back at the funny farm / Shine / Dancing on your grave / Rock it / One track mind / Another perfect day / Marching off to war / I got mine / Tales of glory / Die you bastard / Overkill / Stay clean / (I won't) pay your price / I'll be your sister / Capricorn / No class / Damage case / Tear ya down / Metropolis / Limb from limb.
MC: . . . . TFOMC 8
2LP: . . . . TFOLP 8

ANTHOLOGY - MOTORHEAD.
Tracks: / I got mine / Jailbait / Over the top / Step down / Dirty love / Ace of spades / Hoochie coochie man / Go to hell / Heart of stone / Louie Louie / Stone dead forever / Back at the funny farm / Chase is better than the catch, The / Turn you round again / Another perfect day / Capricorn / Lawman.
LP: . . . . RAWLP 011
MC: . . . . RAWTC 011

BEST OF MOTORHEAD.
MC: . . . . ARLC 1014

BIRTHDAY PARTY.
Tracks: / Iron fist / Mean machine / On the road / We are the road crew / Hammer, The / Metropolis / Ace of spades / Steal your face / Nothing up my sleeve / Bite the bullet / Chase is better than the catch, The / No class / Killed by death (Only on CD.) / Bomber (Only on CD.) / Motorhead (Only on CD.).
LP: . . . . GWLP 101
MC: . . . . GWTC 101

BIRTHDAY PARTY (IMPORT).
LP: 106511
MC: 106514

BLITZKREIG ON BIRMINGHAM.
LP: . . . . RRLP 120

BOMBER.
Tracks: / Dead men tell no tales / Lawman / Sweet revenge / Sharp shooter / Poison / Stone dead forever / All the aces / Step down / Talking head / Bomber.
LP: . . . . BRON 523
LP: . . . . CLALP 227
MC: . . . . CLAMC 227

BOMBER/ACE OF SPADES.
2LP: . . . . TFOLP 24
MC: . . . . TFOMC 24

BORN TO LOSE.
Tracks: / White lion fever / Leaving here / Train kept a rollin' / I'm your witch doctor / Lost Johnny / Keep us on the road / Vibrator / Watcher, The / Beer drinkers and hell raisers / Motorhead / Iron horse / City kids / Fools / On parole.
LP: . . . . DOJOLP 18
MC: . . . . DOJOTC 18

CITY KIDS.
LP: . . . . PLP 28
MC: . . . . PMC 28

COLLECTION: MOTORHEAD (Bear Trap).
Tracks: / Motorhead / Overkill / Talking head / Rock it / Iron fist / I got mine / Steal your face / (We are) the road crew / Swaggletooth / Stay clean / Iron horse / One track mind / Speedfreak / Loser / (Don't need) religion / Stone dead forever / Sweet revenge / Capricorn / Love me like a reptile / Ace of spades.
2LP: . . . . CCSLP 237
MC: . . . . CCSMC 237

DIRTY LOVE.
Tracks: / Hump on your back / Dirty love / Love me like a reptile / Waltz of the vampire / Bastard / We are the road crew / Shoot you in the back / Dirty love (full version) / Fast and loose / Ace of spades (rare version) / Godzilla akimbo.
LP: . . . . RRLP 123

FROM THE VAULTS.
LP: . . . . NEXLP 136
MC: . . . . NEXMC 136

IRON FIST.
Tracks: / Iron fist / Heart of stone / I'm the doctor / Go to hell / Loser / Sex and outrage / America / Shut it down / Speed freak / (Don't let them) grind ya down / (Don't need) religion / Bang to rights.
LP: . . . . CLALP 123
MC: . . . . CLAMC 123
LP: . . . . BRNA 539

LOCK UP YOUR DAUGHTERS (Live in St.Albans).
Tracks: / Motorhead / Leavin' here / Watcher, The / Louie Louie / Iron horse / Instrumental / I'll be your sister / Lost Johnny / Keep us on the road / Tear ya down / White line fever.
LP: . . . . RRLP 130
MC: . . . . RRMC 130

MELTDOWN.
LP: . . . . ESBLP 146

MOTORHEAD.
Tracks: / Motorhead / Vibrator / Lost Johnny / Iron horse / Born to lose / White line fever / Keep us on the road / Watcher, The / Train kept a rollin' / City kids / Beer drinkers and hell raisers / On parole / Instro / I'm your witch doctor.

LP: . . . . WIK 2
MC: . . . . TC-CWK 3008
LP: . . . . WIKM 2

MUSIC AND MEDIA INTERVIEW PICTURE DISC.
LPPD: . . . . MM 1213

NO REMORSE.
Tracks: / Ace of spades / Motorhead / Jailbait / Stay clean / Too late / Killed by death / Bomber / Iron fist / Shine / Dancing on your grave / Metropolis / Snaggletooth / Overkill / Please don't touch / Stone dead forever / Like a nightmare / Emergency / Steal your face / Louie Louie / No class / Iron horse / We are the road crew / Leaving here / Locomotive.
LP: . . . . CLALP 121
MC: . . . . CLAMC 121
LP: . . . . PROLP 5
LP: . . . . MOTOR 1

NO SLEEP AT ALL.
Tracks: / Doctor Rock / Dogs / Built for speed / Deaf forever / Killed by death / Traitor / Ace of spades / Eat the rich / Just cos you got the power / Overkill.
LP: . . . . GWLP 31
MC: . . . . GWTC 31
LP: . . . . RR 9514 1
MC: . . . . RR 9514 4

NO SLEEP TILL HAMMERSMITH.
Tracks: / Ace of spades / Stay clean / Metropolis / Hammer, The / Iron horse / No class / Overkill / Road crew, The / Capricorn / Bomber / Motorhead.
LP: . . . . BRON 535
MC: . . . . BRONC 535
LP: . . . . CLALP 179
MC: . . . . CLAMC 179

ON PAROLE.
Tracks: / Motorhead / On parole / Vibrator / Iron horse / Born to lose / City kids / Fools / Watcher, The / Leaving here / Lost Johnny.
LP: . . . . FA 3009
MC: . . . . TCFA 3009
LP: 1575421
LP: . . . . LBR 1004
LP: . . . . FA 3251
MC: . . . . TCFA 3251

ORGASMATRON.
MC: . . . . GWTC 1
LP: . . . . GWLP 1
LPPD: . . . . GWPD 1
LP: . . . . RR 9677
MC: . . . . RR 49677

OVERKILL.
Tracks: / Overkill / Stay clean / Pay your price / I'll be your sister / Capricorn / No class / Damage case / Tear ya down / Metropolis / Limb from limb.
LP: . . . . BRON 515
LP: . . . . FA 3236
MC: . . . . TCFA 3236
MC: . . . . CLAMC 178
LP: . . . . CLALP 178

RECORDED LIVE.
LP: 20041
MC: 40041

ROCK 'N' ROLL.
LP: . . . . GWLP 14
MC: . . . . GWTC 14
LP: . . . . RR 9594
MC: . . . . RR 4949 4

ST. VALENTINES DAY MASSACRE (See under Headgirl) (Motorhead & Girlschool).

STAND BY YOUR MAN (See under Wendy & Lemmy) (Wendy & Lemmy).

WHAT'S WORDS WORTH.
Tracks: / Watcher, The / Iron horse / Born to lose / On parole / White line fever / Keep us on the road / Leaving here / I'm your witch doctor / Train kept a rollin' / City kids.
LP: . . . . NED 2
MC: . . . . NEDC 2
LP: . . . . WIKM 49

Motors

APPROVED BY.
Tracks: / Airport / Mamma rock 'n' roller / Forget about you / Do you mind / You beat the hell outa me / Breathless / Soul redeemer / Dreaming your life away / Sensation / Today.
LP: . . . . OVED 202
LP: . . . . V 2101

GREATEST HITS: MOTORS.
LP: . . . . V 2204
MC: . . . . TCV 2204

MOTORS, THE.
LP: . . . . V 2089

TENEMENT STEPS.
LP: . . . . V 2151

Motown

20TH ANNIVERSARY ALBUM (Various artists).
LP: . . . . ZL 72132
MC: . . . . ZK 72132

25 USA NO.1 HITS FROM 25 YEARS (Various artists).
Tracks: / Please Mr. Postman: *Marvelettes* / My girl: *Temptations* / You can't hurry love: *Ross, Diana & The Supremes* / I heard it through the grapevine: *Gaye, Marvin* / ABC: *Jackson 5* / Just my imagination (running away with me): *Temptations* / Papa was a rollin' stone: *Temptations* / Let's get it on: *Gaye, Marvin*/ Baby love: *Ross, Diana & The Supremes* / I can't help myself: *Four Tops* / Reach out I'll be there: *Four Tops* / I want you back: *Jackson 5* / Ain't no mountain high enough: *Ross, Diana* / Tears of a clown: *Robinson, Smokey* / What's going on: *Gaye, Marvin* / You are the sunshine of my life: *Wonder, Stevie* / Keep on truckin': *Kendricks, Eddie* / Don't leave me this way: *Houston, Thelma* / Three times a lady: *Commodores* / Give it to me baby: *James, Rick* / Superstition: *Wonder, Stevie* / Got to give it up: *Gaye, Marvin* / Still: *Commodores* / Endless love: *Ross, Diana & Lionel Richie*.
2LP: . . . . TMSP 6018
MCSET: . . . . CTMSP 6018
LP: . . . . WL 72136
MC: . . . . WK 72136

25 YEARS OF MOTOWN CLASSICS (Various artists).
LP: . . . . STMS 5105
MC: . . . . CSTMS 5105
LP: . . . . WL 72127
MC: . . . . WK 72127

32 BIG HITS (Early & late 60's) (Various artists).
2LP: . . . . STMF 7001
MCSET: . . . . CSTMF 7001

150 MOTOWN HITS OF GOLD various artists (Various artists).
LPS: . . . . WL 72410
MCSET: . . . . WK 72410

ALL THE GREAT MOTOWN LOVE DUETS (Various artists).
LP: . . . . WL 72367
MC: . . . . WK 72367

ARTISTS AND SONGS THAT INSPIRED THE MOTOWN 25TH ANNIVERSARY (Various artists).
Tracks: / Reach out I'll be there: *Temptations & Four Tops* / Get ready: *Temptations & Four Tops* / It's the same old song: *Temptations & Four Tops* / Ain't too proud to beg: *Temptations & Four Tops* / Baby I need your loving: *Temptations & Four Tops* / My girl: *Temptations & Four Tops* / I can't get next to you: *Temptations & Four Tops* / I know I'm losing you: *Temptations & Four Tops* / I can't help myself: *Temptations & Four Tops* / Nowhere to run: *Reeves, Martha* / Dancing in the street: *Reeves, Martha* / Heatwave: *Reeves, Martha* / I'm ready for love: *Reeves, Martha* / I heard it through the grapevine: *Knight, Gladys* / Friendship train: *Knight, Gladys* / You need love like I do: *Knight, Gladys* / If I were your woman: *Knight, Gladys* / Daddy could swear, I declare: *Knight, Gladys* / Neither one of us: *Knight, Gladys* / I can't help myself: *Four Tops* / Shake me wake me: *Four Tops* / Standing in the shadows of love: *Four Tops* / Reach out I'll be there: *Four Tops*/ Bernadette: *Four Tops* / Stop in the name of love: *Ross, Diana & The Supremes* / Back in my arms again: *Ross*, Diana & The Supremes / Come see about me: *Ross, Diana & The Supremes* / Love is like an itching in my heart: *Various* original artists / Where did our love go: *Ross, Diana & The Supremes* / I want you back: *Jackson Five* / ABC: *Jackson Five* / Love you save, The: *Jackson Five* / Dancing machine: *Jackson Five* / Never can say goodbye: *Jackson Five* / I'll be there: *Jackson Five* / I know I'm losing you: *Temptations & Four Tops*.
LP: . . . . STMS 5106
MC: . . . . CSTMS 5106

BIG MOTOWN HITS AND HARD-TO-FIND CLASSICS VOL 2 (Various artists).
Tracks: / When I'm gone: *Holloway, Brenda* / Jamie: *Holland, Eddie* / Indiana wants me: *Taylor, R. Dean*/ He was really saying something: *Velvelettes* / Born to wander: *Rare Earth* / With you I'm born again: *Preston*, Billy & Syreeta / Every little bit hurts: *Holloway, Brenda* / Needle in a haystack: *Velvelettes* / Lonely, lonely girl am I: *Velvelettes* / I can't believe you love me: *Terrell, Tammi* / Money (that's what I want): *Strong*, Barrett / Take me in your arms: *Isley Brothers* / I guess I'll always love you: *Isley Brothers* / Here comes the judge: *Long, Shorty* / Function at the junction: *Long, Shorty* / Smiling faces sometimes: *Undisputed Truth*/ I just want to celebrate: *Rare Earth* / River deep, mountain high: *Supremes & Four Tops* / I've never been to me: *Charlene* / What the world needs now is love: *Clay, Tom*.
LP: . . . . WL 72432
MC: . . . . WK 72432

BIG MOTOWN HITS AND HARD-TO-FIND CLASSICS VOL 1 (Various artists).
Tracks: / Helpless: *Weston, Kim* / You've made me so very happy: *Holloway, Brenda* / Love's gone bad: *Clark*, Chris / I got a feeling: *Randolph, Barbara* / Baby I'm for real: *Originals* / Does your mama know about me: *Taylor, Bobby & The Vancouvers* / Bells, The: *Originals* / What becomes of the broken hearted?: *Ruffin, Jimmy*/ I've passed this way before: *Ruffin, Jimmy* / Walk away from love: *Ruffin, David* / My world ended (the moment you left me): *Ruffin, David* / Get ready: *Rare Earth* / I'm losing you: *Rare Earth* / War: *Starr*, Edwin / Twenty five miles: *Starr, Edwin* / It's a shame: *Detroit Spinners* / I'll always love you: *Detroit* Spinners / Darling baby: *Elgins* / Heaven must have sent you: *Elgins* / Just look what you've done: *Holloway, Brenda* / Love's gone bad: *Clark, Chris*.
LP: . . . . WL 72431
MC: . . . . WK 72431

BRITISH MOTOWN CHARTBUSTERS VOL.2 (Various artists).
LP: . . . . WL 72672
MC: . . . . WK 72672

BRITISH MOTOWN CHARTBUSTERS VOL.1 (Various artists).
Tracks: / Blowin' in the wind: *Wonder, Stevie* / You keep me hangin' on: *Ross, Diana & The Supremes* / Standing in the shadows of love: *Four Tops* / It takes two: *Gaye, Marvin & Kim Weston* / When you're young and in love: *Marvelettes* / (I know) I'm losing you: *Temptations* / What becomes of the brokenhearted: *Ruffin, Jimmy*/ Happening, The: *Ross, Diana & The Supremes* / 7 rooms of gloom: *Four Tops* / How sweet it is (to be loved by you): *Walker, Junior & The All Stars* / I'm ready for love: *Reeves, Martha* / Love is here and now you're gone: *Ross, Diana & The Supremes* / Gonna give her all the love I've got: *Ruffin, Jimmy* / I was made to love her: *Wonder, Stevie* / Take me in your arms and love me: *Knight, Gladys & The Pips* / Jimmy Mack: *Reeves, Martha*.
LP: . . . . WL 72671
MC: . . . . WK 72671

EVERY GREAT MOTOWN SONG, VOL 1: THE 60'S (The first 25 years as originally recorded) (Various artists).
Tracks: / Where did our love go?: *Ross, Diana & The Supremes* / Shop around: *Miracles* / Dancing in the street: *Reeves, Martha* / Reach out I'll be there: *Four Tops* / Take me in your arms: *Weston, Kim* / I heard it through the grapevine: *Knight, Gladys & The Pips* / How sweet it is to be loved by you: *Gaye, Marvin* / Heatwave: *Reeves, Martha* / My girl: *Temptations* / You keep me hangin' on: *Ross, Diana & The Supremes* / Ooh baby baby: *Miracles* / Please Mr. Postman: *Marvelettes* / Standing in the shadows of love: *Four Tops*.
LP: . . . . WL 72235
MC: . . . . WK 72235

EVERY GREAT MOTOWN SONG, VOL 2: THE 70'S (The first 25 years as originally recorded) (Various artists).
Tracks: / Ain't no mountain high enough: *Ross, Diana* / If I were your woman: *Knight, Gladys & The Pips* / Never can say goodbye: *Jackson Five* / Just my imagination (running away with me): *Temptations* / Do you know where you're going to?: *Ross, Diana* / Ben: *Jackson, Michael* / Touch me in the morning: *Ross, Diana* / Three times a lady: *Commodores* / Got to give it up: *Gaye, Marvin* / Love hangover: *Ross, Diana* / Sail on: *Commodores*.
LP: . . . . WL 72236
MC: . . . . WK 72236

FROM MOTOWN WITH LOVE (Various artists).
LP: . . . . NE 1381
MC: . . . . CE 2381

GOLDEN SOUND OF MOTOWN, THE (Various artists).
LPS: . . . . ALBUM 68
MCSET: . . . . CASSETTE 68

IT TAKES TWO (Various artists).
2LP: . . . . STD 7
MCSET: . . . . STDK 7

IT TAKES TWO (Various artists).
Tracks: / You're all I need to get by: *Gaye, Marvin & Tammi Terrell* / I'm your puppet: *Houston, Thelma/Jerry Butler* / You ain't livin' till you're lovin': *Houston, Thelma/Jerry Butler* / It's a lifetime thing: *Houston, Thelma/Jerry* Butler / Let's make a deal: *Syreeta & G.C. Cameron* / What good am I without you?: *Gaye, Marvin & Kim Weston*/ It takes two: *Supremes & Four Tops* / Love the one you're with: *Supremes & Four Tops* / River deep, mountain high: *Ross, Diana & Marvin Gaye* / You're a special part of me: *Ross, Diana & Marvin Gaye* / Stand by me: *Ruffin*, David & *Jimmy* / Let's make love now: *Art & Honey* / Oh how happy: *Starr, Edwin & Blinky* / I'm gonna make you love me: *Ross, Diana, The Supremes & The Temptations* / Once upon a time: *Gaye, Marvin & Mary Wells*.
LP: . . . . STMR 9002
MC: . . . . CSTMR 9002

MORE MOTOWN MAGIC (Various artists).
LP: . . . . MFP 50536
MC: . . . . TCMFP 50536

MORE MOTOWN MAGIC VOL 2 (Various artists).
LP: . . . . MFP 50537
MC: . . . . TCMFP 50537

MOST PLAYED OLDIES ON AMERICA'S JUKEBOXES (See under Most Played Oldies) (Various artists).

MOTOWN 20TH ANNIVERSARY ALBUM (Various artists).
Tracks: / Money (that's what I want): *Strong, Barrett* / Shop around: *Miracles* / You've really got a hold on me: *Miracles* / Tears of a clown: *Robinson, Smokey* / Fingertips (part 2): *Wonder, Little Stevie* / You are the sunshine of my life: *Wonder, Stevie* / Living for the city: *Wonder, Stevie* / Uptight: *Wonder, Stevie*/ For once in my life: *Wonder, Stevie* / Superstition: *Wonder, Stevie* / Heatwave: *Reeves, Martha & The Vandellas*/ Dancing in the street: *Reeves, Martha & The Vandellas* / My guy: *Wells, Mary* / Baby love: *Supremes*/ You keep me hangin' on: *Ross, Diana & The Supremes* / Shotgun: *Walker, Junior & The All Stars* / Ben: *Jackson*, Michael / Touch me in the morning: *Ross, Diana* / Do you know where you're going to: *Ross, Diana* / With you I'm born again: *Preston, Billy & Syreeta* / This old heart of mine: *Isley Brothers* / What becomes of the broken hearted?: *Ruffin, Jimmy* / Reach out I'll be there: *Four Tops* / Bernadette: *Four Tops* / You're all I need to get by: *Gaye, Marvin & Tammi Terrell* / I heard it through the grapevine: *Gaye, Marvin* / What's going on: *Gaye, Marvin* / Cloud nine: *Temptations* / Papa was a rollin' stone: *Temptations* / I want you back / I'll be there / War: *Starr, Edwin* / Indiana wants me: *Taylor, R. Dean* / Help me make it through the night: *Knight, Gladys & The Pips*.
2LP: . . . . TMSP 6010
MCSET: . . . . CTMSP 6010

MOTOWN CHARTBUSTERS (Various artists).
LP: . . . . STAR 2283
MC: . . . . STAC 2283

MOTOWN CHARTBUSTERS 80 (Various artists).
LP: . . . . STML 12139
MC: . . . . CSTML 12139

MOTOWN CHARTBUSTERS VOL.1 (Various artists).
Tracks: / Blowin' in the wind: *Wonder, Stevie* / I was made to love her: *Wonder, Stevie* / You keep me hangin' on: *Supremes* / Happening, The: *Supremes* / Love is here and now you're gone: *Supremes* / Standing in the shadows of love: *Four Tops* / Seven rooms of gloom: *Four Tops* / It takes two: *Gaye, Marvin & Kim Weston*/ When you're young and in love: *Marvelettes* / I know Im losing you: *Temptations* / What becomes of the broken hearted?: *Ruffin, Jimmy* / Gonna give her all the love I've got: *Ruffin, Jimmy* / How sweet it is to be loved by you: *Walker, Junior & The All Stars* / I'm ready for love: *Reeves, Martha* / Jimmy Mack: *Reeves, Martha*/ Take me in your arms and love me: *Knight, Gladys & The Pips*.
MC: . . . . CSTML 11055
LP: . . . . STML 11055

MOTOWN CHARTBUSTERS VOL.2 (Various artists).
Tracks: / Ain't nothing like the real thing baby: *Gaye, Marvin & Tammi Terrell* / If I could build my whole world around you: *Gaye, Marvin & Tammi Terrell* / Reflections: *Ross, Diana & The Supremes* / Some things you never get used to: *Ross, Diana & The Supremes* / If you can want: *Various artists* / I second that emotion: *Various artists*/ You keep running away: *Four Tops* / If I were a carpenter: *Four Tops* / I could never love another (after loving you): *Temptations* / You're my everything: *Temptations* / I heard it through the grapevine: *Knight, Gladys* & The Pips / I'm wondering: *Wonder, Stevie* / Shoo-be-doo-be-doo-da-day: *Wonder, Stevie* / I've passed this way before: *Ruffin, Jimmy* / Gotta see Jane: *Taylor, R. Dean* / Honey chile: *Reeves, Martha*.
LP: . . . . STML 11082

MC: . . . . CSTML 11082

MOTOWN CHARTBUSTERS VOL.3 (Various artists).
Tracks: / I heard it through the grapevine: *Gaye, Marvin* / You're all I need to get by: *Gaye, Marvin & Tammi Terrell*/ I'm gonna make you love me: *Ross, Diana & The Supremes* / My cherie amour: *Wonder, Stevie* / For once in my life: *Wonder, Stevie* / No matter what sign you are: *Ross, Diana & The Supremes* / Love child: *Ross, Diana & The* Supremes / This old heart of mine: *Isley Brothers* / Behind the painted smile: *Isley Brothers* / I'll pick a rose for my rose: *Johnson, Marv* / I'm in a different world: *Four Tops* / Dancing in the street: *Reeves*, Martha / Get ready: *Temptations* / Stop her on sight (S.O.S): *Starr, Edwin* / Road runner: *Walker, Junior & The All Stars* / Tracks of my tears: *Various artists*.
LP: . . . . STML 11121
MC: . . . . CSTML 11121
LP: . . . . WL 72673
MC: . . . . WK 72673

MOTOWN CHARTBUSTERS VOL.4 (Various artists).
Tracks: / I want you back / ABC: *Various artists* / Onion song, The: *Gaye, Marvin & Tammi Terrell* / Too busy thinking about my baby: *Gaye, Marvin* / I can't help myself: *Four Tops* / Do what you gotta do: *Four Tops*/ Up the ladder to the roof: *Supremes* / Someday we'll be together: *Ross, Diana & The Supremes*/ Cloud nine: *Temptations*/ I can't get next to you: *Temptations* / I second that emotion: *Temptations with Diana Ross & The Supremes* / Yester-me, yester-you, yesterday: *Wonder, Stevie* / Farewell is a lonely sound: *Ruffin, Jimmy* / What does it take to win your love: *Walker, Junior & The All Stars*.
LP: . . . . STML 11162
MC: . . . . CSTML 11162
LP: . . . . WL 72674
MC: . . . . WK 72674

MOTOWN CHARTBUSTERS VOL.5 (Various artists).
Tracks: / Tears of a clown: *Robinson, Smokey* / War: *Starr, Edwin* / Love you save, The: *Jackson 5* / I'll be there: *Jackson 5* / Ball of confusion: *Temptations* / It's all in the game: *Four Tops* / Still water: *Four Tops* / Heaven help us all: *Wonder, Stevie* / Signed, sealed, delivered (I'm yours): *Wonder, Stevie*/ I'll say forever my love: *Wonder, Stevie* / Ain't no mountain high enough: *Ross, Diana* / Stoned love: *Supremes*/ Abraham, Martin and John: *Gaye, Marvin* / Forget me not: *Reeves, Martha* / It's a shame: *Motown Spinners*/ Never had a dream come true: *Wonder, Stevie*.
LP: . . . . STML 11181
MC: . . . . CSTML 11181
LP: . . . . WL 72675
MC: . . . . WK 72675

MOTOWN CHARTBUSTERS VOL.6 (Various artists).
Tracks: / I'm still waiting: *Ross, Diana* / Remember me: *Ross, Diana* / I don't blame you at all: *Robinson*, Smokey & The Miracles / (Come round here) I'm the one you need: *Robinson, Smokey & The Miracles* / We can work it out: *Wonder, Stevie* / Never can say goodbye: *Jackson 5* / Mama's pearl: *Jackson 5* / These things will keep me loving you: *Velvelettes* / Indiana wants me: *Taylor, R. Dean* / River deep, mountain high: *Supremes & Four* Tops / Simple game: *Four Tops* / Just seven numbers: *Four Tops* / Nathan Jones: *Supremes* / Just my imagination (running away with me): *Temptations* / It's Summer: *Temptations* / Heaven must have sent you: *Elgins*.
LP: . . . . STML 11191
MC: . . . . CSTML 11191
LP: . . . . WL 72676
MC: . . . . WK 72676

MOTOWN CHARTBUSTERS VOL.7 (Various artists).
Tracks: / Automatically sunshine: *Supremes* / Floy Joy: *Supremes* / You gotta have love in your heart: *Supremes* & Four Tops / Surrender: *Ross, Diana* / Doobedood'ndoobe, doobedood'ndoobe: *Ross, Diana* / Just walk in my shoes: *Knight, Gladys & The Pips* / Rockin' robin: *Jackson, Michael* / Ain't no sunshine: *Jackson, Michael*/ Got to be there: *Jackson, Michael* / Take a look around: *Temptations* / Superstar: *Temptations* / If you really love me: *Wonder, Stevie* / Bless you: *Reeves, Martha* / Walk in the night: *Walker, Junior & The All Stars* / Festival time: *San Remo Strings* / My guy: *Wells, Mary*.
LP: . . . . STML 11215
MC: . . . . CSTML 11215
LP: . . . . WL 72677
MC: . . . . WK 72677

MOTOWN CHARTBUSTERS VOL.8 (Various artists).
Tracks: / Superstition: *Wonder, Stevie* / You are the sunshine of my life: *Wonder, Stevie* / Neither one of us: *Knight, Gladys & The Pips*.
LP: . . . . STML 11246
MC: . . . . CSTML 11246

MOTOWN CHARTBUSTERS VOL.9 (Various artists).
Tracks: / All of my life: *Ross, Diana* / Last time I saw him: *Ross, Diana* / My mistake (was to love you): *Ross*, Diana & Marvin Gaye / You are everything: *Ross, Diana & Marvin Gaye* / Baby love: *Ross, Diana & The Supremes*/ High ground: *Wonder, Stevie* / He's misstra know it all: *Wonder, Stevie* / Living for the city: *Wonder*, Stevie / Dancing machine: *Various artists* / Spinnin' and spinnin': *Syreeta* / Keep on truckin': *Kendricks*, Eddie / Boogie down: *Kendricks, Eddie* / There's a ghost in my house: *Taylor, R. Dean* / Just my soul responding: *Robinson, Smokey* / What becomes of the broken hearted?: *Robinson, Smokey* / Machine gun: *Commodores*.
LP: . . . . STML 11270
MC: . . . . CSTML 11270

MOTOWN CHARTBUSTERS VOL.10 (Various artists).
Tracks: / Three times a lady: *Commodores* / Easy: *Commodores* / Sail on: *Commodores* / Love hangover: *Ross, Diana* / Boss, The: *Ross, Diana* / Do you know where you're going to: *Ross, Diana* / Night, The: *Valli, Frankie & Four Seasons* / Got to give it up: *Gaye, Marvin* / Get it up for love: *Vega, Tata* / Big time, Theme from: *Robinson, Smokey* / Your kiss is sweet: *Syreeta* / I'm a sucker for your love: *Marie*, Teena / Love machine: *Miracles* / It should have been me: *Fair, Yvonne* / You and I: *James, Rick*/ Don't leave me this way: *Houston, Thelma*.
LP: . . . . STML 12123
MC: . . . . CSTML 12123

MOTOWN CRUISIN VOL 1 (Various artists).
MCSET: . . . . CTMSP 6016

MOTOWN CRUISIN VOL 2 (Various artists).
MCSET: . . . . CTMSP 6022

MOTOWN DANCE (Various artists).
LP: . . . . WL 72170
MC: . . . . WK 72170

MOTOWN DANCE PARTY (Various artists).
Tracks: / Shotgun: *Walker, Junior & The All Stars* / I can't help myself: *Four Tops* / I want you back: *Jackson* Five / You can't hurry love: *Ross, Diana & The Supremes* / Tears of a clown: *Robinson, Smokey & The Miracles*/ Ain't too proud to beg: *Temptations* / Jimmy Mack: *Reeves, Martha* / Twenty five miles: *Starr, Edwin*/ Uptight: *Wonder, Stevie* / I heard it through the grapevine: *Gaye, Marvin* / You keep me hangin' on: *Ross*, Diana & The Supremes / Do you love me: *Contours* / Ain't that peculiar: *Gaye, Marvin* / Way you do the things like you do, The: *Temptations* / Where did our love go: *Ross, Diana & The Supremes* / ABC: *Jackson Five*/ Mickey's monkey: *Various artists* / Heatwave: *Reeves, Martha* / This old heart of mine: *Isley Brothers*/ It's the same old song: *Four Tops* / Going to a go go: *Various artists* / I'm a road runner: *Walker, Junior* & The All Stars / Nowhere to run: *Reeves, Martha* / Reach out I'll be there: *Four Tops* / My guy: *Wells*, Mary / Come see about me: *Ross, Diana & The Supremes* / Get ready: *Temptations* / Needle in a haystack: *Velvelettes*/ Love you save, The: *Jackson Five* / Love is like an itching in my heart: *Ross, Diana & The Supremes* / Heaven must have sent you: *Elgins* / Dancing in the street: *Reeves, Martha* / Standing in the shadows of love: *Four* Tops / War: *Starr, Edwin* / Stoned love: *Supremes, The* / I can't get next to you: *Temptations* / Brick house: *Commodores* / Superstition: *Wonder, Stevie* / Keep on truckin: *Kendricks, Eddie* / Don't leave me this way: *Houston, Thelma* / He was really saying something: *Various artists* (Available on 12" only) / Take me in your arms (rock me a little while)*: *Weston, Kim*.
LP: . . . . ZL 72700
MC: . . . . ZK 72700

MOTOWN DANCE PARTY, VOL 2 (Various artists).
Tracks: / Stop, in the name of love: *Ross, Diana & The Supremes* / Going to a go go: *Robinson, Smokey & The Temptations*/ Road runner: *Walker, Junior & The All Stars* / Nowhere to run: *Reeves, Martha* / Reach out I'll be there: *Four* Tops / My guy: *Wells, Mary* / Come see about me: *Ross, Diana & The Supremes* / Get ready: *Temptations*/ Needle in a haystack: *Velvelettes* / Love you save, The: *Jackson Five* / Love is like an itching in my heart: *Ross, Diana & The Supremes* / Heaven must have sent you: *Elgins* / Dancing in the street: *Reeves, Martha*/ Standing in the shadows of love: *Four Tops* / You need love like I do: *Knight, Gladys & The Pips* / War: *Starr*, Edwin / Stoned love: *Supremes* / I can't get next to you: *Temptations* / Brick house: *Commodores*/ Superstition: *Wonder, Stevie* / Got to give it up: *Gaye, Marvin* / Keep on truckin': *Kendricks, Eddie*/ Dancing machine: *Jackson Five* / Don't leave me this way: *Houston, Thelma*.
MC: . . . . ZK 72703
LP: . . . . ZL 72703

MOTOWN DISCOMAGIC (Various artists).
LP: . . . . MFP 50448

MOTOWN EXTRA SPECIAL various artists (Various artists).
LP: . . . . STMX 6007
MC: . . . . CSTMX 6007

MOTOWN GIRL GROUPS (Various artists).
LP: . . . . WL 72144
MC: . . . . WK 72144

MOTOWN HEARTBREAKERS (Various artists).
MC: . . . . STAC 2343
LP: . . . . STAR 2343

MOTOWN HITS OF GOLD VOL.1 (Various artists).
LP: . . . . WL 72401
MC: . . . . WK 72401

MOTOWN HITS OF GOLD VOL.2 (Various artists).
MC: . . . . WK 72402
LP: . . . . WL 72402

MOTOWN HITS OF GOLD VOL.3 (Various artists).
LP: . . . . WL 72403
MC: . . . . WK 72403

MOTOWN HITS OF GOLD VOL.4 (Various artists).
LP: . . . . WL 72404
MC: . . . . WK 72404

MOTOWN HITS OF GOLD VOL.5 (Various artists).
LP: . . . . WL 72405
MC: . . . . WK 72405

MOTOWN HITS OF GOLD VOL.6 (Various artists).
LP: . . . . WL 72406
MC: . . . . WK 72406

MOTOWN HITS OF GOLD VOL.7 (Various artists).
LP: . . . . WL 72407
MC: . . . . WK 72407

MOTOWN HITS OF GOLD VOL.8 (Various artists).
LP: . . . . WL 72408
MC: . . . . WK 72408

MOTOWN IN MOTION (Various artists).
Tracks: / Dancin' in the street: *Reeves, Martha* / It's the same old song: *Four Tops* / You ain't livin' till you're lovin': *Gaye, Marvin & Tammi Terrell* / What does it take (to win your love): *Walker, Junior & The All Stars*/ Upside down: *Ross, Diana* / All night long: *Mary Jane Girls* / Love hangover: *Ross, Diana* / All night long: *Richie, Lionel* / Behind the groove: *James, J.* / Rhythm of the night: *DeBarge* / Little bitty pretty one: *Jackson Five* / Skywriter: *Jacksons* / Let's get serious: *Jackson, Jermaine* / Uptight: *Wonder*, Stevie / Just walk in my shoes: *Knight, Gladys & The Pips* / Rockin' robin: *Jackson, Michael* / Nathan Jones: *Supremes, The* / Papa was a rollin' stone: *Temptations* / Don't look any further: *Edwards, Dennis* / Somebody's watching me: *Rockwell* / Give to me baby: *James, Rick* / Let it all blow: *Dazz Band* / Too busy thinking about my baby: *Gaye, Marvin* / Keep on truckin': *Kendricks, Eddie* / Superstar: *Temptations, The*.
LP: . . . . NE 1410
MC: . . . . CE 2410

MOTOWN LOVE SONGS (Various artists).
LP: . . . . WL 72169
MC: . . . . WK 72169
LP: . . . . TMS 3509
MC: . . . . TMC 3509

MOTOWN MALE GROUPS (Various artists).
LP: . . . . WL 72171
MC: . . . . WK 72171

MOTOWN RARE GROOVES (Various artists).
LP: . . . . ZL 72642
MC: . . . . ZK 72642

MOTOWN SINGS THE BEATLES (Various artists).
LP: . . . . WL 72348
MC: . . . . WK 72348
LP: . . . . NSPLP 500
MC: . . . . NSPMC 500

MOTOWN SOLO STARS (Various artists).
LP: . . . . WL 72172
MC: . . . . WK 72172

MOTOWN STORY, THE (The first 25 years (Volumes 1 - 3)) (Various artists).
Tracks: / Please Mr. Postman: *Marvelettes* / Baby I'm for real: *Originals* / Keep on truckin': *Various artists*/ Two lovers: *Wells, Mary* / Dancing machine: *Commodores* / Shop around: *Robinson, Smokey & The Miracles*/ You've really got a hold on me: *Robinson, Smokey & The Miracles* / Tracks of my tears: *Robinson, Smokey & The Miracles*/ I second that emotion: *Robinson, Smokey & The Miracles* / Baby baby don't cry: *Robinson, Smokey & The Miracles*/ Super freak: *James, Rick* / Baby I need your loving: *Four Tops* / I can't help myself: *Four Tops* / Fingertips: *Wonder, Stevie* / I was made to love her: *Wonder, Stevie* / For once in my life: *Wonder, Stevie*/ You're all I need to get by: *Terrell, Tammi & Marvin Gaye* / Love machine: *Miracles* / Three times a lady: *Commodores*/ Cruisin': *Robinson, Smokey* / Heatwave: *Reeves, Martha* / Dancing in the street: *Reeves, Martha* / Nowhere to run: *Reeves, Martha* / Let it whip: *Dazz Band* / Truly: *Richie, Lionel* / My girl: *Temptations*/ I wish it would rain: *Temptations* / What does it take (to win your love): *Various artists* / Let me tickle your fancy: *Jackson, Jermaine* / Endless love: *Ross, Diana & Lionel Richie* / Where did our love go?: *Ross, Diana &* The Supremes / Stop in the name of love: *Ross, Diana & The Supremes* / Love child: *Ross, Diana & The Supremes*/ Someday we'll be together: *Ross, Diana & The Supremes* / I hear a symphony: *Ross, Diana & The Supremes* / You can't hurry love: *Ross, Diana & The Supremes* / Reflections: *Ross, Diana & The Supremes* / Every little bit hurts: *Holloway, Brenda* / Can I get a witness?: *Gaye, Marvin* / Stubborn kind of fellow: *Gaye, Marvin* / How sweet it is to be loved by you: *Gaye, Marvin* / I heard it through the grapevine: *Gaye, Marvin* / I'm gonna make you love me: *Supremes and Temptations* / Intro: *Various artists* / Bad girl: *Robinson, Smokey & The Miracles*/ Money (that's what I want): *Strong, Barrett* / Bye bye baby: *Wells, Mary* / Do you love me: *Contours*/ Way you do the things you do, The: *Temptations* / My guy: *Wells, Mary* / Shotgun: *Walker, Junior & The All* Stars / Stop in the name of love: *Ross, Diana & The Supremes* / I'll be doggone: *Gaye, Marvin* / This old heart of mine: *Isley Brothers* / Beauty is only skin deep: *Temptations* / What becomes of the broken hearted?: *Ruffin, Jimmy* / Reach out I'll be there: *Four Tops* / Jimmy Mack: *Reeves, Martha* / Cloud nine: *Temptations*/ I heard it through the grapevine: *Gaye, Marvin* / I'm gonna make you love me: *Ross, Diana & The Supremes with The* Temptations / My world ended (the moment you left me): *Ruffin, Jimmy* / I want you back: *Jackson Five* / Up the ladder to the roof: *Supremes* / Signed, sealed, delivered (I'm yours): *Wonder, Stevie* / War: *Starr, Edwin*/ Ain't no mountain high enough: *Ross, Diana* / I'll be there: *Jackson Five* / What's going on: *Gaye, Marvin*/ Ben: *Jackson, Michael* / Just my imagination (running away with me): *Temptations* / You are the sunshine of my life: *Wonder, Stevie* / Papa was a rollin' stone: *Temptations* / Neither one of us: *Knight, Gladys & The Pips*/ Let's get it on: *Gaye, Marvin* / Don't leave me this way: *Houston, Thelma* / Sir Duke: *Wonder, Stevie*/ Upside down: *Ross, Diana* / With you I'm born again: *Preston, Billy & Syreeta* / Being with you: *Robinson*, Smokey / All night long: *Richie, Lionel* / Somebody's watching me: *Rockwell* / Rhythm of the night: *DeBarge*/ In my house: *Mary Jane Girls* / Say you, say me: *Richie, Lionel* / Do you know where you're going to: *Instrumental*...(Closing theme from 'Mahogany').
LP: . . . . ZL 72137
MC: . . . . ZK 72137

MOTOWN STORY, THE The first 25 years (Various artists).
LPS: . . . . TMSP 6019
MCSET: . . . . CTMSP 6019

MOTOWN SUPERSTARS SING (Various artists).
LP: . . . . STMS 5100

MOTOWN TRACKIN' (Various artists).
Tracks: / You're what's missing in my life: *Cameron, G.C.* / Our hearts (will always shine): *Ozone* / Fall in love: *King, Bobby* / Gotta find a woman: *Platinum Hook* / Trust me: *Carn, Jean* / Coolin' out: *Edwards*, Dennis / You're all I need to survive: *McNeir, Ronnie* / Ain't nobody straight in L.A.: *Miracles* / To the last drop: *Warp 9* / Everyday love: *Dazz Band* / Dark side of the world: *Gaye,*

Marvin / No one there: *Reeves, Martha (1)* / Date with the rain: *Various artists* / Lovin' fever: *High Jinks*.
MC: . . . . WK 72518
LP: . . . . WL 72518

MOTOWNS GREATEST HITS (Various artists).
MC: . . . . STAC 2375
LP: . . . . STAR 2375

NEVER BEFORE RELEASED MASTERS From Motowns brightest stars (Various artists).
LP: . . . . WL 72425
MC: . . . . WK 72425

POPS, WE LOVE YOU - THE ALBUM (Various artists).
LP: . . . . STML 12114

SPECIAL MOTOWN DISCO ALBUM, VOL. 2 (Various artists).
LP: . . . . STML 12102

THIS IS MOTOWN (Various artists).
LP: . . . . WL 72204
MC: . . . . WK 72204

THREE TIMES A LADY (Motown's Greatest Love Songs) (Various artists).
Tracks: / Love child: *Ross, Diana & The Supremes* / With you I'm born again: *Preston, Billy & Syreeta* / Three times a lady: *Commodores* / I've never been to me: *Charlene* / It's my turn: *Ross, Diana* / Touch me in the morning: *Ross, Diana* / Being with you: *Robinson, Smokey* / Endless love: *Ross, Diana & Lionel Richie*/ All this love: *DeBarge*.
LP: . . . . WL 72603
MC: . . . . WK 72603

VERY BEST OF MOTOWN LOVE SONGS (Various artists).
2LP: . . . . STAR 2239
MC: . . . . STAC 2239

Motown Sounds

SPACE DANCE.
Tracks: / Groove time / Space dance / Easy to love / You don't like to party / Bad mouthin' / Rich love, poor love.
LP: . . . . STML 12105

Mott The Hoople

ALL THE WAY FROM MEMPHIS.
Tracks: / Ballad of Mott the Hoople / One of the boys / Honaloochie boogie / All the young dudes / Sweet Jane / Hymn for the dudes / Violence / Crash Street kids / All the way from Memphis / Drivin's sister / Golden age of rock and roll / Roll away the stone.
LP: . . . . SHM 3055
MC: . . . . HSC 3055

ALL THE YOUNG DUDES.
LP: . . . . CBS 65184

BRAIN CAPERS.
Tracks: / Death may be your Santa Claus / Your own backyard / Darkness, darkness / Journey, The / Sweet Angeline / Second love / Moon upstairs, The / Wheel of the quivering meat conception.
LP: . . . . ILPS 9178

COLLECTION: MOTT THE HOOPLE (Mott The Hoople featuring Ian Hunter).
Tracks: / Golden opportunity / All the way from Memphis / One of the boys / Roll away the stone / Sucker / You nearly did me in / Sweet Jane / All the young dudes / Crash Street kids / Stiff upper lip / Jerkin' crocus / Violence / Once bitten twice shy / Marionette / Drivin' sister / Rose / Hymn for the dudes / Saturday gigs / Where do you all come from.
MC: . . . . CCSMC 174
2LP: . . . . CCSLP 174

DRIVE ON.
LP: . . . . CBS 69154

GREATEST HITS: MOTT THE HOOPLE.
Tracks: / All the way from Memphis / Honaloochie boogie / Hymn for the dudes / Born late '58 / All the young dudes / Roll away the stone / Ballad of Mott the Hoople / Golden age of rock and roll / Foxy foxy / Saturday gigs.
LP: . . . . CBS 32007
MC: 40 32007

HOOPLE, THE.
LP: . . . . CBS 69062

LIVE.
LP: . . . . CBS 69093

MAD SHADOWS.
LP: . . . . ILPS 9119

MOTT.
Tracks: / All the way from Memphis / Whizz kid / Hymn for the dudes / Honaloochie boogie / Violence / Drivin' sister / Ballad of Mott the Hoople / I'm a Cadillac / El camino dolo roso / I wish I was your mother.
LP: . . . . CLALP 138X
MC: . . . . CLAMC 138X
LP: . . . . CBS 69038

MOTT THE HOOPLE.
LP: . . . . ILPS 9108

WILD LIFE.
LP: . . . . ILPS 9144

Mottek

RIOT.
Tracks: / Torture / Moscow / Nothing / Too much is enough / Riot / Mottek, The / Reality / Do it / She / Shout.
LP: . . . . SMR 037UK

Mould, Bob

BLACK SHEETS OF RAIN.
Tracks: / Black sheets of rain / One good reason / Hanging tree, The / Hear me calling / Disappointed / It's too late / Stop your crying / Last night, The / Out of your life / Sacrifice / Let there be peace.
LP: . . . . VUSLP 21
MC: . . . . VUSMC 21

WORKBOOK.
Tracks: / Sunspots / Wishing well / Heartbreak a stranger / See a little light / Poison years / Sinners and their repentances / Brasilia crossed with Trenton / Compositions for the young and old / Lonely afternoon / Dreaming, I am whichever way the wind blows.
LP: . . . . VUSLP 2
MC: . . . . VUSMC 2
LP: . . . . OVED 340
MC: . . . . OVEDC 340

Mouldy Five

MOULDY FIVE-VOLUME 1.
LP: . . . . GHB 181

Moule,Ken

AS TIME GOES BY.
LP: . . . . REC 205

MIDNIGHT MUSIC (Moule,Ken and the Full Score Orchestra).
LP: . . . . REC 305

Mounir, Mohamed

MOHAMED MOUNIR.
LP: 2TM 212
MC: . . . . ZCTM 212

Mounk'a, Pamelo

L'AMOUR ET LA DANSE.
LP: . . . . VME 001

Mounsey, Rob

LOCAL COLOUR (See under Khan, Steve) (Khan, Steve & Rob Mounsey).

Mountain

AVALANCHE.
Tracks: / Whole lotta shakin' goin' on / Sister justice / Alisan / Swamp boy / Satisfaction / Thumb sucker / You better believe it / I love to see you fly / Back where I belong / Last of the sunshine days.
LP: . . . . CLALP 136X
MC: . . . . CLAMC 136X

BEST OF MOUNTAIN.
LP: . . . . BGOLP 33
MC: . . . . BGOMC 33

CLIMBING.
LP: . . . . BGOLP 112
MC: . . . . BGOMC 112

FLOWERS OF EVIL.
LP: . . . . BGOLP 113
MC: . . . . BGOMC 113

NANTUCKET SLEIGHRIDE (Best of Mountain).
Tracks: / Don't look around / You can't get away / Tired angels / My lady / Great train robbery / Taunta (Sammy's tune) / Nantucket sleighride / Animal trainer and the toad, The / Travellin' in the dark.
LP: . . . . BGOLP 32
MC: . . . . BGOMC 32
LP: . . . . ILPS 9148

ROAD GOES ON FOREVER, THE.
LP: . . . . ILPS 9199
LP: . . . . BGOLP 111
MC: . . . . BGOMC 111

Mountain Kidnap

MOUNTAIN KIDNAP (See under Barbie (bk)).

Mountain Top

MOUNTAIN TOP Comhaltas tour 1976 (Various artists).
LP: . . . . CL 14

Mountains Of Mourne

MOUNTAINS OF MOURNE 10 original hits from home (Various artists).
MC: . . . . CHR 02

Mountbatten

LIFE AND TIMES OF LORD MOUNTBATTEN,THE (Various artists).
LPS: . . . . LM 101

Mountford, G

WHY SAVE WILD ANIMALS (G.Mountford/G.Durrell).
MC: . . . . SS 111

Mounting..

MOUNTING EXCITMENT various artists (Various artists).
LP: . . . . NE 1091

Moura, Paulo

MISTURA E MANDA.
LP: 7719

PAULO MOURA.
LP: . . . . BR 4005
MC: . . . . BRC 4005

Mourant, Norman

IT'S HARD TO LIVE ON DREAMS.
Tracks: / I'll never leave my woman's love / Sunday morning coming down / I know you've never been this far before / Pass the glass / If we're not back in love by Monday / It's hard to live on dreams / More like the movies / Night coach out of Dallas / Diana / All in the movies / Two less lonely people / My love for you.
LP: . . . . FHR 100

Mournblade

LIVE FAST, DIE YOUNG.
Tracks: / In the hall of the mountain king / Lolita / Blond, beautiful and dead / My baby left me / Voodoo / I love rock 'n' roll / I can't sleep / Kaw-liga / My girl / I went to see the gypsy / Big brown eyes.
LP: . . . . GILP 333

TIME'S RUNNING OUT.
LP: . . . . SHARP 030

Mouse Butcher

MOUSE BUTCHER, THE (See also Dick King-Smith) (Thorne, Stephen).

Mouse Tales

MOUSE TALES (see Beatrix Potter) (Horden, Sir Michael).

Mousetrap Conspiracy

BOUNDS OF DECENCY.
Tracks: / Waiting for a fire / Cried over you / Rain / Trotsky and the ice picks / Christians / Justify with legislation / Mild fort / Denying / House / Does it matter / Art.
MC: . . . . MTC 001
MC: . . . . MTC 002

Mouskouri, Nana

ALONE.
Tracks: / Recuerdos / I have a dream / Only love / Come on blue / Photographs / All my trials / My rainbow race / Alone / Place in my heart, A / Seeing is believing / Queen of hearts / Amazing grace.
LP: . . . . PHH 3
MC: . . . . PHHC 3

BALLADES.
Tracks: / Mississippi blues / Carry me on / Je t'aime la vie / La ballade du chien loup.
LP: 6399 397
MC: 7199 397

BRITISH CONCERT.
LP: 6651003

CLASSICAL NANA, THE.
Tracks: / Una furtiva lagrima / Serenade leise flehen meine lieder / Dank sei dir, Herr Ogerman / Der lindenbaum / Dis la nostalgie / Mon dieu / Plaisir d'amour / Casta diva / Recuerdos de la althambra / Ave Maria.
2LP: 836 588 1
MC: 836 599 2

COME WITH ME.
Tracks: / Come with me / If it's so easy / Smooth sailing / Lullaby of love / When I dream / Love ain't the question / Love is all that matters / Don't go my love / Someone is looking / If.
LP: . . . . RCALP 5014

EXQUISITE NANA MOUSKOURI, THE.
LP: . . . . STL 5536

GOSPEL.
Tracks: / In the upper room / Are you sure / Go down Moses / Balm in Gilead / Didn't it rain / Nobody knows the troubles I've seen / Oh happy day / Slow train / I got shoes / Sometimes I feel like a motherless... / Precious memories / Rock a my soul.
LP: 848108 1
MC: 848108 4

GREEK SONGS (see Leandros, Vicky) (Mouskouri, Nana/Vicky Leandros/ Demis Roussos).

LIVE AT THE HERODES HATTICUS THEATRE.
LP: 8229971
MC: 8229974

LOVE ME TENDER.
Tracks: / Missing / Taking a child by the hand / I'll remember you / Alleluia / Love me tender / Old paint / All through the night / Why worry / Ave verum corpus / I believe in you / Love is.
LP: 832 019 1
MC: 832 039 4

MAGIC OF NANA MOUSKOURI.
Tracks: / Only love / White rose of Athens, The / Never on a Sunday / Yesterday / Amazing grace / Try to remember / Power of love, The / Bridge over troubled water / Only time will tell / Morning has broken / And I love you so / Ave Maria / Love me tender / Nights in white satin / Song for liberty / Lonely shepherd.
LP: . . . . NMTV 1
MC: . . . . NMTVC 1

NANA (1987 ALBUM).
Tracks: / Unite / Moondance / To me / In my life / Power of love, The / Forgive and forget / Morning angel / Little girl blue / Nights in white satin / Every time we say goodbye.
LP: . . . . PHH 6
MC: . . . . PHHC 6

NANA MOUSKOURI.
Tracks: / Solitaire / Keeping the love alive / Apples won't grow / How can I be sure / Maybe this time / Do I ever cross your mind / When the lovin' goes out of the lovin' / Endlessly / Even a fool would let go / Think it over.
LP: 818 622 1
MC: 818 622 4

OVER AND OVER.
LP: . . . . S 5511

PASSPORT.
Tracks: / Amazing grace / And I love you so / Bridge over troubled water / Cu-cu-rru-cu-cu-paloma / Day is done / Enas mithos / Four and twenty hours / I have a dream / If you love me / Last rose of Summer / Loving song / Milisse Mou / My friend the sea / Never on Sunday / Odos oniron / Over and over / Plaisir d'amour / Seasons in the sun / Try to remember / Turn on the Sun / White rose of Athens, The.
LP: . . . . PRICE 49
MC: . . . . PRIMC 49
LP: 9101 061

RECITAL '70.
LP: 6312003

ROSES AND SUNSHINE.
Tracks: / All over the world / Autumn leaves / Down by the greenwood side / Even now / I never will marry / Love is a rose / Nickels and dimes / Roses love sunshine / Sweet surrender / There is a time / Tomorrow is a long time.
LP: 910 3550

SONG FOR LIBERTY.
Tracks: / Daydreams / Guests / Till all the rivers run dry / Droom droom / Bad old days / On my way to town / Song for Liberty / Loving him was easier / Rose / Every grain of sand / Sweet music man / To Potami.
LP: 6399335
MC: 7199335

SONGS FROM HER T.V. SERIES.
Tracks: / I have a dream / Blow the wind Southerly / Open the door / Morning has broken / Imagine / My colouring book / And I love you so / Let it be / Loch Lomond / Milisse Mou.
MC: 7206 069
LP: 6312036
LP: 6395 069

SPOTLIGHT ON NANA MOUSKOURI.
Tracks: / And I love you so / Blow the wind southerly / Loch Lomond / Bridge over troubled water / Day is done / From both sides now / Imagine / Last rose of summer / Love story / Mamma / Morning has broken / Never on Sunday / Odos oniron / Open your eyes / Over and over / Place in my heart, A / Plaisir d'amour / Put your hand in the hand / Scarborough fair / Scarlet ribbons / Try to remember / Turn on the Sun / Umbrellas of Cherbourg / White rose of Athens, The.
2LP: 6641197

TURN ON THE SUN.
LP: 6312008

WHY WORRY?.
Tracks: / Why worry? / Yesterday / Sweet surrender / Rose, The / Song for liberty (From 'Nabucco' by Verdi.) / Missing / Love me tender / Only love / Time in a bottle / Every grain of sand.
LP: . . . . PHH 4
MC: . . . . PHHC 4

Moustaki, Georges

GEORGES MOUSTAKI.
Tracks: / Pornographie / L'ambassadeur / Sanforneiro / Si cet amour / Pour un ami / Lazy blues / L'aede / Dans la maison ou je suis ne / En regardant ton corps / L'instrument de malheur / Femmes - fleurs - fruits / Pau de chuva.
LP: 2393 285
MC: 3169 285
LP: 823 134-1
MC: 823 134-4

LE METEQUE.

Tracks: / Le meteque / Le facteur / Danse / Joseph / La solitude / Portugal / Flamenco / Declaration / Chanson cri.
LP: **8210471**
MC: **8210474**

TROUBADOR.
LP: **2480 451**

Mouth Music

MOUTH MUSIC.
Tracks: / Bratach bana / Mor a' cheannaich / Chi mi na morbheana / Mile marbh'aisg a'ghaol / Froach a ronaigh / Co ni mire rium / Martin Martin / I bhi a da / Air fair a lail o.
LP: . . . . **TERRA 109**
MC: . . . . **TERRAC 109**

Mouzon, Alphonse

BABY COME BACK.
LP: . . . . **MPS 60 229**

BACK TO JAZZ (Mouzon, Alphonse band).
LP: . . . . **LR 45.001**

BACK TOGETHER (see under Coryell, Larry) (Mouzon, Alphonse & Larry Coryell).

BY ALL MEANS (See under Hancock, Herbie) (Mouzon, Alphonse & Herbie Hancock).

IN SEARCH OF A DREAM.
LP: . . . . **MPS 68 192**

MORNING SUN.
LP: . . . . **SH 8547**

STEP INTO THE FUNK.
LP: **1060 507**

Move

BEST OF THE MOVE.
Tracks: / Blackberry Way / Curly / Yellow rainbow / I can hear the grass grow / Fire brigade / Hey Grandma / Kilroy was here / Night of fear / Feel too good / Brontosaurus / Flowers in the rain / Walk upon the water / Stephanie knows who / Turkish tram conductor blues / Useless information / Weekend / Cherry blossom clinic revisited / So you want to be a rock'n'roll star.
MC: . . . . **MCTC 009**

COLLECTION: MOVE.
Tracks: / Night of fear / I can hear the grass grow / Wave your flag and stop the train / Flowers in the rain / Fire brigade / Wild tiger woman / Blackberry way / Curly / Brontosaurus / So you want to be a rock'n'roll star / Something else / It'll be me / Sunshine help me / When Alice comes back to the farm / Zing went the strings of my heart / Cherry blossom clinic revisited / Hello Susie / Kilroy was here / Last thing on my mind / (Here we go round) the lemon tree / Field's of people / Don't make my baby blue / Yellow rainbow / Walk upon the water.
2LP: . . . . **CCSLP 135**
MC: . . . . **CCSMC 135**

GREATEST HITS: THE MOVE.
LP: . . . . **FUN 9030**
MC: . . . . **FUNC 9030**

GRONGE E MOVE.
LP: . . . . **AD 002**

MOVE.
LP: . . . . **AD 001**
LP: . . . . **SLRZ 1002**

MOVE SHINES ON, THE.
Tracks: / Message from the country / Ella James / No time / Don't mess me up / Until your Momma's gone / Do ya / China Town / It wasn't my idea to dance / Minister / Ben Crawley Steel Company / Words of Arron / My Marge / Tonight / California man.
LP: . . . . **SHSM 2029**

NIGHTRIDING: MOVE.
Tracks: / Flowers in the rain / Fire brigade / Brontosaurus / Blackberry way / Last thing on my mind / Misty on a Monday morning / Lookin' on / What / Open up said the world / Beautiful daughter / Girl outside, The / I can hear the grass grow.
MC: . . . . **KNMC 10011**
LP: . . . . **KNLP 10011**

OFF THE RECORD WITH THE MOVE.
2LP: . . . . **FEDD 1005**
MCSET: . . . . **CFEDD 1005**

PLATINUM COLLECTION.
Tracks: / Flowers in the rain / I can hear the grass grow / Lemon tree / Yellow rainbow / Walk upon the water / Fire brigade / Night of fear / Useless information / Kilroy was here / So you want to be a rock'n'roll star / Stephanie knows who / Brontosaurus / Curly / When Alice comes back to the farm / Something / Hey grandma / Feel too good / Blackberry way / Hello Susie / Wild tiger woman / Weekend / Girl outside, The / Cherry blossom clinic revisited.
2LP: . . . . **PLAT 1001**
MCSET: . . . . **ZCPLT 1001**

SHAZAM.
Tracks: / Hello Susie / Beautiful daughter / Cherry blossom clinic revisited / Fields of people / Don't make my baby blue / Last thing on my mind / Yellow rainbow / Kilroy was here / Lemon tree / Weekend / Walk upon the water / Flowers in the rain / Hey grandma / Useless information / Zing went the strings of my heart / Girl outside, The / Fire brigade / Misty on a Monday morning.
LP: . . . . **TOOFA 5**

Mover, Bob

IN THE TRUE TRADITION.
LP: . . . . **XAN 187**

Movie Musicals

CLASSIC YEARS IN DIGITAL STEREO (see under Classic Years...) (Various artists).

Movies (group)

INDIA.
Tracks: / Must be the angel / Bardot / See through me / Rocket / Love is a sacrifice / From Casablanca / Have another body / India / 8 a.m..
LP: . . . . **GEMLP 105**

MOTOR, MOTOR, MOTOR.
Tracks: / Hello from outer space / Hard heart / Dance some more / Slavery time / Clockwise into the sun / Motor motor motor / Kind of love that shows, The / No tears for this tearaway / Straight no more / Dancing in space.
LP: . . . . **RCALP 5054**
MC: . . . . **RCAK 5054**

Moving Fingers

NATURAL SELECTION.
Tracks: / Final word of history / Karen / Everything changes / Heartlands / Sink like a stone / Rome lies burning / Dreamtime / Subway and the stars / Chlorophyll (in my eyes) / Lock up your heart / Natural selection.
LP: . . . . **SNTF 957**

Moving Hearts

DARK END OF THE STREET.
LP: . . . . **MH 001**
LP: . . . . **WEA 58718**

LIVE HEARTS.
LP: . . . . **IR 0230**

MOVING HEARTS.
Tracks: / Hiroshima / Russian roulette / Irish ways and Irish laws / McBrides / Before the deluge / Landlord / Category / Faithful departed / Lake of shadows / No time for love.
MC: **K4 58387**
LP: . . . . **K 58387**

MOVING HEARTS/DARK END OF THE STREET.
MCSET: . . . . **IR 40607**

STORM, THE.
Tracks: / Lark, The / Storm, The / Tribute to Peardar O Donnell / Titanic, The / Finore / May morning dew, The.
LP: . . . . **TA 3014**
MC: **4TA 3014**
MC: . . . . **BUAC 892**
LP: . . . . **BUAL 892**

Moving Targets

BURNING IN WATER.
LP: . . . . **GOES ON 14**

FALL.
LP: . . . . **TG 93041**

Mowatt, Judy

BLACK WOMAN.
Tracks: / Strength to go through / Concrete jungle / Slave queen / Put it on / Zion chant / Black woman / Down in the valley / Joseph / Many are called / Sisters chant.
LP: . . . . **ILPS 9649**
LP: . . . . **UNKNOWN**
LP: . . . . **GREL 111**
LP: . . . . **SHAN 43011**
MC: . . . . **SHANC 43011**
MC: . . . . **GREEN 111**

LOVE IS OVERDUE.
Tracks: / Sing our own song / Love is overdue / Try a little tenderness / Long long time / Rock me / Get up and chant / Screw face / Hold dem jah / One more time / Who is he.
LP: . . . . **GREL 103**
MC: . . . . **GREEN 103**

MUSIC FOR THE WORLD (see Marley, Rita) (Mowatt, Judy, R. Marley & M. Griffiths).

ONLY A WOMAN.
LP: . . . . **SHAN 43007**
MC: . . . . **SHANC 43007**

WORKING WONDERS.
LP: . . . . **SHAN 43028**
MC: . . . . **SHANC 43028**

Mowrey, Irvin

CONTINENTAL DRIFT.
Tracks: / Fat city / Never come down / Queen of maybe / Tonight tonight / Immigrants, The / Hall of mirrors / Complaint / Is it ever goodbye / Miraculous escape, The / Gullivers fall.
LP: . . . . **IRC 004**

Mox Nix

MOX NIX.
LP: . . . . **AXE 7023**

Moyet, Alison

ALF.
Tracks: / Love resurrection / Honey for the bees / For you only / Invisible / Steal me blind / All cried out / Money mile / Twisting the knife / Where hides sleep.
LP: . . . . **CBS 26229**
MC: **40 26229**

HOODOO.
LP: **4682721**
MC: **4682724**

RAINDANCING.
Tracks: / Weak in the presence of beauty / Ordinary girl / You got me wrong / Without you / Sleep like breathing / Is this love? / Blow wind blow / Glorious love / When I say (no giveaway) / Stay.
LP: **4501521**
MC: **4501524**

Moyo, Jonah

TAXI DRIVER (Moyo, Jonah & Devera Ngwena).
Tracks: / Too cheap / Debbie / Uchazvibvuma / Ratidza chimiro shako / Nyakuzvida / Fundisa umlomon Wakho / Madiro / Taxi driver / Wanguo / Ndinzwei vari Pasi.
LP: . . . . **K-KO 1**

Mozart (composer)

CLARINET QUINTET/OBOE QUARTET/FLUTE QUARTET (MOZART) (K581, K370, K285.) (Prometheus Ensemble).
Tracks: / Clarinet quintet K581 / Oboe quartet K370 / Flute quartet K285.
MC: . . . . **ZC DCA 688**

CONCERTO FOR PIANO AND ORCHESTRA NO. 9 IN E FLAT (Ambache Chamber Orchestra).
Tracks: / Concerto for piano and orchestra No. 9 in E flat / Concerto for piano and orchestra No. 8 in C / Concerto rhondo for piano and orchestra in A.
MC: . . . . **CIMPC 931**

DUOS FOR VIOLIN AND VIOLA (Zimmermann, Tabea/Thomas Zehetmair).
Tracks: / Duo for violin and viola no.1 K423 / Duo for violin and viola no.2 K424 / Duo for violin and viola no.1 (Haydn, M.) (in C major).
MC: **244 192-4**

EINE KLEINE NACHTMUSIK (Various artists).
MC: **426 060-4**

ESSENTIAL MOZART, THE (Various artists).
LP: **4333234**
MC: **4333232**

EXULTATE, JUBILATE (English Chamber Orchestra).
MC: **426 072-4**

FIGARO & COSTI HIGHLIGHTS (Various artists).
MC: **4277124**

FLUTE CONCERTOS IN G & IN D (Concertgebouw Orchestra Amsterdam).
MC: **426 074-4**

FOUR FLUTE QUARTETS (Various artists).
MC: **422 835-4**

HORN CONCERTOS NO. 1 - 4 Jolley & Purvis (Orpheus Chamber Orchestra).
MC: **4278144**

LE NOZZE DI FIGARO - HIGHLIGHTS Marriage of Figaro (Various artists).
MC: . . . . **MC 4277124 GW**

LODRON SERENADES, THE (MOZART) (Camerata Bern).
Tracks: / Divertimento K247 (in F major) / Divertimento K287 (in B flat major).
LP: **150 040-1**
MC: **150 040-4**

MOZART (Various artists).
MC: . . . . **DLCMC 205**

MOZART (Oppitz, Gerhard).
Tracks: / Fantasy K475 (in C minor) / Sonata no.14 K457 (in C minor) / Sonata no.13 K333 (in B flat major) / Rondo K511 (in A minor).
LP: **150 042-1**
MC: **150 042-4**

MOZART FANTASIAS AND SONATAS (Katsaris, Cyprien).
Tracks: / Fantasia K.396 / Fantasia K.397 / Fantasia K.475 / Sonata no.14 K.457 / Sonata no.7 K.309.
MC: **244 191-4**

MOZART OBOE MUSIC (Various artists).
MC: . . . . **CSAR 34**

MOZART: VIOLIN CONCERTO NOS. 1, 2 & 4 (See under London Philharmonic for details).

MOZART: VIOLIN CONCERTOS NOS. 1, 2 & 4 (see under London Philharmonic Orchestra) (London Philharmonic Orchestra).

MOZART WEEKEND (Various artists).
MC: **4255134**

MOZART'S GREATEST HITS (Various artists).
MC: **40 79021**

PIANO CONCERTI NO.12/22 (Rutman, Neil/Academy of London).
Tracks: / Piano concerto no.12, K414 / Piano concerto no.22, K482.
MC: . . . . **ZC QS 6022**

PIANO CONCERTI NO.19/24 (Osorio, Jorge Federico/Royal Philharmonic Orchestra).
MC: . . . . **ZC QS 6015**

PIANO CONCERTOS NOS. 21 & 20 (MOZART) (Various artists).
MC: **4255064**

PIANO CONCERTOS NOS 21 & 25 (London Symphony Orchestra).
MC: **426 077-4**

PIANO CONCERTOS NOS. 21 & 27 (MOZART) (London Symphony Orchestra).
MC: **4278124**

PIANO CONCERTOS NOS. 24 & 20 (MOZART) (Vienna State Opera Orchestra).
MC: . . . . **VETC 6503**

PIANO CONCERTOS NOS. 24 & 25 (Various artists).
MC: **422 331-4**
LP: **422 331-1**

REQUIEM (MOZART) (Various artists).
MC: **4273534**
LP: **4273531**

SERENADES (MOZART) (Various artists).
MC: **4254214**

SYMPHONIES NOS 30 & 35 'HAFFNER' Eine kleine nachtmusik (Vienna Philharmonic Orchestra).
MC: **4278114**

SYMPHONY NO.25/NO.28/NO.29 (MOZART) (Northern Sinfonia of England).
Tracks: / Symphony no.25, K183 / Symphony no.28, K200 / Symphony no.29, K201.
MC: . . . . **ZC QS 6009**

SYMPHONY NO.31/NO.36 (MOZART) (London Philharmonic Orchestra/Royal Philharmonic Orchestra).
Tracks: / Symphony no.31 (Mozart) / Symphony no.36 (Mozart) / Marriage of Figaro overture (Mozart).
MC: . . . . **ZC QS 6033**

SYMPHONY NO. 40 IN G MINOR (See under Solti, Sir George) (Chamber Orchestra of Europe).

SYMPHONY NOS 31, 35 & 36 (MOZART) (Concertgebouw Orchestra Amsterdam).
MC: **426 063-4**

VIOLIN CONCERTOS NOS 1 & 5 (MOZART) (Vienna Philharmonic Orchestra).
MC: **4278134**

VIOLIN SONATAS (Various artists).
MC: **4254204**

WORLD OF MOZART (Various artists).
Tracks: / Eine kleine nachtmusik, K525: *Various artists* (1st movt: Allegro) / Piano concerto No. 21, K467: *Various* artists (2nd movt: Andante) / Le nozze di Figaro - overture: *Various artists* / Dove sono: *Various artists*(Le nozze di Figaro) / Symphony No. 40 in G minor, K550: *Various artists* (1st movt: Molto allegro) / Rondo alla Turca: *Various artists* (from Sonata in A major, K331) / Soave sia il vento: *Various artists* (Cosi fan tutte) / Clarinet concerto (A major, K622): *Various artists* (2nd movt: Adagio) / Ave verum corpus: *Various artists* / Masonic funeral music, K477: *Various artists* / Requiem K626 - Confutatis/Lacrimosa: *Various artists* / Symphony No. 25 in G minor: *Various artists* (1st movt: Allegro con brio) / Musical joke, K522: *Various artists* (4th movt: Presto).
MC: **4304984**

ZAUBERFLOTE HIGHLIGHTS (see under Beethoven's Fidelio) (Various artists).

M'Pongo Love

EXCLUSIVITE YA L'AMOUR.
LP: 8026

Mr. Abie

LITTLE BIT OFF, A.
Tracks: / Kosher cuts / Court cases / Morag and Donald / Pat and Mick / Abie supers / House of ill repute / Horses hoofs / Cannibals / Abie's favourite / Wife / Blackpool / Goodnight.
MC: . . . . ZCKLP 010
LP: . . . . KLP 10

Mr. B

PARTNERS IN TIME (Mr. B & J.C. Herd).
LP: BP-2988

SHINING THE PEARLS.
LP: BP-1886

Mr. B. Detroit

MR B DETROIT SPECIAL.
LP: . . . . OL 8010

Mr. Benn

MR. BENN (See Military bands play favourite themes) (Various artists).

Mr. Big (2)

LEAN INTO IT.
MC: 7567822094
LP: 7567822091

MR BIG (Mr. Big).
Tracks: / Addicted to that rush / Wind me up / Merciless / Had enough / Blame it on my youth / Take a walk / Big love / How can you do what you do / Anything for you / Rock'n'roll over.
LP: 781 990-1
MC: 781 990-4

Mr. Biggs...

MR BIGGS PRESENTS A SUPER CLASH (Bailey, Admiral & Tonto Irie).
Tracks: / News flash time / Moveable man / Neighbour living / Mosquito bite / New York life / Carman style / Cooker / Jail life.
LP: . . . . VIBES 022

Mr. Bungle

MR BUNGLE.
Tracks: / Quote unquote / Slowly growing deaf / Squeeze me macaroni / Carousel / Egg / Stubb (a dub) / My ass is on fire / Girls of porn, The / Love is a fist / Dead goon.
LP: 8282761
MC: 8282764

Mr. Cinders

MR. CINDERS (London revival cast (1983)) (Various artists).
Tracks: / Tennis: *Various artists* / Blue blood: *Various artists* / True to two: *Various artists* / I want the world to know: *Various artists* / One man girl: *Various artists* / On with the dance: *Various artists*/ At the ball: *Various artists* / Spread a little happiness: *Various artists* / Entracte: *Various artists*/ 18th century dance: *Various artists* / She's my lovely: *Various artists* / Please Mr. Cinders: *Various artists*/ On the Amazon: *Various artists* / Every little moment: *Various artists* / I've got you, you've got me: *Various artists* / Honeymoon for four: *Various artists* / Finale: *Various artists.*
LP: . . . . TER 1069
MC: . . . . ZCTER 1069

MR. CINDERS (ORIGINAL) (Original London cast) (Various artists).
LP: . . . . TER 1037
MC: . . . . ZCTER 1037

Mr. Doo

MR. DOO VOL.3 (Various artists).
MC: . . . . DSRC 9992

MR. DOO VOL 2 (Various artists).
LP: . . . . MDLP 002

Mr. Fingers

AMMNESIA.
LP: . . . . FING 2

Mr Hornsman

BLOW.
Tracks: / Jumping Jack / Super Special / Death rides / Run for your life / On the moon / Undertaker's burial / Roll On / Franco Nero / Leaving Rome / Ghost capturer / Nightmare / Judgement warrant / East of the River Nile / Harvest in the East / Va Va Voom / Broken Contract / Butter sefish / If your ready.
LP: . . . . TRLS 257
MC: . . . . ZCTRL 257

Mr. Lee

GET BUSY (ALBUM).
LP: . . . . HIP 98
MC: . . . . HIPC 98

Mr. Lucky

MR.LUCKY (Film Soundtrack) (Mancini, Henry).
MC: 2198.4

Mr. Men (bks)

COUNT TO TEN WITH MR MEN (Read by Arthur Lowe and Roy Castle) (Lowe, Arthur & Roy Castle).
MC: . . . . TBC 9513

MR. MEN (From the TV series) (Lowe, Arthur).
LP: . . . . REC 337
MC: . . . . ZCM 337

MR MEN AND LITTLE MISS, VOL 1 (Lowe, Arthur/John Alderton/Pauline Collins).
Tracks: / Mr. Grumpy / Mr. Tall / Mr. Clumsy / Mr. Skinny / Mr. Worry / Mr. Slow / Little Miss Splendid / Little Miss Shy / Little Miss Sunshine / Little Miss Magic / Little Miss Tiny / Little Miss Naughty.
MCSET: . . . . KIDM 9003

MR MEN AND LITTLE MISS, VOL 2 (Lowe, Arthur/John Alderton/Pauline Collins).
Tracks: / Mr. Busy / Mr. Clever / Mr. Wrong / Mr. Mischief / Mr. Quiet / Mr. Nonsense / Little Miss Neat / Little Miss Helpful / Little Miss Plump / Little Miss Bossy / Little Miss Trouble / Little Miss Scatterbrain.
MCSET: . . . . KIDM 9004

MR MEN SONGS (Various artists).
Tracks: / Mr. Men theme: *Various artists* / Mr. Sneeze: *Various artists* / Mr. Bump: *Various artists*/ Mr. Small: *Various artists* / Mr. Tickle: *Various artists.*
LP: . . . . REC 345
MC: . . . . ZCM 345

MR. MEN STORIES VOL.2 (Lowe, Arthur).
LP: . . . . REC 386
MC: . . . . ZCM 386

MR. MEN STORIES VOL.3 (Lowe, Arthur).
LP: . . . . REC 457
MC: . . . . ZCM 457

MR.MEN RIDE AGAIN, THE (Various artists).
Tracks: / Mr. Tall: *Various artists* / Mr. Grumpy: *Various artists* / Mr. Skinny: *Various artists* / Mr. Slow: *Various artists* / Mr. Worry: *Various artists* / Mr. Clumsy: *Various artists.*
LP: . . . . INGL 001
MC: . . . . INGC 001

PARTY TIME WITH THE MR MEN (Original Cast) (Various artists).
LP: . . . . SMR 8510
MC: . . . . SMC 8510

RETURN OF THE MR. MEN, THE (Lowe, Arthur).
Tracks: / Mr. Wrong / Mr. Nonsense / Mr. Quiet / Mr. Busy / Mr. Mischief / Mr. Clever.
LP: . . . . INGL 002
MC: . . . . INGC 002

VARIOUS MR. MEN RECORDINGS (See under Adventures of...) (Percival, Lance (nar)).

Mr. Mister

GO ON.
Tracks: / Stand and deliver / Healing waters / Dust / Something real / Tube, The / Control / Watching the world / Power over me / Man of a thousand dances / Border, The.
LP: . . . . PL 86276
MC: . . . . PK 86276

I WEAR THE FACE.
Tracks: / Hunters of the night / Code of love / Partners in crime / 32 / Runaway / Talk the talk / I'll let you drive / I get lost sometimes / I wear the face / Life goes on.
LP: . . . . NL 90093
MC: . . . . NK 90093
LP: . . . . PL 84864
MC: . . . . PK 84864

WELCOME TO THE REAL WORLD.
Tracks: / Is it love / Broken wings / Kyrie / Uniform of youth / Welcome to the real world / Tangent tears / Run to her / Into my own hands / Don't slow down / Black-white.
LP: . . . . PL 89647
MC: . . . . PK 89647
LP: . . . . NL 90254
MC: . . . . NK 90254

Mr. Pinkwhistle (bk)

ADVENTURES OF MR. PINKWHISTLE (See under Adventures of...) (Bennett, Clive (nar)).

Mr. Positive

NEW DISH (see Culture, Louie) (Mr. Positive & Louie Culture).

Mr. Review

WALKIN' DOWN BRENTFORD ROAD.
LP: . . . . PHZA 36

Mr. Slob's Spring...

MR. SLOB'S SPRING CLEANING COLLECTION Various artists (Various artists).
MC: . . . . SLOB 004

Mr. Smith

TWO VERY SIMILAR VIEWS OF....
Tracks: / March from a little suite / Society ladies / Barbara Allen / With her head tucked underneath her arm / Buddy can you spare a dime / G-nu, A / She had to go and lose it at the Astor / Star of the County Down / Owl and the pussycat, The / Mock morris / If you were the only girl in the world / Liberty Bell / Half way down the stairs.
LP: . . . . SFA 105

Mr. T

I'M FALLING IN LOVE WITH YOU.
LP: . . . . PMLP 007

MR T'S COMMANDMENTS.
Tracks: / Mr. T's commandments / Don't talk to strangers / Toughest man in the world / M. T Mr T / One and only Mr T / No dope no drugs / You got to go through it.
LP: . . . . CBS 26173

Mrs. Ackroyd Band

ORANGES AND LEMMINGS.
LP: . . . . DOG 007
MC: . . . . DOG 007 C

Mrs. Gerrard's...

MRS GERRARD'S ACCORDION BAND (Mrs Gerrard's Accordion Band).
MC: . . . . ACLMC 6

Mrs. Green

MRS. GREEN.
Tracks: / No time for penance / Happy now / Visions of you / Hurry / Another cold morning / East of Eden / I should care / Already gone / Start again / Tuesday.
LP: . . . . BZ 1001
MC: . . . . BZCA 1001

Mrubat, McCoy

FIREBIRD.
LP: . . . . JAJ 2
MC: . . . . JAJC 2

MTS

MTS.
LP: . . . . LPMTS 1
MC: . . . . ZCMTS 1

Mtukudzi, Oliver

PSSS PSSS HALLO.
Tracks: / Strange isn't it? / Zindoenda / Ngwarai vana vangu / Nditendereiwo / Pwere never lie / Kuzvisunga hugwara / I don't wanna lose you / Tarirai / Munoshusha / Psss psss hallo / Rugare rwamangwana.
LP: . . . . CSLP 5005
MC: . . . . ZCSLC 5005

Mtume

IN SEARCH OF THE RAINBOW SEEKERS.
Tracks: / Give it on up (if you want to) / You can't wait for love / She's a rainbow dancer / We're gonna make it this time / Dance around my naval / Doesn't have to make sense, just cents / So you wanna be a star / Spirit of the dance / Everything good to me / Anticipatin'.
LP: . . . . EPC 84629

JUICY FRUIT (ALBUM).
Tracks: / Green light / Juicy fruit / Hips / Would you like to / Your love's too good / Hip dip skipped a beat / Ready for your love / After 6 mix.
LP: . . . . EPC 25399
MC: 40 25399

THEATER OF THE MIND.
Tracks: / Theater of the mind, Theme from / P.O.P. generation / Breathless / I don't believe you heard me / Body and soul (Take me) / New face Deli / I'd rather be with you / Deep freez (rap-a-song) / Deep freez (tree's thing).
LP: . . . . EPC 26923
MC: 40 26923

YOU, ME AND HE.
Tracks: / C.O.D. (I'll deliver) / You are my sunshine / You, me and he / I simply like / Prime time / Tie me up / Sweet for you and me / To be or not to bop.
LP: . . . . EPC 26077
MC: 40 26077

Mu

BEST OF MU.
MC: . . . . TCRECK 4
LP: . . . . RECK 4

END OF AN ERA.
Tracks: / Land of Mu / Waiting for the sun / Haleaka la / Children of the rainbow / Calling from a star / Drink from the fountain / Make a joyful noise / End of an era / Odd TV occurrence / On our way to hana / Who'll write this song / Daybreak sunshine / Blue jay blue / Love we bare, The / Showering rain / You're not the only one / Awakening, The.
LP: . . . . RECK 7

LAST ALBUM, THE.
LP: . . . . AP 017

Mu, Zvuki

ZVUKI MU.
Tracks: / Source of infection / Forgotten sex / Leave me alone / Gadopiatikna / Traffic policeman / Crazy queen / Zero minus one / Krym / Paper flowers / Zima.
LP: . . . . LAND 007
MC: . . . . LANDC 007

Much Ado About Nothing

MUCH ADO ABOUT NOTHING (see under Shakespeare, William) (Various artists).

Muchin, Sergei

SERGEI MUCHIN QUARTET (Muchin, Sergei Quartet).
LP: . . . . DRLP 135

SERGEI MUCHIN QUARTET VOL.2.
LP: . . . . DRLP 138

Muckram Wakes

DUCHESS OF HAMILTON'S RANT, THE.
Tracks: / Bitter withy / Williams Taylor / T'owd Brahn en / Black boy polka / Two sisters, The / Black boy jig / Farmer's arms, The / Winster wakes / Derby ram, The / Twenty pins / Cromford Mills / Stockinger / Meynel pack, The / Peg og derby / Hugh Stenson the deserter / Owd Joe Biggins.
LP: . . . . LER 2093

MAP OF DERBYSHIRE, A.
LP: . . . . LER 2085

WARBLES JANGLES AND REEDS.
LP: . . . . SHY 7009

Mucky Duck

FROM THE BUSH.
LP: . . . . LRF 154

Mucky Pup

BOY IN A MAN'S WORLD, A.
LP: . . . . RO 94751

CAN'T YOU TAKE A JOKE?.
LP: . . . . RR 9553 1

NOW.
Tracks: / Hippies hate water / Three dead gophers / Jimmy's / Baby / She Quieffed / Feeling sick / Headbangers balls and 120 minutes, A / My hands, your neck / Face / Hotel Penitentiary / Mucky pumpin' beat / I know nobody / Walkin' with the devil / Yesterdays / To be lonely.
LP: . . . . RO 93401

Mud

AS YOU LIKE IT.
Tracks: / Dream lover / It's a show / 1-2 love / Heaven was meant for you / As you like it / You'll like it / So fine / Right between the eyes / Touchdown / Why do fools fall in love / Book of love.
LP: . . . . PL 25256

LET'S HAVE A PARTY (Best of Mud).
Tracks: / Crazy / Hypnosis / Dynamite / Tiger feet / Cat crept in, The / Rocket / Hippy hippy shake / Secrets that you keep, The / Oh boy / Moonshine Sally / One night / Blue moon / End of the world / Tallahassee lassie / Let's have a party / Living doll (CD only.) / Diana (CD only.) / In the mood (CD only.) / Hula love (CD only.).
LP: . . . . EMS 1356
MC: . . . . TCEMS 1356

MUD.
Tracks: / Night has a thousand eyes, The / Teddy bear / Till I kissed you / Save the last dance for me / Only sixteen / Sealed with a kiss / Lipstick on your collar / From a Jack to a King / Lollipop / Ain't that a shame / Don't ever change / Let's dance / Under the boardwalk / Itsy bitsy / Dream lover / She wears red feathers / Poetry in motion / Blueberry Hill / Shakin' all over / Lucille.
LP: 1810 942

MUD ROCK.
LP: . . . . SRAK 508

MUD ROCK, VOL. 2.
LP: . . . . SRAK 513

MUD'S GREATEST HITS.
LP: . . . . SRAK 6755

ROCK ON.
Tracks: / Burn on Marlon / Let me get (close to you) / Walk right back / Who you gonna love / Slow talking boy / Careless love / Drift away / Gotta good reason / Too much of nothing / Cut across Shorty.

LP: PL 25170
MC: PK 25170

USE YOUR IMAGINATION.
LP: PVLP 1003

Mud Acres

MUSIC AMONG FRIENDS.
LP: ROUNDER 3001

Mudboy

MUDBOY & THE NEUTRONS (Mudboy & The Neutrons).
LP: ROSE 98

Mudguards

MUDGUARDS.
LP: CHEAP 1

WESTERN CULTURAL NOISE.
LP: CSCV 1

Mudhoney

EVERY GOOD BOY DESERVES FUDGE.
LP: SP 160

MUDHONEY.
LP: GR 0069

SUPERFUZZ BUGMUFF.
LP: EFA 4472
LP: GR 0034

TOUCH ME I'M SICK (See under Sonic Youth) (Sonic Youth/Mudhoney).

Mudie, Harry

HARRY MUDIE MEETS KING TUBBY (Dub conference Vol 3) (Mudie, Harry & King Tubby).
Tracks: / Where eagles dare / With you in mind / Do this in bed / Peace offering / Nineteen love in dub / Conference theme / Tribal recipe / Mudie's serenade / Dub in paradise.
LP: HM 112

HARRY MUDIE MEETS KING TUBBY (Dub conference Vol 1) (Mudie, Harry & King Tubby).
Tracks: / Full dose of dub / Mad house dub / Dub for the dread / Dub with a difference / Caught you dubbing / Roman dub / Dub conference / Heavy duty dub / Striptease dub / String dub in rema.
LP: HM 108

HARRY MUDIE MEETS KING TUBBY (Dub conference Vol 2) (Mudie, Harry & King Tubby).
Tracks: / World dub conference / Marijuana dub / Heart leap dub / Dub inside out / Melody in dub / Jungle walk dub / Maka back dub / Don't play with dub / Planet dub / Drifting dub.
LP: HM 110

LET ME TELL YOU BOY 1970-71 (Mudie, Harry & Friends).
Tracks: / Drifter, The / Mudies mood / Let me show you boy / Bratah / It may sound silly / Mannix / Who who wha / Serious business / Heart don't leap / Musically red / Power pack / Let's start again / Walking the dead / Give me some more loving / Whispering drums.
LP: TRLS 266
MC: ZCTRL 266

Muhammad, Idris

BOOGIE TO THE TOP.
Tracks: / Boogie to the top / Bread / One with a star / Stick it in your face.
LP: KU 38

FOXHUNTIN'.
Tracks: / Boogie boots / Foxhuntin' / Work your body / Love New Orleans / Are we doin' it / Dancing in the land of lovely ladies.
LP: FT 562

MAKE IT COUNT.
Tracks: / For your love / I'm so glad / Love in the tub / I believe in you / Don't fight the feeling / New Orleans.
LP: F 9598

MY TURN.
Tracks: / Piece o' cake / Free / There is a girl / Dark road / Dracula / This love / Happenstance / Stranger / Where did we go wrong.
LP: 890021
MC: 890024

Muir, Frank

SUPER WHAT-A-MESS.
Tracks: / Super What-a-mess / Rince what-a-mess / What-a-mess the good / What-a-mess goes to school / What-a-mess at the seaside / What-a-mess and the cat next door.
MC: TS 347

WHAT-A-MESS.
Tracks: / What-a-mess / What-a-mess (continued).
MC: 75324

WONDERFUL WHAT A MESS.
MC: TS 353

Muirhead Accordion

RECORDED DELIVERY.
Tracks: / Dashing white sergeant / Girl I left behind me, The / Rattlin' bog / Leather away the wattle'o / Schneewaltzer / Come back to Sorrento / Santa Lucia / Papa Piccolino / Tiree love song / Mother Macree / Rakes of mallow / Cavalleria rusticana / Petronella / Lord Randall's bride / Black boy / Drumleys / Marche und tanze / David's song / Good health and joy / Morning has broken / Annie's song / Winds of Tiree / Highland queen / By cool Siloam's shady rill / My love she's but a lassie yet / East neuk of Fife / Bonnie Banchory.
LP: MSM 1
MC: MSM 1 C

Mukai, Shigeharu

SO AND SO (See under Gilberto, Astrud) (Gilberto, Astrud & Shigeharu, Mukai).

Muldaur, Geoff

BLUES BOY.
LP: FF 201

GEOFF MULDAUR & AMOS GARRETT (Muldaur, Geoff & Amos Garrett).
LP: FF 061

POTTERY PIE (Muldaur, Geoff & Maria).
LP: CGLP 4428
MC: CGC 4428

SLEEPY MAN BLUES.
Tracks: / Jelly roll baker / Rain don't fall on me, The / Sleepy man blues / This morning she was gone / I have had my fun / Good gin blues / Motherless child blues / Georgia skin game / Aberdeen Mississippi blues / Trouble in mind / Everybody ought to make a change / Drop down mama.
LP: WIK 78

Muldaur, Maria

LIVE IN LONDON:MARIA MULDAUR.
LP: SPIN 116

MARIA MULDAUR.
Tracks: / Any old time / Midnight at the oasis / My tennessee mountain home / I never did sing you a love song / Work song / Don't you feel my leg (don't you make me high) / Walking one and only / Long hard climb / Three dollar bill / Vaudeville man / Mad mad mad.
LP: K 44255

OPEN YOUR EYES.
Tracks: / Fall in love again / Finally made love to a man / Birds fly South (when Winter comes) / Heart of fire / Lover man (oh where can you be) / Open your eyes / (No more) dancin' in the street / Eleona / Clean up woman / Love is everything.
LP: K 56634

SOUTHERN WINDS.
Tracks: / I got a man / Here is where your love belongs / That's the way love is / My sisters and brothers / I can't say no / I'll keep my light in my window / Cajun moon / Joyful noise / Say you will / Make love to the music.
LP: K 56463

SWEET AND LOW.
LP: SPIN 109
MC: SPIC 109

SWEET HARMONY.
Tracks: / Sweet harmony / Sad eyes / Lying song / Rockin' chair / I can't stand it / We just couldn't say goodbye / Black by fall / Jon the generator / Wild bird / As an eagle stirred in her nest.
LP: K 54059

THERE IS A LOVE.
Tracks: / Keep my eyes on you / I was made to love you / There is a love / Sundown / I do / Infinite mercy / In the holy name of Jesus / Is my living in vain?.
LP: MYR 1114
MC: MC 1114

TRANSLUCENCY.
LP: UP 27 25

WAITRESS IN A DONUT SHOP.
Tracks: / Squeeze me / Gringo en Mexico / Cool river / I'm a woman / Sweetheart / Honey babe blues / If you haven't any hay get on down the road / Oh papa / It ain't the meat / Backyard blues / Travellin' shoes.
LP: K 54025

Mule (bk)

MULE, THE (Isaac Asimov).
MC: CP 1661

Mulerman, Vadim

FOLK SONG RECITAL.
MC: SM 00355

Muleskinner

MULESKINNER.
Tracks: / Mule skinner blues / Footprints in the snow / Dark hollow / Whitehouse blues / Opus 57 in G minor / Runways of the moon / Roanoake / Rain and snow / Soldier's joy / Blue mule.
LP: ED 219

Mulgrew, John

FIDDLE TUNES.
MC: COAS 3008
LP: OAS 3008

Mulhaire Ceili Band

MULHAIRE CEELI BAND.
LP: HPE 611

Mullan, Ken

I REMEMBER YOU.
LP: A1 LP 1002
MC: A1C 1002

Mullen, Jim

CAPE WRATH (See under Morrissey, Dick) (Mullen, Jim & Dick Morrissey).

INTO THE 90'S.
LP: SAPLP 101
MC: SAPMC 101

THUMBS UP.
Tracks: / Blue Montreaux / Fall / As if you read my mind / Crepuscule / Thumbs up / Herbal scent / Friends / Beauty and the beast.
LP: CODA 4

UP (Mullen, Jim & Dick Morrissey).
Tracks: / Footloose / Sing me softly of the blues / Everything must change / Philip Phuling / What a way to go / You'll know what I mean / Busted fender.
LP: K 50835

Muller, Werner

GOLDEN SOUNDS (Muller, Werner & His Orchestra).
Tracks: / Take the 'A' train / Flying home / Hernando's hideaway / Perlenfischer / Song of the seasons / Clair / Once upon a time in the West / Banana boat song / You are my lucky star / Whiter shade of pale, A.
MC: 4.26649

GYPSY (Muller, Werner & His Orchestra).
Tracks: / Czardas / Hungarian dance No. 5 / Hungarian rhapsody No. 2 / Zorba's dance / Gipsy love / At the Balalaika / Two guitars / Hara Staccato / Mischa / Komm Tzigany / Black eyes / Golden earrings.
LP: DGS 5

TANGOS FOR LOVERS (Muller, Werner & His Orchestra).
Tracks: / Habanera / Elixir of love / Polovisian dances / M'appari / Dance of the hours / Traumerei / Nabucco / Pastorale / Solvig's song / Tango albeniz / Barcarolle / You are my heart's delight.
LP: MORR 522

Mullican, Moon

GREATEST HITS:MOON MULLICAN.
LP: SLP 398
MC: GT 5398

HIS ALL TIME GREATEST HITS.
Tracks: / I'll sail my ship alone / Honolulu rock-a-roll-a / Leaves mustn't fall, The / Mona Lisa / Sugar beet / New Jole Blon / Sweeter than the flowers / Pipeliner's blues / I was sorta wonderin' / Cherokee boogie / You don't have to be a baby to cry / Foggy river.
LP: SING 555

SEVEN NIGHTS TO ROCK.
LP: WESTERN 2001

SWEET ROCKIN' MUSIC.
Tracks: / Jenny Lee / That's me / Sweet rockin' music / Moon's rock / Cush cush ky-yay / Writing on the wall / Wedding of the bugs / Big big city / Pipeliner's blues / I was sorta wonderin' / Early morning blues / Sweeter than flowers / Leaves mustn't fall, The / My baby's gone / Every which a way / I'm waiting for ships that never come in.
LP: CR 30231

Mulligan, Gerry

'63 - THE CONCERT JAZZ BAND.
LP: 837 438 1

ANNIE ROSS SINGS A SONG WITH MULLIGAN (see under Ross, Annie).

BEST OF GERRY MULLIGAN (Compact/Walkman jazz).
Tracks: / Bernie's tune / Festive minor / This lady is a tramp / Blue at the roots / Sweet and lovely / Line for Lyons / Demanton / Spring is sprung / Theme for joblim / Makin' whoopee / Westwood walk / Night lights.
MC: 830 697-4

BLUES IN TIME (Mulligan, Gerry & Paul Desmond).
Tracks: / Blues in time / Body and soul / Stand still / Line for Lyons / Wintersong / Battle hymn of the republic / Fall out.
LP: 2304 329

COLLECTION: GERRY MULLIGAN.
Tracks: / Jeru / Festive minor / I never knew / Rose room / Blue theme / Lady Chatterley's mother / Wee bit of bopita, A / My funny valentine / Chuggin' / Out of this world / Everything happens to me / Bernie's tune.
MC: DVMC 2045

COMPACT JAZZ: GERRY MULLIGAN.
Tracks: / Lady is a tramp, The / Westwood walk.
MC: 831 696-4

CONCERT IN JAZZ.
LP: 2304 424

FABULOUS GERRY MULLIGAN QUARTET (Mulligan, Gerry Quartet).
Tracks: / I may be wrong / Five brothers / Gold rush / Lullaby of the leaves / Makin' whoopee / Laura / Soft shoe / Nearness of you / Limelight / Come out wherever you are / Love me or leave me / Bernie's tune / Walking shoes / Moonlight in Vermont / Lady is a tramp, The / Bark for Barksdale.
2LP: VJD 504
2LP: 400007

GERRY MULLIGAN.
Tracks: / Apple core / Song for Johnny Hodges / Blight of the fumble bee / Gerry meets Hamp / Blues for Gerry / Line for Lyons.
LP: KLJ 20021
LP: JR 123

GERRY MULLIGAN Walkman jazz.
Tracks: / Blueport / Body and soul / Black nightgown / Come rain or come shine / Lady Chatterley's mother / Go home / Let my people be / Barbara's theme / Theme from I want to live / Apple core.
MC: 838 933-4

GERRY MULLIGAN AND JIMMY WITHERSPOON (Mulligan, Gerry & Jimmy Witherspoon).
Tracks: / Time's gettin' tougher than tough / How long blues / Corina Corina / C.C. rider / Roll 'em Pete / Everyday / Outskirts of town / Kansas city / Trouble in mind / St. Louis blues.
LP: SM 3279
MC: MC 3279

GERRY MULLIGAN MEETS BEN WEBSTER (Mulligan, Gerry & Ben Webster).
Tracks: / Chelsea Bridge / Cat walk / Sunday / Who's got rhythm? / Tell me when / Go home.
LP: 8211671
LP: CLP 1373

GERRY MULLIGAN MEETS JOHNNY HODGES (Mulligan, Gerry & Johnny Hodges).
Tracks: / Bunny / What's the rush? / Back beat / What's it all about? / Eighteen carrots for Rabbit / Shady side.
LP: 2304 476

GERRY MULLIGAN-CHET BAKER.
LP: GNPS 56

HOLIDAY WITH MULLIGAN (see under Holiday, Judy) (Mulligan, Gerry & Judy Holiday).

IN SWEDEN 1957.
2LP: CAH 4003/4

JAZZ COMBO FROM 'I WANT TO LIVE' (Original soundtrack) (Mulligan, Gerry & Shelly Manne).
Tracks: / Black nightgown / I want to live, Theme from / Night watch, The / Frisco club / Barbara's theme / Life's a funny thing.
LP: AFF 188

JERU.
Tracks: / Get out of town / Here I'll stay / Inside impromptu / Blue boy / You've come home / Lonely town / Capricious.
LP: CBS 21135
MC: 40 21135

KONITZ MEETS MULLIGAN (See under Konitz, Lee) (Konitz, Lee & Gerry Mulligan).

LA MENACE O (Film soundtrack).
2LP: MRS 506

LITTLE BIG HORN.
Tracks: / Under a star / Sun on stairs / Another kind of Sunday / Bright angel falls / I never was a young man / Little big horn.
LP: GRP 91003

LIVE IN STOCKHOLM, MAY 1957 (Mulligan, Gerry Quartet).
Tracks: / Come out wherever you are / Birth of the blues / Moonlight in Vermont / Lullaby of the leaves / Open country / I can't get started / Frenesi / Baubles, bangles and beads / Yardbird suite.
LP: INGO 3

LIVE IN STOCKHOLM, VOL 2 (Mulligan, Gerry Quartet).
Tracks: / Walking shoes / My funny valentine / Blues at the roots / Bernie's

tune / Lullaby of the leaves / Body and soul / All the things you are.
LP: . . . . **INGO 6**

LONESOME BOULEVARD.
MC: **395 326 4**

MULLIGAN.
Tracks: / Jeru / Festive minor / Rose room / North Atlantic run / Taurus moon / Out back of the barn.
MC: . . . . **MC 7682**

MULLIGAN - BAKER (CARNEGIE CONCERT, VOL. 1&2) (Mulligan, Gerry & Chet Baker).
Tracks: / Carioca / Line for Lyons / Moonlight in Vermont / Bark for Barksdale / Turnstile / Lady is a tramp, The / My funny valentine / Funhouse / Ide's side / Round house / Kaper / Bweebida bobbida / Mullenium / Mulligan's two / Limelight / So easy / Go go / Bevan beeps / Rearin' back.
LP: . . . . **OJCD 504**

MULLIGAN MEETS MONK (See under Monk, Thelonious) (Mulligan, Gerry & Thelonius Monk).

MULLIGAN - VOLUME 1 (see under (Pacific Jazz II collection).

MULLIGAN-BAKER (Mulligan, Gerry & Chet Baker).
Tracks: / Carioca / Line for lYons / Moonlight in Vermont / Bark for Barksdale / Turnstile / Lady is a tramp, The / My funny valentine / Ide's side / Funhouse / Roundhouse / Kaper / Bweebida bobbida / Mullenium / Limelight / Go go / Mulligan's too / So easy / Bevan beeps / Rearin' bacl.
2LP: . . . . **PR 24016**

MY FUNNY VALENTINE.
Tracks: / Catch as catch can / My funny valentine / Blueport / Utter chaos / What is there to say? / Just in time / News from Blueport / Festive minor.
LP: **21102**
MC: **40 21102**

MY FUNNY VALENTINE (VOGUE).
MC: **771511**

NIGHT LIGHTS.
Tracks: / Morning of the carnival / Prelude in E minor / Night lights / Festive minor / Tell me when / In the wee small hours of the morning.
LP: **6336345**
MC: **818 271 4**

SHADOW OF YOUR SMILE (Mulligan, Gerry Quartet).
LP: . . . . **MLP 003**

SOFT LIGHTS AND SWEET MUSIC (Mulligan, Gerry & Scott Hamilton).
Tracks: / Soft lights and sweet music / Gone / Do you know what I see? / I've just seen her / Noblesse / Ghosts / Port of Baltimore blues.
LP: . . . . **CJ 300**
MC: . . . . **CJC 300**

SUMMIT.
Tracks: / Twenty years ago / Close your eyes and listen / Years of solitude / Deus Xango / Twenty years after / Aire de Buenos Aires / Reminiscence / Summit.
LP: . . . . **ORL 8588**

THELONIOUS MONK WITH GERRY MULLIGAN (See under Monk, Thelonious) (Monk, Thelonious & Gerry Mulligan).

TWO OF A MIND (See under Desmond, Paul) (Mulligan, Gerry & Paul Desmond).

WALK ON THE WATER (Mulligan, Gerry & His Orchestra).
Tracks: / For an unfinished woman / Song for strayhorn / 42nd and Broadway / Angelica / Across the track blues / I'm getting sentimental over you.
LP: . . . . **SL 5194**
MC: . . . . **SLC 5194**

WHAT IS THERE TO SAY? (Mulligan, Gerry Quartet).
Tracks: / What is there to say / Just in time / News from blueport / Festive minor / My funny valentine / As catch can / Blueport / Utter chaos.
LP: . . . . **BVL 013**

Mullins, Rich

WINDS OF HEAVEN.
LP: . . . . **RRA R 0036**
MC: . . . . **RRA C 0036**

Mulloy Brothers

COASTLINE OF MAYO, THE.
MC: . . . . **GTDC 073**

Mulqueen, Ann

KERRY'S 25TH.
Tracks: / Kerry's 25th / Slievegallion braes / Rosin dubh / Cliffs of Dooneen / Mick Mackey and his men / Na Connerys / Falls of Doonass / Evelyn Marie / Ca rabhais ar feadh an lae uaim / Bonnie bunch of roses, The / Sweet Dungarvan town / Meet me tonight on the shore.
LP: . . . . **OAS 3022**

Multicoloured Shades

HOUSE OF WAX.
LP: . . . . **HYBLP 7**

SUNDOME CITY EXIT.
LP: . . . . **ABCLP 14**

Multi-Story

EAST-WEST.
Tracks: / East West / Breaking ground / Traveller, The / Ahead of your time / Carrie / Come alive / Wire, The / Heroes.
LP: . . . . **WFKMLP 32**
MC: . . . . **WFKMMC 32**

THROUGH YOUR EYES.
Tracks: / Hold back the night / All out of love / Through your eyes / Rub it off / Heart of mine / Hot seat / Further than now / Spirit of love / Turn me onto.
MC: . . . . **WKFMMC 98**
LP: . . . . **WKFMLP 98**

Mulvihill, Brendan

FLAX IN BLOOM, THE.
LP: . . . . **SIF 1020**
MC: . . . . **CSIF 1020**

Mulvihill, Martin

HUMOURS OF MARTIN MULVIHILL, THE.
MC: . . . . **GVMMC 502**

IRISH FIDDLE, VOL.1.
MC: . . . . **GVMMC 575**

Mummy...

MUMMY, THE (horror classics for ages 7-12) (Unknown narrator(s)).
MC: . . . . **PLBC 175**

Munch

MUNCH.
LP: . . . . **EFA 5860**

Munch Bunch

MUNCH BUNCH STORIES & SONGS (Read by John Noakes/ Peter Purves/ Lesley Judd) (Various artists).
LP: . . . . **STMP 9018**
MC: **STMP4 9018**

MUNCH BUNCH STORIES VOL.1 (Kelly, Matthew (nar)).
MC: . . . . **TBC 9501**

MUNCH BUNCH STORIES VOL.2 (Kelly, Matthew (nar)).
MC: . . . . **TBC 9502**

RORY RHUBARB (Pegram, Nigel (nar)).
MC: . . . . **TTS 9830**

SALLY STRAWBERRY (Pegram, Nigel (nar)).
MC: . . . . **TTS 9829**

SCRUFF GOOSEBERRY (Pegram, Nigel (nar)).
MC: . . . . **TTS 9832**

SPUD (Pegram, Nigel (nar)).
MC: . . . . **TTS 9831**

Mundell, Hugh

AFRICA MUST BE FREE BY 1983 (Mundrell, Hugh).
Tracks: / Let's all unite / My mind / Africa must be free by 1983 / Why do blackmen fuss and fight / Book of life / Run revolution come / Day of judgement / Jah will provide / Ital sip.
LP: . . . . **GREL 94**

ARISE.
LP: . . . . **ATRA 1007**

BLACK MAN FOUNDATION.
LP: . . . . **SHAN 43012**
MC: . . . . **SHANC 43012**

MUNDELL.
Tracks: / Jacqueline / Rasta have the handle / Going places / Red gold and green / Tell I a lie / 24 hours a day / Jah music / Your face is familiar.
LP: . . . . **GREL 36**
MC: . . . . **GREEN 36**

Mundi, Gloria

I INDIVIDUAL.
Tracks: / Pack, The / Condemned to be free / Daughters of rich men / I like some men / I individual / You talk / Park Lane / Split personality / Victim.
LP: . . . . **PL 25157**

WORD IS OUT.
Tracks: / First light of day / What's going on / YY / Do you believe / Temporary hell / Dangerous to dream / Let's pretend / Hill, The / In the blackout / Glory of the world.
LP: . . . . **PL 25244**

Mundon, Tommy

MUNDON MANIA.
LP: . . . . **BRO 135**
MC: . . . . **KBRO 135**

Mundy, Jimmy

FIESTA IN BRASS (Mundy, Jimmy & Orchestra).
LP: . . . . **GELP 15060**

GROOVIN' HIGH (see Wilson, Gerald) (Mundy, Jimmy/Gerald Wilson/Wilbert Baranco).

Muney, David

MING'S SAMBA.
Tracks: / Ming's samba / Nowhere everafter / Walter's waltz / Rememberin' Fats / Spooning.
LP: **4654571**
MC: **4654574**

Mungo Jerry

100 MINUTES OF MUNGO JERRY.
MC: . . . . **ZCTON 123**

ALL THE HITS PLUS MORE.
LP: . . . . **PRST 002**
MC: . . . . **ZPRST 002**

ELECTRONICALLY TESTED.
LP: . . . . **DNLS 3020**

GOLDEN HOUR OF MUNGO JERRY.
MC: . . . . **KGHMC 116**

GOLDEN HOUR PRESENTS MUNGO JERRY'S GREATEST HITS.
Tracks: / In the Summertime / Mighty man / Say goodnight / Lady Rose / Johnny B. Badde / On a Sunday / Open up / You better leave that whisky alone / Baby jump / Maggie / Somebody stole my wife / You don't have to be in the army to fight in the war / She rowed / Have a whiff on me / My girl and me / Northcote Arms / See me.
LP: . . . . **GH 586**

GREATEST HITS: MUNGO JERRY.
LP: **20001**
MC: **40001**

GREATEST HITS: MUNGO JERRY (IMPORT).
LP: **509057**

GREATEST HITS...LADYROSE, ALRIGHT ALRIGHT.
LP: . . . . **VG 509057**

IN THE SUMMERTIME.
Tracks: / In the Summertime / Wild love / Summer's gone / Alright, alright, alright / Hey Rosalyn / Long-legged woman / Dressed in black / Baby jump / On a Sunday / Open up / Lady Rose / Going down the dusty road / You don't have to be in the army to fight in the war.
LP: . . . . **FBLP 8075**
MC: . . . . **ZCFBL 8075**

MUNGO JERRY.
LP: . . . . **DNLS 3008**
MC: **C90**

SIX A SIDE.
LP: **20002**
MC: **40002**

SNAKE BITE.
Tracks: / Snakebite / All I wanna do / Remember me / Sugar in the bowl / Rock'n'roll, rock'n'roll / Heartbreak avenue / Pick a bale o cotton / Red leather and chrome / Jesse James / Right on.
MC: . . . . **ZPREC 5011**

SOUL PARTY.
MC: . . . . **ASK 796**

TOO FAST TO LIVE AND TOO YOUNG TO DIE.
Tracks: / Alright, alright, alright / Long legged woman dressed in black / Open up / 46 and on / Little Miss Hipshake / Too fast to live and too young to die / Gonna bop til I drop / Lady Rose / Mighty man / In the Summertime / My girl and me / Baby jump / You don't have to be in the army to fight in the war / Wild love / My girl and me.
LP: . . . . **PYL 6027**
MC: . . . . **PYM 6027**

Municipio De Arapiraca

LAGOA DE CANOA.
LP: . . . . **RRPL 003**

Munro, Charlie

INTEGRATIONS.
LP: . . . . **LRF 170**

Munro, H.H.

SHOCK TACTICS & OTHER STORIES (Various artists).
Tracks: / Shock tactics: *Various artists* / Stalled ox: *Various artists* / Chaplet, The: *Various artists*/ Bull, The: *Various artists* / Mappined life, The: *Various artists* / Fate: *Various artists* / Gabriel-Ernest: *Various artists* / Holiday task, A: *Various artists* / Unrest-cure, The: *Various artists* / Louise: *Various artists* / Name-day, The: *Various artists.*
MC: **418 048-4**

TOBERMORY & OTHER STORIES (Various artists).
MCSET: **418 024-4**

Munro, John

FAMILY FAVOURITES (Munro, John & Liz).
LP: . . . . **LRF 157**

PLAIN & SIMPLE (see under Bogle, Eric) (Bogle, Eric/John Munro).

Munrow, David

GREENSLEEVES TO A GROUND (Early music).
MC: . . . . **TCCSD 3781**
LP: . . . . **CSD 3781**

Muppets

GREAT MUPPET CAPER, THE (Original soundtrack).
Tracks: / Main title / Hey, a movie / Big red bus / Happiness hotel / Lady Holiday / Steppin' out with a star / Apartment / Night life / First time it happens / Couldn't we ride? / Piggy's fantasy / Great muppet caper / Homeward bound / Finale.
LP: **K56942**

MUPPET MOVIE (Film Soundtrack) (Various artists).
Tracks: / Rainbow connection: *Various artists* / Movin' right along: *Various artists* / Never before never again: *Various artists* / I hope that something better comes along: *Various artists* / Can you picture that: *Various* artists / I'm going to go back there someday: *Various artists* / God bless America: *Various artists* / Come back animal: *Various artists* / Magic stone: *Various artists.*
LP: . . . . **CBS 70170**
MC: **40 70170**

MUPPET SHOW-2, THE.
Tracks: / Muppet show theme, The / Baby face / There's a new sound / Monologue by Fozzie Bear, A / Cuento le gusta / Who / Time in a bottle / Editorial by Sam the eagle, An / Borneo / At the dance / Upidee / Just one person / Happy feet / Pigs in space / I'm five / Sea shanty / New York state of mind / Pig calypso, The / When / Gypsy's violin, A / Wishing song / Animal sings Gershwin / For what it's worth / We got us.
LP: . . . . **NSPH 21**

MUPPET SHOW MUSIC ALBUM, THE.
Tracks: / Muppet show theme, The / Hawaiian war chant / Rhyming song / Blue skies / Eight little notes / Do wah diddy diddy / Jamboree / Henrietta's wedding / Jam / Magic garden / Macho man / Mad about the frog / Pennsylvania 6-5000 / Lime and coconut / Frog kissin' / Dog walk / While my guitar gently weeps / Sixty seconds / It was a very good year.
LP: . . . . **NSPL 18613**
MC: . . . . **ZCP 18613**

MUPPET SHOW, THE.
Tracks: / Muppet show theme, The / Mississippi mud / Mah na mah na / Flight of the bumble bee / Mr. Bass man / Cottleston pie / Muppaphones / Lady of Spain / Pachalafaka / Lydia the tattooed lady / Half way down the stairs / Tenderly / I'm in love with a big blue frog / Tit willow / Soap opera / Vetenarian's hospital / Simon Smith and the amazing dancing bear / What now my love / Fozzie monologue / Hugga wugga / Trees / Sax and violence / Being green.
LP: . . . . **NSPH 19**
MC: . . . . **ZCP 19**

MUPPETS TAKE MANHATTAN.
LP: **9251141**

Murder In The

MURDER IN THE CATHEDRAL (see under Eliot, T.S.) (Pasco, Richard & The Royal Shakespeare Company).

Murder In The...(bk)

MURDER IN THE MEWS (Agatha, Christie) (Hawthorne, Nigel (nar)).
MCSET: . . . . **LFP 7134**
MCSET: . . . . **LFP 417 1345**

Murder Is... (bk)

MURDER IS ANNOUNCED, A (Agatha Christie) (Leach, Rosemary (nar)).
MCSET: . . . . **CAB 297**

Murder On The...

MURDER ON THE ORIENT EXPRESS/ LADY CAROLINE LAMB (Original Soundtrack) (Various artists).
Tracks: / Overture: *Various artists* / Stamboul Ferry: *Various artists* / Orient Express: *Various artists*/ Princess Dragomiroff: *Various artists* / Finale: *Various artists* / Entr'acte: *Various artists* / Caroline: *Various artists* / Honeymoon In Italy: *Various artists* / Caroline and Byron: *Various artists* / Byron's March: *Various artists* / Banquet, The: *Various artists* / William returns home: *Various artists* / Temple, The: *Various artists* / Caroline's ride: *Various artists* / William and Caroline: *Various artists* / End music: *Various artists.*
LP: . . . . **FILM 019**

Murderock
MURDEROCK (See under Emerson, Keith) (Film soundtrack) (Emerson, Keith).

Murdoch, Alistair
FIELDS OF ATHENRY.
MC: . . . CWGR 096

ON THAT BEAUTIFUL SHORE.
LP: . . . WGR 061
MC: . . . CWGR 061

Murdoch, Richard
BAND WAGGON (See Under Askey, Arthur) (Murdoch, Richard & Arthur Askey & Tommy Trinder).

Murdock, Shirley
SHIRLEY MURDOCK.
Tracks: / Be free / No more / Go on without you / Truth or dare / Danger zone / Teaser / As we lay / One I need, The / Tribute.
LP: . . . EKT 32

WOMANS POINT OF VIEW, A.
Tracks: / Husband / Found my way / (Everybody wants) something for nothing / If I know / Spend my whole life / Oh what a feeling / I still love you / Woman's point of view / And I am telling you I'm not going / Modern girls / Instrument of praise.
LP: . . . 9607911
MC: . . . 9607914

Muriel, Linda
BETTER DAY (See under Jonah, Julian) (Muriel, Linda & Julian Jonah).

Murley Silver Band
MURLEY SILVER BAND IN CONCERT.
Tracks: / Colonel Bogey / Nearer my God to thee / Una paloma blanca / Great little army / Rock of ages / Death or glory / Blaze away / Old rugged cross / Territorials / Lead kindly light / Those magnificent men / Cavatina.
LP: . . . STOL 142

Murphey, Michael
MICHAEL MARTIN MURPHEY.
Tracks: / Still taking chances / Two-step is easy / What's forever for / Take it like a man / First taste of freedom / Love affairs / Ring of truth / Interlude / Crystal / Lost river / Hearts in the right place.
LP: . . . LBG 30356

Murphy, Al
THROUGH THE FIELDS.
LP: . . . GVM 305

Murphy, Delia
DELIA MURPHY.
LP: . . . STAL 1055

SPINNING WHEEL (Murphy, Delia The Legendary).
Tracks: / Spinning wheel / If I were a blackbird / I was told by my aunt / I wish that I never was wed / Roving journey man, The / Boston burglar / Thank you ma'am says Dan (Duet with Michael O'Higgins.) / Three lovely lassies / Down by the glenside / Moonshiner / Croppy bar, The / Goodbye Mick, goodbye Pat / Nora Creina (Duet with Michael O'Higgins.).
LP: . . . GRALP 16
MC: . . . GRTC 16

SPINNING WHEEL, THE.
MC: . . . TC STAL 1055

Murphy, Dennis
STAR ABOVE THE GARTER (Murphy, Dennis & Julia Clifford).
LP: . . . CC 5

Murphy, Eddie
COMEDIAN.
LP: . . . CBS 25760

EDDIE MURPHY.
Tracks: / Faggots / Buckwheat / Black movie theaters / Talking cars / Doo doo / Christmas gifts / Myths / Little chinese, A / Boogie in your butt / Drinking fathers / Effrom / Pope and Ronald Reagan, The / Hit by a car / Enough is enough.
LP: . . . CBS 25143

HOW COULD IT BE.
Tracks: / How could it be / Con confused / I wish I could tell you when / Party all the time / I, me, us, we / My god is color blind / Everything's coming up roses.
LP: . . . CBS 26687
MC: . . . 40 26687

SO HAPPY.
Tracks: / Put your mouth on me / Till the money's gone / I got it / So happy / Bubble hill / With all I know / Pretty please / Love moans / Let's get with it / Tonight.
LP: . . . 4624041
MC: . . . 4624044

Murphy, Elliot James
AFFAIRS ETC. (Murphy, Elliot).
LP: . . . FC 066

APRES LE DELUGE.
LP: . . . FC 034

CHANGE WILL COME.
LP: . . . ROSE 158
MC: . . . ROSE 158C

MILWAUKEE.
LP: . . . ROSE 99
MC: . . . ROSE 99C

MURPH THE SMURF.
LP: . . . FC 057

Murphy Gospel Group
BUILD ME A CABIN IN THE CORNER OF GLORYLAND.
Tracks: / Family who prays shall never part, The / I've found a friend in Jesus / Build me a cabin in the corner of Gloryland / Speak my Lord / Take me back to the old fashioned meeting / Living where the healing waters flow / We'll understand it better bye and bye / This train I'm riding / Precious memories / I'm using my Bible for a roadmap / Take your burden to the Lord.
LP: . . . POL 831

Murphy, Jill (aut)
WORST WITCH, THE (See under Worst Witch) (Margolyes, Miriam (nar)).

Murphy, Lyle
NEW ORBIT IN SOUND.
LP: . . . FS 122

Murphy, Mark
ARTISTRY OF MARK MURPHY, THE.
Tracks: / Odd child, The / I don't want to cry anymore / Moody's mood / Trilogy for kids / I remember Clifford / Autumn nocturne / Close enough for love / Long ago and far away.
LP: . . . MR 5286

BOP FOR KEROUAC.
Tracks: / Be-Bop lives (boplicity) / Goodbye pork pie hat / Parker's mood / You better go now / You've proven your point (bongo beep) / Bad and the beautiful / Down St Thomas way / Ballad of the sad young man.
MC: . . . MRC 5253

BRAZIL SONG.
Tracks: / Desafinado / Two kites / island, The / Bolero de sata / She / Someone to light up my life / Nothing will be as it was tomorrow / Outubro / bridges.
MC: . . . MRC 5297

BRIDGING A GAP.
LP: . . . MR 5009

MARK II.
LP: . . . MR 5041

MARK MURPHY.
LP: . . . MR 5078

MARK MURPHY SINGS DOROTHY FIELDS AND CY COLEMAN.
LP: . . . AP 132

SATISFACTION GUARANTEED.
LP: . . . MR 5215

SINGS THE NAT KING COLE SONGBOOK.
Tracks: / Nature boy / Calypso blues / Love letters / Serenata / Oh you crazy moon / 'Tis autumn / I keep going back to Joe's / Tangerine / Lush life / Until the real thing comes along / Baby, baby all the time / Never let me go / These foolish things.
LP: . . . MR 5308

STOLEN MOMENTS.
LP: . . . MR 5012

Murphy, Matt
TOGETHER AGAIN ONE MORE TIME (LIVE IN 85) (See also Slim, Memphis) (Murphy, Matt & Memphis Slim).

WAY DOWN SOUTH.
Tracks: / Way down South / Big six / Gonna be some changes made / Big city takedown / Buck's boogie / Thump tyme / Matt's guitar boogie / Low down and dirty / Gimme somma dat / Blue walls.
MC: . . . ANTMC 13

Murphy, Mike
DREAM OF EVERYDAY HOUSEWIFE, THE.
LP: . . . HPE 604

Murphy, Noel
CAUGHT IN THE ACT.
Tracks: / Boxer, The / Vicar and the frog, The / From Clare to here / Tom Pearce / Breath of fresh air, A / Mursheen durkin' / Bricklayer's song / Glenduloch saint, The / As I roved out / Sailor courted the farmer's daughter, A / Few more for the road, A / Where do you go to my lovely / I walk the line (medley).
LP: . . . PL 25151
MC: . . . PK 25151

NOEL MURPHY PERFORMS.
Tracks: / Folker, The / Good ship Calabar, The / Comical genius / Don't think twice / Medley of a hit / Brian Boru / One eyed Reilly / Sailor courted a farmer's daughter, A / Parting glass, The / Rocky road to Dublin.
LP: . . . PLR 002

Murphy, Pat.J.
PAT MURPHY'S MEADOW.
2LP: . . . HM 045D

Murphy, Peter
DEEP.
Tracks: / Deep ocean vast sea / Crystal wrists / Seven veils / Cuts you up / Roll call / Shy / Marlene Dietrich's favourite poem / Line between the devil's teeth, The / Strange kind of love (version one) / Roll call (reprise).
LP: . . . BEGA 107
MC: . . . BEGC 107

LOVE HYSTERIA.
Tracks: / All night long / His circle and hers meet / Dragnet drag / Socrates the python / Indigo eyes / Time has nothing to do with it / Blind sublime / My last two years / Fun time.
LP: . . . BEGA 92
MC: . . . BEGC 92

SHOULD THE WORLD FAIL TO FALL APART.
Tracks: / Canvas beauty / Light pours out of me, The / Confessions / Should the world fail to fall apart / Never man / God sends / Blue heart / Answer is clear,The / Final solution / Jemal.
LP: . . . BBL 69
MC: . . . BBLC 69
LP: . . . BEGA 69

Murphy, Richard
BATTLE OF AUGHRIM, THE.
LP: . . . CCT 7

Murphy, Rose
OLD TIME IRISH FIDDLE AND ACCORDION.
LP: . . . 12TS 316

ROSE MURPHY WITH RHYTHM SECTION.
LP: . . . AP 70

Murphy, Turk
CONCERT IN THE PARK (Murphy, Turk Jazz Band).
LP: . . . MMRC 117
MC: . . . CMMRC 117

EARTHQUAKE MCGOON RECORDINGS (San Francisco Jazzband).
MC: . . . C-MMRC 105

LIVE AT EASY STREET VOL.1 (Murphy, Turk & His San Francisco Jazz Band).
LP: . . . DC 12015

LIVE AT EASY STREET VOL.2 (Murphy, Turk & His San Francisco Jazz Band).
LP: . . . DC 12018

LIVE AT EASY STREET VOL.3 (Murphy, Turk & His San Francisco Jazz Band).
LP: . . . DC 12019

SAN FRANCISCO JAZZ (Murphy, Turk Jazz Band).
LP: . . . MMRC 114

SAN FRANCISCO JAZZ VOL.2 (Murphy, Turk Jazz Band).
LP: . . . MMRC 115

SAN FRANCISCO MEMORIES (Murphy, Turk Jazz Band).
LP: . . . MMRC 116
MC: . . . CMMRC 116

SEE'S CANDIES PRESENT SONGS OF CHRISTMAS (Murphy, Turk San Fransisco Jazz Band).
LP: . . . SC 1001

SOUTHERN STOMPS (Murphy, Turk Jazz Band).
LP: . . . SOS 1161

TURK AT CARNEGIE (Murphy, Turk Jazz Band).
LP: . . . SOS 1155

TURK MURPHY IN CONCERT VOL.1 (Murphy, Turk & His San Francisco Jazz Band).
LP: . . . GHB 91

TURK MURPHY IN CONCERT VOL.2 (Murphy, Turk & His San Francisco Jazz Band).
LP: . . . GHB 92

TURK MURPHY IN CONCERT VOL.3 (Murphy, Turk & His San Francisco Jazz Band).
LP: . . . GHB 93

TURK MURPHY'S JAZZ BAND (Murphy, Turk Jazz Band).
LP: . . . MMRC 106
MC: . . . CMMRC 106

TURK MURPHY'S SAN FRANCISCO JAZZ BAND (Murphy, Turk San Fransisco Jazz Band).
LP: . . . MMRC 105

Murphy, Walter
DISCOSYMPHONY.
LP: . . . FL 13506

THEMES FROM ET AND MORE (Murphy, Walter & His Orchestra).
Tracks: / E.T., Theme from / Jaws / Poltergeist / Superman / Close Encounters of the Third Kind / Star trek / Raiders of the lost ark.
LP: . . . MCF 3154
MC: . . . MCFC 3154

Murphy, Willy
MR MATURE.
LP: . . . ATR 1101

Murphy's Law
BACK WITH A BONG.
LP: . . . FILER 275
MC: . . . FILECT 275

Murray
INDELICACY.
LP: . . . WW 005

Murray, Amani
AMANI A.W. MURRAY.
Tracks: / Eternal triangle, The / Knarf / A.C Blues / Cheryl / Super funky blues / Ah leu cha / Blues, for the blues / Stranger on the shore / Everywhere calypso, The.
LP: . . . GRP 96331

Murray, Angus
REELY MOVING.
Tracks: / Jigs / Marches / Electronic accordion / Hornpipe / Continental waltz / Continental polka / Reels / Strathspey and reels.
MC: . . . AMC 101

Murray, Anne
BOTH SIDES NOW.
Tracks: / It's all over / For baby / Last thing on my mind / Both sides now / Paths of victory / All the time / Some birds / Buffalo in the park.
LP: . . . SHLP 123
MC: . . . SHTC 123
LP: . . . 20023
MC: . . . 40023
LP: . . . MTM 028

FAVOURITES.
MC: . . . 4XL 9180

HARMONY.
Tracks: / Are you still in love with me / Great divide, The / Tonight (I want to be in love) / Perfect strangers / Give me your love / It happens all the time / Harmony / Natural love / Without you.
LP: . . . EST 2035
MC: . . . TCEST 2035

HEART OVER MIND.
Tracks: / Once you've had it / Time don't run out on me / I don't think I'm ready for you (Film 'Stick.) / Let your heart do the talking / You haven't heard the last of me / Nobody loves me like you do (With Dave Loggins.) / I should know by now / Love you out of your mind / Take good care of my heart / Our love.
LP: . . . EJ 2402241

I'LL ALWAYS LOVE YOU.
Tracks: / I'll always love you / You've got me to hold on to / Stranger at my door / Good old song / Why don't you stick around / Broken hearted me / Easy love / Daydream believer / Wintery feeling / Lovers knot.
LP: . . . EST 12012

LITTLE GOOD NEWS.
Tracks: / That's not the way / I'm not afraid anymore / More we try / Little good news, A / Come on love / Come to me / Sentimental favourite / Just another woman in love / When i can't have you / Heart stealer.
LP: . . . EST7123011

NEW KIND OF FEELING.
Tracks: / Shadows in the moonlight / You've got what it takes / I just fall in love again / Take this heart / Yucatan cafe / You needed me / For no reason at all / Rainin' in my heart / That's why I love you / He's not you / Heaven is here.
LP: . . . EST 11849

SNOWBIRD.
Tracks: / Snowbird / Fire and rain / Break my mind / Just bidin' my time / Put your hand in the hand / Running / Musical friends / Get together / I'll be your baby tonight.
LP: . . . MFP 41 5738 1
MC: . . . MFP 41 5738 4
MC: . . . TCFA 3013
LP: . . . FA 3013

SOMEBODY'S WAITING.

Tracks: / Lucky me / You set my dreams to music / What's forever for / Do you think of me / French waltz / Daydream believer / I'm just happy to dance with you / Moon over Brooklyn / Nevertheless / Beginning to feel like home / Somebody's waiting.
MC: . . . . TC EST 1206 4

SOMETHING TO TALK ABOUT.
Tracks: / Now and forever (you and me) / Who's leaving who / My life's a dance / Call us fools / On and on / Heartaches / Reach for me / When you're gone / You never know / Gotcha.
LP: . . . . EST 2002
MC: . . . . TCEST 2002

SONGMAKERS ALMANAC (Murray, Anne & Graham Johnson).
LP: . . . . A 66176

SPECIAL COLLECTION.
Tracks: / Snowbird / Destiny / Danny's song / Love song, A / You won't see me / He thinks I still care / You needed me / I just fall in love again / Shadows in the moonlight / Broken hearted me / Daydream believer / Time don't run out on me / Just another woman in love / Now and forever (you and me) / I'd fall in love tonight / If I ever fall in love again / Little good news, A / When I fall / Another sleepless night / Blessed are the believers / Nobody loves me like you do.
LP: . . . . EST 2112
MC: . . . . TCEST 2112

TALK IT OVER IN THE MORNING.
LP: 1A 022 58168
MC: 1A 222 58168
LP: 022 58168
MC: 222 58168

TOGETHER (See under Campbell, Glen) (Murray, Anne & Glen Campbell).

VERY BEST OF ANNE MURRAY.
Tracks: / Snowbird / Danny's song / Love song / I just fall in love again / You won't see me / Shadows in the moonlight / Another sleepless night / Where do you go when you dream? / You needed me / Broken hearted me / Daydream believer / Could I have this dance? / I'm happy just to dance with you / Tennessee waltz / Cotton Jenny / Destiny.
LP: . . . . EMTV 31
MC: . . . . TCEMTV 31

WHERE DO YOU GO WHEN YOU DREAM.
Tracks: / Blessed are the believers / It should have been easy / If a heart must be broken / Bitter they are / It's all I can do / We don't have to hold out / Another sleepless night / Where do you go when you dream / Call me with the news / Only love.
LP: . . . . EST 12144

WITH ANNE MURRAY & OTHERS (See under Campbell, Glen).

Murray, Arthur

ARTHUR MURRAY SWINGS FOX TROTS (Murray, Arthur/Anthony, Ray & His Orchestra).
Tracks: / Poor butterfly / Froggy day, A / On the sunny side of the street / This year's kisses / I can't believe that you're in love with me / Can't get out of this mood / You stepped out of this dream / You're the cream in my coffee / I've never been in love before / Gang that sang heart of my heart / let's get lost / Love walked in.
LP: . . . . EMS 1247
MC: . . . . TCEMS 1247

Murray, Bert

ON THE FIDDLE.
MC: . . . . CWGR 091

Murray, David

CONCEPTUAL SAXOPHONE.
LP: . . . . SGC 1007

DAVID MURRAY.
2LP: . . . . SGC 1007/8

FLOWERS FOR ALBERT.
LP: . . . . IN 1026

HOME (Murray, David Octet).
Tracks: / Home / Santa Barbara and Crenshaw / Follies / Choctaw blues / Last of the hipmen / 3-D family.
LP: . . . . BSR 0055

I WANT TO TALK ABOUT YOU (Murray, David Quartet).
LP: 120105-1

INTERBOOGIEOLOGY.
LP: . . . . BSR 0018

LIVE AT SWEET BASIL, VOL 1 (Murray, David Big Band).
Tracks: / Lovers / Bechet's bounce / Silence / Duet for big band.
LP: . . . . BSR 0085

LONDON CONCERT, THE (Live at Collegiate Theatre).
2LP: . . . . SGC 1008/9

LOW CLASS CONSPIRACY.
LP: . . . . AD 5002

MING (Murray, David Octet).
Tracks: / Fast life / Hill, The / Ming / Jasvan / Dewey's circle.
LP: . . . . BSR 0045

ORGANIC SAXOPHONE.
LP: . . . . PALM 31

PENTHOUSE JAZZ VOL.1.
LP: . . . . RK 1887/4

SOLO-LIVE, VOL. 1.
LP: . . . . CECMA 1001

SOLO-LIVE, VOL. 2.
LP: . . . . CECMA 1002

SOLOMON'S SONS (Murray, David & James Newton).
LP: . . . . RK 16177/5

SUR-REAL SAXOPHONE.
LP: . . . . HZ 09

Murray, Gwen

ALL MY RICHES.
LP: . . . . DOVE 39

Murray, Jill

ARROW TO THE HEART (Mitchell, Nancy).
MCSET: . . . . CLT 1012

Murray, Niall

IRISH LOVE SONGS.
MC: . . . . BTC 308

Murray, Paul

IF DANIEL ISN'T COUNTRY (Murray, Paul & Easystreet).
MC: . . . . CASS EAS 103

Murray, Pauline

PAULINE MURRAY & THE INVISIBLE GIRLS (Murray, Pauline & The Invisible Girls).
LP: 2394277

STORM CLOUDS.
LP: . . . . ABB 10
LP: 8344451

Murray, Ruby

BEST OF RUBY MURRAY.
Tracks: / Softly softly / Happy days and lonely nights / Let me go, lover / Get well soon / Slowly with feeling / Real love / Scarlet ribbons / You are my first love / True love / My little corner of the world / Evermore / If anyone finds this, I love you / Heartbeat / Passing strangers / Honestly I do / Goodbye, Jimmy, goodbye / Dear daddy / Mr. Wonderful.
LP: . . . . OU 2084
MC: . . . . TCOU 2084

CHANGE YOUR MIND.
LP: . . . . PTLS 1040

EMI YEARS, THE: RUBY MURRAY (The Best of).
Tracks: / Softly softly / Bambino / Let me go lover / Scarlet ribbons / Little white lies / I'll come when you call / Tammy tell me true / Happy days and lonely nights / Heartbeat / Boy meets girl / Goodbye Jimmy goodbye / Evermore / It's the Irish in me / If anyone finds this I love you / True love / Mr. Wonderful.
LP: . . . . EMS 1339
MC: . . . . TCEMS 1339

HOUR OF RUBY MURRAY, AN.
Tracks: / Softly softly / Happy days and lonely nights / I'll come when you call / When Irish eyes are smiling / If anyone finds this, I love you / Heartbeat / Mr. Wonderful / Danny boy / You are my sunshine / Smile / When I grow too old to dream / Trottin' to the fair / Let me go lover / Let him go, let him tarry / Evermore / Real love / Get well soon / Nevertheless (I'm in love with you) / You are my first love / Goodbye Jimmy goodbye / Cockles and mussels / Button up your overcoat / Pennies from Heaven / Now is the hour.
MC: . . . . HR 8159

VERY BEST OF RUBY MURRAY.
Tracks: / Softly, softly / Heartbeat / Mr wonderful / Danny boy / Evermore / Real love / Get well soon / You are my first love / Nevertheless / If anyone finds this I love you / Let me go lover.
LP: . . . . MFP 4156441

Murray, Sunny

AN EVEN BREAK.
LP: . . . . AFF 30

APPLE CORES.
LP: . . . . PJ 1004

LIVE AT MOERS FESTIVAL.
LP: . . . . MOERS 01054

SUNNY MURRAY.
LP: . . . . ESP 1032

Murvin, Junior

BAD MAN POSSE.
Tracks: / Bad man posse.
LP: . . . . DAT 007

MUGGERS IN THE STREET.
Tracks: / Judas and Jesus / Champagne and wine / Jehovah's children / Strikes and demonstrations / Muggers in the street / Stop the crime / Jamaican girls / Hook, line and sinker / Think twice / I'll follow you.
LP: . . . . GREL 70

POLICE AND THIEVES.
LP: . . . . ILPS 9499

SIGNS AND WONDERS.
LP: . . . . LLLP 30

Musci, Oberto

URBAN AND TRIBAL PORTRAITS (Musci, Oberto & Giovanni Venosta).
LP: . . . . RER 37

Muscle Shoals Horns

BORN TO GET DOWN.
Tracks: / Born to get down / Breakdown / Bump de bump yo boodie / Get it up / Give it to me / Hustle to the music / Open up your heart / Where I'm coming from / Who's gonna love you.
LP: . . . . SHOT 001

Muscles

MUSCLES.
Tracks: / Music is our message / People / Love is all I've got / Muscle hustle / I'm gonna synthesise you / Love fire / No smoke without fire / Jungle strut / Love is you.
LP: . . . . BBR 1001

Muse All Stars

BUDDY TATE AND THE MUSE ALL STARS (see under Tate, Buddy).

Musette

MUSIQUE EN ENVASION.
Tracks: / La java / C'est un mauvais garcon / La plus bath des javas / Ca gaze / Aubade d'oiseaux / La java des dockers / Perles de cristal / Java te revoila / La fille de Dolores / La cumparsita / Le p'tit bal du samedi soir / Ele gato montes / Rue de Lappe / Reine de musette / Ca tourne rond / Accordeon.
MC: 811 958-4

Museum of Devotion

TO THE PINK PERIOD.
LP: . . . . ARTY 6

WANTS VERSUS NEEDS.
LP: . . . . ARTY 029

Music...

MUSICAL HIGHLIGHTS FROM PHILARMONIC 1979 (Various artists).
LP: . . . . UAG 30281

Music Box

MUSIC BOX (Film Soundtrack) (Various artists).
Tracks: / Ann's theme: *Various artists* / Federal building: *Various artists* / Ann studies documents: *Various* artists / Scar, The: *Various artists* / Mirror, The: *Various artists* / Music box: *Various artists*/ Blood red Danube: *Various artists* / Departure from court: *Various artists* / Journey to Budapest: *Various* artists / Ann and Georgina in Talbot: *Various artists* / Remembering: *Various artists* / Newspaper, The: *Various artists*.
LP: . . . . VS 5248
MC: . . . . VSC 5248

Music Emporium

MUSIC EMPORIUM.
LP: . . . . PSYCHO 11

Music For...

MUSIC FOR NATIONS SINGLES ALBUM (Various artists).
2LP: . . . . MFN 71
MC: . . . . TMFN 71

MUSIC FOR ROYAL OCCASIONS (Various artists).
MC: . . . . KCSP 500

MUSIC FOR ROYAL WEDDINGS Various artists (Various artists).
LP: . . . . CBS 73285
MC: 40 73285

Music For Pleasure

BLACKLANDS.
LP: . . . . WHLP 6

INTO THE RAIN.
Tracks: / Light / Switchback / Nostalgia / Time / New day / Lost detail / Winter scene / Aim to life / Warehouse / Underworld.
LP: . . . . POLS 1070
MC: . . . . POLSC 1070

Music for Relaxation

MUSIC FOR RELAXATION (Various artists).
MC: . . . . C 606

Music From...

MUSIC FROM GREAT ROYAL OCCASIONS (Various artists).
LP: . . . . REC 470
MC: . . . . ZCM 470

MUSIC FROM UTOPIA (Various artists).
Tracks: / Old Fulham fertility: *Various artists* / Irden: *Various artists* / Gravity's angel: *Various artists*/ East wind: *Various artists* / Naturliche liebe: *Various artists* / Constellation (part 1): *Various artists*/ Kommunikation hipp-ipp: *Various artists* / Conditioning: *Various artists* / Speed display: *Various artists*/ High on tech: *Various artists* / Eh-ei-joa: *Various artists* / Happy Grenada: *Various artists* / Expedition extra: *Various artists* / Cielouvert: *Various artists* / Ganna plasmid: *Various artists* / Silicon valley: *Various artists* / Interne 1: *Various artists* / Morgen und ein spaziergang: *Various artists* / Tiquetaque: *Various artists* / Annabella: *Various artists* / Exotic defiler: *Various artists* / Later bagatelles 1 & 2: *Various artists* / Hotel reform: *Various artists* / Pujaparwata: *Various artists* / Selig, diegrerchtigkeit willen - tolgt werden: *Various artists*.
LP: 6 28650
LP: . . . . 628650 DW

WICKED LADY (Various artists).
LP: . . . . A 0073

Music Hall

COVENT GARDEN SHOW (Aba Daba) (Various artists).
Tracks: / After the ball: *Holland, Elaine* / Little bit of cucumber, A: *Spraggon, Peter* / All round my hat: *Williams, Bronwen* / I always say hello to a flower: *Heawood, John* / If it wasn't for the 'ouses in between: *Pilgrim, Christine*/ When the summer comes again: *Warwick, Norman* / They're all very fine and large: *Various artists* / That is love: *Warwick, Norman* / Life upon the wicked stage: *Holland, Elaine & Christine Pilgrim* / Have some madeira, m'dear: *Spraggon, Peter* / I want to sing in opera: *Williams, Bronwen* / Fallen star, A: *Heawood, John* / He's all right when you know him: *Pilgrim, Christine* / I fancy I've seen you before: *Heawood, John* / It's all right in the Summertime: *Holland, Elaine* / On Mother Kelly's doorstep: *Warwick, Norman* / Come home, father: *Williams, Bronwen*.
MC: . . . . TT 006

DOWN AT THE OL' BULL AND BUSH (Various artists).
MC: . . . . AM 40

GOLDEN AGE OF MUSIC HALL (Various artists).
Tracks: / Wait till the work comes round: *Elen, Gus* / Riding on top of a motor car: *Victoria, Vesta* / My old dutch: *Chevalier, Albert* / When I take my morning promenade: *Lloyd, Marie* / Robin, The: *Leno, Dan* / My first cigar: *Bradfield, Louis* / Coster girl in Paris: *Lloyd, Marie* / Bang went the chance of a lifetime: *Robey, George* / Where's the count?: *Roberts, Arthur* / When I marry Amelia: *Lytton, Henry* / Fallen star, A: *Chevalier, Albert* / Tower of London: *Leno, Dan* / Territorial, The: *Little Tich* / Anona: *Forde, Florrie*.
LP: . . . . RHA 6014

GOLDEN YEARS OF MUSIC HALL, THE (Various artists).
MC: . . . . CSDL 380

LET'S ALL GO TO MUSIC HALL (Ted Ray & other artists) (Various artists).
2LP: . . . . ZSW 535/6

MUSIC HALL FAVOURITES (Various artists).
MCSET: . . . . DTO 10210

MUSIC HALL TO VARIETY VOL 1 (MATINEE) Various artists (Various artists).
LP: . . . . SH 145

MUSIC HALL TO VARIETY VOL 2 (FIRST HOUSE) Various artists (Various artists).
LP: . . . . SH 149

MUSIC HALL TO VARIETY VOL 3 (SECOND HOUSE) Various artists (Various artists).
LP: . . . . SH 150

MUSIC HALL (TOP OF THE BILL) (Various artists).
LP: . . . . SHB 22

THEY PLAYED THE HACKNEY EMPIRE (Various artists).
LP: . . . . BUR 024
MC: . . . . 4 BUR 024

2LP: . . . . RFLD 23

THEY PLAYED THE HIPPODROME (Various artists).
Tracks: / Japanese sandman: *Adler, Larry* / Somebody stole my gal: *Adler, Larry* / It all belongs to me: *O'Shea, Tessie* / Mister Brown of London town: *Lane, Lupino* / Nice kind Sergeant-Major: *Long, Norman* / Blasted oak, The: *Wallace, Nellie* / Crest of a wave: *Reader, Ralph* / Leaning on a lamp post: *Formby, George* / Underneath the arches: *Scala, Primo & His Banjo & Accordian Band* / Sandy furnishes the home (on hire purchase): *Powell, Sandy* & Company / When you play with fire: *Chester, Charlie & His Gang* / Singing a vagabond song: *O'Connor, Cavan*/ I've got sixpence: *Willmott, Bertha* / In all the world: *James, Dick* / Theophilus and his operation: *Fletcher*, Cyril / Fan: *Fletcher, Cyril* / I like riding on a choo choo: *Sarony, Leslie* / Won't we 'ave a party when it's over: *Waters, Elsie & Doris (Gert & Daisy)* / Reflections on the water (looking down at me): *Browne, Sam*/ I wouldn't take a million for the old grey mare: *Campbell, Big Bill & His Rocky Mountain Rhythm* / We three: *Levis*, Carroll & Eddie Lee / Give me you: *Vaughan, Frankie* / Put your shoes on Lucy: *Shelton, Anne* / Gipsy, The: *Sentimentalists* / Only a glass of champagne: *Handley, Tommy* / Dream: *Dennis, Johnny & His Novelty Swinget*/ My heart isn't in it: *Davis, Beryl* / I'm in love with two sweethearts: *Bonn, Issy* / As time goes by: *Hall*, Adelaide / No one but you: *Whitley, Eric & Joan Butler* / Breathless: *Various artists* / Beware: *Wisdom*, Norman / You're not alone: *Roza, Lita* / I still believe: *Lewis, Archie* / Story of Tina: *Kramer & Wolmer*/ Yes, I'll be here: *Goff, Reggie* / Same old crowd, The: *Wheeler, Jimmy* / Garden in the rain: *Kunz, Charlie*/ Danger ahead: *Kunz, Charlie* / I'll make up for everything: *Kunz, Charlie* / Papa's in bed with his breeches on: *Hatchett's Swingtette* / Don't ever walk in the shadows: *Flanagan & Allen* / Murder: *Gonella, Nat & His New Georgians*.
MCSET: . . . . RECDC 11
2LP: . . . . RECDL 11

THEY PLAYED THE PALLADIUM (Various artists).
MCSET: . . . . DTO 10213
LP: . . . . RFLD 30

THIS IS LONDON (Various artists).
Tracks: / Yeomen of the guard: *Various artists* / With her head tucked underneath her arm: *Various artists* / Old London: *Various artists* / Oranges and lemons: *Various artists* / Piccadilly: *Various artists* / Wot cher!: *Various artists* / Down at the old Bull and Bush: *Various artists* / My old Dutch: *Various artists*/ Queen's horses: *Various artists* / Knightsbridge march: *Various artists* / Nightingale sang in Berkeley Square: *Various artists* / Cockney capers: *Various artists* / Streets of London: *Various artists* / Round the Marble Arch: *Various artists* / Visit to a London East End pub: *Various artists* / London town: *Various artists*.
LP: . . . . SPA 593
MC: . . . . KCSP 593

WORLD OF MUSIC HALL (Various artists).
LP: . . . . SPA 81

YOUR OWN, YOUR VERY OWN (Stars of the music hall) (Various artists).
Tracks: / Don't do it again, Matilda: *Champion, Harry* / Every little movement: *Lloyd, Marie* / Two lovely black eyes: *Coburn, Charles* / Mrs. Kelly: *Leno, Dan* / One of the boys: *Formby, George (Senior)* / Jocular joker, The: *Chergwin, G.H.* / Let's all go where all the crowd goes: *Williams, Billy* / Photo of the girl I left behind me, The: *Merson, Billy* / I'm twenty-one today: *Pleasante, Jack* / Flower of the heather: *Lauder, Harry*/ If the managers only thought the same as mother: *Scott, Maidie* / She sells seashells: *Bard, Wilkie* / By the sea: *Sheridan, Mark* / Don't have any more, Mrs Moore: *Morris, Lily* / Dinah: *Elliott, G.H.* / Hello, sunshine, hello: *Whelan, Albert*.
LP: . . . . AJA 5004
MC: . . . . ZC AJA 5004

Music Is My...

MUSIC IS MY OCCUPATION (See under Ska...) (Various artists).

Music Lovers

MUSIC LOVERS (Film Soundtrack) (Various artists).
Tracks: / Overture - Russian fair: *Various artists* / Piano concerto performance: *Various artists* / Tchaikovsky playing his new opera: *Various artists* / Ballet in St. Petersburg Park: *Various artists* / Night train to Moscow: *Various artists* / Canal sequence: *Various artists* / Dreams at Brailov: *Various artists* / Firework sequence: *Various artists* / Success: *Various artists* / Nina's madness and Tchaikovsky's death: *Various artists*.
LP: . . . . UAS 29134

Music Machine

BEST OF MUSIC MACHINE.
LP: . . . . RNLP 119

TURN ON THE MUSIC MACHINE.
Tracks: / Talk talk / Trouble / Cherry Cherry / Taxman / Some other drum / Masculine intuition / People in me, The / See see rider / Wrong / 96 tears / Come on in / Hey Joe.
LP: . . . . WIK 17

Music Maker

LIVE AT THE HALF WAY TREE.
LP: . . . . DHS 5

Music Man

MUSIC MAN (ORIGINAL ISSUE) (London cast) (Various artists).
LP: . . . . CLP 1444

MUSIC MAN, THE (Film soundtrack) (Various artists).
LP: . . . . WB 4066

MUSIC MAN, THE (FILM) (Original Soundtrack) (Various artists).
LP: . . . . BS 1459
MC: W5 1459

Music Maniac...

MUSIC MANIAC GIMMICK COMPILATION (Various artists).
LP: . . . . MMLP 023

Music Master..

1990 MUSIC MASTER TOP 10 VOL 2 (Various artists).
LP: . . . . DSR 9627

MUSIC MASTER PRESENTS TOP 10 VOL.2 (Various artists).
LP: . . . . MMLP 0020

Music Of....

MUSIC OF O'CAROLAN (Various artists).
LP: . . . . SHAN 95009

Music Of Amadeus

MUSIC OF AMADEUS (Various artists).
LP: 29094
MC: 49094

Music Of Ivor Novello

MUSIC OF IVOR NOVELLO (See under Ivor Novello) (Various artists).

Music Teacher

MUSIC TEACHER (LE MAITRE DE MUSIQUE) (Film soundtrack) (Various artists).
Tracks: / Cortigiani, vil razza dannata: *Various artists* / Alcandro, lo confessa...non so d'onde viene: *Various artists*/ Waltz: *Various artists* / Das lied von der erde: *Various artists* / Symphony no. 4 in g major: *Various artists*/ Deh vieni alla finestra: *Various artists* / Wohl denk ich oft: *Various artists* / Du meine seele, du mein herz: *Various artists* / Stille tranen: *Various artists* / Sorgio, o padre: *Various artists* / An die musik, d547: *Various artists* / Caro nome: *Various artists* / Tanton duol, A: *Various artists* / Ich bin der welt abhanden: *Various artists*.
LP: . . . . PCOM 1109
MC: . . . . PTLC 1109

Music Without...

MUSIC WITHOUT FRONTIERS VOL.1 (See under Jazz) (Various artists).

MUSIC WITHOUT FRONTIERS VOL.2 (See under Jazz) (Various artists).

Musica Miscellanea

MUSICA MISCELLANEA (Various artists).
MC: . . . . CSAR 40

Musica Sveciae

CHILDREN'S SONGS (Musica Sveciae - Sweden).
LP: . . . . PHONT 7414-5

Musical...

CARMEN JONES (Original Broadway cast) (Various artists).
LP: . . . . MCA 1531
MC: . . . . MCAC 1531

CARMEN JONES (1954 Film soundtrack) (Various artists).
Tracks: / Overture: *Various artists* / Opening medley: *Various artists* / Dat's love (habanera): *Various* artists / You talk jus' like my maw: *Various artists* / Dere's a cafe on the corner: *Various artists* / Dis flower: *Various artists* / Beat out dat rhythm on a drum: *Various artists* / Stan' up an' fight: *Various artists*/ Whizzin' away along de track: *Various artists* / Card song: *Various artists* / My Joe: *Various artists*/ Duet and finale: *Various artists*.
LP: AHL1 0046
LP: . . . . BL 80046
MC: 1881.4
MC: . . . . BK 80046

CARMEN JONES (Film Soundtrack) (Various artists).
Tracks: / Overture: *Various artists* / Dere's a cafe on de corner: *Various artists* / You talk jus' like my man: *Various artists* / Dat's love (habanera): *Various artists* / Dis flower: *Various artists* / Beat out dat rhythm on a drum: *Various artists* / Stan' up an' fight: *Various artists* / Whizzin' away along de track: *Various artists* / Card song: *Various artists* / My Joe: *Various artists* / Finale: *Various artists*.
LP: . . . . OU 2005

Musical Boxes

MECHANICAL OPERA (See under Opera...).

MUSICAL BOX DANCES (Various).
MC: . . . . CSDL 359

THREE DISC SYMPHONION (Various).
Tracks: / Tuxedo polka / Old folks at home / After the ball / Monastery bells / Cuckoo's couplet / Carnival of Venice / Bedouin love song / Empire and the Tivoli, The / Vienna hearts / Last rose of summer / Liberty bell / No place like home / Blue Danube / Turkish patrol march / Gavotte d'amour / Hail smiling morn.
LP: . . . . SDL 346
MC: . . . . CSDL 346

Musical Youth

DIFFERENT STYLE.
LP: . . . . YOULP 2
MC: . . . . YOUC 2

UNCONDITIONAL LOVE (See under Summer, Donna) (Musical Youth & Donna Summer).

YOUTH OF TODAY.
Tracks: / Pass the dutchie / Youth of today.
LP: . . . . YOULP 1
MC: . . . . YOUC 1

Musicals...

ANDREW LLOYD WEBBER COLLECTION, THE (Various artists).
Tracks: / Starlight express: *Wayne, Carl* / Unexpected song: *Jones, Paul* / Macavity: The mystery cat: *Lawrence, Stephanie* / Memory: *Lawrence, Stephanie* / Gus: The theatre cat: *Jones, Paul* / Pumping iron: *Conrad*, Jess / Tell me on a Sunday: *Wayne, Carl* / I don't know how to love him: *Hendley, Fiona* / Any dream will do: *Conrad, Jess* / Love changes everything: *Lawrence, Stephanie* / All I ask of you: *Lawrence, Stephanie*/ Oh what a circus: *Conrad, Jess* / Wishing you were somehow here again: *Lawrence, Stephanie*.
MC: . . . . PWKMC 4065

BEST FROM THE MGM MUSICALS (Various artists).
Tracks: / Singin' in the rain: *Kelly, Gene* / Get happy: *Garland, Judy* / Thank heaven for little girls: *Chevalier*, Maurice / Lady is a tramp, The: *Horne, Lena* / I got rhythm: *Kelly, Gene* / Stranger in paradise: *Blyth*, Ann/Vic Damone / I wish I were in love again: *Rooney, Mickey/ Judy Garland* / Ol' man river: *Warfield, William*/ 'S wonderful: *Kelly, Gene/ Georges Guetary* / Over the rainbow: *Garland, Judy* / Bless your beautiful hide: *Keel*, Howard / Make believe: *Grayson, Kathryn/Howard Keel/Ann Miller/Tommy Rall* / Make 'em laugh: *O'Connor, Donald*/ Easter parade: *Garland, Judy & Fred Astaire* / Rose Marie: *Keel, Howard* / Couple of swells, A: *Garland*, Judy & Fred Astaire / Almost like being in love: *Kelly, Gene* / Sometimes I'm happy: *Powell, Jane/Vic Damone*/ Steppin' out with my baby: *Astaire, Fred* / That's entertainment: *Astaire, Fred/Nanette Fabray/Jack Buchanan*.
LP: . . . . EMTV 56
MC: . . . . TCEMTV 56

FIVE GUYS NAMED MOE (Original London Cast) (Various artists).
MC: . . . . CASTC 23
LP: . . . . CAST 23

MAGIC FROM THE MUSICALS (Various artists).
Tracks: / Only you: *Blessed, Brian* / Good morning starshine: *Clark, Petula* / If I were a rich man: *Topol*/ Luck be a lady: *Jones, Paul* / Memory: *Clark, Petula* / Send in the clowns: *Webb, Marti* / Impossible dream, The: *Blessed, Brian* / Bless your beautiful hide: *Keel, Howard* / Thank heaven for little girls: *Topol*/ Lullaby of Broadway: *Jones, Paul* / If he walked into my life: *Webb, Marti* / Annie get your gun medley: *Keel, Howard* / I don't know how to love him: *Webb, Marti* / I've grown accustomed to her face: *Jones, Paul*.
MC: . . . . MCTC 012

MAGIC FROM THE MUSICALS (See under Magic of...) (Various artists).

MAGIC MOMENTS FROM THE MUSICALS VOL. 1 (See under Magic Moments...) (Various artists).

MAGIC MOMENTS FROM THE MUSICALS VOL. 2 (Great MGM Stars) (Various artists).
Tracks: / Thou swell: *Allyson, June* / More than you know: *Martin, Tony* / From this moment on: *Miller, Ann/Bobby* Van/Tommy Rall/Bob Fosse / I remember it well: *Chevalier, Maurice & Hermione Gingold* / March, march: *Kelly, Gene/Dan* Dailey/Michael Kidd / Touch of your hand/Lovely to look at: *Keel, Howard/Kathryn Grayson* / I love you so much: *Dahl*, Arlene / I know that you know: *Powell, Jane/Vic Damone* / Chiribiribee (ciribiribin): *Powell, Jane/Vic Damone*/ Can't help lovin' dat man: *Gardner, Ava* / Stereophonic sound: *Astaire, Fred/Janis Paige* / Night they invented champagne, The: *Caron, Leslie/Louis Jordan/Hermione Gingold* / Too darn hot: *Miller, Ann* / Why is love so crazy: *Keel, Howard* / Leave it to Jane and Cleopatterer: *Allyson, June* / I'll go home with Bonnie Jean: *Johnson, Van*/ John Gustafson / London is London: *Clark, Petula* / Aba daba honeymoon: *Carpenter, Carleton/Debbie Reynolds*/ Merry widow waltz: *Lamas, Fernando/ Trudy Erwin* / Wonderful, wonderful day: *Powell, Jane* / Road to paradise/Will you remember, sweetheart: *Damone, Vic/ Powell, Jane*.
LP: . . . . LPMGM 33
MC: . . . . TCMGM 33

MAGIC MOMENTS FROM THE MUSICALS VOL. 1 (Great MGM Stars) (Various artists).
Tracks: / I'll build a stairway to paradise: *Guetary, Georges* / Yesterdays: *Grayson, Kathryn* / Olive tree, The: *Keel, Howard* / Good morning: *O'Connor, Donald/Gene Kelly/Debbie Reynolds* / Who's sorry now: *De Haven, Gloria*/ Lover come back to me: *Martin, Tony* / Brush up your Shakespeare: *Wynn, Keenan/James Whitmore* / Baubles, bangles and beads: *Blyth, Ann* / Ol' man river: *Warfield, William* / Manhattan: *Rooney, Mickey* / Lady is a tramp, The: *Horne, Lena* / Life upon the wicked stage: *Champion, Marge & Gower* / New sun in the sky/I guess I'll have to change my plans: *Adams, India/Fred Astaire & Jack Buchanan* / Shakin' the blues away: *Miller, Ann* / Night of my nights: *Damone, Vic* / Sometimes I'm happy: *Powell, Jane/Vic Damone* / Mack the black: *Garland, Judy*/ Where's the rainbow: *Southern, Ann* / Thank heaven for little girls: *Chevalier, Maurice* / Bill: *Gardner, Ava* / Serenade: *Olvis, William*.
LP: . . . . LPMGM 32
MC: . . . . TCMGM 32

MUSICAL WORLD OF RICHARD RODGERS (Various artists).
Tracks: / My funny valentine: *Various artists* / There's a small hotel: *Various artists* / I could write a book: *Various artists* / Falling in love with love: *Various artists* / Lady is a tramp, The: *Various artists*/ This can't be love: *Various artists* / Most beautiful girl in the world: *Various artists* / Bewitched: *Various* artists / Where or when: *Various artists* / Some enchanted evening: *Various artists* / Oh what a beautiful morning: *Various artists* / Slaughter on Tenth Avenue: *Various artists* / Shall we dance: *Various artists*/ My favourite things: *Various artists* / Carousel waltz: *Various artists* / Getting to know you: *Various* artists / Do I love you: *Various artists* / Surrey with the fringe on top: *Various artists* / I enjoy being a girl: *Various artists* / Sound of music, The: *Various artists*.
2LP: . . . . CBS 22103

Musichini, Alain

PRINCE DE L'ACCORDEON.
LP: . . . . ILD 42019

Musicians for Missions

HEART CRY.
LP: . . . . WST R 9673
MC: . . . . WST C 9673

Musicians Of Bremen

MUSICIANS OF BREMEN, THE (well loved tales age up to 9) (Unknown narrator(s)).
MC: . . . . PLB 68

Musicians Of The Nile

LUXOR TO ISNA.
Tracks: / Al bahr al gharam wasah (love is a vast river) / Zarhrafat al sai'id / Ya tir a la shadjarah / Horse steps / Al nahla al ali / Kol elle oalboh ankawa / Yunes wa azizah / Al aqsur isna.
LP: . . . . RWLP 8
MC: . . . . RWMC 8

Musique Zen
MUSIQUE ZEN Various artists (Various artists).
LP: AV 4501
MC: AV 5501

Muskat, Thomas
HAMMOND PARTY.
Tracks: / Save your kisses for me / Una paloma blanca / When will I see you again / Love will keep us together / My melody of love / Feelings / Lady Antoinette / Last farewell, The / I'm a travelling man / Don't cry no tears / Kung fu fighting / Sailing / Doctor's orders / Hello and goodbye.
LP: EMB 31323

Muskrats
INSIGHT.
LP: SFA 087

MUSKRATS, THE.
MC: VCA 074
LP: SRTZ 76359

Muslimgauze
BLINDED HORSES.
LP: LIMITED 002

BUDDHIST ON FIRE.
LP: LOOSE 008

COUP D'ETAT.
LP: PDC 005

FLAJELATA.
LP: LIMITED 003

HAJJ.
LP: LIMITED 004

HUNTING OUT WITH AN ARIEL EYE.
LP: LE 1

JAZIRAT-UL-ARAB.
LP: LIMITED 005

RAPE OF PALESTINE, THE.
Tracks: / Rape of Palestine, The.
LP: LIMITED 007

UZI.
LP: 081102

Musselwhite, Charlie
ACE OF HARPS.
Tracks: / Blues overtook me, The / She may be your woman / River hip mama / Leaving your town / Hello pretty baby / Mean ole frisco / Kiddeo / Yesterdays / Hangin' on / My road lies in darkness.
LP: AL 4781

CAMBRIDGE BLUES.
Tracks: / Miss Bessie / Big legged woman / Key to the highway / Take a little walk with me / Up and down / Need my baby / Skinny woman.
LP: BLUH 005

CHARLIE MUSSELWHITE.
MC: C 203

CURTAIN CALL (Musselwhite, Charlie & the Dynatones).
Tracks: / Curtain call blast off / Everybody needs somebody / I'm goin' home / Walk right in / This little voice / She used to be beautiful / Christo redemptor / Tick tock / Trouble no more.
LP: RL 044

GOIN' BACK DOWN SOUTH.
LP: ARHOOLIE 1074

HARMONICA ACCORDING TO CHARLIE MUSSELWHITE, THE.
LP: SNKF 147

MELLOW DEE.
Tracks: / Hey Miss Bessie / Need my baby / I'll get a break / Peach orchard mama / Ask me nice / Come back baby / Coming home baby / Baby please don't go / Lotsa poppa / Steady on your trail / Can't you see what you're doing to me / Christo redemptor.
LP: CCR 1013

MEMPHIS TENNESSEE.
Tracks: / She used to be beautiful / I got to go / Memphis Tennessee / One mint julep / Blues / Wolf, The / Temperature / Arkansas boogie / Willow weep for me / Trouble no more / Done somebody wrong.
LP: CCR 1008

TAKIN' MY TIME.
LP: ARHOOLIE 1056

TELL ME WHERE HAVE ALL THE GOOD TIMES GONE.
LP: BR 103

Musso, Vido
ONE NIGHT STAND.
LP: JLP 1026

THREE KENTON'S BE BOPPERS GROUPS 1947-50 (see Ferguson,Maynard/Vido Musso/Eddie Safranski) (Musso, Vido / Maynard Ferguson / Eddie Safranski).

Mussolini Headkick
BLOOD ON THE FLAG.
LP: WD 6663

GET OUT.
LP: WD 6664

THEMES FOR VIOLENT RETRIBUTION.
LP: WD 6661

Mussolini: His Part...
MUSSOLINI: HIS PART IN MY DOWNFALL (see Milligan, Spike) (Milligan, Spike).

Mussolini, Romano
JAZZ ALBUM.
LP: BBLP 8234

Mussorgsky (composer)
PICTURES AT AN EXHIBITION (See under Solti, Sir George) (Chicago Symphony Orchestra).

PICTURES AT AN EXHIBITION (Jones, Philip Brass Ensemble).
MC: 4250224

Mussulli, Boots
LITTLE MAN.
LP: AFF 67

Mustin, Dene
DENE MUSTIN SINGS FOR HER FRIENDS.
LP: AP 93

DENE MUSTIN SINGS YOUR REQUESTS.
LP: AP 134

Musto & Bones
FUTURE IS OURS, THE.
LP: CBLP 5
MC: CBMC 5

Musto, Tommy
DANCE, MADNESS AND THE BROOKLYN GROOVE (See under Bones, Frankie) (Musto, Tommy & Frankie Bones).

Musy, Jean
FEW AND FAR BETWEEN.
Tracks: / Atalante / Remorse (pourquoi j'ai le mal de toi) / Radiance (child in the rain) / I have no hold on you / Towards morning (La nuit adultere) / Few and far between / Seule a seule.
LP: K 50081

Muta Baruka
ANY WHICH WAY... FREEDOM.
LP: GREL 131
MC: GREEN 131

MYSTERY UNFOLDS,THE.
Tracks: / Leaders speak / Dub poem / Revolutionary words / My great shun / Old cut bruk / Bun dung Babylon / Mystery unfolds / Dis poem / Famine injection / Eyes of liberty / Walkin' on gravel / Voice.
LP: SHAN 43037

OUT CRY.
LP: SHAN 43023
MC: SHANC 43023

Mutant
MUTANT (Original soundtrack) (Various artists).
LP: STV 81209

Mute Beat
JAPANESE DUB.
MC: A 143

Mute Drivers
20000 MILLIONAIRES.
Tracks: / Twenty thousand millionaires / House / Don't / Into the sewer / Motorway, motorway / Don't stop let's go.
LP: MD 002

EVERYONE.
LP: BND 4LP

STOP OR I'LL SCREAM.
LP: MD 003

WAITING FOR WORLD WAR III.
2LP: MD 004

Mutiny!
MUTINY! (Original London cast) (Various artists).
LP: STAR 2261
MC: STAC 2261

Mutiny On The Bounty
MUTINY ON THE BOUNTY (Original soundtrack) (Various artists).
LP: MCA 25007
MC: MCAC 25007

MUTINY ON THE BOUNTY/TARAS BULBA (Various artists).
Tracks: / Mutiny on the bounty theme: *Various artists* / Portsmouth harbour: *Various artists* / Storm at sea: *Various artists* / Girls and sailors: *Various artists* / Mutiny, The: *Various artists* / Follow me (Tahitian): *Various artists* / Leaving harbour: *Various artists* / Arrival in Tahiti: *Various artists* / Pitcairn island: *Various artists* / Follow me (English): *Various artists* / Outrigger chase: *Various artists* / Christian's death: *Various artists* / Taras bulba (overture): *Various artists* / Birth of Andrei, The: *Various artists* / Sleighride, The: *Various artists* / Chase at night: *Various artists* / No retreat: *Various* artists / Ride to Dubno, The: *Various artists* / Wishing star, The - pastorale: *Various artists* / Black plague: *Various artists* / Taras' pledge: *Various artists* / Battle of Dubno and finale: *Various artists.*
LP: LPMGM 26
LP: 794 876 1
MC: TCMGM 26
MC: 794 876 4

Mutton Gun
AMPLEXUS.
Tracks: / Aimless / Thanks, but no thanks / Don't talk to your mother like that / Cutfleisch / Sound track / Kansas / Ruby / Das lied fur dong / Aldgate / Poor unfortunate lovers.
LP: MINT 1

Mutukudzi, Oliver
SUGAR PIE.
LP: CSLP 5001
MC: ZCSLC 5001

Muzsikas
BLUES FOR TRANSYLVANIA.
LP: HNBL 1350
MC: HNBC 1350

HUNGARIAN FOLK MUSIC.
LP: SLPX 18121
MC: MK 18121

PRISONER'S SONG, THE (Muzsikas/ Marta Sebestyen).
LP: HNBL 1341
MC: HNBC 1341

Mwendo Dawa
DIMENSIONS.
Tracks: / Ostinato song / Dimension C / Loop, The / Without shoes / Mwendo / Chords / Blocks.
LP: DRLP 123

HUMAN WALK.
LP: DRLP 155

STRAIGHT LINES.
LP: MVLP 10

M.X. Machine
MANIC PANIC.
LP: GWLP 40

My Beautiful
MY BEAUTIFUL LAUNDERETTE/ SAMMY & ROSY GET LAID/WISH YOU WERE (Original soundtrack) (Various artists).
LP: A 369
MC: C 369

My Bloody Valentine
ECSTASY.
LP: LAZY 08

ECSTASY AND WINE.
LP: LAZY 12

ISN'T ANYTHING.
LP: CRELP 040
MC: CCRELP 040

My Dad Is Dead
LET'S SKIP THE DETAILS.
LP: HMS 109
MC: HMS 109C

My Demon Lover
MY DEMON LOVER (Original Soundtrack) (Various artists).
LP: STV 81322

My Fair Lady
MY FAIR LADY (Original London stage cast) (Various artists).
Tracks: / Overture: *Various artists* / Why can't the English?: *Various artists* / Wouldn't it be loverly?: *Various* artists / With a little bit of luck: *Various artists* / I'm an ordinary man: *Various artists* / Just you wait: *Various artists* / Rain in Spain, The: *Various artists* / I could have danced all night: *Various artists*/ Ascot gavotte: *Various artists* / On the street where you live: *Various artists* / You did it: *Various artists*/ Show me: *Various artists* / Get me to the church on time: *Various artists* / Hymn to him: *Various artists*/ Without you: *Various artists* / I've grown accustomed to her face: *Various artists.*
LP: CBS 32671
MC: 40 32671

MY FAIR LADY (Film soundtrack) (Various artists).
Tracks: / Overture: *Various artists* / Why can't the English?: *Various artists* / Wouldn't it be loverly?: *Various* artists / I'm just an ordinary man: *Various artists* / With a little bit of luck: *Various artists* / Just you wait: *Various artists* / Rain in Spain, The: *Various artists* / I could have danced all night: *Various* artists / Ascot gavotte: *Various artists* / On the street where you live: *Various artists* / You did it: *Various* artists / Show me: *Various artists* / Get me to the church on time: *Various artists* / Hymn to him: *Various artists* / Without you: *Various artists* / I've grown accustomed to her face: *Various artists.*
LP: CBS 32043
MC: 40 32043
LP: BPG 72237

MY FAIR LADY (Studio recording) (Various artists).
Tracks: / Overture...Why can't the English: *Various artists* / Wouldn't it be loverly: *Various artists* / With a little bit of luck: *Various artists* / I'm an ordinary man: *Various artists* / Just you wait: *Various artists*/ Rain in Spain, The: *Various artists* / I could have danced all night: *Various artists* / Ascot Gavotte: *Various* artists / On the street where you live: *Various artists* / Embassy waltz. The: *Various artists* / You did it: *Various artists* / Show me: *Various artists* / Get me to the church on time: *Various artists* / Hymn to Him: *Various artists* / Without you: *Various artists* / I've grown accustomed to her face: *Various artists.*
LP: MFL 1
MC: MFLC 1

MY FAIR LADY (Original Broadway cast - 1959) (Various artists).
MC: PST 02015

MY FAIR LADY (Original 1956 recording) (Various artists).
MC: JST 05090

MY FAIR LADY (ORIGINAL ISSUE) (Original Broadway cast) (Various artists).
LP: RBL 1000

MY FAIR LADY (ORIGINAL ISSUE) (Broadway cast) (Various artists).
LP: BPG 68001

My Friend The
MY FRIEND THE PROFESSOR (Andrews, Lucilla) (Wallace, Jean).
MCSET: SOUND 13

My Girl In...(bk)
MY GIRL IN SKIN TIGHT JEANS (Jarvis, Martin (nar)).
MC: TTDMC 409

My Last Duchess...(bk)
MY LAST DUCHESS & OTHER POEMS (Robert Browning) (Mason, James (nar)).
MC: 1201

My Life With...
I SEE GOOD SPIRITS, I SEE BAD SPIRITS (My Life With The Thrill Kill Kult).
LP: WAXUK 056 LP

My Name Is Nobody
MY NAME IS NOBODY (Film soundtrack) (Various artists).
LP: C'BUS 101

My One and Only
MY ONE AND ONLY (Original Cast Recording) (Various artists).
LP: 7801110 1
MC: 7801110 4

My Prerogative
MY PREROGATIVE: WILD APACHE ALL STARS VOL.1 (Various artists).
MC: WAC 001

My Song Is My Own
MY SONG IS MY OWN Song from women (Various artists).
LP: TPL 000-1

My Square Laddie
MY SQUARE LADDIE (Original cast recording) (Various artists).
LP: AEI 1132

My Stepmother Is ...
MY STEPMOTHER IS AN ALIEN (Film soundtrack) (Various artists).
Tracks: / Pump up the volume: *M/A/R/R/S* / Room to move: *Animotion* / Be the one: *Jackson, Jackie* / One good lover: *Siren* / Klystron, The: *Various artists* / Not just another girl: *Neville, Ivan* / I like the world: *Cameo* / Hot wives: *Aykroyd, Dan* / Enjoy: *Various artists* / Celeste: *Various artists.*
LP: 837 798-1
MC: 837 798-4

Mychals, Robbie
ROBBIE MYCHALS.
LP: D 170952

Myers, Alicia
I APPRECIATE.
LP: MCF 3235

YOU GET THE BEST FROM ME (SAY SAY SAY) (See under Collage/Romeo where's Juliet).

Myers, Amina Claudine

AMINA.
Tracks: / Happiness / Keep on loving / Yes, it's real / Song from the West / Nolan / Arms / B. I. / Nisamethe.
LP: . . . . **PL 83030**

COUNTRY GIRL.
LP: . . . . **MM 1012**

IN TOUCH.
Tracks: / It's alright with me / Cairo / Olaya / First Sunday / My love is strong enough / Electric ice / Ballad for you, A / Natural self.
LP: . . . . **PL 83064**
MC: . . . . **PK 83064**

JUMPING IN THE SUGAR BOWL.
LP: . . . . **MM 002**

SALUTES BESSIE SMITH.
LP: . . . . **LR 103**

SONG FOR MOTHER E.
LP: . . . . **LR 100**

Myers, Louis

I'M A SOUTHERN MAN.
LP: . . . . **ADVENT 2809**

WAILING THE BLUES.
Tracks: / Give me a drink / Mean black spider / Sweet home Chicago / Going down South / Tomorrow night / Wailing the blues / Outskirts of town / Reconsider baby.
LP: . . . . **JSP 1065**

Myers, Sam

MY LOVE IS HERE TO STAY (Myers,Sam & Anson Funderburgh).
LP: . . . . **SPIN 206**
LP: . . . . **BT 1032**
MC: . . . . **BT 1032C**

Mykrophone

MUSIC 2 MAKE U DANCE.
LP: . . . . **UNQLP 2**

Myles, Alannah

ALANNAH MYLES.
Tracks: / Still got this thing / Black velvet / Lover of mine / If you want to / Who loves you / Love is / Rock this joint / Kick start my heart / Just one kiss / Make love.
LP: **781 956-1**
MC: **781 956-4**

Myles, Rayond A.

NEW ORLEANS GOSPEL GENIUS.
LP: **11021**
MC: . . . . **11021 TC**

Mynta

INDIAN TIMES.
Tracks: / Indian time / Yellow fellow / Simply it is / Bala nak / Is it possible / Seventh heaven / Vavop suite / Shurutic / Pahadi.
LP: . . . . **VBR 20371**
MC: . . . . **VBR 20374**

Myofist

HOT SPIKES.
Tracks: / Money / Teenage love affair / What am I to do / Hot spikes / Are you crying / Rock'n'roll suicide / Alimony / Never come back / It's a sin / Lord I miss you.
LP: . . . . **AMLH 64823**

THUNDER IN ROCK.
Tracks: / Double or nothin' / Thunder in rock / Leather 'n' lace / On the radio / It's late / Better way to go / Evil cold / Fleet Street / Open the gates.
LP: . . . . **AMLH 64893**

Myrick, Gary

GARY MYRICK & THE FIGURES (Myrick, Gary & the Figures).
Tracks: / Living disaster / Ever since the world began / She talks in stereo / Model / She's so teenage / You / Party, The / Meaningless / Who'll be next in line / Deep in the heartland.
LP: . . . . **EPC 84450**

Mysterious Island

MYSTERIOUS ISLAND (London Symphony Orchestra).
LP: . . . . **CN 4002**

Mystery Folk

THAT'S HOW I SPELL IRELAND.
MC: . . . . **GTDC 040**

Mystery Girls

SOUR MASH.
LP: . . . . **KICKASS 002**

Mystery Of Edwin Drood

MYSTERY OF EDWIN DROOD (Original Broadway cast) (Various artists).
Tracks: / There you are: *Various artists* / Man could go quite mad, A: *Various artists* / Two kinsmen: *Various* artists / Moonfall: *Various artists* / Wages of sin, The: *Various artists* / Ceylon: *Various artists*/ Both sides of the coin: *Various artists* / Perfect strangers: *Various artists* / No good can come from bad: *Various* artists / Never the luck: *Various artists* / Name of love, The: *Various artists* / Setting up the score: *Various* artists / Off to the races: *Various artists* / Don't quit while you're ahead: *Various artists* / Garden path to hell, The: *Various artists* / Out on a limerick: *Various artists* / Jasper's confession: *Various artists*/ Puffer's confession: *Various artists* / Writing on the wall, The: *Various artists*.
LP: . . . . **POLD 5196**
MC: . . . . **POLDC 5196**

Mystery of the... (bk)

MYSTERY OF THE BURNT COTTAGE, THE (see under Blyton, Enid (author)) (Morgan, Liz & John Baddeley (nars)).

MYSTERY OF THE STRANGE MESSAGES, THE (see under Blyton, Enid) (Morgan, Liz & John Baddeley (nars)).

Mystery Romance

HUMAN SEXUALITY.
Tracks: / All alone / So far away / I had a girl / Eh-oh / Waiting on a train / Stop looking in my window / Cut me some slack / Reason for love / Now that she's gone away / Staring into the rain / Human sexuality.
LP: . . . . **PTLS 1101**

Mystery Slang

VENUS GROVE.
LP: . . . . **V 1645**
MC: . . . . **TCV 1645**

Mystery Train (film)

MYSTERY TRAIN (Various artists).
LP: . . . . **A 509**
MC: . . . . **C 509**

Mystic Eyes

OUR TIME TO LEAVE.
LP: . . . . **GH 1001**

Mystic Forces

TAKE COMMAND.
LP: . . . . **CMFT 7**

Mystic Man

SPEAK SOFTLY (See Junior Wilson) (Mystic Man/Junior Wilson/Sparks, Trevor).

Mystic Merlin

MYSTIC MERLIN.
Tracks: / Burned to learn / Don't you want to be a star / Dreams / Can't stop dancing / Dark side / Got to make the best of a love situation / Just can't give you up.
LP: . . . . **EST 12047**

Mystic Moods Orchestra

COSMIC FORCE.
LP: . . . . **MFSL 1-002**

EMOTIONS.
LP: . . . . **MFSL 1-001**

Mystic Revelations...

GROUNATION (Mystic Revelations Of Rastafari).
LPS: . . . . **MRR**

Mystic Tide

E-TYPES VS MYSTIC TIDE (see E-Types/Mystic Tide) (Mystic Tide/E-Types).

Mystics

COMPLETE MYSTICS.
Tracks: / Hushabye / White cliffs of Dover, The / All through the night / Sunday kind of love / It's only a paper moon / So tenderly / Star crossed lovers / Again / Don't take the stars / Darling I know how / To think of you again / Over the rainbow / Let me steal your heart away / Blue star / Adam and Eve / Goodbye Mr. Blues.
LP: . . . . **CH 157**

Myths

MYTHS 1 (Various artists).
LP: . . . . **SUB 33001-1**

MYTHS 2 (Various artists).
LP: . . . . **SUB 33002-3**

MYTHS 3 (Various artists).
LP: . . . . **SUB 33003-5**

MYTHS VOL.2 Various Artists (Various artists).
LP: . . . . **SUB 33002 1**

Myton, Cedric

FACE THE MUSIC (Myton, Cedric & The Congos).
Tracks: / Can't take it away / Bank of the river / Sinking ship / Love and understanding / Face the music / Woman in the dark / Where he leads me / Dance all night / Scoffers and scorners / Problems.
LP: . . . . **BEAT 4**

N

Na Cabarfeidh

RARE AIR.
LP: . . . . FF 286

Na Casaidigh

FEAD AN IOLAIR.
LP: . . . . CEF 108
MC: . . . . CEFC 108

Na Fili

CHANTER'S TUNE.
LP: . . . . HPE 650
MC: . . . . HPC 650

FAREWELL TO CONNAUGHT.
MC: . . . . COX 1010

KINDLY WELCOME, A.
LP: . . . . BCLP 1

NA FILI 3.
MC: . . . . COX 1017

ONE DAY FOR RECREATION (Na Fili/ Sean O'Sea with Peadar Mercier).
LP: . . . . STAL 8009

TRADITIONAL IRISH MUSIC.
LP: . . . . SOLP 1017

Nabney, Joe

HE LIFTED ME.
Tracks: / Singing I go / It took a miracle / Amazing grace / Then I met the master / Ten thousand angels / Sharan's angel / He lifted me / Under his wings / God did a wonderful thing for me / Old rugged cross, The / It may be today.
MC: . . . . CGSOL 105

HIDING IN THE SHADOW OF THE ROCK.
LP: . . . . PC 858

WALKING IN THE KING'S HIGHWAY.
LP: . . . . PRAISE 38

Nabokov, Vladimir

LOLITA (Mason, James (nar)).
MC: . . . . CDL 51680

Nabucco

NABUCCO (See under Verdi) (Various artists).

NABUCCO (VIDEO) (see under Verdi (composer)) (Various artists).

Nacht Und Nebel

CASABLANCA.
Tracks: / Casablanca.
MC: . . . . ANT 010

Nadens

FOX ON THE RUN.
Tracks: / Does she wish she was single again / Running water / She's a friend of a friend / Who cares about tomorrow / Setting you free / You left the water running / Honky tonk night time man.
LP: . . . . NAD 1

Nadjma

RAPTURE IN BAGHDAD.
LP: . . . . CRAM 027

Naegele, David

DREAMSCAPES.
MC: . . . . C 316

TEMPLE IN THE FOREST (higher consciousness music).
MC: . . . . C 312

Nagata

IT'S GONE (see under Taxman) (Nagata & Taxman).

Nagle, Ron

BAD RICE.
Tracks: / 61 clay / Marijuana hell / Frank's store / Party in LA / That's what friends are for / Dolores / Capricorn queen / Sister Cora / Something's gotta give now / Family style / House of Mandia.
LP: . . . . ED 204

Nail, Jimmy

TAKE IT OR LEAVE IT.
Tracks: / That's the way love is / Airwaves / Walk away / Your decision today / Ladies and gentlemen of South Africa / Rain burns / Same again / Further on / One more day / Love don't live here anymore.
LP: . . . . V 2407
MC: . . . . TCV 2407

Nails

MOOD SWING.
Tracks: / Everytime I touch you / Dark brown / 88 lines about 45 women / Home of the brave / Let it all hang out / Mood swing / Phantom heart / Juanita juanita / She is everything to me / White walls.
LP: . . . . PL 88037
MC: . . . . PK 88037

Naimro, Jean C

EN BALATE.
LP: . . . . GD 026

Najee

DAY BY DAY.
Tracks: / Personality / Day by day / So hard to let go / He's armed 'n' dangerous / Gina / That's the way of the world / Tonight I'm yours / Najee's nasty groove / Sweet sensation / Stand up.
LP: . . . . MTL 1026
MC: . . . . TCMTL 1026
LP: . . . . EL 90096

NAJEE'S THEME.
Tracks: / Feel so good to me / Najee's theme / For the love of you / Can't hide love / We're still family / Sweet love / Betcha don't know / What you do to me / Mysterious.
LP: . . . . AML 3115
MC: . . . . TCAML 3115

Najma

ATISH.
LP: . . . . TERRA 108
MC: . . . . TERRAC 108

QAREEB.
Tracks: / Neend koyi / Har sitani aap ka / Zikar hai apna mehfil mehfil / Karcon na yad magar / Jane kis tarjha / Dil laga ya tha.
LP: . . . . TERRA 103
MC: . . . . TERRAC 103

Nakagawa, Masami

PRELUDE FOR AUTUMN.
MC: . . . . JC 3304

TOUCH OF SPRING.
MC: . . . . JC 3311

Nakai, R.Carlos

SUNDANCE SEASON.
LP: . . . . LPCEL 024
MC: . . . . MCCEL 024

Naked

ONE STEP FORWARD.
LP: . . . . FISH 4

Naked City

TORTURE GARDEN (See under John Zorn) (Naked City & John Zorn).

Naked Eyes

BURNING BRIDGES.
Tracks: / Burning bridges / Voices in my head / I could show you how / Very hard act to follow / Always something there to remind me / Fortune and fame / Could be / Emotion in motion / Low life / Time is now / When the lights go out / Promises promises.
LP: . . . . EMC 3426

Naked Prey

40 MILES FROM NOWHERE.
Tracks: / 40 miles from nowhere / Find my way / Silver train / Carnival, The / Whichita / Lineman / Too far gone.
LP: . . . . ZANE 006

KILL THE MESSENGER.
Tracks: / One even stand / Doctor Brown / Plastic Jesus / I saw the light / Blind man / Yardman / Blue tick hound / Life on Mars / Road crash / Night crew.
LP: . . . . SAVE 73

UNDER THE BLUE MARLIN.
Tracks: / Ride, The / Stranger, A / Dirt / Train whistle / How I felt that day / Come on down / Rawhead / Voodoo Godhead / Fly away / What price for freedom.
LP: . . . . ZONG 011
MC: . . . . ZONGCASS 011

Naked Ray Gun

ALL RISE.
LP: . . . . HMS 045

JETTISON.
LP: . . . . CAROL 1348
MC: . . . . CAROL 1348C

THROB THROB.
LP: . . . . HMS 008

UNDERSTAND.
Tracks: / Treason / Understand? / Bughouse / Never follow / Vagabond dog / Sniper song / Hips swingin' / Entrapment / Wonder beer / Too much of you / O.K. wait / Which side you're on.
LP: . . . . CARLP 6
MC: . . . . CARC 6

Naked & The Dead

NAKED AND THE DEAD (see under Mailer, Norman) (Mailer, Norman).

Naked Voice

FORGOTTEN FRONTIERS.
Tracks: / Politics / Step / Wild frontiers / Too many heads / Ha-ha world / Where was / Four books still negative / Dream house / Why / Original Dixieland one-step / Sweet lorr / Pasadena / Seaport serenade / Sugar blues / I've found a new baby / Frog-I-more rag / Somebody you'll be sorry / Birth of the blues / Sweet Sue / Dreaming the hours away / Ain't she sweet / Pure and easy / Modern cowboy / Reptile man / Tommy / Dangerous / Man / Peeping tom / Out of your reach / Wailing wall / Cliches.
LP: . . . . LTS 12

Name

DANGEROUS TIMES.
Tracks: / Dangerous times / Maybe someday / Calm before the storm / Walk into the world / Great depression / Jesus and the devil / Southern girl / New day / Driving rain / Last war song.
LP: . . . . WOL 6
MC: . . . . ZWOL 6

Name Of The Rose

NAME OF THE ROSE (Various artists).
Tracks: / Beta viscera: *Various artists* / First recognition: *Various artists* / Lesson, The: *Various artists*/ Kyrie: *Various artists* / Scriptorium, The: *Various artists* / Veri sancti spiritus: *Various artists*/ Confession, The: *Various artists* / Flashbacks: *Various artists* / Discovery, The: *Various artists*/ Betrayed: *Various artists* / Epilogue: *Various artists* / Name Of The Rose end title: *Various artists.*
LP: . . . . SCENE 7
MC: . . . . SCENEC 7

Namyslowski, Zbigniew

AIR CONDITION.
Tracks: / Speed limit / Convenient circumstances / Pretty dowseress / Play it to me / Dilemma / Ladderman / We'll have a nice day.
LP: . . . . AFF 83

Nan Tuck Five

RAINWATER RELICS.
LP: . . . . BYLP 3

Nana

NANA (Worth, Irene).
MC: . . . . CDL 51679

Nance, Ray

HOMAGE TO THE DUKE (See under Christie, Keith) (Nance, Ray/John Dankworth/Keith Christie).

JUST A-SITTIN' AND A-ROCKIN' (See under Golsalves, Paul) (Nance, Ray & Paul Gonsalves).

RAY NANCE QUARTET & SEXTET (Nance, Ray-Quartet &Sextet).
LP: . . . . UJ 11

Nandy, Radhakanta

MEDLEY OF PERCUSSIONS.
LP: . . . . S 45 NLP 2041

Nanou

NANOU/CARELESS TALK (Various artists).
LP: . . . . MOMENT 104
MC: . . . . MOMENTC 104

Nanssen, Wolf

GUITAR TALES.
LP: . . . . ISST 140

Napalm

CRUEL TRANQUILITY.
Tracks: / Mind melt / A.O.A. / Shake it off / Gag of steel / Devastation / Combat zone / Immoral society / Attack on America / Reanimate / Act of betrayal / Nightmare administrator / Practice what you preach / Kranked up and out.
LP: 08-7563

ZERO TO BLACK.
LP: 087622

Napalm Beach

FIRE AIR AND WATER.
LP: . . . . RTDL 31

LIQUID LOVE.
Tracks: / Get movin' / Plague / Too much fun / Payin' the price / Livin' on the run / In the sunshine / Can't do that / Takes no fire / She's a carnival / Harmony hill / Down Mexico way.
LP: . . . . EFA 15065

Napalm Death

FROM ENSLAVEMENT TO OBLITERATION.
Tracks: / Evolved as one / It's a M.A.N.'s world / Lucid fairytale / Private death / Unchallenged hate / Uncertainty blurs / Vision, The / Retreat to nowhere / Display to me / From enslavement / Blind to the truth / Emotional suffocation / Practice what you preach / Mentally murdered / Worlds apart.
LP: . . . . MOSH 8
MC: . . . . MOSH 8 MC
LPPD: . . . . MOSH 8 P

HARMONY OF CORRUPTION.
LP: . . . . MOSH 19
MC: . . . . MOSH 19 MC
LPPD: . . . . MOSH 19 P

MOVING TO AND FRO.
LP: . . . . EFA 7202

NAPALM DEATH - TWO COMPLETE SESSIONS.
LP: . . . . SFPSD 049

SCUM.
LP: . . . . MOSH 3
MC: . . . . MOSH 3 MC

Napoleon

NAPOLEON (history for ages 8+) (Unknown narrator(s)).
MC: . . . . PLBH 106

Napoleon of...(bk)

NAPOLEON OF NOTTINGHILL, THE (G.K. Chesterton) (Scofield, Paul (nar)).
MCSET: . . . . SAY 93

Napoleon, Phil

1946-49 (Napoleon,Phil/Frank Signorelli).
Tracks: / Alabama blues / Blue Danube / Margie / Stationary woman / My man o'war / Save it pretty mama.
LP: . . . . HQ 2043

BAILEY'S LUCKY SEVEN.
Tracks: / How many times / Sweet Indiana home / Nobody lied / No wonder I'm lonesome / Tomorrow / Gee but I hate to go home alone / Tomorrow morning / Baby blue eyes / You know you belong to somebody else / Apple sauce / You're in Kentucky sure as you're born / Dear one / Won't you come back to my arms.
LP: . . . . QU 059

PHIL NAPOLEON 1925-27 (Napoleon, Phil/Original Memphis Five).
LP: . . . . IAJRC 26

Napoleon XIV

THEY'RE COMING TO TAKE ME AWAY.
LP: . . . . RNLP 816

Nappe, Neil

JULY.
LP: . . . . SYN 103
MC: . . . . SYNC 103

Napper, Tom

TRIPPING UPSTAIRS (Napper, Tom & Alistair Russel).
LP: . . . . CM 002

Naptali, Raymond

LOVE TRAP (see Campbell, Cornell) (Naptali, Raymond & Cornell Campbell).

TROUBLE POSSEE.
Tracks: / Automatic boom / Give me sensemilia / Loving feeling / Don't cry / Born and grow ina dis / Tek yu hand offa me / You too su su su su / Me no copy / It's you I'm talking to / Trouble possee.
LP: . . . . CSLP 3

Narada

DIVINE EMOTIONS.
Tracks: / Divine emotions / Can't you get outta my head / That's the way I feel about cha / Wild thing / How can I make you stay / Explosion / I belong / But what

up doh? / Jam the night / We still have a dream / Certain kind of lover.
LP: WX 172
MC: WX 172 C

Narayan, Pandit Ram

RAGA PURIA KALYAN.
LP: AMLP 816

Nardella, Steve

IT'S ALL ROCK AND ROLL.
LP: BP-879

Nardini, Peter

IS THERE ANYBODY OUT THERE.
LP: TP 020
MC: CTP 020

Narodna

NARODNA (Various artists).
MC: T 33.7

Nascimento, Milton

MEETINGS AND FAREWELLS (Encontros e Despedidas).
Tracks: / Threshold of colours / Love affair / Nights in the country / Sea of our love / Southern tear / Race / Meetings and farewells / Who asked for me / Morning Star, The / Glass and cut / Radio experience.
LP: 827 638-1
MC: 827 638-4

TRAVESSIA.
LP: 7704

TXAI (Various artists).
Tracks: / Overture: *Various artists* (Narration by Davi Kopenawa Yanomani) / Txai: *Various artists* / Bau Metoro: *Various artists* / Coisas da vida (that's life): *Various artists* / Hoeiepereiga: *Various artists* / Estorias de floresta (stories of the forest): *Various artists* / Yanomani e nos (pacto de vida): Yanomani & us - pact of life: *Various* artists / Awasi: *Various artists* / A terceira margem do rio (third edge of the river): *Various artists* / Benke: *Various artists* (Participation by Leonardo Bretas) / Sertao das aguas (hinterlands of the waters): *Various* artists / Que vira dessa escuridao (what will come out of this dark): *Various artists* / Curi curi: *Various artists*(Narration by River Phoenix) / Nozani na: *Various artists* (Participation by Marlui Miranda) / Baridjumoko: *Various artists* (Interpreted by the Village People).
LP: 4641381
MC: 4641384

YAUARETE (Panther).
Tracks: / Blue planet / Dream merchant / Jaguar / Enchanted city / Heart is my master / Children's dance song / Eldorado / Letter to the republic / Old hill / Mountain / Songs and moments.
LP: 4611411
MC: 4611414

Nash, Cody

LONG RIDE HOME.
Tracks: / Please be kind / From the bottle to bottom / Long ride home / Papa / Grass won't grow / Oklahoma city / Please look over me / Irma Jackson / Nashville queen / Keeping each other satisfied / Circle of tears / Don't think I'll ever love again.
LP: FHR 081

Nash, Dick

NASHVILLE (see Sims, Zoot) (Nash, Dick & Zoot Sims).

ZOOT SIMS/DICK NASH (see Sims, Zoot) (Nash, Dick & Zoot Sims).

Nash, Graham

EARTH AND SKY.
Tracks: / Earth and sky / Love has come / Out on the island / Skychild / Helicopter song / Barrel of pain / T.V. guide / It's all right / Magical child / In the '80's.
LP: EA-ST 12014

INNOCENT EYES.
Tracks: / See you in Prague / Keep away from me / Innocent eyes / Chippin' away / Over the wall / Don't listen to the rumours / Sad Eyes / New Day / Glass and steel / I got a rock.
LP: 781 633-1
MC: 781 633-4

SONGS FOR BEGINNERS.
Tracks: / Military madness / Better days / Wounded birds / I used to be a king / Be yourself / Simple man / Man in the mirror / There's only one / Sleep song / Chicago / We can change the world.
LP: K 40237
LP: 2401 011

WILD TALES.
Tracks: / Wild tales / Hey you / Prison song / You'll never be the same / And so it goes / Grave concern / Oh camile (the winter soldier) / I miss you / On the line / Another sleep song.
LP: K 50025

Nash, Johnny

6 TRACK HITS: JOHNNY NASH.
Tracks: / There are more questions than answers / Tears on my pillow / You got soul / Stir it up / Hold me tight / Cupid.
MC: 7SC 5020

COLLECTION: JOHNNY NASH.
LP: EPC 10008

GOLDEN HIGHLIGHTS OF JOHNNY NASH.
LP: 54740
MC: 40 54740

I CAN SEE CLEARLY NOW.
Tracks: / I can see clearly now / Let's be friends / Cream puff / Reggae on Broadway / Wonderful world / Ooh what a feeling / Birds of a feather / Cupid / Tears on my pillow / Guava jelly / That woman / Dream lover / There are more questions than answers / All I have to do is dream / Nice time / You got soul / My merry go round / Halfway to paradise / Stir it up.
LP: CBS 64860
LP: 4653061
MC: 4653064

JOHNNY NASH.
MCSET: DTO 10098

JOHNNY NASH ALBUM, THE.
Tracks: / I can see clearly now / Dream lover / Hold me tight / Let's be friends / Reggae on Broadway / What a wonderful world / Ooh what a feeling / Cupid / Tears on my pillow / Guava jelly / There are more questions than answers / All I have to do is dream / You got soul / My merry go round / Halfway to paradise / Stir it up.
LP: 40 31779

LET'S GO DANCING.
Tracks: / Wonderful woman / Don't forget / Closer / Mr. Sea / You're the one / Looking over my shoulder / We're lovers / Very special girl / Let's go dancing.
LP: EPC 83043

STIR IT UP.
Tracks: / Stir it up / Ooh what a feeling / Birds of a feather / Hold me tight / Groovin / Cupid / Mellow mood / There are more questions than answers / Tears on my pillow / Guava jelly / Rock it baby / Reggae on Broadway.
LP: SHM 3053
MC: HSC 3053

TEARS ON MY PILLOW.
Tracks: / Why did you do it / Rock it baby / I'm comin' home in the mornin' / Edge of love / Tears on my pillow / Reggae on Broadway / Mellow mood / Let's be friends / Cream puff / Say it ain't true.
LP: 69148

Nash, Ogden

PARENTS KEEP OUT.
MC: 1282

Nash, Paul

JAZZ COMPOSER'S ENSEMBLE, A.
LP: REV 32

Nash, Terry

TERRY NASH COUNTRY.
Tracks: / Six days on the road / Deepening snow, The / Time on my hands / Wheels fell off the wagon / Let me give her the flowers / Walkin' on the other side of Heaven / Hello darlin' / Kiss an angel good morning / I didn't jump the fence / Way it was in '51, The / If my world should end tomorrow / Fighting side of me, The.
LP: BGC 269
MC: KBGC 269

Nash The Slash

AMERICAN BAND-AGES.
LP: HMUSA 40

AND YOU THOUGHT YOU WERE NORMAL.
Tracks: / Pretty folks / RSVP / Vincent's crows / Dance after curfew / Normal / Hynotist, The / Remember when / Animal jamboree / Stalker.
LP: HAI 104

CHILDREN OF THE NIGHT.
LP: DID 9

Nashville...

NASHVILLE NEW YORK (Original London cast) (Various artists).
LP: TER 1001

Nashville All-Stars

BEAUTIFUL COUNTRY MUSIC: VOL 1.
MC: BBM 110

BEAUTIFUL COUNTRY MUSIC: VOL 2.
MC: BBM 111

Nashville Bluegrass

BOYS ARE BACK IN TOWN, THE.
Tracks: / Get a transfer to home / Long time gone / Big river / Hard times / Connie and Buster / Don't let our love die / I'm rollin' through this unfriendly world / Rock bottom blues / Diamonds and pearls / Ghost of Eli Renfro, The / Weary blues from waitin' / Big cow in Carlisle / Dark as the night, blue as the day / Boys are back in town.
LP: SH 3778
MC: SH 3778C

IDLE TIME.
Tracks: / Idle time / Old devil's dream / Two wings / I closed my heart's door / All I want is you / Angeline the baker / Little Maggie / Last night I dreamed of loving you / No one but my darling / My Lord heard Jerusalem when she moaned / Old timey risin' damp / Train carryin' Jimmie Rodgers home.
LP: ROUNDER 0232
MC: ROUNDER 0232C

MY NATIVE HOME.
LP: ROUNDER 0212
MC: ROUNDER 0212C

ORIGINAL BLUEGRASS BAND, THE.
Tracks: / Heavy traffic ahead / I'm going back to old Kentucky / Little cabin on the hill / Bluegrass breakdown / Sweetheart you done me wrong / Molly and Tenbrooks / Toy heart / My Rose of old Kentucky / Wicked path of sin / Summertime is past and gone / When you are lonely / Will you be loving another man.
LP: SS 06
MC: SSC 06

TO BE HIS CHILD.
LP: ROUNDER 0242
MC: ROUNDER 0242C

Nashville Cats

ALL-TIME COUNTRY AND WESTERN HITS: VOL 3.
MC: BBM 137

COWBOYS AND CLOWNS.
MC: BBM 112

Nashville Jazz...

WHERE'S ELI (Nashville Jazz Machine (Big Band)).
Tracks: / Auralsynthes / Love song / Blue Bossa / Nashville connection, The.
LP: AM 14

Nashville Superpickers

LIVE FROM AUSTIN CITY LIMITS.
Tracks: / Canadian sunset / Rollin' in my sweet baby's arms / Fiddlin' around / Long tall Texan / New road under my wheels / Sweet dreams / Shadow of your smile / What a friend we have in Jesus / Orange blossom special.
LP: FF 097

SUPERPICKIN'.
Tracks: / Just a little bit of you / Honky tonk blues / Tennessee waltz / Li'l Red Riding Hood / Move it on over / Short on love / She's a yum yum / Howlin' at the moon / Talk back tremblin' lips / Twelfth of never.
LP: SDLP 021

Nashville Teens

LIVE AT THE RED HOUSE.
LP: HAI 200

Nashville Train

ABBA - OUR WAY.
LP: BUFFG 5001

Nasser, Jimmy

EXPRESSLY ELLINGTON (Nasser, Jimmy Combo).
LP: PJLP 20

Nasty Blues

NASTY BLUES (See under Blues) (Various artists).

Nasty Pop

MISTAKEN I.D..
LP: EGLP 28

Nasty Rox Inc.

CASH.
Tracks: / 9th wonder / 10th wonder / Say it mean it / Escape from New York / Blow / Wooba wubbaa I / Nobby's one / Nasty Rox Inc / Wooba wubbaa II.
LP: ZTT 1
MC: ZTT 1 C

Nasty Savage

ABSTRACT REALITY.
LP: RR 95661
LP: 722441

INDULGENCE.
LP: RR 9630

NASTY SAVAGE.
LP: RR 9752

PENETRATION POINT.
Tracks: / Welcome wagon / Irrational / Ritual submission / Powerslam / Sin eater / Penetration point / Puzzled / Horizertical / Family circus.
LP: RO 94181
MC: RO 94182

Nasty Shock

HEAVY METAL DEVIL WORSHIPPER.
LP: GRO 6

Nat West Jazz Band

HOOKED ON DIXIE.
Tracks: / New Orleans / Fidgety feet / Onions / Chinatown.
LP: NWJB 2
MC: NWJBC 2

YOU CAN BANK ON US.
LP: NWJB 3
MC: NWJBC 3

Natasha

CAPTURED.
LP: TOWLP 2

DON'T WALK AWAY.
LP: TOWLP 9
MC: ZCTOW 9

VEX FOR DAT, A.
LP: NCR 3867

Nathaniel The Grublet

NATHANIEL THE GRUBLET (Various artists).
Tracks: / Diddle-daddle day: *Various artists* / Nathaniel's song: *Various artists* / Hip and a hey: *Various* artists / Risky game: *Various artists* / Father Grublet: *Various artists* / Nathaniel's chorus: *Various* artists / No doggie blues: *Various artists* / In direwood: *Various artists* / Time has come for you, The: *Various artists* / Sunshine: *Various artists* / Majesty was here: *Various artists* / Father Grublet: *Various artists* / Reprise: *Various artists.*
LP: BW R 2018
MC: TC BWR 2018

Nathanson, Roy

BROKEN NIGHT (Nathanson, Roy & Curtis Fowlkes & The Jazz Passengers).
LP: TWI 816

DERANGED AND DECOMPOSED (Nathanson, Roy & Curtis Fowlkes & The Jazz Passengers).
LP: TWI 846

National anthems

NATIONAL ANTHEMS (Various artists).
Tracks: / France - La marseillaise: *Various artists* / Autriche - hymn national Autrichien: *Various artists* / Canada O' Canada: *Various artists* / Finlande - Maamme: *Various artists* / Grece - hymne gec: *Various artists*/ Italie - inno di nameli: *Various artists* / Japon - Kimigayo: *Various artists* / Norvege - hymn national Norvegien: *Various artists* / Suisse 9 cantique suisse: *Various artists* / U.S.A. - The star spangled banner: *Various* artists / Allemagne - Deutsche national hymne: *Various artists* / Belgique - La brabanconne: *Various artists*/ Espagne - marcha reel: *Various artists* / Grande-gretagne - God save the queen: *Various artists* / Hollande -Wilhelmus van nassauowe: *Various artists* / Israel - Hatikva: *Various artists* / Luxembourg - Ons hemecht: *Various* artists / Suede - hymne national de Suede: *Various artists* / U.R.S.S. - Hymne national de l'U.R.S.S.: *Various artists* / Yugoslavie - hej sloveni: *Various artists.*
LP: SCO 9038
MC: SCK 9038
LP: 771 075
MC: 670 075

National Ballet Of

EUGENE ONEGIN (VIDEO) (see under Tchaikovsky).

National Band Of NZ

COLONEL BOGEY ON PARADE (National Band of New Zealand).
MC: SPVP 5043C
LP: SPVP 5043

SPECTACULAR BRASS (National Band of New Zealand).
LP: SPVP 423

THIS IS NEW ZEALAND (National Band of New Zealand).
LP: XPS 5062

National Brass Band

GOLDEN MEMORIES.
LP: ONE 1075

National Health

DD AL CODE.
Tracks: / Flanagan's people / Toad of toad hall / Portrait of a shrinking man / Tales of a Samson knight / Black hat.
LP: LA 02

NATIONAL HEALTH.
Tracks: / Tenemos roads / Brujo / Borogobes (except from 2) / Borogobes (part 1) / Elephants.
LP: AFF 6

NATIONAL HEALTH OF QUEUES AND CURES.
Tracks: / Bryden 2 step (for amphibians) Pt 1, The / Collapso, The / Syuarer for Maud / Dreams wide awake / Binoculars / Phlakaton / Bryden 2 step (for amphibians) pt 2, The.
LP: . . . . **CRL 5010**

National Lampoon

ANIMAL HOUSE (See under Animal House).

THAT'S NOT FUNNY, THAT'S SICK.
Tracks: / Squalor show, The / Confession / Dick Ballentine phone in show No. 1 / Disco hotline / Dick Ballentine phone in show No. 2 / Love birds / Listener sponsored Radio No. 1 / Gymnasty / Dick Ballentine phone in show No. 3 / Yiddishco / Listener sponsored radio No. 2 / Pulp / For $15, 000 / Rapeline / Mr. Roberts No. 1 / Stereos and such / Listener sponsored radio No. 3 / Height report / Dixco / Mr. Roberts No. 2 / Dial a curse / Humpback whales / Listener sponsored radio No. 4 / 2, 015 year old man / Fasten your seatbelts / Listener sponsored radio No. 5 / Monolithic oil.
LP: . . . . **RAD 4**

National Philharmonic

ALIEN (see under Alien, The (film)) (National Philharmonic Orchestra).

BEN-HUR (See under Rozsa, Miklos) (National Philharmonic Orchestra).

CLASSIC SCORES FROM HUMPHREY BOGART FILMS (National Philharmonic Orchestra).
Tracks: / Key largo / Big sleep / Caine mutiny / Casablanca / To have and to have not / Treasure of the Sierra Madre.
LP: . . . . **NL 10422**
MC: . . . . **NK 10422**

CLOSE ENCOUNTERS OF THE 3RD KIND (National Philharmonic Orchestra).
Tracks: / Five tones, The / Experience begins, The (Introduction to 'Close Encounters'.) / Mountain visions / John Williams symphonic suite of 'Close Encounters...' / Conversation / Appearance of the vistors, The / Restoration / First light / Sky ride / Aeromancy.
LP: . . . . **DMT 2002**
LP: . . . . **AL 9500**
MC: . . . . **ACB 6 8365**

ENCHANTED ORCHESTRA, THE (See under Niven, David) (National Philharmonic Orchestra/David Niven).

FILM FANTASY (See under Film Fantasy) (National Philharmonic Orchestra).

GREAT SHAKESPEARE FILMS (See under Shakespeare, William) (National Philharmonic Orchestra).

HIGHLIGHTS FROM HYMNS TRIUMPHANT (National Philharmonic Orchestra of London).
LP: . . . . **WING 517**
MC: . . . . **TC WING 517**

JESUS OF NAZARETH (National Philharmonic Orchestra).
LP: . . . . **NSPH 28504**
MC: . . . . **ZCP 28504**

LA BOHEME/MADAME BUTTERFLY (National Philharmonic Orchestra).
2LP: . . . . **SIV 103**
MC: . . . . **CSIV 103**

RETURN OF THE JEDI (Film Soundtrack) (National Philharmonic Orchestra).
Tracks: / Approaching the death star / Parade of the Ewoks / Luke and Leia / Jabba the Hutt / Return of the Jedi / Ewok battle, The / Han Solo returns / Into the trap - Fight in the dungeon / Heroic Ewok / Battle in the forest / Return of the Jedi finale.
LP: . . . . **RL 14748**
MC: . . . . **RK 14748**

National Wake

NATIONAL WAKE.
Tracks: / Dreams in my head / Time and place / Bollina / Skango / Kalabasn / Mercenaries / Wake of the nation / Supaman / International news / Student life.
LP: . . . . **K 95038**

National Youth...

CONCERT FOR CHRISTMAS, A (National Youth Choir Of Gt. Britain).
Tracks: / Hark the herald angels sing / Mary had a baby (Trad. arr. Brewer.) / Three kings, The / O little town of Bethlehem / Cantata for Christmas (Extract.) / Virgin most pure, A / In dulci jubilo / Christmas is coming (Extracts.) / Away in a manger / Duo seraphin / Little road to Bethlehem, The.
LP: . . . . **MFP 5867**
MC: . . . . **TCMFP 5867**

EXPLORERS, THE (National Youth Band of New Zealand).
Tracks: / Prelude / Cossack patrol / French patrol / French military march / Hymn Thunbury / Slavonic rhapsody / Match of the day / Explorers / Love is in the air / For your eyes only / Hallelujah / Bridge over troubled water / Sailing / Brass spectacular.
LP: . . . . **TRL 041**
MC: . . . . **TCTRL 041**

NATIONAL YOUTH CHOIR (National Youth Choir of New Zealand).
Tracks: / Girl I left behind me, The / O waly, waly / British Grenadiers, The / Golden slumbers / Dashing away with a smoothing iron / Oh to be a wild wind / Soon ah will be done / There is a balm in Gilead / All my trials / Shoot false love / Sweet honey-suckling bees / Lay a garland / I love my love / Nunc dimittis.
LP: . . . . **TRL 044**
MC: . . . . **TCTRL 044**

RITE OF SPRING/FIREBIRD (STRAVINSKY) (see under Stravinsky) (National Youth Orchestra of Great Britain).

National Youth Jazz...

11 PLUS (Live at LWT) (National Youth Jazz Orchestra).
Tracks: / NYJO / Spaghetti junction / Good to be there / Marianne / Wait and see / 11 plus / Who-wray / Yesterday's blues today / Legs eleven / Threshing machine, The / Full house / NYJO reprise.
LP: . . . . **SF 8464**

BIG BAND CHRISTMAS (National Youth Jazz Orchestra).
Tracks: / Deck the halls / Silent night / Christians awake / Maryland, my Christmas tree / In the bleak / At Christmas / I saw six ships / My dancing day / Wenceslas squared / Away in a manger / Thirst, The - No ale / O come all ye faithful / Christmas blues / Take five kings / I left my heart in Royal David's City / Holly and the ivy, The / Hark the herald angels sing.
MC: . . . . **NYJZC 009**

BORN AGAIN (National Youth Jazz Orchestra).
Tracks: / Sweetheart of Sigmund Freud / Infinity promenade / I'm gonna go fishin' / Contours / Topsy / Short stop / Walk don't run / Viva Puente / Boar jibu / Manteca / Un poco loco / Jazz waltz.
MC: . . . . **ZCNYJ 004**

CONCRETE COWS (National Youth Jazz Orchestra).
Tracks: / Concrete cows / Dear John / John's jape / Airedale Sunset / Robbers of Vissenburg / Dialectics (John Dankworth was also soloist on this track.) / Lady Di (John Dankworth was also soloist on this track.) / Dynamo (John Dankworth was also soloist on this track.).
LP: . . . . **NYJ 006**

COOKIN' WITH GAS (National Youth Jazz Orchestra).
Tracks: / Beyond the Hatfield Tunnel / Hot gospel / Step on the gas / Mr B.G. / Be gentle / Behind the gasworks / Cookin' with gas / S'wonderfuel / We care for you / Big girl now / Gasanova / Afterburner / Water babies / Heat of the moment, The.
MC: . . . . **NYJZC 010**

FULL SCORE (National Youth Jazz Orchestra).
Tracks: / Luton hoo / Waltz for Duke / Waiting for Morgan / London / Full score / Bud / Midnight newsroom / Lady can tell, A / Sea beaver, The.
LP: . . . . **NYJ 05**
MC: . . . . **ZCNYJ 05**

IN CAMRA (National Youth Jazz Orchestra).
Tracks: / Opening time / Legless in Garstang / Going for a burton / Ruddle's Rutland reflections / That old peculiar feeling / Fuggles fantastical fugue / Real ale real / Young's make me feel you so / Samuel Smith and his amazing dancing bear / Bitter from the woods / Drink Tolly only / Trip to Jerusalem.
LP: . . . . **PL 25036**

MARY ROSE (National Youth Jazz Orchestra).
Tracks: / Eave-O / Early morning train / Dykes on bikes / Legend of the Mary Rose / Happy katz / Mary Rose / Nothing like a Thane / No flowers by request / Cop this / Cuban thing.
LP: . . . . **N 117**

NYJO DOWN UNDER (National Youth Jazz Orchestra).
Tracks: / Australian opener / Okay with Jay / Schedule D / Barrio / Groover, The / Question time / Out of sight, out of mind / Blenkinsop's blues / As if I cared / Getting down to it / Gynaecology / To set before a queen / Cobwebs / Song to sing by, A / Amazing grace / Tubbs lives / Fox fur / Paying my tax.
2LP: . . . . **DNYJ 502**

PLAYING TURKEY (National Youth Jazz Orchestra).
Tracks: / Istanbul now / Jack of Hart's / Round Robin / Leaving here / And Henry guards the door / Looking back / Three for Tay / Turkish delight.
LP: . . . . **NYJ 003**

PORTRAITS (National Youth Jazz Orchestra).
Tracks: / Blues at the bull / Woody / Basie / Dizzy / Duke / Bird / Quincy / Monk / Duke II / Kenton / Point of no return / Come on the blues / Royal flush / Southern horizons.
MC: . . . . **HHMC 1007**

RETURN TRIP (National Youth Jazz Orchestra).
Tracks: / Return trip / Velvet lady / Blue dolphin / Ballad for Brigitte / Morocco bound / Brahms arms, The / Li'l Jeannie / Gerryatrics / Cockpit / Seven of hearts / Get it right / Independence day celebration / Greasy spoon / Lift off / Tracy's trip / Maybe this time / Bones for Basie / Moon mood / Atropus / Go 'way from here.
LP: . . . . **DPS 2072**

SHERWOOD FOREST SUITE, THE (National Youth Jazz Orchestra).
Tracks: / Fanfare for Robin / Robin's epitaph / Sherwood Forest / All clad in Lincoln green / Lincoln green / She is called Maid Marion / Maid Marion / Sheriff's song / Sheriff of Nottingham, The / Mrs. A'Dales's diary / Minstrel's lay, The / Serving the bishop / Bishop's move / Robin and Marion / Outlaws / Robin's epitaph - reprise / Last arrow, The.
LP: . . . . **NYJ 001**

TO RUSSIA WITH JAZZ (National Youth Jazz Orchestra).
Tracks: / Buffle off to shuffalo / Cruisin' / I wasn't looking for a love affair / Ballad for Bing / Y.H.B. / Blues two / Cannonball / With you in mind / Parkinson's law / Half man / Where is the music / Bristol cream / Home brew, The / Sneaky Pete / As long as there are summers / Summer sands / Black velvet / Girl can't grumble, A / Almost home / To Russia with jazz.
2LP: . . . . **DNYJ 501**

WHY DON'T THEY WRITE SONGS LIKE THIS ANYMORE (National Youth Jazz Orchestra).
Tracks: / Why don't they write songs like this anymore / I'll wait here / Too much, too soon / Don't try and argue with me / When I'm with you / Girl can't grumble, A / Don't go to her / No flowers by request / Wait and see / Rich man / I said there'd be thunder / Accident prone.
LP: . . . . **NYJ 002**

WITH AN OPEN MIND (National Youth Jazz Orchestra).
Tracks: / Cheese'n'Carrots / Revenge of the Amoebae / With an open mind / Rememberance for Jim / Aardvark / Syrup of Phiggs / Fly to me / Midnight oil / Going Dutch.
LP: . . . . **NYJ 007**
MC: . . . . **ZNYJ 007**

Native

NATIVE.
Tracks: / Black tracks / In God we trust / Late September / When the master is dead / King Solomon's mines / Divide and conquer / Time of redemption / Hell hath no fury / Rock stone.
LP: . . . . **NEW 2**

Native Europe

SEARCHING FOR AN ORCHESTRATION.
LP: . . . . **REDLP 38**

Natty Rebels

JAH GLORY (see Blondy,Alpha & Natty Rebels) (Natty Rebels/Alpha Blondy).

Natural

NATURAL, THE (Film soundtrack) (Newman, Randy).
LP: **925116.1**
MC: **925116.4**

Natural Hii

BRIDGING THE GAP.
LP: . . . . **RMM 1151**

Natural Ites

PICTURE ON THE WALL (Natural Ites And The Realistics).
Tracks: / Peace and understanding / Lion inna jungle / Gwan go do it / Sunshine days / Jah works mamma / Picture on the wall / I want your love / I'm in the mood / Black roses / I ain't gonna stop.
LP: . . . . **CSLP 18**
MC: . . . . **ZCSLC 18**

Natural Life

NATURAL LIFE (DIRECT CUT).
LP: . . . . **ASI 5001**

Natural Mystic

GROOVE ROCKING.
Tracks: / Groove rocking.
LP: . . . . **SDLP 914**

Natural Mystics

TILL I KISS YOU (see Barker, Dave & Natural Mystics) (Natural Mystics & Dave Barker).

Natural Rhythm

BLUE BEAT AND SKA.
LP: . . . . **SKANKLP 119**

Natural Roots

NATURAL ROOTS.
LP: . . . . **FS 107**

Natural Touch

COLLECTORS ITEM.
LP: . . . . **NKRLP 003**

Nature Lovers

BEGINNING TO END.
LP: . . . . **INK 7**

Naughtiest Girl In The

NAUGHTIEST GIRL IN THE SCHOOL Blyton, Enid (Various artists).
LP: . . . . **EBLP 012**

Naughty Amelia Jane

ADVENTURES OF NAUGHTY AMELIA JANE (See under Adventures of...) (Pollard, Su (aut)).

Naughty, Hans

PAINT THE TOWN RED.
LP: . . . . **IW 1021**

Naughty Marietta

NAUGHTY MARIETTA (Film soundtrack) (Various artists).
LP: . . . . **HS 413**

Navarro, Fats

1946-49.
LP: . . . . **LPJT 54**

BIRD & FATS - VOL.2 (see Parker, Charlie) (Navarro, Fats Quintet & Charlie Parker).

FABULOUS FATS NAVARRO VOL 1, THE.
Tracks: / Our delight / Squirrel, The / Chase, The / Wail (LP only.) / Bouncing with Bud (LP only.) / Double talk (LP only.) / Dameronia / Chase, The (alt. take) / Squirrel, The (alt. take) / Our delight (alt. take) / Dameronia (alt. take) / Sid's delight (CD only.) / Casbah (CD only.) / John's delight (CD only.) / What's new (CD only.) / Heaven's doors are wide open / Focus.
LP: . . . . **BST 81531**
LP: . . . . **BLP 1531**

FABULOUS FATS NAVARRO VOL 2, THE.
Tracks: / Ladybird (Alternate master.) / Ladybird / Jarbero - alternate master / Jabero / Symphonette - alternate master / Symphonette / Double talk / Bouncing with Bud (LP only.) / Dance of the infidels (LP only.) / Skunk, The / Boperation / Skunk, The (78 Master) (CD only.) / Double talk (alt. take) (CD only.) / I think I'll go away (CD only.).
LP: . . . . **BST 81532**
LP: . . . . **BLP 1532**

FAT GIRL THE SAVOY SESSION.
Tracks: / Boppin' a riff / Fat boy / Everything's cool / Webb city / Calling Dr. Jazz / Fracture / Maternity / Stealin' trash / Just a mystery / Red pepper / Spinal / Hollerin' and screamin' / Fat girl / Ice freezes / Eb pob / Goin' to Mintons / Bebop carroll, A / Tadd walk, The / Gone with the wind / That someone must be you / Nostalgia / Nostalgia (master) / Barry's bop / Barry's bop (master) / Bebop romp / Bebop romp (master) / Fat's blows.
LP: . . . . **SJL 2216**

FATS & TADD AT ROOST (1948) 1.
LP: . . . . **BEP 505**

FATS & TADD AT ROOST (1948) 2.
LP: . . . . **BEP 506**

SATURDAY NIGHT SWING (Navarro, Fats & Allen Eager).
LP: . . . . **GSS 2**

Navigator

NAVIGATOR (Film Soundtrack) (Various artists).
Tracks: / Forging the cross: *Various artists* / Vision: *Various artists* / Ascent, The: *Various artists*/ Plainsong: *Various artists* / Queenfish: *Various artists* / Macedonian pipes: *Various artists* / Paean: The: *Various artists* / Dance: *Various artists* / Refugees: *Various artists* / Connor's return: *Various* artists / Storm: *Various artists* / Work song:

Various artists / Escape: *Various artists* / Fall, The: *Various artists* / Celtic refrain: *Various artists*.
LP: FILM 039
MC: FILMC 039

Navy Lark (Radio)

NAVY LARK, THE (Various artists).
MCSET: ZBBC 1096

NAVY LARK VOLUME 2, THE (Various artists).
MCSET: ZBBC 1173

Nawahi, King Bennie

HOT HAWAIIAN GUITAR 1928-49.
LP: L 1074

Naylor, Oliver

OLIVER NAYLOR'S SEVEN ACES.
LP: FJ 103

Nayobe

PROMISE ME.
Tracks: / I love the way you love me / I'll be around / Can't let go / You are you / You are everything / Who do I call / Some kind of emotion / Promise me / Main squeeze / Have I said I love you lately.
LP: 4671211
MC: 4671214

Nazakat & Salamt Ali

NAZAKAT AND SALAMAT ALI.
LP: HNBL 1332
MC: HNBC 1332

Nazareth

2 X S.
Tracks: / Love leads to madness / Boys in the band / You love another / Gatecrash / Games / Back to the trenches / Dream on / Lonely in the night / Preservation / Take the rap / Mexico.
LP: NIN 001

20 GREATEST HITS: NAZARETH.
LP: SAH 137
MC: SAH 137C

ANTHOLOGY - NAZARETH.
Tracks: / Telegram (part 1) / On your way (part 2) / So you want to be a rock 'n' roll star (part 3) / Sound check (part 4) / Here we go again / Kentucky fried blues / Somebody to roll / Revenge is sweet / Beggars day / Expect no mercy / No mean city (parts 1 & 2) / Silver dollar forger (parts 1 & 2) / Cocaine (live) / Tush (live) / A-shapes of things B-Space safari / Turn on your receiver / Teenage nervous breakdown / Big boy / Go down fighting / Razamanaz / Vigilante man / Hair for the dog / Broken down angel / I want to do everything for you.
LP: RAWLP 039
MC: RAWTC 039

CATCH, THE.
Tracks: / Party down / Ruby Tuesday / Last exit Brooklyn / Moondance / Love of freedom / This month's messiah / You don't believe in us / Sweetheart tree, The / Road to nowhere.
LP: VERL 20
MC: VERLC 20

CLOSE ENOUGH FOR ROCK AND ROLL.
LP: SAH 126
LP: CLALP 182

EXERCISES.
Tracks: / I will not be led / Cats eye, apple pie / In my time / Woke up this morning / Called her name / Fool about you / Love now you're gone / Madelaine / Sad song / 1692 (Glencoe massacre).
LP: SAH 121

EXPECT NO MERCY.
Tracks: / All the king's horses / Expect no mercy / Gimme what's mine / Gone dead train / Kentucky fried blues / New York broken toy / Place in your heart, A / Revenge is sweet / Shot me down.
LP: SAH 123
LP: TOPS 115
LP: CLALP 187

FOOL CIRCLE, THE.
Tracks: / Dressed to kill / Another year / Moonlight eyes / Pop the silo / Let me be your leader / We are the people / Every young man's dream / Little part of you / Cocaine (live) / Victoria.
LP: CLALP 214

FULL CIRCLE, THE.
Tracks: / Dress to kill / Another year / Moonlight eyes / Pop the silo / Let me be your leader / Victoria / We are the people / Every young man's dream / Little part of you / Cocaine (live).
LP: NEL 6019

GREATEST HITS: NAZARETH.
Tracks: / Razamanaz / Holly roller / Shanghaid in Shanghai / Love hurts / Turn on your receiver / Bad bad boy / This flight tonight / Broken down angel / Hair of the dog / Sunshine / My white bicycle / Woke up this morning.
LP: 9279 545
LP: NEL 6022
MC: NEC 6022
LP: TOPS 108
LP: CLALP 149
MC: CLAMC 149

HAIR OF THE DOG.
Tracks: / Hair of the dog / Miss Misery / Guilty / Changing times / Beggars day / Rose in the heather / Whisky drinking woman / Please don't ....
LP: SAH 124
LP: TOPS 107

HAIR OF THE DOG/ RAMPANT.
2LP: TFOLP 13
MCSET: TFOMC 13

LOUD 'N' PROUD.
Tracks: / Go down fighting / Not faking it / Turn on your receiver / Teenage nervous breakdown / Free wheeler / This flight tonight / Child in the sun / Ballad of Hollis Brown, The.
LP: CREST 4
LP: CLALP 174

MALICE IN WONDERLAND.
Tracks: / Holiday / Showdown at the border / Talkin' to one of the boys / Heart's grown cold / Fast cars / Big boy / Talkin' 'bout love / Fallen angel / Ship of dreams / Turning a new leaf.
LP: TOPS 126
LP: CLALP 181
MC: CLAMC 181

NAZARETH.
LP: TOPC 5001

NO MEAN CITY.
Tracks: / Claim to fame / Just to get into it / May the sunshine / No mean city / Simple solutions / Star / Whatever you want babe / What's in it for me.
LP: SAH 120
LP: TOPS 123
LP: CLALP 213

PLAY 'N' THE GAME.
Tracks: / Somebody to roll / Down home girl / Flying / Waiting for the man / Born to love / I want to do everything for you / I don't want to go on without you / Wild honey / L.A. girls.
LP: SAH 131

RAMPANT.
LP: TOPS 106
LP: CREST 15

RAZAMANAZ.
Tracks: / Razamanaz / Alcatraz / Vigilante man / Woke up this morning / Night woman / Bad bad boy / Sold my soul / Too bad, too sad / Broken down angel.
LP: NEL 6023
MC: NEC 6023
LP: 6303085
LP: CREST 1
LP: TOPS 104
LP: CLALP 173

SINGLES COLLECTION, THE.
Tracks: / Broken down angel / Bad bad boy / This flight tonight / My white bicycle / Out of time / Shanghai'd in Shanghai / Love hurts / Hair of the dog / Holy roller / Carry out feelings / You're the violin / Somebody to roll / I don't want to go on without you / Gone dead train / Place in your heart / May the sunshine / Star / Dressed to kill / Morning dew / Games / Love leads to madness.
2LP: CCSLP 280
MC: CCSMC 280

SNAZ.
Tracks: / Telegram / Razamanaz / I want to do everything for you / This flight tonight / Beggar's day / Every young man's dream / Heart's grown cold / Java blues / Cocaine / Big boy / So you want to be a rock 'n' roll star / Holiday / Let me be your leader / Dressed to kill / Hair of the dog / Expect no mercy / Shapes of things / Love hurts / Morning dew / Juicy Lucy / On your way.
LP: NELD 102
LP: CLALP 130
MC: CLAMC 130

SOUND ELIXIR.
Tracks: / All nite radio / Milk and honey / Whippin' boy / Rain on the window / Back room boy / Why don't you read the book / I ran / Rags to riches / Local still / Where are you now?.
LP: SAH 130

Nazareth House Ceili

NAZARETH HOUSE CEILI BAND (Various artists).
MC: CT 103

NAZARETH HOUSE CEILI BAND FROM DERRY.
LP: TOL 103

Nazty

I GOT TO MOVE.
Tracks: / I got to move / It's Summertime / I need love / Look what you've done / Maybe your baby / Bicentennial rock'n'roll / Within / No deposit, no return / Unlucky love / Space boogie.
LP: CLP 542

Nazz

BEST OF NAZZ.
LP: RNLP 116
MC: RNC 116

N'Dour, Youssou

IMMIGRES BITTIM REW.
Tracks: / Immigres bitim rew / Pitche mi / Taaw / Badou.
LP: EWV 10
MC: TCEWV 10
LP: CEL 6709

LION, THE.
Tracks: / Lion, The / Gaiende / Shakin' the tree / Kocc barma / Bamako / Truth, The / Old tucson / Macdy / My daughter (sama doom) / Bes.
LP: V 2584
MC: TCV 2584

NELSON MANDELA.
LP: ERT 1009

SET.
LP: V 2634
MC: TCV 2634

SHAKIN' THE TREE (See under Gabriel, Peter) (N'Dour, Youssou & Peter Gabriel).

Neal, Kenny

BIO ON THE BAYOU.
LP: BEDLP 6

DEVIL CHILD.
LP: AL 4774

WALKING ON FIRE.
Tracks: / Look but don't touch / Truth hurts, The / I put my trust in you / Blues stew / Morning after / I.O.U. / My only good thing / I been missing you too / Caught in the jaws of a vice / Things to get better / Walking on fire / Bad luck card.
MC: AC 4795

Neal, Raful

I BEEN MISTREATED.
Tracks: / I been mistreated / Down in Louisiana / Hard times / I miss you baby / Man, watch your woman / Spill it on me / Starlight diamond / I have eyes for you / Little red rooster / Still in love with you.
LP: ICH 9004
MC: ICH 9004MC

LOUISIANA LEGEND.
Tracks: / Luberta / Steal away / Blues on the moon / Down and out / You don't love me / No cuttin' loose / Been so long / Late in the evening / Honest I do / Let's work together.
LP: BLUH 003

Near Dark

NEAR DARK (See under 'Tangerine Dream') (Tangerine Dream).

Near Holly

JOURNEYS.
LP: RR 405
MC: RC 405

SKY DANCES.
LP: RR 8902

Neary, Paddy

HIGH LEVELS OF PADDY NEARY THE.
LP: C 1006

HIGHLAND SOUVENIR.
Tracks: / 6/8 marches / Strip the willow / Lara's theme / Turkey in the straw / Whistler and his dog, The / Road to Isles Med / Bunch of thyme / Skyeboat / Green hills of Tyrol / Tourist selection / Scottish waltzes / Film themes / Dark Island / Granny's heilan' hame / Scotch.
LP: TC 1008
LP: C 1009
LP: TC 1009

MUSICAL GEMS.
MC: KITV 512

SOUNDS LIKE ACCORDION.
Tracks: / San Antonio rose / Good, the bad and the ugly, The / Nola / Ave Maria / March with hope / Radetzky march / Tuxedo Junction / Stanchen serenade / Blue Danube / Story of a soldier / Zorba's dance.
LP: BGC 247
MC: KBGC 247

Necessaries

EVENT HORIZON.
Tracks: / Rage / More real / Like no other / Driving and talking at the same time / Aeiou / Sahara / Europe / State of the art / Finish line / Detroit tonight / On the run / Paceways.
LP: SRK 3674

Necessitarians

LUNACY IS LEGEND (See under Sudden, Nikki) (Necessitarians/Nikki Sudden/Times).

Necklace Of Raindrops

NECKLACE OF RAINDROPS, A (Aiken, Joan (author)).
MC: 1690

Necrodeath

FRAGMENTS OF INSANITY.
LP: MET 114

Necronomicon

NECRONOMICON.
LP: 805269

Necrophagia

SEASON OF THE DEAD.
LP: NRR 15
MC: NRC 15

Necros

TANGLED UP.
LP: ENIG 22031

Ned Kelly

NED KELLY (Film Soundtrack) (Various artists).
Tracks: / Ned Kelly: *Various artists* / Wild colonial boy: *Various artists* / Son of a scoundrel: *Various* artists / Shadow of the gallows: *Various artists* / Lonigan's widow: *Various artists* / Stoney cold ground: *Various artists* / Kelly's keep comin': *Various artists* / Ranchin' in the evenin': *Various artists* / Blame it on the Kellys: *Various artists* / Pictures of a Sunday afternoon: *Various artists* / Hey Ned: *Various artists*.
LP: UAS 29108

Nederlands

AKKORDEON IN CONCERT (Nederlands Akkordeon Orkest).
LP: KS 7040

Neds Atomic Dustbin

BITE.
LP: 14011831
LP: CHAPLP 058
MC: CHAPC 058

GOD FODDER.
Tracks: / Kill your television / Less than useful / Selfish / Grey cell green / Cut up throwing things / Capital letters / Happy / Your complex / Nothing like until you find out / You / What gives my son.
LP: 4681121
MC: 4681124

Needs, Lyndon

COOL SCHOOL DAYS.
Tracks: / Country Willie / Lovin' my baby / Swingin' daddy / Just love me / Hello sad eyes / School days / Naggin' woman / Rock 'n' roll coat / Goodbye you devil doll / You way you will / Bop off! / Never gonna work again.
LP: MFLP 018

Neegan, Josephine

FIFTY ODD YEARS (See also Powers, Jimmy) (Neegan, Josephine & Jimmy Powers).

Neels, Betty

WISH WITH THE CANDLES (See also Georgina Melville).
MC: PMB 006

Neely, Bill

BLACKLAND FARM BOY.
LP: ARHOOLIE 5014

Neely, Don

HAPPY FEET (Royal Society Jazz Orchestra).
LP: MMRC 110

JAZZ OF THE ROARING 20S (Royal Society Jazz Orchestra).
LP: MMRC 108

JAZZ OF THE ROARING 20S Volume 2 (Royal Society Jazz Orchestra).
LP: MMRC 109

STARDUST (Royal Society Jazz Orchestra).
LP: MMRC 111

Neep, Rod

HEADING FOR THE SUN.
Tracks: / Walls / Mr. Sax / Jimmy Newman / Catch another butterfly / Fire and rain / My song for you / Merlin / To please her / Soldier / Roses for my lady / George / Heading for the sun / Evening lullaby.
LP: FHR 052

Negapadres 3.3

MESSAGE FROM THE ELEMENT.
LP: CIRCLE 1

Negative Fx

NEGATIVE FX.
LP: HOLY 007

Negative Gain

BACK FROM THE DEAD.
LP: PUS 0012-14

Negative Land

ESCAPE FROM NOISE.
LP: RECREC 17
LP: REC 017

JAMCON 8H.
MC: SSTC 233

PASTOR DICK.
MC: SST 901

Negazione

LITTLE DREAMER.
LP: 081262
LP: WEBITE 30

LO SPIRITO CONTINUA.
LP: K 039 101

MUCCHIO MCLVAGGIO (Negazione/ Declino).
LP: GURT 7

WILD BUNCH.
LP: SPV 086112

Negra, Pata

BLUES DE FRONTORA.
LP: HNBL 1309
MC: HNBC 1309

Negro Religious

NEGRO RELIGIOUS MUSIC VOL.2
Sanctified singers II (Various artists).
LP: BC 18

NEGRO RELIGIOUS MUSIC VOL.3
Singing preachers, The (Various artists).
LP: BC 19

Negro Songs...

NEGRO SONGS OF PROTEST (Various artists).
LP: ROUNDER 4004

Neidlinger, Buell

NEW YORK CITY RHYTHM AND BLUES (See under Taylor, Cecil) (Neidlinger, Buell & Cecil Taylor).

Neighbour Hoods

HOODWINKED.
Tracks: / Hangin' / Roxanne / King of the rats / Hate zone / Evil Knievel / Love holiday / Hoodwinked / Anything / Sea of memories / Southern girls / Nancy.
MC: EMC 9462

REPTILE MEN, THE.
LP: EM 9626

Neighbourhood

CERTAIN ATTITUDE, A.
Tracks: / A - the time (B - the inclination) / Certain attitude, A / Life's big mystery / Big long line / Chances are / Tell me something good / Girls like you / Missing out / Forever / I must have faith (CD only.) / That way (CD only.).
LP: PCS 7326
MC: TCPCS 7326

Neighbourhood Rhythms

NEIGHBOURHOOD RHYTHMS (Various artists).
LP: FRWY 213

Neighbours & Lovers

NEIGHBOURS & LOVERS (Original Cast recording) (Various artists).
Tracks: / Isn't it amazing: *Jarvis, Linda & David Cope* / I love you, I really do: *Jarvis, Linda & David Cope*/ You must understand: *Jarvis, Linda & David Cope* / Who cares what people think: *Jarvis, Linda* / Wouldn't it be wonderful: *Jarvis, Linda* / Yes I love him: *Jarvis, Linda* / Bittersweet anguish: *Jarvis, Linda, David* Cope, Alison Barry, Richard Croxford / If only: *Jarvis, Linda & David Cope* / Yes it's true: *Cope, David*/ It's a fantasy: *Cope, David* / What does he see (when he looks at me): *Barry, Alison* / Don't ask me why: *Barry*, Alison / I feel sorry for her (being married to him): *Croxford, Richard* / Top of the tree: *Croxford, Richard*/ It's New Year's Eve!: *Various artists* / George and Dragon, The: *Various artists* / Everyone needs to be needed (finale): *Various artists*.
MC: SGC 1

Neil

NEIL'S HEAVY CONCEPT ALBUM.
Tracks: / Hello vegetables / Hole in my shoe / Heavy potato encounter / My white bicycle / Neil the barbarian / Lentil nightmare / Computer alarm / Wayne / Gnome, The / Cosmic jam / Golf girl / Bad karma in UK / Our tune / Ken / End of the world cabaret, The / God save the Queen / Floating / Hurdy gurdy man / Paranoid mix / Amoeba song, The.
LP: WX 12
MC: WX 12C

Neil, Fred

VERY BEST OF FRED NEIL.
Tracks: / That's the bag I'm in / Badi-da / Fare thee well / Merry go round / Felicity / Everybody's talkin' / Everything happens / Sweet cocaine / Green rocky road / Cynicrustpetefredjohnraga / Please send me someone to love / Fools are a long time coming / Dolphins, The / I've got a secret (didn't we shake sugaree).
LP: SEE 77

Neilson, Chris

LADY FROM VIRGINIA.
LP: MWSL5 508

Nekroplis

LIVE: NEKROPOLIS.
MC: LIKV 4014

Nelken, Laurie

AUDIO BOOK.
MC: K 300379

Nellis, Jimmy

SORT OF NORMAL.
LP: NERV 3
MC: NERVT 3

Nelmes, Graham

HIGH IS THE TOWER (Nelmes, Graham & Sheila).
LP: TSR 042

Nelson

AFTER THE RAIN.
Tracks: / Can't live without your love and affection / After the rain / More than ever / Fill you up / Bits and pieces / I can hardly wait / Tracy's song / Only time will tell / (It's just) desire / Interlude / Everywhere I go / Will you love me?.
LP: WX 394
MC: WX 394C
LP: GEF 24290
MC: GEFC 24290
LP: DGC 24290
MC: DGCC 24290

Nelson Arion Glee

SLICE OF CHRISTMAS.
LP: LKLP 6550

Nelson, Arnett

WHEN THE MUSIC SOUNDS GOOD 1935-38.
LP: PY 1803

Nelson, Bill

ACONOGRAPHY (Orchestra Arcana).
Tracks: / Christ via wires / Clock conscious / Eastern electric / Search and listen / News from nowhere / One man's fetish is another man's faith / Right then left / Iconography / Gods speak, The / Life class / Altar natives / Sex, psyche, etcetera.
LP: JC 18
MC: TCJC 18

CATALOGUE OF OBSESSIONS.
Tracks: / Sex party six / Tune in Tokyo / Promise of perfume / View from a balcony / Test of affection / Birds in two hemispheres / Wider windows for the walls / Boy pilots of Bangkok, The / Talk technique / Glass breakfast / Edge of tears / Erotikon.
LP: JC 9

CHAMBER OF DREAMS.
Tracks: / Blazing memory of innuendo, The / Into the luminous future / Dip in the swimming / Reactor / Tomorrow land (The threshold of 1947.) / Listening to lizards / Endless torsion / My sublime perversion / Eros in autumn / Sleeplessness / Latest skyline, The / Train of thought / Parks and fountains clouds and trees / Golden bough / Forever Orpheus / In Arcadia / Sentimental / Autumn fires / Wild blue yonder.
LP: JC 7

CHANCE ENCOUNTERS IN THE GARDEN OF LIGHT.
Tracks: / West deep / Spirit cannot fail, The / Pilots of kite / Phantom gardens / Angel of hearth and home, The / Villefranche interior / Night tides / First memory / Azure extension / Radiant spires / Evening peal / Threnodia / Short drink from a certain fountain, A / Body of light / At the centre / Self-initiation / Word that became flesh, The / Hermetic garden, The / Revolving globes / Four square citadel, The / Orient of Memphis / Little daughters of light / Angel at the western window / My dark Daemon / Dove consumed, The (the serpent slumbers) / Calling heaven, calling heaven, over / Path of return / Theurgia / Staircase to no place / Evocation of a radiant childhood / Kingdom of consequence, The / Divine raptures of sisterhood / Bright star (moonlight over ocean blue) / Bird of the air shall carry thy voice, A / Clothed in light amongst the stars / Gnosis / Bringers of light to the feast / Hastening the chariot of my heart's desire / Transcendant / Consolamentum.
LPS: JEAN 20
MCSET: JEANTC 20

CHIMERA.
Tracks: / Real adventure, The / Acceleration / Everyday feels like another new drug / Tender is the night / Glow world / Another day, another ray of hope.
LP: MERB 19
MC: MERBC 19
LP: JCS 17

CHIMES AND RINGS.
Tracks: / Lady you're a strange girl / Call of the wild / Dangerous lady / Giving it all away / Wonder where we go / Sell my soul / I wait for you / Playing Jesus to her Judas / Miracle belongs to you, The / Kiss goodbye / Lost to me / Working man / Ice and fire / Dreams of yesterday / Back to dreams / Walk away from paradise / Something's going on.
MC: TCJC 24

DAS KABINET (THE CABINET OF DR CALIGARI.....&).
Tracks: / Asylum / Waltz / Fairground / Doctor Caligari / Cesare the somnambulist / Murder / Funeral, The / Somnambulist and the children, The / Children, The / Caligari disciplines Cesare / Caligari opens the cabinet / Jane discovers Cesare / Attempted murder of Jane, The / Dream dance of Jane and the somnambulist The / Escape over the rooftops / Unmasking, The / Shot, The / Cabinet closes, The / Overture / Family, The / Sisters and sedan chairs / In the forest of storms / Castle, The / Gates, The / Corridor / Great hall, The / Dreams (the merchant sleeps) / Rose and the beast, The / Magnificent (the white horse) / Beauty enters the castle / Door, The / Mirror, The / Candelabra and the gargoyles / Beauty and the beast / Transition (no.1) / Transition (no.2) / Gift, The / Garden, The / Transition (no.3) / Transition (no.4) / Tragedy, The / Transition (no.5) / Enchanted glove, The / Tears as diamonds (the gift reverses) / Beast in solitude, The / Return of magnificent / Transition (no.6) (The journey.) / Pavillion of Diana, The / Transformation (no.1) / Transformation (no.2) / Final curtain.
LP: JC 2

DAS KABINET/BEAUTY & THE BEAST.
2LP: JCD 4

DETAILS.
Tracks: / Maybe it's the future / Wasted lives / Stay with me / Prisoner of love / Man on fire / World to me, The / Everything permitted / One for you / Wondering / Best of you, The / Love and a bucket full of holes / Don't wait / Visionary / Strong enough / Aeroplane wings / Let it all pass you by.
MC: TCJC 27

DUPLEX.
Tracks: / Flaming desire / Acceleration (remix) / Hope for the heartbeat (remix) / Here and now / Life in your hands / Glow world / Blazing memory of innuendo, The / Angel at the western window / Man in the rexine suit, The / Right then left / Half asleep in a hall of mirrors / Opening / Metaphysical jerks / Loving tongues / Radiant spires / Do you dream in colour / Living in my limousine (remix) / October man / Private view / Contemplation / Another day, another ray of hope / Another tricky mission for the celestial pilot / Portrait of Jan with flowers / Wiping a tear from the all seeing eye / Secret ceremony (theme from Brond) / Broadcast news (from Right to Reply) / Loosening up with lady luck / Garden, The / Burning, the groove of Satyre / Set me a seal upon thine heart.
LP: JCD 22
MC: TCJCD 22

GETTING THE HOLY GHOST ACROSS.
Tracks: / Suvasini / Contemplation / Theology / Wildest dreams / Lost in your mystery / Rise like a fountain / Age of reason / Hidden flame / Because of you / Pansophia / Living for the spangled moment / Word for word / Illusions of you / Heart and soul / Finks and stooges of the spirit.
LP: PRT 26602
MC: 40 26602

HEARTBREAKLAND.
MC: TCJC 26

LIVING FOR THE SPANGLED MOMENT.
LP: BN 1

LOVE THAT WHIRLS.
Tracks: / Empire of the senses / Hope for the heartbeat / Waiting for voices / Eros arriving / Bride of Christ in Autumn, The / When your dream of perfect beauty comes true / Flaming desire / Portrait of Jan with flowers / Crystal escalator in the Palace of God Department Store, The / Echo in her eyes / October man, The / Flesh (Extra track on CD) / He and sleep were brothers (Extra track on CD).
2LP: WHIRL 3
MC: CURL 3

MAP OF DREAMS.
Tracks: / Legions of the endless night / Spinning creatures / At the gates of the singing garden / Heavenly message number one / Heavenly message number three / Fellini's picnic / Dark angel / Infernal regions / Dance of the fragrant woman / Alchemy of ecstacy, The / Aphrodite adorned / Wheel of fortune and the hand of fate, The / Forked tongues, mixed blessings / Another tricky mission for the celestial pilot / Water of life (transfiguration).
LP: JC 19
MC: TCJC 19

NORTHERN DREAM.
LP: BUTT 002

NUDITY.
MC: TCJC 25

OPTIMISM (Nelson, Bill Orchestra Arcana).
Tracks: / Exactly the way you want it / Everyday is a better day / Welcome home, Mr Kane / Greeting a new day / Our lady of apparitions / Deva dance / World thru' fast car window / Daughter of dream come true / Why be lonely / Receiver and the fountain pen, The / This is true / Breath in my father's saxophone, The / Whole city between us, The / Always looking forward to tomorrow / Profiles, hearts, stars / Alchemia.
LP: JC 21
MC: TC 21

PAVILLIONS OF THE HEART AND SOUL.
LP: JC 8

PERMANENT FLAME.
LPS: JEAN 1

QUIT DREAMING AND GET ON THE BEAM.
Tracks: / Banal / Living in my limousine / Vertical games / Disposable / Falso alarms / Decline and fall / Life runs out like sand / Kind of loving, A / Do you dream in colour / UHF / Youth of nations on fire / Quit dreaming and get on the beam / Annunication / Ritual echo, The / Sleep / Near East / Emak Bakia / Endless orchard / My intricate image / Heat in the room / Another willingly opened window / Vanishing parade / Glass fish (for the final aquarium) / Cubical domes / Ashes of roses / Shadow garden, The / Opium / White sound (Extra track on compact disc).
LP: 6359 055
MC: 7557 010

SAVAGE GESTURES FOR CHARMS SAKE.
Tracks: / Man in the rexine suit, The / Watching my dreamboat go down in flames / Meat room, The / Another happy thought (carved forever in your cortex) / Portrait of Jan with moon and stars.
LP: JCM 3
MC: JCS 3

SOUND ON SOUND (Nelson, Bill Red Noise).
Tracks: / Don't touch me / For young moderns / Stop go stop / Furniture music / Radar in my heart / Stay young / Out of touch / Better home in the phantom zone / Substitute flesh / Atom age / Art, empire, industry / Revolt into style.
LP: JC 14
MC: CJC 14
LP: SHSP 4095

SOUNDING THE RITUAL ECHO.
Tracks: / Annunciation / Ritual echo, The / Sleep / Near East / Emak bakia / My intricate image / Endless orchard / Heat in the room / Another willingly opened window / Vanishing parades / Glass fish (for the final aquarium) / Cubical domes / Ashes of roses / Shadow garden, The.
LP: JCS 12

SUMMER OF GOD'S PIANO.
Tracks: / Antennae two / Transmission (N.B.C. 97293) / Sleep of Hollywood, The / Celestial bridegroom, The / Under the red arch / Orient pearl / Sacrament / Falling blossoms / Difficulty of being, The / Zanoni / Chinese nightingale, The / Soon September (another enchantment) / Rural shires / Perfidia (incanto) / Lost years, The / Charm of transit, The / Night thoughts (twilight radio) / Wysteria /

Swing / Snowfall / Real of dusk / Over ocean.
LP: . . . . JC 6
MC: . . . . TCJC 6

TRIAL BY INTIMACY.
Tracks: / Falling blossoms / Listening to lizards / Your nebulous smile.
LPS: . . . . JEAN 2

TWOFOLD ASPECT OF EVERYTHING, THE.
Tracks: / Acceleration (remix) / White sound / Living in my limousine (remix) / Flesh / Eros arriving (single version) / Hope for heartbeat (remix) / Passion, The / Ideal homes / Instantly yours / Atom man loves Radium girl / Mr. Magnetism himself / Burning question, The / Haunting in my head / He and sleep were brothers / Connie buys a kodak / Be my dynamo / Touch and glow / Love without fear / Dada guitare / Turn to fiction / Rooms with brittle views / Love in the abstract / Head facts from the fiction department / Hers is a lush situation / When the birds return / All my wives were iron.
LP: . . . . JC 10

Nelson (bk)

NELSON (history for ages 8+) (Unknown narrator(s)).
MC: . . . . PLB 107

Nelson, Eddy

NELSON AND THE LADIES.
LP: . . . . SR 5002

RUSSIAN SONGS AND ARIAS.
LP: . . . . JN 108

Nelson, Erick

FLOW RIVER FLOW.
LP: . . . . HS 28

Nelson, Jackie

TILL WE MEET AGAIN.
Tracks: / I'll be with you in apple blossom time / Two little orphans / Because he lives / When I grow too old to dream / Bringing Mary home / Aloha-oe / Beautiful lady / I overlooked an orchard / Man of calvary / Answer to everything, The / Sad songs / Home along the highway / Walking talking dolly.
LP: . . . . JULEP 29
LP: . . . . KJULEP 29

WITH LOVE.
Tracks: / Dearest mother mine / Sail away / Please don't go / Love is all / Every step of the way / Guilty / Penny arcade / Old lamplighter / If these lips could only speak / Isle of Innisfree / If I only had time / Mansion over the hilltop.
LP: . . . . BGC 355
MC: . . . . KBGC 355

Nelson, Jimmy

JIMMY MR T-99 NELSON.
Tracks: / T-99 blues / Bad habit blues / Big eyed brown eyed girl of mine / Fine little honey dripper / Secondhand fool / Cry hard luck / Mean poor girl / Big mouth / Baby child / Sweetest little girl.
LP: . . . . CH 35

WATCH THAT ACTION! (Nelson, Jimmy 'T-99').
LP: . . . . CHD 228

Nelson, Louis

APRIL IN NEW ORLEANS (Nelson, Louis & New Orleans Band).
LP: . . . . GHB 241

AT SAN JACINTO HALL (See under Bocage, Peter) (Nelson, Louis/Peter Bocage).

EVERYBODY'S TALKING 'BOUT THE....
LP: . . . . GHB 158

IN GERMANY WITH WHITE EAGLE JAZZBAND (Nelson, Louis/Alton Purnell/Barry Martin).
LP: . . . . GHB 204

LOUIS NELSON BIG FOUR VOL.1.
LP: . . . . GHB 25

LOUIS NELSON BIG FOUR VOL.2.
LP: . . . . GHB 26

LOUIS NELSON'S NEW ORLEANS BAND (Nelson, Louis & New Orleans Band).
MC: . . . . TC 007
LP: . . . . NOLA LP 7

NEW ORLEANS PORTRAITS VOL 3.
LP: . . . . SLP 235

SKATER'S WALTZ (Nelson, Louis/ Barry Martin's Serenaders).
LP: . . . . LPS 2
MC: . . . . TCS 2

Nelson, Mark

SOUTHERN LIGHT.
LP: . . . . FF 405

Nelson, Oliver

BACK TALK (Nelson, Oliver/Lou Donaldson).
Tracks: / Hobo flats / Post no bills / Bientot,A / Three plus one / Take me with you / Daylie's double / Teenie's blues / Laz-ie Kate / Tippin' in / L.D. blues / Days of wine and roses / Ignant oil / Rough house blues / Back talk / Huffin' and puffin'.
2LP: . . . . GCH 2-6032

BLUES AND THE ABSTRACT TRUTH.
Tracks: / Stolen moments / Hoe down / Cascades / Yearnin' / Butch and butch / Teenie's blues.
LP: . . . . JAS 20

HAPPENINGS (Nelson, Oliver-Hank Jones).
Tracks: / Broadwalk samba / Winchester Cathedral / Mas que nada / Lullaby of jazzland / Jazztime USA / Cul de sac / Lou's good dues blues / Fugue tune / Spy with the cold nose, The / Funky but blues.
LP: . . . . JAS 61

MEET OLIVER NELSON.
LP: . . . . OJC 227

MORE BLUES AND THE ABSTRACT TRUTH.
Tracks: / Blues and the abstract truth / Blue o'mighty / Mr. Broadway / Midnight blue / Critics choice / One for Bob / Blues for Mr. Broadway / Goin' to Chicago blues.
LP: . . . . JAS 21
MC: . . . . JAS C21

OLIVER NELSON.
Tracks: / Empty ballroom blues / Duke's place / Echoes of Harlem / Disillusion blues / Yearning / Welcome to New York / Black, brown and beautiful / Rockin' in rhythm / Creole love call / Meditation / Mailman bring me no more blues / Skull session / It's glory.
LP: . . . . NL 86993
MC: . . . . NK 86993

SCREAMIN' THE BLUES.
Tracks: / Screamin' the blues / March on, march on / Drive, The / Meetin' The / Three seconds / Alto-itis.
LP: . . . . OJC 080

SOUL BATTLE (Nelson, Oliver/Jimmy Forrest/King Curtis).
Tracks: / Blues at the Five Spot / Anacruses / In passing / Blues for.M.F / Perdido.
LP: . . . . PR 7223
MC: . . . . PRC 7223

STRAIGHT AHEAD (Nelson, Oliver/Eric Dolphy).
LP: . . . . OJC 099

Nelson, Ozzie

OZZIE NELSON, 1937 (Nelson, Ozzie & His Orchestra).
LP: . . . . CLP 27

OZZIE NELSON, 1937 VOL 2.
Tracks: / You can't stop me from dreaming / Ebb tide / I've got my love to keep me warm / Jelly Fish / One rose, The / Satan takes a holiday / Study in Brown, A / Josephine / Big apple, The / Roses in December / Swing high, swing low / Goodnight my love.
LP: . . . . HSR 189

OZZIE NELSON, 1940-42.
Tracks: / Jersey bounce / Moonlight cocktails / Everyone but me / Idaho / Somebody else is taking my place / Sir Walter's serenade / Breathless / Central Avenue shuffle / Tangerine / Autumn nocturne / Broad jump / I don't want to set the world on fire / Cutting classes / Strictly instrumental / Jersey jive / Texas jump.
LP: . . . . HSR 107

OZZIE NELSON AND HIS ORCHESTRA 1940/42 (Nelson, Ozzie & His Orchestra).
Tracks: / Jersey bounce / Moonlight cocktails / Everyone but me / Idaho / Somebody else is taking my place / Sir Walter's serenade / Breathless / Central Avenue shuffle / Tangerine / Autumn nocturne / Broad jump / I don't want to set the world on fire / Strictly instrumental / Cutting classes / Jersey jive / Texas jump.
LP: . . . . HMP 5041

SATAN TAKES A HOLIDAY (1936 - 41) (Nelson, Ozzie & His Orchestra).
LP: . . . . BS 7119

YOUNG AMERICA'S FAVORITE (Nelson, Ozzie & His Orchestra).
Tracks: / Baby don't tell on me / Riff interlude / I'm looking for a guy who plays alto and barit / Do I love you? / It's a blue world / Alice blue gown / Leanin' on the old top rail / John's idea / Shake down the stars / Poor girl / I've got my eyes on you / With the wind and the rain in your hair / Bee bezindt, A / Careless / Cherokee / All the things you are / Make believe dance land.
LP: . . . . AIRCHECK 19

Nelson, Pat

MORE THAN MEETS THE EYE.
LP: . . . . SFA 004

Nelson, Pete

EVERYBODY'S MAKING IT BIG BUT ME.
Tracks: / Beautiful noise / Everybody's making it big but me / Sweet sweet country music / Door is always open, The / Little bit more, A / Back home again / Cover of the Musical Express / Honey my song is slowly killing me / I just found out today / Apples won't grow in Colorado snow / Feeling single, seeing double / California bloodlines.
LP: . . . . SFA 065

I REMEMBER ELVIS.
LP: . . . . BSS 304

Nelson, Phyllis

MOVE CLOSER.
LP: . . . . CAL 203
MC: . . . . CAC 203

Nelson, Red

RED NELSON: 1935-38.
LP: . . . . DLP 545

Nelson, Rick(y)

20 ROCK'N'ROLL HITS: RICKY NELSON.
LP: . . . . IC 064 82749

ALBUM SEVEN BY RICK.
LP: 1A 058 61357

ALL MY BEST.
LP: . . . . SL 801
MC: . . . . MCSL 801

BEST OF RICKY NELSON (Hello Mary Lou, goodbye heart).
Tracks: / Hello Mary Lou (goodbye heart) / Never be anyone else but you / Be bop baby / Stood up / I got a feeling / Someday / Poor little fool / Waitin' in school / It's late / Lonesome town / Sweeter than you / Have I told you lately that I love you / You are the only one / Mighty good / Yes sir that's my baby / Just a little too much / Everlovin' / Young world / It's up to you / Travelin' man / If you can't rock me / Young emotions / Today's teardrops / Wonder like you, A.
LP: . . . . EMC 3603
MC: . . . . TCEMC 3603

BEST OF RICKY NELSON.
Tracks: / Believe what you say / Poor little fool / It's late / Yes sir that's my baby / Just a little too much / Poor loser / Today's teardrops / Hello Mary Lou / Lonesome two / Sweeter than you / Everlovin' travelin' man / It's up to you / Teenage idol / Someday / Be bop baby / Stood up / Waitin' in school / My bucket's got a hole in it / Never be anyone else but you.
LP: . . . . EG 2607581
MC: . . . . EG 2607584

COLLECTION: RICKY NELSON (Live).
Tracks: / Stood up / Waitin' in school / I got a feeling / Travellin' man / Hello Mary Lou / Garden party / You know what I mean / That's alright mama / Believe what you say / Milk cow blues boogie / Never be anyone else but you / Fools rush in / It's up to you / Poor little fool / It's late / Honky tonk women / My bucket's got a hole in it / Boppin' the blues / Lonesome town.
2LP: . . . . CCSLP 211
MC: . . . . CCSMC 211

COMES OF AGE.
Tracks: / Rock and roll lady / Flower opens gently by, A / Life / Last time around, The / We've got a long way to go / Anytime / Down the Bayou country / Sweet Mary / Let it bring you along / Try (try to fall in love) / Someone to love / Wild nights in Tulsa / I don't want to be lonely tonight / California / Feel so fine / Gypsy pilot.
LP: . . . . SEE 217

COUNTRY FEVER, BRIGHT LIGHTS AND COUNTRY MUSIC.
Tracks: / Salty dog / Truck drivin' man / You just can't quit / Louisiana man / Welcome to my world / Kentucky means paradise / Here I am / Bright lights and country music / Hello walls / No vacancy / I'm a fool to care / Congratulations / Night train to Memphis / Take a city bride / Funny how time slips away / Bridge washed out, The / Alone / Big Chief Buffalo Nickel / Mystery train / Things you gave to me / Take these chains from my heart / Lonesome whistle blow (I heard that) / Walkin' down the line / You win again.
LP: . . . . SEE 84
MC: . . . . SEEK 84

GARDEN PARTY.
LP: . . . . BGOLP 38

GOLDEN GREATS: RICK NELSON.
Tracks: / Garden party / Fools rush in / Gypsy woman / She belongs to me / Mystery train / Since I don't have you / Take these chains from my heart / Legend in my time, A / For you / Very thought of you, The / String along / I got a woman / Reason to believe / It doesn't matter anymore / I think it's gonna rain today / Funny how time slips away.
LP: . . . . MCM 5027
MC: . . . . MCMC 5027

GRAFFITI COLLECTION.
MC: . . . . GRMC 07

GREATEST HITS: RICKY NELSON.
LP: . . . . RNLP 215
LPPD: . . . . RNDF 259

HEY PRETTY BABY.
LP: . . . . RSRLP 1010

INTAKES.
Tracks: / You can't dance / One by one / I wanna move with you / It's another day / Wings / Five minutes more / Change your mind / Something you can't buy / Gimme a little sign / Stay young.
LP: . . . . EPC 81802

LIVE IN LAS VEGAS.
MC: . . . . MFC 078

MORE SONGS BY RICKY.
Tracks: / I'm not afraid / Baby won't you please come home / Here I go again / I'd climb the highest mountain / Make believe / Ain't nothin' but love / When your lover has gone / Proving my love / Hey pretty baby / Time after time / I'm all through with you / Again.
LP: 1A 058 61356

PLAYING TO WIN.
Tracks: / Almost Saturday night / Believe what you say / Little Miss American dream / Loser babe is you / Back to schooldays / It hasn't happened yet / Call it what you want / I can't take it no more / Don't look at me / Do the best you can.
LP: . . . . EST 12109

RICKY.
LP: 2C 068 99106

RICKY IS 21.
LP: 2C 068 60542

RICKY NELSON.
LP: 2C 068 99107

RICKY NELSON SINGS RARE TRACKS.
LP: . . . . UF 4086

RICKY SINGS AGAIN.
LP: 2C 068 60543

ROCKIN' ROCK.
LP: . . . . MCA 414049

ROCKIN' WITH RICKY.
Tracks: / Mighty good / Milk cow blues / If you can't rock me / Bebop baby / There's good rockin' tonight / It's late / Waitin' in school / Shirley Lee / There goes my baby / Boppin' the blues / I got a feeling / My babe / Stood up / Down the line / Almost Saturday night / Believe what you say / Little Miss American dream / Loser babe, is you, The / Back to schooldays / It hasn't happened yet / Call it what you want / I can't take it no more / Don't look at me / Do the best you can.
LP: . . . . CH 85

SINGLES ALBUM (1958-1963), THE.
Tracks: / Bebop baby / Have I told you lately that I love you? / Stood up / Waiting in school / Believe what you say / Poor little fool / Lonesome town / Someday / Never be anyone else but you / It's late / Just a little too much / Sweeter than you / Young emotions / Hello Mary Lou / Travellin' man / Everlovin' / Wonder like you, A / It's a young world / Teenage idol / It's up to you.
LP: . . . . FA 3045
MC: . . . . TCFA 3045
LP: . . . . UAK 30246

SONGS BY RICKY.
LP: 2C 068 61358

STRING ALONG WITH RICK.
Tracks: / String along / Just relax / I'm a fool / Stop, look and listen / Mean old world / Since I don't have you / You don't know me / Blue moon of Kentucky / Louisiana man / Night train to Memphis / Take a broken heart / Your kind of lovin' / Mystery train / Take a city bride / Helpless / Fire-breathing dragon.
LP: . . . . CR 30238

Nelson, Romeo

COMPILATION 1928-29-30 (see Smith, Clarence 'Pinetop' & Romeo Nelson) (Nelson, Romeo & Clarence 'Pinetop' Smith).

Nelson, Sandy

20 ROCK'N'ROLL HITS: SANDY NELSON.
Tracks: / Let there be drums / Tequila / My girl Josephine / All night long / What'd I say? / Splish splash / Kansas City / Bebop baby / Honky tonk / Bony Moronie / Let's go / Drums for strippers only / Limbo rock / All shook up / Yakety yak / Rock around the clock / Bongo rock / Clapping song, The / Treat her right / Cool jerk.
LP: . . . . IC 664 82755

VERY BEST OF SANDY NELSON, THE.
Tracks: / Teenbeat / Big noise from the jungle / Honky tonk / All night long / Drums are my beat / Drumming up a storm / Let there be drums / Land of a thousand dances / Drums a go go / Stripper, The / You name it / And then there were drums.
LP: . . . . SLS 50411

Nelson, Sonny Boy

MISSISSIPPI MATILDA 1936.
LP: . . . . WSE 128

Nelson, Tony

OVERNIGHT SENSATION (Nelson, Tony, Cool Country).
LP: . . . . WRS 121

Nelson, Tracy

COME SEE ABOUT ME.
LP: . . . . FF 209

DOIN' IT MY WAY.
LP: . . . . AD 4119

HOMEMADE SONGS.
LP: . . . . FF 052

Nelson, Tyka

ROYAL BLUE.
Tracks: / No promise / Paris / Marc Antony / Try my passion / My friend / Love / Be good to me / Royal blue / This girl is gonna fall in love.
LP: . . . . CTLP 7
MC: . . . . ZCT 7

Nelson, Willie

18 GOLDEN HITS (Nelson, Willie & Waylon Jennings).
LP: . . . . MA 11141183

18 GREAT SONGS.
LP: . . . . DELP 308
MC: . . . . ZCELP 308

20 GOLDEN CLASSICS: WILLIE NELSON.
LP: 20021
MC: 40021

20 GOLDEN HITS: WILLIE NELSON.
LP: . . . . MA 11121183
MC: . . . . MAMC 911121183

20 OF THE BEST: WILLIE NELSON.
Tracks: / Funny how time slips away / Night life / My own peculiar way / Hello walls / Mr. Record man / To make a long story short (she's gone) / Good times / She's still gone / Little things / Pretty paper / Bloody Mary morning / What can you do to me now? / December day / Yesterday's wine / Me and Paul / Good-hearted woman / She's not for you / It should be easier now / Phases and stages / Circles, cycles and scenes.
LP: . . . . NL 89137
MC: . . . . NK 89137
LP: . . . . INTS 5208

20 OUTLAW REUNION HITS (See under Jennings, Waylon) (Nelson, Willie & Waylon Jennings).

ALWAYS ON MY MIND.
Tracks: / Always on my mind / Blue eyes crying in the rain / Do right woman, do right man / Whiter shade of pale / Let it be / Staring each other down / Bridge over troubled water / Old fords and natural stone / Permanantly lonely / Last thing I needed first thing this morning / Party's over.
LP: . . . . CBS 85685
MC: 40 85685

BEAUTIFUL TEXAS 1936-1986.
Tracks: / Dallas / San Antonio / Streets of Laredo / Who put all my ex's in Texas / Hill country theme / Waltz across Texas / San Antonio rose / Travis letter / Remember the Alamo / Texas in my soul / There's a little bit of everything in Texas / Beautiful Texas / San Antonio rose (2) / Home in San Antone.
LP: . . . . BFX 15256

BEST OF WILLIE NELSON, THE.
Tracks: / Will you remember mine / Some other time / I hope so / Is there something on your mind / Broken promises / Blame it on the times / Face of a fighter / Shelter of my arms / End of understanding / Home is where you're happy / And so will you my love / Waiting time / No tomorrow in sight / Everything but you / Happiness lives next door / Right from wrong / Go away / I'll stay around.
LP: . . . . IC 064 82878
MC: 4XLL 9391
MC: . . . . STAC 2317
LP: . . . . STAR 2317
LP: . . . . TCS 2317

BLUE SKIES.
Tracks: / Blue eyes crying in the rain / Georgia on my mind / All of me / Lucky old sun / Whiskey rover / Always / Moonlight in Vermont / On the sunny side of the street / For the good times / Amazing grace / Stardust / Blue skies / My heroes have always been cowboys / Help me make it through the night / On the road again / Tenderly / Summertime / Unchained melody / Funny how time slips away / Red headed stranger.
LP: . . . . CBS 10025
MC: 40 10025

CITY OF NEW ORLEANS.
Tracks: / City of New Orleans / Just out of reach / Good time Charlie's got the blues / Why are you picking on me? / She's out of my life / Cry / Please come to Boston / It turns me inside out / Wind beneath my wings / Until it's time for you to go.
LP: . . . . CBS 26135
MC: 40 26135

CLASSIC WILLIE NELSON.
Tracks: / Funny how time slips away / Hello walls / Wake me when it's over / Crazy / Touch me / Half a man / Darkness of the face of the earth / Mr. Record man / Country Willie / There'll be no teardrops tonight / Right or wrong / Night life / Seasons of my heart / Columbus stockade blues.
LP: . . . . MFP 5602
MC: . . . . TCMFP 5602
LP: . . . . SLS 50430

COLLECTION: WILLIE NELSON.
Tracks: / On the road again / To all the girls I've loved before / Whiter shade of pale, A / They all went to Mexico / Golden earrings / Always on my mind / City of New Orleans / Seven Spanish angels / Georgia on my mind / Highwayman / Over the rainbow / Let it be me.
LP: 4609301
MC: 4609304

COLLECTION: WILLIE NELSON (2).
Tracks: / Blue eyes crying in the rain / Red headed stranger / Crazy / Stormy weather / Blue skies / Homeward bound / Nightlife / Crazy arms / Old friends / Take it to the limit / Trouble in mind / Trouble maker / Healing hands of time / Will the circle be unbroken / Bridge over troubled water / Poncho and Lefty / On the road again / Time of the preacher / Take this job and shove it / Faded love.
2LP: . . . . CCSLP 178
MC: . . . . CCSMC 178

COUNTRY FAVOURITES.
Tracks: / Columbus stockade blues / Seasons of my heart / I'd trade all of my tomorrows (for just one yesterday) / My window faces the south / Go on home / Fraulein / San Antonio rose / I love hyou because / Don't you ever get tired (of hurting me) / Home in San Antone / Heartaches by the number / Making believe.
LP: . . . . NL 90006
MC: . . . . NK 90006

COUNTRY SONGS (I love country).
Tracks: / Me and Bobby McGee / Songwriter / Till I gain control again / Would you lay with me (in a field of stone) / Angel flying too close to the ground / Please come to Boston / Pretend I never happened / Good time Charlie's got the blues / Heart of gold / Railroad lady / Wind beneath my wings / When I dream / We had it all / That's the way love goes / She's not for you / Old five and dimers like me.
LP: 4510081
MC: 4510084

COUNTRY STORE COLLECTION (See under Jennings, Waylon & Willie Nelson).

COUNTRY STORE: WAYLON JENNINGS AND WILLIE NELSON (See under Jennings, Waylon) (Jennings, Waylon & Willie Nelson).

COUNTRY STORE: WILLIE NELSON.
LP: . . . . CST 22
MC: . . . . CSTK 22

COUNTRY WILLIE.
Tracks: / Country Willie / River boy / Darkness on the face of the Earth / Mr. Record man / Night life / I'll walk alone / Take me as I am (or let me go) / Tomorrow night / Take my word / Home motel / Blue must be the colour of the blues / Feed it a memory / Three days / One step beyond / Undo the right / Right or wrong / Columbus stockade blues / Part where I cry, The / Where my house lives / There goes a man.
LP: . . . . EMS 1252
MC: . . . . TCEMS 1252

FAMILY BIBLE.
LP: . . . . IMCA 37167

FAMOUS COUNTRY MUSIC MAKERS.
Tracks: / Mr. Record Man / It could be said that way / Night life / I gotta get drunk / My own peculiar way / Family bible / One step beyond / Hello walls / Me and Paul / Little things / Wabash cannon ball / Wonderful future / Wake me up when it's over / End of understanding / Who do I know in Dallas? / Funny how time slips away / Suffer in silence / Mountain dew / Moment isn't very long / Healing hands of time / Pretty paper / Darkness on the face of the earth / Yesterday's wine / Sweet memories / One day at a time / Ages / There's a little bit of everything in Texas / Party's over, The.
2LP: . . . . DPS 2062

GEORGIA ON MY MIND.
Tracks: / Stardust / Blue skies / All of me / Unchained melody / September song / On the sunny side of the street / Moonlight in Vermont / Don't get around much anymore / Someone to watch over me.
LP: . . . . SHM 3159
MC: . . . . HSC 3159

GREATEST HITS: WILLIE NELSON.
Tracks: / Railroad lady / Heartaches of a fool / Blue eyes crying in the rain / Whisky river / Good-hearted woman / Georgia on my mind / If you've got the money, I've got the time / Look what thoughts will do / Uncloudy day / Mamas don't let your babies grow up to be cowboys / My heroes have always been cowboys / Help me make it through the night / Angel flying too close to the ground / I'd have to be crazy / Faded love / On the road again / Heartbreak hotel / If you could touch her at all / Till I gain control again / Stay a little longer.
2LP: . . . . CBS 88567
MCSET: 40 88567

HALF NELSON.
Tracks: / Pancho & Lefty / Slow movin' outlaw / Are there any more real cowboys / I told a lie to my heart / Texas on a Saturday night / Seven Spanish angels / To all the girls I've loved before / They all went to Mexico / Honky tonk women / Half a man.
LP: . . . . CBS 26596
MC: 40 26596

HELP ME MAKE IT THROUGH THE NIGHT.
Tracks: / Help me make it through the night / I love you because / Heartaches by the number / Both sides now / Have I told you lately that I love you / I'm so lonesome I could cry / Bring me sunshine / What now my love / Born to lose / Everybody's talkin' / Fire and rain / Funny how time slips away / Yesterday / Pretty paper.
LP: . . . . NL 89475
MC: . . . . NK 89475

HIGHWAYMAN (see under Highwayman) (Nelson, Willie & W.Jennings, Johnny Cash, K.Kristofferson).

HOME IS WHERE YOU'RE HAPPY.
Tracks: / Building heartaches / Slow down / Old world / Healing hands of time / And so will you my love / Things to remember / One step beyond / If you can't undo the right undo the wrong / Home is where you're happy / Moment isn't very long, A / Some other time / Blame it on the times / Shelter of my arms / End of an understanding / Will you remember mine / Everything but you / I hope so.
LP: . . . . SHLP 111
MC: . . . . SHTC 111

HONEYSUCKLE ROSE (Original soundtrack).
Tracks: / On the road again / Pick up the tempo / Heaven or hell / Fiddlin' around / Blue eyes crying in the rain / Working man blues / Jumpin' cotton eyed Joe / Whiskey river / Bloody Mary morning / Loving you was easier than anything / I don't do windows / Coming back to Texas / If you want me to love you I will / It's not supposed to be that way / You show me yours and I'll show you mine / If you could touch her at all / Angel flying too close to the ground / I guess I've come to live here in your eyes / Angel eyes / So you think you're a cowboy / Make the world go away / Two sides to every story / Song for you / Uncloudy day.
2LP: . . . . CBS 22080

HORSE CALLED MUSIC.
Tracks: / Nothing I can do about it now / Highway, The / I never cared for you / If I were a painting / Spirit / There you are / If my world didn't have you / Horse called music, A / Is the better part over.
LP: 4654381
MC: 4654384

ISLAND IN THE SEA.
Tracks: / Island in the sea / Wake me when it's over / Little things / Last thing on my mind / There is no easy way (but there is a way) / Nobody there but me / Cold November wind / Women who love too much / All in the name of love / Sky train.
LP: 4510401
MC: 4510404

JAMMIN' WITH JR (See under Chatwell, J.R.) (Nelson, Willie & J.R. Chatwell).

JUST TO SATISFY YOU (see Jennings, Waylon) (Nelson, Willie & Waylon Jennings).

LEGEND BEGINS, THE.
Tracks: / Some other time / I hope so / Will you remember mine? / Is there something on your mind? / Everything but you / Moment isn't very long, A / Blame it on the times / Face of a fighter / Shelter of my arms / End of understanding.
LP: . . . . ALEB 2302
MC: . . . . ZCALB 2302

LONGHORN JAMBOUREE, THE (Nelson, Willie & Friends).
Tracks: / What a way to live / Misery mansion / Rainy day blues / Night life / Man with the blues / Storm was in my heart, The / West Virginia man / Mississippi woman / What'd I say / Save the last dance for me / Honey don't / Blue suede shoes.
LP: . . . . CR 30120

LOVE SONGS: WILLIE NELSON.
Tracks: / To all the girls I've loved before / Blue skies / Let it be me / Tenderly / Harbour lights / Mona Lisa / To each his own / Over the rainbow / Seven Spanish angels / Georgia on my mind / Bridge over troubled water / Without a song / Unchained melody / That lucky old sun / In my mother's eyes / Always on my mind.
MC: 4674514

LOVE SONGS: WILLIE NELSON (ARENA).
Tracks: / Moment Isn't very long, A / Some other time / Blame it on the times / Shelter of my arms / End of understanding / Will you remember mine / Everything but you / I hope so / Face of a fighter / Is there something on your mind / Follow me around / Any old arms won't do / I just don't understand / You'll always have someone / I feel sorry for him / Suffering in silence / You wouldn't cross the street / I didn't sleep a wink.
LP: . . . . ARA 1009
MC: . . . . ARAC 1009

NIGHT LIFE.
Tracks: / Today I started loving you again / Everybody's talkin' / I'm so lonesome I could cry / One day at a time / Sunday morning coming down / Party's over / Night life / Couple more years / Fire and rain / If you can touch her at all / It's not supposed to be that way / Funny how time slips away.
LP: . . . . CBR 1039
LP: . . . . PMP 1015
MC: . . . . PMPK 1015

OFF THE RECORD WITH WILLIE NELSON.
Tracks: / Some other time / I hope so / Will you remember mine / Is there something on your mind / Everything but you / Moment isn't very long, A / Blame it on the times / Face of a fighter / Shelter of my arms / End of understanding / I'm going to lose a lot of teardrops / Waiting time / No tomorropw in sight / New way to cry, A / Both ends of the candle / Broken promises / Happiness lives next door / Right from wrong / Go away / I'll stay around.
2LP: . . . . FEDD 1008
MCSET: . . . . CFEDD 1008

OLD FRIENDS (Nelson, Willie & Waylon Jennings).
Tracks: / We had it all / Why do I have to choose / Blackjack country chains / Till I gain control again / Why baby why / Old friends / Take it to the limit / Would you lay down with me (In a field of stone) / No love at all / Homeward bound.
LP: . . . . SHM 3212
MC: . . . . HSC 3212

ONE FOR THE ROAD (Nelson, Willie & Leon Russell).
Tracks: / Detour / I saw the light / Heartbreak Hotel / Let the rest of the world go by / Trouble in mind / Don't fence me in / Wild side of life / Ridin' down the Canyon / Sioux City Sue / You are my sunshine / Danny boy / Always / Summertime / Because of you / Am I blue / Tenderly / Far away places / That

lucky old sun / Stormy weather / One for my baby.
2LP: CBS 88461

ONE STEP BEYOND.
Tracks: / I let my mind wander / December days / I can't find the time / I didn't sleep a wink / You wouldn't cross the street / Suffering in silence / I feel sorry for him / You'll always have someone / I just don't understand / Pages / Any old arms won't do / Slow down old world / Healing hands of time / And so will you my love / Things to remember / One step beyond / Undo the wrong / Home is where you're happy / Why are you picking on me / I hope so.
LP: SMT 011

OUTLAWS (Nelson, Willie & Allan Coe).
Tracks: / What a way to live / Misery mansion / Rainy day blues / Night life / Man with the blues / Storm has just begun, The / Got you on my mind / These days / Mississippi woman / Why you been gone so long / Mary Magdelene / West Virginia man.
LP: TOP 133
MC: KTOP 133

OUTLAWS' REUNION (Nelson, Willie & Waylon Jennings).
Tracks: / Crying / Sally was a good old girl / Abilene / It's so easy / Love's gonna live here / Don't think twice / Building heartaches / Mean old greyhound / Is there something on your mind? / Face of a fighter.
LP: SDLP 1005

OUTLAWS' REUNION, VOL.2 (Nelson, Willie & Waylon Jennings).
Tracks: / I hope so / Dream baby / Lorena / Everything but you / Burning memories / Moment isn't very long, A / White lightnin' / Big Mamou / Some other time.
LP: SDLP 1007
MC: SDC 1007

POCHO AND LEFTY (see under Merle Haggard).

PORTRAIT IN MUSIC, A.
Tracks: / Face of a fighter / End of understanding / Some other time / Moment isn't very long, A / Blame it on the times / I hope so / Everything but you / Is there something on your mind? / Will you remember mine? / I'm building heartaches / Slow down old world / Healing hands of time / And so will you, my love / Things to remember / One step beyond / If you can't undo the wrong / Home is where you're happy / Why are you picking on me?.
LP: CBR 1016
MC: KCBR 1016

PRETTY PAPER.
Tracks: / Pretty paper / White Christmas / Winter wonderland / Rudolph the red-nosed reindeer / Jingle bells / Here comes Santa Claus / Blue Christmas / Santa Claus is coming to town / Frosty the Snowman / Silent night, holy night / O little town of Bethlehem / Christmas blues.
LP: CBS 83878

PROMISED LAND (Nelson, Willie & Allan Coe).
Tracks: / Living in the promised land / I'm not trying to forget you / Here in my heart / I've got the craziest feeling / No place but Texas / You're only in my arms (to cry on my shoulder) / Pass it on / Do you ever think of me / Old fashioned love / Basin street blues / Bach minuet in G.
LP: CBS 26852
MC: 40 26852

REPLAY ON WILLIE NELSON.
LP: FEDB 5007
MC: FEDC 5007

SAN ANTONIO ROSE (Nelson, Willie & Ray Price).
Tracks: / San Antonio rose / I'll be there / I fall to pieces / Crazy arms / Release me / Don't you ever get tired / This cold war with you / Funny how time slips away / Night life / Deep water / Faded love.
LP: CBS 84358

SLOW DOWN OLD WORLD.
Tracks: / Any old arms won't do / Slow down old world / Healing hands of time / And so will you, my love / Things to remember / One step beyond / If you can't undo the wrong / Home is where you're happy / Why are you picking on me?.
LP: SDLP 1006
MC: SDC 1006

SONG FOR YOU, A.
Tracks: / Song for you, A / Just as I am / For the good times / Amazing grace / Stormy weather / Blue eyes crying in the rain / Help me make it through the night / Thanks again / One for my baby / Loving her was easier / Moonlight in Vermont / That lucky old sun / Do right woman, do right man / Always on my mind / Whiter shade of pale, A / Let it be me / Staring each other down / Bridge over troubled water / Old fords and a natural stone / Permanently lonely / Last thing I needed first thing this morning / Party's over, The.
LP: SHM 3127
MC: HSC 3127

SOUND IN YOUR MIND.
Tracks: / That lucky old sun / If you've got the money I've got the time / Penny for your thoughts / Healing hands of time / Thanks again / I'd have to be crazy / Amazing grace / Sound in your mind / Funny how time slips away / Crazy / Night life.
MC: 40 22144
LP: CBS 31838

STARDUST.
MC: 40 82710

TAKE IT TO THE LIMIT (Nelson, Willie & Waylon Jennings).
Tracks: / No love at all / Why do I have to choose / Why baby why / We had it all / Take it to the limit / Homeward bound / Blackjack country chains / Till I gain control again / Old friends / Would you lay with me.
LP: CBS 25351
MC: 40 25351

THERE'LL BE NO MORE TEARDROPS TONIGHT.
Tracks: / River boy / I'll walk alone / Take me as I am or let me go / Tomorrow night / Am I blue? / Take my word / Home motel / Blue must be the colour of the blues / There'll be no more teardrops tonight / Feed a memory.
LP: UAS 30215

TOUCH ME.
Tracks: / Touch me / Half a man / You took my happy away / Willingly / How long is forever? / Is this my destiny? / There's gonna be love in my house tonight / Way you see me, The / Let me talk to you / Things I might have been, The / Roly poly / Second fiddle / Lonely little mansion / Opportunity to cry / Cabin of love / I hope so / You dream about me / Last letter, The / There'll be no more teardrops tonight / Funny how time slips away.
LP: ED 2606831
MC: ED 2606834

TOUGHER THAN LEATHER.
Tracks: / My love for the rose / Changing skies / Tougher than leather / Little old fashioned karma / Somewhere in Texas / Beer barrel polka / Summer of roses / Convict and the rose, The / I am the forest / Nobody slides / My friend.
LP: CBS 25063

TROUBLEMAKER.
Tracks: / Uncloudy day / When the roll is called up yonder / Whispering hope / There is a fountain / Will the circle be unbroken / Trouble maker / In the garden / Where the soul never dies / Sweet by and by / Shall we gather? / Precious memories.
LP: CBS 32770
MC: 40 32770

WALKING THE LINE (see under Haggard, Merle) (Nelson, Willie/Merle Haggard/George Jones).

WAYLON AND WILLIE (See under Jennings, Waylon) (Jennings, Waylon & Willie Nelson).

WHAT A WONDERFUL WORLD.
Tracks: / Spanish eyes / Moon river / Some enchanted evening / What a wonderful world / South of the border / Ole buttermilk sky / Song from Moulin Rouge / To each his own / Twilight time / Accentuate the positive.
LP: 4625141
MC: 4625144

WILD AND WILLIE.
Tracks: / I'm going to lose a lot of teardrops / Waiting time / No tomorrow in sight / New way to cry, A / Both ends of the candle / Broken promises / Happiness lives next door / Right from wrong / Go away / I'll stay around.
LP: ALEB 2309
MC: ZCALB 309

WILLIE NELSON.
MCSET: DTO 10087

WILLIE NELSON (I Love Country).
Tracks: / No tomorrow in sight / New way to cry, A / I'll stay around / Broken promises / Lets pretend / Take it to the limit / Angel eyes / I'm movin' on / Faded love / Old friends / Jim, I wore a tie today / I gotta get drunk / Reasons to quit / Seven Spanish angels / Loving her was easier / Show me yours (and I'll show you mine) / They all went to Mexico / Hello walls / There stands the glass / Heartbreak Hotel.
LP: CBS 54946
MC: 40 54946
MC: ZCGAS 757

WILLIE NELSON AND FAMILY IN CONCERT.
Tracks: / Whiskey river / Stay a little longer / Funny how time slips away / Crazy / Night life / If you've got the money, I've got the time / Mama's don't let your babies grow up to be cowboys / I can get off on you / If you could touch her at all / Good hearted woman / Red headed stranger medley / Just as I am / Under the double eagle / Till I gain control again / Bloody Mary morning / I'm a memory / Mr. Record man / Hello walls / One day at a time / Will the circle be unbroken / Amazing grace / Take this job and shove it / Uncloudy day / Only daddy that'll walk the line / Song for you / Roll in my sweet baby's arms / Georgia on my mind / I gotta get drunk.
2LP: CBS 88333

WILLIE NELSON & JOHNNY LEE (Nelson, Willie & Johnny Lee).
LP: 20022
MC: 40022

WINNING HAND, THE (see under Parton, Dolly) (Nelson, Willie/Dolly Parton/Kris Kristofferson/Brenda Lee).

WITHOUT A SONG.
Tracks: / Without a song / Once in a while / Autumn leaves / I can't begin to tell you / Harbour lights / Golden earrings / To each his own / As time goes by / Dreamer's holiday.
LP: CBS 25736
MC: 40 25736

WORLD OF WILLIE NELSON, THE.
Tracks: / Will you remember mine / Some other time / I hope so / Is there something on your mind / Broken promises / Blame it on the times / Face of a fighter / Shelter of my arms / End of understanding / Home is where you're happy / And so will you my love / Waiting time / Everything but you / Happiness lives next door / No tomorrow in sight / Right from wrong / Go away / I'll stay around.
LP: WW 2004
MC: WW 20044

YESTERDAY'S WINE.
Tracks: / Where's the show? / Let me be a man / In God's eyes / Family Bible / It's not for me to understand / These are difficult times / Remember the good times / Summer of roses / December day / Yesterday's wine / Me and Paul / Going home.
LP: INTS 5014
MC: INTK 5014

Nemasheva, Galina

RUSSIAN POPULAR SONGS.
MC: M 00178

Nemesis

DAY OF RETRIBUTION, THE.
LP: ATV 15

MUNCHIES FOR YOUR BASS.
LP: FILER 411
MC: FILERCT 411

TO HELL AND BACK.
LP: FILER 283

Nena

IT'S ALL IN THE GAME.
Tracks: / Utopia / It's all in the game / Young as you / Are you awake? / Woman on fire / Warning signs / Let's humanize / Anyplace, anywhere, anytime / You don't know what love is / Auf wiedersehen.
LP: EPC 26578
MC: 40 26578

NENA.
MC: 40 25925
LP: EPC 25925

Neo Arya

ENTIRE L'AMOUR AT LA HAINE.
LP: BIAS 004

Neo Rockabilly Story

NEO ROCKABILLY STORY VOL 1
Various artists (Various artists).
LP: LPM 8705

NEO ROCKABILLY STORY VOL 3
(Various artists).
LP: LPM 8805

NEO ROCKABILLY STORY VOL 4
(Various artists).
LP: LPM 8806

Neon Hearts

POPULAR MUSIC.
Tracks: / Popular music / Armchair theatre / Pretty as a picture / Pin cushions / Body language / Number one fan / Hideaway / Answers / Get so many pains / Party games.
LP: SATL 4012

Neon Judgement

1981-1984.
LP: FACE 007

ALASKA HIGHWAY.
LP: BIAS 167

BLOOD AND THUNDER.
LP: BIAS 135
MC: BIASC 135

GENERAL PAIN AND MAJOR DISEASE.
LP: BIAS 113
MC: BIAS 113MC

HORNY AS HELL.
LP: BIAS 078

INSULT, THE.
LP: BIAS 175

MAFU CAGE.
LP: BIAS 028

MBIH.
LP: ABR 011

Neon Rome

NEW HEROIN.
LP: ROSE 111

Neptune, Jóhn Kaizan

TOKYOSPHERE.
MC: JC 3316

Neren, Bjarne

MORE THAN YOU KNOW.
Tracks: / When your lover has gone / Everything I have is yours / Easy to love / Autumn nocturne / Miss Mopay / More than you know / Gone with the wind / Cabin in the sky / Emaline.
LP: GMLP 56

Nero, Frances

OUT ON THE FLOOR.
LP: MOTCLP 44

Nero, Peter

HAIL THE CONQUERING NERO.
Tracks: / When the world was young / My bonnie lies over the ocean / Midnight in Moscow / What kind of fool am I / Continental holiday / Granada / Never on Sunday / Londonderry air / Anna / Strange music / Gloomy Sunday / Mack the knife.
LP: NL 89056
MC: NK 89056

SOLID GOLD PIANO.
Tracks: / Moon river / Secret love / Midnight in Moscow / I could have danced all night / I'm gonna sit right down and write myself a letter / Yellow rose of Texas / What kind of fool am I? / Mack the knife / Slow boat to China / Three coins in the fountain / Tea for two / St. Louis blues / Hello Dolly / I want to hold your hand / Days of wine and roses / Walk right in / More / Help / This guy's in love with you / Walk on by.
MC: NK 89138

Neruda (composer)

TRUMPET CONCERTOS AND FANFARES (See under Trumpet Music - Classical) (Philharmonia Orchestra).

Nerve

STUNNING GOOD...FUTURE MAKERS.
LP: OFFENCE 9001

Nerve Senta

NERVE SENTA.
LP: SUPLP 2002

Nervous Choir

HOLD EVERYTHING.
LP: NCC 121

Nervous Eaters

HOT STEEL AND ACID.
LP: ROSE 104

Nervous Fellas

BORN TO BE WILD.
LP: NERD 055

Nervous Germans

DESOLATION ZONE.
Tracks: / These boots are made for walking / Watch out / Bogart / Life ain't pretty / Tropic of Capricorn / Things are getting better / Waiting for the next wave / Inside outside / Home town / Germans can't play rock 'n' roll.
LP: ABOUT 3000
MC: CARB 3000

SUMMER OF LOVE.
LP: 814 261 1

Nervous Norvous

TRANSFUSION.
Tracks: / Transfusion / Dig call / Ape call / Wild dogs of Kentucky / Fang, The / Bullfrog hop.
LP: NED 12

Nervus Rex

NERVUS REX.
Tracks: / There she goes / Go go girl / Spies / Real life / Start from the start / God Sheila / Don't look / Incredible crawling eye / Nobody told me / Venus.
LP: **2394270**

Nesbitt, Cathleen

LITTLE MERMAID, THE (See under Little Mermaid).

Nesbitt, E

BOOK OF DRAGONS, THE (Anderson, Dame Judith).
MC: **1427**

FIERY DRAGON, THE/THE BOOK OF BEASTS (Bliss Caroline/Peter Bartlett).
MC: . . . . **TS 354**

FIVE CHILDREN AND IT (Donald, Sheila (nar)).
MCSET: . . . . **COL 3002**

FOUR DRAGON STORIES (Guthrie, Gwyneth).
MCSET: . . . . **COL 3008**

PHOENIX AND THE CARPET, THE (Donald, Sheila (nar)).
MCSET: . . . . **COL 3009**

RAILWAY CHILDREN, THE (Sheridan, Dinah).
MCSET: . . . . **LFP 7436**

Nesmith, Michael

AND THE HITS JUST KEEP ON COMING (Nesmith, Michael & Countryside Band).
LP: . . . . **ILPS 9439**

BEST OF MIKE NESMITH.
Tracks: / Silver moon / Different drum / Harmony constant / Two different roads / Mama Nantucket / Bonaparte's retreat / Some of Shelly's blues / Rainmaker / Listen to the band / Grand ennui / Nevada fighter / Conversations / Joanne / I've just begun to care.
LP: . . . . **RS 1064**

LOOSE SALUTE (Nesmith, Michael & The First National Band).
MC: . . . . **AWT 1024**

MAGNETIC SOUTH (Nesmith, Michael & The First National Band).
MC: . . . . **AWT 1023**

NEVADA FIGHTER (Nesmith, Michael & The First National Band).
MC: . . . . **AWT 1025**

NEWER STUFF, THE.
LP: . . . . **AWL 1014**
MC: . . . . **AWT 1014**

PRETTY MUCH YOUR STANDARD RANCH STASH (Nesmith, Michael & Countryside Band).
LP: . . . . **ILPS 9440**

PRISON, THE.
MC: . . . . **AWT 1020**

Nestico, Sammy

NIGHT FLIGHT (Nestico, Sammy Big Band).
LP: . . . . **SBD 103**

Nettle, David

TWO PIANOS (Nettle, David/Richard Markham).
Tracks: / Scenes from West Side Story / Fantasy on George Gershwin's Porgy and Bess / Four piece suite.
LP: . . . . **EL 7491161**
MC: . . . . **EL 7491164**

Nettles, John (nar)

NO PLACE TO HIDE (See under No Place to Hide).

Netto, Loz

LOZ NETTO.
Tracks: / Walking in the dark / We touch / Dance to the music / No reaction / Silent movies / Fat city / Do what you want / One night out / Substitute.
LP: **781 651-1**

Nettwerk...

FOOD FOR THOUGHT (Nettwerk Sound Sampler Vol.2) (Various artists).
LP: . . . . **NET 008**
MC: . . . . **NET 008C**

Network 7

NETWORK 7 (THEME FROM) (See under Lindsay, Julian) (Lindsay, Julian).

Netzer, Effi

HAVA NAGILA.
LP: . . . . **EULP 1052**
MC: . . . . **EUMC 1052**

Neu

BLACK FOREST GATEAU.
Tracks: / Halloagalld / Isi / E-musik / Negativland / Seeland / Leb wohl / After eight.
LP: . . . . **BRED 37**

HALLOGALLO.
Tracks: / Hallogallo / Sonderangebot / Weissensee / Jahresuberblick / Im gluck / Negativland / Lieber honig.
LP: **0040145**

Neumann, Ulla Sniff

JOY AND FEELINGS.
LP: . . . . **FLC 5086**

Neuronium

CHROMIUM ECHOES.
Tracks: / Prelude / Chromium echoes / Neutron age, The.
LP: . . . . **THBL 057**

FROM MADRID TO HEAVEN.
Tracks: / Intro / Part 1 / Part 2 / Part 3 / Part 4.
LP: . . . . **THBL 2.064**
DAT: . . . . **DTTB 2.064**

HERITAGE.
LP: . . . . **HIP 19**
MC: . . . . **HIPC 19**

NUMERICA.
Tracks: / 500 years / Deep illness of love / Promenade / Power of your smile, The / Numerica / Maze extreme limits / Au revoir.
LP: . . . . **THBL 082**

SUPERNATURAL.
Tracks: / When the goblins invade Madrid / Digitron / Priorite absolue / Europe is Europe / Sundown at Tanah Lot.
LP: . . . . **THBL 055**

Neuroot

PLEAD INSANITY.
LP: . . . . **HR 014**

Neurosis

PAIN OF MIND.
LP: . . . . **VM 105**
MC: . . . . **VM 105C**

Neurotic Arseholes

LIVE: NEUROTIC ARSEHOLES.
LP: . . . . **WS 023**

Neurotics

IS YOUR WASHROOM BREEDING BOLSHOVICS?.
LP: . . . . **FREUD 19**

KICKSTARTING A BACKFIRING NATION.
LP: . . . . **FREUD 10**
MC: . . . . **FREUDC 10**

REPERCUSSIONS.
LP: . . . . **FREUD 07**

Neustadt, Lisa

SHOUT FOR JOY (Neustadt, Lisa/Angel Band/ Jean Redpath).
LP: . . . . **PH 1068**
MC: . . . . **PH 1068C**

Neutron 9000

GREEN HOUSE EFFECT, THE.
Tracks: / Way to heaven, The / Metropolisation / Neuromatrix / Jemblefruit / Concerto on E / Sentinel / Transoceror / Chiba City / Butterfly holocrust / Forward / Cybersculpture / Last world is everything.
LP: . . . . **FILE 293**
MC: . . . . **FILECT 293**

WALRUS.
LP: . . . . **FILER 407**
MC: . . . . **FILERC 407**

Neuwirth, Bob

BACK TO THE FRONT.
Tracks: / Eye on the road / Annabelle Lee / Private eye / Beauty / Heartaches / Pretend / Turn it around / Venice beach / Lucky / Akron / For P.B..
LP: . . . . **VGC 5**
MC: . . . . **TCVGC 5**

Nevada Beach

ZERO DAY.
LP: . . . . **ZORRO 13**
MC: . . . . **TZORRO 13**

Never Been There

AMBIENCE.
LP: . . . . **VBR 20301**

Never Cry Wolf

NEVER CRY WOLF (Film Soundtrack) (Various artists).
Tracks: / Mrs. Soffel: *Various artists* / Times of Harvey Milk, The: *Various artists* / Never cry wolf: *Various artists.*
LP: **371041-1**
MC: **371041-4**

Never Look Back

NEVER LOOK BACK (see Robins, Denise) (Kempton, Victoria).

Never On Sunday

NEVER ON SUNDAY (Film soundtrack) (Various artists).
LP: . . . . **HAT 2309**

Neverending Story

NEVERENDING STORY (Film soundtrack) (Various artists).
Tracks: / Neverending story, The: *Limahl* / Swamps of sadness: *Various artists* / Ivory tower: *Various artists/* Ruined landscape: *Various artists* / Sleepy dragon: *Various artists* / Bastian's happy flight: *Various artists/* Fantasia: *Various artists* / Atreju's quest: *Various artists* / Theme of sadness: *Various artists* / Atreju meets falkor: *Various artists* / Mirrorgate - Southern oracle: *Various artists* / Gmork: *Various artists/* Moonchild: *Various artists* / Auryn, The: *Various artists* / Happy flight: *Various artists.*
LP: . . . . **NES 1**
MC: . . . . **TC NES 1**
LP: . . . . **EJ 240222-1**
MC: . . . . **EJ 240222-4**

Neves, Castro

PEDRO PAULO, CASTRO NEVES & MICHEL LEGRAND (See under Paulo, Pedro) (Neves, Castro/Pedro Paulo/ Michel Legrand).

Nevil, Robbie

C'EST LA VIE.
Tracks: / Just a little closer / Dominoes / Limousines / Back to you / C'est la vie / Wot's it to ya / Walk your talk / Simple life / Neighbours / Look who's alone tonight.
LP: . . . . **MTL 1006**
MC: . . . . **TCMTL 1006**

PLACE LIKE THIS, A.
Tracks: / Who needs somebody like you / Back on holiday / Mary Lou / Getting better / Love and money / Love is only love / Here I go again / Holding on / Too soon / Can I count on you / Dreams (CD and cassette only).
LP: . . . . **MTL 1037**
MC: . . . . **TCMTL 1037**

Nevill Luxury

FEELS LIKE DANCING WARTIME.
LP: . . . . **REDLP 046**

Neville, Aaron

ALL MY LIFE (See under Ronstadt, Linda) (Neville, Aaron/Linda Ronstadt).

DON'T KNOW MUCH (See under Ronstadt, Linda) (Neville, Aaron/Linda Ronstadt).

HUMDINGER.
Tracks: / Over you / I'm waitin' at the station / Everyday / Sweet little mama / Let's live / Humdinger / Wrong number / Reality / How many times / Don't cry / Get out of my life / I found another love / How could I help but love you / Show me the way.
LP: . . . . **SSL 6011**
MC: . . . . **TCSSL 6011**

MAKE ME STRONG.
Tracks: / Struttin' on Sunday / Hercules / Make me strong / All these things / Baby I'm a want you / Performance / Mojo Hannah / Greatest love, The / One fine day / Tell it like it is / Cry me a river / Been so wrong / Speak to me / Wild flower / Feelings / Nadie / For the good times / She's on my mind.
MC: . . . . **TCCRB 1111**
LP: . . . . **CRB 1111**

ORCHID IN THE STORM.
Tracks: / Pledging my love / For your precious love / Ten commandments of love / This is my story / We belong together / Earth angel.
LP: . . . . **VEX 6**

RULER OF HEARTS/SHOW ME THE WAY (see under Thomas, Irma) (Neville, Aaron/Irma Thomas).

SHOW ME THE WAY.
Tracks: / How could I help but love you / Over you / Even though (reality) / Humdinger / Show me the way / I found another love / How many times / Everyday / Hey little Alice / Sweet little mama / Don't cry / Ticks of the clock / For every boy there's a girl / I'm waiting at the station / Wrong number / I've done it again / Let's live / Get out of my life.
LP: . . . . **CRB 1217**
MC: . . . . **TCCRB 1217**

TELL IT LIKE IT IS (ALBUM).
LP: . . . . **CH 301**

WARM YOUR HEART.
LP: **3971481**
MC: **3971484**

Neville, Art

MARDI GRAS ROCK 'N' ROLL.
Tracks: / Zing zing / Oooh-whee baby / Bella Mae / I'm a fool to care / Cha dooky-doo / Back home to me / What's going on / Old time rock'n'roll / Rockin' pneumonia and the boogie woogie flu / Bring it on home to me / Dummy / Let's rock / Arabian love call / Please listen to my song / Whiffenpoof song, The.
LP: . . . . **CHD 188**

ROCK 'N' SOUL HOOTENANNY.
Tracks: / House on the hill / Skeet scat / Little girl from the candy store / Humdinger / All these things / My baby don't love me no more / Darling, don't leave me this way / Come back love / Hook, line and sinker / Too much / Pain in my heart / Heartaches / I need somebody / You won't do right / That rock 'n' roll beat / Bo Diddley.
LP: . . . . **CRB 1177**

Neville Brothers

BROTHERS KEEPER.
Tracks: / Brother blood / Steer me right / Sons and daughters / Jah love / Witness / Sons and daughters (reprise) / Bird on a wire / Brother Jake / Fearless / Fallin' rain / River of life / My brother's keeper / Mystery train.
LP: **395 3121**
MC: **395 3124**

FIYO ON THE BAYOU.
Tracks: / Hey pocky away / Sweet honey dripper / Fire on the Bayou / Ten commandments / Sitting in limbo / Brother John / Iko iko / Mona lisa / Run Joe.
LP: . . . . **FIEND 65**
MC: . . . . **FIENDCASS 65**

LEGACY (A History Of The Nevilles).
Tracks: / Mardi Gras mambo / Over you / Funky miracle / Little girl from the candy store / Show me the way / Sophisticated Cissy / I'm waiting at the station / My baby don't love me anymore / 6v6 LA / Ride your pony / Wrong number / Cardova / I need someone / How could I help but love you / Cissy strut / Humdinger / That rock'n'roll beat / Chicken strut / Don't cry / All these things / Britches / Even though (reality) / Get out of my life / Darling, don't leave me this way / Live wire / House on the hill (rock'n'roll hootenanny) / Tippi toes / Hook line and sinker / For every boy there's a girl / Art / Same old thing / You won't do right / Everyday / Sweet little mama / Pains in my heart / Joog / Tell it like it is / Hercules / I'm gonna put some hurt on you / Make me strong / Look ka py py / All these things / Ease back / Bo Diddley / Speak to me / Cry me a river / Heartaches / Been so wrong / Message from the Meters / Going home.
MCSET: . . . . **TCNEV 1**

LIVE AT TIPITINAS VOL.2.
LP: . . . . **ESSLP 130**
MC: . . . . **ESSMC 130**
LP: . . . . **FIEND 120**

NEVILLE BROTHERS.
Tracks: / Dancing Jones / Washable ink / All night's alright / Audience for my pain / Breakaway / If it takes all night / I'll take my chances / Vieux carre rouge / Arianne / Speed of light.
LP: . . . . **EST 11865**

NEVILLE-IZATION.
Tracks: / Fever / Woman's gotta have it / Mojo Hannah / Tell it like it is / Why you wanna hurt my heart / Fear, hate, envy, jealousy / Caravan / Big chief / Africa.
LP: . . . . **FIEND 31**
LP: . . . . **BT 1031**
MC: . . . . **BT 1031C**

TREACHEROUS-A HISTORY OF THE NEVILLE BROTHERS 1955-1985.
Tracks: / Mardis gras mambo / Cha dooky-doo / Zing, zing / Over you / Let's live / Waiting at the station / All these things / Wrong number / Tell it like it is / Where is my baby / Hercules / Brother John / Meet de boys on de battlefront / Greatest love, The / Dancing Jones / Arianne / Washable ink / I love her too / Her pocky way / Sitting in limbo / Fire on the Bayou / Fever / Fear, hate, envy, jealousy / Amazing Grace / Down by the riverside / Amen.
2LP: . . . . **RNFP 71494**
MC: . . . . **RNFC 71494**

UPTOWN.
Tracks: / Whatever it takes / Forever...for tonight / You're the one / Money back guarantee (my love is guaranteed) / Drift away / Shek-a-na-na / Old habits die hard / I never need no one / Midnight key / Spirits of the world.
LP: . . . . **FA 3255**
MC: . . . . **TCFA 3255**

YELLOW MOON.
Tracks: / My blood / Yellow moon / Fire and brimstone / Change is gonna come, A / Sister Rosa / With God on our side / Wake up / Voodoo / Ballad of Hollis Brown, The / Will the circle be unbroken / Healing chant / Wild injuns.
LP: . . . . **AMA 5240**
MC: . . . . **AMC 5240**

Neville, Ivan

IF MY ANCESTORS COULD SEE ME NOW.

Tracks: / Not just another girl / Falling out of love.
LP: 834 896-1
MC: 834 896-4

Neville, Mike

LARN YERSEL GEORDIE (See under House, George) (Neville, Mike & George House).

RADIO JARRA SLAX (Neville, Mike & George House).
LP: . . . . MWM SP 8
MC: . . . . MWM CSP 8

SON OF GEORDIE.
MC: . . . . MWMC 104
LP: . . . . MWM 1004 S

New Age

ALL THE MONKEYS AREN'T IN THE ZOO.
LP: . . . . TUX 25

DREAM CODE (Various artists).
Tracks: / Return to Russia: *Various artists* / Present voice: *Various artists* / Moments in love-beaten: *Various* artists / Healing place, The: *Various artists* / End of time, The: *Various artists* / Eyes of the wind: *Various* artists / Paradise lost: *Various artists* / Food for fantasy: *Various artists* / Serengeti: *Various artists*/ Sounds and noises: *Various artists* / Reef moods: *Various artists* / Glow energy: *Various artists* / Timber-wave-reflections: *Various artists.*
MCSET: 710.066/67

DREAM HORSES (Various artists).
MC: . . . . BBM LB 5

DREAM MELODIES (Various artists).
LPS: . . . . NML 1013
MCSET: . . . . ZCNML 1013

DREAM SEQUENCE (Various artists).
2LP: . . . . INTEL 4

INTIMATE TEXTURE OF SOUND, THE (Various artists).
Tracks: / Desert sunrise: *Stainsbury, Trevor* / When it's over: *Isbin, Gilbert* / Sanctuary: *Caulfield, Gary*/ Wood nymphs: *Pierce, Dafydd* / Full moon over still waters: *Stainsbury, Trevor* / Paragania: *Gramophone Society* / Heaven's gate: *Coles, Martin* / Dreaming in Azure Forest: *Maxinca* / Chrana: *Tranceport*/ Intimations of immortality: *O'Neill, Kevin* / Dolphin: *Curtis, Jenny* / Surrounded by shadows: *Gestalt, Myth.*
LP: . . . . HWYL 001

KEYS OF LIFE (Various artists).
LP: . . . . LPCEL 017
MC: . . . . MCCEL 017

MIST ON THE RIDGE (Various artists).
LP: . . . . NAGE 1000

NEW AGE MUSIC (Various artists).
Tracks: / Floating: *Various artists* / Julia's dream: *Various artists* / Quelle Dolce: *Various artists*/ Cloudburst flight: *Various artists* / Just a love song: *Various artists* / Nightmist: *Various artists*/ Astralunato: *Various artists* / Chip meditation: *Various artists* / Gymnopedie: *Various artists* / Quick shot: *Various artists* / Souvenir of China: *Various artists* / Sunbeam: *Various artists* / Midnight on Mars: *Various artists.*
2LP: 80.051/52

NIGHT MUSIC (Various artists).
Tracks: / Ships that pass in the night: *Morrissey Mullen* / Love is: *Roach, David* / Two fools in a storm: *Hamill, Claire* / Song from the heart of a boy: *Hubbard's Cubbard* / Whales: *Themis, John* / Back in love again: *Critchinson, John* / Emily: *Themis, John* / 5 for 3: *Critchinson, John* / I won't last a day without you: *Morrissey, Dick* / Thumbs up: *Mullen, Jim.*
LP: . . . . CODA 7
MC: . . . . COCA 7

NIGHT MUSIC COMPILATION (Various artists).
LP: 834 163-1

PIANO ONE (Various artists).
Tracks: / New feelings: *Kuhn, Joachim* / Merry Christmas Mr Lawrence: *Sakamoto, Ryuichi* / Dark room: *Jobson, Eddie* / Housewife's song, The: *Kuhn, Joachim* / Puppet flower: *Watson, Eric* / Ballooning over Texas: *Jobson, Eddie* / Last regrets: *Sakamoto, Ryuichi* / Disturbance in Vienna: *Jobson, Eddie.*
LP: 209640
MC: 409640

PRIVATE SAMPLER (Various artists).
Tracks: / Homeward bound: *O'Hearn, Patrick* / Piece of time, A: *Summers, Andy* / Marakesh: *Tangerine Dream*/ Wing and a prayer, A: *Van Tieghem, David* / Reunion: *O'Hearn, Patrick* / Swept away: *Yanni* / Keys to imagination: *Yanni* / Neverland: *Ciani, Suzanne* / Prarambh: *Shankar, Ravi* / Tears of joy: *Goodman, Jerry* / Joy dancing: *Colina, Michael* / Theme of secrets: *Jobson, Eddie* / Times twelve: *Kottke, Leo.*
LP: 209646
MC: 409646

New Age Dance

DAWN OF A NEW AGE (Various artists).
LP: . . . . BPLP 4

New Age Steppers

NEW AGE STEPPERS.
LP: . . . . STAT LP 9

THREAT TO CREATION (see Creation Rebels/New Age Steppers) (New Age Steppers/Creation Rebels).

New Air

LIVE AT MONTREAL INTERNATIONAL JAZZ FESTIVAL.
Tracks: / Sir Simpleton / Difda dance / Roll on / Tragedy on a Thursday afternoon / Number one.
LP: . . . . BSR 0084

New Amalgam

ANOTHER TIME.
LP: . . . . VS 100

New American Orchestra

MUSIC FROM BLADE RUNNER.
Tracks: / Love theme / Main title / One more kiss dear / Memories of green / End title / Blade Runner blues / Farewell / End title.
LP: . . . . K 99262
MC: . . . . K 499262

New Art Ensemble

SEEKING.
LP: . . . . REV 9

New Asia

NEW ASIA.
LP: . . . . SITU 3

New Avengers

NEW AVENGERS (TV SERIES) (See under Johnson, Laurie) (Johnson, Laurie).

New Bachelors

NOW AND THEN.
Tracks: / Nelly dean / We could have it all / All in love is fair / I'll take you home again kathleen / Sometimes when we touch / You're my best friend / Fairy dance, The / I write the songs / Six in a bed / Even now / Stay / I wouldn't trade you for the world / Diane / No arms can ever hold you / Unicorn / I believe.
LP: . . . . CBS 54877
MC: 40 54877

New Black Eagle...

KID THOMAS & THE NEW BLACK EAGLE JAZZ BAND (see Thomas, Kid & The New Black Eagle Jazz Band) (New Black Eagle Jazz Band).

NEW BLACK EAGLE JAZZ BAND (New Black Eagle Jazz Band).
LP: . . . . GHB 59

New Celeste

HIGH SANDS AND THE LIQUID LAKE.
LP: . . . . SB 372

ON THE LINE.
LP: . . . . BUR 803

New Choice

AT LAST.
Tracks: / People want bass / Funny feeling / Every story / Yo Lisa / That's what he said / Respect / I don't know / At last / No one else but you / Come get some.
LP: 925752 1
MC: 925752 4

New Christs

DISTEMPER.
LP: . . . . CGAS 810

DIVINE RITES.
LP: . . . . MD 7910

New Christy Minstrels

THREE WHEELS ON MY WAGON.
MCSET: . . . . DTO 10246

New City Jazzmen

ANOTHER MAN DONE GONE.
LP: . . . . FLY 207

GOING TO TOWN.
LP: . . . . FLY 203

TO BE COLLECTED.
LP: . . . . FLY 206

New College Choir

CORONATION ANTHEMS (HANDEL) (see under Handel, G.F. (composer)) (New College Choir/King's consort).

New Creation Singers

SWEETER THAN HONEY.
Tracks: / Perfect peace / I will sing / They that trust / Heartily / Hiding place / Perfect peace (reprise) / I am / My soul, wait / What is a man advantaged? / Lord is merciful, The / Not unto us.
LP: . . . . WING 504
MC: . . . . TC WING 504

New Delta Jazzmen '76

NEW DELTA JAZZMEN, THE.
LP: . . . . SLC 28

New Discoveries

NEW DISCOVERIES (Various).
LP: . . . . PUMPKIN 109

New Dublin Orchestra

REFLECTIONS OF IRELAND.
LP: . . . . HM 023

New Edition

ALL FOR LOVE.
Tracks: / Count me in / Little bit of love, A / Sweet thing / With you all the way / Let's be friends / Kick back / Tonight's your night / Whispers in bed / Who do you trust / School / All for love.
LP: . . . . MCF 3305
MC: . . . . MCFC 3305

CANDY GIRL.
Tracks: / Gimme your love / She gives me a bang / Is this the end / Pass the beat / Popcorn love / Candy girl / Ooh baby / Should have never told me / Gotta have your lovin' / Jealous girl.
LP: . . . . SH 8553
MC: . . . . KSAC 8553

EARTH ANGEL.
Tracks: / Million to one, A / Duke of Earl / Hey there lonely girl / Thousand miles away / What's your name / Tears on my pillow / Blue moon / Since I don't have you / Bring back the memories.
LP: . . . . MCF 3356
MC: . . . . MCFC 3356

HEART BREAK.
LP: . . . . MCA 42207

HEARTBEAT.
LP: . . . . MCF 3422
MC: . . . . MCFC 3422

NEW EDITION.
Tracks: / Cool it now / Mr. Telephone man / I'm leaving you again / Baby love / Delicious / My secret (didja gitit yet) / Hide and seek / Lost in love / Kinda girl we like / Amryann.
LP: . . . . MCF 3238
MC: . . . . MCFC 3238

SEASIDE SPECIAL.
Tracks: / Get a little sand between your toes / Sushine Saturday / Get up and boogie / Drive my car / Action express / Ain't nothing but a house party / La booga rooga / Your song / Daydream / God only knows / Rainy day Sunday / Summer song / Just like a woman / Home made sunshine.
LP: . . . . EPC 82089

New Electric Warriors

NEW ELECTRIC WARRIORS (Various artists).
LP: . . . . MOGO 4011

New England

MORE SCOTT JOPLIN RAGS (New England Conservatory Ragtime Ensemble).
LP: . . . . HSU 5009

RED BACK BOOK, SCOTT JOPLIN RAGS (New England Conservatory Ragtime Ensemble).
Tracks: / Cascades / Sunflower slow drag / Chrysanthemum / Entertainer, The / Ragtime dance / Sugar cane / Easy winners / Maple leaf rag.
LP: . . . . ESD 7175
MC: . . . . TCESD 7175

New Era Jazz Band

TIGHT LIKE THAT.
LP: . . . . AWE 2

New Faces Of...

NEW FACES OF... (see Blockbusters) (Welch, Bill).

New Fast Automatic ...

PEEL SESSIONS: NEW FAST AUTOMATIC DAFFODILS (Two Sessions) (New Fast Automatic Daffodils).
MLP: . . . . SFPMA 209

PIGEONHOLE (New Fast Automatic Daffodils).
LP: . . . . BIAS 185
MC: . . . . BIAS 185MC

New Generation...

NEW GENERATION CUBAN ALL STARS-VOLUME 1 (New Generation Cuban All Stars).
Tracks: / Guaracha para los dedos / Cancion de Jose Lazardo / Chango chango / Montuno de monte afuera / Punto neutro / Siglo li de nuestra era.
LP: 1115941

NEW GENERATION CUBAN ALL STARS-VOLUME 2 (New Generation Cuban All Stars).
Tracks: / Elegua soyu / Songo blue / Siglo I A. N. E. / Yemaya asesu / Danzon para las estrellas marinas / Tormenta Africana.
LP: 1115942

New Grass Revival

BARREN COUNTRY.
LP: . . . . FF 083

COMMONWEALTH.
LP: . . . . FF 254

FLY THROUGH THE COUNTRY.
LP: . . . . FLY 0001
LP: . . . . FF 016

FRIDAY NIGHT IN AMERICA.
Tracks: / Friday night in America / You plant your fields / Let's make a baby king / Do what you gotta do / Let me be your man / Lila / Callin' Baton Rouge / Whatever way the wind blows / Big foot / Angel eyes / I'm down.
LP: C1 90739
MC: C4 90739

HOLD ON TO A DREAM.
Tracks: / Hold on to a dream / One way street / Can't stop now / I'll take tomorrow / Before the heartache rolls in / Looking past you / How about you / Metric lips / I can talk to you / Unconditional love.
LP: . . . . EST 2063
MC: . . . . TCEST 2063

NEW GRASS REVIVAL.
Tracks: / What you do to me / Love someone like me / Lonely rider / Sweet release / How many hearts / In the middle of the night / Saw you runnin' / Ain't that peculiar / Seven by seven.
LP: . . . . AML 3116
MC: . . . . TCAML 3116

ON THE BOULEVARD.
LP: . . . . SH 3745

STORM IS OVER, THE.
LP: . . . . FLY 0002

TOO LATE TO TURN BACK.
Tracks: / White freight liner blues / Good woman's love, A / One more love song / Walk in Jerusalem / Watermelon man / Reach / Sapporo.
LP: . . . . SNTF 722
LP: . . . . FF 050

New Guinea

GIZRA AND BINE PEOPLE, THE.
LP: . . . . LLST 7370

GUITAR SONGS OF PAPUA NEW GUINEA (Various artists).
LP: . . . . LLST 7367

VOICES OF THE RAIN FOREST (Various artists).
Tracks: / From morning night to real morning: *Various artists* / Making sago: *Various artists* / Cutting trees: *Various artists* / Clearing the brush: *Various artists* / Bamboo Jew's harp: *Various artists* / From afternoon to afternoon darkening: *Various artists* / Evening rainstorm: *Various artists* / Drumming: *Various artists*/ Song ceremony: *Various artists* / From night to inside night: *Various artists* / Relaxing by the creek: *Various artists.*
MC: . . . . RACS 0173

New Hawaiians

HAWAIIANS IN SEQUENCE (Smith, Bryan & New Hawaiians).
LP: . . . . DS 009

New Hebrides...

PARADE (New Hebrides String Band).
LP: . . . . VP 422

New High Level Ranters

NEW HIGH LEVEL RANTERS, THE.
Tracks: / Fisherman's friend / Black and grey / Ca'hawkie / Old Drove road, The / Kennedy North / Jim Jones / Tynemouth volunteer fire brigade, The / John Peel / Durham regatta / Little Jeannie / Snows they melt the soonest, The / Yellow haired laddie / Glen Coe march, The / New song of the coal / Skipper's wedding / Duke of Eife, The / Maggie Lauder.
LP: 12TS 425

New Hope Singers

NEW HOPE SINGERS.
LP: . . . . PC 422

New Horizon

SOMETIMES ALLELUIA.
LP: . . . . PC 426

New Information

BEGINNINGS (New Information Dixieland Band).
Tracks: / Muskrat ramble / South / Do you know what it means to miss New Orleans / Ain't gonna give nobody none of my jelly roll / Dr.Jazz / Canal Street

blues / That's a plenty / Just a closer walk with thee / Darktown strutters ball / Tin roof blues / Bourbon Street parade.
LP: . . . . AMB 5201

New Jack City

NEW JACK CITY (Original Soundtrack) (Various artists).
LP: 7599244091
MC: 7599244094

New Jersey Mass Choir

LOOK UP AND LIVE (New Jersey Mass Choir/Don Harper).
LP: . . . . LS R 7084
MC: . . . . LS C 7084

New Kids on the Block

HANGIN' TOUGH.
Tracks: / Right stuff, The / Please don't go girl / I'll be loving you / Cover girl / I need you / Hangin' tough / I remember when / What'cha gonna do (about it) (Only on 12" single.) / My favourite girl / Hold on.
LP: 4608741
MC: 4608744

INTERVIEW PICTURE DISC.
LPPD: . . . . BAK 2167

MERRY, MERRY CHRISTMAS.
Tracks: / This one's for the children / Last night I saw Santa Claus / I'll be missin' you come Christmas / I still believe in Santa Claus / Merry, merry Christmas / Christmas song, The / Funky, funky Xmas / White Christmas / Little drummer boy / This one's for the children (reprise).
LP: 4659071
MC: 4659074

NEW KIDS ON THE BLOCK.
LP: 4675041
MC: 4675044

NO MORE GAMES.
Tracks: / Games (the Kids get hard mix) / Call it what you want (C & C pump it up mix) / Please don't go girl / Cover girl / Baby, I believe in you (Love mix) / Hangin' tough (in a funky way) / Step by step (C & C vocal club mix) / My favourite girl / Valentine girl (C & C quiet storm mix) / You got it (the right stuff) / What'cha gonna do (about it) / Never gonna fall in love again (C & C Music Factory mix).
LP: 4674941
MC: 4674944

STEP BY STEP.
Tracks: / Step by step / Tonight / Baby, I believe in you / Call it what you want / Let's try it again / Happy birthday / Games / Time is on your side / Where do I go from here / Stay with me baby / Funny feeling / Never gonna fall in love again.
LP: 4666861
MC: 4666864

TALKIN' TOUGH.
MC: . . . . MBAK 6018
LP: . . . . BAK 6018

New Legend

NEW LEGEND.
Tracks: / No more crazy nightmares / Mean mistreater / High on music / Lowlands / Lonely 1000 nights, A / Paradise(the price you paid) / Felt so good / Angel of mercy / Crazy mama(little white temptress) / All the love in the world.
LP: . . . . PL 74549
MC: . . . . PK 74549

New Life

SOUL SET FREE (see under Jones, Bobby) (New Life/Bobby Jones).

New London Chorale

YOUNG MESSIAH (Original Cast).
Tracks: / Comfort ye / Every valley / Who shall abide? / O thou that tellest / Unto us a child is born / He shall feed his flock / How beautiful are the feet / He was despised / Hallelujah chorus / I know that my Redeemer liveth / Finale.
LP: . . . . PL 70222
MC: . . . . PK 70222
LP: . . . . MYR 1125
MC: . . . . MC 1125
LP: . . . . RCALP 3104

YOUNG WOLFGANG AMADEUS MOZART, THE.
Tracks: / You know him well / Stay with me 'til the morning / Number 21 (piano) / Surrounded by her mystery / Sinfonia concertante / Ave verum corpus / No need to wait / Say goodbye / I remember / Horn concerto / O Isis and Osiris / Rondo alla turk / Hallelujah chorus.
LP: . . . . PL 71161
MC: . . . . PK 71161

New Lost City Ramblers

20TH ANNIVERSARY CONCERT.
Tracks: / Old Joe Clark / Hot corn, cold corn / Barbara Allen / Freight train / Wreck of the old '97 / C & NW railroad blues / Did you ever see the devil / Keep on the sunny side / Soldier and the lady, The / Cold bottom strut / La cassine special / Give the fiddler a dram / Well may the world go / Medley.
LP: . . . . FF 090

TWENTY YEARS.
LP: . . . . FF 102

New LSO

MAGIC OF STRAUSS.
MC: . . . . BRC 2509

New Mayfair Dance

HARMONY HEAVEN (New Mayfair Dance Orchestra).
Tracks: / My Ohio home / All by yourself in the moonlight / Nobody's fault but your own / Good little, bad little you / My southern home / Do something / Deep hollow / Encore / I'm crazy about you / I'll be getting along / She's my slip of a girl / High society blues / We'll build a little world of our own / My heart is saying / Harmony heaven / Anytime's the time to fall in love / Sitting on a rainbow / Baby you've got the right idea / Your sunny disposition and mine / It must be you.
LP: . . . . SVL 162

New Mexborough...

NEW MEXBOROUGH ENGLISH CONCERTINA QUARTET (New Mexborough English Concertina Quartet).
LP: . . . . PLR 071

New Mississippi Sheiks

NEW MISSISSIPPI SHEIKS AND SAM CHATMON.
LP: . . . . ROUNDER 2004

New Model Army

GHOST OF CAIN, THE.
Tracks: / Hunt, The / Lights go out / 51st State / All of this / Poison Street / Western dream / Love songs / Heroes / Ballad / Master race.
LP: . . . . EMC 3516
MC: . . . . TCEMC 3516
LP: . . . . ATAK 136
MC: . . . . TCATAK 136
LP: . . . . FA 3237
MC: . . . . TCFA 3237

IMPURITY.
Tracks: / Get me out / Space / Innocence / Purity / Whirlwind / Marrakech (Not on album.) / Lust for power / Bury the hatchet / 11 years / Lurhstap / Before I get old / Vanity.
LP: . . . . EMC 3581
MC: . . . . TCEMC 3581

MUSIC AND MEDIA INTERVIEW PICTURE DISC.
LPPD: . . . . MM 1242

NO REST FOR THE WICKED.
Tracks: / Frightened / Ambition / Grandmother's footsteps / Better than them / My country / No greater love / No rest / Young gifted and skint / Drag it down / Shot 18 / Attack, The.
LP: . . . . EJ 240 335 1
MC: . . . . EJ 240 335 4
LP: . . . . FA 3198
MC: . . . . TCFA 3198

RADIO SESSIONS.
LP: . . . . ABT 017

RAW MELODY MEN.
Tracks: / Whirlwind / Charge / Space / Purity / White coats / Vagabonds / Get me out / Lib. Ed. / Better than them / Innocence / Lovesongs / Lurhstaap / Archway towers / Smalltown England / Green and grey / World, The.
MC: . . . . TCEMC 3595
2LP: . . . . EMC 3595

SEVEN SONG MINI LP.
Tracks: / My country (live) / Waiting / 51st state / Hunt, The (live) / White coats / Charge / Chinese whispers.
MLP: . . . . CLP 46928

THUNDER AND CONSOLATION.
Tracks: / I love the world / Stupid questions / 225 / Inheritance / Green and grey / Ballad of Bodmin Pill / Family life / Vagabonds / 125 m.p.h. / Archway towers / Charge (CD only.) / Chinese whispers (CD only.) / Nothing touches (CD only.) / White coats (CD only.).
LP: . . . . EMC 3552
MC: . . . . TCEMC 3552
LP: . . . . FA 3257
MC: . . . . TCFA 3257

VENGEANCE (The Independent Story).
MC: . . . . ABTC 008
LP: . . . . ABT 008

New Moon

NEW MOON/ROSE MARIE (Original cast recordings) (Various artists).
LP: . . . . P 13878
MC: . . . . BT 13878

New Music Style

NEW MUSIC STYLE (Various artists).
LP: . . . . NMLP 74217

New Musik

ANYWHERE.
Tracks: / They all run after the carving knife / Areas / Churches / This world of walter / Luxury / While you wait / Changing minds / Peace / Design / Traps / Division / Back to room one.
LP: . . . . GTLP 044

FROM A TO B.
Tracks: / Straight lines / Sanctuary / Map of you, A / Science / On islands / This world of water / Living by numbers / Dead fish (don't swim home) / Adventures / Safe side, The.
LP: . . . . GTLP 041
MC: . . . . GTMC 041

WARP.
Tracks: / Here come the people / Going round again / Train on twisted tracks / I repeat / All you need is love / Kingdoms for horses / Hunting / New evolutionist / Green & red / Planet doesn't mind / Warp.
LP: . . . . EPC 85567

New Order

BROTHERHOOD.
LP: . . . . FACT 150
MC: . . . . FACT 150 C

COMPLETE PEEL SESSIONS: NEW ORDER.
LP: . . . . SFRLP 110
MC: . . . . SFRMC 110

LOW LIFE.
Tracks: / Sooner than you think / Sub culture / Face up / Love vigilantes / Elegie / Perfect kiss, The / This time of night / Sunrise.
LP: . . . . FACT 100
MC: . . . . FACT 100 C

MOVEMENT.
Tracks: / Dreams never end / Truth / Senses / Chosen time / Him, The / I.C.B. / Doubts even here / Denial.
MC: . . . . FACT 50 C
LP: . . . . FACT 50

NEW ORDER: INTERVIEW PICTURE DISC.
LPPD: . . . . BAK 2035

NEW ORDER, THE.
LP: . . . . FCO 31

POWER, CORRUPTION AND LIES.
Tracks: / Your silent face / Ecstacy / Leave me alone / Age of consent / We all stand / Village, The / 5-8-6.
MC: . . . . FACT 75 C
MC: . . . . FACTUS 12C

SUBSTANCE 1987.
LP: . . . . FACT 200
MC: . . . . FACT 200 C
DAT: . . . . FACT 2000

TECHNIQUE.
Tracks: / Fine time / Love less / Run / Vanishing point / All the way / Guilty partner / Mr. Disco / Dream attack.
LP: . . . . FACT 275
MC: . . . . FACT 275C
DAT: . . . . FACT 275 D

New Order (2)

DECLARATION OF WAR.
LP: . . . . FC 031

New Orleans...

NEW ORLEANS TEA PARTY (Various artists).
LP: . . . . NOLA LP 18

New Orleans All Stars

NEW ORLEANS ALL STARS IN CONCERT.
LP: . . . . DJA 502
MC: . . . . DJCD 502

NEW ORLEANS PARADE.
LP: . . . . DJA 518
MC: . . . . DJC 518

WAY DOWN YONDER.
LP: . . . . NOLA LP 2

New Orleans (Film)

NEW ORLEANS (Film soundtrack) (Various artists).
Tracks: / Free as a bird: *Various artists* / When the saints go marching in: *Various artists* / Westend blues: *Various artists* / Do you know what it means to miss New Orleans?: *Various artists* / Brahms' lullaby: *Various* artists / Tiger rag: *Various artists* / Buddy Bolden's blues: *Various artists* / Basin Street blues: *Various artists* / Raymond Street blues: *Various artists* / Melenberg joys: *Various artists* / Where the blues were born in New Orleans: *Various artists* / Farewell to Storyville: *Various artists* / Beale Street stomp: *Various* artists / Dippermouth blues (slow and fast versions): *Various artists* / Shimme sha wobble: *Various artists*/ Ballin' the jack: *Various artists* / King Porter stomp: *Various artists* / Mahogany Hall stomp: *Various artists* / Endie: *Various artists* / Blues are brewin': *Various artists.*
LP: . . . . GOJ 1025
MC: . . . . GOJC 1025

New Orleans Gospel

NEAR THE CROSS.
LP: . . . . NOLA LP 11

New Orleans Jazz

AT THE KITTY HALLS.
LP: . . . . ARHOOLIE 1013

GRACE AND BEAUTY (New Orleans Ragtime Orchestra).
LP: . . . . DS 214

NEW ORLEANS JAZZ SERENADERS VOL.1 (New Orleans Jazz Serenaders).
LP: . . . . GHB 221

NEW ORLEANS JAZZ SERENADERS VOL.2 (New Orleans Jazz Serenaders).
LP: . . . . GHB 222

PUD BROWN'S TENOR FOR TWO.
LP: . . . . LP 001

New Orleans Joymakers

ALGIERS STRUT.
LP: . . . . SNTF 662

New Orleans Ladies

NEW ORLEANS LADIES: FROM THE VAULTS OF RIC AND R (Various artists).
LP: . . . . ROUNDER 2078
MC: . . . . ROUNDER 2078C

New Orleans Nighthawks

NEW ORLEANS NIGHTHAWKS.
LP: . . . . GHB 98

New Orleans Owls

1925/26.
LP: . . . . VLP 21

NEW ORLEANS OWLS/HALFWAY HOUSE ORCHESTRA VOL.2 (see under Halfway House Orchestra) (Halfway House Orchestra & New Orleans Owls).

New Orleans Parade

NEW ORLEANS PARADE (Various artists).
LP: . . . . ZET 709

New Orleans Ragtime

CREOLE BELLES.
LP: . . . . ARHOOLIE 1058

NEW ORLEANS RAGTIME ORCHESTRA.
LP: . . . . SNTF 632
LP: . . . . GHB 210

New Orleans Rascals

NEW ORLEANS RASCALS.
LP: . . . . SOS 1074
LP: . . . . SOS 1113

New Orleans Rhythm...

NEW ORLEANS RHYTHM KINGS 1934/5 (New Orleans Rhythm Kings 1934/5).
MC: . . . . HM 07

RECORDED 1923 (New Orleans Rhythm Kings).
LP: . . . . SM 3092

New Orleans Saxophone

NEW NEW ORLEANS MUSIC, VOL. 2 (NO Saxophone Ensemble/Improvising Arts Quintet).
LP: . . . . ROUNDER 2066
MC: . . . . ROUNDER 2066C

New Ovation

COUNTRY FAVOURITES.
Tracks: / Open up your heart / If I said you had a beautiful body / Snow white dove / You're my best friend / Try a little kindness / Good luck charm / Having daydreams / Do you know you are my sunshine / Please help me, I'm falling / If you're not happy / Happy family / Mr. Music Man.
LP: . . . . NA 117
MC: . . . . NC 117

NEW OVATION.
MC: . . . . NC 110
LP: . . . . NA 110

New Percussion

GO BETWEEN (New Percussion Group Of Amsterdam, The).
Tracks: / Go between / Redbone / Marimba spiritual / Maenaden.
LP: . . . . EGED 54
MC: . . . . EGEDC 54

New Princess...

GERSHWIN OVERTURES (New Princess Theatre Orchestra).
Tracks: / Damsel in distress / Girl crazy / Of thee I sing / Tip-toes / Primrose / Oh Kay.
LP: . . . . EL 270 575 1

MC: . . . . EL 270 575 4

New Race

FIRST & THE LAST, THE.
LP: . . . . STAT LP 16

New Reflections

BEST OF BEAUTIFUL MUSIC.
Tracks: / That ole devil called love / I should have known better / Crying / Chi Mai / Pie Jesu / Flower duet from Lakme, The / Eastenders / Careless Whisper / I just called to say I love you / Hello / Could it be I'm falling in love / Being with you / Thorn birds / Move closer / Arthur's theme / Hard to say I'm sorry / Deer Hunter, Theme from / One more night / Hill Street blues / I want to know what love is.
LP: . . . . WW 2000
MC: . . . . WW 20004

CHART STRINGS.
MCSET: . . . . M 10254

New Reformation...

BEGINNINGS (New Reformation Dixieland Band).
Tracks: / Muskrat ramble / South / Do you know what it means to miss New Orleans / Ain't gonna give nobody none of my jelly roll / Doctor Jazz / Canal street blues / That's a plenty / Just a closer walk with thee / Darktown strutters' ball.
LP: . . . . AMB 5201

New Rhythm & Blues

WILD WEEKEND.
Tracks: / It's a wild weekend / Little floater / Fire works / Boy's life / If I don't have you / Boozoo / Tha's who / Poppin' circumstance / One and only, The / Immortal for a while / Fraction of action / This love is true / Like a locomotive.
LP: . . . . VUSLP 12
MC: . . . . VUSC 12

New Riders Of The...

MARIN COUNTY LINE (New Riders Of The Purple Sage).
Tracks: / Till I met you / Llywelyn / Knights and queens / Green eyes a flashing / Oh what a night / Good woman likes to drink with the boys / Turkeys in a straw / Jasper / Echoes / Twenty good men / Little Miss Bad / Take a red.
LP: . . . . MCF 2820

NEW RIDERS OF THE PURPLE SAGE (New Riders Of The Purple Sage).
Tracks: / I don't know you / Whatcha gonna do / Portland woman / Henry / Dirty business / Glendale train / Garden of Eden / All I ever wanted / Last lonely eagle / Louisiana lady.
LP: . . . . ED 265

PANAMA RED (New Riders Of The Purple Sage).
LP: . . . . BGOLP 26

New Seekers

15 GREAT HITS.
Tracks: / I'd like to teach the world to sing (in perfect harmony) / Never ending song of love / Beg, steal or borrow / You won't find another fool like me.
LP: . . . . ORBLP 101
MC: . . . . ZCORB 101

BEST OF THE NEW SEEKERS.
Tracks: / I'd like to teach the world to sing/(in perfect harmony) / Circles / Nevertheless (I'm in love with you) / Come softly to me / What have they done to my song, Ma? / Pinball wizard - see me, feel me / You won't find another fool like me / Never ending song of love / Goodbye is just another word / I get a little sentimental over you / Your song / Beg, steal or borrow.
LP: . . . . CN 2075
MC: CN4 2075

BEST OF THE NEW SEEKERS (2).
Tracks: / Never ending song of love / What have they done to my song Ma / Here, there and everywhere / Your song / Nickel song / 18 carat friend / Beautiful people / Gentle on my mind / Come softly to me / I'd like to teach the world to sing / Beg steal or borrow / Blowin' in the wind.
LP: 238 412 1

CIRCLES.
LP: 2442 102

MOTIVE SERIES.
LP: 6321 135
MC: 7152 135

NEVER ENDING SONG OF LOVE.
LP: 2383 126

NEW COLOURS.
LP: 2383 066

NOW.
LP: 2383 195

TOGETHER.
LP: 2383 264

WE'D LIKE TO TEACH THE WORLD TO SING.
LP: 2883 103

New Shetl Band

JEWISH/BALKAN DANCE MUSIC.
MC: . . . . GVMMC 121

New Sister Theatre

NEW SISTER THEATRE, THE Andrews, Lucilla (Jermyn, Jane).
MCSET: . . . . SOUND 14

New Squadronaires

IN THE MOOD.
Tracks: / April in Paris / Body and soul / Kid from Red Bank, The / Tangerine (Vocal by Sheila Southern) / Harlem Nocturne / Fever / Moonlight serenade / One o'clock jump / Doin' Basie's thing / In the mood / Li'l darlin' / Begin the beguine / You made me love you (Vocal by Sheila Southern) / American patrol / Woodchoppers ball.
LP: . . . . CBS 54936
MC: 40 54936

New Vaudeville Band

6 TRACK HITS.
MC: 7SC 5044

LIVE VAUDEVILLE.
LP: . . . . SRTXNV 77092

TAP YOUR FEET.
Tracks: / Tap your feet / Peek-a-boo / Holiday Inn / Finchley Central / Green Street Green / Rosie / Shirl / Lili Marlene / Amy / Waiting for Wendy / Reflections / Whispering / So tired / Shine on harvest moon.
2LP: . . . . CR 5148
MCSET: . . . . CRT 5148

WINCHESTER CATHEDRAL.
LP: C5-558

New Victory Band

ONE MORE DANCE AND THEN.
Tracks: / Harper's frolick / Bonnie Kate / Mountain belle / You can't take that on the train / Charles Lynch's waltz / Cajun waltz / Banks of the Dee, The / Pretty little girl from nowhere / Robbie Hobkirk's polka / Hogmany / Mamie May / I'm gonna get my moustache (blacked) / Corn rigs / One more dance and then / Long long trail.
LP: 12TS 382

New Wave

GUILLOTINE (Various artists).
Tracks: / You beat the hell outa me: *Motors* / Don't dictate: *Penetration* / Do the standing still: *Table*/ Strange girl in clothes: *Avant Gardner* / Traffic light rock: *XTC* / Bermuda: *Erickson, Roky* / All wi doin is defendin: *Poet and the Roots* / Oh bondage, up yours!: *X-Ray Spex*.
LP: . . . . OVED 169

LIVE STIFFS (Various artists).
Tracks: / I knew the bride: *Lowe, Nick* / Let's eat: *Various artists* / Semaphore signals: *Various artists*/ Reconnez cherie: *Various artists* / Police car: *Wallis, Larry* / I just don't know what to do with myself: *Costello, Elvis* / Miracle man: *Costello, Elvis* / Wake up and make love with me: *Dury, Ian*/ Billericay Dickie: *Dury, Ian* / Sex and drugs and rock'n'roll: *Various artists* / Chaos: *Various artists*.
LP: . . . . MFP 50445
LP: . . . . GET 1

METHODS OF DANCE VOL.1 (Various artists).
Tracks: / Groove thang: *Heaven 17* / Going under: *Devo* / Der Mussolini: *DAF* / Beat escape, The: *Fingerprintz*/ Soul warfare: *B.E.F.* / Love song: *Simple Minds* / Great man's secrets: *Magazine* / Art of parties, The: *Japan* / Do or die dub (special edit): *Human League*.
LP: . . . . OVED 5
MC: . . . . OVEDC 5

METHODS OF DANCE VOL.2 (Various artists).
LP: . . . . OVED 7
MC: . . . . OVEDC 7

NEW WAVE (Various artists).
LP: 6300 902

NO WAVE (Various artists).
Tracks: / Going down again: *Various artists* / Is she really going out with him?: *Jackson, Joe* / Roxanne: *Police*/ Don't care: *Kent, Klark* / Love in the first degree: *Various artists* / Headcase: *Various artists* / Take me I'm yours: *Squeeze* / You drive me ape: *Dickies* / Lucky lizard: *Various artists* / Bang bang: *Squeeze* / Line shooter I: *Various artists* / Valid or void: *Shrink* / Office girls: *Kent, Klark*/ Sunday papers: *Jackson, Joe* / Can't stand losing you: *Police* / Hideous: *Dickies*.
LP: . . . . AMLE 68505

SIRE MACHINE TURNS YOU UP (Various artists).
Tracks: / Ramona: *Ramones* / Come out and play: *Paley Brothers* / You gotta lose: *Hell, Richard & The Voidoids*/ Get up stand up: *Velez, Martha* / Mighty idy: *DMZ* / Ain't it fun: *Dead Boys* / True confessions: *Undertones*/ You tore me down: *Flamin' Groovies* / Magic love: *Square* / Hey Joe: *Smith, Patti* / Hand of law: *Radio Birdman* / Who's been sleeping here: *Tuff Darts* / Blank generation: *Hell, Richard & The Voidoids* / (My baby) does good sculptures: *Rezillos*.
LP: . . . . SMP 1

STREETS (Various artists).
Tracks: / Trash: *Doll* / Fear on the streets: *Members* / By my prisoner: *Lurkers* / Isgodaman: *Arthur Comics* / Arabs in Arrads: *Art Attacks* / 19: *Dogs* / Talk talk talk: *Reaction* / College girls: *Cane*/ Cranked up really high: *Slaughter & The...* / Ain't bin to no music school: *Nosebleeds* / Lookalikes: *Drones*/ Hungry: *Zeros* / Bend and flush: *Pork Dukes* / Disastermovie: *Exile* / Jerkin: *Drive* / Innocents: *Cooper Clarke, John* / No more rock'n'roll: *Tractor*.
LP: . . . . BEGA 1

WHO PUT THE BOMP (Various artists).
Tracks: / Giving it all: *Various artists* / Drive: *Various artists* / Fun at the beach: *Various artists*/ Shake it up: *Various artists* / Walking out on love: *Various artists* / Tomorrow night: *Various artists*/ Little girl: *Various artists* / You're so much madder than me: *Various artists* / Him or me: *Various artists*/ That kind of feeling: *Various artists* / Kerouac: *Various artists* / Tell it to Carrie: *Various artists*/ Let's swing: *Various artists* / Captain Nemo: *Various artists* / I'd rather you leave me: *Various artists*/ You don't care: *Various artists* / If she cries: *Various artists* / Dancing the night away: *Various artists*/ Unter der Faust: *Various artists* / She don't know why I'm here: *Various artists* / Wimp: *Various artists*/ Busy man: *Various artists* / Life of crime: *Various artists*.
2LP: . . . . DHS 3

New World Philharmonic

ACE OF THEMES VOL 2.
Tracks: / Dynasty / Terms of endearment / No matter what happens / Thorn birds / Hill St. blues / Up where we belong / Bolero / Body walk / Only he has the power to move me / Almost paradise / Seduction / Memory / Sometimes.
LP: . . . . RBD 1102
MC: . . . . ZCRBD 1102

New World Theatre

LET'S DANCE TO THE HITS OF THE 30'S AND 40'S.
LP: . . . . GGL 0026

New York Citizens

STRANGER THINGS HAVE HAPPENED.
LP: . . . . MRE 020

New York City

I'M DOIN' FINE NOW.
LP: . . . . CHELV 1001
MC: . . . . CHELC 1001

New York City La Beat

NEW YORK CITY LA BEAT.
LP: . . . . LECST 1001

New York Community

GATHERING, THE.
LP: . . . . MYR 1110
MC: . . . . MC 1110

MAKE EVERY DAY COUNT.
Tracks: / Make every day count / Song can reach your heart, A / I'll keep my light in my window / World is waiting for a change, The / Rejoice rejoice / Who do you say I am? / This old man / We can make it.
LP: . . . . PL 12782
MC: . . . . PK 12782

New York Cont...

ARCHIE SHEPP/THE NEW YORK CONTEMPORARY FIVE VOL. (see Shepp,Archie/New York etc.) (New York Contemporary Five).

New York Dolls

AFTER THE STORM (New York Dolls & The Original Pistols).
LP: . . . . RRLP 102

LIPSTICK KILLERS.
MC: . . . . A 104

NEW YORK DOLLS, THE.
Tracks: / Babylon / Bad detective / Bad girl / Chatterbox / Don't start me to talkin' / Frankenstein / Human being / It's too late / Jet boy / Lonely planet boy / Looking for a kiss / Personality crisis / Pills / Private world / Puss 'n' boots / Showdown / Stranded in the jungle / Subway train / Trash / Vietnamese baby / Who are the mystery girls?.
2LP: . . . . PRID 12
MCSET: . . . . PRIDC 12

RED PATENT LEATHER.
Tracks: / Girls / Downtown / Pirate love / Personality crisis / Pills / Something else / Daddy rollin' stone / Dizzy Miss Lizzy.
LP: . . . . FC 007

TOO MUCH TOO SOON.
LP: 6463 064

New York Express

HOT ON THE CLUE.
LP: . . . . CR 19364

New York Gong

ABOUT TIME.
LP: . . . . CRL 5021

New York Grassroots...

SACRED BLACK QUARTET TRADITION (New York Grassroots Gospel).
LP: . . . . GVM 206

New York House

NEW YORK HOUSE'N AUTHORITY (New York House'n Authority).
Tracks: / Fantasy / 2 nite's the nite / All you need / Just the little things / Still waiting / Central Park / World Trade Center / Times Square / Park Avenue South / Village, The.
LP: . . . . SBKLP 1002
LP: 795 400 1
MC: . . . . SBKTC 1002
MC: 795 400 4

New York Jazz Quartet

BLUES FOR SARKA.
LP: . . . . ENJA 3025

OASIS.
LP: . . . . ENJA 3083

SONG OF THE BLACK KNIGHT.
Tracks: / Song of the Black Knight / Time for the dancers / After Paris / Romp in the woods somewhere / Estoril soul / Terezia.
LP: . . . . SNTF 753
MC: . . . . ZCSN 753

SURGE.
LP: . . . . ENJA 2094

New York New Wave

MAX'S KANSAS CITY.
Tracks: / Max's Kansas city, 1976 / Fast, The / Boys will be boys / Knots / Final solution / Shake your ashes / Creamin my jeans / Wow pow bash crash / Flip your wig / Man in me, The / Rocket USA.
LP: 82670

MAX'S KANSAS CITY: VOL 2.
Tracks: / Introduction / Night out / Runaround girl / Don't look back / What we need is some rock / Night rider / Phone call / First rock / Star on the moon / Palace of the king / Stitch in time / Finale.
LP: 82858

New York New York

NEW YORK, NEW YORK (Film soundtrack) (Various artists).
Tracks: / You brought a new kind of love to me: *Various artists* / Flip the dip: *Various artists* / V J Stomp: *Various artists* / Opus No. 1: *Various artists* / Once in a while: *Various artists* / You are my lucky star: *Various artists* / Game over: *Various artists* / It's a wonderful world: *Various artists* / Man I love, The: *Various artists* / Hazoy: *Various artists* / Just you, just me: *Various artists* / There goes the ball game: *Various artists* / Blue moon: *Various artists* / Don't be that way: *Various artists*/ Happy endings: *Various artists* / But the world goes 'round: *Various artists* / New York, New York: *Various* artists / Honeysuckle rose: *Various artists* / Once again right away: *Various artists* / Bobby's dream: *Various artists* / Finale: *Various artists*.
2LP: 1A 154 99290/1

New York New York

NEW YORK NEW YORK (Original soundtrack) (Various artists).
LP: 154 99290.1
MC: 254 99290.1

NEW YORK, NEW YORK VOL.1 (Original Soundtrack) (Various artists).
Tracks: / Main title: *Various artists* / You brought a new kind of love to me: *Minnelli, Liza* / Flip the dip: *Auld, Georgie* / V.J. stomp: *Various artists* / Opus one: *Various artists* / Once in a while: *Minnelli, Liza* / You are my lucky star: *Minnelli, Liza* / Game over: *Auld, Georgie* / It's a wonderful world: *Various* artists / Man I love. (The): *Minnelli, Liza* / Hazoy: *Various artists* / Just you, just me: *Minnelli, Liza*.
MCSET: 3C 254 99290

NEW YORK, NEW YORK VOL.2 (Original Soundtrack) (Various artists).

Tracks: / There goes the ball game: *Minnelli, Liza* / Blue Moon: *Place, Mary Kay & Robert De Niro* / Don't be that way: *Various artists* / Happy endings: *Minnelli, Liza & Larry Kert* / But the world goes round: *Minnelli*, Liza / New York, New York: *Auld, Georgie* / New York, New York: *Minnelli, Liza* / New York, New York (orchestral reprise): *Various artists* / Honeysuckle Rose: *Abbott, Diahnne* / Once again right away: *Auld, Georgie*.
MC: **3C 254 99291**

New York Philharmonic

RICHARD RODGERS & N.Y.PHILHARMONIC (see Rodgers,Richard/N.Y.Philharmonic) (N.Y.Philharmonic/Richard Rodgers).

WORLD'S 25 GREATEST MARCHES, THE (New York Philharmonic Orchestra).
Tracks: / Anchors aweigh / Grand march from Aida / Battle hymn of the Republic / Stars and stripes forever / Washington Post / Semper Fidelis / March of the toreadors / La Marseillaise / Rule Britannia.
LP: . . . . **CBS 79257**

New York Port

THREE THOUSAND MILES FROM HOME.
Tracks: / I got it / I used to hate it ('til I ate it) / I don't want to work today / Rainbow / Three thousand miles from home / Guess I'm gonna cry / Twilight zone / Home on a rainy day.
LP: . . . . **INV 81951**

New York Quartet

NEW YORK QUARTET & IMAMU AMIRI BARAKA (New York Quartet/ Imamu Amiri Baraka).
LP: . . . . **ESP 1004**

New York Saxophone

AMERICAN EXPERIENCE, AN (New York Saxophone Quartet).
LP: . . . . **ST 220**

NEW YORK SAXOPHONE QUARTET (New York Saxophone Quartet).
Tracks: / Three improvisations / Chant d'amour / Chantefleur / Bach's fireworks music / Three jays and a bee / OT / La blues.
LP: . . . . **ST 210**

New York Skyy

FROM THE LEFT SIDE.
Tracks: / Givin' it (to you) / Love attack / Non-stop / Song song, The / Big fun / Love illogical / Tell her you care / Jealousitis / Rock it.
LP: . . . . **EST 2014**
MC: . . . . **TCEST 2014**

GREATEST HITS: NEW YORK SKYY.
LP: . . . . **NYS 1**
MC: . . . . **ZCNYS 1**

INNER CITY.
Tracks: / Because of you / Two hearts / Dancin' to be dancin' / Pay up / Passion in the night / I got your number / Love is blind / Slow motion / It's my life.
LP: . . . . **FL 84161**

SKYYJAMMERS.
Tracks: / Movin' violation / Won't you be mine / This song is for you / Miracle / Skyyjammers / Let love shine / Together / Freak outta.
LP: . . . . **EPC 25110**

SKYYLIGHT.
Tracks: / Bad boy / Married man / Questions no answers / Now that we've found love / Hey girl / Show me the way / She's gone / Swing it.
LP: . . . . **EPC 25632**
MC: **40 25632**

SKYYLINE.
Tracks: / Let's celebrate / Call me / Girl in blue / Jam the box / When you touch me / Gonna get it on / Get into the beat.
LP: . . . . **EPC 85494**

SKYYPORT.
Tracks: / Here's to you / I can't get enough / Superlover / No music / Take it easy / Sun won't shine / For the first time / Arrival.
LP: . . . . **EXCLP 5002**

START OF A ROMANCE.
Tracks: / Start of a romance / Sendin' a message / Feeling it now / Let's touch / Love all the way / Sexy minded / Real love / Sunshine.
LP: . . . . **K 781 853 1**
MC: . . . . **K 781 853 4**

New York Stories

NEW YORK STORIES (Film Soundtrack) (Various artists).
LP: **9608521**
MC: **9608574**

New York Studio...

PLAY FOR ME A LOVE SONG (New York Studio Jazz Ensemble).
Tracks: / Play for me a love song / Deep darkness / Mysterioso / My sunshine and my rainbow.
LP: . . . . **J 006**

New York Voices

NEW YORK VOICES.
LP: . . . . **GRP 95891**
MC: . . . . **GRP 95894**

New York's Sweet...

LOVE CHILD (New York's Sweet Sensation).
LP: **7567913071**
MC: **7567913074**

TAKE IT WHILE IT'S HOT (New York's Sweet Sensation).
Tracks: / Never let you go / Sincerely yours / Love games / Let me be the one / Heartbreak / Take it while it's hot / Victim of love / Hooked on you.
LP: . . . . **K 790 917 1**
MC: . . . . **K 790 917 4**

New Zealand...

AUSTRALIAN TOUR (New Zealand National Youth Jazz Band).
Tracks: / Way out west / Loch Lomond / Comin' thro' the rye / Choral and rock out / Waltzing Matilda / Ceramic city festival / Shadow of your smile / Strangers in the night / Shaft / Now is the hour / O my beloved father.
LP: . . . . **VP 430**

BRASS TO GO (New Zealand Army Band).
Tracks: / Fifth of Beethoven, A / Don't cry for me Argentina / Sweet gingerbread man / M.A.S.H., (theme from) / Thingumy bob / After the lovin' / For to go / From Scotland with love / Hot toddy / Mah na mah na / Holly holy / Hustle, The / Homecoming / Jaws / We love you superstar.
LP: . . . . **OU 2206**

COLONEL BOGEY ON PARADE (See under National Band of New Zealand) (National Band of New Zealand).

CONCERT USA (North Shore Accordion Orchestra).
Tracks: / God defend New Zealand / La scala di seta / Tales of Vienna woods / Sound of Philadelphia, The / Carmen suite / Villia (from Merry Widow) / Rock a Jimmy / Perpetuum mobile.
LP: . . . . **L 37020**

NEW ZEALAND SINGS (New Zealand Maori Chorale).
LP: . . . . **VP 431**

ORIGINAL JAZZ COMPOSERS BY N.Z.S (New Zealand Jazz Orchestra).
LP: . . . . **SLC 174**
MC: . . . . **TC SLC 174**

SONGS OF NEW ZEALAND (New Zealand Maori Chorale).
Tracks: / Ebb tide / Stick game / Takua ahou / Poi waka / Song of farewell / Tahi mitri toru e / Kamate kamate / Tera koutou / Pokarekare / Ha ruru ana / He puti puti poi / Karu karu / Pa mai / E rere taku poi / Toia mai te waka nei / He wawata / Now is the hour / Hoki hoki / Waikaremoana / He haere mai.
LP: . . . . **VP 425**
MC: . . . . **VPS 425**

TRIUMPH BRASS (New Zealand, National Band of).
LP: . . . . **VP 427**

TWENTY GOLDEN MAORI SONGS (New Zealand Maori Chorale).
LP: . . . . **VP 406**

New Zealand Airforce

BLUE DEVILS.
Tracks: / Blue devils march / Beguine festival / Amparita roca / Vanguard overture / Norwegian dance No.2 / Aces high / Marche militaire / Latin and lace / Second suite for military band / Rock encounter / R.A.F. march past.
LP: . . . . **SLC 152**

Newberger, Eli

SHAKE IT DOWN (see Mazzy, Jimmy) (Newberger, Eli/Jimmy Mazzy).

Newberry, Booker III

LOVE TOWN.
Tracks: / Love town / Attitude / Shadows / Love drums / Teddy bear / Morning after the night before / Shower of love / Never gonna let you go.
LP: **815 012-1**
LP: . . . . **MALP 001**
MC: . . . . **ZCMAL 1**

LOVE TOWN (OLD GOLD) (See under Cheri/Murphy's law).

Newborn, Phineas Jr.

FABULOUS PHINEAS.
Tracks: / Sugar Ray / What's new? / Forty-five degree angle / No moon at all / I'll remember April / Cherokee / Back home.
LP: . . . . **PL 43163**

HERE IS PHINEAS NEWBORN JR..
Tracks: / Barbados / All the things you are / More I see you / Celia / Dahoud / Newport blues / I'm beginning to see the light / Afternoon in Paris.
LP: . . . . **K 50522**

LOOK OUT - PHINEAS IS BACK.
Tracks: / Salt peanuts / Man I love, The / You are the sunshine of my life / Abber's song / Tamarind blues / Night in Tunisia / Sometimes I'm happy / Donald's dream.
LP: **231 0801**
MC: **K10 801**

NEWBORN PIANO.
Tracks: / Just in time / Blues theme / Chelsea Bridge / Star eyes / Caravan / It's alright with me / Golden earrings / I can't get started / Sweet and lovely / For all we know / Ain't misbehavin' / Take the 'A' train / Real gone guy / Undecided / Ivy League blues / Gee baby ain't I good to you / I've got the world on a string / Midnight sun never sets, The / Love and marriage / Give me the simple life.
LP: . . . . **VJD 561**

WE THREE (see under Haynes, Roy) (Haynes, Roy Trio).

Newbuild

NEWBUILD (Various artists).
LP: . . . . **STATE 002**

Newbury, Mickey

AFTER ALL THESE YEARS.
Tracks: / Sailor, The / Song of sorrow / Let's say goodbye one more time / That was the way it was then / Country boy Saturday night / Truly blue / Just as long as that someone is you / Over the mountain / Catchers in the rye / I still love you (after all these years).
LP: . . . . **SRM 1-4024**

'FRISCO MABEL JOY.
Tracks: / American trilogy / How many times (must the piper be paid) / Future's not what it used to be, The / Mobile blue / Frisco depot / You're not my same sweet baby / Remember the good / Swiss Cottage place / How I love them old songs.
LP: **74107**

HEAVEN HELP THE CHILD.
Tracks: / Heaven help the child / Good morning dear / Sunshine / Sweet memories / Why you been gone so long / Cortelia Clark / Song for Susan / San Francisco Mabel Joy.
LP: **75055**

HIS EYE IS ON THE SPARROW.
Tracks: / Juble Lee's revival / Westphalia Texas waltz / Wish I was / His eye is on the sparrow / Dragon and the mouse, The / Gone to Alabama / It don't matter anymore / I don't know what they wanted me to say / Saint Cecilia / Juble Lee's revival shout.
LP: . . . . **HA 44011**
MC: . . . . **HA 44011C**

I CAME TO HEAR THE MUSIC.
Tracks: / I came to hear the music / Breeze lullaby / You only live once (in a while) / Yesterday's gone if you see her / Dizzy Lizzy / If I could be / Organized noise / Love look at us now / Baby's not home / I an I ain't two.
LP: **7E 1007**

IN A NEW AGE.
Tracks: / Cortelia Clark / I wish I was a willow tree / Sailor, The / Frisco depot / Poison red berries / Lovers / San Francisco Mabel Joy / American trilogy / All my trials.
LP: . . . . **AB 101**

LIVE AT MONTEZUMA HALL/LOOKS LIKE RAIN.
Tracks: / How I love them old songs / Heaven help the child / Earthquake / Cortelia Clark / I came to hear the music / San Francisco Mabel Joy / Bugger red rap / Bugger red blues / How many times (must the piper be paid) / American trilogy / Please send me someone to love / She even woke me up to say goodbye / Write a song / Angeline / She even woke me up to say goodbye / I don't think about her no more / T-total Tommy / 33rd of August, The / When the baby in my lady gets the blues / San Francisco Mabel Joy / Looks like baby's gone.
2LP: . . . . **E 2007**

SAILOR, THE.
Tracks: / Blue sky shinin' / Let's have a party / There's a part of her holding on somehow / Weed is a weed, A / Let it go / Looking for the sunshine / Darlin' take care of yourself / Long gone / Night you wrote that song.
LP: **9311-44017**

SWEET MEMORIES.
Tracks: / American trilogy / Good morning, dear / If you ever get to Houston / She even woke me up to say Goodbye / Dizzy Lizzy / Sweet memories / Remember the good / Sunshine / Future's not what it used to be, The / How I love them old songs.
LP: . . . . **IMCA 945**

Newcastle Grammar

NOWELL, THE (Music for Christmas) (Newcastle/Tyne Royal Grammar School Choir).
Tracks: / Nowell sing we now all and some (Opus 58) / Resonet in laudibus / Natus est nobis / Neugeborne kindelein, Das (Cantata) / Riu riu (Spanish anon 1556) / Gelobet seist du, Jesu Christe (Chorale prelude for trumpet and organ) / Ubers gebirg Maria geht / I saw three ships (Traditional English) / Watchet auf, ruft uns die stimme (Chorale prelude for trumpet and organ) / Psallite unigenito / In dulci jubilo (Old German melody) / Courons a la fete / Entre le beouf et l'ane / Guillo prend ton tambourine / Stille nacht (Silent night) / Christmas is coming (Traditional melodies) / Twelve days of Christmas, The (Traditional English).
LP: . . . . **APS 363**

Newcastle Utd

NEWCASTLE UTD SOUVENIR ALBUM.
LP: . . . . **MWM SP3**
MC: . . . . **MWM CSP 3**

Newcleus

JAM ON REVENGE.
Tracks: / Computer age / Auto-man / I'm not a robot / Destination Earth (1999) / Jam on revenge / Jam on it / Where's the beat? / No more runnin'.
LP: . . . . **SVLP 6600**
MC: . . . . **ZCSVL 6600**

Newhart, Bob

BEST OF BOB NEWHART.
Tracks: / Introducing tobacco to civilisation / Edison's most famous inventions / Bus drivers' school / Kruschev landing rehearsal / Driving instructor, The / Defusing a bomb / Infinitive number of monkeys / Nudist camp expose.
LP: . . . . **K 46001**
MC: **K4 46001**

BEST OF BOB NEWHART (2).
Tracks: / Driving instructor, The / Introducing tobacco to civilisation / Grace L. Ferguson air line, The / Cruise of the USS Codfish / Retirement party, The / Returning a gift / Ledge psychology.
MC: . . . . **HSC 3288**

BOB NEW ART.
MC: . . . . **SSC 3079**

BOB NEWHART.
Tracks: / Driving instructor / Introducing tobacco to civilisation / Returning a gift / Retirement party / Grace L. Ferguson air line, The / Cruise of the USS Codfish / Ledge psychology.
LP: . . . . **SSP 3079**

BUTTON-DOWN MIND OF BOB NEWHART.
LP: . . . . **WM 4010**

MASTERS.
Tracks: / Grace L. Ferguson air line, The / Returning a gift / Driving instructor, The / Cruise of the USS Codfish / Retirement party, The / Introducing tobacco to civilisation / Ledge psychology.
LP: . . . . **K 36003**

Newhouse, Jerry

BEST OF JERRY NEWHOUSE.
2LP: . . . . **T 5001/2**

Newley, Anthony

ANTHONY NEWLEY: MR PERSONALITY.
Tracks: / Personality / Strawberry fair / Why? / I've waited so long / Darlin' / Bee bom / Once in a lifetime / Pop goes the weasel / Do you mind? / That noise / If she should come to you / And the heavens cried / Girls were made to love and kiss / What kind of fool am I?.
LP: . . . . **TAB 84**

LOVE IS A NOW AND THEN THING.
LP: . . . . **LK 4343**

SINGER AND HIS SONGS THE.
LP: . . . . **UAS 30162**

STOP THE WORLD I WANT TO GET OFF (Original cast).
LP: . . . . **SKL 4142**

TONY.
LP: . . . . **CEL 902**

Newlyn Reelers

BIT MORE ROSIN', A.
MC: . . . . SENC 1076

Newman, Alfred

CLASSIC FILM SCORES BY ALFRED NEWMAN (see under Films) (Various artists).

GREATEST STORY EVER TOLD, THE (Film soundtrack) (See under Greatest Story) (Various artists).

Newman, Bob

HANGOVER BOOGIE.
Tracks: / Hangover boogie / Sweet orchard vine / Rover, rover / Haulin' freight / Sand boogie / Doodle bug / Practice what you preach / Around the corner / Quarantined love / Leftover hash / Chic a choo freight / Lonesome truck driver's blues / Baby take me home with you / I'm gonna give you a dose of your own medicine / Phfft you were gone / It hurts me / Turtle dovin / Tonight's the night / Lonesome sailor's dream.
LP: . . . . BFX 15168

Newman, Chris

CHRIS NEWMAN 2.
LP: . . . . COASTAL 7

LIVING WOOD, THE (See under Ni Chathasaigh, Maire) (Newman, Chris/ Maire Ni Chathasaigh).

Newman, Colin

A - Z.
Tracks: / I've waited for ages / And jury / Alone / Order for order / Image / Life on deck / Troisieme / S-S-S Star eyes / Seconds to last / Inventory / But no / B.
LP: . . . . BEGA 20
LP: . . . . BBL 20
MC: . . . . BBLC 20

COMMERCIAL SUICIDE.
LP: . . . . CRAM 045

IT SEEMS.
LP: . . . . CRAM 058
MC: . . . . CRAM 058C

NOTTO.
LP: . . . . CAD 201

RESURGENCE.
Tracks: / Everything must change / Mama Lou / Davey blue / Carnegie blues / Akua ewie / To the holy land.
LP: . . . . MR 5234

Newman, David

HEATHERS (Film Soundtrack).
LP: . . . . VS 5223
MC: . . . . VSC 5223

MR. DESTINY.
LP: . . . . VS 5299
MC: . . . . VSC 5299

SCRATCH MY BACK.
Tracks: / One step at a time / You gotta keep gotta keep dancin' / Two can do it / Scratch my back / Rock me baby / After the ball / Buggs.
LP: . . . . PR 10108

STILL HARD TIMES.
Tracks: / Shana / One for my baby / To love again / Still hard times / Please send me someone to love.
LP: . . . . MR 5283

WIDE OPEN SPACES (Newman, David 'Fathead' & James Clay).
LP: . . . . OJC 257

Newman, Jackie

JACKIE NEWMAN 1938.
LP: . . . . DLP 550

Newman, Jeff

SLIDIN' SMOKE (see under Auldridge, Mike) (Newman, Jeff & Mike Auldridge).

Newman, Jimmy C.

AL TERRY & JIM NEWMAN (see Terry, Al/Jim Newman) (Newman, Jim/Al Terry).

ALLIGATOR MAN.
Tracks: / Alligator man / Big Mamou / Jole blon / Louisiana man / Hollow log / Pretty Texas girl / Good deal Lucille / Bayou talk / Blues stay away from me / D.J. for a day / Everybody's dying for love / Crazy old heart / Just one more night / Finally / Jungles of the world / Temples of Joy / Conflict / Primitivisation / Keep the children alive / Intentions / Realization / Molecatcher, The / Five gallon jar, The / Mr. Lane's maggot / Green ship, The / Other folks' children / Indian lass, The / Pay me my money down / Balance a straw / Dixie's dog / Treadmill song, The / Bungereye / Bonnie Kate of Aberdeen / Lord Carmarthen's march / Wassailing song, The / Gee whoa, Dobbin / Jack the horse courser / Bonnie bunch of roses, The / Haul away the bowline / Bobbing Joan / Ballad of knocking Nelly, The.
LP: . . . . CR 30240

CAJUN AND COUNTRY TOO.
LP: 6052
MC: . . . . 6052 TC

CAJUN COUNTRY.
Tracks: / Sugar bee / Allons a lafayette / Cajun man can, A / Sweet Suzannah / Alligator man / Diggy liggy lo / Louisiana Saturday night / Jole blon / Cry cry darlin' / Big Mamou / Hippy ti yo / Grand chenier.
LP: . . . . TOP 131
MC: . . . . KTOP 131
LP: . . . . INTS 5186
LP: . . . . NL 70438
MC: . . . . NK 70438

CAJUN COUNTRY CLASSICS.
Tracks: / Alligator man / Thibodeaux & his cajun band / Jambalaya / Jole Blon / Boo-dan / Diggy liggy lo / Big Mamou / Louisiana Saturday night / Cajun man can, A / Big Bayou / Colinda / Basile Waltz / Daydreaming / Lache pas la Patate / Happy Cajun, The / Sugar bee.
MC: . . . . TCCR 30208
LP: . . . . CR 30208

FOLK SONGS OF THE BAYOU COUNTRY.
LP: . . . . HAT 3013

HAPPY CAJUN THE.
LP: . . . . CR 30177

JIMMY C. NEWMAN AND CAJUN COUNTRY (Newman, Jimmy C./Cajun Country).
Tracks: / Cochon de lait / Tawna woo woo / Cajun born / Louisiana, the key to my soul / Ragin' cajun (scattin' cajun) / Good ole boys from Louisiana / Laughin' my way back to Lafayette / My toot toot.
LP: . . . . IMCA 39047

JIMMY NEWMAN.
Tracks: / Everybody's dying for love / Big mamou / Sail along silv'ry moon / Good deal lucille / Alligator man / I'll hold you in my heart / My happiness / Blue darlin' / Guess I fooled everybody / Finally / You're the only star / Give me heaven.
LP: . . . . HAT 3060
MC: . . . . HATC 3060

JIMMY NEWMAN & AL TERRY (see under Al Terry) (Newman, Jimmy & Al Terry).

LACHE PAS LA PATATE.
LP: 140

PROGRESSIVE CC.
Tracks: / Alligator man / Boo-dan / Big Mamou / Thibodeaux & his cajun band / Louisiana man / Jambalaya / Diggy liggy lo / Jole blon / Louisiana Saturday night.
LP: . . . . CRL 5005

WILD 'N' CAJUN.
Tracks: / Oh Louisiana / Daddy's in his pirouge / French song / Scattin' Cajun / Sugar cane / Mississippi River / Louisiana woman / Cajun fais do do / Cajun love / Bizzy bayou / That's all you gotta know / Colinda.
LP: . . . . PL 70437
MC: . . . . PK 70437

Newman, Joe

HANGIN' OUT (Newman, Joe & Joe Wilder).
Tracks: / Midgets, The / Here's that rainy day / Duet / Battle hymn of the Republic / Secret love / You've changed / Lypso mania / He was too good to me.
LP: . . . . CJ 262

HAPPY CATS (Newman, Joe Sextet).
Tracks: / Happy cats / Cocktails for two / Later for the happenings / Buttercup / Robbins nest / They can't take that away from me / Feather's nest / Mean to me / Between the Devil and the deep blue sea / Joe's tune / I never knew it.
LP: . . . . JASM 1008

I FEEL LIKE A NEWMAN.
LP: . . . . BLP 60905

IN A MELLOW MOOD (Newman, Joe Quartet).
LP: . . . . ST 219

IN SWEDEN.
LP: . . . . CAH 4002

SHINY STOCKINGS.
LP: . . . . HD 6611

SIMILAR SOULS.
Tracks: / Bassing around / Mambo for Joe / Midnight fantasy / Oh Joe / O shay / Similar souls / Susette / 'Tater pie / Wolafunt's lament / Old devil moon / I'll get by / Out of nowhere / Speak low / Star eyes / Time / Baby, won't you please come home? / Lover man / Nancy / My old flame / You're my thrill / Travellin' light.
2LP: . . . . VJD 563

WAY DOWN BLUES.
LP: . . . . HD 6612

Newman, Nanette (nar)

ADVENTURES OF DUSTY AND THE DINOSAURS (See under Adventures of...).

VARIOUS FAMOUS FIVE BOOKS (see under Blyton, Enid).

Newman, Randy

AWAKENINGS (FILM SOUNDTRACK) (See under Awakenings).

BEST OF RANDY NEWMAN (Lonely at the top).
Tracks: / Love story / Living without you / I think it's going to rain today / Mama told me not to come / Sail away / Simon Smith and the amazing dancing bear / Political science / God's song (that's why I love mankind) / Rednecks / Birmingham / Louisiana 1927 / Marie / Baltimore / Jolly coppers of parade / Rider in the rain / Short people / I love L.A. / Lonely at the top / My life is good (Extra track on cassette and C.D.) / In Germany before the war (Extra track on cassette and C.D.) / Christmas in Capetown (Extra track on cassette and C.D.) / My old Kentucky home (Extra track on cassette and C.D.).
LP: . . . . WX 101
MC: . . . . WX 101C

BORN AGAIN.
Tracks: / It's the money that I love / Story of a rock and roll band, The / Pretty boy / Mr. Sheep / Ghosts / They just got married / Spies / Girls in my life, The / Half a man / William Brown / Pants.
LP: . . . . K 56663
MC: K4 56663

GOOD OLE BOYS.
Tracks: / Rednecks / Marie / Guilty / Every man a king / Naked man / Back on my feet again / Birmingham / Mr. President (have a pity on the working man) / Lousiana 1927 / Kingfish / Wedding in Cherokee county, A / Rollin'.
LP: . . . . K 54022

LAND OF DREAMS.
Tracks: / Dixie flyer / New Orleans wins the war / Four eyes / Falling in love / Something special / Bad news from home / Roll with the punches / Masterman and Baby J / Follow the flag / It's money that matters / I want you to hurt like I do.
LP: . . . . WX 212
MC: . . . . WX 212 C

LITTLE CRIMINALS.
Tracks: / Baltimore / I'll be home / In Germany before the war / Jolly coppers on parade / Kathleen / Old man on the farm / Rider in the rain / Short people / Sigmund Freud's impersonation of Albert Einstein In America / Texas girl at the funeral of her father / You can't fool the fat man.
MC: K4 56404
LP: . . . . K 56404

NATURAL, THE (FILM) (See under 'Natural').

PARENTHOOD (FILM) (See under Parenthood).

RANDY NEWMAN: LIVE.
Tracks: / Mama told me not to come / Tickle me / I'll be home / So long dad / Living without you / Last night I had a dream / I think it's gonna rain today / Lover's prayer / Maybe I'm doing it wrong / Yellow man / Old Kentucky home / Cowboy / Davy the fat boy / Lonely at the top.
LP: . . . . K 44151

SAIL AWAY.
Tracks: / Sail away / It's lonely at the top / He gives us all his love / Last night I had a dream / Simon Smith and the amazing dancing bear / Old man / Burn on big river / Memo to my son / Dayton, Ohio, 1903 / You can leave your hat on / God's song (that's why I love mankind) / Political science.
LP: . . . . K 44185

TROUBLE IN PARADISE.
Tracks: / I love L.A. / Christmas in Capetown / Blues, The / Same girl / Mikey's / My life is good / Miami / Real emotional girl / Take me back / There's a party at my house / I'm different / Song for the dead.
LP: . . . . W 3755
MC: . . . . W 3755 4
LP: . . . . ED 305

TWELVE SONGS.
Tracks: / Have you seen my baby / Let's burn down the cornfield / Mama told me not to come / Suzanne / Lover's prayer / Lucinda / Underneath the Harlem moon / Yellow man / Old Kentucky home / Rosemary / If you need oil / Uncle Bob's midnight blues.
LP: . . . . K 44084

Newman, Richard

POETRY POLITICS & THE ART OF THE ACOUSTIC GUITAR.
Tracks: / On a common or in a park / Mr. Politician / Show me the moon and show me the stars / Fenland boy / North country way / Lost and found / Root / I walked in Piccadilly / Black dog / Tomorrow, today / Let my soul be free.
LP: . . . . CRL 003
MC: . . . . CRL 003C

Newman, Steve

TANANAS.
LP: . . . . AM 1011

Newman, Thomas

WELCOME HOME ROXY CARMICHAEL (Original soundtrack).
LP: . . . . VS 5300
MC: . . . . VSC 5300

Newman, Tom

ASPECTS.
LP: . . . . NAGE 7
MC: . . . . NAGEC 7

BAYOU MOON.
LP: . . . . NAGE 2
MC: . . . . NAGEC 2

Newport Jazz Festival

BERN CONCERT '89 (Various artists).
Tracks: / I want to be happy: *Newport Jazz Festival* / Jeep's blues: *Newport Jazz Festival* / Just a gigolo: *Newport* Jazz Festival (CD only.) / I'm just a lucky so and so: *Newport Jazz Festival* / Johnny come lately: *Newport Jazz* Festival / Blue and sentimental: *Newport Jazz Festival* / In a sentimental mood: *Newport Jazz Festival* (CD only.) / Jumpin' at the woodside: *Newport Jazz Festival.*
MC: . . . . CJ 401C

EUROPEAN TOUR (Various artists).
Tracks: / Tickle toe: *Newport Jazz Festival* / Mood indigo: *Newport Jazz Festival* / Love me or leave me: *Newport* Jazz Festival / These foolish things: *Newport Jazz Festival* / Take the 'A' train: *Newport Jazz Festival*/ Things ain't what they used to be: *Newport Jazz Festival* / Through for the night: *Newport Jazz Festival.*
LP: . . . . CJ 343
MC: . . . . CJC 343

Newport Male Voice

LOVE ME TENDER.
Tracks: / Going home / Long and winding road, The / Seventy-six trombones / Love me tender / Yesterday / Bridge over troubled water / Lara's theme / Maria / Scarborough fair / Still, still, still / If / Battle hymn of the Republic.
LP: 2383 438

News From Babel

LETTERS FROM HOME.
LP: . . . . UNKNOWN

News & The Blues

NEWS AND THE BLUES - TELLING IT LIKE IT IS (Various artists).
MC: 4672494

Newsome, Chubby

ORIGINAL HIP SHAKIN' MAMA.
Tracks: / Hip shakin' mama / Chubby's confession / Back bitin' woman / Bedroom blues / Close to train time / New Orleans lover man / Please throw this poor dog a bone / Better find a job / Hard lovin' mama / I'm still in love with you / Where's the money honey / Little fat woman with the coconut head / Toddle luddle baby / When are you comin' home.
LP: . . . . OFF 6020

Newton, David

GIVEN TIME.
Tracks: / Someday my prince will come / There will never be another you / Given time / How deep is the ocean / I've never been in love before / Katy's song / Prelude to a kiss / Days of wine and roses, The / Last drop blues.
LP: . . . . GFMLP 8003

VICTIM OF CIRCUMSTANCE.
Tracks: / Wishful thinking / Night we called it a day, The / Katy's song / It never entered my mind / Victim of circumstance / One and only / Please come home / Way you look tonight, The.
LP: . . . . AKH 013
MC: . . . . AKC 013

Newton, Frankie

AT THE ONYX CLUB (1937-39).
LP: . . . . M 8017

Newton, Isaac

HISTORY MAKERS (see under History Makers).

Newton, James

AFRICAN FLOWER.
Tracks: / Black and tan fantasy / Virgin jungle / Strange feeling / Fleurette Africaine (the African flower) / Cottontail / Sophisticated lady / Passion flower.
LP: . . . . BT 85109

AXUM.
Tracks: / Dabtara / Malak 'uqabe / Solomon, chief of wise men / Addis Ababa / Choir / Feeling / Axum / Susenyos and werzelya / Neser, The.
LP: . . . . ECM 1214

BINU (Newton, James Quartet).
LP: . . . . RK 21877/11

ECHO CANYON.
LP: . . . . LPCEL 012
MC: . . . . MCCEL 012

FLUTES (Newton, James & Sam Rivers).
LP: . . . . RK 7677/7

IN VENICE.
2LP: . . . . LPCEL 030/31
MCSET: . . . . MCCEL 030/31

JAMES NEWTON.
Tracks: / Daydream / Budapest / Ismene / Persephone / Crips, The.
LP: . . . . IN 1037
LP: . . . . GR 8205

LUELLA.
Tracks: / Not without you / Mr. Dolphy / Anna Maria / Diamonds are for freedom / Luella.
LP: . . . . GR 8304
MC: . . . . GRC 8304

PORTRAITS.
LP: . . . . IN 1051

ROMANCE AND REVOLUTION.
Tracks: / Forever Charles / Meditations of integration / Peace / Evening leans towards you / Tenderly.
LP: . . . . BT 85134

Newton, Juice

CAN'T WAIT ALL NIGHT.
Tracks: / Little love, A / One that gets you / Can't wait all night / Restless heart / Easy way out / Let's dance / He's gone / You don't know me / Eye of the hurricane / Waiting for the sun.
LP: . . . . PL 84995
MC: . . . . PK 84995

COLLECTION: JUICE NEWTON.
LP: . . . . IC 038 85420

COME TO ME (Newton, Juice & Silver Spur).
Tracks: / Come to me / Low down and lonesome / Back down to lonely / Crying too long / Wouldn't mind the rain / Good luck, baby Jane / Save a heart / Fire down below / Good woman at home / You've been around.
LP: . . . . FA 3025
MC: . . . . TCFA 3025

JUICE.
Tracks: / Angel of the morning / Shot full of love / Ride 'em cowboy / Queen of hearts / River of love / All I have to do is dream / Headin' for a heartache / Country comfort / Texas heartache / Sweetest thing.
MC: . . . . TC EST 12136
LP: . . . . EST 12136

QUIET LIES.
Tracks: / Heart of the night / Love's been a little bit hard on me / Break it to me gently / Love sail away / I'm dancing as fast as I can / I'm gonna be strong / Trail of tears / Adios my corazon / Falling in love / Ever true.
LP: . . . . EST 12210

WELL KEPT SECRET.
Tracks: / So many ways / Close enough / I'll never love again / So easy / Love like yours, A / Hey baby / Tell me, baby, goodbye / No reason / It's not impossible / If there could be.
LP: . . . . EST 11811

Newton, Wayne

BEST OF WAYNE NEWTON LIVE.
LP: . . . . CHELV 1006
MC: . . . . CHELC 1006

Newton, William

SET UP,THE.
MC: . . . . SOUND 6

Newton-Howard, James

RAZZLE DAZZLE (See under Jeffries, Michael) (Newton-Howard, James/ Michael Jeffries).

Newton-John, Olivia

BEST OF ME (SINGLE) (See under Foster, David).

COME ON OVER.
Tracks: / Jolene / Pony ride / Come on over / It'll be me / Greensleeves / Blue eyes crying in the rain / Don't throw it all away / Who are you now / Smile for me / Small talk and pride / Wrap me in your arms / Long and winding road, The.
LP: . . . . EMC 3124
MC: . . . . TCEMC 3124

DON'T STOP BELIEVIN'.
Tracks: / Don't stop believin' / Thousand conversations, A / Compassionate man / New born babe / Hey Mr. Dream maker / Every face tells a story / Sam / Love you hold the key / I'll bet you a kangaroo / Last time you loved, The.
LP: . . . . EMC 3162

EARLY OLIVIA.
Tracks: / If not for you / Love song / What is life / Everything I own / Air that I breathe, The / Me and Bobby McGee / Music makes my day / Long live love / Banks of the Ohio / Take me home country roads / Help me make it through the night / If you love me (let me know) / Have you never been mellow / Please Mr., please (CD only.) / Let me be there (CD only.) / I honestly love you (CD only.).
LP: . . . . EMS 1322
MC: . . . . TCEMS 1322

FIRST IMPRESSIONS.
Tracks: / If not for you / Banks of the Ohio / Love song / Winterwood / Everything I own / What is life / Take me home country roads / Amoureuse / Let me be there / Changes / Music makes my day / If you love me (let me know).
LP: . . . . MFP 41 5740 1
MC: . . . . MFP 41 5740 4

GREATEST HITS: OLIVIA NEWTON-JOHN.
Tracks: / Physical / Tied up / Heart attack / Make a move on me / You're the one that I want / What is life / Xanadu / Summer nights / Landslide / Take me home country roads / Little more love, A / Magic / Suddenly / Changes / Hopelessly devoted to you / Sam / If not for you / Banks of the Ohio / Rosewater / I honestly love you.
LP: . . . . EMTV 36
MC: . . . . TV EMTV 36
LP: . . . . EMA 785
MC: . . . . TCEMA 785

HAVE YOU NEVER BEEN MELLOW.
LP: . . . . EMC 3069

LONG LIVE LOVE.
LP: . . . . EMC 3028

LOVE SONGS: OLIVIA NEWTON JOHN.
Tracks: / Please Mr., please / Have you never been mellow / If / Angel of the morning / Behind that locked door (CD only.) / God only knows / Love song / No regrets / If you could read my mind / Little more love, A / I honestly love you / Amoureuse / Where are we going to (CD only.) / Lullaby / I will touch you (CD only.) / Winterwood / If we only have love / Changes.
LP: . . . . MFP 5839
MC: . . . . TCMFP 5839

MAKING A GOOD THING BETTER.
Tracks: / Making a good thing better / Slow dancing / Ring of fire / Coolin' down / Don't cry for me Argentina / Sad songs / You won't see me cry / So easy to begin / I think I'll say goodbye / Don't ask a friend.
LP: . . . . EMC 3192
LP: . . . . FA 3006

MUSIC MAKES MY DAY.
LP: . . . . NSPL 28186

PHYSICAL.
Tracks: / Landslide / Strangers touch / Make a move on me / Falling / Love make me strong / Physical / Silvery rain / Carried away / Recovery / Promise / Dolphin song.
LP: . . . . EMC 3386

RUMOUR, THE.
Tracks: / Rumour, The / Can't we talk it over in bed / Get out / Walk through the fire / Love and let live / It's not heaven / Big and strong / Tutta la vita.
LP: 834957-1
MC: 834957-4

SOUL KISS.
Tracks: / Toughen up / Soul kiss / Queen of the publication / Emotional tangle / Culture shock / Moth to a flame / Overnight observation / You were great, how was I? / Driving music / Right moment, The / Electric (Only on CD and cassette.).
LP: . . . . MERH 77
MC: . . . . MERHC 77

TOTALLY HOT.
Tracks: / Please don't keep me waiting / Dancing round and round / Talk to me / Deeper than the night / Borrowed time / Little more love, A / Never enough / Totally hot / Boats against the current / Gimme some lovin'.
LP: . . . . EMA 789
MC: . . . . TC EMA 789

WARM AND TENDER.
Tracks: / Jenny Rebecca / Rocking (nativity) / Way you look tonight, The / German lullaby / You'll never walk alone / Sleep my princess / Flower, The / Twinkle twinkle little star / Warm and tender / Rock a bye baby / Somewhere over the rainbow / Twelfth of never / All the pretty little horses / When you wish upon a star / Reach out.
LP: 842 145 1
MC: 842 145 4

Newtown Neurotics

45 REVOLUTIONS PER MINUTE.
LP: . . . . FREUD 31

BEGGARS CAN BE CHOOSERS.
Tracks: / Lean on me / Life in their hands / Get up and fight / Living with unemployment / No respect.
LP: . . . . RAZ 6

Next

NEXT.
LP: . . . . EPC 82499

Next Of Kin

NEXT OF KIN (Film Soundtrack) (Various artists).
Tracks: / Brother to brother: *Various artists* / Hillbilly heart: *Various artists* / Paralyzed: *Various artists*/ My sweet baby's gone: *Various artists* / Brothers: *Various artists* / On a Spanish Highway (revised): *Various* artists / Hey backwoods: *Various artists* / Straight and narrow: *Various artists* / Yard sale, The: *Various artists* / Pyramids of cans: *Various artists* / Wailing sax: *Various artists.*
LP: 4662401
MC: 4662404

Nexus

NIGHTRIDING.
LP: . . . . VPA 190

Nexus 21

RHYTHM OF LIFE, THE.
LP: . . . . BLUETEC 2

Ngema, Mbonegeni

MBONGENI NGEMA.
MC: . . . . ICT 9912
LP: . . . . ILPS 9912

Ngobeni, O

MY WIFE BOUGHT A TAXI.
LP: . . . . SHAN 64003

N'Goss Bros.

DANCE OKE-OKE.
LP: . . . . GB 1002
MC: . . . . GB 1002C

Nguema, Hilarion

LA DETENTE.
LP: . . . . MH 118
MC: . . . . MHK 118

Ngukana, Ezra

YOU THINK YOU KNOW.
LP: . . . . JAJ 3
MC: . . . . JAJC 3

Ni Dhonnchadha, Maire

DEORA AILLE (Sean nos singing).
LP: . . . . CC 6

Ni Mhaonaigh, Mairead

CEOL ADUAIDH.
LP: . . . . CEF 102

Niagara

NOW OR NEVER.
Tracks: / Fallen angel / Walking / I will be there / Take my hand / Now or never / I should be stronger / No conversation / You belong to me / Secret lover / Live on the line.
LP: . . . . KILP 4006

RELIGION.
Tracks: / Le ciel s'est dechire / Chemin de croix / Au dela de la riviere / Psychotrope / L'ame des vandales / Ma vie est un serpent au coeur froid / J'ai vu / Pendant que les champs brulent / Chien rouge / La vie est peut etre belle / Pardon a mes ennemis.
LP: 843 446 1
MC: 843 446 4

Nicaragua

NICARAGUAN FOLK MUSIC FROM MASAYA (Various artists).
LP: . . . . FF 474

Nica's Dream

NICA'S DREAM (Various artists).
Tracks: / Woody'n you: *Various artists* / Donna Lee: *Various artists* / Nica's dream: *Various artists*/ Blues march: *Various artists* / Now's the time: *Various artists* / War gewessen: *Various artists* / Original Faubus fables: *Various artists.*
LP: . . . . NW 242

Nice

20TH ANNIVERSARY OF THE NICE.
Tracks: / Bonnie K / Diamond hard blue apples of the moon / Daddy where do I come from? / Flower king of flies / America / Dawn / Cry of Eugene / Thoughts of Emerlist Davjak / Tantalizing Maggie.
LP: . . . . SLP 2
MC: . . . . SC 2
LP: . . . . BTEL 2
MC: . . . . BTEC 2

AMOENI REDIVIVI.
LP: . . . . IML 1003

ARS LONGA VITA BREVIS.
Tracks: / Daddy where do I come from / Little Arabella / Happy Freuds / Intermezzo from 'Karelia suite' / Don Edito el Gruva / Ars longa vita brevis / 1st movement-Awakening / 2nd movement-Realisation / 3rd movement / 4th movement-Denial / Coda-extension to the big note.
MC: . . . . CLAMC 120
LP: . . . . CLALP 120

COLLECTION: NICE.
Tracks: / America / Happy Freuds / Cry of Eugene / Thoughts of Emerlist Davjak / Rondo / Daddy, where do I come from? / Little Arabella / Intermezzo from Ravelia / Hang on to a dream / Diamond hard blue apples of the moon / Angel of death / Ars longa vita brevis.
2LP: . . . . CCSLP 106
MC: . . . . CCSMC 106

ELEGY.
Tracks: / 3rd movement / America / Hang on to a dream / My back pages.
LP: . . . . CHC 1
MC: . . . . CHCMC 1
LP: . . . . CAS 1030

FIVE BRIDGES SUITE.
Tracks: / Fantasia (1st bridge, 2nd bridge) / Chorale (3rd bridge) / High level fugue (4th bridge) / Finale / Intermezzo from 'Karelia suite' / Pathetique (symphony no.6, 3rd movement) / Country pie/Brandenburg concerto No. 6 / One of those people.
LP: . . . . CHC 30
MC: . . . . CHCMC 30
LP: . . . . CAS 1014

FIVE BRIDGES SUITE/AUTUMN 67 AND SPRING 68.
Tracks: / Fantasia (1st bridge, 2nd bridge) / Chorale 3rd bridge / High level fugue 4th bridge / Finale / Intermezzo from 'Karelia suite' / Pathetique (symphony no.6, 3rd movement) / Country pie/Brandenburg Concerto No.6 / One of those people / Thoughts of Emerlist Davjak / Flower king of flies / Bonnie K / Diamond hard blue apples of the moon / Dawn / Tantalising Maggie / Cry of Eugene / Daddy, where do I come from? / America.
MCSET: . . . . CASMC 103

NICE.
LP: . . . . IMSP 026

Nice And Wild

ENERGY LOVE AND UNITY.
Tracks: / Obsession / money can't buy you love / Dangerous in the dark / Oh baby / Diamond girl / Energy, love and unity / Hazel eyes / If you can feel it / Hey y'all we're nice and wild.
LP: 781 719-1
MC: 781 719-4

Nice Enough To Eat

NICE ENOUGH TO EAT (Various artists).
LP: . . . . RRLP 143
MC: . . . . RRLC 143

Nice 'N' Easy

BROADWAY MELODIES (See Under Broadway Melodies) (Various artists).

LOVE STORY - THOSE ROMANTIC 70'S (See under 70's) (Various artists).

SMOKE GETS IN YOUR EYES - THOSE ROMANTIC 50'S (See Under 50's) (Various artists).

YESTERDAY - THOSE ROMANTIC 60'S (See Under 60's) (Various artists).

Nice, Rich

INFORMATION TO RAISE A NATION.
Tracks: / Rhythm, the feeling, The / Outstanding / It's time to get hype / So what you gotta man / Desperado (the Mexican) / Outlaw / Dead to the nation / Trouble man / Information to raise a nation / Two seconds from disaster / Explosion (On CD only.).
LP: . . . . ZL 72692
MC: . . . . ZK 72692

Nice Strong Arm

MIND FURNACE.
LP: . . . . HMS 103

Nicholas, Albert

ALBERT NICHOLAS QUARTET.
LP: .... DL 207

ALBERT NICHOLAS & THE JOHN DEFFERARY JAZZTET (Nicholas, Albert & The John Defferary Jazztet).
LP: .... GHB 64

MEMORIAL.
2LP: 400023

RARE ITALIAN DATES/LIVE AT LOUISIANA DATES 1971 (See under Hackett, Bobby) (Nicholas, Albert & Bobby Hackett).

THIS IS JAZZ VOL 2.
LP: .... SLP 4068

TRADITIONAL JAZZ 2.
Tracks: / Mo pas lemme ca / Memories of you / Les oignons / Embraceable you / How long how long blues / Please don't talk about me / Indiana / Lost hour blues / Rose room / Salee dame / I can't give you anything but love / Albert's blues.
LP: 6459 214

TRIBUTE TO JELLY ROLL MORTON.
LP: .... SLP 4050

Nicholas, Nick

50 SWINGING HONKY TONK FAVOURITES.
2LP: 50DA 312

HONKY TONK FAVOURITES.
MCSET: .... DTO 10231

Nicholas Nickleby

NICHOLAS NICKLEBY (Original cast soundtrack) (Various artists).
Tracks: / London: *Various artists* / Home in Devonshire: *Various artists* / Dotheboys' Hall: *Various artists*/ Journey to Portsmouth: *Various artists* / Farewell waltz, The: *Various artists* / Mantalini chase, The: *Various artists* / Wedding anthem: *Various artists* / Patriotic song: *Various artists* / Milliners' sewing room, The: *Various artists* / Sir Mulberry Hawk: *Various artists* / Mrs. Grudden's goodbye: *Various artists* / Witterly gavotte, The: *Various artists* / At the opera: *Various artists* / Cheerybyle brothers, The: *Various artists*/ Christmas carol: *Various artists*.
LP: .... TER 1029
MC: .... ZCTER 1029

NICHOLAS NICKLEBY (see under Dickens, Charles) (Rees, Roger).

Nicholas, Paul

JUST GOOD FRIENDS.
Tracks: / Just good friends / You don't bring me flowers / I'm not in love / Air that I breathe, The / Boy's in love, The / I made it through the rain / You light up my life / Sometimes when we touch / If you leave now / Always a woman to me / Lady in red / All because of love / Fool (if you think it's over) / Don't wanna go home alone.
LP: .... ONE 1334
MC: .... OCE 2334

PAUL NICHOLAS.
Tracks: / Sunday / Doing it / Earthquake, landslide, hurricane / If you were the only girl in the world / Sway / Reggae like it used to be / Dancing with the captain / Black daddy / When you walk in the room / Heaven on the 7th floor / Do you want my love? / Grandma's party.
LP: 2394 185

SPOT THE DOG (See under Eric Hill).

Nicholls, Billy

UNDER ONE BANNER.
LP: .... EXPAL 3
MC: .... EXPMC 3

Nichols, Grace

CONTEMPORARY LITERATURE READINGS (Nichols, Grace & Samuel Selvon).
MC: .... NSA C4

Nichols, Herbie

HERBIE NICHOLS TRIO.
LP: .... BLP 1519

OUT OF THE SHADOW.
Tracks: / Too close for comfort / Every cloud / Argumentative / Love, gloom, cash, love / Portrait of Ucha / Beyond recall / All the way / Forty-five degree angle / Infatuation eyes / S'crazy pad.
LP: .... AFF 90

THELONIOUS MONK AND HERBIE NICHOLS (see Monk, Thelonious) (Nichols, Herbie/Thelonious Monk).

Nichols, Keith

CHITTERLIN' STRUT.
LP: .... SOS 1159

DOCTORS JAZZ (Nichols, Keith & Red Hot Syncopators).
LP: .... SOS 1135

SHAKIN' THE BLUES AWAY (Nichols, Keith Hot Six).
LP: .... SOS 1063

WITH MOONLIGHT BROADCASTERS. see also under Moonlight Broadcasters (Nichols, Keith & Moonlight Broadcasters).
LP: SOS1193

Nichols, Red

1925 - 1928 (Nichols, Red & Sam Lanin's Orchestra).
LP: .... BR 105
LP: .... FJ 110

1936 (Nichols, Red & Orchestra).
LP: .... CLP 110

BENNY GOODMAN WITH RED NICHOLS' ORCHESTRA (see Goodman, Benny) (Nichols, Red & Benny Goodman).

CLASS OF 39 Radio transcriptions (Nichols, Red/his Five Pennies).
LP: .... BLUE LANTERN 1000

FEELIN' NO PAIN.
Tracks: / Japanese Sandman / China boy / After you've gone / Sally, won't you come back? / Feeling no pain / Wash board blues / Bugle call rag / Eccentric / Ida, sweet as apple cider / Smiles / Buddy's habits / Indiana / That's no bargain / Avalon / Boneyard shuffle / Riverboat shuffle / Sheik of Araby, The.
LP: .... AFS 1038

JACK TEAGARDEN AND RED NICHOLS (See under Teagarden, Jack for full details) (Nichols, Red & Jack Teagarden).

JAZZ CLASSICS IN DIGITAL STEREO (Red Nichols & Miff Mole 1925-1930) (Nichols, Red & Miff Mole).
Tracks: / Darktown strutters' ball / Rhythm of the day / Hurricane / Someday, sweetheart / Wabash blues / Devonport blues / Shimme-sha-wabble / Hot time, A / Riverboat shuffle / Feeling no pain / Original Dixieland / Honolulu blues / Harlem twist / Corina Corina.
LP: .... REB 664
MC: .... ZCF 664

NEGLECTED YEARS 1934-1940 (Nichols, Red & Orchestra).
Tracks: / Rockin' in rhythm / Runnin' wild / Three little words / Harlem / Cream puff / Twilight in Turkey / Hour of parting / Beat me daddy, eight to the bar / Meet Miss eight beat / Lowland blues / Overnight hop / Poor butterfly.
MC: .... NEO 859

RED AND BEN (Nichols, Red & Ben Pollack).
LP: .... BR 103

RED AND MIFF, 1926-31 (Nichols, Red & Miff Mole).
Tracks: / Jersey walk / Clap yo' hands / Wouldn't you / Just the same / Where the wild wild flowers grow / Tap tap / Let a smile be your umbrella / Say yes today / Delirium / Davenport blues / Slippin' around / Feeling no pain / Sugar / Make my cot where the cot-cot-cotton grows / Harlem twist / Five pennies / That's where the south begins / I'm tickled pink / At last I'm happy / If you haven't got a girl.
LP: .... SVL 146

RED NICHOLS AND HIS FIVE PENNIES 1929-32 (Nichols, Red/his Five Pennies).
LP: .... IAJRC 22

RED NICHOLS AND OTHER RADIO TRANSCRIPTIONS.
LP: .... MERITT 18

RED NICHOLS GROUP - 1927-1932 (Nichols, Red Group).
Tracks: / I'm in love again / Sometimes I'm happy / Rosy cheeks / Memphis blues, The / Melancholy Charlie / Hurricane / Sugar / Make my cot where the cot-cot-cotton grows / I can't give you anything but love / Five pennies / Red and his big ten.
MC: .... NEO 861

RED NICHOLS & HIS FIVE PENNIES (Nichols, Red/his Five Pennies).
LP: .... S 838

RED NICHOLS & HIS FIVE PENNIES VOL. 5 (1929) (Nichols, Red Five Pennies).
LP: .... S 840
LP: .... CJM 30

RED NICHOLS NEW YORK JAZZ VOL.1.
MC: .... NEO 710

RED NICHOLS & THE FIVE PENNIES (Nichols, Red & The Five Pennies).
LP: .... J 90

RED NICHOLS & THE FIVE PENNIES, VOL.4 1928-29 (Nichols, Red & The Five Pennies).
LP: .... S 839

RED NICHOLS: VOL 2 (& Miff Mole, Jimmy Dorsey, Adrian Rollini).
Tracks: / Five pennies / Mean dog blues / Riverboat shuffle / Eccentric / Ida / Feeling no pain / Avalon / Japanese sandman / Nobody's sweetheart / My gal Sal / Poor butterfly / Can't you hear me?.
LP: .... CJM 25
LP: .... S 837

RED NICHOLS VOL. 3 1928.
LP: .... CJM 27

RED NICHOLS VOL. 4.
LP: .... S 836
LP: .... CJM 28

RED NICHOLS-VOLUME 5.
LP: .... CJM 30

RHYTHM OF THE DAY (Nichols, Red/his Five Pennies).
Tracks: / Rhythm of the day / Buddy's habits / Boneyard shuffle / Alexander's ragtime band / Alabama stomp / Hurricane / Cornfed / Mean dog blues / Riverboat shuffle / Eccentric / Feeling no pain / Original Dixieland one-step / Honolulu blues / There'll come a time / Harlem twist / Alice blue gown / Corina Corina / Oh Peter, you're so nice / Waiting for the Evening Mail / Sweet Sue.
LP: .... AJA 5025
MC: .... ZC AJA 5025

SYNCOPATED CHAMBER MUSIC (Nichols, Red Five Pennies).
LP: .... AP 2
LP: .... AP 201

Nichols, Roger

SONGWRITERS FOR THE STARS 3 (Nichols, Roger & Bruce Roberts).
Tracks: / Winners theme / I won't last a day without you / So many people / Rainy days and Mondays / Out in the country / We've only just begun / Cool fool / All through the night / Stronger than before / You're moving out today / One star shining.
LP: 6327 080

Nicholson, Lea

CONCERTINA RECORD.
Tracks: / Liberty bell / Kopya / Moonlight serenade / Chattanooga choo choo / In the mood / Lea rig, The / Lasst uns erfreuen / Fourth Brandenburg concerto / Allegro / Andante / Presto.
LP: .... SNKF 165

HORSEMUSIC.
LP: .... LER 3010

Nicholson, Nancy

RHYME AND REASON.
MC: .... GAL 104 C

Nicholson, Roger

DULCIMER PLAYERS, THE.
LP: .... LTRA 502

NONESUCH FOR DULCIMER.
LP: .... LER 3034

TIMES AND TRADITION FOR DULCIMER.
LP: .... LER 2094

Nick & Elaine

LOOK AND LIVE.
LP: .... KLO 44

Nick & Nick

NICK & NICK THE PSYCHOTIC DRIVERS (Nick & Nick The Psychotic Drivers).
LP: .... CONTE 120

Nicks & Buckingham

BUCKINGHAM NICKS.
Tracks: / Crying in the night / Stephanie / Without a leg to stand on / Crystal / Long distance winner / Don't let me down again / Django / Races are run / Lola my love / Frozen love.
LP: 2482 378

Nicks, Stevie

BELLA DONNA.
Tracks: / Bella Donna / Kind of woman / Stop draggin' my heart around / Think about it / After the glitter fades / Edge of seventeen / How still my love / Leather and lace / Highwayman / Outside the rain.
MC: K4 99169
LP: .... K 99169
LP: .... EMC 3562
MC: .... TCEMC 3562
LP: .... ATAK 167
MC: .... TCATAK 167

BEST OF STEVIE NICKS, THE.
Tracks: / Sometimes it's a bitch / Stop draggin' my heart / Whole lotta trouble / Talk to me / Stand back / Beauty and the beast / If anyone falls / Rooms on fire / Love's a hard game to play / Edge of seventeen / Leather and lace / I can't wait / Has anyone ever written anything to you / Desert angel.
LP: .... EMD 1024
MC: .... TCEMD 1024

OTHER SIDE OF THE MIRROR.
Tracks: / Rooms on fire / Long way to go / Two kinds of love / Oh my love / Ghosts / Whole lotta trouble / Fire burning / Cry wolf / Alice / Juliet / Doing the best I can (escape from Berlin) / I still miss someone.
LP: .... EMD 1008
MC: .... TCEMD 1008

ROCK A LITTLE.
Tracks: / I can't wait / Rock a little / Sister honey / I sing for the things / Imperial Hotel / Some become strangers / Talk to me / Nightmare, The / If I were you / No spoken word / Has anyone ever written anything for you?.
LP: .... PCS 7300
MC: .... TCPCS 7300
LP: .... ATAK 123
MC: .... TCATAK 123

WILD HEART.
Tracks: / Stand back / I will run to you (with Tom Petty & The Heart Breakers) / Nothing ever changes / Sable on blond / Beauty and the beast / Wild heart / If anyone falls / Gate and garden / Night bird / Enchanted.
LP: 2500711
MC: 2500714
LP: .... EMC 3563
MC: .... TCEMC 3563
LP: .... ATAK 153
MC: .... TCATAK 153

Nico

BEHIND THE IRON CURTAIN.
Tracks: / All Saints night from a Polish motorway / One more chance / Frozen warnings / Song of the lonely girl, The / Win a few / Konig / Purple lips / All tomorrow's parties / Fearfully in danger / End, The / My funny valentine / 60-40 / Tananoori / Janitor of lunacy / My heart is empty / Femme fatale.
LP: .... DOJOLP 27
MC: .... DOJOTC 27

BLUE ANGEL, THE.
Tracks: / Femme fatale / All tomorrow's parties / I'll keep it with mine / Chelsea girl / Janitor of lunacy / Heroes / One more chance / 60-40 / Waiting for the man / End, The.
LP: .... AUL 731
MC: .... AUC 731

CAMERA OBSCURA.
LP: .... BEGA 63
MC: .... BEGC 63
LP: .... BBL 63
MC: .... BBLC 63

CHELSEA GIRL.
Tracks: / Fairest of the seasons, The / These days / Little sister / Winter song / It was a pleasure then / Chelsea girl / I'll keep it with mine / Somewhere there's a feather / Wrap your troubles in dreams / Eulogy to Lenny Bruce.
LP: 235 302 5

DESERT SHORE.
Tracks: / Janitor of lunacy / Falconer, The / My only child / Le petit chevalier / Abschied / Afraid / Mutterlein / All that is my own.
LP: .... K 44102

DO OR DIE.
MC: .... A 117

DRAMA OF EXILE.
LP: .... AUL 715
LP: .... LILP 400106

EN PERSONNE EN EUROPE.
MC: .... 1/2 CASS 2

HANGING GARDENS.
LP: .... EM 93491
MC: .... EM 93494

LIVE HEROES.
LP: .... PERF 385

LIVE IN DENMARK.
Tracks: / Sayetta / Vegas / 60-40 / Valley of the kings / Janitor of lunacy / I'll keep it with mine / Femme fatale / I'm waiting for my man / Heroes.
LPPD: .... NICO 1

LIVE IN TOKYO.
Tracks: / My heart is empty / Purple lips / Tananore / Janitor of lunacy / You forget to answer / 60-40 / My funny valentine / Sad lied von einsannen madchens / All tomorrow's parties / Femme fatale / End, The.
LP: .... DOJOLP 50

Nicodemus

CABIN STABIN (See under Super Cat) (Nicodemus, Super Cat & Junior Demus).

DJ CLASH - NICODEMUS V TOYAN (Nicodemus/Toyan).

Tracks: / Overseas posse / Bully dread / Tell me your occupation / Wife and sweetheart / Jah love in we heart / Hail nico dread / Shaolin plat / Birdman hunting / Bubble Nicodemus, bubble / Tubbys daddy.
LP: . . . . **GREL 32**

Nicodim, Ion

LA FLUTE TZIGANE (Nicodim, Ion Et Ses Tziganes).
Tracks: / Hora Bidinarilor / Cintec de prietenie pentru Ariana si hora lui / Dragoste, fara noroc / Dimineata inspre ziua / Hora tigancilor / Cintec de dragoste pentru leana / Tiganeasca de joc / Hora lui ion / Cinta cucu de trei zile / Un parinte poate creste / Inimiora cu venim / Mama copil si mei-cintec de pahar / Cuculet de la padure.
LP: . . . . **ARN 33164**

Nicol, Hector

BRAVO JULIET.
LP: . . . . **KLP 42**
MC: . . . . **ZCKLP 42**

COP OF THE NORTH.
LP: . . . . **KLP 17**
MC: . . . . **ZCKLP 17**

GOLDEN YEARS OF, THE.
Tracks: / Policeman, The / Cowboy, The / Convict, The / Prostitute / Hobo, The / Cop, The / Drunk, The / Nurse, The.
LP: . . . . **KLP 53**
MC: . . . . **ZCKLP 53**

HOBO SEXUAL, THE.
LP: . . . . **KLP 24**
MC: . . . . **ZCKLP 24**

I'M A COUNTRY MEMBER (brand x).
Tracks: / Bounty hunter / Hector rides again.
LP: . . . . **KLP 37**
MC: . . . . **ZCKLP 37**

LADY AND THE CHAMP, THE.
LP: . . . . **KLP 03**

LAFFIN ROOM ONLY.
LP: . . . . **KLP 02**

QUEEN OF THE ROAD.
Tracks: / Lady is a tramp, The / Try a little tenderness.
LP: . . . . **KLP 11**

SCOTCH AND FULL OF IT.
LP: . . . . **KLP 07**

Nicol, James

LAST ROSE OF SUMMER.
Tracks: / Dream Angus / Beautiful dreamer / I dream of Jeannie with the light brown hair / Believe me if all those endearing young charms / Danny boy / Lord's my shepherd, The / Whe're you walk / Hail Caledonia / Last rose of summer / Annie's song / Down in the glen / Music of the spey / Ma belle Marguerite / Sally gardens / Baes o'Ballochmyle.
LP: . . . . **LILP 5123**
MC: . . . . **LICS 5123**

SCOTLAND AGAIN.
Tracks: / Bonnie lass o' Fyvie / Barnyards of Delgaty / Anniversary song / Scotland again / Answer me / Old house / Annie Laurie / Mary of Argyll / Cara mia / Gentle maiden, The / Bonnie lass O'Ballochmyle / Lassie who loves me still.
LP: . . . . **LILP 5148**
MC: . . . . **LICS 5148**

Nicol, Jean

MEET ME AT THE SAVOY.
MCSET: . . . . **SOUND 24**

Nicol, Johnny

WHERE THE LOVE IS.
LP: . . . . **LRF 175**

Nicol, R.B.

PIBROCH PIPE-MAJOR R.B. NICOL.
MC: . . . . **TGMMC 503**

Nicol, Simon

BEFORE YOUR TIME.
Tracks: / Over the Lancashire hills / Caught a whisper / Deserter, The / Insult to injury / From a distance / Live not where I love / Before your time/Merry Sherwood rangers / Rosemary's sister.
LP: . . . . **WR 010**
MC: . . . . **WRC 010**

CLOSE TO THE WIND (Nicol, Simon/ Dave Swarbrick).
LP: . . . . **WR 006**

Nicolai, Giancarlo

GIANCARLO NICOLAI TRIO.
LP: . . . . **LR 134**
LP: . . . . **LR 164**

Nicole

JAMPACKED.
Tracks: / Jam packed (at the wall) / Desire / Let's talk about love / So lost without your love / Rock the house / Two hearts are better than one / Everlasting love / Throwdown / He's so romeo.
LP: **4600431**
MC: **4600434**
LP: . . . . **BFE 40575**

LITTLE PEACE, A.
Tracks: / Little peace, A / My first love / Take away the heartaches / Dancing / Where have all my heroes gone / You're the music in me / Give me more time / I have to give you back your freedom / Susanna / Song of love / Away from home / Butterfly.
LP: . . . . **CBS 85011**

NEW YORK EYES (RE-ISSUE) (Thomas,Timmy/Nicole).
Tracks: / New York eyes / Ordinary girl / New York eyes (remix).
MCSET: **CC/026**

WHAT ABOUT ME.
Tracks: / Don't you want my love / New York eyes / Housecalls / What about me / Always and forever / Why you take my love / Ordinary girl / Shy boy / It happens every night / New York eyes (remix).
LP: . . . . **PRT 26844**
MC: **40 26844**

Nicolet, Aurele

HAYDN 'LONDON' TRIOS 1-3/PIANO TRIOS 15 & 16 (see under Haydn (composer)) (Nicolet, Aurele & Christiane /Rocco Filippini/Bruno Canino).

Nicoli, Giancarlo

VIS MUSIC.
2LP: . . . . **LR 406-407**

Nicoll, Helen

MEG & MOG (Lipman, Maureen).
MCSET: **CC/025-6**

MEG'S EGGS (Nicoll, Helen & Jan Piekowski).
MCSET: **CC/025**

Nicols, Maggie

DON'T ASSUME.
LP: . . . . **LR 145**

NICOLS 'N' NU (see Nu/Maggie Nicols) (Nicols, Maggie/Nu).

VOICE (see under Tippetts, J).

Nicolson, Eann

HIGHLAND JOURNEY, A (Nicolson, Eann & The Wick Scottish Dance Band).
LP: . . . . **WGR 013**
MC: . . . . **CWGR 013**

OVER THE ORD (Nicolson, Eann & The Wick Scottish Dance Band).
LP: . . . . **WGR 006**
MC: . . . . **CWGR 006**

Nicra

LISTEN-HEAR.
LP: . . . . **OG 010**

Niebla, Eduardo

CELEBRATION (Niebla, Eduardo/ Antonio Forcione).
Tracks: / For Vic / On return / Celebration / Folk songs / Fuente fresca / Nostalgia / Carousel.
LP: . . . . **VE 7**
MC: . . . . **TCVE 7**

Niehaus, Lennie

OCTET, NO.2., THE.
LP: . . . . **COP 017**

Niels

NIELS AND THE N.Y. STREET PERCUSSIONIST (Niels & The N.Y. Street Percussionist).
LP: . . . . **ITM 1453**

Nielsen, Chris

LET ME DOWN EASY.
LP: . . . . **GES 5001**

Nielsen (composer)

SONATAS FOR VIOLIN & PIANO (Mordkovitch, Lydia & Clifford Benson).
LP: . . . . **ABRD 1288**
MC: . . . . **ABTD 1288**

Nielson, Brigitte

BODY NEXT TO BODY (See under Falco for full details) (Nielson, Brigitte & Falco).

Nieve, Steve

KEYBOARD JUNGLE (Naive, Steve).
Tracks: / Ethnic Erithian / Hooligans and hula girls / Al Green / Spanish guitar / Man with a musical lighter / Outline of a hairdo / End of side one / Liquid looks / Thought of being dad / Pink flamingoes on Coffee Pot Boulevard / Mystery and the majesty / Couch potato rag / Page one of a dead girls diary / End of an era.
LP: . . . . **FIEND 11**

PLAYBOY.
Tracks: / Russians / Pictures from a confiscated camera / Once upon a time in South America / Condition of the heart / Sword fight, The / Ghost town / Walk in Monet's back garden / Life on mars / I'm not in love / Shadows of Paris / Love boat / El rey de sol / 9, The / Hands of Orlac / Birdcage walk / White girl / Divided heart / Careless whisper.
LP: . . . . **FIEND 109**

Niger

MUSIC FROM THE NIGER REGION (Various artists).
MC: **D58006**

Night

LONG DISTANCE.
Tracks: / Doctor Rock / Don't you break my heart / Love on the airwaves / Letter, The / Calling me back / You cried wolf / Stealin' / Miss you / Day after day / Good to be in your arms.
LP: . . . . **K 52251**

NIGHT.
Tracks: / Hot summer nights / Cold wind across my heart / If you gotta make a fool of somebody / Ain't that peculiar / If you remember me / Come around / You ain't pretty enough / Shocked / Love message / Party shuffle.
LP: . . . . **K 52200**

Night Ark

MOMENTS.
Tracks: / Wind / You've got a friend / Offering / Nocturne (i) Dusk / Nocturne (ii) Frezy / Nocturne (iii) After hours / Baby elephant / Over the rainbow / Yazoo-firat / Adolescence / Moments.
LP: . . . . **PL 83028**
MC: . . . . **PK 83028**

PICTURE.
Tracks: / Tree / Blackbird / Of song and silence / Picture / Trilogy / Birth / Malo gato / Looyse / Homecoming.
LP: . . . . **PL 83002**

Night At...

NIGHT AT BIRDLAND (See under Mobley, Hank) (Various artists).

NIGHT AT THE AULD MEAL MILL (Various artists).
LP: . . . . **WGR 064**
MC: . . . . **CWGR 064**

NIGHT AT THE PROMS (Various artists).
MCSET: . . . . **DTO 10061**

Night At The Opera

NIGHT AT THE OPERA 2, A (Various artists).
MC: . . . . **STAC 2436**
LP: . . . . **STAR 2436**

NIGHT AT THE OPERA, A (Various artists).
MC: . . . . **STAC 2414**
LP: . . . . **STAR 2414**

Night Beat

NIGHT BEAT (Various artists).
2LP: . . . . **SMR 8501**
MCSET: . . . . **SMC 8501**

NIGHT BEAT II (Various artists).
Tracks: / Alice I want you just for me: *Full Force* / If you're ready (Come go with me): *Ruby Turner* / I'll be good: *Rene & Angela* / Girls are more fun: *Ray Parker Jr.* / In your car: *Cool Notes* / Mated: *Grant, David & Jaki Graham* / Zapped by love: *Sharp, Debbie* / Say I'm your number one: *Princess* / When the going gets tough (the tough get going): *Ocean, Billy* / Baby love: *Regina* / Oh Sheila - ready for the world - trapped: *Abrams, Colonel* / Your personal touch: *King, Evelyn "Champagne"* / Shaft, Theme from: *Eddy & The Soul Band* / Knock on wood: *Stewart, Amii* / Single life: *Cameo* / I miss you: *Klymaxx* / Cherish: *Kool & The Gang* / Could it be I'm falling in love: *Grant, David & Jaki Graham* / Do what you do: *Jackson, Jermaine* / I'll be your friend: *Wilson, Precious* / Sunshine: *Mills, Warren* / Round and around: *Graham, Jaki* / She's strange: *Cameo* / Inspector Gadget: *Kartoon Krew* / Just for money: *Hardcastle, Paul* / We are the team: *Team* / Dynasty rap: *Dynasty & Mimi* / King heroin (Don't mess with heroin): *Jazzy Jeff* / African breeze: *Masekela, Hugh & Johnathan Butler.*
2LP: . . . . **SMR 8613**
MCSET: . . . . **SMC 8613**

Night Crossing

NIGHT CROSSING (Film Soundtrack) (Various artists).
Tracks: / Main title: *Various artists* / All in vain: *Various artists* / Picnic: *Various artists* / Plans: *Various artists* / Success: *Various artists* / First flight: *Various artists* / Patches, The: *Various artists* / Tomorrow we go: *Various artists* / No time to wait: *Various artists* / Final flight: *Various artists* / In the West: *Various artists.*
LP: . . . . **RVF 6004**

Night Judgement At...

NIGHT JUDGEMENT AT SINOS (see Higgins, Jack) (Talbot, Philip).

Night Moods Orchestra

NIGHT MOODS.
LP: . . . . **ADL 525**
MC: . . . . **ADK 525**

Night of the Comet

NIGHT OF THE COMET (Film soundtrack) (Various artists).
Tracks: / Unbelievable: *Revolver* / Learn to: *Chris Farren & Army Holland* / Strong heart: *Townsend, John* / Let my fingers do the talking: *Stallion* / Whole: *Farren, Chris/Wayne Crawford* / Hard act to follow: *Night* of the Comet / Virgin in love: *Pace, Thom* / Yell me yourself: *Revolver* / Trouble: *SKP Adams* / Lady in love: *Revolver.*
LP: . . . . **CHORD 006**
LP: . . . . **MRC 900**
MC: . . . . **TCMRC 900**

Night Of The Day...

NIGHT OF THE DAY OF THE IMPRISONED WRITER (Various artists).
LP: . . . . **BL 25406**

Night Of The Generals

NIGHT OF THE GENERALS (see Kirst, H.H.) (Croft, Jon).

Night On The Town

NIGHT ON THE TOWN, A (Original soundtrack) (Various artists).
Tracks: / Then he kissed me: *Crystals, The* / What does it take (to win your love): *Collins, Albert* / Albert's smokin' ice: *Collins, Albert* / What does it take (to win your love): *Walker, Junior* / Future in your..: *Southside* Johnny & The Jukes / Twenty five miles: *Starr, Edwin* / Expressway to your heart: *Southside Johnny & The Jukes* / Evil: *Taylor, Koko* / Bring it on home to me: *Cooke, Sam* / Just can't stop...: *Sledge, Percy* / Babysitting blues: *Collins, Albert.*
LP: . . . . **SNTF 999**

Night Ranger

BIG LIFE.
Tracks: / Big life / Color of your smile / Love is standing near / Rain comes crashing down / Secret of my success / Carry on / Better let it go / I know tonight / Hearts away.
LP: . . . . **MCF 3362**
MC: . . . . **MCFC 3362**

DAWN PATROL.
Tracks: / Don't tell me you love me / Sing me away / At night she sleeps / Call my name / Eddie's comin' out tonight / Can't find me a thrill / Young girl in love / Play rough / Penny / Night ranger.
LP: . . . . **EPC 25301**
MC: **40 25301**

GREATEST HITS: NIGHT RANGER.
Tracks: / You can still rock in America / Goodbye / Sister Christian / Secret of my success, The / Rumours in the air / Sing me away / When you close your eyes / Sentimental street / Restless kind / Eddie's comin' out tonight.
LP: . . . . **MCG 6055**
MC: . . . . **MCGC 6055**

MIDNIGHT MADNESS.
Tracks: / Rock in America / Rumours in the air / Why does love have to change? / Sister Christian / Touch of madness / Passion play / When you close your eyes / Chippin' away / Let him run.
LP: . . . . **MCF 3209**
MC: . . . . **MCFC 3209**
LP: . . . . **EPC 25845**
MC: **40 25846**

SEVEN WISHES.
LP: . . . . **MCF 3278**
MC: . . . . **MCFC 3278**

Night Shift

NIGHT SHIFT (Various artists).
LP: . . . . **K 57024**

Night Sky

NIGHT SKY, THE A laymans guide to astronomy (Moore, Patrick).
MC: . . . . **AC 150**

Night Trains

CHECKMATE.
LP: . . . . **BGP 1033**

Night Visitor

NIGHT VISITOR (see Mancini,Henry) (Soundtrack).

Nightbreed

NIGHTBREED (Original Soundtrack) (Various artists).
Tracks: / Nightbreed (main title): *Various artists* / Dream: *Various artists* / Carnival underground: *Various* artists / Into Midian: *Various artists* / Meat for the beast: *Various artists* / Resurrection suite: *Various* artists / Boone

transforms: *Various artists* / Initiation, The: *Various artists* / Scalping time: *Various* artists / Rachel's oratory: *Various artists* / Party in the past: *Various artists* / Poor Babette: *Various* artists / Oh ho Decker: *Various artists* / Then don't say it: *Various artists* / Boone gets a taste: *Various* artists / Breed love: *Various artists* / Mayhem in Midian: *Various artists* / Baphomet's chamber: *Various* artists / Farewell: *Various artists* / 2nd chance: *Various* artists / Nightbreed (end credits): *Various artists* / Country skin: *Various artists*.
LP: . . . . **MCA 8037**
MC: . . . . **MCAC 8037**

Nightcaps

WINE WINE WINE.
LP: . . . . **CR 30183**

Nightflyers

NIGHTFLYERS Original soundtrack (Various artists).
LP: . . . . **STV 81344**

Nighthawk, Robert

BLACK ANGEL BLUES.
Tracks: / Down the line / Handsome lover / My sweet lovin' woman / Sweet black angel / Anna Lee blues / Return mail blues / Sugar papa / She knows how to love a man / Good news / Six three O / Prison bound / Jackson town gal / Sorry my angel / Someday.
LP: . . . . **GCH 8108**

LIVE ON MAXWELL STREET.
LP: . . . . **ROUNDER 2022**
MC: . . . . **ROUNDER 2022C**

Nighthawks

FULL HOUSE.
LP: . . . . **AD 4125**

HARD LIVING.
LP: . . . . **REU 1007**
LP: . . . . **V 022**
MC: . . . . **VRC 022**

HOT SPOT.
LP: . . . . **V 009**
MC: . . . . **V 009C**

JACKS AND KINGS.
LP: . . . . **AD 4120**

LIVE IN EUROPE.
LP: . . . . **CCR 1014**

LIVE: NIGHTHAWKS.
LP: . . . . **AD 4110**

NIGHTHAWKS: 10 YEARS LIVE.
LP: . . . . **VR 001**

NIGHTHAWKS, THE.
LP: . . . . **LPVR 007**

NO MERCY.
Tracks: / Do you wanna play / Dangerous lover / Born to fly / Goddess of the dark / No mercy / Misdemeanant / Lookin' for action / Night of the wolf / We got the power / Nowhere to go.
LP: **080 604**

OPEN ALL NIGHT.
LP: . . . . **AD 4105**

ROCK 'N' ROLL.
LP: . . . . **VR 007**
LP: . . . . **V 007**
MC: . . . . **V 007C**

SIDE POCKET SHOT.
LP: . . . . **AD 4115**

TEN YEARS LIVE.
LP: . . . . **V 001**
MC: . . . . **V 001C**

TROUBLE.
Tracks: / Blind love / Ninety-nine pounds / T-R-O-U-B-L-E / Hard hearted woman / Why why baby / I wouldn't treat a dog / One rock at a time / Get in trouble / Chicken and the hawk, The / You go your way / Ride and roll / Tryin' to get you.
LP: . . . . **POW 4107**
MC: . . . . **POW 4107MC**

Nightingale

NIGHTINGALE (Original London cast) (Various artists).
Tracks: / Prologue: *Various artists* / Perfect harmony: *Various artists* / Why am I so happy?: *Various artists*/ Take us to the forest: *Various artists* / Who are these people: *Various artists* / Never speak directly to an Emperor: *Various artists* / Nightingale: *Various artists* / Emperor is a man, An: *Various artists* / I was lost: *Various artists* / Entr'acte: *Various artists* / Charming: *Various artists* / Singer must be free, A: *Various artists* / Mechanical bird, A: *Various artists* / Please don't make me hear that song again: *Various* artists / Rivers cannot flow upwards: *Various artists* / Death duet: *Various artists* / We are China: *Various artists* / Finale: *Various artists*.
LP: . . . . **TER 1031**
MC: . . . . **ZCTER 1031**

NIGHTINGALE (Dotrice, Michele).
Tracks: / Prologue / Perfect harmony / Why am I so happy / Take us to the forest / Never speak directly to an emperor / Nightingale / Emperor is a man, An / I was lost / Entracte / Charming / Singer must be free, A / Mehanical bird, The / Song again, The / Rivers cannot flow upwards / Death duet / We are China / Finale.
LP: . . . . **LP 200**
MC: . . . . **LPMC 200**
MC: . . . . **STC 307C**

Nightingale, Maxine

BITTERSWEET.
Tracks: / Take your heart / I'm givin' it all to you / Work on it / Just because / All night with me / Never enough / Tight spot / Why did you turn me on?.
LP: . . . . **LBG 30323**

LOVE HIT ME.
LP: . . . . **UAS 30076**
MC: . . . . **CK 30076**

RIGHT BACK WHERE WE STARTED FROM.
Tracks: / Love hit me / Think I want to possess you / Bless you / Right back where we started from / In love we grow / Gotta be the one / One last ride / Reasons / If I ever lose this Heaven / Love enough / You got the love / Life has just begun / Every time I see a butterfly / Goodbye again.
LP: . . . . **UAG 29953**

Nightingale & Thompson

EARTHSCRAPES.
MC: . . . . **LUMCA 5**

Nightingales

HYSTERICS.
LP: . . . . **INK 1**

IN THE GOOD OLD COUNTRY WAYS.
LP: . . . . **YUS 7**

JUST THE JOB.
LP: . . . . **VILP 1**

PIGS ON PURPOSE.
Tracks: / Blood for dirt / Start from scratch / One mistake / Well done underdog / Crunch, The / Hedonists sigh, The / It lives again / Make good / Don't blink / Joking apart / Yeah it's OK / Use your loaf / Blisters.
LP: . . . . **BRED 39**

Nightmare

CHILDREN OF THE NIGHT.
Tracks: / Kung fu, karate and tai kwando / Doctor voodoo / Children of the night / Boogi bogi man / I wanna be a monster in a movie / Drac's back / Young dead heroes / Fly angel fly / Evolution / Video nasties / Schizo psycho homicidal maniac / Cellar, The / Witch woman / Dance of death.
LP: . . . . **RTLP 003**

POWER OF THE UNIVERSE.
LP: . . . . **EBON 30**

Nightmare On Elm St

NIGHTMARE ON ELM STREET (Film Soundtrack) (Various artists).
LP: . . . . **STV 81236**
MC: . . . . **CTV 81236**

NIGHTMARE ON ELM STREET 2 (FREDDIES REVENGE) (Film Soundtrack) (Various artists).
LP: . . . . **STV 81275**
MC: . . . . **CTV 81275**

NIGHTMARE ON ELM STREET 3 (DREAM WARRIORS) (Film Soundtrack) (Various artists).
LP: . . . . **STV 81314**
MC: . . . . **CTV 81314**

NIGHTMARE ON ELM STREET 4 (Film Soundtrack) (Various artists).
Tracks: / Under the night stars: *Sea Hags* / Don't be afraid of your dreams: *Go West* / My way or the highway: *Davis, Jimmie* / Therapist: *Vigil* / Angel: *Love Hate* / Standing over you: *Angels From Angel City*/ Back to the wall: *Divinyls* / Love kills: *Vincent, Vinnie* / Rip her to shreds: *Blondie* / Resurrection: *Safan, Craig*.
LP: . . . . **VS 5203**
MC: . . . . **VSC 5203**
LP: . . . . **CHR 1673**
MC: . . . . **ZCHR 1673**

NIGHTMARE ON ELM STREET 5 (Film soundtrack) (Various artists).
Tracks: / Bring your daughter..to the slaughter: *Dickinson, Bruce* / Savage: *W.A.S.P.* / What do you know: *Slave* Raider / Now I lay me down to sleep: *Fox, Samantha* / Word up doc: *Dr. Ice* / Heaven in the back seat: *Romeo's* Daughter / Can't take the hurt: *Mammoth* / Anyway I gotta swing it: *Whodini* / Let's go: *Kool Moe Dee*/ Livin' in the jungle: *Schoolly D*.
LP: . . . . **VS 5238**
MC: . . . . **VSC 5238**
LP: . . . . **HIP 87**
MC: . . . . **HIPC 87**

NIGHTMARE ON ELM STREET (DREAM CHILD) (Film soundtrack) (Various artists).
LP: . . . . **STV 81238**
MC: . . . . **CTV 81238**

Nightmares

NIGHTMARES-POEM TO TROUBLE YOUR SLEEP (Prelutsky, Jack).
MC: **1705**

Nightmares On Wax

WORD OF SCIENCE, A.
LP: . . . . **WARPLP 4**
MC: . . . . **WARPMC 4**

Nightnoise

AT THE END OF THE EVENING.
LP: **371 076-1**
MC: **371 076-4**

PARTING TIDE, THE.
Tracks: / Blue / Irish carol, An / Jig of sorts / Through the castle garden / Island of hope and tears / Kid in the cot, The / Tryst, The / Snow is lightly falling / Abbot, The.
MC: . . . . **WT 1097**

Nights At The...

NIGHTS AT THE BALLET (Various artists).
MC: **TC2MOM 111**

NIGHTS AT THE OPERA (Various artists).
MC: **TC2MOM 112**

Nights In Vienna

NIGHTS IN VIENNA (Various artists).
LP: . . . . **ADL 516**
MC: . . . . **ADK 516**

Nightwing

NIGHT OF THE MYSTERY ALIVE ALIVE.
LP: . . . . **GULP 1043**

Nihilism Spasm Band

1X - X = X.
LP: . . . . **UD 016**

Nijinsky

NIJINSKY (Film soundtrack) (Various artists).
Tracks: / Invitation to the dance: *Various artists* / Jeux: *Various artists* / Prelude a l'apres midi d'un faune: *Various artists* / Scheherazade: *Various artists* / Carnival: *Various artists* / Le sacre du printemps: *Various artists* / Petrushka: *Various artists*.
LP: . . . . **CBS 73885**
MC: **40 73885**

Nikita

NIKITA (Film Soundtrack) (Serra, Eric).
LP: . . . . **VMM 2**
MC: . . . . **TCVMM 2**

Nikki

NIKKI.
Tracks: / If you wanna / Notice me / Whoa whoa whoa / Ooti oooti / Body rub / Do you love me / Wild boys / We'll be together / Come on over / Shadow man.
LP: . . . . **K 9242231**
MC: . . . . **K 9242234**

NIKKI (WEA).
LP: . . . . **LP 721**

Nikki D

MY LATIN LOVER (see under Q-Pid).

Nile, Willie

GOLDEN DOWN.
Tracks: / Poor boy / Shine your light / Grenade / Can't get you off my mind / I like the way / Golden down / Hide your love / Les Champs Elysee / Shoulders.
LP: . . . . **SPART 1165**

WILLIE NILE.
LP: . . . . **SPART 1126**

Nilsson (Harry)

AERIAL BALLET.
Tracks: / Good old desk / Don't leave me / Mr Richard's favourite song / Little cowboy / Together / Everybody's talkin' / I said goodbye to me / Mr. Tinker / One / Wailing of the willow, The / Bath.
LP: . . . . **SF 7973**

AERIAL PANDEMONIUM BALLET.
Tracks: / 1941 / Daddy's song / Mr. Richland's favourite song / Good old desk / Everybody's talkin' / Bath / River deep, mountain high / Sleep late / My lady friend / Don't leave me / Without her / Together / One / Closing.
LP: . . . . **SF 8326**

ALL FOR YOUR LOVE.
MC: . . . . **ORC 005**

DUIT ON MON DEI.
Tracks: / Jesus Christ you're tall / It's a jungle out there / Down by the sea / Kojak Columbo / Easier for me / Turn out the light / Salmon falls / Puget sound / What's your sign / Home / Good for God.
LP: . . . . **RS 1008**

FLASH HARRY.
Tracks: / Harry / Cheek to cheek / Best move / Old dirt road / I don't need you / Rain / I've got it / It's so easy / How long can disco on / Bright side of life / Jesus Christ you're tall / It's a jungle out there / Down by the sea / Kojak, Columbo / Easier for me / Turn out the light / Salmon falls / Puget sound / What's your sign / Home / Good for God.
LP: **6302 022**

GREATEST HITS: HARRY NILSSON.
Tracks: / Everybody's talkin' / 1941 / I guess the Lord must be in New York City / Me and my arrow / Spaceman / Kojak, Columbo / Who's done it / Coconut / Without you / All I think about is you / Remember (Christmas) / Without her / Makin' whoopee / As time goes by / You made me love you.
LP: . . . . **PL 12798**
LP: . . . . **NL 89081**
MC: . . . . **NK 89081**
LP: . . . . **INTS 5233**

HARRY.
Tracks: / Puppy song, The / Nobody cares about the railroad anymore / Open your window / Mother nature's son / Fairfax rag / City life / Mournin' glory story / Maybe / Marchin' down Broadway / I guess the Lord must be in New York City / Rainmaker / Mr Bojangles / Simon Smith and his amazing dancing bear.
LP: . . . . **SF 8046**
LP: . . . . **NE 1050**

KNNILLSSONN.
Tracks: / All I think about is you / I never thought I'd get this lonely / Who done it / Lean on me / Going down / Old bones / Sweet surrender / Blanket for a sail / Laughin' man / Perfect day.
LP: . . . . **PL 12276**
MC: . . . . **PK 12276**

LITTLE TOUCH OF SCHMILSSON IN THE NIGHT.
Tracks: / For me and my gal / It had to be you / Lazy moon / Always / Makin' whoopee / You made me love you / Lullaby in ragtime / I wonder who's kissing her now / What'll I do? / Nevertheless / This is all I ask / As time goes by.
LP: . . . . **NL 83761**
MC: . . . . **NK 83761**
LP: . . . . **SF 8371**
LP: . . . . **INTS 5083**
MC: **APK1 0097**

NILSSON (Greatest Hits).
Tracks: / Everybody's talkin' / 1941 / I guess the Lord must be in New York City / Me and my arrows / Spaceman / Kojak Columbo / Who's done it / Coconut / Without you / Love story / Remember Christmas / Without her / Makin' whoopee / As time goes by / You made me love you / All I think about is you.
LP: . . . . **NL 89081**
MC: . . . . **NK 89081**

NILSSON SCHMILSSON.
Tracks: / Gotta get up / Driving along / Early in the morning / Moonbeam song, The / Down / Let the good times roll / Jump into the fire / Without you / I'll never leave you.
LP: . . . . **FA 3166**
MC: . . . . **TCFA 3166**
LP: . . . . **NL 83464**
MC: . . . . **NK 83463**
LP: . . . . **SF 8242**
MC: . . . . **PK 1734**

NILSSON SINGS NEWMAN.
Tracks: / Vine street / Love story (you and me) / Yellow man / Caroline / Cowboy / Beehive state / I'll be home / Living without you / Dayton, Ohio, 1903 / So long, dad.
LP: . . . . **PL 42304**
MC: . . . . **NK 90305**
LP: . . . . **NL 90305**

NILSSON'S GREATEST MUSIC.
Tracks: / Everybody's talkin' / 1941 / I guess the Lord must be in New York City / Me and my arrow / Spaceman / Kojak Columbo / Who done it / Coconut / Without you / Love story / Remember Christmas / Without her / Makin' whoopee / As time goes by / You made me love you / All I think about is you.
LP: . . . . **PL 42728**
MC: . . . . **PK 42748**

PANDEMONIUM SHADOW.
Tracks: / Ten little Indians / 1941 / Cuddly toy / She sang hymns out of tune / You can't do that / Sleep late, my lady friend / She's leaving home / There will never be / Without her / Freckles / It's been so long / River deep mountain high.
LP: . . . . **SF 7928**

POINT, THE.

Tracks: / Everything's got 'em / Town, The (narration) / Me and my arrow / Game, The (narration) / Poli high / Trial and banishment (narration) / Think about your troubles / Pointed man, The (narration) / Birds, The (narration) / P.O.V. waltz / Clearing in the woods (narration) / Are you sleeping / Oblio's return (narration).
LP: SF 8166
MC: PK 1623
LP: ED 340
MC: CED 340

SANDMAN.
Tracks: / I'll take a tango / Something true / Pretty soon there'll be nothing left for ... / Ivy covered walls / Here's why I did not go to work today / Flying saucer song, The / How to write a song / Jesus Christ you're tall / Will she miss me.
LP: RS 1015

SCHMILSSON.
Tracks: / Gotta get up / Driving along / Early in the morning / Moonbeam song / Down / Without you / Coconut / Let the good times roll / Jump into the fire / I'll never leave you.
LP: INTS 5002

SON OF DRACULA.
Tracks: / It is he who will be king / Daybreak / At my front door / Count Down meets Merlin and Amber / Moonbeam / Perhaps all this is a dream / Remember / Without you / Count's vulnerability, The / Down / Frankenstein, Merlin and the operation / Jump into the fire / Abdication of Count Down, The / End, The.
LP: APL1 0220

SON OF SCHMILSSON.
Tracks: / Take 54 / Remember Christmas / Joy / Turn on your radio / You're breakin' my heart / Spaceman / Lottery song, The / At my front door / Ambush / I'd rather be dead / Most beautiful world in the world, The.
LP: SF 8297

THAT'S THE WAY IT IS.
Tracks: / That is all / Just one look / Baby I'm yours / Moonshine bandit / I need you / Thousand miles away, A / Sail away / She sits down on me / Daylight has caught me / Zombie jamboree (back to back) / That is all (reprise).
LP: RS 1062

TOUCH MORE SCHMILSSON IN THE NIGHT, A.
Tracks: / Intro / I'm always chasing rainbows / Make believe / You made me love you (I didn't want to do it) / Trust in me / Lullaby in ragtime / All I think about is you / Perfect day / Always / It's only a paper moon / It had to be you / Thanks for the memory / Outro / Over the rainbow.
LP: PL 90251
MC: PK 90251

WITHOUT HER, WITHOUT YOU (The Very Best Of Nilsson, Vol 1).
Tracks: / Over the rainbow / Without her / Cuddly toy / Wailing of the willow, The / Everybody's talkin' / I guess the Lord must be in New York City / Mother Nature's son / Puppy song, The / Mournin' glory story / Daddy's song / Maybe / Down to the valley / Life line / River deep - mountain high / Moonbeam song, The / Without you / Mucho mungo / Mt. Elga / Subterranean homesick blues.
MC: NK 90520

Nimmo, Jenny

SNOW SPIDER, THE (Asher, Jane (nar)).
MC: 3CCA 3062

Nimmons, Phil

ATLANTIC SUITE.
LP: 2008

Nimoy, Leonard

ILLUSTRATED MAN, THE (see under Illustrated Man (bk)).

MARTIAN CHRONICLES, THE (see under Martian Chronicles).

MR SPOCK'S MUSIC FROM OUTER SPACE.
LP: RVLP 1002

Nimsgern, Frank

FRANK NIMSGERN (Nimsgern, Frank feat. Chaka Khan & Billy Cobham).
Tracks: / Last Summer / Just another way out / Catch the time / Take me away / Pretty secrets / Don't you think it's alright / Latin jokes / Pat's prelude / On the trip / Spring.
LP: 890011
MC: 890014

Nina

GOLDEN HOUR PRESENTS NINA.
Tracks: / By the time I get to Phoenix / I won't last a day without you / Open your window / Bird on the wire / Sing children sing / Both sides now / If you go away / Bridge over troubled water / Windmills of your mind / Pocketful of keys / Other side of me, The / Question / This masquerade / Songs / Where's the playground / Love song.
LP: GH 658

Nina & Frederick

NINA AND FREDERICK.
LP: COL 1314

NINA AND FREDERICK (PYE).
LP: NPT 19023

Nine Below Zero

DON'T POINT YOUR FINGER.
Tracks: / One way street / Doghouse / Liquor lover / Helen / Ain't comin' back / I won't lie / Treat her right / Three times enough / Sugar mama / Don't point your finger at the guitar man / Rockin' robin / You can't please all the people all the time.
LP: AMLH 68521
MC: CAM 68521

LIVE AT THE MARQUEE.
Tracks: / Tore down / Straighten her out / Homework / I can't help myself / Can I get a witness / Ridin' on the L & N / I can't quit baby / Stop your naggin' / Hoochie coochie coo, The / Wooly bully / Got my mojo working / Pack fair and square / Watch youself / Swing job.
LP: AMLE 68515
MC: CEM 68515

LIVE AT THE VENUE.
LP: RRLP 121

ON THE ROAD AGAIN.
LP: WOL 1014
MC: WOLMC 1014

THIRD DEGREE.
Tracks: / Eleven plus eleven / Wipe away your kiss / Why can't we be what we want to be? / Tearful eye / True love is a crime / Egg on my face / Sugarbeat (and rhythm sweet) / Mystery man / East Street / You don't love me / You can't say yes and you can't say no.
MC: CAM 68537
LP: AMLH 68537

Nine Inch Nails

PRETTY HATE MACHINE.
LP: ILPS 9973
MC: ICT 9973

Nine Pound Hammer

MUD, THE BLOOD AND THE BEER, THE.
LP: WH 007

Nine (show)

NINE (Original Broadway Cast) (Various artists).
LP: JS 38325
MC: JST 38325

Niney & Friends

BLOOD AND FIRE.
LP: TRLS 263

BRING THE COUCHIE 1974-76.
LP: TRLS 273

Niney The Observer

NINEY THE OBSERVER.
LP: LPHB 68

Ninja

FORGOTTEN SHADOWS.
LP: IW 1012

Ninja Man

MY WEAPON.
MC: DSRC 9732

NINJA MAN VS JOHNNY P (Ninja Man & Johnny P).
LP: PICKLP 05

OUT PON BAIL.
LP: VPRL 1126

SAVE THE LAST DANCE FOR ME (See under Stewart, Tinga) (Ninja Man & Tinga Stewart).

SUNSPLASH.
LP: PICLP 14

SUPER STAR.
LP: MMLP 0015

WARNING YOU.
LP: JMLP 006

ZIG IT UP (See under Flourgon).

Ninja Mr.Palmer

FOREIGN LIVING.
Tracks: / Preacher, The / Nah go deh so / Mix me properly / Bad bwoy habit / Love your woman / Age of the gangster / Nah say nothing / Bounty hunter.
LP: SPLP 001

Ninja Turtle

NINJA TURTLE (PART 2) (Various artists).
LP: PHLP 2000

NINJA TURTLE (PART 3) (Various artists).
LP: PHLP 3000

Nips

BOPS, BABES, BOOZE AND BOVVER.
Tracks: / King of the bop / Nervous wreck / So pissed off / Stavordale Rd. N5 / All the time in the world / Private eye / Gabrielle / Vengeance.
LP: WIKM 66

Nirvana

BLACK FLOWER (LP).
Tracks: / Black flower / I believe in magic / It happened two Sundays ago / Life ain't easy / Pentecost Hotel / World is cold without you / We can make it through / Satellite jockey / Excerpt from The blind and the beautiful / June / Tiny goddess / Illinois / Tres tres bien / Love suite.
LP: KIRI 061

BLEACH.
LP: TUPLP 6

NEVERMIND.
LP: DGC 24425
MC: DGCC 24425

Nistico, Sal

EAST OF ISAR (Nistico, Sal/Benny Bailey).
LP: EGO 4010

JUST FOR FUN.
LP: EGO 4002

NEO/NISTICO.
LP: BH 7006

Nita, Rita & Ruby

ROCK LOVE.
Tracks: / Rock love / Lovey lips / Leroy / Not anymore / Jimmy Unknown / Pledging my love / Last night in my dreams / Whose baby are you? / Give me love / Baby you're the one / I just won't care anymore / Losin' my baby again / You came to the prom alone / No sweet love ain't around / But I love you just the same / My man true to me / At the old town hall / Borrowed diamonds / Hi de ank tum.
LP: BFX 15176

Nite Blues...

CARIBBEAN CARNIVAL (Nite Blues Steel Band).
LP: GH 619

CARNIVAL TIME (Nite Blues Steel Band).
LP: VSLP 4045

Nitecaps

BEST OF CLASSIC DOOWOP VOL.2 (See under Five Keys) (Five Keys/Nitecaps).

GO TO THE LINE.
Tracks: / Same situation / Go to the line / Hot pavement / Can't let one more day go by / Somebody cares / Give me one more chance / Little too long / Black tears / New me / Is this the dream? / Good times.
LP: W 3756

Niteflite

NITEFLITE 3 (Various artists).
Tracks: / Being with you: *Robinson, Smokey* / Just be good to me: *S.O.S. Band* / I need your lovin': *Williams, Alyson* / Always and forever: *Heatwave* / Hold me tighter: *Griffin, Billy* / Me and Mrs. Jones: *Paul, Billy* / Just my imagination: *Temptations* / Rock witcha: *Brown, Bobby (1)* / New York eyes: *Nicole/Timmy Thomas* / Broken heart can mend, A: *O'Neal, Alexander* / Juicy fruit: *Mtume* / All I want is forever: *Taylor/Belle/* Never too much: *Vandross, Luther* / Between the sheets: *Isley Brothers* / Lily was here: *Stewart, David A & Candy Dulfer.*
LP: MOOD 14
MC: MOODC 14

Nite-Lites

I AIN'T DRUNK (see Muldaur, Geoff) (Nite-Lites & Geoff Maldaur).

Niteshift Trio

YOU AIN'T SEEN NOTHIN' YET.
LP: F 3006

Nitros

JUMPIN' BEAT.
LP: NERD 048

STOMPIN' BEAT.
LP: NERD 049

Nits

IN THE DUTCH MOUNTAINS (LP).
Tracks: / In the Dutch mountains / J.O.S. days / Two skaters / Pelican and penguin / In a play / Oom-pah-pah / Panorama man, The / Mountain Jan / One eye open / Eating house, An / Swimmer, The / Goodnight / Strangers of the night* / Moon and stars (Available on cassette only).
LP: 4600711
MC: 4600714

Nitty Gritty

GENERAL PEN, THE.
LP: ADM 080

MUSICAL CONFRONTATION (Nitty Gritty & King Kong).
LP: Unknown

NITTY GRITTY.
LP: MMLP 0014

TURBO CHARGED.
Tracks: / Gimme some of you something / Turbo-charged / Ram up the dance / Key to your heart / Rub-a-dub a kill you / Amazing grace / Cry cry baby / Down in the ghetto / Don't want to lose you / Hog in a minty.
LP: GREL 93

Nitty Gritty Dirt Band

20 YEARS OF DIRT.
LP: 925382 1
MC: 925382 4

ALL THE GOOD TIMES.
LP: BGOLP 93

BEST OF NITTY GRITTY DIRT BAND VOL 2.
Tracks: / Cadillac ranch / I've been looking / Oh what a love / Working man / I love only you / Fishin' in the dark / Baby's got a hold on me / Face on the cutting room floor / Down that road tonight / Home again.
LP: K 925830 1
MC: K 925830 4

BEST OF THE DREAM.
LP: MCG 6106
MC: MCGC 6106

COUNTRY STORE: NITTY GRITTY DIRT BAND.
Tracks: / Battle of New Orleans / All I have to do is dream / Bayou jubilee / Rave on / Mr. Bojangles / Honky tonkin' / House of poor corner / Some of Shelly's blues / Moon just turned blue, The / Make a little magic / American dream / Hey good lookin' / Slim Carter / Diggy liggy lo.
LP: CST 33
MC: CSTK 33

DIRT, SILVER AND GOLD.
Tracks: / Buy for me the rain / Melissa / Collegiana / Mournin' blues / Willie the weeper / Uncle Charlie's interview / Mr. Bojangles / Some of Shelly's blues / Cure, The / House at Pooh corner / Randy Lynn rag / Opus 36 / Clementi / Living without you / Sixteen tracks / Fish song / Creepin' round your back door / Honky tonkin' / Togary mountain / Soldiers joy / Rippling waters / You are my flower / Battle of New Orleans / All I have to do is dream / Rocky top / Gavotte no.2 / Jamaica lady / Mother Earth (provides for me) / Falling down slow / Bowlegs / Doc's guitar / Bayou jubilee / Sally was a goodun' / Cosmic cowboy / Wine or lose / Woody Woodpecker / Visiting an old friend / Will the circle be unbroken / Foggy mountain breakdown.
LPS: UAT 9802

EARLY DIRT 1967-70.
Tracks: / Buy for me the rain / Euphoria / Holding / Song for Julia / Dismal swamp / It's raining here in Long Beach / Shadow dream song / Truly right / Tide of love / Collegiana / Mournin' blues / These days / Some of Shelly's blues / Rave on / Mr. Bojangles / House at Pooh Corner / Living without you.
LP: LIK 3

GOLD FROM DIRT.
Tracks: / Mr. Bojangles / Some of Shelley's blues / Jamaica say you will / Battle of New Orleans / All I have to do is dream.
LP: UAG 30275

LET'S GO.
Tracks: / Heartaches in heartaches / Special look / Shot full of love / Never together / Goodbye eyes / Maryann / Too many heartaches in paradise / Don't get sand in it / Let's go / Dance little Jean.
LP: LBG 400 184 1

NITTY GRITTY DIRT BAND, THE.
MC: 4XLL 9182

UNCLE CHARLIE AND HIS DOG TEDDY.
Tracks: / Some of Shelly's blues / Rave on / Living without you / Uncle Charlie / Mr. Bojangles / Clinch mountain / Back step / Propinquity / Cure, The / Opus 36 / Clementi / Chicken reel / Travellin' mood / Billy in the low / Swanee river / Randy Lynn rag / Santa Rosa / Prodigal's return / Yukon railroad / House at Pooh Corner.
LP: 3C 054 61220
MC: 3C 254 61220

LP: . . . . BGOLP 22

WORKIN' BAND.
LP: 925722 1
MC: 925722 4

Nitzer Ebb

BELIEF, THE.
LP: . . . . STUMM 61
MC: . . . . CSTUMM 61

EBBHEAD.
LP: . . . . STUMM 088
MC: . . . . CSTUMM 088

SHOWTIME.
LP: . . . . STUMM 72
MC: . . . . CSTUMM 72

THAT TOTAL AGE.
Tracks: / Fitness to purpose / Violent playground / Murderous / Smear body / Let your body learn / Let beauty loose / Into the large air / Join in the chant / Alarm / Join in the chant (metal mix) (CD only.) / Fitness to purpose (mix two) (CD only.) / Murderous (instrumental) (CD only.).
LP: . . . . STUMM 45
MC: . . . . CSTUMM 45

Nitzsche, Jack

ST. GILES CRIPPLEGATE.
LP: . . . . IRC 006

Niven, David

BRING ON THE EMPTY HORSES (see under Bring on the... (bk).

ENCHANTED ORCHESTRA, THE (Niven, David/National Philharmonic Orchestra).
LP: . . . . MR 116
MC: . . . . MRC 116

MOON'S A BALLOON, THE.
MCSET: . . . . LFP 7010
MCSET: . . . . LFP 4170105
MCSET: . . . . TCLFP 7010

Nivens

SHAKE.
LP: . . . . DANLP 022
MC: . . . . DANC 022

Nixon, Elmore

SHOUT AND ROCK (See under Harris, Peppermint).

Nixon, Hammie

LIVING COUNTRY BLUES (see under Chatmon, Sam) (Nixon, Hammie & Sam Chatmon).

Nixon, Marti

MARTI NIXON SINGS GERSHWIN.
LP: . . . . RR 19

Nixon, Mojo

BO-DAY-SHUS.
LP: 3272 1

ROOT HOG OR DIE (Nixon, Mojo & Skid Roper).
Tracks: / Debbie Gibson is pregnant (with my two headed / This land is your land / Chicken drop / I'm a wreck / Circus mystery / (619) 239-king / Pirate radio / Louisiana liprock / Legalize it / She's vibrator dependent.
LP: . . . . ENVLP 520
MC: . . . . TCENV 520

UNLIMITED EVERYTHING (Nixon, Mojo & Skid Roper).
Tracks: / Amazing big foot diet, The / Debbie Gibson is pregnant with my two headed love child / Jesus at Mcdonalds / Amsterdam dogshit blues / Stuffin' Martha's muffin / Burn down the malls / Elvis is everywhere / Louisiana liplock / 619 239 king / Burn your money / Rockin' religion / I gotta connect.
LP: . . . . ENVLP 1005
MC: . . . . TCENV 1005

No

GLORY FOR THE SHIT FOR BRAINS.
LP: . . . . ULP 001

No Dice

2 FACED.
Tracks: / Momma do stop your children watching what your momma do / Shooting in the dark / I keep it to myself / Angel with a dirty face / No stone unturned / Come dancing / If you had nothing / Bad boys / Put up 'n' left me.
LP: . . . . EMC 3282

NO DICE.
LP: . . . . EMC 3198

No Easy Walk To

NO EASY WALK TO FREEDOM (THEME FROM) (See under Kay, Janet) (Kay, Janet).

No Entiendes

NO ENTIENDES Live at the ICA.
LP: . . . . AN 1020

No For An Answer

NO FOR AN ANSWER Original cast recording (Various artists).
LP: . . . . AEI 1140

TOUGHT CRUSADE, A.
LP: . . . . HR 9487 1

No Fraud

HARD TO THE CORE.
LP: . . . . NB 7

No Man Is Roger Miller

WIN INSTANTLY.
LP: . . . . SST 243
MC: . . . . SSTC 243

No Man's Land (Film)

NO MAN'S LAND (Film Soundtrack) (Various artists).
Tracks: / Jewel movement: *Various artists* / Medusa's refrain (part 1): *Various artists* / Medusa's refrain (part 2): *Various artists* / Spark from the infinite, A (part 1): *Various artists* / Spark from the infinite, A (part 2): *Various artists* / Return of the dream collector: *Various artists* / Jaipur local: *Various artists*/ Blue anthem: *Various artists*.
LP: . . . . STV 81352
MC: . . . . CTV 81352
LP: . . . . PL 1267 17

No Means No

SEX MAD.
Tracks: / Sex mad / Dad / Obsessed / No f... / She beast / Dead Bob / Long days / Metronome / Revenge / Self pity.
LP: . . . . VIRUS 56

SKY IS FALLING, THE (See under Biafra, Jello) (No Means No & Jello Biafra).

SMALL PARTS ISOLATED AND DESTROYED.
LP: . . . . VIRUS 63

WRONG.
LP: . . . . VIRUS 077
MC: . . . . VIRUS 077MC

No Medals for...

NO MEDALS FOR THE MAJOR (See under Yorke, Margaret) (Yorke, Margaret).

No Mercy

NO MERCY (Film soundtrack) (Various artists).
Tracks: / Main title: *Silvestri, Alan* / Barge, The: *Silvestri, Alan* / Delivery, The: *Silvestri, Alan*/ River crush: *Silvestri, Alan* / Afterglow: *Silvestri, Alan* / Like your friends: *Silvestri, Alan* / Lasado's woman: *Silvestri, Alan* / Michel arrives: *Silvestri, Alan* / Tailed: *Silvestri, Alan* / Blue parrot: *Silvestri, Alan* / I was late: *Silvestri, Alan* / What do you say: *Silvestri, Alan* / No mercury reprise: *Silvestri, Alan*.
LP: . . . . FILM 015
MC: . . . . FILMC 015

No No Nanette

NO NO NANETTE (1971 Revival cast) (Various artists).
LP: . . . . PS 30563
MC: . . . . PST 30563

NO NO NANETTE (Original London cast) (Various artists).
LP: . . . . SH 176

No Other Name

DEATH INTO LIFE.
LP: . . . . LD 5001
MC: . . . . LDC 5001

No Place to Hide (bk)

NO PLACE TO HIDE (Ted Allbeury) (Nettles, John (nar)).
MC: 060056049X

No Smoke

INTERNATIONAL SMOKE SIGNALS.
LP: . . . . WAFLP 3

No Speak Sampler

NO SPEAK SAMPLER (Various).
Tracks: / India / Arabesque / You got me runnin' / Fire and mercy / Equalizer, The / Doctor Brown I presume / No limit / Prisoner, The / Idler, The / Shotgun cha cha / Perfect flight / Glidepath.
LP: . . . . ILP 034

No Sports

KING SKA.
LP: . . . . PHZA 49

No Strings

NO STRINGS (London cast recording) (Various artists).
Tracks: / How sad: *Various artists* / Man who has everything, The: *Various artists* / Orthodox fool: *Various* artists / Loads of love: *Various artists* / You don't tell me: *Various artists* / Love makes the world go: *Various artists* / Eager beaver: *Various artists* / La la la: *Various artists* / Look no further: *Various* artists / Maine: *Various artists* / No strings: *Various artists* / Nobody told me: *Various artists*/ Sweetest sounds: *Various artists*.
LP: . . . . DS 15013

No Surrender

NO SURRENDER (Film soundtrack) (Various artists).
LP: . . . . PACT 12

No Sweat

NO SWEAT.
Tracks: / Heart and soul / Shake / Stay / On the edge / Waters Flow / Tear down the walls / Generation / Lean on me / Stranger / Mover.
LP: 828 206 1
MC: 828 206 4

No Trend

WHEN DEATH WON'T SOLVE YOUR PROBLEM.
LP: . . . . WSP 5

No Way Out (film)

NO WAY OUT/THE YEAR OF LIVING DANGEROUSLY (Film Soundtrack) (Various artists).
Tracks: / No way out: *Jarre, Maurice* / National security: *Jarre, Maurice* / Cover-up: *Jarre, Maurice*/ In the Pentagon: *Jarre, Maurice* / We can interface: *Jarre, Maurice* / Susan: *Jarre, Maurice*.
LP: . . . . TER 1149
MC: . . . . ZCTER 1149

No Y Z

NO Y Z.
LP: . . . . A 112

Noack, Eddie

EDDIE NOACK.
Tracks: / Take it away Lucky / Wind me up / Left over lovin' / Don't trade / Don't worry 'bout me baby / When the bright lights grow dim / It ain' much but it's a home / You done got me / Worm has turned / For you I weep / What's the matter Joe / Think of her now / If it ain't on the menu / Fair today cold tomorrow.
LP: . . . . CH 21

GENTLEMEN PREFER BLONDES.
Tracks: / Scarecrow / Wanderin' oakie / Dust on the river / Walk em off / Man on the wall / Too weak to go / Firewater luke / Price of love.
LP: . . . . CHD 149

Noah House Of Dread

HEART.
LP: . . . . HEART 001

NOAH HOUSE OF DREAD.
Tracks: / Neighbours / More we are together, The / Business is business / Rasta don't fear / Something in my heart / Only Selassie I / Don't let the devil hold you back / Babylon cup / Big shot.
LP: . . . . HEART 002

Noakes, Rab

RAB NOAKES.
LP: . . . . MCF 3083

UNDER THE RAIN.
LP: . . . . CRO 207
MC: . . . . CROC 207

Noble House (tv)

NOBLE HOUSE (TV Soundtrack) (Various artists).
LP: . . . . STV 81360
MC: . . . . CTV 81360

Noble, Ike

IKE NOBLE.
Tracks: / Lonely people / I promise you / Angie / I'm gonna miss your love / Your love / Keep me cryin' / Best years of my life, The / Shake it loose.
LP: . . . . TRLP 100
LP: . . . . TRPL 100

Noble, Ray

1930'S VOLUME 2, THE Complete COTY program (Noble, Ray & Joe Haymes).
Tracks: / Very thought of you, The / Flowers for madame / Way down yonder in New Orleans / Koranga / I never had a chance / Danny boy / Night on the desert / Blue danube / In my country that means love / Two seats in the balcony / Honeysuckle rose / On the good ship lollipop / Nothin' ever happens when Gimbal hits the cymb / London on a rainy night / My melancholy baby / White star of Sigma Nu, The.
LP: . . . . AIRCHECK 2

CLASSIC YEARS IN DIGITAL STEREO (see under Bowlly, Al) (Noble, Ray Orchestra & Al Bowlly).

DINNER MUSIC (Noble, Ray & His Orchestra).
LP: . . . . GELP 15031

GOODNIGHT SWEETHEART (Noble, Ray & His Orchestra).
Tracks: / Blue Danube / Shout for happiness / Put that down in writing / Dreamy Carolina / Lights of Paris / Lady of Spain / It's great to be in love / Lazy day / Give me a tune / One little quarrel / Please don't mention it / Twentieth Century blues / Living in clover / Goodnight sweetheart.
LP: . . . . JOYD 272
MC: . . . . TC JOYD 272

HMV SESSIONS, THE (Noble, Ray Orchestra & Al Bowlly).
Tracks: / Sweet and lovely / Over my shoulder / Close your eyes / When you've got a little springtime in your heart / Did you ever see a dream walking? / I can't get Mississippi off my mind / Remember me / Isle of Capri / Time on my hands / You ought to see Sally on Sunday / Guilty / One morning in May / I'll string along with you / Wanderer / Wagon wheels / You're driving me crazy / I'll be good because of you / Goodnight sweetheart.
LP: . . . . SH 107 822 1
MC: . . . . TCSH 107 822 4

MY SONG GOES ROUND THE WORLD (See under Bowlly, Al) (Noble, Ray & Al Bowlly).

NOTABLE NOBLE.
Tracks: / When the real thing comes your way / South sea rose / You've got to be modernistic / Crazy feel / Sweepin' the clouds away / I've got a feeling / Just imagine / It ain't no fault of mine / Tan-tan-tivvy-tally-ho / Mad about the boy / Blue Danube / Try a little tenderness / Chewing gum / I was in the mood / Sun is round the corner / Repeal the blues.
LP: . . . . EG 2604591
MC: . . . . EG 2604594
LP: . . . . SH 429

OVER ON THE SUNNY SIDE (Noble, Ray & His Orchestra).
LP: . . . . OLD 6
MC: . . . . COLD 6

RAY NOBLE & AL BOWLLY, NO 1 (Noble, Ray & His Orchestra & Al Bowlly).
Tracks: / Love is the sweetest thing / It's bad for me / You're mine, you / Hang out the stars in Indiana / Looking on the bright side of life / With all my love and kisses / I'm glad I waited / What more can I ask? / It's all forgotten now / Midnight, the stars and you / What now? / Love tales / This is romance / Remember me / Hustling and bustling for baby.
LP: . . . . MES 6816

RAY NOBLE & AL BOWLLY, NO. 2 (Noble, Ray & His Orchestra).
LP: . . . . MES 7021

RAY NOBLE & AL BOWLLY, NO 6 (Noble, Ray & His Orchestra & Al Bowlly).
Tracks: / Lady of Spain / This little piggie / On the other side of Lovers' Lane / Got a date with an angel / Twentieth Century blues / If you'll say yes, cherie / Oceans of time / Sailin' on the Robert E. Lee / Isle of Capri / You oughta be in pictures / Lazy day / Grinzing / You're driving me crazy.
LP: . . . . MES 7056

RAY NOBLE ENCORES (Noble, Ray & His Orchestra).
Tracks: / I'll be good because of you / You're twice as nice / Must it end like this? / Spin a little web of dreams / Can't we meet again? / Lady of Madrid / With love in my heart / Roll on, Mississippi, roll on / Japanese sandman / Tiger rag / Mad about the boy / Blue Danube / Evergreen (medley) / Happy ending.
LP: . . . . MES 7070

RAY NOBLE & JOE HAYMES 1935 (see Haymes,Joe & Ray Noble) (Noble, Ray & Joe Haymes).

RAY NOBLE ORCHESTRA 1935-6 (VOLUME 2) (Noble, Ray & His Orchestra).
LP: . . . . HMG 5027

RAY NOBLE'S ENCORES, VOL.3.
LP: . . . . MES 7027

RAY NOBLE'S ENCORES, VOL.4 (Noble, Ray & His Orchestra).
LP: . . . . MES 7039

RAY NOBLE'S ENCORES, VOL.5 (Noble, Ray & His Orchestra).
LP: . . . . MES 7040

WE DANCED ALL NIGHT (Noble, Ray & His Orchestra).
Tracks: / I've got my love to keep me warm / Easy to love / El relicario / Why stars come out at night / Chinatown, my Chinatown / Double trouble / Way down yonder in New Orleans / Soon / Touch of your lips, The / Dinah / I've got you under my skin / Allah holiday.
LP: . . . . NL 89463
MC: . . . . NK 89463

Nobodius, Berbel

WANTON BUT WIND BLOWN.
Tracks: / Leakage / Leit motiv vacuo / Corridors of bureaucracy / Renal birth / Beast of burden / Primevil awakening /

Then emancipation / Miss my leg when skankinging / Brushwood epitaph / Cruise into oblivion / Windblown quiescence / Be our late arrival / Deltoid massacre / Wanton ardour.
LP: HAM 24

Nocenzi, Gianni

EMPUSA.
Tracks: / L'occhio, la luna e il lupo, nell'imputo cosmico / Dance of a bottle / Voodoo bolero / Como dos trenes que se cruzan en la noche.
LP: VE 26
MC: TCVE 26

Nocera

OVER THE RAINBOW.
LP: TLX 11

Nock, Mike

IN OUT AND AROUND (Nock, Mike Quartet).
Tracks: / Break time / Dark light / Shadows of forgotten / Gift, The / Hadrian's wall / In, out and around.
LP: SJP 119

PIANO SOLOS.
Tracks: / Californian country song / Polyhedron / Fallen angel / Break time / Elsewhen / Enchanted garden / Soliloquy / Jackanory / Dolphin dance.
LP: SJP 134

TALISMAN.
LP: ENJA 3071

Nocturna

NOCTURNA (Film soundtrack) (Various artists).
LP: MCG 4004

Nocturnal Emissions

BEFEHLOSNOTSTAND.
LP: SR 5

CHAOS.
LP: CFC LP 2

DEATHDAY.
MC: SRC 003

DROWNING IN A SEA OF BLISS.
LP: SR 4

SHAKE THOSE CHAINS, RATTLE THOSE CAGES.
Tracks: / Shake those chains rattle those cages (Live at the ICA.).
LP: SR 009
MC: SRC 009

SONGS OF LOVE AND REVOLUTION.
LP: SR 7

SPIRIT FLESH.
LP: EARTH 004

STONEFACE.
LP: 081100

TISSUE OF LIES.
LP: EMISS 001

WORLD IS MY WOMB, THE.
LP: EARTH 002

Nocturnal Emissions

NOCTURNAL EMISSIONS (Various artists).
MC: TO 4

Nocturnus

KEY, THE.
LP: MOSH 23
MC: MOSH 23 MC
LPPD: MOSH 23 P

Noddy...

NODDY AND THE MAGIC BOOTS (Bryer, Denise).
MC: TTS 9803

NODDY MAKES EVERYONE CROSS (Bryer, Denise).
MC: TTS 9815

NODDY STORIES.
MCSET: DTO 10536

NODDY STORIES.
MCSET: DTO 10545

NODDY STORIES.
MCSET: DTO 10550

NODDY STORIES (By Enid Blyton) (Briers, Richard).
MC: PTB 605

NODDY STORIES VOL.1.
MCSET: DTO 10500

NODDY STORIES VOL.2.
MCSET: DTO 10507

NODDY STORIES VOL.3.
MCSET: DTO 10542

NODDY'S BIG BALLOON (Bryer, Denise).
MC: TTS 9813

NODDY'S UNLUCKY DAY (Bryer, Denise).
MC: TTS 9814

Nodelijk, Anja & Rene

RENEE.
LP: AKH 001

Noel & Gertie

NOEL AND GERTIE (Original London cast) (Various artists).
Tracks: / Overture: *Noel & Gertie* / Some day I'll find you: *Noel & Gertie* / Mrs. Worthington: *Noel & Gertie*/ Touring days: *Noel & Gertie* / Paisian pierrot: *Noel & Gertie* / Dance little lady: *Noel & Gertie* / Play, orchestra, play: *Noel & Gertie* / We were dancing: *Noel & Gertie* / Man about town: *Noel & Gertie*/ I travel alone: *Noel & Gertie* / Sail away: *Noel & Gertie* / Why must the show go on?: *Noel & Gertie*/ Come the wild, wild weather: *Noel & Gertie* / I'll remember her: *Noel & Gertie* / I'll see you again: *Noel & Gertie* / Curtain music: *Noel & Gertie*.
LP: TER 1117
MC: ZCTER 1117

Noel (Group)

IS THERE MORE TO LIFE THAN DANCING.
LP: V 2126

Noh Rodeo

COOL 'N' GROOVY.
MLP: ANT 047

Noise Unit

GRINDING INTO EMPTINESS.
LP: AS 5001

RESPONSE FREQUENCY.
LP: AS 5029

Noisehunter

SPELL OF NOISE.
LP: 880763

Noiseworks

NOISEWORKS.
Tracks: / Burning feeling / Love somebody / Take me back / No lies / River of tears / Welcome to the world / Edge of darkness / Little bit more, A / Only loving you / It's time.
LP: 4510331
MC: 4510334
LP: 4654961
MC: 4654964

NOISEWORKS/TOUCH.
Tracks: / Burning feeling / Love somebody / Take me back / No lies / River of tears / Welcome to the world / Edge of darkness / Little bit more, A / Only loving you / It's time / Simple man / Touch / Voice of reason / Chained / Home / I can't win / Letter / Tell it like this / Keep me running / Live and die / In my youth.
LP: 4654961
MC: 4654964

TOUCH.
Tracks: / Simple man / Touch / Voice of reason / Chained / Home / I can't win / Letter / Tell it like it is / Keep me running / Live and die / In my youth.
LP: 4631151
MC: 4631154

Nolan, Christopher

UNDER THE EYE OF THE CLOCK (Hefferon, Colm).
MC: IAB 88111

Nolan Struck

HARD WORKING MAN.
Tracks: / Dirty mutha for ya, A / Nine pound steel / Getting married / Welfare problem / Things I used to do, The / Endlessly / Falling in love / Hard working man.
LP: ICH 1045
MC: ICH 1045MC

Noland, Terry

ORIGINAL 1956 DEMOS.
Tracks: / Fabulous love story, The / Puppy love / Oh, baby look at me / Let me be your hero / Oh Judy / Forever loving you / Teenage teardrops / Crazy dream.
LP: BFX 15319

TERRY NOLAND.
LP: BL 54041

Nolans

20 GIANT HITS (TARGET).
Tracks: / Sailing / Don't it make my brown eyes blue / Mull of Kintyre / Don't give up on us baby / Way we were, The / Isn't she lovely / You make me feel brand new / Chanson d'amour / God only knows / Money money money / Bridge over troubled water / Without you / Song sung blue / Your song / He (she) / I'd like to teach the world to sing / When a child is born / Save your kisses for me / Make it with you / Reach out, I'll be there.
LP: TGS 502

ALTOGETHER.
Tracks: / I'm in the mood for dancing / Attention to me / Don't love me too hard / Gotta pull myself together / Don't make waves / Sexy music / Thank you for the music / Dragonfly / Chemistry / Who's gonna rock you / Every home should have one / Touch me in the morning / Crashing down / Spirit, body and soul.
LP: EPC 10037

BEST OF THE NOLAN SISTERS (VOL.2).
Tracks: / Chanson d'amour / Your song / Make it with you / Andy / When a child is born / Without you / Money, money, money / He (she) / You make me feel brand new / Thanks for calling / Mull of Kintyre / Way we were.
LP: SHM 994

BEST OF THE NOLAN SISTERS (VOL.1).
Tracks: / Don't it make my brown eyes blue / Don't give up on us / Song sung blue / Isn't she lovely / God only knows / Reach out I'll be there / Something tells me / Sailing / I'd like to teach the world to sing / Save your kisses for me / Love bandit / Bridge over troubled water / Don't throw your love away.
LP: SHM 993

BEST OF THE NOLANS, THE.
MCSET: DTO 10230

GIRLS JUST WANNA HAVE FUN.
LP: TOWLP 10
MC: ZCTOW 10

HARMONY.
Tracks: / Won't you make a little sunshine smile / Have love will travel / Rain / Love transformation / Oh my darling (end s1) / Thanks for callin' / Back in the world again / Hey what a day / Don't throw your love away / When you are a king.
LP: CBR 1024
MC: KCBR 1024

I'M IN THE MOOD FOR DANCING.
Tracks: / I'm in the mood for dancing / Spirit, body and soul / All the king's horses / I know I'll never love this way again / Don't let me be the last to know / Miss you nights / Who's gonna rock you / Attention to me / More to love / Let's make love / Bright eyes / Thank you for the music.
LP: SHM 3124
MC: HSC 3124

LOVE SONGS: NOLANS.
Tracks: / Chemistry / Touch me in the morning / How do I survive / Don't make waves / Sexy music / Gotta pull myself together / Don't love me too hard / Simple case of loving you, A / If it takes me all night / Out of love with love / Lead me on / Are you thinking of me.
LP: SHM 3169
MC: HSC 3169

MAKING WAVES.
Tracks: / Gotta pull myself together / Don't make waves / Touch me in the morning / Don't stoke the fire / Better late than never / Sexy music / Who's gonna rock you / Attention to me / Old feelings again / Lead me on / Directions of love / Get ready.
LP: EPC 10023
LP: CBS 32409

NOLAN SISTERS.
Tracks: / I'm in the mood for dancing / Spirit / Body and soul / Out of love with love / Bright eyes / Boogie all summer / Miss you nights / All the king's horses / I know I'll never love this way again / Let's make love / Thank you for the music / Don't let me be the last to know / More to love.
LP: EPC 32045
MC: 40 32045
LP: EPC 83892

NOLAN SISTERS COLLECTION, THE.
Tracks: / Don't it make my brown eyes blue / Don't give up on us / Song sung blue / Isn't she lovely / God only knows / Reach out I'll be there / Something tells me / Sailing / I'd like to teach the world to sing / Save your kisses for me / Love bandit / Bridge over troubled water / Don't take your love away / Chanson d'amour / Your song / Make it with you / Andy / When a child is born / Without you.
2LP: PDA 067
MCSET: PDC 067

NOLAN SISTERS, THE.
LP: CBS 83892

NOLANS.
Tracks: / Edelweiss / I'd like to teach the world to sing / White Christmas / Sound of Music, The / Beg, steal or borrow / Danny boy.
LP: NEVLP 145
LP: BD 3003

PORTRAIT: NOLANS.
Tracks: / Don't love me to hard / Chemistry / Don't let it go by / I'm never gonna let you break my heart again / Simple case of loving you / Crashing down / Are you thinking of me / How do I survive / If it takes me all night / Every home should have one / Every little thing / Take it through the night / God knows / Amy.
LP: EPC 10033

TIMES GONE BY.
LP: SRTV 2
MC: SCRTV 2

Nomad

CHANGING CABINS.
LP: RULP 100
MC: RULC 100

Nomad, Naz

GIVE DADDY THE KNIFE, CINDY (Nomad, Naz & The Nightmares).
Tracks: / Nobody but me / Action woman / Wind blows your hair, The / Kicks / Cold turkey / She lied / I had too much to dream last night / Trip, The / I can only give you everything / I can't stand this love, goodbye / Do you know I know? / Just call me Sky.
LP: WIK 21
MC: WIKC 21

Nomads

HARDWARE.
LP: WILP 003
LP: LD 877

NOMADS, THE.
LP: LP 006

OUTBURST.
LP: GOES ON 01

SOMETHING'S BAD (See under Group feat.Cecil Washington).

STAGGER IN THE SNOW.
LP: UNKNOWN

Nomi, Klaus

ENCORE, NOMI'S BEST.
LP: PL 7018

SIMPLE MAN.
Tracks: / From beyond / After the fall / Just one look / Falling in love again / I curok / Rubber band lazer / Wayward sisters / Ding dong / Three wishes / Simple man / Death / Return.
LP: PL 70229
MC: PK 70229
LP: RCALP 6061

Nomo

GREAT UNKNOWN, THE.
Tracks: / We go to sleep believing / Great unknown, The / Dance the dance / Let it come down / What a little true love can do / Wailing wall / Killer love / Red lipstick / Slave for love / Facts of life.
LP: 790 258-1

Non

BEST OF NON.
LP: STUMM 69

BLOOD AND FAME.
LP: STUMM 32

PHYSICAL EVIDENCE.
LP: STUMM 10
MC: CSTUMM 10

Non Credo

RELUCTANT HOSTS.
LP: NML 8814

Non Fiction

NONFICTION.
Tracks: / Dead into West Virginia / Speak the same to everyone / She lived in Memphis once / I got a gun / Simple things / Every nineteen years / If I do dream of you / Madeleine / My character is a card house / Things I want to know when I drink / Lightning rod.
LP: FIEND 76
LP: ARENA 1016

Non Stop..

NON STOP DANCE PARTY (Various artists).
MC: AM 52

NON STOP PASSION VOL. 1 (Various artists).
LP: NOSTO 1

Nontett, Arne Domnerus

BROST TONER.
LP: FLC 5040

Nooks, George

TODAY.
LP: JW&L 842

Noonan, Paddy

MUSICAL TASTE OF IRELAND, A.
LP: 2908 044

Noone, Jimmie

APEX CLUB BLUES.
Tracks: / Apex blues / New Orleans hop scop blues / Blues my naughty sweetie gives to me / Keystone blues / Four or five times / Bump it / Way down yonder in New Orleans / Every evening / My

Monday date / I know that you know / Body and soul / Sweet Lorraine / Sweet Georgia Brown / King Joe / Sweet Joe / Oh Sister, ain't that hot?.
LP: . . . . AFS 1023

JIMMIE NOONE 1931-40.
Tracks: / I need lovin' / It's you / When it's sleepy time down South / Dixie Lee / Inka dinka doo / Delta bound / Like a little bit less / I'd do anything for you / Liza / Soon / Easy to remember / Rump it / Moody melody / They got my number now.
LP: . . . . QU 014

JIMMIE NOONE (1936-41).
LP: . . . . S 1226

JIMMIE NOONE AND HIS ORCHESTRA (Noone, Jimmie & his orchestra).
LP: . . . . IAJRC 18

JIMMIE NOONE & JOHNNY DODDS (Noone, Jimmie & Johnny Dodds).
Tracks: / He's a different type of guy / Way down yonder in New Orleans / Blues jumped a rabbit, The / Sweet Georgia Brown / Shake your can / I'm walkin' this town / Wild man blues / Bump it.
MC: . . . . NEO 856

JIMMIE NOONE, VOL.1 (with Apex Club Orch., & with Stovepipe Johnson).
Tracks: / I know that you know / Sweet Sue / Four or five times / Every evening / Ready for the river / Forever more / Oh sister, / Ain't that hot / I ain't got nobody / Apex blues / Monday date / Blues.
LP: . . . . CJM 29
LP: . . . . S 841

JIMMIE NOONE'S APEX CLUB ORCHESTRA VOL. 3 1929 (Noone, Jimmie Apex Club Orchestra).
LP: . . . . S 843

JIMMIE NOONE'S APEX CLUB ORCHESTRA VOL. 2.
Tracks: / Sweet Lorraine / Sweet Lorraine (2) / Some rainy day / It's tight like that / It's tight like that (2) / Let's sow a wild oat / Let's sow a wild oat (2) / She's funny that way / St.Louis blues / Chicago rhythm / I got a misery / Wake up chill'un, wake up! / Love me or leave me / Love me or leave me (2) / Anything you want.
LP: . . . . S 842

JIMMIE NOONE'S APEX CLUB ORCHESTRA VOL. 4 1929-1930 (Noone, Jimmie Apex Club Orchestra).
LP: . . . . S 844

JIMMY NOONE: 1928-40.
LP: . . . . LPJT 75
MC: . . . . MCJT 75

JIMMY NOONE-VOL.1.
LP: . . . . S 841

KINGS OF NEW ORLEANS (Noone, Jimmie/Johnson, Bunk).
LP: 1010
LP: . . . . JAZ 2018
MC: . . . . ZCJAZ 2018

MERCURY THEATRE, L.A., BROADCASTS (see Ory, Kid) (Noone, Jimmy & Kid Ory).

Noone, Jimmie Jr

JIMMY REMEMBERS JIMMIE.
LP: . . . . SOS 1121

Nooten, Pieter

SLEEPS WITH THE FISHES (Nooten, Pieter & Michael Brook).
LP: . . . . CAD 710

Nordic Jazz Quintet

NORDJAZZ.
LP: . . . . SLP 259

Noren, Fredrik

SNAKE, THE (Noren, Fredrik Band).
LP: . . . . PHONT 7551

Norfolk Jubilee

1927-1938.
Tracks: / When the moon goes down / Moaning in the land / Wonder where the gambling man / When the train comes along / Believe in Jesus / Pure religion / Didn't it rain / No hiding place / Standing by the bedside / You got to live so God can use you / Way down in Egypt land / Jonah in the belly of a whale / Free at last / Jesus is making up my dying bed / Great changes to things I used to do / Beedle de beedle de bop bop.
LP: . . . . HT 310

Norgate, Clifford

AVALANCHE EXPRESS (See also Colin Forbes).

THREE DAY'S TERROR (See under John Creasey).

Noris, Gunter

BEST OF GUNTER NORIS & HIS ORCHESTRA VOL.1.
Tracks: / Fox as fox can / Foxy / Darf ich bitten / La reve / Stranger on the shore / Komm in den park von Sanssouci / Tango erotique / Hold me tight / Simba samba / Jamaican samba / Bambula cha cha cha / Mammy blue / Rasputin.
LP: . . . . DS 037

DANCE RECORD OF THE YEAR '84 (Tanzplatte Des Jahres '84) (Noris, Gunter Big Band).
LP: 6.25601
MC: 425601

DANCE RECORD OF THE YEAR '85 (Tanzplatte Des Jahres '85) (Noris, Gunter Big Band).
Tracks: / Rubin / Topas / Smaragd / Jade / Granat / Tigerauge / Turkis / Diamant / Saphir / Aquamarine / Opal / Amethyst.
LP: 6.25934

DANCE RECORD OF THE YEAR '86 (Tanzplatte Des Jahres '86).
Tracks: / Hibiskus / Jasmin / Amaryllis / Narzissen / Iris / Akelei / Neaken / Lilien / Margeriten / Rosen / Kamelien / Tulpen.
LP: 6.26185
MC: 4.26185

DANCE RECORD OF THE YEAR '87 (Tanzplatte Des Jahres '87) (Noris, Gunter Big Band, Strings & Chorus).
Tracks: / Saxy cha cha / Harmonica romantica / Tropic trumpets / Jiving guitar / Lonesome trumpet / Rock 'n' roll piano / Ballroom memories / Valse pour mandoline / El Bandoneon / Waltzing violins / Golden velvet / Swing in harmony.
LP: 6.26364
MC: 4.26364

DANCE RECORD OF THE YEAR '88 (Tanzplatte Des Jahres '88) (Noris, Gunter Big Band, Strings & Chorus).
Tracks: / Trinidad bikini / Havana by night / Beautiful Brasilia / Chicago a go-go / Dream of New Orleans / Rock around New York / Memories of London / Merci Paris / Melodia-Beunos Aires / Wiener lipizzaner / Sentimental Kopenhagen / Happy birthday Berlin!.
LP: 6.26547
MC: 4.26547

DANCE RECORD OF THE YEAR '89 (Tanzplatte Des Jahres '89) (Noris, Gunter/his gala dance orchestra).
Tracks: / Cha-cha cubana / Rumba in the night / Viva la samba / El torero / Rainbow melody / High life jive / Dirty mambo / I love my foxtrot / Animation / Let's do the tango / Valse elegance / Slowly to Heaven / Step by step.
LP: 6.26850
MC: 4.26850

DANCE RECORD OF THE YEAR '90 (Noris, Gunter/his gala big band).
Tracks: / Samba Baden-Baden / Midnight in Munich / Wuppertal cha-cha-cha / Corrida colonia / Stopover Hannover / Hamburg con salsa / Fantastic Frankfurt / Bonn for lovers / Starlight Berlin / Walzer fur Weimar / Romantic Stuttgart / Happy Dusseldorf.
LP: 246 116-1
MC: 246 116-4

DANCING MELODIES (Noris, Gunter/ his orchestra).
Tracks: / Ballroom memories / Iris blues / Wiener lipizzaner / Topas rumba / Tulpen-quick / Lilien / El bandoneon / Happy birthday, Berlin / Saxy cha cha / Nelken / Golden velvet / Lonesome trumpet.
MC: 4.26626

DANCING THROUGH THE YEAR 1982.
Tracks: / Chico cha-cha / Rumba sentimental / Mamba samba / Come on and jive / Ole ole Dolores / Everybody do the rock / Flic flac fox / Waikiki waltz / Geisha tango / Donnerstags walzer / Alte Liebe / Jogging bird.
LP: . . . . DS 049

EIN BALL-ERLEBNIS (Noris, Gunter/ his orchestra).
Tracks: / Bel ami / Roter mohn / Wenn die weisse flieder wieder bluht / Wir machen musik / Ich kusse ihre hand, Madame / Capri-fischer / Mackie messer / Lili Marlene / Mit musik geht alles besser.
LP: 6.26740
MC: 4.26740

FESTIVAL TROPICAL (Famous Latin-American Dances) (Noris, Gunter Big Band).
Tracks: / Samba d'orphee / Brazil / Tristeza / Amor, amor / Canavelito / Ay, ay, ay / Kingston Town / Banana boat song / Soul limbo / El Cumbanchero / Adios Muchachos / Moliendo cafe / El condor pasa / Todos los Domingos / Mexican hat-dance / Adelita / La Bamba.
LP: 6.26032
MC: 4.26032

PETTICOAT AND BUBBLEGUM (Dance To The 50's And 60's) (Noris, Gunter Nonstop Party-Gang).
Tracks: / Elvis Presley medley / Beatles medley / Twist medley / Bert Kaempfert medley / Glenn Miller Medley, The / Bubblegum medley / Singalong medley / Rock and roll medley / Cha-cha medley / Oldie medley / Whistling medley / Boogie woogie medley / Harry Belafonte medley / Bye bye tunes.
LP: 6.26428
MC: 4.26428

SALUTES '81.
LP: . . . . DS 041

STEP IN GUNTER NORIS PIANO BAR.
Tracks: / Fascination / Autumn leaves / Memory / Romantic rendezvous / La vie en rose / Chanson d'amour / Entertainer, The / As time goes by / Moon river / Summertime / Bilitis / Danke schon.
LP: 6.25769
MC: 425769

WORLD IS DANCING, THE (Greatest Musical Hits).
Tracks: / I could have danced all night / If I were a rich man / Memory / Mack the knife / Summertime / You're the one that I want / Edelweiss / Don't cry for me Argentina / Springtime in Paris / Mame / Cabaret.
LP: 6.26277
MC: 4.26277

Norlanders

BREAKING THROUGH.
Tracks: / Our house is a home / Bonnie border burn / Irish melody / Patsy Fagan / My little son / Busk busk bonnie lassie / Eight more miles to louisville / Banks of the roses / Sands of vatersay / Thief in my bedroom / Softly softly / Eighth argylls / Heroes of Vittoria / My own land / My grass is greener / White cliffs of Dover, The.
MC: . . . . CWGR 108

MOVING ON.
MC: . . . . CWGR 116

Normal

LIVE AT WEST RUNTON (Normal & Robert Rental).
LP: . . . . ROUGH 17

Normal, Henry

OSTRICH MAN.
LP: . . . . NTVLP 18

Norman, Chris

BREAK THE ICE.
Tracks: / Break the ice / Hearts on fire / Night has turned cold, The / One last kiss / Angie don't you love me? / Back again / Sarah / One way love affair / Livin' in a fantasy / These arms of mine / Got me in the palm of your hand / Woman in love.
LP: . . . . PTLP 009
MC: . . . . PTLC 009

STUMBLIN' IN (See under Quatro, Suzi) (Norman, Chris & Suzi Quatro).

Norman, Gene

GENE NORMAN'S JUST JAZZ CONCERTS.
Tracks: / Just you, just me / Perdido / Hot house / Groovin' high / Blue Lou / One o'clock jump / Lover / Body and soul / How high the moon / I got rhythm / Sweet Georgia Brown / C jam blues / Just bop / Yancey special / Swanee River boogie.
LPS: . . . . VJT 3003

Norman, Jessye

60 MINUTES OF MUSIC.
Tracks: / I couldn't hear nobody pray / My Lord, what a morning / Do Lawd, oh do Lawd / There's a man going round / Ev'ry time I feel de spirit / There is a balm in Gilead / Gospel train / Great day / Mary had a baby / Soon ah will be done / Give me Jesus / Ave Maria / Holy City, The / Amazing grace / Greensleeves / Let us break bread together / I wonder if I wonder / Sweet little Jesus boy.
MC: 4169094

AMAZING GRACE (ALBUM).
LP: 651 415 1
MC: 733 715 1

SPIRITUALS AND SACRED SONGS.
Tracks: / I couldn't hear nobody pray / Great day / My Lord, what a morning / Mary had a baby / Were you there / Ave Maria / Amazing grace / Holy City, The / Panis angelicus / Sanctus / O divine redeemer / Excerpts from Great day in the morning.
LP: 412 654-1
MC: 412 654-4

TRIUMPHS OF JESSYE NORMAN, THE.
2LP: 4220251
MCSET: 4220251

WITH A SONG IN MY HEART.
Tracks: / Falling in love with love / In the still of the night / Spring is here / I'm old fashioned / Sleeping bee / I love Paris / All the things you are / Song is you, The / I love you / Love is here to stay / With a song in my heart / Love walked in.
LP: 412 625-1
MC: 412 625-4

Norman, Larry

DOWN UNDER (BUT NOT OUT).
LP: . . . . RMLP 025
MC: . . . . RMC 025

FRIENDS ON TOUR (Norman, Larry/ Alwyn Wall/Barratt Band).
Tracks: / Only one, The / Not the way / Hold on / Dreams on sand / I feel like dying / Why can't you be good / Put your life in His hands / Note from Mr. God / I wish we'd all been ready.
LP: . . . . SRX 1117
MC: . . . . SRC 1117

ONLY VISITING THE PLANET.
LP: . . . . MYR 1170
MC: . . . . MC 1170

REHEARSAL 4 REALITY.
LP: . . . . RMLP 023
MC: . . . . RMC 023

SO LONG AGO THE GARDEN.
LP: . . . . MYR 1169
MC: . . . . MC 1169

SOMETHING NEW UNDER THE SUN.
Tracks: / Hard luck and bad news / Feeling so bad / I feel like dying / Born to be unlucky / Watch what you're doing / Leaving the past behind / Put your life in His hands.
LP: . . . . SRA 1
MC: . . . . SRC 1

STOP THIS FLIGHT.
LP: . . . . RMLP 021
MC: . . . . RMC 021

UPON THIS ROCK.
LP: . . . . DOVE 64

Norman, Neil

GREATEST SCIENCE FICTION HITS, VOL 3 (Norman, Neil & his Orchestra).
Tracks: / E.T., Theme from / War of the worlds / Lost in space / Bladerunner / Flash Gordon / Thing, The / Prisoner, The / Land of giants / Space 1999 / Angry red planet / Capricorn one / Raiders of the lost ark / Invaders, The / UFO / Vena's dance / Return of the jedi.
LP: . . . . GNPS 2163
MC: GNP5 2163

GREATEST SCIENCE FICTION HITS, VOL 2 (Norman, Neil & his Orchestra).
Tracks: / Empire strikes back, The / Twilight zone / Buck Rogers / Time tunnel, The / Doctor Who / Voyage to the bottom of the sea / Dark star / Sinbad and the eye of the tiger.
LP: . . . . NCP 702
MC: . . . . ZCNP 702
LP: . . . . PYL 6043
MC: . . . . PYM 6043
LP: . . . . GNPS 2133
MC: GNP5 2133

GREATEST SCIENCE FICTION HITS, VOL 1 (Norman, Neil & his Orchestra).
Tracks: / Alien / Moonraker / Star wars / Superman / 2001 / Battlestar Galactica / Space 1999 / Star trek / Black hole.
LP: . . . . NCP 1003
LP: . . . . PYL 6042
MC: . . . . PYM 6042
LP: . . . . GNPS 2128
MC: GNP5 2128

NOT OF THIS EARTH (Norman, Neil & his Orchestra).
LP: . . . . GNPS 2111

SECRET AGENT FILE (Norman, Neil & his Orchestra).
Tracks: / Reilly, ace of spies - theme / Octopussy / I spy / Rockford files, The / Man from Uncle, The / Casino Royale / Ipcress file, The / Get smart / Thunderball / Spy who came in from the cold.
LP: . . . . GNPS 2166
MC: GNP5 2166

Normil Hawaiians

MORE WEALTH THAN MONEY.
LP: . . . . JAMS 23

RETURN OF THE LEVELLERS.
LP: . . . . DMLP 1012

WHAT'S GOING ON?.
LP: . . . . JAMS 38

Norregard, Svend Erik

BROWNIE MCGHEE, SONNY TERRY & SVEND ERIK NORREGARD (See under McGhee, Brownie).

Norris, Chuck

LOS ANGELES FLASH, THE.
Tracks: / Los Angeles bounce / In the evening / Shake, rattle and roll / Blues after hours / I know the blues / Chicken

neck shuffle / See see rider / Everyday I have the blues / Honky tonk.
LP: . . . . RJ 201

Norris, John

JOHN NORRIS PLAYS BALDWIN FANTASIA ORGAN.
Tracks: / Up, up and away / Misty / Charade / I don't know how to love Him / Lullaby of Birdland / Song of India / Parade of the sunbeams / Somewhere my love / What would you say? / Where do I begin? / Music to watch girls by / Wave / One note samba.
LP: . . . . GRS 1037

Norris, Walter

DRIFTING.
LP: . . . . ENJA 2044

LIVE AT MAYBECK RECITAL HALL, VOL 4.
Tracks: / Song is you, The / 'Round midnight / Waltz for Walt / Best thing for you, The / Darn that dream (Only on CD) / Scrambled / Modus vivendi (Only on CD) / It's always Spring / Body and soul.
MC: . . . . CJ 425 C

STEPPING ON CRACKS.
Tracks: / Stepping on cracks / Falling in love with love / Cherokee / Giant steps / Child is born, A.
LP: . . . . PRO 7039

SYNCHRONICITY.
LP: . . . . ENJA 3035

WINTER ROSE.
LP: . . . . ENJA 3067

Nort

GAMES OF DANCE AND MUSCLE BLOOD.
Tracks: / It's a dream / Cool on the loop / Angel in my class, An / Ultimate white man, The / Sea is a machine, The / Big daddy / Luther's scream / Sleep for a while / Slow down the insect pest / Looking for the letter.
LP: . . . . CALCLP 044

Norteno Accordion

NORTENO ACCORDION (Various artists).
MC: . . . . C 218

North Atlantic

NORTH ATLANTIC NOISE ATTACK (Various artists).
LP: . . . . ACHE 17

North By Northeast

NORTH BY NORTHEAST (Various artists).
Tracks: / Blaydon races: *Various artists* / Take me up the Tyne: *Various artists* / Here is the news: *Various artists* / Lambton worm, The: *Various artists* / Mally Dunn: *Various artists* / Harrin's heed, Tha: *Various* artists / Keep your feet still Geordie Hinny: *Various artists* / There's more to life than women and beer: *Various* artists / Little cloth cap: *Various artists* / Everything changes: *Various artists* / Here is the news 2: *Various artists* / Cushie butterfield: *Various artists* / Water o' Tyne, The: *Various artists.*
LP: . . . . EC 001
MC: . . . . ECC 001

North By Northwest

NORTH BY NORTHWEST (Film Soundtrack) (London Studio Symphony Orch.).
LP: . . . . DKP 9000

North, Freddie

CUSS THE WIND.
Tracks: / Cuss the wind / My whole world has ended / Love to hate / Sun comes up / Gotta go get your mommy / I loved another woman / Oh Lord, what are you doing / Rainy night in Georgia.
LP: . . . . CLP 544

I'M YOUR MAN.
Tracks: / Do me baby / I'm your man / If this is the last time / Love has it's price / Differently / Don't make me cry / If you're even gonna love me / Everlasting love / (You're killing me) slowly but surely / It's not the spotlight / Someday she'll come along.
LP: . . . . CRB 1220

North, Hugo

WOLFGANG JACOBI (North, Hugo, Saabrucken Madrigal Choir).
Tracks: / Impromptu / Scherzo / Franzosische / Piange Maria / Ich spring an diesm ringe / Es ist ein schnee gefallen / Bet't kinder, bet't / Tanz / Choral / Kinderspiele in Ascoli.
LP: . . . . HS 052

North, Ian

NEO.
Tracks: / If you gotta go / She kills me / Don't dance / Heart / Tran-sister / Heaven on earth / No sound from 25 / Hollywood / Babylon / Girls in gangs / Texas modern / Kamikaze.
LP: . . . . AUL 706

North London

ETERNALLY GRATEFUL (Bible Week highlights) (North London Community Church Singers).
LP: . . . . WRD 3015
MC: . . . . TC WRD 3015

North, Nicky

JAMES BOND 21ST ANNIVERSARY (North, Nicky Orchestra).
Tracks: / Goldfinger / 007 theme / Diamonds are forever / Thunderball / We have all the time in the world / Live and let die / From russia with love.
LP: . . . . VCLP 007

North, Nigel

GUITAR COLLECTION.
LP: . . . . SAR 18
MC: . . . . CSAR 18

North Sea Gas

CALEDONIAN CONNECTION.
MC: . . . . KITV 483

FROM FIELDS A'FAR.
LP: . . . . MK 2
MC: . . . . MKC 2

LIVE FROM EDINBURGH - NORTH SEA GAS IN CONCERT.
LP: . . . . ITV 433
MC: . . . . KITV 433

North & South

NORTH & SOUTH/THE RIGHT STUFF (Film soundtracks) (Various artists).
LP: 704.310
MC: . . . . C 704.310

North Star Band

NORTH STAR BAND.
LP: . . . . AD 2014

Northern Lights

TRIBUTE TO ABBA, A.
MC: . . . . ZCFPA 1019

Northern Pikes

BIG BLUE SKY.
Tracks: / Teenland / You sold the farm / Things I do for money / Just another guy / Dancing in a dance club / Jackie T / Lonely house / Love and a muscle / Never again / Big blue sky.
LP: . . . . V 2494
MC: . . . . TCV 2494

SECRETS OF THE ALIBI.
Tracks: / Place that's insane / Walk away / Wait for me / One good reason / Blood she wants / Let's pretend / Better twice / Hopes go astray / Stars in the sky / Hole in the ground / One good reason (extended mix) (CD only).
LP: . . . . V 2553
MC: . . . . TCV 2553

Northern Sinfonia

CHOPIN/SCHUMANN PIANO CONCERTI (see under Vasary, Tamas) (Northern Sinfonia of England/Tamas Vasary).

CONCERTI GROSSI OP.3 (HANDEL) (see under Handel) (Northern Sinfonia of England).

SYMPHONY NO.3 (BEETHOVEN) (see under Beethoven) (Northern Sinfonia of England).

SYMPHONY NO.25/NO.28/NO.29 (MOZART) (see under Mozart) (Northern Sinfonia of England).

WIND AND STRING SERENADES (see under Dvorak) (Northern Sinfonia of England).

Northern Soul

AFTER THE SESSION (Various artists).
LP: . . . . LPSS 108

BEST OF NORTHERN TRACKS (Various artists).
Tracks: / Superlove: *Wigan's Ovation* / Get out: *Hunt, Tommy* / Love feeling: *McKenna, Val* / Sign on the dotted line: *Latter, Gene* / We ain't here looking for trouble: *Northern Tracks* / Heartbreaker: *Northern* Tracks / Northern soul dancer: *Wigan's Ovation* / Skiing in the snow: *Wigan's Ovation* / Tainted love: *Swann,* Ruth / Honey (I need your love): *Northern Tracks* / Boy, you'd better move on: *Northern Tracks* / I love you: *Northern Tracks* / Stand in line: *Northern Tracks* / Crackin' up: *Hunt, Tommy.*
LP: . . . . SRLM 502

BRAINSTORMERS (Various artists).
Tracks: / Just one more chance: *Bradley, Patrick* / Gee baby I love you: *Malibus* / Stop, leave my heart alone: *2 People* / Getting used to the blues: *Bland, Bobby* / I had a good time: *Taylor, Little Eddie* / Bye bye baby: *Everett, Betty* / Lend a hand: *Hutton, Bobby* / Love runs out: *Hutch, Willie* / Wherever you were: *Harper, Bud* / That's when I need you: *Butler, Freddie* / It's a heartache: *Little Charles & The Sidewinders* / Ain't that good enough: *Green, Garland* / You're too much a part of me: *Austin, Patti* / My heart's not in it anymore: *Steinways* / Kid: *Brasseur, Andre.*
LP: . . . . KENT 042

CAPITOL SOUL CASINO (see under Capitol (label)) (Various artists).

CASINO CLASSICS CHAPTER 1 (Various artists).
Tracks: / Touch of velvet, a sting of brass, A: *Grainer, Ron Orchestra* / Lost summer love: *Silver, Lorraine* / Joe 90: *Grainer, Ron Orchestra* / Panic: *Reparata & The Delrons* / Shake a tail feather: *Purify, James* / I'll do anything: *Gamble, Lenny* / Six by six: *All Night Band* / Joker, The: *All Night Band* / Little darling (I need you): *Flirtations* / I'm gonna share it with you: *Foster, Diana* / I go to pieces: *Granger,* Gerri / Long after tonight is all over: *Radcliffe, Jimmy* / Time will pass you by: *Tobi Legend* / I'm on my way: *Parrish, Dean.*
LP: . . . . CCLP 1001

CASINO CLASSICS CHAPTER 2 (Various artists).
Tracks: / Tainted love: *Jones, Gloria* / Ain't nothing but a house party: *Show Stoppers* / Sliced tomatoes: *Just* Brothers / You got me where you want me: *Hunt, Tommy* / I can't seem to hold you: *Foster, Diana* / I've got a feeling: *Foster, Diana* / Sign on the dotted line: *Latter, Gene* / Better late than never: *Ducane, Diane* / It really hurts me girl: *Carstairs* / Love factory: *Laws, Eloise* / When loves grows cold: *Grainer, Ron* Orchestra / Gonna love you longer stronger baby: *Various artists* / Loving on the losing side: *Hunt, Tommy* / Why'd you put it to me baby: *Short People.*
LP: . . . . CCLP 1002

CLUB SOUL (Various artists).
Tracks: / Dearly beloved: *Montgomery, Jack* / Let's get back together: *Honey Bees* / Honey boy: *Dodds, Nella* / Rainmaker: *Moods* / Since I found you: *Brown, Maxine* / It's me: *Copeland, Johnny* / Two stupid feet: *Jackson, Chuck* / Oh Lord what are you doing to me: *Big Maybelle* / Hand it over: *Jackson, Chuck* / I never want to lose my sweet thing: *Charles, Lee* / Let love win: *Candy & The Kisses* / Too much of a good thing: *Various artists* / You've got the power: *Esquires* / Mr. Schemer: *Wood, Brenton* / I thank you kindly: *Lewis, Diane* / So help me woman: *Tindley, George.*
LP: . . . . KENT 022

COLUMBIA 60'S SOUL (Various artists).
Tracks: / Brand new man: *Wylie, Richard 'Popcorn'* / Little bit of something, A: *Little Richard* / I don't want to discuss it: *Little Richard* / Poor dog: *Little Richard* / Quitter never wins, A: *Williams, Larry & Johnny* Watson / It's an uphill climb to the bottom: *Jackson, Walter* / Everything I touch turns to tears: *St. John, Barry* / Monkey time: *Lance, Major* / Matador, The: *Lance, Major* / Investigate: *Lance, Major* / Ain't no soul: *Lance, Major* / Dance to the music: *Sly & the Family Stone* / You're ready now: *Bennett, Bobby* / Just come closer to me: *Korda, Paul* / One in a million: *Keyes, Karol* / Candy to me: *Raynor, Martin* / These things will keep me loving you: *Carr, Romey* / On the brink: *Vickers, Mike* / Stop and you will become aware: *Shapiro, Helen* / Foxy: *Guest, Earl* / This beautiful day: *Jackson, Levy* / You can't bypass love: *Sue & Sunny.*
2LP: . . . . SX 4231

COOKIN' WITH KENT (Various artists).
Tracks: / Three lonely guys: *Brilliant Corners* / I've been hurt so many times: *Davis, Larry* / New breed, The: *Holiday, Jimmy* / Baby take me back: *Gilliam, Johnny* / I can't stand it (I can't take it no more): *George,* Brenda / I'm lonely for you: *Adams, K. Arthur* / I've gotta get back: *Love, Mary* / No more tears: *Sweethearts* / It's been so long: *Ikettes* / All that shines is not gold: *Windjammers* / One more chance: *Four Tees* / New lease of life: *Universals* / It's crazy baby: *Turner, Ike & Tina* / What's more: *Hill, Z.Z.* / My girl is gone away: *Hammond, Clay* / Better be good: *Woods, Peggy.*
LP: . . . . KENT 053

DANCING 'TIL DAWN (Various artists).
Tracks: / Woman love thief: *Stemmons Express* / I'm your yes man: *Reid, Clarence* / Lost love: *Irma & The* Fascinations / Please stay: *Ivorys* / Come back, baby: *Dodds, Nella* / Show me a man: *Bradshaw, Bobby* / Livin' the nightlife: *Charts* / Out on the streets again: *Candy & The Kisses* / Last minute miracle: *Shirelles* / You busted my mind: *Clay, Judy* / Let me give you my lovin': *Brown, Maxine* / Name it and claim it: *Stewart, Darryl* / Black eyed girl: *Thompson, Billy* / Ain't that peculiar: *Tindley, George* / These chains of love (are breaking me down): *Jackson, Chuck* / Help me: *Wilson, Al.*
LP: . . . . KENT 026

DETROIT A-GO-GO (Various artists).
Tracks: / If it's all the same to you: *Ingram, Luther* / Cool off: *Detroit Executives* / Mighty lover: *Ideals* / Exus trek: *Ingram, Luther* / Get it baby: *Mitchell, Stanley* / Down in the dumps: *Hester, Tony* / Rosemary what happened: *Wylie, Richard 'Popcorn'* / Hanky panky: *Wylie, Richard 'Popcorn'* / Spaceland: *Hester, Tony* / Say it isn't so: *Boo, Betty* / Frantic escape: *Innocent Bystanders* / Saving my love for you: *People's Choice.*
LP: . . . . BURN 11

ESSENTIAL NORTHERN SOUL STORY (Various artists).
2LP: . . . . LPSD 150

GEMS (Jewels from the soul crown) (Various artists).
Tracks: / Evil one: *Sapphires* / Hey girl don't bother me: *Tams* / Boomerang: *Tom & Jerryo* / Treat her right: *Head, Roy* / Competition ain't nothing: *Carlton, Little Carl* / You've been cheating: *Impressions (group)* / Gonzo: *Booker, James* / Hey there lonely girl: *Holman, Eddie* / Tell her: *Parrish, Dean* / It's a crying shame: *Barry, Len* / Girl watcher: *Okaysions* / Homework: *Rush, Otis* / Mama didn't lie: *Fasinations.*
LP: . . . . KENT 021

GREAT DISCO DEMANDS (15 Northern Soul in-demanders) (Various artists).
Tracks: / This man: *Cox, Wally* / Human jungle: *Fugitives* / Can't help loving you: *Breedlove, Jimmy* / I'm so glad: *Fuzz* / I've gotta find me somebody: *Velvets* / Can't help lovin' dat man: *Van, Ila* / Help me: *Wilson, Al* / Dance, dance, dance: *Casualeers* / If you ask me (because I love you): *Williams, Jerry* / Goodbye nothing to say: *Javells.*
LP: . . . . DDLP 5002

IN STYLE (Rare soul uncovered Vol.3) (Various artists).
Tracks: / You'll always be in style: *Barnes, Sidney* / Now I'm in love with you: *Various artists* / That other place: *Flemons, Wade* / I won't stop to cry: *Various artists* / I don't want to hurt nobody: *Various artists* / Why don't you write: *Bates, Lee* / I can't be your part time baby: *Various artists* / You're the dream: *Robinson,* Roscoe / Just like a yo yo: *Winters, Ruby* / My love is gone: *Various artists* / Power of love, The: *Humphrey,* Amanda / I better run: *Various artists* / My man don't think I know: *Various artists* / But I couldn't: *Harper, Willie* / Spanish boy: *Rubies, The.*
LP: . . . . CRB 1166
MC: . . . . TCCRB 1166

IT'S TORTURE & 15 OTHER GREAT SOUL DESTROYERS (Various artists).
Tracks: / It's torture: *Brown, Maxine* / Hey girl: *Porgy & The Monarchs* / Do you love me baby: *Masqueraders* / Bricks, broken bottles & sticks: *Parish, Dean* / My heart is calling: *Wilson, Jackie* / If you can't be true (take a part-time love): *Chandler, Gene* / I've got to keep movin': *Lamont, Charles & The Extremes* / Killer, The: *Fuller, Jerry* / This man: *Cox, Wally* / Stop sign: *Wynn, Mel & The Rhythm Aces* / I'll forgive & forget: *Holden, Ron* / (I need your love) your burning touch of love: *Butler, Billy* / And get away: *Esquires* / Desiree: *Charts* / You are the one I love: *Adams Apples* / I don't have a mind of my own: *Thomas, B.J.*
LP: . . . . KENT 046

JUMPING AT THE GOGO (Various artists).
Tracks: / I'll always need you: *Courtney, Dean* / Ain't no soul: *Paige, Ray* / Blowing up my mind: *Exciters* / Man without a woman: *Michael & Raymond* / I can't help loving you: *Anka, Paul* / You've got your mind on other things: *Beverly Ann* / Moonlight music and you: *Greene, Laura* / What's it gonna be: *Barrett, Susan* / Devil's drive: *Big Boris* / Hold on: *Freeman, Judy* / It didn't take much (for me to fall in love): *Wiggins,* Percy / Change your ways: *Kendricks, Willie* / I can't change: *Chandler, Lorraine* / Crackin' up over you: *Hamilton, Roy* / Stick to me: *Walker, Robert & Soul Strings* / Honest to goodness: *Ward, Herb* / Hold on to my baby: *Cavaliers* / I can't hold on: *Chandler, Lorraine* / Happy go lucky me: *Bobbettes* / I've gotta know right now: *Valentine, Rose.*
LP: . . . . RS 1066

KEEPIN' THE FAITH (Various artists).
Tracks: / Stop what you're doing: *Playthings* / Goodbye, nothing to say: *Javells* / What shall I do?: *Frankie/*

Classicals/ If you ask me (because I love you): *Williams, Jerry* / I'm so glad: *Fuzz / Flasher, (The): Mistura*/ Ask me: *Ecstasy, Passion and Pain* / Love light: *Jackson, Chuck* / Selfish one: *Ross, Jackie* / Landslide: *Clarke, Tony* / Breakout: *Ryder, Mitch* / Footsee: *Wigan's Chosen Few* / Love is getting strong: *Knight, Jason* / Voice your choice: *Radiants*.
LP: . . . . **PRC 5572**
MC: . . . . **ZCPRC 5572**

KEEPIN' THE FAITH VOL 2 (Various artists).
Tracks: / In orbit: *Lovejoy, Joy* / Burning spear: *Soulful Strings* / Hold on: *Radiants* / Emergency (dial 999): *Bown, Alan Set* / Accept my invitation: *Band Of Angels* / You get your kicks: *Ryder, Mitch/Detroit* Wheels / Soul for sale: *Schroeder, John Orchestra* / Dance, dance, dance: *Casualeers* / Can't help lovin' dat man: *Van, Ila* / I can't help loving you: *Breedlove, Jimmy* / Ain't no more room: *Kittens* / Sevens days too long: *Wood, Chuck*.
LP: . . . . **PRC 5573**

KISSING HER AND CRYING FOR YOU (Various artists).
Tracks: / Kissin' her and crying for you: *Checkmates Ltd* / What can I do: *Prophet, Billy* / Li'l lovin' sometimes, A: *Patton, Alexander* / Don't: *Josie, Marva* / I'm only a man: *Tee, Willie* / Drifter, The: *Pollard*, Ray / By yourself: *Martin J.D.* / Right on: *Delory, Al & Mandango* / I hurt on the other side: *Cook*, Jerry / Love is dangerous: *Polk, Frank* / Please keep away from me: *Parker, Elbie* / Hey girl do you love me: *Wilson, Timothy* / I still love you (from the bottom of my heart): *Four Larks* / Don't you care anymore: *Mathis, Jodi* / In your spare time: *Scott, Cindy* / He always comes back to me: *King, Clydie*.
LP: . . . . **KENT 055**

LEAPERS, SLEEPERS & CREEPERS (Various artists).
Tracks: / If you were a man: *King, Clydie* / Tears keep falling: *Solo, Sam E.* / Stay with your own kind: *Holloway*, Patrice / I walked away: *Paris, Bobby* / Baby I need you: *Gee, Marsha* / Ecstacy: *Holloway, Patrice*/ Walk with a winner: *McDaniels, Gene* / I'll never forget you: *O'Jays* / What are you trying to do: *Thomas*, Irma / Look at me, look at me: *Green, Garland* / Let the music play: *Preston, Billy* / Serving a sentence of life: *Douglas, Carl & Big Stampede* / What you gonna do: *Womack, Bobby* / You're on top: *Untouchables*.
LP: . . . . **KENT 031**

LIVIN' THE NIGHTLIFE (Various artists).
LP: . . . . **SINLP 2**

LONDON-AMERICAN NORTHERN SOUL CLASSICS (Various artists).
Tracks: / Real thing, The: *Britt, Tina* / Humphrey stomp: *Harrison, Earl* / You've got too much going for you: *Beaumont, Jimmy* / Weddings make me cry: *Exciters* / My terms: *Ferguson, Helena* / Fortune teller: *Spellman*, Benny / My little red book: *Middleton, Tony* / Our love is in the pocket: *Banks, Darrell* / Up and down the ladder: *Intruders* / Keep him: *Mason, Barbara* / Kick that little foot Sally Ann: *Round Robin* / I'm thru': *Carter, Carolyn* / Pain gets a little deeper: *Fletcher, Darrow* / 365 days: *Height, Donald* / Mr.Bang bang man: *Little Hank* / Talk of the grapevine: *Height, Donald* / In a moment: *Intrigues* / Karate boogaloo: *Jerryo* / Magic potion: *Johnson, Lou* / Unsatisfied: *Johnson, Lou* / Shop around: *Miracles* / She blew a good thing: *Poets* / Good time tonight: *Soul Sisters* / Money: *Strong, Barrett* / We need an understanding: *Turner, Ike & Tina*.
2LP: . . . . **FLLP 1001**

MAGIC TOUCH, THE (Various artists).
Tracks: / Magic touch: *Moore, Melba* / I want a guarantee: *Brown, Maxine* / He's Barbara's guy: *Fawns*/ Girl is not a girl, A: *Shirelles* / Congratulations: *Porgy & The Monarchs* / All the way from heaven: *Chancellors*/ We've gotta keep on: *Hughes, Freddie* / Baby boy: *Hughes, Freddie* / In between tears: *Jackson, Chuck*/ Love it's getting better: *Groove* / Hope we have: *Artistics* / Are you trying to get rid of me baby: *Candy* & The Kisses / You've been in love too long: *Acklin, Barbara* / Do you believe it: *Montgomery, Jack* / Hand it over: *Wand R & B Ensemble*.
LP: . . . . **KENT 057**

MIDNIGHT MOVERS (Various artists).
Tracks: / It's a sad thing: *Pollard, Ray* / Hooked by love: *Banks, Homer* / Hot line: *Garner, Reggie*/ I've got two hearts: *Poets* / Working on your case: *O'Jays* / Groovin' at the gogo: *Four Larks* / Cold wave: *Daisies* / I love you baby: *Scott, Cindy* / Girls got 'it', The: *Preston, Billy* / I feel strange: *Wonderettes* / Now I know what love is: *Wilson, Al* / Trying to keep up with the Joneses: *Polk, Frank*/ Love slipped through my fingers: *Williams, Sam* / Thumb a ride: *Wright, Earl* / Wrong girl, The: *Showmen*/ West Coast: *Lester, Ketty*.
LP: . . . . **KENT 058**
LP: . . . . **CF 3322**

NO, NO, NO, NO, NO NOT MY GIRL (Various artists).
Tracks: / Not my girl: *Platters* / Pretty part of you, The: *Hunt, Tommy* / I'm gonna get you: *Baker, Laverne*/ Upset my heart (got me so upset): *Clay, Judy* / Speed up: *Moorer, Betty* / You can't keep a good man down: *Gentlemen* Four / You brought out the good in me: *Leavill, Otis* / Summer romance (you babe): *Young Holt Unlimited* / Tightrope: *Martin, Bobby* / Chase is on, The: *Howard, Johnny* / Tonight's the night: *Candy & The Kisses*/ Everything is everything: *Waddy, Sandy* / Double life: *Fuller, Jerry* / Nothing but love can save me: *Fawns*/ There comes a time: *Kitt, Eartha* / Tomorrow comes shining: *Bartley, Chris*.
LP: . . . . **KENT 069**

NORTHERN SOUL STORY 1 (Various artists).
Tracks: / I'm gonna get you: *Soulville All Stars* / Stick by me baby: *Salvadors* / Come on and live: *Fabulous* Jades / Sugar pie honey: *Promatics* / Day my heart stood still: *Jackson, Ollie* / Goose pimples: *Scott*, Shirley J. / Breakdown: *Millionaires* / Cross my heart: *Yvonne & The Violets* / Lady love: *Vontastics*/ Don't wanna face the truth: *Radiants* / I'm where it's at: *Jades* / I didn't want to cry: *Gray, Pearlean* & The Passengers / Mind in a bind: *Epsilons* / I know what to do to satisfy you: *Robert, Roy* / Your wish is my command: *Inspirations* / Lonely lover: *McFarland, Jimmy* / Girl across the street, The: *Smith, Moses*/ Another day: *Ascots* / Build your house on a strong foundation: *Gwen & Ray* / Love time: *Kelly Brotherss*/ Love's like a quicksand: *Wynns, Sandy* / I love my baby: *International GTO's* / Heave is in your arms: *Admirations*/ Don't bring me down: *Dacosta, Rita* / Baby that's a groove: *Handy, Roy* / We must be doing something right: *Moody*, Joan / There's nothing else to say: *Incredibles* / There's that mountain: *Tripps* / You got it: *Dealers*/ Never never (will I fall in love): *Herbs* / Job opening: *Del-Larks* / Wash and wear love: *Vernado, Lynn*.
2LP: . . . . **LPSD 107**
MC: . . . . **CPSD 107**

NORTHERN SOUL STORY 2 (Various artists).
Tracks: / Hey little girl: *Del Capris* / Michael (the lover): *C.O.D.'s* / These windows: *Village Sound*/ Sonny: *Cammotions* / I'm comin' home in the mornin': *Pride, Lou* / You got me where you want me: *Santos*, Larry / Is it all gone: *Magicians* / Barefootin' time in Chinatown: *Young, Lester* / There must be roses somewhere in this world: *Taylor, Bobby* / Lord what's happening to your people: *Smith, Kenny* / Easy baby: *Adventurers*/ Make my love a hurtin' thing: *Cummings, William* / I can't take it anymore: *Persians* / Arabia: *Delcos*/ Oh baby: *Creations*.
2LP: . . . . **LPSD 118**
MC: . . . . **CPSD 118**

NORTHERN SOUL STORY 3 (Various artists).
Tracks: / Philly dog around the world: *Raye, Jimmy* / I feel an urge coming on: *Armstead, Jo* / My baby ain't no plaything: *New Holidays* / I don't like it: *Bush, Tommy* / Try to think (what you're doing): *Davis, Court*/ Do it to it: *Funky Sisters* / My life with you: *Traditions* / Sweet magic: *Servicemen, The* / I don't like to lose: *Washington, Cecil* / Oh oh oh what a love this is: *Revlons, The* / Something's bad: *Nomads*/ Baby I dig you: *Anderson, Gene & The Dynamic Psychedelics* / Too much of a good thing: *Ambassadors* / Nothing can compare to you: *Velvet Satins, the* / If you love me (show me): *Monique* / Try my love: *Sequins, The*/ You're not my kind: *Durante, Paula* / Not me baby: *Silhouettes* / You didn't have to leave: *Ellusions*/ Meet me halfway: *Bryant, Lillie* / I must love you: *Wilson, Timothy*.
2LP: . . . . **LPSD 119**
MC: . . . . **CPSD 119**

NORTHERN SOUL STORY 4 (Various artists).
Tracks: / No one else can take your place: *Inspirations* / Baby I'm here just to love you: *Stagemasters* / When I'm not wanted: *Holman, Eddie* / This thing called love: *Wyatt, Johnny* / Gotta draw the line: *Fletcher, Darrow*/ She put the hurt on me: *Martin, Trade* / Set my heart at ease: *Farrow, Mikki* / R & B time: *Jones, E.Rodney*/ Love is the only solution: *Starr, Martha* / On the run: *Accents* / Set my heart at ease: *Farrow, Mikki*.
2LP: . . . . **LPSD 121**

NORTHERN SOUL STORY 5 (Various artists).
2LP: . . . . **LPSD 123**

NORTHERN SOUL STORY 6 (Various artists).
2LP: . . . . **LPSD 124**

NORTHERN SOUL STORY 7 (Various artists).
2LP: . . . . **LPSD 125**

NORTHERN SOUL STORY 8 (Various artists).
2LP: . . . . **LPSD 126**

NORTHERN SOUL STORY 9 (Various artists).
Tracks: / Naughty boy: *Day, Jackie* / Do this for me: *Emotions (group)* / You've got a good thing: *King*, Jeanie / I'm gonna...: *Little Ben/The Cheers* / I'm gonna love you: *Hamilton, Edward* / I'm standing: *Lumley*, Rufus / I'm gonna pick up my toys: *Devonnes* / I'll always love you: *Harris, Quinn* / Love reputation, A: *Lasalle, Denise* / She said goodbye: *Hambrick, Billy* / I found true love: *Hambrick, Billy* / It's just a picture: *Intrepids* / She's so fine: *Topics, The* / Our love will grow: *Showmen* / Black power: *Coit*, James / My little cottage: *Falana, Fluffy* / I don't want a playboy: *Lynn, Barbara* / Free for all: *Mitchell, Phillip* / Pushin' and pullin': *Lovemasters*.
2LP: . . . . **LPSD 127**

NORTHERN SOUL STORY 10 Instrumentals, The (Various artists).
2LP: . . . . **LPSD 128**

NORTHERN SOUL STORY 11 Girl groups (Various artists).
2LP: . . . . **LPSD 129**

NORTHERN SOUL STORY 12 (Various artists).
2LP: . . . . **LPSD 130**

NORTHERN SOUL STORY 13 (Various artists).
2LP: . . . . **LPSD 131**

NORTHERN SOUL STORY 14 (Various artists).
2LP: . . . . **LPSD 132**

NORTHERN SOUL STORY 15 (Various artists).
2LP: . . . . **LPSD 134**

NORTHERN SOUL STORY 16 (Various artists).
2LP: . . . . **LPSD 135**

ON THE UP BEAT (Various artists).
Tracks: / Shing a ling: *Cooperettes* / Raining teardrops: *Demures* / I've lost you: *Wilson, Jackie* / Oh Linda: *Taylor, Linda* / You are: *Various artists* / Just ain't no love: *Young Holt Unlimited* / Have more time: *Smith, Marvin* / California montage: *Young Holt Trio* / Don't take it out on this world: *Adams* Apples / I'm so glad: *Johnson, Herb & The Impacts* / Purple haze: *Jones, Johnny & The King Casuals* / Gotta find me a lover: *Franklin, Erma* / Nothing but blue skies: *Wilson, Jackie* / Chase is on, The: *Artistics*/ I'll bet you: *Butler, Billy* / What goes up (must come down): *Davis, Tyrone*.
LP: . . . . **KENT 020**

OUT ON THE FLOOR TONIGHT (Various artists).
Tracks: / Out on the floor: *Gray, Dobie* / I'll hold you: *Frankie & Johnny* / Tainted love: *Jones, Gloria*/ Love factory: *Laws, Eloise* / You been gone too long: *Sexton, Ann* / Good thing going: *Coulter, Phil Orchestra*/ I'm not strong enough: *Four Perfections* / Gotta get closer to my love: *Show Stoppers* / New York in the dark: *Ad Libs* / If that's what you wanted: *Beverly, Frank* / You don't mean me no good: *Jelly Beans* / Your autumn of tomorrow: *Crow* / It really hurts me girl: *Carstairs* / Queen of fools: *Mills, Barbara* / Touch of venus: *Wynns, Sandy*.
LP: . . . . **INFERNO 001**

PAYING OUR DUES (Various artists).
Tracks: / You hit me where it hurt me: *Clark, Alice* / Something's burnin': *Marvellos* / Go for yourself: *Laster*, Larry / You gotta pay your dues: *Drifters* / Both ends against the middle: *Moore, Jackie* / Take your love and run: *Lynn, Barbara* / My heart needs a break: *Jones, Linda* / I'll be loving you: *Soul Brothers Six*/ Something new to do: *Sheen, Bobby* / Tell me why: *Life* / Since you said you'd be mine: *Ragland, Lou*/ Angel baby: *Banks, Darrell* / Where did I go wrong: *Embers* / That's when the tears start: *Blossoms*/ Just say goodbye: *Phillips, Little Esther*.
LP: . . . . **KENT 093**

RARE NORTHERN SOUL VOL.2 (Various artists).
Tracks: / What more do you want: *Toones, Gene* / Can't we talk it over: *Allen, L* / You can't mean it: *Chapter* Five / Cheatin' kind: *Gardner, Don* / Lady in green: *Magnetics* / Dream my heart: *Edwards, Shirley*/ Showstopper: *Cashmeres* / Love you just can't walk away: *Courtney, Dean* / I'm catching on: *Lloyd, Betty*/ I've arrived: *Flanagan, Steve* / Fireman: *Reegan, Vala & The Valarons* / Chasing my dream all over town: *Wren*, Jenny / Baby I don't need your love: *Chants* / To the ends of the earth: *Middleton, Tony* / There's room for me: *Davis, Jesse* / Breakaway: *Basil, Toni*.
LP: . . . . **RNS 002**

RARE SOUL UNCOVERED (Various artists).
Tracks: / Hung up on your love: *Montclairs, The* / I can't see your love: *Ballads* / Nothing takes the place of you: *Toussaint, Allen* / That's enough: *Robinson, Roscoe* / I hurt the other side: *Barnes, Sidney* / Don't talk like that: *Murray, Clarence* / You gotta pay the price: *Taylor, Gloria* / Medley of soul: *Downing, Big* Al / Breakaway: *Valentines* / Come on train: *Thomas, Don* / I need you more than ever: *Montclairs, The*/ Would you believe?: *Lee, Jacky* / Getting mighty crowded: *Everett, Betty* / Don't let me down: *Hughes, Fred*/ Just another heartbreak: *Little Richie* / You've been gone long: *Sexton, Ann* / Let's go baby (where the action is): *Parker, Robert* / Soul shake: *Scott, Peggy*.
LP: . . . . **CRB 1085**
MC: . . . . **TCCRB 1085**

RARE SOUL UNCOVERED VOL.2 (Various artists).
Tracks: / Lonely for you baby: *Dees, Sam* / I'm your love man: *Lost Souls* / Don't ever leave me: *Williams*, Maurice / Nothing worse than being alone: *Ad Libs* / Unwanted love: *Montclairs, The* / Gonna take a journey: *Strong, Barrett* / What can a man do: *Williams, Maurice* / Night the angels cried, The: *Dynamite, Johnny*/ Touch me, hold me, kiss me: *Inspirations* / I'd think it over: *Fletcher, Sam* / Being without you: *Williams*, Maurice / You're gonna need me: *Ford, Ted* / I keep tryin': *Hughes, Fred* / I'm a teardrop: *Jerms*/ Running for my life: *Shelton, Roscoe* / Till I get it right: *Hobbs, Willie* / Sweet and easy: *McCoy, Van*/ Make up your mind: *Strong, Barrett*.
LP: . . . . **CRB 1109**
MC: . . . . **TCCRB 1109**

RECORD COLLECTOR, VOL 1 (Various artists).
Tracks: / I can't hide it: *Appreciations* / Silent treatment: *Demain, Arin* / Little togetherness, A: *Young* Hearts / Joker, The: *Mylestones* / Love on a rampage: *Kerr, George Orchestra* / So in luv: *Robinson*, Othello / There is nothing else to say: *George, Cassietta* / Looking for you: *Echoes* / You won't say nothing: *Lewis, Tamala* / Bok to Bach: *Father's Angels* / Stronger than her love: *Flirtations* / I never knew: *Foster, Eddie* / These things will keep me loving you: *Blue Sharks*.
LP: . . . . **DS 100001**

RIGHT BACK WHERE WE STARTED FROM (Various artists).
Tracks: / Right back where we started from: *Nightingale, Maxine* / Snake, The: *Wilson, Al* / Better use your head: *Little Anthony & The Imperials* / City lights: *Naylor, Jerry* / Let the music play: *Preston, Billy* / Baby mine: *Houston, Thelma* / This beautiful day: *Jackson, Levy* / Nobody but me: *Human Beinz* / Leap frog: *Nelson, Sandy* / So is the sun: *World Column* / Looking for you: *Mimms, Garnet* / End of our love, The: *Wilson, Nancy* / Number one in your heart: *Goins, Herbie & The Nightimers* / In the midnight hour: *Preston, Billy*.
LP: . . . . **KENT 039**

RIGHT TRACK, THE (Various artists).
Tracks: / Right track: *Butler, Billy* / Angel baby: *Carrow, George* / You don't want me no more: *Lance, Major*/ Where have all the flowers gone: *Jackson, Walter* / Counting on you baby: *McNeil, Landy* / I still love you: *Seven Souls* / Call me tomorrow: *Harris, Major* / Danse a la musique: *French Fries* / Talkin' 'bout poor folks: *Edwards, Lou* / I worship you baby: *Glories* / I'm in a world of trouble: *Sweet Things* / I need you: *Martin, Shane* / Too late: *Williams, Larry & Johnny Watson* / Chain reaction: *Spellbinders* / I don't want to discuss it: *Little Richard*.
LP: . . . . **SINLP 3**

SATISFYING OUR SOULS (Various artists).
Tracks: / Don't pity me: *Sommers, Joanie* / Mr. Creator: *Apollas* / I

remember the feeling: *Lewis, Barbara*/ Contact: *3 Degrees* / Love don't you go through no changes on me: *Sister Sledge* / Afternoon of the rhino: *Post, Mike Coalition* / Feels good: *Wilson, Bobby* / Don't you even care: *Uggams, Leslie* / I just can't live my life (without you babe): *Jones, Linda* / Thank you baby for loving me: *Soul Brothers Six* / Crazy baby: *Coasters*/ Satisfied: *Aiken, Ben* / Catch me I'm falling: *Phillips, Esther* / Bring your love back to me: *Lyndell, Linda* / Stirrin' up some soul: *Markett's* / (I love her so much) it hurts me: *David & Rueben*.
LP: . . . . **KENT 092**

SHOES (Various artists).
Tracks: / Shoes: *Bland, Bobby* / You ought to be in heaven: *Impressions (group)* / Music to my heart: *Austin*, Patti / Gotta have your love: *Sapphires* / I struck it rich: *Barry, Len* / Ain't nothing you can do: *Bland*, Bobby / Image: *Levine, Hank* / I do: *Marvelows* / Be young, be foolish, be happy: *Tams* / Apple of my eye: *Head, Roy & The Traits* / Hide and seek: *Sheep* / I've been hurt: *Whitley, Ray* / Jealous kind of fella: *Green, Garland* / Funny how time slips away: *Hinton, Joe*.
LP: . . . . **KENT 015**

SHRINE - THE RAREST SOUL LABEL (Various artists).
Tracks: / Don't let him hurt you: *Les Chansonettes* / Guess who loves you: *Daye, Eddie & Four Bars* / No other way: *Cautions* / Dream my heart: *Edwards, Shirley* / No more like me: *Pollard, Ray* / I'm a lover: *Hall, Sidney*.
LP: . . . . **HRH 1 LP**

SMART (Various artists).
Tracks: / My little red book: *Middleton, Tony* / Mellow moonlight: *Haywood, Leon* / Take me for a little while: *Mirettes* / Skate: *Parrish, Dean* / One wonderful moment: *Shakers* / Stand by me: *Grant, Earl*/ Great googa mooga: *Tom & Jerryo* / You better move on: *Alexander, Arthur* / Two ways to skin a cat: *Reed*, Jimmy / Love love love: *Barry, Len* / I don't know: *Alaimo, Steve* / Turn on your lovelight: *Bland, Bobby*/ Can't satisfy: *Impressions* / Night life: *King, B.B.* / Someone out there: *Candy & The Kisses*.
LP: . . . . **KENT 052**

SOLD ON SOUL (Various artists).
Tracks: / Be careful girl: *Turner, Betty* / Serving a sentence of life: *Douglas, Carl* / Drifter, The: *Pollard*, Ray / Your eyes may shine: *Short Kuts* / I lost a true love: *Wagner, Danny* / Walk with a winner: *McDaniels*, Gene / Hold on: *O'Jays* / Find me love: *DeShannon, Jackie* / Surrounded by a ray of sunshine: *Jones*, Samantha / My dear heart: *Robinson, Shawn* / Better use your head: *Little Anthony & The Imperials* / Nothing's too good for my baby: *Nelson, Sandy*.
LP: . . . . **LBR 1007**

SOLID SOUL SENSATIONS (Various artists).
LP: . . . . **DDLP 5001**

SOPHISTICATED SOUNDS Soul for the connoisseur (Various artists).
Tracks: / Since I found love: *Hadley, Sandy* / You could be my remedy: *Various artists* / Call on Billy: *Soul*, Billy T. / I'm a lover: *Carter, Chuck* / Hurt, The: *North, Freddie* / I wouldn't change a thing about you: *Wyatt, Johnny* / You say: *Esquires* / You must be losing: *Raye, Jimmy* / Love is a good foundation: *Uggams*, Leslie / I don't want to lose you: *Wynn, Mel* / Change, The: *Eady, Ernestine* / Yesterday's kisses: *Big Maybelle* / You got my love: *Wells, Donnie* / I'm gonna have a party: *Bruce, Ed* / Lover: *Hunt, Tommy*.
LP: . . . . **KENT 079**

SOUL CLASS OF '66 (Various artists).
Tracks: / You've been leading me on: *Steinways* / Give up girl: *Questel, Connie* / Take your time: *Austin*, Patti / I can feel it: *Carlton, Carl* / Girl I love you: *Green, Garland* / Little girl lost: *Sheppards*/ Do it: *Marvellos* / Walkin' uptown: *Prince Arthur & His Knights Of The Round Table* / Baby baby: *Crampton* Sisters / Love ain't love: *Ballard, Florence 'Flo'* / Once upon a time: *Orlons, The* / Baby baby take a chance on me: *Montgomery, Jack* / I'll try: *Sam & Bill* / Gotta get to know you: *Band, Bobby* / I've never loved nobody (like I love you): *Barnes, Ortheia* / I cry alone: *Ruby & The Romantics*.
LP: . . . . **KENT 011**

SOUL OF DETROIT (Various artists).
2LP: . . . . **LPSD 136**

SOUL SERENADE (Various artists).
LP: . . . . **KENT 041**

SOUL SPIN Various artists (Various artists).
Tracks: / That's no way to treat a girl: *Knight, Marie* / I got my heart set on you: *Toys* / You'll fall in love: *Jive Five* / On top of the world: *Soul* / Don't cry (sing along with the music): *Moore, Melba* / My heart cries for you: *Porgy & The Monarchs* / I love you a thousand times: *Platters* / Long after tonight is all over: *Radcliffe, Jimmy* / Hole in the wall: *Stone, George* / This diamond ring: *Ambrose, Sammy* / Try some soul: *Crossen, Ray* / You lie so well: *Knight, Marie* / You got it baby: *Toys* / Sweet sweet lovin': *Platters*/ Live on: *Troy, J B* / Run run roadrunner: *Williams, Jerry*.
LP: . . . . **KENT 024**

SOUL SUPERBOWL-THE SIXTIES V THE SEVENTIES (Various artists).
Tracks: / Please give me one more chance: *Various artists* / Thanks for a little lovin': *Various artists* / Baby boy: *Various artists* / She won't come back: *Various artists* / Skate a while baby: *Various artists* / Keep her guessing: *Various artists* / Hey it's love: *Various artists* / Where does that leave me: *Various* artists / Katrina: *Various artists* / Love's the only way to survive: *Various artists* / What kind of love: *Various artists* / Spread love: *Various artists* / Look up with your mind: *Various artists* / I fooled you this time: *Various artists*.
LP: . . . . **KENT 060**

SOUL TIME (Various artists).
Tracks: / Soul time: *Ellis, Shirley* / Beat, The: *Major Lance* / Quitter never wins, A: *Williams, Larry* & Johnny Watson / I'm coming to your rescue: *Triumphs* / Love trap: *Valentine, T D* / More today than yesterday: *Spiral Staircase* / Little bit of something, A: *Little Richard* / He who picks a Rose: *Carstairs* / This heart of mine: *Artistics* / There's a pain in my heart: *Poppies* / Help me: *Spellbinders* / Walk like a man: *Moore, Johnny* / Lot of love, A: *Taj Mahal* / It's all over me: *Blackwell, Otis* / I need your love so desperately: *Peaches & Herb* / Stranger in my arms: *Randell, Lynne* / Seven the loser: *Lomax, Eric*/ Country roads: *High Voltage*.
LP: . . . . **SINLP 4**

SOULFUL KINDA MUSIC (Various artists).
Tracks: / Do what you gotta do: *Contenders* / Oh baby: *Brown, Phyllis* / Can't lose my head: *Blackwell, George*/ Ain't got nothing but the blues: *Friendly People* / You don't love me: *Epitome Of Sound* / Keep pushing on: *Carpettes*/ Just do the best you can: *Duke & Leonard* / I don't want to lose you: *Bell Boys* / I love her so much it hurts: *Majestics* / Prove yourself a lady: *Bounty, James*.
LP: . . . . **LPSS 103**

SOUND OF THE GRAPEVINE (Various artists).
Tracks: / What: *Street, Judy* / Sidra's theme: *Ronnie & Robyn* / She's wanted in three states: *Clinton, Larry*/ Best thing for you baby: *Parker, Gloria* / Other side: *Five Of A Kind* / Savin' my love for you: *People's Choice* / I've caught you cheatin': *Masqueraders* / I'm gone: *Parker, Eddie* / Paris blues: *Middleton*, Tony / Ho happy day: *Flame'n'King* / Too darn soulful: *Chestnut, Morris* / Easy baby: *Adventurers*/ Keep on going: *Haines, Gary* / Say it isn't so: *Boo, Betty* / I really love you: *Tomangoes* / Yes you did: *Hitson, Herman* / Love you baby: *Parker, Eddie* / As long as you love me: *Ronnie & Robyn* / Let's do the duck: *Motor City Horns* / Sad girl: *Anderson, Carol*.
LP: . . . . **GRAL 1001**

SURE SHOTS (Various artists).
LP: . . . . **KENT 074**

TALK OF THE GRAPEVINE (Various artists).
Tracks: / Ever again: *Woodberry, Gene* / Cool off: *Detroit Executives* / Beggars can't be choosy: *Cooper*, Eula / Spellbound: *Boo, Betty* / I belong to you: *Wright, Milton* / You better gogo: *Lucas, Matt*/ Rosemary what happened: *Wylie, Richard 'Popcorn'* / Look let's make love: *Thomas, Sydney* / Standing by love: *Cooper, Eula* / Stop that boy: *Boo, Betty* / Down in the dumps: *Hester, Tony* / Hanky panky: *Wylie*, Richard 'Popcorn' / Let our love grow higher: *Cooper, Eula* / Quick change artist: *Soul Twins* / Spaceland: *Hester, Tony* / Gallop, The: *Wright, Milton* / Cool jerk 68: *Capitols* / Rosemary what happened (inst.): *Wylie, Richard 'Popcorn'* / Down in the dumps (inst.): *Hester, Tony* / Hanky panky (inst.): *Wylie, Richard 'Popcorn'*.
LP: . . . . **GRAL 1000**

THAT BEATIN' RHYTHM (Various artists).
Tracks: / Don't pretend: *Belles* / Words can't explain: *Belles* / My sugar baby: *Matthews, Sherlie* / My little girl: *Garrett, Bobby* / Oh my darlin': *Lee, Jacky* / I can't get away: *Garrett, Bobby* / Cigarette ashes: *Conwell, Jimmy* / That beatin' rhythm: *Temple, Richard* / Baby do the philly dog: *Olympics*.
LP: . . . . **BURN 1**

THAT DRIVING BEAT (Various artists).
LP: . . . . **LPSS 101**
MC: . . . . **CLPSS 101**

THINK SMART SOUL STIRRERS JERK IT AT THE PARTY I (Various artists).
Tracks: / It's a woman's world (you better believe it): *Gypsies* / Think smart: *Fiestas* / Left out: *Johnson*, Jesse / Baby I need you: *Lorraine & The Delights* / Jerk it: *Gypsies* / Barefootin' time in Chinatown: *Young*, Lester / I want a chance for romance: *Rivera, Hector* / My foolish heart: *Coleman, David* / If I had known: *Houston, Freddie* / You can't trust your best friend: *Height, Freddie* / We're gonna make it: *Reid, Irene*/ Souvenirs of heartbreak: *Jones, Thelma* / Cross my heart: *Yvonne & The Violets* / At the party: *Young, Lester*/ Soul stirrer: *Lou, Bobby & Betty* / You better believe me: *McKay, Beverley*.
LP: . . . . **KENT 064**

THIS IS NORTHERN SOUL (Various artists).
Tracks: / I've got something good: *Sam & Kitty* (Four Brothers records) / To the ends of the earth: *Middleton, Tony*(Licensed from MGM records) / My little cottage: *Falana, Fluffy* / People that's why: *Idle Few* (Licensed from Blue Book Records) / I am nothing: *Williams, Al* (Licensed from La Beat/Palmer Records) / Exus trek: *Ingram, Luther*(Licensed from Hib Records) / How to make a sad man glad: *Capreez* (Licensed from Sound Records) / Eddie's my name: *Holman*, Eddie (Licensed from Parkway Records) / Love slipped thru my fingers: *Williams, Sam* (Licensed from Tower Records) / Baby don't you weep: *Hamilton, Edward* (Licensed from Mary Jane Records) / Rules: *Blanding, Gil* (Licensed from Ready Records) / Lover: *Delites* (Licensed from Cuppy Records) / Trouble: *Agents* (Licensed from Liberty Bell Records) / If it's all the same to you babe: *Ingram, Luther* (Licensed from Hib Records) / Such misery: *Precisions* (Licensed from Drew Records) / This won't change: *Tipton, Lester* (Licensed from La Beat Records) / This man in love: *New Wanderers*.
LP: . . . . **GRAL 1002**

UNTOUCHABLES (Various artists).
Tracks: / What goes up (must come down): *Various artists* / I need a helping hand: *Servicemen, The* / Darling, darling: *Various artists* / I'm gonna hurt you: *Various artists* / I'm getting tired: *Carlettes* / You can forget it: *Sisters Three* / Standing at a standstill: *Various artists* / I want to be free: *Various artists*/ Talking eyes: *Various artists* / You got me in the palm of your hand: *Richardson, Donald Lee* / You left me: *Various artists* / This time you're wrong: *Various artists* / This heart, these hands: *Various artists*/ Where were you: *Epitome Of Sound*.
LP: . . . . **LPSS 109**

UP ALL NIGHT (30 Northern Soul Classics) (Various artists).
Tracks: / Nothing can stop me: *Chandler, Gene* / Getting mighty crowded: *Everett, Betty* / Nothing worse than being alone: *Ad Libs* / That other place: *Flemons, Wade* / I keep tryin': *Hughes, Fred* / You're the dream: *Shelton, Roscoe* / I hurt on the other side: *Barnes, Sidney* / Lonely for you baby: *Dee, Sammy* / Come on train: *Thomas, Don* / Breakaway: *Valentines* / You're gonna need me: *Ford, Ted* / Being without you: *Williams, Maurice* / Why don't you write: *Bates, Lee* / But I couldn't: *Harper, Willie* / Just another heartache: *Little Richie* / Touch me, hold me, kiss me: *Inspirations* / Tear stained face: *Varner, Don*/ Hung up on your love: *Montclairs, The* / Running for my life: *Shelton, Roscoe* / My man don't think I know: *Davies*, Gwen / Hold on: *Beavers, Jackie* / You've been gone too long: *Sexton, Ann* / That's enough: *Robinson*, Roscoe / I'd think it over twice (if I were you): *Fletcher, Sam* / You'll always be in style: *Barnes, Sidney*/ Don't let me down: *Hughes, Fred* / Sweet and easy: *McCoy, Van* / Power of love: *Humphrey, Amanda* / Now I'm in love with you: *Sims, Marvin L.* / I'm a fool, I must love you: *Falcons*.
MCSET: . . . . **TCINSD 5028**

WHOLE LOT OF SOUL IS HERE (Various artists).
Tracks: / Not too old to cry: *Trends* / Your little sister: *Marvelows* / For crying out loud: *Sigler, Bunny*/ Talkin' bout you babe: *Little Charles & The Sidewinders* / Baby I need your love: *Williams, Bobby* / I need you: *Impressions* / Are you trying to cross over: *Mirettes* / Life of the party: *Craig, Anna* / Satisfaction guaranteed: *Burkes, Donnie* / Changing by the minute: *Fletcher, Darrow* / Get off my back: *Sims, Marvin L.*/ Yum yum tree: *Bland, Bobby* / Whole lot of soul is gone, A: *Conerly, Bobby* / Paying the cost to be the boss: *King, B.B.* / It rained 40 days and nights: *Green, Garland* / Young lover: *Little Mr Lee and The Cherokees*.
LP: . . . . **KENT 048**

WINNER TAKES ALL Various artists (Various artists).
LP: . . . . **KENT 035**

Northwest Chamber ...

THREE ENGLISH CLARINET CONCERTOS.
MC: . . . . **KA 66031**

Norum, John

TOTAL CONTROL.
Tracks: / Let me love you / Love is meant / Too many hearts / Someone else here / Eternal flame / Back on the streets / Blind / Law of life / We'll do what it takes together / In chase of the wind.
LP: **4602031**
MC: **4602034**

Norvo, Red

1983 (Norvo, Red & His Orchestra).
LP: . . . . **CLP 3**

COLLECTIONS (Norvo, Red/Pepper, Art/Morello, Joe).
LP: . . . . **FS 224**

FORWARD LOOK, THE (Norvo, Red Quintet).
LP: . . . . **RR 8**

JUST FRIENDS.
LP: . . . . **ST 230**

MISTER SWING - 1943-1944 (Norvo, Red & His Orchestra).
Tracks: / Seven come eleven / Which switch witch / Lagwood walk / Sargeant on Furlough, The / Too marvellous for words / Blue skies / Purple feathers / Bass on the bar room floor, The / In a mellow tone / Flying home.
LP: . . . . **SWH 16**
MC: . . . . **CSWH 16**

NORVO - NATURALLY!.
LP: . . . . **VSOP 35**

RED (Norvo, Red & His Orchestra).
LP: . . . . **HEP 1019**

RED NORVO, CHARLES MINGO, TAL FARLOW 1950-1 (Norvo, Red, Charles Mingo, Tal Farlow).
LP: . . . . **QUEEN 063**

RED NORVO'S FABULOUS JAM SESSION.
Tracks: / Hallelujah / Congo blues / Slam slam blues.
LP: . . . . **SPJ 127**

RED NORVO'S SWINGING BANDS.
Tracks: / Just you, just me / Which switch witch? / Bass on the bar room floor / NRC jump / Seven come eleven / Russian lullaby / Woody's tune / Seal it with a kiss / You ain't gonna bother me no more.
LP: . . . . **RARITIES 23**

RED'S 'X' SESSIONS (Norvo, Red & His Orchestra).
LP: . . . . **FS 182**

SWING THAT MUSIC (see Braff, Ruby) (Norvo, Red & Ruby Braff).

TOWN HALL CONCERT 1 (Norvo, Red & His Orchestra).
LP: . . . . **HMC 5001**

TOWN HALL CONCERT 1945 (See Coleman, Bill) (Norvo, Red/Bill Coleman).

WARTIME VIBE-RATIONS.
LP: . . . . **IARJC 24**

Norwood

I CAN'T LET YOU GO.
Tracks: / I can't let you go / Don't let love / Should have been us together / Lady in love / I can't live without you / Give it up / Feels so good / Glad I found you / Come back my lover.
LP: . . . . **MCF 3374**
MC: . . . . **MCFC 3374**

Norwood B

EVENING WITH NORWOOD B.
Tracks: / My funny valentine / Just the two of us / Here we go again / All at once / Not too strong to cry / Love loving you / You're the one (you're on the money).
LP: . . . . **PWLP 1003**

Norwood Builder

NORWOOD BUILDER, THE (Various artists).
Tracks: / Norwood builder, The: *Various artists* / Lady Frances Carfax: *Various artists*.

MC: . . . . ANV 643

Norwood, Dorothy

DOROTHY NORWOOD & THE COMBINED ATLANTA CHOIR (Norwood, Dorothy & The Combined Atlanta Choir).
LP: . . . . MG 14140

JOHNNY AND JESUS (Norwood, Dorothy Singers).
LP: . . . . MG 14083

LOOK WHAT THEY'VE DONE TO MY CHILD.
LP: . . . . SL 14630

MOTHER'S SON, A.
LP: . . . . IAM R 3813
MC: . . . . IAM C 3813

Norwood (Film)

NORWOOD (Film Soundtrack) (Various artists).
Tracks: / Ol' Norwood comin' home: *Various artists* / Country girl: *Various artists* / Marie: *Various artists/* Brass ensemble of Ralph: *Various artists* / Texas: *Various artists* / Repo man: *Various artists* / Hot wheels: *Various artists* / I'll paint you a song: *Various artists* / Norwood (me and my guitar): *Various artists/* Fring thing: *Various artists* / Down home: *Various artists* / Chicken out: *Various artists* / I'll paint you a song: *Various artists* / Different kind of rock: *Various artists* / Everything a man could ever need: *Various artists.*
LP: . . . . ESW 457

Nose Flutes

SEVERAL YOUNG MEN IGNITE HARDBOARD STUMP.
Tracks: / Perfect cockney hard-on / Romance takes control / Dreamboat / Bullet enters Brad / This is my home / Harmony of dogs, The / Holiday time / Past promise broken in previous life / Why is everyone a man / Sugar buch, The / Cowboy factory.
LP: . . . . LEX 5M

ZIB ZOB AND HIS KIB KOB.
LP: . . . . REAP 001
MC: . . . . CREAP 001

Nosferatu

NOSFERATU (Film soundtrack) (Various artists).
LP: . . . . PLDM 7005
MC: . . . . PMM 705

Nostalgic...

ANOTHER GREAT EAST END SINGALONG (In sequence) (Various artists).
LP: . . . . MTS 18
MC: . . . . CMTS 18

CLASSIC SHOWS, THE (Various artists).
Tracks: / My life belongs to you: *Hart, Dunstan/Mary Ellis* (Ivor Novello at the piano.) / I can give you the starlight: *Ellis, Mary* / My dearest dear: *Ellis, Mary/Ivor Novello* / Primrose: *Beaumont, Roma* (Ivor Novello at the piano.) / Leap year waltz, The: *Various artists* / Three ballet tunes: *Various artists* / Wings of sleep, The: *Various artists* / Waltz of my heart: *Various artists* / Why isn't it you: *Dickson, Dorothy/Walter Crisham/* If you only knew: *Dickson, Dorothy* / Rose of England: *Elmes, Edgar* / Haven of your heart: *Gilbert, Olive/* Music in May: *Dickson, Dorothy* / Why is there ever goodbye?: *Gilbert, Olive* / Studio scene (A bit of opera): *Novello, Ivor/Dorothy Dickson/Olive Gilbert* / Love made the song: *Crawley, Sybil/Eric Starling* / Miracle of Nichaow: *Novello, Ivor* (Temple Ballet Music - Solo: Olive Gilbert.) / Bridge of lovers: *Novello, Ivor* (Solo: Olive Gilbert.).
LP: . . . . SH 521
LP: 794 368 1
MC: . . . . TCSH 521
MC: 794 368 4

CREST OF THE WAVE (Various artists).
Tracks: / Why isn't it you: *Various artists* / Haven of your heart: *Various artists* / If you only knew: *Various artists* / Rose of England: *Various artists.*
LP: . . . . SH 216

D DAY DESPATCHES/VICTORY IN EUROPE (Various artists).
MCSET: . . . . ZBBC 1084

DAY WAR BROKE OUT (Musical and mirthful memories of WW II) (Various artists).
Tracks: / Home guard, The: *Wilton, Robb* / It's that man again: *Handley, Tommy* / Blacking out the flat: *Askey, Arthur/Richard Murdoch* / Imagine me in the Maginot line: *Formby, George* / Londoner and the hun, The: *Flotsam & Jetsam* (Not on CD.) / Lord Haw Haw the humbug of Hamburg: *Western Brothers* (Not on CD.) / In the Quartermaster's stores: *Murgatroyd & Winterbottom* (Not on CD.) / Auxiliary fire service call: *Warner, Jack* (Not on CD.) / War worker, The: *Fletcher, Cyril* (Not on CD.) / Deepest shelter in town, The: *Desmond, Florence* / Could you please oblige me with a Bren gun: *Coward, Noel* (Not on CD.) / Thanks for dropping in Mr. Hess: *Askey, Arthur* (Not on CD.) / Sam goes to it: *Holloway, Stanley (nar)* / I'm one of the Whitehall warriors: *Ritchard, Cyril (nar)* (Not on CD.) / I did what I could with my gas mask: *Formby, George* (Not on CD.) / Munitions worker, The: *Wilton, Robb*(Not on CD.) / Oh you ladies in the forces: *Frankau, Ronald* (Not on CD.) / Max in a air raid (I never slept a wink all night): *Miller, Max* / Can I do yer now sir?: *Summers, Dorothy* (Not on CD.) / Don't let's be beastly to the Germans: *Coward, Noel* / Gracie with the troops: *Fields, Gracie* / We're gonna hang out the washing on the Siegfried line: *Sarony, Leslie* / Somewhere in France with you: *Loss, Joe & His Orchestra* / Nightingale sang in Berkeley Square, A: *'Hutch'* / It's a lovely day tomorrow: *Hale, Binnie* (Not on CD.) / Room 504: *Gibbons, Carroll & Savoy* Hotel Orpheans (Not on CD.) / Ma, I miss your apple pie: *RAOC Blue Rockets* (Not on CD.) / That lovely weekend: *Geraldo* & His Orchestra / White cliffs of Dover, The: *Lynn, Vera* / You are my sunshine: *Roy, Harry & His Band* / Coming in on a wing and a prayer: *Organ, The Dance Band And Me* (Not on CD.) / As time goes by: *Layton, Turner/* This is the army Mr. Jones: *Berlin, Irving* / I'm going to get lit up when the lights go up in London: *Gibbons, Carroll* & Savoy Hotel Orpheans / London pride: *Coward, Noel* / You'll never know: *Loss, Joe & His Orchestra* (Not on CD.) / Lili Marlene: *Andersen, Lale* / No love, no nothin': *Carless, Dorothy* (Not on CD.) / Coming home: *Praeger, Lou & His Orchestra.*
2LP: . . . . EM 1341
MCSET: . . . . TCEM 1341

D-DAY DESPATCHES (War correspondents reports) (Various artists).
LP: . . . . REC 522
MC: . . . . ZCM 522

DOWN THE CUT (Canal Age in song) (Various artists).
LP: . . . . SDL 272

EARLY MINSTREL SHOW (Various artists).
LP: . . . . NW 338

GOLDEN AGE OF BALLADS AND PARLOUR SONGS (Various artists).
Tracks: / Come to the fair: *Wendon, Henry* (From "Songs Of The Fair". Original matrix: CA 18873-1, Columbia DB 2064.) / Grandfather's clock: *Williams, Harold* (Original matrix: CA 14113-1, Columbia DB 1284, 31 October 1933) / Parted: *Booth,* Webster (Original matrix: OEA 10928-1, HMV B 9472, 20 March 1946) / Leanin': *Brannigan, Owen* (Original matrix: 2EA 14244-1, HMV C 4110, 7 October 1949) / Love, could I only tell thee: *Manton, Stephen* / Bloom is on the rye: *Various artists* (Orig matrix numbers : CA 11766-3, Columbia DB 720, 13 July 1931) / Wrap me up in my tarpaulin jacket: *Robertson,* Stuart (Original matrix OB 4416-2, HMV B 4381, 22 October 1932) / Until: *Midgley, Walter with Gladys Vernon* (Original matrix: CA 17497-1, Columbia DB 1871, 9 June 1939) / Volunteer organist, The: *Dawon, Peter* (Original matrix: Bb 19679-1, HMV B 3630, 10 July 1930) / Think on me: *Baillie, Isobel* (Original matrix: CA 18999-7, Columbia DB 2080, 18 June 1942) / Life's dream is o'er: *Hooper, Barrington & Foster Richardson* / As I sit here: *Allin, Norman* (Original matrix: CA 17498-1, Columbia DB 1869, 15 June 1939) / My dreams: *Glynne, Walter* (Original matrix: Bb 17744-5, HMV B 3526, 15 January 1930) / For you alone: *Lloyd, David* (Original matrix: CA 19043-1, Columbia DB 2089, 28 July 1942) / Lo, hear the gentle lark: *Catley, Gwen* / Wrap me up in my Tarpaulin jacket: *Various artists* / Until: *Various artists* / Volunteer organist, The: *Various artists* / Think on me: *Various artists* / Life's dream is o'er: *Various artists* / As I sit here: *Various artists* / My dreams: *Various artists* / For you alone: *Various artists/* Lo, hear the gentle lark: *Various artists* / Come to the fair: *Various artists* (From 'Song of the fair') / Grandfather's clock: *Various artists* / Parted: *Various artists* / Leanin: *Various artists* / Love, could I only tell thee: *Various artists.*
LP: . . . . GX 41 2554
MC: . . . . TCGX 2554

GOLDEN AGE OF FEMALE VOICE (Various artists).
Tracks: / Nightingale sang in Berkeley Square, A: *Welch, Elisabeth* / There goes that song again: *Carless, Dorothy/* When I grow too old to dream: *Laye, Evelyn* / I've told every little star: *Ellis, Mary* / That old feeling: *Hall,* Adelaide / Stormy weather: *Langford, Frances* / Pu-leeze Mr. Hemingway: *Carlisle, Elsie* / Moment I saw you, The: *Courtneidge, Cicely* / Spread a little happiness: *Hale, Binnie* / When you've got a little springtime in your heart: *Matthews, Jessie* / Says my heart: *Becke, Eve* / Night was made for love, The: *Wood, Peggy* / These foolish things: *Welch, Elisabeth* / Nightingale sang in Berkely Square, A: *Welch, Elisabeth* / You've done something to my heart: *Jones, Gwen* / Moon got in my eyes: *Lenner, Anne* / Try a little tenderness: *Williams, Frances/* Wish me luck (as you wave me goodbye): *Fields, Gracie.*
LP: . . . . GX 41 2553
MC: . . . . TCGX 2553
LP: . . . . MFP 5826
MC: . . . . TCMFP 5826

GOLDEN AGE OF MALE VOICE (Various artists).
Tracks: / Goodnight Vienna: *Buchanan, Jack* / Don't let that moon get away: *Trent, Bruce* / Music goes round and around, The: *Elrick, George* / Me and my girl: *Cooper, Jack* / My melancholy baby: *Bowlly, Al* / Best things in life are free, The: *'Hutch'* / Only a glass of champagne: *Askey, Arthur* / On the Amazon: *Howes,* Bobby / Puttin' on the Ritz: *Astaire, Fred* / Change partners: *Henderson, Chick* / Let's face the music and dance: *Dennis, Denny* / Sixty seconds got together: *Melachrino, George* / Dancing in the dark: *Browne, Sam/* I'll see you again: *Coward, Noel* / What a little moonlight can do: *Hulbert, Jack* / You brought a new kind of love to me: *Chevalier, Maurice.*
LP: . . . . GX 41 2552
MC: . . . . TCGX 2552
LP: . . . . MFP 5825
MC: . . . . TCMFP 5825

GOLDEN AGE OF NOEL GAY (Various artists).
Tracks: / Lambeth walk: *Various artists* / Me and my girl: *Various artists* / Fleet's in port again, The: *Various* artists / Ali Baba's camel: *Various artists* / Hold my hand: *Various artists* / Jack o' diamonds: *Various* artists / Love makes the world go round: *Various artists* / Run rabbit run: *Various artists* / Melody maker, The: *Various artists* / Sun has got his hat on, The: *Various artists* / Oh, buddy, I'm in love: *Various artists/* I don't want to go to bed: *Various artists* / Hey little hen: *Various artists* / I took my harp to a party: *Various artists* / You've done something to my heart: *Various artists* / La di da di da: *Various artists.*
LP: . . . . GX 41 2516 1
MC: . . . . GX 41 2516 4

GOLDEN AGE OF VARIETY (Various artists).
Tracks: / Wanderer: *Flanagan & Allen* / Dreaming: *Flanagan & Allen* / Where the arches used to be: *Flanagan & Allen* / Heart and soul: *Mayerl, Billy* / I don't do things like that: *Trinder, Tommy* / Dinah: *Simpson,* Jack / Sweet Sue: *Simpson, Jack* / Bye bye blues: *Simpson, Jack* / Barmaid at the Rose and Crown: *Various* artists / Gert and Daisy and the tandem: *Waters, Elsie & Doris (Gert & Daisy)* / I'm the man who's deputising for the bull: *Howerd, Frankie* / Let it be soon: *O'Shea, Tessie* / Underneath the old pine tree: *Rocky Mountaineers,* featuring Big Bill Campbell / Trail of the lonesome pine: *Rocky Mountaineers, featuring Big Bill Campbell* / Riding down to Dixie: *Reader, Ralph & The Jackdaws* / Can't we meet again?: *Flanagan & Allen* / Million tears, A: *Flanagan & Allen* / Underneath the arches: *Flanagan & Allen* / English as she is spoken: *Howerd, Frankie* / Huntin': *Waters, Elsie & Doris (Gert & Daisy)* / Biggest aspidistra in the world, The: *Fields, Gracie* / Cruising down the river: *Preager, Lou & His Orchestra* / Mockin' Bird Hill: *Ronalde, Ronnie.*
LP: . . . . GX 2560
MC: . . . . TCGX 2560

GOLDEN YEARS OF TIN PAN ALLEY, THE (Various artists).
Tracks: / Stormy weather: *Various artists* / How deep is the ocean: *Various artists* / Heartaches: *Various* artists / All of me: *Various artists* / Blue moon: *Various artists* / Ghost of a chance: *Various artists/* Shoe shine boy: *Various artists* / Music goes round and around, The: *Various artists* / Untill the real thing comes along: *Various artists* / When my dreamboat comes home: *Various artists* / Once in a while: *Various* artists / Undecided: *Various artists* / Heart and soul: *Various artists* / T'aint what you do (it's the way that you do i: *Various artists.*
LP: . . . . NW 248

GREAT SINGERS (Various artists).
LP: . . . . MOIR 509
MC: . . . . CMOIR 509

GREAT SINGERS OF YESTERYEAR (Various artists).
Tracks: / Mad dogs and Englishmen: *Coward, Noel* / Mrs. Worthington: *Coward, Noel* / We'll gather lilacs: *Ziegler,* Anne & Webster Booth / If you were the only girl in the world: *Ziegler, Anne & Webster Booth* / Puttin' on the Ritz: *Astaire, Fred* / My Melancholy baby: *Bowlly, Al* / Goodnight sweetheart: *Bowlly, Al* / Sing as we go: *Fields, Gracie* / Wish me luck (as you wave me goodbye): *Fields, Gracie* / River stay 'way from my door: *Robeson,* Paul / Just a wearyin' for you: *Robeson, Paul* / Louise: *Chevalier, Maurice* / You brought a new kind of love to me: *Chevalier, Maurice* / I'll see you again: *Laye, Evelyn* / Let the people sing: *Laye, Evelyn* / You forgot your gloves: *Buchanan, Jack* / Goodnight Vienna: *Buchanan, Jack* / Red hot Mama: *Tucker, Sophie* / Some of these days: *Tucker, Sophie/* Mr. Wu's an air raid warden now: *Formby, George* / Look for the silver lining: *Matthews, Jessie* / Fascinating rhythm: *Astaire, Fred & Adele.*
MC: . . . . HR 8115
MC: . . . . HR 4181154

GREAT VOICES OF OUR TIME (Various artists).
Tracks: / Ol' man river: *Robeson, Paul* / We'll gather lilacs: *Tauber, Richard* (from 'Perchance to Dream') / Jeanie with the light brown hair: *Various artists* / Floral dance, The: *Dawson, Peter* / Roses of Picardy: *Booth,* Webster (with Fred Hartley's Quintet.) / Lazybones: *Robeson, Paul* / My heart and I: *Tauber, Richard* / Faery song, The: *Booth, Webster* (from 'The Immortal Hour') / At dawning: *Robeson, Paul* / Vienna, city of my dreams: *Tauber, Richard* / Snowy breasted pearl, The: *McCormack, John* / On the road to Mandalay: *Dawson, Peter/* On wings of song: *Booth, Webster* / Swing low, sweet chariot: *Robeson, Paul* / Drink to me only with thine eyes: *McCormack, John* / Boots: *Dawson, Peter* / Come into the garden, Maud: *Booth, Webster* / Rockin' chair: *Robeson, Paul* / Pedro, the fisherman: *Tauber, Richard* (from 'The Lisbon Story'.) / Star of the County Down: *McCormack,* John / Waltzing Matilda: *Dawson, Peter* / One alone: *Tauber, Richard* (from 'The Desert Song') / Trottin' to the fair: *McCormack, John* / Cobbler's song, The: *Dawson, Peter* (from 'Chu Chin Chow') / I leave my heart in an English garden: *Booth, Webster* (from 'Dear Miss Phoebe') / River stay 'way from my door: *Robeson, Paul* / Serenade: *Tauber, Richard* (from 'The Student Prince') / Believe me if all those endearing young charms: *McCormack, John.*
2LP: . . . . DL 1118
MC: . . . . TCDL 1118

GREAT VOICES OF THE CENTURY (Great Tenors) (Various artists).
MC: . . . . CMOIR 405

GREATEST SINGERS, GREATEST SONGS (Various artists).
Tracks: / Blue Danube: *Tauber, Richard* / Beneath thy window (O sole mio): *Tauber, Richard* / Plaisir d'amour: *Tauber, Richard* / Without a song: *Tauber, Richard* / Indian Summer: *Tauber, Richard* / Perfect day: *Tauber,* Richard / I'm in love with Vienna: *Tauber, Richard* / One day when we were young: *Tauber, Richard* / At dawning: *Robeson, Paul* / Rockin' chair: *Robeson, Paul* / Mammy's little kinky headed boy: *Robeson, Paul* / Banjo song: *Robeson, Paul* / Eriskay love lilt: *Robeson, Paul* / River stay 'way from my door: *Robeson, Paul/* Cobbler's song, The: *Robeson, Paul* / Drink to me only with thine eyes: *Robeson, Paul* / Lazybones: *Robeson,* Paul / Honey (dat's all): *Robeson, Paul* / Kerry dance, The: *McCormack, John* / Kashmiri song: *McCormack,* John / Down by the Sally gardens: *McCormack, John* / Jesu, joy of man's desiring: *McCormack, John* / Trees: *McCormack, John* / Mighty like a rose: *McCormack, John* / Bantry Bay: *McCormack, John* / Smilin' through: *McCormack, John* / So deep is the night: *McCormack, John* / God keep you, is my prayer: *McCormack, John/* When the sergeant major's on parade: *Dawson, Peter* / Roses of Picardy: *Dawson, Peter* / Song of the flea: *Dawson,* Peter / Fishermen of England: *Dawson, Peter* / I travel the road: *Dawson, Peter* / Bandolero: *Dawson,* Peter / Boots: *Dawson, Peter* / Somewhere a voice is calling: *Dawson, Peter* / Old Father Thames: *Dawson, Peter* / Song of the volga boatmen: *Dawson, Peter.*
2LP: . . . . MFP 1004
MCSET: . . . . TCMFP 1004

I LOVE TO SING (The other songs of Harold Arlen) (Various artists).

LP: . . . . JASS 7

I'LL ALWAYS REMEMBER, VOL 7 (Various artists).
LP: . . . . RRLP 007

INCOMPARABLE HILDEGARDE: ON THE AIR 1936-44 (Various artists).
Tracks: / Je vous aime, beaucoup: *Various artists* / I'm in a dancing mood: *Various artists* / You are all I wanted: *Various artists* / Eeny meeny miney mo: *Various artists* / Who loves you?: *Various artists* / Wien wien: *Various artists* / Goodnight my love: *Various artists* / Never gonna dance: *Various artists* / I couldn't sleep a wink last night: *Various artists* / I'll be seeing you: *Various artists* / Blue room: *Various artists*/ I love you: *Various artists* / New sun up in a new sky, A: *Various artists* / My shining hour: *Various artists*/ You're the dream: *Various artists* / Zing went the strings of my heart: *Various artists*.
LP: . . . . TOTEM 1036

KEEP SMILING THROUGH (Various artists).
Tracks: / Crash, bang, I wanna go home: *Fields, Gracie* / Follow the white line: *Riscoe, Arthur* / Could you please oblige me with a Bren gun?: *Coward, Noel* / I'm one of the Whitehall warriors: *Richard, Cyril* / Imagine me in the Maginot Line: *Formby, George* / Frank and his tank: *Warner, Jack "Blue Pencil"* / Thingummybob, The: *Askey*, Arthur / I didn't really oughter 'ave went: *Hare, Doris* / Albert evacuated: *Holloway, Stanley (nar)* / Mr. Wu's an air raid warden now: *Formby, George* / Deepest shelter in town: *Desmond, Florence* / I did what I could with my gas mask: *Formby, George* / When can I have a banana again?: *Roy, Harry* / Lord Haw Haw the humbug of Hamburg: *Western Brothers* / Der Fuehrer's face: *Trinder, Tommy* / Oh what a surprise for the Duce: *Desmond, Florence*/ Don't let's be beastly to the Germans: *Coward, Noel* / Jap, the Wop and the Hun: *Frankau, Ronald*.
LP: . . . . GX 41 2532 1
MC: . . . . GX 41 2532 4

KEEP SMILING THROUGH (2) (Various artists).
Tracks: / Deh Fuehrer's face: *Roy, Harry & His Band* / When daddy comes home: *Roy, Harry & His Band* / This is the army Mister Jones: *Roy, Harry & His Band* / Savin' myself for Bill: *Roy, Harry & His Band* / They can't black out the moon: *Roy, Harry & His Band* / When they sound the last all clear: *Roy, Harry & His Band* / I don't want to set the world on fire: *Roy, Harry & His Band* / We mustn't miss the last bus home: *Driver, Betty/Orchestra*/ My A.C.W. 2 (Aircraft woman): *Warner, Jack Orchestra* / We don't know where we're going (until we're there): *Leader*, Harry & His Band / Thanks Mister Roosevelt: *Leader, Harry & His Band* / Bless 'em all: *Formby, George Orchestra*/ Serves you right: *Formby, George Orchestra* / Mr. Wu's an air raid warden now: *Formby, George Orchestra* / Arm in arm: *White, Jack & His Band* / Spitfire song, The: *Loss, Joe & His Orchestra* / Tiggerty boo: *Loss, Joe* & His Orchestra / When that man is dead and gone: *Loss, Joe & His Orchestra* / Five o'clock whistle, The: *Loss*, Joe & His Orchestra / Lili Marlene: *D'Amato, Chappie & His Orchestra* / Hye little hen: *Gonella, Nat/his Georgians*/ It's a pair of wings for me: *Gonella, Nat/ his Georgians* / Badge from your coat, The: *New Mayfair Dance Orchestra*.
2LP: . . . . DL 1182
MC: . . . . TCDL 1182

KEEP THE GREY GULL FLYING 1924-1930 (Various artists).
MC: 042

KEEP THE HOME FIRES BURNING (Various artists).
Tracks: / Here we are, here we are: *Wheeler, F./chorus* (Phonograph cylinder) / Goodbye-ee: *Unknown artist(s)*(Penny piano) / Just before the battle mother: *Oakland, Will/chorus* (Phonograph cylinder) / Your King and country want you: *Clarke, Helen/chorus* (Phonograph cylinder) / Trumpeter, (The): *Newell, Raymond/Ian Swinley* (78rpm record) / Deathless army, The: *Kinniburgh, T.F.* (Phonograph cylinder) / medley: *N.M.B. Flying squadron* (Phonograph cylinder) / Tramp, tramp, tramp: *Harlan & Stanley/chorus* (Phonograph cylinder) / Keep the home fires burning: *Unknown artist(s)*(Penny piano) / Boys of the old brigade: *N.M.B. Flying squadron* (Phonograph cylinder) / Boys in khaki, boys in blue: *Wheeler, F./* chorus (Phonograph cylinder) / Colonel Bogey: *Coldstream Guards Band* (78rpm record - Wembley Military Tattoo 1925 (medley)) / Keep the home fires burning: *Coldstream Guards Band* (ditto) / Pack up your troubles in your old kit bag: *Coldstream* Guards Band (ditto) / It's a long way to Tipperary: *Coldstream Guards Band* (ditto) / Roses of Picardy: *Murray*, Templeton (Pianola) / Passing Review Patrol: *unknown band* (Phonograph cylinder) / What has become of hinkey-dinky-parlay-voo?: *Bernard, Al/chorus* (Edison Diamond Disc 1924).
LP: . . . . SDL 358
MC: . . . . CSDL 358

LEGENDS VOL.1, THE (2) (Various artists).
MC: . . . . MRT 40029

LEGENDS VOL.2, THE (2) (Various artists).
MC: . . . . MRT 40030

LEGENDS VOL.3 (Various artists).
MC: . . . . MRT 40035

LISTEN TO THE BANNED (20 Risque Songs of the Twenties & Thirties) (Various artists).
Tracks: / I've gone and lost my little yo-yo: *Cotton, Billy* / With my little ukelele in my hand: *Formby, George*/ Guy what takes his time, A: *West, Mae* / She was only a postman's daughter, but...: *Durium Dance Band* / Nellie the nudist queen: *Ross & Sargent* / My private affair: *Davies, Dawn* / What's it: *Rodgers, Jimmie (1)*/ He hadn't up 'til yesterday: *Tucker, Sophie* / Winnie the worm: *Frankau, Ronald* / I'm a bear in a lady's boudoir: *Edwards, Cliff* / Everyone's got sex appeal for someone: *Frankau, Ronald/Monte Crick* / All poshed up with my daisies in my hand: *Higgins, Charlie* / Pu-leeze Mr. Hemingway: *Carlisle, Elsie* / Let's all be fairies: *Durium Dance Band* / I'm going to give it to Mary with love: *Edwards, Cliff* / Physician, The: *Lawrence, Gertrude* / No wonder she's a blushing bride: *Fowler, Art* / Flora McDonald: *Byng, Douglas* / Or anything else I've got: *Sutton, Randolph* / And so does he: *Davies, Dawn*.
LP: . . . . AJA 5030
MC: . . . . ZC AJA 5030

LONDON SHOWS (The war years) (Various artists).
Tracks: / Are you having any fun?: *Flanagan & Allen* / Run rabbit run: *Flanagan & Allen* / How beautiful you are: *Ambrose & His Orchestra* / My heart belongs to daddy: *Hall, Adelaide* / Crash, bang, I wanna go home: *Stones*, Lew & His Band / Have you met Miss Jones: *Hall, Adelaide* / Who's taking you home tonight: *Lynn, Vera* / Start the day right: *Daniels, Bebe & Ben Lyon* / As round and round we go-Your company's requested: *Daniels, Bebe* / This can't be love: *Hall, Adelaide* / Let the people sing: *Payne, Jack & His Band/Billy Scott Coomber* / You done some thing to my heart: *Davis, Beryl* / They call me a dreamer: *Rabin, Oscar & His Band* / We'll go smiling along: *Rabin, Oscar & His Band* / Cheerio: *Daniels, Bebe* / Let's be buddies: *Flanagan & Allen* / But in the morning no: *Day, Francis & Bud Flanagan* / Lambeth walk: *Ambrose & His Orchestra* / Me & my girl: *Cotton*, Billy & His Band / Waiting for Sally: *Stones, Lew & His Band* / Wrap yourself in cotton wool: *Hatchett's Swingtette*/ Tahiti rendezvous: *Hatchett's Swingtette* / It's a million to one: *Mantovani* / Smiths and the Jones, The: *Flanagan & Allen* / Yankee doodle came to town: *Cotton, Billy & His Band*.
2LP: . . . . RECDL 1
MCSET: . . . . RECDC 1

LOVE SONGS 1929-1935 (CLassic Years in Digital Stereo) (Various artists).
LP: . . . . REB 651
MC: . . . . ZCF 651

MILLION SELLERS OF THE 30'S AND 40'S (Various artists).
Tracks: / Tiger rag: *Mills Brothers* / Bei mir bist du schon: *Andrews Sisters* / Tisket a tasket, A: *Fitzgerald*, Ella / Over the rainbow: *Garland, Judy* / At the woodchoppers' ball: *Herman, Woody & His Orchestra* / Green eyes: *Dorsey, Jimmy & His Orchestra* / Paper doll: *Mills Brothers* / Oklahoma: *Original stage cast* / Besame mucho: *Dorsey, Jimmy* / You'll never know: *Haymes, Dick & The Songspinners* / Rum and coca cola: *Andrews* Sisters / Swinging on a star: *Crosby, Bing* / Into each life some rain must fall: *Fitzgerald, Ella* / Begin the beguine: *Heywood, Eddie* / Don't fence me in: *Crosby, Bing* / Is you is or is you ain't my baby: *Jordan*, Louis / Little bird told me, A: *Knight, Evelyn & The Stardusters* / MacNamara's band: *Crosby, Bing & The Jesters*/ To each his own: *Ink Spots* / Maybe you'll be there: *Jenkins, Gordon & Charles La Vere* / Beware, brother, beware: *Jordan, Louis* / Easter parade: *Lombardo, Guy* / Little white lies: *Haymes, Dick & Gordon Jenkins* / You always hurt the one you love: *Mills Brothers* / I can dream, can't I: *Andrews, Patti* / Cruising down the river: *Morgan, Russ*.
MCSET: . . . . CRT 033

MUSIC TO REMEMBER (Various artists).
MCSET: . . . . DTO 10085

MUSIC YOU KNOW AND LOVE (Various artists).
MC: . . . . AM 34

NOSTALGIC MEMORIES (Various artists).
LP: . . . . NTS 208
MC: . . . . TCNTS 208

NOSTALGIC MEMORIES VOL.2 (Various artists).
MC: . . . . TCNTS 222
LP: . . . . NTS 222

NOSTALGIC TRIP TO THE STARS VOL.2 (Various artists).
LP: . . . . MES 7031

OPERA 1904-1935 (Classic Years in Digital Stereo) (Various artists).
LP: . . . . REB 653
MC: . . . . ZCF 653

PUTTIN' ON THE RITZ All-time favourites of stage and screen (Various artists).
Tracks: / Puttin' on the Ritz: *Astaire, Fred* / Limehouse blues: *Lawrence, Gertrude* / Makin' whoopee: *Cantor*, Eddie / Lovely to look at: *Dunn, Irene* / Looking at you: *Jolson, Al* / According to the moonlight: *Faye*, Alice / My future is just passed: *Rogers, Charles 'Buddy'* / Lullaby of Broadway: *Shaw, Winifred* / It happened in Monterey: *Boles, John* / Got a bran' new suit: *Powell, Eleanor* / Let yourself go: *Rogers, Ginger*/ I guess I'll have to change my plan: *Vallee, Rudy* / Got to dance my way to heaven: *Matthews, Jessie* / Inka dinka doo: *Durante, Jimmy* / Stompin' at the Savoy: *Garland, Judy* / Love in bloom: *Coward, Noel* / Easy to love: *Langford, Frances* / Sailor, beware: *Crosby, Bing* / Someone to care for me: *Durbin, Deanna*/ With plenty of money and you: *Powell, Dick*.
LP: . . . . SVL 188
MC: . . . . CSVL 188

ROSIE THE RIVETER (Various).
Tracks: / Ferdinand the frantic freak / I've got sixpence / D Day / Rosie the riveter / Der Fuehrer's face / GI jive / Spying is trying / I'm getting corn for my country / Buy stamps and bonds / Here comes the British / You're a sap Mr Jap.
MC: . . . . K 1002

SAUCY SONGS (Classic Years in Digital Stereo) (Various artists).
Tracks: / I like a guy what ...: *West, Mae* / Oh you have no idea: *Tucker, Sophie* / Is there anything wrong: *Kane, Helen* / When I'm cleaning windows: *Formby, George* / I found a new way: *West, Mae* / Say, young lady: *Gardener, Dick* / Bessie couldn't help it: *Randall, Slatz* / O'l man mose: *Norman, Patricia* / It isn't love: *Frankau, Ronald* / You can't blame me: *Miller, Max* / Come up and see: *Edwards, Cliff* / You brought a new: *Waters, Ethel* / I like to do things: *Lang, Jeannie* / Easy rider: *West, Mae* / Pu-leeze Mr. Hemingway: *Suter, Anne* / I'm wild about that thing: *Smith, Bessie* / Life begins at forty: *Tucker, Sophie*/ They call me sister: *West, Mae*.
LP: . . . . REB 728
MC: . . . . ZCF 728

SAY IT WITH MUSIC 100th Birthday tribute to Irving Berlin (Various artists).
Tracks: / Say it with music: *Payne, Jack & The BBC Dance Orchestra* / Alexander's ragtime band: *Casa Loma Orchestra*/ Puttin' on the ritz: *Reisman, Joe & His Orchestra* / How deep is the ocean?: *Blue Lyres* / Easter parade: *Reisman*, Leo Orch. / Maybe it's because I love you too much: *Reisman, Leo Orch.* / Heat wave: *Payne, Jack & His Band/Billy* Scott Coomber / Cheek to cheek: *Stone, Lew & His Band* / Piccolino, The: *Roy, Harry & His Orchestra* / Blue skies: *Goodman, Benny & His Orchestra* / No strings: *Dorsey Brothers Orchestra* / Top hat, white tie and tails: *Dorsey Brothers Orchestra* / I'd rather lead a band: *Himber, Richard & His Orchestra* / Let yourself go: *Noble*, Ray & His Orchestra / Pretty girl is like a melody, A: *Fox, Roy & His Orchestra* / Let's face the music and dance: *Noble, Ray & His Orchestra* / I'm putting all my eggs in one basket: *Casani Club Orchestra* / I've got my love to keep me warm: *Gibbons, Carroll & Savoy Hotel Orpheans*.
LP: . . . . OLD 14
MC: . . . . COLD 14

SECOND WORLD WAR (2) (June 1944 and Spring 1945) (Various artists).
MCSET: . . . . ZBBC 1081

SENTIMENTAL JOURNEY (Various artists).
Tracks: / It's only a paper moon: *Cole, Nat King* / Nightingale can sing the blues, The: *Lee, Peggy* / Along the Navajo trail: *Crosby, Bing & P.Whiteman* / Things ain't what they used to be: *Ellington, Duke* / Stardust: *Shaw*, Artie / May you always: *Stewart, Sandy* / As the world turns: *Gibson, Ginny* / Cherokee canyon: *Miller*, Glenn & His Orchestra / I don't mind: *Boswell, Connie* / Who put the devil in Evelyn's eyes: *Mills Brothers*/ Far from the madding crowd: *Haymes, Dick* / Just another blues: *Cole, Nat King Trio* / Gold cadillac: *Waring*, Fred / And the angels sing: *Goodman, Benny & Orchestra* / In the mood: *Miller, Glenn & The Army Airforce Orchestra*/ Mad about him blues: *Shore, Dinah* / I'll never smile again: *Dorsey, Tommy Orchestra* / On the Atchison Topeka & the Sante Fe: *Herman, Woody* / My very good friend the milkman: *Waller, Fats* / That's how love comes: *Gibson*, Sonny / April fool: *Ellis,Peggy-Anne* / Don't cry cry baby: *Cole, Nat King* / You ain't got nothin': *Boswell*, Connie / (I'm getting) corns for my country: *Andrews Sisters* / It takes a long, long train: *Page, Patti*/ Casanova cricket: *Carmichael, Hoagy* / Finders keepers: *Mitchell, Guy* / I tipped my hat (and slowly rode away): *James, Harry Orchestra*.
MC: . . . . PWKMC 4045

SENTIMENTAL JOURNEY (Various artists).
2LP: . . . . DP 6.28523

SENTIMENTAL JOURNEY '89 (Love Songs From World War II) (Various artists).
2LP: . . . . REQ 751
MC: . . . . ZCQ 751

SILLY SONGS 1922-1935) (Classic years in digital stereo) (Various artists).
LP: . . . . REB 652
MC: . . . . ZCF 652

SONGS OF THE DEPRESSION (Various artists).
LP: . . . . ST 121

SONGS THAT SENT US OFF TO WAR (Various).
Tracks: / We did it before and we can do it again / Praise the Lord & pass the ammunition / Second to none / This is the army / We're shoving right off / There'll be a jubilee / Amphibians battle hymn, The / Scrap your fat / Spirit of the air forces / This is the army / Coming in on a wing and a prayer / Army air corps song.
MC: . . . . K 1001

SOUNDS NOSTALGIC (Various artists).
LP: . . . . MOR 25

STARS FOR VICTORY (Various).
Tracks: / Coming in on a wing and a prayer / He's my guy / Hip hip hooray / See what the boys in the back room will have / We're gonna make sure there's never another war / Bless 'em all / They're either too young or too old / As time goes by / Silver wings / Boogie woogie bugle boy / Thanks for the memory.
MC: . . . . K 1003

STARS OF THE ZIEGFIELD FOLLIES (Various artists).
LP: . . . . SH 2108

STARS OF VARIETY (Various artists).
Tracks: / Wanderer: *Flanagan & Allen* / Dreaming: *Flanagan & Allen* / Where the arches used to be: *Flanagan &* Allen / Heart and soul: *Mayerl, Billy/Dorothy Carless* (from 'A Song Is Born'.) / I don't do things like that: *Trinder*, Tommy (from 'You Lucky People'.) / Dinah: *Simpson, Jack* / Sweet Sue: *Simpson, Jack* / Bye bye blues: *Simpson*, Jack / Barmaid at the Rose And Crown: *Formby, George* (from 'South American George'.) / Gert and Daisy and the tandem: *Waters, Elsie & Doris (Gert & Daisy)* (with orchestral accompaniment.) / I'm the man who's deputising for the bull: *Howerd*, Frankie / Let it be soon: *O'Shea, Tessie* / Zither, The (melody): *Peers, Donald* (Song version of The Harry Lime Theme. BBC Variety Orchestra.) / Someone nice like you: *Kay, Kathie & Billy Cotton* (from 'Stop The World I Want To Get Off'.) / Dummy song, The: *Brough, Peter/Archie Andrews with Max Bygraves* / She was a good girl (as good girls go): *Bygraves, Max* / It's a sin to tell a lie: *Liddle, Gwen* (with the Accordean Buskers) / I used to sigh for the silvery moon: *Elliott, G.H.* / Teasin': *Beverley Sisters* / Too young: *Conway, Steve* (with Chorus and orchestgra conducted by Norrie Paramor.) / Underneath the old pine tree: *Rocky Mountaineers, featuring Big Bill Campbell*(Accompanied by The Bunk House Boys.) / Trail of the lonesome pine: *Rocky Mountaineers, featuring Big Bill Campbell* (Accompanied by The

Bunk House Boys.) / Mockin' Bird Hill: *Ronalde, Ronnie* / Riding down to Dixie: *Reader, Ralph* (from 'The Gang Show of 1937'. With The Jack Daws & Orchestra.) / Can't we meet again: *Flanagan & Allen* / Million tears: *Flanagan & Allen* / Underneath the arches: *Flanagan & Allen* / English as she is spoken: *Howerd, Frankie* (Accompanied by Billy Ternent and his Orchestra.) / Huntin': *Waters, Elsie & Doris (Gert & Daisy)* (with orchestral accompaniment.) / Biggest aspidistra in the world, The: *Fields, Gracie* / Cruising down the river: *Preager, Lou & His Orchestra* (First prize winner of the 'Write A Tune' contest.) / Relatives: *Costa, Sam* (with orchestra accompaniment.) / Just for old times sake: *Roy, Derek & Eve Boswell* / Three bears, The: *Ellington, Ray Quartet* / What a cute little hat: *Ray, Ted & Kitty Bluett* / Yes I'll be here: *Squires, Dorothy* / Some enchanted evening: *Calvert, Eddie* (from 'South Pacific') / Where did the night go: *Brereton, Gerry* (from 'Wish You Were Here'. With Frank Chacksfield and Orchestra.).
2LP: . . . . DL 1155
2LP: 411 155 1
MC: . . . . TCDL 1155
MC: 411 155 4

THERE'LL ALWAYS BE AN ENGLAND (24 war-time songs from 1939) (Various artists).
Tracks: / There'll always be an England: *Various artists* / Wishing: *Various artists* / We must all stick together: *Various artists* / Songs the Tommies sang (medley): *Various artists* (Fall in & follow me#Hello, who's your lady friend?#Mlle from Armentieres) / Adolf: *Various artists* / F.D.R. Jones: *Various artists* / We're gonna hang out the washing: *Various artists* / Handsome territorial, The: *Various artists* / Till the lights of London shine again: *Various artists* / They can't black out the moon: *Various artists* / Kiss me goodnight, Sergeant Major: *Various* artists / We'll meet again: *Various artists* / If a grey haired lady says "How's yer father": *Various artists* / Wish me luck: *Various artists* / Goodnight, children everywhere: *Various artists* / Wings over the navy: *Various* artists / Run, rabbit, run: *Various artists* / I'm sending a letter to Santa Claus: *Various artists* / Nasty Uncle Adolf: *Various artists* / Somewhere in France with you: *Various artists* / Mother's prayer at twilight, A: *Various artists* / Rhymes of the times: *Various artists.*
LP: . . . . AJA 5069
MC: . . . . ZC AJA 5069

THESE FOOLISH THINGS, 1936 (Various artists).
LP: . . . . NOST 7658

UNFORGETTABLE PERFORMANCES OF THE WORLD WAR YEAR (Various artists).
LP: . . . . KAYDEE 2

WE'LL MEET AGAIN (Various artists).
LP: . . . . NE 1188
MC: . . . . CE 2188

WHISPERING GRASS (Various artists).
2LP: . . . . RECDL 19

WORLD OF WORLD WAR 1 (Various artists).
LP: . . . . SPA 27

WORLD WAR II (Various artists).
2LP: . . . . REQ 571
MCSET: . . . . ZCQ 571

WORLD WAR YEARS, 1944 - 45 (Various artists).
Tracks: / Why don't you do right?: *Various artists* / Song of the islands: *Various artists* / Danny boy: *Various* artists / How high the moon: *Various artists* / Rose room: *Various artists* / La Rosita: *Various artists* / Lady be good: *Various artists* / Are you livin' old man?: *Various artists* / High tide: *Various artists* / Play me the blues: *Various artists* / Artie's blues: *Various artists* / Jeep rhythm: *Various artists* / Jubilee jump: *Various artists* / Andy's blues: *Various artists.*
LP: . . . . BS 7132

WORLD WARS 1914/1939 (see under History reflected) (Various artists).

YANKEE CLIPPER (Various).
Tracks: / Hittin' the silk / Keep the home fires burning / Jeep rhythm / Yankee clipper / Army air corps song / Guns in the sky / Burma bomber / There ain't no wings on a foxhole / Army air corps song / Jungle jump.
MC: . . . . K 1005

Not A Penny More

NOT A PENNY MORE, NOT A PENNY LESS (See under Archer, Jeffery (aut)) (Daneman, Paul (nar)).

Not Drowning Waving

CLAIM.
LP: 7599261811
MC: 7599261814

SING SING.
LP: . . . . MLRR 005

Not For Sale

NOT FOR SALE.
LP: . . . . SAVE 014

Not Fragile

WHO DARES WINS.
LP: . . . . OTH 13
MC: . . . . OTH 13C

Not Just Anybody...

NOT-JUST-ANYBODY FAMILY, THE (Betsy Byars) (Fairman, Blain (nar)).
MC: 3CCA 3043

Not Just Mandela

NOT JUST MANDELA (Various artists).
LP: . . . . DLLP 4

Not Quite

NOT QUITE, THE.
Tracks: / Let her go / Get lost girl / Wars or hands of time / I don't know how to tell you / Get away / Mushroom people / You're gonna need me / Just like us / Heaven sent / Fickle wind / Paint me in a corner.
LP: . . . . R 33/8605

OR THE BEGINNING.
LP: . . . . VOXX 20057

Not Quite Jerusalem

NOT QUITE JERUSALEM (Film soundtrack) (Rondo Veneziano).
LP: . . . . RON 4
MC: . . . . ZCRON 4

Nothing But Happiness

DETOUR.
Tracks: / For waitress friends / Striped songs / Battle hymn / Buried in the flowers / Facsimile / Don't laugh / Couldn't make you mine / My summer dress / Blue kiss / Narcotics day.
LP: . . . . REMLP 1

Nothing By Chance

GHOSTS OF LOVE.
Tracks: / Ghosts of love / Crazy eyes / Wild bird / Northern lullaby / Green parrot blues / Fools fool in love too / Killing time, The / All comes down / Maybe I'll forget you / Dark horses dancing / Will not shelter / Green grow the issues o' / Seasons.
MC: . . . . ZDD 27

Nothing In Common

NOTHING IN COMMON (Film Soundtrack) (Various artists).
Tracks: / Nothing in common: *Thompson Twins* / Burning of the heart: *Marx, Richard* / If it wasn't love: *Simon, Carly* / Over the weekend: *Heyward, Nick* / Loving strangers: *Cross, Christopher* / Until you say you love me: *Franklin, Aretha* / Don't forget to dance: *Kinks* / No one's gonna love you: *Real To Reel* / 7 summers: *Cruzados* / Instrumental theme: *Leonard, Pat.*
LP: 207010
MC: 407010

Nothing Like the Sun

EVE OF ST. VENUS/NOTHING LIKE THE SUN (see under Eve of St. Venus (bk).

Noto, Sam

SAM NOTO 2-4-5.
LP: . . . . DDA 1007

Notorious (film)

NOTORIOUS (See under Ketcham, Charles) (Ketcham, Charles).

Notting Hillbillies

MISSING...PRESUMED HAVING A GOOD TIME.
LP: 842 671 1
MC: 842 671 4

Notts Alliance

CHEERFUL 'ORN.
LP: . . . . TSR 011

Nouveau Nation

PARTY TIME LOVERS.
LP: . . . . LPNN 1
MC: . . . . ZCNN 1

Nova

VIMANA.
Tracks: / Night games / Poesia / Thru the silence / Driftwood / Princess and the frog / Vimana.
LP: . . . . ARTY 138

WINGS OF LOVE.
Tracks: / You are the light / Marshall Dillon / Blue lake / Beauty dream - beauty flame / Golden sky boat / Loveliness about you.
LP: . . . . SPARTY 1021

Nova, Aldo

ALDO NOVA.
Tracks: / Fantasy / Hot love / It's too late / Ball and chain / Heart to heart / Foolin' yourself / Under the gun / You're my love / Can't stop lovin' you / See the light.
LP: . . . . PRT 85287

BLOOD ON THE BRICKS.
Tracks: / Blood on the bricks / Medicine man / Bang bang / Someday / Young love / Modern world / This ain't love / Hey Ronnie (Veronica's song) / Touch of madness / Bright lights.
MC: 8485134
LP: 8485131

SUBJECT.
Tracks: / Subject's theme / Armageddon (Race cars) / Monkey on your back / Hey operator / Cry baby cry / Victim of a broken heart / Africa (primal love) / Hold back the night / Always be mine / All night long / Was suite / Prelude to paradise / Paradise.
MC: 40 25482
LP: . . . . PRT 25482

TWITCH.
Tracks: / Tonite (lift me up) / Rumours of you / Surrender / Your heart / If looks could kill / Heartless / Long hot summer / Fallen angel / Stay / Lay your love on me / Twitch.
LP: . . . . PRT 26440
MC: 40 26440

Nova Mob

LAST DAYS OF POMPEII, THE.
LP: . . . . R 261
MC: . . . . CR 261

Nova, Nancy

LIFELINE.
Tracks: / Lifeline / Lookin' to find a way out.
LP: . . . . AMLH 64575

Nova, Paul

TREES WITHOUT LEAVES.
LP: . . . . EXLP 003

Nova Vaga Album

NOVA VAGA ALBUM (Various artists).
LP: . . . . PFLP 201

Novak, Shirley

SEMI-AWARE.
LP: . . . . MYR R 1257
MC: . . . . MYR C 1257

Novalis

BANISHED BRIDGE.
LP: 0061 029

BRANDUNG.
LP: 0060 094

KONZERTE.
LP: 0060 065

NOVALIS.
LP: 0060 1070

SOMMERABEND.
LP: 001 087

VIELLEICHT BIST DU EIN CLOWN.
Tracks: / Der geigenspieler / Zingaresca / Manchmal fallt der regen eben lang / Vielleicht bist du ein clown / City Nord / Die welt wird alt und wieder jung.
LP: 0060 164

Novello, Ivor

DANCING YEARS, THE.
Tracks: / Waltz of my heart / Wings of sleep, The / My life belongs to you / I can give you the starlight / My dearest dear / Primrose / Leap year waltz, The / Three ballet tunes.
LP: . . . . SHB 23

IVOR NOVELLO - SHOWTIME.
Tracks: / Dancing years, The / Careless rapture / Glamorous night / King's rhapsody.
2LP: . . . . MFP 1028
MCSET: . . . . TCMFP 1028

Novelty...

LA-DE-DAH & OTHER NOVELTY HITS (Various artists).
Tracks: / Running bear: *Preston, Johnny* / Alley oop: *Hollywood Argyles* / La de dah: *Billie & Lillie* / Nee nee na na nunu: *Dicky Doo & Don'ts* / Muleskinner blues: *Fendermen* / Telephone man: *Various artists* / Mr. Custer: *Verne, Larry* / Mr. Bass man: *Cymbal, Johnny* / Sgt. Preston of the Yukon: *Stevens, Ray* / Junk food junkie: *Groce, Larry* / Papa oom mow mow: *Rivingtons* / Mr. Livingston: *Verne, Larry.*
LP: . . . . TOP 159
MC: . . . . KTOP 159

MINIATURES A sequence of 51 tiny masterpieces - various art (Various artists).
LP: . . . . PIPE 2
LP: . . . . CBLP 2

RHINO BROTHERS GREATEST FLOPS (Various artists).
Tracks: / 2001: *Temple City Kazoo Orchestra* / Walk on the Kosher side: *Jow, Gefilte & The Fish* / Me and my vibrator: *Seacell, Suzie* / I get around: *Bakersfield Boogie Boys* / Blacklisted (from your heart): *Red Square* / Papa oom mow mow: *Freehold, New Jersey* / I'm the creature from outer space: *Wild Man, JR* / Beverly Hills blues festival: *Various artists* (Featuring Perrier Waters, big Matron Thomberg, Betamax Horowitz, Alfred) / Pipeline: *Bombay Beach Boys* / Beatle rap: *Qworymen* / Wrestlers: *Shannon, Shell Shock* / Just wanna bust heads: *Shannon, Shell Shock* / Sunday, Sunday: *Shannon, Shell Shock* / International Elvis impersonators convention (medley): *Various artists* / Do ya think I'm sexy: *KGB Chicken.*
LP: . . . . RNLP 70827
MC: . . . . RNC 70827

THAT'S MY RABBIT, MY DOG CAUGHT IT (Various artists).
Tracks: / Ground hog: *Various artists* / Old grey horse: *Various artists* / My pretty little pink: *Various* artists / Granny went to the meeting with her old shoes on: *Various artists* / Spanish fandango: *Various artists* / Run banjo: *Various artists* (Justis Begley, bango (1.30)) / Pearly dew: *Various artists* / Blues: *Various* artists / Lights in the valley: *Various artists* / Lost boy blues: *Various artists* / Fe fe phochaux: *Various* artists / Kimball house: *Various artists* / Last of Sizemore: *Various artists* / Hunky dory: *Various* artists / Bigfooted nigger: *Various artists* / That's my rabbit, my dog caught it: *Various artists* / Rymer's favourite: *Various artists* / Le Rille Cajun: *Various artists* / Lost Indian: *Various artists* / Jig: *Various artists* / Bibb County hoe down: *Various artists* / Peakock rag: *Various artists.*
LP: . . . . NW 226

WORLD'S WORST RECORDS VOL. 2, THE (Various artists).
LP: . . . . RNLP 815

Novick, Billy

NEW PENNY WHISTLE ALBUM.
LP: . . . . SIF 1013
MC: . . . . CSIF 1013

Novo Combo

NOVO COMBO.
Tracks: / Up periscope / City bound / We need love / Long road / Tattoo / Don't do that / Sorry / Axis will turn / Light of the world / Do you wanna shake? / Hard to say goodbye.
LP: 2391 523

Now And Then

NOW AND THEN VOL. 1 (Various artists).
LP: . . . . KJLP 002

Now Generation

FOR THE GOOD TIMES.
LP: . . . . TRLS 78

Now Voyager

NOW VOYAGER (OST) (See under Gibb, Barry) (Gibb, Barry).

Nowhere On Earth

NOWHERE ON EARTH (see Elder, Michael) (Elder, Michael).

Nowhere To Hide

NOWHERE TO HIDE (Film soundtrack) (Various artists).
LP: . . . . STV 81336

Nowomowa

WASTED LANDS, THE.
LP: . . . . NAGE 20
MC: . . . . NAGEC 20

Noxious Fumes

NOXIOUS FUMES.
MC: . . . . KC 015

Noyes Brookings,

LYRICS BY ERNEST NOYES BROOKINGS (Various artists).
LP: . . . . SHIMMY 019

NRBQ

ALL HOPPED UP.
LP: . . . . ROUNDER 3029
MC: . . . . ROUNDER 3029C

GOD BLESS US ALL.
MC: . . . . ROUNDER 3108C
LP: . . . . ROUNDER 3108

GROOVES IN ORBIT.
Tracks: / Smackaroo / When things was cheap / Rain at the drive-in / How can I make you love me / Girl like that, A / 12 bar blues / I like that girl / My girlfriend's pretty / Get rhythm / Daddy o / Hit the hay.
LP: . . . . SEE 219

KICK ME HARD.

LP: . . . . ROUNDER 3030
MC: . . . . ROUNDER 3030C

LOU & THE Q (NRBQ/Captain Lou Albano).
LP: . . . . ROUNDER 3098
MC: . . . . ROUNDER 3098C

RC COLA AND A MOON PIE.
LP: . . . . ROUNDER 3090
MC: . . . . ROUNDER 3090C

SCRAPS.
LP: . . . . ROUNDER 3055

TAP DANCIN' BATS.
Tracks: / Captain Lou / I don't think of / You got it / Rats in my room / Bog goodbyes / Tex / Trouble at the henhouse / Ain't it alright / Pretty thing / Dry up and blow away / Dough got low, The / Tapdancin' bats.
LP: . . . . FIEND 51
MC: . . . . FIENDCASS 51
LP: . . . . ROUNDER 3066
MC: . . . . ROUNDER 3066C

THROUGH THE EYES OF A QUARTET.
Tracks: / 12 bar blues / I want you bad / Ridin' in my car / Want you to feel good / You can't hide / Smackaroo (instrumental) / Green lights / Me and the boys / Don't she look good / Never take the place of you / Captain Lou / Get rhythm / This old house.
LP: . . . . FIEND 57

TIDDLYWINKS.
LP: . . . . ROUNDER 3048
MC: . . . . ROUNDER 3048C

Nu, Pete

DON'T ASSUME (See also under Maggie Nicols).

NICOLS 'N' NU (Nu, Pete/ Maggie Nicols).
LP: . . . . LR 127

Nu Shooz

POOLSIDE.
Tracks: / Lost your number / I can't wait / Don't let me be the one / Going through the motions / You put me in a trance / Point of no return / Secret message / Don't you be afraid.
LP: . . . . WX 60
MC: . . . . WX 60 C

TOLD U SO.
Tracks: / Told U so / Should I say yes / Are you lookin' for somebody nu / Wonder / Driftin' / If that's the way you want it / Montecarlo nite / Savin' all my time / Doin' alright / Truth, The (Extra track on cassette only).
LP: . . . . K 781804 1
MC: . . . . K 781804 4

Nu Skavi..

NU SKAVI U A STEJLE (Various artists).
LP: . . . . HJF 3

Nuclear Assault

GAME OVER.
Tracks: / LSD / Cold steel / Betrayal / Radiation sickness / Hang the Pope / After the holocaust / Mr. Softee theme / Stranded in Hell / Nuclear war / My America / Vengeance / Brain death.
LP: . . . . FLAG 5
MC: . . . . TFLAG 5

HANDLE WITH CARE.
LP: . . . . FLAG 35
MC: . . . . TFLAG 35

OUT OF ORDER.
LP: . . . . FLAG 64
MC: . . . . TFLAG 64

PLAGUE, THE.
Tracks: / Game over / Nightmares / Buttf**k / Justice / Plague, The / Cross of iron.
LP: . . . . MFLAG 13
MC: . . . . TMFLAG 13

SURVIVE.
Tracks: / Brainwashed / Great depression / Equal rights / Good times bad times / Survive / Wired / Technology.
LP: . . . . FLAG 21
LPPD: . . . . FLAG 21P
MC: . . . . TFLAG 21

Nuclear Valdez

I AM I.
Tracks: / Summer / Hope / Trace the thunder / If I knew then / Unsung hero / Strength / Eve / Apache / Run through the fields / Where do we go from here / Rising sun.
LP: 4659801
MC: 4659804

Nucleus

NUCLEUS ELASTIC ROCK.
Tracks: / 1916 / Striation / Twisted track / Battle of the boogaloo / Personally, in my own opinion / Elastic rock / Taranaki / Creole blues / Speaking for myself / Persephones jive.
LP: . . . . BGOLP 47
LP: 6360 006

WE'LL TALK ABOUT IT LATER.
LP: 6360 027

Nude

MODERN JAZZ.
LP: . . . . MLCR 100

Nugent, Ted

ANTHOLOGY - TED NUGENT.
Tracks: / Flesh and blood / Weekend warriors / Workin' hard, playin' hard / Snakeskin cowboys / Motor city madness / Scream dream / Come and get it / Smoke screen / Stormtroopin' / Stranglehold / Cat scratch fever / Dog eat dog / Turn it up / Hard as nails / Death by misadventure / State of shock / Where have you been all my life / I love you so I told you a lie / Out of control / Live it up.
2LP: . . . . RAWLP 026
MCSET: . . . . RAWTC 026
MC: . . . . CCSMC 282

CALL OF THE WILD.
Tracks: / Call of the wild / Sweet revenge / Pony express / Ain't it the truth / Renegade / Rot gut / Below the belt / Cannon balls.
LP: . . . . ED 278

CALL OF THE WILD/ TOOTH FANG (Nugent, Ted & Amboy Dukes).
Tracks: / Call of the wild / Sweet revenge / Pony express / Ain't it the truth / Renegade / Rot gut / Below the belt / Cannon balls / Lady luck / Living in the woods / Hibernation / Free flight / Maybellene / Great white buffalo, The / Sacha / No holds barred.
2LP: . . . . K 69202

CAT SCRATCH FEVER.
Tracks: / Cat scratch fever / Wang dang sweet poontang / Death by misadventure / Live it up / Home bound / Workin' hard, playin hard / Sweet Sally / Thousand knives / Fist fightin' son of a gun / Out of control.
LP: . . . . EPC 82010
MC: 40 82010

DOUBLE LIVE GONZO.
2LP: . . . . EPC 88282

FREE FOR ALL.
Tracks: / Free for all / Dog eat dog / Writing on the wall / Turn it up / Together / Street rats / Hammer down / Light my way / I love you so I told you a lie.
LP: . . . . EPC 32065
MC: 40 32065
LP: . . . . EPC 81397

GREAT GONZOS, THE BEST OF TED NUGENT.
Tracks: / Cat scratch fever / Just what the doctor ordered / Free for all / Dog eat dog / Motor city madness / Paralysed / Stranglehold / Baby please don't go / Wango tango / Wang dang sweet poontang.
LP: . . . . EPC 85408

IF YOU CAN'T LICK 'EM, LICK 'EM.
Tracks: / Can't live with 'em / She drives me crazy / If you can't lick 'em lick 'em / Skin tight / Funlover / Spread your wings / Harder they come (the harder I get) / Separate the men from the boys, please / Bite the hand / That's the story of love.
LP: . . . . K 255385 1
MC: . . . . K 255385 4

INTENSITIES-(IN 10 CITIES).
Tracks: / Put up or shut up / Spontaneous combustion / My love is like a tyre iron / Jailbait / I am a predator / Heads will roll / Flying lip lock / Land of a thousand dances / TNT overture / I take no prisoners.
LP: . . . . EPC 84917
MC: 40 84917

JOURNEYS AND MIGRATIONS.
2LP: . . . . MRD 5008

LITTLE MISS DANGEROUS.
Tracks: / High heels in motion / Strangers / Little Miss Dangerous / Savage dancer / Crazy ladies / When your body talks / My little red book / take me away / Angry young man / Painkiller.
LP: 252388 1
MC: 255388 4

MARRIAGE AND ON THE ROCKS (Nugent, Ted & Amboy Dukes).
2LP: 2664 344

ON THE EDGE.
MC: . . . . THBC 120

PENETRATOR.
Tracks: / Tied up in love / Draw the line / Knocking at your door / Don't you want my love / Go down fighting / Thunderthighs / No man's land / Blame it on the night / Lean mean r'n'r machine / Take me home.
LP: 780 125-1

SCREAM DREAM.
Tracks: / Wango tango / Scream dream / Hard as nails / I gotta move / Violent love / Flesh and blood / Spit it out / Come and get it / Terminus Eldora / Don't cry.
LP: . . . . EPC 86111

STATE OF SHOCK.
Tracks: / Paralysed / Take it or leave it / Alone / It doesn't matter / State of shock / I want to tell you / Satisfied / Bite down hard / Snake charmer / Saddle sore / Put up or shut up / Spontaneous combustion / My love is like a tire iron / Jailbait / I am a predator / Heads will roll / Lip rock, The / Land of a thousand dances / T.N.T overture / Take no prisoners.
LP: . . . . EPC 86092
MC: 40 86092

TED NUGENT.
Tracks: / No, no, no / Bound and gagged / Habitual offender / Fightin' words / Good and ready / Ebony / Don't push me / Can't stop me now / We're gonna rock tonight / Tail gunner.
LP: . . . . K 50898
LP: 32028

TOOTH FANG AND CLAW.
Tracks: / Lady luck / Living in the woods / Hibernation / Free flight / Maybelline / Great white buffalo, The / Sasha / No holds barred.
LP: . . . . ED 295

WEEKEND WARRIORS.
LP: . . . . EPC 83036

Null, Lisa

LISA NULL.
LP: . . . . SIF 1006

Numan, Gary

1978/79 (Numan,Gary & Tubeway Army).
Tracks: / That's too bad / Oh I didn't say / Monday troop / Bombers / O.D. receiver / Blue eyes / Crime of passion / Fadeout 1930 / Life machine, The / Random / Crazies, The / Only a downstat / We have a technical / Do you need the service / Game called echo, A / Oceans.
MC: . . . . BEGC 7879

1978/79 VOL.3.
Tracks: / Monday troop / Crime of passion / Life machine / Game called echo, A / Random / Oceans.
MLP: . . . . BEG 124E

BERSERKER.
LP: . . . . NUMA 1001
MC: . . . . NUMAC 1001

COLLECTION: GARY NUMAN.
Tracks: / Cars / Tracks / Down in the park / This wreckage / Random (end s1) / My shadow in vain / She's got claws / Music for chameleons / Remind me to smile / Stories (end s2) / Game called echo, A / Complex / On Broadway (live) / Aircrash bureau, The (end s3) / M.E. / Are 'friends' electric? / Photograph / We are glass.
2LP: . . . . CCSLP 229
MC: . . . . CCSMC 229

DANCE.
Tracks: / Slow car to China / Night talk / Subway called 'You' / Cry, the clock said / She's got claws / Crash / Boys like me / Stories / My brother's time / You are you are / Moral.
LP: . . . . BEGA 28
MC: . . . . BEGC 28
LP: . . . . BBL 28
MC: . . . . BBLC 28

EXHIBITION.
Tracks: / Me, I disconnect from you / That's too bad / My love is a liquid / Music for chameleons / We are glass / Bombers / Sister surprise / Are 'friends' electric / I dream of wires / Complex / Noise noise / Warriors / Everyday I die / Cars / We take mystery to bed / I'm an agent / My centurion / Metal / You are in my vision / I die you die / She's got claws / This wreckage / My shadow in vain / Down in the dark / Iceman comes, The.
LP: . . . . BEGA 88
MC: . . . . BEGC 88

FURY, THE.
Tracks: / Call out the dogs / This disease / Your fascination / Miracles / Pleasure skin / Creatures / Tricks / God only knows / I still remember.
LP: . . . . NUMA 1003
MC: . . . . NUMAC 1003
LPPD: . . . . NUMAX 1003

I ASSASSIN.
Tracks: / White boys and heroes / Dream of Siam, A / This is my house / 1930's rust, The / War song / Music for chameleons / I, assassin / We take mystery to bed.
LP: . . . . BEGA 40
LP: . . . . BBL 40
MC: . . . . BBLC 40

LIVING ORNAMENTS 1979.
Tracks: / Airlane / Cars / We are so fragile / Films / Something's in the house / My shadow in vain / Conversation / Dream police / Metal.
LP: . . . . BEGA 24

LIVING ORNAMENTS 1980.
Tracks: / This wreckage / I die, you die / M.E. / Every day I die / Down in the park / Remind me to smile / Joy circuit / Tracks / Are friends electric? / We are glass.
LP: . . . . BEGA 25

LIVING ORNAMENTS 1979-1980.
LPS: . . . . BOX 1

METAL RHYTHM.
Tracks: / Voix / Respect / Don't call my name / New anger / America / Young heart / Cold metal rhythm / This is emotion / Hunger.
LP: . . . . ILP 35
MC: . . . . ILPC 35

MUSIC AND MEDIA INTERVIEW PICTURE DISC.
LPPD: . . . . GN 2024

NEW MAN NUMAN (THE BEST OF GARY NUMAN).
Tracks: / Are friends electric / Cars / We are glass / Complex / Me, I disconnect from you / Down in the park / I die you die / She's got claws / Love needs no disguise / This wreckage / Stormtrooper in drag / We take mystery to bed / Music for chameleons / White boys and heroes.
LP: . . . . TVA 7
MC: . . . . TVC 7

NUMA RECORDS YEAR 1 (Numan, Gary/Various).
LP: . . . . NUMA 1004
MC: . . . . NUMAC 1004

OUTLAND.
MC: . . . . EIRSCA 1039
LP: . . . . EIRSA 1039

PLAN, THE (Numan,Gary & Tubeway Army).
Tracks: / Basic J / Ice / Something's in the house / Friends / Check it / Steel and you / This is my life / Critics / My shadow in vain / Main street / Bombers / Thoughts no.2.
LP: . . . . BBL 55
MC: . . . . BBLC 55
LPPD: . . . . BEGA 55 P
LP: . . . . BEGA 55

PLEASURE PRINCIPAL/WARRIORS.
Tracks: / Airplane / Metal complex / Films / M.E. / Tracks / Observer / Conversation / Cars / Engineers.
LP: . . . . BEGA 10

PLEASURE PRINCIPLE.
MC: . . . . BEGC 10
LP: . . . . BBL 10
MC: . . . . BBLC 10

RADIO HEART (Numan, Gary with Radio Heart).
Tracks: / Radio Heart / Blue nights / Starlight jingles / Strange thing / All across the nation / I'm alone / Mad about the girl / London times / Victim, The.
LPPD: . . . . NBRP 1
LP: . . . . NBRL 1
MC: NBRK1

SKIN MECHANIC, THE (Live).
Tracks: / Survival / Respect / Call out the dogs / Cars / Hunger / Down in the park / New anger / Creatures / Are friends electric / Young heart / We are glass / I die, you die / I can't stop.
LP: . . . . EIRSA 1019

STORMTROOPER IN DRAG (see Gardiner, Paul) (Numan, Gary with Paul Gardiner).

STRANGE CHARM.
LP: . . . . NUMA 1005
MC: . . . . NUMAC 1005

TELEKON.
Tracks: / This wreckage / Aircrash bureau, The / Telekon / Remind me to smile / Sleep by windows / I'm an agent / I dream of wires / Remember I was vapour / Please push no more / Joy circuit, The.
LP: . . . . BEGA 19
MC: . . . . BEGC 19
LP: . . . . BBL 19
MC: . . . . BBLC 19

WARRIORS.
Tracks: / Warriors / Iceman comes, The / My centurion / Tick tock man / Rhythm of the evening / I am render / This prison moon / Sister surprise / Love is like clock law.
LP: . . . . BBL 47
MC: . . . . BBLC 47
LP: . . . . BEGA 47

WHITE NOISE.
2LP: . . . . NUMAD 1002
MC: . . . . NUMAC 1002

Numarx

OUR TIME.
LP: . . . . **LPBR 7**

Numb

NUMB.
Tracks: / God is dead / Lies / Eat me / Guilt / Hanging key, The / Two faces / Morality of altitude, the / the Blue light, black candle.
LP: . . . . **ARTY 3**

Number 13...

NUMBER 13 AND OTHER GHOST STORIES (see under James, M.R.) (James, M.R. (author)).

Number Ones

NUMBER ONES OF THE SIXTIES (Various artists).
MC: . . . . **STAC 2432**
LP: . . . . **STAR 2432**

Numbers

NUMBERS, THE.
Tracks: / Five letter word / I don't know / Mr. President / Hello / When I get older / Jericho / Modern song, The / Party / Talk to me / OK / Teenage wonderland / Wind.
LP: . . . . **RCALP 3064**

Numbers (Pickwick)

NUMBERS (Various artists).
MC: . . . . **PLB 259**

Numbskull

RITUALLY ABUSED.
LP: . . . . **GWLP 42**

Nunez, Gerardo

FLAMENCOS IN NEW YORK.
Tracks: / Flamencos en Nueva York / Mi Patio / Peunte de los Alunados / Capinetti / A Gil Evans / Canaveral / El ricon del Pali / La Cartuja / Suite de la Golondrina / Queda la Sal.
LP: . . . . **VBRLP 28**
MC: . . . . **VBRMC 28**

Nunn, Bobby

PRIVATE PARTY.
Tracks: / Private party / Do you look that good in the morning / Sex maniac / Ladykiller / Don't knock it / Hangin' out at the mall / Because of you / Too young.
LP: . . . . **STML 12199**
MC: . . . . **CSTML 12199**

Nunn, Gary P

BORDER STATES.
Tracks: / What I like about Texas / I taught her everything she knows / Too many nights in a roadhouse / Money's no good, The / Lesson to be learned from love / Think I'll go to Mexico / Town and county taverns / Old fashion love / Alamogordo / Old home place, The.
LP: . . . . **DFG 8414**

Nunnery, Stu

STU NUNNERY.
LP: . . . . **CREST 6**

Nuns On The Run

NUNS ON THE RUN (Original soundtrack) (Various artists).
Tracks: / Race, The: *Yello* / Comin' to you: *Hidden Faces* / Roll with it: *Winwood, Steve* / Moon on ice: *Yello* / Sacred heart: *Shakespear's Sister* / On the run: *Yello* / Hawaiian chance: *Yello*/ Blow away: *Harrison, George* / Tied up: *Yello* / Dr Van Steiner: *Yello* / Gold rush: *Yello*/ Nun's medley: *Hidden Faces.*
LP: **8460431**
MC: **8460434**

Nunsense

NUNSENSE (Original 1987 London cast) (Various artists).
Tracks: / Nunsense is habit forming: *Various artists* / Difficult transition, A: *Various artists* / Benedicte: *Various artists* / Biggest ain't the best, The: *Various artists* / Playing second fiddle: *Various artists*/ So you want to be a nun: *Various artists* / Turn up the spotlight: *Various artists* / Lilacs bring back memories: *Various artists* / Tackle that temptation with a time step: *Various artists* / Growing up Catholic: *Various artists* / We've got to clean out the freezer: *Various artists* / Just a coupl'a sisters: *Various artists*/ Soup's on: *Various artists* / I just want to be a star: *Various artists* / Drive in, The: *Various artists*/ I could've gone to Nashville: *Various artists* / Gloria in excelsis: *Various artists* / Holier than thou: *Various artists* / Finale: *Various artists.*
LP: . . . . **TER 1132**
MC: . . . . **ZCTER 1132**

NUNSENSE (Original Broadway Cast) (Various artists).
Tracks: / Nunsense is habit forming: *Cast* / Difficult transition, A: *Cast* / Benedicte/Biggest ain't best: *Hubert* and Leo / Playing second fiddle: *Anne, Robert* / So you want to be a Nun: *Amnesia, Mary* / Turn up the spotlight: *Cardelia, Mary* / Lilacs bring back memories: *Cast* / Tackle that temptation with a time-step: *Hubert & Cast*/ Growing up Catholic: *Anne, Robert and Cast* / Drive-in: *Saint Andrew's Sister* / I could've gone to Nashville: *Amnesia, Mary* / Holier than thou: *Hubert & Cast* / Finale: *Cast.*
LP: . . . . **SBL 12589**
MC: . . . . **SBLC 12589**

Nureyev, Rudolf

PERFECT PARTNERSHIP, THE (See under Fonteyn, Margot) (Nureyev, Rudolf & Margot Fonteyn).

Nurnberger

MUSIC FOR ACCORDION ORCHESTRA NO.7 (Nurnberger Accordion Orchestra).
LP: . . . . **HS 069**

MUSIC FOR ACCORDION ORCHESTRA NO.1 (Nurnberger Accordion Orchestra).
LP: . . . . **HS 054**

Nurse With Wound

AUTOMATING Volume 1.
LP: . . . . **UD 019**

AUTOMATING VOL.II.
LP: . . . . **UD 030**

GYLLENSKOLD.
Tracks: / Odd / Dirty fingernails / Brained by falling masonry / Aquarium / Glory hole.
LP: . . . . **LAY 030**

HOMOTOPY FOR MARIE.
LP: . . . . **UD 012**

MISSING SENSE Rasa (Nurse With Wound/Organum).
LP: . . . . **UD 020**

OSTRANENIE 1913.
LP: . . . . **TMR 03**

SPIRAL INSANA.
LP: . . . . **TORSO 33016**

SUCKED ORANGE, A.
Tracks: / Paradise lost / Internal torment II / Autopsy / Stillborn / Deviated instinct / Resurrection encore, The / Doom / Means to an end, A / Confessor / Uncontrolled / Talion / Laws of retaliation / Electro hippies / Freddy's revenge (live) / Toranaga / Dealers in death.
LP: . . . . **UDO 32**

SYLVIE AND BABS HIGH-THIGH COMPANION.
LP: . . . . **LAY 015**

Nursery Rhymes

100 NURSERY RHYMES.
MC: . . . . **PLB 240**

HUMPTY DUMPTY (up to age 5).
MC: . . . . **PLB 150**

JACK AND JILL (up to age 5).
MC: . . . . **PLB 151**

NURSERY RHYMES VOL.1.
MCSET: . . . . **DTO 10503**

NURSERY RHYMES VOL.2.
MCSET: . . . . **DTO 10516**

OLD KING COLE (up to age 5).
MC: . . . . **PLB 152**

PICTURE READING RHYMES.
MC: . . . . **PLB 285**

WALLY WHYTON'S GOLDEN HOUR OF NURSERY RHYMES (Whyton, Wally).
LP: . . . . **GH 560**

WEE WILLIE WINKIE & OTHER NURSERY RHYMES (Unknown narrator(s)).
MC: . . . . **STK 021**

Nutcracker

NUTCRACKER, THE (See under Tschaikowsky) (Tschaikowsky).

Nutcracker Suite

NIGHT BEFORE CHRISTMAS, THE.
LP: . . . . **HDY 1924**
MC: . . . . **ZCHDY 1924**

Nutmeg

ELECTRIC PUTTY.
LP: . . . . **NUT 4**
MC: . . . . **NTUT 4**

Nutmegs

NUTMEGS GREATEST HITS, THE.
LP: . . . . **HERALD 5011**

NUTMEGS, THE (Feat. Leroy Griffin).
LP: . . . . **RELIC 5002**

Nuts

NUTS (FILM) (See under Streisand, Barbra) (Streisand, Barbra).

Nutshell

BEGIN AGAIN.
Tracks: / Love with no limit / Don't let me fall / Caroline / In the father's hand / Starry eyed and laughing / First snow / Take me down / Stay close / Dancer / Heaven in your heart.
LP: . . . . **MYR 1067**
MC: . . . . **MC 1067**

BELIEVE IT OR NOT.
Tracks: / Better take another look / Empty page / Looking for love / Going nowhere / Redeemed / First stone, The / Night flight / Without love / Hard to say goodnight / Thief in the night.
MC: . . . . **MC 1084**
LP: . . . . **MYR 1084**

BEST OF NUTSHELL.
Tracks: / Walking into the wind / Flyaway / Most unusual love / Sara / Redeemed / Bedsitter / Sometimes / Better take another look / Don't let me fall / Thief in the night / Empty page / Looking for love / Love with no limit / Heaven in your heart / Stay close.
LP: . . . . **MYR 1099**
MC: . . . . **MC 1099**

FLYAWAY.
Tracks: / Moonlight / Walking into the wind / Sara / Conversation piece / Flyaway / Feel like a river / Safe and sound / For each other / Bedsitter / Sometimes.
MC: . . . . **MC 1056**
LP: . . . . **MYR 1056**

IN YOUR EYES.
Tracks: / Snowball / Heaven only knows / Most unusual love / In your eyes / Jesus is forever / Stoney ground / Tell me that the sun / Butterfly / Today / Living joy / Black notes white / Redeemed.
LP: . . . . **MYR 1029**
MC: . . . . **MC 1029**

Nutter, Mayf

GOIN' SKINNY DIPPIN'.
LP: . . . . **GNPS 2104**

Nutty Boys

CRUNCH.
LP: . . . . **STR LP 001**
MC: . . . . **STR MC 001**

N.W.A

100 MILES AND RUNNING.
LP: . . . . **EVL 7224**
MC: **E4V 7224**

EFIL4ZAGGIN.
LP: . . . . **BRLP 562**
MC: . . . . **BRCA 562**

STRAIGHT OUTTA COMPTON.
Tracks: / Straight outta Compton / Fu** the police / Gangsta gangsta / If it ain't rough it ain't me / Parental discretion is advised / Express yourself / I ain't the one / Dopeman / Compton's in the house / 8 ball (remix).
MC: **4XL 57102**
MC: . . . . **BRCA 534**
LP: . . . . **BRLP 534**
LP: . . . . **SL 57102**

N.Y. Citizens

POUNDING THE PAVEMENT.
LP: . . . . **SKAR 004**

Nya, Sis

JAH MUSIC.
LP: . . . . **SHAKA 866 LP**

Nyah Fearties

TASTY HEIDFU, A.
Tracks: / Red roller / Glen Ashdale falls / Theme fae the barn / Lugton calling / Rantin' Robbie / When the wind blows cold / Bludgeon man / Apathy / Hallelujah!.
LP: . . . . **DOL LP 001**

Nyam Nyam

HOPE OF HEAVEN (BENEATH RELIGIONS WINGS).
LP: . . . . **SITU 10**

Nyboma

DOUBLE DOUBLE.
LP: . . . . **ROUNDER 5010**
MC: . . . . **ROUNDER 5010C**
LP: . . . . **CEL 6624**

EMPIRE BAKUBA (Nyboma & P Kalle).
LP: . . . . **CEL 8724**

Nyhus, Sven

SVEN NYHUS.
LP: . . . . **SHAN 21003**

Nyland, Tony

UH OH.
Tracks: / I'm giving it up / High rise / Living for the day / 18 to 30 holiday / Back ginnel rag / Busking blues / Someday your prince will come / Fletcher / Kid from New Hall Lane, The / Late freight train, The.
LP: . . . . **HUMAN LP 3**

Nylon, Judy

PAL JUDY.
LP: . . . . **ONULP 16**

Nylons

HAPPY TOGETHER.
Tracks: / Happy together / Dance of love / Crazy in love (morning comes early) / Touch of your hand, The / Kiss him goodbye / It's what they call magic / This island earth / Grown men cry / Chain gang / Face in the crowd.
LP: **370 306 1**
MC: **370 306 4**
LP: . . . . **RR 9623**
MC: . . . . **R 49623**

NYLONS, THE.
LP: . . . . **LAT 1125**
MC: . . . . **CAT 1125**
LP: . . . . **RR 9843**
MC: . . . . **RR 49843**

ONE SIZE FITS ALL.
LP: . . . . **RR 9926**
MC: . . . . **RR 49926**

ROCKAPELLA.
LP: . . . . **RR 9473 1**
MC: . . . . **RR 9473 4**

SEAMLESS.
LP: **370 304-1**
MC: **370 304-4**
LP: . . . . **RR 9856**
MC: . . . . **RR 49856**

Nyman, Michael

AND DO THEY DO# ZOO CAPRICES.
LP: . . . . **TER 1123**
MC: . . . . **ZCTER 1123**

DECAY MUSIC.
Tracks: / One hundred / Bell set No.1.
LP: . . . . **EGED 26**
LP: . . . . **OBS 6**

DROWNING BY NUMBERS (Film Soundtrack).
Tracks: / Trysting fields / Sheep and tides / Great death game / Drowning by number 3 / Wheelbarrow walk / Dead man's catch / Drowning by number 2 / Bees in trees / Fish beach / Wedding tango / Crematorium conspiracy / Knowing the ropes / End game.
LP: . . . . **VE 23**
MC: . . . . **TCVE 23**

KISS AND OTHER MOVEMENTS, THE.
Tracks: / Kiss, The / Nose list song / Tano between the lines / Images were introduced / Water dances (making a splash)-1. Stroking / Water dances (making a splash)-2. Gliding / Water dances (making a splash)-3. Synchronising.
MC: . . . . **EGEDC 40**
LP: . . . . **EGED 40**

MICHAEL NYMAN.
LP: . . . . **SHEET 1**

MICHEAL NYMAN: BOX SET.
Tracks: / Draughtsman's contract, The / Queen of the night / Disposition of the linen / Watery death, A / Garden is becoming a robe room, The / Chasing sheep is best left to shepherds / Eye for optical theory, An / Bravura in the face of grief / Zed and two noughts, A / Angelfish decay / Carcrash / Time lapse / Prawn watching / Bisocosis populi / Swan rot / Delft waltz / Up for crabs / Vermeer's wife / Venus de milo / Lady in the red hat / L'escargot / Drowning by numbers / Trysting fields / Sheep and tides / Great death game / Drowing by number / Wheelbarrow walk / Dead man's catch / Bees in trees / Fish beach / Wedding tango / Crematorium conspiracy / Knowing the ropes / End game / Cook, the thief, his wife and her lover, The / Memorial / Miserere paraphrase / Coupling / Book depository.
2LP: . . . . **VEBN 55**
MCSET: . . . . **TCEBN 55**

Nyro, Laura

CLASSICS.
Tracks: / Wedding bell blues / Stoned soul picnic / And when I die / Save the country / New York tendaberry / You've really got a hold on me / Gibson Street / It's gonna take a miracle / I never meant to hurt you / Jimmy Mack / Eli's comin' / Time and love / Nowhere to run / Lazy Susan / Blackpath / Monkey time : Dancing in the street / Flim flam man / Spanish Harlem / Stoney end.
MC: . . . . **ELITE 015MC**

GONNA TAKE A MIRACLE.
LP: . . . . **BGOLP 27**

IMPRESSIONS.
Tracks: / Wedding bell blues / Stoney end / And when I die / Stoned soul picnic / Sweet blindness / Eli's coming / Emmie / Confession, The / Save the country / Captain Saint Lucifer / Map to the treasure / Beads of sweat / Christmas in my soul.

LP: . . . . **CBS 31864**
MC: **40 31864**

LIVE AT THE BOTTOM LINE.
LP: . . . . **YL 0128**

Nytro

NYTRO.
Tracks: / Atomic funk / Draming / Foolin' around / What it is / Where's the party / Atmosphere / Give me one more chance / Trick bag.
LP: . . . . **K 56373**

RETURN TO NYTROPOLIS.
Tracks: / Nytro express / Return to Nytropolis / Could this be the night / High on disco / People in the country / Makie it / I've paid my dues / Orbit of the sun.
LP: . . . . **K 56614**

O

O Band

WITHIN REACH.
Tracks: / Smile is diamond / Feel alright / Lucia loser / Don't cha wanna / Money talk / Still burning / Paradise blue / Long long way / Within reach.
LP: . . . . **LBR 1980741**

O Kult

O KULT.
LP: . . . . **ST 7511**

O Lucky Man (film)

O LUCKY MAN (Film Soundtrack) (Price, Alan).
Tracks: / O Lucky man / Poor people / Sell sell / Pastoral / Arrival / Look over your shoulder / Justice / My home town / Changes.
LP: . . . . **K 46227**

Oak

WELCOME TO OUR FAIR.
LP: **12TS 212**

Oak Ridge Boys

20 COUNTRY GOSPEL CLASSICS.
LP: **20025**
MC: **40025**

AMERICAN DREAMS.
LP: . . . . **MCA 42311**

AMERICAN MADE.
LP: . . . . **IMCA 5350**

BOBBIE SUE.
LP: . . . . **MCF 3129**

DELIVER.
Tracks: / Ozark mountain jubilee / When you get to the heart / Alice is in Wonderland / Ain't no cure for rock and roll / In the pines / I guess it never hurts to hurt sometimes / Through my eyes / Break my mind / Still holding on / Down deep inside.
LP: . . . . **MCF 3210**
MC: . . . . **MCFC 3210**

FANCY FREE.
LP: . . . . **MCG 4017**

GLORY TRAIN.
Tracks: / Time has made a change in me / Farther along / Someday / Day of rejoicing / Lead me to Calvary / River of life / You'll never walk alone / One of these mornings / When I lay my burden down / At the roll call.
LP: . . . . **SDLP 1014**

GREATEST HITS: OAK RIDGE BOYS, VOL.1.
Tracks: / You're the one / I'll be true to you / Trying to love two women / Crying again / Dream on / Leaving Louisiana in the broad daylight / Heart of mine / Come on in / Sail away / Y'all come back saloon / Elvira / Ozark mountain jubilee / Love song / Fancy free / Everyday / Beautiful you / Thank God for kids / American made / Make my life with you / I guess it never hurts to hurt sometimes.
LP: . . . . **IMCA 5496**

KEEP WALKING.
LP: . . . . **MA 30685**
MC: . . . . **MAMC 930685**

SEASONS.
Tracks: / Seasons / What are you doing in my dream / Don't break the code / Juliet / You made a rock of a rolling stone / Take a step (yesterday waltz) / What you do to me / Everybody wins / Bedtime (on CD only) / Hiding place (on CD only).
LP: . . . . **MCF 3307**
MC: . . . . **MCFC 3307**

SENSATIONAL.
LP: . . . . **SLP 356**
MC: . . . . **GT 5356**

STEP ON OUT.
LP: . . . . **MCF 3271**
MC: . . . . **MCFC 3271**

TOGETHER.
LP: . . . . **MCF 3063**

WHERE THE FAST LANE ENDS.
Tracks: / Love has a mind of its own / Is there any way for us to say goodbye / Where the fast lane ends / It takes a little rain to make love grow / Looking for love / Little late to say goodbye, A / Rainbow at midnight / This crazy love / Little love can go a long, long way, A / Whatever it takes.
LP: . . . . **IMCA 5945**
MC: . . . . **IMCAC 5945**

Y'ALL COME BACK SALOON.
LP: . . . . **ABCL 5241**

YOU'LL NEVER WALK ALONE.
Tracks: / I know / Wonderful saviour / Without God / Old country church / I'll wake up on the other side / Dear Jesus, abide with me / Christian way, The / Hide thou me / I asked the lord / Farther along / Day of rejoicing / Lead me to Calvary / River of life / You'll never walk alone / One of these mornings / When I lay my burden down / At the roll call / Time has made a change in me.
LP: . . . . **SHLP 143**
MC: . . . . **SHTC 143**

Oakband Sound

OAKBAND SOUND.
Tracks: / Canadian 4-step / Reels / Irish waltz selection / Accordion duet / 2/4 Marches / Jigs / Pipe medley / Swedish polka / Fiddle solo / 6/8 pipe marches / Scottish waltz selection.
LP: . . . . **ITV 393**
MC: . . . . **KITV 393**

Oakenshield

ACROSS THE NARROW SEAS.
LP: . . . . **OAK 001**

AGAINST THE GRAIN.
LP: . . . . **OAK 002**

Oakey, Philip

CHROME (Oakey, Philip & Giorgio Moroder).
LP: . . . . **V 2351**
MC: . . . . **TCV 2351**

PHIL OAKEY/GIORGIO MORODER (Oakey, Philip & Giorgio Moroder).
Tracks: / Why must the show go on / In transit (instrumental) / Goodbye bad times / Brand new love (take a chance) / Valerie / Now / Together in electric dreams (From the sountrack of 'Electric Dreams') / Be my lover now / Shake it up.
LP: . . . . **OVED 187**
MC: . . . . **OVEDC 187**

Oakley, Glenroy

THERE'S NO ME WITHOUT YOU (see under McGregor, Freddie).

Oakley, Graham

CHURCH MOUSE & CHURCH CAT (Baker, Tom).
MC: . . . . **CDSC 2**

Oasis

OASIS.
Tracks: / Prelude / If this be the last time / I wonder why / Hold me / Oasis / Sirocco / Who knows? / Weavers of moonbeams / Loved and lost / True love.
LP: . . . . **WX 3**
MC: . . . . **WX 3C**

OASIS (Various artists).
Tracks: / Prelude: *Skellern, Peter* / If this be the last time: *Skellern, Peter* / I wonder why: *Skellern, Peter* / Hold me: *Skellern, Peter* / Oasis: *Skellern, Peter* / Sirocco: *Dalton, Mitch & Marita Phillip* / Who knows: *Skellern, Peter* / Weavers of moonbeams: *Skellern, Peter* / Loved and lost: *Skellern, Peter* / True love: *Porter, Cole.*
MC: . . . . **HSC 3290**

PROMISED LAND.
LP: . . . . **DOVE 52**

SMILE FOR THE SUN.
LP: . . . . **DOVE 45**

Ob Jay Da

AS IF TO SAY.
LP: . . . . **OJD A1**
MC: . . . . **OJD C1**

CIRCUS TIME FOR HEARTS.
MC: . . . . **OJDC 6**

TALES OF THE MYSTERY GIRL.
Tracks: / Mystery girl / For a second / Elysian / Floating on air / Children of stone / Always forever / Kiss of death / Summer / Moon Palace / Love affair (silly version).
LP: . . . . **OJD A3**

O'Banion, John

JOHN O'BANION.
Tracks: / Love you like I never loved before / You're in my life again / Love is blind / Our love can make it / Love is in your eyes / Come to my love / Take a chance on love / Walk away Renee / If you love me / She's not for you.
LP: . . . . **K 52284**
MC: **K4 52284**

Obey, Ebenezer

AIYE WA A TORO.
LP: . . . . **WAPS 48**

GET YOUR JUJUS OUT.
LP: . . . . **RACS 0111**

IN THE 60'S.
LP: . . . . **OC 432**

IN THE 60'S VOLUME 2.
LP: . . . . **OC 436**

JE KA JO.
LP: . . . . **V 2283**
MC: . . . . **TCV 2283**

JUJU JUBILEE.
LP: . . . . **SHAN 43031**
MC: . . . . **SHANC 43031**

MILIKI PLUS.
Tracks: / Ere oloyin momo / Singing for the people / What God has joined together / Happy birthday (celebration) / Eiye to ma ba kowe ke / Eyi yato / Oro mi ti dayo / Ore oluwa a kari / Miliki (Cassette only) / Ojeje (Cassette only) / Je ka jo (Cassette only) / Don't say no (Cassette only) / Abente (Cassette only) / Poto poto (Cassette only) / Paga (Cassette only) / Alu mi (Cassette only).
LP: . . . . **VM 7**
MC: . . . . **VMC 7**

MY VISION.
LP: . . . . **OPS 007**

SECURITY.
LP: . . . . **OPS 006**

SOLUTION Nigeria.
Tracks: / Gbebe mi / Olupese / Ma kuku sise / Oluwa ni mo gbojule / To ba nwa ire / Ibi aiye feni di / O dowa oluwa / Kaiye ma bere pe olorum mi da / Di ro mo / Wai.
LP: . . . . **STERNS 1005**

WHAT GOD HAS JOINED.
LP: . . . . **OTI 528**

Obiedo, Ray

IGUANA.
Tracks: / Boomerang / Terrible beauty / Werewolf / Iguana / Samba Alegre / Mysterious ways / Small talk / At first glance / Emergency exit.
MC: . . . . **WT 0128**

Obituary

CAUSE OF DEATH.
Tracks: / Infected / Chopped in half / Dying / Cause of death / Turned inside out / Bodybag / Circle of the tyrants / Find the arise / Memories remain.
LP: . . . . **RO 93071**
MC: . . . . **RO 93074**

SLOWLY WE ROT.
LP: . . . . **RO 94891**
MC: . . . . **RO 94894**

Objective Burma

OBJECTIVE BURMA (FILM) (See under 'Sunset Boulevard') (Various artists).

Objet D'Art

MUSIC OF MAURO GIULIANI, THE (Objet D'Art/Anisa Angarola/Valerie King).
Tracks: / Serenade for flute and guitar, Opus 127 / I bin a Kohlbauern Bub (variations) (Opus 49) / Grand sonata for flute and guitar, Opus 85.
LP: . . . . **DS 203**

Obliveon

FROM THIS DAY FORWARD.
LP: . . . . **ATV 14**

Oboade

KPANLOGO PARTY (With Mustapha Tettey Addy).
LP: . . . . **TGS 115**

Oboe...

OBOE COLLECTION (Various artists).
Tracks: / Alborada: *Various artists* (Traditional Spanish) / Etenraku: *Various artists* (Traditional Japanese) / An dro nevez: *Various artists* (Traditional Breton) / La quinte estampie real: *Various artists* (Traditional Turkish (C13)) / Variations on 'les folies d'Espagne': *Various artists* (Marais) / Sonata in G minor: *Various artists*(C.P.E. Bach) / Morceau de salon: *Various artists* (Kalliwoda) / Sonatina no. 2 in G: *Various artists* (Walmisley) / Gran concerto: *Various artists* (Pasculli).
LP: . . . . **SAR 22**
MC: . . . . **CSAR 22**

O'Briain, Donncha

DONNCHA O'BRIAIN.
LP: . . . . **CEF 083**

O'Brien, Dermot

20 GREATEST HITS: DERMOT O'BRIEN.
Tracks: / Orange blossom special / Beer barrel polka / Cock o' the north / Whistling Rufus / Laughing accordion / Teddy bear's picnic / 79th Farewell to Gibraltar / Barren rocks of Aden / Marching through Georgia / Battle Hymn of the republic / Peanut vendor / Alpine slopes / Cuckoo waltz / Athole Highlanders, The / Athlone jig / Bluebell polka.
LP: . . . . **PLAT 04**
MC: . . . . **PLAC 04**
LP: . . . . **PLATB 04**
MC: . . . . **PLACB 04**

ACCORDION SOUNDS.
Tracks: / Yellow bird / Whistling Rufus / Cuckoo waltz / Peanut vendor / Bluebell polka.
MC: . . . . **AIM 75**
LP: . . . . **BRL 4022**

ACROSS THE STORMY SEA.
MC: . . . . **GTDC 079**

BUNCH OF THYME.
MC: . . . . **BTC 303**

CEILIDH TIME IN IRELAND.
Tracks: / Reels / Drunken piper / Jigs / Lannigan's ball / Waltz / Hornpipes / Showmans fancy / March / Wearing of the green, The / Set dances / Bonnie Kate / Waltz / Gentle mother / Irish washerwoman, The.
LP: . . . . **HPE 663**

DANCING FINGERS.
Tracks: / Spanish gypsy dance / Dark island / Angelique / Blue Danube / Blaze away / Bel viso / La paloma / Jealousy.
LP: . . . . **BRL 4078**

DEAR OLD IRELAND.
LP: . . . . **HM 041**
MC: . . . . **HMC 041**

DERMOT O'BRIEN.
Tracks: / Fiddlers green / Carrickfergus / Kerry slides / Anna Liffey / And the band played waltzing Matilda.
LP: . . . . **BRL 4103**

FAREWELL TO GALWAY.
LP: . . . . **HPE 600**

HIMSELF.
MC: . . . . **UNKNOWN**

LAUGHING ACCORDION, THE.
Tracks: / Teddy bear's picnic / Orange blossom special / Wheels / Bourasque / Sweet Sue / Carnival of Venice.
LP: . . . . **BRL 4020**

LIVE IN AMERICA.
MC: . . . . **GTDC 080**

MERRY PLOUGHBOY, THE.
Tracks: / Home boys home / Leaving of Liverpool / Ploughboy, The.
LP: . . . . **BRL 4014**

OULD CLADDAUGH RING, THE.
Tracks: / Old Claddagh ring / Connemara rose / Nora / Holy ground / Home boys home / Come to the bower.
LP: . . . . **HPE 628**

ROVING BOY.
Tracks: / Rocky shores of Carna / Green fields of France / Roving boy, The / Bunch of thyme.
LP: . . . . **RITZ 0007**

SONGS OF IRELAND.
Tracks: / Old claddagh ring / Boys of Killybegs / Fiddlers green / Galway shawl / Nora Turfman from Ardee / As I roved out / Merry ploughboy / Cliffs of Dooneen / Home boys home / Slieve na mon / 3 leaf shamrock / Spancil hill / Rocks of Bawn / Carrifergus / Mslieve gallion.
LP: . . . . **PICKTV 2**
MC: . . . . **CPICK 2**

SONGS OF IRELAND, VOL.3.
Tracks: / Sailing home / Logie Bay / Flow sweet river / Mother Malone / Lady grand, The.

LP: . . . . BRL 4075

THREE DIMENSIONS.
Tracks: / Alpine slopes / Colonel Bogey / Old comrades / Alpine herdsmen cuckoo waltz / Marching through Georgia.
LP: . . . . BRL 4033

TRIBUTE TO SCOTLAND.
LP: . . . . BRL 4049

O'Brien, Edna

COUNTRY GIRLS, THE.
MCSET: . . . . CAB 306
MCSET: . . . . SAY 19
MCSET: . . . . ARGO 1256

SOME IRISH LOVING.
Tracks: / Some Irish loving / What is love / Courtship of Etain / Dawning of the day / Young serving man / Poet loves from afar / Her Praise / Eleanor Alexander / He that's dead can do no hurt / Advice to lovers / Love among the Irish / Making of a chapter / Noble lay of Aillinn / Letter to Vanessa / My husband Queen Maeve / Light love / Aileen Aroon / Men improve with the year / Death and the lady / Once I was yellow haired / On the death of his wife / Red rose.
LP: . . . . ZDSW 728

O'Brien, Hod

BITS AND PIECES.
Tracks: / Bits and pieces / Jennifer / Storybook dreams / Through the smoke / Ray's idea / Lovely one in the window / Heaven's doors are open wide / Hi-fly / Toby's song.
LP: . . . . UP 27 08

O'Brien, Kelly

SPROULE.
LP: . . . . SHAN 29015

O'Brien, Maureen (nar)

JANE EYRE (see under Jane Eyre (bk)).

MANSFIELD PARK (See under Austen, Jane).

O'Brien, Michael

CLIFFS OF MOHER, THE.
LP: . . . . FALP 003
MC: . . . . FACS 003

DREAMS OF IRELAND.
LP: . . . . WS 039
MC: . . . . WS 039 C

EVENING WITH MICHAEL O'BRIEN, AN.
MC: . . . . PLAC 331

ONE MORE TIME.
LP: . . . . FALP 004
MC: . . . . FACS 004

SOMETHING FOR EVERYONE.
LP: . . . . KLP 245

WAITING FOR YOU.
LP: . . . . KLP 275

O'Brien, Paddy

EASY LISTENING WITH PADDY O'BRIEN.
MC: . . . . FACS 017

FAVOURITES.
MC: . . . . FACS 016

MAKING FRIENDS.
LP: . . . . FALPTV 5002

MEMORIES.
MC: . . . . FACS 015

SUNNYSIDE.
Tracks: / Keep on the sunny side / Loreena / Close to you / Little town on the Shannon / My wedding band (is a halo of gold) / My lovely Leitrim Shore / Devil woman / Will you think of you / Knock at my window love / She's mine / There goes my everything / Truck driving man / Everybody's reaching out for someone / Sweethearts in heaven / New attraction, A / She taught me how to yodel.
LP: . . . . HM 051

O'Brien, Tim

HARD YEAR BLUES.
LP: . . . . FF 319

TAKE ME BACK (O'Brien, Tim & Mollie).
Tracks: / Leave that liar alone / Sweet sunny South / I loved you a thousand ways / Just someone I used to know / Down to the valley to pray / Wave the ocean, wave the sea / Your long journey / When the roses bloom in Dixieland / Unwed fathers / Nobody's fault but mine / Papa's on the housetop / Dream of the miner's child / Christ was born in Bethlehem.
LP: . . . . SH 3766
MC: . . . . SH 3766C

O'Brien, Tommy

TOMMY'S ENCORE.
LP: . . . . RTE 108

O'Brien, Virginia

SONGS FROM HER MGM FILMS.
LP: . . . . AEI 2117

Obscur, Clair

PLAY.
LP: . . . . CRL 20

Obsession

METHODS OF MADNESS.
LP: 3262 1

SWEET OBSESSION.
LP: . . . . FE 44419

Obsession (bk)

OBSESSION (Charlotte Lamb) (Boyd, Carole (nar)).
MC: . . . . PMB 014

Obsession (film)

OBSESSION (Film Soundtrack) (Various artists).
LP: 16.45029

Obus

PODEROSO COMOEL TRUENO.
LP: . . . . SKULL 8343

O'Canainn, Nuala Agus

BEAL NA TRA.
Tracks: / Lower drum roll / With Marley to Galicia / On the seashore / Fresh stubble of autumn / Ennismore potter, The / Father Michael Ryan's / Creggan churchyard / Little field of barley / Nuala's fiddle / Glamire gallop / Falklands frolics / Stranger, The / Treasure of my heart / Evelyn darling / Johnny's 21st.
LP: . . . . OAS 3040
MC: . . . . COAS 3040

WITH PIPE AND SONG.
Tracks: / Theodore Street / Pope's Quay / Dum ciovais / Francey / Brian McDermot Roe / Deirder's lament / Limerick's lamentation / Grove of Glanmire / Union Quay Tam's jig / Pauline's polka / Claudine's polka / Amen a losa / An sceilpim droighmeach / John Twiss / Saint Anthony's Road / Moss Road to Dungives / Rachad-sa smo Cheaiti / At swim with two birds / Ard Barra jig.
LP: . . . . OAS 3035

Ocasek, Ric

BEATITUDE.
Tracks: / Jimmy Jimmy / Something to grab for / Prove / I can't wait / Connect up to me / Quick one, A / Out of control / Take a walk / Sneak attack / Time bomb.
LP: 9020221
MC: 9020224
LP: . . . . GEF 25282

FIREBALL ZONE.
LP: 7599265521
MC: 7599265524

THIS SIDE OF PARADISE.
Tracks: / Keep on laughin' / True to you / Emotion in motion / Look in your eyes / Coming for you / Mystery / True love / P.F.J. / Hello darkness / This side of paradise.
LP: 9240981
MC: 9240984

O'Casey, Sean

GREEN CROW CAWS, THE.
Tracks: / Down where the bees are humming / My bodice neat & modest / As I wait in the boreen for Maggie / White legg'd Mary / Eros / Since Maggy went away / Niall / Soup soul'd cleric / I tuck'd up my sleeves / Lament for Thomas Ashe / Rare time for death in Ireland / Nora / All round my hat.
LP: . . . . EMA 793

JUNO & THE PAYCOCK (Various artists).
MCSET: 0358

Ocean

OCEAN.
LP: 1200 182

Ocean, Billy

6 TRACK HITS.
Tracks: / Love really hurts without you / Who's gonna rock you / Are you ready / American hearts / Stop me / Red light spells danger.
MC: 7SC 5024

12" TAPE: BILLY OCEAN.
Tracks: / Suddenly / When the going gets tough (the tough get going) / Love zone.
MC: 6509154

BILLY OCEAN.
Tracks: / Tell him to move over / Stop me (if you've heard it all before) / Let's put our emotions in motion / Let's do it all again / Love really hurts without you / Whose little girl are you? / Soul rock / One kiss away / Hungry for love / Eye of a storm / L.O.D. (Love on delivery).
LP: . . . . EPC 32561
MC: 40 32561

CITY LIMIT.
Tracks: / American hearts / Are you ready / Stay the night.
LP: . . . . GTLP 038

COLLECTION: BILLY OCEAN.
Tracks: / Love really hurts without you / Red light spells danger / Are you ready / Don't say stop / Inner feelings / City limit / Calypso funkin' / Soul rock / Mind games / Nights (feel like getting down) / One kiss away / Eye of a storm / Another day won't matter / Stop me / Let's put our emotions in motion / L.O.D. (Love on delivery) / American hearts / Hungry for love / Taking chances / Stay the night / Dance with me / Whose little girl are you.
2LP: . . . . CCSLP 205
MC: . . . . CCSMC 205

GREATEST HITS.
Tracks: / When the going gets tough the tough get going / Caribbean queen / Suddenly / Licence to chill / There'll be sad songs (to make you cry) / Loverboy / Get outta my dreams, get into my car / Love zone / Here's to you / I sleep much better (in someone else's bed) / Colour of love.
LP: . . . . BOTV 1
MC: . . . . BOTC 1

IN MOTION.
Tracks: / On the run / What's gonna happen / Light up the world with sunshine / On the run (hold on brother) / Let's put our emotions in motion / Love really hurts without you / Whose little girl are you / Black as he's painted / Wild beautiful women / On the run (extended remix long).
LP: . . . . MFP 5765
MC: . . . . TCMFP 5765

INNER FEELINGS.
Tracks: / Calypso funkin / Rockabye baby / No matter what / Dance with me / I can't stop / Tryin' to get through / Mind games / Was it you / Inner feelings.
LP: . . . . EPC 32794
MC: 40 32794
LP: . . . . EPC 85568

LOVE REALLY HURTS WITHOUT YOU.
Tracks: / What's gonna happen to our love / On the run / Let's put our emotions in motion / Eye of a storm / Wild beautiful woman / Can you feel it / Light up the world with sunshine / Whose little girl are you? / On the run (The battle is over).
MC: 500107

LOVE ZONE.
Tracks: / When the going gets tough (the tough get going) / Love zone / Without you / There'll be sad songs (to make you cry) / Bittersweet / It's never too late to try / Showdown / Promise me / Love is forever / Love zone (Instrumental mix).
LP: . . . . HIP 35
MC: . . . . HIPC 35

NIGHTS (FEEL LIKE GETTING DOWN).
Tracks: / Are you ready / Don't say stop / Whatever turns you on / Another day won't matter / nights (feel like getting down) / Who's gonna rock you / Stay the night / Everlasting love / Taking chances.
LP: . . . . EPC 32716
MC: 40 32716

RED LIGHT.
MC: 266 226 4

RED LIGHT(IMPORT).
LP: . . . . BRLP 95
MC: . . . . BRMC 95

SUDDENLY.
Tracks: / Caribbean queen / Mystery lady / Syncopation / Long and winding road, The / Loverboy / Lucky man / Dance floor / If I should lose you / Suddenly.
LP: . . . . HIP 12
MC: . . . . HIPC 12
LP: . . . . JIP 12

TEAR DOWN THESE WALLS.
Tracks: / Tear down these walls / Soon as you're ready / Because of you / Gun for hire / Colour of love / Get outta my dreams, get into my car / Pleasure / Here's to you / Stand and deliver / Calypso crazy.
LP: . . . . HIP 57
MC: . . . . HIPC 57

Ocean Blue

OCEAN BLUE.
Tracks: / Between something and nothing / Drifting falling / Frigid Winter days / Love song / Awaking to a dream / Familiar face, A / Vanity fair / Circus animals, The / Just let me know / Ask me Jon / Myron.
LP: . . . . K 9259861
MC: . . . . K 9259864

Oceans, Lucky

LUCKY STEALS THE WHEEL.
LP: BP-1282

Ochs, Phil

ALL THE NEWS THATS FIT TO SING.
Tracks: / One more parade / Thresher, The / Talking Vietnam / Lou Marsh / Power and the glory / Celia / Bells, The / Automation song / Ballad of William Worthy / Knock on the door / Talking Cuban crisis / Bound for glory / Too many martyrs / What's that I hear.
LP: . . . . ED 247
LP: . . . . CGLP 4427
MC: . . . . CGC 4427

CHORDS OF FAME.
Tracks: / I'm going to say it now / Santo Domingo / Changes / Is there anybody here / Love me, I'm a liberal / When I'm gone / Outside of a small circle of friends / Pleasures of the harbor / Tape from California / Chords of fame / Crucifixion / War is over / Jim Dean of Indiana / Power and the glory, The / Flower lady / No more songs.
2LP: . . . . AMLM 64599

GREATEST HITS: PHIL OCHS.
Tracks: / One way ticket home / Jim Dean of Indiana / My kingdom for a car / Boy in Ohio / Gas station women / Chords of fame / Ten cents a coup / Bach, Beethoven, Mozart and me / Basket in the pool / No more songs.
LP: . . . . ED 201

I AIN'T MARCHING ANYMORE.
LP: . . . . CGLP 4422
MC: . . . . CGC 4422

THERE BUT FOR FORTUNE.
LP: . . . . K 9608321
MC: . . . . K 9608324

TOAST TO THOSE WHO ARE GONE, A.
Tracks: / Do what I have to do / Ballad of Billie Sol / Coloured town / A M A song / William Moore / Paul Crump / Going down to Mississippi / I'll be there / Ballad of Oxford / No Christmas in Kentucky / Toast to those who are gone, A / I'm tired.
LP: . . . . ED 242

O'Connell, Helen

GREEN EYES.
Tracks: / Star eyes / Not mine / Tangerine / Green eyes / Yours / When the sun comes out / All of me / Jim / Amapola / Time was / Embraceable you / Brazil.
LP: . . . . NL 90037
MC: . . . . NK 90037

HELEN O'CONNELL AND PAGE CAVANAUGH TRIO, VOL. 2 (O'Connell, Helen & Page Cavanaugh Trio).
LP: . . . . HSR 228

HELEN O'CONNELL SINGS GREAT SONGS IN HIGH STYLE.
LP: . . . . AP 74

O'Connell, Maura

JUST IN TIME.
Tracks: / Scholar, The / If you love me / Feet of a dancer / Isle of Malachy, The / New Orleans / Water is wide, The / Leaving Neidin / Crazy dreams / Loves old sweet song / Another morning / I will / Just in time.
LP: 831 184-1
MC: 8311844
LP: . . . . PH 1124
MC: . . . . PH 1124C
LP: . . . . RGLP 10

MAURA O'CONNELL.
LP: . . . . BLB 5007

WESTERN HIGHWAY.
Tracks: / Trouble in the fields / Cast a long shadow / Summerfly / Bed for the night / Isn't it always love / Helpless heart / Can't stop the girl / Just like the blues / Only a fool / Western highway / You'll never know.
LP: . . . . RGLP 9
MC: . . . . RGMC 9

O'Connell, Moloney

KILKELLY (O'Connell, Moloney & Keane).
LP: . . . . SIF 1072
MC: . . . . CSIF 1072

O'Connell, Robbie

CLOSE TO THE BONE.
LP: . . . . SIF 1038
MC: . . . . CSIF 1038

O'Connor, Cavan

DOWN MEMORY LANE.
Tracks: / I travel the road / Daybreak / Come back my love / Fleur d'amour / Sing me a song of the morning / Life's desire / She moved through the fair / My prayer / Sunshine of Paradise Alley / Old turf fire / Just for today / Eileen O'Grady / Home / Goodnight.

LP: PRX 25

I'M JUST A VAGABOND.
Tracks: / World is mine tonight / Danny boy / There's something in your eyes / If you want to touch an irish heart / Could you be true to eyes of blue / Rose of kilarney / That tumbledown shack in athlone / Love is like a cigarette / I'll take you home again kathleen / Daybreak / Fool with a dream / Singing a vagabond song / When i leave the world behind / Round the bend of the road / Kathleen Mavoureen / Starlight serenade / Let us live for tonight / Godnight.
LP: RFL 26

IN THE STILL OF THE NIGHT.
Tracks: / One alone / Where the river shannon flows / Round the bend of the road / My wild Irish rose / Pretty girl is like a melody, A / I'll take you home again Kathleen / Starlight serenade / When I leave the world behind / Desert song, The / Rose of Tralee, The / Shannon river / Let us live for tonight / Kathleen Mavoureen / Daybreak / Bantry Bay / My Irish song of songs / There's a blue haze on the mountains / I hear your voice / White cliffs of Dover, The / Little town in the ould County Down / God will remember / Old oak tree, The / Mountains of Mourne / When evening comes / Two hands against the moon / When April comes again / Mother Machree / At the close of a long long day / Goodnight (Full title: Goodnight (I'm only a strolling vagabond)(Ich bin nur ein ar) / In the still of the night / Singing a vagabond song / Fool with a dream, A.
MCSET: RECDC 13
2LP: RECDL 13

O'Connor, Des

ANYTIME.
Tracks: / When you're smiling / Everybody's talkin' / Raindrops keep falling on my head / For the good times / You always hurt the one you love / Careless hands / One two three O'Leary / Your cheatin' heart / Didn't we / I pretend / Dream a little dream of me / With love / Anytime / Dick a dum dum / Tip of my fingers, The / I'll go on hoping / Loneliness / Something / All I need is you / Heartaches / Try to remember / Red roses for a blue lady / My thanks to you.
MC: HR 8105
MC: HR 4181054

BEST OF THE EMI YEARS: DES O'CONNOR.
Tracks: / When you're smiling / I had the craziest dream / Careless hands / Danny boy / You always hurt the one you love / Red roses for a blue lady / I pretend / Other man's grass is always greener, The / Never my love / Dream a little dream of me / One, two, three O'Leary / With pen in hand / Quiet nights of quiet stars / Good life / There goes my heart / Dick-a-dum-dum (King's road) / Raining in my heart / Loneliness (Non sono Maddalena) / Importance of your love, The / It had to be you / There I've said it again / I'll get by (as long as I have you) / Tip of my fingers, The / I'll go on hoping / To be the one you love / Neighbours.
MC: TCEMS 1401

CARELESS HANDS.
MC: TCIDL 1

CHRISTMAS WITH....
LP: HMA 270
MC: HSC 349

DES O'CONNOR COLLECTION.
2LP: PDA 049

DES O'CONNOR NOW.
Tracks: / Bilitis / Lately / To all the girls I've loved before / Arthur's theme / Our love / Key largo / Isn't it strange / Sad songs / Fool if you think it's over / Hello / I just called to say I love you / Drive / She's always a woman / Waiting game, The / I honestly love you / If ever you're in my arms again.
LP: STAR 2245
MC: STAC 2245

DES O'CONNOR REMEMBER ROMANCE.
LP: WW 5100

GOLDEN HITS: DES O'CONNOR.
Tracks: / One two three O'Leary / Loneliness / World of dreams / Something / Everyone / My thanks to you / Tip of my fingers, The / Other man's grass, The / I pretend / Careless hands / Dick a dum dum / I'll go on hoping / For love or money / With love / You've done something to my heart / Danny boy / This guy's in love with you / Sunshine of love / Thinking of you / All I need is you / Happiness and heartaches / Didn't we / Never my love.
2LP: MFP 1027
MCSET: TCMFP 1027

GREAT SONGS, THE.
Tracks: / Imagine / When I fall in love / It's impossible / Unchained melody / She / Air that I breathe, The / Feelings / Begin the beguine / This guy's in love with you / Strangers in the night / Something / Stardust / Three times a lady / Spanish eyes / What I did for love / I get a kick out of you.
LP: STAR 2260
MC: STAC 2260

I PRETEND.
LP: SCX 6295

JUST FOR YOU.
LP: WW 5071

LOVING FEELING.
Tracks: / That's all I ask of you / Lady in red / Together again / You've lost that lovin' feeling / On my own / Miss you like crazy / Certain smile, A / Night and day / How deep is your love / Wind beneath my wings / Some day I'll fly away / You're so beautiful / My love / Never never never / Wonderful tonight / Every time we say goodbye.
LP: STAR 2368
MC: STAC 2368

SING A FAVOURITE SONG.
LP: NSPL 18390

SKYE BOAT SONG (See under Whittaker, Roger) (O'Connor, Des & Roger Wittaker).

THIS IS DES O CONNOR.
Tracks: / Careless hands / For the good times / Dick a dum dum / Everybody's talkin' / Tip of my fingers / Importance of your love, The / I'll go on hoping / Raindrops keep fallin' / One two three O' Leary / All I need is you / You always hurt the one you love / Any time / Heartaches / Didn't we / Loneliness / I pretend.
LP: THIS 11

TRUE LOVE WAYS.
Tracks: / True love ways / Too young / Long ago and far away / Honey / For ever and ever / I won't send roses / I feel fine / Power of love, The / Can't help falling in love / I wanna wake up with you / Love letters / Always / Moonlight serenade / All the way.
LP: 208685
MC: 408685

WITH FEELINGS.
LP: HMA 255
MC: HSC 257

WITH LOVE.
LP: SCX 6417

O'Connor, Hazel

BREAKING GLASS (SOUNDTRACK) (see under Breaking Glass).

COVER PLUS.
Tracks: / Cover plus - we're all grown up / Hanging around / Ee-i-adio / Not for you / Hold on / So you're born / Dawn chorus / Animal farm / Runaway / Do what you gotta do / Men of good fortune / That's life.
LP: ALB 108
MC: CALB 108
LP: ALLP 400010

GLASS HOUSES.
LP: DAI 002

SMILE.
Tracks: / Just good friends / Don't touch me / I'm so sorry / Tell me a story / Cuts too deep / Man I love, The / I don't know / Mystified / Bring it on home to me / Spancil Hill.
LP: PL 70268
MC: PK 70268

SONS AND LOVERS.
Tracks: / D-days / Waiting / Who will care / Zoo / Gigolo / Do what you do / Glass houses / Sons and lovers / Ain't it funny / Danny boy / Bye bye / Time.
LP: ALLP 400030
LP: ALB 104

O'Connor, John

SONGS FOR OUR TIMES.
LP: FF 331

O'Connor, Mark

FALSE DAWN.
LP: ROUNDER 0165
MC: ROUNDER 0165C

MARK O'CONNOR.
LP: ROUNDER 0046
MC: ROUNDER 0046C

MARKOLOGY.
Tracks: / Dixie breakdown / Markology / Kit's waltz / Fluid drive / Blackberry blossom / Pickin' the wind / Banks of the Ohio / Berserkeley / On top of the world.
LP: ROUNDER 0090
MC: ROUNDER 0090C

ON THE RAMPAGE.
LP: ROUNDER 0118
MC: ROUNDER 0118C

PICKIN' IN THE WIND.
Tracks: / Pickin' in the wind / Midnight on the water / Tom and Jerry / Cotton patch rag / Tammy's waltz / Lonesome fiddle blues / Daybreak in Dixie / Mark's waltz / Grey eagle / Dixie hoedown / Goodbye waltz / Herman's rag / Faded love / Dixie breakdown.
LP: ROUNDER 0068
MC: ROUNDER 0068C

SOPPIN' THE GRAVY.
LP: ROUNDER 0137
MC: ROUNDER 0137C

O'Connor, Martin

PERPETUAL MOTION.
LP: CCF 26
MC: 4CCF 26

O'Connor, Mary

MY OWN NATIVE LAND.
LP: FRC 007

O'Connor, Sinead

I DO NOT WANT WHAT I HAVEN'T GOT.
LP: CHEN 14
MC: ZCHEN 14

LION AND THE COBRA, THE.
Tracks: / Jackie / Mandinka / Jerusalem / Just like u said it would b / Never get old / Troy / I want your (hands on me) / Drink before the war / Just call me Joe.
LP: CHEN 7
MC: ZCHEN 7

O'Connor, Tom

ACE OF CLUBS.
Tracks: / Introduction / Lord had Mersey on me, The / Proud people / Cruise / Kids / Beauty contest / Cup final, The / Coming home / What is a wife? / T.V. adverts / Finale (Includes: The Lord had Mersey on me, The Bill, My old home town.).
MC: DJM 42055

LOOK AT LIFE, A.
Tracks: / Let's look at life / Cash in your pocket / I'm coming back / Me and my gang / Comedy sketches.
LP: PRCV 140
MC: TCPRCV 140

October Cherries

WORLD HITS '76.
Tracks: / December 63 / Let your love flow / Movie star / Moonlight feels right / Baby blue / Sailing / Arms of Mary / Afternoon delight / Love to love you baby / All by myself / More more more / Get up and boogie.
LP: BE 603

October File

OCTOBER FILE.
LP: TGLP 7

Octopus

AN OCEAN OF ROCKS.
LP: SKY 016

Octopussy

OCTOPUSSY (Film soundtrack) (Various artists).
Tracks: / All-time high: *Coolidge, Rita* / Bond look-alike: *Various artists* / 009 gets the knife: *Various artists* / Gobinda attacks: *Various artists* / That's my little Octopussy: *Various artists* / Arrival at the island of Octopussy: *Various artists* / Bond at the Monsoon Palace: *Various artists* / Bond meets Octopussy: *Various artists* / Yo-yo fight: *Various artists* / Death of Vijay: *Various artists* / Chase bomb theme, The: *Various artists* / Palace fight, The: *Various artists*.
LP: AMLX 64967
MC: CXM 64967

O'Cuthbert, Martin

FOR ALIEN EARS.
LP: MARTOC 001

REJECTED BY A CRYSTAL SIGH.
LP: MARTOC 002

O'Day, Anita

ANITA O'DAY 1949-50.
LP: TJ6003

BIG BAND SESSIONS.
Tracks: / Up state / Night bird / Ballad of the sad young man / It had to be you / Hershey bar / Come rain or come shine / Easy come, easy go / You're a clown / Don't explain / I hear music / Crazy he calls me / Ten cents a dance / Have you met Miss Jones / Get out of town / I get a kick out of you / Johnny one note.
2LP: 2632083

COMPACT JAZZ (see under Blakey, Art) (Blakey, Art/Chet Baker/Anita O'Day/Memphis Slim).

HIGH STANDARDS.
MC: SLC 5209
LP: SL 5209

LEGENDARY VOL.2, THE.
LP: GLS 6001

MELLO DAY.
LP: GNPS 2126

ONCE UPON A SUMMERTIME.
Tracks: / Sweet Georgia Brown / Love for sale / S'Wonderful / Tea for two / Once upon a summertime / Night and day / Anita's blues.
LP: GLS 6000
LP: JASM 2531
MC: JASMC 2531

PICK YOURSELF UP.
Tracks: / Don't be that way / Let's face the music and dance / I never had a chance / Stompin' at the Savoy / Pick yourself up / Stars fell on Alabama / Sweet Georgia Brown / I won't dance / Man with a horn / I used to be color blind / There's a lull in my life / Let's begin.
LP: OFF 3015

SINGS THE WINNERS.
Tracks: / Take the 'A' train / Tenderly / Night in Tunisia / Four / Early Autumn / Four brothers / Sing, sing, sing / My funny valentine / Frenesi / Body and soul / What's your story, morning glory? / Peanut vendor.
LP: 2304 255
MC: 837939 4

TRAVELLIN' LIGHT.
Tracks: / Travellin' light / Moon looks down and laughs / God bless the child / If the moon turns green / I hear music / Lover come back to me / Crazy, he calls me / Miss Brown to you / Don't explain / Remember / Some other spring / What a little moonlight can do.
LP: 2304 584

WAVE (Live at Ronnie Scott's).
Tracks: / Wave / You'd be so nice to come home to / On Green Dolphin street / I can't get started / It don't mean a thing if it ain't got that swing / Street of dreams,The / 'S wonderful / They can't take that away from me / Is you is or is you ain't my baby / My funny valentine / I cried for you / Four brothers / Wave.
MC: ESMMC 019

O'Day, Molly

SOUL OF MOLLY O'DAY VOL.1.
LP: OHCS 312

SOUL OF MOLLY O'DAY VOL.2.
LP: OHCS 313

Odd Socks

MEN OF THE MOMENT.
LP: SFA 030

Odds Against (bk)

ODDS AGAINST (see Francis, Dick) (Powell, Robert (nar)).

Odenhall, Staffan

BIG EARS BIG BAND.
LP: DRLP 144

Odessa File (bk)

ODESSA FILE, THE (see under Forsyth, Frederick) (Allen, Patrick (nar)).

Odessa, Jacob FR

DEVIL'S FIDDLE, THE.
LP: EULP 1007

Odetta

CHRISTMAS SPIRITUALS.
MC: VBR 20384

ESSENTIAL, THE.
2LP: VSD 43/44
MCSET: CVSD 43/44

HOLE IN THE BUCKET (See under Belafonte, Harry) (Odetta & Harry Belafonte).

IT'S IMPOSSIBLE.
LP: FLC 5007

ODETTA AND THE BLUES.
Tracks: / Hard, oh Lord / Believe I'll go / Oh papa / How long blues / Hogan's alley / Leavin' this mornin' / Oh, my babe / Yonder come the blues / Make me a pallet on the floor / Weeping willow blues / Go down sunshine / Nobody knows you (when you're down and out).
LP: OBC 509

O'Dette, Paul

SONGS FOR TENOR AND LUTE BY JOHN DOWLAND (see under Rogers, Nigel) (O'dette, Paul & Nigel Rogers).

O'Domhnaill, Michael

NIGHTNOISE (see Oskay, Bill) (O'Domhnaill, Michael & Bill Oskay).

O'Donnell, Al

AL O'DONNELL.
LP: LER 2073

AL O'DONNELL 2.
LP: LTRA 501

O'Donnell, Conal

AN BHANALTRA (Folksongs in Irish Gaelic).

Tracks: / An bhanaltra / Brid bhan / Brid og ni mhaille / An cailin gaelach / Chuaigh me 'na rosann / Donall o maolaine / Eirigh's cuir ort do chuid eaeaigh / Rise up my darling / Gardai'n ri / In aimsir bhaint an fheir / Is iomaidh coiscein fada / Ma theid tu' unaonaigh / Maire chonnacht agus Seamus O'Donaill / Nion a'bhaoilligh / An t-oilean ur / An seamduine doighte / Seimidh eoghainin duib duibh / Thios i dteach a'torrairm / Tiochfiadh an samhrdh.
MC: 60-003

O'Donnell, Daniel

BOY FROM DONEGAL, THE.
Tracks: / Donegal shore / Old rustic bridge / Galway bay / Forty shades of green / My side of the road / 5,000 miles from Sligo / Old bog road / Slievenamon / Noreen Bawn / Ballyhoe.
LP: IHLP 04
MC: IHMC 04

DON'T FORGET TO REMEMBER.
Tracks: / I don't care / Old loves never die / I wonder where you are tonight / Don't be angry / Roses are red / Before I'm over you / Take good care of her / Pretty little girl from Omagh / Green willow / Don't let me cross over / Good old days / Pat Murphy's meadow / I just can't make it on my own.
LP: RITZLP 0043
MC: RITZLC 043

FAVOURITES.
Tracks: / Bed of roses / Excuse me / Geisha girl / Home sweet home / Home is where the heart is / Forever you'll be mine / Streets of Baltimore, The / Bringin' Mary home / Banks of my own lovely Lee, The / Green hills of Sligo.
LP: RITZLP 0052
MC: RITZLC 0052

FROM THE HEART.
Tracks: / Minute you're gone, The / Mary from Dungloe / Wasting my time / Things / It doesn't matter anymore / Bye bye love / Kelly / Old rugged cross, The / Act naturally / Honey / Wooden heart / It keeps right on a-hurtin' / My bonnie Maureen / I know that you know / Old Dungarvan oak / Danny boy.
LP: STAR 2327
MC: STAC 2327

I NEED YOU.
Tracks: / Sing an old Irish song / I need you / From a jack to a king / Lovely rose of Clare / Stand beside me / Irish eyes / Dear old Galway town / Three leaf shamrock / Veil of white lace / Kickin' each others hearts around / Medals for mothers / Wedding bells / Snowflake / Your friendly Irish way / Lough Melvin's rocky shore / I love you because.
LP: RITZLP 0038
MC: RITZLC 0038
MC: HMC 17

IRISH FAVOURITES.
MC: SMAC 9011

LAST WALTZ, THE.
Tracks: / Here I am in love again / We could / Last waltz of the evening / When only the sky was blue / Heaven with you / You know I still love you / Talk back trembling lips / Shelter of your eyes, The / When we get together / Ring of gold / Fool such as I, A / Memory number one / Look both ways / Little patch of blue / Marianne (Only on CD.).
LP: RITZLP 0058
MC: RITZLC 0058

THOUGHTS OF HOME.
Tracks: / My shoes keep walking back to you / Mountains of Mourne, The / London leaves / Blue eyes crying in the rain / Old days remembered / Send me the pillow you dream on / Moonlight and roses / Little piece of Heaven, A / Far far from home / Isle of Innisfree / My heart skips / I know one / I'll take you home again Kathleen / Second fiddle / My favourite memory / Forty shades of green.
LP: STAR 2372
MC: STAC 2372

TWO SIDES OF DANIEL O'DONNELL, THE.
Tracks: / Green glens of Antrim / Blue hills of Breffni / Any Tipperary town / Latchyco, The / Home town on the Foyle / These are my mountains / My Donegal shore / Crying my heart out over you / My old pal / Our house is a home / Your old love letters / 21 years / Highway 40 blues / I wouldn't change you if I could.
LP: RITZLP 0031
MC: RITZLC 0031

VERY BEST OF DANIEL O'DONNELL, THE.
LP: RITZBLP 700
MC: RITZBLC 700

O'Donnell, Eugene

SLOW AIRS & SET DANCES.
LP: SIF 1015
MC: CSIF 1015

O'Donnell, Liam

SONGS OF TIPPARARY (Counties of Ireland Vol.1).
MC: EI 811

O'Donnell, Triona

TRIONA O'DONNELL.
LP: CEF 043

O'Donohue, Michael

FEIS.
LP: EI 803

O'Doors, Patti

WORLD TURNED UPSIDE DOWN, THE.
LP: MEK 2

O'Dowd, Barry

20 IRISH FAVOURITES.
LP: KGEC 1159

20 IRISH PARTY SONGS (O'Dowd, Barry And The Shamrock Singers).
Tracks: / If your Irish come into the parlour / With my shillelagh under me arm / Galway Bay / Peggy O'Neil / Unicorn / Isle of Innisfree / Did your mother come from Ireland / Too-ra-loo-ra-loo-ra / Dear old Donegal / Little bit of heaven, A / It's a great day for the Irish / Stone outside Dan Murphy's door, The / My wild Irish rose / Goodbye Johnny / When Irish eyes are smiling / I'll take you home again Kathleen / Danny boy / Phil the fluter / How can you buy Killarney / MacNamara's band.
MC: KBER 022

IRISH MEMORIES.
Tracks: / Galway bay / That old Irish mother of mine / Gypsy, The / Dear old shamrock, The / Macushla / Mickey / Dear old Donegal / Last rose of summer / My girl's an Irish girl / If you ever go to Ireland / Kelly / Come back to Erin / Mother Macree / Star of the County Down / How are things in Glocca morra? / I'll take you home again Kathleen.
LP: GES 1230
MC: KGEC 1230

O'Dowda, Brendan

FISHERMEN OF GALWAY.
LP: STAL 8007

HOLLOW IN THE PARK.
LP: STAL 8007

IMMORTAL PERCY FRENCH.
LP: STAL 1041

IRISH FAVOURITES OF PERCY FRENCH.
Tracks: / Phil the fluters ball / Mountains of Mourne, The / Whislin' Phil McHugh / Wait for a while now Mary / Drum colliner / Sweet Marie / Eileen oge / Come back Paddy Reilly / Carmody's Mare / Fortunes of Finnegan, The / Slattery's mounted fut / Gortnomona / Are you right there Michael / Emigrants letter, The / Donegans daughter / Irish mother / That's why we're burying him / Mary Anne McHugh, The / Inishmeela / Father O'Callaghan.
MC: HR 8199

SPECIAL REQUEST.
LP: STAL 6013

WORLD OF PERCY FRENCH.
LP: STAL 6026

O'Duffy, Michael

IRISH REQUESTS.
LP: MODC 1

IRISH REQUESTS, VOL.2.
LP: MODC 2

SPECIAL THOMAS MOORE COMMEMORATION ISSUE.
Tracks: / Minstrel boy / Meeting of the waters / Last rose of summer / When love is kind / Bendemeer's stream / Harp that once through Tara's halls / Believe me if all those endearing young charms / Avenging and bright / Oft in the stilly night / She is far from the land / 'Tis sweet to think / Let Erin remember.
LP: PKL 5579

O'Duibheannaigh, Aodh

AODH O'DUIBHEANNAIGH.
LP: CEF 048

Odyssey

BEST OF ODYSSEY.
Tracks: / Use it up wear it out / Easy come, easy go / Hold de mota down / Follow me / If you're looking for a way out / Lucky star / Native New Yorker / Going back to my roots / Hang together / I got the melody / Ever lovin' Sam / It will be alright / Don't tell me, tell her.
LP: RCALP 6023
MC: RCAK 6023
LP: PL 89541

GREATEST HITS (RCA).
Tracks: / Going back to my roots / Inside out / Magic touch / Oh no not my baby / Weekend lover / Don't tell me tell her / Native New Yorker / Use it up and wear it out / Hang together / It will be alright / Follow me (play follow the leader) / Easy come easy go / When you love somebody / If you're looking for a way out / Native New Yorker (Brooklyn club mix) (CD only).
MC: NK 90436
LP: NL 90436

GREATEST HITS (STYLUS).
Tracks: / Native New Yorker / Weekend lover / When you love somebody / Inside out / It will be alright / Ever lovin' Sam / If you're looking for a way out / Use it up, wear it out / Don't tell me, tell her / Easy come, easy go / Hold de mota down / Going back to my roots / Magic touch / Follow me (Play follow the leader) / Hang together.
LP: SMR 735

HANG TOGETHER.
Tracks: / Hang together / Never had it all / Don't tell me, tell her / Down boy / Follow me / Use it up wear it out / If you're looking for a way out / Rooster loose in the barnyard.
LP: RCALP 3045
MC: RCAK 3045
LP: PL 13526

HAPPY TOGETHER.
Tracks: / Together / Happy people / Inside out / Happy together / When you love somebody / Love's alright / Magic touch.
LP: RCALP 6036

HOLLYWOOD PARTY NIGHT.
Tracks: / Single again / What time does the balloon go up / Pride / You wouldn't know a real live true love... (Full title: You wouldn't know a real live true love if it walked right u) / Hey Bill / Lilly and Harvey, late to the party again / Lucky star / Comin' back for more / I dare ya / I got the melody / Roots suite / Ajomara / Going back to my roots / Baba awa / Holding back my love / Baby that's all I want / It will be alright / Oh no not my baby / Hold on to love.
LP: PL 13031

I GOT THE MELODY.
LP: RCALP 5028
MC: RCAK 5028

MAGIC MOMENTS WITH ODYSSEY.
Tracks: / Native New Yorker / If you're looking for a way out / Follow me / Oh no not my baby / Roots suite / Don't tell me, tell her / Magic touch / Hang together / Use it up wear it out / It will be alright / Easy come easy go / Happy together / Weekend lover / Ever lovin' Sam / Inside out / When you love somebody.
MC: NK 89405

MAGIC TOUCH OF ODYSSEY.
Tracks: / Use it up wear it out / Going back to my roots / Inside out / Native New Yorker / When you love somebody / If you're looking for a way out / Easy come, easy go / Hold de mota down.
LP: STAR 2223
MC: STAC 2223

ODYSSEY.
Tracks: / Native New Yorker / Ever lovin' Sam / Weekend lover / You keep me dancin' / Woman behind the man, The / Easy come, easy go / Hold de mota down / Golden hands / Thank you, God, for one more day.
LP: PL 12204

PIPING JOURNEY, A.
LP: MMC 001

Of Cabbage & Kings

FACE.
LP: PURGE 024

Ofarim, Esther & Abi

2 IN 3.
LP: SBL 7825

CINDERELLA ROCKEFELLA (OLD GOLD) (See under Horst Jankowski - Walk In The Black).

OFARIM CONCERT-LIVE '69.
LP: XL 4

O.F.B.

SATURDAY NIGHTS AND SUNDAY MORNINGS (O.F.B. (Our Favourite Band)).
Tracks: / Lost and lonely / Exile on main street / leavin' Louisiana / Funnel of love / Woman needs a fiddle / Tennessee ain't heaven / Dreamin' of eternity / Stop your fussin' / Drownin' in another pool of love / Girl made in Japan / Waste of a woman / My truck (drove me out of your love) / Road and the miles to dundee, The / Banjo / Pipes medley / Round Scotland medley / Star Wars / Irish medley / Dallas (Dallas dreams), Theme from / Burns medley / Bridge over troubled water / Jacobean medley / Abide with me.
LP: ROSE 120

Off The Record With...

OFF THE RECORD WITH...THEMES (TV themes) (Various artists).
Tracks: / Cats' eyes: *Kongos, John* / Me and my girl: *Skellern, Peter* / Deer hunter, Theme from the: *Williams, John (Guitarist)* / Waltons - theme: *Giltrap, Gordon* / Tales from...: *Grainer, Ron Orchestra* / Onedin line: *Keating John* / Song of freedom: *Mansell Chorale* / Love for Lydia: *London Film Orchestra* / Bouquet of flowers: *South Bank Orchestra* / Paris was made for...: *Legrand, Michel* / Mapp and Lucia: *South Bank Orchestra* / Married man, A: *South Bank Orchestra* / Drummonds: *South Bank Orchestra* / Dempsey & Makepeace: *South Bank Orchestra* / Atlantis: *South Bank Orchestra* / Upstairs, downstairs: *South Bank Orchestra* / Black beauty: *King, Denis* / Lillie: *South Bank Orchestra* / Dick Turpin: *King, Denis Orchestra* / Love story: *Lai, Frances Orchestra* / Man and a woman, A: *Lai, Frances Orchestra* / Windmills of your mind: *Legrand, Michel.*
2LP: FEDD 1010
MCSET: CFEDD 1010

Offerings Of Isca

OFFERINGS OF ISCA (Various artists).
LP: MIC 15 001

Offhooks

OFF THE HOOK.
LP: DISPLP 18

Office Boy

WITH A WOMAN LIKE YOU (see under "Campbell, Gordon").

Office Ladies

BRAINS IN BED, BRAINS AND BOOTS, NO BOOTS IN BED.
LP: NAR 042
MC: NARC 042

Officer & a Gentleman

OFFICER AND A GENTLEMAN, AN (Film soundtrack) (Various artists).
Tracks: / Officer and a gentleman, An: *Ritenour, Lee* / Up where we belong: *Cocker, Joe & Jennifer Warnes* / Hungry for you love: *Morrison, Van* / Tush: *ZZ Top* / Treat me right: *Benatar, Pat* / Be real: *Sir Douglas Quintet* / Tunnel of love: *Dire Straits.*
LP: ISTA 3
MC: ICT 3
MC: ICM 2041
MC: 842 715 4

Official...

OFFICIAL MUSIC OF THE 1984 GAMES (Various artists).
LP: CBS 26048
MC: 40 26048

Officiers of

FULL STEAM AHEAD (see Tchico & Les Officiers of African Music) (Officiers of African Music & Tchico).

O'Flatharta, Vail

BLATH NA NAIRNI (Sean nos singing).
LP: CC 45
MC: 4CC 45

O'Flynn, Liam

BRENDAN VOYAGE (O'Flynn, Liam & Orchestra).
LP: TA 3006
MC: 4TA 3006

Ofwerman, Rune

BAD BOYS FROM BRAZIL (Ofwerman, Rune Trio).
LP: AMLP 857

Ogden, Nigel

IT'S A MUSICAL WORLD.
Tracks: / It's a musical world / Dance in the twilight / Clog dance / Cachucha / Swingle jingle / When sunny gets blue / Besame mucho / March, The / Up, up and away / Bluesette / Leicester Square looks round / Noddy's holiday / Minuet for Melinda / Shopping spree / As long as he needs me / Amor amor / Gypsy in my soul.
LP: AML 312

Ogdon, John

MORE PIANO FAVOURITES (Ogdon, John/Daniel Adni).
MC: TC2MOM 113

PIANO MOODS (Ogdon, John/Daniel Adni).
MC: TC2MOM 122

Ogerman

CITYSCAPE (Ogerman & Brecker).
LP: K 57014

GOLDEN HIGHLIGHTS OF AKKERMAN & OGERMAN (See under Akkerman, Jan) (Akkerman & Ogerman).

Ogermann, Claus

CLAUS OGERMANN ORCHESTRA WITH MICHAEL BRECKER (Ogermann, Claus Orchestra & Michael Brecker).
Tracks: / Corfu / Lyricosmos / After the fight / Adonia / Boulevard tristesse.
LP: . . . . **GRP 96321**
MC: . . . . **GRP 96324**

O'Grada, Conal

TOP OF COOM, THE.
LP: . . . . **CCF 27**
MC: **4CCF 27**

O'Grady, Geraldine

QIET LAND OF ERIN.
LP: . . . . **STAL 8006**

Oh Boy

OH BOY.
LP: . . . . **N 109**

Oh Calcutta

OH CALCUTTA (Original Australian Cast) (Various artists).
Tracks: / Oh Calcutta: *Various artists* / Coming together, going together: *Various artists* / Sincere replies: *Various artists* / Dick and Jane: *Various artists* / Clarence and Mildred: *Various artists* / Exchanges of information: *Various artists* / I like the look: *Various artists* / Jack and Jill: *Various artists*/ Green pants: *Various artists* / Much too soon: *Various artists* / Reprise: *Various artists.*
LP: . . . . **INTS 1178**

Oh Captain

OH CAPTAIN (Original Broadway cast) (Various artists).
LP: . . . . **AOS 2002**

Oh Dev

YOU GET WHAT YOU DESERVE.
LP: . . . . **SCHEMER 8904**

Oh Happy Days

OH HAPPY DAYS.
LP: . . . . **WH 5004**

Oh No...

OH NO, IT'S MORE FROM RAW.
LP: . . . . **RAWLP 2**

Oh Well

FIRST ALBUM, THE.
Tracks: / Hit you / Mad day in London / Radar love / Don't waste my time / Day by day / Stop the world / I'll be forever your man / Downtown / We will rock you / I'll be forever your man (12" mix) (CD only.).
LP: . . . . **PCS 7340**
MC: . . . . **TCPCS 7340**

Oh What A Lovely War

OH WHAT A LOVELY WAR (Original London Cast) (Various artists).
Tracks: / Overture: *Various artists* / Row row row: *Various artists* / Your king and country want you: *Various* artists / Belgium put the kibosh on the Kaiser: *Various artists* / Are we downhearted? No: *Various artists*/ Hold your hand out you naughty boy: *Various artists* / I'll make a man of you: *Various artists* / Pack up your troubles: *Various artists* / Hitchy koo: *Various artists* / Heilige nacht: *Various artists* / Christmas day in the cookhouse: *Various artists* / Goodbye-ee: *Various artists* / Oh it's a lovely war: *Various artists*/ Gassed last night: *Various artists* / There's a long long trail: *Various artists* / Hush, here comes a whizzbang: *Various artists* / They were only playing leapfrog: *Various artists* / I wore a tunic: *Various artists*/ Forward, Joe Soap's army: *Various artists* / When this lousy war is over: *Various artists* / Wash me in the water: *Various artists* / I want to go home: *Various artists* / Bells of hell, The: *Various artists* / Keep the home fires burning: *Various artists* / La chanson de Craonne: *Various artists* / I don't want to be a soldier: *Various artists* / They didn't believe me: *Various artists.*
LP: . . . . **TER 1043**
MC: . . . . **ZCTER 1043**

OH WHAT A LOVELY WAR (ORIGINAL 1914-18 RECORDINGS) (Various artists).
Tracks: / Oh it's a lovely war: *Various artists* / Goodbye-ee: *Various artists* / Belgium put the kibosh on the Kaiser: *Various artists* / Your king and country want you: *Various artists* / I'll make a man of you: *Various* artists / When the moon shines bright on Charlie Chaplin: *Various artists* / Pack up your troubles in your old kit bag: *Various artists* / Conscientious objector: *Various artists* / Marie Lloyd: *Various artists* / Now you've got yer khaki on: *Various artists* / Oh boy, when you're home on leave: *Various artists* / Over there: *Various* artists / When the war is over: *Various artists* / Mother dear: *Various artists* / Till the boys come home: *Various artists* / Roses of Picardy: *Various artists* / America answers the call: *Various artists* / They didn't believe me: *Various artists.*
LP: . . . . **SH 130**

O'Hagan, Patrick

22 GOLDEN SHAMROCKS.
Tracks: / I'll take you home again Kathleen / Mountains of Mourne / There's a little bit of Irish (in everybody's heart) / My wild Irish rose / Where the river Shannon flows / Garden where the praties grow / Mother Machree / Isle of Innisfree / Wearing of the green, The / Galway Bay / If your Irish come into the parlour / With my shillelagh under me arm / Stone outside Dan Murphy's door, The / Little town in the ould County Down / Dear old Donegal / When Irish eyes are smiling / Danny boy / Too-ra-loo-ra-loo-ra / MacNamara's band / It's a great day for the Irish / Rose of Tralee, The / Dear little shamrock.
MC: . . . . **KBER 023**

O'Hagan, Sean

HIGH LLAMAS.
LP: . . . . **FIEND 192**
MC: . . . . **FIENDCASS 192**

O'Halloran Brothers

MEN OF THE ISLAND, THE Irish traditional music and song.
Tracks: / Music in the glen / Green fields of America / Lark in the morning, The / Connaught man's rambles, The / Lowlands of Holland, The / Stack of barley / Johnny, will you marry me? / Martin Byrne's waltz / Hundred pipers, A / Dingle regatta / Granuaile / Sailor on the rock, The / Maid I ne'er forget, The / Limerick lasses, The / Lake shore, The / Exile's return, The / Eel in the sink, The / Larry Redigan's reel / Moorlough Mary / Bucks of Oranmore, The / Wind that shakes the barley, The.
LP: **12TS 305**

O'Hara, Dan

IRISH FAVOURITES.
LP: . . . . **RBA 108**

ROVIN' IRISHMAN.
LP: . . . . **RBA 133**

O'Hara, Mary

AT THE ROYAL FESTIVAL HALL.
Tracks: / Morning has broken / Tapestry / Heridean milking song, A / Among silence / Bring me a shawl from Galway / Bridge over troubled water / Forty five years / Una Bhan / Scarlet ribbons / Song for a winter's night / When I need you / Lord of the dance.
LP: . . . . **CHR 1159**
MC: . . . . **ZCHR 1159**
LP: . . . . **MFP 41 5664 1**
MC: . . . . **TCMFP 4156644**

CELEBRATION OF LOVE.
Tracks: / El Shaddai / Forever young / Any dream will do (and other tracks).
LP: . . . . **WST R 9702**
MC: . . . . **WST C 9702**

COLOURS.
Tracks: / Colours of my life / Blow the wind southerly / My favourite things / Mr. Tambourine man / Greensleeves / Rose, The / You needed me / Jesu, joy of man's desiring / Being green / English country garden / Last rose of summer / In my life.
LP: . . . . **IMG 0001**
MC: . . . . **IMGC 0001**

FAREWELL, BUT WHENEVER.
LP: . . . . **HMR 9004**

FOCUS ON MARY O'HARA.
MC: . . . . **KFOC 28089**

IN HARMONY ALBUM.
Tracks: / Plaisir D'amour / Rainy day people / Clown, The / Sun is burning, The / Too much magic / Pussy willows cat tails / Sliabh na mban / Friend of mine, A / Wee cooper o' Fife, The / Mon pays / Spinning wheel.
LP: . . . . **CHR 1217**

INSTRUMENTAL COLLECTION, THE.
Tracks: / Way we were, The / Londonderry air / Skye boat song / Pamela Brown / Bunch of thyme, A / Scarborough fair / For the good times / Bright eyes / Walking in the air / Three times a lady / Going home / Greensleeves / In an English country garden / Memory / Annie's song / One day at a time.
LP: . . . . **VAL 8059**
MC: . . . . **VAL 68059**

LAST ROSE OF SUMMER, THE.
Tracks: / Annie Laurie / Last rose of summer / Cucuin a chuaichin (cuckoo,little cuckoo) (Cuckoo little cuckoo) / Trotting to the fair / Lord Randal / Shetland lullaby, A / My Aunt Jane (end s1) / Roisin dubh (Dark Rosaleen) / Child of the woodland (Na hao ri u - ghost song) / Wee cooper o' Fife, The / Seansa bhriste leathair (John and his leather breeches) / Parting, The / Deirin de (lullaby) / Cogai a gagog.
LP: . . . . **CBR 1028**
MC: . . . . **KCBR 1028**

LIVE AT CARNEGIE HALL.
Tracks: / Rainy day people / Spanish lady, The / Ulst castle croon / Chanson pour les petits enfants / Perhaps love / Kitty of Coleraine / Oaken ashes / Judas and Mary / In an English country garden / Rose, The / Song of Glensdun / Willie's gone to Melville castle / Scent of roses, The / Riddle song, The / Face to face / Snail, The / Say that I'll be sure to find you / Tis a gift to be simple / Lord of the dance / Greensleeves.
LP: . . . . **VAL 8056**
MC: . . . . **VAL 68056**

MARY O'HARA.
Tracks: / Plaisir d'amour / Rainy day people / Clown, The / Sun is burning, The / Too much magic / Pussy willows cat tails / Silabh na mban / Friend of mine, A / Wee cooper o' Fife, The / Spinning wheel.
MC: . . . . **SSC 3083**
LP: . . . . **SHM 3092**
MC: . . . . **HSC 3092**

MARY O'HARA double cassette.
MCSET: . . . . **DTO 10217**

MARY O'HARA'S WORLD OF MUSIC.
Tracks: / Minstrel of the dawn / Song for Ireland, A / A la Claire Fontaine / Zavara katra nemia / Cancion de cuno para dormir a un negrito / Take it on the chin / In Trutina / Unusual way / Wiengenlied lullaby / Traguoudo tragoudo / Song for the Myra, A / Oceans away / All through the night / Minstrel boy.
LP: . . . . **MFP 5870**
MC: . . . . **TCMFP 5870**

MUSIC SPEAKS LOUDER THAN WORDS.
Tracks: / Music speaks louder than words / Annie's song / Cucuin a chuaichin (cuckoo, little cuckoo) / Oceans away / Dust in the wind / Snail, The / I'll have to say I love you in a song / Home in the meadow / Scorn not his simplicity / Ceol a phiobaire / Never my love / Roisin dubh.
LP: . . . . **SSP 3083**

SCALLYWAG GANG (8 CANINE RASCALS) (Read by Mary O'Hara).
MC: . . . . **TBC 9505**

SCENT OF THE ROSES, THE.
Tracks: / You are the new day / Prayer of the badger, The / Rainbow connection, The / Child of the woodland / Greenfinch and Linnet bird / Scent of the roses, The / Try to remember / Garden song / Ye banks and braes / As I walked forth on summer's day / Chanson pour le petits enfants / I gave my love a cherry.
LP: . . . . **CHR 1308**
MC: . . . . **ZCHR 1308**

SONG FOR IRELAND, A.
Tracks: / My Lagan love / Kitty of Coleraine / Soft day, A / Danny boy / Spanish lady / She moved through the fair / Gartan mothers lullaby / Down by the Sally gardens / Song of Glendun, The / Quiet land of Erin, The.
LP: . . . . **VAL 8053**
MC: . . . . **VAL 68053**

SONGS OF IRELAND.
MC: . . . . **BTC 309**

SPREAD A LITTLE HAPPINESS.
Tracks: / Both sides now / Isn't this a lovely day / You light up my life / El condor pasa / Annie Laurie / Do you know where you're going to (Theme from Mahogany) / Here, there and everywhere / Flower duet from Lakme, The / Umbrella man / Always / Spread a little happiness / Pie Jesu / Follow me / Danny boy / Morning has broken / We're all alone / T'was a lover and his lass / If.
LP: . . . . **STAR 2255**
MC: . . . . **STAC 2255**

TRANQUILITY 20 SONGS OF LIFE.
LP: . . . . **WW 5072**

O'Hara, Mary Margaret

MISS AMERICA.
Tracks: / To cry about / Year in song, The / Body's in trouble / Dear darling / New day, A / When you know why you're happy / My friends have / Help me lift you up / Keeping you in mind / Not be alright / You will be loved again.
LP: . . . . **V 2559**
MC: . . . . **TCV 2559**

O'Hearn, Patrick

BETWEEN TWO WORLDS.
Tracks: / Rain maker / Sky juice / Cape perpetual / Gentle was the night / Fire ritual / 87 dreams of a lifetime / Dimension D / Forever the optimist / Journey to Yoroba / Between two worlds.
LP: **209.963**
MC: **409.963**

ELDORADO.
Tracks: / Amazon waltz / Nepalese tango / Black Delilah / Chattahoochee field day / Illusionist, The / One eyed jacks / Hear our prayer / Delicate / Eldorado / There's always tomorrow.
LP: **210102**
MC: **410102**

MIX UP.
Tracks: / Fire ritual / April fool / Journey to Yoroba / Black Delilah / Illusionist, The / Mixed up / Chatahochee field day / So saxy.
LP: **211143**
MC: **411143**

RIVERS GONNA RISE.
Tracks: / Homeward bound / Stroll, The / Glory for tomorrow / Acadia / Forgiveness / April fool / Reunion / Brief repose, A / Subtle persuasion / Portobello locks.
LP: **209645**
MC: **409645**

Ohio Express

SWEETER THAN SUGAR.
LP: **2636531**
MC: **2636534**

Ohio Players

ECSTASY.
LP: . . . . **SEW 026**
MC: . . . . **SEWC 026**

FIRE.
Tracks: / Fire / I want to be free / It's all over / Runnin' from the devil / Smoke / Together / What the hell.
LP: **9100 009**

GOLD.
Tracks: / Fire / Skin tight / Who'd she coo / Love rollercoaster / Sweet sticky thing / Angel / Far east Mississippi / Feel the beat / Fopp / I want to be free / Jive turkey / Only a child can love.
LP: **824461 1**
MC: **824461 4**
LP: . . . . **JABB 26**
MC: . . . . **JABBC 26**
LP: **9100 030**

GRADUATION.
LP: . . . . **AIR 7601**
MC: . . . . **AIRZC 7601**

OHIO PLAYERS.
LP: . . . . **SM 11291**

OUCH!.
Tracks: / Do your thing / Star of the party / Sweet lil lady / Everybody dance / My baby gets the best of my love / Just me / Thinkin'bout you / Devoted / I'd better take a coffee break.
LP: . . . . **EPC 85562**

PAIN.
Tracks: / Pain / Never had a dream / Players balling (players doin' their own thing) / I wanna hear it from you / Reds, The / Singing in the morning.
LP: . . . . **SEW 004**
MC: . . . . **SEWC 004**

PLEASURE.
Tracks: / Pleasure / Laid it / Pride and vanity / Walt's first trip / Varee is love / Walked away from you / Paint me / Funky worm / Our love has died.
LP: . . . . **SEW 014**
MC: . . . . **SEWC 014**

TENDERNESS.
Tracks: / Try a little tenderness / Sometimes I cry skinny / Try to be a man / Board walkin' / Call me / (Sittin' on) the dock of a bay / It takes a while / Hard to love your brother.
LP: . . . . **EPC 85041**

Ohlson, Curtis

BETTER THAN EVER.
LP: . . . . **ENVLP 518**
MC: . . . . **TCENV 518**

SO FAST.
Tracks: / Half nelson / Love's school / I'm dreaming of you (As I sing...) / Johnson family, The / Verbal abuse / You / So fast / Village chant.
LP: **3274 1**

Ohrensausen

OHRENSAUSEN (Various artists).
LP: . . . . **DOM V77-03**

Ohrlin, Glenn

WILD BUCKAROO, THE.
LP: . . . . **ROUNDER 0158**

'Oi'

CARRY ON OI (Various artists).
Tracks: / United: *Johnson, Gary* / Dambusters: *JJ Alstars* / Suburban rebels: *Business* / Each dawn I die: *Infa Riot* / Arms race: *Partisans* / East end kids: *Ejected* / Transvestite: *Peter & The Test Tube Babies* / Nation on fire: *Blitz (group)* / King of the jungle: *Last Resort* / Tuckers ruckers ain't no suckers:

Gonads / Evil: *4 Skins* / Product: *Business* / SPG: *Red Alert* / Maniac: *Peter & The Test Tube Babies* / What am I gonna do: *Ejected* / No U-turn: *Partisans* / Youth: *Blitz (group)*/ Mob chorus: *Various artists.*
LP: . . . . SEC 2
MC: . . . . TSEC 2

CARRY ON OI (2) (Various artists).
LP: . . . . LINKLP 067

OI - CHARTBUSTER, VOL.1 (Various artists).
LP: . . . . LINK LP 03

OI CHARTBUSTERS VOL.2 (Various artists).
LP: . . . . LINK LP 016

OI CHARTBUSTERS VOL.5 (Various artists).
LP: . . . . LINK LP 081

OI GLORIOUS OI (Various artists).
Tracks: / Work it out: *Section 5* / I wanna knighthood: *Angelic Upstarts* / Holding on: *Burial* / Some fun: *Anti Heros* / Where were you: *Glory* / Willing to kill: *Vendetta* / Rip off: *Cockney Rebel*/ Lost on highway 46: *Sham 69* / One thing on our minds: *Vicious Rumours* / Bank holidays: *Indecent exposure*/ Turncoat: *Youth defence league* / Action man: *Strike* / I'd rather be down the pub: *Close Shave* / Rebel: *Intensive Care.*
LP: . . . . LINK LP 023

OI OF SEX, THE (Various artists).
LP: . . . . SYNLP 4
LP: . . . . LINK LP 036

OI OI OI (Various artists).
LP: . . . . LINKLP 130

OI OI THAT'S YER LOT (Various artists).
LP: . . . . LINKLP 068
LP: . . . . RR 9945

OI THAT'S YER LOT (Various artists).
Tracks: / Real enemy, The: *Business* / Doctor Crippens: *5-O* / White flag: *Oppressed* / Stick together: *Sub Culture* / Liddle towers: *Crux* / Horror show: *Warriors* / Big brother: *Attack* / Revenge: *Black Flag* / Arthur's theme: *Arthur & The Afters* / On your bike: *Frankie & The Flames* / Getting pissed: *Magnificent Gonads* / Willie Whitelaw's willie: *Attila The Stockbroker* / Belle of Snodland Town, The: *Judge Dread* / Oi oi music: *Skingraft* / Awayday: *Attila The Stockbroker* / Such fun: *Coming blood.*
LP: . . . . SEC 5
MC: . . . . TSEC 5

OI THAT'S YOUR LOT (Various artists).
Tracks: / Oi, oi, oi: *Cockney Rejects* / Here we go again: *Cockney Rejects* / Rob a bank: *Peter & The Test Tube Babies* / Intensive care: *Peter & The Test Tube Babies* / Wonderful world: *4 Skins* / Chaos: *4 Skins*/ Have a cigar: *Postmen* / Beardsmen: *Postmen* / Daily news: *Exploited* / I still believe in anarchy: *Exploited* / Generation of scars: *Terrible twins* / Guns for the Afghan rebels: *Angelic Upstarts* / Last night another soldier: *Angelic Upstarts* / Sunday stripper: *Cock Sparrer* / Isubeleeene: *Splodge. Max/Desert Island Joe* / Where have all the bootboys gone?: *Slaughter & The...* / Boot boys: *Barney & the Rubbles.*
LP: . . . . ZIT 1

OI - THE PICTURE DISC (Various artists).
LP: . . . . LINK LP 014

OI, THE PICTURE DISC VOL 2 (Various artists).
LP: . . . . LINK LP 037

OI-THE RESURRECTION (Various artists).
LP: . . . . LINK LP 01

SON OF OI! various punk artists (Various artists).
Tracks: / Onwards: *Kraut with Steve Jones* / Andy is a corporatist: *Attila The Stockbroker* / I understand: *Angelic* Upstarts / Chip on my shoulder: *Cock Sparrer* / Generation landslide: *Prole* / Boy about town: *Johnson, Gary* / Young conservatives: *Johnson, Gary* / On the streets: *4 Skins* / Jobs not jails: *Gonads* / Something they don't understand: *Paranoid Pictures* / Violent playground: *Clockwork Destruction* / This is your loife: *Vicious Rumours* / Molotov: *Maniac Youth* / Sing something swindle: *Orgasm Guerillas* / Jerusalem: *L.O.L.S* / Manifestdi: *Oi The Robot/The Business.*
LP: . . . . SYNLP 3

SOUND OF OI! The hills are alive with the... (Various artists).
Tracks: / Coventry: *Business* / Surfin' in Newquay: *Vicious Rumours* / My life's fine: *Skin Deep* / Sheila: *Burial* / Fictional kicks: *Renegade* / Battle: *Condemned 84* / Old: *Cock Sparrer* / Norman: *4 Skins* / Headcase: *Section 5* / Coming on strong: *Magnificent* / Best, The: *5-O* / Confusion: *Van Del & The Hooligans* / Law, The: *Close Shave* / Beginning of the end: *Cockney Rejects.*
LP: . . . . LINK LP 011

STRENGTH THROUGH OI (Various artists).
LP: . . . . WOW LP 3

THIS IS OI (A street punk compilation) (Various artists).
LP: . . . . OIR 004

UNITED SKINS (Various artists).
LP: . . . . SKREW LP 1

Oi Polloi

ATOMIC MENACE.
LP: . . . . WOWLP 13

SKINS AND PUNKS VOLUME 2 (Oi Polloi/Betrayed).
LP: . . . . OIR 008

UNITE AND WIN.
LP: . . . . OIR 011

YOU ARE NOT ALONE(EP) (see under Hex) (Hex/ Oi Polloi/ Stalag 17/ Symbol Of Freedom).

Oihid, Jimmy

JIMMY OIHID.
LP: 106101
MC: 106102

Oil A World Crisis

OIL A WORLD CRISIS (See under UNESCO reports).

Oil City Symphony

OIL CITY SYMPHONY (Stage Show Soundtrack) (Various artists).
LP: . . . . SBL 12594
MC: . . . . SBLC 12594

Oil In The Eye

SURGICAL FATHERLAND, THE.
LP: . . . . EBA 003

Oingo Boingo

NOTHING TO FEAR.
Tracks: / Private life / Wild sex.
LP: . . . . AMLH 64903

ONLY A LAD.
Tracks: / Little girls / Perfect system / On the outside / Capitalism / You really got me / Only a lad / What you see / Controller / Imposter / Nasty habits.
LP: . . . . AMLH 64863

Oisin

BEALOIDEAS.
LP: . . . . TA 2011
MC: 4TA 2011

JEANNIE C., THE.
LP: . . . . TA 2013

OISIN.
LP: . . . . TA 2010
MC: 4TA 2010

OVER THE MOOR TO MAGGIE.
LP: . . . . TA 2012
MC: 4TA 2012

WINDS OF CHANGE.
LP: . . . . TA 2016
MC: . . . . UTA 2016

WINDS OF CHANGE.
LP: . . . . TA 2016
MC: 4TA 2016

O'Jays

6 TRACK HITS: O'JAYS.
MC: 7SC 5053

COLLECTOR'S ITEMS Greatest hits.
Tracks: / Love train / 992 arguments / Message in our music / Give the people what they want / Livin' for the weekend / I love music (part 1) / For the love of money / Put your hands together / Darlin' darlin' baby (sweet tender love).
LP: . . . . PIR 32189
MC: 40 32189

EMOTIONALLY YOURS.
Tracks: / Don't let me down / Sosmething for nothing / Emotionally yours (R & B version) / Respect / Keep on lovin' me / Love and trust / Don't you know true love / Emotionally yours (Gospel version) / That's how love is / Closer to you / If I find love again / Keep on pleasing me / Lies / Make it feel good.
LP: . . . . MTL 1060
MC: . . . . TCMTL 1060

EXTRAORDINARY GIRL.
LP: . . . . CXMB 7200

FROM THE BEGINNING.
Tracks: / One night affair / You're the best thing since candy / Branded bad / Losing touch / I should be your lover / Deeper in love with you / Let me in your world / I can't get enough / I've got the groove / There's someone waiting / It's too strong.
LP: . . . . GCH 8087

GREATEST HITS: O'JAYS.
Tracks: / For the love of money / Back stabbers / Forever mine / Stairway to heaven / Love train / Sunshine / Let me make love to you / Used to be my girl / Darlin' darlin' baby / I love music.
LP: . . . . PIR 32441
MC: 40 32441
LP: . . . . PIR 32189

HEART AND SOUL OF THE O'JAYS.
Tracks: / Love train / Sing a happy song / Put our heads together / Time to get down / 992 arguments / Work on me / Used ta be my girl / I love music / Darlin' darlin' baby / Message in our music / Girl don't let it get you down / I just want to satisfy / Livin' for the weekend / Brandy.
LP: . . . . KNLP 12052
MC: . . . . KNMC 12052

IDENTIFY YOURSELF.
Tracks: / Sing a happy song / Get on out and party / Identify yourself / So nice I tried it twice / Hurry up and come back / Forever mine / I want you here with me / One in a million.
LP: . . . . PIR 83666
MC: 40 83666

LET ME TOUCH YOU.
Tracks: / Don't take your love away / Loving you / True love never dies / Still missing / I just want somebody to love me / Let me touch you / Undercover lover / No lies to cloud my eyes / Don't let the dream get away / 'Cause I want you back again.
LP: . . . . PHIL 4002
MC: . . . . TCPHIL 4002
LP: . . . . MTL 1014
MC: . . . . TCMTL 1014

LOVE AND MORE.
LP: . . . . PIR 25998
MC: 40 25998

MESSAGE IN THE MUSIC.
Tracks: / Message in our music / Prayer / Make a joyful noise / Desire me / Darlin' darlin' baby / I swear / I love no one but you / Let life flow.
LP: . . . . PIR 81460

MY FAVOURITE PERSON (ALBUM).
Tracks: / I just want to satisfy you / Your body's here with me / My favourite person / One on one / I like to see us get down / Your true heart / Out in the real world / Don't walk away / Mad.
LP: . . . . PIR 85712

O'JAYS 4 track cassette EP.
Tracks: / Love train / I love music / Used to be my girl / Darlin' darlin' baby.
MC: . . . . PIRA 402628

PEACE.
Tracks: / Now he's home / Little brother / Crossroads of life / La de dah / Peace / Shattered man / Your turn this time / Just to be with you / Gotta get my broom out / Never can say goodbye / Year 2000, The / To prove I love you / You'll never know / You're the girl of my dreams / You won't feel / Girl don't let it get you down / Answer's in you / Once is not enough.
LP: . . . . PHX 1001

REFLECTIONS IN GOLD (1973-1982).
Tracks: / Ship ahoy / Now that we found love / Don't call me brother / Survival / How time flies / You and me / She is only a woman / Cry together / This time baby / Brandy / Help somebody please / Hurry up and come back / Your body's here with me.
2LP: . . . . CDX 28
MC: . . . . TCCDX 28

SERIOUS.
Tracks: / Out of my mind / Leave it alone / Have you had your love today / Serious hold on me / Friend of a friend / Never been better / Rainbow / Fading / Pot can't call the kettle black.
LP: . . . . MTL 1041
MC: . . . . TCMTL 1041
LP: . . . . E 190921

WHEN WILL I SEE YOU AGAIN.
Tracks: / I can't stand the pain / Betcha don't know / When will I see you again / House of fire / Letter to my friends / Put our heads together / Ain't nothin' wrong with good lovin' / Nice and easy.
LP: . . . . PIR 25290
MC: 40 25290

WORKING ON YOUR CASE.
Tracks: / Lipstick traces (on a cigarette) / How does it feel / You're the one / Rented tuxedo / Let it all out / You're on top / No time for you / My dearest beloved / Working on your case / Hold on / Lonely drifter / Today and tomorrow / Storm is over, The / Stand in for love / Dotted line / Stand tall.
LP: . . . . EG 2604821
MC: . . . . EG 2604824

YEAR 2000, THE.
Tracks: / Year 2000 / To prove I love you / You'll never know / You're the girl of my dreams / You won't fail / Girl don't let it get you down / Answer's in you / Once is not enough.
LP: . . . . PIR 84221
MC: 40 84221

OK Jive

LIVE AT THE BLUE CHONJO SKY DAY & NIGHT CLUB.
Tracks: / Anyway / Take it easy / Why won't you dance with me / Bongos / Magic man Brown / Richard / Detective / Benga special / White lie.
LP: . . . . EPC 85908

O'Kanes

IMAGINE THAT.
LP: 4663461
MC: 4663464

O'KANES, THE.
Tracks: / Oh darlin' (why don't you care for me no more) / Just loving you / Daddies need to grow up too / Can't stop my heart from loving you / Bluegrass blues / Oh lonesome you / When we're gone' long gone / That's alright mama / Gonna walk that line / When I found you.
LP: 4500691
MC: 4500694

TIRED OF THE RUNNIN'.
Tracks: / One true love / All because of you / If I could be there / Blue love / Rocky road / Highway 55 / Tired of the runnin' / In my heart / I'm lonely / Isn't that so.
LP: 4608311
MC: 4608314

O'Keefe, Danny

DAY TO DAY, THE.
LP: . . . . 8235201 ME

Okeh...

OKEH BLACK ROCK 'N' ROLL (Various artists).
LP: . . . . ED 283

Okin, Earl

EARL OKIN HIMSELF.
Tracks: / Gee baby ain't I good to you / Tooting / When the music fades away / Black beauty / Ludwig baby / I want us to last / Quiet nights / Nightingale / Miss Otis regrets / Tulip or turnip?.
LP: . . . . WP 107
MC: . . . . WP 107LPC

EARL'S CAUGHT.
LP: . . . . WF 027
MC: . . . . WF 027C

MR OKIN COMES TO TOWN.
LP: . . . . FL 1016

Okines, Ken

CLOSE RELATIONS (Okines, Ken/Sue Ashby).
Tracks: / False fox, The / Blackberry fall / Fires of hell / Tommy the proud / Little Mohee / Jenny in the morning / Just a dream / June apple / Fly away / David / G.O.D. / Down in the city / Commonsense.
LP: . . . . BURL 012

Oklahoma

OKLAHOMA (London stage cast) (Various artists).
Tracks: / Overture: *Various artists* / Oh what a beautiful morning: *Various artists* / Surrey with the fringe on top: *Various artists* / Kansas City: *Various artists* / I can't say no: *Various artists* / Many a new day: *Various artists* / People will say we're in love: *Various artists* / Poor Jud is dead: *Various artists*/ Lonely room: *Various artists* / Out of my dreams: *Various artists* / Farmer and the cowman: *Various artists*/ All er nothin': *Various artists* / Oklahoma: *Various artists* / Finale: *Various artists.*
LP: . . . . OAK 1
MC: . . . . ZOAK 1

OKLAHOMA (Original stage cast) (Various artists).
Tracks: / Oh what a beautiful morning: *Various artists* / Surrey with the fringe on top: *Various artists* / Out of my dreams: *Various artists* / Kansas City: *Various artists* / I can't say no: *Various artists* / People will say we're in love: *Various artists* / Farmer dance, The: *Various artists* / Poor Jud is dead: *Various* artists / It's a scandal, it's an outrage: *Various artists* / Many a new day: *Various artists* / All er nothin': *Various artists* / Oklahoma: *Various artists.*
LP: . . . . SH 393
LP: . . . . MCL 1658
MC: . . . . MCLC 1658

OKLAHOMA (Revival original Broadway cast) (Various artists).
LP: . . . . CBL 1 3572
MC: . . . . CBK 1 3572
LP: . . . . BL 13572
MC: . . . . BK 13572

Okossun, Sonny

AFRICAN SOLDIERS.
LP: . . . . FILER 414
MC: . . . . FILERCT 414

FIRE IN SOWETO.
LP: NEMI 0330

LIBERATION.
LP: SHAN 43019
MC: SHANC 43019

WHICH WAY NIGERIA.
LP: HIP 18

WIND OF CHANGE.
LP: IVR 001

O.K.s

DESIRE.
LP: 400 245

Okukuseku

ODE YE DE.
LP: RASLPS 052

Old...

OLD LADY DRIVERS.
LP: MOSH 7

Old Gold...

BEST OF 12 SYNTH (Various artists).
LP: OG 1802
MC: OG 2802

Old Grey Whistle Test

OLD GREY WHISTLE TEST (Various artists).
LP: BELP 017

Old Gringo

OLD GRINGO (Film Soundtrack) (Various artists).
Tracks: / Ride to the hacienda: *Various artists* / Battle, The: *Various artists* / Harriet's theme: *Various* artists / Bitter's last ride: *Various artists* / Mirrors, The: *Various artists* / Nightime: *Various artists*/ Bell tower, The: *Various artists* / Sigh, The: *Various artists* / Battle (resolution), The: *Various artists*/ Bitter's destiny: *Various artists* / Finale: *Various artists*.
LP: GNPS 8017
MC: GNP5 8017

Old & In The Way

OLD AND IN THE WAY.
Tracks: / Pig in the pen / Old and in the way / Hobo song, The / Wild horses / White dove / Midnight moonlight / Knockin' on your door / Panama red / Kissimmee kid / Land of the Navajo.
LP: GDV 4014
MC: GDTC 4014

Old Man Of Lochnagar

OLD MAN OF LOCHNAGAR (Original cast recording) (Various artists).
MC: SCENEC 5

Old Man & The Sea

OLD MAN AND THE SEA, THE (Film Soundtrack) (Various artists).
LP: ACS 8013

Old Music Box...

OLD MUSIC BOX WALTZ MELODIES Swiss music boxes - Bornand collection.
Tracks: / Invitation to the dance / Artists life waltz / Treasure waltz / Merry widow / Faust waltz / Little fisher maiden / Skater's waltz / Estudiantina / Chimes of Normandy / Tales of Vienna woods / Blue Danube / Carnival of Venice / On a Sunday afternoon / In the good old summertime / Edelweiss glide / When the leaves begin to turn / After the ball / Southern roses / Wine, women and song / Mikado waltz.
LP: RCB 4
MC: RCBC 4

Old & New Dreams

PLAYING.
Tracks: / Happy house / Mopti / New dream / Rushour / Broken shadows / Playing.
LP: ECM 1205

Old School

OLD SCHOOL (Various artists).
LP: LICLP 40

Old Skull

GET OUTTA SCHOOL.
LP: LS 94481

Old Swan Band

GAMESTERS,PICKPOCKETS AND HARLOTS.
LP: DIN 322

NO REELS.
LP: FRR 011

OLD SWAN BAND.
Tracks: / Matelot. / Michael Turner's jig no. 3 / Captain Lemo's quick march / King of the gypsies, The / Can't stop polka / Evesham stick dance / Jack Tarr on the shore / Stoney's waltz / Neriah Benfield's waltz / Jack Robinson / April morning / British man of war / Redower Polka / Scan's stepdance no. 2 / Crabfish / Step dance / Bunch of violets blue / Symondsbury mummers' tune / Doctor Casey's fin book / My love my love / Fare thee well, dearest Nancy / Trip to the forest / Triumph, (The) / Bourton six / Speed the plough.
LP: FRR 028

Old Swinging Bridge

OLD SWINGING BRIDGE, THE (Various artists).
LP: ROUNDER 0020

Old Time...

OLD TIME GREATS TRUK 4 (Various artists).
MC: VCA 622

REINE RIMON IN NEW ORLEANS (Various artists).
LP: LPS 15

Old Vs Young

OLD VS YOUNG (Various artists).
LP: RMM 1020

Old Wives' Tale

OLD WIVES' TALE, THE (see under Bennett, Arnold) (Calvert, Phyllis).

Oldfield, Mike

AMAROK.
LP: V 2640
MC: TCV 2640

BOXED.
Tracks: / Tubular bells (part 1) / Tubular bells (part 2) / Hergest ridge (part 1) / Ommadawn (part 1) / Ommadawn (part 2) / Phaeacian games, The / Star's end (extract) / Rio Grande / First excursion / Algiers / Portsmouth / In dulci jubilo / Speak (tho you only say farewell) / Hergest ridge (part 2).
MCSET: TCVX 1

COMPLETE MIKE OLDFIELD (Best Of Compilation).
Tracks: / Arrival / In dulci jubilo / Portsmouth / Jungle gardenia / Guilty / Blue Peter / Waldberg (the peak) / Etude / Wonderful land / Moonlight shadow / Family man / Mistake / Five miles out / Crime of passion / To France / Shadow on the wall / Excerpt from Tubular bells / Sheba / Mirage / Platinum / Mount Teide / Excerpt from Ommadawn / Excerpt from Hergest Ridge / Excerpt from Incantations / Excerpt from The killing fields.
2LP: MOC 1
MC: CMOC 1

CRISIS.
Tracks: / Crisis / Moonlight shadow / In high places / Foreign affair / Taurus three / Shadow on the wall.
LP: V 2262
MC: TCV 2262
MC: OVEDC 351
LP: OVED 351

DISCOVERY.
Tracks: / To France (Vocals - Maggie Reilly) / Poison arrows (Vocals - Barry Palmer) / Crystal gazing (Vocals - Maggie Reilly) / Tricks of the light (Vocals - Maggie Reilly & Barry Palmer) / Discovery (Vocals - Barry Palmer) / Talk about your life (Vocals -Maggie Reilly) / Saved by a bell (Vocals - Barry Palmer) / Lake, The (Instrumental).
LP: V 2308
MC: TCV 2308

EARTH MOVING.
Tracks: / Holy / Far country / Runaway son / Earth moving / Nothing but / Nostage / Innocent / See the light / Blue night / Bridge to paradise.
LP: V 2610
MC: TCV 2610

EXPOSED.
Tracks: / Incantations (parts 1 & 2) / Incantations (parts 3 & 4) / Tubular bells (part 1) / Tubular bells (part 2) / Guilty.
2LP: VD 2511
MC: TCVD 2511

FIVE MILES OUT.
Tracks: / Taurus II / Family man / Orabidoo / Mount Teidi / Five miles out.
LP: V 2222
MC: TCV 2222
LP: OVED 293
MC: OVEDC 293
LP: VVIP 106
MC: VVIPC 106

FIVE MILES OUT (See also Mike Oldfield CD Box Set Vol.2).

HEAVEN'S OPEN.
LP: V 2653
MC: TCV 2653

HERGEST RIDGE.
Tracks: / Hergest ridge (part 1) / Hergest ridge (part 2).
LP: OVED 163
MC: OVEDC 163
LP: V 2013

HERGEST RIDGE (See also Mike Oldfield CD Box Set Vol.1).

INCANTATIONS.
Tracks: / Incantations (parts 1 & 4) / Guilty.
2LP: VDT 101
MC: TCVDT 101

ISLANDS.
Tracks: / Wind chimes, The (part 1) / Wind chimes, The (part 2) / Islands / Flying start / Northpoint / Magic touch / Time has come, The / When the night's on fire (CD only).
LP: V 2466
MC: TCV 2466

KILLING FIELDS, THE (Film Soundtrack).
Tracks: / Pran's theme / Requiem for a city / Evacuation / Capture / Execution / Bad news / Pran's departure / Work site / Year zero / Blood sucking / Pran's escape / Trek, The / Boy's burial, The/ Pran sees the red cross / Good news / Etude / Pran's theme -2 / Year zero (2).
LP: V 2328
MC: TCV 2328
LP: OVED 183
MC: OVEDC 183

MUSIC WONDERLAND.
Tracks: / Tubular bells / Portsmouth / Blue Peter / Guilty (live) / Arrival / In dulci jubilo / Punkadiddle.
LP: 204 000

OMMADAWN (See also Mike Oldfield CD Box Set Vol.1).

OMMADAWN.
Tracks: / Ommadawn (parts 1 & 2).
LP: OVED 208
MC: OVEDC 208
LP: V 2043

ORCHESTRAL TUBULAR BELLS.
LP: OVED 97
MC: OVEDC 97
LP: VVIP 101
MC: VVIPC 101

ORCHESTRAL TUBULAR BELLS (See also Mike Oldfield CD Box Set Vol.1).

PLATINUM (See also Mike Oldfield CD Box Set Vol.2).

PLATINUM.
Tracks: / Platinum (part 1)-Airborne / Platinum (part 2)-Platinum / Platinum (part 3)-Charleston / Platinum (part 4)-North star/Platinum finale / Woodhenge / Sally / Punkadiddle / I got rhythm.
LP: PLAT 1007
LP: V 2141
MC: TCV 2141
LP: OVED 233
MC: OVEDC 233

QE2.
Tracks: / Q.E.2. / Taurus / Sheba / Conflict / Arrival / Wonderful land / Mirage / Celt / Molly / Q.E.2. Finale.
LP: V 2181
MC: TCV 2181
LP: OVED 235
MC: OVEDC 235

QE 2 (See also Mike Oldfield CD Box Set Vol.2).

TUBULAR BELLS.
Tracks: / Tubular Bells (Part 1) / Tubular Bells (Part 2).
LP: V 2001
LPPD: VP 2001
MC: TCV 2001

Oldfield, Sally

CELEBRATION.
Tracks: / Mandela / Morning of my life / Woman of the night / Celebration / Blue water / My damsel heart / Love is everywhere.
LP: CLALP 103
MC: CLAMC 103

COLLECTION: SALLY OLDFIELD.
Tracks: / Mirrors / Water bearer / Path with a heart / River of my childhood / Sons of the free / Mandela / Sun in my eyes / My damsel heart / Easy / Song of the lamp / You set my gypsy blood free / Woman of the night / Answering you / Love of a lifetime / Song of the healer / Morning of my life / Meet me in Verona / Celebration / Weaver / Love is everywhere.
2LP: CCSLP 125
MC: CCSMC 125

EASY.
Tracks: / Sun is in my eyes / You set my gypsy blood free / Answering you / Boulevard song / Easy / Sons of the free / Hide and seek / First born of the earth / Man of storm.
LP: CLALP 102
MC: CLAMC 102
LP: BRON 522

FEMME.
Tracks: / Silver dagger / This is my song / Marlene / Strangers in the dawn / I'm leaving / Andromeda rising / Sometimes I'm a woman / Two different drummers / Giving all my love.
LP: 4510341
MC: 4510344

NIGHTRIDING: SALLY OLDFIELD.
Tracks: / Mirrors / Broken Mona Lisa / Talks like a lady / Million light years away from home, A / Rare lightning / Man I love, The / Manchild / Never knew love could get so strong / Let it all go / Playing in the flame / I sing for you / For all time / It's a long time / Mandala.
MC: KNMC 10021

STRANGE DAY IN BERLIN.
Tracks: / Path with a heart / Million light years away from home / She talks like a lady / Meet me in Verona / Strange day in Berlin / Never knew love could get so strong / This could be a lover.
LP: BRON 549
MC: BRONC 549

WATER BEARER.
Tracks: / Water bearer / Songs of the quendi (Night theme, Wampum song, Nenya, Land of the sun.) / Weaver / Mirrors / Night of the hunter's moon / Child of Allah / Song of the bow / Fire and honey / Song of the healer.
LP: CLALP 101
MC: CLAMC 101

Oldfield, Terry

CASCADE.
MC: C 140

IN SEARCH OF THE TROJAN WAR (TV soundtrack).
Tracks: / Trojan War, The / Mycenae / Journey to war, The / Troy / Trojan theme / Epitaph / Sea people / Nesas waspas / Hittites / Great railway journeys:Boy on a bicycle / Great river journeys:Maji mengi / Great river journeys:Leaving Kishasa / Helen's song.
LP: REB 553
MC: ZCF 553

IN THE PRESENCE OF LIGHT.
MC: C 139

REVERENCE.
MC: C 141

Oldham, Andrew

RARITIES (Oldham, Andrew 'Orchestra & Chorus').
Tracks: / Da doo ron ron / Memphis, Tennessee / I wanna be your man / La bamba / Funky and fleopatra / 365 rolling stones / Maggie Maggie May (parts 1 and 2) / Oh I do like to be on the B side / There are but five rolling stones / Rise of the Brighton surf, The / You better move on / Theme for a rolling stone / Tell 'em (you're coming back) / Last time, The / Needles and pins / Want to hold your hand / Right of way / I can't get no satisfaction / Carry on.
LP: C5-518
MC: C5K-518
LP: SEE 36

ROLLING STONES SONGBOOK,THE (Oldham, Andrew 'Orchestra & Chorus').
Tracks: / Blue turns to grey / I can't get no satisfaction / You better move on / Time is on my side / Heart of stone / As tears go by / Theme for a rolling stone / Tell me (you're coming back) / Congratulations / Last time, The.
LP: DOA 9

Oldham Tinkers

BEST O'T' BUNCH.
Tracks: / Rochdale mashers, The / Seeing double / Pennine rangers, The / Two jews, The / Piecer's tale, A / Best o' t' bunch / Lancashire toreador, The / Cob coaling medley, A / Four loom weaver, (The) / John Willie's ragtime band / Platt's good time coming / I mean to wait for Jack / Ski-ing, Oldham style / Man like thee, (A).
LP: 12TS 237

FOR OLD TIMES SAKE.
Tracks: / Signora / Eaur Joe's lad / John Willie's horse / Barefoot days / Lancashire witches / Come whoam to thi childer an' me / Johnny Bugger / Billy Winker / Bits o' Bromley Street / Condemned cell, The / Maypole, The / For old time's sake.
LP: 12TS 276

OLDHAMS BURNING SANDS.
Tracks: / Success to the weaver / Lancashire miller, The / Charlie Chaplin / Eawr market neet / Owdham chap's visit to th' queen, The / In our town / Oldham's burning sands / Fine old English gentleman, A / Peterloo / We're off in a motor car / Oldham pensioner, The / Stockport strike, The / Childer's holiday / Owl of Oldham, The.
LP: 12TS 206

SIT THEE DOWN.
Tracks: / Maid in the calico dress, The / Elsie Bell / Pity me my darling / Talking dog, The / To Sarah / Tall tales medley / Sit thee down / Deserter, The / Poor little hauve timer / Dad's medals / Fishing / Jumping Jack / Jim's medley.

LP: 12TS 323

THAT LANCASHIRE BAND.
Tracks: / Old May song / John Willie's performing newt / Nowt about owt / Children's chants and songs / Eawr house as was / Oh Lancashire jazz band / Lark, The / John Wille's grand dad / Tribute to owd Paddy / Old king Cole / Steeple Jack / Crime Lake Boggart, The / McCarthy's party.
LP: 12TS 399

Oldimers, Jenaer

MIT BANJO UND TUBA.
LP: 855 266

Oldland Montano

TIME HAS COME, THE.
Tracks: / My world / Ocean of emotion / Just a game / Sometimes black, sometimes white / Skin deep / Time has come, The / Sugar mummy / Am I hooked? / Love dimension / Sunken love / Problems / Forbidden fruit.
MC: . . . . SRNMC 17
LP: . . . . SRNLP 17

Olds, Jerome

NO DISGUISE.
LP: . . . . SS R 8129
MC: . . . . SS C 8129

O'Leary, Johnny

MUSIC FOR THE COMPLETE POLKA SET.
LP: 12TS 357

Olenn, Johnny

JUST ROLLIN' WITH JOHNNY OLENN.
Tracks: / Candy kisses / My idea of love / Pipeliner's blues / Sally let your bangs hang down / Twenty four hours / Someday you'll want me to want you / When my dreamboat comes home / Gypsy, The / I ain't gonna cry no more / Oh what a dream / Because you love me / Yeah yeah yeah.
LP: . . . . CH 48

Oliver

OLIVER (Original Cast) (Various artists).
MC: . . . . KCSP 30

OLIVER (Film Soundtrack) (Various artists).
Tracks: / Overture: *Various artists* / Food glorious food: *Various artists* / Boy for sale: *Various artists*/ Where is love: *Various artists* / You've got to pick a pocket or two: *Various artists* / Consider yourself: *Various* artists / I'd do anything: *Various artists* / Be back soon: *Various artists* / As long as he needs me: *Various* artists / Who will buy: *Various artists* / It's a fine life: *Various artists* / Reviewing the situation: *Various artists* / Oom pah pah: *Various artists* / Finale: *Various artists.*
LP: . . . . PL 85501
MC: . . . . PK 85501
LP: . . . . COSD 5503
MC: . . . . OKCG 1003
LP: . . . . NL 90311
MC: . . . . NK 90311
LP: . . . . SB 6777
MC: . . . . VCS 67277

OLIVER (Original London Cast) (Various artists).
Tracks: / Food glorious food: *Various artists* / Oliver: *Various artists* / I shall scream: *Various artists*/ Boy for sale: *Various artists* / That's your funeral: *Various artists* / Where is love?: *Various artists*/ Consider yourself: *Various artists* / You've got to pick a pocket or two: *Various artists* / It's fine life: *Various artists* / Be back soon: *Various artists* / Oom pah pah: *Various artists* / My name: *Various* artists / As long as he needs me: *Various artists* / I'd do anything: *Various artists* / Who will buy?: *Various artists* / Reviewing the situation: *Various artists* / Finale: *Various artists.*
LP: . . . . TER 1042
MC: . . . . ZCTER 1042

OLIVER (Various artists).
Tracks: / Oliver: *Various artists* / I'd do anything: *Various artists*/ Food glorious food: *Various artists*/ Oom pah pah: *Various artists* / Boy for sale: *Various artists* / Who will buy?: *Various artists* / It's a fine life: *Various artists* / You've got to pick a pocket or two: *Various artists* / As long as he needs me: *Various artists* / Reviewing the situation: *Various artists* / Consider yourself: *Various artists.*
LP: . . . . BD 3012

OLIVER (Original Broadway Cast 1963) (Various artists).
Tracks: / Food, glorious food: *Various artists* / Oliver: *Various artists* / I shall scream: *Various artists*/ Oom pah pah: *Various artists* / Boy for sale: *Various artists* / Where is love: *Various artists* / Consider yourself: *Various artists*/ You've got to pick a pocket or two: *Various artists* / It's a fine life: *Various artists* / I'd do anythisng: *Various artists* / Be back soon: *Various artists* / Oom-pah-pah: *Various artists* / My name: *Various* artists / As long as he needs me: *Various artists* / Who will buy: *Various artists* / Reviewing the situation: *Various artists* / As long as he needs me (reprise): *Various artists* / Reviewing the situation (reprise: *Various artists* / Oliver (finale): *Various artists.*
MC: . . . . GK 84113

OLIVER (ORIGINAL ISSUE) (London cast) (Various artists).
LP: . . . . LK 4359

OLIVER (RE-ISSUE) (London cast) (Various artists).
LP: . . . . SPA 30

Oliver & Company

OLIVER AND COMPANY (Various artists).
LP: . . . . PLD 450
MC: . . . . PBC 450

OLIVER AND COMPANY (Unknown narrator(s)).
MC: . . . . DIS 010

Oliver Cromwell

OLIVER CROMWELL (history for ages 8+) (Unknown narrator(s)).
MC: . . . . PLBH 103

Oliver, Gene

TRIBUTE TO NEIL DIAMOND,A.
MC: . . . . ZCFPA 1025

Oliver, Jane

STAY THE NIGHT.
Tracks: / Stay the night / Honesty / He's so fine / Solitaire / Can't leave you cause I love you / Let's make some memories / Can't we make it right again / You're the one I love / Song for my father / Right garden.
LP: . . . . CBS 82934

Oliver, King

1923 (Oliver, King & His Creole Jazz Band).
LP: . . . . S 1257

1923-30.
LP: . . . . LPJT 21

CHIMES BLUES.
LP: . . . . LPJT 21
MC: . . . . MCJT 21

CLASSIC JAZZ (Oliver, King & His Creole Jazz Band).
LP: 22023
MC: 42023

CREOLE JAZZ BAND (Oliver, King & His Creole Jazz Band).
Tracks: / Alligator hop / I'm going away to wear you off my mind / Froggie Moore / Snake rag / Chimes blues / Just gone / Canal street blues / Mandy Lee blues / Weather bird rag / Dippermouth blues / Krooked blues.
LP: . . . . SM 3089

FAREWELL BLUES (1926-7).
LP: . . . . SM 3809

FRANKIE & JOHNNY (1926-7).
LP: . . . . SM 3811

GENNETT SIDES OF APRIL & OCTOBER, 1923 (Oliver, King & His Creole Jazz Band).
Tracks: / Just gone / Canal Street blues / Mandy Lee blues / I'm going away to wear you off my mind / Chimes blues / Weather bird rag / Dippermouth blues / Froggie Moore / Snake rag / Alligator hop / Zulus' ball / Working man blues / Krooked blues.
LP: . . . . RHA 6023

HOMETOWN BLUES.
Tracks: / Kiss me sweet ((Composed: S.Lewis#A.J.Piron)) / Construction gang ((Composed; J & S Edwards)) / Home town blues / Sorrow valley blues ((Composed: I.Scruggs)) / Empty bed blues (part 1) ((Composed: J.C.johnson)) / Empty bed blues (part 2) ((Composed: J.C.johnson)) / You're such a cruel papa to me ((Composed: Piron#Williams#Perrault)) / My diff'rent kind of man ((Composed: J.Palmer)) / My handy man ((Composed: A.Razaf)) / Organ grinder blues ((Composed: C.Williams)) / I'm busy and you can't come in ((Composed: C.Williams)) / Jeannine ((Composed: L.Wolfe Gilbert)) / In the bottle blues ((Composed: Williams#Oliver#Lang)) / What do you want me to do ((Composed: C.Williams)) / Blue blood blues ((Composed: J.C.Johnson)).
LP: . . . . RHA 6032

I'M CRAZY 'BOUT MY BABY (1930-31).
LP: . . . . SM 3812

KING AND MISTER JELLY LORD, THE (Oliver, King & Jelly Roll Morton).
LP: . . . . PAR 2303

KING OLIVER.
LP: . . . . CJM 19

KING OLIVER 1929-30.
LP: . . . . SFR DP 657

KING OLIVER AND HIS ORCHESTRA (Oliver, King & his Orchestra).
2LP: . . . . PM 42411

KING OLIVER COLLECTION (20 Golden Greats).
Tracks: / Don't you think I love you? / Trumpet's prayer / Too late / My good man, Sam / New Orleans shout / Rhythm club stomp / Frankie and Johnny / Boogie woogie / Can I tell you? / Olga / I'm lonesome, sweetheart / You're just my type / West End blues / Nelson stomp / I must have it / What you want me to do? / Mule face blues / Sweet like this / St. James' Infirmary / I can't stop loving you.
LP: . . . . DVLP 2085
MC: . . . . DVMC 2085

KING OLIVER & HIS DIXIE SYNCOPATORS (1926-28 Vol. 2).
LP: . . . . S 283

KING OLIVER & HIS DIXIE SYNCOPATORS (1926-28).
LP: . . . . S 822

KING OLIVER & HIS DIXIE SYNCOPATORS (1926).
LP: . . . . S 821

KING OLIVER & HIS ORCHESTRA 1929-30.
Tracks: / West end blues / I've got that thing / Call of the freaks, The / Trumpet's prayer / Freakish light blues / Can I tell you? / My good man Sam / What you want me to do / Sweet like this / Too late / I'm lonesome, sweetheart / I want you just myself / I can't stop loving you / Everybody does it in Hawaii / Frankie and Johnny / New Orleans shout / St. James Infirmary / I must have it / Rhythm club stomp / You're just my type / Edna / Boogie woogie / Mule face blues / Struggle bunny / Don't you think I love you / Olga / Shake it and break it / Stingaree blues / What's the use of living without you / You were only passing time with me / Nelson stomp / Stealing.
MCSET: . . . . NK 89770

KING OLIVER VOL. 1 1928 & 31.
LP: . . . . CJM 21

KING OLIVER'S CREOLE JAZZ BAND (1923).
LP: . . . . VLP 49

NEW YORK SESSIONS.
Tracks: / What you want me to do / Sweet like this / Too late / I'm lonesome, sweetheart / Frankie and Johnny (take 3) / New Orleans shout / Everybody does it in Hawaii / Frankie and Johnny (take 4) / I must have it / Rhythm Club stomp / You're just my type / Edna / Mule face blues / Struggle buggy / Don't you think I love you / Olga (take 1) / Olga (take 2) / Shake it and break it / Stingaree blues / Nelson stomp (take 2) / Nelson stomp (take 3) / Stealing love.
MC: . . . . NK 90410
LP: . . . . NL 90410
LP: . . . . NL 90414
MC: . . . . NK 90414

OKEH SESSIONS, THE (Oliver, King & His Creole Jazz Band).
Tracks: / Snake rag / My sweet lovin' man / High society rag / Sobbin' blues / Where did you stay last night / Dipper mouth blues / Jazzin' babies blues / Buddy's habits / Tears / I ain't gonna tell nobody / Room rent blues / Sweet baby doll / Working man blues / Mabel's dream.
LP: . . . . EG 2605791
MC: . . . . EG 2605794
LP: . . . . SH 358

SNAG IT.
LP: . . . . SFR DP 696

SNAG IT (1926-7).
LP: . . . . SM 3808
LP: . . . . SFR DP 696

SWEET LIKE THIS.
Tracks: / West end blues / I've got that thing / Call of the freaks, The / Trumpet's prayer / Freakish light blues / Can I tell you? / My good man Sam / What you want me to do? / Sweet like this / Too late / I'm lonesome sweetheart / I want you just myself / I can't stop loving you / New Orleans shout / Everybody does it in Hawaii / Frankie and Johnny / St. James' infirmary / When you're smiling.
LP: . . . . HDL 106
MC: . . . . CHDL 106

WEST END BLUES 1929.
LP: . . . . SM 3810

Oliver, Sy

ANNIE LAURIE.
LP: 500069
LP: . . . . JL 69

EASY WALKER.
LP: 500085

JULY 7TH 1960 & OCTOBER 18TH 1962.
Tracks: / I've been working on the railroad / I like you / Old time religion / Mixed doubles / Five flats furnished / Lazy / Easy walker / Oh them golden slippers / This is love / Blue tail fly / I'll fly away / Intermezzo / I found the one I love.
LP: . . . . JV 105

SENTIMENTAL SY.
Tracks: / On the sunny side of the street / Then I'll be happy / Stardust / Without a song / Yes indeed / Opus one / We'll git it / Chicago / East of the sun / Blue skies / For you / Swanee river.
LP: . . . . JASM 1513

Oliver Twist

OLIVER TWIST (see Dicken's, Charles) (Unknown narrator(s)).

OLIVER TWIST/MALTA G.C. (Film soundtracks) (Royal Philharmonic Orchestra).
Tracks: / Prelude / Storm, The / Fight, The / Oliver's sleepless night / Oliver and the Artful Dodger / Fagin's romp / Chase, The / Oliver and Brownlow / Nancy and Browlow / Finale / Prelude / Convoy / Old valletta / Air raid / Ruins / Quick march / Intermezzo / Work and play / Finale.
LP: . . . . CN 7012

Oliver's Story

OLIVER'S STORY (Film soundtrack) (Various artists).
LP: . . . . MCF 3003
MC: . . . . MCFC 3003

Olivier, Jim

CAJUN MUSIC FOR EVERYONE.
LP: 6042
MC: . . . . 6042 TC

I LOVE CAJUN MUSIC.
LP: 6039
MC: . . . . 6039 TC

LE MUSIQUE DE JIM OLIVIER.
LP: 6059
MC: . . . . 6059 TC

LET'S KEEP IT CAJUN.
LP: 6048
MC: . . . . 6048 TC

SINGS THE CAJUN WAY.
LP: 6044
MC: . . . . 6044 TC

Olney, David

CONTENDER (Olney, David & The X-Rays).
LP: . . . . ROUNDER 3064
MC: . . . . ROUNDER 3064C

DEEPER WELL.
LP: . . . . PH 1117
MC: . . . . PH 1117C

EYE OF THE STORM.
LP: . . . . ROUNDER 3099
MC: . . . . ROUNDER 3099C

Olomide, Koffi

TCHA TCHO.
Tracks: / Tcha tcho du sorcier / Elle et moi / V.I.P. / Mannequin / Henriquet / Mal aime / Experience / La ruta.
LP: . . . . STERNS 1031
MC: . . . . STC 1031

Olson, Carla

CARLA OLSON.
LP: 089206

MICK TAYLOR & CARLA OLSON LIVE (See under Taylor, Mick for details) (Olson, Carla & Mick Taylor).

Olsson, Ingemar

I FEEL FREE.
LP: . . . . DAY R 4029
MC: . . . . DAY C 4029

Olsson, Kai

CRAZY LOVE.
Tracks: / Every inch a lady / Gloria trail / Sierra Leone / Heart to heart / Livin' in your heart / New day / Bishops and queens / Fools cry / Crazy love / Playing tonight.
LP: . . . . CHR 1226

Olsson, Kvintetten

LATT PA SNE Featuring Olsson Quintet).
Tracks: / Det ska vi sjunga / Fridolins darskap / Greensleeves / Om Beethoven / Inte ens en gra litne fagel / Vilse / Liten froken vid himlaporten / Balladen om herr Rosenbloms speleman / Yesterday / Sa lunka vi sa smaning om / Dixie / Per spelman / Trad fram du nattens gud / Varkonsert / Nu tror vi det kan vara tid.
LP: . . . . PHONT 7524

Olympia Brass Band

NOLA SINGLES ALBUM.
MC: . . . . TC 025

OLYMPIA BRASS BAND.

LP: . . . . **NOLA LP 4**

OLYMPIA BRASS BAND OF NEW ORLEANS, THE.
LP: . . . . **AP 108**

Olympic Orchestra

REILLY - ACE OF SPIES (see under Reilly - Ace Of Spies).

Olympic Runners

HOT TO TROT.
Tracks: / Say what you wanna but it sure is funky / Just enough / One step at a time / Just funkin' around / Straight St. strut / Personal thang / World record / Just a little lick / Bahama mama / Love on my mind.
LP: . . . . **NORT 1**

IT'S A BITCH.
Tracks: / Bitch / 130 beats a minute / Crazy talk / Make it happen / Closer to paradise / Betcha can't dance / Making it better / Disco smash.
LP: **2383549**

KEEP IT UP.
Tracks: / Solar heat / Down to the bone / Guacamole getdown / Interference free / Hash browns / Keep it up / Swamp lizard / Boogie line.
LP: . . . . **PL 25124**
MC: . . . . **PK 25124**

OUT OF THE GROUND.
Tracks: / Whatever it takes / Back on the track / Out of the ground / Don't let up / Party time is here to stay / In the can / Pacapaco-wa-wa / Kool gent, The.
LP: . . . . **PL 25195**

PUTTING IT ON YA.
Tracks: / Sir Dancealot / Wooden head / When you're dancing / God bless you / Energy beam / Get it while you can / Breakout / Onya.
LP: . . . . **POLD 5015**

Olympic Sideburns

OLYMPIC SIDEBURNS.
LP: . . . . **ROSE 60**

Olympics

DOIN' THE HULLY GULLY.
Tracks: / Big boy Pete / Little Pedro / Stay away from Joe / Big Chief, Little Puss / Stay where you are / What'd I say / Private eye / Baby it's hot / Dooley / Baby hully gully / Dodge City / I'll never fall in love again / Working hard.
LP: . . . . **CH 56**

OLYMPICS MEET THE MARATHONS, THE.
Tracks: / C. Percy Mercy of Scotland Yard / Oink Jones / Chicken spaceman / Nothing in the world / Gee / Tight sweater / Talkin' trash / Peanut butter / Shimmy like Kate / Slop / Party popper / Scotch / Mash them taters / Stomp / Boo-dee green / Dance by the light of the moon.
LP: . . . . **CH 123**

Olympus On My Mind

OLYMPUS ON MY MIND (Film soundtrack) (Various artists).
Tracks: / Welcome to Greece: *Chorus, The* / Heaven on earth: *Jupiter, Alchmene* / Gods on tap, The: *Delores*, Jupiter / Surprise: *Sosia and Mercury* / Love - what...: *Jupiter, mercury and dolores* / Enter the husband: *Chorus, The* / I know my wife: *Amphitryon* / It was me: *Sosia and Amphitryon* / Back so soon: *Amphitryon*, Sosia and orch / Wonderful: *Alchmene* / At liberty...: *Charis and the chorus* / Jupiter slept here: *Jupiter* and all / Something of yourself: *Mercury* / Star is born, a: *Delores & all* / Final sequence: *Amphitryon, alchmene.*
LP: . . . . **TER 1131**

Om

CEREBUS.
LP: . . . . **JAPO 60032**

OM (Om with Dom Um Roamoa).
LP: . . . . **JAPO 60022**

RAUTIONAHA.
LP: . . . . **JAPO 60016**

Om Kalsoum

AGHAR MEN HASNET EL GANOUB.
MC: . . . . **MC 7247**

AL NILE.
MC: . . . . **MC 7244**

AOULEK EIK.
MC: . . . . **MC 7245**

WOLEDA EL HODA.
MC: . . . . **MC 7246**

YALLI KAN YEEHGEEK ANEENI.
MC: . . . . **MC 7248**

ZELAMNA EL HOB.
MC: . . . . **MC 7243**

Omar

BLUES BAG.
LP: . . . . **PRL 70281**
MC: . . . . **PRLC 70281**

THERE'S NOTHING LIKE THIS.
Tracks: / There's nothing like this / Don't mean a thing / You and me / Positive / I'm in love / Meaning of life / Stop messing around / Serious style / I don't mind the waiting / Fine (acapella).
LP: **510021-1**
MC: **510021-4**

THERE'S NOTHING LIKE THIS.
LP: . . . . **KDLP 2**
MC: . . . . **KDMC 2**

Omar & The Howlers

HARD TIMES IN THE LAND OF PLENTY.
Tracks: / Hard times in the land of plenty / Dancing in the canebrake / Border girl / Mississippi hoo doo man / Don't rock me the wrong way / Don't you know / Same old grind / You ain't foolin' nobody / Shadow man.
LP: **4509481**
MC: **4509484**

I TOLD YOU SO.
LP: . . . . **DFG 8417**

MONKEY LAND.
Tracks: / Monkey land / Big town shakedown / Night shadows / She's a woman / Dirty people / Next big thing / Tonight I think of you / Fire in the jungle / Modern man / Loud mouth woman / Ding dong clock.
LP: . . . . **PRL 70131**
MC: . . . . **PRC 70134**

WALL OF PRIDE.
Tracks: / Wall of pride / Rattlesnake shake / Don't lead me on / Rock it while you can / Down in Mississippi / Movin' / We gotta get out of this place / Bad seed / King's ransom / Dimestore hoo doo / Meet me down at the river.
LP: **4625131**
MC: **4625134**

Omartian, Michael

ADAM AGAIN.
Tracks: / Ain't you glad / No matter what shape you're in / See this house / Whachersign / Annie the poet / Telos suite: Prelude / Alive and well / Adam again / Here he comes.
LP: . . . . **MYR 1058**
MC: . . . . **MC 1058**

BUILDER, THE (Omartian, Michael & Stormie).
Tracks: / Charlie's dream / Only thing missing is you / Builder, The / Mr. Trash man / Anything you ask of me / Doctor Jesus / Big time / Half past three / End times.
LP: . . . . **MYR 1088**
MC: . . . . **MC 1088**

CONVERSATIONS.
Tracks: / Homeland / Soldier, The / Rest is now, The / Feast, The / Right at the start / Desert, The / Call, The / Rest, The.
LP: . . . . **RRA R 0017**
MC: . . . . **RRA C 0017**

SEASONS OF THE SOUL.
Tracks: / Ms. Past / Travel on with me / Gonna write me a song / More like you / Where I been / It all comes down to you / Heaven will wait for me / Seasons of the soul.
LP: . . . . **MYR 1073**
MC: . . . . **MC 1073**

WHITE HORSE.
Tracks: / Jeremiah / Fat city / Orphan, The / Silver fish / Add up the wonders / Take me down / Right from the start / Rest is up to you, The / White horse.
LP: . . . . **MYRA 1048**
MC: . . . . **MC 1048**

Ombale, Bimi

BALLE DE MATCH.
LP: . . . . **LD 01**

O.M.D.

ARCHITECTURE AND MORALITY.
Tracks: / New Stone Age, The / She's leaving / Souvenir / Sealand / Joan of Arc / Joan of Arc / Architecture and morality / Georgia / Beginning and the end, The.
LP: . . . . **DID 12**
MC: . . . . **DIDC 12**
LP: . . . . **OVED 276**
MC: . . . . **OVEDC 276**

ARCHITECTURE & MORALITY (See under O.M.D. CD Box Set for details).

BEST OF O.M.D..
Tracks: / Electricity / Messages / Enola Gay / Souvenir / Joan Of Arc / Maid Of Orleans / Talking loud and clear / Tesla girls / Locomotion, The / So in love / Secret / If you leave / (Forever) live and die / Dreaming / Telegraph (CD only) / We love you (12" version) (CD only) / La femme accident (12" version) (CD only) / Genetic engineering (CD only).
LP: . . . . **OMD 1**
MC: . . . . **TCOMD 1**

CRUSH.
Tracks: / So in love / Secret / Bloc bloc bloc / Women 111 / Crush / 88 seconds in Greensboro' / Native daughters of the Golden West, The / La femme accident / Hold you / Lights are going out, The.
LP: . . . . **V 2349**
MC: . . . . **TCV 2349**

DAZZLE SHIPS.
Tracks: / Radio Prague / Genetic engineering / ABC auto indistry / Telegraph / This is Helena / International / Romance of the telescope, The / Silent running (on dangerous ground) / Radio waves / Time zones / Of all the things we've made / Dazzle ships.
LP: . . . . **V 2261**
MC: . . . . **TCV 2261**
LP: . . . . **OVED 106**
MC: . . . . **OVEDC 106**

JUNK CULTURE.
Tracks: / Junk culture / Tesla girls / Locomotion, The / Apollo / Never turn away / Love and violence / Hard day / All wrapped up / White trash / Talking loud and clear.
LP: . . . . **OVED 215**
MC: . . . . **OVEDC 215**
LP: . . . . **V 2310**

O.M.D. (See under O.M.D. CD Box Set for details).

ORCHESTRAL MANOEUVRES IN THE DARK.
Tracks: / Bunker soldiers / Almost / Mysterreality / Electricity / Messerschmit twins, The / Messages / Julia's song / Red frame/White light / Dancing / Pretending to see the future.
LP: . . . . **OVED 96**
MC: . . . . **OVEDC 96**
LP: . . . . **DID 2**

ORGANISATION (See under O.M.D. CD Box Set for details).

ORGANISATION.
Tracks: / Enola gay / 2nd thought / VCL X1 / Motion and heart / Statues / Misunderstanding, The / More I see you, The / Promise, The / Stanlow.
LP: . . . . **DID 6**
MC: . . . . **DIDC 6**
LP: . . . . **OVED 147**
MC: . . . . **OVEDC 147**

PACIFIC AGE.
Tracks: / Stay (The black rose and the universal wheel) / (Forever) live and die / Pacific age, The / Dead girls, The / Shame / Southern / Flame of hope / Goddess of love / We love you / Watch us fall.
LP: . . . . **V 2398**
MC: . . . . **TCV 2398**

SUGAR TAX.
LP: . . . . **V 2648**
MC: . . . . **TCV 2648**

Omega

GAMBLER.
MC: . . . . **MEGA 2**

GOD LOVES TO ROCK AND ROLL.
MC: . . . . **MEGA 1**

PROPHET, THE.
LP: . . . . **MACH 1**

Omega Tribe

LIVE AT THE CLARENDON.
MC: **96 11**

NO LOVE LOST.
LP: . . . . **CHRIST ITS 5**

Omen

BATTLE CRY.
LP: . . . . **RR 9818**

CURSE, THE.
LP: . . . . **RR 9661**

ESCAPE TO NOWHERE.
Tracks: / It's not easy / Radar love / Escape to nowhere / Cry for the morning / Thorn in your flesh / Poisoned / Nomads / King of the hill / No way out.
LP: . . . . **RR 95441**

NIGHTMARES.
LP: . . . . **RR 9617**

WARNING OF DANGER.
LP: . . . . **RR 9738**

Omen (Film)

DAMIEN: OMEN 2 (1978 Film Soundtrack) (Various artists).
Tracks: / Main title: *Various artists* / Runaway train: *Various artists* / Claws: *Various artists* / Thoughtful night: *Various artists* / Broken ice: *Various artists* / Fallen temple: *Various artists* / I love you, Mark: *Various artists* / Shafted: *Various artists* / Knife, The: *Various artists* / All the power (end title): *Various artists.*
LP: . . . . **FILM 002**
MC: . . . . **FILMC 002**

FINAL CONFLICT - OMEN III (1985 film soundtrack) (Various artists).
LP: . . . . **CST 8020**
LP: . . . . **STV 81272**
MC: . . . . **CTV 81272**
MC: . . . . **VSC 5282**

OMEN, THE (Film Soundtrack) (Various artists).
MC: . . . . **VSC 5281**

Omnibus Big Band

MEMORIES OF YOU (Omnibus Big Band & Putte Wickman).
LP: . . . . **DRLP 122**

On A Clear Day ...

ON A CLEAR DAY YOU CAN SEE FOREVER (Film Soundtrack) (Various artists).
LP: . . . . **AS 30086**
MC: . . . . **BT 30086**

On Golden Pond

ON GOLDEN POND (Film soundtrack) (Various artists).
LP: . . . . **MCA 1497**
MC: . . . . **MCAC 1497**

On Her Majesty's...

ON HER MAJESTY'S SECRET SERVICE (see under Fleming, Ian) (Fleming, Ian).

ON HER MAJESTY'S SECRET SERVICE (Film Soundtrack) (Various artists).
MC: . . . . **E 41 E 90618**
2LP: . . . . **UAD 60027/8**

On Moonlight Bay

ON MOONLIGHT BAY/TEA FOR TWO (Film Soundtrack) (Various artists).
LP: . . . . **P 17660**
MC: . . . . **BT 17660**

On The Avenue

ON THE AVENUE/THANKS A MILLION (See under Thanks a million) (Various artists).

On The Big Hill

ON THE BIG HILL (Film Soundtrack) (Various artists).
Tracks: / Opening shot: *Various artists* / Best laid plans: *Various artists* / Mountain madness: *Various* artists / Thru the window: *Various artists* / Try not to fall: *Various artists* / Higher ground: *Various* artists / There are times: *Various artists* / Things look different: *Various artists* / Take a short walk: *Various artists* / Some people get hurt: *Various artists* / Long walk: *Various artists* / Across the bridge: *Various artists* / Dougie's march: *Various artists* / Each night you die a little: *Various artists* / In the back of your mind: *Various artists* / Home Dougie, home: *Various artists.*
LP: . . . . **ORELP 501**
MC: . . . . **OREC 501**

On The Rocks

ON THE HALLS (Various artists).
2LP: . . . . **SHB 43**

ON THE ROCKS.
Tracks: / Stop red eye / Baga trouble / Gun / Jah is watching you / Riddim of life / What is your meaning / Ishen tree / Don't burn baby.
LP: . . . . **TPL 99**

ON THE SPOT VOL.2 (Various artists).
LP: . . . . **DANLP 2**

On The Steps...

ON THE STEPS OF THE DOLE OFFICE (Various artists).
LP: . . . . **LRF 15**

On The Town

ON THE TOWN (Broadway cast) (Various artists).
Tracks: / New York, New York: *Various artists* / Dance: *Various artists* / Miss Turnstiles: *Various artists*/ Taxi number: *Various artists* / Come up to my place: *Various artists* / Carried away: *Various artists*/ Lonely town: *Various artists* / I can cook too: *Various artists* / Lucky to be me: *Various artists*/ Times Square: *Various artists* / Night club sequence: *Various artists* / Ballet: *Various artists* / Imaginary Coney Island: *Various artists* / Some other time: *Various artists* / Finale: *Various artists.*
LP: . . . . **CBS 32315**
MC: **40-32315**
MC: . . . . **JST 02038**

ON THE TOWN Original Broadway cast (Various artists).
LP: . . . . **AS 31005**
MC: . . . . **BT 31005**

ON THE TOWN (Film Soundtrack) (Various artists).
LP: . . . . **DS 15029**

On The Twentieth ...

ON THE TWENTIETH CENTURY (Original Broadway Cast) (Various artists).
LP: ATS 35330
MC: BT 35330

On The Waterfront

WEST SIDE STORY/ON THE WATERFRONT (Film soundtracks) (See under West Side Story) (Various artists).

On Top

UNITY.
LP: BCM 424

On Your Toes

ON YOUR TOES (1983 Original Broadway cast) (Various artists).
Tracks: / Overture: *Various artists* / Two a day for Keith: *Various artists* / It's got to be love: *Various* artists / Too good for the average man: *Various artists* / There's a small hotel: *Various artists* / Heart is quicker than the eye, The: *Various artists* / Quite night: *Various artists* / Questions and answers: *Various* artists / Glad to be unhappy: *Various artists* / On your toes: *Various artists* / Princess Zenobia ballet (edited): *Various artists* / Slaughter on Tenth Avenue (edited): *Various artists.*
LP: TER 1063
MC: ZCTER 1063

ON YOUR TOES (Studio Cast) (Various artists).
LP: COS 2590

Onaje

WALTZ FOR STELLA.
LP: LRF 174

Once Around

ONCE AROUND (Film Soundtrack) (Various artists).
LP: VS 5308
MC: VSC 5308

Once Bitten

ONCE BITTEN (Film soundtrack) (Various artists).
LP: RD 001
LP: IMCA 6154

Once Upon...

ONCE UPON A MATTRESS (Various artists).
LP: DS 15026

Once Upon A Time

ONCE UPON A TIME & HAPPY EVER AFTER (Various artists).
LP: RTLD 2068 A/B
MC: 4CRTLD 2068 A/

ONCE UPON A TIME IN AMERICA (Film Soundtrack) (Various artists).
Tracks: / Once upon a time in America: *Various artists* / Poverty: *Various artists* / Deborah's theme: *Various* artists / Childhood memories: *Various artists* / Amapola: *Various artists* / Friends: *Various artists*/ Prohibition dirge: *Various artists* / Cockeye's song: *Various artists* / Childhood poverty: *Various artists*/ Photographic memories: *Various artists* / Friendship and love: *Various artists* / Speakeasy: *Various artists*/ Deborah's theme: *Various artists* / Amapola: *Various artists.*
LP: MERH 45
MC: MERHC 45

ONCE UPON A TIME IN THE WEST (See under Morricone, Ennio) (Morricone, Ennio).

One

ONE OF EACH (Various artists).
LP: DIXIE 10

UPSTREAM.
LP: CHR 1710
MC: ZCHR 1710

One 2 Many

MIRROR.
Tracks: / Another man / Nearly there / Writing on the wall / Man on the run / Answer / Downtown / In my heart / Hawk / You're the reason / Mirror.
LP: AMA 9003
MC: AMC 9003

One Big Happy Family

ONE BIG HAPPY FAMILY (Various artists).
LP: IRSP 1

One Blood

ONE BLOOD IN LOVE.
LP: NKRLP 001

SUPER SHOWCASE.
LP: NKRLP 002

One Corpse Too Many

ONE CORPSE TOO MANY (A Mediaeval Whodunnit) (Houston, Glyn).
MCSET: LFP 7508

One Flew Over...

ONE FLEW OVER THE CUCKOO'S NEST (Film soundtrack) (Various artists).
LP: MPF 4531

ONE FLEW OVER THE CUCKOO'S NEST (Moriarty, Michael).
MCSET: LFP 7264

ONE FLEW OVER THE CUCKOO'S NEST (see under Kesey,Ken).

One From The Heart

ONE FROM THE HEART (Film Soundtrack) (Various artists).
Tracks: / Opening montage: *Various artists* / Tom's piano: *Various artists* / Once upon a town: *Various artists*/ Wages of love, The: *Various artists* / Is there any way out of this dream?: *Various artists* / Presents: *Various* artists / Picking up after you: *Various artists* / Old boy friends: *Various artists* / Broken bicycles: *Various* artists / I beg your pardon: *Various artists* / Little boy blue: *Various artists* / Instrumental montage: *Various artists* / Tango, The: *Various artists* / Circus girl: *Various artists* / You can't unring a bell: *Various artists* / This one's from the heart: *Various artists* / Take me home: *Various artists.*
LP: CBS 70215
MC: 40 70215
LP: 4676091
MC: 4676094

One In A Million

ONE IN A MILLION (Various artists).
LP: GALP 007

One Love

SOUNDS JAMAICA.
MC: CHV 314

One Minute To Pray

ONE MINUTE TO PRAY, ONE SECOND TO DIE (Film Soundtrack) (Various artists).
LP: SP 8023

One Mo' Time

ONE MO' TIME (Original cast) (Various artists).
Tracks: / Down in Honky Tonk town: *Various artists* / Kiss me sweet: *Various artists* / Miss Jenny's ball: *Various* artists / Cake walkin' babies from home: *Various artists* / I got what it takes: *Various artists* / CC rider: *Various artists* / Graveyard: *Various artists* / He's funny that way: *Various artists* / Kitchen man: *Various artists* / Wait till you see my baby do the Charleston: *Various artists* / Love: *Various artists*/ Louise: *Various artists* / New Orleans hop scop: *Various artists* / Blues: *Various artists* / Everybody loves my baby: *Various artists* / You've got the right key but the wrong keyhole: *Various artists* / After you've gone: *Various artists* / My man blues: *Various artists* / Papa de da da: *Various artists* / Muddy water: *Various artists* / There'll be a hot time in the old town tonight: *Various artists.*
LP: K56850

One Nation

BIG LIFE, BIG TEARS.
Tracks: / What good is love? / Touch tonite / Purpose of pain / Big life / This is as far as I go / Love's rock / Big tears / Voice of America / As long as I'm alive / Stability / Child's play.
LP: EIRSLP 1060
MC: EIRSTC 1060

STRONG ENOUGH.
Tracks: / Love is an emotion / What you see is what you've got / This is different / Strong enough / Inspiration / Equality / My commitment / Passion / Blinded.
LP: EIRSA 1008
MC: EIRSAC 1008

One Night Stand

KEYBOARD EVENT.
Tracks: / Charleston rag / After the rain / Pentagonal / Sunshower / Calypso / Mirabella / Princess / When Johnny comes marching home / Winding river / Doom / Memory of mine / Common cause / DCH / Hexagon.
2LP: 88527

One Of A Number...

ONE OF A NUMBER, PART OF A WHOLE (Various artists).
LP: ANT 071

One Plus One

IVY ROOM, THE.
LP: HMS 018

One Plus Two

ONCE IN A BLUE MOON.
LP: HMS 050

One Silver Dollar

ONE SILVER DOLLAR (Film Soundtrack) (Various artists).
LP: PHCAM 02

One The Juggler

NEARLY A SIN.
Tracks: / Enjoy yourself / Mr. Wolf / Passion killer / O no you're not the same / Sister soul / Junkie for love / Blind old senator / Minor eff, A / Barnaby / Damage is done / Django's coming / Patience of a saint / Are you the one / Damage reprise.
LP: PL 70256
MC: PK 70256

SOME STRANGE FASHION.
Tracks: / Everyday / Hours and hours / Soldier / Snake shed skin / Good morning / Freaks / Total control / Mr. Muscle / Sleeper / Beat a retreat.
LP: PL 70606

One Touch Of Venus

ONE TOUCH OF VENUS (Original Broadway Cast) (Various artists).
LP: AEI 1136

One Way

LADY.
LP: MCF 3219

MUSIC (OLD GOLD) (See under Dynasty/I don't wanna be a freak).

WILD NIGHT (One Way (featuring Al Hudson)).
LP: MCF 3153

One Way System

WRITING ON THE WALL.
Tracks: / Corrupted world / This is the age / One day soon / Nightmare / Neurotix / Reason why / Into the fires / Days are numbered / On the line / Life on the outside.
LP: GRAM 08

One Way Ticket

TIME IS RIGHT.
Tracks: / Time is right / Sing along / Take a ride / Reason why / Everybody's been / Fall out / Lusty eyes / Money / Right or wrong / Outroduction.
LP: PTLS 1069

One World

ONE WORLD, ONE VOICE (Various artists).
LP: V 2632
MC: TCV 2632

O'Neal, Alexander

ALEXANDER O'NEAL.
Tracks: / Broken heart can mend, A / If you were here tonight / Do you wanna like I do / Look at us now / Innocent / You were meant to be my lady (not my girl) / Alex 99 / What's missing.
LP: TBU 26485
MC: 40 26485
LP: 460187 1
MC: 460187 4

ALEXANDER O'NEAL - THE 12" TAPE.
Tracks: / Hersay '89 / Critcize / Whats missing / You were meant to be my lady (not my girl) / If you were here tonight.
MC: 4689874

ALL TRUE MAN.
Tracks: / Time is running out / Yoke (G.U.O.T.R.) / Every time I get up / Somebody changed your mind / Midnight run / Used / All true man / Sentimental / What is this thing called love? / Morning after, The / Hang on / Shame on me.
LP: 4658821
MC: 4658824

HEARSAY.
Tracks: / To make you love me (what can I say) / Hearsay / Lovers, The / Fake / Criticize / Never knew love like this / Sunshine / Crying overtime / When the party's over.
LP: 450936 1
MC: 450936 4

HEARSAY ALL MIXED UP.
Tracks: / Fake 88 (house mix) / (What can I say) to make you love me (Hateful club mix) / Never knew love like this (extended version) / Criticize (Ben Liebrand remix) / Lovers, The (extended version) / Criticize (remix) / (What can I say) to make me love me (Ben Liebrand remix) / Fake (extended version) / You were meant to be my lady (88 Keith Cohen extended remix) (Only on CD.) / Innocent (88 Keith Cohen House mix) (Only on CD.).
LP: MIXUP 1
MC: MIXUP 4
MC: 4631964

HEARSAY/ALL MIXED UP (SPECIAL DEAL).
Tracks: / What can I say to make you love me / Hearsay / Lovers, The / Fake / Criticize / Never knew love like this / Crying overtime / When the party's over / Fake 88 (House mix) / What can I say to make you love me (Hateful club mix) / Never knew love like this (ext. version) / Criticize (Ben Liebrand remix) / Lovers, The (ext. version) / Criticize (remix) / What can I say to make you love me / Fake (ext. version).
LP: 466 123 1
MC: 466 123 4

MY GIFT TO YOU.
Tracks: / My gift to you / Sleigh ride / Our first Christmas / Remember (why it's Christmas) / Little drummer boy / Christmas song, The / This Christmas / Winter wonderland / Thank you for a good year / Remember (why it's Christmas) (reprise).
LP: 463152 1
MC: 463152 4

O'Neal, Johnny

COMING OUT.
Tracks: / It could happen to you / If I should lose you / Blues in F / They say it's wonderful / Sometimes I'm happy / Joan's gospel blues / Just the way you are / Just squeeze me.
LP: CJ 229

LIVE AT BAKER'S KEYBOARD LOUNGE.
LP: PARKWOOD 105

O'Neill, Dennis

DENNIS O'NEILL SINGS.
LP: REN 626
MC: ZCN 626

I'LL NEVER WALK ALONE.
Tracks: / You'll never walk alone / Maria (West Side Story) / Funiculi, funicula / Una furtiva lagrima / Shenandoah / Caro mio Ben / Flower song (Carmen) / These are my songs / Be my love / Exodus song.
LP: DENNS 1
MC: DENNC 1

O'Neill, Eugene

EMPEROR JONES, THE (Various artists).
MCSET: 0341

ICE MAN COMETH, THE (Various artists).
MCSET: 0359

LONG DAY'S JOURNEY INTO NIGHT (Various artists).
MCSET: 0350

O'Neill, Sarah

ON THE SHORES OF LOUGH NEAGH (see Hanna, George) (O'Neill, Sarah & George Hanna).

O'Neill, Sean

50 IRISH FAVOURITE PUB SONGS.
LP: KLP 260

IRISH DRINKING SONGS (O'Neill, Sean Band).
MC: OCE 2470

IRISH PARTY SINGSONG.
LP: UNKNOWN

Oneness Of Juju

ELECTRIC JUJU NATION.
LP: MVLP 14

One-Trick Pony (film)

ONE-TRICK PONY (Film soundtrack) (See under Simon, Paul) (Simon, Paul).

Ongala, Remmy

MALILIA MINANA (Ongala, Remmy & Orchestra).
LP: WOMAD 010
MC: WOMCAS 010

SONGS FOR THE POOR MAN (Ongala, Remmy & Orchestra).
Tracks: / Nasikitka / Karola / Kependa roho / Sauti ya mnyonge / Usingizi / Pamella / Muziki asili yake wapi / Mariam wangu / Kifo (Only on CD and MC.) / Muziki asili yake wapi (version) (Only on CD and MC.).
LP: RWLP 6
MC: RWMC 6

Onix

STRESS.
LP: FS 300

Only Alternative

AS FATE WOULD HAVE IT - THE ONLY ALTERNATIVE.
LP: CHIME 0013 M

Only Child

ONLY CHILD.
LP: LPVAG 002
MC: CASSVAG 002

Only Ones

ALONE IN THE NIGHT.
Tracks: / Why don't you kill yourself / Another girl another planet / From here to eternity / Strange mouth / Fools / Out

there in the night / Me and my shadow / Flaming torch / Trouble in the world / Imortal story / Deadly nightshade / You've got to pay / Big sleep / My way out of here.
LP: . . . . DOJOLP 43

BABY'S GOT A GUN.
Tracks: / Happy pilgrim, The / Why don't you kill yourself? / Me and my shadow / Deadly nightshade / Strange mouth / Big sleep / Oh Lucinda / Re-union / Trouble in the world / Castle built on the sand / Fools / My way out of here.
LP: 84089

EVEN SERPENTS SHINE.
Tracks: / From here to eternity / Flaming torch / You've got to pay / No solution / In betweens / Out there in the night / Curtains for you / Programme / Someone who cares / Miles from nowhere / Instrumental.
LP: . . . . CBS 83451

ONLY ONES LIVE, THE.
Tracks: / Trouble in the world / Beast, The / Lovers of today / Why don't you kill yourself / As my wife says / Big sleep / City of fun / Programme / Happy pilgrim, The (Available on CD only) / Strange mouth (Available on CD only) / No peace for the wicked / Miles from nowhere / Another girl, another planet / Me and my shadow.
MC: 40 82830
LP: 82830
LP: . . . . MAU 603

PEEL SESSIONS: ONLY ONES.
Tracks: / Oh Lucinda / No peace for the wicked / Beast, The / In betweens / Oh no / Prisoners / From here to eternity / Why don't you kill yourself / Miles from nowhere / Telescopic love / Another girl, another planet / Language problem / Happy pilgrim, The / Big sleep.
LP: . . . . SFRLP 102
MC: . . . . SFRMC 102

REMAINS.
LP: . . . . CL 012

Only The Rivers...

ONLY THE RIVERS RUN FREE (Various artists).
LP: . . . . CGLEN 010

Ono, Seigen

COMME DES GARCONS.
Tracks: / Something to hold on to / Have you seen it yet? / All men are heels / Round the globe / Hunting for lions / Look for an afternoon / Pessoa quase certa / After you / 5.40 a.m., view of empire.
MC: . . . . TCVE 51
LP: . . . . VE 51

COMME DES GARCONS VOL 2.
Tracks: / Julia / Carnation / If only you knew / You will be all right / Pastorinhas bandeira branca / Mascara negra / Galope / Roman marching band / Ta ta ta / Louis San / Staying on the beach all day / Another groove / On the sunny side of the street / Finale.
MC: . . . . TCVE 52
LP: . . . . VE 52

GREEN CHINESE TABLE, THE.
Tracks: / Seon in Macau / Pink room, the / World collision / La tete dans ma tete / Green chinese table, The.
LP: . . . . VE 10
MC: . . . . TCVE 10

SEIGEN.
LP: . . . . NEWLP 100
MC: . . . . NEWMC 100

Ono, Yoko

IT'S ALRIGHT.
Tracks: / My man / Never say goodbye / Speck of dust / Loneliness / Tomorrow may never come / It's alright / I see rainbows / Dream love / Let the tears dry / Wake up.
LP: . . . . POLD 5073

MILK AND HONEY: A HEART PLAY (see Lennon, John) (Ono, Yoko & John Lennon).

SEASON OF GLASS.
Tracks: / Goodbye sadness / Mindweaver / Even when you're far away / Nobody sees me like you do / Turn of the wheel / Dogtown / Silver horse / I don't know why / Extension 33 / No, no, no / Will you touch me? / She gets down on her knees / Toy boat / Mother of the universe.
LP: . . . . K 99164
MC: . . . . K 499164

STARPEACE.
Tracks: / Hell in paradise / I love all of me / Children power / Rainbow revolution / King of the zoo / Remember raven / Cape clear / Sky people / You and I / It's gonna rain (living on tiptoe) / Starpeace / I love you, Earth.
MC: 827 530-4
LP: 827 530-1

Onset

POOL OF LIFE, THE.
LP: . . . . PROBE 19
MC: . . . . PROBE 19C

Onslaught

FORCE, THE.
LP: . . . . FLAG 1
MC: . . . . TFLAG 1

IN SEARCH OF SANITY.
Tracks: / Asylum / Shellshock / Let there be rock / Welcome to dying / In search of sanity / Lightning war / Blood upon the ice / Powerplay.
LP: 828 142 1
MC: 828 142 4

POWER FROM HELL.
Tracks: / Damnation / Onslaught (Power from hell) / Thermo neuclear devastation / Skullcrusher 1 / Lord of evil / Death metal / Angels of death / Devil's legion, The / Street meets steel / Skullcrusher 2 / Witch hunt / Mighty empress.
LP: . . . . FLAG 7
LP: . . . . GURT 2

Onuora, Oku

PRESSURE DROP.
LP: . . . . BM 103
LP: . . . . HB 26

Opafire

OPAFIRE.
Tracks: / Kalimbahari / Taos in mind / Wajumbe / Somewhere in between / Walk like rain / Tell me slowly / Rattle in the bush / As children.
LP: . . . . PL 83034
MC: . . . . PK 83034

Opal

EARLY RECORDINGS.
LP: . . . . R 128
MC: . . . . CR 128

Open Mind

OPEN MIND.
LP: . . . . ANTAR 2

Open Mind Surgery

OPEN MIND SURGERY (Various artists).
LP: . . . . FISH 15

Open Road

OPEN ROAD, THE (see Grahame, Kenneth) (Grahame, Kenneth).

Open Space

WE CALL IT CHRISTMAS (see under Johnson,JC & J Kitchener.

Open Winds

OPEN WINDS (Various artists).
LP: . . . . DRLP 146

Opera

CLASSIC YEARS IN DIGITAL STEREO (See under Classic years...) (Various artists).

MECHANICAL OPERA (Musical Boxes).
Tracks: / Il Trovatore (Verdi) / Ernani (Verdi) / La traviata (Verdi) / Rigoletto (Verdi) / Nabucco (Verdi) / Mikado (Gilbert/Sullivan) / Pirates of Penzance (Gilbert/Sullivan) / H.M.S. Pinafore (Gilbert/Sullivan) / Les huguenots (Meyerbeer) / Robert La Diable (Meyerbeer) / La fille du regiment (Donizetti) / Linda di Chamounix (Donizetti) / Lucia di Lammermoor (Donizetti) / William Tell (Rossini) / Barber of Seville (Rossini) / Puritani, I (Bellini) / La sonnambula (Bellini) / Norma (Bellini) / Faust (Gounod) / Carmen (Bizet) / Czar and carpenter (Lortzing) / Marriage of Figaro (Mozart) / La dame blanche (Boieldieu) / Mignon (Thomas) / Lohengrin (Wagner) / Tannhauser overture (Wagner) / Les cloches de Corneville (Planquette) / Midsummer night's dream, A (Mendelssohn).
LP: . . . . SDL 354
MC: . . . . CSDL 354

NEW YORK CITY OPERA CHILDREN'S CHORUS (New York City Opera Childrens Choir).
LP: . . . . TC 1558
MC: . . . . CDL 51558

Opera For Africa

OPERA FOR AFRICA (Various artists).
Tracks: / Andrea Chenier: *Various artists* / Carmen: *Various artists* / Norma: *Various artists* / Requiem: *Various artists* / Cats: *Various artists* / Showboat: *Various artists* / West side story: *Various* artists / La traviata: *Various artists* / La donna del lago: *Various artists* / Un ballo in maschera: *Various artists* / Magic flute: *Various artists* / Nabucco: *Various artists*.
LP: 419 280-1
MC: 419 280-4

Operating Theatre

MISS MAUGER.
LP: . . . . KAOT 6

Operetta

OPERETTA (Various artists).
LP: . . . . REH 716
MC: . . . . ZCR 716

OPERETTA 2 (Vintage collection) (Various artists).
LP: . . . . REH 755
MC: . . . . ZCR 755

Operette

OPERETTE (SHOW) (See under Coward, Noel 'Great shows') (Coward, Noel).

Ophelia Ragtime

ECHOES FROM THE SNOWBALL CLUB.
LP: . . . . SOS 1108

Ophelias

NIGHT OF HALLOWEEN.
LP: . . . . ROUGHUS 28

Ophiuchus

PRONOUNCED O-FEE-ICK-US.
LP: . . . . PROBE 23

Oppitz, Gerhard

MOZART (see under Mozart).

Opposites

OPPOSITES (Various artists).
MC: . . . . PLB 274

Opposition

EMPIRE DAYS.
Tracks: / Five minutes / Abusing words / Fool for you, A / First suspect / Susan gets by on love / If that wasn't love / Someone to talk to me / Mr. Cleanam / War zone / Who's been telling you lies / World's first Vitaphone announcement, The / Empire days.
LP: . . . . OPLP 2
MC: . . . . OPMC 2
LP: . . . . CHC 76
MC: . . . . CHCMC 76

INTIMACY.
Tracks: / Life's blood / Sand and glue / My room is white / New house / Big room / Small view / Voice has changed, The / Day in the future, A / Aching arms / I became a new man / In the heart.
LP: . . . . CAS 1161
MC: . . . . CASMC 1161

PROMISE.
Tracks: / Fall into line / Small talk / I already know / Innocent / Alternatives / Searching for a home / Factory gate / Don't forget to leave the light on in the hall / I dream in colour / Stranded.
LP: . . . . CHC 75
MC: . . . . CHCMC 75
LP: . . . . OPLP 1
MC: . . . . OPMC 1

Oppressed

DEAD AND BURIED.
Tracks: / Victims / Work Together / Urban soldiers / Ultra Violence / Run from you / Riot / Leave Me Alone / Joe Hawkins / Government out / It Ain't Right / We're the opressed.
LP: . . . . OIR 012

FATAL BLOW.
LP: . . . . CREW 1

OI OI MUSIC.
LP: . . . . OPLP 1

Opus

LIVE IS LIFE.
Tracks: / Opus pocus / Positive / No job / Opusition / Again and again / Double bubbles / Live is life / Flyin' high / Follow me / Eleven / Keep your mind / Last note, The.
LP: 825 542-1
MC: 825 542-4

OPUS ELEVEN.
LP: 6 26132

Oral

SEX.
LP: . . . . QUEST 6

Orange

MADBRINGER.
Tracks: / Honey let me feel your pussy / Get away / Don't stop I'm stoned again / Release / Madbringer / Got to be / Blood lips / Your eyes call me back to Tokyo / Let the child be born.
LP: 2121 344

Orange Bicycle

LET'S TAKE A TRIP ON AN ORANGE BICYCLE.
Tracks: / Hyacinth threads / Dropping out / Rennaissance fair / Sing this all together / Amy Peate / So long Marianne / Jenskadajka / Soft winds / Laura's garden / Trip on an orange bicycle / Competition / L.A. / Nicely / Sister Sharon / Box 49 / Lavender girl.
LP: . . . . MBT 5003

Orange Juice

IN A NUTSHELL.
Tracks: / Falling and laughing / Poor old soul / L.O.V.E. / Felicity / In a nutshell / I can't help myself / Hokoyo / Rip it up / Flesh of my flesh / Place in my heart / Bridge / Out for the count / Artisans / What presence.
LP: . . . . OJLP 3
MC: . . . . OJMC 3

ORANGE JUICE.
Tracks: / Lean period / I guess I'm just a little too sensitive / Burning desire / Scaremonger / Artisans / What presence / Out for the count / Get while the gettings good / All that ever mattered / Salmon fishing in New York / Rip it up / Love sick / Flesh of my flesh.
LP: . . . . SPELP 102
MC: . . . . SPEMC 102
LP: OJHP2

ORANGE JUICE/ CAN'T HIDE YOUR LOVE FOREVER.
MC: 8477274

RIP IT UP.
Tracks: / Rip it up / Mud in your eye / Breakfast time / Flesh of my flesh / Hokoyo / Million pleading faces, A / Turn away / I can't help myself / Louise Louise / Tenterhook.
LP: . . . . POLS 1076
MC: . . . . POLSC 1076
MC: 839 768 2

TEXAS FEVER.
Tracks: / Bridge / Craziest feeling / Punch drunk / Day I went down to Texas / Place in my heart / Sad lament.
LP: . . . . OJMLP 1
MC: . . . . OJMMC 1

YOU CAN'T HIDE YOUR LOVE FOREVER.
Tracks: / Falling and laughing / Untitled melody / Wan light / Tender object / Dying day / L.O.V.E. / Intuition told me / Upwards and onwards / Satellite city / Three cheers for our side / Consolation prize / Felicity / In a nutshell.
LP: . . . . POLS 1057
MC: . . . . POLSC 1057

Orb

ADVENTURES BEYOND THE ULTRAWORLD.
2LP: . . . . DLP 5
MCSET: . . . . DMC 5

Orbison, Roy

ALL TIME GREATEST HITS.
Tracks: / Only the lonely / Leah / In dreams / Uptown / It's over / Crying / Dream baby / Blue angel / Working for the man / Candy man / Running scared / Falling / Claudette / Ooby dooby / I'm hurting / Mean woman blues / Lana / Blue bayou / Oh pretty woman.
LP: . . . . SL 805
MC: . . . . MCSL 805

ALL-TIME GREATEST HITS.
Tracks: / Only the lonely (know the way I feel) / Leah / In dreams / Uptown / It's over / Crying / Dream baby / Blue angel / Working for the man / Candy man / Running scared / Falling / Love hurts / I'm hurtin' / Mean woman blues / Pretty paper / Crowd, The.
2LP: . . . . MNT 67290

...AT ROCK HOUSE.
LP: . . . . CRM 2007

BALLADS.
Tracks: / You got it / Too soon to know / She's a mystery to me / Crawling back / In dreams / Love so beautiful, A / Running scared / Blue bayou / Actress, The / I'm hurtin' / Good night / Only the lonely / California blue / It's over / Evergreen / Crying / Falling / Leah / Love hurts / Blue angel / Penny arcade / Oh pretty woman.
MC: . . . . STAC 2441
LP: . . . . STAR 2441

BEST LOVED STANDARDS.
Tracks: / I can't stop loving you / Distant drums / No one will ever know / Beautiful dreamer / Great pretender, The / Let the good times roll / Bye bye love / Dream / (I'd be a) legend in my own time / All I have to do is dream / Cry / What'd I say.
LP: 463 419 1
MC: 463 419 4

BEST OF ROY ORBISON.
2LP: . . . . ADEP 19

BIG O COUNTRY.
Tracks: / Kaw-liga / You win again / I can't help it (if I'm still in love with you) / I'm so lonesome I could cry / Your cheatin' heart / I heard you crying in your sleep / (I'd be a) legend in my own time / Hey good lookin' / Your cold cold heart / Mansion on the hill / There'll be no

teardrops tonight / I can't stop loving you / Too soon to know / Jambalaya.
LP: TAB 72
MC: KTBC 72

BIG O, THE.
Tracks: / Rock house / It's too late / You're gonna cry / Ooby dooby / You're my baby / Mean little mamma / Fool's hall of fame / Cause of it all, The / True love goodbye / Lovestruck / Clown, The / One more time / Problem child / Chicken hearted / I like love / Domino.
MC: CFK 1018
LP: CR 30008
MC: HSC 3264

BIG O, THE (MAGNUM FORCE).
Tracks: / Go go go / I never knew / It's too late / Chicken hearted / Devil doll / Domino / Ooby dooby / Trying to get to you / You're gonna cry / You're my baby.
LP: MFM 024

BLACK & WHITE NIGHT (Orbison, Roy & Friends).
Tracks: / Oh pretty woman / Only the lonely / In dreams / Dream baby (how long must I dream) / Leah / Move on down the line / Crying / Mean woman blues / Running scared / Blue bayou / Candy man / Uptown / Ooby dooby / Comedians, The / (All I can do is) Dream of you / It's over.
MC: TCV 2601
LP: V 2601
MC: OVEDC 369

CLASSIC ROY ORBISON, THE.
Tracks: / Ooby dooby / Trying to get to you / Go go go / This kind of love / You're gonna cry / You're my baby / Rock house / Claudette / Domino / Sweet and easy to love / Devil doll / Chicken hearted / I like love / It's too late / Mean little mama.
LP: OCN 2017WL
MC: OCN 2017WK

CLASSIC ROY ORBISON, THE (DECCA).
LP: HAU 8297

COLLECTION: ROY ORBISON.
Tracks: / Trying to get to you / Ooby dooby / Go go go / You're my baby / Domino / Sweet and easy to love / Devil doll / Cause of it all, The / Fools hall of fame / True love goodbye / Chicken hearted / I like love / Mean little mama / Problem child / This kind of love / It's too late / I never knew / You're gonna cry / One more time (Demo) / Lovestruck (Demo) / Clown / Claudette.
2LP: CCSLP 147
MC: CCSMC 147

CRYING.
LP: HAU 2437

DANCIN' WITH ROY ORBISON.
LP: SP 243

DREAMING WITH ROY ORBISON.
LP: SP 250

EARLY YEARS, THE.
Tracks: / Domino / Ooby dooby / Claudette / Devil doll / Rockhouse / Problem child / Chicken hearted / Mean little mama / Love struck / Cause of it all, The / Clown, The / You're gonna cry / Fools hall of fame / This kind of love.
LP: INS 5010
MC: TCINS 5010

EXCITING SOUND OF ROY ORBISON.
Tracks: / This kind of love / Devil doll / You're my baby / Trying to get to you / It's too late / Rock house / You're gonna try / I never knew / Sweet and easy / Mean little mama / Ooby dooby / Problem child.
LP: NR 5013

FOCUS ON ROY ORBISON.
Tracks: / Twinkletoes / Harlem woman / Lonesome number one / I fought the law / Sugar man / Run, baby, run / Remember the good / Run the engines up high / Shy away / Sweet dreams / Beaujolais / I can't stop loving you / I'm the man on Susie's mind / Memories / Memphis, Tennessee / Take care of your woman / Claudette / Heartache / Land of a thousand dances / Crawling back / Cry softly, lonely one / Cheyenne / Blue blue day / Penny arcade.
2LP: FOS U15/16

GOLDEN DAYS.
LP: MNT 10026
MC: 40 10026

GOLDEN DECADE BOX SET (1960-1970).
LPS: ROYLP 47002
MCSET: ROYMC 47002

GREATEST HITS: ROY ORBISON.
Tracks: / Crowd, The / Love star / Crying / Evergreen / Running scared / Mama / Candy man / Only the lonely / Dream baby / Blue angel / Uptown / I'm hurtin'.
LP: 64 663

LP: SMO 5007

HITS 1, THE.
Tracks: / Only the lonely (know the way I feel) / Candy man / You're my girl / Working for the man / Bye bye love / In dreams / Dream baby (how long must I dream) / Crowd, The / Great pretender, The / Blue Avenue / Party heart / Blue bayou.
LP: SHM 3303
MC: HSC 3303

HITS 2, THE.
Tracks: / Running scared / Blue angel / Mean woman blues / Loneliness / Lana / Pretty paper / It's over / Love hurts / I'm hurtin' / Dream / House without windows / Goodnight.
LP: SHM 3305
MC: HSC 3305

HITS 3, THE.
Tracks: / Oh pretty woman / My prayer / She wears my ring / All I have to do is dream / Uptown / Born on the wind / Crying / Distant drums / Leah / Raindrops / Here comes that song again / Falling.
MC: PWKMC 4024

IN DREAMS (The Greatest Hits).
Tracks: / Only the lonely / Leah / In dreams / Uptown / It's over / Crying / Dream baby / Blue angel / Working for the man / Candy man / Running scared / Falling / I'm hurtin' / Claudette / Oh pretty woman / Mean woman blues / Ooby dooby / Lana / Blue bayou.
2LP: VGD 3514
MC: VGDC 3514

IN DREAMS.
LP: HAU 8108

LAMINAR FLOW.
Tracks: / Easy way out / Love is a cold wind / Lay it down / I care / We're into something good / Movin' / Poor baby / Warm spot hot / Tears / Friday night / Hound dog man.
LP: K 53092

LEGEND, THE.
Tracks: / Too soon to know / (Yes) I'm hurting / Loner, The / Breaking up is breaking my heart / What about me / Far far away / Big hearted me / Blue blue day / Sweet dreams / Oh, such a stranger / Maybe / Lonesome number one / Why hurt the one who loves you / Crawling back / Same street, The / (I'd be a) legend in my time.
MC: HSC 3266
MC: PWKMC 4036P

LEGENDARY ROY ORBISON, THE.
Tracks: / It's over / Only the lonely / Goodnight / Lana / Crowd, The / All I have to do is dream / Crying / Dream baby / Mean woman blues / Oh pretty woman / Love hurts / My prayer / Falling / Blue angel / In dreams / Blue bayou / Great pretender, The / Pretty paper.
LP: STAR 2330
MC: STAC 2330

LEGENDARY ROY ORBISON, THE (2).
LP: XELLP 112
MC: XELMC 112

LONELY AND BLUE.
LP: HAU 2342

MAGIC OF ROY ORBISON, THE.
Tracks: / Chicken hearted / Domino / Go go go / Trying to get to you / You're my baby / Devil doll / I never knew / It's too late / You're gonna cry.
MC: VENUMC 6

MYSTERY GIRL.
Tracks: / You got it / Real world / Dream you / Love so beautiful, A / California blue / She's a mystery to me / Comedians, The / Windsurfer / Careless heart.
LP: V 2576
MC: TCV 2576

OH PRETTY WOMAN.
LP: HAU 8207

ONLY THE LONELY.
LPPD: AR 30041

ORBISON WAY, THE.
LP: HAU 8279

ORBISONGS.
LP: SMO 5004

OTHER SIDE OF, THE.
LP: LSP 1063

OUR LOVE SONG.
Tracks: / Born to love me / (I get so) Sentimental / Evergreen / Mama / Indian wedding / Yo te amo maria / Sleepy hollow / Love star / Borne on the wind / Old love song / Goodnight / (Say) you're my girl.
LP: MNT 4634171
MC: 463 417 4

PROBLEM CHILD.
Tracks: / Problem child / This kind of love / I never knew / It's too late / You're gonna cry / Chicken hearted / Trying to get to you / Problem child (2) / It's too late (2) / Mean little mama / This kind of love (2) / Claudette.
LP: Z 2006

RARE ORBISON COLLECTION.
Tracks: / Actress, The / Paper boy / With the bug / Today's teardrops / Here comes that song again / Only with you / Pretty one / No chain at all / Blues in my mind / Drifting away / Wings of glory / Belinda.
LP: 463 418 1
MC: 463 418 4

ROY ORBISON.
Tracks: / Domino / Ooby dooby / Go go go (down the line) / Rockhouse / You're my baby / Trying to get to you / Cause of it all, The / I was a fool / Problem child / You're gonna cry / Mean little mama / This kind of love / I like love / Chicken hearted.
LP: SUNLP 1050

ROY ORBISON: VINTAGE INTERVIEW PIC DISC.
LPPD: VBAK 3002

SINGLES COLLECTION, THE.
LP: 839 234 1
MC: 839 234 4

SUN YEARS, THE.
Tracks: / Ooby dooby / Trying to get to you / Go go go / You're my baby / Rock house / Domino / Sweet and easy / Devil doll / Cause of it all, The / Fools' hall of fame / True love goodbye / Chicken hearted / I like love / Mean little mama / Problem child / I was a fool / This kind of love / It's too late / I never knew / You're gonna cry / You tell me / I give up / One more time / Lovestruck / Clown, The / Claudette / Jenny / Find my baby for me.
2LP: CDX 4

THERE IS ONLY ONE ROY ORBISON.
LP: HAU 8252

TWENTY CLASSIC HITS.
LP: MA 221185
MC: MAMC 9221185

Orbit, William

ORBIT.
Tracks: / Love my way / Fool to myself / Heartbroken highway / Escape to Mexico / Rider in black / Swamp dog / Feel like jumping / Blue Street / Cluny Ann / Night runs forever, The / Cry one more tear.
LP: MIRF 1020
MC: MIRFC 1020

STRANGE CARGO.
Tracks: / Via Caliente / Jump jet / Secret garden / Scorpion / Jimmy's jag / Theme dream / Fire and mercy / Silent signals / Out of the ice / Riding to Rio / Mighty Limpopo, The.
LP: MCF 1030
MC: MCFC 1030
LP: MIRF 1030

STRANGE CARGO II.
LP: EIRSA 1041
MC: EIRSAC 1041

Orcadian Poet

ORCADIAN POET, THE (see under Browne, George Mackay).

Orchestra

MUSIC FOR THE END (Orchestra of the eighth day).
LP: FF 292

Orchestra Baobab

PIRATE'S CHOICE.
LP: WCB 014
MC: WCC 014

Orchestra Des Hauses..

MUSIC FOR ACCORDION ORCHESTRA NO.4.
Tracks: / Pastorale Francaise / Kompositionen fur akkordeon orchestra.
LP: HS 059

Orchestra Harlow

SALSA! (Orchestra Harlow feat. Junior Gonzalez).
Tracks: / No quiero / La cartera / Popo pa' mi / No hay amigo / Sueltame / El paso de encarnacion / Wampo / Silencio.
LP: HOT 104
MC: TCHOT 104

Orchestra Jazz

PLAYS THE MUSIC OF CARLA BLEY.
Tracks: / 440 / Lone arranger, The / Dreams so real / Baby baby / Joyful noise / Egyptian / Blunt object.
LP: XTRAWATT 4

Orchestra Makassy

AGWAYA.
Tracks: / Mambo bado / Zimababwe / Kufiliska sio kilema / Nakolela cherie / Mosese / Athumani / Mke wangu / Molema.
LP: OVED 94
LP: V 2236

Orchestra Marrabenta

INDEPENDENCE.
LP: PIR 12

Orchestra Super

KAIVASKA.
Tracks: / Mbanda ya mobange / Kassongo / Ji ji / Nanga / Banana / Samba / Malaba d'amour / Mokano / Mwana nyiau.
LP: OVED 126
LP: V 2263

MALOBA D'AMOR.
Tracks: / Kassongo / Shauri yako / Salima (parts 1 and 2) / Mwana nyiau (parts 1 and 2) / Nabinakate / Maloba d'amor / Samba (parts 1 and 2).
LP: AFRILP 007

Orchestra Tango Cafe

TANGO ARGENTINO.
LP: ATSS 1001
MC: TAC 1

Orchestra Virunga

MALAKO.
LP: ERT 1006

Orchestral Splendour

ORCHESTRAL SPLENDOUR (Various artists).
2LP: 268 100 9

Orchestre Jazira

NOMADIC ACTIVITIES.
LP: BEGA 56
MC: BEGC 56

Orchestre Victoria

SANS PREAVIS.
LP: EVVI 20

Orchids

ORCHIDS.
LP: MCF 3067

UNHOLY SOUL.
MC: SARAH 605MC

Ordinaires

ONE.
LP: BND 7LP

ORDINAIRES.
LP: ST 7509

Oregon

45TH PARALLEL.
LP: VBR 20481
MC: VBR 20484

CROSSING.
Tracks: / Queen of Sydney / Pepe Linque / Alpenbridge / Travel by day / Kronach waltz / Glidj / Amaryllis / Looking glass / Crossing, The.
LP: ECM 1291

DISTANT HILLS.
LP: VNP 5318
MC: VNP 6318

ECOTOPIA.
Tracks: / Twice around the sun / Innocente / WBAI / Zephyr / Ecotopia / Leather cats / Redial / Song of the morrow.
LP: ECM 1354

MUSIC OF ANOTHER PLANET.
Tracks: / North Star / Sail / Children of God / Shard / Bell spirit / Touchstone / Silence of a candle, The / Rough places plain, The / At the Hawk's well / Opening / Spring is really coming / Land of heart's desire / Swan, The / Baku the dream maker.
MC: CV 79326

OREGON.
Tracks: / Rapids, The / Beacon / Toast / Beside a brook / Ariana / There was no Moon that night / Skyline / Impending bloom.
LP: ECM 1258

OUT OF THE WOODS.
Tracks: / Yellow bell / Fall 77 / Reprise / Cane fields / Dance to the morning star / Vision of a dancer / Story-telling / Water wheel / Witchi tai to.
LP: K 52101

Oreo Moon

WALK DON'T SCREAM.
Tracks: / Hard luck / Walk don't scream / Futurama / In the darkest part of you / Don't hold back / Freedom's curve / Nine old men / Jungle life.
LP: SNTF 898

Orff (composer)

CARMINA BURANA (Berlin Philharmonic Orchestra).
MC: 422 363-4
LP: 422 363-1

Organ Music...

50 HAMMOND ORGAN FAVOURITES (Various artists).
MCSET: TR 1536

MCSET: . . . . TR 4114365

101 KEY MORTIER DANCE ORGAN FAVOURITES (Various artists).
MC: . . . . KAFL 105

FOUR COLUMNS (Various artists).
Tracks: / American patrol: *Mortier Show Organ* / Rambling rose of my childhood: *Mortier Show Organ* / I dreamt I dwelt in marble halls: *Mortier Show Organ* / Then you'll remember me: *Mortier Show Organ* / When other lips: *Mortier Show Organ* / Aquarious: *Mortier Show Organ* / Joseph polka: *Mortier Show Organ* / Toot toot tootsie goodbye: *Mortier Show Organ* / I'm sitting on top of the world: *Mortier Show Organ* / Malaguena: *Mortier Show* Organ / Entry of the gladiators: *Mortier Show Organ* / Vienna bloos: *Mortier Show Organ* / Gilbert and Sullivan, Highlights: *Mortier Show Organ* / Loudly let the trumpets bray: *Mortier Show Organ* / Poor wandering one: *Mortier* Show Organ / When a felon's not engaged: *Mortier Show Organ* / Behold the Lord High Executioner: *Mortier Show* Organ / Wandering minstrel: *Mortier Show Organ* / Flowers that bloom in the spring: *Mortier Show Organ* / I'm called little buttercup: *Mortier Show Organ* / Dance a cachucha: *Mortier Show Organ* / Down yonder: *Mortier* Show Organ / Avalon: *Mortier Show Organ* / Who's sorry now: *Mortier Show Organ* / Alexander's ragtime band: *Mortier Show Organ* / When you're smiling: *Mortier Show Organ* / Tico tico: *Mortier Show Organ* / Gold and silver waltz: *Mortier Show Organ.*
LP: . . . . JOYS 257

GOLDEN HAMMOND ORGAN FAVOURITES (Various artists).
Tracks: / Calcutta: *Various artists* / Top of the world: *Various artists* / Snowbird: *Various artists*/ Big spender: *Various artists* / Pink panther, Theme from: *Various artists* / Stripper, The: *Various artists*/ Big country: *Various artists* / Good, the bad and the ugly, The: *Various artists* / Magnificent seven, The: *Various* artists / Mexico: *Various artists* / Chihuahua: *Various artists* / Those lazy, hazy, crazy days of summer: *Various artists* / Cuando sali de Cuba: *Various artists* / Guantanamera: *Various artists* / Hustler, The: *Various artists* / Carioca: *Various artists* / Coffee song, The: *Various artists* / Brazil: *Various* artists / Eso beso: *Various artists* / Charade: *Various artists* / Felicidade: *Various artists* / Moonglow: *Various artists* / Wives and lovers: *Various artists* / Freedom come, freedom go: *Various artists*/ Love story theme: *Various artists* / All I ever need is you: *Various artists* / Adagio from Venetian Anonymous: *Various artists* / San Antonio rose: *Various artists.*
LP: . . . . NTS 213
MC: . . . . TCNTS 213

GREAT ORGAN FAVOURITES (Various artists).
MC: TC2MOM 115

INTRODUCING THE YAHAMA ORGAN STARS (Various artists).
LP: . . . . ADOR 2

KNOW YOUR ORGAN (Various artists).
LP: . . . . DEROY 1413

ORGAN MUSIC FROM CAMBRIDGE No.4.
LP: . . . . GRS 1041

ORGANIST ENTERTAINS YOU (Various artists).
LP: . . . . MOR 536
MC: . . . . KMORC 536

SING AND DANCE WITH THE MORTIER ORGAN (Various artists).
LP: . . . . MORR 503

SONG OF A DUTCH STREET ORGAN various artists (Various artists).
LP: . . . . GM 2007

TURNERS MERRY-GO-ROUND VOL.1 Organ music (Various artists).
Tracks: / Lady of Spain: *Various artists* / I'm in the mood for dancing: *Various artists* / Dinah: *Various* artists / When the lilac blooms again: *Various artists* / Alexander's ragtime band: *Various artists* / Making your mind up: *Various artists* / Birdie song, The: *Various artists* / New York, New York: *Various artists*/ Winner takes all: *Various artists* / But I do: *Various artists* / Flic flac: *Various artists* / Woodpecker song, (The): *Various artists* / Chattanooga choo choo: *Various artists* / Pennsylvania 6-5000: *Various artists*/ Elmer's tune: *Various artists* / Little brown jug: *Various artists* / Moonlight serenade: *Various artists*/ In the mood: *Various artists* / Day trip to Bangor: *Various artists* / Post horn galop: *Various artists*/ Rock around the clock: *Various artists* / Thank you for the music: *Various artists* / My blue Heaven: *Various* artists / Some of these days: *Various artists* / After you've gone: *Various artists* / Somebody stole my gal: *Various artists* / St. Louis blues: *Various artists* / Chinatown: *Various artists.*
LP: . . . . GRS 1132
MC: . . . . KGRS 1132

Organum

IN EXTREMIS.
LP: . . . . LAY 19

SUBMISSION.
LP: . . . . UD 023

O'Riada, Reader

GOMBEANNAITEAR DUIT.
LP: . . . . CEF 125

READAR O'RIADA.
LP: . . . . UNKNOWN

O'Riada, Sean

MISE EIRE.
LP: . . . . CEF 080

O RIADA.
LP: . . . . CEF 032

O'RIADA'S FAREWELL.
LP: . . . . CC 12
MC: 4CC 12

PLAYBOY OF THE WESTERN WORLD, THE.
LP: . . . . CEF 012

Oriental Wind

BAZAAR.
LP: . . . . SNTF 864

SANKIRNA (Oriental Wind & The Karnataka College Of Percussion).
LP: . . . . SNTF 930

Original...

ORIGINAL SOUNDTRACKS (Various artists).
MC: 1A 222 1582754

ORIGINAL STALAG 17-18 AND 19 (Various artists).
LP: . . . . WR 1684

ORIGINALS (Various artists).
2LP: . . . . TVDLP 14
MCSET: . . . . ZCTVD 14

Original 5 Blind Boys

PRECIOUS MEMORIES.
LP: . . . . MCA 28002

Original Camelia

ORIGINAL CAMELIA JAZZ BAND (Original Camelia Jazz Band).
LP: . . . . NOR 7207

Original Concept

STRAIGHT FROM THE BASEMENT OF KOOLEY HIGH.
Tracks: / Legend / Charlie sez / Runnin' yo mouth / Knowledge / Pump that bass (live) / Jonnie wuza gangsta / Here comes the 5-oh / Prejudice / Psychodustrip / Can you feel it '88 / Get stupid ... again / Cause we're original / Fat lady / To the beat y'all / She's got a moustache / Stranded / Total confusion / Gottanotha funky break 4 U hit it (On cassette only.).
LP: 4629781
MC: 4629784

Original Dixieland...

1943 (Original Dixieland Jazz Band).
LP: . . . . GHB 100

NUMBER TWO BLUES (Original Dixieland Jazz Band).
LP: . . . . GAPS 190

ORIGINAL DIXIELAND JAZZ (Original Dixieland Jazz Band & Louisiana Five).
LP: . . . . FJ 101

ORIGINAL DIXIELAND JAZZ BAND REVISITED (Original Dixieland Jazz Band).
LP: . . . . RARITIES 36

SENSATION (Original Dixieland Jazz Band).
Tracks: / Livery stable blues / Sensation rag / Dixie jazz band one-step / That teasin' rag / Tiger rag / Bluein' the blues / Fidgety feet / Clarinet marmalade / Lazy daddy / At the Jazz Band Ball / Look at 'em doing it / Ostrich walk / Satanic blues / 'Lasses candy / Tell me / I've got a captain working for me now / Mammy o'mine / I've lost my heart in Dixieland / Margie / Singing the blues.
LP: . . . . AJA 5023
MC: . . . . ZC AJA 5023

Original Jazz Hounds

ORIGINAL JAZZ HOUNDS & GULF COAST 7.
LP: . . . . VLP 45

Original Memphis..

ORIGINAL MEMPHIS BLUES BROTHERS, THE (See under Blues for details) (Various artists).

Original Mirrors

HEART, TWANGO & RAW BEAT.
Tracks: / Heart, twango and raw beat / Dancing with the rebels / Teen beat / When you're young / Things to come / Darling .... in London / Don't cry baby / Please don't wear red / Swing together / Time has come.
LP: 6359046

Original Ramblers

ORIGINAL RAMBLERS (Theo Uden Masman).
LP: . . . . RFC 100

Original Salty Dogs

DOWN IN HONKY TONKY TOWN.
LP: . . . . SOS 1115

RHYTHM KINGS ON THE RIGHT TRACK.
LP: . . . . GHB 62

Original Sin

SIN WILL FIND YOU OUT.
LP: . . . . RR 9679

Original Sins

SELF DESTRUCT.
LP: . . . . MMLP 035

Original Soul Stirrers

DIVINE LOVE.
LP: . . . . MAL 04384

NOBODY'S CHILD.
LP: . . . . MGS 4369

Original Stalag 20

ORIGINAL STALAG 20 (Various artists).
LP: . . . . WRLP 28

Original Unknown DJ's

BREAK BEATS 2.
Tracks: / Funky beat 1 / Shaft in Africa / Freestyle II / Jazzies groove / Buffalo beats II / Isaac II / House it up / Granny scratch / How ya living / Swing beat I / Chief / Films / Funky beat II / Swing beat II / Dope / Samples and effects.
LP: . . . . WRRLP 011

Orioles

JUMP CHILDREN (Recorded 1953-56) (Orioles/Moonglows/Flamingos).
Tracks: / Jump children / Real gone mama / Live it up / Cross over the bridge / Baby please / Fools will be fools / Golden teardrops / Ooh rockin' daddy / I just got lucky / My gal / Someday, someway / Happy till the letter / 219 train / Carried away / Never leave me baby / Whistle my love.
LP: . . . . CRB 1060

Orion

REBORN.
LP: . . . . CRL 5020

Orion, Lore Coyote

LORE COYOTE ORION.
Tracks: / Born to roll / I wish in Texas / You and me, woman and man / My fantasies / Runnin' wild / Mustang Canyon / Once you cross the line / She takes my breath away / On the horizon / Eldorado / She likes to drive me crazy / Texas ain't the same / They got Jesse / Tickin' away.
LP: . . . . PTLP 004

Orion the Hunter

ORION THE HUNTER.
LP: . . . . PRT 25906
MC: 40 25906

Orissa

ETERNAL INDIA (See under 'India' for details).

ETERNAL INDIA.
Tracks: / Mangala charan / Batu nrutya / Pallavi / Abhinaya / Yugma dwanda / Moksha nata / Mangala.
LP: . . . . ARN 33287

Orkney Strathspey...

ORKNEY FIDDLE MUSIC (Orkney Strathspey & Reel Society).
Tracks: / Signature tune of The Orkney Strathspey & Reel Soc. / Marwick Bay ((a) Marwick Bay (b) The Churchill Barriers (c) Miss Muriel Harvey) / Churchill barriers, The ((a) The Deerness jig (b) Graemeshall Bay (c) R.Aims compliments to J.C) / Miss Muriel Harvey ((a)The Stronsay Waltz (b) Jock Halcro) / Deerness jig, The ((a) Gairsay (b) R.Aims compliments to A.Robertson (c) Road to Orkney) / Graemeshall bay ((a) Peter Pratt's polka (b) Norwegian polka (c) Jimmy o' the bu's polka) / Aim's compliments to J. Craigie, Rousay ((a) Orkney's compli's to R.Appleyard (b) Lamb Holm (c) Elspeth's march) / Jock Halcro ((a) St Mary's waltz) / Stronsay waltz, The / Gairsay / R. Aim's compliments to Arthur Robertson / Road to Orkney, The / Peter Pratt's polka / Norwegian polka / Jimmy o' the bu's polka / Orkney's compliments to Reuben Appleyard / Lamb Holm / Elspeth's wedding march / Scapa Flow / Deerness reel / Old polka, The / Maggie Watson's farewell to Blackhammar / St. Mary's waltz / Orkney Strathspey & Reel Society's compliments / Helliar Holm / Brinkie's brae / Mirlind's polka / Inganess.
LP: . . . . MFP 41 5752 1
MC: . . . . MFP 41 5752 4
LP: . . . . OU 2157

Orlando, Tony

BLESS YOU.
LP: . . . . BN 611

Orleans

FOREVER.
LP: . . . . MCL 1698

Ormiston, Billy

BORDER SPIRIT (Ormiston, Billy & Clive Ryder).
Tracks: / Willie Moore / Border spirit / Campbell's black heid / Brafferton Village / Rowin' foula doon / Miss Catherine Brosnan (Kilcoy's march) / Pride of Glencoe / Bantry Bay / Gipsy laddie / Kielderburn, The (stronsay waltz).
MC: . . . . FSMC 7

Ornberg, Tomas

COME BACK, SWEET PAPA (Ornbergs, Tomas Blue Five).
LP: . . . . SOS 1043

THOMAS ORNBERG'S BLUE FIVE (Ornbergs, Tomas Blue Five).
LP: . . . . OP 8003

O'Rourke, Jim

JIM O'ROURKE AR HOELION WYTH.
Tracks: / Tomen o wallt / Chwarelwyr / Malvinas / Gwelais I ti / Cowboi / Pentigili.
LP: . . . . LOCO 1016

Y BONT.
LP: . . . . SAIN 1425 M

Orphan

PHOBIAS.
Tracks: / Phobias / Nervous / I don't want it like that / Time bomb / R.S.V.P.U. / Dream boat / Julie isn't Julie in the bath / Mouth to mouth / 7 teen / Ambition / Little England / Love on the Lichfield line.
LP: . . . . ORF 1

Orpheon Celesta

LA GARE DE LYON.
LP: . . . . SOS 1083

ORPHEON CELESTA VOLUME 2.
LP: . . . . SOS 1095

Orpheus

PSYCHOTRONIC SOUND.
MC: . . . . CXC 01

Orquestra Reve

LA EXPLOSION DEL MOMENTO.
Tracks: / Rundera (son) / La gente no se puede aguantar (changui son) / De mayo / Changui clave / Mas viejo que ayer, mas joven que manana / El palo de anon / Que te importa a ti / Espero que pase el tiempo / You no quiero que seas celosa / El ron pa despue / Que cuento es ese / Que lastima me da contigo mi amor.
LP: . . . . RWLP 4
MC: . . . . RWMC 4

Orquestra Ritmo

LA RITMO ORIENTAL TE ESTA LLAMANDO! (Ritmo Oriental is calling you).
Tracks: / Nena, asi no se vale / Yo traigo panatela / Que rico bailo yo / Maritza / La ritmo suena a areito / Maria baila el son / El que no sabe, sabe / Advertencia para todos / Si no hay posibilidad me voy.
LP: . . . . ORB 034

Orr, Benjamin

LACE, THE.
Tracks: / Too hot to stop / In circles / Stay the night / Skyline / When you're gone / Spinning / Hold on / Lace, The / That's the way / This time around.
LP: 9604601
MC: 9604604

Orrall, Robert Ellis

FIXATION.
Tracks: / Something to tell you / Baby go / She's all grown up / Girls gotta listen / White noise / How can she (even like that guy) / Hit man / Actually / But no / Only love / Call the uh-oh squad / Problem with woman.
LP: . . . . WHO 2
MC: . . . . WHOK 2

Orson Family

BUGLES GUITARS AND AMPHETAMINES.
LP: . . . . CRIMLP 127

RIVER OF DESIRE.
MLP: . . . . NEW 22

Orsted-Pederson, N.H.

JUST THE WAY YOU ARE (see Gustafsson, Rune) (Orsted-Pederson, Hiels-Henning & Rune Gustafsson).

Ortega, Anthony

JAZZ FOR YOUNG MODERNS.
LP: FS 153

NEW DANCE.
Tracks: / New dance / Shadow of your smile / Sentimentalize / Conversation piece.
LP: REV 3

NEW DANCE.
LP: REVM 3

PERMUTATIONS.
Tracks: / My buddy / Pizzicato / G the key / I love you / Arco / 'Tis Autumn.
LP: REV 7

RAIN DANCE (Ortega, Anthony Quintet).
LP: DS 788
MC: DSC 788

Orthodox Church Music

RUSSIAN ORTH CHUR MUS (VOL 3)/ FINNISH ORTH MUS (IKO 4F & IKO 15) (Various artists).
MCSET: CIKO 22D

Ortiz, Pertico

IN TRADITION.
LP: 1115947

Orwell, George

1984 (Jacobi, Derek (nar)).
MCSET: TCLFP 417140 5

ANIMAL FARM.
MC: LFP 41 7178 5

Ory, Kid

1944 - 1945 (Ory, Kid & His Creole Jazz Band).
LP: FL 9008

1955 (Kid Ory's creole jazz band).
Tracks: / Savoy blues / Good man is hard to find, A / Closer walk with thee, A / Shake that thing / Copenhagen / Royal garden blues / Mississippi mud / Tin roof blues / Indiana.
LP: 1012 008

AT CLUB HANGOVER VOL. 6 (Ory, Kid & His Creole Jazz Band).
LP: SLP 4070

AT THE JAZZBAND BALL Live in concert (Ory, Kid & His Creole Jazz Band).
Tracks: / Panama rag ((Composed: Tyers)) / At the jazz band ball / Peoria ((Composed: Fripp#Collins#Burrell#Wallace)) / Basin Street blues ((Composed: Williams)) / St. James Infirmary blues ((Composed: J.Primrose)) / Wolverine blues ((Composed: Morton#spikes#Spikes)) / Savoy blues ((Composed: Edward Ory)) / Tin roof blues ((Composed: Brunies#Rappolo#Mares#Spitzel#Pollack#Mirose)) / That's a plenty ((Composed: Pollack#gilbert)) / Aunt Hagar's blues ((Composed: W.C.Handy#I.T.J.Brinn)).
LP: RHA 6034

GREATEST (Kid Ory's creole jazz band).
Tracks: / South rampart street parade / Girls go crazy, The / How come you do me like you do / Four or five times / St. James infirmary / Bill Bailey won't you please come home / Milenberg joys / Creole song / Bucket's got a hole in it / Creole love call / Ballin' the jack / Aunt Hagar's blues.
LP: 1012 045

KID ORY AT THE BEVERLY CAVERN
That's all, folks!.
LP: SOUNDS 1208

KID ORY & CREOLE BAND AT DIXIELAND JUBILEE (Ory, Kid & His Creole Jazz Band).
LP: DJA 519

KID ORY & CREOLE JAZZBAND (Ory, Kid & His Creole Jazz Band).
LP: LPJT 48

KID ORY PLAYS THE BLUES.
Tracks: / Savoy blues / Snag it / Royal Garden blues / Yellow dog blues.
LP: SLP 4064

KID ORY'S CREOLE BAND.
Tracks: / Original Dixieland one-step / I wish I were in Peoria / Careless love / Won't you come home Bill Bailey / St. James Infirmary / That's a plenty.
LP: QU 052

KID ORY'S CREOLE JAZZ BAND.
LP: 1012 004

KID ORY'S CREOLE JAZZ BAND 1955.
Tracks: / Savoy blues / Good man is hard to find, A / Closer walk with thee, A / Shake that thing / Copenhagen / Royal Garden blues / Missippi mud / Tin roof blues / Indiana.
LP: 1012 008

LIVE AT CLUB HANGOVER VOL.1 (Ory, Kid & His Creole Jazz Band).
LP: DC 12013

LIVE AT CLUB HANGOVER VOL.2 (Ory, Kid & His Creole Jazz Band).
LP: DC 12014

LIVE AT CLUB HANGOVER VOL.3 (Ory, Kid & His Creole Jazz Band).
LP: DC 12016

LIVE AT CLUB HANGOVER VOL.4 (Ory, Kid & His Creole Jazz Band).
LP: DC 12017

MERCURY THEATRE, L.A., BROADCASTS (Ory, Kid & Jimmy Noone).
Tracks: / High Society / Muskrat ramble / That's a plenty / Panama rag / Sugar foot stomp / Jimmy's blues / Savoy blues / Weary blues / Kid Ory Creole Jazz Band blues.
LP: SM 3085

NEW ORLEANS (Ory, Kid & His Creole Jazz Band).
Tracks: / Savoy blues / Creole song / Glory of love / Mahogany Hall stomp / Blues for Jimmy / At a Georgia camp meeting / Go back where you stayed last night / Yaaka hula hickey dula / Tiger rag / My bucket's got a hole in it / Eh la bas / Joshua fit de battle of Jerico / World's jazz crazy / Lawdy so am I / Farewell to Storyville / Creole bo bo / Bill Bailey, won't you please come home?.
LP: CBS 21061
MC: 40 21061

NEW ORLEANS LEGENDS (see Johnson, Bunk) (Ory, Kid & Bunk Johnson).

SONG OF THE WANDERER.
Tracks: / Song of the wanderer / Tailgate ramble / Mahogany Hall stomp / Baby won't you please come home? / St. Louis blues / Toot toot tootsie / Sheik of Araby, The / Tiger rag.
LP: 2304 542

THIS KID'S THE GREATEST (Ory, Kid & His Creole Jazz Band).
Tracks: / South Rampart street parade / Girls go crazy, The / How come you do me like you do / Four or five times / St. James infirmary / Bill Bailey won't you please come home / Milneberg joys / Creole song / Bucket's got a hole in it / Creole love call / Ballin' the Jack / Aunt Hagar's blues.
LP: 1012 045

WE'VE GOT RHYTHM (Ory, Kid & Red Allen).
LP: 2304 504

Oryema, Geoffrey

EXILE.
LP: RWLP 14
MC: RWMC 14

Osadebe, Osita

OSONDI OSWENDI.
LP: POLP 120

Osborn, Michael

GOLD HEARTED GIRL.
LP: CCR 1020

Osborne, Brian

AE FOND KISS.
LP: TRS 024
MC: TRS 024/CS

Osborne Brothers

BLUEGRASS COLLECTION.
Tracks: / Kentucky waltz / Pain in my heart / Blue ridge cabin home / When are you lonely / Some old day / I hear a sweet voice calling / Cabin in Caroline / It's a long, long way to the top of the world / Sunny side of the mountain / Head over heel / Don't that road look rough and rocky / I'm going back to old Kentucky / Your sweet love is like a flower / Sweethearts again / Little cabin home on the hill / No mother or Dad / Toy heart / Rank strangers / Vision of mother, A / Lonesome day / My rose of old Kentucky / This heart of mine can never say goodbye / Thinking about you / White dove.
2LP: CMH 9011
MC: CMH 9011C

BLUEGRASS CONCERTO.
Tracks: / Bluegrass concerto / Tina Rene waltz / Bandy's 109 / Shawnee / I'll fly away / Homecoming, The / Jesse James / Bobby Van Waltz / Black mountain drive / Sure-fire / Uncloudy day, The.
LP: CMH 6231

BOBBY & HIS MANDOLIN.
LP: CMH 6260

ESSENTIAL BLUEGRASS ALBUM, THE (Osborne Brothers/Mac Wiseman).
Tracks: / Midnight flyer / Shackles and chains / Bluebirds are singing for me / Family bible / Don't let your sweet love die / I wonder how the old folks are at home / Little white church, The / It's goodbye and so long to you / Four walls around me / Mother Maybelle / I'll still write your name in the sand / Poison love / Take me back to Renfro Valley / Shenandoah waltz / Mountain fever / Are you coming back to me / I'm a stranger here / You're the girl of my dreams / Pins and needles in my heart / I've always wanted to sing in Renfro Valley / Travellin' this lonesome road / Tis sweet to be remembered.
2LP: CMH 9016
MC: CMH 9016C

FROM ROCKY TOP TO MUDDY BOTTOM (The songs of Boudleaux & Felice Bryant).
Tracks: / Rocky top / Georgia mules and county boys / Don't ever tell me you love me / Hey Joe / All I ever have to do is dream / Packing up your heart / Tell it to your old Grandpa / Little boy / Banjo's going home / Georgia piney woods / Just another dream / I can't see the rainbow / Take me as I am / Tennessee hound dog / Where did the sunshine / Country boy / Love hurts / Fortune, fortune / Muddy bottom.
2LP: CMH 9008
MC: CMH 9008C

I CAN HEAR KENTUCKY CALLING ME.
LP: CMH 6244

MODERN SOUNDS OF BLUE GRASS MUSIC, THE.
Tracks: / Kind of woman I got, The / Hard times / Walking the floor over you / Roll muddy water / One tear / Lonesome feeling / One kiss away from you / Memories / Someone before me / Let's say goodbye / World of forgotten people / I'm leaving.
LP: HAT 3063
MC: HATC 3063

NUMBER ONE.
Tracks: / Leavin's heavy on my mind / Say old man (can you play the mandolin) / Guide me home my Georgia moon / Memories never die / Each season changes you / Rueben / Last time, The / Bent, broken and blue / Fair and tender ladies / Hobo on a freight train to heaven / Rutland's reel.
LP: CMH 6206

ONCE MORE VOL.1.
LP: SH 3754

ONCE MORE VOL.2 (Favorite memories).
LP: SH 3758

OSBOURNE BROTHERS & RED ALLEN (Osborne Brothers & Red Allen).
LP: SS 03
LP: HAT 3129

OSBOURNE BROTHERS, THE.
LP: SS 04
MC: SSC 04

SINGING, SHOUTING PRAISES.
Tracks: / Jesus cares what happens / Medals for Mother / Saviour, Lord and guide / Are you so afraid to speak our Saviour's name / What a friend we have in Jesus / Old brush arbors / Still waters / Where no-one stands alone / Nearer my God to thee / Singing, shooting praises / Hide me rock of ages.
LP: SH 3764
MC: SH 3674C

SOME THINGS I WANT TO SING ABOUT.
Tracks: / How much does it cost to ride this train / February in my heart / Always you / So doggone lonesome / Somehow tonight / Rosie Bokay / Wreck of the old 97 / If you're gonna do me wrong, do it right / Some things I want to sing about / Harvest of my heart / Too long / Can't you hear that whistle blow.
LP: SH 3740
MC: SH 3740MC

VOICES IN BLUEGRASS.
Tracks: / Take this hammer / Cottonfields / Me and my old banjo / Pathway of teardrops / Kentucky / Bluegrass express / This heart of mine / Cuckoo bird / Don't ever look at me / Charlie Cotton / Bugle on the banjo / Salty dog blues.
LP: HAT 3003
MC: HATC 3003

Osborne, Jeffrey

DON'T STOP.
Tracks: / Don't stop / Let me know / Border lines / Power / Is it right? / You can't be serious / Crazy 'bout cha / Hot coals / Live for today.
LP: AMA 5017
MC: AMC 5017

EMOTIONAL.
Tracks: / We belong to love / You should be mine / Soweto / In your eyes / Room with a view / Emotional / Second chance / Love's not ready / Who would have guessed / Come midnight.
LP: AMA 5103
MC: AMC 5103

JEFFREY OSBORNE.
Tracks: / New love / Eeny meeny / I really don't need no light / On the wings of love / Ready for your love / Who you talkin' to / You were made to love / Ain't nothin' missin' baby / Congratulations.
LP: AMLH 64896
MC: CAM 64896

ONE LOVE ONE DREAM.
Tracks: / She's on the left / Can't go back on a promise / True believers / One love one dream / All because of you / La cuenta, por favor / Family, The / My heart can wait forever / You can't wait forever / Cindy.
LP: AMA 5205
MC: AMC 5205

ONLY HUMAN.
Tracks: / If my brother's in trouble / Only human / Good things come to those who wait / Morning after, The / Lay your head / Baby wait a minute / Sending you a love / Feel like makin' love / Back in your arms / Nightime (Only on cassette and CD.) / Getting better all the time.
LP: 210920
MC: 410920

STAY WITH ME TONIGHT.
Tracks: / Don't you get so mad / We're going all the way / Stay with me tonight / Greatest love affair / Plane love / Other side of the coin / I'll make believe / When are you coming back / Two wrongs don't make a right.
LP: AMLX 64940
MC: CXM 64940

TAKE GOOD CARE OF YOU AND ME (See under Warwick, Dionne) (Osborne, Jeffrey & Dionne Warwick).

Osborne, John

LUTHER (Various artists).
MCSET: 0363

Osborne, Mike

ALL NIGHT LONG (Osborne's, Mike Trio).
LP: OG 700

BORDER CROSSING.
LP: OG 300

MARCEL'S MOUSE (Osborne, Mike Quintet).
LP: OG 810

ORIGINAL (See under Tracey, Stan) (Osborne, Mike & Stan Tracey).

Osborne, Will

1936 (Osborne, Will & His Orchestra).
LP: HSR 197

HALLELUJAH (Osborne, Will & His Orchestra).
LP: GELP 15035

WILL OSBORNE ON THE AIR (Osborne, Will & His Orchestra).
Tracks: / Gentleman awaits, The / Charming little faker / Let there be love / Way back in 1939 AD / It was written in the stars / Tales from the Vienna Woods / Leanin' on the old top rail / Out of the mood / Little fox, The / Missouri scrambler / Imagination / Mr. Jackson Alexander Wolcott Brown / Too romantic / Bolero my dream / Tuxedo Junction.
LP: AIRCHECK 37

Osbourne, Johnny

BRING THE SENSI COME.
LP: Unknown

DANCING TIME.
LP: LDLP 005

FALLY LOVER.
Tracks: / Fally lover / You're too sexy / Two bad daughter / Ice cream love / Man of Jehoviah / Mushroom / No lollipop no sweet so / Love so strong / He can surely turn the tide / Come back darling.
LP: GREL 12

IN THE AREA.
Tracks: / In the Dutch mountains / J.O.S. days / Two skaters / Pelican and penguin / In a play / Oom-pah-pah / Panorama man, The / Mountain jan / One eye open / Eating house, An / Swimmer, The / Goodnight / Strangers of the night (Extra track on cassette.) / Moon and stars (Extra track on cassette.).
LP: UNKNOWN
MC: UNKNOWN

JOHNNY OSBOURNE.
Tracks: / I forgot to say I love you till I'm gone / Cool down / What about me / Come a little bit closer / Baby, I love your way / You sexy thing / True confession /

What's love got to do with it / Groovy kind of love / I'm missing you.
LP: UNKNOWN

JOHNNY OSBOURNE.
LP: LIXLP 300

MICHAEL PALMER MEETS JOHNNY OSBOURNE (Osbourne, Johnny & Michael Palmer).
LP: VV 001

NEVER STOP FIGHTING.
Tracks: / Never stop fighting / Love is universal / In your eyes / Over 31 under 21 / Sister mister / Give a little love / Freelance lover / Curly locks girl / Baccara / Words of the ghetto.
LP: GREL 38

NUH DIS (COME YA FE DRINK MILK).
LP: SSBLP 004

REALITY.
LP: SELLP 01

REGGAE ON BROADWAY.
LP: VSLP 4062

ROCK ME, ROCK ME.
LP: TRA 6004

RUBADUB SOLDIER.
LP: J 005

WATER PUMPING.
Tracks: / Give a little love / Trouble maker / Water pumping / Rolling reggae / Purify your heart / Get up / Fire down below / Dance with you / Love you tonight / Na look nobody / Angel in my arms.
LP: GREL 61

Osbourne, Ozzy

BARK AT THE MOON.
Tracks: / Rock 'n' roll rebel / Bark at the moon / You're no different / Now you see it (now you don't) / Forever / So tired / Waiting for darkness / Spiders.
LP: EPC 32780
MC: 40 32780
LP: EPC 25739
LP: 32780

BLIZZARD OF OZ.
LP: 4504531
MC: 4504534
LP: JETLP 234

CHRIS TETLEY INTERVIEWS OZZY OSBOURNE.
LPPD: CT 1010

CLOSE MY EYES FOREVER (See under Ford, Lita) (Osbourne, Ozzy & Lita Ford).

DIARY OF A MADMAN.
LP: JETLP 237
MC: JETCA 237
LP: 4630861
MC: 4630864

JUST SAY OZZY.
Tracks: / Miracle man / Bloodbath in paradise / Shot in the dark / Tattooed dancer / Sweet leaf / War pigs.
LP: 4659401
MC: 4659404

MUSIC AND MEDIA INTERVIEW PICTURE DISC.
LPPD: MM 1201

NO REST FOR THE WICKED.
Tracks: / Miracle man / Devil's daughter (Holy war) / Crazy babies / Breakin' all the rules / Bloodbath in paradise / Fire in the sky / Tattooed dancer / Demon alcohol.
LP: 4625811
MC: 4625814

OZZY OSBOURNE: INTERVIEW PICTURE DISC.
LPPD: BAK 2053

TALK OF THE DEVIL.
Tracks: / Symptom of the Universe / Snow blind / Black Sabbath / Fairies wear boots / War pigs / Wizard, The / N.I.B / Sweatleaf / Never say die / Sabbath bloody Sabbath / Iron man / Children of the grave / Paranoid.
2LP: 4511241
MCSET: 4511244
2LP: JETDP 401
MC: CCSMC 296

TRIBUTE (Osbourne, Ozzy & Randy Rhodes).
Tracks: / I don't know / Crazy train / Believer / Mr. Crowley / Flying high again / Revelation (mother earth) / Steal away (the night) / Suicide solution / Iron man / Children of the grave / Paranoid / Goodbye to romance / No bone movies / Dee (Randy Rhodes studio out-takes).
LP: 4504751
MC: 4504754

ULTIMATE SIN.
Tracks: / Ultimate sin / Secret loser / Never know why / Thank God for the bomb / Never / Lightning strikes / Killer of giants / Fool like you, A / Shot in the dark.
LP: EPC 26404
MC: 40 26404
LPPD: EPC 11 26404
LP: 462496 1
MC: 462496 4

URPNEY SONG, THE (See under Connolly, Billy) (Connolly, Billy/Bruno, Frank/Osbourne, Ozzy/Batt, Mike).

Osbourne, Tony

NICE AND EASY LISTENING.
MC: AM 41

Osby, Greg

GREG OSBY AND SOUND THEATRE (Osby, Greg And Sound Theatre).
Tracks: / You big / Daigoro / Return to now / Shohachi bushi - oyamako bushi / Calculated risk / For real moments / Gyrhthmitoid.
LP: JMT 870011

MIND GAMES.
LP: 834 422 1

SEASON OF RENEWAL.
Tracks: / Sapphire / Enchantment / For the cause / Life's truth / Dialogue x / Season of renewal / Mischief makers / Word / Constant structure / Eye witness / Spirit hour.
LP: 843 435 1
MC: 843 435 4

Oscar, Lee

BEFORE THE RAIN.
Tracks: / Before the rain / Steppin' / San Francisco bay / Feeling happy / More than words can say / Sing song / Haunted house.
LP: MCF 2870

LEE OSCAR.
LP: MCF 3060

O'Se, Sean

BANKS OF MY OWN LOVELY LEE.
LP: STAL 8008

ONE DAY FOR RECREATION (see under Na Fili).

O'Shamrock, Barney

16 SINGALONG FAVOURITES.
LP: PLAT 17
MC: PLAC 17

IRISH ACCORDION, THE.
Tracks: / Slievenamon / Old flames / Doonaree / Rose of Tralee, The / Rose of Mooncoin / Wild colonial boy / Irish American (medley) / How can you buy Killarney / Maggie / Fields of Athenry / Galway Bay / Molly Malone / Bunch of thyme / Danny boy / Hannigan's hooley / Banks of my own lovely Lee, The / When Irish eyes are smiling / Did your mother come from Ireland / Old bog road / Forty shades of green / Irish medley.
LP: PLA 011
MC: Unknown
LP: PLAT 11
MC: PLAC 11

IRISH ACCORDION, THE (2).
LP: IHLP 12
MC: IHMC 12

SCOTTISH ACCORDION, THE.
MC: PLAC 26

O'Shea, Sean

HERITAGE.
MCSET: HMC 010D

Osibisa

BEST OF OSIBISA.
Tracks: / Beautiful seven / Music for gong gong / Y sharp / Akwaaba / Wango wango / Dawn / Phallus C / Kokoroko / Woyaya.
LP: MCL 1693
MC: MCLC 1693

BEST OF OSIBISA (BBC).
Tracks: / Welcome home / Odensu / Seaside meditation / Do it / Kolomashie / Warrior, The / Cherry field / Ohah awake / Hamattan / Time is right / Gumbe / Jumbo / Kyrie Eleison / Lost fisherman / Sunshine day / Choboi / Right now / Uhuru / Coffee song, The / Flying bird / Dance the body music / Keep on trying / Sakaba / Get up / Soldier / Abele / Africa we go go / Sakura.
LP: REF 776
MC: ZCD 776

BLACK MAGIC NIGHT.
Tracks: / Introduction / Welcome home / Living loving feeling / Spirits up above / Fire / Beautiful seven / Encore / Dawn, The / Ayiko bia / Woyaya / Ke le le / Music for gong gong / Sunshine day / Survival.
MC: ZCF 777

HAPPY CHILDREN.
Tracks: / Happy children / We want to know / Kotuku / Adwoa / Bassa-Bassa / Somaja / Fire.
LP: K 56022

LIVE AT THE MARQUEE, 1983.
Tracks: / Fire / Life / Ayioka / Who's got the paper / Woyaya (end s1) / Music for Gong gong / Too much going on / Happy children / Warrior / Sunshine day.
LP: CBR 1035
MC: KCBR 1035

MYSTIC ENERGY.
Tracks: / Meeting point / Celebration / Africa we go go / Orebo (magic people) / Moving on / Mama (I will be back) / (I feel) pata pata / Fatima / Obinkabimame.
LP: CABLP 1002
MC: ZCCZB 1002

OSIBISA.
LP: MDKS 8001

OSIBISA UNLEASHED.
Tracks: / Raghupati raghava ragaram / Time is right / Kelele / We bring you love / Happy children / Move your body / Why / Get up and dance / Beautiful India.
LP: MAGL 5053
MC: ZCMAG 5053

OSIBROCK.
Tracks: / Who's got the paper / Why / Osibrock / Celele / Atinga bells / African jive / We belong / Komfo (High Priest) / Kangaroo / Home affairs.
LP: K 56048

WOYAYA.
LP: MDKS 8005

Osiris

WAR ON THE BULLSHIT.
LP: LPATTACK 1

Oskay, Bill

NIGHTNOISE (Oskay, Bill & Michael O'Domhnaill).
LP: TAC 1031

Oskorri

ADIO KATTALINA.
LP: ELKAR 50

ALEMANIAN EUSKERAZ.
LP: ELKAR 76

HAU HERMOSURIE.
LP: ELKAR 78

Oslin, K.T.

EIGHTIES LADIES.
Tracks: / Wall of tears / I'll always come back / Younger men / Eighties ladies / Do ya' / Two hearts / Doctor Doctor / Lonely but only for you / Old pictures.
LP: PL 85924
MC: PK 85924

LOVE IN A SMALL TOWN.
Tracks: / Come next Monday / Oo-wee / Mary and Willie / Love is strange / Momma was a dancer / New way home / Cornell Crawford / Still on my mind / You call everybody darling.
MC: PK 90545
LP: PL 90545

THIS WOMAN.
Tracks: / This woman / Money / Round the clock lovin' / Where is a woman to go / Hold me / Hey Bobby / She don't talk like us no more (CD only) / Jealous (CD only) / Didn't expect it to go down this way / Truly blue (CD only).
LP: PL 88369
MC: PK 88369

Osmond Boys

OSMOND BOYS.
LP: 4680421
MC: 4680424

Osmond Brothers

TODAY.
Tracks: / I think about your lovin' / It's like falling in love (over and over) / Never ending song of love / Take this heart / Ease the fever / Your leaving was the last thing on my mind / Blue all over you / She's ready for someone to love her / If every man had a woman like you / What do the lonely do / We work hard (to make love easy) / Where does an angel go when she cries / She's back in town again / One way rider.
LP: RANGE 7005
MC: SDC 5118
MC: RANGE 67005

Osmond, Donny

ALONE TOGETHER.
LP: 2315 210

DISCOTRAIN.
LP: 2391 226

DONNY.
LP: 2315 314

DONNY OSMOND.
Tracks: / Soldier of love / Sacred emotion / Faces in the mirror / I'm in it for love / Only heaven knows / If it's love that you want / Inner rhythm / My secret touch / Groove / Hold on.
LP: V 2469
MC: TCV 2469
LP: OVED 301
MC: OVEDC 301

EYES DON'T LIE.
Tracks: / My love is a fire / Eyes don't lie / Love will survive / Sure lookin' / Private affair / Take another try (at love) / Make it last forever / Never too late for love / Just between you and me / Before it's too late.
LP: EST 2135
MC: TCEST 2135

GOIN' COCONUTS (Osmond, Donny & Marie).
Tracks: / On the shelf / Don't play with the one who loves you / You don't have to say you love me / Baby, now that I've found you / Gimme some time / Let's fall in love / You bring me sunshine / Fallin' in love again / Doctor dancin' / You never can tell / May tomorrow be a perfect day.
LP: 239 137 1

I'M LEAVING IT ALL UP TO YOU (Osmond, Donny & Marie).
LP: 2315 307

MAKE THE WORLD GO AWAY (Osmond, Donny & Marie).
LP: 2315 343

PORTRAIT OF DONNY.
LP: 2315 108

TIME FOR US, A.
LP: 2315 273

TOO YOUNG.
LP: 2315 113

Osmond, Donny & Marie

DEEP PURPLE.
LP: 2391 220

NEW SEASON.
Tracks: / Ain't nothing like the real thing / Anytime sunshine / It's all been said before / Which way you goin' Billy / Show me / You broke my heart / Now we're together / Hold me, thrill me, kiss me / Sing / We got love.
LP: 2391 245

Osmond, Jimmy

KILLER JOE.
LP: 2315 157

Osmond, Marie

ALL IN LOVE.
Tracks: / I'm in love and he's in Dallas / Raining tears / My hometown boy / Baby's blue eyes / Lonely as the night is long / 99% of the time / Somebody else's moon / Sweet life / All in love / Without a trace.
LP: EST 2068
MC: TCEST 2068

DEEP PURPLE (see under Osmond, Donny) (Osmond, Marie & Donny).

DEEP PURPLE (SINGLE) (See under Osmond, Donny) (Osmond, Marie & Donny).

I ONLY WANTED YOU.
Tracks: / Cry just a little / I only wanted you / You're still new to me / Making magic / I know the feeling / Your love carries me away / We're gonna need a love song / New love / More than dancing / Everybody's crazy 'bout me baby.
LP: EST 2020
MC: TCEST 2020

I'M LEAVING IT ALL UP TO YOU (see under Osmond, Donny) (Osmond, Marie & Donny).

I'M LEAVING IT ALL UP TO YOU (SINGLE) (See under Osmond, Donny) (Osmond, Marie & Donny).

MAKE THE WORLD GO AWAY (see under Osmond, Donny) (Osmond, Marie & Donny).

MAKE THE WORLD GO AWAY (SINGLE) (See under Osmond, Donny) (Osmond, Marie & Donny).

MORNING SIDE OF THE MOUNTAIN (See under Osmond, Donny) (Osmond, Marie & Donny).

ON THE SHELF (See under Osmond, Donny) (Osmond, Donny & Marie).

PAPER ROSES.
LP: 2315 262

THERE'S NO STOPPING YOUR HEART.
Tracks: / There's no stopping your heart / Needing a night like this / Read my lips / Best of you, The / I'll be faithful to you / Meet me in Montana / That old devil moon / Love will find it's way to you / Until I fall in love again / Blue sky / Shining.
LP: EST 2000
MC: TCEST 2000

Osmonds

AROUND THE WORLD Live in concert.
2LP: 2659 044

CRAZY HORSES.
LP: 2315 123

I CAN'T LIVE A DREAM.
LP: 2391 236

I'M STILL GONNA NEED YOU.
LP: 2315 342

LOVE ME FOR A REASON.
LP: 2315 312

OSMONDS' GREATEST HITS.
Tracks: / One bad apple / Proud one, The / Ain't nothing like the real thing / Love me for a reason / Are you lonesome tonight / C'mon Marianne / Puppy love / Down by the lazy river / This is the way I feel / Long haired lover from Liverpool / Let me in / I'm leaving it all up to you / Go away little girl / Crazy horses / Deep purple / Too young / Going home / Paper roses / Hold her tight / Morning side of the mountain / Having a party / Twelfth of never.
MC: . . . . BRC 2522
2LP: 2675 153

OSMONDS LIVE.
LP: 2315 117

OUR BEST TO YOU.
LP: 2315 300

PLAN, THE.
LP: 2315 251

Osorio, Jorge Federico

PIANO CONCERTI NO.19/24 (see under Mozart) (Osorio, Jorge Federico/ Royal Philharmonic Orchestra).

Ossian

BORDERS.
LP: . . . . IR 007
MC: . . . . IRC 007

DOVE ACROSS THE WATER.
LP: . . . . IR 004
MC: . . . . IRC 004

FERGUSSON'S AULD REIKIE (Ossian & Jock Tamsons Bairns).
LP: . . . . IR 003

LIGHT ON A DISTANT SHORE.
LP: . . . . IR 009
MC: . . . . IRC 009

OSSIAN.
Tracks: / Corncrake, The / I hae a wife o ma ain / Sitting in the stern of the boat / Ma rovin' eye / O mo dhuthaich (Oh my country) / Ossian's lament / 72nd Highlanders farewell to Aberdeen / Favourite dram, The / Ae fond kiss / Brose and butter / Monaghan jig / Jackson's bottle of brandy / Music of Spey / Let me in this ae night / Spootaskerry / Willow Kishie, The / Simon's wart / Oidhche mhath leibh (goodnight to you).
LP: . . . . SPR 1004
MC: . . . . SPRC 1004

SEAL SONG.
LP: . . . . IR 002
MC: . . . . IRC 002

ST KILDA WEDDING.
LP: . . . . IR 001
MC: . . . . IRC 001

WELLPARK SUITE, THE (See under Jackson, Billy).

Osterman Weekend

OSTERMAN WEEKEND, THE (Film soundtrack) (Various artists).
LP: . . . . TER 1084
MC: . . . . CTV 81198

Osterwald, Hazy

KRIMINAL TANGO (Osterwald, Hazy Sextet).
LP: . . . . BTS 943405

Ostrogoth

DON'T POINT YOUR FINGER.
LP: . . . . SKULL 8374

ECSTASY AND DANGER.
MC: . . . . TAPE 78319
LP: . . . . SKULL 8319

FEELING OF FURY.
LP: . . . . ULT 331804

Ostroushko, Peter

DOWN THE STREETS OF MY OLD NEIGHBOURHOOD.
LP: . . . . ROUNDER 0227
MC: . . . . ROUNDER 0227C

SLUZ DUZ MUSIC.
LP: . . . . ROUNDER 0204
MC: . . . . ROUNDER 0204C

O'Suilleabhain,

DOLPHIN WAY, THE.
Tracks: / Christmas Eve / Plains of Boyle, The / Gentle fair Elly (Eibhi gheal chiuin) / Old grey goose, The / Pretty milkmaid, The / Snowy breasted pearl, The (Pearls an bhrollaig bhain) / Carolan's concerto / Merrily kiss the quaker / Little fair haired child, The / Fox chase, The / Molly Halpin (Mollai ni ailpin) / Planxty Irwin / Gentle maiden, The.
LP: . . . . VE 1
MC: . . . . TCVE 1

O'Sullevan, Peter

PETER O'SULLEVAN TALKS TURF.
LP: . . . . CAS 1160
MC: . . . . CASMC 1160

O'Sullivan, Bernard

CLARE CONCERTINAS (O'Sullivan, Bernard & Tommy McMahon).
Tracks: / Babes in the wood / Cooraclare polka / Clare dragoons / Sandy groves of Piedmont / Humours of Ennistymon / Old torn petticoat / Tommy People's favourite / Mount Fabus hunt / Ollie Conway's selection / Kilrush races / Clogher reel / Burren reel / Bonaparte's retreat / Bonaparte's march / Barron's jig / Jackson's jig / Miltown jig / Rodney's glory / Tommy McMahon's reel / Over the waves / Girl I left behind me, The / Maggie in the wood / Martin Taltry's jig / Thomas Friel's jig / Joe Cunnean's jig / Sean Ryans hornpipe / Danganella hornpipe / Job of journeywork / Ash plant, The / Maid of Mount Cisco, The.
LP: 12FRS 502

IRISH TRADITIONAL MUSIC OF COUNTY.
Tracks: / I have a bonnet trimmed with blue / Rakes of mallow / Farmer Moroney's reel / Mulvill's reel / Maud Millar's reel / Bucks of Oranmore, The / My heart's in the highlands / Dewdrop, The / Blooming meadows / Mullagh jig / Ballinakill jig / Merry sisters / Quilty reel / Cliff, The / Derry hornpipe / Rose in the heather / Flowery mountains / Kiss the maid behind the barrel / Milliners daughter, The / Trip to Durrow, A / Stack Ryan's polka / Set dance / Garden of daisies, The / Andy Keone's jig / Three sea captains / Boys of Ballysadare, The / Five mile chase.
LP: 12FRS 505

O'Sullivan, Cathie

ARTESIAN WATERS.
LP: . . . . LRF 047

HIGH PLACES.
LP: . . . . LRF 128

SUMMERHAZE.
LP: . . . . LRF 183

O'Sullivan, Gilbert

20 GOLDEN GREATS: GILBERT O'SULLIVAN.
Tracks: / Nothing rhymed / No matter how I try / We will / Alone again, naturally / Oooh wakka doo wakka day / Clair / I love it, but / Hello, it's goodbye / Underneath the blanket go / What's in a kiss? / Matrimony / Ooh baby / Why oh why / Happiness is me and you / Woman's place, A / Christmas song, The / Susan Van Heusen / Can't get enough of you / I don't love you but I think I like you.
LP: . . . . NE 1133
MC: . . . . CE 2133

20 GOLDEN PIECES: GILBERT O'SULLIVAN.
Tracks: / Alone again, naturally / Matrimony / I don't love you but I think I like you / Who was it? / I hope you'll stay / I've never loved you as much as I love you today / Why oh why / I'm in love with you / I, of course, replied / Marriage machine / My love and I / Happiness is me and you / If you love me like I love you / Niceness of it all, The / If I don't get you back again / That's love / Just as you are / Friend of mine, A.
LP: . . . . BDL 2050
MC: . . . . BDC 2050

20 OF THE VERY BEST.
Tracks: / Clair / We will / Ooh baby / Get down / Who was it? / Matrimony / Nothing rhymed / Alone again, naturally / Why oh why / Too much attention / Out of the question / No matter how I try / I'm a writer not a fighter / Oooh wakka doo wakka day / Where peaceful waters flow / If you love me like I love you / Always somebody / Golden rule / But I'm not / My father.
LP: . . . . SHM 3090
MC: . . . . HSC 3090

BACK TO FRONT.
LP: . . . . MAMS 502

COLLECTION: GILBERT O'SULLIVAN.
2LP: . . . . NETV 1001
MC: . . . . NETVC 1001

GILBERT O'SULLIVAN.
Tracks: / Clair / Who was it? / Friend of mine, A / That's love / I don't love you but I think I like you / No more / My love and I / Nothing rhymed / Get down / No matter how I try / I have never loved you as much as I love you today / Alone again, naturally / Oooh wakka doo wakka day / What could be nicer? / Marriage machine / Golden rule / You are you / Nothing to do about much / Who knows? / Perhaps maybe / Out of the question / Why oh why / If I can't have you all to myself / If I don't get you back again / Oh baby / Victor E. / I'll believe it when I see it / Matrimony.
MCSET: . . . . CRT 001

GILBERT O'SULLIVAN'S GREATEST HITS.
Tracks: / Alone again, naturally / Clair / Christmas song, The / We will / Nothing rhymed / Why oh why / Get down / Matrimony / Oooh wakka doo wakka day / No matter how I try / Ooh baby / Out of the question.
LP: . . . . MAMA 2003

GREATEST HITS: GILBERT O'SULLIVAN (IMPORT).
LP: . . . . BRLP 46
MC: . . . . BRMC 46

GREATEST HITS: O' SULLIVAN.
LP: 2215227
MC: 2115227

HIMSELF.
LP: . . . . MAMS 501

I'M A WRITER NOT A FIGHTER.
LP: . . . . MAMS 505

IN THE KEY OF 'G'.
LP: . . . . CHR 1747
MC: . . . . ZCHR 1747
LP: . . . . ADO 11

LIFE AND RHYMES.
Tracks: / Live now pay later / Bear with me / You don't own me / Minute of your time / Is it a crime / Got to be that way / Has been / I promise honest / Wonder why / Looking / If I know you / At least I'm honest.
LP: . . . . CBS 85668

NOTHING BUT THE BEST.
Tracks: / Nothing rhymed / Matrimony / We will / No matter how I try / Permissive twit / Alone again (naturally) / Ooh-wakka-doo-wakka day / Out of the question / Clair / Get down / Friend of mine, A / Ooh baby / Why oh why oh why / Happiness is me and you / Woman's place, A / Christmas song / I don't love you but I think I like you / What's in a kiss.
2LP: . . . . CTVLP 107
MCSET: . . . . CTVMC 107

OFF CENTRE.
Tracks: / I love it, but / What's in a kiss? / Hello, it's goodbye / Why pretend? / I'm not getting any younger / Things that go bump in the night / Help is on the way / For what it's worth / Niceness of it all, The / Can't get enough of you / Break it to me gently / Or so they say.
LP: . . . . CBS 84524
MC: 40 84524

SPOTLIGHT ON GILBERT O'SULLIVAN.
Tracks: / Get down / Ooh baby / Friend of mine, A / Woman's place, A / I don't love you but I think I like you / Underneath the blanket go / Clair / Nothing rhymed / Out of the question / If I don't get you back again / Where peaceful waters flow / Christmas song, The / Alone again, naturally / Why oh why / We will / What could be nicer? / It's so easy to be sad / Permissive twit / Oooh wakka doo wakka day / Matrimony / No matter how I try / Susan Van Heusen / Marriage machine / Bye bye.
2LP: . . . . SPOT 1002
MCSET: . . . . ZCSPT 1002

STRANGER IN MY OWN BACK YARD.
LP: . . . . MAMS 506

UNFORGETTABLE: GILBERT O'SULLIVAN (16 Golden Classics).
Tracks: / Nothing rhymed / Matrimony / We will / No matter how I try / Alone again (naturally) / Clair / Get down / Ooh baby / Friend of mine, A / They've only themselves to blame / Where peaceful waters flow / Happiness is me and you / Why oh why / I don't love you but I think I like you / Miss my love today / What's in a kiss.
LP: . . . . UNLP 004
MC: . . . . UNMC 004

VERY BEST OF GILBERT O'SULLIVAN, THE.
LP: . . . . SHM 3156
MC: . . . . HSC 3156

O'Sullivan, Jerry

INVASION, THE.
LP: . . . . SIF 1074
MC: . . . . CSIF 1074

Otello

OTELLO (Film Soundtrack) (Various artists).
LPS: . . . . EX 270 461 3
MCSET: . . . . EX 270 461 5

OTELLO (See under Verdi) (Various artists).

Othello

OTHELLO (see under Shakespeare, William) (Various artists).

OTHELLO (VIDEO) (see under Verdi (composer)) (Various artists).

Other Ghost Stories

OTHER GHOST STORIES (see under James, M.R.) (Horden, Sir Michael).

Other Music

INCIDENTS OUT OF CONTEXT.
LP: . . . . FF 302

Other Ones

LEARNING HOW TO WALK.
LP: . . . . V 2569
MC: . . . . TCV 2569

OTHER ONES, THE.
Tracks: / Another holiday / Stay with me / We are what we are / Losing it / Moments / He's a man / All the love / All day all night / Makes me higher / Stranger.
LP: . . . . V 2404
MC: . . . . TCV 2404

Other Song

OTHER SONG OF THE SOUTH (Various artists).
Tracks: / Breaking up is hard to do: *Various artists* / Poor me: *Various artists* / Go on, go on: *Various* artists / I cried: *Various artists* / Just a memory: *Various artists* / Shedding teardrops over you: *Various* artists / Secret of love: *Various artists* / Please accept my love: *Various artists* / Cool down baby: *Various* artists / Mathilda finally came back: *Various artists* / Part of everything: *Various artists* / All of my life: *Various artists* / Love me, love me: *Various artists* / Bald head: *Various artists* / Oncoming train: *Various artists* / Sea of love: *Various artists*.
LP: 6463 086

Othermothers

NO PLACE LIKE HOME.
LP: . . . . SPIN 303

Otis Brothers

STICK TO THE PROMISE.
MC: . . . . GVMMC 201

Otis, Byron

MISSING YOUR LOVE.
LP: . . . . CSLP 003

Otis, Johnny

BARRELHOUSE STOMP.
Tracks: / Omaha flash / Jeff-hi stomp / Miss Mitchell / Ultra-violet / Sgt. Barksdale / Love's nocturne / Barrelhouse stomp / Pay day blues / Hog jaws / Jelly roll, The / Happy new year baby / That's your last boogie / Alligator meat / Stardust / One nighter blues.
LP: . . . . JB 611
MC: . . . . JBC 611

GEE BABY (Otis, Johnny & Co.).
Tracks: / Gee baby / Alimony boogie / My heart tells me / Crazy 'bout your cookin' / Square dance / New love / Baby baby blues / Voodoo / Call operator / Goomp blues / What's your name / Gypsy blues / Chittlin' switch / Brown skin butterball / Why don't you believe me / Wishing well.
LP: . . . . JB 617

GOOD LOVIN' BLUES (Otis, Johnny Show).
Tracks: / Ida Mae / Ice water in your veins / Your last boogie / Pop and sons boogie / In the driver's seat / Loving you is all I know / Listen women / Time to say 'bye bye' / Open house at my house / Good good lovin' blues / Come on over baby / Hey, Mr Bartender / Rock me baby.
LP: . . . . CH 299

GREAT RHYTHM AND BLUES VOL.3.
Tracks: / Willie and the hand jive / Barrelhouse blues / Please don't leave me / Bad luck shadow / Fannie Mae / Signifying monkey, The / Harlem nocturne / Stack-a-lee / Don't start me to talkin' / Baby, I've got news for you / Country girl / Bye bye baby.
LP: . . . . BDL 1002

INTO THE EIGHTIES.
Tracks: / Rock and roll wedding / Stand by me / Love (makes me do foolish things) / Hit that jive, jack rollin' / Do it again, baby / In the still of the night / Hide away / Will you love me tomorrow / Soothe me baby / When something is wrong with my baby / I found you / Fine and mellow / I'm gonna leave these women alone.
LP: . . . . CRB 1110

JOHNNY OTIS SHOW, THE.
LP: 2C 068 86528

LIVE AT MONTEREY (Otis, Johnny Show).

Tracks: / Willie and the hand jive / Cry me a river / Cleanhead's blues / I got a gal / Baby you don't know / Preacher's blues / Good rockin' tonight / Time machine / Margie's boogie / Little Esther's blues / Blowtop blues / T-Bone blues / Jelly, jelly / Kidney stew / Things I used to do, The / The R.M. blues / Shuggies blues / You better look out / Goin' back to L.A. / Plastic man / Boogie woogie bye bye.
2LP: . . . . **DED 266**

NEW JOHNNY OTIS SHOW, THE.
Tracks: / Drinkin' wine spo-dee-o-dee / Every beat of my heart / Jonella and Jack / What else can I do? / Half steppin' woman / Why don't you do right? / Big time scoop / I never felt this way before / Don't deceive me / So fine.
LP: . . . . **SNTF 878**
MC: . . . . **AC 4726**

ORIGINAL JOHNNY OTIS SHOW, THE.
LP: . . . . **SJL 2230**

ORIGINAL JOHNNY OTIS VOL 2, THE.
LP: . . . . **SJL 2252**

ROCK AND ROLL HIT PARADE.
LP: . . . . **FLY 550**

ROCK 'N' ROLL REVUE.
Tracks: / Shake it Lucy baby / Willie and the hand jive / Ring-a-ling-a-ling / Bye bye baby / Light still shines, The / Tell me so / Telephone baby / Mumblin' moise / Good golly / Ma, he's making eyes at me / Crazy country hop / Hum ding a ling / You just kissed me goodbye / In the dark / Can't you hear me callin' / Castin' my spell.
LP: . . . . **CRB 1041**

Otito

TRUTH, (THE) (see Ade, King Sunny) (Otito/King Sunny Ade)).

Ottah, Rogana

UDIE CHUKU.
LP: . . . . **MLPS 010**

Ottawan

OTTAWAN.
Tracks: / D.I.S.C.O. / Hello Rio / Sha-la-la song / Tant que durera la nuit / Help, get me some help / Comme aux USA / D.I.S.C.O. (French version).
LP: . . . . **CAL 118**

OTTAWAN (4TRACK EP).
Tracks: / Hands up / Disco / You're OK / Sha la la song.
MC: . . . . **RCXK 010**

OTTAWAN'S GREATEST HITS.
Tracks: / Hands up / Hello Rio / Crazy music / Sha-la-la song / Aie is my song / D.I.S.C.O. / Help, get me some help / You're OK / Siesta for two.
LP: . . . . **CAL 132**
MC: . . . . **CAC 132**

Otters

OTTERS FIRST SONG COLLECTION.
Tracks: / Hallo there hi / One cat, two cats / Another alphabet song / Keep on dancing / Excuse me, please / We met on sunday / Yellow banana / Barn dance / London bridge / I like food / Seasons / In my room / What's that thing / Pets / Otter rag / Barn dance (reprise).
MC: . . . . **OTT 001**

Otto's Chemical Lounge

SPILLOVER.
LP: . . . . **HMS 023**

Otway & Barrett

WAY BAR.
Tracks: / Birthday boy / DK 50-80 / Cry cry / 21 days / Medieval dance / Body talk / Man who shot Liberty Valance, The / Loves in bloom / Day after day / Come back darling.
LP: **2383 581**

Otway, John

ALL BALLS AND NO WILLY.
Tracks: / Nothing's gone / Mass communication / In dreams / Too much air, not enough oxygen / Montreal / Middle of winter / Turn off your dream / Telex.
LP: . . . . **HAM LP 1**

DEEP AND MEANINGLESS (Otway, John & Wild Willie Barrett).
Tracks: / Place farm way / To Ann / Beware of the flowers(cos I'm sure they're going to get you) / Alamo, The / Oh my body is making me / Josephine Schnot / Riders in the sky / I wouldn't wish it on you / Can't complain.
LP: **2382 501**

GONE WITH THE BIN OR THE BEST OF OTWAY AND BARRE (Otway, John & Wild Willie Barrett).
Tracks: / Beware of the flowers(cos I'm sure they're going to get you) / Racing cars / Oh my body is making me / Running from the law / Riders in the sky / Cheryl's goin' home / Birthday boy / Geneve / Really free / DK 50/80 / Louisa on a horse / Body talk / Man who shot Liberty Valance, The / Baby's in the club / I did it Otway.
LP: . . . . **POLS 1039**
MC: . . . . **POLSC 1039**

GREATEST HITS:JOHN OTWAY.
LP: . . . . **SBR 4 LP**
MC: . . . . **SBR 4C**

JOHN OTWAY AND WILD WILLIE BARRETT (Otway, John & Wild Willie Barrett).
Tracks: / Misty mountain / Murder man / If I did / Racing cars / Louisa on a horse / Gypsy / Really free / Bluey green / Cheryl's goin' home / Trying times / Geneve.
LP: **2383 453**

WHERE DID I GO RIGHT.
Tracks: / Makes good music / It's a pain / Blue eyes of the belle / Best dream / What a woman / Frightened and scared / Waiting (waiting for you) / Hurting her more / Highwayman.
LP: **2385 532**

Ouardia

ASSIREM.
Tracks: / Chedh Hime Dh'Loumayere / Yougui quiazizene / Assirem / Quine Hemlegh / Dhalnikh / Thayrikh / Ouliw Dhamejrouh / Yirthayri.
LP: . . . . **ORB 030**

Ouled Nail

LES HAUTS PLATEAUX D'ALGERIE.
Tracks: / En arrivant a Charef / Air bedoin / Aidi / Zatout nailia / Soir sous la tente / Oulet-nail / Chant de l'oued / Saadaoui / Chant d'adoration / Quand la caravane se leve / Saihi / El ain zarga / Ameur / Oh! Mohammed / Bagarra Kheira / Jour de fete a Charef / Alai Saharaoui / Air de fantasia.
LP: . . . . **ARN 33437**

Our Daughters Wedding

MOVING WINDOWS.
Tracks: / Auto music / She was someone / Elevate her / Track me down / Daddy's slave / Longitude 60 degree's / Love machine / Always be true / Moving windows / Paris / Buildings.
LP: . . . . **AML 3025**

Our Kate

OUR KATE Cookson, Catherine (Blakiston, Caroline).
MCSET: . . . . **TCLFP 417138 5**

Our Man Flint

OUR MAN FLINT (Film soundtrack) (Various artists).
LP: . . . . **FILM 046**
MC: . . . . **FILMC 046**

Our Man In Havana

OUR MAN IN HAVANA (Various artists).
MCSET: . . . . **ZBBC 1067**

Our Story (bk)

OUR STORY (Reg & Ron Kray with Fred Dinenage) (Blake, Roger/Jim McManus (nar)).
MCSET: . . . . **LFP 7445**

Ousley, Harold

HAROLD OUSLEY.
LP: . . . . **FS 242**

SWEET DOUBLE HIPNESS.
LP: . . . . **MR 5141**

Out Loud

OUT LOUD.
Tracks: / Outloud / It's love this time / Am I on your mind / Square business / Kak / Feeling good / Camouflage / Good together / Fundamental / Circle of love/ Music lover.
LP: **925632 1**
MC: **925632 4**

Out of Africa (bk)

OUT OF AFRICA (Karen Blixen) (James, Geraldine (nar)).
MCSET: . . . . **LFP 7272**
MCSET: . . . . **TCLFP 7272**

Out Of C.I.T.E

OUT OF C.I.T.E (Various artists).
LP: . . . . **MOY 1**

Out Of Order

OUT OF ORDER (ABWARTS) (Film soundtracks) (Various artists).
LP: . . . . **RG 1018**

Out Of The Blue

INSIDE TRACK.
Tracks: / Inside track / Cherry pickens / Hot house / E force / Nathan Jones / Isolation / Elevation.
LP: . . . . **BT 85128**

LIVE AT MT.FUJI.
Tracks: / Parisian thoroughfare / Blue pearl / Nathan Jones / Elevation / OTB / Celia / Over the rainbow.
LP: . . . . **BT 85141**

OUT OF THE BLUE.
Tracks: / RH factor / Eastern love village / Output / Reunited / Git in there / Blue Hughes / OTB.
LP: . . . . **BT 85118**
MC: . . . . **TCBT 85118**

OUT OF THE BLUE (Various artists).
Tracks: / I'll make the living if you make the loving worthwhile: *Chandler, Gene* / It's cool: *Jackson, Walter*/ L.A. nights: *Agawa, Yasuko* / Oh darlin': *Brothers by Choice* / Share my love with you: *Magnum Force*/ I'll never love the same way twice: *Mason, Barbara* / Rose of Sharon: *Bridges, Calvin* / One more time: *Dante*.
LP: . . . . **AN 03**
MC: . . . . **ANC 03**

Out Of The Darkness

OUT OF THE DARKNESS Songs of survival (Various artists).
LP: . . . . **F 4001**

Out of the Rain (bk)

OUT OF THE RAIN (Ciaran Madden (auth)) (Cadell, Elizabeth (nar)).
MC: . . . . **CAB 309**

Out Of The Ruins

OUT OF THE RUINS (Film soundtrack) (Various artists).
MC: . . . . **FILMC 063**

Out Of The Unknown

OUT OF THE UNKNOWN.
LP: . . . . **PENCV 1001**

Out Of This World

OUT OF THIS WORLD (Original Broadway Cast) (Various artists).
LP: . . . . **CML 4390**

Out The Lights

OUT THE LIGHTS, VOLUME 1 (Various artists).
LP: . . . . **DTLP 4**

Out West At Berkeley

OUT WEST AT BERKELEY (Various artists).
LP: . . . . **ARHOOLIE 4001**

Outback

BAKA.
Tracks: / Air play / Baka / An dro nevez / Other side, The / Hold on / On the streets / Buenaventura / Dingo go.
LP: . . . . **HNBL 1357**
MC: . . . . **HNBC 1357**

DANCE THE DEVIL AWAY.
LP: . . . . **HNBL 1369**
MC: . . . . **HNBC 1369**

Outcasts

BLOOD AND THUNDER.
LP: . . . . **ABT 004**
LP: . . . . **ROSE 16**

Outfield

BANGIN'.
Tracks: / Somewhere in America / Bangin' on my heart / No surrender / Moving target / Long way home / Playground / Alone with you / Main attraction / Better than nothing / Since you've been gone.
LP: **45056091**
MC: **4506094**

DIAMOND DAYS.
LP: . . . . **MCA 10111**
MC: . . . . **MCAC 10111**

PLAY DEEP.
Tracks: / Say it isn't so / Your love / I don't need her / Everytime you cry / 61 seconds / Mystery man / All the love in the world / Talk to me / Taking my chances / Nervous alibi.
LP: . . . . **CBS 26594**
MC: **40 26594**

VOICES OF BABYLON.
Tracks: / Voices of Babylon / My paradise / Part of your life / Shelter me / Night ain't over, The / No point / Taken by surprise / Reach out / Makin' up / Inside your skin.
LP: **4634451**
MC: **4634454**

Outland (film)

OUTLAND (Film soundtrack) (Goldsmith, Jerry).
LP: . . . . **K 56921**

Outlaw Blues

OUTLAW BLUES (Film Soundtrack) (Various artists).
Tracks: / Everybody's goin' on the road: *Various artists* / Jailbirds don't fly: *Various artists* / I dream of highways: *Various artists* / Outlaw on the run: *Various artists* / Beyond these walls: *Various artists*/ Outlaw blues: *Various artists* / Outlaw blues love theme: *Various artists* / Water for my horses: *Various artists* / Whisper in a velvet night: *Various artists* / Little more holy: *Various artists*.
LP: . . . . **EST 11691**

Outlaw Posse

MY AFRO'S ON FIRE.
LP: . . . . **GEEA 6**
MC: . . . . **GEEMC 6**

Outlaws

DREAM OF THE WEST.
LP: . . . . **BGOLP 118**

Outlaws (60's)

RIDE AGAIN (SINGLES A'S & B'S).
LP: . . . . **SEE 303**

ROCKIN' GUITAR (rare items).
LP: **3178**

Outlaws (Group)

BRING IT BACK ALIVE.
Tracks: / Stick around for rock 'n' roll / Loverboy / There goes another love song / Freeborn man / Prisoner, The / I hope you don't mind.
2LP: . . . . **DARTY 5**

GHOST RIDERS IN THE SKY.
Tracks: / Ghost riders in the sky / White horses / Angels hide / Devil's road / Can't stop loving you / Wishing wells / Sunshine / Freedom walk.
LP: . . . . **SPART 1160**

HURRY SUNDOWN.
Tracks: / Gunsmoke / Hearin' my heart talkin' / So afraid / Holiday / Hurry sundown / Cold and lonesome / Night wines / Heavenly blues.
LP: . . . . **SPART 1010**

IN THE EYE OF THE STORM.
Tracks: / Long gone / It's all right / Miracle man / Comin' home / Blueswater / Dance with me / Too long without her / I'll be leaving soon.
LP: . . . . **SPART 1112**

LADY IN WAITING.
Tracks: / Breaker-breaker / South Carolina / Ain't so bad / Freeborn man / Girl from Ohio / Loverboy.
LP: . . . . **ARTY 126**

LOS HOMBRES MALO.
Tracks: / Don't stop / Foxtail Lilly / Rebel girl / Goodbye / Back from eternity / Won't come out of the rain / Running / Easy does it / All roads.
LP: **204558**

ON THE RUN AGAIN.
Tracks: / Ghost riders in the sky / Green grass and high tides / There goes another love song / You are the show / Stick around for rock 'n' roll / I can't stop loving you / Devil's Road / Real good feeling / Breaker-breaker / Loverboy / Foxtail Lilly.
LP: . . . . **RAWLP 028**
MC: . . . . **RAWTC 028**

OUTLAWS.
Tracks: / There goes another love song / Song for you, A / Song in the breeze / It follows from your heart / Cry no more / Waterhole.
LP: . . . . **ARTY 115**

PLAYING TO WIN.
Tracks: / Take it anyway you want it / Cry some more / You are the show / You can have it / If dreams come true / Real good feelin' / Love at first sight / Falling rain / Dirty city.
LP: . . . . **ARTY 156**

SOLDIERS OF FORTUNE.
Tracks: / One last ride / Soldiers of fortune / Night cries, The / Outlaw / Cold harbour / Whatcha don't do / Just the way I like it / Saved by the bell / Lady luck / Racin' for the red light.
LP: **4501351**
MC: **4501354**

Outline of a Hairdo

OUTLINE OF A HAIRDO (THEME FROM) (See under Nieve, Steve).

Outlines

BLIND ALLEY.
LP: . . . . **L 8909202**

Outnumbered

HOLDING THE GRENADE TOO LONG.
LP: . . . . **HMS 051**

WHY ARE ALL THE GOOD PEOPLE GOING CRAZY?.
LP: . . . . **HMS 019**

Outnumbered By Sheep

OUTNUMBERED BY SHEEP (Various artists).
LP: . . . . **BFM 001**

Outram, Ken

PLAYS THE HAMMOND COMMODORE.
LP: . . . . **GRS 1179**

Outrider

NO WAY OUT.
MC: . . . . **CASSGP 001**

Outside Edge

RUNNING HOT.
Tracks: / Heartbeat away / Wait / Louella / Don't be a hero / Running hot / Don't leave me tonight / You / Heartbreaker / Hold on.
LP: . . . . **DIX 24**
MC: . . . . **CDIX 24**

Outsiders

I'M NOT TRYING TO HURT YOU.
LP: . . . . **KIRI 101**

SKIN.
Tracks: / Skin.
LP: . . . . **PLAN 002**
MC: . . . . **PLANMC 002**

Outsiders (Film)

OUTSIDERS (Film soundtrack) (Various artists).
LP: . . . . **FILM 051**

Outskirts

HEAVEN'S ON THE MOVE.
LP: . . . . **MGLALP 14**

Outskirts Of Infinity

LORD OF THE DARK SKIES.
Tracks: / Invocation (warning) / Gemini machine / Eastern spell / Stoned crazy / Tales of brave Ulysees / Eyes in the back of my head / Lord of the dark skies / Reaching upwards / Celebration.
LP: . . . . **W 007**

SCENES FROM THE DREAMS OF ANGELS.
LP: . . . . **INF 001**

STONE CRAZY.
LP: . . . . **INF 002**

Outta Place

WE'RE THE OUTTA PLACE.
LP: . . . . **MIR 102**

Ova

OUT OF BOUNDS.
Tracks: / Self-defence / Madness of a memory / Helium ballon / Walking in mercury / Nuclear madness / We can share our visions / Rainbowomon / Bloodstream / Auto-erotic blues / Full moonlight dance / Either gives in / Neither gives in.
LP: . . . . **SC 666**

OVA.
Tracks: / I can see the dream / Rock 'n' roll fever / Woman at the crossroads / Little girls / Voci 01 Donne / Lesbian fighting song / Offer that decision / Woman behind bars / Early in the evening.
LP: . . . . **SC 222**

POSSIBILITIES.
Tracks: / Moving inside / Tidal dream / Possibilities / Travelling spirit / Granny song / Language for lovers / Far beyond the dawn / Happy drumming / Earthquake.
LP: . . . . **SC 444**

Oval Emotion

GO GO.
LP: . . . . **HB 002**

Ovaltineys

OVALTINEYS SING YOUR ALL-TIME FAVOURITES.
LP: . . . . **OVALP 1**

Ovation

OVATION Best of Andrew Lloyd Webber, The (Various artists).
Tracks: / Don't cry for me Argentina: *Various artists* / Another suitcase in another hall: *Various artists* / I don't know how to love him: *Various artists* / Take that look off your face: *Various artists* / Tell me on a Sunday: *Various artists* / King Herod's song: *Various artists* / One more angel in heaven: *Various artists*/ Pumping iron: *Various artists* / Starlight express: *Various artists* / Pie Jesu: *Various artists* / Old deuteronomy: *Various artists* / Introduction: variations: *Various artists.*
MC: . . . . **OCE 1311**
LP: . . . . **ONE 1311**

Over The Brooklyn

OVER THE BROOKLYN BRIDGE (Film soundtrack) (Various artists).
Tracks: / Changes: *Various artists* / In the heat of the night: *Various artists* / Over a bridge: *Various* artists / Pino Donaggio: *Various artists* / Over the Brooklyn Bridge: *Various artists* / Streets of Manhattan: *Various artists* / Honey cake: *Various artists* / Alby's a blues: *Various artists* / Uncle Benjamin: *Various* artists / Brooklyn to Broadway: *Various artists* / Problems for Alby: *Various artists* / Son of the Godfather: *Various artists* / On Seventh Avenue: *Various artists* / Which way to go?: *Various artists* / I'd like to hold you through the night: *Various artists.*
LP: . . . . **BUST 1200**
MC: . . . . **ZCBUST 1200**

Over The Moon

BLACK HOLE (THEME FROM 'OVER THE MOON') (See under Nova) (Nova).

Over The Top

OVER THE TOP (Film soundtrack) (Various artists).
Tracks: / Winner takes it all, The: *Hagar, Sammy* / In this country: *Zander, Robin* / Take it higher: *Greene,* Larry / All I need is you: *Big Trouble* / Bad nite: *Stallone, Frank* / Meet me half way: *Loggins, Kenny*/ Gypsy soul: *Asia* / Fight, The: *Various artists* / Mind over matter: *Greene, Larry* / I will be strong: *Money, Eddie.*
LP: **4504841**
MC: **4504844**

Overcoming Shyness

OVERCOMING SHYNESS
Zimbardo,Philip.
MC: . . . . **PT 36**

Overkill

FEEL THE FIRE.
LP: . . . . **N 0035**
LP: . . . . **NUK 035**

FU YOU.**
MLP: **781 792-1**

TAKING OVER.
Tracks: / Deny the cross / Wrecking crew / Fear his name / Use your head / Fatal if swallowed / Powersurge / In union we stand / Electro-violence / Overkill II.
LP: **781 735-1**
MC: **781 735-4**
MC: . . . . **ZCNUK 069**
LP: . . . . **NUK 069**
LP: . . . . **N 0069**
MC: . . . . **N 0070**

TRIUMPH OF WILL.
LP: . . . . **SST 038**

UNDER THE INFLUENCE.
Tracks: / Shred / Never say never / Hello from the gutter / Mad gone world / Brainfade / Drunken wisdom / End of the line / Head first / Overkill III.
LP: . . . . **K 781 865 1**
MC: . . . . **K 781 865 4**

YEARS OF DECAY.
LP: **K7 82045 1**
MC: **K7 82045 4**

Overlord X

CHARGIN' WARRIOR (see under M.C. Smart).

WEAPON IS MY LYRIC.
Tracks: / Rough in Hackney / Two bad / Clap your hands / Now my day begins / Visa to rock / Kickbag / Go it's like World War 3 / Weapon is my lyric / Brutal bass / Fourteen days in May.
MC: . . . . **ICT 9924**
LP: . . . . **ILPS 9924**
MC: . . . . **ICM 9924**
LP: . . . . **ILPM 9924**

X VERSUS THE WORLD.
LP: . . . . **MLPS 1048**
LP: **846 502 1**
MC: . . . . **MCT 1048**
MC: **846 502 4**

Overstreet, Paul

SOWIN' LOVE.
Tracks: / Love helps those / All the fun / Call the preacher / Richest man on Earth / Sowin' love / Love never sleeps / Dig another well / Seein' my father in me / What God has joined together / Homemaker / 'Neath the light of your love (Only on CD.).
LP: . . . . **PL 89717**
MC: . . . . **PK 89717**
LP: . . . . **PL 90354**
MC: . . . . **PK 90354**

Overstreet, Rev Louis

REV LOUIS OVERSTREET, HIS GUITAR & CONGREGATION.
LP: . . . . **ARHOOLIE 1014**

Overstreet, Tommy

SOLID GOLD HITS.
Tracks: / Heaven is my woman's love / Gwen / Jeannie Marie, you were a lady / If I miss you again tonight / Send me no roses / I'll never break these chains / Ann, don't go runnin' / That's when my woman begins / Dream maker / Heart of Dixie.
LP: . . . . **BDL 1063**

Overton, Hal

DUAL PIANO JAZZ (see under Dave McKenna) (Overton, Hal/Dave McKenna).

Overtone

OVERTONE 1 - THE MODERN ALBUM (Various artists).
LP: . . . . **OVLP 1**

OVERTONE 2 - THE PROGRESSIVE ALBUM (Various artists).
LP: . . . . **OVLP 2**

OVERTONE 3 - THE ROCK ALBUM (Various artists).
LP: . . . . **OVLP 3**

Overtures...

YOUR FAVOURITE OVERTURES (Various artists).
MCSET: . . . . **DTO 10058**

Overweight Pooch

FEMALE PREACHER.
LP: **394349 1**
MC: **394349 4**

Owen, Beti Mary

GOOD TIDINGS.
Tracks: / Child in a manger / Dwell with me / O Jesu, King most wonderful / Breathe on me, breath of God / Prayer for Wales / Jesu lover of my soul / Jesu, the very thought of me / I hear the voice of Jesus say.
LP: . . . . **SCLP 628**
MC: . . . . **CRC 628**

OUR SONG IS JESUS.
LP: . . . . **SCLP 621**
MC: . . . . **CRC 621**

SONGS WE LOVE.
Tracks: / My mother's picture / When night comes / Night / My little Welsh home / Palm Sunday / For our sake / Just as I am / Heaven / Good Friday / In excelsis gloria.
LP: . . . . **SCLP 650**
MC: . . . . **CRC 650**

WELSH FOLK SONGS AND THE LIKE.
Tracks: / Lazy robin / Tending the white wheat / If my lover comes / Hue of sunshine / As long as there are two / By the sea shore / My grandmother's cottage / Loom / David of the white rock / All through the night / Where are you going / Lullaby / Red robin / Hearsay / Llangollen market / Mother and her babe / Let us go to Bethlehem / Rejoicing / Let every Christian come.
LP: . . . . **SCLP 649**
MC: . . . . **CRCP 649**

Owen, Bill

NORA BATTY'S STOCKINGS (see also Kathy Staff) (Owen, Bill & Kathy Staff).

Owen, Dilys

SOPHY.
MC: . . . . **SOUND 39**

Owen, Jack

YOUNG OWEN.
LP: . . . . **DIN 318**

Owens, Bonnie

JUST BETWEEN THE TWO OF US (Owens, Bonnie & Merle Haggard).
Tracks: / Just between the two of us / House without love is not a home, A / Slowly but surely / Our hearts are holding / I wanta live again / Forever and ever / I'll take a chance / Stranger in my arms / Too used to being with you / So much for me, so much for you / Wait a little longer, please Jesus.
LP: . . . . **HAT 3073**
MC: . . . . **HATC 3073**

Owens, Buck

12 GREAT NUMBER 1 COUNTRY HITS.
LP: . . . . **MFP 50357**

ACT NATURALLY.
Tracks: / Tijuana lady / Gonna have love / Out there chasing rainbows / I was there / Act naturally / Playboy / Rock hard love / Crying time / Brooklyn Bridge / Take me back again.
LP: . . . . **EST 2119**
MC: . . . . **TCEST 2119**
MC: **792 893 4**

BLUE LOVE.
Tracks: / House down the block, The / You're fer me / Down on the corner of love / Blue love / It don't show on me / Pease don't take her from me / Three dimension love / Why don't mommy stay with daddy and me / When I hold you / Country girl / I will love you always / Right after the dance / I'm gonna blow / Higher and higher and higher.
LP: . . . . **SDLP 055**

BUCK OWENS.
MC: . . . . **ZCGAS 755**

HOT DOG.
Tracks: / Don't let her know / A-11 / Summertime blues / Memphis / Hot dog / Put a quarter in the jukebox / Under your spell again / Second fiddle / Sweethearts in heaven / Keys in the mailbox, The.
LP: . . . . **EST 2082**
MC: . . . . **TC EST 2082**

Owens, Charles

PLAYS THE MUSIC OF HARRY WARREN, VOL.1 (Owens, Charles & The New York Ensemble).
Tracks: / More I see you, The / I wish I knew / September in the rain / I only have eyes for you / Serenade in blue / You'll never know.
LP: . . . . **DS 811**

TWO QUARTETS, THE.
LP: . . . . **DS 787**
MC: . . . . **DSC 787**

Owens, Jimmy

COME TOGETHER (Owens, Jimmy & Carol/Pat Boone).
Tracks: / Come together / His Name is Jesus / He is here / Turn your hearts / Clap your hands / Hallelujah, His blood avails for me / Doxology / Holy, holy / Freely, freely / Greet somebody in Jesus' name / People of God / Blessed be the tie that binds / May I introduce you to a friend? / All we like sheep / God so loved the world / Is He coming for you? / Finale.
LP: . . . . **LS 7006**
MC: . . . . **LC 7006**

COME TOGETHER AGAIN (Gospel musical '86) (Owens, Jimmy & Carol).
LP: . . . . **OAK R 3006**
MC: . . . . **OAK C 3006**

GLORY OF CHRISTMAS, THE (Owens, Jimmy & Carol).
Tracks: / Overture / Christmas isn't Christmas / Such wise men / Sing, rejoice / He shall feed His flock / Special Lady / I know him / How should a king come? / Shepherds beside themselves / O little town of Bethlehem / No sleep for the serpent / Joy to the world / O come all ye faithful / I will love Him / Run, run, run / He is born.
LP: . . . . **LS 7058**
MC: . . . . **LC 7058**

IF MY PEOPLE (Owens, Jimmy & Carol).
Tracks: / If my people will pray / Children of the Kingdom / We are family / Behold the man / Father, we thank you / Make a joyful noise unto the Lord / Lift up your hands in holiness / By a new and living way / We worship Thee / You shall be holy / Thank you, Lord / Turn to the Lord / Keep looking down / Lord, achieve your holy purpose.
LP: . . . . **LS 7022**
MC: . . . . **LC 7022**

VICTOR, THE (Owens, Jimmy & Carol).
LP: . . . . **OAK R 3001**
MC: . . . . **OAK C 3001**

Owens, Robert

RHYTHMS IN ME.
LP: **846327-1**
LP: . . . . **BRLP 549**
MC: **846327-4**
MC: . . . . **BRCA 549**

Owens-Collins, Jamie

GIFT OF CHRISTMAS, THE.
MC: . . . . **OAK C 3008**

GROWING PAINS.
Tracks: / Hard times / Never had to go this far / Father's song, (The) / Singin' hallelujah / New Jerusalem / Victor, The / Fly away with me / My prayer for you / Many times / My Jesus, I love Thee.
LP: . . . . **LSX 7027**
MC: . . . . **LC 7027**

LAUGHTER IN YOUR SOUL.
Tracks: / You'll start falling in love / Peace / I'm so happy / Charity / Love is / Walk in the sunshine / Living light / We're looking upwards / Sweet dying Lamb / May I introduce you to a friend?.
LP: . . . . **LS 7012**
MC: . . . . **LC 7012**

LOVE EYES.
Tracks: / Love eyes / Daniel / Radio man / Hidden treasure / It's been quite a year / Pleasure servin' you / Only you / New day / Waters of rest / Mighty river.
LP: . . . . **LS 7049**
MC: . . . . **LC 7049**

STRAIGHT AHEAD.
Tracks: / Fooled by a feeling / Look how far you've come / I have / Liar on the loose / Walkin' on / How could I ever say no / I'm yours / Perfect heart, A / Holy fire / Shine through me.
LP: . . . . **BIRD 125**
MC: . . . . **TC BIRD 125**

O'Williams, Wendy

KOMMANDER OF CHAOS.
LP: . . . . **ZEB 7**

MAGGOTS (Film soundtrack) (O'Williams, Wendy/Plasmatics).
Tracks: / Overture / Introduction (Spoken word) / You're a zombie / White's apartment, The / Four meal dinner (Spoken) / Day of the humans is gone, The / Central research laboratory, The / Valerie and Bruce on the phone /

Destroyers / Bruce's bedroom / Brain dead / Propogators / White's bedroom fire escape, The / Finale.
LP: . . . . **GWLP 8**

REFORM SCHOOLGIRLS (FILM) (See under 'Reform Schoolgirls').

W.O.W..
LP: . . . . **PB 6034**
MC: . . . . **PBC 6034**
LP: . . . . **MFN 24**

Owl & The Pussycat
OWL & THE PUSSYCAT, THE (Film Soundtrack) (Various artists).
LP: . . . . **AS 30401**
MC: . . . . **BT 30401**

Own Goal
OWN GOAL (Various artists).
LP: . . . . **GOAL 1**

Oxala, Nezinho de
NEZINHO DE OXALA.
LP: **2494 597**

Oxbow
FUCKFEST.
LP: . . . . **PATH 002**

Ox-Bow Incident (bk)
OX-BOW INCIDENT (Walter Van Tilbury Clark) (Fonda, Henry (nar)).
MC: . . . . **CDL 51620**
LP: . . . . **TC 1620**

Oxen Killer
MONSTERS OF STEEL.
LP: . . . . **KKR 1006**

Oxenbury, Helen
HELEN OXENBURY'S NURSERY RHYMES.
MC: **0 00 109032 1**

HELEN OXENBURY'S NURSERY STORIES.
MC: **0 00 109031 3**

Oxford Marmalade
OXFORD MARMALADE (see under Hayes, Lesley) (Hayes, Lesley).

Oxford United
MY OH MY (Oxford United & Prism).
LP: . . . . **OXF 1**

Oxford, Vernon
20 OF THE BEST: VERNON OXFORD.
Tracks: / Redneck / Clean your own tables / Shadows of my mind / Watermelon time in Georgia / This woman is mine / Old folks home, The / Woman, let me sing you a song / Forgetfulness for ale / Fields of flowers / Touch of God's hand / Good old-fashioned Saturday night honky-tonk barroom brawl,A / Redneck roots / Only the shadows know (Wot, even Hank? (sorry)) / Your wanting for me is gone / Baby sister / I've got to get Peter off my mind / Stone by stone / Little sister (throw your red shoes away) / Let's take a cold shower / She's always there.
LP: . . . . **NL 89373**
MC: . . . . **NK 89373**

BETTER WAY OF LIFE, A.
Tracks: / Lord, I've tried everything but you / Dust on the bible / Sweeter than the flowers / Uncloudy day / House of gold / Wings of a dove / O come, angel band / Better way of life, A / Family bible / Mother's not dead / Where the soul never dies.
LP: . . . . **SDLP 035**
MC: . . . . **SDC 035**
LP: . . . . **ROUNDER 0138**
MC: . . . . **ROUNDER 0138C**
LP: . . . . **JULEP 24**

HIS AND HERS.
LP: . . . . **ROUNDER 0123**
MC: . . . . **ROUNDER 0123C**

I LOVE TO SING.
Tracks: / I love to sing / Walkin' my blues away / If kisses could talk / Gonna ease my worried mind / No-one is listening / Turn the record over / I think living is sweet / Blanket of stars / Great stoneface, The / Rainy day / (I just want) somebody to love me / Let your love shine.
LP: . . . . **BFX 15050**

IF I HAD MY WIFE TO LOVE OVER.
LP: . . . . **ROUNDER 0091**

KEEPIN' IT COUNTRY.
Tracks: / You're the reason / Baby sister / Busiest memory in town / Honky tonk troubles / Bringing Mary home / Early morning rain / I feel chained / Sad situation / Long black veil / Outlaws again / Last letter, The.
LP: . . . . **SDLP 019**
MC: . . . . **SDC 019**
LP: . . . . **ROUNDER 0156**
MC: . . . . **ROUNDER 0156C**

POWER IN THE BLOOD.
Tracks: / Intercessary prayer / Where the roses never fade / At calvary / What a friend I have in Jesus / Daughter of the wine / Redneck / Be careful of stones that you throw / Power in the blood / Lord I've tried everything but you / I'll fly away / Little sister throw your red shoes away / Saviour saviour / They'll never take her love from me / Go home.
LP: . . . . **REN 729**
MC: . . . . **ZCN 729**

TRIBUTE TO HANK WILLIAMS, A.
LP: . . . . **SKYL 7002**

Oxley, Dave
HARVEST (see Raven, Jon/Nigel Jones/Dave Oxley) (Oxley, Dave/Nigel Jones/Jon Raven).

Oxley, Tony
SECOND ALBUM.
LP: . . . . **INCUS 18**

SONG FOR SOMEONE (see also D Bailey, E Parker) (Oxley, Tony, D Bailey, E Parker).

TONY OXLEY.
LP: . . . . **INCUS 8**

Oxo
OXO.
Tracks: / Whirly girl / Dance all night / My ride / Wanna be your love / In the stars / You make it sound so easy / Waiting for you / Back in town / I'll take you back / Love I need her / Runnin' low.
LP: . . . . **GEF 25425**
MC: **4025425**

Oxtot, Dick
DICK OXTOT'S GOLDEN AGE JAZZ BAND (Oxtot's, Dick Golden Age Jazz Band).
LP: . . . . **ARHOOLIE 4007**

DOWN IN HONKY TONKY TOWN (Oxtot's, Dick Golden Age Jazz Band).
LP: . . . . **ARHOOLIE 4010**

Oyster Band
ENGLISH ROCK AND ROLL THE EARLY YEARS (1800-1850).
LP: . . . . **YOP 1**

FREEDOM AND RAIN (See Tabor, June) (Oyster Band & June Tabor).

LIBERTY HALL.
LP: . . . . **YOP 7**
MC: . . . . **YOPC 7**

LIE BACK AND THINK OF ENGLAND.
LP: . . . . **YOP 6**

LITTLE ROCK TO LEIPZIG.
Tracks: / Jail song two / Gonna do what I have to do / Galopede / I fought the law / New York girls / Oxford girl, The / Too late now / Red barn stomp / Coal not dole / Johnny Mickey Barry's.
LP: . . . . **COOK 032**
MC: . . . . **COOKC 032**

RIDE.
Tracks: / Too late now / Polish plain / Heaven to Calcutta / Tincans / This year, next year / New York girls / Gamblers / Take me down / Cheekbone City / Love vigilantes / My dog (CD only.) / Sins of a family, The (CD only.).
LP: . . . . **COOK 020**
MC: . . . . **COOKC 020**

STEP OUTSIDE.
Tracks: / Hal-an-Tow / Flatlands / Another quiet night in England / Milly Bond / Bully in the alley / Day that the ship goes down, The / Gaol song, The / Old dance, The / Bold Riley / Ashes to ashes (CD only.).
LP: . . . . **COOK 001**
MC: . . . . **COOKC 001**
LP: . . . . **BAKE 001**
MC: . . . . **BAKEC 001**

WIDE BLUE YONDER.
Tracks: / Generals are born again, The / Pigsty Billy / Oxford girl / Following in father's footsteps / Lost and found, The / Coal creek mine / Rose of England, The / Careless life, A / Early days of a better nation, The / Lakes of Coolfin / Between the wars / Hal-an-tow (CD only.) / Flatlands (CD only.) / Another quiet night in England (CD only.).
LP: . . . . **COOK 006**
MC: . . . . **COOKC 006**

Oyster Ceilidh Band
JACK'S ALIVE.
LP: . . . . **DIN 309**

Oyuki Conjugate
INTO DARK WATER.
LP: . . . . **FIB 004**

SCENE IN MIRAGE.
LP: . . . . **NUMB 1818**
LP: . . . . **FIC 007**

Ozark Mountain
HEART OF THE COUNTRY.
LP: . . . . **DFG 8409**

MODERN HISTORY.
Tracks: / Everywhere she goes / Love is calling / I'm still dreaming / Turn it up / True love / Lonely knight / Over again / Heating up / River, The / Heart of the country / Wild the days.
LP: . . . . **RR 303**
MC: . . . . **MCRR 303**

OZARK MOUNTAIN DAREDEVILS.
Tracks: / Take you tonight / Jump at the chance / Sailin' around the world / Lovin' you / Tuff luck / Oh darlin' / Empty cup / Rosalie / Runnin' out / Fools gold.
LP: . . . . **CBS 84193**

Ozila
OZILA 2001.
Tracks: / Odila 2001 / Honey honey / From blacks to blacks / Sweet music / Jesus / Dance / Free people / Dad and mam.
LP: . . . . **NSPL 28529**

Ozo
LISTEN TO THE BUDDAH.
LP: . . . . **DJF 20488**

MUSEUM OF MANKIND.
LP: . . . . **DJF 20517**
MC: . . . . **DJH 40517**

SPIRITS OF AFRICA.
LP: . . . . **BBSPLP 01**

Ozone, Makoto
AFTER.
Tracks: / Yellow fever / If you knew sushi / After / Merry go round / Katos revenge / Waltz for Ronko / Improvisation.
LP: . . . . **CBS 26889**
MC: **40 26889**

MAKOTO OZONE.
Tracks: / Crystal love / I need you here / Flight / Endless session / Improvisation.
LP: . . . . **CBS 26198**
MC: **40 26198**

Ozric Tentacles
ERPLAND.
2LP: . . . . **DOVELP 1**

PUNGENT EFFULGENT.
LP: . . . . **DMLP 1017**

STRANGEITUDE.
LP: . . . . **DOVELP 3**
MC: . . . . **DOVEMC 3**

Ozz II
ASSASSIN, THE.
Tracks: / Sail on / Checkin' it out (baby don't you cry) / I've been looking / Exploited / Electric gliding nails / Castle plan, The / Brain and backer / Rack room, The / Drowning, The / Hendrix revenge / Can you imagine that.
LP: . . . . **ZEB 2**

P

Paaras

PURE GOLD.
MC: .... CMUT 1046

Pablo All Stars

PABLO ALL STARS JAM.
Tracks: / Cote d'azur / Pennies from Heaven / Samba de Orfeu / God bless the child.
LP: 2308 210
MC: .... K 08 210

Pablo, Augustus

AFRICA MUST BE FREE BY 1983 DUB.
Tracks: / Unity dub / Africa dub / My mind dub / Western Kingston style / Levi (dub) / Revolution dub / Judgement dub / Sufferer dub.
LP: .... GREL 98

BLOWING WITH THE WIND.
LP: .... GREL 149
MC: .... GREEN 149

EARTHS RIGHTFUL RULER.
LP: .... MESS 1005
MC: .... MESSC 1005

EAST MAN DUB.
Tracks: / Only Jah Jah dub / Eastman dub / Look within dub / Isn't it time (dub) / It up to Jah dub / Big yard connection / African step / Original scientist / Corner stone (chapter 3).
LP: .... GREL 109
MC: .... GREEN 109

EAST OF THE RIVER NILE.
LP: .... MESS 1003
MC: .... MESSC 1003

ISRAEL IN HARMONY.
LP: .... AB 1

ITAL DUB.
Tracks: / Big rip off, The / Road block / Curly dub / Well red / Gun trade / Shake up / Hillside airstrip / Barbwire disaster / Mr. Big / Ell's move / House raid / Shake down.
LP: .... TRLS 115

KING TUBBY MEETS ROCKERS UPTOWN.
LP: .... MESS 1007
MC: .... MESSC 1007
LP: .... RLP 001
MC: .... RLC 001

ONE STEP DUB.
LP: .... AP 003
MC: .... APC 003

ORIGINAL ROCKERS.
Tracks: / Rockers dub / Up Warrikka Hill / Cassava piece / Tubby's dub song / Jah dread / Brace a boy / Thunder clap / Park Lane special / New style / AP special.
LP: .... GREL 8
MC: .... GREEN 8

RISING SUN.
Tracks: / Dub wiser / Hopi land / Rising sun / Fire red / Jah wind / Pipers of Zion / Day before the riot, The / African frontline / Melchesedec (the high priest) / Signs and wonders.
LP: .... GREL 90
MC: .... GREEN 90
MC: .... SHMC 44009

ROCKERS COMES EAST.
Tracks: / Pablo meets P. Smart in L.I. / Progression dub / Revelino dub / Babylon loosing dub / Sun ray dub / Jah D special / Rockers comes east / Dubbing the oppressors / Zion seals dub.
LP: .... GREL 106
MC: .... GREEN 106

ROCKERS MEET KING TUBBY IN A FIRE HOUSE.
LP: .... SHAN 43001
MC: .... SHANC 43001

THIS IS AUGUSTUS PABLO (Rebel rock reggae).
LP: .... HB 34
MC: .... HBC 34
LP: .... TRLS 243

THRILLER.
Tracks: / Striker / Fat girl Jean / Rocky road.
LP: .... STLP 102
MC: .... VSMC 002

Pablo Cruise

PABLO CRUISE.
Tracks: / Island woman / Denny / Sleeping dogs / What does it take (to win your love) / Rock 'n' roller / Not tonight / In my quiet way / Ocean breeze.
LP: .... AMLH 64528

PLACE IN THE SUN, A.
Tracks: / Place in the sun, A / Whatcha gonna do / Raging fire / I just wanna believe / Tonight my love / Can't you hear the music / Never had a love / Atlanta June / El verano.
LP: .... AMLH 64625

REFLECTOR.
Tracks: / This time / Cool love / Don't let the magic disappear / One more night / Jenny / Slip away / That's when / Inside - outside / Paradise (let me take you into) / Drums on the night.
LP: .... AMLK 63726

WORLDS AWAY.
Tracks: / Worlds away / Love will find a way / Family man / Runnin' / Don't want to live without it / You're out to lose / Always be together / Sailing to paradise / I go to Rio.
LP: .... AMLH 64697

Pac Man

ADVENTURES OF PAC MAN, THE (Pac Man- The adventures of).
MC: .... PTB 638

Pace, Johnny

CHET BAKER INTRODUCES JOHNNY PACE (See under Baker, Chet) (Pace, Johnny & Chet Baker).

Pace, Thom

MAYBE.
Tracks: / Don't kid yourself / Belong to someone / Don't look now / Easy with you / She cheers me up / Don't mistake this loneliness for love / Title track / I wrote it in a song / One of a kind / Waiting for their time.
LP: .... EST 12053

Pacheco, Johnny

CONDE RODRIGUEZ (Pacheco, Johnny & Pete).
LP: .... SLP 625

GOLD.
LP: .... CLP 133

INTRODUCING JOHNNY PACHECO.
Tracks: / Alto songo / Esa prieta / Azucar mami / El Panazo / Caramelo / Acuyuye / Solo estoy / Ileana / Dakar punto final / Me voy pa moron.
LP: .... HOT 121
MC: .... TCHOT 121

JICAMO.
LP: .... JM 638

Pacheco, Tom

EAGLE IN THE RAIN.
LP: .... TPLP 1
MC: .... TPMC 1

SUNFLOWERS AND SCARECROWS.
LP: .... RTMLP 30
MC: .... RTMMC 30

Pacific

INFERENCE.
LP: .... CRELP 087
MC: .... CCRE 087

Pacific 1860

PACIFIC 1860 (Original London cast) (Various artists).
Tracks: / If I were a man: *Various artists* / His excellency regrets: *Various artists* / Uncle Harry: *Various artists* / Dear Madam Salvador: *Various artists* / My horse has cast a shoe: *Various artists* / Bright was the day: *Various artists* / One, two, three: *Various artists* / I never knew: *Various artists* / I saw no shadow: *Various artists* / Invitation to the waltz: *Various artists* / I wish, I wasn't quite such a big girl: *Various artists* / Pretty little bridesmaids: *Various artists* / Mothers' lament: *Various artists* / This is a changing world: *Various artists* / This is a night for lovers: *Various artists* / Fumfumbolo: *Various artists* / Toast music and finale: *Various artists.*
LP: .... TER 1040
MC: .... ZCTER 1040

Pacific Coast ...

PACIFIC COAST RAGTIME ORCHESTRA (Pacific Coast Ragtime Orchestra).
LP: .... CLP 137

Pacific Heights

PACIFIC HEIGHTS (Original Soundtrack) (Various artists).
LP: .... VS 5286
MC: .... VSC 5286

Pacific Overtures

PACIFIC OVERTURES (Original Broadway cast) (Various artists).
MC: .... BK 84407
LP: .... BL 84407

PACIFIC OVERTURES (LONDON CAST) (Various artists).
LP: TER2 1151
MC: .... ZCTER 1151

Pacific Rim...

PACIFIC RIM DULCIMER PROJECT, THE (Various artists).
LP: .... FF 307

Pack

STAND AND FIGHT (See under Benn, Nigel) (Pack featuring Nigel Benn).

Packham, Greg

ACTION REACTION (Packham, Greg Group).
LP: .... ST 242

Packham, Kit

SHADY SIDE OF THE STREET.
MC: .... SPJCS 903

Paco De Lica

PACO DE LICA.
LP: 6358 085

Pad Anthony

NUFF NICENESS.
LP: .... J 004

Paddington Bear

BEAR CALLED PADDINGTON, A (Michael Bond).
MC: 1580

BIRTHDAY TREAT AND OTHER STORIES, A (Michael Bond).
MC: 1767

MORE ABOUT PADDINGTON BEAR (Michael Bond) (Cribbins, Bernard (nar)).
MC: .... P 90025

PADDINGTON (Horden, Sir Michael).
MC: 39557

PADDINGTON ABROAD (Cribbins, Bernard (nar)).
MC: .... P 90029

PADDINGTON AND THE DISAPPEARING TRICK (Michael Bond (aut)) (Cribbins, Bernard (nar)).
MC: 1599

PADDINGTON AT LARGE (Cribbins, Bernard (nar)).
MC: .... P 90030

PADDINGTON AT THE STATION (Horden, Sir Michael).
MC: .... 0 00 109081 X

PADDINGTON BEAR, VOL.1 (Cribbins, Bernard (nar)).
LP: .... LP 8304

PADDINGTON BEAR VOL 2 (Cribbins, Bernard (nar)).
MC: .... P 90024

PADDINGTON DOES IT HIMSELF (Horden, Michael Sir).
MC: 00 103529

PADDINGTON GOES TO THE SALES (Horden, Sir Michael).
MC: 0 00 102189 3

PADDINGTON GOES TO TOWN (Cribbins, Bernard (nar)).
MC: .... P 90037

PADDINGTON HELPS OUT (Cribbins, Bernard (nar)).
MC: .... P 90026

PADDINGTON HITS OUT (Horden, Sir Michael).
MC: 00 1034510

PADDINGTON MARCHES ON (Cribbins, Bernard (nar)).
MC: .... P 90035

PADDINGTON TAKES A BATH (Horden, Sir Michael).
MC: 0 00 109084 4

PADDINGTON'S GOLDEN RECORD.
LP: .... ATXLP 7
MC: .... ZCATX 7

PADDINGTON'S NEW ROOM (Horden, Sir Michael).
MC: 0 00 102190 7

TROUBLE AT THE AIRPORT AND OTHER STORIES (Michael Bond).
MC: 1780

VISIT TO THE DENTIST, A (Michael Bond).
MC: 1773

Padilla, Pedro

PUERTO RICAN TRADITIONAL MUSIC (Padilla, Pedro Y Su Conjunto).
LP: .... ROUNDER 5003

Pagan

PAGAN.
LP: .... US 18

Pagan Babies

NEXT.
LP: .... HR 9545 1

Pagans

GODLIKE POWER OF PAGANS, THE.
LP: .... TR 004

STREET WHERE NOBODY LIVES (LIVE).
LP: .... R 33 8921

Page, Cleo

LEAVING MISSISSIPPI.
LP: .... JSP 1003

Page, Elizabeth

PLAYING THE RECORDER.
LP: .... MFP 41 5661 1
LP: .... MFP 41 5661 4
LP: .... CFP 4513

Page, Hot Lips

BUCK CLAYTON, HOT LIPS PAGE & BUD FREEMAN (See under Clayton, Buck) (Page, Hot Lips/Buck Clayton/ Bud Freeman).

HOT LIPS PAGE 1938-1940.
Tracks: / Good old bosom bread / He's pulling his whiskers / Down on the levee / Old man Ben / I would do anything for you / I ain't got nobody / Porter's love song to a chambermaid, A / Gone with the gin / Walk it to me / It won't be here long / Lafayette / South / Harlem rhumbain' the blues / No matter where you are.
LP: .... OFF 3047

JUMPIN' STUFF (see Jordan, Louis) (Page, Hot Lips/Louis Jordan/Don Byas).

SWING STREET (Page, Hot Lips and His Orchestra with Jonah Jones & Orch.).
LP: AG6 25524

Page, Jim

HOT TIMES.
LP: .... W 03

SHOT OF THE USUAL, A.
LP: .... W 01

VISIONS IN MY VIEW.
LP: .... FF 367

Page, Jimmy

1972 INTERVIEW PART 2.
LP: .... RAMBLE 4

DEATHWISH II (Film soundtrack).
Tracks: / Who's to blame / Chase, The / City sirens / Jam sandwich / Carol's theme / Release, The / Hotel rats and photostats / Shadow in the city, A / Jill's theme / Deathwish: prelude / Big band / Sex and violence / Hypnotizing ways(Oh mamma).
LP: .... SSK 59415

JAM SESSION (Page, Jimmy, Sonny Boy Williamson & Brian Auger).
Tracks: / Don't send me no flowers / I see a man downstairs / She was so dumb / Goat, The / Walking little girl / How old are you? / It's a bloody life / Getting out of town.
LP: .... CR 30193

NO INTRODUCTION NECESSARY (Page, Jimmy & Friends).

Tracks: / Lovin' up a storm / Everything I do is wrong / Think it over / Boll weevil / Livin' lovin' wreck / One long kiss / Dixie fried / Down the line / Fabulous / Breathless / Rave on / Lonely weekends / Burn up.
LP: THBL 007
MC: THBC 007

OUTRIDER.
Tracks: / Wasting my time / Wanna make love / Writes of winter / Only one, The / Liquid mercury / Hummingbird / Emerald eyes / Prison blues / Blues anthem.
LP: WX 155
MC: WX 155C
MC: GEFC 24188

SESSION MAN.
LP: AIP 10041

SESSION MAN VOL 2.
LP: AIP 10053

SMOKE AND FIRE.
Tracks: / Wailing sounds / 'Cause I love you / Flashing lights / Gutty guitar / Would you believe / Smoke and fire / Thumping beat / Union Jack car / One for you baby / L-O-N-D-O-N / Brightest lights / Baby come back.
LP: THBL 2.022
MC: THBC 2.022

WHATEVER HAPPENED TO 1214 A.D. (See under Harper, Roy) (Page, Jimmy with Roy Harper).

Page, Larry

KINKY MUSIC (Page, Larry Orchestra).
Tracks: / Tired of waiting / Come on now / Something better beginning / You really got me / Don't ever change / Got my feet on the ground / All day and all of the night / One fine day / I go to sleep / Just can't go to sleep / Revenge / I took my baby home / Everybodys gonna be happy.
LP: C5-521
MC: C5K-521

RESTLESS SENORITA (Page, Larry Orchestra).
LP: PRCV 134

Page, Patti

BEST OF PATTI PAGE.
Tracks: / Tennessee waltz / I went to your wedding / Cross over the bridge / Allegheny moon / Mockin' Bird Hill / Old Cape Cod / Detour / With my eyes wide open, I'm dreaming / Changing partners / Mr. & Mississippi / How much is that doggie in the window? / Rock of ages.
MC: 16-22

PATTI PAGE WITH LOU STEIN'S MUSIC (1949).
LP: HSR 223

Page, Stu

HONEYSUCKLE DREAMING (Page, Stu/Remuda).
MC: CSTON 8604

STU PAGE (Page,Stu & Restless Wheels).
Tracks: / Restless wheels / I got drove to it / Just another country / Slave to the wheel / Drift away / Are you still in love with me / He made the whole world sing.
LP: BGE LP 1006
MC: BGE C 1006

SYLVANTONE SHOWCASE, THE (see Goodacre, Tony) (Page, Stu/Tony Goodacre).

Page, Tommy

FROM THE HEART.
LP: 7599265831
MC: 7599265834

TOMMY PAGE.
LP: 925740 1
MC: 925740 4

Pahinui, Gabby

GABBY PAHINUI HAWAIIAN BAND.
Tracks: / Alhoa ka manini / Ku 'U pua lei mokihana / Pu' uanahulu / Moani ke'ala / Blue Hawaiian moonlight / Moonlight lady / E nihi ka hele / Hawaiian love / Wahini U'I / Oli komo -chant / Ipo lei manu.
LP: ED 241

Paice, Ashton, Lord

MALICE IN WONDERLAND.
Tracks: / Ghost story / Remember the good times / Arabella / Silas and Jerome / Dance with me, baby / On the road again / Again / Sneaky Private Lee / I'm gonna stop drinking / Malice in Wonderland.
LP: 2482 485

Paice, Ian

MALICE IN WONDERLAND (See under Paice Ashton Lord) (Paice, Ashton, Lord).

Paich, Marty

HOT PIANO.
LP: VSOP 27

I GET A BOOT OUT OF YOU (Paich, Marty Big Band).
Tracks: / It don't mean a thing / Love for sale / Violets for your furs / Things ain't what they used to be / Moanin'.
LP: DS 829
MC: DSC 829

IN CONCERT - TOKYO (see under Torme, Mel) (Paich, Marty Dek-tette/Mel Torme).

JAZZ CITY WORKSHOP.
LP: FS 235

LULU'S BACK IN TOWN (See Torme, Mel & the Marty Paich Dek-Tette) (Marty Paich Dek-Tette & Mel Torme).

MARTY PAICH OCTET (Paich, Marty Octet).
LP: FS 287

NEW YORK SCENE, THE.
Tracks: / It's alright with me / I love Paris / Too close for comfort / Lazy afternoon.
LP: DS 844

PICASSO OF BIG BAND JAZZ, THE.
LP: CS 9031

SWING SCHUBERT ALLEY (See under Torme, Mel) (Paich, Marty/Mel Torme).

WEST COAST SCENE (see Giuffre, Jimmy) (Paich, Marty Octet & Jimmy Giuffre).

WHAT'S NEW (Paich, Marty Big Band).
LP: DS 857

Paige, Elaine

BARRIER (Paige, Elaine with Peter Oliver).
2LP: WHS 1001/2
2LP: WHI 1001/2

CHRISTMAS.
Tracks: / Walking in the air / Peace on Earth / Father Christmas eyes / Ave Maria / Wishing on a star / Santa Claus is coming to town / Coventry carol / Coldest night of the year / Light of the stable / I believe in Father Christmas / Thirty two feet and eight little tails / Winters tale, A.
LP: WX 80
MC: WX 80C

CINEMA.
Tracks: / Windmills of your mind / Out here on my own / Prisoner, The / Sometimes / Do you know where you're going to (Theme from 'Mahogany') / Up where we belong / Unchained melody / Bright eyes / Alfie / Missing / Way we were, The / Rose, The.
LP: 240511 1
MC: 240511 4
LP: NE 1282
MC: CE 2282
LP: SHM 3285
MC: HSC 3285

COLLECTION.
Tracks: / Sometimes / Rose, The / MacArthur Park / Windmills of your mind, The / Without you / Walking in the air / Secrets / Last one to leave, The / Memory / Winter's tale, A / Ave Maria / Another suitcase in another hall / So sad (to watch good love go bad) / If you don't want my love / Hot as sun / Way we were, The.
LP: PWKLPS 4021
MC: PWKMCS 4021

ELAINE PAIGE.
Tracks: / If you don't want my love for you / Far side of the bay / So sad (to watch good love go bad) / Secrets / I want to marry you / Second time, The / Falling down to earth / Hot as sun / Last one to leave, The / How the heart approaches what it yearns / Miss my love today.
LP: K 58385
MC: K4 58385

FOR I KNOW HIM SO WELL (See under Dixon, Barbara) (Paige, Elaine & Barbara Dickson).

LOVE CAN DO THAT.
LP: PL 74932
MC: PK 74932

LOVE HURTS.
Tracks: / Love hurts / Sorry seems to be the hardest word / This is where I came in / All things considered / MacArthur Park / For you / My man and me / Without you / Apple tree, The / Shaking you / I know him so well.
LP: WX 28
MC: WX 28 C
LP: SHM 3240
MC: HSC 3240

MEMORIES.
Tracks: / I don't know how to love him / Love hurts / Second time, The / Tomorrow / On my own / I know him so well / Way we were, The / Rose, The / Walking in the air / If you don't want my love for you / Missing / Another suitcase in another hall / Don't cry for me Argentina.
LP: STAR 2313
MC: STAC 2313

QUEEN ALBUM, THE.
Tracks: / Bohemian rhapsody / Kind of magic, A / Love of my life / Who wants to live forever / My melancholy blues / You take my breath away / Las palabras de amor (the words of love) / One year of love / Is this the world we created / Radio ga ga.
LP: SRNLP 22
MC: SRNMC 22
MC: VVIPC 108
LP: VVIP 108

SITTING PRETTY.
Tracks: / Is anyone there? / Don't walk away till I touch you / Memories / Shining / Daybreak / Right side of the morning / Dancing close / Whose baby blue are you? / We're home again (From the film Boys from Brazil.) / Something ain't right.
LP: MFP 41 5704 1
MC: MFP 41 5704 4
LP: NTS 221

STAGES.
Tracks: / Memory / Be on your own / Another suitcase in another hall / Send in the clowns / Running back for more / Good morning, starshine / Don't cry for me Argentina / I don't know how to love him / What I did for love / One night only / Losing my mind / Tomorrow.
LP: 240228 1
MC: 2402284
LP: NE 1262
MC: CE 2262

Paige, Kevin

KEVIN PAIGE.
Tracks: / Anything I want / Don't shut me out / Love of the world / Touch of paradise, A / Hypnotize / Stop messin' with me / Believe in yourself / (You put me in) another world / I realise / Black and white.
LP: CHR 1683
MC: ZCHR 1683

Pain

PAIN.
LP: N 0039

Pain Teens

BORN IN BLOOD.
Tracks: / Basement, The / Shotguns / Way love used to be, The / Lady of flame / She shook me / My desire / Pleasures of the flesh / Bad in my head / Secret is sickness / Desu evol yaw / Christo / Noh jam.
LP: TR 03

Painkiller

GUTS OF A VIRGIN.
LP: MOSH 045
MC: MOSH 045 MC

Paint Your Wagon

PAINT YOUR WAGON (Musical show 1951 version) (Various artists).
Tracks: / I'm on my way: *Various artists* / Rumson: *Various artists* / What's goin' on here: *Various artists*/ I talk to the trees: *Various artists* / They call the wind Maria: *Various artists* / I still see Elisa: *Various* artists / How can I wait: *Various artists* / In between: *Various artists* / Whoop-ti-ay: *Various artists*/ Carino mio: *Various artists* / There's a coach comin' in: *Various artists* / Hand me down that can o' beans: *Various artists* / Another autumn: *Various artists* / All for him: *Various artists* / Wandrin' star: *Various artists.*
MC: GK 60243

PAINT YOUR WAGON (Original London cast) (Various artists).
Tracks: / I'm on my way: *Various artists* / Rumson: *Various artists* / What's goin' on here?: *Various artists*/ I talk to the trees: *Various artists* / They call the wind Maria: *Various artists* / I still see Elisa: *Various* artists / How can I wait?: *Various artists* / In between: *Various artists* / Whoop ti ay: *Various artists*/ Carino mio: *Various artists* / There's a coach comin' in: *Various artists* / Hand me down that can o' beans: *Various artists* / Another Autumn: *Various artists* / All for him: *Various artists* / Wanderin' star: *Various artists.*
LP: TER 1061
MC: ZCTER 1061

PAINT YOUR WAGON (ORIGINAL ISSUE) (Film soundtrack) (Various artists).
LP: SPFL 257

Painted Willie

PAINTED WILLIE.
LP: SST 107

Painted Word

LOVELIFE.
Tracks: / That's the reason I'm alive / Lovelife / Wilderness / Frances / Joie de vivre / 24 hours / Worldwide / I want it here and I want it now / 77 / Pleasure inside, The.
LP: PL 74165
MC: PK 74165

Painting The Town Red

PAINTING THE TOWN RED (Various artists).
LP: TOTEM 2

Paisley Abbey

CAROLS FOR CULZEAN CASTLE (Paisley Abbey Choir/Neil Mackie).
Tracks: / O come all ye faithful / Unto us a boy is born / It came upon a midnight clear / Holy boy, The / Seven joys of Mary, The / Whence is that goodly fragrance flowing? / Benedicamus Domino / Once in royal David's city / O little town of Bethlehem / In Bethlehem City / Three kings, The / In the bleak mid winter / Ecce novum gaudium / Shepherd's pipe carol / Hark the herald angels sing.
LP: APS 356

GREAT ORGAN MUSIC (Paisley Abbey, Organ of).
LP: LILP 5067

IN QUIRES AND PLACES NO. 24 (Paisley Abbey Choir).
LP: LPB 789

WORLD OF SACRED MUSIC, THE (Paisley Abbey Choir).
LP: SPA 62

Paisley, Bob

BOB PAISLEY AND THE SOUTHERN GRASS (Paisley, Bob & The Southern Grass).
LP: ROUNDER 0142
MC: ROUNDER 0142C

LOVE SICK AND SORROW (see Lundy, Ted) (Paisley, Bob/Ted Lundy/Southern Mountain Boys).

Paisley, Ronnie

SMOKING MIRROR (Paisley, Ronnie Band).
Tracks: / Celtic lullaby / Walteaser / Captain Bligh / Widelife / Lady D / Bust / Traveller / God / Everything / Jumping gas flash.
LP: NSPL 18592

Paisleys

COSMIC MIND AT PLAY.
LP: PSYCHO 7

Pajama Game

CALAMITY JANE/PAJAMA GAME (Film soundtracks) (See under Calamity Jane) (Various artists).

PAJAMA GAME (Original 1955 London Cast) (Various artists).
Tracks: / Overture: *Various artists* / Pajama game, The: *Various artists* / Racing with the clock: *Various artists* / New town is a blue town, A: *Various artists* / I'm not at all in love: *Various artists* / I'll never be jealous again: *Various artists* / Hey there: *Various artists* / Her is: *Various artists* / Once a year day: *Various artists* / Small talk: *Various artists* / There once was a man: *Various artists* / Steam heat: *Various artists* / Think of the time I save: *Various artists* / Hernando's hideaway: *Various artists*/ Seven and a half cents: *Various artists* / Finale: *Various artists.*
LP: TER 1058
MC: ZCTER 1058
MC: PST 32606

PAJAMA GAME, THE (Original soundtrack) (Various artists).
LP: AOL 5212
MC: BT 5210

SONGS FROM PAJAMA GAME AND CALAMITY JANE (See under Day, Doris) (Day, Doris).

Pajama Slave Dancers

BLOOD, SWEAT AND BEAR.
LP: GWLP 46

Pakistan

KAWWALI MUSICIANS OF PAKISTAN (Featuring Brothers Sabri) (Various artists).
Tracks: / Saazina: *Various artists* / Jamale kibriya main hoon: *Various artists* / Roona ach-cha lagta hai: *Various artists* / Ali dam dam kay ander: *Various artists* / Mera piya ghar aya: *Various artists.*
LP: ARN 33654

L'ALGOZA DU SIND (Various artists).
Tracks: / Rano: *Various artists* / Malkauns: *Various artists* / Mor thotele: *Various artists* / Danse du sind: *Various artists* / Mange: *Various artists* / Loraho:

Various artists / Djamalou: *Various artists* / Bhairavi: *Various artists* / Aiman: *Various artists*.
LP: . . . . ARN 33483

PAKISTAN - THE MUSIC OF THE QAWAL (Various artists).
MC: . . . . AUD 580278

Pal

TRUTH FOR THE MOVEMENT.
Tracks: / Man about town / Like it / Her husband / On the edge / Everybody's nasty / Panic / Talk we don't, spellbound / Strange dreams / Checkin' u out.
LP: . . . . ZL 72398

Pal Joey

PAL JOEY (1981 London Revival cast) (Various artists).
Tracks: / What is a man?: *Various artists* / Chicago: *Various artists* / Flower garden of my heart: *Various* artists / Zip: *Various artists* / In our little den of iniquity: *Various artists* / I could write a book: *Various artists* / You mustn't kick it around: *Various artists* / That terrific rainbow: *Various artists*/ Bewitched: *Various artists*.
LP: . . . . TER 1005
MC: . . . . ZCTER 1005

PAL JOEY (Original cast recording) (Various artists).
MC: . . . . JST 04364

PAL JOEY (ORIGINAL ISSUE) (Film soundtrack) (Various artists).
Tracks: / That terrific rainbow: *Various artists* / I didn't know what time it was: *Various artists* / Do it the hard way: *Various artists* / Great big town: *Various artists* / There's a small hotel: *Various artists*/ Zip: *Various artists* / Bewitched: *Various artists* / I could write a book: *Various artists* / Lady is a tramp, The: *Various artists* / Plant you now, dig you later: *Various artists* / My funny valentine: *Various* artists / You mustn't kick it around: *Various artists* / Strip number: *Various artists* / What do I care for a dame: *Various artists*.
LP: . . . . LCT 6148
LP: . . . . T 912

Palace Of Light

BEGINNING HERE AND TRAVELLING OUTWARDS.
LP: . . . . KIRI 058

Paladins

LET'S BUZZ.
LP: . . . . AL 4782

PALADINS.
Tracks: / Hold on / Make it / Honky tonk all night / Let's go / Lucky man / Lover's rock / Daddy yar / Come on home / Bad case of love / Let 'er roll / Slow down.
LP: . . . . WIK 64
LP: . . . . WR 1687
MC: . . . . WRC 1687

YEARS SINCE YESTERDAY.
LP: . . . . AL 4762

Palais Schaumburg

LUPA.
Tracks: / 3 nach 9 / Nett sein / Lupa / Sprung uber vier Pferde / Sieg auf Knien / Rosen / Nationen / Der Tiger und die Stimme / Stich auf stich / Europa / Papperazzo.
LP: 643 518 2

Palass

QUEEN OF THE WORLD.
Tracks: / Queen of the world / Last Friday, The / Love is life / Mutant, The / Devil girl / Get out / Heroes / End, The.
LP: . . . . POWLP 5506

Pale Fountains

FROM ACROSS THE KITCHEN TABLE.
Tracks: / Shelter / Stole the love / Jean's not happening / Bicycle thieves / Limit / 27 ways to get back home / Bruised arcade / These are the things / It's only hard / From across the kitchen table / Hey / September sting.
LP: . . . . OVED 164
MC: . . . . OVEDC 164
LP: . . . . V 2333
MC: . . . . TCV 2333

PACIFIC STREET.
Tracks: / Reach / Something on my mind / Unless / Southbound excursion / Natural / Faithful pillow (part 1) / You'll start a war / Beyond Friday's field / Abergele next time / Crazier / Faithful pillow (part 2).
LP: . . . . V 2274
MC: . . . . TCV 2274
LP: . . . . OVED 143
MC: . . . . OVEDC 143

Pale Saints

COMFORTS OF MADNESS.
Tracks: / Way the world is / Sea of sound / Little hammer / Deep sleep for Steven, A / Fell from the sun / Time thief / You tear the world in two / True coming dream / Insubstantial / Language of flowers / Sight of you.
LP: . . . . CAD 0002
MC: . . . . CAD 0002C

Palermo, Ed

ED PALERMO ORCHESTRA (Palermo, Ed Orchestra).
Tracks: / Papier mache / Complete control / Before Max / Dusty (another cowboy song) / Different people differently / Escape nonetheless, An.
LP: . . . . VHR 001

Palestine

MUSIC OF THE INTIFADA (Various artists).
Tracks: / Min al mukhayyam etc: *Sabaya Al Intifada* / Al raba'yye: *In A'd Rifaki* / Al kassam al filistini: *In A'd Rifaki* / Jirah lan tamout: *Al-Amal Ashabi* / Alrass al lutisar: *Abnaa El-Balad* / Al intifada was etc: *Palestinian Student Karmel Group* / Kulluna Fil Tareeg: *In A'd Rifaki* / Watani lafsahakiba: *Palestinian Student* Karmel Group / Al fajir: *Muhiddine Al Baghdadi* / Jabal al zaytoun: *Sabaya Al Intifada* / Bism Ilhurriya: *Al-Amal Ashabi* / Umma al wabiba: *Sabaya Al Intifada* / Al hegran: *Muhiddine Al Baghdadi* / In A'd Rifaki: *In A'd Rifaki*.
LP: . . . . VE 29
MC: . . . . TCVE 29

Paley Brothers

PALEY BROTHERS, THE.
Tracks: / You're the best / Too good to be true / I heard the bluebirds sing / Magic power / Turn the tide / Stick with baby / Tell me tonight / Lovin' eyes can't lie / Come out and play / Down the lime.
LP: . . . . SRK 6052

Paley, Tom

WHO'S GOING TO SHOE YOUR PRETTY LITTLE FOOT?... (Paley,Tom & P.Seeger).
Tracks: / Who's that knocking at my window / Love Henry / Lass of Roch royal / Who's going to shoe your pretty little foot? / Pretty Polly / Englewood mine / Buck dancer's choice / Just as the tide was flowing / Kicking mule, The / Heartless lady, The / Fiddling soldier, The / Tittery nan / Loving Reilly / Cuckoo, The / If he'd be a buckeroo / Girl on the greenbriar shore, The.
LP: 12T 113

Paligap

WINTER.
LP: . . . . UNKNOWN

Palin, Joe

LIVE AT THE AVGARDE GALLERY (See under Rendell, Don) (Palin, Joe Trio & Don Rendell).

Palin, Michael

MOWGLI'S BROTHERS.
MC: . . . . LP 205
MC: . . . . LPMC 205

Palladin, Patti

COPY CATS (See Thunders, Johnny) (Palladin, Patti & Johnny Thunders).

SHE WANTS TO MAMBO (See Thunders, Johnny) (Palladin, Patti & Johnny Thunders).

Pallas

ARRIVE ALIVE.
Tracks: / Heart attack / Crown of thorns / Queen of the deep / Ripper.
LP: . . . . CKLP 002

WEDGE, THE.
Tracks: / Dance through the fire / Throwing stones at the wind / Win or lose / Executioner (Bernie Goetz a gun) / Million miles away, A (imagination) / Ratracing / Just a memory.
LP: . . . . SHVL 850
MC: . . . . TCSHVL 850

Pallas, Laura

SENTINEL, THE.
Tracks: / Eyes in the night / Cut and run / Rise and fall / Shock treatment / Art of infinity / Atlantis.
LP: . . . . SHSP 2400121
MC: . . . . TCSHSP 240012

Palm, Anna

ARRIVING AND CAUGHT UP.
LP: . . . . TPLP 10

Palm Beach Orchestra

PLAY GLENN MILLER (BIG BAND VOLUME 1).
MC: . . . . BBM 145

Palm Court...

DOWN PEACOCK VALLEY (Palm Court Theatre Orchestra).
Tracks: / Haunting rag / Say a little prayer for me / Love for sale / Poem / Coon band contest / Charleston / Down south.
LP: . . . . LBRD 010
MC: . . . . LBTD 010

HITTING THE HIGH SPOTS (Palm Court Orchestra).
LP: . . . . LRF 155

PICNIC PARTY, THE (Palm Court Theatre Orchestra).
Tracks: / There's a ring around the Moon / Black eyes / Grasshopper's dance, The / Silver bird / Fiddlesticks rag / I'm forever blowing bubbles / Petite tonkinoise / Whistle for me / In the shadows / Polly / Down in Zanzibar / Ragtime bass player, The / Two little sausages / In a Persian market.
LP: . . . . LBR 002
MC: . . . . LBT 002
LP: . . . . ABRD 1022

PUTTIN' ON THE RITZ (Palm Court Theatre Orchestra).
Tracks: / Puttin' on the ritz / It must be true / Tot toot tootsie / Sheik of Araby, The / Let's get friendly / Honeymoon lane / Happy feet / Oh what a night / Roll along covered wagon / Ain't misbehavin' / She's a Latin from Manhattan / Horatio Nicholls' Californian serenade / Loving you / Tiger rag.
LP: . . . . LBRD 015
MC: . . . . LBTD 015

SECOND SERENADE (Palm Court Trio).
LP: . . . . RES 008

SERENADE (Palm Court Trio).
LP: . . . . RES 004

VINTAGE PARADE (CHILDHOOD MEMORIES) (Palm Court Theatre Orchestra).
Tracks: / He'd have to get under, get out and get under / Parade of the tin soldiers, The / Humpty Dumpty / Cinderella's wedding / Rag doll / Teddy bears' picnic / Childhood memories / Happy frog, The / Pattering feet / Policeman's holiday / Dainty Miss / Vintage galop.
LP: . . . . LBRD 012
MC: . . . . LBTD 012

Palma, Triston

JOKER SMOKER.
Tracks: / Innocent man, An / Babylon / Give me, give me your love / Lonely man / Got to praise Jah Jah / Joker smoker / Peace and love in the ghetto / Two timer / Ghetto king / Lover man.
LP: . . . . GREL 43

ON THE ATTACK.
LP: . . . . BMLP 009

REGGAE '85 (See under Campbell, Al) (Palma, Triston & Al Campbell).

SETTLE DOWN GIRL.
LP: . . . . TRLS 215

SHOW CASE.
LP: . . . . VSLP 4006
LP: . . . . MRLP 90000

TOUCH ME, TAKE ME.
Tracks: / Raving / Heart breaker / Sad news.
LP: . . . . STLP 1017
MC: . . . . VSMC 004

TRISTON PALMER MEETS EARLY B (Palmer, Triston & Early B).
LP: . . . . Unknown

WOUNDED.
LP: . . . . BG 1004

Palmer, Barry

WITHOUT AIM.
LP: . . . . VENLP 1
MC: . . . . ZCVEN 1

Palmer, David

MUSIC OF GENESIS, THE (Palmer, David/London Symphony Orchestra).
LP: . . . . PL 86242
MC: . . . . RK 86242

MUSIC OF JETHRO TULL (Palmer, David/LSO).
Tracks: / Locomotive breath / Thick as a brick / Elegy / Bouree / Fly by night / Aqualung / Too old to rock 'n' roll / Teacher / Bungle in the jungle / Rainbow blues / Living in the past / War child.
LP: . . . . RL 71134
MC: . . . . RK 71134

OBJECTS OF FANTASY (Palmer, David & RPO).
LP: . . . . RK 87960
LP: . . . . RL 87960

Palmer, Gladys

HIGH PRIESTESS OF JIVE.
Tracks: / Strangest feeling / You alone / In the rain / Palmer's boogie / If I didn't have you / Later on / Song man / Fool that I am / I'm pulling through / Tonight you belong to me / Where the lazy river goes by / After you've gone / I'm living in a great big way / In the middle of a kiss / Get behind me satan, and push / Trees.
LP: . . . . OFF 6048

Palmer, Jeff

LASER WIZZARD.
LP: . . . . SLP 8081

Palmer, Joe

PLACE IN YOUR HEART (ISLAND) (Palmer, Joe & Joe Giltrap).
Tracks: / Cliffs of Dooneen / Galway bay / Boys from the County Armagh / Bally James Duff / Rose of Tralee / Gurragh of Kildare / Rose of Mooncoin / Isle of Innisfree / Mountains of Mourne / Connemara cradle song / Blackwater side / Mary from Dunloe / In Dublin's fair city / Carrickfergus / Bunclody / Limerick you're a lady.
LP: . . . . ETLP 1001
MC: . . . . ETCS 1001

Palmer, Michael

ANGELLA.
LP: . . . . VSLP 4064

GHETTO LIVING.
LP: . . . . BB 092

LICK SHOT.
MC: . . . . Unknown

MICHAEL PALMER MEETS JOHNNY OSBOURNE (see Osbourne, Johnny) (Palmer, Michael & Johnny Osbourne).

MICHAEL PALMER MEETS KELLY RANKS (Palmer, Michael & Kelly Ranks).
LP: . . . . DFLP 3003

PULL IT UP NOW.
Tracks: / Pull it up now / We rule / She give me fever / Mixing and blending / Don't stay out late / Flirt around / My Susan / Pon your toe / Don't push me / I've been to many places.
LP: . . . . GREL 83
MC: . . . . GREEN 83

SHOWCASE - I'M STILL DANCING.
LP: . . . . Unknown

STAR PERFORMER.
LP: . . . . TONLP 001

SWEET DADDY.
LP: . . . . BLSCLP 002

WE RULE.
LP: . . . . Unknown

Palmer, Poli

HUMAN ERROR.
LP: 6. 26208

Palmer, Robert

ADDICTIONS VOL.1.
Tracks: / Bad case of lovin' you (doctor doctor) / Pride / Addicted to love / Sweet lies / Woke up laughing / Looking for clues / Some guys have all the luck / Some like it hot / What's it take / Every kinda people / Johnny and Mary / Simply irresistable / Style kills.
LP: . . . . ILPS 9944
MC: . . . . ICT 9944

ADDICTIONS VOL.2.
MC: . . . . ICTTV 4
LP: . . . . ILPTV 4

CLUES.
Tracks: / Looking for clues / Sulky girl / Johnny and Mary / What do you care / I dream of wires / Woke up laughing / Not a second time / Found you now.
LP: . . . . ILPM 9595
MC: . . . . ICM 9595
LP: . . . . ILPS 9595
MC: 842 553 4

DON'T EXPLAIN.
Tracks: / Your mother should have told you / Light-years / You can't get enough of a good thing / Dreams to remember / You're amazing / Mess around / Happiness / History / I'll be your baby tonight / Housework / Mercy mercy me/ I want you / Don't explain / Aeroplane / People will say we're in love / Not a word / Top 40 / You're so desirable / You're my thrill.
2LP: . . . . EMDX 1018
MC: . . . . TCEMDX 1018

DOUBLE FUN.
Tracks: / Every kinda people / Best of both worlds / Where can it go / Night people / Love can run faster / You overwhelm me / You really got me / Your gonna get what's coming.
LP: . . . . ILPM 9476
MC: . . . . ICM 9476
MC: 842 592 4

EARLY YEARS, THE (Palmer, Robert with The Alan Bown).
Tracks: / My friend / Strange little friend / Perfect day / Children of the night / Gypsy girl / Elope / All I can do / Still as stone / Prisoner, The / Kick me out / Wrong idea, The / Strange little friend / Friend in St. Louis.
LP: C5-501
MC: C5K 501

HEAVY NOVA.
Tracks: / Simply irresistible / More than ever / Change his ways / Disturbing

behaviour / Early in the morning / It could happen to you / She makes my day / Between us / Casting a spell / Tell me I'm not dreaming.
LP: . . . . EMD 1007
MC: . . . . TCEMD 1007

MAYBE IT'S LIVE.
Tracks: / Every kinda people / Sneaking Sally through the alley / Some guys have all the luck.
LP: . . . . ILPS 9665
MC: . . . . ICM 9665

PRESSURE DROP.
Tracks: / Give me an inch girl / Work to make it work / Back in my arms / Riverboat / Pressure drop / Here with you tonight / Trouble / Fine time / Which of us is the fool.
LP: . . . . ILPM 9372
MC: . . . . ICM 9372
MC: 842 594 4

PRIDE.
Tracks: / Pride / Deadline / Want you more / Dance for me / You are in my system / It's not difficult / Say you will / You can have it (take my heart) / What you waiting for / Silver gun.
LP: . . . . ILPM 9720
MC: . . . . ICM 9720
LP: . . . . ILPS 9720
MC: 811 322 4

RIPTIDE.
Tracks: / Riptide / Hyperactive / Addicted to love / Trick bag / Get it through your heart / I didn't mean to turn you on / Flesh wound / Discipline of love / Riptide (reprise).
LP: . . . . ILPS 9801
MC: . . . . ICT 9801
MC: . . . . ICM 9801
LP: . . . . ILPM 9801

SECRETS.
Tracks: / Bad case of lovin' you (doctor doctor) / Too good to be true / Can we still be friends / In walks love again / Mean ol' world / Love stop / Jealous / Under suspicion / Woman you're wonderful / What's it take / Remember to remember.
LP: . . . . ILPM 9544
MC: . . . . ICM 9544
LP: . . . . ILPS 9544
MC: 842 354 4

SNEAKIN' SALLY THROUGH THE ALLEY.
Tracks: / Sailing shoes / Hey Julia / Sneakin' Sally through the alley / Get outside / How much fun / From a whisper to a scream / Through it all there's you.
LP: . . . . ILPM 9294
MC: . . . . ICM 9294
MC: 842 607 4

SOME PEOPLE CAN DO WHAT THEY LIKE.
Tracks: / One last look / Keep in touch / Man smart (woman smarter) / Spanish moon / Have mercy / Gotta get a grip on you (part 2) / What can you bring me? / Hard head / Off the bone / Some people can do what they like.
LP: . . . . ILPS 9420
MC: . . . . ICT 9420

Palmer, Singleton

DIXIE BY GASLIGHT.
LP: . . . . DJA 511

Palmieri, Eddie

BAMBOLEATE (Palmieri, Eddie/Cal Tjader).
Tracks: / Bamboleate / We've loved before / Resemblance / Mi montuno / Samba do suenho / Guarjira candela / Pancho's seis por ocho / Come an' get it.
LP: . . . . HOT 130
MC: . . . . TCHOT 130

LA VERDAD (The truth).
Tracks: / El cuarto / Congo yambumba / La verdad / Lisa / Noble cruise / Buscandote.
LP: . . . . HOT 118
MC: . . . . TCHOT 118

SUENO.
Tracks: / Variations on a given theme / Azucar / Just a little dream / Covarde / Humpty Dumpty / La liberatad.
LP: . . . . INT 30081
MC: . . . . INT 30084

Palmvist, Claes

RAGTIME GUITAR DUETS (Palmvist, Claes & L.Johansson).
LP: . . . . SNKF 120

Palookas

HIT THE BOTTLE.
Tracks: / Hit the bottle / Quality street / Girl with everything, The / Loggo land / Chicken in a basket / Doctor No / Run rabbit run / Black pebo / Rubber Johnny.
LP: . . . . CON 00032

Pameijer, Pam

JELLY ROLL MORTON - 100 YEARS.
LP: . . . . SOS 1134

LONDON BLUES (Pameijer, Pam Trio).
LP: . . . . SOS 1172

PAM PAMEIJER AND HIS CLASSIC JAZZ ACES (Pameijer, Pam & His Classic Jazz Aces).
LP: . . . . SOS 1194

Pammi, Parmijit

SHE'S BAD.
LP: . . . . MUT 1101
MC: . . . . CMUT 1101

Pamplemousse

SWEET MAGIC.
Tracks: / Sweet magic / Slow down / Do you have any / I wanna make music with you / Deeper / No sweat.
LP: . . . . AVLP 501

Pan Assembly

SPIRIT, THE (Pan Assembly Pan Calypso).
LP: . . . . C 01688

Pan Pipes

GOLDEN PAN FLUTE (Various artists).
LP: 29098
MC: 49098

GOLDEN PAN FLUTE VOL 2 (Various artists).
MC: 49110

PAN PIPES PLAY LOVE SONGS (Various artists).
Tracks: / If you leave me now: *Various artists* / Something: *Various artists* / Do you know where you're going to: *Various artists* (Theme from Mahogany) / Feelings: *Various artists* / I'm stone in love with you: *Various* artists / Unchained melody: *Various artists* / She's out of my life: *Various artists* / Softly as I leave you: *Various artists* / First time ever I saw your face, The: *Various artists* / Endless love: *Various artists*/ True love ways: *Various artists* / Light my fire: *Various artists* / Why can't it wait till morning: *Various artists* / Godfather love theme: *Various artists.*
LP: . . . . CFTC 545
MC: . . . . MCFRC 545

Panama (country)

STREET MUSIC OF PANAMA (See under Street Music Of Panama) (Various artists).

STREET MUSIC OF PANAMA (Various artists).
MC: . . . . OMA 401C

Panatella, Slim

SLIM PANATELLA AND THE MELLOW VIRGINIANS (Panatella, Slim & The Mellow Virginians).
MC: . . . . ACS 005
LP: . . . . ASC 005

Panaunie

PANAUNIE (Various artists).
LP: . . . . RRTG 7705
MC: . . . . RRTGC 7705

Pandemonium

HOLE IN THE SKY.
LP: . . . . RR 9727

KILL, THE.
LP: . . . . RR 95371

Pandoras

IT'S ABOUT TIME.
LP: . . . . VOXX 200021

ROCK HARD.
LP: . . . . GWLP 38

STOP PRETENDING.
LP: . . . . RNLP 70857

Pandora's Box

ORIGINAL SIN.
Tracks: / Invocation / Original sin (the natives are restless tonight) / Twentieth century fox / Safe sex (when it comes 2 loving U) / Good girls go to heaven (bad girls go everywhere) / Requiem metal / I've been dreaming up a storm lately / It's all coming back to me now / Opening of the box, The / Want ad, The / My little red book / It just won't quit / Pray lewd / Future ain't what it used to be, The.
LP: . . . . V 2605
MC: . . . . TCV 2605

Panic

EPIDEMIC.
LP: . . . . ZORRO 24
MC: . . . . TZORRO 24

Panic Brothers

IN THE RED.
Tracks: / Bivouac / No news / I made a mess of a dirty weekend / Repo man / Almost as blue as Hank Williams / In debt / Later than you think / I'm broke in everything but my heart / Late night picture show / I've forgotten what it is that I was drinking to forget.
LP: . . . . SPD 1003

Panic Buttons

TELEPHONE BOX (EP) (See under Hayward, Andrew) (Panic Buttons & Andrew Hayward).

Pankow

FREIHEIT FUR DIE SKLAVEN.
Tracks: / Gimme more (dub) / Girls and boys / In Heaven / Sickness takin' over / Freiheit fur die sklaven / Gimme more / She's gotta be mine / Nice bottom (schoener arsch) / Touch (I'm your bastard) / Nice bottom (nice dub).
LP: . . . . CONTE 113

GISELA.
LP: . . . . LD 8936

OMNE ANIMAL TRISTE POST COITUM.
LP: . . . . CONTE 161
MC: . . . . CONTAPE 161

Panol, Dominque

PLUS PLEZIW.
LP: . . . . GD 037

Panorama Du Jazz

LES GEANTS DU JAZZ.
LP: 504152

Pantera

COWBOYS FROM HELL.
Tracks: / Cowboys from hell / Primal concrete sledge / Psycho holiday / Cemetery gates / Shattered / Medicine man / Sleep, The / Heresy / Domination / Clash with reality / Message in blood / Art of shredding.
LP: 7567913721
MC: 7567913724

POWER METAL.
LP: . . . . MMR 1988

Panther Burns

BEHIND THE MAGNOLIA CURTAIN.
Tracks: / Come on little mama / She's the one that got it / Hey high school baby / Brazil / You're undecided / Oo wee baby / River of love / Snake drive / Blind man / Where the Rio de Rosa flows / Snatch it back / Bourgeois blues / St. Louis blues / Moving on down the line.
LP: . . . . ROUGH 32

NOW.
MC: . . . . NBTFZ 001

Pantry, John

EMPTY-HANDED.
LP: . . . . DOVE 56

Panzer

SALVESE QUIEN PUEDA.
LP: . . . . SKULL 8342

Papa Dee

LETTIN' OFF STEAM.
Tracks: / Lettin' off steam / Real thing, The / Ain't no stoppin' us now / Wake up / Beautiful woman / Thrill night / Take it easy / Chosen one, The / Young gifted and black / Earthquake dub / What's going on (what ah gwan) / Microphone poet / Hypocrites (Only on cassette and CD).
LP: 211322
MC: 411322

Papa Noel

SELIA ZOZO.
LP: . . . . AP 048

Papa Peacock

PAPA PEACOCK (Various artists).
MC: . . . . ANV 623

Papa San

ANIMAL PARTY.
LP: . . . . Unknown

BUCK WILD (See under Paul, Frankie) (Papa San & Frankie Paul).

LYRIC SHOP.
LP: . . . . BSLP 015

MC CLASH (Papa San & Tippa Irie).
Tracks: / Gal bring it come / Write me a letter / It's a hit / Gals love money man / Long time friend / Predominant / Sweetness lyrics / It a de talking / Time for reality / Look how jah great.
LP: . . . . FADLP 007

STYLE AND FASHION.
LP: . . . . BSLP 23189

WOULDA, SHOULDA, COULDA (See under Red Rose 'Girl watcher') (Papa San & Peter Mann).

Papa Wemba

L'ESCLAVE.
LP: . . . . GIP 004
MC: . . . . C 1024

Papadimitriou,Sakis

FIRST MOVE.
LP: . . . . LR 128

PIANO ORACLES.
LP: . . . . LR 163

PIANO PLAYS.
LP: . . . . LR 111

Papasov, Ivo

BALKANOLOY.
Tracks: / Miladeshki dance / Hristianova kopanitsa / Istoria na edna / Ivo's ruchenitsa / Song for Baba Nedelya / Ergenski dance / Mominsko horo / Tziganska ballada / Veseli Zborni / Proleten dance / Kasapsko horo.
LP: . . . . HNBL 1363
MC: . . . . HNBLBC 1363

ORPHEUS ASCENDING (Papasov, Ivo & His Bulgarian Wedding Band).
LP: . . . . HNBL 1347
MC: . . . . HNBC 1347

Papathanassiou,Vangeli

IGNACIO.
LP: 900531

Paper Garden

PRESENTS THE PAPER GARDEN.
LP: . . . . ANTAR 3

Paper House

PAPER HOUSE (Film soundtrack) (Various artists).
LP: . . . . A 374
MC: . . . . AC 374

Paper Lace

PAPER LACE COLLECTION.
Tracks: / Night Chicago died, The / Billy, don't be a hero / Like a rolling stone / Early one morning / Games people play / Black eyed boys, The.
MCSET: . . . . PDC 023
2LP: . . . . PDA 023

Paperwate

MEMORIES DE PLAISER.
LP: . . . . BSS 136

Papetti, Fausto

AMBIENCE SAX.
2LP: 432 013
MC: 832 013

GOLDEN SAX.
MC: 260 905 4

J'AIME LE BAL.
LP: 508 671
MC: 709 671

MEDLEY IN SAX.
LP: 508 670
MC: 709 670

Papillon

PAPILLON (Film soundtrack) (Various artists).
Tracks: / Pipillon, Theme from: *Various artists* / Camp, The: *Various artists* / Reunion: *Various artists*/ New friend: *Various artists* / Freedom: *Various artists* / Gift from the sea: *Various artists* / Antonio's death: *Various artists* / Cruel sea: *Various artists* / Hospital: *Various artists* / Survival: *Various artists.*
LP: . . . . FILM 029

Pappa Tollo

MOTHER LIZA MEETS PAPPA TOLLO (see Mother Liza) (Pappa Tollo/Mother Liza).

Para

ZENTESE.
LP: A5 5016

Parable

ILLUSTRATIONS.
LP: . . . . HS 34

MORE THAN WORDS.
LP: . . . . HS 22

Parachute Club

PARACHUTE CLUB, THE.
LP: . . . . MAGL 5059
MC: . . . . ZCMAG 5059

SMALL VICTORIES.
Tracks: / Tearing the veil / Love is fire / Secret heart (wild zone) / Walk to the rhythm of your heartbeat / Love & compassion / Small victories / Journey, The / Cheat the prophecy / Waves.
LP: . . . . PL 71186
MC: . . . . PK 71186

Parachute Men

EARTH, DOGS AND EGGSHELLS.
MC: . . . . FIREMC 24
LP: . . . . FIRELP 24

INNOCENTS, THE.
LP: . . . . FIRELP 14

Parade Ground

CUT UP.
Tracks: / Hollywood / Modern hunting / I will talk / Moans / Moist hands / Such is the bow / Cut up the neck tie / Cut throat business / Strange world.
LP: . . . . BIAS 93

Paradis, Vanessa

MARILYN AND JOHN.
Tracks: / Marilyn and John / Maxou / Le bon dieu est un marin / Mosquito / Soldat / Joe le taxi / Cut cut brothers / Chat Ananas / Scarabee.
LP: . . . . **POLD 5232**
MC: . . . . **POLDC 5232**

Paradise

DESIGNED IN HEAVEN.
LP: . . . . **BBSLP 004**

LOVE IS THE ANSWER.
Tracks: / Love is the answer / One mind two hearts / Back together / Just can't stop.
LP: . . . . **PLP 1**
MC: . . . . **PCAS 1**

Paradise Express

PARADISE EXPRESS.
Tracks: / Dance / Poinciana / Reverend Lee / Star in my life / Hold on.
LP: . . . . **FT 557**

Paradise Lost

GOTHIC.
LP: . . . . **VILE 26**

LOST PARADISE.
Tracks: / Intro / Deadly inner sense / Paradise lost / Our saviour / Rotting misery / Frozen illusion / Breeding fear / Lost paradise.
LP: . . . . **VILE 17**
MC: . . . . **VILE 17 MC**

PARADISE LOST (see under Milton, John) (Various artists).

Paradise Postponed

PARADISE POSTPONED (TV soundtrack) (Webb, Roger Orchestra (The)).
Tracks: / Paradise postponed (Title theme from Thames TV series from Elgar cello concerto) / Main theme / In the Chilterns / Meadows and streams / Romance / Pastorale / Encounters / Letter, The / Lady Grace's waltz / Love theme / Journey to London / Picton Hall.
LP: . . . . **SCX 6706**
MC: . . . . **TC-SCX 6706**

SIR MICHAEL HORDERN (See under Hordern, Sir Michael).

Paradise Regained

PARADISE REGAINED (Various artists).
LP: . . . . **LICLP 020**
MC: . . . . **LICMC 020**

Paradise, Sal

SHIMMER.
Tracks: / Living in a dreamboat / Beat of my heart / Andiamo / Made in heaven / Sahara no way / There was a universe / Mantra / Legion / Baby of the world / Olipopo kalimar.
LP: **206156**
MC: **406156**

Paradise Vendor

PARADISE FOR WHO?.
LP: . . . . **UNKNOWN**

PARADISE VENDOR.
LP: . . . . **PLASLP 20**

THIS IS PARADISE.
LP: . . . . **PLASLP 020**

Paradox

HERESY.
LP: . . . . **RO 95061**

PRODUCT OF IMAGINATION.
LP: . . . . **RR 9593**

Paragon Brass Band

LIVE ON THE STREETS OF ROUEN.
LP: . . . . **GHB 87**

Paragonne

ASPECTS OF.
Tracks: / Hope for the future / 24 hours / Gentle giant / Difference of opinion / 71890 / Doubtful / Agression and regression / Weathertop / Unbelievable / Monica and the pirate / River, The / Before and after / Zara.
LP: . . . . **MMC 010**
MC: . . . . **TCMMC 1010**

Paragons

NOW.
LP: . . . . **SDLP 909**

ON THE BEACH.
LP: . . . . **TILP 1007**
MC: . . . . **CAS 1007**

ORIGINAL PARAGONS, THE.
Tracks: / Blackbird singing / Silver bird / Same song, The / You mean the world to me / Mercy, mercy, mercy / Riding high on a windy day / All my life / I am a worried man / Land of sea and sun / My best girl.
LP: . . . . **TILP 007**

PARAGONS.
LP: . . . . **ILPS 9631**
MC: . . . . **ICT 9631**

Paralamas

BORA BORA.
Tracks: / O Beco / Bundale le / Bora bora / Sanfona / Um a um / Fingido / Don't give me that / Uns dias / Quase um segundo / Dois elefantes / Tres / Impressao / O fundo do coracoa / Can, The.
LP: . . . . **INT 30141**
MC: . . . . **INT 30144**

Paramor, Norrie

BEST OF NORRIE PARAMOR.
Tracks: / My little friend / Wonderful land / Walk in love / Just the way you are / Summer of '42 / Scarborough fair / Solitaire / Big country, The / She / You don't bring me flowers / Summer place, A theme from / Annie's song / Whistle down the wind / Aria.
LP: . . . . **REC 512**
MC: . . . . **ZCM 512**

BY REQUEST (Paramor, Norrie Orchestra).
MC: . . . . **ZCF 326**

BY REQUEST VOLUME 4 (see Midland Radio Orchestra) (Paramor, Norrie/ Midland Radio Orchestra).

CLASSICAL RHYTHM (Paramor, Norrie Orchestra).
Tracks: / Beethoven's fifth / Habanera / Dance of the hours / Rachmaninov / Hungarian dance no. 1 / Poet and peasant / Hora staccato / Moto perpetuo / Ballet Egyptian no 1 / Orpheus in the underworld / Schubert 5 / Estudiantina / Fantasie - impromptu / Skaters waltz.
LP: . . . . **NSPLX 41058**

RAGTIME (Paramor, Norrie/Big Ben Banjo Band).
Tracks: / Temptation rag / Entertainer, The / Swipesy / Janie / Rialto ripples / Easy winners / Peacherine rag / Maple leaf rag / Bohemia rag / Elite syncopations / Pick 'n' mix / Euphonic sounds / Smokey mokes / Chimes of Dixie.
LP: . . . . **FBLP 8090**
MC: . . . . **ZCFBL 8090**

THANK YOU FOR THE MUSIC.
Tracks: / Copacabana / Bright eyes / Music box dancer / Cavatina / Just the way you are / I will survive / American popular song / Annie's song / Penmarric / Does your mother know / You don't bring me flowers / Thank you for the music.
LP: . . . . **REB 370**
MC: . . . . **ZCF 370**

Paramount...

PARAMOUNT OLD TIME TUNES (Various artists).
LP: . . . . **JEMF 103**

Paramount Jazzband...

AIN'T CHA GLAD? (Paramount Jazzband Of Boston).
LP: . . . . **SOS 1205**

Paramounts

WHITER SHADES OF R & B.
Tracks: / Poison Ivy / I feel good all over / Little bitty pretty one / Certain girl, A / I'm the one who loves you / It won't be long / Bad blood / Do I / Blue ribbons / Cuttin' in / You never had it so good / Don't ya like my love / Draw me closer / Turn on your lovelight / You've got what I want / Freedom.
LP: . . . . **ED 112**

Paranoia

SHATTERED GLASS.
LP: . . . . **ASS 11**

Paranoics

BANANAS!.
LP: . . . . **BIAS 143**

SOMETIMES TEENAGE IS SPELT TNT.
Tracks: / Song for Debbie H / Frantic romantic / I gotta go / Summer's here / Lovely days are gone / Be my baby.
LP: . . . . **BIAS 91**

WE'RE THE TEENAGE LOVERS.
Tracks: / We're the teenage lovers.
LP: . . . . **LD 8710**

Paranoid Visions

GET OFF THE MAP.
LP: . . . . **FOAD 1000**

SCHIZOPHRENIA.
Tracks: / Other half lives, The / Outside in / New townism / Chicken song, The / Ignore it / Death to the poor / Rhythm of injustice / Visions.
LP: . . . . **FOAD 2**

Parasite

PARASITE.
LP: . . . . **SWORDLP 003**

Parc & Dare Band

PARC AND DARE BAND.
Tracks: / March of the peers / Cornet roundabout / Black magic woman / I wish you love / Suite for brass / Hob y derri dando / McArthur march / Tuba tabestry / Horseman riding by / Concertino for tenor horn and band / Chorale and rock out.
LP: . . . . **SB 336**

Parcel O'Rogues

PARCEL O'ROGUES.
MC: . . . . **CTP 033**

Parchment

REHEARSAL FOR A REUNION.
LP: . . . . **PC 105**

Pardesi Music Machine

NASHAY DIYE BAND BOTLAY.
LP: . . . . **SSRLP 5067**
MC: . . . . **SC 5067**

PUMP UP THE BHANGRA.
LP: . . . . **SSRLP 5077**
MC: . . . . **SC 5077**

SHAKE YOUR PANTS.
LP: . . . . **SSRLP 5097**

Pardon, Walter

BRIGHT GOLDEN STORE.
LP: . . . . **LP 301**

COUNTRY LIFE, A.
Tracks: / Raggle taggle gypsies / Peggy Bawn / Bold Princess Royal, The / One cold morning in December / Devil and the farmer's wife, The / Old man's advice, An / Uncle Walter's tune / Country life, A / Cupid the ploughboy / Dandy man, The / Jack Hall / I wish, i wish / Broomfield Hill / Hungry army, The.
LP: **12TS 392**

OUR SIDE OF THE BAULK.
Tracks: / Pretty ploughboy, The / Up to the rigs / I'll beat the drum again / Down by the dark arches / Grace Darling / Generals all / I'll hang my heart on a willow tree / Wreck of the ramillies, The / Joan's ale / Old miser, The / Balaclava.
LP: . . . . **LED 2111**

PROPER SORT, A.
LP: . . . . **LED 2063**

Pardoner's Tale (bk)

GENERAL PROLOGUE, THE / PARDONER'S TALE, THE (see under Chaucer, Geoffrey (aut)).

Parent Trap...

PARENT TRAP/ SUMMER MAGIC/ IN SEARCH ... (Film Soundtrack Excerpts) (Various artists).
Tracks: / For now, for always: *Various artists* / Let's get together: *Various artists* / Whistling at the boys: *Various artists* / Cobbler, cobbler: *Various artists* / For now, for always: *Various artists* / Parent trap: *Various artists* / Enjoy it: *Various artists* / Castaway: *Various artists* / Flitterin': *Various* artists / Beautiful Beulah: *Various artists* / Ugly bug ball: *Various artists* / On the front porch: *Various artists*.
LP: . . . . **DQ 1318**

Parenthood (film)

PARENTHOOD (Film soundtrack) (Newman, Randy).
Tracks: / I love to see you smile / Helen and Julie / Gary's in trouble / Drag race / I love to see you smile (end title) / Kevin's graduation / Kevin's party (cowboy Gil) / Father and son / Karen and Gill.
LP: . . . . **K 9260011**
MC: . . . . **K 9260014**

Parenti's Liberty...

MIDWAY DANCE ORCHESTRA AND OTHERS, THE (Parenti's Liberty Syncopators).
LP: . . . . **VLP 34**

Parenti,Tony

FINAL BAR (Parenti, Tony & His Jazz Stars).
LP: . . . . **J 71**

WNYC JAZZ FESTIVAL (See under Williams, Clarence) (Parenti,Tony, Clarence Williams & Albert Nicholas).

Parga, Mario

MAGICIAN, THE.
MC: . . . . **PTLC 1116**

Parham, Tiny

FROM THE LATE 1920'S (Parham, Tiny and His Musicians).
LP: . . . . **FL 9028**

TINY PARHAM AND MUSICIANS VOL. 1 (1928-29) (Parham, Tiny and His Musicians).
LP: . . . . **S 831**

TINY PARHAM VOL. 2.
LP: . . . . **CC 40**

TINY PARHAM VOL. 2 - 1929-1930.
Tracks: / Pig's feet slaw / Bombay / Fat man blues / Golden lilly / Steel string blues / Sud busters dream / Dixieland doings / Cathedral blues / After all I've done for you / Squeeze me.
MC: . . . . **NEO 860**

Pariah

BLAZE OF OBSCURITY.
Tracks: / Missionary of mercy / Puppet regime / Canary / Retaliate! / Hypochondriac / Enemy within.
LP: **087594**

KINDRED, THE.
LP: **087526**

TAKE AND WALK.
LP: **20002**

Paris All Stars

TRIBUTE TO CHARLIE PARKER, A.
Tracks: / Jumpin' blues, The / Moten swing / I'm just a lucky so and so / Lonely boys blues / Parker's mood / Say forward, I'll march / Tender touch / Swingin' the blues / Have you ever had the blues / Sebastian / Vine street boogie / Hootie blues.
LP: **820 833-2**

Paris France Transit

PARIS FRANCE TRANSIT.
Tracks: / Crime in your town, A / Child / Paris france / Voices of jupiter / Paintings / Souvenir from rio / Ego / Beyond your mind.
LP: . . . . **N 5015**
MC: . . . . **ZCN 5015**

Paris, Jackie

JACKIE PARIS.
LP: . . . . **AP 158**

Paris, Jeff

WIRED UP.
Tracks: / Saturday night / One night alone / Trial by fire / Crying / Wired up / Charmed life / I can't let go / Heart to the flame / Matter of time / Illusions.
LP: . . . . **VERH 45**
MC: . . . . **VERHC 45**

Paris, Mica

CONTRIBUTION.
LP: . . . . **BRLP 558**
LP: **846 814 1**
MC: . . . . **BRCA 558**
MC: **846 814 4**

SO GOOD.
Tracks: / Where is the love / My one temptation / Like dreamers do / Breathe life into me.
MC: . . . . **BRCA 525**
LP: . . . . **BRLP 525**

Paris Reunion Band

FOR KLOOK.
Tracks: / Work song / For Klook / Man from Potter's Crossing / Jamaican hot nights / Gaby / Locksley.
LP: . . . . **SNTF 977**

FRENCH COOKING.
LP: . . . . **SNTF 945**

HOT LICKS.
LP: . . . . **SNTF 1002**

Paris, Texas

PARIS, TEXAS (Film soundtrack) (Cooder, Ry).
Tracks: / Paris, Texas / Brothers / Nothing out there / Cancion mixteca / No safety zone / Houston in two seconds / She's leaving the bank / On the couch / I knew this people / Dark was the night.
LP: **925270 1**
MC: **925270 4**

Paris, Twila

IT'S THE THOUGHT.
MC: . . . . **SS C 8128**

SAME GIRL.
Tracks: / Prince of Peace / Running to the rescue / Let no man take your crown / Send me / Same girl / I feel it / Bonded together / Holy is the Lord / Praise and worship medley.
LP: . . . . **SSR 8078**
MC: . . . . **SSC 8078**

Paris Washboard

WHEN WE'RE SMILING.
LP: . . . . **SOS 1182**

Parisienne Walkways

PARISIENNE WALKWAYS (see under swing collection) (Various artists).

Park, Dean

CELTIC FAVOURITES.
Tracks: / Celtic song / Holy ground / Three leaves of emerald green / Danny boy / John Thomson / Sailing / We shall not be moved / You'll never walk alone / Wild rover / Celtic celtic / Boys from the County Armagh / Over and over.
LP: . . . . **KMLP 307**

Park, John

IF WINTER COMES.
LP: .... JAZZ MARK 105

Park Mains School

SOUNDS OF PARK MAINS HIGH, THE (Various artists).
LP: .... KMLP 302

Park, Simon

DANGER UXB (See under Danger UXB) (Park, Simon Orchestra).

MUSIC OF THE STARS - PISCES.
LP: .... BIRTHLP 5
MC: .... BIRTHMC 5

Parker, Allan

WAVES ACROSS THE SAND.
LP: .... ISST 148

Parker, Billie Jean

TRUTH ABOUT BONNIE AND CLYDE, THE.
LP: .... NL 89460
MC: .... NK 89460

Parker, Cecil

CHIRPIN.
Tracks: / Get on up / Love is / I think it's time / You were there / I've been missin' your lovin' / What it is / Your love keeps me going / You put some fun in my life.
LP: .... EMC 3353

Parker, Charlie

1949 CONCERT AND ALL STARS 1950-51.
MC: .... UMK 99009

1947-1948.
Tracks: / Koko / Hot house / I surrender, dear / Fine and dandy / Sunny side of the street / How deep is the ocean? / Tiger rag / 52nd Street theme / Lullaby in rhythm / Yardbird suite / Dee Dee's dance / Donna Lee / Everything I have is yours / Fats flats / Tea for two / Don't blame me / Groovin' high / Ornithology / Cheryl / Bird of paradise.
2LP: .... ALB 376

ALIVE AND KICKIN' VOL 1.
LP: 500204

ALIVE AND KICKIN' VOL 2.
LP: 500205

ALTERNATIVE MASTERS (Vol. 1 and 2).
LPS: .... DIAL 904/905

ANTHOLOGY - CHARLIE PARKER.
LPS: .... AM 008/9/10

ANTHROPOLOGY.
Tracks: / Donna Lee / Everything I have is yours / Fats flats / Tea for two / Don't blame me / Groovin' high / Koko / Anthropology / Now's the time / Lady be good / Just you, just me.
LP: .... SPJ 108

APARTMENT SESSIONS.
Tracks: / Little Willie leaps / All the things you are / Bernie's tune / Donna Lee / Out of nowhere / Half Nelson / Fine and dandy / Cherokee / Scrapple from the apple / Star eyes.
LP: .... SPJ 146

APEX OF BE BOP VOL 2.
LP: .... LPJT 41

AT THE PERSHING BALLROOM.
Tracks: / Indiana / I can't get started / Anthropology / Out of nowhere / Get happy / Hot house / Embraceable you / Body and soul / Cool blues / Stardust / All the things you are / Billie's bounce / Pennies from Heaven.
LP: .... ZM 1003

BALLADS AND BIRDLAND.
Tracks: / Ornithology / 52nd Street theme / How high the moon / Bewitched / Summertime / I cover the waterfront / Gone with the wind / Easy to love / Just friends / April in Paris.
LP: .... ZZ 1002

BAND THAT NEVER WAS, THE (Parker, Charlie & The Gene Roland Orchestra).
Tracks: / It's a wonderful world / Just you, just me / Stardust / 52nd Street theme / Dizzy atmosphere / My old flame (excerpt) / All the things you are / Half nelson / Big Foot.
LP: .... SPJ 141

BIRD AND PRES CARNEGIE HALL 1949 (Parker, Charlie & Lester Young).
LP: .... LP VRV 5

BIRD AT THE ROOST.
LP: .... SJL 1108

BIRD (FILM) (Film soundtrack).
Tracks: / Lester leaps in / I can't believe that you're in love with me / Laura / All of me / This time the dream's on me / Koko / Cool blues / April in Paris / Now's the time / Ornithology / Parker's mood.
LP: 4610021
MC: 4610024

BIRD FLIES DEEP (Live performance).
Tracks: / Groovin' high / Move / Ornithology / Out of nowhere / Hot house / How high the moon / Bebop / Scrapple from the apple / Street beat / Round midnight / Koko.
LP: .... ATS 12
MC: .... TCATS 12

BIRD IN PARIS.
Tracks: / Scrapple from the apple / Out of nowhere / Barbados / 52nd Street theme / Salt peanuts / Allen's alley / Untitled blues / Ladybird.
LP: .... SPJ 118

BIRD IS FREE.
Tracks: / Rocker / Sly mongoose / Moose the mooche / Star eyes / This time the dream's on me / Cool blues / My little suede shoes / Lester leaps in / Laura.
LP: .... RHAP 7

BIRD MEETS BIRKS, VOL.2.
LP: .... ZZ 1003

BIRD ON TENOR 1943.
Tracks: / Sweet Georgia Brown / Three guesses / Boogie woogie / Embraceable you / Indiana / Sweet Georgia Brown (2) / Lover come back to me / Billie's bounce / Caravan / Drifting on a reed / Ornithology / Barbados / Cool blues.
LP: .... ST 260

BIRD ON VERVE, VOL 1.
Tracks: / Repetition / No noise / Mango mangue / Okie doke / Bird, The / Cardboard / Visa / Segment / Passport No. 1 / Passport No. 2 / Diverse / Just friends / Everything happens to me / April in Paris / Summertime / I didn't know what time it was / If I should lose you.
LP: 817 442-1

BIRD ON VERVE, VOL 2.
Tracks: / Star eyes / Blues / I'm in the mood for love / Mohawk / Melancholy baby / Leap frog.
LP: 817 443-1

BIRD ON VERVE, VOL 3.
Tracks: / Relaxin' with Lee / Dancing in the dark / Out of nowhere / Laura / East of the sun / They can't take that away from me / Easy to love / I'm in the mood for love / I'll remember April.
LP: 817 444-1

BIRD ON VERVE, VOL 4.
Tracks: / Repetition / What is this thing called love? / April in Paris / Easy to love / I'll remember April / Celebrity / Ballade / Cancion mambo 1 / Cancion mambo 2 / 6/8 jazz / Rhumba Abierta.
LP: 817 445-1

BIRD ON VERVE, VOL 5.
Tracks: / Au privave / She rote / K.C. blues / Star eyes / My little suede shoes / Un poquito de tu amor / Tico tico / Fiesta / Who do I love you? (three takes).
LP: 817 446-1

BIRD ON VERVE, VOL 6.
Tracks: / Blues for Alice / Si si / Swedish schnapps / Back home blues / Lover man / Temptation / Lover / Autumn in New York / Stella by starlight / Mama Inez / La cucaracha / Estrellita / Begin the beguine / La paloma.
LP: 817 447-1

BIRD ON VERVE, VOL 7.
Tracks: / Night and day / Almost like being in love / I can't get started / What is this thing called love? / Song is you, The / Laird baird / Cosmic rays (Two takes) / In the still of the night / Old folks / If I love again / Chi chi (Three takes).
LP: 817 448-1

BIRD ON VERVE, VOL 8.
Tracks: / I remember you / Now's the time / Confirmation / I get a kick out of you / Just one of those things / My heart belongs to daddy / I've got you under my skin / Love for sale (two takes) / I love Paris (two takes).
LP: 817 449-1

BIRD SONG.
LP: .... SJAZZ 5
MC: .... SJAZZC 5

BIRD SYMBOLS.
Tracks: / Moose the mooche / Yardbird suite / Ornithology / Night in Tunisia / Bird's nest / Cool blues / Bird of paradise / Embraceable you / My old flame / Scrapple from the apple / Out of nowhere / Don't blame me.
LP: .... RHAP 5

BIRD, THE.
LP: 20100
MC: 40100

BIRD, THE SAVOY RECORDINGS (Master Takes).
LP: .... SJL 2201

BIRD (VERVE).
LP: 837 176-1
MC: 837 176-4

BIRD WITH STRINGS.
Tracks: / Easy to love / Jumping with Symphony Sid / Just friends / Everything happens to me / East of the sun / Laura / Dancing in the dark / What is this thing called love / Laura / They can't take that away from me.
LP: .... CBS 82292

BIRD YOU NEVER HEARD, THE.
LP: .... ST 280

BIRDS AND FATS (Parker, Charlie Quintet).
LP: .... BLJ 8029

BIRDS AND FATS - VOL.2 (Parker, Charlie & Fats Navarro Quintet).
LP: .... BLJ 8030

BIRDS EYES, VOL. 1.
LP: 214W 5

BIRD'S EYES, VOL. 2 (Pershing Hotel 1949).
LP: 214W 12

BIRD'S EYES VOL 4.
LP: 214W 18

BIRD'S EYES VOL 5.
LP: 214W 19

BIRD'S EYES VOL 6.
LP: 214W29

BIRTH OF BE BOP 1944-47.
LP: .... LPJT 31

BOSS BIRD.
Tracks: / Swingmatism / Jumpin' blues, The / Red cross / Groovin' high / Now's the time / Koko / Slim's jam / Lady be good / Moose the mooche / Yardbird suite / Ornithology / Night in Tunisia / Cool blues / Relaxin' at Camarilla / Hymn, The / Bird of paradise / Klactoveesedstein / Out of nowhere / Bluebird / Bird gets the worm / Barbados / Parker's mood / Bird, The / Segment / Just friends / Relaxin' with Lee / She wrote / Star eyes / My little suede shoes / Laird baird / Cosmic rays / I remember you.
LP: .... OFF 3011-2
MC: .... OFF 43011-2

CHARLIE PARKER.
Tracks: / Bloomido / My little suede shoes / Lover man / In the still of the night / Au privave / Repetition / Blues for Alice / Just friends.
MC: 833 288-4
MC: .... ZCGAS 751

CHARLIE PARKER (1949-53).
LP: .... QUEEN 002

CHARLIE PARKER: 1949-52.
LP: .... LPJT 71

CHARLIE PARKER AND DIZZY GILLESPIE (Parker, Charlie & Dizzy Gillespie).
Tracks: / Night in Tunisia / Confirmation / Groovin' high / Champ, The / They can't take that away from me / Good bait / I've got the bluest blues / Birks works.
LP: .... JR 101
LP: 2M 056 64847
MC: 2M 256 64847
MC: .... JRC 101

CHARLIE PARKER AND MILES DAVIS (Parker, Charlie & Miles Davis).
LP: .... SJAZZ 7
MC: .... SJAZC 7

CHARLIE PARKER AT STORYVILLE.
Tracks: / Moose the mooche / I'll walk alone / Ornithology / Out of nowhere / Now's the time / Don't blame me / Dancing on the ceiling / Cool blues / Groovin' high.
LP: .... BT 85108

CHARLIE PARKER COLLECTION (20 golden greats).
Tracks: / Night in Tunisia / Ornithology / Moose the mooche / Bebop / Cool blues / Lover man / Gypsy, The / White Christmas / Bird of paradise / Bongo bop / Stupendous / Relaxin' at Camarillo / Out of nowhere / My old flame / Yardbird suite / Klactoveesedstein / Drifting on a reed / Scrapple from the apple / Bird feathers / Embraceable you.
LP: .... DVLP 2017
MC: .... DVMC 2017

CHARLIE PARKER IN SWEDEN.
Tracks: / Anthropology / Cheers / Lover man / Cool blues / Scrapple from the apple / Embraceable you / Star eyes / All the things you are / Strike up the band / How high the moon / Body and soul / Fine and dandy.
2LP: .... SPJ 124/5

CHARLIE PARKER (JOKER).
LP: .... SM 3288
MC: .... MC 3288

CHARLIE PARKER - LIVE AT BIRDLAND.
LP: 500 905

CHARLIE PARKER, MILES DAVIS AND DIZZY GILLESPIE, VOL 2 (Parker, Charlie/Miles Davis/Dizzy Gillespie).
Tracks: / Bird feathers / Dewey square / Quasimodo / Crazeology / Bongo bop / Swing low sweet cadillac / My man / Klactoveesedstein / Dizzy atmosphere / Air conditioning.
LP: .... JR 124

CHARLIE PARKER (PRESTIGE).
Tracks: / 52nd Street theme / Shaw 'nuff / Out of nowhere / Hot house / This time the dream's on me / Night in Tunisia, A / My old flame' / Way you look tonight, The / Chasin' the bird / Dizzy atmosphere / How high the moon / I didn't know what time it was / Ornithology / Embraceable you / Visa / I cover the waterfront / Scrapple from the apple / Star eyes / Theme / Confirmation / Smoke gets in your eyes / Now is the time.
2LP: .... PR 24009

CHARLIE PARKER, VOL 1.
Tracks: / Moose the mooche / Yardbird suite / Ornithology / Night in Tunisia / Bird's nest / Blowtop blues / I didn't know what time it was / Embraceable you / Bird of paradise / My old flame / Scrapple from the apple / Out of nowhere / Don't blame me / April in Paris.
LP: .... JR 116
LP: .... SM 3866

CHARLIE PARKER, VOL 2.
Tracks: / Rocker / Sly mongoose / Moose the mooche / Star eyes / Just friends / Summertime / This time the dream's on me / Cool blues / My little suede shoes / Lester leaps in / Laura.
LP: .... JR 139

CHARLIE PARKER WITH THE ORCHESTRA.
Tracks: / Fine and dandy / These foolish things / Light green / Thou swell / Willis / Don't blame me / Something to remember you by / Blue room / Round house.
LP: .... K 52359

CHOICE BIRD.
LP: .... JAZ 2008
MC: .... ZCJAZ 2008

COLE PORTER SONGBOOK.
Tracks: / Easy to love / Begin the beguine / Night and day / What is this thing called love? / In the still of the night / I get a kick out of you / Just one of those things / My heart belongs to daddy / I've got you under my skin / Love for sale / I love Paris.
LP: .... VRV 10
LP: 8232501
MC: 8232504

COMPLETE ROYAL ROOST PERFORMANCES, VOL. 2 (Bird at the roost).
Tracks: / How high the moon / Scrapple from the apple - 1 / Be-bop - 1 / Hot house / Oop bop sh'bam / Scrapple from the apple -2 / Scrapple from the apple - 3 / Scrapple from the apple - 4 / Salt peanuts - 1 / Salt peanuts - 2 / Salt peanuts - 3 / Groovin' high - (1) / Groovin' high - (2) / Barbados - 1 / Barbados - 2 / Confirmation / Be-bop - 2.
MCSET: .... WK 70825
LP: .... WL 70825

COMPLETE ROYAL ROOST PERFORMANCES, VOL. 3 (The Savoy Years).
Tracks: / Deedle - 1 / Deedle - 2 / Cheryl- 1 / Half Nelson / Night in Tunisia / Scrapple from the apple / What's this? / Anthropology / Hurry home / Royal roost bop (all the things you are) / Cheryl - 2 / Slow boat to China / Chasin' the bird.
LP: .... WL 70831
MC: .... WK 70831

COMPLETE ROYAL ROOST PERFORMANCES, VOL. 1.
Tracks: / Fifty second street theme / Koko / Groovin' high / Big boot / Ornithology / Slow boat to China / Hot house / Salt peanuts / Chasin' the bird / Out of nowhere / How high the moon / Half Nelson / White Christmas / Little Willie leaps / Be bop / East of the sun / Cheryl.
LP: .... WL 70541
MC: .... WK 70541

COMPLETE SAVOY SESSIONS.
LP: .... SJL 5500

COMPLETE SAVOY SESSIONS 1.
Tracks: / Tiny's tempo / I'll always love you just the same / Romance without finance / Red cross / Billie's bounce / Warming up a riff.
LP: .... WL 70520
MC: .... WK 70520

COMPLETE SAVOY SESSIONS 2.
Tracks: / Billie's bounce / Now's the time / Thriving / Meandering / Koko / Flat

foot floogie / Dizzy's boogie / Poppity pop / Slim's jam.
LP: WL 70527
MC: WK 70527

COMPLETE SAVOY SESSIONS 3.
Tracks: / Donna Lee / Chasin' the bird / Cheryl / Buzzy / Milestones / Little Willie leaps.
LP: WL 70548
MC: WK 70548

COMPLETE SAVOY SESSIONS 4.
Tracks: / Half Nelson / Sippin' at bells / Another hair-do / Bluebird / Klaunstance / Bird gets the worm / Barbados / Ah leu cha / Constellation.
LP: WL 70813
MC: WK 70813

COMPLETE SAVOY SESSIONS 5 (1948).
Tracks: / Parker's mood (Takes 3 & 4) / Parker's mood (Take 5) / Perhaps (take 1) / Perhaps (takes 2 & 3) / Perhaps (takes 4, 5, & 6) / Perhaps (take 7) / Marmaduke (Takes 1, 2, & 3) / Marmaduke (Takes 4 & 5) / Marmaduke (Takes 6, 7, 8 & 9) / Marmaduke (Takes 10, 11, & 12) / Steeplechase (Takes 1 & 2) / Merry go round (Take 1) / Merry go round (Take 2) / Parker's mood (Takes 1 & 2).
LP: WL 70832
MC: WK 70832

CONCERT - MASSEY HALL, TORONTO (See Gillespie, Dizzy) (Parker, Charlie & Dizzy Gillespie).

COOL BLUES.
LP: BLJ 8014

DIAL MASTERS 1.
LPS: SPJBOX 6

DIAL MASTERS, VOL 1.
Tracks: / Diggin' for Diz / Moose the mooche (three takes) / Yardbird suite (two takes) / Ornithology (three takes) / Famous alto break, The / Night in Tunisia (two takes) / Max making wax / Lover man / Gypsy, The / Bebop.
LP: SPJ 101

DIAL MASTERS, VOL 2.
Tracks: / This is always (two takes) / Bird's nest (three takes) / Cool blues (Four takes).
LP: SPJ 102

DIAL MASTERS, VOL 3.
Tracks: / Relaxin' at Camarillo / Cheers / Carvin' the bird / Home cooking (three takes).
LP: SPJ 103

DIAL MASTERS, VOL 4.
Tracks: / Dexterity (two takes) / Bongo bop / Deway Square (three takes) / Hymn (two takes) / Bird of paradise (Three takes) / Embraceable you (two takes).
LP: SPJ 104

DIAL MASTERS, VOL 5.
Tracks: / Bird feathers / Klactoveesedstein (two takes) / Scrapple from the apple / My old flame / Out of nowhere (three tapes) / Don't blame me / Moose the mooche / Dark shadows / Hallelujah.
LP: SPJ 105

DIAL MASTERS, VOL 6.
Tracks: / Drifting on a reed (three takes) / Quasimodo (two takes) / Charlie's wig (three takes) / Bongo beep / Crazeology (two excerpts) / How deep is the ocean? (two takes).
LP: SPJ 106

DIAL MATERIAL VOL 1.
LP: LPUP 5156

DIAL MATERIAL VOL 2.
LP: LPUP 5157

DIAL MATERIAL VOL 3.
LP: LPUP 5158

DIZZY GILLESPIE AND CHARLIE PARKER (see Gillespie, Dizzy) (Parker, Charlie & Dizzy Gillespie).

DIZZY GILLESPIE/SARAH VAUGHAN/CHARLIE PARKER (See under Gillespie, Dizzy) (Parker, Charlie / Dizzy Gillespie / Sarah Vaughan).

ENCORES.
LP: SJL 1107

ENCORES VOL 2.
LP: SJL 1129

EVERY BIT OF IT.
Tracks: / Seven-eleven / Do nothing till you hear from me / Don't blame me / Perdido / Nightcap / Saturday night / Floogie boo / St. Louis blues / What's the matter now? / I want every bit of it / That's the blues / G.I. blues / 4F blues / Dream of you / Seventh Avenue / Sorta kinda / Oh, oh, my, my / What more can a woman do? / I'd rather have a memory than a dream / Mean to me / Taking off / If I had you / 20th century blues / Street beat / Dizzy boogie (two takes) / Flat foot floogie / Poppity pop / Slim's jam.
2LP: SPJ 150D

FABULOUS BIRD BLOWS, THE (Modern Jazz Collectors series).
LPS: DIAL LP 901
LPS: SPJBOX 3

FRAGMENTS.
LP: CP 508

GREATEST DIAL CUTS.
LP: JU6-7333

GREATEST HITS: CHARLIE PARKER.
LP: MA 25983
MC: MAMC 925983

HALLELUJAH (Parker, Charlie & Dizzy Gillespie).
Tracks: / Hallelujah.
LP: KLJ 20007

HAPPY BIRD, THE.
Tracks: / Happy bird blues / I'll remember April / Scrapple from the apple / I may be wrong.
LP: RHAP 6

HEAVENLY HORNS.
Tracks: / Ornithology / Night in Tunisia / Birds nest / Long time / Pure delight / Blue lament / It's a sin to tell a lie / Dance time.
LP: MAN 5016

IN SWEDEN 1950.
LP: SLP 1007

IT HAPPENED ONE NIGHT (Parker, Charlie / Dizzy Gillespie / Ella Fitzgrald).
LP: NAT:ORG:7000

JAZZ TIME VOL.4.
LP: 502704

LIVE AT BIRDLAND.
LP: VG 500905

LIVE AT THE CAFE SOCIETY.
LP: CP 509

LIVE AT THE ROCKLAND PALACE.
LP: CP 502
MC: ZCCP 502

LULLABY IN RHYTHM.
Tracks: / Koko / I surrender, dear / Fine and dandy / Sunny side of the street / How deep is the ocean? / Tiger rag / 52nd Street theme / Lullaby in rhythm / Yardbird suite / Dee Dee's dance.
LP: SPJ 107

MAGNIFICENT BIRD.
Tracks: / I can't get started / Lover man / They can't take that away from me / Laird baird / Old folks / I'm in the mood for love / April in Paris / I get a kick out of you / Au privave / An oscar for treadwell / Ballade / Cosmic rays.
LP: MTM 013

MEMORIAL 1920-1955.
LP: 500 753

MILES DAVIS, DIZZY GILLESPIE AND CHARLIE PARKER (see Davis, Miles) (Parker, Charlie /Dizzy Gillespie/Miles Davis).

MILES OF JAZZ (see Davis,Miles/ Charlie Parker) (Parker, Charlie & Miles Davis).

MONK AND BIRD (See under Monk, Thelonious) (Parker, Charlie & The Gene Roland Orchestra).

MOVE (Parker, Charlie/Fats Navarro/ Bud Powell).
LP: KLJ 20010

NEW BIRD.
LP: LP 10

NEW BIRD, VOL 2.
LP: LP 12

NOW'S THE TIME.
Tracks: / Song is you, The / Laird baird / Kim / Cosmic rays / Chi chi / I remember you / Now's the time / Confirmation.
LP: 2304 095

ONCE THERE WAS BIRD.
Tracks: / Hallelujah / Get happy / Slam slam blues / Congo blues.
LP: RHAP 4

ONE NIGHT IN CHICAGO.
LP: SJL 1132

ORIGINAL BIRD.
MC: ZK 71854

ORNITHOLOGY.
LP: JJ 610

PARKER STREET.
Tracks: / Bird of paradise / Embraceable you / Bird song / Cool bird / Inside out / Soul time / Blue diamond / Soul interlude.
LP: MAN 5026

QUARTET, QUINTET AND SEXTET.
LP: LPJT 60

QUINTET OF THE YEAR, THE (see Gillespie, Dizzy/Parker/Powell/Mingus & Roach) (Parker, Charlie/Powell/ Mingus/Roach & Gillespie).

SESSIONS LIVE, VOL.1.
LP: ZET 703

SESSIONS LIVE, VOL.2.
LP: ZET 712

SIMPLY CHARLIE.
Tracks: / Moose the mooch / Yardbird suite / My old flame / Charlie's theme / Train stop / Big foot / Blue soul / Delight.
LP: MAN 5017

TROIS GEANTS DU JAZZ (Parker, Charlie/Miles Davis/Dizzy Gillespie).
2LP: 400008

YARDBIRD.
LP: VGM 0009

YARDBIRD IN LOTUS LAND.
Tracks: / Shaw 'nuff / Groovin' high / Dizzy atmosphere / Salt peanuts / Tea for two / Body and soul / Cherokee / Ornithology / Anthropology / Billie's bounce / Blue 'n' boogie / All the things you are.
LP: SPJ 123

Parker, Dennis

LIKE AN EAGLE.
Tracks: / High life / I need your love / I'm a dancer / Why don't you boogie time / Like an eagle / New York by night.
LP: 9109622

Parker, Dorothy

DOROTHY PARKER STORIES (Booth, Shirley).
MC: 1136

Parker, E

SONG FOR SOMEONE (see under Oxley, Tony) (Parker, E/Oxley, Tony).

Parker, Evan

AT THE UNITY THEATRE (Parker, Evan & Paul Lytton).
LP: INCUS 14

COLLECTIVE CALLS (URBAN) (Parker, Evan & Paul Lytton).
LP: INCUS 5

FROM SAXOPHONE AND TROMBONE (See under Lewis, George) (Parker, Evan & George Lewis).

LONDON CONCERT (see under Derek Bailey) (Parker, Evan & Derek Bailey).

LONGEST NIGHT, VOL 1 (see Stevens, John) (Parker, Evan & John Stevens).

LONGEST NIGHT, VOL 2 (see Stevens, John) (Parker, Evan & John Stevens).

RA 1 + 2 (See under Lyttleton, Paul) (Parker, Evan & Paul Lytton).

SAXOPHONE SOLOS.
LP: INCUS 19

SECOND EVAN PARKER SOLO A1.
LP: INCUS 27

TOPOGRAPHY OF THE LUNGS (Parker, Evan & Derek Bailey).
LP: INCUS 1

Parker, Graham

ALONE IN AMERICA (LIVE).
Tracks: / White honey / Black honey / Soul corruption / Gypsy blood / Back in time / Change is gonna come, A / Watch the moon come down / Protection / Back to schooldays / Durban poison / You cant' be too strong / Don't let it break you down.
LP: FIEND 141
MC: FIENDCASS 141

ANOTHER GREY AREA.
Tracks: / Temporary beauty / Another grey area / No more excuses / Dark side of the bright lights / Can't waste a minute / Big fat zero / You hit the spot / Its all worth nothing alone / Crying for attention / Thankless task / Fear not / Beating and screaming - part II / Magnum force / Sex and glory / Angel face.
LP: RCALP 6029
LP: PIPLP 026
MC: PIPMC 026

BEST OF GRAHAM PARKER AND THE RUMOUR, THE (Parker, Graham & the Rumour).
Tracks: / Soul shoes / Heat treatment / Howling wind / Hold back the night / Back to schooldays / You can't be too strong / Kansas city / Stick to me / New York shuffle / Local girls / White honey / Hotel chambermaid / Between you and me / Hey Lord / Don't ask me questions.
LP: VERB 001
MC: VERBC 001
LP: 9102042

HEAT TREATMENT.
Tracks: / Heat treatment / Turned up too late / Hotel chambermaid / Back door love / Help me shake it / That's what they all say / Black honey / Pourin' it all out / Something you're goin' thru / Fools' gold.
LP: 6360 137

HOWLIN'.
LP: BGOLP 48

HUMAN SOUL.
Tracks: / Little Miss Understanding / My love's strong / Dancing for money / Call me your doctor / Big man on paper / Soultime / Everything goes / Sugar gives you energy / Daddy's a postman / Green monkeys / I was wrong / You got the word (right where you want it) / Slash and burn.
LP: FIEND 163
MC: FIENDCASS 163

IT DON'T MEAN A THING IF IT AIN'T GOT THAT SWING (Parker, Graham & the Rumour).
Tracks: / White honey / Soul shoes / Stick to me / Fool's gold / Hey Lord don't ask me questions / I want you back / Protection / Hold back the night / New York shuffle / Between you and me / Silly thing / You can't be too strong / Mercury poisoning.
LP: PRICE 62
MC: PRIMC 62

MONA LISA'S SISTER.
Tracks: / Don't let it break you down / Under the mask of happiness / Back in time / I'm just your man / OK Heironymous / Get started, start a fire / Girl isn't ready, The / Blue highway / Success / I don't know / Cupid.
LP: FIEND 122
MC: FIENDCASS 122

PARKERILLA.
LP: 6641 797

REAL MACAW, THE.
Tracks: / You can't take love for granted / Glass jaw / Passive resistance / Sound like chains / Just like a man / Life gets better / Last couple on the dance floor / Miracle a minute, A.
LP: RCALP 6086
MC: RCAK 6086
LP: PIPLP 027
MC: PIPMC 027

SQUEEZING OUT SPARKS.
Tracks: / Discovering Japan / Don't get excited / Local girls / Love gets you twisted / Nobody hurts you / Passion is no ordinary word / Protection / Saturday nite is dead / Waiting for the UFO's / You can't be too strong.
LP: 9102 030

STEADY NERVES (Parker,Graham & The Shot).
Tracks: / Break them down / Might rivers / Lunatic fringe / Wake up (next to you) / When you do that to me / Weekend's too short / Take everything back / Black Lincoln Continental / Canned laughter / Everyone's hand is on the switch / Locked into green.
LP: EKT 4
MC: EKT 4C

STICK TO ME (Parker, Graham & the Rumour).
LP: 9102 017

STRUCK BY LIGHTNING.
LP: FIEND 201
MC: FIENDCASS 201

UP ESCALATOR, THE.
Tracks: / No holding back / Devil's sidewalk / Stupefaction / Love without greed / Julie, Julie / Endless night / Paralysed / Manoeuvres / Empty lives / Beating of another heart.
LP: SEEZ 23
MC: ZSEEZ 23
LP: FIEND 121

Parker, Johnny

BOOGIE WOOGIE.
LP: DC 33003
LP: DCS 33003

JOHNNY PARKER'S BOOGIE WOOGIE TRIO.
LP: CLUB 33003

Parker, Junior

BAREFOOT ROCK (see Bland, Bobby).

I WANNA RAMBLE (Parker, Junior & the Blue Flames).
Tracks: / I wanna ramble / Please baby blues / Dirty friend blues / Can't understand / Sittin', drinkin' and thinkin' / Driving me mad / I'm tender / Pretty baby / Sweet home Chicago / Long years / Can you tell me, baby? / Backtracking / There better be no feet / Mother-in-law blues / That's alright.
LP: CH 42

LEGENDARY SUN PERFORMERS (Parker, Junior & Billy 'Red' Love).
Tracks: / Feeling good / Mystery train / Love my baby / Fussin' and fightin' blues / Sittin' at the window / Sittin' at the bar / Sittin', drinkin' and thinkin' / Feel so bad / Gee I wish / Hearts bread boogie /

News is all around town, The / Blues leave me alone / If you want to make me happy / There's no use / Early in the morning / Dream, A.
LP: . . . . CR 30135

MEMPHIS BLUES BROTHERS (Parker, Junior & Bobby Bland).
Tracks: / Good lovin' / Drifting from town to town takes 1 & 2 / Dry up baby / Crying all night long / Love me baby / You're my angel / Bad women, bad whiskey / Whole heap of mama / I wronged to a woman / I can't forgive you / Sad and lonely / Rumpus romp / Trouble and me / I cried / Midnight hours journey.
LP: . . . . CHAD 265

Parker, Ken

GLINT OF GOLD, A.
LP: . . . . PS 5007

I SHALL NOT BE MOVED.
LP: . . . . PS 5003

JESUS ON THE MAIN LINE.
LP: . . . . PS 5006

KEY, THE.
LP: . . . . KEN 01

LOVERS PARADISE.
LP: . . . . TRLS 234

TOUCH OF INSPIRATION, A.
LP: . . . . PS 5002

Parker, Knocky

EIGHT ON EIGHTY-EIGHT - VOL.15.
LP: . . . . ESR 1215

FROM CAKEWALK TO RAGTIME.
LP: . . . . JCE 81

TEXAS JAZZ VOL. 4 (Smokey & The BearKats) (Parker, Knocky & Smokey Montgomery).
LP: . . . . CLP 10004

TEXAS SWING - AND THE BLUES (Parker, Knocky & Smokey Montgomery).
LP: . . . . CLP 10003

TEXAS SWING - BOOGIE WOOGIE (Parker, Knocky & Smokey Montgomery).
LP: . . . . CLP 10002

TEXAS SWING - THE BARRELHOUSE (Parker, Knocky & Smokey Montgomery).
LP: . . . . CLP 10001

Parker, Leo

BACK TO BACK BARITONES (Parker, Leo/Sax Gill).
Tracks: / Woody / Rolling with Parker / Leo leaps in (2) / Solitude / Rolling with Parker (2) / Leo leaps in / Leo leaps in (3) / Crisco jump / That's the groovy thing / Shortnin' bread / Off beat jump / Mel's jump / Bullfrog bounce / Dancer's delight.
LP: . . . . KK 829

LET ME TELL YOU 'BOUT IT.
Tracks: / Glad lad / Blue Leo / Let me tell you 'bout it / VI / Parker's pals / Low Brown / Low Brown (Long version) / TCTB / Lion's roar, The.
LP: . . . . BST 84087

ROLLIN' WITH LEO.
Tracks: / Lion's roar, The / Bad girl / Rollin' with Leo / Music hall beat / Jumpin' Leo / Stuffy (This track is taken from the 'Mainstream' album from the boxed set.) / Talkin' the blues / Mad lad returns / Daphne.
LP: . . . . BST 84095

Parker, Little Junior

LITTLE JUNIOR PARKER.
MC: . . . . MC 9002

Parker, Maceo

ROOTS REVISITED.
MC: 8437514
LP: 8437511

WHAT GOES AROUND COMES AROUND (see also under: Byrd, Bobby & Wesley, Fred) (Byrd, Bobby/Maceo Parker/Fred Wesley).

Parker, Ray Jnr.

AFTER DARK.
Tracks: / I don't think that man should sleep / Over you / Loving you / You shoulda kept a spare / Past, The / You make my nature a spare / Perfect lovers / After midnite / I love your daughter.
LP: . . . . WX 122
MC: . . . . WX 122 C

BEST OF RAY PARKER JNR (Parker, Ray Jnr.& Raydio).
Tracks: / Ghostbusters / You can't change that / Woman needs love (just like you do) / More than one way to love a woman / Stay the night / Let me go / Betcha can't love me just once / Jack and Jill / Other woman, The / Two places at the same time / (I still can't get over) loving you / Girls are more fun / Is this a love thing / For those who like to groove.
MC: 410.365

OTHER WOMAN, THE.
Tracks: / Other woman, The / Streetlove / Stay the night / It's our own affair / Let me go / Let's get off / Stop, look before you love / Just having fun.
LP: . . . . SPART 1190
MC: . . . . TCART 1190

SEX AND THE SINGLE MAN.
LP: 207252
MC: 407252

VERY BEST OF RAY PARKER JNR..
Tracks: / Other woman, The / You can't change that / Is this a love thing? / Woman needs love, A / Jack and Jill / Bad boy / Two places at the same time / For those who like to groove / That old song / People next door, The.
LP: 205078
MC: 405078

WOMAN NEEDS LOVE, A (Parker, Ray Jnr.& Raydio).
Tracks: / Woman needs love, A / It's your night / That old song / All in the way you get down / You can't fight what you feel / Old pro / Still in the groove / So into you.
LP: . . . . SPART 1152

WOMAN OUT OF CONTROL.
Tracks: / Woman out of control / I still can't get over loving you / Electronic lover / In the heat of the night / I don't wanna know / She still feels the need / Invasion / N2U2.
LP: 205752
MC: 405752

Parker, Robert

BAREFOOTIN' (RE-ISSUE).
Tracks: / Barefootin' / Duke of earl / Let's go baby (where the action is) / Hiccup, The (on 12" only.).
LPS: . . . . CS 9010

GET TA STEPPIN'.
Tracks: / Barefootin' / Let's go baby (where the action is) / Little bit of something, A / Sneaking Sally thru the alley / Better luck in the summertime / You see me / Give me the country side of life / Get right down / Get ta steppin / Hiccup, The / Hot and cold / Skinny dippin' / I like what you do to me / Disco doctor.
LP: . . . . CRB 1174
MC: . . . . TCCRB 1174

Parker, Rupert

ROMANTIC HARP OF, THE.
MC: . . . . KNMC 16018

Parker, Wesley

GOOD TIME TONIGHT.
Tracks: / Good time tonight / Baby it's you / Her heart got in the way / Family of man / What love can do / Love must know hard times / Love song / All the things America should be / Valley song / I only wanna be your friend.
LP: . . . . PRCV 113

I'LL TAKE YOU THERE AGAIN.
LP: . . . . GIR 506 15

Parkhouse, David

BABAR THE LITTLE ELEPHANT (see under Rippon, Angela) (Parkhouse, David/Angela Rippon/Orch. of St. John's Smith Sq.).

Parkin, Eric

CHANGING MY TUNE (23 Gershwin standards).
Tracks: / Foggy day, A / 'S wonderful / Bess you is my woman now.
LP: . . . . ACN 6002
MC: . . . . BCN 6002

MARIGOLD (Piano impressions of Billy Mayer).
Tracks: / Legends of King Arthur, The / Almond blossom / April's fool / Harp of the winds, The / Marigold / Railroad rhythm / Shallow waters / From a Spanish lattice / Song of the fir tree / Nimble fingered gentleman / Evening primrose / Ace of diamonds / Ace of hearts / Joker, The.
LP: . . . . LBRD 018
MC: . . . . LBTD 018

Parkins, Molly

PURPLE PASSES.
MC: . . . . ZCMOLI

Parkinson, C.

JEEVES - A GENTLEMAN'S PERSONAL GENTLEMAN (Various artists).
MCSET: . . . . SAY 20
MCSET: . . . . ARGO 1133

Parkinson, Michael

PARKINSON MEETS THE GOONS.
LP: . . . . REC 259

Parkinson, Robin

TWO STORIES FROM BUTTON MOON.
MC: . . . . ZCRDB 1152

Parks, Van Dyke

CLANG OF THE YANKEE REAPER.
Tracks: / Clang of the Yankee reaper / City on the hill / Pass that stage / Another dream / You're a real sweetheart / Love is the answer / Iron man / Tribute to Spree / Soul Train / Cannon in D.
LP: . . . . ED 213

DISCOVER AMERICA.
Tracks: / Jack Palance / Introduction / Bing Crosby / Steelband music / Four Mills brothers, The / Be careful / John Jones / F.D.R. in Trinidad / Sweet Trinidad / Occapella / Sailin' shoes / Riverboat / Ode to Tobago / Your own comes first / G-man hoover / Stars and stripes forever.
LP: . . . . ED 210

SONG CYCLE.
Tracks: / Vine Street / Palm desert / Widow's walk / Laurel Canyon Boulevard / All golden / Van Dyke Parks / Public domain / Donovan's colours / Attic, The / By the people / Potpourri.
LP: . . . . ED 207

TOKYO ROSE.
Tracks: / America / Tokoyo rose / Yankee go home / Cowboy / Manzanar / Calypso / White chrysanthemum / Trade war / Out of love / One home run.
LP: . . . . K 925 968 1
MC: . . . . K 925 968 4

Parlan, Horace

BLUE PARLAN (Parlen, Horace Trio).
LP: . . . . SCS 1124

HAPPY FRAME OF MIND.
Tracks: / Home is Africa / Tune for Richard, A / Back from the gig / Dexi / Kucheza blues / Happy frame of mind.
LP: . . . . BST 84134

JOE VAN ENKHUIZEN MEETS THE RHYTHM SECTION.
LP: . . . . SJP 249

MUSICALLY YOURS.
LP: . . . . SCS 1141

PANNONICA (Parlen, Horace Trio).
LP: . . . . ENJA 4076

REUNION (See under Shepp, Archie) (Parlan, Horace & Archie Shepp).

SANDRA JEAN (See under Pender, Don) (Parlan, Horace/Don Pender).

TROUBLE IN MIND (Parlan, Horace & Archie Shepp).
LP: . . . . SCS 1139

US THREE.
LP: . . . . BLP 4037

Parlet

INVASION OF THE BODY SNATCHERS.
Tracks: / Ridin' high / No rump to bump / Don't ever stop / Booty snatchers / You're leaving / Huff'n'puff.
LP: . . . . CAL 2052

Parliament

GLORYHALLASTOOPID.
LP: . . . . NBLP 7195

MOTHERSHIP CONNECTION.
LP: 824 502-1
MC: 824 502-4

MOTOR BOOTY AFFAIR.
Tracks: / Mr. Wiggles / Rumpopsteelskin / Water sign / Aqua boogie / One of those funky things / Liquid sunshine / Motor booty affair / Deep.
LP: . . . . CALH 2043

RHENIUM.
Tracks: / Breakdown, The / Call my baby pussycat / Little ole country boy / Moonshine Heather / Oh Lord, why Lord - prayer / Red hot mama / My automobile / Nothing before me but thang / Funky woman / Come in out of the rain / Silent boatman, The.
LP: . . . . HDH LP 008
MC: . . . . HDH MC 008

TROMBIPULATION.
Tracks: / Trombipulation / Crush it / Long way round / Agony of defeat / New doo review / Let's play house / Body language / Peek-a-groove.
LP: . . . . NBLP 7249

UNCUT FUNK-THE BOMB (The best of Parliament).
Tracks: / P-funk (wants to get funked) / Give up the funk / Up for the down stroke / Chocolate city / Big bang theory / Flashlight / Gloryhallastoopid (Pin the tail on the Funk) / Aqua boogie.
LP: . . . . JABB 18
MC: . . . . JABBC 18

Parnell, Jack

50 BIG BAND FAVOURITES (see under Loss, Joe) (Parnell, Jack & His Orchestra/Joe Loss & His Orchestra).

BIG BAND STEREO SPECTACULAR (Parnell, Jack & His Orchestra/Joe Loss & His Orchestra).
Tracks: / Skyliner / Peanut vendor / Swingin' shepherd blues / In a sentimental mood / I've got a gal in Kalamazoo / Sing, sing, sing / South Rampart Street parade / Opus one / Li'l darlin' / American patrol / Mood indigo / On the sunny side of the street / Satin doll / Hot toddy / Trumpet blues and cantabile / Take the 'A' train / Tuxedo Junction / Skin deep / Darktown poker club / St. Louis blues march / Blues in the night / Manhattan spiritual / Big noise from Winnetka / Caravan / Tristeza / Viramundo / Carnival / Deixa isso pra la / Brazil.
2LP: . . . . MFP 1007
MCSET: . . . . TCMFP 1007

MEMORIES.
Tracks: / Memories / Stardust / Touch of your lips, The / Shadow of your smile / I can't get started / Very thought of you, The / Serenade / I'll never smile again / Yesterdays / I had the craziest dream / Serenata / All the things you are / Remember / Way we were, The / Laura / Street of dreams.
LP: . . . . MEM 1
MC: 4MEM 1

Parr, John

JOHN PARR.
Tracks: / Magical / Naughty naughty / Love grammar / Treat me a like an animal / She's gonna love you to death / Revenge / Heartbreaker / Somebody stole my thunder / Don't leave your mark on me / St. Elmo's fire.
LP: . . . . LONLP 12
MC: . . . . LONC 12

RUNNING THE ENDLESS MILE.
Tracks: / Two hearts / Don't worry 'bout me / King of lies / Running the endless mile / Don't leave your mark on me / Scratch / Do it again / Blame it on the radio / Story still remains the same / Steal you away.
LP: . . . . LONLP 23
MC: . . . . LONC 23

Parr, Sheila

LONDON REVUE HIGHLIGHTS (Parr, Sheila & The National Philharmonic Orchestra).
Tracks: / I've got the urge / Wind in the willows / Oceans of time / Nightingale sang in Berkeley Square, A / I'm dancing with a ghost / My love for you / Transatlantic lullaby / Little cooperation from you, A / Another dream gone wrong / Your heart and mine / Lost without your love / Night may have its sadness.
LP: . . . . RSCT 112521
MC: . . . . RSCT 5223/1

Parra, Violeta

LE CHILI DE VIOLETA PARRA - UN RIO DE SANGRE (Parra, Violeta, Isabel et Angel).
Tracks: / Santiago penando estas / Segun el favor del viento / El santo padre / Hasta cuando estas / Cantos a lo divino / La carta / En los jardines humanos / Un rio de sangre / Que vamos a hacer? / Tename en tu corazon / Arauco tiene una pena.
LP: . . . . ARN 34222
MC: . . . . ARN 434222

Parrish, Mick

WELCOME BACK TO MICK PARRISH.
LP: . . . . JIN 4009

Parry, Bernie

SAILING TO THE MOON.
LP: . . . . FRR 026

Parry, Harry

PARRY OPUS (Parry, Harry & His Radio Rhythm Club Sextet).
Tracks: / I've found a new baby / Black eyes / Boog it / Softly as in a morning sunrise / Dim blues / Parry opus / It don't count / I'm young and healthy / Champagne / Honeysuckle rose / Bounce me brother with a solid four / Don't be that way / Java joint / Oceans and motions / My melancholy baby / I may be wrong / Blues for eight / Thrust and parry / Someday sweetheart / Sheik of araby.
LP: . . . . EG 2602941
MC: . . . . EG 2602944

Parsons, Alan Project

ALAN PARSONS PROJECT BOX SET, THE.
MCSET: . . . . NK 74374

ALAN PARSONS XMAS.
MCSET: 504100

AMMONIA AVENUE.

Tracks: / Prime time / Let me go home / One good reason / Since the last goodbye / Don't answer me / Dancing on a high wire / You don't believe / Pipeline / Ammonia Avenue.
LP: 206100
MC: 406100
LP: 208885
MC: 408885

BEST OF ALAN PARSONS PROJECT.
Tracks: / I wouldn't want to be like you / Eye in the sky / Games people play / Time / Pyramania / You wouldn't believe / Lucifer / Psychobabble / Damned if I do / Don't let it show / Can't take it with you / Old and wise.
LP: APP1
MC: . . . . . TCAPP 1

EVE.
Tracks: / Lucifer / You lie down with the dogs / I'd rather be a man / You won't be there / Winding me up / Damned if I do / Don't hold back / Secret garden / If I could change your mind.
LP: . . . . . FA 3071
MC: . . . . . TCFA 3071
LP: 208981
MC: 408981
LP: . . . . . SPARTY 1100

EYE IN THE SKY.
Tracks: / Syrius / Eye in the sky / Children of the moon / Gemini / Silence and I / You're gonna get your fingers burned / Psychobabble / Mammagamma / Step by step / Old and wise.
LP: 208718
MC: 408718
LP: 204666
MC: 404666

GAUDI.
Tracks: / La sagrada familia / Too late / Closer to heaven / Standing on higher ground / Money talks / Inside looking out / Paseo de gracia.
LP: 208084
MC: 408084
LP: 210 171
MC: 410 171

I ROBOT.
Tracks: / I wouldn't want to be like you / Some other time / Breakdown / Don't let it show / Voice, The / Nucleus / Day after day / Total eclipse / Genesis CH 1 V 32 / I, robot.
LP: 209651
MC: 409651
LP: . . . . . SPARTY 1012
MC: . . . . . TCARTY 1012

INSTRUMENTAL WORKS.
Tracks: / Pipeline / Where's the walrus / I, robot / Mammagamma / Hawkeye / Voyager / Paseo De Gracia / Urbania / Gold bug, The / Genesis.
LP: 209237
MC: 409237

LIMELIGHT (Best of the Alan Parsons Project, Vol 2).
Tracks: / Limelight / Same old song / Ammonia Avenue / Mammagamma / Since the last goodbye / I, robot / Prime time / Hawkeye / Return of a friendly card / Silence and I.
LP: 208634
MC: 408634

PYRAMID.
Tracks: / Voyager / What goes up... / Eagle will rise again, The / One more river / Can't take it with you / In the lap of the gods / Pyramania / Hyper-gamma-spaces / Shadow of a lonely man.
LP: 208983
MC: 408983
LP: . . . . . SPART 1054
MC: . . . . . TCART 1054

STEREOTOMY.
Tracks: / Stereotomy / Beaujolais / Urbania / Limelight / In the real world / Where's the walrus? / Light of the world / Chinese whispers / Stereotomy two.
LP: 207463
MC: 407463
MC: 409050
LP: 209050

TALES OF MYSTERY.
Tracks: / Dream within a dream, A / Raven, The / Tell-tale heart, The / Cask of Amontillado, The / Doctor Tarr and Professor Fether / Fall of the House of Usher, The / To one in Paradise.
LP: . . . . . LONLP 48
MC: . . . . . LONC 48

TALES OF MYSTERY AND IMAGINATION (EDGAR ALLEN POE).
Tracks: / Dream within a dream / Raven / Tell-tale heart / Cask of Amontillado / System of Dr Tarr and Professor Fether / Fall of the House of Usher, The / To one in paradise.
LP: . . . . . CDS 4003
MC: . . . . . CDSMC 4003

TURN OF A FRIENDLY CARD.
Tracks: / Turn of a friendly card / Gold bug, The / Time / Games people play / I don't wanna go home / Nothing left to lose / May be a price to pay.
LP: 208982
MC: 408982
MC: . . . . . TCART 1
LP: . . . . . DLART 1

VULTURE CULTURE.
Tracks: / Let's talk about me / Separate lives / Days are numbers (The traveller) / Sooner or later / Vulture culture / Hawkeye / Somebody out there / Same old song.
LP: 206577
MC: 406577
LP: 208884
MC: 408884

Parsons, David

HIMALAYA.
MC: . . . . . MCFOR 17059-4

Parsons, Gene

GENE PARSONS.
LP: . . . . . SRS 8703

Parsons, Gram

EARLY YEARS 1963-65, THE.
LP: . . . . . SRS 8702

EARLY YEARS THE.
Tracks: / I may be right / Big country / Zah's blues / Mary don't you weep / Bells of Rhymney / Goin' away / Don't you want to go / They shall go down / On my journey home / Surfin' Anny / Oh didn't they crucify my Lord.
LP: . . . . . SDLP 1010
MC: . . . . . SDC 1010

G.P.
Tracks: / Still feeling blue / We'll sweep out the ashes in the morning / Song for you, A / Streets of Baltimore / That's all it took / New soft shoes, The / Kiss the children / Cry one more time / How much I've lied / Big mouth blues / She.
LP: . . . . . K 44228

GRAM PARSONS.
Tracks: / We'll sweep out the ashes in the morning / Hearts on fire / Kiss the children / That's all it took / Love hurts / In my hour of darkness / Return of the grievous angel / Still feeling blue / $1000 wedding / Las Vegas / New soft shoes / How much I've lied / Cash on the barrelhead / Hickory wind.
LP: . . . . . SHILOH 4088
LP: . . . . . K 57008
MC: K4 57008

GRIEVOUS ANGEL.
Tracks: / Love hurts / Las Vegas / In my hour of darkness / Return of the grievous angel / Hearts on fire / I can't dance / Brass buttons / 1, 000 dollar wedding.
LP: . . . . . K 54018

LIVE: GRAM PARSONS (Parsons, Gram/Emmylou Harris).
Tracks: / We'll sweep out the ashes in the morning / Big mouth blues / New soft shoe / Streets of Baltimore / Cry one more time / California cottonfields / Love hurts / Country baptizing / Drug store truck driving man / That's all it took / Six days on the road.
LP: . . . . . SDLP 003
MC: . . . . . SDC 003
LP: 625 106
LP: . . . . . GP 1973

LUXURY LINER.
LP: . . . . . SHILOH 4086

MELODIES.
Tracks: / My kingdom for a car / Melodies from a bird in flight / Mama papa / Won't last long / Hot burrito no.1 / No fire here tonight / Pastime / Little jewels / Why you been gone so long.
LP: . . . . . SDLP 008
MC: . . . . . SDC 008

SAFE AT HOME (Parsons, Gram International Submarine Band).
Tracks: / Blue eyes / I must have been somebody else / You've known a satisfied mind / Folsom Prison blues / That's all right / Millers cave / I still miss someone / Luxury liner / Strong boy / Do you know how it feels to be lonesome?.
LP: . . . . . STATLP 26
MC: . . . . . SDC 071

SNEAKY PETE KLENIOW.
LP: . . . . . SHILOH 4087

Parson's Pleasure

PARSON'S PLEASURE (See under Hardwick, Mollie) (Hardwick, Mollie).

Parsons, Stephen

PASSION.
LP: . . . . . TET 6
MC: . . . . . CTET 6

Parsons, Steve

DREAMS OF GOLD.
Tracks: / Dreams of gold, (Part 1) / Astral wild life / Dreams of gold, (Part 2) / Beneath the earth / Sticky threads / Helios, (Parts 1 & 2).
LP: . . . . . KNEWL 05
MC: . . . . . KNEWMC 05

Part

MISERERE.
LP: . . . . . ECMI 430
MC: 8475394

Part 1

PICTURES OF PAIN.
LP: 0012-04

Part, Arvo

ARBOS.
Tracks: / Arbos / An den wassern zu babel / Pari Intervallo / De Profundis / Es sang vor langen Jahren / Summa / Stabat Mater.
LP: . . . . . ECM 1325
MC: 8319594

PASSIO (Part, Arvo & The Hilliard Ensemble).
LP: . . . . . ECM 1370
MC: 8371094

Partisans

PARTISANS THE.
LP: . . . . . PUNK 4

TIME WAS RIGHT THE.
LP: . . . . . PART LP 1

Partners In Crime

ORGANISED CRIME.
Tracks: / Hollywood dreams / Miracles / Fools / Hold on / Gypsy tricks / Heat of the night / No way out of here / I can't forget / What does it take / She's got eyes.
LP: . . . . . EPC 26356

Partners In Kryme

TURTLE RHAPSODY (see under Orchestra On The Half Shell) (Orchestra On The Half Shell/Partners In Kryme).

Parton, Dolly

9 TO 5 AND ODD JOBS.
Tracks: / 9 to 5 / Hush-a-bye hard times / House of the rising sun / Deportees (Plane wreck at Los Gatos) / Sing for the common man / Working girl / Detroit City / But you know I love you / Dark as a dungeon / Poor folks town.
LP: . . . . . RCALP 3047
MC: . . . . . RCAK 3047
LP: . . . . . PL 13852

ALL I CAN DO.
Tracks: / All I can do / Fire that keeps you warm / When the sun goes down tomorrow / I'm a drifter / Falling out of love with me / Shattered image / Boulder to Birmingham / Preacher Tom / Life's like poetry / Hey, lucky lady.
LP: . . . . . RS 1068
MC: . . . . . PK 11737

ANTHOLOGY - DOLLY PARTON.
MC: . . . . . VSOPMC 165

BARGAIN STORE.
Tracks: / Bargain store / Kentucky gambler / When I'm gone / Only hand you'll need to hold, The / On my mind again / I want to be what you need / Love to remember / You'll always be special to me / He would know / I'll never forget.
LP: . . . . . LSA 3217
MC: . . . . . PK 10950

BEST OF DOLLY PARTON.
Tracks: / Mule skinner blues / Down from Dover / My Blue Ridge Mountain boy / In the good old days / Gypsy, Joe and me / In the ghetto / Just because I'm a woman / Daddy come and get me / How great Thou art / Just the way I am.
LP: . . . . . LSA 3101

BEST OF DOLLY PARTON VOL2.
Tracks: / Jolene / Travelling man / Lonely comin' down / Bargain store / Touch your woman / I will always love you / Love is like a butterfly / Coat of many colours / My Tennessee mountain home / When I sing for him.
LP: . . . . . NL 85146
MC: . . . . . NK 85146
LP: . . . . . LSA 3236
MC: . . . . . MPK 245

BEST OF PORTER WAGONER AND DOLLY PARTON, THE (Parton, Dolly/Porter Wagoner).
Tracks: / Just someone I used to know / Daddy was an old time preacher man / Tomorrow is forever / Jeannie's afraid of the dark / Last thing on my mind / Pain of loving you, The / Better move it on home / Holding on to nothin' / Run that by me one more time / We'll get ahead someday.
LP: . . . . . LSA 3046
MC: . . . . . PK 42008

BOTH SIDES.
LP: . . . . . WH 5006

BURLAP AND SATIN.
Tracks: / Ooo-eee / Send me the pillow you dream on / Jealous heart / Gamble either way / Appalachian memories / I really don't want to know / Potential new boyfriend / Cowboy's ways / One of those days / Calm on the water.
LP: . . . . . PL 84691
MC: . . . . . PK 84691
LP: . . . . . RCALP 6080

COUNTRY GIRL.
Tracks: / Jolene / My Tennessee mountain home / Bargain store, The / Love is like a butterfly / Just the two of us / I will always love you / Touch your woman / Seeker, The / Travelling man / Daddy come and get me / My blue tears / Coat of many colours / Joshua / Washday blues / Mule skinner blues (Blue yodel No. 8) / Coming for to carry me home / Afraid to love again (CD only.) / I wash my face in the morning dew (CD only.).
MC: . . . . . TCMFP 5914

DOLLY.
Tracks: / We used to / Love I used to call mine, The / My heart started breaking / Most of all why / Bobby's arms / Seeker, The / Hold me / Because I love you / Only the memory remains / I'll remember you as mine.
LP: . . . . . LSA 3260
MC: . . . . . MPK 250

DOLLY, DOLLY, DOLLY.
Tracks: / Starting over again / Same old fool / Old flames can't hold a candle to you / You're the only one I ever needed / Say goodnight / Fool for your love / Even a fool would let go / Sweet agony / I know you when / Packin' it up.
LP: . . . . . PL 13546

DOLLY PARTON.
Tracks: / Down on music row / Letter, The / I remember / Doctor Roberts F. Thomas / Daddy's working boots / All I can do / Hey lucky lady / In the good old days / Wrong direction home, The / Better part of life, The / Back home / Old black kettle.
LP: . . . . . CDS 1164
LP: . . . . . CDS 1208
MC: . . . . . CAM 1208

DOLLY PARTON COLLECTION, THE (MONUMENT VERSION).
Tracks: / Dumb blonde / Your ole handy man / I don't want to throw rice / Put it off until tomorrow / I wasted my tears / Something fishy / Fuel to the flame / Giving and the taking, The / I'm in no condition / Company you keep, The / I've lived my life / Little things / Why why why / I wound easy / I don't want you around me anymore / Hillbilly Willy / This boy has been hurt / Daddy won't be home anymore / As long as I love / Habit I can't break, A / I'm not worth the tears / I don't trust me around you / I couldn't wait forever / Too lonely too long.
2LP: . . . . . MNT 22105
MCSET: 40 22105

DOLLY PARTON COLLECTION, THE (PICKWICK).
Tracks: / D.I.V.O.R.C.E. / Love and learn / Big wind / Mule skinner blues / Daddy / She never met a man / I wish I felt this way at home / Love isn't free / Only way out, The / Try being lonely / You're gonna be sorry / We had all the good things going / Mine / Don't let trouble make up your mind / More than their share / Little bird / Mama say a prayer / In the ghetto / Chas / But you loved me then.
2LP: . . . . . PDA 053
MCSET: . . . . . PDC 053

DOLLY PARTON STORY, THE.
Tracks: / Fuel to the flame / I don't want you around me anymore / As long as I love / Giving and the taking, The / I'm in no condition / I couldn't wait forever / I've lived my life / Something fishy / Dumb blonde / I would easy / I don't want to throw rice / Why why why / Too lonely too long / Daddy won't be home anymore / This boy has been hurt / Hillbilly Willy.
LP: . . . . . CBS 31582

EAGLE WHEN SHE FLIES.
Tracks: / If you need me / Rockin' years / Country road / Silver and gold / Eagle when she flies / Best woman wins / What a heartache / Runaway feelin' / Dreams do come true / Family / Wildest dreams.
LP: 4678541
MC: 4678544

GREAT BALLS OF FIRE.
Tracks: / Star of the show / Down / You're the only one / Help / Do you think that time stands still / Sweet summer lovin' / Great balls of fire / Almost in love / It's not my affair anymore / Sandy's song.

LP: . . . . PL 13361

GREAT DOLLY PARTON VOL.1, THE.
Tracks: / D.I.V.O.R.C.E. / Love and learn / Big wind / Mule skinner blues / Daddy / She never met a man she didn't like / I wish I felt this way at home / Love isn't free / Only way out, The / Try being lonely / You're gonna be sorry / We all had a good thing going.
LP: . . . . CDS 1171

GREAT DOLLY PARTON VOL.2, THE.
Tracks: / I'm doing this for your sake / Mama say a prayer / When possession get too strong / In the ghetto / But you loved me then / Carroll County accident / Don't let it trouble your mind / More than their share.
LP: . . . . CDS 1184
MC: . . . . CAM 489

GREAT PRETENDER, THE.
Tracks: / Save the last dance for me / I walk the line / Turn, turn, turn (to everything there is a season) / Downtown / We had it all / She don't love you (like I love you) / We'll sing in the sunshine / I can't help myself / Elusive butterfly / Great pretender, The.
LP: . . . . PL 84940
MC: . . . . PK 84940

GREATEST HITS: DOLLY PARTON.
Tracks: / 9 To 5 / But you know I love you / Heartbreak express / Old flames can't hold a candle to you / Applejack / Me and little Andy / Here you come again / Hard candy Christmas / Two doors down / It's all wrong but it's all right / Don't I ever cross your mind / I will always love you.
LP: . . . . PL 84422
MC: . . . . PK 84422
LP: . . . . RCALP 6058

GREATEST HITS: DOLLY PARTON (2).
Tracks: / Here you come again / Think about love / Baby I'm burning / Love is like a butterfly / Save the last dance for me / Heartbreaker / But you know I love you / 9 to 5 / Islands in the stream (duet with Kenny Rogers) / Don't call it love / Old flames can't hold a candle to you / Bargain store / Real love (duet with Kenny Rogers) / Potential new boyfriend / Jolene / I will always love you (from Best Little Whorehouse in Texas) / I really got the feeling (MC & CD only) / Starting over again (MC & CD only) / We had it all (CD only) / You're the only one (CD only).
LP: . . . . PL 90407
MC: . . . . PK 90407

HEARTBREAK EXPRESS.
Tracks: / Heartbreak express / Single woman / My blue ridge mountain / Boy / As much as always / Do I ever cross your mind / Act like a fool / Prime of our love / Hollywood potters.
LP: . . . . PL 84289
MC: . . . . PK 84289
LP: . . . . RCALP 3076

HEARTBREAKER.
Tracks: / I really got the feeling / It's too late to love me now / We're through forever ('til tomorrow) / Sure thing / What am I gonna do with you gone / Baby, I'm burning / Nickels and dimes / Man / Heartbreaker.
LP: . . . . PL 12797
MC: . . . . PK 12797

HERE YOU COME AGAIN.
Tracks: / Here you come again / Baby, come out tonight / It's all wrong, but it's all right / Me and little Andy / Lovin' you / Cowgirl and the dandy / Two doors down / God's colouring book / As soon as I touched him / Sweet music man.
LP: . . . . PL 12544
MC: . . . . PK 12544

HITS OF DOLLY PARTON.
Tracks: / Jolene / My Tennessee mountain home / Touch your woman / Seeker, The / Travelling man / Daddy come and get me / My blue tears / Coat of many colours / Bargain store / Joshua / Love is like a butterfly / Washday blues / We used to / Mule skinner blues / I will always love you / Coming for to carry me home.
LP: . . . . PL 89090
MC: . . . . PK 89090
LP: . . . . PL 42192
MC: . . . . PK 42192

IN THE GOOD OLD DAYS (When times were bad).
Tracks: / Don't let it trouble your mind / He's a go getter / In the good old days / It's my time / Harper Valley PTA / Little bird / Mine / Carroll County accident, The / Fresh out of forgiveness / Mama say a prayer / Always the first time / D.I.V.O.R.C.E..
LP: . . . . NL 90007
MC: . . . . NK 90007

ISLANDS IN THE STREAM (See under Rogers, Kenny) (Parton, Dolly & Kenny Rogers).

JOLENE.
Tracks: / Jolene / When someone wants to leave / River of happiness / Early morning breeze / Highlight of my life / I will always love you / Randy / Living on memories of you / Lonely comin' down / It must be you.
LP: AFL1 0473
MC: . . . . PK 10473

JUST BECAUSE I'M A WOMAN.
Tracks: / You're gonna be sorry / I felt this way at home / False eye lashes / I'll oil wells love you / Only way out (is to walk over me), The / Little bit slow to catch on / Bridge, The / Love and learn / I'm running out of love / Just because I'm a woman / Baby sister / Try being lonely.
LP: . . . . NL 89853
MC: . . . . NK 89853

JUST THE TWO OF US (Parton, Dolly/ Porter Wagoner).
Tracks: / Closer by the hour / I washed my face in the morning dew / Jeannie's afraid of the dark / Holding on to nothin' / Slip away today / Dark end of the Street / Just the two of us / Afraid to love again / We'll get ahead someday / Somewhere between / Party, The / I can.
LP: . . . . LSA 3023

LOVE ALBUM, THE.
Tracks: / You are / Heartbreaker / Bargain store / I will always love you / Love is like a butterfly / Coat of many colours / Islands in the stream / Here you come again / Send me the pillow (that you dream on) / It's all wrong but it's all right / Jolene / One of those days.
LP: . . . . NL 90307
MC: . . . . NK 90307

LOVE ALBUM, THE VOL.2.
Tracks: / We used to / You're the only one / But you know I love you / We had it all / Sweet music man / My girl (my love) / Almost in love / Sandy's song / I really don't want to know / Sweet summer lovin' / Love I used to call mine, The / Starting over again.
MC: . . . . NK 90455

LOVE IS LIKE A BUTTERFLY.
Tracks: / Love is like a butterfly / In the ghetto / We had all the good things going / Daddy / Mama say a prayer / My Tennessee mountain home / Chicken every Sunday / I wish I felt this way at home / Joshua / Don't let it trouble your mind / Carroll County accident, The / Mule skinner blues.
LP: . . . . CDS 1202
MC: . . . . CAM 1202
LP: . . . . LSA 3195
MC: . . . . PK 10712

LOVE IS LIKE A BUTTERFLY (M.F.P).
Tracks: / Love is like a butterfly / If I cross your mind / My eyes can only see you / Take me back / Blackie, Kentucky / Gettin' happy / You're the one that taught me how to swing / Highway headin' South / Once upon a memory / Sacred memories.
LP: . . . . MFP 5774
MC: . . . . TCMFP 5774

MAGIC MOMENTS WITH DOLLY PARTON.
Tracks: / Mule skinner blues (blue yodel No. 8) / Down from Dover / My blue ridge mountain boy / In the good old days / Gypsy Joe and me / In the ghetto / Just because I'm a woman / Daddy come and get me / How great Thou Art / Just the way I am / Jolene / Travelling man / Lonely comin' down / Bargain store / Touch your woman / I will always love you / Love is like a butterfly / Coat of many colours / My Tennessee mountain home / When I sing for him / We used to / Seeker, The / You are / Here you come again.
MC: . . . . NK 89620

MAKING PLANS (Parton, Dolly/Porter Wagoner).
Tracks: / Making plans / If you go I'll follow you / Hide me away / Someone just like you / Little David's harp / Beneath the sweet magnolia tree / Touching memories / Daddy did his best / If you say I can.
LP: . . . . PL 13700

MY TENNESSEE MOUNTAIN HOME.
Tracks: / Letter, The / I remember / Old black kettle / Daddy's working boots / Doctor Robert F. Thomas / In the good old days / My Tennessee mountain home / Wrong direction home, The / Back home / Better part of life, The / Down on music row.
LP: . . . . LSA 3178

NEW HARVEST - NEW GATHERING.
Tracks: / Light of a clear blue morning / Applejack / My girl / Holdin' on to you / You are / How does it feel / Where beauty lives in memory / (Your love has lifted me) Higher and higher / Getting in my way / There.
LP: . . . . PL 12188
MC: . . . . PK 12188

ONCE UPON A CHRISTMAS (Parton, Dolly & Kenny Rogers).
Tracks: / I believe in Santa Claus / Sleighride / Winter wonderland / Christmas without you / Christmas song, The / Christmas to remember / With bells on / Silent night / Greatest gift of all / White Christmas / Once upon a Christmas.
LP: . . . . PL 85307
MC: . . . . PK 85307

QUEENS OF COUNTRY (Parton, Dolly/ Donna Fargo).
Tracks: / Honky tonk angels / Making believe / Letter to heaven / Release me / Little blossom / Two little orphans / Daddy / Sticks and stones / All that's keeping me alive / Wishful thinking.
LP: . . . . SDLP 1001
MC: . . . . ZCSD 1001

RAINBOW.
Tracks: / River unbroken, The / I know you by heart (Duet with Smokey Robinson) / Dump the dude / Red hot screaming love / Make love work / Everyday hero / Two lovers / Could I have your autograph / Savin' it for you / More than I can say.
LP: 4604511
MC: 4604514

REAL LOVE.
Tracks: / Think about love / Tie our love / We got too much / It's such a heartache / Don't call it love / Real love / I can't be true / I hope you're never happy / Once in every blue moon / Come back to me.
LP: . . . . PL 85414
MC: . . . . PK 85414

RHINESTONE (Film Soundtrack).
LP: . . . . BL 85032
MC: . . . . BK 85032

SAVE THE LAST DANCE FOR ME.
Tracks: / Save the last dance for me / Potential new boyfriend / Love is like a butterfly / Bargain store / I can't help myself / Jolene / Here you come again / Seeker, The / Baby I'm burning / Two doors down / Downtown / 9 to 5.
LP: . . . . CDS 1225
MC: . . . . CAM 1225

TRIO, THE (Parton, Dolly/Linda Ronstadt/Emmylou Harris).
Tracks: / Pain of loving you / Making plans / To know him is to love him / Hobo's meditation / Wilflowers / Telling me lies / My dear companion / Those memories of you / I've had enough / Rosewood casket.
LP: . . . . K 925491 1
MC: . . . . K 925491 4

VERY BEST OF DOLLY PARTON, THE.
Tracks: / Down from Dover / Joshua / Coat of many colours / Heartbreaker / Jolene / I will always love you / Love is like a butterfly / Bargain store / Seeker, The / We used to / You are / All I can do / Shattered image / Me and little Andy / My Tennessee mountain home / Touch your woman / Two doors down / Here you come again / Baby, I'm burning / Lonely comin' down.
LP: . . . . PL 89007
MC: . . . . PK 89007
LP: . . . . RCALP 5052

WHITE LIMOZEEN.
Tracks: / Time for me to fly / Why'd you come in here / Slow healing heart / Wait 'til I get you home / Moon, the stars and me, The / Yellow roses / Lookin' like that / What is it my love / Take me back to the country / He's alive.
LP: 4651351
MC: 4651354

WINNING HAND, THE (Parton, Dolly/ Kris Kristofferson/Willie Nelson/Brenda Lee).
Tracks: / You're gonna love someone (in the morning) / Ping pong / You'll always have someone / Here comes that rainbow again / Bigger the fool, The / Help me make it through the night / Happy birthday baby / You left a long time ago / To make a long story short (she's gone) / Everything is beautiful.
2LP: . . . . MNT 88611
MCSET: 40 88611

YOU ARE.
Tracks: / You are / Applejack / Down from Dover / Shattered image / Me and little Andy / All I can do / Jeannie's afraid of the dark / We used to / Boulder to Birmingham / Just because I'm a woman / Joshua / Lonely comin' down.
LP: . . . . INTS 5044
MC: . . . . INTK 5044

Parton, Stella

COUNTRY SWEET.
Tracks: / Easy to love / Charlie's baby / Little bitty tear, A / If you're a dream / I'm not that good at goodbye / Standard lie number one / Danger of a stranger, The / I've got to have you for mine / It's the little things / More the change, The.
LP: . . . . K 52060

I WANT TO HOLD YOU....
LP: . . . . JULEP 1

LOVE YA.
Tracks: / I cried for the lady / Long lost love / Room at the top of the stairs, The / Someone / Little inconvenient / Steady as the rain / I want to hold you in my dreams, tonight / Honey come home / Rest of the way / Stormy weather.
LP: . . . . K 52136

STELLA PARTON.
Tracks: / Four little letters / Undercover lovers / Late late late late show, The / Love is a word / There's a rumour going round / Haven't you heard / Lie to Linda / Wishing well / Fade my blues away / Down to earth.
LP: . . . . K 52069

Partridge, Andy

TAKE AWAY (The lure of salvage).
Tracks: / Commerciality / Day they pulled the North Pole down, The / Forgotten language of light, The / Steam fist futurist / Shore leave ornithology (another 1950) / Cairo / Rotary, The / Madnattan / I sit in the snow / Work away Tokyo day / New broom.
LP: . . . . V 2145
LP: . . . . OVED 130
MC: . . . . OVEDC 130

Partridge Family

CHRISTMAS CARD.
LP: . . . . BELLS 214

GREATEST HITS: PARTRIDGE FAMILY.
Tracks: / Come on get happy / I think I love you / Doesn't somebody want to be wanted / I'll meet you halfway / Cherish / It's one of those nights (yes love) / I can feel your heartbeat / Am I losing you / Could it be forever / Point me in the direction of Alberquerque / Echo Valley 2-6809 / Summer days / Looking thru the eyes of love / How long is too long / One night stand.
MC: 410364

PARTRIDGE FAMILY SOUND MAGAZINE, THE.
LP: . . . . BELLS 206

SHOPPING BAG.
LP: . . . . BELLS 212

UP TO DATE.
LP: . . . . SBLL 143

Party Boppers

ROCK 'N' ROLL PARTY ALBUM.
Tracks: / Rock around the clock / Shake, rattle and roll / See you later alligator / Bye bye love / Wake up little Susie / All I have to do is dream / Bird dog / Everyday / Heartbeat / Oh boy / That'll be the day / Peggy Sue / Rave on / Raining in my heart / It's my party / Locomotion, The / Stupid cupid / Sweet nothin's / Lipstick on your collar / Ma he's making eyes at me / Ain't that a shame / Blueberry Hill / Great balls of fire / Tutti frutti / Long tall Sally / Good golly Miss Molly / Whole lotta shakin' goin' on / C'mon everybody / Weekend / Summertime blues / Three steps to heaven / Hound dog / All shook up / Teddy bear / Blue suede shoes / Jailhouse rock / Return to sender / Wooden heart / Love me tender / Wonder of you, The.
LP: . . . . MFP 5834
MC: . . . . TCMFP 5834

Party Classics

PARTY CLASSICS Various artists (Various artists).
2LP: . . . . STAR 2003
MCSET: . . . . STAC 2003

Party Day

GLASSHOUSE.
LP: . . . . FXLP 401

IT'S ALL SIMPLICITY.
LP: . . . . POLP 501

Party Fever

PARTY FEVER (Various artists).
LP: . . . . BD 3005

Party For The World

PARTY FOR THE WORLD (Various artists).
LP: . . . . STAR 2336
MC: . . . . STAC 2336

Party Music

PARTY MUSIC VOL. 11 (Various artists).
LP: . . . . SGLP 008

Party Party Party

PARTY PARTY PARTY ALBUM (Various artists).
LP: . . . . QUALP 2

MC: . . . . QUALPTC 2

Party Poppers

SINGALONG 60'S PARTY.
Tracks: / Sergeant Pepper's lonely hearts club band / Mighty Quinn / Downtown / Summer holiday / When I'm sixty four / Little loving, A / With a little help from my friends / King of the road / I want to hold your hand / Winchester Cathedral / Sugar, sugar / Hard days night, A / Ob-la-di, ob-la-da / World without love / Ferry 'cross the Mersey / Yellow submarine / Can't buy me love / Carnival is over, The / Hey Jude / Have I the right / Baby now that I've found you / Oh pretty woman / Release me / Green green grass of home / I can't stop loving you / Crying in the chapel / Young ones, The / I like it / There's a kind of hush / I only want to be with you / How do you do it / Bachelor boy / Delilah / You'll never walk alone / Are you lonesome tonight / Last waltz, The.
MC: . . . . **TCMFP 5892**

SING-ALONG CHRISTMAS PARTY.
Tracks: / White Christmas / I saw mommy kissing Santa Claus / Let it snow, let it snow, let it snow / Frosty the snowman / Happy holiday / That's what I'd like for Christmas / When Santa got stuck up the chimney / It's the most wonderful time of the year / We three kings of Orient are / Jingle bells / Good King Wenceslas / Kings' horses, The / Santa Claus is coming to town / Rudolph the red nosed reindeer / Holiday season, The / Mary's boy child / When a child is born / Silent night / Deck the halls / Stop the cavalry / Have yourself a merry little Christmas / Christmas song, The / Do you hear what I hear / Christmas dreaming / Little donkey / Winter wonderland / It's beginning to look like Christmas / I saw three ships / All I want for Christmas (is my two front teeth) / Silver bells / Sleigh ride / Joy to the world / I wish it could be Christmas every day / Merry Christmas everybody / We wish you a merry Christmas / Auld lang syne / Christmas alphabet (CD only.) / Fairy on the Christmas tree (CD only.) / Jolly old St. Nicholas (CD only.) / Mister Santa (CD only.) / Mistletoe and wine (CD only.) / Little drummer boy (CD only.) / O little town of Bethlehem (CD only.) / It came upon a midnight clear (CD only.) / God rest ye merry gentlemen (CD only.).
LP: . . . . **MFP 5795**
MC: . . . . **TCMFP 5795**

Party Posse

IT'S PARTY TIME.
LP: . . . . **HIP 82**
MC: . . . . **HIPC 82**

Party Singalong

PARTY SINGALONG (Various artists).
MC: . . . . **BRC 2523**

PARTY SING-ALONG (Various artists).
LP: . . . . **SHM 812**
MC: . . . . **HSC 198**

Party Time

PARTY TIME (Various artists).
MC: . . . . **STC 005**

Parvez, Shahid

INTRODUCING SHAHID PARVEZ AND ZAKIR HUSSAIN (Parvez, Shahid & Zakir Hussain).
LP: **2393963**

Pasadena Roof

16 GREATEST HITS: PASADENA ROOF ORCHESTRA.
LP: . . . . **FUN 9034**
MC: . . . . **FUNC 9034**

ANTHOLOGY - PASADENA ROOF ORCHESTRA.
LP: . . . . **MTRA 2009**

C'MON ALONG AND LISTEN.
Tracks: / Don't be that way / Honey pie / I'm on the crest of a wave / Duke steps out / Show must go on / She's a latin from Manhattan / Josephine Baker / Introducing Josephine Charleston / What is this thing called love / Sing, sing, sing / As time goes by / Skokiaan / Lullaby of Broadway.
LP: . . . . **CFRC 516**
MC: . . . . **MCFRC 516**

COLLECTION: PASADENA ROOF ORCHESTRA.
Tracks: / It don't mean a thing / Bye bye blackbird / Black bottom / Charleston / Temptation rag / Blue skies / What is this thing called love? / Lullaby of Broadway / Nobody's sweetheart / You're the cream in my coffee / Singing in the rain / Top hat, white tie and tails / I won't dance / Three little words / Stormy weather / Don't be that way / I'll see you again / Pasedena / Georgia / Whispering / Paddlin' Madelin' home / Varsity drag / Here's to the next time / Cheek to cheek.
MC: . . . . **CCSMC 189**
2LP: . . . . **CCSLP 189**

EVERYTHIN' STOPS FOR TEA.
Tracks: / Lullaby of Broadway / As time goes by / Varsity drag / Charleston / Pasadena / Three little words / Cheek to cheek / Holding hands / Sing, sing, sing / Stormy weather / Black bottom / Top hat / I won't dance / Singing in the rain.
2LP: . . . . **CR 135**
MCSET: . . . . **CRT 135**

FIFTEEN YEARS ON.
Tracks: / I can't dance / Yes yes (my baby says yes) / You took advantage of me / Varsity drag / Very thought of you, The / Casa loma stomp / Pasadena / Lambeth walk / Solitude / I heard / Don't bring Lulu / Ain't she sweet / Five foot two, eyes of blue / Charleston / Here's to the next time.
LP: . . . . **ARC 1018**
MC: . . . . **ARCT 1018**

GOOD NEWS.
Tracks: / Good news / Vo do do de o blues / Stormy weather / My canary has circles under his eyes / Choo-choo / Three little words / Home / Everything stops for tea / Pasadena / Sugarfoot stomp / Sing Holly, Go whistle, hey hey / Georgia / That's my weakness now / King's horses, The / Mooche, The / Here's to the next time.
LP: . . . . **TRA 301**

HAPPY FEET.
Tracks: / Happy feet / Nightingale sang in Berkeley Square, A / I got rhythm / Georgia on my mind / Cotton Club stomp / I'm crazy 'bout my baby / When it's sleepy time down South / Oh Donna Clara / Makin' wickey wackey down in Waikiki / Just squeeze me / Bei mir bist du schon.
LP: . . . . **PROOF 1**
MC: . . . . **TCPRO 1**

ISN'T IT ROMANTIC.
Tracks: / Isn't it romantic / I won't dance / I've told every little star / Cheek to cheek / Hey Miss Moonlight / Singing in the rain / Whispering / I'll see you again / Dream a little dream of me / Creole love call / Soft shoe shuffle blues / Sunday.
LP: . . . . **TRA 335**

NIGHT OUT.
LP: . . . . **CBS 83220**
MC: **40 83220**

ON TOUR.
Tracks: / Black bottom / Top hat white tie and tails / East St. Louis toodle-oo / Mississippi mud / Blue skies / Ball and chain / It don't mean a thing / Bye bye blackbird / Clarinet marmalade / Meadow lark / Temptation rag / Nagasaki / Pasadena.
LP: . . . . **TRA 314**

PASADENA ROOF ORCHESTRA (DITTO).
MCSET: . . . . **DTO 10253**

PASADENA ROOF ORCHESTRA, THE.
Tracks: / Paddlin' Madelin' home / You've got me crying again / Wo-ba-ly walk / Love in bloom / Me and Jane in a plane / Savoy Christmas medley / Nagasaki / Muddy water / Varsity drag / Can't we be friends / Eccentric / Charleston / Come on baby.
LP: . . . . **TRA 286**
MC: . . . . **TRAC 314**

PUTTIN' ON THE RITZ.
Tracks: / Young and healthy / I've found a new baby / Mean to me / You're never fully dressed without a smile / Am Sonntag will mein susser mit segein gehn / Going Hollywood / Hooray for Hollywood / There's a rainbow round my shoulder / Isn't this a lovely day / Puttin' on the Ritz / Keep young and beautiful / Little orphan Annie / Yes sir, that's my baby.
LP: . . . . **SPR 8528**
MC: . . . . **SPC 8528**

STEPPING OUT.
Tracks: / Who walks in? / My melancholy baby / How 'm doin? / Creole love call / Sahara / Skirts / Pennies from Heaven / Latin from Manhattan / Business in 'F' / I can't get started / Louisiana / Golden wedding / I only have eyes for you / Minnie the moocher / Stepping out / Pasadena.
LP: . . . . **PROOF 2**
MC: . . . . **TCPRO 2**

TALKING PICTURE, A.
MC: **40 82751**

TOP HAT, WHITE TIE AND TAILS.
MCSET: . . . . **DTO 10220**

Pasadenas

ELEVATE.
Tracks: / Reeling / South Africa / Love thing / I'd die for you / Bridge over troubled water / Another lover / I'd die for you (reprise) / Strong enough / Cry my tears (posthumously yours) / I want to be / More time / For love / Base is slipping, The / Love changes / I want to be (uk mix) (Only on MC and CD).
LP: **4670231**
MC: **4670234**

TO WHOM IT MAY CONCERN.
Tracks: / Funny feeling / Living in the footsteps of another man / Enchanted lady / New love / Riding on a train / Give a little peace / Tribute (right on) / I really miss you / Justice for the world / Something else.
LP: **4628771**
MC: **4628774**

Pascali's Island

PASCALI'S ISLAND (Film soundtrack) (Various artists).
Tracks: / Pascali's theme (Pritouritze planinata): *Various artists* / Pasha's castle, The: *Various artists* / Nisi by night: *Various artists* / Jealous pursuit: *Various artists* / Izzet effendi: *Various artists*/ Pascali's passion: *Various artists* / Nightmares: *Various artists* / Sultan's spy, The: *Various artists*/ Fear of Greeks: *Various artists* / Deal complete, The: *Various artists* / Mysterious Englishman: *Various* artists / Discovery: *Various artists* / Growing despair: *Various artists* / Under cover of night: *Various artists* / Lydia's death: *Various artists* / Pascali's grief: *Various artists.*
LP: . . . . **V 2557**
MC: . . . . **TCV 2557**
LP: **90976.1**
MC: **90976.4**

Pasco, Richard (nar)

BEST LOVED VERSE (see under Best Loved Verse (bk)) (Watson, Gwen (nar) & Richard Pasco (nar)).

CLASSIC GHOST STORIES (see under Classic Ghost... (bk).

GREAT EXPECTATIONS (See under Dickens, Charles).

Pascoal, Hermeto

BRASIL UNIVERSO.
LP: . . . . **RRPL 002**

Pascoe, Freddy

TAKE IT.
LP: **BLP001**

Paso Doble

PASO DOBLE (Various artists).
Tracks: / Morena de mi copla: *Various artists* / Mi jaca: *Various artists* / En er mundo: *Various artists*/ Puerto del sol: *Various artists* / Coplas: *Various artists* / El gato montes: *Various artists* / Espana cani: *Various artists* / El galito: *Various artists* / El relicario: *Various artists* / El beso: *Various artists* / Cumuna: *Various artists.*
LP: . . . . **IMS 8161671**

Pass, Joe

A SALLE PLEYEL (see Peterson, Oscar) (Pass, Joe & Oscar Peterson).

AT THE MONTREUX JAZZ FESTIVAL 1975.
Tracks: / You are the sunshine of my life / Very thought of you, The / Nobs / Li'l darlin' / Blues for Nina / How long has this been going on? / More than you know / Grete / Nuages / I'm glad there is you / Willow weep for me.
LP: **2310 752**

BEST OF JOE PASS.
Tracks: / Foxy chick and a cool cat, A / How high the moon? / What are you doing the rest of your life? / Que que ha? / Summertime / Blues for Alican / Satin doll / On Green Dolphin Street.
LP: **2310 893**

BIG THREE, THE (See Jackson, Milt) (Pass, Joe/ Milt Jackson/ Ray Brown).

BLUES FOR FRED.
Tracks: / Cheek to cheek / Night and day / Blues for Fred / Oh lady be good / Foggy day, A / Be myself / They can't take that away from me / Dancing in the dark / I concentrate on you / Way you look tonight.
LP: . . . . **PAB 005**

BLUES FOR TWO (See under Sims, Zoot) (Pass, Joe & Zoot Sims).

CHECKMATE (Pass, Joe/Jimmy Rowles).
Tracks: / What's your story, morning glory? / So rare / As long as I live / Marquita / Stardust / We'll be together again / Can't we be friends? / Deed I do / 'Tis Autumn / God bless the child.
LP: . . . . **D 2310 865**
MC: **K10 865**

CHOPS (Pass, Joe and Niels Pederson).
Tracks: / Have you met Miss Jones? / Oleo / Lover man / Five pound blues / Come rain or come shine / Quiet nights / Tricrotism / Old folks / Yardbird suite / Your own sweet way.
LP: **2310 830**
MC: **K10 830**

COMPLETE 'CATCH ME' SESSIONS.
Tracks: / Catch me / You stepped out of a dream / No cover, no minimum / Just friends / Walkin' up / Summertime / But beautiful / Falling in love with love / Mood indigo / Days of wine and roses.
LP: . . . . **LBR 1035**

DIGITAL III AT MONTREUX (see Fitzgerald, Ella) (Pass, Joe/Ella Fitzgerald/Count Basie).

EASY LIVIN (See under Fitzgerald, Ella) (Pass, Joe & Ella Fitzgerald).

FITZGERALD AND PASS...AGAIN (see Fitzgerald, Ella) (Pass, Joe & Ella Fitzgerald).

GIANTS, THE (see under Peterson, Oscar) (Pass, Joe/Oscar Peterson/Ray Brown).

I REMEMBER CHARLIE PARKER.
Tracks: / Just friends / Easy to love / Summertime / April in Paris / Everything happens to me / Laura / They can't take that away from me / I didn't know what time it was / If I should lose you / Out of nowhere (concept 1) / Out of nowhere (concept 2).
LP: **2312 109**
MC: . . . . **K 12 109**

INTERCONTINENTAL.
Tracks: / Chloe / Meditation / I cover the waterfront / I love you / Stompin' at the Savoy / Watch what happens / Joe's blues / El gento / Ode to Billy Joe / Li'l darlin'.
LP: . . . . **MOIR 105**
MC: . . . . **CMOIR 105**

IRA, GEORGE, AND JOE.
Tracks: / Bidin' my time / How long has this been going on? / Soon / Lady be good / But not for me / Foggy day, A / It ain't necessarily so / Love is here to stay / 'S wonderful / Nice work if you can get it / Embraceable you.
LP: **2312 133**
MC: . . . . **K 12133**

JOE PASS.
Tracks: / Blues for Yano San / Blues for Sitges / Blues for Val / Wait till you see her / She's funny that way / Blues for Martin / Masquerade.
LP: **2308 212**
MC: . . . . **K 08 212**

LIVE AT DONTE'S (Pass, Joe Trio).
Tracks: / What have they done to my song? / You stepped out of a dream / Time for love, A / Donte's inferno / You are the sunshine of my life / Secret love / Sweet Georgia Brown / Stompin' at the Savoy / Darn that dream / Milestones / Lullaby of the leaves / What are you doing the rest of your life? / Blues for Pam.
LP: **2620 114**

LIVE AT LONG BEACH COLLEGE.
Tracks: / Wave / Blues in G / All the things you are / Round midnight / Here's that rainy day / Duke Ellington's sophisticated lady melange / Blues dues / Bluesette / Honeysuckle rose.
LP: **230 8239**
MC: . . . . **K 08 2239**

LIVE IN COPENHAGEN (see Grappelli,Stephane) (Pass, Joe / Stephane Grappelli).

LIVE IN THE NETHERLANDS (see Thielemans,Toots) (Pass, Joe/Toots Thielemans).

LIVING LEGENDS, THE (Pass, Joe & Robert Conti).
Tracks: / Hello young lovers / Stella by starlight / Little girl blue / My romance / Nuages.
LP: . . . . **DS 906**

NORTHSEA NIGHTS (Pass, Joe and Niels Pederson).
Tracks: / If I were a bell / 'Round about midnight / How deep is the ocean? / Stella by starlight / I can't get started / Blues for the Hague.
LP: **2308 221**
MC: . . . . **K 08 221**

PARIS CONCERT, THE (See under Peterson, Oscar) (Pass, Joe, Oscar Peterson, Niels Pederson).

PORGY & BESS (See under Peterson, Oscar) (Pass, Joe & Peterson, Oscar).

PORTRAITS OF DUKE ELLINGTON.
Tracks: / Satin doll / I let a song go out of my heart / Sophisticated lady / I got it bad and that ain't good / In a mellow tone / Solitude / Don't get around much anymore / Do nothing till you hear from me / Caravan.
LP: **231 0716**
MC: **K10 716**

QUADRANT.
Tracks: / Concorde / Joe's tune / Lady be good / Ray's tune / Grooveyard / Man I love, The / Blues for the stone.
LP: **2310837**

STONE JAZZ, THE.
Tracks: / Play with fire / 19th nervous breakdown / I am waiting / Lady Jane / Not fade away / Mothers little helper / I can't get no satisfaction / Paint it black / What a shame / As tears go by / Stone jazz.
LP: . . . . **MOIR 505**
MC: . . . . **CMOIR 505**

TAKE LOVE EASY (See under Fitzgerald, Ella) (Pass, Joe & Ella Fitzgerald).

TIVOLI GARDENS, COPENHAGEN (See under Grappelli, Stephane) (Pass, Joe/Stephane Grappelli/Niels Pedersen).

TRIO, THE (see Peterson,Oscar/Niels Pederson/Joe Pass) (Pass, Joe, Oscar Peterson, Niels Pederson).

TUDO BEM (see Da Costa,Paulinho & Joe Pass) (Pass, Joe/Paulinho Da Costa).

TWO FOR THE ROAD (see under Ellis, Herb for full details) (Pass, Joe & Herb Ellis).

VIRTUOSO.
Tracks: / Night and day / Stella by starlight / Here's that rainy day / My old flame / How high the moon / Cherokee / Sweet Lorraine / Have you met Miss Jones? / Round midnight / All the things you are / Blues for Alican / Song is you, The.
LP: **231 0708**
MC: **K10 708**

VIRTUOSO NO.2.
Tracks: / Giant steps / Five hundred miles / Grooveyard / Misty / Joy spring / Blues for O. P. / On Green Dolphin Street / Windows / Blues for Basie / Feelings / If / Limehouse blues.
LP: **231 0788**
MC: **K10 788**

VIRTUOSO NO.3.
Tracks: / Off beat / Trinidad / Nina's blues / Sevenths / Ninth / Dissonance / Minor detail / Pablo de Lucia / Sultry / Passanova / Pasta blues / Dissonance no. 2.
LP: **231 0805**
MC: **K10 805**

VIRTUOSO NO.4.
Tracks: / Lush life / Indian Summer / Autumn leaves / Yesterdays / Come Sunday / Lover man (oh where can you be) / Come rain or come shine / My shining hour / I'll remember April / Some day my prince will come / Acoustic blues / Now's the time / I can't get started / It's a wonderful world / Man I love, The / Nearness of you, The / Limehouse blues / Easy living.
LP: **2640 102**
MC: **K40 102**

WE'LL BE TOGETHER AGAIN (see under Johnson, J. J.) (Pass, Joe/J J Johnson).

WHITESTONE.
Tracks: / Light in your eyes / Shuffle city / Estate / Daquilo que eu sei / Whitestone / Lovin' eyes / Amancer / I can't help it / Tarde / Fleeting moments.
LP: **2310 912**
MC: **K10 912**

Pass The Time

PASS THE TIME (An Anthology of Donegal Fiddling) (Various artists).
LP: **12TS 397**

Passage

DEGENERATES.
Tracks: / Xoyo / Revelation / Love is as / Born every minute / Go to seed / Armour / Time will tell / Empty words.
LP: . . . . **BRED 29**

ENFLAME.
Tracks: / Sharp tongue / Clear as crystal / Drugface / Man of war / Half of it (twats), The / Half of it (Sissies), The / Dogstar - A th day / Horseplay / BRD USA DDR JFK / Sunburn.
LP: . . . . **BRED 45**
MC: . . . . **CBRED 45**

FOR ALL AND NONE.
LP: . . . . **PMAM 2300**

THROUGH THE PASSAGE.
Tracks: / Xoyo / Sharp tongue / Devils and angels / Good and useful life / Taboos / Born every minute / Sixteen houses / Watching you dance / Love is as / Carnal / Wave.
LP: . . . . **BRED 56**

Passage Four

VLAD SPEAKS TO IMMANUEL.
Tracks: / Vlad speaks / Sleep the night / Your name / Garden of Mr. Mann / Sexual trance / Killing desire.
LP: . . . . **ST 7545**

Passage to India

PASSAGE TO INDIA (see under Forster, E.M.) (Kingsley, Ben).

PASSAGE TO INDIA, A (Film soundtrack) (Jarre, Maurice).
LP: . . . . **EJ 2403021**
MC: . . . . **EJ 2403024**
MC: **92059.4**

PASSAGE TO INDIA, A (See Forster, E.M.) (Spoken Word (Group)).

Passion

SONGS FROM THE ANTI-HILL (Passion of a Primitif, The).
MLP: . . . . **ANT 055**

Passion Day

PURITAN LEFT, THE.
MC: . . . . **CEP 1**

Passion (film)

PASSION (see under Gabriel, Peter) (Gabriel, Peter).

Passion Fodder

FAT TUESDAY.
Tracks: / Extra extra / I.O.U. / So this is love / My world is empty without you / I want it to be real / Dream, The / Move / Luz blanca / St. Helens / Heart hunters / Mardi gras / Skin poetry / In the echo / Hot waltz away / In the moodswing / Hard work / As you dig your hole / Tomorrow is a long time (Cassette only.) / Paname song / Violations (Cassette only.) / Dirt (Cassette only.) / God couldn't fight his way out of a wet brown bag.
LP: . . . . **BEGA 83**
MC: . . . . **BEGC 83**
LP: . . . . **BBL 83**
MC: . . . . **BBLC 83**

HARD WORDS FROM A SOFT MOUTH.
Tracks: / Red legs / Coal / Pigeons / Peter O'Toole / In the smooth / Before hitlist / Red orange blue / Big fat obstacle.
LP: . . . . **UPLP 10**

LOVE, WALTZES AND ANARCHY.
Tracks: / Polished off / Pascal's waltz / Kill me Hannah / Hunger burns / Orwell cooks / Spokane / Struggle for love (rent, painting...) / Pray, anarchist / Girl that I marry, The.
MC: . . . . **BEGC 94**
LP: . . . . **BEGA 94**

WOKE UP THIS MORNING.
LP: . . . . **BEGA 105**
MC: . . . . **BEGC 105**

Passion Play

UNKNOWN HEIGHT.
MC: . . . . **PP 1**

Passion Puppets

BEYOND THE PALE.
Tracks: / Beyond the pale / Like dust / Terminal culture / New way / Playground / Voices / Fear of being touched / Child / Memories / In your eyes.
LP: . . . . **SEEZ 54**
MC: . . . . **ZSEEZ 54**

Passion Sources

DESERT AND HER DAUGHTERS, THE (See under Gabriel, Peter) (Gabriel, Peter Passion Sources & John Hassell).

Passion Tracking

PASSION TRACKING VOLUME 7 (Various artists).
LP: . . . . **PADLP 107**

Passionate Deception

PASSIONATE DECEPTION (Mary Lyons) (Boyd, Carole (nar)).
MC: . . . . **PMB 017**

Passionell

OUR PROMISE.
LP: **2093 1**

Passions

MICHAEL AND MIRANDA.
Tracks: / Pedal fury / Oh no it's you / Snow / Love song / Man on the tube / Miranda / Obsession / Suspicion / Palava / Absentee / Brick wall / Why me.
LP: . . . . **FIX 3**

PASSION PLAYS.
Tracks: / I'm in love with a German film star / Runaway / Swimmer, The / Someone special / Bachelor girls / Skin deep / African mine / Jump for joy / Letter, The / Love is essential / Your friend / Sanctuary.
LP: . . . . **SPELP 85**

SANCTUARY.
Tracks: / Jump for joy / Letter / Into night / Small talk / White lies / Sanctuary / Love is essential / Your friend / Hold on, don't go / Cars driven fast.
LP: . . . . **POLS 1066**

THIRTY THOUSAND FEET OVER CHINA.
Tracks: / I'm in love with German film star / Someone special / Swimmer, The / Strange affair / Small stones / Runaway / Square, The / Alice's song / Bachelor girls / Skin deep.
LP: . . . . **POLS 1041**
MC: . . . . **POLSC 1041**

Passmore Sisters

FIRST LOVE, LAST RITES.
Tracks: / Difficult / Every child in Heaven / Goodbye Billy Wild / Shatter / Sally Way / Safe place to hide, A / Dance the house down / June in the water / Foundry of lies / Grim English joke / Red star blue heart / All I need is change.
LP: . . . . **CALP 001**

Passport

ATARAXIA.
Tracks: / Ataraxia (Part 1) / Ataraxia (Part 2) / Sky blue / Mandrake / Reng ding dang dong / Loco-motive / Secret, The / Louisiana / Alegrias.
LP: . . . . **K 50456**

CROSS COLLATERAL.
LP: . . . . **K 50111**

GARDEN OF EDEN.
Tracks: / Big bang, The / Garden of Eden / Snake / Gates of paradise / Dreamware / God earth smile / Children's dance.
LP: . . . . **K 50586**

INFINITY MACHINE.
Tracks: / Ju ju man / Morning sun / Blue aura / Infinity machine / Ostinato / Contemplation / Homunculus / Cross collateral / Jadoo / Willo the wisp / Albatross / Damais.
LP: . . . . **K 50254**

OCEAN LINER.
Tracks: / Departure / Allegory / Ancient saga / Oceanliner / Rub-a-dub / Uptown rendezvous / Bassride / Seaside.
LP: . . . . **K 50688**

Past, Present & Future

DARRYL PAYNE: 'PAST, PRESENT & FUTURE' (Various artists).
Tracks: / I need you now (88 re-make): *Sinnamon* / Why can't you (believe in me): *Sadane, Mark* / I can't believe it's over: *Payne, Darryl & Will Downing* / Touch me (love me tonite): *Keith, Brian* / It's alright: *NV*/ You can do it (it's so easy): *Terrell, Dino* / Dancing in the street: *Kreamcicle & Barbara Harris* / Can you love me: *Strick, Billy.*
LP: . . . . **LIPS 4**
MC: . . . . **TCLIPS 4**

Pastels

SITTING PRETTY.
LP: . . . . **CHAPLP 43**
MC: . . . . **CHAPMC 43**
LPPD: . . . . **CHAPLP 43 P**

SUCK ON THE PASTELS.
LP: . . . . **CRELP 031**

UP FOR A BIT WITH THE PASTELS.
Tracks: / Up for a bit / I'm alright with you / Hichin' a ride / Get round town / Automatically yours / Baby honey / If I could tell you.
LP: . . . . **GLALP 021**

Pastor, Guy

THIS IS IT.
LP: . . . . **DS 918**

Pastor, Tony

1944-1947: TONY PASTOR (Pastor, Tony & His Orchestra).
LP: . . . . **CLP 31**

CONFESSIN' (1940-1949) (Pastor, Tony & His Orchestra).
LP: . . . . **BS 7114**
MC: . . . . **BS 7114C**

LET'S DANCE WITH T.P. (Pastor, Tony & His Orchestra).
LP: . . . . **FS 131**

LIVE: TONY PASTOR AND ORCHESTRA 1947 (Pastor, Tony & His Orchestra).
LP: . . . . **LP 42-142**

MR. PASTOR GOES TO TOWN.
Tracks: / Funiculi funicula / Hollywood bowl / Mr. Pastor goes to town / Deed I do / Don't worry 'bout strangers / King Porter stomp / That's good enough for me / Paradiddle Joe / 'S wonderful / Dancing room only / Swinging on a star / I learned a lesson.
LP: . . . . **SWH 36**

RADIO DISCS OF TONY PASTOR (The Late 1940's).
LP: . . . . **JLP 2001**

WITH ROSEMARY AND BETTY CLOONEY 1942-47 (Pastor, Tony & His Orchestra).
LP: . . . . **CLP 121**

Pastorius, Jaco

JAZZ STREET (Pastorius, Jaco/Brian Melvin).
Tracks: / No clack / Miles modes / Wedding waltz / Drums of Yadzarah / Jazz Street / May day / Out of the night.
LP: . . . . **SJP 258**

NIGHT FOOD (FEATURING JACO PASTORIUS) (See under Melvin, Brian's Nightfood) (Pastorius, Jaco/Brian Melvin).

TRILOGUE-LIVE (See under Danielson) (Pastorius, Jaco/Danielson/ Mangelsdorff).

WORD OF MOUTH.
Tracks: / Crisis / Three views of X secret / Liberty city / Chromatic fantasy / Blackbird / Word of mouth / John and Mary.
LP: . . . . **K 56897**

Pastourelle

PASTOURELLE (Various artists).
Tracks: / Pastourelle: *Various artists* / Mirabel Bridge: *Various artists* / Spinner, The: *Various artists*/ Young shepherdess, The: *Various artists* / Shepherd's song: *Various artists* / Three bourrees: *Various artists*/ Bailero: *Various artists* / Come follow me: *Various artists* / I am so sad: *Various artists* / Unhappy the man: *Various artists* / Lullaby: *Various artists* / Forsaken shepherdess: *Various artists.*
LP: . . . . **RL 25413**
MC: . . . . **RK 25413**

Pat Garret (film)

PAT GARRET AND BILLY THE KID (Film soundtrack) (See under Dylan, Bob) (Dylan, Bob).

Patches

DON'T THINK TWICE.
Tracks: / Don't think twice / Where does the good times go? / Gambler, The / This time of the year / Four strong winds / Looking for love / City of New Orleans / Dream / Sleepin' alone / Tobermory Bay / Me and you and a dog named Boo.
LP: . . . . **BGC 322**
MC: . . . . **KBGC 322**

Patchwork

INTRAMENTO.
LP: . . . . **COB 37016**

Patent Pending

TROUBLES AND TRIALS.
LP: . . . . **FF 371**

Paterson, Cynthia

FOXWOOD TALES: FOXWOOD KIDNAP (Paterson, Cynthia & Brian).
MC: **0 00 102193 1**

FOXWOOD TALES: FOXWOOD REGATTA (Paterson, Cynthia & Brian).
MC: . . . . **0 00 102194 X**

FOXWOOD TALES: FOXWOOD TREASURE (Paterson, Cynthia & Brian).
MC: **0 00 102195 8**

FOXWOOD TALES: ROBBERY AT FOXWOOD (Paterson, Cynthia & Brian).
MC: **0 00 102196 6**

Paterson, Frances

SUN AND SHADOW.
LP: . . . . **LRF 194**

Paterson, P.

VIEW FROM THE HILL.
LP: . . . . **ZMRB 6**

Paterson, Rod

SMILING WAVED GOODBYE.
Tracks: / Roll that boulder away / Le garcon malheureux / Lord Gordon's kitchen boy / Flying up to London / You / Smiling waved goodbye / Earl Richard / Dowie dens of Yarrow, The / Wee flingette, A.
MC: . . . . **CTRAX 016**
LP: . . . . **TRAX 016**

TWO HATS.
Tracks: / My funny valentine / Every time we say goodbye / Willie Wassle / My Nannie / Pierre le Bateau / Wrong joke again / I do it for your love / Steggie / Bleacher lass o' Kelvinhaugh.
LP: . . . . **TRAX 004**
MC: . . . . **CTRAX 004**

Pathological

PATHOLOGICAL COMPILATION (Various artists).
Tracks: / Genital grinder: *Carcass* / John F Poodle: *Terminal Cheesecake* / Contains a disclaimer: *Coil*/ Dum dum slug: *God* / Hepatic tissue fermentation: *Carcass* / Internal animosity: *Napalm Death* / Live is a dog from hell: *Godflesh* / Three pottery owls: *Stretcheads* / Head's human: *Terminal Cheesecake*/ Groin death: *Stretcheads* / My own light: *Godflesh.*
LP: . . . . **PATH 01**

MC: . . . . PATH 01C

Patience

PATIENCE (see under Gilbert & Sullivan).

Patients

EMERGENCY MEASURES.
LP: . . . . COD 6

Patillo, Leon

BRAND NEW.
LP: . . . . BIRD R 191
MC: . . . . BIRD C 191

DANCE, CHILDREN, DANCE.
Tracks: / Dance, children, dance / High on You / These signs / Born again / Temple to the sky / Trinity / He is comin' / Come.
LP: . . . . MM 0049
MC: . . . . TC MM 0049

DON'T GIVE IN.
Tracks: / Blessed is / Have faith / Flesh of My flesh / We must believe / Your love is lifting me higher and higher / Star of the morning / Don't give in / How can I begin? / My sweet Lord / Go.
LP: . . . . MYR 1091
MC: . . . . MC 1091

LOVE AROUND THE WORLD.
LP: . . . . MYR R 1184
MC: . . . . MYR C 1184

SKY'S THE LIMIT, THE.
LP: . . . . MYR 1167
MC: . . . . MC 1167

Patinkin, Mandy

DRESS CASUAL.
Tracks: / Doodle doodle doo (medley) / On the atchinson / Topeka and Santa Fe / Bein' green / Triplets / I'm always chasing rainbows / Evening primrose / Pal Joey (suite) / Sorry grateful / Being alive / Ya got trouble (in River City) / Giants in the sky / Mr. Arthur's place / Yossel, yossel / Hollywood (medley).
MC: 4045998

MANDY PATINKIN.
Tracks: / Over the rainbow / Coffee in a cardboard cup / Pretty lady / Brother, can you spare a dime? / Love unrequited / No more / Me and my shadow / No one is alone / Sonny boy / Rockabye your baby with a Dixie melody / Casey (medley) / And the band played on / Marie / Once upon a time / Anyone can whistle / Soliloquy / I'll be seeing you / There's a rainbow round my shoulder / Top hat, white tie and tails / Puttin' on the ritz / Alexander's ragtime band / Swanee / My mammy / Handful of keys / Pennies from Heaven.
LP: 44943
MC: 40 44943

Patitucci, John

JOHN PATITUCCI.
Tracks: / Growing / Wind spirit / Searching, finding / Baja bajo / Change of seasons / Our family / Peace and quiet time / Crestline / Zaragoza / Then and now (Bonus track on CD only.) / Killeen (Bonus track on CD only.) / View, The (Bonus track on CD only.).
LP: . . . . GRP 91049
MC: . . . . GRPM 91049

ON THE CORNER.
LP: . . . . A 9583
MC: . . . . C 9583
LP: . . . . GRP 95831
MC: . . . . GRP 95834

SKETCHBOOK.
Tracks: / Spaceships / Joab / If you don't mind / Scophile / Greatest gift / From a rainy night / Junk man / Two worlds / Backwoods / They heard it twice / Trane / Through the clouds.
LP: . . . . GRP 96171
MC: . . . . GRP 96174

Paton, Alan

CRY, THE BELOVED COUNTRY.
MC: . . . . CDL 51605

CRY, THE BELOVED COUNTRY (Kingsley, Ben).
MCSET: . . . . LFP 7288

Patriach

PROPHECY.
LP: . . . . SHARK 16

Patrick, Keith

KEITH PATRICK.
Tracks: / Be my girl / How far / All my love / Sail away / Heaven / Reach for the sky / You're the one / Love U now / Night to remember.
LP: . . . . K 781 815 1
MC: . . . . K 781 815 4

Patrick, Rikki

BREAKPOINT.
Tracks: / I never thought it would come to this / Night moves / So much in love / Take a raincheck / Save us / Breakpoint / Clear the way / Don't you wanna / You've got it all / Never too late.
LP: . . . . CBS 25924

Patriots

PHARAOH'S LAND/ SECOND THOUGHTS.
LP: . . . . MARI 057

Pat's Big Band

SWING IT AGAIN, PAT.
LP: . . . . SP PB 83 0171

Patten, Brian

BRIAN PATTEN READING HIS POEMS.
MC: 1300

POEMS AND SONGS.
LP: . . . . TGS 116

Patterson, Bobby

BOBBY PATTERSON.
MC: . . . . BLP 101

KYLE CREED WITH BOBBY PATTERSON & THE CAMP CREEK (See Creed, Kyle) (Patterson, Bobby/ Kyle Creed/Camp Creek Boys).

Patterson, Don

MOVIN' UP.
LP: . . . . MR 5121

Patterson, Frank

AT CHRISTMAS.
Tracks: / Little drummer boy / White Christmas / O holy night / Jingle bells / Silent night / Adeste Fideles / Joy to the world / When a child is born / O little town of Bethlehem / Mary's boy child / Scarlet ribbons / Nazareth.
LP: 8228441
MC: 8228444

DREAMING THE HAPPY HOURS.
LP: . . . . KSXC 7005

FAREWELL MY DERRY LOVE.
MC: . . . . OCE 2468

FAVOURITE TENOR ARIAS.
Tracks: / Serenade / Che gelida manina / Una furtiva lagrima / Questa o quella / La fleur que tu m'avais jetee / Ach so fromm / Sound an alarm / Dies bildnis ist bezaubernd schon / Mit wurd und hoheit angetan / If with all your hearts / Le repos de la sainte famille / Tribute to Jimmy Shand.
LP: 8149 751
MC: 8149 754

FOR YOUR PLEASURE, VOLUME 2.
Tracks: / Tipperary / Silent worship / How great Thou art / Love me tender / Annie's song / Mary most glorious / When a child is born / Love Thee dearest / Take a pair of sparkling eyes / Home sweethome / Mary's boy child / Amazing grace.
LP: 7233 002
LP: 9108004

FRANK PATTERSON.
MC: . . . . RTE 62

FRANK PATTERSON SINGS.
LP: 830 324 4

GOLDEN VOICE OF FRANK PATTERSON.
Tracks: / O sole mio / Can't help falling in love / Cara mia / Try to remember / Be my love / True love / Impossible dream, The / Perhaps love / Granada / Memory / You'll never walk alone / Vaja con dios / Twelfth of never / You needed me / Moon river / Galway Bay / I'll take you home again, Kathleen / How great thou art.
LP: 826 484-1
MC: 826 484-4

IRELAND'S BEST LOVE BALLADS.
Tracks: / Fields of Athenry / Raglan Road / Tipperary so rare / Slievenamon / Irish ballad, An (tooralooral) / Galway Bay / Lady of Knock, Queen of Ireland / Lass of Aughrim, The / Town I loved so well, The / When you and I were young Maggie / Lonesome waters / Danny Boy / Four green fields / I'll take you home again Kathleen.
LP: . . . . RGLP 7
MC: . . . . RGMC 7

IRISH FAVOURITES.
Tracks: / Eily O'Grady / Banks of my own lovely Lee, The / Dublin's fair city / Portlairge / Last rose of summer / Hills of Donegal / Rose of Mooncoin / Believe me if all those endearing young charms / Remember all the glories of Brian Brave, (The) / An Chuileann / Peigi leitir moir / Down by the glenside.
MC: 723 0107

JOHN MCCORMACK FAVOURITES.
LP: . . . . SXL 7005
MC: . . . . KXCL 7005
LP: 9500 218
LP: 7399 042

MY DEAR NATIVE LAND.
LP: 6599 227

PEACE AND JOY.
LP: 6373 015

ROSE OF TRALEE, THE.
Tracks: / When you and I were young Maggie / Old rustic bridge / Rose of Tralee, The / Believe me if all those endearing young charms / My wild Irish rose / Danny boy / Banks of my own lovely Lee, The / When Irish eyes are smiling / My Mary of the curling hair / I hear you calling me / Old house / Last rose of summer.
LP: 824 847 1
MC: 824 847 4

SINGS FOR YOUR PLEASURE.
LP: 6392 016

THOMAS MOORE'S IRISH MELODIES.
LP: 6392 024

VOICE OF ERIN, THE.
LP: 6588 009

Patterson, Ottilie

BACK IN THE OLD DAYS (Patterson, Ottilie with Chris Barber).
Tracks: / There'll be a hot time in the old town tonight / Lordy Lord / Basin Street blues / T'aint what you do / Bad spell blues / Squeeze me.
LP: . . . . CBJBLP 4001
MC: . . . . ZCBJB 4001

MADAME BLUES AND DOCTOR JAZZ (Patterson, Ottilie with Chris Barber).
Tracks: / Georgia grind / There'll be a hot time in the old town tonight / Baby, won't you please come home / Stumbling block / I'm a salty dog / I'm a salty dog / Doctor Jazz / A.U..
LP: . . . . BLM 51101

Patterson, Sir Les

12 INCHES OF LES.
LP: . . . . TOWLP 13
MC: . . . . ZCTOW 13

Patterson, Sunshine

LINES (See under Maelov, Eddie) (Maelov,Eddie and Sunshine Patterson).

Patterson, Uncle John

PLAINS GEORGIA ROCK.
LP: . . . . ARHOOLIE 5018

Pattersons

PATTERSONS FROM DONGAL THE.
LP: . . . . HPE 619
MC: . . . . HPC 619

Patti, Guesch

NOMADE (Patti, Guesch & Encore).
Tracks: / L'homme au tablier vert - (Fleurs carnivores) / Dans l'enfer / Comment dire / Il va loin le malheur / Et meme (CD only.) / Nomade / J'veux pas m'en meler / Opera / Raler / Piege de lumiere / Libido (CD only.) / Encore / Merci (CD only.).
LP: . . . . PM 240
LP: 793 876 1
MC: . . . . TCPM 440
MC: 793 876 4
LP: . . . . EMC 3575
MC: . . . . TCEMC 3575

Patti, Sandi

GIFT GOES ON, THE.
Tracks: / Worship the King / Worship the gift / It came upon a midnight clear / Away in a manger / What child is this? / O little town of Bethlehem* / Gift goes on, The / Christmas was meant for children / Jesu Bambino: O holy night / Worship the King (reprise) / Celebrate the gift / Rejoice; for unto us a child is born / Hark the herald angels sing / Joy to the world / I wonder as I wander / O magnify the Lord / Bethlehem morning / Merry Christmas with love / Have yourself a merry little Christmas.
LP: . . . . WST R 9690
MC: . . . . WST C 9690

MAKE HIS PRAISE GLORIOUS.
LP: . . . . WST R 9064
MC: . . . . WST C 9064

MORNING LIKE THIS.
LP: . . . . WST R 9672
MC: . . . . WST C 9672

NO OTHER NAME.
LP: . . . . LD 5002
MC: . . . . LDC 5002

SANDI PATTI AND THE FRIENDSHIP COMPANY (Patti, Sandi/Friendship Company).
LP: . . . . WST R 9059
MC: . . . . WST C 9059

Pattinson, James

FLIGHT TO THE SEA.
MC: . . . . SOUND 25

Patto, Michael

TIME TO BE RIGHT.
Tracks: / So much for the lovin' / Calling / Few good moments / Hold on / Paradise has gone / (I've got) love enough for two / Time to be right / Very thought of you, The / What can I do / Don't say a word.
LP: . . . . ZL 74976
MC: . . . . ZK 74976

Patton

PATTON (Film soundtrack) (Various artists).
Tracks: / Patton speech: *Various artists* / Main title: *Various artists* / Battleground: *Various artists*/ First battle: *Various artists* / Attack: *Various artists* / Funeral: *Various artists* / Winter march: *Various artists* / Patton march: *Various artists* / No assignment: *Various artists* / German advice: *Various artists* / Hospital: *Various artists* / Payoff: *Various artists* / End title/Speech: *Various artists.*
LP: 810366.1
MC: 810366.4
LP: . . . . SSL 10302

PATTON (Film soundtrack) (Various artists).
LP: . . . . FILM 047
MC: . . . . FILMC 047

Patton, Charlie

FOUNDER OF DELTA BLUES.
2LP: . . . . L 1020

REMAINING TITLES 1929-34.
LP: . . . . WSE 103

Patton, John

BLUE JOHN.
Tracks: / Hot sauce / Bermuda clay house / Dem dirty dues / Country girl / Nicety / Blue John.
LP: . . . . BST 84143

SOUL CONNECTION.
LP: . . . . NQ 3406

Patton, Robbie

ORDERS FROM HEADQUARTERS.
Tracks: / Victim of your love / Louise / It's your heart / Lonely nights / Feel the flow / Orders from headquarters / Tell her goodbye / Smiling islands / All because of you / Look away.
LP: 780 006-1

Patton, Sims

PATTON, SIMS & BERTHA LEE (Patton, Sims & Bertha Lee).
LP: . . . . HER 213

Patton, Wayland

GULF STREAM DREAMIN'.
Tracks: / Gulf stream dreamin' / Fellow travellers / Rockin' the boat / Eight years down the road / Rock my chair / One horse town / We should only have time for love / Hoka hey / Evangelina / Knowin' when to leave the past behind.
MC: C4 93872

Pattullo, Gordon

ACCORDION FAVOURITES.
MC: . . . . CWGR 045
LP: . . . . WGR 045

ALL THE BEST.
Tracks: / Traveller, The / More luck to us / Rose in the garden / Mother-in-law / Come to the bottlehouse / Claybraes two step / Samba polka / Crags of Tumbledown Mountain / Falkland palace / Glencoe march / Braemar reel / Norwegian waltz / Banks of the Avon / Lady Elspeth Cameron / Doug Boyd's favourite / Pipe Major George Allan / Torrance's teaser / Margaret's waltz / Mormor's polka / Finstrom's polka / Vendome hornpipe / Comin' thro' the rye / Green grow the rushes-o / Scots wha' hae / My ain kind dearie / Susan C.MacLean / Achnashee fiddler / More toast for the boys / Tour of Mull / Auberge des cafards.
LP: . . . . LAP 118
MC: . . . . LAP 118 C

GORDON FOR YOU A.
LP: . . . . OU 2141

HERE'S TAE A GORDON.
Tracks: / Bluebird polka / Soldier boy / Laird of Drumblair, The / Mason's apron / Green hills of Tyrol / Road and the miles to Dundee, The / Take me back / Campbeltown Loch / Muckin' o' Geordie's byre / Donald, where's yer troosers / Wild rover / Old rustic bridge / Battle of the Somme / Black bear, The / Plaza polka / Flowers of Edinburgh / Miss Monaghan / Far from home / Bottom of the punchbowl / Seven stars / My Dungannon sweetheart / Jean's reel / Mull of Kintyre / Polka des as / There was a lad / Duncan Gray / Man's a man, A / Corn rigs / Star o' Rabbie Burns, The / Pipe Major William McLean / Kenneth MacDonald's jig / Brolum / Annie's song / High level, The.
LP: . . . . GES 1215
MC: . . . . KGEC 1215

NORTHLANDS - A SELECTION OF SCOTTISH MUSIC, THE.
LP: . . . . OU 2207

SCOTCH ON THE BOX.
LP: .... WGR 094
MC: .... CWGR 094

SCOTLAND'S FAVOURITE.
Tracks: / Bluebird polka / Andy Stewart medley / Plaza polka / Strathspey / Mull of Kintyre / March jig and reel / Soldier boy / Old rustic bridge / Flowers of Edinburgh / Hornpipe jig and reel / Marching with Burns / Annies song.
MC: .... 4 HOM 009
LP: .... GES 1204

Patty Hearst

PATTY HEARST (Film soundtrack) (Various artists).
Tracks: / Mom dad: *Various artists* / Cinque's vision: *Various artists* / My real crime: *Various artists*/ Rest home: *Various artists* / Persistence of vision: *Various artists* / Pen chorale: *Various artists*/ Closet: *Various artists* / Young once: *Various artists* / Motel: *Various artists* / Pistol rope: *Various artists* / Dad mom: *Various artists.*
LP: .... K 9791861
MC: .... K 9791864

Paul, Andrew

SOUND BOY BURIAL (See under General, Mikey) (Paul, Andrew & Mikey General).

Paul, Billy

6 TRACK HITS.
Tracks: / Me & Mrs Jones / Let's make a baby / Thanks for saving my life / Let 'em in / Don't give up on us / Brown baby.
MC: 7SC 5019

BEST OF.
Tracks: / Let 'em in / Only the strong survive / Don't give up on us / July july july / Without you / Bring the family back / Me and mrs jones / Let's make a baby / You're my sweetness / Thanks for saving my life / I trust you / Your song.
LP: .... PIR 84169

BILLY PAUL'S GREATEST HITS.
LP: .... PIR 32347
MC: 40 32347

FIRST CLASS.
Tracks: / False faces / Bring the family back / Game of life / It's critical / Thank you / What a way to love / So glad to see you again / Treasure of my life / I gotta put this life down.
LP: .... PIR 83481

LATELY.
Tracks: / Fire in her love / Sexual therapy / Lately / I search no more / I only have eyes for you / Hot date / Get down to lovin' / Let me in / Me and you / On a clear day.
LP: .... PL 85711
MC: .... PK 85711

LET 'EM IN.
Tracks: / Let 'em in / We all got a mission / How good is your game / Love won't come easy / Without you / Word sure gets around / I trust you / I think I'll stay home today.
LP: .... PIR 81695

ONLY THE STRONG SURVIVE.
Tracks: / Only the strong survive / Takin' it to the streets / Sooner or later / One man's junk / Everybody's breakin' up / Times of our lives / Don't give up on us / Where I belong.
LP: .... PIR 82236

SOUND OF SOUL, THE.
LP: .... BLATLP 14
MC: .... BLATMC 14

WHEN LOVE IS NEW.
Tracks: / People power / America (we need the light) / Let the dollar circulate / Malorie / When love is new / I wantcha baby / Let's make a baby.
LP: .... PIR 69207

WIDE OPEN.
LP: .... ICH 1025
MC: .... ZCICH 1025

Paul, Eugene

SENTIMENTAL REASON.
LP: .... WIR 12L 703

Paul, Frankie

AT HIS BEST.
LP: WRLP26

BARRINGTON LEVY MEETS FRANKIE PAUL (See under Levy, Barrington) (Paul, Frankie & Barrington Levy).

BE MY LADY.
Tracks: / Not a pretty gal / Stormy night / Out of the darkness / Just be my lady / She no ready yet / Level vibes / Come home baby / Memories.
LP: .... BMLP 053
LP: .... JGML 60077

CAN'T GET YOU OUT OF MY MIND.
MC: .... RRTGC 7780

CASANOVA.
LP: .... LALP 23
MC: .... LALC 23

CHAMPIONS CLASH, THE (Paul, Frankie & Leroy Sibbles).
Tracks: / I am in love / I don't know / Don't worry yourself / Weep and moan / I need your love / Broken heart / Sence for sale / Tug of war / We big / 16 lovers (remix).
LP: .... KVL 9024

CHATTE CHATTE (see under Brother D's nengeh nengeh).

CLASSIC, THE.
LP: .... TZLP 1001

CLOSE TO YOU.
LP: .... JMLP 003

DOUBLE TROUBLE (Paul, Frankie/ Michael Palmer).
Tracks: / It's too late / I'm attractive / Hold me / Better she go on / Them a chat / Pass the dub plate / Love is like a candy / Zion train / Where is that love / Tell me why.
LP: .... GREL 77
MC: .... GREEN 77

EASY MOVER.
LP: .... VALP 2

ELISHA.
LP: .... DSR 8616

GIVE ME THAT FEELING.
Tracks: / Tato / Tickle me / Don't pressure me / Ragamuffin / Hungrybelly / Warning / She's a maniac / Give me what we want / Rock you / Lady love.
LP: .... MR 1004

HEARTICAL DON.
LP: .... SPLP 104

LOVE AFFAIR.
LP: .... WRLP 22

LOVE LINE.
LP: .... GGLP 003

PASS THE TU-SHENG-PENG.
Tracks: / Pass the tu-sheng-peng / Jump no fence / Hot number / Hooligan / Only you / War is in the dance / Don't worry yourself / Prophet, The / Them a talk about / If you.
LP: .... GREL 75
MC: .... GREEN 75

REACHING OUT.
Tracks: / Jam it up / Skank with Frankie Paul / Dance have fi nice / Ethiopia here I come / I love you / Legal / Lover medley / People of the world / Watch the fool dem.
LP: .... BMLP 023
MC: .... BMC 023

RICH AND POOR.
LP: .... SALLP 1

RIPE MANGO.
LP: .... BDLP 001

RUB-A-DUB MARKET.
Tracks: / Rub-a-dub market / Little bit more, A / You're my love / Don man / Come in the dance / Here we go again / I'm missing you / Willi walli.
LP: .... ILPS 9882
MC: .... ICT 8992

SARAH.
LP: .... LALP 17
MC: .... LALC 17

SHOWDOWN VOLUME 6 (Paul, Frankie & Little John).
LP: .... JJ 168

SHUT UP B'WAY.
Tracks: / Touch me / Version / Shut up / We rule, A / Call the brigade / Don't go changing.
LP: .... RMM 1386

SIZZLING.
LP: .... SKDLP 009

SLOW DOWN.
LP: .... VPREL 1034
MC: .... VPREC 1034
LP: .... REDLP 14

STRANGE FEELING.
LP: .... Unknown

STRICTLY REGGAE MUSIC.
LP: .... LDR LP 008

TIDAL WAVE.
Tracks: / Dem a go feel it / Beat down the fence / Baby come home / Music is the staff of life / She's got style / Tidal wave / Your love is amazing / King champion / You too greedy / Hold me.
LP: .... GREL 79
MC: .... GREEN 79

TRUE.
LP: .... BSLP 8801

TURBO CHARGE (Paul, Frankie & Pinchers).
Tracks: / I need you / Kuff / Chat mi back / Life is a gamble / Traveller, The / I'm in love again / Musical calamity / Memories of love.
LP: .... SUPLP 1
MC: .... SUPLC 1

WARNING.
Tracks: / Tato / Tickle me / Don't pressure me / Ragamuffin / Hungry belly / Warning / She's a maniac / Give me what we want / Rock you / Lady love.
LP: .... RAS 3027
MC: .... RASC 3027

Paul, Les

16 ORIGINAL HITS (Paul, Les & Mary Ford).
MC: .... MC 1630

ALL TIME GREATEST HITS (Paul, Les & Mary Ford).
Tracks: / How high the moon / Jazz me blues / I'm sitting on top of the world / Nola / Bye bye blues / Chicken reel / Jealous / Lover / Little Rock getaway / I'm forever blowing bubbles / Goofus / St. Louis blues / La Rosita / World is waiting for the sunrise, The / Carioca / Vaya con Dios / Johnny is the boy for me / Walkin' and whistlin' blues / Tiger rag / Lady of Spain / Mockin' Bird Hill / Whispering / Tico tico / Meet Mr Callaghan / Mr. Sandman / Tennessee waltz / I'm a fool to care / 12th Street rag / Falling in love with love / Best things in life are free, The.
LP: 5C 134 53027/28

ALL-TIME HITS (Paul, Les & Mary Ford).
MC: 4XL 9101

CAPITOL YEARS, THE: LES PAUL AND MARY FORD (Best of) (Paul, Les & Mary Ford).
Tracks: / Whispering / World is waiting for the sunrise, The / Lover / Mockin' Bird Hill / Nola / That old feeling / Little Rock getaway / Bye bye blues / Twelfth St. rag / I'm sitting on top of the world / Chicken reel / How high the moon / Walkin' and whistlin' blues / How deep is the ocean / Tico tico / Vaya con dios.
LP: .... EMS 1309
MC: .... TCEMS 1309

CHESTER AND LESTER (see under Atkins, Chet) (Paul, Les & Chet Atkins).

FEEDBACK (1944-1945) (Paul, Les & His Trio).
LP: .... CLP 67

GUITAR MONSTERS (see under Atkins, Chet) (Paul, Les & Chet Atkins).

LES PAUL AND MARY FORD (EMI) (Paul, Les & Mary Ford).
Tracks: / Mississippi blues / Carry me on / Je t'aime la vie / La ballade du chien loup.
LP: 1A 022 58099
MC: 1A 222 58099

LES PAUL AND MARY FORD (ENTERTAINERS) (Paul, Les & Mary Ford).
Tracks: / Three little words / I can't give you anything but love / Vaya con Dios / Just one more chance / Carioca / In the good old Summertime / Moon of Manakoora, The / Lover / How high the moon / I'm confessin' / Bye bye blues / Whispering / Lonesome road / Don'cha hear them bells / How deep is the ocean / World is waiting for the sunrise, The.
LP: .... ENT LP 13014
MC: .... ENT MC 13014

NEW SOUND VOLUME II, THE (Paul, Les & Mary Ford).
Tracks: / In the good old summertime / Three little words / Lonesome road / Chicken reel / I'm confessin' / Carioca / I can't give you anything but love / Just one more chance / I'm forever blowing bubbles / Moon of Manakoora / Don'cha hear them bells / La rosita.
LP: .... EMS 1138
MC: .... TCEMS 1138

VERY BEST OF LES PAUL AND MARY FORD (Paul, Les & Mary Ford).
Tracks: / How high the moon / I'm sitting on top of the world / I'm forever blowing bubbles / Nola / Bye bye blues / Chicken reel / Jealous / Lover / Little rock getaway / Goofus / Jazz me blues / St. Louis blues / La Rosita / World is waiting for the sunrise, The / Carioca / Vaya Con Dios.
LP: .... MFP 5604
MC: .... TCMFP 5604

Paul, Owen

AS IT IS.
Tracks: / Pleased to meet you / Somebody's angel / My favourite waste of time / Sonny / Just another day / One world / Only for the young (Remix) / Prime time / Paraoh / Bring me back that spark.
LP: .... EPC 57114
MC: 40 57114

MY FAVOURITE WASTE OF TIME (OLD GOLD) (See under Wilder, Matthew - Break My Stride).

Paul & Sharon

TAKE THE TIME.
LP: .... PC 121

Paulas Country

WELCOME TO PAULA'S COUNTRY.
LP: .... BSS 206

Paulin, Tom

CORNET SOLOS.
Tracks: / Maid of the mist / Berceuse / Stars in a velvety sky / Twilight dreams / My regards / David of the white rock / Sounds from the Hudson / Castles in the air / Venus waltz / Hebe lullaby / Grand Russian fantasia.
LP: .... LKLP 7050

Paulo, Michael

FUSEBOX.
Tracks: / Story of O, The / Fusebox / Don't let go / Love will come again / In the spirit / Miles calling / Stolen lover No. 4 / Rainbow room / When I need you / Story of O, The - reprise (rap version).
LP: .... GRP 96231
MC: .... GRP 96234

ONE PASSION.
LP: .... MCA 42295
MC: .... MCAC 42295

Paulo, Pedro

PEDRO PAULO, CASTRO NEVES AND MICHAEL LEGRAND (Paulo, Pedro, Castro Neves & Michel Legrand).
LP: 7703

Pauly, Danielle

FLEUR DU JURA.
Tracks: / Reve gourmand (Waltz) / L'epatante (Polka) / Ballade matinale (March) / Delice Catalan (Tango) / Rapide digitale (Polka) / Carte postale (Waltz) / Ballade Vosgienne (Polka) / Clin d'oeil (Java) / File Indienne (March) / Piccolo rag (Rag) / Fleur du Jura (Polka) / Exotic samba (Samba) / Souffle Andalou (Tango) / Matin tonique (Not a military march,more suited to bombing along a m-way at an early hr) / Eclats de rire (Novelty foxtrot) / Melody bolero (Bolero) / Valse des lucioles (Waltz).
LP: .... SDL 353
MC: .... CSDL 353

Paupers

MAGIC PEOPLE.
Tracks: / Magic people / It's your mind / Black thank you package / Let me be / Think I care / White song / One rainy day / Tudor impressions / My love hides from your view / You and me / South Down Road / Cairo hotel / Can't go on / Another man's hair on my razor / Numbers / Oh that she might / Yes I know / Ask her again / Juliana.
2LP: .... DED 253

Pauvros, Jean-Francois

LE GRAND AMOUR.
Tracks: / Cri du coeur / Juste un peu de brume / Other side, The / Los paranoidos / Philippine / Chante nix / Alors / Arithmetique amoureuse / Pas decales soixante-deux.
LP: .... NATO 599

Pavane

LIKE ODYSSEUS.
MC: .... FC 09

Pavarotti, Luciano

60 MINUTES OF MUSIC.
Tracks: / Vesti la giubba / Celeste aida / O mes amis....pour mon ame / E Lucevan le stelle / Che gelida manina / Di quella pira / Panis angelicus / Una furtiva lagrima / O Fede negar potessi....Quando sere al placido / Questa o quella / Cielo e mar / Nessun dorma / Che faro senza euridice.
MC: 4173984

COLLECTION, THE.
Tracks: / Quand le sere al Palcido / Fra poco a me ricovero / Questa o quella / La Donna e mobile / Ouverture / Mamma / Rondine al nido / Lolita / Il volo del calabrone / Amor ti vieta / Non ti scordar di me / Che gelida manina / O sole mio / Torna a surriento/ Nessuno dorma.
MC: .... CCSMC 288

ESSENTIAL PAVAROTTI, THE.
LP: 4302101
MC: 4302104
MC: 4302102

GREATEST HITS: PAVAROTTI.
LP: .... D 2362

IN CONCERT (WITH CARRERAS, DOMINGO AND MEHTA) (See under Carreras, Jose).

MAMMA (Popular Italian Songs).
Tracks: / Mamma / Non ti scordar di me / Lolita / Musica probita / Firenze sogna / Vivere / Par lami d'amour / In un palco della scala / Addio sogni di Gloria / Voglio vivere cosi / Chitarra Romana / Rondine al nido / La Ghirlandeina / La

mia canzone al vento / Vieni sul mar / La campana di San Giusto.
LP: 4119591
MC: 4119594

NEW PAVAROTTI COLLECTION, THE (Live).
Tracks: / Peccia Lolita Riocardi / Amor ti vieta / Vesti la giubba / Chitarra romana / Il volo del calabrone (flight of the bumble bee) / La mia canzone al vento / Overture (La Gazza Ladra) / Ole sole mio / Che gelida manina / Quando lesere of Placido / Fra poco a me ricovero / Questa o quella / La donna e mobile / Non ti scorda di me / Cherubini momma / Rondine al nido / Torna a Surriento / Nessun dorma.
2LP: . . . . SMR 857
MCSET: . . . . SMC 857

PAVAROTTI COLLECTION.
Tracks: / La donna mobile / 'M' Appari' / Celeste Aida / Parmi veder leagrime / Che faro senza euridice / O paradiso / Donna mon vidi mai / Mattinata / La serenata / Luna d'estate / Vaga luna / Lamento di federico / Saluti demeure / Questa o quella / Messun dorma / Pourquoi me reveiller / Vesti la giubba / Cujus animam / Caro mio ben / Mari Chiare / Di quella pira / O sole mio / A vucchella / Panis Angelicus / Spirito gentil / Flower song / Torna a surriento.
2LP: . . . . SMR 8617
MCSET: . . . . SMC 8617

PAVAROTTI FAVOURITES.
Tracks: / Oh fede negar potessi...quando le sere al Placido (From "Luisa Miller") / Una furtiva lagrima (L'elisir d'amore) / Torna a surriento / Lucia, perdona...addio! (Lucia de Lammermoor) / Ingemisco (Requiem) / Ave Maria / Questa o quella (Rigoletto) / La Donna e Mobile (Rigoletto) / Che gelida manina (La Boheme) / Cielo e mar (La Gioconda) / Ogni mortal...giunto sul passo (Mefistofele) / E lucevan le stelle (Tosca) / Che faro senza euridice (Orfeo ed euridice) / La danza / Nussun dorma (Turandot).
LP: 417 240-1
MC: 417 240-4

VOLARE.
Tracks: / Volare / Occhi di fata / La strade del bosco / La girometta / Malinconia d'amore / Chi e piu felice di me? / Luna marinara / Fra tanta gente / Fiorin fiorello / Ti voglio tanto bene / Una chitarra nella notte / La canzone dell' amore / Cantate con me / Serenata / Dimmi tu primavera / Un amore cosi grande.
LP: 4210521
MC: 4210524

Paverty, Franklin B.

SONGS FROM THE AUSTRALIAN GOLDRUSH.
LP: . . . . LRF 173

Pavlov's Dog

AT THE SOUND OF THE BELL.
Tracks: / She came shining / Standing here with you (Megan's song) / Mersey / Valkene / Try to hang on / Gold nuggets / She breaks like a morning sky / Early morning on / Did you see him cry?.
LP: . . . . CBS 81163

PAMPERED MENIAL.
Tracks: / Julia / Late November / Song dance / Fast gun / Natchez trace / Subway Sue, Theme from / Episode / Preludin / Of once and future kings.
LP: . . . . CBS 80872

Pawlak, Andy

SHOEBOX FULL OF SECRETS.
LP: 836904-1
MC: 836904-4

Pawnbroker

PAWNBROKER (See under Klugh, Earl 'Night songs') (Klugh, Earl).

Paxton, George

GEORGE PAXTON, 1944-45.
Tracks: / Screamliner / Gotta be this or that / All of me / Clear out of this world / Solid mahogany / Blue Lou / Paxonia / This can't be love / I'm gonna see my baby / Anytime / I'm coming Virginia / Jug night.
LP: . . . . HSR 183

Paxton, Tom

AND LOVING YOU.
Tracks: / Last hobo, The / Nothing but time / Home to me / Love changes the world / Missing you, the / You are love / And lovin' you / Every time / Bad old days / Panhandle wind / When we were good / All coming together.
LP: . . . . FF 414

COMPLEAT TOM PAXTON, THE.
Tracks: / Clarissa Jones / Things I notice now / Jennifer's rabbit / Give you the morning / Marvellous toy, The / Leaving London / Angie / All night long / Bayonet rap / Pot luck blues / Jimmy Newman / Outward bound / Morning again / I can't help but wonder where I'm bound / My lady's a wild flying dove / Now that I've taken my life / About the children / Ballad of Spiro Agnew / Mr. Blue / I wish I had a troubadour / Every time / When we are gone / Cindy's crying / Hooker / My rambling boy / Last thing on my mind.
2LP: . . . . K 62004
MC: . . . . K 462004
2LP: . . . . EKD 2003

EVEN A GREY DAY.
Tracks: / Even a grey day / I give you the morning / Love of loving you, The / When Annie took me home / Dance in the shadows / Annie's going to sing her song / Corrymeela / Outward bound / Wish I had a troubador / Hold on to me babe / Last thing on my mind.
LP: . . . . SDLP 027
LP: . . . . FF 280

HEROES.
LP: . . . . VSD 79411

IN THE ORCHARD.
Tracks: / Bottle of wine / Thank you Republic Airlines / Only a game / Not tonight Marie / Dear diary / Perfect bomb, The / Little bitty gun, A / I thought you were an A-rab / I'm changing my name to Chrysler / Mail will go through, The / I don't want a bunny wunny.
LP: . . . . PIPLP 711
MC: . . . . ZCPIP 711
LP: . . . . SDLP 062

MARVELLOUS TOY AND OTHER GALLIMAUFRY, THE.
Tracks: / Englebert the elephant / Jennifer's rabbit / Katy / Going to the zoo / Grey mares.
LP: . . . . PIPLP 701
MC: . . . . ZCPLP 701
LP: . . . . FF 408
LP: . . . . SDLP 065

NEW SONGS FOR OLD FRIENDS.
Tracks: / Hobo in my mind / When we were good / Who's been passing dreams around / When Annie took me home / Katy / Fred / Wasn't that a party / Faces and places / When you shook your long hair down / Silent night / When princes meet.
LP: . . . . K 44237

NEW SONGS FROM THE BRIER PATCH.
MC: . . . . VMTC 5313
LP: . . . . VNLP 6313

NO. 6.
LP: 2469-003

ONE MILLION LAWYERS AND OTHER DISASTERS.
LP: . . . . FF 356

PAXTON REPORT, THE.
Tracks: / We all sound the same / I don't want a bunny wunny / I'm changing my name to Chrysler / Be a sport / Afghanistan / She sits on the table / He may be slow / I thought you were an Arab / Mary got a new job / All clear in Harrisburg / We live on the water / Gas line romance.
LP: . . . . EVLP 5
MC: . . . . EVK 5

PEACE WILL COME.
LP: . . . . K 44182

POLITICS - LIVE.
LP: . . . . FF 486

STORYTELLER.
LP: . . . . STFL 4
MC: . . . . STFC 4

UP AND UP.
Tracks: / Has Annie been in tonight? / That's the way it seems to me / My favourite spring / Home to me / Feed the children / Bad old days / Hush old man / Life / Outlaw / Let the sunshine.
LP: . . . . EVLP 2

VERY BEST OF TOM PAXTON.
LP: . . . . STL 14
MC: . . . . STC 14
LP: . . . . FF 519

Pay Any Price (bk)

PAY ANY PRICE (Ted Allbeury) (Harte, Jerry).
MC: . . . . CAB 307

Paycheck, Johnny

APARTMENT NO 9.
Tracks: / Apartment No.9 / My baby don't love me anymore / Just between you and me / Yesterday, today and tomorrow / Here we go again / He's in a hurry (to get home to my wife) / Handcuffed to love / Big town baby / Understanding makes love / Fools' hall of fame / Tell me your troubles (I'll tell you mine) / Make me one more memory.
LP: . . . . PRCV 100
LP: . . . . PRC 100

ARMED AND CRAZY.
Tracks: / Friend, lover, wife / Armed and crazy / Mainline / Thanks to the cathouse / Leave it to me / Me and the IRS / Let's have a hand for the little lady / Just makin' love don't make it love / Look what the dog drug in / Outlaw's prayer.
LP: . . . . EPC 83499

BACK ON THE JOB.
LP: 20031
MC: 40031

BIGGEST HITS.
Tracks: / She's all I got / Someone to give my love to / Love is a good thing / Something about you I love / Mr. Love maker / Song and dance man / My part of forever / Outlaws prayer / Take this job & shove it / Slide off your satin sheets / I'm the only hell / Me & the I.R.S. / Friend, lover, wife / Cocaine train / Drinkin' and drivin' / For a minute there.
MC: 40 32305
LP: . . . . EPC 32305

DOUBLE TROUBLE (See under Jones, George) (Jones, George & Johnny Paycheck).

EVERYBODY'S GOT A FAMILY, MEET MINE.
Tracks: / Cocaine train / Ragged old truck / Drinkin' and drivin' / Who was that man that beat me so / Billy Bardo / Fifteen beers / Low class reunion / I never met a girl I didn't like / Save your heart for me / Roll in my sweet baby's arms.
LP: . . . . EPC 84112

GOLDEN CLASSICS.
LP: . . . . GT 0098

HONKY TONK AND SLOW MUSIC.
Tracks: / Honky tonk and slow music / Nowhere to run / I feel like crying / I'm remembering / Coming home to my heart / Make me one more memory / I'm a coward / Keeping up with the Joneses / I don't know when that will be / Johnsons of Turkey Ridge, The.
MC: . . . . SDC 1047
LP: . . . . SDLP 1047

I DON'T NEED TO KNOW THAT RIGHT NOW.
Tracks: / Happy hour / I've had mine / Georgia in a jug / She's all I got / Song and dance man / I don't need to know that right now / Take this job and shove it / Slide off your satin sheets / Somebody loves me / Jeannie in a bottle.
LP: . . . . ALEB 2301
MC: . . . . ZCALB 2301

JOHNNY PAYCHECK.
MC: . . . . ZCGAS 753

JUKEBOX CHARLIE.
Tracks: / Jukebox Charlie / I never had the one I wanted / Everything you touch turns to hurt / Wildfire / Talk to my children mama / If I'm gonna sink / Help me Hank, I'm fallin' / California dreams / Billy Jack Washburn / Lovin machine, The / There's no easy way to die / It's for sure I can't go on / My worst is the best I can give / These things I'm not.
LP: . . . . PRCV 109

MR. HAG TOLD MY STORY.
Tracks: / Turnin' off a memory / I've got a yearning / Carolyn / I'll leave the bottle on the bar / All night lady / I can't hold myself in line / Yesterdays's news just hit home today / You don't have very far to go / No more you and me / Someone told my story.
LP: . . . . EPC 84847

Payere

PEYERE (Various artists).
MC: . . . . PEY 86

Payne, Anthony

PHOENIX MASS (ANTHONY PAYNE).
LP: . . . . REH 297

Payne, Cecil

BIRD GETS THE WORM.
LP: . . . . MR 5061

BRIGHT MOMENTS.
Tracks: / Violets for your furs / Skylark / Lover man / Equinoxe / Disorder at the border / Bright moments / Solar / Speak low.
LP: . . . . SPJ LP 21

BROOKFIELD ANDANTE.
Tracks: / Opener, The / Sterling place / Brookfield andante / Azoff blues.
LP: . . . . CP 2

CONNECTION, THE (Payne, Cecil/ Clark Terry & Bennie Green).
Tracks: / Stop and listen / Born again blues / Dear people / Kenny's one / Sister Carol / Mighty fine wine / It's your life.
LP: . . . . JR 105

Payne, Cy

CHEEK TO CHEEK (Payne, Cy Band).
LP: . . . . FKLP 101

LATIN MAGIC OF CY PAYNE.
LP: . . . . MTS 15

Payne, Devin

EXCUSE ME.
LP: 2302 105

Payne, Freda

BANDS OF GOLD.
LP: . . . . HDH LP 002

DEEPER AND DEEPER (The Best of Freda Payne).
Tracks: / Unhooked generation / I left some dreams back there / Rock me in the cradle of love / Cherish what is dear to you / Mama's gone / Bring the boys home / You brought the joy / I'm not getting any better / You've got to love somebody / Road we didn't take, The / He's my life / Band of gold / Deeper and deeper / Easiest way to fall, The / Now is the time to say goodbye / Just a woman / Through the memory of my mind / World don't owe you a thing, The / Suddenly it's yesterday / How can I live without my life / Odds and ends / You're the only bargain I've got.
LP: . . . . HDH LP 005

GREATEST HITS: FREDA PAYNE.
LP: . . . . BRLP 62
MC: . . . . BRMC 62

Payne, Gordon

GORDON PAYNE.
Tracks: / Down on love / Blackmail / Fool proof / Babe naked / Oklahoma posse / Go ask her / Redlight / Fumblin' with the blues / Green eyes / Flow river flow.
LP: . . . . SP 4725

Payne, Jack

GOLDEN AGE OF JACK PAYNE THE.
LP: . . . . GX 41 2535 4

I'LL STRING ALONG WITH YOU.
Tracks: / This'll make you whistle / My song for you / Tina / I'll string along with you / Little valley in the mountains / Over my shoulder / Guilty / Isle of Capri / Close your eyes / Until the real thing comes along / Nun-yuff and sun-yuff / Juba, The / Organ grinder's swing / Shadows on the pavement / When your hair has turned to silver / When it's Springtime in the Rockies / Just imagine / Sunny days.
LP: . . . . BUR 008
MC: . . . . 4 BUR 008

IMPERIAL DAYS, THE.
Tracks: / Smile and sing your cares away / Paradise / Love is the sweetest thing / Was that the human thing to do? / Good morning Mr. Sun / Love me tonight / Lullaby of the leaves / By the sycamore tree / Good evening / Auf wiedersehen my dear / While we danced at the Mardi Gras / I'll do my best to make you happy / Wanderer / She didn't say yes / Ooh that kiss / Where the blue of the night.
LP: . . . . JOY 273
MC: . . . . TC JOY'D 273
LP: . . . . D 273

JACK PAYNE.
LP: . . . . SH 143

RADIO NIGHTS, 1928-31 (Payne, Jack & His BBC Dance Orchestra).
Tracks: / Radio nights / I've got a feeling I'm falling / Anything you say / If I could be with you one hour tonight / Old Italian love song / I'm crazy over you / Sweet Sue / Moonlight saving time / Down by the old front gate / Here comes Emily Brown / My baby just cares for me / Make yourself a happiness pie / You're driving me crazy / Dicky bird told me so / She's my slip of a girl / Exactly like you / Haven't I? / Haven't heard a single word from baby / Look in her eyes / I like a little girl like that.
LP: . . . . SVL 152
MC: . . . . CSVL 152

RHYTHMATITIS.
Tracks: / Yes sir, that's my baby / Sally's come back / Out of the dawn / Sweet Sue / Little dicky bird told me so, A / I faw down an' go boom / Blondy / When it's Springtime in the Rockies / Moochi, The / My baby just cares for me / If I could be with you (one hour tonight) / Lady of Spain / River stay 'way from my door / Miss Elizabeth Brown / Lazy day / When the moon comes over the mountain / Rhythmatitis / Guilty / Love letters in the sand / Hot coffee.
LP: . . . . SH 508
MC: . . . . TC SH 508

Payne, John

RAZOR'S EDGE THE (Payne, John Band).
LP: . . . . FLP 41036

Payolas

IN A PLACE LIKE THIS.
Tracks: / In a place like this / I'm sorry / Jukebox / Whiskey boy / Good job / You

can't walk away / Too shy to dance / Hot tonight / Female hands / Comfortable / China boys.
LP: . . . . **SP 70017**

NO STRANGER TO DANGER.
Tracks: / Romance / Mystery to me.
LP: . . . . **AMLH 64908**

Pays Catalan

COBLA PRINCIPAL DFE GERONA (Cobla Pe).
LP: . . . . **VG 400634**

Payton, Walter

NEW ORLEANS MUSIC OF WALTER PAYTON, THE.
MC: . . . . **TC 024**

WOLVERINE BLUES (See also under Teddy Riley & Jim Duggan).

Paz

ALWAYS THERE.
Tracks: / Right moment, The / Big shot / Angels delight / For art / I can see you / You've got something / Be natural / Hold back / Always there.
LP: . . . . **CODA 21**
MC: . . . . **COCA 21**

KANDEEN LOVE SONG.
Tracks: / Crotales / Solar wind / Bell tree / Yours is the light / Buddha / Time stood still / Kandeen.
LP: . . . . **SPJ 507**

LOOK INSIDE.
Tracks: / AC/DC / Cravo e canela / One hundred / Sunny day / Making smiles / Bags / Look inside / Three blonde mice / Nightbird.
MC: . . . . **PALC 001**
LP: . . . . **CODA 18**
LP: . . . . **PALP 001**

MESSAGE, THE.
Tracks: / Xenon / Message, the / Party, The / Citron presse / Slide time / Nylon stockings.
LP: . . . . **CHELP 6**
MC: . . . . **CHEMC 6**

PAZ ARE BACK.
Tracks: / Laying eggs / Horrors / AC/DC / Where is Ron? / Moonchild / I can't remember / Iron works / Everywhere Calypso, The / Dancing in the dark.
LP: . . . . **SPJ 518**

Peabody, Dave

AMERICANA.
Tracks: / On a monday / What are they doing in heaven today? / Sewing machine blues / Boot that thing / Lonesome man blues / Tu partida / Great dreams of heaven / Cincinnati underworld woman.
LP: . . . . **WF 033**

COME AND GET IT.
LP: . . . . **AP 019**

DOWN THE ROAD APIECE (see Hall, Bob) (Hall, Bob & Dave Peabody).
LP: . . . . **AP 025**

PAYDAY.
LP: . . . . **WF 001**

ROLL AND SLIDE (see Hall, Bob) (Peabody, Dave & Bob Hall).

P.E.A.C.E. Compilation

P.E.A.C.E. COMPILATION (Various artists).
LP: . . . . **RR 1984**

Peace In The Valley

PEACE IN THE VALLEY (22 Religious Favourites).
LP: . . . . **RTL 2043**
MC: . . . . **RTLC 2043**

Peaceful Revolution

PEACEFUL REVOLUTION By Laurens Van Der Post.
MC: . . . . **SS 117**

Peaches & Herb

SAYIN' SOMETHING.
LP: . . . . **PD 16332**

TWICE THE FIRE.
Tracks: / Roller skatin' mate / I pledge my love / Gypsy lady / Howzabout some love / Gettin' down, gettin' down / Put it there / Back together / Love lift.
LP: **2391433**

TWO HOT.
Tracks: / We've got love / Shake your groove thing / Reunited / All your love / Love it up tonight / Four's a traffic jam / Star of my life / Easy as pie.
LP: **239 237 8**

WELL WORTH THE WAIT.
LP: **2391 484**

Peacock, Annette

ABSTRACT CONTACT.
LP: . . . . **IRONIC 5**

BEEN IN THE STREETS TOO LONG.
Tracks: / Been in the streets too long / So hard, it hurts / Song to seperate, A / Half broken / Safe inside the fantasy / Pillow lined prison / No winning, no losing.
LP: . . . . **IRONIC 3**

I HAVE NO FEELINGS.
Tracks: / Nothing ever was, anyway / Butterflies / I'm not perfect / I have no feelings / Cynic,The / Carousel / You've left me / Sincereless / Freefall / This almost spring / Feeling's free, The / Personal revolution, A / Not enough.
LP: . . . . **IRONIC 4**

I'M THE ONE.
Tracks: / I'm the one / Seven days / Pony / Been and gone / Blood / One way / Love me tender / Gesture without plot / Did you hear me mommy.
LP: . . . . **NL 89900**
MC: . . . . **NK 89900**

PERFECT RELEASE.
Tracks: / Love's out to lunch / Solar systems / American sport / Loss of consiousness / Rubber hunger / Succubus / Survival.
LP: . . . . **AUL 707**

SKY-SKATING.
LP: . . . . **IRONIC 2**

X-DREAMS.
Tracks: / My mama never taught me how to cook / Real and defined androgens / Dear Bela / This feeling within / Too much in the skies / Don't be cruel / Questions.
LP: . . . . **AUL 702**
LP: . . . . **LILP 400490**

Peacock, Charlie

LIE DOWN IN THE GRASS.
LP: . . . . **ER 0008**
MC: . . . . **TC ER 0008**

Peacock, Gary

DECEMBER POEMS.
LP: . . . . **ECM 1119**

GUAMBA.
Tracks: / Guamba / Requiem / Celina / Thyme time / Lila / Introending / Gardenia.
LP: . . . . **ECM 1352**

SHIFT IN THE WIND.
Tracks: / So green / Fractions / Last first / Shift in the wind centers / Caverns beneath the zoth / Valentine.
LP: . . . . **ECM 1165**

TALES OF... (Peacock, Gary, K. Jarrett & J. DeJohnette).
LP: . . . . **ECM 1101**

TALES OF ANOTHER.
Tracks: / Vignette / Tone field / Major / Trilogy / Trilogy (II) / Trilogy (III).
MC: **7104659**

VOICES FROM THE PAST - PARADIGM.
LP: . . . . **ECM 1210**

Peak

EBONDAZZAR.
LP: . . . . **KS 80044**

Peak Folk

PEAK FOLK, THE.
Tracks: / Banks of Newfoundland / Arabella's reef / Whistle's blowin' / Casey's last ride / Hangman and the Papist / Stanton drew / Fine hunting day / Backwaterside / King comes riding, The / Mr. Sax / Rout of the blues, The / Parting glass, The.
LP: . . . . **FHR 082**

Peanut Butter

TURN ON A FRIEND.
Tracks: / It's a happening thing / Then came love / Twice is life / Why did I get so high / Dark on you now / Market place, The / You should now / Most up til now, The / Turn on a friend / Too many do / Living, loving, life / Invasion of the poppy people / Living dream / Ecstacy / Time is after you / Wonderment.
LP: . . . . **DO 2000**

Pearce, Alison

LAND OF HEART'S DESIRE.
LP: . . . . **E 77088**

MY LAGAN LOVE (AND OTHER SONGS OF IRELAND) (Pearce, Alison/ Susan Drake).
Tracks: / Castle of Dromore, The / She moved through the fair / Next market day / Gartan mothers lullaby / I have a bonnet trimmed with blue / Little boats / I will walk with my love / Star of the County Down.
MC: . . . . **KH 88023**
LP: . . . . **A 66023**

SONGS OF THE HEBRIDES (Pearce, Alison/Susan Drake).
Tracks: / Isle of my heart / Leaping galley / Spinning song / Sea longing / Crone's reel / Caristiona / Ullapool sailor's song / Eriskay lullaby / Reiving ships / O heartling of my heart / Birlinn of the white shoulders / Islay reapers' song / Ailein Duinn / Ship at sea / Loch Broom love song / Kirsteen / Sea wandering / Uncanny mannikin of the cattlefold / Death farewell.
MC: . . . . **KH 88024**
LP: . . . . **A 66024**

Pearce, Bob

HEY HEY THE BLUES IS ALRIGHT (Pearce, Bob & His Blues Band).
LP: . . . . **BLUH 012**

Pearce, Monty

EVERYONES A WINNER (The M.P Sound).
LP: . . . . **BTS 1009**

KING OF THE ROAD.
Tracks: / Heartaches by the number / Shades of gold / Crystal chandeliers / Welcome to my world / King of the road / One has my name, the other my heart / Hello Mary Lou / Oh Lonesome me / I love you so much it hurts / After all these years / From a jack to king / Candy kisses / Take these chains from my heart.
LP: . . . . **BTS 1014**
LP: . . . . **SAV 158**

LET'S BE HAPPY (Pearce, Monty Sound).
LP: . . . . **SAV 159**
MC: . . . . **SAVC 159**

MAGIC MOMENTS (Pearce, Monty & His Musicians).
Tracks: / Magic moments / Arm in arm / Girl of my dreams / You were meant for me / Sweet Georgia Brown / Teddy bears' picnic / Sunset in Menorca / Thorn birds / Spain / La rosa blanca / Sweet and gentle / My man / Eye level / Always in my heart.
LP: . . . . **DS 066**

MONTY PEARCE SOUND, THE.
LP: . . . . **BTS 1011**

Pearce, Philippa (nar)

BATTLE OF BUBBLE AND SQUEAK, THE (See under Battle of Bubble ....

Pearce-Pickering

1975-76 (Pearce-Pickering Barrelhouse Jazz Band).
LP: **2LP 001**

BARRELHOUSE JB.
LP: . . . . **S 1404**

FLANAGAN'S SHENANIGANS (1971-72) (Pearce-Pickering Ragtime Five).
LP: . . . . **S 1309**

RED HOT AND BLUE (Pearce-Pickering Barrelhouse Jazz Band).
LP: . . . . **CFPS 122**

TIN LIZZIE DAYS (1970-71) (Pearce-Pickering Ragtime Five).
LP: . . . . **S 1293**

Pearl of Babar Shah,

PEARL OF BABAR SHAH, THE (Various artists).
Tracks: / Pearl of Babar Shah: *Various artists* / Elephant: *Various artists* / Bird who told lies, The: *Various artists* / Queen precious pearl: *Various artists* / Clever jackal, The: *Various artists* / Man who loved horses, The: *Various artists.*
MC: . . . . **ANV 638**

Pearls Before Swine

BEST OF PEARLS BEFORE SWINE.
2LP: . . . . **AD 4111**

Pears, Peter

FOLK SONGS (Pears, Peter & Benjamin Britten).
Tracks: / Brisk young widow / O waly, waly / Sweet Polly Oliver / Early one morning / Bonnie Earl o'Moray, The / Ash grove, The / Come you not from Newcastle? / Le roi s'en va - t'en chasse / La Belle est au jardin d'amour / Minstrel boy / How sweet the answer / Last rose of summer / Evening and bright / Oft in the stilly night / Miller of Dee, The / Ca' the yowes / Ploughboy, The.
LP: **4118021**
MC: **4118024**
LP: . . . . **REGL 417**

Pearson, Brian

TAM LIN (see Armstrong, Frankie) (Pearson, Brian/Frankie Armstrong/ Blowzabella/Jon Gillaspie).

Pearson, Chris

CHRIS PEARSON.
LP: . . . . **DID 716**

Pearson, Duke

WAHOO.
Tracks: / Amanda / Bedouin / Farewell Machelle / Wahoo / E.S.P. (extra sensory perception) / Fly, little bird fly.
LP: . . . . **BST 84191**

Pearson, Johnny

BRIGHT EYES (Pearson, Johnny Orchestra).
Tracks: / You don't bring me flowers / Don't cry for me Argentina / Raining in my heart / Just the way you are / You are the one / Cavatina / Bright eyes / You needed me / Loving you is easy / Annie's song / Stay with me forever / House of Caradus theme.
LP: . . . . **RAMP 7**

GOLDEN HOUR OF SOUNDS ORCHESTRAL WITH ... (Pearson, Johnny Orchestra).
Tracks: / Cast your fate to the wind / What a wonderful world / Moon river / Stranger on the shore / Guantanamera / Chopin's nocturne in E flat, Opus 8 / Petite fleur / Moonglow / Picnic (theme from) / Carnival imanha de carnava from Black Orpheus / Many moons ago / Good morning starshine / Do you know the way to San Jose / Poor people of Paris, The / Canadian sunset / Romance on the North Sea / Starblow / Red roses for a blue lady / Pretty flamingo / Waltz of the flowers 'Valee des fleurs' / Exodus (Main theme).
MC: . . . . **KGHMC 136**

ON GOLDEN POND (Pearson, Johnny Orchestra).
Tracks: / On golden pond / For youe eyes only / Waiting for you / Sukiyaki / Together / I wish I knew how it feels to be free / Chariots of fire / One day ion your life / White sands / Cast your fate to the wind / Love match / Chi mai.
LP: . . . . **PAGS 701**

THEMES AND DREAMS (Pearson, Johnny Orchestra).
Tracks: / Godfather, The / House of Caradus (theme) / All creatures great and small / Love dream / Chi mai / First love / Triangle (love theme and intro) / Chariots of fire (theme) / You are the one / Seduction, The / Love dreamer / Cavatina / I wish I knew how it feels to be free / Love story (theme).
LP: . . . . **PRCV 132**
MC: . . . . **TCPCRV 132**

Pearson, Keith

KEITH PEARSON RIGHT HAND BAND (Pearson, Keith Right Hand Band).
LP: . . . . **ERON 014 LP**
MC: . . . . **ERON 014 CA**

Peasants All

BROADSIDE ON.
Tracks: / Fanfare / Queen at Tilsburie, The / Cradle, The / New years' gift / You traitors all / All in a garden green / Sturdy oak, The / Allemande / Fantasia que contrahaze la harpa en la manera de Luduvico / Great galleazo, The / Fortune, my foe / We be three poor mariners / Pavanne de la guerre / Galliarde de la guerre.
LP: . . . . **PLR 024**

COUNTRIE FAIRE (Peasants All/ Benjamin Luxon).
Tracks: / Parson's farewell / St. Martin's / In eighty eight / Greensleeves / All the flowers of the bloom / He that will an alehouse keep / Soldiers three / Watkin's ale / Brawl / Goddesses / Little Musgrave / Buffens / Spanish ladies / Wolsey's wild / When cannons are roaring.
LP: . . . . **PLR 016**

HANDFUL OF PLEASANT DELITES, A.
Tracks: / O admirable veneris ydolum / Bryd one brere / Pleasant ballad of King Henry II and the miller of Mansfield / Trotto / Downfall of dancing, The / Ronde / Hunt is up, (The) / Blow thy horn, hunter / Ohne fels / La mourisque / Martin said to his man / English dance / Allemande / Lord Willoughby.
LP: . . . . **PLR 008**

Peaston, David

INTRODUCING DAVID PEASTON.
Tracks: / Two wrongs / Take me now / We're all in this together / Eyes of love / Thank you for the moment / God bless the child / Tonight / Can I? / Don't say no.
LP: . . . . **K 9242281**
MC: . . . . **K 9242284**

Pebbles, Rikki

ONLY THE LIGHT.
LP: . . . . **OKLP 3006**
MC: . . . . **ZCOK 3006**

Pebbles (Singer)

ALWAYS.
LP: . . . . **MCG 6108**
MC: . . . . **MCGC 6108**

DO ME RIGHT.
LP: . . . . **MCA 8040**

PEBBLES.
LP: . . . . **MCF 3418**
MC: . . . . **MCFC 3418**

Peck, Bob (nar)

BODY POLITIC, THE (See under Body Politic).

Peck, Gregory

LYRICS FACTORY.
2LP: . . . . JMLP 002

Pecos Bill

PECOS BILL (Williams, Robin & Ry Cooder).
MC: . . . . WT 0709

Pedaljets

PEDALJETS.
Tracks: / Dead dogs / Place in the race, A / Looking out of my window / Bulletins / Agnes mind / Burgundy / Small towns / Giants of May / Mrs. Green / Stipple County / Kings highway / Red boots / Long distance.
LP: . . . . COMM 013

Peddlers

BIRTHDAY.
LP: . . . . SBPG 63682

FREE WHEELERS.
LP: . . . . SBPG 61383

Pedersen, Herb

LONESOME FEELING.
Tracks: / Last thing on my mind / Childish love / Fields have turned brown, The / Homecoming, The / Easy ride / Lonesome feeling / Willow garden / It's worth believing / Even the worst of us / Your love is like a flower.
LP: . . . . SH 3738
MC: . . . . SH 3738C

Pedersen, Niels

CHOPS (Pedersen, Niels & Joe Pass).
LP: 231 0830
MC: K10 830

ETERNAL TRAVELLER, THE.
Tracks: / Moto perpetu / En elefant kom marcherende / Jeg gik mig ud en sommerday at hore / Det haver sa nyeligen regnet / His hvor vejen slar en bugt / Jeg ved en Laerkerede / Sig manen langsomt haever / Dawn / Eternal traveller / Skul gammel venskab / Rejn forgo / Moto perpetuo.
LP: 2310 910
MC: K10 910

NEW WORLD (see Lockwood, Didier etc.) (Pedersen, Niels/Didier Lockwood/Gordon Beck/Tony Williams).

NORTHSEA NIGHTS (See under Pass, Joe) (Pedersen, Niels & Joe Pass).

PARIS CONCERT, THE (See under Peterson, Oscar) (Pederson, Niels, Oscar Peterson & Joe Pass).

PEDERSON, NIELS, OSCAR PETERSON, JOE PASS (See under Peterson, Oscar) (Pederson, Niels, Oscar Peterson & Joe Pass).

PRIZE WINNERS (See Under Drew, Kenny) (Pedersen, Niels/ Drew/ Henning/ Asmussen/ Thigpen).

TIVOLI GARDENS, COPENHAGEN (See under Grappelli, Stephane) (Pedersen, Niels / Stephane Grappelli / Joe Pass).

VIKING, THE.
Tracks: / Puzzle, The / My funny valentine / Marie / Nuages / Air power / Dancing girls / September start / Little train / Stella by starlight / I fall in love too easily.
LP: 2310 894

Pederson, Orsted

PAUL BLEY, NIELS HENNING, ORSTED PEDERSEN (See Under Bley, Paul) (Pederson, Orsted, Paul Bley & Niels Henning).

Pedicin, Mike

ROCK 'N' ROLL WITH MIKE PEDICIN.
LP: . . . . REV 3003

Pedlar's Pack

FRANK KIDSON'S TRADITIONAL TUNES.
MC: . . . . BH 8607 C

Pee Wee (Film)

PEE WEE'S BIG ADVENTURE/BACK TO SCHOOL (Film soundtrack) (Various artists).
LP: 704.370
MC: . . . . C 704.370

PEE WEE'S BIG TOP (Film soundtrack) (Various artists).
LP: . . . . AL 8568
MC: . . . . ALC 8568

Pee Wee & The Specials

PEE WEE AND THE SPECIALS.
LP: . . . . LPL 8004

Peebles, Ann

99 LBS.
Tracks: / 99 lbs / Walk away / Give me some credit / Heartaches / Somebody's on your case / I still love you / Part time love / I'll get along / Generation gap between us / Slipped, tripped and fell in love / Trouble / Heartaches and sadness / I feel like breaking up somebody's home / I pity the fool / Do I need you / I can't let you go / One way street.
LP: . . . . HIUKLP 402

CALL ME.
LP: 269 509 1
MC: 269 509 4

I CAN'T STAND THE RAIN.
Tracks: / I can't stand the rain / Do I need you? / Until you came into my life / Hangin' on / Run, run, run / If we can't trust each other / Love vibration, (A) / You got to feed the fire / I'm gonna tear your playhouse down / One way street.
LP: . . . . SHU 8468

I'M GONNA TEAR YOUR PLAYHOUSE DOWN.
Tracks: / I can't stand the rain / Beware / Love vibration, A / Doctor love power / Love played a game / It was jealousy / What you laid on me / Being here with you / I'm gonna tear your playhouse down / When I'm in your arms / Good day for lovin', A / Come to mama / Old man with young ideas / I needed somebody / If this is heaven.
LP: . . . . HIUKLP 422
MC: . . . . HIUKCASS 422

Peech Boys

LIFE IS SOMETHING SPECIAL.
LP: . . . . ILPS 9761
MC: . . . . ICT 9761

Peek, Kevin

AWAKENING.
Tracks: / Awakening / City on the water / Sidewinder / For those we left behind / Spanish blues / Manitou / Sailplane / Starship suite / Infinite dreams / Arrival.
LP: . . . . ARL 5065

GUITAR JUNCTION.
Tracks: / Guitar junction / Don't lose your heart / Romance d'amour / Bunny chase / Highland in the sun / Forward march / Girl alone, A / High Sierra / Reggae guitar / Slot machine / Fresh as a daisy / Missing quaver.
LP: . . . . ISST 110

LIFE AND OTHER GAMES.
Tracks: / Drifting / Pacific run / Viewfinder / In the time / Capricorn II / Hunter's theme / Epsilon / East of Suez / Hey Joe.
LP: . . . . ARL 5067
MC: . . . . ZCARL 5067

Peelers

BANISH MISFORTUNE.
LP: . . . . BACL 001
MC: . . . . BACC 001

Peeping Tom

IT SENDS YOU BLIND.
LP: . . . . COT 911

LARK RISE.
Tracks: / Bonnie Kate / Lemady / Arise and pick a posy / Harvest work song / Young Sally's song / John Barleycorn / Skylark, The / Tommytoes / John Dory / Poor old soldier / Sam's song / Harbinger / Old woman from Cumberland / Witch elder / Lemmy Brazil's no.2 / Cheapjack song / Jo Jo's jig / People's William / Have you ever been in the Peninsular / Roxburgh Castle.
MC: . . . . FSMC 9

Peer Gunt

BACK SEAT.
Tracks: / Backseat / Let her in / Hole in the door / Lonely little spies / Ya walk alone / Bad boys are here / Lock's on the wrong side / I take your money (And honey) / Down by the shadow / Liquere and drugs.
LP: . . . . NEAT 1039

Peers, Donald

DONALD PEERS COLLECTION, THE.
Tracks: / Faraway places / Twelfth St. rag / Powder your face with sunshine / For you / Lavender blue / Everywhere you go / Last mile home / Rolling round the world / Dear hearts and gentle people / Music, music, music / Harry Lime theme / Daddy's little girl / Down in the glen / Beloved, be faithful / I remember the cornfields / My heart cries for you / Tennessee waltz / Mistakes / She wears red feathers / Your cheatin' heart.
LP: . . . . ONCM 505

GOLDEN AGE OF DONALD PEERS.
Tracks: / Powder your face with sunshine / For you / Far away places / Lavender blue / Dear hearts and gentle people / Music, music, music (Put another nickel in) / If I knew you were coming I'd've baked a cake / Daddy's little girl / Enjoy yourself / It's later than you think / Tennessee waltz / My heart cries for you / Get out those old records / Mistakes / Encore / Walkin' my baby back home / Let the rest of the world go by / I love the sunshine of your smile / She wears red feathers / Please don't go.
LP: . . . . GX 2559
MC: . . . . TCGX 2559

WORLD OF DONALD PEERS, THE.
MC: . . . . KCSP 320

Peg

PEG (Original London cast) (Various artists).
LP: . . . . TER 1024
MC: . . . . ZCTER 1024

Pegasus

PEGASUS THE WINGED HORSE (Various artists).
MC: . . . . TS 317

Pegg, Bob & Carole

COMPLETE MR FOX.
LP: . . . . TRA 303

HE CAME FROM THE MOUNTAINS.
LP: . . . . LER 3016

Pegg, Dave

COCKTAIL COWBOY GOES IT ALONE, THE.
LP: . . . . WR 003

Peggy Sue

GENTLY HOLD ME.
LP: . . . . BRA 1003
MC: . . . . BRC 1003

Peggy Sue Got Married

PEGGY SUE GOT MARRIED (Film soundtrack) (Various artists).
Tracks: / Did we break up?: *Various artists* / Charlie's unplayed guitar: *Peebles, Ann* / Peggy Sue's homecoming: *Peebles, Ann* / Charlie, I had the strangest experience: *Various artists* / Peggy Sue got married: *Holly, Buddy* / I wonder why: *Dion & The Belmonts* / He don't love you: *Cage, Nicolas & Pride & Joy* / Teenager in love: *Dion & The Belmonts* / You belong to me: *Crenshaw, Marshall.*
LP: . . . . TER 1126
MC: . . . . ZCTER 1126

Pegler, Tony

AS REQUESTED (THE LOWRY CONTILLION ORGAN).
Tracks: / Happening, The / Spanish flea / Java / I was a fool / Cherokee / Baby elephant walk / One voice / Through the years / Cavaquinho / Amor, amor / We'll meet again / Dick Turpin / Once in a while / East of the sun / T.V. disco.
LP: . . . . GRS 1126

CORONADO CASCADE (PLAYING THE CORONADO CASCADE 297).
Tracks: / Devils gallop / Londonderry air / Dancing queen / Badinerie / Chanson de matin / Barnacle Bill / I'm in the mood for dancing / Y.M.C.A. / Romantica / Blue tango / Even now / Galloping home.
LP: . . . . GRS 1091

Pegram, George

BANJO AND FIDDLE 1967.
LP: . . . . ROUNDER 0001

Pehchan, Chirag

CHILLI MAAL.
LP: . . . . MUT 1045
MC: . . . . CMUT 1045

JAT SOORMEY.
MC: . . . . CMUT 1056

Peiffer, Bernard

AND HIS ST GERMAINE DES PRES ORCHESTRA.
LP: . . . . FS 188

Pekka

MATHEMATICIANS AIR DISPLAY.
Tracks: / Perceived journey-lantern / Hands straighten the water / Mathematician's air display, The / Consequences of head bending (part 1-The pain left melting) / Consequences of head bending (part 2-The plot thickens) / False start of the shadows.
LP: . . . . OVED 201

Pelham, Ruth

LOOK TO THE PEOPLE.
LP: . . . . FF 399

Pell, Chris Orchestra

50 HIT SOUNDS OF BIG BANDS.
2LP: 50DA 310

BIG BAND FAVOURITES.
Tracks: / Songs of India / I could write a book / Sophisticated lady / And the angels sing / It's been a long long time / Christopher Columbus / Jersey bounce / Just a gigolo / Yesterdays / I let a song go out of my heart / I concentrate on you / Green eyes.
MCSET: . . . . DTO 10033

Pell, Dave

PLAYS AGAIN (Pell, Dave Quartet).
LP: . . . . FS 49

PLAYS IRVING BERLIN (Pell, Dave Octet).
LP: . . . . FS 174

PREZ AND JOE (Pell, Dave/Joe Williams).
Tracks: / Oh lady be good / Getting some fun out of life / You can depend on me / Fooling with myself / Boogie woogie / How high the moon / If I could be with you / If dreams come true / Easy living / When you're smiling.
LP: . . . . GNPS 2124
MC: GNP5 2124
LP: . . . . N 5006

PREZ CONFERENCE.
Tracks: / I never knew / Sometimes I'm happy / Lester leaps in / Jumpin' with symphony Sid / Jumpin' at the Woodside / One o'clock jump / Just you, just me / Lester leaps again / Taxi war dance / Jump Lester jump.
LP: . . . . NSPL 28274

Pelle The Conquerer

PELLE THE CONQUERER (Original Soundtrack) (Various artists).
LP: A364

Pelletier, Jean-Claude

HAMMOND ORGAN (Slow, Dance and Blues).
LP: . . . . VG SLVLX 677

Pellmell Rhyming

FOR YEARS WE STOOD.
MC: . . . . KC 011

PELLMELL RHYMING GUITARS.
LP: . . . . SST 241
MC: . . . . SSTC 241

Pemberton, Victor

NIGHT OF THE WOLF (Price, Vincent & Coral Browne).
MC: . . . . ZCF 502

Pembroke Male Choir

PEMBROKE MALE VOICE CHOIR.
LP: . . . . BM 37

Pena, Paco

ART OF FLAMENCO GUITAR, THE.
Tracks: / Alegrias de Cordoba / De levante / Bulerias cortas / Zambra mora / Patio cordobes / Cantes por bulerias / Punta y tacon / Tristeza gitana / El garrotin / Campina andaluza.
LP: . . . . DGS 1

LIVE IN LONDON (GUITAR).
Tracks: / Junqueras / La union / Saluquena / Jerezana / Atardecer / Pura metal / Picachos / El nuevo dia / Amanecer arabel / Zapateado en re.
LP: . . . . MOR 524

LIVE IN MUNICH.
LP: . . . . CORD 5945

PACO PENA FLAMENCO COMPANY LIVE AT SADLERS WELLS.
Tracks: / La Esencia / Horas de Ausencia / Las morearas / Antologia minera / Venta a la fragua / Isla De Plata / Ritmo y fiesta / Lai lo lai.
LP: . . . . MOR 528

Pendarvis, Tracy

BISON BOP.
LP: . . . . BBLP 2004

TRACEY PENDARVIS.
Tracks: / Give me loving / All you gotta do / It don't pay / One of these days / Philadelphia filly / School days / Johnny B. Goode / So tenderly / Get it / Crazy baby / Wierd feeling / Hard luck / Blueberry Hill / My girl Josephine.
LP: . . . . BB 2004

Pendemia

NARCOTIC RELIGION.
LP: . . . . CMFT 4

Pender, Don

SANDRA JEAN (Pender, Don/Horace Parlan).
LP: . . . . SD 1002

Pendergrass, Teddy

GREATEST HITS: TEDDY PENDERGRASS.
Tracks: / Turn off the lights / Love TKO / I don't love you anymore / More I get the more I want, The / Only you / Close the door / When somebody loves you back / You can't hide from yourself / Come go with me.
LP: . . . . PIR 32442
MC: 40 32442

HEAVEN ONLY KNOWS.
Tracks: / Crazy about your love / Judge for yourself / I want my baby back / Life

is for living / You and me for right now / Just because you're mine / Heaven only knows / Don't ever stop.
MC: 40 25691
LP: PIR 25691

HOLD ME (See also Houston, Whitney) (Pendergrass, Teddy & Whitney Houston).

IT'S TIME FOR LOVE.
Tracks: / I can't live without your love / You're my latest greatest inspiration / Nine times out of ten / keep on lovin' me / It's time for love / She's over me / I can't leave your love alone / You must live on.
LP: PIR 85220

JOY.
Tracks: / Joy / 2 a.m. / Good to you / I'm ready / Love is the power / This is the last time / Through the falling rain / Can we be lovers.
LP: 9607751
MC: 9607754
LP: EKT 48
MC: EKT 48C

LIFE IS A SONG WORTH SINGING.
Tracks: / Life is a song worth singing / Only you / Cold, cold world / Get up, get down, get funky, get loose / Close the door / It don't hurt now / When somebody loves you back.
LP: PIR 32309

LIVE COAST TO COAST.
Tracks: / Life is a song worth singing / Only you / If you don't know me by now / Love I lost / Bad luck / Wake up everybody / When somebody loves you back / Ger up get down get funky get loose / LA Rep / Come go with me / Close the door / Turn off the lights / Do me / Where did all the lovin' go / It's you I love / Shout & scream.
2LP: PIR 88474

LOVE LANGUAGE.
Tracks: / In my time / So sad the song / Hot love / Stay with me / Hold me / You're my choice tonight / Love / This time is yours.
LP: 960 317-1
MC: 960 317-4

READY FOR TEDDY.
Tracks: / Whole town's laughing at me, The / Turn off the lights / Love TKO / Somebody told me / I just called to say / Close the door / You can't hide from yourself / More I get the more I want, The / Only you / Life is a song worth singing / Be sure / Take me in your arms tonight.
LP: PIR 84903
MC: 40 84903

SOUND OF SOUL.
LP: BLATLP 12
MC: BLATMC 12

TEDDY.
Tracks: / Come go with me / Turn off the lights / I'll never see heaven again / All I need is you / If you know like I know / Do me / Set me free / Life is a circle.
MC: 40 83656
LP: PIR 83656

TEDDY PENDERGRASS.
LP: PIR 32127

T.P.
Tracks: / Is it still good to ya / Take me in your arms tonight / I just called to say / Can't we try / Feel the fire / Girl you know / Love TKO / Let me love you.
LP: PIR 84542

TRULY BLESSED.
LP: EKT 82
MC: EKT 82C

WORKING IT BACK.
Tracks: / Love 4/2 / One of us fell in love / Never felt like dancing / Closer / Lovely colour blue / Want you back in my life / Working it back / Reach out and touch (somebody's hand).
LP: EKT 26
MC: EKT 26C

Pendragon

9.15 LIVE.
Tracks: / Victims of life / Circus / Leviathan / Red shoes / Alaska / Black Knight / Please / Fly high fall far / Higher circles.
LP: AWL 4042
MC: AWT 4042

FIRE IN HARMONY.
LP: ARRLP 100

FLY HIGH FALL FAR.
LP: ARRMP 001

JEWEL.
Tracks: / Higher circles / Pleasure of hope, The / Leviathan / At home with the earth / Snowfall / Circus / Oh Divineo / Black night, The / Fly high fall far / Victims of life.
LP: AWL 4041
MC: AWT 3031
LP: ARRLP 101

KOWTOW.
Tracks: / I walk the rope / Solid heart / Am / Time for a change / Total recall / Haunting, The / Kowtow.
LP: PEND 1

Pendyrus Male Choir

FAVOURITE HYMNS.
Tracks: / Praise, my soul, the King of Heaven / Lord's my shepherd, The / Now thank we all our God / Glorious things of Thee are spoken / Abide with me / Holy holy holy / Jesus shall reign / When I survey the wondrous cross / Onward Christian soldiers / Mine eyes have seen the glory of the coming of the Lord.
LP: WST 9606
MC: WC 9606

SHEEP MAY SAFELY GRAZE.
Tracks: / Lord's prayer, The / Sheep may safely graze / Steal away / O Father, whose almighty power / Gwahoddiad / Sound an alarm / Michael row the boat ashore / Largo / Deus salutis / Kwmbayath / Cwm Rhondda.
LP: WST 9603
MC: WC 9603

Penetration

COMING UP FOR AIR.
Tracks: / Shout above the noise / She is the slave / Last saving grace / Killed in the rush / Challenge / Come into the open / What's going on / Party's over, The / On reflection / Lifeline / New recruit.
LP: OVED 203
LP: V 2131

MOVING TARGETS.
Tracks: / Future daze / Life's a gamble / Lovers of outrage / Vision / Silent community / Stone heroes / Movement / Too many friends / Reunion / Nostalgia / Freemoney.
LP: OVED 40
LP: V 2109

Penfold, Rebecca

SWEET PRIMROSES.
Tracks: / Nightingales sing / Meeting in a pleasant place / Poor orphan boy / Little old log cabin, The / Banks of the sweet Dundee.
MC: 30-042

Pengilly, Mark

STRAYER FROM AUSTRALIA, A.
LP: LRF 063

Penguin Cafe Orchestra

BROADCASTING FROM HOME.
Tracks: / Music for a found harmonium / Prelude and yodel / More milk / Sheep dip / White mischief / In the back of a taxi / Music by numbers / Another one from the colonies / Air / Heartwind / Isle of view (music for helicopter pilots) / Now nothing.
LP: EGED 38
MC: EGEDC 38

MINI ALBUM.
Tracks: / Penguin Cafe single / Air a danser / Toy / Number 1-4 / Salty bean fumble / Piano music.
LP: EGMLP 2
MC: EGMMC 2

MUSIC FROM THE PENGUIN CAFE.
Tracks: / Chartered flight / Hugebaby / Penguin Cafe single / Sound of someone you love, The / Zopf (from the colonies) / Zopf (coronation) / Zopf (Giles Farnaby's dream) / Zopf (in a Sydney motel) / Zopf (pig) / Zopf (surface tension) / Zopf (milk).
LP: EGED 27
MC: EGEDC 27

PENGUIN CAFE ORCHESTRA.
Tracks: / Air a danser / Number 1-4 / Salty bean fumble / Yodel 1 / Telephone and rubber band / Cutting branches for a temporary shelter / Pythagoras' trousers / Yodel 2 / Paul's dance / Ecstasy of dancing fleas, The / Walk don't run / Flux / Simon's dream / Harmonic necklace / Steady state.
MC: EGEDC 11
LP: EGED 11

SIGNS OF LIFE.
Tracks: / Bean fields / Southern jukebox music / Horns of the bull / Oscar tango / Snake and the lotus, The / Rosasolis / Sketch / Perpetuum mobile / Swing the cat / Wildlife / Dirt.
LP: EGED 50
MC: EGEDC 50

WHEN IN ROME - LIVE.
Tracks: / Air a danser / Yodel 1 / From the colonies / Southern jukebox music / Numbers 1-4 / Bean fields / Paul's dance / Oscar tango / Music for a found harmonium / Isle of view (music for helicopter pilots) / Prelude and yodel / Giles Farnaby's dream / Air (CD & Cassette only) / Dirt (CD & cassette only) / Cutting branches for a temporary shelter (CD & cassette only) / Telephone and rubber band (CD & Cassette only).
LP: EGED 56
MC: EGEDC 56

Penguins

EARTH ANGEL.
Tracks: / Don't do it / Promises, promises, promises / She's gone, gone, gone / Okey ook / Walkin down Broadway / Hey senorita / Cool baby cool / Ice / Jingle jangle / Christmas prayer, A / Earth angel / It only happens with you / Be mine / My troubles are not at an end / Love will make your mind go wild / Dealer of dreams / Will you be mine / Devil that I see / Peace of mind / Earth angel (2).
LP: BFX 15222
LP: CH 249

Penitent

PENITENT (Film soundtrack) (Various artists).
LP: STV 81331
MC: CTV 81331

Penitentiary III

PENITENTIARY III (Film Soundtrack) (Various artists).
Tracks: / You and I: *Payne, Freda & Lenny Williams* / Special: *Yarbrough & Peoples* / Can't let it go: *Larue*/ Bustin' out: *Franklin, Rodney* / Do the prep: *Midnight Star* / Sweeter than candy: *Gap Band* / Cold stupid: *New Choice* / No mission's impossible: *Shawnie* / I know you are: *Dotti, Lottie* / Just a touch: *Reese, James.*
LP: PL 86663
MC: PK 86663

Penn, Michael

MARCH.
Tracks: / No myth / This and that / Innocent one / Bedlam boys / Cupid's got a brand new gun / Battle room / Half harvest / Brace new world / Disney's a snow cone / Invisible / Big house / Even fall.
LP: PL 90421
MC: PK 90421

Pennies From Heaven

MORE PENNIES FROM HEAVEN (Various artists).
LP: SH 276

PENNIES FROM HEAVEN (TV soundtrack) (Various artists).
LP: SH 266

PENNIES FROM HEAVEN (Various artists).
2LP: DDV 5007/8
2LP: K 66109

PENNIES FROM HEAVEN (48 original recordings featured in the BBC TV s (Various artists).
Tracks: / Down Sunnyside Lane: *Various artists* / Clouds will soon roll by, The: *Various artists* / Roll along prarie moon: *Various artists* / Seein' is believin': *Various artists* / You rascal you: *Various artists*/ Pennies from Heaven: *Various artists* / Zing went the strings of my heart: *Various artists* / You've got me crying again: *Various artists* / Cheek to cheek: *Various artists* / That's a plenty: *Various artists* / Without that certain thing: *Various artists* / You couldn't be cuter: *Various artists* / Yes, yes, my baby said yes: *Various* artists / Just let me look at you: *Various artists* / You and the night and the music: *Various artists* / Garden of weed: *Various artists* / Love is good for anything that ails you: *Various artists* / I only have eyes for you: *Various artists* / Oh you nasty man: *Various artists* / I love you truly: *Various artists* / Radio times: *Various artists* / Life begins at Oxford Circus: *Various artists* / Easy come, easy go: *Various* artists / Better think twice: *Various artists* / We'll make hay when the sun shines: *Various artists* / Riptide: *Various artists* / Indian love call: *Various artists* / How's chances: *Various artists* / Echo of a song, The: *Various artists* / Okay toots: *Various artists* / Painting the clouds with sunshine: *Various artists*/ Serenade in the night: *Various artists* / My woman: *Various artists* / I've found the right girl: *Various* artists / On the other side of the hill: *Various artists* / Anything goes: *Various artists* / Hands across the table: *Various artists* / You sweet so and so: *Various artists* / Moon got in my eyes, The: *Various artists*/ In the middle of a kiss: *Various artists* / March winds and April showers: *Various artists* / Says my heart: *Various artists* / Roll along covered wagon: *Various artists* / Whistling in the dark: *Various artists*/ I like to go back in the evening: *Various artists* / In the dark: *Various artists* / Glory of love: *Various artists* / Pennies from Heaven: *Various artists.*
LPS: REF 768
MCSET: ZCD 768

PENNIES FROM HEAVEN (GOLDEN AGE) (Various artists).
Tracks: / Roll along, prairie moon: *Various artists* / Seeing is believing: *Various artists* / You rascal you: *Various artists* / You and the night and the music: *Various artists* / Yes yes (my baby says yes): *Various* artists / Love is good for anything that ails you: *Various artists* / We'll make hay while the sun shines: *Various* artists / It's got to be love: *Various artists* / Pop, goes your heart: *Various artists* / Painting the clouds with sunshine: *Various artists* / Moon got in my eyes: *Various artists* / Haunting me: *Various artists*/ Roll along, covered wagon: *Various artists* / I like to go back in the evening: *Various artists* / Says my heart: *Various artists* / Pennies from Heaven: *Various artists.*
LP: GX 41 2501
MC: TC GX 2501

PENNIES FROM HEAVEN II (Various artists).
LP: REN 824
MC: ZCN 824

Pennington, Barbara

MIDNIGHT RIDE.
Tracks: / Midnight ride / All time loser / Trusted friend / Spend a little time with me / Can't help being guilty / Twenty four hours a day / It's so hard getting over / You are the music within me.
LP: UAS 30144

OUT OF THE DARKEST NIGHT.
LP: SOHOLP 9
MC: SOHOTC 9

Penny, Dave

IN FOR A PENNY.
Tracks: / That stranger is a friend / Little lost dog / Love has made you beautiful / What colour is my valley? / Come home Rhondda boy.
LP: EMS 240 1021

Penny, Hank

ROMPIN', STOMPIN', SINGIN', SWINGIN'.
Tracks: / Catch em' young, treat 'em rough, tell 'em nothin' / What she's got is mine / White shotguns / I like molasses / I want my rib / Hold the phone / No muss, no fuss, no bother / Taxes, taxes / You're bound to look like a monkey / Won't ride you in) my little red wagon / Hadacillin boogie / Fan it / You can't pull the wool over my eyes / That's my weakness now / Mink on her back, The / You played on my piano.
LP: BFX 15102

TOBACCO STATE SWING (Penny, Hank & His Radio Cowboys).
Tracks: / Back up a little bit / Tobacco state swing / Mama's getting younger / Lonesome train blues / Hot time mama / Hawaiian honeymoon / Rose's sister / Won't you ride in my little red wagon / Cowboy's swing / Sweet talkin mama / Hesitation blues / All night and all day long / Oh yes take another guess / Blue ridge blues.
LP: RAMBLER 103

Penny Serenade

PENNY SERENADE (Various artists).
Tracks: / Stormy weather: *Various artists* / It's a sin to tell a lie: *Various artists.*
LP: HAL 13
LP: JOY 278

Pentagram

DAY OF RECKONING.
LP: FLAME 6

PENTAGRAM.
LP: DEVIL 4

Pentangle

BASKET OF LIGHT.
Tracks: / Light flight / Once I had a sweetheart / Springtime promises / Lyke wyke dirge / Train song / Hunting song / Sally go round the roses / Cuckoo, The / House carpenter.
LP: TRS 114
MC: KTRS 114
LP: TRANDEM 7
LP: TRA 205

COLLECTION: PENTANGLE.
Tracks: / Let no man steal your thyme / Bells / Hear my call / Turn your money green (live) / I've got a feeling / Bruton Town (studio version) / Goodbye pork pie hat (live) / When I was in my prime / Sweet child (live) / Light flight (Theme: Take Three Girls) / Once I had a sweetheart / Sally go round the roses / Maid that's deep in love / Lord Franklin / When I get home / Rain and snow / Will the circle be unbroken?.
2LP: CCSLP 184
MC: CCSMC 184

CRUEL SISTER.
LP: TRA 228
LP: 44.005

IN THE ROUND.
2LP: . . . . **TALP 2001**
MC: . . . . **TAMC 2001**

IN YOUR MIND.
MC: **495942**

MAID THAT'S DEEP IN LOVE, A.
LP: . . . . **SHAN 79066**
MC: . . . . **SHANC 79066**

OPEN THE DOOR.
LP: . . . . **SPIN 111**
LP: . . . . **VR 017**
MC: . . . . **VR 017C**

PENTANGLE - AT THEIR BEST.
Tracks: / I've got a feeling / Bells / Market song / No more my Lord / House carpenter / Once I had a sweetheart / Miss Heather Rosemary Sewell / Bruton Town / In time / Sally go round the roses / Earl of Salisbury / Time has come, The / Pentangling / So early in the spring / Rain and snow / Light flight / Three part thing / Lord Franklin / Haitian fight song / When I get home.
2LP: . . . . **CR 054**
MCSET: . . . . **CRT 054**

PENTANGLE IN THE ROUND.
Tracks: / Play the game / Open sea / She moved through the fair / Set me free / When the night is over come to me baby / Sunday morning blues / Saturday movie, The / Suil agrar / Circle the moon / Let me be.
LP: . . . . **2TA LP 1**

PENTANGLE, THE.
LP: . . . . **TRA 162**

PENTANGLING.
Tracks: / I've got the feeling / Helping hand / Pentangling / When I get home / Rain and snow / Lyke wyke dirge / Trees they do grow high, The / Maid that's deep in love / Once I had a sweetheart.
LP: . . . . **TRS 106**
MC: . . . . **KTRS 106**

SO EARLY IN THE SPRING.
LP: . . . . **PLANE 88648**

Pentecostal Praise

GENERAL CONFERENCE.
LP: . . . . **PC 318**

Penthouse Paupers

PENTHOUSE PAUPERS.
LP: . . . . **WRONG 2**

People, Animals &...

PEOPLE, ANIMALS AND OTHER MONSTERS Jack Prelutsky (Prelutsky, Jack).
MC: . . . . **CP 1699**

People Band

BROTHERS AND SISTERS (see Zabandis People Band) (People Band & Zabandis).

People Like Us

PEOPLE LIKE US.
Tracks: / Ressurection / Deliverance / Hiroshima / Two to tango / Prayer for you / Heart in the night / Fight for you / Love will survive / Midnight lover.
LP: . . . . **PAPX 104**

People Of Destiny

ARISE.
Tracks: / Rejoice / Jesus light of the nations / Lord of the harvest / Oh most high / Jesus, King and Conqueror / I stand in awe / Go forth / I long for you, O Lord / Raise up an army / We are your people / You have been given.
LP: . . . . **SOP R 2022**
MC: . . . . **SOP C 2022**

People's ...

EARTH DANCER (People's International Silver String Macedonian Band).
LP: . . . . **BAY 205**

PEOPLE'S INTERNATIONAL SILVER STRING MACEDONIAN BAND (People's International Silver String Macedonian Band).
LP: . . . . **BAY 201**

People's Carol

PEOPLE'S CAROL (Various artists).
LP: . . . . **LEE 4065**

Peoples Choice

WE GOT THE RHYTHM.
Tracks: / Here we go again / Jam, jam, jam / All night long / We got the rhythm / Cold-blooded and downright funky / Movin' all directions / Opus de funk / Mellow mood, A.
LP: . . . . **PIR 81370**

Peoples, Tommy

IRONMAN, THE (Peoples, Tommy With Daithi Sproule).
LP: . . . . **SHAN 79044**

MOLLOY, BRADY, PEOPLES (see Molloy, Matt/Paul Brady/Tommy Peoples) (Peoples, Tommy/Matt Molloy/ Paul Brady).

Peoria Jazzband

NEW SIDES.
LP: . . . . **OP 7911**

PASSPORT TO JAZZ.
LP: . . . . **OP 7802**

Pepe (film)

PEPE (FILM) (See under Crush, Bobby 'First love') (Crush, Bobby).

Pepito, Don

A ERA DE OURO (Pepito, Don Y Su Ritmo Tropical).
LP: **6470 568**

Pepl, Harry

CRACKED MIRRORS (Pepl, Harry/ Herbert Joos/ Jon Christensen).
Tracks: / Wolkenbilder 1 / Reflections in a cracked mirror / Schikaneder delight / Die alte mar und das mann / More far out than east / Wolkenbilder 2 / Tintenfisch inki / Purple light.
LP: . . . . **ECM 1356**

Peplowski, Ken

DOUBLE EXPOSURE.
Tracks: / I would do anything for you / There's no you / Lava / Blame it on my youth / Segment / High and flighty / Don't you know I care / Jubilee / Careless love / Imagination.
LP: . . . . **CJ 344**
MC: . . . . **CJ 344 C**

ILLUMINATIONS.
Tracks: / June night / Trubbel / Panama / Between the Devil and the deep blue sea / How long has this been going on? / Jim Dawg / Smada / Alone together (Only on CD.) / Did I remember? / Nancy (with the laughing face) / Best things in life are free, The / If we never meet again (Only on CD.).
MC: . . . . **CJ 449C**

MR. GENTLE AND MR. COOL (Peplowski, Ken Quintet).
Tracks: / Mr. Gentle and Mr. Cool / Please be kind / You do something to me / Body and soul / Makin' whoopee (Only on CD.) / Stray horn (Only on CD.) / Follow your heart / On a misty night / Syeeda's song flute / There'll be some changes made / Count your blessings instead of sheep / When day is done.
MC: . . . . **CJ 419 C**

SONNY SIDE (Peplowski, Ken Quintet).
LP: . . . . **CJ 376**
MC: . . . . **CJ 376 C**

Peppe, Rodney

HUXLEY PIG AT THE CIRCUS.
MC: **39567**

Pepper, Art

AMONG FRIENDS (IMPORT).
Tracks: / What is this thing called love / 'Round about midnight / What's new / I'll remember April.
LP: . . . . **DS 837**
MC: . . . . **DSC 837**
LP: . . . . **FLY 211**
LP: . . . . **IP 7718**

ART OF PEPPER, THE.
LP: . . . . **VSOP 30**

ART OF PEPPER VOL 2, THE.
LP: . . . . **VSOP 33**

ART PEPPER MEETS THE RHYTHM SECTION.
Tracks: / You'd be so nice to come home to / Red pepper blues / Imagination / Waltz me blues / Straight life / Jazz me blues / Tin tin deo / Star eyes / Birk's works.
LP: . . . . **COP 004**

BLUES FOR THE FISHERMAN/TRUE BLUES (See under Leviev, Milcho) (Leviev, Milcho, Quartet with Art Pepper).

COLLECTION: ART PEPPER.
Tracks: / Deep purple / Chili pepper / Art's oregano / Way you look tonight / Thyme time / Cinnamon / Nutmeg / Suzy the poodle / Straight life / What's new? / Everything happens to me / Tickle toe / Salute / Be easy, be tender / Dynaflow / Harlem folk dance / Unison riff.
LP: . . . . **DVLP 2094**
MC: . . . . **DVMC 2094**

DISCOVERIES, THE SAVOY SESSIONS.
LP: . . . . **SJL 2217**

FRIDAY NIGHT AT THE VILLAGE VANGUARD.
LP: **1007 643**

GETTIN' TOGETHER (Pepper, Art & Conte Candoli).
LP: . . . . **COP 023**

INTENSITY.
Tracks: / I can't believe that you're in love with me / I love you / Come rain or come shine / Long ago and far away / Gone with the wind / I wished on the moon / Too close for comfort.
LP: . . . . **COP 010**

IT HAPPENED IN PESCARA 1969-89 (see under Evans, Bill) (Evans, Bill/Art Pepper).

LANDSCAPE.
Tracks: / True blues / Sometime / Avalon / Over the rainbow / Straight life / Landscape.
LP: . . . . **GXY 5128**

LIVE AT SONTE'S VOL 1.
LP: . . . . **FS 309**

LIVING LEGEND.
Tracks: / Orphelia / Here's that rainy day / What Laurie likes / Mr. Yohe / Lost life / Samba mom-mom.
LP: . . . . **COP 014**

MODERN ART (Complete Aladdin recordings vol. II) (Pepper, Art Quartet).
Tracks: / Blues in / Bewitched, bothered and bewildered / Stompin' at the Savoy / What is this thing called love / Blues out / When you're smiling / Cool bunny / Diane's dilemma / Diane's dilemma (alt. take) / Summertime / Fascinating rhythm (alt. take) / Begin the beguine / Webb City (alternate take).
LP: . . . . **FS 223**

MORE FOR LES.
LP: . . . . **COP 025**

NO LIMIT.
LP: . . . . **COP 019**

OMEGA ALPHA.
Tracks: / Surf ride / Body and soul / Too close for comfort / Summertime / Fascinating rhythm / Begin the beguine / Webb city.
LP: . . . . **LBR 1039**

ONE SEPTEMBER AFTERNOON.
Tracks: / Mr. Big falls his J.G. hand / Close to you alone / There will never be another you / Melolev / Goodbye, again / Brazil.
LP: . . . . **GXY 5141**

PLAYBOYS (see Baker, Chet & Art Pepper) (Pepper, Art & Chet Baker).

PLUS ELEVEN.
Tracks: / Move / Groovin' high / Opus de funk / Shaw nuff / Round midnight / Four brothers / Bernie's tune / Walkin' shoes / Airegin / Anthropology / Walkin' / Donna Lee.
LP: . . . . **COP 007**

POPO (Pepper, Art & Shorty Rogers).
LP: . . . . **XAN 148**

REDISCOVERIES.
Tracks: / Chili pepper (Take 3) / Suzy the poodle (Take 3) / Everything happens to me (Take 2) / Nutmeg (Take 6) / Cinnamon / What's new / Thyme time / Straight line / Art's oregano / Chili pepper (Take 5) / Suzy the poodle (Take 5) / Everything happens to me (Take 3) / Everything happens to me (Take 6) / Nutmeg (Take 7).
LP: . . . . **WL 70828**
MC: . . . . **WK 70828**

ROADGAME.
Tracks: / Roadgame / Road waltz / When you're smiling / Everything happens to me.
LP: . . . . **GXY 5142**

SATURDAY NIGHT AT THE VILLAGE VANGUARD.
LP: **1007 644**

SMACK UP.
Tracks: / Smack up / Las guevas de Mario / Bit of basic / How can you lose / Maybe next year / Tears inside.
LP: . . . . **COP 031**

STRAIGHT LIFE.
Tracks: / Chili pepper / Cinnamon / Tickle toe / Suzy the poodle / Everything happens to me / Nutmeg / Deep purple / What's new / Thyme time / Art's oregano / Way you look tonight / Straight life.
LP: . . . . **GXY 5127**

TODAY.
Tracks: / Miss you / Mambo koyama / Lover come back to me / Patricia / These foolish things / Chris's blues.
LP: . . . . **OJC 3002**

TRIP, THE.
Tracks: / Trip / Song for Richard / Sweet love of mine / Junior cat / Summer knows / Red car.
LP: . . . . **COP 032**

TRUE BLUES (See Leviev, Milcho).

WAY IT WAS, THE.
Tracks: / I can't believe that you're in love with me / All the things you are / What's new / Tickle toe / Man I love, The / Autumn leaves / Way you look tonight.
LP: . . . . **COP 041**

WINTER MOON.
Tracks: / Our song / Here's that rainy day / That's love / Winter moon / When the sun comes out / Blues in the night / Prisoner, The (love theme from 'Eyes of Laura Mars').
LP: . . . . **GXY 5140**

Pepper, Jim

COMIN' AND GOIN'.
Tracks: / Witchitiato / Ya na ho / Squaw song / Goin' down to Muskogee / Comin' and goin' / Lakota song / Water / Custer gets it / Malinyea.
LP: . . . . **AN 8706**
MC: . . . . **ANC 8706**

Peppermint Harris

HOUSTON CAN'T BE HEAVEN.
Tracks: / I got to go / Let's go to the chicken shack / Married woman / Love at first sight / Bye bye fare thee well / All for you / Lonesome / Twenty four hours / Smiles / Houston can't be heaven / I don't care / Foot loose / Black cat bone / I'll wipe away your tears / I had a dream.
LP: . . . . **CHD 267**

SITTIN' IN WITH HISTORICAL RECORDINGS.
LP: **L2M 2003**

Peppe's Jolly Sax

JOLLY JOE JOKER.
LP: . . . . **ISST 166**

Pepping, Henk

HENK PEPPING AND THE ATTACKS (Pepping, Henk & the Attacks).
Tracks: / Spring in April / Dark room boogie / Feeling like a suitcase / Boogie bop / Don't get around much anymore / Riders in the sun / You / Bodyguard boogie / Rockin' the boogie / Ridin' on my stallion / Little joke / Crazy 'J' / Blue heart / Happy cowboy / Madman / Butterfly boogie.
LP: . . . . **DS 9244**

ROCKIN' THE BOOGIE WOOGIE.
Tracks: / Wildman boogie / Johnson's boogie / Boogie woogie power / Ragtime boogie / Mrs. J. Boogie / Swinging thing, The / Beer boogie / Can't stay this way / Turbo boogie / Boogie woogie me / Real boogie woogie / No time for resting / Finger talking / Rockin' the boogie / Don't want to go / Break up / For all time / Real swingin'.
LP: . . . . **DS 9235**

Pepsi & Shirlie

ALL RIGHT NOW.
Tracks: / Heartache / Lover's revolution / Can't give me love / High time / What's going on inside your head / Goodbye stranger / Surrender / Crime of passion / All right now.
LP: . . . . **POLH 38**
MC: . . . . **POLHC 38**

Pepys, Samuel

DIARY OF SAMUEL PEPYS (Richardson, Ian).
MC: **1464**

Percival, Lance (nar)

VARIOUS MR. MEN RECORDINGS (See under Adventures of...).

Percy

PERCY (Film soundtrack) (Kinks).
Tracks: / God's children / Lola / Way love used to be, The / Completely / Running round town / Moments / Animals in the zoo / Just friends / Whip lady / Dreams / Helga / Willesden Green / End title.
LP: . . . . **PYL 6011**
MC: . . . . **PYM 6011**
LP: . . . . **NSPL 18365**

Perdurabo

PERDURABO (Various artists).
Tracks: / Watch world weal: *Primary Industry* / Ectasy (Inst): *Wolfgang Press* / My baby: *Legendary Pink Dots* / Shades of love: *Heavenly Bodies* / Glorious morning: *Bands Of Holy Joy* / Die front: *Bunker, Die* / Coil: *Heads On Sticks* / Adam and Eva: *Attrition* / "V": *Sturm Group* / Blues, heaven or hell: *Muerte, La*.
LP: . . . . **CABLA 2**

Perdute, Speranze

ITALIAN FOLK, MAZURKAS AND POLKAS.
MC: . . . . **GVMMC 603**

Pere Ubu

390 DEGREES OF SIMULATED STEREO (Live Volume 1).
LP: . . . . **ROUGH 23**

ARCHIVAL COLLECTION (Pere Ubu/ Terminal Tower).
LP: . . . . **ROUGH 83**

ART OF WALKING, THE.
LP: . . . . **ROUGH 14**

CLOUDLAND.

Tracks: / Breath / Cry / Waiting for Mary / Bus called Happiness / Lost Nation Road / Flat / Pushin' / Race the sun / Why go it alone / Ice cream truck / Love love love / Nevada! / Waltz / Monday night.
LP: 8382371
MC: 8382374

DATAPANIK IN THE YEAR ZERO.
Tracks: / Heart of darkness / 30 seconds over Tokyo / Cloud 149 / Untitled heaven.
LP: RDR 1

MODERN DANCE, THE.
Tracks: / Non-alignment pact / Modern dance, The / Laughing / Street waves / Chinese radiation / Life stinks / Real world / Over my head / Sentimental journey / Humor me.
LP: SFLP 3
MC: SFMC 3

NEW PICNIC TIME.
LP: CHR 1248

TENEMENT YEAR, THE.
Tracks: / Something's gotta give / George had hat / Talk to me / Busman's honeymoon / Say goodbye / Universal vibration / Miss you / Dream the moon / Rhythm kind / Hollow earth, The / We have the technology.
LP: SFLP 5
MC: SFMC 5

WORLDS IN COLLISION.
Tracks: / Oh Catherine / I hear they smoke the barbecue / Turpentine / Goodnite Irene / Mirror man / Cry cry / Worlds in collision / Life of Riley / Over the moon / Don't look back / Playback / Nobody knows / Winter in the Netherlands.
MC: 848 564 4
LP: 848 564 1

Peregoyo Y Su Combo

TROPICALISMO.
LP: WCB 015
MC: WCC 015

Perennial Divide

PURGE.
LP: SAX 016

Perez, Freddie

I'M A WINNER (see Gypsy) (Perez, Freddie & Gypsy).

Perfect

PERFECT (Film soundtrack) (Various artists).
Tracks: / (Closest thing to) Perfect: *Jackson, Jermaine* / I sweat (going through the motions): *Hendryx, Nona*/ All systems go: *Pointer Sisters* / Shock me: *Houston, Whitney & Jermaine Ja* / Wham rap (enjoy what you do): *Wham* / Wear out the grooves: *Stewart, Jermaine* / Hot hips: *Reed, Lou* / Talking to the wall: *Hartman, Dan* / Masquerade: *Berlin* / Lay your hands on me: *Thompson Twins*.
LP: 207203
MC: 407203

Perfect, Christine

CHRISTINE PERFECT.
LP: 32198
MC: 40 32198

Perfect Day

WORLD TONIGHT, THE.
LP: 828 132 1
MC: 828 132 4

Perfect Daze

BUBBLEGUM.
Tracks: / Bubblegum / Picture of you / She revs me up / Blue horizon / Love you kill the bomb drops.
MLP: SOL 1

Perfect Disaster

ASYLUM ROAD.
LP: FIRELP 11

HEAVEN SCENT.
LP: FIRELP 27

PERFECT DISASTER.
LP: GLALP 027

UP.
LP: FIRELP 18
MC: FIREMC 18

Perfect Match

PERFECT MATCH.
LP: BGC 288
MC: KBGC 288

Perfect Murder

PERFECT MURDER, A (See under Archer, Jeffrey) (Jarvis, Martin & Rosalind Ayres).

Perfect Partnership

PERFECT PARTNERSHIP, THE (See under Fonteyn, Margot) (Fonteyn, Margot & Rudolph Nureyev).

Perfect Vision

DEMONSTRATION.
MC: PV 003

TONGUES OUT.
LP: NCHMLP 9

Perfect Weight

PERFECT WEIGHT (see under 'Sutphen, Dick') (Sutphen, Dick).

Perfect World

HAVE A GOOD LOOK.
Tracks: / Vacation in black / Twist and shout / Stolen idol / Never never / Have a good look.
LP: SBR 11LP

Perfect Zebras

MIXING WITH WILDLIFE.
Tracks: / Touching my heart again / Blond boys in blue denim / I don't dream anymore / Love's an illusion / In for the kill / Running with Zebras / Another love story / Man or machine / Standby to Shangri-La / Terrorists.
LP: FOLP 1

Performance

MEXICO SUNDOWN BLUES (see Ray, James) (Performance/James Ray).

Performance (Film)

PERFORMANCE (See under Jagger, Mick) (Jagger, Mick).

Performance (Various)

PERFORMANCE (Best of Andrew Lloyd Webber, The) (Various artists).
Tracks: / Jesus Christ Superstar: *Head, Murray* / I dont know how to love him: *Head, Murray* / Oh what a circus: *Essex, David* / Close every door: *Miles, John* / Another suitcase in another hall: *Collins, Judy* / High flying adored: *Essex, David* / Pity the child: *Miles, John* / Don't cry for me Argentina: *Paige, Elaine*/ Memory: *Paige, Elaine* / Mr. Mistoffelees: *Ellington, Lance* / One night in Bangkok: *Head, Murray* / Least of my troubles, The: *Wilkinson, Colm* / Take that look off your face: *Terry, Helen* / I am the starlight: *Helms, Jimmy* / Running back for more: *Head, Murray* / I know him so well: *Paige, Elaine & Barbara Dickson*.
LP: STAR 2262
MC: STAC 2262

Performing Ferrets

FERRETABLE THING, THE.
MC: DHC 2

Perfume - The Story...

PERFUME - THE STORY OF A MURDERER (Barrett, Sean (aut)).
MC: IAB 88072

Pericles

PERICLES (see under Shakespeare, William) (Various artists).

Perishers

PERISHERS SING, THE.
LP: RES 801

Perkins, Betty

ELIJAH ROCK.
Tracks: / Elijah rock / Trusting everyday / God of our Father / I've got to make it / It took a miracle / I love him / Keeping me alive / You can't hide / Why do you wait.
LP: OUTSTANDING 32

Perkins, Bill

BILL PERKINS QUARTET with Claude Williamson (Perkins, Bill Quartet).
LP: FS 321

CONFLUENCE (Perkins, Bill & Pepper Adams).
LP: IP 7721

MANY WAYS TO GO (Perkins, Bill Quartet).
LP: SB 2006

PEPPER ADAMS.
LP: FLY 214

REMEMBRANCE OF DINO'S.
LP: IP 8606

WEST COAST CONFERENCE (Perkins, Bill/Paul Chambers/Philly Joe Jones).
LP: AFF 56

Perkins, Carl

20 GOLDEN PIECES: CARL PERKINS.
Tracks: / I don't like what I'm seeing in you / Rise and shine / Hallelujah special / This ole house / Blue suede shoes / All mama's children / Country soul / When you are 21 / Sundays are fundays / Redneck / Every road / Don't get off getting it on / Standing in the need of love / I don't want to fall in love / Sweeter than candy / Hurt put on by you, The / That's right / Dixie fried.
LP: BDL 2034

BEST OF AND THE REST OF, THE.
Tracks: / Rock around the clock / That's alright mama / Kawliga / Tutti frutti / Yes it's me and I'm in love again / Blue suede shoes / Be bop a lula / Maybelline / Whole lotta shakin' / Hang up my rock 'n' roll shoes / Shake rattle and roll / Rock around the clock.
MC: ARLC 1025

BLUE SUEDE SHOES (LP).
Tracks: / Blue suede shoes / Honey don't / Everybody's trying to be my baby / Boppin' the blues / Wrong yo yo / Cat clothes / Let the juke box keep on playing / Dixie bop / Gone gone gone / You can't make love to somebody / Tennessee / Sure to fall.
LP: SUN 1014

BOPPIN' THE BLUES.
Tracks: / Blue suede shoes / I'm sorry, I'm not sorry / Let the juke box keep on playing / All Mama's children / Honey don't / Dixie fried / Boppin' the blues / Your true love / That's alright / Matchbox / Lend me your comb / Gone gone gone.
LP: TOP 107
MC: KTOP 107

BORN TO ROCK.
LP: UVL 76001
MC: UVLC 76001

CARL PERKINS.
Tracks: / Matchbox / If I had 'a known / Green green grass of home / Texas woman / Signs / Blue suede shoes / Honey don't / I'm walking / Matchbox / Suzie Q / Memphis / Maybellene / Slippin' and slidin' / Be bop a lula / Roll over Beethoven / Hound dog / Whole lotta shakin' goin' on / Lucille / Jailhouse rock / All shook up / That's alright mama / Bird dog / Rock Island line.
LP: MCF 3315
MC: MCFC 3315

CARL PERKINS (CAMBRA).
2LP: CR 101
MCSET: CRT 101

CARL PERKINS (DITTO).
MCSET: DTO 10089

CARL PERKINS ROCK'N'ROLL PARTY, THE.
LP: WW 5139
MC: WW 45139

CLASSIC CARL PERKINS, THE.
MC: OCN 2036WK
LP: OCN 2036WL

COUNTRY STORE: CARL PERKINS.
Tracks: / Ruby don't take your love to town / Love sweet love / Just as long / (Let's get) dixie fried / Lord I sinned again last night / Help me dream / Sing my song / You tore my Heaven all to Hell / One more loser going home / Never look back / Honky tonk song / Going to Memphis / Sunday dinner / Big bad blues.
LP: CST 53
MC: CSTK 53

DANCE ALBUM.
Tracks: / Blue suede shoes / Movie magg / Sure to fall / Gone gone gone / Honey don't / Only you / All mama's children / Tennessee / Wrong yo yo / Everybody's trying to be my baby / Matchbox / Your true love / Boppin' the blues.
LP: CRM 2012

DISCIPLINE IN BLUE SUEDE SHOES.
LP: 20090
MC: 40090

EVERY ROAD.
LP: SM 3995
MC: MC 3995

GOIN' BACK TO MEMPHIS.
Tracks: / Twenty one / Georgia court room / Hallelujah special / Sweeter than candy / I don't want to fall in love / Hurt put on by you, The / Rise and shine / Take me back / Sing a song / I want you back again.
LP: MFLP 1042

GOING BACK TO MEMPHIS Vol. 2.
LP: SM 3996

HEART AND SOUL OF CARL PERKINS, THE.
Tracks: / I don't want to fall in love / Hurt put on by you, The / I want you back again / Country soul / Redneck / I dont like what I'm seeing in you / We did it in '54 / Don't get off getting it on / 21 / Standing in the need of love.
LP: ALEB 2308
MC: ZCALB 2308

HONKY TONK GAL.
LP: SS 27

LEGENDARY, THE.
Tracks: / Born to boogie / I can feel it / Don't get off gettin' it on / Take me back / Redneck / Hurt put on by you, The / Sweeter than candy / Boppin' the blues / We did in '54 / Mama / Standing in the need of love / What am I living for / '21' / Country soul / Georgia court room / I didn't want to fall in love again.
MC: PWKMC 4037

MAN AND THE LEGEND, THE.
Tracks: / Blue suede shoes / Honey don't / I'm walking / Matchbox / Suzie Q / Memphis / Maybellene / Slippin' and slidin' / Be bop a lula / Roll over Beethoven / Hound dog / Whole lotta shakin' goin' on / Lucille / Jailhouse rock / All shook up / That's alright mama / Bird dog / Rock island line / Singing the blues / Got my mojo working.
LP: MFLP 2039

MR COUNTRY ROCK.
LP: DEMAND 0015

OL'BLUE SUEDES IS BACK.
LP: UATV 30146

ORIGINAL CARL PERKINS, THE.
Tracks: / Movie Magg / Turn around / Let the juke box keep on playing / Gone gone gone / Blue suede shoes / Honey don't / Boppin' the blues / All mama's children / I'm sorry I'm not sorry / Dixie fried / Matchbox / You true love / Forever yours / That's right / Glad all over / Lend me your comb.
LP: CR 30110

PUT YOUR CAT CLOTHES ON.
Tracks: / Sweethearts or strangers / You can do no wrong / Caldonia / Roll over Beethoven / Matchbox / Put your cat clothes on / Her love rubbed off / Pink pedal pushers / That's right / Look at that moon / Glad all over / Lend me your comb / Your true love.
LP: SUN 1046

ROCKIN' GUITARMAN.
Tracks: / Blue suede shoes / Roll over Beethoven / Sweethearts and strangers / Perkins wiggle / Honky tonk gal / You can do no wrong / What do you want when you're crying? / Boppin' the blues / Caldonia / Lonely street / I care / Y.O.U. / Glad all over / Honey don't / Dixie fried / Her love rubbed off.
LP: CR 30003

ROCKIN' THE HOUSE DOWN.
2LP: NETV 1002
MCSET: NETVC 1002

SUN YEARS, THE.
Tracks: / Honky tonk gal / Movie Magg (2 takes) / Turn around (2 takes) / You can't make love to somebody / Gone gone gone / Let the juke box keep on playing / What ya doin' when you're cryin' / Drink up and go home / Blue suede shoes (3 takes) / Honey don't (2 takes) / Sure to fall / Tennessee / Perkins wiggle / Boppin' the blues (2 takes) / All mama's children / Everybody's trying to be my baby (plus Carl Perkins in Richmond - radio plug) / Somebody tell me (plus Carl Perkins in Memphis - radio plug) / Dixie fried / I'm sorry I'm not sorry / Sweethearts or strangers / Keeper of the key / Be honest with me / That don't move me / Lonely street / Pink pedal pushers (2 takes) / Matchbox (2 takes) / Your true love (2 takes) / Caldonia / Her love rubbed off / You can do no wrong / Roll over Beethoven / Put your cat clothes on (2 takes) / Only you / That's right (2 takes) / Forever yours / I care / Y.O.U. / Look at that moon / Lend me your comb (2 takes) / Glad all over / Right string baby but the wrong yo / Honky tonk babe.
LPS: SUN BOX 101

SURVIVORS, THE (see Cash, Johnny) (Perkins, Carl/Johnny Cash/Jerry Lee Lewis).

SWEETER THAN CANDY.
LP: 20092
MC: 40092

TENNESSEE BOP.
Tracks: / Blue suede shoes / Honky tonk gal / Glad all over / Perkins wiggle / Honey don't / Matchbox / Put your cat clothes on / Everybody's trying to be my baby / Lend me your comb / Dixie fried / Boppin' the blues / Tennessee / Gone gone gone / All mama's children.
LP: INS 5019
MC: TCINS 5019

THAT ROCKIN' GUITAR MAN.
Tracks: / Born to boogie / Daddy sang bass / Redneck / Standing in the need of love / Mama / We did it in '54 / Disciple in blue suede shoes / I can feel it / What am I living for / Don't get off getting it on.
LP: MFLP 1024

TRIO PLUS (see Lewis, Jerry Lee/ Charlie Rich/Carl Perkins) (Perkins, Carl/Jerry Lee Lewis/Charlie Rich)).

TURN AROUND.
LP: CP 2003

Perkins, Carl (jazz)

INTRODUCING.....
Tracks: / Way cross town / You don't know what love is / Lady is a tramp, The / Marblehead / Woodyn you / Westside / Just friends / It could happen to you / Lilacs in the rain / Carl's blues.
LP: . . . . BOP 008

Perkins, Jonathan

SNAKE TALK (Perkins, Jonathan & The Flame).
Tracks: / Hey little girl / I can't say no / Stella / Last day of Summer, The / This time tomorrow / Impatient angel (Track on cassette/ CD only.) / Little hate (makes love much better), A / Joe Lean / Snake talk / X-streams / Move the moon / Fishing for wreaths (Track on cassette/ CD only.).
LP: . . . . ZL 74814
MC: . . . . ZK 74814

Perkins, Pinetop

AFTER HOURS.
LP: . . . . BP 3088

CHICAGO BOOGIE BLUES PIANO MAN (Pinetop Perkins).
LP: . . . . JSP 1107

Perkins, Tony

ON A RAINY AFTERNOON.
LP: . . . . FS 113

Perks, Katie

HAT MUSIC.
LP: 003

SEA OF AIR.
LP: . . . . PLASLP 022

SHINE THE LIGHT.
Tracks: / Shine the light / Cut the rope / Beauty / Rambling shambling man / Golden city / Let it rain / Angel says / Blues, The / Naming of the game, The / Shake hands / Floating world, The.
LP: . . . . PLASLP 010

Perlemuter, Vlado

COMPLETE PIANO WORKS VOLUMES 1 & 2 (see under Ravel for full details).

ETUDES (See under Chopin for full details).

PIANO SONATAS - CHOPIN (See under Chopin for full details).

PRELUDES, BERCEUSE (See under Chopin for full details).

Perlman, Itzhak

TRADITION (Perlman, Itzhak/Israel Zohar/Israel Philharmonic).
Tracks: / Jewish mother, The (Yiddische mamme) / When the Rabbi Elimelech becomes so very merry (As de Rebbe Elimelech is gevoym saoi freylach) / Reyzele / At the fireplace (Oif'n pritpetchik brennt a feier'l) / Doyna / Raisins and almonds (Rozhinkes mit mandelen) / By the wayside stands a tree / Song, A (A dudele) / Where shall I go.
MC: . . . . EL 7479044

Permanent Record

PERMANENT RECORD (Film Soundtrack) (Various artists).
Tracks: / Trash City: *Strummer, Joe* / Baby the trans: *Strummer, Joe* / Nefertiti rock: *Strummer, Joe* / Nothin' 'bout nothin': *Strummer, Joe* / Permanent record, Theme from: *Unknown* / 'Cause I said so: *Godfathers* / Waiting on love: *BoDeans* / Wishing on another lucky star: *Souther, J.D.* / All day and all of the night: *Stranglers* / Something happened: *Reed, Lou*.
LP: . . . . SE 40879
LP: 4611611
MC: 4611614

Peron, Carlos

IMPERSONATOR II.
LP: . . . . BIAS 116

Perras, Anita

ANITA AND TIM (Perras, Anita & Tim Taylor).
MC: . . . . SVMC 9401

TOUCH MY HEART.
LP: . . . . UNKNOWN

Perri

CELEBRATE.
LP: . . . . MCF 3325
MC: . . . . MCFC 3325

INFLIGHT.
Tracks: / I'm the one / No place to go / Flight / Secret weapon / Caves of Altmira / Upside down / Fall in love / I don't wanna lose your love / Travels / Eternal life.
LP: . . . . MCF 3434
MC: . . . . MCFC 3434

TRADE WINDS.
Tracks: / Someone like you / You taught me how / Talk to me / Crazy / No way to treat a lady / It's been you / Tradewinds / You're the one / Mary Mary / Say you will.
LP: . . . . MCG 6104
MC: . . . . MCGC 6104

Perri, Joel

EL CONDOR DEL INDIO.
LP: . . . . EULP 1067
MC: . . . . EUMC 1067

EL CONDOR PASA.
LP: . . . . EULP 1055
MC: . . . . EUMC 1055

MANDOLINE.
LP: . . . . EULP 1047
MC: . . . . EUMC 1047

SOUFFLE DE VENTE.
LP: . . . . EULP 1029
MC: . . . . EUMC 1029

TARANTELLA DEL DIAVOLO.
LP: . . . . EULP 1077
MC: . . . . EUMC 1077

Perry, Demetrius

ANOTHER WORLD.
Tracks: / Another world / Can do can do (anything for you) / Breathless / Betcha don't know / Use me / I'll take you there / Are you lonely / I'll be true / Everything a man could want.
LP: 466 878 1
MC: 466 878 4

Perry, Eden

CHRISTMAS ELVIS PRESLEY STYLE.
MC: . . . . CHV 321

Perry, Frank

BALANCE.
LP: . . . . INCUS 11

Perry, Jeff

LOVE DON'T COME NO STRONGER (See under Taylor, Debbie/Just don't pay).

Perry, Joe Project

LET THE MUSIC DO THE TALKING (Joe Perry Project).
Tracks: / Let the music do the talking / Conflict of interest / Discount dogs / Shooting star / Break song / Rockin' train / Mist is rising / Ready on the firing line / Life at a glance.
LP: . . . . CBS 84213

ONCE A ROCKER,ALWAYS A ROCKER.
Tracks: / Once a rocker, always a rocker / Black velvet pants / Woman in chains / Guns West / Crossfire / Adrianna / King of the Kings / Get it on (bang a gong) / Walk with me Sally / Never wanna stop.
LP: . . . . MCF 3205
MC: . . . . MCFC 3205

Perry, King

KING PERRY 1947-54.
Tracks: / Keep a dollar in your pocket / Rocks in my bed / Perry's wiggle boogie / Hold your gold / I am the blues / San Quentin quail / 18th and Vine St. blues / Leona's boogie / Fat mama / Pitching a party / Wait now / Going to California / Christopher columbus / Kilroy was here / Back to Kansas City / Things ain't what they used to be.
LP: . . . . KK 7438

Perry, Lee

BEST OF LEE PERRY & THE UPSETTERS VOL.2 (Perry, Lee 'Scratch' And the Upsetters).
LP: . . . . PTLP 1028

BLACK ARK, VOL.2 (Perry, Lee 'Scratch').
LP: . . . . BALP 4001

BLOOD VAPOUR (Perry, Lee 'Scratch').
LP: . . . . LALP 007

BUILD THE ARK (Perry, Lee & The Upsetters).
Tracks: / My little Sandra / Dubbing Sandra / Long long time / White belly rat / Freedom street / Land of love / Cross over / Travelling / Green Bay incident / Thanks and praise / Feelings / Wah dat, A / White belly rat (version) / Peace and love / Think so / At the feast / Ethiopian land / Brother nosh / Mr Money Man.
LPS: . . . . PERRY 3

CHICKEN SCRATCH (Perry, Lee 'Scratch').
LP: . . . . HB 53
MC: . . . . HBC 53

CLOAK AND DAGGER (Perry, Lee 'Scratch' & The Dub Syndicate).
LP: . . . . TSLP 9001

FROM THE SECRET LABORATORY.
LP: . . . . MLPS 1035

GIVE ME POWER (Perry, Lee & Friends).
Tracks: / Sick & tired / Rasta no pickpocket / Don't cross the nation / Give me power / News flash / Justice to the people / Babylon's burning / Ring of fire / Dig the grave / Thanks we get, The / Public enemy no.1 / Mid-East rock / Forward up / Hot tip / To be a lover.
LP: . . . . TRLS 254
MC: . . . . ZCTRL 254

GOD MUZICK.
LP: . . . . NETLP 018

HEART OF THE ARK (Perry, Lee 'Scratch').
LP: . . . . SLLP 1

LEE PERRY (Perry, Lee 'Scratch').
MC: . . . . PERRYC 3

LEE PERRY MEETS MAD PROFESSOR IN DUB 2 (Perry, Lee 'Scratch').
LP: . . . . ANG 009

MAGNETIC MIRROR MASTER MIX (Perry, Lee 'Scratch' & The Dub Syndicate).
Tracks: / Voodooism / Wolf out deh / Better future / Bafflin' smoke signals / Dub cap / Living y life / Voodoo dub / Shepherd rod / Future dub / Captive / Different experience.
LP: . . . . AAS 9003

MEGATON DUB 2 (Perry, Lee 'Scratch').
LP: . . . . SLLP 5

MILLIONAIRE LIQUIDATOR (Battle of Armagideon) (Perry, Lee 'Scratch' And the Upsetters).
Tracks: / Introducing myself / Drum song / Grooving / All things are possible / Show me that river / I'm a madman / Joker / Happy birthday / Sexy lady / Time marches on.
LP: . . . . TRLS 227
MC: . . . . ZCTRL 227

MYSTIC MIRACLE STAR (Perry, Lee & The Majestics).
LP: . . . . HB 06
MC: . . . . HBC 06

MYSTIC WARRIOR (Perry, Lee 'Scratch').
LP: . . . . ARI LP 054

MYSTIC WARRIOR (DUB) (Perry, Lee 'Scratch').
LP: . . . . ARI LP 055

OPEN THE GATES (Perry, Lee 'Scratch' & Friends).
LPS: . . . . PERRY 2

OUT OF MANY - THE UPSETTER.
LP: . . . . TRLS 297
MC: . . . . ZCTRL 297

PUBLIC JESTERING 1974-76.
LP: . . . . ATLP 108

REGGAE GREATS.
MC: . . . . RRCT 10

RETURN OF THE SUPER APE (Perry, Lee 'Scratch').
MC: . . . . LPIRC 0001
LP: . . . . LPIR 0001

REVOLUTION DUB (Perry, Lee 'Scratch').
LP: . . . . CTLP 112
LP: . . . . TSLP 9006

ROAST FISH COLLIE WEED & CORN BREAD (Perry, Lee 'Scratch' And the Upsetters).
LP: . . . . LPIR 0000
MC: . . . . LPIRC 0000

SATAN KICKED THE BUCKET (Perry, Lee 'Scratch').
LP: . . . . W 2740

SENSI DUB VOLUME 2 (Perry, Lee/ King Tubby).
LP: . . . . OMLP 15

SOME OF THE BEST (Perry, Lee 'Scratch' And the Upsetters).
LP: . . . . HB 37
MC: . . . . HBC 37

SPIRITUAL HEALING.
LP: . . . . EFA 14998

TIME BOOM (Perry, Lee 'Scratch').
LP: . . . . ONULP 43
MC: . . . . ONULP 43C

TIME BOOM X DE DEVIL DEAD (Perry, Lee 'Scratch').
Tracks: / S.D.I. / Blinkers / Jungle / De devil dead / Music and science lovers / Kiss the champion / Allergic to lies / Time conquer.
LP: . . . . SYLP 6000
MC: . . . . TCSYLP 6000

TURN AND FIRE.
LP: . . . . AAS 9004

UPSETTER BOX SET, THE (Perry, Lee 'Scratch').
LPS: . . . . PERRY 1

Perry, Lee 'Scratch'

LORD GOD MUZIK.
LP: ZSII0

Perry, Mark

SNAPPY TURNS.
LP: . . . . DLP 06

Perry, Phil

HEART OF THE MAN.
Tracks: / Amazing love / Say anything / Forever / Woman / More nights / Call me / (Forever in the) arms of love / Best of me, The / God's gift to the world / Goodbye / Who do you love (CD & cassette only).
LP: C1 92115
MC: C4 92115

Perry, Roy

MANCUNIAN WAY, THE (Perry, Roy and Roy Wood).
LP: . . . . DEROY 1199

Perry, Steve

STREET TALK.
Tracks: / Oh Sherrie / I believe / Go away / Foolish heart / It's only love / She's mine / You should be happy / Running alone / Captured by the moment / Strung out.
LP: . . . . CBS 25967
MC: 40 25967

Perryman, Willie

WILDFIRE.
LP: . . . . MB 902

Persian Risk

RISE UP.
LP: . . . . METALLP 2

Persian Rugs

DROWNING POOL.
LP: . . . . PSP LP 3

Persip, Charlie

SUPERBAND (Persip, Charlie & Gerry McFurns).
LP: . . . . ST 209

Person, Houston

BIG HORN, THE.
LP: . . . . MR 5136

HEAVY JUICE.
Tracks: / Heavy juice / Summertime / Loveboat theme / Never let me go / Let the feeling flow / Please send me someone to love / Texas shuffle / Blue hue.
LP: . . . . MR 5260

NEARNESS OF YOU, THE.
LP: . . . . MR 5178

SOMETHING IN COMMON (Person, Houston & Ron Carter).
Tracks: / Blue seven / It thought about you / Mack the knife / Joy Spring / Good morning heartache / Anthropology / Once in a while / Blues for two.
LP: 600633

STOLEN SWEETS.
LP: . . . . MR 5110

SUSPICIONS.
LP: . . . . MR 5199

Person To Person

STRONGER THAN REASON.
Tracks: / High time / Love on the rebound / Turning back the pages / Reputation / Right from wrong / Still on my mind / Poison street / 4 a.m. / Wrong side of midnight / Running out.
LP: . . . . EPC 26513
MC: 40 26513

Personal Effects

MANA FIESTA.
LP: . . . . GWLP 50

Personality Crisis

PERSONALITY CRISIS (Various artists).
LP: . . . . ARLP 101

Perspico Acumine

PERFECT ACTION, A (Perspico Acumine (Holdings)).
Tracks: / Pre match tension / Robinson Moxon / Thin man from Orpington / Sir Derek, The Retford Prince / Thin man (reprise) / Lubo (visor Crunch) / I.T.Man Preview / Sow Coda / Movement (Off the perch through the air) / Colchester Express, The / Son of Ivanhoe / Twelfth just man, The.
LP: . . . . ACME 4

Persson

LIVIN' HIGH (Persson's London Stompers).
LP: . . . . SOS 1167

Persson, Bent

LOUIS ARMSTRONG 50 HOT CORNET CHORUS 1.
LP: . . . . KS 2044

LOUIS ARMSTRONG 50 HOT CORNET CHORUS 2.
LP: . . . . KS 2045

Persuaders

PERSUADERS (THEME FROM) (See under Barry, John).

Persuasion (bk)

PERSUASION (See under Austen, Jane) (Massey, Anna (nar)).

PERSUASION (See under Austen, Jane) (Scales, Prunella (nar)).

Persuasions

ACAPELLA.
Tracks: / Intro / Searchin' for my baby / I just can't work no longer / Ol' man river / Monologue / Don't look back / Drip drop / Whole world is a stage, The / Up on the roof / Bounce, The / Since I fell for you / Too late / It's all right.
LP: . . . . ED 296

CHIRPIN.
LP: . . . . K 52057

COMIN' AT YA.
LP: . . . . FF 093

GOOD NEWS.
LP: . . . . ROUNDER 3053
MC: . . . . ROUNDER 3053C

NO FRILLS.
Tracks: / You can have her / Under the boardwalk / Sand in my shoes / I was wrong / I woke up in love this morning / I wonder do you love the Lord like I do / Still ain't got no band / Victim / Treasure of love / Sweet was the wine / What are you doing New Years Eve / Slip slidin' away.
LP: . . . . ROUNDER 3083
LP: . . . . FIEND 46
MC: . . . . ROUNDER 3083C

STARDUST.
LP: . . . . CATA 905

Pertwee, Jon

ADVENTURES OF WORZEL GUMMIDGE, THE (See under Adventures of... (Spoken Word)).

JOHNNY TOMORROW.
MC: . . . . VCA 097

WORZEL GUMMIDGE.
Tracks: / New friends for worzel / Village fete.
MCSET: . . . . KC 001

WORZEL GUMMIDGE SINGS.
Tracks: / Worzel's song / Sulking / Scarecrow's party, The / Owor k wo dip / I might we'll see / Acting / Scarecrows on parade / If I was you and you was me / Singalonga Worzel / Who'd be a scarecrow / Oh what a day this is / Worzel walk, The.
LP: . . . . CROW 1
MC: . . . . KCROW 1

WORZEL GUMMIDGE, VOL. 1.
Tracks: / Scarecrow hop / Tea party, The.
MCSET: . . . . KC 002

WORZEL GUMMIDGE, VOL. 2.
Tracks: / Saucy nancy / Worzel's 'ansome 'ead.
MCSET: . . . . KC 003

WORZEL GUMMIDGE, VOL. 3.
Tracks: / Fair old pullover, A / Little learning, A.
MCSET: . . . . KC 004

WORZEL GUMMIDGE, VOL. 4.
Tracks: / Worzel's nephew / Trial or Worzel, The.
MCSET: . . . . KC 005

WORZEL GUMMIDGE, VOL. 5.
Tracks: / Worzel gives a lecture / Worzel's wedding.
MCSET: . . . . KC 006

Peru

INCA HARP - LAMENTS AND DANCES (Various artists).
LP: . . . . LLST 7359

MUSIC FROM THE LAND OF MACCHU PICCHU (Various artists).
LP: . . . . LLST 7294
MC: . . . . LLCT 7294

MUSIC OF THE INCAS (Various artists).
LP: . . . . LLST 7348
MC: . . . . LLCT 7348

REAL MUSIC OF PERU, THE (See Under Huaynos & Huaylas) (Huaynos & Huaylas).

VIRACOCHA - LEGENDARY MUSIC OF THE ANDES (Various artists).
LP: . . . . LLST 7264
MC: . . . . LLCT 7264

Peruna Jazzmen

DOCTOR JAZZ.
LP: . . . . SLP 438

PERUNA JAZZMEN, VOL. 2.
LP: . . . . SOS 1020

PERUNA JAZZMEN, VOL. 3.
LP: . . . . SOS 1105

Pesniary

PESNIARY.
Tracks: / Olesya / Why should she need a garden / Inheritance / Mountain here and mountain there / Earrings / Love / Black eyes / There is a pussy willow / Rose blossom / Lad ploughs the soil.
LP: . . . . UAS 30201

Pestalozzi

SONGS OF JOY (Pestalozzi School Choir).
Tracks: / I'd like to teach the world to sing / Piper, The / I had a dream / Sing a song of freedom / Amazing grace / Morning has broken / Black and white / Mary's boy child / Kumbaya / Imagine / Give peace a chance / Everything is beautiful / Sailing / When a child is born / Happy Xmas (war is over).
LP: . . . . NE 1140
MC: . . . . CE 2140

Pestilence

CONSUMING IMPULSE.
LP: . . . . RO 94211
MC: . . . . RO 94214

MALLEUS MALEFICARUM.
Tracks: / Malleus Maleficarum / Subordinate to the domination / Commandments / Bacterial surgery / Osculum inflame / Parricade / Extreme unction / Chemo therapy / Cycle of existance / Systematic instruction.
LP: . . . . RR 95191

TESTIMONY OF THE ANCIENTS.
LP: . . . . RC 92851
MC: . . . . RC 92854

Pet Hate

BAD PUBLICITY.
Tracks: / I'm not the one / Girls grow up too fast / Cry of the wild / Street fighting man / She's got the action.
LP: . . . . HMRLP 23
LP: . . . . HMRLP 23 W
MC: . . . . HMRMC 23

BRIDE WORE RED, THE.
Tracks: / Bride wore red, The / Moya's comim' out / How can I carry on / Love me madly / Wanting you / Caught (red handed) / Party's over, The / Roll away the stone / First kiss / Real good time.
LP: . . . . HMRLP 17
MC: . . . . HMRMC 17

Pet Sematary (film)

PET SEMATARY (Original soundtrack) (Various artists).
LP: . . . . VS 5227
MC: . . . . VSC 5227

Pet Shop Boys

ACTUALLY.
Tracks: / One more chance / Shopping / Rent / Hit music / What have I done to deserve this? / It couldn't happen here / It's a sin / I want to wake up / Heart / King's Cross.
LP: . . . . PCSD 104
MC: . . . . TCPCSD 104

ACTUALLY/ALWAYS ON MY MIND.
LP: E190263

BEHAVIOUR.
Tracks: / Being boring / This must be the place I waited years to leave / To face the truth / How can you expect to be taken seriously? / Only the wind / My October symphony / So hard / Nervously / End of the world / Jealousy.
LP: . . . . PCSD 113
LP: 794 310 1
MC: . . . . TCPCSD 113
MC: 794 310 4

DISCO.
Tracks: / In the night / Suburbia / Opportunities / Paninaro / Love comes quickly / West End girls.
MC: . . . . TCPRG 1001
LP: . . . . PRG 1001
LP: . . . . ATAK 129
MC: . . . . TCATAK 129

DISCOGRAPHY - THE COMPLETE SINGLES COLLECTION.
Tracks: / West end girls / Love comes quickly / Opportunities (let's make lots of money) / Suburbia / It's a sin / What have I done to deserve this / Always on my mind / Heart / Domino dancing / Left to my own devices / It's alright / So hard / Being boring / Where the streets have no name / Jealousy / DJ culture / Was it worth it?.
2LP: . . . . PMTV 3
MC: . . . . TCPMTV 3

INTROSPECTIVE.
Tracks: / Left to my own devices / I want a dog / Domino dancing / I'm not scared / Always on my mind / It's alright / In my house.
LP: . . . . PCS 7325
MC: . . . . TCPCS 7325
LP: . . . . PCSX 7325

LOSING MY MIND (See under Minelli, Liza) (Pet Shop Boys & Liza Minelli).

PET SHOP BOYS: INTERVIEW PICTURE DISC.
LPPD: . . . . BAK 2064

PLEASE.
Tracks: / Two divide by zero / West End girls / Opportunities (Lets make lots of money) / Love comes quickly / Suburbia / Tonight is forever / Violence / I want a lover / Later tonight / Why don't we live together.
LP: . . . . PSB 1
MC: . . . . TCPSB 1
LP: . . . . PCS 7303
MC: . . . . TCPS 7303

SUBURBIA.
Tracks: / Suburbia / Jack the lad / Love comes quickly / Paninaro.
MC: . . . . TCR 6140

Petards

BURNING RAINBOWS.
Tracks: / And you all talk about heaven / All right, tonight you'll be a woman / One more chance / To be blue (burning rainbows) / Green eyes paradise / Speed freak / Today is my birthday / Alone / Dust of my way, The / Some day I'll cry / Come to me / Come to you / You better move right now / Goky and me / Who will sell his dreams / Roses.
LP: . . . . BFX 15088

GOLDEN GLASS.
Tracks: / Golden glass / Tiger rider / Sun came out at seven / Firetree / Summerwind / If you want to go away / Drive / I won't come back / Shoot me up to the moon / Lazy moon / Deeper blue, A / My little heart / Love all around / Baby / Roses for Kathy / Confusion all day.
LP: . . . . BFX 15086

HITSHOCK.
Tracks: / Take me, shake me / Blue fire light / Dream, The / Special sunset for a lady / Pictures / Mekka / Keep on / My world / Sunday rainshine / Ruins of Tookamoon / Stone by now / Rover on the roam.
LP: . . . . BFX 15085

Petchersky, Alma

GRAND SONATA (TCHAIKOVSKY)/ SCRIABIN.
Tracks: / Grand sonata op.37 (in G major) / Piano sonata no.3 (Scriabin) / Poemes (2) op.32 (Scriabin).
LP: . . . . DCA 671
MC: . . . . ZC DCA 671

SPANISH PIANO MUSIC.
LP: . . . . ALH 949
MC: . . . . ZC ALH 949

Pete Kelly's Blues

PETE KELLY'S BLUES (OST) (See under Lee, Peggy) (Lee, Peggy).

Peter & Gordon

BEST OF PETER & GORDON.
Tracks: / True love ways / Five hundred miles / My little girl's gone / Lady Godiva / I go to pieces / Nobody I know / I don't want to see you again / Woman / Let it be me / Lucille / World without love / Crying in the rain / Hurtin' is loving / To know you is to love you / Someone ain't right / You've had better times / Baby I'm yours / Exodus song / High noon.
LP: 1A 022 58030
LP: C5-502
MC: C5K 502

BEST OF THE EMI YEARS: PETER AND GORDON.
Tracks: / World without love, A / Freight train / Leave my woman alone / Nobody I know / Tell me how / Long time gone, A / I don't want to see you again / I go to pieces / True love ways / Crying in the rain / to know you is to love you / Homeward bound / Baby I'm yours / Green leaves of Summer / Woman / When I fall in love / Lady Godiva / Somewhere / Knight in rusty armour / Sunday for tea / Memphis / Send me the pillow (that you dreamed on).
MC: . . . . TCEMS 1409

HITS AND MORE.
Tracks: / World without love / Nobody I know / I don't want to see you again / I go to pieces / True love ways / To know you is to love you / Let it be me / Crying in the rain / Baby I'm yours / There's no living without your loving / Lady Godiva / Knight in rusty armour / Sunday for tea / Lucille / Leave my woman alone.
LP: . . . . EMS 1146
MC: . . . . TCEMS 1146

PETER & GORDON.
LP: 33SX 1630

SOMEWHERE.
LP: 1A 220 1583234

WORLD WITHOUT LOVE.
Tracks: / True love ways / Five hundred ways / My little girl's gone / Lady Godiva / I go to pieces / Nobody I know / I don't want to see you again / Woman / Let it be me / Lucille / World without love / Crying in the rain / Hurtin' is loving / To know him is to love him / Someone ain't right / You've had better times / Baby I'm yours / Exodus song / High noon.
LP: . . . . CM 106
MC: . . . . CMK 106

Peter Grimes (opera)

PETER GRIMES (see under Britten, Benjamin) (Various artists).

Peter Pan

PETER PAN (TV Cast with Jean Arthur and Boris Karloff) (Various artists).
LP: . . . . AOL 4312
MC: . . . . PST 4312

PETER PAN (Royal Shakespeare Cast).
LP: . . . . RSP 1

PETER PAN (Original Soundtrack) (Various artists).
Tracks: / Main title: *Peter Pan* / Second star to the right: *Peter Pan* / You can fly: *Peter Pan* / Pirate's life: *Peter Pan* / Following the leader: *Peter Pan* / What made the red man red: *Peter Pan* / Your mother and mine: *Peter Pan* / Elegant Captain Hook, The: *Peter Pan* / Following the leader: *Peter Pan* / Never smile at a crocodile: *Peter Pan* / You can fly: *Peter Pan* / Your mother and mine: *Peter Pan* / Finale: *Peter Pan* / You can fly: *Peter Pan*.
LP: . . . . WD 014
MC: . . . . WDC 014
LP: . . . . DQ 1206

PETER PAN (Various artists).
MC: . . . . GK 83762

PETER PAN (Original Broadway cast) (Various artists).
MC: . . . . JST 04312

PETER PAN (Original Broadway Cast) (Various artists).
LP: . . . . AYKI 3762

PETER PAN/CINDERELLA (Film soundtracks) (Various artists).
Tracks: / Second star to the right, The: *Various artists* / You can fly, you can fly: *Various artists* / Pirate's life, A: *Various artists* / Never smile at a crocodile: *Various artists* / Following the leader: *Various artists*/ What made the red man red?: *Various artists* / Your mother and mine: *Various artists* / Elegant Captain Hook, The: *Various artists* / Finale: *Various artists* / Cinderella: *Various artists* / Dream is a wish your heart makes, A: *Various artists* / Oh sing sweet nightingale: *Various artists* / Work song, The: *Various artists*/ Bibbidi bobbidi boo: *Various artists* / Cinderella arrives at the ball: *Various artists* / So this is love: *Various artists* / Cinderella (finale): *Various artists*.
LP: . . . . REC 577
MC: . . . . ZCM 577

Peter Pan (bk)

PETER PAN (Children's Classics).
MC: . . . . PLBC 138

PETER PAN.
MC: 0 00 109030 5

PETER PAN (J.M. Barrie) (Craig, Wendy (nar)).
MCSET: . . . . LFP 7086
MCSET: . . . . TCLFP 7086

STORY OF PETER PAN (J.M. Barrie) (Johns, Glynis (nar)).
MC: 1395

Peter, Paul & Mary

BEST OF PETER, PAUL & MARY.
Tracks: / Blowin' in the wind / Don't think twice / Early in the morning / This land is your land / For lovin' me / If I had a hammer / Lemon tree / Puff (the magic dragon) / Cruel war / Betty and Dupree / Tell in on the mountain / 500 miles.
LP: . . . . K 46012

IN CONCERT VOL.1.
LP: . . . . WM 8158

IN THE WIND.
LP: . . . . WM 8142

NO EASY WALK TO FREEDOM.
Tracks: / Weave me the sunshine / Right field / I'd rather be in love / State of the heart / No easy walk to freedom / Greenland whale fisheries / Whispered words / El Salvador / Greenwood / Light one candle.
LP: . . . . VGC 2
MC: . . . . TCVGC 2
MC: . . . . OVEDC 374

PETER, PAUL & MARY.
LP: . . . . WM 4064

REUNION.
LP: . . . . K 56554

TEN YEARS TOGETHER.
Tracks: / Blowin' in the wind / Too much of nothing / Lemon tree / Stewball / Early morning rain / 500 miles / I dig rock 'n' roll / Leaving on a jet plane / Puff (the magic dragon) / For lovin' me / Don't think twice / It's alright / If I had a hammer / Day is done.
LP: . . . . K 46051
LP: . . . . WS 2552

Peter & The Test....

3 X 45 (Peter & The Test Tube Babies).
LP: . . . . NO FEARS 1

ANOTHER NOISY PUNK ROCK LP (Peter & The Test Tube Babies).
LP: . . . . HP 1

BEST OF PETER AND THE TEST TUBE BABIES (Peter & The Test Tube Babies).
Tracks: / Banned from the pub / Moped lads / Run like up yer bun / Elvis is dead / Maniac / Zombie creeping flesh / September part 2 / Wimpeez / Jinx / Blown out again / Keys to the city / Louise wouldn't like it / Every second counts.
LP: . . . . DOJOLP 57

JOURNEY TO THE CENTRE OF JOHNNY CLARKE'S HEAD (Peter & The Test Tube Babies).
MC: . . . . OD 1

MATING SOUNDS OF THE SOUTH AMERICAN FROG, THE (Peter & The Test Tube Babies).
LP: . . . . THIN 1
LP: . . . . CHIN 001

PISSED AND PROUD (Peter & The Test Tube Babies).
Tracks: / Moped lads / Banned from the pub / Elvis is dead / Up yer bum / Smash and grab / Run like hell / Shit stirrer / Intensive care / Keep Britain untidy / Transvestite / Maniac / Disco / I'm the leader of the gang (I am).
MC: . . . . CPUNK 3
LP: . . . . RR 9938

SOBERPHOBIA (Peter & The Test Tube Babies).
Tracks: / Keys to the city / Louise / Spirit of keith moon / Allergic to life / All about love / He's on the whiskey / Boozanza / Every time I see her / Ghost in my bedsit / Every second counts.
LP: . . . . DOJOLP 49
LP: . . . . HP 002

Peter & The Wolf (bk)

PETER AND THE WOLF (Unknown narrator(s)).
LP: . . . . PLB 271

Peters, Brian

FOOLS OF FORTUNE.
LP: . . . . HAR 005
MC: . . . . HARC 005

PERSISTENCE OF MEMORY.
Tracks: / Miner's lockout, The / Ninian south / Bloddaur drain / Merch Megan / Lankin / Bring the sea to Manchester / No dough blues / Demon lover, The / Cunning cobbler, The / Jenny Bell / Herd on the hill / Farewell to the brine.
LP: . . . . FE 051

Peters, Chris

BODY MUSIC.
LP: . . . . MXLP 01

BUBBLEGUM BOY.
Tracks: / Phantom of the bassline, The / Mess on your hands / Don't go breaking my heart / Foggy day, A / Take a chance to dance / Bad attitude / Doctor DJ / Your love spells danger.
LP: . . . . TNALP 2

CAUGHT IN THE ACT.
Tracks: / Caught in the act / Susy rings my bell / Love insurance / Runaround love / Love trap / Round and round / Easier said than done.
LP: . . . . TNALP 1

Peters, Cyndee

BLACK IS THE COLOUR.
LP: . . . . OP 7706

Peters, Ellis

MORBID TASTE FOR BONES, A (Mediaeval Whodunnit) (Houston, Glyn).
MCSET: . . . . LFP 7481

ONE CORPSE TOO MANY (see under One Corpse Too Many) (Houston, Glyn).

Peters, Frans

HAMMOND ORGAN OF FRANS PETERS, THE.
MC: . . . . AIM 101

Peters, Hal

FOLLOW THRU (Peters, Hal Trio).
LP: . . . . LP 8801

Peters, John

SOMETHING FOR NOTHING.
MC: . . . . WHYC 6

Peters & Lee

ALL I EVER NEED IS YOU.
Tracks: / All I ever need is you / By your side / Everybody needs a rainbow / Loving baby / If / Nevertheless / Old fashioned way, The / Raining in my heart / She's a mover / Stars fell on Alabama / United we stand / Until it's time for you to go.
LP: . . . . SPR 8570
MC: . . . . SPC 8570

BEST OF PETERS & LEE.
MCSET: . . . . DTO 10071

BY YOUR SIDE.
LP: 6308 192

FAREWELL ALBUM.
Tracks: / Sing me a memory / Ocean and blue sky / Come softly to me / Can't you hear the song / Way you look tonight / Release me / Yesterday just passed my way again / Together again / Punch and Judy man / We love each other / What have I got / Twelfth of never / Don't throw it all away.
LP: . . . . ACLP 006

FAVOURITES.
Tracks: / Closer / Come to me / Comin' home baby / Crying game, The / Don't blame me / Don't stay away too long / Guess you'll never know / If I fell / I'll be your baby tonight / I'm confessin' / Killing me softly with his song / Last happy song, The / Mayday / Oh baby I love you / Old fashioned way, The / Only you / Our song / Remembering / Welcome home / Wonderful baby.
LP: 9109 205

INVITATION.
LP: . . . . UNKNOWN

PETERS AND LEE.
LP: . . . . PTLS 1098
MC: . . . . PTLC 1098

RAINBOW.
LP: 6308 208

REMEMBER WHEN.
Tracks: / Welcome home / Closer / Seasons in the sun / Only you / Tie a yellow ribbon / Butterfly / Our song / Hey Mr. Music man / Something stupid / Smile / Suspicious minds / Remember when / Last happy song, The / Bye bye blues.
LP: 6391024

SMILE.
Tracks: / Bye bye blues / Bye bye love / Can't smile without you / I got a thing about you / Let love come between us / Pretend / Remember when / Share your love with me / Smile / Suspicious minds / Walk softly / Welcome home.
LP: 9109 219

SPOTLIGHT ON PETERS AND LEE.
Tracks: / When somebody thinks you're wonderful / Good morning freedom / If / Don't stay away too long / Only you / Welcome home / Hey Mr. Music man / Closer / Raining in my heart / All I want to do / Old fashioned way / Bye bye blackbird / I'm confessin' / Save your kisses for me / By your side / Another somebody done somebody wrong song / Can't keep my mind on the game / Oh baby I love you / All I ever need is you / Send in the clowns / Butterfly / Rainbow / If I fell / My cherie amour / You are the sunshine of my life / Everything is beautiful.
2LP: 6625040

WE CAN MAKE IT.
LP: 6308 165

YESTERDAY AND TODAY.
Tracks: / Together again / Punch and Judy man / We love each other / What have I got / Twelfth of never / Don't throw it all away / Sing me a memory / Ocean and blue sky / Everybody knows / Way you look tonight / Sing me a memory / Come softly to me / Release me / Yesterday just passed my way again / New York, New York / Joanna / Nature boy / These empty arms / Hurt / When your old wedding ring was new / Something 'bout you baby I like / Your cheatin' heart / Unforgettable / I wish you love / Just out of reach / Imagine.
2LP: . . . . CR 074
MCSET: . . . . CRT 074

Peters, Lennie

UNFORGETTABLE.
Tracks: / Something 'bout you baby I like / Your cheatin' heart / Unforgettable / I wish you love / Just out of reach / Imagine / New York, New York / Joanna / Nature boy / These empty arms / Hurt / When your old wedding ring was new.
LP: . . . . ACLP 012

Peters, Mike

DJANGO'S MUSIC (Peters,Mike/Bob Wilberg/Birelli Lagrene).
LP: . . . . ST 253

Peters, Sir Shina

SHINAMANIA.
LP: . . . . CBS N 1006

Peters Sisters

TERRIFIC PETERS SISTERS, THE.
Tracks: / Without a song / I feel a song coming on / Mean to me / Glory of love / Sing baby sing / Only you / T'aint what you do (it's the way that you do it) / Best things in life are free, The / Till / Who stole the jam / Maybe it's because (I love you too much) / It's de-lovely / Please don't talk about me when I'm gone.
LP: 2C 068 65085

Peters, Thomas. J.

IN SEARCH OF EXCELLENCE (Secrets of Success series).
MC: 0600560678

Petersen, Kari

VAELFERDAR VISUR.
LP: . . . . HJF 5

Petersen, Pete

JAZZ JOURNEY (Petersen, Pete & Collection Jazz Orchestra).
LP: . . . . PAUSA 7163

PLAYIN' IN THE PARK (Petersen, Pete & Collection Jazz Orchestra).
LP: . . . . PAUSA 7191

STRAIGHT AHEAD (Petersen, Pete & Collection Jazz Orchestra).
LP: . . . . CM 8020
MC: . . . . CMMC 8020

TEXAS STATE OF MIND (Petersen, Pete & Collection Jazz Orchestra).
LP: . . . . PAUSA 7143

Peterson, Billy

NO METHOD (See under Goodwin, Bill) (Peterson, Billy/ Bill Goodwin/ Hal Galper).

Peterson, Colleen

BASIC FACTS.
Tracks: / Weather the storm / Let's try / I had it all / Gently lay down / Mr. Conductor / Basic fact of love / 1942 / What a fool I'd be / Love scares me / Ghost of Maggie's sailor.
LP: . . . . BSR 33-66

COLLEEN.
Tracks: / Dynamite rock'n'roll band / Go thru the motions / Beginning to feel like home / Delaney / Stealing away / Bucket to the south / You make it look so easy / Startin' out clean / Closest thing to you, The / Dim lights / Thick smoke and loud loud music.
LP: . . . . ST 11714

TAKIN' MY BOOTS OFF.
Tracks: / I go to pieces / Angelina / Last time I saw you / Need your lovin' / Going going gone / Run to her / Maybe it's love / One horse town / Booze the blues away.
LP: . . . . EST 11835

Peterson, James

ROUGH AND READY.
Tracks: / I fell in love with a prostitute / Chicken biddy / Takin' inventory / All on account of you / Bait cost more than the fish / Can't teach an old dog new tricks / Mind is a terrible thing to waste, A / Sing the blues until I die / Up for adoption / Clothesline.
LP: . . . . KIN 4031
MC: . . . . KIN 4031 MC

Peterson, John

NIGHT OF MIRACLES.
LP: . . . . PC 872

Peterson, Lucky

LUCKY STRIKES.
Tracks: / Over my head / Can't get no loving on the telephone / Lucky strikes / Bad feeling / Earlene / Pounding of my heart / She spread her wings / Dead cat on the line / Heart attack.
LP: . . . . AL 4770

TRIPLE PLAY.
Tracks: / Let the chips fall where they may / Your lies / Six o'clock blues / Repo man / I found a love / Jammin' in the jungle / Locked out of love / I'm free / Don't cloud up on me / Funky Ray.
MC: . . . . AC 4789

Peterson, Marvin

ANGELS OF ATLANTA, THE (Peterson, Marvin 'Hannibal').
LP: . . . . ENJA 3085

HANNIBAL IN ANTIBES (Peterson, Marvin 'Hannibal').
LP: . . . . ENJA 3011

POEM SONG (Peterson, Marvin 'Hannibal').
LP: . . . . MOLE 6

Peterson, Oscar

ACTION.
LP: . . . . MPS 68 073

AIN'T BUT A FEW OF US LEFT (see Jackson, Milt) (Peterson, Oscar/ Milt Jackson/ Grady Tate/ Ray Brown).

ALONE TOGETHER (see Carter, Benny) (Peterson, Oscar & Benny Carter).

ALTERNATE BLUES (See under Clark, Terry) (Peterson, Oscar/Clark Terry/ Freddie Hubbard/Dizzy Gillespie).

ANOTHER DAY (Peterson, Oscar Trio).
Tracks: / Blues for Martha / I'm old fashioned / All the things you are / Too close for comfort / JAMFS are coming, The / It never entered my mind / Carolina shout.
LP: . . . . MPS 68 083

AT THE MONTREUX JAZZ FESTIVAL, 1975 (Peterson, Oscar Big Six).
Tracks: / Au privave / Here's that rainy day / Poor butterfly / Reunion blues.
LP: 231 0747
MC: K10 747

AT THE OPERA HOUSE (see Modern Jazz Quartet) (Peterson, Oscar Trio & Modern Jazz Quartet).

AT THE STRATFORD SHAKESPEARIAN FESTIVAL (Oscar Peterson Trio).
Tracks: / Falling in love with love / How about you / Flamingo / Swinging on a star / Noreen's nocturne / Gypsy in my soul / How high the moon / Love you madly / 52nd Street theme.
LP: 2304223

BEST OF OSCAR PETERSON (Compact/Walkman jazz).
MC: 830 698-4

CARIOCA.
Tracks: / Carioca / Samba sensitive / Amanha / Meditation / Mas que nada / Samba de Orfeu / Manha de carnaval / Soulville samba / How insensitive.
LP: . . . . B 90110
MC: . . . . MB 990110

COLLECTION: OSCAR PETERSON.
Tracks: / How high the moon / Falling in love with love / Sometimes I'm happy / Big fat mama / Should I love you so? / Swinging on a star / Love you madly / In the wee small hours of the morning / I've never been in love before / Joy spring / Gypsy in my soul.
MC: . . . . DVMC 2041

COMPACT JAZZ: OSCAR PETERSON.
Tracks: / Let's fall in love / Mack the knife.
MC: 831 698-4

DIGITAL AT MONTREUX.
Tracks: / Old folks / Soft winds / Indiana / That's all / Younger than Springtime / Caravan / Rockin' in rhythm / C jam blues / Solitude / Satin doll / Caravan (reprise) / On the trail.
LP: . . . . D 230 8224
MC: . . . . K 08 224

ELLA & OSCAR (See Fitzgerald, Ella) (Peterson, Oscar & Ella Fitzgerald).

EVENING AT THE HOLLYWOOD BOWL, AN (Peterson, Oscar & Ella Fitzgerald).
2LP: 2610058

'EXTRAORDINARY' CANADIAN CONCERT OF..., THE (Peterson, Oscar & Ray Brown).
LP: . . . . CA 1400

FIORELLO (1959 show) (Peterson, Oscar Trio).
Tracks: / When did I fall in love? / Little tin box / Home again / 'Til tomorrow / Politics and poker / Gentleman Jimmy / Unfair / On the side of the Angela / Where do I go from here?.
LP: 8171 081

FREEDOM SONG (Peterson, Oscar Big 4).
Tracks: / 'Round midnight / Watch what happens / For debby / Easy living / Move / Hymn to freedom / Fallen warrior / Sweet lorraine / You look good to me / Now's the time / Future child / Mississauga rattler / Nigerian market place / Emily / Tenderly / Nightchild / Cake walk, The.
LP: 2640 101
MC: . . . . K 40 101

GEORGE GERSHWIN SONGBOOK.
Tracks: / Man I love, The / Fascinating rhythm / It ain't necessarily so / Somebody loves me / Strike up the band / I've got a crush on you / I was doin' alright / 'S wonderful / Lady be good / I got rhythm / Foggy day, A / Love walked in.
LP: 823 249-1

GIANTS, THE (Peterson, Oscar/Ray Brown/Joe Pass).
Tracks: / Riff blues / Who cares? / Jobim / Blues for Dennis / Sunny /

Getting sentimental over you / Caravan / Eyes of love.
LP: 231 0796
MC: K10 796

GIRL TALK.
LP: . . . . MPS 68 074

GOOD LIFE, THE.
LP: 230 8241
MC: . . . . K 8241

GREAT CONNECTION (Peterson, Oscar Trio).
Tracks: / Younger than Springtime / Where do we go from here / Smile / Soft winds / Just squeeze me / On the trail / Wheatland.
LP: . . . . MPS 68 086

HARK (see De Franco, Buddy) (Peterson, Oscar Quartet & Buddy De Franco).

HELLO HERBIE (Peterson, Oscar & Herb Ellis).
LP: . . . . MPS 68 080

HISTORY OF AN ARTIST.
Tracks: / R.B. blues / I wished on the moon / You can depend on me / This is where it's at / Okie blues / I want to be happy / Texas blues / Main stem / Don't get around much anymore / Swamp fire / In a sentimental mood / Greasy blues / Sweety blues / Gay's blues / Good life / Richard's round / Lady of the lavender mist.
2LP: 262 5702
MCSET: . . . . K 25 702

HISTORY OF AN ARTIST, VOL 2.
Tracks: / Wes' tune / Reunion blues / When your lover has gone / Five o'clock whistle / Old folks / Ma, he's making eyes at me / Tenderly.
LP: 2310 895

IF YOU COULD SEE ME NOW.
Tracks: / Weird blues / If I should lose you / On Danish shores / L'Impossible / If you could see me now / Limehouse blues.
LP: 231 0918
MC: K10 918

IN RUSSIA.
Tracks: / I got it bad and that ain't good / I concentrate on you / Hogtown blues / Place St Henri / On Green Dolphin Street / You stepped out of a dream / Wave / On the trail / Take the 'A' train / Summertime / Just friends / Do you know what it means to miss New Orleans? / I loves you, Porgy / Georgia on my mind / Li'l darlin' / Watch what happens / Hallelujah trail / Someone to watch over me.
2LP: 262 5711
MCSET: . . . . K 25 711

JOUSTS (Peterson, Oscar & The Trumpet Kings).
Tracks: / Danish pastry / Crazy rhythm / Stella by starlight / Satin doll / Oakland blues / There is no greater love / Summertime / Makin' whoopee / Trust in me.
LP: 231 0817
MC: K10 817

LIVE AT THE NORTH SEA JAZZ FESTIVAL, 1980.
Tracks: / Caravan / Straight, no chaser / Like someone in love / There is no you / You stepped out of a dream / City lights / I'm old fashioned / Time for love, A / Bluesology / Goodbye / No greater love.
2LP: 262 0115
MCSET: . . . . K 20 115

LONDON CONCERT, THE (Peterson, Oscar/John Heard/Louis Bellson).
Tracks: / It's a wonderful world / People / Ain't misbehavin' / Jitterbug waltz / Pennies from Heaven / I get along without you very well / Sweet Georgia Brown / Falling in love with love / Hogtown blues / Emily / Satin doll / I got it bad and that ain't good / Do nothing till you hear from me / C jam blues / Lush life / Take the 'A' train / Caravan / Cute.
2LP: 2620 111
MCSET: . . . . K 20 111

MASTERS OF JAZZ.
LP: . . . . CL 42265

MELLOW MOOD.
LP: . . . . MPS 68 077

MOTIONS AND EMOTIONS.
Tracks: / Sally's tomato / Sunny / By the time I get to Phoenix / Wanderin' / This guy's in love with you / Wave / Dreamsville / Yesterday / Eleanor Rigby / Ode to Billy Joe.
LP: 8212891
LP: . . . . MPS 68 079

MY FAVOURITE INSTRUMENT.
LP: . . . . MPS 68 076

NIGERIAN MARKETPLACE (Peterson, Oscar Trio).
Tracks: / Nigerian marketplace / Au privave / Nancy with the laughing face / Misty / Waltz for Debbie / Cake walk, The / You look good to me.
LP: . . . . D 2308 231
MC: . . . . K 08231

NIGHT CHILD (Peterson, Oscar Quartet).
Tracks: / Solar winds / Dancin' feet / Soliloquy / Night child / Charlie / Teenager.
LP: 231 2108
MC: . . . . K 12 108

NIGHT RIDER (See under Basie, Count) (Peterson, Oscar & Count Basie).

NIGHT TRAIN.
Tracks: / Night Train / C jam blues / Georgia on my mind / Bag's groove / Moten swing / Easy does it / Honeydripper / Things ain't what they used to be / I got it bad and that ain't good / Band call / Hymn to freedom.
MC: 8217244
LP: 8217241

ONE O'CLOCK JUMP 1953 (see under Brown,Ray) (Peterson, Oscar & Ray Brown).

OSCAR PETERSON (Peterson, Oscar Trio).
Tracks: / Royology / Love for sale / Tenderly / Swingin' on a star / Marshmallow moon / Should I / Heatwave / You go to my head / Surrey with the fringe on top / Continental, The.
LP: . . . . KLJ 20022

OSCAR PETERSON AND CLARK TERRY (Peterson, Oscar & Clark Terry).
Tracks: / On a slow boat to China / But beautiful / Shaw 'nuff / Satin doll / Chops / Makin' whoopee / No flugel blues / Mack the knife.
LP: 231 0742
MC: K10 742

OSCAR PETERSON AND DIZZY GILLESPIE (Peterson, Oscar & Dizzy Gillespie).
Tracks: / Caravan / Mozambique / Autumn leaves / Close your eyes / Blues for Bird / Dizzy atmosphere / Alone together / Con Alma.
LP: 231 0740
MC: K10 740

OSCAR PETERSON AND FRIENDS (Peterson, Oscar & Friends).
Tracks: / Tea for two / Wonderful guy, A / You turned the tables on me / Scrapple from the apple / Foggy day, A / No strings / Three little words / Topsy / 'S wonderful / Touch of your lips, The / Lush life.
MC: 835 315-4

OSCAR PETERSON AND HARRY EDISON (Peterson, Oscar & Harry Edison).
Tracks: / Easy living / Days of wine and roses / Gee baby ain't I good to you / Basie / Mean to me / Signify / Willow weep for me / Man I love, The / You go to my head.
LP: 231 0741
MC: K10 741

OSCAR PETERSON AND JON FADDIS (Peterson, Oscar & Jon Faddis).
Tracks: / Things ain't what they used to be / Autumn leaves / Take the 'A' train / Blues for Birks / Summertime / Lester leaps in.
LP: 231 0743
MC: K10 743

OSCAR PETERSON AND ROY ELDRIDGE (Peterson, Oscar & Roy Eldridge).
Tracks: / Little Jazz / She's funny that way / Way you look tonight / Sunday / Bad hat blues / Between the Devil and the deep blue sea / Blues for Chu.
LP: 231 0739
MC: K10 739

OSCAR PETERSON AND THE BASSISTS.
Tracks: / No greater love / You look good to me / People / Reunion blues / Teach me tonight / Sweet Georgia Brown / Soft winds.
LP: 2308 213
MC: . . . . K 08 213

OSCAR PETERSON IN CONCERT.
Tracks: / Bag's groove / I've got the world on a string / Daahoud / Gai / Sweet Georgia Brown / Tenderly / C jam blues / Pompton turnpike / Seven come eleven / Love for sale / Lollobrigida / Swingin' 'til the girls come home / Nuages / Avalon / Come to the Mardi Gras / Baby, baby all the time / Easy does it / Sunday / Falling in love with love / Noreen's nocturne / Gypsy in my soul / Flamingo / Love you madly / 52nd Street theme.
2LP: 2683 063
LP: 1635 206

OSCAR PETERSON JAM.
Tracks: / Ali and Frazier / If I were a bell / Things ain't what they used to be / Just in time.
LP: 2308 208
MC: . . . . K 08 208

OSCAR PETERSON PLAYS JAZZ STANDARDS (Compact/Walkman jazz).
Tracks: / Swingin' 'til the girls come home / Con Alma / Joy Spring / I remember Clifford / Love you madly / Bag's groove / When lights are low / Waltz for Debbie / 52nd Street theme.
LP: 833 283-4

OSCAR PETERSON & STEPHANE GRAPPELLI (Peterson, Oscar & Stephane Grappelli Quartet).
Tracks: / Them there eyes / Blues for musidisc / Makin' whoopee / Thou swell / Walkin' my baby back home / Autumn leaves / Looking at you / Folks who live on the hill, The / I won't dance / Time after time / My one and only love / My heart stood still / Flamingo / If I had you / Let's fall in love.
2LP: . . . . ALB 329

OSCAR PETERSON TRIO WITH CLARK TERRY (Peterson, Oscar Trio & Clark Terry).
Tracks: / Brotherhood of man / Jim / Blues for Smedley / Roundalay / Mumbles / Mack the knife / They didn't believe me / Squeaky's blues / I want a little girl / Incoherent blues.
LP: 6336 342

PARIS CONCERT, THE (Peterson, Oscar/Joe Pass/Niels Pedersen).
Tracks: / Please don't talk about me when I'm gone / Who can I turn to? / Benny's bugle / Soft winds / Goodbye / Place St. Henri / Manha de carnaval / If / Ornithology / Blue Lou / How long has this been going on? / Gentle tears / Lover man / Samba de Orfeu / Donna Lee / Sweet Georgia Brown.
2LP: 262 0112
MCSET: . . . . K 20 112

PORGY AND BESS (Peterson, Oscar & Joe Pass).
Tracks: / Summertime / Bess, you is my woman now / My man's gone now / It ain't necessarily so / I got plenty o' nuttin' / Oh, Bess, oh where's my Bess? / I loves you, Porgy / They pass by singin' / There's a boat that's leaving shortly for New York / Strawberry woman.
LP: 231 0779
MC: K10 779

REUNION BLUES (Peterson, Oscar & Milt Jackson).
Tracks: / Satisfaction / Dream of you / Some day my prince will come / Time for love, A / Reunion blues / When I fall in love / Red top.
LP: . . . . MPS 68 087

ROMANCE.
Tracks: / I'm glad there is you / Polka dots and moonbeams / One for my baby / I hear music / Autumn in New York / I can't give you anything but love / Spring is here / These foolish things / From this moment on / Things we did last summer, The / Too marvellous for words / But not for me.
LP: 2304 473

ROYAL WEDDING SUITE, A.
Tracks: / Announcement / London gets ready / When summer comes / It's on / Heraldry / Royal honeymoon / Lady Di's waltz / Let the world sing / Empty cathedral.
LP: 231 2129
MC: . . . . K 12 129

SALLE PLEYE, A (Peterson, Oscar & Joe Pass).
LP: 262 5705
MCSET: . . . . K 25 705

SATCH AND JOSH (Peterson, Oscar & Count Basie).
Tracks: / Bun's blues / These foolish things / R.B. burning / Exactly like you / Jumpin' at the woodside / Louis B. / Lester leaps in / Big stockings / S and J blues.
MC: K10 722
LP: 231 0722

SATCH AND JOSH AGAIN (Peterson, Oscar & Count Basie).
Tracks: / Roots / Red wagon / Home run / Sweethearts on parade / Li'l darlin' / Time is right / Cherry / Lester leaps in / She's funny that way / Lady Fitz.
LP: 231 0802
MC: K10 802

SILENT PARTNER.
Tracks: / Theme for Celine / Happy hour / Party time USA / Elliot (the silent partner) / Theme for Susannah / Blues for Chris (the fox).
LP: 231 2103
MC: . . . . K 12 103
MC: 3119 103

SKOL (Peterson, Oscar/Stephane Grappelli/Joe Pass).
Tracks: / Nuages / How about you? / Someone to watch over me / Makin' whoopee / That's all / Skol blues.
LP: 230 8232
MC: K08 232

SOMETHING WARM.
Tracks: / There is no greater love / I remember Clifford / Autumn leaves / Blues for Big Scotia / Swamp fire / I love you.
LP: 2352 195

SWING THE GREAT STANDARDS (Peterson, Oscar Trio).
Tracks: / Surrey with the fringe on top / Serenade in blue / Pick yourself up / You're a sweetheart / Foggy day, A / It's alright with me / Stormy weather / Lady is a tramp, The / Great day / Between the devil and the deep blue sea / They all laughed / Night and day / I won't dance / Song is ended, The / Blue moon / I feel a song coming on.
LP: . . . . MOIR 130
MC: . . . . CMOIR 130

THIS IS OSCAR PETERSON, VOL.1.
Tracks: / I got rhythm / Louise / My blue heaven / Sheik of Araby, The / Flying home / C jam blues / If I could be with you one hour tonight / Humoresque / Blue moon / In a little Spanish town / Time on my hands / China boy / Runnin' wild / Sweet Lorraine / Honeydripper / East of the sun.
LP: . . . . OFF 3037

THIS IS OSCAR PETERSON, VOL.2.
Tracks: / Back home again in Indiana / Margie / I surrender dear / I don't stand a ghost of a chance with you / Oscar's boogie / Smiles / Stairway to the stars / Poor butterfly / Oop-bop sh-bam / Sweet Georgia Brown / Sleepy time gal / Rockin' in rhythm / Fine and dandy / My heart stood still / Somebody loves me / At sundown.
LP: . . . . OFF 3039

TRACKS.
LP: . . . . MPS 68 084

TRAVELLIN' ON.
LP: . . . . MPS 68 078

TRIBUTE TO MY FRIENDS, A.
Tracks: / Blueberry Hill / Sometimes I'm happy / Stuffy / Birk's works / Cottontail / Lover man / Tisket a tasket, A / Rockin' chair / Now's the time.
LP: 231 0902
MC: K10 902

TRIO IN TRANSITION.
Tracks: / Children's tune / Younger than springtime / Misty / Django / Shadow of your smile / Shelley's world / Let's fall in love / Blues etude / Smudge / Autumn leaves / Moanin' / Lover's romance / L'impossible / If i were a bell / Stella by starlight / I know you oh so well / Bossa beguine.
2LP: 6641 577

TRIO LIVE FROM CHICAGO, THE.
LP: 2304 194
MC: 823 008-4

TRIO, THE.
Tracks: / Blues etude / Chicago blues / Easy listening blues / Come Sunday / Secret love.
MC: K10 701
LP: 2310 701

TRISTEZA ON PIANO.
Tracks: / Tristeza / Nightingale / Porgy / Triste / You stepped out of a dream / Watch what happens / Down here on the ground / Fly me to the moon.
LP: . . . . MPS 68 081

TRUMPET SUMMIT MEETS THE OSCAR PETERSON BIG FOUR (Peterson, Oscar Big 4).
Tracks: / Daahoud / Chicken wings / Just friends / Champ, The.
LP: 231 2114
MC: . . . . K 12 114

TWO OF THE FEW (See under Jackson, Milt) (Peterson, Oscar & Milt Jackson).

VERY TALL (see Jackson, Milt & Oscar Peterson) (Peterson, Oscar & Milt Jackson).

VOCAL STYLING OF OSCAR PETERSON.
Tracks: / I'm glad there is you / Polka dots and moonbeams / One for my baby / I hear music / Autumn in New York / I can't give you anything but love / These foolish things / From this moment on / Things we did last summer / Too marvellous for words / But not for me / Spring is here.
LP: 2352 169

WALKING ON THE LINE.
LP: . . . . MPS 68 082

WAY I REALLY PLAY, THE.
LP: . . . . MPS 68 075

WE GET REQUESTS.

Tracks: / Quiet nights of quiet stars / Days of wine and roses / My one and only love / People / Have you met Miss Jones / You look good to me / Girl from Ipanema / D and E blues / Time and again / Goodbye JD.
LP: 2352 065
MC: 311 204-4

WILL TO SING, THE.
MCSET: 8472034

YESSIR THAT'S MY BABY (See under Basie, Count) (Peterson, Oscar & Count Basie).

Peterson, Ralph

V (Peterson, Ralph Quintet).
Tracks: / Enemy within / Monief / Short end of the stick, The / Soweto 6 / Viola's dance / Bebopskerony.
LP: 7917301

Peterson, Ray

ALL HIS HITS.
Tracks: / Corina Corina / I'm gone / Doggone it / I'm tired / Shirley Purly / Is it wrong / Promises / Patricia / Fever / Tell Laura I love her / Tell Tommy I miss him / Give us your blessing / Wonder of you, The / Missing you / We're old enough to cry / Teenage heartache / Come and get it / Be my girl.
LP: . . . . . BFX 15245

Pete's Dragon

PETE'S DRAGON (Original Soundtrack) (Various artists).
Tracks: / Pete's dragon (title): *Various artists* / Candle on the water: *Various artists* / I saw a dragon: *Various* artists / It's not easy: *Various artists* / Every little pieces: *Various artists* / Happiest home in these hills, The: *Various artists* / Brazzle dazzle day: *Various artists* / Boo bop bop bop bop (I love you too): *Various* artists / There's room for everyone: *Various artists* / Passamashloddy: *Various artists* / Bill of sale: *Various artists* / Candle on the water (reprise): *Various artists*.
LP: . . . . . EA ST 11704

PETE'S DRAGON (Various artists).
Tracks: / Pete's dragon: *Various artists*.
LP: . . . . . D 369
MC: . . . . . D 19DC

Petipa/Tchaikovsky

STORY OF SWAN LAKE (Bloom, Claire (nar)).
MC: 1673

Petit, Jean Claude

CYRANO DE BERGERAC (See Under Cyrano de Bergerac).

MANON DES SOURCES Film soundtrack.
LP: . . . . . A 241
MC: . . . . . C 241

RETURN OF THE MUSKETEERS (See Under Return Of...).

Petit Pays

TROUVER LA VIE.
LP: . . . . . AT 087

Petitjean, Dave

CAJUN CAPERS.
LP: 5004
MC: . . . . . 5004 TC

CAJUN HUMOR.
LP: 5002
MC: . . . . . 5002 TC

HUMOR FROM CAJUN COUNTRY.
LP: 5003
MC: . . . . . 5003 TC

MY FANS.
LP: 5001
MC: . . . . . 5001 TC

REAL AND FUNNY CAJUN, A.
LP: 5005
MC: . . . . . 5005 TC

Petra

BACK TO THE STREET.
LP: . . . . . SR R 2073
MC: . . . . . SR C 2073

BEAT THE SYSTEM.
LP: . . . . . SR R 2057
MC: . . . . . SR C 2057

CAPTURED IN TIME AND SPACE.
LP: . . . . . SR R 2065
MC: . . . . . SR C 2065

COME AND JOIN US.
LP: . . . . . Unknown
MCSET: . . . . . TWIN C 108

MORE POWER TO YA.
LP: . . . . . SR R 397
MC: . . . . . SR C 397

NEVER SAY DIE.
LP: . . . . . SR R 357
MC: . . . . . SR C 357

NOT OF THIS WORLD.
LP: . . . . . SR R 418
MC: . . . . . SR C 418

ON FIRE.
LP: . . . . . SS R 8106
MC: . . . . . SS C 8106

PETRA.
LP: . . . . . Unknown
MCSET: . . . . . TWIN C 108

PETRA PRAISE (the rock cries out).
LP: . . . . . DAY R 4184
MC: . . . . . DAY C 4184

THIS MEANS WAR!.
LP: . . . . . SR R 8084
MC: . . . . . SR C 8084

WASHES WHITER THAN SNOW.
LP: . . . . . SR R 327
MC: . . . . . SR C 327

Petri, Michala

MODERN RECORDER, THE.
MC: . . . . . RK 87946

Petric, Faith

FAITH PETRIC.
LP: . . . . . BAY 216

Petrie, Robin

CONTINENTAL DRIFT (Petrie, Robin & Danny Carnahan).
LP: . . . . . FF 442

TWO FOR THE ROAD (Petrie, Robin & Danny Carnahan).
LP: . . . . . FF 364

Petrol & Pollution

PETROL AND POLLUTION (See under UNESCO reports).

Petrov, A

RUSSIAN SONGS-SONGS & INSTRUMENTAL PIECES.
MC: . . . . . SM 00205

Petrucciani, Michel

100 HEARTS.
Tracks: / Turn around / Three forgotten magic words / Silence / St. Thomas / Potpourri / Very early / Some day my prince will come / Child is born, A / 100 hearts.
LP: . . . . . GW 3001

LIVE AT THE VILLAGE VANGUARD.
LP: . . . . . GW 3006

MICHEL PLAYS PETRUCCIANI.
Tracks: / She did it again / One for us / Sahara / 13th / Mr. K. J. / One night at Ken and Jessica's / It's a dance / La champagne / Brazilian suite.
LP: B1 48679

MUSIC.
Tracks: / Looking up / Memories of Paris / My bebop tune / Brazillian suite No. 2 / Bite / Lullaby / O nana oye / Play me / Happy birthday Mr. K (CD only.) / Thinking of Wayne (CD only.).
LP: B1 92563
LP: 792 563 1

PIANISM.
Tracks: / Prayer, The / Our tune / Face's face / Night and day / Here's that rainy day / Regina.
LP: . . . . . BT 85124
LP: 785 124 1

POWER OF THREE (Petrucciani, Michel/Wayne Shorter/Jim Hall).
Tracks: / Limbo / Careful / Morning blues / Waltz new / Beautiful love / In a sentimental mood / Bimini.
LP: . . . . . BT 85133

TRIO RECORDING.
LP: . . . . . OWL L025

Pettiford, Oscar

BLUES BROTHERS.
LP: . . . . . BLP 30135

BOHEMIA AFTER DARK.
Tracks: / Another one / Minor seventh heaven / Stardust / Bohemia after dark / Oscalypso / Scorpio / Don't squawk / Kamman's a comin'.
LP: . . . . . AFF 117

EARLY DAYS, THE (SCANDINAVIA) (see Getz, Stan) (Pettiford, Oscar & Stan Getz).

IN HI-FI.
Tracks: / Nican's tempo / Deep passion / Sunrise sunset / Perdido / Two french fries / Pendulum at Falcon's Lair / Gentle art of love / Not so sleepy / Speculation / Smoke signal.
LP: . . . . . JASM 1034

JAZZ ON THE AIR Volume 6 (Pettiford, Oscar & His Birdland Big Band).
Tracks: / Theme / Aw c'mon / Nica's tempo / Seventh heaven / Perdido / Two french fries / He's my guy / Smoke signals / I remember Clifford / Not so sleepy.
LP: . . . . . SPJ 153

LEGENDARY OSCAR PETTIFORD, THE.
LP: . . . . . BLP 30185

MONTMARTRE BLUES.
LP: . . . . . BLP 60124

OSCAR RIDES AGAIN (Pettiford, Oscar-Quintet & Nonet).
Tracks: / Sextet / Golden touch / Cable car / Trictatism / Edge of love / Oscar rides again / Jack the bear / Tamalpais / Swing t'll the girls come home / Mood indigo / Chuckles / Time on my hands.
LP: . . . . . AFF 160

VIENNA BLUES -- THE COMPLETE SESSION.
Tracks: / Cohn's limit / Gentle art of love / All the things you are / Stalag 414 / Vienna blues / Oscar's blues / Stardust / There will never be another you / Blues in the closet.
LP: . . . . . BLP 60104

Pettinger, Peter

STRAD JAZZ (see Kennedy, Nigel/ Peter Pettinger) (Pettinger, Peter/Nigel Kennedy).

Pettis, Alabama Jr

CHICAGO BLUES SESSION 4 (Pettis, Alabama Jr & Teardrops).
LP: . . . . . WOLF 120 850

Pettis, Jack

JACK PETTIS.
LP: . . . . . FJ 129

Pettus, Giorge

GIORGE PETTUS.
Tracks: / My night for love / Can you wait / I'm good for you / One track mind / Trouble in paradise / You're perfect / Make it right / I can fix-U-up / One time affair.
LP: . . . . . MCF 3406
MC: . . . . . MCFC 3406

Petty, Tom

DAMN THE TORPEDOES.
Tracks: / Refugee / Here comes the girl / Even the losers / Century city / Don't do me like that / What are you doin' in my life? / Louisiana rain.
LP: . . . . . MCF 3044
MC: . . . . . MCFC 3044

FULL MOON FEVER.
LP: . . . . . MCG 6034
MC: . . . . . MCGC 6034

GIANT IN THE SKY.
Tracks: / Giant in the sky.
LP: . . . . . MCA 10317
MC: . . . . . MCAC 10317

HARD PROMISES.
Tracks: / Waiting, The / Woman in love / Nightwatchman / Something big / Kings Road / Letting you go / Thing about you, A / Insider / Criminal kind, The / You can still change your mind / Refugee / Here comes my girl / Shadow of a doubt / Century city / Don't do me like that / You tell me / What are you doing in my life / Louisiana rain.
LP: . . . . . MCL 1817
MC: . . . . . MCLC 1817
LP: . . . . . MCF 3098

HARD PROMISES/DAMN THE TORPEDOES.
Tracks: / Waiting, The / Woman in love / Nightwatchman / Something big / Kings Road / Letting you go / Thing about you, A / Insider / Criminal kind, The / You can still change your mind / Refugee / Here comes my girl / Even the losers / Shadow of a doubt (Complex kid) / Century City / Don't do me like that / You tell me / What are you doin' in my life? / Louisiana rain.
MCSET: . . . . . MCA 2 105

INTO THE GREAT WIDE OPEN.
LP: . . . . . MCA 10317
MC: . . . . . MCAC 10317

LET ME UP (I'VE HAD ENOUGH) (Petty, Tom & The Heartbreakers).
Tracks: / Jammin' me / Runaway train / Damage you've done, The / It'll all work out / My life / Think about me / All mixed up / Self-made man, A / Ain't love strange / How many more days / Your world / Let me up (I've had enough).
LP: . . . . . MCG 6014
MC: . . . . . MCGC 6014

LONG AFTER DARK.
Tracks: / One story town, A / You got lucky / Deliver me / Change of heart / Finding out / We stand a chance / Straight into darkness / Same old you, The / Between two worlds / Wasted life, A.
LP: . . . . . MCL 1818
MC: . . . . . MCLC 1818
LP: . . . . . MCF 3155

PACK UP THE PLANTATION (LIVE).
Tracks: / Needles and pins / So you want to be a rock 'n' roll star / Waiting, The / Breakdown / American girl / It ain't nothin' to me / Insider / Rockin' around (with you) / Refugee / I need to know / Southern accents / Rebels / Don't bring me down / You got lucky / Shout / Stories we can tell.
2LP: . . . . . MCMD 7001
MCSET: . . . . . MCMDC 7001

SOUTHERN ACCENTS.
Tracks: / Rebels / It ain't nothin' to me / Don't come around here no more / Southern accents / Make it better / Spike / Dogs on the run / Mary's new car / Best of everything, The.
LP: . . . . . MCF 3260
MC: . . . . . MCFC 3260

STOP DRAGGIN' MY HEART AROUND (See under Nicks, Stevie) (Petty, Tom/ Stevie Nicks & The Heartbreakers).

TOM PETTY AND THE HEARTBREAKERS.
Tracks: / Rockin' around (with you) / American girl / Luna / Mystery man / Fooled again (I don't like it) / Stranger in the night / Anything that's rock 'n' roll / Forever / Wild one / Home town blues / Breakdown.
LP: . . . . . ILPS 5014
MC: . . . . . ICTA 5014
MC: . . . . . MCLC 1715
MC: . . . . . MCAC 10135

TOM PETTY - INTERVIEW PICTURE DISC.
LPPD: . . . . . BAK 2143

TOO HARD TO HANDLE (See under Dylan, Bob) (Petty, Tom & Bob Dylan).

YOU'RE GONNA GET IT (Petty, Tom & The Heartbreakers).
LP: . . . . . ISA 5017
MC: . . . . . MCAC 10134

Petula & The Clarks

PETULA & THE CLARKS.
LP: . . . . . AM 68

Petway, Robert

COMPLETE RECORDINGS 1941-42.
LP: . . . . . WSE 108

Peyr

AS ABOVE....
LP: . . . . . LX 001

Peyton, K.M.

GOING HOME.
MCSET: 086 222 0504

Peyton Place

PEYTON PLACE (Film soundtrack) (Various artists).
LP: . . . . . ERS 6515

Pezband

LAUGHING IN THE DARK.
Tracks: / Love goes underground / I'm leaving / Stop, wait a minute / Come on Madeline / I'm the one / Better way to win / On and on / Lovesmith / Black magic / Gimme gimme / Crash and burn.
LP: . . . . . RAD 6

Pfeifer, Diane

DIANE PFEIFER.
Tracks: / Free to be lonely again / Second hand heart / Just when I needed a love song / Wishful drinkin' / Sing you to sleep / Roses ain't red / Blue from your little white lies / I believe in fairy tales too / Do you mind (if I fall in love with you) / Oh no not love again.
LP: . . . . . EST 12046

Pfister Sisters

NEW ORLEANS.
LP: 11010
MC: . . . . . 11010 TC

PFM

CHOCOLATE KINGS.
Tracks: / From under / Harlequin / Chocolate kings / Out of the roundabout / Paper charms.
LP: . . . . . K 53508
LP: . . . . . PIPLP 009
MC: . . . . . PIPMC 009

COOK.
Tracks: / Four holes in the ground / Dove...quando / Just look away / Celebration / Mr. Nine 'till five / Ata Loma five till nine.
LP: . . . . . K 53506

JET LAG.
Tracks: / Penninsula / Jet lag / Storia in L.A. / Breakin' in Verco la lingua / Meridian / Left handed theory / Traveller, The.
LP: . . . . . K 53511

PER UN AMICO.
LP: . . . . . PIPLP 012
MC: . . . . . PIPMC 012

PHOTOS OF GHOSTS.
Tracks: / River of life / Celebration / Photos of ghosts / Old rain / Il banchetto / Mr. 9 'till 5 / Promenade the puzzle.
LP: . . . . . K 43502
LP: . . . . . PIPLP 010
MC: . . . . . PIPMC 010

STORIA DI UN MINUTO.
LP: . . . . **PIPLP 011**
MC: . . . . **PIPMC 011**

WORLD BECAME THE WORLD, THE.
Tracks: / Mountain, The / Just look away / World became the world, The / Four holes in the ground / Is my face on straight / Have your cake and beat it.
LP: . . . . **K 53502**

P-Funk All Stars

P. FUNK ALL-STARS LIVE.
2LP: **SEW2 031**
MCSET: **SEWC2 031**

P.F.X.

PERNICIOUS NONSENSE.
LP: . . . . **NBX 2**
MC: . . . . **NBX 2C**

Phaedra

PHAEDRA (Film Soundtrack) (Various artists).
Tracks: / Love theme from Phaedra: *Various artists* / Rendezvous: *Various artists* / Ship to shore: *Various* artists / London's fog: *Various artists* / One more time: *Various artists* / Agapimou: *Various artists*/ Only you: *Various artists* / Fling: *Various artists* / Candlelight: *Various artists* / Rodostimo: *Various artists* / Love theme from Phaedra: *Various artists* / Goodbye John Sebastion: *Various artists*.
LP: . . . . **SLS 50173**

Phalon

RISING TO THE TOP.
LP: **7559609661**
MC: **7559609664**

Phantasm

PHANTASM (Film Soundtrack) (Various artists).
LP: . . . . **GEMM 1**
LP: . . . . **VC 81105**

PHANTASM (Songs From The Film) (Various artists).
LP: . . . . **GEMLP 102**

Phantom

DEAD OR ALIVE.
Tracks: / Dead or alive / Under the gun / Punish the sinner / Stand, The / Black widow / Take me down slow / Dead of night / Turbo-charged.
LP: . . . . **US 12**
LP: . . . . **NRR 14**
MC: . . . . **NRC 14**

Phantom 309

SINISTER ALPHABET, A.
LP: . . . . **TUPLP 003**

SPLIT LP (Phantom 309 & The Sun Also Rises).
Tracks: / Mother's army / 8 ball crowe / Prayer, A / Crush / Shout you fascist / Buffy's mitt / Rats, lice and history.
LP: . . . . **TUPEP 005**

Phantom Blue

PHANTOM BLUE.
LP: . . . . **RR 9469 1**
MC: . . . . **RR 9469 4**

Phantom Of Paradise

PHANTOM OF PARADISE, THE (Film soundtrack) (Various artists).
LP: . . . . **SP 3176**
MC: . . . . **CS 3176**

Phantom Of The Opera

HIGHLIGHTS FROM THE PHANTOM OF THE OPERA (Various artists).
Tracks: / Overture: *Various artists* / Angel of music: *Various artists* / Mirror, The: *Various artists*/ Phantom of the opera, The: *Various artists* / Music of the night: *Various artists* / Prima donna: *Various* artists / All I ask of you: *Various artists* / Masquerade: *Various artists* / Wishing you were somehow here again: *Various artists* / Point of no return: *Various artists* / Down once more: *Various artists*.
LP: . . . . **POLH 33**
MC: . . . . **POLHC 33**

PHANTOM OF THE OPERA (Original London Cast) (Various artists).
Tracks: / Phantom of the opera (overture): *Various artists* / Think of me: *Various artists* / Angel of music: *Various artists* / Little Lotte: *Various artists* / Mirror, The: *Various artists* / Phantom of the opera, The: *Various artists* / Music of the night, The: *Various artists* / I remember: *Various artists* / Stranger than you dreamt it: *Various artists* / Magical lasso: *Various artists* / Prima donna: *Various artists*/ Poor fool, he makes me laugh: *Various artists* / All I ask of you: *Various artists* / Entr'acte: *Various* artists / Masquerade: *Various artists* / Why so silent: *Various artists* / Twisted every way: *Various* artists / Wishing you were somehow here again: *Various artists* / Wandering child: *Various artists* / Point of no return, The: *Various artists* / Down once more: *Various artists* / Phantom of the opera (finale): *Various artists*.
2LP: . . . . **PODV 9**
MC: . . . . **PODVC 9**

PHANTOM OF THE OPERA (Film soundtrack) (Various artists).
LP: . . . . **FILM 069**

PHANTOM OF THE OPERA (1943) (Various artists).
2LP: . . . . **STK 114**

Phantom, Rocker &

PHANTOM, ROCKER AND SLICK.
Tracks: / What you want / My mistake / Hollywood distractions / No regrets / Well kept secret / Men without shame / Runnin' from the hounds / Time is on my hands / Sing for your supper / Lonely actions.
LP: . . . . **AML 3100**
MC: . . . . **TCAML 3100**

Phantom Tollbooth (bk)

PHANTOM TOLLBOOTH, THE (Juster, Norman) (Carroll, Pat (nar)).
MC: **1703**
LP: . . . . **HMS 067**

Phantoms

PHANTOMS IN SWEDEN, THE.
LP: **33.8604.01**

Phar Lap...

PHAR LAP - HEART OF A NATION (Film soundtrack) (Various artists).
LP: . . . . **EJ 2403191**
MC: . . . . **EJ 2403194**

Pharaohs

BLUE EYGPT.
LP: . . . . **NERD 020**

Pharaon, Kid

LOVE BIKES (Pharaon, Kid & The Lonely Ones).
LP: . . . . **CL 0076**

Pharoah Sisters

BLACK UNITY.
LP: . . . . **AS 9219**
MC: . . . . **ASC 9219**

TAUHID.
MC: . . . . **ASC 9138**

THEMBI.
MC: . . . . **ASC 9206**
LP: . . . . **AS 9206**

Phase One

PHASE ONE: COLLECTORS' EDITION (Various artists).
LP: . . . . **PRFLP 003**
MC: . . . . **PRFC 003**

PHASE ONE: DUBWISE (Various artists).
LP: . . . . **PRFLP 004**
MC: . . . . **PRFC 004**

Phasslayne

CUT IT UP.
Tracks: / Think it over / Picture me / Don't walk away / Run for guns / Down and out / Minute men / Get it right / Feels on wheels / King Creole / Who's losing now.
LP: . . . . **NEAT 1022**

PhD

IS IT SAFE?.
Tracks: / I didn't know / Pretty ladies / Johnny / Shotgun romance / Changing partners / No right to be sad / Fifth of May / No happy endings / Beautiful day / New york city.
LP: . . . . **WEA U0050**

PHD.
Tracks: / Little suzie's on the up / War years / Oh Maria / Oo sha sha / I won't let you down / There's no answer to it / Poor city / Up down / Hollywood signs / Radio to on.
LP: . . . . **K 99150**

Phenomena II

DREAM RUNNER.
Tracks: / Stop / Surrender / Did it all for love / Hearts on fire / Jukebox / Double 6, 55, 44... / Move - you lose / Emotion mama / It must be love.
LP: **208697**
MC: **408697**

Phil & John

DON'T LOOK NOW - IT'S THE HALLELUJAH BROTHERS.
LP: . . . . **WHA R 1259**
MC: . . . . **WHA C 1259**

LONELY DANCER.
LP: . . . . **WHAR 1236**
MC: . . . . **WHAC 1236**

Phil & The ...

ACID BURNS (Phil & The Acid Houses Of London).
LP: . . . . **MICRODOT 1**

Philadelphia Experiment

PHILADELPHIA EXPERIMENT (Film soundtrack) (Various artists).
LP: . . . . **RNSP 306**

Philharmonia Hungarica

HAYDN SYMPHONIES (See under Haydn (composer)).

Philharmonia Orchestra

AN HOUR OF POPULAR WALTZES.
MC: . . . . **HR 8132**

CHAMPIONS (Original Soundtrack).
LP: . . . . **ISTA 7**
MC: . . . . **ICT 7**

LONDON SYMPHONY, A.
Tracks: / Cockaigne overture / London symphony, A / London overture, A.
LP: . . . . **DCA 634**
MC: . . . . **ZC DCA 634**

SYMPHONY NO.9 (SCHUBERT) (see under Schubert).

SYMPHONY NO. 1 IN E MINOR, OP 39 (See under Sibelius (composer)).

TRUMPET CONCERTOS AND FANFARES (See under Trumpet Music - Classical).

WAGNER HIGHLIGHTS V3 (see under Wagner).

Philharmonic...

ALL IN THE APRIL EVENING (Philharmonic Chamber Choir).
Tracks: / All in the April evening / Isle of Mull / Steal away / Dashing white sergeant / Were you there / Banks o' Doon, The / Peat fire / Smooring prayer / Loch Lomond / King Arthur / Belmont / Iona boat song / Herdmaiden's song / Bluebird, The / Faery song from "The Immortal Hour" / An eriskay love lilt.
MC: . . . . **KH 88008**
LP: . . . . **A 66064**

BLUE NILE CONCERTO (Philharmonic Pop Orchestra).
LP: . . . . **ISST 161**

CASTLES IN THE AIR (Philharmonic Pop Orchestra).
LP: . . . . **ISST 146**

DISCONCERTO.
Tracks: / Disconcerto / Swan song / G-string boogie / Paradise lost / Hallelujah hustle / 1912/76 / New world / Moonshine / Bees knees / Song & dance / Big apple / Save our soul.
LP: **6381074**

POP SINFONIETTA (Philharmonic Pop Group).
LP: . . . . **ISST 179**

POP TO THE PAST (Philharmonic Pop Orchestra).
LP: . . . . **ISST 195**

Philippe, Louis

APPOINTMENT WITH VENUS.
Tracks: / La pluie fait des claquettes / Man down the stairs / When I'm an astronaut / We live on an island / Orchard, The / Heaven is above me / Rescue the Titanic / Touch of evil / Ballad of Sophie Sololl / Angelica my love / I will / Exporado tales / Apertivo / Fires rise and die / La pluie fait des claquettes.
LP: . . . . **ACME 5**

IVORY TOWER.
Tracks: / Guess I'm dumb / Chocolate soldiers / Domenica / Anna / Sixteen / Mindreader / Ulysses and the siren / Monsieur Leduc / All stands still / Smash hit wonder / Sleep angry beauty / Night talk / Ivory tower / Everyword meant goodbye / Hot summer evenings (Available on CD only) / Cantilena (Available on CD format only.) / House of 1000 windows (Available on CD format only.) / Endless September / Cavaliere servente (on CD only.) / Perfume / Simon Bolivar airport (Available on CD only).
LP: . . . . **ACME 15**

METHODE DE POUR LA FLUTE.
LP: . . . . **TWI 703**

YURI GAGARIN.
Tracks: / Diamond / Did you say her name was Peg? / She's great / Endless September / Vision, A / Goodbye again / Anna s'en va / Jean and me / I collect stamps / Sunday morning Camden Town / Another boy / Yuri Gagarin.
LP: . . . . **ACME 23**

Philippine Gong Music

PHILIPPINE GONG MUSIC FROM LANAO.
LP: . . . . **LLST 7322**

PHILIPPINE GONG MUSIC FROM LANOA VOL.2.
LP: . . . . **LLST 7326**

Philips, Flip

SOUND INVESTMENT, A (Philips, Flip & Hamilton).
LP: . . . . **CJ 334**

Philips, Glen

ELEVATOR.
Tracks: / Micro / Sex messiah / Inca silver metallic / Ario / John marshall / Vista cruiser / D.N.A. I ran / Rememory / Tower of babel / Rain tonight / Death ship, The.
LP: . . . . **SST 136**

Philips, Paul

SINCERELY.
Tracks: / Most beautiful girl in the world, The / La vie en rose / La goualante du pauvre Jean / Les trois cloches / Padam padam / Autumn leaves / L'accordeoniste / Sous le ciel de Paris / Milord / Exodus / Hymne a l'amour / Mon manege a moi / Bravo pour le clown / Comme moi / La foule / Non, je ne regrette rien.
LP: . . . . **KLP 61**
MC: . . . . **ZCKLP 61**

Phillinganes, Greg

PULSE.
Tracks: / Behind the mask / Won't be long now / Playin' with fire / I have dreamed / Come as you are / Lazy Nina / Signals / Countdown to love / Shake it.
LP: . . . . **PL 84698**
MC: . . . . **PK 84698**
LP: . . . . **FL 84698**
MC: . . . . **FK 84698**
MC: . . . . **NK 90554**

SIGNIFICANT GAINS.
Tracks: / Girl talk / Baby I do love you / Takin' it up all night / Forever now / Big man / I don't want to be the one / Maxxed out / Do it all for love / Call, The.
LP: . . . . **K 52299**

Phillipe, Brun

1930-38.
LP: . . . . **PM 155281**

Phillipinos

DOO WADDA DOO WOP.
LP: . . . . **SWFLP 009**

Phillips, Anthony

1984.
Tracks: / Prelude 84 / 1984 part 1 / 1984 part 2 / Anthem 1984.
LP: . . . . **RCALP 5036**
MC: . . . . **RCAK 5036**

ANTIQUES.
Tracks: / Motherforest / Hurlingham suite / Suite in D minor / Danse nude / Esperansa / Elegy / Otto's face / Sand dunes / Old wives tale.
LP: . . . . **INTS 5228**
MC: . . . . **INTK 5228**

GEESE AND THE GHOST, THE.
LP: . . . . **HIT&RUN 001**

HARVEST OF THE HEART.
Tracks: / Trail of tears / Esperansa / Salmon leap / Flapjack / Bouncer / Beauty and the beast / Amorphous, cadaverous and nebulous / Salmon's last sleepwalk / Erotic strings / Bandido / Sistine / Lindsay / Over the gate / Sean and the armadillo, The / Lights on the hill.
LP: . . . . **BRED 66**

INVISIBLE MEN.
Tracks: / Sally / Golden bodies / Going for broke / It's not easy / Traces / Guru / My time has come / Love in a hot air balloon / I want your heart / Falling for love / Women were watching, The.
LP: . . . . **STLP 013**
MC: . . . . **STC 0013**

PRIVATE PARTS AND PEICES VII.
LP: . . . . **SYN 308**
MC: . . . . **SYNC 308**

SLOW DANCE.
LP: . . . . **V 2638**
MC: . . . . **TCV 2638**

WISE AFTER THE EVENT.
LP: . . . . **SPART 1063**

Phillips, Barre

CALL ME WHEN YOU GET THERE.
Tracks: / Grants pass / Craggy slope / Amos crowns / Barn / Pittmans rock / Highway 37 / Winslow cavern / Riverbend / Brewestertown.
LP: . . . . **ECM 1257**

MOUNTAINSCAPES.
LP: . . . . **ECM 1076**

MUSIC BY.
LP: . . . . **ECM 1178**

THREE DAY MOON.
LP: . . . . **ECM 1123**

Phillips, Ben "Bach"

O'R GWCW (THE CUCKOO) Songs from Pembrokeshire (Phillips, Ben & Andrew Thomas).
Tracks: / O'r gwcw (the cuckoo) / Hen ladi fowr benfelen / Dywetse'r hen ddyn wrth ei ferch / Bugeiles y wyddfa / Y deuddeg dydd o'r gwyliau / Jeremiah / Can y bardd wrth farw / Hen ffon fy nain / Pentry mathry lan / Canyr ychen / Ar lan y mor / Y ferch o blwyf penderwyn / Yr hogen goch / Fy morwyn ffein i / Yr eboles / O Milford daeth hen bria pwr / Boneddwr mawr o'r bala / Ar ryw nos fercher / Y saith rhyfeddod / Y lodes lwyd / Gini melyn bach / My boy Willy / Father father build me a boat / Working on the railway / Wild man of Borneo.
MC: 60-052

Phillips, Brewer

INGLESIDE BLUES (Chicago 1982).
LP: . . . . WOLF 120 608

WHOLE LOTTA BLUES.
Tracks: / Whisky headed woman / Poison ivy / Watermelon man / Poor boy blues / Whole lotta lovin' / Okee dokee stomp / Woke up this morning / Everyday I have the blues / Cleo.
LP: . . . . JSP 1048

Phillips, Bryars

IRMA - AN OPERA (Phillips, Bryars & Orton).
Tracks: / I tell you that's Irma herself / First interlude / Irma you will be mine / Second interlude / Love is help mate / Postlude.
LP: . . . . OBS 9
LP: . . . . EGED 29

Phillips, Dave

BEST OF ROCKS.
LP: . . . . LP 8603

DAVE PHILLIPS.
LP: . . . . MLP 8420
LPPD: . . . . PLP 8414

UNDERSTATEMENTS.
LP: KIX4U 3334
LP: . . . . PLAT 3334

WILD YOUTH (Phillips, Dave & Hot Road Gang).
LP: . . . . LPL 8201

Phillips, Esther

CAPRICORN PRINCESS.
Tracks: / Magic's in the air / I haven't got anything better to do / Boy I really tried one on / Candy / Beautiful friendship, A / Higher and higher / All the way down / Dream.
LP: . . . . KU 31

COMPLETE SAVOY RECORDINGS (Phillips, Little Esther).
2LP: . . . . SJL 2258
LP: . . . . SJL 2258

CONFESSIN' THE BLUES.
Tracks: / I'm gettin' 'long alright / I wonder / Confessin' the blues / Romance in the dark / C.C. Rider / Cherry red / In the evenin' / I love Paris / It could happen to you / Bye bye blackbird / Blow top blues / Jelly jelly blues / Long John blues.
LP: . . . . K 50521

ESTHER PHILLIPS.
Tracks: / What a difference a day made / Home is where the hatred is / Use me / I feel the same / I've never found a man (to love me like you do) / Boy I really tried one on / One night affair / From a whisper to a scream / Justified / Living alone / Candy.
LP: . . . . SKU 001

GOOD BLACK IS HARD TO CRACK.
LP: . . . . SRM 14005

HERE'S ESTHER-ARE YOU READY.
Tracks: / Mr. Melody / Philadelphia freedom / I hope you'll be very unhappy without me / Love makes a woman / Our day will come / Bedtime stories / Oo oop oo oop / I'll close my eyes.
LP: 9100 065

WAY TO SAY GOODBYE, A.
Tracks: / It's all in the game / Mama said / Going in circles / Nowhere to run / We are through / Fa fa fa fa fa (sad song) / Mr. Bojangles / Shake this off / Way to say goodbye, A.
MC: . . . . MRC 5302

WHAT A DIFFERENCE A DAY MADE.
Tracks: / One night affair / What a difference a day made / Hurtin' house / Oh papa / Turn around, look at me.
LP: . . . . CTI 9023
MC: . . . . CTK 9523

Phillips, Flip

MELODY FROM THE SKY, A.
Tracks: / Melody from the sky, A / Stompin' at the Savoy / Sweet and lovely / Swingin' for Popsie / Bob's belief / Why shouldn't I? / Lover come back to me / Popolloma / Skyscraper / 1-2-3-4 jump / More than you know / Without Woody.
LP: . . . . ASLP 806
MC: . . . . ZCAS 806

REAL SWINGER, A.
Tracks: / Hashimoto's blues / Vol vistu gailey star / It was a very good year / Cottontail / Poor butterfly / I want to be happy / Tricotism / September song / Symphony / I got a right to sing the blues / Christian scientist.
LP: . . . . CJ 358
MC: . . . . CJ 358 C

SWINGING WITH FLIP (Phillips, Flip & Orchestra).
LP: . . . . ST 1019
MC: . . . . SC 1019

Phillips, Gene

GENE PHILIPS, VOL.1 (Phillips, Gene & His Rhythm Aces).
Tracks: / Hey lawdy mama / Short haired ugly woman / I could make you love me / Slippin' and slidin' / Honey chile / Gene jumps the blues / Superstitious woman / I've been fooled before / I wonder what the poor folks are doing / Getting down wrong / Boogie everywhere / Gene's guitar blues / Women, women, women / It's a lonely world / Hey now / Honky tonk train (take one) / Honky tonk train (take two).
LP: . . . . CHD 169

I LIKE 'EM FAT (Cool R'n'B, late 40's, early 50's.) (Phillips, Gene & His Rhythm Aces).
Tracks: / Big legged woman / See see rider / Rock bottom / Stinking drunk / I want a little girl / How long how long blues / 304 boogie / Rambling woman / My mama told me / My baby's mistreating me / To each his own, brother / Snuff dippin' mama / You can't come back home / Crying won't help you none / You gotta toe the line / Honky tonk train blues.
LP: . . . . CHD 245

Phillips, Glenn

SCRATCHED BY THE RABBIT.
Tracks: / Scotland / Theme from (dawn of the prehistoric Newton) / Calling back / Berlin Wall / Go to sleep / Howl / Rain's to blame, The / 22nd of May / Lover's leap.
LP: . . . . FIEND 180

Phillips, John

WOLFKING OF L.A..
Tracks: / April Anne / Topanga Canyon / Malibu people / Someone's sleeping / Drum / Captain - The mermaid / Let it bleed, Genevieve / Down the beach / Mississippi / Holland tunnel.
LP: . . . . LIK 42

Phillips, Ken

I'M OLD FASHIONED.
MC: . . . . KENPH 1

Phillips, Leslie

BLACK AND WHITE IN A GREY WORLD.
LP: . . . . MYR R 1212
MC: . . . . MYR C 1212

DANCING WITH DANGER.
LP: . . . . MYR 1174
MC: . . . . MC 1174

RECOLLECTION.
Tracks: / Your kindness / No one but you / Heart of hearts / Walls of silence / Liberate me / Love is not lost / Answers don't come easy / You're the same / I'm finding / When the world is new / Be my spirit / Strength of my life.
LP: . . . . MYR R 1248
MC: . . . . MYR C 1248

TURNING, THE.
Tracks: / River of love / Love is not lost / Turning, The / Libera me / Carry you / Beating heart / Expectation / Down / Answers don't come easy / God is watching you.
LP: . . . . MYR R 1235
MC: . . . . MYR C 1235

Phillips, Little

BAD BAD GIRL.
Tracks: / Ring-a-ding doo / I'm a bad bad girl / Deacon moves in, The / Looking for a man / Hound dog / Cherry wine / Turn the lamps down low / Flesh blood and bones / Last laugh blues / You took my love too fast / Saturday night daddy / Mainliner / Hollerin' and screamin' / Storm, The / Ramblin' blues / Aged and mellow blues.
LP: . . . . CRB 1100
MC: . . . . TCCRB 1100

I PAID MY DUES.
Tracks: / Better beware / Hold me / Somebody new / Bring my lovin' back to me / I paid my dues / Sweet lips / Love oh love / I'll be there (at your beck and call) / Street lights / Heart to heart / Tell him that I need him / Summertime / Cryin' blues, The / Other lips, other arms / Don't make a fool out of me / Cryin' and singin' the blues.
LP: . . . . SING 1156
MC: . . . . SING 41156

Phillips, Lloyd

LLOYD'S MOODS.
LP: . . . . 77 SEU 12/43

Phillips, Sam

INDESCRIBABLE WOW, THE.
Tracks: / I don't want to fall in love / I don't know how to say goodbye to you / Flame / Remorse / What do I do / I can't stop crying / Holding on to the earth / She can't tell time / What you don't want to hear / Out of time.
LP: . . . . SRNLP 21
MC: . . . . SRNMC 21

Phillips, Shawn

TRANSCENDENCE.
Tracks: / Take it easy / I'm an American child on a nuclear pile / Lady in violet / Implications / Good evening madam / Lament pour l'enfant mort / Motes of dust / Ease your mind.
LP: . . . . PL 13028

Phillips, Sid

GOLDEN HOUR PRESENTS SID PHILLIPS H'ORS D'OUVRES.
Tracks: / Hors d'ouvres / Alexander's ragtime band / All of me / Bluin' the blues / Canadian capers / Deed I do / Farewell blues / Goody goody / High society / I cried for you / I never knew / Ain't misbehavin' / It had to be you / Indiana / Lazy river / Mississippi mud / Moonglow / My honey's lovin' arms / Nagasaki / Nobody's sweetheart / Sleepy time gal / Rose room / Twelfth St. rag / You came a long way from St Louis.
LP: . . . . GH 622

GOODY GOODY.
Tracks: / Basin Street blues / Hors d'ouvres / Just one of those things / Lady is a tramp, The / Is it true what they say? / Red silken stockings / You're gonna be sorry / Stardust / Deed I do / I'm a ding dong daddy / Forty cups of coffee / Frankie and Johnny / Indiana / Disillusioned / You turned the tables on me / Goody, goody.
LP: . . . . PLE 502
MC: . . . . TC-PLE 502

I GOT RHYTHM.
Tracks: / Hors d'oevres / Night ride / Clarinet cadenza / Basin Street blues / Cotton pickers congregation.
2LP: . . . . DL 1173
MC: . . . . TCDL 1173

SPOTLIGHT ON SID PHILLIPS 1936-37.
LP: . . . . HQ 3025

STARDUST (Phillips, Sid & With His Orchestra & Quintet).
Tracks: / Clarinet marmalade / Pretty girl is like a melody, A / Lulu's back in town / That's my home / Copenhagen / Stardust / Sugar foot stomp / Cocktails for two / Woodchoppers ball / Confessin' / Without that certain thing / Avalon / Careless love / Sweet Georgia Brown / Riff raff / Can't help lovin' dat man / I surrender, dear / Hors d'ouvres / Gorgeous gal / I'll remember her / All alone / By heck / Anything goes.
LP: . . . . HAL 20

Phillips, Simon

PROTOCOL.
Tracks: / Streetwise / Protocol / V8 / Red rocks / Slofunk / Wall Street.
LP: . . . . GRUB 10 M
MC: . . . . GRUB 10 MD

Phillips, Sonny

I CONCENTRATE ON YOU.
LP: . . . . MR 5157

MY BLACK FLOWER.
LP: . . . . MR 5118

Phillips, Steve

BEST OF STEVE PHILLIPS.
LP: . . . . BRAVE 5

STEEL RAIL BLUES.
LP: . . . . BRAVE 9
MC: . . . . BRAVE 9 C

Phillips, Todd

RELEASED.
LP: . . . . V 011
MC: . . . . V 011C

Phillips, Utah

ALL USED UP AND A SCRAP BOOK.
LP: . . . . PH 1050

EL CAPITAN.
LP: . . . . PHILO 1016

GOOD THOUGH.
LP: . . . . PHILO 1004
MC: . . . . PH 1004C

WE HAVE FED YOU ALL THESE YEARS.
LP: . . . . PH 1076
MC: . . . . PH 1076C

Phillips, Van

VAN PHILLIPS AND HIS BAND:1928-1934 (Phillips, Van & His Band).
Tracks: / Sometimes / I'm a dreamer, aren't we all / If I had a talking picture of you / I'm like a sailor / High and low / Goodbye to all that / Reach out for a rainbow / I'm in the market for you / Just like in a story book / Living a life of dreams / Nobody cares if I'm blue / Oh Donna Clara / Go home and tell your mother / I'm doing that thing / It's all forgotten now / Breeze.
LP: . . . . SH 277

Philly Cream

NO TIME LIKE NOW.
Tracks: / No time like now / What cha puttin' down / Slow down / Cowboys to girls / Fun fun fun / Devil / So much to talk about / Who do you do.
LP: . . . . WMLP 5001

PHILLY CREAM.
Tracks: / Sly hi / Motown review / Doin' it to death / Jammin' at the disco / Soul man / Join the army.
LP: . . . . FT 559

Phish

LAWN BOY.
LP: . . . . AGO 1992
MC: . . . . AGO 1992MC

Phobia/Gruel

SPLIT UP.
LP: . . . . JHI 109

Phoenix

ANY OLD TIME.
Tracks: / Reels / Hornpipes / Field behind the plough, The / Slides / Polkas / Bantry girl's lament / Courting is a pleasure / Jigs / Times (are not what they used to be).
LP: . . . . DARA 025
MC: . . . . DARAC 025

IN FULL VIEW.
LP: . . . . CAS 1150

SONGS ELVIS MIGHT HAVE SUNG.
Tracks: / Walk of life / I just called to say I love you / Woman / I'm on fire / Lucille / Crazy little thing called love / I'm not ready / Three times a lady / If I said you had a beautiful body / Shame on the moon / Some things are better left unsaid / Rock this town.
MC: . . . . MFBC 002

Phoenix & The Carpet

PHOENIX AND THE CARPET, THE (see Nesbitt, E) (Donald, Sheila (nar)).

Phontastic Dixieland

DIXIE DISC (From Basin Street to Louisiana).
LP: . . . . PHONT 7523

Photoglo, Jim

FOOL IN LOVE WITH YOU.
Tracks: / Fool in love with you / Tonight will last forever / More to love / Won't let you do it to me / Ruled by my heart / Angelina / I can't let go of you / Run to me / Try it again / There's always another chance left for love.
LP: . . . . T 621
MC: . . . . C 621

Photos

PHOTOS.
Tracks: / Do you have fun / Irene / Barbarellas / Now you tell me that we're through / Look at the band / Friends / Loss of contact / She's artistic / All I want / Maxine / Evelyn II / I just don't know what to do with myself.
LP: . . . . PHOTO 5

Phranc

FOLKSINGER.
Tracks: / Noguchi / Mary Hooley / Ballad of the dumb hairdresser / Caped crusader / One o' the girls / Female mudwrestling / Lonesome death of Hattie Carroll, The / Amazons / Liar liar / Handicapped / Carolyn / Lifelover.
LP: . . . . SEEZ 60
LP: . . . . RNDA 856

I ENJOY BEING A GIRL.
Tracks: / Folksinger / I enjoy being a girl / Double decker bed / Bloodbath / Individuality / Rodeo parakeet / Take off your swastika / Toy time / M-A-R-T-I-N-A / Myriam and Esther / Ballad of Lucy and Ted / Moonlight becomes you.
MC: . . . . ICT 9940
LP: . . . . ILPS 9940
MC: . . . . ICM 2042
MC: 842 579 4

POSITIVELY PHRANC.
MC: . . . . ICT 9981
LP: . . . . ILPS 9981

Physics

PHYSICS (COURSE) (see under G.C.S.E.) (Longman/Pickwick Pass Packs).

Pia

DANCE OUT OF MY HEAD (see under Zadora, Pia).

Piacentini, Paul

OUT OF MY BOX.
LP: . . . . **ASA 01**

Piaf, Edith

25TH ANNIVERSAIRE.
Tracks: / Mon legionnaire / Le fanion de la legion / Sans y penser / Dans ma rue / La vie en rose / J'm'en fous pas mal / Les trois cloches / Les amants de Paris / Bal dans ma rue / Hymne a l'amour / Jezebel / Padam padam / Bravo pour le clown / Johnny, tu n'es pas un ange / La goualante du pauvre Jean / Le ca ira / L'accordeoniste / C'est a Hambourg (**) / L'homme a la moto / Les amants d'un jour / La foule / Mon manege a moi / Je sais comment / Milord / Non, je ne regrette rien / Les flons flons du bal / Le vieux piano / Mon vieux lucien (Extra tracks available on CD only.) / Mon dieu / Les amants / A quoi ca sert l'amour / Une valse / Emporte-moi / L'homme de Berlin / Je hais les dimanches / Je t'ai dans la peau / Sous le ciel de Paris / Marie la Francaise / Les prisons du Roy / Marie-Trottoir.
2LP: . . . . **EN 5008**
MCSET: . . . . **TCEN 5008**
LP: **790555 1**

BEST OF EDITH PIAF VOL 1.
Tracks: / L'accordeoniste / C'etait une histoire d'amour / C'est toujours la meme histoire / Le disque use / Le petit monsieur triste / De l'autre cote de la rue / Mon legionnaire / C'etait un jour de fete / C'est lui que mon coeur a choisi / Entre saint - queen et clingnancourt / C'est un monsieur tres distinque / Ding din don.
LP: **824 073 1**
MC: **824 073 4**

BEST OF EDITH PIAF VOL 2.
Tracks: / Y a pas d' printemps / Elle frequentait La Rue Pigalle / Mon amant de la coloniale / L'Julie jolie / Un jeune homme chantait / Fais-moi valser / J'entends la sirene / Le vagabond / L'entranger / Va danser / Tout fout le camp.
LP: **826 617-1**
MC: **826 617-4**

BOBINO 1963 - LES AMANTS.
LP: **2C062 15306**

COLLECTION: EDITH PIAF (20 golden greats).
Tracks: / La vie en rose / Non, je ne regrette rien / Les amants d'un jour / Mon dieu / C'est pour ca / Mon vieux Lucien / C'est a Hambourg / Hymne a l'amour / Un jeune homme chantait / L'accordeoniste / Je t'ai dans la peau / La belle histoire d'amour / Les feuilles mortes / Les flons flons du bal / La ville inconnue / Les grognards / Le petit homme / Bravo pour le clown / Les mots d'amour / Misericorde.
LP: . . . . **DVLP 2062**
MC: . . . . **DVMC 2062**

COMPLETE PIAF.
LPS: **2C 150 72085/98**

DE BRAVO LE CLOWN A J'M'EN FOUS PAS MAL.
LP: **2C 062 15303**

DE L'ACCORDEONISTE A MILORD.
Tracks: / L'accordeoniste / La vie en rose / Je sais comment / Mon dieu! / Toi tu l'entends pas / Hymne a l'amour / Non, je ne regrette rien / Le trois cloches / Milord / La foule / A quoi ca sert l'amour / Con theo sarapo / Le droit d'aimer.
LP: **2C 062 15301**

DE L'ACCORDEONISTE A MILORD (VOL.2).
Tracks: / Les amants de Venise / Johnny tu n'es pas un ange / Un etranger / C'est a Hambourg / Je hais les dimanches / C'est l'amour / Les amants de Paris / Pour moir tout seule / Le chevalier de Paris / L'homme au piano / C'est un gars / Bravo pour le clown.
LP: **3C 054 10358**
MC: . . . . **BC 054 10358**
LP: **3C 054 10797**

DISQUE D'OR (COLLECTION) VOL 1.
LP: **2C 070 72007**

DISQUE D'OR (COLLECTION) VOL 2.
LP: **2C 070 72013**

DROIT D'AIMER.
LP: . . . . **2 C 178 14960/61**

EDITH ET MARCEL (See under Edith et Marcel).

EDITH PIAF.
Tracks: / Cri du coeur / Ouragan / Non la vie n'est pas trist / Quand tu dors / Les gens / Traque / La vie en rose / Don't cry / Chante-moi / Cause I love you / I shouldn't care / One little man / Legende / Bravo pour le clown / Hymne a l'amour / Les amants d'un jour / Les tambours / Dans les prisons de Nantes / Celine / Si si si si / Ca gueule ca madame / Quoi ca sert l'amour, A / Les amants.
LP: **2C 156 72596**
MC: **2C 450 72598**

EDITH PIAF - 60 MINUTES OF MUSIC.
Tracks: / Mon legionnaire / Les momes de la cloche / Je n'en connais pas la fin / La fanion de la legion / Les marins ca fait des voyages / Il riait / Madeleine qu'avait du coeur / Embrasse-moi / Mon coeur est au coin d'une rue / L'accordeoniste / La java en mineur / Y'avait du soleil / Dans un bouge du vieux port / Ou sont-ils mes petits copains? / Un monsieur me suit dans la rue / Les deux rengaines / On danse sur ma chanson.
MC: **826 798 4**

EDITH PIAF (83).
LP: . . . . **2 C 068 72174**

EDITH PIAF AT THE PARIS OLYMPIA.
Tracks: / Milord / Heureuse / Avec ce soleil / C'est a Hambourg / Legende / Enfin le printemps / Padam...padam / Hymne a l'amopur / L'accordeoniste / Mon manege a moi / Bravo pour le clown / Les mots d'amour / Les flons flons du bal / T'es l'homme qu'il me faut / Mon dieu / Mon vieux Lucien / Non, je ne regrette rien / La ville inconnue (CD only.) / La belle histoire d'amour (CD only.) / Les blouses blanches (CD only.).
LP: . . . . **EMS 1362**
MC: . . . . **TCEMS 1362**

EDITH PIAF (EMI FRANCE).
LP: . . . . **2 C 156 72596/7**
MC: . . . . **TC 2 C 450 72598**

EDITH PIAF STORY, THE.
Tracks: / Misericorde (heaven have mercy) / La fete continue / Telegramme / L'accordeoniste / Bravo pour le clown / La goualante du pauvre Jean / Padam padam / Les feuilles mortes / Heureuse / Hymne a l'amour(if you love me really love me) / C'est a hambourg / Les grognards / L'homme a la moto / Je t'ai dans la peau / C'est pour ca / Non, je ne regrette rien / Les blouses blanches / T'es l'homme qu'il me faut / La ville inconnue / Les flons flons du bal / Mon dieu / Les mots d'amour / Mon vieux luchen / La belle histoire d'amour.
MCSET: . . . . **DVREMC 21**

EDITH PIAF VOLUME 1.
Tracks: / L'accordeoniste / La vie en rose / Je sais comment / Mon dieul / Toi tu l'entends pas / Hymne a l'amour / Non je ne regrette rien / Le trois cloches / Milord / La foule / Quoi ca sert l'amour / Le droit d'aimer.
LP: . . . . **PM 1153011**
MC: . . . . **PM 1153034**
LP: **3C054 10358**
MC: **3C254 10358**

EDITH PIAF VOLUME 2.
Tracks: / Les amants de Venise / Johnny tu n'es pas un ange / Un etranger / C'est a Hambourg / Je hais les dimanches.
LP: . . . . **PM 1153021**
MC: . . . . **PM 1153024**
LP: **3C054 10797**
MC: **3C254 10797**

EDITH PIAF VOLUME 3.
Tracks: / La giyalante / T'es beau, tu sais / Les Croix / Cri du coeur / Padam padam / C'est un homme terribi / Exodus / Mea Culpa / Je me souviens d'une chanson / Et Pourtant / Le da ira / Mon Manece A Mor.
LP: **3C 054 10796**
MC: **3C 254 10796**
LP: . . . . **PM 1153031**
MC: . . . . **PM 1153034**

EDITH PIAF VOLUME 4.
Tracks: / Mariagr / Qu'as tu tait John / Notre Dame de Parie / Monsieur et Madam / Pout pourrt / Misericorde / Toi qua sais / Unde dame / C'est mer vulletre / Sous le ciel de Paris.
LP: **3C 054 72413**
MC: **3C 254 72413**
LP: . . . . **PM 1153041**
MC: . . . . **PM 1153044**

EDITH PIAF VOLUME 5.
LP: . . . . **PM 1153051**
MC: . . . . **PM 1153054**

EDITH PIAF VOLUME 6.
LP: . . . . **PM 1153061**
MC: . . . . **PM 1153064**

GREAT EDITH PIAF, THE.
Tracks: / La vie en rose / Padam, Padam / C'est d'la faute / Je m'en fous pas mal / Une enfant / Les feuilles mortes / L'accordeoniste / Chante moi / Hymne a l'amour / I won't care / Du matin jusqi au soir.
LP: . . . . **CBS 85007**

GREATEST HITS: EDITH PIAF.
LPPD: . . . . **AR 30042**

HEART AND SOUL.
Tracks: / No regrets / La vie en rose / La coualante du pauvre Jean / Les trois cloches / Padam padam / Autumn leaves / L'accordeoniste / Sous le ciel de Paris / Milord / Exodus / Hymne a l'amour / Mon manage a moi / Bravo pour le clown / Comme moi / La foule / Non, je ne regrette rien.
2LP: . . . . **SMR 736**
MCSET: . . . . **SMC 736**

HER LEGENDARY LIVE RECORDINGS.
Tracks: / Heureuse / Avec ce soleil / Legende / Padam padam / Une dame / Milord / L'accordeoniste / Les grognards / Autumn leaves / Le petit homme / Telegramme / La vie en rose / Comme moi / La foule / Mon dieu / Non je ne regrette rien / M. Incognito / Chant d'amour / C'etait pas moi.
LPS: . . . . **SCXSP 662**

I REGRET NOTHING.
Tracks: / Non, je ne regrette rien / Bravo pour le clown / L'accordeoniste / Enfin le printemps / C'est a Hambourg / Hymne a l'amour / Mon manege a moi / Le goualante du pauvre Jean / Je t'ai dans la peau / Heureuse / La foule / L'homme a la moto / Milord / A quoi ca sert l'amour / Le droit d'aimer.
LP: . . . . **SCX 6477**

JE VOUS AIME Original cast recording.
LP: . . . . **NSPD 503**

LA MOME PIAF VOL.1.
Tracks: / Les momes de la cloche / L'etranger / Reste / La fille et le chien / La julie jolie / Moi valser / Mon amant de la coloniale / Il n'est pas distingue / La java de cezique / Mon apero / Les hiboux / J'suis mordue / Fais / Va danser / Y avaid du soleil / Les deux menetriers.
MC: . . . . **MU 451**

LA VIE EN ROSE AND OTHER FAVS..
MC: **4XL 57007**

LEGENDARY EDITH PIAF, THE.
Tracks: / Heureuse / Non, Je ne regrette rien / La goualante du pauvre Jean / Padam, padam / L'accordeoniste / La vie en rose / Les amants d'un jour / A quoi ca sert l'amour (CD only.) / Mon manege a moi (CD only.) / La foule (CD only.) / Les mots d'amour (CD only.) / Comme moi (CD only.) / Le droit d'aimer (CD only.) / Les feuilles mortes / Les flons flons du bal / Enfin le printemps / Mon dieu / C'est a Hambourg / Milord / Hymne a l'amore (If you love me, really love me).
LP: . . . . **MFP 5869**
MC: . . . . **TCMFP 5869**

MASTER SERIES: EDITH PIAF.
Tracks: / Mon legionnaire / C'est lui que mon coeur a choisi / Elle frequentait La Rue Pigalle / C'etait une histoire d'amour / La Julie Jolie / Ou sont-ils mes petits copains? / De l'autre cote de la rue / Y'a pas d'printemps / L'accordeoniste / Un jeune homme chantait / Fais-moi valser / Le disque use / Vagabond / J'ai dance avec l'amour / C'etait un jour de fete / Le fanion de la legion.
MC: **832189 4**

MILORD.
Tracks: / Milord / Padam padam / Bal dans ma rue / Mon dieu / Les flons flons du bal / Heureuse / L'homme a la moto / Bravo pour le clown / Le chant d'amour / Les feuilles mortes / Non je ne regrette rien / La vie en rose / L'accordeoniste / Enfin le printemps / C'est merveilleux / Non manege a moi / Les gens / La foule / Les amants d'un jour / Exodus.
LP: . . . . **IDL 13**
MC: . . . . **TCIDL 13**

MON LEGIONNAIRE.
Tracks: / Le momes de la choche / L'etranger / Fais moi valser / Mon amant de la coloniale / Le fanion de la legion / Mon legionnaire / Entre saint - queen et clingnancourt / Un jeune homme chantait / Ding din don / J'entends la sirene / Les marins ca fait des voyages / C'est lui que mon coeur a choisi / Elle frequentait La Rue Pigalle / Le petit Monsieur Triste / L'accordeoniste / J'ai dance avec l'amour / C'etait une histoire d'amour / Le vagabond / Il riait / Cmest tojours la meme historie / Y'a pas d'printemps / De l'autre cote de la rue.
LP: **6680 258**
MC: **7581 235**

OLYMPIA 1961 - NON, JE NE REGRETTE RIEN.
LP: . . . . **2 C 062 15304**

OLYMPIA 1955/56.
LP: . . . . **ONCR 529**

PATHE MARCONI Edith Piaf Vol 1.
Tracks: / La vie en rose / Les trois cloches / Hymne a l'amour / Johnny, tu n'es pas un ange / Sous le ciel de Paris / Mon manege a moi / C'est a Hambourg / L'accordeoniste / L'homme a la moto / Les amants d'un jour / La foule / Milord / Mon, je ne regrette rien / A quoi ca sert l'amour.
LP: . . . . **PM 261**

PIAF ALBUM, THE.
Tracks: / Non, je ne regrette rien / Milord / Sous le ciel de Paris / Mon manage a moi / Bravo pour le clown / Autumn leaves / Les flons flons du bal / Comme moi / La foule / La vie en rose / Padam padam / La goualante du pauvre Jean / L'accordeoniste / L'homme a la moto / Mon dieu / C'est a Hambourg / Exodus / Hymne a l'amour / A quoi ca sert l'amour / No regrets.
LP: . . . . **EMS 1727891**
MC: . . . . **TCEMS 1727894**

PORTRAIT OF EDITH PIAF.
2LP: . . . . **DUO 109**
MC: **TC2EXE 1018**

THIS IS EDITH PIAF.
Tracks: / La vie en rose / Hymne a l'amour / Sous le ciel de Paris / La fete continue / C'est un gars / Mon manege a moi / La belle histoire d'amour / L'accordeoniste / Padam, padam / Milord / A quoi ca sert l'amour / Comme moi / Les flons flons du bal / L'homme a la moto / Marie Trottoir / Mon Dieu / Exodus / Non, je ne regrette rein.
LP: . . . . **THIS 17**

TOP SIXTEEN.
MC: . . . . **PM 1562544**

TWENTY FRENCH HIT SINGLES.
Tracks: / Les trois cloches / La vie en rose / Bal dans ma rue / Hymne a l'amour / Padam, padam / Je m'en fous pas mal / Johnny, tu n'es pas un ange / Bravo pour le clown / La goualante du pauvre Jean / L'accordeoniste / C'est a Hambourg / Les amants d'un jour / L'homme a la moto / La foule / Mon manege a moi / Milord / Non, je ne regrette rien / Mon dieu / Exodus / A quoi ca sert l'amour.
LP: . . . . **SCX 6606**

VERY BEST OF EDITH PIAF.
Tracks: / La vie, l'amour / La vie en rose / Milord / Comme moi / Le vieux piano / Polichinelle / Toujours aimer / L'effet qu'tu m'fais / Mom manege a moi / Mon dieu / Hymne a l'amour / T'es beau, tu sais / Bravo pour le clown / C'est l'amour / Non, je ne regrette rien.
LP: . . . . **EMC 3142**
MC: . . . . **TCEMC 3142**

Piano...

GUNFIRE AND PIANO'S (Various artists).
LP: . . . . **SITU 17**
MC: . . . . **SITC 17**

Piano Blues

PIANO BLUES, VOL.18: ROOSEVELT SYKES/LEE GREEN 1 (Way I Feel) (Various artists).
LP: . . . . **PY 4418**

Piano Pops

PIANO POPS (Various artists).
MC: **TC2MOM 1546549**
MC: **TC2MOM 130**

Piano Red

AIN'T GOIN' TO BE YOUR LOW DOWN DOG NO MORE.
LP: . . . . **BLP 30162**

DOCTOR FEELGOOD.
Tracks: / Sloppy drunk / Blues, blues, blues / Pinetop's boogie / Doin' it / When things go wrong with you / Doctor Feelgood / Red's boogie / Dupree blues / Just another world goin' round / Whisky / You 'got the thing on me / Goodbye.
LP: . . . . **BLP 30171**

DOCTOR FEELGOOD ALONE.
LP: . . . . **ARHOOLIE 1064**

DOCTOR FEELGOOD - JUMPING TO THE BOOGIE.
LP: . . . . **OL 2821**

FLAT FOOT BOOGIE (Piano Red & His Chicago Blues Band).
LP: **9901**

ORIGINAL DR. FEELGOOD, THE.
LP: . . . . **JSP 1100**

Piano Slim

MEAN WOMAN BLUES.
LP: **2103**

Piano & Swing

PIANO AND SWING (1935-1938) (Various artists).
LP: . . . . **PM 1552561**

Piano Two

PIANO TWO (Various artists).
Tracks: / Nostalgia: *Yanni* / Velocity of love, The: *Ciani, Suzanne* / Fifth wave, The: *Ciani, Suzanne*/ Read your eyes: *Kuhn, Joachim* / Mother night: *Yanni* / Marching season: *Yanni* / Aria: *Riesman, Michael* (From act III of Satyagraha).
LP: 209643
MC: 409643

Pianola Roll

KITTEN ON THE KEYS.
Tracks: / Bye bye blackbird / Thora / Miss Annabelle Lee / For me and my gal / Stars and stripes forever / Sweet Genevieve / J'en ai marre / Alexander's ragtime band / I want to be happy / Doll dance / Moon river / Lovable and sweet / Me and Jane in a plane / Kitten on the keys / Stealing / Tippy canoe / Among my souvenirs / More we are together / Three o'clock in the morning.
LP: . . . . SDL 355
MC: . . . . CSDL 355

PIANOLA JAZZ.
Tracks: / Skip along / Maple leaf rag / Blame it on the blues / For me and my gal / Aunt Hagar's blues / I'll dance till de sun breaks through / Rose of Washington Square / Georgia camp meeting / Stumbling / French trot / Alabama dream / Creole belles / Old-fashioned girl.
MC: . . . . CSDL 117
LP: . . . . SDL 117

PIANOLA RAGTIME (Piano rolls 1895-1916).
Tracks: / Temptation rag / Ragtime skedaddle / Wabash blues / 1915 rag / Grizzly bear rag / Walhalla (two step craze) / Florida rag / Coon band contest / Smokey mokes / Tickled to death / Buzzer rag / Panama rag / Bow wow blues / Ragtime Oriole.
LP: . . . . SDL 132
MC: . . . . CSDL 132

Pianorama

LET YOURSELF GO.
Tracks: / Let's face the music and dance / Is it true what they say about dixie? / You brought a new kind of love / Swinging down the lane.
MC: . . . . DLCT 111

PIANORAMA (Harold Rich and Colin Campbell).
LP: . . . . REH 674
MC: . . . . ZCR 674

SENSATIONAL SIXTIES, THE (2).
MC: . . . . DLCT 108

WARTIME FAVOURITES.
Tracks: / We're gonna hang out the washing on the Siegfried line / Run rabbit run / Hey little hen / Let the people sing / I've got sixpence / Roll out the barrel / Praise the lord and pass the ammunition / Maizy doats and dozy doats / In the quartermaster's stores / I left my heart at the stage door canteen / If I had my way / I don't want to set the world on fire / You are my sunshine / Sgt Major's serenade, The / Don't sit under the apple tree / Dearly beloved / I'll be seeing you / Something to remember you by / Sailor with the navy blue eyes, The / Coming in on a wing and a prayer / I'm gonna get lit up / Fleet's in, The / That lovely weekend / Room 504 / Nightingale sang in Berkeley Square, The / It's foolish but it's fun / Elmer's tune / Lili Marlene / Yours / Jingle jangle / Deep in the heart of Texas / Oh Johnny, oh / Wishing (will make it so) / Tangerine / Long ago and far away / Our love affair / It's a lovely day tomorrow / Wish me good luck as you wave me goodbye / Kiss me goodnight Sergeant Major / Nursie, nursie / Ma, I miss your apple pie / You'll never know (Available CD only) / Beneath the lights of home (Available CD only) / Silver wings in the moonlight (Available CD only) / Moonlight becomes you (Available CD only) / When the lights go on again (Available CD only) / All over the place (Available CD only) / Down forget-me-not lane (Available CD only) / White cliffs of Dover, The / We'll meet again.
LP: . . . . DLCL 106
MC: . . . . DLCT 106

Pianosauras

GROOVY NEIGHBOURHOOD.
LP: . . . . ROUNDER 9010
MC: . . . . ROUNDER 9010C
LP: . . . . ROSE 107

Piazza, Rod

HARPBURN.
LP: . . . . SPIN 129
LP: . . . . MB 1008

SO GLAD TO HAVE THE BLUES.
LP: . . . . SPD 1015
MC: . . . . SPD 1015C

Piazzolla, Astor

LA CAMORRA.
Tracks: / La Camorra 1 / La Camorra 2 / La Camorra 3 / Soledad / Fugata / Sur: Los Suenos / Sur: Regresso al amor.
LP: . . . . AMCL 10211
MC: . . . . AMCL 10214

LIVE IN VIENNA.
Tracks: / Fracanapa / Verano Porteno / Caliente / Decarisimo / Libertango / Revirado / Invierno porteno / Adois nonino.
LP: 115916

MARIA DE BUENOS ARIES.
LP: . . . . A 391
MC: . . . . C 391

ROUGH DANCER AND THE CYCLICAL NIGHT.
LP: . . . . AMCL 10191
MC: . . . . AMCL 10194

SADNESS OF A DOUBLE A, THE.
LP: 15969

TANGO: ZERO HOUR.
Tracks: / Tanguedia III / Milonga del angel / Concierto para quinteto / Milonga loca / Michelangelo '70 / Countrabajissimo / Mumuki.
LP: 461156 1
MC: 461156 4
LP: . . . . AMCL 10131
MC: . . . . AMCL 10134

Pic & Bill

GIVIN' IT TO YOU.
Tracks: / Don't leave me / Moments like these / Soul of a man / You walk so fine / Just a tear / How many times / Talk about love / Yesterday / Talking 'bout nobody but my baby / When something is wrong with my baby / It's not you / This is my story / Sad world without you / Gonna give it to you / All I want is you / Love is a many splendoured thing.
LP: . . . . CRB 1172

TAKING UP THE SLACK.
LP: . . . . BAN 4109
MC: . . . . BAN 4109MC

Picante, Salsa

AND SOMETIMES VOICES (see Fischer, Clare) (Picante, Salsa & Clare Fischer & Two Plus Two).

Picante Y Caliente

LA SONORA DINAMITA.
MC: . . . . MCT 1031
LP: . . . . MLPS 1031

Picassos

PICASSOS, THE.
LP: . . . . TEK 001

Piccadilly Dance...

LET YOURSELF GO (Piccadilly Dance Orchestra).
MC: . . . . LLK 126
LP: . . . . LLP 126

Piccadilly Hotel Bands

PICCADILLY REVELS BANDS (Various artists).
LP: . . . . SH 250

Pick It Up Showcase

PICK IT UP SHOW CASE (Various artists).
LP: . . . . CAP LP 1

Pick & The Malt Shovel

PICK & THE MALT SHOVEL (Various artists).
LP: . . . . TSR 017

Pickens, Edwin Buster

EDWIN BUSTER PICKENS.
LP: . . . . FLY 536

Pickens, Slim

FIDDLIN' FOOL, THE.
Tracks: / I'm a ladies' man / Uncle Harvey's plane / Up cat pole cat / I won't go huntin' with you Jake / Cousin Pauline / I couldn't spell **** / Boil them cabbage down / Hoot and holler bar and grill / Fifteen beers ago / Stutterin' bum / Kansas City star / Make me a star.
LP: . . . . WRS 086

Pickering, David

CHORAL MUSIC FROM YORKSHIRE (See under St. Edmund, Roundhay) (Pickering, David/St. Edmund, Roundhay).

Pickering, Donald

ADVENTURES OF SHERLOCK HOLMES, THE (see under Sherlock Holmes (bk)).

Pickett, Charlie

ROUTE 33.
LP: . . . . SPIN 121

WILDERNESS, THE (Pickett, Charlie & The MC3).
Tracks: / In the wilderness / Religion or pleasure / Death letter / Party till noon / On the river in '59 / Tell me (that you don't) / Destry rides again / John the revelator / If this is love can I get my money back / Four wise men.
LP: . . . . SAVE 066

Pickett, Dan

1949 - COUNTRY BLUES.
Tracks: / Baby how long / You got to do better / Ride to a funeral in a V-8 / Decoration day / Drivin' that thing / 99 1/2 won't do / That's grieving me / Baby don't you want to go / Chicago blues / Something's gone wrong / Early one morning / Number writer / Laughing rag.
LP: . . . . KK 811

Pickett, Lenny

LENNY PICKETT & THE BORNEO HORNS (Pickett, Lenny & The Borneo Horns).
Tracks: / Dance music for Borneo Horns (1-5) / Solo for saxophone / Septer £2 / Dance suite / Landscape.
LP: . . . . HNBL 1321
MC: . . . . HNBC 1321

Pickett, Philip

ALCHEMIST, THE.
MC: 4252094
LP: 4252091

Pickett, Wilson

AMERICAN SOUL MAN.
Tracks: / Thing called love, A / When your heart speaks / Love never let me down / Man of value, A / (I wanna) make love to you / In the midnight hour / Don't turn away / Just let her know / Can't stop now.
LP: . . . . ZL 72615
MC: . . . . ZK 72615

BEST OF WILSON PICKETT.
Tracks: / In the midnight hour / 634 5789 / I found a love / Mustang Sally / Ninety nine and one-half (won't do) / Everybody needs somebody to love / Don't fight it / I'm a midnight mover / Funky Broadway / Soul dance number three / I'm in love / Land of a thousand dances.
LP: 780 170-1
MC: 780 170-4

EXCITING WILSON PICKETT, THE.
LP: SD8129

GREATEST HITS: WILSON PICKETT.
Tracks: / In the midnight hour / I found a love / 634-5789 / If you need me / Mustang Sally / Everybody needs somebody to love / It's too late / Ninety nine and one half (won't do) / Funky broadway / Soul dance number three / Land of a thousand dances / Don't let the green grass fool you / Sugar sugar / Get me back on time / I'm a midnight mover / Man and a half, A / Mama told me not to come / She's looking good / I'm in love / Don't knock my love - part 1 / Hey Jude you keep me hanging on / I found a true love.
LP: . . . . K 60038

HEART AND SOUL.
MC: . . . . KNMC 12062

I WANT YOU.
Tracks: / Groove city / You are the love of my life.
LP: . . . . AML 3007

RIGHT TRACK, THE.
Tracks: / Back on the right track / If you can't beat em' join em' / Help me be without / I ain't gonna give you no more / Maybe this time / Don't underestimate the power of love / It's you.
LP: . . . . AML 3016

Pickford, Ed

SONGWRITER.
LP: . . . . ROF 001

Pickles, Nigel

MEXBOROUGH ENGLISH CONCERTINA PRIZE BAND.
LP: . . . . PLR 055

Pickwick

PICKWICK (ORIGINAL ISSUE) (London cast) (Various artists).
LP: . . . . AL 3431

Pickwick Papers (bk)

PICKWICK PAPERS (Orchard, Julian).
MC: . . . . P 90011

Picky Picnic

HA HA TARACHINE.
LP: . . . . WR 31

Picnic

PICNIC (Film soundtrack) (Various artists).
LP: . . . . MCA 1527
MC: . . . . MCAC 1527

Picnic At Hanging Rock

PICNIC AT HANGING ROCK, THEME FROM (See under Zamfir, Gheorghe) (Zamfir, Gheorghe).

Picnic At The...

DOORS ARE OPEN, THE (Picnic At The Whitehouse).
Tracks: / Human outro / Eternal / Doors are open, The / East River / Success / We need protection / Little lady / Intro of human / Human / Clockwork blue / Heaven / All I need.
LP: 4502621
MC: 4502624

Picone, Vitto

ELEGANTS' GREATEST HITS (Picone, Vitto & The Elegants).
LP: . . . . APT 1000

Picture

DIAMOND DREAMER.
Tracks: / Lady lightning / Night hunter / Hot lovin' / Diamond dreamer / Message from hell / You're all alone / Lousy lady / Hangmen / Get me rock and roll / You're touching me.
LP: 6350 065

ETERNAL DARK.
MC: . . . . CAC 217
LP: . . . . CAL 217

HEAVY METAL EARS.
LP: 6530 058

MARATHON.
Tracks: / Breakaway / Vampire of the new age / Money / Desperate call / I'm on my way / S.O.S. / Get out of my sight / We just can't lose / Don't keep me waiting.
LP: . . . . CAL 228

NIGHT HUNTER.
Tracks: / Lady lightning / Night hunter / Hot lovin' / Diamond dreamer / Message from hell / You're all alone / Lousy lady / Hangmen / Get me rock and roll / You're touching me.
LP: . . . . CAL 146
MC: . . . . CAC 146

TRAITOR.
LP: 824 806 1

Picture Frame

HAND OF THE RIDER.
LP: . . . . PFS 001

Picture Music

PICTURE MUSIC INSTRUMENTAL VOL.4 (Various artists).
LPPD: . . . . SKYP 092

Picture Of Dorian (bk)

PICTURE OF DORIAN GRAY, A (NARRATIVE) (see also under Wilde, Oscar) (Hatfield, Hurd).

Pictures

PICTURES.
Tracks: / Lullaby / Nursery rap / Dancing mind to mind / Skrahs / Battle of the leaves / Black tiger / Loneliness / Child in a sweet shop / Adventure lost / Voodoo.
LP: . . . . EGED 32

Pidgeon, Fred

LADIES BREAST-KNOT.
Tracks: / Plain schottische / Heel and toe polka / Double change side / Polka mazurka / Circassian circle / Highland fling / Triumph / Scotch polka / Double schottische / Galopede / Barn dance / Varsoviana / Danish waltz / Lancers / Plain quadrille / Church Stratton waltz / Ring the bell, watchman / Pop goes the weasel.
MC: 45-087

Piece Of Steak

PIECE OF STEAK, A (see London, Jack) (Bryce, James).

Pieces

COULD IT BE YOU (see Jones, Vivian) (Pieces/Vivian Jones).

PIECES.
LP: . . . . UAG 30252

Pieces Of A Dream

AIN'T MY LOVE ENOUGH.
LP: . . . . EL 48740

'BOUT DAT TIME.
Tracks: / 'Bout dat time / I just want your love / What can I do / Can't be alone / For you / Pick up the pieces / Lonely hearts of love / Take me tonight / Kicking / Surrender.
LP: . . . . MTL 1048
MC: . . . . TCMTL 1048

JOYRIDE.
Tracks: / Save some time for me / Say la la / I can give you want you want / Joy ride / Love of my life / Careless whisper / Outside in / Winning streak / Sunshine.
LP: . . . . MTL 1004
MC: . . . . TCMTL 1004

MAKES YOU WANNA.
Tracks: / Ain't my love enough / We belong to each other / Makes you wanna / Rising to the top / Round midnight /

Mellow magic / Feeling for you / Holding back the years.
LP: MTL 1030
MC: TCMTL 1030

PIECES OF A DREAM.
Tracks: / All about love / Easy road home / Lovers / Body magic / Warm weather / Steady glide / Touch me in the spring / Pieces of a dream.
LP: 960 270-1
LP: K 52320

Pied Piper of Hamelin

PIED PIPER OF HAMELIN story tape (Various artists).
MC: TS 304

PIED PIPER OF HAMELIN & OTHER FAMOUS POEMS (Various artists).
MC: TS 328

PIED PIPER OF HAMELIN, THE (Various artists).
MC: STC 306C

PIED PIPER OF HAMELIN, THE (well loved tales age up to 9).
MC: PLB 180

Pied Pipers

GOOD DEAL MACNEAL 1944-1946.
LP: HEP 33

Pienkowski, Jan

MEG & MOG (see Nicoll, Helen) (Lipman, Maureen).

MEG ON THE MOON (See under Nicoll, Helen) (Pienkowski,Jan & Helen Nicoll).

MEG'S EGGS (See under Nicoll, Helen) (Pienkowski,Jan & Helen Nicoll).

Pieranunzi, Enrico

NEWLANDS.
LP: SJP 211

NO MAN'S LAND.
LP: 121 221 1
MC: 121 221 4

Pierce, Billie

BILLIE & DE DE PIERCE (Pierce, Billie & De De).
LP: JCE 25

WILLIAM THE CONQUEROR.
Tracks: / Blue nostalgia / Pannonica / Color blind / Over the edge / William the Conqueror / Sudan blue / We'll be together / Nature folksong.
LP: SSC 1013
MC: SSC 1013D

Pierce, Billie & De De

NEW ORLEANS MUSIC.
LP: ARHOOLIE 2016

Pierce, Bobby

PIERCING.
LP: MR 5304

Pierce, Jeffrey Lee

WILDWEED.
Tracks: / Sensitivity / Hey Juana / Love circus / Wildweed / Midnight promise, The / Fertility goddess, The / Open the door / Osiris / Portrait of the sticks in hell / Chris and Maggie meet blind Willie McTell / Love and desperation (long and short versions) / Sex killer / Cleopatra dreams on / From temptation to you.
LP: STATLP 25
MC: STATC 25

Pierce, Joshua

PORTRAIT OF BROADWAY, A (Pierce, Joshua & Dorothy Jonas).
MC: ZPREC 5003

Pierce, Monty

GREATEST HITS OF FLANAGAN & ALLEN (See under Smith, Bryan) (Pierce, Monty/ Bryan Smith & Roy Hudd).

Pierce, Nat

5400 NORTH (Pierce, Nat Quintet).
LP: HEP 2004

1948-1950 (Pierce, Nat Orchestra).
LP: ZM 1005

AT THE SAVOY BALLROOM (Pierce, Nat Big Band).
LP: FS 118

BALLAD OF JAZZ STREET (Pierce, Nat Orchestra).
LP: HEP 2009

BOSTON BUSTOUT.
Tracks: / King Edward the flatted fifth / Pat / Indian Summer / Lonesome crowd / King for a day / Crazy moon / You may not love me / Kind girl / Sheba / Babylon / What can I say / Whats new / You were meant for me / Paradise.
LP: HEP 13

EVERYTHING'S COMING UP ROSIE (see under Clooney, Rosemary) (Pierce, Nat Quintet/Rosemary Clooney).

JUGGERNAUT (See Under Capp, Frank) (Capp-Pierce Orchestra).

Pierce, Webb

CROSS COUNTRY.
Tracks: / Heartaches by the number / You are my life / Cry cry darlin' / Waterloo / Free of the blues / I'm letting you go / Take time / Someday you'll call my name / All my love / Crazy wild desire / I'm falling in love with you / I close my eyes.
LP: HAT 3004
MC: HATC 3004

GREAT SONGS OF WEBB PIERCE, THE.
Tracks: / I'm walking the dog / Slowly / It's been so long / There stands the glass / Even tho' / I'm gonna fall out of love with you / I'm in the jailhouse now / Wondering / You can't be true / I'm not in love with you.
LP: BDL 1026

I AIN'T NEVER.
Tracks: / I ain't never / Teenage boogie / Sittin' alone / Bye bye love / In the jailhouse now / Honky tonk song / After the boy gets the girl / New panhandle rag / California blues / You scared the love right out of me / I'm walking the dog / More and more / I'm gonna see my baby tonight / Sparkling brown eyes / Sneakin' all around / Why baby why.
LP: CR 30235

WEBB!.
LP: HAT 3019
MC: HATC 3019

WONDERING BOY, THE.
LP: HAT 3119

Pierre, Marie

LOVE AFFAIR.
Tracks: / Choose me / Can't go through (with life) / I believe / Somebody else's man / Nothing gained (for loving you) / Humanity / Rowing / My best friend / Walk away / Over reacting.
LP: TRLS 177

Pierson, Kate

CANDY (See under Pop, Iggy) (Pop, Iggy & Kate Pierson).

Pig

POKE IN THE EYE, A.
LP: EFA 2228

PRAISE THE LARD.
LP: CPRODLP 017

Pig Bros

FROM NOW ON THIS WILL BE YOUR IDEAL LIFE.
Tracks: / Face of baby / Past caring / Cheap life / From now on this will be your ideal life / Skin deep theories / Still goes on / Stones / Dunus question / All or nothing / Way things currently are, The.
LP: LPCAKE 1

TIME TO UNMASK.
LP: PIECE LP 6

Pig, Clive

TIME TO GET TOUGH.
Tracks: / Him + her + baby / I must be mad / World is so, The / Various friends for various times / Time to get tough / At a church outside the village / First jump of love, The / Say something simple she said.
LP: TGT 018

Pigalle, Anne

ANNE PIGALLE.
MC: ZCIQ 7

EVERYTHING COULD BE SO PERFECT.
Tracks: / Why does it have to be this way / Via vagabond / Looking for love / He stranger / Intermission / Souvenir d'un Paris / Crack in the ocean, A / 1000 colours waltz, The.
LP: ZTTIQ 7
MC: ZCIQ 7

HOT SEGAS (EP) (see under Plytas, Nick) (Pigalle, Anne & Nick Plytas).

Pigbag

BEST OF PIGBAG.
Tracks: / Papa's got a brand new pigbag / Weak at the knees / Hit the O deck / Getting up / Brazil nuts / Jump the line / Another orangutango / Sunny day / Big bean / Can't see for looking / Six of one / Big bag / Listen listen little man.
MC: KAZ MC 3

DOCTOR HECKLE & MR. JIVE.
LP: Y 17

LEND AN EAR.
LP: YLP 501
MC: YK 501

PIG BAG - LIVE.
LP: YMP 1001
MC: YK 1001

Pigface

DEVOTION.
LP: DVN 2
MC: TDVN 2

GUB.
Tracks: / Tapeworm / Bushmaster / Cylinder head world / Point blank / Suck / Symphony for taps / Greenhouse / Little sisters / Tailor made / War ich nicht immer ein guter junge / Blood and sand / Weightless.
LP: GRAM 47

Pigg, Billy

BORDER MINSTREL, THE.
LP: LER 2006

Piggleswick Folk

PIG IN THE MIDDLE.
LP: CF 256

Pigor Och Drangar

PIGOR OCH DRANGAR.
LP: PHONT 7508

Pigwig (bk)

PIGWIG.
MC: LL 41 8023 4

PIGWIG AND THE PIRATES.
MC: LL 41 8024 4

Pike, Dave

DAVE PIKE AND CHARLES MCPHERSON (See also McPherson, Charles) (Pike, Dave/Charles McPherson).
Tracks: / Scrapple from the apple / Off minor / Piano trio medley / Embraceable you / Up jumped Spring / Big foot.
LP: SJP 302

DAVE PIKE,VIBES WITH CEDAR WALTON TRIO.
LP: XX 1021

LET THE MINSTRELS PLAY ON.
LP: MR 5203

MOON BIRD.
LP: MR 5261

PIKE'S GROOVE (Pike, Dave/Cedar Walton Trio).
LP: CRISS 1021

TIMES OUT OF MIND.
LP: MR 5092

Pikes In Panic

KEEP IT COOL AND DRY.
Tracks: / Sunday love / Pikemen's shake / Burglars / Sunshine / Summer girl / Ghost rider / Some kinda fun / She sang the blues / My lovers like a TV screen / Floppy boy / Break the sound barrier / Little by little.
LP: CONGAS 116

Piledriver

METAL INQUISITION.
Tracks: / Metal inquisition / Sex with Satan / Sodomize the deed / Witch hunt / Pile driver / Human sacrifice / Alien rape.
LP: RR 9762

STAY UGLY.
LP: RR 9701

Pilgrim Jubilee

BACK TO BASICS.
LP: MAL 4431
MC: MALC 4431

OLD SHIP OF ZION.
LP: MCA 28010

PUT YOUR TRUST IN JESUS.
LP: SL 14728

Pilgrim Souls

IS THIS ALL OF US?.
Tracks: / For the big country / C'mon baby / Letterbox / 5.38 to Alcatraz / She keeps me happy / Train's gotta roll on / Gimme back my home / 2 lanes / Parish in the woods / Redemption day.
LP: 4634671
MC: 4634674

Pilgrim's Progress

PILGRIM'S PROGRESS, THE (John Bunyan) (Gielgud, Sir John (nar)).
MCSET: SAY 111
MCSET: ARGO 1100

PILGRIM'S PROGRESS, THE (John Bunyan) (Mason, James (nar)).
MC: CP 1666

Pillar, Michele

LOOK WHO LOVES YOU NOW.
LP: BIRD 157
MC: TC BIRD 157

Pillow, Ray

ONE TOO MANY MEMORIES.
Tracks: / One too many memories / Livin' in the sunshine of your love / How do I hide from a memory / Wasted again / Please don't leave me / Days of you and me, The / You're one memory I'd like to make again / How much can love take /

Julie loved Boston more than me / We're together again.
LP: ALEB 2307
MC: ZCALB 2307

Pilot

BEST OF PILOT.
Tracks: / Sooner or later / Girl next door / Just a smile / You're my no.1 / Call me round / January / Magic / High in the sky / Passion piece / Penny in my pocket / Canada / Trembling / Never give up / Auntie Iris.
LP: NUT 29

BEST OF PILOT, THE (2).
LP: C5-563

SECOND FLIGHT.
LP: EMC 3075

Pilot Error

PILOT ERROR.
MC: ETA 1

Piltzecker, Ted

DESTINATIONS.
LP: SB 2027

Pinaudres

VOSGES ETERNELLES.
Tracks: / La ronde lorraine / La soyotte / L'alouette / La toilette du galant / La ronde des bacelles / Valse de la Camarelle / He be sagar / M'y allant promener / La valse des moissonneurs / Branle vosgien / La fiancee fidele / Le pauver colas / Les cerceils / Trimazo / Juronde.
LP: ARN 33372

Pinchers

AGONY.
MC: LALC 13

GOT TO BE ME.
Tracks: / Take some time / Lyric none stop / Dollyman / Boops / Nuh worry yourself / I love you / I am gonna be there / Lift it up again.
LP: LALP 13

LIFT IT UP AGAIN.
LP: DSR 8608

MASS OUT.
Tracks: / Pot of coffee / Meant to be / Grammy / Nuthing no deh / Turn over / Mass out / Take some time / No worry yourself / Who say what / Christian lady.
LP: RAS 3023

PINCHERS MEETS SANCHEZ (Pinchers & Sanchez).
LP: Unknown

RAGGA MUFFIN RISE AGAIN (See under Isaaacs, Gregory) (Isaacs, Gregory and Pinchers).

RETURN OF THE DON.
LP: VPRL 1065

TURBO CHARGE (see under Paul, Frankie) (Pinchers & Frankie Paul).

Pinchers With Pliers

PINCHERS WITH PLIERS.
LP: BSLP 001

Pinckney, St. Clair

PRIVATE STOCK.
Tracks: / Private stock / From the book / Joy life / Stranded / Night stroller / From the head / Summer night / I'm in love with you.
LP: ICH 1036
MC: ZCICH 1036

Pine, Courtney

ANGEL HEART (See under Angel heart (film)) (Pine, Courtney/Trevor Jones).

CLOSER TO HOME.
Tracks: / Get busy / I don't care / Be mine tonight / Closer to home / In time (all will know) / Blue tide / Kingston / I'm still waiting / Never be lonely / Home song.
LP: MLPS 1046
LP: 846 528 1
MC: MCT 1046
MC: 846 528 4

DESTINY'S SONG AND THE IMAGE OF PURSUANCE.
Tracks: / Beyond the thought of my last reckoning / In pursuance / Vision, The / Guardian of the flame / Round midnight / Sacrifice / Prismic omnipotence / Alone / Raggamuffin's tale, A / Mark of the time.
LP: AN 8725
MC: ANC 8725
MC: ICM 2043
LP: ILPM 2043

JOURNEY TO THE URGE WITHIN.
Tracks: / Mis-interpret / I believe / Peace / Delores St. S.F / As we would say / Children of the ghetto / When, where, how and why / C.G.C. / Seen / Sunday song.
LP: ILPS 9846
MC: ICT 9846
MC: ICM 9846

LP: ILPM 9846

VISION'S TALE, THE.
Tracks: / Introduction / In a mellow tone / Just you, just me / Raggamuffin's stance, A / No greater love / Skylark / I'm an old cowhand from the Rio Grande / God bless the child / And then (a warrior's tale) / Our descendants' descendants / CP's theme.
MC: ANC 8746
LP: AN 8746

WITHIN THE REALMS OF OUR DREAMS.
MC: ANC 8756
LP: AN 8756

Pine Island

LIVE INSIDE.
LP: FR 124

Pinewood

HEARTACHE AND PROMISES.
Tracks: / Bandido / I should have known better / Everybody's talkin' / If you can't be loved / Raining in my heart / Run for home / Power cut / Living next door to Alice / Till there was you / It's a heartache / Love of my life / Heartaches and promises.
LP: FHR 108

Pinhas, Richard

CHRONOLYSE.
LP: COB 37015

RHIZOSPERE.
LP: COB 37005

Pini, Mick "Wildman"

MICK WILDMAN PINI.
Tracks: / Collector, The / Onion rings / You can make it / Unknown destination / It's got to be the blues / More than I could chew / Free load / Like mother like daughter / Freddy's midnite dream / Too many mountains.
LP: BLUH 009

Pink

SOUL FLIGHT.
LP: SPIN 121

Pink Cadillac

PINK CADILLAC (Film Soundtrack) (Various artists).
MC: 925922.4

Pink Fairies

BEST OF THE PINK FAIRIES, THE.
MC: 8438944

KILL EM 'N EAT' EM.
Tracks: / Broken statue / Fear of love / Undercover of confusion / Waiting for the ice cream to melt / Taking LSD / White girls on amphetamine / Seeing double / Fool about you / Bad attitude / I might be lying.
LP: FIEND 105

LIVE AT THE ROUNDHOUSE.
Tracks: / City kids / Waiting for the man / Lucille / Uncle Harry's last freakout / Going down.
LP: WIK 14

NEVER NEVER LAND.
LP: 2383 045

PINK FAIRIES.
Tracks: / Snake, The / Well well well / Do it / Pigs of Uranus.
MC: 843 894 4

PREVIOUSLY UNRELEASED.
Tracks: / As long as the price is right / Waiting for the lightning to strike / Can't find the lady / No second chance / Talk of the devil / I think it's coming back again.
LP: NED 9

WHAT A BUNCH OF SWEETIES.
LP: 2383 132

Pink Floyd

ANIMALS.
Tracks: / Pigs on the wing (part one) / Dogs / Pigs (three different ones) / Sheep / Pigs on the wing (part two).
LP: SHVL 815
MC: TCSHVL 815
LP: Q4SHVL 815

ATOM HEART MOTHER.
Tracks: / Rise and shine / Sunny side up / Morning glory / Remergence / Father's shout / Breast milky / Mother fore / Funky dung / Mind your throats please / If / Summer '68 / Fat old sun / Alan's psychedelic breakfast.
LP: SHVL 781
MC: TCSHVL 781

COLLECTION OF GREAT DANCE SONGS, A.
Tracks: / One of these days / Money / Another brick in the wall (part 2) / Wish you were here / Shine on you crazy diamond / Sheep.
LP: ATAK 31
MC: TCATAK 31
LP: FA 41 3144 1
MC: FA 41 3144 4
LP: FA 3144
MC: TCFA 3144
LP: SHVL 822

DARK SIDE OF THE MOON.
Tracks: / Speak to me / Breath in the air / On the run / Time / Great gig in the sky, The / Money / Us and them / Any colour you like / Brain damage / Eclipse.
LP: SHVL 804
MC: TCSHVL 804

DELICATE SOUND OF THUNDER.
Tracks: / Shine of you crazy diamond / Learning to fly / Yet another movie / Round and around / Sorrow / Dogs of war / On the turning away / One of these days / Timed / Wish you were here / Us and them (Cassette & CD only.) / Money (Album & CD only.) / Another brick in the wall (part 2) / Comfortably numb / Run like hell.
MCSET: TCEQ 5009
2LP: EQ 5009

FINAL CUT, THE.
Tracks: / Postwar dream / Your possible / One of the few / Hero's return / Gunner's dream / Paranoid eyes / Get your filthy hands off my desert / Fletcher memorial home / Southampton dock / Final cut / Not now John / Two suns in the desert.
LP: SHPF 1983
MC: TCSHPF 1983

MASTERS OF ROCK.
LP: 05404299
LP: 3C054 04299
MC: 3C254 04299

MEDDLE.
Tracks: / One of these days / Pillow of winds, A / Fearless (Interpolating) / You'll never walk alone / San Tropez.
LP: ATAK 35
MC: TCATAK 35
LP: SHVL 795
MC: TCSHVL 795

MOMENTARY LAPSE OF REASON, A.
Tracks: / Signs of life / Learning to fly / Dogs of war / One slip / On the turning away / Yet another movie / Round and around / New machine (part 1) / Terminal frost / New machine (part 2) / Sorrow.
LP: EMD 1003
MC: TCEMD 1003
LP: EMDS 1003

MOMENTARY LASPE OF REASON, A.
Tracks: / Signs of life / Learning to fly / Dogs of war / One slip / On the turning away / Yet another movie / Round and around / New machine (part 1) / Terminal frost / New machine (part 2).
MC: TCEMD 1003

MORE (Original Soundtrack).
Tracks: / Cirrus minor / Nile song, The / Crying song / Up the Khyber / Green is the colour / Cymbaline / Party sequence / Main theme / Ibiza bar / More blues / Quicksilver / Spanish piece, A / Dramatic theme.
LP: SCX 6346
MC: TCSCX 6346

NICE PAIR, A.
Tracks: / Astronomy domine / Lucifer Sam / Matilda mother / Flaming / Take up thy stethoscope and walk / Interstellar overdrive / Gnome, The / Chapter 24 / Scarecrow / Bike / Let there be more light / Remember a day / Set the controls for the heart of the sun / Corporal Clegg / Saucerful of secrets, A / See-saw / Jugband blues.
2LP: SHDW 403
MC: TC2EXE 1013

OBSCURED BY CLOUDS.
Tracks: / Obscured by clouds / When you're in / Burning bridges / Gold it's in the, The / Wots...uh the deal / Mudmen / Childhood's end / Free four / Stay / Absolutely curtains.
LP: SHSP 4020
MC: TCSHSP 4020

PINK FLOYD: INTERVIEW PICTURE DISC.
LPPD: BAK 2028

PIPER AT THE GATES OF DAWN, THE.
Tracks: / Astronomy domine / Lucifer Sam / Matilda mother / Flaming / Pow r toc h / Take up thy stethoscope and walk / Interstellar overdrive / Gnome, The / Chapter 24 / Scarecrow / Bike.
LP: FA 3065
MC: TCFA 3065
LP: SCX 6157

RELICS.
Tracks: / Arnold Layne / Intersellar overdrive / See Emily play / Remember a day / Paintbox / Julia dream / Careful with that axe, Eugene / Cirrus minor / Nile song, The / Bidin' my time / Bike.
LP: MFP 50397
MC: TCMFP 50397
LP: SRS 5071

SAUCERFUL OF SECRETS, A.
Tracks: / Let there be more light / Remember a day / Set the controls for the heart of the sun / Corporal Clegg / Saucerful of secrets, A / See-saw.
LP: FA 3163
MC: TCFA 3163
LP: SCX 6258
MC: TC SCX 6258

THERE'S SOMEBODY OUT THERE (Interview album).
LPPD: BAK 6003

UMMAGUMMA.
Tracks: / Astronomy domine / Careful with that axe, Eugene / Set the controls for the heart of the sun / Saucerful of secrets, A / Sysyphus (parts 1-4) / Grantchester meadows / Several species of small furry animals gathered together... / Narrow way, The / Grand Vizier's garden party, The.
2LP: SHDW 1
MCSET: TC2SHDW 4501

WALL, THE (Original soundtrack).
Tracks: / In the flesh / Thin ice / Happiest days of our lives / Another brick in the wall (part 2) / Mother / Goodbye blue sky / Empty spaces / Young lust / One of my turns / Don't leave me now / Another brick in the wall (part 3) / Goodbye cruel world / Hey you / Is there anybody out there? / Nobody home / Comfortably numb / Show must go on / Run like hell / Waiting for the worms / Stop / Trial, The / Outside the wall.
2LP: SHDW 411
MCSET: TC 2S HDW 411

WISH YOU WERE HERE.
Tracks: / Shine on you crazy diamond (Parts 1-9) / Welcome to the machine / Have a cigar / Wish you were here.
LP: SHVL 814
MC: TCSHVL 814

Pink Industry

LOW TECHNOLOGY.
LP: ZULU 2

NEW BEGINNINGS.
LP: ZULU 7

PINK INDUSTRY.
LP: CRL 18

WHO TOLD YOU YOU WERE NAKED.
Tracks: / Extremes / Not moving / Situation / Taps / Raft, The / Two cultures / Urban jazz / Anyones fashion.
LP: ZULU 4

Pink Military

DO ANIMALS BELIEVE IN GOD?.
Tracks: / Degenerated man / I cry / Did you see her / Wild west / Back on the London stage / After Hiroshima / Living in the jungle / Dreamtime / Wargames / Heaven/Hell / Do animals believe in God?.
LP: ERICS 004
LP: OVED 231

Pink Panther (film)

PINK PANTHER (Film soundtrack) (Various artists).
Tracks: / Pink Panther theme: *Various artists* / It had better be tonight: *Various artists* / Royal blue: *Various* artists / Champagne and quail: *Various artists* / Village Inn, The: *Various artists* / Tiber twist, The: *Various* artists / It had better be tonight: *Various artists* / Cortina: *Various artists* / Lonely princess, The: *Various* artists / Something for Sellers: *Various artists* / Piano and strings: *Various artists* / Shades of Sennett: *Various artists.*
LP: NL 80832
MC: NK 80832

PINK PANTHER THEME (see under Mancini, Henry).

RETURN OF THE PINK PANTHER, THE (Mancini, Henry & His Orchestra).
Tracks: / Pink Panther, Theme from / Greatest gift (instrumental), The / Here's looking at you, kid / Summer in Gstaad / So smooth / Return of the Pink Panther, The / Greatest gift (vocal) / Orange float, The / Dreamy / Disco / Navel manoeuvre / Belly belly, bum bum / Wet look, The.
LP: RS 1010

REVENGE OF THE PINK PANTHER (Film soundtrack) (Various artists).
Tracks: / Pink panther (theme from): *Various artists* / Simone: *Various artists* / Give me some mo'l: *Various* artists / Thar she blows: *Various artists* / Balls caprice: *Various artists* / Move 'em out: *Various* artists / Touch of red, A: *Various artists* / After the shower: *Various artists* / Hong Kong fireworks: *Various artists* / Almond eyes: *Various artists.*
LP: UAK 30176
MC: E 41 E 91113

SHOT IN THE DARK, A (see Henry Mancini at the movies).

TRAIL OF THE PINK PANTHER (Film soundtrack) (Mancini, Henry & His Orchestra).
Tracks: / Trail of the pink panther / Greatest gift / Hong Kong fireworks / Shot in the dark / Simone / It had better be tonight / Easy life in Paris / Come to me / Bierfest polka / After the shower / Inspector Clouseau theme / Return of the Pink Panther.
LP: LBG 30355
MC: TC LBG 30355
MC: E 41 E 90627

Pink Peg Slax

12 SONGS NEVER RECORDED BY FRANK SINATRA.
Tracks: / I feel I'm getting old / We can still be friends / Such a fool / Mr. Fiddle / Arkansas mountain man / Last cigarette, The / Big body, The / Le fou's blues / Our spark became a dud / One hand loose / Just trust in me / Liquid paradise.
LP: CALCLP 027

BELTING OUT A TUNA.
LP: HC 61

Pink Turns Blue

META.
Tracks: / First, The / Curse, The / Your master is calling / Darkness / Cult of the beautiful / Celebration's day / Touch the skies / Marcella / Faces of the gone / Church of choice, The.
LP: FUNFACL 3913

Pinkees

PINKEES, THE.
Tracks: / Danger games / I'll be there / Say what you're thinking / Thinking of her / You don't love her anymore / Girl in a million / Holding me tight / I'm feeling lonely / One step / Gonna be lonely again / I love you / Maybe I'm a fool / I want you here tonight / Rocking with the band.
LP: CRLP 516
MC: CRLC 516

Pinkney, Bill

LIVE: BILL PINKNEY & THE ORIGINAL DRIFTERS (Pinkney, Bill & The Original Drifters).
Tracks: / Up on the roof / Twist, The / Under the boardwalk / Please stay / Money honey / Some kind of wonderful / Sand dancers / This magic moment / I count the tears / Save the last dance for me.
LP: BDL 1041

Pinkney, Fayette

ONE DEGREE.
LP: CHOPE 3

Pinkney, St Clair

DO YOU LIKE IT.
LP: ICH 1014
MC: ZCICH 1014

Pinnacle Boys

PINNACLE BOYS, THE.
LP: ROUNDER 0049

Pinns, Suzi

JERUSALEM (See under Ant, Adam).

Pinocchio (bk)

PINOCCHIO.
LP: D 311
MC: D 2DC
LP: D 3905
LPPD: D 3102
MC: PLB 69

PINOCCHIO.
MC: STK 013

PINOCCHIO (Carlo Collodi) (Cribbins, Bernard (nar)).
MC: TS 332
MCSET: SAY 9

PINOCCHIO (Carlo Collodi) (Ritchard, Cyril (nar)).
MC: 1262

PINOCCHIO.
MC: DIS 003

Pinocchio (film)

PINOCCHIO (Film soundtrack) (Various artists).
Tracks: / When you wish upon a star: *Various artists* / Jiminy Cricket theme: *Various artists* / Little wooden head: *Various artists* / Blue fairy theme: *Various artists* / Give a little whistle: *Various artists*/ Pinocchio goes to school: *Various artists* / I've got no strings: *Various artists* / Hi diddle dee dee: *Various* artists / Whale chase, The: *Various artists* / Turn on the old music box: *Various artists* / Pinocchio (finale): *Various artists.*
LP: WD 002
MC: WDC 002
LP: REC 540
MC: ZCM 540
MC: HSC 344
LP: DQ 1202

Pinodo, Bon

LOVE IS LOVE.
LP: . . . . **PADA 0025**

Pins & Needles

PINS AND NEEDLES (Original Broadway Cast) (Various artists).
LP: . . . . **AOS 210**

Pinski Zoo

EAST RAIL EAST.
Tracks: / Search mode / Potlatch boogie / Glamour jungle / Rosa / Slip drip / East rail east / Fireside baby / Jimi Quoshi / Later that same day / Safe house / Slab / Easy attack / Breeze block brain / Rosa / Fireside baby too.
LP: . . . . **JCR 904**
MC: . . . . **JCRMC 904**

RARE BREEDS.
LP: . . . . **PINS 006**

Pinter, Harold

HOMECOMING, THE (Various artists).
MCSET: **0361**

NO MAN'S LAND (Various artists).
MC: **0369**

Pinza, Ezio

GREAT VOICES OF THE CENTURY.
MC: . . . . **CMOIR 404**

Pioneers

CLASSIC TRACKS (See under Collins, Dave & Ansel) (Pioneers/Dave & Ansell Collins).

GREATEST HITS: PIONEERS.
Tracks: / I need your sweet inspiration / Papa was a rollin' stone / At the discotheque / Feeling high / Let it all hang out / Long shot kick de bucket / Simmer down quashie / Let your yeah be yeah / Time hard / Jamaica jerk off / Battle of the giants / Dem a wolf.
LP: . . . . **TRLS 172**

I BELIEVE IN LOVE.
LP: . . . . **TRLS 48**

I'M GONNA KNOCK ON YOUR DOOR.
LP: . . . . **TRLS 98**

LONG SHOT.
LP: . . . . **TBL 103**

MORE REGGAE FOR LOVERS VOL.3.
LP: . . . . **STLP 1028**

MORE REGGAE FOR LOVERS VOL.4.
LP: . . . . **STLP 1029**

PUSHER MAN.
Tracks: / Bust them shut / Pusher man / Riot in Notting Hill / Ohio / Tears on my pillow / Bad to worse / Ahuma / Feeling high / Ghetto, The / Goodnight my love / Sabotage / Them a wolf.
LP: . . . . **TRLS 156**

REGGAE FOR LOVERS VOL.1.
LP: . . . . **STLP 1019**

REGGAE FOR LOVERS VOL.2.
LP: . . . . **STLP 1021**

SO FINE.
LP: . . . . **PILP 91**

WHAT A FEELING.
LP: . . . . **PILP 30**

Pipe Bands...

25 YEARS OF WORLD PIPE CHAMPIONS (Various artists).
MC: . . . . **LDDC 8011**

BEST OF THE PIPES AND DRUMS OF SCOTLAND (Various artists).
Tracks: / Scotland the brave: *Grantown & District Pipe Band* / Crooked bawbee: *Dysart & Dundonald Pipe Band* / Baro of Armagh: *Dysart & Dundonald Pipe Band* / Piper's waltz: *Dysart & Dundonald Pipe Band* / Pretty Marion: *Shotts &* Dykehead Caledonia Pipe Band / Atholl highlanders: *Macleod, Pipe Major Donald* / I am a young man: *Glasgow &* Strathclyde University OTC Pipe Band / Muckin' o' Gorgie's byre: *Glasgow & Strathclyde University OTC Pipe Band* / Cock o' the north: *Glasgow & Strathclyde University OTC Pipe Band* / Bonnie Dundee: *Glasgow & Strathclyde University* OTC Pipe Band / Lament for Alasdair Dearg MacDonnell: *MacNeill, Seamas* / Drum salute: *Dysart & Dundonald Pipe* Band / Green hills of Tyrol: *Grantown & District Pipe Band* / Battle's o'er, The: *Grantown & District Pipe Band*/ Highland brigade at Magersfontein, The: *Grantown & District Pipe Band* / Cullen bay: *Shotts & Dykehead Caledonia* Pipe Band / Rose among the heather: *Glasgow & Strathclyde University OTC Pipe Band* / Smith's a gallant fireman, The: *Glasgow & Strathclyde University OTC Pipe Band* / Circassian circle: *Glasgow & Strathclyde University OTC Pipe Band*/ Petronella: *Glasgow & Strathclyde University OTC Pipe Band* / Paddy whack: *Glasgow & Strathclyde University OTC Pipe* Band / Connaught man's rambles, The: *Glasgow & Strathclyde University OTC Pipe Band* / Archie McKinlay: *Shotts* & Dykehead Caledonia Pipe Band / Black isle, The: *Shotts & Dykehead Caledonia Pipe Band* / Banks of the Lossie: *Shotts &* Dykehead Caledonia Pipe Band / Battle of the Somme: *Shotts & Dykehead Caledonia Pipe Band* / Heights of Dargai, The: *Shotts & Dykehead Caledonia Pipe Band* / Lord is my shepherd, The: *Dysart & Dundonald Pipe Band* / By cool Siloam's shady rill: *Dysart & Dundonald Pipe Band* / Day has ended, The: *Dysart & Dundonald Pipe Band.*
LP: . . . . **LILP 5114**
MC: . . . . **LICS 5114**

DIAMOND JUBILEE PIPE BAND CHAMPIONSHIPS (Various artists).
MC: . . . . **ZCMON 809**

GRANTS PIPING CHAMPIONSHIP (Ceol mor - piobaireachda) (Various artists).
Tracks: / Battle of Auldearn (No. 1 setting): *Stoddart, Pipe Major* / MacKintosh of Borlum Salute: *Morrison, Pipe Major Iain* / MacDougall's gathering: *Livingstone, Pipe Major Bill* / Beloved Scotland: *MacCallum, Hugh A..*
LP: . . . . **LILP 5134**
MC: . . . . **LICS 5134**

GRANTS PIPING CHAMPIONSHIP VOL.2 (March strathspey and reel) (Various artists).
Tracks: / Marchioness of Tulliebardine: *Various artists* / Rejected suitor: *Various artists* / Major Manson at Clachantrushal: *Various artists* / Ewie wi' the crookit horn: *Various artists* / Bessie McIntyre: *Various* artists / Bonnie Anne: *Various artists* / Lady Loudon: *Various artists* / Lochiel's away: *Various artists*/ Rosshire volunteers: *Various artists* / Bogan lochan: *Various artists* / John Mackechnie's reel: *Various* artists / Kantara to el arish: *Various artists* / Inverary Castle: *Various artists* / Lachlan MacPhail of Tiree: *Various artists* / R.U.Brown's farewell to Ballochbuie: *Various artists* / MacBeth's Strathspey: *Various artists* / Willie Cumming's rant: *Various artists.*
LP: . . . . **LILP 5135**
MC: . . . . **LICS 5135**

GRANTS WHISKY PIPING CHAMPIONSHIPS VOLUME 1 (Various artists).
Tracks: / MacDougall's gathering: *Various artists* / Unjust incarceration: *Various artists* / Rory MacLeod's lament: *Various artists* / Lament for the Viscount of Dundee: *Various artists.*
LP: . . . . **LIDL 6001**

GRANTS WHISKY PIPING CHAMPIONSHIPS VOLUME 2 (Various artists).
LP: . . . . **LIDL 6002**

IMMIGRANTS (78th Fraser Highlanders Pipe Band).
MC: . . . . **LDDC 8013**

NORTHERN ISLAND WORLD CHAMPION PIPE BANDS (Various artists).
Tracks: / No awa tae bide awa: *Robert Armstrong Memorial Pipe Band* / Police tattoo 1976: *McNeillstown Pipe Band*/ Minnie Hynd: *McNeillstown Pipe Band* / Old tasty: *McNeillstown Pipe Band* / Rose among the heather: *McNeillstown* Pipe Band / High road to Linton: *McNeillstown Pipe Band* / Jock Wilson's ball: *McNeillstown Pipe Band* / Schiehallion: *McNeillstown Pipe Band* / 51st Highland division: *Robert Armstrong Memorial Pipe Band* / Rowan tree: *Robert* Armstrong Memorial Pipe Band / Meeting of waters: *Robert Armstrong Memorial Pipe Band* / Loch Rannoch: *Ballycoan* Pipe Band / Louden's bonnie woods: *Ballycoan Pipe Band* / Orange and blue: *Ballycoan Pipe Band* / Magersfontein: *Ballycoan Pipe Band* / Auld hoose, The: *McNeillstown Pipe Band* / Lee rig: *McNeillstown Pipe Band* / Lilliecrankie: *McNeillstown Pipe Band* / Cock o' the north: *Robert Armstrong Memorial Pipe Band* / Glendaurel Highlanders: *Robert* Armstrong Memorial Pipe Band / Bonawe Highlanders, The: *Robert Armstrong Memorial Pipe Band* / Green hills of Tyrol: *Ballycoan Pipe Band* / Battle's o'er, The: *Ballycoan Pipe Band* / City of Hastings: *McNeillstown Pipe Band*/ Waters of Kylesku: *McNeillstown Pipe Band* / London's bonnie woods & braes: *McNeillstown Pipe Band* / Orange and blue: *McNeillstown Pipe Band* / Castle Kennedy: *McNeillstown Pipe Band* / Archie McKinlay: *Ballycoan Pipe* Band / Black Isle: *Ballycoan Pipe Band* / Banks of the Lossie: *Ballycoan Pipe Band* / Flowers of the forest: *Robert Armstrong Memorial Pipe Band* / Within a mile of Edinburgh toon: *Ballycoan Pipe Band* / Black Watch polka: *Ballycoan Pipe Band* / Highland whiskey: *Ballycoan Pipe Band* / Shetland fiddler, The: *Ballycoan Pipe Band*/ Willie Roy's looming house: *Ballycoan Pipe Band* / Blackthorn stick: *Ballycoan Pipe Band* / Abide with me: *McNeillstown* Pipe Band / Jesus lover of my soul: *McNeillstown Pipe Band* / Work for the night is coming: *McNeillstown Pipe Band.*
MC: . . . . **CHRL 215**

PIPERS CALL (Various artists).
LP: . . . . **MFP 50480**
MC: . . . . **TCMFP 50480**

PIPES & DRUMS OF SCOTLAND (Various artists).
Tracks: / Flower of Scotland: *Various artists* / Scotland the brave: *Various artists* / Westering home: *Various* artists / Road to the isles: *Various artists* / Green hills of Tyrol: *Various artists* / Black bear, The: *Various artists* / Spinning wheel: *Various artists* / Ae fond kiss: *Various artists* / Rowan tree: *Various* artists / Rustic brig: *Various artists* / Crooked bawbee: *Various artists* / Lovely Stornoway: *Various artists.*
LP: . . . . **LOCLP 1031**
MC: . . . . **ZCLOC 1031**

PIPES & STRINGS OF SCOTLAND.VOL.2. (Various artists).
MC: . . . . **KITV 394**

SOUND OF THE PIPES (Various artists).
MC: . . . . **TCMFP 5615**

WORLD PIPE BAND CHAMPIONSHIPS (1990) (Various artists).
MC: . . . . **ZCMD 2810**

WORLD PIPE BAND CHAMPIONSHIPS 1987 (Various artists).
Tracks: / Selection: *78th Fraser Highlanders* / March strathspey and reel: *78th Fraser Highlanders* / Selection: *Scotrail Vale Of Atholl Pipe Band* / Selection: *Strathclyde Police Pipe Band* / March strathspey and reel: *Toronto & District Caledonian* / Selection: *Montgomery, Field Marshall Ban* / Selection: *Fraser, Simon University Pipe* Band / March strathspey and reel: *Royal Ulster Constabulary* / Selection: *Boghall & Bathgate Caledonia* / March strathspey and reel: *Strathclyde Police Pipe Band* / Selection: *City Of Victoria* / March strathspey and reel: *Babcock Renfrew* / March strathspey and reel: *Boghall & Bathgate Caledonia.*
2LP: . . . . **LDDL 8002**
MCSET: . . . . **LCDM 8002**

WORLD PIPE BAND CHAMPIONSHIPS (1989) (Various artists).
Tracks: / March strathspey and reel: *Strathclyde Police Pipe Band* / Selection: *Strathclyde Police Pipe Band*/ Selection: *Scotrail Vale Of Atholl Pipe Band* / March strathspey and reel: *Scotrail Vale Of Atholl Pipe Band*/ Selection: *78th Fraser Highlanders* / March strathspey and reel: *78th Fraser Highlanders* / Selection: *Lothian* & Borders Police Band / March strathspey and reel: *Power Of Scotland Pipe Band* / Selection: *Power Of Scotland* Pipe Band / March strathspey and reel: *Shotts & Dykehead Caledonia Pipe Band* / Selection: *Shotts & Dykehead Caledonia* Pipe Band / March strathspey and reel: *Lothian & Borders Police Band* / March strathspey and reel: *Fraser, Simon University Pipe Band* / Selection: *Toronto & District Caledonian* / March strathspey and reel: *Royal Ulster Constabulary.*
LP: . . . . **LDDL 8009**

WORLD PIPE BAND CHAMPIONSHIPS 1980 (Various artists).
LP: . . . . **REC 401**
MC: . . . . **ZCM 401**

WORLD PIPE BAND CHAMPIONSHIPS 1983 (Various artists).
LP: . . . . **REC 490**
MC: . . . . **ZCM 490**

WORLD PIPE BAND CHAMPIONSHIPS (1988) (Various artists).
Tracks: / Young MacGregor, The: *Strathclyde Police Pipe Band* / Barry Ewing: *Strathclyde Police Pipe Band* / Links of forth: *Scotrail Vale Of Atholl Pipe Band* / Ragtime pipers: *Toronto & District Caledonian* / Shepherd's crook, The: *Royal Scots Dragoon Guards* / Copperhill: *78th Fraser Highlanders Pipe Band* / Argyllshire gathering, The: *78th Fraser Highlanders Pipe Band* / Helen Black of Inveran: *Scotrail Vale Of Atholl Pipe Band* / Clan MacRae, The: *Pipes & Drums Of British* / Lord Alexander Kennedy: *Royal Ulster Constabulary* / Murdoch MacAllister: *Fraser,* Simon University Pipe Band / Lord Alexander Kennedy: *Fraser, Simon University Pipe Band* / Noel Slagle: *Shotts* & Dykehead Caledonia Pipe Band / Highland wedding, The: *Memorial, Graham Pipe Band* / 24th gds br'de at Anzio, The: *Pipes & Drums Of British* / Lord Alexander Kennedy: *Boghall & Bathgate Caledonia* / Arfon stag, The: *Boghall &* Bathgate Caledonia / Donald Cameron: *Shotts & Dykehead Caledonia Pipe Band* / Rathven Market: *Memorial, Graham Pipe Band* / Highland wedding, The: *Montgomery, Field Marshall Ban.*
2LP: . . . . **LDDL 8007**
MCSET: . . . . **LDDC 8007**

WORLD PIPE BAND CHAMPIONSHIPS (1986) (Various artists).
LP: . . . . **LILP 5149**
MC: . . . . **LICS 5149**

Pipe Music

WORLD'S GREATEST PIPERS VOL. 1 (MacDonald,Pipe Major Angus).
Tracks: / Lord MacPherson of Drumochter / Major John MacLennan / Susan MacLeod / Mrs MacPherson of Inveran / Bobs of Balmoral / I laid a herring in saut / Fair maid of Barra, The / Pinney's of Scotland / Caledonian Society of London, The / Cameron highlanders, The / Banks of Allan water / Highland brigade at Magersfontein, The / Road to Sham Shui Poh, The / Jim Tweedie's sea legs / High level, The / Flowers of the forest,The / 93rd, of Modder river, The / Braes of Castle Grant, The / Wiseman's exercise / Fiddler's joy, The / Smith's a gallant fireman, The / Laird of Drumblair, The / Brolum / Kalabakan / Tam bain's lum / Willie's brogues / Liverpool hornpipe / Kesh jig / Rocking the baby / Give me a drink of water / Conundrum, The / P/M Willie Gray's farewell to the Glasgow Police / Lament for the children.
LP: . . . . **LILP 5143**
MC: . . . . **LICS 5143**

WORLD'S GREATEST PIPERS VOL. 2 (MacCallum, Hugh A.).
Tracks: / MacNeils of Ugadale / Sweet maid of Mull, The / Arniston castle / Caberfeidh / Grey bob, The / Willie Murray / Iain Rhuadh's lament / Donald, Hugh and his dog / Ross-shire volunteers, The / John MacFadyen of Melfort / Joe McGann's fiddle / P/M George Allan / Clan MacColl, The / Tulloch castle / Major D. Manson / Mhairi van og (Fair young Mary) / Battle of the Somme / Archie McKinlay / Miss Ada Crawford / Captain Home / Duke of Gordon's birthday, The / Sleepy Maggie / Dancing feet / Tail toddle / Allan MacPherson of Mosspark / Herring wife / Lament for Mary MacLeod.
LP: . . . . **LILP 5147**
MC: . . . . **LICS 5147**

WORLD'S GREATEST PIPERS VOL. 3 (Stoddart, Pipe Major GNM).
Tracks: / Colin Thompson / Crags of Stirling, The / Man from Skye, The / Brae riach / Turf lodge / Lady Loudon / Maggie Cameron / Smith of Chilliechassie, The / Grey bob, The / MacLeod of Mull / Jean Mauchline / Ladies of the Alamo, The / Donald MacLennan's tuning phrase / Arniston castle / Caberfeidh / Caledonian Society of London, The / Mrs MacPherson of Inveran / Anon / Highland wedding, The / Blair Drummond / Sheepwife, The / Abercairney highlanders / Braes of Brecklet, The / Bonnie Anne / Ronald MacDonald of Morar's lament.
LP: . . . . **LILP 5151**
MC: . . . . **LICS 5151**

WORLD'S GREATEST PIPERS VOL. 4 (Henderson, Murray).
LP: . . . . **LILP 5159**
MC: . . . . **LICS 5159**

WORLD'S GREATEST PIPERS VOL. 5 (Wilson, John).
Tracks: / 6/8 marches / Gaelic air and 2/4 marches / Hornpipe and jigs / Strathspeys and reels / Slow air strathspeys and reels / Lowland air and 2 irish reels / March strathspey and reel / Gaelic airs and jigs / Glengarry's march / 9/8 marches / Hornpipes and jigs.
LP: . . . . **LILP 5170**
MC: . . . . **LICS 5170**

WORLD'S GREATEST PIPERS VOL. 6 (MacLeod, Roderick J).
Tracks: / 6/8 Marches / Strathspeys and reels / Gaelic air and jigs / 2/4 marches / Hornpipes / March strathspey and reel / Jigs / 9/8 marches / Strathspeys and reels (2) / Slow air and reels / Piobaireachd.
LP: . . . . **LILP 5177**
MC: . . . . **LICS 5177**

WORLD'S GREATEST PIPERS VOL. 7 (MacFadyen, Iain).
Tracks: / March, strathspey and reel / 6/8 marches / Gaelic air and hornpipes / Jigs / 9/8 marches / Piobaireachd / 6/8 march and jig / 2/4 marches / Gaelic air and hornpipes / 6/8 marches (2) / Strathspeys and reels / Piobaireachd (2).
LP: . . . . **LILP 5180**
MC: . . . . **LICS 5180**

WORLD'S GREATEST PIPERS VOL. 8 (McDougall, John).
Tracks: / 2/4 marches / Strathspeys and reels / Slow air and jigs / 6/8 marches / Strathspeys and reels (2) / Lady Margaret MacDonald's salute / 2/4 marches (2) / Hornpipe / Slow air and march / Strathspeys and reels (3) / 6/8 marches (2) / Battle of the Pass of Crieff.
LP: . . . . **LILP 5189**
MC: . . . . **LICS 5189**

Piper Alpha Benefit

PIPER ALPHA BENEFIT (Various artists).
2LP: . . . . **BGE LP 1008**
MC: . . . . **BGE C 1008**

Piper, Wardell

WARDELL PIPER.
Tracks: / Super sweet / Win your love / Captain boogie / Don't turn away from me baby / If you want to make love to me.
LP: **2310664**

Pips

AT LAST...THE PIPS.
LP: . . . . **CAL 2022**

CALLIN'.
LP: . . . . **CAL 2031**

Piranhas

PIRANHAS.
Tracks: / Getting beaten up / Pleasure / Do you? / Saxophone / Love game / Tom Hark / Tension / Fiddling while Babylon burns / Green don't suit me / Something / Coffee / I don't want my body / Final straw.
LP: . . . . **SRK 6098**

Pirate (Film)

PIRATE, THE/PAGAN LOVE SONG (Film Soundtrack) (Various artists).
LP: . . . . **MCA 39080**
MC: . . . . **MCAC 39080**

Pirate Movie

PIRATE MOVIE (Various artists).
LP: . . . . **POLD 5074**
MC: . . . . **POLDC 5074**

Pirates

FISTFUL OF DUBLOONS, A.
Tracks: / Linda Lu / Honey hush / Put your cat clothes on / Sweet love on my mind / Lonesome train / Milk cow blues / Casting my spell / Tricky Dicky / Tear it up / Kaw-Liga.
LP: . . . . **ED 102**

HAPPY BIRTHDAY ROCK'N'ROLL.
Tracks: / Happy birthday rock'n'roll / You can't sit down / Hey Mary / Golden oldies / Alarmer / Lady put the light on me / Going back home / Lemonade / Hard ride / 1.30, 2.30.
LP: . . . . **HIFLY 33**

OUT OF THEIR SKULLS.
Tracks: / Please don't touch / I can tell / Peter Gunn / Lonesome train / Shakin' all over / Milk cow blues / Drinkin' wine spo-dee-o-dee / Do the dog / Gibson Martin Fender / Don't munchen it / That's the way you are / You don't own me.
LP: . . . . **K 56411**

SKULL WARS.
Tracks: / Long journey home / Doctor Feelgood / All in it together / Johnny B.Goode's good / Johnny B.Goode (live) / Talking about you (live) / I'm in love again (live) / Voodoo / Four to the bar / Honey hush (live) / Diggin' my potatoes / Shake hands with the devil.
LP: . . . . **K 56468**
MC: **K4 56468**

STILL SHAKIN'.
Tracks: / Ain't got no money / Going back home / Money honey / I can't tell / Honey hush / All by myself / Milk cow blues / Lonesome train / Shakin' all over / Don't munchen it / Lights out / Let it rock.
LP: . . . . **THBL 063**

Pirates (Film)

PIRATES (Film soundtrack) (Various artists).
Tracks: / Pirates: *Various artists* / Sauves mais captifs: *Various artists* / Linares se meurt: *Various artists*/ Mutinerie a bord: *Various artists* / C'ptain red maitre du galion: *Various artists* / Red, la grenouille et le requin: *Various artists* / Dolores (theme d,amour'): *Various artists* / Don alfonso s'evade: *Various artists*/ Red, la grenouille, le tronde, boomako et le b: *Various artists* / C'ptain red's empare du tresor tendis que la g: *Various artists* / Red et la grenouille voguent vers de nouvelles: *Various artists.*
LP: . . . . **A 233**
MC: . . . . **C 233**

Pirates of Penzance

PIRATES OF PENZANCE (Original Broadway cast) (Various artists).
Tracks: / Poor, o pour the pirate sherry: *Various artists* / When Frederic was a little lad: *Various artists*/ Oh better far to live and die: *Various artists* / Oh false one you have deceived me: *Various artists* / Climbing over rocky mountain: *Various artists* / Stop ladies pray: *Various artists* / Oh is there not one maiden breast: *Various artists* / Poor wandering one: *Various artists* / What ought we to do: *Various artists* / How beautiful blue the sky: *Various artists* / Stay, we must not lose our senses: *Various artists* / Hold monsters: *Various artists* / I am the very model of a modern Major General: *Various artists* / Oh men of dark and dismal fate: *Various artists* / Oh dry the glistening tear: *Various artists* / Then Frederic: *Various artists*/ When the foreman bares his steel: *Various artists* / Now for the pirates lair: *Various artists* / When you had left our pirate fold: *Various artists* / My eyes are fully open: *Various artists* / Away away: *Various artists*/ My heart's on fire: *Various artists*/ All is prepared: *Various artists* / Stay: *Various artists* / Frederic stay: *Various artists* / Sorry her lot: *Various artists* / No I am brave: *Various artists* / When a felon's not engaged in his employment: *Various artists* / Rollicking band of pirates we, A: *Various artists*/ With cat like treat upon our prey we steal: *Various artists* / Hush hush not a word: *Various artists* / Sighing softly to the river: *Various artists* / Pirates of Penzance (finale): *Various artists.*
2LP: . . . . **K 62035**

PIRATES OF PENZANCE, THE (see under Gilbert & Sullivan).

Pirchner, Werner

EU.
Tracks: / Sonate vom rauhen leben / Streichquartett fur blaserquintett / Good news from the Ziller family / Kammer-symphonie 'Soiree Tyrolienne' / Do you know Emperor Joe / Two war & peace choirs / Kleine mes um 'c' fur den lieben gott / Solo sonata for bass-vibes.
LP: . . . . **ECM 1314**

Piron, A.J.

A.J. PIRONS NEW ORLEANS ORCHESTRA (Piron,A.J.'s New Orleans orchestra).
LP: . . . . **FJ 128**

Pirozzoli, Tom

EYES AND FOOTPRINTS.
LP: . . . . **MENULP 3**

Pisces

PISCES.
LP: . . . . **LER 2025**

Pistol For Two/Hazard

PISTOL FOR TWO/HAZARD (See Heyer, Georgette) (Cazenove, Christopher).

Pitch Shifter

INDUSTRIAL.
LP: . . . . **DEAF 5**
MC: . . . . **DEAF 5MC**

Pitney, Gene

16 EVERGREENS.
LP: . . . . **SM 3958**

20 GOLDEN PIECES: GENE PITNEY.
Tracks: / Misty / More / My prayer / Only you / Smoke gets in your eyes / Great pretender, The / Twilight time / Crying / Town without pity / Every breath I take / She's a heartbreaker / If I didn't have a dime / Louisiana man / You've lost that lovin' feeling / Autumn leaves / Man who shot Liberty Valance, The / 24 hours from Tulsa / Half heaven half heartache / I'll be seeing you / I can't stop loving you.
LP: . . . . **BDL 2028**
MC: . . . . **AJKL 2028**

20 GREATEST HITS: GENE PITNEY (Original Recordings).
LP: . . . . **PLAT 3904**
MC: . . . . **PLAC 3904**

20 GREATEST HITS: GENE PITNEY.
LP: . . . . **MA 1129683**
LP: **5C 052 97853**

24 HOURS FROM TULSA.
Tracks: / 24 hours from Tulsa / Mecca / Every breath I take / I'm gonna be strong / Town without pity / (I wanna) love my life away / Only love can break a heart / Man who shot Liberty Valance, The / It hurts to be in love / Looking through the eyes of love / Something's gotten hold of my heart / Backstage.
LP: . . . . **TOP 141**
MC: . . . . **KTOP 141**

ANTHOLOGY - GENE PITNEY 1961-1968.
2LP: . . . . **RNDA 1102**

BACKSTAGE (The Greatest Hits and More).
Tracks: / Something's gotten hold of my heart / 24 hours from Tulsa / That girl belongs to yesterday / I'm gonna be strong / I must be seeing things / Looking thru the eyes of love / Princess in rags / Nobody needs your love / Just one smile / In my life / Only one woman / First cut is the deepest / We've got tonight / Let the heartaches begin / There is no distance / Fool if you think it's over / All by myself / Town without pity (Only on CD and cassette.) / Somethings gotten hold of my heart (original) (Only on CD and cassette).
LP: **847 119 1**
MC: **847 119 4**

BEST OF GENE PITNEY.
Tracks: / Looking through the eyes of love / Only love can break a heart / 24 hours from Tulsa / It hurts to be in love / It's gonna be strong / She's a heartbreaker / Town without pity / Man who shot Liberty Valance, The / Twenty four hours from Tulsa.
MC: **16-8**
LP: **1A 022 58076**
LP: . . . . **SSL 10286**

BLUE GENE.
LP: . . . . **ULP 1061**

COLLECTION: GENE PITNEY.
MC: . . . . **CCSMC 239**

EP COLLECTION: GENE PITNEY.
LP: . . . . **SEE 313**
MC: . . . . **SEEK 313**

GENE PITNEY.
Tracks: / Twenty four hours from Tulsa / Looking through the eyes of love / Backstage / That girl belongs to yesterday / Town without pity / Something's gotten hold of my heart / I'm gonna be strong / I must be seeing things / Love my life away / Princess in rags / Nobody needs your love / Just one smile.
LP: . . . . **COUNT 1**
MC: . . . . **ZC CNT 1**

GENE PITNEY.
MC: . . . . **ZCGAS 719**

GENE PITNEY COLLECTION.
Tracks: / Twenty four hours from Tulsa / It hurts to be in love / Half heaven half heartache / Billy you're my friend / True love never runs smooth / Not responsible / Yesterday's hero / Tower tall / Every breath I take / Street called hope, A / Teardrop by teardrop / Only love can break a heart.
MCSET: . . . . **DTO 10007**

GENE PITNEY COLLECTION, THE.
2LP: . . . . **PDA 004**
MCSET: . . . . **PDC 004**

GENE PITNEY COLLECTION VOL.2.
2LP: . . . . **PDA 034**
MCSET: . . . . **PDC 034**

GENE PITNEY'S BIG SIXTEEN.
LP: . . . . **SL 10118**
LP: . . . . **SSL 10199**

GREATEST HITS: GENE PITNEY.
LP: **2636271**
MC: **2636274**

GREATEST HITS: GENE PITNEY.
Tracks: / Something's gotten hold of my heart / 24 Sycamore / 24 hours from Tulsa / Looking through the eyes of love / I must be seeing things / Just one smile / It hurts to be in love / Man who shot Liberty Valance, The / Street called hope, A / Only love can break a heart / (In the) cold light of day / Somewhere in the country / Backstage / I'm gonna be strong / She's a heartbreaker / I wanna love my life away / Nobody needs your love / Maria Elena / Yours until tomorrow / Last chance to turn around / Town without pity / Princess in rags / Half heaven half heartache / That girl belongs to yesterday.
MC: . . . . **HSC 3261**
LP: . . . . **SHM 3261**
2LP: . . . . **ADEP 22**

GREATEST HITS OF ALL TIME.
Tracks: / Town without pity / Man who shot Liberty Valance, The / Only love can break a heart / Every breath I take / Looking through the eyes of love / Twenty four hours from Tulsa / It hurts to be in love / Backstage / Half heaven half heartache / I'm gonna be strong.
LP: . . . . **PHX 1017**

HALF HEAVEN-HALF HEARTACHE.
Tracks: / Princess in rags / 24 hours from Tulsa / It hurts to be in love / I'm gonna be strong / Somewhere in the country / That girl belongs to yesterday / Half heaven half heartache / Backstage / I must be seeing things / Nobody needs your love / 24 Sycamore / Maria Elena / Love my life away / Louisiana mama / Man who shot Liberty Valance, The / Town without pity / Mecca / Street called hope, A / Every breath I take / Only love can break a heart / Something's gotten hold of my heart / Just one smile / I didn't have a dime / Looking through the eyes of love / She lets her hair down / Billy you're my friend.
2LP: . . . . **CR 041**
MCSET: . . . . **CRT 041**

HITS OF GENE PITNEY, THE.
LP: . . . . **SPR 8566**
MC: . . . . **SPC 8566**

I'M GONNA BE STRONG.
LP: . . . . **SL 10120**

LOOKIN' THRU THE EYES OF LOVE.
LP: . . . . **SL 10148**

LOVE MY LIFE AWAY.
MC: . . . . **ORC 004**

NOBODY NEEDS YOUR LOVE.
LP: . . . . **SL 10183**

PROFILE: GENE PITNEY.
LP: **6.24472**
MC: **CL4 624472**

SOMETHING'S GOTTEN HOLD OF MY HEART.
Tracks: / Green green grass of home / If I only had time / Groovy kind of love / Stop in the name of love.
MCSET: . . . . **DTO 10055**

SOMETHING'S GOTTEN HOLD OF MY HEART (see under Almond, Marc).

VERY BEST OF GENE PITNEY, THE.
Tracks: / Town without pity / Mecca / 24 hours from Tulsa / Backstage / Just one smile / Yours until tomorrow / (I wanna) love my life away / If I didn't have a dime / (The man who shot) Liberty Valance / It hurts to be in love / I'm gonna be strong / That girl belongs to yesterday / Something's gotten hold of my heart / Looking thru' the eyes of love / I must be seeing things / Nobody needs your love (like I do).
LP: . . . . **ACT 004**
MC: . . . . **ACTC 004**

WALKIN' IN THE SUN.
Tracks: / It's over it's over / Walkin' in the sun / We wrote the show / Dedication / Love on our hands / Sandman / Something's gotten hold of my heart / Town without pity / I'm gonna be strong / Twenty four hours from Tulsa / Looking through the eyes of love / I must be seeing things / That girl belongs to yesterday / Only love can break a heart / Backstage / Just one smile.
LP: **4651041**
MC: **4651044**

YOUNG WARM AND WONDERFUL.
LP: . . . . **SSL 10194**

Pitre, Austin

BACK TO THE BAYOU.
LP: . . . . **SNTF 815**

EVANGELINE PLAYBOYS.
LP: **6041**

SWALLOW RECORDINGS, THE (See Under D.L. Menard) (Pitre, Austin & D.L. Menard).

Pittman, Barbara

I NEED A MAN.
Tracks: / I need a man / No matter who's to blame / I'm getting better all the time / Two young fools in love / Everlasting love / Cold cold heart / Handsome man / Eleventh commandment, The / Just one day / Sentimental fool / Voice of a fool / I'm getting better all the time (2) / Sentimental fool (2) / Love is a stranger / Take my sympathy / I'm getting better all the time / I forgot to remember to forget / Sentimental fool (3) / I'll never let you go.
LP: . . . . **BFX 15359**

TEXAS BOOGIE.
Tracks: / Diggin' the boogie / You're undecided / Everlasting love / I'm getting better all the time / Money honey / Right behind you baby / Honey hush / Trying to get to you / Big boss man / I need a man / Long tall Sally / Rockin' daddy.
LP: . . . . **MFLP 050**

Pitts, Zasu

PITTS BEAR DOWN, THE: RECORDED LIVE (Pitts, Zasu Memorial Orchestra).
LP: . . . . **F 23**
MC: . . . . **C 23**

Pixies

BOSSANOVA.
Tracks: / Cecilia Ann / Velouria / Is she weird / All over the world / Down to the well / Blown away / Stormy weather /

Rock music / Allison / Ana / Dig for fire / Happening, The / Hang wire / Havalina.
LP: CAD 0010
MC: CADC 0010

COME ON PILGRIM.
MLP: MAD 709

DOOLITTLE.
Tracks: / Debaser / Wave of mutilation / Dead / Mr. Grieves / La la I love you / There goes my gun / Silver / Tame / Here comes your man / Monkey gone to heaven / Crackity Jones / Number 13 baby / Hey / Gouge away.
LP: CAD 905
MC: CADC 905

PIXIES: INTERVIEW PICTURE DISC.
LPPD: BAK 2151

SURFER ROSA.
Tracks: / Bone machine / Something against you / Gigantic / Where is my mind / Tony's theme / Vamos / Brick is red / Break my body / Broken face / River Euphrates / Cactus / Oh my golly / I'm amazed.
LP: CAD 803
MC: CADC 803

TROMPE LE MONDE.
LP: CAD 1014
MC: CADC 1014

Pizarro, David

PLAYS ORGAN OF ST. PETERS CATHEDRAL CHURCH, BRADFORD.
LP: GRS 1017

Pizzarelli, Bucky

2 X 7 = PIZZARELLI.
LP: ST 207

BUCKY PLAYS BIX.
LP: MES 7066

BUCKY'S BUNCH.
LP: MES 7082

CAFE PIERRE TRIO, THE.
LP: MES 7093

DOUG AND BUCKY (see under Jernigan, Doug) (Pizzarelli, Bucky & Doug Jernigan).

GREEN GUITAR BLUES.
LP: MES 7047

LOVE SONGS: BUCKY PIZZARELLI.
LP: ST 213

SOLO FLIGHT - UNACCOMPANIED GUITAR.
LP: ST 263

SWINGING SEVENS (Pizzarelli,Bucky & John).
LP: ST 239

Pizzarelli, John

HIT THAT JIVE, JACK (Pizzarelli, John Jr).
LP: ST 256

I'M HIP (Pizzarelli, John & Bucky Pizzarelli Trio).
LP: ST 226

SING SING SING.
LP: ST 267

Pizzi, Ray

ESPRESSIVO.
Tracks: / In a sentimental mood / 'Round about midnight / Spinnes / Ode to a toad / In and out / Killer Kowalski / Ballad for jazz bassoon / Espressivo.
LP: DS 853

LOVE LETTER, THE.
Tracks: / Buzzard's bay / Aicia / My funny Valentine.
LP: DS 801

Placebo

ENGLAND'S TRANCE.
LP: AUL 721

Places In The Heart

PLACES IN THE HEART (Film Soundtrack) (Various artists).
LP: A 269
LP: STV 81229
MC: CTV 81229

Plague

NARAKA.
LP: PL 001

Plague Dogs

PLAGUE DOGS (Film Soundtrack) (Various artists).
LP: CBS 70227

Plaickner, Konrad

BAL CHAMPETRE TYROLIEN (Plaickner, Konrad & Burggrafler).
Tracks: / Festtag in Tirol / Meran 2000 / Haflinger / Heute lustig / Auslese '75 / Abschied / Lieseiotte / Auf'n tanzbod'n / Landler / Wiesen polka / Hochzeit / Die lustige harmonika / Zum kuchuck / Petersberger jodler.
LP: ARN 33363
MC: ARN 433363

CONCERT CHAMPETRE TYROLIEN (Plaickner, Konrad & Burggrafler).
Tracks: / Mein heimatland / Junges sudtirol / Der grosse tag / Hoch axams / Konig ortler / Mein schones sudtirol / Festiche fanfarenklange / Sepp thaler marsch / Blasermusik / Platzkonzert in meran / Tisner marsch / Hymne der blasmusik.
LP: ARN 33685
MC: ARN 433685

Plaidy, Jean (aut)

SIXTH WIFE, THE (Read by Marie Palmer).
MC: SOUND 29

Plain Characters

INVISIBLE YEARNINGS.
LP: ABT 001

Plain Sailing

DANGEROUS TIMES.
LP: CHR 1282

Plains Indians

POW WOW SONGS.
Tracks: / Slow war dance songs / Contest songs for straight dancers / Contest songs for fancy dancers / Round dance / Sioux flag song / War dance song / Slow war dance, Vietnam song / War dance song / Grass dance song.
LP: NW 343

Plainsong

IN SEARCH OF AMELIA EARHART.
Tracks: / For the second time / Yo yo man / Louise / Call the tune / Diesel on my tail / Amelia Earhart's last flight / I'll fly away / True story of Amelia Earhart / Even the guiding light / Side roads / Raider.
LP: K 42120

Plan 9

ANYTIME, ANYPLACE, ANYWHERE.
LP: ENIGMA 21821

FRUSTRATION.
LP: VOXX 200007

HAM AND SAM JAMMIN'.
LP: LS 94471

KEEP YOUR COOL.
LP: 2034 1

SEA HUNT.
LP: 3248 1

TRY TO RUN.
LP: ROSE 41

Planes, Trains & ...

PLANES, TRAINS AND AUTOMOBILES (Film soundtrack) (Various artists).
Tracks: / I can take anything: *E.T.A* / Ba-na-na-bam-boo: *Westworld* / I'll show you something special: *Balaam* & The Angel / Modigliani (lost in your eyes): *Book Of Love* / Power to believe: *Dream Academy* / Six days on the road: *Steve Earle & the Dukes* / Gonna move: *Edmunds, Dave* / Back in baby's arms: *Harris, Emmylou*/ Red river rock: *Silicon Teens* / Wheels: *Stars Of Heaven.*
LP: IMCA 6223
MC: IMCAC 6223

Planet Earth

PLANET EARTH.
LP: NSPL 18556

Planet Of The Apes

PLANET OF THE APES (Film Soundtrack) (Various artists).
LP: PR 5023
MC: PRC 5023

Planet of the Elves

PLANET OF THE ELVES, THE (Unknown artist(s)).
MC: PLB 145

Planet Of The Hoojibs

PLANET OF THE HOOJIBS (Various artists).
LP: D 454
MC: D 154 DC

Planet P Project

PINK PROJECT.
2LP: MCSP 311
MCSET: MCSPC 311

PLANET P PROJECT.
Tracks: / Static / King for a day / I won't wake up / Top of the world / Armageddon / Why me? / Power tools / Send it in a letter / Adam and Eve / Only you and me.
LP: 9040001
MC: 9040004
LP: GEF 25367

Planet Pacific...

PLANET PACIFIC, PACIFIC PLANET (Various artists).
LP: LP 1

Planet Patrol

PLANET PATROL.
Tracks: / Cheap thrills / Danger zone / I didn't know I loved you till I saw you rock'n'roll / Play at your own risk / It wouldn't have made a bit of difference / Don't tell me.
LP: POLD5106

Planet Wilson

IN THE BEST OF ALL POSSIBLE WORLDS.
Tracks: / Flap the bird / Big wheel / Rolling balls / Distraction / Sinister Dexter / Seven days / Love by hand / Wish it was so / White lies / Vision on (CD only) / I remain outside (CD only).
LP: V 2508
MC: TCV 2508

NOT DROWNING BUT WAVING.
Tracks: / Truth hurts / Taken for a ride / I remain outside / Golden touch / Honeymoon / Fly by night / How do I feel? / Mouth to mouth / Night swimming.
LP: PLAN 003

Planets

GOONHILLY DOWN.
Tracks: / Iron for the iron / Mile high / Minute ago / Lines / Break it to me gently / Too late / Secret / Ball and chain / I'm on fire.
LP: TENOR 102
MC: ZCTEN 102

SPOT.
Tracks: / I can't stop / Let me fall / Intensive care / You gave your love / Want to touch you / Don't look down / Earth / Follow the leader / Forgone conclusion / C.R.A.Z.Y..
LP: ALTO 102
MC: ZCALT 102

Plant, Richard

BETTER BE SANE.
LP: TSR 022

Plant, Robert

24K (see under Band of Joy) (Band Of Joy).

MANIC NIRVANA.
Tracks: / Hurting kind (I've got my eyes on you) / S S S and Q / Nirvana / Your ma said you cried in your sleep / Liars dance / Big love / I cried / Tie dye on the highway / Anniversary / Watching you.
LP: WX 229
MC: WX 339C

NOW AND ZEN.
Tracks: / Heaven knows / Dance on my own / Tall cool one / Way I feel, the / Helen of Troy / Billy's revenge / Ship of fools / Why / White, clean and neat.
LP: WX 149
MC: WX 149C

PICTURES AT ELEVEN.
Tracks: / Burning down one side / Moonlight in Samosa / Pledge pin / Slow dancer / Worse than Detroit / Fat lip / Like I've never been gone / Mystery title.
LP: SSK 59418
MC: SK4 59418

PRINCIPAL OF MOMENTS.
Tracks: / Other arms / In the mood / Messin' with the Mekon / Wreckless love / Through with the two step / Horizontal departure / Big log / Stranger here than over there.
LP: 790101 1
MC: 790101 4

ROBERT PLANT: INTERVIEW PICTURE DISC.
LPPD: BAK 2097

SHAKEN 'N' STIRRED.
Tracks: / Hip to hoo / Kallalou / Too loud / Trouble your money / Pink and black / Little by little / Doo doo a do do / Easily lead / Sixes and sevens.
LP: 790265 1
MC: 790265 4

Planxty

AFTER THE BREAK.
LP: TA 3001
MC: 4TA 3001

ARIS.
Tracks: / Slip jig / Kid on the mountain, The / After McBride / Reels / Old torn raincoat, The / Wind that shakes the barley, The / Yarmouth town / Johnny Cope / Only our rivers / Dogs among the bushes, The / Jenny's wedding / Cliffs of Dooneen / Si eheag si mhor / Fisherman's lilt / Cronin's hornpipe / Well below the valley, The.
LP: 815 229-1
MC: 815 229-4

COLD BLOW AND THE RAINY NIGHT.
LP: SHAN 79011
LP: 2383 301
MC: SH 79011 C

COLLECTION: PLANXTY.
LP: SHAN 79012
LP: 2382 397

PLANXTY.
LP: SHAN 79009
LP: 2383 186

WELL BELOW THE VALLEY, THE.
LP: SHAN 79010
LP: 2382 232
MC: SH 79010 C

WOMAN I LOVED SO WELL, THE.
LP: TA 3005
MC: 4TA 3005

WORDS AND MUSIC.
Tracks: / Queen of the rushes / Paddy Fahy's jig / Thousands are sailing / Taimse I'm Chodladh / Lord Baker / Accidentals / Aragon mill / Aconry lasses, The / Old wheels of the world, The / Spike island lasses, The / I pity the poor immigrant / Irish marche, The.
LP: K 0101
MC: K 0101 4
LP: SHAN 79035
LP: 240 101 1

Plasmatics

COUP D'ETAT.
Tracks: / Put your love in me / Stop / Rock'n'roll / Lightning breaks / No class / Mistress of taboo / Country fairs / Path of glory / Just like on TV / Damned.
LP: REV LP 78
MC: REV MC 78
LP: EST 12237

MAGGOTS (see O'Williams, Wendy) (Plasmatics/Wendy O'Williams).

NEW HOPE FOR THE WRETCHED.
Tracks: / Tight black pants / Monkey suit / Living dead / Test tube babies / Won't you / Concrete shoes / Squirm (live) / Want you baby / Dream lover / Sometimes / Corruption / Butcher baby.
LP: SEEZ 24

VALLEY OF 84 + METAL PRIESTESS.
LP: PVC 8929
MC: PVCC 8929

Plastic Dolls

BLINDFOLDED.
LP: TV 5679

MORNING LASTS FOREVER, THE.
LP: TV 5680

WHERE IS THE WORLD.
LP: COL 269501

Plastic Ono Band

LIVE PEACE IN TORONTO.
Tracks: / Blue suede shoes / Money (that's what I want) / Dizzy Miss Lizzy / Yer blues / Cold turkey / Give peace a chance / Don't worry Kyoko / John John let's hope for peace.
LP: CORE 2001

SOMETIME IN NEW YORK CITY (John & Yoko With The Plastic Ono Band).
Tracks: / Sisters, O sisters / Attica state / Born in a prison / New York City / Sunday bloody Sunday / Luck of the Irish, The / John Sinclair / Angela / We're all water / Cold turkey / Don't worry Kyoko (With Frank Zappa and The Mothers of Invention.) / Well (baby please don't go) (With Frank Zappa and The Mothers of Invention.) / Jamrag (With Frank Zappa and The Mothers of Invention.) / Scumbag (With Frank Zappa and The Mothers of Invention.) / Au (With Frank Zappa and The Mothers of Invention.) / Woman is the nigger of the world.
2LP: PCSP 716

Plasticland

PLASTICLAND.
LP: KIRI 034

SALON.
LP: ENIG 21791
LP: 72179 1

Plastics

WELCOME BACK.
LP: ILPS 9627

Plater, Alan (aut)

BEIDERBECKE AFFAIR, THE (Bolam, James (nar)).
MCSET: LFP 7385

BEIDERBECKE TAPES, THE (See under Beiderbecke Tapes) (Bolam, James (nar)).

Plath, Sylvia

READING HER POETRY.
LP: TC 1544
MC: CDL 51544

Platinum Album

PLATINUM ALBUM (Various artists).
LP: NE 1134
MC: CE 2134

Platinum Blonde

ALIEN SHORES.
Tracks: / Situation critical / Crying over you / Red light / It ain't love anyway / Somebody, somewhere / Lost in space / Temple of the new born / Holy water / Animal / Hungry eyes.
LP: . . . . **EPC 26658**
MC: **40 26658**

STANDING IN THE DARK.
Tracks: / Doesn't really matter / Standing in the dark / Sad sad rain / Take it from me / Cast a shadow / Leaders in danger / Not in love / Video disease / All fall down / Cinderella story.
LP: . . . . **EPC 25997**

Platinum Dance

STRICT TEMPO (64 great dance melodies).
Tracks: / Quickstep medley / Slow fox-trot medley / Samba medley / Barn dance medley / Tango medley / Palma waltz medley / Gipsy tap medley / Old time waltz medley / Rhumba medley / Pride of Erin / Cha-cha medley.
2LP: . . . . **PLAT 03**
MCSET: . . . . **PLAC 03**

Platinum Hook

IT'S TIME.
Tracks: / Give me time to say / Time / Be not a long time / Play with you / One more day / It's for you / Love makes me feel good.
LP: . . . . **STML 12110**

Platoon

PLATOON (Film soundtrack) (Various artists).
Tracks: / Village, The - Adagio for strings: *Vancouver Symphony Orchestra* / Tracks of my tears: *Robinson, Smokey*/ Okie from Muskogee: *Haggard, Merle* / Hello, I love you: *Doors* / White rabbit: *Jefferson Airplane*/ Barnes shoots Elias: *Vancouver Symphony Orchestra* / Respect: *Franklin, Aretha* / (Sittin' on) the dock of the bay: *Redding, Otis* / When a man loves a woman: *Sledge, Percy* / Groovin': *Rascals* / Adagio for strings: *Vancouver Symphony Orchestra.*
LP: . . . . **WX 95**
MC: . . . . **WX 95 C**

Platoon Leader

PLATOON LEADER (Film soundtrack) (Various artists).
LP: . . . . **GNPS 8013**
MC: **GNP5 8013**

Platters

6 TRACK HITS.
Tracks: / Great pretender, The / Only you / Smoke gets in your eyes / I'm sorry / Twilight time / My prayer.
MC: **7SC 5006**

18 ORIGINAL HITS: PLATTERS.
LP: . . . . **K 5002**

20 CLASSIC HITS: PLATTERS.
LP: **9100 049**

20 GOLDEN PIECES: PLATTERS.
Tracks: / Only you / Hey now / I need you all the time / Maggie doesn't work here anymore / You made me cry / Tell the world / Voo vee ah vee / Give thanks / Shake it up mambo / Love all night / I believe / World is not my home, The / Put Crying in the chapel / My prayer / Put your hand in the hand / How great Thou art / Loving you / He's my friend / Heading home / Sweet inspiration.
LP: . . . . **BDL 2037**

20 GREATEST HITS: PLATTERS.
LP: . . . . **MA 101285**
MC: . . . . **MAMC 101285**

BEST OF THE PLATTERS.
Tracks: / My prayer / Smoke gets in your eyes / Sweet sweet love / Red sails in the sunset / Only you / Harbour lights / Unchained melody / Magic touch.
MC: **16-4**
LP: . . . . **NE 1380**
MC: . . . . **CE 2380**

EARLY YEARS, THE.
Tracks: / Only you / Hey now / I need you all the time / Maggie doesn't work here anymore / You made me cry / Tell the world / Voo vee ah vee / Give thanks / Shake it up mambo / Love all night.
LP: . . . . **BDL 1036**

ENCORE OF GOLDEN HITS.
Tracks: / Great pretender, The / Twilight time / Smoke gets in your eyes / Magic touch / Enchanted / My prayer / Only you / Remember when / Heaven on earth / I'm sorry / You'll never never know / It isn't right.
LP: **6463 062**
MC: **7145 062**

GOLDEN HIT COLLECTION.
Tracks: / Washed ashore (on a lonely island in the sun) / Lovely / If I had a love / I'll be home / I'm sorry / Harbour lights / Twilight time / I love you because / Heaven on earth / Great pretender, The / If I had you / I love you a thousand times.
MCSET: . . . . **DTO 10003**

GOLDEN HITS COLLECTION.
MC: . . . . **HSC 3405**

GOLDEN HITS: PLATTERS.
Tracks: / Great pretender, The / Only you / I love you a thousand times / With this ring / My prayer / You've got the magic touch / Harbour lights / Smoke gets in your eyes / I'm sorry / Twilight time.
LP: . . . . **PHX 1014**

GRAFFITI COLLECTION.
MC: . . . . **GRMC 08**

GREAT PRETENDER.
Tracks: / My prayer / Great pretender, The / Smoke gets in your eyes / Harbour lights / Only you / Pledging my love / I'll be home / Red sails in the sunset / With this ring / Twilight time / I'm sorry / If I had you.
LP: **463 092**
MC: **7145 092**
LP: . . . . **TOP 123**
MC: . . . . **KTOP 123**

GREAT PRETENDER, THE'.
Tracks: / One in a million / Great pretender, The / With this ring / Pledging my love / Washed ashore (on a lonely island in the sun) / Twilight time / I'm sorry / You've got the magic touch.
LP: . . . . **MFM 025**

GREAT PRETENDER, THE (2).
LP: . . . . **RMB 5614**

GREATEST HITS: PLATTERS.
MC: **2636754**

GREATEST HITS: THE PLATTERS.
LP: . . . . **FUN 9041**
MC: . . . . **FUNC 9041**

INKSPOTS, THE/THE PLATTERS (See under Inkspots) (Platters/Inkspots).

JUKE BOX GIANTS.
Tracks: / Great pretender, The / Harbour lights / Only you / One in a million / Pledging my love / Love letter, The / Washed ashore (on a lonely island in the sea) / With this ring / I love you a thousand times / Smoke gets in your eyes / Twilight time / You've got the magic touch / Heaven on earth / If I had you / I'll be home / Sweet sweet lovin' / How beautiful our love is / Red sails in the sunset / I'm sorry.
LP: . . . . **AFEMP 1007**

MORE I SEE YOU, THE.
Tracks: / Wonder of you, The / One in a million / All my love belongs to you / On the top of my mind / I can't get used to sharing you / What name shall I give you, my love? / I love you, yes I do / Love letters / Going back to Detroit / Love must go on / Wish it were me.
LP: . . . . **SPR 8500**
MC: . . . . **SPC 8500**

MUSIC FOR THE MILLIONS.
Tracks: / Only you / She's mine / My prayer / Remember when / Red sails in the sunset / You've got the magic touch / Thanks for the memory / You'll never know / Sincerely / One in a million / Stormy weather / Mack the knife / Love me tender / Sentimental journey / September song / Great pretender, The / Smoke gets in your eyes / Twilight time / I'm sorry / It's magic / Ebb tide / Trees / Song for the lonely / Summertime / Heaven on earth / Moonlight beach / My dream / Harbour lights / I'll never smile again / My blue Heaven.
LP: **6463 152**
MC: **7145 152**
2LP: **818 412 1**
MCSET: **818 412 4**

ONLY YOU.
Tracks: / Only you / I'm sorry / Harbour lights / Remember when / Smoke gets in your eyes / You'll never know / Red sails in the sunset / Enchanted / It's magic / Ebb tide / On a slow boat to China / Thanks for the memory.
LP: **2872 246**
MC: **3472 246**
MC: . . . . **BRC 2527**

PLATTERAMA.
Tracks: / Platterama medley / Red sails in the sunset / Twilight time / You've got the magic touch / Only you / Great pretender, The / My prayer / Harbour lights / Enchanted / Smoke gets in your eyes.
MC: . . . . **MCR 414050**
LP: . . . . **SRM 14050**

PLATTERS.
Tracks: / Great pretender, The / Only you / Smoke gets in your eyes / Red sails in the sunset / Harbour lights / I'll be home / My prayer / Twilight time / I'm sorry / Pledging my love / With this ring / Washed ashore (on a lonely island in the sea).
LP: . . . . **COUNT 3**
MC: . . . . **ZC CNT 3**

PLATTERS COLLECTION (20 golden greats).
Tracks: / Only you / Smoke gets in your eyes / Great pretender, The / My prayer / Red sails in the sunset / I love you because / Twilight time / Sweet sweet lovin' / Harbour lights / My way / I'm sorry / With this ring / Unchained melody / Heaven on earth / I love you a thousand times / Magic touch / Why? / Doesn't ring a bell / Alone in the night / If I had love.
LP: . . . . **DVLP 2055**
MC: . . . . **DVMC 2055**

PLATTERS COLLECTION, THE.
2LP: . . . . **PDA 003**
MCSET: . . . . **PDC 003**

PLATTERS MEET THE DRIFTERS, THE (Platters, The & The Drifters).
MC: . . . . **U 3014-2**

PLATTERS, THE.
MC: . . . . **ZCGAS 718**
LP: . . . . **BID 8002**
LP: . . . . **SM 3886**
MC: . . . . **MC 3886**

TWENTY CLASSIC HITS.
Tracks: / Only you / Great pretender, The / You've got the magic touch / My prayer / Heaven on earth / You'll never never know / One in a million / I'm sorry / My dream / Twilight time / I wish / Smoke gets in your eyes / Enchanted / Remember when / Harbour lights / Sleepy lagoon / Ebb tide / Red sails in the sunset / To each his own.
LP: . . . . **PRICE 56**
MC: . . . . **PRIMC 56**

Play

PLAY, LISTEN AND SINGALONG.
MCSET: . . . . **DTO 10544**

Play (band)

RED MOVIES.
LP: . . . . **SURB 1**

Play Dead

CAUGHT FROM BEHIND.
Tracks: / Break / Last degree / Solace / Shine / Isabel / Sin of sins / Torn on desire / This side of heaven / Sacrosanct / Tenant, The.
LP: . . . . **DOJOLP 34**

COMPANY OF JUSTICE.
LP: . . . . **TANZLP 1**

FINAL EPITAPH.
LP: . . . . **FREUD 15**

FIRST FLOWER, THE.
MC: . . . . **FREUDC 03**
LP: . . . . **FREUD 03**

FROM THE PROMISED LAND.
LP: . . . . **CLAYLP 11**

INTO THE FIRE.
LP: . . . . **CLAYLP 16M**

SINGLES '82-'85.
LP: . . . . **CLAYLP 20M**
LP: . . . . **CLAYLP 207**

Play It Again, Sam

PLAY IT AGAIN, SAM (Film Soundtrack) (Various artists).
Tracks: / Bogart - that's strictly in the movies: *Various artists* / Don't take it personal: *Various artists*/ Dames are shrimple: *Various artists*/ She wanted to swing: *Various artists* / Date for Allan: *Various artists*/ What about Sharon: *Various artists* / You ashamed to sweat: *Various artists* / I love the rain: *Various* artists / Bogart fantasy: *Various artists* / Blues for Allan Felix: *Various artists* / One two one two: *Various* artists / How'd it go with Julie: *Various artists* / Homosexual panic: *Various artists* / Allan, did you say you love me: *Various artists* / Slide: *Various artists* / Casablanca revisited: *Various artists.*
LP: . . . . **SPFL 279**

Play Misty for Me

PLAY MISTY FOR ME (See under Garner, Errol 'Misty') (Garner, Erroll).

Playbox

LIZ AND THE SANDPIPERS.
MC: . . . . **CDSC 3**

Playboys

INVITATION TO DEATH.
LP: . . . . **F 3008**

LIVE: PLAYBOYS.
LP: . . . . **BSS 170**

MADE IN THE COUNTRY.
LP: . . . . **BSS 118**

Player

DANGER ZONE.
Tracks: / Love in the danger zone / Silver lining / I just wanna be with you / Forever / I've been thinkin' / Prisoner of your love / Join in the dance / Wait until tomorrow / Let me down easy.
LP: . . . . **RSS 3**

PLAYER.
LP: **2394 193**

ROOM WITH A VIEW.
Tracks: / Room with a view / It's for you / Upside down again / Who do you think you are / Bad news travels fast / All tied up / Givin' it all / It may never happen / Tip of the iceberg.
LP: . . . . **NBLP 7217**

Players Association

LET YOUR BODY GO.
Tracks: / Get on up now / Groovin' on home / Let your body go / R & R bop-bop / Things you get me to do / Life is just a song.
LP: . . . . **VSD 79434**

TURN THE MUSIC UP.
Tracks: / Turn the music up / Closer I get to you, The / Everybody dance / I wish / More than a little bit / Ride the groove.
LP: . . . . **VSD 79421**

Players (group)

CHRISTMAS (PLAYERS).
LP: . . . . **PACLP 1**
MC: . . . . **PACMC 1**

Playground

SLEEPING DOGS.
LP: . . . . **DYL 1**

Playgroup

EPIC SOUND BATTLES.
Tracks: / Bombs scare / Epic sound battles / Crunch / Slither, The / Burn up / Deep and mintyful / Silent mover / Epic one drop / Shock absorbers / No speed limit / Boggs might fly / Ballroom control (Only available on CD) / Going overdrawn (Only available on CD) / Going for a song (Only available on CD) / Haphazard (Only available on CD) / Squeek squawk (Only available on CD) / Shoot out (Only available on CD) / Lost in L.A. (Only available on CD).
LP: . . . . **BRED 28**

Playing For Keeps

PLAYING FOR KEEPS (Film soundtrack) (Various artists).
Tracks: / Life to life: *Townshend, Pete* / It's not over: *Thompson, Chris* / Distant drums: *Frampton, Peter*/ It's getting hot: *Wilde, Kim* / Think we're gonna make it: *Battle, Hinton* / We said hello goodbye: *Collins, Phil* / Here to stay: *Sister Sledge* / Say the word: *Arcadia* / Make a wish: *Cruz, Joe* / Stand by me: *Lennon, Julian.*
LP: . . . . **PCS 7306**
MC: . . . . **TCPCS 7306**

Playing The Halls

PLAYING THE HALLS (Various artists).
LP: . . . . **SH 350**

Playmates

BODY AND SOUL (see Gibbons, Carroll).

LONG SWEET DREAMS.
LP: . . . . **GOES ON 03**

Playn Jayn

5 GOOD EVILS.
LP: . . . . **ABCLP 5**

FRIDAY THE 13TH AT THE MARQUEE CLUB.
Tracks: / You weren't born you were created / In your eyes / I'm the only one for me / Crystal ball / If I stayed where I was I wouldn't be where I am / Bits of gold / Strange...but true / Pleasant surprises / Rockin' hearse / La premiere fille / Dans l'eau de la Claire Fontaine / Le vieux Leon / Penelope / A l'ombre de coeur de ma mie / Uncle Archibald / La route aux 4 chansons / Les amourex des bancs publics / L'orange / Le 22 Septembre / Les passantes.
LP: . . . . **JAYN 13**

Playschool

PLAYSCHOOL - STORIES.
LP: . . . . **RBT 10**

Playtime

PLAYTIME.
MCSET: . . . . **DTO 10569**

Playtime (group)

PLAYTIME.
LP: . . . . **CON 002**

Plaza, Martin

PLAZA SUITE.
Tracks: / Pit stop / I could be so good / Concrete and clay / Out the door / Best foot forward / Miss you like mad / Chalk and cheese / Use me all over / Rollerina / Bats and balls.
LP: . . . . **EPC 57005**
MC: **40 57006**

Pleasance, Donald

BRAVE LITTLE TAILOR (see under Brave Little Tailor (bk)).

Please, Peter

UFFINGTON.
LP: . . . . **PLR 060**

Please Warm...

PLEASE WARM MY WEINER (Various artists).
LP: . . . . **L 1043**

Pleasure

PLEASURE.
Tracks: / Yellowfield / Takin' a chance on you / Could it be love / Please / Pain / Yield not to temptation / Beautiful day / You gotta nerve / Tuesday's child / Leaves / Remember you're not perfect either babe.
LP: . . . . **NERVLP 2**
MC: . . . . **NERVMC 2**

Pleasure Starts Here

PLEASURE STARTS HERE (Various artists).
LP: . . . . **PLZL 841**

Pleasure Zone

FUCK CHARLEY (see : "Two Of A Kind 'somewhere in west hall'").

Pleasureheads

HARD TO SWALLOW.
Tracks: / Sold / Whip it up / Crystal clear / Something you're above / Hit the ground / Frankly (I'm not H.P.) / Treasure / Harvey's cane is out / Kind but blind.
LP: . . . . **CALCLP 043**

SOLD.
LP: . . . . **CALCLP 045**

Pleasures...

PLEASURES AND TREASURES (A kaleidoscope of sound) (Various artists).
Tracks: / March by Mr Handel: *Hacker, Alan* (Boxwood clarinet.) / Mira O Norma: *Polyphon musical box* / Jean's reel: *Tickell, Kathryn* (Northumbrian small pipes.) / Lezghinka: *Best Of Brass* / Prelude to lute suite in E major: *North, Nigel* (Baroque lute.) / Colette: *Whiteman, Paul & His Orchestra* (From 78rpm record.) / John come kiss me now: *Townsend, Dave* (English concertina) / Music from Compline: *Stanbrook Abbey Nuns/Prinknash Abbey Monks*(Plainsong) / Le coucou: *Preston, Stephen* (Ivory flute) / Whistling Rufus: *Sound in Brass Handbells* (Handbells) / Limerick's lamentation: *Monger, Eileen* (Celtic harp) / La quinte estampie real: *Canter, Robin* (Treble shawm) / I've got a lovely bunch of coconuts: *Barrel Organ...* / Love at the fair: *Jing Ying Soloists* (Chinese Er-hu) / Miss Annabelle Lee: *Pianola Roll* / Scherzo: *Holmes, Ralph* (Stradivarius violin) / Wibbly wobbly walk, The: *Charman, Jack* (Phonograph cylinder) / Jenny Lind medley: *Couza, Jim* (Hammer dulcimer) / Turkish rondo: *Burnett*, Richard (Viennese fortepiano) / O Sanctissima: *Schmitt, Georges* (Pan pipes and organ) / Reve gourmand: *Pauly, Danielle* (French accordion) / Sportive little trifler: *Canterbury Clerkes/ London Serpent Trio* (English glee with serpents).
LP: . . . . **SDLC 362**
MC: . . . . **CSDLC 362**

Plethyn

BLAS Y BRIDD.
LP: . . . . **SAIN 1145**

BYD A BOD.
LP: . . . . **SAIN 1393 M**

CANENON GWERIH I BLANT.
LP: . . . . **SAIN 1309 M**

GOLAU TAN GWMWL.
LP: . . . . **SAIN 1188**

RHOWN GARREG.
LP: . . . . **SAIN 1226**

TENLU'R TIR.
LP: . . . . **SAIN 1274**

Pleyer, Frank

JUST FOR PLEASURE (Pleyer, Frank/ Orchestra).
Tracks: / Unforgettable / Liebestraum / Vilia / Barcarolle / Can't stop loving you / Can't forget you / Schwarze Augen / Rumba magico / Guantanamera / Gioconda / Belo horizonte / La bamba / La Coruwa / Nifty.
LP: . . . . **DSO 63**

Pliers

CLASH OF THE 90'S (Pliers & J Moore).
LP: . . . . **SP 002LP**

HEARTICAL DON MAN.
LP: . . . . **PICKLP 09**

Plimsouls

EVERYWHERE AT ONCE.
Tracks: / Shaky city / Magic touch / Oldest story in the world / Lie, beg, borrow and steal / Play the breaks / How long will it take / Million miles away / My life ain't easy / Inch by inch / I'll get lucky / Everywhere at once.
LP: . . . . **GEF 25509**

ONE NIGHT IN AMERICA.
Tracks: / Hush hush / How long will it take / I want what you got / In this town / Help yourself / I'll get lucky / Now / Million miles away, A / Time won't let me / One more heartache / Dizzy Miss Lizzy / Come on now.
LP: . . . . **FC 048**
MC: . . . . **FC 048C**

Ploughboy Lads

THEY DIED FOR IRELAND.
LP: . . . . **DOLM 5032**

Plow

PLOW (Various artists).
LP: . . . . **ORG 85/1**

Plummer, Christopher

AROUND THE WORLD IN 80 DAYS (See under Around the World in 80 Days).

Plunky Branch

TROPICAL CHILL.
LP: . . . . **NB 19881**

Pluto

OVERTURE.
MC: . . . . **SRLP 106C**

PLUTO...PLUS.
Tracks: / I really want it / Crossfire / And my old rocking horse / Down and out / She's innocent / Road to glory / Stealing my thunder / Beauty queen / Mister Westwood / Something that you loved / Rag a bone Joe / Bare lady.
LP: . . . . **SEE 265**

Plyers

SWEET SHERENE.
LP: . . . . **DSLP 8901**
MC: . . . . **DSC 8901**

PM

1 PM.
Tracks: / Dynamite / You've got me rockin' / Green velvet splendour / Dreamers / Go on carry on / Do you go all the way / Go for it / Madeleine / You're too much / Children of the air age.
LP: . . . . **ARL 5048**

PM Dawn

OF THE HEART, OF THE SOUL, OF THE CROSS.
LP: . . . . **GEEA 7**
MC: . . . . **GEEMC 7**

P'O

LITTLE STONES.
LP: . . . . **RUTLP 1**

WHILST CLIMBING THIEVES VIE FOR POSITION.
LP: . . . . **COURT 1**

Poacher

POACHER.
LP: . . . . **RKLP 5002**

Poacher, Cyril

BROOMFIELD WAGER, THE.
LP: **12TS 252**

Pocket Change

RANDOM AXIS.
LP: . . . . **PJ 88018**
MC: . . . . **PJC 88018**

Poco

FROM THE INSIDE.
LP: **64 543**

GHOST TOWN.
Tracks: / Ghost town / How will you feel tonight / Shoot for the moon / Cry no more / Midnight rodeo / Break of hearts / Love's so cruel / Special care / When hearts collide / High sierra.
LP: . . . . **K 50902**

LEGACY.
Tracks: / When it all began / Call it love / Nature of love, The / What do people know / Nothin' to hide (Only on cassette and CD.) / Look within / Rough edges / Who else / Lovin' you every minute / If it wasn't for you / Follow your dreams.
LP: . . . . **PL 90395**
MC: . . . . **PK 90395**

LEGEND.
Tracks: / Boomerang / Spellbound / Barbados / Little darlin' / Crazy love / Love comes, love goes / Heart of the night / Last goodbye / Legend.
MC: . . . . **CAB 5264**
LP: . . . . **ABCL 5264**

PICKING UP THE PIECES.
LP: . . . . **XED 161**

ROSE OF CIMARRON.
Tracks: / Stealaway / Just like me / Rose of Cimarron / Company's coming / Slow poke / Too many nights too long / When you come around / Starin' at the sky / All alone together / Tulsa turnaround.
LP: . . . . **MCL 1638**

SONGS OF RICHIE FURAY.
Tracks: / Good feelin' to know / Hurry up / Don't let it pass by / What if I should say I love you / Pickin' up the pieces / Crazy eyes / Settin' down / C'mon / What am I gonna do.
LP: . . . . **CBS 31781**
MC: **40 31781**

Podmore, J. F.

KITCHENETTE (See under Hope, Peter) (Podmore, J. F. & Peter Hope).

Poe, Edgar Allan (aut)

FALL OF THE HOUSE OF USHER (Rathbone, Basil (nar)).
MC: **1195**

PIT AND THE PENDULUM AND OTHER WORKS (Rathbone, Basil (nar)).
MC: **1115**

PURLOINED LETTER AND OTHER WORKS, THE (Quayle, Anthony (nar)).
MC: **1288**

RAVEN AND OTHER WORKS, THE (Rathbone, Basil (nar)).
MC: **1028**

SHORT STORIES, VOL 1 (Donegan, Martin).
LP: . . . . **PRCS 117**

TALES OF HORROR (Lee, Christopher).
MCSET: . . . . **LFP 7454**

TALES OF MYSTERY AND IMAGINATION (Mitchell, Bill).
MCSET: . . . . **SAY 54**

TELLTALE HEART, THE (See under Samuels, Arthur - Repossession).

Poems from the...(bk)

POEMS FROM THE BARRIER BLOCK (Wild Billy Childish).
LP: . . . . **WORDUP 003**

Poems of Laughter (bk)

POEMS OF LAUGHTER AND VIOLENCE (Wild Billy Childish).
Tracks: / People don't need poetry / Warts grown like flys / Talking lites, The / Me 'n' my father / Hawk and spitfire / Heaven she said / In here we believe / Terrible buti, The / Catastrophy / Mercy.
LP: . . . . **HANG 16 UP**

Poems & Pints

ANOTHER ROUND OF POEMS AND PINTS.
LP: . . . . **NTS 150**

Poems without Rhyme

POEMS WITHOUT RHYME (Wild Billy Childish).
LP: . . . . **WORDUP 004**

Poesie Noir

EN GRANDE COUTURE.
Tracks: / Beat about the bush / Earth / Turn turtle / Poesie noire / Restraint / Fait accompli / Trophy.
MLP: . . . . **ANT 092**

HUM AND HAW.
Tracks: / Hum and haw.
LP: . . . . **ANT 040**

LOVE IS COLDER THAN DEATH.
LP: . . . . **AS 5006**
MC: . . . . **AS 5006MC**

PITY FOR THE SELF OR WE'LL TEACH YOU TO DANCE.
MLP: . . . . **ANT 103**

POESIE NOIRE.
MC: . . . . **ANT 099 MC**

TALES OF DOOM.
Tracks: / Tales of doom.
LP: . . . . **ANT 053**

TETRA.
Tracks: / Tragedy / Earth / Travel / Rain / Air / Tame / Escape / Tower / Rescue / Adaptation / Agony / Restraint (Extra track on CD only.) / Timber (Extra track on CD only.) / White night (Extra track on CD only.).
LP: . . . . **ANT 074 LP**

Poetry...

ANTHOLOGY - POETRY READINGS (see under Burton, Richard) (Burton, Richard).

BURNS SUPPER, A (see under Burns, Robert) (Various artists).

FOUR TWENTIETH CENTURY POETS (W.H. Auden) (Lewis, C. Day (nar)).
Tracks: / Ecstatic, The / My love is a tower / You that love England / From the Georgics of Virgil / Now the full-throated daffodils / With me, my lover makes / Beauty's end is in sight / Learning to talk / On not saying everything / Pegasus / Room, The / Elegy for a woman unknown / Christmas tree / Fox, The / Failure / Episode, An / Derelict, The / Final instructions / Departure in the dark / Homage to Clio / Shield of Achilles / Sext / Nones / Vespers / Compline / Metalogue to the magic flute / Hard question / Song / Lady weeping at the crossroads / More loving one, The / Walk after dark, A / Wanderer / First things first / Alonso to Ferdinand / Word / Hawk, The / Not to you I sighed / And I can never be a great man / Beethoven's death mask / My parents kept me from children who were rough / What I expected was / Who live under the shadow of war / Express, The / Landscape near an aerodrome / Prisoners / I think continually / Elementary school classroom / Elegy for Margaret / Song / Four short poems about children / Earth treading stars / Seascape.
MCSET: **414 727-4**

MORE FAVOURITE POEMS (Various artists).
MCSET: . . . . **SAY 80**

POEMS YOU LOVE (Various artists).
MCSET: **418 165-4**
MCSET: . . . . **ARGO 1181**

POET SPEAKS, THE (Various artists).
MCSET: . . . . **SAY 60**

POETRY OF ROBERT BURNS, THE (see under Burns, Robert) (Various artists).

POETRY OLYMPICS VOL 1 (Various artists).
LP: . . . . **ARRLP 1**

POETRY PLEASE (Various artists).
MCSET: . . . . **ZBBC 1034**

POETRY PROSE AND PIANO (Various artists).
LP: . . . . **KPM 7015**

PORTRAIT OF FOUR POETS, A (Owen, Read, Thomas & Davies) (Various artists).
MCSET: **414 757-4**
MCSET: . . . . **ARGO 1250**

RHYME AND RHYTHM (A collection of poetry & song for children) (Various artists).
MCSET: . . . . **SAY 102**

SELECTION OF FAVOURITE POETRY, A (Barkworth, Peter & Tim Pigott-Smith).
MCSET: . . . . **LFP 7302**

TAKE MY YOUTH (AN ANTHOLOGY OF POETRY FROM THE G (Various artists).
MC: . . . . **TTC/FWO 1**

TEMPO FAVOURITE POEMS (23 traditional poems for children) (Various artists).
MCSET: **00 103 211 9**

TEN POETS OF THE 20TH CENTURY (Various artists).
MCSET: **414 769-4**

TREASURY OF LOVE POEMS, THE (Various artists).
MC: . . . . **ARGO 1280**

TREASURY OF ROMANTIC POETRY, THE (Various artists).
MCSET: . . . . **ARGO 1169**

TREASURY OF VICTORIAN POETRY, THE (Various artists).
MCSET: . . . . **ARGO 1115**

TWELVE POETS OF THE 20TH CENTURY (Various artists).
MCSET: **414 772-4**

YOUR FAVOURITE POEMS (Various artists).
MCSET: . . . . **SAY 18**
MCSET: . . . . **ARGO 1139**

Poetry In Motion

POETRY IN MOTION (Various artists).
LP: . . . . **MDKR 1**
MC: . . . . **MDKRC 1**

Poetry of Catullus

POETRY OF CATULLUS (Mason, James (nar)).
MC: . . . . **CDL 51611**

Poets

POETS, THE.
Tracks: / Subversive / Spies in the rain / Manson / Peak / Collision of love / Absentee / Don't waste your roses / Death angels of Israel / I met you / Silver girl / Down down / Canvas.
MC: . . . . **PK 74431**
LP: . . . . **PL 74431**

Pogues

HELL'S DITCH.
LP: . . . . **WX 366**
MC: . . . . **WX 366 C**

IF I SHOULD FALL FROM GRACE WITH GOD.
Tracks: / If I should fall from grace with God / Turkish song of the damned / Bottle of smoke / Fairytale of New York / Metropolis / Thousands are sailing / South Australia* / Fiesta / Recruiting sergeant, The / Rocky road to Dublin (medley) / Galway races (medley) / Streets of sorrow/Birmingham six / Lullaby of London / Battle march, The / Sit down by the fire / Broad majestic Shannon / Worms.
MC: TCNYR 1
LP: NYR 1
LP: WX 243
MC: WX 243C

PEACE AND LOVE.
Tracks: / Gridlock / Young Ned of the hill / Cottonfields / Down all days / Lorelei / Boat train / Night train to Lorca / White city / Misty morning Albert Bridge / Blue heaven / USA / Gartioney rats / Tombstone / London you're a lady.
LP: WX 247
MC: WX 247 C

POGUES: INTERVIEW PICTURE DISC.
LPPD: BAK 2160

RED ROSES FOR ME.
Tracks: / Transmetropolitan / Battle of Brisbane, The / Auld triangle, The / Waxie's dargle / Sea shanty / Dark streets of London / Streams of whiskey / Poor Paddy / Dingle regatta / Greenland whale fisheries / Down in the ground where the dead men go / Kitty.
LP: WX 240
MC: WX 240C
LP: SEEZ 55

RUM, SODOMY AND THE LASH.
LP: SEEZ 58
MC: ZSEEZ 58
LP: WX 241
MC: WX 241C

Poi Dog Pondering

WISHING LIKE A MOUNTAIN AND THINKING LIKE A SEA.
Tracks: / Bury me deep / Watermelon song, The / U li la lu / Everybody's trying / Big beautiful spoon / Ancient Egyptians, The / Spending the day in the shirt you wore / Thanksgiving / Praise the lord / Me that was your son, The / Fruitless / Big walk / Sugarbush cushman.
LP: 4666741
MC: 4666744

Poindexter, Buster

BUSTER POINDEXTER.
Tracks: / Smack dab in the middle / Bad boy / Hot hot hot / Are you lonely for me baby / Screwy music / Good morning judge / Oh me oh my (I'm a fool for you baby) / Whadaya want? / House of the rising sun / Cannibal / Heart of gold.
LP: PL 86633
MC: PK 86633

Point Blank

ON A ROLL.
Tracks: / On a roll / I just want to know / Love on fire / Don't look now / Great white line / Let her go / Gone Hollywood / Take me up.
LP: MCF 3141
MC: MCFC 3141

Point of Ayr...

BLUE AND THE GRAY, THE (Point of Ayr Colliery Band).
Tracks: / Opus 99 / Pastorale / Tired trombones / Dove, The / Anyone can whistle / Elen Fwyn / Cranberry Corner U.S.A. / Army of the Nile / Tuba smarties / Nuts & wine / Myfanwy / Blue and the gray, The.
LP: PRL 029D
MC: CPRL 029D

Point of Honour

POINT OF HONOUR, THE Maugham, Somerset (Burden, Hugh (nar)).
MC: TTC/WSM 3

Point (show)

MAGIC CIRCLE.
LP: LOLITA 5011

POINT, THE (Original Soundtrack) (Various artists).
Tracks: / Overture: everything's got 'em: *Various artists* / Me and my arrow: *Various artists* / Poli high: *Various* artists / Remember: *Various artists* / To be a king: *Various artists* / He's leaving here this morning: *Various* artists / Think about your troubles: *Various artists* / Blanket for a sail: *Various artists* / Lifeline: *Various* artists / Thursday: *Various artists* / It's a jungle out there: *Various artists* / P.O.V. waltz: *Various* artists / Are you sleeping: *Various artists* / Gotta get up: *Various artists* / Reprise overture: *Various artists.*
LP: MCF 2826

Pointer, Anita

LOVE FOR WHAT IT IS.
Tracks: / Overnight success / Love me like you do / Pledge, The (the duet with Philip Bailey) / You don't scare me / More than a memory / Have a little faith in love / Love for what it is / Temporarily blue / Beware of what you want.
LP: 64191 R
LP: PL 86419
MC: PK 86419

Pointer, Bonnie

BONNIE POINTER.
Tracks: / When I'm gone / Free me from my freedom / Tie me to a tree / Heaven must have sent you / More and more / I love to sing to you / I wanna make it / My everything.
LP: STML 12101

BONNIE POINTER II.
Tracks: / I can't help myself / Jimmy Mack / Heaven must have sent you / When the lovelight starts shining through his eyes / Deep inside my soul / Come see about me / Nowhere to run.
LP: STML 12129

IF THE PRICE IS RIGHT.
Tracks: / Premonition / Johnny / Come softly to me / Under the influence of love / Your touch / Tight blue jeans / There's nobody quite like you / If the price is right.
LP: EPC 26128
MC: 40 26128

Pointer, June

BABY SITTER.
Tracks: / Ready for some action / I will understand / To you, my love / New love, true love / I'm ready for love / You can do it / Always / My blues have gone / Don't mess with Bill.
LP: RPLP 3001
MC: RPK 3001

Pointer, Noel

ALL MY REASONS.
Tracks: / Classy lady / East St. Louis melody / All the reasons why / Brookline / Savin' it up / Virgie / I feel your soul / Oh what a beautiful city / Land of make believe.
LP: LBG 30340

FEEL IT.
LP: UAG 30278

Pointer Sisters

BEST OF POINTER SISTERS.
Tracks: / You gotta believe / Black coffee / Wang dang doodle / Salt peanuts / Steam heat / Cloudburst / Easy days / Ja da / That's a plenty / Little pony / Sugar / Yes we can can / Sleeping alone / Fairytales / Shakey flat / Going down slowly / How long.
2LP: ABCD 611

BLACK AND WHITE.
Tracks: / Sweet lover man / Someday we'll be together / Take my heart, take my soul / Slow hand / We're gonna make it / What a surprise / Got to find love / Fall in love again / Should I do it.
LP: NL 89378
MC: NK 89378
LP: K 52300

BREAK OUT.
Tracks: / Jump (for my love) / Automatic / I'm so excited / I need you / Dance electric / Neutron dance / Easy persuasion / Baby come and get it / Telegraph your love / Operator.
LP: FL 89450
MC: FK 89450
LP: NL 90206
MC: NK 90206
LP: FL 84705

COLLECTION: POINTER SISTERS.
Tracks: / Cloudburst / Lonely girl / Sugar / Chainy do / Wang dang doodle / Salt peanuts / Bring your sweet stuff home to me / Grinning in your face / Save the bones for Henry Jones... / Shakey flat blues / Naked foot / I need a man / Sleeping alone / Pains and tears / Yes we can / Fairytale / How long / Black coffee / Going down / Little pony.
MC: CCSMC 175
2LP: CCSLP 175

CONTACT.
Tracks: / Twist my arm / Hey you / Pound, pound, pound / Back in my arms / Burn down the night / Bodies and souls / Contact / Dare me / Freedom.
LP: NL 90089
MC: NK 90089
LP: PL 85457

ENERGY.
Tracks: / Happiness / Fire / Angry eyes / Echoes of love / Everybody is a star / Lay it on the line / Dirty work / Hypnotized / As I come of age / Come and get your love.
LP: NL 85091
MC: NK 85091
LP: K 52107

FROM THE POINTER SISTERS WITH LOVE.
Tracks: / Slow hand / I'm in love / All I know is the way I feel / Moonlight dancing / Easy persuasion / Someday we will be together / He's so shy / Fire / I feel for you / Dirty work / See how the love goes / Got to find love / I will be there / I need you.
MC: NK 90541

GREATEST HITS: POINTER SISTERS.
Tracks: / He's so shy / Fire / Should I do it / Someday we'll be together / Happiness / Slow hand / Could I be dreamin' / Love too good to last / Take my heart, take my soul / Special things.
LP: 9602031

HOT TOGETHER.
Tracks: / My life / Mercury rising / Goldmine / Say the word / Hot together / Sexual power / Set me free / Tast / Eyes don't lie.
LP: PL 85609
MC: PK 85609

JUMP (ALBUM) (Best of the Pointer Sisters).
Tracks: / Jump (for my love) / Someday we'll be together / Automatic / He's so shy / Should I do it / Slow hand / Heart to heart / Telegraph your love / I'm so excited / Goldmine / Back in my arms / I need you / Neutron dance / Dare me / See how the love goes / Overnight success (Only on cassette and CD.) / I'm ready for love (Only on cassette and CD.) / Fire (Only on CD.).
LP: PL 90319
MC: PK 90319

PRIORITY.
Tracks: / Who do you love / All you love / Dreaming as one / Turned up too late / Happy / Blind faith / Don't let a thief steal into your heart / She's got the fever / Shape I'm in.
LP: K 52161

RETROSPECT.
Tracks: / Yes, we can can / Sleeping alone / Fairytale / Easy days / Chainey do / That's a plenty / Surfeit USA / Old songs, The / Salt peanuts / Cloudburst / Ain't got nothing but the blues / Rocks in my bed / Creole love song / Satin doll / I got it bad and that ain't good / Mood indigo.
LP: MCL 1636
MC: MCLC 1636

RIGHT RHYTHM.
Tracks: / Friend's advice (don't take it) / Man with the right rhythm / Real life / After you / You knocked the love (right outta my heart) / Billy said Yes / Insanity / What a woman wants / Where have you been? / (We just wanna)Thank you (Not on Album).
LP: ZL 72704
MC: ZK 72704

SERIOUS SLAMMIN'.
Tracks: / Serious slammin' / Shut up and dance / Moonlight dancing / He turned me out / Flirtations / My life / I'm in love / Pride / Uh uh / I will be there.
LP: PL 86562
MC: PK 86562

SO EXCITED.
Tracks: / I'm so excited / See how the love goes / All of you / Heart beat / If you wanna get back your lady / I feel for you / Heart to heart / American music.
LP: NL 90255
MC: NK 90255

SPECIAL THINGS.
Tracks: / Could I be dreamin' / He's so shy / Love too good to last, The / Evil / Save this night for love / We've got the power / Where did the time go / Special things / Here is where your love belongs.
LP: K52242
MC: K4 52242
LP: NL 85088
MC: NK 85088

Poirot ...(bk)

POIROT INVESTIGATES VOL. 1 (Agatha Christie) (Suchet, David (nar)).
MCSET: LFP 7421

POIROT INVESTIGATES VOL. 2 (Agatha Christie) (Suchet, David (nar)).
MCSET: LFP 7460

Poison

FLESH AND BLOOD.
Tracks: / Strange days of uncle Jack / Valley of lost souls / (Flesh and blood) sacrifice / Swampjuice (soul-o) / Unskinny bop / Let it play / Life goes on / Come hell or high water / Ride the wind / Don't give up an inch / Something to believe in / Ball and chain / Life loves a tragedy / Poor boy blues.
LP: EST 2126
LP: 791 813 1
MC: TCEST 2126
MC: 791 813 4

LOOK WHAT THE CAT DRAGGED IN.
Tracks: / Cry tough / I want action / I won't forget you / Play dirty / Look what the cat dragged in / Talk dirty to me / Want some, need some / Blame it on you / No.1 bad boy / Let me go to the show.
MC: TMFN 69
LP: MFN 69
LPPD: MFN 69P
LP: CMP 1003
LP: 746 735 1
MC: TCCMP 1003
MC: 746 735 4
LP: ATAK 162
MC: TCATAK 162

OPEN UP AND SAY AHH.
Tracks: / Love on the rocks / Nothin' but a good time / Back to the rocking horse / Good love / Tearin' down the walls / Look but you can't touch / Fallen angel / Every rose has it's thorn / Your mama don't dance / Bad to be good.
LP: EST 2059
MC: TCEST 2059
LPPD: ESTP 2059

POISON: INTERVIEW PICTURE DISC.
LPPD: BAK 2047

SWALLOW THIS LIVE.
Tracks: / Intro / Look what the cat dragged in / Look but you can't touch / Good love / I want action / Something to believe in / Poor boy blues / Unskinny bop / Every rose has it's thorn / Fallen angel / Your mama don't dance / Nothin' but a good time / Talk dirty to me / So tell me why / Souls on fire / Only time will tell / No more lookin' back (Poison jazz).
LP: ESTU 2159
MC: TCESTU 2159

Poison Girls

7 YEAR SCRATCH.
LP: RM 101

BLOODY REVOLUTIONS/PERSONS UNKNOWN (See under Crass) (Poison Girls/Crass).

CHAPPOQUIDICK BRIDGE.
LP: 421984/2

SONGS OF PRAISE.
LP: XN 2008

WHERE'S THE PLEASURE.
LP: XN 2006

Poison Idea

FEEL THE DARKNESS.
MC: SOL 25 C

KINGS OF PUNK.
LP: 0012-10
LP: TG 9284 1

POISON IDEA.
LP: FACE 6

RECORD COLLECTORS ARE PRETENTIOUS ASSHOLES.
LP: TG 9299 1

WAR ALL THE TIME.
LP: VM 106
MC: VM 106 C

Poisoned Electric Head

DRINK ME.
Tracks: / Apollo II / Diana's gyroscope / Dream of me / Astral tchunk / Poisoned Electric Head / 20th century man presidents reply / Elephant's song / Ticker tape.
MC: HEAD 003

Pokkela, Martti

OLD AND NEW KANTELE.
LP: EULP 1040
MC: EUMC 1040

Poland

DANSES DE POLOGNE (Various artists).
Tracks: / Na srodku pola stoi topola: *Various artists* / Oberek: *Various artists* / A wy muzykanty grajta powolniaka: *Various artists* / Szla dziewczyna koto mtyna: *Various artists* / Polka a l'ancienne: *Various artists*/ Nie chodzjasui dzis do dziewczyny: *Various artists* / Zaborowska warsawianka: *Various artists* / Taczko zielona: *Various artists.*
LP: ARN 33667

Poland, Chris

RETURN TO METALOPOLIS.
LP: RR 9348-1
MC: RR 9348-4

Polanski, Roman

PIRATES (See under Pirates).

Polar Praxis

FIREWORKS.
Tracks: / Fireworks IV / Fireworks V / Fireworks VI / Fireworks VII / Fireworks III.
LP: CIRCLE 4
LP: FACE 18
LP: FACE 010

Polcer, Ed

ED POLCER & EDDIE CONDONS ALL-STARS (Polcer, Ed & Eddie Condon).
LP: .... J 150

Polecats

CULT HEROES.
LP: .... NERD 001

LIVE AND ROCKIN'.
LP: .... LINKLP 069

POLECATS ARE GO.
Tracks: / How high the moon / Red ready amber / Don't cry baby / Marie Celeste / Black magic / Don't push / We say yeah! / Little pig / Running back / Big green car / Rockabilly guy / Baby doll / All night long / John I'm only dancing.
LP: 6359 057

WON'T DIE.
LP: .... ASKLP 1

Police

EVERY BREATH YOU TAKE (The singles).
Tracks: / Roxanne / Can't stand losing you / Message in a bottle / Walking on the moon / Don't stand so close to me '86 / De do do do de da da da / Every little thing she does is magic / Invisible sun / Spirits in the material world / Every breath you take / King of pain / Wrapped around your finger / So lonely (Only on Cassette & CD).
LP: .... EVERY 1
MC: .... EVERC 1

GHOST IN THE MACHINE.
Tracks: / Spirit in the material world / Every little thing she does is magic / Invisible sun / Hungry for you / Demolition man / Too much information / Rehumanise yourself / One world (not three) / Omega man / Secret journey / Darkness.
LP: .... AMLK 63730
MC: .... CKM 63730

OUTLANDOS D'AMOUR.
Tracks: / Next to you / So lonely / Hole in my life / Roxanne / Peanuts / Can't stand losing you / Truth hits everybody / Born in the 50's / Be my girl - Sally / Masoko Tango.
LP: .... AMLH 68502
MC: .... CAM 68502

REGATTA DE BLANC.
Tracks: / Message in a bottle / Reggatta de blanc / It's alright for you / Bring on the night / Deathwish / Walking on the moon / On any other day / Bed's too big without you, The / Contact / Does everybody stare / No time this time.
LP: .... AMLH 64792
MC: .... CAM 64792

REGATTA DE BLANC/ SYNCRONICITY.
MC: .... AMC 24103

SYNCHRONICITY.
Tracks: / Synchronicity 1 / Walking in your footsteps / Oh my God / Mother / Miss Gradenko / Synchronicity II / Every breath you take / King of pain / Wrapped around your finger / Tea in the Sahara.
LP: .... AMLX 63735
MC: .... CXM 63735

ZENYATTA MONDATTA.
Tracks: / Don't stand so close to me / Driven to tears / When the world is running down, you make the best of what's / Canary in a coalmine / Voices inside my head / Bombs away / De do do do De da da da / Behind my camel / Man in a suitcase / Shadows in the rain / Other way of stopping, The.
LP: .... AMLH 64831
MC: .... CAM 648331

Police Academy

POLICE ACADEMY FOUR 'CITIZENS ON PATROL' (Film soundtrack) (Various artists).
Tracks: / Rock the house: *Duncan, Daryll* / It's time to move: *S.O.S. Band* / Dancin' up a storm: *Lattisaw, Stacy* / Let's go to heaven in my car: *Wilson, Brian* / High flyers, The: *Folk, Robert* / Citizens on patrol: *Winslow, Michael & the L.A. Dream Team* / Rescue me: *Family Dream* / I like my body: *DeBarge, Chico* / Winning streak: *Glenn, Gary* / Shoot for the top: *Southern Pacific.*
LP: .... ZL 72586
MC: .... ZK 72586

Polish American..

POLISH-AMERICAN DANCE MUSIC Early recordings 1927-1933 (Various artists).
LP: .... FL 9026

Polish Radio National

VIOLIN CONCERTI (see under Brodski, Vadim) (Polish Radio National Symphony Orchestra/Vadim Brodski)).

Polite, Nick

NICK POLITE'S JAZZMEN (Melbourne NOR jazzband).
LP: .... S 1332

Political Asylum

SOMEDAY.
LP: .... WEBITE 18

Politics Of Experience

POLITICS OF EXPERIENCE.
LP: .... KK 010

Polka..

POLKA'S GREATEST HITS (Various artists).
LP: .... PC 364

Polkemmet Grorud

FROM CELTIC ROOTS (Polkemmet Grorud Pipe Band).
LP: .... LILP 5150
MC: .... LICS 5150

PIPE BANDS OF DISTINCTION (Polkemmet Grorud Pipe Band).
MC: .... ZC MON 808

Pollack, Ben

BEN POLLACK & HIS ORCHESTRA 1933/4.
LP: .... VLP 43

FUTURISTIC RHYTHM 1928-1929 (Pollack, Ben & His Park Central Orchestra).
Tracks: / Futuristic rhythm / Buy buy for baby / She's one sweet show girl / Then came the dawn / Sentimental baby / Let's sit and talk about you / Louisa / Wait till you see ma cherie / My kinda love / On with the dance / In the hush of the night / Won't cha / Bashful baby / Where the sweet forget-me-nots remember / Song of the blues / True blue Lou / Sweetheart / You've made me happy today / From now on / Keep your undershirt on.
LP: .... SVL 154
LP: .... HDL 117
MC: .... CHDL 117

RED AND BEN (see under Nichols, Red) (Pollack, Ben & Red Nichols).

Pollard, Chuck

CHUCK POLLARD AND OTHERS.
LP: .... JIN 9011

Pollard, Su (aut)

ADVENTURES OF NAUGHTY AMELIA JANE (See under Adventures of... (spoken word)).

SU.
Tracks: / Starting together / Perhaps love / You never done it like that / Once you lose your heart / Falling for you / Lies (la la lies) / You've lost that lovin' feeling / Wives will always be the last to know / Band of gold / Never thought I'd be losing you / Come to me I am a woman.
LP: .... NE 1327
MC: .... CE 2327

Pollen

COLOURS AND MAKE BELIEVE.
LP: .... DANLP 028
MC: .... DANC 028

CONTRASTS.
LP: .... DANMLP 007
MC: .... DANC 712

Pollution & Industry

POLLUTION AND INDUSTRY (See under UNESCO reports).

Poltergeist

BEHIND THE MASK.
LP: 0897151

DEPRESSION.
LP: 089 704

Poltergeist (Film)

POLTERGEIST (Film soundtrack) (Various artists).
LP: 2315 439

POLTERGEIST II (Film soundtrack) (Various artists).
Tracks: / Power, The: *Various artists* / Late call: *Various artists* / Smoke, The: *Various artists* / Worm, The: *Various artists* / Reaching out: *Various artists.*
MC: .... ACS 2001
LP: .... TER 1116

POLTERGEIST III (Film soundtrack) (Various artists).
LP: 704.620
MC: .... C 704.620

Poly Styrene

TRANSLUCENCE.
Tracks: / Dreaming / Talk in toytown / Skydive / Day that time forgot / Shades / Essence / Hip city hip / Bicycle song / Sub tropical / Translucence / Age / Goodbye.
LP: .... UAG 30320

LP: .... RRLP 128
MC: .... RRLC 128

Polyphonic Size

LIVE FOR EACH MOMENT.
LP: .... ROSE 12

OVERNIGHT DAY, THE.
LP: .... ROSE 150
MC: .... ROSE 150C

Polyrock

NO LOVE'S LOST.
MC: .... A 144

POLYROCK.
Tracks: / No love lost / Green for go / Bucket rider / Go West / Your dragging feet / Romantic me / Shut your face / Body me / This song / Sound alarm / No. 7.
LP: .... PL 43502

Pomeroy, Herb

LIFE IS A MANY SPLENDORED GIG (Pomeroy, Herb Orchestra).
LP: .... FS 85

TRUMPETS OUT FRONT (see ferguson, Maynard &Herb Pomeroy) (Pomeroy, Herb & Maynard Ferguson).

Pompey, Ron

BANANA POLICE.
LP: .... GS 2291

YUH LOOK NICE.
LP: .... GS 2306

Pomus, Doc

SEND FOR THE DOCTOR.
LP: .... KM 700

Ponce, Daniel

ARAWE.
Tracks: / Arawe / No comprendo / Reputation / Oromi / Holiday / Pachanga.
LP: .... AN 8710
MC: .... ANC 8710

CHANGA TE LLAMA.
MC: .... MCT 1071
LP: .... MLPS 1071

Pondles

PONDLES, VOL 1, THE.
Tracks: / Puddletown parade / Rain dance / Puddletown puffer / Three little jackdaws / Pip's birthday / Daisy saves the day / Conker's song / Grandad's shed / Bangers and mash / Jackdaw song / Happy birthday / Daisy will do it.
MCSET: .... KIDM 9001

PONDLES, VOL 2, THE.
Tracks: / Concertina, The / Pondleberry robbers / Tortoise and the puffer / Purple thingy / Mustard's mystery machine / Boat race, The / Wheezy squeezy / Earthworm song / Hedgehog's song, The / Travellin' light / Woodland song.
MCSET: .... KIDM 9002

Ponomarev, Valery

MEANS OF IDENTIFICATION.
LP: .... RSR 101

Ponomarev, Viocheslav

FAURE VIOLIN CONCERTO (see under Faure (composer)) (Orquesta Filarmonica de la Ciudad de Mexico).

Ponomareva, Valentina

FORTUNE TELLER.
LP: .... LR 136

INTRUSION.
LP: .... LR 156

Ponsar, Serge

BACK TO THE LIGHT.
Tracks: / Out in the night / I want money / Gotta get outside / Back to the light / Keep it hot / Life time / V.I.D.E.O.
LP: 9239141

Ponselle, Rosa

ROSA PONSELLE.
LP: .... GVC 506

ROSA PONSELLE (Verdi, Meyerbeer, Bellini, Ponchielli).
MC: .... GK 87810

Pontarddulais Male

SOFTLY AS I LEAVE YOU.
Tracks: / Softly as I leave you / Ride the chariot / Doilch I'r 'or / Finnish forest, The / Windmills of your mind / Thanks be to God / Evening's pastorale, An / Bryn myrddin / Christus redemptor (hyfrydol) / My Lord, what a morning / Memory / Lord's prayer, The / Bywyd y bugail / Mil harddach wyt na'r rhosyn gwyn / Comrades in arms.
LP: .... GRALP 8
MC: .... GRTC 8

Pontiac Brothers

DOLL HUT
.LP: .... FLP 1014

FIESTA EN LA BIBLIOTECA.
LP: .... SHIG LP1

JOHNSON.
LP: 46141

Ponty, Jean-Luc

AURORA.
Tracks: / Is once enough / Renaissance / Aurora (part 1) / Aurora (part 2) / Passenger of the dark / Lost forest / Between you and me / Waking dream.
LP: .... K 50228

CIVILIZED EVIL.
Tracks: / Demagomania / In case we survive / Forms of life / Peace crusaders / Happy robots / Shape up your mind / Good guys bad guys / Once a blue planet.
LP: .... K 50744

COSMIC MESSENGER.
Tracks: / Cosmic messenger / Art of happiness / Don't let the world pass you by / I only feel good with you / Puppets' dance / Fake paradise / Ethereal mood / Egocentric molecules.
LP: .... K 50505

ENIGMATIC OCEAN.
Tracks: / Overture / Trans love express, The / Mirage / Enigmatic ocean (parts 1 & 2) / Nostalgic lady / Struggle of the turtle to the sea parts 1,2,3.
LP: .... K 50409

FABLES.
Tracks: / Infinite pursuit / Elephants in love / Radioactive legacy / Cats tales / Perpetual rondo / In the kingdom of peace / Plastic idols.
LP: 781 276-1
MC: 781 276-4

GIFT OF TIME, THE.
Tracks: / Prologue / New resolutions / Faith in you / No more doubts / Between sea and sky / Metamorphosis / Introspective / Perceptions / Gift of time, The.
LP: 4604361
MC: 4604364

IMAGINARY VOYAGE.
Tracks: / New country / Gardens of Babylon / Wandering on the milky way / Once upon a dream / Tarantula / Imaginary voyage part 1 / Imaginary voyage part II.
LP: .... K 50317

INDIVIDUAL CHOICE.
Tracks: / Computer incantations for world peace / Far from the beaten paths / In spiritual love / Eulogy to Oscar Romero / Nostalgia / In spite of all / Individual choice.
LP: .... POLD 5138

JEAN-LUC PONTY & STEPHANE GRAPPELLI (Compact/Walkman Jazz) (Ponty, Jean-Luc/Stephane Grappelli).
Tracks: / Pent-up house / La chanson de rue / Carole's garden / Undecided / Sweet Lorraine / Cat coach / Summit soul / Flamingo / Sunday walk / Swing guitars / Tangerine.
MC: 835 320-4

KING KONG.
Tracks: / King Kong / Idiot bastard son / Twenty small cigars / How would you like to have a head like that / Music for electric violin and low budget orchestra / America drinks and goes home.
LP: .... EMS 1254
MC: .... TCEMS 1254
LP: 3C054 91651
MC: 3C254 91651
LP: .... ATAK 102
MC: .... TCATAK 102

MYSTICAL ADVENTURES.
Tracks: / Mystical adventures / Rhythms of hope / As / Final truth / Jig.
LP: .... K 50872

OPEN MIND.
Tracks: / Open mind / Solitude / Watching birds / Modern times blue / Orbital encounters / Intuition.
LP: 823 581 1
MC: 823 581 4

SONATA EROTICA.
Tracks: / Preludio / Pizzicato con fuoco e con echo / Con sensualito appassionato / Accelerando rallentando.
LP: .... AFF 133
LP: .... IRI 5008

STEPHANE GRAPPELLI WITH JEAN LUC PONTY (See under Grappelli, Stephane) (Ponty, Jean-Luc/Stephane Grappelli).

UPON THE WINGS OF MUSIC.
Tracks: / Upon the wings of music / Question with no answer / Now I know / Polyfolk dance / Waving memories / Echoes of the future / Bowing bowing / Fight for life.
LP: .... K 50149

Pony

THORNS AND CUTLERY.
LP: . . . . **CLP 225**

Ponzel, Peter

PRISM.
LP: . . . . **VS 114**

Pooh Sticks

FORMULA ONE GENERATION.
LP: . . . . **FRIGHT 37**

GREAT WHITE WONDER, THE.
LP: . . . . **CHEREE 18 LP**
MC: . . . . **CHEREE 18 MC**

ON TAPE.
LP: . . . . **FRIGHT 028**

ORGASM.
LP: . . . . **AGAMC 5**

PEEL SESSIONS: POOH STICKS.
LP: . . . . **OVER 018**

POOH STICKS.
LP: . . . . **FRIGHT 034**

Pookiesnackenburger

AS ADVERTISED ON TV.
LP: . . . . **MSTALK 1**
MC: . . . . **MSTALKC 1**

Pool Sharks

FINAL ADJUSTMENTS.
Tracks: / Moth to a flame / Destination unknown / Honeymoon with a heartache / Love is a dangerous thing / Collison / Sunshine / I remember / Welcome to the city / Shadows in the dark / Be lucky.
LP: . . . . **FIN 1**
MC: . . . . **FIN 1K**

Poole, Brian

GREATEST HITS: BRIAN POOLE.
MC: . . . . **ASK 773**

GREATEST HITS: BRIAN POOLE.
LP: . . . . **BPCV 1**

REMEMBERING BRIAN POOLE & THE TREMELOES (Poole, Brian & the Tremeloes).
LP: . . . . **REM 5**

TWIST AND SHOUT (Poole, Brian & the Tremeloes).
LP: . . . . **SPR 8579**
MC: . . . . **SPC 8579**
LP: . . . . **TAB 42**
MC: . . . . **KTAB 42**

Poole, Charlie

CHARLIE POOLE 1926-1930.
LP: . . . . **HLP 8005**

Poopshovel

I CAME, I SAW.
LP: . . . . **COMM 39191**

OPUS LENTHEMUS.
Tracks: / Young people in love / African bees / Raw / Tube rose / Sausage / Plethora / Fine / Earliness factor / Queller / Little pictures / Moshra / Ouija board.
LP: . . . . **COMM 39041**

Poor Man, Rich Man

POOR MAN, RICH MAN.
LP: . . . . **ROUNDER 1026**

Poor People of

POOR PEOPLE OF BEVERLEY HILLS (Various artists).
LP: . . . . **VSOP 40**

Poor Righteous

HOLY INTELLECT.
Tracks: / Can I start this? / Strictly ghetto / Time to say peace / So many teachers / Butt naked booty bless / Rock dis funky joint / Holy intellect / Style dropped / Word from the wise / Poor righteous teachers.
LP: . . . . **FILE 289**
MC: . . . . **FILECT 289**

PURE POVERTY.
LP: . . . . **FILER 415**
MC: . . . . **FILERCT 415**

Poors Of Reign

WRECKED.
LP: . . . . **FUCTLP 1**
MC: . . . . **FUCTMC 1**

Poovey, Groovey Joe

TWO SIDES, THE.
Tracks: / Move around / Careful baby / Ten long fingers / Thrill of love, The / Livin' alone / You may seek / I dreamed about the blues / My life's ambition / Ole Louella / Jamaica Jill / Silence baby / Two young hearts / It's a lonely night / What have I got to lose?.
LP: . . . . **SJLP 562**

YESTERDAY AND TODAY.
Tracks: / Ten long fingers / Sweet Louella / Careful baby / Move around / Part time hero / My life's ambition / Silence baby / Nursery rock / Don't blame it on me / Baby let's rock / Little Miss Linda / Cold margarita, A / Last stroke of midnight / Dream, dream baby / To get from there to here / Lost in the shuffle / All dressed up for the blues / Boogie woogie weekend.
LP: . . . . **BB 2054**
LP: . . . . **DJLP 2054**

Pop

12 SUPER HITS (Various artists).
MC: . . . . **BBMM 62**

20 GOLDEN HITS OF THE ROLLING STONES (Various artists).
MC: . . . . **AM 35**

20 HOLIDAY HITS (Various artists).
Tracks: / Dolce vita: *Paris, Ryan* / Words: *David, F.R.* / Hands up: *Ottowan* / Superman: *Various* artists / Hooray hooray it's a holi holiday: *Boney M* / Y viva Espana: *Sylvia* / Barbados: *Typically* Tropical / Clap clap sound, The: *Klaxon 5* / I want you: *Low, Gary* / Sunshine reggae: *Estapona*/ Birdie song, The: *Tweets* / Una paloma blanca: *King, Jonathan* / Brown girl in the ring: *Boney M* / D.I.S.C.O.: *Ottawan* / Live is life: *Sierras* / La bamba: *Antonia* / El bimbo: *Bimbo Jet* / Vamos a la playa: *Righeira* / Kalimba de luna: *Esposito, Tony* / Nitespot: *Anderson, Ricky.*
LP: . . . . **CTV 1**
MC: . . . . **ZC CTV 1**

20 SUPER HITS (Various artists).
LP: . . . . **PLE 7000**
MC: . . . . **PLC 7000**

40 NON STOP NUMBER ONES (Various artists).
MCSET: . . . . **MFP 4110409**
MCSET: . . . . **TCMFP 1040**
MC: . . . . **TCDL 1040**
2LP: . . . . **MFP 4110403**
MCSET: . . . . **TCMFP 411040 5**

40 UNFORGETTABLE MEMORIES (Various artists).
2LP: . . . . **PLD 8017**
MCSET: . . . . **PLDC 8017**

100 MINUTES OF DANCE PARTY HITS (Various artists).
MC: . . . . **ZCTON 122**

GREAT BRITISH NUMBER ONES (VOL.2) (Various artists).
Tracks: / Tie a yellow ribbon: *Dawn* / Everything I own: *Boothe, Ken* / Sweets for my sweet: *Searchers*/ Puppet on a string: *Shaw, Sandie* / Seasons in the sun: *Jacks, Terry* / Gamblin' man: *Donegan, Lonnie*/ Israelites: *Dekker, Desmond* / Give a little love: *Bay City Rollers* / Cumberland gap: *Donegan, Lonnie*/ Sailor: *Clark, Petula* / Wand'rin' star: *Marvin, Lee* / Double barrel: *Collins, Dave & Ansel* / Save your kisses for me: *Brotherhood Of Man* / Back home: *England World Cup Squad* / Bye bye baby: *Bay City Rollers*/ I'm a believer: *Monkees* / When: *Kalin Twins* / Knock three times: *Dawn* / Where are you now?: *Trent*, Jackie / Tired of waiting: *Kinks* / Long live love: *Shaw, Sandie* / Baby come back: *Equals* / Baby jump: *Jerry, Mungo* / Putting on the style: *Donegan, Lonnie* / If: *Savalas, Telly.*
MCSET: . . . . **CRT 084**
2LP: . . . . **CR 084**

GREAT BRITISH NUMBER ONES (VOL.1) (Various artists).
Tracks: / What do you want to make those eyes at me for?: *Ford, Emile & The Checkmates* / Sunny afternoon: *Kinks*/ Mony mony: *James, Tommy & The Shondells* / Don't throw your love away: *Searchers* / Barbados: *Typically* Tropical / That'll be the day: *Crickets* / Baby, now that I've found you: *Foundations* / Why do fools fall in love?: *Lymon, Frankie & The Teenagers* / Always something there to remind me: *Shaw, Sandie* / Have I the right?: *Honeycombs* / Kung fu fighting: *Douglas, Carl* / My old man's a dustman: *Donegan, Lonnie* / Rock around the clock: *Haley, Bill & The Comets* / What a wonderful world: *Armstrong, Louis* / Michelle: *Overlanders*/ Sad sweet dreamer: *Sweet Sensation* / Angelo: *Brotherhood Of Man* / This is my song: *Clark, Petula*/ Let the heartaches begin: *Baldry, Long John* / Matchstalk men and matchstalk cats and dogs: *Brian & Michael*/ In the Summertime: *Mungo Jerry* / You really got me: *Kinks* / It doesn't matter anymore: *Holly, Buddy*/ Needles and pins: *Searchers* / Blue moon: *Marcels* / I'll be home: *Boone, Pat* / You to me are everything: *Real Thing.*
2LP: . . . . **CR 044**
MCSET: . . . . **CRT 044**

GREAT BRITISH NUMBER ONES (VOL.3) (Various artists).
Tracks: / Rock and roll waltz: *Starr, Kay* / Jealous mind: *Stardust, Alvin* / Little things mean a lot: *Kallen*, Kitty / Chirpy chirpy cheep cheep: *Middle Of The Road* / Catch a falling star: *Como, Perry* / Mary's boy child: *Belafonte, Harry* / With a girl like you: *Nilsson (Harry)* / Here comes summer: *Keller, Jerry* / Ms. Grace: *Tymes* / Cabaret: *Various artists* / Amazing grace: *Royal Scots Dragoon Guards* / Day that the rains came down, The: *Morgan, Jane* / In the year 2525: *Zager/Evans* / Cherry pink and apple blossom white: *Prado, Perez*/ Yes sir, I can boogie: *Baccara* / Hold my hand: *Cornell, Don* / My ding a ling: *Berry, Chuck* / Blockbuster: *Various original artists* / Magic moments: *Como, Perry* / Billy don't be a hero: *Paper Lace* / Distant drums: *Reeves, Jim* / Young love: *Hunter, Tab* / Don't cry for me Argentina: *Covington, Julie.*
2LP: . . . . **CR 088**
MCSET: . . . . **CRT 088**

GREAT BRITISH NUMBER ONES (VOL.4) (Various artists).
2LP: . . . . **CR 089**
MCSET: . . . . **CRT 089**

GREATEST STARS ON 45 (Various artists).
LP: . . . . **CBS 25048**

HEART OF SOUL (Various artists).
Tracks: / I just can't stop loving you: *Jackson, Michael* / Shake you down: *Abbott, Gregory* / You got it all: *Jets (American)* / Don't make me wait for love: *Kenny G.* / Respect yourself: *Willis, Bruce* / Smoking gun: *Cray, Robert Band* / Lost in emotion: *Lisa Lisa* / Rhythm is gonna get you: *Estefan, Gloria* / (You gotta) fight for your right (to party): *Beastie Boys.*
LP: **4629931**
MC: **4629934**

HEARTS AND KNIVES.
LP: . . . . **RNEP 510**

HERE COMES SUMMER (Rediscover the 50's and 60's) (Various artists).
Tracks: / Summer Place, A, Theme from: *Faith, Percy* / Big bad John: *Dean, Jimmy* / Bless you: *Orlando, Tony*/ Tower of strength: *Vaughan, Frankie* / Sea of love: *Wilde, Marty* / Halfway to paradise: *Fury, Billy*/ Only the lonely: *Orbison, Roy* / Running bear: *Preston, Johnny* / Here comes summer: *Keller, Jerry*/ Take five: *Brubeck, Dave Quartet* / Let it be me: *Everly Brothers* / Handy man: *Jones, Jimmy (singer)*/ Lion sleeps tonight, The: *Tokens* / Happy birthday sweet sixteen: *Sedaka, Neil* / Language of love: *Loudermilk*, John D. / I will follow him: *March, Little Peggy* / Romeo: *Clark, Petula* / Devil woman: *Robbins, Marty*/ Sheila: *Roe, Tommy* / Speedy Gonzales: *Boone, Pat* / Little town flirt: *Shannon, Del* / (Dance with) the guitar man: *Eddy, Duane* / Peggy Sue got married: *Holly, Buddy* / It's my party: *Gore, Lesley.*
MCSET: . . . . **OG 2203**

I AM WOMAN (Various artists).
LP: . . . . **WOMTV 1**
MC: . . . . **WOMMC 1**

I WRITE THE SONGS (Various artists).
Tracks: / I write the songs: *Various artists* / Fantasy: *Various artists* / January, February: *Various artists*/ Heart on my sleeve: *Various artists* / I won't last a day without you: *Various artists* / I could have been a sailor: *Various artists* / Pretty girls: *Various artists* / Kiss on my list: *Various artists* / Dust in the wind: *Various artists* / Harry: *Various artists* / Souvenirs: *Various artists* / Lay lady lay: *Various artists* / Time passages: *Various artists* / Song for a winters night: *Various artists* / Solitaire: *Various artists* / Spaceman came travelling, A: *Various artists* / Somewhere in the night: *Various artists* / Say you don't mind: *Various artists* / Shine silently: *Various artists* / Lady of the dawn: *Various artists* / I just wanna stop: *Various artists* / I know there's something going on: *Various artists* / Love among the ruins: *Various artists* / Candle in the wind: *Various artists* / It never rains in Southern California: *Various artists*/ I'll never fall in love again: *Various artists* / Will you: *Various artists* / All by myself: *Various artists.*
2LP: . . . . **STD 4**
MCSET: . . . . **STDK 4**

IN THE HEAT OF THE NIGHT (Various artists).
Tracks: / Use it up, wear it out: *Odyssey* / Keep in touch: *Various artists* / Dancing in outer space: *Atmosphere*/ Do you feel my love?: *Grant, Eddy* / Love is in the air: *Young, John Paul* / You can do it: *Hudson, Al*/ Falcon: *Ram Band* / This feelin': *Hooker, Frank* / Can you feel the force?: *Real Thing* / Rock the boat: *Hues Corporation* / Dancin' easy: *Williams, Danny* / Amigo: *Black Slate* / You little trust maker: *Tymes*/ Morning dance: *Spyro Gyra* / Slowdown: *Miles, John* / Slide: *Rah Band* / Whenever you want my love: *Real Thing* / Starship trooper: *Brightman, Sarah* / Can't get enough of you: *Grant, Eddy* / We can do it: *Stone, R & J.*
MCSET: . . . . **CRT 011**

IS THIS LOVE (Various artists).
Tracks: / Is this love: *Whitesnake* / Everywhere: *Fleetwood Mac* / Valerie: *Winwood, Steve* / China in your hand: *T'Pau* / Never tear us apart: *INXS* / What's love got to do with it: *Turner, Tina* / Missing you: *Waite, John* / Drive: *Cars* / Layla: *Derek & The Dominoes* (Full length version.) / Since you've been gone: *Rainbow (Group)* / Stuck with you: *Lewis, Huey & The News* / Kayleigh: *Marillion* / Don't stand so close to me: *Police* / Little wing: *Hendrix, Jimi Experience* / Wonderful tonight: *Clapton, Eric.*
LP: . . . . **EMTV 47**
MC: . . . . **TCEMTV 47**

ISLAND STORY, THE (Various artists).
Tracks: / With or without you: *U2* / Higher love: *Steve Winwood* / Virginia plain: *Roxy Music* / Living in the past: *Jethro Tull* / All right now: *Free* / Keep on running: *Davis, Spencer Group* (Not on CD.) / Paper sun: *Traffic* (Not on CD.) / Addicted to love: *Palmer, Robert* / Slave to the rhythm: *Jones, Grace*/ Annie I'm not your daddy: *Kid Creole & The Coconuts* / Cuba: *Gibson Brothers* / Harlem shuffle: *Bob & Earl*/ Israelites: *Dekker, Desmond & The Aces* (Not on CD.) / My boy lollipop: *Millie* (Not on CD.) / Now that we've found love: *Third World* (Not on CD.) / No woman, no cry: *Marley, Bob & The Wailers* / Love hurts: *Capaldi*, Jim (Not on CD.) / Up where we belong: *Cocker, Joe & Jennifer Warnes* (Not on CD.) / Smoke gets in your eyes: *Ferry*, Bryan / Wild world: *Cliff, Jimmy* (Not on CD.) / Eighteen with a bullet: *Wingfield, Pete* / Si tu dois partir: *Fairport Convention* / Morning has broken: *Stevens, Cat* / World shut your mouth: *Cope, Julian* / Kissing with confidence: *Will Powers* / Too good to be forgotten: *Amazulu* / Video killed the radio star: *Buggles*(Not on CD.) / This town ain't big enough for the both of us: *Sparks* (Not on CD.) / Do anything you wanna do: *Eddie & The Hot Rods* / Forgotten Town: *Christians* / Rage hard: *Frankie Goes To Hollywood.*
2LP: . . . . **ISL 25**
MCSET: . . . . **ISLC 25**

ISLE OF WIGHT: ATLANTA POP FESTIVAL (Various artists).
LPS: **66311**

IT STARTED WITH A KISS (Various artists).
MC: . . . . **ARC 910304**
LP: . . . . **ARC 910301**

IT'S COOL (Various artists).
Tracks: / Lovely day: *Withers, Bill* / Club Tropicana: *Wham* / Walking on sunshine: *Katrina & The Waves*/ La bamba: *Los Lobos* / Wouldn't it be nice: *Beach Boys* / Beach baby: *First Class* / Here comes the sun: *Harley, Steve & Cockney Rebel* / Summertime blues: *Cochran, Eddie* / Summer in the city: *Lovin' Spoonful*/ On the beach: *Rea, Chris* / Summer breeze: *Isley Brothers* / Long hot summer: *Style Council* / Groovin': *Young Rascals* / Take it easy: *Eagles* / Sunny afternoon: *Kinks* / Under the boardwalk: *Drifters*/ Rhythm of the rain: *Cascades* / Summer (the first time): *Goldsboro, Bobby* / Girl from Ipanema, The: *Gilberto, Astrud* / Summertime: *Fitzgerald, Ella.*
LP: . . . . **PCSTV 1**
MC: . . . . **TCPCSTV 1**

JUKE BOX COLLECTION - DANCING ON A SATURDAY NIGH (Popular hits of the 60's & 70's) (Various artists).
Tracks: / Son of my father: *Chicory Tip* / Banner man: *Blue Mink* / Snoopy Vs the Red Baron: *Royal Guardsmen*/ Mouldy old dough: *Lieutenant Pigeon* / Beautiful Sunday: *Boone, Daniel* / Venus: *Shocking Blue* / Puppet on a string: *Shaw, Sandie* / Bridget the midget: *Stevens, Ray* / Sugar sugar: *Archies* / Beach baby: *First* Class / Dancing on a Saturday night: *Blue, Barry* / Simon says: *1910 Fruitgum Co* / Is this the way to Amarillo: *Christie, Tony* / Little arrows: *Lee, Leapy.*
LP: . . . . **OG 1713**
MC: . . . . **OG 2713**

JUKE BOX GEMS (Various artists).
MCSET: . . . . **DTO 10218**

JUKE BOX SATURDAY NIGHT (Various artists).
Tracks: / Sweet little sixteen: *Berry, Chuck* / Good golly Miss Molly: *Little Richard* / Venus in blue jeans: *Clanton, Jimmy* / See you later alligator: *Haley, Bill* / I'm a man: *Chicago* / Chapel of love: *Dixie Cups* / Volare: *Rydell, Bobby* / Rock 'n' roll music: *Berry, Chuck* / Come see about me: *Knight, Gladys* & The Pips / Soul man: *Sam & Dave* / Hold on I'm coming: *Sam & Dave* / Blue Monday: *Domino, Fats*/ 25 or 6 to 4: *Chicago* / Forget him: *Rydell, Bobby* / Girl can't

help it, The: *Little Richard* / Under the boardwalk: *Drifters* / Sweet pea: *Roe, Tommy* / Wild one: *Rydell, Bobby* / Memphis: *Berry, Chuck*.
MCSET: . . . . **DTO 10270**
MCSET: . . . . **DTOL 10270**

JUNIOR SAW IT HAPPEN (Various artists).
Tracks: / Get it on: *T. Rex* / Flowers in the rain: *Move* / Shapes of things: *Yardbirds* / Tin soldier: *Small Faces* / You really got me: *Kinks* / America: *Nice* / 2nd amendment: *Various artists* / Down the dustpipe: *Status Quo* / Needles and pins: *Searchers* / Have I the right: *Honeycombs* / Homburg: *Procul Harum* / With a little help from my friends: *Cocker, Joe* / If paradise is half as nice: *Amen Corner*/ Blackberry Way: *Move* / Lazy Sunday: *Small Faces* / Hot love: *T. Rex* / For your love: *Yardbirds*/ Waterloo sunset: *Kinks* / Melting pot: *Blue Mink* / Catch the wind: *Donovan* / Whiter shade of pale: *Procul Harum*.
LP: . . . . **FBL 1001**

LA VIE EN ROSE VOL. 1 (Various artists).
LP: . . . . **ERECT 1**
MC: . . . . **ERECTC 1**

LAND OF MAKE BELIEVE (Various artists).
MC: . . . . **STC 011**

LEGENDS (Various artists).
2LP: . . . . **CR 5162**
MCSET: . . . . **CRT 5162**

LEGENDS AND HEROES (Various artists).
LP: . . . . **SMR 987**
MC: . . . . **SMC 987**

LEGENDS (SOLITAIRE COLLECTION) (Various artists).
2LP: . . . . **STD 8**
MCSET: . . . . **STDK 8**

LEGENDS VOL.1, THE (Various artists).
LP: . . . . **AMULP 1**
MC: . . . . **ZCAMU 1**

LEGENDS VOL.2, THE (Various artists).
LP: . . . . **AMULP 2**
MC: . . . . **ZCAMU 2**

LENNON AND MCCARTNEY SONGBOOK (Various artists).
Tracks: / Lucy in the sky with diamonds: *John, Elton* / Let it be: *Franklin, Aretha* / Here, there and everywhere: *Harris, Emmylou* / Anytime at all: *Lofgren, Nils* / Day tripper: *Redding, Otis* / With a little help from my friends: *Cocker, Joe* / Hey Jude: *Pickett, Wilson* / In my life: *Collins, Judy* / I call your name: *Mamas & Papas* / Got to get you into my life: *Bennett, Cliff & The Rebel Rousers* / Tomorrow never knows: *Monsoon*/ Get back: *Ike & Tina Turner* / I saw him standing there: *Tiffany* / Please please me: *Flamin' Groovies*/ Things we said today: *Richard, Cliff* / Nowhere man: *Three Good Reasons* / I've just seen a face: *Dillards*/ From me to you: *McFerrin, Bobby* / She came in through the bathroom window: *Cocker, Joe* / It's for you: *Three* Dog Night / Step inside love: *Black, Cilla* / Bad to me: *Kramer, Billy J. & The Dakotas* / Yesterday: *Faithfull, Marianne* / You've got to hide your love away: *Silkie*.
LP: . . . . **VSOP LP 150**
MC: . . . . **VSOPMC 150**

LENNON AND MCCARTNEY SONGBOOK, THE (K-TEL) (Various artists).
LP: . . . . **NE 1317**
MC: . . . . **CE 2317**

LET'S HEAR IT FROM THE GIRLS (Various artists).
Tracks: / Cloudbusting: *Bush, Kate* / We don't need another hero: *Turner, Tina* / Someone for me: *Houston*, Whitney / You look good to me: *Cherrelle* / Dare to dream: *Wills, Viola* / Pain: *Wright, Betty* / Light my fire: *Stewart, Amii* / Holding out for a hero: *Tyler, Bonnie* / After the love has gone: *Princess*/ One dance won't do: *Hall, Audrey* / This is my life: *Kitt, Eartha* / Sugar walls: *Easton, Sheena* / Smooth operator: *Sade* / Love is a battlefield: *Benatar, Pat* / That ole devil called love: *Moyet, Alison*/ See the day: *Lee, Dee C* / Together we are beautiful: *Kinney, Fern* / Power of love, The: *Rush, Jennifer*/ I'll be your friend: *Wilson, Precious* / Misty blue: *Moore, Dorothy* / Stir it up: *Labelle, Patti* / Integrity: *Franklin, Aretha* / Automatic: *Pointer Sisters* / I will survive: *Gaynor, Gloria* / If you're ready (come go with me): *Turner, Ruby* / Let the four winds blow: *Lasalle, Denise* / In the shelter of your arms: *Rustie* / Round and around: *Graham, Jaki*.
MCSET: . . . . **SMR 8614**
MCSET: . . . . **SMC 8614**

LOOK OF LOVE, THE (Various artists).
MC: . . . . **MCTC 039**

MAGNETIC HITS (Various artists).
Tracks: / Duke of Earl: *Darts* / Red dress: *Stardust, Alvin* / I'm stone in love with you: *Sherman Brothers*/ I got to sing: *J.A.L.N. Band* / To the beat: *Grant, Carrie* / Walking in the sunshine: *Bad Manners*/ Buzz buzz a diddle it: *Matchbox* / Get up and boogie: *Silver Convention* / Hurt so good: *Cadogan, Susan*/ Starfighter theme, The: *Starfighters* / Gimme some: *Brendon* / Sherry: *Baker, Adrian* / There's a whole lot of loving: *Guys & Dolls* / Gee baby: *Shelley, Peter* / Love me tonight: *Walters, Trevor* / Move your body: *Farrow, Gene* / Shanga lang song, The: *Pearl, Ruby & The Dreamboats* / Tell me why: *Stardust, Alvin*/ Let's hang on: *Darts* / When you ask about me: *Matchbox* / Drive safely darlin': *Mason, Barry* / My girl lollipop: *Bad Manners* / Oh what a night: *Thompson, Linda* / It's raining: *Darts* / Goodbye-ee: *14-18*/ Just one cornetto: *Count Giovani di Regina* / Disco music: *J.A.L.N. Band* / How can you mend a broken heart: *Various artists*.
2LP: . . . . **CR 108**
MCSET: . . . . **CRT 108**

MASSIVE HITS (Various artists).
LP: . . . . **STAR 2505**

MEMORIES ARE MADE OF THESE... (Various artists).
MC: . . . . **CC 501**

MOST COLLECTION, THE (Various artists).
Tracks: / Jailhouse rock: *Stewart, Rod* / All shook up: *Stewart, Rod* / Little games: *Yardbirds* / Ten little indians: *Yardbirds* / Friends: *Reid, Terry* / Superlungs: *Reid, Terry* / We've gotta get out of this place: *Animals* / House of the rising sun (Trad. arr Price): *Animals* / Beck's bolero: *Beck, Jeff*/ Hi ho silver lining: *Beck, Jeff* / Whole lotta love: *CCS* / Tap turns on the water: *CCS*.
LP: . . . . **MFP 50015**

MUSIC MACHINE (Various artists).
MCSET: . . . . **DTO 10057**

MUSIC ON THE MOVE (20 ORIGINAL POP HITS) (Various artists).
MC: . . . . **INTK 9002**

NIGHT MOVES (Various artists).
LP: . . . . **NE 1255**
MC: . . . . **CE 2255**

NIGHT MOVES (Various artists).
LP: . . . . **NE 1065**

NUMBER ONE HITS VOL.2 (Various artists).
MC: . . . . **ASK 772**

NUMBER ONES OF THE 80'S (Various artists).
MCSET: . . . . **STAC 2382**
2LP: . . . . **STAR 2382**

OLD GOLD'N'JUKEBOX (Various artists).
MC: . . . . **NK 42754**
LP: . . . . **NL 42754**

ONE HUNDRED DANCING PARTY FAVOURITES (Various artists).
MCSET: . . . . **TR 41 15515**
MCSET: . . . . **TR 1551**

ORIGINAL STARTRACKS (Various artists).
Tracks: / December '63 (oh what a night): *Four Seasons* / Lonely boy: *Gold, Andrew* / Chanson d'amour: *Manhattan* Transfer / Nature boy: *Benson, George* / Welcome back: *Sebastian, John* / Takin' it to the streets: *Doobie* Brothers / Nights on Broadway: *Staton, Candi* / Disco inferno: *Trammps* / Feel the need: *Detroit Emeralds*/ Happy days: *Pratt & McClain* / Let your love flow: *Bellamy Brothers* / Midnight at the Oasis: *Muldaur, Maria*/ Sundown: *Lightfoot, Gordon* / Le freak: *Chic* / Patches: *Carter, Clarence* / Ma baker: *Boney M*/ Cathy's clown: *Everly Brothers* / 59th Street bridge song: *Harpers Bizarre* / Polk salad Annie: *White, Tony Joe* / I must be in love: *Rutles*.
MC: **K4 58039**

ORIGINAL TOP HITS (VOL.4) (Various artists).
Tracks: / Blue world: *Moody Blues* / Nightmares: *Flock Of Seagulls* / Sporcati: *Arcangeli, Marina* / Where did we go wrong: *Liquid Gold* / That's the way: *Marley, Rita* / Love to love: *Bimbo Jet* / No news: *Chico & The Chile Sisters* / To hell with him: *Taka Boom* / Vamos a la playa: *Richeira* / Maybe one day: *Creatures* / Turn to me: *Rickfors, Mikael* / Magic touch: *Simmons, Leroy* / Just one more kiss: *Renee* & Renato / Tango: *Maanam* / Danger games: *Pinkees* / Downtown rock 'n' roll discotheque: *Blizzard*/ Number one contender: *Bertucci, Anne*.
MC: **425847**

OUT OF THE BOX (Various artists).
LP: . . . . **HOP 213**
MC: . . . . **HOPC 213**

PENS GUNS AND RIFFS (Various artists).
LP: . . . . **PACT 1**

POP CLASSICS (Various artists).
LP: . . . . **ARC 944421**
MC: . . . . **ARC 944424**

POWERPLAY (Various artists).
LP: . . . . **DISCO 208**

RAK PAK, THE (Various artists).
Tracks: / Brother: *CCS* / Dance with the devil: *Powell, Cozy* / Some girls: *Racey* / Tiger feet: *Mud*/ Brother Louie: *Hot Chocolate* / I don't want to lose you: *Kandidate* / Kara Kara: *New World* / Journey: *Browne, Duncan* / Oh you pretty things: *Noone, Peter* / Tap turns on the water: *CCS* / Tear me apart: *Quatro, Suzi* / Dynamite: *Mud* / Forty eight crash: *Quatro, Suzi* / Na na na: *Powell, Cozy* / Man from Nazareth: *Jones, John Paul* / Tom Tom turnaround: *New World* / Emma: *Hot Chocolate* / Cambodia: *Wilde, Kim* / If I could: *Felix, Julie*.
2LP: . . . . **VSOPLP 117**
MC: . . . . **VSOPMC 117**

RAK'S - GREATEST HITS (Various artists).
Tracks: / House of the rising sun: *Animals* / I'm into something good: *Herman's Hermits* / Tobacco road: *Nashville* Teens / Hi ho silver lining: *Beck, Jeff* / To sir with love: *Lulu* / I've been drinking: *Beck, Jeff* & Rod Stewart / Whole lotta love: *CCS* / Oh you pretty thing: *Noone, Peter* / Dance with the devil: *Powell*, Cozy / Journey: *Browne, Duncan* / Tiger feet: *Mud* / So you win again: *Hot Chocolate* / Can the can: *Quatro, Suzi* / Bump, The: *Kenny* / Motor bikin': *Spedding, Chris* / Lay your love on me: *Racey*/ Kids in America: *Wilde, Kim* / Tom, Tom turnaround: *New World* / Classic: *Gurvitz, Adrian* / You sexy thing: *Hot Chocolate*.
LP: . . . . **SRAK 545**
MC: . . . . **TCSRAK 545**

REMEMBER WHEN (MEMORIES OF 50S & 60S) (Various artists).
2LP: . . . . **PDA 076**
MCSET: . . . . **PDC 076**

ROCK 'N' ROLL YEARS (1968-1971) (Various artists).
Tracks: / This wheel's on fire: *Driscoll, Julie* / Fire: *Brown, Arthur* / Crossroads: *Hatch, Tony* / Nights in white satin: *Moody Blues* / Voodoo chile: *Hendrix, Jimi* / Pinball Wizard: *John, Elton* / I'm the urban spaceman: *Bonzo Dog Band* / Going up the country: *Canned Heat* / I'd rather go blind: *Various artists*/ Games people play: *South, Joe* / Instant Karma: *Lennon, John* / Rag mama rag: *Band* / Black night: *Deep* Purple / Witches promise: *Jethro Tull* / All right now: *Free* / My sweet lord: *Harrison, George*/ Your song: *John, Elton* / Get it on: *T. Rex* / Malt and barley blues: *McGuinness Flint* / Maggie may: *Stewart, Rod*.
LP: . . . . **REN 634**
MC: . . . . **ZCN 634**

ROCK, POP, GLAM AND SOUL (A Selection from Bell) (Various artists).
Tracks: / Cry like a baby: *Box Tops* / Can you hear me: *Dorsey, Lee* / Sweet inspiration: *Johnson, Johnny &* Bandwagon / Love grows where my Rosemary goes: *Edison Lighthouse* / (Blame it) on the pony express: *Johnson*, Johnny & Bandwagon / Didn't I (blow your mind this time): *Delfonics* / Something old something new: *Fantastics*/ La la means I love you: *Delfonics* / Knock three times: *Dawn* / Johnny Reggae: *Piglets* / Rock'n'roll (part 1): *Glitter, Gary* / Third finger left hand: *Pearls* / Dancing on a Saturday night: *Blue, Barry*/ I'm the leader of the gang (I am): *Glitter, Gary* / Do you wanna dance: *Blue, Barry* / Angel face: *Glitter* Band / Hey rock'n'roll: *Showaddywaddy* / Tell him: *Hello* / Seasons in the sun: *Jacks, Terry* / There goes my first love: *Drifters* / New York groove: *Hello* / Hello happiness: *Drifters* / Under the moon of love: *Showaddywaddy* / People like you and people like me: *Glitter Band*.
2LP: . . . . **VSOPLP 122**
MC: . . . . **VSOPMC 122**

ROCK RHYTHM AND BLUES (Various artists).
Tracks: / I'm ready: *John, Elton* / For your precious love: *McDonald, Michael* / Ten commandments: *Hewett*, Howard / It's just a matter of time: *Travis, Randy* / Roll with my Henry: *McVie, Christine* / This magic moment: *James, Rick* / Fever: *Khan, Chaka* / I wanna be your girl: *Manhattan Transfer* / Mr. Lee: *Pointer Sisters* / Goodnight my love: *DeBarge*.
LP: . . . . **WX 255**
MC: . . . . **WX 255 C**

ROOTS REGGAE ROCK (Various artists).
Tracks: / Wonderful world, beautiful people: *Cliff, Jimmy* / Young gifted and black: *Bob and Marcia* / Double barrel: *Collins, Dave & Ansel* / Israelites: *Dekker, Desmond* / Let your yeah be yeah: *Pioneers* / Black and white: *Greyhound* / Suzanne beware of the devil: *Livingstone, Dandy* / Rivers of Babylon: *U-Roy* / Up town top ranking / Kaya: *Marley, Bob* / Everything I own: *Boothe, Ken* / Liquidator: *Harry J. All Stars*/ Hurt so good: *Cadogan, Susan* / Help me make it through the night: *Holt, John* / Why must I cry: *Tosh, Peter*/ Funky Kingston: *Toots & The Maytals* / Love of the common people: *Thomas, Nicky* / Red red wine: *UB40*/ Can't get used to losing you: *Beat* / Do you feel my love: *Grant, Eddy* / Amigo: *Black Slate* / Money in my pocket: *Brown, Dennis* / On my radio: *Selector* / Tide is high: *Blondie* / Reggae for it now: *Lovelady*, Bill / Tears on my pillow / Do you really want to hurt me: *Culture Club* / Youth of today, The: *Musical Youth*/ I shot the sheriff: *Light Of The World* / So here I am: *UB40* / Special brew: *Bad Manners* / Iko iko: *Retriever* / Try Jah love: *Third World* / Love of the common people: *Young, Paul*.
2LP: . . . . **STAR 2233**
MC: . . . . **STAC 2233**

SALUTE TO THE BEE GEES (Various artists).
MC: . . . . **AM 8**

SATURDAY NIGHT'S ALRIGHT (Various artists).
2LP: . . . . **CR 5159**
MCSET: . . . . **CRT 5159**

SHANGRI LA - A TRIBUTE TO THE KINKS (Various artists).
LP: . . . . **ILLUSION 003**

SIMON BATES' PARTY ALBUM (Various artists).
Tracks: / Rock around the clock: *Haley, Bill & The Comets* / Great balls of fire: *Lewis, Jerry Lee* / Singing the blues: *Mitchell, Guy* / Yes tonight Josephine: *Ray, Johnnie* / Bye bye love: *Everly Brothers* / At the hop: *Danny & The Juniors* / When: *Kalin Twins* / C'mon everybody: *Cochran, Eddie* / It's late: *Nelson*, Rick(y) / Teenager in love: *Wilde, Marty* / Hound dog: *Presley, Elvis* / Lollipop: *Mudlarks* / Hard day's night, A: *Beatles* / I only want to be with you: *Springfield, Dusty* / It's my party: *Stewart, Dave* & Barbara *Gaskin* / Locomotion, The: *Little Eva* / Needles and pins: *Searchers* / Just one look: *Hollies*/ Down town: *Clark, Petula* / My tambourine man: *Byrds* / San Francisco: *Mackenzie, Scott* / Monday Monday: *Mamas & Papas* / Onion song, The: *Gaye, Marvin*.
LP: . . . . **SHM 3295**
MC: . . . . **HSC 3295**

SINGER AND THE SONG, THE (Various artists).
Tracks: / Chelsea morning: *Mitchell, Joni* / Baker street: *Rafferty, Gerry* / You're so vain: *Simon, Carly*/ Streets of London: *McTell, Ralph* / Walk on the wild side: *Reed, Lou* / Last thing on my mind: *Paxton, Tom*/ Fool (If you think it's over): *Rea, Chris* / Cathedral song: *Tikaram, Tanita* / Your song: *John, Elton*/ How men are: *Aztec Camera* / Fire and rain: *Taylor, James* / Vincent: *McLean, Don* / Orinoco flow: *Enya*/ Catch the wind: *Donovan* / If you could read my mind: *Lightfoot, Gordon* / Where do you go to my lovely: *Sarstedt*, Peter / It never rains in Southern California: *Hammond, Albert* / Me and Bobby McGee: *Kristofferson, Kris*/ Suzanne: *Cohen, Leonard* / Kid: *Pretenders*.
LP: . . . . **SMR 975**
MC: . . . . **SMC 975**

SMASH HITS - VOL.3 (Various artists).
MC: . . . . **AM 46**

SOFTLY AS I LEAVE YOU (Various artists).
Tracks: / Softly as I leave you: *Monro, Matt* / Cry me a river: *Gayle, Crystal* / And I love you so: *Hill*, Vince / By the time I get to Phoenix: *Campbell, Glen* / I (who have nothing): *Bassey, Shirley* / Honey: *Goldsboro*, Bobby / I apologise: *Proby, P.J.* / Woman: *Peter & Gordon* / Till there was you: *Lee, Peggy* / If not you: *Dr. Hook* / Summer (the first time): *Goldsboro, Bobby* / Anyone who had a heart: *Black, Cilla*/ Where do I begin?: *Hill, Vince* / Maria: *Proby, P.J.* / Still: *Dodd, Ken* / Talking in your sleep: *Gayle*, Crystal / Walk away: *Monro, Matt* / Funny how time slips away: *Nelson, Willie* / Don't let it die: *Smith, Hurricane* / God only knows: *Beach Boys*.
LP: . . . . **MFP 41 5667 1**
MC: . . . . **MFP 41 5667 4**

SONGS OF THE BEATLES (Various artists).

Tracks: / Get back: *Various artists* / And I love her: *Various artists* / Eleanor Rigby: *Various artists*/ Fool on the hill: *Various artists* / You never give me your money: *Various artists* / Come together: *Various* artists / I want you: *Various artists* / Blackbird: *Various artists* / Something: *Various artists*/ Here, there and everywhere: *Various artists* / Long and winding road: *Various artists* / Yesterday: *Various artists* / Hey Jude: *Various artists.*
LP: . . . . **K 50792**

SOUNDS BOUNCY (Various artists).
Tracks: / Puppet on a string: *Various artists* / Y viva Espana: *Various artists* / Waterloo: *Various artists*/ Up up and away: *Various artists* / Tie a yellow ribbon: *Various artists* / Yellow rose of Texas: *Various* artists / Poor people of Paris: *Various artists* / La bamba: *Various artists* / Jersey bounce: *Various* artists / Sugar sugar: *Various artists* / Ob la di ob la da: *Various artists* / Hey look me over: *Various artists* / Seventy six trombones: *Various artists* / Down town: *Various artists.*
LP: . . . . **MOR 28**

SOUNDS LIKE ABBA (Various artists).
MC: . . . . **VCA 090**

SOUNDS OF BONEY M (Various artists).
MC: . . . . **AM 27**

SPIRIT OF PEACE (Various artists).
Tracks: / Higher love: *Winwood, Steve* / Biko: *Gabriel, Peter* / Passengers: *John, Elton* / I believe: *Tears For Fears* / No one is to blame: *Jones, Howard* / Pipes of peace: *McCartney, Paul* / Strange fruit: *Sting* / Brothers in arms: *Dire Straits* / Pink Houses: *Cougar, John Mellencamp* / Ghost dancing: *Simple Minds* / Tonight: *Adams, Bryan.*
2LP: . . . . **SMR 743**
MCSET: . . . . **SMC 743**

SPOTLIGHT ON STATESIDE (Various artists).
LP: . . . . **SPOT 1033**
MC: . . . . **ZCSPT 1033**

STAX GOLD (Hits 1968-1974) (Various artists).
LP: . . . . **SXD 043**
MC: . . . . **SXDC 043**

STEVIE WONDER SONGBOOK (Various artists).
LP: . . . . **STLD 0020**

STREET SCENE (Various artists).
Tracks: / Heartbreaker: *Warwick, Dionne* / I wanna do it with you: *Manilow, Barry* / Knock me out: *Gary's* Gang / Changes: *Imagination* / Back on the chain gang: *Pretenders* / Jack and Diane: *Mellencamp, John* Cougar / Don't pay the ferryman: *De Burgh, Chris* / I don't want to be the one: *Searchers* / Danger games: *Pinkees* / Give me your heart tonight: *Various artists* / Save your love: *Renee & Renato* / Young guns (go for it): *Wham* / Wishing: *Flock Of Seagulls* / Cry boy cry: *Blue Zoo* / Let's go to bed: *Cure*/ Here you come again: *Convertibles* / Samson and Delilah: *Bad Manners* / Pata pata: *Natasha* / Life in Tokyo: *Japan* / Lies: *Thompson Twins* / Classic rock classics: *Various artists* / Best years of our lives: *Modern Romance.*
LP: . . . . **NE 1183**
MC: . . . . **CE 2128**

TODAYS SMASH HITS VOL.3 (Various artists).
MC: . . . . **AIM 57**

TON OF HITS, A (Various artists).
Tracks: / Sealed with a kiss: *Donovan, Jason* / Beyond your wildest dreams: *Gordon, Lonnie* / Packjammed with the party possee: *Stock/Aitken/Waterman* / Roadblock: *Stock/Aitken/Waterman* / After the love has gone: *Princess*/ Say I'm your number one: *Princess* / New York afternoon: *Mondo Cane* / Let's get together tonite: *Walsh,* Steve / No fool (for love): *Dean, Hazell* / Wouldn't change a thing: *Minogue, Kylie* / Never gonna give you up: *Astley, Rick* / Whenever you need somebody: *Astley, Rick* / Can't forget you: *Sonia* / Together forever: *Astley, Rick* / They say it's gonna rain: *Dean, Hazell* / I should be so lucky: *Minogue, Kylie* / Cross my broken heart: *Sinitta* / Got to be certain: *Minogue, Kylie* / Je ne sais pas pourquoi: *Minogue, Kylie*/ That's the way it is: *Mel & Kim* / Blame it on the boogie: *Big Fun* / Showin' out (get fresh at the weekend): *Mel & Kim* / When you come back to me: *Donovan, Jason* / Counting every minute: *Sonia* / Heartache: *Pepsi* & Shirlie / Get ready: *Hitchcock, Carol* / Every day (I love you more): *Donovan, Jason* / I only wanna be with you: *Fox, Samantha* / He ain't no competition: *Brother Beyond* / You think you're a man: *Divine*/ I haven't stopped dancing yet: *Pat 'n' Mick* / Loco-motion, The: *Minogue, Kylie* / Back in my arms (once again): *Dean, Hazell* / I'm so beautiful: *Divine* / Harder I try, The: *Brother Beyond* / Whatever I do (wherever I go): *Dean, Hazell* / Tears on my pillow: *Minogue, Kylie* / Especially for you: *Minogue, Kylie & Jason Donovan*/ Ferry 'cross the Mersey: *Various artists* / End of the world: *Sonia* / In the heat of a passionate moment: *Princess*/ You'll never stop me loving you: *Sonia* / Never too late: *Minogue, Kylie* / Better the devil you know: *Minogue,* Kylie / I don't believe in miracles: *Sinitta* / All of me: *Sabrina* / Take me to your heart: *Astley,* Rick / Maybe (we should call it a day): *Dean, Hazell* / Toy boy: *Sinitta* / G.T.O.: *Sinitta* / All the way: *England Football Team* / Nothing can divide us: *Donovan, Jason* / Let's all chant: *Pat 'n' Mick*/ Hand on your heart: *Minogue, Kylie* / SS Paparazzi: *Stock/Aitken/Waterman* / Success: *Sigue Sigue Sputnik*/ Love's about to change my heart (Edit): *Summer, Donna* / Happenin' all over again: *Gordon, Lonnie* / Can't shake the feeling: *Big Fun* / Use it up and wear it out: *Pat 'n' Mick* / Love is war: *Brilliant* / Tell me tomorrow: *Princess* / Heaven I need, The: *3 Degrees* / Another night: *Donovan, Jason* / When love takes over you (remix): *Summer, Donna* / Somebody: *Brilliant* / Rhythm of the rain: *Donovan, Jason* / Turn it into love: *Dean, Hazell* / I'll keep on loving you: *Princess* / My arms keep missing you: *Astley, Rick* / Hang on to your love: *Donovan, Jason* / Who's leaving who: *Dean, Hazell* / Nothing's gonna stop me now: *Fox, Samantha*/ Too many broken hearts: *Donovan, Jason* / F.L.M.: *Mel & Kim* / Respectable: *Mel & Kim* / Just don't have the heart: *Richard, Cliff* / Ain't nothing but a house party: *Fearon, Phil* / I'd rather jack: *Reynolds Girls* / Listen to your heart: *Sonia* / Handful of promises: *Big Fun.*
2LP: . . . . **ADD 19**
MCSET: . . . . **ZDD 19**

TOUCH RADIO 2 (Various artists).
MC: . . . . **VAULT 2**

TRANSATLANTIC NUMBER ONES (Various artists).
2LP: . . . . **CR 137**
MCSET: . . . . **CRT 137**

TRIBUTE TO ANDY WILLIAMS (Various artists).
MC: . . . . **DY 12**

TRIBUTE TO BUDDY HOLLY (Various artists).
LP: **1A 022 1583681**
MC: **1A 222 1583684**

TRIBUTE TO DIANA ROSS (Various artists).
MC: . . . . **AIM 14**

TRIBUTE TO ELVIS (Various artists).
MC: . . . . **AIM 45**

TRIBUTE TO GLEN CAMPBELL (Various artists).
MC: . . . . **OAK C 167**

TRIBUTE TO HARRY CHAPIN (Various artists).
LP: **4677261**
MC: **4677264**

UNFORGETTABLE (Various artists).
Tracks: / When I fall in love: *Cole, Nat King* / Love letters: *Lester, Ketty* / That ole devil called love: *Holiday,* Billie / My baby just cares for me: *Simone, Nina* / Fever: *Lee, Peggy* / Wonderful world: *Cooke, Sam*/ Moon river: *Williams, Danny* / Smoke gets in your eyes: *Platters* / Every time we say goodbye: *Fitzgerald,* Ella / Always on my mind / I just don't know what to do with myself: *Springfield, Dusty* / You've lost that lovin' feeling: *Righteous Brothers* / Sun ain't gonna shine anymore, The: *Walker Brothers* / Stand by me: *King, Ben E.* / When a man loves a woman: *Sledge, Percy* / True love ways: *Holly, Buddy* / Crazy: *Cline, Patsy*/ Unforgettable: *Various artists.*
LP: . . . . **EMTV 44**
MC: . . . . **TCEMTV 44**

UNFORGETTABLE II (Various artists).
Tracks: / Something's gotten hold of my heart: *Pitney, Gene* / I only want to be with you: *Springfield, Dusty*/ I say a little prayer: *Franklin, Aretha* / I get the sweetest feeling: *Wilson, Jackie* / Lovely day: *Withers,* Bill / Wild world: *Cliff, Jimmy* / (Sittin' on) The dock of the bay: *Redding, Otis* / What a wonderful world: *Armstrong, Louis* / Crying: *Orbison, Roy* / Groovy kind of love: *Mindbenders* / God only knows: *Beach Boys* / Baby I love your way: *Frampton, Peter* / He ain't heavy, he's my brother: *Hollies* / Nights in white satin: *Moody Blues* / Miss you nights: *Richard, Cliff* / Halfway to paradise: *Fury, Billy* / It doesn't matter anymore: *Holly, Buddy.*
LP: . . . . **EMTV 46**
MC: . . . . **TCEMTV 46**

VERY BEST OF TRASH HORROR (Various artists).
Tracks: / Jack the ripper: *Sutch, Screaming Lord* / Cemetery girls: *Barnes & Barnes* / Addams family, The: *Fiends*/ Blob, The: *Little Stevie & The McQueens* / Purple people eater: *Wooley, Sheb* / Monster mash: *Pickett, Bobby* Boris & Krypt Kickers / Haunted house: *Jumpin' Gene Simmons* / Twilight zone: *Norman, Neil* / Till the following night: *Sutch, Screaming Lord* / Out of limits: *Challengers.*
LP: . . . . **JOCK LP 8**

VINTAGE PERFORMANCES Various artists (Various artists).
2LP: . . . . **CR 119**
MCSET: . . . . **CRT 119**

VITAL VINYL (VOL.1) (Various artists).
LP: . . . . **SHM 3036**
MC: . . . . **HSC 3036**

VITAL VINYL (VOL.2) (Various artists).
LP: . . . . **SHM 3037**
MC: . . . . **HSC 3037**

WORDS (Various artists).
Tracks: / Wonderful tonight: *Clapton, Eric* / Fields of fire: *Big Country (group)* / Time passages: *Stewart, Al* / It never rains in Southern California: *Hammond, Albert* / Making love: *Air Supply* / Music: *Miles,* John / Souvenirs: *Fogelberg, Dan* / All by myself: *Carmen, Eric* / Sorry seems to be the hardest word: *John,* Elton / Say you don't mind: *Blunstone, Colin* / Hold me now: *Logan, Johnny* / Blue guitar: *Hayward, Justin* & John Lodge / Words: *Bee Gees* / Candle in the wind: *John, Elton* / Small town talk: *Charles, Bobby*(Not available on CD.) / Pretty girls: *Edelman, Randy* (Not available on CD.) / Lady of the dawn: *Batt, Mike* (Not available on CD.) / Harry: *Howe, Catherine* / Homburg: *Procul Harum* (Not available on CD.) / With a little help from my friends: *Cocker, Joe* (Not available on CD.) / You're my soul and inspiration: *Righteous Brothers* (Not available on CD.) / Fantasy: *Kenny, Gerard* (Not available on CD.) / Seasons in the sun: *Jacks, Terry* (Not available on CD.) / Chestnut mare: *Byrds* (Not available on CD.) / Look of love, The: *ABC* / Time in a bottle: *Croce, Jim* (Not available on CD.) / Promises: *Clapton, Eric & His Band* (Not available on CD.).
2LP: . . . . **STDLP 25**
MC: . . . . **STDMC 25**

YOU HEARD IT HERE FIRST (Various artists).
Tracks: / Ain't that a shame: *Domino, Fats* / Stack a lee part 1: *Archibald* / I hear you knocking: *Lewis,* Smiley / Sick and tired: *Kenner, Chris* / Toy bell: *Bees* / Hurt so bad: *Little Anthony & The Imperials*/ Do wah diddy diddy: *Exciters* / Jeannie, Jeannie, Jeannie: *Maddin, Jimmie* / After midnight: *Cale, J.J.*/ Gambler, The: *Schitz, Don* / Elvira: *Frazier, Dallas* / Minute you're gone, The: *James, Sonny* / Everybody's talkin': *Neil, Fred* / More than I can say: *Vee, Bobby* / Thinkin' 'bout you baby: *Marie, Sharon* / Killing me softly with his song: *Lieberman, Lori.*
LP: . . . . **EG 2605751**
MC: . . . . **EG 2605754**

YOUNGBLOOD STORY, VOL.1 (Various artists).
Tracks: / Do wah diddy: *Dave Dee, Dozy, Beaky, Mick & Tich* / Brandy: *English, Scott* / Get ready for love: *Easybeats*/ Planetary cruiser: *McGlynn, Pat Band* / Sea trip: *Shelley, Peter* / On the run: *Ocean, Billy* / Rhythm on the radio: *ABC* / True love forgives: *Kissoon, Mac & Katie* / Crazy feeling: *Douglas, Carl* / Ain't nothing but a house party: *Show Stoppers* / Personality crisis: *New York Dolls* / Take a heart: *Fardon, Don*/ Mr. Station Master: *Harper, Roy* / Morning bird: *Damned* / C'mon round to my place: *Wayne, Carl* / When I was 16: *Page, Jimmy* / Captain man: *Powell, Jimmy* / Let the live live: *Fardon, Don* / (You keep me) hanging on: *Kissoon, Mac* (Available on CD only) / Don't ever change: *Berry, Mike* (Available on CD only) / Spread myself around: *King, Ben E.* (Available on CD only) / Can you feel it?: *Ocean, Billy* (Available on CD only) / Sleepwalk: *Los Indianos* (Available on CD only).
LP: **C5-549**

Pop Art

SNAP CRACKLE POP ART.
LP: . . . . **LPBM 3001**

Pop Box

POP BOX (Various artists).
LPS: **303796**
MCSET: **503796**

Pop Concert

SOUND SENSATIONS.
LP: . . . . **TMP 9014**

Pop Group

HOW MUCH LONGER MUST WE TOLERATE THIS MASS MURDER.
LP: . . . . **ROUGH 9**

IN THE BEGINNING (See under Slits) (Pop Group & Slits).

WE ARE TIME.
LP: . . . . **ROUGH 12**

Y.
Tracks: / Thief of fire / Snowgirl / Blood money / Savage sea / We are time / Words disobey me / Don't call me pain / Boys from Brazil / Don't sell your dreams.
LP: . . . . **RAD 20**

Pop Guns

EUGENIE.
LP: . . . . **CHIME 108**
MC: . . . . **CHIME 108 C**

SNOG.
LP: . . . . **CHIME 01.15**
MC: . . . . **CHIME 01.15C**

Pop, Iggy

BLAH BLAH BLAH.
Tracks: / Real wild child / Baby, it can't fall / Shades / Fire girl / Isolation / Cry for love / Blah, blah, blah / Hideaway / Winners and losers.
LP: . . . . **AMA 5145**
MC: . . . . **AMC 5145**

BRICK BY BRICK.
Tracks: / Home / I won't crap out / Butt town / Moonlight lady / Neon forest / Pussy power / Brick by brick / Main Street eyes / Candy / Undefeated, The / Something wild / Starry night / My baby wants to rock and roll / Livin' on the edge of the night.
LP: . . . . **VUSLP 19**
MC: . . . . **VUSMC 19**

CHOICE CUTS.
LP: . . . . **PL 84957**

IDIOT, THE.
Tracks: / Sister midnight / Nightclubbing / Funtime / Baby / China girl / Dum dum boys / Tiny girls / Mass production.
LP: . . . . **PL 12275**
MC: . . . . **PK 12275**
LP: . . . . **OVED 277**
MC: . . . . **OVEDC 277**

IGGY POP: INTERVIEW PICTURE DISC.
LPPD: . . . . **BAK 2061**

INSTINCT.
Tracks: / Cold metal / High on you / Strong girl / Tom Tom / Easy rider / Power and freedom / Lowdown / Instinct / Tuff baby / Squarehead.
LP: . . . . **AMA 5198**
MC: . . . . **AMC 5198**

KILL CITY (Pop, Iggy/James Williamson).
Tracks: / Kill City / Sell your love / Beyond the law / I got nothing / Johanna / Night theme / Consolation prizes / No sense of crime / Lucky moments / Master charge.
LP: . . . . **RAD 2**

LUST FOR LIFE.
Tracks: / Lust for life / Sixteen / Some wierd sin / Passenger, The / Tonight / Success / Turn blue / Neighbourhood threat / Fall in love with me.
LP: . . . . **NL 82488**
MC: . . . . **NK 82488**
LP: . . . . **PL 12488**
LP: . . . . **INTS 5114**
LP: . . . . **OVED 278**
MC: . . . . **OVEDC 278**

NEW VALUES.
Tracks: / Tell me a stay / New values / Girls / I'm bored / Don't look down / Endless sea / Five foot one / How do you fix a broken heart / Angel / Curiosity / African man / Billy is a runaway.
LP: **1201144**
LP: . . . . **SPART 1092**
LP: **210997**
MC: **410997**

PARTY.
Tracks: / Pleasure / Rock and roll party / Eggs on plate / Sincerity / Houston is hot tonight / Pumpin' for Jill / Happy man / Bang bang / Sea of love / Time won't let me.
LP: **203806**
MC: **403806**
LP: . . . . **SPART 1158**

RAW POWER (Pop, Iggy & The Stooges).
Tracks: / Search and destroy / Gimme danger / Your pretty face is going to hell / Penetration / Raw power / I need somebody / Shake appeal / Death trip.
LP: . . . . **CBS 31464**

LP: . . . . ESSLP 005
MC: . . . . ESSMC 005
LP: . . . . CBS 32083

SOLDIER.
Tracks: / Loco mosquito / Ambition / Take care of me / Get up and get out / Play it safe / I'm a conservative / Dog food / I need more / Knocking 'em down (in the city) / Mr. Dynamite / I snub you.
LP: 210160
LP: . . . . SPART 1117
MC: 410160

TV EYE (1977 LIVE).
Tracks: / TV eye / Funtime / Sixteen / I got a right / Lust for life / Dirt / Nightclubbing / I wanna be your dog.
LP: . . . . PL 12796
MC: . . . . PK 12796

WELL, DID YOU EVAH (See Under Harry, Deborah) (Pop, Iggy & Deborah Harry).

ZOMBIE BIRDHOUSE.
Tracks: / Run like a villain / Villagers, The / Angry hills / Life of work / Ballad of Cookie McBride / Ordinary bummer / Eat or be eaten / Bulldozer / Platonic / Horse song, The / Watching the news / Street crazies.
LP: . . . . CHR 1399
MC: . . . . ZCHR 1399

Pop Machine

SING AND PLAY ABBA.
MC: . . . . BRC 2526

Pop Masters

POP MASTERS, THE.
LP: . . . . BLJ 8017

Pop Negatif Wastad

POP NEGATIF WASTAD.
LP: . . . . SLATE 9

Pop Rai...

POP RAI & RACHIO STYLE (Various artists).
LP: . . . . EWV 15
MC: . . . . TCEWV 15

Pop Rivits

LIVE IN GERMANY '79.
LP: . . . . HANG 35 UP

ORIGINAL FIRST ALBUM.
LP: . . . . HANG 27UP

POP RIVETS GREATEST HITS.
LP: . . . . HIP 007

Pop Tarts

AGE OF THE THING.
LP: . . . . WOW 23

Pop Will Eat Itself

BOX FRENZY.
Tracks: / Grebo guru / Beaver patrol / Let's get ugly / U.B.L.U.D. / Inside you / Evelyn / There is no love between us anymore / She's surreal / Intergalactic love mission / Love missile F1-11 / Hit the hi tech groove / Razorblade kisses.
LP: . . . . CHAPLP 18
MC: . . . . CHAPC 18

CURE FOR SANITY.
Tracks: / Incredible PWEI vs the moral majority / Dance of the mad bastards / 88 seconds and still counting / X, Y and Zee / City Zen Radio 1990/2000 FM / Dr. Nightmare's medication time / Touched by the hand of Cicciolina / 1000 x no / Psychosexual / Axe of men / Another man's rhubarb / Medicine man speaked with forked tongue / Nightmare at 20,000 feet / Very metal noise pollution / 92 degrees F (the 3rd degree) / Lived in splendour, died in chaos / Beat that refused to die, The.
LP: . . . . PL 74828
MC: . . . . PK 74828
LP: . . . . PL 75023
LPPD: . . . . PL 75041
MC: . . . . PK 75023

NOW FOR A FEAST.
Tracks: / Black Country chainstore massacre / Monogamy / Oh Grebo I think I love you / Titanic clown / B-6-B-6 / Breakdown / Sweet sweet pie / Like an angel / I'm sniffin' with you hoo / Sick little girl / Mesmerized / There's a psychopath in my soup / Candydiosis / Devil inside / Orgone accumulator.
LP: . . . . CHAPLP 33
MC: . . . . CHAPC 33
LP: . . . . ROUGHUS 22

THIS IS THE DAY, THIS IS THE HOUR.
Tracks: / PWEI is a four letter word / Preaching to the perverted / Wise up sucker / Sixteen different flavours of hell / Inject me / Can u dig it / Fuses have been lit, The / Poison to the mind / Def con one / Radio PWEI / Shortwave transmission on up to the minuteman / Satellite ecstatica / Now now James we're busy / Wake up, time to die / Wise up sucker (12" youth remix) (Only on CD format.).
LP: . . . . PL 74106
MC: . . . . PK 74106

Popcorn Explosion

HUNGER AFTER DINNER.
LP: . . . . VOW 012

Popdy

POPDY SHOWREEL (Various artists).
MC: . . . . POPDY AP1

Pope, Dave

BEST OF DAVE POPE.
Tracks: / Broken up people / Love / It only goes to show / Love song / Dying embers / We're all one / Kind of a thank you / Piece of your time / My hope / Take my life / Still waters / Do you believe he's coming.
LP: . . . . MYR 1094
MC: . . . . MC 1094

ROYAL PRAISE (Pope, Dave/Saltmine Band).
LP: . . . . DAY R 4024

SAIL AWAY.
Tracks: / It only goes to show / Love song / Once again / Lord I love you / Sail away / Couldn't care less / Dying embers / Lord, I miss the rain / It's you / We're all one.
LP: . . . . MYR 1068
MC: . . . . MC 1068

TASTE AND SEE.
LP: . . . . MYR 1192
MC: . . . . MC 1192

Pope John-Paul II

HIS HOLINESS POPE JOHN PAUL II.
LP: . . . . POPE 11

HISTORICAL VISIT TO IRELAND.
LP: . . . . IRL 1979

LIVERPOOL 30TH MAY 1982.
Tracks: / Solemn Mass of Pentecost (Live recordings.).
LP: . . . . LPM 30582
MC: . . . . CLPM 30582

PILGRIM POPE, THE.
LP: . . . . REB 445
MC: . . . . ZCF 445

RECORDED SOUVENIR OF THE HISTORIC VISIT OF HIS HOLINESS, A (England, May 28th 1982 - June 2nd 1982).
LP: . . . . EV 001

Popealopes

ADDERS TALE, AN.
LP: . . . . RES 338814

POPEALOPES.
LP: . . . . R 33-8814

Popeye

POPEYE (Original soundtrack) (Various artists).
Tracks: / I yam what I yam: *Various artists* / He needs me: *Various artists* / Swee'pea's lullaby: *Various artists* / Din' we?: *Various artists* / Sweethaven: *Various artists* / Blow me down: *Various artists* / Sailin': *Various artists* / It's not easy being me: *Various artists* / He's large: *Various artists* / I'm mean: *Various artists* / Kids: *Various artists* / I'm Popeye the sailor man: *Various artists*.
LP: . . . . EPC 70203
MC: 40 70203

Popinjays

BANG UP TO DATE WITH THE POPINJAYS.
LP: . . . . TPLP 28
MC: . . . . TRMC 28

Popp, Lucia

LUCIA POPP.
MC: . . . . GK 69015

Poppi UK

MAKESHIFT HOME MUSIC.
Tracks: / Bonsai / Everybody's trying / This house / GMA 4 / Lions eat tamer / Human meat / PMST / You're not the same / Rambo's girlfriend / Requiem.
LP: . . . . SCHEMER 8908

MISFIT HOME MUSIC.
LP: . . . . SCH 8908

POPPI UK.
Tracks: / Crusader / Walkman walk / Disco soweto / Riot / Fire consuming your heart, The / Ghosts / Ramadam / Multi-purpose coffin / Great man's apes.
LP: . . . . DMC 018

Poppie Nongena

POPPIE NONGENA (Original Cast Recording) (Various artists).
Tracks: / Amen: *Various artists* / Taru bawo: *Various artists* / Wenzeni na: *Various artists* / U Jehova: *Various artists* / Uzubale: *Various artists* / Makoti: *Various artists* / Lalasana: *Various artists* / Jerusalem: *Various artists* / Nkosi Sikela l'Afrika: *Various artists* / Zisana abantwane: *Various artists* / Bantwena besikolo: *Various artists* / Liza Lisi Dinga: *Various artists* / Mampondo mse: *Various artists*.
LP: . . . . HNBL 6301
MC: . . . . HNBC 6301

Poppy

POPPY (Royal Shakespeare Company's stage production) (Various artists).
LP: 2500001
MC: 2500004

Poppy, Andrew

ALPHABED (A mystery dance).
Tracks: / 45 is / Goodbye Mr. G / Amusement, The.
LP: . . . . ZTTIQ 9
MC: . . . . ZCIQ 9

BEATING OF WINGS.
Tracks: / Object is a hungry wolf / 32 frames for orchestra / Listening in / Cadenza.
LP: . . . . ZTTIQ 5
MC: . . . . ZCIQ 5

Pop-Rock Symphonia

ORCHESTRAL POPS COLLECTION.
Tracks: / Mickey / Take it away / Girl crazy / Fantasy island / Head over heels / Jive talkin' / Come on Eileen / Rockin' all over the world / Super trouper / Hi fidelity / I could be so good for you / I will survive / Modern girl / Nine to five / Can't smile without you / Arthur's theme / Begin the beguine / Copacabana / One of us / Hill Street blues / Fame / Hands up / Stayin alive / Just another broken heart / If I should love again / I write the songs.
2LP: . . . . CR 093
MCSET: . . . . CRT 093

Popul Vuh

AGAPE AGAPE.
LP: . . . . U 015

BRUDER DES SCHATTENS SOHNE DES LICHTS.
LP: 0060 167

COBRA VERDE (1988 film soundtrack).
Tracks: / Der tod des Cobra Verde / Nachts: schnee / Der marktplatz / Eine andere welt / Grab der mutter / Die singenden madchen von ho, ziavi / Sieh nicht uberm meer ist's / Ha'mut bis dass die nacht mit ruh.
LP: . . . . A 353
MC: . . . . C 353

FITZCARALDO (1982 film soundtrack).
LP: . . . . ZYX 20017

MUSIC FROM COEUR DE VERRE.
LP: 900536

MUSIC FROM NOSFERATU.
Tracks: / Mantra 1 and 2 / Morning sunrays / Venus principle / On the way / Through pains to heaven / To a little way / Zwiestrache der rohrsolette mit der saengerin / Die nacht derhimmel / Der rus der rohrosolette.
LP: 900573

SPIRIT OF PEACE.
LP: . . . . C 001
MC: C-0014

Popular Front

BIG BANG, THE.
MC: . . . . BRIEF 2000

HEARTBEAT OF LAUGHING, A.
LP: . . . . CHIME 00 23

Popular History Of...

COMRADES (Popular History Of Signs).
LP: . . . . FREUD 05

ENGLAND IN THE RAIN (Popular History Of Signs).
LP: . . . . FREUD 21

TASTE (Popular History Of Signs).
LP: . . . . FREUD 17

Populi, Vox

BURN BABY.
Tracks: / Nothing more than this / Animals, The / Burn baby burn / Cover / Swimming in the shallow end.
LP: . . . . VOX 001

Porcelain Bus

FRAGILE.
LP: . . . . CGASS 14

STEEL BROS.
LP: . . . . CITLP 508

TALKING TO GOD.
LP: . . . . CGAS 804

Porcino, Al

IN OBLIVION.
LP: . . . . JAZZ MARK 106

Porgy & Bess

PORGY AND BESS (ORIGINAL ISSUE) (Film soundtrack) (Various artists).
LP: . . . . ABL 3282

PORGY & BESS Various artists (Various artists).
LPS: . . . . SET 609/11

PORGY & BESS (Original 1942 Broadway cast) (Various artists).
Tracks: / Overture and summertime: *Various artists* / Woman is a sometime thing: *Various artists* / My man's gone now: *Various artists* / It takes a long pull to get there: *Various artists* / O got plenty o' nuttin': *Various* artists / Buzzard song: *Various artists* / Bess, you is my woman now: *Various artists* / It ain't necessarily so: *Various artists* / What you want wid Bess: *Various artists* / Strawberry woman's call - crab man's call: *Various* artists / I loves you, Porgy: *Various artists* / Requiem, The: *Various artists* / There's a boat that's leavin' soon for New Yor: *Various artists* / Porgy's lament and finale: *Various artists*.
LP: . . . . MCL 1662
MC: . . . . MCLC 1662

PORGY & BESS (Original soundtrack) (Various artists).
LP: 70007
LP: . . . . PS 2016
MC: . . . . PST 2016

PORGY & BESS REVISITED Various artists (Various artists).
LP: . . . . SW 8414

Pork Dukes

PIG IN A POKE.
LP: . . . . PORK 001

PIG OUT OF HELL.
Tracks: / Devil driver / House of the rising sun / Three men in an army truck / My mother / Gin sin / Let's spend the night together / I'm a guitar / Day tripper / Do you love me / Marxist ceninist feminist / Stop / Around and around.
LP: . . . . PORK 2

Porky's

PORKY'S (Original Soundtrack) (Various artists).
LP: 2488 858
MC: 3199 326

PORKY'S REVENGE (Film soundtrack) (Various artists).
LP: . . . . CBS 70265
MC: 40 70265

Porno Sect

NOOSE AND THE SPEAR, THE.
LP: 081 104

OF VIBRATIONS, RESONANCE.
Tracks: / Slave / White boy / Trash / Medium is the edit, The / Ire becomes truth, The / Subvert/subject / Subjugation / Year zero / Fresh fields / Pure / Combat zone.
LP: . . . . PKLP 0053

Porres, Nannie

SANGER MED SONJA.
LP: . . . . DRLP 52

Porridge

PORRIDGE (With original cast) (Various artists).
MC: . . . . ZCF 270
LP: . . . . REB 270

Porteous, Lindsay

PORTRAIT OF A JEW'S-HARP PLAYER (Porteous, Lindsay and friends).
Tracks: / Reel of Tulloch, The / Duke of Peth's reel / Cuttie's waddin' / Duke of Fife's welcome to Deeside / Banks hornpipe / Farewell to the creeks / Athole highlanders, The / Fairy reel / Bratach bana / Beeswing hornpipe / Freedom come all ye / Merry blacksmith / Willafjord / Sleep soond ida morning / Braes of Tullymet / Inverness gathering, The / Plaidie awa' / White cockade, The / Flowers of Edinburgh / Soldiers joy / Timour the tartar / I'll ay ca' in by yon toun / Drops of brandy / Tail toddle / Hen's march / Speed the plough / Spey in spate / Ale is dear, The.
MC: . . . . CTRAX 022

Porter

PORTRAIT OF PORTER.
LP: . . . . PHONT 7561

Porter, Cole

ANYTHING GOES - CAPITOL SING COLE PORTER (Various artists).
Tracks: / All of you: *Ross, Annie/Gerry Mulligan* / Always true to you in my fashion: *Lee, Peggy & George Shearing* / Anything goes: *Bennett, Tony & Count Basie* / Begin the beguine: *MacRae, Gordon* / Blow, Gabriel, blow: *Tilton,* Martha / Ev'ry time we say goodbye: *Christy, June & Stan Kenton* / From now on: *Lee, Peggy* / I get a kick out of you: *Connor, Chirs & Stan Kenton* / I happen to like New York: *Garland, Judy* / In the still of the night: *O'Connell, Helen* / It's alright with me: *Shore, Dinah & The Red Norvo Quintet* / I've got you under my skin: *Prima,* Louis & Keely Smith / Just one of those things: *Cole, Nat King* / Looking at you: *Minelli, Liza* / Miss Otis regrets (she's unable to lunch today):

Faye, Frances / So in love: *Raitt, John* / True love: *Martin, Dean* & Nelson Riddle / What is this thing called love: *Smith, Keely & Nelson Riddle* / Why shouldn't I?: *Whiting, Margaret*/ Wunderbar: *Stafford, Jo & Gordon MacRae* / You'd be so nice to come home to: *Wilson, Nancy* / You're the top: *Turner, Jean & Stan Kenton* / Let's do it (let's fall in love): *Richards, Trudy & Billy May* / Get out of town: *Southern, Jerry & Billy May* / You do something to me: *Andrews Sister & Billy May*.
MC: **C4 96361**

COLE PORTER COLLECTION (Various artists).
LP: . . . . **ST 127**

COLE PORTER SONGBOOK (Night And Day) (Various artists).
Tracks: / I've got you under my skin: *Washington, Dinah* / Love for sale: *Horn, Shirley* / Let's do it: *Armstrong*, Louis / Anything goes: *Fitzgerald, Ella* / What is this thing called love: *Torme, Mel* / You'd be so nice to come home to: *Merrill, Helen* / At long last: *Henderson, Bill* / I love you: *O'Day, Anita* / Just one of those things: *Armstrong, Louis* / It's de-lovely: *Vaughan, Sarah* / Always true to you in my fashion: *Dearie*, Blossom / I concentrate on you: *Astaire, Fred* / I get a kick out of you: *Washington, Dinah* / In the still of the night: *Eckstine, Billy* / Easy to love: *Holiday, Billie* / Night and day: *Fitzgerald, Ella* / Every time we say goodbye: *Carter, Betty*.
MC: **847 202-4**

DREAM DANCING (see Fitzgerald, Ella) (Porter, Cole & Ella Fitzgerald).

GREAT BRITISH DANCE BANDS PLAY COLE PORTER (See under Dance Bands...).

IN LONDON.
LP: . . . . **SHB 26**

NYMPH ERRANT (World premiere complete recording) (Various artists).
MC: . . . . **EL 754 079 4**

SONG IS...COLE PORTER (Various artists).
Tracks: / Just one of those things: *Himber, Richard & His Orchestra* / Anything goes: *Porter, Cole* / I'm in love again: *Bernie, Ben/his Hotel Roosevelt Orchestra* / I get a kick out of you: *Merman, Ethel* / How could we be wrong?: *Bowly, Al* / Miss Otis regrets: *Byng, Douglas* / Lady fair: *Anything Goes Foursome* / I'm a gigolo: *Porter, Cole* / Let's do it: *Crosby, Bing* / Night and day: *Astaire, Fred* / They all fall in love: *Hylton, Jack* & His Orchestra / You're the top: *Porter, Cole* / Love for sale: *Holman, Libby* / All through the night: *Ambrose* & His Orchestra (7) / Be like the bluebird: *Porter, Cole* / Experiment: *Lawrence, Gertrude* / Thank you so much, Mrs Lowsborough-Goodbye: *Porter, Cole* / What is this thing called love: *Reisman, Joe & His Orchestra*.
LP: . . . . **AJA 5044**
MC: . . . . **ZC AJA 5044**

TRIBUTE TO COLE PORTER, A (Various artists).
Tracks: / I get a kick out of you: *Bassey, Shirley* / Just one of those things: *Bassey, Shirley* / Easy to love: *Bassey, Shirley* / You're sensational: *Monro, Matt* / My heart belongs to daddy: *Kirkwood, Pat* / Anything goes: *'Hutch'* / Let's do it (let's fall in love): *'Hutch'* / Always true to you in my fashion: *Wilson, Julie/Freddie* Brethert / Why can't you behave: *Wilson, Julie/Freddie Brethert* / It's alright with me: *Hockridge, Edmund/ Charles* Pren / I am in love: *Hockridge, Edmund/Charles Pren* / I've got my eyes on you: *Martin, Millicent* / Ev'ry time we say goodbye: *Four Freshmen* / So in love: *Lee, Vanessa* / In the still of the night: *Geraldo* & His Orchestra / Don't fence me in: *Geraldo & His Orchestra* / I concentrate on you: *Dawn, Julie* / It's de-lovely: *Loss, Joe & His Orchestra* / You're the tops: *Loss, Joe & His Orchestra* / Get out of town: *Squires, Rosemary*/ Do I love you?: *Young, Jimmy* / You'd be so nice to come home to: *Young, Jimmy* / True love: *Martin, Dean*/ You do something to me: *Cogan, Alma* / Never give anything away: *Hilda, Irene* / Live and let live: *Hilda*, Irene / I love Paris: *Harris, Ronnie* / I am loved: *Coupland, Diana* / Hey, good-lookin': *Gibbons, Carroll* & The Savoy Hotel Orpheans / I love you Samantha: *King's Singers* / Swingin' the jinx away: *Gonella, Nat & His* Georgians (CD only) / Ridin' high: *Geraldo & His Orchestra* (CD only) / Night and day: *Geraldo & His Orchestra*(CD only) / How could we be wrong: *Bowlly, Al* (CD only) / Begin the beguine: *Hughes, David* (CD only) / Miss Otis regrets (she's unable to lunch today): *King Brothers* (CD only) / Let's be buddies: *Roy, Harry & His Orchestra*/ What is this thing called love: *Cordell, Frank & His Orchestra* (CD only) / I've got you under my skin: *Bassey, Shirley*(CD only).
MC: . . . . **TCDL 1203**

Porter, Eddie Ray

DANCE ON THE EARTH.
LP: . . . . **ROSE 168**

WHEN THE MORNING FALLS.
Tracks: / Through the night / Slow motion dancer / After the fall / Daddy's cadillac / Lightning over water / Angelina / End of the line / Tonight (said and done) / When the morning falls.
LP: . . . . **ROSE 124**

Porter, Jerry

DON'T BOTHER ME.
LP: . . . . **Unknown**

Porter, King

SPECIAL REQUEST (Porter, King & His Orchestra).
Tracks: / Russel St Hussel / Porter's ball / Shuffling boogie / Russell Street hustle / King Porter special / Barfly / Come on in / Battle axe / Charlie the boogie man / Bumps boogie / Hey little brownie / Should have rationed myself / Chidtlin ball / Don't let Fletcher getcha / Special request / I've tried.
LP: . . . . **OFF 6056**

Porter, Royce

ROCKABILLY MEETING (See under Williams, Wayne) (Porter, Royce and Wayne Williams).

Porter-Brown, Reginald

REGINALD PORTER-BROWN.
LP: . . . . **DEROY 1020**
LP: . . . . **DEROY 1001**

Porthos, Pablo

PABLO PABLO.
Tracks: / Ngai locataire / Na mituni / Motema ebouge / Osuki wapi.
LP: . . . . **ORB 008**

Portion Control

ASSAULT.
MC: . . . . **ALL 186**

HIT THE PULSE.
LP: . . . . **EZ 2**

PSYCHO BOD SAVES THE WORLD.
LP: . . . . **DMC 008**

PURGE.
LP: . . . . **DMC 001**

SIMULATE SENSUAL.
LP: . . . . **PHA 5**

STEP FORWARD.
LP: . . . . **JAMS 44**

Portland Bill (bk)

ADVENTURES OF PORTLAND BILL (See under Adventures of...) (Rossington, Norman (nar)).

PORTLAND BILL & A..... (Rossington, Norman (nar)).
MC: . . . . **TTS 9816**

PORTLAND BILL & THE STORM (Rossington, Norman (nar)).
MC: . . . . **TTS 9818**

PORTLAND BILL'S BUSY DAY (Rossington, Norman (nar)).
MC: . . . . **TTS 9802**

PORTLAND BILL'S IMPORTANT MESSAGE (Rossington, Norman (nar)).
MC: . . . . **TTS 9817**

STORIES AND SONGS OF PORTLAND BILL, (THE) (see under Grace, John) (Grace, John).

Portland Stone

PORTLAND STONE QUARRIES WORK CHANTS.
MC: **30 203**

Portsmouth Sinfonia

20 CLASSIC ROCK CLASSICS.
Tracks: / Apache / Bridge over troubled water / Day in the life, A / Don't cry for me Argentina / Glad all over / God only knows / Heartbreak Hotel / It's only make believe / Leader of the pack / My boy lollipop / Nights in white satin / Nut rocker / Pinball wizard / Rock around the clock / Satisfaction / Telstar / Uptown top ranking / Whiter shade of pale / You really got me / You should be dancing.
LP: **9109 231**

Portugal

SONNETS FROM THE PORTUGUESE (Various artists).
MC: **1071**

TRADITIONAL MUSIC OF ALENTEJO (Various artists).
LP: . . . . **KP 9089**

TRADITIONAL PORTUGUESE MUSIC (Various artists).
MC: **D58008**

Portuguese

PORTUGUESE STRING MUSIC (Various artists).
LP: . . . . **HT 323**

Portway Peddlars

IN GREENWOOD SHADES.
LP: . . . . **GVR 229**

Poser

MY TIME.
LP: . . . . **GS 2280**

Posey, Sandy

BEST OF SANDY POSEY & SKEETER DAVIS (Posey, Sandy/Skeeter Davis).
LP: . . . . **GT 0005**

BORN A WOMAN.
LP: . . . . **MGM CS 8035**

VERY BEST OF SANDY POSEY.
LP: . . . . **SPELP 60**
MC: . . . . **SPEMC 60**

Posh Hits

GOD BLESS AMERICA Posh hits Vol.1 (Various artists).
LP: . . . . **FALL LP 032**

POSH HITS, VOL 1 Various artists (Various artists).
LP: . . . . **PBS 8138**

Posies

DEAR 23.
Tracks: / My big mouth / Apology / You avoid parties / Help yourself / Everyone moves away / Golden blunders / Any other way / Suddenly Mary / Mrs Green / Flood of sunshine.
LP: **7599243051**
MC: **7599243054**

Posit, Jean Pierre

FLUTE D'AMOUR.
LP: . . . . **JPPLP 300**
MC: . . . . **ZCJPP 300**

Position Alpha

CREDO.
Tracks: / Tati / Friday The 13th / Spirits Rejoice / Credo.
LP: . . . . **DRLP 134**

DON'T BRING YOUR DOG.
LP: . . . . **DRLP 50**

GREAT SOUND OF SOUND, THE.
2LP: . . . . **DRLP 101/102**

MOTE MONSUNEN.
Tracks: / Calle schewens vals / Mote I Monsunen/ Kinesiska muren / Nocturne.
LP: . . . . **DRLP 149**

Positive 2

POSITIVE TWO FEATURING SPINMASTER J.L. (Positive 2 & Spinmaster JL).
Tracks: / Beware / In God we trust / It's too funky in here / Heart of stone / Diamonds and gold / Nasty girls / D.F.A.D.F.D. (dreaming for a drug free day) / Come into my house of love / Bug out.
LP: . . . . **KEY 4037**
MC: . . . . **KEY 4037 MC**

Positive Noise

CHANGE OF HEART.
LP: . . . . **STAT LP 8**

DISTANT FIRES.
LP: . . . . **STATLP 23**

HEART OF DARKNESS.
LP: . . . . **STATLP 1**

Positively ....

POSITIVELY ELIZABETH STREET (Various artists).
LP: . . . . **CGAS 803**

Posse, George

SMILE (see Adekile, Toyin) (Posse, George/Toyin Adekile).

Possessed

BEYOND THE GATES.
Tracks: / Heretic / Tribulation / March to die / Phantasm / No will to live / Beyond the gates / Beast of the Apocalypse / Seance / Restless dead / Dog fight.
LP: . . . . **FLAG 3**

EYES OF HORROR, THE.
LP: . . . . **MFLAG 16**

SEVEN CHURCHES.
Tracks: / Exorcist / Burning in hell / Seven churches / Holy hell / Fallen angel / Pentagram / Evil warriors / Satan's curse / Twisted minds / Death metal.
LP: . . . . **RR 9757**

Possession

THIN WHITE ARMS.
LP: . . . . **LEV 1823**

Post, Jim

AND FRIENDS.
LP: . . . . **FF 419**

MAGIC.
LP: . . . . **FF 216**

SHIPSHAPE.
LP: . . . . **FF 240**

Post, Mike

A-TEAM, THE.
Tracks: / St elsewhere / Cast your fate to the wind / Think of laura / Against all odds / Terms of endearment / A team / I like chopin / Beat it / Do you really want to hurt me / Footloose.
LP: . . . . **PL 85183**
MC: . . . . **PK 85183**

FUSED (Post, Mike Coalition).
Tracks: / Briarwood express / Lovingly / Big mouth harp / Not A blade of grass / Great guitar hoax / Country ode / Bubble gum breakthrough / Shady grove / Afternoon of the rhino / Noble underground / Overground fusion.
LP: . . . . **K 56163**

T.V. THEME SONGS.
Tracks: / Hill Street Blues / Greatest American hero / White shadow / Magnum p.i. / School's out / Rockford files.
LP: . . . . **K 52372**

Post Mortem

CORONER'S OFFICE.
LP: . . . . **NRR 11**
MC: . . . . **NRC 11**

MISSING LINK.
LP: . . . . **NRR 19**
MC: . . . . **NRC 19**

Postcard From Paradise

POSTCARD FROM PARADISE (Various artists).
LP: . . . . **EDENLP 001**

Postman Pat

ADVENTURES OF POSTMAN PAT, THE (Cunliffe, John (auth)).
MC: . . . . **UNKNOWN**

ADVENTURES OF POSTMAN PAT, THE (See also Ken Barrie) (Barrie, Ken (nar)).

FUN AND GAMES WITH POSTMAN PAT (Cunliffe, John (auth)).
MC: **00 103 44 99**

MORE POSTMAN PAT STORIES (Cunliffe, John (auth)).
MC: . . . . **TS 341**

POSTMAN PAT (see Cunliffe, John) (Barrie, Ken (nar)).

POSTMAN PAT.
Tracks: / Postman Pat / Jesse the cat / Walking in Greendale / Mobile shop / Reverend Timms / Travelling music / Handyman song / Valley waltz / Miss Rebecca Hubbard / Farmer's song / Dawn and countryside waltz / Greendale jig / Busy day.
LP: **PPLP101**
MC: . . . . **ZCPLP 101**

POSTMAN PAT GOES ON SAFARI (See also Cunliffe, John) (Barrie, Ken (nar)).

POSTMAN PAT MAKES A SPLASH (See also John Cunliffe) (Barrie, Ken (nar)).

POSTMAN PAT PLAYS FOR GREENDALE (See also John Cunliffe) (Barrie, Ken (nar)).

POSTMAN PAT STORIES, THE (see John Cunliffe) (Barrie, Ken (nar)).

POSTMAN PAT & THE CHRISTMAS PUDDING (See also John Cunliffe) (Barrie, Ken (nar)).

POSTMAN PAT & THE DINOSAUR BONES (See also John Cunliffe) (Barrie, Ken (nar)).

POSTMAN PAT & THE GREENDALE GHOST (See also John Cunliffe) (Barrie, Ken (nar)).

POSTMAN PAT'S 123 STORY (see Cunliffe, John) (Barrie, Ken (nar)).

POSTMAN PAT'S ABC STORY (see Cunliffe, John) (Barrie, Ken (nar)).

POSTMAN PAT'S DAY IN BED (See also John Cunliffe) (Barrie, Ken (nar)).

POSTMAN PAT'S MESSY DAY (See also John Cunliffe) (Barrie, Ken (nar)).

POSTMAN PAT'S PARCEL OF FUN (See also John Cunliffe) (Barrie, Ken (nar)).

POSTMAN PAT'S WET DAY (See also John Cunliffe) (Barrie, Ken (nar)).

SING-A-LONG WITH POSTMAN PAT (Barrie, Ken (nar)).
MC: . . . . **RKC 13**

Potamus

CHAMBERPOT.
LP: . . . . **BEAD 2**

Potato Five

FIVE ALIVE.
LP: . . . . **PHZA 073**

POTATO 5 MEET LAUREL AITKEN (See under Aitken, Laurel) (Potato Five/ Laurel Aitken).

POTATO FIVE.
LP: . . . . **PHAZ 32**

TRUE FACT.
LP: . . . . **MASH 001**

Potent Brew

BLUES ON THE BOIL.
LP: . . . . **LRF 187**

Potential Threat

DEMAND AN ALTERNATIVE.
LP: . . . . **MORT 24**

Potter, Beatrix (aut)

BEATRIX POTTER STORIES VOL 1 (Leigh, Vivien).
Tracks: / Tale of Peter Rabbit / Tale of Benjamin Bunny, The / Tale of the Flopsy bunnies / Tale of Mrs. Tiggywinkle.
MC: . . . . **TC-SRS 5096**

BEATRIX POTTER STORIES VOL 2 (Leigh, Vivien).
Tracks: / Tale of Jemima Puddle-Duck / Tale of Squirrel Nutkin / Tale of Johnny Town-Mouse.
MC: . . . . **TC SRS 5097**

MOUSE TALES (Horden, Sir Michael).
MC: **881662**

MRS TIGGY-WINKLE & FRIENDS (Horden, Sir Michael & Patricia Routledge).
MC: **881751**

TAILOR OF GLOUCESTER, THE.
Tracks: / Tailor of Gloucester / Tale of Mrs. Tittlemouse / Tale of Mr.Tod.
MC: . . . . **TSP 405**

TALE OF BENJAMIN BUNNY.
MC: . . . . **TSP 404**

TALE OF JEMIMA PUDDLE-DUCK (Unknown narrator(s)).
MC: . . . . **PLBN 226**

TALE OF JEMIMA PUDDLE-DUCK & OTHER STORIES (Unknown narrator(s)).
Tracks: / Tale of Jemima Puddle-Duck / Tale of Samuel Whiskers & the Roly-Poly Pudding (cont.) / Tale of the Pie & the Patty Pan.
MC: . . . . **TSP 403**

TALE OF LITTLE PIG ROBINSON.
MC: . . . . **TSP 406**

TALE OF PETER RABBIT & OTHER STORIES.
Tracks: / Tale of the Flopsy Bunnies / Tale of Mrs. Tiggywinkle / Appley Dapply's Nursery Rhymes / Tale of two bad mice / Tale of Mr Jeremy Fisher / Tale of Ginger & Pickles / Tale of Peter Rabbit.
MC: . . . . **TSP 401**
MC: . . . . **TLP 411**

TALE OF PETER RABBIT, THE (age 3+) (Unknown narrator(s)).
MC: . . . . **PLBN 224**

TALE OF SQUIRREL NUTKIN, THE (for age 3+) (Unknown narrator(s)).
MC: . . . . **PLBN 225**

TALE OF TOM KITTEN & OTHER STORIES.
Tracks: / Cecily Parsley's nursery rhymes / Tale of Timmy Tiptoes / Tale of Johnny Town-Mouse / Tale of Squirrel Nutkin / Tale of Tom Kitten.
MC: . . . . **TSP 402**

TALE OF TUPPENY & OTHER STORIES.
Tracks: / Tale of the Faithful Dove (cont.) / Tale of the Faithful Dove / Sly old cat, The / Tale of Tuppeny.
MC: . . . . **TSP 412**

YOURS AFFECTIONATELY PETER RABBIT.
Tracks: / Peter Rabbit's correspondence / Squirrel Nutkin's Correspondence / Lucinda Doll's Correspondence / Mrs. Tiggywinkle's Correspondence / Correspondence concerning Jeremy Fisher / Mr. Alderman PT Tortoise, Invitations / Ribby's Invitation / Mr. Samuel Whisker's correspondence / Sally Henny Penny's Invitations / Rebecca Puddleduck's correspondence / Bird's correspondence, The / Flopsy bunnies correspondence.
MC: . . . . **TSP 413**

Potter, Don

OVER THE RAINBOW.
LP: . . . . **MIRROR 6**

Potter, John

ROCKIN' THE 88'S.
Tracks: / High school confidential / Blue moon of Kentucky / Mean woman blues / I'll make it all up to you / Got a lot of livin' to do / Rockin' the 88's / Ubangi stomp / All aboard / Jambalaya / Mailtrain / Ballad of Billy Joe / When thew boogie breaks.
LP: . . . . **CH 49**

Potter, Nic

BLUE ZONE, THE.
LP: . . . . **VP 103**

DREAMS IN VIEW 81-87.
Tracks: / Dimension Z / Bird can take flight / Cuban dance / Future contemplation / Gone wild (remix version) / Goddess of Ios / Morning suite / Planet of paradise (I) / Planet of paradise (II) / Planet of paradise (III) / Paradise journey / Forest, The / Die grossenwahn / Night falls over Europe.
2LP: . . . . **Unknown**
LP: . . . . **EPI 001**

LONG HELLO 2.
LP: . . . . **NOTT 004**

MOUNTAIN MUSIC.
LP: . . . . **ZOMART 001**
MC: . . . . **ZOMART 001C**

SKETCHES IN SOUND.
LP: . . . . **ZOMART 002**

Pottinger, Sonia

PUT ON YOUR BEST DRESS.
LP: . . . . **ATLP 109**

Potts, Bill

555 FEET HIGH (Potts, Bill Big Band).
LP: . . . . **JAZZ MARK 107**

Potts, Sean

BAKERSWELL.
LP: . . . . **CCF 20**
MC: **4CCF 20**

Potts, Steve

LIVE IN BUDAPEST (See under Lacy, Steve) (Potts, Steve & Steve Lacy).

Potts, Tommy

LIFFEY BANKS, THE.
LP: . . . . **CC 13**

Poulenc (composer)

GLORIA#STABAT MATER (Various artists).
MC: **4273044**

Pound, Ezra (nar)

CANTICO DEL SOLE, CANTO 99... (see under Cantico Del Sole...).

Pourcel, Franck

CLASSICAL FAVOURITES IN DIGITAL.
LP: . . . . **TWOD 2002**

CLASSICAL IN DIGITAL VOL.3.
LP: **2C 063 73148**
MC: **7C 063 73148**

CLASSICS.
Tracks: / Thus spake Zarathustra / Carmen overture / Intermezzo (From "Cavalleria Rusticana".) / Norwegian dance no. 2 / Sicilian Vespers (overture) / Tango / Ritual fire dance / Sicilienne / Sabre dance / Largo / Czardas / Gymnopedie no.3 / La danza / Le lac de come / Can can (From " La Vie Parisienne".) / Reve d'amour / Valse, opus 39.
MC: . . . . **TCEMS 1263**
LP: . . . . **EMS 1263**

DIGITAL AROUND THE WORLD (Pourcel, Franck & His Orchestra).
Tracks: / Bette Davis eyes / Memory / Lay all your love on me / Logical song / Morning train.
LP: **2C 068 73551**

EDITH AND POURCEL.
LP: . . . . **2 C 068 73555**
MC: . . . . **TC-2 C 068 73555**

FRANCK POURCEL & ORCHESTRA (Pourcel, Franck & His Orchestra).
MC: . . . . **TC IDL 18**

FRANK POURCEL PLAYS ABBA.
Tracks: / Dancing queen / Knowing me, knowing you / Summer night city / I wonder / Fernando / Name of the game / Money, money, money / Eagle / Hole in your soul / I do, I do, I do / Thank your for the music.
LP: . . . . **TWOX 10077**

GREAT FILM MUSICALS (Pourcel, Franck & His Orchestra).
Tracks: / Hello Dolly / Tonight / C'est magnifique / I love Paris / I've got you under my skin / In the still of the night / Easy to love / True love / Singin' in the rain / Top hat, white tie and tails / Summertime / Sound of music / Jesus Christ superstar / I don't know how to love Him / Day by day / Aquarius / Sunrise, sunset / If I were a rich man / Secret love / Chitty chitty bang bang / Night and day / Just one of those things / So in love / Don't fence me in / Tip-toe through the tulips / Begin the beguine.
MC: . . . . **TCEMS 1351**

LA FEMME ROMANTIQUE.
LP: **2C 068 15590**

LES HITS CLASSIQUES.
Tracks: / La danza / Badinerie (Extrait de la suite en Si Mineur BWV 1067) / Bolero / Danse horgroise de Brahms no. 5 / Carmina burana / Marche turque / La moldau / Allegro du concerto en re mineur / Marche de Radetsky / Theme du lac des cygnes / Carmen (air du toreador) / Valse no 6 en re majeur, opus 64 (No 1 dite 'du petit chien') / Aida 'Marche triomphale' (trompettes) / Marche hongroise de 'La damnation de faust' / Can-Can (Exrait de 'La vie Parisienne') / Adagio pour cordes et orgue.
LP: **1735941**
MC: **1735944**

NEW SOUND TANGOS.
LP: **2C 068 721 62**

NOSTALGIA MOOD.
Tracks: / Cry me a river / Puttin' on the Ritz / Flamingo / Tweedle Dee / Fascination / Mona Lisa / All of me / Answer me / In a nostalgia mood / I'm getting sentimental over you / I love you / September in the rain / Unforgettable.
LP: . . . . **PM 1735 641**
MC: **1735944**

PALMES D'OR.
LP: **2C 070 73553**

THIS IS POURCEL.
LP: . . . . **STWO 7**

Poussez

LEAVE THAT BOY ALONE.
Tracks: / I'm in love with you / Do it for the sake of love / You made my dream come true / Leave that boy alone / Let's rollerskate / I'm never gonna give my love again / I'll always be your friend / Don't stop, keep movin'.
LP: . . . . **VSD 79433**

POUSSEZ.
Tracks: / Come on and do it / Boogie with me / You're all I have / Never gonna say goodbye.
LP: . . . . **VSD 79412**
MC: . . . . **ZCVS 79412**

Powaqqatsi

POWAQQATSI (See under Glass, Philip) (Glass, Philip).

Powder Blues

RED HOT/TRUE BLUE.
LP: . . . . **FF 343**

UNCUT.
Tracks: / Boppin' with the blues / Hear that guitar ring / Just a little / Rockchopper / Doin' it right / Buzzard luck / What've I been drinking / Personal manager / Sweet little girl.
LP: . . . . **PL 10365**

Powell, Andrew

BEST OF THE ALAN PARSONS PROJECT (Powell, Andrew/ Philharmonic Orchestra).
Tracks: / Lucifer / Time / Games people play / I robot suite / Damned if i do / Pavane / What goes up / Eye in the sky / Old and wise.
LP: . . . . **EMTV 1077291**

Powell, Baden

APAIXONADO.
LP: . . . . **MPS 68 090**

BADEN POWELL.
LP: . . . . **SM 3991**
MC: . . . . **MC 3991**

CANTO ON GUITAR.
LP: . . . . **MPS 68 157**

ESTUDOS.
LP: . . . . **MPS 68 092**

IMAGES ON GUITAR.
LP: . . . . **MPS 68 091**

POEMA ON GUITAR.
LP: . . . . **MPS 68 089**

TRISTEZA ON GUITAR.
Tracks: / Tristeza / Canto de zango / Round about midnight / Sarava / Canto de ossanha / Manha de carnaval / Invencao em 71-2 / Das rosas / Som do carnaval / Astronauta.
LP: . . . . **MPS 68 093**

Powell, Benny

LIVE AT THE 1990 CONCORD JAZZ FESTIVAL (See Under McConnell, Rob) (Powell, Benny & Rob McConnell & Al Grey).

Powell, Bobby

FOOL FOR YOU, A.
Tracks: / Spread your love / Fool for you, A / Sweet sixteen / I can't stop loving you / Queen size woman / When you move you lose / Night time is the right time / Let me love you / Drifting blues / Glory of love (part 1).
LP: . . . . **CRB 1185**

Powell, Bud

ALTERNATE TAKES.
Tracks: / Bouncing with Bud / Wail / Dance of the infidels / Reets and I / Collard greens and black-eyed peas / Blue pearl / John's abbey / Comin' up / Like someone in love / Our love is here to stay.
LP: . . . . **BST 84430**

AMAZING BUD POWELL, VOL 1.
Tracks: / Un poco loco (first take) / Un poco loco (second take) / Dance of the infidels / 52nd Street theme / It could happen to you (LP only.) / Night in Tunisia (LP only.) / Wail / Ornithology / Bouncing with Bud / Parisian thoroughfare (LP only.) / Bouncing with Bud ((Alt take 1) CD only.) / Bouncing with Bud ((Alt take 2) CD only.) / Wail (alt. take) (CD only.) / Dance of the infidels (alt. take) (CD only.) / You go to my head (CD only.) / Ornithology (alt. master) (CD only.) / Un poco loco (alt. take 2) (CD only.) / Over the rainbow (CD only.).
LP: . . . . **BST 81503**
LP: . . . . **BLP 1503**

AMAZING BUD POWELL, VOL 2.
Tracks: / Reets and I / Autumn in New York / I want to be happy / It could happen to you / Sure thing / Polka dots and moonbeams / Glass enclosure / Collard greens and black-eyed peas / Over the rainbow (LP only.) / Audrey / You go to my head (LP only.) / Ornithology (LP only.) / Night in Tunisia, A (CD only.) / Night in Tunisia, A (alt. master) (CD only.) / It could happen to you (alt. master) (CD only.) / Reets and I (alt. take) (CD only.) / Parisian thoroughfare (CD only.) / Collard greens and black-eyed peast (alt. take) (CD only.).
LP: . . . . **BST 81504**
LP: . . . . **BLP 1504**
LP: . . . . **BNS 40006**

AMAZING BUD POWELL, VOL 3.
Tracks: / Some soul / Blue pearl / Frantic fancies / Bud on Bach / Keepin' in the groove / Idaho / Don't blame me / Moose the mooche / Blue pearl (alt. take).
MC: **4BN 81571**
LP: . . . . **BST 81571**

AT THE BLUE NOTE CAFE PARIS 1961.
LP: . . . . **ESP 1066**

AT THE GOLDEN CIRCLE VOL 4.
LP: . . . . **SCC 6014**

AUTUMN SESSION 1953.
LP: . . . . **BASE 3035**

BEST OF BUD POWELL.
Tracks: / Bouncing with Bud / 52nd Street theme (CD only.) / Un poco loco / Parisian thoroughfare / Collard greens and black-eyed peas / Glass enclosure / Reets and I (CD only.) / Blue pearl / Bud on Bach / John's abbey / Monopoly / Buster rides again (CD only.) / Scene changes, The / Cleopatra's dream / Like someone in love (CD only.).
LP: **B1 93204**
LP: **793 204 1**

BEST YEARS, THE.
LP: . . . . **VJD 546**
2LP: **421010**

BLUES FOR BOUFFEMONT.
Tracks: / In the mood for a classic / Una noche con frances / Relaxin' at Camarillo / Moose the mooche / Blues for Bouffemont / Little Willie leaps / My old flame / Star eyes / There will never be another you.
LP: . . . . **KLJ 20019**
LP: . . . . **BLP 60135**

BOUNCING WITH BUD (Powell, Bud Trio).
LP: . . . . **SLP 4113**

BUD POWELL TRIO PLAYS, THE (Powell, Bud Trio).
Tracks: / I'll remember April / Indiana / Somebody loves me / I should care / Bud's bubble / Off minor / Nice work if you can get it / Everything happens to me / Embraceable you / Burt covers Bud / My heart stood still / You'd be so nice to come home to / Bag's groove / My devotion / Stellar by starlight / Woody'n you.
LP: . . . . **ROU 1011**
LP: **793 902 1**

BUD POWELL VOL. 1.

Tracks: / I'll remember April / Everything happens to me / Indiana / I should care / Nice work if you can get it / Off minor / Bud's bubble / Somebody loves me / Embraceable you / My heart stood still / You'd be so nice to come home to / Burt covers Bud / My devotion / Stella by starlight / Bag's groove / Woodyn' you.
LP: . . . . JR 112

BUD POWELL VOL 2.
Tracks: / Buttercup / John's abbey / Sweet & lovely / Crossin' the channel / I know that you know / Best thing for you / Just one of those things / I remember Clifford / Hallucinations / If I loved you / On Green Dolphin Street / Someone to watch over me.
LP: . . . . JR 131

COMPLETE ESSENTIAL JAZZ FESTIVAL CONCERT, THE.
Tracks: / Shaw 'nuff / Blues in the closet / Willow weep for me / John's abbey / Salt peanuts / All the things you are / Just you, just me / Yesterdays / Stuffy.
LP: . . . . BLP 760105

GENIUS OF BUD POWELL.
Tracks: / Tempus fugit / Celia / Cherokee / I'll keep loving you / Strictly confidential / All God's chillun got rhythm / So sorry please / Get happy / Sometimes I'm happy / Sweet Georgia Brown / Yesterdays / April in Paris / Body and soul / Tea for two / Hallelujah / Parisian thoroughfare / Oblivion / Dusk at Saudi / Hallucinations / Fruit / Last time I saw Paris, The / Just one of those things / Nightingale sang in Berkeley Square.
2LP: 2532051

GENIUS OF BUD POWELL THE.
Tracks: / Parisienne thororfare / Oblivion / Dusk in sandi / Hallucinations / Fruit / Tea for two / Hallelujah / Last time I saw Paris, The / Just one of those things / Nightingale sang in berkeley square.
LP: 2304 112

GENIUS OF..., THE.
LP: . . . . LPJT 44

HAWKINS IN GERMANY (see Hawkins, Coleman) (Powell, Bud & Coleman Hawkins).

IN EUROPE.
LP: . . . . D 1012

IN PARIS (Powell, Bud Trio).
Tracks: / How high the moon / Body and soul / Satin doll / Jor-Du / I can't get started.
LP: . . . . DS 830

INVISIBLE CAGE, THE.
Tracks: / Blues for Bouffemont / Little Willie leaps / My old flame / Moose the mooche / In the mood for a classic / Like someone in love / Una noche con Francis / Relaxin' at Camarillo.
LP: . . . . BLP 30120

JAZZ GIANT.
LP: 829 937-1

LIVE AT BIRDLAND.
LP: . . . . QU 024

MOVE (See under Parker, Charlie) (Powell, Bud/Charlie Parker/Fats Navarro).

MY DEVOTION.
MC: 771512

ORNITHOLOGY.
LP: . . . . BLJ 8034

PORTRAIT OF THELONIOUS.
Tracks: / Off minor / There will never be another you / Ruby / My dear / No name blues / Thelonious / Monk's mood / I ain't fooling / Squattyroo.
LP: . . . . CBS 54301

QUINTET OF THE YEAR, THE (see Gillespie, Dizzy/Parker/Powell/Mingus & Roach) (Powell/Mingus/Roach/Parker & Gillespie).

RETURN OF BUD POWELL.
LP: . . . . FS 226

SALT PEANUTS.
LP: . . . . BLP 60121

SPRING SESSIONS 1953.
LP: . . . . BASE 3033

SUMMER SESSIONS 1953.
LP: . . . . BASE 3034

SWINGIN WITH BUD.
2LP: . . . . PM 45137

Powell, Cozy

FORCEFIELD III (see under Bonnet, Graham) (Powell, Cozy/Graham Bonnet/Ray Fenwick/Jan Akkerman).

OCTOPUSS.
Tracks: / Up on the downs / 633 squadron / Title track / Big country / Formula one / Princetown / Dartmoor / Rattler.
MC: . . . . POLDC 5093
LP: . . . . POLD 5093

OVER THE TOP.
Tracks: / Theme one / Killer / Heidi goes to town / El sid / Sweet poison / Loner / Over the top.
LP: . . . . FA 3056
MC: . . . . TCFA 3056
LP: . . . . ARL 5036

TILT.
Tracks: / Right side / Jekyll and Hyde / Sooner or later / Living a lie / Cat moves / Sunset / Blister / Hot rock.
LP: . . . . POLD 5047

Powell, Dick

16 CLASSIC TRACKS.
LP: . . . . MCL 1691

LEGENDARY, THE.
MC: . . . . MRT 40047

LULLABY OF BROADWAY.
Tracks: / Lullaby of broadway / I'm sitting high on a hilltop / I'm goin' shoppin' with you / Lulu's back in town / Words are in my heart, The / Don't give up the ship / Down sunshine lane / Pop goes your heart / Happiness ahead / Rose in her heart, The / Mr. & Mrs. is the name / Flirtation walk / Don't say goodnight / Wonder bar / Thanks a million / I've got a pocket full of sunshine.
LP: . . . . RECOL 6
MC: . . . . RECMC 6

LULLABY OF BROADWAY (LIVING ERA).
Tracks: / Fair and warmer / Young and healthy / Wonder bar / Lulu's back in town / Outside of you / Lonely gondolier / Why do I dream those dreams? / I'll string along with you / I only have eyes for you / Mr. and Mrs. is the name / Flirtation walk / Rose in her hand, The / Waterfall, A / Thanks a million / I'm going shopping with you / Lullaby of Broadway.
LP: . . . . AJA 5045
MC: . . . . ZC AJA 5045

ON THE AVENUE.
Tracks: / I'm like a fish out of water / With plenty of money and you / I've got my love to keep me warm / Let's put our heads together / 'Cause my baby says it's so / You've got something there / Two hearts divided / There's two sides to every story / Speaking of the weather / You can't stop me from dreaming / I've hitched my wagon to a star / This year's kisses / All's fair in love and war / Moonlight on the campus / You can't run away from love tonight / In your own quiet way / Don't give up the ship / Roses in December / You're laughing at me / Song of the marines.
LP: . . . . CHD 147
MC: . . . . MCHD 147

RARE RECORDINGS 1934-1951.
LP: . . . . SH 2048
MC: . . . . CSH 2048

Powell, Doc

LOVE IS WHERE IT'S AT.
LP: . . . . JABH 28
MC: . . . . JABHC 28

Powell, Mel

BOUQUET (Powell, Mel Trio).
Tracks: / Quin and sonic / If dreams come true / Cross your heart / Avalon / Borderline / Makin' whoopee / What's new / Thigamagic / You're my thrill / Button up your overcoat / Don-que-de / Bouquet / Ain't she sweet / Take me in your arms / California here I come.
LP: . . . . VJD 572

PIANO FORTE (Powell, Mel & His Uptown Hall Gang).
LP: . . . . NOST 7649

WORLD IS WAITING 1942-46 (See Buskin, Joe) (Powell, Mel & Joe Buskin).

Powell, Patsy

FOR THE GOOD TIMES (Powell, Patsy & The Goodtimers).
LP: . . . . FHR 066

THANK YOU FOR LOVING ME.
LP: . . . . FHR 073

THAT'S WHAT THE WORLD NEEDS (Powell, Patsy & The Goodtimers).
LP: . . . . FHR 099

Powell, Peter

KEEP FIT AND DANCE.
LP: . . . . NE 1167
MC: . . . . CE 2167

Powell, Polly

ALL OF ME.
LP: . . . . AP 136

Powell, Robert (nar)

KIND HEARTS AND CORONETS/ ARSENIC AND OLD LACE (See under 'Kind hearts & cornets').

SCARLET PIMPERNEL, THE (See under Scarlet Pimpernel (bk)).

STUDY IN SCARLET, A (see under Sherlock Holmes (bk)).

THIRTY-NINE STEPS, THE (see under Thirty-Nine Steps (bk)).

Powell, Roger

AIR POCKET.
Tracks: / Lunar plexus / Landmark / Air pocket / Windows / Emergency splash down / Morning chorus / March of the Dragonslayers / Prophecy / Sands of Arrakis / Dragons 'n' griffins / Mr. Triscuit's theme.
LP: . . . . ILPS 9607

CONNECTIONS TO THE WORLD.
LP: . . . . SYN 107
MC: . . . . SYNC 107

Powell, Seldon

SELDON POWELL SEXTET (Powell, Seldon Sextet).
LP: . . . . FS 286

Powell, Verna Lee

SIGNS OF THE TIMES.
LP: . . . . TRULP 001

Powell, Will

GREAT SIGFELD, THE (Powell, Will/ Various).
LP: . . . . CIF 3005

Power

POWER.
LP: . . . . MAL 7408

Power, Duffy

MARY OPEN THE DOOR.
LP: . . . . MACH 5

Power (film)

POWER, THE (See Under Q - The Winged Serpent) (Various artists).

Power, Jimmy

FIFTY ODD YEARS (Power Jimmy & Josephine Neegan).
LP: . . . . TP 001
LP: 0001

IRISH FIDDLE PLAYER.
LP: 12TS 306

IRISH MUSIC FROM THE FAVOURITE also see Tony ledwith.
LP: . . . . LEA 2051

Power Mad

ABSOLUTE POWER.
Tracks: / Slaughterhouse / Nice dreams / Test the steel (Powermad) / B.N.R. / Brainstorms / Absolute power / Return from the fear / Plastic town / Failsafe / Final frontier.
LP: . . . . K 9259371
MC: . . . . K 9259374

Power Of Dreams

IMMIGRANTS, EMIGRANTS AND ME.
Tracks: / Jokes on me, The / Does it matter / Had you listened / Never told you / Never been to Texas / Maire I don't love you / Mothers eyes / Talk / Much too much / Stay / Bring you down / Where is the love / 100 ways to kill a man / My average day.
LP: 843 258 1
MC: 843 258 4

Power of Love (The)

POWER OF LOVE (Various artists).
LP: . . . . WEF 4
MC: . . . . ZCWEF 4

POWER OF LOVE (THE) Various artists (Various artists).
LP: 6.26144
MC: 4.26144

Power Pack Orchestra

'A' IS FOR ACTION.
Tracks: / Superman (theme) / Hill Street blues / T.J. Hooker (theme).
LP: . . . . MFP 5705
MC: . . . . TCMFP 5705
LP: . . . . MFP 41 5705 1
MC: . . . . MFP 41 5705 6

CRIMEBUSTERS.
Tracks: / Cagney and Lacey / Miami Vice / Scarecrow and Mrs.King / Gentle touch, The / Hunter, The / Miss Marple / Remington Steele / Hart to Hart / Mike Hammer theme / Highway patrol / Airwolf / Crazy like a fox / Murder She Wrote / Magnum / Juliet Bravo / Sweeney, The / Fall guy, The / Chinese detective, The / Bill, The (Overkill) / Z Cars.
LP: . . . . MFP 5768
MC: . . . . TCMFP 5768

FAVOURITE SPORTS THEMES.
Tracks: / Match of the day / BBC snooker theme (Drag racer) / ITV's big match live (Aztec gold) / Sportsnight / BBC golf theme (Chase side shoot up) / Ski Sunday (Pop goes Bach) / Question of sport / Sports report (Out of the blue) / Boxing / BBC cricket theme / Wimbledon (Light and tuneful) / Saint and Greavsie theme / BBC Grandstand / Rugby special / ITV's world of sport / 1987 world championship athletic theme / Chain, The (Grand Prix) / Chariots of fire / Kick start (be my boogie woogie baby) / Shuffle, The.
LP: . . . . MFP 5818
MC: . . . . TC MFP 5818

GREAT WAR THEMES.
Tracks: / Winds of war, The / Longest day, The / Where eagles dare / Six three three squadron / Dambusters / Operation crossbow / Cavatina / Colonel Bogey / Death before dishonor (theme) / Washington post / In the mood / Great escape march / Guns for San Sebastian (love theme) / Reach for the sky / Battle of Britain / Aces high (CD only.).
MC: . . . . TCMFP 5885

MUSIC OF ANDREW LLOYD WEBBER.
Tracks: / Jesus Christ superstar / Phantom of the opera / Tell me on a Sunday (from 'Song and Dance') / Starlight express (from 'Starlight Express') / Mr. Mistoffelees (from 'Cats') / Music of the night (from 'Phantom of the Opera') / Take that look off your face (from 'Song and Dance') / Another suitcase in another hall (from 'Evita') / I don't know how to love Him (from 'Jesus Christ Superstar') / Any dream will do (from 'Joseph and The Amazing Technicolour Dreamcoat') / Don't cry for me Argentina (From 'Evita') / Old Deuteronomy (from 'Cats') / All I ask of you (from 'The Phantom of the Opera') / Pumping iron (CD only.) / King Herod's song (CD only.) / One more angel in heaven (CD only.) / Love changes everything (CD only.).
LP: . . . . MFP 5808
MC: . . . . TCMFP 5808

SOAPS (TV Themes).
Tracks: / Soap / Coronation Street / Eastenders / Dynasty / Crossroads / Knots Landing / Sons and daughters / Colbys, The / Brookside / Waltons - theme / Dallas / Emmerdale Farm / Falcon Crest / Alice / Albion Market, Theme from / Hotel / Take the High Road / St. Elsewhere / Sullivans, The / Barwick Green.
LP: . . . . MFP 5759
MC: . . . . TCMFP 5759

YOUR 40 ALL-TIME DANCE HITS.
Tracks: / In the mood / Opus one / Don't get around much anymore / I'm beginning to see the light / American patrol / Touch of your lips, The / Spanish harlem / My cherie amour / Shadow of your smile / Guitar boogie shuffle / Nut rocker / Goody goody / Deep in the heart of Texas / Hoots mon / Lara's theme / Moon river / Green leaves of summer / You made me love you / Limehouse blues / St. Louis Blues / Body and soul / Stranger on the shore / Moonlight serenade / Mood indigo / Tuxedo Junction / It happened in Monterey / String of pearls / Brazil / Sucu sucu / Caravan / Copacabana / Lipstick on your collar / Let there be drums / Never on a Sunday / Spanish flea / Hernando's hideaway / New fangled tangle / Get happy / Continental, The / Last waltz, The.
LP: . . . . MFP 5866
MC: . . . . TCMFP 5866

Power Station

POWER STATION.
Tracks: / Some like it hot / Murderess / Lonely tonight / Communication / Get it on / Go to zero / Harvest for the world / Still in your heart.
LP: . . . . POST 1
MC: . . . . TCPOST 1
LP: . . . . FA 3206
MC: . . . . TCFA 3206
LP: . . . . EJ 2402971
MC: . . . . EJ 240297

Power Themes '90

POWER THEMES '90 (Various artists).
Tracks: / Thunderbirds are go: *Various artists* / Joe 90: *Various artists* / UFO: *Various artists* / Captain Scarlet: *Various artists* / Space 1999: *Various artists* / Stingray: *Various artists* / Prisoner, The: *Various artists* / Saint, The: *Various artists* / Avengers, The: *Various artists* / Danger man: *Various artists* / Department S: *Various artists* / Persuaders, The: *Various artists.*
MCSET: . . . . STAC 2430
LP: . . . . STAR 2430

Power Tools

STRANGE MEETING.
MC: . . . . ANC 8715
LP: . . . . AN 8715

Powerhouse...

POWERHOUSE.
LP: 40 1003

POWERHOUSE PRESENTS STRICTLY LIVESTOCK (Various artists).
LP: . . . . GREL 81

POWERHOUSE REPRESENTS FINAL MISSION (Various artists).
LP: . . . . Unknown

Powerlord

AWAKENING, THE.
Tracks: / Masters of death / Malice / Silent terror / Invasion of the Lords / Merciless Titans / Powerlord.
LP: . . . . SHARK 008

Powermixer

POWERMIXER (Various artists).
LP: . . . . PMM 001

Powers, Chris

CHRIS POWERS & HIS ORCHESTRA (Powers, Chris & His Orchestra).
LP: . . . . CLP 89

Powers, Johnny

CAN'T RESIST THAT ROCK'N'ROLL.
Tracks: / Mama rock / Indeed I do / Waitin' for you / Don't go away / Trouble (I'm evil) / Don't lie to me / Waiting for you / Won't you please pretty baby / Rosalee / Corina, Corina / Rest of my days are lonely ones, The / I believe she loves me too / I need your lovin' baby / I got a girl who knows how to live / Everybody says I'm a lucky guy / Well I got troubles / I'll take that chance / It's now or never little one / I just got to know now / You didn't care.
LP: . . . . ROLL 2017

LET IT ROCK.
LP: . . . . SJLP 587

ROCK ROCK ROCK.
Tracks: / Long blonde hair / Rock rock / Honey let's go (to a rock 'n' roll show) / Your love / I'm walking / Treat me right / Be bop a lula / Mean mistreater / I'm evil / With your love, with your kiss / Be mine all mine / Me and my rhythm guitar / Waiting for you / Oh so far away / Kiss me baby / Falling star / Bigger they are (the harder they fall in love), The / Please return my love / Someone's gonna hurt you / Seventeen.
LP: . . . . ROLL 2010

Powers, Will

DANCING FOR MENTAL HEALTH.
Tracks: / Adventures in success / Dancing for mental health / Opportunity / Kissing with confidence / Will power / All thru history / Happy birthday / Smile.
LP: . . . . ILPS 9765
MC: . . . . ZCL 9765

Powersurge

POWERSURGE.
LP: . . . . RR 93111
MC: . . . . RR 93114

Powertrax

POWERTRAX (Various artists).
LP: . . . . NEAT 1033

Powrie, Ian

AT HOME.
Tracks: / Ian Powrie's compliments to Sir Thomas Wardle / Jimmy Shand's welcome to Corrieburn / Lass from Glasgow town / Lunan bay / Mary Shaw / Sir Kenneth Alexander / Clan MacColl / Mrs. Hamilton of Pencaitland / Scotty Wilson / Donald MacLellan of Rothesay / Jimmy and Mickie / Highland cathedral / Gaelic reel / In the gloaming / Tigh-na-gorm / Mackworth / Kemmel hill / Catherine and John Fraser's diamond wedding / Old Scottish waltz / Kenny Thomson's compliments to Ian Powrie / Tribute to Stan Hamilton, A / Peerie Willie / Ellenbrook / Black boy, The / Georgina Catherine MacDonald's fancy / C.M. Hall / Annie's song / Take me home country roads / Thank God I'm a country boy / Crags of Tumbledown mountain.
LP: . . . . GRALP 27
MC: . . . . GRTC 27

LEGENDS OF SCOTLAND (Powrie, Ian Band).
Tracks: / St. Johnstoun reel / Lass o' paties mill / Doctor Robertson's reel Margaret-Anne Robertson / Lochaber gathering, The / Tam Bain's lum / Stool of repentance / David Ross / Irish washerwoman, The / Bandboys / Bonnie lass o' Bon Accord / Tushker, The / St. Ann's / Callum Donaldson / Dancing the baby / Gloomy winter / Silver city waltz / Old maid in a garret / Flower of the queen, The / Merry boys of Greenland / Willfijord / Leveneep head.
MC: . . . . ZCLLS 706

P.O.X.

VOODOO POWER.
LP: KIX4U 2225
LP: . . . . PLAT 2225

Pozo Seco Singers

POZO SECO SINGERS (Pozo Seco Singers feat.Don Williams).
Tracks: / Take my hand for a while / There's never never a time / Where do I go from here / On her way to be a woman / Follow me back to Louisville / Spend some time with me / There's always something there to remind me / Ruby Tuesday / Storybook children / Coming apart / Tears'.
LP: . . . . SHM 3021
MC: . . . . HSC 3021

Prado, Perez

GUANTANAMERA.
LP: . . . . WS 4068

PEREZ PRADO.
LP: . . . . BO 712

PEREZ PRADO & ORCHESTRA (Prado, Perez & His Orch).
LP: . . . . SM 4029

Praeger, Lou

DANCING CLOSE TOGETHER.
LP: . . . . JOY 245

ON THE SUNNY SIDE OF THE STREET (Praeger, Lou & His Orchestra).
Tracks: / Peg o' my heart / Bring on my drums / Until / There's no one but you / Sophisticated lady / Don't be a baby baby / First day of summer, The / First floor jump / I want to learn to dance / I'm comin' a courtin' / Doggin' around / Two can dream as cheaply as one / Shoemaker's serenade, The / Third floor jump / Good, good, good / Saturday night is the loneliest night of the week / Carolina / On the sunny side of the street.
LP: . . . . PLE 500
MC: . . . . TC-PLE 500

Praise The Lord...

PRAISE THE LORD AND PASS THE AMMUNITION (Various artists).
Tracks: / Let's all be Americans now: *American Quartet, Studio Orchestra* / When the Lusitania went down: *Stuart, Herbert studio orchestra* / I didn't raise my boy to be a soldier: *Harvey, Morton Studio Orchestra* / Over there: *Various artists* / Hello central: *Johnson, Al Studio Orchestra* / There's a vacant chair in every home tonight: *Shannon Four Studio Orchestra* / I've got a captain working for me now: *Jolson/Dreyer/Rose* / My dream of the big parade: *Peerless Quartet Studio Orchestra* / Defuehrer's face: *Jones, Spike & His City Slickers* / He's 1-A in the army and he's 1-A in my heart: *Bonney, Betty/Les Brown and his Orchestra* / Stalin wasn't stallin' (a modern spiritual): *Golden Gate Quartet* / We did it before and we can do it again: *Robertson, Dick Studio Orchestra* / I left my heart at the stage door canteen: *Baker, Kenny Orchestra* / Goodbye, mama (I'm off to Yokohama): *Robertson, Dick Studio Orchestra* / No love, no nothing: *Long, Johnny & His Orchestra/Patti Dugan* / Praise the Lord and pass the ammunition: *Kyser, Kay & His Orchestra & Glee Club* / My guy's come back: *Forrest, Helen Studio Orchestra.*
LP: . . . . NW 222

Prams

WHAT'S THE TIME MR WOLF.
LP: . . . . WWL 101A

Prats, Jorge Luis

PIANO CONCERTO NO.3 (RACHMANINOV) (see under Rachmaninov) (Prats, Jorge Luis/ Mexico City Symphony Orchestra).

Pratt, Andy

SHIVER IN THE NIGHT.
Tracks: / All I want is you / Rainbow / I want to see you dance / My love is so tender / So faint / Keep your dream alive / Landscape / What's important to you / Mama's getting love / Dreams / Born to learn.
LP: . . . . SSK 59400

Pratt, Graham

CLEAR AIR OF THE DAY (Pratt, Graham & Eileen).
Tracks: / Merrie hostess, The / Ned of the hills / Love is come again / Nothing but the blood of Jesus / Lark in the clear air / Woman woman / Greenwood laddie / Merlins song / Murdered serving man / Gay green gown / Dancing days.
LP: . . . . FSLP 2

HIEROGLYPHICS (Pratt, Graham & Eileen).
LP: . . . . PLR 068

MAGIC PEAR TREE (Pratt, Graham & Eileen).
Tracks: / Pilgrim fathers, The / Pied piper / Lady Howard's coach / Devil's bridge / Black fox, The / Tramp's song, The / Lumley Kettlewell / Minstrel, The / Nobleman and the thresher, The / Campbell's servant / High mettled racer, The / Northill May song / Lord Nelson's lament / Ol' bangum / Broomfield hill.
MC: 60-048

TO FRIEND AND FOE (Pratt, Graham & Eileen).
LP: . . . . DIN 308

Pravda

LESSON ONE.
MC: . . . . TASC 1

Prayer Boat

OCEANIC FEELING.
Tracks: / Stopping the world / Oceanic feeling / Millionaire hero / Don't make me breathe you in / Love and possession / Upside down / Out of mind / Still only one / Hunger for the beautiful / Mercy / Among madmen (Track on CD only.).
LP: . . . . PL 74818
MC: . . . . PK 74818

Praying Mantis

TIME TELLS NO LIES.
Tracks: / Cheated / All day and all of the night / Running for tomorrow / Rich city kids / Lovers to the grave / Panic in the streets / Beads of ebony / Flirting with suicide / Children of the earth.
LP: . . . . SPART 1153

Preacher

HARDCORE DEMO SERIES.
LP: . . . . WRR 004

Preacher Jack

3000 BARROOMS LATER.
LP: . . . . ROUNDER 3077
MC: . . . . ROUNDER 3077C

ROCK 'N' ROLL PREACHER.
Tracks: / Going to the river / Preacher's boogie woogie / Almost persuaded / Who will buy the wine / Can't believe you wanna leave / All for the love of a girl / Lovin' up a storm / Singing waterfall / Say you'll stay until tomorrow / All by myself.
LP: . . . . SNTF 836
LP: . . . . ROUNDER 3033
MC: . . . . ROUNDER 3033C

Preachers

REAL GONE.
LP: . . . . SLR 3301

Precious Metal (group)

PRECIOUS METAL (Precious Metal).
LP: . . . . MCF 3069

RIGHT HERE, RIGHT NOW.
Tracks: / This girl / Right here, right now / Bad guys / Pretty boy / Emily / Shakin' / Girls night out / You do something special / Cheesecake / Rembering old times.
LP: 826146 1

THAT KIND OF GIRL.
LP: . . . . LPVAG 001
MC: . . . . CASSVAG 001

Predator

PREDATOR.
LP: . . . . RR 9714

Predator (film)

PREDATOR 2 (Film Soundtrack) (Various artists).
LP: . . . . VS 5302
MC: . . . . VSC 5302

Prefab Sprout

FROM LANGLEY PARK TO MEMPHIS.
Tracks: / King of rock and roll / Cars and girls / I remember that / Enchanted / Nightingales / Hey Manhattan / Knock on wood / Golden calf, The / Nancy let your hair down for me / Venus of the soup kitchen, The.
LP: . . . . KWLP 9
MC: . . . . KWC 9

JORDAN - THE COMEBACK.
Tracks: / Looking for Atlantis / Wild horses / Machine gun Ibiza / We let the stars go / Carnival 2000 / Jordan: The comeback / Jesse James symphony / Jesse James bolero / Moon dog / All the world loves lovers / All boys believe anything / Ice maiden, The / Paris Smith / Wedding march, The / One of the broken / Michael / Mercy / Scarlet nights / Doo wop in Harlem.
LP: . . . . KWLP 14
MC: . . . . KWC 14

PROTEST SONGS.
Tracks: / World awake, The / Life of surprises / Horsechimes / Wicked things / Dublin / Tiffanys / Talkin' scarlet / Till the cows come home / Pearly gates.
LP: . . . . KWLP 4
MC: . . . . KWC 4
MC: 4651184

STEVE MCQUEEN.
Tracks: / Faron young / Bonny / Appetite / When love breaks down / Goodbye Lucille / Hallelujah / Moving the river / Horsing around / Desire as / Blueberry pies / When the angels.
LP: . . . . KWLP 3
MC: . . . . KWC 3
LP: 4663361
MC: 4663364

SWOON.
Tracks: / Don't sing / Cue fanfare / Green Isaac / Here on the eerie / Cruel / Couldn't bear to be special / I never play basketball now / Ghost town blues / Elegance / Technique.
LP: 460908 1
MC: 460908 4
LP: . . . . KWLP 1

Pregnant Neck

SHENANIGANESQUE RAPSCALLIANISMZ.
LP: . . . . OOEER 1

Preiss, Byron

VAMPIRE STATE BUILDING & THE CRYING COMPUTOR.
MC: 1766

Preister, Julian

KOPUTAI (See under Clayton, Jay) (Preister, Julian/ Jay Clayton/ Ralph Townes).

Prelude

P.R.E.L.U.D.E..
LP: . . . . AFT LP 1
MC: . . . . AFT MC 1

PRELUDE 1 (Various artists).
LP: 21008
MC: 41008

Premi

AT THE FRONT LINE.
Tracks: / Happy birthday / Ik mutiar kuri / Agh sabh de siney lanwe ni / Pyaar mere naal palay / Sapni di kanj warga / Chunni lakey / Tere warga narm patola / Giddhe wich nach kuriay.
LP: . . . . MUT 1053
MC: . . . . CMUT 1053

MEIN TERI HOGAYEE.
Tracks: / Paliey Punjean Waliey / Saun mahiney / Mein teri hogayee / Tere lakh de hularey / Yaar mere di chaal / Kagara swadey menoon haniaan / Ban mohrni / Aj mein peenia / Aj di mehfil.
LP: . . . . MUT 1019
MC: . . . . CMUT 1019

NACHDI DO GOOTH KHULGAYE.
LP: . . . . MUT 1034
MC: . . . . CMUT 1034

NUMBER ONE.
LP: . . . . MUT 1062
MC: . . . . CMUT 1062

PREMI STRIKES AGAIN.
LP: . . . . MUT 1093
MC: . . . . CMUT 1093

Premier Sampler (Word

PREMIER SAMPLER-CONTEMPORARY V2 (Various artists).
MC: . . . . MOM C 11

PREMIER SAMPLER-PRAISE & WORSHIP (Various artists).
MC: . . . . MOM C 10

PREMIER SAMPLER-PRAISE & WORSHIP V2 (Various artists).
MC: . . . . MOM C 12

Premiere Accordian

GO HAWAIIAN.
Tracks: / Clap clap sound, The / Aloha oe / Highland hulu / Beyond the reef / Now is the hour.
LP: . . . . ITV 463
MC: . . . . KITV 463

Premiere Collection

PREMIERE COLLECTION, THE (Best of Andrew Lloyd Webber) (Various artists).
Tracks: / Phantom of the opera: *Harley, Steve & Sarah Brightman* / Take that look off your face: *Webb, Marti* / All I ask of you: *Richard, Cliff & Sarah Brightman* / Don't cry for me Argentina: *Covington, Julie* / Magical Mr. Mistoffeles: *Nicholas, Paul* / Variations 1-4: *Lloyd Webber, Julian* / Superstar: *Head, Murray* / Memory: *Paige, Elaine* / Starlight express: *Shell, Ray* / Tell me on a Sunday: *Webb, Marti* / Music of the night: *Crawford, Michael* / Another suitcase in another hall: *Dickson, Barbara* / I don't know how to love him: *Elliman, Yvonne* / Pie Jesu: *Brightman, Sarah & Paul Miles Kingston.*
LP: . . . . ALWTV 1
MC: . . . . ALWTC 1

Pre-Mixture

PRE-MIXTURE (Various artists).
LP: . . . . CHAMP 2

Prendergast, Kevin

GREEN HILLS OF SLIGO, THE.
MC: . . . . FACX 3001
LP: . . . . FALPX 3001

LET'S GO BACK TO MAYO.
MC: . . . . FACS 006
LP: . . . . FALP 006

PRIDE OF THE WEST, THE.
MC: . . . . FACS 007
LP: . . . . FALP 007

WHO'S GOING TO KEEP THE HOME FIRES BURNING.
LP: . . . . FALPTV 5001

Prento, Gussie

RAW RUB A DUB INNA FASHION.
LP: . . . . TOPLP 001

Presencer, Alain

SINGING BOWLS OF TIBET.
Tracks: / Invocation / Bowl voices / Shepherd's song / Lullaby / Bon-po chant / Lamentation / Symphony of the bowls.
LP: . . . . SDL 326
MC: . . . . CSDL 326

Present Laughter

PRESENT LAUGHTER Coward, Noel (Scofield, Paul/Fenella Fielding/ Margoles/Routledge).
MC: TCC/NCW2

Presenting Lily Mars

PRESENTING LILY MARS (Film soundtrack) (Various artists).
LP: . . . . STK 117

President

BRING YOUR CAMERA.
Tracks: / Hearts are broken / Our hands of water / Andre's wood / Wish the children would come / Clear the bridge / Philip / Ride the wide streets / Bad dream / 3 crows.
LP: . . . . K 960777 1
MC: . . . . K 960779 4

Presidentti,

LAMBERTLAND.
LP: . . . . SNTF 636

MILKY WAY MOSES.
Tracks: / Milky way Moses / Caught from the air / Jelly: confusing the issue / How to start a day / Piece of mind.
LP: . . . . SNTF 658

Presley, Elvis

20 GOLDEN HITS: ELVIS PRESLEY (VOL. 3).
MC: 40165

20 GREATEST HITS: ELVIS PRESLEY (VOL.1).
Tracks: / My baby left me / Heartbreak hotel / Blue suede shoes / Hound dog / Love me tender / Got a lot of livin' to do / Teddy bear / Party / All shook up / Old Shep / Don't / Hard headed woman / King Creole / Jailhouse rock / Big hunk o' love, A / I got stung / One night / Fool such as I, A / I need your love tonight / Stuck on you.
LP: . . . . NL 89024
MC: . . . . NK 89024
LP: . . . . INTS 5115

20 GREATEST HITS: ELVIS PRESLEY (VOL.2).
Tracks: / Fever / It's now or never / Are you lonesome tonight / Wooden heart / Surrender / His latest flame / Wild in the country / There's always me / Rock a hula baby / Can't help falling in love / Good luck charm / She's not you / Return to sender / Devil in disguise / Crying in the chapel / Guitar man / In the ghetto / Suspicious minds / There goes my everything / Don't cry daddy.
LP: . . . . NL 89168
MC: . . . . NK 89168
LP: . . . . INTS 5116

32 FILM HITS VOL. 1.
Tracks: / Fun in Acapulco / Mexico / Marguerita / Bossa nova baby / Blue Hawaii / Can't help falling in love / Rock a hula baby / Ku-u-i-po / King Creole / Hard headed woman / Trouble / Dixieland rock / Frankie and Johnny / Please don't stop loving me / Easy come, easy go / Sing you children / Tonight's alright for love / Frankfurt special / Wooden heart / G.I. blues / Blue suede shoes / Doin' the best I can / Dog's life / Charro / Roustabout / Little Egypt / Poison ivy league / Girls, girls, girls / Where do you come from / Return to sender / Follow that dream / Angel.
2LP: . . . . NL 89388
MCSET: . . . . NK 89388

32 FILM HITS VOL. 2.
Tracks: / Jailhouse rock / Young and beautiful / Baby I don't care / They remind me too much of you / Beyond the bend / Relax / One broken heart for sale / I'm falling in love tonight / No more / Island of love / Moonlight swim.
2LP: . . . . NL 89550
MCSET: . . . . NK 89550

'56 SESSIONS VOL.1, THE.
Tracks: / I got a woman / Heartbreak hotel / Money honey / I'm counting on you / I was the one / Blue suede shoes / My baby left me / One-sided love affair / I'm so glad you're mine / I'm gonna sit right down and cry over you / Tutti frutti / Lawdy Miss Clawdy / Shake rattle and roll / I want you I need you I love you / Hound dog / Don't be cruel.
LP: . . . . PL 42101
MC: . . . . PK 42101
LP: . . . . RCALP 3025
MC: . . . . RCAK 3025

'56 SESSIONS VOL.2, THE.
Tracks: / Anyway you want me / Love me tender / We're gonna move / Poor boy / Let me / Playing for keeps / Love me / Paralysed / How do you think I feel? / How's the world treating you? / When my blue moon turns to gold again / Long tall Sally / Old Shep / Too much / Any place is paradise / Ready Teddy / First in line / Rip it up.
LP: . . . . RCALP 3030
MC: . . . . RCAK 3030
LP: . . . . PL 42102
MC: . . . . PK 42102

1935-1977.
MC: . . . . VCA 044

ALL TIME GREATEST HITS, THE.
Tracks: / Heartbreak hotel / Blue suede shoes / Hound dog / Love me tender / Too much / All shook up / Teddy bear / Paralysed / Party / Jailhouse rock / Don't / Wear my ring around your neck / Hard headed woman / King Creole / One night / Fool such as I, A / Big hunk o' love, A / Stuck on you / Girl of my best friend / It's now or never / Are you lonesome tonight? / Wooden heart / Surrender / His latest flame / Can't help falling in love / Good luck charm / She's not you / Return to sender / Devil in disguise / Crying in the chapel / Love letters / If I can dream / In the ghetto / Suspicious minds / Don't cry Daddy / Wonder of you, The / I just can't help believing / American trilogy / Burning love / Always on my mind / My boy / Suspicion / Moody blue / Way down / It's only love.
2LP: . . . . PL 90100
MCSET: . . . . PK 90100

ALMOST IN LOVE.
LP: . . . . INTS 1206

ALOHA FROM HAWAII.
Tracks: / What now my love / Fever / Welcome to my world / Suspicious minds / See see rider / Burning love / Hound dog / I'll remember you / Long tall Sally / Whole lotta shakin' goin' on / American trilogy / Big hunk o' love, A / Can't help falling in love / Burning love / Something / You gave me a mountain / Steamroller blues / My way / Love me / Johnny B. Goode / It's over / Blue suede shoes / I'm so lonesome I could cry / I can't stop loving you.
LP: . . . . PL 82642
LP: . . . . DPS 2040
MC: . . . . PK 5144

ALTERNATIVE ALOHA.
Tracks: / Also sprach Zarathustra (Introduction) / See see rider / Burning love / Something / You gave me a mountain / Steamroller blues / My way / It's over / Blue suede shoes / I'm so lonesome I could cry / What now my love / Fever / Welcome to my world / Suspicious minds / I'll remember you / American trilogy / Big hunk o' love, A / Can't help falling in love / Blue Hawaii / Hound dog / Hawaiian wedding song / Ku-u-i-po (Available on Compact Disc only).
LP: . . . . PL 86985
MC: . . . . PK 86985

ALWAYS ON MY MIND.
Tracks: / Separate ways / Don't cry daddy / My boy / I miss you / Bitter they are / Solitaire / Hurt / Pieces of my life / It's midnight / I've lost you / Unchained melody / You gave me a mountain / Burning love / Always on my mind.
LP: . . . . PL 85430
MC: . . . . PK 85430

ARE YOU LONESOME TONIGHT.
Tracks: / Are you lonesome tonight / Girl of my best friend / Rock a hula baby / There's always me / Wild in the country / Fool such as I, A / Can't help falling in love / Hard headed woman / Don't cry daddy / Blue Hawaii / Wooden heart / Surrender.
LP: . . . . CDS 1207
MC: . . . . CAM 1207

BALLADS.
Tracks: / Can't help falling in love / In the ghetto / Moody blues / Suspicion / Are you lonesome tonight / Girl of my best friend / Don't / Wooden heart / It's now or never / Wonder of you, The / There goes my everything / Crying in the chapel / My boy / It's only me / Don't cry daddy / Hawaiian wedding song / Suspicious minds / My way.
LP: . . . . STAR 2264
MC: . . . . STAC 2264

BEST OF ELVIS.
LP: 130 250

BEST OF ELVIS, THE.
Tracks: / Heartbreak hotel / I don't care if the sun don't shine / Blue moon / Tutti frutti / All shook up / Hound dog / Too much / Anyway you want me / Don't be cruel / Playing for keeps.
LP: . . . . DLP 1159

BLUE HAWAII (See under Blue Hawaii (film)) (Various artists).

BLUE HAWAII (1961 Film Soundtrack).
Tracks: / Blue Hawaii / Almost always true / Aloha-oe / No more / Can't help falling in love / Rock a hula baby / Moonlight swim / Ku-u-i-po / Ito eats / Slicin' sand / Hawaiian sunset / Beach boy blues / Island of love / Hawaiian wedding song.
LP: . . . . NL 83683
MC: . . . . NK 83683
LP: . . . . RD 27238
LP: . . . . SF 8145
MC: . . . . PK 11561

BLUE RHYTHMS.
Tracks: / Trouble / Reconsider baby / Mess of blues, A / Give me the right / Such a night / When it rains it really pours / Trying to get to you / Like a baby / Mean woman blues / Ain't that loving you baby / One night / Little sister / Big boss man / Baby what you want me to do / Stuck on you / Tomorrow night / It feels so right.
LP: . . . . EPC 1000
MC: . . . . EPK 1000

BLUE RHYTHMS (DOUBLE).
Tracks: / Trouble / Reconsider baby / Mess of blues, A / Give me the right / Such a night / When it rains it really pours / Trying to get to you / Like a baby / I want to be free / Mean woman blues / Ain't that loving you baby / One night / Little sister / So glad you're mine / Big boss man / I want you with me / Baby what you want me to do / Santa Claus is back in town / Stuck on you / I feel so bad / What'd I say / Tomorrow night / It feels so right / Merry Christmas, baby.
2LP: . . . . PPD 2001
MC: . . . . PPK 2001

BLUE SUEDE SHOES.
Tracks: / Blue suede shoes.
MC: 40169

CALIFORNIA HOLIDAY (Film Soundtrack).
Tracks: / Stop look and listen / Adam and evil / All that I am / Never say yes / Am I ready / Beach shack / Spinout / Smorgasbord / I'll be back / Tomorrow is a long time / Down in the valley / I'll remember you.
LP: . . . . INTS 5038
MC: . . . . INTK 5038
LP: . . . . RD 7820
LP: . . . . NL 82560

CAN'T HELP FALLING IN LOVE & OTHER GREAT MOVIE HITS.
Tracks: / Can't help falling in love / Rock a hula baby / Follow that dream / What a wonderful life / Easy come, easy go / Rubberneckin' / One broken heart for sale / Girls, girls, girls / G.I. blues / Roustabout / Frankie and Johnny / Charro / I got lucky / Home is where the heart is.
LP: . . . . CDS 1210
MC: . . . . CAM 1210

CLAMBAKE (Film Soundtrack).
Tracks: / Clambake / Who needs money / House that has everything / Confidence / Hey hey hey / You don't know me / Girl I never loved, The / Guitar man / How can you lose what you never had / Big boss man / Singing trees / Just call me lonesome.
LP: . . . . NL 82565
MC: . . . . NK 82565
LP: . . . . SF 7917
LP: . . . . INTS 5040

C'MON EVERYBODY.
LP: . . . . INTS 1286

COLLECTOR'S GOLD.
Tracks: / G.I blues / Pocketful of rainbows / Big boots / Black star / Summer kisses, winter tears / I slipped, I stumbled, I fell / Lonely man / What a wonderful life / Whistling tune, A / Beyond the bend / One broken heart for sale / You're the boss / Roustabout / Girl happy / So close, yet so far / Stop, look and listen / Am I ready / How can you lose what you never had / Like a baby / There's always me / I want you with me / Gently / Give me the right / I met her today / Night rider / Just tell her Jim said hello / Ask me / Memphis, Tennessee / Love me tonight / Witchcraft / Come what may (you are mine) / Love letters / Going home / Blue suede shoes / I got a woman / Heartbreak hotel / Love me tender / Baby, what you want me to do / Runaway / Surrender/Are you lonesome tonight / Rubber neckin' / Memories / Introduction by Elvis Presley / Jailhouse rock/Don't be cruel / Inherit the wind/ This is the story / Mystery train / Tiger man / Funny how time slips away / Loving you/Reconsider baby / What I'd say.
LPS: . . . . PL 90574
MCSET: . . . . PK 90574

COMPLETE BONUS SONGS.
Tracks: / I slipped, I stumbled, I fell / Love me tonight / Slowly but surely / Echoes of love / Long lonely highway / You'll be gone / Animal instinct / Wisdom of the ages / Sand castles / Tomorrow is a long time / Down in the alley / I'll remember you / It won't be long / Never ending / Blue river / What now, what next, where to? / Guitar man / Big boss man.
2LP: . . . . NL 45180
MC: . . . . NK 45180

COMPLETE SINGLES (11 album box set).
LPS: . . . . RPL 2504 14

COMPLETE SUN SESSIONS, THE.
Tracks: / That's alright mama / Blue moon of Kentucky / Good rockin' tonight / I don't care if the sun don't shine / Milkcow blues boogie / You're a heartbreaker / Baby, let's play house / Im left you're right she's gone / Mystery train / I forgot to remember to forget / I love you because / Blue moon / Tomorrow's night / I'll never let you go / Just because / Trying to get to you / Harbour lights / When it rains, It really pours.
2LP: . . . . PL 86414
MCSET: . . . . PK 86414
MCSET: . . . . NK 89107
2LP: . . . . NL 89107

CONFIDENTIALLY ELVIS.
2LP: . . . . ARAD 1008
MC: . . . . ARADC 1008

DATE WITH ELVIS, A.
Tracks: / Blue moon of Kentucky / Young and beautiful / Baby I don't care / Milk cow blue boogie / Baby let's play house / Good rockin' tonight / Is it so strange / I forgot to remember to forget.
LP: . . . . NL 89097
MC: . . . . NK 89097
LP: . . . . RD 27128
LP: . . . . NL 90360
MC: . . . . NK 90360
LP: . . . . INTS 5032

DOUBLE DYNAMITE COLLECTION.
Tracks: / Old Shep / Fools fall in love / Burning love / Mama / Follow that dream / I'll be there / Flaming star / Tender feeling / Yellow rose of Texas / You'll never walk alone / Easy come easy go / Frankie and Johnny / US male / Big boss man / Charro / Separate ways / Rubberneckin' / It's a matter of time / If you think I don't need you / Peace in the valley.
2LP: . . . . PDA 057
MCSET: . . . . PDC 057

DOUBLE DYNAMITE VOL.1.
Tracks: / Old Shep / Fools fall in love / Burning love / Mama / Follow that dream / I'll be there / Flaming star / Tender feeling / Yellow rose of Texas / You'll never walk alone.
LP: . . . . CDS 1182
MC: . . . . CAM 494

DOUBLE DYNAMITE VOL.2.
Tracks: / Easy come, easy go / Frankie and Johnny / US male / Big boss man / Charro / Separate ways / Rubberneckin' / It's a matter of time / If you think I don't need you / Peace in the valley.
LP: . . . . CDS 1188
MC: . . . . CAM 499

DOUBLE TROUBLE (Film soundtrack).
Tracks: / Double trouble / Baby, if you'll give me all your love / Could I fall in love / Long legged girl / City by night / Old McDonald / I love only one girl / There is so much world to see / It won't be long / Never ending / Blue river / What now, what next, where to.
LP: . . . . SF 7892
LP: . . . . INTS 5039
LP: . . . . NL 82564

EARLY YEARS.
LP: . . . . R&C 1004

EASY COME EASY GO.
Tracks: / C'mon everybody / Santa Lucia / Guadalajara / Little less conversation, A / Long legged girl with the short dress on.
LP: . . . . CDS 1146
MC: . . . . CAM 1146

ELVIS.
Tracks: / That's all right / Lawdy Miss Clawdy / Mystery train / Playing for

keeps / Poor boy / Money honey / I'm counting on you / My baby left me / I was the one / Shake, rattle and roll / I'm left, you're right / You're a heartbreaker / Tryin' to get to you / Blue suede shoes.
MC: . . . . **PK 11529**
LP: . . . . **CDS 1201**
MC: . . . . **CAM 1201**
LP: **26.21008**
LP: . . . . **SF 8378**

ELVIS' 40 GREATEST HITS.
Tracks: / My baby left me / Heartbreak hotel / Blue suede shoes / Hound dog / Love me tender / Got a lot of livin' to do / Teddy bear / Party / All shook up / Old Shep / Don't / Hard headed woman / King Creole / Jailhouse rock / Big hunk o' love, A / I got stung / One night / Fool such as I, A / I need your love tonight / Stuck on you / Fever / It's now or never / Surrender / Are you lonesome tonight? / Wooden heart / His latest flame / Wild in the country / There's always me / Rock-a-hula-baby / Can't help falling in love / Good luck charm / She's not you / Return to sender / Devil in disguise / In the ghetto / Crying in the chapel / Guitar man / Suspicious minds / There goes my everything / Don't cry Daddy.
2LP: . . . . **ADEP 12**
2LP: . . . . **PL 42691**
MC: . . . . **PK 42691**

ELVIS AARON PRESLEY.
Tracks: / Jailhouse rock / Blue Christmas / My way / Follow that dream / Shoppin' around / Heartbreak hotel / Fool such as I / Love me / I got a woman / Such a night / One night / Money honey / Hound dog / Wonder of you / It's still here / See see rider / I'm leavin' / Rags to riches / It's only love / Polk salad Annie / Sweet Caroline / Kentucky rain / My babe.
LPS: . . . . **ELVIS 25**

ELVIS' CHRISTMAS ALBUM.
Tracks: / Santa Claus is back in town / White Christmas / Here comes Santa Claus / I'll be home for Christmas / Blue Christmas / Santa bring my baby back to me / O little town of Bethlehem / Silent night / Peace in the valley / I believe / Take my hand precious Lord / It is no secret.
LP: . . . . **CDS 1155**
MC: . . . . **CAM 1155**
LP: . . . . **NL 89116**
MC: . . . . **NK 89116**
MC: . . . . **CAM 462**
LP: . . . . **INTS 1126**
LP: . . . . **NL 90300**
MC: . . . . **NK 90300**
LP: . . . . **PL 85486**

ELVIS FOR EVERYONE.
Tracks: / Your cheatin' heart / Summer kisses, Winter tears / Finders keepers / In my way / Tomorrow night / Memphis Tennessee / For the millionth and the last time / Forget me never / Sound advise Santa Lucia / Met her today / When it rains it really pours.
LP: . . . . **NL 84232**
MC: . . . . **NK 84232**
LP: . . . . **RD 7782**
LP: . . . . **SF 8232**

ELVIS FOREVER-96 HITS.
Tracks: / My baby left me / Heartbreak hotel / Blue suede shoes / Hound dog / Love me tender / Got a lot of livin' to do / Teddy bear / All shook up / Don't / Hard headed woman / King Creole / Jailhouse rock / Big hunk o' love, A / I got stung / One night / Stuck on you / Fever / Are you lonesome tonight / Wooden heart / Surrender / Wild in the country / Rock a hula baby / Can't help falling in love / Good luck charm / Return to sender / Crying in the chapel / Guitar man / In the ghetto / Suspicious minds / There goes my everything / Don't be cruel / I want you, I need you, I love you / Too much / Loving you / Treat me nice / I beg of you / Ain't that loving you baby / Wear my ring around your neck / Such a night / Mess of blues, A / I gotta know / Kiss me quick / Little sister / No more / I feel so good / King of the whole wide world / (Such an) easy question / Bossa nova baby / Mexico / Witchcraft / What'd I say / Kissin' cousins / Viva Las Vegas / Ask me / It hurts me / I've lost you / I just can't help believing / Love letters / You don't have to say you love me / Wonder of you, The / Burning love / My way / Blue moon / Money honey / I got a woman / Tutti frutti / Long tall Sally / Blueberry Hill / Mean woman blues / Your cheatin' heart / Dixieland rock / Fool such as I, A / Lover doll / Doncha' think it's time / Make me know it / Fame and fortune / Girl of my best friend / Lonely man / Blue Hawaii / His latest flame / Anything that's part of you / Aloha-oe / Night rider / Suspicion / She's not you / Santa Lucia / (It's a) long lonely highway / Please don't drag that string around / Memphis Tennessee / Little Egypt / Do the clam / Indescribably blue / Gentle on my mind / Any day now.
LPS: . . . . **NL 89830**
MCSET: . . . . **NK 89930**

ELVIS FOREVER VOL.2.
Tracks: / Don't be cruel / I want you, I need you, I love you / Too much / Loving you / Treat me nice / I beg of you / Ain't that loving you baby / Wear my ring around your neck / Such a night / Mess of blues, A / I gotta know / Kiss me quick / Little sister / No more (la paloma) / I feel so bad / King of the whole wide world / Easy question / Bossa nova baby / Mexico / Witchcraft / What'd I say / Kissin' cousins / Viva Las Vegas / Ask me / It hurts me / I've lost you / I just can't help believing / Love letters / You don't have to say you love me / Wonder of you, The / Burning love / My way.
2LP: . . . . **CL 42853**

ELVIS FOREVER VOLUME 4.
LP: . . . . **NL 89870**

ELVIS' GOLDEN RECORDS VOL.1
(Original issue).
Tracks: / Hound dog / I love you because / All shook up / Heartbreak hotel / You're a heartbreaker / Love me / Too much / Don't be cruel / That's when your heartaches begin / I'll never let you go / Love me tender / I forgot to remember to forget / Anyway you want me / I want you, I need you, I love you.
LP: . . . . **RB 16069**

ELVIS' GOLDEN RECORDS VOL.1
(Re-issue).
Tracks: / Hound dog / Loving you / All shook up / Heartbreak hotel / Teddy bear / Jailhouse rock / Love me tender / Treat me nice / Anyway you want me / I want you I need you I love you.
LP: . . . . **NL 81707**
MC: . . . . **NK 81707**
LP: . . . . **SF 8129**
LP: . . . . **INTS 5143**
MC: . . . . **INTK 5143**
MC: . . . . **PK 11602**

ELVIS' GOLDEN RECORDS VOL.2.
Tracks: / I need your love tonight / Wear my ring around your neck / My wish came true / I got stung / Loving you / Teddy bear / One night / Hunk o love, A / I beg of you / Fool such as I, A / Doncha think it's time / Jailhouse rock / Treat me nice / Don't.
LP: . . . . **RD 27159**
LP: . . . . **SF 8151**
LP: . . . . **INTS 5144**
MC: . . . . **INTK 5144**
MC: . . . . **PK 11531**

ELVIS' GOLDEN RECORDS VOL.3.
Tracks: / It's now or never / Stuck on you / Fame and fortune / I gotta know / Surrender / I feel so bad / Are you lonesome tonight / His latest flame / Little sister / Good luck charm / Anything that's part of you / She's not you.
LP: . . . . **INTS 5145**
MC: . . . . **INTK 5145**
LP: . . . . **RD 7630**
LP: . . . . **SF 7630**
LP: . . . . **NL 82765**
MC: . . . . **NK 82765**
MC: . . . . **PK 11570**

ELVIS' GOLDEN RECORDS VOL.4.
Tracks: / Love letters / It hurts me / What I'd say / Please don't drag that string around / Indescribably blue / Devil in disguise / Lonely man / Mess of blues, A / Ask me / Ain't that loving you baby / Just tell her Jim said hello / Witchcraft.
LP: . . . . **NL 83921**
MC: . . . . **NK 83921**
LP: . . . . **SF 7924**
MC: . . . . **PK 11571**

ELVIS' GOLDEN RECORDS VOL.5.
Tracks: / Suspicious minds / Kentucky rain / In the ghetto / Clean up your own backyard / If I can dream / Burning love / If you talk in your sleep / For the heart / Moody blue / Way down.
LP: . . . . **PL 84941**
MC: . . . . **PK 84941**

ELVIS IN CONCERT.
Tracks: / Elvis fans comment / Opening riff / 2001 / See see rider / That's alright / Are you lonesome tonight / You gave me a mountain / Jailhouse rock / How great thou art / I really don't want to know / Elvis introduces his father / Hurt.
2LP: . . . . **PL 82587**
MCSET: . . . . **PK 82587**

ELVIS IN DEMAND.
Tracks: / Suspicion / High heel sneakers / Got a lot of livin' to do / Have I told you lately that I love you / Please don't drag that string around / It's only love / Sound of your cry, The / Viva Las Vegas / Do not disturb / Tomorrow is a long time / It's a long lonely highway / Puppet on a string / First time ever I saw your face, The / Summer kisses and winter tears / It hurts me / Let it be me.
LP: . . . . **RCALP 3018**
MC: . . . . **RCAK 3018**
LP: . . . . **PL 42003**
MC: . . . . **PK 42003**

ELVIS IN GERMANY.
Tracks: / Wooden heart / I love only one girl / C'mon everybody / Frankfurt special / Tonights alright for love / Today / Tomorrow and forever / G.I. blues / Tonight is so right for love / Five sleepy heads / Fool / Elvis sails.
LP: . . . . **NL 43730**
MC: . . . . **NK 43730**

ELVIS IN HOLLYWOOD.
Tracks: / Jailhouse rock / Rock a hula baby / G.I. blues / Kissin' cousins / Wild in the country / King Creole / Blue Hawaii / Fun in Acapulco / Follow that dream / Girls girls girls / Viva Las Vegas / Bossa nova baby / Flaming star / Girl happy / Frankie and Johnny / Roustabout / Spinout / Double trouble / Charro / They remind me too much of you.
LP: . . . . **CBR 1014**
MC: . . . . **KCBR 1014**

ELVIS IS BACK.
Tracks: / Make me know it / Fever / Girl of my best friend / I will be home again / Dirty dirty feeling / Thrill of your love, The / Soldier boy / Such a night / It feels so right / Girl next door, The / Like a baby / Reconsider baby.
LP: . . . . **NL 89013**
MC: . . . . **NK 89013**
LP: . . . . **RD 27171**
LP: . . . . **SF 5060**
MC: . . . . **PK 11532**

ELVIS LIVE AT MADISON SQUARE GARDEN.
Tracks: / 2001 / That's alright mama / Proud Mary / Never been to Spain / You don't have to say you love me / You've lost that lovin' feeling / Polk salad Annie / Love me / All shook up / Heartbreak hotel / Impossible dream, The / Hound dog / Suspicious minds / For the good times / American trilogy / Funny how time slips away / I can't stop loving you / Can't help falling in love / Why me Lord / How great thou art / Blueberry Hill / Can't stop loving you / Help me / Let me be there / My baby left me / Lawdy, Miss Clawdy / Closing - vamp.
LP: . . . . **SF 8296**
MC: . . . . **PK 2054**

ELVIS LOVE SONGS.
LP: . . . . **NE 1062**
MC: . . . . **CE 2062**

ELVIS NBC SPECIAL (TV soundtrack).
Tracks: / Trouble / Guitar man / Lawdy Miss Clawdy / Baby what you want me to do / Heartbreak hotel / Hound dog / All shook up / Can't help falling in love / Jailhouse rock / Love me tender / Where could I go but to the Lord / Up above my head / Saved / Blue Christmas / One night / Memories / Nothingville / Big boss man / Little Egypt / If I can dream.
LP: . . . . **NL 83894**
MC: . . . . **NK 83894**
LP: . . . . **RD 8011**
LP: . . . . **INTS 5093**
LP: . . . . **PL 42370**
MC: . . . . **PK 42370**

ELVIS NOW.
Tracks: / Help me make it through the night / Miracle of the rosary / Hey Jude / Put your hand in the hand / Until it's time for you to go / We can make the morning / Early mornin' rain / Sylvia / Fools rush in (where angels fear to tread) / I was born ten thousand years ago.
LP: . . . . **SF 8266**

ELVIS PRESLEY.
Tracks: / Blue suede shoes / I love you because / Tutti frutti / I'll never let you go / Money honey / I'm counting on you / I got a woman / One-sided love affair / Just because / Trying to get to you / I'm gonna sit right down and cry over you / Blue moon.
LP: . . . . **NL 89046**
MC: . . . . **NK 89046**
LP: **26.21007**

ELVIS PRESLEY - BOX SET.
Tracks: / Hound dog / Loving you / All shook up / Heartbreak hotel / Jailhouse rock / Love me / Too much / Don't be cruel / That's when your heartaches begin / Teddy bear / Love me tender / Treat me nice / Anyway you want me (that's how I will be) / I want you, I need you, I love you / I need your love tonight / Don't, wear my ring around your neck / My wish came true / I got stung / Loving you / Teddy bear / One night / Big hunk o' love, A / I beg of you / Fool such as I, A / Don'cha think it's time / Jailhouse rock / Treat me nice / It's now or never / Stuck on you / Fame and fortune / I gotta know / Surrender / I feel so bad / Are you lonesome tonight / (Marie's the name) his latest flame / Little sister / Good luck charm / Anything that's part of you / She's not you.
MCSET: . . . . **NK 74375**

ELVIS PRESLEY COLLECTION.
Tracks: / Peace in the valley / It is no secret / Swing down sweet Chariot / Frankie and Johnny / Guitar man / Big boss man.
2LP: . . . . **PDA 009**
MCSET: . . . . **PDC 009**

ELVIS PRESLEY COLLECTION VOL.2.
Tracks: / Separate ways / C'mon everybody / Santa Lucia / Old shep / Little less conversation, A / Long legged girl (with the short dress on).
2LP: . . . . **PDA 042**
MCSET: . . . . **PDC 042**

ELVIS PRESLEY COLLECTION VOL.3.
Tracks: / What every woman lives for / Please don't stop me loving you / Change of habit / Come along / Shout it out / Beginners luck / Clean up your own backyard / Rubberneckin' / Edge of reality / Petunia, the gardener's daughter / Hard luck / Have a happy / Flaming star / Wonderful world / All I needed was the rain / Too much monkey business / Tiger man.
2LP: . . . . **PDA 054**
MCSET: . . . . **PDC 054**

ELVIS PRESLEY (DOUBLE ALBUM).
Tracks: / Blue suede shoes / That's alright / Blue moon of Kentucky / Anyway you want me / Mystery train / Long tall Sally / Shake, rattle and roll / Lawdy Miss Clawdy / I don't care if the sun don't shine / Old Shep / Good rockin' tonight / Heartbreak hotel / Separate ways / Are you lonesome tonight / Fool such as I, A / Crying in the chapel / How great thou art / Rip it up / Wonder of you, The / Sweet Caroline / American trilogy.
2LP: . . . . **NL 43054**

ELVIS PRESLEY: INTERVIEW PICTURE DISC.
LPPD: . . . . **BAK 2086**

ELVIS PRESLEY & JANIS MARTIN
(Presley, Elvis & Janis Martin).
LPPD: . . . . **PD 1085**

ELVIS PRESLEY LIVE ON STAGE IN MEMPHIS.
Tracks: / See see rider / I got a woman / Love me / Trying to get to you / Long tall Sally (medley) / Flip flop and fly / Jailhouse rock / Hound dog / Why me, Lord / How great Thou art / Blueberry Hill (medley) / Help me / American trilogy / Let me be there / My baby left me / Lawdy Miss Clawdy / Can't help falling in love / Closing vamp.
LP: **APL1 0606**

ELVIS PRESLEY SINGS LEIBER & STOLLER.
Tracks: / Hound dog / Love me / Loving you / Hot dog / I want to be free / Jailhouse rock / Treat me nice / Baby I don't care / Santa Claus is back in town / Don't trouble / King Creole / Steadfast loyal and true / Dirty dirty feeling / Just tell her Jim said hello / Girls, girls, girls / Bossa nova baby / Little Egypt / Fools fall in love / Saved.
LP: . . . . **NL 89099**
MC: . . . . **NK 89099**
LP: . . . . **INTS 5031**

ELVIS PRESLEY SUN COLLECTION.
Tracks: / That's alright mama / Blue moon of Kentucky / I don't care if the sun don't shine / Good rockin' tonight / Milk cow blue boogie / You're a heartbreaker / I'm left you're right she's gone / Baby let's play house / Mystery train / I forgot to remember to forget / I love you because / Trying to get to you / Blue moon / Just because / I'll never let you go.
LP: . . . . **NL 42757**
MC: . . . . **NK 42757**
LP: . . . . **HY 1001**

ELVIS PRESLEY WITH BILL HALEY
(Presley, Elvis & Bill Haley).
LPPD: . . . . **PD 1084**

ELVIS SINGS HITS FROM HIS MOVIES.
Tracks: / Down by the riverside / When the saints go marching in / Guitar man / Frankie and Johnny / How would you like to be big boss man.
LP: . . . . **CDS 1110**
MC: . . . . **CAM 423**

ELVIS SINGS THE WONDERFUL WORLD OF CHRISTMAS.
Tracks: / Oh come all ye faithful / First Noel, The / On a snowy Christmas night / Winter wonderland / Wonderful world of Christmas, The / It won't seem like Christmas (without you) / I'll be home on Christmas day / If I get home on Christmas day / Holly leaves and Christmas trees / Merry Christmas baby / Silver bells.
LP: . . . . **PL 42371**
MC: . . . . **PK 42371**
LP: . . . . **NL 81936**
MC: . . . . **NK 81936**

ELVIS TAPES, THE.
LP: . . . . **RED 1**

ELVIS, THE MOVIE (See under Elvis, The Movie).

ELVIS THE PELVIS (50th anniversary album).
Tracks: / Tutti frutti / Money honey / Trying to get to you / Mystery train / Heartbreak hotel / I got a woman / Treat me nice / One-sided love affair / Don't be cruel / Shake, rattle and roll / I want you, I need you, I love you / Good rockin' tonight / Lawdy Miss Clawdy / I'm gonna sit right down and cry over you / I was the one / I want to be free / Ready Teddy / Blue moon of Kentucky / Baby let's play house / Long tall Sally / I'm left your right she's gone / How do you think I feel / I love you because / Blue suede shoes / When my blue moon turns to gold again / Young and beautiful.
2LP: . . . . **NL 89515**
MCSET: . . . . **KA 89515**

ELVIS-THE ULTIMATE PERFORMANCE.
Tracks: / Also sprach Zarathustra / See see rider / Blue suede shoes / Johnny B. Goode / Are you lonesome tonight / Never been to Spain / You don't have to say you love me / Impossible dream, The / American trilogy / In the ghetto / Suspicious minds / Love me / Burning love / Words / Polk salad Annie / I can't stop loving you / Can't help falling in love.
LP: . . . . **NE 1141**
MC: . . . . **CE 2141**

ESSENTIAL ELVIS.
Tracks: / Teddy bear / Loving you / Mean woman blues / Got a lot of livin' to do / Lonesome cowboy / Jailhouse rock / Treat me nice / Young and beautiful / Don't leave me now / I want to be free / Baby I don't care / Love me tender (With the Jordanaires) / Let me / Poor boy / We're gonna move / Party / Hot dog.
LP: . . . . **PL 89979**
MC: . . . . **PK 89979**

ESSENTIAL ELVIS VOL.3 (Hits like never before).
Tracks: / King Creole / Fool such as I, A / Your cheatin' heart / Dontcha' think it's time / Lover doll / Danny / Crawfish / Ain't that loving you baby / Your cheatin' heart / I need your love tonight / I got stung / As long as I have you / I got stung / Wear my ring around your neck / Big hunk o' love, A / Steadfast, loyal and true / King Creole (instrumental).
LP: . . . . **PL 90486**
MC: . . . . **PK 90486**

ESSENTIAL ELVIS VOL. 2 (Stereo 57).
Tracks: / I beg of you / Have I told you lately that I love you / Blueberry Hill / Peace in the valley / Is it so strange / It is no secret / Mean woman blues / That's when your heartaches begin.
LP: . . . . **PL 90250**
MC: . . . . **PK 90250**

FIFTIES INTERVIEWS, THE.
Tracks: / Truth about me, The / Jacksonville, Florida / WMPS, Memphis / Witchita Falls, Texas / LaCrosse, Wisconsin / Little Rock, Arkansas / KLAC-TV, Memphis / New Orleans / New Orleans (2) / St. Petersburg, Florida.
LP: . . . . **MFLP 074**

FILM HITS.
LPS: . . . . **NL 89797**

FIRST LIVE RECORDINGS.
Tracks: / I wanna play house with you / Maybellene / Tweedle dee / That's alright / Recollections by Frank Page / Hound dog.
LP: . . . . **PG 89387**
MC: . . . . **PH 89387**

FIRST TEN YEARS,THE.
LP: . . . . **CDS 1213**
MC: . . . . **CAM 1213**

FIRST YEAR, THE (Presley, Elvis/Bill Black/Scotty Moore).
Tracks: / Bill Collie interview / Good rockin' tonight / Baby let's play house / Blue moon of Kentucky / I got a woman / That's alright mama / Elvis Presley interview / Scotty Moore tells the story of the first year.
LP: . . . . **SUN 1007**

FLAMING STAR.
Tracks: / Flaming star / Wonderful night / Night life / All I needed was the rain / Too much monkey business / Yellow rose of Texas / Eyes of Texas, The / She's a machine / Do the vega / Tiger man.
LP: . . . . **CDS 1185**
MC: . . . . **CAM 490**
LP: . . . . **RD 7723**
LP: . . . . **INTS 1012**

FOLLOW THAT DREAM (VIDEO) (See under Follow that dream) (Various artists).

FOR LP FANS ONLY.
Tracks: / That's all right / Lawdy Miss Clawdy / Mystery train / Playing for keeps / Poor boy / Money honey / I'm counting on you / My baby left me / I was the one / Shake rattle and roll / I'm left, you're right, she's gone / You're a heartbreaker / Tryin' to get to you / Blue suede shoes.
LP: . . . . **NL 90359**
MC: . . . . **NK 90359**

FOR THE ASKING.
Tracks: / Long lonely highway / Western union / Witchcraft / Love me tonight / What now, what next, where to? / Please don't drag that string around / Blue river / Never ending / Devil in disguise / Finders keepers / Echoes of love / Slowly but surely / It hurts me / Memphis Tenessee / Ask me.
LP: . . . . **NL 90513**
MC: . . . . **NK 90513**

FOREVER.
Tracks: / My baby left me / Heartbreak hotel / I got stung / Hound dog / Teddy bear / Love me tender / Guitar man / In the Ghetto / Suspicious minds / Don't / One night / Stuck on you / Surrender / Wooden heart / All shook up.
2LP: . . . . **NL 89004**
MCSET: . . . . **NK 89004**

FRANKIE & JOHNNY (Film soundtrack).
Tracks: / Frankie and Johnny / Come along / Petunia, the gardner's daughter / Chesay / What every woman lives for / Look out Broadway / Beginners luck / Down by the riverside / When the saints go marching in / Shout it out / Hard luck / Please don't stop loving me.
LP: . . . . **NL 82559**
MC: . . . . **NK 82559**
LP: . . . . **RD 7793**
LP: . . . . **INTS 5036**

FROM ELVIS IN MEMPHIS.
Tracks: / Wearin' that loved on look / Only the strong survive / I'll hold you in my heart / Long black limousine / It keeps right on a-hurtin' / I'm moving on / Power of my love / Gentle on my mind / After loving you / True love travels on the gravel road / Any day now / In the ghetto.
LP: . . . . **SF 8029**
LP: . . . . **NL 90548**
MC: . . . . **NK 90548**

FROM ELVIS PRESLEY BOULEVARD, MEMPHIS, TENNESSEE.
Tracks: / Hurt / Never again / Blue eyes crying in the rain / Danny boy / Last farewell, The / For the heart / Bitter they are / Solitaire / Love coming down / I'll never fall in love again.
LP: . . . . **PL 89266**
LP: . . . . **RS 1060**
MC: . . . . **PK 89266**
MC: . . . . **PK 11729**

FROM MEMPHIS TO VEGAS.
Tracks: / Blue suede shoes (Elvis at the International Hotel, Las Vegas.) / Johnny B. Goode / All shook up / Are you lonesome tonight / Hound dog / I can't stop loving you / Me babe / Mystery train / Tiger man / Words / In the ghetto / Suspicious minds / Can't help falling in love / Elvis back in Memphis / Inherit the wind / This is a story / Stranger in my own home town / Little bit of green, A / And the grass won't pay no mind / Do you know who I am / From a Jack to a king / Fair's moving on / You'll think of me / Without love.
2LP: . . . . **NL 89068**
2LP: . . . . **SF 8080/1**

FUN IN ACAPULCO (FILM) (Film soundtrack).
Tracks: / Fun in Acapulco / Vino / Dinero Y amor / Mexico / El toro / Marguerita / Bullfighter was a lady / No room to rhumba in a sports car / I think I'm gonna like it here / Bossa nova baby / You can't say no in Acapulco / Guadalajara / Love me tonight / Slowly but surely.
LP: . . . . **RD 7609**
LP: . . . . **INTS 5106**
LP: . . . . **PL 42357**
MC: . . . . **PK 42357**
LP: . . . . **NL 89014**

G.I.BLUES (Film soundtrack).
Tracks: / Tonight is so right for love / What's she really like? / Frankfurt special / Wooden heart / G.I. blues / Pocketful of rainbows / Shopping around / Big boots / Didja ever? / Blue suede shoes / Doin' the best I can.
LP: . . . . **NL 83735**
MC: . . . . **NK 83735**
LP: . . . . **RD 27192**
LP: . . . . **SF 5078**
LP: . . . . **INTS 5104**
MC: . . . . **PK 5078**

GIRL HAPPY (Film Soundtrack).
Tracks: / Girl happy / Spring fever / Fort Lauderdale / Chamber of Commerce / Startin' tonight / Wolf call / Do not disturb / Cross my heart and hope to die / Meanest girl in town / Do the clam / Puppet on a string / I've got to find my baby / You'll be gone.
LP: . . . . **NL 83338**
MC: . . . . **NK 83338**
LP: . . . . **RD 7714**
LP: . . . . **INTS 5034**

GIRLS GIRLS GIRLS (Film Soundtrack).
Tracks: / Girls, girls, girls / I don't wanna be tied / Where do you come from / I don't want to / We'll be together / Boy like me, a girl like you, A / Earth boy / Return to sender / Because of love / Thanks to the rolling sea / Song of the shrimp / Walls have ears / We're coming in loaded.
LP: . . . . **NL 89048**
MC: . . . . **AK 89048**
LP: . . . . **INTS 5107**
LP: . . . . **PL 42354**
MC: . . . . **PK 42354**
LP: . . . . **CDS 1221**
MC: . . . . **CAM 1221**
LP: . . . . **RD 7534**

GIRLS GIRLS GIRLS (VIDEO) (See under Girls Girls ...).

GOLDEN CELEBRATION.
Tracks: / Harbour lights / That's all right / Blue moon of Kentucky / I don't care if the sun don't shine / I'm left, you're right, she's gone / I'll never let you go (little darling) / When it rains, it really pours / Shake, rattle and roll / Flip flop and fly / I got a woman / Baby let's play house / Tutti frutti / Blue suede shoes / Heartbreak Hotel / I was the one / Hound dog / I want you I need you, I love you / I want you I need you, I love you (dialogue) / Long tall Sally / Introductions and presentations / I got a woman / Don't be cruel (to a heart's that's true) / Ready Teddy / Love me tender / Love me / Too much / When my blue moon turns to gold again / Peace in the valley / Danny boy / Soldier boy / Fool, The / Earth angel / He's only a prayer away / My heart cries for you / Dark moon / Write to me from Naples / Suppose / Tiger man / That's all right / Lawdy Miss Clawdy / Baby, what you want me to do? / Are you lonesome tonight / Blue Christmas (Monologue) / One night / Trying to forget you.
LPS: . . . . **PL 85172**
MCSET: . . . . **PK 85172**

GOOD TIMES.
Tracks: / Take good care of her / Loving arms / I got a feelin' in my body / If that isn't love / She wears my ring / I got a thing about you baby / My boy / Spanish eyes / Talk about the good times / Good time Charlie's got the blues.
LP: . . . . **NL 80475**
LP: **APL1 0475**

GREAT PERFORMANCES.
Tracks: / My happiness / That's all right / Shake, rattle and roll / Flip flop and fly / Heartbreak hotel / Blue suede shoes / Ready teddy / Don't be cruel / Got a lot of livin' to do / Jailhouse rock / Treat me nice / King Creole / Trouble / Fame and fortune / Return to sender / Always on my mind / American trilogy / If I can dream / Unchained melody / Memories.
LP: . . . . **PL 82227**
MC: . . . . **PK 82227**

GREATEST HITS: ELVIS PRESLEY.
Tracks: / Heartbreak hotel / Jailhouse rock / It's now or never / All shook up / Wooden heart / Are you lonesome tonight?.
MC: . . . . **THPA 1234**

GUITAR MAN.
Tracks: / Guitar man / After loving you / Too much monkey business / Just call me lonesome / Lovin' arms / You asked me to / Clean up your own backyard / She thinks I still care / Faded love / I'm movin' on.
LP: . . . . **RCALP 5010**

HAREM HOLIDAY (Film Soundtrack).
Tracks: / Harem holiday / My desert serenade / Go West young man / Mirage / Shake that tambourine / Hey little girl / Golden coins / So close yet so far / Animal instinct / Wisdom of the ages.
LP: . . . . **NL 82558**
MC: . . . . **NK 82558**
LP: . . . . **RD 7767**
LP: . . . . **INTS 5035**

HAREM HOLIDAY (FILM) (See under Harem holiday) (Various artists).

HE TOUCHED ME.
Tracks: / He touched me / I've got confidence / Amazing grace / Seeing is believing / He is my everything / Bosom of Abraham / Evening prayer, An / Lead me, guide me / There is no God but God / Thing called love / I, John / Reach out to Jesus.
LP: . . . . **SF 8275**

HE WALKS BESIDES ME.
Tracks: / He is my everything / MIracle of the rosary / Where did they go Lord? / Somebody bigger than you and I / Evening prayer, An / Impossible dream, The / If I can dream / Padre / Known only to Him / Who am I? / How great Thou art.
LP: . . . . **PL 12772**
MC: . . . . **PK 12772**

HEARTBREAK HOTEL.
Tracks: / Heartbreak Hotel / Jailhouse rock / Blue suede shoes / All shook up / Hound dog / King Creole / I got stung / Guitar man / My baby left me / Whole lotta shakin' goin' on / His latest flame / I slipped, I stumbled, I fell.
LP: . . . . **CDS 1204**
MC: . . . . **CAM 1204**
LP: . . . . **PLP 18**
MC: . . . . **PMC 18**

HIS HAND IN MINE.
Tracks: / His hand in mine / I'm gonna walk dem golden stairs / My father's house / Milky white way / Known only to him / I believe / Joshua fit de battle of Jerico / Jesus knows what I need / Swing down sweet chariot / Mansion over the hilltop / If we never meet again / Working on the building.
LP: . . . . **NL 83935**
MC: . . . . **NK 83935**
LP: . . . . **RD 27211**
LP: . . . . **INTS 5105**
LP: . . . . **SF 8207**

HISTORY OF ROCK AND ROLL.
MC: . . . . **HRC 001**
LP: . . . . **HRL 001**

HITS OF THE 70'S.
Tracks: / Wonder of you, The / I'm leaving / Burning love / Always on my mind / I just can't help believing / You don't have to say you love me / There goes my everything / Rags to riches / Until it's time for you to go / I've lost you / Kentucky rain / American trilogy.
LP: . . . . **LPL 17527**
MC: . . . . **LPK 17527**

HOUND DOG.
MC: **40170**

HOW GREAT THOU ART.
Tracks: / How great Thou art / In the garden / Somebody bigger than you and I / Farther along / Stand by me / Without him / So high / Where could I go but to the Lord / By and by / If the Lord wasn't walking by my side / Run on / Where no one stands alone / Crying in the chapel.
LP: . . . . **NL 83758**
MC: . . . . **NK 83758**
LP: . . . . **SF 7867**
LP: . . . . **SF 8206**

I CAN HELP.
Tracks: / I can help / Moody blue / If you talk in your sleep / Sweet Angeline / Only the strong survive / Hurt / Promised land / My boy / Green green grass of home / Raised on rock / Fool / Way down / T.R.O.U.B.L.E. / Take good care of her.
LP: . . . . **PL 89287**
MC: . . . . **PK 89287**

I GOT A WOMAN.
MC: **40172**

I GOT LUCKY.
Tracks: / I got lucky / Yoga is as yoga does / Fools fall in love / I need somebody / You gotta stop / Love machine.
LP: . . . . **CDS 1154**
MC: . . . . **CAM 496**
LP: . . . . **INTS 1322**

I WAS THE ONE.
Tracks: / I was the one / Baby let's play house / Shake rattle and roll / Flip flop and fly / Don't / Paralyzed / Your cheating heart / Baby i don't care / Don't be cruel / Wear my ring around your neck / My baby left me / Little sister / Heartbreak hotel / Ready teddy / Young and beautiful / Rip it up / Hound dog.
LP: . . . . **RCALP 3105**

I'M 10,000 YEARS OLD (Elvis Country).
Tracks: / Snowbird / Tomorrow never comes / Little cabin on the hill / Whole lotta shakin' goin' on / Funny how time slips away / I really don't want to know / There goes my everything / It's your baby / Fool, The / Faded love / I washed my hands in muddy water / Make the world go away / I was born ten thousand years ago.
LP: . . . . **NL 83956**
MC: . . . . **NK 83956**
LP: . . . . **SF 9172**
LP: . . . . **INTS 5111**
MC: . . . . **INKT 5111**

IMAGES: ELVIS PRESLEY.
Tracks: / That's alright / Blue moon of Kentucky / Good rockin' tonight / I don't care if the sun don't shine / Mystery train / Money honey / My baby left me / Blue suede shoes / All shook up / I'm gonna sit right down and cry over you / Paralysed / Rip it up / I got stung / Big

hunk o' love, A / Make me know it / So glad you're mine / It feels so right / Mess of blues, A / Hard luck / Like a baby / Big boss man / Reconsider baby / Steamroller blues / Release me / Fool / Help me make it through the night / I'm leaving / Rags to riches / Do you know who I am / And the grass won't pay no mind.
2LP: . . . . **CR 061**
MCSET: . . . . **CRT 061**

IN HOLLYWOOD.
Tracks: / Jailhouse rock / Rock a hula baby / GI blues / Kissin' cousins / Wild in the country / King Creole / Fun in Acapulco / Blue Hawaii / Follow that dream / Viva Las Vegas / Girls girls girls / Bossa nova baby / Flaming star / Girl happy / Frankie and Johnny / Double trouble / Roustabout / Spinout / They remind me too much of you / Charro.
LP: . . . . **PMP 1011**
MC: . . . . **PMPK 1011**

IN PERSON (Presley, Elvis/Scotty Moore/Bill Black).
LP: . . . . **NR 8973**

IN THE BEGINNING (Elvis, Scotty & Bill).
Tracks: / Biff Collie interview / There's good rockin' tonight / Baby let's play house / Blue moon of Kentucky / I got a woman / That's alright mama / Elvis Presley interview / Tweedlee dee / Maybellene.
LP: . . . . **TOP 106**
MC: . . . . **KTOP 106**
LP: . . . . **KING 1**

INSPIRATION.
LP: . . . . **NE 1101**
MC: . . . . **CE 2101**

IT HAPPENED AT THE WORLD'S FAIR (Film soundtrack).
Tracks: / Beyond the bend / Relax / Take me to the fair / They remind me too much of you / One broken heart for sale / I'm falling in love tonight / Cotton candy land / World of our own, A / How would you like to be big boss man / Happy ending.
LP: . . . . **NL 82568**
MC: . . . . **NK 82568**
LP: . . . . **RD 7565**
LP: . . . . **INTS 5033**

IT WON'T SEEM LIKE CHRISTMAS WITHOUT YOU.
Tracks: / It won't seem like Christmas without you / On a snowy Christmas night / If every day was like Christmas / Where no one stands alone / I'll be home on Christmas day / If we never meet again / Wonderful world of Christmas, The / He touched me / Merry Christmas baby / Reach out to Jesus / If I get home on Christmas day / His hand in mine / O come all ye faithful / Holly leaves and Christmas trees / Christmas message from Elvis / Silent night.
LP: . . . . **NL 89025**
MC: . . . . **NK 89025**

IT'S NOW OR NEVER.
Tracks: / It's now or never / Surrender / Love me tender / Don't / Stuck on you / She's not you / Teddy bear / Fools fall in love / Crying in the chapel / Have I told you lately that I love you / I need your love tonight / There goes my everything / One broken heart for sale.
LP: . . . . **CDS 1203**
MC: . . . . **CAM 1203**

JAILHOUSE ROCK/LOVE IN LAS VEGAS.
LP: . . . . **RCALP 9020**

JANIS AND ELVIS.
LP: **130253**

KID GALAHAD AND EASY COME EASY GO.
LP: . . . . **PL 42791**
MC: . . . . **PK 42791**

KING.
Tracks: / Blue Hawaii / Early morning rain / No more / Relax / So close yet so far / Happy ending.
LP: . . . . **CDS 1190**
MC: . . . . **CAM 500**

KING CREOLE (Film soundtrack).
Tracks: / King Creole / As long as I have you / Hard headed woman / Trouble / Dixieland rock / Don't ask me why / Lover doll / Crawfish / Young dreams / Steadfast, loyal and true / New Orleans.
MC: **40173**
LP: . . . . **NL 83733**
MC: . . . . **NK 83733**
LP: . . . . **RD 27086**
LP: . . . . **INTS 5013**
LP: . . . . **SF 8231**

KING SPEAKS, THE.
LP: . . . . **HMR 9005**

KISSIN' COUSINS (Film Soundtrack).
Tracks: / Kissin' cousins / Smokey mountain boys / Catchin' on fast / Tender feeling / Anyone could fall in love with you / Barefoot ballad / Once is enough / Echoes of love / It's a long lonely highway.
LP: . . . . **NL 84115**
MC: . . . . **NK 84115**
LP: . . . . **RD 7645**
LP: . . . . **INTS 5108**
LP: . . . . **PL 42355**
MC: . . . . **PK 42355**

LEGEND BEGINS, THE (Elvis live).
LP: . . . . **OCN 2031WL**
MC: . . . . **OCN 2031WK**

LEGEND, THE.
Tracks: / Heartbreak hotel / Blue suede shoes / Hound dog / Teddy bear / Jailhouse rock / King Creole / Fool such as I, A / My wish came true / Girl of my best friend / Wooden heart / Rock a hula baby / Return to sender / Devil in disguise / Such a night / Love letters / US male / Rags to riches / It's only love.
LP: . . . . **CDS 1212**
MC: . . . . **CAM 1212**

LEGEND, THE '68-'70.
LPS: . . . . **ELR 4**

LEGENDARY ELVIS PRESLEY, THE.
LP: . . . . **ENT LP 13040**
MC: . . . . **ENT MC 13040**

LEGENDARY PERFORMER VOL.1.
Tracks: / That's alright / I love you because / Heartbreak hotel / Elvis (excerpt from an interview) / Don't be cruel / Love me / Trying to get to you / Love me tender / Peace in the valley / Elvis (further excerpts from an interview) / Fool such as I, A / Tonight is so right for love / Are you lonesome tonight / Can't help falling in love.
LP: **CPL1 0341**
MC: **APK1 0341**

LEGENDARY PERFORMER VOL.2, A.
Tracks: / Harbour lights / I want you, I need you, I love you / Blue suede shoes / Interview with Elvis by Jay Thompson (Interview with Elvis backstage following a live performance) / Blue Christmas (With The Jordanaires.) / Jailhouse rock / It's now or never (With The Jordanaires.) / Cane and high starched collar / Presentation of awards to Elvis (Excerpt from press conference, Pearl Harbour, Hawaii, March 25th 1961.) / Blue Hawaii (With J D Sumner & The Stamps & The Imperials Quartet.) / Such a night (With The Jordanaires.) / Baby what you want me to do / How great thou art / If I can dream.
LP: **CPL1 1349**
MC: . . . . **PK 11717**

LEGENDARY PERFORMER VOL.3, A.
Tracks: / Hound dog / Danny / Fame and fortune / Frankfurt special / Britches / Crying in the chapel / Surrender / Guadalajara / It hurts me / Let yourself go / In the ghetto / Let it be me.
LP: . . . . **PL 13082**

LEGENDARY PERFORMER VOL.4.
LP: . . . . **PL 84848**
MC: . . . . **PK 84848**

LIVE A LITTLE, LOVE A LITTLE (VIDEO) (See under Live a little).

LOVE LETTERS FROM ELVIS.
Tracks: / Love letters / When I'm over you / If I were you / Get my mojo working / Heart of Rome / Only believe / This is our dance / Cindy Cindy / I'll never know / It ain't no big thing (but it's growing) / Life.
LP: . . . . **NL 89011**
MC: . . . . **NK 89011**
LP: . . . . **SF 8202**
LP: . . . . **INTS 5081**

LOVE ME TENDER.
LP: . . . . **CL 89518**

LOVE SONGS: ELVIS PRESLEY.
Tracks: / Always on my mind / If I'm a fool for lovin' you / Tender feeling / Girl of my best friend / Tonight is so right for love / Fools fall in love / I slipped, I stumbled, I fell / Burning love / I love only one girl / Almost in love / Have I told you lately that I love you / Hawaiian wedding song.
LP: . . . . **CDS 1211**
MC: . . . . **CAM 1211**

LOVING YOU (Film Soundtrack).
Tracks: / Mean woman blues / Teddy bear / Got a lot of livin' to do / Lonesome cowboy / Hot dog / Party / Blueberry Hill / True love / Don't leave me now / Have I told you lately that I love you? / I need you so / Loving you.
LP: . . . . **NL 81515**
MC: . . . . **NK 81515**
LP: **130 251**
LP: . . . . **PL 42358**
LP: . . . . **INTS 5109**
MC: . . . . **PK 42358**
LP: . . . . **RC 24001**

LOVING YOU (FILM) (See under Loving You).

MAGIC MOMENTS.
Tracks: / Always on my mind / If I'm a fool for lovin' you / I just can't help believing / Love letters / Kentucky rain / Clean up your own backyard / Hey Jude / Wonder of you, The / Charro / In the ghetto / Your time hasn't come yet, baby / Until it's time for you to go / If I can dream / From a jack to a king / Separate ways / Are you lonesome tonight? / It keeps right on a-hurtin' / It's only love / Any day now / Make the world go away / Jailhouse rock / Teddy bear / Hound dog / Don't be cruel / Suspicious minds / Gentle on my mind / I'll be there if you ever want me / Bridge over troubled water / Edge of reality.
MC: . . . . **NK 89400**

MEMPHIS ALBUM, THE.
Tracks: / Stranger in my own home town / Power of my love / Only the strong survive / Any day now / Suspicious minds / Long black limousine / Wearin' that loved on look / I'll hold you in my heart / After loving you / Rubberneckin' / I'm movin' on / Gentle on my mind / True love travels on a gravel road / It keeps right on a-hurtin' / You'll think of me / Mama liked the roses / Don't cry daddy / In the ghetto / Fair is movin' on, The / Inherit the wind / Kentucky rain / Without love (there is nothing) / Who am I?.
2LP: . . . . **PL 86221**
MCSET: . . . . **PK 86221**

MESS O BLUES (24 Classic tracks) .
LP: . . . . **PFP 2000**
MC: . . . . **PFC 2000**

MOODY BLUE.
Tracks: / Unchained melody / If you love me (let me know) / Little darlin' / He'll have to go / Let me be there / Way down / Pledging my love / Moody blue / She thinks I still care.
LP: . . . . **RCALP 3021**
MC: . . . . **RCAK 3021**
LP: . . . . **PL 12428**
MC: . . . . **PK 12428**
LP: . . . . **NL 90252**
MC: . . . . **NK 90252**

MUSIC AND MEDIA INTERVIEW PICTURE DISC.
LPPD: . . . . **ELV 1001**

ON STAGE (February 1970).
Tracks: / See rider blues / Release me (and let me love again) / Sweet Caroline / Runaway / Wonder of you, The / Polk salad Annie / Yesterday / Proud Mary / Walk a mile in my shoes / Let it be me.
LP: . . . . **SF 8128**
LP: . . . . **NL 90459**
MC: . . . . **NK 90459**

OUR MEMORIES OF ELVIS.
LP: . . . . **PL 13279**

OUR MEMORIES OF ELVIS VOL 2.
Tracks: / I got a feelin' in my body / Green green grass of home / For the heart / She wears my ring / I can help / Way down / There's a honky tonk angel / Find out what's happening / Thinking about you / Don't think twice, it's alright.
LP: . . . . **PL 13448**

PARADISE HAWAIIAN STYLE (Film Soundtrack).
Tracks: / Paradise Hawaiian style / Queenie Wamine's papaya / Scratch my back (then I'll scratch yours) / Drums of the islands / Datin' / Dog's life / House of sand / Stop where you are / This is my heaven / Sand castles.
LP: . . . . **NL 89010**
MC: . . . . **NK 89010**
LP: . . . . **RD 7810**
LP: . . . . **INTS 5037**

PICTURES OF ELVIS.
Tracks: / Return to sender / Roustabout / Little Egypt / Paradise Hawaiian style / Girls, girls, girls / Double trouble / Do the clam / Fun in Acapulco / Bossa nova baby / Clambake / Girl happy / Rock a hula baby.
LP: . . . . **INTS 5001**
MC: . . . . **INTK 5001**
LP: . . . . **HY 1023**

PICTURES OF ELVIS (II).
Tracks: / I was the one / Blue suede shoes / Tutti frutti / Blue moon / Lawdy Miss Clawdy / Love me tender / Teddy bear / Loving you / Jailhouse rock / Trying to get to you / Anyway you want me / Just because.
LPPD: . . . . **AR 30 002**

PLEASE DON'T STOP LOVING ME.
Tracks: / What every woman lives for / Please don't stop loving me / Change of habit / Come along / Shout it out / Beginners luck / Clean up your own backyard / Rubberneckin' / Edge of reality / Petunia, the gardener's daughter / Hard luck / Have a happy.
LP: . . . . **CDS 1175**
MC: . . . . **CAM 485**

PORTRAIT IN MUSIC (IMPORT).
LP: . . . . **SRS 558**

POT LUCK WITH ELVIS.
Tracks: / Kiss me quick / Just for old time's sake / Gonna get back home some how / Such an easy question / Steppin' out of line / I'm yours / Something blue / Suspicion / I feel I've known you forever / Night rider / Fountain of love / That's someone you never forget.
LP: . . . . **NL 89098**
MC: . . . . **NK 89098**
LP: . . . . **RD 27265**
LP: . . . . **INTS 5074**

PROMISED LAND.
Tracks: / Promised land / There's a honky tonk angel (who will take me) / Help me / Mr. Songman / Love song of the year / It's midnight / Your love's been a long time coming / If you talk in your sleep / Thinking about you / You ask me to.
LP: **APL1 0873**

RARE ELVIS VOL.1.
Tracks: / Early mornin' rain / Hawaiian wedding song / Ku-u-i-po / No more / It's only love / Come what may / I'm yours / First time ever I saw your face, The / Patch it up / Don't cry daddy / High heel sneakers / Lover doll / Doncha' think it's time / Sound of your cry, The / Elvis Presley interview.
LP: . . . . **PL 89003**
MC: . . . . **PK 89003**

RARE ELVIS VOL.2.
Tracks: / Datin' / Shopping around / Beyond the reef / Sweet Caroline / Are you lonesome tonight / Shake, rattle and roll / Heartbreak hotel / Flip flop and fly / Long tall Sally / Blue suede shoes / Hound dog.
LP: . . . . **PL 89119**
MC: . . . . **PK 89119**
LP: . . . . **PL 45297**

RARE ELVIS VOL.3.
Tracks: / Judy / Little sister / G.I. blues / Viva Las Vegas / What'd I say / Long lonely highway / Life / Almost in love / His latest flame / Good luck charm / Doin' the best I can.
LP: . . . . **PL 89051**
MC: . . . . **PK 89051**

READY TEDDY.
MC: **40168**

RECONSIDER BABY.
Tracks: / Reconsider baby / Tomorrow night / So glad you're mine / When it rains, it really pours / My baby left me / Ain't that loving you baby / I feel so bad / Down in the alley / High heel sneakers / Stranger in my own home town / Merry Christmas baby.
LP: . . . . **PL 85418**
MC: . . . . **PK 85418**

RETURN OF THE ROCKER, THE.
LP: . . . . **PL 85600**

RETURN TO SENDER.
Tracks: / Return to sender / Have I told you lately that I love you / Roustabout / Hard headed woman / Girls, girls, girls / Whole lotta shakin' goin' on / Girl of my best friend / Do the clam / Once is enough / Steadfast, loyal and true / Slowly but surely / G.I. blues.
LP: . . . . **CDS 1200**
MC: . . . . **CAM 1200**

ROCK HITS, THE.
LP: . . . . **CDS 1215**
MC: . . . . **CAM 1215**

ROCK 'N' ROLL NO.1.
Tracks: / Blue suede shoes / I got a woman / I'm counting on you / I'm left you're right she's gone / That's all right mama / Money honey / Mystery train / I'm gonna sit right down and cry over you / One-sided love affair / Lawdy Miss Clawdy / Shake rattle and roll / Trying to get to you.
LP: . . . . **CLP 1093**
LP: . . . . **SF 8233**
MC: . . . . **PK 11620**
LP: . . . . **NL 89125**
MC: . . . . **NK 89125**

ROCK 'N' ROLL NO.2.
Tracks: / Rip it up / Love me / When my blue moon turns to gold again / Long tall Sally / First in line / Paralysed / So glad you're mine / Old Shep / Ready Teddy / Any place is paradise / How's the world treating you / How do you think I feel.
LP: . . . . **NL 81382**
MC: . . . . **NK 81382**
LP: . . . . **RD 7528**
LP: . . . . **CLP 1105**
MC: . . . . **PK 11530**
LP: . . . . **SF 7528**

ROCK 'N' ROLL REBEL (20 rock 'n' roll originals).
Tracks: / Good rockin' tonight / Ready Teddy / Hard headed woman / Shake, rattle and roll / Mystery train / I got a

woman / One night / Lawdy Miss Clawdy / King Creole / Jailhouse rock / Dixieland rock / Rip it up / Baby I don't care / I'm left you're right she's gone / Paralysed / Poor boy / Blue moon of Kentucky / I don't care if the sun don't shine / My baby left me / Party.
LP: NE 1170
MC: CE 2170

ROCKER ELVIS.
Tracks: / Blue suede shoes / Tutti frutti / Lawdy Miss Clawdy / I got a woman / Money honey / Jailhouse rock / Ready Teddy / Rip it up / Shake, rattle and roll / Long tall Sally / Hound dog / Baby I don't care.
LP: PL 85182
MC: PK 85182

ROMANTIC ELVIS (20 LOVESONGS)/ ROCKIN' ELVIS.
Tracks: / Doin' the best I can / You don't know me / Anything that's part of you / It hurts me / Love me tonight / Ask me / I don't want to / World of our own, A / There's always me / I met her today / Indescribably blue / All that I am / Boy like me, a girl like you, A / Starting today I'm yours / Echoes of love / I feel that I've known you forever / Something blue / Mine / Make me know it / Devil in disguise / Finders keepers / One broken heart for sale / I want you with me / Please don't drag that string around / Memphis, Tennessee / Western union / Witchcraft / Return to sender / Long lonely highway / His latest flame / Such a night / I gotta know / Little sister / Shopping around / Judy / I'll be back / US male / I'm coming home / For the millionth and the last time.
2LP: PL 89124
MCSET: PK 89124
2LP: RCALP 1000

ROUSTABOUT (Film Soundtrack).
Tracks: / Roustabout / Little Egypt / Poison ivy league / Hard knock / It's a wonderful world / Big love, big heartache / One-track heart / It's carnival time / Carny town / There's a brand new day on the horizon / Wheels on my heels.
LP: NL 89049
MC: NK 89049
LP: RD 7678
LP: INTS 5110
LP: PL 42356
MC: PK 42356

ROUSTABOUT (VIDEO) (See under Roustabout) (Various artists).

SEPARATE WAYS.
Tracks: / Separate ways / In my way / What now, what next, where to? / Old Shep / I slipped, I stumbled, I fell / It is so strange.
LP: CDS 1118
MC: CAM 428

SINGS MORT SHUMAN.
LP: NL 89504

SINGS WORLD HITS.
LP: NL 89309
MC: NK 89309

SOMETHING FOR EVERYBODY.
Tracks: / There's always me / Give me the right / It's a sin / Sentimental me / Starting today I'm yours / Gently / I'm coming home / In your arms / Put the blame on me / Judy / I want you with me / I slipped, I stumbled, I fell.
LP: NL 84116
MC: NK 84116
LP: RD 27224
LP: SF 5106

SOUND OF YOUR CRY.
Tracks: / It's only love / Suspicious minds / Angel / What'd I say / Sound of your cry, The / Big hunk o' love, A / Are you lonesome tonight / Steamroller blues / Don't cry daddy / Burning love / You'll never walk alone / Kentucky rain.
LP: RCALP 3060

SPEEDWAY (Film soundtrack).
Tracks: / Speedway / There ain't nothing like a song / Your time hasn't come yet, baby / Who are you, who am I? / He's your uncle, not your dad / Let yourself go / Your groovy self / Five sleepy heads / Western Union / Mine / Going home / Suppose.
LP: NL 85012
MC: NK 85012
LP: INTS 5041

SPEEDWAY (VIDEO) (See under Speedway) (Various artists).

STAY AWAY JOE (VIDEO) (See under Stay Away Joe).

SUN YEARS, THE.
LP: SUNLP 1001

SUSPICIOUS MINDS.
Tracks: / Suspicious minds / Got a lot of livin' to do / Return to sender / Big hunk o' love, A / In the ghetto / One night / Good luck charm / US male / Party / Fever / Old Shep / Devil in disguise.
LP: CDS 1206
MC: CAM 1206

THAT'S THE WAY IT IS (Film soundtrack).
Tracks: / I just can't help believing / Twenty days and twenty nights / How the web was woven / Patch it up / Mary in the morning / You don't have to say you love me / You've lost that lovin' feeling / I've lost you / Just pretend / Stranger in the crowd / Next step is love, The / Bridge over troubled water.
LP: NL 84114
MC: NK 84114
LP: SF 8162
MC: PK 11566

THIS IS ELVIS.
Tracks: / His latest flame / Moody blue / That's alright / Shake, rattle and roll / Flip flop and fly / Heartbreak hotel / Hound dog / Hy Gardner interview excerpts / My baby left me / Merry Christmas, baby / Mean woman blues / Don't be cruel / Teddy bear / Jailhouse rock / Army swearing-in / G.I. blues / Departure for Germany:press conference excerpt / Home from Germany: press conference excerpt / Too much monkey business / Love me tender / I got a thing about you, baby / I need your love tonight / Blue suede shoes / Viva Las Vegas / Suspicious minds / JC's award to Elvis excerpt / Promised land / Madison Square Gardens press conference excerp / Are you lonesome tonight? / My way / American trilogy / Memories.
LP: BL 84031
MC: BK 84031
LP: RCALP 5029

TODAY.
Tracks: / T-R-O-U-B-L-E / And I love you so / Susan when she tried / Woman without love / Shake a hand / Pieces of my life / Fairytale / I can help / Bringing it back / Green green grass of home.
LP: RS 1011
MC: PK 11682

U.S. MALE.
LP: CDS 1150
MC: CAM 457

VOICE OF THE KING (Interviews).
Tracks: / Texarkana 1955 / St. Petersburg 1956 / Witchita Falls 1956 / New Orleans 1956 / Memphis 1961 / Houston 1970 / New York 1972.
LP: OCN 2024WL
MC: OCN 2024WK

VOLUME ONE.
LP: ENT LP 13011
MC: ENT MC 13011

VOLUME TWO.
LP: ENT LP 13019
MC: ENT MC 13019

WELCOME TO MY WORLD.
Tracks: / Welcome to my world (With J D Sumner & The Stamps) / Help me make it through the night / Release me / I really don't want to know (With the Imperials Quartet.) / For the good times / Make the world go away / Gentle on my mind / I'm so lonesome I could cry (With J D Sumner & The Stamps) / Your cheatin' heart (With the Jordanaires) / I can't stop loving you.
LP: RCALP 3020
MC: RCAK 3020
LP: PL 12274
MC: PK 12274

WONDERFUL WORLD OF ELVIS.
Tracks: / Fools fall in love / Hard luck / What a wonderful life / Santa Lucia / Come along / Old Shep / Yellow rose of Texas / Rubberneckin' / Please don't stop loving me / It's a matter of time / Too much monkey business / I got lucky / Burning love / If you think I don't need you / Wonderful world / Clean up your own backyard / Tender feeling / Home is where the heart is / Little less conversation, A / US male / Let's be friends / Flaming star / Long legged girl with the short dress on / Today, tomorrow and forever.
2LP: PDA 073
MCSET: PDC 073

WORLD WIDE 25 GOLD AWARD HITS - VOL 4.
Tracks: / My baby left me / When my blue moon turns to gold again / Mean woman blues / Lonesome cowboy / Got a lot of livin' to do / Young dreams / Trouble / As long as I have you / Lover doll / Let me / Don'cha think it's time / My wish came true / Wild in the country / (You're so square) Baby I don't care / I want to be free / I need your love tonight / Just tell her Jim said hello / Ask me / Tell me why / Wonder of you, The / Please don't drag that string around / You'll think of me / Next step is love, The / You don't have to say you love me / I really don't want to know.
MC: DPTK 5012

WORLD WIDE 25 GOLD AWARD HITS - VOL 3.
Tracks: / Rip it up / Paralysed / Love me / We're gonna move / Poor boy / Hot dog / New Orleans / Dixieland rock / Crawfish / Don't ask me why / King Creole / One night / His latest flame / They remind me too much of you / Young and beautiful / Fame and fortune / Lonely man / Witchcraft / It hurts me / Puppet on a string / I believe / Any day now / I've lost you / Patch it up / There goes my everything.
MCSET: DPTK 5011

WORLD WIDE 25 GOLD AWARD HITS - VOL 2.
Tracks: / Are you lonesome tonight / I gotta know / I feel so bad / Surrender / Don't cry daddy / Kentucky rain / Little sister / Can't help falling in love / Rock a hula baby / Anything that's part of you / Good luck charm / She's not you / Return to sender / Where do you come from / Bossa nova baby / Kissin' cousins / Vive Las Vegas / Ain't that loving you baby / Crying in the chapel / In the ghetto / If I can dream / One broken heart for sale / You're the devil in disguise / Wooden heart / Suspicious minds / Excerpts from a press interview.
MCSET: DPTK 5001

WORLD WIDE 25 GOLD AWARD HITS - VOL 1.
Tracks: / Heartbreak hotel / I was the one / I want you, I need you, I love you / Mess of blues, A / Hound dog / Love me tender / Anyway you want me / Big hunk o' love, A / Playing for keeps / All shook up / That's when your heartaches begin / Loving you / Teddy bear / Jailhouse rock / I got stung / I beg of you / Don't / Wear my ring around your neck / Hard headed woman / Don't be cruel / Too much / Treat me nice / (Now and then there's) A fool such as I / Stuck on you / It's now or never.
MCSET: DPTK 5000

WORLD WIDE 50 GOLD AWARD HITS - VOL.1.
Tracks: / Heartbreak Hotel / I was the one / I want you, I need you, I love you / Don't be cruel / Hound dog / Love me tender / Anyway you want me / Too much / Playing for keeps / All shook up / That's when your heartaches begin / Loving you / Teddy bear / Jailhouse rock / Treat me nice / I beg of you / Don't / Wear my ring around your neck / Hard headed woman / I got stung / (Now and then there's) a fool such as I / Big hunk o love, A / Stuck on you / Mess of blues, A / It's now or never / I gotta know / Are you lonesome tonight / Surrender / I feel so bad / Little sister / Can't help falling in love / Rock a hula baby / Anything that's part of you / Good luck charm / She's not you / Return to sender / Where do you come from? / One broken heart for sale / You're the devil in disguise / Bossa nova baby / Kissin' cousins / Viva Las Vegas / Ain't that loving you baby / Wooden heart / Crying in the chapel / If I can deram / In the ghetto / Suspicious minds / Don't cry daddy / Kentucky rain / Excerpts from a press interview.
LPS: LPM 6401

WORLD WIDE 50 GOLD AWARD HITS - VOL.2.
Tracks: / Puppet on a string / Witchcraft (With the Jordanaires.) / Trouble / Poor boy / I want to be free / Doncha think it's time / Young dreams / Next step is love, The / You don't have to say you love me / Paralysed / My wish came true (With The Jordanaires.) / When my blue moon turns to gold again / Lonesome cowboy (With The jordanaires.) / My baby left me / It hurts me / I need your love tonight / Tell me why / Please don't drag that string around / Young and beautiful / Hot dog / New orleans (With The Jordanaires.) / We're gonna move / Crawfish / King Creole / I believe / Dixieland rock (With The Jordanaires.) / Wonder of you, The (With The Imperials Quartet.) / They remind me too much of you (With The Mello Men.) / Mean woman blues / Lonely man (With The Jordanaires.) / Any day now / Don't ask me why (With The Imperials Quartet.) / Baby I don't care (With The Jordanaires.) / I've lost you / Let me / Love me / Got a lot of livin' to do / Fame and fortune / Rip it up / There goes my everything (With The Imperials Quartet.) / Lover doll / One night / Just tell her Jim said hello / Ask me (With The Jordanaires.) / Patch it up / As long as I have you (With The Jordanaires.) / You'll think of me / Wild in the country (With The Jordanaires.).
LPS: LPM 6402

YOU'LL NEVER WALK ALONE.
Tracks: / You'll never walk alone / Peace in the valley / I believe / It is no secret / Take my hand precious Lord / Swing low sweet chariot.
LP: CDS 1088
MC: CAM 415

50,000,000 ELVIS FANS CAN'T BE WRONG.
Tracks: / Big hunk o' love, A / My wish came true / Fool such as I, A / I need your love tonight / Don't / I beg of you / Santa bring my baby back to me / Party / Paralysed / One night / I got stung / King Creole / Wear my ring around your neck / Doncha' think it's time.
LP: NL 89429
MC: NK 89429

Press Gang

ROGUES.
LP: VOX 022

Presser, Gabor

ELECTROMANTIC.
Tracks: / Title track / 2000 dioptria / Z op. 1 / Electromance / Valvola / La balletta / Adagio electrico / Rondo a la terror / D.D..
LP: EMC 3428

Pression X

PRESSION X.
LP: EES 012

Pressure

PRESSURE.
LP: MCF 3055

Pressure Company

LIVE IN SHEFFIELD 19TH JANUARY 1982.
LP: SOLID 1

Pressure Point

DREAMING (ALBUM).
Tracks: / Dreaming / Coming back / Gave me up / Maybe / Leave right now / Everything to me / Stay with me / Do you love me.
LP: VICELP 1
MC: VICEMC 1

THIS IS LONDON.
LP: VICELP 1
MC: VICEMC 1

Prestige

CHEATIN'.
LP: 780 105-1

Prestige All-Stars

ROOTS.
LP: OJC 062

Preston, Billy

BEHOLD.
Tracks: / I'm giving my life to christ / Heavenly / Born again / All to Jesus I surrender / He will see you through / He brought me out / Motherless child / Yes my God is real / Behold / For you my lord.
LP: MYR 1070
MC: MC 1070

BILLY PRESTON.
MCSET: DTO 10096

BILLY PRESTON & SYREETA (Preston, Billy & Syreeta).
Tracks: / Someone special / Searchin' / Just for love / It's so easy / Long and lasting love, A / Love / One more try / Hey you / New way to say I love you, A / What we did for love.
LP: STML 12155
MC: CSTML 12155

BILLY'S BAG.
Tracks: / Billy's bag / Steady gettin' it / Let me know / Soul meeting / Octopus / Slippin' and slidin' / Lowdown / I am coming through / My girl / Shotgun / Stop in the name of love / Can't you hear my heartbeat / Downtown / Eight days a week / King of the road / If I had a hammer.
LP: TOP 164
MC: KTOP 164

COLLECTION: BILLY PRESTON.
Tracks: / Bus, The / How long has the train been gone / It's alright ma (I'm only bleeding) / Blackbird / Let's make love / Will it go round in circles / Outa space / Let it be / I can't stand it (live) / You are so beautiful / Should've known better / You got me buzzin' / Billy's bag / Listen to the wind (Live) / I'm so tired / Struttin' / Space race / It's my pleasure / Nothing from nothing / Disco dancin' / Get back.
2LP: CCSLP 210
MC: CCSMC 210

FAST BREAK (Film soundtrack) (Preston, Billy & Syreeta).
Tracks: / More than just a friend / He didn't say / Go for it / Welcome to Cadwallader / With you I'm born again / Books and basketball half time / Big game, The.
LP: STML 12107

LATE AT NIGHT.
Tracks: / Give it up / Hot / Late at night / All I wanted was you / You / I come to rest in you / It will come in time / Lovely

lady / With you I'm born again / Sock it rocket.
LP: STML 12116
MC: CSTML 12116

PRESSIN' ON.
Tracks: / Pressing on / I'd like to go back home again / Lovin' you is easy / Turn it out / I'm never gonna say goodbye / Thanks but no thanks / Don't try to fight it / I love you so.
LP: SRML 12177
MC: CSTML 12177

THAT'S THE WAY GOD PLANNED IT.
Tracks: / Do what you want / I want to thank you / Everything's all right / She belongs to me / It doesn't matter / Morning star / Hey brother / What about you? / Let us all get together right now / This is it / Keep to yourself / That's the way God planned it / Through all times / As I get older / That's the way God planned it (alternate).
2LP: SAPCOR 91
MC: TCSAPCOR 9

WAY I AM, THE.
Tracks: / Hope / Good life boogie / Keep on truckin' / Change is gonna come, A / Let your feeling on me / I won't mistreat your love / Baby I'm yours / Until then / Way I am, The.
LP: STML 12148
MC: CSTML 12148

Preston, Don

SACRE BLUES.
Tracks: / Boogie woogie woman / I've got a right to love my baby / Lookin' for my baby / Do what you want / Come into my kitchen / Farther up the road / I found love / I wonder why do things happen to me / Skid row blues / Shake your money maker.
LP: RAG 1005

Preston, Jimmy

JIMMY PRESTON 1949-1950.
Tracks: / Swingin' in the groove / They call me the champ / I'm lonesome / Hang out tonight / Potato salad / Oh Mr. Possum / Hey everybody / Hey everybody (alternative take) / Early morning blues / Hay ride / Estellina bim bam / Credit blues / Swingin' in the groove / Going away.
LP: KK 806

ROCK THE JOINT (Jimmy Preston vol 2).
Tracks: / Rock the joint / Drinking woman / Hucklebuck Daddy / Sugar baby / They call me the champ / Let me call you sweetheart / Messin' with Preston / Numbers blues / Chop suey Louie / Home cookin' mama / Hold me baby / Do the bump / They call me the champ (2) / Let's hang out tonight.
LP: KK 827

Preston, Johnny

COME ROCK WITH ME.
LP: DEMAND 0035
LP: SR 60609

HIS TOP HITS.
MC: 824

Preston, Simon

WORLD OF THE ORGAN.
Tracks: / Toccata from symphony No. 5 (Widor) / Wachet auf BWV 645 (J.S. Bach) / Fantasia in F minor, K608 (Mozart) / Crown imperial / Prince of Denmark's march (Clarke) / Dead march from Saul (Handel) / Trumpet tune (Purcell) / Imperial march / Symphony No. 1 (finale) (Vierne) / Pilgrims' chorus from Tannhauser (Wagner) / March on a theme of Handel (Guilmant) / Study No. 5 (Schumann) / March triomphale (Klarg-Elert).
MC: 4300914

Preston, Stephen

FLUTE COLLECTION (Preston, Stephen/Lucy Carolan).
Tracks: / Le coucou (Daquin) / Air de Mr de Luly (Arr. Hotteterre) / Sonata in D (Quantz) / La de Drummond (Duphly) / Sonata in E minor (Devienne) / Fantaisie brillant sur 'La Fee aux roses' (Tulou) / Home, sweet home / Gute nacht (Schubert arr. Bohm).
LP: SAR 19
MC: CSAR 19

Prestor, Joey

ROCK 'N' ROLL RIOT - CANADIAN ROCK'N'ROLL (See King, Bob) (Prestor, Joey & Bob King).

Presumed Innocent

PRESUMED INNOCENT (Film Soundtrack) (Williams, John).
LP: VS 5280
MC: VSC 5280

Pretenders

EXTENDED PLAY.
Tracks: / Message of love / Talk of the town / Porcelain / Cuban slide.
LP: MINI 3563

GET CLOSE.
Tracks: / My baby / When I change my life / Light of the moon / Dance / Tradition of love / Don't get me wrong / I remember you / How much did you get for your soul? / Chill factor / Hymn to her / Room full of mirrors.
LP: WX 64
MC: WX 64C

LEARNING TO CRAWL.
Tracks: / Middle of the road / Back on the chain gang / Time the avenger / Show me / Watching the clothes / Thumbelina / My city was gone / Thin line between love and hate / I hurt you / 2,000 miles.
LP: WX 2
MC: WX 2C

PACKED.
LP: WX 346
MC: WX 346 C

PRETENDERS 2.
Tracks: / Adultress, The / Bad boys get spanked / Message of love / I go to sleep / Birds of paradise / Talk of the town / Pack it up / Waste not, want not / Day after day / Jealous dogs / English rose / Louie Louie.
LP: SRK 3572
MC: SRC 3572

PRETENDERS: INTERVIEW PICTURE DISC.
LPPD: BAK 2027

PRETENDERS, THE.
Tracks: / Precious / Phone call / Up to the neck / Tattooed love boys / Space invader / Wait, The / Stop your sobbing / Kid / Private life / Lovers of today / Brass in pocket / Mystery achievement.
LP: REAL 3
MC: REALC 3

SINGLES, THE.
Tracks: / Stop your sobbing / Kid / Brass in pocket / Talk of the town / I go to sleep / Day after day / Message of love / Back on the chain gang / Middle of the road / 2000 miles / Show me / Thin line between love and hate / Don't get me wrong / Hymn to her / My baby / I got you babe / What you gonna do about it.
LP: WX 135
MC: WX 135 C

Pretty Boy

PRETTY BOY.
LP: MAL 7428

Pretty Boy Floyd

LEATHER BOYZ WITH ELECTRIC TOYS.
LP: MCG 6076
MC: MCGC 6076

Pretty Green

PRETTY GREEN.
LP: NTL 30014

Pretty In Pink

PRETTY IN PINK (Film soundtrack) (Various artists).
Tracks: / Left of centre: *Vega, Suzanne* / Get to know ya: *Johnson, Jesse* / Do wot you do: *INXS* / Pretty in pink: *Psychedelic Furs* / Shellshock: *New Order* / Round round: *Some, Belouis* / Wouldn't it be good: *Hutton, June* / Bring on the dancing horses: *Echo & the Bunnymen* / Please, please let me get what I want: *Smiths*/ If you leave: *O.M.D.*.
LP: AMA 5113
MC: AMC 5113

WAKE UP.
Tracks: / Boys do lie / All about you / Girls night out / I wanna be your girlfriend / Kiss and tell / Two hearts, one love / Home by midnight / Boy is mine / Dreams / Wake up everybody / All about you / Testin' my love / Boy I think you're cute.
LP: ZL 72756
MC: ZK 72756

Pretty Maids

FUTURE WORLD.
Tracks: / Future world / Loud 'n' proud / Love games / Yellow rain / Rodeo / We came to rock / Needles in the dark / Eye of the storm / Long way to go.
LP: 4502811
MC: 4502814

PRETTY MAIDS.
LP: CULP 1

RED HOT AND HEAVY.
Tracks: / Fortuna / Back to back / Red hot and heavy / Waitin' for the time / Cold killer / Battle of pride / Night danger / Place in the night, A / Queen of dreams / Little darlin'.
LP: PC 26207
MC: 40 26207

Pretty Poison

CATCH ME (I'M FALLING).
Tracks: / Hold me / Nightime / Closer / When I look in your eyes / Let freedom ring / Catch me (I'm falling) / Look, The / Don't cry baby / Shine on me / Heaven.
LP: V 2512
MC: TCV 2512

Pretty Things

1967-1971.
Tracks: / Defecting Grey / Mr. Evasion / Talkin' about the good times / Walking through my dreams / Private sorrow / Balloon burning / Good Mr. Square, The / Blue serge blues / October 26 / Cold stone / Summertime / Circus mind / Stone hearted mama.
LP: CM 103
MC: CMK 103

CLOSED RESTAURANT BLUES.
LP: KIRI 032

CRIES FROM THE MIDNIGHT CIRCUS.
Tracks: / S F sorrow is born / Journey, The / I see you / Well of destiny / Old man going / Cries from the midnight circus / Grass / She's a lover / What's the use / Cold stone / October 26 / Stone-hearted mama.
LP: EMS 1119
MC: TCEMS 1119

CROSS TALK.
Tracks: / I'm calling / Edge of the night / Sea of blue / Lost that girl / Bitter end / Office love / Falling again / It's so hard / She don't / No future.
LP: K 56842

GET THE PICTURE.
Tracks: / You don't believe me / Buzz the jerk / Get the picture / Can't stand the pain / Rainin' in my heart / We'll play house / You'll never do it baby / I had a dream / I want your love / London town / Cry to me / Gonna find me a substitute.
LP: 6438214

LET ME HEAR THE CHOIR SING.
Tracks: / Rosalyn / Big boss man / Don't bring me down / Road runner / Judgement day / Big city / Mama, keep your big mouth shut / 13 Chester Street / Honey I need / I can never say / Oh baby doll / She's fine, she's mine / Get a buzz / We'll play house / You'll never do it baby / I want your love.
LP: ED 139

LIVE AT HEARTBREAK HOTEL.
Tracks: / Big boss man / Midnight to six man / I'm a king bee / Honey I need / Shakin' all over / Rosalyn / Road runner / Mama keep your big mouth shut / Raining in my heart / Reelin' and rockin' / Don't bring me down / Mona.
LP: WIK 24

PARACHUTE.
Tracks: / Scene one / Good Mr. Square, The / She was tall, she was high / In the square / Letter, The / Rain / Miss Fay regrets / Cries from the midnight circus / Grass / Sickle clowns / She's a lover / What's the use / Parachute.
LP: ED 289
LP: SHVL 774

PRETTY THINGS, THE.
Tracks: / Road runner / Judgement day / 13 Chester Street / Big city / Unknown blues / Mama, keep your big mouth shut / Honey, I need / Oh baby doll / She's fine, she's mine / Don't you lie to me / Moon is rising, The / Pretty thing.
LP: 6438212
LP: TL 5239
LP: 8460541
MC: 8460544

PRETTY THINGS, THE (2).
LP: HORN 004

S.F. SORROW.
Tracks: / S F sorrow is born / Bracelets of fingers / She says good morning / Private sorrow / Balloon burning / Death / Baron Saturday / Journey, The / I see you / Well of destiny / Trust / Old man going / Loneliest person.
LP: XED 236

S.F. SORROW/PARACHUTE.
2LP: SHDW 406

SILK TORPEDO.
Tracks: / Dream / Joey / Maybe you tried / Atlanta / L.A.N.T.A. / Is it only love / Come home momma / Bridge of God / Singapore silk torpedo / Belfast cowboys / Bruise in the sky.
LP: SSK 59401

Pretty Woman

FAME 90 (See under Bowie, David).

KING OF WISHFUL THINKING (See under Go West).

PRETTY WOMAN (Film soundtrack) (Various artists).
Tracks: / Wild women do: *Cole, Natalie* / Fame 90: *Bowie, David* / King of wishful thinking: *Go West*/ Tangled: *Wiedlin, Jane* / It must have been love: *Roxette* / Life in detail: *Palmer, Robert* / No explanation: *Cetera, Peter* / Real wild child (wild one): *Otcasek, Christopher* / Fallen: *Wood, Lauren* / Oh pretty woman: *Orbison, Roy* / Show me your soul: *Red Hot Chili Peppers.*
LP: MTL 1052
LP: 793 492 1
MC: TCMTL 1052
MC: 793 492 4

Previn, Andre

COLLABORATION (see Rogers,Shorty/ Andre Previn) (Previn, Andre/ Shorty Rogers).

DIFFERENT KIND OF BLUES, A.
Tracks: / Look at him go / Little face / Who reads reviews / Night thoughts / Different kind of blues, A / Chocolate apricot / Five of us / Make up your mind.
LP: ASD 3965
MC: TC ASK 3965

DORIS DAY AND ANDRE PREVIN (See under Day, Doris) (Previn, Andre & Doris Day).

DUET (see Day, Doris) (Previn, Andre & Doris Day).

GENIUS OF ANDRE PREVIN, THE.
Tracks: / Ain't misbehavin' / Honeysuckle rose / Black and blue / I've got a feeling / Oh, you sweet thing / That's where the west begins / Fatstuff / Stealin' apples.
LP: ALEB 2311
MC: ZCALB 2311

GIGI.
Tracks: / Parisians / I remember it well / A toujours / It's a bore / Aunt Alicia's march / Thank heaven for little girls / Gigi / She is not thinking of me.
LP: 1007 548

IT'S A BREEZE (Previn, Andre/Itzhak Perlman).
Tracks: / It's a breeze / Rain in my head / Catgut your tongue / It's about time / Quiet diddling / Tune for Heather / Bowing and scraping / Red bar.
LP: EMD 5537

MACK THE KNIFE & OTHER KURT WEILL SONGS (Previn, Andre & JJ Johnson).
LP: CBS 61352

MY FAIR LADY (see Manne,Shelly) (Previn, Andre/Shelly Manne/Leroy Vinnegar).

NICE WORK IF YOU CAN GET IT (see Fitzgerald,Ella) (Previn, Andre & Ella Fitzgerald).

PAL JOEY.
LP: 1007 543

PLAYS FATS WALLER.
MC: ORC 014

PLAYS WEST SIDE STORY/PLAYS MY FAIR LADY (see Brubeck,Dave/ Andre Previn) (Previn, Andre/Dave Brubeck).

PREVIN AT SUNSET.
Tracks: / I got it bad and that ain't good / Body and soul / Sunset in blue / All the things you are / Something to live for / Good enough to keep / That old blue magic / Blue skies / I found a new baby / Variations on a theme / Mulholland Drive.
LP: BLP 30121

PREVIN PLAYS GERSHWIN (Previn, Andre and the London Symphony Orchestra).
Tracks: / Rhapsody in blue / Concerto in F / American in Paris, An.
LP: EG 2908491
MC: EG 2908494

SOUND STAGE (Under The Direction Of Johnny Williams).
Tracks: / You oughta be in pictures / Way you look tonight,The / Zip-a-dee-doo-dah / Swinging on a star / Only have eyes for you,I / Around the world / Someday my prince will come / There will never be another you / When you wish upon a star / Stella by starlight / Summertime / That old black magic.
LP: BPG 62394

WEST SIDE STORY (Previn, Andre/ Shelly Manne/Leroy Vinnegar).
LP: COP 046

Previn, Dory

DORY AND ANDRE PREVIN.
LP: MRS 503

DORY PREVIN.
Tracks: / Lover lover be my cover / Cold water canyon / Atlantis / Mama mama comfort me / Brando / New rooms / Empress of China, The / Obscene phone

call, The / Crooked Christmas star '73 / Did Jesus have a baby sister.
LP: . . . . **K 56066**

MARY C.BROWN & THE HOLLYWOOD SIGN.
Tracks: / Mary C Brown & the Hollywood sign / Holy man on Malibu bus number 3, The / Midgets lament, The / When a man loves a woman / Cully surroga he's almost blind / Left hand lost / Perfect man, The / Starlet starlet on the screen / Who will follow Norma Jean / Don't put him down / King kong / Morning star / Evening evening star / Jesus was a androgyne / Anima / Animus.
LP: . . . . **BGOLP 3**

MYTHICAL KINGS AND IGUANAS.
Tracks: / Mythical kings and iguanas / Yada yada la scala / Lady with the braid / Her mother's daughter / Angels and devils the following day / Mary C Brown and the Hollywood sign / Lemon haired ladies / Stone for Bessie Smith / Game / Going home.
LP: . . . . **GO 2019**

WE'RE CHILDREN OF COINCIDENCE & HARPO MARX.
Tracks: / Children of convenience / I wake up slow / Woman soul / Comedian, The / Fours / So much trouble / Wild roses / How'm I gonna keep myself together / Owl and the pussycat, The.
LP: . . . . **K 56213**
MC: **K4 56213**

Previn, Lovely

SHATTERPROOF.
LP: . . . . **SEC 6**

Previte, Bobby

CLAUDE'S LATE MORNING.
LP: **188811 1**
MC: **188811 4**

DULL BANG, GUSHING SOUND, HUMAN SHRIEK.
LP: . . . . **ST 7532**

Prevost, Eddie

NOW HERE THIS THEN (Prevost, Eddie Band).
LP: . . . . **SPJ 505**

Prey, Herman

PORTRAIT: HERMAN PREY.
Tracks: / Paloma / Somewhere / Monn river.
2LP: **DP6 28551**
MC: **CO4 28551**

WORLD FULL OF MUSIC, A (Eine welt voll musik).
Tracks: / Am brunnen vor dem tore / Was frag ich viel nach geld und gut / Kommt a Vogerl geflogen / Dank sei dir, Herr Ogerman / Somewhere / La Montanara / Moon river / O taler weit, o hohen / etc.
MC: **4.26646**

Price, Alan

16 GOLDEN CLASSICS.
Tracks: / Simon Smith and the amazing dancing bear / Cherie / Don't stop the carnival / If I could / Slow down / Shame / People are talking / Angel eyes / Jarrow song / Don't slam that door / Nobody can / Too much / Jump children / Mama divine / Please / I'll put a spell on you.
LP: . . . . **UNLP 011**
MC: . . . . **UNMC 011**

ALAN PRICE COLLECTION, THE.
Tracks: / Simon Smith and the amazing dancing bear / In times like these / Too many people / Falling in love again / I put a spell on you / Barefootin' / O lucky man / House that Jack built, The / Don't stop the carnival / Poor people / Tickle me / My old Kentucky home / Hi lili hi lo / Trimdon Grange explosion, The / Shame.
LP: . . . . **MFP 5757**
MC: . . . . **TCMFP 5757**

BEST OF ALAN PRICE, THE.
LP: . . . . **ARLP 104**
MC: . . . . **ZCAR 104**

BEST OF AND THE REST OF, THE.
Tracks: / Jarrow song / In times like these / Don't stop the carnival / Nobody can / Angel eyes / Hi lili hi lo / Just got love, I / Simon Smith and the amazing dancing bear / Mama divine / I'll put a spell on you / Don't try / Shame / House that Jack built, The / Cherie.
MC: . . . . **ARLC 1010**

BETWEEN TODAY AND YESTERDAY.
LP: . . . . **K 56032**

FOCUS ON.
2LP: . . . . **FOS 65/6**

GEORDIE ROOTS & BRANCHES.
Tracks: / Lambton worm, The / There's more to life than women and beer / Bobby Shaftoe / Girl from the north country / Billy boy / Dance ti' thi' daddy / Water o' Tyne, The / Cushie Butterfield / Keep your feet still Geordie Hinny / My home town / Keel row, The / Blaydon races.
LP: . . . . **MWM SP1**
MC: . . . . **MWMC SP1**

GEORGIE FAME WITH ALAN PRICE (see Georgie, Fame & Alan Price) (Price, Alan & Georgie Fame).

GREATEST HITS: ALAN PRICE.
LP: . . . . **NE 1371**
MC: . . . . **CE 2371**

GUESS WHO.
LP: . . . . **SAP 001**

LIBERTY.
Tracks: / Fools in love / Everything but love / Days like these / Bad dream / Double love / Changes / Mania urbania / Liberty / Say it isn't true / Free with me (Only on CD.) / Man overboard (Only on CD.).
LP: **210.042**
MC: **410.042**
LP: **211390**
MC: **411319**

PROFILE.
Tracks: / House that Jack built / Sunshine & rain / Simon Smith & the amazing dancing bear / Living without you / To Ramona / TGckle me / I put a spell on you / Going down slow / Come and dance with me / Don't stop the carnival / Hi lili hi lo.
LP: **AL6 24284**

PROFILE: ALAN PRICE.
Tracks: / House that Jack built, The / Sunshine and rain / Simon Smith and the amazing dancing bear / Living without you / To Ramona / Tickle me / I put a spell on you / Going down slow / Come and dance with me / Don't stop the carnival / Hi lili hi lo.
LP: **6.24284**
MC: **CL4 24284**

RISING SUN.
LP: **JETLP227**

ROCK 'N' ROLL NIGHT AT THE ROYAL COURT.
LP: . . . . **KEY 1**

ROSETTA (see Fame, Georgia & Alan Price) (Price, Alan & Georgie Fame).

TOGETHER (Price, Alan & Georgie Fame).
Tracks: / Rosetta / Yello man / Dole song / Time I move on / John and Mary / Here and now / Home is where the heart is / Ballad of Billy joe / That's how strong my love is / Blue condition / I can't take it much longer.
LP: . . . . **CBS 32509**
MC: **40 32509**

TRAVELLIN' MAN.
LP: . . . . **APB 101**
MC: . . . . **ZCAPB 101**

WORLD OF ALAN PRICE, THE.
LP: . . . . **SPA 77**

Price, Bill

FINE OLD YORKSHIRE GENTLEMAN, THE.
Tracks: / Fine old Yorkshire gentleman, The / Pony driving song / Simon John / Cropper lads / Rothwell debtors prison song / Kirby malzeard calling on song / Weavers, The / Keepers and the drivers, The / Fisher lads of Whitby, The / Spence Broughton / T'owd farmer and his shrew / Forster's mill / Master Smith said to John / Methody parson.
LP: . . . . **FHR 038**

Price, David

ACCORDION MAGIC.
Tracks: / Delilah / Memory / Tijuana taxi / Autumn leaves / Whiter shade of pale, A / I'll wait for you / Spanish eyes / Guantanamera / Charade / Chanson d'amour / Windmills of your mind / March post / La vie en rose / Girl from Ipanema / So nice / Petite fleur / If / She.
MC: . . . . **PD 004 A**

Price Killers

DETENTE.
Tracks: / Losers / It's your fate / Shattered illusions / Widows walk / Russian roulette / Catelepsy / Blood I bleed / Vultures in the sky.
LP: . . . . **RO 96951**
MC: . . . . **SPV 7832702**

Price, Leontyne

RIGHT AS THE RAIN (Price, Leontyne & Andre Previn).
Tracks: / Right as rain / Sunrise, sunset / It's good to have you near again / It never entered my mind / Nobody's heart / My melancholy baby / Sleepin' bee, A / They didn't believe me / Hello, young lovers / Love walked in / Where, I wonder.
MC: . . . . **GK 82983**

Price, Lloyd

JUKE BOX GIANTS.
Tracks: / Stagger Lee / Just because / Lawdy Miss Clawdy / I'm gonna get married / I'll be a fool for you / Try a little tenderness / Hooked on a feeling / Me and a dog named Poo / Personality / Question / Imagination / Misty / Mr. & Mrs. Untrue / You're nobody till somebody loves you / Ready for Betty / Where were you (on our wedding day).
LP: . . . . **AFEMP 1009**

LAWDY MISS CLAWDY.
Tracks: / Lawdy Miss Clawdy / Mailman blues / Ain't it a shame / Restless heart / What's the matter now / Baby don't turn your back on me / SS Heart / Lord Lord amen / Walkin' the track / Woe ho ho / L yi yi gomen a sai / Trying to find some one to love / Frog legs / Oo wee baby / Baby please come home / Breaking my heart / Rock 'n' roll dance.
LP: . . . . **CH 127**

LLOYD AT ANY PRICE.
LP: . . . . **JOY 179**

MR. PERSONALITY REVISITED.
Tracks: / Stagger Lee / Mailman blues / Have you ever had the blues / Question / You need love / What do you do to my heart / Come into my heart / I'm gonna get married / Where were you (on our wedding day) / Oh, oh, oh, why / I wish your picture was you / Lady Luck / Just because / Lawdy Miss Clawdy / Personality.
LP: . . . . **CRB 1052**

WALKIN' THE TRACK.
LP: . . . . **SP 2163**

Price, Louis

LOUIS PRICE.
Tracks: / Distant lover / Play it by heart / Heart's devotion / Flesh and blood / What becomes of the brokenhearted / Nobody but you / Just one thing / How can I make you love me / Try it baby / I believe in you (Cassette & CD only).
LP: . . . . **ZT 72746**
MC: . . . . **ZK 72746**

Price, Malcolm

AND THEN WE ALL GOT UP.....
LP: . . . . **SFA 017**

BOURGEOIS BLUES.
LP: . . . . **WF 003**

IN AN OLD DUTCH HOUSE.
LP: . . . . **MU 7437**

Price Of Fear

PRICE OF FEAR, THE (With Vincent Price) (Various artists).
MCSET: . . . . **ZBBC 1118**

Price, Ray

DIAMONDS IN THE STARS.
Tracks: / Diamonds in the stars / Let it rain let her cry / Something to forget you by / It don't hurt me half as bad / Forty and fadin' / When you gave your love to me / She's the right kind of woman / Circle driveway / Getting over you again / I'm still not over you.
LP: . . . . **YBLP 121**

HONKY TONK YEARS 1951-53, THE.
LP: . . . . **SS 22**

Price, Ronnie

DANCING PIANO, THE.
LP: . . . . **MTS 3**

RONNIE PRICE PLAYS MUSIC MUSIC MUSIC WITH THE (Price, Ronnie/ Ronnie Price Quartet).
LP: . . . . **MTS 20**

Price, Ruth

RUTH PRICE.
LP: . . . . **FS 285**

Price, Sam

DO YOU DIG MY JIVE.
Tracks: / Nasty but nice / Cow cow blues / How 'bout that mess / Blow Katy blow / Teed-up / Eiffel Boogie / Blue rhythm stomp / Oh lawdt mama / Lead me daddy straight to the bear / I know how to do it / Pigalle blues.
LP: . . . . **KM 704**

PLAY IT AGAIN SAM.
Tracks: / After hours at the Copley bar / Room 509 / Trouble in mind / 509 boogie / Empty bed blues / Do your duty / Box car shorty's return / Back bay bounce / Ain't nobody's business / Bean town boogie / Movin' that thing / Good old wagon / Back water blues.
LP: . . . . **KM 702**

RIB JOINT.
2LP: . . . . **SJL 2240**

SINGING WITH SAMMY.
LP: . . . . **BT 2002**

Price, Sammy

BARRELHOUSE & BLUES.
LP: . . . . **BLP 30130**

BLUE & BOOGIE.
LP: **500103**

BLUES & BOOGIE (see McShann, Jay) (Price, Sammy & Jay McShann).

BLUES ON MY MIND.
LP: . . . . **BLP 30201**

BOOGIE WOOGIE TWINS, THE (Price, Sammy & Torben Plys Peterson).
LP: . . . . **SLP 278**

COPENHAGEN BOOGIE (Price, Sammy With Fessor's Big City Band).
LP: . . . . **SLP 266**

DOC & SAMMY (see Cheatham, Doc & Sammy Price) (Price, Sammy & Doc Cheatham).

KING JAZZ VOLUME 5 (see Mezzrow-Bechet Quintet Septet) (Price, Sammy & Mezzrow-Bechet Quintet Septet).

ORIGINAL PIANO SOLO.
LP: . . . . **SM 3538**

ROCKIN' BOOGIE.
LP: **33560**

SAMMY PRICE AND HIS BLUESICIANS 1944 (Price, Sammy and His Bluesicians).
LP: . . . . **CLP 73**

SAMMY PRICE PIANO SOLOS.
Tracks: / In a mezz / Those mellow blues / Gully loves blues / Cow cow blues / 133rd Street boogie / I finally gotcha / Boogin' with Mezz / Callin' 'em home / Step down, step up / Shakin' loose / Boogin' with Big Sid.
LP: . . . . **SM 3075**

SWEET SUBSTITUTE.
LP: **3024**

Price, Smitty

COLOURS OF PRAISE (see under Rogers, Harlan) (Price, Smitty/Harlan Rogers).

COLOURS OF PRAISE II (See under Rogers, Harlan) (Price, Smitty/Harlan Rogers).

HYMNS IN COLOUR (Price, Smitty/ Harlan Rogers).
Tracks: / Joyful, joyful we adore Thee / For the beauty of the Earth / How great Thou art / Take my life / Just as I am (six more tracks, then) / Joy to the world.
LP: . . . . **MM R 0269**
MC: . . . . **MM C 0269**

Prick Up Your Ears

PRICK UP YOUR EARS (Film soundtrack) (Various artists).
Tracks: / Prick up your ears: *Various artists* / Song for a joke: *Various artists* / Keep your socks on: *Various artists* / This one's on me: *Various artists* / Dancing hearts: *Various artists* / We're all friends here: *Various artists* / Boys will be boys: *Various artists* / Mr. Right: *Various artists* / Love in Islington: *Various artists* / By the beautiful sea: *Various artists*.
LP: . . . . **FILM 014**
MC: . . . . **FILMC 014**

Pride, Charley

20 OF THE BEST: CHARLEY PRIDE.
Tracks: / All I have to offer you is me / Wonder could I live there anymore / I can't believe that you stopped loving me / I'd rather love you / I'm just me / It's gonna take a little bit longer / Amazing love / Then who am I / Hope you're feelin' me (like I'm feelin' you) / My eyes can only see as far as you / She's just an old love turned memory / Someone loves you honey / Where do I put her memory / You're my Jamaica / Honky tonk blues / You win again / Never been so loved (in all my life) / You're so good when you're bad / Why baby why / Night games.
LP: . . . . **NL 89848**
MC: . . . . **NK 89848**

AFTER ALL THIS TIME.
Tracks: / Even knowin' / Have I got some blues for you / Looking at a sure thing / After all this time / Next to you, I like me / If you still want a fool around / On the other hand / One of these days / Look in your mirror / You took me there.
LP: . . . . **RITZLP 0042**
MC: . . . . **RITZLC 042**

AMAZING LOVE.
Tracks: / Comin' down with love / If she just helps me (get over you) / I'm only losin' everything I threw away / Footprints in the sands of time / Amazing love / Blue Ridge Mountains turning green / I've just found another reason for loving you / Old photographs / I'm glad it was you / Mr. Joe Henry's happy hand-clappin' open air.
LP: **AFL1 0397**
MC: **AFK1 0397**

AMY'S EYES.

Tracks: / White house's / Moody woman / Amy's eyes / After me, after you / I made love to you in my mind / Whole lotta love on the line / Nickles and dimes and love / Look who's looking / I wrote the songs that broke her heart / You hold my world together / Right one, The / Plenty good lovin'.
MC: RITZ LC 0057

BEST OF CHARLEY PRIDE.
Tracks: / Just between you and me / Does my ring hurt your finger / Is anybody going to San Antone / Snakes crawl at night, The / (In my world) you don't belong / Easy part's over, The / I'm just me / I know one / Gone, on the other hand / Before I met you / Too hard to say I'm sorry / Kiss an angel good morning / Place for the lonesome, A / I'd rather love you / Kaw-liga / Let the chips fall / All I have to offer you (is me) / (There's still) someone I can't forget / Day the world stood still, The / Let me live / (I'm so) afraid of losing you again / You'll still be the one.
MCSET: DPTK 5009

BEST OF CHARLEY PRIDE.
Tracks: / Just between you and me / Does my ring hurt your finger / Kaw-liga / Snakes crawl at night, The / All I have to offer you is me / Easy part's over, The / Day the world stood still, The / I know one / Gone, on the other hand / Before I met you / Too hard to say I'm sorry / Let the chips fall.
MC: PK 42014
LP: PL 42014

BEST OF CHARLEY PRIDE VOL 2.
Tracks: / Place for the lonesome, A / I'd rather love you / Is anybody going to San Antone / Kiss an angel good morning / (In my world) you don't belong / (There's still) someone I can't forget / I'm just me / Let me live / (I'm so) afraid of losing you again / You'll still be the one.
MC: PK 42009
LP: LSA 3105

BEST OF CHARLEY PRIDE VOL 3.
Tracks: / I don't deserve a mansion / My eyes can only see as far as you / Happiness of having you, The / Hope you're feelin' me (like I'm feelin' you) / I ain't all bad / Then who am I? / Mississippi cotton picking delta town / Searching for the morning sun / Amazing love / Don't fight the feelings of love / Oklahoma morning.
LP: LSA 3283
MC: MPK 254

BURGERS AND FRIES.
Tracks: / Burgers and fries / Best in the world / Whose arms are you in tonight / Nothing's prettier than Rose is / Mem'ries / When I stop leaving / I can see the lovin' in your eyes / One on one / Where do I put her memory / You snap your fingers.
LP: PL 12983

CHARLEY.
Tracks: / Hope you're feelin' me (like I'm feelin' you) / Searching for the morning sun / Hardest part of livin's loving me, The / Now and then / Fools / I ain't all bad / She's as close as I can get to loving you / One mile more / You're the woman behind everything / Lovin' understandin' man.
LP: LSA 3246

CHARLEY PRIDE COLLECTION.
Tracks: / I'd rather love you / Time / Jeannie Norman / Anywhere / When the trains come in / Piroque Joe / Was it all worth losing you / Instant loneliness / This highway leads to glory / Time out for Jesus / Yonder comes a sucker / Able bodied man / What money can't buy / Billy Bayou / Detroit city / Me and Bobby McGee / Act naturally / Banks of the Ohio / That's my way / Last thing on my mind.
MCSET: PDC 058
2LP: PDA 058

CHARLEY PRIDE GOLDEN COLLECTION, THE.
LP: NE 1056

CHARLEY PRIDE SINGS HEART SONGS.
Tracks: / You'll still be the one / Anywhere (just inside your arms) / I'm beginning to believe my own lies / Kiss an angel good morning / What money can't buy / No one could ever take me from you / Jeannie Norman / Once again / Miracles, music and my wife / Pretty houses for sale.
LP: LSA 3052

CHARLEY PRIDE SPECIAL.
Tracks: / Able bodied man / Through the years / Is anybody going to San Antone / Thought of losing you / I think I'll take a walk / Things are looking up / Special / Poor boy like me, A / (There's) Nobody home to go home to / This is my year for Mexico.
LP: SF 8171
LP: PL 42013
MC: PK 42013

CHARLEY SINGS EVERYBODY'S CHOICE.
Tracks: / I don't think she's in love anymore / I see the devil in your deep blue eyes / You're so good when you're bad / When she dances / Mountain of love / Oh what a beautiful love song / I haven't loved this way in years / Cup of love / Love is a shadow / I hope (you never cry again).
LP: RCALP 3075
MC: RCAK 3075
MC: PK 84287
LP: PL 84287

CHARLIE PRIDE SONG BOOK.
MC: AM 115

CHRISTMAS IN MY HOMETOWN.
Tracks: / Christmas in my home town / Deck the halls with boughs of holly / They stood in silent prayer / Santa and the kids / Silent night / Little drummer boy / Happy Christmas day / First Christmas morn, The / Christmas and love / O holy night.
LP: LSA 3185

COUNTRY CHARLEY PRIDE.
Tracks: / Busted / Distant drums / Detroit City / Yonder comes a sucker / Green, green grass of home / That's the chance I'll have to take / Snakes crawl at night, The / Miller's cave / Atlantic coastal line, The / Got leavin' on her mind.
LP: LSA 3143
MC: MPK 183

COUNTRY FEELIN'.
Tracks: / Which way do we go? / We could / It amazes me / All his children / Streets of gold / I don't see how I can love you anymore / Singin' a song about love / Man I used to be, The / Let my love in / Love put a song in my heart.
LP: AFL1 0534
MC: AFK1 0534

COUNTRY GREATS.
Tracks: / Busted / Distant drums / Detroit City / Yonder comes a sucker / Green, green grass of home / That's the chance I'll have to take / Before I met you / Folsom Prison blues / Snakes crawl at night, The / Miller's cave / Atlantic coastal line, The / Got leavin' on her mind.
LP: MFP 5816
MC: TCMFP 5816

COUNTRY STORE: CHARLEY PRIDE.
LP: CST 24
MC: CSTK 24

COUNTRY WAY, THE.
Tracks: / Too hard to say I'm sorry / Little folks, The / Crystal chandeliers / Act naturally / Does my ring hurt your finger / Mama don't cry for me / Day the world stood still, The / Gone, on the other hand / You can tell the world / I'll wander back to you / Life turned her that way / I threw away the rose.
LP: LSA 3145
MC: MPK 185

DID YOU THINK TO PRAY.
Tracks: / Did you think to pray / I'll fly away / Time out for Jesus / Angel band / Jesus, don't give up on me / Let me live / Whispering hope / This highway leads to glory / Church in the wildwood, The / Lord, build me a cabin in glory.
LP: LSA 3156
MC: MPK 188

GREATEST HITS: CHARLEY PRIDE VOL.2.
Tracks: / Let a little love come in / Every heart should have one / You're so good when you're bad / Why baby why / Power of love, The / Down on the farm / Night games / I don't think she's in love anymore / Mountain of love / Now and then.
LP: PL 85426
MC: PK 85426

HAPPINESS OF HAVING YOU, THE.
Tracks: / Happiness of having you, The / I can't keep my hands off you / Everything I am / My eyes can only see as far as you / I've got a woman to lean on / Right back missing you again / Help me make it through the night / Oklahoma morning / Everything she touches turns to love / Signs of love.
LP: LSA 3262

HITS OF CHARLEY PRIDE, THE.
Tracks: / Happiness of having you, The / Then who am I / Kiss an angel good morning / I ain't all bad / It's gonna take a little bit longer / I'd rather love you / She's too good to be true / Did you think to pray / Mississippi cotton picking delta town / Hope you're feelin' me (like I'm feelin' you) / I'm just me / Amazing love / Don't fight the feelings of love / Shoulder to cry on, A / All his children / We could.
LP: PL 42178
MC: PK 42178

I'M GONNA LOVE HER ON THE RADIO.
Tracks: / I'm gonna love her on the radio / She's soft to touch / Your used to be / Come on in and let me love you / There ain't lovin' / Little piece of Heaven, A / If we're just killing time (Let's love it to death).
LP: RITZLP 0048
MC: RITZLC 048

I'M JUST ME.
Tracks: / On the Southbound / (In my world) you don't belong / You never gave up on me / I'd rather love you / Instant loneliness / I'm just me / Place for the lonesome, A / Hello darlin' / You're still the only one I'll ever love / That's my way.
LP: LSA 3050
MC: MPK 194

IN CONCERT WITH HOST CHARLEY PRIDE (See under In Concert) (Various artists).

IN PERSON.
Tracks: / Last thing on my mind / Just between you and me / I know one / Lovesick blues / Image of me, The / Kaw-liga / Shutters and boards / Six days on the road / Streets of Baltimore / Crystal chandeliers / Introduction by Po Bowell.
LP: INTS 5026
MC: INTK 5026
MC: NK 80996
LP: NL 80996
LP: LSA 3100
MC: PK 42007

JUST PLAIN CHARLEY.
Tracks: / Me and Bobby McGee / Good chance of tear fall tonight, A / One time / (I'm so) Afraid of losing you again / Brand new bed of roses, A / That's why I love you so much / If you'd have only taken the time / Gone, gone, gone / Happy Street / I'm a lonesome fugitive / It's all right.
LP: LSA 3146
MC: MPK 186

MAGIC MOMENTS WITH CHARLEY PRIDE.
Tracks: / Crystal chandeliers / Just between you and me / All I have to offer you is me / I'm so afraid of losing you again / Is anybody going to San Antone / Wonder could I live there anymore / I can't believe that you've stopped loving me / I'd rather love you / I'm just me / Kiss an angel good morning / Don't fight the feelings of love / Amazing love / Hope you're feelin' me (like I'm feelin' you) / Happiness of having you, The / My eyes can only see as far as you / She's just an old love turned memory / Someone loves you honey / Easy part's over, The / I know one / Kawliga / Does my ring hurt your finger / (there's still) someone I can't forget / Day the world stood still, The / Let the chips fall.
MC: NK 89621

MAKE MINE COUNTRY.
Tracks: / Now I can live again / Word or two to Mary, A / If you should come back today / Guess things happen that way / Before the next teardrop falls / Banks of the Ohio / Wings of a dove / Girl I used to know, A / Lie to me / Why didn't I think of that / Above and beyond / Baby is gone.
LP: LSA 3049
MC: MPK 181

NIGHT GAMES.
Tracks: / Draw the line / Love on a blue rainy day / Late show, The / Night games / Down in Louisiana / Ev'ry heart should have one / Thanks for wakin' me up this mornin' / Lovin' it up (livin' it down) / Just can't leave that woman alone / I could let her get close to me.
LP: PL 84822
MC: PK 84822

POWER OF LOVE.
LP: PL 85031
MC: PK 85031

PRIDE OF AMERICA.
Tracks: / Then who am I / I still can't leave your memory alone / Hard times will be the best times, The / Completely helpless / Mississippi cotton picking delta town / She loves me the way that I love you / Mary go round / That was forever ago / Thorns of life / North wind.
LP: LSA 3202
MC: MPK 236

PRIDE OF COUNTRY MUSIC.
Tracks: / In the middle nowhere / Last thing on my mind / Just between you and me / Apartment No.9 / Spell of the freight train / I know one / I'm not the boy I used to be / Good woman's love, A / Silence / Take me home / Touch my heart / Best banjo picker.
LP: LSA 3144
MC: MPK 184

ROLL ON MISSISSIPPI.
Tracks: / Roll on, Mississippi, roll on / I used to be that way / Taking the easy way out / She's as good as gone / He can be an angel / Fall back on me / Make it special again / You beat 'em all / Ghost written love letters / You almost slipped my mind.
LP: RCALP 5019
MC: RCAK 5019

SENSATIONAL CHARLEY PRIDE.
Tracks: / Louisiana man / She's still got a hold on you / Let the chips fall / Come on home and sing the blues to Daddy / Never more than I / Let me live / Take care of the little things / Even after everything's she's done / (It's just a matter of) making up my mind / It's the little things / Billy Bayou / We had all the good things going.
LP: PL 42023
MC: PK 42023

SHE'S JUST AN OLD LOVE TURNED MEMORY.
Tracks: / She's just an old love turned memory / Rhinestone cowboy / Hunger, The / Whole lotta things to sing about, A / I feel the country callin' me / I'll be leaving alone / We need lovin' / Country music / Rose is for today, The / Get up off your good intentions.
LP: PL 12261
MC: PK 12261

SOMEONE LOVES YOU HONEY.
Tracks: / Someone loves you honey / Georgia keeps pulling on my ring / I love you / Play, guitar, play / Another 'I love you' kind of day / More to me / Days of our lives / Daydreams about night things / Heaven watches over fools like me / Days of sand and shovels, The.
LP: PL 12478
MC: PK 12478

SONGS OF LOVE BY CHARLEY PRIDE.
Tracks: / Too weak to let you go / She's too good to be true / She's that kind / You were all the good in me / Give a lonely heart a home / Good hearted woman / I love you more in memory / My love is deep, my love is wide / (Darlin' think of me) every now and then / I'm building bridges.
LP: LSA 3155

SONGS OF PRIDE.
Tracks: / Someday you will / She made me go / Right to do wrong, The / Easy part's over, The / Day you stop loving me, The / I could have saved you the time / One of these days / All the time / My heart is a house / Let me help you work it out / Both of us love you / Top of the world, The.
MC: PK 42015
LP: PL 42015

SUNDAY MORNING WITH CHARLEY PRIDE.
Tracks: / I don't deserve a mansion / Be grateful / He's the man / In Jesus' name I pray / Without mama here / Little Delta church / Next year finally came / Jesus is your saviour child / He took my place / Brush arbour meeting.
LP: LSA 3267

SWEET COUNTRY.
Tracks: / Along the Mississippi / Happiest song on the jukebox, The / Shelter of your eyes, The / I'm learning to love her / Don't fight the feelings of love / Just to be loved by you / Tennessee girl / Love unending / Pass me by / Shoulder to cry on, A.
LP: LSA 3181
MC: MPK 214

THAT'S MY WAY.
LP: CDS 1166
MC: CAM 1166

THERE'S A LITTLE BIT OF HANK IN ME.
Tracks: / There's a little bit of Hank in me / My son calls another man daddy / Moanin' the blues / Mansion on the hill / Mind your own business / I can't help it / Honky tonk blues / I'm so lonesome I could cry / Low down blues / I could never be ashamed of you / Why don't you love me / You win again.
LP: PL 13548

TO ALL MY WONDERFUL FANS FROM ME TO YOU.
Tracks: / That's the only way life's good to me / I can't believe that you've stopped loving me / There's still someone I can't forget / Sweet promises / Was it all worth losing you / Fifteen years ago / Wonder could I live there anymore / Piroque Joe / Time (you're not a friend of mine) / Today is that tomorrow.
LP: LSA 3147

VERY BEST OF CHARLEY PRIDE, THE.

Tracks: / I'd rather love you / Is anybody going to San Antone / I'm so afraid of losing you again / Kiss an angel good morning / Just between you and me / All I have to offer you is me / Wonder could I live there anymore / I can't believe that you're stopped loving me / I'm just me / Crystal chandeliers / Amazing love / Happiness of having you, The / Easy part's over, The / I know one / Does my ring hurt your finger / For the good times / Kaw-liga / My eyes can only see as far as you / She's just an old love turned memory / Someone loves you honey.
LP: RCALP 5049
MC: RCAK 5049
MC: PK 89088
LP: PL 89088

YOU'RE MY JAMAICA.
Tracks: / What're we doing, doing this again / No relief in sight / Playin' around / Missin' you / You're my Jamaica / Heartbreak mountain / To have and to hold / Let me have a chance to love you / I want you / When the good times outweighed the bad.
MC: PK 13441
LP: PL 13441

Pride, Lou

GONE BAD AGAIN.
Tracks: / Gone bad again / So far away / Been so long / I didn't take your woman / I found a love / We're only fooling ourselves / Very special / I'm not through loving you.
LP: CUR 2009
MC: CURMC 2009

I WAS BORN TO LOVE YOU.
MC: SPAR 003

Pride Of Erin Ceili

HARVEST TIME IN IRELAND.
MC: COX 1036

Pride Of London Big

GEE WHIZ.
LP: ISST 177

Pride of Murray Pipe

BEST OF SCOTTISH PIPES AND DRUMS.
LP: EULP 1164
MC: EUMC 1164

Pride & Prejudice (bk)

PRIDE AND PREJUDICE (See under Austen, Jane) (Johnson, Celia (nar)).

PRIDE AND PREJUDICE (See under Austen, Jane) (Sutcliffe, Irene (nar)).

PRIDE AND PREJUDICE (See under Austen, Jane) (Bloom, Claire (nar)).

PRIDE & PREJUDICE (see Austen, Jane) (Sutcliffe, Irene (nar)).

PRIDE & PREJUDICE (see Austen, Jane) (Bloom, Claire (nar)).

PRIDE & PREJUDICE (see Austen, Jane) (Johnson, Celia (nar)).

Pride & The Passion

PRIDE & THE PASSION, THE (Film Soundtrack) (Various artists).
LP: AUSLP 1005

Priest, Maxi

BONAFIDE.
Tracks: / Just a little bit longer / Close to you / Never did say goodbye / Best of me, The / Space in my heart / Human work of art / Temptress / Peace throughout the world / You / Sure fire love / Life / Prayer for the world.
LP: DIX 92
MC: CDIX 92

INTENTIONS.
Tracks: / Love train / Woman in you / Crazy love / Jehovan / Cry me a river / Strollin' on / Pretty little girl / Let me know / Festival time / Must be a way.
LP: DIX 32
MC: CDIX 32
LP: OVED 337
MC: OVEDC 337

MAXI.
Tracks: / Wild world / Suzie - you are / Goodbye to love again / You're only human / Same old story / Marcus / How can we ease the pain / It ain't easy / Some guys have all the luck / Problems (CD & Cassette only) / Reasons (CD & Cassette only).
2LP: DIXG 64
LP: DIX 64
MC: CDIX 64
MC: CDIXG 64
LP: OVED 347

YOU'RE SAFE.
Tracks: / Should I / Hey little girl / Dancin' mood / Sensi / Caution / Stand up and fight / In the Springtime / Fatty fatty / You're safe / Throw me corn.
LP: DIX 11
MC: CDIX 11
LP: OVED 284
MC: OVEDC 284

Priest Of Love

PRIEST OF LOVE (film soundtrack) (Various artists).
Tracks: / Lawrence: *Various artists* / English hotel trio: *Various artists* / Variations: *Various artists*/ Mabel's tango: *Various artists* / Frieda's theme (part 1): *Various artists* / Frieda's theme (part 2): *Various* artists / Italy: *Various artists* / Cornwall: *Various artists* / Fugue: *Various artists* / Lawrence's death: *Various artists* / Priest of love (finale): *Various artists* / Way we get it together, The: *Various artists.*
LP: TER 1014
LP: DSLP 1003

Priestley, Brian

LOVE YOU GLADLY dedicated to the Duke (Priestley, Brian Special Septet).
Tracks: / Everything but you / Mooche, The / Ducalypso / Mood indigo / Band call / Blooz for dook / Downtown uproar / Love you gladly / Angelica.
LP: SGC 1021

Prima Dona

PRIMA DONA.
LP: COB 37018

Prima, Louis

ANGELINA.
Tracks: / Oh Marie / Hey boy hey girl / Pennies from Heaven / San Fernando Valley / Do a little business on the side / Kentucky / That's how much I love you / Stella by starlight / Buona sera / Angelina / Lip, The / Sleepy time gal / Bacci goldo / It takes time / Roses in the rain / Chinatown.
MC: 40183
LP: 20180

BEST OF LOUIS PRIMA.
Tracks: / Buona sera / Angelina / Oh Marie / Hey boy.
LP: 1A 022 8158
MC: 1A 222 8158

BUONA SERA.
Tracks: / Buona sera.
MC: ENT MC 13026

CALL OF THE WILDEST, THE.
Tracks: / When you're smiling / Sheik of Araby, The / Autumn leaves / I've got the world on a string / Blow red blow / Pump song, The / Pennies from Heaven / Birth of the blues / Closest to the bone.
MC: JAS C306
LP: JAS 306

HEY BOY, HEY GIRL (Prima, Louis and Keely Smith).
Tracks: / Hey boy, hey girl / Banana split for my baby, A / You are my love / Fever / Oh Marie / Lazy river / Nitey-nite / When the saints go marching in / Autumn leaves.
LP: T 1160

JIMMIE LUNCEFORD & LOUIS PRIMA 1945 (see Lunceford, Jimmie) (Prima, Louis/Jimmie Lunceford).

JUMP, JIVE AN' WAIL.
Tracks: / Jump, jive and wail / Oh Marie / You rascal you (I'll be glad when you're dead) / Buona sera / I've got the world on a string / Fee fie foo / Gigolo / I ain't got nobody / Pennies from Heaven / Angelina / Zooma zooma / Don't worry bout me / I'm in the mood for love / Them there eyes / Honeysuckle rose / Ya gotta see baby tonight.
MC: TCCRB 1116
LP: CRB 1116

JUST A GIGOLO 1945 - 50 (Prima, Louis & His Orchestra).
LP: BS 7139
MC: BS 7139C

LIVE FROM LAS VEGAS.
Tracks: / Oh Marie / Buona sera / Imagination / I love Paris / Up jumped the rabbit / Georgia on my mind / I want you to be my baby / Baby won't you please come home / When the saint's go marching' in / Cold cold heart / Robin Hood / Going to Kansas City / Goody goody / Tiger rag / Night train / That old black magic / Sing sing sing.
LP: EB 406

LOUIS PRIMA AND KEELY SMITH (Prima, Louis & Keely Smith).
LP: ENT LP 13026

LOUIS PRIMA WITH KEELY SMITH GREATEST HITS.
MC: 4XL 9277

PLAY IT PRETTY FOR THE PEOPLE (Prima, Louis/his big Band).
LP: GELP 15055

PLAYS PRETTY FOR THE PEOPLE.
LP: MASO 120003

REMEMBER.
Tracks: / Robin Hood / Saint Louis blues / I'll walk alone / Angeline / Some Sunday morning / I don't wanna be loved / You gotta see baby tonight / White cliffs of Dover, The / Just a gigolo / I aint got nobody.
LP: AWE 12

STRICTLY PRIMA (Prima, Louis with Sam Butera & The Witnesses).
Tracks: / If you were the only girl in the world / Judy / 5 months, 2 weeks, 2 days / That's my home / Sing, sing, sing / Gotta see baby tonight / Felicia no capacia / Moonglow / Bourbon Street blues / Fie fie foo.
LP: EMS 1135
MC: TCEMS 1135
LP: EMS 12135

WILDEST SHOW AT TAHOE, THE (Prima, Louis and Keely Smith).
LP: PM 155 299-1
MC: PM 155 299-4

WILDEST, THE.
Tracks: / Just a gigolo / I ain't got nobody / Nothing's too good for my baby / Lip, The / Body and soul / Five months, two weeks, two days / Basin street blues / When it's sleepy time down South / Jump, jive and wail / Buona sera / Night train / You rascal you.
LP: 2C 062 80271
MC: 2C 244 80271
LP: JAS 300
MC: JAS C300

Prima Tanz Musik

PRIMA TANZ MUSIK (Various artists).
LP: 1040 232
MC: 1640 232

Primal Scream

PRIMAL SCREAM.
Tracks: / Imperial / Gentle Tuesday / Silent spring / Rock / Country / I love you / Leaves / Tomorrow ends today / Aftermath / Sunshine bright / What's the matter?.
LP: ELV 2
MC: ELV 2 C
LP: CRELP 054
MC: CREC 054

SCREAMADELIC.
2LP: CRELP 076
MC: CCRELP 076

SONIC FLOWER GROOVE.
LP: WLV 2
MC: WLV 2C

Primary Industry

ULTRAMARINE.
LP: SAX 015

Prime Design

TIME DESIGN.
LP: CDP 85002

Prime Movers

MATTERS OF TIME (Prime Movers, Boston).
LP: CLO 059

SINS OF THE FOREFATHERS.
LP: CND 1

Prime Time

BABY CONFESS IT.
Tracks: / Guilty / What's that you slipped into my wine / I bet 'cha / Sex-o-logical / Confess it baby / Baby don't break my back / Come into my love life / Give me a chance / Remote control.
LP: FL 85712
MC: FK 85712

Primer, John

CHICAGO BLUES SESSION 6.
LP: WOLF 120.852

Primevals

CHICKEN FACTORY.
LP: GPR 127

ETERNAL HOTFIRE.
LP: ROSE 47

LIVE A LITTLE.
Tracks: / St. Jack / Justify / Cottonhead / Fertile mind / Prairie chain / Heya / Sister.
LP: ROSE 123
MC: ROSE 123C

NEON OVEN - LIVE AT THE REX, PARIS.
LP: DISPLP 21

SOUND HOLE.
LP: ROSE 80

Primitives

LAZY 86-88.
Tracks: / Thru the flower (originals) / Lazy / (We've) found the way to the sun / Stop killing me / Laughing up my sleeve / Thru the flowers / She don't need you / Across my shoulder / Really stupid / Where the wind blows / Buzz buzz buzz / Shadow (guitar version) / Everything shining bright.
LP: LAZY 15
MC: LAZY 15C

LOVELY.
Tracks: / Crash / Spacehead / Carry me home / Shadow / Thru' the flowers / Dreamwalk baby / I'll stick with you / Nothing left / Stop killing me / Out of reach / Ocean blue / Run, baby, run / Don't want anything to change / Buzz buzz buzz.
LP: PL 71688
MC: PK 71688

PRIMITIVES: INTERVIEW PICTURE DISC.
LPPD: BAK 2130

PURE.
Tracks: / Outside / Summer rain / Sick of it / Shine / Dizzy heights / All the way down / I'll be your mirror / Secrets / Keep me in mind / Lonely streets / Can't bring me down / Way behind me / Never tell / Noose / All the way down (beat version) (CD only.) / I almost touched you (CD only.).
LP: PL 74252
MC: PK 74252

Primitons

HAPPY ALL THE TIME.
Tracks: / On or off the bus / Deception / Don't go away / Gabriel / Happy / Riddle / You are learning / Pope, The / Little wail.
LP: GOES ON 09

Primo Scala

SING AS WE GO.
Tracks: / Whistling waltz, The / At the close of a long long day / When did you leave heaven / Little man you've had a busy day / I dream of San Marino / Love thy neighbour / Three of us / There's a home in Wyomin' / Sing as we go / Street in old Seville, A / One night in Napoli / Wheel of the wagon is broken, The / Lonely villa / I want to hear those old time melodies / Tonight / Shoe shine boy.
LP: BUR 012
MC: 4 BUR 012

Primrose, Christine

S TU NAM CHUIMNHE.
LP: TP 024
MC: CTP 024

Primus

FRIZZLE FRY.
Tracks: / To defy the laws of tradition / Too many puppies / Frizzle fry / You can't kill Michael Malloy / Pudding time / Spaghetti western / To defy / Ground hog's day / Mr. Knowitall / John the fisherman / Toys go winding down, The / Sathington Willoby / Harold of the rocks.
LP: CARLP 10
MC: CARC 10

Prince

1999.
Tracks: / 1999 / Little red corvette / Delirious / Let's pretend we're married / D.M.S.R. / Automatic / Something in the water / Free / Lady cab driver / All the critics love you in New York / International lover.
2LP: 923720 1
MCSET: 923720 4
LP: W 3809

AROUND THE WORLD IN A DAY.
Tracks: / Around the world in a day / Paisley Park / Condition of the heart / Raspberry beret / Tambourine / America / Pop life / Ladder, The / Temptation.
LP: 925286 1
MC: 925286 4

BATMAN (Film soundtrack).
Tracks: / Future, The / Electric chair / Arms of orion, The / Partyman / Vicking waiting / Trust / Lemon crush / Scandalous / Batdance.
LP: WX 281
MC: WX 281C

CONTROVERSY.
Tracks: / Private joy / Ronnie talk to Russia / Let's work / Annie Christian / Jack u off / Sexuality / Controversy / Do my baby.
LP: K 56950

DIRTY MIND.
Tracks: / Dirty mind / When you were mine / Do it all night / Gotta broken heart again / Uptown / Head / Sister / Party up.
LP: K 56862
MC: K4 56862

FOR YOU.
Tracks: / For you / In love / Soft and wet / Crazy you / Just as long as we're together / Baby / My love is forever / So blue / I'm yours.
LP: K 56989
MC: K4 56989

GETT OFF (Prince & The New Power Generation).
LP: 9401382

GRAFFITI BRIDGE (Original Soundtrack).

Tracks: / Can't stop this feeling / Question of U, The / Round and round / Joy in rejection / Tick, tick, bang / Thieves in the temple / Melody cool / Graffiti bridge / Release it / Elephants and flowers / We can funk / Love machine / Shake / Latest fashion, The / Still would stand all time / New power generation (part II).
LP: WX 361
MC: WX 361 C

KISSES 4 U.
MC: MBAK 6013

LOVESEXY.
Tracks: / I no / Alphabet Street / Glam slam / Anna Stesia / Dance on / Lovesexy / When 2 r in love / I wish U heaven / Positivity.
LP: WX 164
MC: WX 164C

MUSIC AND MEDIA INTERVIEW PICTURE DISC.
LPPD: PRINCE 1001

PARADE (Original soundtrack) (Prince & The Revolution).
Tracks: / Christopher Tracey's parade / New position / I wonder u / Under the cherry moon / Girls and boys / Life can be so nice / Venus de Milo / Mountains / Do u lie / Kiss / Anotherloverholenyohead / Sometimes it snows in April.
LP: WX 39
MC: WX 39C

PRINCE.
Tracks: / I wanna be your lover / Why do you want to treat me so bad / Sexy dancer / When we're dancing / With you / Bambi / Still waiting / I feel for you / It's gonna be lonely.
LP: K 56772
MC: K4 56772

PRINCE: INTERVIEW PICTURE DISC.
LPPD: BAK 2056

PURPLE RAIN (Film soundtrack) (Prince & The Revolution).
Tracks: / Let's go crazy / Take me with u / Beautiful ones / Computer blue / Darling Nikki / When doves cry / I would die 4 u / Baby I'm a star / Purple rain.
LP: 925110 1
MC: 925110 4

SIGN OF THE TIMES.
Tracks: / Play in the sunshine / Housequake / Ballad of Dorothy Parker / It / Starfish and coffee / Slow love / Hot thing / Forever in my life / U got the look / If I was your girlfriend / Strange relationship / I could never take the place of your man / Cross, The / It's gonna be a beautiful night / Adore.
2LP: WX 88
MCSET: WX 88C

Prince At Black..(bk)

PRINCE AT BLACK PONY INN.
MCSET: DTO 10546

Prince Attila's

PRINCE ATTILA'S JOURNEY (Various artists).
Tracks: / Prince Attila's journey: *Various artists* / King, the dog and the golden bowl, The: *Various artists*/ Lady who came out of a cupboard, The: *Various artists* / Poor birdcatcher, The: *Various artists*.
MC: ANV 609

Prince Barakadi

PRINCE BARAKADI.
LP: AP 006

Prince Buster

BIG FIVE.
LP: SKABBLP 3
MC: SKABBMC 3

FABULOUS GREATEST HITS.
Tracks: / Earthquake / Texas hold-up / Freezing up Orange Street / Free love / Julie / Take it easy / Judge dread / Too hot / Ghost dance / Ten commandments / Al Capone / Barrister pardon.
LP: SPLP 007
MC: SPLC 007
LP: MSCD 1
MC: MSLC 1

JUDGE DREAD.
LP: BBLP 809

JUDGE DREAD, ROCK STEADY.
LP: SKABBLP 4
MC: SKABBMC 4

MEMORY LANE.
LP: TC 1002

ORIGINAL GOLDEN OLDIES VOL 1.
LP: PB 9
MC: PBLC 9

ORIGINAL GOLDEN OLDIES VOL 2.
LP: PB 10
MC: PBLC 10

PRINCE BUSTER ON TOUR.
LP: SKABBLP 1
MC: SKABBMC 1

PRINCE BUSTER'S FABULOUS GREATEST HITS.
LP: MS 1

SHE WAS A ROUGH RIDER.
LP: BBLP 820
LP: SKABBLP 2
MC: SKABBMC 2

WRECK A PUM PUM.
LP: BBLP 821

Prince Charles

COMBAT ZONE (Prince Charles & The City Beat Band).
Tracks: / Stone cold killers / More money / Jailhouse rock / I need you / Skintight Tina / I want (to satisfy you) / City life / Combat zone.
LP: OVED 145
MC: OVEDC 145

STONE KILLERS (Prince Charles & The City Beat Band).
Tracks: / Don't fake the funk / Cash (cash money) / Big chested girls / Cold as ice (NYC blues) / I'm a fool for love / Jungle stomp / Bush beat / Video freak (defend it).
LP: OVED 128
MC: OVEDC 128
MC: A 115
LP: V 2271

Prince Far-I

BLACKMAN LAND.
Tracks: / Message from the king / Dream, The / Reggae music moving / Black man land / Marble stone / Wish I have a wing / Armageddon / Commandment of drugs / Badda card / Moses Moses / Some with roof / Foggy road / Put it out / King of kings / Ghetto living / River of Jordan.
MC: FLC 9005

CRY TUFF DUB ENCOUNTER - CHAPTER III (Prince Far-I & The Arabs).
LP: DKLP 15

CRY TUFF DUB ENCOUNTER - CHAPTER IV (Prince Far-I & The Arabs).
Tracks: / Foundation stepper / Deadly command / Time stone turning / Sound gesture / Earth stone shake down / Stone Africa ground / Destruction sound battle.
LP: TRLS 205
MC: A 129

CRY TUFF DUB ENCOUNTER - CHAPTER II.
LP: FLX 4002

FREE FROM SIN.
Tracks: / Free from sin / When Jah ready you got to move / Call on I in trouble / Don't deal with the folly / Light of fire / Reggae music / Go home on the morning train / Siren / I and I are the chosen one.
LP: TRLS 175

JAMAICAN HEROES.
LP: TRLS 190

LIVITY.
Tracks: / Reggae music moving / Badda card / Some with roof / Marble stone / Put it out / King of kings / River Jordan / Ghetto living / Give me for my continent / Wish I have a wing.
LP: PREX 7

MUSICAL HISTORY.
LP: TRLS 214

SHOWCASE IN A SUITCASE.
Tracks: / Throw away your gun / Buds bush / How love divine / Lovers frock / If you want to know your friend / Farm drunk / Can't take su pon dread / Prince Far I dub / Mighty ruler / Jah do that.
LP: PREXF 003

SPEAR OF THE NATION (Umkhonto we sizwe).
Tracks: / Survival / Ask ask / African queen / Stop the war / Jerry doghead / Special request.
LP: KVL 9016
LP: TWLP 1013

UNDER HEAVY MANNERS.
LP: JGM 23

VOICE OF THUNDER.
Tracks: / Ten commandments / Tribute to Bob Marley / Hold the fort / Everytime I hear the word / Head of the Buccaneer / Shall not dwell in wickedness / Give I strength / Kingdom of God / Coming from the rock / Skinhead.
LP: TRLS 204

Prince Hammer

VENGEANCE.
LP: BCS 2

Prince Ivan

PRINCE IVAN AND THE FROG PRINCESS - A FAIRY TALE (Makarova, Natalia).
MC: 13491 6003 4

Prince Jammy

COMPUTERISED DUB.
Tracks: / Synchro start / Interface / 32 bit chip / Auto rhythm / Peek and poke / Megabyte / Wafer scale integration / Crosstalk / Modern / 256K ram.
LP: GREL 92

DUB WAR, VOL.1.
LP: VSLP 4039

HIS MAJESTY'S DUB (Prince Jammy & King Tubby).
LP: SJ 03

KAMIKAZI DUB.
Tracks: / Throne of blood / Brothers of the blade / Shoalin temple / Kamikaze / Oragami black belt / Fist of fury / Opium den / Swords of vengeance / Downtown Shangai rock / Waterfront gang war.
LP: TRLS 174

OSBOURNE IN DUB.
Tracks: / Loving tonight / Reggae stylee / Dance dub / Jah is with you / Chopping dub / Pumping dub / Double trouble / See no evil / Pure is the soul / Rise up.
LP: CSLP 10

PRESENTS MUSIC MAKER (Jammy, Prince & the Striker Lee Posse).
LP: DHS 005

PRINCE JAMMY DESTROYS THE INVADERS.
Tracks: / Conspiracy on Neptune / Martian encounter / Saturn bombardment / Attack on Ganymede / War in the asteroid belt / Great red spot, The / Life on Uranus / Final destruction.
LP: GREL 29

Prince Jazzbo

ITAL CORNER.
LP: LPCT 0103

Prince, Jesse

JUMP IT WITH A SHUFFLE.
Tracks: / Jump it with a shuffle / You satisfy / Froggy bottom / Kansas City mama / You can't take it with you / Whirly gig / Just another day wasted / Frettin' for some pettin' / Nagasaki / I'm the drummer man / That's the way she feels / Big town blues / My baby done left me / Tippin' out / Blue book boogie / Baby, let's be friends.
LP: JB 620

Prince Of Darkness

PRINCE OF DARKNESS (Film soundtrack) (Various artists).
LP: TER 1157
MC: ZCTER 1157

Prince Of The City

PRINCE OF THE CITY (Film soundtrack) (Various artists).
LP: TER 1012

Prince Of Wales...

YORKIES ON TOUR, THE (Prince Of Wales Yorkshire Regiment).
LP: MM 0574

Prince Regent

PRINCE REGENT (TV Soundtrack) (Various artists).
LP: SKL 5313
MC: KSKC 5313

Prince, Roland

COLOUR VISIONS.
Tracks: / Samba de unity / Iron band dance / Red pearl / Giant steps / Al don B / Eddie A / Genevieve.
LP: VSD 79371

Prince & The Pauper

PRINCE AND THE PAUPER (see Twain, Mark) (Unknown narrator(s)).

PRINCE AND THE PAUPER, THE (Various artists).
MC: VSC 5207

Prince & the Pekingese

PRINCE AND THE PEKINGNESE, THE (Barbara Cartland) (Rodska, Christian (nar)).
MC: IAB 88083

Princess

ALL FOR LOVE.
Tracks: / Red hot / Shoot the moon / Risky business / Where are the stars / I cannot carry on / Programmed to love you (CD & Cassette only) / All for love / Jammin' with your love / I wish you love.
LP: POLH 35
MC: POLHC 35

PRINCESS.
Tracks: / In the heat of a passionate moment / I'll keep on loving you / After the love has gone / Say I'm your number one / If it makes you feel good / Tell me tomorrow / Anytimes the right time / Just a tease.
LP: SU 1
MC: ZCSU 1

Princess &..

PRINCESS AND THE FROG (well loved tales age up to 9) (Unknown narrator(s)).
MC: PLB 64

PRINCESS AND THE GOBLIN (see MacDonald, George) (McBain, Rose).

PRINCESS AND THE PEA (well loved tales age up to 9) (Unknown narrator(s)).
MC: PLB 62

PRINCESS AND THE PEA/THE THREE MUSICIANS (Fullerton, Fiona).
MC: LP 202

Princess Bride (film)

PRINCESS BRIDE, THE (Film soundtrack) (Knopfler, Mark).
Tracks: / Once upon a time...storybook love / I will never love again / Florin dance / Morning ride / Friends' song, The / Cliffs of insanity, The / Sword fight, The / Guide my sword / Fire swamp and the rodents of unusual size, The / Revenge / Happy ending, A / Storybook love.
LP: VERH 53
MC: VERHC 53

PRINCESS BRIDE (THEME FROM) (See under Knopfler, Mark) (Knopfler, Mark).

Princess Ferozshah...

PRINCESS FEROZSHAH & THE HORSE PRINCE (Various artists).
Tracks: / Princess Ferozshah & The Horse Prince: *Various artists* / Weaver and the devh, The: *Various artists*/ Water carrier and the three walnuts, The: *Various artists* / Rustum and the iron fortress: *Various artists* / Shah's ring, The: *Various artists* / Magnificent slippers, The: *Various artists*.
MC: ANV 602

Princess Ida

PRINCESS IDA (See under Gilbert & Sullivan) (Various artists).

Princess Pang

PRINCESS PANG.
LP: RO 9471-1
MC: RO 9471-4

Princess Snowdrop

PRINCESS SNOWDROP (Various artists).
Tracks: / What a wonderful world we live in: *Various artists* / You're welcome: *Various artists* / Handful of flowers, A: *Various artists* / Poor little moon: *Various artists* / Always together: *Various artists*.
LP: ERON 018 LP
MC: ERON 018 CA

Principato, Tom

BLAZING TELECASTERS (Principato, Tom & Friends).
Tracks: / Honey hush (talkin' woman) / Blue mood / Quiet village / Cherokee / If you only knew / Didn't think twice / It's all right / Been 'n' gone.
LP: POW 4036
MC: POW 4036 MC

HOT STUFF.
Tracks: / Congo square / Rolene / Here I come / Blue lights / My baby worships me / Never make your love too soon / I know what your thinkin' / Try to reach you / Slipped, tripped, fell in love.
LP: POW 4106
MC: POW 4106MC

IN ORBIT (Principato, Tom & Powerhouse).
Tracks: / Nobody / In orbit / Arms around my honey / Deep in the heart of Texas / Same old blues / My baby don't love no-one but me / You slipped up / In a dream / You're not alone / All she wants to do is rock / Mama, your daughter lied.
LP: POW 4032
MC: POW 4032 MC

SMOKIN'.
Tracks: / Slipped, tripped and fell in love / My baby worships me / Blue mood / Lipstick, powder and paint / Fish dry / Here I come / Talkin' trash / I'm on fire / Well oh well / Hard livin'.
LP: EM 9608

Principle, Peter

REVAUX AU BONGO.
LP: MTM 2

SEDIMENTAL JOURNEY.
LP: MTM 4

TONE POEMS.
LP: MTM 18

Prine, John

AIMLESS LOVE.
Tracks: / Be my friend / Tonight / Aimless love / Me myself and I / Oldest baby in the world / Slow boat to China / Bottomless lake / Maureen Maureen / Somewhere, someone's falling in love /

People putting people down / Unwed fathers / Only love.
LP: FIEND 84
MC: OOBR 002

BRUISED ORANGE.
Tracks: / Fish and whistle / There she goes / If you don't want my love / That's the way the world goes round / Bruised orange / Sabu visits the twin cities alone / Aw heck / Crooked piece of time / Iron ore Betty / Hobo song, The.
LP: K 53084

DIAMONDS IN THE ROUGH.
Tracks: / Everybody / Torch singer, The / Souvenirs / Late John Garfield blues, The / Sour grapes / Billy the bum / Frying pan / Yes I guess they oughta name a drink after you / Take the star out of the window / Great compromise, The / Clocks and spoons / Rocky mountain time / Diamonds in the rough.
LP: K 40427

GERMAN AFTERNOONS.
Tracks: / I just want you to dance with me / Love love love / Bad boys / They'll never take her love from me / Paradise / Lulu walls / Speed of the sound of loneliness / Sailin' around / If she were you / Linda goes to Mars.
LP: FIEND 103

JOHN PRINE LIVE.
Tracks: / Come back to us Barbara Lewis / Hare Krishna beauregard / Six o'clock news / Oldest baby in the world / Angel from Montgomery / Grandpa was a carpenter / Blue umbrella / Fish and whistle / Sabru visits the twin cities alone / Living in the future / Illegal smile / Mexican home / Speed of the sound of lonliness / Accident (things could be worse) / Sam Stone / Souvenirs / Aw heck / Donald and Lynda / That's the way the world goes round.
MC: OBRC 005
2LP: OBR 005

PINK CADILLAC.
Tracks: / Chinatown / Automobile / Killing the blues / No name girl / Saigon / Cold war / Baby let's play house / Down by the side of the road / How lucky / Ubangi stomp.
LP: K 52164

SWEET REVENGE.
LP: K 40524

Pringle, Chris

SPIRIT OF FAITH.
MC: MYR C 1199

Prinknash Abbey...

MUSIC FROM PRINKNASH ABBEY (Prinknash Abbey Monks).
Tracks: / Introit / Alleluia / Christe Redemptor / Vexilla regis / Veni creator spiritus / Adore Te devote / Virgo dei genitrix / Ave Maria / Montes gelboe / Ave verum corpus / Salve Regina / Magnificat / Compline / Blessed be the God and Father / Angel came and stood at the altar, An / Christ our Saviour / Into the silence of our hearts / Eternal living Lord of all / Spiritus Domini / I thank you, Lord, with all my heart / We greet you, Holy Queen / God is for us a refuge and strength.
LP: SDL 330
MC: CSDL 330

O GIVE THANKS TO THE LORD (Prinknash Abbey Monks/Stanbrook Abbey Nuns).
Tracks: / Gaudeamus / Mass - Cum jubilo / Media vita / Music from Compline / Keep in your minds / Like as the deer / Let all creation / Into your hands / To the lamb of God / O give thanks unto the Lord / Daughter of the king, The / Send forth Your Spirit / Alleluia / Te Deum.
LP: SDL 349
MC: CSDL 349

Prior, Andy

SHOT IN THE DARK, A (Prior, Andy & His Night Owls).
Tracks: / River stay away from my door / Hot toddy / Nightingale sang in Berkeley Square, A / Naked gun / I wish I were in love again / South Rampart Street parade / That old black magic / Too little time / Peter Gunn / Putting on the Ritz / Dragnet / Where or when / Warm breeze, A / Mack the knife / Victor and Hugo / Serenade in blue / Pennsylvania 6-5-0-0-0 / Learning the blues.
LP: CMV 1001
MC: CMT 1001

Prior, Maddy

CHANGING WINDS.
Tracks: / To have and to hold / Pity the poor / Night porter / Bloomers / Accappella Stella / Canals / Sovereign prince, The / Ali Baba / Mountain, The / In fighting / Another drink.
LP: CHR 1203
MC: ZCHR 1203

GOING FOR GLORY (Prior, Maddy & The Answers).
LP: SPIN 104

HAPPY FAMILIES (ALBUM) (Prior, Maddy & Rick Kemp).
LP: PRKA 4
MC: PRKC 4

HOOKED ON WINNING (Prior, Maddy Band).
Tracks: / Hooked on winning / Anthem to failure / Long holiday / Nothing but the best.
LP: PLR 036

SILLY SISTERS (Prior, Maddy & June Tabor).
Tracks: / Burnin' o'Auchidoon / Lass of roch royal / Seven joys of Mary, The / My husband's got no courage in him / Singing the travels / Silver whistle / Grey funnel line / Geordie / Seven wonders / Four loom weaver / Game of cards, The / Dame Durden.
LP: CHR 1101

SING FOLK SONGS OF OLD ENGLAND VOL.2 (see Hart, Tim & Maddy Prior) (Prior, Maddy & Tim Hart).

SING LUSTILY AND WITH GOOD COURAGE (Prior, Maddy & The Carnival Band).
Tracks: / Who would true valour see / As pants the hart / How firm a foundation / Light of the world / O worship the king / O for a thousand tongues / Lo he comes.
MC: CSDL 383

SUMMER SOLSTICE (see Hart, Tim) (Prior, Maddy & Tim Hart).

TAPESTRY OF CAROLS, A (Prior, Maddy & The Carnival Band).
Tracks: / Sans Day carol / In dulci jubilo / God rest ye merry, gentlemen / It came upon a midnight clear / Holly and the ivy, The / Coventry carol / Ding dong merrily on high / Angel Gabriel, The / Angels from the realms of glory / Infant Holy / Virgin most pure, A / Unto us a boy is born / Rejoice and be merry / Joseph dearest / Personent Hodie / On Christmas night (Sussex Carol.).
LP: SDL 366
MC: CSDL 366

WOMAN IN THE WINGS.
Tracks: / Woman in the wings / Cold flame / Mother and child / Gutter geese / Rollercoaster / Deep water / Long shadows / I told you so / Rosettes / Cats' eyes / Baggy pants.
LP: CHR 1185
MC: ZCHR 1185

Prior, Snooky

CHICAGO BLUES SESSION 1.
LP: WOLF 120 847

SHAKE YOUR BOOGIE.
LP: BRP 2033

Prism

ARMAGEDDON.
Tracks: / Coming home / Jealousy / Virginia / You walked away again / Take it or leave it / Armageddon / Night to remember / Mirror man.
LP: EST 12051

SMALL CHANGE.
Tracks: / Don't let him know / Turn on your radar / Hole in paradise / Rain / When will I see you again / Heart and soul / When love goes wrong / In the jailhouse now / Wings of your love.
LP: EST 12184

YOUNG AND RESTLESS.
Tracks: / American music / Young and restless / Satellite / Party lime / Acid rain / Here comes another world / Visitor / Deception / Hideaway / Runnin' for cover.
LP: EST 12072

Prison

PRISON (Film soundtrack) (Various artists).
LP: STV 81361

Prison Work Songs

PRISON WORK SONGS (Various artists).
LP: ARHOOLIE 2012

Prisonaires

FIVE BEATS BEHIND BARS.
LP: CR 30176

Prisoner

PRISONER, THE (Original TV soundtrack) (Various artists).
Tracks: / Arrival: *Various artists* / A,B and C: *Various artists* / Free for all: *Various artists* / General, The: *Various artists* / Many happy returns: *Various artists* / Dance of the dead: *Various artists*/ Checkmate: *Various artists* / Hammer into anvil: *Various artists* / Girl who was death, The: *Various artists*/ Once upon a time: *Various artists* / Prisoner, The (closing credits): *Various artists* / Arrival 2: *Various artists* / Chimes: *Various artists.*
LP: KIRI 066
LP: FILM 042
MC: FILMC 042

Prisoner Of A Promise

PRISONER OF A PROMISE (see Tilbury, Quenna) (Spouse, Isobel).

Prisoner Of Zenda

PRISONER OF ZENDA (BK) (see under Hope, Anthony) (Jacobi, Derek (nar)).

Prisoners

IN FROM THE COLD.
Tracks: / More that I teach you,The / Wish the rain / Find and seek / Mourn my health / Ain't no telling / Lesser evil, The / All you gotta do is say / Be on your way / I know how to please you / Deceiveng eye / Come closer / In from the cold.
LP: DOWN 2

LAST FOURFATHERS, THE/ TASTE OF PINK, A.
LP: OWN-UP U2

LAST NIGHT AT THE MIC CLUB, THE (see under Milkshakes) (Prisoners & Milkshakes).

MILKSHAKES V PRISONERS LIVE (see under Milkshakes) (Prisoners & Milkshakes).

RARE AND UNISSUED.
LP: HANG 23 UP

WISERMISERDEMELZA, THE.
Tracks: / Go go / Hurricane / Somewhere / Think of me / Love me lies / Tonight / Here come the misunderstood / Dream is gone, The / For now and forever / Unbeliever, The / Far away.
LP: WIK 19

Pritchard, Bill

BILL PRITCHARD.
Tracks: / Black souls under white skies / Sheltered life / Pas de plaisanterie / White city / Arsenic and old lace / Dimanche soir / Grey parade / Greek street / Impact of the cities.
LP: TMLP 19

HALF A MILLION.
LP: TMLP 23

JOLIE.
LP: BIAS 176
MC: BIAS 176MC

THREE MONTHS, THREE WEEKS AND TWO DAYS.
Tracks: / Tommy & co. / Invisible state / Sometimes / Pillow talk / Cosy evenings / We were lovers / Romance sans paroles / Je n'attendais que toi / Nineteen / Kenneth Baker / Better to be bitter.
LP: BIAS 106

Pritchard, Chris

SWEET ROTHIE VALE (Pritchard, Chris & Terry Taylor).
MC: CWGR 018

Private Eye

PRIVATE EYE.
Tracks: / What do you want from me / Your place or mine / Good girl gone bad / Beneath the wheels / Changes / I hate to tell you / Everybody knows / Stay until the morning / Come my way.
LP: EST 11980

Private Investigations

P.I. PRIVATE INVESTIGATIONS (See under P.I.).

Private, Jo

DU SWING AU MUSETTE.
Tracks: / La Marseillaise / Mains de velours / Love for sale / Caravane gitane / Montagne St,Genevieve / Undecided / Mister 'B' / Romanella / Poinciana / Swing-Charleston / Confessin' / Douce ambiance.
LP: 742069

Private Life

SHADOWS.
Tracks: / Put out the fire / Last heartbeat / Don't blame it on love / Don't let go / Rockabye angel / Spirit free / Hold on / Runnin' the race / Spider (the funk tune) / Amazing grace.
LP: 925803 1
MC: 925803 4

Private Lives

PREJUDICE AND PRIDE.
Tracks: / From a river to a sea / No chance you'll pay / Living in a world / Stop / God only knows / Break the chains / Don't wanna cry / Win / Break the whole thing down / Prejudice and pride.
LP: LIV 1
MC: TCLIV 1
LP: EJ2401361

PRIVATE LIVES Coward, Noel (Various artists).
MC: TCC/NCW1

PRIVATE LIVES (Coward, Noel) (Scofield, Paul/Fenella Fielding/ Margoles/Routledge).
MC: TTC/NCW1

Private Popsicle

PRIVATE POPSICLE (Film Soundtrack) (Various artists).
LP: CBS 70235
MC: 40 70235

Privates On Parade

PRIVATES ON PARADE (Original London Cast) (Various artists).
LP: EMC 3233

Privilege

PRIVILEGE (FILM) (See 'Flashback to the sixties') (Various artists).

Pro Arte Orchestra

TRIBUTE TO ERIC COATES.
LP: NCP 705
MC: ZCNCP 705

Probert, George

INCREDIBLE, THE.
LP: GHB 70

Problem Children

LONG WEEKEND.
LP: EFA 15118

Problemist

NINE TIMES SANITY.
LP: SSLP 007

Proby, P.J.

BEST OF P.J.PROBY VOL.1.
MC: SEEK 72

BEST OF P.J.PROBY VOL.2.
MC: SEEK 82

CLOWN SHOES.
Tracks: / She's helping me get over you / Handsome guy / Memories of you / Cinderella's fool / Ain't gonna kiss ya / In a moment / What did I do to you / Like all the times before / Hold me / Tonight / Clown shoes / Place for girls like you, A / Life you offered me, The / Maria / Somewhere / I apologise / Niki Hoeky.
LP: MTM 026

I'M P.J. PROBY.
LP: LBY 1235

LEGENDARY P.J. AT HIS VERY BEST, THE , VOL.2.
Tracks: / Rockin' pneumonia and the boogie woogie flu / Masquerade is over, The / I'll go crazy / You don't love me no more / Just call and I'll be there / Cuttin' in / Hold me / Together / Nicki hoeky / Honey hush / Butterfly high / She's looking good / You can't come home again (if you leave me now) / Pretty girls everywhere / Hold what you've got / Sweet summer wine / That's the tune / Work with me Annie.
LP: SEE 82

LEGENDARY P.J. PROBY AT HIS VERY BEST.
Tracks: / When love has passed you by / I'm coming home / Give me time / Turn her away / Why baby why / I've got my eyes on you / I apologise baby / Somewhere / That means a lot / Maria / Rain on snow / My prayer / To make a big man cry / I can't make it alone / What's wrong with my world / Day Lorraine came down, The / Today I killed a man I didn't know / Zing went the strings of my heart.
LP: SEE 72

SOMEWHERE.
Tracks: / Somewhere / Just call, and I'll be there / Que sera sera / Stagger Lee / Linda Lu / Together / Rockin' pneumonia and the boogie woogie flu / Glory of love / Masquerade is over, The / Zing went the strings of my heart / Question / Hold me.
LP: EG 2606291
MC: EG 2606294

THANKS.
Tracks: / Someone from somewhere / Sentimental over you / Thanks / I'm alright / Stage of fools / Wherever you are / Love song to you / I will always be in love with you / I will be your mountain / I'm alright (extended mix) / Stage of fools (narration).
MC: TTON.001 LMC

THREE WEEK HERO.
LP: BGOLP 87

YOU'VE GOT IT ALL (see under Brown,Polly) (Proby, P.J/Polly Brown).

Proce, David

ELKAVOX ORCHESTRA, THE.
Tracks: / (They long to be) close to you / For all we know / Somewhere my love / More / Many splendoured thing / Hungarian dance no. 5 / Can can /

Funiculi / One day in your life / Hello Dolly / Bye bye blues / Born free / Michelle / Yesterday / Spanish eyes.
MC: . . . . DPOO 6 A

Proclaimers

SUNSHINE ON LEITH.
LP: . . . . CHR 1668
MC: . . . . ZCHR 1668

THIS IS THE STORY.
Tracks: / Throw the 'r' away / Over and done with / Misty blue / Part that really matters, The / (I'm gonna) burn your playhouse down / Letter from America / Sky takes the soul / It broke my heart / First attack / Make my heart fly / Beautiful truth / Joyful Kilmarnock blues, The.
LP: . . . . CHR 1602
MC: . . . . ZCHR 1602

Proctor, Chris

DELICATE DANCE, THE.
LP: . . . . FF 357

HIS JOURNEY HOME.
LP: . . . . FF 471

Procul Harum

20 GREATEST HITS: PROCUL HARUM.
LP: . . . . FUN 9028
MC: . . . . FUNC 9028

BROKEN BARRICADES.
LP: . . . . ILPS 9158

COLLECTION: PROCUL HARUM.
Tracks: / Whiter shade of pale, A / Homburg / Too much between us / Salty dog / Devil came from Kansas, The / Whaling stories / Good Captain Clack / All this and more / Quite rightly so / Shine on brightly / Grand hotel / Bringing home the bacon / Toujours l'amour / Broken barricades / Power failure / Conquistador (Live) / Nothing but the truth / Butterfly Boys / Pandora's box / Simple sister.
2LP: . . . . CCSLP 120
MC: . . . . CCSMC 120

EXOTIC BIRDS AND FRUIT.
Tracks: / Nothing but the truth / Beyond the pale / As strong as Samson / Idol, The / Thin end of the wedge, The / Monsieur R.Monde / Fresh fruit / Butterfly boys / New lamps for old.
LP: . . . . CHR 1058
MC: . . . . ZCHR 1058

GREATEST HITS: PROCUL HARUM.
LP: . . . . PLP 33
MC: . . . . PMC 33

HOME.
LP: . . . . SLRZ 1014
LP: . . . . CLALP 142
MC: . . . . CLAMC 142

NIGHTRIDING: PROCUL HARUM.
Tracks: / Whiter shade of pale, A / Homburg / Shine on brightly / Ramblin' on / Devil came from Kansas, The / All this and more / Lime street blues / Quite rightly so / About to die / Whisky train / Seem to have the blues / Salty dog.
MC: . . . . KNMC 10005
LP: . . . . KNLP 10005

OFF THE RECORD WITH PROCOL HARUM.
2LP: . . . . FEDD 1004
MCSET: . . . . CFEDD 1004

PLATINUM COLLECTION.
Tracks: / Whiter shade of pale, A / Salty dog / Too much between us / Boredom / Devil came from Kansas, The / Pilgrims progress / Quite rightly so / Shine on brightly / Kaleidoscope / Salad days are here again / Skip softly my moonbeams / Whisky train / Conquistador / She wandered through the garden fence / Magdalena / Dead's man's dream, The / Wreck of the Hesperus / Long gone geek / Homburg / Nothing that I didn't know / Barnyard story / All this and more / Repent walpurgis / Whaling stories.
LP: . . . . PLAT 1003
MC: . . . . ZCPLT 1003

PROCUL HARUM.
Tracks: / Whiter shade of pale, A / Salty dog / Shine on brightly / Wreck of the Hesperus / Long gone geek / Whaling stories / Homburg / Conquistador / Whisky train / Good Captain Clack / Barnyard story / Kaleidoscope.
LP: 6886 555
MC: 7486 552
LP: . . . . COUNT 13
MC: . . . . ZC CNT 13

PROCUL HARUM LIVE.
Tracks: / Conquistador / Whaling stories / Salty dog / All this and more / In held 'twas in I.
LP: . . . . CHR 1004
MC: . . . . ZCHR 1004

PROCUL'S NINTH.
LP: . . . . CHR 1080

SALTY DOG.
Tracks: / Salty dog / Milk of human kindness, The / Too much between us / Devil came from Kansas, The / Boredom / Juicy John Pink / Wreck of the Hesperus / All this and more / Crucifiction Lane / Pilgrims progress.
LP: . . . . FEDB 5012
MC: . . . . CFEDB 5012
LP: . . . . SLRZ 1009

SHINE ON BRIGHTLY.
Tracks: / Quite rightly so / Shine on brightly / Skip softly my moonbeams / Wish me well / Rambling on / Magdalena / In held 'twas in I / Glimpses of Nirvana / Twas tea time at the circus / In the Autumn of my madness / Look to your soul / Grand finale / Whisky train / Dead man's dreams / Still there'll be more / Nothing that I didn't know / About to die / Barnyard story / Piggy pig pig / Whaling stories / Your own choice.
LP: . . . . TOOFA 10
MC: . . . . ZCTOF 10
LP: . . . . FEDB 5026
MC: . . . . CFEDB 5026

SHINE ON BRIGHTLY/A SALTY DOG.
Tracks: / Quite rightly so / Shine on brightly / Skip softly my moonbeams / Wish me well / Rambling on / Magdalena / In held 'twas in I / Salty dog / Milk of human kindness / Too much between us / Devil came from Kansas, The / Boredom / Juicy John Pink / Wreck of the Hesperus / All this and more / Crucifiction lane / Pilgrims progress.
MC: . . . . TFOMC 5
2LP: . . . . TFOLP 5

WHITER SHADE OF PALE, A.
Tracks: / Whiter shade of pale, A / Conquistador / She wandered through the garden fence / Something following me / Mabel / Cerdes / Christmas camel / Kaleidoscope / Salad days / Good Captain Clack / Repent / Walpurgis.
LP: . . . . FEDB 5008
MC: . . . . CFEDB 5008
LP: . . . . TOOFA 7
MC: . . . . ZCTOF 7
LP: . . . . CLALP 188
MC: . . . . CLAMC 188
MC: . . . . CLACD 188

WHITER SHADE OF PALE/SALTY DOG.
2LP: . . . . TOOFA 7/8

Producers (film)

PRODUCERS, THE (Film soundtrack) (Various artists).
LP: . . . . INTS 5075
MC: . . . . INTK 5075

Product 2378

PRODUCT 2378 (Various artists).
LP: . . . . STAR 2378
MC: . . . . STAC 2378

Product, Clive

FINANCIAL SUICIDE.
LP: . . . . UTIL 002

STRETCHING ARMS AND LEGS (Product, Clive & Gary Williams).
Tracks: / Bloody funny monkey / Everything you've ever wanted / I am the devil / Two feet in one leg / You say things with your eyes / Falling up the stairs / Disco unfunk yourself / Another bloody funny monkey.
LP: . . . . CLEAR 015

VILLAGE TOURS START HERE.
Tracks: / Puffin club / Penguins / Peter Curtains / From here to asparagus / Ribbons / Orchestra man / Lobster girls / Aeroplanes to put it mildly / Snail talk / Jelly dance (every jelly girl and every jelly boy) / Here they come / In celebration of Mr Robinson's winter warmer.
LP: . . . . CLEAR 011

Profane, Benny

DUMBLUCK CHARM.
Tracks: / Time bomb / Maureen / Devil laughing / Walkaway / Perfect girl / Everything / Hey waste of space / Beam me up / Imaginary / Ghoul friend / She.
LP: . . . . ILLUSION 008

TRAPDOOR SWING.
LP: . . . . DEC 25

Professionals

AFRICAN DUB (1) (see Gibbs, Joe) (Professionals/Joe Gibbs).

AFRICAN DUB (2) (see Gibbs, Joe) (Professionals/Joe Gibbs).

I DIDN'T SEE IT COMING.
LP: . . . . V 2220
MC: . . . . TCV 2220

Professionals (tv)

PROFESSIONALS (See under Johnson, Laurie) (Johnson, Laurie).

Professor Griff

PAWNS IN THE GAME.
Tracks: / Pawns in the game / Verdict, The / Suzi wants to be a rock star / Real African people (pt 1) / Pass the ammo / Real African people (pt 2) / Love thy enemy / Rap terrorist / 1-900 stereotype / Last Asiatic disciples / Word of God, The / 5th amendment, The / Interview, The / It's a blax thanx.
LP: . . . . XR 111
MC: . . . . CXR 111

Professor Longhair

CRAWFISH FIESTA.
LP: . . . . SNTF 830

HOUSEPARTY NEW ORLEANS STYLE (The lost sessions 1971-72).
Tracks: / No buts and maybes / Gone so long / She walked right in / Thank you pretty baby / 501 boogie / Tipitina / Gonna leave this town / Cabbagehead / Hey little girl / Big chief / Cherry pie / Junco partner / Everyday I have the blues / 'G' jam / Doctor Professor Longhair.
LP: . . . . REU 1022
LP: . . . . ROUNDER 2057
MC: . . . . ROUNDER 2057C

LIVE ON THE QUEEN MARY.
Tracks: / Tell me pretty baby / Mess around / Everyday I have the blues / Tipitina / I'm movin' on / Mardi Gras in New Orleans / Cry to me / Gone so long / Stagger Lee.
LP: . . . . SSL 6004
MC: . . . . TCSSL 6004

LONDON CONCERT, THE.
LP: . . . . JSP 1025

MARDI GRAS IN NEW ORLEANS.
Tracks: / Mardi Gras in New Orleans / Tipitina / She walks right in / Mess around / Gone so long / Big chief / Hey little girl / Yancey's mixture / Well alright / Everyday I have the blues / Rockin' with Fes / Pinetop's boogie woogie.
LP: . . . . NH 108
LP: . . . . KK 7408

NEW ORLEANS PIANO.
LP: . . . . SD 7225

Professor Playtime

ALL ABOUT MUSIC.
MC: . . . . PE 303

KNOW YOUR COLOURS.
MC: . . . . PE 304

LEARN THE ALPHABET.
MC: . . . . PE 305

LEARNING TO COUNT.
MC: . . . . PE 306

MUSICAL TIMES TABLES.
MC: . . . . PE 301

PRIMARY FRENCH.
MC: . . . . PE 308

SIMPLE SUMS.
MC: . . . . PE 307

TELLING THE TIME.
MC: . . . . PE 302

Professor X

YEARS OF THE 9, ON THE BLACKHAND SIDE.
MC: . . . . BRCA 555
LP: . . . . BRLP 555

Proffitt, Frank

NORTH CAROLINA SONGS AND BALLADS.
LP: 12T 162

Profit, Clarence

COMPLETE 1939-40.
LP: . . . . MERITT 15

Profundo Rosso

PROFUNDO ROSSO/ SUSPIRIA (Film soundtrack) (Various artists).
LP: . . . . CIA 5005
MC: . . . . CIAK 75005

Project

PROJECT 1 (Various artists).
LP: . . . . PKLP 0010

Project D

SYNTHESIZED 2.
MC: . . . . STAC 2428
LP: . . . . STAR 2428

Prokofiev (composer)

CAROLE FARLEY SINGS PROKOFIEV (Farley, Carole/Roger Vignoles).
Tracks: / Ugly duckling, The (Prokofiev) / Childrens songs / Russian songs op.104 (2) (Prokofiev) / Poems op.23 (5) (Prokofiev) / Melodies op.35 (5) (Prokofiev).
LP: . . . . DCA 669
MC: . . . . ZC DCA 669

PETER AND THE WOLF/CARNIVAL OF THE ANIMALS, THE (see under Royal Philharmonic) (Royal Philharmonic Orchestra/Angela Rippon).

PETER & THE WOLF (Rippon, Angela (nar)).
LP: . . . . ACM 2005
MC: . . . . ZC ACM 2005

PETER & THE WOLF (Bowie, David).
LP: . . . . RL 82743
MC: . . . . RK 92743

PETER & THE WOLF (Geilgud, Sir John).
LP: . . . . VC 790786 1
MC: . . . . VC 790786 4

PETER & THE WOLF (Channing, Carol).
MC: . . . . CDL 51623

ROMEO AND JULIET - SUITE (London Symphony Orchestra).
MC: 4250274

SYMPHONY CONCERTANTE.
MC: . . . . MCE 75485

TWO VIOLIN SONATAS, THE (Fujikawa, Mayumi/Craig Sheppard).
Tracks: / Violin sonata no.1 (Prokofiev) / Violin sonata no.2 (Prokofiev) (Originally a flute sonata) / Melodies op.35 (5) (Prokofiev) (Originally vocal melodies.).
LP: . . . . DCA 667
MC: . . . . ZC DCA 667

Proletariat

INDIFFERENCE.
LP: . . . . HMS 052
MC: . . . . HMS 52 C

Promenaders

PROMENADERS, THE.
LP: . . . . Y 31 LP

Prometheus Ensemble

CLARINET QUINTET/OBOE QUARTET/FLUTE QUARTET (MOZART) (see under Mozart (composer)).

TROUT QUINTET (ETC) (SCHUBERT) (see under Schubert (composer)).

Promised Land

CHEYENNE (See under Creation - I get the fever) (Promised Land & Creation).

Prong

BEG TO DIFFER.
Tracks: / For dear life / Steady decline / Beg to differ / Lost and found / You fear / Intermenstrual DSB / Right to nothing / Prime cut / Just the same / Take it in hand.
LP: 4663751
MC: 4663754

FORCE FED.
LP: . . . . SPT 2
MC: . . . . SPT 2C

PRIMITIVE ORIGINS.
Tracks: / Disbelief / Watching / Cling to life / Denial / Dreams like that / In my view / Climate control / Persecution.
LP: . . . . SPT 1

Propaganda

1, 2, 3, 4.
Tracks: / Vicious circle / Heaven give me words / Your wildlife / Only one word / How much love / Vicious (reprise) / Ministry of fear / Wound in my heart / La carne, la morte e il diavolo.
LP: . . . . V 2625
MC: . . . . TCV 2625

SECRET WISH, A.
Tracks: / Dream within a dream / Murder of love,The / Jewel duel / P machinery / Power force push drive / Doctor Mabuse (The first love) / Sorry for laughing.
LP: . . . . ZTTIQ 3
MC: . . . . ZCIQ 3

WISHFUL THINKING (DISTURB DANCES).
Tracks: / Dr Mabuse. / P. Machinery / Sorry for laughing / Jewelled / Murder of love.
LP: . . . . ZAS 20
MC: . . . . CZAS 20
LP: . . . . ZTTIQ 20

Propaganda (Various)

PROPAGANDA (Various artists).
Tracks: / Goodbye girl: *Various artists* / Throw it away: *Various artists* / Come on: *Various artists*/ Landlord: *Various artists* / Next to you: *Various artists* / Don't wanna be like that: *Various artists*/ Doll: *Various artists* / Hollow sound: *Various artists* / Wrong way: *Various artists* / Weather station: *Various artists* / Joey: *Various artists*.
LP: . . . . AMLE 64786

Proper Little Madams

PROPER LITTLE MADAMS.
LP: . . . . SWL 2004

Prophecy Of Doom

ACKNOWLEDGE THE CONFUSION MASTER.
Tracks: / Prophetic believers prepare / Hybrid thought / Rhetorical fusion / Calculated mind rape / Rancid oracle / Insanity reigns supreme / Earth reality victim / Prophetic believers act / Acknowledge the confusion master.

LP: DEAF 002
MC: DEAF 002 MC

PEEL SESSIONS: PROPHECY OF DOOM.
MC: SFRMC 080

Prophet

CYCLE OF THE MOON.
MC: K 781822-4
LP: K 781822-1

Prophet, Chuck

BROTHER ALDO.
LP: FIRELP 22
MC: FIREMC 22

Prophet, Michael

CEASE FIRE.
LP: MVLP 2

CERTIFY.
LP: BS 1056

JOINT FAVOURITES (Prophet,Michael & Half Pint).
Tracks: / Crazy girl / What's going down / Tell me this tell me that / Day I can't forget / Freedom fighters / You're safe / Belly lick / Read your Bible / I don't know why / Saw you at the dance.
LP: GREL 89

LOVE IS AN EARTHLY THING.
Tracks: / Rich man poor man / Instructions / Never fall in love / Baby baby / Reggae music all right / Love is an earthly thing / It's a girl / Pretty face / Fussing and fighting.
LP: CSLP 7

MICHAEL PROPHET.
Tracks: / Hold on to what you've got / Guide and protect you / Youthman gunman / Turn them around / Upside down / Love and unity / Never leave me lonely / Help them please / Sweet loving.
LP: GREL 27

RIGHTEOUS ARE THE CONQUEROR.
Tracks: / Righteous are the conquerer / You are a no good / Long long tribulation / Conscious dreadlocks / Make me a romance / Cassandra / Originally / What is the difference / Gypsy woman / Happy days.
LP: GREL 18

SERIOUS REASONING.
Tracks: / Fight to the top / Hear I prayer / Turn me loose / Gates of Zion / Praise you jah jah / Love and unity / Warn them / Conscious man / Give thanks / Serious reasoning.
LP: ILPS 9606

SETTLE YU FE SETTLE.
Tracks: / Settle yu fe settle / Change your ways / Give me a little soul / Jamming / Jean / She says no / Conquer the dragon / Cop a raid / Rosale / Jack a day.
LP: LLLP 23

Prophet, Ronnie

RONNIE PROPHET.
Tracks: / Sanctuary / It wouldn't be so bad if it hadn't been so / Shine on / Last night I felt the whole world changing / Big big world / Phone call from Allyson / I want to be touched by you / Feel the magic / It's enough / Day by day (I'm getting over you).
LP: PL 10164

RONNIE PROPHET.
Tracks: / Don't take her to heart / No holiday in L.A. / If you're up for love / Please don't go / Fire in the feeling / Stealer of hearts / Are you real or am I dreaming / You've got me right where I want me / Breaking up ain't hard to do / For the children.
LP: NL 71837
MC: NK 71837

RONNIE PROPHET COUNTRY.
Tracks: / It ain't easy lovin' me / Misery loves company / Nothing sure look good on you / Who's gonna worry 'bout you now / Tuesday night local / She's an outlaw / Alabama dream girl / Lusty lady / How can anything that feels so good hurt so bad / Hangin' on to what I got.
LP: PL 40677

Prophets Of Doom

ACCESS TO WISDOM.
LP: VOV 672

Propis, David

DAVID PROPIS.
MC: GVMMC 120

Prospects

PROSPECTS (Film soundtrack) (Various artists).
Tracks: / Prospects: *Made in England* / Stay sharp: *Made in England* / Heist, The: *Glasman, Joseph* / Work hard, play hard: *Glasman, Joseph* / This is the news: *I Catch I* / My darlin': *I Catch I* / Who were you thinking of?: *Wynter, Valerie* / Today could be so good: *O'Connor, Hazel* / You gotta get up: *Chisholm, Colin* / Listen to me: *Y* / Keep on looking: *US* / Just an illusion: *Imagination*.
LP: RBLP 1011
MC: ZCRB 1011

Prosper Poati-Poati

MUANA SUKH.
LP: 2452

Protagonist

CONTENT TO WRITE IN I DINE WEATHERCRAFT.
Tracks: / White field (in isis) / Seance of a kondalike / Blue glide / Out of the dark, into the dawn / Young colatic child / Fox / Melting grey / Whale / Emma Wild / Dead rose, A / Vixen / Room.
LP: MAGL 5066

Protection

EGG IS BREAKING OPEN, AN.
Tracks: / Blue wind / Four doors / Painted faces / Making desperate sign language... / Birthday, The / IPKR.
LP: T 33

Protector

ARM THE MAD.
Tracks: / Capitascism / Nothing has changed / Antagonist of life / Arm the mad / Atrocities / Sliced, hacked and grinded / Most repungent / Quasimodo / Decadence / Molotov cocktail.
LP: ATOMH 10

GOING PLACES.
LP: GS 2294
MC: GSC 2294

GOLEM.
LP: ATOMH 007

MISANTHROPY.
2LP: ATOMH 001

Protrudi, Link

DRIVE IT HOME (Protrudi, Link & The Jaymen).
LP: MMLP 009

Proud, Malcolm

HARPSICHORD (Plays Bach, Byrd, Couperin, Froberger).
LP: CSM 59

Proust, Marcel (aut)

REMEMBRANCE OF THINGS PAST (Richardson, Sir Ralph (nar)).
MCSET: 2017

Providence

PROVIDENCE (Film soundtrack) (Various artists).
LP: SL 9502

Provine, Dorothy

ROARING TWENTIES-SONGS FROM THE TV SERIES.
LP: WM 4035

VAMP OF THE ROARING TWENTIES.
LP: WM 4053

Prowizorka Dzezz Bed

MOON LIGHTING.
LP: TTD 526

Prowlers

LIVING OUTSIDE THE LAW.
Tracks: / Horse doctor / Boulevard of broken dreams / Messin' with evil / Barbed wire heart / High plane baby / Alamo, The / Life's a mystery / Crawling up my spine / Buried alive / Tounge tied johnny / No lip / Living outside the law / Satin sheets.
LP: BREADTH 3
LP: BRAVE 3
MC: BRAVE 3C

RIDE A WHIRLWIND.
LP: CALCLP 055

Proysen, Alf

MRS. PEPPERPOT STORIES (Gallimore, Patricia).
Tracks: / Mrs. Pepperpot tries to please her husband / Mrs. Pepperpot minds the baby / Mrs. Pepperpot's penny watchman / Mrs. Pepperpot & the moose / Mrs. Pepperpot finds hidden treasure / Mr. Pepperpot.
MC: TS 345

Prudes

DESIGNER KARMA.
LP: ILLUSION 030

PS I'M LEAVING.
LP: COX 016

Prudhoe Gleemen

PRUDHOE GLEEMEN PRESENT.
LP: MWM 1032

Pruess, Craig

MUSIC OF THE STARS - SAGITTARIUS (The eye of Jupiter).
Tracks: / Into the eye of Jupiter suite / Fountain of fortune / Rings of Saturn / Ayre for trumpet / Fountain of heritage / Fountain of heaven and earth / Cloudburst / Superradiant / Journey of transformation suite.
LP: BIRTHLP 2
MC: BIRTHMC 2

Pruett, Jeanne

ENCORE.
Tracks: / Back to back / Every now and then / Temporarily yours / Star studded nights / Wild side of life / Waitin' for the sun to shine / Ain't we sad today / Love is a fading rose / Love all the leavin' out of you / Please sing satin sheets for me.
LP: PL 25290

JEANNE PRUETT.
Tracks: / Satin sheets / I've been around enough to know / Back to back / Best kept secret in town, The / You're all the man I'll ever need / Let's fall to pieces together / Heart first / I told you so / Rented room.
LP: IMCA 39031
MC: IMCAC 39031

Prunes

BLOSSOMS AND BLOOD.
LP: BABY 014

Pruvot, Michel

DEL DUCASS AU BAL MUSETTE VOL.2 (Pruvot, Michel et ses Picards).
Tracks: / Trumpet echo / Banda,A / Rendezvous au the dansant / Melodie d'amour / Jolis quartiers de Paris / Vive campeurs / Les refraines tricolores / Si la valse m'etait chantee / Maria la Portugaise / Radio Montmarte / Mediteranee March.
LP: MLD 222

DEL DUCCASS AU BAL MUSETTE.
Tracks: / Rosi Rosita / Chanson des becs sales / Faut pas craquer / Azur / Depart en piste / Rendezvous au the dansant / Si tu reviens danser ce soir / Du sacre coeur a la grande bleue / Melodia d'amore / Accordeon a la carte.
LP: MLD 218

RECORD MUSETTE.
Tracks: / Train d'enfer / Les guinguettes / Clap clap sound, The / Pedrillo / La java du loto / Buvons un coup marins pecheurs / Le fana du Charleston / Record musette / Et ca repart / Variations auvergnates / Tango des cocus / March des mineurs / Moulin Rouge.
LP: ILD 42045

Pryde, Jimmy

PIPE DREAMS.
MC: CWGR 059
LP: 2386 086

Pryor, Arthur

1907-1919 (see Europe,Jim & Arthur Pryor Bands) (Pryor,Arthur & Jim Europe Bands).

Pryor, Richard

IS IT SOMETHING I SAID.
Tracks: / Eulogy / Shorter of white people / New niggers / Cocaine / Just us / Mudbone - intro / Mudbone - little feets / When your woman leaves you / Goodnight kiss, The / Women are beautiful / Our text for today.
LP: K 54052

LIVE IN CONCERT - WANTED.
Tracks: / Heart attacks / Ali / Keeping in shape / Leon Spinks / Nature / Things in the woods / Deer hunter / Chinese food / Being sensitive / Dogs and horses / Jim Brown / Monkeys / Kids / New Year's eve / White and black people / Black funerals / Discipline.
2LP: K 66091

Pryor, Snooky

SNOOKY.
LP: BP-2387

SNOOKY PRYOR.
LP: PY 1813

SNOOKY PRYOR & MOODY JONES Job series vol.3 (Pryor, Snooky & Moody Jones).
LP: FLY 565

Prysock, Arthur

ROCK 'N' ROLL.
Tracks: / Jump, Red jump / Happy feet / Blow your horn / Little Jamie / Zonked / Rock 'n' roll / Zip / Fat's place / Alright, okay you win / That's the groovy thing / Jumbo / Hand clappin'.
LP: OFF 6017

ROCKIN' GOOD WAY, A.
Tracks: / Baby (you've got what it takes) / I want to thank you, girl / Bloodshot eyes / Teach me tonight / Every morning baby / Passing strangers / Next time you see me / Rockin' good way, A.
LP: M 9139

Prysock, Red

CRYIN' MY HEART OUT.
LP: BP 502

Psalty

PSALTY'S FAMILY CHRISTMAS (Various artists).
MC: MM C 0245

PSALTY'S MIGHTY MINI MUSICALS (Various artists).
LP: MM R 0199
MC: MM C 0199

PSALTY'S NON-STOP SINGALONGATHON (Various artists).
MC: MM C 0247

PSALTY'S SINGALONGATHON (Various artists).
MC: TC MAC 5102
LP: MAC 5102

Pseudo Echo

AUTUMNAL PARK.
Tracks: / Beat for you / See through / From the shore / Stranger in me / Dancing until midnight / Listening / His eyes / Walkaway / Fast cars / Destination unknown.
LP: EJ 2402921
MC: EJ 2402924

LONG PLAYS 83-87.
LP: EMX 430048

LOVE AND ADVENTURE.
Tracks: / Beat for you / Living in a dream / Try / Listening / I will be you / Love an adventure / Destination unknown / Funky town / Lonely without you / Lies are nothing.
LP: PL 90024
MC: PK 90024

Psyche

INSOMNIA THEATRE.
LP: ROSE 78

MYSTERY HOTEL.
LP: ROSE 145
MC: ROSE 145C

UNLEASHED.
MC: ALL 287

UNRELEASED.
MC: ALL 288

UNVEILING THE SECRET.
LP: ROSE 108

Psychedelia

CIRCUS DAYS VOL.1 (Various artists).
Tracks: / Ice cream man: *Clover* / Money lender: *Rhubarb Rhubarb* / Honey machine: *Lomax All Stars* / Someday: *Head West* / I'll be there: *Talor, Duffy Blues* / I see the morning: *Penny Peeps* / Wheel of fortune: *Garrie, Nick* / Garden of earthly delights: *Arzachel* / Bedazzled: *Moore, Dudley* / Fluffy: *High Tide Formation* / Follow me: *Fruit Machine* / Dreams of dreams: *Smoke* / Circus with a female clown: *Fingers*/ Doves, The: *Wire Machine* / Circles: *Blonde On Blonde* / Nobody wants you back: *Los Brincos* / Baby let your hand down: *Foce Five* / Auntie Annie's place: *Stars* / Why may I not know: *Waterloo* / Shapes and shadows: *Tandem* / Alice: *Plum, John* / Running to the convent: *Dry Ice* / I'd like to walk around: *Vashti* / Pole vault man: *Burton, Johnny* / Psychedelic wilderness: *Green Scarab* / I got no time: *Orange Peel* / Bird, The: *Nimrod* / Castles in the sky: *Blonde On Blonde* / You're still mine: *Eggy*.
LP: STZ 5001

CIRCUS DAYS VOL.2 (Various artists).
LP: STZ 5002

TEXAS PSYCHEDELIA FROM THE 60'S (Various artists).
LP: EVA 12057

Psychedelic

BEST OF AND THE REST OF BRITISH PSYCHEDELIA (Various artists).
Tracks: / Morning Morgantown: *Jude* / Shirley: *Wade, Cliff* / House of many windows: *Motherlight* / Baby you've gotta stay: *Angel Pavement* / My friend Jack: *Smoke* / It never stays the same: *Grimm, Bob* / Green Mellow Hill: *Magic Worms* / Look at me I've fallen in a teapot: *Wade, Cliff* / Keep a hold of what you do: *Shots*/ Peru: *Chimmera* / Saga of a wrinkled man: *Fortes Mentum* / Laura's garden: *Orange Bicycle* / All of my life: *Pussy* / Leilla the flatterer: *Neogy, Chitra*.
MC: ARLC 1024

BEST OF AND THE REST OF BRITISH PSYCHEDELIA (See under British Psychedelia) (Various artists).

BRITISH PSYCHEDELIC TRIP 4 (Various artists).
Tracks: / That's the way it's gotta be: *Poets* / I lied to Auntie May: *Neat Change* / Movin' in: *Toby Twirl*/ Glass house green, splinter red: *Kinsmen* / Lazy day: *Tinkerbell's Fairydust* / Water woman: *Pacific Drift*/ Paper chase: *Love Children* / Whisper her name: *Ice* / Peacefully

asleep: *Life 'n' Soul* / Turn to earth: *Stewart, Al* / Baby get your head screwed on: *Double Feature* / Eight-and-a-half hours of Paradise: *Elastic* Band / Fade away Maureen: *Cherry Smash* / Gotta wait: *Game* / 8.35 on the dot: *Stirling, Peter Lee*/ All our Christmases: *Majority* / Requiem: *Chocolate Watch Band* / Water woman: *Amazingly Friendly Apple*/ I'll be home (in a day or so): *Dream Police* / Walking through the streets of my mind: *Timebox*.
LP: . . . . **SEE 206**

CLOUDS HAVE GROOVY FACES (Rubble Six) (Various artists).
Tracks: / Lovely people: *Fairytale* / Glass house green, splinter red: *Kinsmen* / I am so blue: *Poets*/ Anniversary of love: *Ice* / Shades of orange: *End* / Tales of Flossie Fillet: *Turquoise* / Magic bus: *Pudding* / Neville thumbcatch: *Attack* / Red sky at night: *Accent* / 8 1/2 hours to ...: *Elastic* Band / Created by Clive: *Attack* / Surburban early morning...: *Two And A Half* / Peacefully asleep: *Life & Soul* / I'll cry with the moon: *Poets* / Beggards parade: *Falling Leaves* / 20-10: *Tinkerbell's Fairydust*.
LP: . . . . **KIRI 049**

ELECTRIC CRAYON SET (Rubble five) (Various artists).
Tracks: / That's the way it's got to be: *Poets* / Anymore than I do: *Attack* / I'm not your stepping stone: *Flies*/ Please please me: *Score* / I'm leaving: *Mark Four, The* / Father's name is dad: *Fire* / Mothers little helper: *Letter, Gene* / House of love: *Flies* / Hey Gyp, dig the slowness: *Shields, Keith* / Try it: *Attack*/ I love her still: *Poets* / Living is easy: *Dream Police* / Gonna get me someone: *Game* / Run and hide: *Fairytale* / Hurt me (if you will): *Mark Four, The*.
LP: . . . . **KIRI 044**

ILLUSIONS FROM THE CRACKLING VOID (Various artists).
LP: . . . . **MARX 085**

INTERNATIONAL ARTISTS SINGLES COLLECTION (Various artists).
Tracks: / Tried to hide: *13th Floor Elevators* / Rejected: *Sterling Damon* / Help murder police: *Thursday's* Children / Ever ever land: *Rubayyat* / Thinkin' about thinkin': *Bubble Puppy* / When will you come through: *Lost & Found* / Ginger: *Ginger Valley* / Tell me one more time: *Endle St Cloud* / You can forget about that: *Thursday's Children* / If I had a reason: *Bubble Puppy* / Quest for beauty: *Endle St Cloud* / Professor Black: *Lost & Found* / Times gone by: *Disciples of Shaftesbury* / Country life: *Ginger Valley* / What do you see: *Bubble Puppy*.
LP: . . . . **LIK 53**

IT'S ONLY A PASSING PHASE (Various artists).
Tracks: / Tamaris khan: *Onyx, The* / My clown: *July* / Steam: *Mandrake Paddle Steamer* / Hippy gumbo: *Johns Children* / If (would it turn out wrong): *Esprit de corps* / Anymore than I do: *Attack* / Just a good show: *Gants* / Liquidy headbox: *Kings Of Oblivion* / Pink purple yellow and red: *Sorrows* / Satellite jockey: *Nirvana* / Pictures in the sky: *Orange seaweed* / When you're dead: *Ghost* / It's just a fear: *Answers* / Wind blows your hair, the: *Seeds* / I take it we're through: *Riot Squad*.
LP: . . . . **MARX 100**

LIVE AT ALICE IN WONDERLAND (Various artists).
LP: . . . . **SHARP 035**
MC: . . . . **SHARP 035 C**

MORGAN BLUE TOWN (Various artists).
Tracks: / Morning Morgan town: *Jude* / Keep hold of what you've got: *Shots* / Shirley: *Wade, Cliff* / House of many windows: *Motherlight* / Peru: *Chimera* / Saga of a wrinkled man: *Fortes Mentum* / My friend Jack: *Smoke* / Laura's garden: *Orange Bicycle* / It never stays the same: *Grimm, Bob* / All of my life: *Pussy* / Green Mellow Hill: *Magic Worms* / Leila: *Neogy, Chitra* / Look at me: *Wade, Cliff*.
LP: . . . . **MBT 5002**

NIGHTMARES IN WONDERLAND Rubble Three (Various artists).
Tracks: / Nightmares in red: *Brain* / 10,000 years behind my mind: *Focus Three* / Talkin' about the good times: *Pretty Things* / Fox has gone to ground: *Bamboo Shoot* / Visions in a plaster sky: *Wild Silk* / He's our dear old weatherman: *Wirtz, Mark* / William Chaulker's time machine: *Lemon Tree* / Barricades: *Koobas*/ 10,000 words in a cardboard box: *Aquarian Age* / Mr. Evasion: *Pretty Things* / Gardena dreamer: *Executive*/ Fragile child: *Chances Are* / Hold on: *Ipsissimus* / Shades of grey: *Rumbold, Edwick* / Model village: *Penny Peeps* / Revolution: *Tomorrow*.
LP: . . . . **KIRI 026**

PERFUMED GARDEN, THE (1) (Various artists).
LP: . . . . **PSYCHO 6**

PERFUMED GARDEN, THE (2) (Various artists).
LP: . . . . **PSYCHO 15**

PICTURES IN THE SKY Rubble seven (Various artists).
Tracks: / Pictures in the sky: *Orange seaweed* / Real life permanent: *Orange Machine* / So sad inside: *Onyx, The* / My world fell down: *Ivy League* / Better make up your mind: *Koobas* / Within the night: *Velvett fogg* / You didn't have...: *Glass Menagerie (film)* / Jump and dance: *Carnaby* / Flying machine: *Flying machine, the* / Cloudy: *Factotums* / I'm a hog for you baby: *Grant Erky/Earwigs*.
LP: . . . . **KIRI 083**

POP SIKE PIPE DREAMS Rubble Two (Various artists).
Tracks: / Eastern music: *Mode* / World spinning sadly: *Parking Lot* / Marmalade hair: *Wimple Wrinch*/ Defecting grey: *Pretty Things* / Kid was a killer: *West, Keith* / Indian thing: *Shotgun Express* / Trace took a trip: *Executive* / Lollipop minds: *Wimple Wrinch* / You break my heart: *Tailsmen* / Walking through my dreams: *Pretty Things* / Sweet love: *Various artists* / Bluebell wood: *Wimple Wrinch* / Knocking nails into my house: *Idle Race* / After tea: *Spencer Davis group* / Rosecrans bud: *Various artists*.
LP: . . . . **KIRI 025**

PROFESSOR JORDAN'S MAGIC SOUND SHOW Rubble ten (Various artists).
Tracks: / Tamaris khan: *Onyx, The* / We didn't kiss: *Clique* / Linda loves Lin: *Floribunda rose* / Riding on a wave: *Turnstyle* / Running wild: *Fresh air* / Hungry: *5 AM event* / She's a rainbow: *Glass Menagerie* (film) / Buffalo: *Writing on the wall* / Frederick Johnson: *Glass Menagerie (film)* / Step in the right direction: *Montanas* / Lady Caroline: *Velvett fogg* / Frosted panes: *Kytes* / Stay a while: *Orange seaweed*/ Keep on moving baby: *Game* / Stay indoors: *New formula* / You can all join in: *Orange Machine*.
LP: . . . . **KIRI 098**

PSYCHEDELIC SMASHES (Various artists).
2LP: . . . . **CR 086**
MCSET: . . . . **CRT 086**

PSYCHEDELIC SNARL (THE) Rubble One (Various artists).
Tracks: / Atmospheres: *Wimple Winch* / Faster than light: *Mirror* / Woman of distinction: *Caleb* / It's all over now: *Cure, Martin & The Peeps* / Always with him: *Living Daylights* / Never had a girl like you before: *Misunderstood* / Cast a spell: *Open Mind* / Spider and the fly, The: *Dakotas* / Rumble on Mersey Square South: *Wimple Winch* / Magic potion: *Open Mind* / Let's live for today: *Living Daylights* / I must be mad: *Craig* / I will: *Unit 4 + 2* / Grey: *Hush* / Save my soul: *Wimple Winch* / Morning after: *Mindbenders*.
LP: . . . . **KIRI 024**

PSYCHEDELIC TRIP 1966-1969 (Various artists).
Tracks: / Muffin man: *World of Oz* / Anniversary (of love): *Ice* / Shades of orange: *End* / Iceman: *End*/ Run and hide: *Fairytale* / Come on back: *Paul & Ritchie & The Cryin' Shames* / Vacuum cleaner: *Tintern Abbey*/ Love: *Virgin Sleep* / Saynia: *Turquoise* / Romeo and Juliet: *Twirl, Toby* / Magician: *Amazing Friendly* Apple / Beeside: *Tintern Abbey* / Fathers name is dad: *Fire* / I'm not your stepping stone: *Flies*/ Red sky at night: *Accent* / Tales of Flossie Fillet: *Turquoise* / Created by Clive: *Attack* / Baked jam roll in your eye: *Timebox* / In your tower: *Poets* / Leave me here 23rd turnoff: *Turnoff*.
LP: . . . . **SEE 66**

PSYCHEDELIC UNKNOWNS (Various artists).
MC: . . . . **PSY 101**

PSYCHEDELIC YEARS, THE (Various artists).
Tracks: / Eight miles high: *Byrds* / White rabbit: *Jefferson Airplane* / For what it's worth: *Buffalo Springfield*/ Happy together: *Turtles* / Green tambourine: *Lemon Pipers* / Along comes Mary: *Association* / You keep me hangin' on: *Vanilla Fudge* / Somebody to love: *Jefferson Airplane* / Psychotic reaction: *Count Five*/ I had too much to dream (last night): *Electric Prunes* / Little girl: *Syndicate Of Sound* / (We ain't got) nothin' yet: *Blues Magoos* / In a gadda da vida: *Iron Butterfly* / Time has come today: *Chambers Brothers* / Fresh garbage: *Spirit* / Electricity: *Captain Beefheart* / Lemon princess: *Leaves* / You're gonna miss me: *13th Floor* Elevators / I won't leave my wooden wife for you, sugar: *United States Of America* / On the road again: *Canned* Heat / Get together: *Youngbloods* / Alone again or: *Love (band)* / White bird: *It's A Beautiful Day*/ Cabinessence: *Beach Boys* / I got a line on you: *Spirit* / Buzzin' fly: *Buckley, Tim* / House at Pooneil corner, The: *Jefferson Airplane* / Expecting to fly: *Buffalo Springfield* / Spin, spin, spin: *HP Lovecraft*/ Hey Grandma: *Moby Grape* / Venus in furs: *Velvet Underground* / Mona: *Quicksilver Messenger Service*/ Darkness, darkness: *Youngbloods* / Sunshine Superman: *Donovan* / Shapes of things: *Yardbirds* / Whiter shade of pale, A: *Procul Harum* / Strange brew: *Cream* / San Franciscan nights: *Burdon, Eric & The Animals*/ Itchycoo park: *Small Faces* / Kites: *Dupree, Simon & The Big Sound* / Fire!: *Brown, Arthur* / Flowers in the rain: *Move* / My white bicycle: *Tomorrow* / Dandelion seeds: *July* / S.F. sorrow is born: *Pretty* Things / Skeleton and the roundabout: *Idle Race* / (Tell me) have you ever seen me: *Apostolic Intervention*/ Shy boy: *Kippington Lodge* / Painting box: *Incredible String Band* / Sunshine of your love: *Cream*.
LPS: . . . . **PSDLP 47003**
MCSET: . . . . **PSDMC 47003**

STAIRCASE TO NOWHERE (Rubble twelve) (Various artists).
Tracks: / Portcullis gate: *Bulldog Breed* / Secret: *Virgin Sleep* / Vacuum cleaner: *Tintern Abbey* / Michaelangelo: *23rd Turnoff* / Day in my mind's mind: *Human Instinct* / Northern hemisphere: *East Of Eden*/ Peter's birthday (black & white rainbows): *World of Oz* / Catherine's wheel: *Laine, Denny* / Beeside: *Tintern Abbey* / Pink dawn: *Human Instinct* / Gone is the sad man: *Timebox* / Glastonbury: *People* / Help me please: *Outer Limits* / Like a tear: *World of Oz* / Nite is-a-comin: *Warm Sounds*.
LP: . . . . **KIRI 070**

THROUGH THE LOOKING GLASS - 1966 (Various artists).
LP: . . . . **ILLUSION 023**

THROUGH THE LOOKING GLASS 1967 (Various artists).
LP: . . . . **ILLUSION 010**
MC: . . . . **ILLC 010**

Psychedelic Furs

12" TAPE: PSYCHEDELIC FURS.
Tracks: / Pretty in pink / Love my way / Heaven / Heartbeat / Ghost in you.
MC: **4501304**

ALL OF THIS AND NOTHING.
Tracks: / President gas / All that money wants / Imitation of Christ / Sister Europe / Love my way / Highwire days / Dumb waiters / Pretty in pink / Ghost in you / Heaven / Heartbreak beat / All of this and nothing.
LP: **4611101**
MC: **4611104**

BOOK OF DAYS.
LP: **4659821**
MC: **4659824**

FOREVER NOW.
Tracks: / President gas / Love my way / Run and run / Merry go round / Forever now / Sleep comes down / Danger / You and I / Goodbye / No easy street / Shadow (Extra track on cassette only.).
LP: . . . . **CBS 32777**
MC: **40 32777**

MIDNIGHT TO MIDNIGHT.
Tracks: / Heartbreak beat / Shock / Shadow in my heart / Angels don't cry / Midnight to midnight / One more word / Torture / All of the law / Pretty in pink / No release (Extra track on cassette only).
LP: **4502561**
MC: **4502564**
LP: **4633991**
MC: **4633994**

MIRROR MOVES.
Tracks: / Ghost in You / Here come cowboys / Heaven / Heartbeat / My time / Like a stranger / Alice's house / Only a game / Highwire days.
LP: **4503561**
MC: **4503564**
LP: **25950**

MUSIC AND MEDIA INTERVIEW PICTURE DISC.
LPPD: . . . . **MM 1257**

PSYCHEDELIC FURS.
Tracks: / India / Sister Europe / Imitation of Christ / Fall / Pulse / We love you / Wedding song / Blacks/Radio / Flowers.
LP: . . . . **CBS 32299**
MC: **40 32299**
LP: . . . . **CBS 84084**

PSYCHEDELIC FURS (4 TRACK CASSETTE EP).
MC: **40 2909**

TALK, TALK, TALK.
Tracks: / Dumb waiters / Pretty in pink / I wanna sleep with you / No tears / Mr. Jones / Into you like a train / It goes on / So run down / All of this and nothing / She is mine.
LP: . . . . **BS 32539**
MC: **40 32539**
LP: **84892**

Psychic Amp

PEOPLE OF THE BOOK (UGLY AS POWER).
LP: . . . . **PROBE 18**
MC: . . . . **PROBE 18C**

Psychic TV

ALLEGORY AND SELF.
LP: . . . . **TOPY 38**

ALLERGORY AND SELF.
LP: . . . . **TOPY 038**

BERLIN ATONAL VOL.1.
LP: . . . . **ST 3001**

BEYOND THE INFINITE BEAT.
LP: . . . . **TOPY 049DJ**
MC: . . . . **TOPY 049CC**

DREAMS LESS SWEET.
Tracks: / Hymn 23 / Orchids, The / Botanica / Iron glove / Always is always / White hights / Finale / Eleusis / Medmenham / Ancient lights / Proof of survival / Eden 1 / Eden 2 / Eden 3 / Clouds without water / Black moon / Silver and gold / In the nursery / Circle.
LP: . . . . **CBS 25737**
MC: **40 25737**

FORCE THE HAND OF CHANCE.
Tracks: / Just drifting / Terminus / Stolen kisses / Caresse / Guiltless / No go go / Ov power / Message from the temple.
LP: . . . . **PSY 1**

KONDOLE/COPYCAT.
LP: . . . . **TOPY 46**
MC: . . . . **TOPYC 46**

LIVE AT MARDI GRAS.
LP: . . . . **TOPY 36**

LIVE AT THE CIRCUS.
LP: . . . . **TOPY 042**

LIVE AT THE PYRAMID.
LP: . . . . **TOPY 047**

LIVE AT THEE RITZ.
LP: . . . . **TOPY 45**

LIVE EN SUISSE.
LP: . . . . **TOPY 27**

LIVE IN BREGENZ.
LP: . . . . **TOPY 020**

LIVE IN GLASGOW.
LP: . . . . **TOPY 016**

LIVE IN GOTTINGEN.
LP: . . . . **TOPY 29**

LIVE IN HEAVEN.
Tracks: / I hear vocals / Leg song, The / Paradise lost / Lies and spies / Revenge on God / Stolen lightning / Seat of broken glass / Radium.
LP: . . . . **TOPY 018**

LIVE IN PARIS.
LP: . . . . **TOPY 014**

LIVE IN REYJAVIK.
LP: . . . . **TOPY 26**

LIVE IN TOKYO 1986.
LP: . . . . **TOPY 015**

LIVE IN TORONTO.
LP: . . . . **TOPY 28**

MOUTH OF THE NIGHT.
LP: . . . . **TOPY 010**
LPPD: . . . . **TOPIC 010**
MC: . . . . **TOPY C010**

NEW YORK SCUM HATERS.
LP: . . . . **TOPY 002**

PAGAN DAY.
Tracks: / Catalogue / W kiss / Opium / Cold steel / Los Angeles / Iceland / Translucent carriages / Paris / Baby's gone away / Alice / New sexuality / Farewell.
LP: . . . . **TOPY 017**
LP: . . . . **TOPY 003**

PSYCHIC TV.
LPPD: . . . . **TOPY 31**

TEMPORARY TEMPLE.
LP: . . . . **TOPY 30**

THEMES.
LP: . . . . **TOPY 4**

THEMES 3.
LP: . . . . **TOPY 019**

TOWARDS THEE INFINITE BEAT.
LP: . . . . **TOPY 049**
MC: . . . . **TOPY 049CC**

Psycho

HOSEBAGS FROM HELL.
LP: . . . . ACHE 09

Psycho (bk)

PSYCHO (Robert Bloch) (McCarthy, Kevin (nar)).
MCSET: . . . . LFP 7343

Psycho Daisies

SONICLY SPEAKING.
Tracks: / Rubber legs / Dead wood / Demotion daze / Caged bird things / Spider baby / What you gonna do about it? / She went shopping / Bad amusements.
LP: . . . . R 33-8819

Psycho (Film)

PSYCHO (Film soundtrack) (Various artists).
LP: . . . . ACH 022
MC: . . . . CCH 022

PSYCHO/NORTH BY NORTHWEST (Film soundtracks)(See under North By Northwest) (Various artists).

Psycho II

PSYCHO II (Film soundtrack) (Various artists).
LP: . . . . MCA 6119
MC: . . . . MCAC 6119
MC: . . . . VSC 5252

Psycho III

PSYCHO III (Film soundtrack) (Various artists).
Tracks: / Scream of love: *Various artists* / Maureen in the desert: *Various artists* / Dirty street: *Various* artists / Before and after shower: *Various artists* / Warm as a cry for help: *Various artists* / Mother?: *Various artists* / Sisters: *Various artists* / Catherine Mary: *Various artists* / Bad boys and body bags: *Various artists* / Revenge of the thankless child: *Various artists* / Electroshock waiting room: *Various artists.*
LP: . . . . IMCA 6174
MC: . . . . IMCAC 6174

Psycho Surgeons

MAD HOUSE.
LP: . . . . QTA 2

Psycho Tendencies

PSYCHO TENDENCIES (Various artists).
LP: . . . . RAUCLP 001

Psycho-attack

PSYCHO-ATTACK OVER EUROPE Various Artists (Various artists).
LP: KIX4U 3335
LP: . . . . PLAT 3335

PSYCHO-ATTACK OVER EUROPE VOL.3 (Various artists).
LP: KIX4U 3345
LP: . . . . ROCK 3345

Psychobilly...

BEST OF STOMPING AT THE KLUB FOOT (Various artists).
LP: . . . . DOJOLP 53

BLOOD ON THE CATS/REVENGE OF THE KILLER PUSSIES (Various artists).
2LP: . . . . DGRAM 002

GRAVEYARD STOMP (Various artists).
Tracks: / Graveyard stomp: *Various artists* / Teenage werewolf's bride: *Various artists* / My brain is in the cupboard above the kitchen sink: *Various artists* / Psychobilly Jekyll & Mr. Hyde: *Various artists* / Headchange: *Various artists* / Return of the cannibal zombie businessman: *Various artists* / Vampire bat: *Various artists*/ Love zombies: *Various artists* / Witch girl: *Various artists* / Devil call: *Various artists* / Flesh eater: *Various artists* / Wolfman howl: *Various artists* / Zombies: *Various artists.*
LP: . . . . GRAM 39

MONSTER A GO-GO (Japanese Psychobilly) (Various artists).
LP: KIX4U 2227
LP: . . . . ROCK 2227

REVENGE OF THE KILLER PUSSIES (Various artists).
Tracks: / Hellhag shuffle: *Various artists* / Werewolf blues: *Various artists* / She's got fever: *Various* artists / Escalator: *Various artists* / Long necked daddy o: *Various artists* / Red monkey, The: *Various* artists / Alligator: *Various artists* / Hills have eyes, The: *Various artists* / Psychotic reaction: *Various* artists / Shearing machine: *Various artists* / She's my witch: *Various artists* / Dawn of the flies: *Various* artists / Goldfish: *Various artists* / Zulu beat: *Various artists* / I wanna get thin: *Various artists*/ I wanna be like you: *Various artists.*
LP: . . . . GRAM 17
MC: . . . . CGRAM 17

ROCKABILLY PSYCHOSIS (Various artists).
Tracks: / Surfin' bird: *Trashmen* / Psycho: *Sonics* / Crusher, The: *Novas* / Paralysed: *Legendary* Stardust Cowboy / She said: *Adkins, Hasil* / My daddy is a vampire: *Meteors* / Radioactive kid: *Meteors*/ Dateless nites: *Falco, Tav & The Panther Burns* / Jack on fire: *Gun Club* / Folsom prison blues: *Geezers*/ Catman: *Stingrays* / Just love me: *Guana Batz* / Love me: *Phantom* (Not available on CD) / Red headed woman: *Dickinson, Jimmy & the Cramps* / Scream!: *Nielsen, Ralph & The Chancellors* (Available on CD only) / Hidden charms: *Wray, Link* (Available on CD only) / Run chicken run: *Milkshakes* (Available on CD only).
LP: . . . . WIK 18
MC: . . . . WIKC 18

STOMPIN' AT THE KLUB FOOT VOL 3 (Various artists).
LP: . . . . ABCLP 8

STOMPIN' AT THE KLUB FOOT VOL 1 (Live at the Klub Foot) (Various artists).
Tracks: / I got a feeling: *Wigsville Spliffs* / Rockjet: *Torment* / Uncle Sam: *Torment* / Psycho disease: *Coffin Nails* / Coffin nails: *Coffin Nails* / Ball and chain: *Caravans* / De-frocked priest: *Rochee & The Sarnos* / Ballroom blitz: *Batmobile* / Cold sweat: *Batmobile.*
LP: . . . . ABCLP 3

STOMPIN' AT THE KLUB FOOT VOL 2 (Various artists).
LP: . . . . ABCLP 6

STOMPING AT THE KLUB FOOT VOL.5 (Various artists).
LP: . . . . ABCLP 15

THESE CATS AIN'T NOTHIN' BUT TRASH (Various artists).
Tracks: / Before the night is through: *Milkshakes* / Nothing said: *Milkshakes* / Please don't tell my baby: *Milkshakes*/ It's gonna be: *Milkshakes* / I want my woman: *Stingrays* / Cat, The: *Stingrays* / Dinosaurs: *Stingrays*/ Math of trend: *Stingrays* / Light bulb blues: *Cannibals* / Can't seem to make you mine: *Cannibals* / Weekend on Mars: *Cannibals* / Come see me (I'm your man): *Cannibals.*
LP: . . . . WIKM 28
LP: . . . . NED 3

ZORCH FACTOR ONE Various artists (Various artists).
LP: . . . . NERD 023

ZORCH FACTOR THREE (Various artists).
Tracks: / House on haunted hill: *Coffin Nails* / Route 66: *Torment* / Restless: *Ghost Town* / I can't stay: *Quakes* / Broken home: *Broken Home* / That's the way it is: *Caravans* / I hear the pounding: *Surfin' Wombatz* / Crying state: *Skitzo* / I heard it through the grapevine: *Caravans* / Reaper grim: *Spook & The Ghouls* / Crazy and wild: *Pharoahs* / What's you papa gonna say: *Get Smart* / Live and raw: *Spook & The Ghouls* / Safe surf: *Frantic Flintstones.*
LP: . . . . NERD 042

ZORCH FACTOR TWO Various Artists (Various artists).
LP: . . . . NERD 029

Psychology

DREAMS AND DREAMING (Evans, Dr. Christopher).
MC: . . . . SS 107

NEW LOOK AT PSYCHOLOGISTS (By Liam Hudson) (New Look At Psychologists).
MC: . . . . PT 35

Psycho's Mum

SIBILANT SIN, A.
LP: . . . . W 011

Psychosurgery

CASE AGAINST IT.
MC: . . . . SS 118

Psychotic Waltz

SOCIAL GRACE, A.
Tracks: / Social grace, A.
LP: 942202

Psychotron

PSYCHOTRON O.
MC: . . . . MMATT 60

Psyclones

ANOTHER BRIDGE.
Tracks: / Another bridge / Pour avlon / He who falls... / Slabyard / La fin des debut (how many rights) / Hardcore soundtrack / Between space / 100 miles abob wire / Between space.
LP: . . . . DMC 024

PSY 231.
LP: . . . . BNIA FOUR

Psycoplasma

RADIO FLIES.
LP: . . . . M 8903

Psylons

PSYLONS IS GOLDEN.
MC: . . . . BB 016

Pub songs

FIFTY CLASSIC PUB SONGS (Various artists).
LP: . . . . PUB 001
MC: . . . . PUBC 001

FIFTY CLASSIC PUB SONGS (A & R LABEL) (Various artists).
LP: . . . . PUB 50
MC: . . . . PUBC 50

Public Enemy

FEAR OF A BLACK PLANET.
Tracks: / Contract on the world love jam / Brothers gonna work it out / 911 is a joke / Incident at 66.6 FM / Welcome to the terrordome / Meet the G that killed me / Pollywanacraka / Anti-nigger machine / Burn Hollywood burn / Power to the people / Who stole the soul / Fear of a black planet / Revolutionary generation / Can't do nuttin' for ya man / Reggie jax / Leave this off your fu**in' charts / B side wins again / War at 33 and a third / Final count of the collision between us and them.
LP: 4662811
MC: 4662814

IT TAKES A NATION OF MILLIONS TO HOLD US BACK.
Tracks: / Countdown to Armageddon / Bring the noise / Don't believe the hype / Flavor flav cold lampin' / Terminator X to the edge of panic / Mind terrorist / Louder than a bomb / Caught, can we get a witness / Show 'em whatcha got / She watch channel zero? / Night of the living baseheads / Black steel in the hour of chaos / Security of the first world / Rebel without a pause / Prophets of rage / Party for your right to fight.
LP: 4624151
MC: 4624154
LP: . . . . BFW 44303

PUBLIC ENEMY: INTERVIEW PICTURE DISC.
LPPD: . . . . BAK 2113

YO, BUM RUSH THE SHOW.
Tracks: / You're gonna get yours / Sophisticated bitch / Miuzi weighs a ton / Time bomb / Too much posse / Rightstarter (message to a black man) / Public enemy no.1 / M.P.E. / Yo, bum rush the show / Raise the roof / Megablast / Terminator X speaks with his hands.
LP: 4504821
MC: 4504824

Public Image Ltd (PIL)

9.
Tracks: / Happy / Disappointed / Warrior / U.S.L.S. / Sand castles in the snow / Worry / Brave new world / Just like that / Same old story / Armada.
LP: . . . . V 2588
MC: . . . . TCV 2588
MC: . . . . OVEDC 348
LP: . . . . OVED 348

ALBUM.
Tracks: / F.F.F. / Rise / Fishing / Round / Bags / Home / Ease.
LP: . . . . V 2366
MC: . . . . TCV 2366
LP: . . . . OVED 245
MC: . . . . OVEDC 245

FLOWERS OF ROMANCE.
Tracks: / Four enclosed walls / Track 8 / Phenagen / Flowers of romance / Under the house / Hymies him / Banging the door / Go back / Francis massacre.
LP: . . . . OVED 51
MC: . . . . OVEDC 51
LP: . . . . V 2189

GREATEST HITS: PUBLIC IMAGE LTD (Greatest hits so far).
Tracks: / Public image / Death disco / Memories / Careering / Flowers of romance / This is not a love song / Rise / Home / Seattle / Body, The / Rules and regulations / Disappointed / Warrior / Don't ask me.
LP: . . . . V 2644
MC: . . . . TCV 2644

HAPPY?.
Tracks: / Seattle / Rules and regulations / Body, The / Save me / Hard times / Open and revolving / Angry / Fat chance hotel.
LP: . . . . V 2455
MC: . . . . TCV 2455
LP: . . . . OVED 299
MC: . . . . OVEDC 299

LIVE IN TOKYO.
Tracks: / Annalisa / Religion / Low life / Flowers of romance / Death Disco / Solitaire / (This is not a) love song / Bad life / Banging the door / Under the house.
2LP: . . . . VGD 3508
MC: . . . . VGDC 3508

METAL BOX.
Tracks: / Albatross / Memories / Swan lake / Poptones / Careering / No birds / Graveyard / Suit, The / Bad baby / Socialist / Chant / Radio 4.
LP: . . . . METAL 1

PARIS AU PRINTEMPS (PARIS IN SPRING).
Tracks: / Theme / Chant / Careering / Bad baby / Attack / Poptones / Lowlife.
LP: . . . . OVED 50
MC: . . . . OVEDC 50

PIL: INTERVIEW PICTURE DISC.
LPPD: . . . . BAK 2045

PUBLIC IMAGE.
Tracks: / Theme / Religion 1 / Religion 2 / Annalisa / Fodderstompt / Low life / Public image / Attack.
LP: . . . . OVED 160
MC: . . . . OVEDC 160
LP: . . . . V 2114
MC: . . . . TCV 2114

SECOND EDITION.
Tracks: / Albatross / Memories / Swan lake / Pop tones / Careering / Socialist / Graveyard / Suit, The / Bad baby / No birds do sing / Chant / Radio 4.
2LP: . . . . VD 2512
2LP: . . . . VGD 3513
MC: . . . . MBCAS 1

THIS IS WHAT YOU WANT..THIS IS WHAT YOU GET.
Tracks: / Bad life / This is not a love song / Solitaire / Tie me to the length of that / Pardon, The / Where are you? / 1981 / Order of death, The.
MC: . . . . TCV 2309
LP: . . . . OVED 176
MC: . . . . OVEDC 176
LP: . . . . V 2309

Puccini (composer)

BOHEME & TRAVIATA HIGHLIGHTS (Various artists).
MC: 4277184

MADAMA BUTTERFLY (See under Madama Butterfly for details).

PUCCINI'S BEST (Various artists).
LP: . . . . BES 1004
MC: . . . . BESC 1004

Pucho

TOUGH (Pucho & His Latin Soul Brothers).
LP: . . . . PR 7471

Puckett, Gary

UNION GAP.
LP: 63342

YOUNG GIRL (Puckett, Gary & The Union Gap).
MCSET: . . . . DTO 10254

Puckett, Riley

OLD TIME GREATS VOL. 2.
LP: . . . . OHCS 174

RED SAILS IN THE SUNSET.
Tracks: / Tie me to your apron strings / Margie / Nobody's business / Playmates / When I'm back in Tennessee / Get out and get under the moon / Walkin' my baby back home / Red sails in the sunset / Railroad boomer / South of the border / Oh Johnny, oh Johnny oh / Whistle and blow your blues away / Old fashioned locket / Tuck me to sleep in my old Kentucky home / Where the shy little violets grow / In a little garden.
LP: . . . . BFX 15280

Puddle Lane

CLOCK STRUCK THIRTEEN, THE (for ages 3-6) (Unknown narrator(s)).
MC: . . . . PLBP 215

HICKORY MOUSE (for ages 3-6) (Unknown narrator(s)).
MC: . . . . PLBP 218

LITTLE MONSTER, THE (for ages 3-6) (Unknown narrator(s)).
MC: . . . . PLBP 169

MAGIC BOX, THE (for ages 3-6) (Unknown narrator(s)).
MC: . . . . PLBP 162

MAGIC PENNY, THE (for ages 3-6) (Unknown narrator(s)).
MC: . . . . PLBP 217

MAGICIAN'S PARTY, THE (for ages 3-6) (Unknown narrator(s)).
MC: . . . . PLBP 216

MRS. PITTER PATTER & THE MAGICIAN (for ages 3-6) (Unknown narrator(s)).
MC: . . . . PLBP 168

OLD MR. GOTOBED (for ages 3-6) (Unknown narrator(s)).
MC: . . . . PLBP 221

TESSA AND THE MAGICIAN (for ages 3-6) (Unknown narrator(s)).
MC: . . . . PLBP 166

TESSA IN PUDDLE LANE (for ages 3-6) (Unknown narrator(s)).
MC: **PLBP 219**

TIM CATCHAMOUSE (for ages 3-6) (Unknown narrator(s)).
MC: **PLBP 161**

TOBY SPELLDRAGON AND THE MAGICIAN (for ages 3-6) (Unknown narrator(s)).
MC: **PLBP 222**

VANISHING MONSTER, THE (for ages 3-6) (Unknown narrator(s)).
MC: **PLBP 163**

WHEN THE MAGIC STOPPED (for ages 3-6) (Unknown narrator(s)).
MC: **PLBP 170**

WIDEAWAKE MICE GO TO MARKET (for ages 3-6) (Unknown narrator(s)).
MC: **PLBP 220**

WIDEAWAKE MICE, THE (for ages 3-6) (Unknown narrator(s)).
MC: **PLBP 167**

Puegamoides

BAILANDO (See under Alaska) (Puegamoides, The / Alaska).

Puente, Tito

AZUQUITA CE MAGNIFIQUE.
LP: **JMTS 1440**

BEST OF THE SIXTIES (Puente, Tito & His Orchestra).
Tracks: / Vete pa' la luna / Fat mama / Ay carino / Ran kan kan / Fancy feet / Babarabatoro / Cuando calienta el sol / T.P.'s shing a ling / Caramelos / Noro morales, A / Azukiki.
LP: **HOT 105**
MC: **TCHOT 105**

DANCEMANIA 80'S.
LP: **JMTS 1439**

EL REY (Puente, Tito & His Latin Ensemble).
Tracks: / Oye como va / Autumn leaves / Ran kan kan / Rainfall / Giant steps / Linda Chicana / Medley: Stella by starlight / Delirio / Equinoxe / El rey del timbal.
LP: **CJP 250**
MC: **CJPC 250**

GOZA MI TIMBAL.
Tracks: / Airegin / Cha cha cha / Pent up house / Picadillo a lo Puente / All blues / Ode to Cachao / Straight, no chaser / Lambada timbales.
MC: **CJPC 399**

HOMENAJE A BENY MORE VOLUME 3 (See under Cruz, Celia) (Puente, Tito & Celia Cruz).

MAMBO DIABLO (Puente, Tito & His Latin Ensemble).
Tracks: / Mambo diablo / Take five / Lush life / Pick yourself up / Lullaby of Birdland / No pienses asi / China / Eastern joy dance.
LP: **CJP 283**

ON BROADWAY (Puente, Tito & His Latin Ensemble).
Tracks: / T.P.'s special / Sophisticated lady / Bluesette / Soul song / On Broadway / Maria Cervantes / Jo je ti / First light.
LP: **CJP 207**
MC: **CJPC 207**

OUT OF THIS WORLD.
Tracks: / Descarga / In walked Bud / Sweet Georgia Brown / Amanecer guajira / S' wonderful / Lucky dog / Out of this world / Along came Betty / Latin percussion summit.
MC: **CJP 448C**

PUENTE IN PERCUSSION.
LP: **JMTS 1422**

PUENTE NOW.
LP: **516 002**
LP: **GNPS 2048**
MC: **GNP5 2048**

SALSA MEETS JAZZ.
LP: **CJP 354**
MC: **CJP 354 C**

SENSATION.
Tracks: / Fiesta a la king / Guajira for cal / Round Midnight / Que sensacion / Jordu / Cantigo en la distancia / Morning / Spain.
LP: **CJP 301**
MC: **CJPC 301**

UN POCO LOCO (Puente, Tito & His Latin Ensemble).
Tracks: / Un poco loco / Swinging shepherd blues (goes Latin) / Alma con alma / El timbalon / Chang / Machito forever / Prelude to a kiss / Killer Joe / Triton.
LP: **CJP 329**
MC: **CJPC 329**

Puerto Rico

PUERTO RICO (1929-46) (Various artists).
LP: **HQ 2075**

Puff The Magic Dragon

PUFF THE MAGIC DRAGON (Various artists).
MC: **STC 015**
MC: **STC 308b**

Puffalumps

PUFFALUMPS & THE CAVES (Buxton, Judy).
MC: **0 00 102182 6**

PUFFALUMPS & THE WIZARD, THE (Buxton, Judy).
MC: **0 00 102181 8**

Puget Sound...

PUGET SOUND GUITAR WORKSHOP Anthology (Various artists).
LP: **KM 128**

Pugh, John

RONNIE & JOHNNY (See under Morton, Ronnie) (Pugh, John/Ronnie Morton).

Pukwana, Dudu

COSMICS CHAPTER 90.
Tracks: / Mra khali / Hamba (go away) / Big apple / Cosmics / Blues for Nick / Zwelistsha.
MC: **AHUM 0054**

IN THE TOWNSHIPS (Pukwana, Dudu & Spear).
Tracks: / Baloyi / Ezilalini / Zukude / Sonia / Angel Nemali / Nobomyu / Sekela khuluma.
LP: **EWV 5**
MC: **TCEWV 5**

LIFE IN BRACKNELL & WILLISAU (Pukwana, Dudu & Zila).
Tracks: / Hug pine / Mahlomole / Lafente (Ntabeni - In the mountains) / Baqanga / Freely / Funk them up to Erika / Ziyekeleni(Let them be) / Big (pine)apple / Zama khwalo (try again).
LP: **ZL 2**

RADEBE-THEY SHOOT TO KILL (Pukwana, Dudu & John Stevens).
Tracks: / Mbizo Radebe Pt. 1 / Mbizo Radebe Pt.2.
LP: **AFF 179**

ZILA 86 (Pukwana, Dudu & Zila).
Tracks: / Madodana (the young ones) / Hamba (Go away) / Mra / Khali / Harare / Nonceba (merciful) / Nompongo / Let's get together / August one.
LP: **ZL 3**

Puleo, Johnny

JOHNNY PULEO.
MC: **ZCGAS 748**

Pull Both Ends

PULL BOTH ENDS (Original London cast) (Various artists).
Tracks: / Prelude (Every morning): *Various artists* / What about people: *Various artists* / After all (we're women): *Various artists* / Tiny touch, A: *Various artists* / Particular woman, A: *Various artists* / Some kind of love: *Various artists* / Decisions: *Various artists* / Put a little smile: *Various artists* / Wallowers: *Various artists* / If you knew the way I feel: *Various artists* / Get the world to dance: *Various artists*/ Here am I: *Various artists* / Strike: *Various artists* / Little leather book: *Various artists* / There's something about her: *Various artists* / Oh, Joe: *Various artists* / Can this be love?: *Various artists*/ We're ready: *Various artists* / Pullin' together: *Various artists.*
LP: **TERS 1028**

Pullen, Don

ALL THAT FUNK (See under Adams, George for details) (Pullen, Don/George Adams).

BREAKTHROUGH (Pullen, Don & Adams, George Quartet).
Tracks: / Mr. Smoothie / Just foolin' around / Song from the old country / We've been here all the time / Time for sobriety, A / Necessary blue, The (or thank you very much, Mr Monk).
LP: **BT 85122**

CAPRICORN RISING.
LP: **BSR 004**

CITY GATES (See under Adams, George for details) (Pullen, Don/George Adams).

DECISIONS (See under Adams, George) (Pullen, Don Quartet).

DON PULLEN PLAYS MONK.
LP: **K 28P 6368**

DON'T LOSE CONTROL (See under Adams, George) (Pullen, Don/George Adams).

EARTH BEAMS (See under Adams, George) (Pullen, Don/George Adams).

GEORGE ADAMS AND THE DON PULLEN QUARTET (see under Adams, George) (Adams, George & Don Pullen Quartet).

HEALING FORCE.
LP: **BSR 0010**

LIFE LINE (Pullen, Don Quartet).
MC: **SJP 1154**

LIVE AT MONTMARTRE (see under Adams, George) (Pullen, Don Quartet).

LIVE AT VILLAGE VANGUARD (See under Adams, George) (Pullen, Don/George Adams).

MONTREUX CONCERT.
LP: **K 50499**

MORE FUNK (See under Adams, George) (Pullen, Don/George Adams).

NEW BEGINNINGS.
Tracks: / Jana's delight / Once upon a time / Warriors / New beginnings / At the Cafe Centrale / Reap the whirlwind / Silence-death (CD only.).
LP: **B1 91785**
LP: **791 785 1**

RESOLUTION (Pullen, Don/H. Bluiett).
LP: **BSR 0014**

SOLO PIANO ALBUM.
LP: **3008**

SONG EVERLASTING (Pullen, Don & Adams, George Quartet).
Tracks: / Another reason to celebrate (Extra track on CD only) / Sunwatchers / Serenade for Sarah / 1529 Gunn Street / Warm up / Sing me a song everlasting.
LP: **BT 85143**
LP: **BLJ 46907**

WARRIORS.
LP: **BSR 0019**

Pullens, Vern

MINI LP COLLECTION.
LP: **MLP 8415**

Pullerman

PULLERFRAU.
LP: **084551**

Pulling Faces

DANCE OF GHOSTS.
LP: **PF 2**
MC: **PFC 2**

Pullins, Leroy

I'M A NUT.
Tracks: / I'm a nut / Knee deep / Out in the Smokehouse taking a bath / Tatersville auxiliary sewing circle, The / Meter maid / What's his name / I love you drops / Swimming at the bottom of the pool / I done you wrong song / Tickled pink / Okeefenokee / Billy Roy and Jackson Sam / Yellow / S tree towers / World what have I done.
LP: **BFX 15216**

Pullum, Joe

BLACK GAL.
LP: **AB 2012**

Pulp

FREAKS.
LP: **FIRELP 5**

IT.
LP: **REDLP 29**

Pulse 8

PULSE 8 (Various artists).
LP: **SURLP 010**
MC: **ZCSUK 10**

Puma, Joe

SHINING HOUR.
LP: **RSR 102**

Pump

DECORATION, THE.
LP: **FIB 003**

JUST WANT TO DANCE.
MC: **SRC 002**

Pump Blenders

FUNK THE PEOPLE LIVE.
Tracks: / Work that sucker to death / All the freaks are freaking now / Funk the people / Get, get, get on down y'all / Love boat / Talking about freakbody / Dip.
LP: **CHR 1501**
MC: **ZCHR 1501**

Pump Boys & Dinettes

PUMP BOYS & DINETTES (Original Broadway cast) (Various artists).
Tracks: / Highway 57: *Various artists* / Taking it slow: *Various artists* / Serve yourself: *Various artists*/ Menu song: *Various artists* / Best man, The: *Various artists* / Fishermans prayer: *Various artists*/ Catfish: *Various artists* / Mamaw: *Various artists* / Be good or be gone: *Various artists* / Drinkin' shoes: *Various artists* / Pump boys: *Various artists* / Mona: *Various artists* / Night Dolly Parton was nearly mine, The: *Various artists* / Tips: *Various artists* / Sister: *Various artists* / Vacation: *Various artists* / No holds barred: *Various artists* / Farmer Tan: *Various artists* / Closing time: *Various artists.*
LP: **FM 37790**
MC: **FMT 37790**

Pump Up The Noise

PUMP UP THE NOISE D.J. Rhythm tracks.
LP: **HOP 228**

Pumping Iron

PUMPING IRON 2 (THE WOMEN) (Various artists).
LP: **ISTA 9**

Punannu Tegreg

PUNANNU TEGREG (VOLUME 1) (Various artists).
LP: **VPRL 1119**

Punany Train

PUNANY TRAIN (Various artists).
LP: **DSR 9561**

Punch, Kid

CALIFORNIA CRUSADERS, VOL. 2 (Punch, Kid & Captain John Hardy).
LP: **GHB 192**

CALIFORNIA CRUSADERS, VOL. 3 (Punch, Kid & Captain John Hardy).
LP: **GHB 193**

KID PUNCH & CAPTAIN JOHN HANDY.
LP: **JCE 12**

Punchline

PUNCHLINE (Film soundtrack) (Various artists).
LP: **SP 392 2**
MC: **CS 392 2**

Pungent Stench

FOR GOD YOUR SOUL.
LP: **082973**

PUNGENT STENCH.
LP: **082 932**

SPLIT LP (Pungent Stench/Disharmonic Orchestra).
LP: **NB 019**

Punilux

SEVEN.
LP: **REDLP 034**

Punishment of luxury

LAUGHING ACADEMY (ALBUM).
LP: **UAG 30258**

Punjab

FLUTE DU PENDJAB (Various artists).
Tracks: / Raga jog: *Various artists* / Nat bhairava: *Various artists* / Dhun pahari: *Various artists.*
LP: **ARN 33344**

Punk ...

ALLE 24 GOED (Various artists).
LP: **TORPO 002**

ANGELS WITH DIRTY FACES (Various artists).
LP: **MPUNK 8**

BEST OF 20 OF ANOTHER KIND (Various artists).
Tracks: / In the city: *Jam* / Borstal breakout: *Sham 69* / Gary Gilmore's eyes: *Adverts* / Homicide: *999* / First time: *Boys* / No more heroes: *Stranglers* / No entry: *Sham 69* / No excuses: *Jolt*/ I'm on heat: *Lurkers* / 'A' bomb in Wardour Street: *Jam* / Emergency: *999* / Out in the dark: *Lurkers*/ Now it's gone: *Chords* / If the kids are united: *Sham 69* / Strange town: *Jam* / Hersham boys: *Sham 69* / Lost love: *Carpettes* / Butterfly collector, The: *Jam* / Down in the park: *Tubeway Army* / Tracks: *Tubeway Army.*
2LP: **CCSLP 215**
MC: **CCSMC 215**

BULLSHIT DETECTOR (Various artists).
LP: **221984/3**

BURNING AMBITIONS (History of punk) (Various artists).
Tracks: / Boredom: *Buzzcocks* / Bingo master's breakout: *Fall* / 12XU: *Wire* / Life: *ATV* / Keys to your heart: *101'ers* / I'm alive / Gary Gilmore's eyes: *Adverts* / (Get a) grip (on yourself): *Stranglers*/ Baby baby: *Vibrators* / Oh bondage, up yours!: *X-Ray Spex* / I'm stranded: *Saints* / Chinese rocks: *Heartbreakers* / Love song: *Damned* / In a rut: *Ruts* / Stranglehold: *UK Subs* / Flares and slippers: *Cockney Rejects* / Wait, The: *Killing Joke* / Holiday in Cambodia: *Dead Kennedys* / Last rockers: *Vice Squad* / Someone's gonna die: *Anti Pasti* / City baby attacked by rats: *G.B.H.* / Russians

in the DHSS: *Attila The Stockbroker* / Lust for glory: *Angelic Upstarts*.
LP: .... BRED 3

DAFFODILS TO THE DAFFODILS HERE'S THE DAFFODILS (Various artists).
LP: .... PAX 19

DIGGING THE WATER (Various artists).
Tracks: / Our production: *Disorder* / Kill your baby: *Chaos UK* / Senil fools: *Concrete Sox* / Single ticket to hell: *Ripcord* / Coconut song: *Vicious Circle* / Ultracool: *CCM* / Bullshit propoganda: *Extreme* Noise / Life: *Electro Hippies* / Oldest trick in the book: *Generic* / Slumber party: *Stupids* / Firing line: *Dpraved* / Truth: *Bad Dress Sense* / Mr. Poison / Fairer sex, The: *Civilised Society* / Face the facts: *Eyes On You* / Miseravle bastards: *Potential Threat* / Pigs for the slaughter: *Oi Polloi*.
LP: .... ACHE 003

DIMINISHED RESPONSIBILITY (Various artists).
LP: .... BBPLP 01

FAREWELL TO THE ROXY (Various artists).
Tracks: / Strange boy: *Blitz (group)* / Smile and wave goodbye: *Acme Sewage Co.* / Relics from the past: *Karloff*, Billy / I live in a car: *UK Subs* / Get yourself killed: *Tickets* / Never wanna leave: *Red Lights*/ Here comes the knife: *XL5's* / TV drink: *Jets (British)* / Sniper: *Streets...* / Tough on you: *Plastix*/ Fun fun fun: *Bears* / Vertigo: *Open Sore* / Lullabies lie: *Crabs*.
LP: .... LIP 2

FEAR OF A PUNK PLANET (Various artists).
LP: .... TX 92781

FURTHER CHANGES (Various artists).
LP: .... GRAM 001

KICK UP THE ARSE, VOL 1 (Various artists).
LP: .... ASS 21

LET'S GET PISSED (Various artists).
LP: .... CULT 001

LET'S GET PISSED ITS CHRISTMAS PART 2 (Various artists).
LP: .... CULT 002

LIFE'S A RIOT AND THEN YOU DIE (Various artists).
LP: .... CITY 009

LIVE AT THE RAT (Various artists).
LP: .... RAT 528

LIVE AT THE ROXY (Various artists).
LP: .... RRLP 132
MC: .... RRLC 132

LIVE AT THE ROXY (Various artists).
LP: .... FNARRLP 003

MAGGIE MAGGIE MAGGIE OUT OUT OUT (Various artists).
Tracks: / Open your eyes: *Action Pact* / Government stinks: *Violators* / Woman in disguise: *Angelic Upstarts*/ F**k religion, f**k politics, f**k the lot of you: *Chaotic Dischord* / Flood of lies: *UK Subs* / You'll never know: *Vice Squad* / Crisis: *Red Alert* / Government policy: *Expelled* / Warning: *Discharge* / Kill the poor: *Dead Kennedys* / Government downfall: *Samples* / Burn 'em down: *Abrasive Wheels* / Keep Britain untidy: *Peter & The Test Tube Babies* / Government's to blame: *Varukers* / Police story: *Partisans*/ Give us a future: *One Way System*.
LP: .... GRAM 28
MC: .... CGRAM 28

MOONLIGHT TAPES (Various artists).
LP: .... DANCE 1

MOTHER OF A PUNK (Various artists).
LP: .... CON 13

NEW YORK HARDCORE (Various artists).
MC: .... BL 001C

NO MORE HEROES (Music that influenced a generation) (Various artists).
Tracks: / Going underground: *Jam* / Promises: *Buzzcocks* / Rat trap: *Boomtown Rats* / My perfect cousin: *Undertones* / If the kids are united: *Sham 69* / Teenage kicks: *Undertones* (CD only.) / Something better change: *Stranglers* (CD only.) / No more heroes: *Stranglers* / Eton rifles: *Jam* / Ever fallen in love (with someone you shouldn't've): *Buzzcocks* / I don't like Mondays: *Boomtown Rats* / Jimmy Jimmy: *Undertones*/ Hersham boys: *Sham 69* / Peaches: *Stranglers*.
LP: .... FA 3233
MC: .... TCFA 3233

OOPS, WRONG STEREOTYPE (Various artists).
LP: .... VIRUS 68

PARTY POOPING PUNK ROCK PROVOCATION (Various artists).
LP: .... DOZENTH 1

PUNK (Various artists).
Tracks: / What do I get (live): *Buzzcocks* / E.M.I.: *Sex Pistols* / Personality crisis: *New York Dolls*/ Angels with dirty faces (live): *Sham 69* / Born to lose (live): *Thunders, Johnny* / Bored teenagers (live): *Adverts*/ Looking for a kiss: *New York Dolls* / Rip off (live): *Sham 69* / One track mind (live): *Thunders, Johnny*/ Boston babies (live): *Slaughter & the Dogs* / Pretty vacant (live): *Sex Pistols* / To time to be 21 (live): *Adverts*/ Hear nothing, see nothing, say nothing: *Discharge* / Brickfield nights (live): *Boys* / Time's up (live): *Buzzcocks*.
MC: .... MCTC 015

PUNK AND DISORDERLY (Various artists).
LP: .... AABT 100
MC: .... AABTC 100

PUNK LIVES LET'S SLAM (Various artists).
LP: .... SLAM 002

PUNK LIVES LET'S SLAM 2 (Various artists).
LP: .... SLAM 003

PUNK ON THE ROAD (Various artists).
LP: .... SKUNXLP 1

PUNK ROCKERS (Various artists).
MC: .... ARLC 1016

RAW COMPILATION VOL.1 (Various artists).
LP: .... FNARRLP 009

RIOTOUS ASSEMBLY (Various artists).
LP: .... ASSEMBLY ONE

ROT IN HELL (77) (Various artists).
LP: .... ASS 15

ROXY, LONDON WC2 (JAN-APR 77) (Various artists).
Tracks: / Runaway: *Slaughter & The...* (Slaughter & the dogs) / Boston babies: *Slaughter & The...* (Slaughter & the dogs (Rossi/Barrett)) / Freedom: *Unwanted* / Lowdown: *Wire* / 1.2.X.U.: *Wire* / Bored teenagers: *Adverts* / Hard lovin' man: *Moped, Johnny* / Don't need it: *Eater* / Oh bondage, up yours!: *X-Ray Spex* / Breakdown: *Buzzcocks* / Love battery: *Buzzcocks*.
LP: .... EMS 1189
MC: .... TCEMS 1189

SECRET LIFE OF PUNKS (Various artists).
Tracks: / Dogs of war: *Exploited* / One law for them: *4 Skins* / Kids of the 80's: *Infra Riot* / No U turns: *Partisans* / Employers black list: *Business* / Youth: *Blitz (group)* / Harry may: *Business*/ Jet boy jet girl: *Chron Gen* / King of the jungle: *Last Resort* / Maniac: *Peter & The Test Tube Babies*/ Catch 22: *Infra Riot* / Yesterdays heroes: *4 Skins* / Army life: *Exploited* / I lost my love to a UK sub: *Gonads*.
LP: .... SEC 10
MC: .... TSEC 10

SHORT CIRCUIT - LIVE AT THE ELECTRIC CIRCUS (Various artists).
Tracks: / Stepping out: *Fall* / (You never see a nipple in the) Daily Express: *Cooper Clarke, John* / At a later date: *Joy Division* / Persecution complex: *Drones* / Makka splaff (The colly man): *Steel Pulse* / I married a monster from outer space: *Cooper Clarke, John* / Last orders: *Fall* / Time's up: *Buzzcocks*.
MLP: .... OVED 170
MLP: .... VCL 5003

THERE IS NO FUTURE (Various artists).
LP: .... PUNK 9

THEY ONLY COME OUT AT NIGHT (Various artists).
LP: .... CLAYLP 17M

TRANSWORLD..VOL. 2 (1964-66) (Various artists).
LP: .... TW 65

UK/DK (Original soundtrack) (Various artists).
Tracks: / U.S.A.: *Exploited* / Joker in the pack: *Various artists* / No security: *Chaos UK* / Life: *Disorder*/ Blind justice: *Business* / Things that need: *Various artists* / Fighter pilot: *Vibrators* / Ignite: *Damned* / You talk, we talk: *Pressure* / Viva la revolution: *Various artists* / Jerusalem: *One Way System* / Soldier boy: *Varukers* / 42nd Street: *Angelic Upstarts* / Stand strong, stand proud: *Vice Squad*.
LP: .... GRAM 06

ULTIMATE HISTORY OF THE PUNK UNIVERSE (Various artists).
LPS: .... JOCK BOX 2

VINYL SOLUTION (Various artists).
Tracks: / Orgasm addict: *Buzzcocks* / Valley of the dolls: *Generation X* / Peaches: *Stranglers* / I'm stranded: *Saints* / Straw dogs: *Stiff Little Fingers* / Little Red Riding Hood: *999* / Kill the poor: *Dead Kennedys* / Ever fallen in love (with someone you shouldn't've): *Buzzcocks* / One hundred punks: *Generation* X / Go buddy go: *Stranglers* / Stranglehold: *UK Subs* / Greatest cockney rip off: *Cockney Rejects*/ White riot: *Angelic Upstarts* / Jet boy, jet girl: *Damned* / Wildkat ways: *Meteors* / You crack me up: *Meteors*.
LP: .... DOJOLP 17

WARGASM (Various artists).
LP: .... PAX 4

WE DON'T WANT YOUR FUCKING LAW (Various artists).
LP: .... FIGHT 7

WE DON'T WANT YOUR FUCKING WAR (Various artists).
LP: .... FIGHT 5

WE WON'T BE YOUR FUCKING POOR (Various artists).
Tracks: / Casulty, The: *Post Mortem* / Apathy: *Political Asylum* / Please help: *Kulturkampf* / Tortured agony: *Distrust* / Kick back, question, Disobey: *Stagnant Era* / America out: *Corpse* / Animal instincts: *AOA* / How many more lies: *Conflict* / Unjustified actions: *Shrapnel* / Victim: *Revulsion* / Sheer funk: *Toczek, Nick* / Skin deep: *Stone The Crows* / Nuclear attack: *Death Sentence* / Music for the streets: *Classified protest* / Death trades: *Systematic Annex* / Aids charade: *Fallout* / General strike: *D.O.A.* / Rough justice: *Miasma* / Insult to injury: *Indian Dream* / Dig your own grave: *Sacrilege*/ Turkey, The: *Virus* / Drugged up to the state of....: *Abreaction* / Dig up the Duke: *Waste* / I'm your leader: *Diatribe* / No filthy nuclear power: *Polloi, Oi*.
2LP: .... MORT 13

WET DREAMS (Various artists).
LP: .... ASS 4

WHAT ARE YOU DOING? (Various artists).
LP: .... HOLEIN 1

WORLD CLASS PUNK (Various artists).
MC: .... A 131

WORLD WAR III (Various artists).
LP: .... WW 001

Purbrook, Colin

COLIN PURBROOK TRIO With Peter King (Purbrook, Colin/Peter King).
MC: .... SPJCS 538

Purcell (composer)

CHACONY (English Chamber Orchestra).
MC: 4251604

Pure Gold

PURE GOLD VOL.1 (Various artists).
LP: .... SUCCESS 162

Pure Overkill

PURE OVERKILL (Various artists).
LP: .... GRC 2162

Pure Prairie League

CAN'T HOLD BACK.
Tracks: / Can't hold back / I can't believe / Rude rude awakening / White line / Misery train / Restless woman / I'm going away / Jerene / Livin' it alone / Fool fool / Goodbye so long.
LP: .... PL 13335

DANCE.
Tracks: / Dance / In the morning / All the way / Livin' each day at a time / Fade away / Tornado warning / Catfishin' / Help yourself / San Antonio / All the lonesome cowboys.
LP: .... PL 11924

FIRIN' UP.
Tracks: / I'm almost ready / Give it up / Too many heartaches in paradise / She's all mine / You're my true love / Let me love you tonight / I can't stop the feelin' / Lifetime of nightmare / I'll be damned / Jenny Lou.
LP: .... NBLP 7212

JUST FLY.
Tracks: / Place in the middle / Slim pickin's / Love will grow / You don't have to be alone / Love is falling / Just fly / Lifetime / Working in the coal mine / My young girl / Bad dream.
LP: .... PL 12590
MC: .... PK 12590

PURE PRAIRIE COLLECTION.
Tracks: / Tears / You're between me / Woman / It's all on me / Early morning riser / Falling in and out of love / Amie / Jazzman / Boulder skies / Angel / Call me, tell me / Two lane highway / Just can't believe it / That'll be the day / Going home.
LP: .... INTS 5101
MC: .... INTK 5101

LP: .... NL 89335
MC: .... NK 89335

SOMETHING IN THE NIGHT.
Tracks: / Don't keep me hangin' / Love me again / Hold on to our hearts / Something in the night / Do you love truly Julie / You're mine tonight / Still right here in my heart / I wanna know your name / Feel that fire / Tell me one more time.
LP: 6480 016
MC: 7190 016

Pure Rock

PURE ROCK - 10 BEST FROM THE WEST (Various artists).
LP: .... RNLP 70082

Purely Physical

BEAUTIFUL (See Under Powell, Jenny).

Purify, James

100% PURIFIED SOUL (Purify, James & Bobby).
Tracks: / I take what I want / Untie me / I've got everything I need (I've got you) / Wish you didn't have to go / Do unto me / You left the water running / I don't want to have to wait / I'm your puppet / Shake a tail feather / So many reasons / I've been loving you too long / Sixteen tons / Change is gonna come, A / Let love come between us / Blame me (don't blame my heart) / You can't keep a good man down.
MC: .... TCCRB 1182
LP: .... CRB 1182

Purim, Flora

500 MILES HIGH.
Tracks: / O cantador / Bridge / 500 miles high / Craro E canels / Baia / Un / Jive talk.
LP: .... M 9070

COLOURS OF LIFE, THE (See under Moreira, Airto) (Purim, Flora & Airto Moreira).

HUMBLE PEOPLE (Purim, Flora & Airto).
Tracks: / 20 years blue / Move it on up / Jogral / Bad jive / Humble people / Nvula ieza / Humbiumbi / Jungle cry / New flora / Shoulder (Ombro).
LP: .... GW 3007
MC: .... GWC 3007

MAGICIANS, THE (Purim, Flora & Airto).
Tracks: / Sweet baby blues / Garimpo / Esquinas / Bird of paradise / Magicians, The / Jennifer / Jump / Two minutes of peace / Love reborn.
LP: .... CCR 5001
MC: .... CRC 5001

MIDNIGHT SUN, THE.
Tracks: / Angel eyes / Light as a feather / Midnight sun, The / Nothing will be as it was / Las olas / Flora nova / A Esperanca / Good morning heartache / Bodas de prata.
MC: .... TCVE 21
LP: .... VE 21

MILESTONE MEMORIES.
Tracks: / Moon Dreams / Vera Cruz / Windows / Cravo E Canela / What Can I Say? / Casa Forte / Samba Michel / Open your eyes you can fly / Overture.
LP: .... BGP 1008
MC: .... BGPC 1008

SUN IS OUT, THE (Purim, Flora & Airto Moreira).
Tracks: / Samba do cantor / Viver de arnor / Sun is out, The / Asas do imaginacao / Midday sun / Hope / Pablo sereno / Lua Flora / Forever friends / Olivia (changes).
LP: .... CR 5003
MC: .... CR 5003C

Purim, Yana

BIRD OF BRAZIL.
LP: .... SNTF 1010

HARVEST TIME (Purim, Yana and Herbie Hancock).
Tracks: / It happens every day / Gentle rain, The / You must believe in Spring / Amazonas / Harvest time / Malaguena / Non-stop to Brazil / Monster and the flower, The.
LP: .... SNTF 1036

Purnell, Alton

ALTON PURNELL: 1958.
LP: .... C 5528

ALTON PURNELL - LIVE.
LP: .... CLPS 1018

ALTON PURNELL MEETS HOULIND.
Tracks: / Four or five times / I'll always be in love with you / Little coquette / Lady be good / Exactly like you / Runnin' wild / Melancholy blues / Altons blues.
MC: .... MC 101

Purple Cow & Goops

PURPLE COW & GOOPS G. Burgess (Channing, Carol).
MC: .... CP 1656

Purple Gang

GRANNY TAKES A TRIP.
LP: . . . . **RAZ 22**

Purple Hearts

BEAT THAT.
Tracks: / Jimmy / Perfect world / Something you can't have / Beat that / Nothin's left / Frustration / If you need me / Can't stay here / Can't help thinking about me / Slay it with flowers / I've been away.
LP: . . . . **FIX 2**

POP-ISH FRENZY.
LP: . . . . **RAZS 19**

Purple Helmets

RIDE AGAIN.
Tracks: / Brand new cadillac / I'm crying / Rosalin / She's not there / First I look at the purse / Get yourself home / Oh pretty woman / Homework / Don't you like what I do / Money / Under the sun / Baby let me take you home / She la la (Only on CD.) / Baby (Only on CD.) / Everything's alright (Only on CD.).
LP: . . . . **GRAM 42**
MC: . . . . **CGRAM 42**
LP: . . . . **ROSE 160**
MC: . . . . **ROSE 160C**

Purple Outside

MYSTERY LANE.
LP: . . . . **NAR 052**
MC: . . . . **NARC 052**

Purple Rain

PURPLE RAIN (See under Prince) (Prince & The Revolution).

Purple Rose Of Cairo

PURPLE ROSE OF CAIRO (Film soundtrack) (Hyman, Dick).
LP: **2522251**
MC: **2522254**

Purple Things

PURPLE THINGS.
LP: . . . . **FREELP 1**

Purpleman

PURPLEMAN SAVES PAPPA TOLLO IN A DANCE HALL STYLE.
LP: . . . . **VSLP 4024**

Pursey, Jimmy

ALIEN ORPHAN.
Tracks: / First deadly sin / Why / I'm a human being / Who's making who happy / Jungle west one / On invite only / Spies / Oh isn't it a weird weird world / Alien orphan / One night in Paris / Technical / Naughty boys like naughty girls.
LP: . . . . **EPC 85235**

IMAGINATION CAMOUFLAGE.
Tracks: / Moon morning funday / Have a nice day / Freak show / Situation's vacant / Your mother should have told you / Playground soldier / Just another memory / White trash / Fifty fifty / You never can tell / Lucky man.
LP: **2442 180**

Pursuit

PURSUIT (Original Soundtrack) (Various artists).
LP: . . . . **POLS 1055**
MC: . . . . **POLSC 1055**

Pursuit Of Happiness

LOVE JUNK.
Tracks: / Hard to laugh / She's so young / Walking in the woods / Looking for girls / Tree of knowledge / Ten fingers / Consciousness raising / Beautiful white / Man's best friend / Killed by love.
LP: . . . . **CHR 1675**
MC: . . . . **XCHR 1675**

ONE SIDED STORY.
LP: . . . . **CHR 1757**
MC: . . . . **ZCHR 1757**

Purves, Libby

ONE SUMMERS GRACE.
MCSET: . . . . **ZBBC 1167**

Purvis, Geoff

BORDER FIDDLER, THE (Purvis, Geoff & The Border Country Dance Band).
Tracks: / Ian's fancy / Jean's reel / Richard Brannan's favourite / Kings favourite / Portree jig / Colley's / Colonel Rodney / Sheehan's reel / Tom Billy's / Doonside up / Nab hornpipe / Rialto, The / Professor Blackie / Rambling pitchfork, The / Swallows nest / Cherish the ladies / Humours of Glendart / Capt. Cameron's / Scotlandwell / Tricia's tune / Beeswing, The / Tykeside, The / Cuckoo waltz / Sally gardens / O'Rourke's / Silver spear / Down in the broom / Yellow haired laddie / Master MacDermot's / Dillon Brown / Ron McDonald's / Joan C MacKenzie / Cork Hill.
LP: . . . . **FE 003**

Purvis, Pam

HEART SONG (Purvis, Pam / Bob Ackerman).
LP: . . . . **BKH 51201**

Push Button Pleasure

LAST DISSONANCE, THE.
LP: . . . . **HAM 19**

VAST DIFFERENCE, THE.
LP: . . . . **HAM 14**

Pushtwangers

PUSHTWANGERS.
LP: . . . . **BC 9008**

Puss In Boots

PUSS IN BOOTS (well loved tales age up to 9) (Unknown narrator(s)).
Tracks: / Puss 'n' boots / Bearskin / One eye, two eyes and three eyes / Cinderella / Little farmer, The.
MC: . . . . **ANV 621**
MC: . . . . **PLB 54**

PUSS IN BOOTS & JACK & THE BEANSTALK (Graham, J).
MC: . . . . **TS 330**

PUSS IN BOOTS & OTHER STORIES
For children aged 3-7 (Various artists).
MC: . . . . **VCA 603**

Pussy Galore

DIAL 'M' FOR MOTHERF*CKER.
Tracks: / Understand me / Kicked out / Undertaker / Dick Johnson / Eat me / Evil eye / Hang on / SM 57 / Solo sex / Dwda / 1 hour later / Waxhead / Adwd 2.
LP: . . . . **INCLP 001**
MC: . . . . **INCMC 001**

GROOVY HATE FK.**
LP: . . . . **SUK 001**

HISTORIA DELLA MUSICA-ROCK.
LP: . . . . **ROUGH 149**
MC: . . . . **ROUGHC 149**

RIGHT NOW.
LP: **33PROD 19**

SUGAR SHIT SHARP.
Tracks: / Yu gung / Adolescent wet dream / Brick / Handshake / Sweet little hi-fi / Renegade.
LP: . . . . **M PROD 15**
MC: . . . . **M PRODC 15**

Put On Your Dancing

PUT ON YOUR DANCING SHOES (Various artists).
LP: . . . . **EG 2605721**
MC: . . . . **EG 2605724**

Puthli, Asha

DEVIL IS LOOSE.
Tracks: / Flying fish / Devil is loose, The / Hello everyone / Wonder why / My buddy and me / Say yes / Space talk / Our love is making me sing / Goodnight.
LP: . . . . **CBS 81443**

Putnam String County

PUTMAN STRING COUNTY BAND.
LP: . . . . **ROUNDER 3003**

Pyatt, Rosina

TO CATCH AN EARL.
MC: . . . . **PMB 005**

Pyewackett

7 TO MIDNIGHT.
LP: . . . . **FAM 47**

MAN IN THE MOON DRINKS CLARET, THE.
LP: . . . . **FAM 43**

PYEWACKETT.
LP: . . . . **DIN 312**

THIS CRAZY PARADISE.
LP: . . . . **FAM 59**
MC: . . . . **FAM 59C**

Pyjama Sutra

KILLING TIME.
LP: . . . . **PLASLP 004**

Pyle, Howard

MEN OF IRON (Richardson, Ian).
MC: **1704**

Pylon

CHOMP.
Tracks: / K / Yo-Yo / Beep / Italian movie theme / Crazy / M-Train / Buzz / No clocks / Reptiles / Spider / Gyrate / Altitude.
LP: . . . . **DB 65**
MC: . . . . **DBC 65**

GYRATE.
LP: . . . . **ARM 5**

Pyne, Mick

ALONE TOGETHER (piano/cornet duets).
LP: . . . . **SPJ 506**

JON EARDLEY & MICK PYNE (See Eardley, Jon & Mick Pyne) (Pyne, Mick & Jon Eardley).

LITTLE BLUE, A (Pyne, Mick Quartet).
Tracks: / Another nice mess / Space in time / Di's waltz / Red zinger / Little blue, A / Nothing less than love.
LP: . . . . **MM 073**

MICK PYNE QUARTET (Pyne, Mick Quartet).
LP: . . . . **MM 003**

ONCE IN A WHILE (Pyne, Mike & Humphrey Littleton).
LP: . . . . **BLP 12149**

Pyrolator

WUNDERLAND.
LP: . . . . **WR 26**

Python Lee Jackson

IN A BROKEN DREAM (Python Lee Jackson(feat. Rod Stewart)).
LP: . . . . **GNPS 2066**
MC: **GNP5 2066**
MC: . . . . **VCA 025**

Q5

STEEL THE LIGHT.
MC: . . . . **TMFN 39**
LP: . . . . **MFN 39**

STEEL THE LIGHT/WHEN THE MIRROR CRACKS (See When the mirror cracks for CD).

WHEN THE MIRROR CRACKS.
LP: . . . . **MFN 64**
MC: . . . . **TMFN 64**

Q The Winged Serpent

Q - THE WINGED SERPENT/ THE POWER (Original Soundtracks) (Various artists).
LP: . . . . **C'BUS 206**

Q.B.VII

Q.B.VII (QUEEN'S BENCH NO.7) (Various artists).
LP: **254890.1**

Q.E.D.

Q.E.D. (Various artists).
Tracks: / Organofonia ramovs: *Laibach* / Ataxia: *Dieform* / Untitled excerpt: *2'EV* / Ebony tower in the Orient water: *Radio Rabotnik TV* / Kennen sie koein ?: *Der Plan* / Delerium 2: *Chris & Cosey* / HLA: *Non Toxique Lost* / Tribal noise 2: *Het Zweet* / Anyway, don't do the sport fuck: *Spring As Der Wolken*/ Call, The: *Banabila, Michel* / Restimulation: *Hafler Trio* / Mutation waltz: *Manoton, K. B.* / Menegins: *Einsturzende Neubauten* / 11: *De Executie/Klec* / E & E: *Pig D4* / Getuich der miljoenen: *Zegueld*, Peter / L'espirit domine l'etoile: *Etant Donnes* / Oirat: *Various artists* / I wanna be injured, l'ace d'or: *Club Moral* / Liberal 1:13: *Zero Kama* / C.B.A.: *S.B.O.T.H.I* / Demonomania: *Test Department*.
LPS: . . . . **NLC 001**

Q-Tips

Q-TIPS (Q-Tips featuring Paul Young).
Tracks: / Some kinda wonderful / Tracks of my tears / Please don't stay at home / You are the life inside of me / In crowd, The / Beautiful memory, (Now I'm left with a) / Sysljfm (the letter song) / Man can't lose, A / Uncle Willy / Different world / Keep your shoes on.
LP: . . . . **MFP 5770**
MC: . . . . **TCMFP 5770**
LP: . . . . **CHR 1255**
MC: . . . . **ZCHR 1255**

Quadrant

TOASTS DUKE ELLINGTON.
Tracks: / Caravan / Sophisticated lady / All too soon / I'm beginning to see the light / Mood indigo / Solitude / Take the 'A' train / Main stem / In a sentimental mood / Just a sittin' and a rockin' / Rocks in my bed.
LP: **2312 117**

Quadrophonia

COZMIC JAM.
Tracks: / Quadrophonia / Man with the masterplan / Djoum 1000 / Hardhead / Cozmic jam / Find the time (part 1) / Schizophrenia -the worst day of my life / Wave of the future, The / Original statement / Cozm' and Ovo / Quadrophonia (remix) / 9 lives of Pitou, The / Find the time (part II) / Theme from Quadrophonia.
LP: **4683221**
MC: **4683224**

Quakes

QUAKES, THE.
Tracks: / Pack our bags and go / You're dead / Other side of the tracks / Where did it go / You are the scene / Psycho attack / Show me / Nine lives / Deal, The / Psychobilly Jekyll and Mr Hyde / Hangman's noose / Satan on my side.
LP: . . . . **NERD 037**

VOICE OF AMERICA.
LP: . . . . **NERD 058**

Quando Quango

PIGS AND BATTLESHIPS.
LP: . . . . **FACT 110**
MC: . . . . **FACT 110 C**

Quantum Jump

BARRACUDA.
Tracks: / Don't look now / Seance, The / Barracuda / Starbright park / Love crossed / Blue mountain / Europe on a dollar a day / Neighbours.
LP: . . . . **TRIX 3**
MC: . . . . **ZCTRIX 3**

MIXING.
Tracks: / Captain Boogaloo / Lone ranger / Barracuda / No American starship / Don't look now / Blue mountain / Over Rio / Neighbours.
LP: . . . . **TRIX 11**

Quarter Pounders

TRIBUTE TO THE GENIUS OF GLEN "MAD" EROS.
LP: . . . . **BLOB 1**

Quarterflash

BACK INTO BLUE.
Tracks: / Walking on ice / Caught in the rain / Back into blue / Talk to me / I want to believe its you / Love without a net / Come to me / Grace under fire / Just for you / Welcome to the city.
LP: . . . . **GEF 26650**

QUARTERFLASH.
Tracks: / Harden my heart / Find another fool / Critical times / Valerie / Try to make it true / Right kind of love / Cruisin with the deuce / Love should be so kind / Williams Avenue.
LP: **9020031**
MC: **9020034**
LP: . . . . **GEF 96008**

TAKE ANOTHER PICTURE.
Tracks: / Take me to heart / Take another picture / Shane / Eye to eye / It don't move me / Shakin' the jinx / Make it shine / One more round to go / Nowhere left to hide / It all becomes clear.
LP: **9040111**
MC: **9040114**
LP: . . . . **GEF 25507**

Quartet Muntu

ATHENS CONCERT, THE (see Moondoc,Jemel/Quartet Muntu) (Quartet Muntu/Jemel Moondoc).

Quartz (dance)

PERFECT TIMING.
LP: **8487391**
MC: **8487394**

Quartz, Jakie

EMOTION AU PLURIEL.
LP: **4606601**
MC: **4606604**

Quartz (rock)

AGAINST ALL ODDS.
Tracks: / Tell me why / Too hot to handle / Buried alive / Avalon.
LP: . . . . **HMRLP 9**

QUARTZ-LIVE.
Tracks: / Street fighting lady / Good times / Mainline rider / Belinda / Count Dracula / Around and around / Roll over Beethoven.
LP: . . . . **MOGO 4007**

Quatro, Suzi

AGGRO-PHOBIA.
Tracks: / Heartbreak hotel / Don't break my heart / Make me smile / What's it like to be loved / Tear me apart / Honky tonk downstairs / Half as much as me / Close the door / American lady / Wake up little Susie.
LP: . . . . **SRAK 525**

GREATEST HITS: SUZI QUATRO.
Tracks: / Can the can / She's in love with you / 48 crash / Wild one / Too big / I may be too young / If you can't give me love / Devil Gate Drive / Daytona demon / Mama's boy / Tear me apart / Race is on / Your mama won't like me / I've never been in love.
LP: . . . . **EMTV 24**

MAIN ATTRACTION.
Tracks: / Heart of stone / Main attraction / Cheap shot / She knows / Two miles out of Georgia / Candy man / Remote control / Fantasy in stereo / Transparent / Oh baby.
LP: **2311 159**

ROCK HARD.
Tracks: / Rock Hard / Glad all over / Love is ready / State of mind / Woman cry / Lipstick / Hard headed / Ego in the night / Lonely is the hardest / Lay me down / Wish upon me.
LP: **911 304**
MC: **911 311**
LP: . . . . **CSAPLP 102**
MC: . . . . **CSAPMC 102**

SATURDAY NIGHT SPECIAL.
LP: . . . . **BIFF 4**

SUZI AND OTHER FOUR LETTER WORDS.
Tracks: / I've never been in love / Mind demons / She's in love with you / Hollywood / Four letter words / Mama's boy / Starlight lady / You are my love / Space cadets / Love hurts.
LP: . . . . **SRAK 538**

SUZI QUATRO.
LP: . . . . **SRAK 505**

WILD ONE, THE (ALBUM) (Greatest hits, The).
Tracks: / Can the can / 48 crash / Daytona demon / Devil Gate Drive / Too big / Wild one, The / Your mama won't like me / I bit off more than I could chew / I may be too young / Tear me apart / Roxy roller / If you can't give me love / Race is on / She's in love with you / Mama's boy / I've never been in love / Rolling stone (CD only.) / All shook up (CD only.) / Keep a knockin' (CD only.) / Wake up little Susie (CD only.).
LP: . . . . **EMS 1357**
MC: . . . . **TCEMS 1357**

Quayle, Anthony (nar)

CANTERVILLE GHOST, THE (see under Canterville Ghost).

EXPLOITS OF DON QUIXOTE (see under Don Quixote (bk)).

TWELVE LABOURS OF HERACLES, THE (see under Twelve Labours (bk)).

Quebec, Ike

BLUE AND SENTIMENTAL.
Tracks: / Blue and sentimental / Minor impulse / Don't take your love from me / Blues for Charlie / Like / Count every star / That old black magic (CD only.) / It's alright with me (CD only.).
LP: . . . . **BST 84098**
MC: . . . . **TCBST 84098**

EASY LIVING.
Tracks: / See see rider / Congo lament / Que's pill / I've got a crush on you / Nancy (with the laughing face) / Easy living / B.G's groove two (On CD only) / I.Q. shuffle (On CD only).
LP: . . . . **BST 84103**

Queen

COMPLETE WORKS.
LPS: . . . . **QB 1**
LPS: . . . . **QBX 1**

DAY AT THE RACES, A.
Tracks: / Long away / Millionaire waltz, The / You and I / Somebody to love / White man / Good old-fashioned lover boy / Drowse / Teo torriate (let us cling together) / Tie your mother down / You take my breath away.
LP: . . . . **ATAK 28**
MC: . . . . **TCATAK 28**
LP: . . . . **EMTC 104**
MC: . . . . **TCEMTC 104**

FLASH GORDON (1980 film soundtrack).
Tracks: / Flash's theme / In the space capsule (the love theme) / Ming's theme (in the court of Ming the merciless) / Ring, The (hypnotic seduction of Dale) / Football fight / In the death cell (love theme reprise) / Execution of Flash / Kiss, The (Aura resurrects Flash) / Arboria (planet of the tree men) / Escape from the swamp / Flash to the rescue / Vultan's theme (attack of the hawk men) / Battle theme / Wedding march, The / Marriage of Dale and Ming (and Flash approaching) / Crash dive on Mingo city / Flash's theme reprise (victory celebrations) / Hero, The.
LP: . . . . **ATAK 26**
MC: . . . . **TCATAK 26**
LP: . . . . **EMC 3351**
MC: . . . . **TCEMC 3351**

GAME, THE.
Tracks: / Play the game / Dragon attack / Another one bites the dust / Need your loving tonight / Crazy little thing called love / Rock it (prime jive) / Don't try suicide / Sweet sister / Coming soon / Save me.
LP: . . . . **ATAK 21**
MC: . . . . **TCATAK 21**
LP: . . . . **EMA 795**
MC: . . . . **TCEMA 795**

GREATEST HITS: QUEEN.
Tracks: / Bohemian rhapsody / Another one bites the dust / Killer queen / Fat bottomed girls / Bicycle race / You're my best friend / Don't stop me now / Save me / Crazy little thing called love / Now I'm here / Good old-fashioned lover boy / Play the game / Flash / Seven seas of Rhye / We will rock you / We are the champions / Somebody to love.
LP: . . . . **EMTV 30**
MC: . . . . **TCEMTV 30**
LP: . . . . **EMC 3350**

HOT SPACE.
Tracks: / Staying power / Dancer / Back chat / Body language / Action this day / Put out the fire / Life is real (song for Lennon) / Calling all girls / Las palabras de amor (the words of love) / Cool cat / Under pressure.
LP: . . . . **ATAK 25**
MC: . . . . **TCATAK 25**
LP: . . . . **EMA 797**
MC: . . . . **TCEMA 797**
LP: . . . . **FA 3228**
MC: . . . . **TCFA 3228**

INNUENDO (ALBUM).
Tracks: / Innuendo / I'm going slightly mad (edit) (LP only.) / I'm going slightly mad (Cassette and CD only.) / Headlong / I can't live with you / Ride the wild wind / All God's people / These are the days of our lives / Delilah / Don't try so hard (edit) (LP only.) / Don't try so hard (Cassette & CD only.) / Hitman, The (edit) (LP only.) / Hitman, The (Cassette & CD only.) / Bijou (edit) (LP only.) / Bijou (Cassette & CD only.) / Show must go on.
LP: . . . . **PCSD 115**
MC: . . . . **TCPCSD 115**

JAZZ.
Tracks: / Mustapha / Fat bottomed girls / Jealousy / Bicycle race / If you can't beat them / Let me entertain you / Dead on time / In only seven days / Dreamers ball / Fun it / Leaving home ain't easy / Don't stop me now / More of that jazz.
LP: . . . . **ATAK 24**
MC: . . . . **TCATAK 24**
LP: . . . . **EMA 788**
MC: . . . . **TCEMA 788**

KIND OF MAGIC, A.
Tracks: / Princes of the universe / Kind of magic, A / One year of love / Pain is so close to pleasure / Friends will be friends / Who wants to live forever / Gimme the prize / Don't lose your head / One vision / Kind of magic, A (Available on CD only) / Friends will be friends will be friends... (Available on CD only) / Forever (Available on CD only).
LP: . . . . **EU 3509**
MC: . . . . **TCEU 3509**

LIVE IN CONCERT.
LP: **603431**
LP: . . . . **OC 40285**

LIVE KILLERS.
Tracks: / We will rock you / Let me entertain you / Death on two legs (dedicated to...) / Killer queen / Bicycle race / I'm in love with my car / Get down make love / You're my best friend / Now I'm here / Dreamers ball / Love of my life / '39 / Keep yourself alive / Don't stop me now / Spread your wings / Brighton rock / Bohemian rhapsody / Tie your mother down / Sheer heart attack / We will rock you / We are the champions / God save the Queen.
2LP: . . . . **ATAK 23**
MC: . . . . **TCATAK 23**
2LP: . . . . **EMSP 330**
MCSET: **TC2EMSP 330**

LIVE MAGIC.
Tracks: / One vision / Tie your mother down / Seven seas of Rhye / Another one bites the dust / I want to break free / Is this the world we created / Bohemian rhapsody / Hammer to fall / Radio ga ga / We will rock you / Friends will be friends / We are the champions / God save the Queen / Kind of magic, A / Under pressure.
LP: . . . . **EMC 3519**
MC: . . . . **TCEMC 3519**

MESSAGE FROM THE PALACE (Interview picture disc).
LPPD: . . . . **BAK 6014**
MC: . . . . **MBAK 6014**

MIRACLE, THE.
Tracks: / Party / Khashoggi's ship / Miracle, The / I want it all / Invisible man, The / Breakthru / Rain must fall / Scandal / My baby does me / Was it all

worth it / Hang on in there (Available on CD only) / Chinese torture (Available on CD only).
LP: PCSD 107
LP: 792 357 1
MC: TCPCSD 107
MC: 792 357 4

MUSIC AND MEDIA INTERVIEW PICTURE DISC.
LPPD: MM 1218

NEWS OF THE WORLD.
Tracks: / We will rock you / We are the champions / Sheer heart attack / All dead all dead / Spread your wings / Fight from the inside / Get down make love / Sleeping on the sidewalk / Who needs you / It's late / My melancholy blues.
MC: TCATAK 20
LP: ATAK 20
LP: EMA 784
MC: TCEMA 784

NIGHT AT THE OPERA, A.
Tracks: / Death on two legs (dedicated to...) / Lazing on a Sunday afternoon / You're my best friend / I'm in love with my car / Sweet lady / Seaside rendezvous / Good company / '39 / Prophet's song, The / Love of my life / Bohemian rhapsody / God save the Queen.
LP: ATAK 27
MC: TCATAK 27
LP: EMTC 103
MC: TCEMTC 103

QUEEN.
Tracks: / Keep yourself alive / Doing alright / Great King Rat / My fairy King / Liar / Night comes down, The / Modern times rock 'n' roll / Son and daughter / Jesus / Seven seas of Rhye.
LP: FA 3040
MC: TCFA 3040
LP: EMC 3006

QUEEN AT THE BEEB.
Tracks: / My fairy King / Keep yourself alive / Doing alright / Liar / Ogre battle / Great King Rat / Modern times rock 'n' roll / Son and daughter.
LP: BOJLP 001
MC: BOJMC 001

QUEEN GREATEST HITS 2.
Tracks: / Kind of magic, A / Under pressure / I want it all / I want to break free / Innuendo / Breakthrou' / Who wants to live forever / Headlong / Miracle, The / I'm going slightly mad / Invisible man, The / Hammer to fall / Friends will be friends / Show must go on, The.
2LP: PMTV 2
MC: TCPMTV 2

QUEEN II.
Tracks: / Procession / Father to son / White Queen (as it began) / Some day one day / Loser in the end, The / Ogre battle / Fairy feller's master-stroke, The / Nevermore / March of the black Queen, The / Funny how love is / Seven seas of Rhye.
LP: FA 4130991
MC: FA 4130994
LP: FA 3099
MC: TCFA 3099
LP: EMA 767

QUEEN: INTERVIEW PICTURE DISC.
LPPD: BAK 2014

SHEER HEART ATTACK.
Tracks: / Brighton rock / Tenement funster / Flick of the wrist / Lily of the valley / Now I'm here / In the lap of the gods / Stone cold crazy / Bring back that Leroy Brown / She makes me (stormtrooper in stilettos) / In the lap of the gods...revisited / Killer queen / Dear friends / Misfire.
LP: ATAK 22
MC: TCATAK 22
LP: EMC 3061
MC: TCEMC 3061

WORKS, THE.
Tracks: / Radio ga ga / Tear it up / It's a hard life / Man on the prowl / Machines (or Back to humans) / I want to break free / Keep passing the open windows / Hammer to fall / Is this the world we created.
LP: WORK 1
MC: TC WORK 1
LP: EMC 240 014 1
MC: TCEMC 2400144

Queen City...

EVERYBODYS RAG (Queen City Ragtime Ensemble).
LP: SOS 1138

Queen Ida

CAUGHT IN THE ACT (QUEEN IDA) (Queen Ida and Her Zydeco Band).
LP: SNTF 951
LP: GNPS 2181
MC: GNP5 2181

COOKIN' WITH QUEEN IDA.
LP: SNTF 1021

LIVE IN SAN FRANCISCO (Queen Ida and Her Zydeco Band).
Tracks: / Fais deaux deaux / Bad moon rising / Every now and then / La porte / Zydeca taco / Back door / Raywood / Vaporsa / My girl Josephine / Jambalaya.
LP: SNTF 901
LP: GNPS 2158
MC: GNP5 2158

NEW ORLEANS (Queen Ida & The Bon Temps Zydeco Band).
Tracks: / Capitaine Gumbo / Mon paradis / La vierge / La Louisiane / Corps solide / Grand basile / Papiers dans mes souliers / Madame Ben / La femme du doight.
LP: SNTF 846
LP: GNPS 2131
MC: GNP5 2131

ON A SATURDAY NIGHT (Queen Ida & The Bon Temps Zydeco Band).
Tracks: / Capitaine Gumbo / La Louisiane / Le Mazuka / Grand Basile / P'tit fille o'paradis / Madame Ben / Frisco zydeco / La femme du doight / Vieux Paris / On a Saturday night / Bonjour tristesse / Creole de lake Charles / Celimene / Mal d'amour / Chere duloone / My tu tu / Hey negress / Jolie Blon / Cotton eyed Joe.
LP: SNTF 916
LP: GNPS 2172
MC: GNP5 2172

ON TOUR.
Tracks: / Capitaine Gumbo / Grand Basile / Mazurka / La Louisiane / P'tit fille o paradis / Madame Ben / Bayou polka / Corps solide / La vierge / La femme du doight / Vieux Paris / C'est la vie.
LP: SNTF 871

QUEEN IDA & BON TEMPS BAND ON TOUR (Queen Ida & The Bon Temps Zydeco Band).
LP: GNPS 2147
MC: GNP5 2147

UPTOWN ZYDECO (Queen Ida & The Bon Temps Zydeco Band).
Tracks: / Uptown Zydeco / Creole de Lake Charles / Moi mademoiselle / Rosa Majeur / Frisco Zydeco / Lucille Kanai / Moi tit feye o'paradis / Mazurka / On' teres / Tayo Zydeco / Mal d'amour / C'est la vie.
LP: SNTF 884

ZYDECO (Queen Ida & The Bon Temps Zydeco Band).
LP: GNPS 2101
MC: GNP5 2101

ZYDECO ALA MODE (Queen Ida & The Bon Temps Zydeco Band).
LP: GNPS 2112
MC: GNP5 2112

Queen Latifah

ALL HAIL THE QUEEN.
LP: GEEA 005
MC: GEEAC 005

ALL HAIL THE QUEEN (RE-ISSUE).
MC: GEEMC 5
LP: GEEA 5

NATURE OF A SISTA.
MC: GEEMC 8
LP: GEEA 8

Queen Of Clubs

QUEEN OF CLUBS.
LP: SVLM 7500

Queen Sylvia

MIDNIGHT BABY.
LP: LR 42.057

Queens College

CHOIR OF QUEENS COLLEGE, CAMBRIDGE (Queens College Choir, Cambridge).
Tracks: / O Lord, in Thy wrath / When David heard / Ascendit Deus / O nata lux / Rejoice in the Lord always (Anon. (16th century).) / O clap your hands / Nunc dimittis (short service) (Gibbons) / Lord, let me know mine end / Faire is the Heaven / Valiant-for-truth / Nunc Dimittis (evening service in C) (Stanford).
LP: ACA 549

Queens Dragoon Guards

QUEENS DRAGOON GUARDS.
Tracks: / Fanfare alpha and omega / Sounding brass / Big bang bash / Latin lullaby / Music makers / Regimental quick march / Fanfare victory / Sinatra in concert / Trombone king / Fanfare & soliloquy / Regmental slow march.
LP: MM 0602

Queen's Lancashire...

LANCASHIRE BANDSTAND VOL.2 (Queens' Lancashire Regiment).
Tracks: / Calling all workers / George formby medley / Can't buy me love / Alfie / Cavalier / Spitfire perlude / Facade suite / World of sport / Cossack / Count your blessings.
LP: MM 0598

LANCASHIRE BANDSTAND VOL.3 (Queens' Lancashire Regiment).
Tracks: / Strike up the band / Music of Albeniz / Johnny comes marching home / Bluesette / Silver salute / Prelude to a festival / Blues for band / Peanut vendor / Colditz march / Fanfare and soliloquy.
LP: MM 0599

Queens Own Highlanders

CEILIDH LINES.
Tracks: / Monte Catarelto / Murdo Mackenzie of Blughasary / Banks of the Skiach, The / Balmoral Highlanders, The / Atholl cummers, The / Brown haired maiden, The / Cutting bracken / Spirits of Old Pulteney, The / Modder river / Bridge of Bogie / Kissing reel, The / O'rourkes / Black mill, The / Swallows tail / Raigmore / Single petre, The / Alex Robertson's limp / Shona's jig / Lads from Glendale, The / Shawbost is dear to me / Leaving Barra / Kiss me sweetheart / Old favourite, The / One horned cow / Gudgeon of Morris's motorcar, The / Four courts, The / Lillie Long-Wades welcome to Inverness / Eighth army, The / An Eileen Ard / MacPhail of Bunnessan / Hills of Kintail / Redcoat, The / Yesterhouse / Gravel walk / Rakish paddy / Scarce O'tatties / Rabs loon / Ceilidh lines / Robertson's lament / Kyly Alexander / Weaver / Paddy be easy / Foxhunter, The / Angelena's lullaby / Wee man from South Uist, The / Hi ho hirum / Kiwi, The / Cromdale hornpipe, The / Dick Gossips / Maid behind the bar, The.
LP: GRALP 22
MC: GRTC 22

QUEENS OWN HIGHLANDERS.
Tracks: / Pipes & drums sets / Around the Scotish Isles / British legion / Colchester castle / Old Panama / Champion / Sons of the brave / Liberty bell / Garb of old gaul / Regimental march.
LP: MM 0600

Queen's Royal Lancers

QUEEN'S ROYAL LANCERS.
Tracks: / Fanfare royale / Old comrades / Sons of the brave / Holyrood / Stable jacket / Old grey mare / Post horn galop / Thin red line / Light calvary / Goodbye Dolly Gray / Soldiers of the Queen / With sword & lance / Queen Charlotte.
LP: MM 0597

Queensland Irish...

QUEENSLAND IRISH... (Queensland Irish Association Pipe Band).
Tracks: / Kenneth Macleod / Wc Bellour Campbell / Leaving Lismore / King George V's Army / Royal Scottish Pipers society / Waltzing Matilda / Dr Ross's 50th welcome to the Argllshire / Jimmy Findlater / Believe me if all those endearing young charms / Shilly shally / Willie Gray's farewell to the Glasgow Police.
LP: LILP 5145
MC: LICS 5145

Queensryche

EMPIRE.
Tracks: / Best I can / Thin line, The / Jet city woman / Della Brown / Another rainy night (without you) / Empire / Resistgance / Silent lucidity / Hand on heart / One and only / Anybody listening?.
2LP: MTL 1058
MC: TCMTL 1058

OPERATION: MINDCRIME.
Tracks: / I remember now / Anarchy X / Revolution calling / Operation: Mindcrime / Speak / Spreading the disease / Mission, The / Suite Sister Mary / Needle lies, The / Electric requiem / Breaking the silence / I don't believe in love / Waiting for 22 / My empty room / Eyes of a stranger.
LP: MTL 1023
MC: TCMTL 1023
LP: AML 3126
MC: TCAML 3126
LP: SPRO 1413637

RAGE FOR ORDER.
Tracks: / Walk in the shadows / I dream in infrared / Whisper / Gonna get close to you / Killing words, The / Surgical strike / Neue regal / Chemical youth (We are rebellion) / London / Screaming in digital / I will remember.
LP: AML 3105
MC: TCAML 3105

WARNING, THE.
Tracks: / Warning / En force / Deliverance / No sanctuary / NM 156 / Take hold of the flame / Before the storm / Child of fire / Roads to madness.
LP: ATAK 108
LP: EJ 2402201
LP: QY 1
MC: EJ 2402204

Quemener, Jean

CHANTS PROFOUNDS DE BRETAGNE VOL.1 (Quemener, Jean-Francois).
Tracks: / An anjelus / Gwerz zkolvan / Ar verjelenn / Kichen chapel Sant Laorans / Ar basion vras / Iwan Gamus / Ar miliner.
LP: ARN 34386

CHANTS PROFOUNDS DE BRETAGNE VOL.2 (Quemener, Jean-Francois).
Tracks: / Janedig er rouz / Un de'a oen e pourmen / Er paotr anrajet / O lo le / Bo, bo, bo ke li bo, o / Er prins yaouank / Bolom koz / Er plarh iverniet / Er breur hag er hoar.
LP: ARN 34476

CHANTS PROFOUNDS DE BRETAGNE VOL.3 (Quemener, Jean-Francois).
Tracks: / Er Plarh demeet gand en Diaoul / Bai en Hennbont'zo un iliz / Sant Sulian / Mab er Brigant / Gouspereu er raned / En tad moualh / Er sorserez.
LP: ARN 34587
MC: ARN 434587

CHANTS PROFOUNDS DE BRETAGNE VOL.4 (Quemener, Jean-Francois).
Tracks: / Olole / Pa oan ar mintin man / Ar jouiz / Ar plac'hik hag ine hi mamm / Ar pla'hig hag ar marc'hataer yaouank / An hini a garan / Disul en oferenn / Me zo ganet e-kreiz er mor / Me'm eus choazet evit mestrez / Mari Madelen / Deut ganin da ma bro / Pa oen me bihanik.
LP: ARN 34789
MC: ARN 434789

Quemener,

KAN HA DISKAN - CHANTS A DANSER.
Tracks: / Konskried Sant Nikolas / D'an traon gant / Konskried Logivi / Mag c'han me d'an arme / Ne oeran ket petra / Konskried Saint-Trefin / Silvestric / Ar c'hentan gwezh / Ar c'hallez vihan / An desertour / 'Barzh un enez / Mari-Louise.
LP: ARN 34702

Quern

LIFE, POETRY AND SONGS OF ROBERT BURNS, THE.
Tracks: / Opening instrumental selection / Comin' thro' the Rye / Ca' the Yowes / Man's a man for a' that, A / Bonnie lass o' Ballochmyle / O a' the airts / O wert thou in the cauld blast / Sweet afton / Closing instrumental selection / Willi brewed a peck o' maut / Last May a braw wooer / Scots wha' hae / Ae fond kiss / John Anderson my jo / De'il's awa', The / There'll never be peace till Jammie comes home.
MC: LC 001

Quest

LIVE AT THE MONTMARTRE.
LP: SLP 4121

Quest For Fire

QUEST FOR FIRE (Original Soundtrack) (Various artists).
LP: RCALP 6034

Question Mark

96 TEARS FOREVER (Question Mark & The Mysterians).
Tracks: / Don't tease me / Love me baby / You're tellin' me lies / Make you mine / Got to / 96 tears / I'll be back / Smokes / Ten o clock / Girl (you captivate me) / Do something to me / Midnight hour / I can't get enough of you, baby.
MC: A 137
LP: DANLP 032

Question Of Love

QUESTION OF LOVE, A (Various artists).
LP: GALP 010

Questions

BELIEF.
Tracks: / Belief / All the time in the world / Bottom line / Month of Sundays / Someone's got to lose / Body and soul / Tuesday sunshine / December / Learning tree, The / Drom that burdan / Everything I see.
LP: RRL 503
MC: RRC 503

Qui C'est Ce Garcon

QUI C'EST CE GARCON (Film soundtrack) (Sarde, Philippe).
LP: A 312

Quick

FASCINATING RHYTHM.
Tracks: / Rhythm of the jungle / Katy can't / Young men drive fast / One light in a black out / To prove my love / Zulu /

Small blonde box / Twisted / Sharks are cool, jets are hot / Don't take me for granted.
LP: . . . . **EPC 85569**

INTERNATIONAL THING.
Tracks: / It's an international thing / This city / Missing you / Love in motion / Where is the lion in you / Listen to your heart / Do not erase this heart / No day at the beach / Biggest factor / All hung up on you.
LP: . . . . **EPC 25923**

WAH WAH.
Tracks: / Adventures tonight / Down the wire / We can learn from this / Cry baby / Poise / I needed you, you needed me / Big decision / Last victim / Sharon / Bed of nails.
LP: . . . . **AMA 5140**
MC: . . . . **AMC 5140**

Quick, Benny

MOTOR BIENE.
Tracks: / Motorcycle / Yummie yama papa / Hello Josephine / Twistin' Patricia / Hello goodbye / California sun twist girl / Hey Daisy / Just the two of us / This diamond ring / I think I'm falling in love / But you're mine / I got you babe.
LP: . . . . **BFX 15047**

Quick Change

CIRCUS OF DEATH.
Tracks: / Will you die / Show no mercy / Sea witch / Circus of death / Injected / What's next / Sludge / A.T.L. / Leave it to the beaver / Battle your fear / Death games / Plowed.
LP: . . . . **RR 950 31**

Quickflight

DECENT BEAT.
LP: . . . . **SR R 442**
MC: . . . . **SR C 442**

Quicksilver (film)

QUICKSILVER (Film soundtrack) (Various artists).
Tracks: / Quicksilver lightning: *Quicksilver* / Casual thing: *Quicksilver* / Nothing at all: *Quicksilver* / Shortcut to somewhere: *Quicksilver* / Love song from Quicksilver: *Quicksilver* / One sunny day/Duelling bikes from Quicksilver: *Quicksilver* / Motown song, The: *Quicksilver* / Suite streets from Quicksilver: *Quicksilver* / Quicksilver suite I-rebirth: *Quicksilver* / Quicksilver suite II-crash landing: *Quicksilver*.
LP: **781 631-1**
MC: **781 631-4**

Quicksilver

COMIN' THROUGH (Quicksilver Messenger Service).
LP: . . . . **BGOLP 88**

HAPPY TRAILS (Quicksilver Messenger Service).
Tracks: / Who do you love (part one) / When you love / Where you love / How do you love / Which do you love / Who do you love (part two) / Mona / Maiden of the cancer moon / Calvary / Happy trails.
LP: . . . . **GO 2012**

QUICKSILVER MESSENGER SERVICE (Quicksilver Messenger Service).
Tracks: / Pride of man / Light your windows / Dino's song / Gold and silver / It's been too long / Fool, The.
LP: . . . . **ED 200**
LP: . . . . **CZ 151**

SHADY GROVE (Quicksilver Messenger Service).
Tracks: / Shady grove / Flute song / 3 or 4 feet from home / Too far / Holy moly / Joseph's coat / Flashing lonesome / Words can't say / Edward (The mad shirt grinder).
LP: . . . . **XED 208**

ULTIMATE JOURNEY (Quicksilver Messenger Service).
Tracks: / Who do you love / Pride of man / Codine / Dino's song / Gold and silver / Joseph's coat / Shady grove / Fresh air / Too far / Stand by me / What about me / Mona.
LP: . . . . **SEE 61**

WHAT ABOUT ME (Quicksilver Messenger Service).
LP: . . . . **BGOLP 58**

Quiet Earth

QUIET EARTH, THE (Film soundtrack) (Various artists).
LP: . . . . **ACH 028**
MC: . . . . **CCH 028**

Quiet Force

FLOW.
Tracks: / Hard bodies / Cool Jude jive / African chip dance / Master of night / My dreams / Childhood memories / Listen to the music / Grande finale.
LP: **80.068**

Quiet Riot

CONDITION CRITICAL.
Tracks: / Sign of the times / Mama weer all crazee now / Party all night / Stomp your hands, clap your feet / Winners take all / Condition critical / Scream and shout / Red alert / Bad boy / Born to rock.
LP: . . . . **EPC 26075**

METAL HEALTH.
Tracks: / Metal health / Cum on feel the noize / Don't wanna let you go / Slick black cadillac / Love's a bitch / Breathless / Run for cover / Battle axe / Let's get crazy / Thunderbird.
LP: **4500841**
MC: **4500844**
LP: . . . . **EPC 25322**

POWER AND GROOVE.
Tracks: / Stay with me tonight / Calling the shots / Run to you / I'm king of the hill / Joker, The / Lunar obsession / Don't wanna be your fool / Coppin' a feel / In a rush / Empty promises.
LP: **4628961**
MC: **4628964**

QUIET RIOT 3.
Tracks: / Main attraction / Wild and the young / Twilight hotel / Down and dirty / Rise or fall / Put up or shut up / Still of the night / Pump, The / Slave to love / Helping hand / Bass care.
LP: . . . . **EPC 26945**
MC: **40 26945**

WILD, YOUNG AND CRAZEE.
Tracks: / Metal health / Cum on feel the noize / Love's a bitch / Mama weer all crazee now / Winner takes all / Condition critical / Bad boy / Main attraction / Wild and the young / Put up or shut up / Slave to love / Let's get crazy.
LP: . . . . **RAWLP 033**
MC: . . . . **RAWTC 033**

Quiet Sun

MAINSTREAM.
Tracks: / Bargain classics / Mummy was an asteroid, daddy was a non-stick kitchen utensil / RFD / Rongwrong / Sol caliente / Trot, The / Trumpets with motherhood.
LP: . . . . **EGED 4**

Quigg, Stephen

CATCH ME IF YOU CAN.
Tracks: / Hiking song, The / Mason's apron / Dumbarton's drums / Killiecrankie / Dark island / Catch me if you can / Isle of Mull / Mingulay boat song / Working for MacBraynes / Island of Arran / He left them / Eriskay love lilt / Barnyards of Delgaty / Mountains of Mourne / Uist tramping song / Mari's wedding.
MC: . . . . **KITV 386**

Quik, DJ

QUIK IS THE NAME (See under DJ Quik) (D.J. Quik).

Quill, Gene

PHIL & QUILL WITH PRESTIGE (see Woods, Phil/Gene Quill Quintet) (Quill, Gene / Phil Woods Quintet).

Quillian, Rufus

RUFUS & BEN QUILLIAN 1929-31 (Quillian, Rufus & Ben).
LP: . . . . **MSE 217**

Quincicasm

QUINCICASM.
LP: . . . . **SDL 249**

Quincy

TURN THE OTHER WAY AROUND.
Tracks: / Turn the other way around / Critics choice / Don't knock on my door / Always in the news / Dime store lies / Can't live in a dream / Stop now / Just a tragedy / Grow up / Roamin' Catholic / Stuck on you / Ordinary town.
LP: . . . . **CBS 84451**

Quine, Robert

BASIC (Quine, Robert & Fred Maher).
Tracks: / Pick up / Bluffer / Fala / Stray / Summer storm / Sixty five / Dark place / Despair / Village / Bandage bait.
LP: . . . . **EGED 36**

Quinichette, Paul

CHASE IS ON, THE (see Rouse, Charlie).

KID FROM DENVER, THE.
LP: . . . . **FS 265**
LP: . . . . **MTLP 021**

ON THE SUNNY SIDE.
Tracks: / Blue dots / Circles / On the sunny side of the street / Cool-lypso.
LP: . . . . **OJC 076**

Quinn, Brendan

BRENDAN QUINN COLLECTION.
Tracks: / After sweet memories play born to lose again / I'll bet all my love on you / Lucille / How great thou art / Cowboys ain't supposed to cry / Ruby don't take your love to town / Judy and me / Mother's love's a blessing, A / If the shoe fits / Bandy the rodeo clown / Let me take you in my arms again / Till you can make it on your own / Rollin' in the aisles / When you and I were young Maggie / Almost persuaded / My wild Irish rose / Daddy's little girl / Before I'm fool enough to give it one more try / Most of all why / I can almost see my home town from here.
LP: . . . . **BER 018**
MC: . . . . **KBER 018**

HITS OF BRENDAN QUINN.
Tracks: / Blanket on the ground / Help me make it through the night / Wedding bells / Four in the morning / Behind closed doors / Find on your finger / You're my best friend / Back home again / Ride me down easy / Backstreet affair / Forever was the name of our sunshine / Ravishing Ruby.
LP: . . . . **PHL 429**
MC: . . . . **CPHL 429**

HUSTLER.
MC: . . . . **MBLP 1011**

JUST AN ORDINARY MAN.
LP: . . . . **RITZLP 0035**
MC: . . . . **RITZLC 0035**

REST YOUR LOVE ON ME.
MC: . . . . **BTC 302**

Quinn, Denis

OPEN SECRET.
MC: . . . . **C 147**

Quinn Family

MUSIC FROM THE GLENS.
LP: . . . . **OAS 3016**

Quinn, Freddy

EDITION 1: HEIMWEH... DORT WO DIE BLUMEN BLUH'N.
Tracks: / Heimweh / Sie heiss Mary Ann / Rosalie / Bel sante / Hallo Joe / Karte Genugt / Baiao medley / Samba medley / So geht das jede nacht / At the hop / Stood up / Endlose nachte / Wer das vergisst / Heimatlos / Einmal in Tampico / Ein armer mulero.
LP: . . . . **BFX 15311**

EDITION 2: HAVE I TOLD YOU LATELY THAT I LOVE YO.
Tracks: / You're gonna change / Have I told you lately that I love you / Magic moments / Bouquet of roses / Echo of your footsteps, The / Twenty six miles / My heart is waiting / Ain't misbehavin' / Love me ever - leave me never / I'm coming home / Don't forbid me / Banana boat song / No letter today / On the sunny side of the street / Waltz of the wind / Let's say goodbye like we said hello.
LP: . . . . **BFX 15312**

EDITION 3: DIE GITARRE UND DAS MEER.
Tracks: / Ich bin ein vagabund / Sabrina / Der legionar / Bleib' bei mir / Ich bin bald wieder hier / Noch immer allein / Cigarettes and whisky / De nacht vergeht so schnell / Die gitarre und das meer / Du brauchst doch immer wieder einen freund / Unter fremden sternen / Du musst alles vergessen (Ay-ay-ay amigo) / Guitar playing Joe / Melodie der nacht / Irgendwann gibt's ein wiedersehn.
LP: . . . . **BFX 15313**

EDITION 4: WEIT IST DER WEG.
Tracks: / Weit ist der weg / La guitarra Brasiliana / Botella, La / Samba fieber / Nur der wind / Einmal oben, einmal unten / Wenn die sehnsucht nicht war' / So viele traume / Irish inn / Rosalie / Zonder thuis / Het verlangen was groot / In zijn dromen / Eenmal toch / Melodie der nacht / Lang ist die weg.
LP: . . . . **BFX 15314**

EDITION 5: SEUL AU MONDE.
Tracks: / Day O / Le Seul pays / Rosalie / Seul au monde / Le guitarra Brasiliana / Melodie du soir / Pres de mon coeur / N'importe ou / Dans le vent / J'ai besoin de ton amour / Que toutre commence / La chitarra Brasiliana / Nostalgia di marinaio / Qualcuno da amare / Non c'e' lavoro.
LP: . . . . **BFX 15315**

HEIMWEH NACH ST.PAULI.
Tracks: / Auf der Reeperbahn nachts um halb eins / In Hamburg an der Waterkant / Seemann, oh Seemann / Scheun mutt dat sien / Lonesome star, The / Was will das meer von mir / Homesick for St. Pauli / Fishmarket von St. Pauli / Lonesome star, The (2) / Tell sailor, tell me a story / Mein Hamburg / Das gibt's nur auf der Reeperbahn / Du bist die Liebe / Heimweh nach St.Pauli / Junge komme bald wieder / Wo ist der Mann / Snicksnack snuckelchen / Makkaroni von Pams.
LP: . . . . **BFX 15355**

Quinn, Hugh

DOFFIN MISTRESS.
Tracks: / Mill-doffer's song / Rover's song / You might easily know a doffer / Over there / B for Barney / I am the wee falorie man / Poor woman from Sandy Row / Jenny Jo / Varsoviana: will you wallace / Flowery garden / My son John / O love is pleasing / Talk about James Joyce (Spoken word.) / May queen songs / Our Qu. can burl her leg / Lizzie Moore / There she stands / Brogie Mor / Sick lover / Knifegrinder's chant / What is my Mary weeping for / Till apples grow / Go ye in by yonders town / I'll tell me ma / 5 o'clock is striking / Polka song / Three Lords / Jeannie McGinn / He said he was County Tyrone / All around the loney-o.
MC: **60-072**

Quinn, John

COUNTRY DREAM.
Tracks: / Katy did / Some day my day will come / Charlie's picture / I'm all she's got / Crown of thorns / Two lonely people / I guess I had a real good time last night / Couldn't love have picked a better place to die / Bic flicking baby / Lightening the load / Where love begins / Was it all worth loosing you.
LP: . . . . **BGC 323**
MC: . . . . **KBGC 323**

YOU KNOW I AM A STRANGER.
Tracks: / Everyone does it but you / Go and leave me if you wish it / Nanny goat / Wedding above in Glencree / Lady in her father's garden / Big hiring fair in Newtownhamilton / You know I am a stranger / Gay ploughboy / Willie was her sailor boy / At the foot of Davitt's mountain / Young apprentice boy / My father's servant boy.
LP: . . . . **OAS 3018**

Quinn, Paul

ONE DAY (see Clarke, Vince) (Quinn, Paul & Vince Clarke).

Quinn, Philomena

BEST OF PHILOMENA QUINN (Ireland's country colleen).
Tracks: / Wild flowers / Forty shades of green / Last thing on my mind / If we only had old Ireland over here / Behind the footlights / When Irish eyes are smiling / Old country dance / Moonlight in Mayo / My heart cries for you / Too-ra-loo-ra-loo-ra / Where the grass grows the greenest / Mother's Bible.
MC: . . . . **CPHL 499**

IT'S A COWBOY LOVIN' TONIGHT.
Tracks: / I think I'll say goodbye / It's a cowboy lovin' tonight / Jealous heart / Two little orphans / She's got you / Ashes of love / Heaven's just a sin away / Old country dance / Mother's bible / One day at a time / Sing the blues, bluebirds / It's no secret.
LP: . . . . **GES 5014**

Quinn The Eskimo

MOUNTAIN IS A DANDY, THE.
Tracks: / Samantha Rain / Breathing / Big hedge / Haymaker, The / Like a flame / Eternity / Once upon a day / Wreck, The / Eastward / Importance of being honest, The.
LP: . . . . **SUML 002**

Quintessence

DIVE DEEP.
LP: . . . . **ILPS 9143**

QUINTESSENCE.
LP: . . . . **ILPS 9128**

SELF.
LP: . . . . **SF 8273**

Quintet Of The...

1935 AND 1936 IN PARIS (Quintet Of The Hot Club Of France).
LP: . . . . **OLD 12**
MC: . . . . **COLD 12**

CINQUANTIEME ANNIVERSAIRE (Quintet Of The Hot Club Of France).
2LP: **425019**

PARISIAN SWING (Quintet Of The Hot Club Of France).
LP: . . . . **ACL 1189**

SWING '35-'39 (Quintet Of The Hot Club Of France).
Tracks: / Limehouse blues / I got rhythm / St Louis blues / I've found a new baby / It was so beautiful / China boy / Moonglow / It don't mean a thing / Billets doux / Swing from Paris / Them there eyes / Three little words / Appel direct / Swing '39.
MC: . . . . **KECC 2051**
LP: . . . . **ECM 2051**

Quinton

PROPELLOR.
Tracks: / Rake, The / Weird emotional scar / Flying very fast / End of a good idea / She / Surrealing / Operation rise /

Rediscover me / Love shine down on me / Propeller.
LP: . . . . **PGLP 1**

Quireboys

LITTLE BIT OF WHAT YOU FANCY, A.
Tracks: / 7 o'clock / Man on the loose / Whippin' boy / Sex party / Sweet Mary Ann / I don't love you anymore / Hey you / Misled / Long time comin' / Roses and rings / There she goes again / Take me home.
LP: . . . . **PCS 7335**
MC: . . . . **TCPCS 7335**
LP: . . . . **PCSX 7335**
MC: . . . . **TCPCSX 7335**

LIVE: QUIREBOYS (Recorded Around The World).
Tracks: / Hey you / Sex party / Whipping boy / Sweet Mary Ann / Heartbreaker / I don't love you anymore / Hold on I'm coming / There she goes again.
LP: . . . . **PRG 1002**
LP: **795 413 1**
MC: . . . . **TCPRG 1002**
MC: **795 413 4**

QUIREBOYS: INTERVIEW PICTURE DISC.
LPPD: . . . . **BAK 2166**

Quiristers

LEAD ME, LORD (Quiristers/ Winchester College Chapel Choir).
Tracks: / Up good Christian folk / In the bleak mid winter / Quem Vidistis / Sir Christemas / There shall a star / Ave Maria / Libera me / Jubilate Deo / Lead me, Lord / Te Lucis / Christ rising / Jerusalem / I was glad.
LP: . . . . **ACA 551**

Quisqueya

QUISQUEYA (Various artists).
LP: . . . . **VPA 8399**
MC: . . . . **VC 4950**

Quiver Full...

QUIVER FULL OF ARROWS (See under Archer, Jeffrey).

Quo Vadis

QUO VADIS (Film Soundtrack) (Various artists).
Tracks: / Marcus and Lygia: *Various artists* / Fertility hymn: *Various artists* / Burning of Rome: *Various artists* / Petronius' banquet, meditation and death: *Various artists* / Ave Caesar: *Various artists* / Chariot chase: *Various artists* / Assyrian dance: *Various artists* / Aftermath (Death of Peter): *Various artists*/ Death of Poppaea, Nero's suicide: *Various artists* / Hail Galba: *Various artists* / Miracle and finale, The: *Various artists* / Epilogue: *Various artists.*
LP: . . . . **GM 30716**
MC: **4212654**

R

Raag Raag

QADAM QADAM.
MC: . . . . **BIP 205**

Rabbath, Francois

TOULAI & FRANCOIS RABBATH (See under 'Toulai' for details).

Rabbit

DREAM JUNGLE.
MC: . . . . **LUMCA 2**

Rabbitt, Eddie

COUNTRY STORE: EDDIE RABBITT.
Tracks: / Step by step / I don't know where to start / Early in the morning / You and I / Good night for falling in love / You can't run from love / Someone could lose a heart tonight / You put the beat in my heart / Dim the lights / Rivers / Our love will survive / Years after you / Laughing on the outside / Nothing like falling in love.
LP: . . . . **CST 2**
MC: . . . . **CSTK 2**

EDDIE RABBITT.
Tracks: / I'm a little bit lonesome / I can't help myself / Stop look and listen / Girl on my mind / You make love beautiful / Sure thing / Jewellery store / We can't go on living like this / Is there a country song on the jukebox / She loves me like she means it.
LP: . . . . **K 52054**

GREATEST HITS.
Tracks: / I love a rainy night / Drivin' my life away / Step by step / You and i / Suspicions / You put the beat in my heart / Nothing like falling in love / Someone could lose a heart tonight / You can't run from love / Gone too far.
LP: **8143641**

HORIZON.
Tracks: / I love a rainy night / 747 / Drivin' my life away / Short road to love / Rockin' with my baby / I need to fall in love / What will i write / Pretty lady / Just the way it is.
LPS: . . . . **K 52225**

LOVELINE.
Tracks: / Pour me another tequila / Gone too far / Loveline / One and only one / Suspicious / So fine / I will never let you go again / Amazing love / It's always like the first time / I don't wanna make love with anyone else.
LP: . . . . **K 52135**

RABBIT TRAX.
Tracks: / Threw it away / Singing in the subway / This moment / World without love / Gotta have you / Repetitive regret / Both to each other (friends and lovers) / When we make love / Letter from home.
LP: . . . . **PL 87041**
MC: . . . . **PK 87041**

RADIO ROMANCE.
Tracks: / You can't run from love / Years after you / Good night for falling in love / You and I / You got me now / Our love will survive / Stranger in your eyes / Bedroom eyes / Laughing on the outside (crying on the inside) / All my life, all my love.
LP: . . . . **MERL 13**
MC: . . . . **MERLC 13**

ROCKY MOUNTAIN MUSIC.
Tracks: / Do you right tonight / I can't get this ring off my finger / Rocky mountain music / Two dollars in the jukebox / I don't wanna make love with anyone but you / I just got to have you / Tullohoma dancing pizza man / Ain't I something / There's someone she lies to / Could you love a poor boy dolly / Drinkin' my baby (off my mind).
LP: . . . . **K 52037**

STEP BY STEP.
Tracks: / Early in the morning / Bring back the sunshine / Skip-a-beat / Dim dim the lights / Rivers / Step by step / Someone could lose a heart tonight / I don't know where to start / Nobody loves me like my baby / My only wish.
LP: **6302152**

Rabelais, Francois

HISTORIES OF GARGANTUA & PANTAGRUEL (Mason, James (nar)).
MC: **1675**

Rabin, Oscar

ESPECIALLY FOR YOU (Rabin, Oscar & His Band).
Tracks: / I let a song go out of my heart / Proud of you / Especially for you / Sing my heart / At the woodchoppers ball / They say / Could be / I fall in love with you every day / Wrappin' it up / Begin the beguine / This time it's real / Ain't cha comin' out? / I hear a dream / I understand / Exactly like you / Where the blue begins / Starlight serenade / We'll go smiling along.
LP: . . . . **RFL 15**

RABIN, OSCAR & HIS BAND (see British Dance Bands of the Forties) (Rabin, Oscar & His Band).

TRY A LITTLE TENDERNESS.
Tracks: / It's gonna be you / Moon song / Try a little tenderness / Morning, noon and night / Shadows on the swanee / Shadow waltz / Rockabye moon / Rambling down the lane together / Horses carry tails / I can't remember / Pettin' in the park / Wear a great big smile / Hiawatha's lullaby / This is the rhythm for me / Willow weep for me / Two little windows / Waltzing in a dream / Hyde Park corner.
LP: . . . . **BUR 017**
MC: . . . . **4 BUR 017**

Rabin, Trevor

CAN'T LOOK AWAY.
Tracks: / Can't look away / Sorrow (your heart) / Promises / Eyes of love / Hold on to me / I miss you now / Something to hold on to / Cover up / Etoile noir / I didn't think it would last / Sludge / Cape, The.
LP: . . . . **EKT 58**
MC: . . . . **EKT 58C**

FACE TO FACE.
Tracks: / I'll take the weight / Don't you ever lose / I'm old enough / Wanderer / You / Now / Ripper / Candy's bar / Always the last one.
LP: . . . . **CHR 1221**
MC: . . . . **ZCHR 1221**

TREVOR RABIN.
Tracks: / Getting to know you / Finding me a way back home / All I want is your love / Live a bit / Fantasy / Stay with me / Red desert / Painted picture / Love life.
LP: . . . . **CHR 1196**
MC: . . . . **ZCHR 1196**

WOLF.
Tracks: / Open ended / Heard you cry / Wolf / Do ya want me / Stop turn / Lost in love / Looking for a lady / Pain / Take me to a party / She's easy / Long Island sound.
LP: . . . . **CHR 1293**
MC: . . . . **ZCHR 1293**

Race, Hugo

EARLS WORLD (Race, Hugo & The True Spirit).
LP: . . . . **NORMAL 125**

RUE MORGE BLUES.
LP: . . . . **NORMAL 118**

Racer X

EXTREME VOLUME.
LP: . . . . **RR 9530 1**

SECOND HEAT.
LP: . . . . **RR 9601**

STREET LETHAL (Racer X, with Paul Gilbert).
Tracks: / Frenzy / Street lethal / Into the night / Blowin' up the radio / Hotter than fire / On the loose / Loud and clear / Y.R.O. / Dangerous love / Getaway / Rock it.
LP: . . . . **RR 9705**

Racey

SMASH AND GRAB.
Tracks: / Love's a riot / Such a night / There's a party going on / Lay your cards on the table / She's a winner / Some girls / Lay your love on me / Kitty / Rah stateway / Boy oh boy / We are Racey.
LP: . . . . **SRAK 537**

Rachabane, Barney

BARNEY'S WAY.
LP: . . . . **JAJ 1**
MC: . . . . **JAJC 1**

Rachell, Yank

BLUES MANDOLIN MAN.
LP: **BP-1986**

CHICAGO STYLE.
LP: . . . . **DS 649**

COMPLETE RECORDINGS 1934-38.
LP: . . . . **WSE 106**

COMPLETE RECORDINGS 1938-41.
LP: . . . . **WSE 107**

LIVE IN AUSTRIA, 1966 (See under Estes, Sleepy John) (Rachell, Yank & Sleepy John Estes).

YANK RACHELL'S TENNESSEE JUG BUSTERS (Rachell, Yank & His Tenessee Jug Busters).
LP: . . . . **UNKNOWN**

Rachmaninov (composer)

PIANO CONCERTO NO.3 (RACHMANINOV) (Prats, Jorge Luis/ Mexico City Symphony Orchestra).
Tracks: / Piano concerto no.3 (Rachmaninov) / Vocalise (Rachmaninov) / Prince Rostislav (Rachmaninov) (Based on Tolstoy).
LP: . . . . **DCA 668**
MC: . . . . **ZC DCA 668**

RACHMANINOV AND CHOPIN CELLO SONATAS (see under Gregor-Smith, Bernard) (Gregor-Smith, Bernard/ Yolande Wrigley).

Racing Cars

DOWNTOWN TONIGHT.
LP: . . . . **CHR 1099**

Rackham, Neil

PSYCHOLOGY OF NEGOTIATING, THE (Secrets of Success series).
MC: **060056066X**

Radar, Don

WALLFLOWER (Radar, Don Quintet).
LP: . . . . **DS 796**

Radcliff, Bobby

DRESSES TOO SHORT.
Tracks: / Ugh! / Bonehead / Stick around / You haven't hurt me / Going home tomorrow / Next woman I marry / Dresses to short / Keep loving me baby / Alimony blues / Hard road to travel / Kool and the gang.
LP: . . . . **FIEND 152**

Radcliffe, Jimmy

LONG AFTER TONIGHT IS ALL OVER (See under Parrish, Dean).

Radiators

BUYING GOLD IN HEAVEN.
LP: . . . . **HWLP 8503**

GHOSTOWN.
Tracks: / Johnny jukebox / They're looting in the town / Confidential / Million dollar hero / Under Cleary's clock / Faithful departed / Let's talk about the weather / Who are the strangers / Kitty Ricketts / Plura belle / Walking home alone again / Dead the beast, dead the poison.
LP: . . . . **WIK 85**
MC: . . . . **WIKC 85**
LP: . . . . **CWK 3003**

RADIATORS FROM SPACE.
LP: . . . . **HWLP 8503**
MC: . . . . **CSHW 8503**

Radical Dance Faction

BORDERLINE CASES.
Tracks: / Surplus people / Borderline / 4 chuck chant / Riverwise / Sorepoint for a sickman / Chinese poem / Rogue trooper (live mix) / Back in the same place / Hot on the wire / Firepower.
LP: . . . . **EZ 001**

LANDING PARTY.
Tracks: / Landing party / Landing party (version) / Riverwise II.
LP: . . . . **EZ 002**

Radio...

50 DJ JINGLES (Various artists).
MC: . . . . **ZCDJ 50**

50 YEARS OF ROYAL BROADCASTS (Various artists).
2LP: . . . . **REJ 187**
MC: . . . . **HRMC 187**

BEST OF FAMILY FAVOURITES (Various artists).
Tracks: / With a song in my heart: *Various artists* / Think of me: *Various artists* / Hands across the sea: *Various* artists / Green green grass of home: *Various artists* / Dambusters march: *Various artists* / With a little bit of luck: *Various artists* / Happy anniversary: *Various artists* / We'll meet again: *Various artists*/ Sailing: *Various artists* / You need hands: *Various artists* / Anniversarty waltz: *Various artists*/ We'll keep a welcome: *Various artists* / Climb every mountain: *Various artists* / 633 squadron: *Various artists* / May each day: *Various artists* / Welcome home: *Various artists.*
LP: . . . . **REB 335**

BEST OF ROUND THE HORNE (Various artists).
LP: . . . . **REH 193**
MC: . . . . **RMC 4018**

BEYOND OUR KEN (Excerpts From BBC Radio Series) (Various artists).
LP: . . . . **NTSM 195**

CASABLANCA (Radio Adaptation) (Various artists).
LP: . . . . **MR 1099**
MC: . . . . **CMR 1099**

DECEIVER, THE (Various artists).
MCSET: . . . . **ZBBC 1254**

EIGHTEEN OF THE BEST (From Radio Scotland's 'Take the Floor') (Various artists).
Tracks: / Marches: *Various artists* / Bonnie lass: *Various artists* / Eva three step: *Various artists*/ Modern gaelic waltz: *Various artists* / Reels: *Various artists* / Strip the willow: *Various artists*/ Strathspey: *Various artists* / Red house reel: *Various artists* / Dashing white sergeant: *Various artists*/ Baron's piper, The: *Various artists* / Canadian barn dance: *Various artists* / Speed the plough: *Various* artists / Old tyme waltz: *Various artists* / Campbell's frolic: *Various artists* / Roxborough castle: *Various artists* / Gay gordons: *Various artists.*
LP: . . . . **REH 762**
MC: . . . . **ZCF 762**

FAMILIES AND HOW TO SURVIVE (Various artists).
MCSET: . . . . **ZBBC 1244**

FLYWHEEL, SHYSTER AND FLYWHEEL (Various artists).
MCSET: . . . . **ZBBC 1225**

FORSYTE SAGA, THE (Various artists).
MCSET: . . . . **ZBBC 1252**

GARDEN PARTY, THE (Various artists).
MCSET: . . . . **ZBBC 1265**

HOBBIT, THE (4 hour dramatisation) (Various artists).
MCSET: . . . . **ZBBC 1038**

HUMAN FACTOR, THE (Various artists).
MCSET: . . . . **ZBBC 1150**

IN MY WILDEST DREAMS (Various artists).
MCSET: . . . . **ZBBC 1216**

INDIAN SUMMER, AN (Various artists).
MCSET: . . . . **ZBBC 1247**

J KINGSTON PLATT (Various artists).
MCSET: . . . . **ZBBC 1246**

JANE AUSTEN COLLECTION (Various artists).
MCSET: . . . . **ZBBC 1207**

JENNINGS (Various artists).
MCSET: . . . . **ZBBC 1226**

LONDON CALLING (Famous Themes: Vol.3) (Various artists).
Tracks: / London calling: *Coates, Eric* (Theme for BBC radio overseas service) / On the sea shore (players cigarettes TV commercial): *Farnon, Robert* / Shadow waltz: *Dubois, Paul* (from "the Teckman biography") / Picture parade: *Beaver, Jack* / Swiftly(from 'a place in the sun'): *Arel, Jack/Jean-Claude Petit* / Rippling waters (BBC-TV angel fish interlude): *Thorne, Donald* / Royal review: *Steck, Arnold* / Shopping centre: *Green, Philip* / Seascape: *Lowry,* Tony (From 'the windjammers') / Jamboree: *Richardson, Clive* / Openings and endings: *Farnon, Robert* / Trapeze waltz: *Torch, Sidney* (From Guy De Maupassant) / Jockey on the carousel (from 'Mainly for women'): *Farnon, R./Buchel,P.* / Dalilia (the desperadoes): *Roger, Roger* (From 'Desperate People') / Autumn love: *Lewis, Paul* (from 'Spring and Autumn') / Bring on the girls: *Torch, Sidney* / Proscenium (from 'armchair theatre'): *Farnon, Robert* / Pastoral montage:BBC-TV windmill interlude: *Fagan, Gideon* / Jolly juggler: *Ellis,*

Vivian / Sentimental: *Foley, Adrian/ Daley, Ronnie* (Theme from "Richard Attenbourgh presents".) / Metropolitan march(from'calling all sportsmen'): *Barsotti, Roger.*
LP: GRALP 30
MC: GRTC 30

LORD OF THE RINGS, THE (13 hour dramatisation) (Various artists).
MCSET: ZBBC 1050

MONK'S HOOD (Various artists).
MCSET: ZBBC 1209

MORE OF THE BEST OF ROUND THE HORNE (Various artists).
LP: REH 240
MC: RMC 4044

MY UNCLE SILAS (Various artists).
MCSET: ZBBC 1243

NAVY LARK, VOL. 3 (Various artists).
MCSET: ZBBC 1250

ON THE AIR (60 years of BBC theme music) (Various artists).
Tracks: / On the air: *Various artists* / In town tonight: *Various artists* / I.T.M.A.: *Various artists*/ Take it from here: *Various artists* / Much binding in the marsh: *Various artists* / In the mood: *Various* artists / You're dancing on my heart: *Various artists* / Meet the Huggets: *Various artists* / Paul Temple: *Various artists* / Dick Barton: *Various artists* / Music while you work: *Various artists* / Say it with music: *Various artists* / T.V. newsreel: *Various artists* / Toytown: *Various artists* / Muffin the mule: *Various artists* / Sooty: *Various artists* / Housewives choice: *Various artists* / Down your way: *Various* artists / Have a go: *Various artists* / Sports report: *Various artists* / Billy Cotton Band show: *Various* artists / Mrs. Dale's diary: *Various artists* / Archers, The: *Various artists* / Listen with mother theme: *Various artists* / Children's choice: *Various artists* / Top of the form: *Various artists* / Tonight: *Various artists* / Six five special: *Various artists* / Jukebox jury: *Various artists* / Sing something simple: *Various artists* / Pick of the pops: *Various artists* / Roundabout: *Various artists* / Doctor Kildare theme: *Various artists* / Grand hotel: *Various artists* / Desert island discs: *Various artists*/ Nationwide: *Various artists* / Doctor Finlay's casebook: *Various artists* / Monitor: *Various artists*/ Two way family favourites: *Various artists* / Dixon of Dock Green: *Various artists* / Maigret: *Various artists*/ Z Cars: *Various artists* / Tomorrows world: *Various artists* / Sky at night, The: *Various artists* / Grandstand: *Various artists* / Match of the day: *Various artists* / That was the week that was: *Various artists*/ Steptoe and son: *Various artists* / Monty Python: *Various artists* / Fawlty Towers: *Various artists*/ Dad's army: *Various artists* / Blue Peter: *Various artists* / Magic roundabout: *Various artists* / Forsyte saga, The: *Various artists* / Onedin line: *Various artists* / All creatures great and small: *Various artists*/ Juliet Bravo: *Various artists* / Dallas: *Various artists* / Here's to the next time: *Various artists.*
2LP: REF 454
MC: ZCD 454

ONE HUNDRED DEEJAY INSERTS VOL 1 (Various artists).
LP: EAP 1003 SLP
MC: EAP 1003 CAS

ONE HUNDRED DISCOTHEQUE JINGLES VOL 4 (Various artists).
LP: EAP 1008 SLP
MC: EAP 1008 CAS

ONE HUNDRED DISCOTHEQUE JINGLES VOL 2 (Various artists).
LP: EAP 1002 SLP
MC: EAP 1002 CAS

ONE HUNDRED DISCOTHEQUE JINGLES VOL 1 (Various artists).
LP: EAP 1001 SLP
MC: EAP 1001 CAS

ONE HUNDRED DISCOTHEQUE JINGLES VOL 3 (Various artists).
LP: EAP 1005 SLP
MC: EAP 1005 CAS

ONE HUNDRED SONOVOX JINGLES (Various artists).
LP: EAP 1004 SLP
MC: EAP 1004 CAS

POETRY PLEASE, VOL. 2 (Various artists).
MCSET: ZBBC 1241

RADIO (Story of the development of radio) (Various artists).
MCSET: C 10

ROUND THE HORNE (Various artists).
MCSET: ZBBC 1010

ROUND THE HORNE 2 (Various artists).
MCSET: ZBBC 1092

ROUND THE HORNE VOL.3 (Various artists).
LP: REH 296
MC: ZCF 296
MCSET: ZBBC 1093

RUGBY UNION (Various artists).
MCSET: ZBBC 1251

SILENT PARTNER (Various artists).
MCSET: ZBBC 1231

STAR IS BORN, A (Various artists).
MC: CMR 1155

SUMMONED BY BELLS (Various artists).
MCSET: ZBBC 1249

TEN YEARS OF OFFSHORE RADIO (Various artists).
2LP: JUMBO R 100/1
MCSET: JUMBO C 100

THOSE WONDERFUL RADIO YEARS (Various artists).
Tracks: / Itma: *Various artists* / Henry Hall's guest night: *Various artists* / Romance in rhythm: *Various* artists / In town tonight: *Various artists* / Variety bandbox: *Various artists* / Grand hotel: *Various* artists / Hi gang: *Various artists* / Meet the Huggetts: *Various artists* / Our Gracie: *Various artists*/ Piano playtime: *Various artists* / Over to you: *Various artists* / Rocky mountain rhythm: *Various artists*/ Stand easy: *Various artists* / Mid day music hall: *Various artists* / Music while you work: *Various artists*/ Worker's playtime: *Various artists* / Ray's a laugh: *Various artists* / Take it from here: *Various artists*/ Music from the movies: *Various artists* / Goon show, The: *Various artists* / Billy cotton band show: *Various artists* / 'Appy 'arf 'our: *Various artists* / Jazz club: *Various artists.*
2LP: RFLD 34

UNSUITABLE ATTACHMENT, AN (Various artists).
MCSET: ZBBC 1214X

VAMPIRE'S HOLIDAY/DR. JEKYLL & MR. HOLLINS (Various artists).
MCSET: ZBBC 1205

WELL SCHOOLED IN MURDER (Various artists).
MCSET: ZBBC 1260

WOMAN'S HOUR (Various artists).
MCSET: ZBBC 1115

WORLD OF MEDIUM WAVE RADIO STATIONS (Various artists).
2LP: R 106/107
MCSET: C 103

WORLD OF MEDIUM WAVE RADIO STATIONS (Various artists).
2LP: R 106/7

YEAR IN PROVENCE, A (Various artists).
MCSET: ZBBC 1218

Radio Big Band

SPECIAL EDITION.
LP: RBB 002LP
MC: RBB 002MC

Radio Birdman

RADIOS APPEAR.
Tracks: / What gives / Non-stop girls / Do the op / Man with golden helmet / Descent into the maelstrom / New race / Aloha Steve and Danno / Anglo girl desire / Murder city nights / You're gonna miss me / Hand of law / Hit them again.
LP: SRK 6050

Radio Caroline

RADIO CAROLINE STORY 1964-74 (Various artists).
2LP: R 104/5

RADIO CAROLINE STORY 1964-84 (Various artists).
LPS: R111/116

RADIO CAROLINE STORY 1964-84, THE (Various artists).
LPS: R 111-6

RADIO CAROLINE - THE OFFICIAL STORY (Various artists).
2LP: R 102/103
MCSET: C 101

Radio Collection

ASIMOV FOUNDATION TRILOGY (8 hour dramatisation) (Various artists).
MCSET: ZBBC 8001

DIANA'S STORY (Various artists).
MCSET: ZBBC 1112

DIARY OF A SOMEBODY (Various artists).
MCSET: ZBBC 1111

FASHION IN SHROUDS, THE.
MCSET: ZBBC 1166

FATHER BROWN (Various artists).
MCSET: ZBBC 1175

MUCH BINDING IN THE MARSH (Various artists).
MCSET: ZBBC 1197

TAKE IT FROM HERE (Various artists).
MCSET: ZBBC 1113

TITUS GROAN (Various artists).
MCSET: ZBBC 1114

Radio Days (film)

RADIO DAYS (Film Soundtrack) (Various artists).
Tracks: / Frenesi: *Shaw, Artie & His Orchestra* / Donkey serenade, The: *Jones, Allan* / You and I: *Dorsey*, Tommy Orchestra/Frank Sinatra / Remember Pearl Harbour: *Kay, Sammy* / That old feeling: *Lombardo, Guy/his Royal Canadians* / White cliffs of Dover, The: *Miller, Glenn & His Orchestra* / Goodbye: *Goodman, Benny & Orchestra/Helen* Ward / I'm gettin' sentimental over you: *Dorsey, Tommy & His Orchestra* / American patrol: *Miller, Glenn & His Orchestra* / Take the 'A' train: *Ellington, Duke And His Orchestra* / One,two,three, kick blues: *Cugat, Xavier & His Waldorf-Astoria Orchestra* / Opus one: *Dorsey, Tommy & His Orchestra.*
LP: PL 83017
MC: PK 83017

Radio Freedom

RADIO FREEDOM (Commentary & Music) (Various artists).
LP: REU 1010

VOICE OF THE AFRICAN NATIONAL CONGRESS (Various artists).
MC: ROUNDER 4019C
LP: ROUNDER 4019

Radio Heart

RADIO HEART (see under Numan, Gary).

Radio Jingles

LASER, MONIQUE & CAROLINE JINGLES (Various artists).
MC: C 7

Radio Laser

LASER 558 STORY, THE (Various artists).
2LP: R 119/120
MCSET: C 119/120

LASER "HOT HITS" JINGLES (Various artists).
MC: C 8

LASER MASTERS TAPE, THE (Various artists).
MC: C 9

Radio Leicester

RADIO LEICESTER BIG BAND & FRIENDS (Radio Leicester Big Band).
Tracks: / Take the 'A' train / Senorita blues / Twin town trip / Back to the barracks / Feels so good / Big dipper / Cute / Lucky for some / Bone free / Teddy the toad / More than Froleswoth.
LP: RLBB 103

Radio Nordsee

RADIO NORDSEE - INTERNATIONAL STORY (Various artists).
2LP: R 104/105
MCSET: C 102

Radio One

10 YEARS OF HITS - RADIO ONE (Various artists).
2LP: BEDP 002

ONES ON 1 (Various artists).
Tracks: / Baby now that I've found you: *Foundations* / Everlasting love: *Love Affair* / Do it again: *Beach* Boys / Mighty quinn: *Manfred Mann* / Albatross: *Fleetwood Mac* / Something in the air: *Thunderclap Newman*/ In the Summertime: *Mungo Jerry* / Get it on: *T. Rex* / Maggie May: *Stewart, Rod* / Mama weer all crazee now: *Slade* / School's out: *Cooper, Alice* / See my baby jive: *Wizzard* / Seasons in the sun: *Jacks, Terry* / Down down: *Status Quo* / Make me smile (come up and see me): *Harley, Steve & Cockney Rebel* / Bohemian rhapsody: *Queen* / Don't go breaking my heart: *John, Elton & Kiki Dee* / Dancing queen: *Abba* / Way down: *Presley, Elvis* / Wuthering heights: *Bush, Kate* / Heart of glass: *Blondie* / Brass in pocket: *Pretenders*/ Going underground: *Jam* / Every little thing she does is magic: *Police* / Land of make believe: *Bucks Fizz*/ Karma chameleon: *Culture Club* / I'm your man: *Wham* / Don't leave me this way: *Communards* / Never gonna give you up: *Astley, Rick* / I should be so lucky: *Minogue, Kylie.*
2LP: REF 693
MCSET: ZCD 693

Radioactive

RADIO ACTIVE (Various artists).
Tracks: / Police file and shipping forecast: *Various artists* / Commercial break: *Various artists* / Radiothon: *Various artists* / S.O.S. message: *Various artists* / Thought for the day: *Various artists* / Results service: *Various artists.*
LP: REH 471
MC: ZCR 471

RADIOACTIVE (Various artists).
LP: FALL LP 040

Radium Cats

MUNSTER MADNESS.
LP: FLATOP 002

Radulesco, Gheorghe

LE CYMBALUM ROUMAIN.
Tracks: / Le traineau de Bucarest / Les tsiganes de Felentari / Melodie de Pargari / Joc de Costanta / Primavera de Craiova / Joc du mouchoir / Souvenir de Olt / Joc de Gheorghe / Escale en Transylvanie / Nicolas, Nicolet / La petite fille au miroir / Montagne de Sinaia / Murele / Chanson, danse de Jianu / La sirba de Ploiesti / La chanson de lon Albabi.
LP: ARN 30121

Rae, Dashiell

MUSIC OF THE STARS (See under Kirsch, Barry) (Rae, Dashiell & Kirsch, Barry).

SONG WITHOUT WORDS.
LP: NAGE 4
MC: NAGEC 4

Rae, Jesse

THISTLE, THE.
Tracks: / Inside out / That kind o' girl / Hou-di-ni / Don't give up / Friend-ship / Thistle, The / Be yer sel / Rusha / Over the sea / Scotland the brave / Open all night / Follow the night / Heavy shit / Windsong / Tears / Radio romance / Rainyday / Island of blue.
LP: WX 97
MC: WX 97 C

Raeburn, Boyd

1943 - 1948 (Raeburn, Boyd & His Musicians).
LP: FH 8

EXPERIMENTS IN BIG BAND JAZZ 1945 (Raeburn, Boyd Orchestra).
Tracks: / Night in Tunisia / Summertime / Prisoner of love / Out of nowhere / Blue prelude / This heart of mine.
LP: MVS 505

GEP BOYDS (Raeburn, Boyd & His Orchestra).
LP: GELP 15014

JEWELS.
2LP: SJL 2250

MEMPHIS IN JUNE.
LP: HEP 22

MORE 1944-45 (Raeburn, Boyd Orchestra).
LP: CLP 113

NEW SOUNDS IN THE FORTIES (see under Tristano, Lennie) (Raeburn, Boyd/ Lennie Tristano).

ON THE AIR VOLUME 1 (Raeburn, Boyd Orchestra).
Tracks: / Tonsillectomy / Picnic in the wintertime / Rip Van Winkle / Yerxa / Night in Tunisia / Eagle flies / Boyd meets Stravinsky / Tone poem in four movements.
LP: HEP 1

ON THE AIR VOLUME 2 (Raeburn, Boyd Orchestra).
Tracks: / Boyd meets Stravinsky / Where you at / Tea for two / Caravan / High tide / Bagdad / Hep Boyds / Boyds nest / There's no you / Duck waddle / Two spoons / St. Louis blues / How high the moon / Begin the beguine / Tonsillectomy.
LP: HEP 3

RHYTHMS BY RAEBURN (Raeburn, Boyd & His Orchestra).
Tracks: / There must be a way / Night in Tunisia / He's home for a little while / Boyd meets girl / If I loved you / Hep Boyd's / Out of this world / Bagdad / Stranger in town / There's no you / Who started love? / How deep is the ocean / Blue moon.
LP: AIRCHECK 20

Raeburn, Ray

1944: RAY RAEBURN (Raeburn, Ray & His Orchestra).
LP: CLP 22

Raes

DANCING UP A STORM.
Tracks: / Little lovin' / I only wanna get up and dance / Gonna burn my boogie shoes / Honest I do / Don't turn around / Don't make waves / School.
LP: AMLH 64754

R.A.F. (group)

HEAT'S ON.
Tracks: / Easy come is easy go / You can't hold back now / Stop her on sight / Heat's on / Tightrope / I can't get started / Borrowed time / Talking pictures / Miracles / Holocaust.
LP: . . . . **AMLH 68525**

R.A.F..
Tracks: / Sweet Melinda / Give me a little time / Warm welcome on a cold night / Don't take sweets from strangers / Take me to your leader / Change your ways / More crazy now / Blue / She used to be mine / Waiting for the weekend.
LP: . . . . **AMLH 64816**

RESTLESS SPIRIT.
Tracks: / Dream boy / Only the heart can tell / Steal your love / Faces in the windshield / Woman like you, A / Stranger in the mirror / We can only dream / It's only love / Restless spirit (reprise).
LP: . . . . **AUL 733**
MC: . . . . **AUC 733**

Rafferty, Gerry

BEST OF STEALERS WHEEL (Rafferty, Gerry & Joe Egan).
Tracks: / Stuck in the middle with you / Who cares / Benediction / Go as you please / Late again / Everything will turn out fine / Blind faith / Star / Outside looking in / Found my way to you / Right or wrong / You put something better inside me.
LP: . . . . **MFP 50501**

BLOOD AND GLORY.
Tracks: / Please sing a song for us / Rick-rack / Patrick / Shoeshine boy / Song for Simon / Steamboat row / Look over the hill and far away / Blood and glory / New Street blues / Didn't I / Mr. Universe / Mary Skeffington / Long way round / To each and everyone / Can I have my money back / Sign on the dotted line.
LP: . . . . **TRANDEM 3**

CAN I HAVE MY MONEY BACK.
Tracks: / New street blues / Didn't I / Mr. Universe / Mary Skeffington / Long way round / Can I have my money back / Sign on the dotted line / Make you break you / To each and everyone / One drink down / Don't count me out / Half a chance / Where I belong.
MC: . . . . **ASK 769**
LP: . . . . **TRS 112**
MC: . . . . **KTRS 112**

CITY TO CITY.
Tracks: / Ark, The / Baker street / Right down the line / City to city / Sealin' time / Mattie's rag / Whatever's written in your heart / Home and dry / Island / Waiting for the day.
LP: . . . . **FA 413119 1**
MC: . . . . **FA 413119 4**
LP: . . . . **FA 3119**
MC: . . . . **TCFA 3119**
LP: . . . . **UAS 30104**

FIRST CHAPTER, THE.
Tracks: / Patrick / Rick rack / Blood and glory / Coconut tree / Steam boat row / Shoe shine boy / Song for Simon / My singing bird / Didn't I / Long way round / Mr. Universe / One drink down / Mary Skeffington / Half a chance.
2LP: . . . . **CR 132**
MCSET: . . . . **CRT 132**

HUMBLEBUMS, THE (see Connolly, Billy) (Rafferty, Gerry & Billy Connolly).

NIGHT OWL.
Tracks: / Days gone down / Night owl / Way that you do it, The / Why won't you talk to me / Get it right next time / Take the money and run / Family tree / Already gone / Tourist, The / It's gonna be a long night.
LP: . . . . **FA 41 3147 1**
MC: . . . . **FA 41 3147 4**
LP: . . . . **ATAK 37**
MC: . . . . **TCATAK 37**
LP: . . . . **FA 3147**
MC: . . . . **TCFA 3147**
LP: . . . . **UAK 30238**

NORTH AND SOUTH.
Tracks: / North and South / Moonlight and gold / Tired of talking / Hearts run dry / Dangerous age / Shipyard town / Winter's come / Nothing ever happens down here / On a night like this / Unselfish love.
LP: . . . . **LONLP 55**
MC: . . . . **LONC 55**

PORTFOLIO.
2LP: . . . . **CHR 1638**
MC: . . . . **ZCHR 1638**

RIGHT DOWN THE LINE (Best of Gerry Rafferty).
Tracks: / Baker Street / Whatever's written in your heart / Bring it all home / Right down the line / Get it right next time / Way that you do it, The (CD only.) / Tired of talking (CD only.) / Garden of England, The (CD only.) / Sleepwalking (CD only.) / Night owl / As wise as a serpent (CD only.) / Dangerous age / Family tree / Shipyard town / Right moment, The / Look at the moon (Not on CD.).
LP: . . . . **UAG 30333**
MC: . . . . **TCUAG 30333**

SLEEPWALKING.
Tracks: / Standing at the gates / Good intentions / Change of heart, A / On the way / Sleepwalking / Cat and mouse / Right moment, The / As wise as a serpent.
LP: . . . . **EMS 1190**
MC: . . . . **TCEMS 1190**
LP: . . . . **FA 41 3113 1**
MC: . . . . **FA 41 3113 4**
LP: . . . . **ATAK 84**
MC: . . . . **TCATAK 84**
LP: . . . . **LEG 30352**

SNAKES AND LADDERS.
Tracks: / Royal mile / I was a boy scout / Welcome to Hollywood / Wastin' away / Look at the moon / Bring it all home / Garden of England, The / Johnny's song / Didn't I / Syncopatin' Sandy / Cafe le cabotin / Don't close the door.
MC: . . . . **TCK 30298**
LP: . . . . **UAK 30298**

STUCK IN THE MIDDLE (See under Egan, Joe) (Rafferty, Gerry & Joe Egan).

Rafferty, Jim

SOLID LOGIC.
Tracks: / Keep it in the family / Look in your eyes / Stepping out / Tomorrow's another day / Oh Lucy / Home away from home / Saturday night / Get down to the rhythm / Underwood Lane / Any port in a storm.
LP: . . . . **SKLR 5314**

Raffles

RAFFLES - BLACK MASK VOL 1 (see Hornung, E.W.) (Elder, Michael).

RAFFLES - BLACK MASK VOL 2 (see Hornung, E.W.) (Elder, Michael).

RAFFLES VOL.1 (see Hornung, E.W.) (Elder, Michael).

RAFFLES VOL.2 (see Hornung, E.W.) (Elder, Michael).

Rage

EXECUTION GUARANTEED.
LP: . . . . **N 0073**
LP: . . . . **NUK 073**
MC: . . . . **ZCNUK 073**

EXTENDED POWER.
LP: . . . . **NO 1695**

NICE 'N' DIRTY.
Tracks: / American radio stations / Wasted years / Woman / Heartbreaker / Silver and gold / Long way from home / Only child / Blame it on the night / Wild cat woman / Ready to go.
LP: . . . . **CAL 138**
MC: . . . . **CAC 138**

OUT OF CONTROL.
Tracks: / Out of control / What have I done wrong / She's on fire / Roll the dice / Fallen idol / Money / I didn't want to leave / Rage / Thank that woman.
MC: . . . . **CAC 124**
LP: . . . . **CAL 124**

PERFECT MAN.
Tracks: / Don't fear the winter / Death in the afternoon / Pilgrim's path / Time and place / Round trip / Between the lines / Wasteland / In the darkest hour / Animal instinct / Perfect man, The / Sinister thinking / Supersonic hydromatic.
LP: . . . . **N 0112**
MC: . . . . **N 0112-2**

REFLECTIONS OF A SHADOW.
Tracks: / Introduction (a bit more green) / That's human bondage / True face in everyone / Flowers that fade in my hand / Reflections of a shadow / Can't get out / Waiting for the moon / Saddle the wind / Dust / Nobody knows.
LP: . . . . **NUK 160**
MC: . . . . **ZCNUK 160**

REIGN OF FEAR.
LP: . . . . **N 0038**
LP: . . . . **NUK 038**

RUN FOR THE NIGHT.
Tracks: / Cry from a hill / Fantasy / Can't say no / Light years / Ladykiller / No prisoners / Run for the night / Badlands / Never before / Rock fever.
LP: . . . . **CAL 149**
MC: . . . . **CAC 149**

SECRETS IN A WEIRD WORLD.
LP: . . . . **NUK 137**
MC: . . . . **ZCNUK 137**
LP: . . . . **N 0137 1**
MC: . . . . **N 0137 4**

Rage Of ...

RAGE OF THE HEART (Various artists).
LP: . . . . **ROLE 1**
MC: . . . . **ROLEC 1**

Ragga Twins

REGGAE OWES ME MONEY.
LP: . . . . **SUADLP 002**
MC: . . . . **SUADMC 002**

Ragged Child

RAGGED CHILD, THE (Original London cast) (Various artists).
LP: . . . . **CAST 12**
MC: . . . . **CASTC 12**

Ragged Heroes

RAGGED HEROES ANNUAL.
LP: . . . . **CM 013**

Raggedy Rawney

RAGGEDY RAWNEY (Film soundtrack) (Various artists).
Tracks: / Tribe, The: *Various artists* / You should see Nellie pass water: *Various artists* / Caravans: *Various artists* / Horse race, The: *Various artists* / Farmyard: *Various artists* / Rolling home: *Various artists*/ Jessie and Tom: *Various artists* / Daisy chain: *Various artists* / Wedding dress: *Various artists* / Bullroarer: *Various artists* / Band of lace: *Various artists* / Peacock polka (Darky's polka): *Various artists*/ Simon drowned: *Various artists* / Funeral lament: *Various artists* / Prayer: *Various artists* / Officer, The: *Various artists* / Children, The: *Various artists* / Raggedy rawney, The: *Various artists*.
LP: . . . . **FILM 033**
MC: . . . . **FILMC 033**

Raggerty

BORROWED TIME.
LP: . . . . **SFA 032**

Raging Death

RAGING DEATH (Various artists).
LP: . . . . **GRX 001**

Raging Moon

RAGING MOON (Film Soundtrack) (Various artists).
Tracks: / Time for winning: *Various artists* / Together: *Various artists* / Disoriented: *Various artists*/ Tenderness: *Various artists* / Alone: *Various artists* / Music to wake up the whole house to: *Various artists*/ Loving: *Various artists* / Many loving things: *Various artists* / Playing: *Various artists* / Rage: *Various artists* / Apart: *Various artists* / Touching: *Various artists* / Remembering: *Various artists*.
LP: . . . . **SCX 6447**

Raging Slab

ASSMASTER.
Tracks: / Mr. Lucky / Rocks off is rocks off.
LP: . . . . **BOR 12011**

RAGING SLAB.
Tracks: / Don't dog me / Jaynde / Sorry's all I got / Waiting for the potion / Get off my jollies / Shiny mama / Geronimo / Bent for silver / When love comes loose / Dig a hole / San Loco.
LP: . . . . **PL 90396**
MC: . . . . **PK 90396**

Raging Sun

RAGING SUN (Various artists).
LP: . . . . **RANT 1**
MC: . . . . **RUSK 006**

Ragtime

CONTEMPORARY RAGTIME GUITAR (Various artists).
Tracks: / Wild cherries: *Leibman, Dave* / Maple leaf rag: *Marcus, Tony* / Grace and beauty: *Wynkamp, Leo Jnr.* / Piano roll blues: *Schoenberg, Rick* / Grandpa's spells: *Leibman, Dave* / Georgia camp meeting: *Wynkamp,* Leo Jnr. / Buck dancer's choice: *Sandberg, Larry* / 10th Street scratch: *Mann, Woody* / Oh papa: *Schoenberg,* Rick / Nola: *Leibman, Dave* / Singing in the country: *Schoenberg, Rick* / Original rags: *Gillfellow, Tom* / Blackberry rag: *Miller, Dale Jnr.* / Slippery elm: *Schoenberg, Rick* / Dill pickle rag: *Schoenberg, Rick* / Somebody loves me: *Miller, Dale Jnr.* / Bye bye blackbird: *Miller, Dale Jnr.*.
LP: . . . . **SNKF 100**
LP: . . . . **KM 107**

MAPLE LEAF RAG (Various artists).
LP: . . . . **NW 235**

MASTERS OF THE RAGTIME GUITAR (Various artists).
LP: . . . . **SNKF 130**

PIANO RAGTIME OF THE 20'S & 30'S (Vol. 3) (Various artists).
LP: . . . . **HERWIN 406**

PIANO RAGTIME OF THE 20'S & 30'S (Vol. 1) (Various artists).
LP: . . . . **HERWIN 405**

RAGTIME (Film soundtrack) (Various artists).
LP: . . . . **K 52342 1**
MC: . . . . **K 52342 4**

RAGTIME BLUES GUITAR (1928-30) (Various artists).
Tracks: / One way gal: *Moore, William* / Ragtime crazy: *Moore, William* / Midnight blues: *Moore, William*/ Ragtime millionaire: *Moore, William* / Tillie Lee: *Moore, William* / Barbershop rag: *Moore, William*/ Old country rock: *Moore, William* / Raggin' the blues: *Moore, William* / Brownie blues: *Gay, Tarter*/ Unknown blues: *Gay, Tarter* / Jamestown exposition: *Baylesse Rose* / Black dog blues: *Baylesse Rose*/ Original blues: *Baylesse Rose* / Frisco blues: *Baylesse Rose* / Dupree blues: *Walker, Willie* / Sould Caroline rag: *Walker, Willie*.
LP: . . . . **MSE 204**

RAGTIME COLLECTION (20 Original Greats, 1906-1930) (Various artists).
Tracks: / Buffalo rag: *Various artists* / Dill pickle rag: *Various artists* / At a Georgia camp meeting: *Various artists* / Black and white rag: *Various artists* / Temptation rag: *Various artists* / Alexander's ragtime band: *Various artists* / Ragtime drummer: *Various artists* / Hungarian rag: *Various artists* / You're here and I'm here: *Various artists* / Desecration rag: *Various artists* / Ragging the scale: *Various artists* / Bullfrog blues: *Various artists* / Dixie jass band one-step: *Various artists* (Track title is correct: ie Dixie jass...) / Slippery Hank: *Various artists* / Yah-de-dah: *Various artists* / Laughing rag: *Various artists*/ Ross juba: *Various artists* / Waiting for the Evening Mail: *Various artists* / I wonder where my baby is tonight: *Various artists* / Maple leaf rag: *Various artists*.
LP: . . . . **DVLP 2120**
MC: . . . . **DVMC 2120**

RAGTIME MEMORIES (Various artists).
LP: . . . . **VLP 51**

THOSE RAGTIME YEARS 1899-1916 (Various artists).
Tracks: / Hot foot Sue: *Various artists* / Rice's ragtime opera: *Various artists* / Ragtime skedaddle: *Various artists* / Mississippi river song: *Various artists* / Ain't yer gwine say: *Various artists* / St. Louis rag: *Various artists* / Peaceful Henery: *Various artists* / American rag: *Various artists* / Operatic rag: *Various artists* / St. Louis tickle: *Various artists* / Wild cherries: *Various artists* / Red rose rag: *Various artists* / Tickled to death: *Various artists* / Fiddlesticks rag: *Various artists* / Turkey trot: *Various artists* / Powder rag: *Various artists* / Be my little baby bumble bee: *Various artists* / I'll dance till de sun breaks through: *Various artists* / College rag: *Various artists* / Rum-tum-tiddle: *Various* artists / Red pepper rag: *Various artists* / I want to be in Dixie: *Various artists* / You made me love you: *Various artists* / On San Francisco bay: *Various artists* / Land of cotton: *Various artists* / Hiawatha: *Various artists* / Lumbrin' Luke: *Various artists* / Gaby glide, The: *Various artists* / Wedding glide: *Various artists* / I want a dancing man: *Various artists* / Hors d'ouvres: *Various artists* / You can't get away from it: *Various artists* / Are you from Dixie: *Various artists* / Dear old Shepherds Bush: *Various artists* / Down home rag: *Various artists*.
2LP: . . . . **SHB 41**

Ragtime Banjo

RAGTIME BANJO COMMISSION, THE.
LP: . . . . **GHB 154**

Ragtime Charlie

EVENING WITH RAGTIME CHARLIE AND SISTER KATE (Ragtime Charlie & Sister Kate).
LP: . . . . **BR 201**

Rah Band

CRUNCH AND BEYOND, THE.
Tracks: / Crunch, The / Electric fling / Concrete / Is anybody there / Beyond / Spacerace / Turkey roll / Vampire vamp / Woogie boogie / Crunch, The (reprise).
LP: . . . . **EBY 1001**
MC: . . . . **EBK 1001**

MYSTERY.
Tracks: / Clouds across the moon / Night wind / Sorry doesn't make it anymore / Float / Mystery boy / Are you satisfied / Shadow of your love / Out on the edge.
LP: . . . . **PL 70640**

PAST PRESENT AND FUTURE.
Tracks: / What'll become of the children / Star dance / Perfumed garden / Rock me down to Rio / Are you satisfied / Clouds across the moon / Messages

from the stars / Falcon / Sam the samba man / Crunch, The.
LP: PL 70888
MC: PK 70888

RAH BAND.
Tracks: / Falcon / Downside up / Dream on / Slide / Blue horizon drifter / Dancing on the moon / Ride.
LP: DJF 20573
MC: DJH 40573

SOMETHING ABOUT THE MUSIC.
Tracks: / Run 4 the sun / Something about the music / Take some thyme / Nothing in the world / Woman's life, A / Adventures of E man, The / Life after love / Jammin' on the byte / Across the bay / Road of no return.
LP: PL 71560

UPPER CUTS.
LP: SNDLP 601

Raheem

VIGILANTE, THE.
LP: AMA 5212
MC: AMC 5212

Rahim, Emanuel K.

TOTAL SUBMISSION.
LP: MR 5122

Rai, Raina

HADA CHEMAL.
MC: LVS 1021

Raices Incas

FLAUTAS ANDINAS.
Tracks: / Fiesta para Sikuris / El Arriero chola cuencana / Kacharpari / Fiesta aimara / Sikuriadas / Ojitos chuquenos / Es una lisura / Patajaliphapi / Aires de tarka / Peregrino.
LP: 104 7092

MUSIC FROM THE ANDES.
Tracks: / Casarjeta / Mariposa / An oranzas / Patajaliphapi / Waca waca / Kacharpari / Peregrino / Buscado / Es un lisura / Peregrinacion / Los carnavales / La diablada / Huayruro / El condor pasa.
LP: NL 70168
MC: NK 70168

Raiders of...

RAIDERS OF THE LOST ARK (Film soundtrack) (Various artists).
Tracks: / Raiders of the lost ark: *Various artists* / Flight from Peru: *Various artists* / Map room, The: *Various artists* / Dawn: *Various artists* / Basket game, The: *Various artists* / Well of souls, The: *Various artists*/ Desert chase: *Various artists* / Marion's theme: *Various artists* / Miracle of the ark, The: *Various artists*/ Raiders march, The: *Various artists.*
LP: CBS 70205
MC: 40 70205
LP: 8215831
MC: 8215834
LP: POLD 5146

RAIDERS OF THE LOST ARK (Various artists).
LP: D 452

Railway

CLIMAX.
LP: RR 9667

RAILWAY.
Tracks: / Hell soldiers / Heavy metal fever / Nightrider.
LP: RR 9821

RAILWAY 2.
LP: RR 9760

Railway Cat (bk)

RAILWAY CAT, THE (Phyllis Arkle) (Branch, Andrew (nar)).
MC: 881980

Railway Children

NATIVE PLACE.
Tracks: / Every beat of the heart / Music stop / You're young / Because / Cotton counting / It's heaven / Something so good / Collide / Native place / Fall on / Harbour force / Blue sky.
LP: V 2627
MC: TCV 2627

RECURRENCE.
Tracks: / Somewhere south / Pleasure / Swallowed / Merciless / My word / In the meantime / Over and over / Monica's light / Chrysalis / No great objections.
LP: V 2525
MC: TCV 2525

REUNION WILDERNESS.
Tracks: / Gentle sound / Content / Another town / Railroad side / Brighter / Listen on / First notebook / Careful / Hands of freedom.
LP: 906 361
LP: FACT 185
MC: FACT 185 C

Railway Children (bk)

RAILWAY CHILDREN, THE (children's classics) (Unknown narrator(s)).
MC: PLBC 177

RAILWAY CHILDREN, THE (see under Nesbit, E.) (Sheridan, Dinah).

Railway Children

RAILWAY CHILDREN, THE (Film soundtrack) (Various artists).
Tracks: / Overture: *Various artists* / Roberta's theme: *Various artists* / Mother's theme: *Various artists*/ Robbers: *Various artists* / More than ever now: *Various artists* / Paper chase: *Various artists* / Kindly old gentleman: *Various artists* / Perks must be about it: *Various artists* / Birthday waltz: *Various artists*/ Finale: *Various artists.*
LP: SCX 6446

Railway Stories

FURTHER RAILWAY STORIES (Rev. W. Awdry, (aut)) (Rushton, Willie (nar)).
Tracks: / Main line engines / Small railway engines / Enterprising engines / Oliver the western engine / Duke the lost engine / Tramway engines.
MCSET: SAY 100

MORE RAILWAY STORIES (1) (Rev. W. Awdry) (Rushton, Willie (nar)).
Tracks: / Twin engine, The / Branch line engines / Gallant old engine / Stepney / Mountain engines / Very old engines.
MCSET: SAY 75
MCSET: ARGO 1151

MORE RAILWAY STORIES (2) (Morris, Johnny (nar)).
Tracks: / Troublesome engines / Henry the green engine / Toby the tram engine / Gordon the big engine.
MCSET: SAY 90

RAILWAY STORIES (Rushton, Willie (nar)).
Tracks: / Edward the blue engine / Four little engines.
LP: SPA 559

RAILWAY STORIES (Featuring Thomas the Tank Engine) (Morris, Johnny (nar)).
MC: 0600560872

RAILWAY STORIES (Rushton, Willie (nar)).
Tracks: / Percy the small engine / Eight famous engines.
LP: SPA 560

RAILWAY STORIES (Rushton, Willie (nar)).
Tracks: / Duck the diesel engine / Little old engine.
LP: SPA 561

RAILWAY STORIES (1) (Rev. W. Awdry) (Rushton, Willie (nar)).
MCSET: SAY 29
MCSET: ARGO 1058

RAILWAY STORIES (2) (Rev. W. Awdry) (Morris, Johnny (nar)).
MCSET: SAY 87

RAILWAY STORIES VOL. 3 (Rev. W. Awdry) (Morris, Johnny (nar)).
MCSET: ARGO 1235

Rain

TASTE OF RAIN.
Tracks: / All I want / Going / Beat goes on, The / Lemonstone desired / Hold on / Here they are / Taste of rain / She's on fire / Mother earth / Inside out / Outback blues (Only on cassette & CD).
LP: 4684421
MC: 4684424

TO THE CITADEL (Rain, The).
LP: CITRUS 001

Rain Dogs

LOST SOULS.
Tracks: / I'm not scared / Phantom flame / Too many stars / Cry for mercy / This is the place / I believe / May your heart keep beating / Higher road, The / Nobdoy's getting out / Adventure / Under the rainbow / Something wouldn't be the same.
LP: 7912971
MC: 7912974

Rain Gods

IN SOME WAKING HOUR.
LP: SLICE 8

LOST WORLDS.
Tracks: / Deep blue sea / I believe in you / Beach / Armour / Raining hearts / Come back / From the horses mouth / Tears in the rain / Pressure me up / Worshipping the sun.
LP: PL 71672
MC: PK 71672

Rain Man

IKO IKO (FROM RAINMAN) (See under Belle Stars).

RAIN MAN (Film Soundtrack) (Various artists).
Tracks: / Iko Iko: *Belle Stars* / Scatterlings of Africa: *Clegg, Johnny & Savuka* / Dry bones: *Delta Rhythm* Boys / At last: *James, Etta* / Lonely Avenue: *Gillan, Ian & Roger Glover* / Nathan Jones: *Bananarama*/ Leaving Wallbrook: *Zimmer, Hans* / Las Vegas (end credits): *Zimmer, Hans* / Stardust: *Wasserman, Rob/Aaron Neville* / Beyond the blue horizon: *Christie, Lou* / On the road: *Various artists.*
LP: EST 2091
MC: TCEST 2091

Rain Parade

BEYOND THE SUNSET.
LP: IMA 17
MC: IMC 17

CRASHING DREAM.
LP: ILPS 9805
MC: ICT 9805

EMERGENCY THIRD RAIL POWER TRIP.
Tracks: / Talking in my sleep / I look around / This can't be today / 1 hr 1/2 ago / Carolyn's song / What she's done to your mind / Look at Merri / Saturday's asylum / Kaleidoscope / Look both ways.
LP: ENIGMA 19
LP: ZONG 001

EXPLOSIONS IN THE GLASS PLACE.
Tracks: / You are my friend / Prisoners / Blue / Broken horse / No easy way down.
LP: ZANE 003

Rain People

RAIN PEOPLE.
Tracks: / Tell me what you want / Little bit of time / I won't give up on you / Love lies waiting / Children in the rain / Clockwork / Miracle man / I'm changing / Hiding out / Distance.
LP: 4634901
MC: 4634904

Rain Tree Crow

RAIN TREE CROW.
LP: V 2659

Rainbirds

CALL ME EASY, SAY I'M STRONG.
Tracks: / Love is a better word / Better than before.
LP: 838176-1
MC: 838176-4

RAINBIRDS.
Tracks: / Boy on the beach / Compartments / On the balcony / No greater love / We make love falling / Fire works / Bird up there, The / Apparently.
LP: MERH 125
MC: MERHC 125

TWO FACES.
Tracks: / Two faces / Ha ha Houdini's laughing / World is growing old, The / Real / Head over heels / Big fat cat / Invisible / Mystery train / Woman with a golden eye / Things change / Two faces (string).
LP: 848 554-1
MC: 848 554-4

Rainbow

BENT OUT OF SHAPE.
Tracks: / Stranded / Can't let you go / Fool for the night / Fire dance / Anybody there / Desperate heart / Street of dreams / Drinking with the devil / Snowman / Make your move.
LP: POLD 5116

BEST OF RAINBOW.
Tracks: / All night long / Man on the silver mountain / Can't happen here / Lost in Hollywood / Since you've been gone / Stargazer / Catch the rainbow / Kill the king / Sixteenth century greensleeves / I surrender / Long live rock 'n' roll / Eyes of the world / Starstruck / Light in the black, A / Mistreated.
2LP: POLDV 2
MCSET: PODVC 2
MCSET: 800 074-4
2LP: 800 074-1

DIFFICULT TO CURE.
Tracks: / I surrender / Spotlight kid / No release / Magic / Vielleicht das nachster zeit (Maybe next time.) / Can't happen here / Freedom fighter / Midtown tunnel vision / Difficult to cure.
LP: SPELP 76
MC: SPEMC 76
MCSET: 3574 141
LP: POLD 5036

FINYL VINYL.
Tracks: / Spotlight kid / I surrender / Miss Mistreated / Jealous lover / Can't happen here / Tearin' out my heart / Since you've been gone / Bad girl / Difficult to cure / Stone cold / Power / Long live rock 'n' roll / Weiss heim / Man on the silver mountain.
2LP: PODV 8
MCSET: PODVC 8

LIVE IN GERMANY 1976.
Tracks: / Kill the king / Mistreated / Sixteenth century greensleeves / Catch the rainbow / Man on the silver mountain / Stargazer / Still I'm sad / Do you close your eyes.
2LP: DPVSOPLP 155
MCSET: DPVSOPMC 155

LONG LIVE ROCK 'N' ROLL.
Tracks: / Long live rock 'n' roll / Lady of the lake / L.A. connection / Gates of Babylon / Sensitive to light / Kill the King / Shed, The / Rainbow eyes.
LP: SPELP 34
MC: SPEMC 34
LP: POLD 5002

ON STAGE.
Tracks: / Kill the king / Man on the silver mountain / Blues / Starstruck / Catch the Rainbow / Mistreated / 16th century Greensleeves / Still I'm sad.
2LP: 2657 016
2LP: SPDLP 6

RAINBOW RISING.
Tracks: / Tarot woman / Run with the wolf / Starstruck / Do you close your eyes / Stargazer / Light in the black, A.
LP: SPELP 35
MC: SPEMC 35
LP: 2490 137

RITCHIE BLACKMORE'S RAINBOW.
Tracks: / Man on the silver mountain / Self portrait / Black sheep of the family / Catch the rainbow / Snake charmer / Temple of the king / If you don't like rock'n'roll / 16th century greensleeves / Still I'm sad.
LP: SPELP 7
MC: SPEMC 7
LP: OYA 2001
LP: 2490 141

STRAIGHT BETWEEN THE EYES.
Tracks: / Death Alley driver / Stone cold / Bring on the night / Tite squeeze / Tearin' out my heart / Power / Miss Mistreated / Rock fever / Eyes on fire.
LP: POLD 5056

Rainbow Brite

RAINBOW BRITE (Various artists).
Tracks: / Rainbow Brite saves the day: *Various artists* / Rainbow Brite and the colour kids: *Various artists*/ Happy birthday Twink: *Various artists* / Rainbow Brite and the blue lake: *Various artists.*
LP: REC 566
MC: ZCM 566

Rainbow, Chris

WHITE TRAILS.
Tracks: / Love you eternally / Don't take the night away / Song of the earth / Be like a woman / Ring ring / Streetwise / White trails / In love with love.
LP: EMC 3305

Rainbow (film)

RAINBOW, THE (Film Soundtrack) (Davis, Carl).
Tracks: / Prelude and opening titles / Walking home / Swingboats, The / Ursula and Winifred / Seduction: The lettuce patch / Exam results / School assembly / Mr. Harby / Wedding, The / Moonlight lovers / Military two-step / Waterfull, The / Cottage Idyll / Pursuit through the forest / Ursula's dream / Rainbow, The.
LP: FILM 040
MC: FILMC 040

Rainbow (Group)

DOWN TO EARTH.
Tracks: / All night long / Eyes of the world / No time to lose / Making love / Since you've been gone / Love's no friend / Danger zone / Lost in Hollywood.
LP: SPELP 69
MC: SPEMC 69
LP: POLD 5023

Rainbow Remiped...

TAHITI SYNDROME, THE (Rainbow Remiped Dance Band).
LP: EAT 1

Rainbow Rhymes

RAINBOW RHYMES (TV soundtrack) (TV Cast).
Tracks: / Ride a cock horse / One two three four five once I caught a fish alive / Twinkle twinkle little star / Little Tommy Tucker / There was a crooked man / Mary, Mary, quite contrary / Cock-a-doodle-doo / Girls and boys come out to play / See-saw, Margery Daw / Little Jack Horner / Grand old Duke of York, The / Pray open your umbrella / Five little ducks / Dingle-dangle scarecrow / Here we go round the Mulberry bush / Milkman's song, The / Honey bee song, The / Doggy song, The.
LP: RBBLP 7300
MC: ZCRBB 7300

Rainbow Songtime

RAINBOW SONGTIME (Various artists).
LP: . . . . **TMP 9016**
MC: **TMP4 9016**

Raincoats

KITCHEN TAPES, THE.
MC: . . . . **A 120**

MOVING.
Tracks: / Overheard / Animal rhapsody / Dreaming in the past / Body, The / Honey mad woman / Dance of hopping mad / I saw a hill / Rainstorm.
LP: . . . . **ROUGH 66**

ODY SHAPE.
LP: . . . . **ROUGH 13**

RAINCOATS, THE.
LP: . . . . **ROUGH 3**

Raindance

RAINDANCE.
LP: . . . . **XIS 121**
MC: . . . . **XIS 121 C**

Rainer & Das Combo

BAREFOOT ROCK WITH....
LP: . . . . **SPIN 211**

Rainey, Ma

COMPLETE RECORDINGS - VOL.1 (1923-1924).
LP: . . . . **VLP 81**

MA RAINEY - COMPLETE RECORDINGS VOL.2 (August 1924-July 1925).
Tracks: / Shave 'em dry / Farewell Daddy blues / Booze and blues / Toad frog blues / Jealous hearted blues / See see rider blues / Jelly bean blues / Countin' the blues (Takes 2 and 3.) / Cell bound blues / Army camp harmony blues / Explaining the blues (Takes 1 and 2.) / Louisiana hoo doo blues / Goodbye daddy blues / Rough and tumble blues / Night time blues.
LP: . . . . **VLP 82**

MA RAINEY'S BLACK BOTTOM.
Tracks: / Ma rainey's black bottom / Don't fish in my sea / Booze and blues / Farewell daddy blues / Oh papa blues / Blues oh blues / Shave 'em dry / Lucky rock blues / Screetch owl blues / Georgia cake walk / Sleep talking blues / Yonder come the blues.
LP: . . . . **L 1071**
LP: . . . . **YAZOO 1071**

OH MY BABE BLUES.
Tracks: / Jealousy blues / Shave 'em dry / Oh my babe blues / Soon this morning / Farewell daddy blues / Don't fish in my sea / Countin' the blues / Sissy blues / Jog camp blues / Hustlin' blues / Ma and pa poorhouse blues / Big feeling blues.
LP: . . . . **BMLP 1048**

PARAMOUNT SESSIONS CHRONOLOGICALLY, VOL 1, THE.
LP: . . . . **WCH 12001**

Rainey, Willie Guy

KEEP ON TRUCKING.
LP: . . . . **SLP 7**

Rainmakers

GOOD NEWS AND THE BAD NEWS,THE.
LP: **8382321**
MC: **8382324**

RAINMAKERS.
Tracks: / Rockin' at the T-dance / Downstream / Let my people go go / Doomsville / Big fat blonde / Long gone long / One that got away, The / Government cheese / Nobody knows / Drinkin' on the job / Information.
LP: . . . . **MERH 96**
MC: . . . . **MERHC 96**
LP: **8302141**
MC: **8302144**

TORNADO.
Tracks: / Snakedance / Tornado of love / Wages of sin, The / Small circles / No romance / One more Summer / Lakeview man, The / Rainmaker / I talk with my hands / Other side of the world.
LP: . . . . **MERH 118**
MC: . . . . **MERHC 118**

Raintree County

7 DAY WEEKEND.
LP: . . . . **NTVLP 061**

SEVEN DAY WEEKEND.
LP: . . . . **NTVLP 61**

Rainwater, Marvin

ESPECIALLY FOR YOU.
Tracks: / Lonesomest guy in town / Darling where are you / Whole lotta woman / Cold woman / Looking good / I dig you baby / Happiness for me / Indian momma / I saw a bluebird / Old rivers / I miss you already / Follow me / Empty pond, The / Oh George / Village blacksmith, The / Sad witch / There's only one of you / Christmas time / Wobbling song / Little flower / Cardboard train / Cinderella / Mr. Snowman / Soft toys / Circus song / What's behind the Moon.
LP: . . . . **WRS 101**

ROCKIN' ROLLIN'.
Tracks: / I dig you baby / Don't be late for love / Whole lotta woman / Get off the stool / Love me baby like there's no tomorrow / Baby don't go / In the valley of the moon / She's gone / Roving gambler / Dance me Daddy / Hard luck blues / Mister blues / So you think you've got troubles / My brand of blues / Moanin the blues / Hot and cold.
LP: . . . . **BFX 15079**

WITH A HEART WITH A BEAT.
Tracks: / Boo hoo (Original Warwick recording.) / Can't forget (Original Warwick recording.) / Rough top cat (Original Warwick recording.) / That's the way I feel (Previously unissued.) / Last time, The (Previously unissued.) / (There's always) a need for love / Down in the cellar (Previously unissued.) / There's a honky tonk in your heart (Original Warwick recording.) / That's when I'll stop loving you / Two fools in love / Gonna find me a bluebird / Can I count on your love / Because I'm a dreamer / You my darling you / Crazy love (Previously unissued.) / Look for me (I'll be waiting for you).
LP: . . . . **BFX 15132**

Rainy Day

RAINY DAY.
LP: . . . . **ROUGH 70**

Raising Arizona (film)

RAISING ARIZONA/BLOOD SIMPLE (Film soundtrack) (Various artists).
LP: . . . . **TER 1140**
MC: . . . . **ZCTER 1140**

Raitt, Bonnie

BONNIE RAITT.
Tracks: / Bluebird revisited / I'm a mighty tight woman / Thank you / Finest lovin' man / Any day woman / Big road (walking blues) / Danger heartbreak dead ahead / Since I fell for you / I ain't blue / Woman be wise.
LP: . . . . **K 56255**

COLLECTION: BONNIE RAITT.
Tracks: / Finest lovin' man / Women be wise / Love me like a man / I feel the same / Angel from Montgomery / My first night alone without you / Louise / Runaway / (Goin') wild for your baby / True love is hard to find / Give it up or let me go / Under the falling sky / Love has no pride / Guilty / What is success / Sugar mama / About to make me leave home / Glow / Willya wontcha / No way to treat a lady.
LP: **9257911**
MC: **9257914**
LP: **7599262421**
MC: **7599262424**

GIVE IT UP.
Tracks: / Give it up or let me go / Nothing seems to matter / I know / If you gotta make a fool of somebody / Love me like a man / Stayed too long at the fair / Under the falling sky / You got to know how / You told me baby / Love has no pride.
LP: . . . . **K 46189**

GLOW, THE.
Tracks: / I thank you / Your good thing / Standin' by the same old love / Sleep's dark and silent gate / Glow / Bye bye baby / Boy can't help it / Best old friend / You're gonna get what's comin' / Wild for you baby.
LP: . . . . **K 56706**

GREEN LIGHT.
Tracks: / Keep this heart in mind / River of tears / Can't get enough / Willya wontcha / Let's keep it between us / Me & the boys / I can't help myself / Baby come back / Talk to me / Green light.
LP: . . . . **K 56980**

HOME PLATE.
Tracks: / What do you want the boy to do / Good enough / Run like a thief / Fool yourself / My first night alone without you / Walk out the front door / Sugar mama / Pleasin' each other / I'm blown away / Your sweet and shiny eyes.
LP: . . . . **K 56160**

LUCK OF THE DRAW.
Tracks: / Something to talk about / Good man, good woman / I can't make you love me / Tangled and dark / Come to me / No business / One part be my lover / Not the only one / Papa come quick (Jody and Chico) / Slow ride / Luck of the draw / All at once.
LP: . . . . **EST 2145**
MC: . . . . **TCEST 2145**

NICK OF TIME.
Tracks: / Nick of time / Thing called love, A / Love letters / Cry on my shoulder / Real man / Nobody's girl / Have a heart / Too soon to tell / I will not be denied / I ain't gonna let you break my heart again / Road's my middle name, The.
LP: . . . . **EST 2095**
LP: **791268 1**
MC: . . . . **TCEST 2095**
MC: **791268 4**

NINE LIVES.
Tracks: / No way to treat a lady / Runnin' back to me / Who but a fool / Crime of passion / All day, all night / Stand up to the night / Excited / Frezin' (for a little human love) / True love is hard to find / Angel.
LP: **925486 1**
MC: **925486 4**

STREETLIGHTS.
Tracks: / That song about the midway / Rainy day man / Angel from Montgomery / I got plenty / Streetlights / What is success / Ain't nobody home / Everything that touches you / Got you on my mind / You gotta be ready for love (if you wanna be).
LP: . . . . **K 56075**

SWEET FORGIVENESS.
Tracks: / Sweet forgiveness / Gamblin' man / Two lives / Runaway / About to make me leave home / Three time loser / My opening farewell / Takin' my time / Home / Louise.
LP: . . . . **K 56323**

TAKIN' MY TIME.
Tracks: / You've been in love too long / I gave my love a candle / Let me in / Everybody's cryin' mercy / Cry like a rainstorm / Wah she go do / I feel the same / I thought I was a child / Write me a few of your lines / Kokomo blues / Guilty.
LP: . . . . **K 56254**

Rakes

RAKES, THE.
LP: . . . . **LED 2071**

Rakes Progress

RAKES PROGRESS (VIDEO) (see under Stravinsky (composer)) (Various artists).

Raksin, David

LAURA, FOREVER AMBER (Raksin, David & New Philharmonia Orchestra).
Tracks: / Laura forever Amber suite / Amber / King's mistress, The / Whitefriars / Great fire / End title / Forever Amber / Bad and the beautiful / Love is for the very young / Acting lesson / Quickies and the sneak preview, The / Nocturne and theme.
MC: . . . . **GK 81490**

Rallo, Tony

BURNIN' ALIVE (Rallo, Tony & The Midnight Band).
Tracks: / Holdin' on / Burnin' alive / Fais l'amour / Travelin' flights of m mind / Say you believe.
LP: . . . . **CABLP 5001**

Ralls, Tony

LIFE.
LP: . . . . **LD 5003**
MC: . . . . **LDC 5003**

Ralphs, Mick

TAKE THIS.
LP: . . . . **MACH 3**

Ramage, Andy

TWO FOR THE ROAD (Ramage, Andy/ Mathieson, Neil).
MC: . . . . **MR 1006**

Ramazzotti, Eros

IN OGNI SENSO.
Tracks: / Se bastasse una canzone / C'e una strada in cielo / Amore contro / Dammi la luna / Taxi story / Dolce Barbara / Amarti e l'immenso per me / Canzoni lontane / Cara prof / Cantico / Oggi che giorno e' / Andare...in ogni senso.
LP: . . . . **PL 74765**
MC: . . . . **PK 74765**

Rambler, Het

THEO UDEN MASMAN (Rambler's, Het Dansorkest).
LP: . . . . **H 2002**

Ramblers

ZUIDERZEE BLUES (1938-39).
LP: . . . . **H 2013**

Ramblin' Thomas

RAMBLIN' THOMAS (1928-32).
Tracks: / So lonesome / Hard to rule woman blues / Lock and key blues / Sawmill moan / No baby blues / Ramblin' mind blues / No job blues / Back gnawing blues / Jig head blues / Hard Dallas blues / Ramblin' man / Poor boy blues / Good time blues / New way of living blues / Ground hog blues / Shake it gal.
LP: . . . . **MSE 215**

Rambo

RAMBO II: FIRST BLOOD (Film Soundtrack) (Various artists).
Tracks: / Main title: *Various artists* / Preperation: *Various artists* / Jump, The: *Various artists*/ Snake, The: *Various artists* / Stories: *Various artists* / Cage, The: *Various artists* / Betrayed: *Various artists* / Peace in our life: *Various artists* / Escape from torture: *Various artists* / Ambush: *Various* artists / Revenge: *Various artists* / Bowed down: *Various artists* / Pilot over: *Various artists*/ Home flight: *Various artists* / Day by day: *Various artists.*
LP: . . . . **TER 1104**
MC: . . . . **ZCTER 1104**

RAMBO III (Original Soundtrack) (Various artists).
Tracks: / It's our destiny: *Medley, Bill* / Preparations: *Various artists* / Afghanistan: *Various artists*/ Game, The: *Various artists* / Another time: *Various artists* / He ain't heavy, he's my brother: *Medley*, Bill / Aftermath: *Various artists* / Questions: *Various artists* / Bridge, The: *Moroder, Giorgio & Joe Pizullo* / Final battle: *Various artists.*
LP: . . . . **POLD 5227**
MC: . . . . **POLDC 5227**
LP: . . . . **RVF 6006**

Rambow, Philip

JUNGLE LAW.
Tracks: / Don't come / Jungle law / Magnificent obsession / Star / Jessica / Snakes and ladders / Creature comforts / Bike boys / Beyond the naked and the dead / Mansion on the hill / Love is a hard time.
LP: . . . . **PCS 7216**

SHOOTING GALLERY.
Tracks: / Strange destinies / Fallen / Don't call me Tonto / Victim / Sound and the fury / Rebel kind / Privilege / Young lust / Deep river.
LP: . . . . **EMC 3304**

Ramedios, Ramon

SUITE OF GODS (See under Wakeman, Rick) (Ramedios, Ramon & Rick Wakeman).

Ramey, Samuel

SAMUEL RAMEY SINGS RODGERS & HAMMERSTEIN (Ramey, Samuel/ National Philharmonic Orchestra).
Tracks: / June is bustin' out all over (from Carousel.) / When the children are asleep (from Carousel.) / You'll never walk alone (from Carousel.) / I have dreamed (from The King And I.) / Some enchanted evening (from South Pacific.) / This nearly was mine (from South Pacific.) / Younger than Springtime (from South Pacific.) / Man I used to be, The (from Pipe Dream.) / Climb every mountain (from The Sound Of Music.) / Oh what a beautiful morning (from Oklahoma.) / Surrey with the fringe on top (from Oklahoma.) / You are beautiful (from Flower Drum Song.) / Do I love you because you're beautiful (from Cinderella) / Fella needs a girl, A (from Allegro.).
LP: . . . . **EL 749 581 1**
MC: . . . . **EL 749 581 4**

Ramifications

RAMIFICATIONS (Various artists).
LP: . . . . **OG 500**

Ramirez, Louie

TRIBUTE TO CAL TJADER.
Tracks: / Latin blues / Milestones / It could happen to you / Mambo for Cal / Soul sauce / Lullaby of Birdland / El titere / Noche de salsa.
LP: . . . . **BGP 1013**

Ramirez, Ramon

RAMPANT RAM.
LP: . . . . **S 1356**

Ramm, Ken

DRAGON.
LP: . . . . **RAG 1011**

Ramones

ALL THE STUFF.
Tracks: / Blitzkrieg bop / Beat on the brat / Judy is a punk / Now I wanna sniff some glue / Don't go down the basement / Loudmouth / Havana affair / 53rd and 3rd / I don't wanna walk around with you / I wanna be sedated / Glad to see you go / I remember you / Sheena is a punk rocker / Glad to see you go / Sheena is a punk rocker / Pinhead / Swallow my pride / California sun / I wanna be your boyfriend / You're gonna kill that girl / Babysitter / Listen to my heart / Let's dance / Today your love, tomorrow the world / I can't be / Gimme gimme shock treatment / Oh oh I love her so / Suzy is a headbanger / Now I

wanna be a good boy / What's your game / Commando / Chainsaw / You should never have opened that door / California sun (live).
LP: 759926201
MC: 759926202

ANIMAL BOY.
Tracks: / Somebody put something in my drink / Animal boy / Love kills / Ape man hop / She belongs to me / Crummy stuff / Bonzo goes to Bitburg / Metal hell / Eat that rat / Freak of nature / Hair of the dog / Something to believe in.
LP: BEGA 70
MC: BEGC 70

BRAIN DRAIN.
Tracks: / I believe in miracles / Punishment fits the crime / Pet Semetary / Merry Christmas / Learn to listen / Zero zero UFO / All screwed up / Can't get you outta my mind / Ignorance is bliss.
LP: CHR 1725
MC: ZCHR 1725

END OF THE CENTURY.
Tracks: / Do you remember rock 'n' roll radio? / I'm affected / Danny says / Chinese rocks / Return of Jackie and Judy, The / Let's go baby / Baby I love you / I can't make it on time / This ain't Havanna.
MC: SRC 6077
LP: SRK 6077

HALFWAY TO SANITY.
Tracks: / Wanna live / Bop 'till you drop / Garden of serenity / Weasel face / Go lil' Camaro go / I know better now / Death of me / I lost my mind / Real cool time, A / I'm not Jesus / Bye bye baby / Worm man.
LP: BEGA 89
MC: BEGC 89

IT'S ALIVE.
Tracks: / Rockaway beach / Teenage labotomy / Blitzkrieg bop / I wanna be well / Glad to see you go / Gimme gimme shock treatment / You're gonna kill that girl / I don't care / Sheena is a punk rocker / Havana affair / Commando / Here today gone tomorrow / Surfin' bird / Cretin hop / Listen to my heart / California sun / I don't wanna walk around with you / Pinhead / Suzy is a headbanger / Let's dance / Oh oh I lover her so / Now I wanna sniff some glue / We're a happy family.
2LP: SRK 26074
MC: SRC 26074

LEAVE HOME.
Tracks: / Glad to see you go / Gimme gimme shock treatment / I remember you / Oh oh I love her so / Carbona not glue / Suzy is a headbanger / Pinhead / Now I wanna be a good boy / Shallow my pride / What's your game / California sun / Commando / You're gonna kill that girl / You should never have opened that door.
LP: SR 6031
LP: MAU 602

LET'S GO (See under Paley Brothers) (Paley Brothers/Ramones).

PLEASANT DREAMS.
Tracks: / We want the airwaves / All's quiet on the eastern front / KKK took my baby away, The / Don't go / You sound like you're sick / It's not my place / She's a sensation / 7-11 / You didn't mean anything to me / Come on now / This business is killing me / Sitting in my room.
MC: SRC 3571
LP: SRK 3571

RAMONES MANIA.
Tracks: / I wanna be sedated / Teenage lobotomy / Do you remember rock 'n' roll radio? / Gimme gimme shock treatment / Beat on the brat / Sheena is a punk rocker / I wanna live / Pinhead / Blitzkrieg bop / Cretin hop / Rockaway beach / Commando / I wanna be your boyfriend / Mamma's boy / Bop 'till you drop / We're a happy family / Bonzo goes to Bitburg / Outsider, The / Psycho therapy / Wart hog / Animal boy / Needles and pins / Howlin' at the moon / Somebody put something in my drink / We want the airwaves / Chinese rocks / I just want to have something to do / KKK took my baby away, The / Indian giver / Rock 'n' roll high school.
2LP: 925709 1
MC: 925709 4

RAMONES, THE.
Tracks: / Blitzkrieg bop / Beat on the brat / Judy is a punk / I wanna be your boyfriend / Chain saw / Now, I wanna sniff some glue / I don't wanna go down in the basement / Loud mouth / Havana affair / Listen to my heart / 53rd and 3rd / Let's dance / I don't wanna walk around with you / Today your love, tomorrow the world.
LP: SR 6020

ROAD TO RUIN.
Tracks: / I just want to have something to do / I wanted everything / Don't come close / I don't want you / Needles and pins / I'm against it / I wanna be sedated / Go mental / Questioningly / She's the one / Bad brain / It's a long way back.
LP: SRK 6063

ROCKET TO RUSSIA.
Tracks: / Cretin' hop / Rockaway beach / Here today, gone tomorrow / Locket loe / Don't care / Sheena is a punk rocker / We're a happy family / Teenage lobotomy / Do you wanna dance / I wanna be well / I can't give you anything / Ramona / Surfin' bird / Why is it always this way / Cretin hop / Rockaway beach / Here today, gone tomorrow / Locket love / Don't care / Sheena is a punk rocker / We're a happy family / Teenage lobotomy / Do you wanna dance / I wanna be well / I can't give you anything / Ramona / Surfin' bird / Why is it always this way.
LP: SR 6042
MC: 7222 102
LP: 9102 255

SUBTERRANEAN JUNGLE.
Tracks: / Little bit o' soul / I need your love / Outsider / What'd ya do? / Highest trails above / Somebody like me / Psycho therapy / Time has come today / My kind of a girl / In the park / Time bomb / Everytime I eat vegetables....
LP: W 3800

TOO TOUGH TO DIE.
LP: BEGA 59
MC: BEGC 59

Rampage

RAMPAGE (see under Morricone, Ennio) (Various artists).

Rampal, Jean Pierre

FASCINATIN' RAMPAL.
Tracks: / I got rhythm / Fascinating rhythm / Someone to watch over me / Nice work if you can get it / Man I love, The / Liza / Porgy and Bess medley / Foggy day / American in Paris, An / Preludes.
LP: FM 39059

SCOTT JOPLIN.
Tracks: / Maple leaf rag / Elite syncopations / Bathena / Combination march / Entertainer, The / Cascades / Cleopha / Ragtime dance / Chrysanthemum / Favourite ragtime two step / Original rags / Harmony club waltz / Great crush' collision march.
LP: CBS 73865
MC: 40 73865

SUITE FOR FLUTE AND JAZZ PIANO.
LP: CBS 73900

Ramsay, Fay

MASTER'S WIFE (Olsson, Diana).
MCSET: CLT 1009

Ramsby, Walter

MORNING SONG.
LP: SNTF 759

Ramsey, Bill

OHNE KRIMI GEHT DIE MIMI NIE INS BETT.
Tracks: / Ohne Krimi geht die Mimi nie ins Bett / Maskenball bei Scotland Yard / Feuerwasser und Liebe / Flotter dampfer / Sagst du alles deiner frau / Hallo, hallo Boss / Zwei alte Freude / Mimi needs a thriller when she goes to bed / Chug a lug / Bin nur ein Tramp / Canary blues / Bossa nova baby / Wer heisst heir Johnny? / Molly / Es gibt immer wieder arger / Kapt'n Brown von Clipper / Ich lese Abends keinen Krimi.
LP: BFX 15358

SOUVENIRS.
Tracks: / Yes Fanny ich tu das / So ein stroll in tirol / Casa bambu / Wumba tumba schokoladeneisverkaufer / Cecilia / Er war vom konstantinopelitanischen gesangsverein / Souvenirs / Mach keinen heck-meck / Telefon aus Paris / Hier konn' matrosen vor anker gehn' / Jeden tag 'ne andre partie / Weit weg von hier / De welt ist rund / Go man go / Rockin' mountain / Gina Gina.
LP: BFX 15325

Ranaldo, Lee

FROM HERE TO INFINITY.
LP: BFFP 9
MC: BFFP 9C

Rancid Hell Spawn

RANCID HELL SPAWN.
Tracks: / Siamese sextuplets / Bicycle shed girls / Sixteen cans of Stella / Botulism babies / Waste not want more / Farm night / Fifteen seconds fame / Cancerous cowboys / Ketchup boys / Sledgehammer job / Homunculus stumps / Monstrous man / Football special to Grimsby / Drinking myself to death / Eye in my stomach / Scalpel party / Jumpin' Jack flash / Going down to Croydon / Emphysema Eddie / Shane MacGowan's brain / Dirt city / Washout / Great expectations / Sex in a butchers' shop.
LP: STUNCH 002

Randall, Alan

GREAT COMEDY WAR SONGS (BLESS 'EM ALL).
MC: KGRS 1225

WORLD OF ALAN RANDALL, THE.
Tracks: / I blew a little blast on my whistle / Pleasure cruise / Mr. Wu's a window cleaner now / Baby show, The / Hi tiddly hi ti island / Super Ukulele / What ever you do keep fit / I'm one of the guests at the guest house / Hill billy Willie / Grandad's flannelette nightshirt / Sweet Georgia Brown / With my little stick of Blackpool rock.
LP: SPA 492

Randall, Frankie

SWINGIN' TOUCH, A.
LP: FS 106

Randall, Freddy

FREDDY RANDALL AND HIS BAND (Randall, Freddy & His Band).
LP: DM 5

SOMETHING BORROWED, SOMETHING BLUE.
Tracks: / Struttin' with some barbecue / Ain't misbehavin' / Birth of the blues / Something old, something new / Blues my naughty sweetie gives to me / Moonglow / Love is just around the corner / Lonesome road / Something new / She's funny that way / Keepin' out of mischief now / Limehouse blues.
LP: AJ 4503

Randazzo, Teddy

WE'RE GONNA ROCK TONIGHT.
LP: DLP 1003

Randell, Helen

COUNTRY CLASS.
LP: BGC 164
MC: KBGC 164

SOMEBODY STOLE MY HAPPY SONGS.
LP: BGC 146

Randells

SING COUNTRY.
MC: ZCFPA 1013

Randi, Don

NEW BABY (Randi, Don & The Quest Jazz Sextet).
LP: LAB 12

Randolph, Elsie

ORIGINAL LONDON CAST RECORDINGS (See under Buchanan, Jack) (Randolph, Elsie & Jack Buchanan).

Random, Eric

ISHMAEL (Random, Eric & The Bedlamites).
Tracks: / Demolition man / Done it again.
LP: BED 7

TIME SPLICE (Random, Eric & The Bedlamites).
LP: DVR 11

Random Hold

BURN THE BUILDINGS.
Tracks: / City clean / Toys / Walking on the edge / Dance feeling / Palmreader / March / Missing the boat / Future kids / Is there light / In the centre / We can work it out / Burn the buildings.
LP: RCALP 3062

Raney, Doug

GUITAR, GUITAR, GUITAR.
LP: SCS 1212

MEETING THE TENORS (Raney, Doug Sextet).
LP: CRISS 1006

STOLEN MOMENTS (see under Raney, Jimmy) (Raney, Jimmy & Doug Raney Quartet).

Raney, Jimmy

IN THREE ATTITUDES.
LP: JASM 1049

JIMMY RANEY TRIO (Raney, Jimmy Trio).
LP: XX 1019

MASTER, THE (Raney, Jimmy Quartet).
LP: CRISS 1009

RANEY 1981.
LP: CRISS 1001

SPECIAL BREW (see under Haig, Al) (Raney, Jimmy 4 & Al Haig).

STOLEN MOMENTS (Raney, Jimmy & Doug Raney Quartet).
LP: SCS 1118

TED BROWN & JIMMY RANEY (see Brown, Ted/Jimmy Raney) (Raney, Jimmy / Ted Brown).

TWO GUITARS (See Burrell, Kenny) (Raney, Jimmy & Kenny Burrell).

VISITS PARIS.
LP: FS 282

WISTARIA (Raney, Jimmy Trio).
LP: CRISS 1019

Raney, Sue

FLIGHT OF FANCY.
Tracks: / Summer me / Winter me / Sure as you're born / Nice 'n' easy / Piece of sky, A / Make me rainbows.
LP: DS 931
MC: DSC 931

RIDIN' HIGH (Raney, Sue with The Bob Florence Group).
Tracks: / How's that for openers / This happy madness / Stardust / Baseballs / I let a song go out of my heart / Pure imagination / Tea for two / Ridin' high / Body and soul / No more blues.
LP: DS 913
MC: DSC 913

SINGS THE MUSIC OF JOHNNY MANDEL (Raney, Sue & The Bob Florence Trio).
Tracks: / Emily / Time for love, A / Shadow of your smile / Suicide is painless (Theme from M*A*S*H) / Close enough for love.
LP: DS 875

Raney, Wayne

MORE HOT BOOGIE.
Tracks: / Why don't you haul off and love me (one more time) / Gone with the wind this morning / I ain't nothing but a tom cat, kitten / Powerful love / Falling / I want a home in Dixie / I've done sold my soul / Lonesome wind blues / Roosters are crowing, The / Pardon my whiskers / I'd feel like a millionaire / Gonna row my boat / I'm really needin' you / When they let the hammer down / Old fashioned matrimony in mind / No one's crying but me.
LP: CR 30263

REAL HOT BOOGIE.
Tracks: / Jack and Jill Boogie / Lost John Boogie / Real hot boogie / Catfish baby / Bootleg boogie / I was there / You better treat your man right / Adam / I had my fingers crossed / If you've got the money I've got the time / Heads or tails I win / Blues at my door / I'm on my way / Undertaking daddy / Real good feeling / Beating around the bush.
LP: CR 30247

Range

VALLEY ROAD, THE (see under Hornsby, Bruce) (Range/Bruce Hornsby).

Rangell, Nelson

NELSON RANGELL.
Tracks: / Rain forest / Tomorrow (better you, better me) / N.Y.C. / Prelude to a kiss / Starlight whispers / Brasilia / Givin' the hi' sign / Carousel, The / Stone cold / Wishes for you / If I could.
LP: GRP 96241
MC: GRP 96244

PLAYING FOR KEEPS.
LP: GRP 95931

TO BEGIN AGAIN.
LP: 1390071
MC: 1390074

Ranglin, Alvin

HOLY GROUND.
LP: HB 62

Ranglin, Ernie

TRUE BLUE (Raglin, Ernie).
LP: RRI 1202
MC: KRRI 1202

Rani Soho Road Dee

RANI SOHO ROAD DEE.
LP: SC 5082

Rank & File

LONG DEAD GONE.
Tracks: / Rank & File / John Brown / Tell her I love her / I'm an old man / Saddest girl in the world / Amanda Ruth.
LP: SLAP 2
MC: SMAC 2

SUNDOWN.
MC: SMMC 18
LP: SLMP 18
MC: SLMC 18

Rankin, Joe

DISCO SKATE.
LP: COP LP 3

Rankin, Kenny

HIDING IN MYSELF.
LP: YL 0114

INSIDE.

Tracks: / Creepin' / Inside / Lost up to loving you / Sunday kind of love / She's a lady / Roll-a-round / Feeling / Up from the skies / Marie / You.
LP: . . . . K 59653

Rankine, Alan

SHE LOVES ME NOT.
Tracks: / Beat fit / Days and days / Loaded / Last bullet / Your very last day / Sandman / Lose control / Break for me / World begins to look her age, The.
LP: . . . . V 2450
MC: . . . . TCV 2450

WORLD BEGINS TO LOOK HER AGE.
LP: . . . . TWI 672

Ranking, Ann

SLICE OF ENGLISH TOAST, A.
LP: . . . . ARILP 002

SOMETHING FISHY GOING ON.
LP: . . . . ARILP 010

Ranking Devon

YOU DON'T CARE FOR ME (see under Technics) (Ranking Devon/Technics).

Ranking Dread

LOTS OF LOVING.
LP: . . . . FSLOP 1

YOU REALLY DON'T LOVE ME (See under Delgado, Junior) (Ranking Dread & Junior delgado).

Ranking Joe

ARMAGEDDON.
Tracks: / Oh what a night / Music alone shall live / Can't stop the natty dread / Plait she plaits / You Mr. Finnigan / Armageddon / Can't stand it / Talk too much / Everybody bawling / Just a one night love affair.
LP: . . . . KVL 9010

DUB IT IN DANCE.
Tracks: / Clarks booty style / Choice of colour / Beg you to be true / Cold blood / Slackness style / Cock man / Dub it in a dance / Mr. Walker / Miss Lou / Loving girl.
LP: . . . . TRLS 194

NATTY SUPERSTAR.
Tracks: / Pork in the corner / Sister Pam / Jump the fence / Rock it on / Something on my mind / Natty superstar / Physical fitness / See a girls face / Ariena.
LP: . . . . BMLP 043

SATURDAY NIGHT JAMDOWN STYLE.
Tracks: / Step it down shepherds bush / Lift up your frock / Rub sister rub it / Christine / Spead propaganda / River Jordan / Hooligan / Sex maniac / Dreadlocks time / Love it like a lightpost.
LP: . . . . GREL 16

WEAKHEART FADEAWAY.
Tracks: / Dub sister dub it / Rock pon the rock / Dread earthquake, A / Natty dread a trademan / Nine months belly / Weakheart fadeaway / Natty the collie smoker / Queen tell / Honest living / Milkman coming.
LP: . . . . GREL 2

Ranking Rayvon

STAND BY ME (See under Mystic Man) (Ranking Rayvon & Mystic Man).

Ranking Roger

RADICAL DEPARTURE.
Tracks: / Falling down / One minute closer (to death) / Time to mek a dime / Smashing down another door / So excited / Mono gone to stereo / Your problems / I told you / Point of view / I'll be there / In love with you.
LP: . . . . MIRF 1035
MC: . . . . MIRFC 1035

Ranking, Santa

ROUGH DJ.
LP: . . . . TJPLP 004

ROUGHNECK CHICKEN.
LP: . . . . W 2732

Ranks, Cutty

DIE PART (PART 1).
LP: . . . . DGLP 22

STOPPER, THE.
LP: . . . . FADLP 020

Ranks & Demus

ROUGH AND RUGGED.
MC: . . . . DSBC 4205
LP: . . . . SPLP 10

Ranks, Nardo

ME NO LIKE RIKERS ISLAND (See under Coco Tea) (Ranks, Nardo & Coco Tea).

Ranks, Shaba

SHOCK OUT YU SELF (See under Flougan) (Ranks, Shaba/Flourgan).

Ranks, Shabba

AS RAW AS EVER.
Tracks: / Trailor load a girls / Where does slackness come from / Woman tangle / Gun pon me / Gone up / Ambi get scarce / Housecall / Flesh axe / A mi di girls dem love / Fist a ris / Jame, The / Park yu benz.
LP: 4681021
MC: 4681024

GOLDEN TOUCH.
LP: . . . . GREL 141
MC: . . . . GREEN 141

HOLDING ON (See under Home, T) (Ranks, S. & C. Tea/Home).

JUST REALITY.
LP: . . . . BMLP 041
MC: . . . . BMLC 041

RAPPING WITH THE LADIES.
LP: . . . . GREL 150
MC: . . . . GREEN 150

STAR OF THE '90'S.
LP: . . . . SPL 102

Ransome, Arthur (aut)

SWALLOWS AND AMAZONS (Cribbins, Bernard (nar)).
MCSET: . . . . LFP 7090
MCSET: . . . . LFP 417 090 5

Rantanplan

TWO WORLDS AT ONCE.
LP: . . . . LINKLP 131

Ranting Sleazos

NEVER LOST FOR WORDS.
LP: . . . . DRGN 892

Rap

ENJOY-STORY OF RAP SET (Greatest hits from the birth of the Zulu nation (Various artists).
LPS: . . . . ENJOY 1
MC: . . . . ZCEJOY 1

GENIUS OF RAP (The Sugarhill Story) (Various artists).
Tracks: / Rappers delight: *Sugarhill Gang* / White lines (don't do it): *Grandmaster Flash & The Furious Five*/ It's nasty (genius of love): *Grandmaster Flash & The Furious Five* / Spoonin' rap: *Spoonie Gee* / Drop the bomb: *Trouble Funk* / Message, The: *Grandmaster Flash & The Furious Five* / Gotta rock: *Treacherous Three* / Jesse: *Grandmaster Flash & Melle Mel* / Message II (survival): *Melle Mel & Duke Bootee* / Pump me up: *Trouble Funk* / That's the joint: *Funky 4 Plus 1.*
LP: . . . . BLATLP 1
MC: . . . . BLATMC 1
MC: . . . . CCSMC 284

GENIUS OF RAP 2 (Various artists).
Tracks: / Adventures of Grandmaster Flash on the wheels of steel, The: *Grandmaster Flash & The Furious Five* / Flash to the beat (part 1): *Grandmaster Flash & The Furious Five* / Birthday party: *Grandmaster Flash & The Furious Five*/ Simon says: *Sequence* / Monster jam: *Spoonie Gee and Sequence* / Showdown: *Furious Five, The Meets The Sugarhill* Gang / Rapping and rocking the house: *Funky Four Plus One* / Supergrit: *Trouble funk* / Spoonie is back: *Spoonie Gee* / Apache: *Sugarhill Gang* / 8th wonder: *Sugarhill Gang* / Funk box: *Sugarhill Gang.*
2LP: . . . . BLATLP 6
MC: . . . . BLATMC 6

GET ON DOWN (Various artists).
Tracks: / Think about me: *Instant Funk* / Little love, A: *Aurra* / Whikka rap: *Evasions* / Jock's rap: *Evasions* / Mr. D.J.: *Indeep* / Barbados: *Typically Tropical* / Lone Ranger, The: *Quantum Jump*/ Lucky number: *Lovich, Lene* / How high: *Cognac* / Whiter shade of pale, A: *Procul Harum* / Pappadum pappadum: *Indian Monks.*
LP: . . . . BATLM 1
MC: . . . . ZCBTM 1

GIANTS OF RAP (Various artists).
LP: 35026

GREAT BRITISH MC'S (Various artists).
LP: . . . . FADLP 001

GREATEST RAP HITS, VOL.2 (Various artists).
Tracks: / Eighth wonder: *Sugarhill Gang* / Freedom: *Grandmaster Flash & The Furious Five* / Monster jam: *Gee, Spoonie & Sequence* / Birthday party: *Grandmaster Flash & The Furious Five* / That's the joint: *Funky Four Plus One.*
LP: . . . . SHLP 1002
MC: . . . . ZCSH 1002

JIVE RAP ATTACK (Various artists).
LP: . . . . HOP 211
MC: . . . . HOPC 211

MACHINE GUN POETRY (Various artists).
MC: . . . . BRCA 541
LP: . . . . BRLP 541
MC: . . . . ICM 2064
MC: 842 377 4

MR. MAGIC'S RAP ATTACK VOL.3 (Various artists).
2LP: . . . . PRO 1249

N.W.A. AND POSSE (Various artists).
Tracks: / Boyz-the-hood: *E, Eazy* / 8 ball: *N.W.A* / Dunk the funk: *Fila Fresh Crew* / Scream: *Rappingstine*/ Drink it up: *Fila Fresh Crew* / Panic Zone: *N.W.A* / L.A. is the place: *E., Eazy & Ron-De-Vu* / Dope man: *N.W.A* / Tuffest man alive: *Fila Fresh Crew* / Fat girl: *E., Eazy & Ron-De-Vu* / 3 the hard way: *Fila Fresh Crew.*
LP: . . . . RHR 5134

RAP ACADEMY (Various artists).
MC: . . . . BRCA 564
LP: . . . . BRLPD 564

RAP ATTACK (Various artists).
Tracks: / Hey DJ: *Beatmasters* / Stop the violence: *Boogie Down Productions* / Talkin' all that jazz: *Stetsasonic*/ Don't scandalize mine: *Sugar Bear* / Pump up the jam: *Technotronic* / Set it off: *Big Daddy Kane* / Go on girl: *Shante, Roxanne* / Bang zoom (let's go go): *Shante, Roxanne* / Turn up the bass: *Tyree* / They want money: *Kool Moe Dee* / Let it rock: *Lazy, Doug* / Say no go: *De La Soul* / Got to keep on: *Cookie Crew* / It takes two: *Base, Rob & D.J. E-Z Rock* / Wee rule: *Wee Papa Girl Rappers* / Nightmare on my street: *D.J. Jazzy Jeff.*
LP: . . . . NE 1450
MC: . . . . CE 2450

RAP ATTACK (Various artists).
Tracks: / Nasty, The: *Fe-La Antoine* / Love is blind: *Def Squad* / Give the people what they want: *Dr. Ease* & The Easetown Posse / Peter Paul: *33 & A Third* / Don't rush my beat: *Second Power* / Original tramp, The (street version): *Sweetenlo* / Keep that booty clean (scrub that butt): *Supersonic Syd* / Push and shove: *44* Max / Diamonds and gold: *Positive 2 & Spinmaster JL* / What's going on: *Slamm Syndicate* / Crack is in the mirror: *Ayers, Roy.*
LP: . . . . ICH 1067
MC: . . . . ICH 1067MC

RAP GRAFFITI (Various artists).
Tracks: / Une sal histoire: *Various artists* / Change the beat: *Various artists* / Roxy, The: *Various artists*/ Grandmixer (cuts it up): *Various artists* / Krush groove: *Various artists* / Smurf for what it's worth: *Various artists* / Escapades of futura 2000: *Various artists.*
LP: . . . . CRM 2031
MC: . . . . TCCRM 2031

RAP IT UP (Various artists).
Tracks: / Message, The: *Grandmaster Flash & The Furious Five* / Planet rock: *Bambaataa, Afrika & The Soul Sonic Force*/ Magic's wand: *Whodini* / Mr. D.J.: *Concept, The* / Rapper's delight: *Sugarhill Gang* / (Nothing serious) Just buggin': *Whistle* / White lines (don't don't do it): *Grandmaster Flash & Melle Mel* / Fat Boys are back, The: *The Fat Boys* / Rock box: *Run D.M.C.* / Breaks, The: *Blow, Kurtis.*
LP: . . . . NE 1324
MC: . . . . CE 2324

RAP IT UP (Various artists).
LP: . . . . HIP 97
MC: . . . . HIP 97 C

RAP PACK VOL 1 (Various artists).
LP: . . . . SBUKLP 11
MC: . . . . SBUKMC 11

RAP: THE NEXT GENERATION (Various artists).
LP: . . . . MODEF 2

RAP TRACKS (Various artists).
Tracks: / Calling Doctor Ice: *Various artists* / Enjoy with me: *Midnight Blue* / Put the boogie in your body: *Treacherous Three* / Do it, do it: *Disco Four* / Double Dutch bus: *Smith, Frankie* / Can you feel it: *Funk Fusion Band* / Station brake: *Captain Sky* / Here to stay (Me and Mr Double R.R): *Count Coolout.*
LP: . . . . V 2225

RAP TRAX (Various artists).
Tracks: / Only way is up, The: *Yazz & The Plastic Population* / Superfly guy: *S. Express* / Heat it up: *Wee* Papa Girl Rappers/2 Men And A Drum Machine / I need you: *B.V.S.M.P.* / How ya like me now: *Kool Moe Dee* / My Adidas: *Run D.M.C.* / Parents just don't understand: *D.J. Jazzy Jeff & Fresh Prince* / Jack that house built, The: *Jack 'n' Chill* / Bass (how low can you go?): *Harris, Simon* / I need love: *L.L. Cool J* / Don't believe the hype: *Public Enemy* / I know you got soul: *Eric B & Rakim* / Strictly business: *E.P.M.D.*/ Get up, I feel like a sex machine: *Brown, James* / Do this my way: *Kid 'N Play* / My philosophy: *Boogie* Down Productions / Friday night & Saturday morning: *Einstein* / Naturally: *Top Billin'* / Rock you again (again & again): *Whodini* / Megablast: *Bomb The Bass.*
LP: . . . . SMR 859
MC: . . . . SMC 859

RAPPED UPTIGHT (Various artists).
Tracks: / Message, The: *Grandmaster Flash & The Furious Five* / Disco dream: *Mean Machine* / Hey fellas: *Trouble* Funk / It's good to be Queen: *Sylvia* / Sunshine of our love, The: *Staton, Candi* / Simon says: *Sequence*/ Rapper's delight: *Sugarhill Gang* / Do you want to rock (before I let go): *Funky Four* / Whip it: *Treacherous Three* / Apache: *Sugarhill Gang* / Check it out: *Wayne And Charlie.*
LP: . . . . SHLD 1001
MC: . . . . ZCSHD 1001

RAPPED UPTIGHT VOL.2 (Various artists).
Tracks: / White lines (don't don't do it): *Grandmaster Melle Mel* / Yes we can can: *Treacherous Three* / Breakdancin' electric boogie: *West Street Mob* / Message II: *Melle Mel & Duke Bootee* / Kick it live from 9 till 5: *Sugarhill* Gang / Everybody's uptight: *Jocko* / New York, New York: *Grandmaster Flash & The Furious Five* / Aah dance: *Fine Quality featuring Cuz* / We are known as emceees (we turn the party's out): *Crash Crew* / Adventures of Grandmaster Flash on the wheels of steel, The: *Grandmaster Flash & The Furious Five* / All night long (Waterbed): *Kevie Kev*/ Simon says dance: *Farrari.*
LP: . . . . SHLD 5551
MC: . . . . ZCSHD 5551

RAPPERS DELIGHT (Various artists).
2LP: . . . . KWEST 2074
MCSET: . . . . KWEST 4074

RAPPIN' (Film soundtrack) (Various artists).
Tracks: / Rappin': *Various artists* / Snack attack: *Various artists* / Fight rap, The: *Various artists*/ Neighbourhood walk: *Various artists* / Itchin' for a scratch: *Various artists* / Flame in the fire: *Various* artists / Call me: *Various artists* / If you want to: *Various artists* / Golly gee: *Various artists*/ First love never dies: *Various artists.*
LP: 781 252-1
MC: 781 252-4

RAPPIN' UP THE HOUSE (Various artists).
LP: . . . . NE 1428
MC: . . . . CE 2428

STREET BEATS, VOL 1 (Various artists).
Tracks: / White lines (don't don't do it): *Grandmaster Flash & Melle Mel* / On the radio: *Crash Crew* / I can't stop: *West Street Mob* / Showdown: *Furious Five & Sugarhill Gang* / Breakdancin' electric boogie: *West Street Mob* / Get up: *Treacherous Three* / Scorpio: *Grandmaster Flash* / Living in the fast lane: *Sugarhill Gang.*
LP: . . . . SHLP 7151
MC: . . . . ZCSHB 7151

WE WILL RAP YOU (Various artists).
LP: . . . . SGLP 9002

WEST COAST RAP ALL STARS (Various artists).
LP: 7599262411
MC: 7599262414

Raped

PHILES AND SMILES.
LP: . . . . PILLAGED 1

Rapeman

TWO NUNS AND A PACK MULE.
LP: . . . . BFFP 33
MC: . . . . BFFP 33C

Rapheal, Jean

LE TEMPS DU TANGO (Acc/Song).
Tracks: / Le temps du tango / Adios pampa mia / Non je ne veux pas revior tes yeux / Chemin de ta maison / J'ai pleure sur tes pas / Tango de Marilou / Le plus beau tango du monde / Paloma, La / Partir un jour / Serenade a violetta etc..
LP: . . . . ILD 42062

Rapids

TURNING POINT.
LP: . . . . NERD 019

Rapiers

RAPIERS 1961, THE.
Tracks: / Venture, The / I pretend I'm with you / Phamtom widow, The / (I feel like) I'm loosing you / Think it over / Jinx / Hippy hippy shake / I've got you under my skin / I'll never get over you / Shadow land / Don't leave now / In the hall of the mountain king.
LP: . . . . WIK 67

STRAIGHT TO THE POINT.

Tracks: / Green jeans / I'm a moody guy / Do you really love me too / Out of this world / It's been nice / Haunting guitar / Straight to the point / Husky team / Still i cry / Baby sittin' / Lonesome fella / Deep feeling.
LP: .... WIK 40

Rapone, Al

C'EST LA VIE! (Rapone, Al & The Zydeco Express).
LP: .... LR 44.012

LET'S HAVE A ZYDECO PARTY (Rapone, Al & The Zydeco Express).
Tracks: / Tit fille / Rosa Majeur / Camden zydeco / Sa mio fait du mal / Pu ils sa / Mazuka / Joe Peter / La vierge / Corps solide / Baby let me ride you home / Tu le ton son ton.
LP: .... JSP 1092

Rappin is Fundamental

DOO HOP LEGACY, THE.
LP: 3953411
MC: 3953414

Rapunzel (bk)

RAPUNZEL (Well Loved Tales up to Age 90) (Rapunzel).
MC: .... PLB 112

Rare Air

HARD TO BEAT.
LP: .... SIF 1073
MC: .... CSIF 1073

MAD PLAID.
LP: .... FF 333

Rare Bird

SYMPATHY.
Tracks: / Sympathy / You went away / Nature's fruit / Bird on a wing / What you want to know / Beautiful scarlet / Hammerhead / I'm thinking / As your mind flies by.
LP: .... CHC 6
MC: .... CHCMC 6

Rare Earth

GET READY.
LP: .... STML 11165

Rarebell, Herman

HERMAN ZE GERMAN.
LP: .... WKFMLP 80
MC: .... WKFMMC 80

NIP IN THE BUD.
Tracks: / Messing around / Two timer / Havin' a good time / Rock your balls / Triangle / Slob / Junk junk / Do it / Pancake / I'll say goodbye.
LP: .... SHSP 4118

Ras Iley

SPRING GARDEN ON FIRE.
LP: .... RI 3302

Ras Michael

RALLY ROUND.
LP: .... SHAN 43027
MC: .... SHANC 43027

Ras Tesfa

VOICE OF THE RASTAMAN.
LP: .... ML 401
MC: .... MLC 401

Rascoe, Moses

BLUES: RECORDED LIVE AT GODFREY DANIELS.
LP: .... FF 454

Rasmussen, Peter

DANISH JAZZ VOL.5 (1943 -44).
LP: .... SLP 414

Rasoul Gibran Trio

JUST A MOMENT.
MC: .... BIP 301

Raspberries

BEST OF THE RASPBERRIES, THE.
Tracks: / Go all the way / Tonight / Ecstacy / I wanna be with you / I can remember / Overnight sensation / Let's pretend / Drivin' around / Starting over / Don't want to say goodbye.
LP: .... CAPS 1026

OVERNIGHT SENSATION (Very Best of The Raspberries).
Tracks: / Overnight sensation / Go all the way / Let's pretend / Driving around / On the beach / Ecstasy / I reach for the light / All through the night / I wanna be with you / Cruisin' music / Tonight / I don't know what I want / Rose coloured glasses / Waiting / Starting over.
LP: .... ZAP 1

Raspe, Rudolf Erich

BARON MUNCHAUSEN TRULY TALL TALES (Ustinov, Peter).
MC: 1409

Rasses

EXPERIENCE.
LP: .... UAG 30259

Rasses Band

HARDER NA RASS.
Tracks: / Interstellar over dub / Second sight / Modular dub / Time warp / Universally dubbed / Terrestial dub / Gravitational echo's / Dub vortex / Regenerated dub / Cosmic silence.
LP: .... LBR 1031

Rat Race

RAT RACE (see Ogilvy, Ian) (Francis, Dick (author)).

Ratcat

BLIND LOVE.
Tracks: / Yes I wanna go / Run and hide / Baby baby / Hopeless mind / Pieces / Racing / That ain't bad / Wonder of you, The / Don't go now / Strange / End, The.
LP: 8485231
MC: 8485234

RATCAT.
LP: .... DAMP 66

TINGLES.
Tracks: / That ain't bad / Tingles (Only on 12" Single.) / Getting away (from this world) / Skin / My bloody valentine.
LP: 868573-1
MC: 868573-4

Rathbone, Basil (nar)

SHERLOCK HOLMES STORIES (see under Sherlock Holmes (bk)).

Rathbone, Jools

PULU PSHU (see under Monkman, Francis) (Rathbone, Jools & Francis Monkman).

Rather Nasty Dream...

RATHER NASTY DREAM ON PAPPLEWICK POND (Various artists).
LP: .... CMO 191

Rational Emotive

RATIONAL EMOTIVE THERAPY (Ellis, Albert).
MC: .... PT 26

Rational & Intuitive

RATIONAL & THE INTUITIVE BRAIN (Ornstein, Rbt./D.Galin).
MC: .... SS 119

Ratmen

LIVE FAST DIE YOUNG.
LP: .... NERD 041

Ratt

DANCIN' UNDER COVER.
Tracks: / Dance / Body talk / Take a chance / Looking for love / Seventh avenue / Drive me crazy / Slip of the lip / One good lover / Enough is enough / It doesn't matter.
LP: 781 683-1
MC: 781 683-4

DETONATOR.
LP: 7567821271
MC: 7567821274

INVASION OF YOUR PRIVACY.
Tracks: / You're in love / Never use love / Lay it down / Give it all / Closer to my heart / Between the eyes / What you give me is what you get / Gome me on the line / You should know by now / Dangerous but worth the risk.
LP: 781 257-1
MC: 781 257-4

OUT OF THE CELLAR.
Tracks: / Wanted man / You're in the money / Round and round / In your direction / She wants money / Lack of communication / Back for more / Morning after, The / I'm insane / Scene of the crime.
LP: 780 143-1
MC: 780 143-4

RATT.
Tracks: / Sweet cheater / You think you're tough / U got it / Tell the world / Back for more / Walking the dog.
LP: 790245 1
MC: 790245 4
LP: .... MFN 2

RATT: INTERVIEW PICTURE DISC.
LPPD: .... BAK 2092

REACH FOR THE SKY.
Tracks: / What I'm after / Chain reaction / City to city / I want a woman / No surprise / Don't bite the hand that feeds / Bottom line / What's it gonna be / No one can stop you now / Way cool JR / I want to love you tonight.
LP: 781 929-1
MC: 781 929-4

Rattigan, Terence

BROWNING VERSION, THE (Various artists).
MCSET: 0370

TERENCE RATTIGAN DOUBLE BILL (The Browning version & The Winslow boy) (Stock, Nigel/Michael Aldridge).
MCSET: .... ZBBC 1037

Rattle & Hum (film)

RATTLE & HUM (See under 'U2' for details) (U2).

Rattle, Simon

SIMON RATTLE SAMPLER (Various artists).
MC: .... TCRATT 1

Rattlers

NEVER SAY DIE.
LP: .... NERD 052

ROCKIN'.
LP: .... LM LP 007EX

SCARE ME TO DEATH.
Tracks: / Scare me to death / Little red / Mine all mine / Cat crept in, The / Blue zoot / Hey baby / Always yours / You're my baby / Rattlin' boogie, The / Knife edge baby.
LP: .... LM LP 001B

TAKE A RIDE.
LP: .... LM LP 007

Rattlers N.Y.C.

RATTLED.
LP: .... PVCL 601

Rattlesnake Annie

COUNTRY LIVIN'.
LP: .... RATTLE 2020

RATTLESNAKE ANNIE.
Tracks: / Funky country livin' / Sixteen tons / Country music hall of pain / Somewhere south of Macon / Goodbye to a river / Outskirts of town / Callin' your bluff / Long black limousine / Been waitin' that long / Lonesome, on'ry and mean.
LP: 4500441
MC: 4500444

Rattray, Mark

MARK RATTRAY PERFORMS THE SONGS OF THE MUSICALS.
MC: .... STAC 2458
LP: .... STAR 2458

Rattus

STOLEN LIFE.
LP: .... NEGFX 007

Rauber, Francois

CIRCUS MUSIC.
LP: .... AV 4730
MC: .... AV 5730

Raul, Orellana

GUITARRA (T.V. Soundtrack).
LP: .... BCM 314 LP
MC: .... BCM 314 MC

Raunch Radley

GUITAR CITY.
LP: .... REDITA 103

Raunchy Business

RAUNCHY BUSINESS - HOT NUTS AND LOLLIPOPS (See Under Blues) (Various artists).

Rava

STRING BAND.
Tracks: / Verde que eu te quero ver / String band / Operatta / Note is a note, A / Still life / Chanana / More from Giulietta / Sensatez.
LP: .... SN 1114

Rava, Enrico

IL GIRO DEL GIORNO IN 80.
LP: .... BSR 0011

OPENING NIGHT (Rava, Enrico Quartet).
LP: .... ECM 1224

VOLVER (Rava, Enrico/Dino Saluzzi Quintet).
Tracks: / A bout de souffle / Minguito / Luna-volver / Tiempos de ausencias / Ballantine for valentine visions.
LP: .... ECM 1343

Ravage

WRECKING BALL.
LP: .... RR 9672

Ravan, Genya

AND I MEAN IT.
Tracks: / Pedal to the metal / I won't sleep on the wet spot no more / Steve / Stubborn kinda girl / It's me / Junkman / Love isn't love / I'm wired wired wired / Roto root her / Night owl.
LP: .... T 595

URBAN DESIRE.
LP: .... BTH 8007

Ravazza, Carl

CARL RAVAZZA, 1940-44.
Tracks: / Vieni su / I wish I had a sweetheart / Violets for your furs / Sing me a song / Ollie Ollie outs in free / Cancel the flowers / Would it make any difference to you / Got something in my eye / I hadn't anyone till you / Put your arms around me honey / Very thought of you, The / It all depends on you / I got it bad and that ain't good / Paper doll / For the first time / On the alamo.
LP: .... HSR 117

Rave From the Grave

RAVE FROM THE GRAVE VOL.1 Transfusion (Various artists).
LP: .... UP 003

Ravel (composer)

BOLERO (See under Solti, Sir George) (Chicago Symphony Orchestra).

BOLERO (Various artists).
LP: .... ADL 506
MC: .... ADK 506

BOLERO - PAVANE POUR UNE INFANTE DEFUNTE ETC. (Various artists).
MC: 4278154

STRING QUARTETS (See under Medici String Quartet for details) (Medici String Quartet).

Raven

ALL FOR ONE.
Tracks: / Take control / Mind over metal / Sledgehammer rock / All for one / Run silent, run deep / Hung drawn and quartered / Break the chain / Take it away / Seek and destroy / Athletic rock.
LP: .... NEAT 1011
MC: .... NEATC 1011

DEVIL'S CARRION, THE.
Tracks: / Hard ride / Bring the hammer down / Inquisitor / All for one / Hellraiser / Action (Medley) / Live at the inferno / Crash, bang, wallop / Ballad of Marshall Stack / Crazy world / Rock until you drop / Don't need your money / Hell patrol / Rock hard / Faster than the speed of light / Wiped out / Break the chain / Read all about it / Firepower / Athletic rock / Run silent, run deep.
2LP: .... RAWLP 003
MC: .... RAWTC 003

LIFE'S A BITCH.
Tracks: / Savage and the hungry, The / Pick your window / Life's a bitch / Never forgive / Iron league / On the wings of an eagle / Overload / You're a liar / Fuel to the fire / Only the strong survive / Juggernaut / Playing with the razor / Finger on the trigger (extra track on cassette only.).
LP: 781 734-1
MC: 781 734-4

LIVE AT THE INFERNO.
Tracks: / I don't need your money / Break the chain / Hell patrol / Live at the inferno / Crazy world / Let it rip / I.G.A.R.B.O. / Wiped out / Fire power / All for one / Forbidden planet / Star war / Tyrant of the airways / Run silent, run deep / Take control / Mind over metal / Crash bang wallop / Rock until you drop / Faster than the speed of light.
2LP: .... NEAT 1020
2LP: .... RR 9808

NOTHING EXCEEDS LIKE EXCESS.
LP: .... FLAG 28
MC: .... TFLAG 28

PACK IS BACK, THE.
Tracks: / Pack is back, The / Gimme some lovin' / Screamin' down the house / Young blood / Hyperactive / Rock dogs / Don't let it die / Get into your car / All I want / Nightmare ride.
LP: 781 629-1
MC: 781 629-4

ROCK UNTIL YOU DROP.
Tracks: / Hard ride / Hell patrol / Don't need your money / Over the top / 39-40 / For the future / Rock until you drop / Nobody's hero / Hellraiser / Action / Lambs to the slaughter / Tyrant of the airways.
LP: .... NEAT 1001
LPPD: .... NEATP 1001
MC: .... NEATC 1001
LP: .... RC 93871

STAY HARD.
Tracks: / Stay hard / When the going gets tough / On and on / Get it right / Restless child / Power & the glory / Pray for the sun / Hard ride / Extract the action / Bottom line.
LP: 7812411

WIPED OUT.
Tracks: / Faster than the speed of light / Bring the hammer down / Fire power / Read all about it / To the limit / To the top / Battle zone / Live at the inferno / Star war / UXB / 20/21 / Hold back the fire / Chain saw.
LP: .... NEAT 1004

Raven, Eddy

EDDY RAVEN.
LP: 127

TEMPORARY SANITY.
LP: .... UVL 76003
MC: .... UVLC 76003

Raven, Jon

HARVEST.
Tracks: / Factory girl / City song / Spare parts city / Smoke and fire / Harvest / Shadows / Down the way / Hawk.
LP: BRO 117
MC: KBRO 117

SONGS OF A CHANGING WORLD (Raven, Jon/Nic Jones/Tony Rose).
LP: LER 2083

Raven, Marsha

WHY DON'T YOU COME BACK (see under Kakoulli, Harry) (Raven, Marsha & Harry Kakoulli).

Raven, Michael

GYPSY- A VARIETY OF GUITAR MUSIC.
Tracks: / Dark eyes / Farruca / Three renaissance dances / Staines Morris / Zarabanda / Mistress Winter's jump (downland) / Flamenco song / Soleares / Americana - Guido's rag: Melancholy pavan / Willow rag / Lichfield Greenhill bower processional, The / Vals (Aguado) / Caribbean dance - Rhumba cubana / Lady Mary's delight - Lady Mary / Argent / Cambria - Wrth fynd efo deio i dywyn / Three Spanish dances (bolero) / My lady Vals / Fandango de Almeria / Iberia - Lagrima (Tarrega) / Chula / Gypsy (part II) - Troseg y gareg / Rakes of mallow / Tanguillio.
LP: SCLP 610

JOLLY MACHINE, THE (Raven, Michael/Joan Mills).
Tracks: / Chartist's anthem / Nailmaker's lament / Charlie's song / Needlemaker's lamentation / Landlord don't you cry / Freedom and reform / John Whitehouse / Waiting for wages / Wednesbury town / Jolly machine / Colliers' rant, The / Tommy Note / Dudley canal tunnel song.
LP: FHR 053

MISCELLANY OF GUITAR MUSIC, A.
Tracks: / Suite in D: Prelude / Warriors welcome home / Comical fellow, The / Bushes and briars / Two butchers / Leonora / Aymara / New mown hay / McKinnon's lament and jig / Suite in E: Sarabande / Fanfare / Hymn / Waltz / Lakes of Ponchartrain, The / Jonathan Wild's jig / Tarantos / Black joke, The / To the weavers / Rough music.
LP: BRO 124
MC: KBRO 124

Ravenna

ROCKABILLY FOOLS (Ravenna & The Magnetics).
Tracks: / Bound to the sound / Rockabilly fool / Mean little mama / Waterproof love / I like your kind of love / Hypnotized / Headaches & heartaches / Rock around with Ollie Vee / Bang bang / Willin and ready / Good love / Hot pink cowboy boots / Changing all those changes / I need your love / Swamp Sally / Mean, mean man.
LP: ABOUT 1001

TENNESSEE AND TEXAS (Ravenna & The Magnetics).
Tracks: / Tennessee and Texas / Find my baby for me / Turning tide / Surefire shaker / Lonely weekends / Waiting to come back / I never lie / Night owl / Feel so good / Baby that's alright / 6918 peach / Vibrate.
LP: ABOUT 8

Ravens

GREATEST VOCAL GROUP OF THEM ALL.
Tracks: / Mahzel / For you / Would you believe me / Write me a letter / Until the real thing comes along / September song / Always / Searching for love / I'm afraid of you / Fool that I am / Together / There's no you / How could I know / It's too soon to know / White Christmas / Silent night / Deep purple / There's nothing like a woman in love / Careless love / If you didn't mean it / Someday / Lilacs in the rain / I've been a fool / I'm gonna paper my walls with your love letters / Sylvia / Tea for two / Without a song / It's the talk of the town / No more kisses for baby / Moonglow / Who's sorry now / I've got the world on a string.
2LP: SJL 2227

RAVEN COUNTRY.
Tracks: / Darlin' / Ebony eyes / Little church / Where my Eileen is waiting / Back home again / I would like to see you again / Four strong winds / Happy anniversary / Medals for mothers / Kelly / Save the last dance for me / Hymn I knew as a boy.
LP: STOL 139
MC: CT 139

Rave-ups

TOWN AND COUNTRY.
Tracks: / Positively lost me / Remember (Newman's love song) / Better world / Class tramp / In my gremlin / Radio / By the way / Not where you're at / You ain't goin' nowhere / Rave-up / Shut up.
LP: FIEND 62
MC: FIENDCASS 62

Ravin' Auto

GRAB BAG.
MC: FLASH 1

Raw Deal (film)

RAW DEAL (Film soundtrack) (Various artists).
LP: STV 81286
MC: CTV 81286

Raw Material

WALLIN ROSS REID.
LP: DRLP 48

Raw Power

AFTER YOUR BRAIN.
LP: TXLP 08

MINE TO KILL.
LP: MOTR 35
MC: MOTR 35C

SCREAMS FROM THE GUTTER.
LP: TXLP 03

Rawhead, Jason

BACKFIRE.
LP: FLAG 34

COLLISON HYPE.
LP: KK 61

JASON RAWHEAD.
LP: KK 024

Rawhide

RAWHIDE (THEME FROM) (See under Laine, Frankie) (Laine, Frankie).

Rawicz/Landauer

MAGIC PIANOS OF RAWICZ & LANDAUER, THE.
MCSET: DTO 10233

Rawle, Len

LEN RAWLE GOES NORTH.
2LP: CF 245

Rawlings, Marjorie

YEARLING, THE (Wayne, David).
MCSET: 2057

Rawlins, Steve

STEP RIGHT UP.
LP: SB 3003

Rawls, Lou

ALL THINGS IN TIME.
Tracks: / You're the one / Need you forever / This song will last forever / Let's fall in love all over again / From now on / Pure imagination / You'll never find another love like mine / Time / Groovy people.
LP: PIR 81368

AT LAST.
Tracks: / At last / Two years of torture / Fine brown frame / Good intentions / That's where it's at / If I were a magician / You can't go home / Room with a view / After the lights go down low / She's no lady / Oh what a night.
LP: B1 91937
LP: 791 937 1
MC: TCB1 91937
MC: 791 937 4

BEST OF LOU RAWLS.
Tracks: / Dead end street / Tobacco road / Soul serenade / Trouble down here below / Down here on the ground / It was a very good year / Trouble in mind / Beautiful friendship, A / Love is a hurtin' thing / World of trouble / Nobody by me / One for my baby / Stormy weather / God bless the child / Three o'clock in the morning / Your good thing.
LP: CAPS 1027
LP: 1A 022 1583831
MC: 1A 222 1583834

CLASSIC SOUL.
Tracks: / Sad song / Trying as hard as I can / I love you yes I do / Season of the witch / I wonder / I want to be loved / Your good thing is about to end / When a man loves a woman / Gentle on my mind.
LP: BMM 005

CLOSE COMPANY.
Tracks: / All time lover / In the middle of the night / Close company / Pretty eyes / When we were young / Ready or not / Forever i do / Lady in my life, The / ay it again / Sunshine.
LP: EPC 26127

HEART AND SOUL OF LOU RAWLS.
Tracks: / You'll never find another love like mine / Way you look tonight, The / Let me be good to you / It never entered my mind / Sit down and talk to me / Love all your blues away / Wind beneath my wings / Lady love / You're my blessing / Willow weep for me / One life to live / We'll be together again / See you when I get there / Groovy people.
LP: KNLP 12053
MC: KNMC 12053

IT'S SUPPOSED TO BE FUN.
Tracks: / It's supposed to be fun / Don't let me be misunderstood / All around the world / Good morning blues / Moonglows / Any day now / This bitter earth / If you gotta make a fool of somebody (CD only.) / One more time / You're the one / I wonder where our love has gone / But I do (CD only.) / Good night my love / Last night of the world, The.
LP: B1 93841
LP: 793 841 1
MC: B4 93841
MC: 793 841 4

LET ME BE GOOD TO YOU.
Tracks: / Time will take care of everything / What's the matter with the world / Tomorrow / We keep getting closer / Bark, bite / Let me be good to you / Lover's holiday / Sweet tender nights.
LP: PIR 83658

LOU RAWLS (LIVE).
Tracks: / Lady love / I wish it were yesterday / One life to live / Dollar green / Trade winds / There will be love / Unforgettable / That would do it for me / If I coulda, woulda, shoulda / Not the staying kind / This song will last forever / 'Tribute' medley / See you when I git there / We understand each other / Early morning love / When you say Budweiser, you've said it all / Send in the clowns / You'll never find another love like mine / Lovely way to spend an evening.
2LP: PIR 88316

LOVE ALL YOUR BLUES AWAY.
Tracks: / Change your mind / Are you with me / Love all your blues away / Stop me from starting this feeling / Learn to love again / Willow weep for me / We'll be together again / Way you look tonight / It never entered my mind.
LP: EPC 26809
MC: 40 26809

LOVE SONGS: LOU RAWLS.
MC: 4XL 9040

MERRY CHRISTMAS HO HO HO.
Tracks: / Little drummer boy / Good time Christmas / Little boy dear / Christmas is / Have yourself a merry little Christmas / Santa Claus is coming to town / Merry Christmas, baby / Christmas song, The / Christmas will really be Christmas / What are you doing New Year's Eve / Child with a toy, A.
MC: C4 94703
MC: 794 703 4

NOW IS THE TIME.
Tracks: / Kiss me one more time / Let me show you how / Ain't that love / Baby / While the rain comes down / Now is the time for love / Watch your back / It's too late / Back to you / This love.
LP: PRT 85193

SHADES OF BLUE.
Tracks: / Did you ever love a woman / Cottage for sale / Be anything / You've lost that lovin' feeling / I go crazy / Think / Hoochie coochie man / Baby watcha want me to do.
LP: PIR 84572
MC: 40 84572

SIT DOWN AND TALK TO ME.
Tracks: / One day soon you'll need me / Heartaches / Ain't that loving you baby / When you get home / Sit down and talk to me / You're my blessing / Old times / You are.
LP: PIR 84024

SOUL SERENADE.
Tracks: / Dead end street / Down here on the ground / I'd rather drink muddy water / Love is a hurtin' thing / Your good thing is about to end / Wade in the water / Chained and bound / For what it's worth / Stormy Monday / Tobacco Road / They don't give medals / Please send me someone to love / My ancestors / Evil woman / I'm gonna use what I got (to get what I need) / Hard to get / Thing called love, A.
LP: EG 2606681
MC: EG 2606684

STORMY MONDAY (Rawls, Lou & Les McCann Limited).
Tracks: / Stormy Monday / God bless the child / See see rider / Willow weep for me / I'm gonna move to the outskirts of town / In the evening / T'aint nobody's business if I do / Lost and lookin' / I'd rather drink muddy water / Sweet lover / Blues is a woman (CD only.) / Little Les of Lou's blues, A (CD only.) / Stormy Monday (alternate) (CD only.).
LP: SEE 51
LP: B1 91441
LP: 791 441 1

UNMISTAKABLY LOU.
Tracks: / See you when I get there / Spring again / Early morning love / Somefolks never learn / Someday you'll be old / Secret tears / We understand each other / It's our anniversary today / All the way.
LP: PIR 81873

WHEN THE NIGHT COMES.
Tracks: / Upside down / Wind beneath my wings / If your gonna love me / Couple more years / One I sing my songs to / You can't take it with you / When the night comes / Midnight sunshine / That's when the magic begins / I been him.
LP: EPC 25305

Rawsthorne, Noel

ORGAN SPECTACULAR.
Tracks: / Pomp and circumstance march / Hallelujah chorus / Stars and stripes forever / Grand march from Aida / Ride of the Valkyries / Trumpet voluntary / Londonderry air / Mendelssohn's wedding march / Marche militaire / Lost chord, The / Air on a G string.
LP: EL 2701651
MC: EL 2701654

Ray, Alan

ALAN RAY'S INTERNATIONAL ALBUM.
Tracks: / Rollin' in my sweet baby's arms / Crystal chandeliers / Kaw-liga / Green green grass of home / Kansas city / Six days on the road / I wonder where you are tonight / Put another log on the fire / Daydreams about night things / Old dogs, children and watermelon wine.
LP: WRS 137

Ray, Bobby

COUNTRY WAY, THE.
LP: BSS 140

SOMETHING IN THE AYRE.
LP: BSS 336

Ray, Danny

SAME ONE, THE.
LP: TRLS 84

WHY DON'T YOU SPEND THE NIGHT (featuring Shirley James).
LP: BJLP 03

Ray, Fay

CONTACT YOU.
Tracks: / Different morning / Heatwave / Love is strange / Modern lovers / Contact you / Family affairs / Cold as steel / Consequences / Clean lines / Wargames.
LP: K 99188

Ray, Goodman & Brown

II.
LP: 6359 038

MOOD FOR LOVIN'.
Tracks: / Where did you get that body...baby? / Mood for lovin' / Where are you now? / Say it / Electrified / Next time I'll know / Never stop lovin' you / Don't make me wait.
LP: MTL 1038
MC: TCMTL 1038

RAY, GOODMAN & BROWN.
Tracks: / Inside of you / Special lady / Slipped away / Way it should be / Treat her right / Thrill/friends / Deja vu / Another day.
LP: 9109800

STAY.
Tracks: / Stay / Good ole days / How can love so right (be so wrong) / Pool of love / Till the right one comes along / Heaven in the rain / Only you / Midnight lady / When the lovin' goes out of the lovin' / Lover's night.
LP: 6359 093

TAKE IT TO THE LIMIT.
Tracks: / Take it to the limit / Baby, let's make love tonight / Good love / Celebrate your love / Why must I wait / Waiting for Dawn / We've got tonight / Someone's missing your love.
LP: AML 3113
MC: TCAML 3113

Ray, Harry

IT'S GOOD TO BE HOME.
Tracks: / It's good to be home / You ain't been loved / Love is a game / Sweet baby / I'm willin' / You're killing me / Lost affair / I will love you anyway.
LP: SHLP 1008
MC: ZCSH 1008

Ray, James

ITTY BITTY PIECES.
Tracks: / One by one / Marie / Come rain or come shine / Old man & the mule / Lazybones / Guilty / On that day / If you gotta make a fool of somebody / Itty bitty pieces / It's been a drag / St James Infirmary / Put me in your diary / You remember the face / Things are gonna

be different / We got a thing going on / I'm gonna keep on trying.
LP: CRB 1065

Ray, John

BIG IF SMILES AGAIN, THE (Ray, John Collective).
LP: IR 900
MC: IRC 900

Ray, Johnnie

AMERICAN LEGEND, AN.
Tracks: / Cry / Yes tonight, Josephine / Song of the dreamer / Just walking in the rain / All of me / Please Mr. Sun / Such a night / Look homeward angel / Walkin' my baby back home / Littlw white cloud that cried / Build your love / Hey there / Faith can move mountains / Who's sorry now / Somebody stole my girl / Hernando's hideaway.
LP: CBS 31696
MC: 40 31696

AMERICAN LEGENDS VOL.1 (See under American legends) (Ray, Johnnie/ Frankie Laine/Guy Mitchell).

BEST OF JOHNNIE RAY.
Tracks: / Cry / Song of the dreamer / Little white cloud that cried, The / All of me / Please Mr. Sun / Just walking in the rain / Hernando's hideaway / Such a night / Yes tonight, Josephine / Build your love / Walkin' my baby back home / Faith can move mountains / Hey there / Somebody stole my gal / Who's sorry now / Look homeward angel.
LP: SPR 8507
MC: SPC 8507

GOOD EVENING FRIENDS (See under Laine, Frankie) (Ray, Johnny & Frankie Laine).

GREATEST HITS: JOHNNIE RAY.
Tracks: / Just walkin' in the rain / Broken hearted / Hey there / Alexander's ragtime band / Paths of paradise / Little white cloud that cried, The / Please Mr Sun / Walkin' my baby back home / All of me / Tell the lady I said goodbye / Yes tonight, Josephine.
LP: 32418

HIS TOP HITS.
MC: 806

MA SAYS PA SAYS (See under Day, Doris) (Day, Doris & Johnnie Ray).

PORTRAIT OF A SONG STYLIST.
Tracks: / Just walking in the rain / Hey there / I'm beginning to see the light / If you believe / Nethertheless I'm in love with you / Hands across the table / Walkin' my baby back home / Cry / I'm confessin' / All of me / Too marvellous for words / They can't take that away from me / Little white cloud that cried, The / Alexanders Ragtime Band / Yes tonight Josephine / Shake a hand / Who's sorry now / It all depends on you.
LP: HARLP 103
MC: HARMC 103

REMEMBER JOHNNIE RAY.
Tracks: / Mame / It's impossible / Glad rag doll / I'll cry in my sleep / Tie a yellow ribbon round the old oak tree / Cry / Yesterday / Little white cloud that cried, The / Walking my baby back home / It's all over / Goodnight sleepyhead.
LP: CSAP LP 100
MC: CSAP MC 100

VERY BEST OF JOHNNIE RAY, THE (double cassette).
MCSET: DTO 10280

YESTERDAY, TODAY AND TOMORROW.
Tracks: / Mame / It's impossible / Glad rag doll / I'll cry in my sleep / Tie a yellow ribbon / Cry / Yesterday / Little white cloud that cried, The / If you go away / Until it's time for you to go / Walking my baby back home / It's all over / Goodnight sleepyhead.
LP: ACLP 009

Raybeats

GUITAR BEAT.
Tracks: / Calhoun surf / Tight turn / Big black sneakers / Holiday in Spain / Tone zone / International operator / Guitar beat / Searching / Pirahana salad / Andy's plus 1 / Backstroke, The.
LP: X 7

IT'S ONLY A MOVIE.
Tracks: / Jack the ripper / Sad little caper, The / Doin' the dishes.
LP: SHAN 82003

Raydio

JACK AND JILL (OLD GOLD) (See under Parker Jnr, Ray/Ghostbusters).

RAYDIO.
Tracks: / Is this a love thing / You need this to satisfy that / Betcha can't love me just once / Honey I'm rich / Jack and Jill / Me / Let's go all the way / Get down.
LP: SPART 1041

ROCK ON.
Tracks: / What you waiting for / Hot stuff / You can't change that / Rock on / More than one way to love / Woman / When you're in the need of love / Goin' thru school and love / Honey I'm a star.
LP: SPART 1087

TWO PLACES AT THE SAME TIME.
LP: SPART 1121

Raye, Sol

COME HOME LOVE.
LP: DAYL 001
LP: CUS 1004

Raymonde

BABELOGUE.
Tracks: / No one can hold a candle to you / Stop kickin' my heart around / Been too many years / Solid state soul / Gospel song, A / Oh hellish choir / Milk train doesn't stop here anyone / Fool of fortune / Every single night / Rock 'n' roll ancesty / Son of the soil.
LP: AZLP 3
MC: ZAZLP 3

Raymonde (2)

LA PERLE ORIENTALE VOLUME 1.
MC: 83133

LA PERLE ORIENTALE VOLUME 2.
MC: 83134

LA PERLE ORIENTALE VOLUME 3.
MC: 83135

Rayne, Janie (nar)

ADVENTURES OF MILLY MOLLY MANDY (See under Adventures of...).

Ray-O-Vacs

SESAME MUCHO.
Tracks: / Besame mucho / Take me back to my boots and saddle / If you ever should leave me / My baby's gone / Let's / What's mine is mine / I still love you / She's a real lovin' baby / Start lovin' me / Outside of paradise / I still love you / All about daddy / I'm the baby now / Party time / Crying all alone / Wine-o.
LP: OFF 6047

Ray's A Laugh

RAY'S A LAUGH (Ray, Ted).
MCSET: ZBBC 1117

Raze

RAZE - THE LP.
LP: CHAMP 1020
MC: CHAMPK 1020

Razor

CUSTOM KILLING.
LP: FPL 3042

EVIL INVADERS.
Tracks: / Nowhere fast / Legacy of doom / Iron hammer / Cut throat / Tortured skull / Cross me fool / Evil invaders / Instant death / Speed merchants / Thrashdance.
LP: RR 9732

EXECUTIONER'S SONG.
LP: RR 9778

MALICIOUS INTENT.
LP: RR 9698

VIOLENT RESTITUTION.
LP: 087 569

Razor Baby

TOO HOT TO HANDLE.
Tracks: / Danger / Rock this place / Downtown / Outta hand sister / Move me / Too hot to handle / Got me running / Low down and dirty.
LP: HMUSA 102
MC: HMAMC 102

Razor sharp cuts

RAZOR SHARP CUTS (Various artists).
LP: RAZS 12

Razorbacks

CRUISIN' DOWN.
LP: F 3013

Razorcuts

STORY TELLER, THE.
LP: CRELP 026

WORLD KEEPS TURNING, THE.
LP: CRELP 045

Razors Edge

RAZORS EDGE (Film soundtrack) (Various artists).
LP: SCRS 1009

R.D.P.

ANARKOPHOBIA.
LP: RO 93261
MC: RO 93264

Re Quarterly

RE QUARTERLY NO.3 (Various artists).
LP: RE 103

RE QUARTERLY NO.4 (Various artists).
LP: RE 104

RE QUARTERLY VOL.2 (Various artists).
LP: RE 0203

RE RECORDS QUARTERLY NO.1 Various Artists (Various artists).
LP: RE 101

RE RECORDS QUARTERLY NO.2 Various Artists (Various artists).
LP: RE 102

Rea, Chris

AUBERGE (ALBUM).
Tracks: / Auberge / Gone fishing / You're not a number / Heaven / Set me free / Red shoes / Sing a song of love to me / Every second counts / Looking for the summer / And you my love / Mention of your name, The.
LP: WX 407
MC: WX 407C

CHRIS REA.
Tracks: / Loving you / If you choose to go / Guitar Street / Do you still dream? / Every beat of my heart / Goodbye little Columbus / One sweet tender touch / Do it for your love / Just want to be with you / Runaway / When you know your love has died.
LP: WX 187
MC: WX 187 C
LP: MAGL 5040

DANCING WITH STRANGERS.
Tracks: / Joys of Christmas / I can't dance to that / Windy town / Gonna buy a hat / Curse of the traveller / Let's dance / Que sera / Josie's tune / Loving you again / That girl of mine / September blue / I don't care anymore (Extra track on CD only) / Donahue's broken wheel (Extra track on CD only.) / Danielle's breakfast (Extra track on CD only.).
LP: WX 180
MC: WX 180 C
LP: MAGL 5071

DELTICS.
Tracks: / Twisted wheel / Things lovers should do, The / Dance (don't think) / Raincoat and a rose / Cenotaph - letter from Amsterdam / Deltics / Diamonds / She gave it away / Don't want your best friend / No qualifications / Seabird.
MC: WX 185 C
LP: WX 185
LP: MAG 5028

NEW LIGHT THROUGH OLD WINDOWS (Best of Chris Rea).
Tracks: / Let's dance / Working on it / Ace of hearts / Josephine / Candles / On the beach / Fool if you think it's over / I can hear your heartbeat / Shamrock diaries / Stainsby girls / Windy town / Driving home for Christmas / Steel river.
LP: WX 200
MC: WX 200 C

ON THE BEACH.
Tracks: / On the beach / Little blonde plaits / Giverney / Lucky day / Just passing through / It's all gone / Hello friend / Two roads / Light of hope / Auf immerund ewig / Bless them all (Casette and compact disc only) / Freeway (Casette and compact disc only) / Crack that mould (Casette and compact disc only).
LP: WX 191
MC: WX 191 C
LP: MAGL 5069

ROAD TO HELL (LP).
LP: WX 317
MC: WX 317C

SHAMROCK DIARIES.
Tracks: / Steel river / Stainsby girls / Chisel Hill / Josephine / One golden rule / All summer long / Stone / Shamrock diaries / Love turns to lies / Hired gun.
LP: WX 190
MC: WX 190 C
LP: MAGL 5062

TENNIS.
Tracks: / Tennis / Sweet kiss / Since I don't see you anymore / Dancing girls / No work today / Every time I see you smile / For ever and ever / Good news / Friends across the water / Distant summers / Only with you / Stick it.
LP: WX 186
MC: WX 186 C
LP: MAG 5032

WATER SIGN.
Tracks: / Nothing's happening by the sea / Deep water / Candles / Love's strange ways / Texas / Let it loose / I can hear your heartbeat / Midnight blue / Hey you / Out of the darkness.
LP: WX 188
MC: WX 188 C
LP: MAGL 5048

WHATEVER HAPPENED TO BENNY SANTINI?.
Tracks: / Whatever happened to Benny Santini? / Closer you get / Because of you / Dancing with Charlie / Bows and bangles / Fool (if you think it's over) / Three angels / Just one of those days / Standing in your doorway / Fires of spring, The.
LP: WX 184
MC: ZCMAG 5021
MC: WX 184C

WIRED TO THE MOON.
Tracks: / Bombollini / Touche d'amour / Shine shine shine / Wired to the moon / Reasons / I dont know what it is but I love it / Ace of hearts / Holding out / Winning.
LP: WX 189
MC: WX 189 C
LP: MAGL 5057

Rea, John

IRISH MUSIC ON THE HAMMER DULCIMER.
Tracks: / Whistle o'er the levet / Braes of Tullymet / Scudding through the whins / Bundle and go / Jug of punch / Galway reel, The / Donny O'Brien's / Ladies of France, The / Jackson's trip to Aughrim / Jackson's return from Dover / Belfast, The / Rights of man, The / Sailor on the rope, The / Bonnie bunch of roses, The / Three sea captains / Kitty's fancy / Lady Anne Hope / Boys of Ballycastle, The / Kinnegad slashers / Tenpenny bit, The / Plains of Boyle, The / Jackson's slippers / Roaring Mary - Stormy weather / Tim Moloney / Set dance and highland / St. Patrick's day / Duncan Davidson.
LP: 12TS 373

Reach for the Sky

REACH FOR THE SKY (Paul Brickhill) (Britton, Tony (nar)).
MCSET: LFP 7146

Reactions

CRACKED MARBLE.
LP: HMS 066

Read, Al

AL READ SHOW.
MCSET: ZBBC 1012

Read, Cheese

CAJUN HOUSE PARTY.
LP: ARHOOLIE 5021

Reading, Bertice

BERTICE.
Tracks: / Paper moon / My funny valentine / I wish you love / Little girl blue / How about you / Someone to watch over me / Day in, day out / Glad to be unhappy / Everybody's somebody's fool / Lover man / Right to be wrong, The / When the world was young / That's my desire / Time after time.
LP: VIR 83001
MC: ZCVIR 83001

FIFTIES, THE.
Tracks: / Sweet goody / I'd gladly do it again / I gotta know / I'm alone / Tears of joy / Judgement of love, The / Can't be satisfied / Beantown boogie / I wash my hands / Little things mean a lot / Goodbye for the last time / Rock and roll / It's almost like being in love / No more in life / Old fashioned love / Rock baby rock.
LP: OFF 6003

Ready For The World

LONG TIME COMING.
LP: MCF 3352
MC: MCFC 3352

READY FOR THE WORLD.
LP: MCF 3298
MC: MCFC 3298

Ready Made

URO BREAK BEATS.
LP: WAMLP 004X

Reagan, Ronald

ON RADIO.
LP: MR 1118

WIT AND WISDOM OF RONALD REAGAN.
LP: ABRA 1

Reagon, Bernice

RIVER OF LIFE.
LP: FF 411

Real Ale & Thunder

AT VESPERS.
Tracks: / Battle hymn of the republic / His eye is on the sparrow / Bye & bye / Old rugged cross, The / Royal telephone / Down by the riverside / What a friend we have in Jesus / Take my hand, precious Lord / Amazing grace / Just a closer walk with thee / Swing low - sweet chariot / Peace in the valley / When the saints go marching in.
LP: HAL 22

JUST A LITTLE WHILE.
MC: VJMAC 11
LP: VJMALP 11

RATS.

Tracks: / Just a little while to stay here / Bournemouth bell / Bugle boy march / There'll be hot time in the old town tonight / That lucky old sun / Route 66 / Joe Averys' piece / I thought I heard Buddy Bolden say.
LP: ALP 11
MC: AC 11

Real Blend

GOLDEN MEMORIES.
Tracks: / Jeanie with the light brown hair / Moonlight bay / Shine on harvest moon / By the light of the silvery moon / Danny boy / Beautiful dreamer / Toot toot tootsie goodbye / Swanee / Loch Lomond / Silver threads among the gold / Red red rose / Annie Laurie / Let me call you sweetheart / When I grow too old to dream / I'll be with you in apple blossom time / Mary of Argyll / Maggie / Rose of Tralee, The / Kathleen / Abide with me / Tonsillectomy / Memphis in June / I don't care who knows / How deep is the ocean / Black night in fog / Caravan / Please let me forget / C jam blues / In the still of the night / And so would I / Blue skies / Stormy weather / Sheherazade.
LP: KLP 49
MC: ZCKLP 49

WHITE CHRISTMAS.
Tracks: / White Christmas / Winter wonderland / Mary's boy child / Silent night / Ding dong merrily on high / When a child is born / Have yourself a merry little Christmas / God rest ye merry gentlemen / O come all ye faithful / Jingle bells / Sleigh ride / Deck the halls / We wish you a merry Christmas.
LP: KLP 55
MC: ZCKLP 55

Real Crazy

REAL CRAZY (18 action packed rockers 1955-61).
LP: SIN ALLEY 1

Real Fairies (bk)

REAL FAIRIES.
MCSET: DTO 10570

Real Fans Of Africa

SEVEN MILES HIGH.
LP: BIG 1

Real Ghostbusters

GHOSTBUSTER OF THE YEAR.
MC: 39579

Real Kids

ALL KINDA JERKS LIVE.
LP: ROSE 21

HIT YOU HARD.
LP: ROSE 24

OUTTA PLACE.
LP: ROSE 14

REAL KIDS.
LP: FC 010

Real Life

REAL LIFE (Film soundtrack) (Mindel, David).
LP: VFRLP 001

Real Milli Vanilli

MOMENT OF TRUTH.
Tracks: / Keep on running / Tell me where it hurts / Crazy cane / When I die / Body slam / Nice 'n' easy / Hard as hell / In my life / Too late (True love) / End of good times, The / I'll be loving you / Big brother.
LP: CHR 1819
MC: ZCHR 1819

Real People

REAL PEOPLE, THE.
Tracks: / Window pane / I can't wait / For you / Truth, The / Everyday's the same / Wonderful / Open up your mind (let me in) / She / In your hands / Looking at you / Words / Another day.
LP: 4680841
MC: 4680844

Real Roxanne

REAL ROXANNE, THE.
LP: SEL 21627
LP: 839 665 1
MC: 839 665 4

Real Sound..

REAL SOUND OF COUNTRY, THE (See under Country..) (Various artists).

Real Sounds

HARARE.
LP: ZML 1015

WENDE ZAKO.
Tracks: / Wende Zako / Tsi tsi wangu / Mujiknga / Tornados vs Dynamos / Esha / Walk for the world (Only on CD.).
LP: COOK 004
MC: COOKC 004
MC: ROUNDER 5029C
LP: ROUNDER 5029

Real Sounds Of Africa

GET REAL.
Tracks: / Chamunorwa / Nakuja / Omba / Bafineliye ngai liso / Musao / Oh ye (Only on CD) / Soccer fan (Only on CD) / Moselebende (Only on CD) / Nalala naloto (Only on CD) / Maifa (Only on CD) / Sophie (Only on CD) / Nakei napoto (Only on CD).
LP: BRED 89

Real Thing

100 MINUTES OF THE REAL THING.
MC: ZCTON 109

BEST OF THE REAL THING.
Tracks: / You to me are everything (remix) / Rainin' through my sunshine / She's got a groovy freak / (We've gotta take it to the) second stage / You'll never know what you're missing / Can you feel the force? / Can't get by without you (remix) / Won't you step into our world? / Love takes tears / Whenever you want my love / Children of the ghetto / Whatcha say watcha do.
LP: NRT 1
MC: ZCNRT 1

CAN YOU FEEL THE FORCE.
Tracks: / Watcha say, watcha do / We gonna take it to the second stage / Can you feel the force / Lady, I love you all the time / Rainin' through my sunshine / Whatcha say, whatcha do / Give me the chance / We gotta take it to the second stage / Won't you step into my world / Whenever you want my love / You gotta keep holding on / Love me right.
LP: NSPH 18601

GOLDEN HOUR OF THE REAL THING, A.
MC: KGHMC 153

GREATEST HITS: REAL THING.
LP: NE 1073

HEART AND SOUL OF THE REAL THING.
Tracks: / You to me are everything / You'll never know what you're missing / Raining through my sunshine / Love's such a wonderful thing / Hard times / Can you feel the force / I can't help myself / I can't get by without you / Mystique / Let's go disco / Children of the ghetto / Boogie down / Straight to the heart.
LP: KNLP 12051
MC: KNMC 12051

REAL THING, THE.
Tracks: / Hallelujah man / You to me are everything / Topsy turvy / He's just a moneymaker / Young and foolish / Flash / Can't get by without you / Why oh why / Keep an eye (on your best friend) / You'll never know what you're missing.
LP: NSPL 18507
MC: C 908

SAINTS OR SINNERS.
Tracks: / Boogie down / Saints or sinners / Story of my life / Thank you for loving me / You can't force the funk / Give me your love / One girl in my life.
LP: CABLP 100

Reale, Roger C.

RADIOACTIVE.
Tracks: / High society / Dead dad / Stop and go / Pain killer / Rescue me / Kill me / Reach for the sky / Madonna's last stand / Please believe me / Close inspection / Inside outside / I can't control myself.
LP: SHY 8528

Really Free Band

JESUS OUR LOVE.
Tracks: / Following you / Jesus our love / Looking at you / Children of the nation.
MC: PCN 113

NEVER SURRENDER.
Tracks: / Following you / Here inside / Never surrender / Reverence for the Lord / Children of the nation / Only want to be with you / Looking at you / Sabena's song / Hangin' / Jesus our love / Following you (reprise).
MC: PCN 119

REVERENCE.
Tracks: / Only want to be with you / Reverence for the Lord / Sabena's song / Hangin'.
MC: PCN 112

Really Rosie

REALLY ROSIE (Broadway Cast) (Various artists).
MC: CDL 5368

Realm

ENDLESS WAR.
LP: RO 9509 1

SUICIETY.
LP: RO 94061
MC: RO 94064

Re-Animator

CONDEMNED TO ETERNITY.
Tracks: / Don't eat the yellow snow / St. Alphonzo's pancake breakfast / Cosmik debris / Apostrophe / Stink foot / I'm the slime / 50/50 / Dinah moe hum / Nanook rubs it / Father O'Blivion / Excentrifugal forz / Uncle Remus / Camarillo brillo / Dirty love / Zomby woof / Montana.
LP: FLAG 37
MC: TFLAG 37

DENY REALITY.
Tracks: / Deny reality / Fatal descent / Re-animator / Follow the masses / O.P.C. / D.U.A.F.
LP: MFLAG 32

LAUGHING.
LP: FLAG 53
MC: TFLAG 53

Re-Animator (Film)

RE-ANIMATOR, THE (Film soundtrack) (Various artists).
LP: STV 81261
MC: CTV 81261

Reaves, Giles

WUNJO.
Tracks: / Wunjo / Sowelu / Uruz (strength) / Eithwaz / Eihwaz (Defense) / Odin (the unknowable) / Kano (opening).
LP: IMCA 5819
MC: IMCAC 5819

Reavy, Ed

IRISH FIDDLER.
LP: ROUNDER 6008

Reba

SANGEET.
MC: BIP 203

SANGEET TWO.
MC: BIP 406

Reba & Tridib

NORTH INDIAN CLASSICAL VOCAL MUSIC.
MC: BIPMAR 002

RAGA SANGEET North Indian classical music.
MC: BIP 402

Rebb, Johnny

COME ON LET'S GO.
LP: KK 781

Rebearth Corporatio

VERSES.
LP: CIRCLE 2

Rebecca

REBECCA (Du Maurier, Daphne) (Bloom, Claire (nar)).
MCSET: TC FP 417118-5

Rebekka Frame

HAYSTACKS.
Tracks: / Sensitive boys / Stray away / Haystacks / Speak in rhymes / Jealous of youth / False prophet.
LP: REVLP 77

Rebel

REBEL FAVOURITES (Various artists).
MC: TP 7002

Rebel Cats

REBEL CATS.
LP: IND 001

Rebel Heels

ONE BY ONE BY ONE.
Tracks: / On rebel heels / In hot pursuit / World of mirrors / Empty love / Love changes this / Break the chain / Perfect day for rain, A / Low hum of machines, The / Rise / My only enemy.
LP: K 781 571 1
MC: K 781 571 4

Rebel Kind

REBEL KIND (Various artists).
LP: LOLITA 5007

Rebel MC

21 MIXES (Rebel MC & Double Trouble).
LP: LUVLP 4

BLACK MEANING GOOD.
LP: LUVLP 12
MC: LUVMC 12

REBEL MUSIC.
LP: LUVLP 5
MC: LUVMC 5

Rebel Pebbles

GIRLS TALK.
Tracks: / Dream lover / How do you feel / Girl's talk / Anthony's attic / Toy soldier / No more cryin' / Groovy love / Without you / Eskimo and butterfly / Elephant's revenge / Wild weekend.
LP: EIRSLP 1053
MC: EIRSTC 1053

Rebel Rock Quality

REBEL ROCK QUALITY (Various artists).
LP: KOMA 788 024

Rebel Soca

WHEN THE RIGHT TIME COMES.
LP: SHAN 64010

Rebello, Jason

CLEARER VIEW, A.
Tracks: / Back to back / Medusa seducer / Ship to shore / Punch and Judy / Golden fleece / 1st instinct / Clearer view, A / Siobhan / Tone row / Memorial.
LP: PL 74805
MC: PK 74805

Rebels Without A Cause

NAKED LUNCH.
LP: EES 007

Reber, Heinz

CELLORGANICA (See under Demenga, Thomas) (Reber, Heinz/Thomas Demenga).

Rebirth Brass Band

FEEL LIKE FUNKIN' IT UP.
LP: SPD 1040
MC: SPDC 1040

Rebirth Jazz Band

HERE TO STAY.
MC: C 1092

REBIRTH JAZZ BAND OF NEW ORLEANS.
LP: ARHOOLIE 1092

Rebles

ALL NATURAL SOCA VOL.3.
Tracks: / Happy / Bacchanal lady / This party is it / Wet me down / Soca in the palace / We can make it.
LP: GS 2286

SOCA PARTY COMBINATION.
LP: GS 2302
MC: GSC 2302

Rebroff, Ivan

BEST OF IVAN REBROFF.
Tracks: / Cossacks must ride / Gypsy drinking song / Oh, Natascha / Girls in the fields / Cossack patrol / Untroubled / Ol' man river / Lara's theme / Hey Andruschka / Play, gypsy / Hey O dessa / Kalinka / Dark eyes / First light of the morning / Moscow lights / Ave Maria.
LP: 193531
MC: 193534

FESTLICHE WEIHNACHT (XMAS).
MC: 317412

GLASNOST PERESTROIKA.
LP: 317421
MC: 317422

GREATEST HITS.
LP: 4667591
MC: 4667594

IVAN REBROFF.
Tracks: / Evening chimes / Two guitars / Dark eyes / Song of the volga boatmen / Nightingale, The / Volga boat song / Meadowland / Bublitschki / Lara's theme / Over the steppes / Taspaschol.
LP: 64 460

MY RUSSIAN HOMELAND.
LP: 317321
MC: 317322

SOMEWHERE MY LOVE (Ivan Rebroff sings in English).
Tracks: / Russia is my homeland / Kalinka / Midnight in Moscow / Cossacks must ride / Somewhere my love / Hey Andrushka / Meadowland / Reins held fast in the hand, The / Old man's dreams / Play on gypsy / Song of the volga boatmen / Black eyes.
LP: 64658

TAIGA TRAUME.
LP: 25438
MC: 40 25438

VERY BEST OF IVAN REBROFF.
Tracks: / Evening chimes / Song of the Volga boatmen / Hava nagila / Im tiefen keller / Two white doves / Perestroika / Grosser alter don / Dark eyes / Schto nam gorje / Poj zyganka / Somewhere my love / Ol' man river / Kalinka malinka / La calunnia / Ach natascha / On the way from Petersburgh to Nowgorod / Cossack patrol.
LP: REB 778
MC: ZCF 778

VERY BEST OF IVAN REBROFF VOLUME II, THE.
LP: REB 848
MC: ZCF 848

ZAUBER EINER GROSEN STIMME.
LP: 317401
MC: 317402

Recipe

SKINNY DIPPING.
LP: DMC 014

Recipients Of Death

FINAL CONFLICT.
LP: .... **WRE 9051**

Reckless

HEART OF STEEL.
Tracks: / Hot 'n' ready / Heart of steel / Drivin' you mad / Feel the fire / Need you next to me / In the night / Only after dark / Shadows of you / Don't walk away.
LPPD: .... **HMAPD 6**
MC: .... **HMAMC 6**
LP: .... **HMUSA 6**

NO FRILLS.
Tracks: / Nitty gritty / Wild in the streets / Deadly game / Voices in the night / Crazy over you / Breakin' up / Night after night / Railroad alley / Eye for an eye / Holdin' on.
LP: **790564 1**
MC: **790564 4**

RECKLESS.
Tracks: / Victim of time / Giving it all away / Ready for action / Heartache rock and roll / Too much to bear / Reckless / Child of the night / All night woman / Could this be love / Yesterday's news / Passion and pain / Searching for a dream.
LP: .... **EMC 3362**

Reckless Sleepers

BIG BOSS SOUNDS.
Tracks: / Tried to please her / I wake up loving you / If we never meet again / Mary Lou / Notting Hill Gate / This heart / Mesmerised / Big before it bursts / Big Boss sounds / It came quick (and didn't stay long).
LP: .... **EIRSA 1016**
MC: .... **EIRSAC 1016**

Recoil

HYDROLOGY.
Tracks: / Grain / Stone / Sermon.
LP: .... **STUMM 51**
MC: .... **CSTUMM 51**

RECOIL 1&2.
LP: .... **STUMM 31**

Recollections

RECOLLECTIONS NO. 2; LIFE ON THE CANAL (Richards, Frank).
MC: .... **AC 149**

RECOLLECTIONS NO. 3; SILENT DAYS OF THE CINEMA (Mellor, Tom).
MC: .... **AC 147**

RECOLLECTIONS NO. 5; BRITISH MOTORCYCLE INDUSTRY (Turner, Edward/Val Page).
MC: .... **AC 146**

Record City

RECORD CITY (Music From The Original Soundtrack) (Various artists).
LP: **2391 299**

Record Of Singing

RECORD OF SINGING VOL. 1 (Various artists).
LPS: .... **RLS 7705**

RECORD OF SINGING VOL. 2 (Various artists).
LPS: .... **RLS 7706**

RECORD OF SINGING VOL. 3 (Various artists).
LPS: .... **EX 2901693**

Records

CRASHES.
Tracks: / Rumour sets the woods alight / Hearts in her eyes / I don't remember your name / Man with a girl proof heart / Same mistakes / Girl in golden disc / Spent a week with you last night / Hearts will be broken / Worriers / Guitars in the sky.
LP: **V2155**

MUSIC ON BOTH SIDES.
Tracks: / Imitation jewellery / Heather and hell / Selfish love / Clown around town / Not so much time / Keeping up with the Joneses / Third hand information / Real life / King of kings / Cheap detective music / Everyday nightmare.
LP: .... **V 2206**

ON A SUNNY AFTERNOON IN WATERLOO.
LP: .... **WF 042**

SHADES IN BED.
Tracks: / Girl / Teenarama / Girls that don't exist / Starry eyes / Up all night / All messed up and ready to go / Insomnia / Affection rejected / Phone / Another star.
LP: .... **V 2122**

Rectonob

SPANK THAT LOBSTER.
MC: .... **EBS 9**

Rector, Red

ANOTHER HAPPY DAY (Rector, Red & Bill Clifton).
LP: .... **BD 001**

ARE YOU FROM DIXIE? (Rector, Red & Bill Clifton).
Tracks: / Are you from Dixie? / Down in the old cabin home / Spirit of love watches over me, The / Fourteen days in Georgia / Are you my best friend / Dixie cannonball / Keep that wheel a turning / Sugartree stomp / Valley of peace / It takes a long tall brown skin gal to make a preacher... / Old man's story, The / Ashdown waltz / She has forgotten / On the sea of Galilee / There's no other love for me / Tall pines.
LP: .... **BF 15013**

RED RECTOR & FRIENDS.
LP: .... **RS 931**

Red

CRACK.
LP: .... **LM LP 011**

IN MOTION.
Tracks: / Naomi / Let her go.
LP: .... **RGMLP 2001**

RED.
LP: .... **SAW 2**

Red Alert

WE'VE GOT THE POWER.
Tracks: / We've got the power / They came in force / Crisis / You've got nothing / SPG / Art of brutality, The / Industrial slide.
LP: .... **PUNK 5**

Red Army Choir

RED ARMY CHOIR, THE.
LP: .... **LDX 74353**
LP: .... **LDX 74768/9**
MC: **K63**
MC: **K265**

Red Army Ensemble

RED ARMY ENSEMBLE AT THE ROYAL ALBERT HALL.
Tracks: / British national anthem / Russian national anthem / Russian fields / Volga boat song / Festive overture / My motherland / Parade on Red Square / Barinya / Live and don't be sad / Above clear fields / Yesterday / Di quella pira / La donna e mobile / No, John, no / Brave soldiers / Unharness your horses, oh guys / Cossack dance / Variyag / Quiet, quiet / Korobeiniki / Serenade of the stutterer / Cossack goes to the Danbube / O sole mio / Amapola / Kalinka / Soldiers friendship (dance) / Auld lang syne / Kalinka (reprise).
2LP: **303.278**
MCSET: **503.278**

Red Bandit

COOL LOVER BOY.
Tracks: / Cool lover boy / Please don't cry / Movin' on / I want you to be my girl / I'm back / It's not over / House people / Red Bandit is here / Nothing to be played with / Let's keep it mellow / Can I get a little.
LP: .... **ZL 72722**
MC: .... **ZK 72722**

Red Bank Rockers

RESCUE (see under Clemons, Clarence) (Red Bank Rockers / Clarence Clemons).

Red Beans & Rice

LIVE AT THE DUBLIN CASTLE.
Tracks: / Too tired / T-Bone shuffle / That will do / Hallelujah I love her so / Mary Anne / Two bones and a pick / Treat her right / Funk shun / Sadie Green / Dripper's boogie / Don't touch me / We wanna boogie / Caldonia / Chicken shack boogie.
LP: .... **CH 72**

Red Beards From Texas

HAVIN' A BALL.
LP: .... **RRLP 108**

Red Box

CIRCLE AND THE SQUARE.
Tracks: / For America / Heart of the sun / Billy's line / Bantu / Living in domes / Lean on me / Chenko / Saskatchewan / Leaders in the seventh heaven / Walk walk / Amen.
LP: .... **WX 79**
MC: .... **WX 79 C**

Red Byrd Vocal

ELIZABETHAN CHRISTMAS ANTHEMS.
Tracks: / This is the record of John / Sing unto God / Upon my lap / O ye little flock / Sweet was the song the virgin sung / Starre anthem, The / Lullaby / See, see the word is incarnate.
MC: .... **CSAR 46**

Red Chair Fadeaway

RED CHAIR FADEAWAY.
Tracks: / Let it happen / Myra / Dragonfly / Red chair fadeaway.
LP: .... **CTA 103**

Red Clay Ramblers

CHUCKIN' THE FRIZZ.
LP: .... **FF 089**

HARD TIMES.
LP: .... **FF 246**

IT AIN'T RIGHT.
LP: .... **FF 334**

LIE OF THE MIND, A.
LP: .... **SH 8501**

MERCHANTS LUNCH.
LP: .... **FF 055**

STOLEN LOVE.
LP: .... **FF 009**

TWISTED LAUREL.
LP: .... **FF 030**

Red Cloud

DARK END OF THE STREET.
LP: .... **SNTF 1024**

RED CLOUD IN DUB.
Tracks: / I can see the light / You're for real / Long hard road.
LP: .... **STLP 1009**

Red Crayola

BLACK SNAKES.
LP: .... **ALRC 1849**

GOD BLESS RED KRAYOLA.
Tracks: / Say hello to Jamie Jones / Music / Shirt / Listen to this / Save the house / Victory garden / Coconut hotel / Sheriff Jack / Free Piece / Ravi Shankar: Parachutist / Piece for piano and electric bass / Dairy maids lament / Big / Leejol / Sherlock Holmes / Dirth of Tilth / Tina's gone to have a baby / Jewels of the Madonna / Green of my pants / Night song.
LP: .... **LIK 29**

GOD BLESS THE RED CRAYOLA AND ALL WHO SAIL IN IT.
Tracks: / Say hello to Jamie Jones / Music / Shirt, The / Listen to this / Save the house / Victory garden / Coconut hotel / Sheriff Jack / Free piece / Ravi Shankar / Parachutist / Dairy maids lament / Big / Leejol / Sherlock Holmes / Dirth tilth / Tina's gone to have a baby / Jewels of the Madonna / Green of my pants / Night song.
LP: .... **RAD 16**

MALEFACTOR, ADE.
LP: .... **GLALP 035**

PARABLE OF ARABLE LAND.
Tracks: / Free form freakout / Hurricane fighter plane / Transparent radiation / War sucks / Pink stainless tail / Parable of arable land / Former reflections enduring doubt.
LP: .... **LIK 20**
LP: .... **RAD 12**

SOLDIER TALK.
Tracks: / March no. 12 / On the brink / Letter-bomb / Conspirators' oath / March no.14 / Soldier talk / Discipline / X / Opposition spokesman, An / Uh knowledge dance / Wonderland.
LP: .... **RAD 18**

Red Dawn

RED DAWN (Film Soundtrack) (Various artists).
Tracks: / Invasion: *Various artists* / Drive-in, The: *Various artists* / Let it turn: *Various artists*/ Woverines: *Various artists* / Flowers: *Various artists* / Eulogy: *Various artists* / Robert's end: *Various artists* / Death and freedom: *Various artists* / End title: *Various artists.*
LP: .... **RVF 6001**

Red Dogs

RED DOGS.
LP: .... **LUSLP 5**
MC: .... **LUSMC 5**

WRONG SIDE OF TOWN, THE.
LP: .... **LUSMLP 6**

Red Flag

NAIVE ART.
LP: .... **ENVLP 534**

Red Guitars

SLOW TO FADE.
Tracks: / Remote control / Dive / Astronomy / Cloak and dagger / Shaken not stirred / Crocodile tears / Sting in the tail / Marimba / Slow to fade.
LP: .... **SCARLP 001**
MC: .... **SCARC 001**

TALES OF THE EXPECTED.
Tracks: / Be with me / Suspicion & fear / Love and understanding / House of love / Storyville / Trains on time / Marianne / Baby's got a gun / Sweet water ranch / National Avenue (Sunday afternoon).
LP: .... **OVED 224**
MC: .... **OVEDC 224**

Red Gun

IF YOU DON'T FIGHT YOU LOSE.
Tracks: / I've been to Bali too / Diamantina drover, The / I was only 19 / Gladstone pier / Long run, The / It doesn't matter to me / Still life / Asio / Where you gonna run to? / Killing floor.
LP: .... **CBS 26527**
MC: **40 26527**

Red Hackle Pipers

BLEND OF RED HACKLE.
LP: .... **GBS 1019**
MC: .... **KGBC 1019**

PRIDE O' SCOTLAND.
Tracks: / Scotland the brave / Teribus / Corriechoillies's welcome / 51st Highland division / 79th Farewell to Gibraltar / Highland whiskey / Stirling castle / Louden's bonnie woods / Orange and blue / High road to Linton / Piper O'Drummond / Tall toddle / Mrs. MacLeod of Raasay / Longueval / Gairloch / Skye boat song / Jigs jigo slurs / Duncan Mackillop / McPherson of Mosspark, A / Drum salute / Rowan tree, The / Dream valley of Glendaruel, The / Old rustic bridge / Canadian highlanders / Farewell to the creeks / Dovecote park / Retreat airs / Green hill of Tyrol / Battle is o'er, The / Lochanside / Balmoral Highlanders, The / Dora Macleod / Champion piper / Slow air / Kylesku / Bloody fields of Flanders, The / Raasay house.
LP: .... **NL 70124**
MC: .... **NK 70124**
LP: .... **INTS 5244**
LP: .... **NL 25214**

Red Hadley

STEP IT UP & GO (See under Smokey Joe) (Red Hadley and Smokey Joe).

Red Harvest

SAVED.
LP: .... **DOM 004**

STRANGE.
LP: .... **AFT 5**

Red Heads

RED HEADS, SIX HOTTENTOTS & LANIN'S ARCADIANS.
2LP: .... **DFJ 110**

Red Hot & Blue (Show)

RED HOT & BLUE/STARS IN YOUR EYES Original Broadway cast (Various artists).
LP: .... **AEI 1147**

Red Hot Chili Peppers

FREAKY STYLEY.
Tracks: / Jungle man / Hollywood (Africa) / American ghost dance / If you want me to stay / Nevermind / Freaky styley / Blackeyed blonde / Brothers cup, The / Battle ship / Lovin' and touchin' / Catholic school girls rule / Sex rap / Thirty dirty birds / Yertle the turtle.
LP: .... **MTL 1057**
LP: **790 617 1**
MC: .... **TCMTL 1057**
MC: **790 617 4**

MOTHER'S MILK.
Tracks: / Good time boys / Higher ground / Subway to Venus / Magic Johnson / Nobody weird like me / Knock me down / Taste the pain / Stone cold bush / Fire / Pretty little ditty / Punk rock classic / Sexy Mexican maid / Johnny kick a hole in the sky.
LP: .... **MTL 1046**
LP: **792 152 1**
MC: .... **TCMTL 1046**
MC: **792 152 4**

RED HOT CHILI PEPPERS.
Tracks: / True men don't kill coyotes / Baby appeal / Buckle down / Get up and jump / Why don't you love me / Green heaven / Mommy where's daddy / Out in L.A. / Police helicopter / You always sing / Grand pappy du plenty.
LP: .... **MTL 1056**
LP: **790 616 1**
MC: .... **TCMTL 1056**
MC: **790 616 4**

UPLIFT MOFO PARTY PLAN.
Tracks: / Fight like a brave / Funky crime / Me and my friends / Backwoods / Skinny sweaty man / Behind the sun / Subterranean homesick blues / Special secret song inside / No chump love sucker / Walkin' on down the road / Love trilogy / Organic anti-beat box band.
LP: .... **AML 3125**
MC: .... **TCAML 3125**

Red Hot Mammas

RED HOT MAMMAS (Various artists).
Tracks: / You've got to see mamma ev'ry night: *Kay, Dolly* / I loved you once: *Kay, Dolly* / Lovey came back: *Harris, Marion* / Charleston Charley: *Harris,*

Marion / Big boy: *Young, Margaret* / Red hot Henry Brown: *Young, Margaret* / On the Z-R-3: *Patricola, Isabella* / Big Bad Bill (is Sweet William now): *Patricola, Isabella*/ Honey bunch: *Green, Jane* / Ya gotta know how to love: *Walker, Esther* / Hard-to-get-Gertie: *Walker, Esther*/ One sweet letter from you: *Smith, Kate* / I'm gonna meet my sweetie now: *Smith, Kate* / What'll you do: *Tucker, Sophie* / Virginia (there's a blue ridge in my heart): *Tucker, Sophie* / That's my weakness now: *Challis, Beth*/ I'm the last of the red hot mammas: *Dyson, Belle* / He's a good man to have around: *Dyson, Belle*.
LP: . . . . **FV 207**

Red Hot Max

LONESOME ROCKER.
LP: . . . . **LP 8311**

WHY CHANGE? (Red Hot Max & Cats). Tracks: / Fractured / Eyes like a cat / Crackerjack / Lose control / Live it up / Crazy / Count down boogie / I got a woman / I'm a hobo / Hey baberiba / Weary blues goodbye.
LP: . . . . **SJLP 566**

Red Hot 'n' Blue

WAIT 'N' SEE.
LP: . . . . **NWLP 1005**

Red Hot & Ragtime

RED HOT & RAGTIME (Various artists).
MCSET: . . . . **DTO 10211**

Red Jasper

ENGLAND'S GREEN AND PLEASANT LAND.
LP: . . . . **VIX 101**

STING IN THE TALE.
Tracks: / Faceless people / Guy Fawkes / TV screen / Second coming / Old Jack / Company director / Secret society / Magpie / I can hew.
LP: . . . . **HTD LP 3**

Red Lemon Electric...

RED LEMON ELECTRIC BLUES BAND.
LP: . . . . **MMLP 1036**

Red Letter Day

SOFT LIGHTS AND LOUD GUITARS (see under Sect, The) (Sect, The/Red Letter Day).

Red London

OUTLAWS.
Tracks: / New kids on the block / Go for it / Chase it up / Day they tore the old school down / Coming home / 48 reasons / Shades of 34 / It's never too late / Livin' for the weekend / Voices / Desolation / Day they tore the old school down (reprise).
LP: . . . . **NLP 010**

PRIDE AND PASSION.
LP: . . . . **GM 015**

Red Lorry Yellow Lorry

BLOW.
LP: . . . . **SITU 25**
MC: . . . . **SITUC 25**

NOTHING WRONG.
Tracks: / Nothing wrong / Do you understand / Calling (Extra track on 12".) / Big stick / Hands off me / She said / Sayonara / World around / Hard-away / Only dreaming / Never know / Pushing on / Time is tight.
LP: . . . . **SITU 20**
MC: . . . . **SITC 20**
LP: . . . . **SITL 20**

PAINT YOUR WAGON.
LP: . . . . **REDLP 65**
MC: . . . . **REDC 65**

SMASHED HITS.
Tracks: / Beating my head / He's red / Monkeys on juice / Spinning round / Cut down / Take it all / Hollow eyes / Generation / Hold yourself down / Chance.
LP: . . . . **REDLP 086**
MC: . . . . **REDC 86**

TALK ABOUT THE WEATHER.
LP: . . . . **REDLP 50**

Red Mill

RED MILL (Various artists).
LP: . . . . **TV 34766**

Red Moon Joe

ARMS OF SORROW.
LP: . . . . **RRA 013**
MC: . . . . **RRAMC 013**

Red Onion Jazz Babies

1924: RED ONION JAZZ BABIES (see under Armstrong, Louis).

RED ONION JAZZ BABIES AND COOK'S DREAMLAND ORCHESTRA.
LP: . . . . **FJ 107**

Red Onions & Ottilie

RED ONIONS AND OTTILIE.
LP: . . . . **SOS 1090**

Red Plastic Bag

PAINTING THE TOWN RED.
LP: . . . . **RI 3303**

RED ALERT.
LP: . . . . **RRTG 2232**

Red Pony

RED PONY, THE (Film soundtrack) (Various artists).
LP: . . . . **STV 81259**
MC: . . . . **CTV 81259**

Red Rider

AS FAR AS SIAM.
Tracks: / Lunatic fringe / Cowboy's in Hong Kong / Only game in town / Thru' the curtain / What have you got to do / Ships / Caught in the middle / Don't let go of me / Laughing man.
LP: . . . . **EST 12145**

DON'T FIGHT IT.
Tracks: / Don't fight it / How's my little girl tonight / White hot / Just the way it goes / Look out again / Make myself complete / Avenue A / Iron in the soul.
LP: . . . . **EST 12028**

Red Riding Hood

RED RIDING HOOD (Various artists).
MC: . . . . **STC 302A**

Red River

RED RIVER.
Tracks: / Broke again / Mercury / Lucky tonight / Fools paradise / Cheap thrills / City doesn't weep, The.
LP: . . . . **ROSE 167**

TEXAS ADVICE.
Tracks: / Ride - ride - ride / Comin' to you live / 8 chrome and wings / Come on over / Dry country blues / Ain't workin' no more / Broke again / Lucky tonight / Cheap thrills / Texas advice / At the roadhouse tonite / I'll drink you're booze / Talkin' to me / Something's gotta give / Goin' down / Mercury / Fools paradise / City doesn't weep, The.
LP: . . . . **ROSE 210**

Red River Runs

RED RIVER RUNS (Various artists).
LP: . . . . **FLY 259**

Red Rockers

GOOD AS GOLD.
Tracks: / China / Good as gold / Dreams fade away / Change the world around / Answers to the questions / Till it all falls down / Running away from you / Fanfare for Metropolis / (Come on into) my house / Home is where the war is.
LP: . . . . **CBS 25388**
MC: **40 25388**

SCHIZOPHRENIC CIRCUS.
Tracks: / Just like you / Blood from a stone / Shades of '45 / Another day / Freedom row / Good thing i know her / Eve of destruction / Both hands in the fire / Burning bridges.
LP: . . . . **CBS 26142**

Red Rodney

3 R'S, THE (Rodney, Red/Richie Cole/ Ricky Ford).
LP: . . . . **MR 5290**

BIRD LIVES.
LP: . . . . **MR 5034**

HI JINX AT VANGUARD (Rodney, Red & Ira Sullivan).
LP: . . . . **MR 5267**

HOME FREE.
LP: . . . . **MR 5135**

LIVE AT THE VILLAGE VANGUARD (featuring Ira Sullivan).
LP: . . . . **MR 5209**

MODERN MUSIC FROM CHICAGO (Rodney, Red Quintet).
LP: . . . . **OJC 048**

RED RODNEY.
Tracks: / Shaw 'nuff / Red hot and blue / I remember / 5709 / Two by two / Whirlwind / Jordu / Shelley.
LP: . . . . **JR 158**

RED RODNEY WITH THE BEBOP PRESERVATION SOCIETY.
Tracks: / Merry-go-round / March of Ides / Tenderly / Sid's delight / Blue to boogie / Seven dials / Esmerelda / If you could see me now.
LP: . . . . **SPJ LP 7**

RED TORNADO.
LP: . . . . **MR 5088**

RED, WHITE AND BLUES.
LP: . . . . **MR 5111**

SPRINT.
LP: **9602611**

SUPERBOP.
LP: . . . . **MR 5046**

YARD'S PAD.
Tracks: / Yard's pad / Red hot / Informality / S.A.S. / Here at last / Fourth of March / Don't remember April.
LP: . . . . **SNTF 698**
MC: . . . . **ZCSN 698**

Red Rose Ragtime Band

ROSE IS A ROSE IS A ROSE, A.
LP: . . . . **SOS 1128**

Red Roseland...

HANDFUL OF KEITH (Red Roseland Cornpickers & Keith Nichols).
LP: . . . . **SOS 1133**

RED HOT BAND (Red Roseland Cornpickers & Keith Nichols).
LP: . . . . **SOS 1153**

RED ROSELAND CORNPICKERS-VOL.1 (Red Roseland Cornpickers).
LP: . . . . **SOS 1101**

RED ROSELAND CORNPICKERS-VOLUME 2 (Red Roseland Cornpickers).
LP: . . . . **SOS 1102**

Red Rum

FIVE GRAND NATIONALS 1973-1977 (Various artists).
LP: . . . . **REP 1**

Red Scorpion

RED SCORPION (Film Soundtrack) (Various artists).
LP: . . . . **VS 5230**
MC: . . . . **VSC 5230**

Red Shift

BACK IN THE RED.
Tracks: / Up the walls of Valencia Harbour / Waves of Tory, The / No cause, no cause for alarm / Sold down the river again / Lancashire emigrant's farewell, The / Last dance.
LP: . . . . **BASH 41**

Red Sonja

RED SONJA (Film soundtrack) (Various artists).
LP: . . . . **JMP 4011**
LP: . . . . **STV 81248**
MC: . . . . **CTV 81248**

Red, Sonny

OUT OF THE BLUE.
LP: . . . . **BLP 4032**

Red Temple Spirits

DANCING TO RESTORE AN ECLIPSED SUN.
LP: . . . . **SAVE 74**

Red Tent

RED TENT (Film Soundtrack) (Various artists).
Tracks: / Love theme: *Various artists* / Do dreams go on: *Various artists* / Death at the Pole: *Various artists*/ Love like the snow: *Various artists* / Message from Rome: *Various artists* / They're alive: *Various artists*/ Farewell: *Various artists* / Others, who will follow us: *Various artists.*
LP: **255064.1**
LP: . . . . **SPFL 275**

Red Wave

RED WAVE (Various artists).
Tracks: / Ashes: *Aquarium* / Tonight: *Aquarium* / Thirst, The: *Aquarium* / Saw a night: *Kino*/ Films: *Kino* / City: *Kino* / Streetcar headed east: *Kino* / Experimentor: *Alisa* / Doctor boogie: *Alisa* / Juice squeezer: *Alisa* / Metamorphoses: *Strange games* / If you think: *Strange games*/ No telephone: *Strange games* / Paper flowers: *Strange games.*
LP: . . . . **ZL 71331**
MC: . . . . **ZK 71331**

Red Wing Blackbirds...

TWO STEP BALL (Red Wing Blackbirds Ragtime Band).
LP: . . . . **SOS 1018**

Redbone, Leon

BRANCH TO BRANCH.
Tracks: / Te na na / Hot time in the old town tonight / Sweet mama, papa's getting mad / Step it up and go / Your cheatin' heart / Seduced / Why / My blue heaven / Extra blues / When you wish upon a star / Prairie lullaby.
LP: . . . . **K 50778**

CHRISTMAS ISLAND.
Tracks: / White Christmas / Winter wonderland / Frosty the snowman / Blue Christmas / There's no place like home for the holidays / Toyland / Christmas Island / That old Christmas moon / I'll be home for Christmas / Let it snow, let it snow, let it snow / Christmas ball blues.
LP: **211.203**
MC: **411.203**

DOUBLE TIME.
Tracks: / Diddy wah diddy / Nobody's sweetheart / Shine on harvest moon / Crazy blues / Mississippi Delta blues / Mr. Jelly Roll Baker / Melancholy baby / Sheik of Araby, The / Mississippi river blues / Winin boy blues / If we never meet again / This side of heaven.
LP: . . . . **K 56301**

NO REGRETS.
LP: . . . . **SH 3761**

ON THE TRACK.
Tracks: / Sweet mama hurry home or I'll be gone / Ain't misbehavin (I'm savin' my love for you) / My walking stick / Lazybones / Marie / Desert blues (big chief buffalo nickel) / Lulu's back in town / Some of these days / Big time woman / Haunted house / Polly wolly doodle.
LP: . . . . **K 56173**

RED TO BLUE.
LP: . . . . **AS 8888**

SUGAR.
Tracks: / Ghost of the Saint Louis blues / Roll along Kentucky moon / Right or wrong / Laughing blues / Breeze / Whistling colonel, The / Sugar / Pretty baby / When I take my sugar to tea / What you want me to do / Messin' around / So relax / 14th Street blues.
LP: **210 555**
MC: **410 555**

Redbridge Brass

REDBRIDGE PHENOMENON.
LP: . . . . **GRS 1018**

Redcap James

PLAYS BROADWAY & UHURU.
LP: . . . . **AFRB 1001**

Redcoats

COULD I HAVE THIS DANCE.
Tracks: / When you get to heaven / Banks of the roses / Could I Have This Dance / Oh Boy / Bally James Duff / Help Me Make It Through The Night / If those lips could only speak / My world's come down / Before the next teardrop falls / Gypsy woman.
MC: . . . . **CDN 001**

Redd, Freddie

STRAIGHT AHEAD.
LP: . . . . **IP 7715**

UNDER PARIS SKIES.
LP: . . . . **SWING 03**

Redd, Jeff

QUIET STORM, A.
LP: . . . . **MCA 42299**
LP: . . . . **MCG 6086**
MC: . . . . **MCGC 6086**

Redd Kross

BORN INNOCENT.
LP: **46091L**

NEUROTICA.
Tracks: / Neurotica / Play my song / Frosted flake / Janus, Jeanie and George Harrison / Love is you / Peach kelli pop / McKenzie / Ballad of a love doll / What they say / Gandhi is dead (I'm the cartoon man) / Beautiful bye byes.
LP: . . . . **ZL 71427X**
MC: . . . . **ZK 71427X**

Redd, Sharon

BEAT THE STREET.
Tracks: / Can you handle it / Never give you up / Love how you feel / You're a winner / In the name of love / Beat the street / Somebody save the night / You got my love.
LP: . . . . **PRSLP 6002**
MC: . . . . **PRSK 6002**

LOVE HOW YOU FEEL(ALBUM).
Tracks: / Activate / You're a winner / Got ya where I want ya / Liar on the wire / Sweet sensation / Somebody save the night / Love how you feel.
LP: . . . . **PRL 25776**

REDD HOTT.
Tracks: / Never give you up / You're the one / Send your love / Beat the street / In the name of love / Takin' a chance on love / We're friewnds again.
LP: . . . . **PRL 25056**

SHARON REDD.
Tracks: / You got my love / Can you handle it / It's a lie / Try my love on for size / Leaving you is easier said than done / Love is gonna get ya / You stayed on my mind / Never give you up / Love how you feel / You're a winner / In the name of love / Beat the street / Somebody save the night.
LP: . . . . **EPC 84894**
MC: **40 84894**

THAT'S FUNK.
LP: **6 25470**

Redder Than Red

REDDER THAN RED (Various artists).
LP: . . . . **CJ 3021**

Redding, Jacqui

TICKLE ON THE TUM (see under McTell, Ralph) (Redding, Jacqui & Ralph McTell).

Redding, Otis

BEST OF OTIS REDDING.
Tracks: / Mr. Pitiful / My girl / Respect / I've been loving you too long / Love man / Cigarettes and coffee / I can't get no satisfaction / Try a little tenderness / I can't turn you loose / Hard to handle / Fa fa fa fa fa (sad song) / (Sittin' on) the dock of the bay / Shake / Ole man trouble / Good to me / Tell the truth / Down in the valley / These arms of mine / Tramp / Just one more day / Pain in my heart / My lover's prayer / Chain gang / You don't miss your water / Rock me baby / That's how strong my love is / Change is gonna come, A.
2LP: . . . . **K 60016**
LP: **780 171-1**
MC: **780 171-4**
MC: **K4 60016**

COME TO ME.
Tracks: / These arms of mine / Hey hey baby / That's what my heart needs / Mary's little lamb / Pain in my heart / Something is worrying me / Security / Lucille / Come to me / Don't leave me this way / I want to thank you / Chained and bound / Your one & only man / I'm depending on you.
LP: . . . . **CRB 1077**
MC: . . . . **TCCRB 1077**

DOCK OF THE BAY (The Definitive Collection).
Tracks: / Shake / Mr. Pitiful / Respect / Love man / I can't get no satisfaction / I can't turn you loose / Hard to handle / Fa fa fa fa fa (sad song) / My girl / I've been loving you too long / Try a little tenderness / My lover's prayer / That's how strong my love is / Pain in my heart / Change is gonna come, A / (Sittin' on) the dock of the bay / Cigarettes and coffee (Extra track available on C.D. only) / These arms of mine (Extra track available on C.D. only) / Tramp (Extra track available on C.D. only).
LP: **2411171**
MC: **241 117-4**
LP: **231-001**
LP: **241 118-1**
MC: **241 118-4**

GREAT OTIS REDDING SINGS SOUL BALLADS, THE.
LP: . . . . **SD 33248**

HEART AND SOUL.
MC: . . . . **KNMC 12060**

HISTORY OF OTIS REDDING.
Tracks: / I've been loving you too long / Try a little tenderness / These arms of mine / Pain in my heart / My lover's prayer / Fa fa fa fa fa (sad song) / Respect / Satisfaction / Mr. Pitiful / Security / I can't turn you loose / Shake.
LP: . . . . **K 40066**
LP: . . . . **S 418**
MC: **K4 40066**

IMMORTAL OTIS REDDING.
LP: **588-113**

KING AND QUEEN (Redding, Otis & Carla Thomas).
LP: . . . . **SD 7716**
LP: **589-007**

LIVE: OTIS REDDING.
Tracks: / Destiny / Good to me / Chained and bound / Ol' man trouble / I can't turn you loose / I've been loving you too long / Security / Hard day's night, A.
LP: **K50881**

LOVE MAN.
LP: . . . . **K 40078**

OTIS BLUE.
Tracks: / I can't get no satisfaction / Respect / Shake / I've been loving you too long / My girl / You don't miss your water.
LP: . . . . **K 40003**
MC: . . . . **K 440 003**
LP: . . . . **ATL 5041**
LP: **587 036**

OTIS REDDING DICTIONARY OF SOUL.
LP: . . . . **SD 33249**
LP: **588-050**

OTIS REDDING IN EUROPE.
LP: **589-016**

OTIS REDDING STORY, THE.
Tracks: / These arms of mine / That's what my heart needs / Mary's little lamb / Pain in my heart / Something is worrying me / Security / Come to me / I've been loving you too long / Change is gonna come, A / Shake / Rock me baby / Respect / You don't miss your water / Satisfaction / Chain gang / My lover's prayer / It's growing / Fa fa fa fa fa (sad song) / I'm sick y'all / Sweet Lorene / Try a little tenderness / Day tripper / Stay in school / You left the water running / Happy song / Hard to handle / Amen / I've got dreams to remember / Champagne and wine / Direct me / Your one & only man / Chained and bound / That's how strong my love is / Mr. Pitiful / Keep your arms around me / For your precious love / Woman, a lover, a friend, A / Home in your heart / Ole man trouble / Down in the valley / I can't turn you loose / Just one more day / Papa's got a brand new bag / Good to me / Cigarettes and coffee / Ton of joy / Hawg for you / Tramp / Knock on wood / Lovey dovey / New year's resolution / Ooh Carla ooh Otis / Merry Christmas baby / White Christmas / Love man / Free me / Look at that girl / Match game, The / Tell the truth / (Sittin' on) The dock of the bay.
LPS: . . . . **K 781 762 1**
MCSET: . . . . **K 781 762 4**

OTIS REDDING STORY, VOL 1.
2LP: . . . . **SD 2807**

OTIS REDDING STORY, VOL 2.
2LP: . . . . **SD 2808**

PAIN IN MY HEART.
LP: **587 042**

PURE OTIS.
Tracks: / Respect / Down in the valley / I've been loving you too long / Shake / My girl / Wonderful world / (I can't get no) satisfaction / Try a little tenderness / That's how strong my love is / Love man / Mr. Pitiful / Higher and higher / Stand by me / Louie Louie / Hard to handle / These arms of mine / Fa fa fa fa fa (sad song) / (Sitting on the) Dock of the bay / Big blue eyes / You send me.
LP: . . . . **K 50564**

SOUL ALBUM.
LP: **587-011**

SOUL BALLADS.
LP: . . . . **ATL 5029**

Reddings

AWAKENING, THE.
Tracks: / Remote control / Funkin' on the one / Come in out of the rain / It's Friday night / Awakening, The (part 1) / I want it / Doin' it / Lady be my lovesong / Awakening, The (part 2).
LP: . . . . **EPC 84767**

IF LOOKS COULD KILL.
Tracks: / In my pants / Where did our love go / Didn't want to fall in love / Parasite / I don't understand it / Talk's all over town / If looks could kill / Third party.
LP: **823 324 1**

STEAMIN' HOT.
Tracks: / I know you got another / Dock of the Bay / You bring me joy / Follow me / Steamin' hot / For you / You can be a star / Time won't wait.
LP: . . . . **EPC 85725**

Reddy, Helen

BEST OF HELEN REDDY.
Tracks: / I am a woman / I don't know how to love him / Leave me alone / Delta dawn / You and me against the world / Angie baby / Emotion / Keep on singing / Peaceful / Ain't no way to treat a lady.
LP: . . . . **EST 11467**
MC: . . . . **TCEST 11467**

FEEL SO YOUNG (The Helen Reddy Collection).
Tracks: / Angie baby / You make me feel so young / Let's go up / I am woman / That's all / Ain't no way to treat a lady / Lost in the shuffle / Looks like love / Here in my arms / You and me against the world.
MC: . . . . **PWKMC 4072**

FREE AND EASY.
LP: . . . . **EST 11348**

I AM WOMAN.
Tracks: / Peaceful / I am woman / This masquerade / I didn't mean to love you / Where is my friend / And I love you so / What would they say / Where is the love / Hit the road Jack / Last blues song.
LP: . . . . **MFP 41 5739 1**
MC: . . . . **MFP 41 5739 4**
LP: . . . . **FA 3024**

IMAGINATION.
LP: . . . . **MCF 3158**

LIVE IN LONDON:HELEN REDDY.
Tracks: / Rhythm rhapsody / This masquerade / Bluebird / Candle on the water (From 'Pete's dragon'.) / Hold me in your dreams tonight / I believe in music / Crazy love / Peaceful / You and me against the world / Delta dawn / Ain't no way to treat a lady / Leave me alone / Last blues song / I am woman / I'll be your audience / Angie baby / Poor little fool / Ready or not / West wind circus / We'll sing in the sunshine / Mama / You're my world / I can hear you no more / Entertainer, (The).
2LP: . . . . **ESTSP 20**

PLAY ME OUT.
LP: . . . . **MCF 3115**

REDDY.
Tracks: / Trying to get to you / Perfect love affair / Magic is still there, The / Make love to me / Minute by minute / Let me be your woman / You're so good / Words are not enough / Sing my heart out.
LP: . . . . **EST 11949**

TAKE WHAT YOU FIND.
Tracks: / Take what you find / Killer barracuda / Way with ladies / Love's not the question / Last of the lovers / One I sing my love songs to / Wizard in the wind / All I really need is you / Midnight sunshine / That plane.
LP: . . . . **EST 12068**

WE'LL SING IN THE SUNSHINE.
Tracks: / Ready or not / All I ever need / Poor little fool / One after 909 / I'd rather be alone / Lady of the night / We'll sing in the sunshine / Blue / If I ever had to say goodbye to you / Catch my breath.
LP: . . . . **EST 11759**

Redell, Teddy

ROCKIN' ON THE "88" IN '88.
LP: . . . . **WLP 8933**

TEDDY REDELL IS BACK (New recordings).
Tracks: / Brain cloudy rock / China river / Stop your rolling / Cow cow blues / Roll in my sweet baby's arms / California blues / Teddy's boogie / Country man / Lie, lie, lie / Back in the U.S.A / Pipeliner, 1979 / Too young to die / It'll be me.
LP: . . . . **WLP 8815**

TEDDY REDELL SOUND.
Tracks: / Knocking on the backside / Judy / Gold dust / I see the moon / Pipeliner / I want to hold you / I'll sail my ship alone / Before it began / Don't grow old alone / Can't you see / Crawlin' back to you / Corina Corina.
LP: . . . . **WLP 8813**

Redgrave, Sir Michael

TALES OF HANS CHRISTIAN ANDERSEN (See under Andersen, Hans).

Redgrave, Vanessa

IGOR STRAVINSKY'S THE SOLDIER'S TALE (see under Sting) (Redgrave, Vanessa/ Sting/ Ian McKellan).

Redhead Kingpin

SHADE OF RED, A (Redhead Kingpin & The FBI).
Tracks: / Do the right thing / Pump it hottie / We rock the mic right / Superbad superslick / Redhead one, The / Scram / Kilimanjaro style / Do that dance / Speaking on everything / Shade of red, A.
LP: . . . . **DIX 85**
MC: . . . . **CDIX 85**

Redman, Dewey

IN WILLISAU (Redman, Dewey/Ed Blackwell).
Tracks: / Willisee / We hope / F I / Communication / S 126 T.
LP: . . . . **BSR 0093**

LIVING ON THE EDGE (Redman, Dewey Quartet).
LP: **1201231**

STRUGGLE CONTINUES, THE (Redman, Dewey Quartet).
LP: . . . . **ECM 1225**

Redman, Don

1932-1936 REDMAN'S RED BOOK (Redman, Don & His Orchestra).
LP: . . . . **M 8002**

DOIN' THE NEW LOWDOWN (Redman, Don & His Orchestra).
LP: . . . . **HEP 1004**

DON REDMAN.
LP: . . . . **JR 160**

DON REDMAN ALL-STARS, THE VOL. 1.
LP: **500066**
LP: . . . . **JL 66**

DON REDMAN ALL-STARS, THE VOL. 2 (Redman, Don All Stars).
LP: . . . . **JL 82**

DON REDMAN VOL.3 (Redman, Don & His Orchestra).
LP: . . . . **HEP 1026**

JULY 22ND & 26TH,1957 (Redman, Don All Stars).
Tracks: / Last night in town / To the river / Ballad 'n' bounce / Dreamy melody / Christmas in the valley / Ain't gonna get fooled again / Donnybrook / Peetni petite / My dream of yesterday / Free and easy / Coffee light / Echoing.
LP: . . . . **JV 112**

SHAKIN' THE AFRICAN (Redman, Don & His Orchestra).
LP: . . . . **HEP 1001**

SMOKE RINGS.
LP: . . . . **NOST 7641**

Redman Super Power

REDMAN SUPER POWER VOL.1 (Various artists).
LP: . . . . **REDLP 13**

REDMAN SUPER POWER VOL.2 (Various artists).
LP: . . . . **REDLP 15**

Redpath, Jean

ANGELS HOVERIN' ROUND (Redpath, Jean/Lisa Neustadt).
LP: . . . . **FR 138**

ANYWHERE IS HOME (Redpath, Jean/ Lisa Neustadt).
LP: . . . . **FR 154**

FATHER ADAM.
LP: . . . . **PH 1061**

FINE SONG FOR SINGING, A.
Tracks: / I will make you brooches / Up the Noran water / Captive song of Mary Stuart / Wild geese / Capernaum / Now the die is cast / South wind / Song of wandering aengus / Rohallion / Tryst, The / John O'Dreams / Broom o'the Cowdenknowes / Annie Laurie / Broken brook.
LP: . . . . **PH 1110**
MC: . . . . **CPH 1110**
MC: . . . . **CTRAX 032**

FIRST FLIGHT.
LP: . . . . **R 11556**

JEAN AND GUESTS (Redpath,Jean & Guests).
MC: . . . . **ZCM 293**

JEAN REDPATH.
LP: . . . . **PH 2015**
MC: . . . . **PH 2015C**

LADY NAIRNE (Redpath, Jean & Abby Newton).
LP: . . . . **PH 1087**
MC: . . . . **PH 1087C**

LEAVING THE LAND.
Tracks: / Leaving the land / Miss Admiral Gordon's Strathspey / Scarborough settler's lament / Un Canadien errant / Last minstrel show / Snow goose / Next time round / Sonny's dream / Maggie / Hallow'een / Leaving Lerwick harbour / Now I'm easy / Wild lass, The.
MC: . . . . **CTRAX 029**

LOWLANDS.
LP: . . . . **PH 1066**
MC: . . . . **PH 1066C**

MILLER'S REEL (Redpath, Jean & Rod Paterson).
Tracks: / Mill, mill o, The / My ain kind dearie / This is no my ain lassie / Green grow the rushes-o / O can ye labour lea / My love is like a red, red rose / Ploughman lad, The / Corn rigs / Jamie, come try me / Lass o' ecclefechan, The / Collier laddie, The / Laddie lie near me / Bonnie briar bush, The / O steer her up / My nanie o / My love is like a red, red rose / Here's his health in water / Thou has left me ever, Jamie / Wantonness / Mill, mill o, The (version).
LP: . . . . **REH 737**
MC: . . . . **ZCR 737**

MUSIC AND SONGS OF THE SCOTTISH FIDDLE.
Tracks: / Cradle song / Gow's lamentation for Abercarny / Lowlands of Holland, The / Through the wood laddie / Gow's lament for the death of his brother / Willie Duncan / Mrs. Dundas of Arniston / Birks o' Aberfeldy, The / I'm a doun for lack o' Johnnie / Caledonia's wail for Niel Gow / Heiress / Wee bird cam' to our ha' door, A / Highland Harry / Flower o' the Quern / Gow's lament for the death of his second wife.
LP: . . . . **LIFL 7009**
MC: . . . . **LIFC 7009**

SONG OF THE SEALS.
LP: . . . . **PH 1054**
MC: . . . . **PH 1054C**

SONGS OF ROBERT BURNS VOLUME 5.
MC: . . . . **CTRAX 008**
LP: . . . . **TRAX 008**
LP: . . . . **PH 1093**
MC: . . . . **PH 1093C**

SONGS OF ROBERT BURNS VOLUME 4.
Tracks: / Wha is that at my bower door? / Address to the woodlark / There grows a bonie brier-bush / Taylor fell thro' the bed, The / Here's his health in water / Behold, my love / Rattlin' roarin' Willie / Tam glen / Thou hast left me ever, Jamie / I'll ay ca' in by yon toun / Lea rig, The / My collier laddie / O, this is no my ain lassie / O can ye labour lea / Long winter night, A.
LP: . . . . **TRAX 007**

MC: CTRAX 007
LP: PH 1072
MC: PH 1072C

SONGS OF ROBERT BURNS VOLUME 7.
Tracks: / Mauchline lady, The / O, merry hae I been / Gallant weaver, The / Young highland rover, The / Cauld is the e'enin blast / My father was a farmer / My love / She's but a lassie yet / Ode to Spring / O' guid ale comes / Bonnie lass o' Albanie / O, for ane-and-twenty, Tam / Where are the joys.
MC: CTRAX 039

SONGS OF ROBERT BURNS VOLUME 2.
LP: TRAX 018
MC: CTRAX 018
LP: PH 1048
MC: PH 1048C

SONGS OF ROBERT BURNS VOLUME 6.
Tracks: / Killiecrankie / Galloway Tam / Srathalan's lament / Fornicator / Here's to thy health / Last may a braw woo'er / Gloomy December / Jamie come try me / White cockade, The / Cardin O'T / Sandy and Jockie / Hey ca' through.
MC: CTRAX 005
LP: TRAX 005

SONGS OF ROBERT BURNS VOLUME 1.
LP: TRAX 017
MC: CTRAX 017
LP: PH 1037
MC: PH 1037C

SONGS OF ROBERT BURNS VOLUME 3.
Tracks: / Lass o' Ecclefechan, The / Banks o' Doon, The / Slave's lament / O fare ye weel my auld wife / Belles of Mauchline, The / Duncan Davidson / Ploughman, The / Phillis the fair / Deuk's dang o'er my daddie, The / Will ye go the Indies, my Mary / Song, composed in August / Reel o' Stumpie, The / Green grow the rushes-o.
MC: CTRAX 006
LP: TRAX 006
LP: PH 1071
MC: PH 1071C

THERE WERE MINSTRELS.
Tracks: / Dumbarton's drums / Rattlin' roarin' Willie / My love she's but a lassie yet / Robin Shure in hairst / West Virginia mine disaster / Gilderoy / Sheath and knife / Yellow yorlin / Rob Roy / No, sir / Clerk Cloven / Caroline of Edinburgh town / Davie & Jeannie.
LP: LER 2106

Redriff Primary School

CHILDREN'S SINGING GAMES.
LP: IMPA 101

Reds

REDS.
LP: AMLH 64772

STRONGER SILENCE.
Tracks: / Danger / Stronger silence / Try it on you / Don't let go / It's not the same thing / I don't know / Do you play the game / Dilling you / No more / Driving me crazy / Just a second / Signal.
LP: KVL 9005

Reds (film)

REDS (Film Soundtrack) (Stephen Sondheim/ Dave Grusin).
LP: CBS 70213

Redskins

NEITHER WASHINGTON NOR MOSCOW.
LP: FLP 1
MC: FC 1

Redway, Mike

MY KINDA MUSIC.
Tracks: / You'll never know / More I see you, The.
LP: GALP 105
MC: ZC GALP 105

OUR ANNIVERSARY OF LOVE.
LP: AVECCA 004

THOSE BEAUTIFUL BALLAD YEARS.
Tracks: / Lark in the clear air / Rose of Killarney / Passing by / On the banks of the Wabash / I love the moon / Barbara Allen / I dream of Jeannie with the light brown hair / Just awearyin' for you / I'll be your sweetheart / When you and I were young Maggie / Mighty like a rose.
LP: RKL 7
MC: RKC 7

Redwood (label)

REDWOOD COLLECTION - A SAMPLER (Various artists).
LP: RR 411

Redwoods

PLEASE....
Tracks: / Don't mind / (Please be) Good to me / Sunday / At the hop / Separates / I know, it's wrong, you're gone / Hint of irony / I belong to you / Story bedtime / Much better now....
LP: DLLP 17

Reece, Colin

WELL KEPT SECRETS.
LP: DAM 009

Reece, Dizzy

BLOWIN' AWAY (Reece, Dizzy & Ted Curson).
LP: IP 7716

MANHATTAN PROJECT.
LP: BH 7001

MOOSE THE MOOCHE.
Tracks: / Stella by starlight / Walkin' / All the things you are.
LP: DS 839

POSSESSION, EXORCISM, PEACE.
LP: HD 6619

PROGRESS REPORT.
Tracks: / Now / Basie line / Gipsy, The / Scrapple from the apple / Rivera / Chorous / You came along from out of nowhere / Momentum.
LP: JASM 2013

Reed, A.C.

I'M IN THE WRONG BUSINESS.
Tracks: / I'm in the wrong business / I can't go on this way / Fast food Annie / This little voice / My buddy buddy friends / She's fine / These blues is killing me / Miami strut / Things I want you to do, The / Don't drive drunk / Hard times / Going to New York / Moving out of the ghetto.
LP: SNTF 994

Reed, Blind Alfred

HOW CAN A POOR MAN STAND.
LP: ROUNDER 1001

Reed, Buddy

TOUGH ENOUGH (Reed, Buddy and the Rip It Up's).
Tracks: / (Buddy's) big legged woman / Rock me / Blues for Mud / You so fine / You shop / Rialto rock / Meet me in the moonlight / Sugar bee / Lonely no more / I'm a hog for you (baby) / Kiss my ass.
LP: RL 0085

Reed, Dan

DAN REED NETWORK (Reed, Dan Network).
Tracks: / World has a heart too / Resurrect / Get to you / Baby don't fade / Ritual / Human / Forgot to make her mine / Halfway round the world / Tamin' the wild nights / Rock you all night long / I'm so sorry.
LP: 834 309-1
MC: 834 309-4

HEAT, THE (Reed, Dan Network).
LP: 848855-1
MC: 848855-4

SLAM (Reed, Dan Network).
Tracks: / Make it easy / Slam / Tiger in a dress / Rainbow child / Doin' the love thing / Stronger than steel / Cruise together / Under my skin / Lover / I'm lonely / Please stay / Come back baby / All my lovin' / Seven Sisters Road.
LP: 838 868 1
MC: 838 868 4

Reed, Fred

NORTHUMBRIAN VOICE.
LP: WM 001

Reed, Jerry

20 OF THE BEST: JERRY REED.
Tracks: / Guitar man / U.S. male / Georgia sunshine / When you're hot you're hot / Amos Moses / Ko ko Joe / Smell the flowers / Alabama wild man / You took all the rambling out of me / Uptown poker club / Good woman's love, A / Lord Mr. Ford / Crude oil blues / Friend, A / Mind your love / You got a lock on me / Gator / Sweet love feelings / Eastbound and down / Texas bound and flyin'.
LP: INTS 5117
MC: INTK 5117
LP: NL 89855
MC: NK 89855

HITS OF JERRY REED, THE.
Tracks: / Alabama wild man / Mind your love, Lord, Mr. Ford / Smell the flowers / When you're hot, you're hot / You got a lock on me / Boogie woogie rock and roll / Ko ko Joe / You took all the ramblin' out of me / Uptown poker club, The / Good woman's love, A / Telephone, The / Let's sing our song / Crude oil blues, The / Another puff.
LP: PL 42180
MC: PK 42180

Reed, Jimmy

12 GREATEST HITS.
Tracks: / Sun is shining, The / Honest I do / Down in Virginia / Baby what you want me to do / Found love / Hush hush / Bright lights big city / Close together / Big boss man / Aw shucks / Good lover / Shame shame shame.
LP: TOP 174
MC: KTOP 174

BEST OF JIMMY REED.
2LP: GNPS 2-10006
MCSET: GNP5 2-10006

BOOGIE IN THE DARK.
Tracks: / Honest I do / Oh John / Go on to school / Boogie in the dark / I'm nervous / Caress me baby / My baby's so sweet / Little rain / I was so young / Shame shame shame.
LP: BMM 001

COLD CHILLS 1967-1970.
Tracks: / My baby told me / Just can't sleep at night / If the four winds don't change / I'll be home one day / Honey, it's time for love / Why can't I come in? / Tribute to a friend / Poor country boy / Texas is so doggone big / Cold chills / Somebody help me / Don't cry / Crazy 'bout that miniskirt.
LP: KK 786

FUNKY FUNKY SOUL (Reed, Jimmy & Screamin' Jay Hawkins).
Tracks: / Hard walkin' Hannah / Cry before I go / Can't stand to leave / Big legged woman / Funky funky soul / Africa gone funky / Ashes / I need you / Sweet Ginny.
LP: MAN 5041

GOT ME DIZZY.
Tracks: / I'm a love you / Hush hush / Take out some insurance / I wanna be loved / Caress me baby / Boogie in the dark / I'll change my style / When you're doin' alright / You got me dizzy / Come love / Meet me / Odds and ends / Can't stand to see you go / Going by the river / You don't have to go / Crazy love.
LP: CRB 1028

HIGH AND LONESOME.
LP: CRB 1013

HONEST I DO.
LP: CL 281283
MC: CLMC 9281283

I'M THE MAN (DOWN THERE).
Tracks: / I found my baby / Roll and rhumba / Shoot my baby / Come on baby / Rockin' with Reed / When you left me / State street boogie / Signals of love / I'm the man down there / Tell me you love me / Let's get together / Looking for you baby / Don't think I'm through / When girls do it / Left handed woman / New leaf, A.
LP: CRB 1082

SHAME SHAME SHAME VOL.1.
Tracks: / If you don't want me, baby / I'm leaving / When I woke up / I got to keep rolling / High yellow good lovin' / Cry before I go / Shame shame shame / Life is funny / Run here to me, baby / Two in love / Down at the grocery store / Big legged woman.
LP: KK 781

UPSIDE YOUR HEAD.
Tracks: / Shame shame shame / I'm gonna get my baby / I ain't got you / Ain't that loving you baby / Down the road / Bright lights / Big city / Too much / Big boss man / I'm goin' upside your head / Goo lover / Honest I do / Down in Virginia / Aw Shucks / Hush your mouth / Found love / Baby, what you want me to do? / Going to New York.
LP: CRB 1003
MC: TCCRB 1003

Reed, Les

WORLD OF LOVE (Reed, Les Orchestra).
MCSET: DTO 10073

Reed, Lou

BELLS, THE.
LP: SPART 1093

BERLIN.
Tracks: / Berlin / Lady Day / Men of good fortune / Caroline says / How do you think it feels / Oh Jim / Caroline says II / Kids, The / Bed (The) / Sad song.
LP: NL 84388
MC: NK 84388
LP: RS 1002

BLUE MASK.
Tracks: / My house / Women / Underneath the bottle / Gun / Blue mask / Average guy / Heroine / Waves of fear / Day John Kennedy died / Heavenly arms.
LP: RCALP 6028

CONEY ISLAND BABY.
Tracks: / Crazy feeling / Charley's girl / She's my best friend / Kicks / Gift / Oooh baby / Nobody's business / Coney Island baby.
LP: NL 83807
MC: INTK 5082
MC: NK 83807
LP: RS 1035
LP: INTS 5082

GRANDES EXITOS DE.
LP: NL 42488

GRANDES EXITOS DE VOL.2.
LP: NL 42489

GROWING UP IN PUBLIC.
Tracks: / How do you speak to an angel / My old man / Keep away / Standing on ceremony / So alone / Love is here to stay / Power of positive drinking, The / Smiles / Think it over / Teach the gifted children.
LP: SPART 1131

I CAN'T STAND IT.
Tracks: / Perfect day / Vicious / Men of good fortune / How do you think it feels? / White light / White heat / I can't stand it / Andy's chest / Sally can't dance / Satellite of love / Blue mask.
LP: CL 42841
MC: CK 42841
LP: NL 89312
MC: NK 89312

LEGENDARY HEARTS.
Tracks: / Legendary hearts / Don't talk to me about work / Make up / Martial law / Last shot, The / Turn out the light / Pow wow / Betrayed / Bottoming out / Home of the brave / Rooftop garden.
LP: NL 89843
MC: NK 89843
LP: RCALP 6071

LIVE IN ITALY.
Tracks: / Sweet Jane / I'm waiting for my man / Marshal Law / Satellite of love / Kill your sons / Betrayed / Some kinda love / Sister Ray / Walk on the wild side / Heroin / Sally can't dance.
LP: PL 89156
MC: PK 89156

LIVE: LOU REED.
Tracks: / Walk on the wild side / I'm waiting for the man / Vicious / Oh Jim / Satellite of love / Sad song.
LP: NL 83752
MC: NK 83752
LP: INTS 5071

LOU REED.
Tracks: / I can't stand it / Going down / Walk and talk it / Lisa says / Berlin / I love you / Wild child / Love makes you feel / Ride into the sun / Ocean.
LP: 26 21088
LP: SF 8281

LOU REED BOX SET.
MCSET: NK 74376

LOU REED LIVE.
Tracks: / Vicious / Satellite of love / Walk on the wild side / I'm waiting for the man / Oh Jim / Sad song.
LP: RS 1007

LOU REED & VELVET UNDERGROUND.
Tracks: / I'm waiting for the man / Sister Ray / Lady Godiva's operation / Heroin / Sunday morning / All tomorrow's parties / There she goes again / White light, white heat / Femme fatale.
LP: 231 525 8

MAGIC MOMENTS.
Tracks: / Vicious / Perfect day / Walk on the wild side / Satelite of love / New York telephone conversation / Lady Day / Caroline says / Caroline says (II) / Sad song / Charley's girl / Coney Island baby / Animal language / Kill your sons / Sally can't dance / Ennui / Heroin / White light white heat.
MC: NK 89895

MAN, THE - INTERVIEW PICTURE DISC.
LPPD: VBAK 3003

METAL MACHINE MUSIC.
2LP: PIPDL 023
MC: PIPDM 023

MISTRIAL.
Tracks: / Mistrial / No money down / Outside / Don't hurt a woman / Video violence / Spit it out / Original wrapper / Mama's got a lover / I remember you / Tell it to your heart.
LP: PL 87190
MC: PK 87190
LP: NL 90253
MC: NK 90253

NEW SENSATIONS.
Tracks: / I love you Suzanne / Endlessly jealous / My red joystick / Turn to me / New sensations / Doin the things that we want to / What becomes a legend most / Fly into the sun / My friend George / High in the city / Down at the arcade.
LP: PL 84998
MC: PK 84998

NEW YORK.
Tracks: / Romeo and Juliet / Halloween parade / Dirty boulevard / Endless cycle / There is no time / Last great American whale / Beginning of a great mystery, The / Busload of faith / Sick of you / Hold

on / Good evening Mr. Waldheim / Xmas in February / Strawman / Dime store mystery.
LP: . . . . WX 246
MC: . . . . WX 246 C

NEW YORK SUPERSTAR.
Tracks: / Walk on the wild side / Vicious / Charley's girl / Berlin / Lady Day / Gift / Intro to sweet Jane / Sweet Jane / Caroline says / Billy / Goodnight ladies.
LP: . . . . FA 3164
MC: . . . . TCFA 3164

RETRO.
Tracks: / Walk on the wild side / Satellite of love / I love you Suzanne / Wild child / How do you think it feels / Lady Day / Coney Island baby / Sweet Jane (live) / Vicious / Sally can't dance / Berlin / Caroline says II / Perfect day / Kill your sons / White light/White heat (live) / I'm waiting for the man (CD only.) / Heroin (CD only.).
LP: . . . . PL 90389
MC: . . . . PK 90389

ROCK AND ROLL DIARY, 1967-1980.
Tracks: / Waiting for the man / White light / White heat / I heard her call my name / Pale blue eyes / I'm beginning to see the light / Sweet Jane / Rock and roll / Heroin / Femme fatale / Walk on the wild side / Berlin / Men of good fortune / Kids, The / Coney Island baby / Temporary thing / All through the night / So alone / How do you speak to an angel? / Keep away / Street hassle.
2LP: . . . . DARTY 8

ROCK AND ROLL HEART.
Tracks: / I believe in love / Banging on my drum / Follow the leader / You wear it so well / Ladies pay / Rock and roll heart / Temporary thing.
LP: . . . . ARTY 142

ROCK GALAXY.
Tracks: / Vicious / Andy's chest / Perfect day / Hangin' around / Walk on the wild side / Make up / Satellite of love / Wagon wheel / New York telephone conversation / I'm so free / Goodnight ladies / Berlin / Lady Day / Men of good fortune / Caroline says / How do you think it feels? / Oh Jim / Kids, The / Bed, The / Sad song.
LP: . . . . CL 43214

ROCK 'N' ROLL ANIMAL.
Tracks: / Intro- sweet Jane / White light, white heat / Heroin / Lady Day / Rock and roll.
LP: . . . . NL 83664
MC: . . . . NK 83664
LP: APL1 0472

SALLY CAN'T DANCE.
Tracks: / Ride, Sally, ride / Animal language / Baby face / NY stars / Kill your sons / Billy / Sally can't dance / Ennui.
MC: . . . . NK 90308
LP: . . . . NL 90308
LP: APL1 0611

SONGS FOR DRELLA (See under Cale, John) (Reed, Lou and John Cale).

SOUL MAN (see under Moore, Sam) (Reed, Lou & Sam Moore).

STREET HASSLE.
Tracks: / Gimme some good times / Dirt / Street hassle / I wanna be black / Real good time together / Shooting star.
LP: . . . . SPART 1045
LP: . . . . AL 8499

TAKE NO PRISONERS.
Tracks: / Sweet Jane / I wanna be black / Satellite of love / Pale blue eyes / Berlin / I'm waiting for the man / Coney Island baby / Street hassle / Walk on the wild side / Leave me alone.
LP: . . . . XL 03066

TALK ON THE WILD SIDE, A.
LP: . . . . POW 006

TRANSFORMER.
Tracks: / Vicious / Andy's chest / Perfect day / Hangin' around / Walk on the wild side / Make up / Satellite of love / Wagon wheel / New York telephone conversation / I'm so free / Goodnight ladies.
LP: . . . . NL 83806
MC: . . . . NK 83806
LP: . . . . PC 9852
LP: . . . . INTS 5061
MC: . . . . PK 2095
LP: . . . . SP 4807

WALK ON THE WILD SIDE (Best of Lou Reed).
Tracks: / Satellite of love / Wild child / I love you / How do you think it feels? / New York telephone conversation / Walk on the wild side / Sweet Jane / White light, white heat / Sally can't dance / Nowhere at all / Coney Island baby / Vicious.
LP: . . . . NL 83753
MC: . . . . NK 83753
LP: . . . . PL 12001
MC: . . . . PK 12001

WITH THE VELVET UNDERGROUND 1969.
Tracks: / Beginning to see the light / Femme fatale / Heroin / I'll be your mirror / I'm waiting for the man / Lisa says / New age / Ocean / Over you / Pale blue eyes / Rock 'n' roll / Some kinda love / Sweet Bonnie Brown / It's just too much / Sweet Jane / We're gonna have a real good time together / What goes on / White light / White heat.
2LP: 6641 900

Reed, Lulu

I'M GONE, YES I'M GONE.
Tracks: / Sick and tired / Jealous love / Watch dog / You key don't fit it no more / Going back to Mexico / Bump on a log / Three men / Sample man / Troubles on your mind / Wild stage of life, The / Ain't it a shame / Without love / I'm gone, yes I'm gone / Why don't you come on home / I'll upset you baby / Caught me when my love was down.
LP: . . . . SING 1157

Reed, Ola Belle

OLA BELLE REED.
LP: . . . . ROUNDER 0021

OLA BELLE REED & FAMILY (Reed, Ola Belle & family).
LP: . . . . ROUNDER 0077

Reed, Preston

PLAYING BY EAR.
LP: . . . . FF 324

POINTING UP.
LP: . . . . FF 244

ROAD LESS TRAVELLED, THE.
LP: . . . . FF 423

Reed, Tony

BLACK BOOK.
LP: . . . . CRELP 666

Reed, Waymon

46TH & 8TH.
LP: . . . . AH 10

Reedy, Winston

CROSS OVER.
Tracks: / Romantic girl / Word, The / Love is a treasure / Judah's dream / For the music / Ambition / Humours of love / Baby love / Superstar / World crisis.
LP: . . . . LPDEP 7
MC: . . . . CADEP 7

DIM THE LIGHT.
LP: . . . . ONLP 001

Reegs

RETURN OF THE SEA MONKEY.
LP: . . . . ILLUSION 029
MC: . . . . ILLCASS 029

Reel Murder (bk)

REEL MURDER (Marian Babson) (Leach, Rosemary (nar)).
MCSET: . . . . CAT 4025

Reel World String Band

IN GOOD TIME.
LP: . . . . FF 335

Reeman, Douglas

IRON PIRATE, THE (Massey, Daniel (nar)).
MCSET: . . . . LFP 7349

Rees, Angharad (nar)

EMMA VOL. 1 (See under Austen, Jane).

EMMA VOL. 2 (See under Austen, Jane).

Reese, Della

3 GREAT GIRLS (see Three great girls) (Reese, Della/Ann Margret/Kitty Kallen).

CLASSIC DELLA.
Tracks: / Story of a starry night / These are the things I love / If you are but a dream / My reverie / Take my heart / Stranger in Paradise / Gone / Serenade / Moon love / Softly my love / Till the end of time / Don't you know?.
LP: . . . . INTS 5046
MC: . . . . INTK 5046

DELLA.
Tracks: / Lady is a tramp, The / If I could be with you one hour tonight / Let's get away from it all / Thou swell / You're driving me crazy / Goody goody / And the angels sing / Baby won't you please come home? / I'm beginning to see the light / I'll get by / Blue skies / Someday.
LP: . . . . NL 89054
MC: . . . . NK 89054

DELLA BY STARLIGHT.
Tracks: / Touch of your lips / He was too good to me / That old feeling / I had the craziest dream / I wish I knew / Lamplight / How did he look ? / More than you know / These follish things / Deep in a dream / Embraceable you / Two sleeepy people.
LP: . . . . INTS 5194

DELLA DELLA CHA-CHA-CHA.
Tracks: / Diamonds are a girl's best friend / Come on...a my house / Why don't you do right / My heart belongs to daddy / Let's do it / Whatever Lola wants (Lola gets) / Daddy / Tea for two / Always true to you in my fashion / It's so nice to have a man around the house / There's a small hotel / Love for sale.
LP: . . . . NL 90039
MC: . . . . NK 90039

I LIKE IT LIKE DAT.
Tracks: / Travellin' light / If it's the last thing I do / T'aint nobody's business if I do / Ev'ry evening blues / Stranger on earth / I ain't ready for that / Fool that I am / If I ever get to heaven / Drinking again / Man with a horn / In the dark / Nobody knows the way I feel this morning.
LP: . . . . JASM 1504

SURE LIKE LOVIN' YOU.
Tracks: / When I fall in love / That's all / Come rain or come shine / Love me tender / Touch me again / Morning comes too soon / Air that I breathe, The / Wrapped up in the comfort of you / Two together / Sure like lovin' you / It's over now.
LP: . . . . PRCV 126

THREE GREAT GIRLS (Reese, Della/ Ann Margret/Kitty Kallen).
Tracks: / How lovely to be a woman / I'm in the mood for love / Begin the beguine / Misty / What is there to say / When a woman loves a man / Best is yet to come, The / I really don't want to know / It amazes me / True / I hadn't anyone till you / I get the blues when it rains.
LP: . . . . NL 89455
MC: . . . . NK 89455

Reeve, Douglas

PACK UP YOUR TROUBLES.
LP: . . . . CF 255

PERFECT COMBINATION, A.
Tracks: / Pack up your troubles in your old kit bag / Old comrades / Bal masque / Ragtime memories / Bye bye blackbird / If you knew Susie / Swanee / Waiting for the Robert E. Lee / California here I come / Forgotten dreams / Music of Richard Rodgers / Lover / Mountain greenery / Sound of music, The / June is bustin' out all over / Oklahoma / Trumpet tune and air / Song for the seaside / Stranger on the shore / On the crest of a wave / Sussex by the sea / Song of paradise / Pirates of Penzance (selection) / Lost chord, (The) / Bunch of evergreens, A / Threepenny opera, Theme from / When you're smiling / Somebody stole my gal / Sunshine of your smile, The / Tiger rag.
LP: . . . . GRS 1098

SAY IT WITH MUSIC.
Tracks: / Colonel Bogey / Gold and silver / Tik tak polka / All in the April evening / Umbrella man / Run rabbit run / Underneath the arches / South Rampart Street parade / Bless this house / Grand march from Aida / Temptation rag / As time goes by / I can't give you anything but love / Nobody's sweetheart / Beer barrel polka / Say it with music / Girl that I marry, The / Everybody's doing it now / Pretty girl is like a melody, A / Cheek to cheek / Alexander's ragtime band / There's no business like show business.
LP: . . . . GRS 1137

Reeves, Del

BABY I LOVE YOU.
Tracks: / One life to live / You're not the changing kind / Love love love / Baby I love you / My baby loves to rock and roll / Cool drool / Trot, The / Two teen hearts / He stands real tall / Empty house / As far as I can see / Be quiet mind / Love she offered me / I closed my eyes and saw the light / Only girl I can't forget, The / Once a fool.
LP: . . . . BFX 15269

Reeves, Dianne

DIANNE REEVES.
Tracks: / Sky islands / I'm OK / Better days / Harvest time / Chan's song / Yesterdays / I got it bad and that ain't good / That's all.
LP: . . . . BLJ 46906
MC: . . . . TCBLJ 46906

FOR EVERY HEART.
LP: . . . . PA 203

I REMEMBER.
Tracks: / Afro blue / Nearness of you, The/Misty / I remember / Love for sale / Softly as in the morning sunrise / Like a lover / How high the moon / You taught my heart to sing / For all we know.
LP: B1 90264

NEVER TOO FAR.
Tracks: / Hello, haven't I seen you before / Never too far / Come in / How long / Eyes on the prize / Bring me joy / Fumilayo / More to love (than making love) / We belong together / Company.
LP: . . . . DIANNE 1
LP: 792 401 1
MC: . . . . TCDIANNE 1
MC: 792 401 4

WELCOME TO MY LOVE.
MC: . . . . PAC 8026
LP: . . . . PA 8026

Reeves, Jack

WHO WILL BUY THE WINE.
Tracks: / Wabash cannonball / Extra love affair / Me and Bobbie McGee / Sing me back home / Come on out and see the sunshine / Truck drivin' man and wife / Why not take the time / Happy travellin' man / Message from home / Truck drivin' man's comin' home.
LP: . . . . MAN 5037

Reeves, James

CASTLE OF THE GOLDEN SUN, THE
See also Georgina Melville.
MC: . . . . TTC/K 10

Reeves, Jim

12 SONGS FOR CHRISTMAS.
Tracks: / Jingle bells / Blue Christmas / Senor Santa Claus / Old Christmas card, An / Merry Christmas polka, The / White Christmas / Silver bells / C-H-R-I-S-T-M-A-S / O little town of Bethlehem / Mary's boy child / O come all ye faithful / Silent night.
LP: . . . . CDS 1160
MC: . . . . CAM 463
LP: . . . . CL 81927
MC: . . . . CK 81927
MC: . . . . NK 82758

20 OF THE BEST: JIM REEVES.
Tracks: / I won't come in while he's there / Storm, The / I heard a heart break last night / That's when I see the blues / When you're gone / When two worlds collide / Nobody's fool / Angels don't lie / Gypsy feel / Writing on the wall / Missing you / Am I that easy to forget / I'd fight the world / It's nothin' to me / Little ole dime / You're the only good thing that's happened to me / Don't let me cross over / Oh, how I miss you tonight / Take me in your arms and hold me / Have you ever been lonely.
LP: . . . . NL 898 52
MC: . . . . NK 898 52

25 ALL TIME WORLD WIDE FAVOURITES - VOL 2.
Tracks: / Welcome to my world / I love you because / I can't stop loving you / You're the only good thing (that's happened) / I won't forget you / Mary's boy child / When two worlds collide / Is it really over / I won't come in while he's there / In the misty moonlight / Fool such as I, A / Angels don't lie / Stranger's just a friend, A / Distant drums / Nobody's fool / That's when I see the blues (in your pretty) / How can I write on paper / When you are gone / But you love me daddy / Oh how I miss you tonight / Not until the next time / Guilty / Storm, The / My cathedral / Adios amigo.
MC: . . . . DPTK 5003

25 ALL TIME WORLD WIDE FAVOURITES - VOL 1.
Tracks: / There's a heartache following me / Danny boy / Yonder comes a sucker / Four walls / Bimbo / Partners / I'm gonna change everything / I know one / Little ole you / Am I losing you / Billy Bayou / Wreck of the number nine, The / Make the world go away / He'll have to go / Stand at your window / It hurts so much / I'm gettin' better / I fall to pieces / Blizzard / Mexican Joe / Anna Marie / This world is not my home / Just out of reach / Letter to my heart, A / Snow flake.
MC: . . . . DPTK 5002

40 GOLDEN GREATS: JIM REEVES.
2LP: . . . . ADEP 16

50 ALL TIME WORLD FAVOURITES.
Tracks: / There's a heartache following me / Mexican Joe / Yonder comes a sucker / Four walls / Bimbo / Partners / I'm gonna change everything / Anna Marie / I know one / Little ole you / Billy Bayou / This world is not my home / He'll have to go / Stand at your window / Am I losing you / I'm gettin' better / I fall to pieces / Blizzard / Just out of reach / Wreck of the number nine, The / Make the world go away / It hurts so much / Letter to my heart, A / Danny boy / Snow flake / Welcome to my world / I love you because / I can't stop loving you / You're the only good thing / I won't forget you / When two worlds collide / Guilty / Is it really over / I won't come in while he's in there / In the misty moonlight / Fool such as I, A / Angels don't lie / Mary's boy child / Distant drums / Nobody's fool / That's when I see the blues / How can I

write on paper (what I feel in ...) / When you are gone / But you love me daddy / Oh, how I miss you tonight / Not until the next time / Stranger's just a friend, A / Storm, The / My cathedral / Adios amigo.
LPS: . . . . **LSP 7403**

ABBOTT RECORDINGS, VOL 1.
Tracks: / I'll follow you / Where does a broken heart go? / Drinking tequila / Mexican Joe / Give me one more kiss / Shall we gather at the river? / Hillbilly waltz / Butterfly love / It's hard to love just one / Penny candy / Gypsy heart / Red eyed and rowdy / Beatin' on the ding dong / Wilder your heart beats the sweeter you love / Are you the one? / El rancho del Rio / Bimbo.
LP: . . . . **INTS 5222**
MC: . . . . **INTK 5222**
LP: . . . . **NL 89052**
MC: . . . . **NK 89052**

ABBOTT RECORDINGS, VOL 2.
Tracks: / Let me remember / How many? / Woman's love / Tahiti / Padre of Old San Antone / My rambling heart / Echo bonita / Each beat of my heart / Then I'll stop loving you / Let me love you just a little / I could cry / Heartbreaking baby / Wagonload of love / You're the sweetest thing / What were you doing last night? / Whispering willow / I'll always love you / Spanish violins / If you love me don't leave me / I'll tell the world I love you.
LP: . . . . **NL 89311**
MC: . . . . **NK 89311**
LP: . . . . **INTS 5223**

ACCORDING TO MY HEART.
LP: . . . . **INTS 1013**

BEST OF JIM REEVES.
Tracks: / He'll have to go / Four walls / Guilty / Blue boy / I'm getting better / Blizzard / Am I losing you? / Billy bayou / Anna Marie / Adios amigo / Danny boy.
LP: . . . . **NL 83678**
MC: . . . . **NK 83678**
LP: . . . . **RD 7666**
LP: . . . . **SF 8147**
MC: . . . . **PK 11506**

BIMBO.
Tracks: / Bimbo / Echo bonita / Penny candy / Mexican Joe / Then I'll stop loving you / Drinking tequila.
LP: . . . . **CDN 1080**

COLLECTION: JIM REEVES.
Tracks: / From a jack to a king / Fool such as I / White cliffs of Dover, The / I can't stop loving you / Moonlight and roses / That's my desire / You belong to me / Blue skies / Carolina moon / Not until the next time / When two worlds collide / Moon river / Adios amigo / I love you because / Welcome to my world / I won't forget you / There's a heartache following me / It hurts so much / I won't come in while he's there / You're the only good thing that's happened to me / Is it really over / But you love me, daddy / Shifting, whispering sands / Danny boy.
2LP: . . . . **CCSLP 183**
MCSET: . . . . **CCSMC 183**

COUNTRY GENTLEMAN.
LP: . . . . **NE 1088**

COUNTRY SIDE OF JIM REEVES.
Tracks: / Railroad bum / Blue side of lonesome / When two worlds collide / Waiting for a train / My lips are sealed / Yonder comes a sucker.
LP: . . . . **CDS 1000**
LP: . . . . **CDN 5100**

COUNTRY STORE: JIM REEVES.
LP: . . . . **CST 21**
MC: . . . . **CSTK 21**

DISTANT DRUMS.
Tracks: / Distant drums / I won't forget you / Is it really over? / I missed me / Snowflake / Letter to my heart, A / Losing your love / This is it / Not until the next time / Good morning self / Where does a broken heart go? / Overnight / Gods were angry with me, The.
LP: . . . . **NL 89317**
MC: . . . . **NK 89317**
LP: . . . . **RD 7814**
LP: . . . . **SF 7814**
MC: . . . . **VCS 67119**

DON'T LET ME CROSS OVER.
Tracks: / Don't let me cross over / When two worlds collide / I fall to pieces / Take me in your arms and hold me / Oh how I miss you tonight / Guilty / I'm a fool to care / I've enjoyed as much of this as I can stand / Have you ever been lonely / After loving you.
MC: . . . . **PK 13454**

FABULOUS JIM REEVES, THE.
Tracks: / Welcome to my world / Yonder comes a sucker / According to my heart / Bimbo / Mexican Joe / Am I losing you / One dozen roses / Anna Marie / Golden memories and silver tears / Gypsy feet / Have I told you lately that I love you / Scarlet ribbons / He'll have to go / Blizzard / I fall to pieces / Distant drums / Storm, The / Memories are made of this / Make the world go away / Missing you / Roses are red / Four walls / Hawaiian wedding song / How can I write on paper (what I feel in my heart).
2LP: . . . . **CR 048**
MCSET: . . . . **CRT 048**

FOREVER.
Tracks: / Make the world go away / Deep dark water / Welcome to my world / One dozen roses / Hawaiian wedding song / Penny Candy / Four walls / I won't forget you / Wreck of the number nine, The / Missing you / Bimbo / When you are gone / Angels don't lie / According to my heart / Missing angel / Auf wiederseh'n sweetheart / Memories are made of this / Guilty / Have I told you lately that I love you / Distant drums / Gypsy feet / Storm, The / Scarlet ribbons / But you love me daddy / He'll have to go / Roses are red / Is it really over / Blizzard / Am I losing you / Mexican Joe / You're the only good thing that's happened to me / Crying in my sleep.
2LP: . . . . **NL 89366**
MCSET: . . . . **NK 89366**

GENTLEMAN JIM.
Tracks: / Memories are made of this / Roses are red / After loving you / Waltzing on top of the world / When you are gone / Just out of reach / I love you because / I'd fight the world / One that got away, The / Once upon a time / I never pass there anymore.
LP: . . . . **SF 7541**
LP: . . . . **RD 7541**
MC: . . . . **PK 11533**

GIRLS I HAVE KNOWN.
Tracks: / Marie / Mona Lisa / My Juanita / Charmaine / Margie / Anna Marie / Sweet Sue / Linda / Ramona / Maria Elena / My Mary / Goodnight Irene.
LP: . . . . **NL 89996**
MC: . . . . **NK 89996**
LP: . . . . **INTS 1256**

GOD BE WITH YOU.
Tracks: / How long has it been / Teach me how to pray / Padre of Old San Antone / Precious memories / God be with you till we meet again / It is no secret.
LP: . . . . **CDS 1092**
LP: . . . . **RD 7636**

GOLDEN RECORDS (IMPORT).
LP: . . . . **NL 89340**
MC: . . . . **NK 89340**
MC: . . . . **CAM 449**
LP: . . . . **CDS 1145**

GOOD 'N' COUNTRY.
Tracks: / Don't let me cross over / Talking walls, The / Little ole dime / World you left behind, The / You kept me awake last night / I've enjoyed as much of this as I can stand.
LP: . . . . **CDM 1075**
LP: . . . . **CDN 5114**

GREATEST HITS: PATSY CLINE & JIM REEVES (see Cline, Patsy) (Reeves, Jim/ Patsy Cline).

HAVE I TOLD YOU LATELY THAT I LOVE YOU.
Tracks: / Have I told you lately that I love you? / Waltzing on top of the world / Roly poly / Beyond the shadow of a doubt / Your old love letters / Highway to nowhere.
LP: . . . . **CDM 1049**
LP: . . . . **CDN 5112**

HE'LL HAVE TO GO (LP).
LP: . . . . **RD 27176**

HIS BEST LOVE SONGS.
LP: . . . . **CDS 1224**
MC: . . . . **CAM 1224**

HITS OF JIM REEVES, THE.
Tracks: / Am I that easy to forget / Gypsy feet / Missing you / You belong to me / Nobody's fool / Writing's on the wall, The / I'd fight the world / I love you because / You'll never know / Angels don't lie / That's when I see the blues / When two worlds collide / When you are gone / Why do I love you (melody of love).
LP: . . . . **PL 42179**
MC: . . . . **PK 42179**

I LOVE YOU BECAUSE.
Tracks: / When two world's collide / Take me in your arms and hold me / You're free to go / I won't come in while he's there / From a Jack to a king / I love you because / Shifting whispering sands, The / I know one / Fool such as I, A / Someday (you'll want me to want you).
LP: . . . . **PL 11224**
MC: . . . . **PK 11224**

I LOVE YOU MORE (Live).
Tracks: / If you were only mine / I love you more / Have I told you lately that I love you / Everywhere you go / Sweet evening breeze / Oklahoma hills where I was born, The / Evening prayer, An / Dear hearts and gentle people / I've lived a lot in my time / If heartaches the fashion / Home / How's the world treating you / I'm beginning to forget you / Rolypoly / Wind up, The / Your old love letters / Till the end of the world / Making believe / Just call me lonesome / Highway to nowhere / Beyond the shadow of a doubt.
LP: . . . . **ATOM 3**
MC: . . . . **CATOM 3**

I'LL ALWAYS LOVE YOU.
Tracks: / I'll always love you / Spell of the Yukon / I'm a fool to care / Streets of Laredo / Wreck of the number nine, The / White cliffs of Dover, The.
LP: . . . . **CDS 1163**

INTERNATIONAL JIM REEVES.
Tracks: / Auf wiederseh'n sweetheart / Old Kalahari, The / White cliffs of Dover, The / True / I'm crying again / Guilty / Blue Canadian Rockies / Hawaiian wedding song / You are my love / Heartbreak in silhouette / Tahiti / Golden memories and silver tears.
LP: . . . . **RD 7577**
MC: . . . . **PK 11536**

INTIMATE JIM REEVES, THE.
LP: . . . . **RD 27193**

IT'S NOTHIN' TO ME.
Tracks: / It's nothin' to me / You are my love / Talking walls, The / Little ole you / Trying to forget / World you left behind, The / Crying is my favourite mood / Gypsy feet / Once upon a time / There's that smile again / Deep dark water.
LP: . . . . **PL 12309**
MC: . . . . **PK 12309**

JIM REEVES.
Tracks: / You're the only good thing / Before I died / Little ole dime / There's a heartache following me / Dark moon / Missing angel / Roses / Talking walls, The / I never pass there anymore / There's a new moon over my shoulder.
LP: . . . . **PL 12720**
MC: . . . . **PK 12720**

JIM REEVES AND SOME FRIENDS.
LP: . . . . **SF 8022**

JIM REEVES COLLECTION.
Tracks: / Have I told you lately that I love you? / Letter to your heart / Your old love letters / I love you because / I'm a fool to care / Welcome to my world.
2LP: . . . . **PDA 010**
MCSET: . . . . **PDC 010**

JIM REEVES COLLECTION VOL 2.
Tracks: / Welcome to my world / Danny boy / Letter to my heart, A / Dear hearts and gentle people / I won't forget you / You're the only good thing.
2LP: . . . . **PDA 039**
MCSET: . . . . **PDC 039**

JIM REEVES GOLDEN RECORDS.
LP: . . . . **INTS 1070**

JIM REEVES ON STAGE.
Tracks: / Mexican Joe / Yonder comes a sucker / Four walls / I missed me / Tennessee waltz / I really don't want to know / He'll have to go / Walking the floor over you / There stands the glass / One by one / Guess things happen that way / I want to be with you always / Wildwood flower / Blizzard / Your old love letters / Am I losing you? / Bimbo / Stand at your window / Danny boy.
MC: . . . . **PK 1383**

JIM REEVES WAY, THE.
Tracks: / Make the world go away / In the misty moonlight / You'll never know / There's that smile again / Bolandse nooientjie / It hurts so much / I can't stop loving you / Nickel piece of candy, A / Where do I go to throw a picture away / Maureen / Ek verlang na jou / Somewhere along the line.
LP: . . . . **RD 7694**
MC: . . . . **VCS 67072**

JIM REEVES WRITES YOU A RECORD.
LP: . . . . **SF 8176**

LEGENDARY PERFORMER, A.
Tracks: / Mexican Joe / Yonder comes a sucker / Four walls / Teach me how to pray / He'll have to go / Danny boy / You're slipping away from me / Welcome to my world / Guilty / Roving gambler / I guess I'm crazy / Is it really over / Distant drums.
LP: . . . . **RS 1078**
MC: . . . . **PK 11751**

MAGIC MOMENTS.
Tracks: / He'll have to go / Distant drums / When two worlds collide / I missed me / Blizzard / This is it / Moonlight and roses / You're the only good thing that's happened to me / I love you because / I won't forget you / There's a heartache following me / It hurts so much / Not until the next time / Is it really over? / Snowflake / Guilty / I'd fight the world / Trying to forget / Nobody's fool / Welcome to my world / Four walls / Blue boy / I'm getting better / Am I losing you? / Billy Bayou / Anna Marie / Stand at your window / Adios amigo / Danny boy.
MC: . . . . **NK 89402**

MEMORIES ARE MADE OF THIS.
MC: . . . . **CAM 1228**

MOONLIGHT AND ROSES.
Tracks: / Moonlight and roses / Mexicali rose / Carolina moon / Rosa Rio / Oh what it seemed to be / What's in it for me? / Roses / One dozen roses / Moon river / There's a new Moon over my shoulder / It's only a paper moon / When I lost you.
LP: . . . . **RD 7639**
LP: . . . . **SF 7639**
MC: . . . . **VCS 67037**
LP: . . . . **NL 89016**

MY CATHEDRAL.
LP: . . . . **SF 8146**

MY FRIEND.
LP: . . . . **SF 8258**

OLD TIGE.
Tracks: / Old Tige / Angels don't lie / When two worlds collide / Nobody's fool / What would you do / Read this letter / Writing's on the wall / There's a heartache following me / Wild rose / After loving you / Trying to forget / Seven days.
LP: . . . . **CDS 1216**
MC: . . . . **CAM 1216**
LP: . . . . **INTS 5021**

ON STAGE.
LP: . . . . **SF 8047**

PURE GOLD VOL.1.
Tracks: / Four walls / Goodnight Irene / Melody of love / Auf wiederseh'n sweetheart / Hawaiian wedding song / Welcome to my world / From a jack to a king / My happiness / Mona Lisa / You'll never know.
LP: . . . . **NL 13014**

REMEMBERING (see under Cline, Patsy) (Reeves, Jim/ Patsy Cline).

SONGS FROM THE HEART.
Tracks: / Someday you'll want me to want you / Just call me lonesome / Throw another log on the fire / Fool such as I, A / How's the world treating you? / Dear hearts and gentle people / Till the end of the world / Satan can't help me / May the good Lord bless and keep you / Making believe / Am I losing you? / Scarlet ribbons.
LP: . . . . **CDS 1099**
MC: . . . . **CAM 1099**
MC: . . . . **CAM 437**

SONGS OF LOVE.
Tracks: / You'll never know / Blue skies / Oh what it seemed to be / (It's no) sin / Moon river / You belong to me / White cliffs of Dover / That's my desire / Moonlight and roses / Oh how I miss you tonight.
LP: . . . . **PL 11037**
MC: . . . . **PK 11037**

THERE'S ALWAYS ME.
Tracks: / There's always me / Room full of roses / Moon river / All dressed up and lonely / Blue skies / After loving you / Somewhere along the line / Blue side of lonesome / What would you do / I can't stop loving you.
LP: . . . . **PL 13827**

TOUCH OF SADNESS, A.
Tracks: / Where do I go to throw a picture away? / You kept me awake last night / I'm cryin' again / Oh, how I miss you tonight / Lonesome waltz / Your wedding / When you are gone / Missing you / Honey, won't you please come home? / In a mansion stands my love / I'm glad you're better.
LP: . . . . **SF 7978**
MC: . . . . **PK 11537**

TOUCH OF VELVET, A.
Tracks: / Have you ever been lonely / There's always me / Just walking in the rain / Be honest with me / I fall to pieces / It's no sin / Welcome to my world / Am I that easy to forget / Blue skies / All dressed up and lonely / Wild rose, The / I'm a fool to care.
LP: . . . . **MFP 5775**
MC: . . . . **TCMFP 5775**
LP: . . . . **RD 7521**
LP: . . . . **INTS 1089**

VERY BEST OF JIM REEVES, THE.
Tracks: / He'll have to go / Distant drums / When two world's collide / I missed me / Blizzard / This is it / Moonlight and roses / You're the only good thing that's happened to me / I love you because / I won't forget you / There's heartache following me / I hurt so much to see you go / Not until the next time / It is really over / Snowflake /

Guilty / I'd fight the world / Trying to forget / Nobody's fool / Welcome to my world.
LP: . . . **NL 89017**
MC: . . . **NK 89017**
LP: . . . **RCALP 5047**

VERY BEST OF JIM REEVES, VOL. 2, THE.
Tracks: / Bimbo / Yonder comes a sucker / My lips are sealed / Four walls / Anna Maria / Billy Bayou / (How can I write on paper) What I feel in my heart / Losing your love / Adios amigo / I'm gonna change everything / Blue side of lonesome / I won't come in while he's there / I heard a heart break last night / That's when I see the blues (in your pretty brown eyes) / Angels don't lie / Missing you / How long has it been / This world is not my home / But you love me daddy / Old tige / Jim Reeves medley, The.
MC: . . . **NK 90568**

VERY SPECIAL LOVE SONGS.
Tracks: / I love you because / When two worlds collide / Just out of reach / In the misty moonlight / Fool such as I, A / Am I that easy to forget? / He'll have to go / Moonlight & roses / You're the only good thing / I can't stop loving you / Just call me lonesome / Make the world go away.
LP: . . . **PMP 1016**
MC: . . . **PMPK 1016**
LP: . . . **PFP 1010**
MC: . . . **PFC 1010**
LP: . . . **CBR 1040**

WE THANK THEE.
Tracks: / We thank thee / Have thine own way / Lord the night watch / I'd rather have Jesus / Take my hand precious Lord / This world is not my home.
LP: . . . **CDS 1111**
LP: . . . **RD 7637**

WELCOME TO MY WORLD.
Tracks: / Welcome to my world / Adios amigo / I'm a fool to care / Never take no for an answer / I love you because / Old tige / I could cry.
LP: . . . **CDS 1152**
MC: . . . **CAM 461**

Reeves, Martha

ANTHOLOGY - MARTHA REEVES (Reeves, Martha & The Vandellas).
Tracks: / Come and get these memories / Heatwave / Quicksand / In my lonely room / Dancing in the street / Nowhere to run / You've been in love too long / My baby love me / I'm ready for love / Jimmy Mack / Love bug leave my heart alone / Honey chile / I can't dance to that music you're playing / (We've got) honey love / Forget me not / I gotta let you go / Bless you / In and out of my life.
LP: . . . **STMR 9017**
MC: . . . **CSTMR 9017**
LP: . . . **ZL 72166**
MC: . . . **ZK 72166**

GREATEST HITS: MARTHA & THE VANDELLAS (Reeves, Martha & The Vandellas).
Tracks: / My baby loves me / Come and get these memories / Heatwave / Dancing in the street / Quicksand / Live wire / You've been in love too long / In my lonely room / Love (makes me do foolish things) / Love like yours, A / Nowhere to run / Wild one.
LP: . . . **WL 72089**
MC: . . . **WK 72089**
LP: . . . **STMS 5042**

HEATWAVE (Reeves, Martha & The Vandellas).
Tracks: / Heatwave / Then he kissed me / Hey there, lonely boy / More / Danke schon / If I had a hammer / Hello stranger / Just one look / Wait till my Bobby gets home / My boyfriend's back / Mockingbird / Quicksand.
LP: . . . **STMS 5009**
MC: . . . **CSTMS 5009**
LP: . . . **WL 72070**

Reeves, Reuben 'River'

RIVER BOYS 1929 (Reeves, Reuben 'River' & His Tributaries).
LP: . . . **FJ 126**

Reeve's Tale (bk)

GENERAL PROLOGUE, THE / REEVE'S TALE, THE (see under Chaucer, Geoffrey (aut)).

Reflections

IMAGINATIONS - FURTHER REFLECTIONS (Various artists).
Tracks: / American gigolo: *Various artists* / To the unknown man: *Various artists* / Harry's game, Theme from: *Various artists* / Ordinary people: *Various artists* / Picnic at hanging rock: *Various artists* / Local hero: *Various artists* / Facades: *Various artists* / Song for Guy: *Various artists* / Stranger: *Various* artists / Once upon a time in the west: *Various artists* / Merry Christmas Mr. Lawrence: *Various artists*/ Officer and a gentleman: *Various artists* / Kari: *Various artists* / Ballade pour Adeleine: *Various artists*/ Reilly: *Various artists* / Flight of the condor: *Various artists* / Focus 1: *Various artists* / Concierto de Aranjuez: *Various artists* / Belledonna: *Various artists.*
LP: . . . **CBS 10044**
MC: . . . **40 10044**

LIKE ADAM AND EVE (See under August & Duneen).

REFLECTIONS (Various artists).
Tracks: / Brideshead Revisited: *Various artists* / Chariots of fire: *Various artists* / Flame trees of Thika: *Various artists* / Light of experience: *Various artists* / Cosmos: *Various artists* / Deer hunter: *Various* artists / Bilitis: *Various artists* / Midnight express: *Various artists* / Trois Gymnopedies: *Various artists* / Shepherds song: *Various artists* / Albatross: *Various artists* / Don't cry for me Argentina: *Various* artists / Annie's song: *Various artists* / Samba Pati: *Various artists* / Aria: *Various artists*/ Chi Mai: *Various artists* / Hands and clouds: *Various artists* / Arrival: *Various artists.*
LP: . . . **CBS 10034**
MC: . . . **40 10034**

SLUGS AND TOADS.
Tracks: / Tight rope walker / Zigzagging / Keep it easy / Toy dog ripped by cat / Demon of my desires / Human touch / Interpreter / Oh baby look out / I had love in my hands / Clamming up / Nag takes a ride / Parting.
LP: . . . **BRED 22**

Re-Flex

POLITICS OF DANCING, THE.
Tracks: / Praying to the beat / Hit line / Hurt / Couldn't stand a day / Politics of dancing / Something about you / Pointless / Jungle / Sensitive / Keep in touch.
LP: . . . **EMC 2400181**

Reflex Compilation, A

REFLEX COMPILATION, A Various artists (Various artists).
LP: . . . **LEX 4M**

Reflexionen

REFLEXIONEN LIVE.
LP: . . . **SFP 264**

Reflexus

REFLEXUS DA MAE AFRICA.
MC: . . . **MCT 1076**
LP: . . . **MLPS 1076**

Reform Schoolgirls

REFORM SCHOOLGIRLS (Film soundtrack) (O'Williams, Wendy).
LP: . . . **ZEB 7**

Refugee

AFFAIRS IN BABYLON.
Tracks: / Affairs in Babylon / Thunder of another night / Listen to your heart / Hot words / Dream on Anastasia / Exiles in the dark / No survivors / Body to body / (Jane) Here we go again / These are the good times.
LP: . . . **CHR 1493**

Regal Slip

BANDSTAND.
LP: . . . **DIN 319**

Regan, Joan

JOAN REGAN COLLECTION, THE.
LP: . . . **NRP 102**
MC: . . . **NRTC 102**

Regent Chamber Choir

THORA HIRD'S FAVOURITE HYMNS AND CAROLS.
Tracks: / Praise my soul the king of heaven / Lord's my shepherd, The / Morning has broken / Jerusalem / Onward Christian soldiers / I vow to thee my country / All people that on Earth do dwell / O sacred head / Day thou gavest Lord is ended, The / Abide with me / Ding dong merrily on high / Once in Royal David's city / In dulci jubilo / Rocking / In the bleak mid winter / While shepherd's watch / O little town of Bethlehem / Deck the hall / We wish you a merry Christmas / When I survey the wondrous cross / My song is love unknown / Love divine, all love excelling / City of God / There is a green hill far away / Lead us, heavenly Father, lead us / Jerusalem the golden / Dear Lord and Father / Guide me, o thou great redeemer / O come all ye faithful / Silent night / Sussex carol / God rest ye merry gentlemen / I saw three ships / Shepherd's pipe carol / Coventry carol / Away in a manger / Hark the herald angel sing.
2LP: . . . **TRX 705**
MCSET: . . . **TRXC 705**

Regents

7 TEEN (See under Mobiles/Drowning in Berlin).

Reggae

2 SEXES CLASH (Linval Thompson presents...) (Various artists).
Tracks: / Where do broken hearts go: *Jones, Barbara* / Sweet for my sweets: *Lady Junie* / Moonlight lover: *Jones,* Barbara & Barker B / Raggamuffin love: *Niceness, Tracey & Chris Wayne* / Ebony eyes: *Jones, Barbara* / Mix up: *Little John* / Bless my soul: *Rowe, Michael* / Sing an old song: *King Everal* / If I didn't love you: *Thompson, Linval* / Old pan sound: *King Everal.*
LP: . . . **CSLP 27**
MC: . . . **ZCSLC 27**

6 TRACK HITS: REGGAE CHARTBUSTERS (Various artists).
MC: . . . **7SC 5042**

007 (SHANTY TOWN) (See under Pressure Drop) (Various artists).

16 REGGAE ROCKERS (Various artists).
LP: . . . **TRLS 168**

20 CLASSIC REGGAE TRACKS (Various artists).
Tracks: / Ain't that lovin' you: *Various artists* / Equal rights: *Various artists* / Should I: *Various artists*/ Slave driver: *Various artists* / Milk and honey: *Various artists* / Wolves and leopards: *Various artists*/ Jah love: *Various artists* / Love me always: *Various artists* / Concrete castle king: *Various artists*/ Yabby you: *Various artists* / Money in my pocket: *Various artists* / Man next door: *Various artists*/ Three meals a day: *Various artists* / Home sweet home: *Various artists* / Open your eyes: *Various artists*/ Cup of tea, A: *Various artists* / Oh what a day: *Various artists* / Say what you say: *Various artists*/ Whip them jah: *Various artists* / Stay at home: *Various artists.*
LP: . . . **SMT 002**
MC: . . . **SMC 002**

20 REGGAE BLOCKBUSTERS (Various artists).
MC: . . . **ZCTRL 176**

20 REGGAE BLOCKBUSTERS (Various artists).
LP: . . . **TRLS 176**

20 REGGAE CLASSICS (Various artists).
Tracks: / Red red wine: *Tribe, Tony* / Sweet sensation: *Melodians* / Love of the common people: *Thomas, Nicky*/ Johnny too bad: *Slickers* / Pressure drop: *Maytals* / Liquidator: *Harry J. All Stars* / Skinhead moonstomp: *Simaryp* / Long shot kick de bucket: *Pioneers* / Please don't make me cry: *Groovy, Winston* / Many rivers to cross: *Cliff, Jimmy* / 007 (shanty town): *Dekker, Desmond & The Aces* / Rudy, a message to you: *Livingstone,* Dandy / Version girl: *Friday, Boy* / Cherry oh baby: *Donaldson, Eric* / Fattie fattie: *Eccles, Clancy*/ Keep on moving: *Various artists* / Rivers of Babylon: *Melodians* / Train to Skaville: *Ethiopians.*
LP: . . . **TRLS 222**
MC: . . . **ZCTRL 222**

20 REGGAE CLASSICS VOL.2 (Various artists).
Tracks: / 54-46 was my number: *Maytals* / Phoenix city: *Alphonso, Roland* / Love I can feel: *Holt, John*/ Java: *Pablo, Augustus* / Reggae in your jeggae: *Livingstone, Dandy* / Pop a top: *Capp, Andy* / Double barrel: *Collins, Dave & Ansel* / Wear you to the ball: *U Roy And John Holt* / Herbsman shuffle: *King Stitt* And The Dynamites / Small axe: *Various artists* / Battle axe: *Upsetters* / Israelites: *Dekker, Desmond* & The Aces / Law, The: *Capp, Andy* / Fat man: *Morgan, Derrick* / So easy: *Groovy, Winston* / Whip, The: *Ethiopians* / Pomps and pride: *Maytals* / Further you look, The: *Holt, John* / Return of Django: *Upsetters* / Soul shakedown party: *Marley, Bob & The Wailers* / Fire corner: *King Stitt* / Next corner: *Dynamites.*
LP: . . . **TRLS 224**
MC: . . . **ZCTRL 224**

20 REGGAE CLASSICS VOL.3 (Various artists).
MC: . . . **ZCTRL 256**

ABSOLUTE REGGAE (Various artists).
Tracks: / Everything I own: *Boothe, Ken* / Let your yeah be yeah: *Pioneers, the* / You make me feel: *Gardiner,* Boris / Eighteen with a bullet: *Harriott, Derrick* / Return of Django: *Upsetters* / Love of the common people: *Thomas, Nicky* / Cherry oh baby: *Donaldson, Eric* / Black and white: *Greyhound* / Reggae man: *Dekker, George* / Walk away: *Pierre, Marie* / Rain: *Ruffin, Bruce* / Young gifted and black: *Bob and Marcia*/ Suzanne beware: *Livingstone, Dandy* / Lively up yourself: *Marley, Bob* / Then he kissed me: *Marvels*/ Heart made of stone: *Hall, Audrey* / Johnny too bad: *Slickers* / Many rivers to cross: *Cliff, Jimmy*/ Israelites: *Dekker, Desmond & The Aces* / Oh what a feeling: *Simon, Tito* / Hurt so good: *Cadogan, Susan*/ Rivers of Babylon: *Melodians* / First time ever I saw your face, The: *Griffiths, Marcia* / Help me make it through the night: *Holt, John* / Suzanne beware the devil: *Livingstone, Dandy.*
2LP: . . . **VSOPLP 104**
MC: . . . **VSOPMC 104**

ADAM'S RIB (Various artists).
LP: . . . **ARILP 049**

AFRICA CALLING (See under Africa) (Various artists).

AFRICAN REGGAE (See under Africa) (Various artists).

AGE OF REGGAE (Various artists).
LP: . . . **NG 752**

AGE OF REGGAE VOLUME 2 (Various artists).
Tracks: / Welcome everybody: *Various artists* / Who is the king of kings?: *Various artists* / Zion I love: *Various* artists / Zion high: *Various artists* / One more river to cross: *Various artists* / Try a little love: *Various* artists / One black love: *Various artists* / Hard to believe: *Various artists* / It gwine dreada: *Various artists.*
LP: . . . **NG 509**

BABYLON A FALL DOWN (Various artists).
LP: . . . **TRLS 290**
MC: . . . **ZCTRL 290**

BE THANKFUL - AN ATTACK SAMPLER (Various artists).
LP: . . . **ATLP 115**
MC: . . . **MCAT 115**

BEST OF AND THE REST OF, THE (Greatest original reggae hits) (Various artists).
Tracks: / To be young gifted and black: *Bob & Marcia* / Let your yeah be yeah: *Pioneers* / Everything i own: *Boothe,* Ken / Black pearl: *Faith, Horace* / Love of the common people: *Thomas, Nicky* / Hit the road Jack: *Big* Youth / Pied piper: *Bob & Marcia* / Israelites: *Dekker, Desmond* / Help me make it through the night: *Holt,* John / Liquidator: *Harry J. All Stars* / This monday morning feeling: *Simon, Tito* / You can it if you really want it: *Dekker, Desmond* / Black and white: *Greyhound* / Double barrel: *Collins, Dave & Ansel.*
MC: . . . **ARLC 1006**

BEST OF BEVERLEYS (Masterpieces from the works of Leslie Kong) (Various artists).
LP: . . . **TRLS 199**

BEST OF REGGAE DANCEHALL VOLUME 2 (Various artists).
LP: . . . **FILER 291**
MC: . . . **FILECT 291**

BEST OF STUDIO ONE (Various artists).
LP: . . . **HB 07**
MC: . . . **HBC 07**

BEST OF STUDIO ONE VOL. 2 (Various artists).
LP: . . . **HB 14**
MC: . . . **HBC 14**

BEST OF STUDIO ONE VOL. 3 (Inst. Downbeat) (Various artists).
LP: . . . **HB 38**
MC: . . . **HBC 38**

BLUEBEAT, SKA AND REGGAE REVOLUTION (Various artists).
LP: . . . **SEE 319**

BREAKING DOWN THE BARRIERS WITH SOUND (Vol.1 - Captured by the vibes) (Various artists).
Tracks: / Captured by the vibes: *Robotiks* / Didn't I: *Kofi* / I just want to love you: *Simmonds, Leroy*/ Dancing time: *Aisha* / Roots and culture: *B, Macka* / Let's make it work: *Cross, Sandra* / And now you're gone: *McLean,John* / Baby, baby, my love's all for you: *Tajah, Paulette* / Mellow: *Intense* / Daylight and darkness: *Sister Audrey* / Captured by the dub: *Mad Professor.*
LP: . . . **ARILP 040**

BREAKING THE BARRIERS - VINYL MANIAX PART 3 (Various artists).
LP: . . . **ARILP 046**

BUBBLERS ROCK VOL.1 (Various artists).
LP: . . . **TTLP 3**

BUSTIN' OUT (Various artists).
LP: . . . **VPRL 1046**

CABIN STABBIN (Various artists).
LP: . . . **WALP 006**

CALLING RASTAFARI (Various artists).
LP: . . . **NH 304**

CAN'T DO THE WORK (Various artists).
Tracks: / Can't do the work: *Ranks, Shaba* / Fight over request: *Daddy*

Lizard / Can't wash and cook: *Johnny P* / Jamaican girls: *Irie, Henkel* / She nah tell me no: *Ranks, Nardo* / Inna the business long: *Daddy* Blue / Watch your friends them: *Little Twitch* / You nuh woman yet: *Untouchable Cris* / Version: *Steely & Cleevie*.
LP: UPRL 1045

CATCH THIS BEAT (Rocksteady Years 1966-68) (Various artists).
Tracks: / Train to glory: *Various artists* / Got my bugaloo: *Various artists* / Shake it: *Various artists*/ New boss: *Various artists* / Save a bread: *Various artists* / I'm a winner: *Various artists* / Train is coming: *Various artists* / Swing easy: *Various artists* / Set them free: *Various artists* / Rasta put it on: *Various artists* / Napoleon solo: *Various artists* / River jordan: *Various artists* / I caught you: *Various artists* / Tonight: *Various artists* / Last train to expo 67: *Various artists* / Do I worry: *Various artists*.
LP: IRSP 7
MC: TC IRSP 7

CHAPTER THREE (Various artists).
Tracks: / Chapter three: *African Dub* / Rema dub: *African Dub* / Tribesman rockers: *African Dub* / Freedom call: *African Dub* / Jubilation dub: *African Dub* / Entebbe affair, The: *African Dub* / Angolian chant: *African Dub* / Zion gate: *African Dub* / Jungle dub: *African Dub* / Dub three: *African Dub*.
LP: LIP 12

CHAPTER TWO (African Dub All-Mighty) (Various artists).
LP: JGM 0014

CHECK THE WINNER (Pantomime Instrumental Collection) (Various artists).
LP: GREL 603

CLASSIC LOVERS VOLUME 1 (Various artists).
LP: BJLP 005

CLASSIC ROCKERS (Various artists).
Tracks: / Baby I love you so: *Various artists* / Isn't it time to see: *Te Track* / Can't keep a good man down: *Immortals* / Earth wind and fire: *Blackman, Paul* / Jah in the hills: *Various artists* / Changing world: *Sixteen, Earl* / Blackman's heart: *Delgado, Junior* / Jah say the time has now come: *Mundell, Hugh* / Just as long: *Andy, Horace*.
LP: ILPS 9886

CLASSIC ROCKERS (Various artists).
MC: RLC 002

CLUB PLAYS (Various artists).
LP: Unknown

CLUB REGGAE (Various artists).
LP: TRLS 97

CLUB REGGAE VOL. 1 (Various artists).
Tracks: / Holly holy: *Various artists* / 54-36: *Various artists* / Double barrel: *Various artists* / Rivers of Babylon: *Various artists* / I need your sweet inspiration: *Various artists*.
LP: TBL 159

CLUB REGGAE VOL. 2 (Various artists).
Tracks: / Cherry oh baby: *Various artists* / Sweet Jamaica: *Various artists* / It's too late: *Various artists*/ Small axe: *Various artists* / Knock three times: *Various artists* / My sweet Lord: *Various artists*.
LP: TBL 164

CLUB REGGAE VOL 4 (Various artists).
LP: TBL 188

CLUB REGGAE VOL. 5 (Various artists).
Tracks: / Feeling high: *Various artists* / Nice one Cyril: *Various artists* / Reggae makossa: *Various artists*/ Brother Louie: *Various artists* / Cherry baby: *Various artists*.
LP: TBL 205

COLLECTION OF GOLD CHAPTER 1 (Various artists).
LP: BSMLP 103

COMPUTER CORN (Various artists).
LP: RMM 412

COSMIC FORCE DANCEHALL VOL 1 (Various artists).
LP: CFR 8002

COUGHING UP FIRE (Saxon studio international) (Various artists).
LP: LICKWOOD 1
MC: C-LICKWOOD 1

CREATION ROCKERS, VOL.1 (Various artists).
LP: TRLS 180

CREATION ROCKERS, VOL.2 (Various artists).
LP: TRLS 181

CREATION ROCKERS, VOL.3 (Various artists).
LP: TRLS 182

CREATION ROCKERS, VOL.4 (Various artists).
LP: TRLS 183

CREATION ROCKERS, VOL.5 (Various artists).
LP: TRLS 184

CREATION ROCKERS, VOL.6 (Various artists).
LP: TRLS 185

CRUCIAL COLLECTION (Reggae Superstars) (Various artists).
LP: VSLP 4028

CRUCIAL REGGAE (Various artists).
Tracks: / Music is my desire: *Moses, Pablo* / New age music: *Inner Circle* / Just like that: *Toots & The* Maytals / Saturday evening: *Third World* / Reggae fever: *Steel Pulse* / One love jamdown: *Various artists*/ Rainbow culture: *Aswad* / Jogging: *McGregor, Freddie* / Happiness: *Uhuru* / Some guys have all the luck: *Tucker, Junior*.
LP: ILPS 9640
LP: ILPS 9730

CSA COLLECTION VOL.1 (Reggae music all night) (Various artists).
Tracks: / Tu sheng peng: *Brown, U* / Unity is strength: *Chaplin, Charlie & Don Carlos* / Rich man poor man: *Prophet, Michael* / Automatic boom: *Naptali, Raymond* / Out a hand: *Buro* / Saturday night at the movies: *Sinbad*, Captain & Little John / Water Jelly: *Metro, Peter* / Ain't nobody love nobody/Girl it's over: *Viceroys* / True love: *Undivided Roots* / Picture on the wall: *Holt, John* / Burning sun: *Natural Ites* / Nice time (Late night blues): *Carlos, Don*.
LP: CSLP 9

CSA COLLECTION VOL.2 (Various artists).
LP: CSLP 17

CSA COLLECTION VOL.3 (Chant rub-a-dub) (Various artists).
Tracks: / Metric system: *Metro, Peter* / Walk with jah love: *Brown, U* / Sammy dead: *Sinbad, Captain & Little* John / If you break the curfew: *Smalling, Milton* / Gwan go do it: *Natural Ites* / My love: *Viceroys*/ Betcha by golly wow: *Dunkley, Errol* / You move me: *Douglas, Keith* / Chant rub-a-dub: *Campbell, Al*/ Give me: *Tuff, Tony* / Without love: *Tamlins* / How can I: *Holt, John* / Carrot and onion: *Anthony, Pad* / Picture on the wall: *Natural Ites*.
LP: CSLP 20

D J GOVERNMENT (Various artists).
LP: DSR 9897

DANCE ALL NIGHT (Various artists).
LP: TRLS 287
MC: ZCTRL 287

DANCE HALL LIFE (Various artists).
2LP: Unknown

DANCE HALL MASTERS VOL.1 (Various artists).
LP: DGLP 01

DANCE HALL MASTERS VOL.2 (Various artists).
LP: DGLP 009

DANCE HALL SESSION (Various artists).
LP: RASSO 9001

DANCE HALL SHOWCASE VOL.1 (Various artists).
MC: MDHSC 1
LP: MDHS 1

DANCE HALL SHOWCASE VOL.2 (Various artists).
LP: MDHS 2
MC: MDHSC 2

DANCE HALL SHOWCASE VOL.3 (Various artists).
Tracks: / No jolly pals: *Minott, Echo* / Don't let me down: *French, Robert* / Don't let me down (dub): *Various* artists / Wine your body: *Various artists* / Flood Ina Jamdown: *Junior Wilson* / Ragamuffin beat: *Crew H C F* / Rock and come in: *Various artists* / Rock and come in dub: *Asher, Tony* / Prod: *Henry, Witty*.
LP: MDGH 3
MC: MDHSC 3

DANCE HALL THRILLER (Various artists).
LP: BLKMX 01

DANCEHALL REGGAE - A NEW BEGINNING (Various artists).
LP: RRTG 7738

DAY 1 BEST OF THE REGGAE SUNSPLASH (Various artists).
LP: VSLP 8904

DEE JAY EXPLOSION (Various artists).
LP: HB 04

DEE-JAY SUPERCLASH! (Various artists).
LP: CSLP 16

DIGITAL ENGLISH PRESENTS DUB PLATE STYLE Vol. 1 (Various).
LP: DELP 002

D.J. BATTLE (Various artists).
Tracks: / Oh what a night: *Various artists* / One night loving: *Various artists* / Ann Marie: *Various artists*/ Everybody bawling: *Various artists* / Mini skirt: *Various artists* / Youthman: *Various artists* / I can't stand it: *Various artists* / Boll weevil: *Various artists* / Air is polluted: *Various artists* / Talk too much: *Various artists*.
LP: KVC 6002

DJ CHOICE (Various artists).
LP: ARILP 053

DJ CONFRONTATION (Various artists).
LP: DSR 9349

DJ CONNECTION (Various artists).
LP: DSR 9517

DJ GREATEST (Various artists).
Tracks: / X rated country: *Bailey* / Lt. Stitchie's remedy: *Stitchie Lt* / We a'say one: *Higgs & Twins*/ Bank ha' fe luck: *Junior Demos* / Needle eye pum pum: *Shabble Ranks* / Bam bam: *Tiger* / In the ghetto: *Higgs & Twins* / Respect due: *Little Twitch* / Put your feet in: *Bailey*.
LP: WALP 20

DJ SHOWCASE (Various artists).
LP: MLLP 006
MC: MLC 006

DJ SHOWDOWN (Various artists).
LP: VPRL 1049

D.J.'S GREATEST, VOL. 2 (Various artists).
LP: LALP 27

DOUBLE TWINSPIN VOL.1 (Various artists).
Tracks: / Deh wid yuh: *Super Black* / Your eyes only: *Pinchers* / Send fi Spanish fly: *Little Twitch*/ Murderer: *Anthony, Pad* / If you were here with me: *Roach, Collie* / Ain't nothing but the rent: *Smith*, Conroy / Yes mama: *Little John* / Love feeling: *Angelo, Don* / Gi mi di money: *Benjy, Risto* / No borrow gun: *Pinchers* / Punaany: *Bailey, Admiral* / Wrong move: *Wales, Josey*.
LP: STLP 1

DUB POETS DUB (Various artists).
LP: HB 30

DUBBLE ATTACK - DEE-JAY COLLECTION 1972-74 (Various artists).
Tracks: / No. 1 in the world: *U-Roy* / Opportunity rock: *Big Youth* / Meaning of one: *Prince Jazzbo*/ Rasta on a Sunday: *I-Roy* / Father's call: *Beckford, Dean* / This is a year for rebels: *Godsons* / Spider to the fly: *Big Youth* / Brother Toby is a movie from London: *I-Roy* / Mr. Harry Skank: *Prince Jazzbo*/ Dubble attack: *Big Youth* / Whole lot of sugar: *Prince Hammer* / Festive season: *I-Roy* / Mr. Want All: *Prince Jazzbo* / Butter bread: *Young, Lloyd*.
LP: GREL 601
MC: GREEN 601

DUCK DANCE COMPETITION (Various artists).
LP: VPRL 1037
MC: VPRC 1037

DUCK DANCE V'S CHINA TOWN (Various artists).
LP: VPRL 1043

DYNAMIC ROCKERS (Various artists).
Tracks: / Truth has come again: *Various artists* / Babylonian: *Various artists* / Cuban cutlass: *Various* artists / Leaving Babylon: *Various artists* / Fulfillment: *Various artists* / Follow that man: *Various* artists / Be wise: *Various artists* / Weekend cowhand: *Various artists* / Real natty dreadlock: *Various artists* / For I: *Various artists* / Bless the sunshine: *Various artists* / Join hands and heart: *Various artists*.
LP: DYLP 3009

EARLY YEARS (Various artists).
LP: WBRLP 801

ENFORCER ONE (Various artists).
LP: DSR 9288

EQUAL RIGHTS (Various artists).
LP: WRLP 23

ETERNAL LOVE (Various artists).
LP: WBRLP 01

EXTERMINATOR VOL 3 (Various artists).
LP: EXLP 6
MC: VPCT 1127

FASHION REVIVES VOL.3 (Various artists).
LP: FADLP 010

FAST CAR (Various artists).
LP: VPRL 1058
MC: VPRC 1058

FEEL LIKE JUMPIN' (Various artists).
LP: RRLP 111

FIFTEEN BIG ONES (Various artists).
LP: STLP 1036

FRESH REGGAE HITS (Various artists).
LP: PW 7406

GATHERING (Various artists).
LP: TRSLP 1

GEMINI SOUND LIVE AT SKATELAND (Various artists).
LP: DHS 002

GET READY ROCK STEADY (Various artists).
Tracks: / Never love again: *Ellis, Alton* / My last love: *Termites* / Hound dog: *Frazer, Norma* / Big mistake: *Bassies* / Won't you come home now: *Ken & Delroy* / Oh babe: *Ken & Delroy* / Darker shade of black: *Soul Vendors* / Fat fish: *Soul Vendors* / If you got soul: *Young, Pete* / Soul and inspiration: *Hamlins* / Get ready rock steady: *S.O.U.L. Agents* / Groove to the beat: *Keith & Ken*.
LP: CSL 8007

GHETTO DUB (Various artists).
Tracks: / Ghetto (dub): *Various artists* / Station dub: *Various artists* / Fire (dub): *Various artists*/ Moving Dub: *Various artists* / Magnet dub: *Various artists* / World dub: *Various artists* / Danger dub: *Various artists* / Tribuation Dub: *Various artists* / Blazing dub: *Various artists*.
LP: RDL 900

GOOD INSTRUCTIONS (Various artists).
LP: SJ 09

GREAT BRITISH DJ'S ROLL CALL 89 (Various artists).
LP: GTLP 2

GREATEST ORIGINAL REGGAE HITS (Various artists).
LP: RMLP 1
MC: RMMC 1

GREATEST ORIGINAL REGGAE HITS (Various artists).
LP: KTR 127

GREATEST ORIGINAL REGGAE HITS (Various artists).
LP: TRLS 127

GREENSLEEVES SAMPLER (Various artists).
Tracks: / Crazy list: *Brown, Dennis* / Feel the rydim: *Minott, Sugar* / Zungguzungguguzungguzeng: *Yellowman*/ Pass the Tu-Sheng-Peng: *Paul, Frankie* / Let off supm: *Isaacs, Gregory* / Africa must be free by 1983: *Mundell*, Hugh / I love King Selassie: *Black Uhuru* / They don't know Jah: *Wailing Souls* / Dematerialise: *Scientist*/ Ganja smuggling: *Eek-A-Mouse* / Stop that train: *Eastwood & Saint* / We are going: *Burning Spear*.
LP: GREZ 1
MC: GREZC 1

GREENSLEEVES SAMPLER 2 (Various artists).
LP: GREZ 2
MC: GREZC 2

GREENSLEEVES SAMPLER 3 (Various artists).
LP: GREZ 3
MC: GREZC 3

GREENSLEEVES SAMPLER 4 (Various artists).
LP: GREZ 4
MC: GREZC 4

GREENSLEEVES SAMPLER 5 (Various artists).
LP: GREZ 5
MC: GREZC 5

HAVE A DREADFUL SUMMER (Various artists).
MC: RACS 0178

HEARTBEAT REGGAE (SAMPLER) (Various artists).
LP: HB 39801
MC: HBC 39801

I SHALL SING (Various artists).
LP: TRLS 289
MC: ZCTRL 289

IN A DANCE HALL (Various artists).
LP: DSR 9351

IN THE MOOD (Various artists).
Tracks: / I need a love: *Paul, Frankie* / In the mood: *James, Hopeton* / Sweet feeling: *Stewart, Tinga*/ Falling in love: *Franklyn, Chevel* / Just once: *Thriller U* / Come in: *Wilson, Ernest* / Your love: *Clarendonians* / I'm lonely: *James, Hopeton* / Exterminator: *Thriller U* / Lets wait awhile: *Franklyn, Chevel*.
MC: ITMC 1
LP: WRLP 19
MC: WRLC 19

INSTRUMENTAL REGGAE HITS (see under Instrumental...) (Various artists).

IYAH BINGHI ROCKERS SHOWCASE (Various artists).
LP: . . . . **IBR 005**

JAH SHAKA PRESENTS DUB MASTERS VOL 1 (Various artists).
LP: . . . . **MLPM 1001**
MC: . . . . **MCTM 1001**

JAM SESSION VOLUME 1 (Various artists).
LP: . . . . **VPRL 1031**

JAM SESSION VOLUME 2 (Various artists).
LP: . . . . **VPRL 1032**

JAMAICA AFFAIR VOL.2 (Various artists).
LP: . . . . **JDLP 004**

JAMAICA AFFAIR VOL 3 (Various artists).
Tracks: / Bad jamma: *Mercian, Mickey* / Take me back home: *King Kong* / Nothing for nothing: *Big Youth*/ Can't live a England: *Big Youth* / Further east: *Lionheart* / Eva: *Everados* / Social friend: *Palmer*, E / Family affair: *Mercian, Mickey* / Trouble on the road: *Big Youth* / Free Nelson Mandela: *Decosta, Glen*.
LP: . . . . **JDLP 006**

JAMAICA'S FINEST VOL. 1 (Various artists).
LP: . . . . **FADLP 012**

JAMAICA'S GREATEST (Various artists).
LP: . . . . **MLP 12-158**

JAMMIN' (Various artists).
Tracks: / Jamming: *Marley, Bob and The Wailers* / 54-46 (was my number): *Toots & Maytals* / You can get if you: *Cliff, Jimmy* / Johnny too bad: *Slickers* / Israelites: *Dekker, Desmond* / Somebody's watching you: *Black Uhuru* / Now that we've found love: *Third World* / Don't turn around: *Aswad* / Wonderful world: *Kotch*/ Electric boogie: *Griffiths, Marcia* / Baltimore: *Tamlins* / Long shot kick de bucket: *Pioneers*.
MC: . . . . **MCT 1010**
LP: . . . . **MLPS 1010**

JAMMY BUT NICE (Various artists).
LP: . . . . **JRLP 01**

JAPANESE AND A JAMAICAN IN COMBINATION (Various artists).
LP: . . . . **STMLP 003**

JUNJO PRESENTS A LIVE SESSION WITH ACES INTERNAT (Various artists).
LP: . . . . **GREL 48**
MC: . . . . **GREEN 48**

JUNJO PRESENTS TWO BIG SOUND (Various artists).
LP: . . . . **GREL 54**

JUST MY IMAGINATION (Various artists).
LP: . . . . **TRLS 286**
MC: . . . . **ZCTRL 286**

KEEP ON COMING THROUGH THE DOOR (Various artists).
Tracks: / Dance beat: *Various artists* / Jack of my trade: *Various artists* / Sounds of Babylon: *Various artists* / Fire corner: *Various artists* / Heart don't leap: *Various artists* / To the fields: *Various* artists / Mosquito one: *Various artists* / Mr. Harry Skank: *Various artists* / Alpha & omega: *Various artists*.
LP: . . . . **TRLS 255**
MC: . . . . **ZCTRL 255**

KING KONG COMPILATION (Various artists).
Tracks: / Israelites: *Various artists* / Monkey girl: *Various artists* / Sweet sensation: *Various artists*/ Freedom street: *Various artists* / Let them talk: *Various artists* / Samfie man: *Various artists* / It's my delight: *Various artists* / Peepin' Tom: *Various artists* / Rivers of Babylon: *Various artists*/ Gave you my love: *Various artists* / Bitterness of life: *Various artists* / Night flight: *Various artists*/ Long shot kick de bucket: *Various artists* / It mek: *Various artists* / Why baby why: *Various artists*/ Monkey man: *Various artists*.
LP: . . . . **IRSP 12**

KING TUBBY ON THE MIX (Various artists).
LP: . . . . **OMLP 022**

KING TUBBY PRESENTS SOUNDCLASH DUB PLATE STYLE (Various artists).
LP: . . . . **KT 001**

KING TUBBYS FAST CAR (Various artists).
LP: . . . . **SSBLP 00002**

LASER REGGAE HITS (Various artists).
Tracks: / Uptown top ranking: *Various artists* / Ina jah children: *Various artists* / Hole in my bucket: *Various* artists / I'm not ashamed: *Various artists* / Love one another: *Various artists* / Slave driver: *Various artists* / Two sevens clash: *Various artists* / You never know what you've got: *Various artists* / Ain't that lovin' you: *Various artists* / Calico suit: *Various artists* / Money in my pocket: *Various artists* / Bubbling love: *Various artists*.
LP: . . . . **BMLP 1003**

LEGENDS OF REGGAE MUSIC (Various artists).
LP: . . . . **RRTG 7718**
MC: . . . . **RRTGC 7718**

LEGENDS OF REGGAE MUSIC (See under Legends Of...) (Various artists).

LION ATTACK (Various artists).
LP: . . . . **VPRL 1141**

LIVE AND LEARN SMASHING ALL STARS (Various artists).
LP: . . . . **CSLP 22**

LO JAI (Various artists).
LP: . . . . **SHAN 21008**

LOVER'S CHOICE VOL.1 (Various artists).
LP: . . . . **OLP 32**

LOVERS FOREVER (Various artists).
LP: . . . . **LMLP 1000**

LOVERS FOREVER VOL.3 (Various artists).
LP: . . . . **LMLP 5000**

LOVERS REGGAE VOL.1 (Various artists).
LP: . . . . **STLP 169**

LOVERS ROCK COLLECTION VOLS. 1 & 2 (Various artists).
LP: . . . . **STLP 112**

LOVERS & ROCKERS (Various artists).
Tracks: / Point of view: *Various artists* / Conscious man: *Various artists* / Don't look back: *Various artists*/ Baltimore: *Various artists* / Self service love: *Various artists* / Moving target: *Various artists*/ Little way different, A: *Various artists* / African teacher: *Various artists* / Wolf and leopards: *Various artists* / Same song: *Various artists* / Unconventional people: *Various artists* / Living in SUS: *Various artists* / Electrocharge: *Various artists*.
LP: . . . . **RDM 3001**

LOVERS ROOTS VOL.2 (Various artists).
LP: . . . . **STLP 164**

MAFIA & FLUXY DANCEHALL COLLECTION VOL.1 (Various artists).
LP: . . . . **MFLP 001**

MAGIC REGGAE (See under Magic reggae) (Various artists).

MAGNIFICENT 14, THE (Various artists).
LP: . . . . **TRLS 283**
MC: . . . . **ZCTRL 283**

MASSIVE VOL. 1 (Various artists).
Tracks: / Cockney translation: *Smiley Culture* / 'Allo tosh: *Pato* / Walk & skank: *Jah Screechy* / Here I come: *Levy, Barrington* / Pass the tu-sheng-peng: *Paul, Frankie* / Billy Jean/Mama used to say: *Shinehead*/ Should I (put my trust in you): *Priest, Maxi/Caution* / Need your love (each and every day): *Aswad* / Running around: *One Blood* / Just can't get you out of my mind: *Brown, A. J* / Keep on searching: *Riccs, Glen*/ Cottage in Negril: *Taylor, Tyrone*.
LP: . . . . **OVED 217**
MC: . . . . **OVEDC 217**

MASSIVE VOL. 2 (Various artists).
Tracks: / Kool noh: *Aswad* / In the Springtime: *Priest, Maxi* / Heartbeat: *Irie, Tippa* / Call on me: *Hartley, Trevor* / Tonight: *Thompson, Carroll* / Who the cap fits: *Shinehead* / Every Thursday night: *Isaacs, Gregory* / Hurt me: *Minott, Sugar* / She loves me know: *Hammond, Beres* / Am I the same girl: *Winsome* / Magic feeling: *Gordon, Michael* / (It's a) romance: *One Blood* / No puppy love: *Tiger*/ Do you believe: *Home T-4* / Until you come back to me: *Dale, Just and the Robotics* / Selector him good: *Little Clarkie And The Offbeat Posse*.
LP: . . . . **V 2405**
MC: . . . . **TCV 2405**
LP: . . . . **OVED 258**
MC: . . . . **OVEDC 258**

MASSIVE VOL. 3 (Various artists).
Tracks: / Ragamuffin girl: *Hunningale, Peter & The Night Flight Band* / Come back to me: *Malvo, Anthony & Tiger*/ Why do fools fall in love: *Leo, Phillip & C.J. Lewis* / (No more) nine til five: *Hartley, Trevor & Clement Irie*/ Roughneck fashion: *Tenor Fly* / Don't test: *Tucker, Junior* / Making love: *Room, Barry* / Dial my heart: *Paul, Frankie* / Give me that touch: *Glasgow, Deborahe* / I'm still in love with you: *Kofi & John McLean*/ Too good to be true: *Isaacs, Gregory* / Push push: *Batson, Slim* / On and on: *Aswad & Sweetie Irie*/ Step up in love: *Levy, Barrington & Sasafras* / Telephone love: *Lodge, J.C.* / Fast car: *Brown, Foxy*/ Nice every time: *Irie, Clement* / Ickie fashion: *Pepper & Daddy Freddie* / It's over: *Thriller U* / We ain't been getting along: *Instigators* / Two-timing lover: *Davis, Janet* / My best friend's man: *Cross, Sandra* / Crash crash: *Anthony, Mike* / Smile: *McGregor, Freddie*.
2LP: **828 173 1**
MC: **828 173 4**

MASSIVE VOL. 4 (Various artists).
Tracks: / Twice my age: *Krystal & Shabba Ranks* / Worried over you: *Davis, Janet & CJ Lewis* / Poco man jam: *Peck*, Gregory / Shaka on the move: *Demus, Shaka* / Holy water: *Admiral Bailey* / New talk: *Sweet Irie & Joe* 90 / I know love: *Priest, Maxi & Tiger* / Mr. Lover Man: *Deborahe & Shaba* / Good thing going: *Leo, Phillip* & C.J. Lewis / One blood: *Reid, Junior* / Proud of Mandela: *Macka B & Kofi* / Guidance: *Nerious, Joseph*/ Dub be good to me: *Beats International, featuring Lindy Layton* / I wanna rock: *Paul, Frankie* / First date: *Cocoa Tea* / Tears: *Sanchez* / Glide gently: *Anthony, Mike* / If you want it: *Hunningale, Peter*/ Hurry over: *Boom, Barry* / Dancing with my baby: *Foster, Royden* / Let's start over: *Winsome & Frankie Paul*/ Are you going my way: *Home-T* / Baby don't go too far: *Hartley, Trevor* / Paradise: *Smith, Karen* / You are the one: *Intense*.
2LP: **828 2101**
MCSET: **828 2104**

MATRIX DUB (Various artists).
LP: . . . . **CENTURY 1000**

MELODICA MELODIES (Various artists).
Tracks: / Bass and drum version: *Various artists* / Kenyatta: *Various artists* / Smokey eyes: *Various artists*/ Loving you: *Various artists* / African queen: *Various artists* / Merry up: *Various artists* / Two wedding skank: *Various artists* / Blackboard jungle: *Various artists* / Java: *Various artists* / Cheer up: *Various artists* / Call me Trinity: *Various artists* / Naked spectrum: *Various artists*.
LP: . . . . **TRLS 200**

MIX MAN SERIES 1 (Various artists).
LP: . . . . **BLKMX 02**

MIX UP AND BLEND (Various artists).
LP: . . . . **LALP 33**

MONKEY BUSINESS (Various artists).
Tracks: / Tighten up: *Untouchables* / Fatty fatty: *Eccles, Clancy* / 54-36 was my number: *Maytals* / 007 shanty town: *Dekker, Desmond* / Liquidator: *Harry J. All Stars* / Fire corner: *Eccles, Clancy* / Double barrel: *Collins, Dave & Ansel* / Birth control: *Lee, Byron* / Herbsman: *Various artists* / Elizabethan reggae: *Gardiner, Boris* / Return of django: *Upsetters* / Monkey spanner: *Collins, Dave & Ansel* / Long shot kick the bucket: *Pioneers* / Young gifted and black: *Bob & Marcia* / Monkey man: *Maytals* / Dollar in the teeth: *Upsetters* / Barbwire: *Dean, Nora* / Shocks of mighty: *Collins, Dave & Ansel* / Them laugh and kiki: *Soulmates* / Cherry oh baby: *Donaldson, Eric*.
LP: . . . . **TRLS 188**

MORE POCO (Various artists).
LP: . . . . **VPRL 1142**

MUDIES MOOD (Various artists).
Tracks: / Mudies mood: *Rhythm Rulers* / Heart don't leap: *Walks, Dennis* / Power pack: *Rhythm Rulers*/ Rome: *Jones, Lloyd* / Mannix: *Rhythm Rulers* / Musically red: *Rhythm Rulers* / Let me tell you boy: *Ebony Sisters* / Let's start again: *Coral, Don & The Eternals* / Waking the dead: *Rhythm Rulers* / Drifter, The: *Walks, Dennis* / Run for your life: *Rhythm Rulers* / Serious business: *Rhythm Rulers*.
LP: . . . . **HM 101**

MUSIC WORKS '88 AND '89 (Various artists).
LP: . . . . **GREL 503**
MC: . . . . **GREEN 503**

MUSIC WORKS PRESENTS TWICE MY AGE (Various artists).
LP: . . . . **GREL 144**
MC: . . . . **GREEN 144**

MUSIC WORKS SHOWCASE 88 (Various artists).
LP: . . . . **GREL 117**
MC: . . . . **GREEN 117**

MUSIC WORKS SHOWCASE 89 (Various artists).
LP: . . . . **GREL 123**
MC: . . . . **GREEN 123**

MUSICAL CONSORTIUM (Various artists).
LP: . . . . **AT 1008**

MUSICAL FEVER 1967-1968 (Various artists).
Tracks: / Bad mind grudgeful: *Winston & Robin* / Puppy love: *Bennett & Dennis* / Bad treatment: *Cannon &* Soul Vendors / Get a lick, A: *Oakley, Bumps* / Hip hug her: *Sultans* / Let me love you: *Miller, Jacob*/ Rub up, push up: *Termites* / Wailing time: *Winston & Robin* / Venus: *Frater, Eric* / Norwegian wood: *Williams, Marshall* / Love me girl: *Soul Vendors* / You shouldn't be the one: *Holness, Winston* / Ram jam: *Jackie & Soul Vendors* / You gonna lose: *Octaves* / Get with it: *Soul Vendors* / Fat fish: *Viceroys*/ Grooving steady: *Jackie & Soul Vendors* / Bye bye baby: *Simms, Zoot* / Soul junction: *Soul Vendors*/ Mercy mercy: *Slim & Freedom Singers* / Baba boom: *Jackie & Soul Vendors* / Love and unity: *Viceroys*/ I don't mind: *Bob & Ty* / Zigaloo: *Sterling, Lester* / Contemplating mind: *Spence, Barrington* / Good girl: *Nangle, Ed* / Musical fever: *Enforcers* / Wiser than Solomon: *Sterling, Lester*.
2LP: . . . . **TRLD 408**

MUSICAL FEVER 1967-1968 (see under Dodd, Clement Coxsone) (Various artists).

MUSICWORKS SHOWCASE 90 (Various artists).
Tracks: / Too good to be true: *Various artists* / Fatal attraction: *Various artists* / Can't make a slip: *Various* artists / I.O.U.: *Various artists* / Hard road to travel: *Various artists* / Big all around: *Various* artists / Jealousy: *Various artists* / Fall for you again: *Various artists* / What's the matter: *Various artists* / Report to me: *Various artists* / Express love: *Various artists* / Break the ice: *Various artists*/ Easy life: *Various artists*.
LP: . . . . **GREL 139**
MC: . . . . **GREEN 139**

NATTY REBEL ROOTS (Various artists).
MC: . . . . **FLC 9013**

NICE UP DANCEE (Various artists).
MC: . . . . **RACS 0202**

NOW THIS IS WHAT I & I CALL VERSION (Various artists).
LP: . . . . **TRLS 276**

OLDIES BUT GOODIES VOL.1 (Various artists).
LP: . . . . **GW 0002**

ONE AWAY STYLE (Various artists).
LP: . . . . **Unknown**

ONE MAN ONE VOTE (Various artists).
LP: . . . . **GREL 160**
MC: . . . . **GREEN 160**

ONE OUT OF MANY (Trojan Sampler) (Various artists).
LP: . . . . **TRS 1**

ORIGINAL REGGAE HITS (Various artists).
LP: . . . . **WF 101**

OTHER REGGAE SUPERSTARS, THE (Various artists).
LP: . . . . **STLP 0111**

OUT OF MANY, ONE - VOLUME 2 (Various artists).
LP: . . . . **TRS 2**
MC: . . . . **ZCTRS 2**

PAY DOWN PON IT (Various artists).
LP: . . . . **BMLP 039**

PAY IT ALL BACK, VOL. 1 (Various artists).
LP: . . . . **ONULP 37**

PAY IT ALL BACK, VOL. 2 (Various artists).
LP: . . . . **ONULP 42**

PICK OUT ALLSTARS VOL 1 (Various artists).
LP: . . . . **PICKLP 02**

POPULAR ROOTS (Various artists).
Tracks: / Right track: *Dillon, Phillis* / Cry tough: *Ellis, Alton & The Flames* / Your ace from space: *U-Roy*/ Version galore: *U-Roy* / Come on little girl: *Melodians* / Things you say you love: *Jamaicans* / Tide is high, The: *Paragons* / Right time, The: *Mighty Diamonds* / I need a roof: *Mighty Diamonds* / MPLA: *Zukie, Tappa* / Oyo dub: *Prince Far-I* / Train to Rhodesia: *Big Youth* / Uptown top ranking / Mix up: *Gladiators* / Never get weary: *Culture* / Plastic smile: *Black Uhuru* / This land is for everyone: *Abbysinians*/ Stepping razor: *Tosh, Peter* / Universal tribulation: *Isaacs, Gregory* / John Public: *Isaacs, Gregory*/ Let's dance: *Isaacs, Gregory* / Crazy bald head: *Clarke, Johnny* / Stick a bush: *Gladiators* / Country living: *Mighty Diamonds*.
2LP: . . . . **VGD 3512**
MC: . . . . **VGDC 3512**

PRESSURE DROP (Various artists).
MCSET: . . . . **MBOXC 25**

LPS: MBOX 25

PRINCE JAMMY PRESENTS VOL.1 (Various artists).
LP: LALP 002

PRINCE JAMMY PRESENTS VOL.3 (Various artists).
LP: LALP 12

PURE LOVERS VOL.2 (Various artists).
LP: CLP 102
MC: CLC 102

PURE LOVERS VOL.3 (Various artists).
LP: CLP 103
MC: CLC 103

PURE LOVERS VOL 1 (Various artists).
LP: CLP 101

QUAD STAR REVOLUTION (Various artists).
Tracks: / Let me tell you boy: Mudies All Stars / Spanish town rock: Prince Heron / African home: Mudies All Stars / Woodcutter skank: Big Joe / Woodcutter dub: Mudies All Stars / Margaret dub: Mudies All Stars / Drifter: Roy, I. / Drifter dub: Mudies All Stars / Black stick rock: Big Joe / Black stick rock dud: Mudies All Stars / Grass root dub: Mudies All Stars.
LP: HM 104

QUAD STAR REVOLUTION VOL 2 (Various artists).
Tracks: / What do you do: Count Sticky / Heart don't leap: Roy, I. / Dub them heart: Mudies All Stars/ Lick them face: Big Joe / Dub them face: Big Joe / Musical pleasure: Roy, I. / Hot pop: Bennett, Jo Jo / Dub girl: Big Joe / T bone girl: Mudies All Stars / Bitter water rock: Big Joe.
LP: HM 106

RAGGAMUFFIN DUB (Various artists).
MC: APC 001

RAIDERS OF THE LOST DUB (Various artists).
LP: ILPS 9705

RAM DANCEHALL (Various artists).
Tracks: / Hurricane: Lodge, J.C. / Bad love affair: Coco Tea / Lonely am I: Lady Patra / Caution: Fraser, Dean / True loving: Barrington, Hugo / Maniac: Gold, Brian & Tony / Never let go: Tiger/ Don't throw our love away: Home-T / Ring a roses / Madman: Tibet, Admiral.
MC: MCT 1018
LP: MLPS 1018

RARE REGGAE FROM THE VAULTS OF STUDIO ONE (Various artists).
LP: HB 47
MC: HBC 47

RAS RECORDS PRESENTS A REGGAE CHRISTMAS (Various artists).
Tracks: / We wish you a merry Christmas: Various artists / Jingle bells: Carlos, Don & Glenice Spencer / Joy of the world: Lodge, June / Come all ye faithful: McGregor, Freddie / Drummer boy: Michigan & Smiley/ Twelve days of Christmas, The: Broggs, Peter / Silent night: Black, Pablo / Feliz Navidad: McGregor, Freddie/ Night before Christmas, The: Eek-A-Mouse.
LP: RAS 3101
MC: RASC 3101

RAS, REGGAE AND RYKODISC (Various artists).
MC: RACS 0151

RASTA HAVE AMBITION (Various artists).
LP: LALP 001

RAVE ON BROTHER (Various artists).
LP: AT 1012

RAVERS ROCK VOL.1 (Various artists).
Tracks: / Money is not all: Various artists / Brothers killing brothers: Various artists / Bum ball: Various artists.
LP: VSLP 4004

RAVERS ROCK VOL.2 (Various artists).
LP: VSLP 4037

RAW GROOVE (Various artists).
LP: FADLP 017

REAL AUTHENTIC SAMPLER (Various artists).
LP: RAS 3301
MC: RASC 3301

REBEL MUSIC (An Anthology of Reggae Music) (Various artists).
Tracks: / You don't know: Andy, Bob / Loser, The: Harriott, Derrick / High school dance: McKay, Freddie/ Russians are coming, The: Bennett, Val / Tonight: Keith & Tex / Ain't that lovin' you: U-Roy / Them a fe get a beatin': Tosh, Peter / God helps the man: Smart, Leroy / Hypocrite: Heptones / S90 skank: Big Youth / Hard tighter: Little Roy / Eedding skank: Brown, Glen / Anywhere but nowhere: White, K.C. / Beat down Babylon: Byles, Junior / Concentration: Brown, Dennis / Screaming target: Big Youth/ Slaving: Parkes, Lloyd / You are my angel: Andy, Horace / Melody maker: Hudson, Keith / Money in my pocket: Brown, Dennis / Cheater: Brown, Dennis / Blackman time: I-Roy / Satan side: Andy, Horace & Earl Flute / Give praises: Big Youth / Rock away: Isaacs, Gregory / Saturday night special: Dyke, Michael / Cool rasta: Heptones.
2LP: TRLD 403

REBEL ROCK (Various artists).
LP: TWLP 103

REBEL TENG (Various artists).
LP: 430 26

REGGAE 14 Various artists (Various artists).
LP: SDLP 913

REGGAE AMBASSADORS (Various artists).
LP: DGLP 008

REGGAE ATTACK (Various artists).
LP: ATLP 113
MC: MCAT 113

REGGAE BIBLE (Book of drifters) (Various artists).
Tracks: / Drifter: Walks, Dennis / Car pound drifter: Herman, Bongo / Midnight drifter: M.B.V. / DJ drifter: Roy, I. / Reggae foundation: Tubby, King / Drifter bratah: Rhythm Rulers / Drifter on the ball: Big Joe / Dub in red: Mudies All Stars / Rocking the drifter: Anderson, Gladstone / Drifting with a flute: McCook, Tommy/Mudies All Stars / Drifter in fly style: Walks, Dennis.
LP: HM 118

REGGAE BLASTERS (Various artists).
MC: CE 2299
LP: NE 1299

REGGAE CHARTBUSTERS: VOLUME III (Various artists).
LP: TBL 169

REGGAE CHRISTMAS (Various artists).
Tracks: / Silent night: Various artists / I saw mommy kiss a dreadlocks: Various artists / Dub it for Christmas: Various artists / Santa claus: Various artists / Flash your dread: Various artists / Sensimillia: Various artists.
LP: BMLP 051

REGGAE CLASSICS (Various artists).
MC: ARLC 1021

REGGAE CLASSICS VOL. 3 (Various artists).
LP: TRLS 256

REGGAE CLASSICS VOL. 4 (Various artists).
LP: TRLS 284
MC: ZCTRL 284

REGGAE COLLECTION - BEND DOWN LOW (Various artists).
LP: OCN 2029WL
MC: OCN 2029WK

REGGAE CONFUSION BOOPS (Various artists).
LP: WENLP 3023

REGGAE CROSSING (Various artists).
LP: BS 1042

REGGAE DANCE HALL (Various artists).
LP: RRTG 7731
MC: RRTGC 7731

REGGAE DANCE PARTY (Various artists).
Tracks: / Nice up dance: Natural Beauty / Do the dance: Levy, Barrington / Reggae ska: Michigan & Smiley/ Springheel skanking: Carlos, Don / Teach me to dance: Smith, Wayne / Great train robbery: Black Uhuru/ Get flat: Blake, Paul & The Blood Fire Posse / Rub-a-sound: Minott, Sugar / Elementary: Andy, Horace/ You can dance: Lodge, J.C. / Private beach party: Isaacs, Gregory.
LP: RAS 7019
LP: RAS 3018
MC: RASC 3018

REGGAE DANCE PARTY (Various artists).
Tracks: / Dennis the menace: Pinnock, Dennis / Honest I do: Rondo, Gene / Got to come back: English, Junior/ Why why?: Tradition / Confusion: Ellis, Alton / We do it: Tyrone & Aurora / Sky larking: Horace, Andy / Moving on (instrumental): Tradition / Don't it make my brown eyes blue: York, Aurora / Ride on: Pinnock, Dennis / Way we were, The: Rondo, Gene / Rastafaria: Tradition / Forget me now: Davis, Ronnie/ I love to love: Lovington, Grace / Can I change my mind: Ellis, Alton / Summertime: Tradition.
LP: PL 25162
MC: PK 25162

REGGAE DANCEHALL LIMOUSINE (Various artists).
LP: VPRL 1053

REGGAE FROM AROUND THE WORLD (Various artists).
LP: RAS 3050

REGGAE GOLD (Various artists).
LP: RGLP 001

REGGAE GREATEST HITS (Various artists).
2LP: DLP 2068
MCSET: DMC 4068

REGGAE GREATS (Various artists).
Tracks: / Runaway girl: U-Roy / Barnabas Collins: Lone Ranger / One love jamdown: Michigan, Papa & General Smiley / Draw your brakes: Scotty / Soldier take over: Yellowman / Mi God Mi King: Levi, Papa/ Wa do dem: Eek-A-Mouse / C.B.200: Dillinger / Drunken master: General Echo / Wicked she wicked: Boyo, Billy.
LP: IRG 4
MC: IRGC 4

REGGAE GREATS (Various artists produced by Lee Perry) (Various artists).
Tracks: / Party time: Heptones / Police and thieves: Murvin, Junior / Groovy situation: Rowe, Keith/ Soul fire / War in a Babylon: Romeo, Max / Wisdom: Jah Lion / To be a lover: Faith, George / Roast fish & corn bread / Croaking lizard: Prince Jazzbo / Dreadlocks in moonlight.
LP: IRG 12
MC: IRGC 12

REGGAE HISTORY VOL 1 (Various artists).
Tracks: / Knocking on my door: Ashmeade, Roy / Poison ivy: Bennett, Jo Jo / Forward home from Rome: Big Joe / African shuffle: Count Ossie/The African Drums / Love without feelings: Heptones / Let me tell you boy: Ebony Sisters / Bud conference theme: Mudies dub stars / Push me in the corner: Various artists/ Don't walk alone: McCook, Tommy/ Mudies All Stars / Stick by me: Isaacs, Gregory / Swinging for joy: Count Ossie/ The African Drums / God is standing by: Wilson, Ernie / African eyes: Bennett, Jo Jo.
LP: HM 116

REGGAE HITS OF THE 80'S (Various artists).
Tracks: / Pass the dutchie: Various artists / I'm getting married: Various artists / Diseases: Various artists / Boxing around: Various artists / More than I can say: Various artists / One draw: Various artists / Mr. Chin: Various artists / Bam bam: Various artists / Rent man: Various artists.
LP: BMLP 041
MC: BMC 041

REGGAE HITS VOL.2 (Various artists).
Tracks: / Wildfire: Holt, John & Dennis Brown / I'll be on my way: Isaacs, Gregory / Inferiority complex: Various artists / Country living: Mighty Diamonds / Curly locks: Byles, Junior / Senci addick: Fergeson, Horace/ Baby be true: Thompson, Carroll / Caught you in a lie: Reid, Sandra / I love you: Sister Audrey / Jazzy: Paula / I'm gonna fall in love: Stewart, Tinga / Horsemove (giddiup): Horseman / House is not a home, A: Minott, Sugar.
LP: JELP 1002
MC: JELC 1002

REGGAE HITS VOL.3 (Various artists).
Tracks: / Sweet reggae music: Nitty Gritty / Shub in: Paul, Frankie / Watch how the people dancing: Knots, Kenny / Greetings: Half Pint / Dear Boopsie: Hall, Pam / Boops: Supercats / Girlie girlie: George, Sophia / Members only (copyright control): Taylor, Tyrone / One dance won't do: Hall, Audrey / Sixth street: Wilson, Jack / Hello darling: Irie, Tippa / Be my lady: Hunningale, Peter / It's you: Cross, Sandra/ Party nite: Undivided Roots / Guilty: Gardiner, Boris.
LP: JELP 1003
MC: JELC 1003

REGGAE HITS VOL.4 (Various artists).
Tracks: / Wings of love: Sparks, Trevor / Girlfriend: Various artists / She's mine: Levy, Barrington/ She's my lady: Administrators / Holding on: Cross, Sandra / If I give my heart to you: McLean,John/ Guilty for loving you: St. Clair, Carl / Dangerous: Smith, Conroy / Chill out: Tenor saw/Doggie / Debi Debi girl: Metro, Peter/Charmaine / Bad boy: Melody, Courtney / Get ready: Paul, Frankie / Tears: Turner, Chuck / Big in bed: Melody, Lilly.
LP: JELP 1004
MC: JELC 1004

REGGAE HITS VOL.5 (Various artists).
Tracks: / Woman of moods: Dixon, Trevor / Black pride: Kofi / No way no better than yard: Bailey, Admiral/ Am I losing you: Schloss, Cynthia / Ooh la la: LJM / Mi love mi girl bad: Flourgan & Sanchez / Proud to be black: Crucial Robbie / Power of love, The: Gibbons, Leroy / Cover me: Stewart, Tinga & Ninga Man/ Very best, The: Intense / Life: Frighty & Colonel Mite / I still say yes: Parkings, Juliet / Man in the mirror: Little Kirk.
LP: JELP 1005
MC: JELC 1005

REGGAE HITS VOL.6 (Various artists).
Tracks: / My commanding wife: Gardiner, Boris / Bun and cheese: Irie, Clement & Robert French / Looking over love: Kofi / Baby can I hold you tonight: Sanchez / New way to say I love you: Wonder, Wayne / Stick by me / I want to get next to you: Manifest / Love me ses: Top Cat / On my mind: Intense / Lovers' affair: Roni / Fatal attraction: Taxman / Baby can I hold you tonight: Brown, Foxy / Mix up: Madoo, U.U. & Captain Barky / Sweet and nice: Douglas, Lambert & Wayne Fire.
LP: JELP 1006
MC: JELC 1006

REGGAE HITS VOL.7 (Various artists).
LP: JELP 1007
MC: JEMC 1007

REGGAE HITS VOL 1 (Various artists).
Tracks: / Under me sensi: Levy, Barrington / Herbman hustling: Minott, Sugar / Mix me down: Tuff, Tony/ Haul and pull up: Brown, Neville / Lovers magic: Isaacs, Gregory / Someone special: Brown, Dennis/ Gimme good loving: Natural Touch / Feel so good: Reid, Sandra / Between me and you: Campbell, Carol/ Cos you love me baby: Tajah, Paulette / Roots rockin': Aswad / Woman I need your loving: Investigators.
LP: JELP 1001
MC: JELC 1001

REGGAE HITS VOL 8 (Various artists).
LP: JELP 1008
MC: JEMC 1008

REGGAE HITS VOL. 10 (Various artists).
MC: JELC 1010
LP: JELP 1010

REGGAE HITS VOLUME 9 (Various artists).
LP: JELP 1009
MC: JELC 1009

REGGAE INVASION VOL.1 (Various artists).
LP: WBLP 003

REGGAE JAMAICA (Various artists).
LP: TBL 181

REGGAE JAMAICA: VOLUME III (Various artists).
LP: TBL 204

REGGAE PLATINUM, HIT 1 (Various artists).
Tracks: / Private number: Campbell, Bill / This time: Campbell, Pete / Golden touch: Harrison, Valerie/ On my own: Campbell, Bill / Please Mr., please: Campbell, Ann / For the love of you: Campbell, Bill/ Make me yours: Campbell, Bill / I don't want to be alone: Johnson, Carl / It's been so long: Mattick, George / Sharing the nights together: Campbell Brothers / As long as you love me: Williams, Ginger / Just a little bit more: Campbell, Bill.
LP: BBLP 0014

REGGAE RAPPERS (Various artists).
LP: CSLP 28
MC: ZCSLC 28

REGGAE RECIPE (Various artists).
LP: MFP 50511
MC: TCMFP 50511

REGGAE REFRESHERS (SAMPLER) (Various artists).
MC: RRCTS 101
MC: 846269 4

REGGAE, REGGAE, REGGAE (Various artists).
LP: RRLP 105
MC: RRLC 105

REGGAE REPLAY (Various artists).
Tracks: / Liquidator: Harry J. All Stars / Soul shakedown party / Love of the common people: Thomas, Nicky / Crying over you: Boothe, Ken / Red red wine: Tribe, Tony / Skinhead moonstomp: Simaryp / Dollar in the teeth: Upsetters / Double barrel: Collins, Dave & Ansel / Train to Skaville: Ethiopians / Suzanne, beware of the Devil: Livingstone, Dandy / Israelites: Dekker, Desmond / Monkey man: Maytals / Many rivers to cross: Cliff, Jimmy.
LP: ARLP 107
MC: ZCAR 107

REGGAE ROCKERS (Various artists).

LP: . . . . DHLP 2007

REGGAE SHOWCASE VOL.1 (Various artists).
Tracks: / Stop that train: *Eastwood, Clint & General Saint* / Tidal wave: *Paul, Frankie* / I like it: *Carlos, Don* / Slow down woman: *Brown, Dennis* / Big ship: *McGregor, Freddie* / Wa-do-dem: *Eek-A-Mouse* / Roots rock reggae: *Minott, Sugar* / Private beach party: *Isaacs, Gregory* / Zunguguzungguseng: *Yellowman*/ Boom shack a lack: *Reid, Junior* / Fat she fat: *Holt, John.*
LP: . . . . MR 117
MC: . . . . MRC 117

REGGAE STAR JAM VOL.1 (Various artists).
LP: . . . . RCLP 001

REGGAE STARS EXPLOSION, VOL 1 (Various artists).
LP: . . . . KVL 9022

REGGAE STARS VOL.1 (Various artists).
LP: . . . . WER/LP 113

REGGAE, STEADY, GO VOL.1 Various artists (Various artists).
Tracks: / I want to wake up with you: *Various artists* / Police officer: *Various artists* / Am I the same girl: *Various artists* / Man in a house: *Various artists* / Rub-a-dub soldier: *Various artists* / Wet look crazy: *Various artists* / Cherish: *Various artists* / Come back Charlie: *Various artists* / Girlie girlie: *Various* artists / Monday morning feeling: *Various artists* / No good girl: *Various artists* / As if I didn't know: *Various artists* / Dreaming of a little island: *Various artists* / What one dance can do: *Various artists*/ Dynamic: *Various artists* / Kool & Deadly: *Various artists* / Sideshow: *Various artists* / Everything I own: *Various artists* / You can get it if you really want: *Various artists* / Impossible love: *Various artists*/ Young gifted & black: *Various artists* / Ire feelings: *Various artists* / Help me make it through the night: *Various artists* / Double Barrel: *Various artists* / Liquidator: *Harry J. All Stars* / Israelites: *Various* artists / Mad about you: *Various artists* / Hurt so good: *Various artists* / Love of the common people: *Various* artists / Wonderful world, beautiful people: *Various artists* / Midnight rider: *Various artists* / Tree ring circus: *Various artists.*
LP: . . . . RHIN 4

REGGAE STRINGS (Various artists).
LP: . . . . TRLS 54

REGGAE SUNSPLASH (Various artists).
2LP: . . . . K 62037

REGGAE SUPERSTARS (Various artists).
LP: . . . . RRTG 7732
MC: . . . . RRTGC 7732

REGGAE SUPERSTARS OF THE 80'S (Various artists).
LP: . . . . BSL 12003
MC: . . . . BSLC 12003

REGGAE SWEET AND SMOOTH (Various artists).
LP: . . . . TAK LP 003

REGGAE TO THE HEART (Various artists).
LP: . . . . SJ 0019LP

REGGAE TO THE HEART (Various artists).
LP: . . . . SJ 19

REGGAE TREASURE (Various artists).
LP: . . . . PALM TREE 1

REGGAEMANIA VOL.1 (Various artists).
Tracks: / Life story: *Stiff, Lloyd* / Must have fi come: *Curry Don* / Wiz kid version: *Raphael* / Matic: *Stewart, Roman* / Gun man: *Bobo General* / Musically: *T, Erroll* / Say what you're saying: *Burrell, Roland* / We have fi sparks: *Zeekie, Papa* / Version: *Lynn, Robbie.*
LP: . . . . PH 007

REVENGE OF THE SLENG TENG (Various artists).
LP: . . . . Unknown

REVIVES CLASSIC LOVERS VOL.1 (Various artists).
LP: . . . . FADLP 008

REVIVES MORE CLASSIC LOVERS VOL.2 (Various artists).
LP: . . . . FADLP 009

REWARD, LIVE FROM JAMAICA (Various artists).
LP: . . . . DHS 006

RHYTHM DISTRESS (Various artists).
LP: . . . . GREL 137

RIDE THE RHYTHM (Various artists).
LP: . . . . Unknown

RIGHT WAY, THE (Various artists).
LP: . . . . SHAKA 846

ROCKERS ALL STAR EXPLOSION (Various artists).
LP: . . . . AL 8310

ROMANTIC NIGHTS (20 SONGS FOR LOVERS) (Various artists).
Tracks: / Funny feeling: *Brown, Dennis* / How could I let you get away: *Dunkley, Errol* / Betcha by golly wow: *Dunkley, Errol* / Vaya con dios: *Holt, John* / My devotion: *Brown, Junior* / My time: *Isaacs, Gregory*/ What a feeling: *Minott, Sugar* / You move me: *Douglas, Keith* / True love: *Undivided Roots* / I never knew love: *Chalice* / Aware of your love: *Various artists* / Nice time: *Carlos, Don* / Shine eye girl: *Levy, Barrington* / It's you gal: *Prophet, Michael* / No time to lose: *Campbell, Al* / My love: *Viceroys*/ Sticky wicket: *Tuff, Tony* / Peek-a-boo: *Various artists* / I'm in the mood: *Natural Ites* / Girl is mine, The: *Yellowman & Peter Metro.*
LP: . . . . CSLP 24
MC: . . . . ZCSLC 24

ROMANTIC REGGAE - 24 GREAT REGGAE LOVE SONGS (Various artists).
Tracks: / I wanna wake up with you: *Holt, John* / Choose me: *Pierre, Marie* / Moon river: *Greyhound*/ You are everything: *Chosen Few* / Stand by me: *Junior Soul* / Sweet inspiration: *Pioneers* / Everything I own: *Boothe, Ken* / Side show: *Biggs, Barry* / Hurt so good: *Cadogan, Susan* / Only a smile: *Brown,* Dennis / Prisoner of love: *Barker, Dave* / All I have is love: *Isaacs, Gregory* / Black pearl: *Faith,* Horace / Spanish harlem: *Edwards, Jackie* / First time ever I saw your face, The: *Griffiths, Marcia* / Runaway with love: *Chambers, Lloyd* / Crying over you: *Boothe, Ken* / Everybody plays the fool: *Chosen Few* / You make me feel brand new: *Gardner, Boris* / Still in love: *Ellis, Alton* / Montego bay: *Notes, Freddie & The Rudies* / You are everything to me: *Holt, John* / Let us be: *Thomas, Nicky* / Save the last dance for me: *Heptones.*
2LP: . . . . VSOPLP 133
MC: . . . . VSOPMC 133

ROOTS DAUGHTERS (Various artists).
Tracks: / Guide and protect: *Aisha* / Catch the boat: *Live Wya* / English girl: *Sister Audrey* / Free South Africa: *Cross, Sandra* / Fire: *Faybienne* / Until you come back to me: *Just Dale/Robotniks* / Place in the sun, A: *Kofi* / Mr. Roots man: *Rasheda.*
LP: . . . . ARILP 039

ROOTS OF REGGAE (Music from Jamaica) (Various artists).
LP: . . . . LLST 7314
MC: . . . . LLCT 7314

ROOTS OF REGGAE, THE (Various artists).
Tracks: / Soul shakedown party: *Marley, Bob* / Everything I own: *Boothe, Ken* / You can get it if you really want it: *Dekker, Desmond* / Black and white: *Greyhound* / Hurt so good: *Cadogan, Susan* / Man in the street: *Drummond, Don* / Barber saloon: *Dread, Mikey* / Let me down easy: *Brown, Dennis* / I'm a madman: *Perry, Lee* / Israelites: *Dekker, Desmond* / Help me make it through the night: *Holt, John* / 54 46 was my number: *Toots & The Maytals* / Kaya: *Marley, Bob* / Let your yeah be yeah: *Pioneers* / To be young gifted and black: *Bob & Marcia* / Rock me in dub: *Thompson, Linval* / Java: *Pablo, Augustus* / What you gonna do on judgement day: *Prince Far-I.*
MC: . . . . MCTC 014

ROOTS OF REGGAE VOL. 2 (Various artists).
MC: . . . . MCTC 041

ROOTS ROCK REGGAE (Various artists).
LP: . . . . CTLP 124

ROOTS ROCK REGGAE, VOL 2 (Various artists).
LP: . . . . SAVL 1001

ROOTS ROCKERS (Various artists).
LP: . . . . ATLP 112
MC: . . . . MCAT 112

ROOTS ROCKERS (Various artists).
LP: . . . . ARLP 102
MC: . . . . ZCAR 102

ROUGH MEAN AND IRIE (Various artists).
LP: . . . . REDLP 13
LP: . . . . VPREL 2003
MC: . . . . VPREC 2003

ROUGH ROAD (Various artists).
LP: . . . . BS 1018

ROUGHNECK FASHIONS (Various artists).
Tracks: / No drugs allowed: *Daddy Freddie* / Don't lick no rock: *Tuffy, Ricky* / Bike rider: *Top Cat*/ Rough house no ramp: *Mannix, Joe* / Original ade key: *Crystal, Conrad* / Respect a champion: *Ninja Mr.Palmer*/ Rough girl fashions: *Lady Mackerel* / DJ anthem: *Irie, Devon* / Respect woman: *Momma Sonia* / Remedy: *Milo* / Love her to death: *Ranking, Ricky* / Send them come: *Junior chin* / Respect woman: *Schekles, Shanki.*
LP: . . . . BDLP 003

RUB-A-DUBBLE REGGAE VOL. 1 (Various artists).
Tracks: / Picture on the wall (original mix): *Natural Ites* / Declaration of rights: *Carlos, Don & Gold* / Carrot and onion: *Anthony, Pad* / Fighting spirit: *Smalling, Milton* / Rich man poor man: *Prophet, Michael* / Unity is strength: *Chaplin, Charlie & Don Carlos* / Jam it tonight: *Brown, U* / Mr. Wicked Man: *Levy, Michael*/ Tug-o-war games: *Castell, Lacksley* / African culture: *Sly & Robbie* / Angel: *Douglas, Keith* / Feeling inside: *Skanga* / My devotion: *Brown, Junior* / I won't hurt your feelings: *Brown, Carol & Jackie Mittoo*/ Love and understanding: *Natural Ites* / Rise in the morning: *Sixteen, Earl* / Get up: *Carlos, Don* / How could I let you get away: *Dunkley, Errol* / Never fall in love: *Prophet, Michael.*
2LP: . . . . CSAP 102
MCSET: . . . . ZCSAP 102

RUB-A-DUBBLE REGGAE VOL. 2 (Various artists).
Tracks: / Lion inna jungle: *Natural Ites* / Bad boy: *Campbell, Al* / Tu sheng peng: *U-Brown* / Plantation: *Carlos, Don* / Nice time (late night blues): *Carlos, Don* / Girl is mine, The: *Yellowman & Peter Metro*/ Me no inna it: *Cotton, Joseph* / Leggo me shirt gate man: *Chaplin, Charlie (Reggae)* / Dibi dibi sound: *Tipper* Lee & Rappa Robert / Dibi dibi girl: *Metro, Peter/Sister Charmaine* / You move me: *Douglas, Keith* / Little action, A: *Brown, Carol* / True love: *Undivided Roots* / Peek-a-boo: *Sixteen, Earl* / I've gotta feeling: *Minott, Sugar* / Julia: *Sixteen, Earl* / 9 to 5: *Bevedoo* / Ebony eyes: *Evral, King* / Betcha by golly wow: *Dunkley, Errol.*
2LP: . . . . CSAP 103
MCSET: . . . . ZCSAP 103

RUBBING THE WALLPAPER (Various artists).
LP: . . . . ARILP 044

RUBBLE DUB-MC'S CHOICE (Various artists).
LP: . . . . RUBLP 001

SANTIC COLLECTION VOL.2 (Various artists).
LP: . . . . ST 001LP
MC: . . . . ST 001MC

SAY I LOVE YOU (Various artists).
Tracks: / Just the two of us: *Wilson, Ernest* / Over and over: *Malibu* / What's going down: *Fagann, Lloyd*/ Sweet loving: *Wilson, Ernest* / I wanna say I love you: *Paul, Frankie* / Angel in the morning: *Brown, Foul*/ Greatest love affair: *Brown, Foul & Frankie Paul* / I need a true love: *Brown, Foul* / What am I to do: *James, Hopeton* / I want to love you non stop: *Malibu.*
MC: . . . . ITMC 2
LP: . . . . WRLP 20
MC: . . . . WRLC 20

SCOTTY UNBELIEVABLE SOUNDS (Various artists).
LP: . . . . TRLS 264

SCRATCH ON THE WIRE (Various artists).
Tracks: / Vibrate on: *Various artists* / Soldier and police war: *Various artists* / Diana: *Various artists*/ John Public: *Various artists* / In these times: *Various artists* / Bird in hand: *Various artists* / Big neck police man: *Various artists* / Soul fire: *Various artists* / No peace: *Various artists* / War in a Babylon: *Various artists.*
LP: . . . . ILPS 9583

SEDUCER DUBWISE (Various artists).
LP: . . . . JJ 082

SELEKTA SHOWCASE '89 (Various artists).
Tracks: / My prerogative: *Sanchez* / Enquirer: *One-two crew* / Lick out: *Ninja Man* / Jah is the way: *Minott, Sugar* / Nice and cute: *Johnny P* / Special lady: *Gel, Ny* / Vanity crazy: *Demus, Shaka*/ Rawborn rub a dub: *Meakes, Carl* / Me no know why: *General Trees* / Step it up: *Antony, Pad.*
LP: . . . . GREL 130
MC: . . . . GREEN 130

SERIOUS DUB (Various artists).
Tracks: / Mission impossible: *Radics, Jack* / Sodom dub: *Sly & Robbie* / Mi love dub: *Chemist, Peter*/ Dub-ology: *A Class Crew* / Chemist special: *Chemist, Peter* / Stiff mix: *Chemist, Peter* / Rambo salute: *Roots, Chessey* / Reverse dub: *Mills, Kevin* / Eastern dub: *Pablo, Augustus* / Digital bumps: *Caractacus.*
LP: . . . . ILPS 9878
MC: . . . . ICT 9878

SHANK I SHECK Various artists (Various artists).
LP: . . . . VSLP 2003

SHANKIN' ROUND THE WORLD, VOLUME 3 (Various artists).
LP: . . . . PHZA 52

SHOCKS OF MIGHTY (1969-74) (Various artists).
Tracks: / Pound get a blow: *Upsetters* / No bread and butter: *Morris, Milton* / Tackro, The: *Upsetters*/ Set me free: *Barker, Dave* / Shocks of a mighty: *Barker, Dave & Upsetters* / Dark moon: *Upsetters* / Civilization: *Classics* / French Connection (chapter 2): *Upsetters* / Black mans time: *Grant, Neville*/ Three blind mice: *Graham, Leo* / Three times three: *King Tubby/The Upsetters* / Be thankful: *Clarke, Bunny*/ Dubbing in the back seat: *Upsetters* / Woman's gotta have it: *Riley, Jimmy* / Gotta have dub: *Upsetters*/ Move out of my way: *Clarke, Bunny* / Move out dub: *Upsetters.*
LP: . . . . ATLP 104

SHUFFLING ON BOND STREET (Various artists).
LP: . . . . TRLS 275

SKINHEAD CLASSICS (Various artists).
LP: . . . . TRLD 407

SKINHEAD CLASSICS EP (See under Trojan Explosion vol.9) (Various artists).

SKINHEAD CLASSICS VOL.2 (See under Trojan Explosion vol.13) (Various artists).

SLIM BELLY MAN (Various artists).
LP: . . . . JLLP 021

SOLID GOLD FROM THE VAULTS (Various artists).
LP: . . . . TRLS 291
MC: . . . . ZCTRL 291

SOME GUYS HAVE ALL THE LUCK (All Time Reggae Classics) (Various artists).
Tracks: / Some guys have all the luck: *Harriott, Derrick* / Everything I own: *Boothe, Ken* / Israelites: *Decker,* Desmond / Young, gifted and black: *Bob & Marcia* / Let your yeah be yeah: *Pioneers* / Rivers of Babylon: *Melodians*/ First time ever I saw your face, The: *Griffiths, Marcia* / I shot the sheriff: *Inner Circle* / Take me home country roads: *Toots & The Maytals.*
LP: . . . . OCN 2023WL
MC: . . . . OCN 2023WK

SONIC PRESENTS VOLUME 1... D.J. STYLE (Various artists).
MC: . . . . SSDJ 001

SONIC PRESENTS VOLUME 2... THE SINGERS (Various artists).
MC: . . . . SSC 002

SONIC PRESENTS VOLUME 3... THE SINGERS & DJ'S (Various artists).
MC: . . . . SSDJ 003

SOUNDCLASH '89 (Various artists).
LP: . . . . SPLP 13

SOUNDCLASH DUBPLATE STYLE (Various artists).
LP: . . . . DSR 4401

SOUNDCLASH SOUND 1 (Various artists).
LP: . . . . SPLP 12

SOUNDCLASH SPECIAL VOL 1 (Various artists).
LP: . . . . RMM 1662

SOUNDCLASH SPECIAL VOL 2 (Various artists).
LP: . . . . DSLP 8903

STEPPA PRODUCTIONS ALL STARS, VOLUME 1 (Various artists).
LP: . . . . STEPPALP 01

STREET CORNER (Ital food) (Various artists).
LP: . . . . GG 0127

STRICTLY FOR LOVERS (Various artists).
Tracks: / Dim the lights: *Reedy, Winston* / Roots rockin': *Aswad* / Have you ever been in love?: *Brown, Dennis*/ Wide awake in a dream: *Biggs, Barry* / Love and devotion: *Riley, Jimmy* / Show and tell: *Boothe, Ken*/ Key to the world: *Thomas, Ruddy* / Some guys have all the luck: *Tucker, Junior* / Rocky music: *Struggle*/ Go away dream: *Tamlins* / Rent-a-car: *Various artists.*
LP: . . . . IRG 8
MC: . . . . IRGC 8

STRICTLY FOR ROCKERS (Various artists).

Tracks: / Moulding: *I Jahman* / Ballistic affair: *Smart, Leroy* / King Tubby meets the rockers uptown: *Pablo*, Augustus / Bredda: *Wailing Souls* / Go deh right: *Desi Roots* / Battering down sentence: *Wailer, Bunny*/ Love and unity: *Prophet, Michael* / Two sevens clash: *Culture* / Jogging: *McGregor, Freddie* / Black woman: *Mowatt, Judy* / Trouble you a trouble me: *Various artists* / Rud-a-dub sound: *Sugar Minott*.
LP: . . . . **IRG 16**
MC: . . . . **IRGC 16**

SUFFERERS CHOICE (Various artists).
LP: . . . . **ATLP 101**
MC: . . . . **MCAT 101**

SUNSHINE MIX (Various artists).
Tracks: / Some guys have all the luck: *Priest, Maxi* / Calypso crazy: *Ocean, Billy* / Amigo: *Black Slate*/ To be young gifted and black: *Bob & Marcia* / Pied piper: *Bob & Marcia* / I am what I am: *Greyhound*/ Skinhead moonstomp: *Simaryp* / You can get it if you really want: *Dekker, Desmond & The Aces* / Money in my pocket: *Brown, Dennis* / Hello darling: *Irie, Tippa* / Israelites: *Dekker, Desmond & The Aces* / It mek: *Dekker*, Desmond & The Aces / Ram goat liver: *Pluto* / Monkey spanner: *Collins, Dave & Ansel* / Elizabethan reggae: *Lee, Byron & Boris Gardiner* / Do you really want to hurt me: *Culture Club* / Everything I own: *Boy George*/ Work all day: *Biggs, Barry* / Help me make it through the night: *Holt, John* / Crying over you: *Boothe*, Ken / Everything I own: *Boothe, Ken* / Red red wine: *Tribe, Tony* / Three ring circus: *Biggs, Barry*/ Sideshow: *Biggs, Barry* / You are my life: *Biggs, Barry* / It must be love: *Madness* / Moon River: *Greyhound*/ Mad about you: *Ruffin, Bruce* / Black pearl: *Faith, Horace* / Black and white: *Greyhound* / Wee rule: *Wee Papa Girl Rappers* / Reggae got soul: *Big One Crew* / Tomorrow people: *Marley, Ziggy & The Melody Makers*/ Tide is high, The: *Blondie* / Real fashion reggae style: *Johnson, Carey* / Think about that: *Livingstone*, Dandy / Big city: *Livingstone, Dandy* / Train tour to rainbow city: *Pyramids* / 007 (shanty town): *Dekker*, Desmond & The Aces / Love of the common people: *Thomas, Nicky* / Barbados: *Lee, Rustie* / Companero: *Mighty* Gabby / We want more Grynner: *Mighty Grynner* / Bend down: *Lee, Rustie* / Hot hot hot: *Arrow* / If you're ready (come go with me): *Turner, Ruby* / Hip hop reggae: *Asher D & Daddy Freddy* / Life: *Frighty &* Colonel Mite / Police officer: *Smiley Culture* / Mental hospital: *Hunter, Tad* / Wild world (long & saxy): *Priest, Maxi* / Rumours: *Isaacs, Gregory* / Girlie girlie: *George, Sophia* / Liquidator: *Harry J.* All Stars / Suzanne beware of the devil: *Livingstone, Dandy* / Midnight rider: *Davidson*, Paul / Double barrel: *Collins, Dave & Ansel* / Return of Django: *Upsetters* / This is ska: *Longsy D & Buster Bloodvessel* / Dollar in the teeth: *Upsetters*.
2LP: . . . . **SMR 986**
MCSET: . . . . **SMC 986**

SUNSPLASH (Various artists).
LP: . . . . **NE 1229**
MC: . . . . **CE 2229**

SUNSPLASH SHOWCASE (Various artists).
LP: . . . . **KVL 9007**

SUPERFRESH (Various artists).
LP: . . . . **WRLP 9**

SUPERROCK (Various artists).
LP: . . . . **WR LP 10**

SUPERSTAR HIT PARADE (Various artists).
Tracks: / Material girl: *Brown, Dennis* / No warrior: *Delgado, Junior* / If you a warrior: *Osbourne, Johnny*/ Can't take the pressure: *Campbell, Al* / Rosie: *Angelo, Don* / More rub-a-dub: *Jarrett, Eccleton* / Dance hall serious thing: *Anthony, Pad* / Move to the top: *King Kong*.
LP: . . . . **GREL 96**

SUPERSTAR HIT PARADE VOL 5 (Various artists).
LP: . . . . **SPLP 14**

SUPERSTARS HIT PARADE VOL.1 (Various artists).
LP: . . . . **LALP 01**

SUPERSTARS HIT PARADE VOL.2 (Various artists).
LP: . . . . **LALP 006**

SUPERSTARS HIT PARADE VOL.4 (Various artists).
Tracks: / Groovin': *Wales, Josey* / Run come gi me: *Chicken Chest* / D.J. a look fi me: *Lecturer* / Wake up little Susie: *Love, Courtney* / Shakey shakey love: *Buckley, Michael* / Woo woo song: *Gold, Brian & Tony*/ Let's give it a try: *Isaacs, Gregory* / Bye bye love: *Sparks, Trevor* / Old time something: *Admiral Bailey*/ Dean in Chinatown: *Frazer, Dean*.
LP: . . . . **LALP 26**

SUPERSTARS HIT PARADE VOL.7 (Various artists).
LP: . . . . **SPLP 16**

SURE SHOT VOL. 1 (Various artists).
MC: . . . . **VPRC 1039**
LP: . . . . **VPRL 1039**

TAMOKI AND WAMBESI SHOWCASE (Various artists).
LP: . . . . **TWLP 1019**

TAXI CONNECTION LIVE IN LONDON (Various artists).
Tracks: / Red hot: *Sly & Robbie* / When you're hot you're hot: *Sly & Robbie* / Trouble you a trouble me: *Kamoze*, Ini / Call the police: *Kamoze, Ini* / One in a million: *Sensimillia & Half Pint* / Mr. Landlord: *Half Pint* / Greetings: *Half Pint* / Reggae calypso: *Yellowman*.
LP: . . . . **ILPS 9862**
MC: . . . . **ICT 9862**

THEY TALK ABOUT LOVE (Various artists).
LP: . . . . **TRLS 277**

THIRD WORLD DISCO - VOL.1 (Various artists).
LP: . . . . **TWLP 204**

THIRD WORLD DISCO - VOL.3 (Various artists).
LP: . . . . **TWLP 206**

THIS IS LOVERS REGGAE (Various artists).
LP: . . . . **ARILP 061**

THIS IS ROOTS MUSIC-VOL.1 (Various artists).
Tracks: / Call me anytime: *Johnson, Anthony* / Youthman fight on: *Johnson, Anthony* / Need to be loved: *Fraser*, Philip / Get happy: *Zero, Earl* / Blood a go run: *Prince Allah/Nazarines* / Bucket bottom: *Prince Allah*/ New civilization: *Campbell, Clifton* / Come Ethiopians: *Fraser, Philip* / Love you: *Fullwood, George*/ Son be careful: *White, Silvon* / Free up the blackman: *Earl-Locks, Joseph*.
LP: . . . . **VGLP 003**

TIGHT ROCK: VOLUME I (Various artists).
LP: . . . . **TMLP 1**

TIGHTEN UP BOX SET (Various artists).
LPS: . . . . **TALL 300**

TIGHTEN UP VOL. 2 (Various artists).
LP: . . . . **TBL 145**

TIGHTEN UP VOL. 5 (Various artists).
LP: . . . . **TBL 165**

TIGHTEN UP VOL. 6 (Various artists).
LP: . . . . **TBL 185**

TIGHTEN UP VOL. 7 (Various artists).
LP: . . . . **TBL 196**

TIGHTEN UP VOL. 8 (Various artists).
LP: . . . . **TBL 207**

TOKYO REGGAE CLASH (Various artists).
LP: . . . . **W 250003**

TOP 12 '89 REGGAE, 2 (Various artists).
LP: . . . . **SPLP 15**

TOP TEN SOUND CLASH (Various artists).
LP: . . . . **DSR 11114**

TRIBUTE TO MARCUS GARVEY (Various artists).
MC: . . . . **GREEN 147**
LP: . . . . **GREL 147**

TROJAN EXPLOSION (20 Reggae Hits) (Various artists).
Tracks: / You can get it if you really want it: *Desmond Dekker & The Aces* / Reggae in your jeggae: *Livingstone, Dandy*/ Johnny too bad: *Slickers* / Liquidator: *Harry J. All Stars* / Wonderful world, beautiful people: *Cliff, Jimmy* / Them a laugh and a kiki: *Soulmates* / 54-46 was my number: *Maytals* / Cherry oh baby: *Donaldson*, Eric / Let your yeah be yeah: *Pioneers* / Dollar of soul: *Ethiopians* / Young gifted and black: *Bob* & Marcia / Sweet sensation: *Melodians* / Elizabethan reggae: *Gardiner, Boris* / Mama look deh: *Pioneers*/ Double barrel: *Collins, Dave & Ansel* / Small axe: *Marley, Bob* / Pomps and Pride: *Maytals* / Return of Django: *Upsetters* / 007 (Shanty town): *Dekker, Desmond & The Aces* / Phoenix city: *Alphonso, Roland*.
LP: . . . . **TRLS 246**
MC: . . . . **ZCTRL 246**

TROJAN STORY, THE (Various artists).
Tracks: / Guns of Navarone: *Skatalites* / Phoenix City: *Alphonso, Roland* / Oh ba-a-by: *Techniques* / Rock steady: *Ellis, Alton* / Do the reggae: *Maytals* / Stand by your man: *Webber, Marlene* / Red red wine: *Tribe, Tony* / Miss Jamaica: *Cliff, Jimmy* / Version galore: *Roy, U* / Screaming target: *Big Youth*/ Cassius Clay: *Alcapone, Dennis* / Black man time: *Roy, I.* / Silhouette: *Brown, Dennis* / Jimmy Brown: *Parker, Ken* / Just can't figure it out: *Diamonds* / Enter into his gates with praise: *Clark, Johnnie*/ Pretty African: *Dekker, Desmond* / Save the last dance for me: *Heptones* / Nice nice time: *Zap Pow*/ Take me home country roads: *Toots & The Maytals* / Time is the master: *Simon, Tito* / Mama look deh: *Pioneers*/ Big 8: *Judge Dread* / Them a fe get a beatin': *Tosh, Peter* / Montego Bay: *Notes, Freddie & The Rudies*/ Elizabethan reggae: *Lee, Byron & The Dragonaires* / 007 (shanty town): *Dekker, Desmond* / Crying over you: *Boothe*, Ken / Return of Django: *Upsetters* / Mr. Bojangles: *Holt, John* / Reggae in your jeggae: *Livingstone, Dandy* / Long shot kick de bucket: *Pioneers*.
2LP: . . . . **TRLD 402**

TROJAN STORY, VOL 1 (Various artists).
Tracks: / Bartender: *Aitken, Laurel* / Humpty dumpty: *Morris, Eric* / Housewives choice: *Derrick & Patsy*/ Don't stay out too late: *Patrick, Kentrick* / Rough and tough: *Cole, Stranger* / Man to man: *Patrick, Kentrick*/ Confucius: *Drummond, Don* / Soon you'll be gone: *Blues Busters* / Yeah, yeah: *Riots* / Dreader than dread: *Martin, Honeyboy* / Syncopate: *Astronauts* / Keep the pressure on: *Winston, George* / Oh babe: *Techniques* / Train to Skaville: *Ethiopians* / Pretty Africa: *Cliff, Jimmy* / Rock steady: *Ellis*, Alton / Perfidia: *Dillon, Phillis* / Way of life: *Tait, Lynn* / Second fiddle: *Tennors* / Nana: *Slickers*/ Black and white: *Various artists*.
LPS: . . . . **TALL 100**
MCSET: . . . . **ZCTAL 100**

TRUMP JACK IN DUB (Various artists).
LP: . . . . **TJPLP 003**

TRUTH, JUSTICE & THE RAGAMUFFIN WAY (Various artists).
LP: . . . . **ARCLP 1**

TWELVE THE HARD WAY (Various artists).
LP: . . . . **TMLP 001**

TWO FRIENDS TING AND TING (Various artists).
Tracks: / Sound ting: *Gold, Brian & Tony* / Idle talk ting: *Ranks, Cutty* / Keeping a fat ting: *Red Rose*/ Gun ting: *Lindo, Hopeton* / Pretend ting: *Papa San* / Love ting: *Home-T* / Oil ting: *Cocoa Tea*/ Bow ting: *Flourgan* / Procrastinate ting: *Mann, Peter* / Bun ting: *Pink Panther (film)* / Cheat ting: *Chevelle* / Gyow ting: *Sister Charmaine*.
LP: . . . . **GREL 155**
MC: . . . . **GREEN 155**

UPRISING (Black Scorpio Volume 2) (Various artists).
LP: . . . . **DSR 9743**

UPSETTER BOX SET (Various artists).
Tracks: / Tighten up: *Dillinger* / Django shoots first: *Sir Lord Comic* / Uncle Charley: *Upsetters* / Sokup: *Upsetters* / Double power: *Upsetters* / Lover's version: *Upsetters* / Rumpelsteelskin: *Upsetters*/ Skankgin: *Dillinger* / Kuchy skank: *Upsetters* / Connection: *Dillinger* / Operation: *Upsetters*/ Do your thing: *Barker, Dave* / Dream land: *Upsetters* / Long sentence: *Upsetters* / Not guilty: *Upsetters*/ Cool and easy: *Upsetters* / Well dread version three: *Addis Ababa children* / My girl: *Upsetters* / Saw dust: *Upsetters* / Place called Africa version 3: *Prince, Winston* / Isn't it wrong: *Hurricanes* / Go slow: *Upsetters* / Bad luck: *Upsetters* / Move me: *Upsetters* / Surplus: *Upsetters* / Kentucky skank: *Upsetters* / Double six: *Roy, U* / Just enough: *Isaacs, David* / In the iaah: *Upsetters*/ Jungle lion: *Upsetters* / We are neighbours: *Isaacs, David* / Soul man: *Upsetters* / Stick together: *U-Roy* / High fashion: *Roy, U* / Hail stones: *Upsetters* / Ironside: *Upsetters* / Cold weather: *Upsetters* / Waap you aww: *Various artists*.
LPS: . . . . **PERRY 1**

VERSION LIKE RAIN (Various artists).
Tracks: / I want a wine: *Graham, Leo* / Double wine: *Upsetters* / Hot and cold version 1: *Pablo & Upsetters*/ Fever: *Cadogan, Susan* / Beat down Babylon: *Byles, Junior* / Outformer version: *Upsetters* / Beat version: *Upsetters* / Iron wolf: *Upsetters* / Stick together: *U-Roy* / Fever: *Byles, Junior* / This world: *Henry, Milton* / Influenza version: *Upsetters* / Informer man: *Byles, Junior* / Babylon's burning: *Maxie*/ Freedom fighter: *Bunny & Ricky* / Bet you don't know: *Duffus, Shenley*.
LP: . . . . **TRLS 278**

VERSION TO VERSION (Various artists).
LP: . . . . **TBL 182**

VERSION TO VERSION: VOLUME III (Various artists).
LP: . . . . **TBL 206**

VINTAGE REGGAE VOL 2 (Various artists).
LP: . . . . **DGLP 286**

VISION OF REGGAE (Various artists).
LP: . . . . **TWLP 1007**

WAMBESI ALL- STAR (Various artists).
LP: . . . . **TWDV 1002**
LP: . . . . **TWLP 1002**

WHOLE NEW GENERATION OF DJ (Various artists).
Tracks: / What about righ oink: *Eastwood, Clint & General Saint* / Push baby push: *Shorter, Errol* / Man live it: *Captain Sinbad* / Jean Green: *Ranking Dread* / Gow: *Mundy, Glen* / Special request to all Isle Vendor: *Toyan* / Girls of today: *Tullo, Pappa* / Can't take the running: *Mikes, Jah* / Qualified girl: *Smart, Nicker* / Better your life: *Sinbad, lincoln*.
LP: . . . . **GREL 26**

WISER DREAD (Various artists).
LP: . . . . **NH 301**

WORKS FOR THE FUTURE PART 2 (Various artists).
LP: . . . . **JTLP 022**

WORRIES IN THE DANCE (Various artists).
LP: . . . . **JJ 191**

YARD STYLE CHRISTMAS Various artists (Various artists).
LP: . . . . **Unknown**

YESTERDAY ONCE MORE (Various artists).
LP: . . . . **TRLS 294**
MC: . . . . **ZCTRL 294**

Reggae George

FIGHT ON MY OWN.
LP: . . . . **SJ 005**

MIX UP.
LP: . . . . **TRLS 213**

NO MORE FRIEND (see under Meditations).

Reggae Nomix

REGGAE NOMIX.
LP: . . . . **CLAYLP 13**

Reggae Philharmonic...

LOVELY THING (Reggae Philharmonic Orchestra).
Tracks: / Lovely thing / Lovely thing (Instrumental) (On 7", CD, MC and 12 MNX 742 only.) / Lovely thing (Version) (On CD and 12 MNG 742 only.) / Lovely thing (Dub mix) (On CD and 12 MNG 742.) / Lovely thing (Rap) (On 12 MNX 742 only.).
MCSET: . . . . **MNT 742**

REGGAE PHILHARMONIC ORCHESTRA (Reggae Philharmonic Orchestra).
Tracks: / Minnie the moocher / Sharpeville / Work, eat, sleep / Best friend / As time goes by / Love and hate / Working class / Fool, The / Dangling / Scrounger.
MC: . . . . **ICT 9898**
LP: . . . . **ILPS 9898**

TIME (Reggae Philharmonic Orchestra).
LP: . . . . **MLPS 1047**
LP: **846 274 1**
MC: . . . . **MCT 1047**
MC: **846 274 4**

Reggae Regulars

GHETTO ROCK.
Tracks: / Ghetto rock / Aristocrat / Violence in the streets / Black skin boys / Praise Jah love / Don't let money rule your head / Jah bring them come / Tribute to the D.J. / Jah festival (instrumental) / Natty camp / Check for him.
LP: . . . . **GREL 64**

REGGAE REGULARS.
LP: . . . . **JDLP 005**

Regulars

VICTIM.
Tracks: / Fools game / Hey girl / Weed stalk / Not any more / Victim / Jah jah children / Friends of tomorrow / Ital club / Where is jah.
LP: . . . . **CBS 83541**

Rehak, Frank

JAZZVILLE VOL.2 (Rehak, Frank Sextet & Alex Smith Quintet).
LP: . . . . **FS 283**

Rei, Panta

PANTA REI.
LP: . . . . **DRLP 131**

Reich, Steve

DESERT MUSIC, THE.
LP: 9791011

DIFFERENT TRAINS (Reich, Steve & The Kronos Quartet).
Tracks: / Different trains / Electric counterpoint.
LP: 979176 1
MC: 979176 4

DRUMMING.
Tracks: / Part 1 / Part 2 / Part 3 / Part 4.
LP: . . . . K 979170 1
MC: . . . . K 979170 4

EARLY WORKS.
Tracks: / Come out 1966 / Piano phrase / Clapping music / It's gonna rain.
LP: . . . . K 979169 1
MC: . . . . K 979169 4

FOUR ORGANS-PHASE PATTERNS.
LP: . . . . SHAN 83511

MUSIC FOR 18 MUSICIANS.
LP: . . . . ECM 1129

SIX MARIMBAS.
LP: 979 1381
MC: 979 1384

TEHILLIM.
Tracks: / Parts I & II (Performed by Steve Reich and Musicians conducted by George Manahan.) / Parts III & IV.
LP: . . . . ECM 1215

Reichman, Joe

JOE REICHMAN 1944-49.
Tracks: / Pagliacci and variations in G / You made me love you / Kashmiri love song / Chopsticks / Music stopped, The / Dancing in the dark / Lovely way to spend an evening, The / Liza / Don't sweetheart me / I've had this feeling before / Johnson rag / It could happen to you / Featherhead / There I've said it again / Mama's gone goodbye / Joe jumps with joy / Little thoughts.
LP: . . . . HSR 166

PAGLIACCI OF THE PIANO (Reichman, Joe & His Orchestra).
LP: . . . . CLP 84

Reid, Alan

SIDETRACKS (Reid, Alan/ Brian McNeill).
LP: 12TS 417

Reid, Duke

BA BA BOOM.
LP: . . . . TRLS 265

GOLDEN HITS: DUKE REID.
LP: . . . . TILP 003

IT'S ROCKIN' TIME.
LP: . . . . TRLS 279

Reid, Irene

LADY FROM SAVANNAH (Reid, Irene & Mike Carr Quartet).
Tracks: / I'm walkin' / S'posin' / Don't get around much anymore / Easy living / Fever / Rainy day / I get a kick out of you / Blues medley.
LP: . . . . MC 589

Reid, Jim

I SAW THE WILD GEESE.
LP: . . . . SPR 1015
MC: . . . . SPRC 1015

Reid, Jimmy

ARE YOU READY.
LP: . . . . LDR LP 009

Reid, Junior

BACK TO BACK (Reid, Junior/Leroy Smart).
LP: . . . . UP RL 1019

BOOM SHACK A LACK.
Tracks: / Cross over the border / Mother move / Big timer / Row your boat / There will be no darkness / Boom shack a lack / Drink out me royalty / Strange things / Sitting in the park / False rumours.
MC: . . . . GREEN 78
LP: . . . . GREL 78

ONE BLOOD.
Tracks: / One blood / Nuh so, A / Who done it / When it shows / Searching for better / Married life / Eleanor Rigby / Gruppie Diana / Sound / Dominant.
LP: . . . . RMUSIC 01
LP: . . . . JRLP 1
MC: . . . . JRMC 1

ORIGINAL FOREIGN MIND.
LP: . . . . LM LP 002

TWO OF A KIND (Reid, Junior & Teasy).
LP: . . . . TWLP 1009

Reid, Mike

GOLDEN HOUR OF MIKE REID.
MC: . . . . KGHMC 123

GOLDEN HOUR PRESENTS MIKE REID.
Tracks: / Ugly duckling / Knocked 'em in the Old Kent Road / Three bells / Flash, bang, wallop / High hopes / Old Shep / Get me to the church on time / Thing, The / Swinging on a star / Marrow song / When I leave the world behind / King's new clothes, The / My old dutch / Purple people eater / That's who / Spaniard that blighted my life / My Yiddisha, momma / Winkle picking Annie / Oom pah pah / Sweeny Todd / He's going there every night / Bye bye blackbird.
LP: . . . . GH 672

Reid, Neil

NEIL REID.
LP: . . . . SKL 5122

SMILE.
LP: . . . . SKL 5136

Reid, Patti

PATTI REID COLLECTION.
Tracks: / Lord Derwentwater / Lowlands of Holland, The / Rambling boys of pleasure, The / Garden gate / Bonnie Annie / Pretty saro / Cold / Haily windy night / Snows, The / Craigie hill / Ten thousand miles / Where the moorcock crows / Farewell farewell.
LP: . . . . FE 061

Reid, Roy

WHAP'N'BAP.
Tracks: / Whap'n'bap / Alphabet / Union call / Ladies man / London / Get up / Sweet pussy cat / Conscious argument / Jive time / Injection.
LP: . . . . V 2164

Reid, Rufus

SEVEN MINDS (Reid, Rufus Trio).
Tracks: / Seven minds / Along came Betty / You make me smile / Tones for Joan's bones / Struttin' about.
LP: . . . . SSC 1010

TOO MARVELLOUS FOR WORDS (see Carter, Joe) (Reid, Rufus/Joe Carter).

Reid, Sandra

FEELS SO GOOD.
LP: . . . . SGLP 004

IF DREAMS WERE REAL.
LP: . . . . SGLP 001

Reid, Steve

RAW MATERIAL (see Wallen,Per Henrik) (Reid, Steve/Per Henrik Wallen/ Kevin Ross).

Reid, Tam

KING OF THE BOTHY BALLAD SINGERS.
Tracks: / Trampin lass / Bogie's bonnie belle / Muckle Friday fair / Prince and Jean / Hash of Bennagoak / Big Kilmarnock bonnet / Drummallochie / Twa recruiting sergeants / Buchan ploorman, The / Nicky tams / Muckle gauket gype / Braes of Braenall / Buchan vet, The.
MC: . . . . CWGR 119

OOR FAIRM TOON.
Tracks: / Oor fairm toon / Buchan gairdener, The / Sleepytoon / New lum hat, The / Kissing in the dark / Im-hm / Road and the miles to Dundee, The / It's afa' like its father / Tobacco pipes / Country geordie / Bandy's roup / Corncake amang the whinney knowes, The / Auld Grace / Drunkard's ragged wean, The / Buchan Bobby, The / Lang lang syne.
MC: . . . . CWGR TV11

TAM REID'S CEILIDH.
Tracks: / Festival o' Keith / Mucking of Geordie's byre, The / Atholl highlanders / Kenmore's up and awa' / Dancing dustmas, The / Glen Isla and Glenshee / Pear tree, The / Bonnie lass o' Fyvie / Headlands, The / Peter Fair / Bride in the morning / Forty shades of green / Dancing fingers / Trampin' lass / It's lonely in the bothy / Three laddies and their faithers / Nod and a wink, A / Affection / Laird o' Tomintoul, The / Flech, The / Im-hm / Up the Noran Water / Kelty clippie / Once a man / Twa bicycles, The / Lum hat, The.
MC: . . . . CWGR 130

Reid, Terry

DRIVER, THE.
LP: . . . . WX 426
MC: . . . . WX 426C

HAND DON'T FIT THE GLOVE, THE.
Tracks: / Hand don't fit the glove, The / Superlungs my supergirl / Silver white light / July / Better by far / Marking time / Stay with me baby / This time / Fires alive / Highway 61 revisited / Friends highway 61 revisited / Speak now or forever hold your peace / Rich kid blues.
LP: . . . . SEE 50

ROUGE WAVES.
Tracks: / Ain't no shadow / Baby, I love you / Stop and think it over / Rogue waves / Walk away Renee / Believe in the magic / Then I kissed her / Bowangi / All I have to do is dream.
LP: . . . . EST 11857

Reidel, George

GEORGE REIDEL.
LP: . . . . PHONT 7552
LP: . . . . FLC 5906

Reidy, Winston

ON DE ROCK part 2 (Reidy, Winston & The Cimarons).
Tracks: / Wake up Jah-man-can (on the rock) / Jah no dead / Soul and inspiration / Rooting for a cause / Rock rock reggae rhapsody / Dim the light / Paul Bogle / Take heed / Greedy man / Ship took us away.
LP: . . . . ONLY 4

Reilly, John

BONNY GREEN TREE.
LP: 12TS 359

Reilly, Paddy

20 GOLDEN IRISH BALLARDS.
MC: . . . . DCX 9006

COME BACK PADDY REILLY.
MC: MCCOOL001

FIELDS OF ATHENRY.
Tracks: / Town I loved so well, The / Farewell to Nova Scotia / Galtee mountain boy / Farewell to the Rhonda / John O'Dreams / Scorn not his simplicity / Crack was ninety in the Isle of Man, The / Dancing at Whitsun / Mulligan and me / Jim Larkin / Bunch of Thyme / Fields of Athenry.
LP: . . . . RITZLP 0027
MC: . . . . RITZLC 0027
LP: . . . . DOLX 9002
MC: . . . . DOCX 9002

GREEN SHAMROCK SHORE.
LP: . . . . DOLM 5040

LIFE OF PADDY REILLY, THE.
Tracks: / Spancil Hill / Coming of the road / Sam Hall / Come to the bower / Deportees / Dollymount Strand / Irish soldier boy / Matt Hyland / Orange and the green, The / James Larkin / James Connolly / Lark in the morning, The.
LP: . . . . DOLM 5001
MC: . . . . DOCM 5001

OLD REFRAIN, THE.
Tracks: / Old refrain, The / Beautiful dreamer / Champion at keeping them rolling / Galway races / This town is not their own / Paddy's green shamrock shore / Farewell to Dublin / Only our rivers / Derroll in the rain / Old man song / Bunclody / Lark in the morning, The.
LP: . . . . DOLX 9003
MC: . . . . DOCX 9003

PADDY REILLY AT HOME.
Tracks: / Come out ye black and tans / Four green fields / Silver in the stubble / Peggy Gordon / Foggy dew, The / Kelly the boy from Killane / Joe Hill / Nation once again, A / Blackwater side / Limerick rake / Anach Cuin / Salford Town.
LP: . . . . DOLM 5006
MC: . . . . DOCB 5006

PADDY REILLY LIVE.
MC: . . . . RTE 78

PADDY REILLY NOW.
LP: . . . . JBLP 007

PADDY REILLY'S GREATEST HITS.
2LP: . . . . HM 002D
MC: . . . . HMC 002

PADDY REILLY'S IRELAND.
2LP: . . . . HM 011D

SONGS OF IRELAND.
MC: . . . . ARANC 0013

TOWN I LOVED SO WELL, THE.
Tracks: / Flower of sweet Strabane / Cliffs of Dooneen / Hills of Kerry / Galway races / Ratcliffe highway / Come up the stairs, Molly O / Town I loved so well, The / Arthur McBride / Autumn has come / I once loved a lass / Bold tenant farmer / Sweet Carnlough Bay / There has to be an end to it someday / Movin' along song, The.
LP: . . . . DOLM 5010
MC: . . . . DOCM 5010

TWENTY GOLDEN IRISH BALLADS.
Tracks: / Fields of Athenry / Bunch of thyme / Spancil hill / Galway races / Lark in the morning, The / Peggy Gordon / Joe Hill / Four green fields / Come out ye black and tans / Cliffs of Dooneen / Hills of Kerry / Arthur McBride / Matt Hyland / Galtee Mountain boy / Bunclody / Crack was ninety in the Isle Of Man, The / Sweet Carnlough Bay / Jim Larkin / Nation once again, A.
MC: . . . . DOCX 9006

TWENTY GOLDEN IRISH BALLADS VOLUME 2.
Tracks: / Town I loved so well, The / There has to be an end to it someday / Irish soldier boy / Sam Hall / Limerick rake / Silver in the stubble / James Larkin / Blackwater side / Kelly the boy from Killane / I once loved a lass / Flower of sweet Strabane / Bold tenant farmer / Come to the bower / Autumn has come / Ratcliffe highway / Annerchuain / Dollymount strand / Moving along song / Orange and the Green, The / Deportees.
MC: . . . . DOCX 9009

Reilly, Peter

IRISH TINKER BALLADS.
MC: 60-175

Reilly, Robert

TEMPTATION.
Tracks: / Half a chance / Gone too long / Praying for rain / Long distance / North wind / Temptation / Towns like mine / Save me / After all these years / All I want.
LP: . . . . SCARTLP 3
MC: . . . . SCARTMC 3

Reilly, Tommy

THANKS FOR THE MEMORY (Reilly, Tommy & James Moody).
LP: . . . . LBRD 020
MC: . . . . LBTD 020

Reilly, Vinny

ANOTHER SETTING.
MC: . . . . FACT 74 C

Reinhardt, Babik

ALL LOVE.
MC: . . . . MODEMC 1008
LP: . . . . MODEM 1008

Reinhardt, Django

50TH ANNIVERSARY CONCERT (Reinhardt, Django & Stephane Grappelli).
Tracks: / I saw stars / Confessin' / Dinah / Tiger rag / Lady be good / Lily Belle May June / Sweet Sue / Continental / Simplement / Fumee aux yeux / Cocktails for two / Blue drag / Swanee river / Ton doux sourire / Ultra fox / Si j'avais ete.
LP: . . . . VJD 6950

50TH ANNIVERSARY OF THE QUINTET OF THE HOT CLUB OF FRANCE (see Grappelli, Stephane) (Reinhardt, Django & Stephane Grappelli).

AU CLUB ST GERMAIN DES PRES.
LP: 502008

AVEC STEPHANE GRAPPELLI ET H. ROSTAING.
LP: 500 813

CLUB ST GERMAIN (February 1951).
LP: . . . . HR 5003

CRAZY RHYTHM.
Tracks: / How high the moon / Fine and dandy / Yesterdays / Lover / Apple honey / Manoir de mes reves / Dream of you / Crazy rhythm.
LP: . . . . TOP 128
MC: . . . . KTOP 128

DEUX GEANTS DU JAZZ (See under Bechet, Sidney) (Reinhardt, Django/ Sidney Bechet).

DJANGO.
Tracks: / Lady be good / Dinah / Confessin' / I saw stars / Tiger rag / Continental / Blue drag / Sweet Sue / Sunshine of your smile / Nuages / Swanee river / Night and day / September song / Testament / Brazil / Manoir de mes reves / Blues for Ike / Insensiblement / Gypsy with a song.
LP: . . . . OJC 057
LP: . . . . CBS 22186
MC: 40 22186

DJANGO - 1934.
LP: . . . . GNPS 9031

DJANGO - 1935.
LP: . . . . GNPS 9023
MC: GNP5 9023

DJANGO - 1936-37.
LP: . . . . S 1399

DJANGO - 1937-39.
LP: . . . . S 1400

DJANGO - 1943-50.
LP: . . . . S 1401

DJANGO ET COMPAGNIE.
LP: 2489 188

DJANGO REINHARDT.
MC: . . . . CCH 538

DJANGO REINHARDT, 1934-53.
LP: 2MJP 1052

DJANGO REINHARDT BOX SET, THE.
Tracks: / I'se a muggin' / I can't give you anything but love / Oriental shuffle / After you've gone / Are you in the mood? / Limehouse blues / Nagasaki / Swing guitars / Georgia on my mind / Shine / In the still of the night / Sweet chorus / Exactly like you / Charleston / You're driving me crazy / Tears / Solitude / Hot lips / Ain't misbehavin' / Rose room /

Body and soul / When day is done / Runnin' wild / Chicago / Liebestraum No. 3 / Miss Annabelle Lee / Little love, a little kiss, A / Mystery Pacific / In a sentimental mood / Sheik of Araby, The / Improvisation / Parfum / Alabamy bound / Crazy rhythm / Honeysuckle rose / Out of nowhere / Sweet Georgia Brown / Bugle call rag / Between the Devil and the deep blue sea / I got rhythm / Sweet Sue / Hangin' around Boudon / Japanese sandman / St. Louis blues / Bouncin' around / Eddie's blues / Lady be good / Dinah / Daphne / You took advantage of me / I've found a new baby / I ain't got nobody / Baby, won't you please come home? / Big boy blues / Bill Coleman blues / Somebody loves me / I can't believe that you're in love with me / Concerto in D Minor - first movement / Fiddle blues / Swingin' with Django / Paramount stomp / Bolero de Django / Mabel / My serenade / You rascal you / Stephen's blues / Sugar / Tea for two / Blues / Easy going / College stomp / Harlem swing / It had to be you / I'm coming, Virginia / Farewell blues / Blue light blues / Montmartre / Low cotton / Finesse / I know that you know / Solid old man / Stockholm / Younger generation, The / I'll see you in my dreams / Echoes of Spain / Naguine / At Jimmy's bar / Rhythme futur / Begin the beguine / Indecision / Swing 41 / Nuages / Pour vous (exactly like you) / Fantaisie sur une dance Norvegienne / Vendredi 13 / Liebesfreud / Petit mesonges (Little white lies) / Les yeux noirs / Swing de Paris / Oiseaux des isles / All of me / Belleville / Lentement, Mademoiselle / Douce ambiance / Manoir de mes reves / Oui / Fleur d'ennui / Blues Clair / Improvisation no.3 (part 1) / Improvisation no.3 (part 2) / If dreams come true / Stompin' at the Savoy / Hallelujah / How high the moon / Djangology / Coquette / Django's tiger / Embraceable you / Echoes of France (La Marseillaise) / R-vingt-six / Lover man / Blue Lou / Swing dynamique / Festival 48 / Brick top / Time on my hands / Blue skies.
LPS: . . . . **BOX 107**
LPS: . . . . **PM 1728833**
MCSET: . . . . **PM 1728839**
LPS: . . . . **ALBUM 64**
MCSET: . . . . **CASSETTE 64**

DJANGO REINHARDT COLLECTION (20 Golden Greats).
Tracks: / Double whisky / Dream of you / Porto cabello / Duke and Dukie / I saw stars / Nuages / I can't give you anything but love / September song / Swing guitars / Stormy weather / I got rhythm / All the things you are / Sophisticated lady / It's only a paper moon / Daphne / Djangology / Tisket a tasket, A / St. Louis blues / Honeysuckle rose / Royal Garden blues.
LP: . . . . **DVLP 2067**
MC: . . . . **DVMC 2067**

DJANGO REINHARDT & QUINTET OF HOT CLUB OF FRANCE (Volume 1) (Reinhardt, Django & Quintet Of Hot Club Of France).
LP: . . . . **S 1305**

DJANGO REINHARDT & QUINTET OF HOT CLUB OF FRANCE (Volume 2) (Reinhardt, Django & Quintet Of Hot Club Of France).
LP: . . . . **S 1306**

DJANGO REINHARDT & QUINTET OF HOT CLUB OF FRANCE (Volume 3) (Reinhardt, Django & Quintet Of Hot Club Of France).
LP: . . . . **S 1389**

DJANGO REINHARDT, VOL 1.
Tracks: / Daphne / Tears / Dinah / Tiger rag / Them there eyes / Improvisation / Uptown blues / Clair de Lune / Lentement Mademoiselle / Melodie au Crepuscule / How high the moon / Manoir de mes Reves / Danse nuptiale / I can't give you anything but love.
LP: . . . . **JR 119**

DJANGO REINHARDT VOL 2.
MC: . . . . **NEO 844**

DJANGO REINHARDT WITH STEPHANE GRAPELLI (1947-49) (Reinhardt, Django & Stephane Grappelli).
LP: . . . . **S 1371**

DJANGO REINHARDT/HOT CLUB DE FRANCE.
LP: . . . . **ALB 322**

DJANGO REINHARDT/SIDNEY BECHET (See under Bechet, Sidney for information) (Reinhardt, Django/Sidney Bechet).

DJANGO RHYTHM.
LP: . . . . **S 1251**

DJANGO SWING.
LP: . . . . **S 1252**

DJANGO/HOT CLUB OF FRANCE (Reinhardt, Django & Quintet Of Hot Club Of France).
LP: . . . . **GNPS 9019**

DJANGOLOGY.
Tracks: / After you've gone / Limehouse blues / Nagasaki / Honeysuckle rose / Crazy rhythm / Out of nowhere / Chicago / Georgia on my mind / Shine / Sweet Georgia Brown / Bugle call rag / Between the devil and the deep blue sea / Exactly like you / Charleston / You're driving me crazy / Farewell blues / I got rhythm / I know that you know / Ain't misbehavin' / Rose room / Japanese sandman / Swing guitars / Minor swing / Nuages.
LP: . . . . **LPJT 8**

DJANGOLOGY 49.
Tracks: / World is waiting for the sunrise, The / Hallelujah / I'll never be the same / Honeysuckle rose / All the things you are / Djangology / Daphne / Beyond the sea / Lover man / Marie / Minor swing / Ou est tu mon amour / Swing 42 / After you've gone / I got rhythm / I saw stars / Heavy artillery (artillerie lourde) / It's only a paper moon / Bricktop.
LP: . . . . **NL 90448**
MC: . . . . **NK 90448**

DJANGOLOGY, VOL 1.
LP: **2C 054 16001**

DJANGOLOGY, VOL 2.
LP: **2C 054 16002**

DJANGOLOGY, VOL 3.
LP: **2C 054 16003**

DJANGOLOGY, VOL 4.
LP: **2C 054 16004**

DJANGOLOGY, VOL 5.
LP: **2C 054 16005**

DJANGOLOGY, VOL 6.
LP: **2C 054 16006**

DJANGOLOGY, VOL 7.
LP: **2C 054 16007**

DJANGOLOGY, VOL 8.
LP: **2C 054 16008**

DJANGOLOGY, VOL 9.
LP: **2C 054 16009**

DJANGOLOGY, VOL 10.
LP: **2C 054 16010**

DJANGOLOGY, VOL 11.
LP: **2C 054 16011**

DJANGOLOGY, VOL 12.
LP: **2C 054 16012**

DJANGOLOGY, VOL 13.
LP: **2C 054 16013**

DJANGOLOGY, VOL 14.
LP: **2C 054 16014**

DJANGOLOGY, VOL 15.
LP: **2C 054 16015**

DJANGOLOGY, VOL 16.
LP: **2C 054 16016**

DJANGOLOGY, VOL 17.
LP: **2C 054 16017**

DJANGOLOGY, VOL 18.
LP: **2C 054 16018**

DJANGOLOGY, VOL 19.
LP: **2C 054 16019**

DJANGOLOGY, VOL 20.
LP: **2C 054 16020**

DJANGOLOGY/USA VOLS 1-7 (Reinhardt, Django & The Quintet of the Hot Club of France).
LPS: . . . . **SW 8420/26**

DJANGO'S CASTLE.
Tracks: / Minor swing / Manoir de mes reves / Saw star (I) / Nuages / Swing guitars / Artillerie lourde / Djangology / Daphne / After you've gone / Swing 42 / Bricktop / Honeysuckle rose.
LP: . . . . **CL 70907**
MC: . . . . **CK 70907**

ET LE QUINTETTE DU 'HOT CLUB DE FRANCE'.
Tracks: / Ma reguliere / Par correspondance / Rossetta / Limehouse blues / Nagasaki / Charleston / Runnin' wild / Improvisation / Honeysuckle rose / Eddie's blues / Bill Coleman blues / Swingin' with Django / Minor's swing / Bolero / Christmas swing / I got rhythm / Younger generation / Tears / Swing 41 / Nuages / Les yeux noirs / La cigale et la fourmi / Belleville / Welcome / Ol' man river / Just a Gigolo / Manoir de mes reves.
2LP: **1568023**
MC: **1568029**

GOLDEN AGE OF DJANGO REINHARDT.
Tracks: / Nuages / Sweet Sue / Limehouse blues / Place de Broukere / Black eyes / Daphne / Mabel / Djangology / Swing '41 / Swing '42.
LP: . . . . **GX 2506**
MC: . . . . **TCGX 2506**

HOT CLUB DE FRANCE (see under Grappelli, Stephane) (Grappelli, Stephane/Django Reinhardt).

I GOT RHYTHM.
Tracks: / I got rhythm / Crazy rhythm / My melancholy baby / Jeepers creepers / Sweet Georgia Brown / Honeysuckle rose / Liza / Nauges / Nuits de saint germain de press / Just one of those things / I cover the waterfront / I wonder where my baby is tonight.
LP: . . . . **MTM 012**

IMMORTAL DJANGO REINHARDT.
LP: . . . . **GNPS 9038**

INDISPENSABLE DJANGO REINHARDT (1949-50).
Tracks: / Minor swing / Beyond the sea / World is waiting for the sunrise, The / Django's castle / Dream of you / Menilmontant / It's only a paper moon / I saw stars / Nuages / Swing guitars / All the things you are / Tisket a tasket, A / September song / Heavy artillery (Artillerie lourde) / Improvisation / Djangology / Daphne / I'll never be the same / Marie / Jersey bounce / I surrender dear / Hallelujah / Anniversary song / After you've gone / Swing 42 / Stormy weather / Brick top / Lover man / I got rhythm / Honeysuckle rose / St. Louis blues.
2LP: . . . . **NL 70929**
MCSET: . . . . **NK 70929**
2LP: . . . . **PM 45362**

INEDITS VOL.1.
LP: **502010**

INEDITS, VOL 2.
LP: . . . . **VOGUE 502010**

JAZZ TIME VOL.13.
LP: **502713**

LA GRANDE PARADE.
2LP: **400005**

LE DISQUE D'OR.
LP: **509031**

LE DOUBLE DISQUE D'OR.
2LP: **416003**

LEGENDARY DJANGO REINHARDT.
LP: . . . . **GNPS 9039**

LERE PUBLICATION.
2LP: **406505**

L'INOUBLIABLE.
LPS: **000315**

MASTERS OF JAZZ.
LP: . . . . **CL 42342**

NUAGES.
LP: **20102**
MC: **40102**
LP: **500100**

PARIS 1945' DJANGO REINHARDT.
Tracks: / If dreams come true / Stompin' at the Savoy / Hallelujah / How high the moon / Hommage a Fats Waller / Hommage a Debussy / After you've gone / Shoemaker's apron / China boy / Sugar / Don't blame me / Poor Miss Black.
LP: . . . . **BVL 046**

PARISIAN SWING.
LP: . . . . **GNPS 9002**

QUINTET HOT CLUB OF FRANCE.
LP: . . . . **GNPS 9001**

RHYTHM IS OUR BUSINESS (Reinhardt, Django & Stephane Grappelli).
Tracks: / Jeepers creepers / Sweet Sue / Noel brings the swing / Jive bomber / Dinah / Chasing shadows / Some of these days / Believe it, beloved / Clouds / Japanese sandman / Twelfth year / Au revoir / Stardust / Avalon / Swing '39 / I never knew.
LP: . . . . **TAB 55**
MC: . . . . **KTBC 55**

ROME 1949 VOL.1 (Reinhardt, Django/Stephane Grappelli).
LP: . . . . **S 1390**

ROME 1949 VOL.2 (Reinhardt, Django/Stephane Grappelli).
LP: . . . . **S 1391**

RYTHME FUTUR (Radio Sessions 1947).
LP: **500108**

SAME (Reinhardt, Django/Stephane Grappelli).
MC: . . . . **KACC 1158**

STRUTTIN' OUT (Reinhardt, Django & Stephane Grappelli).
Tracks: / HCQ strut / Nuages / It don't mean a thing / I wonder where my baby is tonight / It was so beautiful / Them there eyes / Limehouse blues / Some of these days / Appel direct / I've found a new baby / Undecided / Improvisation no.2 / I've got my love to keep me warm / Chasing shadows / Swing '39 / If I had you / Don't worry 'bout me / My sweet / Duke and Dukie / Believe it, beloved / China boy / I've had my moments / Ultra fox / Del Salle / St. Louis blues / Nocturne / Songe d'automne / Moonglow / Just one of those things / Black and white / Sweet Georgia Brown / It had to be you / Daphne / Lambeth walk / Night and day / Liza.
2LP: . . . . **DPA 3098**

SWING FROM PARIS (Reinhardt, Django/Stephane Grappelli).
Tracks: / Miss Annabelle Lee / Chasing shadows / Stomping at Decca / Solitude / Appel direct / J'attendrai / After you've gone / Nagasaki / Night and day / Avalon / Runnin' wild / Djangology / Shine / Sweet chorus / Them there eyes / Some of these days / If I had you / Three little words / Little love, a little kiss, A / Swing from Paris.
LP: . . . . **CHD 165**
MC: . . . . **MCHD 165**

SWING IN PARIS (Reinhardt, Django & Stephane Grappelli).
Tracks: / I got rhythm / St Louis blues / Appel direct / Honeysuckle rose / Black and white / Limehouse blues / Moonglow / Billets doux / Daphne / China boy / Night and day / My sweet / It don't mean a thing / Sweet Georgia Brown / Swing from Paris / I've found a new baby / Lambeth walk / Them there eyes / It was so beautiful / Three little words / HCQ strut / Swing 39.
LP: . . . . **AJA 5070**
MC: . . . . **ZC AJA 5070**

SWINGING WITH DJANGO.
LP: . . . . **S 1370**

TOGETHER (Reinhardt, Django/Stephane Grappelli/Eddie South).
LP: **2M 056 78140**
MC: **2M 256 78140**

UNISSUED TITLES 1937-47.
LP: . . . . **KC 109**

VERSATILE GIANT, THE.
LP: **500064**

Reininger, Blaine

BOOK OF HOURS.
LP: . . . . **TWI 845**

BYZANTIUM.
Tracks: / Rolf and Florian go Hawaiian / Blood of a poet / Teenage theatre / Some fine day / Japanese dream / Too cool to die / Bird on the wire / Rosebud.
LP: . . . . **TWI 767**

COLORADO SUITE (Reininger, Blaine/Mikel Rouse).
LP: . . . . **MTM 3**

INSTRUMENTALS 1982-86.
LP: . . . . **IM 008**

LIVE IN BRUSSELS (LP).
Tracks: / Volo / Night air / Birthday song / What use indeed ? / Uptown (concert version) / Broken fingers.
LP: . . . . **MASO 33038**

PARIS EN AUTOMNE (Reininger, Blaine/Alain Goutier).
LP: . . . . **TWI 380**
LP: . . . . **MASO 12003**

Reiser, Harry

BANJO CRACKERJAX 1922-30.
LP: . . . . **YAZOO 1048**

BANJO VIRTUOSO VOL.2.
LP: . . . . **BR 152**

Reisman, Joe

PARTY NIGHT AT JOE'S (Reisman, Joe & His Orchestra).
LP: . . . . **FS 180**

Reiter, Joerg

FUN KEY 2.
LP: . . . . **ISST 172**

FUN KEY 3 - THE PIANO CONCEPTION.
LP: . . . . **ISST 185**

NIGHT GROOVE, THE.
LP: . . . . **ISST 198**

SUN RIVER see also under Diez, Stefan (Reiter, Joerg & Stefan Diez).
LP: . . . . **ISST 155**

SUNSET KISSES (Reiter, Joerg & band).
LP: . . . . **ISST 162**

Reith, Pieter

POWER PLANT.
LP: . . . . **ISST 193**

Reithmuller, Heinrich

HAPPY ORGAN PLAYER, THE.
LP: . . . . **JOY 243**

Reivers

SATURDAY.
LP: . . . . **CKT 46926**

Rejects

QUIET STORM.
LP: HMRLP 22
MC: HMRMC 22
LP: HMRLP 22B

Re-Joyce

RE-JOYCE (SOUNDTRACK) (See under Lipman, Maureen) (Lipman, Maureen).

Rektum

SAKREDANUS.
LP: PSI 001

Relations

PATRICK.
LP: WELLP 001

Relative Band

RELATIVE BAND '85.
LP: HOT 1017

Relatives

JIM MORRISON.
LP: RC 003

Relativity

GATHERING PACE.
Tracks: / Blackwell court / Gathering pace / Rose catha na mumhan / Miss Tara Macadam / Ma theid tu unaonaigh / Siun ni dhuibhir / When she sleeps / Monday morning reel, The / Ceol Anna.
LP: SIF 1076
MC: CSIF 1076

Religious

COME SUNDAY (Various artists).
MC: AMP 003

COMMUNION (Various artists).
LP: WING 505
MC: TC WING 505

COMMUNION CONTINUED (Various artists).
LP: WING 513
MC: TC WING 513

CONGREGATIONAL SINGING 1927-9 (Vol. 1 - The 20s) (Various artists).
LP: ELE 6-200

CRUSADE MEMORIES (Graham, Billy).
Tracks: / I've discovered the way of gladness / Mighty fortress is our God, A / Ye gates lift up your heads / Tis marvellous and wonderful / Jesus whispers peace / To God be the glory / My Lord knows the way through the wilderness / It is no secret / Crown him with many crowns / Just as I am / Blessed assurance / How great thou art / Sunlight / What a friend we have in Jesus / His eye is on the sparrow / It is well with my soul / Singing I go / Jesu, joy of man's desiring / Lord's prayer, The.
LP: TWE 6004
MC: TC TWE 6004

EMMANUEL (Various artists).
Tracks: / Come let us worship and bow down: *Various artists* / Love of the ages: *Various artists* / Emmanuelle: *Various artists* / King of kings: *Various artists* / Worthy: *Various artists* / What child is this?: *Various* artists / O come, o come Emmanuel: *Various artists* / God rest ye merry gentlemen: *Various artists* / Hark the herald angels sing: *Various artists* / Silent night: *Various artists* / Joy to the world: *Various artists.*
LP: MM 0071
MC: TC MM 0071

GOD LOVES COUNTRY MUSIC (See under Country...) (Various artists).

GREAT CATHEDRAL ORGANS (Various artists).
MC: TC2MOM 1546509
MC: TC2MOM 126

GUITAR EVANGELISTS VOL 1 (Various artists).
LP: TLP 1002

GUITAR EVANGELISTS VOL 2 (Various artists).
LP: TLP 1003

HYMNS FOR ALL SEASONS VOL. 1 (Various artists).
Tracks: / When morning gilds the skies: *Various artists* / Praise my soul, the King of Heaven: *Various artists*/ Rejoice, the Lord is King: *Various artists* / Great is Thy faithfulness: *Various artists* / God of Abraham praise, The: *Various artists* / O love that wilt not let me go: *Various artists* / Jesus shall reign: *Various artists.*
LP: WST R 9659

HYMNS FOR ALL SEASONS VOL. 2 (Various artists).
LP: WST R 9668

HYMNS FOR ALL SEASONS VOL. 3 (Various artists).
LP: WST R 9669
MC: WST C 9669

IN EVERYTHING GIVE THANKS (SCRIPTURE SONGS) (Various artists).
LP: DOVE 48

INCARNATION (Various artists).
LP: ML R 7013
MC: ML C 7013

INTERNATIONAL PRAISE (Various Salvation Army Participants) (Various artists).
LP: BAB 3515

JESUS IS THE ANSWER (Various artists).
Tracks: / Walk with me: *Highway QC'S* / It's me: *Highway QC'S* / How I got over: *Swan Silvertones* / That day on Calvary: *Swan Silvertones* / My religion: *Caravans* / It's Jesus in me: *Caravans* / I'm going through: *Caravans* / I can see everybody's mother: *Five Blind Boys Of Alabama* / What he's done for me: *Five* Blind Boys Of Alabama / He has a way: *Greater Harvest Choir* / Jesus is the answer: *Argo Singers* / See how he kept me: *Argo Singers* / When tears are falling: *Harmonizing Four*/ Wade in the water: *Harmonizing Four*/ Uncloudy day: *Staple Singers* / Two wings: *Staple Singers.*
LP: CRB 1083

JOHN PAUL II IN POLAND (Various artists).
Tracks: / Fanfare for the Pope: *Various artists* / Raftsmen: *Various artists* / Moment of the entire life: *Various* artists / Oh God, I place my trust in you: *Various artists* / Queen, black Madonna: *Various artists* / Hazulen song: *Various artists* / Peter's song: *Various artists* / Our Father: *Various artists* / Blessing: *Various* artists / Prayer to the Mother of God: *Various artists* / Brown Madonna: *Various artists* / Do not be afraid Mary, you Lily: *Various artists* / Temple is our house: *Various artists* / We are never alone like skipping stones: *Various artists* / Little cantata: *Various artists* / On a December night: *Various artists.*
LP: EMC 3317

JUST FOR TODAY (Various artists).
Tracks: / Love is a gift: *Various artists* / Actors in prayer: *Various artists* / Nun's prayer: *Various artists*/ Prayers for peace: *Various artists* / 23rd psalm: *Various artists* / Love divine, all loves excelling: *Various artists* / Lord's prayer: *Various artists* / Lord of the dance: *Various artists.*
LP: 297264 8

KIDS' PRAISE 1 (Various artists).
Tracks: / Amen, praise the Lord: *Various artists* / Behold, what manner of love: *Various artists* / Jesus, name above all names: *Various artists* / If I were a butterfly: *Various artists* / Seek ye first: *Various artists*/ Heaven is a wonderful place: *Various artists* / Wa wa song, The: *Various artists* / Father I adore you: *Various artists* / Children of the Lord: *Various artists.*
LP: MAC 5098
MC: TC MAC 5098

KIDS' PRAISE 2 (Various artists).
Tracks: / Matthew 16:24 (if any man): *Various artists* / Sandyland: *Various artists* / Say to the Lord I love you: *Various artists* / Jesus: *Various artists* / Arky arky: *Various artists* / Make a joyful noise: *Various artists* / Clap de hands: *Various artists.*
LP: MAC 5099
MC: TC MAC 5099

KIDS' PRAISE 3 (Various artists).
MC: TC MAC 5100

KIDS' PRAISE 4 (Various artists).
MC: TC MAC 5101

KIDS' PRAISE 5 (Various artists).
MC: MAC C 5104

KIDS' PRAISE 6 (Various artists).
MC: MMC 0180

KIDS' PRAISE 7 (Various artists).
LP: MM R 0241
MC: MM C 0241

KIDS' PRAISE 8 (Various artists).
LP: MM R 0255
MC: MM C 0255

LET THE WORLD REJOICE (Various artists).
LP: MM 0122

MADE IN HEAVEN (18 songs of pure inspiration) (Various artists).
LP: NE 1298
MC: CE 2298

MEADOWLARK SAMPLER '86, THE (Various artists).
LP: MLR 7014
MC: MLC 7104

MEADOWLARK SAMPLER 1985 (Various artists).
LP: ML R 7006
MC: ML C 7006

MISFIT (Erick & Michele) (Various artists).
Tracks: / Misfit, The: *Various artists* / Carry me along: *Various artists* / Sail on: *Various artists*/ Can't find my way home: *Various artists* / Moon is a harsh mistress, The: *Various artists* / He's asleep: *Various* artists / Hurting people: *Various artists* / Take me to the light: *Various artists* / First prayer: *Various artists* / Love hurts: *Various artists* / He gave me love: *Various artists* / Martyr song: *Various artists.*
LP: MM 0057
MC: TC MM 0057

MISSION ENGLAND VOL.2 (Various artists).
LP: WST 9661
MC: WC 9661

MORE FOLK IN WORSHIP (Various artists).
LP: REC 176

MUSIC FROM THE 11TH WORLD PENTECOSTAL CONFERENCE (Various artists).
LP: PC 857

MUSIC OF THE GREEK ORTHODOX LITURGY (Various artists).
Tracks: / Chrysanthine chants: *Various artists* / Trisagion Asmtikon chant: *Various artists* / Hymn settings: *Various artists.*
LP: LLST 7159

OBERAMMERGAU PASSION PLAY (1634-1984 - Highlights from 1984 production) (Various artists).
LP: 8211231
MC: 8211234
LP: 243 782 0

OH PRAISE YE THE LORD (Various artists).
LP: MVP 808

ONE THOUSAND TONGUES TO SING (Various artists).
Tracks: / O joy of the justified: *Various artists* / O love that wilt not let me go: *Various artists* / At the cross: *Various artists* / Am I a soldier of the Cross?: *Various artists* / Guide me o thou great Jehovah: *Various artists* / Prince of peace: *Various artists* / Onward, Christian soldiers: *Various artists* / He hideth my soul: *Various artists* / Christ liveth in me: *Various artists* / Like men that wait: *Various artists*/ What a friend we have in Jesus: *Various artists* / Lover of my soul: *Various artists* / Praise my soul: *Various artists.*
LP: WST 9591
MC: WC 9591

ORTHODOX VIGIL SERVICE (Various artists).
2LP: IKO 16/17
MCSET: CIKO 16/17

PREMIER SAMPLER-CONTEMPORARY (Various artists).
MC: MOM C 09

PSALMS ALIVE INSTRUMENTAL (Various artists).
LP: MM 0121
MC: TC MM 0121

READINGS FROM THE PSALMS (Various artists).
MCSET: 418 006-4

RELIGIOUS AS HELL (Various artists).
LP: HELL 036

RELIGIOUS GOLD (Various artists).
LPS: EGS 4 5004
MC: EC EGS 4 5004

RELIGIOUS MUSIC OF INDIA (Various artists).
LP: PS 33523

SAINTS IN PRAISE V1 (Various artists).
LP: SP R 1189
MC: SP C 1189

SANCTIFIED VOL.3 (Various artists).
LP: HER 207

SAY AMEN SOMEBODY (Film Soundtrack) (Various artists).
Tracks: / Highway to heaven: *Various artists* / Singing in my soul: *Various artists* / What manner of man is this: *Various artists* / When I've done my best: *Various artists* / Take my hand, precious Lord: *Various artists*/ I'm his child: *Various artists* / He chose me: *Various artists* / No ways tired: *Various artists* / Jesus dropped the charges: *Various artists* / I'll never turn back: *Various artists* / Storm is passing over, The: *Various artists* / It's gonna rain: *Various artists* / He brought us: *Various artists* / Canaan: *Various artists.*
2LP: SB2L 12584
MCSET: SB2LC 12584

SECOND SUNDAY SINGALONG (Various artists).
MC: MMC 0188

SONGS FOR A MODERN CHURCH (Various artists).
Tracks: / Traveller, The: *Ward, Clifford T.* / Prayer before birth: *McGuiness, Joan & Anawin* / Refugees: *Hammill,* Peter & Van Der Graaf / Sympathy: *Rare Bird* / Go placidly every which way: *Bell, Graham* / Clear white light: *Lindisfarne* / Christmas: *Betjeman, Sir John* / Nunc Dimittis: *Phoenix, Paul & St Paul's Cathedral Boys' Choir*/ My name is Rain: *Emerson, Keith & West Park School Choir* / Jesus: *Rowe, Kenny* / I'd like to teach the world to sing: *St. Paul's Cathedral School Choir* / Poor and clean: *Isaacs, Gregory.*
LP: CAS 1159
MC: CASMC 1159

SONGS OF PRAISE (Various artists).
LP: ADL 518
MC: ADK 518

SONGS OF PRAISE VOL.2 from BBC TV (Various artists).
LP: REC 338
MC: ZCM 338

SONGS OF THE NEW REDEMPTION HYMNAL (live) (Various artists).
Tracks: / And can it be?: *New Redemption Hymnal* / Bind us together: *New Redemption Hymnal* / Great is Thy faithfulness: *New Redemption Hymnal* / Just as I am: *New Redemption Hymnal* / Old rugged cross, The: *New Redemption Hymnal*/ Thine be the glory: *New Redemption Hymnal* / When I survey the Wondrous Cross: *New Redemption Hymnal.*
LP: WRD R 3029
MC: WRD C 3029

SORROW COME PASS ME AROUND Rural black religious music (Various artists).
LP: ADVENT 2805

SOUNDS OF YORK MINSTER (Various artists).
Tracks: / Great Peter: *Various artists* / Dies irae: *Various artists* / Grieve not, the Holy Spirit of God: *Various* artists / Overture to the occasional oratorio: *Various artists* / Lord, I call upon thee: *Various artists*/ Trumpet tune: *Various artists* / He that is down: *Various artists* / Call changes (Queens): *Various artists*/ Plain Bob Triples: *Various artists* / Through the day: *Various artists* / Os justi: *Various artists*/ Largo, allegro, aria and variations: *Various artists* / Hymn of St. Columba: *Various artists* / Jesu, the very thought of thee: *Various artists* / Toccata: *Various artists* / Heavy octave and Great Peter: *Various artists.*
MC: YORK MC 103

SPIRIT OF PRAISE V2 (Various artists).
Tracks: / Don't you know it's time: *Various artists* / Jesus my Lord: *Various artists* / Praise ye the Lord: *Various* artists / Lord you are more precious: *Various artists* / My Lord let me be: *Various artists* / Pierce my ear: *Various artists* / Ah Lord god: *Various artists* / Oh Lord you've done great things: *Various artists*/ Jesus, Jesus, Jesus: *Various artists* / Thine be the glory: *Various artists* / Jesus is King: *Various artists*/ What kind of love is this: *Various artists* / O breath of life: *Various artists* / I delight greatly: *Various* artists / My peace: *Various artists* / Spirit of the living God: *Various artists* / Be still and know: *Various artists* / I will sing: *Various artists.*
LP: SOP R 2002
MC: SOP C 2002

SPIRIT OF PRAISE V3 (Various artists).
LP: SOP R 2013
MC: SOP C 2013

SPIRIT OF PRAISE VOL. 4 (Various artists).
Tracks: / Be bold, be strong: *Various artists* / Behold the King: *Various artists* / Holy spirit we welcome you: *Various artists* / I will bless the Lord: *Various artists* / I will give thanks to Thee: *Various artists*/ I will arise: *Various artists* / Name which is exalted above all names: *Various artists* / O come and worship the Lord: *Various artists* / Praise be to the Lord: *Various artists* / Put on the garments of praise: *Various artists* / Rejoice, rejoice, rejoice: *Various artists* / Lord the light of Your love: *Various artists* / There is a redeemer: *Various artists* / When I look into your holiness: *Various artists* / With a clean heart: *Various artists* / Won the victor's crown: *Various artists.*
LP: SOP R 2023
MC: SOP C 2023

SPRING HARVEST '87 (Where truth & justice meet) (Various artists).
Tracks: / Lord is marching out, The: *Various artists* / Rejoice, rejoice, rejoice: *Various artists* / He has showed you o man what is good: *Various artists* / Be still, for the presence of the Lord:

Various artists / Here is love: *Various artists* / Glorie Co. medley: *Various artists* / Jesus Thou art precious: *Various artists* / Hosanna: *Various artists* / Whizz kids song: *Various artists* / O lord the clouds are gathering: *Various artists*/ Jesus, You are the radiance: *Various artists* / He that is in us: *Various artists* / Spirit of God show me Jesus: *Various artists* / Jesus, You are changing me: *Various artists* / Holy is the Lord: *Various artists* / Lord the light of your love: *Various artists*.
LP: SOP R 2017
MC: SOP C 2017

SPRING HARVEST : THANK YOU (Various artists).
Tracks: / We'll sing a new song: *Various artists* / I hear the sound of rustling: *Various artists* / Battle hymn: *Various artists* / Servant king (from heaven you came): *Various artists* / This is your God (Meekness and Majesty): *Various artists* / Shine, Jesus, shine: *Various artists* / Our God reigns: *Various artists* / Lights to the world: *Various artists* / Rejoice, rejoice, rejoice: *Various artists* / O come let us adore Him: *Various artists* / All Heaven declares the glory: *Various artists*.
LP: SOP R 2025
MC: SOP C 2025

SUNDAY EVENING'S FAVOURITE HYMNS (Various artists).
LP: GES 1129
MC: KGEC 1129

THIS IS YOUR GOD (Various artists).
LP: SOP R 2012
MC: SOP C 2012

TOP TEN HYMNS (Various artists).
Tracks: / Praise my soul the King of Heaven: *Various artists* / Dear Lord and Father of mankind: *Various artists*/ Lord's my shepherd, The: *Various artists* / Abide with me: *Various artists* / Guide me o thou great Jehovah: *Various artists* / O Jesus I have promised: *Various artists* / Love divine: *Various artists* / When I survey the wondrous cross: *Various artists* / Thine be the glory: *Various artists* / Day thou gavest, Lord is ended, The: *Various artists*.
LP: REC 556
MC: ZCM 556

VICTOR, THE (Original cast) (Various artists).
Tracks: / Song of praise: *Various artists* / Everything that love can give: *Various artists* / He is alive: *Various artists* / Easter song: *Various artists* / Can't take my eyes off the clouds: *Various artists* / Victor, The: *Various artists* / Together: *Various artists* / Song of praise (reprise): *Various artists* / Warrior: *Various artists* / Battle belongs to the Lord, The: *Various artists* / He that overcomes: *Various artists*/ We shall stand: *Various artists* / Here he comes: *Various artists*.
LP: OAK 3001
MC: OAK C 3001

WITH MY HANDS LIFTED UP (Scripture songs) (Various artists).
LP: DOVE 13

WORD FAMILY CHRISTMAS ALBUM (Various artists).
LP: WST 9613
MC: WC 9613

Reluctant Paragon (bk)

RELUCTANT PARAGON (Catherine George) (Boyd, Carole (nar)).
MC: PMB 004

Reluctant Stereotypes

LABEL, THE.
Tracks: / Factory wit / Side with him / Back to the Greek / Plans for today / Sunday's tears / Reluctant / Lofaska / Reverend Green / Visual romance / Confused action / M.O.D. / Label.
LP: K 58201
MC: K4 58201

R.E.M.

BEST OF R.E.M, THE.
LP: MIRH 1
MC: MIRHC 1

CHRONIC TOWN.
LP: ILP 26097

DEAD LETTER OFFICE.
Tracks: / Crazy / There she goes again / Burning down / Voice of Harold / Burning hell / White Tornado / Toys in the attic / Windout / Ages of you / Pale blue eyes / Rotary ten / Bandwagon / Femme fatale / Walters theme / King of the road.
LP: SP 70054
MC: CS 70054

DOCUMENT.
Tracks: / Finest worksong / Welcome to the occupation / Exhuming McCarthy / Disturbance at the heron house / Strange / It's the end of the world as we know it (and I feel fine) / One I love, The / Fireplace / Lightnin' Hopkins / King of birds / Oddfellows local 151.
LP: MIRG 1025
MC: MIRGC 1025

DOCUMENT NO 5.
MC: MIRLC 1508

EPONYMOUS.
Tracks: / Gardening at night / So central rain / Driver 8 / Fall on me / Finest worksong / Talk about the passion / Can't get there from here / Romance / One I love, The / Its the end of the world as we know it.
LP: MIRG 1038
MC: MIRGC 1038

FABLES OF THE RECONSTRUCTION.
Tracks: / Feeling gravity's pull / Maps and legends / Driver 8 / Life and how to live it / Old man Kensey / Can't get there from here / Green grow the rushes-o / Kohoutek / Auctioneer (another engine) / Good advice / Wendell Gee.
LP: MIRF 1003
MC: MIRC 1003

GREEN.
Tracks: / Pop song 89 / Get up / You are the everything / Stand / World leader pretend / Wrong child, The / Orange crush / Turn you inside out / Hairshirt / I remember California / Untitled song.
LP: WX 234
MC: WX 234C

LIFE'S RICH PAGEANT.
LP: MIRG 1014
MC: MIRGC 1014

MURMOUR / RECKONING.
MC: AMC 24109

MURMUR.
Tracks: / Radio free Europe / Pilgrimage / Laughing / Talk about the Passion / Moral kiosk / Perfect circle / Catapult / Sitting still / 9-9 / Shaking through / We walk / West of the fields.
LP: SP 70604
MC: CS 70604

OUT OF TIME.
Tracks: / Radio song / Losing my religion / Low / Near wild Heaven / Endgame / Shiny happy people / Belong / Half a world away / Texarkana / Country feedback / Me in honey.
LP: WX 404
MC: WX 404C

RAPID MOUTH MOVEMENT.
LP: POW 001

RAPID MOUTH MOVEMENT PART 2.
LP: POW 003

RECKONING.
Tracks: / Harborcoat / Seven Chinese brothers / South central rain / Pretty persuasion / Time after time / Second guessing / Letter never sent / Camera / Don't go back to Rockville / Little America.
LP: IRSA 7045
MC: IRSC 7045

R.E.M: INTERVIEW PICTURE DISC.
LPPD: BAK 2057

Rem Records

BOB MOONEY AND 'REM RECORDS' (Various artists).
LP: WLP 8948

Remains

REMAINS.
2LP: FC 012

Remember....

REMEMBER THESE (Various artists).
LP: SOLP 1009
MC: SOCAS 1009

REMEMBER WHEN (Various artists).
LP: CBR 1032
MC: KCBR 1032

REMEMBER WHEN... (Various artists).
MC: CC 502

REMEMBER....VOLUME 2 (Various artists).
2LP: CR 138
MCSET: CRT 138

Reminiah Dub

REMINIAH DUB.
Tracks: / Iron gate dub / Long sentence (dub) / Jah live (dub) / Ratatata dub / Heavy revolution dub / No tennants dub / Babylon war dub / Reminiah dub / Naked city dub / Prophecy dub.
LP: OMLP 0011

Remipeds

REMIPEDS.
Tracks: / Hawaii five-O / Zimbabwe / In the mood / Just for kicks / This is the law / Heavy wetness / Ain't no day / Rainbow remiped / Relami / Tropical milk / Negative zone, The / SEMO / It's alright.
LP: TENOR 106

Remler, Emily

CATWALK.
Tracks: / Mocha spice / Catwalk / Gwendolyn / Antonio / Pedals / Five years / Mozambique.
LP: CJ 265

EAST TO WEST.
Tracks: / Daahoud / Sweet George fame / East to West / Snowfall / Hot house / Softly as in a morning sunrise.
LP: CJ 356
MC: CJ 356 C

TAKE TWO (Remler, Emily Quartet).
Tracks: / Cannonball / In your own sweet way / For regulars only / Search for peace / Pocket west / Waltz for my grandfather / Afro blue / Eleuthra.
LP: CJ 195

TOGETHER (Remler, Emily & Larry Coryell).
Tracks: / Arabian nights / Joy spring / Ill wind / How my heart sings / Six beats, six strings / Gerri's blues / How insensitive.
LP: CJ 289
MC: CJC 289

TRANSITIONS.
Tracks: / Nunca mais / Serchin' / Transitions / Del sasser / Coral / Ode to Mali.
LP: CJ 236

Remuda

HONEYSUCKLE DREAMING (see Page, Stu) (Remuda/Stu Page).

SYLVANTONE SHOWCASE, THE (see Goodacre, Tony) (Remuda/Tony Goodacre).

Remue, Charles

CHARLES REMUE AND THE NEW STOMPER ORCHESTRA 1927.
LP: FG 401

Rena, Kid

DOWN ON THE DELTA (see Johnson, Bunk) (Rena, Kid/Bunk Johnson/ Celestin's Tuxedo Orchestra).

Rena Rama

RENA RAMA.
LP: DRLP 118

Renaissance

ASHES ARE BURNING.
LP: SVNA 7261

AZURE D'OR.
Tracks: / Jekyll and Hyde / Winter tree, The / Only angels have wings / Golden key / Forever changing / Secret mission / Kalynda / Discovery, The / Friends / Flood at Lyons, The.
MC: K4 56633
MC: THBC 045
LP: THBL 045
LP: K 56633

CAMERA CAMERA.
Tracks: / Camera camera.
LP: ILP 008

ILLUSION.
LP: HELP 27

LIVE AT CARNEGIE HALL.
LP: 26 28146

NOVELLA.
Tracks: / Can you hear me / Sisters, The / Midas man / Captive heart, The / Touching once (is so hard to keep).
MC: K4 56422
LP: K 56422

PROLOGUE.
LP: SVNA 7253

RENAISSANCE.
LP: ILPS 9114

RENAISSANCE LIVE AT CARNEGIE HALL.
Tracks: / Prologue / Ocean gypsy / Can you understand? / Carpet of the sun / Running hard / Mother Russia / Song of Scheherazade / Fanfare / Betrayal, The / Sultan, The / Love theme / Young prince and princess, The / Festival preparations / Fugue for the Sultan / Festival, The / Finale / Ashes are burning.
2LP: BTM 2001

ROCK GALAXY.
2LP: CL 25282

SCHEHERAZADE AND OTHER STORIES.
Tracks: / Tip to the fair / Vultures fly high, The / Ocean gypsy / Song of Scheherazade / Fanfare / Betrayal, The / Sultan, The / Love theme / Young prince and princess, The / Festival preparations / Fugue for the Sultan / Festival, The / Finale.
LP: BTM 1006

SCHEREZADE.
LP: 26 21554

SONG FOR ALL SEASONS, A.
Tracks: / Opening out / Day of the dreamer, The / Closer than yesterday / Kindness (at the end) / Back home once again / She is love / Northern lights / Song for all seasons, A.
LP: K 56460
MC: K4 56460

TIME LINE.
Tracks: / Flight / Missing persons / Chagrin Boulevard / Richard the IX / Entertainer, The / Electric avenue / Majik / Distant horizons / Orient express / Auto tech.
LP: SP 70033

TURN OF THE CARDS.
Tracks: / Running hard / I think of you / Things I don't understand / Black flame / Cold is being / Mother Russia.
LP: 26 21490
LP: BTM 1000

Renaissance Choir

SEBASTIAN DE VIVANCO.
Tracks: / Canite tube in Sion (Motet.) / Quis dabit capiti meo aquam (Motet.) / O Domine Jesu Christe (Motet.) / Circumdederunt me dolores mortis (Motet.) / Ecce sacerdos magnus (Motet. (end s1)) / Missa in festo Beatae Mariae Virginis (Incl: Kyrie Eleison, Gloria in excelsis Deo, Credo in unum Deum, Sanctus) / Missa in festo Beatae Mariae Virginis (cont'd) (Benedictus, Agnus Dei I, Agnus Dei II.).
LP: ACA 550

Renaissance Group...

MUSIC OF LIGHT AND SHADOW (Renaissance group of University of Saint Andrews).
LP: APS 337
MC: CAPS 337

Renaissance Players

MEMORIES OF ENGLISH MINSTRELSY.
LP: VP 457

Renaldo & The Loaf

ARABIC YODELLING.
Tracks: / Kimbolton gnome song / Green candle / Critical dance, A / Leery looks / Vitamin song.
LP: RL 8308

ELBOW IS TABOO, THE.
Tracks: / Street called straight, A / Boule / Hambo hodo / Dance for Sonambulist / Here's to the oblong boys / Bread song / Critical dance, A / Extracting the re-re.
LP: RD 5

OLLEH OLLEH ROTCOD.
LP: RD-3

SONGS FOR SWINGING LARVAE.
LP: RIDE 6

Renato

SAVE YOUR LOVE.
Tracks: / Save your love / She wears my ring / If / Solitaire / Ave Maria / Danny boy.
LP: LEG 9
MC: LEGC 9

TASTE OF ITALY, A.
Tracks: / Caruso / Santa Lucia / Come prima / La mattinata / Loveliest night of the year / Mama / Till / Wedding, The / La donna e mobile / Torna a Sorriento / Save your love / Because / Ave Maria / Be my love / I'll walk with God / Arrevederci Roma.
LP: PL 74473
MC: PK 74473

Renaud, Henri

NEW SOUND AT THE 'BEOUF SUR LE TOIT' (Renaud, Henri & Son Orchestre).
LP: FS 262

Renbourn & Grossman

RENBOURN & GROSSMAN (Renbourn, John & Stefan Grossman).
LP: KM 152

Renbourn, John

BLACK BALLOON, THE.
Tracks: / Moon shines bright, The / English dance / Bouree / Mist covered mountains of home, The / Orphan, The / Tarboulton, The / Pelican, The / Black balloon, The.
LP: UMM 1002
LP: KM 163

ENCHANTED GARDEN (Renbourn, John Group).
LP: TRA 356

FOLK BLUES OF JOHN RENBOURN.
Tracks: / Another monday / Lady Nothinge's toye puffe / I know my babe / Waltz / Lost lover blues / Train tune / National seven / In captivity / One for William / Buffalo / Song / Down on the barge / Sugar babe / Debbie Anne / Can't keep from cryin' / Day at the seaside / Winter is gone / Plainsong / Nobody's fault but mine.
LP: TRANDEM 2

JOHN RENBOURN & BERT JANSCH (Renbourn, John & Bert Jansch).
Tracks: / Buffalo / So clear John's tune / Back on the road again / Seven up / Watch the stars / Another Monday / Willie o' Winsbury / I know my babe / My dear boy / Noah and the rabbit / Goodbye pork pie hat / Soho / Birthday blues / Come back baby / First time ever I saw your face, The / Reynardine / Time has come, The / Woman like you, A / No exit / Tie-tocative / Angie / Needle of death / Bird song.
2LP: . . . . **CR 056**
MCSET: . . . . **CRT 056**

JOHN RENBOURN & STEFAN GROSSMAN (Renbourn, John & Stefan Grossman).
LP: . . . . **SNKF 139**

KICKING MULE (see Grossman, Stefan) (Renbourn, John & Stefan Grossman).

LIVE.....IN CONCERT (Renbourn, John & Stefan Grossman).
2LP: . . . . **SPIN 401**

MAID IN BEDLAM, A (Renbourn, John Group).
LP: . . . . **SHAN 79004**

MEDIAEVAL ALMANACK, THE.
Tracks: / Earl of Salisbury / Trotto / Saltarello / Veri floris / Triple ballade / Bransie gay / Bransie de Bourgogne / Alman / Melancholy Galliard / Westron Wynde / Lamento di Tristan / La Rotta / Sarabande / Shaeffertanz / Lady Nothinge's toye puffe / Lady goes to church / Lady and the unicorn, The / Princess and the puddings / Pavanne / Toye, A / Lord Willoughby's welcome home.
LP: . . . . **TRANDEM 6**

NINE MAIDENS.
LP: . . . . **FF 378**
LP: . . . . **SPIN 102**

SHIP OF FOOLS.
LP: . . . . **FF 466**
LP: . . . . **RRA 009**
MC: . . . . **RRAMC 009**

THREE KINGDOMS (Renbourn, John & Stefan Grossman).
LP: . . . . **SNTF 981**
LP: . . . . **SHAN 95006**

Rendall, Ruby

IN PORTRAIT.
Tracks: / Just in case you change your mind / Guitar town / Your free to go / Never like this before / South gonna rattle again, The / Blue moon of Kentucky / Girl like Emmylou, A / Evangeline / Two more bottles of wine / Even now / American trilogy.
LP: . . . . **AT 013**
MC: . . . . **ATC 013**

NEVER LOOK BACK.
LP: . . . . **WGR 095**
MC: . . . . **CWGR 095**

STRAIGHT FROM THE HEART.
LP: . . . . **WGR 079**
MC: . . . . **CWGR 079**

Rendell, Don

EARTH MUSIC (Rendell, Don Nine).
Tracks: / Genesis jump / Meridian mango / Land lovers / Seven sea rock / Blues tones / Tenor firma / Strata dance / Ground finale.
LP: . . . . **SPJ 515**

JUST MUSIC (Rendell, Don & Barbara Thompson).
Tracks: / Wensleydale suite / Well, make it up / Sands of time / Blues for Adolphe Sax / Penta gone / Gab and Ben / Out of my window / Mina impact.
LP: . . . . **SPJ 502**

LIVE AT THE AVGARDE GALLERY (Rendell, Don & Joe Palin Trio).
Tracks: / On the way / Euphrates / I can't get started / Antibes / Summer song.
LP: . . . . **SPJ 501**

SET 2 (Rendell, Don Five).
Tracks: / Becclesology / Devon dance / Waltz / It could've happened to you / Unicorn.
LP: . . . . **SPJ 516**

Rendell, Ruth (author)

HEARTSTONES/THORNAPPLE (James, Geraldine (nar)).
MCSET: . . . . **ZC SWD 362**

INSPECTOR WEXFORD - MEANS OF EVIL (See under Inspector Wexford) (Baker, George).

INSPECTOR WEXFORD ON HOLIDAY (Baker, George).
MCSET: . . . . **LFP 7499**

Rene & Angela

STREET CALLED DESIRE.
Tracks: / Save your love (for number 1) / I'll be good / No how-no way / You don't have to cry / Street called desire / Your smile / Who's foolin' who / Drive my love.
LP: . . . . **JABH 12**
MC: . . . . **JABHC 12**

WALL TO WALL.
Tracks: / Wall to wall / Just friends / Secret rendezvous / Wanna be close to you / I love you more / Love's alright / Imaginary playmates / Come my way.
LP: . . . . **EMS 1118**
MC: . . . . **TCEMS 1118**

Renee & Renato

JUST ONE......
LP: . . . . **HLP 001**
MC: . . . . **HCS 001**

Renegade Soundwave

RENEGADE SOUNDWAVE IN DUB.
LP: . . . . **STUMM 85**
MC: . . . . **CSTUMM 85**

SOUNDCLASH.
LP: . . . . **STUMM 63**
MC: . . . . **CSTUMM 63**

Reney, Diane

NAVY BLUE.
LP: . . . . **TFM 3133**

Renner, Mark

PAINTER'S JOY.
LP: . . . . **EM 9540 1**

Reno, Don

DEAR OLD DIXIE (Reno, Don & Bill Harrell).
Tracks: / Dear old Dixie / One morning in May / It's a long, long way from the bottom / Hobo's song / Please keep remembering / At last I'm free / Where would over flowers grow? / B.G. / Chase, The / Wind blew across the wild moor, The / Make believe / Into these hills.
LP: . . . . **CMH 6201**

FAMILY AND FRIENDS.
Tracks: / Your love is dying / No longer a sweetheart of mine / Clear skies / Lonesome wind blues / Chokin' the strings / Freight train boogie / Country boy rock 'n' roll / Eastbound freight train / I'm the talk of the town / John Hardy / I want to know / Dixie breakdown.
LP: . . . . **F 34**
MC: . . . . **C 34**

FASTEST FIVE STRINGS ALIVE.
LP: . . . . **KLP 1065**
MC: . . . . **GT 51065**

HOME IN THE MOUNTAINS (Reno, Don & Bill Harrell).
Tracks: / Home in the mountain / Miss Elsie's place / Follow the leader / Pretty angel tree, A / If today was tomorrow / Banjo Bill / I want to go back to the mountains / Walking catfish / Once in a while / Booked up in advance / Going back to church with mama.
LP: . . . . **CMH 6210**

Reno, Johnny

BORN TO BLOW (Reno, Johnny and The Sax Maniacs).
Tracks: / Born to blow.
LP: . . . . **BT 1025**

FULL BLOWN (Reno, Johnny and The Sax Maniacs).
LP: . . . . **ROUNDER 9001**
MC: . . . . **ROU 9001C**

Reno & Smiley

16 GREATEST HITS: RENO & SMILEY.
LP: . . . . **SLP 3001**
MC: . . . . **GT 53001**
LP: . . . . **SD 3001**

20 BLUEGRASS SPECIALS.
LP: . . . . **SLP 5025**
MC: . . . . **GT 55025**

BEST OF RENO & SMILEY.
LP: . . . . **SLP 961**
MC: . . . . **GT 5961**

COUNTRY SINGING AND INSTRUMENTALS.
LP: . . . . **KLP 776**
MC: . . . . **GT 5776**

COUNTRY SONGS.
LP: . . . . **KLP 701**
MC: . . . . **GT 5701**

LAST TIME TOGETHER.
LP: . . . . **SLP 485**
MC: . . . . **GT 5485**

RENO & SMILEY VOL 2 (83 Collectors edition).
LP: . . . . **GT 0111**

RENO & SMILEY VOL 3 (83 collectors edition).
LP: . . . . **GT 0112**

RENO & SMILEY VOL 4 (83 collectors edition).
LP: . . . . **GT 0113**

SONGS OF YESTERDAY.
LP: . . . . **REBEL 1661**

WORLD'S BEST FIVE STRING BANJO.
LP: . . . . **KLP 861**
MC: . . . . **GT 5861**

Rent Party

HONK THAT SAXOPHONE.
LP: . . . . **WF 022**

Rent Party Revellers

SHAKE THAT THING.
LP: . . . . **GHB 186**

Rent-A-Cop

RENT-A-COP (Film Soundtrack) (Various artists).
Tracks: / Rent a cop: *Various artists* / Bust, The: *Various artists* / Lonely cop: *Various artists* / Russian roulette: *Various artists* / Station, The: *Various artists* / Worth a lot: *Various artists* / Lights out: *Various artists* / This is the Guy: *Various artists* / They need me: *Various artists* / Room, The: *Various artists* / Lake forest: *Various artists* / Jump: *Various artists.*
LP: . . . . **FILM 025**

Rental, Robert

LIVE AT WEST RUNTON (see Normal) (Rental, Robert & Normal).

Renzi, Mike

BEAUTIFUL FRIENDSHIP, A (Renzi, Mike Quartet).
LP: . . . . **ST 273**

REO Speedwagon

6 TRACK HITS.
Tracks: / Only the strong survive / Meet me on the mountain / Shakin' it loose / In your letter / I need you tonight / Roll with the changes.
MC: **7SC 5049**

BEST FOOT FORWARD.
Tracks: / Roll with the changes / Take it on the run / Don't let him go / Live every moment / Keep on loving you / Back on the road / Wherever you're goin' (it's alright) / Can't fight this feeling / Shakin' it loose / Time for me to fly / Keep pushin' / I wish you were there.
LP: . . . . **EPC 26640**
MC: **40 26640**

DECADE OF ROCK & ROLL.
Tracks: / Sophisticated lady / Music man / Golden country / Son of a poor man / Lost in a dream / Reelin' / Keep pushin' / Our time is gonna come / Breakaway / Lightning / Like you do / Flying turkey trot / 157 Riverside Avenue / Ridin' the storm out / Roll with the changes / Time for me to fly / Say you love me or say goodnight / Only the strong survive / Back on the road.
2LP: . . . . **EPC 22131**

EARTH, A SMALL MAN, HIS DOG AND A CHICKEN, A.
Tracks: / Love is a rock / Heart survives, The / Live it up / All heaven broke loose / Love in the future / Halfway / Love to hate / You won't see me / Can't lie to my heart / L.I.A.R. / Go for broke.
LP: **4670131**
MC: **4670134**

GOOD TROUBLE.
Tracks: / Keep the fire burning / Sweet time / Girl with the heart of gold / Every now and then / I'll follow you / Key, The / Back in my heart again / Let's be-bop / Stillness of the night / Good trouble.
LP: . . . . **EPC 32789**
LP: . . . . **EPC 85789**

HI-INFIDELITY.
Tracks: / Don't let him go / Keep on loving you / Follow my heart / In your letter / Take it on the run / Tough guys / Out of season / Shakin' it loose / Someone tonight / I wish you were there.
LP: . . . . **EPC 32538**
MC: **40 32538**
LP: . . . . **EPC 84700**

HITS, THE.
Tracks: / I don't want to lose you / Here with me / Roll with the changes / Keep on loving you / That ain't love / Take it on the run / Don't let him go / Can't fight this feeling / Keep pushin' / In my dreams / Time for me to fly / Ridin' the storm out.
LP: **4608561**
MC: **4608564**

KEEP ON LOVING YOU (OLD GOLD) (See under Tyler, Bonnie/Total eclipse of...).

LIFE AS WE KNOW IT.
Tracks: / New way to love / That ain't love / In my dreams / One too many girlfriends / Variety tonight / Screams and whispers / Can't get you out of my heart / Over the edge / Accidents can happen / Tired of getting nowhere.
LP: **4503801**
MC: **4503804**

NINE LIVES.
Tracks: / Heavy on your love / Drop it / Only the strong survive / Easy money / Rock and roll music / Take me / I need you tonight / Meet me on the mountains / Back on the road.
LP: . . . . **EPC 83647**

REO SPEEDWAGON.
LP: . . . . **CBS 32096**

WHEELS ARE TURNIN'.
Tracks: / I do'wanna know / One lonely night / Thru the window / Rock and roll star / Live every moment / Can't fight this feeling / Gotta feel more / Break his spell / Wheels are turning.
LP: . . . . **EPC 26137**
MC: **40 26137**

YOU CAN TUNE A PIANO.
LP: . . . . **EPC 32115**

YOU GET WHAT YOU PLAY FOR.
Tracks: / Like you do / Lay me down / Any kind of love / Being kind (can hurt someone sometimes) / Keep pushin' / Only a summer love / Son of a poor man / I believe our time is gonna come (flying turkey trot) / Gary's guitar solo / 157 Riverside Avenue / Ridin' the storm out / Music man / Little Queenie / Golden country.
2LP: . . . . **EPC 88265**

Replacements

ALL SHOOK DOWN.
Tracks: / Merry go round / Nobody / Sadly beautiful / When it began / Attitude / Torture / Last, The / One wink at a time / Bent out of shape / Someone take the wheel / All shook down / Happy town / My little problem.
LP: **7599262981**
MC: **7599262984**

BOINK.
LP: . . . . **GLALP 016**
MC: . . . . **GLAMC 016**

DON'T TELL A SOUL.
Tracks: / Talent show / Back to back / We'll inherit the earth / Achin' to be / They're blind / Anywhere's better than here / Asking me lies / I'll be you / I won't / Rock 'n' roll ghost / Darlin' one.
LP: . . . . **K 925721 1**
MC: . . . . **K 925721 4**

HOOTENANNY.
LP: . . . . **GOES ON 021**

LET IT BE.
Tracks: / I will dare / Favourite thing / We're comin' out / Tommy gets his tonsils out / Androgynous / Black diamond / Unsatisfied / Seen your video / Gary's got a boner / Sixteen blue / Answering machine.
LP: . . . . **ZONG 002**
LP: . . . . **ROSE 42**

PLEASED TO MEET ME.
Tracks: / I.O.U. / Alex Chilton / I don't know / Nightclub jitters / Ledge, The / Never mind / Valentine / Shooting dirty pool / Red red wine / Skyway / Can't hardly wait.
LP: . . . . **K 925557 1**
MC: . . . . **K 925557 4**

SORRY MA FORGOT TO TAKE OUT THE TRASH.
LP: . . . . **GOES ON 17**

STINK.
Tracks: / Kid's don't follow / F**k school / Stuck in the middle / God damn job / White and lazy / Dope smokin' moran / Go / Gimme noise.
LP: . . . . **GOES ON 020**

TIM.
Tracks: / Hold my life / I'll buy / Kiss me on the bus / Dose of thunder / Waitress in the sky / Swingin' party / Bastards of young / Lay it down clown / Left of the dial / Little mascara / Here comes a regular.
LP: **925330 1**

Repo Man

REPO MAN (Film soundtrack) (Various artists).
LP: . . . . **MCF 3223**
MC: . . . . **MCFC 3223**

Repression

REPRESSION.
LP: . . . . **A 37**

Reprise Repertory

SOUTH PACIFIC (Original cast).
Tracks: / Younger than springtime / Carefully taught / There is nothing like a dame / Bloody Mary / Younger than springtime / Happy talk / Dites-moi / Honey bun / I'm gonna wash that man right outta my hair / Some enchanted evening / This nearly was mine / I'm in love with a wonderful man / Bali Ha'i / Cock-eyed optimist / Twin soliloquies / Overture.
LP: . . . . **K 54115**

Reptile

FAME AND FOSSILS.
LP: PLAY LP 13

Reptiles At Dawn

DRESSED IN FLESH.
LP: ROSE 133

NAKED IN THE WILDERNESS.
LP: ROSE 91

Reptilicus

CRUSHER OF BONES.
LP: CATNO 002

Republic (label)

REPUBLIC REMIX LP (Various artists).
LP: LICTLP 35
MC: LICMC 35

Republica

1984.
LP: MEGATONLP 1

Repulsion

HORRIFIED.
Tracks: / Stench of burning death, The / Acid bath / Radiation sickness / Splattered cadavers / Festering boils / Eaten alive / Slaughter of the innocent / Pestilent decay / Decomposed.
LP: NECRO 2

Requiem (musical)

REQUIEM (ROCK REQUIEM) (See under 'Lloyd Webber, Andrew') (Lloyd Webber, Andrew).

Rescuers

RESCUERS (Film soundtrack) (Various artists).
MC: D 14DC

STORY OF THE RESCUERS (Film Soundtrack) (Various artists).
LP: WD 023
MC: WDC 023

Research

SOCIAL SYSTEMS.
Tracks: / Trails to Olympia / Stone free / River art / Tough / Rapid eye movement / Social systems.
LP: ST 7533

Residents

13TH ANNIVERSARY SHOW Live in Japan.
LP: TORSO 33018

CENSUS TAKER, THE (See under Census Taker).

COMMERCIAL ALBUM.
LP: PREX 2

GEORGE AND JAMES.
Tracks: / Rhapsody in blue / I got rhythm / Summertime / I'll go crazy / Try me / Think / I don't mind / Lost someone / Please please please / Night train.
LP: KODE 9

GOD IN THREE PERSONS.
Tracks: / Hard and tenderly / Devotion / Thing about them, The / Their early years / Loss of a loved one / Touch, The / Service, The / Confused / Fine fat flies / Time / Silver sharp / Kiss of flesh / Pain and pleasure.
2LP: TORSO 33061
DAT: TORSODAT 055
LP: 33055

MEET THE RESIDENTS.
LP: 40016

NIBBLES (Residents & Snakefinger).
LP: VR 3

PAL TV LP.
LP: DVR 17

RALPH BEFORE '84 VOLUME 1.
Tracks: / It's a man's man's man's world / Diskomo / Hello skinny / I left my heart in San Francisco / Happy home / Smack your lips clap your teeth / You yes yes yes / Jailhouse rock / Monkey and bunny / Festival of death.
LP: KODE 10
MC: CODE 10

RALPH BEFORE '84 VOLUME 2.
Tracks: / Eva's warning / Halloween / Evolution / What use / Mahogany wood / Same ole me / Tritone / Melvyn's repose / Yeti: what are you / Nelda danced at day break / Norrgarden nyvia.
LP: KODE 12

SNAKE.
LP: TORSO 33033

STARS AND HANK FOREVER.
LP: TORSO 33022

TITLE IN LIMBO (Residents & Renaldo & The Loaf).
LP: RR 8351

TUNES OF TWO CITIES, THE.
Tracks: / Mousetrap / Smack your lips clap your teeth / Maze of jigsaws, A / God of darkness / Secret seed, The / Evil disposer, The.
LP: RZ 8202

VILENESS FATS.
LP: RZ 8452

Resistance

BLACK COMEDY.
Tracks: / Black comedy / Don't fraternise with the fraternity / Musical chairs / Blah blah units / All purpose hermaphrodite / Invisible man, The / Ego / Perfect / One famous nudge master / Days of wine and roses / Survival kit / Unwilling soldiers / Nuclear family.
LP: 6359059

THOROUGHBRED MEN.
LP: ASS 14

Resistant Militia

HARDCORE DEMO SERIES.
LP: WRR 003

Resort

1989.
LP: LINKLP 088

Respighi (composer)

PINES OF ROME - THE BIRDS - SUITE (London Symphony Orchestra).
MC: 4255074

Rest In Pieces

UNDER MY SKIN.
Tracks: / Five golden rings / Divided / Cries of the ghetto / MCM / No mans land / Forty years on / I got the fire / Right through me / Hooked up / Under my skin.
LP: RO 95101
MC: RO 95104

Restaurant at... (bk)

RESTAURANT AT THE END OF THE UNIVERSE (Douglas Adams) (Moore, Stephen (nar)).
MCSET: LFP 7115
MCSET: LFP 4171155
MCSET: TCLFP 7115

Restivo, Johnny

SHAPE I'M IN.
Tracks: / Shape I'm in, The / Ya ya / I like girls / Girl scout / I make the love / I wanna play house with you / Thing, The / That's good - that's bad / Last night at the back porch / Come closer / Dear someone / I looked for love / Our wedding day / High school play / Boy crazy / Jealous.
LP: BFX 15171

Restless

AFTER MIDNIGHT.
LP: ABCLP 7
MC: ABCK 7

BEAT MY DRUM.
LP: NUTA LP 001
MC: NUTACASS 001

DO YOU FEEL RESTLESS ?.
LP: NERD 015
LP: LP 8409

EARLY YEARS.
LP: NERD 026

LIVE AND KICKING.
LP: ABCLP 12

WE ROCK THE NATION.
LP: 941 305

WHY DON'T YOU.....JUST ROCK!.
LP: NERD 004

Restless Heart

FAST MOVIN' TRAIN.
Tracks: / Fast movin' train / Dancy's dream / Sweet auburn / I've never been so sure / Long lost friend / Little more coal on the fire, A / When somebody loves you / Lady luck / River of stone (Only on CD.) / Truth hurts, The.
LP: PL 90456
MC: PK 90456

Restless Natives

RESTLESS NATIVES (See under Big Country 'Look away') (Big Country (group)).

Resurrection Band

COLOURS.
Tracks: / Autograph / Colours / N.Y.C. / Hidden man / Amazing / American dream / Benny & Sue / City street / Beggar in the alleyway / Struggle, The.
LP: LSX 7059
MC: LC 7059

DMZ.
LP: LS 7064

LIVE BOOTLEG.
LP: BIRD 153
MC: MC 153

MOMMY DON'T LOVE DADDY ANYMORE.
Tracks: / Stark / Spare / Elevator muzik / Alienated / Can't get you outta my mind / Chair, The / Can't do it on my own / First degree apathy / Mommy don't love daddy anymore / Crossing, The / Little children / Loving you.
LP: LSX 7064
MC: LC 7064

Reswick, Art

ART RESWICK.
Tracks: / This is new / Gift / Goose is loose, The / Just one of those things / Close enough for love / Touch of your lips, The / Mon p'tit bijou.
LP: CAP 74015-1

Rethberg, Elisabeth

SOPRANO - RADIO PERFORMANCES.
LP: GL 8003

Retribution

RETRIBUTION/ LOST EMPIRE (See under Lost Empire) (Various artists).

Return Journey...

RETURN JOURNEY TO SWANSEA (Various artists).
LP: TC 354
MC: SWC 1354

Return Of...

RETURN OF MARTIN GUERRE/JULIA (Original Soundtrack) (Various artists).
LP: SL 9514
MC: SLC 9514

RETURN OF THE BEAT MENACE (Various artists).
LP: CHEEP 006

RETURN OF THE JEDI (Various artists).
LP: D 455
MC: D 155DC

RETURN OF THE JEDI (Film soundtrack) (Various artists).
Tracks: / Main title: *Various artists* / Into the trap: *Various artists* / Luke and Leia: *Various artists*/ Bot got Jarraz: *Various artists* / Han Solo returns: *Various artists* / Parade of the Ewoks: *Various artists*/ Forest, The: *Various artists* / Rebel briefing: *Various artists* / Emperor, The: *Various artists* / Return of the Jedi: *Various artists* / Ewok celebration and finale: *Various artists*.
LP: RSD 5023

RETURN OF THE JEDI (See under National Philharmonic Orchestra) (National Philharmonic Orchestra).

RETURN OF THE JEDI (The Ewoks Join The Fight) (Various artists).
LP: D 460
MC: D 160DC

RETURN OF THE LIVING DEAD (Film Soundtrack) (Various artists).
Tracks: / Surfin' dead: *Cramps* / Partytime (zombie version): *45 Grave* / Nothing for you: *T.S.O.L.*/ Eyes without a face: *Flesh Eaters* / Burn the flames: *Erickson, Roky* / Dead beat dance: *Damned* / Take a walk: *Tall Boys* / Love under will: *Jet Black Berries* / Tonight (we'll make love until we die): *SSQ*/ Trash's theme: *SSQ*.
LP: WIK 38
MC: WIKC 38
LPPD: ROSE 66P
LP: ROSE 66

RETURN OF THE LIVING DEAD (PART 2) (Various artists).
Tracks: / Space hopper: *Cope, Julian* / I'm the man: *Anthrax* / Monster mash: *Big O* / A.D. 1: *Anthrax*/ Dead return: *Robinson, J Peter* / High priest of love: *Mindwarp, Zodiac* / Big band boy: *Mantronix*/ Alone in the night: *Leatherwolf* / Flesh to flesh: *Lamo&t.*
MC: ICT 17
LP: ISTA 17

RETURN OF THE SOLDIER (Film soundtrack) (Various artists).
Tracks: / Main title (dream, The): *Various artists* / Chris and Jenny: *Various artists* / Old house, The: *Various* artists / Chris and Margaret: *Various artists* / Memories: *Various artists* / Hallucinations: *Various* artists / Anyone home: *Various artists* / Love letters: *Various artists* / After the ball: *Various artists*/ Chris at the window: *Various artists* / Return to Monkey Island: *Various artists* / Chris, Jenny and Margaret: *Various artists* / Piano interlude: *Various artists* / Return of the soldier, The: *Various artists* / End titles (Love theme): *Various artists*.
LP: TER 1036

Return Of Sherlock...

RETURN OF SHERLOCK HOLMES, THE (see under Sherlock Holmes (bk)) (Hardy, Robert (nar)).

Return Of Superfly

RETURN OF SUPERFLY (Film Soundtrack) (Various artists).
Tracks: / Superfly 1990: *Mayfield, Curtis & Ice-T* / Eazy Street: *Eazy-E* / Cheeba cheeba: *Tone Loc*/ Funky in the joint: *Mellow Man Ace* / On the real tip: *Def Jef* / Showdown: *Mayfield, Curtis* / Forbidden: *Mayfield, Curtis* / Superfly 1990 (Hip hop instrumental): *Mayfield, Curtis* / For the love of you: *Mayfield, Curtis* / Take you home: *King Tee* / There's a riot jumpin' off: *King Tee* / Somethin' like dis: *C.P.O.*.
LP: EST 2129
MC: TCEST 2129
LP: 794 244 1
MC: 794 244 4

Return of the ...

RETURN OF THE DINOSAURS (See under Action Force (tv)).

Return Of The Jedi

RETURN OF THE JEDI (STAR WARS 3) (Film Soundtrack) (Various artists).
LP: POLD 5105
MC: POLDC 5105

STORY OF THE RETURN OF THE JEDI (Various artists).
LP: D 62103

Return Of The

RETURN OF THE MUSKETEERS (Original Soundtrack) (Various artists).
LP: A383

Return Of The Native

RETURN OF THE NATIVE, THE (see Hardy, Thomas) (Rickman, Alan).

RETURN OF THE NATIVE, THE (see under Hardy, Thomas) (Jeffrey, Peter (nar)).

Return To Forever

BEST OF RETURN TO FOREVER.
Tracks: / Musician / Romantic warrior / So long Mickey Mouse / Majestic dance / Music magic / Hello again / Sorceress.
LP: CBS 84292

Return To Oasis

RETURN TO OASIS An anthology of poetry from the Second World War.
MC: TCC/OAS1

Return To Snowy ...

RETURN TO SNOWY RIVER (Film Soundtrack) (Various artists).
LP: 704 510
MC: 704 510 C

Return To The...

RETURN TO THE FORBIDDEN PLANET (Original Soundtrack) (Various artists).
Tracks: / Wipeout: *Various artists* / Great balls of fire: *Various artists* / Good vibrations: *Various artists*/ I'm gonna change the world: *Various artists* / She's not there: *Various artists* / Gloria: *Various artists*/ Tell her: *Various artists* / Shake, rattle and roll: *Various artists* / Only the lonely: *Various artists*/ We've gotta get out of this place: *Various artists* / Hey Mr. Spaceman: *Various artists* / Great balls of fire (reprise): *Various artists* / It's a man's world: *Various artists* / Don't let me be misunderstood: *Various* artists / Ain't gonna wash for a week: *Various artists* / Teenager in love: *Various artists* / All shook now: *Various artists* / Robot man: *Various artists* / Go now: *Various artists* / Young ones, The: *Various artists* / Wipeout (reprise): *Various artists* / Monster mash: *Various artists*.
LP: V2631
MC: TCV 2631

Reunion

BE BORN AGAIN.
Tracks: / I saw the light / I didn't stop dancing / Pass me not / Born again / There's no need for a heaven / Jesus hears, He cares, He can / Had it not been / Little spot in heaven, A / If we forget God / My bible / Oh what a happy day.
LP: PC 335

COOL CHANGE, A A cappella series vol.6.
LP: CL 1006

Rev, Martin

CLOUDS OF GLORY.
LP: ROSE 52

Revanche

MUSIC MAN.
Tracks: / You get high in N.Y.C. / Revenge / Music man / 1979 it's dancing time.
LP: K 50639

Revard, Jimmie

OH SWING IT!.
LP: RAMBLER 108

Revelation

BOOK OF REVELATION.
LP: BS 1030

VARIATION ON A THEME.
LP: BBV 1007

Revell, Graeme

INSECT MUSICIANS, THE.
LP: . . . . **BR 001**

NECROPOLIS AMPHIBIAN & REPTILES.
Tracks: / Necropolis, amphibians & reptiles / Countless saladine / Chimpnas-apes of the union Canada / Allgebrah / Ebony tower in the Orient water / Balli, The / St. Adolfs comet / Natural form of the holy light / Rhama margarine / Lea tantaaria / Great God father nieces.
LP: . . . . **BRU 002**

Revenge

7 REASONS (See under Hook, Peter).

ONE TRUE PASSION.
LP: . . . . **FAC 230**
MC: . . . . **FAC 230C**

SWEET AND SOUR.
LP: . . . . **SP 003**

WARTIME.
LP: . . . . **BIAS 023**

Revenge (Film)

REVENGE (Film Soundtrack) (Various artists).
Tracks: / Love theme: *Various artists* / Friendship: *Various artists* / Miryea: *Various artists* / Betrayal: *Various artists* / Jeep ride: *Various artists* / On the beach: *Various artists* / Illicit love: *Various artists* / Tibey's revenge: *Various artists* / Whorehouse and healing: *Various artists* / Dead Texan: *Various artists* / Confrontation: *Various artists* / Miryea's death: *Various artists.*
MC: . . . . **FILMC 065**

Revenge Of...

REVENGE OF THE NINJA (Film soundtrack) (Walsh, Rob).
LP: . . . . **STV 81195**

Revere, Paul

GREATEST HITS: PAUL REVERE (Revere, Paul & The Raiders).
LP: **2636061**
MC: **2636064**

KICKS (Revere, Paul & The Raiders).
Tracks: / Great airplane strike, The / Him or me / 1001 Arabian nights / Steppin' out / Just like me / Kicks / Gone moving on / Tighter / Undecided man / Hungry / I'm not your stepping stone / Why why why / Louise / Good thing / Louie go home / Ups and downs.
LP: . . . . **ED 123**

PAUL REVERE & THE RAIDERS (Revere, Paul & The Raiders).
MC: **811**

ROCK 'N' ROLL.
LP: . . . . **GARDENIA 1000**

Reverend

WORLD WON'T MISS YOU.
LP: . . . . **CUSLP 2**
MC: . . . . **CUSMC 2**

Revillos

REV UP.
Tracks: / Secret of the shadow / Rev up! / Rock a boom / Voodoo / Bobby come back to me / Scupa boy bop / Yeah yeah / Hungry for love / Jukebox sound / On the beach / Cool jerk / Hippy hippy sheik / Motorbike beat.
LP: . . . . **OVED 53**
LP: . . . . **DID 3**

Revival

GREAT HUDSON REVIVAL, THE (Various artists).
LP: . . . . **FF 214**

WHEN THE STORM IS OVER.
LP: . . . . **FF 032**

Revival Time Choir

20 BEST LOVED CAROLS - VOL.2.
Tracks: / Good Christian men, rejoice / Hark the herald angels sing / Away in a manger / Holly and the ivy, The / See, amid the winter's snow / Angel song / Peace / Mary lay down in a stable / In the bleak mid winter / God rest ye merry gentlemen / First Noel, The / Brightest and best / Sweet Christmas bells / What child is this / And his name was Jesus / Who is he in yonder stall / We three kings of Orient are / Joy joy joy / I saw three ships / Good King Wenceslas.
LP: . . . . **PC 326**

HAPPY REVIVAL TIME CHRISTMAS, A.
Tracks: / Joy joy joy / Good Christian men rejoice / As with gladness men of old / And his name was Jesus / See, amid the winter's snow / O little town of Bethlehem / Joy to the world / Peace / Angels from the realms of glory / Mary lay down in a stable / Sweet Christmas bells / Silent night.
LP: . . . . **PC 839**

HE'S THE ONE.
Tracks: / Great is Emmanuel / Way that he loves, The / I've found the answer / No one understands / How sweet the name / I have a home / Somebody bigger than you and I / Come and dine with me / He knows just what I need / He's the one / His hands were pierced / All that I need / Be thou exalted.
LP: . . . . **PC 816**

IT'S REVIVAL TIME.
Tracks: / My king of all kings / Hallelujah amen / Meeting in the air, The / Soldiers of Emmanuel / He reigns / All hail to thee Emmanuel / Shepherd of love / Count your blessings / If any man will follow / Reach out to Jesus / I'll walk with his hands in mine / I'm very very glad / They that wait upon the lord / Jesus saves / Let the whole world know / My task / What a friend we have in Jesus / Overshadowed / Answer yes / Deep down in my heart / You can if you will / Blessed assurance / Let thy mantle fall on me / Trust and obey / He giveth more grace.
LP: . . . . **PC 751**

IT'S REVIVAL TIME (ALBUM 2).
Tracks: / He touched me / Do you know my Jesus / Jesus is all I need / I will pilot thee.
LP: . . . . **PC 752**

IT'S REVIVAL TIME (ALBUM 3).
LP: . . . . **PC 753**

SHOW A LITTLE BIT OF LOVE AND KINDNESS.
Tracks: / Show a little bit of love and kindness / Every time I feel the Spirit / He hath blotted out my sin / Christ is coming back again / I know my redeemer lives / At the lamb's high feast we sing / King is coming / I have decided to follow Jesus / We are climbing Jacob's ladder / I'm happy now / Coming again / Through it all / Love, His love remains the same / My Lord arose.
LP: . . . . **PC 328**

Revolting Cocks

BEERS, STEERS AND QUEERS.
LP: . . . . **WAX 063 LP**
MC: . . . . **WAX 063 MC**

BIG SEXY LAND.
LP: . . . . **WAXUK 017**

YOU GODDAMNED SON OF A BITCH.
2LP: . . . . **WAXUK 037**

Revolutionaries

BLACK ASH DUB.
Tracks: / Marijuana / Herb / Collie / Lambsbread / Rizla / LSD / Acapulco / Cocaine.
LP: . . . . **TRLS 186**

GOLDMINE DUB.
Tracks: / Calico Jack / Big foot / Goldmine / Bitter blood / Red river dub / Musketeer dub / Jamintel / Heartburn / Sore mouth / Pepper dub.
LP: . . . . **GREL 4**

NEGREA LOVE DUB (See under Thompson, Lynval).

OUTLAW DUB.
Tracks: / 79 rock / Danger rockers / African free up / Wicked (dub) / Dub I dub / Roots man dub / Fisherman (dub) / Shockin' rock / Thompson sound incorporated.
LP: . . . . **TRLS 169**

REVOLUTIONARIES SOUNDS - VOL.2.
Tracks: / Tension / Pressure / Strain / Severe / Rigid / Intense / Retribution / Drastic / Energy / Urgency.
LP: . . . . **UAK 30237**

SOUNDS VOL 2.
Tracks: / Tension / Pressure / Strain / Severe / Rigid / Intense / Retibution / Drastic / Energy / Urgency.
LP: . . . . **UAG 30237**

Revolutionary Army

GIFT OF TEARS (Revolutionary Army Of The Infant Jesus).
LP: . . . . **PROBE 12**
MC: . . . . **PROBE 12 C**

Revolutionary Ensemble

MANHATTAN CYCLES.
LP: . . . . **IN 1023**

PEOPLES REPUBLIC, THE.
Tracks: / New York / Trio for trio / Chinese rocks / People's republic, The / Ponderous planets.
LP: . . . . **AMLJ 708**

REVOLUTIONARY ENSEMBLE.
LP: . . . . **ESP 2007**

Revolver

NORTHERN SONGS.
LP: . . . . **ROXLP 001**

Revolving Paint Dream

GREEN SEA BLUE / SUN, SEA, SAND.
LP: . . . . **CRELP 062**

MOTHER WATCH ME BURN.
LP: . . . . **CRELP 039**

OFF TO HEAVEN.
LP: . . . . **CRELP 018**

Rew, Kimberley

BIBLE OF BOP.
Tracks: / Nightmare / Stomping / Nothing is gonna change / Fighting someone's war / My baby does her hairdo long / Walking in the dew / Fishing / Hey war pig.
LP: . . . . **P 2003**

Rewind

REWIND (Various artists).
LP: . . . . **DHS 6**

REX

BEST OBSESSIONS.
Tracks: / Too pretty too soon / Come back to the five and dime / Far cry / Walking on water / Back on parade / Sleepwalking / 13 frightened girls / Curious / Television / Country dance.
LP: . . . . **CHR 1707**
MC: . . . . **ZCHR 1707**

Rexroth, Kenneth

POETRY AND JAZZ AT THE BLACKHAWK.
Tracks: / Married blues / Nicholas / Deserted courtesan, The / Shadows, The / Quietly / State and 32nd / Go lovely Rose / Orchard, The.
LP: . . . . **BGP 1019**

POETRY IN THE CELLAR (Rexroth, Kenneth & Lawrence Ferlinghetti).
Tracks: / Thou shalt not kill / Statue of St. Francis, The / Autobiography / Junkman's obbligato.
LP: . . . . **BGP 1024**

Rey, Alvino

1946 (Rey, Alvino & His Orchestra).
Tracks: / How high the moon / Bumble boogie / From the land of the sky blue water / You've got me crying again / April in Paris / Yesterdays / Dardanella / Hey frantic, relax / Stocking horse / Sheik of Araby / Just you, just me / Between the devil and the deep blue sea / Should I / Russian lullaby / High octane / Blue Lou.
LP: . . . . **HMP 5057**

1940/1 - VOL.3 (Rey, Alvino & His Orchestra).
LP: . . . . **HSR 196**

ALVINO REY AND ORCHESTRA 1946 (Rey, Alvino & His Orchestra).
Tracks: / How high the moon / Bumble boogie / Land of the sky blue water / You've got me crying again / April in Paris / Yesterdays / Dardanella / Stocking horse / Sheik of Araby / Just you, just me / Between the devil and the deep blue sea / Should I / Russuan lullaby / Hey frantic, relax / High octane / Blue Lou.
LP: . . . . **HSR 121**

ALVINO REY, VOL 2, 1946.
Tracks: / Blue Rey / Who's sorry now / Ghost of a chance / Lullaby of Broadway / I dont know why / I'm so right tonight / Dreamland / Kickapoo joy juice jolt / Chinese lullaby / I'm in the mood for love / Two guitars / Something sentimental / I can't believe that you're in love with me / Stormy weather / In an 18th century drawing room / Nighty night.
LP: . . . . **HSR 167**

BIG BAND SOUNDS (Dance With Me).
LP: . . . . **R 1000**

Rey, Chico

CRYING (IN THE DARK) (see Bowie, Angie & Chico Rey) (Rey, Chico & Angie Bowie).

Rey, H.A.

CURIOUS GEORGE (Harris, Julie).
MC: **1420**

Rey, Monte

DONKEY SERENADE & OTHER FAVOURITES.
Tracks: / Donkey serenade / O sole mio / Kiss me again / Annie Laurie / Frenesi / Boa noite / ntermezzo / Romanesca / Besame mucho / Don't ask me why / You belong to my heart / One day when we were young / Play gypsy play / Pablo the dreamer / Santa Lucia / Perhaps perhaps perhaps.
LP: . . . . **SH 330**

GOLDEN AGE OF MONTE REY.
Tracks: / So deep is the night / When our dreams grow old / World is waiting for the sunrise, The / Love's last word is spoken / Darling / Song of the rose / O lonely moon (Cielito lindo) / My serenade / love is a song / Kiss in the night, A / Sweetheart, we'll never grow old / Stars in your eyes / Carmelita / My lovely world and you / Stars will remember, The / Rose I bring you, The.
LP: . . . . **GX 2555**
MC: . . . . **TCGX 2555**

SONG OF SONGS.
Tracks: / Smoke gets in your eyes / Can I forget you / World is mine tonight, The / Yira Yira / Without a song / Love is mine / Vida mia / My heart will never sing / Beyond the blue horizon / I surrender dear / Song of songs / Love I give you my all / Donde / Shine through my dreams / In my little red book / O maiden, my maiden / Balloons / Rose of tralee (The).
LP: . . . . **CHD 130**

Rey, Tonto

A YA WE DEH (see Johnson, Anthony) (Rey, Tonto & Anthony Johnson).

Reyes, Walfredo De Los

ECUE (See Under Bellson, Louis) (Reyes, Walfredo De Los & Louis Bellson).

Reynard

FRESH FROM THE EARTH.
Tracks: / Well met / Ode to joy / Summer and winter / Faith hope and love / Greenwood gamble / Gold frankincense and myrrh / Abram and Isaac / Shepherd's carol / Song for a carpenter, A / Golden game / Lord of my blood / My song / Fiddler, the juggler and the clown, The / Beginnings.
LP: . . . . **PC 818**

Reyne, James

JAMES REYNE.
Tracks: / Fall of Rome / Hammerhead / Mr. Sandman / Counting on me / Always the way / Land of hope and glory / Motor's too fast / Heaven on a stick / Rip it up / Burning wood / Traveller, The.
LP: . . . . **EST 2066**
MC: . . . . **TC EST 2066**

Reynolds, Ambrose

GREATEST HITS: AMBROSE REYNOLDS.
LP: . . . . **ZULU 3**

Reynolds, Debbie

DEBBIE.
Tracks: / Love is a simple thing / S'posin' / You won't be satisfied / Moonglow / Hooray for love / Every time / You couldn't be cuter / Mean to me / Blue room / Here I am in love again / I like the likes of you / Time after time.
LP: . . . . **JASM 1512**

Reynolds, Jody

ENDLESS SLEEP.
LP: . . . . **MFLP 066**
LP: . . . . **SJLP 579**

Reynolds, John

TIMES AND SEASONS AT HAMPTON COURT (see under Hampton Court Chapel) (Reynolds, John/Hampton Court Chapel Royal choir).

Reynolds, L.J.

LOVIN' MAN.
Tracks: / Lovin' man / Don't give up on us / Don't let nobody hold you down / Don't worry / Touch down / Love take 2 / Weigh all the facts / Love me all over.
LP: . . . . **JABL 4**

TELL ME YOU WILL.
LP: . . . . **FAX 508**

Reynolds, Margaret

THINK ABOUT IT BABY.
LP: . . . . **MAL 7442**
LP: . . . . **ST 1027**

Rez Band

BETWEEN HEAVEN AND HELL.
LP: . . . . **SPR R 1111**
MC: . . . . **SPR C 1111**

HOSTAGE.
LP: . . . . **BIRD 163**
MC: . . . . **TC BIRD 163**

SILENCE SCREAMS.
LP: . . . . **OCE R 8123**
MC: . . . . **OCE C 8123**

Rezanova, Svetlana

RUSSIAN POPULAR SONGS.
MC: . . . . **SM 00371**

Rezillos

ATTACK.
LP: . . . . **SV 4001**

CAN'T STAND THE REZILLOS.
Tracks: / Flying saucer attack / No / Someone's gonna get their head kicked in tonight / Top of the pops / 2000 AD / It gets me / Can't stand my baby / Glad all over / My baby does good sculptures / I like it / Gettin' me down / Cold wars / Bad guy reaction.
LP: . . . . **K 56530**

MC: **K4 56530**

MISSION ACCOMPLISHED BUT THE BEAT GOES ON.
Tracks: / Top of the pops / Mystery action / Somebody's gonna get their head kicked in / Thunderbirds are go / Cold wars / Teenbeat / No / Land of a thousand dances / I need you / Gettin' me down / Culture shock / Ballroom blitz / (My baby does) good sculptures / Destination venus.
LP: . . . . **SRK 6069**
MC: . . . . **SRC 6089**

TOP OF THE POPS.
Tracks: / Top of the pops / Destination Venus.
MC: . . . . **SPC 3**

Rhapsodie

RHAPSODIE.
LP: . . . . **JHI 102**

Rhapsody In Blue

RHAPSODY IN BLUE (Various artists).
Tracks: / Rhapsody in blue: *Various artists* / Street music: *Various artists* / Entertainer, The: *Various* artists / Sugar cane rag: *Various artists* / Maple leaf rag: *Various artists* / Charleston rag: *Various* artists / Alexander's ragtime band: *Various artists* / 12th Street rag: *Various artists* / Darktown strutter's ball: *Various artists.*
LP: **2535666**

Rhead Brothers

BLACK SHAHEEN.
Tracks: / Black shaheen / Strange mercy / Sweet sweet heartache / No surprise / Love's a crazy game / Dark and quiet walls / Oh darling / Song of a sadder side of town / When the seagul flies.
LP: . . . . **EMC 3228**

Rhiannon

BIRDS OF RHIANNON.
Tracks: / TWA corbies / Rince Briotanach(Gavotten ar menez) / Galloping trots / Lovely Joan / Will ye go to Flanders / Apples in winter / Fhir / Spanish ladies.
LP: . . . . **FE 046**
MC: . . . . **FE 046 C**

Rhinestone

RHINESTONE (OST) (See under Parton, Dolly) (Parton, Dolly).

Rhino Bucket

RHINO BUCKET.
LP: **7599263171**
MC: **7599263174**

Rhino Teen Magazine

RHINO TEEN MAGAZINE (Various artists).
LP: . . . . **RNLP 059**

Rhodes, Emitt

FRESH AS A DAISY.
Tracks: / With my face on the floor / Somebody made for me / She's such a beauty / Long time no see / Lullaby / Fresh as a daisy / Live till you die / Promises I've made / You take the dark out of the night / You should be ashamed / Ever find yourself running / You must have / Blue horizon / Only lovers decide / Love will stone you / Better side of life / Mirror / Really wanted you.
LP: . . . . **SEE 74**

Rhodes, Eugene

TALKIN' ABOUT MY TIME.
LP: . . . . **C 5522**

Rhodes, Kimmie

ANGELS GET THE BLUES.
LP: . . . . **HLD 010**
MC: . . . . **HLD 010C**

MAN IN THE MOON.
Tracks: / Man in the moon, The / Daddy's song / Earth shakin' thing / Just someone I used to know / When you wish upon a star / 1000 musicians / What a love's supposed to be / It'll do / How long.
LP: . . . . **HLD 007**

WITH THE JACKALOPE BROS.
LP: **HLD008**

Rhodes, Roy

COUNTRY HEARTBREAK.
Tracks: / I never miss a day missing you / Coward of the county / Today I started loving you again / To daddy / Dream / Crying time / One day at a time / Four in the morning / Walk on by / Answer to everything, The / Almost persuaded.
LP: . . . . **BGC 263**
MC: . . . . **KBGC 263**

COUNTRY SIDE OF ROY RHODES.
MC: . . . . **CWGR 102**

Rhodes, Sonny

DISCIPLE OF THE BLUES.
Tracks: / You can look for me / Blue funky down / Ain't nothing but the blues / Cigarette blues / Are we losing our thing / Ain't no blues in town / Ya ya / Blue shadows falling / Blue thunder.
LP: . . . . **ICH 9002**
MC: . . . . **ICH 9002 MC**

I DON'T WANT MY BLUES COLOURED.
LP: . . . . **AMLP 821**

IN EUROPE.
LP: . . . . **AP 023**

Rhodes, Todd

DANCE MUSIC THAT HITS THE SPOT.
LP: . . . . **ST 1020**
LP: . . . . **SC 1020**

YOUR DADDY'S DOGGIN' AROUND.
Tracks: / Flying disco / Anitra's jump / Red boy at the mardi gras / I'm just a fool in love / Beulah / Evening breeze / Good man / Comin' home / Your daddy's doggin' around / I shouldn't cry but I do / I shouldn't cry but I do / Pig latin blues / Hog maw and cabbage slaw / Lost child / Your mouth got a hole / Must I cry alone.
LP: . . . . **JB 615**

Rhonda

BLACK & STRANGE.
MC: . . . . **BIP 201**

Rhos Male Voice Choir

COR MEIBION ORFFIWS Y RHOS.
LP: . . . . **SCLP 579**

GREAT OPERA CHORUSES.
LP: . . . . **TXDS 502**
MC: . . . . **KTXDC 502**

JIM REEVES - WE THANK THEE.
Tracks: / Welcome to my world / Just out of reach / He'll have to go / In the misty moonlight / I won't forget you / Distant drums / Little ole you / Adios amigo / I love you because / Anna Marie / You're the only good thing that's happened to me / We thank thee.
LP: . . . . **MOR 510**

MUSIC OF WALES.
Tracks: / Fantasia on welsh hymn tunes / Jesu, lover of my soul / I will sing the wondrous story / In heavenly love, abiding / Judge eternal / Guid me, o thou great Jehovah / Hunting the hare / David of the White Rock / All through the night / Calon lan / Ash grove, The / New years eve / Men of Harlech.
LP: . . . . **ETMP 8**

RHOS MALE VOICE CHOIR.
Tracks: / Land of my fathers / My little Welsh home / God bless the Prince of Wales / Going home / David of the white rock / Men of Harlech / All through the night / 23rd psalm / Dove, The / Bless this house / Ash grove, The.
LP: . . . . **GH 520**

SING JIM REEVES FAVOURITES.
LP: . . . . **SPR 8580**
MC: . . . . **SPC 8580**

Rhyme Syndicate

COMIN' THROUGH.
Tracks: / Comin' through / Think you can hang / Bustin' Loose / Syndication / TDF Connection / T D F / Ghettoish / I need a rolex / While you've been.
LP: **925774-1**
MC: **925774-4**

Rhys Jones, Griff

BITTER AND TWISTED (See under Smith & Jones).

Rhythm & Blues

20 GREAT RHYTHM & BLUES OF THE 50'S (Various artists).
Tracks: / Rockin' pneumonia and the boogie woogie 'flu: *Smith, Huey "Piano" & The Clowns* / Ain't a better story told: *Littlefield, Little Willie* / B.B. boogie: *King, B.B.* / Good rockin' daddy: *James, Etta* / Rock house boogie: *Hooker, John Lee* / Let the good times roll: *Shirley & Lee* / Bop hop: *Crayton, Pee Wee* / Don't you know Yockomo: *Smith, Huey & The Clowns* / Oop shoop: *Queens, The* / Reelin' & rockin': *McCracklin, Jimmy*/ Who's been jivin with you: *Witherspoon, Jimmy* / Road I travel, The: *Turner, Ike's Rhythm Kings* / Morning at midnight: *Howlin' Wolf* / Is everything alright: *King, Earl* / Love bandit: *Cadets* / Goodbye baby: *James,* Elmore / No more doggin: *Gordon, Roscoe* / Early times: *Turner, Ike's Rhythm Kings* / Gee baby: *Joe & Ann* / Kansas City blues: *Turner, Big.*
LP: . . . . **DROP 1001**
MC: . . . . **CROP 1001**

50'S: R & B VOCAL GROUPS, THE (See under 50's) (Various artists).

1983 R & B JAMBOREE (Various artists).
Tracks: / Wow wow: *Egans, Willie* / Driftin' blues: *Egans, Willie* / Lawdy Miss Clawdy: *Egans, Willie*/ Pachuko hop: *Higgins, Chuck* / Baby what you want me to do?: *Higgins, Chuck* / Aw shucks: *Higgins, Chuck*/ It's love, baby: *Young Jessie* / It don't happen no more: *Young Jessie* / Lonesome desert: *Young Jessie*/ Night train: *McNeely, Big Jay* / There is something on your mind: *McNeely, Big Jay* / 3-D: *McNeely, Big Jay.*
LP: . . . . **CH 89**

ALL THESE THINGS (Sound of New Orleans, The) (Various artists).
Tracks: / Barefootin': *Parker, Robert* / Tell it like it is: *Neville, Aaron* / Mother in law: *K-Doe, Ernie*/ Working in a coal mine: *Dorsey, Lee* / I like it like that: *Kenner, Chris* / Ooh poo pah doo: *Hill, Jessie*/ It will stand: *Showman* / You always hurt the one you love: *Henry, Clarence 'Frogman'* / Fortune teller: *Spellman,* Benny / All these things: *Neville, Art* / Iko iko: *Dixie Cups* / Ruler of my heart: *Thomas, Irma*/ Rockin' pneumonia and the boogie woogie flu: *Smith, Huey "Piano"* / Chicken strut: *Meters* / Release me: *Adams, Johnny* / Something you got: *George, Barbara.*
LP: . . . . **INS 5024**
MC: . . . . **TCINS 5024**

ATLANTIC R & B SERIES (See under Atlantic (label)) (Various artists).

BEST OF BATON R & B (Various artists).
LP: . . . . **FLY 552**

BEST OF NEW ORLEANS RHYTHM AND BLUES (Various artists).
Tracks: / Loud mouth Annie: *Various artists* / Rhythmatic rhythum: *Various artists* / Jockomo: *Various artists*/ Mardi gras: *Various artists* / Country boy: *Various artists* / Flat foot Sam: *Various artists* / Ding dong darling: *Various artists* / Lawdy mama: *Various artists* / What can I do: *Various artists* / Joke, The: *Various artists* / Walk that walk: *Various artists* / I cried all the way home: *Various artists*/ Foolish woman: *Various artists* / Oh oh: *Various artists* / This should go on forever: *Various artists*/ Needing your love: *Various artists* / Baby please: *Various artists.*
LP: . . . . **CXMP 2055**

BEST OF RIC RECORDS VOL. 1 (Various artists).
Tracks: / Carnival Time: *Johnson, Al* / Cotton candy: *Capello, Lenny* / Check Mr. Popeye: *Bo, Eddie*/ Check Mr. Popeye: *Adams, Johnny* / I don't talk too much: *Nelson, Martha* / Let's stop and talk it over: *Ridgley,* Tommy / Lena: *Johnson, Al* / 90 pound weakling: *Capello, Lenny* / Losing battle, A: *Adams, Johnny*/ Let's Get It: *Blanchard, Edgar* / She's got what it takes: *Ridley, Tommy* / Feeling right Sat: *Velvetiers.*
LP: . . . . **ED 257**

BORDER TOWN JIVE (Chicago R & B from San Antonio 1960's) (Various artists).
LP: . . . . **KK 7436**

BOSS VOCAL GROUPS OF THE 60'S (Various artists).
Tracks: / Daddy rollin' stone: *Various artists* / Ol' man river: *Various artists* / Deep river: *Various artists*/ Homesick: *Various artists* / Oh' what a feeling: *Various artists* / You've got just what I need: *Various* artists / Poor baby: *Various artists* / Sincerely: *Various artists* / Some of this, some of that: *Various* artists / So long: *Various artists* / Night and day: *Various artists* / Love bound: *Various artists*/ Kisses: *Various artists* / In my dream: *Various artists* / Dreaming: *Various artists.*
LP: . . . . **RL 065**

BRITISH R & B ARCHIVE, THE (See under British R & B Archive) (Various artists).

BRITISH R & B SCENE (Various artists).
Tracks: / Meanie genie: *Brook, Tony/ Breakers* / You better let him go: *Powell, Keith & The Valets* / Once upon a time: *Untamed* / Down in Mexico: *Boston Crabs* / Sporting life: *Finn, Mickey* / Bald headed woman: *Sneekers*/ I just don't understand: *Cresters* / Baby what you want me to do: *Sons of Fred* / Ooh poo pah doo: *Brook,* Tony/Breakers / How: *Jynx* / Jack o' diamonds: *Carruthers, Ben & The Deep* / Jean Dorothy: *Five Chesternuts*/ It's so easy: *Toggery Five* / Baby not like you: *Whirlwinds* / Yes I do: *Tony's defenders* / Right behind you: *Carruthers, Ben & The Deep* / Hole in my soul: *Preachers* / Cupid: *Haydocks Rockhouse* / Can't stop: *Senate* / Bye bye Johnny: *Wayne, Pat/ Beachcombers.*
LP: . . . . **SEE 33**

CARNIVAL TIME: THE BEST OF RIC RECORDS vol. 1 (Various artists).
LP: . . . . **ROUNDER 2075**
MC: . . . . **ROUNDER 2075C**

CHARLY R & B PARTY (See under Charly (label)) (Various artists).

CHESS MASTERS (Various artists).
2LP: . . . . **CXMD 4010**

CHESS NEW ORLEANS R&B (Various artists).
LP: . . . . **DET 205**

CHESS SAMPLER (Various artists).
Tracks: / My babe: *Little Walter* / Help me: *Williamson, Sonny Boy* / Smokestack lightning: *Howlin' Wolf*/ Mannish boy: *Waters, Muddy* / Sugar mama: *Hooker, John Lee* / Dust my broom: *James, Elmore* / Walking by myself: *Rodgers, Jimmie (1)* / Road runner: *Diddley, Bo* / Brown eyed handsome man: *Berry, Chuck* / Wang dang doodle: *Taylor, Koko* / We're gonna make it: *Little Milton* / High heel sneakers: *Little Tommy Tucker*/ Soulful dress: *Sugar Pie Desanto* / Security: *James, Etta.*
LP: . . . . **CXSP 7250**
MC: . . . . **ZCCXSP 7250**

CHESS STORY 1954-1969 (Various artists).
Tracks: / Bye bye Johnny: *Berry, Chuck* / Suzie Q: *Hawkins, Dale* / Rinky dink: *Cortez, Dave 'Baby'*/ In the mood: *Hooker, John Lee* / Madison blues: *James, Elmore* / Ain't got no home: *Henry, Clarence 'Frogman'*/ Sincerely: *Moonglows* / Sneakin' around: *Little Milton* / Rescue me: *Fontella Bass* / Stop around: *Guy,* Buddy / Bring it to Jerome: *Diddley, Bo* / High heel sneakers: *Tucker, Tommy* / Mannish boy: *Waters,* Muddy / Smokestack lightning: *Howlin' Wolf* / In crowd, The: *Lewis, Ramsey Trio* / Peanut butter: *Marathons*/ Only time will tell: *James, Etta* / Get closer together: *Tex, Joe* / Selfish one: *Ross, Jackie.*
2LP: . . . . **VSOPLP 130**
MC: . . . . **VSOPMC 130**

CHESS:THE RHYTHM AND THE BLUES (Various artists).
LP: . . . . **SAM 500**
MC: . . . . **TCSAM 500**

CONDITION YOUR HEART (Various artists).
Tracks: / My baby don't need changing: *Kinglets* / Pretty please: *Kinglets* / Tell me why: *Rockers* / Condition your heart: *Little Herbert & The Arabians* / Rumblin' tumblin' baby: *Emeralds* / Wham slam bam: *Green,* Fred / My love: *Turner, Ike & The Kings of Rhythm* / That's all I need: *Turner, Ike & The Kings of Rhythm*/ Bye bye baby: *Love, Clayton* / Mistreated: *Love, Clayton* / I don't hurt anymore: *Bass, Fontella* / Honey bee: *Bass, Fontella* / It's alright: *Lassiter, Art* / Eastside blues: *Sain, Oliver* / Workin' again: *Smith, Robert T.*
LP: . . . . **RL 0069**

DOWN BEHIND THE RISE, 1947-1953 (Various artists).
LP: . . . . **NH 105**

DOWN IN THE GROOVY (Texas rhythm and blues 1949-1952) (Various artists).
LP: . . . . **KK 7418**

DRIVING R'N'B & BOOGIE WOOGIE (Various artists).
Tracks: / Choo choo ch' boogie: *Jordan, Louis* / Six wheel chaser: *Lewis, Meade Lux* / Hamp's boogie woogie: *Hampton, Lionel* / Oh boy that's where my money goes: *Four Blazes.*
MC: . . . . **CONE 9**

DUKES OF RHYTHM 1960 (Featuring Joe Carl) (Various artists).
Tracks: / Those eyes: *Various artists* / For love: *Various artists* / Before I grow too old: *Various artists*/ Ooh poo pah doo: *Various artists* / Holy one: *Various artists* / Tell it like it is: *Various artists*/ Don't leave me again: *Various artists* / One little dream: *Various artists* / Somebody's cheatin': *Various* artists / You broke my heart: *Various artists* / Everybody's rockin': *Various artists* / I've found my love: *Various artists* / Defeated: *Various artists* / Don't leave me again: *Various artists.*
LP: . . . . **KK 788**

GOING DOWN TO LOUISIANA (Various artists).
Tracks: / Joe Hill: *Louis, Joe Hill* / Forth & Beale: *Louis, Joe Hill* / Ruthy Mae: *Louis, Joe Hill*/ Going down to Louisiana: *Louis, Joe Hill* / Get up off it: *Louis, Joe Hill* / Sweetest woman: *Louis, Joe Hill* / Beautiful, beautiful love: *Cleve, Schoolboy* / Mean old world: *Crudup, Arthur 'Big Boy'* / Baby I've been mistreated: *Crudup, Arthur 'Big Boy'* / Boogie all the time: *Crudup, Arthur 'Big Boy'* / I wonder where my baby's gone: *Crudup, Arthur 'Big Boy'* / My baby done gone: *Cleve, Schoolboy* / Smokestick

lightning: Bad Smitty / Rhythm with me: Meyers, Sam.
LP: WLP 9955

GOOD TO THE LAST DROP (Various artists).
Tracks: / Duster Benton: Various artists / Good to the last drop: Various artists / Sweet 94: Various artists/ Money is the name of the game: Various artists / My back scratcher: Various artists / Curtis Griffin: Various artists / Baby have your way: Various artists / John Lee Hooker: Various artists / I feel good: Various artists.
LP: **CRB 1203**

GOTHAM HOUSE PARTY (Various artists).
Tracks: / Drinking beer: Summers, J.B. / Stomp: Jennings, Bill / Roly Poly Mama: Crafton, Harry / That's right: Cole, Eddie / Mel's jump: Gill, Sax / Dual trumpet blues: Motley, Frank / I'm free: Gonzales, Charlie / Hey Everybody: Preston, Jimmy / I ain't mad at you: Jones Boys / House party: Tribble, T.N.T./ Corn pone: Mae, Daisy & Hepcats / Danny's blues: Turner,Danny / Red hot boogie: Tribble, T.N.T..
LP: **KK 803**

GREAT BRITISH RHYTHM & BLUES, BARRELHOUSE (Various artists).
LP: **TAB 54**

GREAT GATES 1949-1952 (EARLY WEST COAST R&B) (Various artists).
Tracks: / Rocking time: Various artists / Farewell baby: Various artists / Ain't got no money: Various artists / Race track blues: Various artists / Change your ways: Various artists / Rock me: Various artists / Blue after hours: Various artists / Central rocks: Various artists / Rock me baby: Various artists / Checkin' up blues: Various artists / Home town boy: Various artists / Teadrops are falling: Various artists / Come back home: Various artists / Sad and lonesome: Various artists / Evening blues: Various artists / Later after hours: Various artists.
LP: **KK 7435**

GROOVE JUMPING (Various artists).
Tracks: / Ride and roll: Terry, Sonny / No good lover: Mickey & Sylvia / Strange kind of feeling: Kennedy, Tiny / Bottle it up and go: Green, Big John / Boot 'em up: Du-Droppers / Dead broke: Du-Droppers/ Speed King: Du-Droppers / Smack dab in the middle: Du-Droppers / Lawdy Miss Mary: Five Keys / Worried 'bout you baby: Gaines, Roy 'Mr Guitar' / Dat dat de dum dum: Gaines, Roy 'Mr Guitar' / Mr. Bear: Gaines, Roy 'Mr Guitar' / Radar: Gaines, Roy 'Mr Guitar' / How come?: Gaines, Roy 'Mr Guitar'.
LP: **DT 33003**

HISTORY OF...,A VOL.1(1950-1958) (Various artists).
Tracks: / Let the good times roll: Shirley & Lee / Rockin' pneumonia and the boogie woogie flu: Various artists/ Lawdy Miss Clawdy: Price, Lloyd / Bald head: Professor Longhair / Later alligator: Charles, Bobby/ Those lonely lonely nights: King, Earl / Walkin' with Mr.Lee: Allen, Lee / Ain't got no home: Henry, Clarence 'Frogman' / Just because: Price, Lloyd / Jock-a-mo: Crawford, James 'Sugarboy' & His Canecutters / Don't you just know it: Smith, Huey "Piano" & The Clowns / Feel so good: Shirley & Lee / Things that I used to do: Guitar Slim / Mardis gras mambo: Hawketts.
LP: **RNLP 70076**
MC: **RNC 70076**

HISTORY OF...,A VOL.2(1959-1962) (Various artists).
Tracks: / Ooh poo pah doo(part 1): Hill, Jessie / Certain girl, A: K-Doe, Ernie / Fortune teller: Spellman, Benny / Trick bag: King, Earl / I know (you don't love me no more): George, Barbara / All these things: Neville, Art / It will stand: Showmen / Ya ya: Dorsey, Lee / Mother-in-law: K-Doe, Ernie/ Over you: Neville, Aaron / I like it like that (part1): Kenner, Chris / Sea cruise: Ford, Frankie/ There's something on your mind (part 2): Marchan, Bobby / But I do: Henry, Clarence 'Frogman'.
LP: **RNLP 70077**
MC: **RNC 70077**

HISTORY OF...,A VOL.3(1962-1970) (Various artists).
Tracks: / Ride your pony: Dorsey, Lee / Lipstick traces (on a cigarette): Spellman, Benny / Time is on my side: Thomas, Irma / Release me: Adams, Johnny / Down home girl: Robinson, Alvin / You'll lose a good thing: Lynn, Barbara / Working in a coalmine: Dorsey, Lee / Barefootin': Parker, Bobby / Get out of my life woman: Dorsey, Lee / Tell it like it is: Neville, Aaron / Something you got: Robinson, Alvin / Wish someone would care: Thomas, Irma / I won't cry: Adams, Johnny / Iko iko: Dixie Cups.
LP: **RNLP 70078**
MC: **RNC 70078**

IF IT'S NOT A HIT I'LL EAT MY HAT (Various artists).
Tracks: / Hound dog: Thornton, Big Mama / Pledging my love: Various artists / I love my baby: Little Richard with Johnny Otis Orchestra / I wanna ramble: Little Junior Parker & The Blue Flames / Farther up the road: Bland, Bobby / Keep on diggin': Gordon, Roscoe / To the end: Sensational Nightingales / Texas flood: Davis, Larry / Okie dokie stomp: Brown, Gatemouth with Pluma Davis Orchestra / Taxi blues: Little Frankie Lee and the Saxons / Spunky onions: Davis, Billy & The Legends & Hank Moore Band / Blue Monday: Davis, James / Funny how time slips away: Hinton, Joe / Treat her right: Head, Roy.
LP: **CH 154**

IN THE STILL OF THE NIGHT (Various artists).
Tracks: / Glory of love: Five Keys / You're so fine: Falcons / In the still of the night: Five Satins/ Tonite tonite: Mello Kings / I didn't want to do it: Spiders / Oh Julie: Crescendos / Try the impossible: Andrews, Lee & The Hearts / Close your eyes: Five Keys / Love potion No.9: Clovers / Western movies: Olympics / When you dance: Turbans / Ling-ting-tong: Five Keys / Get a job: Silhouettes / Wonderful dream, A: Majors / Pama Oom Mow Mow: Rivingtons / Stay: Williams, Maurice.
LP: **CGB 1004**
MC: **TC CGB 1004**

JM VOL.1 - TAG ALONG (Legendary Jay Miller sessions) (Various artists).
LP: **FLY 516**

JM VOL.2 - GONNA HEAD FOR HOME (Various artists).
LP: **FLY 517**

JM VOL.3 - ROOSTER CROW'D FOR DAYS (Various artists).
LP: **FLY 518**

JM VOL.4 - SLIM HARPO Blues hangover (Various artists).
LP: **FLY 20**

JM VOL.15 - ROCKIN' FEVER (Various artists).
LP: **FLY 540**

JM VOL.17 - BOPPIN' IT (Various artists).
LP: **FLY 554**

JM VOL.18 - THE GIRL IN THE TIGHT BLUE JEANS (Various artists).
LP: **FLY 555**

JUKE BOX (Various artists).
MC: **CHDC 335**

LIVE IN LONDON - VOL.1 (Various artists).
Tracks: / Down to the doctors: Mickey Jupp Band / All night worker: Red Beans & Rice / Somebody's changed the lock: Diz & The Doormen / Bluebird two step: Electric Bluebirds / Square dancin' Momma: Electric Bluebirds/ Shame shame shame: Red Beans & Rice / Whistlin' Joe: Red Beans & Rice / Five guys named Moe: Chevalier Brothers / Jumpin' at the woodside: Chevalier Brothers / Kansas city: Mickey Jupp Band / Call me the breeze: Electric Bluebirds / Messaround: Diz & The Doormen.
LP: **CH 91**

LOADED DOWN WITH THE BLUES (Various artists).
Tracks: / Loaded down: Various artists / Tight like that: Various artists / Nervous condition: Various artists / I'm gonna make you eat them words: Various artists / Moanin' and screamin' (parts 1 & 2): Various artists/ Ain't broke, ain't hungry: Various artists / Early morning blues: Various artists / Way in the middle of the night: Various artists / Bad luck and trouble: Various artists / Somebody's doin' me wrong: Various artists/ (If I only had a) chance for your love: Various artists / It's a thing you gotta face: Various artists / What is life?: Various artists / Fooler, The: Various artists.
LP: **CRB 1170**
MC: **TCCRB 1170**

LOST DREAMS New Orleans vocal groups (Various artists).
Tracks: / Drunk drunk drunk: Kidds / Why fool yourself: Williams, Bernie / Bluesy me: Collis, Dave/Scubbs/ Lost dreams: Dukes / Sunny side of the street: Bees / Eternally yours: Barons / Cotton pickin' hands: Dukes / Later baby: Matthews, Fat Man/4 kittens / Boom boom: New Orleans Vocal Groups / Teardrop eyes: Dukes / Ain't gonna do it: Pelicans / Shake the dice: Barons / Darling please: Bees / Last ride, The: Dukes.
LP: **SSL 6024**
MC: **TCSSL 6024**

LOUISIANA R AND B (Various artists).
Tracks: / Life problem: Various artists / Sick & tired: Various artists / Don't touch me, baby: Various artists / Humpty dumpty heart: Various artists / Crawl: Various artists / Shed so many tears: Various artists / I'm gonna have to pass: Various artists / I've been your fool: Various artists / Nobody knows: Various artists / Help me forget her: Various artists / My life is a lonely one: Various artists / Mexican shoeshine boy: Various artists / Let's stick together: Various artists / Drifting cloud: Various artists.
LP: **RP 702**

LYONS AVENUE JIVE (Various artists).
Tracks: / Hattie Green: Various artists / Mr. Ticket agent: Various artists / Creole gal blues: Various artists / I cried: Various artists / She'll be mine after a while: Various artists / Coming back home: Various artists / R B boogie: Various artists / New kind of loving: Various artists / Irene's boogie: Various artists / Tired of this life I'm living: Various artists / Make her see things my way: Various artists / I'm not suspicious, but: Various artists / Summer's coming on: Various artists / Hepcat's advice: Various artists / You see me smiling: Various artists / Alabama blues: Various artists.
LP: **CHD 171**

MORE POWER TO YA (Various artists).
Tracks: / More power to ya: Various artists / Heaven help me (I'm falling in love with you): Various artists/ Please don't break my heart (like you did): Various artists / All I need is you: Various artists / It's a man's world: Various artists / Gentle on my mind: Various artists / Sweetest story, The: Various artists/ It sure was fun: Various artists / I met her in church: Various artists / Mighty long way, A: Various artists / What the world needs now is love: Various artists / Headman: Various artists / My man (my sweet man): Various artists / Home for the summer: Various artists / Don't let go: Various artists / To make my life beautiful: Various artists.
LP: **CRB 1224**

MR JOE'S JAMBALAYA (Various artists).
Tracks: / Beverly baby: Allen & Allen / Ooh poo pah doo: Hill, Jessie / Lottie mo: Dorsey, Lee / Over you: Neville, Aaron / Mother-in-law: K-Doe, Ernie / Mudd: Montrell, Roy / Always naggin': Del-Royals/ I need money: Diamond, Lee / I like it like that: Kenner, Chris / All these things: Neville, Art/ It will stand: Showmen / New kind of love: Harper, Willie / Everything happens at night: August, Joseph 'Mr. Google Eyes' / I'm gonna put some hurt on you: Lewis, Raymond.
2LP: **CDX 26**
MC: **TCCDX 26**

NASHVILLE R&B VOL.1 (Various artists).
LP: **KK 7431**

NASHVILLE R&B VOL.2 (Various artists).
Tracks: / L and N special: Various artists / Sittin' here drinking: Various artists / Every day in the week: Various artists / Evil-eyed woman: Various artists / I ain't nothing but a fool: Various artists / Old man you're slippin': Various artists / I'll help you baby: Various artists / Lord have mercy: Various artists / I'm just what you're looking for: Various artists / Price you pay for love: Various artists / Snake in the grass: Various artists / Heartache blues: Various artists / You ain't nothing but trouble: Various artists / Slave to love: Various artists / Gotta stop loving you: Various artists.
LP: **KK 7432**

NASHVILLE R&B VOL.3 (Various artists).
LP: **KK 7433**

NEW JERSEY BURNERS (Various artists).
Tracks: / Little Eva: Green, Johnny / That's all I wanna do: Rollins, Bird / Pretty little school girl: Rollins, Bird / Forgive me: Carson, Eddie / Barracuda: Carson, Eddie / Walkin' & cryin': Carson, Eddie/ Ever lovin' baby: Little Luther / Just let me be: Rollins, Bird / Green champaign: Green, Johnny/ I'm leaving: Love Bug / Loaded guitar: Tubbs, Joe / Best wishes: Tubbs, Joe / Oh babe: Orlon, Terry / Soft lights: Clowney, David / Crying blues: Little Luther / Hackensack: Franklin, Gene.
LP: **KK 7442**

NEW ORLEANS RHYTHM & BLUES (Various artists).
LP: **1019**
MC: **1019 TC**

NEW ORLEANS RHYTHM & BLUES OFFICIAL ANNIVERSARY Various artists (Various artists).
LP: **SNTF 937**

NEW ORLEANS R'N'B 1949-67 (Various artists).
LP: **KK 7403**

NEW ORLEANS VOLUME 1 (Various artists).
Tracks: / Eternity: Various artists / I want you: Various artists / Bouncing the boogie: Various artists/ Do you really love me baby: Various artists / I need your love: Various artists / Say baby: Various artists/ Heavy sugar: Various artists / I s everything alright: Various artists / Who's ben fooling you: Various artists / Hopeless love: Various artists / Mr. Bumps: Various artists / My dreams are in vain: Various artists / Got a gal in Nashville: Various artists / Long lost stranger: Various artists / Looked at the moon: Various artists / Preachin' & teachin': Various artists.
LP: **CH 165**

NEW ORLEANS VOLUME 2 Various artists (Various artists).
LP: **CH 181**

NEW YORK R 'N' B (Various artists).
LP: **PY 1817**

OKEH RHYTHM AND BLUES (Various artists).
2LP: **EPC 22125**
MC: **40 22125**

OLD KING GOLD, VOL 1 (Various artists).
Tracks: / Finger poppin' time: Ballard, Hank / Only you: Platters / Daddy o: Lou, Bonnie / Since I don't have you: Flamingos / Ivory tower: Williams, Otis & The Charms / Flamingo: Bostic, Earl / Tossin' and turnin': Lewis, Bobby / Last kiss, The: Cochran, Wayne / Seventeen: Bennett, Boyd / These foolish things: Ward, Billy & The Dominoes / Sleep: John, Little Willie / Slow walk: Austin, Sil.
LP: **BID 8027**

OLD KING GOLD, VOL 2 (Various artists).
Tracks: / Honky tonk (part 1): Doggett, Bill / Honky tonk (part 2): Doggett, Bill / Talk to me: John, Little Willie / Sixty minute man: Ward, Billy & The Dominoes / Down the aisle: Labelle, Patty & The Bluebells / White cliffs of Dover, The: Checkers / Harlem nocturne: Bostic, Earl / Beside you: Swallows / Sexy ways: Midnighters / Dedicated to the one I love: Five Royales / Well oh well: Bradshaw, Tiny / It hurts to be in love: Laurie, Annie.
LP: **BID 8028**

OLD KING GOLD, VOL 3 (Various artists).
Tracks: / Have mercy, baby: Ward, Billy & The Dominoes / Let them talk: John, Little Willie / Let's go, let's go, let's go: Ballard, Hank & The Midnighters / Guess who: Hunter, Ivory Joe / This little girl of mine: Hurricanes/ Soft: Bradshaw, Tiny / Hearts of stone: Williams, Otis & The Charms / I love you, yes I do: Jackson, Bull Moose / Think: Five Royales / Tomorrow night: Johnson, Lonnie / Over the rainbow: Checkers / Tonk game: Marr, Hank.
LP: **BID 8029**

OLD KING GOLD, VOL 4 (Various artists).
Tracks: / Hideaway: King, Freddie / Fever: John, Little Willie / Little things mean a lot: Ward, Billy & The Dominoes / Good rockin' tonight: Harris, Wynonie / Trying: Rhodes, Todd & Laverne Baker / September song: Bostic, Earl / Chica boo: Glenn, Lloyd / Kansas City: Ballard, Hank & The Midnighters / All my love belongs to you: Jackson, Bull Moose / Another woman's man: Tex, Joe / Shout bamalaya: Redding, Otis/ Tenderly: Hope, Lynn.
LP: **BID 8030**

OLD KING GOLD, VOL 5 (Various artists).
Tracks: / Ling-ting-tong: Various artists / What can I do?: Elbert, Donnie / No, no, no: Chanters/ Yours: Hurricanes / Long gone, Part 1: Thompson, Sonny / Long gone, Part 2: Thompson, Sonny / Work with me, Annie: Ballard, Hank & The Midnighters / Black night: Brown, Charles / All around the world: John, Little Willie / I do the shimmy shimmy: Freeman, Bobby / Moondust: Doggett, Bill / Swingin' shepherd blues: Pate, Johnny.
LP: **BID 8031**

OLD KING GOLD, VOL 6 (Various artists).

Tracks: / Twist, The: *Ballard, Hank* / Bells, The: *Ward, Billy & The Dominoes* / Bloodshot eyes: *Harris, Wynonie* / Walkin' with Mr.Lee: *Pate, Johnny* / Come home: *Johnson, Bubber* / Hold it: *Doggett, Bill* / Gumdrop: *Williams, Otis & The Charms* / My friends: *Strangers* / Goof, The: *McNeely, Big Jay* / Somebody done stole my cherry red: *Vinson, Eddie "Cleanhead"* / Big boy: *Jennings, Bill.*
LP: . . . . **BID 8032**

OLD KING GOLD, VOL 7 (Various artists).
Tracks: / That's what you're doing to me: *Ward, Billy & The Dominoes* / Don't take it so hard: *King, Earl* / Greasy spoon: *Marr, Hank* / Don't throw your love on me so strong: *King, Albert* / I want a bow-legged woman: *Jackson, Bull Moose* / I won't be this way always: *King Pins* / Annie had a baby: *Ballard, Hank & The Midnighters* / Dearest: *Swallows* / Mellow blues, Part 1: *Thompson, Sonny* / Mellow blues, Part 2: *Thompson, Sonny* / I'm tore up: *Gayles, Billy* / Diamonds and pearls: *Escos.*
LP: . . . . **BID 8033**

OLD KING GOLD, VOL 8 (Various artists).
Tracks: / Heaven only knows: *Williams, Otis & The Charms* / Ram-bunk-shush: *Doggett, Bill* / It shouldn't happen to a dog: *Gene & Ruth* / I'll drown in my own tears: *Reed, Lule & Sonny Thompson* / Boogie at midnight: *Brown, Roy* / Every beat of my heart: *Ballard, Hank* / Do something for me: *Ward, Billy & The Dominoes* / Ping pong: *Bradshaw, Tiny* / Cherry wine: *Phillips, Little Esther* / Cuttin' in: *Watson, Johnny 'Guitar'* / I'm waiting just for you: *Millinder, Lucky* / You've got to love her with a feeling: *King, Freddie.*
LP: . . . . **BID 8034**

OLD KING GOLD, VOL 9 (Various artists).
Tracks: / Heavy juice: *Bradshaw, Tiny* / My pillow stays wet: *Duncan, James* / Tennessee wig walk: *Lou, Bonnie* / Need your love so bad: *John, Little Willie* / Shake that thing: *Harris, Wynonie* / Hard luck blues: *Brown, Roy* / Sleep: *Bostic, Earl* / Big blue diamonds: *King, Earl* / Rock love: *Reed, Lule & Sonny Thompson* / Have you ever loved a woman?: *King, Freddie* / It's love baby: *Ballard, Hank* / Tears of joy: *Five Royales.*
LP: . . . . **BID 8035**

OLD KING GOLD, VOL 10 (Various artists).
Tracks: / Smokie: *Doggett, Bill* / Have I sinned?: *Elbert, Donnie* / Teardrops on your letter: *Ballard, Hank* & The Midnighters / Love don't love nobody: *Brown, Roy* / Looking for a man: *Phillips, Little Esther* / Temptation: *Bostic, Earl* / Stumble, The: *King, Freddie* / Walking after midnight: *Williams, Otis & The Charms* / I'm sorry: *Martin, Kenny* / We'll build a bungalow: *Long, Johnny* / Right around the corner: *Five Royales* / Old time shuffle: *Glenn, Lloyd.*
LP: . . . . **BID 8036**

OOH POO PAH DOO Early sixties soul 1960/1965 (Various artists).
Tracks: / Fool in love, A: *Turner, Ike & Tina* / Ooh poo pah doo: *Hill, Jessie* / Cry baby: *Mimms, Garnet/Enchanters* / That's how heartaches are made: *Washington, Baby* / Hurt so bad: *Little Anthony & The Imperials* / I know: *George*, Barbara / Over you: *Neville, Aaron* / It's gonna work out fine: *Turner, Ike & Tina* / Mother-in-law: *K-Doe*, Ernie / I love the way you love: *Johnson, Mary* / Lipstick traces (on a cigarette): *O'Jays* / Mockingbird: *Foxx, Inez & Charlie* / Think: *McCracklin, Jimmy* / Wish someone would care: *Thomas, Irma* / Certain girl, A: *K-Doe, Ernie* / She's with her other love: *Hayward, Leon.*
LP: . . . . **CGB 1012**
MC: . . . . **C CGB 1012**

ORIGINAL RHYTHM'N'BLUES (Various artists).
LP: **522 017**
MC: **722 017**

PEACOCK CHICKS & DUCHESSES SING THE BLUES (Various artists).
Tracks: / Mr. Thrill: *Jones, mildred* / New orleans: *Johnson, Gwen* / Bettye Jean: *Washington, Bettye Jean* / Why oh why: *Washington, Bettye Jean* / He's my kind of man: *Ford, Valli* / No you can't...: *Brown, Jewel* / Don't touch my bowl: *Hill, Gladys* / Bad shape blues: *Mitchell, Joe Ann* / Trumpet blows away, A: *Johnson, Gwen* / Young Boy: *Johnson, Gwen* / Roll like a big wheel: *Brown, Olive* / Letter to my girlfriend: *Brown, Olive* / Looking for a home: *Brown, Olive* / Bonita's blues: *Cole, Bonita* / Life is like that: *Cole, Bonita.*

LP: . . . . **CHD 233**

PEPPER HOT BABY Baton R&B (Various artists).
LP: . . . . **KK 7449**

R AND B CLASSICS (Various artists).
Tracks: / Mannish boy: *Waters, Muddy* / High heel sneakers: *Tucker, Tommy* / Bright lights big city: *Reed, Jimmy* / Smokestack lightnin': *Howlin' Wolf* / My babe: *Little Walter* / Dust my broom: *James, Elmore* / Dimples: *Hooker, John Lee* / Kansas City: *Harrison, Wilbert* / Boom boom: *Hooker, John Lee* / Shame shame shame: *Reed, Jimmy* / Got my mojo working: *Waters, Muddy* / Shake your money maker: *James, Elmore* / Feeling good: *Parker, Little Junior* / Spoonful: *Howlin' Wolf.*
LP: . . . . **KNLP 15002**
MC: . . . . **KNMC 15002**

R AND B CONFIDENTIAL NO.1 - THE FLAIR STORY (Various artists).
Tracks: / Romp and stomp blues: *Dee, Mercy* / Baby beat it: *Henderson, Duke* / Cuban getaway: *Turner, Ike* Orchestra / Please find my baby: *James, Elmore* / You better hold me: *Reed, Jimmy* / Night howler: *Gale*, Billy / This is the night for love: *Flairs* / Let's make with some love: *Flairs* / Go Robbie go: *Robinson*, Robbie with Binky / Send him back: *Gunter, Shirley* / Baby I love you so: *Gunter, Shirley* / Oop shoop: *Gunter*, Shirley / Hey Dr Kinsey: *Henderson, Duke* / Next time, The: *Berry, Richard* / Hard times: *Fuller, Johnny* / Chop house: *Allen, Blinky* / Have you ever: *Dee, Mercy* / My baby left town: *Dixie Blues Boys* (Available on CD only) / People are wonderin': *Parham, Baby 'Pee Wee'* (Available on CD only) / Baby please: *Cockrell, Mat* / Quit hangin' around: *King, Saunders* (Available on CD only).
LP: . . . . **CHD 258**

R & B LAFF BLASTS FROM THE PAST (Various artists).
Tracks: / He sure could hypnotize: *Clovers* / Snatchin' peaches: *Chanteclairs* / Down at Ling Ting Laundry: *Chanteclairs* / Cecilia: *Ravens* / Do the zombie: *Symbols* / Sh-he-be: *Essentials* / Back trail: *Blackwell, Otis* / Daddy can I go to the hop: *Cashmeres With Eddie Jones* / Baby monkey's song (yes we have no bananas), The: *Jarmolettes* / Sardines: *Magnetics* / Earth cousins: *Middleton, Tony & Jack Hammer* / Invasion: *Dovers.*
LP: . . . . **RL 059**

R & B MATINEE (Various artists).
LP: . . . . **LTD 602**

R & B SOUND OF DETROIT, THE (Various artists).
LP: . . . . **TRPL 124**

R&B SCENE VOLUME 2 (1963-1969) (Various artists).
Tracks: / Hound dog: *Duffy's Nucleus* / Feeling blue: *Kim Davis* / Boom boom: *Blues By Five* / I'm gonna move to the outskirts of town: *Rod Stewart* / Anytime at all: *Fairies* / Heart of stone: *Hi-Numbers, The* / Breakdown blues: *Bread & Beer Band* / Can I get a witness: *Aldo, Steve* / Hoochie coochie man: *Graham Bond* Organisation / Talkin' about you: *Redcaps, The* / Hurt me if you will: *Mark Four, The* / I feel so blue: *Knight*, Tony & The Livewires / Dancing in the street: *Hi-Numbers, The* / Baby what you want me to do: *Cruisers* / Not fade away: *Berry, Dave* / Stu-Ball: *Stewart, Ian & The Railroaders* / I can only give you everything: *Them.*
LP: . . . . **SEE 73**

R&B VOLTS FROM THE VJ VAULTS (Various artists).
LP: . . . . **CRB 1106**

RCA VICTOR R & B REVUE (Various artists).
Tracks: / Romance in the dark: *Green, Lil* / Why don't you do right?: *Green, Lil* / After hours: *Hawkins*, Erskine & His Orchestra / Stormy Monday blues: *Hines, Earl & His Orchestra* / Jelly jelly: *Hines, Earl & His Orchestra* / I sold my heart to the junkman: *Jones, Etta with J.C. Heard & His Band* / Hot rod: *Jacquet, Illinois & His Orchestra* / Dry bones: *Delta Rhythm Boys* / Take the 'A' train: *Delta Rhythm Boys* / Rock with it: *Moore, Johnny's Three Blazers* / Two guitar boogie: *Hall, Rene* / Rooming house boogie: *Calloway, Cab/his Cab Jivers* / Moanin' the blues: *Millinder, Lucky & His Orchestra* / Hey, pretty baby: *Basie, Count & His Orchestra* / Did you see Jackie Robinson hit that ball?: *Basie, Count & His Orchestra* / Natural blues: *Millinder, Lucky & His Orchestra* / Coleslaw: *Stone, Jesse & His Orchestra* / Butcher boy: *Mr. Sad Head* / Reliefin' blues: *Lynn, Blow-Top & His House Rockers* / Get rich quick: *Little Richard* / Squeeze me: *Trenier, Milt & His Sound Six* / Thinkin' 'bout my mother: *Little Richard* / Rockin' daddy-o: *Heartbreakers* / All night baby: *Robins* / Bam balam: *Du-Droppers* / Boot 'em up: *Du-Droppers* / Open up: *King Curtis* / Shout: *Isley Brothers.*
2LP: . . . . **PL 86279**

RED HOT 'N' BLUE (Various artists).
LP: . . . . **CRB 1061**

RHYTHM AND BLUES HOUSEPARTY (Various artists).
Tracks: / Let the doorbell ring: *Dale, Larry* / I'll never let you go (boo-hoo-hoo): *Little Richard* / Stranded in the jungle: *Cadets* / Harbour lights: *Beasley, Jimmy* / Who's been fooling you: *Myles, Big Boy* / Chop chop: *Chimes* / Hey fine mama: *Five Notes* / How long she's been gone: *Phillips, Marvin* / Ay la bah: *Cooper, Dolly* / Pretty soon: *Young Jessie* / Great pretender, The: *Fran, Carol* / These golden rings: *Jive Five* / Hole in the wall: *Dixon, Floyd* / Drag race: *Houston, Joe* / W-O-M-A-N: *James, Etta* / Ooh-Bop-She-Bop: *Dukes* / Come on little children: *Gaddy, Bob* / Every time I hear that mellow saxophone: *Montrell, Roy.*
LP: . . . . **CH 179**
MC: . . . . **CHC 179**

RHYTHM & BLUES BOOGIE WOOGIE, VOL.1 (Various artists).
Tracks: / Caldonia: *Various artists* / Oh boy, that's where my money goes: *Various artists* / Down the road apiece: *Various artists* / Loumel's boogie: *Various artists* / Hamp boogie woogie, The: *Various artists* / Kansas City boogie woogie: *Various artists* / Four months, three weeks, two days & one hour blues: *Various artists* / St. Louis blues: *Various artists* / Chicago blues: *Various artists* / Six wheel chaser: *Various artists* / I ain't mad at you: *Various artists* / Why don't you do it right?: *Various artists* / Jam boogie: *Various artists.*
LP: . . . . **SWH 8**
MC: . . . . **CSWH 8**

RHYTHM & BLUES BOOGIE WOOGIE VOL.3 (Various artists).
LP: . . . . **SWH 43**

RHYTHM & BLUES BOOGIE WOOGIE VOL.2 (Various artists).
Tracks: / Basie boogie: *Various artists* / Hey lawdy mama: *Various artists* / Roll em: *Various artists* / Dollhouse boogie: *Various artists* / Baranco boogie: *Various artists* / Bumble boogie: *Various artists* / Zoot Gibson stride again: *Various artists.*
MC: . . . . **CSWH 30**
LP: . . . . **SWH 30**

RHYTHM & BLUES IN THE 1940'S & 50'S (Various artists).
LP: . . . . **RB 401**

RHYTHM & BLUES, THE (Various artists).
LP: . . . . **LP 101**

RHYTHM & BOOZE - VOL.2 (Various artists).
LP: **L2M 2004**

RHYTHM IN RHYTHM & BLUES, THE 1951-62 (Various artists).
Tracks: / I hear you knocking: *Lewis, Smiley* / Snag-a-tooth Jeanie: *Smith, Huey* / That's how you got killed before: *Bartholomew, Dave* / Domino stomp: *Domino, Fats* / I've been walkin': *Eaglin, Ford* / Bobby sox ramble: *Houston, Joe* / Deacon rides again: *McNeely, Big Jay* / Blue Monday: *Domino, Fats* / Shufflin' fox: *Bartholomew, Dave* / Bumpity bump: *Lewis, Smiley* / Sleepwalking woman: *Smilin' Joe* / Great big eyes: *Archibald* / Come on: *King, Earl.*
LP: . . . . **SSL 6030**
MC: . . . . **TCSSL 6030**

RHYTHM 'N' BLUES AT ITS BEST (Various artists).
Tracks: / Voodoo: *Farlowe, Chris/ Thunderbirds* / Ride your pony: *Dorsey, Lee* / Ya ya: *Dorsey, Lee* / Dimples: *Hooker, John Lee* / For your precious love: *Butler, Jerry & The Impressions* / Getting mighty crowded: *Everett, Betty* / You threw a lucky punch: *Chandler, Gene* / It's in his kiss: *Everett, Betty* / Shake your moneymaker: *James, Elmore* / Oh little girl: *Clark, Dee & The Upsetters* / Just keep it up: *Clark, Dee* & The Upsetters / You got me dizzy: *Reed, Jimmy* / Let it be me: *Everett, Betty & Jerry Rubler* / At my front door: *Eldorados* / I'm gonna hit ya: *Harris, Betty* / Shame shame shame: *Reed, Jimmy* / Hush your mouth: *Reed, Jimmy* / First love blues: *Walker, T-Bone* / In between tears: *Thomas, Irma* / Let the love flow: *Burke, Solomon* / Stoolpigeon blues: *Hopkins, Lightnin'* / E.T. blues: *Taylor, Eddie.*
2LP: . . . . **CR 106**
MCSET: . . . . **CRT 106**

RHYTHM & ROCK (Best of Chess, Checker, Cadet) (Various artists).

LP: . . . . **CXMP 2002**

RIDIN' THE RIFF (Various artists).
Tracks: / Big Bob's boogie: *Various artists* / Ridin' the riff: *Various artists* / Tom,Dick & Harry: *Various artists* / Tina's canteen: *Various artists* / 125th Street, New York: *Various artists* / Tan skin lad: *Various* artists / Buttermilk and beans: *Various artists* / Please Mr. Jive: *Various artists* / Hi ho: *Various artists* / I need my baby: *Various artists* / I ain't mad no more: *Various artists* / Come home baby: *Various artists* / Tra la la: *Various artists* / Anything but love: *Various artists* / I wanna go steady with you: *Various artists* / Baby don't cry: *Various artists.*
LP: . . . . **CRB 1128**

RISKY BLUES (Various artists).
Tracks: / Big 10-inch record: *Jackson, Bull Moose* / It ain't the meat: *Swallows* / Annie had a baby: *Midnighters* / Wasn't that good?: *Harris, Wynonie* / Don't stop Dan: *Checkers* / Lovin' machine: *Harris, Wynonie* / Silent George: *Millinder, Lucky* / Sixty minute man: *Dominoes* / Somethin's gone wrong with my lovin' machine: *Henry, Robert* / Walkin' blues: *Powell, Jesse & Fluffy Hunter* / Keep on churnin' (till the butter comes): *Harris, Wynonie* / I want a bow-legged woman: *Jackson, Bull Moose* / Rocket 69: *Rhodes, Todd* / Mountain oysters: *Davis, Eddie 'Lockjaw'.*
LP: . . . . **BID 8026**

R'N'B FROM JOE DAVIS 1952-53 (see under Davis, Joe) (Various artists).

ROCKIN' BLUES PARTY (Various artists).
Tracks: / Now you know: *Guitar Junior* / Goin' crazy, baby: *Guitar Junior* / Clawtelia: *Jackson, Ivory Lee* / Make up my mind: *Good Rockin' Bob* / Got it made (when I marry Shirley Mae): *Guitar Junior* / Family rules: *Guitar Junior* / Fuss too much: *Semien, Ivory Lee* / That wouldn't satisfy: *Wilson, Hop & Ivory Lee Semien* / Love's got me all fenced in: *Wilson, Hop & Ivory Lee Semien* / Chicken stuff: *Wilson, Hop & His Two Buddies* / Rockin' in the coconut top: *Various artists* / Rockin' with hop: *Wilson, Hop & His Two Buddies.*
LP: . . . . **GCL 115**

ROOTIN' AND TOOTIN' (Vee Jay Honkers) (Various artists).
Tracks: / Right now: *King Kolax* / Give it up: *Watts, Noble* / Foolin' around slowly: *Various artists* / Last call: *Various artists* / What have you done to me: *Various artists* / Buttermilk: *Various artists* / Fussing 'n' loving: *Various artists* / South shore drive: *Various artists* / Pass the buck: *Watts, Noble* / Those crazy rhythm 'n' blues: *King Kolax* / Big Jay's hop: *Various artists* / Goodnite blues: *King Kolax* / Zero: *Various artists* / Off time: *Various artists* / Kansas City: *Various artists* / Bit two four: *Various artists.*
LP: . . . . **CRB 1043**

SEE Y'ALL Y'HEAR (Various artists).
Tracks: / I'm gonna put some hurt on you: *Various artists* / But I couldn't: *Various artists* / Sooner you realise, The: *Various artists* / Fair play: *Various artists* / Cloudy weather: *Various artists* / C.C. rider: *Various* artists / Ruthless lover: *Various artists* / Too many pots: *Various artists* / I've got to keep on trying: *Various artists* / If I say goodbye you're gonna cry: *Various artists* / New kind of love: *Various artists* / I'm gonna see y'all y'hear: *Various artists* / Be my baby: *Various artists* / She's far away: *Various artists* / Help yourself: *Various artists* / Begging for your love: *Various artists.*
LP: . . . . **CRB 1179**
MC: . . . . **TCCRB 1179**

SEHORN'S SOUL FARM (Various artists).
Tracks: / Star revue: *Lee, Warren* / Why you wanna do it?: *Harper, Willie* / Blues, tears and sorrow: *Williams*, John (Guitarist) / Sinner girl: *Spellman, Benny* / Love affair: *Holmes, Eldridge* / Let's make it: *Haywood*, Joe / Get low down: *Moore, Curley* / Hercules: *Neville, Aaron* / Struttin' on Sunday: *Neville, Aaron* / Climb the ladder: *Lee, Warren* / Don't pity me: *Moore, Curley* / Oh love, this is Sonny: *Fisher, Sonny* / All my love: *King, Earl* / That's what you need: *Harper, Willie* / Gossip, gossip: *Diamond Joe* / Hotcha mama: *Doe, Ernie K..*
LP: . . . . **CRB 1032**

SOUND OF THE GULF COAST (Various artists).
Tracks: / Schoolday blues: *Johnny/ Jammers* / Let me come your way: *Boykin, Burl* / Sweet Lilly: *Roy 'Boogie Boy'* / True love: *Roy 'Boogie Boy'* / Good lovin': *Chas & Gene* / Baby don't go: *Charles, Andy & The Blues Kings* / Woke up this morning: *Canfil, Chase* / I had a dream: *Canfil, Chase* / No one else

will do: *Mitchell, Joey* / Penalty of love: *Velvetones.*
LP: . . . . **CH 20**

SOUTHEND ROCK (Various artists).
Tracks: / Tears of a clown: *Various artists* / I do what I do: *Various artists* / I'm going mad: *Various* artists / I'm not like everybody else: *Various artists* / Ging gang goolie: *Various artists* / Prisoner: *Various* artists / I'm looking for you: *Various artists* / Guitar pickin' slim: *Various artists* / Route 66: *Various* artists / Monica: *Various artists* / Nobody but you: *Various artists* / Down to the doctor's: *Various artists* / Another pair of boots: *Various artists.*
LP: . . . . **SNTF 806**

SPECIALTY STORY VOL 1, THE (Various artists).
Tracks: / Silly dilly: *Pentagons* / Till the well runs dry: *Carr, Wynona* / Brand new baby: *Williams, Lester*/ Country boy rock: *Price, Lloyd* / Honey dew melon: *Gipson, Byron 'Slick'* / Twitchy: *Hall, Rene* / Please don't go: *Dixon, Floyd* / Nursery rhyme rock: *Carr, Wynona & The Bumps Blackwell Band* / Oh Rooba Lee: *Maye,* Arthur Lee & The Crowns / Lights out: *Byrne, Jerry* / I'll come running back to you: *Cooke, Sam* / Who's been fooling you: *Myles, Big Boy* / Foolish fool, A: *Zeppa, Ben Joe & The Zephyrs* / I'm so tired: *Milton, Roy*/ Rip it up: *Little Richard* / Ooh-bop-she-bop: *Dukes.*
LP: . . . . **CH 134**

STILL GROOVE JUMPING (Various artists).
Tracks: / High low Jack: *Lucas, Buddy* / Mr. Bear comes to town: *Mr. Bear* / I'm gonna keep my good eye on you: *Mr. Bear* / Peek-a-boo: *Mr. Bear* / Bear hug, The: *Mr. Bear* / When I get married: *Dupree, Champion* Jack / Rockin with red (she knows how to rock me): *Piano Red* / Jump man jump: *Piano Red* / She's got no hair: *Crudup, Arthur* / Country boy: *Kennedy, Tiny* / You better heed my warning: *Dale, Larry* / Down in the bottom: *Dale, Larry* / Midnight hours: *Dale, Larry* / Right now baby: *Gaines, Roy* / All my life: *Gaines, Roy* / Drink up: *Du-Droppers.*
LP: . . . . **DT 33006**

STONED ALCHEMY (Various artists).
Tracks: / Come on: *Berry, Chuck* / Red rooster, The: *Howlin' Wolf* / Fortune teller: *Spellman, Benny*/ I just want to make love to you: *Waters, Muddy* / Road runner: *Diddley, Bo* / Down home girl: *Robinson,* Alvin / Bright lights, big city: *Reed, Jimmy* / Down the road apiece: *Berry, Chuck* / Around and around: *Berry,* Chuck / Ruler of my heart: *Thomas, Irma* / I can't be satisfied: *Waters, Muddy* / Fannie Mae: *Brown,* Buster / Cops and robbers: *Diddley, Bo* / Down in the bottom: *Howlin' Wolf* / You can't catch me: *Berry,* Chuck / Diddley daddy: *Diddley, Bo* / I'm your hoochie coochie man: *Waters, Muddy* / Honest I do: *Reed,* Jimmy / How many more years: *Howlin' Wolf* / You can make it if you try: *Allison, Gene* / Route 66: *Berry,* Chuck / Carol: *Berry, Chuck* / I need you baby: *Diddley, Bo* / Susie Q: *Hawkins, Dale* / Pretty thing: *Diddley, Bo* / Got my mojo working: *Waters, Muddy* / It's all over now: *Womack, Bobby.*
2LP: . . . . **INSD 5016**
MCSET: . . . . **TCINSD 5016**

STRAIGHTEN UP AND FLY RIGHT (Various artists).
Tracks: / Flying home: *Hampton, Lionel & His Orchestra* / Roll 'em Pete: *Turner,Joe/Pete Johnson* / Sun didn't shine,The: *Golden Gate Quartet* / Straighten up and fly right: *Cole, Nat King* / I Wonder: *Grant, Cecil*/ Choo choo ch' boogie: *Jordan, Louis* / Call it stormy Monday: *Walker, T-Bone* / Good rockin' tonight: *Harris,* Wynonie / Give me a simple prayer: *Ravens* / Well,oh well: *Bradshaw, Tiny & His Orchestra* / Hello central: *Hopkins, Lightnin'* / One Mint Julep: *Clovers* / Hound Dog: *Thornton, Willie Mae 'Big Mama'* / Mama, he treats your daughter mean: *Brown, Ruth* / Crying in the Chapel: *Till, Sonny & The Orioles* / Hoochie Coochie man: *Waters, Muddy.*
LP: . . . . **NW 261**

SUPER RHYTHM 'N' BLUES (Various artists).
Tracks: / Keep on knowin': *Various artists* / I found my baby there: *Charles, Ray* / Letter, The: *King, B.B.*/ Could this be love: *Tex, Joe* / I thank God: *Cooke, Sam* / Big fine woman: *Hooker, John Lee* / Lovin' woman: *Simone, Nina* / Blues are bluer: *Holiday, Billie* / Cry baby cry: *Angels* / Need him: *Various* artists / Wild child: *Phillips, Esther* / Walkin' and talkin': *Charles, Ray* / Please love me: *King,* B.B. / I'm tramping: *Various artists* / Porgy: *Simone, Nina* / Deep river: *Cooke, Sam* / My man: *Holiday, Billie* / See what you have done: *Charles, Ray* / Blues for Christmas: *Hooker, John Lee* / That's heaven to me: *Cooke, Sam* / Feel like I wanna cry: *Phillips, Esther* / I just can't take it: *Tex, Joe*/ I'm wondering: *Charles, Ray* / Milky white way: *Various artists* / Maybellene: *Berry, Chuck* / Memphis: *Berry, Chuck* / Lover come back to me: *Holiday, Billie* / Did you cry the blues: *Charles, Ray* / Peace breaker: *Pickett, Wilson* / Why don't you love me: *Hendrix, Jimi & Little Richard* / Long tall Sally: *Various artists* / Baby call on me: *Pickett, Wilson* / Let the good times roll: *Shirley & Lee* / My prayer: *Platters*/ Goodnight Irene: *Hendrix, Jimi & Little Richard* / Sweet little sixteen: *Berry, Chuck.*
LP: **2M 126 54315/16/17**

SWAMPLANDS BEAT (Various artists).
Tracks: / Rock a way blues: *Various artists* / Who's baby are you baby: *Various artists* / Freight train: *Various* artists / I'm just a mender: *Various artists* / Let's go boppin' tonight: *Various artists* / Thought I found love: *Various artists* / Girl left alone: *Various artists* / Never had the blues: *Various artists* / Feels so good: *Various artists* / What is that thing you call love: *Various artists* / Honey baby: *Various artists*/ Oh, baby: *Various artists* / Too tired to rock: *Various artists* / Wrapped around your finger: *Various artists.*
LP: . . . . **GCL 117**

TESTIFYIN' (Various artists).
Tracks: / My great loss (ashes to ashes): *Smith, Charles* / Glad to be home: *Smith, Charles* / I'm useless: *Smith,* Charles / Why can't I cry: *Smith, Charles* / The only time you say you love me: *Smith, Charles* / Stand up and take it like a man: *Smith, Charles* / Pull me out of the water: *Smith, Charles* / Two pillows: *Smith,* Charles / Why does it hurt so bad: *Armstrong,Chuck* / How sweet it is: *Armstrong,Chuck* / I'm gonna forget about you: *Armstrong,Chuck* / Keep your mind on me: *Armstrong,Chuck* / She's gonna come back: *Ford, Ted*/ Pretty girls everywhere: *Ford, Ted* / You're gonna need me: *Ford, Ted* / Please give me another chance: *Ford, Ted.*
LP: . . . . **CRB 1155**

TEXAS RHYTHM AND BLUES (Various artists).
Tracks: / Love me, pretty baby: *Booker, Connie Mack* / All alone: *Booker, Connie Mack* / Whoopin' and hollerin': *Stevens, Preacher* / Blue memories: *Kimble, Quinn* / Feel my broom: *Kimble, Quinn* / I'll be there: *Daniels,* Melvin & The King Curtis Orchestra / If you don't want my lovin': *Daniels, Melvin & The King Curtis Orchestra* / Boogie in the moonlight: *Daniels, Melvin & The King Curtis Orchestra* / Hey hey little girl: *Daniels, Melvin & The King Curtis Orchestra* / Craw fishin': *Garlow, Clarence Bonton* / Route 90: *Garlow, Clarence Bonton.*
LP: . . . . **CH 29**

THIS IS CHARLY RHYTHM AND BLUES (See under Charly (label)) (Various artists).

THUNDERBOLT Searing R & B sax instrumentals (Various artists).
Tracks: / Paradise rock: *Various artists* / Thunderbolt: *Various artists* / Paradise roll: *Various artists*/ Fish bait: *Various artists* / Melancholy horn: *Various artists* / Jay bird: *Various artists* / Strollin' out: *Various artists* / Flying with the king: *Various artists* / King is blue: *Various artists* / Big wind: *Various artists* / Royal crown blues: *Various artists* / Sweet Georgia Brown: *Various artists* / Easy ridin': *Various artists* / Joy ride: *Various artists.*
LP: . . . . **KK 778**

TOUGH STUFF (Various artists).
LP: . . . . **CR 30186**

TWIST AND SHOUT (Various artists).
LP: **241 690-1**
MC: **241 690-4**

TWIST AND SHOUT AT THE CAMDEN PALACE (Various artists).
Tracks: / Your love is lifting...: *Wilson, Jackie* / 1-2-3: *Barry, Len* / One fine day / Clapping song, The: *Ellis,* Shirley / Little bit of soul: *Music Explosion* / Treat her right: *Head, Roy* / Wipe out: *Surfaris, The*/ Twist and shout: *Isley Brothers* / Wanderer: *Dion* / Reet petite: *Wilson, Jackie* / Tequila: *Champs*/ Louie, louie: *Kingsmen* / Peaches and cream: *Ikettes* / When the boy's happy (the girl's happy too): *Four Pennies* / Little bit of soap, a: *Jarmels* / Baby it's you: *Shirelles.*
LP: . . . . **ACT 005**
MC: . . . . **ACTC 005**

VOCAL GROUP R'N'B FROM JOE DAVIS VOL.1 (Various artists).
LP: . . . . **KK 797**

VOCAL GROUP R'N'B FROM JOE DAVIS VOL.2 1954-56 (Various artists).
LP: . . . . **KK 798**

WEST COAST WINNERS (R & B 1953-67) (Various artists).
LP: . . . . **BLP 103**

WHEN GIRLS DO IT (Various artists).
Tracks: / When girls do it: *Bennett, Bobby (guitar)* / Things I do for you: *Junior Wells* / Suicide blues: *Stricklin,* Little Oscar / Down and out: *Turner, Ike* / How low is low: *Harmonica Fats* / Love me baby: *Magic Slim*/ Sweet little angel: *Baker, Sam* / Evil hearted woman: *Drifting Charles* / Drifting cloud: *Drifting Charles*/ Blue and lonesome: *Various artists* / Street walking woman: *Jacobs, Donnie* / My heart's full of pain: *T.V. Slim* (Wills) / Don't knock the blues: *TV Slim* / Hard but fair: *Guy, Buddy* / My love is your love: *Magic* Sam / Wild woman: *Danny Boys* / Kokomo me baby: *Danny Boys* / Farewell: *McCracklin, Jimmy* / Take a chance: *McCracklin, Jimmy* / I ain't gonna suffer: *Mr. Bo* / If trouble was money: *Mr. Bo* / I'm a stranger: *Wells, Junior* / Hilli Billy blues: *Clear Waters* / Boogie woogie baby: *Clear Waters* / Don't cut out on me: *Slim, Tender* / I'm checkin' up: *Slim, Tender* / Little girl: *Williamson, Sugar Boy* / Five long years: *Williamson, Sugar Boy.*
2LP: . . . . **RL 006**

WHITE LIGHTNING (30 original hits that lit up the sixties) (Various artists).
Tracks: / Roll over Beethoven: *Berry, Chuck* / Boom boom: *Hooker, John Lee* / Road runner: *Diddley, Bo*/ Spoonful: *Howlin' Wolf* / Walkin' thru the park: *Waters, Muddy* / My babe: *Little Walter* / I wish you would: *Arnold, Billy Boy* / Kansas city: *Harrison, Wilbert* / Dust my broom: *James, Elmore* / I'm talking about you: *Berry, Chuck* / Reconsider baby: *Fulson, Lowell* / Certain girl, A: *K-Doe, Ernie* / Dimples: *Hooker, John Lee* / Smokestack lightning: *Howlin' Wolf* / You can't judge a book by the cover: *Diddley, Bo*/ I ain't got you: *Arnold, Billy Boy* / No more doggin': *Gordon, Roscoe* / First time I met the blues: *Guy,* Buddy / Too much monkey business: *Berry, Chuck* / I like it like that: *Kenner, Chris* / Go now: *Banks,* Bessie / Baby what do you want me to do: *Reed, Jimmy* / Rollin' and tumblin': *James, Elmore* / Help me: *Williamson,* Sonny Boy / Night time is the right time: *Turner, Joe* / I'd rather go blind: *James, Etta* / Pretty thing: *Diddley, Bo* / Going down slow: *Howlin' Wolf* / Standing at the crossroads: *James, Elmore* / I can't quit you baby: *Rush, Otis.*
2LP: . . . . **INSD 5017**
MC: . . . . **TCINSD 5017**

WILD (Various artists).
Tracks: / Shtiggy boom: *Anne, Patti* / Snatch and grab it: *Lee, Julia* / That's a plenty: *Lutcher, Nellie*/ Fever: *Lee, Peggy* / Baby please don't go: *Mitchell, Rose* / Cleo's boogie: *Brown, Cleo* / This joint's too hip for me: *Hall Jones, Betty* / Take a chance on me: *Allen, Annisteen* / Slow smooth and easy: *Tucker,* Anita / Fujiyama Mama: *Allen, Annisteen* / For you my love: *Lutcher, Nellie* / Why don't you do right: *Lee, Peggy* / Lake Charles boogie: *Lutcher, Nellie* / I love my baby: *Crystals* / Somebody put a jukebox in the study hall: *Shirley & Lee* / It's raining: *Thomas, Irma* / Buddy stay off that wine: *Hall Jones, Betty*/ Last call: *Unknown.*
LP: . . . . **SSL 6033**
MC: . . . . **TCSSL 6033**

WRINKLES (Classic And Rare Chess Intrumentals) (Various artists).
Tracks: / Lucky Lou: *Williams, Jody* / Wrinkles: *Big Three Trio, The* / Blue midnight: *Little Walter*/ How high the moon: *Berry, Chuck* / Driving home (part 2): *Gayten, Paul* / Soft, sweet and mellow blues (take 2): *Brown, Earl* / Five spot: *Span, Otis* / Little Eva: *Glenn, Lloyd* / Ram bunk shush (ain't got no money): *Gene The Hat* / Shimmy shimmy walk (part 1): *Megatons* / Coolin' out: *Davis, J C* / Mess around: *Diddley, Bo.*
LP: . . . . **CH 9293**

Rhythm Cadillacs
SHAKE THIS SHAK.
LP: . . . . **LP 8808**

Rhythm Devils
APOCALYPSE NOW SESSIONS.
Tracks: / Compound / Trenches / Street gang / Beast, The / Steps / Tar / Lance / Cave / Hell's bells / Kurtz / Napalm for breakfast.
MC: . . . . **RACS 10109**

Rhythm Divine
RHYTHM DIVINE, THE (Various artists).
MC: . . . . **DINMC 22**
LP: . . . . **DINTV 22**

Rhythm is Rhythm
FULL MOON.
LP: . . . . **UNKNOWN**
MC: . . . . **UNKNOWN**

Rhythm Kings
SETTING FIRE TO MY HEART.
Tracks: / Setting fire to my heart / Ain't no saint / Baby don't you worry 'bout a thing / Little things / Easy action / Turn up your radio / She's nineteen / Private guy / How come I was the last to know? / 54-46 (was my number) / Tell it like it is.
LP: . . . . **MAGL 5065**

Rhythm Makers
RHYTHM MAKERS OF BUENOS AIRES (1938-1948 Unissued titles).
LP: . . . . **HQ 2064**

Rhythm Mode D
SO DAMN TOUGH (REISSUE).
LP: . . . . **BLUERMLP 1**

Rhythm Of The Sun
RHYTHM OF THE SUN (Various artists).
LP: . . . . **STAR 2362**
MC: . . . . **STAC 2362**

Rhythm Pigs
CHOKE ON THIS.
LP: . . . . **K 001 105**

I'M NOT CRAZY, I'M AN AIRPLANE.
Tracks: / Peanuts / Doctor Harley / Break of well / Break or we'll break your face / Red snapper / Arkansas / Get it now / Baal / Quest, The / Conditional love / Marlboroman / I can fly / New saviour / Killer beat yammin' / Satan tuned my snare drum / Cactus pants / More yams.
LP: . . . . **K 007/107**

RHYTHM PIGS.
LP: . . . . **MDR 2**

Rhythm Plus One
RHYTHM PLUS ONE.
LP: . . . . **FS 24**

Rhythm Rascals
CROWN JEWELS 1935-1936.
Tracks: / Temptation rag / Tiger rag / Nobodys sweetheart / Bugle call rag / Music goes round and around, The / Talking it over / Dinah / My sweetie went away / I'm tickled to death I'm me / When a lady meets a gentleman down south / Keep smiling / Wah hoo!.
LP: . . . . **HQ 3017**

Rhythm Sisters
ROAD TO ROUNDHAY PIER.
LP: . . . . **REDLP 87**
MC: . . . . **REDC 87**

WILLERBY.
LP: . . . . **ILLUSION 027**
MC: . . . . **ILLCASS 027**

Rhythm Zone
RHYTHM ZONE 2.
LP: . . . . **KOOLLP 002**
MC: . . . . **KOOLMC 002**

Rhythmaires
LOSIN' OUT.
Tracks: / Who ya gonna choose / I hate you / Christina / Demolition man / Forbidden fruit / Come back to me / Keep your hands off my baby / I'm burning / Losing out again / Red hot rockin' blues / Her love rubbed off / By the time you read this letter.
LP: . . . . **NERD 030**

Rias Orchestra
PLEASE SMILE AGAIN.
LP: . . . . **ISST 126**

Ribera, Bruno
PARIS COLLECTION VOL.1.
MC: . . . . **MODEMC 1022**

PARIS COLLECTION VOL.2.
MC: . . . . **MODEMC 1023**

PARIS COLLECTION VOL.3.
MC: . . . . **MODEMC 1024**

Ribot, Marc
ROOTLESS COSMOPOLITANS.
MC: . . . . **ANC 8749**
LP: . . . . **AN 8749**

Ricardos Jazzmen
WONDERFUL COPENHAGEN.
LP: . . . . **ML 104**

Ricchi & Poveri
NO.1S, MADE IN ITALY, THE.
LP: **60592**
MC: . . . . **C 60592**

Rice, Boyd
BOYD RICE.
LP: . . . . **STUMM 4**

EASY LISTENING FOR THE HARD OF HEARING (Rice, Boyd & Frank Tovey).
LP: . . . . **STUMM 20**

Rice Brothers

RICE BROTHERS, THE.
Tracks: / Grapes on the vine / This old house / Original unlimited / Teardrops in my eyes / You're drifting away / Don't think twice / Let it ride / Keep the light on Sadie / Soldier's joy / Whisper my name / Life is like a mountain railroad.
LP: . . . . **ROUNDER 0256**
MC: . . . . **ROUNDERC 0256**

Rice, Daryle

I WALK WITH MUSIC (Rice, Daryle & The Loonis McGlohon Quartet).
LP: . . . . **AP 141**

Rice, Gene

JUST FOR YOU.
Tracks: / Love is calling you / You're gonna get served / No one can love you like I love you / Let's do it again / Let's get away / You're a victim / I believe / It's too late / So far away / I'll be right here waiting on you.
LP: . . . . **PL 83159**
MC: . . . . **PK 83159**

Rice, Larry

HURRICANES AND DREAMS.
Tracks: / Four wheel drive / Deportee / You've got a crazy heart / Starbound heroes (the space shuttle song) / Used to be / Finish line / It's hard to run away (from the storm) / Tabasco / Hurricane Elena / I cried again / Dad's old coat / Move along.
LP: . . . . **REB 1646**
MC: . . . . **REBMC 1646**

TIME MACHINE.
LP: . . . . **REB 1656**
MC: . . . . **REBMC 1656**

Rice, Rev. D.C.

REV. D.C. RICE AND CONGREGATION (Rice, Rev. D.C. & Congregation).
LP: . . . . **HER 212**

TRADITIONAL JAZZ AND SANCTIFIED SINGING.
LP: . . . . **HERWIN 212**

Rice, Tony

ACOUSTICS.
LP: . . . . **K 10**

BACKWATERS (Rice, Tony Unit).
LP: . . . . **ROUNDER 0167**
MC: . . . . **ROUNDER 0167C**

CALIFORNIA AUTUMN.
Tracks: / California Autumn / Bullet man / Mr. Poverty / Billy in the law ground / Red haired boy / Good woman's love, A / You don't know my mind / Alone and forsaken / Bugle call rag / Georgia on my mind / Scarborough fair / Beaumont rag.
LP: . . . . **SDLP 045**
LP: . . . . **REB 1549**
MC: . . . . **REBMC 1549**

CHURCH STREET BLUES.
Tracks: / Church Street blues / Cattle in the cane / Streets of London / One more night / Gold rush / Any old time / Orphan Annie / House carpenter / Jerusalem Ridge / Last thing on my mind / Pride of man.
LP: . . . . **SH 3732**
MC: . . . . **ZCSH 3732**

COLD ON THE SHOULDER.
Tracks: / Cold on the shoulder / Wayfaring stranger / John Hardy / Fare thee well / Bitter green / Muleskinner blues / Song for life / Why don't you tell me so / If you only knew / Likes of me / I think it's gonna rain today.
LP: . . . . **ROUNDER 0183**
MC: . . . . **ROUNDER 0183C**

GUITAR.
LP: . . . . **REB 1582**
MC: . . . . **REBMC 1582**

MANZANITA.
LP: . . . . **ROUNDER 0092**
MC: . . . . **ROUNDER 0092C**

MAR WEST (Rice, Tony Unit).
LP: . . . . **ROUNDER 0125**
MC: . . . . **ROUNDER 0125C**

ME AND MY GUITAR.
LP: . . . . **ROUNDER 0201**
MC: . . . . **ROUNDER 0201C**

NATIVE AMERICAN.
Tracks: / Shadows / St. James hospital / Night flyer / Why you been so long / Urge for going / Go my way / Nothin' like a hundred miles / Changes / Brother to the wind / John Wilkes Booth / Summer wages.
LP: . . . . **ROUNDER 0248**
MC: . . . . **ROUNDER 0248C**

NORMAN BLAKE AND TONY RICE (See under Blake, Norman) (Rice, Tony & Norman Blake).

RICKY SKAGGS & TONY RICE (Rice, Tony & Ricky Skaggs).
LP: . . . . **ROUNDER 0108**

STILL INSIDE (Rice, Tony Unit).
LP: . . . . **ROUNDER 0150**
MC: . . . . **ROUNDER 0150C**

TONY RICE.
LP: . . . . **ROUNDER 0085**
MC: . . . . **ROUNDER 0085C**

Rice, Wyatt

NEW MARKET GAP.
LP: . . . . **ROU 272**
MC: . . . . **ROUC 272**

Rich, Buddy

47/48.
Tracks: / I've got news for you / Man could be such a wonderful thing, A / Good bait / Budella / Just you and me / I believe / What is this thing called love? / Little white lies / You go to my head / Queer Street / That's rich / Fine and dandy / I may be wrong / Robbins' nest.
LP: . . . . **HEP 12**

AT RONNIE SCOTTS (Rich, Buddy & His Orchestra).
Tracks: / Moments notice / St. Mark's Square / Little train / Time being / Word / Dancing men / In a mellow tone / Two bass hit.
LP: . . . . **INTS 5012**

BACK TO BACK (Rich, Buddy & Gene Krupa).
MCSET: . . . . **DTO 10222**

BUDDY AND SOUL.
LP: . . . . **BGOLP 23**

BUDDY RICH Compact/Walkman jazz.
Tracks: / Jumpin' at the Woodside / Broadway / Yardbird suite / Toot toot toosie goodbye / Between the devil and the deep blue sea / Bloody Mary / From the sticks / Late date / Jump for me / Night in Tunisia.
MC: **833 295-4**

BUDDY RICH AND HIS GREATEST BAND (1946-7).
LP: . . . . **FH 5**

BUDDY RICH AND HIS ORCHESTRA (Rich, Buddy & His Orchestra).
LP: . . . . **MCF 3101**

BUDDY RICH AT RONNIE SCOTTS.
Tracks: / Moments notice / St. Marks Square (a special day) / Little train / Time being / Milestones / Word, The / Dancing men / In a mellow tone / Two bass hit.
LP: . . . . **NL 89339**
MC: . . . . **NK 89339**

BUDDY RICH BAND (Rich, Buddy Band).
Tracks: / Never can say goodbye / Fantasy / Listen here goes funky / Slo-funk / Good news / Beulah witch.
LP: . . . . **IMCA 853**
MC: . . . . **IMCAC 5853**

BUDDY RICH PLAYS AND PLAYS AND PLAYS.
Tracks: / Ya gotta try / Time out / 'Round midnight / Tales of Rhoda rat / No jive / Lush life / Party time / Kong / Mickey Mouse mambo.
LP: . . . . **PL 12273**

COOL BREEZE.
Tracks: / Cool breeze / Carioca / Four rich brothers / Sunday kind of love, A / What is this thing called love? / Nellie's nightmare / Handicap / Mind my business / I cover the waterfront / Poor little rich kid / Goof and I, The / Let's blow / Poon Tang / Rags to Riches.
LP: . . . . **F 20128**
LP: **20128**
MC: **40128**

DRUM BATTLE (see Krupa, Gene) (Rich, Buddy & Gene Krupa).

EASE ON DOWN THE ROAD (Rich, Buddy Big Band).
Tracks: / Time check / Backwoods sideman / Nuttville / Playhouse / Senator Sam / Big Mac / Three day sucker / Ease on down the road / Tommy (medley) / Pieces of dreams / Lush life / Nik-nik / Layin' it down.
MC: . . . . **MC 8511**

EXCITING BUDDY RICH JAZZ SPECIAL, THE.
LP: . . . . **CL 42786**

GENE KRUPA AND BUDDY RICH (See under Krupa, Gene) (Krupa, Gene & Buddy Rich).

GENE KRUPA & BUDDY RICH Compact/Walkman jazz (see under Krupa,Gene).

GENE KRUPA & BUDDY RICH - THE DRUM BATTLE (see Krupa, Gene) (Rich, Buddy & Gene Krupa).

GREAT MOMENTS-1946.
LP: . . . . **GELP 15021**

IN LONDON.
Tracks: / Moment's notice / Love story / Time being / That's enough / Dancing men / Milestones / In a mellow tone / St. Mark's Square / Two bass hit.
LP: . . . . **PL 43695**

JAZZ OFF THE AIR VOL.5 (The Cinch) (Rich, Buddy Quintet).
Tracks: / Four / If I were a bell / In a prescribed manner / Cinch, The / I don't wanna be kissed / Everyday / Our delight.
LP: . . . . **SPJ 149**

KEEP THE CUSTOMER SATISFIED (Rich, Buddy Big Band).
Tracks: / Keep the customer satisfied / Long days journey / Midnight cowboy / He quit me man / Everybody's talkin' / Tears and joys / Celebration.
LP: . . . . **EMS 1187**
MC: . . . . **TCEMS 1187**

KRUPA & RICH (see Krupa, Gene) (Rich, Buddy & Gene Krupa).

LIONEL HAMPTON PRESENTS BUDDY RICH (Rich, Buddy & Lionel Hampton).
Tracks: / Moment's notice / Giant steps / Buddy's Cherokee / Take the 'A' train / I'll never be the same / Latin silk / Buddy's rock (CD only.) / My funny valentine (CD only.).
LP: . . . . **GATE 7011**
MC: . . . . **CGATE 7011**

MAN FROM PLANET JAZZ, THE.
Tracks: / Beulah witch / Grand concourse / Blues a la 88 / Saturday night / Slow funk / Good news.
LP: . . . . **NSLP 18620**

ORIGINAL DRUM BATTLE (see Krupa, Gene) (Rich, Buddy & Gene Krupa).

RICH AND FAMOUS.
Tracks: / Red snapper / Time will tell / Ballad of the matador / Dancing man / Cottontail / One and only love / Manhattan-the city / Manhattan-central park.
LP: . . . . **MTLP 004**
MC: . . . . **MTC 004**

RICH RIOT (Rich, Buddy & His Orchestra).
Tracks: / Theme quiet riot / Day by day / Nellie's nightmare / Great moments / Daily double / Just a sittin and a rockin / Rags to riches / Goof and I, The / Man could be such a wonderful thing, A / Little handicap, A.
LP: . . . . **FH 27**
MC: . . . . **CFH 27**

TOGETHER AGAIN.
MC: . . . . **ZCJC 833**

TOGETHER AGAIN - FOR THE FIRST TIME (Rich, Buddy & Mel Torme).
Tracks: / When I found you / Here's that rainy day / Blues in the night / Bluesette / You are the sunshine of my life / I won't last a day without you / Oh lady be good.
LP: . . . . **PL 25178**

TUFF DUDE.
Tracks: / Donna Lee / Chameleon / Second Avenue blue / Jumpin' at the woodside / Sierra lonely / Nica's dream / Billie's bounce.
MC: . . . . **MC 7972**

Rich, Charlie

BEHIND CLOSED DOORS.
LP: . . . . **EPC 32047**
LP: **65716**

CHARLIE RICH (I love country).
Tracks: / Big boss man / River stay 'way from my door / Big Jack / Mountain dew / She loved everybrody but me / Let me go my merry way / Ol' man river / Grass is always greener, The / Ways of a woman in love, The / Why oh why / Rosanna / Are you still my baby / Behind closed doors / Most beautiful girl, The / Daddy don't you walk so fast / My elusive dreams / I love my friend / Sunday kind of woman, A / Papa was a good man / Spanish eyes (A) / Very special love song, A / Rollin' with the flow / Life has it's little up's and downs / Every time you touch me (I get high) / Since I fell for you / On my knees / Somebody wrote that song for me / That's the way a cowboy rocks and rolls.
LP: . . . . **NL 89999**
MC: . . . . **NK 89999**
LP: . . . . **EPC 54939**
MC: **40 54939**

CHARLIE RICH.
MCSET: . . . . **DTO 10044**
MCSET: . . . . **DTO 10092**

COUNTRY STORE: CHARLIE RICH.
Tracks: / Behind closed doors / Almost persuaded / Sunday kind of woman, A / We love each other / Very special love song, A / I love my friend / Amazing grace / Most beautiful girl, The / Everytime you touch me I get high / Daddy don't you walk so fast / I take it on home / Sometimes I feel like a motherless child / She / My elusive dreams / Life has its little ups and downs (Only on CD.) / Rollin' with the flow (Only on CD.) / On my knees (Only on CD.) / Woman left lonely, A (Only on CD.).
LP: . . . . **CST 3**
MC: . . . . **CSTK 3**

DON'T PUT NO HEADSTONE ON MY GRAVE.
Tracks: / Don't put no headstone on my grave (complete session) / Goodbye Mary Ann / Long way from Tennessee / Stop faking your love / Lonely weekends / It's too late / Juanita / Finally find out / Who will the next fool be / My heart cries for you / There's another place I can't go / C.C. rider / Home with me / How's the world treating you / Show me the way back to your heart.
LP: . . . . **Z 2002**

FOOL STRIKES AGAIN, THE.
Tracks: / Fool strikes again, The / I'd even let you go / Born to love me / Lady / Somewhere there's a love song / She knows just how much to touch me / Life goes on / Standing tall / I love you that way.
LP: . . . . **UAS 30219**

FULLY REALISED.
Tracks: / Mohair Sam / I can't go on / Dance of love / Field of yellow daisies / I washed my hands in muddy water / Everything I do is wrong / She's a yum yum / It ain't gonna be that way / Just a little bit of you / Moonshine Minnie / Down and out lonely weekends / No home / So long / Best years, The / Party girl / You can have her / Have I stayed away too long / Hawg jaw / Something just came over me / Double dog dare me / Just a little bit of time / Blowin' town / Tears a go-go.
LP: **6641 199**

GREATEST HITS: CHARLIE RICH.
Tracks: / Most beautiful girl, The / Very special love song, A / Since I fell for you / My elusive dreams / Every time you touch me (I get high) / Behind closed doors / Life has its little ups and downs / All over me / I love my friend / America the beautiful / We love each other.
MC: **40 81478**
MC: **40 32568**

I'LL SHED NO TEARS.
Tracks: / When something is wrong with my baby / Don't tear me down / Hurry up freight train / Pass on by / Can't get right / I'll shed no tears / To fool a fool / Love is after me / Who will the next fool be / You win again / Cold, cold heart / Nobody's lonesome for me / They'll never take her love from me / My heart would know.
LP: . . . . **HIUKLP 418**

LONELY WEEKENDS.
MC: . . . . **BRC 2525**

MY ELUSIVE DREAMS.
Tracks: / Most beautiful girl, The / My elusive dreams / Rolling with the flow / Set me free / July 12th 1939 / I love my friend / Life's little ups and downs / Woman left lonely, A / Very special love song, A / Nice and easy / Raggedy Ann / I take it on home / On my knees / Part of your life / Since I fell for you / Behind closed doors.
LP: . . . . **PMP 1005**
MC: . . . . **PMPK 1005**

NOBODY BUT YOU.
LP: . . . . **UAG 30284**

ONCE A DRIFTER.
Tracks: / Once a drifter / Man just don't know what a woman goes through / Angelina / I love my lady / Wonderful night / When it's gone (it's just gone) / Marie / Dream on me / Good time Charlie's got the blues / Are we dreamin' the same dream?.
LP: . . . . **K 52264**

ORIGINAL CHARLIE RICH, THE.
Tracks: / Whirlwind / Philadelphia baby / Rebound / Big man / Lonely weekends / Everything I do is wrong / Sad news / Red man / Who will the next fool be? / Caught in the middle / Easy money / Midnite blues / Sittin' and thinkin' / I finally found out / There's another place I can't go / I need your love.
LP: . . . . **CR 30112**

ORIGINAL HITS AND MIDNIGHT DEMOS.
Tracks: / Whirlwind / Philadelphia baby / Rebound / Big man / Lonely weekends / Everything I do is wrong / School days / Ascap / Gonna be waitin' / Stay / Who will the next fool be / Caught in the middle / It's too late / Just a little bit sweet / Midnight blues / Easy money / Sittin' and thinkin' (2 takes) / I finally found out / I need your love / There's another place I can't go / Little woman friend of mine / Ain't it a shame / Thanks a lot / My baby done left me / There won't be anymore / Juicehead baby / Everyday / Charlie's boogie / You made a hit / Now everybody knows / Baby I

need you / Stop thief / Too many tears / Ways of a woman in love, The / Popcorn polly.
2LP: . . . . CDX 10

ROLLIN' WITH THE FLOW.
Tracks: / Rollin' with the flow / Somebody wrote that song for me / Windsong / That's what love is / Night talk / Beautiful woman / To sing a love song / Love survived / Somewhere in my lifetime / That's the way a cowboy rocks and rolls.
LP: . . . . EPC 82229

SONGS OF LOVE.
Tracks: / Somebody wrote this song for me / That's what love is / Beautiful woman / Night talk / To sing a love song / Love summer / That's the way a cowboy rocks and rolls / Rollin' with the flow / Love survived / Somewhere in my lifetime.
LP: . . . . SHM 3025
MC: . . . . HSC 3025

VERY SPECIAL LOVE SONGS.
LP: 80031

Rich, Denise

SWEET PAIN OF LOVE.
Tracks: / Do you wanna dance / Sweet pain of love / Frankie / Too good for you / Show her / We walked away from a love affair / Do ya wanna dance / Silent majority / Years go by so quickly, The / Talking love / Wind in my soul.
LP: . . . . MCG 6008
MC: . . . . MCGC 6008

Rich, Freddie

DANCE THE DEPRESSION AWAY (Rich, Freddie & His Orchestra).
Tracks: / He's so unusual / Dixie jamboree / Collegiate love / Accordian Joe / I was made to love you / Wasting my love on you / Sweetheart of my student days / You're lucky to me / I got rhythm / Cheerful little earful / Little things in life, The / I'm tickled pink with a blue-eyed baby / I'm so afraid of you / Would you like to take a walk / Please don't talk about me when I'm gone / When I take my sugar to tea / Little girl / It's the girl.
LP: . . . . SH 410

FREDDIE RICH ON THE AIR-VOL.1.
Tracks: / I've got five dollars / Copenhagen / Bugle call rag / Japanese sandman / Roll on, Mississippi, roll on / Dinah / Some of these days / Somebody stole my gal / Goin' to town / Zanky / Dixie jamboree / Nobody's sweetheart / San.
LP: . . . . AIRCHECK 12

FREDDIE RICH ON THE AIR-VOL.2.
Tracks: / I've got five dollars / One man band / I know that you know / Alabamy bound / Happy landing, A / Hiding in the shadows of the moon / You try somebody else / Sugar / Too late / Sweet and lovely / What is it? / Bend down sister / This is the missus / Waiting for the Robert E. Lee.
LP: . . . . AIRCHECK 13

Rich In Paradise

GOING BACK TO MY ROOTS (See under F.P.I. Project for details) (Rich In Paradise/F.P.I. Project).

Rich Kids

GHOSTS OF PRINCES IN TOWERS.
Tracks: / Strange one / Hung on you / Ghosts of princes in towers / Cheap emotion / Marching men / Put you in the picture / Young girls / Bullet-proof lover / Rich kids / Lovers and fools / Burning sounds.
LP: . . . . FA 4130771
MC: . . . . TCFA 41 30771
LP: . . . . EMC 3263
LP: . . . . EMS 1010

Rich Kids On LSD

GREATEST HITS LIVE : RICH KIDS ON LSD.
LP: . . . . EFA 5143

ROCK AND ROLL NIGHTMARES.
MC: . . . . VM 104 C
LP: . . . . VM 104

Rich, Lisa

LISTEN HERE.
Tracks: / Shaker song / Spring can really hang you up the most / Can't buy me love / Morning / Wine of May, The.
LP: . . . . DS 908

TOUCH OF THE RARE (Rich, Lisa with Clare Fischer).
Tracks: / Love for sale / Invitation / Some other time / Novios / Minor sights / Gaviota.
LP: . . . . TR 541
MC: . . . . TRC 541

Rich, Richie

I CAN MAKE YOU DANCE.
MC: . . . . GEEMC 3
LP: . . . . GEEA 3

Rich, Young & Pretty

RICH, YOUNG AND PRETTY (See under Nancy Goes To Rio for details) (Various artists).

Richard, Cliff

20 GREATEST HITS: CLIFF RICHARD.
LP: 1A 058 1073201
MC: 1A 258 1073204

20 ROCK'N'ROLL HITS: CLIFF RICHARD.
LP: . . . . IC 064 07145

21 TODAY.
LP: 33SX 1384
LP: 1A 046 05074

32 MINUTES & 17 SECONDS.
LP: 33SX 1431

40 GOLDEN GREATS.
Tracks: / Move it / Living doll / Travellin' light / Fall in love with you / Please don't tease / Nine times out of ten / Theme for a dream / Gee whiz it's you / When the girl in your arms is the girl in your heart / Girl like you, A / Young ones, The / Do you wanna dance? / I'm lookin' out the window / It'll be me / Bachelor boy / Next time, The / Summer holiday / Lucky lips / It's all in the game / Don't talk to him / Constantly / On the beach / I could easily fall in love with you / Minute you're gone, The / Wind me up (let me go) / Visions / Blue turns to grey / In the country / Day I met Marie, The / All my love / Congratulations / Throw down a line / Goodbye Sam, hello Samantha / Sing a song of freedom / Power to all our friends / You keep me hangin' on / Miss you nights / Devil woman / I can't ask for anymore than you / My kinda life / Thief in the night.
2LP: . . . . EMTVS 6
MCSET: . . . . TC EMTVS 6

ALADDIN AND HIS WONDERFUL LAMP.
LP: 5C 052 06962
LP: 33SX 1676

ALWAYS GUARANTEED.
Tracks: / One night / Once upon a time / Some people / Forever / Two hearts / Under your spell / This time now / My pretty one / Remember me / Always guaranteed.
LP: . . . . EMD 1004
MC: . . . . TCEMD 1004
LPS: . . . . EMDB 1004
LP: . . . . ATAK 131
MC: . . . . TCATAK 131

AN HOUR OF CLIFF RICHARD.
Tracks: / I could easily fall (In love with you) / Gee whiz it's you / Travellin' light / Unchained melody / Beat out that rhythm on a drum / Blueberry Hill / Got a funny feeling / Spanish harlem / It is no secret / We say yeah / Day by day / Dancin' shoes / Blue turns to grey / Voice in the wilderness, A / When my dreamboat comes home / D in love / So I've been told / Fire and rain (live) / With the eyes of a child / Good news / Sing a song of freedom / Mr. Business man (Live).
MC: . . . . HR 8122
MC: . . . . HR 4181224

BEST OF CLIFF.
LP: . . . . SCX 6343

BEST OF CLIFF VOL.2.
LP: . . . . SCX 6519

CAROLS.
Tracks: / Little Town / In the bleak mid winter / Unto us a child is born / Sweet little Jesus boy.
LP: . . . . WRD R 3034
MC: . . . . WRD C 3034

CINDERELLA.
LP: 5C 052 06967
LP: 33SCX 6103

CLIFF.
Tracks: / Apron strings / My babe / Down the line / I got a feeling / Jet black / Baby I don't care / Donna / Move it / Ready Teddy / Too much / Don't bug me baby / Driftin' / That'll be the day / Be bop a lula / Danny / Whole lotta shakin' goin' on.
LP: 33SX 1147
LP: . . . . FA 3064

CLIFF IN JAPAN.
LP: . . . . SCX 6244

CLIFF IN THE 60'S.
Tracks: / Nine times out of ten / I love you / Girl like you, A / Young ones, The / I'm lookin' out the window / Bachelor boy / Summer holiday / Lucky lips / I'm the lonely one / On the beach / Twelfth of never / Visions / Time drags by / It's all over / All my love / Day I met Marie, The.
LP: . . . . MFP 41 5656 1
MC: . . . . MFP 41 5656 4
LP: . . . . MFP 5656
MC: . . . . TCMFP 5656

CLIFF RICHARD.
LP: 33SX 1709

CLIFF RICHARD (BOX SET).
Tracks: / Minute you're gone, The / Living doll / Day I met Marie, The / Move it / Look homeward angel / Young ones, The / Bachelor boy.
LPS: 4M 128 54042/44
LPS: 4MI 2854042/3

CLIFF RICHARD: INTERVIEW PICTURE DISC.
LPPD: . . . . BAK 2063

CLIFF RICHARD LIVE.
LP: . . . . MFP 50307
MC: . . . . TCMFP 50307

CLIFF RICHARD SONGBOOK, THE.
Tracks: / Take me high / Bachelor boy / Young ones, The / Twelfth of never / Move it / Living doll / F.B.I. / Apache / Corina Corina / Wild wild woman / Whisky river / Rock baby rock it / You made me love you / That's the way I love / I'll wait / Run come see / Trudy.
LPS: . . . . ALBUM 26
MCSET: . . . . CASSETTE 26

CLIFF RICHARD STORY, VOL 1 : CLIFF.
Tracks: / Apron strings / My babe / Down the line / I got a feeling / Baby I don't care / Jet black / Donna / Move it / Ready Teddy / Too much / Don't bug me, babe / Be bop a lula / That'll be the day / Danny / Whole lotta shakin' goin' on.
LP: 5C 052 05071

CLIFF RICHARD STORY, VOL 2 : CLIFF SINGS.
Tracks: / Blue suede shoes / Snake and the bookworm, The / I gotta know / Here comes summer / I'll string along with you / Embraceable you / As time goes by / Touch of your lips, The / Twenty flight rock / Pointed toe shoes / Mean woman blues / I'm walking / I don't know why / Little things mean a lot / Somewhere along the way / That's my desire.
LP: 1A 052 05072

CLIFF RICHARD & THE SHADOWS (Richard, Cliff & The Shadows).
LP: 1A 052 05019

CLIFF SINGS.
LP: 33SX 1192

CLIFF & THE SHADOWS (20 original greats) (Richard, Cliff & The Shadows).
Tracks: / On the beach / Do you wanna dance / Lucky lips / Don't talk to him / Voice in the wilderness, A / Girl like you, A / Fall in love with you / Gee whiz it's you / Mean streak / In the country / Move it / Nine times out of ten / Dancing shoes / Theme for a dream / Willie and the hand jive / I'm the lonely one / When the girl in your arms is the girl in your (Tepper/Bennett) / Time drags by / I could easily fall in love with you (Marvin/Welch/Bennett/Rostill.) / We say yeah.
LP: . . . . CRS 1
LP: . . . . EG 2601481
MC: . . . . EG 2601484
MC: . . . . TCCRS 1
LP: . . . . ATAK 132
MC: . . . . TCATAK 132

CLIFF'S HIT ALBUM.
Tracks: / Move it / Living doll / Travellin' light / Voice in the wilderness, A / Fall in love with you / Please don't tease / Nine times out of ten / I love you / Theme for a dream / Girl like you, A / Young ones, The / Do you wanna dance? / When the girl in your arms is the girl in your heart / I'm lookin' out the window.
LP: . . . . SCX 1512
LP: 33SX 1512

DON'T STOP ME NOW.
LP: . . . . SCX 6133

DRESSED FOR THE OCCASION (Richard, Cliff/Philharmonic Orchestra).
Tracks: / Green light / We don't talk anymore / True love ways / Softly as I leave / Carrie / Miss you nights / Galadriel (spirit of starlight) / Maybe someday / Thief in the night / Up in the world / Treasure of love / Evil woman (reprise).
LP: . . . . ATAK 53
MC: . . . . TCATAK 53
MC: . . . . TCEMC 3432
LP: . . . . EMC 3432

EP COLLECTION, THE: CLIFF RICHARD.
Tracks: / Look in my eyes, Maria / If I give my heart to you / Maria / Secret love / Love letters / I only have eyes for you / All I do is dream of you / When I grow too old to dream / My heart is an open book / Boom boom (that's how my heart beats) / Moonlight bay / Forever kind of love, A / La mer / J'attendrai / Shrine on the second floor, The / Where the four winds blow / Solitary man / Things we said today / Carnival (from Black Orpheus) / Little rag doll.
LP: . . . . SEE 280
MC: . . . . SEEK 280

EVENT BOXSET, THE.
LPS: . . . . CRTVB 31
MCSET: . . . . TCCRTVB 31

EVERY FACE TELLS A STORY.
LP: . . . . EMC 3172

FINDERS KEEPERS.
LP: 5C 052 06966
LP: . . . . SX 6079

FROM A DISTANCE (THE EVENT).
Tracks: / Zing went the strings of my heart / Always / When / Glory of love (Not on CD.) / Hoots mon (Not on CD.) / Don't look now / Girl can't help it, The / Sea cruise / From a distance / Some people / We don't talk anymore / Shake, rattle and roll / Silhouettes / Move it / Summer holiday (Not on CD.) / Young ones, The / In the country (Not on CD) / Good golly Miss Molly (Not on CD) / Fighter/ Thief in the night / Share a dream / All the time you need / Saviours day.
2LP: . . . . CRTV 31
MC: . . . . TCCRTV 31

GOOD NEWS.
LP: . . . . SCX 6167

GREEN LIGHT (LP).
LP: . . . . EMC 3231

HIS LAND (See under His Land).

HYMNS AND INSPIRATIONAL SONGS.
Tracks: / What a friend we have in Jesus / High ground / King of love my shepherd is, The / All glory, laud and honour / When I survey the wondrous cross / Just a closer walk with thee / Take my hand / Amazing grace / Lord's my shepherd, The / It is no secret / May the good Lord bless and keep you.
LP: . . . . WRD R 3017
MC: . . . . WRD C 3017

I LOVE YOU.
LP: 1A 022 1583421
MC: 1A 222 1583424

I'M NEARLY FAMOUS.
Tracks: / I can't ask for anymore than you / It's no use pretending / I'm nearly famous / Lovers / Junior cowboy / Miss you nights / I wish you'd change your mind / Devil woman / Such is the mystery / You've got to give me all your lovin' / If you walked away / Alright, it's alright.
LP: . . . . FA 3010
MC: . . . . TCFA 3010
LP: . . . . EMC 3122

I'M NO HERO.
Tracks: / Take another look / Anything I can do / Little in love, A / Here (so doggone blue) / Give a little bit more / In the night / I'm no hero / Dreamin' / Heart will break, A / Everyman.
LP: . . . . FA 41 3148 1
MC: . . . . FA 41 3148 4
LP: . . . . FA 3148
MC: . . . . TCFA 3148
LP: . . . . EMA 796

IT'S A SMALL WORLD.
Tracks: / Tiny planet / Small world / Devil woman / Moving in / It has to be you / La gonave / I will follow you / Only way out, The / Rock 'n' roll juveniles / Where do you go from here?.
LP: . . . . MYR R 1209
MC: . . . . MYR C 1209

KENDRICK COLLECTION, THE (see under All Souls, Langham Place) (Richard, Cliff/All Souls' Orchestra/Choir).

KINDA LATIN.
LP: . . . . SX 6039

LISTEN TO CLIFF.
Tracks: / What'd I say? / Blue moon / True love will come to you / Lover / Unchained melody / Idle gossip / First lesson / Almost like being in love / Beat out that rhythm on a drum / Memories linger on / Temptation / I live for you / Sentimental journey / I want you to know me / We kiss in a shadow / It's you / It'll be me / So I've been told / How long is forever? / I'm walkin' the blues / Turn around / Blueberry Hill / Let's make a memory / When my dreamboat comes home / I'm on my way / Spanish Harlem / You don't know / Falling in love with love / Who are we to say? / I wake up crying.
2LP: . . . . MFP 1011
MCSET: . . . . TCMFP 1011
LP: 33SX 1320

LOVE IS FOREVER.
LP: 33SX 1769

LOVE SONGS: CLIFF RICHARD.
Tracks: / Miss you nights / Constantly / Up in the world / Carrie / Voice in the wilderness, A / Twelfth of never / I could easily fall in love with you / Day I met Marie, The / Can't take the hurt anymore / Little in love, A / Minute you're gone, The / Visions / When two worlds drift

apart / Next time, The / It's all in the game / Don't talk to him / When the girl in your arms is the girl in your heart / Theme for a dream / Fall in love with you / We don't talk anymore.
LP: EMTV 27
MC: TCEMTV 27

ME AND MY SHADOWS (Richard, Cliff & The Shadows).
LP: 1A 052 05073
LP: 33SX 1261

MORE HITS BY CLIFF.
LP: 33SX 1737

NOW YOU SEE ME, NOW YOU DON'T.
Tracks: / Only way out, The / First date / Thief in the night / Where do we go from here? / Son of thunder / Little town / It has to be you / Water is wide, The / Now you see me, now you don't / Be in my heart / Discovering.
LP: ATAK 36
MC: TCATAK 36
LP: EMC 3415
MC: TCEMC 3415

PRIVATE COLLECTION (His Personal Best 1979-1988).
Tracks: / Some people / Wired for sound / All I ask of you / Carrie / Remember me (Album & Cass. only.) / True love ways / Dreamin' / Green light (Album & cassette only.) / She means nothing to me / Heart user (Album & Cassette only.) / Little in love, A / Daddy's home / We don't talk anymore / Never say die (give a little bit more) / Only way out, The / Suddenly / Slow rivers (Album & cassette only.) / Please don't fall in love / Little town / My pretty one / Ocean deep / She's so beautiful / Two hearts (Album & cassette only.) / Mistletoe & wine.
2LP: CRTV 30
MC: TCCRTV 30

ROCK AND ROLL JUVENILE.
Tracks: / Monday thru' Friday / Doing fine / Cities may fall / You know that I love you / My luck won't change / Rock 'n' roll juveniles / Sci-fi / Falling in love / Carrie / Hot shot / Language of love / We don't talk anymore / Count me out.
LP: ATAK 54
MC: TCATAK 54
LP: EMC 3307
MC: TCEMC 3307

ROCK CONNECTION, THE.
Tracks: / Heart user / Willie and the hand jive / Lovers and friends / Never be anyone else but you / La gonave / Over you / Shooting from the heart / Learning how to rock and roll / Lucille / Be bop a lula / Donna / Dynamite / She means nothing to me / Making history.
LP: CLIF 2
MC: TCCLIF 2

ROCK ON WITH CLIFF RICHARD.
Tracks: / Move it / High class baby / My feet hit the ground / Living doll / Mean streak / Never mind / Apron strings / Dynamite / Blue suede shoes / Twenty flight rock / Mean woman blues / Willie and the hand jive / Please don't tease / Nine times out of ten / "D" in love / Mumblin' Mosie / Gee whiz it's you / What'd I say? / Got a funny feeling / Forty days / Tough enough / We say yeah / Do you wanna dance? / It'll be me / Dancing shoes.
LP: 1A 022 58054
MC: 1A 222 58054
LP: MFP 50467
MC: TCMFP 50467

SEINE GROSSEN ERFOLGE.
Tracks: / Gut, dass es Freunde gibt / Wenn du lachst, lachst das gluck / Ich traume deine Traume / Goodbye Sam, hello Samantha / Sag no zu ihm / Man gratuliet mir / Rote lippen soll man kussen / Du, du gefallest mir so / Ein sonntag mit Marie / Das ist die frage aller fragen / Es war keine so wunderbar wie du.
LP: IM 048 05358

SHE MEANS NOTHING TO ME (see Everly, Phil) (Richard, Cliff/Phil Everly).

SILVER.
Tracks: / Silver's home tonight / Hold on / Never say die (give a little bit more) / Front page / Ocean deep / Locked inside your prison / Please don't fall in love / Baby you're dynamite / Golden days are over, The / Love stealer / Making history / Move it / Donna / Teddy bear / It'll be me / Lucille / Little bitty pretty one / Never be anyone else but you / Be bop a lula / Tutti frutti.
LP: EMC 1077871
MC: TCEMS 1077874

SINCERELY.
LP: SCX 6357

SLOW RIVERS (see under John, Elton) (Richard, Cliff/Elton John).

SMALL CORNERS.
Tracks: / Why should the Devil have all the good music? / I love / Why me? / I've got news for you / Hey, watcha say? / I wish we'd all been ready / Good on the Sally Army / Going home / Up in Canada / Yes, He lives / When I survey the wondrous cross.
LP: MFP 50539
MC: TCMFP 50539
LP: EMC 3219
LP: WRD R 3036
MC: WRD C 3036

STARS OF ROCK AND ROLL (Richard, Cliff & The Shadows).
LP: 1A 054 04740

STRONGER.
Tracks: / Stronger than that / Who's in love / Best of me, The / Clear blue skies / Lean on you / Keep me warm / I just don't have the heart / Joanna / Everybody knows / Forever you will be mine / Better day / Share a dream.
LP: EMD 1012
MC: TCEMD 1012

SUMMER HOLIDAY (Richard, Cliff & The Shadows).
Tracks: / Seven days to a holiday / Summer holiday / Let us take you for a ride / Les girls / Round and round / Foot tapper / Strange in town / Orlando's mime / Bachelor boy / Swingin' affair / Really waltzing / All at once / Dancing shoes / Yugoslav wedding / Big news.
LP: 5C 052 06965
LP: EMS 1009
MC: TCEMS 1009

SUMMER HOLIDAY (Film Soundtrack) (Richard, Cliff & The Shadows).
Tracks: / Seven days to a holiday / Summer holiday / Let us take you for a ride / Les girls / Foot tapper / Round and round / Stranger in town / Orlando's mime / Bachelor boy / Swingin' affair, A / Really waltzing / All at once / Dancing shoes / Yugoslav wedding / Next time, The / Big news.
LP: MFP 5824
MC: TCMFP 5824
LP: 33SX 1472

SUPERGOLD (Richard, Cliff & The Shadows).
2LP: IC 134 05316/17

TAKE ME HIGH.
LP: EMC 3016

THANK YOU VERY MUCH... (London Palladium reunion concert) (Richard, Cliff & The Shadows).
Tracks: / Young ones, The / Do you wanna dance? / Day I met Marie, The / Shadoogie / Atlantis / Nivram / Apache / Please don't tease / Miss you nights / Move it / Willie and the hand jive / All shook up / Devil woman / Why should the Devil have all the good music? / End of the show.
LP: MFP 41 5677 1
MC: TCMFP 4156774
LP: 5C 062 06939
LP: MFP 5677
MC: TCMFP 5677
LP: EMTV 15

TOGETHER.
Tracks: / Have yourself a merry little Christmas / O come all ye faithful / We should be together / Mistletoe and wine / Christmas never comes / Christmas alphabet / Saviours day / Christmas song, The (Merry Christmas to you) / Scarlet ribbons / Silent night / White Christmas / This New Year.
LP: EMD 1028
MC: TCEMD 1028

TRACKS 'N' GROOVES.
LP: SCX 6435

TWO A PENNY.
LP: 5C 052 06964

WALKING IN THE LIGHT.
Tracks: / Better than I know myself / Such is the mystery / Every face tells a story / Love and a helping hand / You got me wondering / Walking in the light / Why should the Devil have all the good music? / Under the influence / Lost in a lonely world / You, me and Jesus / Summer rain / Deep in the night.
LP: MYRR 1176
MC: MYRC 1176

WE'RE LOST ERRE.
LP: 1A 062 07320

WHEN IN FRANCE.
Tracks: / Two a penny / Power to all our friends / Questions / Congratulations.
LP: 1A 062 06234

WHEN IN GERMANY, VOL 1.
LP: 1A 062 07203

WHEN IN GERMANY, VOL 2.
LP: 1A 062 07204

WHEN IN ROME.
LP: 1A 052 07147

WHEN IN ROME & WHEN IN SPAIN.
2LP: EDP 1546303
MCSET: TC2 EDP 1546309

WHEN IN SPAIN.
LP: 1A 052 06728
LP: 33SX 1541

WIRED FOR SOUND.
Tracks: / Wired for sound / Once in a while / Better than I know myself / Oh no don't let me go / Cos I love that rock 'n' roll / Broken doll / Lost in a lonely world / Summer rain / Young love / Say you don't mind / Daddy's home.
LP: FA 3159
MC: TCFA 3159
LP: ATAK 40
MC: TCATAK 40
LP: EMC 3377

WONDERFUL LIFE (Film Soundtrack).
LP: 5C 052 06961
LP: 33SX 1628

YOUNG ONES, THE (Film Soundtrack) (Richard, Cliff & The Shadows).
Tracks: / Friday night / Peace pipe / Young ones / No one for me but Nicky / Vaudeville routine / Living doll / When the girl in your arms / Savage / We say yeah.
LP: EMS 1008
MC: TCEMS 1008
LP: 33SX 1384

YOUNG ONES, THE (2) (Original soundtrack) (Richard, Cliff & The Shadows).
Tracks: / Friday night / Got a funny feeling / Peace pipe / Nothing's impossible / Young ones, The / All for one / Lessons in love / No one for me but Nicky / What d'you know, we've got a show / Vaudeville routine / Mambo / Savage, The / We say yeah.
LP: MFP 5823
MC: TC-MFP 5823
LP: 5C 052069 63

Richard & Cosima

RICHARD AND COSIMA (Film about Richard Wagner) (Various artists).
LP: A 297
MC: C 297

Richard II

RICHARD II (see under Shakespeare, William) (Various artists).

Richard III

RICHARD III (see under Shakespeare, William) (Various artists).

Richard & Maureen

RICHARD & MAUREEN.
Tracks: / Somebody done somebody wrong song / You needed me / Hasta manana / Coat of many colours / Aye ready / When I need you / Dear god / Just a closer walk with thee / Old rugged cross / Can't smile without you / Sunday school to broadway / One day atb a time / My life.
LP: KMLP 304
MC: ZCMLP 304

Richard, Zachary

MARDI GRAS MAMBO.
LP: ZS 94

ZACK'S BON TON.
LP: ZS 96

Richards, Angela

SECRET ARMY (Richards, Angela/Ken Moule).
Tracks: / Je suis seul ce soir / Lili Marlene / Memories come gently / Nuages / Einmal wirst du wieder bei mir sein / That lovely weekend / For all our yesterdays / J'attendrai / Blues in the night / I bet you've heard this one before / Velvet blue / I'll be seeing you / If this is the last time I see you / When we can live in peace once more.
LP: REC 412
MC: ZCM 412

Richards, Ann

I'M SHOOTING HIGH.
Tracks: / I'm shooting high / Moanin' low / Nightingale / Blues in my heart / I've got to pass your house to get to my house / Deep night / Poor little rich girl / Should I / I'm in the market for you / Absence makes the heart grow fonder / Lullaby of Broadway / Will you still be mine.
LP: JAS 310
MC: JAS C310

TWO MUCH.
LP: ST 1067

Richards, Digby

WHISKEY SUNDOWN.
Tracks: / Samantha / Whiskey sundown / Losing you / Where there's smoke / Suzanne / Play, mama, play / Too long gone / In his songs / Hymn for Rosie / Falling / Louise.
LP: PL 25154
MC: PK 25154

Richards, Frank (aut)

BILLY BUNTER GETS THE BOOT (see under Billy Bunter...(bk)) (Biggins, Christopher (nar)).
MCSET: LFP 7490

Richards, Goff

GOFF RICHARDS & BURNISHED BRASS (Richards, Goff & Burnished Brass).
Tracks: / Stop the cavalry / Busy doing nothing / Shadow of your smile / Puttin' on the Ritz / Change Partners / Someone to watch over me / Let yourself go / Tritsch Tratsch Polka / Doin' the racoon / My cherie amour / Spread a little happiness / One day / Get out of your lazy bed / Sweet & Low / Super Trouper.
LP: PRZ 002
MC: CPRZ 002

Richards, Johnny

AIJALON (Richards, Johnny & His Orchestra).
Tracks: / Waltz anyone? / For all we know / Dimples / Band aide / Turn about / Burrito borracho / Long ago and far away / Aijalon.
LP: DS 895

AQUI HABLA ESPANOL.
Tracks: / Long live fats / Nothing more / Brass hat / Silver blue / Little apple / Perfume jungle / I go / Fort outside Mexico city / Spanish drink.
LP: JR 148

ARRANGER'S TOUCH, THE.
Tracks: / Get me to the church on time / On the street where you live / I could have danced all night / Wouldn't it be loverly? / Show me / Rain in Spain, The / I've grown accustomed to her face / With a little bit of luck / Omo ado / Kele kele / La pecadora / Ochun / Oluo anu / Ofo.
2LP: VJD 566
MCSET: ZC VJD 566

JE VOUS ADORE (Richards, Johnny & His Orchestra).
Tracks: / Concerto to end all concertos / What is there to say / How are things in Glocca Morra / This time / No moon at all.
LP: DS 915

MY FAIR LADY - MY WAY (Richards, Johnny & His Orchestra).
LP: FS 304

NO SQUARES ALLOWED.
LP: GELP 15047

SOMETHING ELSE (Richards, Johnny & His Orchestra).
Tracks: / Waltz anyone? / For all we know / Dimples / Band aside / Turn about / Burrito Borracho / Long ago & far away / Aijalon.
LP: AFF 155

WALK SOFTLY - RUN WILD (Richards, Johnny & His Orchestra).
Tracks: / Walk softly / Way you look tonight / Laura / Sunday's child / Alone together / You go to my head / Run wild / Tempest on the Charles / Three cornered hat / Yemaya.
LP: JASM 1500

WIDE RANGE (Richards, Johnny & Orchestra).
LP: ST 1052

Richards, Jonathon

GOLDEN FLUTE, THE.
MC: ZCFPA 1017

Richards, Keith

INTERVIEW ROME 1988.
LPPD: SYMPA 34666

TALK IS CHEAP.
Tracks: / Big enough / Take it so hard / Struggle / I could have stood you up / Make no mistake / You don't move me / How I wish / Rockawhile / Whip it up / Locked away / It means a lot.
LP: V 2554
MC: TCV 2554
LP: OVED 338
MC: OVEDC 338

Richards, Nansi

ART OF NANSI RICHARDS, THE.
Tracks: / Cainc Dafydd broffwyd / Morfa frenhines / Pwt ar y bys / Piddawns gwyr Wrecsam / Count Sax's minuet and variations / Aria / Morfa Rhuddlan / Clychau Aberdyfi / Pant Corlan yr wyn / Sicilian mariner - minuet / Dwr glan / Cainc Ifan ddal / Gorhoffedd gwyr Harlech / Y gaeaf / Mathafarn / Sandon / Cainc Dona / Rhif wyth / Cwrw melyn / Ffidl ffadl / Fairy dance, The / Irish reels / Melfyn / Codiad yr enedydd / Gwenynen Gwent / Cainc y datgeiniad / Cychau'r cantref / Cainc Lona / Pen rhaw / Wyres Megan / Llwyn Onn / Lldaw / Moel yr wyddfa / Nos galan.
LP: SQUAD 115

HARPS AND HORNPIPES Memories of Welsh gipsies.
Tracks: / Clog hornpipes / Romany conversation & words / Nos galen / Fairy reel, The / Fishing stories / Moel yr wyddfa / Talk about poachers / Men of Harlech / Was you ever see / Wrexham hornpipe / Y lyfant a mediodd / Gipsy hornpipe / Y ferch o blwyf penderwyn / Napoleon's grand march / Bargaining song / Tavern in the town / 3 men went a-hunting / Rising of the lark, the / I was in the hayshed / Rhyf wyth / Romany song.
MC: 60-053

JOYOUS VOICE OF NANSI RICHARDS, THE.
Tracks: / Mor fawr wyt ti / Ynys y plant / Ysbryd y myndd / Sing joyous bird / Homing / Lord is my light, The / Mawr yw Jehofa / There is no death / Broken heart.
LP: . . . . SCLP 611

SONGS OF PRAISE.
Tracks: / Cof am y cyfiawn Iesu / In the garden / Dim ond Iesu / I need Thee every hour / O liefara addfwyn Iesu / There is a green hill / Dyma feibl / Lord, I am coming home / Mi glywaf dyner lais / My God I love Thee / Mi dafla maich / Pwyso ar ei friach.
LP: . . . . SQUAD 118

Richards, Noel

DANGER LINE, THE.
LP: . . . . PR R 7502
MC: . . . . PR C 7502

LIONHEART.
MC: . . . . PR C 7503

Richards, Paul

MYRIAD SOUNDS OF PAUL RICHARDS.
LP: . . . . GRS 1181
MC: . . . . KGRS 1181

Richards, Red

I'M SHOOTING HIGH (Richards, Red & George Kelly Quintet).
LP: 2017

Richards, Regina

REGINA RICHARDS & RED HOT (Richards, Regina & Red Hot).
Tracks: / Ton of bricks / Company girl / Tyger / Don't want you back / Daytime dream / Jealous / You better go / Main chick / Shoulda done something / Tug of war.
LP: . . . . AMLH 68524

Richards, Reuben

FROM MY HEART.
Tracks: / From my heart / Special kind of love / Closer to me / I'll choose you / My love is true / I found love / Because I love you / Rolling on.
LP: . . . . OLP 027

Richards, Sam

ENGLISH FOLKSINGER, THE (Richards, Sam & Tish Stubbs).
Tracks: / We poor labouring men / Old man he courted me / Game of football / See it come down / Hopping down in Kent / Dying airman / Sheffield grinders song / Punch and Judy / Diddling song / Ware our mother / Jackie's building site / Drunken man / Bold archer / Still he slumbered / Cottage for sale / Time to be moving on / Shepton beauchamp wassail song.
LP: . . . . MTRA 2011

INVITATION TO NORTH AMERICA (See under Stubbs, Tish) (Richards, Sam & Tish Stubbs).

Richards, Trevor

NEW ORLEANS TRIO (Richards, Trevor & Louis Nelson).
LP: . . . . WAMO NO.11

Richardson, Betty

STORY BOOK CHILDREN (See under Junior Soul) (Richardson, Betty/ Junior Soul).

Richardson, Ian

TALES OF HOFFMAN (Councillor Krespel).
MC: . . . . CDL 51671

TALES OF KING ARTHUR.
MC: . . . . CDL 51609

Richardson, Jim

DON'T GET EMOTIONAL - UN POCO POGO.
Tracks: / Scoops / Soul eyes / Giant steps / I mean you / Blue water beach / Sitting bull / Chandra / Afro blue / Monk's dream.
LP: . . . . SPJ 537

Richardson, John

CALLING, THE.
MC: . . . . C 608

CIRRUS.
MC: . . . . C 603

DEVOTION.
MC: . . . . C 607

RESPONSE, THE.
MC: . . . . C 609

SOLSTICE.
MC: . . . . C 604

WITH A LITTLE HELP.
MC: . . . . C 606

Richardson, Miranda

SECRET GARDEN, THE (see under Secret Garden).

Richardson, Sir Ralph

POETRY OF WILLIAM BLAKE (see under Blake, William).

Richenel

YEAR HAS MANY DAYS, A.
Tracks: / Dance around the world / Don't save your love / Temptation / Secret wish / Higher ground / Tell me / 50/50 (makes 100%) / Don't fear / Take it to the max / Can't give it up.
LP: 4504341
MC: 4504344

Richey, Paul

DEVIL INSIDE.
LP: . . . . LP 1072

Richie, Lionel

CAN'T SLOW DOWN.
Tracks: / All night long / Stuck on you / Penny lover / Hello / Love will find a way / Running with the night / Only one, The / Can't slow down.
LP: . . . . STMA 8041
MC: . . . . CSTMA 8041

DANCING ON THE CEILING.
Tracks: / Sela / Ballerina girl / Don't stop / Deep river woman / Love will conquer all / Tonight will be alright / Say you, say me / Night train (Smooth alligator) (Cassette and Compact Disc only.) / Dancing on the ceiling / Love will find a way.
LP: . . . . ZL 72412
MC: . . . . ZK 72412

ENDLESS LOVE (See under Ross, Diana for details) (Richie, Lionel & Diana Ross).

LIONEL RICHIE.
Tracks: / Serves you right / Wandering stranger / Tell me / My love / Round and round / Truly / You are / You mean more to me / Just put some love in your heart.
LP: . . . . STMA 8037
MC: . . . . CSTMA 8037

ROCKIN AND ROMANCE.
LP: . . . . ROUGH 72

Richies

WINTER WONDERLAND.
LP: 086 119

Richman, Jonathan

23 GREAT RECORDINGS BY JONATHAN RICHMAN (Richman, Jonathan & The Modern Lovers).
Tracks: / Road runner / Dignified and old / Pablo Piccasso / Astral plane / Girl friend / Government centre / New teller / It will stand / Morning of our lives / Abominable snowman in the market / Important in your life / My little kookenhaken / Dodge veg-o-matic / Lonely financial zone / Roller coaster by the sea / New England / Egyptian reggae / Ice cream man / Buzz buzz buzz / Abdul and Cleopatra / Party in the woods tonight / Road runner (twice) / She cracked (Not on CD.) / Hospital (Not on CD.).
2LP: . . . . ESDLP 128
MCSET: . . . . ESDMC 128

BACK IN YOUR LIFE (Richman, Jonathan & Modern Lovers).
Tracks: / Abdul and Cleopatra / She's gonna respect me / Lover please / Affection / Buzz buzz buzz / Back in your life / Party in the woods tonight / My love is a flower (just beginning to bloom) / I'm natures mosquito / Emaline / Lydia / I hear you calling me.
LP: . . . . BZ 0060
LP: . . . . LILP 400466
LP: . . . . BSERK 17

IT'S TIME FOR JONATHAN RICHMAN & THE MODERN LOVERS (Richman, Jonathan & Modern Lovers).
LP: . . . . ROUGH 92
MC: . . . . ROUGHC 92

JONATHAN GOES COUNTRY.
Tracks: / Since she started to ride / Reno / You're the one for me / Your good girl's gonna go bad / I must be king / You're crazy for taking the bus / Rodeo wind / Corner store / Neighbours, The / Man walks among us / I can't stay mad at you / Satisfied mind.
LP: . . . . SPD 1037
MC: . . . . SPDC 1037

JONATHAN RICHMAN.
Tracks: / Malaguena de Jojo / Everyday clothes / Blue moon / I eat with gusto, damn you bet / Sleepwalk / Mistake today for me, A / Action packed / Fender Statocaster / Closer / Miracles will start to happen / Que reste t'll de nos amours / Cerco.
MC: . . . . SPD C 1024
LP: . . . . SPD 1024

JONATHAN RICHMAN SONGBOOK.
LP: BSERK19

JONATHAN RICHMAN & THE MODERN LOVERS (LIVE) (See under Modern Lovers for details) (Richman, Jonathan & Modern Lovers).

JONATHAN RICHMAN & THE MODERN LOVERS (Richman, Jonathan & Modern Lovers).
Tracks: / Rockin' shopping centre / Back in the U.S.A. / Important in your life / New England, A / Lonely financial zone / Hi dear / Abominable snowman in the market / Hey there little insect / Here comes the Martian Martians / Springtime / Amazing Grace.
LP: . . . . BZ 0048

JONATHAN RICHMAN & THE MODERN LOVERS (Richman, Jonathan & Modern Lovers).
Tracks: / Ice cream man / Egyptian reggae / Abdul and Cleopatra / My love is a flower / Dodge veg-o-matic / Summer morning.
LP: . . . . BSERK 2

JONATHAN SINGS (Richman, Jonathan & Modern Lovers).
LP: . . . . ROUGH 52
MC: . . . . ROUGHC 52

MODERN LOVERS 88 (Richman, Jonathan & Modern Lovers).
Tracks: / Dancin' late at night / When Harpo played his harp / Gail loves me / New kind of neighborhood / African lady / I love hot nights / California desert party / Everything's gotta be right / Circle 1 / I have come out to play / Moulin rouge, Theme from.
LP: . . . . FIEND 106
MC: . . . . ROUNDER 9014C
LP: . . . . ROUNDER 9014

ROCK 'N' ROLL WITH MODERN LOVERS (See under Modern Lovers for details) (Richman, Jonathan & Modern Lovers).

Richman, Richie

HARRY RICHMAN AND SOPHIE TUCKER.
LP: . . . . MES 7048

Richmond, Danny

HAND TO HAND (See under Adams, George) (Richmond, Danny/George Adams).

LAST MINGUS BAND PLAYS CHARLES MINGUS.
Tracks: / Fabour is fabous / Goodbye pork pie / Nostalgia in times square / Noddin' your head blues / Duke Ellington's sound of love / Wee.
LP: . . . . SJP 148

Richmond, Robin

FROM A SEAT IN THE STALLS.
LP: . . . . CF 265

NOSTALGIA IN RHYTHM.
Tracks: / Up with the curtain / Leap frog / South rampart Street Parade / Blue star / Vibrollini / 920 special / Love parade / Poodles on parade / I had a ball / Bats in the belfry / Dancing tambourine / Stompin' at the Savoy / Nice cup of tea, A / Powder your face with sunshine / Some like it hot / Mediterranean dawn / Doin' the racoon / Maple leaf rag / Entertainer, The / Easy winner, The / Gladiolus rag / Pineapple rag / Paragon rag / Solace (a Mexican serenade) / Magnetic rag.
LP: . . . . GRS 1086

Richmond Strings

MUSIC OF AMERICA (Richmond Strings/Mike Sammes Singers).
LP: . . . . TRD 2016

Rickets, Glen

I FOUND A LOVE.
LP: . . . . DK 7773

JUST CAN'T GET OVER YOU.
LP: . . . . PR 7777

MORE LOVE.
LP: . . . . JCLP 003

Rick's

RICK'S (Various artists).
LP: . . . . FF 079

Ricks, Jimmy

OLD MAN RIVER.
Tracks: / Old man river / Green eyes / It ain't necessarily so / Our love / Say it isn't so / You'll never know / Love is the thing / Zing went the strings of my heart / Summertime / Everything I have is yours / Darktown strutters' ball / She's funny that way.
LP: . . . . OFF 6035

Ricks, Phil Jerry

LOW LIGHT BLUES (Ricks, Phil Jerry & Oscar Klein).
LP: . . . . LR 42.007

Rico

JAMA RICO.
Tracks: / Destroy them / We want peace / Jam rock / Someday / Distant drums / Love and justice / Java / Do the reload / Easter island.
LP: . . . . CHRTT 5006
MC: . . . . ZCHRT 5006

RICO AND HIS CREOLE BAND - 1932/34 (Rico & His Creole Band).
Tracks: / Vision de Venus / Mi Chiquita / Don Lengua / See saw / Cancion a guarina / Lamento esclavo / Shangai / Son de amor / Pobre corazon / Mon aime douudou moin.
LP: . . . . HQ 2080

THAT MAN IS FORWARD.
Tracks: / Easy snappin' / Fiesta / Chang Kai Shek / Stay out late / Red top / X / Ganja / That man is forward.
LP: . . . . CHR TT 5005
MC: . . . . ZCHR T 5005

Ricochets

MADE IN THE SHADE.
LP: . . . . NERD 005

Ricotti, Frank

BEIDERBECKE CONNECTION (TV Soundtrack) (Ricotti, Frank All Stars).
Tracks: / Connection,The / Viva le van / Morgans mystery / Tulips for Chris / Barney's walk / Boys in blue / Hobson's chase / Tiger jive / Scouting ahead / Jennie's tune / Live at the Limping Whippet / Russian over / Dormouse delights / Cryin' all day.
LP: . . . . DM 20
MC: . . . . DMC 20

Riddim Force

HOW SWEET IT IS TO BE LOVED.
LP: . . . . PILP 031

NOTHING BUT LOVE SONGS.
LP: . . . . TTLP 001

Riddle, Almelda

BALLADS AND HYMNS FROM THE OZARKS.
LP: . . . . ROUNDER 0017

MORE BALLADS AND HYMNS FROM THE OZARKS.
LP: . . . . ROUNDER 0083

Riddle, Nelson

BEST IS YET TO COME (See under Fitzgerald, Ella) (Riddle, Nelson/Ella Fitzgerald).

CAN-CAN (Riddle, Nelson & His Orchestra).
Tracks: / It's alright with me / Allez-vous-en / Go away / You do something to me / Maidens typical of France / Let's do it / Just one of those things / I love Paris / C'est magnifique / Come along with me / Live and let live / Montmart's / Can-can.
LP: . . . . CAPS 2400161
MC: . . . . TCCAPS 2400164

HEY LET YOURSELF GO (Riddle, Nelson & Orchestra).
Tracks: / You and the night and the music / You leave me breathless / You are my lucky star / I get along without you very well / Then I'll be happy / Have you got any castles, baby / You're an old smoothie / Darn that dream / Let's face the music and dance / Let yourself go / Younger than Springtime / I can't escape from you.
LP: 2C 068 54578
MC: . . . . PM 1545784

JOY OF LIVING, THE (Riddle, Nelson & His Orchestra).
Tracks: / Life is just a bowl of cherries / You make me feel so young / Makin' whoopee / Bye bye blues / It's so peaceful in the country / Joy of living / It's a big wide wonderful world / June in January / Isn't this a lovely day / Indian Summer / It's a grand night for singing / I got the sun in the morning.
LP: . . . . EG 2606081
MC: . . . . EG 2606084

LOOK OF LOVE, THE (Riddle, Nelson & His Orchestra).
Tracks: / I wish you love / In the arms of love / I love how you love me / Wonder of you, The / And when I die / Rainy night in Georgia / Love grows where my Rosemary goes / Hey there lonely girl / Stay (reste) / Tonight I'll say a prayer / Until it's time for you to go / My elusive dreams / Can't take my eyes off you / Look of love, The / My cup runneth over /

Pick up the pieces / Ghetto man / Jah Jah knows / Sufferer of the ghetto / If I were you / When you are wrong / Promised land / Only for a time / Blacker black / Peace & love / My sweat turns to blood / Come a long way / Stand & give praise / Freedom fighters / Israel be wise / If you want good / Happy Tim / Never be a tomorrow before today.
LP: . . . . BDL 1039
MC: . . . . AJKL 1039

ROMANCE, FIRE AND FANCY (Riddle, Nelson & His Orchestra).
Tracks: / Beautiful sunrise / Costa mesa / Don't break my heart / Chemise noir / Midironde / Dancing shadows / Sun spots / Twilight romance / Fireflies / Night winds / Talk about music / Night tangle.
LP: . . . . ISST 115

WONDERFUL NAT KING COLE SONGS, THE.
Tracks: / Too young / It's only a paper moon / Nature boy / Walkin' my baby back home / Mona Lisa / Night Lights / Dance Ballerina dance / Sweet Lorraine / Ramblin' Rose.
LP: . . . . CBS 32666
MC: 40 32666

Riddle of the...(bk)

RIDDLE OF THE SANDS, THE (Childers, Erskine (aut)) (Sinden, Leon (nar)).
MCSET: . . . . COL 2024

Riddles, Nat

JOHNSON. WHERE DID YOU GET THAT SOUND? (see under Johnson, Larry) (Riddles, Nat & Larry Johnson).

Ride

NOWHERE.
Tracks: / Seagull / Kaleidoscope / In a different place / Polar bear / Dreams burn down / Decay / Paralysed / Vapour trail / Taste / Here and now / Nowhere.
LP: . . . . CRELP 074
MC: . . . . CCRE 074

Rider On The Rain

RIDER ON THE RAIN (Film Soundtrack) (Various artists).
Tracks: / Rider on the rain: *Various artists* / Dobbs duality: *Various artists* / Marriage waltz: *Various* artists / American theme: *Various artists* / Mellie and the American: *Various artists* / Arrest: *Various* artists / Meeting house: *Various artists* / Setting the scene: *Various artists* / Car theme: *Various* artists / Mellie's theme: *Various artists* / Bestial theme: *Various artists* / Marriage: *Various artists*/ Momento of melancholy: *Various artists* / Anguish: *Various artists* / Dobbs at the station: *Various artists*/ Rape: *Various artists* / Duality and Dobbs: *Various artists* / Mellie's theme: *Various artists.*
LP: . . . . UAS 29137

Riders In The Sky

COWBOY JUBILEE.
LP: . . . . ROUNDER 0147
MC: . . . . ROUNDER 0147C

LIVE.
Tracks: / Cowboy jubilee / Yodel blues, The / When the bloom is on the sage / After you're gone / Cowboy song / Varmit dancing / Hold that critter down / Cielito lindo / Last roundup, The / I grab my saddlehorns and blow / Blue bonnet lady / When the payday rolls around / So long saddle pals.
LP: . . . . ROUNDER 0186
MC: . . . . ROUNDER 0186C

NEW TRAILS.
LP: . . . . ROUNDER 0220
MC: . . . . ROUNDER 0220C

PRAIRIE SERENADE.
LP: . . . . ROUNDER 0170
MC: . . . . ROUNDER 0170C

SADDIE PAIS.
LP: . . . . ROUNDER 8011
MC: . . . . ROUNDER 8011C

THREE ON THE TRAIL.
LP: . . . . ROUNDER 0102
MC: . . . . ROUNDER 0102C

WEEDS AND WATER.
Tracks: / Cool water / West Texas cowboy / La cucaracha / Streets of Laredo / Singing a song in the sky / Tumbling tumbleweeds / Pecos bill / That's how the yodel was born / Wasteland / Bound to hit the trail.
LP: . . . . ROUNDER 1038
MC: . . . . ROUNDER 1038C

Ridgeley, Andrew

SON OF ALBERT.
Tracks: / Red dress / Shake / Price of love, The / Flame / Hangin' / Mexico / Big machine / Kiss me / Baby Jane.
LP: 4667171
MC: 4667174

Ridgley, Tommy

NEW ORLEANS KING OF THE STROLL, THE.
Tracks: / New Orleans king of the stroll, The / Doubled eyed whammy / Is it true? / Should I ever love again / My ordinary girl / I've heard that story before / Heavenly / Girl from Kooka Monga, The / In the same old way / Three times / Only girl for me, The / I love you yes I do / Please hurry home.
LP: . . . . ED 260
LP: . . . . ROUNDER 2079
MC: . . . . ROUNDER 2079C
LP: . . . . FLY 519

Ridgway, Stan

BIG HEAT.
Tracks: / Salesman / Pick it up / Can't stop the show / Pile driver / Drive she said / Walking home alone / Twisted / Big heat / Camouflage.
LP: . . . . MIRF 1008
MC: . . . . MIRFC 1008

DON'T BOX ME IN (See under Copeland, Stewart for details) (Ridgway, Stan/Stewart Copeland).

MOSQUITOS.
Tracks: / Heat takes a walk / Lonely town / Goin' Southbound / Dogs / Can't complain / Peg and Pete and me / Newspapers / Calling out to Carol / Last honest man, The / Mission in life, A.
LP: . . . . EIRSA 1010
MC: . . . . EIRSAC 1010

PARTYBALL.
Tracks: / Watch your step / Jack talked (like a man on fire) / I wanna be a boss / Mouthful of sand / Roadblock, The / Snaketrain / Right through you / Gumbo man, The / Harry Truman / Venus is hell / Overlords / Uba;s house of fashions / Bad news at the dynamite ranch / Beyond tomorrow.
LP: . . . . EIRSLP 1058
MC: . . . . EIRSTC 1058

Ridin' In Rhythm

RIDIN' IN RHYTHM (Various artists).
2LP: . . . . SHB 42
2LP: . . . . SW 8453/4

Riding High

RIDING HIGH (Original soundtrack) (Various artists).
LP: . . . . JAM 2

Riedy, Bob

JUST OFF HALSTED (Riedy, Bob & his blues band).
LP: . . . . FF 006

LAKE MICHIGAN AIN'T NO RIVER (Bob Riedy Chicago Blues Band).
LP: . . . . ROUNDER 2005

Rieman, Kurt

ELECTRONIC NIGHTWORKS.
LP: . . . . KS 80047

Riethmuller, Heinrich

ZWEI IN EINER GROSSEN STADT (Two in a big city).
Tracks: / Kauf dir einen bunten luftballon / Glaube mir / Tulpen aus Amsterdam (Tulips from Amsterdam) / Es leuchten die stern / Nimm uns mit, Kapitan / Vor meinem vaterhaus steht eine linde / Goodbye Johnny / So ein tag / Abends in der taverne / Zwei in einer grossen stadt (Two in a big city) / Bel ami / Auf der Reeperbahn nachts um halb eins etc.
LP: 6.26412

Riff

MISSION LOVE.
Tracks: / No mercy / Elaine / Paradise in dreams / Thrilling days / Sally dear / All or nothing / Promise don't cry / Station to station / No one waits forever / Time to live.
LP: . . . . MFN 97

RIFF.
Tracks: / Everytime my heart beats / My heart is failing me / All or nothing / If you're serious / I can't believe we just met / Baby it's wonderful / Temporary insanity / Little girls / Read my eyes / April's fool.
LP: . . . . SBKLP 13
MC: . . . . SBKTC 13

WHO WANTS IT.
LP: . . . . SKUMKLP 112

Riff Raff

VINYL FUTURES.
Tracks: / Nina / Shades of blue / Treat me right / I ain't gonna run anymore / Mary lou / My, my / Love in vain / Heroes / Time riff / Hall of mirrors.
LP: . . . . K 50819

Rifkin, Joshua

SCOTT JOPLIN-DIGITAL RAGTIME.
Tracks: / Maple leaf rag / Entertainer, The / Easy winners / Gladiolus rag / Pineapple rag / Heliotrope bouquet / Paragon rag / Solace / Magnetic rag.
LP: . . . . EMD 5534
MC: . . . . TCCEMD 5534

Rift, Zoogz

LOOSER THAN CLAMS.
Tracks: / Idiots on the minature golf course / Lobotomy 2 / Dinkle dance / Heart attack / Art band / Secret marines - The sequel / No use / With the necessary changes having.. / Mutatis mutandis / Island of living puke / Torture sequence / You're killing me / High fidelity.
LP: . . . . SST 088

TORMENT.
LP: . . . . SST 251
MC: . . . . SSTC 251

Rigadoon

SEA, FRESH AND FAIR.
Tracks: / Reels / Medley / Moulin Rouge / Moon river / Jigs / Five foot two, eyes of blue / March/Strathspey / Carillon / Hayfield twostep / Bulgarian folk tunes / Flight of the bumble bee.
LP: . . . . JEL 2001

TARTAN LASSIES, THE.
Tracks: / Weaver and his wife, The / Cornerhouse jig / Donald Iain Rankine / Loch Ruan / Leslie Angus / Heights of casino / Rosshire volunteers, The / Duke of Edinburgh / Blackberry bush / Battle of the Somme / Earl of Mansfield / Leaving Port Askaig / Headlands, The / Sheena's wedding / Irish washerwoman, The / Rollicking Irishman / Corn rigs / My love she's but a lassie yet / Highland lassie / There was a lad / Lynda's waltz / Accordion samba / Drunken piper / Barren rocks of Aden / Athole Highlanders, The.
LP: . . . . LOCLP 1022
MC: . . . . ZCLOC 1022

Rigby, Robert

ROCK STAR.
LP: . . . . FUS 7000

Rigby, Will

SIDEKICK PHENOMENON.
LP: . . . . E 02

Rigg, Diana

PYGMALION (see Shaw, George Bernard) (Rigg, Diana & Alec McCowen).

Riggs

RIGGS.
Tracks: / Ready or not / One night affairs / Over and over / Take it off / Depending on love / Girls on the loose / Christine / Don't walk away / Too strong.
LP: . . . . K 99197

Riggs, Chuck

LIVE HOT JAZZ (See under Davern, Kenny) (Riggs, Chuck/Kenny Davern).

Right Choice

RIGHT CHOICE, THE.
LP: . . . . MOT 6257

Right Stuff (film)

RIGHT STUFF / NORTH & SOUTH (See under 'North & South') (Conti, Bill).

Right Stuff (group)

WA WA.
Tracks: / That's right / Girl's all go, The / Ministry of love / Right stuff / Ghost in my life / One man band / Scissors / Sympathetic / Mission / Priceless / Girl's all go, The (Ipcress mix) / 24 + (Only on CD).
LP: 210460
MC: 410460

Righteous Brothers

BEST OF RIGHTEOUS BROTHERS.
Tracks: / You've lost that lovin' feeling / That lucky old sun / So many lonely nights ahead / Go ahead and cry / Soul and inspiration / Hold on I'm coming / Unchained melody / Drown in my own tears / In the midnight hour / Hung on you / Harlem shuffle / I just want to make love to you / Mine all mine / He / Angels listened in, The / What'd I say.
LP: 831 996-1
MC: 831 996-4

GREATEST HITS: RIGHTEOUS BROTHERS.
Tracks: / You've lost that lovin' feeling / White cliffs of Dover, The / For sentimental reasons / Georgia on my mind / You'll never walk alone / Just once in my life / Unchained Melody / See that girl / Ebb tide / Guess who / Hung on you / Great pretender, The.
LP: . . . . SPELP 47
MC: . . . . SPEMC 47

REUNION.
Tracks: / Unchained melody / Just once in my life / Rock and roll heaven / (You're my) soul and inspiration / You've lost that lovin' feelin' / Hung on you / Try to find another woman / Little Latin lupe lu / Ebb tide / My babe / Unchained melody (timeless love extended).
LP: 467 957 1
MC: 467 957 4

THEIR TOP HITS (Righteous Brothers & Bill Medley).
MC: 821

UNCHAINED MELODY - THE VERY BEST OF.
LP: 847 248 1
MC: 847 248 4

Righteous Pigs

LIVE AND LEARN.
LP: . . . . NB 12
LP: 082 944

STRESS RELATED.
LP: . . . . NB 035

Rigoletto

RIGOLETTO (VIDEO) (see under Verdi (composer)) (Various artists).

Rikky & Pete

RIKKY & PETE (Original Soundtrack) (Various artists).
LP: SBL12593

Rilcy, Claude

ATMOSPHERES.
LP: 5790

Riley

IMPROVISATIONS ARE FOREVER NOW (Riley/Wachsmann/Guy).
LP: . . . . VS 113

Riley, Billy Lee

BILLY LEE RILEY & THE LITTLE GREEN MEN (Riley, Billy Lee And The Little Green Men).
Tracks: / Trouble bound / Rock with me baby / Pearly Lee / Red hot / Flyin' saucers rock and roll / I want you baby / One more time / Baby please don't go / Wouldn't you know / Rock with me honey / No name girl / When a man gets the blues.
LP: . . . . SUNLP 1049

BILLY RILEY & THE LITTLE GREEN MEN.
Tracks: / Red hot / Dark muddy bottom (Featuring Lightnin' Leon) / Repossession blues (Featuring Lightnin' Leon) / Mud Island / My baby's got love / That's what I want to do / Columbus Stockade blues (Featuring Martin Willis) / San Antonio rock (Featuring Martin Willis) / Beat-nik (Featuring J.M.Van Eaton) / Foggy (Featuring J.M.Van Eaton) / Jump back (Featuring J.M.Van Eaton) / Out-standing (Featuring J.M.Van Eaton) / Something else (Featuring J.M.Van Eaton) / Too much woman for me.
LP: . . . . BFX 15272

LEGENDARY SUN PERFORMERS.
Tracks: / Red hot / Rock with me baby / Flyin' saucers rock 'n' roll / No name girl / I want you baby / Wouldn't you know / Got the water boiling / Down by the riverside / That's right / Baby please don't go / Open the doors / Richard / Sun goin' down on Frisco / Workin' on the river / Looking for my baby / Pilot town Louisiana.
LP: . . . . CR 30131

RED HOT RILEY (Riley, Billy Lee And The Little Green Men).
2LP: . . . . CDX 9

SUN SOUNDS SPECIAL.
Tracks: / Pearly Lee / Swanee river rock / She's my baby / Just one more time / Let's talk about us / Searchin' / Betty and Dupree / Sweet Williams / Troubled bound / Wouldn't you know / Itchy / Nitty gritty / Mississippi / Tallahassee lassie / San Fransico lady / Kay / Old home place.
LP: . . . . CR 30151

Riley, Cheryl Pepsii

ME MYSELF AND I.
Tracks: / Me myself and I.
LP: . . . . FC 44409
LP: 4632831
MC: 4632834

Riley, Doug

DREAMS.
LP: . . . . PM 007

Riley, Howard

ENDGAME (see Guy, Barry) (Riley, Howard & Barry Guy & John Stevens & Trevor Watts).

FOR FOUR ON TWO TWO.
Tracks: / Pedal points / Four four on two two / Somethings / Activate / Unfold.
LP: . . . . AFF 110

HOLYWELL CONCERT, THE (See under Coxhill, Lol) (Coxhill, Lol/Haslam/Rutherford/Riley).

IN FOCUS (Riley, Howard & Keith Tippett).

LP: . . . . AFF 137

INTERWINE (MUSIC OF 2 PIANOS).
LP: . . . . GCM 771

OTHER SIDE, THE (Solo Piano).
Tracks: / Agitate / Yesterday's friends / Deflection / Furthest point, The / Trajectory / Returning.
LP: . . . . SPJ 511

SHAPED.
LP: . . . . GCM 781

SYNOPSIS.
LP: . . . . INCUS 13

TORONTO CONCERT.
LP: . . . . VS 112

Riley, Jeannie C.

GIRL FROM TEXAS, THE.
Tracks: / Price I pay to stay, The / I'll be a woman of the world / How can anything so right be so wrong / No one ever lost more / One slightly used wedding band / You got me singing nursery rhymes / What about them / Heart he kicks around, The / I don't know what I'm doing here / Deaf, dumb and blind / Hey cheatin' man / Faded ribbon / Did you ever / You're for me.
LP: . . . . PRCV 110

HARPER VALLEY PTA.
Tracks: / Harper Valley PTA / Yearbooks and yesterdays / Things go better with love / Country girl / Generation gap, The / Back side of Dallas, The / Girl most likely, The / Duty not desire / He made a woman out of me / Help me make it through the night / Macom Georgia ban girl / Will the real Jesus please stand up.
LP: . . . . TOP 130
MC: . . . . KTOP 130

JEANNIE C.RILEY.
LP: . . . . SPR 8582
MC: . . . . SPC 8582

TOTAL WOMAN.
Tracks: / Total woman / Love vacation / Shall I sing forever of yesterday / Limousine lovers / Too late for regrets / Gone with the West Texas wind / David play your harp / White as snow / Back to your heart / Return to Harper Vlley.
LP: . . . . SDLP 039

Riley, Jimmy

PUT THE PEOPLE FIRST.
LP: . . . . SHAN 43005
MC: . . . . SHANC 43005

RYDIM DRIVEN.
LP: . . . . ILPS 9671

TELL THE YOUTHS THE TRUTH.
Tracks: / Tell the youths the truth / Give thanks and praise / Price, The / Nyah bingi / Feeling is believing / Change your ways / Statue of a fool / Somebody told me / Majority rule / Hard headed Israelites.
LP: . . . . TRLS 167

WORLD FOR EVERYONE.
LP: . . . . BMLP 002

Riley, Marc

CULL.
LP: . . . . IT 005

FANCY MEETING GOD.
LP: . . . . IT 015

GROSS CUT (Riley, Marc & The Creepers).
LP: . . . . IT 007

Riley, Teddy

HONKY TONK TOWN '79.
LP: . . . . LPS 3
MC: . . . . TCS 21
LP: . . . . NOLA 21
MC: . . . . TC 021

MY FANTASY (See also Guy).

WENDELL EUGENE AND FRIENDS (See Under Eugene, Wendell) (Riley, Teddy, Wendell Eugene, Michael White, Kid Sheik Cola).

WOLVERINE BLUES (See also under Jim Duggan & Walter Payton).

Riley, Terry

CADENZA ON THE NIGHT PLAIN (Riley, Terry & The Kronos Quartet).
LP: 187014 1
MC: 187014 4

CHURCH OF ANTHRAX (see Cale, John) (Riley, Terry & John Cale).

HARP OF NEW ALBION.
2LP: . . . . LPCEL 018/19
MCSET: . . . . MCCEL 018/19

IN C.
LP: . . . . ED 314
LP: . . . . CBS 61237
LP: . . . . LPCEL 130261
MC: . . . . MCCEL 130264

PERSIAN SURGERY DERVISHES.
2LP: . . . . SHAN 83501/2

RAINBOW IN CURVED AIR.
LP: . . . . CBS 32099

SHRI CAMEL.
Tracks: / Anthem of the Trinity / Celestial valley / Across the lake of the ancient world / Desert of ice.
LP: . . . . CBS 73929

SONGS FOR THE TEN VOICES OF THE TWO PROPHETS.
LP: . . . . LPKUCK 067

Rimac, Ciro

CIRO RIMAC - 1936 TO 1937.
Tracks: / La conga mi rosa / Cachita / La rumba el viandero / Habanera flor / Cubanacan.
LP: . . . . HQ 2077

Rimarimba

CHICAGO DEATH EXCRETION GEOMETRY.
LP: . . . . HAM 20

Rimbaud, Mike

MUTINY IN THE SUBWAY.
LP: . . . . STOP 010

Rimmington, Sammy

EXCITING SAX OF SAMMY RIMMINGTON.
LP: . . . . PRO 7077

GEORGE LEWIS CLASSICS.
LP: . . . . GHB 94

IN TOWN WITH SAM LEE.
LP: . . . . GHB 213

NEW ORLEANS SESSION WITH SAMMY RIMMINGTON, A.
LP: . . . . GHB 209

ONLY A LOOK.
LP: . . . . DC 12027

RED WING (See under Easy Riders Jazz Band) (Rimmington, Sammy/Easy Riders Jazz Band).

REED ALL ABOUT IT (Rimmington, Sammy/Ian Wheeler Band).
Tracks: / J / My darling / Am I to blame / Once in a while / Something is gonna give way / Shoeshine boy / Decatur street / Hymn to freedom / Save your sorrows.
LP: . . . . HJ 104

SAMMY RIMMINGTON A NEW ORLEANS QUARTET (Rimmington, Sammy & Nre Orleans Quartet).
LP: . . . . ML 114

SAMMY RIMMINGTON AND BARRY MARTYN (Rimmington, Sammy & Barry Martyn).
LP: . . . . GHB 214

WAY DOWN YONDER IN NEW ORLEANS (see Smith, Keith) (Rimmington, Sammy & Keith Smith).

Rimpianto

ITALIAN MUSIC IN AMERICA 1915-29.
MC: . . . . GVMMC 601

Rimsky-Korsakov

RIMSKY-KORSAKOV (Various artists).
MC: . . . . DLCMC 218

SCHEHERAZADE - SADKO Musical picture (London Symphony Orchestra).
MC: 4214004

SHEHERAZADE (Various artists).
MC: 4278164
MC: . . . . VETC 6509

Rinder, Laurin

SEVEN DEADLY SINS (Rinder, Laurin/ Michael Lewis).
LP: . . . . NSPL 28252

Ring O' Bells

BARN DANCIN' AND COUNTRY DANCIN' (Ring O' Bells Country Dance Band).
LP: . . . . BEE 006
MC: . . . . BEE 006C

CEILIDH SATURDAY NIGHT (Ring O' Bells Country Dance Band).
LP: . . . . BEE 004
MC: . . . . BEE 004 C

HOEDOWN SATURDAY NIGHT (Ring O' Bells Country Dance Band).
LP: . . . . BEE 023
MC: . . . . BEE 023 C

SQUARE DANCE SATURDAY NIGHT (Ring O' Bells Country Dance Band).
LP: . . . . BEE 002
MC: . . . . BEE 002 C

Ring Of Bright Water

RING OF BRIGHT WATER Maxwell, Gavin (Timothy, Christopher (nar)).
MC: . . . . TC LFP 7075

RING OF BRIGHT WATER/GOD TOLD ME TO (Film soundtrack) (Various artists).
LP: . . . . DGS 1004

Ringer, Jim

ANY OLD WIND THAT BLOWS.
LP: . . . . PHILO 1021

ENDANGERED SPECIES.
Tracks: / Roseville fair / Bugler / Wild horses / Wild women / Dusty desert wind / Still got that look / Family tree / Brand new Jole Blon / Linda's out there on her own / Bayou blues / Whiskey and cocaine.
LP: . . . . FF 242

GOOD TO GET HOME.
LP: . . . . PHILO 1012

TRAMPS AND HAWKERS.
LP: . . . . PH 1047

Ringing The Changes

RINGING THE CHANGES/LAZARUS RISING (Various artists).
MC: . . . . NF 12

Ringo, Johnny

ASHER SENATOR V JOHNNY RINGO (See under Senator, Asher) (Ringo, Johnny & Asher Senator).

Ringo The Texan

RINGO THE TEXAN/IN A COLTS SHADOW (Original Soundtracks) (Various artists).
LP: . . . . SP 8014

Rini, Anthony Galla

ANTHONY GALLA RINI IN CONCERT.
Tracks: / Toccata / Three preludes / Waltz of the flowers / Little white donkey, The / Lesginka / Caprice viennoise / Dance of the hours.
LP: . . . . OMLP 1001

Rink

RINK,THE (Original Broadway Cast) (Various artists).
Tracks: / Colored lights: *Various artists* / Chief cook and bottle washer: *Various artists* / Don't ah ma me: *Various artists* / Blue crystal: *Various artists* / Under the roller coaster: *Various artists* / Not enough magic: *Various artists* / Here's to the rink: *Various artists* / We can make it: *Various artists* / After all these years: *Various artists* / Angel's rink...: *Various artists* / What...: *Various artists* / Marry me: *Various artists* / Mrs. A: *Various artists* / Rink, The: *Various artists* / Wallflower: *Various artists* / All the children: *Various artists* / Coda: *Various artists.*
LP: . . . . TER 1091
MC: . . . . ZCTER 1091

Rintoul, David

BONES IN THE SAND (See also Kenneth Royce).

ODESSA FILE, THE (See also Frederick Forsyth).

Rio

BORDERLAND.
LP: . . . . MFN 53
MC: . . . . TMFN 53

SEX CRIMES.
Tracks: / Pay for love / Under pressure / Atlantic radio / High school rock / Guilty / When the walls come down / Danger zone / Sex crimes / Dirty movies / Bad blood.
LP: . . . . MFN 65

Rio, Bob

TASTE OF COUNTRY, A.
Tracks: / Rocky mountain high / Amanda / Old Red / Galveston / Charlie is my name / Spiders and snakes / Wreck of the old '97 / I'd rather love you / Movin' on / Old Shep / You are my best friend / One piece at a time.
LP: . . . . SFA 104

Rio Bravo (film)

RIO BRAVO (TITLE THEME) (See under Martin, Dean) (Martin, Dean).

Rio Grande Band

RIO GRANDE BAND.
LP: . . . . ROUNDER 0105
MC: . . . . ROUNDER 0105C

Rio Tone

RIO TONE (Original Soundtrack) (Various artists).
LP: . . . . A 352

Riopelli, Jerry

LIVIN' THE LIFE.
Tracks: / Livin' the life / Naomi's song / Shoulder to the wheel / Blues on my table / Doodley doo / Silly old gigolo / Roll with the feelin' / Take a chance / River on the run / Hey old friend / Me and the fox / Valentine / Cryin' out loud / Talk to me / Walking on the water / Steppin' out.
LP: . . . . SEE 70

Riot

BORN IN AMERICA.
LP: . . . . SLAM 6

FIRE DOWN UNDER.
Tracks: / Swords and tequila / Fire down under / Feel the same / Outlaw / Don't bring me down / Don't hold back / Altar of the king / No lies / Run for your life / Flashbacks.
LP: . . . . K 52315

NARITA.
Tracks: / Waiting for the taking / 49er / Kick down the wall / Narita / Here we come again / Do it up / Hot for love / White rock / Born to be wild / Road racin'.
LP: . . . . EST 12081

PRIVILEGE OF POWER.
Tracks: / On your knees / Metal soldiers / Runaway / Killer / Dance of death / Storming the gates of hell / Maryanne / Little Miss Death / Black leather and glitter steel / Race with the devil on a Spanish highway.
LP: 4664861
MC: 4664864

RESTLESS BREED.
Tracks: / Restless breed / Hard lovin' man / CIA / When I was young / Loved by you / Loneshark / Over to you / Showdown / Dream away / Violent crimes.
LP: . . . . K 52398

THUNDERSTEEL.
Tracks: / Thundersteel / Fight or fall / Sign of the crimson storm / Flight of the warrior / On wings of eagles / Johnny's back / Bloodstreets / Run for your life / Buried alive (tell-tale heart).
LP: 460976 1
MC: 4609764

Riot Rockers

RIOT ROCKER, THE.
LP: . . . . CR 30158
LP: . . . . LP 8809

Riot Squad

ANYTIME.
Tracks: / I take it we're through / Bittersweet love / How is it done / Jump / It's never too late to forgive / Working man / Not a great talker / Anytime / Try to realise / Gonna make you mine / Gotta be the first time / Nevertheless / I wanna talk about my baby.
LP: . . . . KIRI 080

NO POTENTIAL THREAT.
LP: . . . . ASS 13

R.I.P.

GIVE ME THOUGHT.
LP: . . . . HM 01

Rip Chords

HEY, LITTLE COBRA.
LP: . . . . STC 8951

Rip Rig & Panic

ATTITUDE.
Tracks: / Keep the sharks from your heart / Sunken love / Rip open, but oh so long thy wounds take to heal / Do the tightrope / Intimacy, just gently shimmer / How that spark sets me aglow / Alchemy in this cemetry / Beat the beast / Eros, what brings colour up the stem / Push your tiny body as high as your desire can take you / Viva dreams / Birth pangs of spring, The.
LP: . . . . OVED 63
MC: . . . . OVEDC 63
LP: V2268

GOD.
Tracks: / Constant drudgery is harmful to soul, spirit and health / Wilhelm show me the diagram (function of the orgasm) / Through nomad eyeballs / Change your life / Knee deep in shit / Totally naked (without lock or key) / Try box out of this box / Need (deschool you) / Howl caged bird / Those Eskimo women speak frankly / Blue blue third, The / Shadows only there because of the sun / Beware (our leaders love the smell of napalm) / Miss Pib / It don't mean a thing.
LP: . . . . OVED 118
LP: . . . . V 2213

I AM COLD.
Tracks: / Storm the reality asylum / Warm to the if in life / Liars shape up or ship out / Epi epi arp woosh! / Nurse increase the sedatives (the torment's no better) / Take a donkey to mystery / Tax sex / Hunger (the ocean roars it bites) / You're my kind of climate / Here gathers nameless energy (volcanoes covered by snow) / Misa luba lone woolf.
LP: . . . . OVED 119
LP: . . . . V 2228

KNEE DEEP IN HITS (Best of Rip Rig & Panic).
LP: . . . . OVED 329
MC: . . . . OVEDC 329

Rip Stip &.....

MONTH IN BOHEMIA IS WORTH TWO IN THE BUSH, A.
LP: . . . . DISPLP 1

Ripcord

DEFIANCE OF POWER.
LP: . . . . ACHE 05

POETIC JUSTICE.
LP: . . . . RAGE 001

Riperton, Minnie

LOVE LIVES FOREVER.
Tracks: / Here we go / I'm in love again / Strange affair / Island in the sun / Give me time / You take my breath away / Song of life.
LP: . . . . EST 12097

MINNIE.
Tracks: / Memory lane / Lover and friend / Return to forever / Love hurts / Dancin' and actin' crazy / Never existed before / I'm a woman / Light my fire.
LP: . . . . FA 3027
MC: . . . . TCFA 3027
LP: . . . . EST 11936

MINNIE RIPERTON, THE BEST OF.
Tracks: / Perfect angel / Memory lane / Loving you / Can you feel what I'm saying / Here we go / Inside my love / Lover and friend / Woman of heart and mind / Young, willing and able / You take my breath away / Adventures in paradise.
LP: . . . . EST 12189
MC: . . . . TC EST 12189

PERFECT ANGEL.
LP: . . . . EPC 80426

STAY IN LOVE.
LP: . . . . EPC 81457

Ripley Wayfarers

CHIPS AND BROWN SAUCE.
LP: . . . . TSR 006

GENTLEMEN OF HIGH RENOWN.
LP: . . . . TSR 018

Ripon Cathedral

ORGAN FAVOURITES FROM RIPON CATHEDRAL (Perrin, Ronald).
Tracks: / Toccata and fugue in D minor (J.S. Bach) / Adagio / Allelujah (Preston) / Three chorale preludes (Reger) / Voluntary in E Min. (Stanley) / Finale from symphony II (Widor) / Radetzky march (Strauss) / Lied to the Sun ana Aria / Spanish toccata (Perrin) / Folk tune (Whitlock) / Carillon-Sortie (Mulet).
MC: . . . . YORKMC 102

RIPON CATHEDRAL CHOIR (Ripon Cathedral Choir).
Tracks: / On this day earth shall ring / My soul, there is a country / Litany to the Holy Spirit / Hail, gladdening light / O Lorde, the maker of all thing / Adoramus te / Turn back, O man / Trumpet minuet, A / Lo star-led chiefs / Beati quorum / Evening hymn / Heavens are telling, The.
MC: . . . . HAC 802

RIPON CATHEDRAL CHOIR & ORGAN 2 (Ripon Cathedral Choir).
Tracks: / Ascribe unto the Lord / Trumpet tune and air / Elves / Loving shepherd of thy sheep / War march of the priest / Lord is my shepherd, The / Fiat lux / It is a thing most wonderful / Hallelujah chorus.
MC: . . . . HAC 834

Ripping Corpse

DREAMING WITH THE DEAD.
Tracks: / Dreaming with the dead.
LP: . . . . FLAG 57
MC: . . . . TFLAG 57

SPLATTERED REMAINS.
Tracks: / Splattered remains.
LP: . . . . CCG 006

Rippingtons

CURVES AHEAD.
Tracks: / Curves ahead / Aspen / Santa Fe Trail / Take me with you / North Star / Miles away / Snowbound / Nature of the beast / Morning song.
MC: . . . . GRP 96514

KILIMANJARO.
Tracks: / Morocco / Dream of the Sivens / Kilimanjaro / Love notes / Oceansong / Northern lights / Katrina's dance / Backstabbers / Los Cabos.
LP: . . . . PJ 88042

MOONLIGHTING.
Tracks: / Moonlighting / She likes to watch / Angela / Dreams / Mirage / Calypso Cafe / Open all night / Intimate stranger.
LP: . . . . PJ 88019
MC: . . . . PJC 88019

TOURIST IN PARADISE.
LP: . . . . GRP 95881
MC: . . . . GRP 95884

WELCOME TO THE ST. JAMES' CLUB.
Tracks: / Welcome to The St James Club / Soul mates / I watched her walk away / Affair in San Miguel / Who's holding her now / Kenya / Wednesday's child / Tropic of Capricorn / Passion fruit / Victoria's secret.
LP: . . . . GRP 96181
MC: . . . . GRP 96184

Rippon, Angela (nar)

BABAR THE ELEPHANT.
LP: . . . . K 53598

BABAR THE LITTLE ELEPHANT (Rippon, Angela/David Parkhouse/St. John's Smith Square Orch.).
Tracks: / Toy symphony / Three German dances.
LP: . . . . ACM 2033
MC: . . . . ZC ACM 2033

BLACK BEAUTY (see under Black Beauty (bk)).

PETER AND THE WOLF/CARNIVAL OF THE ANIMALS, THE (see under Royal Philharmonic) (Rippon, Angela/ Royal Philharmonic Orchestra).

READS VICTORIA PLUM STORIES.
MC: 7215 043

STORIES FROM THE BALLET.
LP: . . . . REC 344
MC: . . . . ZCM 344

Risca Male Voice Choir

SING LENNON & McCARTNEY.
LP: . . . . BM 54

SOUND OF WALES.
Tracks: / Hallelujah chorus / Power and glory / Little horses, The / Ching a ring chaw / Deus salutis / Steal away / Chorus of robbers / Marrianina / Flowers of joy / Gwahoddiad / Eleanor Rigby / Bright eyes / Feast of feast.
LP: . . . . ALM 4006
MC: . . . . ZC ALM 4006

Rise & Fall of a

RISE AND FALL OF A DECADE (Various artists).
LP: . . . . ARTY 033

Rising Force

HEAVEN TONIGHT (see under Malmsteen, Yngwie J.) (Rising Force/ Yngwie J. Malmsteen).

Risk

BACK TO THE FUTURE.
LP: . . . . PHZA 20

BITTER SWEET.
LP: . . . . PHZA 25

DIRTY SURFACES.
LP: 0876231
MC: 8476232

HELL'S ANIMALS.
Tracks: / Monkey business / Perfect kill / Dead or alive / Secret of our destiny / Sicilian showdown / Torture and pain / Mindshock / Megalomania / Russian nights / Epilogue.
LP: 08-7592

OUT AND ABOUT (Risk and the Threads).
MC: . . . . PHZC 16

Risky Business (Film)

RISKY BUSINESS (Film Soundtrack) (Various artists).
Tracks: / Old time rock'n'roll: *Seger, Bob* / Dream is always the same, The: *Tangerine Dream* / No future: *Tangerine* Dream / Mannish boy: *Waters, Muddy* / Pump, The: *Beck, Jeff* / D.M.S.R.: *Prince* / After the fall: *Journey (Group)* / In the air tonight: *Collins, Phil* / Love on a real train: *Tangerine Dream* / Guido the killer pimp: *Tangerine Dream* / Lana: *Tangerine Dream.*
LP: . . . . V 2302
MC: . . . . TCV 2302
LP: . . . . OVED 240
MC: . . . . OVEDC 240

Rita, Sue & Bob Too

RITA, SUE & BOB TOO (OST) (See under Kamen, Michael) (Kamen, Michael).

Ritchard, Cyril (nar)

PINOCCHIO (see under Pinocchio (bk)).

Ritchie, Brian

BLEND, THE.
LP: . . . . SST 141

SONIC TEMPLE AND THE COURT OF BABYLON.
LP: . . . . SST 202

Ritchie Family

AMERICAN GENERATION.
Tracks: / American generation / Big spender / Good in love / I feel disco good / Musicman.
LP: 9109 618

RITCHIE FAMILY.
Tracks: / Put your feet to the beat / Bad reputation / It's a man's world / Where are the men / Sexy man.
LP: 9109 627
LP: . . . . QUAMP 1
MC: . . . . QUAMPC 1

Ritchie, Jean

NONE BUT ONE.
Tracks: / Fair Nottamun Town / Too many shadows / Black waters / None but one / Orphan's lament / Flowers of joy / See that rainbow shine / Riddle song / Sweet sorrow in the wind / Wondrous love / Now is the cool of the day.
LP: . . . . SRK 6025

Ritenour, Lee

AMERICAN FLYERS (Film Soundtrack) (Ritenour, Lee & Greg Mathieson).
Tracks: / American flyers / Travelling music / Brand new day / Gone ridin' / Bad moon rising / Brothers, The (part 1) / 'J' factor, The / Breakaway / Brothers, The (part 2) / Treadmill / Epilogue (third race).
LP: . . . . GRPA 2001
MC: . . . . GRPC 2001

BANDED TOGETHER.
Tracks: / Operator / Other love / Sunset drivers / Mandela / Amaretto / Rit variations II / Be good to me / I'm not responsible / Shadow dancing / Heavenly bodies.
LP: 9603581

CAPTAIN'S JOURNEY, THE.
Tracks: / Captain's journey, The (part 1) / Captain's journey, The (part 2) - The storm / Morning glory / Sugarloaf express / Matchmakers / What do you want / That's enough for me / Etude.
LP: . . . . K 52094

COLLECTION.
Tracks: / Early a.m. attitude / Rio funk / Night rhythms / White water / San ysidro / Asa / Dolphin dreams / Is it you / 24th street blues / Latin lover / Sauce, The / Malibu / Waltz for Carmen (Only on CD.).
LP: . . . . GRP 96451
MC: . . . . GRP 96454

COLOR RIT.
LP: . . . . GRP 95941
MC: . . . . GRP 95942

EARTH RUN.
Tracks: / Soaring / Earth run / If I'm dreamin' (don't wake me) / Watercolours / Sauce, The / Butterfly / Sanctuary / Water from the moon.
LP: . . . . GRP 91021
MC: . . . . GRPM 91021

FEEL THE NIGHT.
Tracks: / Feel the night / Market place / Wicked wine / French roast / You make me feel like dancing / Midnight lady / Uh oh.
LP: . . . . K 52141

FESTIVAL.
LP: . . . . GRPA 9570-1
MC: . . . . GRPM 9570-4

FIRST COURSE.
MC: 4670944

FRIENDSHIP.
LP: . . . . VIDC 3

GENTLE THOUGHTS.
LP: . . . . VID CIE

HARLEQUIN (See under Grusin, Dave) (Ritenour, Lee & Dave Grusin).

ON THE LINE.
Tracks: / Rit variations / Starbright / Pedestrian / Dolphin dreams / California roll / Heavenly bodies / On the line / Tush.
LP: 960 310 1

PORTRAIT: LEE RITENOUR.
Tracks: / Route 17 (Available on CD only) / Portrait / Asa / Windmill / G-rit / White water / Turn the heat up / Children's games / Run away / Shades in the shade.
LP: . . . . GRP 91042
MC: . . . . GRPM 91042

RIO.
Tracks: / Rainbow / San Juan sunset / Rio funk / It happens every day / Ipanema sol / Simplicidad / Little bit of this and a little bit of that,A.
LP: . . . . GRP 91017
MC: . . . . C 1017

RIT.
Tracks: / Mr. Briefcase / Tell me pretty lies / No sympathy / Is it you? / Dream walk / Countdown / Good question / On the slow glide.
LP: . . . . K 52273

RIT 2.
Tracks: / Cross my heart / Voices / Dreamwalkin' / Keep it alive / Malibu / Tied up / Road runner / Promises, promises / On the Boardwalk / Fantasy.
LP: . . . . E 0186

STOLEN MOMENTS.
Tracks: / Uptown / Stolen moments / 24th Street blues / Haunted heart / Waltz for Carmen / St. Bart's / Blue in green / Sometime ago.
LP: . . . . GRP 96151
MC: . . . . GRP 96154

SUPER LIVE 2 (See Grusin, Dave) (Ritenour, Lee/Chick Corea/Dave Grusin).

WHERE GO THE BOATS (See under Handy, John).

Rites Of Spring

SPRING.
LP: . . . . DISCHORD 16

Ritmia

FORSE IL MARE.
LP: . . . . RD 003

Ritmo De Bahia

RITMO DE BAHIA (Various artists).
LP: 171001
MC: 271001

Ritmo, Nuevo

HEART OF CUBA.
LP: . . . . GNPS 47

Rito, Danza E Teatro

RITO, DANZA E TEATRO (Various artists).
LP: . . . . VPA 8484

Ritter, Tex

FRIENDLY VOICE OF TEX RITTER, THE.
LP: . . . . HAT 3114
MC: . . . . HATC 3114

HIGH NOON.
Tracks: / High noon (1) (Movie soundtrack - rare British Capitol recording.) / Boogie woogie cowboy / Pecos Bill / Dallas darling / Eyes of Texas, The / Night Herding song / Pony express / High noon (2) (1st Capitol recording) / He's a cowboy auctioneer / Billy the kid / Texas rangers, The / Cattle call / Goodbye my little cherokee / There's a goldstar in her window / In case you change your mind (Previously unissued.) / I was out of my mind (Previously unissued.) / Dark days in Dallas (Previously unissued.Tribute to J.F.Kennedy).
LP: . . . . BFX 15126
MC: 4XL 9296

LADY KILLIN' COWBOY.
Tracks: / Sam Hall / Get along little doggies / Thirty three years in prison / Lady killin' cowboy / I'm a do right cowboy / Bill the bar fly / Nobody's darlin' but mine / My brown eyed Texas rose / Take me back to my boots and saddle / Oregon trail, The / Answer to nobody's darling but mine / Melody from the sky, A / Hills of old Wyomin', The / We'll rest at the end of the trail.
LPPD: . . . . BDP 15209

SINGIN' IN THE SADDLE.
Tracks: / High wide and handsome / Headin' for the Rio Grande / Out on the lone prairie / Arizona days / My sweet Chiquita / Jailhouse lament / I'm hittin' the trail (for home) / I'm a natural born cowboy / Ride, ride, ride / Ridin' down, the trail of Albuquerque / Sing cowboy sing / Down the Colorado trail / When it's lamplighting time in the valley / Singin' in the saddle / Sundown on the prairie / Ai viva tequila.
LPPD: . . . . BDP 15231

SONGS FROM THE WESTERN SCREEN.
Tracks: / Bandit, The / Wichita / I leaned on a man / Brave man / Searchers, The / Last frontier, The / Remember the Alamo / High noon / Marshal's daughter, the / Prairie home / Trooper hook.
LP: . . . . HAT 3041
MC: . . . . HATC 3041

STREETS OF LAREDO.
Tracks: / Blood on the saddle / Barbara Allen / Samuel Hall / Bury me not on the lone prairie / Little Joe the wrangler / When the work's all done this fall / Face on the bar room floor, The / Boll weevil / Billy the kid / Streets of Laredo / Sam Bass / Rye whiskey.
LP: . . . . BDL 1022
MC: . . . . BDC 1022

Ritual Tension

EXPELLED.
LP: . . . . SAVE 076

I LIVE HERE.
LP: . . . . SAVE 049

Ritz

PUTTIN' ON THE RITZ.
Tracks: / Dance until you drop / Wake up nights / Started out dancing, ended up making love / Anyone who had a heart / Soul tripping / Locomotion / Ain't no doubt / Love vibrations / Lazy love.

LP: . . . . EPC 63769

RITZ, THE.
Tracks: / All the things you are / Saturday night fish fry / Summer burn / Walkin' / It never entered my mind / Invitation / Scrapple from the apple / Child is born, A / Old folks / Golden rule / Ooh yah / Music in the air / Best is yet to come, The / It ain't necessarily so.
MC: . . . . CC 22

River Boys

MY ROOF COMES TUMBLING DOWN.
LP: . . . . SLC 002

River City People

SAY SOMETHING GOOD.
Tracks: / What's wrong with dreaming? / Walking on ice / Under the rainbow / Carry the blame / Say something good / Thirsty / When I was young / No doubt / I'm still waiting / Home and dry / Huskisson St. (CD only.) / Find a reason (CD only.).
LP: . . . . EMC 3561
MC: . . . . TCEMC 3561
LP: . . . . EMCX 3561

River Detectives

SATURDAY NIGHT SUNDAY MORNING.
LP: . . . . WX 295
MC: . . . . WX 295C

River (Film)

RIVER, THE (Original Soundtrack) (Various artists).
LP: . . . . MCA 6138
MC: . . . . MCAC 6138

Rivera, Luis

BATTLE OF THE ORGANS.
Tracks: / DB / Hay ride / Soft one / Grinding / Deep purple / I want a little girl / Memories of you / LR / Tangerine / Fat stocking / Heavy hips / Bobby sox / Manhattan / Milano blues.
LP: . . . . SING 631

Rivera, Martin

FOR DANCERS ONLY (See under Mance, Junior) (Rivera, Martin & Junior Mance).

Rivers, Ben Lee

SUNSHINE ON THE SNOW.
Tracks: / Jody and the kids / Great mail robbery, The / Behind closed doors / She's in love with a rodeo man / Billy Bayou / Funny how time slips away / Sunshine on the snow / Corner of my life / No hiding place / Make the world go away / Dreaming my dreams with you / Bad guitars players son, The.
LP: . . . . BSS 344

Rivers, Blue

BLUE BEAT IN MY SOUL (Rivers, Blue & His Maroons).
Tracks: / Guns of Navarone / Too much / Mercy mercy mercy / Phoenix city / Witchcraft man / Searching for you baby / I've been pushed around.
LP: . . . . BRMLP 024
LP: . . . . SEE 318

Rivers, Debbie

LONELY TALKIN' AGAIN, THE (see under King, Terry's "Tears on my pillow").

Rivers, Jimmy

BRISBANE BOP 1961-64 (Rivers, Jimmy & The Cherokees).
LP: . . . . WESTERN 2003

Rivers, Joan

CAN WE TALK.
LP: . . . . GEF 25676
MC: 4025676

Rivers, Johnny

LAST BOOGIE IN PARIS.
Tracks: / Sea cruise / Over the line / Barefootin' / Summer rain / Long tall Sally / Walkin' blues / Take me in your arms (rock me a little while) / John Lee Hooker.
LP: . . . . K 50033

ROAD.
Tracks: / Lights on the highway / Wait a minute / Geronimo's cadillac / I like your music / Sitting in Limbo / Six days on the road / See you then / Good love is like a good song, A / Artists and poets / Breath.
LP: . . . . K 50063

ROCK 'N' ROLL YEARS.
LP: 5787

Rivers, Mavis

WITH MATT CATINGUB BIG BAND (see under Catingub, Matt) (Rivers, Mavis with Catingub, Matt).

Rivers, Sam

DIMENSIONS AND EXTENSIONS.
Tracks: / Precis / Paean / Effusive melange / Involution / Afflatus / Helix.
LP: . . . . BST 84261

FLUTES (See under Newton, James) (Rivers, Sam & James Newton).

FUCHSIA SWING SONG.
LP: . . . . BST 84284

RIVERS AND HOLLAND VOL.2 (Rivers, Sam & Dave Holland).
LP: . . . . IAI 373848

SAM & DAVE- VOLUME 1 (See under Holland, Dave) (Rivers, Sam & Dave Holland).

SAM & DAVE-VOLUME 2 (See under Holland, Dave) (Rivers, Sam & Dave Holland).

STREAMS.
LP: . . . . MCA 39120

TUBA TRIO VOL 1 (Rivers, Sam & J Daley & W Smith).
LP: . . . . RK 2976/1

TUBA TRIO VOL 2 (Rivers, Sam & J Daley & W Smith).
LP: . . . . RK 2976/2

TUBA TRIO VOL 3 (Rivers, Sam & J Daley & W Smith).
LP: . . . . RK 2976/3

WAVES.
Tracks: / Shockwaves / Torch / Pulse / Flux / Surge.
LP: . . . . AFF 186

Riverside Ceilidh Band

HORSES FOR COURSES.
MC: . . . . LICS 5196

Riverside Jazz Band

30 YEARS ON.
LP: . . . . BURL 025

IN AT THE DEEP END.
LP: . . . . BURL 016

Riverside, Maros

FOLK MUSIC FROM LORINCREVE.
Tracks: / Duljon le a Botfalvi var, / Invirtita / Haidau / Falu vegen van egy valyu (there is a trough) / Let the castle in Botfalva fall.
LP: . . . . SLPX 18102

Riverside Trio

FLAT BROKE.
LP: . . . . NWLP 1004

RIVERSIDE TRIO, THE.
Tracks: / Just another day / Please give me something / Postman song, The / I ain't lovin' / Showpiece / Gotta keep movin' / Love me baby love me / Way she walks, The / Am I wrong / I'm gonna.
MC: . . . . TPC 3

Rivey, Alain

LUNATIK COMBO.
LP: . . . . DFG 8405

Riviera

RIVIERA.
LP: . . . . JUNGLE 70063

Riviera Boys

BOOLA BOOLA.
LP: . . . . BOG 002

Rivits

MULTIPLAY.
Tracks: / Some vision / Multiplay / Look all you like / Oo she do / Old Broadway / Nail it down / Lookin' / Future soon / Red light on.
LP: . . . . ILPS 9617

Rizzetta, Sam

SEVEN VALLEYS - HAMMERED DULCIMER.
LP: . . . . FF 489

Rizzi, Tony

DISCO PACIFIC.
Tracks: / On the atchison / Topeka and the Santa Fe / Take the 'A' train / Long train runnin' / Blues in the night / Chattanoogo choo choo / Night train / Love train / Sentimental journey.
LP: . . . . MORRHYTHM 6

RJ's Latest Arrival

TRULY YOURS.
Tracks: / What becomes of the broken hearted? / Off the hook / Truly yours / Could have been you / I'll always love you / Miracles / Time 4 love / Nights / Water pump / Terri's place.
LP: . . . . MTL 1035
MC: . . . . TCMTL 1035

R.M.F.

ROUTE 666.
LP: . . . . REDR 050

R.M.O.

BEYOND THE LIMIT.
LP: 0060 115

GARUDA.
LP: 0001 072

R.M.S.

CENTENNIAL PARK.
Tracks: / Broadway rundown / Tootin' Beck / After all these years / Truck / Hoover the duvet / First love / Juna the last / Memories of Crete / Centennial park.
MC: . . . . TCMMC 1004

GET THE BALL.
Tracks: / Broadway rundown / Tootin' beck / After all these years / Truck centennial / Hoover the duvet / First love / Juma the last / Memories of Crete.
LP: 001 083
MC: . . . . MMC 004
LP: . . . . MMR 004

Roach, David

I LOVE SAX.
LP: . . . . NML 1006

RUNNING WITH THE RIVER.
Tracks: / Running with the river / Move it / Innocent child / Love is / Back to back / Hot line / Rocketta / Every morning / Letter.
LP: . . . . CODA 6
MC: . . . . COCA 6
LP: 834 164-1

TALKING CITY, THE.
Tracks: / Emotional jungle / That's all it takes / Sleepwalker / Tell me / Reach for it / New dog / Nerja / Taking city, The / Tinsel Town / Tinsel.
LP: . . . . CODA 14
MC: . . . . COCA 14

Roach, Hal

AUDIENCE WITH HAL ROACH, AN.
MC: . . . . GRA 1002

BEST OF IRISH HUMOUR.
LP: . . . . CAB 101
MC: . . . . CCAB 101

HE MUST BE JOKING.
MC: . . . . GRA 1001

KING OF BLARNEY.
MC: . . . . GMC 5015

WE IRISH TALK LIKE THAT.
LP: . . . . EVE 5017
MC: . . . . EVC 5017
MC: . . . . GMC 5017

WRITE IT DOWN.
LP: . . . . EVE 5014
MC: . . . . EVC 5014
MC: . . . . GRA 5014

Roach, Max

AT BASIN STREET (See under Brown, Clifford) (Roach, Max & Clifford Brown).

BIRTH AND REBIRTH (Roach, Max & Anthony Braxton).
LP: . . . . BSR 0024

BOP SESSION, THE (See under Gillespie, Dizzy) (Roach, Max/Dizzy Gillespie/Sonny Stitt/John Lewis).

CHICAGO GOLDEN YEARS (See Blakey, Art) (Roach, Max & Art Blakey).

CONVERSATIONS.
Tracks: / Speak brother speak / Variation, A / You stepped out of a dream / Filide / It's you or no one / Jodies cha cha / Deeds, not words / Larry Larne / Conversations.
LP: . . . . M 47061

DRUMMIN THE BLUES (Roach Max & Stan Levy).
LP: . . . . LRP H3064

DRUMS UNLIMITED.
Tracks: / Drum also waltzes / Nommo / Drums unlimited / St. Louis blues / For big Sid / In the red.
LP: . . . . K 50519

EUROPEAN TOUR (See under: Thelonius Monk).

FORCE (see Shepp, Archie) (Roach, Max & Archie Shepp).

FREEDOM NOW SUITE.
LP: . . . . AMLP 810

GRAZ CONCERT 1963 (Roach, Max Quintet & Sonny Rollins Trio).
LP: . . . . JC 108

HARDBOP ACADEMY (See under Blakey, Art) (Roach, Max Quintet/Art Blakey/Jazz Messengers).

HISTORIC CONCERTS (Roach, Max & Cecil Taylor).
LP: . . . . SN 1100

IN THE BEGINNING (Roach, Max & Clifford Brown).
LP: 500097
LP: . . . . JL 97

IT'S TIME.
LP: . . . . AS 16
MC: . . . . ASC 16

LONG AS YOU'RE LIVING.
LP: . . . . ENJA 4074

MAX ROACH AGAIN.
2LP: . . . . AFFD 32

MAX ROACH & ANTHONY BRAXTON (see also Anthony Braxton) (Roach, Max & Anthony Braxton).

MAX ROACH COLLECTION.
Tracks: / Now's the time / Donna Lee / S'il vous plait / Stop motion / To Lady / Drum variations.
LP: . . . . DVLP 2127
MC: . . . . DVMC 2127

NEWPORT REBELS (See under Mingus, Charles) (Roach, Max/Charles Mingus/Eric Dolphy/Roy Eldridge/Jo Jones).

PERCUSSION DISCUSSION (See under Blakey, Art) (Roach, Max & Art Blakey).

QUINTET OF THE YEAR, THE (see Gillespie, Dizzy/Parker/Powell/Mingus & Roach) (Roach, Max/Powell/Powell/ Mingus & Gillespie).

SCOTT FREE.
Tracks: / Scott free (part 1) / Scott free (part II).
LP: . . . . SN 1103

SOUND AS A ROACH (Roach, Max & Abbey Lincoln).
LP: . . . . LPPS 111 17

STUDY IN BROWN (See also Brown, Clifford) (Roach, Max & Clifford Brown).

SURVIVORS.
Tracks: / Survivors / Third eye, The / Billy the kid / Jasme / Drum also waltzes,The / Sassy Max (self portrait) / Smoke that thunders,The.
LP: . . . . SN 1093

WE INSIST (Freedom Now Suite).
Tracks: / Driva' man / Freedom day / Triptych (With: Prayer/Protest/Peace.) / All Africa / Tears for Johannesburg.
LP: . . . . CS 9002

Roach, Steve

DREAMTIME RETURN.
2LP: 18055-1
MC: 18055-2

EMPETUS.
LP: . . . . LPFOR 036
MC: . . . . MCFOR 036

STRUCTURES FROM SILENCE.
LP: . . . . LPFOR 024
MC: . . . . MCFOR 024

Roachford

GET READY (LP).
Tracks: / Get ready / Survival / Funkee chile / Stone city / Wanna be loved / Bayou / Innocent eyes / Hand of fate, The / Takin' it easy / Higher / Vision of the future / Get ready (reprise).
LP: 4681361
MC: 4681362

ROACHFORD.
Tracks: / Give it up / Family man / Cuddly toy / Find me another love / No way / Kathleen / Beautiful morning / Living again / Since / Nobody but you.
LP: 4606301
MC: 4606304

Road Block

THREE DIMENSION.
LP: . . . . NRLP 3

Road Works Ahead

NIGHT AND DAY.
Tracks: / El museo / For Woff / Man I love, The / Chorus for Horace / Night and day / Table for two, away from the band please.
LP: . . . . TR 520
MC: . . . . TRC 520

Roadhouse

ROADHOUSE (Film soundtrack) (Various artists).
Tracks: / Road house blues: *Healey, Jeff Band* / Blue Monday: *Seger, Bob* / I'm tore down: *Healey, Jeff Band* / These arms of mine: *Redding, Otis* / When the night comes falling from the sky: *Healey, Jeff Band* / Rad gumbo: *Little Feat* / Raising heaven (in hell tonight): *Swayze, Patrick* / Good heart, A: *McKay, Kris* / Hoochie coochie man: *Healey, Jeff Band* / Cliff's edge: *Swayze, Patrick.*
LP: 209948
MC: 409948

Roadie

ROADIE (Film soundtrack) (Various artists).
Tracks: / Everything works if you let it: *Cheap Trick* / You better run: *Benatar, Pat* / Brainlock: *Ely, Joe* / Road rats: *Cooper, Alice* / Pain: *Cooper, Alice* / Can't we try: *Pendergrass, Teddy* / Drivin' my life away: *Rabbitt, Eddie* / Your precious love: *Bishop, Stephen* / Man needs a woman: *Ferguson, Jay* / Crystal ball: *Styx* / Double yellow line: *Saad, Sue & The Next* / Ring of fire:

Blondie / That lovin' you feelin' again: *Orbison, Roy & Emmylou Harris* / Hot damn, I'm a one woman man: *Lewis, Jerry Lee* / Texas me and you: *Asleep At The Wheel* / American way: *Williams, Hank Jr.*.
2LP: . . . . **K 66093**
MC: **K4 66093**

Roadknight, Margaret

BLUESMAKERS.
LP: . . . . **LRF 055**

Roadside Picnic

FOR MAD MEN ONLY.
Tracks: / Sometimes I get very sad / For mad men only / Lonely wolf / Premonition (adventures in the magic theatre) / Song for Elaine / No blues / Victoria Park forever / Visitation, The / Steve at the beach.
MC: . . . . **PK 74581**
LP: . . . . **PL 74581**

ROADSIDE PICNIC.
Tracks: / Morning song / Cairo / Kindred spirit / Never too late / You get wet sleeping in the park / In the maze / New Canterbury tale, A / Berlin / There was a place / Celebration / 8th May 1945 / Phoenix from the ashes.
MC: . . . . **PK 74002**
LP: . . . . **PL 74002**

Roar

ROAR (Original Motion Picture Soundtrack) (Various artists).
LP: . . . . **GT 1600**
MC: . . . . **GTC 1600**

Roar of the...

ROAR OF THE GREASEPAINT, THE SMELL OF THE CROWD (Original Broadway Cast) (Various artists).
Tracks: / Roar of the greasepaint...(overture): *Various artists* / Beautiful land, The: *Various artists* / Wonderful day like today, A: *Various artists* / It isn't enough: *Various artists* / Things to remember: *Various artists*/ Put it in the book: *Various artists* / With all due respect: *Various artists* / This dream: *Various artists*/ Where would you be without me?: *Various artists* / My first love song: *Various artists* / Look at that face: *Various artists* / Joker, The: *Various artists* / Who can I turn to? (When nobody needs me): *Various artists*/ That's what it is to be young: *Various artists* / What a man: *Various artists* / Feeling good: *Various artists*/ Nothing can stop me now: *Various artists* / Things to remember (reprise): *Various artists* / My way: *Various artists* / Who can I turn to? (reprise): *Various artists* / Beautiful land, The (reprise): *Various artists*/ Sweet beginning: *Various artists*.
MC: . . . . **GK 60351**

Roaring Jack

STREET CREDIBILITY.
LP: . . . . **MBEP 0002**

Roaring Jelly

IN THE ROAR.
Tracks: / Beethoven bluebeat / Bucketful of mud / Maybe it's just as well / Irretrievable breakdown / Cajun gumbo / Valerie Wilkins / Maracas in Caracas / Dirty little stop out / Thundercloud / Ides of March / Not for the soul / Christmas in Australia / Bed bug.
LP: **12TS 420**

ROARING JELLY'S GOLDEN GRATES.
LP: . . . . **FRR 013**

Roaring Seven Jazz...

ROARING SEVEN JAZZ BAND (Roaring Seven Jazz Band).
LP: . . . . **SOS 1019**

Roaring Twenties

CLASSIC YEARS IN DIGITAL STEREO (see under Classic Years...) (Various artists).

Rob 'N' Raz

ROB 'N' RAZ FEATURING LEILA K (Rob 'N' Raz featuring Leila K).
Tracks: / Got to get / Rok the nation / On tour / Just tell me / Love for love.
LP: **210672**
MC: **410672**

Robbins, Hargus 'Pig'

PIG IN A POKE.
LP: . . . . **K 52071**

Robbins, Kate

KATE ROBBINS.
Tracks: / More than in love / Run wild / Goodnight / I'll never love this way again / Now / I want you back / You're the only one that I ever needed / Anytime at all / Cassie's song / Crowds of you.
LP: . . . . **RCALP 6013**
MC: . . . . **RCAK 6013**

Robbins, Marty

AFTER MIDNIGHT.
Tracks: / I'm in the mood for love / Misty / Looking back / September in the rain / Don't throw me away / Pennies from Heaven / Summertime / It had to be you / All the way / I'm having a ball / If I could cry / On the sunny side of the street.
LP: . . . . **SHM 3197**
MC: . . . . **HSC 3197**
LP: . . . . **CBS 32421**

ALL AROUND COWBOY.
Tracks: / All around cowboy / Dreamer, The / Pride and the badge / Restless cattle / When I'm gone / Buenos dias Argentina / Lonely old bunkhouse / San Angelo / Tumbling tumbleweeds / Ballad of a small man.
LP: . . . . **SHM 3174**
MC: . . . . **HSC 3174**
LP: . . . . **CBS 83917**

BIGGEST HITS.
Tracks: / Singing the blues / White sports coat / Story of my life / El Paso / You gave me a mountain / Ribbon of darkness / Tonight Carmen / My woman, my woman, my wife / Padre / Devil woman / She's just a drifter / Jenny / My greatest memory / Occasional rose, An / Completely out of love / Teardrops in my heart.
LP: . . . . **CBS 32301**
MC: **40 32301**

BORDER TOWN AFFAIR.
Tracks: / El Paso / Tonight Carmen / Gardenias in her hair / Have I told you lately that I love you / La Paloma / Girl from Spanish town / Maria Elena / Camellia / Bound for old Mexico / Spanish lullaby / In the valley of the Rio Grande / Feleena.
LP: . . . . **CBS 31536**

BY THE TIME I GET TO PHOENIX.
Tracks: / By the time I get to Phoenix / Until we meet again / As time goes by / That old feeling / Am I that easy to forget / Love is in the air / To be in love with her / Love is blue / Yesterday / Virginia / You made me love you.
LP: . . . . **SHM 989**
MC: . . . . **HSC 386**

COME BACK TO ME.
Tracks: / Some memories just won't die / It's not all over / American dream / Here your memory comes again / First song that wasn't the blues / Prayin' for rain / That's all she wrote / Tie your dreams to mine / If her eyes don't get you / Lover lover.
LP: . . . . **CBS 85794**

COUNTRY STORE: MARTY ROBBINS.
Tracks: / Devil woman / Cool water / El Paso / Have I told you lately that I love you / Adios amigo / Big iron / Streets of Laredo / I did what I did for Maria / Maria Elena / By the time I get to Phoenix / Air that I breathe, The / Singing the blues / Ballad of the Alamo / Ruby Ann / Some memories just won't die (Only on CD.) / Honky tonk man (Only on CD.) / El Paso City (Only on CD.) / Yellow roses (Only on CD.).
LP: . . . . **CST 7**
MC: . . . . **CSTK 7**

COWBOYS, THE (see Cash, Johnny) (Robbins, Marty & Johnny Cash).

DON'T LET ME TOUCH YOU.
Tracks: / Don't let me touch you / There's no more you and me / To get to you / Way I loved you best, The / Try a little tenderness / Return to me / Harbour lights / More than anything I miss you / Tree in the meadow, A / Tomorrow, tomorrow, tomorrow.
LP: . . . . **CBS 82429**

DOUBLE-BARRELLED MARTY ROBBINS, THE.
2LP: . . . . **CBS 88152**
MC: **40 88152**

EL PASO.
LP: . . . . **SHM 726**

EVERYTHING I'VE ALWAYS WANTED.
Tracks: / Woman in my bed / Completely out of love / There's no wings on my angel / Holding on to you / Gene Autry, my hero / My greatest memory / I'll go on alone / Another cup of coffee / Occasional rose / Crossroads of life.
LP: . . . . **CBS 84816**

FASTEST GUN AROUND, THE.
LP: . . . . **SHM 878**

GREAT YEARS, THE.
Tracks: / Twentieth century drifter / Mother knows best / I heard the bluebirds sing / Way I'm needing you, The / Darling come home / You're an angel disguised as a girl / Georgia blood / Don't you think / I'm wanting to / I couldn't believe it was true / Love needs.
LP: . . . . **SHM 3208**
MC: . . . . **HSC 3208**

GUNFIGHTER BALLADS.
LP: . . . . **TFL 5063**

HAWAII'S CALLING ME.
Tracks: / Lovely Hula hands / Sea and me, The / Night I came to shore, The / Echo island / Kuu ipo Lani (my sweetheart Lani) / Beyond the reef / Hawaiian wedding song / Drowsy waters / Hawaiian bells / My wonderful one / Blue sand / Hawaii's calling me / Hawaiian wedding song / Ku lu a (love song of kalua) / Drowsy waters (Wailana) / Hawaii's calling me / Hawaiian bells / Song of the islands / Don't sing aloha when i go / Crying steel guitar waltz / My isle of golden dreams / Now is the hours (Maori Farewell song) / Sweet leilani / Down where the tradewinds blow / Aloha oe (farewell to thee) / Island echoes / Moonland / Constancy (Ua like no more).
LP: . . . . **BFX 15123**

IN THE WILD WEST PART 1.
Tracks: / Cool water / In the valley / Running gun / El Paso / El Paso city / Big iron / Master's call, The / Little green valley / Hundred and sixty acres, A / Billy the kid / Utah Carol / They're hanging me tonight.
LP: . . . . **BFX 15145**

IN THE WILD WEST PART 2.
Tracks: / Strawberry roan, The (Cover & label erroneously give this track as Utah carol.) / Saddle tramp / She was young and she was pretty / Streets of Laredo / Little Joe / Wrangler, The / I've got no use for women / Billy Venero (Previously unissued.) / This peaceful sod / Five brothers / San Angelo / Song of the bandit / Wind (Previously unissued.) / My love / Ride, cowboy, ride / Red River valley / Prairie fire.
LP: . . . . **BFX 15146**

IN THE WILD WEST PART 3.
Tracks: / Ballad of the Alamo / Bend in the river, The / Abilene Rose / Dusty winds / Doggone cowboy / Red hills of Utah, The / Tall handsome stranger / Jimmie Martinez / Ghost train / Fastest gun around, The / San Angelo / Old red / Man walks among us.
LP: . . . . **BFX 15147**

IN THE WILD WEST PART 4.
Tracks: / When the work's all done this fall / Old red / I'm gonna be a cowboy / Rich man, poor man / I've got a woman's love / Small man / Hanging tree, The / Night time on the desert / Yours / Adios mariquita Linda.
LP: . . . . **BFX 15183**

IN THE WILD WEST PART 5.
Tracks: / Master's call, The / Cowboy in the continental suit, The / Cry stampede / Oh, Virginia / Meet me tonight in Laredo / Take me back to the prairie / Wind goes, The / Never tie me down / Cottonwood tree, The / Mister shorty / Chant of the wanderer, The / Ghost riders in the sky.
LP: . . . . **BFX 15213**

JUST ME AND MY GUITAR.
Tracks: / Little rosewood casket, The / Letter edged in black / Twenty one years (Previously unissued.) / Convict and the rose, The / Dream of the miner's child / Little box of pine in the 7:29, The (Previously unissued.) / Wreck of the number nine, The (Previously unissued.) / Sad lover, The (Previously unissued.) / Shirt my mother made for me, The (Previously unissued.) / My mother was a lady (Previously unissued.) / When it's lamplighting time in the valley (Previously unissued.) / Wreck of the 1256, The (Previously unissued.) / Just before the battle mother (Previously unissued.) / Long, long ago (Previously unissued.) / Beautiful dreamer (Previously unissued.).
LP: . . . . **BFX 15119**

LEGEND.
Tracks: / Jumper cable man / Lady, I love you / It's not too hard / Good hearted woman / Air that I breathe, The / My all time high / Honeycombe / Simple little love song / I'm here to get my baby out of jail / Teardrops in my heart.
LP: . . . . **CBS 85308**

LIFETIME OF SONG A (1951-1982).
Tracks: / Tomorrow you'll be gone / I'll go on alone / That's alright / Knee deep in the blues / Singing the blues / White sports coat / Story of my life / Don't worry / Ruby Ann / Devil woman / El Paso / Big iron / Hanging tree, The / Ribbon of darkness / El Paso city / I walk alone / My woman, my woman, my wife / Among my souvenirs / Return to me / Some memories just won't die.
MC: **40 22165**
2LP: . . . . **CBS 22165**

LONG LONG AGO.
Tracks: / Long long ago / It finally happened / Reach for me / People's valley / When the works all done this fall / I'm gonna be a cowboy / Last night about this time / Address unknown / Lonely old bunkerhouse / Where could I go.
LP: . . . . **CBS 88649**
MC: **40 88649**

MARTY ROBBINS.
MCSET: . . . . **DTO 10267**
MCSET: . . . . **DTO 10046**
MCSET: . . . . **DTO 10093**

MARTY ROBBINS (I love country).
Tracks: / Some memories just won't die / My woman, my woman, my wife / Good hearted woman / Air that I breathe, The / My elusive dreams / Oh mein papa / She's made of faith / I'm just here to get my baby out of jail / El Paso City / Sometimes when we touch / Return to me / Among my souvenirs / 18 yellow roses / Don't let me touch you / Honky tonk man / Performer, The.
LP: . . . . **CBS 54940**
MC: **40 54940**

MARTY ROBBINS (2).
LP: . . . . **SHM 662**
LP: . . . . **SPR 8506**
MC: . . . . **SPC 8506**

MARTY ROBBINS COLLECTION.
Tracks: / El Paso / Streets of Laredo / Fastest gun around, The / San Angelo / Cool water / Red river valley.
2LP: . . . . **PDA 018**
MCSET: . . . . **PDC 018**

MARTY ROBBINS COLLECTION (LOTUS).
LP: . . . . **WH 5009**

MARTY ROBBINS FILES, VOL 1: 1951-1953.
Tracks: / Tomorrow you'll be gone / I wish somebody loved me / Love me or leave me alone / Crying cause I love you / I'll go on alone / Pretty words / You're breaking my heart (while you're holding my hand) / I can get along (without you very well) (Previously unissued.) / I couldn't keep you from crying / Just in time (Previously unissued.) / Crazy little heart (Previously unissued.) / After you leave me / Lorelei / Castle in the sky, A / Your heart's turn to break / Why keep wishing (you don't care) (Previously unissued.) / Halfway chance with you, A.
LP: . . . . **BFX 15095**

MARTY ROBBINS FILES, VOL 2: 1953-1954.
Tracks: / Sing me something sentimental / At the end of a long, lonely day / Blessed Jesus, should I fall don't let me lay / Kneel and let the Lord take your load / Don't make me ashamed / It's a long, long ride / It looks like I'm just in your way (Previously unissued.) / I'm happy 'cause you're hurtin' (Previously unissued.) / My isle of golden dreams / Have Thine own way / God understands / Aloha-oe / What made you change your mind? (Previously unissued.) / Way of a hopeless love (Previously unissued.) / Juarez (previously unissued.) / I'm too big to cry.
LP: . . . . **BFX 15096**

MARTY ROBBINS FILES, VOL 3: 1954-1956.
Tracks: / Call me up / It's a pity what money can do / Time goes by / This broken heart of mine / It looks like I'm just in your way / I'll love you 'til the day I die / Don't let me hang around (if you don't care) / Pray for me, mother of mine / Daddy loves you / I'll know you're gone / How long will it be? / Where d'ya go? / Most of the time (Previously unissued.) / Same two lips (Previously unissued.) / Your heart of blue is showing through (Previously unissued.).
LP: . . . . **BFX 15118**

MARTY ROBBINS FILES, VOL 4: 1957-1958.
Tracks: / It's too late now (to worry anymore) / I never let you cross my mind / I'll step aside / Bouquet of roses / I'm so lonesome I could cry / Lovesick blues / Moanin' the blues / Rose of ol' Pawnee / I hang my head and cry / Have I told you lately that I love you? / All the world is lonely now / You only want me when you're lonely / Beautiful Ohio (Previously unissued.) / Faded petal from a beautiful bouquet (Previously unissued.) / Then I turned and slowly walked away / Jodie.
LP: . . . . **BFX 15138**

MARTY ROBBINS FILES, VOL 5: 1958/1959/1962.
Tracks: / House with everything but love / Nothing but sweet lies / Baby I need you (like you need me) / Kaw-liga / Paper face / Many tears ago (Previously unissued.) / Address unknown / Waltz of the wind / Hands you're holding now, The / Shackles and chains / Oh, how I miss you (since you went away) / Wedding bells / Sweet Cora (Previously unissued.) / Ain't life a crying shame? (Previously unissued.) / Silence and

tears (Previously unissued.) / Roving gambler (Previously unissued.).
LP: . . . . BFX 15139

MARTY ROBBINS SONG BOOK.
MC: . . . . AM 112

MARTY ROBBINS VOL.2 (double cassette).
MCSET: . . . . DTO 10286

PERFORMER, THE.
Tracks: / Please don't play a love song / Confused and lonely / Look what you've done / You're not ready for me yet / Another pack of cigarettes, another glass ... / My elusive dreams / Jenny / Oh, Regina / Touch me with magic / Performer.
LP: . . . . CBS 83488
MC: 40 83488

PIECES OF YOUR HEART.
Tracks: / Ribbons of darkness / Pieces of your heart / I'm not ready yet / I feel another heart break coming on / Too far gone / Not so long ago / Ain't I right / My own native land / Girl from Spanish town / Kingston girl / Girl from Spanish town (2) / Never look back.
LP: . . . . BFX 15212

ROCKIN ROLLIN' ROBBINS VOL.1.
Tracks: / Footprints in the snow ((Previously unissued)) / It's driving me crazy ((Previously unissued)) / Baby I need you (like you need me)(rock'n'roll version) ((Previously unissued)) / Mean mama blues / That's alright / Mabellene / Pretty mama / I can't quit (I've gone too far) / Long tall Sally / Singing the blues / Knee deep in the blues / Respectfully Miss Brooks / Mister teardrop / Tennessee Toddy / Pain & misery ((Previously unissued)) / You don't owe me a thing / Long thing gone lonesome blues.
LP: . . . . BFX 15045

ROCKIN' ROLLIN' ROBBINS VOL.3.
Tracks: / Ruby Ann (chart version) / Sometimes I'm tempted / No signs of loneliness here / While you're dancing / Teenager's Dad / Ruby Ann / Cap and gown (fast) / Last night about this time / I hope you learn a lot / Love can't wait / Cigarettes and coffee / Little rich girl / Hello baby (goodbye baby) / Baby's gone / Cap and gown (slow) / A whole lot easier / She was young and whe was pretty / Cap and gown (New york recording) / Sweet cora / Ain't live a cryin' shame / Silence and tears / You've been so busy baby.
LP: . . . . BFX 15184

ROCKIN ROLLIN' ROBBINS VOL 2 (Ray Conniff recordings).
Tracks: / Jeannie and Johnnie (Previously unissued.) / Just married / Stairway of love / Please don't blame me / Grown up tears / Teenage dream / Foolish decision / Once a week date / Story of my life / Sport coat and a pink carnation, A / Ain't I the lucky one / Hanging tree, The / Sittin' in a tree house / She was only seventeen (and he was one year more) / Last time I saw my heart, The / Blues country style, The.
LP: . . . . BFX 15105

SOME MEMORIES JUST WON'T DIE.
Tracks: / Some memories just won't die / Change of heart / What if I said I love you / I'm saving all the good times for you / Devil in a cowboy hat / Angelina / I miss you the most / How to make love to a woman / Baby that's love / Honky tonk man.
MC: . . . . SPC 8577
LP: . . . . CBS 25380

SONG OF THE ISLANDS.
Tracks: / Song of the Islands / Don't sing Aloha when I go / Beyond the reef / Crying steel guitar waltz / My Isle of Golden Dreams / Now is the hour / Sweet Leilani / Down where the trade wind blows / Constancy (Ua like no a like) / Island echoes / Moonland / Aloha-oe.
LP: . . . . BFX 15130

TWENTIETH CENTURY DRIFTER.
Tracks: / Twentieth century drifter / This much a man / Love me / Don't you think / Crawling on my knees / Walking piece of Heaven / Man and a train,A / Two gun daddy / It takes faith / Life.
LP: . . . . IMCA 27060

WITH LOVE MARTY ROBBINS.
Tracks: / She's made of faith / I can't wait until tomorrow / Slipping from me / One man's trash / All I want to do / Sometimes when we touch / I'll go to pieces / Wonderful world of you / Misery in my soul / Oh my papa.
LP: . . . . CBS 84427
MC: 40 84427

Robbins, Rockie

WE BELONG TOGETHER.
LP: . . . . MCF 3259

Robe (Soundtrack)

ROBE, THE (Film Soundtrack) (Various artists).
Tracks: / Farewell to Diana: *Various artists* / Palm Sunday: *Various artists* / Carriage of the cross, The: *Various artists* / Marcellus returns to Capri: *Various artists* / Village of Cana: *Various artists* / Redemption of Marcellus, The: *Various artists* / Miriam: *Various artists* / Catacombs, The: *Various artists* / Rescue of Demetrius, The: *Various artists* / Better kingdom, The: *Various artists*.
LP: . . . . MODEM 1011
MC: . . . . MODEMC 1011
LP: . . . . MCA 1529
MC: . . . . MCAC 1529

Robert & Elizabeth

ROBERT AND ELIZABETH (Chichester Festival Cast) (Various artists).
Tracks: / Here on the corner of Wimpole Street: *Various artists* / Family Moulton-Barrett, The: *Various artists*/ World outside, The: *Various artists* / Moon in my pocket, The: *Various artists* / I said love: *Various artists*/ You only to love me: *Various artists* / Real thing, The: *Various artists* / In a simple way: *Various artists*/ I know now: *Various artists* / Escape me never: *Various artists* / Sololoquy: *Various artists* / Pass the eau-de-cologne: *Various artists* / I'm the master here: *Various artists* / Hate me, please: *Various artists*/ Girls that boys dream about, The: *Various artists* / Long ago I loved you: *Various artists* / What the world calls love: *Various artists* / Woman and man: *Various artists* / Frustration: *Various artists*.
LP: . . . . CAST 8
MC: . . . . CASTC 8

ROBERT & ELIZABETH (Original London cast) (Various artists).
Tracks: / Robert and Elizabeth (overture): *Various artists* / Wimpole Street song: *Various artists* / Family Moulton Barrett, The: *Various artists* / Moon in my pocket: *Various artists* / World outside: *Various artists*/ I said love: *Various artists* / Real thing: *Various artists* / You only to love: *Various artists* / In a simple way: *Various artists* / I know now: *Various artists* / Sololoquy: *Various artists* / Pass the eau de Cologne: *Various artists* / I'm the master here: *Various artists* / Escape me never: *Various artists*/ Hate me please: *Various artists* / Girls that boys dream about, The: *Various artists* / Woman and man: *Various artists* / Fustration: *Various artists*.
LP: . . . . ONCR 532
LP: . . . . AEI 1111

Robert & Johnny

WE BELONG TOGETHER.
LP: . . . . CH 172

Robert, Rappa

NUH TROUBLE WE (See under Lee, Tippa) (Robert, Rappa & Tippa Lee).

Robert Service Story

ROBERT SERVICE STORY, THE (See Service, Robert) (Cairney, John).

Robert The Bruce

ROBERT THE BRUCE (history for ages 8+) (Unknown narrator(s)).
MC: . . . . PLBH 149

Roberta

ROBERTA (Original Soundtrack) (Various artists).
LP: . . . . SH 2061

ROBERTA (Studio cast) (Various artists).
LP: . . . . COS 2530

Roberts, Al Jr.

FROGABILLY.
LP: . . . . FROG 002

ROCKABILLY GUITAR MAN.
LP: . . . . FROG 001

Roberts, Alan

CALEDONIA (Roberts, Alan & Dougie Maclean).
Tracks: / Plooboy laddie / Johnny Teasie weasle / Over my mountains / Rowan tree / Mistress MacKinley's breakfast surreals / Caledonia / Mormond braes / To tomorrow / Jennifer's tunes / Sleepy toon.
LP: . . . . PLR 012

Roberts, Andy

FROM TIME TO TIME.
LP: . . . . BBX 503

LOOSE CONNECTIONS (Film soundtrack).
LP: . . . . V 2306

Roberts, Bob

BREEZE FOR A BARGEMAN.
LP: . . . . SS 054

SONGS FROM THE SAILING BARGES.
Tracks: / Candlelight fisherman, The / Grey hawk, The / Stormy weather / Boys / Waltz with me / Haul away, Joe / Oily rig, The / Little ball of yarn, The / Single sailor, The / Young Collins / Fish and chip ship, The / While gamekeepers lie sleeping / Windy old weather / London waterman, The / Bob Roberts' waltz / Whisky Johnny / Foggy dew, The / Bell bottom trousers / Black shawl, The / Little boy Billy / Collier brig, The / Leave her Johnny.
LP: 12TS 361

STORMY WEATHER, BOYS.
Tracks: / When I was single / Foggy dew, The / Smuggler boy / Bold Princess Royal, The / Worst old ship / Bargemen's alphabet / Little boy Billy / Maggie May / Bold Henry Martin / High Barbaree / Will watch.
MC: 60-047

Roberts, Bruce

BRUCE ROBERTS.
Tracks: / I don't break easily / Our night / I don't wanna go / I'd rather be alone / Starmaker / This boy / Me and my love / Car song, The / Steal away again / I'm comin' home again.
LP: . . . . K 52061

WEST COAST JAZZ.
Tracks: / Isn't it romantic / Trickeydiddler / Oh play that thing / Not really the blues / Martians go home / My heart stood still / Michele's meditation / That's what I'm talking about.
LP: . . . . K 50247

Roberts, Dave

MIRROR IMAGES.
Tracks: / One nightmare city / Ferry across the Styx / Requiem for the common man / Swarm / Music in them their hills / Chasing a dream / Hart of the wood / Merry go round / M 25 / Rain of sadness / Narcissus revealed / Quiet morning, A / User hostile / Orchid / Last frontier, The / Voyage home, The.
LP: . . . . FF 001

Roberts, David Thomas

EARLY FOLK RAGS.
LP: . . . . SOS 1021

RAGS.
LP: . . . . SOS 1132

THROUGH THE BOTTOM LANDS.
LP: . . . . SOS 1072

Roberts, Fiddlin' Doc

KENTUCKY COUNTRY.
LP: . . . . ROUNDER 1037

Roberts, Hank

BIRDS OF PREY.
Tracks: / Comin' home / Seven generations / Scream / Hear me / Pretty boy Tom / Angels and mud / Touch.
LP: 8344371
MC: 8344374

MINATURE (See Under Baron, Joey) (Baron,Joey/Tim Berne/Hank Roberts).

Roberts, Howard

GOOD PICKINS.
Tracks: / Will you still be mine / When the sun comes out / All the things you are / Lover man / God bless the child / Easy living / Between the devil and the deep blue sea / More I see you, The.
LP: 2304 459

TURNING TO SPRING (Roberts, Howard Quartet).
LP: . . . . DS 812

Roberts, Judy

OTHER WORLD, THE.
LP: . . . . IC 1088

Roberts, Kane

KANE ROBERTS.
Tracks: / Rock doll / Women on the edge of love / Triple X / Gorilla / Outlaw / If this is heaven / Out for blood / Full pull / Too much (for anyone to touch) / Tears of fire / Strong arm needs a stronger heart, A.
LP: . . . . IMCA 5787
MC: . . . . IMCAC 5787

SAINTS AND SINNERS.
LP: . . . . DGC 24320
MC: . . . . DGCC 24320

Roberts, Kenny

INDIAN LOVE CALL.
LP: . . . . SLP 336
MC: . . . . GT 5336

Roberts, Larry

I WANT TO GO BACK (Roberts, Larry & The Trinity).
Tracks: / I want to go back / All he wants / Something special / Are you willing / I'll fly away / Refresh spirit / Remember me / Take control / Are you ready / Serving God / I love Jesus / Give God the praise.
LP: GCR2 4901
MC: GCR2 4901MC

Roberts, Lee

SOULIN' (Roberts, Lee & The Sweaters).
LP: . . . . BS 4703

Roberts, Luckey

HARLEM PIANO (See Smith, Willie) (Roberts, Luckey & Willie 'The Lion' Smith).

Roberts, Malcolm

THIS IS MALCOLM ROBERTS.
Tracks: / Love is all / We can make it girl / Lovingly / I love her / Without a song / After the rain / My way / May I have the next dream with you / Sophia / How does a man become a puppet / This is my beloved / Because you're mine / Cantiga por Luciana / More.
LP: . . . . THIS 28

Roberts, Marcus

ALONE WITH THREE GIANTS.
Tracks: / Jungle blues / Mood indigo / Solitude / I got it bad and that ain't good / Trinkle tinkle / Misterioso / Pannonica / New Orleans blues / Prelude to a kiss / Shout 'em Aunt Tillie / Black 'n' tan fantasy / Monk's mood / In walked Bud / Crepuscule with Nellie / Crave, The.
LP: . . . . PL 83109
MC: . . . . PK 83109

BEHIND THE SHED.
Tracks: / Governor, The / Nebuchadnezzar / Spiritual awakening / Behind the shed / Mysterious interlude / E. Dankworth.
LP: . . . . PL 83078
MC: . . . . PK 83078

TRUTH IS SPOKEN HERE, THE.
Tracks: / Arrival, The / Blue monk / Maurella / Single petal of a rose / Country by choice / Truth is spoken here, The / In a mellow tone / Nothin' but the blues.
LP: . . . . PL 83051
MC: . . . . PK 83051

Roberts, Paddy

PADDY ROBERTS TRIES AGAIN.
LP: . . . . LK 4358

STICTLY FOR GROWN-UPS.
LP: . . . . LF 1322

WORLD OF PADDY ROBERTS.
LP: . . . . SPA 37

Roberts, Paul

CITY WITHOUT WALLS.
LP: . . . . SNTF 949

KETTLE DRUM BLUES.
Tracks: / King of your heart / Slowdown / Working for the good times / Out of the blue / Sexual chemistry / Hand of fate, The / Kettle drum blues / Ready for me now / Words are not enough / Refugee.
LP: . . . . SNTF 991
MC: . . . . ZCSN 991

ON STAGE AT THE PARK.
Tracks: / I want to be happy / I hear music / Murder on the Orient Express (Waltz: Theme music from the film,"Murder on the Orient Express".) / Let's go live in the country / Pied piper / I know him so well (From the Musical "Chess".) / That ole devil called love / Serenade to a Japanese tea bag / Things we did last summer, The / Dad's army (theme) / Upstairs downstairs / Alley cat song / Tales of the unexpected (From the T.V. Series of the same name.) / Jolly Coppersmith, The / Run rabbit run (Full title: Run rabbit run/ Things ain't wot they used to be/ I want to).
LP: . . . . SUJ 223

ON YOUR TOES.
Tracks: / I want to be happy / Happy talk / Let's face the music and dance / I'm putting all my eggs in one basket / Spoonful of sugar, A / Supercalifragilisticexpialidocious / On your toes / Honey bun / Small hotel / Out of my dreams / This nearly was mine / Tammy / Affair to remember, An / Rain in Spain, The / Younger than Springtime / I have dreamed / I can't get started / Life upon the wicked stage / Blue room / Hey look me over / Wedding of the painted doll, The.
LP: . . . . SUS 522

Roberts, Steve

DO YOU KNOW WHO I AM.
LP: . . . . EXPLP 2002

Robertson, Alasdair

FRIENDS AND COMPANIONS.
Tracks: / Time and trouble / Session, The / Shooting star at the dawn / Blantyre disaster / Down by the shoreline / Cumbrian girl / Ballad of a young anarchist / Rising, The / Chaz and Eileen's wedding / Coach house girls, The / Star, The / Region of dreams.
LP: . . . . FE 066

MC: . . . . FE 066 C

Robertson, Arthur

REHEARSES HIS OWN FIDDLE COMPOSITIONS.
MC: . . . . CTRAX 044

Robertson, B.A.

B.A. ROBERTSON.
Tracks: / dot dot dot / Ready or not / Moscow rules / Nothing like a great romance / Four minutes to midnight / Hold me / Legislate for love / Son of a gunn / One plus one / Asleep with a stranger / Just like a rash.
LP: . . . . K 52383

BULLY FOR YOU.
Tracks: / Saint Saens / Bully for you / Maggie / Growing old's unhealthy / Please Miss / In the bar at the Munich Hilton / Dart Vader / Hey presto / Flight 19 / Only one / Turn the volume down / Home sweet home.
LP: . . . . K 52275

INITIAL SUCCESS.
Tracks: / Gonzo for my girlfriend / Man or a mouse / Goosebumps / Fallin' in luv / Kool in the kaftan / Bang bang / Eat your heart out Sandy Nelson / To be or not to be / She's a beezer / England's green and pleasant land / Walking rover / Knocked it off / Here I sit.
LP: . . . . K 52216

TIME (See under Frida) (Robertson, B.A./Frida).

Robertson, Eric

PIANO MAGIC.
LP: . . . . NE 1228
MC: . . . . CE 2228

Robertson, George R

THE WILLOUGHBY OBSESSION (See under Bailey, Don - No Admittance, no exit) (Various artists).

Robertson, Harry

HAWK THE SLAYER (Film soundtrack) (See under Hawk The Slayer).

WHALE CHASING MEN.
LP: . . . . LRF 049

Robertson, Herb

SHADES OF BUD POWELL (Robertson, Herb Brass Ensemble).
Tracks: / Un poco loco / I'll keep loving you / Hallucinations / Glass enclosure / Fruit, The / Shades of Bud.
LP: 834420-1

Robertson, Jeannie

JEANNIE ROBERTSON.
Tracks: / Bonnie wee lassie who never said no, The / What a voice / My plaidie's awa' / Gypsy laddie, The / When I was no' but sweet sixteen / MacCrimmon's lament / Roy's wife of Aldivalloch / Lord Lovat.
LP: 12T 96

MONUMENTAL FIGURE OF WORLD FOLKSONG, A (1908-1975).
Tracks: / Overgate, The / Battle of Harlaw, The / Busk bonnie lassie / Laird o' the windy wa', The / Jolly beggar, The / I saw my own bonnie lass / Ten o'clock is ringing / For I will lay you doon / Twa' recruiting sergeants / Busk and go (Cuttie's wedding) / Dottered auld Carle, A / Far over the forth / Eenst upon a time / Auld man cam courtin me, An / Gallowa' hills / My son David / Bonnie lass come o'er the burn / Jeannie my dear / Braes o' Killecrankle, The.
LP: . . . . LIFL 7001
MC: . . . . LIFC 7001

WHAT A VOICE.
Tracks: / Loch O'Shallin / Never wed a' auld man / Go away from my window / Old witch woman, The (Spoken word) / Blin' drunk, A / Bonnie lassie-o / Maggie / Rub-a-dub-dub / Flashy dashy petticoats / Eenst upon a time / Crooked house / Eenty peenty / My daddy woudna / Cuckoo's nest, The / Bonnie wee highland man / Susan Pyatt / Overgate, The / Braes o'Balquhidder, The / Four Maries, The / Lord Lovatt / Moon shined on my bed last night, the.
MC: 60-067

Robertson, Ken

SONGS OF AUSTRALIA.
LP: . . . . BF 15026

Robertson, Kim

CELTIC CHRISTMAS.
MC: . . . . C 368

MOONRISE.
MC: . . . . C 362

WATER SPIRIT.
MC: . . . . C 361

WIND SHADOWS - CELTIC HARP.
MC: . . . . C 360

WIND SHADOWS - SOLO HARP, VOL. II.
MC: . . . . C 366

Robertson, Liz

SOMEBODY'S GIRL.
LP: . . . . VIR 83004
MC: . . . . ZCVIR 83004

Robertson, Nick

BULLETPROOF BOY.
LP: . . . . CIRCA 13
MC: . . . . CIRC 13

Robertson, Paul

OLD FRIENDS, NEW FRIENDS.
LP: . . . . PA 8013

SONG IS YOU, THE.
LP: . . . . PA 8002

Robertson, Robbie

ROBBIE ROBERTSON.
Tracks: / Fallen angel / Showdown at big sky / Broken arrow / Sweet fire of love / American roulette / Somewhere down the crazy river / Hell's half acre / Sonny got caught in the moonlight / Testimony.
LP: . . . . WX 133
MC: . . . . WX 133C
MC: . . . . GEFC 24160
LP: . . . . GEF 24160

STORYVILLE.
LP: . . . . GEF 24303
MC: . . . . GEFC 24303

Robertson, Stanley

NIPPIT FIT, CLIPPIT FIT Traditional songs, stories and ballads.
Tracks: / Wee bannock, The / Twa humpies, The / Laird o' drum, The / Gipsy children, The / Battle o' Harlaw / Nippit fit clippit fit / I choked on a tattie / Burnin' o' Auchindoon / Silly Jack and the factor / Twelve o' clock is ringing / Old woman and the vinegar bottle, The.
MC: . . . . ACLMC 3

Robeson, Paul

BEST OF PAUL ROBESON.
Tracks: / Summertime / It ain't necessarily so / Woman is a sometime thing / Ongo lullaby / Love song / Canoe song / Ol' man river / It still suits me / Sleepy river / Deep river / Just a wearyin' for you / Swing low, sweet chariot / Ma curly headed baby / Trees / Steal away / Mighty like a rose / Joshua fit de battle ob Jericho / Mah Lindy Lou / Short'nin' bread / Water boy.
LP: . . . . NTS 181
MC: . . . . TCNTS 181

ESSENTIAL PAUL ROBESON, THE.
LP: . . . . VMLP 5303
MC: . . . . VMTC 6303

ESSENTIAL, THE.
Tracks: / Every time I feel the Spirit / Balm in Gilead / Volga boat song / Monologue from Shakespeare's Othello / O thou silent night / Chinese children's song / My curly headed baby / Ol' man river / Going home / Monologue from Boris Godunov / Orphan, The / Christ lag in Todesbanden / Didn't my Lord deliver Daniel / Lullaby / O no, John / Joe Hill / Jacob's ladder / Ballad for Americans / Deep river / John Brown's body / Jerusalem / Londonderry Air / Water boy / Shenandoah / Sometimes I feel like a motherless child / Git on board, li'l chilun / House I live in, The / Loch Lomond / Drink to me only with thine eyes / Joshua fit de battle of Jerico / All through the night.
2LP: . . . . VSD 57

GLORIOUS VOICE OF PAUL ROBESON, THE.
Tracks: / Lonesome road / River, stay 'way from my door / Mighty lak' a rose / Ma curly headed baby / Ol' man river / Round the bend of the road / Lazybones / Water boy / Song of freedom / Sleepy river / Carry me back to green pastures / Canoe song / I still suits me / Lonely road / Passing by / My way / Summertime / It ain't necessarily so / All through the night / Just a-wearying for you / Perfect day, A / Deep river.
LP: . . . . SH 522
MC: . . . . TCSH 522

GOLDEN AGE OF PAUL ROBESON, THE.
Tracks: / At dawning / Rockin' chair / Mammy's little kinky headed boy / Banjo song / Eriskay love lilt / River stay 'way from my door / Just a-wearing' for you / Cobbler's song, The / Drink to me only with thine eyes / Lazybones / She is far from the land / Gloomy Sunday / Canoe song / Honey (dat's all).
LP: . . . . GX 2514
MC: . . . . TCGX 2514
LP: . . . . MFP 5829
MC: . . . . TCMFP 5829

GREEN PASTURES.
Tracks: / St. Louis blues / Rockin' chair / Mary had a baby, yes Lord / Love song / All God's chillun got wings / Banjo song / Bear the burden / When it's sleepy time down South / Killing song / High water / Lazybones / Carry me back to green pastures / Congo lullaby / Shortnin' bread / Snowball / Fat li'l feller with his mammy's eyes / Canoe song / River stay 'way from my door.
LP: . . . . AJA 5047
MC: . . . . ZC AJA 5047

LONESOME ROAD, A.
Tracks: / Ol' man river / My curly headed baby / Water boy / I'm goin' to tell God all o' my troubles / Oh didn't it rain, little pal / There's no hiding place / Poor old Joe / Scandalize my name / Ezekiel saw de wheel / Sinner, please don't let this harvest pass / Jus' keepin' on / Mah Lindy Lou / Steal away / Mighty lak' a rose / Deep river / Hear the lambs a-cryin' / Git on board, li'l chilun / Old folks at home (Swanee river) / Witness / Oh rock me Julie / Li'l gal / I got a home in that rock / Lonesome road.
LP: . . . . AJA 5027
MC: . . . . ZC AJA 5027

MIGHTY VOICE OF PAUL ROBESON, THE.
MC: 1A 220 1583264

PAUL ROBESON COLLECTION 20 golden greats.
Tracks: / Volga boat song / Ol' man river / Oh no, John / Jacob's ladder / Joe Hill / My curly headed baby / Every time I feel the Spirit / Lullaby / Swing low, sweet chariot / Killing song / Summertime / Shortnin' bread / It ain't necessarily so / Sleepy river / Canoe song / Songs my mother taught me / Mah Lindy Lou / Joshua fit de battle of Jerico / Congo lullaby / Mood indigo.
LP: . . . . DVLP 2082
MC: . . . . DVMC 2082

...SINGS 'OL' MAN RIVER' AND OTHER FAVOURITES.
Tracks: / Ol' man river / Roll away clouds / Lonesome road / Got the South in my soul / Hush-a-lullaby / Round the bend of the road / Carry me back to green pastures / Blue prelude / Wagon wheels / So shy / St. Louis blues / Little man you've had a busy day / I ain't lazy, I'm just dreaming / Shenandoah / All through the night / Solitude / Song of the volga boatmen / Dear old Southland / Nothin' / Perfect day.
LP: . . . . EG 2604771
MC: . . . . EG 2604774

SONGS OF FREE MEN.
Tracks: / From border to border / Oh, how proud our quiet Don / Purest kind of guy, The / Joe Hill / Peat bog soldiers, The / Four insurgent generals, The / Native land / Go down Moses / Balm in Gilead / By and by / Sometimes I feel like a motherless child / John Henry / Water boy / Nobody knows de trouble I've seen / Joshua fit de battle of Jerico.
LP: . . . . MP 39512
MC: . . . . MPT 39512

SONGS OF MY PEOPLE.
Tracks: / Git on board, li'l chilun / Were you there / Dere's no hidin' place / Deep river / Witness / Water boy / On ma journey / Swing low, sweet chariot / Ezekiel saw de wheel / Nobosy knows de trouble I've seen / I want to be ready / Sometimes I feel like a motherless child / Joshua fit de battle ob Jericho / Hear de lam's a cryin' / Bye and bye / Weepin' Mary / Steal away / I'm goin' to tell God all my troubles / Li'l gal / I've got a home in that rock.
LP: . . . . LSA 3097

SONGS OF THE MISSISSIPPI (20 great hits).
Tracks: / Ol' man river / Were you there when they crucified my Lord / Shortnin' bread / Swing low, sweet chariot / Love song / Fat li'l feller with his mammy's eyes / Round the bend of the road / Don't you cry my honey / Tke me away from the river / Mighty lak' a rose / Rockin' chair / Old kentucky home / Piccaninny slumber song / My Lindy Lou / My curly headed baby / Killing song / Carry me back to green pastures / Lonesome road / Git on board, li'l chilun / Just keepin' on.
LP: . . . . PLAT 19
MC: . . . . PLAC 19

Robic, A.

OLD TIME MUSIC DANCE PARTY (Robic, A. & The Exertions).
LP: . . . . FF 415

Robic, Ivo

MORGEN.
LP: . . . . BFX 15347

Robichaux, Joe

1933 (Robichaux, Joe & His New Orleans Boys).
LP: . . . . CJM 37

COMPLETE J.ROBICHAUX, THE.
2LP: . . . . T 1007/8

JOE ROBECHAUX AND HIS NEW ORLEANS BOYS (Robichaux, Joe & His New Orleans Boys).
LP: . . . . FL 9032

Robillard, Duke

DUKE ROBILLARD (Robillard, Duke & The Pleasure Kings).
Tracks: / Let me love you / Baby please come home / My plea / It's my own business / Tore up / If this is love / Oh babe / What that means to me / Just kiss me / One more time.
LP: . . . . FIEND 16

DUKE ROBILLARD AND THE PLEASURE KINGS (Robillard, Duke & The Pleasure Kings).
LP: . . . . ROUNDER 3079
MC: . . . . ROUNDER 3079C

SWING.
Tracks: / Cadillac Slim / Jumpin' blues / Exactly like you / Glide on / ZOT / I'll always be in love with you / Shuffin' with some barbeque / Durn tottin' / You'd better change your ways / Jim jam.
LP: . . . . REU 1019
LP: . . . . ROUNDER 3103
MC: . . . . ROUNDER 3103C
LP: . . . . CD 191

TOO HOT TO HANDLE (Robillard, Duke & The Pleasure Kings).
Tracks: / Someone / Anything it takes / Duke's mood / Too hot to handle / Give me your attention / She made my mind / She's sweet / T-Bone boogie / Rickin' blues / Give me all the love you got.
LP: . . . . FIEND 48
LP: . . . . ROUNDER 3082
MC: . . . . ROUNDER 3082C

YOU GOT ME (Robillard, Duke/Various).
LP: . . . . ROUNDER 3100
MC: . . . . ROUNDER 3100C
LP: . . . . ZS 062

Robin Hood

ROBIN HOOD (Film Soundtrack) (Various artists).
Tracks: / Whistle stop: *Various artists* / Oo-de-lally: *Various artists* / Love: *Various artists* / Phoney King of England, The: *Various artists* / Not in Nottingham: *Various artists.*
LP: . . . . REC 575
MC: . . . . ZCM 575

Robin Hood (bk)

ROBIN HOOD (Woolf, Gabriel & David Brierly (nar)).
MC: . . . . SQRL 13

ROBIN HOOD (Jarvis, Martin (nar)).
MC: . . . . P 90038

ROBIN HOOD (for ages 7-12) (Unknown narrator(s)).
MC: . . . . PLBC 178

ROBIN HOOD (Unknown narrator(s)).
MC: . . . . DIS 008

ROBIN HOOD (Various artists).
Tracks: / Robin Hood: *Various artists* / Childe Roland: *Various artists* / Young Bekie: *Various artists*/ Tomas the Rhymer: *Various artists* / Little Lord Lorn: *Various artists.*
MC: . . . . ANV 662

ROBIN HOOD (Various artists).
MC: . . . . TS 327

ROBIN HOOD (Various artists).
MC: . . . . STC 301B

ROBIN HOOD & OTHER FAVOURITE STORIES FOR CHILDRE (Various artists).
MC: . . . . VCA 604

Robins

BEST OF THE ROBINS.
LP: . . . . GNPS 9034

COMPLETE SAVOY RECORDINGS, THE.
LP: . . . . SJL 1188

Robins, Butch

FIFTH CHILD, THE.
LP: . . . . ROUNDER 0130

FORTY YEARS LATE.
LP: . . . . ROUNDER 0086

FRAGMENTS OF MY IMAGINATION.
LP: . . . . ROUNDER 0104

Robins, Cantor Stephen

CANTOR STEPHEN ROBINS (With London Jewish Male Choir).
MC: . . . . L 005 161C

Robins, Denise

INFATUATION (Latimer, Sheila).
MCSET: . . . . CLT 1005

NEVER LOOK BACK (See Kempton, Victoria) (Kempton, Victoria).

STRANGE RAPTURE (Guthrie, Gwyneth).
MCSET: . . . . CLT 1006

Robinson, Alvin

SHINE ON.
Tracks: / Lazy Mary / Truly / Wake up / They said it couldn't be done / Baby, don't blame me / Im leaving you today / Haul offand die over you / Pain in my heart / Og red / Dedicated to Domino / Something you got / Searchin' / Fever / Down home girl / How can I get over you / Im gonna put some hurt on you / Bottom of my soul / Let the good times roll.
LP: CRB 1181
MC: TCCRB 1181

Robinson, Banjo Ikey

1929-35 - BLUES, SKIFFLE AND JAZZ.
LP: DOC 509

Robinson, Bert

NO MORE COLD NIGHTS.
LP: CLX 46921

Robinson Crusoe (bk)

ROBINSON CRUSOE (Norgate, Clifford).
MC: SQRL 32

ROBINSON CRUSOE (Danie Defoe (aut)) (Andrews, Harry (nar)).
MCSET: 414 766-4
MCSET: ARGO 1073

ROBINSON CRUSOE Daniel Defoe (aut)) (Unknown narrator(s)).
MCSET: DTO 10579

ROBINSON CRUSOE (Duncan, Frank).
MC: P 90010

ROBINSON CRUSOE (Richardson, Ian).
LP: TC 1461
MC: 1461

ROBINSON CRUSOE & OTHER FAVOURITE STORIES FOR CH (Various artists).
MC: VCA 610

ROBINSON CRUSOE/MAN FRIDAY (TV Soundtrack) (Various artists).
LP: PST 501

Robinson, Elzadie

ELZADIE ROBINSON (1926-29).
LP: BD 2081

Robinson, Fenton

BLUES IN PROGRESS.
LP: BM 9005

I HEAR SOME BLUES DOWNSTAIRS.
Tracks: / I hear some blues downstairs / Just a little bit / West side baby / I'm so tired / I wish for you / Tell me what's the reason / Going West / Killing floor / As the years go passing by.
LP: SNTF 712

MELLOW FELLOW.
Tracks: / Somebody loan me a dime / Little turch / Leave you in the arms (of your other man) / Let me come on home / She's a wiggler / Laughin cryin blues / I wanna ooh / I fell in love one time / Sky is crying, The / Getaway / Sideman / Mellow fellow.
LP: CRB 1131

SOMEBODY LOAN ME A DIME.
Tracks: / Somebody loan me a dime / Getaway / Directly from my heart / Going to Chicago / You say you're leaving / Checking on my woman / You don't know what love is / I've changed / Country girl / Gotta wake up / Texas flood.
LP: SNTF 686

Robinson, Jackie

CONSIDER ME.
LP: KPLP 002

Robinson, James

GUILTY.
Tracks: / Can we do it again / Guilty / Pretend / Feel like going on / Seems so long / Lord's prayer, The / Kind of love, A / Just what I've been missing / When you'll be mine / You're the one I've been dreaming of.
LP: BFZ 40823
LP: 460091 1
MC: 460091 4

Robinson, Jim

JIM ROBINSON WITH.....
LP: SMOKEY MARY 197J

Robinson, Joan

BEST OF TEDDY ROBINSON.
Tracks: / Teddy Robinson goes to hospital / Teddy Robinson's night out / Teddy Robinson is put in a book.
MC: TS 306

Robinson, Keith

WORLD NEEDS LOVE, THE (Robinson, Keith & some mates).
LP: WIVLP 1002

Robinson, L.C.

UPS AND DOWNS.
LP: ARHOOLIE 1062

Robinson, Martell

I STILL LOVE YOU.
Tracks: / I still love you / Let it be known / Call on me / Memories of you / Endlessly / Promises / Sincerely / Tired man.
LP: OLP 30
LP: RALP 24

Robinson, Nambo

SANITY.
LP: UNKNOWN

Robinson, Robbie

TIME IS RIGHT, THE.
Tracks: / Time is right / Rise Africa rise / Light up your fire / Bright light / Problems problems / Jamaica Jamaica / I'm in love with you / Love and hate / Love and hate (organ instrumental) / Time is right (organ instrumental).
LP: CPRA 1001

Robinson, Robin

LOVE SMOKEY.
Tracks: / Love is the light / (It's the) same old love / Love 'n life / I can't find / Take me through the night / Everything you touch / Don't wanna be just physical / Come to me soon / You made me feel love / Jasmin / Easy / Just another kiss (Only on CD.) / Unless you do it again (Only on CD.).
LP: ZL 72666
MC: ZK 72666

Robinson, Roscoe

HIGH ON JESUS.
LP: SL 14733

WHY MUST IT END?.
Tracks: / Let me know / Why are you afraid / Fox hunting on a weekend / You don't move me no more / Darling please tell me / I'm burning and yearning / Why must it end / How many times must I knock / We got a good thing going / Standing in the safety zone / Prove it / You and me / You qualify / Trust me / Yesterday is gone tomorrow is too late.
LP: CRB 1154

Robinson, Smokey

ANTHOLOGY - SMOKEY ROBINSON (Robinson, Smokey & The Miracles).
Tracks: / Got a job / Bad girl / Way over there / You can depend on me / Shop around / Who's loving you? / What's so good about goodbye? / I'll try something new / I've been good to you / You've really got a hold on me / Love she can count on, A / Mickey's monkey / I gotta dance to keep from crying / I like it like that / That's what love is made of / Come on do the jerk / Ooo baby baby / Tracks of my tears / My girl has gone / Choosey beggar / Going to a go go / I'm the one you need / Save me / Love I saw in you was just a mirage, The / More love / I second that emotion / If you can want / Yester-love / Special occasion / Baby baby don't cry / Doggone right / Here I go again / Abraham, Martin and John / Darling dear / Point it out / Who's gonna take the blame? / Tears of a clown / I don't blame you at all / Satisfaction / We've come too far to end it now / I can't stand to see you cry / Crazy about the la la la / Do it baby / Don't cha love it / Love machine.
2LP: TMSP 6014
MCSET: CTMSP 6014
2LP: ZL 72134

BEING WITH YOU.
Tracks: / Being with you / Food for thought / If you wanna make love / Who's sad? / Can't fight love / You are forever / As you do / I hear the children singing.
LP: WL 72256
MC: WK 72256
LP: STML 12151

BLAME IT ON LOVE (Greatest hits).
Tracks: / Blame it on love / Being with you / Cruisin' / Just my soul responding.
LP: STML 12193
MC: CSTML 12193

BLAME IT ON LOVE AND ALL THE GREAT HITS.
Tracks: / Blame it on love / Just like you / Don't play another love song / Tell me tomorrow / Being with you / Cruisin' / If you wanna make love (come 'round here) / Just a touch away / Baby come close / Let me see the clock.
MC: WK 72542

ESSAR.
Tracks: / And I don't love you / Train of thought / I can't find / Why are you running from my love / Gone forever / Close encounters of the first kind / Little girl, little girl / Girl I'm standing there / Driving thru life in the fast lane.
LP: ZL 72152
MC: ZK 72152

HOT SMOKEY.
Tracks: / Just my soul responding / Responding / Let me be the clock / Vitamin U / Heavy on the pride (light of love) / What's in your life for me? / I love the nearness of you.
LP: TMS 3510
MC: TMC 3510

LOVE SONGS: MARVIN GAYE & SMOKEY ROBINSON (See under Gaye, Marvin) (Robinson, Smokey & Marvin Gaye).

ONE HEARTBEAT.
Tracks: / It's time to stop shoppin' around / Why do happy memories hurt so bad / You don't know what it's like / What's too much / Love bought us here tonight / Love don't give no reason / Keep me / One heartbeat / Just to see her.
LP: ZL 72580
MC: ZK 72580

POPS, WE LOVE YOU (See under Ross, Diana) (Ross, Diana/Stevie Wonder/ Marvin Gaye/Smokey Robinson).

PURE SMOKEY.
Tracks: / It's her turn to live / Love between me and my kids / Asleep on my love / I am, I am / Just passing through / Virgin man / She's only a baby herself / Fulfil your need / Tattoo.
LP: STMS 5043
MC: CSTMS 5043

QUIET STORM, A.
Tracks: / Quiet storm / Agony and the ecstasy / Baby that's backatcha / Wedding song, The / Happy love letters / Coincidentally.
LP: STMS 5044
MC: CSTMS 5044

SMOKE SIGNALS.
Tracks: / Some people (will do anything for love) / Sleepless nights / Because of you (it's the best it's ever been) / Be kind to the growing mind / Te quiero como si no hubiera un manana / Hold on to your love / Photograph in my mind / No time to stop believing / Wishful thinking / Hanging on by a thread.
LP: ZL 72394
MC: ZK 72394

SMOKEY.
Tracks: / Holly / Never my love / Never can say goodbye / Silent partner in a three-way love affair / Just my soul responding / Sweet harmony / Will you love me tomorrow / Wanna know my mind? / Family song / Baby come close.
LP: STMS 5011
MC: CSTMS 5011

SMOKEY ROBINSON STORY THE.
LP: NE 1175
MC: CE 2175

TEARS OF A CLOWN (Robinson, Smokey & The Miracles).
Tracks: / My girl / Composer, The / It will be alright / You must be love / We had a love so strong / Something / Something you got / More, more, more of your love / I can't stand to see you cry / I'm the one you need / Hunter gets captured by the game / You ain't livin' until you're lovin'.
MC: TMC 3501
LP: WL 72071
LP: STMS 5010

TEARS OF A CLOWN (MFP) (Robinson, Smokey & The Miracles).
LP: MFP 50422

TOUCH THE SKY.
Tracks: / Touch the sky / Gimme what you want / Even tho' / Gone again / All my life's a lie / Sad time / Dynamite / I've made love to you a thousand times.
LP: STML 12175
MC: CSTML 12175

WARM THOUGHTS.
Tracks: / Let me be the clock / Heavy on the pride (light of love) / Into each life some rain must fall / Wine, women and song / Melody man / What's in your life for me / I want to be your love / Travellin' through.
LP: STML 12134

WHERE THERE'S SMOKE.
Tracks: / Smoke / It's a good night / I love the nearness of you / Hurt in you, The / Ever had a dream? / Fire get ready / Share it / Cruisin'.
LP: STML 12115
MC: CSTML 12115

YES IT'S YOU, LADY.
Tracks: / Tell me tomorrow / Yes it's you, lady / Old-fashioned love / Are you still there? / Only game in town, The / International baby / Merry-go-ride / I'll try something new / Destiny.
LP: STML 12165
MC: CSTML 12165

Robinson, Spike

AT CHESTERS VOLS 1 & 2 (See under Thompson Eddie).

GERSHWIN COLLECTION.
Tracks: / Oh lady be good / I've got a crush on you / Foggy day, A / Summertime / Soon / Who cares / Someone to watch over me / Somebody loves me / How long has this been going on / They can't take that away from me / I got rhythm.
LP: HEP 2042

IN TOWN (See under Elaine Delmar).

MUSIC OF HARRY WARREN (Robinson, Spike Quartet).
Tracks: / This is always / This heart of mine / More I see you, The / Chattanooga choo choo / Cheerful little earful / I only have eyes for you / Lulu's back in town / I wish I knew.
LP: DS 870

SPIKE ROBINSON/TOMMY POLLARD'S DOWNBEAT FIVE/ VICTOR FELDMAN (Robinson, Spike/ Tommy Pollard's Downbeat Five/Victor Feldman).
LP: ESQ 318

Robinson, Sugar Chile

GO BOY GO.
LP: OL 2828

JUNIOR JUMP.
Tracks: / Go boy go / Say little girl / Bases were loaded / Sticks and stones / Whop whop / Yancey special / I'll eat my spinach / Caldonia / Numbers boogie / Frustration boogie / Lazy boys boogie / Bounding ball boogie / After school blues / Christmas boogie.
LP: CRB 1126

Robinson, Tom

BACK IN THE OLD COUNTRY.
Tracks: / Listen to the radio: Atmospherics / Too good to be true / Up against the wall / Northern rain / I shall be released / Mary Lynne / 2.4.6.8 motorway / Drive all night / Don't take no for an answer / Where can we go tonight / Back in the old country / Alright all night / War baby / Power in the darkness / Crossing over the road / Rikki don't lose that number / Bitterly disapointed / Looking for a bonfire / Hard cases / Still loving you / Not ready / Bully for you / Long hot summer.
2LP: VSOPLP 138
MC: VSOPMC 138

CABARET '79.
LP: 6.25304
LP: ROBBO 2

COLLECTION-'77-'87 (Robinson, Tom Band).
Tracks: / 2-4-6-8 motorway / Grey Cortina / Don't take no for an answer / Martin / Too good to be true / Up against the wall / Bully for you / War baby / Atmospherics / Never gonna fall in love (again) / Back in the old country / Old friend / Glad to be gay '87' / Still loving you.
LP: EMC 3540
MC: TCEMC 3540
LP: ATAK 126
MC: TCATAK 126

HARD CASES (See under 'Hard Cases').

HOPE AND GLORY.
Tracks: / Murder at the end of the day / Prison / Rikki don't lose that number / Old friend / Looking for a bonfire / War baby / Listen to the radio: Atmospherics / Cabin boy / Blond and blue / Hope and glory.
LP: ZL 70483
MC: ZK 70483

LIVE- MIDNIGHT AT THE FRINGE (Robinson, Tom and Crew).
Tracks: / Atmospherics / Night time, The / Cabin boy / Surabaya Johnny / Bonfire / Back in the old country / Old friend / War baby / Never gonna fall in love (again) / Blond and blue.
LP: DOJOLP 51

NORTH BY NORTHWEST.
Tracks: / Now Martin's gone / Atmospherics / Can't keep away (part 2) / Looking for a bonfire / Merrily up on high / Those days / In the cold / Night tide, The / Duncannon / Love comes.
MC: CLAMC 128
LP: CLALP 128

POWER IN THE DARKNESS (Robinson, Tom Band).
Tracks: / Up against the wall / Grey Cortina / Too good to be true / Ain't gonna take it / Long hot summer / Winter of '79 / Man you never saw / Better decide which side you're on / You gotta survive / Power in the darkness.
LP: EMS 1066681
MC: TCEMS 1066684
LP: EMC 3226

SECTOR 27.
Tracks: / Invitation / Not ready / Mary Lynne / 523 / Looking at you / Total recall / One fine day / Take or leave it.
MC: . . . . TC ZONO 102
LP: . . . . ZONO 102

STILL LOVING YOU.
Tracks: / Feel so good, hurt so bad / Nothing like the real thing / Still loving you / Take me home again / You tattooed me / Drive all night / Living in a love town / Spain / This little romance / Wedding.
LP: . . . . ZL 71129
MC: . . . . ZK 71129
LP: . . . . PL 71129

TOM ROBINSON BAND (Robinson, Tom Band).
Tracks: / 2-4-6-8 motorway / Bully for you / Never going to fall in love again / Getting tighter / Our people / I shall be released / Glad to be gay / Don't take no for an answer / Winter of '79 / Martin / Right on sister / I'm alright Jack.
LP: . . . . EMS 1005
LP: . . . . FA 3028

TRB TWO (Robinson, Tom Band).
Tracks: / Alright all night / Why should I mind / Black angel / Let my people be / Blue murder / Bully for you / Crossing over the road / Sorry Mr Harris / Law and order / Days of rage / Hold out.
LP: . . . . EMS 1652151
MC: . . . . TCEMS 1652154
LP: . . . . EMC 3296

WE NEVER HAD IT SO GOOD (Robinson, Tom & Jakko M Jakszyk).
LP: 106661
MC: 106664

Robinson, Vicki Sue

HALF AND HALF.
Tracks: / Feels so good it must be wrong / Jealousy / Freeway song / Don't try to win me back again / Trust in me / Hold tight / We found each other / Half and half.
LP: . . . . PL 12294
MC: . . . . PK 12294

MOVIN' ON.
Tracks: / Can't accept the fact / Never stop loving me / Hope your feelings are like mine / What's happening in my life / Shine your love on me / High on your love / More complete in the night time / Movin on.
LP: . . . . PL 13080

NEVER GONNA LET YOU GO.
Tracks: / Turn the beat around / Common thief / Never gonna let you go / Wonderland of love / We can do almost anything / Lack of respect / When you're lovin' me / Act of mercy.
LP: . . . . RS 1051

Robinson's Jacinto...

ROBINSON'S JACINTO BALLROOM ORCHESTRA (Robinson's Jacinto Ballroom Orchestra).
LP: . . . . GHB 28

Robles, Marisa

NARNIA SUITE, THE.
LP: . . . . DCA 513
MC: . . . . ZC DCA 513

Robocop

ROBOCOP (Film Soundtrack) (Various artists).
LP: . . . . TER 1146
MC: . . . . ZCTER 1146

ROBOCOP 2 (Original Soundtrack) (Various artists).
Tracks: / Robocop - overture: *Various artists* / City mayhem: *Various artists* / Happier days: *Various artists* / Robo cruiser: *Various artists* / Robo memories: *Various artists* / Robo and Nuke: *Various artists* / Robo fanfare: *Various artists* / Robo and Cain chase: *Various artists* / Creating the monster: *Various artists* / Robo I vs Robo II: *Various artists*.
LP: . . . . VS 5271
MC: . . . . VSC 5271

Robot

DISCOMEDY A.
LP: . . . . NSPL 28258

Robotiks

MAN AND MACHINE.
LP: . . . . ARILP 019

MY COMPUTER'S ACTING STRANGE.
LP: . . . . ARILP 027

Robots of Dawn (bk)

ROBOTS OF DAWN, THE (Isaac Asimov).
MC: . . . . CDL 51732

Robson, Carolyn

BANKS OF TYNE.
LP: . . . . DIN 316

Rocca, John

EXTRA EXTRA.
LP: . . . . CBLP 001
MC: . . . . CBMC 001

ONCE UPON A TIME.
LP: . . . . BEGA 52
MC: . . . . BEGC 52

Rocha, Sebastiao

BRAZIL 99.
Tracks: / Lambaio / Saia rodada / Bicho cabeludo / Aguas do amazonas / Ghinawa / Bahia boa terra / Capoeira de angola / Bachoros.
LP: . . . . PS 605

Rochdale Band

CRUSADERS.
LP: . . . . GRS 1054

Rochdale Wilsons Band

BRASS BAND ON THE MARCH.
LP: . . . . PRD 2011
MC: . . . . PRD 4 2011

Roche, Betty

TAKE THE 'A' TRAIN.
Tracks: / Take the 'A' train / Something to live for / In a mellow tone / Time after time / Go away blues / Can't help lovin' dat man / Route 66 / All my life / I just got the message, baby / All too soon / You don't love me no more / September in the rain.
LP: . . . . AFF 175

Roche, David

ALL IRELAND CHAMPION BUTTON ACCORDION.
Tracks: / My Lagan love / Jacqueline waltz / Alpine slopes / Masons apron / O sole mio / Foxhunters reel / Ship's for sale, The / Kesh jig / Andrew's welcome home / Amazing grace / Peter Street / God speed the plough / Lonesome boatman, The / Green groves of Erin, The / Lord McDonald's / Sunshine hornpipe / Yellow bird / She wears my ring / Sally gardens / Sligo maid, The / Dingle regatta.
LP: . . . . GVR 213

Rochee & The Sarnos

UNDERSTANDING SARNOS.
LP: . . . . NERD 018

Rochereau

TABU LEY.
LP: . . . . SHAN 43017
MC: . . . . SHANC 43017

Roches

KEEP ON DOING.
Tracks: / Halleluljah chorus, The / Losing true / Steady with the maestro / Largest Elizabeth in the world, The / On the road to Fairfax country / I fell in love / Scorpion lament, The / Want not want not / Sex is for children / Keep on doing what you do / Jerks on the loose.
LP: . . . . K 57027
MC: K4 57027

NURDS.
Tracks: / Nurds / It's bad for me / Louis / Bobby's song / Boat family / My sick mind / Death of Suzzy Roche / Factory girl / One season / This femine position.
LP: . . . . K 568 55

ROCHES, THE.
Tracks: / We / Hammond song / Mr. Sellack / Damned old dog / Troubles, The / Train, The / Married men, The / Runs in the family / Quitting time / Pretty and high.
LP: . . . . K 56683

SPEAK.
LP: . . . . MCG 6071
MC: . . . . MCGC 6071

WE THREE KINGS.
LP: . . . . MCG 6122
MC: . . . . MCGC 6122

Rochester

VEASLEY BAND.
LP: . . . . GR 8505

Rock

20 GOLDEN ROCKERS (Various artists).
LP: 28028
MC: 48028

20 ORIGINAL ROCK HITS (Various artists).
LP: . . . . PLE 7001
MC: . . . . PLC 7001

20 YEARS OF ROCK (VIDEO) (See under Rolling Stone) (Various artists).

21 YEARS OF ALTERNATIVE RADIO 1 (Various artists).
Tracks: / Hey Joe: *Hendrix, Jimi* / Whiter shade of pale, A: *Procul Harum* / Delta lady: *Cocker, Joe*/ My father's gun: *John, Elton* / Fat man: *Jethro Tull* / Mandolin king: *Lindisfarne* / Keep yourself alive: *Queen* / No love for free: *Armatrading, Joan* / New rose: *Damned* / Dancing in the moonlight: *Thin Lizzy* / Overground: *Siouxsie & Banshees* / Read it in books: *Echo & the Bunnymen* / Can't stand losing you: *Police* / It's better this way: *Associates* / 5-8-6: *New Order* / What difference does it make: *Smiths*/ Sally MacLannan: *Pogues* / Inside me: *Jesus & Mary Chain* / My favourite dress: *Wedding Present* / Ruby red lips: *Gaye Bykers On Acid* / Strong enough to change: *Unseen Terror*.
2LP: . . . . SFRLP 200
MCSET: . . . . SFRMC 200

24 CARAT ROCK (Various artists).
LP: . . . . CARAT 1
MC: . . . . ZCZRT 1

ABSOLUTION (Various artists).
Tracks: / Spellbound: *Siouxsie & Banshees* / Don't let me down gently: *Wonder Stuff* / Deliverance: *Mission*/ Eloise: *Damned* / Never enough: *Cure* / Ziggy stardust: *Bauhaus* / Love like blood: *Killing Joke*/ European female: *Stranglers* / Some candy talking: *Jesus & Mary Chain* / Cutter: *Echo & the Bunnymen*/ Love my way: *Psychedelic Furs* / Enjoy the silence: *Depeche Mode* / Martha's harbour: *All About Eve*/ Baby I love you: *Ramones* / Miss the girl: *Creatures* / No rest: *New Model Army* / Heartache: *Gene Loves Jezebel* / Moonchild (first seal): *Fields Of The Nephilim*.
LP: 845 747 1
MC: 845 747 4

BEST OF SCANDINAVIAN ROCK (Various artists).
LP: . . . . SWORDLP 005

BEST OF THE ROCK MACHINE TURNS YOU ON, THE (Various artists).
Tracks: / Can't be so bad: *Moby Grape* / Fresh garbage: *Spirit* / I won't leave my wooden wife for you: *United States Of America* / Turn on a friend: *Peanut Butter Conspiracy* / Sisters of mercy: *Cohen, Leonard* / My days are numbered: *Blood, Sweat & Tears* / Killing floor: *Electric Flag* / Come away Melinda: *Rose, Tim* / More and more: *Blood, Sweat & Tears* / Stoned soul picnic: *Nyro, Laura* / Stop: *Bloomfield, Mike/Al Cooper*/ You ain't goin' nowhere: *Byrds* / Somebody to love: *Slick,Grace & The Great Society* / Hey that's no way to say goodbye: *Cohen, Leonard* / See to your neighbour: *Electric Flag* / Ball and chain: *Big Brother & Holding Co.*/ Time: *Valente, Dino* / Lot of love, A: *Taj Mahal* / Tired of waiting for you: *Flock* / White bird: *It's A Beautiful Day* / Dolphins smile: *Byrds*.
2LP: . . . . CCSLP 224
MC: . . . . CCSMC 224

BRUM BEAT LIVE AT THE BARRELL ORGAN (Various artists).
2LP: . . . . BRUM 1

CHRISTENDOM ROCK (Various artists).
MC: . . . . CR 1

CLASSIC ROCK (ATLANTIC) (Various artists).
Tracks: / In the midnight hour: *Young Rascals* / For what it's worth: *Buffalo Springfield* / You keep me hangin' on: *Vanilla Fudge* / Dazed and confused: *Led Zeppelin* / Stairway to heaven: *Led Zeppelin* / Highway to hell: *AC/DC* / Back in black: *AC/DC* / Rough boys: *Townshend, Pete* / Suite Judy blue eyes: *Crosby*, Stills & Nash / Whole lotta love: *Led Zeppelin* / Ohio: *Crosby, Stills & Nash* / I've seen all the good people: *Yes* / Urgent: *Foreigner* / You can't stop rock 'n' roll: *Twisted Sister* / Round and round: *Ratt*/ All I need is a miracle: *Mike & The Mechanics* / Heaven knows: *Plant, Robert*.
2LP: . . . . K 781 935 1
MC: . . . . K 781 935 4

COAST TO COAST (Various artists).
Tracks: / Voice of America: *Dark Star* / American fool: *Green, Jack* / Better late than never: *XS* / How far Jerusalem: *Magnum* / Call of the wild: *Sabu* / Hold back the night: *Multi-Story* / Stand me up: *Statetrooper* / Dancin' on midnight: *White Sister* / Shoot for the heart: *Lawrence, Karen* / Surrender: *Joshua*.
LP: . . . . WKFMLP 96
MC: . . . . WKFMMC 96

DEADICATED (A Grateful Dead Tribute Compilation) (Various artists).
Tracks: / Bertha: *Los Lobos* / Jack Straw: *Hornsby, Bruce & The Range* / U.S. blues: *Harshed Mellows*/ Ship of fools: *Costello, Elvis* / China doll: *Vega, Suzanne* / Cassidy: *Vega, Suzanne* / Truckin': *Yoakam, Dwight* / Casey Jones: *Zevon, Warren & David Lindley* / Uncle John's band: *Indigo Girls* / Friend of the devil: *Lovett, Lyle* / To lay me down: *Cowboy Junkies* / Wharf rat: *Midnight Oil* / Estimated prophet: *Burning Spear* / Deal: *Dr. John* / Ripple: *Jane's Addiction*.
LP: 304179
MC: 504179

DEATH LEAVES AN ECHO (Various artists).
LP: . . . . TWI 653

DEF AMERICAN SAMPLER - TIL DEF DO US PART (See Under Def America) (Various artists).

DEFIANTE POSE (Various artists).
LP: . . . . ILP 013

DIAMONDS & PORCUPINES (Various artists).
LP: . . . . EFA 4341

DON'T LET THE HOPE CLOSE DOWN (Various artists).
Tracks: / Underestimated man, The: *Vibes* / Hush: *Prisoners* / Mona: *Milkshakes* / What the new breed say: *Stingrays* / Double tracking the dog: *Screaming Blue Messiahs* / Let there be more darkness: *Hitchcock, Robyn* / Pillars of society: *Serious Drinking* / Favourite things: *Turkey Boys & The Wild Dogs* / Crazy when I hear that beat: *Dead Beats* / Tears in my beer: *Tearjerkers.*. / I don't want to get thin: *Blubbery Hellbellies*/ Whisky with me giro: *Men They Couldn't Hang* / Last chance baby: *Restless* / I fell in love last night: *Hackney 5-0* / Band played waltzing Matilda, The: *Pogues* / Don't let the hope close down: *Boothill Foot Tappers*.
LP: . . . . HOPE 1

DRIVE TIME USA (Various artists).
Tracks: / Drive: *Cars* / You can do magic: *America (Group)* / After the fire: *Loggins, Kenny* / I can dream about you: *Hartman, Dan* / Chuck E's in love: *Jones, Rickie Lee* / Heat is on, The: *Frey, Glen*/ Secrets in the street: *Lofgren, Nils* / Rock and roll dreams come through: *Steinman, Jim* / Rocky Mountain way: *Walsh, Joe* / Jack and Diane: *Mellencamp, John Cougar* / Hotel California: *Eagles* / Cocaine: *Cale, J.J.* / Willing: *Little Feat* / Roll on down the highway: *Bachman-Turner Overdrive* / Well all right: *Santana*/ Joker, The: *Miller, Steve* / Little sister: *Cooder, Ry* / Ride like the wind: *Cross, Christopher* / Sweet home Alabama: *Lynyrd Skynyrd* / Ramblin' man: *Allman Brothers* / What a fool believes: *Doobie Brothers*.
2LP: . . . . NE 1321
MC: . . . . CE 2321

DRIVIN' MUSIC (Various artists).
MC: . . . . JHC 64

DRIVIN' ROCK (Various artists).
MC: . . . . JHC 61

EARTHQUAKE ALBUM, THE (Various artists).
Tracks: / Smoke on the water: *Rock Aid Armenia* / Spirit of radio: *Rush* / Headless cross: *Black Sabbath*/ Owner of a lonely heart: *Yes* / Fool for your loving: *Whitesnake* / We built this city: *Starship* / Run to the hills: *Iron Maiden* / Silent running: *Mike & The Mechanics* / Since you been gone: *Rainbow (Group)*/ Turn it on again: *Genesis* / Fanfare for the common man: *Emerson, Lake & Palmer* / Heat of the moment: *Asia*/ Jukebox hero: *Foreigner* / Black night: *Deep Purple*.
LP: . . . . AIDLP 001
MC: . . . . AIDMC 001

ELECTRIC SUGAR CUBE FLASHBACKS (Various artists).
LP: . . . . AIP 1008

ELECTRIC SUGAR CUBE FLASHBACKS VOL.2 (Various artists).
LP: . . . . AIP 10010

ELECTRIC SUGAR CUBE FLASHBACKS VOL.4 (Various artists).
LP: . . . . AIP 10052

ELECTRIC SUGAR CUBE FLASHBACKS VOL.3 (Various artists).
LP: . . . . AIP 10050

ENDLESS JOURNEY PHASE 1 (Various artists).
LP: . . . . PSYCHO 1

ENDLESS JOURNEY PHASE 2 (Various artists).
LP: . . . . PSYCHO 3

ENDLESS JOURNEY PHASE 3 (Various artists).
Tracks: / Close the barn door: *Forty-ninth parallel* / Tribute to Hendrix: *Swift, T./Electric bag* / Hearts to cry: *Fruminous Bandersnatch* / Forest of black: *Dirty filthy mud* / Ruler of the universe: *Strange*.
LP: . . . . PSYCHO 19

ENTERTAINMENT FROM THE USA (Various artists).
2LP: . . . . SMR 8612
MCSET: . . . . SMC 8612

EXPLOSIVE ROCK (Various artists).
LP: **OG 1803**
MC: **OG 2803**

FAREWELL TO MAX'S (Various artists).
Tracks: / Treat me like a dog: *Mendis/ Mossop* / Heart full of soul: *Gouldman, Graham* / Call me: *Gem, Robert* & Reg Presley / She don't care: *Alexander, Joe* / It's only natural: *Setzer, Brian* / Go go getter: *Setzer*, Brian / This I know: *Alexander, Joe* / That's alright: *Crudup, Arthur* / Take it easy: *Prince Buster*/ I do do I do: *Gem, Robert & Reg Presley*.
LP: **MKC 101**

GOLDEN DAYS OF ROCK (Various artists).
MC: **AMP 016**

GREASY TRUCKERS PARTY (Various artists).
LP: **UDX 203/4**

GUITAR EXPLORATION (Various artists).
LP: **WKFMLP 169**
MC: **WKFMMC 169**

GUITAR MASTERS (Various artists).
LP: **RR 94831**

IN GOOD COMPANY (Various artists).
Tracks: / Someday: *Chicago* / Dark eyed woman: *Spirit* / Save the country: *Nyro, Laura* / White bird: *It's A Beautiful Day* / Way to power, The: *Black Widow* / Albert Shuffle: *Bloomfield, Mike/Al Cooper*/ Evil ways: *Santana* / Freefall: *Argent* / Hustled down in Texas: *Winter, Johnny* / Ballad of easy rider: *Byrds* / Head in the clouds: *Gun* / Nothing special: *Trees*.
LP: **WSR 945**

IN THE FOREST (Various artists).
Tracks: / Adriatic sea view: *Plant, Robert/The Band Of Joy* / Elmer's out: *Bowel, Bill & The Movements* / Hold on: *Webb, Stan 'Chicken Shack'* / Wheels are turning: *Rouen* / Bam boom bam: *Roden, Jess* / Feel so good: *Hayriders* / Annie Laurie: *Swift, Duncan* / Change of heart: *Ward, Clifford T.* / Key to the highway: *Cool, Ricky* / Blood on the moon: *Cartwright, Dave* / Till the day I die: *Clippers* / Wobble, The: *Big Town Playboys* / Little Joe: *Maiden, Brian* / Sheik of Araby, The: *Swift, Duncan*.
MC: **C 01**

INTERNATIONAL ROCKERS (Various artists).
LP: **EF 4419**

IRS - THE SINGLES USA/UK (Various artists).
LP: **MIRL 1501**
MC: **MIRLC 1501**

IS IT ANY WONDER? (Dunhill folk/rock, Vol 1) (Various artists).
Tracks: / Things I should have said, The: *Various artists* / Is happy this way: *Various artists* / Eve of destruction: *Various artists* / April Anne: *Various artists* / Child of our times: *Various artists* / From a distance: *Various artists* / Creeque alley: *Various artists* / Monday Monday: *Various artists* / Look through my window: *Various artists* / Out of touch: *Various artists* / Let me be: *Various artists* / Topanga: *Various artists* / Is it any wonder: *Various artists*.
LP: **WIK 74**

ISLAND LIFE (Various artists).
Tracks: / Hard rain's gonna fall: *Ferry, Bryan* / Baby's on fire: *Eno* / Do the Strand: *Roxy Music* / 21st century schizoid man: *King Crimson* / Feel like makin' love: *Bad Company* / Heartbreak Hotel: *Cale, John*/ I'm ready: *Kossoff, Paul* / You're gonna get: *Palmer, Robert* / May I?: *Ayers, Kevin* / Matty Groves: *Fairport Convention* / Traffic: *Martyn, John & Beverley* / Now be thankful: *Fairport Convention* / River man: *Drake, Nick* / Poor ditching, The: *Thompson, Richard* / Cuckoo's nest, The: *Hutchings/Thompson/Mattacks*/ Albion Surprise: *Albion Band* / Love's made a fool of you: *Bunch* / Hokey pokey: *Thompson, Richard*/ John Barleycorn: *Traffic* / Whole of the moon, The: *Waterboys* / Island: *Renaissance* / 16 shells from A 30.6: *Waits, Tom* / Spacehopper: *Cope, Julian* / Sailing: *Sutherland Brothers* / Peace Train: *Stevens*, Cat / Bury me deep in love: *Triffids* / Dear old...: *Incredible String Band* / ...And that's why: *Christians*/ Trouble: *Trouble funk* / Say it ain't so Joe: *Head, Murray* / Let's Rock: *Sly & Robbie* / King and Queen of England: *Denny, Sandy* / You can discover: *Martyn, John*.
LPS: **IBX 25**
MCSET: **IBXC 25**

JAMMING WITH EDWARD (Various artists).
Tracks: / Boudoir stomp, The: *Various artists* / It hurts me too: *Various artists* / Edwards thrump up: *Various* artists / Blow with Ry: *Various artists* / Interlude a la el hopo: *Various artists* / Lovliest night of the year, The: *Various artists* / Highland fling: *Various artists*.
LP: **COC 39100**

JUST IN TIME FOR CHRISTMAS (Various artists).
MC: **EIRSAC 1046**

KINGS OF ROCK (Various artists).
LP: **2872 215**
MC: **3472 215**

KNEBWORTH - THE ALBUM (Various artists).
Tracks: / Everybody wants to rule the world: *Tears For Fears* / Dirty water: *Status Quo* / Rockin' all over the world: *Status Quo* / Do you wanna dance: *Richard, Cliff & The Shadows* / Liar's dance: *Plant, Robert*/ Wearing and tearing: *Plant, Robert & Jimmy Page* / Turn it on again (medley): *Genesis* / Sunshine of your love: *Clapton, Eric* / Money for nothing: *Dire Straits* / Saturday night's all right for fighting: *John, Elton*/ Hey Jude: *McCartney, Paul* / Run like hell: *Pink Floyd* / Badman's song: *Tears For Fears* / Whatever you want: *Status Quo* / On the beach: *Richard, Cliff & The Shadows* / Hurting kind: *Plant, Robert* / Tall cool one: *Plant, Robert* / Mama: *Genesis* / Sussudio: *Collins, Phil* / Think I love you too much: *Dire* Straits / Sad songs (say so much): *John, Elton* / Coming up: *McCartney, Paul* / Comfortably numb: *Pink Floyd*.
MC: **843 921 4**
LP: **843 921 1**

LA VIE EN ROSE (Various artists).
LP: **ROSE 50**

LADIES GET THE BLUES (Various artists).
Tracks: / Can't get even the blues no more: *McEntire, Reba* / Today all over again: *McEntire, Reba* / Someday when things are good: *Williams, Leona* / You take me for granted: *Williams, Leona* / Love at the five and dime: *Mattea, Kathy* / Walk the way the wind blows: *Mattea, Kathy* / For every inch I've laughed I've cried a mile: *Hensley*, Teri / Hard baby to rock: *Hensley, Teri* / Funny face: *Fargo, Donna* / Happiest girl in the whole USA: *Fargo, Donna*.
LP: **834 199-1**
MC: **834 199-4**

LEATHER AND LACE (The Men and Women of Rock) (Various artists).
LP: **DINTV 9**
MC: **DINMC 9**

LEATHER AND LACE - THE SECOND CHAPTER (Various artists).
Tracks: / Radio ga ga: *Queen* / Black velvet: *Myles, Alannah* / Road to hell, The: *Rea, Chris* / Rooms on fire: *Nicks, Stevie* / Hurting kind (I've got my eyes on you): *Palmer, Robert* / Edge of a broken heart: *Vixen*/ Better days: *Gun* / I don't want a lover: *Texas* / Run to you: *Adams, Bryan* / Big love: *Fleetwood* Mac / Radar love: *Golden Earring* / Get your love: *Black Velvette* / From out of nowhere: *Faith No More*/ Martha's harbour: *All About Eve* / I'm a believer: *Giant* / First time: *Beck, Robin* / Centrefold: *Geils, J. Band*.
LP: **DINTV 12**
MC: **DINMC 12**

LEATHER CHAPS AND LACE PETTICOATS (Various artists).
Tracks: / Hootin' and a howlin': *Leather Chaps &...* / Free Mexican air force: *Leather Chaps &...* / Kickin' som': *Leather Chaps &...* / Foundations of love: *Leather Chaps &...* / Get your feet out of my shoes: *Leather Chaps &...* / Magic toy missing: *Leather Chaps &...* / Rye whiskey: *Leather Chaps &...* / Your good girl's gonna go bad: *Leather Chaps &...* / Freight train: *Leather Chaps &...* / I've only just turned 21: *Leather Chaps &...* / Mystery blonde: *Leather Chaps &...* / Two little orphans: *Leather Chaps &...* / Pointed bra: *Leather Chaps &...* / Stomp it: *Leather Chaps &...*.
LP: **GRAM 20**

LIFE IN THE EUROPEAN THEATRE (Various artists).
Tracks: / London calling: *Various artists* / Little boy soldiers: *Various artists* / I am your flag: *Various* artists / Man at C & A: *Various artists* / Living through another Cuba: *Various artists* / I don't remember: *Various artists* / Reasons to be cheerful: *Various artists* / Grey day: *Various artists* / Psychedelic Eric: *Various artists* / Nuclear device: *Various artists* / It's going to happen: *Various artists* / All that jazz: *Various artists* / Diet: *Various artists*.
LP: **K 58412**

LIFE IN THE FAST LANE (Various artists).
LP: **STAR 2315**
MC: **STAC 2315**

LIVE AT THE 101 (Various artists).
2LP: **INTEL 1**
MCSET: **ZCINT 1**

LIVE AT THE KREMLIN VOL. 1 (Various artists).
LP: **ROSE 247**
MC: **ROSK 247**

LIVE AT THE KREMLIN VOL. 2 (Various artists).
LP: **ROSE 248**
MC: **ROSE 248 C**

LIVE FOR IRELAND (Various artists).
Tracks: / Maggie's farm: *U2* / Seven into the sea: *In Tua Nua* / Many rivers...: *Costello/The Attractions*/ Dirty old town: *Pogues* / Don't pay the ferryman: *De Burgh, Chris* / Harry's game (theme from): *Clannad*/ Bridge, The: *Cactus World News* / Looking after no. 1: *Boomtown Rats* / Here's comes the night: *Morrison*, Van / Don't believe a word: *Thin Lizzy* / Steel river: *Rea, Chris* / Make it work: *Moore, Chris & Paul Doran*.
LP: **MCG 6027**
MC: **MCGC 6027**

LIVING LEGENDS (Various artists).
Tracks: / Rain: *Various artists* / 4500 times: *Various artists* / Rocks off: *Various artists* / Junior's eyes: *Various artists* / Die young: *Various artists* / Rocker: *Various artists* / Suicide: *Various* artists / Satellite: *Various artists* / Temples of Syrinx: *Various artists* / What you're doing: *Various artists*.
LP: **6498 092**

LOST HITS (Various artists).
LP: **SKYDOG 2230**

MAKE A DIFFERENCE (Various artists).
LP: **842 093 1**
MC: **842 093 4**

MARQUEE 30 LEGENDARY YEARS (32 Classic Rock tracks) (Various artists).
Tracks: / Pride (in the name of love): *U2* / Solid rock: *Dire Straits* / Turn it on again: *Genesis* / Run to you: *Adams, Bryan* / White wedding: *Idol, Billy* / Love song: *Simple Minds* / Don't stand so close to me: *Police* / Going underground: *Jam* / No more heroes: *Stranglers* / Rat trap: *Boomtown Rats*/ Matthew and son: *Stevens, Cat* / Living in the past: *Jethro Tull* / Dreamer: *Supertramp* / Another brick in the wall: *Pink Floyd* / Kayleigh: *Marillion* / Killer queen: *Queen* / Saturday night's alright (for fighting): *John, Elton* / Get it on: *T. Rex* / All the young dudes: *Mott The Hoople* / You wear it well: *Stewart, Rod* / Boys are back in town: *Thin Lizzy* / Caroline: *Status Quo* / Layla: *Derek & The Dominoes*/ Substitute: *Who* / All right now: *Free* / Badge: *Cream* / Gimme some lovin': *Spencer Davis group*/ Need your love so bad: *Fleetwood Mac* / For your love: *Yardbirds* / Sha-la-la-la-lee: *Small Faces* / Purple haze: *Hendrix, Jimi* / Space oddity (original version): *Bowie, David*.
2LP: **MQTV 1**
MCSET: **MQTVC 1**

MARQUEE THE COLLECTION 1958-1983 - VOL.3 (Various artists).
Tracks: / Turn it on again (Live): *Genesis* / Ride a white swan: *T. Rex* / Shapes of things: *Yardbirds*/ Something in the air: *Thunderclap Newman* / Sounds from the street: *Jam* / Man of the world: *Fleetwood Mac*/ From the underworld: *Herd, The* / Go now: *Moody Blues* / Love is the drug / Sultans of swing: *Dire Straits*/ America: *Nice* / Lady Eleanor: *Lindisfarne* / He knows you knows (Live): *Marillion* / London boys: *Bowie, David* / Pick up the pieces: *Average White Band* / Cool for cats: *Squeeze*.
LP: **MAR 3**
MC: **MARC 3**

MARQUEE THE COLLECTION 1958-1983 - VOL.1 (Various artists).
Tracks: / My generation (live): *Who* / Whiter shade of pale, A: *Procul Harum* / Maggie May: *Stewart, Rod*/ All right now: *Free* / For your love: *Yardbirds* / Get it on: *T. Rex* / Daydream: *Lovin' Spoonful*/ With a little help from my friends: *Cocker, Joe* / Layla: *Derek & The Dominoes* / Itchycoo Park: *Small Faces*/ Nights in white satin: *Moody Blues* / Show me the way: *Frampton, Peter* / Your song: *John, Elton* / I know what I like (in your wardrobe): *Genesis* / Out of time: *Farlowe, Chris* / No particular place to go: *Berry, Chuck*.
LP: **MAR 1**
MC: **MARC 1**

MARQUEE THE COLLECTION 1958-1983 - VOL.2 (Various artists).
Tracks: / Hey Joe: *Hendrix, Jimi Experience* / Here comes the night: *Them* / Strange brew: *Cream* / Boys are back in town: *Thin Lizzy* / Fire: *Brown, Arthur (The crazy world of)* / Silver machine (Live): *Hawkwind*/ Broken down angel: *Nazareth* / Delta lady: *Cocker, Joe* / Whatever you want: *Status Quo* / Love like a man: *Ten Years After* / Paranoid: *Black Sabbath* / Devil's answer: *Atomic Rooster* / I need a lover: *Cougar, Johnny* / Darlin': *Miller, Frankie* / Don't bring me down: *Animals* / Natural born boogie: *Humble Pie*.
LP: **MAR 2**
MC: **MARC 2**

MARQUEE THE COLLECTION 1958-1983 - VOL.4 (Various artists).
Tracks: / Rocket man: *John, Elton* / If paradise is half as nice: *Amen Corner* / With a girl like you: *Troggs*/ Matthew and son: *Stevens, Cat* / Pictures of matchstick men: *Status Quo* / Let the heartaches begin: *Baldry*, Long John / This town ain't big enough for the both of us: *Sparks* / Flowers in the rain: *Move* / Reflections of my life: *Marmalade* / How come: *Lane, Ronnie* / Coz I luv you: *Slade* / It's a mystery: *Toyah*/ Heart on my sleeve: *Gallagher & Lyle* / Hold tight: *Dave Dee, Dozy, Beaky, Mick & Tich* / Stuck in the middle with you: *Stealers Wheel* / Eighth day: *O'Connor, Hazel* / Part of the union: *Strawbs* / Blackberry way: *Move* / In the Summertime: *Mungo Jerry* / Young Parisians: *Adam & The Ants*.
LP: **MAR 4**
MC: **MARC 4**

MILESTONES (20 Rock Operas) (Various artists).
Tracks: / Bohemian rhapsody: *Queen* / I don't like Mondays: *Boomtown Rats* / Bat out of hell: *Meatloaf*/ Don't let the sun go down on me: *John, Elton* / Samba pa ti: *Santana* / Hotel California: *Eagles* / I'm not in love / 10538 overture: *E.L.O.* / Wuthering heights: *Bush, Kate* / Oxygene IV: *Jarre, Jean Michel*/ Vienna: *Ultravox* / Nights in white satin: *Moody Blues* / Let's work together: *Canned Heat* / Layla: *Derek & The Dominoes* / Tubular bells: *Oldfield, Mike* / Smoke on the water: *Deep Purple* / Whiter shade of pale, A: *Procul Harum* / Music: *Miles, John* / Albatross: *Fleetwood Mac* / Drive: *Cars*.
LP: **STAR 2379**
MC: **STAC 2379**

MODERN ROCKERS (Various artists).
LP: **WW 5135**
MC: **WW 4 5135**

MONUMENT TO BRITISH ROCK (Various artists).
LP: **EMTV 17**

MORE ROCK FROM THE GREAT EARLY DAYS (Various artists).
Tracks: / Swanee River shake: *Scuderi, Leon* / Blues in the night: *Scuderi, Leon* / Berry's bounce: *Smith*, Berry / I'm lost without your love: *Lee, Wibbe* / I don't believe I'll fall in love today: *Lee, Al* / Secret lover: *Stone, Charlie* / Frankie and Johnny: *Durham, Jerry* / Out of a clear blue sky: *Frizzell, Billy*/ Tiddley Diddley: *Hopkins, Leon* / Linda: *Starfires* / Ponderosa rock: *White, Lucky* / Tall skinny Annie: *Watson, Clayton* / Everybody boppin': *Watson, Clayton* / I saw you standing: *Howell, Leigh* / Wind and the sea, The: *Howell, Leigh*.
LP: **WLP 8901**

MUSIC FOR UNICEF CONCERT (Various artists).
LP: **2335214**

NEW GLADIATORS (Various artists).
Tracks: / Fortuna: *Pretty Maids* / Get out: *Vengeance* / I shall return: *Trust* / Autoblast: *Black'n'Blue*/ High school: *Hanoi Rocks* / Heavy Christmas: *200* / Come one, come all: *Madam X* / Heavy metal shuffle: *Kick Axe* / Party all night: *Quiet Riot* / All fired up: *Fastway* / I need your love: *Horizon*/ Without you: *Stevie*.
LP: **EPC 32783**
MC: **40 32783**

NEW ROSE '82 COMPILATION (Various artists).
LP: **ROSE 9**

NEW ROSE '83 COMPILATION (Various artists).
LP: **ROSE 17**

NIGHT OF THE GUITAR (Various artists).
Tracks: / Doctor Brown I presume: *Haycock, Pete* / Lucienne: *Haycock, Pete* / Hey Joe: *California, Randy*/ King will come, The: *Wishbone Ash* / Never in my life: *West, Leslie* / Wurm: *Howe, Steve* / Ain't nothin' shakin': *Lee, Alvin* / Idler, The: *Hunter, Steve* / Groove thing: *California, Randy* / Love me two times: *Kreiger, Bobby* / Theme from an imaginary western: *West, Leslie* / Clap medley: *Howe, Steve* / No limit: *Lee, Alvin* / Whole lotta shakin' goin' on: *Various artists* / Johnny B. Goode: *Various artists* / Bye bye Johnny:

Various artists / All along the watchtower: *Various artists* / Dizzy Miss Lizzy: *Various artists*/ Rock and roll music: *Various artists*.
2LP: . . . . **EIRSDA 1005**
MC: . . . . **EIRSAC 1005**

NO NUKES (Various artists).
2LP: . . . . **K 62027**

NYLON JUICE (Various artists).
Tracks: / High noon part 2: *Various artists* / Be bop rock part 2: *Various artists* / For the same man: *Various artists* / Get the money: *Various artists* / Prepare to energise: *Various artists* / Pictures: *Various artists* / Pioneer girl: *Various artists* / We love you: *Various artists*.
LP: . . . . **IRSA 7050**

OLD GREY WHISTLE TEST TAKE 2 (Various artists).
2LP: . . . . **BEEDP 001**

PEOPLE'S CONCERT FOR KAMPUCHEA (Various artists).
LP: . . . . **K 60153**

PLAY NEW ROSE FOR ME (Various artists).
LP: . . . . **ROSE 100**

POKE IN THE EYE (Various artists).
MCSET: . . . . **ESDMC 153**

POWER AND THE GLORY, THE (Various artists).
Tracks: / Suicide blonde: *INXS* / Would I lie to you: *Eurythmics* / Best, The: *Turner, Tina* / Road to hell, The: *Rea, Chris* / Listen to your heart: *Roxette* / Black velvet: *Myles, Alannah* / Hard to handle: *Black Crowes* / Hey you: *Quireboys* / Blaze of glory: *Bon Jovi, Jon* / Everybody wants to the rule the world: *Tears For Fears* / Good morning Britain: *Aztec Camera & Mick Jones* / Joker, The: *Miller, Steve* / I can't go for that: *Hall & Oates* / Power of love, The: *Lewis, Huey & The News* / Love is a battlefield: *Benatar, Pat* / Dedication: *Thin Lizzy* / All right now: *Free* / Wind of change: *Scorpions*.
MC: **5103604**
LP: **5103601**

PRECIOUS METAL (Various artists).
LP: . . . . **SMR 976**
MC: . . . . **SMC 976**

PRINCES TRUST COLLECTION (Various artists).
LP: . . . . **STAR 2275**
MC: . . . . **STAC 2275**

PRINCE'S TRUST SOUNDTRACK, THE (Various artists).
Tracks: / Money for nothing: *Various artists* / Call of the wild: *Various artists* / Marlene on the wall: *Various* artists / In the air tonight: *Various artists* / Fields of fire: *Various artists* / No one is to blame: *Various* artists / Something about you: *Various artists* / I'm still standing: *Various artists* / Reach out: *Various* artists / Better be good to me: *Various artists* / Sailing: *Various artists* / Get back: *Various artists*/ Long tall Sally: *Various artists*.
LP: . . . . **AMA 3906**
MC: . . . . **AMC 3906**

PRINCES' TRUST, THE (Various artists).
Tracks: / Running in the family: *Various artists* / If I was: *Various artists* / Behind the mask: *Various* artists / You've lost that lovin' feeling: *Collins, Phil & Paul Young* / Stand by me: *Various artists* / Misfit: *Various artists* / Wonderful tonight: *Various artists* / Don't look down: *Various artists* / Invisible: *Various artists* / Through the barricades: *Various artists* / So strong: *Various artists* / Run to you: *Various artists* / Saturday night's alright (for fighting): *Various artists* / It's the same old song: *Various* artists / I can't help myself: *Various artists* / Reach out I'll be there: *Various artists* / Your song: *Various* artists / Wanderer: *Edmunds, Dave & Bryan Adams* / While my guitar gently weeps: *Various artists* / Here comes the sun: *Various artists* / With a little help from my friends: *Various artists* / God save The Queen: *Various artists*.
LP: . . . . **PTA 1987**
MC: . . . . **PTC 1987**

PURE SOFT METAL (It takes your breath away) (Various artists).
Tracks: / Kind of magic, A: *Queen* / (I just) died in your arms: *Cutting Crew* / Missing you: *Waite, John*/ Kyrie: *Mr. Mister* / Summer of '69: *Adams, Bryan* / Forget me not: *Bad English* / Every rose has it's thorn: *Poison* / Rosanna: *Toto* / Can't fight this feeling: *REO Speedwagon* / Take my breath away: *Berlin*/ Crying: *Vixen* / Forever free: *W.A.S.P.* / Over the hills and far away: *Moore, Gary* / Modern girl: *Meatloaf* / Play for your life: *Wasch* / Bad times: *Mammoth* / True: *Spandau Ballet* / China in your hand: *T'Pau*.
LP: . . . . **SMR 996**
MC: . . . . **SMC 996**

PURPLE RAINBOWS (Various artists).
Tracks: / Black night: *Deep Purple* / Speed king: *Deep Purple* / Child in time: *Deep Purple* (Extra track on CD and cassette.) / Strange kind of woman: *Deep Purple* / Fireball: *Deep Purple* / Smoke on the water: *Deep Purple* / Highway star: *Deep Purple* / Woman from Tokyo: *Deep Purple* (Extra track on CD and cassette.) / Perfect strangers: *Deep Purple* / Hush ('88 version): *Deep Purple* / Since you been gone: *Rainbow* / I surrender: *Rainbow* / Fool for your loving (original version): *Whitesnake* / Here I go again (US remix): *Whitesnake*/ Night games: *Bonnet, Graham* / Rock 'n' roll children: *Dio*.
LP: **845534-1**
MC: **845534-4**

Q - THE ALBUM VOL. 1 (Various artists).
MC: . . . . **STAC 2522**
LP: . . . . **STAR 2522**

RAINBOW WARRIORS (Various artists).
Tracks: / Pride (in the name of love): *U2* / Heaven is a place on earth: *Carlisle, Belinda* / Love is the seventh wave: *Sting* / Let's go forward: *D'arby, Terence Trent* / Ship of fools: *World Party* / Don't stop the dance: *Ferry, Bryan* / Last great American whale: *Reed, Lou* / When tomorrow comes: *Eurythmics* / Middle of the road: *Pretenders* / Throwing stones: *Grateful Dead* / This time: *INXS* / Lay your hands on me: *Thompson Twins* / Small world: *Lewis, Huey & The News* / City of dreams: *Talking Heads* / Waterfront (live): *Simple Minds* / Whole of the moon, The: *Waterboys* / It's the end of the world as we know it: *R.E.M.* / You're the voice: *Farnham, John* / Set them free: *Aswad* / Somebody: *Adams, Bryan* / Miles away: *Basia*/ Red rain: *Gabriel, Peter* / Look out any window: *Hornsby, Bruce & The Range* / Wholly humble heart: *Stephenson*, Martin & The Daintees / I will be your friend: *Sade* / We are the people: *Cougar, John Mellencamp* / Why worry: *Dire Straits* / Balance: *Little Steven* (Only on CD.) / Scottish rain: *Silencers* (Only on CD.) / Hard rain: *Hothouse Flowers* (Only on CD.) / Somewhere down the crazy river: *Robertson, Robbie* (Only on CD.).
2LP: . . . . **PL 74065**
MCSET: . . . . **PK 74065**

RAISED ON ROCK, VOL. 1 (Various artists).
MCSET: . . . . **RORMC 37001**

RAISED ON ROCK VOL. 2 (Various artists).
Tracks: / With a little help from my friends: *Cocker, Joe* / Here comes the night: *Them* / Pictures of matchstick men: *Status Quo* / For your love: *Yardbirds* / We've gotta get out of this place: *Animals* / I feel free: *Cream* / You really got me: *Kinks* / Out of time: *Farlowe, Chris* / Man of the world: *Fleetwood Mac*/ America: *Nice* / Natural born boogie: *Humble Pie* / Got to get you into my life: *Bennett, Cliff & The Rebel* Rousers / Hi ho silver lining: *Beck, Jeff* / Fire: *Crazy World of Arthur Brown* / I don't like Mondays: *Boomtown* Rats / Lola: *Kinks* / Rubber bullets: *10 CC* / Hold your head up: *Argent* / Paranoid: *Black* Sabbath / Take on the world: *Judas Priest* / Show me the way: *Frampton, Peter* / You wear it well: *Stewart*, Rod / Layla: *Derek & The Dominoes* / Question: *Moody Blues* / Roll away the stone: *Mott The Hoople*/ Who do you love: *Juicy Lucy* / Bad bad boy: *Nazareth* / Part of the union: *Strawbs* / Come on Eileen: *Dexy's Midnight Runners & Emerald Express* / Unchain my heart: *Cocker, Joe* / Night games: *Bonnet, Graham*/ Garden party: *Marillion* / Killer on the loose: *Thin Lizzy* / I want candy: *Bow Wow Wow* / Wanderer, The: *Status Quo* / Wild boys: *Duran Duran* / Shot in the dark: *Osbourne, Ozzy* / Love and pride: *King*/ Take the situation: *Heyward, Nick* / Breaking the law: *Judas Priest* / Holding out for a hero: *Tyler, Bonnie*/ Golden brown: *Stranglers*.
MCSET: . . . . **RORMC 37002**

RARE STUFF (Various artists).
LP: . . . . **SHSM 2028**

READING FESTIVAL '73 (Various artists).
LP: . . . . **MQCLP 001**
MC: . . . . **MQCMC 001**

READING FESTIVAL '82 (Various artists).
LP: . . . . **MNLP 82**

RED HOT AND BLUE (Various artists).
Tracks: / Well did you evah?: *Harry, Deborah & Iggy Pop* / Who wants to be a millionaire?: *Thompson Twins* / I love Paris: *Les Negresses Vertes* / Love for sale: *Fine Young Cannibals* / After you: *Watley, Jody* / So in love: *Lang, K.D.* / You do something to me: *O'Connor, Sinead* / Down in the depths: *Stansfield, Lisa*/ Night and day: *U2* / It's alright for me: *Waits, Tom* / Miss Otis regrets: *MacColl, Kirsty*/ *Pogues*/ I get a kick out of you: *Jungle Brothers* / Just one of those things: *MacColl, Kirsty*/ *Pogues* / Begin the beguine: *Keita, Salif* / From this moment on: *Somerville, Jimmy* / Too darn hot: *Erasure* / Every time we say goodbye: *Lennox, Annie* / Do I love you?: *Aztec Camera* / Don't fence me in: *Byrne, David* / In the still of the night: *Neville Brothers* / So in love: *Lang, K.D.* / I've got you under my skin: *Cherry, Neneh*.
2LP: . . . . **CHR 1799**
MC: . . . . **ZCHR 1799**

REQUIEM FOR THE AMERICAS (Various artists).
LP: . . . . **ENVLP 529**
MC: . . . . **TCENV 529**

REVELATIONS - ANTHOLOGY FOR GLASTONBURY FAYRE (Various artists).
LPS: . . . . **REV 1/3**

REVENGE OF THE UNDERDOG (Various artists).
LP: . . . . **SITU 4**

ROCK ANTHEMS (Various artists).
Tracks: / Rockin' all over the world: *Status Quo* / Bat out of hell: *Meatloaf* / Get it on: *T. Rex* / All the young dudes: *Mott The Hoople* / All day and all of the night: *Kinks* / Born to be wild: *Steppenwolf*/ All right now: *Free* / Gimme some lovin': *Spencer Davis group* / Conquistador: *Procul Harum* / I hear you knocking: *Edmunds, Dave* / Blinded by the light: *Manfred Mann's Earthband* / This flight tonight: *Nazareth*/ You ain't seen nothing yet: *Bachman-Turner Overdrive* / Hold your head up: *Argent* / With a little help from my friends: *Cocker, Joe* / Milk and alcohol / Sweet home Alabama: *Skynard, Lynard* / Whisky in the jar: *Thin Lizzy* / Hush: *Deep Purple* / Gypsy: *Uriah Heep* / Rocky mountain way: *Walsh, Joe* / On the road again: *Canned Heat* / Weight, The: *Band* / Black magic woman: *Santana*.
LP: . . . . **NE 1309**
MC: . . . . **CE 2309**

ROCK ANTHEMS II (Various artists).
Tracks: / Walk on the wild side: *Reed, Lou* / Don't fear the reaper: *Blue Oyster Cult* / Hot blooded: *Foreigner*/ Black Betty: *Ram Jam Band* / Radar Love: *Golden Earring* / School's out: *Cooper, Alice* / All along the watchtower: *Hendrix, Jimi* / Badge: *Cream* / White light, white heat: *Velvet Underground* / For your love: *Yardbirds* / Here comes the night: *Them* / Nutbush city limits: *Turner, Ike & Tina* / Fire: *Crazy* World of Arthur Brown / Layla: *Derek & The Dominoes* / One & one is one: *Medicine Head* / Spanish stroll: *Various artists* / Mockingbird: *Hart, Tim & Maddy Prior* / In a broken dream: *Python Lee Jackson* / Paranoid: *Black Sabbath* / Silver machine: *Hawkwind* / Rock and roll star: *Various artists* / American woman: *Guess Who* / We gotta get out of this place: *Animals* / Hi ho silver lining: *Beck, Jeff*.
LP: . . . . **NE 1319**
MC: . . . . **CE 2319**

ROCK AROUND THE CLOCK (PREMIER) (Various artists).
Tracks: / Rock around the clock: *Haley, Bill & The Comets* / Teenager in love: *Sha Na Na* / Great balls of fire: *Lewis, Jerry Lee* / Party doll: *Knox, Buddy* / Lucille: *Little Richard* / Why do fools fall in love?: *Lymon, Frankie & The Teenagers* / Whole lotta shakin' goin' on: *Lewis, Jerry Lee* / Ooby dooby: *Orbison, Roy*(end s1) / Good golly Miss Molly: *Little Richard* / Boy from New York City: *Ad Libs* / Shake, rattle and roll: *Haley, Bill & The Comets* / Mary Lou: *Hawkins, Ronnie* / Tell Laura I love her: *Sha Na Na* / Sweet little sixteen: *Lewis, Jerry Lee* / Boppin' the blues: *Perkins, Carl* / See you later alligator: *Haley, Bill & The Comets*.
LP: . . . . **CBR 1025**
MC: . . . . **KCBR 1025**

ROCK CITY NIGHTS (Various artists).
Tracks: / One vision: *Queen* / You give love a bad name: *Bon Jovi* / Big area: *Then Jerico* / King of emotion: *Big Country (group)* / Red sky: *Status Quo* / Incommunicado: *Marillion* / Satisfied: *Marx*, Richard / Some like it hot: *Power Station* / Rock the night: *Europe* / Need you tonight: *INXS* / I don't want a lover: *Texas* / I won't back down: *Petty, Tom* / Silent running: *Mike & The Mechanics*/ Africa: *Toto* / More than a feeling: *Boston* / Go your own way: *Fleetwood Mac* / I surrender: *Rainbow (Group)* / Eye of the tiger: *Survivor*.
MC: . . . . **RCNTC 1**
LP: . . . . **RCNTV 1**

ROCK CLASSICS (Various artists).
2LP: **303800**
MCSET: **503800**

ROCK EXPRESS (Various artists).
Tracks: / Hambone: *Haley, Bill & The Comets* / I'll make it all up to you: *Lewis, Jerry Lee* / That's right: *Perkins*, Carl / Mr. Five by five: *Morse, Ella Mae* / Shake it Lucy baby: *Otis, Johnny* / Problem child: *Orbison*, Roy / Buttermilk baby: *Moore, Merrill E.* / Love all night: *Platters* / Skinny Minnie: *Haley, Bill & The* Comets / Believe me when I say rock 'n' roll is here to stay: *Esquerta* / No kissin' and a huggin': *Berry, Richard And The Pharoahs* / Let's all rock together: *Jodimars*.
LP: . . . . **BDL 1008**

ROCK FROM THE CAROLINAS (Various artists).
Tracks: / My hot mama: *Gittens, Louis* / Gonna leave: *Gittens, Louis* / Puppet: *Gittens, Louis* / Rebel rouser: *Gittens, Louis* / Take up the slack, Daddy O: *Gittens, Louis* / Spider walk: *Gittens, Louis* / Bobby sox bop: *Whitaker, Gene & Kelly Sears* / You're just right for me: *Don's Rockers* / Moonlight stroll: *Don's* Rockers / Pacific honky tonk: *Ray, Don* / Big big truck: *Crosby, Harold* / I will mend your heartaches tomorrow: *Crosby, Harold* / Bright lights: *Crosby, Harold* / How bad can bad luck be: *Miller, Joseph June*.
LP: . . . . **WLP 8912**

ROCK FURY (Various artists).
Tracks: / Radar love: *Golden Earring* / Boys are back in town: *Thin Lizzy* / Freebird: *Lynyrd Skynyrd*/ Cat scratch fever: *Nugent, Ted* / Hold your head up: *Argent* / What you're proposing: *Status Quo* / Career of evil: *Blue Oyster Cult* / Hit me with your best shot (live): *Benatar, Pat* / Funk no.48: *James Gang*/ Spaceman: *Journey (Group)* / Natural born boogie: *Humble Pie*.
LP: . . . . **RAWLP 002**
MC: . . . . **RAWTC 002**

ROCK GUITAR LEGENDS (Various artists).
LPS: . . . . **RGLLP 47001**
MCSET: . . . . **RGLMC 47001**

ROCK GUITAR LEGENDS VOL. 2 (Various artists).
Tracks: / Mercury blues: *Lindley, David* / Over and over: *Walsh, Joe* / Juke box hero: *Foreigner* (Mick Jones) / Lost in the shuffle: *Kortchmar, Danny* / Long time til' I get over you: *Little Feat* (Paul Barrere/Fred Tackett) / River of tears: *Raitt, Bonnie* / Ashphalt jungle: *Felder, Don* / So wrong: *Simmons, Patrick*(Pat Simmons) / Stainsby girls: *Rea, Chris* / Spirit of radio: *Rush* (Alex Lifeson) / I can see for miles: *Who*(Pete Townshend) / Cocaine: *Cale, J.J.* / Sky high: *Atlanta Rhythm Section* (Barry Bailey) / Waiting for the man: *Velvet Underground* (Lou Reed) / Whisky in the jar: *Thin Lizzy* (Phil Lynott/Eric Bell) / From little things big things grow: *Edmunds, Dave* / Confidence man: *Healey, Jeff* / We can be together: *Jefferson Airplane*(Jorma Kaukonen) / Built for speed: *Stray Cats* (Brian Setzer) / Roll with the changes: *REO Speedwagon* (Gary Rickrath) / Don't stop believing: *Journey (Group)* (Neal Schon) / Honey don't leave L.A.: *Taylor, James* (Danny Kortchmar) / Sweet potato pie: *Taylor, James* / Rock 'n' roll hoochie coo: *Winter, Johnny* (Johnny Winter/Rick Derringer) / East of Eden's gate: *Thorpe, Billy* / Need your love so bad: *Fleetwood Mac* (Peter Green) / Where have you been all my life: *Nugent, Ted* / Ready for love: *Mott The Hoople* (Mick Ralphs) / Once bitten twice shy: *Hunter*, Ian (Mick Ronson) / American girl: *Petty, Tom* / Sweet home Alabama: *Lynyrd Skynyrd* (Gary Rossington/Ed King/Allen Collins) / Gotta hurry: *Yardbirds* (Eric Clapton) / No particular place to go: *Berry, Chuck* / Natural born boogie: *Humble Pie* (Peter Frampton) / Parisienne walkways (live): *Moore, Gary* / I'm your witch doctor: *Clapton*, Eric Allstars / Laundromat: *Gallagher, Rory* / Bleeding heart: *Hendrix, Jimi* / You won't see me anymore: *Green, Peter* / Breakdown: *Coverdale, David* (Mickey Moody) / I've been born again: *Frey, Glen* / Who do you love: *Juicy Lucy* (Glen Campbell/Neil Hubbard) / Paranoid: *Black Sabbath* (Tony Iommi) / Rocky mountain way: *Walsh, Joe* / Drift away: *Gray, Dobie* (Reggie Young) / I came to dance: *Lofgren, Nils* / Show me the way: *Frampton, Peter* / Dear Mr. Fantasy: *Traffic* (Dave Mason).

MCSET: RGLMC 47006

ROCK HEROES (Various artists).
2LP: PLD 8001
MCSET: PLDC 8001

ROCK HOUSE (Various artists).
LP: RTL 2061
MC: 4 CRTL 2061

ROCK LEGENDS (Various artists).
2LP: STAR 2290
MCSET: STAC 2290
MCSET: SSDC 8032
2LP: SSD 8032
MC: MCTC 045

ROCK MACHINE (Various artists).
LP: ARLP 106
MC: ZCAR 106

ROCK MACHINE VOL 1 (Various artists).
Tracks: / Beg to differ: *Various artists* / Burning tree: *Various artists* / Future tense: *Various artists*/ Dirty weapons: *Various artists* / Solitary solitude: *Various artists* / Hey kid: *Various artists* / Paris calling: *Various artists* / Devil wears lingerie, The: *Various artists* / Maryanne: *Various artists*/ Summer: *Various artists* / Shot in the dark (live): *Various artists* / Only my heart talkin': *Various artists*/ Guilty: *Various artists.*
LP: 4669341
MC: 4669344

ROCK MACHINE...STILL TURNS YOU ON (Various artists).
2LP: EPC 22228
MC: 40 22228

ROCK ME ALL NIGHT LONG (Various artists).
LP: FLY 606

ROCK 'N' ROLL HIGH SCHOOL (Various artists).
Tracks: / Rock 'n' roll high school: *Ramones* / I want you around: *Ramones* / Come on let's go: *Ramones*/ Blitzkrieg bop: *Ramones* / Teenage lobotomy: *Ramones* / She's the one: *Ramones* / California sun: *Ramones*/ Pinhead: *Ramones* / So it goes: *Lowe, Nick* / Energy fools the magician: *Eno, Brian* / Rock'n'roll high school: *Soles, P.J.* / Come back Jonee: *Devo* / Teenage depression: *Eddie & The Hot Rods* / Smoking in the boys room: *Brownsville Station* / School days: *Berry, Chuck* / Dream goes on forever: *Rundgren, Todd*/ School's out: *Cooper, Alice.*
LP: SRK 6070

ROCK OF AGES (Various artists).
Tracks: / Hey Joe: *Hendrix, Jimi* / Africa: *Toto* / State of independence: *Jon & Vangelis* / Broken wings: *Mr. Mister* / Take it on the run: *REO Speedwagon* / Wooden ships: *Jefferson Airplane* / Burnin' for you: *Blue Oyster Cult* / In a lifetime: *Clannad* / White room: *Cream* / You're the voice: *Farnham, John*/ Dead ringer for love: *Meatloaf* / Rock of life: *Springfield, Rick* / Talking all night: *Hall & Oates*/ Dust in the wind: *Kansas* / Flame, The: *Cheap Trick* / Diamond dust: *Beck, Jeff* / Presence of the Lord: *Blind Faith* / More than a feeling: *Boston* / Because the night: *Smith, Patti Group.*
MC: STDMC 32

ROCK OF AMERICA (Various artists).
Tracks: / Don't come around here no more: *Petty, Tom & The Heartbreakers* / Because the night: *Smith, Patti* / Maneater: *Hall & Oates* / This little girl: *Bonds, Gary U.S.* / I love you Suzanne: *Reed, Lou* / Rush hour: *Wiedlin, Jane* / Deadringer for love: *Meatloaf* / More than a feeling: *Boston* / Call me: *Blondie*/ Centrefold: *J.Geils Band* / Rosanna: *Toto* / Bette Davis eyes: *Carnes, Kim* / Some weird sin: *Pop, Iggy* / Jessie's girl: *Springfield, Rick.*
LP: MODEM 1036
MC: MODEMC 1036

ROCK ON (Various artists).
LP: THIS 29

ROCK ON BRAIN (Various artists).
Tracks: / Anyone's daughter: *Various artists* / Novalis: *Various artists* / Accept: *Various artists*/ Jane: *Various artists* / SFF: *Various artists* / Guru Guru: *Various artists* / Sunband: *Various artists* / Birth control: *Various artists* / Epitaph: *Various artists* / RMO: *Various artists.*
LP: 0040 119

ROCK ON THROUGH THE SIXTIES (Various artists).
LP: MFP 50469

ROCK PRETTY (Various artists).
Tracks: / Two hearts: *Various artists* / Rock en roll chicken: *Various artists* / Gettin' sticky (over the girl next door): *Various artists* / Flesh of the devil: *Various artists* / Little Miss Teazer: *Various artists*/ You better believe it: *Various artists* / Beard song, The: *Various artists* / Suzy (was a live wire): *Various artists* / Respect the dead: *Various artists* / Tension: *Various artists.*
LP: HMRLP 25

ROCK REVIVAL (Various artists).
2LP: NE 634

ROCK REVOLUTION VOL 1 (Various artists).
LP: SHM 933
MC: HSC 304

ROCK REVOLUTION VOL 2 (Various artists).
LP: SHM 951
MC: HSC 326

ROCK SHOP (Various artists).
LP: SHM 3107
MC: HSC 3107

ROCK SOCK THE BOOGIE (Various artists).
Tracks: / Sapphire: *Various artists* / In the bottom of my heart: *Various artists* / 49th State blues: *Various* artists / Handle with care: *Various artists* / I stand accused: *Various artists* / I walk a lonely mile: *Various* artists / Knock kneed Nellie from Knoxville: *Various artists* / Rock sock the boogie: *Various artists* / Too much boogie: *Various artists* / Come dance with me: *Various artists* / Big rock inn: *Various artists*/ Ain't that just like a woman: *Various artists* / Shut the door baby: *Various artists.*
LP: CR 30237

ROCK SOLID (Various artists).
LP: LBR 100
MC: CLBR 100

ROCK SUPERSTARS VOL 1 (Various artists).
LP: SHM 957
MC: HSC 332

ROCK THE CITY (Various artists).
LP: 0146022
MC: 0146141

ROCK THE FLAG (Various artists).
Tracks: / We say yeah!: *Various artists* / 10 cats down: *Various artists* / Eeny Meeny: *Various artists*/ You're so fine: *Various artists* / Red sails in the sunset: *Various artists* / Maria Elena: *Various artists*/ If I had my life to live over: *Various artists* / Swanee river rock: *Various artists* / Oh you babe: *Various* artists / Rockabily rose: *Various artists* / Will you: *Various artists* / Gonna be a star: *Various artists*/ Rockabilly: *Various artists* / Hey little girl: *Various artists* / Blue day: *Various artists* / Stompin' with the wildcats: *Various artists.*
LP: MFM 014

ROCK THE NATION (The Chart Show) (Various artists).
Tracks: / Crazy crazy nights: *Kiss* / Addicted to love: *Palmer, Robert* / Mony mony: *Idol, Billy* / Incommunicado: *Marillion* / Listen like thieves: *INXS* / Wanted dead or alive: *Bon Jovi* / Is this love: *Whitesnake*/ Valerie: *Winwood, Steve* / Power of love, The: *Lewis, Huey & The News* / Satellite: *Hooters* / Li'l devil: *Cult* / Girls girls girls: *Motley Crue* / Love is a battlefield: *Benatar, Pat* / In the army now: *Status Quo* / Battleship chains: *Georgia Satellites* / Comin' on strong: *Broken English* / Crazy: *Icehouse*/ I want to know what love is: *Foreigner* / Final countdown, The: *Europe* / St. Elmo's fire: *Parr, John*/ Let my people go go: *Rainmakers* / Don't shed a tear: *Carrack, Paul* / Said she was a dancer: *Jethro Tull*/ Drive: *Cars.*
2LP: ADD 2
MCSET: ZDD 2

ROCK, TICK, TOCK (Various artists).
LP: 37650

ROCKIN' ALL OVER THE WORLD (Rediscover the 70's and 80's) (Various artists).
Tracks: / Walk on the wild side: *Reed, Lou* / Witch queen of New Orleans: *Redbone* / Jeepster: *T. Rex*/ Layla: *Derek & The Dominoes* / You wear it well: *Stewart, Rod* / American woman: *Guess Who* / All the way from Memphis: *Mott The Hoople* / Wall Street shuffle / Radar love: *Golden Earring* / How long: *Ace*/ Play that funky music: *Wild Cherry* / Pick up the pieces: *Average White Band* / Glass of champagne: *Sailor*/ Hanging on the telephone: *Blondie* / Hold the line: *Toto* / More than a feeling: *Boston* / Everyday hurts: *Sad Cafe* / Run for home: *Lindisfarne* / Year of the cat: *Stewart, Al* / Philadelphia freedom: *John, Elton* / Rockin' all over the world: *Status Quo* / Black Betty: *Ram Jam* / 5-7-0-5: *City Boy*/ Going underground: *Jam.*
MCSET: OG 2206

ROCKIN' AND ROLLIN' (Various artists).
Tracks: / Whole lotta shakin' goin' on: *Little Richard* / I didn't know I loved you till I saw you rock'n'roll: *Glitter*, Gary / Rock on: *Essex, David* / Frankenstein: *Winter, Edgar* / And when I die: *Blood, Sweat & Tears*/ Lucille: *Various artists* / Free electric band: *Hammond, Albert* / Rock 'n' roll hoochie koo: *Winter, Johnny*/ Stardust: *Essex, David* / God gave rock 'n' roll to you: *Argent* / Hold your head up: *Argent* / Don't fear the reaper: *Blue Oyster Cult* / All the way from Memphis: *Mott The Hoople* / I'm the leader of the gang (I am): *Glitter, Gary* / Blue suede shoes: *Perkins, Carl* / Hold the line: *Toto* / More than a feeling: *Boston*/ All the young dudes: *Mott The Hoople* / Say you love me or say goodbye: *REO Speedwagon* / So you want to be a rock 'n' roll star: *Byrds.*
MCSET: DTO 10062

ROCK-ON-ROLL-ON (Various artists).
Tracks: / Rock a little bit: *Vikings* / Chicken session: *De Rieux, Larry* / High school blues: *Vickery, Mack*/ Moon dawg: *Gamblers* / Going my way: *Vidone, Bob* / I like to go: *McDaniel, Floyd* / Dozen diamond man: *Stephens, Billy* / Why was I blue?: *Robbins, Webb* / Oreo: *Cooper, Johnny* / Travelling Sam: *Smith*, Robert / Devil's run: *Kleibe, Herb* / Come to my house: *Logsdon, Bill* / B-52: *Gibson, Bobby* / I've lost you: *Draper, Joseph June* / Rockin' Parts, part 1: *Rockin' Parts.*
LP: WLP 8865

RUBAIYAT (Various artists).
Tracks: / Hello I love you: *Cure* / House of the rising sun: *Chapman, Tracy* / Tokoloshe man: *Happy Mondays*/ You're so vain: *Faster Pussycat* / Hotel California: *Gipsy Kings* / Seven and seven is: *Bragg, Billy*/ Motorcycle mama: *Sugarcubes* / Born in Chicago: *Pixies* / Marquee moon: *Kronos Quartet* / You belong to me: *Baker, Anita* / I want to make it with you: *Pendergrass, Teddy* / These days: *10,000 Maniacs* / One more parade: *They Might Be Giants.*
LP: EKT 78
MC: EKT 78 C

SCREAM - THE COMPILATION (Various artists).
LP: GHS 24177
MC: K 9241774
LP: K 9241771

SECOND FRAMES (Various artists).
Tracks: / Sweet Russian: *Argent, Rod* / Light in your eyes: *Foster, Mo* / Irish girl, The: *Legg, Adrian*/ Back against the wall: *Armstrong, Herbie* / Rainmaker: *Wood, Mark* / Spellbound: *Chatton, Brian* / Woman of Ireland: *Davis, Andy* / Jabe: *Davis, Andy* / I remember: *Lynn, Ian.*
MC: TCMMC 1018

SECRET TEAM, THE (Various artists).
LP: VXS 300039

SGT. PEPPER KNEW MY FATHER (Various artists).
Tracks: / With a little help from my friends': *Wet Wet Wet* / She's leaving home: *Bragg, Billy.*
LP: PEPLP 100
MC: PEPMC 100

SINGLES (Various artists).
MC: A 116

SISTERS ARE DOIN' IT (Various artists).
2LP: TVLP 11
MC: ZCTV 11

SLASH CUTS (Various artists).
LP: SLAP 8

SOFT METAL (Various artists).
LP: SMR 862
MC: SMC 862

SOFT METAL BALLADS (Various artists).
2LP: ARC 933501
MCSET: ARC 933504

SOFT ROCK (Various artists).
MC: STAC 2397
LP: STAR 2397

SONGS FROM THE BOSS (Various artists).
Tracks: / Blinded by the light: *Manfred Mann's Earthband* / Pink cadillac: *Cole, Natalie* / This little girl: *Bonds, Gary U.S.* / From small things, big things come: *Edmunds, Dave* / Born to run: *Clarke, Allan* / Reason to believe: *Beat Farmers, The* / Fire: *Pointer Sisters* / 4th July Ashbury Park: *Hollies* / Dancing in the dark: *Big Daddy* / Fever: *Ford, Dean* / Spirit in the night: *Manfred Mann's Earthband.*
LP: ADD 3
MC: ZDD 3

SONGS OF BOB DYLAN, THE (Various artists).
Tracks: / Blowin' in the wind: *Cooke, Sam* / Hard rain's gonna fall: *Ferry, Bryan* / Don't think twice: *Bare*, Bobby / Tomorrow's a long time: *Presley, Elvis* / Dusty old fairgrounds: *Blue Ash* / It ain't me babe: *Cash*, Johnny / Mama you been on my mind: *Stewart, Rod* / If you gotta go go now: *Flying Burrito Brothers* / Mr. Tambourine man: *Byrds* / Farewell Angelina: *New Riders Of The Purple Sage* / It's all over now baby blue: *Them*/ It takes a lot to laugh, it takes a train to cry: *Stills/Kooper/Bloomfield* / From a Buick 6: *Bonds, Gary U.S.*/ Just like Tom Thumb's blues: *Collins, Judy* / Absolutely sweet Marie: *Jason & The Scorchers* / This wheel's on fire: *Siouxsie & Banshees* / I shall be released: *Robinson, Tom Band* / I pity the poor immigrant: *Havens*, Richie / All along the watchtower: *Hendrix, Jimi* / Lay lady lay: *Axton, Hoyt* / Tonight I'll be staying here with you: *Turner, Tina* / Wanted man: *Thorogood, George* / Champaign Illinois: *Perkins, Carl* / When I paint my masterpiece: *Band* / Watching the river flow: *Cocker, Joe* / Knockin' on heaven's door: *Clapton*, Eric / Simple twist of fate: *Baez, Joan* / Rita Mae: *Lewis, Jerry Lee* / Abandoned love: *Everly Brothers*/ Seven days: *Wood, Ronnie* / Need a woman: *Cooder, Ry* / Let's keep it between us: *Raitt, Bonnie.*
2LP: STDL 20
MCSET: STDC 20

SOUND OF DEEP ELLUM, THE (Various artists).
Tracks: / No more love: *Three on a hill* / Six gun: *Decadent Dub Team* / Snatch rap: *Buck Pets, The*/ Paint the flowers all black: *Shallow Reign* / Devil's chasin' me, The: *Reverend Horton Heat* / Jamaican lady: *New Bohemians* / Cattlecar: *Trees* / My dark earth edge (end over end): *End Over End* / Man o' war: *Daylights*/ Sales tax: *Legendary Revelations.*
LP: ILPS 9888
MC: ICT 9888

SOUND OF THE SUBURBS, THE (Various artists).
Tracks: / Eton rifles, The: *Various artists* / Antmusic: *Various artists* / Ever fallen in love (with someone you shouldn't 've): *Various artists* / Another girl, another planet: *Various artists* / Teenage kicks: *Various* artists / Echo beach: *Various artists* / Happy birthday: *Various artists* / Oliver's army: *Various artists*/ 2-3-6-8 Motorway: *Various artists* / Hit me with your rhythm stick: *Various artists* / Call me: *Various artists* / Reward: *Various artists* / I don't like Mondays: *Various artists* / Pretty in pink: *Various* artists / No more heroes: *Various artists* / Turning Japanese: *Various artists* / Do anything you wanna do: *Various artists* / Sound of the suburbs, The: *Various artists.*
LP: MOOD 18
MC: MOOD C18

STATE OF THINGS (Various artists).
LP: BBB 1

STONED AGAIN (Tribute to The Rolling Stones) (Various artists).
LP: ILLUSION 006

SWEET DREAMS (Various artists).
Tracks: / Age of reason: *Farnham, John* / All by myself: *Carmen, Eric* / Broken wings: *Mr. Mister* / Walk on the wild side: *Reed, Lou* / Don't talk to strangers: *Springfield, Rick* / Dancing on a high wire: *Parsons*, Alan Project / All out of love: *Air Supply* / Closer to your heart: *Clannad* / On the air tonight: *Southside* Johnny / First we take Manhatten: *Warnes, Jennifer* / Don't forget to dance: *Kinks* / Midnight blue: *Tucker, Louise* / Living inside myself: *Vannelli, Gino* / Stairway to heaven: *Far Corporation.*
MC: NK 74590

TAKE IT EASY - THE SOUND OF CALIFORNIA (Various artists).
Tracks: / On the way home: *Buffalo Springfield* / Doctor my eyes: *Browne, Jackson* / Willin': *Little Feat*/ Return of the grievous angel: *Harris, Emmylou/ Gram Parsons* / Hotel California: *Eagles* / Cinderella: *Firefall*/ Life's been good: *Walsh, Joe* / I love L.A.: *Newman, Randy* / Hot burrito: *Flying Burrito Brothers*/ Take it easy: *Eagles* / Cry like a rainstorm: *Raitt, Bonnie* / Fallin' in love: *Souther* / It's so easy: *Ronstadt, Linda* / Werewolves of London: *Zevon, Warren* / Little sister: *Cooder, Ry.*
LP: 229241981
MC: 229241984

THATS LIVE (Various artists).
LP: METALPM 125

TOP 40 ROCK CLASSICS (See under Top 40 ...) (Various artists).

TOUCHDOWN (Various artists).
Tracks: / Touchdown: *Various artists* / Soft drink: *Various artists* / Life: *Various artists* / W.A.S.P. town: *Various artists* / Do it today: *Various artists* / Flowers for Ingrid: *Various artists* / Red ribbon day: *Various artists* / Stand me up: *Various artists* / Put your ghost shirt on: *Various artists.*
LP: TOUCH 1

TRASH ON DELIVERY (Various artists).
LP: . . . . SHARP 011

TROUSER PRESS COMPILATION (Various artists).
MC: . . . . A 124

TUATARA (Various artists).
LP: . . . . ED 193

V Various artists-Robert Wyatt, Mike Oldfield, etc (Various artists).
LP: . . . . VD 2502
MC: . . . . TCVD 2502

VERTIGO CLASSICS AND RARITIES (1969-1973 Vol. 1) (Various artists).
LP: 8465221
MC: 8465224

VISION SHARED, A: FOLKWAYS (Various artists).
Tracks: / Sylvie: *Sweet Honey in the Rock* / Pretty boy Floyd: *Dylan, Bob* / Do-re-mi: *Mellencamp, John Cougar*/ I ain't got no home: *Springsteen, Bruce* / Jesus Christ: *U2* / Rock Island line: *Little Richard/Fishbone*/ East Texas red: *Guthrie, Arlo* / Philadelphia lawyer: *Nelson, Willie* / Hobo's lullaby: *Harris, Emmylou*/ Bourgeois blues: *Taj Mahal* / Gray goose: *Sweet Honey in the Rock* / Goodnight Irene: *Wilson, Brian*/ Vigilante man: *Springsteen, Bruce* / This land is your land: *Seeger, Pete* (with Sweet Honey In The Rock, Doc Watson & The Little Red School House).
LP: 4609051
MC: 4609054

WALL, THE (21st July 1990 Berlin Wall) (Various artists).
2LP: 846 611 1
MCSET: 846 911 4

WE WILL ROCK YOU (Various artists).
LP: . . . . DINTV 26
MC: . . . . DINMC 26

WILD ONE, THE (Various artists).
Tracks: / Breakthru: *Queen* / Crazy crazy nights: *Kiss* / Poison: *Cooper, Alice* / Tattooed millionaire: *Dickinson, Bruce* / No more Mr. Nice Guy: *Megadeth* / Dirty love: *Thunder* / Battleship chains: *Georgia* Satellites / Heaven knows: *Plant, Robert* / Hey you: *Quireboys* / Piece of me: *Skid Row* / Real me, The: *W.A.S.P.* / Kickin' up dust: *Little Angels* / Epic: *Faith No More* / Walk this way: *Run D.M.C.*/ Glamour boys: *Living Colour* / Crying: *Vixen*.
LP: . . . . EMTV 52
MC: . . . . TCEMTV 52

WILLIE AND THE POOR BOYS (Various artists).
LP: . . . . BILL 1
MC: . . . . KBILL 1

WOODSTOCK ONE (Music from the film) (Various artists).
Tracks: / I had a dream: *Sebastian, John B* / Going up the country: *Canned Heat* / Freedom: *Havens, Richie*/ Rock and soul music: *Country Joe & The Fish* / Coming into Los Angeles: *Guthrie, Arlo* / At the hop: *Sha Na Na* / Fish cheer, The: *McDonald, Country Joe* / I feel like I'm fixin' to die rag: *Various artists* / Drug store truck drivin' man: *Baez, Joan* / Sea of madness: *Crosby, Stills & Nash* / Wooden ships: *Crosby, Stills* & Nash / We're not gonna take it: *Who* / With a little help from my friends: *Cocker, Joe* / Crowd rain chant: *Cocker, Joe* / Soul sacrifice: *Santana* / I'm going home: *Ten Years After* / Volunteers: *Jefferson* Airplane / Rainbows all over your blues: *Sebastian, John* / Love march: *Butterfield Blues Band* / Star spangled banner, The: *Hendrix, Jimi*.
LPS: . . . . K 60001
MCSET: K4 60001

WOODSTOCK TWO (Music from the film) (Various artists).
Tracks: / Jam back at the house: *Hendrix, Jimi* / Izabella: *Hendrix, Jimi* / Get my heart back together: *Hendrix*, Jimi / Saturday afternoon: *Jefferson Airplane* / Eskimo blue day: *Jefferson Airplane* / Everything's gonna be alright: *Butterfield Blues Band* / Sweet Sir Galahad: *Baez, Joan* / Guinevere: *Crosby, Stills, Nash & Young*/ 4 + 20: *Crosby, Stills, Nash & Young*/ Marakesh express: *Crosby, Stills, Nash & Young* / My beautiful people: *Melanie* / Birthday of the sun: *Melanie* / Blood of the sun: *Mountain* / Theme for an imaginary western: *Mountain* / Woodstock boogie: *Canned Heat* / Let the sun shine in: *Audience*.
2LP: . . . . K 60002

Rock A Teens

WOOHOO.
Tracks: / Woo hoo / Doggone it baby / I'm not afraid / That's my mama / Dance to the bop / Story of a woman / Twangy / Janis will rock / Pagan / Lotta boppin' / Oh my nerves / I was born to rock.
LP: . . . . SR 25109
LP: . . . . ROLL 3001

Rock City Angels

YOUNG MAN'S BLUES.
Tracks: / Deep inside my heart / Hard to hold / Mary / Our little secret / Damned don't cry / Wild tiger / These arms of mine / Rumblefish / Boy from Hell's kitchen / Liza Jo / Beyond Babylon / Hush child / Ya gotta swear / Rough'n'tumble / South of the border.
2LP: . . . . WX 204
MC: . . . . WX 204C

Rock, Dickie

20 GREATEST HITS - DICKIE ROCK.
Tracks: / Every step of the way / Yours / Till / I'll hide my teardrops / There's always me / Coward of the county / Angeline / Candy store / Mandy / Just for old times sake / Come back to stay / I left my heart in San Francisco / She believes in me / You're my world / Love me tender / Back home again / You don't have to say you love me / How could you go / I write the songs / Wonder of you, The.
LP: . . . . DHL 717
MC: . . . . CDHL 717

DICKIE.
LP: . . . . SOLO 7008

DICKIE ROCK IN STYLE.
LP: . . . . SOLO 7011

TILL.
LP: . . . . HPE 624
MC: . . . . HPC 624

Rock Follies

ROCK FOLLIES (Various artists).
LP: 2302 054
LP: . . . . EGLP 23
LP: . . . . ILPS 9362

ROCK FOLLIES OF 1977.
LP: 2302 072
LP: . . . . EGLP 29

Rock From Arkansas

ROCK FROM ARKANSAS (See under Rock 'n' Roll) (Various artists).

Rock Goddess

HELL HATH NO FURY.
Tracks: / Hold me down / No more / Gotta let your hair down / Don't want your love / In the night / Visitors are here / I've seen it all before / You've got fire / It will never change / God be with you.
MC: . . . . CXM 68560
LP: . . . . AMLX 68560

ROCK GODDESS.
Tracks: / Heartache / Back to you / Love lingers still / To be betrayed / Take your love away / My angel / Satisfied then crucified / Start running / One way love / Make my night / Heavy metal rock 'n' roll.
LP: . . . . AMLH 68554
MC: . . . . CAM 68554

Rock Hard Hits

ROCK HARD HITS (Various artists).
LP: . . . . SHM 3113

Rock & Hyde

UNDER THE VOLCANO.
Tracks: / Dirty water / I will / Blind, the deaf and the lame, The / Knocking on closed doors / What children say / Talk to me / Middle of the night / There is always someone tougher / It's always raining / Oh Ruby.
LP: . . . . EMC 3525
MC: . . . . TCEMC 3525

Rock It

ROCK IT VOL 1 (Various artists).
LP: . . . . LP 8411

ROCK IT VOL 2 (Various artists).
LP: . . . . LP 8503

Rock It Baby Rock It

ROCK IT BABY ROCK IT (Original Soundtrack) (Various artists).
LP: . . . . RNDF 309

Rock Melons

TALES OF THE CITY.
LP: . . . . K 781 949 1
MC: . . . . K 781 949 4

Rock 'n' Roll

10 YEARS' COLLECTOR RECORDS (Various artists).
Tracks: / Eager boy: *Lonesome Drifter* / Teardrop valley: *Lonesome Drifter* / Wait a little baby: *Roby, Jimmy*/ Be boppin' baby: *Roby, Jimmy* / Walking and strolling: *Wayne, Billy* / I love my baby: *Wayne, Billy*/ Bad, bad boy: *Lollar, Bobby* / Servant of love (take 1): *Van Bros* / Spin the bottle, 1955: *Joy, Benny*/ Piano man: *Redell, Teddy* / Why worry: *Crain, Jimmy* / It's the way you are: *Mask, James* / Too old to rock 'n' roll: *Taylor, Carmol* / Parking in the dark: *Dean, Charles* / Itchy: *Dean, Charles* / Train whistle boogie: *Dean, Charles*.
LP: . . . . WLP 8816

14 GREAT ALL-TIME JIVERS, VOL 2 (Various artists).
LP: . . . . JIVIN 183

14 GREAT ALL-TIME JIVERS, VOL 1 (Various artists).
LP: . . . . JIVIN 182

14 GREAT ALL-TIME JIVERS, VOL 4 (Various artists).
LP: . . . . JIVIN 185

20 GOLDEN PIECES: VINTAGE ROCK 'N' ROLL (Various artists).
Tracks: / House of blue lights: *Slack, Freddie/Ella Mae Morse* / Bonnie B: *Lewis, Jerry Lee* / Ooby dooby: *Orbison*, Roy / Rock rockola: *Moore, Merrill E.* / Stranded in the jungle: *Cadets* / Voo vee ah vee: *Platters*/ Well now dig this: *Jodimars* / Heartbreak Hotel: *Jones, George* / Hole in my heart: *Berry, Richard/Pharoahs*/ Esquerita: *Berry, Richard/Pharoahs* / Louie Louie: *Berry, Richard/Pharoahs* / Good golly: *Otis, Johnny*/ Rock house: *Orbison, Roy*/ *Teen Kings* / Rock rock rock: *Berry, Richard/Pharoahs* / Down the line: *Lewis*, Jerry Lee / Rockin' the joint: *Esquerita* / Do you wanna rock?: *Cadets* / Rock everywhere: *Teen Queens*/ Dixie fried: *Perkins, Carl* / Poppin' Johnny: *Miller, Frankie* / Guitar shuffle: *Fulson, Lowell*.
LP: . . . . BDL 2018
MC: . . . . AJKL 2018

20 GREAT BALLS OF FIRE VOL.2 (Various artists).
LP: 2636912

20 GREAT ROCK 'N' ROLL HITS OF THE 50'S (Various artists).
Tracks: / Sea cruise: *Ford, Frankie* / When my dreamboat comes home: *Olenn, Johnny* / Stranded in the jungle: *Cadets* / Eddie my love: *Teen Queens* / Tossin and turnin: *Lewis, Bobby* / Goodnight my love: *Belvin*, Jesse / Don't you just know it: *Smith, Huey & The Clowns* / Baby hully gully: *Olympics* / Go Jimmy go: *Clayton, Jimmy* / Rumble: *Wray, Link & His Raymen* / Hippy hippy shake: *Romero, Chan* / Ooh my head: *Valens, Richard*/ Good golly Miss Molly: *Various artists* / Be bop a lula: *Everly Brothers* / Charlie Brown: *Chordettes*/ My true story: *Jive Five with Joe Rene & His Orchestra, The* / Cut it out: *Tex, Joe* / Hot banana: *McLollie, Oscar* / Everybody rock: *Stone, Jeff* / Batman: *Wray, Link & His Raymen*.
LP: . . . . DROP 1002
MC: . . . . CROP 1002

20 GREATEST HITS: ROCK 'N' ROLL STORY (Various artists).
MC: . . . . MAMC 9241285

20 ORIGINAL ROCK AND ROLL CLASSICS (Various artists).
LP: . . . . PLE 7004
MC: . . . . PLC 7004

24 ROCK'N'ROLL HOUSE SHAKERS (Various artists).
Tracks: / Whole lotta shakin' goin' on: *Lewis, Jerry Lee* / What'd I say?: *Lewis, Jerry Lee* / Good golly Miss Molly: *Various artists* / Long tall Sally: *Little Richard* / Be bop a lula: *Vincent, Gene* / Say mama: *Vincent, Gene* / Ain't that a shame: *Domino, Fats* / I'm gonna be a wheel someday: *Domino, Fats* / Maybellene: *Berry, Chuck* / Rock house: *Orbison, Roy* / Lotta lovin': *Blue Caps* / Jungle rock: *Mizzell, Hank*/ Tear it up: *Stevens, Shakin'* / Ready Teddy: *Stevens, Shakin'* / Dancin' party: *Showaddywaddy* / Remember then: *Showaddywaddy* / Midnight dynamos: *Matchbox* / Rockabilly rebel: *Matchbox* / Shout shout (knock yourself out): *Sharpe, Rocky & The Replays* / Rama lama ding dong: *Sharpe, Rocky & The Replays* / Rockabilly baby: *Jets (British)* / Crazy little teddy girl: *Crazy Cavan & The Rhythm Rockers* / Hey you guys: *Lee, Freddie Fingers* / Maybe that's why I care: *Rock Island Line*.
LP: . . . . WW 2002
MC: . . . . WW 20024

25 ROCK 'N' ROLL GREATS (Various artists).
MC: . . . . AM 17

50 ROCK'N'ROLL FAVOURITES (Various artists).
MCSET: . . . . TR 1518
MCSET: . . . . MFP 4115185

ABSOLUTE ROCK'N'ROLL (Various artists).
Tracks: / Rock around the clock: *Haley, Bill & The Comets* / Summertime blues: *Cochran, Eddie* / Be bop a lula: *Vincent, Gene* / Shakin' all over: *Kidd, Johnny & The Pirates* / Chantilly lace: *Big Bopper* / Blue suede shoes: *Perkins, Carl* / Blueberry hill: *Domino, Fats* / That'll be the day: *Holly, Buddy & The Crickets*/ Peggy Sue: *Holly, Buddy* / Great balls of fire: *Lewis, Jerry Lee* / Apache: *Shadows* / Rubber ball: *Vee, Bobby* / Western movies: *Olympics* / Only sixteen: *Cooke, Sam* / Dance with the guitar man: *Eddy*, Duane / Blue moon: *Marcels* / Come softly to me: *Fleetwoods* / Young love: *Hunter, Tab* / It's all in the game: *Edwards, Tommy* / Smoke gets in your eyes: *Platters* / I'm sorry: *Lee, Brenda* / It's my party: *Gore, Lesley* / It's almost tomorrow: *Dream Weavers* / Sea of heartbreak: *Gibson, Don* / Diana: *Anka, Paul* / Oh Carol: *Sedaka, Neil* / On the rebound: *Cramer, Floyd* / What do you want?: *Faith*, Adam / Locomotion, The: *Little Eva* / Ma, he's making eyes at me: *Otis, Johnny Show* / Nut rocker: *Bumble, B & The Stingers* / Stupid cupid: *Francis, Connie*.
2LP: . . . . SLTD 15
MC: . . . . SLTK 15

ACE ROCK'N'ROLL (Various artists).
LP: . . . . R&C 1012

AGE OF ROCK AND ROLL (Various artists).
MC: . . . . GM 0217

AGE OF ROCK 'N'ROLL, THE (Various artists).
LP: . . . . MCF 3096

ALADDIN 14 MAGIC LAMPS (Various artists).
LP: . . . . PM 1546741
MC: . . . . PM 154674 4

ALADDIN MAGIC (Various artists).
Tracks: / King Kong: *Various artists* / Everybody's rockin': *Various artists* / Yak yak: *Various artists*/ Rockin' too much: *Various artists* / Everyday of the week: *Various artists* / Bom born Lulu: *Various artists*/ Fat back and corn liquor: *Various artists* / Do what you did: *Various artists* / Be baba leba: *Various artists*/ One, two let's rock: *Various artists* / Boogie woogie king: *Various artists* / Flirt: *Various artists*/ New born ton roulet: *Various artists* / Jump, jump, jump: *Various artists* / No one can love: *Various artists*/ One scotch, one bourbon, one beer: *Various artists* / Hootchy kootchy: *Various artists* / Sadie Green: *Various artists*.
LP: 1566281
LP: . . . . UAS 30187

ALADDIN ROCKS AND ROLLS (Various artists).
LP: . . . . PM 1561321

ALADDIN'S ROCK 'N' ROLL "SOCK HOP" (Various artists).
LP: 2C 068-64791

ALAN FREED ROCK 'N' ROLL COLLECTION (Various artists).
Tracks: / Why do fools fall in love?: *Lymon, Frankie* / Ruby baby: *Drifters* / Ivory tower: *Williams, Otis*/ Little girl of mine: *Cleftones* / Speedo: *Cadillacs* / Mr. Sandman: *Chordettes* / Eddie my love: *Chordettes*/ I almost lost my mind: *Hunter, Ivory Joe* / Hound dog: *Vincent, Gene* / Be bop a lula: *Vincent, Gene*/ Tweedle Dee: *Baker, Laverne* / Dance with me Henry: *James, Etta* / Magic touch: *Platters* / My prayer: *Platters* / Treasure of love: *MacPhatter, Clyde* / Maybellene: *Berry, Chuck* / Roll over Beethoven: *Berry, Chuck* / Earth angel: *Penguins* / Rock around the clock: *Haley, Bill & The Comets*.
LP: . . . . DVLP 2130
MC: . . . . DVMC 2130

BEST OF AND THE REST OF, THE (Various artists).
Tracks: / All by myself: *Stevens, Shakin'* / I'm movin' on: *Vincent, Gene* / Lucille: *Ravis, Dave & Bad River*/ I don't wanna discuss it: *Crimes, Carol & The Red Price Band* / My babe: *Tracy, Lee & The Tributes* / Lovin' up a storm: *Memphis Index* / I'm walking: *Rock 'n' Roll Allstars* / Say mama: *Vincent, Gene* / Odessa: *Wild Angels* / Wee Dock and Doris: *Price, Red Band* / Right behind you baby: *Houseshakers* / Let the good times roll: *Moore, Merrill* / Lotta lovin': *Impalas*.
MC: . . . . ARLC 1026

BEST OF CHESS ROCK 'N' ROLL/ CHESS JAZZ (Various artists).
MC: . . . . TCAD 25

BEST OF RON RECORDS, VOLUME 1 (We got a party) (Various artists).
Tracks: / Goofer dust: *Big Lucky Carter* / I've been hurt: *Big Lucky Carter* / Please don't leave me: *Big Lucky Carter* / You'd better mind: *Big Lucky Carter* / Don't turn your back on me: *Bryant, Don* / Call of distress, The: *Bryant, Don* / Is that asking too much?: *Bryant, Don* / There is something on your mind: *Bryant, Don*.
LP: . . . . ED 258

BEST ORIGINAL ROCK IN TOWN (Various artists).
Tracks: / Chick, The: *Moore, Mike* / Skateboard granny: *Dee, Jerry* / It's cool: *Edwards, Al* / Riverboat blues:

Phillips, Buddy / Coffee baby: *Phillips, Buddy* / Spinning my wheel: *Coates, Don* / Jiggedy wiggedy wolly: *Coates, Don* / You are my sunshine: *Coates, Don* / Rockin' piano: *Ruby, Don* / Little Suzanne: *Jerry & The Del-Fi's* / Let's make it real: *Bryan, Dave* / Island of regret: *Baker, Sam* / Wait a minute, Lennie: *Globe, Johnny* / Steamer: *Bellomo, Joey* / Five, ten, fifteen hours: *Tyler, Chris* / All-American hillbillies: *Boppin' Billies* / Key of love: *Boppin' Billies*.
LP: . . . . **WLP 8891**

BIG D JAMBOREE (Various artists).
LP: . . . . **SJLP 588**

BISON BOP (Various artists).
LP: . . . . **BBLP 2000**

BISON BOP STRICTLY INSTRUMENTAL (Various artists).
LP: . . . . **BBLP 2002**

BISON BOP VOL.2 (Various artists).
LP: . . . . **BBLP 2001**

BISON BOP VOL.33 (Various artists).
LP: . . . . **BBLP 2041**

BISON BOP VOL.34 (Various artists).
LP: . . . . **BBLP 2042**

BISON BOP, VOL 51 Various artists (Various artists).
LP: . . . . **BBLP 2067**

BISON BOP, VOL 52 Various artists (Various artists).
LP: . . . . **BBLP 2068**

BOP BABY BOP (Various artists).
LP: . . . . **RR 2010**

BOP BOOGIE IN THE DARK (Various artists).
LP: . . . . **GCL 105**

BOP'N'ROLL PARTY (Various artists).
2LP: . . . . **BBR 1004/5**

BOPPIN' ROCK'N'ROLL (Various artists).
LP: . . . . **WLP 8941**

BRITISH ROCK'N'ROLL (The early years) (Various artists).
Tracks: / We're gonna rock tonight: *Crombie, Tony and his Rockets* / Rock 'n' roll coaster: *Crombie, Tony and his Rockets* / Short'nin' bread rock: *Crombie, Tony and his Rockets* / Big beat, The: *Lang, Don & His Frantic 5* / Rock pretty baby: *Lang, Don & His Frantic 5* / Six five special: *Lang, Don & His Frantic 5* / Rock Mister Piper: *Lang, Don & His Frantic 5* / Rockin' shoes: *King Brothers* / Wake up little Susie: *King Brothers* / Baby sittin': *Angelo, Bobby & The Tuxedos* / Skinny Lizzie: *Angelo, Bobby & The Tuxedos* / Cool and cosy: *Avons* / Rubber ball: *Avons* / I'm a moody guy: *Fenton, Shane & The Fentones* / Five foot two eyes of blue: *Fenton, Shane & The Fentones* / Saturday nite at the duckpond: *Cougars* / Ain't misbehavin': *Bruce, Tommy & the Bruisers* / Got the water boilin': *Bruce, Tommy & the Bruisers* / That rock 'n' rollin' man: *Ellington, Ray Quartet* / Walk don't run: *Barry, John Seven* / You can't say I love you to a rock'n'roll tune: *Small, Joan* / Cruel sea, The: *Dakotas* / Shakin' all over: *Kidd, Johnny & The Pirates* / Rock 'n' roll opera: *Lawrence, Lee* / Trambone: *Krew Kats* / Gypsy beat: *Packabeats*.
2LP: . . . . **DL 1164**
MC: . . . . **TCDL 1164**

BRITISH ROCK'N'ROLL 1955-1960 (Various artists).
Tracks: / Ninety nine ways: *James, Ricky* / Baby talk: *Landis, Bill & Brett* / Five days, five days: *Eager, Vince* / If you're so smart: *Sproud, Billy* / Summertime blues: *Vipers* / Later: *Cuddly Dudley* / Lot's more love: *Cuddly Dudley* / Living doll: *Ellington, Ray* / Mercy, mercy: *Taylor, Neville* / Cool shake: *Page, Larry* / Rough and smooth: *Webb, Dean* / Ain't that a shame: *Southlanders* / Baby talk: *Landis, Bill & Brett* / Cool cool: *Todd, Sharky & The Monsters* / Betty Betty: *Pride, Dickie* / Dynamo: *Les Hobeaux* / Crazy little daisy: *Taylor, Neville* / No more: *Eager, Vince* / Don't let nobody move: *Lawrence, Lee* / Rock 'n' roll opera: *Lawrence, Lee* / Slim Jim tie: *Wayne, Terry*.
LP: . . . . **SEE 38**

BUSY ROCK & ROLL (Various artists).
LP: . . . . **WLP 8927**

CHICKEN ROCK (Various artists).
LP: . . . . **EAGLE 301**

CHICKEN ROCK VOL.3 (Various artists).
LP: . . . . **EAGLE 306**

CHICKEN ROCK VOL.4 (Various artists).
LP: . . . . **EAGLE 307**

CINCINNATI ROCK 'N' ROLL, 1950'S (Various artists).
LP: . . . . **RLP 006**

CLASS OF '55 (Various artists).
Tracks: / Birth of rock and roll: *Various artists* / Sixteen candles: *Various artists* / Class of '55: *Various artists* / Waymore's blues: *Various artists* / We remember the king: *Various artists* / Coming home: *Various artists* / Rock 'n' roll (fais-do-do): *Various artists* / Keep my motor runnin': *Various artists* / I will rock and roll with you: *Various artists* / Big train (from Memphis): *Various artists*.
LP: . . . . **USAH 1**
MC: . . . . **USAC 1**
MC: **830 002-4**

CLASSIC ROCK'N'ROLL (Various artists).
Tracks: / Breathless: *Lewis, Jerry Lee* / Rock house: *Orbison, Roy* / Pearly Lee: *Riley, Billy Lee* / Right behind you baby: *Smith, Ray* / Red cadillac and a black moustache: *Smith, Warren* / Blue suede shoes: *Perkins, Carl* / Mona Lisa: *Mann, Carl* / Weekends: *Rich, Charlie*.
LP: . . . . **OCN 2026WL**
MC: . . . . **OCN 2026WK**

COLLEGE HOP (Various artists).
Tracks: / Slick chick: *Northern Lights* / Shortnin' bread: *Northern Lights* / Do you know?: *Kole, Fred & The Northern Lights* / Please tell me: *Taylor, Bill* / Too many times: *Beehler, Doug* / Borderline: *Sunshine Boys* / Car, A: *Chick, Tony* / Albino bat: *Jordan, Jim* / I'm a madman: *Ward, Willie* / My baby's casual: *Flaharty, Sonny* / I can't get up: *Sena, Tommy* / Choo choo train: *Sena, Tommy* / My baby's fine: *Bobby & The Fifths* / Bamboo baby: *Carlton, Johnny*.
LP: . . . . **WLP 8906**

COOL BABY COOL (Various artists).
LP: . . . . **EAGLE 310**

CRUISIN' (See under Cruisin') (Various artists).

DANCE TO THE BOP (Various artists).
LP: . . . . **BLK 7703**

DESPERATE ROCK 'N' ROLL VOL. 2 (Various artists).
LP: . . . . **FLAME 002**

DESPERATE ROCK'N'ROLL VOL.1 (Various artists).
LP: . . . . **FLAME 001**

DESPERATE ROCK'N'ROLL VOL.3 (Various artists).
LP: . . . . **FLAME 003**

DESPERATE ROCK,N,ROLL VOL.4 (Various artists).
LP: . . . . **FLAME 004**

DESPERATE ROCK'N'ROLL VOL.5 (Various artists).
LP: . . . . **FLAME 005**

DESPERATE ROCK'N'ROLL VOL.6 (Various artists).
LP: . . . . **FLAME 006**

DESPERATE ROCK'N'ROLL VOL.7 (Various artists).
LP: . . . . **FLAME 007**

DESPERATE ROCK'N'ROLL VOL.8 (Various artists).
LP: . . . . **FLAME 008**

DESPERATE ROCK'N'ROLL VOL.9 (Various artists).
LP: . . . . **FLAME 009**

DESPERATE ROCK'N'ROLL VOL.10 (Various artists).
LP: . . . . **FLAME 010**

DIXIE BOP (Various artists).
LP: . . . . **CFM 508**

DON'T YOU STEP ON MY BLUE SUEDE SHOES (Sun's Greatest Hits) (Various artists).
Tracks: / Whole lotta shakin' goin' on: *Lewis, Jerry Lee* / Great balls of fire: *Lewis, Jerry Lee* / High school confidential: *Lewis, Jerry Lee* / Matchbox: *Perkins, Carl* / Blue suede shoes: *Perkins, Carl* / Honey don't: *Perkins, Carl* / I walk the line: *Cash, Johnny* / Folsom Prison blues: *Cash, Johnny* / Whirlwind: *Rich, Charlie* / Rebound: *Rich, Charlie* / We wanna boogie: *Burgess, Sonny* / Red hot: *Riley, Billy Lee* / Mona Lisa: *Mann, Carl* / After the hop: *Pinkney, Bill* / Miss Froggie: *Smith, Warren*.
LP: . . . . **CR 30119**
MC: . . . . **CFK 1003**

DORE ROCK'N'ROLL VOL.1 (Various artists).
LP: . . . . **R&C 1009**

DORE ROCK'N'ROLL VOL.2 (Various artists).
LP: . . . . **R&C 1017**

DOWN ON BROADWAY AND MAIN (Various artists).
Tracks: / Peg leg woman: *King, Willie* / Mistreating me: *King, Willie* / Rock 'n' roll deacon: *Neal, Screaming Joe* / Tell me pretty baby: *Neal, Screaming Joe* / East St. Louis: *Aaron, Little* / Teach me how: *Williams, Johnny (The Twist)* / St. Louis sunset twist: *Sharp, Benny* / My baby has gone: *Jessie, Little Miss* / She's my baby: *Neal, Screaming Joe* / Don't quit me baby: *Neal, Screaming Joe* / Nona baby: *Williams, Johnny Lee* / Look out pretty baby: *Williams, Johnny Lee*.
LP: . . . . **RL 064**

EARLY ROCKIN' IN ARKANSAS (Various artists).
LP: . . . . **WLP 8947**

EASYRIDING: ROCK 'N' ROLL KINGS (Various artists).
Tracks: / Great balls of fire: *Lewis, Jerry Lee* / Let the four winds blow: *Domino, Fats* / Donna: *Wilde, Marty* / Let the good times roll: *Jordan, Louis* / Hucklebuck, The: *Bell, Freddy & The Bellboys* / Long tall Sally: *Lewis, Jerry Lee* / Rock & roll: *Prysock, Red* / I'm on fire: *Lewis, Jerry Lee* / Caldonia: *Jordan, Louis* / Whole lotta shakin' goin' on: *Various artists* / What'd I say: *Lewis, Jerry Lee* / Handclappin': *Prysock, Red* / Blueberry Hill: *Domino, Fats* / Good golly Miss Molly: *Lewis, Jerry Lee* / Please don't leave me: *Domino, Fats* / Landy Miss Clandy: *Various artists* / Breathless: *Lewis, Jerry Lee* / Giddy up a ding dong: *Bell, Freddy & The Bellboys* / Jambalaya: *Domino, Fats* / Hound dog: *Bell, Freddy & The Bellboys* / Corina Corina: *Lewis, Jerry Lee* / Whole lotta shakin' goin' on: *Lewis, Jerry Lee* / Lawdy Miss Clawdy: *Prysock, Red*.
MC: . . . . **KNMC 11002**
LP: . . . . **KNLP 11002**

ELVIS CONNECTION (Various artists).
Tracks: / My boy Elvis: *Martin, Janis* / Elvis Presley for President: *Monte, Lou* / Tupelo Mississippi flash: *Reed, Jerry* / Elvis: *Barlby, Steve* / Heartbreak hotel: *Homer & Jethro* / All American boy: *Bare, Bobby* / Elvis blues: *Bash, Otto* / Hound dog: *Homer & Jethro* / Elvis and me: *Kids* / Wonder of you, The: *Peterson, Ray* / Fool such as I, A: *Snow, Hank* / That's alright: *Crudup, Arthur 'Big Boy'* / My baby left me: *Crudup, Arthur 'Big Boy'* / Guitar man: *Reed, Jerry* / US male: *Reed, Jerry* / Crying in the chapel: *Glenn, Darrell*.
LP: . . . . **INTS 5078**
MC: . . . . **INTK 5078**

ELVIS HITS IN GERMAN VOL.1 (Various artists).
Tracks: / Du liebst nicht heisse rhythmen (Baby I don't care): *Bennett, Robert* ((Originally on Harmona Label)) / Ohne dich (loving you): *Mucke, Maria* ((Originally on phillips)) / O baby, mach dich schon (treat me nice): *Various artists*((Originally on Opera Aufnahmen label)) / Ich brauch' keinen ring: *Herold, Ted* ((Originally on Polydor)) / Wunderbar wie du heut' wieder kusst: *Herold, Ted* ((Originally on Polydor)) / Dixieland rock: *Herold, Ted* ((Originally on Polydor)) / Unser haus: *Charlie & Co.* ((Originally on Polydor)) / Hotel zur einsamkeit: *Overheidt, Werner*((Original on Polydor)) / Tuuti Fruitt: *Kraus, Peter* ((Originally on Polydor)) / O wie gut: *Kraus, Peter*((Originally on Polydor)) / Teddybar (teddy bear): *Kraus, Peter* ((Originally on Polydor)) / Immer wieder lieb' ich dich (love me tender): *Wenland, Gerhard* ((Originally on Polydor)) / Total veruckt (all shook up): *Bennett, Robert*((Originally on Harmona Label)).
LP: . . . . **BFX 15218**

ELVIS HITS IN GERMAN VOL.2 (Various artists).
Tracks: / Bist du einsam heut nacht (Are you lonesome tonight): *Alexander, Peter* / Ein fremder mann (Lonely man): *Jonny* / Ich find kein bett (I feel so bad): *Gluck, Harry* / Ich suche dich (His latest flame): *Black, Roy* / Mach dich schon: *Kraus, Peter* / Ich brauche dich dazu: *Kent, Tommy* (I need your love tonight.) / Ab und zu (A fool such as I): *Backus, Gus* / Wooden heart: *Herold, Ted* / Hey baby: *Herold, Ted* / Herz ohne gluck (wild in the country): *Herold, Ted* / Little Linda (little sister): *Herold, Ted* / Sie war all sein gluck (His latest flame): *Herold, Ted* / Mein wunsch wird wahr (My wish came true): *Graf, Wolfgang* / Tut mir lied (stuck on you): *Reimar*, Johnny / Ich komme wieder: *Terry, Jack* (It's now or never.) / Adieu, lebewohl, goodbye (tonight is so right for love): *Beil, Peter*.
LP: . . . . **BFX 15219**

ELVIS HITS IN GERMAN VOL.3 (Various artists).
Tracks: / Hotel zur einsamkeit: *Bendix, Ralf* / Heute geh ich nicht nach haus: *Bendix, Ralf* / Blaue wildlederschuh': *Kuhn, Paul* / Einsamer cowboy: *Kuhn, Paul* / Ich such dich, Ich brauch dich, Ich lieb dich: *Hansen Quartett*((I want you, I need you, I love you)) / Immer wieder lieb 'ich dich (love me tender): *Hansen Quartett* / Mach dich schon: *Dietmar, Lutz* / Komm' (Don't): *Brandes, Will* / King Creole: *Brandes, Will* / Ja so'ne party: *Sanders*, Billy / Wer weiss warum (Don't ask me why): *Blum, Hans* / Hey baby: *Various artists* / Lach' nicht so (stuck on you): *Various artists* / Leibe kalter als eis (Devil in disguise): *Gildo, Rex* / Bossa nova baby: *Ramsey, Bill* / Wer heisst hier Johnny: *Ramsey, Bill*.
LP: . . . . **BFX 15220**

ELVIS HITS IN GERMAN VOL.4 (Various artists).
Tracks: / Manitou (Flaming star): *Rizz, Bobby* / Das lied von der liebe (wild in the country): *Holm, Michael* / Die junge liebe ist suss: *Holm, Michael* / Weit, so weit (Can't help falling in love): *Assia, Lys* / Rock a hula baby: *Bottcher, Gerd & Detlef Engel* / Was ist schon dabei (Moonlight swim): *Roland, Jo* / Du gehorst auf's titelbuild (Good luck charm): *Ulrik, John* / Der King (King of the whole wide world): *Die Missouris* / Und mit blumen im haar (the fair is moving on): *Hardt, Oliver* / Das ist rock and roll (hound dog): *Various artists* / Ich brauche dich dazu: *Gutmann, Ferry* (I need your love tonight.) / Ich komme wieder: *Bottcher, Gerd* (It's now or never.) / Adieu, lebewohl, goodbye (tonight is so right for love): *Bottcher, Gerd* / Ich such dich auf allen wegen (Surrender): *Bottcher*, Gerd / Du schaust mich an (She's not you): *Bottcher, Gerd* / Bist du einsam heut nacht (Are you lonesome tonight): *Hoop, Wyn*.
LP: . . . . **BFX 15221**

EVERYDAY IS A HOLLYDAY (Various artists).
LP: . . . . **ROSE 175**
MC: . . . . **ROSE 175C**

FEEL LIKE ROCKIN' (Various artists).
Tracks: / Rockin' love: *Mann, Carl* / Some enchanted evening: *Mann, Carl* / Take these chains from my heart: *Mann, Carl* / Hey baby doll: *Bush, Eddie* / No more cryin' the blues: *Alton & Jimmy* / Tied to your apron string: *Hoback, Curtis* / I fell in love: *Cooke, Ken* / Walkin' with my best friend: *Hoback, Curtis* / Apron strings: *Hoback, Curtis* / Crazy baby: *Cooke, Ken* / I feel in love: *Cook, Ken* / Lordy hoody: *Blake, Tommy* / Feel like rockin': *Parchman, Kenny* / Tennessee zip: *Parchman, Kenny* / Love crazy baby: *Parchman, Kenny* / You call everybody darlin': *Parchman, Kenny* / Treat me right: *Parchman, Kenny*.
LP: . . . . **SUN 1038**

GEORGIA MUSIC (Various artists).
LP: . . . . **WLP 8936**

GIRLS ARE ROCKIN', THE (Various artists).
Tracks: / Big midnight special: *Armstrong, Joan & The Shakers* / Rock, baby, rock: *Tennant, Barbara* / He's my man: *Gunter, Launa* / Big Daddy Rabbit: *Bennett, Barbara* / Ballin' keen: *Lee, Sandy* / Jackpot: *Fredericks*, Dolores / Baby doll: *Wells, Ardis* / Real gone: *Acorn Sisters* / You treat me like a baby: *Lovett, Glenda* / Let's trade a little: *Bryant, Audrey* / Needle in a haystack: *West, Penny* / Leaving you this time: *Roy*, Thelma / Hey good lookin': *Rogers, Betty* / Jukebox on the moon: *Millay, Ginny* / Lover man: *Sherman, Nancy* / Baby oh honey: *Emerson, Jeannie* / What for?: *Dolly & The Deans*.
LP: . . . . **WLP 8919**

GOLDEN AGE OF ROCK'N'ROLL (Various artists).
LP: . . . . **OAK R 128**

GOTTA ROCK ME DADDY (Various artists).
Tracks: / Little Willy: *Deram, Richie* / Girl and a hot rod: *Deram, Richie* / She's gone, gone, gone: *Davis*, Dale / Gotta rock me daddy: *Davis, Dale* / Shady lady: *Shades* / I'm not moving: *Wheatley, Paul* / Rockin' the blues: *Griffith, Peggy* / It looks like a dead end to me: *Van Winkle, Arnold* / Woke up this morning: *Spivey, Kenny* / Waitin' in line: *Rutledge, Bobby* / Go slow, fatso: *Rutledge, Bobby* / Think it over, baby: *Cleary, Eddie* / Crawdad song: *Haney, Bill* / Richmond, Chicago, Mexico and home: *Miller, Sonny* / Sweet lies: *Chapparrals*.
LP: . . . . **WLP 8862**

GREAT BRITISH ROCK'N'ROLL & ROCKABILLY VOL.II (Various artists).
Tracks: / Setting the woods on fire: *Various original artists* / Feels so bad (matchbox): *Various original artists* / Train of love: *Various original artists* / Crazy stomp, The: *Crazy Cavan & The Rhythm Rockers* / Earthquake: *Various original artists* / Fast Eddie: *Storm, Johnny & Memphis* / Sweet little sixteen: *Various original* artists / Silver wings / Last train to San Fernando: *Various original artists* / Maybe that's why I care

(Rock Island Line): *Rock Island Line* / As you like it: *Various original artists* / Give me some of it: *Deltas*.
MC: . . . . **INTK 5102**
LP: . . . . **INTS 5102**

GREAT BRITISH ROCK'N'ROLL & ROCKABILLY (Various artists).
MC: . . . . **INTK 5042**
LP: . . . . **INTS 5042**

GREAT DAMES OF ROCK 'N' ROLL (Various artists).
LP: . . . . **SPA 2**

GREAT RARITIES (Various artists).
Tracks: / Looking for money: *Dove, Johnny* / Sanny Ann: *Wayne, Bobby* / Warpaint: *Wayne, Bobby* / 9lf-ton mama: *Joe, Ron & George* / Reachie: *Joe, Ron & George* / Honky tonk boogie: *Miller, Eddie* / Blue, blue, blue: *Duke & Null* / Trance: *Shelton, Gary* / Midnight sun rock: *Oster, Al* / Next boat: *Oster, Al* / Fatty Patty: *Ox Tones* / Mickey: *Ox Tones* / 'Cause I love you: *Allen, Little Joe* / Mom, pop, start to rock: *Briggs, Gail & Steve*.
LP: . . . . **WLP 8850**

GREAT ROCK'N'ROLL LOVE SONGS (Various artists).
MC: . . . . **GM 0207**

GREATEST EVER ROCK 'N' ROLL MIX (Various artists).
Tracks: / Great balls of fire: *Lewis, Jerry Lee* / Move it: *Richard, Cliff* / Good golly Miss Molly: *Little* Richard / Blue suede shoes: *Perkins, Carl* / Chantilly lace: *Big Bopper* / Bye bye love: *Everly Brothers* / Please don't touch: *Kidd, Johnny & The Pirates* / Why do fools fall in love: *Lymon, Frankie & The Teenagers* / Long tall Sally: *Little Richard* / Shake rattle and roll: *Haley, Bill & The Comets* / When: *Kalin Twins* / At the hop: *Danny & The Juniors* / Oh boy: *Crickets* / Nut rocker: *B. Bumble & The Stingers* / Mr Bass man: *Cymbal, Johnny* / I dig you baby: *Rainwater, Marvin* / Handy man: *Jones, Jimmy (singer)* / Whole lotta woman: *Rainwater, Marvin* / Poor me: *Faith, Adam* / Somethin' else: *Cochran, Eddie* / Pistol packin' mama: *Vincent, Gene* / Runaround Sue: *Dion* / Rave on: *Holly, Buddy* / Here comes Summer: *Keller*, Jerry / Breathless: *Lewis, Jerry Lee* / Rockin' Robin: *Day, Bobby* / Party doll: *Knox, Buddy* / Wake up little Susie: *Everly Brothers* / Rock around the clock: *Haley, Bill & The Comets* / High class baby: *Richard*, Cliff & The Shadows / Be bop a lula: *Vincent, Gene* / That'll be the day: *Crickets* / Stupid cupid: *Francis*, Connie / Bird dog: *Everly Brothers* / Lucille: *Little Richard* / Peggy Sue: *Holly, Buddy & The Crickets* / Little darlin': *Diamonds* / You're sixteen: *Burnette, Johnny* / Summertime blues: *Cochran, Eddie* / Teenager in love: *Dion & The Belmonts* / Lipstick on your collar: *Francis, Connie* / Whole lotta shakin' goin' on: *Lewis, Jerry Lee* / Let's have a party: *Jackson, Wanda* / Mona Lisa: *Twitty, Conway* / Cradle of love: *Preston, Johnny* / Maybe tomorrow: *Fury, Billy* / It's all in the game: *Edwards, Tommy* / Great pretender, The: *Platters* / Earth angel: *Crew Cuts* / It's almost tomorrow: *Dream Weavers* / Born too late: *Poni-Tails* / It's only make believe: *Twitty, Conway* / Blueberry hill: *Domino, Fats* / Love letters in the sand: *Boone, Pat* / Teen angel: *Dinning, Mark* / Young love: *Hunter, Tab* / Western movies: *Olympics* / Ain't that a shame: *Domino, Fats* / Halfway to paradise: *Fury, Billy* / Stagger Lee: *Price, Lloyd*.
2LP: . . . . **SMR 858**
MCSET: . . . . **SMC 858**

GT.LABELS OF SOUTH (Trepur/ Ridgecrest) (Various artists).
Tracks: / Elvis in the army: *Wasden, Jaybee* / De castrow: *Wasden, Jaybee* / Let's rock: *Howard, Rusty* / I'm gonna do you like you are doing me: *Howard, Rusty* / Milkman blues: *Joyce, Chuck* / Bounce baby bounce: *Lofton*, Fuzzy / I've been down this road: *Wydemon, Jimmie* / Vulcan song, The: *Wydemon, Jimmie* / Don't cry little darling: *Carpenter Bros.* / Day I heard you say goodbye, The: *Worley, David* / I'm being haunted: *Melson*, Lee 'Red' / Rockin' through the tunnel of love: *Melson, Lee 'Red'* / Mean ole bartender blues: *Melson, Lee 'Red'* / Carmen Sue rock: *Melson, Lee 'Red'*.
LP: . . . . **WLP 8834**

HEART & SOUL OF ROCK & ROLL, THE (Various artists).
LP: . . . . **STAR 2351**
MC: . . . . **STAC 2351**

HI-FI ROCK 'N' ROLL PARTY (Various artists).
Tracks: / Lights out: *Byrne, Jerry* / Roll hot rod roll: *McLollie, Oscar* / Runaround sue: *Dion* / Sea cruise: *Ford, Frankie* / Little bit of soap, A: *Jarmels* / Thinking of you: *Beasley, Jimmy* / Maybellene: *Dee, Mercy* / Poetry in motion: *Tillotson, Johnny* / Tutti frutti: *Little Richard* / Wake up little Susie: *Everly Brothers* / Peanut butter: *Marathons* / Promised land: *Allan, Johnnie* / Wanderer: *Dion* / Deuces wild: *Wray, Link* / Hush-a-bye: *Mystics* / Teenager in love: *Dion & The Belmonts* / Lollipop: *Chordettes* / My true story: *Jive Five* / Goodnight my love: *Belvin, Jesse* / He's so fine: *Chiffons* / Way I like it, The: *Gunter, Shirley* / Reet petite: *Wilson, Jackie*.
MC: . . . . **CHC 904**

I WANT A ROCK & ROLL GUITAR (Various artists).
LP: . . . . **REDITA 112**

IF IT AIN'T A HIT I'LL EAT MY....BABY (Various artists).
LP: . . . . **Z 2009**

ISLAND RECORDINGS, THE (Various artists).
Tracks: / Don't push, don't shove: *Browning, Bill* / Down in the holler where Sally lives: *Browning, Bill* / Love left over: *Browning, Bill* / Gonna be a fire: *Browning, Bill* / Answer your telephone: *Browning, Bill* / Hula rock: *Browning, Bill* / Mountain guitar: *Thacker, Rudy* / Boppin' to Grandfather's clock: *Lewis, Sidney* Jo / Jukebox play for me: *Cook Bros* / You gotta go: *Cook Bros* / Birmingham bounce: *Gunter, Hardrock* / Rock a bop baby: *Gunter, Hardrock* / Vera Lee: *Lou & The Monarchs* / Chopstick rock: *Lou & The Monarchs*.
LP: . . . . **WLP 8814**

IT'S ONLY ROCK 'N' ROLL (1957-1964) (Various artists).
LP: . . . . **NUTM 19**

IT'S ONLY ROCK'N'ROLL 1957-62 VOL 2 (Various artists).
LP: . . . . **NUTM 26**

IT'S ROCK 'N' ROLL (Various artists).
LP: . . . . **BEMP 001**
MC: . . . . **ZCR 001**

IT'S ROCK 'N' ROLL (VOL. 2) (Various artists).
LP: . . . . **BEMP 004**
MC: . . . . **ZCR 004**

JAKE PORTERS COMBO RECORDS STORY VOL.1 (Various artists).
LP: . . . . **CH 84**

JAKE PORTERS COMBO RECORDS STORY VOL.2 (Various artists).
Tracks: / Baby baby take a look: *Ray, Robbin* / It's a lonesome old world: *Ray, Robbin* / Girl of my dreams: *Ray*, Robbin / I love my baby: *Ray, Robbin* / Cool daddy's blues: *Booker, Sherman & His bluenotes* / Echo blues: *Carter, Tal* / Mad as a man can be: *Carter, Tal* / Things we used ta do (we can do no more), The: *Houston*, Joe / I tried: *Various artists* / Worries and troubles: *Young Wolf* / Cotton picker: *Higgins, Chuck* / Beer drinking woman: *Harrison, Cledus* / I miss my baby: *Jenkins, Gus* / You lied: *Ree, Mamie* / Caught: *Ree, Mamie*.
LP: . . . . **CHD 104**

JEWEL SPOTLIGHTS, VOL.1 (Various artists).
LP: . . . . **JEWEL 5051**

JIVE JIVE, JIVE (Various artists).
Tracks: / O yes das ist musik: *Oliver, Dorit* / Green door: *Bruck, Inge* / See you later alligator: *Franke*, Renee / Crazy man crazy: *Various artists* / Spiel hula hoop: *Bendorff, Monika* / There's never been a night: *Bendorff, Monika* / Expresso bar: *Bendorff, Monika* / Be mine: *Leandros, Leo* / Rock around the clock: *Asmussen, Svend (dup0)* / Warenhaus rock bei der firma rock'n'roll: *Haensch, Delle* / Rock baby rock: *Quick*, Conny / Rock and roll so wei noch nie midnight: *Overheidt, Werner* / Angel smile: *Herwig, Claus* / Rock a baby: *Die Rockies* / Love and kisses: *Kitty Sisters*.
LP: . . . . **BFX 15144**

JIVE JIVE JIVE IN DEN SOER VOLUME 2 (Various artists).
Tracks: / Bim bam: *Wust, Harry* / Die Lilly mit dem himmelblauen pulli: *Palmer, Teddy* / My baby hast du heute frei: *Palmer, Teddy* / Woo Hoo: *Woo Hoo's* / Tinga tanga rock: *Hinnen, Peterli* / Ding dong: *Mo*, Billy / Mr. Rhythm King: *Mo, Billy* / Oh Marie: *Mo, Billy* / Hey hey rock rock: *Ohio's* / Mondschein rock: *Schmid, Geschwister* / Ding dang danglin': *Die Serenaders* / Too hoop: *Palmer, Teddy/ Werner Hass* / Rocky violins: *Muller, Werner* / Guitar boogie shuffle: *Muller, Werner* / Siebenmal in der woche: *Torriani, Vico* / Jingeling jang Judy: *Die Stefanos*.
LP: . . . . **BFX 15286**

JIVE, JIVE, JIVE, VOL 3 (Various artists).
LP: . . . . **JIVIN' 188**

JIVE, JIVE, JIVE, VOL 4 (Various artists).
LP: . . . . **JIVIN' 139**

JIVE, JIVE, JIVE, VOL 5 (Various artists).
LP: . . . . **JIVIN' 190**

JIVE, JIVE, JIVE, VOL 6 (Various artists).
LP: . . . . **JIVIN' 191**

JIVE, JIVE, JIVE, VOL 7 (Various artists).
LP: . . . . **JIVIN 192**

JIVE, JIVE, JIVE, VOL 8 (Various artists).
LP: . . . . **JIVIN 193**

JIVIN' GIRLS' PARTY, VOL 1 (Various artists).
LP: **84121**

JIVIN' GIRLS' PARTY, VOL 2 (Various artists).
LP: **84122**

JIVIN' GIRLS' PARTY, VOL 3 (Various artists).
LP: **84123**

JIVIN' GIRLS' PARTY, VOL 4 (Various artists).
LP: **84124**

JOHNNY OTIS PRESENTS.... (Various artists).
LP: . . . . **CH 88**

JUKE BOX COLLECTION - BLUE SUEDE SHOES (Rock 'n' roll classics) (Various artists).
Tracks: / La bamba: *Valens, Ritchie* / Wake up little Susie: *Everly Brothers* / Good golly Miss Molly: *Little* Richard / Tequila: *Champs* / Come go with me: *Del Vikings* / Endless sleep: *Reynolds, Jody* / Great balls of fire: *Lewis, Jerry Lee* / Blue suede shoes: *Perkins, Carl* / Raunchy: *Justis, Bill* / Rockin' robin: *Day, Bobby* / Bony Moronie: *Williams, Larry*.
MC: . . . . **OG 2701**
LP: . . . . **OG 1701**

JUKE BOX FAVOURITES (Various artists).
MC: . . . . **GM 0223**

JUKE BOX HEROES, VOL 1 (Various artists).
LP: **240626 1**
MC: **240626 4**

JUKE BOX HEROES, VOL 2 (Various artists).
LP: **240627 1**
MC: **240627 4**

JUKE BOX JIVE (Various artists).
MC: . . . . **GM 0221**

JUKE BOX JIVE MIX (Rock'n'roll greats) (Various artists).
LP: . . . . **SMR 993**
MC: . . . . **SMC 993**

JUKE BOX PARTY (Various artists).
LP: . . . . **CD 2457**

JUKE BOX ROCK (Various artists).
MC: . . . . **GM 0222**

JUKE BOX ROCK'N'ROLL (Various artists).
LP: . . . . **NE 1211**
MC: . . . . **CE 2211**

JUKE BOX SATURDAY NIGHT (Various artists).
MC: . . . . **GM 0224**

JUMP BABY JUMP (Various artists).
LP: . . . . **LP 8402**

JUMP THE BOOGIE (Various artists).
LP: . . . . **RR 2020**

JUST GO WILD OVER ROCK 'N' ROLL (Various artists).
LP: . . . . **CRM 2016**

KANSAS CITY ROCKERS (Various artists).
LP: . . . . **REDITA 106**

KINGS OF MEMPHIS TOWN (Various artists).
LP: . . . . **RL 333**

KINGS OF ROCK 'N' ROLL (Various artists).
MCSET: . . . . **PLDC 8016**
2LP: . . . . **PLD 8016**

KINGS OF ROCK'N'ROLL, THE (Various artists).
Tracks: / Rock around the clock: *Haley, Bill & The Comets* / See you later alligator: *Haley, Bill & The Comets* / Blue suede shoes: *Perkins, Carl* / Roll over Beethoven: *Perkins, Carl* / High school confidential: *Lewis*, Jerry Lee / Great balls of fire: *Lewis, Jerry Lee* / Ooby dooby: *Orbison, Roy* / Rock house: *Orbison*, Roy / Mona Lisa: *Mann, Carl* / Kansas City: *Mann, Carl* / Luther played the boogie: *Cash, Johnny* / Get rhythm: *Cash, Johnny*.
LP: . . . . **SPR 8567**
MC: . . . . **SPC 8567**

LEGENDARY GUITARISTS OF GENE VINCENT, THE (Various artists).
LP: . . . . **MFLP 068**

LEGENDARY SESSIONS (Delta sessions) (Various artists).
LP: . . . . **RSE 5**

LEGENDARY SESSIONS (Memphis style) (Various artists).
LP: . . . . **RSE 2**

LEGENDARY SPECIALITY MISSING MASTERS (Various artists).
Tracks: / Oh babe: *Milton, Roy* / Wah-bop-sh-wah: *Twilighters* / Jump Jack jump: *Carr, Wynona* / Bouncin' the boogie: *Royal Kings* / Brand new baby: *Williams, Lester* / Hey fine mama: *Pierce, Henry* / Jelly bean: *Don & Dewey* / Let it lay: *Moore, Kenzie* / I've got my sights on someone new: *Jackson, Roddy* / Just to hold my hand: *Myles, Big Boy* / Bangin' the boogie: *Howard, Camille* / Rock & roll fever: *Monitors* / Ooh bop she bop: *Dukes* / Boogie woogie lou: *Liggins, Joe* / Check yourself baby: *Allen, Tony* / Goodbye baby goodbye: *Lowbry, Sonny*.
LP: . . . . **SNTF 5029**

LEGENDS OF ROCK'N'ROLL, THE (Various artists).
LP: . . . . **MMLP 1037**

LEMBO RECORDINGS, THE (Various artists).
Tracks: / Bye bye baby: *Dusters* / Oh why?: *Dusters* / She's mine: *Dusters* / Rock at the hop: *Dusters* / I wanna go: *Rhodes, Jimmy* / Honeybee: *Fearsley, Dwarless* / You talk too much: *Fearsley, Dwarless* / Seventh Heaven: *Gamble, Johnny* / Wicked woman: *Gamble, Johnny* / Blue ink: *Shuffles* / There she goes: *Allstars* / I'm sorry: *Allstars* / Betty Jo: *Brazell, Nicky* / Linda Jean: *Satellites* / Rockateen: *Satellites* / Custer's last stand: *Sultans*.
LP: . . . . **WLP 8917**

LET THE GOOD TIMES ROLL (Various artists).
Tracks: / Rock around the clock: *Haley, Bill* / At the hop: *Danny & The Juniors* / Personality: *Price, Lloyd* / Tequila: *Champs* / Sweet nothin's: *Lee, Brenda* / Good golly Miss Molly: *Little Richard* / Oh boy: *Holly*, Buddy / Jungle rock: *Mizell, Hank* / That'll be the day: *Holly, Buddy* / Long tall Sally: *Little Richard* / Wake up little Susie: *Everly Brothers* / Lawdy Miss Clawdy: *Price, Lloyd* / Chapel of love: *Dixie Cups* / Duke of Earl: *Chandler, Gene* / Born too late: *Poni-Tails* / Great balls of fire: *Lewis, Jerry Lee* / Chantilly lace: *Big Bopper* / Shake, rattle and roll: *Haley, Bill* / Charlie Brown: *Coasters* / Leader of the pack: *Shangri-Las* / Pretty little angel eyes: *Lee, Curtis* / Rock 'n' roll is here to stay: *Danny* & The Juniors / Only you: *Platters* / Tutti frutti: *Little Richard* / Peggy Sue: *Holly, Buddy* / Alley oop: *Hollywood Argyles* / Poison ivy: *Coasters* / Blue suede shoes: *Perkins, Carl* / Remember then: *Earls* / Whole lotta shakin' goin' on: *Lewis, Jerry Lee*.
MCSET: . . . . **CRT 020**
LP: . . . . **MFP 50465**
MC: . . . . **GL 1956**

LET THE GOOD TIMES ROLL: EARLY ROCK CLASSICS, 19 (Various artists).
Tracks: / Let the good times roll: *Shirley & Lee* / Ain't that a shame: *Domino, Fats* / Great balls of fire: *Lewis*, Jerry Lee / Sittin' in the balcony: *Cochran, Eddie* / House of blue lights: *Moore, Merrill* / I hear you knocking: *Lewis, Smiley* / Rockin' the joint: *Esquerita* / Short fat Fanny: *Williams, Larry* / Blueberry Hill: *Domino*, Fats / Willie and the hand jive: *Otis, Johnny Show* / Bony Moronie: *Williams, Larry* / I'm gone: *Shirley* & Lee / Blue Monday: *Domino, Fats* / Little bitty pretty one: *Harris, Thurston* / One night: *Lewis, Smiley* / Over and over: *Harris, Thurston*.
LP: . . . . **CGB 1001**
MC: . . . . **TC CGB 1001**

LET'S FLAT GET IT (Various artists).
Tracks: / Let's flat get it: *Various artists* / Billy boy: *Various artists* / Baby lets play house: *Various* artists / Such a night: *Various artists* / Once with you: *Various artists* / Shape I'm in, The: *Various* artists / Can'tcha see: *Various artists* / Little ole you: *Various artists* / I'd rather be lucky: *Various* artists / Pretty blue jean baby: *Various artists* / Mama mama: *Various artists* / When I'm alone with you: *Various artists* / You've got me lyin': *Various artists* / Satisfaction guaranteed: *Various artists* / Where did you stay last night: *Various artists* / Talk about my baby: *Various artists*.
LP: . . . . **CR 30253**

LET'S GO ROCK AND ROLL (Various artists).
Tracks: / Let's go rock and roll: *Cookie Charley* / Hot rod: *Moore, Oscar* / Rock,

rock, rock: *Blue Jays*/ Sixteen teens: *Jackson Q, Hey* / R' n' roll march: *Jackson Q, Hey* / Cow jumped over, The: *Isley Brothers*/ Rock me a boogie: *Dougherty, B. Bob* / 24 boyfriends: *Clark, Dee* / Number 9 train: *Slim, Tarheel* / Wildcat tamer: *Slim, Tarheel* / Susie and Pat: *McCracklin, Jimmy* / Hey Hester: *Tucker, Frankie* / My girl across town: *Robertson, Lester* / Take it home to Grandma: *Robertson, Lester.*
LP: . . . . **RR 2008**

LET'S GO ROCKING AT THE HIGH SCHOOL HOP (Various artists).
LP: **5917**

LET'S ROCK TONIGHT (Various artists).
Tracks: / Let's rock tonight: *Grubbs, Jimmy* / Six foot down: *Ski, Gene* / Fool about you: *Darren, Danny*/ Bitter feelings: *Phillipson, Larry* / Venus rock: *Rollettes* / Shake bop: *Garland, Dickie* / Ce'ny: *Jerry & The Silvertones* / Mystery train: *Waleen, Johnny* / Take my everything: *Cay, Phil* / You shake me: *Lane, Bobby* / Blacksmith rock: *Short, Bill* / Here we go again: *Short, Bill* / Budd's bounce: *Clarke, Gene* / Never: *Jones, Sweetie* / Dark eyes: *Chessmen* / Oh baby: *Jackson, Bobby.*
LP: . . . . **WLP 8843**

LIGHT UP DYNAMITE AND BLOW UP THE STEREO (Various artists).
Tracks: / On the street: *Various artists* / Have you seen my baby: *Various artists* / Little queenie: *Various artists* / That's alright mama: *Various artists* / Down: *Various artists* / Train train: *Various artists*/ Justine: *Various artists* / Exciting accident: *Various artists* / Mumblin' mosie: *Various artists* / Something's going on: *Various artists* / Truth drug: *Various artists* / Blue skies and sunshine: *Various artists*/ Frisco band: *Various artists.*
LP: . . . . **MFLP 006**

LITTLE JUMP JOINT (Various artists).
Tracks: / I get the blues when it rains: *Payne, Jimmy & Dick Barton* / Whatcha gonna say?: *Miller, Rich* / Hep, 2, 3, 4: *Manis, Georgie* / Hang up my rock 'n' roll shoes: *Oldham, Ronnie* / Good good lovin': *Bissett, Jim*/ Please come back: *Starfires* / Rocky bop: *Starfires* / Hold me tight tonight: *Starfires* / Jungle boogie: *Starfires* / Blonde headed woman: *Lee, Harold* / Little jump joint: *McKinnon, Harold* / You don't love me, baby: *McKinnon, Harold* / Krunchy: *Boy, Donnie* / Flippin' over you: *Pearson, Ronnie* / Wigwam Willie: *Phillips, Carl* / Salty dog blues: *Phillips, Carl.*
LP: . . . . **WLP 8909**

LIVE AT THE STAR CLUB (Various artists).
Tracks: / Money: *Various artists* / Lucille: *Various artists* / Shot of rhythm and blues, A: *Various artists*/ Red river rock: *Various artists* / Bony Moronie: *Various artists* / It's only make believe: *Various artists*/ Baby says: *Various artists* / Son of Jack The Ripper: *Various artists* / Hold on I'm coming: *Various artists*/ Rip it up: *Various artists* / Blue suede shoes: *Various artists* / Get the right string baby: *Various artists*/ Star club rock: *Various artists.*
LP: . . . . **MFLP 1.058**

LOOSE ENDS - ANTHOLOGY (Various artists).
Tracks: / Space guitar: *Watson, Young John* / Have guitar will travel: *Moore, Scotty Trio* / Electrode: *Cunningham, B.B. Jnr* / Scratchin': *Cunningham, B.B. Jnr* / Cury: *Skelton, Eddie* / Guitar boogie shuffle: *Virtues*/ Eclipse: *Vigilantes* / In the moon: *Hawk* / Harlem nocturne: *Viscounts* / Caravan: *Eddy, Duane*/ Loose ends: *Ronnie & The Rainbows* / Torture: *Fendermen* / Good soul: *Fireballs.*
LP: . . . . **UP 005**

LOTS OF ROCKIN' (Various artists).
Tracks: / Just for tonight: *Trent, Tommy* / Spider, The: *Lee, Eddie* / Everybody rock: *Lee, Eddie* / Show boat boogie: *Winkler, Al* / High steppin' woman: *Hardin, Jim* / Lowdown feeling: *Blair, Retus* / Scroungy man: *Aldrich, Charlie* / Don't move me more no: *Cavallo, Jimmy* / Lot of shakin', lot of jivin': *Piano Red* / Key jammer: *Piano Red* / Rockin' down Mexico way: *Clingman, Loy* / Don't stop the rockin': *Richmond, Pat* / Tommy: *Richmond, Pat* / Can't I have you tonight?: *Deltones* / Beatnik: *Royal Jokers* / Vibrations: *Royal Jokers.*
LP: . . . . **WLP 8871**

LUCKEY LABEL, THE (Various artists).
Tracks: / Look what I found: *Hubbard, Orangie* / Is she sore?: *Hubbard, Orangie* / Missed the workhouse: *Watkins, Bill* / I got troubles: *Watkins, Bill* / Creepin' and crawlin': *Browning, Bill Zekie* / I'll pay you back: *Browning, Bill Zekie* / Spinning wheel rock: *Browning, Bill Zekie* / Bad case of the blues: *Browning, Bill Zekie* / If it's lovin' that you want: *Martin, Billy* / Love is just that way: *Brady, Pal* / When you're gone: *Brady, Pal* / Rock old sputnik: *Young, Nelson* / Charlie Brown's mule: *Young, Nelson* / Jealous dreams: *Grove, Bobby* / Black train: *Dale, Larry & Rudy Thacker.*
LP: . . . . **WLP 8857**

MADNESS INVASION: TRASH TRACKS OF THE LATE 50'S, (Various artists).
LP: . . . . **GMG 75026**

MADNESS INVASION, VOL 2: LATE 50'S, EARLY 60'S (Various artists).
LP: . . . . **GMG 75030**

MAKE IT ROCK 'N' ROLL (Various artists).
LP: . . . . **REC 460**
MC: . . . . **ZCM 460**

MEDWAY POWERHOUSE VOL.1 (Various artists).
LP: . . . . **HANG 4 UP**

MEDWAY POWERHOUSE VOL.2 (Various artists).
Tracks: / Cadlina: *Milkshakes* / You did her wrong: *Milkshakes* / Red monkey, The: *Milkshakes* / Joe 90: *Prisoners* / Little Miss Misfit: *Discords* / 2nd to no one (part 2): *Discords* / I've got everything..: *Delmonas* / Uncle Willy: *Delmonas* / Stroll on: *Auntie vegetable* / Cat, The: *Taylor Quartet, The*/ Your love: *Mighty Caesars* / Johnny guitar: *Tremolo, Timmy* / Bourgeois blues: *Wild Billy & Big Russ*/ Laughing at you: *Pop rivers* / M.T. Sounds: *Pop rivers* / Hurt me: *Mindreaders.*
LP: . . . . **HANG 8 UP**

MEDWAY POWERHOUSE VOL.3 (Various artists).
Tracks: / Love me lies: *Prisoners* / Johnny pay day: *Barkers bandits* / Dearest darling: *Milkshakes*/ Dirty water: *Gruffmen* / Jack the ripper: *Auntie vegetable* / Traindrivers lament: *Rocking Richard*/ Nothing shak: *Barkers bandits* / Pretty baby: *Mighty Caesars* / So happy: *Discords* / Dangerous charms: *Delmonas* / Incendiary device: *Pop Rivits* / Lonesome city: *Tremolo, Timmy* / Yellow skinned: *Natural born lovers* / Boredom: *Ketch, Jack & The Crewmen.*
LP: . . . . **HANG 17 UP**

MEDWAY POWERHOUSE VOL.4 (Various artists).
LP: . . . . **HANG 25 UP**

MEMPHIS (Rock'n'roll capital of the world vol.1) (Various artists).
Tracks: / Bop hop jamboree: *Ellis, Rex* / Wondering if you still care: *High, Billie* / Train's done gone, The: *Scott, Ray* / Just behind your smile: *Scott, Ray* / Bo be ah be: *Coburn, Kimball* / Search: *Monarchs*/ Yes, uh huh or even maybe: *Monarchs* / How can I go?: *Raleigh, Chuck* / You can lead me to the water but you can't make me drink: *Eads, Larry* / Standing in your window: *Johnson, Hoyt* / Big Johnny blues: *Barnes, Johnny*/ Memphis rocking: *Toran, Rex* / Stormy: *King, Billy* / No one but you: *Perry, Happ* / Hello Memphis: *Dixon, Tex* / Two timin' lover: *Gattis, Ben.*
LP: . . . . **WLP 8904**

MEMPHIS AREA, THE (Various artists).
LP: . . . . **RL 307**

MEMPHIS BEAT (Various artists).
Tracks: / Sorry I lied: *Thomas, Cliff* / Treat me right: *Thomas, Cliff* / I'm on my way home: *Thomas, Cliff*/ Stairway to nowhere: *Barton, Ernie* / Trouble in mind: *Adams, Billy* / Betty and Dupree: *Adams, Billy*/ Got my mojo working: *Adams, Billy* / There won't be anymore: *Rich, Charlie* / Bobaloo: *Johnson, Bill*/ Honey bee: *Hinton, Don* / Fire: *Vel-tones* / I'm getting better all the time: *Pitman, Barbara* / I ain't never: *Stuart, Jeb* / Uncle Jonah's place: *Dorman, Harold* / Rockin' bandit: *Smith, Ray* / Raining the blues: *Barton, Ernie.*
LP: . . . . **CR 30149**

MEMPHIS LABEL STORY, THE (Various artists).
Tracks: / Rockin' at the Y: *Ingle, Thomas* / Wild wild party: *Feathers, Charlie* / Prom, The: *Roundabouts*/ I couldn't make...: *Arnold, Lloyd* / Sugaree: *Arnold, Lloyd* / I've waited too long: *Christian, Jody*/ Tomorrow I'll..: *Boyd, Eddie* / Go go go: *Longhairs* / Rockin' boppin' teenager: *Shaw, Jim* / Love don't...: *Feathers, Charlie* / What's the matter: *Shaw, Jim* / Hey rena: *Maupin, Ramon* / Today and tomorrow: *Feathers, Charlie* / I'll cry today: *Ingle, Thomas* / Next to me: *Arnold, Lloyd* / Night surfing: *Rebel Rousers.*
LP: . . . . **CHAD 197**

MEMPHIS ROCKS THE COUNTRY (Various artists).
LP: . . . . **REDITA 104**

MEMPHIS SATURDAY NIGHT (Various artists).
LP: . . . . **Z 2005**

MEMPHIS SHAKEDOWN (Various artists).
LP: . . . . **PY 1810**

MEMPHIS-ROCK 'N' ROLL CAPITAL OF THE WORLD VOL.6 (Various artists).
Tracks: / It's all your fault: *Smith, Jerry Lee* / Girl can't help it, The: *Smith, Jerry Lee* / Cocklebur: *Fuller, Tiny* / I am a pilgrim: *Fuller, Tiny* / Running wild: *Starks, Blackie* / What's on your mind?: *Smith, Shelby* / Since my baby said goodbye: *Smith, Shelby* / You have this and more: *Moore, Ronnie* / Firefly: *Wammack, Travis* / Honky tonk ways: *Turney, Carvis* / Jimmy the kid: *Stone, Doug* / Memphis yodel blues: *Stone, Doug* / She moved to Kansas City: *Stone, Doug* / Pick me up on your way down: *Stone, Doug* / Boll Weevil Junction: *Blankenship, Sonny.*
LP: . . . . **WLP 8920**

MEMPHIS-ROCK'N'ROLL CAPITAL OF THE WORLD (Various artists).
Tracks: / Let's talk about us: *Various artists* / Strength of love: *Various artists* / Rockin' guitars: *Various artists* / Diamond of my heart: *Various artists* / Rock bottom boogie: *Various artists* / Doin' it live: *Various artists* / Memphis Tennessee: *Various artists* / Wash my hands in a muddy stream: *Various artists* / My rock & roll daddy: *Various artists* / Witchapoo: *Various artists* / Big fat mama: *Various artists* / My bonny: *Various artists* / Walkin' Charlie: *Various artists* / My friends call me shorty: *Various artists* / Don't be angry: *Various artists.*
LP: . . . . **WLP 8914**

MEMPHIS-ROCK'N'ROLL CAPITAL OF THE WORLD VOL.5 (Various artists).
Tracks: / Dudley do rite: *Evans, Jimmy* / Messy Bessy: *Evans, Jimmy* / Pink cadillac: *Evans, Jimmy* / J & E twist: *Evans, Jimmy* / Call me Mr Lonesome: *Evans, Jimmy* / Kassavubu boogie: *Skylarks* / Drop it: *Skylarks* / Look coming yonder: *Hogan, Joel* / Go on and say goodbye: *Hogan, Joel* / Spinning top: *Graves, Glenn* / Quicksand love: *Skipper, Macy* / Who put the squeeze on Eloise?: *Skipper, Macy* / Midnight train: *Rocco, Tommy* / Battle of Earl K. Long: *Barton, Bart* / Ain't I a mess?: *Barton, Bart* / Walk with me: *Barton, Bart* / Man with the heart of gold: *Barton, Bart.*
LP: . . . . **WLP 8918**

MISSOURI AND TENNESSEE (Various artists).
LP: . . . . **RL 310**

MISTER ROCK 'N' ROLL (Various artists).
Tracks: / Matchbox: *Netherton, Fred* / You are the one: *Volk, Dennis* / I hear thunder: *Ballenger, Paul*/ Annie Mae: *Dewitt, Bobby* / Rockin' the blues: *Bowman, Leon & Jerry Parker & His Buddies* / Baby tonight: *Harmony Brothers* / Saturday night bop: *Harmony Brothers* / You'll come running back to me: *Collier, Ralph* / Long lost John: *Owens, Kenny* / My queen and me: *Lenny & The Star Chiefs* / Ruby baby: *Boni, Johnny* / Train rock: *Boni, Johnny* / Mister rock 'n' roll: *Star Combo* / Love flame: *Kilgore Brothers & Howard Vokes*/ Hot rod race: *Williams, Bob.*
LP: . . . . **WLP 8859**

MODERN ROCK'N'ROLL AND ROCKABILLY (Various artists).
LP: . . . . **CH 185**

MONSTER HOP (Various artists).
LP: . . . . **WLP 8930**

MONSTER ROCK 'N' ROLL (Various artists).
LP: . . . . **CRYPT 181**

MOONLIGHT ROCK (Various artists).
Tracks: / Billy boy: *Dotson Brothers* / Moonlight rock: *Dotson Brothers* / Swingin': *Dotson Brothers*/ My baby: *Dotson Brothers* / How could you do this to me: *Dotson Brothers* / Hi lift: *Dotson, James*/ I wanna do it: *Excorts* / Main drag: *Excorts* / It's you: *Shelton, Johnny* / Mama may: *Rex & Herb*/ I come back big Bertha: *Rex & Herb* / Baby don't leave me: *Rex & Herb* / Little Bob's boogie: *Little Bob*/ Night riders drag: *Little Bob* / Big noise, The: *Harper, Harold* / Bingo blues: *Wert, Jimmy* / Cry baby cry: *Denhams* / Nitebeats are rockin': *Nitebeats* / Big beat, The: *Seachrist, Norm.*
LP: . . . . **WLP 8949**

MORE GEORGIA MUSIC (Various artists).
LP: . . . . **WLP 8942**

MORE GREAT RARITIES (Various artists).
Tracks: / Hey baby: *Denton, Johnny & Harold Sharp* / Strange woman's love: *Wortham, Johnny* / Hanky panky: *Brown, Jay* / Rockin' the guitar: *Brown, Jay* / Look who's lonely: *Junior, Carl* / Raining teardrops: *Jeffers, Jimmy* / World belongs to me: *Little, Olen* / It's love: *Fanning, Jay* / Is this the place?: *Royal Lancers*/ Rock with the mambo: *Fraser, Johnny* / You're no good for me: *Sudduth, Dorie* / Come on: *Stewart, Wynn*/ It'd surprise you: *Smith, Jan* / Flip over you: *Allen, Ronnie* / Ronnie's swannee: *Allen, Ronnie.*
LP: . . . . **WLP 8851**

MORE HOME MADE EARLY ROCK & ROLL (Various artists).
Tracks: / She's mine: *Adkins, Hasil* / Chicken walk: *Adkins, Hasil* / Hunch, The: *Adkins, Hasil* / Have mercy: *Hobock, Curtis* / Whole town's talking, The: *Hobock, Curtis* / I can't stay mad at you: *Friar, Hugh*/ Hey, hey, don't tease me: *Ratliff, Bo* / I just learned to rock: *King, Jack* / Two ruby lips: *King, Jack*/ Ooh yeah baby: *Tyler, Kip* / Jungle hop: *Tyler, Kip* / Don't try to get away: *Trowbridge, Cliff* / Man, what a party: *Walton & The Silver Lake Boys* / Cheretta rock: *Jasper, Bob* / Hillbilly hop: *Prevette, Colin.*
LP: . . . . **WLP 8868**

MORE PENNSYLVANIA BOPPERS (Various artists).
Tracks: / You fit me like a glove: *Sizemore, Gordon & Rex Roat* / Anything: *Sizemore, Gordon & Rex Roat* / 3 0 3: *Foley, Nick* / If you stayed: *Neat, Bill* / Squirmin' at the Sherman: *Anthony, Chuck* / Hydrogen, nitrogen, potassium: *Hall, Jim* / You found a new love: *Patrick, Sue* / Impact, The: *Impacts* / Light my rockets: *Alan, Neil* / Send me to the moon: *Alan, Neil* / Pizza pizza pizza pie: *Alan, Neil* / Eager lips: *Huckaby*, Gary & Joyce Duval / Fat mama: *Sharpe, Buddy* / White house rock: *Sharpe, Buddy* / Tommy Teen: *Colin & Jerry* / Little bit of lovin': *Pcono Playboys* / Wild stallion: *Wilson, Billy.*
LP: . . . . **WLP 8910**

MORE PRIMITIVE SOUND (Various artists).
Tracks: / You are my sunshine: *Woodard, Jerry* / You don't love me: *Woodard, Jerry* / Downbeat: *Woodard*, Jerry / Mean woman blues: *Woodard, Jerry* / Six long weeks: *Woodard, Jerry* / Our love & romance: *Woodard*, Jerry / Who's gonna rock my baby (1 & 2): *Woodard, Jerry* / Midnight train: *Newman, Wayne* / Rita Juanita: *Newman, Wayne* / Eeny meeny miney mo: *Davis, Jim* / Free ride: *Davis, Rebel & Big Hoe* / Big Daddy rock: *Watts, Hunter* / Whirlin' twerlin' rock: *Duncan, Bill* / Rosalie: *Lett, Roy* / Big fat papa: *Boyer, Tommy & Carl & Bill.*
LP: . . . . **WLP 8833**

MORE RARE ROCK (Various artists).
LP: . . . . **WLP 8870**

MORE RARE ROCKIN' GIRLS (Various artists).
Tracks: / I'm not gonna do it anymore: *Hunt Sisters* / You're not doin' me right: *Darlene, Donna* / Move over, tall woman: *Hubbard, Doris M.* / Long sideburns: *Barry, Boelean* / Chilli dippin' baby: *Poynter, Joyce*/ Record hop dream: *Mae, Lonnie* / Babysitter's blues: *Paul, Bunny* / Gonna spend my time: *Myers, Orella*/ Give a little, take a little: *Myers, Orella* / Ask Lucille: *Myers, Orella* / Rock 'n' roll thunderbird: *Burt* Sisters / Yeah baby: *Smith, Betty* / Two timin' woman: *Lee, Bella* / Going to hold my baby: *Wheeler*, Karen / Wait till I'm sixteen: *Wheeler, Karen* / Red thunderbird: *Howard, Lynn* / I wanna be free: *Harlene, Evelyn* / Rockin' the blues: *Griffith, Peggy* / Stagger Lee: *Johnson, Kay* / If again: *Neal, Abbie.*
LP: . . . . **WLP 8899**

MORE SUNDOWN ROCKERS (Various artists).
Tracks: / I was a fool: *Cook, Ken* / Why do I love you?: *Alton & Jimmy* / I just don't know: *Alton & Jimmy*/ Don't you know: *Parchman, Kenny* / Treat me right: *Parchman, Kenny* / Problem child: *Cook, Ken* / I'll wait forever: *Honeycutt, Glenn* / Heartbreak's girl: *Ballman, Wanda* / Ain't got a worry on my mind: *Ballman*, Wanda / Hey Mr. Blues: *Woods, James* / Somehow we'll find a way: *Fakes, Roger* / Gonna give a party: *Woods, James* / Lock you in my heart: *Woods, James* / Be wise don't cry: *Honeycutt, Glenn.*
LP: . . . . **SUN 1036**

MORE TENNESSEE ROCKIN' (Various artists).
Tracks: / I ain't gonna do it no more: *Pritchett, Dubb* / Five o'clock hop: *Pritchett, Dubb* / I don't know how to

cook: *Pritchett, Dubb* / Bill's special: *Lyle, Bill* / Get off my toe: *Blakley, Cliff* / I'm not going steady anymore: *Blakley, Cliff* / High steppin': *Blakley, Cliff* / Want to be with you: *Blakley, Cliff*/ Linda Lu: *Ford, Bubba* / Wiggling blonde: *Ford, Bubba* / Tiger: *Allen, Little Joe* / Nancy: *Tedder, Randy* / Good gosh gal: *Beasly, Phil* / Bedlam: *Sounds* / Ain't got a nickel: *Lowe, Max.*
LP: . . . . **WLP 8840**

MORE WILD ROCKIN' (Various artists).
Tracks: / Don't be that way: *Lawson, Bobby* / If you want my love: *Lawson, Bobby* / Petty blue: *Alexander, Charles* / Unknown riders: *DeWayne, Dick* / Witchcraft: *DeWayne, Dick* / Short stuff: *Jenkins, Gene*/ Janet: *Martin, Jerry* / If you're gonna shake it: *Carter, Bobby* / Weird: *Vidone, Bob* / Ain't that a dilly: *Grisham, Marlon* / Sugarfoot: *Grisham, Marlon* / Wiggle: *Chearlanders* / Saturday night: *Stephens*, Big Will / She left me crying: *Harris, Dinky* / Pig pen boogie: *Bowers, Chuck* / You tore your playhouse down: *Sanders, Rabon.*
LP: . . . . **WLP 8858**

NASHVILLE JUMPS (Various artists).
LP: . . . . **KK 783**

NEW ORLEANS ROCK'N'ROLL (Various artists).
LP: . . . . **RARIN' 555**

NIGHT & DAY U.S.A. (Various artists).
Tracks: / Night and day USA: *Gracie, Charlie* / Midnight hassle: *Virtue, Frank Combo* / Bossa nova stomp: *Fabulous dials* / King, The: *Madden, Greg* / Boca raton: *Mitchell, Ronnie* / I ask you: *Desires, The* / Pitter patter: *Five Fleets* / Story tellin' baby: *Jodimars & Marshall Lytle* / Street, The: *Terry & The Tunisians*/ King steps out, The: *King, Sleepy* / Pop corn baby: *Nuggets* / Be kind: *Ronnie & The Hi-Lites* / Exchange student: *Martin, Jerry* / You're still my baby: *Wade, Earl* / I am yours: *Barrett, Richard & The Sevilles*/ Ooh baby ooh: *Appel, Dave, & His Applejacks.*
LP: . . . . **SEL 6**

OLD TIME ROCK 'N' ROLL (Various artists).
Tracks: / Old time rock'n'roll: *Various artists* / Snake and the bookworm, The: *Various artists* / I ain't gonna be your dog no more: *Various artists* / Silly Willy: *Various artists* / Real wild child: *Various artists*/ Baby I'm bugged: *Various artists* / Dangerous doll: *Various artists* / Like wow: *Various artists* / Knock knock: *Various artists* / Short hair and turtle necked sweater: *Various artists* / Pucker paint: *Various artists* / You were mean baby: *Various artists* / Box of candy and a piece of fruit: *Various artists* / Livin' high: *Various artists* / I'm glad I waited so long: *Various artists* / Doodlebug: *Various artists.*
LP: . . . . **CR 30252**

ORDINARY ROCKIN' GIRLS (Various artists).
LP: . . . . **WLP 8932**

ORIGINAL EARLY ROCK INSTRUMENTALS (Various artists).
Tracks: / Madison blues: *Raging Storms* / High octane: *Raging Storms* / Rhythm rock: *Carter, Johnny*/ Drum shuffle: *Carter, Johnny* / Grazin': *Robens, Ronnie* / Earthquake boogie: *Earthquakes* / Twitchin': *Pastel Six* / Chopper, The: *Tempomen* / Honky tonk guitar: *Dee, Joe* / Jamboo: *Vulcans* / Shimmy shuffle: *Vulcans* / Black lightning: *Royaltones* / Midnight express: *Dawnbeats* / Panic: *Noise Makers*/ Zoobee: *Noise Makers* / Mad Beavers: *Hollywood Hurricanes* / Mad surfer: *Stingrays* / Surfer's walk: *Stingrays.*
LP: . . . . **WLP 8884**

ORIGINAL ROCK AND ROLL (Various artists).
LP: . . . . **WLP 8928**

ORIGINAL ROCK'N'ROLL CLASSICS (Various artists).
LP: **522 016**
MC: **722 016**

PENNSYLVANIA ROCKS (Various artists).
Tracks: / Come in world: *Ellis, Don & The Royal Dukes* / Half of me: *Ellis, Don & The Royal Dukes* / Navajo: *Ellis*, Don & The Royal Dukes / Blue fire: *Ellis, Don & The Royal Dukes* / Party doll: *Ellis, Don & The Royal Dukes*/ Big Daddy: *Rays, Del* / Radar: *Rays, Del* / Duke, The: *Rays, Del* / Slim little Annie: *Genos*/ Hey hot rod: *Herman, Hermy* / Eight days a week: *Herman, Hermy* / Rock all night with me: *Tacker, Dick*/ Jet: *Royal Rockers* / My bird dog: *Denver Bill & His Ranch Hands* / Susie or Mary Lou: *Barr, Chuck & The Rockabillies* / Come on back: *Barr, Chuck & The Rockabillies.*
LP: . . . . **WLP 8897**

PIKE RECORDINGS (Various artists).
Tracks: / Shake bop: *Garland, Dickie* / Breakin': *Thomas, Freddie* / Like thunder: *Thomas, Freddie* / Ring round your neck: *Hollister, Bobby* / Keep a knockin': *Sessions, Little Ronnie* / I got a lot on my conscience: *Sessions, Little Ronnie* / What a man: *Flowers, Cancie* / Karate: *Rialtos* / Monkey bite: *Hendrix, Al* / Rhonda Lee: *Hendrix, Al* / Toolin' around: *Hendrix, Al* / Jumping Johnny: *Hendrix, Al* / Go, daddy, go rock: *Hendrix, Al* / Bingo's bongo bingo party: *Baby Bugs* / Sheep: *Dee, Tommy & Gene Moles.*
LP: . . . . **WLP 8888**

PLAY THOSE OLDIES MR. D.J. - VOL.1 Giddy up a ding dong (Various artists).
LP: **6498 183**
MC: **7133 183**

PLAY THOSE OLDIES MR. D.J. - VOL.2 Whole lotta shakin' goin' on (Various artists).
LP: **6498 184**
MC: **7133 184**

PLAY THOSE OLDIES MR. D.J. - VOL.3 Brokenhearted melody (Various artists).
LP: **6498 185**
MC: **7133 185**

PLAY THOSE OLDIES MR. D.J. - VOL.4 Twistin' the night away (Various artists).
LP: **6498 186**
MC: **7133 186**

PLAY THOSE OLDIES MR. D.J. - VOL.5 All night worker (Various artists).
LP: **6498 187**
MC: **7133 187**

PRIMITIVE SOUND (Various artists).
Tracks: / Only cowgirl in town: *Barr, Glen & Roger Harrison* / I'm in no position: *Barr, Glen & Roger Harrison*/ Country rock 'n' roll: *Harrison, Roger* / How I love you: *Speck, Darrell* / Take me back: *Speck, Darrell*/ Lies, lies, lies: *Bullock, Norman* / Moanin' the blues: *Bullock, Norman* / My ramblin's over: *Johnson, Dan*/ Just over a girl: *Renfro Bros.* / Ever ready: *Renfro Bros.* / Lover man: *Cox, Jerry* / Rock & roll daddy O: *Castle, Joey* / Look coming yonder: *Scott, Ray* / Tennessee shake: *Scott, Ray* / He's a headed South: *Hopper, Evelyn.*
LP: . . . . **WLP 8830**

RABBIT ACTION (Various artists).
Tracks: / Blue suede shoes: *Various artists* / Rhythm called rock and roll: *Various artists* / Honey don't: *Various artists* / Rabbit action: *Various artists* / Everybody's trying to be my baby: *Various artists* / How come you do me: *Various artists* / Rock-me-baby: *Various artists* / Dixie fried: *Various artists* / Cat clothes: *Various artists* / You can't make love to somebody: *Various artists* / Cat clothes (version 2): *Various artists*/ That don't move me: *Various artists* / Honey don't (2): *Various artists.*
LP: . . . . **SUN 1018**

RARE COLLECTION OF ROCK (Various artists).
Tracks: / Goshamody whatabody: *Goza, Glen* / Little girl: *Lara, Sammy* / Silly Sally: *Lara, Sammy* / So lonely: *Sunday, Salty* / Hard hat: *Worley, Jim* / I'm a long-gone daddy: *Wright, Rebel* / Eeny meeny miney mo: *Davis, Jimmie* / El Diablo: *Lofton, Ronny* / Tell me: *Ronnie & The Regals* / Baggy Maggie: *Levoy*, Henry / Pretty baby: *Angel, Johnny* / Boogie man: *Angel, Johnny* / Top string boogie: *Jackson, Marvin*/ Amazon dance: *Dean, Bobby* / Path of regrets: *Ross, Jack* / Little bull and buttercup: *Homer, Chris.*
LP: . . . . **WLP 8894**

RARE ROCK FROM CANADA (Various artists).
Tracks: / Mary Lou: *Daigle, Ted* / Cut across Shorty: *Daigle, Ted* / No-one else: *Daigle, Ted* / Sweet little sixteen: *Daigle, Ted* / Red hen hop: *Daigle, Ted* / Farewell Adelita: *Daigle, Ted* / Ballad of a teenage queen: *Daigle, Ted* / It may be silly: *Daigle, Ted* / Rockin' the jukebox: *King, Bob* / Party hop: *King, Bob* / Rock 'n' roll lullaby: *Smith, Reg* / Baggy pants: *Smith, Reg* / Let's make hay: *Smith, Reg* / Red hot boogie: *Stevenson, Scotty* / No help wanted: *Canadian Sweethearts.*
LP: . . . . **WLP 8860**

RARE ROCKING GIRLS (Various artists).
Tracks: / Gotta rock: *Carter Kids* / Satellite: *Aguirre, J.* / Boy watcher: *Parker, Pat* / Everybody's trying to be my baby: *Stevens, Rosie* / Wrong yo yo: *Stevens, Rosie* / Crazy little heart: *Holly, Brenda*/ Squeeze box rock: *Browning Sisters* / Dallas chiggers: *Martin, Mamie* / Never gonna let you go: *Wells, Karen*/ Rockin' in the nursery: *Starr, Sally* / Eeny meeny miney mo: *Herren, Joyce* / I'm a bop: *Parr, Lona*/ Walking papers: *Anderson, Dot* / Jealous hearted woman: *Anderson, Dot* / What for?: *Dolly & The Deans*/ Someone to love: *Kelley, Jean.*
LP: . . . . **WLP 8885**

RARE, WILD, PRIMITIVE EARLY INSTRUMENTALS (Various artists).
Tracks: / Battle of the three blind mice: *Jerry & The Casuals* / Dennis boogie: *Volk, Dennis* / Mad gas: *Royal* Teens / Ghost train: *Swanks* / Boss: *Dial Tones* / Dreaming: *Various artists* / Dead man: *Prince* Tons Five / Graveyard: *Phantom Five* / Springtime rock: *Volk, Jimmie* / Blitzkrieg: *Dissonaires*/ Spitfire: *Logsdon, Bill* / Lariat: *Legends* / Flintales rock: *Flintales* / Clip clop: *Royaltones*/ Jambo: *Vulcans* / Shimmy shuffle: *Vulcans.*
LP: . . . . **WLP 8861**

RAZORBACK ROCK'N'ROLL (Various artists).
LP: . . . . **R&C 1018**

REAL 50'S ROCK & ROLL (Various artists).
LP: **2004**

REAL FINE PRIMITIVE ORIGINALS (Various artists).
LP: . . . . **WLP 8931**

REAL ROCK INSTRUMENTALS (Various artists).
Tracks: / Round rock boogie: *Rel-yeas* / Rugged rock: *Rel-yeas* / Whirly bird: *Rel-yeas* / Spartan stomp: *Treblemakers* / Breaker: *Polaras* / Cricket: *Polaras* / Gary's boogie: *Shadows Five* / Dynamite drums: *Shadows Five* / Four on the floor: *Rangers* / Joe's shuffle: *Shades* / Swampwater: *Pierce*, Alan & The Tonekings / Stampede: *Scarlets* / Pierman stomp: *Piermen* / Shoo shoo: *Jerry & Reggie*/ Scorpion: *Carnations* / Growl: *Pierce, Alan.*
LP: . . . . **WLP 8907**

REAL TENN, ROCK & COUNTRY ROCK, VOL.3 (Various artists).
Tracks: / Walk, spin, shake & rock: *Griffith, Joe* / She's my woman: *Griffith, Joe* / Big Sandy: *Griffith*, Joe / Little Hilda: *Griffith, Joe* / Crazy sack: *Griffith, Joe* / Annabelle Lee: *Griffith, Joe* / Drifter, The: *Tennessee Drifters* / If you ain't lovin' (you ain't livin'): *Rolison, Red* / Good rockin' tonight: *Rolison, Red* / Blue moon of Kentucky: *Rolison, Red* / Gonna roll and rock: *Rolison, Red* / Up and down that road before: *Moore, Charles* / Three way boogie: *Roach, Charlie.*
LP: . . . . **WLP 8810**

REED RECORDINGS (Various artists).
Tracks: / You hit the nail on the head: *Perry, Bill* / Go fly a kite: *Perry, Bill* / Thunder: *Starliners*/ Static: *Starliners* / Go, cat, go: *Bowman, Leon* / Rockin' the blues: *Bowman, Leon* / Black widow spider: *Bowman, Leon* / Panama City blues: *Larry & The Loafers* / Teenage bop: *Quinn, Botie* / Barbara Allen: *Smith, Eddie Arnold* / Mason Dixon: *Smith, Eddie Arnold* / Queen of my heartaches: *Smith, Eddie Arnold*/ I want my baby back: *Smith, Eddie Arnold* / Somebody else is taking my place: *Smith, Eddie Arnold* / Same thing: *Mizzell, Bobby* / Heart and soul: *Mizzell, Bobby* / Atomic fallout: *Mizzell, Bobby & J. Woodward* / Seven times Heaven: *Ballenger, Paul.*
LP: . . . . **WLP 8872**

ROADHOUSE ROCK (Various artists).
Tracks: / Elaine: *Hall, Sam* / Roadhouse rock: *Hanyel, Arbis* / Cross-eyed Susie wakeup: *Bob & Vic* / Funky: *Wallace, Vince* / Let's take a chance: *Dawson, Jimmie* / Froggie went a-courtin': *Dawson, Jimmie*/ I'm in love with you and my honda: *Mighty Four* / Satellite baby: *Stanley, Skip* / Stella got a fella: *Fireflies*/ Party date: *Canida, Carl* / Rock that rhythm: *Whisnant, Ray* / Gals don't mean a thing: *Whisnant, Ray* / How much do you miss me: *Montgomery, Harold* / Glynns hop: *Bittle, Walker (Arbie)* / Go go Gertrude: *Dodge, Percy* / Don't touch me: *Cupit, Earl* / Baby don't knock: *Mike & Jim* / Dungaree cutie: *Mike & Jim.*
LP: . . . . **WLP 8937**

ROCK ALONG .... (Various artists).
Tracks: / Tennessee rhythm: *Newton, Ted* / Walkin' down the road: *Newton, Ted* / Long, long ponytail: *Tharpe*, Chuck / Tennessee border: *Work, Jimmy* / Baby I'm sorry: *Stange, Howie* / I need your love: *Morgan, Bill*/ Pow wow: *Glentells* / Uprisin': *Glentells* / Tennessee Saturday night: *Smith, Chester* / Can't you see it in my eyes?: *Reagan, Jimmy* / Lonely, lonely heart: *Reagan, Jimmy* / Baby what you want me to do?: *Mick*, Fred / Daddy o goose and the three little piggies: *Mick, Fred* / Loose juice: *Law, Tommy* / Come to your Tommy now: *Clark, Leon* / I love my baby: *Savoys* / Caffeine, nicotine and gasoline: *Royal, Bill* / If you can spare the time (I won't miss the money): *Dubois, Morey.*
LP: . . . . **WLP 8886**

ROCK AND ROLL AT THE CAPITOL TOWER (VOL 2) (Various artists).
2LP: **2C 150 85029/3**

ROCK AND ROLL AT THE CAPITOL TOWER (VOL 1) (Various artists).
2LP: **2C 150 81970/1**

ROCK AND ROLL AT THE CAPITOL TOWER (VOL 3) (Various artists).
2LP: **2C 150 85345/6**

ROCK AND ROLL CLASSICS (Various artists).
MC: . . . . **ZCTON 116**

ROCK AND ROLL DANCE PARTY (Various artists).
MC: . . . . **AM 48**

ROCK AND ROLL PILLS (Various artists).
LP: . . . . **SUNLP 1023**

ROCK AND ROLL PILLS (Various artists).
Tracks: / Wild woman: *Various artists* / Bop pills: *Various artists* / Fire engine red: *Various artists*/ Sonny boy: *Various artists* / Watch that stuff: *Various artists* / Sentimental fool: *Various artists*/ Tootsie: *Various artists* / Slow rock and roll: *Various artists* / I won't be rockin' tonight: *Various artists*/ Red velvet: *Various artists* / Welcome to the club: *Various artists* / Rock 'n' roll cinnamon tree: *Various artists* / Call me anything but call me: *Various artists* / Voice of a fool: *Various artists.*
LP: . . . . **SUN 1023**

ROCK AND ROLL RADIO 1956 (Various artists).
LP: . . . . **RADIOLA 1087**

ROCK AND ROLL' (THE EARLY DAYS) (Various artists).
Tracks: / Sh'boom: *Chords* / Good rockin' Tonight: *Wynonie 'Mr Blues' Harris* / Hound dog: *Mae, Willie'Big Mama'* / I'm your Hoochie Coochie man: *Waters, Muddy* / Shake, rattle and roll: *Turner, Big Joe* / Rock around the clock: *Haley, Bill & The Comets* / That's alright: *Presley, Elvis* / Blue suede shoes: *Perkins, Carl*/ Maybellene: *Berry, Chuck* / Bo Diddley: *Diddley, Bo* / Tutti frutti: *Little Richard* / Great balls of fire: *Lewis, Jerry Lee.*
LP: . . . . **PL 85463**
MC: . . . . **PK 85463**
LP: . . . . **NL 90085**
MC: . . . . **NK 90085**

ROCK AROUND THE TOWN (Various artists).
LP: . . . . **BOPCAT 700**

ROCK, BABY, ROCK (Various artists).
Tracks: / Snake-eyed woman: *Sundowners* / Sundown stomp: *Sundowners* / Ubangi stomp: *Sundowners* / Savage: *Bernicoat, Alan* / Trip to the Orient: *Bernicoat, Alan* / Screamin' Mimi: *Roy, Ricky* / My baby's gone: *Ranado, Chuck* / Studio blues: *Highlights* / Rag roof roadster: *Foster, Jim* / Rock and roll daddy o: *Castle, Joey* / Baby I don't care: *Gregg, O. David* / Picture yourself: *Gregg, O. David* / Rock, baby, rock: *Milo Choir* / Go, girl, go: *Powers, Jet* / Teena: *Carney, Sandy* / She's a fine cat: *Darrow, Neil* / I'm a wile ol' cat: *Mitchell, Thomas.*
LP: . . . . **WLP 8890**

ROCK BABY,ROCK IT (Original soundtrack) (Various artists).
Tracks: / Hot rock: *Various artists* / Stop the world: *Various artists* / Your love is all I need: *Various artists* / Eat your heart out: *Various artists* / Chicken in the rough: *Various artists* / Bop it: *Various* artists / Crazy crazy lovin' wild wild women: *Various artists* / Lonesome: *Various artists* / Love me baby: *Various artists* / Saint song, The: *Various artists* / Roogie doogie: *Various artists* / Love never forgets: *Various artists* / Rockin' maybelle: *Various artists* / Hey Huanita: *Various artists* / Sugar baby: *Various artists.*
LP: . . . . **MFLP 040**

ROCK BOP BOOGIE (Various artists).
Tracks: / Hula baby: *Various artists* / Sentimental fool: *Various artists* / Ten cats down: *Various artists*/ Rakin' and scrapin': *Various artists* / I need your lovin' kiss: *Various artists* / When you're gone: *Various* artists / She's a woman: *Various artists* / Paul Rivere: *Various artists* / I'm sorry I'm not sorry: *Various* artists / It's me baby: *Various artists* / Rock and roll with my baby: *Various artists* / Signifying monkey, The: *Various artists* / Listen to me: *Various artists.*
LP: . . . . **SUN 1021**

ROCK FROM ARKANSAS (Various artists).
Tracks: / Please, please baby: *Brown, Bobby (1)* / Bobby's blues: *Brown, Bobby (1)* / Down at big Mary's house: *Brown, Bobby (1)* / I get the blues when it rains: *Brown, Bobby (1)* / Black Cadillac: *Green, Joyce* / Saddle rag: *Redell, Teddy* / Country girl: *Moore, Johnny* / Frog man hop: *Owens, K.* / Come back baby: *Owens, K.* / Knocking on the backside: *Duniven, Bill* / Black river bay: *Smith, Earl* / Little more lovin': *Comer, Chuck*.
LP: . . . . **WLP 8818**

ROCK FROM EAST TO WEST (Various artists).
Tracks: / Flea circus: *Baxter, Bobo* / She wore pink pedal pushers: *Circo, Re & Row* / Dangerous redhead: *Raines*, Jerry / Crawdad song: *Harrod, Chuck* / Don't you go chicken: *Preston, Rudy* / Four-tyred car: *Preston*, Rudy / Alone with a memory: *Scott, Tommy* / School's out: *James, Bill* / Juke joint honey: *Gosnell, Leo*/ Shake it over sputnik: *Hogan, Billy* / That's love: *Wendell & The Dreamers* / Rockabilly boogie: *Rockabilly Three* / Hey doll baby: *Patey Brothers* / Jeannie: *Patey Brothers*.
LP: . . . . **WLP 8846**

ROCK FROM MEMPHIS (Various artists).
LP: . . . . **REDITA 102**

ROCK FROM RARE LITTLE LABELS (Various artists).
Tracks: / That's alright: *Hines, Ronnie* / I got a woman: *Hines, Ronnie* / Green stamps: *Flynn, Freddie*/ Hazel: *Flynn, Freddie* / Big Chief Buffalo Nickel: *Ross, Macey* / Black Jack: *Werley, Coy* / Bubblegum boogie: *McBride, Jim/Curly Rash/South Texas Playboys* / Speedway rock: *Woodard, Jerry* / That's alright: *Louis*, Dwain / Gamblin' man: *Starvin' Marvin* / Party line: *May, Haskell* / Tears: *England, Hank* / Space needle: *Starfires* / Ginger: *Parker, Wayne* / PM rock: *Ginsburg, Arnie & The Three D's* / Arnie's theme: *Ginsburg, Arnie & The Three D's*.
LP: . . . . **WLP 8898**

ROCK FROM THE OTHER SIDE, VOL 2 (Various artists).
Tracks: / Girl in the teddy bear coat: *Hewitt, Red* / Is a bluebird blue?: *Hewitt, Red* / Tennessee waltz: *Hewitt*, Red / Betty Lou's got a new pair of shoes: *Hewitt, Red* / Don't you leave me: *Two Davies* / Big girl: *Paris*, Bob Combo / Bar X boogie: *Zito* / Just because: *Zito* / Spaceman: *Zito* / All I can do is cry: *Zito*/ Teenage beat: *Jess, Will* / Mean woman blues: *Sundin, Ronnie* / Moo cow boogie blues: *Sundin, Ronnie*/ Way I walk, The: *Sundin, Ronnie* / Be bop a Lula: *Fisher, Ivor* / Hot rod Lincoln: *Butler, Eddie*.
LP: . . . . **DS 9212**

ROCK FROM THE OTHER SIDE, VOL 4 (Various artists).
Tracks: / Mama rock: *Brown, Johnny Scat* / Cross my heart: *Arthur, Malcolm & The Knights* / Saturday night: *Blue* Jays / Hound dog: *Welch, Les* / Rumble: *Popcorn* / Great balls of fire: *Miller, Bob* / Geronimo: *Convairs* / Jukebox hop: *Wayne, Dale* / Tallahassee lassie: *Harmony Flames* / Reet petite: *McLean*, Peter / My bucket's got a hole in it: *Trailblazers* / Prettiest baby: *Wicker, Grade* / Go man go: *Thomas, Bob*.
LP: . . . . **DS 9215**

ROCK FROM THE OTHER SIDE, VOL 1 (Various artists).
Tracks: / Four city rock: *Lewis, Peter* / Money honey: *Lewis, Peter* / D.J. blues, The: *Hewitt, Red*/ Gravediggers' rock: *Scott, Clyde* / Bluebird: *Scott, Clyde* / Able Mabel: *Davis, Bobby* / Tallahassee lassie: *Davis, Bobby* / I'm in love: *Tucker, Clyn/Ian Lowe/Tornadoes* / Carol: *Tucker, Clyn/Ian Lowe/Tornadoes*/ Cool 'n' crazy: *Maxman, Ron* / Moo cow boogie: *Callaher, Vince & Will Jess* / Gone but not forgotten: *Riggir, Jack* / Pretty baby: *Riggir, Jack* / Hippy hippy shake: *Howell, Eddie & Ben Tawhiti*.
LP: . . . . **DS 9211**

ROCK FROM THE OTHER SIDE, VOL 3 (Various artists).
Tracks: / Everlovin' honey bee: *Bryant, Bix* / Let's have a party: *Bryant, Bix* / Judy: *Lincoln & The Lawmen*/ Cool it, baby: *Lincoln & The Lawmen* / Lotta lovin': *Richard & The R'Jays* / Nature boy: *Raiders* / Nightmare: *Raiders* / Cloudburst: *Wades, Laurie* / Cincinnati fireball: *Benton, Marv* / Nervous breakdown: *Benton, Marv* / Love bug blues: *Buckley, Colin* / My baby calls: *Buckley, Colin* / Board boogie: *Aztecs &* Billy Thorpe / Shakin' in the Shaky Isle: *Maori Troubadours* / Meet me in the alley, Sally: *Thunderbirds/Billy O'Rourke/Billy Owens* / Warrant for arrest: *Thunderbirds/Billy O'Rourke/Billy Owens*.
LP: . . . . **DS 9213**

ROCK MOON ROCK (Various artists).
LP: . . . . **WLP 8924**

ROCK 'N' ROLL CANNIBALS (Various artists).
Tracks: / Rock 'n' roll cannibals: *Coffee, Red & B.Jones* / Jungle hop: *Tyler, Kip* / Come on: *Stewart, Wynn*/ Uncle Tom got caught: *Stewart, Wynn* / School bus love affair: *Stewart, Wynn* / Nancy: *Barker Bros., The*/ Cute: *Coburn, Kimball* / My little girl: *Coburn, Kimball* / Boo be ah be: *Coburn, Kimball* / Down on the farm: *Downing, Big Al & The Poe Kats* / Oh babe!: *Downing, Big Al & The Poe Kats* / Wail man wail: *Coffee*, Red & B.Jones / Nothing but tough: *Tyler, Kip* / Ooh yeah baby: *Tyler, Kip* / She got eyes: *Tyler, Kip*/ Shadow street: *Tyler, Kip* / Hello Mr. Dee-Jay: *Tyler, Kip* / Make her love me: *Barker Bros., The*.
LP: . . . . **BFX 15233**

ROCK 'N' ROLL CLASSICS (Various artists).
Tracks: / Great balls of fire: *Lewis, Jerry Lee* / Ooby dooby: *Orbison, Roy* / Rockin' pneumonia/Woogie flu: *Smith*, Huey "Piano" / Good golly Miss Molly: *Little Richard* / Rock'n'roll music: *Berry, Chuck* / Jungle rock: *Mitzell*, Hank / Breathless: *Lewis, Jerry Lee* / Maybelline: *Berry, Chuck* / Bo Diddley: *Diddley, Bo* / Suzie Q: *Hawkins, Dale* / Boppin' the blues: *Perkins, Carl* / Raunchy: *Justis, Bill* / Flying saucers rock'n'roll: *Riley, Billy Lee* / Whole lotta shakin' goin' on: *Lewis, Jerry Lee*.
LP: . . . . **KNLP 15001**
MC: . . . . **KNMC 15001**

ROCK 'N' ROLL CLASSICS - CHESS MASTERS (Various artists).
LP: . . . . **CHXL 107**
MC: . . . . **CHXT 107**

ROCK 'N' ROLL COLLECTION (Various artists).
Tracks: / Rock around the clock: *Haley, Bill* / Whole lotta shakin' goin' on: *Lewis, Jerry Lee* / Lucille: *Little* Richard / Roll over, Beethoven: *Perkins, Carl* / Memphis: *Berry, Chuck* / Blue Monday: *Domino, Fats*/ Tutti frutti: *Little Richard* / Shake, rattle and roll: *Haley, Bill* / Hound dog: *Lewis, Jerry Lee*/ Long tall Sally: *Little Richard* / Great balls of fire: *Lewis, Jerry Lee* / Sweet little sixteen: *Berry*, Chuck / See you later alligator: *Haley, Bill* / Good golly Miss Molly: *Little Richard* / Blueberry Hill: *Domino*, Fats / Blue suede shoes: *Perkins, Carl* / Hail, hail rock'n'roll: *Berry, Chuck* / Maybellene: *Lewis, Jerry Lee* / Honey don't: *Perkins, Carl* / Be bop a lula: *Vincent, Gene*.
LP: . . . . **DVLP 2053**
MC: . . . . **DVMC 2053**

ROCK 'N' ROLL FEVER (Various artists).
LP: . . . . **REDITA 125**

ROCK 'N' ROLL FOREVER 1 (Various artists).
MC: **64030**

ROCK 'N' ROLL FOREVER 2 (Various artists).
MC: **64031**

ROCK 'N' ROLL GIANTS (Various artists).
MC: . . . . **GL 1952**

ROCK 'N' ROLL GIRLS (Various artists).
Tracks: / Hot dog: *Hickel, Betty* / Gonna be loved: *Linda & The Epics* / Going, going, gone: *Carson, Colleen*/ Claire's boogie: *Cook, Clair* / Rockin' tree: *Trina, Marguerite* / Stop your running around: *Morgan, Maggie*/ Sugar blues: *Morgan, Maggie* / I'll take back that heartache: *Neal, Abbie* / Square from nowhere: *Thompson*, Loretta / Rovin' lady: *Darlin, Brenda* / You can have my love: *Capps, Judy* / Polka wheel: *Merrill, Genia*/ Real gone Okie: *Hicks, Renie* / Eskimo boogie: *Betty Jo & Johnny Starr* / Rock a bop: *Lynn, Lorelei*/ Mean: *Collins, Boots* / Rockin' lady: *Candy, Penny*.
LP: . . . . **WLP 8866**

ROCK 'N' ROLL GOLD (Various artists).
2LP: . . . . **CR 5155**
MCSET: . . . . **CRT 5155**

ROCK 'N' ROLL GREATS (Various artists).
Tracks: / Great balls of fire: *Lewis, Jerry Lee* / Ooby dooby: *Orbison, Roy* / Blue suede shoes: *Perkins*, Carl / Lonely weekends: *Rich, Charlie* / Raunchy: *Justis, Bill* / Flying saucers rock 'n' roll: *Riley*, Billy Lee / We wanna boogie: *Burgess, Sonny* / Jungle rock: *Mizell, Hank* / Red cadillac and black moustache: *Smith, Warren* / Slow down: *Earls, Jack* / Bottle to the baby: *Feathers, Charlie* / Pink pedal pushers: *Perkins, Carl* / Domino: *Orbison, Roy* / Breathless: *Lewis, Jerry Lee*.
LP: . . . . **INS 5013**
MC: . . . . **TCINS 5013**

ROCK 'N' ROLL GREATS (Various artists).
Tracks: / Matchbox: *Perkins, Carl* / Blueberry hill: *Domino, Fats* / Tutti frutti: *Little Richard*.
MCSET: . . . . **DTO 10026**

ROCK 'N' ROLL GREATS VOL.1 (Various artists).
Tracks: / Tutti frutti: *Little Richard* / That'll be the day: *Holly, Buddy & The Crickets* / Blueberry Hill: *Domino*, Fats / Take good care of my baby: *Vee, Bobby* / Walk don't run: *Ventures* / Say mama: *Vincent, Gene*/ Bird dog: *Everly Brothers* / Sweet little sixteen: *Berry, Chuck* / Something else: *Cochran, Eddie* / Rock around the clock: *Haley, Bill & The Comets* / I'm walking: *Domino, Fats* / Oh boy: *Holly, Buddy & The* Crickets / Don't ever change: *Crickets* / Why do fools fall in love: *Lymon, Frankie & The Teenagers* / Be bop a lula: *Vincent, Gene* / Summertime blues: *Cochran, Eddie* / You're sixteen: *Burnette, Johnny* / Rubber ball: *Vee, Bobby*.
LP: . . . . **MFP 41 5744 1**
MC: . . . . **MFP 41 5744 4**
LP: . . . . **MFP 5744**
MC: . . . . **TC MFP 5744**

ROCK 'N' ROLL GREATS VOL.2 (Various artists).
Tracks: / C'mon everybody: *Cochran, Eddie* / Ain't that a shame: *Domino, Fats* / Willie and the hand jive: *Otis*, Johnny Show / Memphis Tennessee: *Berry, Chuck* / Dreamin': *Burnette, Johnny* / Red river rock: *Johnny &* The Hurricanes / Git it: *Vincent, Gene* / I'm not a juvenile delinquent: *Lymon, Frankie & The Teenagers*/ Whole lotta shakin' goin' on: *Lewis, Jerry Lee* / At the hop: *Danny & The Juniors* / Great balls of fire: *Lewis*, Jerry Lee / Peggy Sue: *Holly, Buddy & The Crickets* / Claudette: *Everly Brothers* / Three steps to heaven: *Cochran, Eddie* / Blue Monday: *Domino, Fats* / Blue jean bop: *Vincent, Gene* / Johnny B. Goode: *Berry, Chuck* / Good golly Miss Molly: *Little Richard*.
LP: . . . . **MFP 41 5745 1**
MC: . . . . **MFP 41 5745 4**
LP: . . . . **MFP 5745**
MC: . . . . **TCMFP 5745**

ROCK 'N' ROLL GREATS VOL.3 (Various artists).
Tracks: / Be my guest: *Domino, Fats* / Night has a thousand eyes, The: *Vee, Bobby* / Pistol packin' mama: *Vincent*, Gene / Cincinnati fireball: *Burnette, Johnny* / She's gone: *Knox, Buddy* / Piltdown rides again: *Piltdown* Men / Let's have a party: *Jackson, Wanda* / Get a job: *Silhouettes* / Ma he's making eyes at me: *Otis*, Johnny (The Johnny Otis Show with Marie Adams & The Three Tons Of Joy) / Weekend: *Cochran, Eddie* / Perfidia: *Ventures*/ Bony Moronie: *Williams, Larry* / Mother-in-law: *K-Doe, Ernie* / Love potion No.9: *Clovers* / Runaway: *Shannon, Del* / You've got what it takes: *Johnson, Marv* / Stay: *Williams, Maurice & The Zodiacs* / Baby baby: *Lymon, Frankie & The Teenagers* (As sung in the film 'Rock, Rock, Rock'.).
LP: . . . . **MFP 5809**
MC: . . . . **TCMFP 5809**

ROCK 'N' ROLL GREATS VOL.4 (Various artists).
Tracks: / Hello Mary Lou: *Nelson, Rick(y)* / Shakin' all over: *Kidd, Johnny & The Pirates* / Run to him: *Vee*, Bobby / Shake, rattle and roll: *Haley, Bill* / Rave on: *Holly, Buddy* / I'm in love again: *Domino, Fats*/ Move it: *Richard, Cliff* / No particular place to go: *Berry, Chuck* / Little town flirt: *Shannon, Del*/ Only sixteen: *Douglas, Craig* / See you later alligator: *Haley, Bill* / It's late: *Nelson, Rick(y)*/ Rock and roll music: *Berry, Chuck* / Wild cat: *Vincent, Gene* / Say man: *Diddley, Bo* / Sweetie pie: *Cochran, Eddie* / Hey little girl: *Shannon, Del* / It doesn't matter anymore: *Holly, Buddy*.
LP: . . . . **MFP 5846**
MC: . . . . **TC-MFP 5846**

ROCK 'N' ROLL HITS VOL 1 (Various artists).
Tracks: / Rock around the clock: *Haley, Bill* / Dig your baby: *Rainwater, Marvin* / I saw Linda yesterday: *Lee, Dickey* / Great balls of fire: *Lewis, Jerry Lee* / Wooly bully: *Sam The Sham & The Pharaohs* / Whole lotta twistin' going on: *Taylor, Vince* / Heartbreak hotel: *Twitty, Conway* / Move it on over: *Williams, Hank*/ Blue jean bop: *Taylor, Vince* / Roll over, Beethoven: *Vincent, Gene* / See you later alligator: *Haley, Bill*/ Let the four winds blow: *Domino, Fats*.
LP: **819 307-1**
MC: **819 307-4**

ROCK 'N' ROLL HITS VOL 2 (Various artists).
Tracks: / Shake, rattle and roll: *Haley, Bill* / Whole lotta woman: *Rainwater, Marvin* / Sweet little sixteen: *Taylor, Vince* / Maybellene: *Lewis, Jerry Lee* / Chantilly lace: *Big Bopper* / Say Mama: *Vincent*, Gene / Long black train: *Twitty, Conway* / Be bop a lula: *Vincent, Gene* / Corina Corina: *Lewis, Jerry* Lee / Lover please: *McPhatter, Clyde* / Rock this joint tonite: *Haley, Bill* / C'mon everybody: *Taylor, Vince*.
LP: **819 308-1**
MC: **819 308-4**

ROCK 'N' ROLL IS HERE TO STAY (2) (Various artists).
LP: . . . . **WAX 1**

ROCK 'N' ROLL IS STILL ALIVE (Various artists).
LP: . . . . **CRL 5002**

ROCK 'N' ROLL ITCH (Various artists).
LP: . . . . **WLP 8935**

ROCK 'N' ROLL JAMBOREE (Various artists).
LP: . . . . **SJLP 822**

ROCK 'N' ROLL JAMBOREE VOL 2 (Various artists).
LP: . . . . **SJLP 831**

ROCK 'N' ROLL LEGENDS RECORDED LIVE IN LONDON (Various artists).
LP: . . . . **SHSM 2024**

ROCK 'N' ROLL -- LET'S GO (Various artists).
Tracks: / Let's go: *Manning, Chuck* / Live it up: *Martin & The Sundowners* / Pretty woman blues: *Moore, Lattie*/ Jukebox Johnny: *Moore, Lattie* / No doze blues: *Leonard, Sonny* / Wow, wow: *Love, Tommy* / Mister Blues: *Kross, Jack* / Billy Boy hop: *Sounds* / Street walkin': *Sounds* / I wanna rock now: *Blockbusters*/ Rock all night: *Blockbusters* / Baby, baby, baby: *Wesley, Chuck* / Be my baby: *Orrell, David* / You're the one: *Orrell, David* / Chattanooga drummer man: *Flying Tornados* / Paper moon: *Robinson, Jerry*.
LP: . . . . **WLP 8922**

ROCK 'N' ROLL LOVE SONGS (Various artists).
LP: . . . . **DINTV 13**
MC: . . . . **DINMC 13**

ROCK 'N' ROLL MAMAS (Various artists).
Tracks: / Rock 'n' roll mama: *Various artists* / Business woman: *Various artists* / In the bag boogie: *Various* artists / Skillet's gonna fry: *Various artists* / Rainy morning blues: *Various artists* / Hands off: *Various* artists / Spare man: *Various artists* / Everything's alright: *Various artists* / Rockin' good way, A: *Various* artists / Like a baby: *Various artists* / I ain't givin' up nothing: *Various artists* / Sittin' and drinkin': *Various artists* / Mr. Big wheel: *Various artists* / Next door to the blues: *Various artists* / Nobody's fault: *Various artists* / I'm a woman: *Various artists*.
LP: . . . . **CRB 1079**

ROCK 'N' ROLL MEDICINE (Various artists).
Tracks: / Do you dig me, little mama?: *Scott, Tommy* / Cats and dogs: *Scott, Tommy* / Cat music: *Scott, Tommy*/ Dance with me Henry: *Scott, Tommy* / Jumpin' from six to six: *Scott, Tommy* / Nobody but you: *Scott, Tommy*/ Juke joint girl: *Scott, Tommy* / Talkin' to myself: *Scott, Tommy* / Bad bad way: *Roger & The Tempests*/ Carla blues: *Tolleson, Tommy* / Second and San Antone: *Ball, Earl* / Desert boots: *Six Kings* / Hound dog boogie: *Hound Dogs* / Hey little crayfish: *Michel, Don* / Barbie, Barbie: *Milton, Fred* / Linda baby: *Fitzhugh, Sammy*.
LP: . . . . **WLP 8903**

ROCK 'N' ROLL MEETING (Various artists).
LP: . . . . **RLP 001**

ROCK 'N' ROLL NUMBER ONES OF THE FIFTIES (OLD GOLD (Various artists).
Tracks: / Singing the blues: *Steele, Tommy* / Diana: *Anka, Paul* / Stupid cupid: *Francis, Connie* / Claudette: *Everly Brothers* / It's only make believe: *Twitty, Conway* / All shook up: *Presley, Elvis* / Rock around the clock: *Haley, Bill & The Comets* / Great balls of fire: *Lewis, Jerry Lee* / Jailhouse rock: *Presley, Elvis*/ Cumberland gap: *Donegan, Lonnie* / Yes tonight Josephine: *Ray, Johnnie* / Rockabilly: *Mitchell, Guy*/ Hoots mon: *Lord Rockingham's XI* / That'll be the day: *Crickets*.
LP: . . . . **OG 1502**
MC: . . . . **OG 2502**

ROCK 'N' ROLL ORIGINALS VOL. 1 (See under Sun Records) (Various artists).

ROCK 'N' ROLL PARTY (Various artists).
LP: **33.8009**

ROCK 'N' ROLL PARTY (Various artists).
MC: . . . . **AM 62**

ROCK 'N' ROLL PARTY VOL.1 (Mit Ted Harold & Anderen) (Various artists).
Tracks: / Poor me: *Herold, Ted* / Blue moon: *Gluck, Harry* / Jingle bell rock: *Makulis, Jimmy* / Johnny angel: *Kessler, Alice & Ellen* / Corina, Corina: *Kent, Tommy* / Endless sleep: *James Brothers* / Fool such as I, A: *Backus, Gus* / Elvis Peter: *Main, Micky* / Plenty good lovin': *Mann, Danny* / Lion sleeps tonight, The: *Salvidor, Henry* / Be mine: *Kraus, Peter* / You're my baby doll: *Berg, Jorg Maria* / Red river rock: *Geissler, Ladi* / Save the last dance for me: *Robic, Ivo* / Baby oh baby (don't forbid me): *Die Teddies.*
LP: . . . . **BFX 15055**

ROCK 'N' ROLL PARTY VOL.2 (Mitt Ted Herold) (Various artists).
Tracks: / Trouble in paradise: *Herold, Ted* / Peggy Sue: *Bob & Eddy* / Let's think about living: *Gluck, Harry* / Charlie Brown: *Honey Twins* / Susie darlin': *Kent, Tommy* / Wenn du heut ausgehst: *Kraus, Peter* / Running bear: *Backus, Gus* / Here comes Summer: *Paulsen, Ralf* / Purple people eater: *Ramsey, Bill* / Hello Mary Lou: *Kollo, Rene* / Young ones, The: *Kraus, Peter* / Kisses sweeter than wine: *Berg, Jorg Maria* / Are you lonesome tonight: *Alexander, Peter* / Halfbreed: *Halbblut* / Things: *Brandes, Will* / Singing the blues: *Die Montecarlos.*
LP: . . . . **BFX 15056**

ROCK 'N' ROLL PARTY VOL.3 (Mit Ted Herold & Anderen) (Various artists).
Tracks: / Whatever happened to Judy: *Herold, Ted* / Black boy: *Wurges, Paul* / Don't you just know it: *Cremer,* Hannelore / Wonderful time up there, A: *Simson, Rolf* / Yes tonight Josephine: *Roland, Jo* / Rocky tocky baby: *Sanders, Billy* / Witch doctor: *Hass, Werner* / Wild wind: *Timmer-Mann, Gerd* / Home on the range: *Bottcher, Gerd* / Oh lonesome me: *Williams, Roland & Christa* / Lollipop: *Solar, Ria* / My happiness: *Lind, Gitta.*
LP: . . . . **BFX 15058**

ROCK 'N' ROLL PARTY VOL.4 (Various artists).
Tracks: / Bird dog: *Quick, Conny* / I remember you: *Petersen, Hank* / Everybody loves a lover: *Gualdi, Nana* / Roses are reds: *Padre Twins* / Michael: *Leandros, Leo* / Fools rush in: *Beil, Peter* / Heartbreak hotel: *Overheidt, Werner* / Annabella Susan I'm gonna knock on your door: *Candy Kids* / Mandolins in the moonlight: *Hagara, Willy* / Come softly to me: *Segler, Manfred* / Never be anyone else but you: *Bruhl, Heidi* / Hey little Lucy: *Herwig, Claus* / I saw Linda yesterday: *Marino* / Lovers Lane: *Beil, Peter.*
LP: . . . . **BFX 15091**

ROCK 'N' ROLL PARTY VOL.5 (Various artists).
Tracks: / Hag: *Twist, Oliver* / Norman: *Mann, Danny* / King Creole: *Brandes, Will* / Along came Jones: *Blum, Hans* / White sports coat: *Kuhn, Paul* / Peggy Sue: *Olaf, Teddy* / Rock boogie: *Rock, Benny* / Big man: *Hansen Boys & Girls* / Generation: *Lang, Sunny* / Susie darlin': *Howland, Chris* / Baby sittin' boogie: *Bendix, Ralf* / Stomp and whistle: *Bobejan* / Da doo ron ron: *Herold, Ted.*
LP: . . . . **BFX 15094**

ROCK 'N' ROLL PARTY VOL.6 (Various artists).
LP: . . . . **CH 175**

ROCK 'N' ROLL PARTY VOL 5 (Various artists).
LP: . . . . **CH 158**

ROCK 'N' ROLL PARTY VOL 7 (Various artists).
Tracks: / Crazy man crazy: *Various artists* / Free and easy: *Various artists* / Whistlin' Joe: *Various artists* / Nite life boogie: *Various artists* / Dance the thing: *Various artists* / Little bit more, A: *Various artists* / Bim bam: *Various artists* / Hey boy, hey girl: *Various artists* / Bad mousie yes: *Various artists* / Zig zig zaggin': *Various artists* / Heebie jeebies: *Various artists* / I found a new girl: *Various artists* / Daddy, daddy: *Various artists* / Do the bop bop bop: *Various artists* / Bluebird, The buzzard & the oriole, The: *Various artists.*
LP: . . . . **CH 221**

ROCK 'N' ROLL RADIO (Various artists).
MC: . . . . **CMR 1087**

ROCK 'N' ROLL STORY (Various artists).
LP: . . . . **MA 241285**

ROCK 'N' ROLL STORY VOL.1 (Various artists).
Tracks: / Good golly Miss Molly: *Little Richard* / I'm ready: *Domino, Fats* / Flip flop and fly: *Lewis, Jerry Lee* / Back to Memphis: *Berry, Chuck* / Jailhouse rock: *Celentano, Adriano* / See you later alligator: *Haley,* Bill / Blue Monday: *Domino, Fats* / Thirty days: *Berry, Chuck* / Johnny B. Goode: *Lewis, Jerry Lee* / Buona sera: *Celentano, Adriano* / Kansas City: *Domino, Fats* / Shake, rattle and roll: *Haley, Bill* / Tutti frutti: *Little Richard* / Yes, it's me, and I'm in love again: *Domino, Fats* / Going down slow: *Charles,* Ray / Breathless: *Lewis, Jerry Lee* / Back in the U.S.A.: *Berry, Chuck* / Long tall Sally: *Little Richard* / Jambalaya: *Domino, Fats* / Hound dog: *Lewis, Jerry Lee* / Reelin' and rockin': *Berry, Chuck* / Roll over, Beethoven: *Lewis, Jerry Lee* / My blue Heaven: *Domino, Fats.*
LP: . . . . **DO 50030**

ROCK 'N' ROLL STORY VOL.2 (Various artists).
Tracks: / Rock around the clock: *Haley, Bill* / Lucille: *Little Richard* / Blueberry Hill: *Domino, Fats* / Back in the U.S.A.: *Berry, Chuck* / Beatnik fly: *Johnny & The Hurricanes* / Sweet little rock 'n' roller: *Berry,* Chuck / All around the world: *Little Richard* / I'm walking: *Domino, Fats* / Back to Memphis: *Berry,* Chuck / Keep a knockin': *Little Richard* / Ooh my soul: *Little Richard* / See you later alligator: *Haley,* Bill / Thirty days: *Berry, Chuck* / Red River rock: *Johnny & The Hurricanes* / Jenny, Jenny: *Little Richard* / I do really love you: *Berry, Chuck* / I'm ready: *Domino, Fats* / Baby face: *Little Richard* / Slippin' and slidin': *Little Richard.*
LP: . . . . **DB 80030**

ROCK 'N' ROLL STORY VOL.3 (Various artists).
Tracks: / Miss Ann: *Little Richard* / Beatnik fly: *Johnny & The Hurricanes* / My heart will always belong to you: *Berry, Chuck* / So long: *Domino, Fats* / At the hop: *Danny & The Juniors* / Long tall Sally: *Lewis,* Jerry Lee / Reveille rock: *Johnny & The Hurricanes* / Ready Teddy: *Little Richard* / Why don't you do it right: *Domino, Fats* / Charlie Brown: *Coasters* / High heel sneakers: *Lewis, Jerry Lee* / Hippy hippy shake: *Swinging Blue Jeans* / Runaway: *Shannon, Del* / Oh baby doll: *Berry, Chuck* / Susie darlin': *Luke, Robin* / Roll over, Beethoven: *Lewis, Jerry Lee* / Please don't leave me: *Domino, Fats* / Bama lama bama loo: *Little Richard* / Stagger Lee: *Price, Lloyd* / When the saints go marching in: *Domino, Fats* / Maybellene: *Lewis, Jerry Lee* / Girl can't help it, The: *Lewis, Bobby* / Mary Lou: *Lewis, Bobby* / Goodnight, it's time to go: *Berry, Chuck.*
LP: . . . . **DB 80057**
MC: . . . . **MDB 980057**

ROCK 'N' ROLL SUPERSTARS (Various artists).
MCSET: . . . . **DTO 10013**

ROCK 'N' ROLL SURVIVAL SHOW (Various artists).
LP: . . . . **BULL 1002**

ROCK 'N' ROLLING BRITAIN (Various artists).
Tracks: / Rock with the caveman: *Steele, Tommy & The Steelemen* / Baby she's gone: *Dene, Terry* / Rockin' at the 2-I's: *Harris, Wee Willie* / Swagger: *Brown, Joe & The Bruvvers* / Wee Tom: *Lord Rockingham's XI* / Rebel rock: *Steele, Tommy & The Steelemen* / Mole in the hole, The: *Southlanders* / Darktown strutters' ball: *Brown,* Joe & The Bruvvers / Rock Island line: *Donegan, Lonnie* / Hoots, mon: *Lord Rockingham's XI* / Six five special: *Cort, Bob* / Back to school again: *Harris, Wee Willie* / Start movin': *Dene, Terry* / Elevator rock: *Steele, Tommy & The Steelemen.*
LP: . . . . **TAB 85**

ROCK 'N' ROLL'N'JIVE, VOL 1 (Various artists).
LP: **60 590**

ROCK 'N' ROLL'N'JIVE, VOL 2 (Various artists).
LP: **60 591**

ROCK 'N' ROLL..VOL. 2 (Various artists).
MC: **8802**

ROCK 'N' ROLL..VOL. 4 (Various artists).
MC: **8804**

ROCK 'N' ROLL..VOL. 5 (Various artists).
MC: **8805**

ROCK 'N' ROLL..VOL. 6 (Various artists).
MC: **8806**

ROCK 'N' ROLL..VOL. 7 (Various artists).
MC: **8807**

ROCK 'N' ROLL..VOL. 8 (Various artists).
MC: **8808**

ROCK ORIGINALS (Various artists).
Tracks: / Uncle Sam's call: *Woodall, Jimmy* / Woody's rock: *Woodall, Jimmy* / Lorena: *Lemons, Bill* / Walkin' talkin' baby doll: *Boykin, Jerald* / If you call that love: *Boykin, Jerald* / Little Billy Boy: *Hulin, T.K.* / Thunder: *Storms* / Darlin' Ann: *Belden, Jimmie* / I never felt this way: *Lee, Wally* / Eeny meeny: *Lee, Wally* / Aquagell blues: *Burch, Woody* / Jumping: *Teen Tones* / Moon won't tell, The: *Reno, Jack* / That blonde-headed, blue-eyed baby of mine: *Whitney, Everett* / Count down: *Shifters.*
LP: . . . . **WLP 8844**

ROCK ORIGINALS (Various artists).
Tracks: / Zzztt, zzztt, zzztt: *Lewis, Wink* / Gee whiz Liz: *Senns, Charles* / Dig me a crazy record: *Senns,* Charles / Hey yea baby: *Plamer, Dom* / Easy going: *Nomads* / One melt, two straws: *Hall, Ron* / I'm so lonesome, baby: *Smith, Kenny* / Alabama jailhouse: *Morris, Rod* / This old bomb of mine: *Stange, Howie* / Real gone daddy: *Stange, Howie* / Little Annie: *Halo, Johnny* / Silly Sally: *Lara, Sammy* / Rockin' chair roll: *Cavalier, Johnny* / Knock off the rock: *Cavalier, Johnny* / Rockateen: *Satellites* / Linda Jean: *Satellites* / How does it feel to be lonely?: *Mores, Echo & Betty Lee.*
LP: . . . . **WLP 8841**

ROCK & RHYTHM (Various artists).
Tracks: / I got it made: *Lott, Alton* / I can't stand it: *Rogers, Buck* / Forbidden love: *Donelly, Jimmy* / Look out: *Bird, Bobby* / Tootsie: *Truck, James* / Every time I see you: *Lee, Harry* / Call the law: *White, Danny* / Education fool: *White, Danny* / Rock & roll bells: *Seacrest, Eddie* / I'm winning now (take 1): *Harris, Ray* / Love me: *Ray, Danny* / Just you and me: *Millet, Lou* / Baby it's love: *Angels, Johnny* / Atlanta, Georgia: *Hebb, Bobby.*
LP: . . . . **WLP 8801**

ROCK ROCK ROCK (Various artists).
Tracks: / Baby, baby, baby: *Holler, Dick* / Let's get it on: *Almond, Hershel* / I love you baby: *Almond, Hershel* / Looking for a woman: *Almond, Hershel* / That's what I call love: *Dee, Jimmy* / Who do you love: *Carroll, Alton* / What I learned about you: *Caine, Jeanne* / I love you: *Ray & Lamar* / Love don't treat me right: *Feathers, Charlie* / Every woman I know likes an automobile: *Vance, Al* / Memphis: *Smith, Mack Allen* / Sick & tired: *Smith, Mack Allen* / You better move on: *Smith, Mack Allen* / King of rock and roll: *Smith, Mack Allen.*
LP: . . . . **GCH 8020**
MC: . . . . **GCHK 78020**
LP: . . . . **WLP 8805**

ROCK ROCK ROCK VOL 1 (Various artists).
LP: . . . . **USA 1957-59-1**

ROCK ROCK ROCK VOL 2 (Various artists).
LP: . . . . **USA 1957-59-2**

ROCK ROCK ROCK VOL 3 (Various artists).
LP: **563 00**
LP: . . . . **USA 1957-59-3**

ROCK & ROCKABILLY AGAIN (Various artists).
Tracks: / Sun would never shine, The: *Johnson, Brownie* / Ray's theme: *Awalt, Ray* / Rowdy: *Awalt, Ray* / My woman: *Witter, Jimmy* / Aaaaaaaahh: *Witter, Jimmy* / Joint bank account: *Lancaster, Bill* / Tapping that thing: *Shagnasty, Boliver* / Bumble boogie: *Fraley, Dale* / Date at eight, A: *King, Ray* / Silence baby: *Kriss, Bobby* / Judy Judy: *Chancellers* / Hey bop bop: *Phantom* / Rock & roll rock: *Kelly, Roy* / You shake me: *Wayne, Jimmy.*
LP: . . . . **WLP 8822**

ROCK & ROLL BLUES (Various artists).
LP: . . . . **REDITA 124**

ROCKIN' 50'S (Various artists).
Tracks: / Hey Miss Fannie: *Various artists* / Worrying kind, The: *Various artists* / Mabellene: *Various artists* / I'll sail my ship alone: *Various artists* / Fort Worth jail: *Various artists* / Gone and left me blues: *Various* artists / Sugaree: *Various artists* / Try me: *Various artists* / My baby loves to rock: *Various artists* / Rockin' in the Congo: *Various artists* / Deep elm: *Various artists* / Blue jean bop: *Various artists* / Race with the devil: *Various artists* / Rocky road blues: *Various artists* / I gotta know: *Various artists* / Let's have a party: *Various artists.*
LP: . . . . **MFLP 048**

ROCKIN' AGAIN AT THE 2 I'S (Various artists).
Tracks: / Rock, baby, rock: *Reading, Bertice* / Girl like, A: *Peters, Janice* / Right behind you baby: *Taylor,* Vince & Playboys / Ubangi stomp: *Shannon, Dean* / Slippin' and slidin': *Pride, Dickie* / Let's you and I rock: *Crombie, Tony* / So what: *Kidd, Johnny & The Pirates* / Baby sittin': *Angelo, Bobby & The Tuxedos* / Long stringy baby: *Crawford, Jimmy* / If you need me: *Sampson, Dave and The Hunters* / Hey Miss Fannie: *Webb, Dean* / Teen street: *Eden, Toni* / This little girl's gone rockin: *Peters, Janice* / Brand new cadillac: *Taylor, Vince & Playboys.*
LP: . . . . **CHA 77**

ROCKIN' AND BOPPIN' (Various artists).
Tracks: / Dis a itty bit: *Brians, R.H.* / Makin' love with...: *Turley, Richard* / Rock on baby: *Sherrell,* Bill / Cool baby: *Cole, Lee* / Rhythm guitar: *Miller, Carl* / Boppin' guitar: *Melton, Ray* / I'm out: *Surf Riders* / Batman: *Wray, Link* / Sweet rockin' mama: *Hi Tombs* / Chicken rock: *Holmes, Fat Daddy* / Yeah, yeah, my baby: *Farmer, Wayne* / My minds make up: *Various artists* / Funny feeling: *Various artists* / Long legged Linda: *Various artists.*
LP: . . . . **RR 2004**

ROCKIN' AT THE HOP VOL.1 (Various artists).
MC: . . . . **VCA 012**

ROCKIN' AT THE HOP VOL.2 (Various artists).
MC: . . . . **VCA 095**

ROCKIN' CHRISTMAS THE 50'S (Various artists).
LP: . . . . **RNLP 066**

ROCKIN' IN LOUISIANA VOL. 1 (Various artists).
Tracks: / Rock 'n' roll angel: *Chevalier, Joe* / Big cloud: *Chevalier, Joe* / Better do it now: *Wray, Jimmy* / Then you'll know: *Dante, Joe* / Nothing but love: *Wainwright, Happy* / Waiting all alone: *Templet, Doyle* / Gotta right to want to love you: *Elledge, Jimmy* / Peanut Paddy: *John's Boy.*
LP: . . . . **WLP 8889**

ROCKIN' IN LOUISIANA VOL. 3 (Various artists).
Tracks: / End of the hunt: *Darnell, Bozo* / I shouldn't forget you: *Bell, Reuben* / Happy's tune: *Bell, Reuben* / Happy's love song: *Bell, Reuben* / Shake a hand: *Cain, Mike* / Late at night: *Perrywell, Charles* / Mama, mama, mama: *Hobbs, Louis* / Honey don't you listen: *Wayne, Roy* / Any way you do: *Wayne, Roy* / Allons rock 'n' roll: *Walker, Lawrence* / Martin's special: *Martin & The Rockers* / My Suzie Q: *Segura, Allen* / Barefoot rock: *Raines, Jerry* / Sha Marie: *Kerry, Marvin* / One boy, one girl: *Evans, Dean* / Geraldine: *Casanova & The Chants.*
LP: . . . . **WLP 8893**

ROCKIN' IN THE 50'S (Various artists).
Tracks: / Been away too long: *Blihovde, Marv* / Nobody's darlin' but you: *Blihovde, Marv* / Sweet little wife: *Blihovde, Marv* / Pickles: *Blihovde, Marv* / Cigarette and coffee blues: *Blihovde, Marv* / Teenage partner: *Hanson, Ronnie* / I got a baby: *Roubik, Jack* / Live it up: *Roubik, Jack* / Shake a leg: *Hodges,* Sonny / Date with you, A: *Hodges,* Sonny / Big dog, little dog: *Hodges,* Sonny / That's alright: *Faile, Tommy* / Little girl: *Ramistella, Johnny* / Two by two: *Ramistella, Johnny* / Party party: *T.J.'s.*
LP: . . . . **WLP 8839**

ROCKIN' & JIVIN' (Various artists).
LP: . . . . **RR 2016**

ROCKIN' JIVIN', THE (Various artists).
LP: **1287**

ROCKIN' JUMPIN' SHOUTIN' (Various artists).
Tracks: / Sound the bell: *Garlow, Clarence Bonton* / Bon ton roulet: *Garlow, Clarence Bonton* / Wicked old fever: *Sheffield, Charles 'Mad Dog'* / Mad dog: *Sheffield, Charles 'Mad Dog'* / Cool cat: *Sheffield, Charles 'Mad Dog'* / Got the news this morning: *Jackson, Ivory Lee* / Ball game: *Sheffield, Charles 'Mad Dog'* / Clear my nights of miserie: *Sheffield, Charles 'Mad Dog'* / One hour thirty minutes too long: *Sheffield, Charles 'Mad Dog'* / Sunday morning: *Garlow, Clarence Bonton* / Pretty little dollie: *Garlow, Clarence Bonton* / You move me: *Sheffield, Charles 'Mad Dog'* / Don't think I can make it: *Jackson, Ivory Lee.*
LP: . . . . **GCL 112**

ROCKIN' ON TOP (Various artists).

Tracks: / Oh baby please don't go: *Various artists* / Crawl, The: *Various artists* / Goin' to Louisiana: *Various artists* / Love me love me Mary Ann: *Various artists* / Lovin' huggin' kissin' my baby: *Various artists* / Rockin' in the coconut top: *Various artists* / Rock and roll jolie blonde: *Various artists* / Hey little Shyrel: *Various artists* / I wanna rock rock roll: *Various artists* / Bye bye baby: *Various artists* / I'm a country boy: *Various artists* / Sticks shuffle boogie: *Various artists*.
LP: . . . . **GCL 113**

ROCKIN' ORIGINAL ARTISTS (Various artists).
Tracks: / Sweet love on my mind: *Burnette, Johnny* / Honey hush: *Burnette, Johnny* / Drinkin' wine: *Burnette, Johnny* / Dum dum: *Lee, Brenda* / Sweet nothin's: *Lee, Brenda* / Jambalaya: *Lee, Brenda* / Razz dazzle: *Haley, Bill & The Comets* / See you later alligator: *Haley, Bill & The Comets* / Rip it up: *Haley, Bill* & The Comets / Maybe baby: *Holly, Buddy* / Rave on: *Holly, Buddy* / Peggy Sue got married: *Holly, Buddy*/ I fought the law: *Crickets* / Rockin' pneumonia: *Crickets*.
LP: . . . . **MFP 50466**

ROCKIN' PEG (Various artists).
Tracks: / You're just that kind: *Jones, Little Montie* / Rockin' Peg: *Redd, Johnny* / Early one morning: *Gillen*, Jack / Wrapped in green, made for ten: *Ferguson, Bobby* / I've been seasick: *Meadows, Bill* / Moonshine: *Garrison*, Red / You're gonna reap what you sow: *Strong, Ray* / That cat: *Brown, Tommy* / Wicked: *Rudy & Vince*/ Nite beat: *Edwards, Slim* / Jerico rock: *Mysterians* / Screamin' and dyin': *Blass, Charles* / Judy's clown: *Lee, Dennis (nar)* / Raw deal: *Dickens, Doug* / Hep cat baby: *Criss, Gene* / Please don't say goodbye: *Criss, Gene*.
LP: . . . . **WLP 8950**

ROCKIN' RHYTHMS (Various artists).
MC: . . . . **GM 0209**

ROCKIN' ROLLIN' COUNTRY STYLE (Various artists).
Tracks: / Drivin': *Vickery, Mack* / Foolproof: *Vickery, Mack* / Have you ever been lonely: *Vickery, Mack*/ My one desire: *Williams, Jimmy* / All I want is you: *Williams, Jimmy* / Walkin' shoes: *Wheeler, Onie*/ That's all: *Wheeler, Onie* / Tell 'em off: *Wheeler, Onie* / Jump right out of this jukebox: *Wheeler, Onie*/ Bonaparts retreat (instr.): *Wheeler, Onie* / Trumpet: *Yelvington, Malcolm* / First and last love: *Yelvington*, Malcolm / Mr.Blues: *Yelvington, Malcolm* / What I tell my heart: *McDaniel, Luke* / Don't come crying: *Ruick, Tommy*.
LP: . . . . **SUN LP 1030**

ROCKIN' ROLLIN' HIGH SCHOOL VOL.3 (Various artists).
Tracks: / Rock 'n' roll that hula hoop: *LeGarde Twins* (Available on 12" only) / Little brother: *Lane Brothers*/ Somebody sweet: *Lane Brothers* / Boppin' in a sack: *Lane Brothers* / Goodbye she's gone: *Sprouts* / Every little once in a while: *Sprouts* / Shake me up again: *Sprouts* / Luscious lovin' Lucy: *Sprouts*/ I'll never tell: *Orbison, Roy* (Previously unissued.) / Young love (original version): *Cartey, Ric* / Crying goodbye: *Cartey, Ric* (Previously unissued.) / Hey little ducky: *James, Sonny* (Previously unissued.) / Apache: *James, Sonny* (Previously unissued.) / Stand in: *Robertson, Doc* (Previously unissued.) / Edge of town, The: *Clement, Jack* (Previously unissued.) / Whole lotta lookin' all over this world: *Clement, Jack* (Previously unissued.).
LP: . . . . **BFX 15111**

ROCKIN' ROLLIN' HIGH SCHOOL VOL.5 (Various artists).
Tracks: / Red sweater: *Rich, Dave* / School blues: *Rich, Dave* / Sunshine in my heart: *Rich, Dave* / Dream boat: *Inman, Autrey* / Hard way, The: *Inman, Autrey* / Teenage wonderland: *Pruitt, Tommy* / Remember the night: *Fagan,Tom* / You look good to me: *Clay, Joe* / Doggone it: *Clay, Joe* / Goodbye goodbye: *Clay*, Joe / Slipping out and sneaking in: *Clay, Joe* / Keep a lovin' me baby: *Endsley, Melvin* / I like your kind of love: *Endsley, Melvin* / I got a feeling: *Endsley, Melvin* / I ain't gettin' nowhere with you: *Endsley, Melvin*.
LP: . . . . **BFX 15113**

ROCKIN' ROLLIN' HIGH SCHOOL VOL.7 (Various artists).
Tracks: / Man in the moon is a lady, The: *Robinson, Floyd* / Ooba ooba ooba: *Burton, Dave* / Rock 'n' roll Ruby: *Burton, Dave* / Oh baby: *Dell, Jimmy* (Previously unissued.) / Nite rock: *Nite Rockers* / Dear Tommy: *Teeners (Teen Queens)* / King of rock 'n' roll: *Teeners (Teen Queens)* (Previously unissued.) / Ring around the rock: *Teeners (Teen Queens)* (Previously unissued.) / Oh, oh baby: *Dell, Jimmy* (Previously unissued.) / Chicken hearted: *Dell, Jimmy* (Previously unissued.) / Left right here: *Dell, Jimmy* (Previously unissued.) / Me and big mouth: *Dell, Jimmy* (Previously unissued.) / Tuggin' on my heart strings: *Rich, Dave* / Burn on love fire: *Rich, Dave* / I believe in love: *Robinson, Floyd* (Previously unissued.) / Back in school again: *Robinson, Floyd*.
LP: . . . . **BFX 15115**

ROCKIN' ROLLIN' HIGH SCHOOL VOL.6 (Various artists).
Tracks: / Jamboree: *Allen, Milt* / Youthful lover: *Allen, Milt* (Previously unissued.) / One love too many: *Allen*, Milt (Previously unissued.) / Land of tomorrow: *Allen, Milt* (Previously unissued.) / Lovin' at night: *Salvo*, Sammy / My perfect love: *Salvo, Sammy* / Oh Julie: *Salvo, Sammy* / Julie doesn't love me anymore: *Salvo*, Sammy / Wake up little Susie: *Lane Brothers* / Uh uh honey: *Lane Brothers* / Ding dang danglin': *Lane* Brothers / Lips of wine: *Lane Brothers* / Come a little bit closer baby: *Castle, Joey* / Shake hands with a fool: *Castle, Joey* (Previously unissued.) / Please love me: *Castle, Joey* (Previously unissued.).
LP: . . . . **BFX 15114**

ROCKIN' ROLLIN' HIGH SCHOOL VOL.1 (Various artists).
Tracks: / Pig Latin song: *Luman, Bob* / Shopping centre: *Lord, Bobby* / Barbara: *Melson, Joe* / Shook up: *Melson, Joe* / What should I do: *Jensen, Kris* / There came a tear: *Folger, Dan* / Tell her for me: *Folger, Dan* / Girl in the night: *Folger, Dan* / Mary is my little lamb: *Folger, Dan* / Love is all I'm asking for: *Mitchell, Sinx (Earl Sinx)* / Ring around my Rosie: *Mitchell, Sinx (Earl Sinx)* ((Previously unissued)) / Return to Thunder road: *Mitchell, Sinx (Earl Sinx)* / Run Opic run: *Dinning, Mark* / Should we do it: *Dinning, Mark* / Last rose, The: *Dinning, Mark* / I love to dance with Annie: *Ashworth, Ernest*.
LP: . . . . **BFX 15064**

ROCKIN' ROLLIN' HIGH SCHOOL VOL.4 (Various artists).
Tracks: / Teeny weeny: *Dell, Jimmy* / Cool it, baby: *Dell, Jimmy* / Message, The: *Dell, Jimmy* / It's simply grand: *Allen, Milt* / Love a, love a lover: *Allen, Milt* / Just look, don't touch, she's mine: *Allen*, Milt / Half loved (1st recording): *Allen, Milt* (Previously unissued.) / Love twister: *Denson, Lee* / It took too long: *Denson, Lee* (Previously unissued.) / Heart of a fool: *Denson, Lee* / Pied piper: *Denson, Lee*/ Let me tell you about love: *Cartey, Ric* / Born to love one woman: *Cartey, Ric* / Heart throb: *Cartey, Ric*.
LP: . . . . **BFX 15112**

ROCKIN' ROLLIN' HIGH SCHOOL VOL. 2 (Various artists).
LP: . . . . **BFX 15065**

ROCKIN' ROLLIN' VOCAL GROUPS, VOL 1 (Various artists).
LP: . . . . **CHAM 181177**

ROCKIN' ROLLIN' VOCAL GROUPS, VOL 4 (Various artists).
LP: . . . . **CHAM 80505**

ROCKIN' ROLLIN' VOCAL GROUPS, VOL 3 (Various artists).
LP: . . . . **CHAM 80430**

ROCKIN' ROLLIN' VOCAL GROUPS, VOL 2 (Various artists).
LP: . . . . **CHAM 80423**

ROCKING DESS & POOR BOY MASTERS (Various artists).
Tracks: / Rock & roll joys: *Bowshier, Little Donnie* / I thought I heard you call my name: *Baker, Rob 'Boy'* / Impact: *Ramblin' Rebels* / Lost safari, The: *Ramblin' Rebels* / Grandma rock 'n' roll: *Sisco, Gene* / Turning the tables: *Sisco, Gene* / Mind your own business: *White, Evelyn* / Servant of love: *Van Bros* / Sweet Marie: *Van Bros* / Uncle Jim Riggs will: *Van Bros* / Wake me: *Witcher, Norman* / Somebody's been rocking my boat: *Witcher, Norman* / Doing things: *Richmond Boys*.
LP: . . . . **WLP 8811**

ROCKING RUFUS (Various artists).
Tracks: / Rocking Rufus: *Mauphin, Ramon* / What's the use?: *Mauphin, Ramon* / 'Cause I love you: *Allen, Little* Joe / When mom and pop started to rock: *Briggs, Gail & Steve* / Red lips: *Mondo* / Everybody needs somebody: *Mondo* / She's a square: *St. Germaine, Ray* / Hound dog guitar: *D'Valiant, Ronnie* / Iggy Joe: *Ward*, Willie / Meanest blues: *Thomas, Jake* / Iftic: *Emcees* / Born to ramble: *Loren, Keith* / Row boy: *O'Mary, Slim* / Sink or swim: *O'Mary, Slim* / I cried: *Purdy, Steve* / Walking in my sleep: *Dean, Jerry* / Not for love or money: *Hodge, Gary*.
LP: . . . . **WLP 8856**

ROLLERCOASTER ROCKERS, VOL 1 (Various artists).
Tracks: / Crazy man crazy: *Haley, Bill & The Comets* / Ten long fingers: *Poovey, Groovey Joe* / I'm gonna tell on you: *Fleming, George* / Sinful woman: *Browning, Bill* / Say hey little lover: *Sullivan, Niki* / Whoo, I mean whee: *Gunter, Hardrock* / Guitar boogie: *Gracie, Charlie* / Flip flop and fly: *King, Sid & The Five* Strings / Sleep rock'n'roll baby: *Wayne, Alvis* / Boo hoo: *Rainwater, Marvin* / Boppin' to grandfather's clock: *Lewis, Sidney Jo* / Big bounce, The: *Caddell, Shirley* / Wash machine boogie: *Echo Valley Boys* / Peggy Sue got married: *Lord, Kenny* / Whispering bells: *Chip & The Chimes* / Cruisin': *Crickets* / My baby scares me: *Morra, Tony & The Belltones* / Rappin' the bass: *Day, Jack & Haley's Comets*.
LP: . . . . **ROLL 2008**

ROLLIN' THE ROCK VOL.1 (Various artists).
LP: . . . . **LP 009**

ROLLIN' THE ROCK VOL.2 (Various artists).
LP: . . . . **LP 012**

ROLLIN' THE ROCK VOL.3 (Various artists).
LP: . . . . **LP 015**

ROULETTE ROCK 'N' ROLL COLLECTION (Various artists).
Tracks: / Where the Rio de Rosa flows: *Lloyd, Jimmy* / You've gone, baby: *Lloyd, Jimmy* / She's mine: *Strickland*, Johnnie / Woo hoo: *Rock A Teens* / Doggone it, baby: *Rock A Teens* / My baby's gone: *Bowen, Jimmy*/ Rock a bon a lina: *Hart, Billy & Don* / Long long walk: *Rivers, Johnny* / Goin' back to St Louis: *Vickery*, Mack / Baby take me back: *Larue, Roc* / Rocket in my pocket: *Lloyd, Jimmy* / You've got what it takes: *Strickland, Johnnie* / Leapin' guitar: *Chaparrals* / Janis will rock: *Rock A Teens* / Lotta boppin': *Rock A Teens*/ Goin' wild: *Isle, Jimmy* / Never anymore: *Davies, Bob* / Baby come back: *Rivers, Johnny* / Only one, The: *Roberts, Don "Red"* / You're driving me mad: *Campbell, Jo Ann*.
LP: . . . . **NSPL 28245**

SARG RECORDS STORY (Various artists).
Tracks: / Everybody rock: *Various artists* / Gonna be better times: *Various artists* / Let me have your love: *Various artists* / My money's gone: *Various artists* / Rockin' & a-bopping: *Various artists* / Broke up: *Various artists* / Little Alice: *Various artists* / No love in you: *Various artists* / Lookin' for money: *Various artists* / Moonshine: *Various artists* / Walkin' fever: *Various artists* / Long black train: *Various artists* / I'm gonna rock with my baby tonight: *Various artists* / Strange kinda feelin': *Various artists*.
LP: . . . . **CH 36**

SCREAMIN' HOWLERS (Various artists).
LP: . . . . **SCR LP 001**

SCREAMIN' ROCK 'N' ROLL (Various artists).
LP: . . . . **RR 2015**

SHAKE AROUND (Various artists).
Tracks: / Rockin' bandit: *Smith, Ray* / Judy: *Grayzell, Rudy* / Shake around: *Blake, Tommy* / You better believe it: *Blake, Tommy* / That's the way I feel: *Pritchett, Jimmy* / Don't you worry: *Watson, Sid* / With your love, with your kiss: *Powers, Johnny* / Dear John: *Smith, Warren* / Sweet sweet girl: *Smith, Warren*/ Sweet woman: *Bruce, Edwin* / I dig you baby: *Blake, Tommy* / Sweetie pie: *Blake, Tommy* / Be mine, all mine: *Powers, Johnny* / Doll baby: *Bruce, Edwin* / I'm evil: *Powers, Johnny*.
LP: . . . . **SUN 1029**

SHAKE, RATTLE AND ROLL (Various artists).
Tracks: / Shake, rattle and roll: *Turner, Joe* / Clock, The: *Ace, Johnny* / Have mercy baby: *Ward, Billy*/ Shake a hand: *Adams, Faye* / See you later alligator: *Haley, Bill & The Comets* / Maybellene: *Berry, Chuck*/ Mailman blues: *Price, Lloyd* / I can't go on: *Domino, Fats* / Every hour: *Little Richard* / Get a job: *Silhouettes* / That'll be the day: *Holly, Buddy & The Crickets* / Good golly Miss Molly: *Lewis, Jerry Lee*/ Reet petite: *Wilson, Jackie* / I met him on a sunday: *Shirelles* / At my front door: *Clark, Dee* / I'm movin on: *Charles, Ray* / What about us: *Coasters* / New Orleans: *Bonds, Gary U.S.* / Shake rattle and roll: *Turner, Joe*.
LP: . . . . **NW 249**

SHE'S JUST ROCKIN' (Various artists).
LP: . . . . **F 3001**

SIMPLY ROCKIN' (Various artists).
LP: . . . . **WLP 8943**

SOMETHING TO SHOUT ABOUT (Various artists).
Tracks: / Something to shout about: *Maresca, Ernie* / 8 o' clock scene: *Casals* / Cheer up: *Five Fleets*/ Feel so bad: *Wade, Earl* / Bongo stomp: *Little Joey & The Flips* / Wheel and deal: *Roxy, Bill* / Pretty baby: *Gracie, Charlie* / Shoo Sue: *Jodimars & Marshall Lytle* / Rock 'n' roll story, The: *Appel, Dave, & His Applejacks* / Wounded (in the battle of love): *Shaw, Ricky* / Manhunt: *Frank Virtue Combo* / Twisting and kissin: *Ronnie & The Hi-Lites* / Love wheel: *Foster, Millie* / Happy music: *Sleepy King* / Slow dance: *Kelly, Karol* / Shake a take a: *Martin, Jerry*.
LP: . . . . **SEL 4**

SOUTHERN ROCKIN' (Various artists).
Tracks: / You'll never change me: *Allen, Lonnie* / Verbena: *Smith, Lanier* / Can't stand to be alone: *Guy*, Dewey / Rock a while: *Guy, Dewey* / Have a tear on me: *Wilson, Jim* / I'm the wrong one: *Hunt, Kenneth*/ Teenage tease: *Hunt, Kenneth* / Packing my dud: *Marvin, Eddie* / Tutti frutti: *Shaul, Lawrence* / Hey little mama: *Shaul, Lawrence* / Loco choo choo: *Miller Bros.* / G.I. Blues: *Knull, Roger* / Country boy shuffle: *Sewell, Homer Lee* / I want my baby back: *Dixon, Mason*.
LP: . . . . **WLP 8835**

SPECIALITY ROCK'N'ROLL (Various artists).
Tracks: / Lights out: *Bryne, Jerry* / Moose on the loose: *Jackson, Roddy* / Bim bam: *Don & Dewey* / Don't you just know it: *Titans* / Rock around the clock: *Millet, Lil* / My baby's rockin': *Monitors* / Hickory dickory dock: *Myles, Big Boy* / Flip: *Marvin & Johnny* / Good golly Miss Molly: *Little Richard* / Rocking pneumonia: *Neville, Art* / Goodbye baby goodbye: *Lowery, Sonny* / Short fat Fannie: *Williams, Larry* / Rock'n'roll dance: *Price, Lloyd* / Girl can't help it, The: *Little Richard* / Haunted house: *Fuller, Jerry*/ Slow down: *Williams, Larry* / Cherokee dance: *Landers, Bob* / Hiccups: *Jackson, Roddy* / Zing zang: *Neville, Art* / Carry on: *Byrne, Jerry*.
LP: . . . . **CH 291**

SPOKEN WORD OF ROCK'N'ROLL, THE (See under Spoken Word...) (Various artists).

SPOKEN WORD OF ROCK'N'ROLL, THE (Various artists).
LP: . . . . **STAR 2486**
MC: . . . . **STAC 2486**

SPOTLIGHT ON ROCK 'N' ROLL (Various artists).
Tracks: / Remember then: *Earls* / Blue moon: *Marcels* / Do you wanna dance?: *Freeman, Bobby* / Why do fools fall in love?: *Lymon, Frankie & The Teenagers* / Tallahassee lassie: *Cannon, Freddy* / Kisses sweeter than wine: *Rodgers, Jimmie (2)* / Let's dance: *Montez, Chris* / I fought the law: *Fuller, Bobby Four* / Sweet little sixteen: *Berry, Chuck* / Party doll: *Knox, Buddy* / Hey baby: *Chanel, Bruce* / Stagger Lee: *Price*, Lloyd / Poetry in motion: *Tillotson, Johnny* / Cradle of love: *Preston, Johnny* / Rockin' robin: *Day*, Bobby / Mule skinner blues: *Fendermen* / Endless sleep: *Reynolds, Jody* / Pretty little angel eyes: *Lee*, Curtis / All I have to do is dream: *Everly Brothers* / Sea cruise: *Ford, Frankie* / To know him is to love him: *Teddy Bears* / Donna: *Valens, Ritchie* / But I do: *Henry, Clarence 'Frogman'* / Stay: *Williams, Maurice & The Zodiacs*.
2LP: . . . . **SPOT 1019**
MCSET: . . . . **ZCSPT 1019**

STEWED MOONBEAMS IN WAVY GRAVY (Okeh Black Rock'n'Roll) (Various artists).
LP: . . . . **ED 283**

STILL GOING STRONG (Various artists).
Tracks: / Honey baby: *Miller, Buddy* / Little bo Pete: *Miller, Buddy* / I found my love: *Miller, Buddy*/ Blonds, brunettes or redheads: *Arnold, Jerry* / Sarsaparilla: *Harris, Burton* / She loves me better: *Crabtree*, Riley / Those brown eyes: *Miller, Buddy* / Hot rod Kelly: *Sabres* / Bobcat: *Sabres* / Right now: *Montgomery, Gray* / Mean mouthin' momma: *Ol' Thoroughbred* / Rock while we ride: *Dockery, Chuck* / Knock on your door: *King, Tommy* / Bop diddle in the jungle: *King, Tommy*.
LP: . . . . **WLP 8837**

STOP THEN ROCK (Various artists).
LP: . . . . **WLP 8925**

SUN INTO THE SIXTIES (Various artists).

Tracks: / As long as I live: Lewis, Jerry Lee / Bonnie B: Lewis, Jerry Lee / What'd I say: Lewis, Jerry Lee / Don't drop it: Lewis, Jerry Lee / Great speckled bird, The: Lewis, Jerry Lee / You can't help it: Lewis, Jerry Lee / Old black Joe: Lewis, Jerry Lee / Baby baby bye bye: Lewis, Jerry Lee / My blue heaven 1: Lewis, Jerry Lee / My blue heaven 2: Lewis, Jerry Lee / I feel so good (i've been twisting): Lewis, Jerry Lee / Good golly miss Molly: Lewis, Jerry Lee / Waiting for a train: Lewis, Jerry Lee / I can't trust me: Lewis, Jerry Lee / I can't seem to say goodbye: Lewis, Jerry Lee / Carry me back to old Virginia: Lewis, Jerry Lee / Even tho': Mann, Carl / Canadian sunset: Mann, Carl / Chinatown my Chinatown: Mann, Carl/ Because of you: Mann, Carl / Baby I don't care: Bush, Eddie / Eddie's blues: Bush, Eddie / Blue suede shoes: Austin, Tony / Hambone: Anthony, Rayburn / Girls like you: Anthony, Rayburn / Alice blue gown: Anthony, Rayburn / St.Louis blues: Anthony, Rayburn / There's no tomorrow: Anthony, Rayburn / Who's gonna shoe your pretty little feet: Anthony, Rayburn / Big dream: Anthony, Rayburn / How well I know: Anthony, Rayburn/ Travelin' salesman: Smith, Ray / I won't miss you: Smith, Ray / Candy doll: Smith, Ray / Hey bossman: Smith, Ray / Raining the blues: Barton, Ernie / Open the door Richard: Barton, Ernie / Shut your mouth: Barton, Ernie / Herd of turtles: Barton, Ernie / Little by little: Rich, Charlie / Time and again: Rich, Charlie / Midnight blues: Rich, Charlie / I wanna make sweet love: McGill, Jerry / Honey bee: Hinton, Don / Me and my blues: Reddell, Teddy / Belle of Suwanee: Pendarvis, Tracy / Wait til' Saturday night: Dorman, Harold / Tragedy: Wayne, Thomas / Satisfied: Bond, Eddie / Rockin' daddy: Bond, Eddie / Double duty lovin': Bond, Eddie / Backstreet affair: Bond, Eddie / I can't quit: Bond, Eddie/ You nearly lose your mind: Bond, Eddie / One more memory: Bond, Eddie / They'll never take her love from me: Bond, Eddie / My buckets gotta hole in it: Bond, Eddie / Guess I'd better go: Strength, Texas Bill / Call of the wild: Strength, Texas Bill / Drunken gambler: Scaife, Don / Gone and left me blues: Louis, Jimmy / I'll wait forever: Wood, Anita / Shot out of the saddle: Stinit, Dane / Don't knock what you don't understand: Stinit, Dane / Muddy old river: Stinit, Dane / Bobaloo: Johnson, Bill / You better dig it: Johnson, Bill / Shake 'em up baby: Ballard, Frank / No-one to call your own: Ballard, Frank / Move on down the line: Ballard, Frank / If that's the way it is (you better move on): Ballard, Frank / I see trouble down the road: Ballard, Frank / I just can't help it: Ballard, Frank / Just walkin' in the rain: Stuart, Jeb/ Coming down with the blues: Stuart, Jeb / I betcha gonna like it: Stuart, Jeb / I'm in love again: Stuart, Jeb / I ain't never: Stuart, Jeb / Will I ever be free: Stuart, Jeb / All my weakness: Climates/ No you for me: Climates / Breakin' up again: Climates / Stop, wait and listen: Yates, Bill / Don't step on my dog: Yates, Bill / Poison ivy: Adams, Billy / Rock me baby: Adams, Billy / Trouble in mind: Adams, Billy / Reconsider: Adams, Billy / Too late to right my wrong: Yates, Bill / Big big world: Yates, Bill/ Cadillac man: Jesters, The / My babe: Jesters, The / Night train from Chicago: Jesters, The / Jim Dandy and sweet 16: Jesters, The / Heartbreak hotel: Jesters, The / Boppin' the blues: Jesters, The/ What's so good about goodbye: Jesters, The & Jimmie Day / Caddilac man 2: Jesters, The / I'm tired: Anderson, Brother James / My soul needs resting: Anderson, Brother James / Gonna move in the room with the lord: Anderson, Brother James / Workin' diggin' deeper: Anderson, Brother James / Hush hush (somebody call my name): Anderson, Brother James / Nobody's bloodstains: Anderson, Brother James / What can I do: Anderson, Brother James / Going home with Jesus: Anderson, Brother James / On my appointed time: Anderson, Brother James / Jelly roll king: Frost, Frank / Crawl back: Frost, Frank / Take the pain from my heart: Stidham, Arbee / Please let it be me: Stidham, Arbee / My heart belongs to you: Stidham, Arbee / Can't live in this world by myself: Stidham, Arbee / Nine below zero: Jackson, Cliff / Frank this is it: Jackson, Cliff & Jellean Delk / Kay / Lookin' for my baby / Pilot town, LA / Workin' on the river / Sun goin'down on Frisco / Nitty gritty Mississippi: Various artists / San Francisco lady / Tallahasse / Old home place, The / Will the circle be unbroken: Dyke, Jerry / Blackland farmer: La Beef, Sleepy/ I'm rugged but I'm right: La Beef, Sleepy / Stormy Monday blues: La Beef, Sleepy / There ain't much left after taxes: La Beef, Sleepy / Jenny Lee: Trammell, Bobby Lee / It's all your fault: Trammell, Bobby Lee/ Memphis Slim: Kellum, Murray.

LPS: . . . . **SUN BOX 109**

SUN RECORDS - THE ROCKING YEARS (Various artists).
Tracks: / I don't mind: Bernero, Johnny Band / Sentimental fool: Pittman, Barbara / I need a man: Pittman, Barbara / Voice of a fool: Pittman, Barbara / I'm getting better all the time: Pittman, Barbara / Bop bop baby: Moore, Wade & Dick Penner / Don't need your lovin': Moore, Wade & Dick Penner / Wild woman: Moore, Wade & Dick Penner / Don't need your lovin': Penner, Dick / Cindy Lou: Penner, Dick / Honey love: Penner, Dick / Fine little baby: Penner, Dick / Move baby move: Penner, Dick / Ooby dooby: Orbison, Roy/ Go go go: Orbison, Roy / Rock house: Orbison, Roy / Domino: Orbison, Roy / Sorry I lied: Thomas, Cliff / Rockabilly gal: Thompson, Hayden with Roy Orbison and Slim Rhodes / Flat foot Sam: Blake, Tommy/ Rakin' and scrapin': Beard, Dean / Long time gone: Beard, Dean / I dig you baby: Blake, Tommy / Rock boppin' baby: Bruce, Edwin / That's the way I love: Carroll, Johnny / Why why why: Smith, Ray / Walkin' (the stroll): Pride, Charley / With your love, with your kiss: Powers, Johnny / No more cryin' the blues: Alton & Jimmy / No name girl: Riley, Billy Lee / Got your water boiling: Riley, Billy Lee / Blues at midnight: Simmons, Gene / You can't make love to somebody: Perkins, Carl / Everybody's trying to be my baby: Perkins, Carl / Dixie fried: Perkins, Carl / Put your cat clothes on - 1: Perkins, Carl / That don't move me: Perkins, Carl / Only you: Perkins, Carl / Pink pedal pushers: Perkins, Carl / That's right: Perkins, Carl/ Crawdad hole: Earls, Jack / If you don't mind: Earls, Jack / Slow down: Earls, Jack / Fool for loving you: Earls, Jack / Whole lotta shakin' goin' on: Lewis, Jerry Lee / Sign it on the dotted line: Earls, Jack/ All night rock: Honeycutt, Glenn / I'll be around: Honeycutt, Glenn / I'll wait forever: Honeycutt, Glenn/ Be wise, don't cry: Honeycutt, Glenn / Breakup: Lewis, Jerry Lee / Sally's got a sister: Justis, Bill & His Orchestra / Come on little mama - 1: Harris, Ray / Where'd you stay last night: Harris, Ray / Love dumb baby: Harris, Ray / Greenback dollar: Harris, Ray / Foolish heart: Harris, Ray / Lonely wolf: Harris, Ray / Greenback dollar: Harris, Ray / Cotton pickin' boogie: Bernero, Johnny Band / Rockin' at the wood choppers ball: Bernero, Johnny Band / It makes no difference now: Bernero, Johnny Band / Bernero's boogie: Bernero, Johnny Band / Put your cat clothes on - 2: Perkins, Carl / Sign on the dotted line: Earls, Jack / Come on little mama - 2: Harris, Ray / Rock baby, rock it: Carroll, Johnny / Tennessee zip: Parchman, Kenny / I feel like rockin': Parchman, Kenny / Love crazy baby: Parchman, Kenny / Treat me right: Parchman, Kenny / Get it off your mind: Parchman, Kenny / What's the reason: Parchman, Kenny / You call everybody darlin': Parchman, Kenny / Go ahead baby: McDaniel, Luke / Huh babe: McDaniel, Luke / High high high: McDaniel, Luke / My baby don't rock: McDaniel, Luke / That's what I tell my heart: McDaniel, Luke / Born to sing the blues: Jenkins, Harold / I need your lovin' kiss: Jenkins, Harold / Goin' crazy: Self, Mack / Mad at you: Self, Mack / Good lookin' woman: Williams, Jimmy / Rockabye baby: Williams, Jimmy/ Sweet rocking mama: Williams, Jimmy / Sonny boy: Williams, Jimmy / Fire engine red: Williams, Jimmy/ All I want is you: Williams, Jimmy / My one desire: Williams, Jimmy / Tomorrow: Williams, Jimmy / Please don't cry over me: Williams, Jimmy / That depends on you: Williams, Jimmy / Down on the border: Simmons, Gene / Don't let me down: Simmons, Gene / Shake, rattle and roll: Simmons, Gene / It's me baby: Yelvington, Malcolm / Rocking with my baby: Yelvington, Malcolm / Trumpet: Yelvington, Malcolm / Ten cats down: Miller Sisters / Fools hall of fame: Richardson, Rudi / Cheese and crackers: Gordon, Roscoe / Sally Jo: Gordon, Roscoe / We wanna boogie: Burgess, Sonny / Red headed woman: Burgess, Sonny / Ain't got a thing: Burgess, Sonny / Feeling good: Burgess, Sonny / Truckin' down the avenue: Burgess, Sonny / Restless: Burgess, Sonny / Find my baby for me: Burgess, Sonny / Sadie Brown: Burgess, Sonny / Itch: Burgess, Sonny/ Rock 'n' roll Ruby: Smith, Warren / Stop the world: Smith, Warren / Uranium rock: Smith, Warren / Dear John: Smith, Warren / Flyin' saucers rock 'n' roll: Riley, Billy Lee / I want you baby: Riley, Billy Lee / Red hot: Riley, Billy Lee / Pop and mama: Simmons, Gene / Chains of love: Simmons, Gene/ Juicy fruit: Simmons, Gene / Drinkin' wine: Simmons, Gene / I done told you: Simmons, Gene / Crazy woman: Simmons, Gene / I don't love you baby: Simmons, Gene / Money money money: Simmons, Gene / If I'm not wanted: Simmons, Gene / Love my baby - 1: Thompson, Hayden / Love my baby (take 2): Thompson, Hayden/ One broken heart: Thompson, Hayden / Fairlane rock: Thompson, Hayden / Blues blues blues: Thompson, Hayden/ Madman 1: Wages, Jimmy / Heartbreakin' love: Wages, Jimmy / Miss Pearl: Wages, Jimmy / Take me (from this garden of evil): Wages, Jimmy / Madman 2: Wages, Jimmy / You win again: Lewis, Jerry Lee / High school confidential: Lewis, Jerry Lee / Crazy heart: Lewis, Jerry Lee / Charlie's boogie: Rich, Charlie/ Blue suede shoes: Rich, Charlie / My baby done left me: Rich, Charlie / Rebound: Rich, Charlie / Lonely weekends: Rich, Charlie / Stairway to nowhere: Barton, Ernie / She's gone away: Barton, Ernie/ Did you tell me you don't care: Felts, Narvel / I wanta rock: Holcomb, Patsy / Memories of you: Priesman, Magel / Judy: Brayzell, Rudy / Drive in: Vickery, Mack / Fool proof: Vickery, Mack / Have you ever been lonely: Vickery, Mack / Lordy hoody: Blake, Tommy / You better believe it-1: Blake, Tommy/ Sweetie pie: Blake, Tommy / Shake around: Blake, Tommy / You better believe it-2: Blake, Tommy / Eight wheel: Bruce, Edwin / Sweet woman: Bruce, Edwin / Baby that's good: Bruce, Edwin / King of fools: Bruce, Edwin / Memories never grow old: Lee, Dicky / Good lovin': Lee, Dicky / Fool fool fool: Lee, Dicky / Dreamy nights: Lee, Dicky / Hey heart: Lee, Dicky / Right behind you baby: Smith, Ray/ So young: Smith, Ray / Sail away: Smith, Ray / Breakup: Smith, Ray / Rockin' bandit: Smith, Ray / Willing and ready: Smith, Ray / Shake around: Smith, Ray / You made a hit: Smith, Ray / Forever yours: Smith, Ray / Mona Lisa: Mann, Carl / Rockin' love: Mann, Carl / Pretend: Mann, Carl / Too young: Mann, Carl / Thousand guitars, A: Pendarvis, Tracy / Is it too late?: Pendarvis, Tracy / Southbound line: Pendarvis, Tracy / Beat it: Pendarvis, Tracy / Is it me?: Pendarvis, Tracy/ Your lovin' man: Taylor, Vernon / Today is blue day: Taylor, Vernon / Breeze: Taylor, Vernon / Hey little girl: Taylor, Vernon / Mystery train - 1: Taylor, Vernon / This kind of love: Taylor, Vernon/ Sweet and easy to love: Taylor, Vernon / Mystery train - 2: Taylor, Vernon / Thinkin' of me: Gilley, Mickey/ Have a little party: Gilley, Mickey / Whole lotta shakin' goin' on: Gilley, Mickey / I'll change my ways: Stewart, Danny / This old heart of mine: Bond, Eddie / Love is my business: Gleaves, Cliff / I lost my baby: Hall, Roy / Raunchy: Justis, Bill & His Orchestra / Midnight man: Justis, Bill & His Orchestra / Somehow we'll find a way: Justis, Bill & His Orchestra / Wild rice: Justis, Bill & His Orchestra / College man: Justis, Bill & Billy Riley / Scrounge: Justis, Bill & His Orchestra / After the hop: Justis, Bill & Bill Pinkney/ Bop train: Justis, Bill & His Orchestra / Flip flop and bop: Justis, Bill & His Orchestra / Little Rolando: Janes, Roland Band / Little bitty pretty girl: Janes, Roland Band / Hey good lookin': Janes, Roland Band / Sugarfoot rag: Willis, Martin / Hey bo diddley: Van Eaton, Jimmy / That's the way I feel: Cannon, Johnny 'Ace' Band/ Tuff (cattywampus): Cannon, Johnny 'Ace' Band / That's just too bad: Cannon, Johnny 'Ace' Band / 706 union: Suggs, Brad / Crawdad hole: Earls, Jack / Rock all night: Honeycutt, Glenn / You don't care: Felts, Narvel / I wanna rock: Holcomb, Patsy.

LPS: . . . . **SUN BOX 106**

SUN'S GOLD HITS (Various artists).
Tracks: / Whole lotta shakin' goin' on: Lewis, Jerry Lee / You win again: Lewis, Jerry Lee / Breathless: Lewis, Jerry Lee / I walk the line: Cash, Johnny / Guess things happen that way: Cash, Johnny / Blue suede shoes: Perkins, Carl / Boppin' the blues: Perkins, Carl / Mona Lisa: Mann, Carl / I'm coming home: Mann, Carl / Lonely weekends: Rich, Charlie / Stay: Rich, Charlie / Raunchy: Justis, Bill.

LP: . . . . **CRM 2010**

SUN'S GREATEST HITS (Various artists).

LP: . . . . **RNDF 256**

SUNSET SPECIAL (Various artists).
Tracks: / Your honey love: Penner, Dick / Willing and ready: Smith, Ray / Judy: Grayzell, Rudy / Shake around: Smith, Ray / You made a hit: Smith, Ray / Behind you baby: Smith, Ray / Why why why: Smith, Ray / Show me: Bond, Eddie / Broke my guitar: Bond, Eddie / Break up: Smith, Ray / This old heart of mine: Bond, Eddie / Christine: Hall, Roy / Sweet love on my mind: Hall, Roy / I lost my baby: Hall, Roy.

LP: . . . . **SUN 1035**

SUPER ROCK INSTRUMENTALS (Various artists).

LP: . . . . **WLP 8926**

SWINGING THE ROCK (Various artists).
Tracks: / Puppy dog love: Braham, Ronnie / Please, please, baby: Lindsay, Larry / Teenage doll: Lindsay, Larry / Square rock: Squares / Davey's drag: Squares / Baby love: Bingham, Howard / Do you love another?: Weis, Doug / I'm buggin' out, little baby: Moore, Donny Lee / Rolly poly: Schurb, Duane / Ooh bee: Atha, Chuck / Hopin' and prayin': Marino, Sandy / Mailman blues: Moreland, Little Richard/ Fascinating baby: Scott, Sherree / Lonely Street: Williams, Cee Vee.

LP: . . . . **WLP 8869**

TANK TOWN BOOGIE (Various artists).
Tracks: / Tank town boogie (Take 1 & 3): Harral, Hank / She's gone: Harral, Hank / Dream band boogie: Harral, Hank / Oklahoma land: Harral, Hank / D.J. blues, The: Harral, Hank / Dilly dally doodle: Harral, Hank/ Summit ridge drive: Nix, Hoyle / Without you: Haggett, Jimmy / That's the way it goes: Daly, Durwood/ Little Rome: Alexander, Max & Hank Harral / Rock, rock everybody rock: Alexander, Max & Hank Harral / Casanova: Tate, Jack / Blue tomorrow: New, Roy / I've lost again: Ball, Ace / You can't stop me from dreaming: Dolly, Andy / Hey ba ba re bop: Dolly, Andy / Boogie walk: Dolly, Andy / Gotta have you: Dolly, Andy / Rollin' rhythm: Dolly, Andy / Oodabegga wow: Dolly, Andy / Stockade rock: Dolly, Andy / Honky tonk queen: Hankins, Bobby / Wild side of life: Thurn, Ike/Andy Doll / If I had me a woman: Vale, Blacky / Star of love: Vale, Blacky / Tattle tale: Dane, Jimmy / Please have mercy: Dane, Jimmy/ Honky tonkin' baby: Smith, Bob / Meet me in the barnyard: Cay, Phil / Mutha: Bing, Jim.

LP: . . . . **WLP 8831**

TEENAGE ROCK 'N' ROLL PARTY VOLUME 3 (Various artists).
Tracks: / Here she comes again: Uptowns / Schoolday blues: Johnny/ Jammers / Can't let you go I love you so: Scott, Albert / Bluebird two step: Electric Bluebirds / Carry on: Barron, Ronnie / Hot banana: McLollie, Oscar / Let's ride ride ride: McVea, Jack / Keep a knockin': Everly Brothers / Heebie jeebies: Little Richard / Big fat mama: Higgins, Chuck / I can't go on: Dion & The Belmonts / My little Ruby: Romero, Chan / Bopper 486609: Dameron, Donna / Is it a dream: Flamingo, Johnny / Boppin' the rock: Chenier, Clifton / Rock 'n' roll dance: Price, Lloyd.

LP: . . . . **CH 106**

TEENAGE ROCK'N'ROLL PARTY VOL 1 (Various artists).
Tracks: / Sea cruise: Ford, Frankie/ Huey 'Piano' Smith/his orchestra / All night long: Houston, Joe / Hit, git and split: Young Jessie / Roll, hot rod, roll: McLollie, Oscar / Let's get it on: Almond, Hershel/Al Good/his band / I can't find the doorknob: Jimmy and Johnny / Slippin' and slidin': Little Richard / Night of the werewolf: Kristofferson, Lee / Eddie my love: Teen Queens / Say another word: Milton, Buddy/ Twilighters/ Those lonely, lonely nights: Watson, Johnny 'Guitar' / Goodnight my love: Belvin, Jesse / Tell me, thrill me: Chanters / Goodnight my love: Various artists.

LP: . . . . **CH 25**

TEENAGE ROCK'N'ROLL PARTY VOL 4 (Various artists).
Tracks: / Johnny never knew: Jive Five / Blow Joe blow: Houston, Joe / Real gone hound dog: Hatchetmen/ He's my baby: Hightower, Donna / Surch, The: Various artists / Grasshopper rock: Davis, Link / Maybe: Four Closures / Big fat mama: Higgins, Chuck / Ay la bah: Cooper, Dolly / Whistlin' Joe: Lambert, Lloyd / Jungle hop: Don & Dewey / Keep a walking: Knight, Sonny / Wine woogie: Phillips, Marvin/ Don't stop loving me: Cliques / Make a little love: Harper Brinson Band / Harper's express: Various artists/ When you wish upon a star: Dion & The Belmonts / In the still of the night: Dion & The Belmonts / Lover's prayer: Dion & The Belmonts / My private joy: Dion & The Belmonts / My day: Dion & The Belmonts / Swinging on a star: Dion & The Belmonts / Every little thing I do: Dion & The Belmonts / All the things you are: Dion & The Belmonts / It's only a paper moon: Dion & The

Belmonts / Fly me to the moon: *Dion & The Belmonts* / I'm through with love: *Dion & The Belmonts* / When the red, red robin comes bob, bob, bobbin' along: *Dion & The Belmonts*/ September song: *Dion & The Belmonts* / Faith: *Dion & The Belmonts*.
LP: CH 137

TEENAGE ROCK'N'ROLL PARTY VOLUME 2 (Various artists).
Tracks: / Jump Jack jump: *Carr, Wynona* / Boo hoo hoo: *Little Richard* / Rock everybody: *Teen Queens*/ Something is going on in my room: *Cleanhead, Daddy & The Chuck Higgins Band* / Bluecoat man: *Diz & The Doormen*/ Please understand: *Milton, Buddy/Twilighters* / I've got nothing working now: *Cole, Ann with Chorus and orchestra*/ I'm in love with a girl: *Cliques* / Miss Ann: *Little Richard* / Since I don't have you: *Skyliners with Lenny* Martin's Orchestra / I love you for sentimental reasons: *Belvin, Jesse* / Right now: *Hightower, Donna* / Another sleepless night: *Clanton, Jimmy* / She wants to Mambo: *Chanters* / Hands off: *Hightower, Donna* / My desire: *Cliques*.
LP: CH 46

TEENTOWN HOP (The other kings vol. 2) (Various artists).
LP: LP 1180

TENNESSEE ROCKIN' (Various artists).
Tracks: / Oh love: *Wade, Don* / Bust head gin: *Wade, Don* / Gone gone gone: *Wade, Don* / Forever yours: *Wade, Don* / Loving on my mind: *Barnes, David* / Corina Corina: *Lipford, Preston* / I'll sail my ship alone: *Lipford, Preston* / Midnight piano rock: *Lipford, Preston* / Flip flop and fly: *Lipford, Preston*/ High school love: *Allen, Ronnie* / River of love: *Allen, Ronnie* / Juvenile delinquent: *Allen, Ronnie*/ This love of yours: *Allen, Ronnie*.
LP: WLP 8820

TEXAS DANCE HALL FAVOURITES (Various artists).
Tracks: / Big boss man: *Christy, Charles & The Crystals* / Tell me: *Carrasco, Joe 'King' & The El Molino Band*/ You upset me, woman: *Meyers, Augie* / Just a gigolo: *Ron-Dels* / I ain't got nobody: *Ron-Dels* / It's only make believe: *Christy, Charles & The Crystals* / Mathilda: *Meyers, Augie* / For your love: *Christy, Charles* & The Crystals / Fannie Mae: *McLinton, Delbert & The Ron-Dels* / Prosperity Street: *Meyers, Augie* / In my room: *Christy, Charles & The Crystals* / Rockesta noche: *Carrasco, Joe 'King' & The El Molino Band* / You cannot tell a lie: *Ron-Dels* / Justine: *Christy, Charles & The Crystals* / I'm a fool to care: *Meyers, Augie*/ Searchin': *McLinton, Delbert & The Ron-Dels*.
LP: WIK 13

THANK YOUR LUCKY STARS (Various artists).
LP: TAB 51

THAT GOOD OL' ROCK'N'ROLL SOUND (Various artists).
Tracks: / Brush pile burn: *Keller, Jimmy* / Juke: *Downbeats* / Going down: *O'Bannon, Charley* / She's cool: *Six Kings* / Rock it on Mars: *Dunavan, Terry* / There's the blues: *Goode, Larry* / Train whistle: *Boys & Girls* / It will be me: *Bounty, Rick* / My woman: *Moreland, Tommy* / Mean mean mama blues: *Moreland*, Tommy / That's the way: *Clendening, Jimmie* / Move: *Keetie & The Kats* / Koosey coo: *Long, Curtis*/ Going out on the town: *Long, Curtis* / Rockin' out the blues: *Linn, Carroll* / Indian rock: *Linn, Carroll*.
LP: WLP 8902

THEN CAME ROCK 'N' ROLL (Various artists).
2LP: THEN 1
MCSET: TCTHEN 1

THEY CALLED IT ROCK'N'ROLL (Various artists).
MCSET: DTO 10262

THIS IS ROCK 'N' ROLL (Various artists).
2LP: IMP 0100
MCSET: IMPC 0100

THOSE OLDIES BUT GOODIES FROM DEL FI (Various artists).
Tracks: / Hippy hippy shake: *Romero, Chan* / High dive: *Lewis, Bill* / My babe: *Holden, Ron* / Love you so: *Holden, Ron* / Little deuce coupe: *Defenders* / Come on, let's go: *Valens, Ritchie* / Ooh my head: *Valens, Ritchie* / My little Ruby: *Romero, Chan* / Under stars of love: *Carlos Brothers* / It's love: *Addrisi Brothers* / Cherry stoned: *Addrisi Brothers* / Fast freight: *Allens, Arvee*.
LP: CH 63

TOP SIXTEEN ROCK AND ROLL (Various artists).
MC: PM 1562604

UNIVERSAL ROCK & ROLL (Various artists).
LP: WLP 8929

UNKNOWN ROCK & ROLL (Various artists).
Tracks: / Mama, mama: *Stevens, Jesse* / No bluebirds in the sea: *Stevens, Jesse* / Go boy go: *Stevens, Jesse*/ Live it up: *Moon, Joe* / She's gone: *Moon, Joe* / Future I hold, The: *Meers, Arvil* / Muddy river: *Meers*, Arvil / Tennessee boogie: *Pittman, Clyde* / Ittie bitty rockabilly: *Boppers* / Pull it man: *Boppers*/ Love me, hug me: *Boppers* / That's alright: *Stone, Tommy* / That's what makes the world go round: *Stone, Tommy* / Honey, you talk too much: *Fox, Orville* / Let's do that again: *Eastwood, Johnny*.
LP: WLP 8812

VICTOR ROCK'N'ROLLERS (Various artists).
Tracks: / Duck tail: *Various artists* / Drugstore rock'n'roll: *Various artists* / Blue suede shoes: *Various* artists / Hip couple: *Various artists* / Mary Nell: *Various artists* / That ain't nothing but right: *Various* artists / Ooh wee: *Various artists* / Teen Billy baby: *Various artists* / TV hop: *Various artists*/ Sixteen chicks: *Various artists* / Sugar sweet: *Various artists* / New shoes: *Various artists* / Crackerjack: *Various artists* / Get on the right track: *Various artists* / Rosie let's get cozy: *Various artists* / Lovin' honey: *Various artists* / Will you Willyum: *Various artists* / It's called rock and roll: *Various artists*/ I've got a dollar: *Various artists* / Don't bug me baby: *Various artists*.
LP: PL 42809

VIN ROCK'N'ROLL (Various artists).
LP: R&C 1019

WE GOT A PARTY (Best of Ron Records vol.1) (Various artists).
LP: ROUNDER 2076
MC: C 2076

WELCOME TO 1984 (Various artists).
LP: MRR 001

WELTY RECORDINGS, THE (Various artists).
LP: WLP 8938

WEST COAST TEEN ROCK 1958-64 (Various artists).
LP: CGB 1006

WILD ROCKIN' (Various artists).
Tracks: / My rockin' baby: *Watson, Gene* / Interplanetary rock: *Watson, Gene* / Life's valley: *Watson, Gene*/ Drummer boy rock: *Watson, Gene* / Don't be cruel: *Watson, Gene* / School day: *Watson, Gene* / Whole lotta shakin' goin' on: *Watson, Gene* / Tick tock: *Calloway, Bob* / What's the matter with you: *Calloway*, Bob / Bonfire: *Piper, Jimmy* / Love me, love me: *Piper, Jimmy* / Summertime rock: *Rodney & The Blazers*/ Oriental nightmare: *Rodney & The Blazers* / Warpaint: *Rodney & The Blazers*.
LP: WLP 8829

YUKKA RECORDS & OTHER THINGS (Various artists).
Tracks: / Green gator: *Sims, Al* / You giggle too much: *Sims, Al* / Here comes that train: *Sims, Al*/ If you've got a lot of dough: *Sims, Al* / Taylor's rock: *Taylor, Bob* / Sky diver: *Cooper, Steve* / Your lovin' get's the best of me: *Vine, Steve* / Boo boo bear: *Vine, Steve* / Jungle bunny: *Bell, Jerry*/ Bacardi: *Bell, Jerry* / Pretty baby: *Bell, Jerry* / Pretty baby: *Pruitt, Lewis* / China doll: *Smith*, Dappa / Rockin' with Joe: *Renaults* / March to eternity: *Renaults* / You're my baby: *Nighthawks*/ Jim's jive: *Bright, Jerry*.
LP: WLP 8836

Rock 'n' Roll Circus

AT LAST.
Tracks: / Rockin' Robin / Blueberry Hill / Come go with me / Oh boy / Good vibrations / Only the lonely - pretty woman / Walk like a man / Unchained melody / Wanderer / Help me Rhonda.
LP: LOCO 1015

Rock, Pretty Baby

PRETTY BABY (Film soundtrack) (Various artists).
Tracks: / Rock, pretty baby: *Various artists* / Dark blue: *Various artists* / Free and easy: *Various artists*/ What's it gonna be: *Various artists* / Rockin' the boogie: *Various artists* / Rockabye lullaby blues: *Various artists* / Teenage bop: *Various artists* / Most, The: *Various artists* / Can I steal a little love: *Various* artists / Jukebox rock: *Various artists* / Saints rock 'n' roll: *Various artists* / Picnic by the sea: *Various* artists / Young love: *Various artists* / Happy is a boy named me: *Various artists* / Hot Rod: *Various artists* / Big band rock and roll: *Various artists*.
LP: JASM 1028

Rock Steady Crew

READY FOR BATTLE.
Tracks: / Up rock / Me and baby brother / She's fresh / B-boys b-girls / It's just begun / Hey you (the rock steady crew) / Digital boogie.
LP: CHC 78
MC: CHCMC 78
LP: RSC LP 1

Rockabilly...

20 GREAT ROCKABILLY HITS OF THE 50'S VOL.2 (Various artists).
Tracks: / I'm through: *La Beef, Sleepy* / I'm a hobo: *Reeves, Danny* / Gee whiz: *Dee & Patty* / Rock candy rock: *Crawford, Fred* / Raw deal: *Thompson, Junior* / It's Saturday night: *Mack, Billy* / Shadow my baby: *Barber, Glen* / That ain't it: *Rogers, Rock* / My big fat baby: *Hall, Sonny & The Echoes* / I don't know when: *Harris, Hal* / Hollywood party: *Busch, Dick* / If I had a woman: *Glenn, Glen* / Rockin' and rollin': *Fisher, Sonny* / Little bit more, A: *La Beef, Sleepy* / True affection: *Johnson, Blind Willie*/ Rock, roll and rhythm: *McGinnis, Wayne* / Tongue tied Jill: *Feathers, Charlie* / Pink cadillac: *Todd, Johnny*/ Strange kinda feeling: *Dugosh, Eddy & The Ah-Ha Playboys* / Maybe little baby: *Jones, George*.
LP: DROP 1009
MC: CROP 1009

20 GREAT ROCKABILLY HITS OF THE 50'S (Various artists).
Tracks: / Pink cadillac: *Todd, Johnny* / My baby left me: *Rogers, Rock* / Everybody's movin': *Glenn, Glen*/ Let's get it on: *Almond, Hershel/Al Good/his band* / Red hot rockin' blues: *James, Jesse* / Baby doll: *Dale*, Jimmie / Snake eyed Mama: *Cole, Don* / I'm gonna rock with my baby tonight: *McIntyre, Chester* / Move baby move: *Urban, Al* / Prettiest girl at the dance: *Wyatt, Gene* / All the time: *La Beef, Sleepy* / Spin the bottle: *Joy, Benny* / Jitterbop baby: *Harris, Hal* / Be boppin Daddy: *Cole, Les & The Echoes* / Rockin Daddy: *Fisher, Sonny* / Rock it: *Jones, George* / Circle rock: *Matchbox* / Blue jeans: *Glenn, Glen*/ I walk the line: *Barnes, Benny*.
LP: DROP 1003
MC: CROP 1003

50'S: ROCKABILLY FEVER, THE (See under 50's) (Various artists).

AAAAHHHH ROCKABILLY (Various artists).
Tracks: / Track down baby: *James, Tom* / Hey baby: *James, Tom* / Rock and roll baby: *Round Up Boys* / Let's jive it: *Ebert, Lee* / Tom cat boogie: *Ebert, Lee* / Weird session: *Stephens, Steve* / Blues for Oklahoma: *Bozman, Virgil* / Please be mine: *Kid Rock* / Don't knock it: *Dickerson, Dub* / T.N.T.: *Rikki* & The Rikatones / Part time hero: *Poovey, Joe* / Sie Simon shuffle: *Owen, Jim* / I've got the right key baby: *Nettles, Norman*.
LP: WLP 8821

ACETATE SESSIONS, THE (Various artists).
Tracks: / Whisky river: *Carroll, Johnny* / You two timed me two times too often: *Carroll, Johnny* / You made me love you: *Carroll, Johnny* / What I'll do: *Curtis, Mac* / Mean mean daddy: *French, Loretta* / He's just aggravatin': *French, Loretta* / Skinner blues: *Doug & Dubby* / Hoochie coochie man: *Burgess, Sonny* / Hanging round my gal: *Burgess, Sonny* / Oh look at that baby: *Aquirre, Jim* / Satellite: *Aquirre, Jim*/ Wildcat daddy: *Aquirre, Jim* / Nobody knows where: *Jimmy & Johnny* / I've nothing but love: *Burgess, Sonny*.
LP: WLP 8896

AMERICAN NEO-ROCKABILLIES (Various artists).
LP: LPL 8204

BEST OF ACE ROCKABILLY (Various artists).
Tracks: / Rockin' daddy: *Fisher, Sonny* / Everybody's movin': *Glenn, Glen* / I can't find the doorknob: *Jimmy & Johnny* / My big fat baby: *Hall, Sonny & The Echoes* / How come it: *Jones, Thumper* / Trucker from Tennessee: *Davis, Link* / Little bit more, A: *La Beef, Sleepy* / Jitterbop baby: *Harris, Hal* / Let's get on with it: *Almond, Hershel* / One cup of coffee: *Glenn, Glen* / I'm a hobo: *Reeves, Danny* / Rock it: *Jones, George* / Sneaky Pete: *Fisher, Sonny* / I'm through: *La Beef, Sleepy*.
LP: CH 45

BEST OF BRITISH ROCKABILLIES (Various artists).
LP: CRM 2002

BEST OF BRITISH ROCKABILLIES VOL.2 (Various artists).
LP: LPL 8212

BEST OF BRITISH ROCKABILLIES VOL.1 (Various artists).
LP: MLP 7901

BEST OF BRITISH ROCKABILLY (Various artists).
LP: SNTF 787

BEST OF SUN ROCKABILLY VOL 1 (Various artists).
Tracks: / Ten cats down: *Various artists* / Jump right out of this jukebox: *Various artists* / Gonna romp and stomp: *Various artists* / Domino: *Orbison, Roy* / Rakin' and scrapin': *Various artists* / Slow down: *Various* artists / Red cadillac and a black moustache: *Various artists* / Break up: *Various artists* / Greenback dollar: *Various artists* / Red headed woman: *Various artists* / Flyin' saucers rock 'n' roll: *Various artists*/ Crawdad hole: *Earls, Jack* / Love my baby: *Various artists* / Red hot: *Various artists* / We wanna boogie: *Various artists* / Come on little mama: *Various artists* / Right behind you baby: *Various artists* / Ubangi stomp: *Various artists* / Let's bop: *Various artists* / Rabbit action: *Various artists* / Put your cat clothes on: *Various artists* / Rocking with my baby: *Various artists*.
LP: CR 30123

BEST OF SUN ROCKABILLY VOL 2 (Various artists).
Tracks: / Got love if you want it: *Smith, Warren* / That don't move me: *Perkins, Carl* / Itchy: *Burgess*, Sonny / Drinkin' wine: *Simmons, Gene* / How come you do me: *Thompson, Junior* / Gimme some lovin': *Jenkins*, Harold / Johnny Valentine: *Anderson, Andy* / Baby please don't go: *Riley, Billy Lee* / Sentimental fool: *Pittman*, Barbara / Rebound: *Rich, Charlie* / Miss Froggie: *Smith, Warren* / Rock around the town: *Beard, Dean*/ Wild one: *Lewis, Jerry Lee* / My baby don't rock: *McDaniel, Luke* / Find my baby for me: *Burgess, Sonny*/ My gal Mary Ann: *Earls, Jack* / Me and my rhythm guitar: *Powers, Johnny* / All night rock: *Honeycutt, Glenn*/ Your loving man: *Taylor, Vernon* / Madman 1: *Wages, Jimmy* / Fairlane rock: *Thompson, Hayden* / I need your loving kiss: *Jenkins, Harold* / Perkins wiggle: *Perkins, Carl* / Ain't got a thing: *Burgess, Sonny*.
LP: CR 30124

BOPPIN' HILLBILLY VOL. 1 (Various artists).
LP: WLP 2801

BOPPIN' HILLBILLY VOL. 2 (Various artists).
LP: WLP 2802

BOPPIN' HILLBILLY VOL. 3 (Various artists).
LP: WLP 2803

BOPPIN' HILLBILLY VOL. 4 (Various artists).
LP: WLP 2804

BOPPIN' HILLBILLY VOL. 5 (Various artists).
LP: WLP 2805

BOPPIN' HILLBILLY VOL. 6 (Various artists).
LP: WLP 2806

BOPPIN' HILLBILLY VOL. 7 (Various artists).
LP: WLP 2807

BOPPIN' HILLBILLY VOL. 8 (Various artists).
LP: WLP 2808

BOPPIN' HILLBILLY VOL. 9 (Various artists).
LP: WLP 2809

BOPPIN' HILLBILLY VOL. 10 (Various artists).
LP: WLP 2810

BOPPIN' HILLBILLY VOL. 11 (Various artists).
Tracks: / Nursery rhyme blues: *Miller Bros.* / When the band played: *Noack, Eddie* / Your big beaver: *Jones*, Paul & Jimmie Short / Down the road: *Whitney, Don* / Cherokee rose: *Scott, Tommy* / Super market day: *Key, Jimmy* / Slick chick boogie: *Maston's Music Makers* / Juke box baby: *Ward, Reggie* / Clean town blues: *Leaders*, Benny / Hey Miss Fannie: *Leaders, Benny* / Flour, lard, coffee, sugar: *Lucky White* / Freeport blues: *Woytek*, Lester / Spanish fireball: *Hendon, R.D.* / Cotton pickin' boogie: *Bryant, Doc* / Highball boogie: *Prine, Richard* / K Bar blues: *Adams, Dub* / Old jalopy bounce: *Alexander, Murl*.
LP: WLP 2811

BOPPIN' HILLBILLY VOL. 12 (Various artists).
Tracks: / You've got to give me what's mine: *Bruner, Cliff* / Out of business: *Bruner, Cliff* / Guitar shuffle: *Frontiersmen* / Honky tonk hop: *Frontiersmen* / Man in the moon, The:

Carl, Utah / Silver sage stomp: *Manning, Bob* / Love made a wreck out of me: *Red River Dave* / Nacogdoches county line: *Torok, Mitchell* / Fisherman blues: *Ham, Claudie* / Who flung that 'mater: *Jordan, Troy* / Jelly roll blues: *Thompson, Cotton* / Crying my heart out over you: *Armstrong, Gene* / Tennessee Avenue: *Phelps, Helen* / Look what love has done to me: *Wilcox, Coye* / Backin' up: *Johnson, Mark* / Juvenile love: *Colbert, Tiny* / Love me baby: *Willet, Slim* / Blues won't bother me: *Crabbe, Gene*.
LP: . . . . **WLP 2812**

CALIFORNIA ROCKABILLIES (Various artists).
Tracks: / Don't you love me: *Glenn, Glen* / Blue suede shoes: *Glenn, Glen* / Jailhouse rock: *Glenn, Glen* / I'm gonna sit right down and cry over you: *Glenn, Glen* / Mystery train: *Brooks, Tommy* / Be bop a lula: *Brooks*, Tommy / Hound dog: *Brooks, Tommy* / Breathtaking baby: *Brooks, Tommy* / I wish I knew: *Brooks, Tommy* / Love me tender: *Brooks, Tommy* / Lonely town: *Brooks, Tommy* / Dixie: *Cochran, Eddie & Gary Lambert* / Boogie woogie breakdown: *Cochran, Eddie & Gary Lambert* / Gary's tune: *Cochran, Eddie & Gary Lambert* / Beginning of the end: *Lambert, Gary* / I'll never stop loving you: *Lambert, Gary* / Wait wait: *Lambert, Gary*.
LP: . . . . **SJLP 582**

CAPITOL ROCKABILLY ORIGINALS (see under Capitol (label)) (Various artists).

CAT TALK (Best of Imperial Rockabilly) (Various artists).
Tracks: / Make with the lovin': *Herrold, Dennis* / Cat talk: *Williams, Lew* / Warm love: *Burnette, Brothers* / Oh la baby: *Perkins, Laura Lee* / Rockin' by myself: *Gowans, Sammy* / Everybody's got a baby but me: *Miller*, Warren / Please give me something: *Allen, Bill* / All night long: *Luman, Bob* / So long good luck and goodbye: *Rogers, Weldon* / Gone ape man: *Williams, Lew* / Buddy: *Dee, Jackie* / Hey baby: *Lawrence, Bill* / Red hot: *Luman, Bob* / Hip hip baby: *Herrold, Dennis* / Sweet baby doll: *Burnett, Johnny* / If you can't rock me: *Strikes* / Something I said: *Williams, Lew* / Bop bop ba doo bop: *Williams, Lew* / Rockin' baby: *Henslee, Gene* / Chew tobacco rag No. 2: *Briggs, Billy* / Rockin': *Strikes* / Dirty dog: *Banks, Dick* / Centipede: *Williams, Lew* / Hip shakin' baby: *Brown, Roy* / Play my boogie: *Mack, Billy* (CD only.) / Let's go baby: *Eldridge, Billy* (CD only.) / Don't wait up: *Perkins, Laura Lee* (CD only.) / Baby I'm sorry: *Strikes* (CD only.) / It's late: *Burnette, Dorsey* (CD only.) / Everybody needs a little lovin': *Kilgore, Merle* (CD only.).
LP: . . . . **GO 2020**
MC: . . . . **TCGO 2020**

CBS ROCKABILLY VOL. 1 (Various artists).
LP: . . . . **CBS 82401**
MC: **40 82401**

CBS ROCKABILLY VOL. 2 (Various artists).
LP: . . . . **CBS 82993**

CBS ROCKABILLY VOL. 3 (Various artists).
Tracks: / That's all she wrote: *Various artists* / Romp stompin' boogie: *Various artists* / Flip out: *Various* artists / It's a great big day: *Various artists* / Sugar diet: *Various artists* / Purr, Kitty purr: *Various* artists / Teenage wedding: *Various artists* / Honky tonk man: *Various artists* / Black land blues: *Various* artists / Bump, The: *Various artists* / Boogie blues: *Various artists* / I like it: *Various artists* / Petrified: *Various artists* / Hurricane: *Various artists*.
LP: . . . . **CBS 83911**
MC: **40 83911**

CHESS, CHECKER, CADET ROCKABILLIES (Various artists).
LP: **9124213**

CHESS ROCKABILLIES (Various artists).
Tracks: / Man: *Sisco, Bobby* / Suzie Q: *Hawkins, Dale* / Cool off baby: *Barrix, Billy* / True love: *Diamond*, Larry / Sweet talk: *York, Rusty* / Save it: *Robbins, Mel* / Why did you leave me: *Josie, Lou* / Just go wild over rock 'n' roll / Roses are blooming: *Silvatones* / Sugaree: *York, Rusty* / Jet tone boogie: *Tones*, Jet / Rock yea: *Saint, Del the devils* / Go go go: *Sisco, Bobby* / Vacation's over: *Josie, Lou* / Are you with me: *Robbins, Mel* / All night long: *Fuller, Johnny* / Love me: *Lee, Jimmy* / Look out Mabel: *Crockett, G.L.*.
LP: . . . . **DET 204**

CLASSIC ROCKABILLY (Various artists).
MC: . . . . **OCN 2035WK**
LP: . . . . **OCN 2035WL**

CRAZY ALLIGATOR (Various artists).
Tracks: / Crazy alligator: *Russ, Irvin* / My imagination: *Russ, Irvin* / Speed limit: *Twisters* / Countdown 1, 2, 3: *Twisters* / Bandstand rocket: *Twisters* / Kat walk: *Twisters* / One way ticket: *Lumpkin, Bobby* / Your conscience: *Lumpkin, Bobby* / That Jim: *Beers, Mackey* / Lorilee: *Beers, Mackey* / Crying over you: *Dale, Larry* / Wombie zombie: *Taylor, Billy* / I'm long gone: *Belew, Carl* / Gertrude: *Neal, Meredith* / Lookie, lookie, lookie: *Grand, K.C.*.
LP: . . . . **WLP 8877**

DANCE BABY DANCE (Glo-lite rockabilly from Memphis) (Various artists).
Tracks: / What am I gonna do: *Evans, Jimmy* / Your pilot light went out: *Jones, Roy* / Dance baby dance: *Hadley, J.* / Crazy memories: *Alden, Roy* / I hate to say goodbye: *Evans, Jimmy* / She won't let me down: *Little*, Curtis / Rockabilly baby: *Kline, John* / Get with it: *Van Storey, Marcus* / Pink cadillac: *Evans, Jimmy* / Little Susie: *Evans, Jimmy* / She knows how to rock me: *Hadley, Red* / Way down blues: *Yelvington, Malcolm* / Goodbye Marie: *Yelvington, Malcolm* / Moving south: *Davis, Bill Scott*.
LP: . . . . **CHD 264**

EVERYBODY IN THE WHOLE CELL BLOCK (Various artists).
Tracks: / We're gonna teach you to rock: *Various artists* / They call me the rockin' lady: *Various artists* / Bop street: *Various artists* / Rockabilly land: *Various artists* / If you remember me: *Various artists* / Flaming star: *Various artists* / Big bad Billy: *Various artists* / Don't you ever leave me again: *Various artists* / Wig wam Willie: *Various artists* / In the mood: *Various artists*.
LP: . . . . **HYBLP 4**

FEDERAL ROCKABILLIES (Various artists).
LP: . . . . **BID 8041**

FERNWOOD ROCKABILLIES VOL.1 (Various artists).
LP: . . . . **REDITA 118**

FERNWOOD ROCKABILLIES VOL.2 (Various artists).
LP: . . . . **REDITA 119**

GOLDBAND ROCKABILLY (Various artists).
LP: . . . . **R&C 1015**

GOOD ROCKIN' TONIGHT (Various artists).
Tracks: / Number one: *Various artists* / You bring me down: *Various artists* / Am I losing you: *Various artists* / Long black train: *Various artists* / If you don't know how to dance: *Various artists* / Rockabilly party: *Various* artists / Somebody else: *Various artists* / Never felt like this: *Various artists* / Boys are here, The: *Various artists* / She's mine: *Various artists* / Draggin': *Various artists* / Dance to the boogie: *Various artists* / Let's make love: *Various artists* / I'm on my own: *Various artists* / Good rockin' tonight: *Various artists*.
LP: . . . . **DLP 2019**

GYPSY GIRL (Various artists).
LP: . . . . **F 3003**

I WANT ROCK (Various artists).
Tracks: / Run, baby, run: *King, Claude* / Ella Rea: *Leon & James* / I'll be there: *Tucker, Rick* / Whoo ooee: *Jones, Charles* / Ponderosa rock: *White, Lucky* / My babe: *Stafford, Roger & The Royal Monarchs* / Great balls of fire: *Stafford, Roger & The Royal Monarchs* / Finding you: *Kubiak, Jack* / Devil or angel: *Montana*, Tex / Minor chads: *Row, Steve* / Trip to the Moon: *Reynolds, Wesley* / Shake it up: *Rand, D.C.* / Rolling stone: *O'Keefe, Larry* / Tall Texas woman: *Paxton, Les*.
LP: . . . . **WLP 8875**

IMPERIAL ROCKABILLIES, VOL 2 (Various artists).
Tracks: / Sweet baby doll: *Various artists* / Oh la baby: *Various artists* / Kiss me sweet: *Various artists* / Rockin': *Various artists* / Abracadabra: *Various artists* / Ernie: *Various artists* / Loretta: *Various* artists / Rockin' baby: *Various artists* / I don't want to cry over you: *Various artists* / Hey baby: *Various* artists / Hip hip baby: *Various artists* / Kiss me baby: *Various artists* / All night long: *Various artists* / Baby, I'm sorry: *Various artists* / Cat talk: *Various artists* / Ride Jesse ride: *Various artists* / Be my love tonight: *Various artists* / Dig'n and datin': *Various artists* / Lies: *Various artists* / Willa Mae: *Various artists*.
LP: . . . . **UAS 30173**
LP: **2C 068 83097**

IMPERIAL ROCKABILLIES, VOL 3 (Various artists).
Tracks: / Loverboy: *Lewis, Wally* / It's late: *Burnette, Dorsey* / I only came here to dance: *Venet, Nick* / Love in bebop time: *Venet, Nick* / Long black hearse: *Greaves, Cliff* / Gone ape man: *Williams, Lew* / Something I said: *Luman, Bob* / Make up your mind, baby: *Luman, Bob* / My poor heart: *Strikes* / Buddy: *Dee, Jackie* / Chew tobacco rag: *Briggs, Billy* / Number two: *Banks, Dick* / Dirty dog: *Banks, Dick* / Get off my back: *Blue, Jay* / Speed crazy: *Slavin, Slick* / Only teenagers allowed: *Walker, Jackie*.
LP: . . . . **UAG 30312**
LP: **2c 068 83096**

JIN ROCKABILLY (Various artists).
LP: . . . . **R&C 1016**

KENTUCKY ROCK-A-BILLY (Various artists).
Tracks: / Be bop battlin' ball: *Gaines, Eddie* / Man alive: *Pate, Gus* / Kick off: *Pate, Gus* / Wild side of life: *Rothering, Dewey* / Long black shiny car: *Page, Mike* / Baby you done flubbed your dub with me: *Tag* & Effie / Rock 'n' roll on a Saturday night: *Bell, Dwain* / I'm gonna ride: *Bell, Dwain* / Hula hoop boogie: *Orr, J.D.* / Come to me baby: *Oller, Shady* / You sure look good to me: *Oller, Shady* / Wildfire: *Herman, Norman* / Don't play around with my heart: *Piper, Jimmy*.
LP: . . . . **WLP 8802**

KING-FEDERAL ROCKABILLIES (Various artists).
LP: . . . . **K 5016**

KINGS OF ROCKABILLY (Various artists).
MCSET: . . . . **DTO 10236**

KINGS OF ROCKABILLY VOL 1 (Various artists).
LP: **10CH 18**

KINGS OF ROCKABILLY VOL 2 (Various artists).
LP: **10CH 19**

L.A. ROCKABILLY (Various artists).
LP: . . . . **LP 8707**

LET'S ALL GO WILD (The Famous Rollin' Rockabilly Sound) (Various artists).
LP: . . . . **DIAL LP 003**

MEMPHIS HONKY TONK HILLBILLY (Various artists).
LP: . . . . **CH 168**

MEMPHIS ROCKABILLY (Various artists).
Tracks: / Jukebox mama: *Various artists* / Got the blues from waiting: *Various artists* / Boppin' wigwam Willie: *Various artists* / Here comes that train: *Various artists* / Joints really jumping, The: *Various artists* / Got you on my mind: *Various artists* / How can I go: *Various artists* / Lowdown feeling: *Various artists* / Standing in your window: *Various artists* / Eenie meenie minie mo: *Various artists* / Boo be ah be: *Various* artists / Baby don't you know me any more: *Various artists* / Short skirts: *Various artists* / I'm asking but I'm not getting: *Various artists* / Goodbye she's gone: *Various artists* / Slowly dying: *Various artists*.
LP: . . . . **CH 167**
LP: . . . . **SJLP 568**

MEMPHIS ROCKABILLY VOL 2 (Various artists).
Tracks: / Rockin' at the Y: *Various artists* / Wild wild party: *Various artists* / Tomorrow I'll be gone: *Various artists* / Hey Rena: *Various artists* / Night surfing: *Various artists* / Make my dreams come true: *Various* artists / What's the matter with my heart: *Various artists* / Tennessee twist: *Various artists* / Zombie walks, The: *Various artists* / Let's make the party sweet: *Various artists* / Prom, The: *Various artists* / Rockin' boppin' teenager: *Various artists* / I'll cry today: *Various artists* / Tomorrow we'll know: *Various artists* / Go go go: *Various artists*.
LP: . . . . **SJLP 578**

MERCURY ROCKABILLIES (Various artists).
Tracks: / Flip flop mama: *Various artists* / Boppin Bonnie: *Various artists* / You nearly lose your mind: *Various* artists / You're my big baby now: *Various artists* / That's my reward: *Various artists* / Mean mistreatin' baby: *Various artists* / Burning the wind: *Various artists* / You're the one that done it: *Various artists* / Slip slip slippin' in: *Various artists* / Baby, baby, baby, what'm I gonna do: *Various artists* / Born to sing the blues: *Various artists* / Lonesome train: *Various artists* / Wild wild mind: *Various artists* / Crazy blues: *Various artists* / Draggin': *Various artists* / Sittin' on top of the world: *Various artists*.
LP: **6463 084**

MGM ROCKABILLY COLLECTION (Original Artists) (Various artists).
LP: **2315 394**

MGM ROCKABILLY COLLECTION VOL.2 (Various artists).
LP: **2354147**

MGM ROCKABILLY KINGS (Various artists).
LP: . . . . **MID 1001**

MIAMI ROCKABILLY, VOL 1 (Various artists).
LP: **1001**

MIAMI ROCKABILLY, VOL 2 (Various artists).
LP: **1002**

MIAMI ROCKABILLY, VOL 3 (Various artists).
LP: **1003**

MINNESOTA ROCKABILLY ROCK VOL.1 (Various artists).
Tracks: / Record hop: *Scott, Tom* / I dig: *Don & Jer* / Rock the blues away: *Jack & The Knights* / Mean mama blues: *Ray, Ronnie* / Vulture, The: *Ray, Ronnie* / Sally Jol: *Thaxter, Jim* / Cyclone: *Thaxter*, Jim / Three bad habits: *Fritz, Hal* / Goin' out on you: *Fritz, Hal* / Switchblade: *Thompson, Ron* / Queen bee: *Harmony Twins* / Queen bee: *Orbits* / Barnyard rock 'n' roll: *Harmony Twins* / Moonlight rock: *Carson, Chuck* / Downbeat rock: *Randall, Eddie*.
LP: . . . . **WLP 8852**

MINNESOTA ROCKABILLY ROCK, VOL 4 (Various artists).
Tracks: / Baby, baby: *Waggoner, Mike & The Bops* / Basher number five: *Waggoner, Mike & The Bops* / Hey mama: *Waggoner, Mike & The Bops* / Good rockin' tonight: *Waggoner, Mike & The Bops* / Coming up: *Waggoner, Mike* & The Bops / Guitar man: *Waggoner, Mike & The Bops* / Bye bye Johnny: *Waggoner, Mike & The Bops* / Three little pigs, The: *Waggoner, Mike & The Bops* / Work with me, Annie: *Waggoner, Mike & The Bops* / Scramble: *Barkdall*, Eddie / Wailin' wailin' party: *Barkdall, Eddie* / I still love her: *Buchwitz, Junior* / Revel rock: *Buchwitz, Junior*.
LP: . . . . **WLP 8855**

MINNESOTA ROCKABILLY ROCK, VOL 2 (Various artists).
Tracks: / My little Sue: *Lee, Terry & The Poorboys* / Driftin': *Lee, Terry & The Poorboys* / Dream night: *Houle* Brothers / Homicide: *Lee, Myron* / Mary's swinging lamb: *Lee, Myron* / Aw c'mon baby: *Lee, Myron* / Watch your step: *Galaxies* / Minus one blast off: *Sonics* / Marlene: *Sonics* / Wild party: *Vilados* / Bloodshot: *String Kings* / Bash, The: *String Kings* / Hush hush little baby: *Dennis, Bob & Denny* / Guitar boogie: *Walsh, Andy* / Flyin' high: *Thundermen*.
LP: . . . . **WLP 8853**

MINNESOTA ROCKABILLY ROCK, VOL 5 (Various artists).
Tracks: / Hurry: *Robbins, Robbie* / Easy rhythm: *Glenrays* / Haunted by reception: *Glenrays* / That's alright mama: *James, Deviny* / Ivy League baby: *Garcia, Augie* / Be my guest: *Garcia, Augie* / Hi ho Silver: *Garcia, Augie* / Goin' to Chicago: *Garcia, Augie* / Lili Marlene: *Jades* / Little girl: *Leonard*, Ben / Congo bongo: *Leonard, Ben* / Buggin' the boogie: *Delricos* / Voodoo: *Delricos* / Rockin' the blues: *Flames* / Arabian caravan: *Flames* / Minor chaos: *Treasures* / Black rock: *Five Spots* / Mr. Fortune: *Five Spots* / Minor chaos: *Row, Steve*.
LP: . . . . **WLP 8878**

MORE REAL ROCKABILLY AND COUNTRY (Various artists).
Tracks: / Long gone lonesome blues: *Champion, Hollis* / Big beat, The: *Champion, Hollis* / Sundown boogie: *Clour*, Deral & Charly Drake / Poor me: *McRill, Chandos* / Teddle, The: *McRill, Chandos* / Money lovin' woman: *McRill*, Chandos / Flat foot Sam: *Scoggins, Johnny* / Learning how to live: *Draper, Joseph June* / When you kissed me: *McPeak, Henry*.
LP: . . . . **WLP 8819**

NEO ROCKABILLY STORY VOL. 2 Various artists (Various artists).
LP: . . . . **LPM 8706**

ORIGINAL ROCKABILLY COLLECTION (Various artists).
Tracks: / Long black train: *Twitty, Conway* / My brand of blues: *Rainwater, Marvin* / Rockin' rollin' stone: *Starr*, Andy / One more time: *Starr, Andy* / Round and round: *Starr, Andy* / Stutterin' papa: *Griffin, Buck* / Rockin' chair: *Campbell, Cecil* / Rock and roll fever: *Campbell, Cecil* / My square dancin' mama: *Gallion*, Bob / Rock doll: *Early, Bernie* / Rollin' the boogie: *Hyman, Dick* / Rockin' and rollin' with grandmaw: *Robinson*, Carson / Latch on: *Hargrave, Ron* / Midnight line: *Riley, Bob* / I ain't studyin' you, baby: *Gibson, Don* / Who shot Willie?: *Smith, Arthur*.

LP: **2486 257**
MC: **3186 092**

OUTRAGE VOL.1 (Various artists).
LP: . . . . **RAGELP 104**

OUTRAGE VOL 2 (Various artists).
LP: . . . . **RAGELP 105**

RARE ROCK-A-BILLY BOPPIN' (Various artists).
LP: . . . . **RR 2023**

RARE ROCKABILLY VOL.1 (Various artists).
Tracks: / Cast iron arm: *Wilson, Peanuts* / Be bop baby: *Inman, Autrey* / Sweet love on my mind: *Jimmy & Johnny* / Hot rock: *Carroll, Johnny* / Rock 'n' roll Ruby: *Carroll, Johnny* / Wild wild women: *Carroll,* Johnny / Trying to get to you: *Carroll, Johnny* / Alligator come across: *Duff, Arlie* / Crazy baby: *Maltais,* Gene / Barking up the wrong tree: *Woody, Don* / Make like a rock and roll: *Woody, Don* / Morse code: *Woody,* Don / Bird dog: *Woody, Don* / Ruby pearl: *Cochran, Jackie Lee* / Teenage boogie: *Pierce, Webb* / Whole lotta shakin' goin' on: *Hall, Roy* / Diggin' the boogie: *Hall, Roy* / Offbeat boogie: *Hall, Roy* / Shakin' the blues: *Young, Donny* / Three alley cats: *Various artists.*
LP: . . . . **MCL 1755**
MC: . . . . **MCLC 1755**

RARE ROCKABILLY VOL.2 (Various artists).
Tracks: / Mama don't you think I know: *Cochran, Jackie Lee & Jimmy Pruett* / Ten little women: *Noland, Terry* / Cool it baby: *Fontaine, Eddie* / Shake baby shake: *Raney, Wayne* / Here comes the night: *Guitar, Billy* / All by myself: *Hall, Roy* / See you later alligator: *Hall, Roy* / Behave, be quiet, or be gone: *Hall, Roy* / Flip flop and fly: *Ball, Johnny* / Rock it on down to my house: *Tubb, Justin* / Tennessee rock'n'roll: *Helms,* Bobby / Crazy crazy lovin': *Carroll, Johnny* / Corina Corina: *Carroll, Johnny* / Wee Willy Brown: *Graham,* Lou / Crazy chicken: *Gallagher, James* / Is that all to the ball, Mr Hall?: *Riley, Billy Lee* / She wanna rock: *Derksen, Arnie* / Don't go baby: *Coker, Al* / Hypnotised: *Noland, Terry.*
MC: . . . . **MCLC 1756**
LP: . . . . **MCL 1756**

RARE ROCKABILLY VOL.3 (Various artists).
Tracks: / Lorraine: *Covell, Buddy* / It would be a dog-gone lie: *Inman, Autrey* / Everybody's trying to be my baby: *York Brothers* / Moon's rock: *Mullican, Moon* / Teenage love is a misery: *Kennedy, Jerry* / Don't stop me now: *Hall, Roy* / Move on: *Hall, Roy* / You gotta move: *Smith, Chester* / Juke joint Johnny: *Sovine,* Red / Way out there: *Chuck & Bill* / Cheat on me baby: *Rockin' Saints* / I wanna bop: *Harlan, Billy* / Schoolhouse rock: *Harlan, Billy* / Knock knock rattle: *Allen, Rex* / Crazy little guitar man: *Foley, Red* / Pan American boogie: *Glosson, Lonnie* / Sputnik: *Engler, Jerry* / Baby's gone: *Claud, Vernon* / Hey Ruby: *Osbourne, Arthur* / Let's go downtown: *Therien, Joe Jnr..*
MC: . . . . **MCLC 1757**
LP: . . . . **MCL 1757**

RARE ROCKABILLY VOL.4 (Various artists).
Tracks: / Tennessee Toddy: *Grey, Billy & His Western Okies* / Baby don't leave me: *Five Charles Brothers* / Uncle John's bongos: *Johnnie & Jack* / Jenny Lee: *Mullican, Moon* / One and only: *Fontaine, Eddie* / Rockabilly boogie: *Therien, Joe Jnr & His Rockets* / Come back to me: *Therien, Joe Jnr & His Rockets* / Touch of loving: *Sykes,* Bobby / Crazy bullfrog: *Pruitt, Lewis* / You've got me where I wanna be: *Walker, Wayne P.* / Rock around the world: *Reeves, Glenn* / Rock a boogie Lou: *Reeves, Glenn* / Got a lot of rhythm in my soul: *Cline, Patsy* / Be my bride: *Phillips, Charlie* / Show me how: *Hackett, Veline* / You played on my piano: *Gunter, Hardrock* / California blues: *Pierce, Webb* / Falling in love: *Warner, Mack* / It hurts the one who loves you: *Doggett, Ray* / All nite boogie: *Sosebee, Tommy* / You played on my piano: *Various artists.*
MC: . . . . **MCLC 1758**
LP: . . . . **MCL 1758**
LP: . . . . **MCF 3035**

RAREST ROCKABILLY & HILLBILLY BOOGIE (Various artists).
Tracks: / Nothin' but a nuthin': *Stewart, Jimmy* / Darlin': *Dale, Jimmie* / Baby doll: *Dale, Jimmie* / Pretending is a game: *Jeffers, Sleepy & The Davis Twins* / Don't sweep that dirt on me: *Shaw, Buddy* / My baby left me: *Rogers, Rock* / Little dog blues: *Price, Mel* / Henpecked daddy: *Johnson, Ralph & The Hillbilly Show* Boys / Um boy, you're my baby: *Johnson, Bill & The Dabblers* / Stoney mountain boogie: *Stoney Mountain Playboys* / My blackbirds are bluebirds now: *Jeffers, Sleepy & The Davis Twins* / No more: *Shaw, Buddy* / Big black cat: *Hendon, R.D. & The Western Jamboree Cowboys* / It's Saturday night: *Mack, Billy.*
LP: . . . . **CH 44**

RARIN' ROCKABILLIES (Various artists).
LP: . . . . **RARIN' 666**

RAUNCHY ROCKABILLY (Sun Sounds Special) (Various artists).
Tracks: / How come you do me: *Thompson, Junior* / Jukebox help me find my baby: *Rhythm Rockers* / Truckin' down the avenue: *Burgess, Sonny* / Daddy blues: *Burgess, Sonny* / Listen to me: *Baugh, Smokey Joe* / Your lovin' man: *Taylor, Vernon* / Blues blues blues: *Thompson, Hayden* / Fairlane rock: *Thompson, Hayden* / Willing and ready: *Smith, Ray* / Shake around: *Smith, Ray* / Baby that's good: *Bruce, Edwin* / Miss Pearl: *Wages,* Jimmy / Fine little baby: *Penner, Dick* / I'll change my ways: *Stewart, Danny* / Never did I: *Hosea, Don* / John Henry: *Hosea, Don.*
LP: . . . . **CR 30147**

REAL ROCKIN' NOW (Various artists).
Tracks: / Girl named Sue, A: *Tolleson, Tommy* / Cindy: *Fay, Johnny* / Rock 'n' roll rover: *King, Jesse Lee* / Nervous wreck: *King, Jesse Lee* / Cuddles: *Butterball, Maximilian* / One little kiss: *Newsome, C.* / So long, baby: *Newsome, C.* / Barracuda: *Fausz, Gary L.* / Walking the blues: *Beacg, Ray* / Shame: *Brown,* Johnny / Angel eyes: *Warr, Doug* / Guitar boogie: *Faulkner, G. & D.* / Tom cat: *Gaggard, J.C.* / I want you now: *Gaggard, J.C.* / Honey doll: *Gaggard, J.C.* / I will ask, I will plead: *Gaggard, J.C..*
LP: . . . . **WLP 8881**

REBEL ROCKABILLY (Various artists).
LP: . . . . **CRM 2015**

RED HOT ROCKABILLIES (Various artists).
Tracks: / My pink cadillac: *Various artists* / Watch your mouth: *Various artists* / Judy: *Various artists* / Rave on: *Various artists* / Swingin' baby doll: *Various artists* / I wanna rock: *Various artists* / Drinkin' wine spo dee o dee: *Various artists* / Piano Nellie: *Various artists* / Party party: *Various artists* / Ding dong dandy: *Various artists* / She's sumpin' else: *Various artists* / Sugar: *Various artists* / Can't you see: *Various artists* / Walkin' 'n' talkin': *Various artists* / Bop a dee: *Various artists* / Rockin' country style: *Various artists* / Baby please don't go: *Various artists* / Rockin' redwing: *Various artists.*
LP: . . . . **K 58344**

RED HOT ROCKABILLY (Various artists).
Tracks: / Hip shakin' mama: *Various artists* / Bip bop boom: *Various artists* / Look out Mabel: *Various artists* / Grits: *Various artists* / Sunglasses after dark: *Various artists* / Okies in the pokie: *Various artists* / Hot dog: *Various artists* / Made in the shade: *Various artists* / Down on the farm: *Various artists* / Fool, The: *Various artists* / Oakie boogie: *Various artists* / Blue swingin' mama: *Various artists.*
LP: . . . . **MFLP 030**

RED HOT ROCKABILLY VOL 2 (Various artists).
Tracks: / 49 women: *Various artists* / One way ticket: *Various artists* / Jackson dog: *Various artists* / Satellite hop: *Various artists* / Roll over Beethoven: *Various artists* / You don't mean to make me cry: *Various* artists / Clickety clack: *Various artists* / Go go heart: *Various artists* / Rock on Mabel: *Various artists* / Puppy love: *Various artists* / Tore up: *Various artists* / Move over Rover: *Various artists.*
LP: . . . . **MFLP 043**

RED HOT ROCKABILLY VOL 3 (Various artists).
Tracks: / Jitterbuggin' baby: *Various artists* / No.9 train: *Various artists* / Dig that crazy driver: *Various* artists / You bet I do: *Various artists* / Oh little girl: *Various artists* / Long tall Sally: *Various* artists / That'll get it: *Various artists* / No doubt about it: *Various artists* / Live your life with care: *Various artists* / Fool about you: *Various artists* / Elvis stole my gal: *Various artists* / Lonely heart: *Various artists.*
LP: . . . . **MFLP 055**

RED HOT ROCKABILLY VOL 4 (Various artists).
Tracks: / My baby's still rockin': *Various artists* / It hurts the one who loves you: *Various artists* / Your conscience: *Various artists* / Your cheatin' heart: *Various artists* / I forgot to forget: *Various artists* / Somebody's gonna hurt you: *Various artists* / Crawdad hole: *Various artists* / Blue suede shoes: *Various artists* / I'm walking: *Various artists* / Last night I cried: *Various artists* / Big boss man: *Various artists* / I'll never let you go: *Various artists.*
LP: . . . . **MFLP 056**

RED HOT ROCKABILLY VOL 5 (Various artists).
Tracks: / Bop hop jamboree: *Various artists* / Wondering if you still care: *Various artists* / Train's done gone, The: *Various artists* / I just don't love you anymore: *Various artists* / Last time, The: *Various artists* / Spanish rock and rolla: *Various artists* / Surge: *Various artists* / No one but you: *Various artists* / Midnight train: *Various artists* / How can I go: *Various artists* / Rainbow love: *Various artists* / Standing in your window: *Various artists* / Hello Memphis: *Various artists* / Big Johnny blues: *Various artists* / Just behind your smile: *Various artists* / Two timing lover: *Various artists.*
LP: . . . . **MFLP 060**

RED HOT ROCKABILLY VOL 6 (Memphis) (Various artists).
Tracks: / Boo be ah be: *Various artists* / My life's desire: *Various artists* / That's the reason I'm leaving town today: *Various artists* / Look coming yonder: *Various artists* / Guess I'll cry instead: *Various artists* / Blues got to me, The: *Various artists* / Go on and say goodbye: *Various artists* / I'm leavin' this town: *Various* artists / Lowdown feeling: *Various artists* / Just skip it: *Various artists* / Got you on my mind: *Various* artists / Three long years: *Various artists* / Walk with me: *Various artists* / What's in store for me: *Various artists* / J & E twist: *Various artists* / Ain't I'm a mess: *Various artists.*
LP: . . . . **MFLP 062**

RED HOT ROCKABILLY VOL 7 (Various artists).
Tracks: / Rock 'n' roll on a Saturday night: *Various artists* / Rock a socka hop: *Various artists* / Grandma rock 'n' roll: *Various artists* / Servant of love: *Various artists* / Knocking on the backside: *Various artists* / Walking and a' strolling: *Various artists* / Black Cadillac: *Various artists* / D.J. blues, The: *Various* artists / Don't cry little darling: *Various artists* / Linda Lou: *Various artists* / Teenage lover: *Various* artists / So help me gal: *Various artists* / Snake eyed woman: *Various artists* / Depression blues: *Various artists* / Quick sand love: *Various artists* / Nicotine: *Various artists.*
LP: . . . . **MFLP 069**

RETURN OF ROCKAPHILLY (Various artists).
Tracks: / Sixteen cats: *Wellington, Rusty* / Rock with me baby: *Coleman, Ray* / Rockin' jamboree: *Raye, Michael & Judy* Shaye / Wee willy waterdilly: *Keefer Sisters* / Jukebox cannonball: *Rogers, Jesse* / Go man go get gone: *Zario, Rex* / Rockin' in the nursery: *Starr, Sally* / I gotta go: *Rex, Al* / Jumpin' Jackie: *Lee,* Jacky / Buzz buzz buzz: *Satellites* / Philadelphia baby: *Hatcher, Ray* / Bitter tears: *Tanner Bros* / Bulldoggin' the steel: *Nastos, Nick* / I ain't a movin' on no more: *Wellington, Rusty* / Jump, jump honey: *Wellington,* Rusty / Rock chicken rock: *Coleman, Ray* / ABC rock: *Starr, Sally* / I'm rockin': *Coleman, Ray* / Toodle oo bamboo: *Coleman, Ray.*
LP: . . . . **ROLL 2004**

ROCK & COUNTRY ROCKABILLY VOL.1 (Various artists).
LP: . . . . **R&C 1006**

ROCKABILLY (Various artists).
LP: **6498 142**
MC: **7133 142**
MC: **8803**

ROCKABILLY BASH (Various artists).
LP: . . . . **BOPL 100**

ROCK-A-BILLY BLUES (Various artists).
Tracks: / Blues at midnight: *Simmons, Gene* / Hey Slim: *Earls, Jack* / Bottle to the baby: *Feathers, Charlie* / Drinkin' scotch: *Simmons, Gene* / Pop and mama: *Simmons, Gene* / You can't make love to somebody: *Perkins,* Carl / Crawdad hole: *Earls, Jack* / They can't keep me from you: *Earls, Jack* / Fool for loving you: *Earls,* Jack / Hey Jim: *Earls, Jack* / Uh babe: *McDaniel, Luke* / Go ahead baby: *McDaniel, Luke* / Slow down: *Earls, Jack* / Sign on the dotted line: *Earls, Jack.*
LP: . . . . **SUN 1019**

ROCKABILLY BOOGIE Rare Items vol. 1 (Various artists).
LP: . . . . **REV 4001**

ROCKABILLY BOOGIE Rare items vol.3 (Various artists).
LP: . . . . **REV 4003**

ROCKABILLY BOOGIE (Rare items vol.2) (Various artists).
LP: . . . . **REV 4002**

ROCKABILLY BOP VOL.1 (Various artists).
Tracks: / Look kat: *Sherrell, Bill* / Little jewels: *Heap, Jimmy* / Hard hearted girl: *Davis, Cliff* / Rocky road blues: *Davis, Cliff* / Flat top box: *Jackson, Tommy* / Got rockin' on my mind: *Griffin, Curley* / Got the best of me: *Bowser, Donny* / Hey Mr. Porter: *Pruitt, Ralph* / Rocket on the moon: *Caves, John Wesley* / Curfew cop: *Cole, Sonny* / Robinson Crusoe bop: *Cole, Sonny* / Hey doll baby: *Kelly, Pat* / Cloud 13: *Kelly, Pat* / Rockin' Rochester: *Tempests.*
LP: . . . . **RR 2002**

ROCKABILLY BOP VOL.2 (Various artists).
Tracks: / Alley cat: *Brown, Walter* / Jelly roll rock: *Brown, Walter* / Teenage ball: *Deitzel, Elroy* / Night club r'n'roll: *Parsons, Gene* / Come to your Tommy now: *Clark, Leonard* / Dig me a crazy record: *Senns,* Charles / Gee whiz Liz: *Senns, Charles* / Saturday night party: *Perkins, Reggie* / Pretty Kitty: *Perkins,* Reggie / Big Sandy: *Roberts, Bobby* / Rattle shakin' mama: *McGonnigle, Mel* / That big old moon: *Burke, Buddy* / Rockin' with r'n'b: *Haig, Ronnie* / Calypso boogie: *Hager, Don.*
LP: . . . . **RR 2003**

ROCKABILLY BOP VOL.3 (Various artists).
Tracks: / Cat all night: *Finn, Lee* / It's night: *Finn, Lee* / Jukebox Johnny: *Moore, Lattie* / Pretty woman blues: *Moore, Lattie* / How about me?: *Johnson, Jimmy* / Cat daddy: *Johnson, Jimmy* / 21 carpenters: *Roberts, Marty* / Let's all go wild: *Pullen, Whitey* / Drinkin' wine: *Pullen, Whitey* / Walk me back home: *Pullen, Whitey* / Moonshine liquor: *Pullen, Whitey* / Tuscaloosa Lucy: *Pullen, Whitey* / Tight slacks: *Pullen, Whitey* / I dreamed I was Elvis: *Cole, Sonny.*
LP: . . . . **RR 2006**

ROCKABILLY BOPPIN' (Various artists).
Tracks: / Rock 'n' roll fever: *Ray, Gene* / I'm going to Hollywood: *Ray, Gene* / Too old to rock 'n' roll: *Sloan,* Chucklin' Chuck / You gotta show me: *Lane, Ralph* / Bartender's blues: *Buskirk, Kenny* / Get with it: *Buskirk,* Kenny / Thermostat baby: *Dorn, Dick* / My screamin' screamin' Mimi: *Campi, Ray* / Waddle, The: *Slades* / I'll give you all my love: *Berry, Ron* / Tell me, baby: *Smith, Billy* / Rock a long time: *Ratcliff, Bozo* / Let me in: *Ratcliff, Bozo* / I wanna go steady with you: *Armstrong, Dick* / At the high school dance: *Taylor, R. Dean.*
LP: . . . . **WLP 8842**

ROCKABILLY CLASSICS VOL. 1 (Various artists).
LP: . . . . **MCA 25088**

ROCKABILLY & COUNTRY (Various artists).
Tracks: / Have you heard the gossip: *Charlie Brown* / Mean mean mama: *Charlie Brown* / My hungry heart: *Charlie* Brown / Boogie woogie mama: *Charlie Brown* / Pickin': *Charlie Brown* / Don't put the blame on me: *Charlie* Brown / Milkcow blues boogie: *Charlie Brown* / Hound dog: *Banks, Mack* / Be Boppin' daddy: *Banks, Mack* / They don't come in droves like me: *Banks, Mack* / Mack's boogie: *Banks, Mack* / You're so dumb: *Banks, Mack* / They raided the joint: *Banks, Mack.*
LP: . . . . **WLP 8804**

ROCKABILLY CRAZY (Various artists).
LP: . . . . **CFM 506**

ROCKABILLY FEVER (Various artists).
LP: . . . . **CFM 510**

ROCKABILLY FROM TENNESSEE VOL.2 (Various artists).
Tracks: / Swing it, little Katy: *Owens, Clyde* / Last bouquet, The: *Owens, Clyde* / Rocket city rock: *Hillis,* Clayton / Don't you know I love you: *Hillis, Clayton* / Hoochie coochie man: *Long, Curtis* / After all: *Long,* Curtis / Mystic Madonna: *Jay Dee's* / Old red devil: *Champion, Hollis* / Little rock: *Four Sons (The* Johnson Boys) / Good times in Memphis: *Delmore, Alton* / What's going on: *Moore, Marvin* / Jumpin' the boogie: *Moore, Marvin* / I'm on this rocket: *Moore, Marvin.*
LP: . . . . **WLP 8808**

ROCKABILLY FROM TENNESSEE VOL.1 (Various artists).
Tracks: / Dreamer boy: *Hardin, Bobby* / I'm loving you baby: *Hardin, Bobby* / Sweet, sweet dreams: *Hardin,* Bobby / Gettin' better: *Hardin, Bobby* / My old lonesome love: *Rickman, Joe* / Lonely

heart: *Rickman, Joe* / Puppy love: *Snyder, Tony* / Jackson dog: *Brinkley, Larry* / Move over Rover: *Brinkley, Larry*/ I hate to leave you: *Brinkley, Larry* / All night long: *Brinkley, Larry* / Tornado: *Brinkley, Larry*/ Pins and needles: *Stevenson, N.A.* / Boogie woogie country girl: *Stevenson, N.A.*.
LP: WLP 8806

ROCKABILLY GREATEST HITS (Various artists).
LP: 20004
MC: 40004

ROCKABILLY HEROES (Various artists).
LP: RLP 005

ROCKABILLY INFLUENCE 1950-60 (Various artists).
LP: CGB 1008

ROCKABILLY JAMBOREE (Various artists).
LP: CFM 505

ROCK-A-BILLY LEGENDS (Various artists).
MC: AIM 108

ROCKABILLY PARTY (Various artists).
Tracks: / Jitterbop baby: *Various artists* / Rock little baby: *Various artists* / Looking: *Various artists*/ Little rock rock: *Various artists* / Be boppin' daddy: *Various artists* / By big fat baby: *Various artists*/ Trucker from Tennessee: *Various artists* / That ain't it: *Various artists* / I don't know when: *Various artists* / One of these days: *Various artists*.
LP: CH 17

ROCKABILLY REBELS (CAMBRA RELEASE) (Various artists).
Tracks: / Going home: *Burgess, Sonny* / Yakety yak: *Vevington, Malcolm* / Tootsie: *McVoy, Carl* / Cadillac man: *Jesters, The* / Rockin' Daddy: *Bond, Eddie* / I've been deceived: *Feathers, Charlie* / Dear John: *Smith, Warren* / Rock with me baby: *Riley, Billy Lee* / Drinking wine: *Simons, Gene* / Pink pedal pushers: *Perkins, Carl* / Caldonia: *Perkins, Carl*/ Flyin' saucers rock 'n' roll: *Riley, Billy Lee* / Hillbilly music: *Lewis, Jerry Lee* / Teddy jive: *Various artists* / Jungle rock: *Mizell, Hank* / Sadie's back in town: *Burgess, Sonny* / Domino: *Orbison, Roy* / Ten cats down: *Miller Sisters* / Red cadillac and a black moustache: *Smith, Warren* / Milkshake mademoiselle: *Lewis, Jerry Lee* / Let's bop: *Earls, Jack* / Love my baby: *Thompson, Hayden*.
2LP: CR 104
MCSET: CRT 104

ROCKABILLY REBELS (HALLMARK RELEASE) (Various artists).
Tracks: / Girl in red: *Stevens, Shakin'/ Sunsets* / Heavenly: *Showaddywaddy* / Buzz buzz a diddle it: *Matchbox*/ Come on let's go: *Sharpe, Rocky & The Replays* / James Dean: *Jets (British)* / Crazy little teddy girl: *Crazy Cavan & The Rhythm Rockers* / If I ain't home: *Rock Island Line* / When I see my baby: *Sneekers* / Jungle rock: *Stevens, Shakin'/Sunsets* / King of the jive: *Showaddywaddy* / Rockabilly rebel: *Matchbox* / Shout, shout: *Sharpe, Rocky & The Replays* / Rockabilly baby: *Jets (British)* / Put a light in the window: *Crazy Cavan & The Rhythm Rockers* / Barking up the wrong tree: *Rock Island Line* / Good good rockin': *Sneekers*.
LP: SHM 3147
MC: HSC 3147

ROCKABILLY ROCK (Various artists).
Tracks: / Cool cool baby: *Yarborough, Lafayette* / Living doll: *Yarborough, Lafayette* / I'd rather make love: *Green, Thomas* / Fort Worth rock: *Gilliland, Don* / Dallas rock: *Gilliland, Don* / Sweet Louella: *Couch, Orville* / Wild girl: *Couch, Orville* / Strictly fake: *Rim Shots & Dennis Lynn* / Native dance, The: *Rim Shots & Dennis Lynn* / Tom cat boogie: *Haynes, Jimmy* / Wake up little boy blue: *Calloway, Bob* / Look at me eyes: *Walls, Jimmy* / Live & learn: *Jowers, Jerry/ Jimmy Trucks* / There's no use in me loving you: *Murphy, Jimmy* / Humpty Dumpty: *Burnette, Al* / Lookie here baby: *Burnette, Al*.
LP: WLP 8824

ROCKABILLY RULES U.K. (Various artists).
LP: CR 30138

ROCKABILLY SHAKEOUT - NUMBER 1 (Various artists).
Tracks: / Shadow my baby: *Barber, Glen* / Atom bomb: *Barber, Glen* / I don't know when: *Harris, Hal*/ My little baby: *Jimmy & Johnny* / True affection: *Johnson, Byron* / Slipping and sliding: *Davis, Link*/ Hey hey little boy blue: *Lindsay, Merle* / Gee whiz: *Dee & Patty* / All the time: *La Beef, Sleepy* / Spin the bottle: *Joy, Benny* / Chicken bop: *Truitt Forse* / My big fat baby: *Hall, Sonny & The Echoes*/ Cat's just got back in town: *Mack, Billy* / Tennessee rock: *Scoggins, Hoyt* / Uranium fever: *Gaddis, Ruddy*/ Prettiest girl at the dance: *Wyatt, Gene*.
LP: CH 191
MC: CHC 191

ROCKABILLY SOUVENIR (Various artists).
Tracks: / Get away: *Landon, Bud* / Six mile climb: *Landon, Bud* / Wicked woman: *Gamble, Johnny* / Hey pretty mama: *Killen, Ked* / Baby I won't keep waitin': *Blevins, Bill* / Crazy blues: *Blevins, Bill* / Rock & roll boogie: *Raper Bros.* / Rock, hop, hop: *Raper Bros.* / Jorris boogie: *Hennessee, Jorris* / McMinnville rock, The: *Hennessee, Jorris* / Jorris stomp: *Hennessee, Jorris* / Lonely heart: *Kelly, Sterling*/ Let me be your man: *Moore, Roy E.* / Black out: *Moore, Roy E.* / Little Betty rock: *Clark, Ray*.
LP: WLP 8838

ROCKABILLY STARS VOL.1 (Various artists).
LP: EPC 12165

ROCKABILLY STARS VOL.2 (Various artists).
2LP: EPC 22116

ROCKABILLY STARS VOL.3 (Various artists).
2LP: EPC 22100

ROCK-A-BILLY TIME (Best of Linn & Kliff) (Various artists).
Tracks: / Jitterbuggin' baby: *Ray, David* / Lonesome baby blues: *Ray, David* / Lonesome feeling: *Ray, David*/ Swinging boogie: *Smith, D. Ray* / Gone baby gone: *Smith, D. Ray* / Tell me why: *Starr, Frank "Andy"*/ Disc jockey fever: *Chuck A Lucks* / Guitar smoke: *Brinkley, Jay* / Rough tough man: *Curtis, Don* / Rockin' hall: *McClarey, Butch* / Knees shakin': *Terry, Don* / Dog fight: *Jokers* / Meadowlark boogie: *Griffin, Buck* / It don't make no never mind: *Griffin, Buck* / Let's elope baby: *Griffin, Buck* / Bawlin' and squallin': *Griffin, Buck*.
LP: WLP 8827

ROCKABILLY TUNES (Various artists).
Tracks: / I was a fool: *Orbison, Roy* / Rockabilly gal: *Thompson, Hayden* / Johnny Valentine: *Anderson, Andy*/ Tough tough tough: *Anderson, Andy* / Love dumb baby: *Harris, Ray* / Heart breakin' love: *Wages, Jimmy*/ Take me: *Wages, Jimmy* / Thinkin' I am to-night of blue eyes: *Carter* / Don't come crying: *Ruick, Tommy*/ Prisoner of the blues: *Ruick, Tommy* / Let 'em know: *Ruick, Tommy* / Lonely river: *Felts, Narvel* / Foolish thoughts: *Various artists* / Lonesome feeling: *Various artists*.
LP: SUN 1026

ROCKABILLY ...VOL. 2 (Various artists).
LP: MCA 25089

ROCKABILLY WORLD (Various artists).
Tracks: / Bug boat song, The: *Mac, Johnny* / Go, cats, go: *Rhodes, Texas Red* / Boogie rock: *Ringhiser & Rhythm Drifters* / Uranium miner's boogie: *Walker, Riley* / Shakedown: *Thomas, Bill* / Sputnik story, The: *Thomas, Bill* / Steel guitar rag: *McCann, Dennis* / Hadacol boogie: *Sims, Babe* / Permit blues: *Davis, Link* / Airliner: *Davis, Link* / Dance, baby, dance: *Crum, Tom* / Lonesome guitar: *Garland, Bill*/ Guitar blues: *Garland, Bill* / I stubbed my toe: *Walker, Bryan* / Trick or treat: *Walker, Bryan* / Annie Mae: *Dewitt, Bobby*.
LP: WLP 8908

ROCKAPHILLY - PHILADELPHIA ROCK 'N' ROLL (Various artists).
Tracks: / Sky rock - jukebox rock 'n' roll: *Coleman, Ray* / Everybody's rockin' tonight: *Coleman, Ray* / You look like something that the cat drug in: *Moss, Bill* / Rockabilly hop: *Moss, Bill* / Ducktail: *Wellington, Rusty*/ Rockin' the blues: *Wellington, Rusty* / Rock 'n' roll Ruby: *Wellington, Rusty* / It should have been me: *Kingsmen*/ Hot to trott: *Highliters* / Four alarm boogie: *Collett, Jimmy* / Beetlebug boogie: *Collett, Jimmy* / Rock around the clock: *Dae, Sonny & His Knights ((Original version))* / Jump cats jump: *Rogers, Jesse* / Hydrogen bomb: *Rex, Al* / Buck fever boogie: *Herdman, Curly* / Chuck's boogie: *Hess, Chuck*.
LP: ROLL 2001

ROCKAROLLA AHILLABILLY WING DING DO (Red hot rockabilly 1955-62) (Various artists).
LP: SIN ALLEY 2

SARG ROCKABILLY (Various artists).
LP: R&C 1011

SPADE ROCKABILLY (Various artists).
LP: R&C 1007

STARDAY DIXIE ROCKABILLIES (Various artists).
LP: K 5017

STARDAY DIXIE ROCKABILLIES - VOL.2 (Various artists).
LP: GD 5031

TEXAS HILLBILLY BOOGIE (Various artists).
LP: RR 2018

TEXAS ROCKABILLY (Various artists).
Tracks: / Love come back to me: *Patton, Jimmy* / Let me slide: *Patton, Jimmy* / I'm not skukin: *Patton, Jimmy*/ Oakies in the pokie: *Patton, Jimmy* / High class feelin: *Finn, Lee* / Pour me a glass of wine: *Finn, Lee*/ Sleep rock'n'roll baby: *Wayne, Alvis* / Swing bop boogie: *Wayne, Alvis* / I gottum: *Wayne, Alvis* / Lay your head on my shoulder: *Wayne, Alvis* / Don't mean maybe,baby: *Wayne, Alvis* / Oklahoma blues: *Chapman, Gene* / Don't come cryin': *Chapman, Gene*.
LP: RR 2001

TEXAS ROCKABILLY VOL. 2 (Various artists).
LP: RR 2012

VIRGINIA ROCK-A-BILLY & COUNTRY (Various artists).
Tracks: / I ain't gonna rock tonight: *Saul, Hender* / Hard right to my heart: *Saul, Hender* / Where have you been all night: *Martin Bros* / That was yesterday: *Martin Bros* / Rock & roll baby: *Spangler, Randy* / My Spanish senorita: *Spangler, Randy* / Rock run blues: *Leon & Carlos* / Rock everybody: *Leon & Carlos* / Bip bop boom: *Mullins, Moon & Mickey Hawks* / Rock & roll rhythm: *Mullins, Moon & Mickey Hawks* / Reel it and roll it: *Mullins, Moon & Mickey Hawks* / One step away: *Saul, Hender & Billy Foley*.
LP: WLP 8807

YUCCA ROCKABILLY (Various artists).
LP: R&C 1010

Rockabilly Rebs.

REBELS TILL THE END.
Tracks: / Stop talking / Angel angel / Your daddy's got a gun / Eddie say your prayers / Trust nobody these days / Ain't nothing shakin' / Mean evil daddy / Ain't she sweet / It'll be alright / Rebel till the end / Watchdog / Better things to do / Tell me baby / Honey don't / Leroy / Blues stay away from me.
LP: JSP 1045

ROCKABILLY REBS.
Tracks: / Telephone baby / Rockabilly Romeo / State line / Go away hound dog / Haunted house / Runaway lover / Tore up / Tongue tied Jill / Caroline / Rockabilly baby / Sweet talkin' woman / One way train / Boot Hill boogie / Rockabilly angel.
LP: NTS 220

Rockats

LIVE AT THE RITZ.
LP: ILPS 9626

Rockers

ROCKERS (Film soundtrack) (Various artists).
Tracks: / We 'a' rockers: *Inner Circle* / Money worries: *Maytones* / Police and thieves: *Murvin, Junior*/ Book of rules: *Heptones* / Stepping razor: *Tosh, Peter* / Tenement yard: *Miller, Jacob* / Fade away: *Byles, Junior* / Rockers: *Wailer, Bunny* / Slave master: *Isaacs, Gregory* / Dread lion: *Scratch & Upsetters* / Graduation in Zion: *Kiddus 1* / Jah no dead: *Burning Spear* / Satta masagana: *Third World*/ Natty takes over: *Hines, Justin & The Dominos*.
LP: ILPS 9587
MC: ZCI 9587

Rockers & Balladeers

ROCKERS AND BALLADEERS 1 (Various artists).
MC: PLAC 341

ROCKERS AND BALLADEERS 2 (Various artists).
MC: PLAC 342

Rockers International

ROCKERS INTERNATIONAL (Various artists).
LP: ML 001

Rocket 88

ROCKET 88.
Tracks: / Talking about Louise / Roadhouse boogie / Swindon swing / Roll 'em Pete / Waiting for the call / St. Louis blues / Rocket 88.
LP: K 50776

Rockets

BACK TALK.
Tracks: / Back talk / Jealous / Lift you up / Shanghaied / Love for hire / I can't get satisfied / Tired of wearing black / I'll be your lover / American dreams / Lie to me.
LP: K 52309

LOVE TRANSFUSION.
Tracks: / Fast thing in Detroit / Fell out of love / My heart needs you / Lookin' for love / I got to move / Ramona / Fly little bird / Love transfusion / She's a pretty one.
LP: FL 12572
MC: FK 12572

NO BALLADS.
Tracks: / Desire / Don't hold on / Restless / Sally can't dance / Takin' it back / Time after time / Sad songs / I want you to love me / Is it true / Troublemaker.
LP: RSS 20

ROCKETS.
Tracks: / Can't sleep / Turn up the radio / Oh well / Lost forever, left for dreaming / Long long gone / Love me once again / Something ain't right / Lucille / Feel alright.
LP: RSS 7

Rockett, Garth

IAN GILLAN'S GARTH ROCKETT & THE MOONSHINERS STO (Rockett, Garth & The Moonshiners).
LPPD: ROHALP 3
MC: ROHAMC 3

Rockfella

ROCKAFELLA (Various artists).
LP: JBLP 301

Rockfile 11

ROCKFILE 11 (Various artists).
LP: MFM 015

Rockie

KNOCK OUT.
LP: MUT 1058
MC: CMUT 1058

Rockin' At The..

ROCKIN' AT THE TAKE 2 (Various artists).
LP: LINKLP 089

Rockin' Berries

BOWL OF ROCKIN' BERRIES, A.
LP: PYL 4016
MC: PYM 4016

IN TOWN.
LP: NPL 38013

Rockin' Chair

PAS UN CADEAU.
LP: A 120 050

STOP A LA DEPRIME.
LP: A 198

Rockin' Civil Servant

BOOGIE WOOGIE PIANO.
Tracks: / Steeplechase boogie / Dub boogie / Stompin' / Black gal makes it thunder / Upright boogie / Real train boogie / Bird boogie / Medium boogie / From the beginning / Easy going / Boogie trying / Boogie forever.
LP: DS 9202

ROCK, RHYTHM AND BOOGIE.
Tracks: / Feeling down / Jump boogie / Perfect love / Simple boogie / Comin' back / Misery blues / Going home / Thank you / Speedin' bird boogie / No more ramblin' around / Renewed boogie / Sleepless night / Same thing might happen to you, The.
LP: DS 9201

Rockin' Dopsie

BIG BAD ZYDECO (Rockin' Dopsie & His Cajun Twisters).
Tracks: / Me and my chauffer / Jambalaya / Trouble in mind / Sugar bee / On my way back home / Ma Negresse / Colinda / T'ant na na / Ay-tete fee / Zydeco two step.
LP: SNTF 851
LP: GNPS 2154
MC: GNP5 2154

CLIFTON CHENIER AND ROCKIN' DOPSIE (See under Chenier, Clifton) (Rockin' Dopsie & Clifton Chenier).

CROWN PRINCE OF ZYDECO.
Tracks: / Back door / Old time Zydeco / I got a woman / Do right tonight / Flip flop and fly / Something on your mind / Make it hot / I'm in the mood baby / Crazy 'bout that married woman / Why you do the things you do / Hey, hey, hey / Zydecool.
LP: SNTF 982

DOIN' THE ZYDECO (Rockin' Dopsie And The Twisters).
Tracks: / Who's loving you? / Ma negresse / Please come home / Joile blonde / Doin' the zydeco / Jump up / Rock me baby / Josephine / Grand ol mamou / Please don't leave me / Me & my chauffer / Jambalaya / Trouble in mind / Sugar bee / On my way back home / Colinda / T'ant na na / Ay-tete fee / Zydeco two step.
LP: SNTF 718

FRENCH STYLE (Rockin' Dopsie & His Cajun Twisters).
Tracks: / Shopick two step / Ti ne / Hound dog / I'm in the mood / Tu connais / Alvina / I passed in front of your door / Flames of hell / Where were you last night / What'd I say.
LP: SNTF 872

GOOD ROCKIN' (Rockin' Dopsie & His Cajun Twisters).
LP: SNTF 905
LP: GNPS 2167
MC: GNP5 2167

HOLD ON (Rockin' Dopsie & His Cajun Twisters).
Tracks: / Hold on / Baby bye bye / My baby she's gone / Marie / That gets it / Times done gone / Opelousas waltz / You promised me love / Tanya / Tire in the street.
LP: SNTF 800
LP: GNPS 2156
MC: GNP5 2156

ROCKIN' DOPSIE AND THE TWISTERS (Rockin' Dopsie And The Twisters).
LP: ROUNDER 6012
MC: ROUNDER 6012C

ROCKIN' WITH DUPSEE.
Tracks: / Woman I don't want your troubles / Things I used to do, The / Night and day / You told me baby / Ma Negresse / She's my little girl / Rockin' with Dupsee / Don't you want a man like me / Oh negresse / Dupsee shuffle / Don't let the green grass fool you.
LP: FLY 592

SATURDAY NIGHT ZYDECO.
LP: 1025

ZY-DE-BLUE (Rockin' Dopsie And The Twisters).
Tracks: / See see rider / My little girl / Lucille / When I lost my little girl / Cold cold night / Things I used to do, The / It's all right / Worried life blues / This loneliness (about to drive me out of my mind).
LP: SNTF 761

Rockin' Guitar

ROCKIN' GUITAR INSTRUMENTALS, VOL 5 (Various artists).
LP: 3177

Rockin' It Up

ROCKIN' IT UP (Various artists).
LP: LNLP 012

ROCKIN' IT UP VOL.2 (Various artists).
LP: LM LP 017

Rockin' Jimmy

BY THE LIGHT OF THE MOON (Rockin'Jimmy And The Brothers Of Night).
Tracks: / Stand back / Slow pace / Little Rachel / Crazy / Wind at your back, The / Can't jive enough / Raging storm / Leave my woman alone / Why you doin' what you do / Another chance / Ride it easy / Call on me.
LP: SNTF 857

ROCKIN' JIMMY AND THE BROTHERS OF THE NIGHT (Rockin'Jimmy And The Brothers Of Night).
Tracks: / Rockin' all nite / You got it made / Sugar babe / Beat of my heart / Right on time / Angel eyes / It's a mystery / Mood music / We got love / You got me.
LP: SNTF 889

Rockin' Kats...

THEY ARE ALL ROCKIN' KATS (Various artists).
LP: WLP 8934

Rockin' Lord Lee

SHAME (Rockin' Lord Lee & The Outlaws).
LP: ROCK 8902

Rockin' Louie

IT WILL STAND (Rockin' Louie & Mama Jammers).
LP: CR 30185

Rockin' Rebels

WILD WEEKEND.
LP: SWAN 509

Rockin' Sidney

BOOGIE BLUES 'N' ZYDECO.
LP: 1008
LP: KK 787
MC: 1008 TC

CREOLA.
LP: 102
MC: 102 TC

CROWNED PRINCE OF ZYDECO.
LP: 1020
MC: 1020 TC

GIVE ME A GOOD TIME WOMAN.
LP: 1007
MC: 1007 TC

HOLIDAY CELEBRATION, A.
Tracks: / Party this Christmas / I'm not gonna spend this Christmas alone / It's Christmas / Goin' home for Christmas / Christmas waltz / Christmas celebration / Christmas time is the time / My sweet thing / Christmas without you / Birthday celebration / She's a beautiful bride.
LP: 100
MC: 100 TC

HOTSTEPPIN.
LP: 101
MC: 101 TC
LP: JSP 1119

MY TOOT TOOT.
Tracks: / My toot toot / My zydeco shoes / Joy to the south / Don't be a wallflower / Alligator waltz / Rock and roll me baby / Joe Pete is in the bed / You ain't nothing but fine / If it's good for the gander / Twist to the zydeco / Dance and show off / Let me take you to zydeco / I got the blues for my baby / Louisiana creole man.
LP: CH 160

MY ZYDECO SHOES (Got the zydeco blues).
LP: 1009
MC: 1009 TC

THEY CALL ME ROCKIN'.
LP: FLY 515

Rockin' With Raucous

ROCKIN' WITH RAUCOUS (Various artists).
LP: RAUCLP 2

Rocking..

ROCKIN' WON'T STOP (Various artists).
LP: LM LP 003

ROCKING FROM HOLLYWOOD TO GRONINGEN various artists (Various artists).
LP: DIAL LP 002

ROCKING IT UP (Various artists).
LP: LM LP 012

Rocking Horse..(bk)

ROCKING HORSE SECRET, THE.
MCSET: DTO 10559

Rocking Richard

TEA AND BACCY (Rocking Richard & Whistling Vic Templar).
Tracks: / Blue Moon / Choice to choose / Come on now girl / Lonesome Town / Ghosts of Jesse Garon, The / I feel like giving in / World keeps going round / Peggy Sue / Long Black Train / Bastard sons of Elvis / Little Red Riding Hood / I Put A Spell On You / Cry Me A River.
LP: HANG 14 UP

Rockpile

SECONDS OF PLEASURE.
Tracks: / Teacher teacher / If sugar was sweet as you / Heart / Now and always / Knife and fork / Play that fast thing / Wrong way / Pet you and hold you / Oh what a thrill you / When I write the book / Fool too long, A / You ain't nothin' but fine.
LP: PILE 1
MC: XXC 7
LP: FIEND 28
LP: XXLP 7

Rocks, Noel

ADAM AMOS & NOEL ROCKS (see Amos,Adam & Noel Rocks) (Rocks, Noel/Adam Amos).

CASUAL ON THE BALCONY (see Amos,Adam & Noel Rocks) (Rocks, Noel/Adam Amos).

Rocks World Revolution

ROCKS WORLD REVOUTION: THE ROOTS (Various artists).
LP: LG 1000

Rocksnax

ROCKSNAX (Various artists).
LP: GRC 80

Rockwell

CAPTURED.
Tracks: / Peeping Tom / He's a cobra / T.V. psychology / We live in a jungle / Captured / Don't it make you cry / Tokyo / Costa Rica.
LP: ZL 72339
MC: ZK 72339

GENIE, THE.
Tracks: / That's nasty / Carme / Baby on the corner / Grown up / Nervous condition / Concentration / Man from mars / Genie of love.
LP: ZL 72442
MC: ZK 72442

SOMEBODY'S WATCHING ME.
LP: ZL 72147
MC: ZK 72147

Rockwell, Bob

ON THE NATCH (Rockwell, Bob Quartet).
LP: SCS 1229

Rockwell, Gene

MAKIN' SWEET MUSIC.
Tracks: / Love that country music / Sweetest love I've ever had, The / Hey Mr. Macho / Love wonderful love / Do you know her? / It's good to be home again / I like it, like it was / Lonely all the time / Makin' sweet music / I got the funny feelin' / You really wouldn't care if I went home / I'm sorry, just isn't gonna make it anymore / Never quiet in the city.
LP: MORRHYTHM 43

Rocky

ROCKY I (Original Soundtrack) (Various artists).
Tracks: / Gonna fly now: *Various artists* / Philadelphia morning: *Various artists* / Going the distance: *Various* artists / Reflections: *Various artists* / Marine's hymn/yankie doodle: *Various artists* / Take you back: *Various artists* / First date: *Various artists* / You take my heart away: *Various artists* / Fanfare for Rocky: *Various* artists / Butkus: *Various artists* / Alone in the ring: *Various artists* / Final bell, The: *Various artists*/ Rocky's reward: *Various artists.*
LP: 182 707.1
MC: 182 707.4
MC: TCK 30039

ROCKY II (Original Soundtrack) (Various artists).
Tracks: / Redemption: *Various artists* / Gonna fly now: *Various artists* / Conquest: *Various artists*/ Vigil: *Various artists* / All of my life: *Various artists* / Overture: *Various artists* / Two kinds of love: *Various artists* / All of my life: *Various artists.*
LP: UAG 30257
LP: 182720-1
MC: 182720-4

ROCKY III (Original Soundtrack) (Various artists).
Tracks: / Eye of the tiger: *Various artists* / Take you back (Tough Gym): *Various artists* / Pushin': *Various* artists / Reflections: *Various* artists / Mickey: *Various artists* / Take you back: *Various artists*/ Decision: *Various artists* / Gonna fly now: *Various artists* / Adrian: *Various artists* / Conquest: *Various artists.*
LP: LBG 30351
MC: TCLBG 30351

ROCKY IV (Original Soundtrack) (Various artists).
Tracks: / Burning heart: *Survivor* / Heart's on fire: *Gafferty, John* / Double or nothing: *Loggins, Kenny* & Gladys Knight / Eye of the tiger: *Survivor* / War fanfare from Rocky: *Dicola, Vince* / Living in America: *Brown, James* / No easy way out: *Tepper, Robert* / One way street: *Go West* / Sweetest victory, The / Training montage: *Dicola, Vince.*
LP: SCT 70272
MC: 40 70272

ROCKY STORY, THE (Various artists).
Tracks: / Eye of the tiger: *Survivor* / Burning heart: *Survivor* / Living in America: *Brown, James* / No easy way out: *Tepper, Robert* / Hearts of fire: *Cafferty, John* / Gonna fly now (Rocky theme): *Rocky Orchestra*/ War: *Dicola, Vince* / Training montage: *Dicola, Vince* / Gonna fly now (inst.): *Rocky Orchestra.*
LP: 848 242-1
MC: 848 242-4

ROCKY V (Music from and inspired by The Motion Picture) (Various artists).
Tracks: / That's what I said: *M.C. Hammer* / All you gotta do is sing: *Ellis, Joey B.* / No competition: *M.C.* Tab / Go for it (heart and fire): *Ellis, Joey B.* & *Tynetta Hare* / Take you back (home sweet home): *Seven A 3*/ Measure of a man, The: *John, Elton* / Can't stop the fire: *John, Elton* / I wanna rock: *Base, Rob* / Thought U were the one for me: *Ellis, Joey B.* / Keep it up: *Snap* / Feel my power: *M.C. Hammer.*
LP: EST 2137
MC: TCEST 2137

Rocky Horror Show

ROCKY HORROR BOX SET, THE (Original Soundtrack) (Various artists).
LPS: RHBXLP 1

ROCKY HORROR PICTURE SHOW (Original Soundtrack) (Various artists).
Tracks: / Science fiction: *Various artists* / Double feature (plus reprise): *Various artists* / Dammit Janet: *Various artists* / Over at the Frankenstein place: *Various artists* / Time warp, The: *Various artists*/ Sweet transvestite: *Various artists* / I can make you a man: *Various artists* / Hot patootie: *Various artists*/ Bless my soul: *Various artists* / Touch-a, touch-a, touch me: *Various artists* / Eddie: *Various artists*/ Rose tint my world: *Various artists* / Floor show: *Various artists* / Don't dream it: *Various artists*/ Wild and untamed thing: *Various artists* / I'm going home: *Various artists* / Super heroes: *Various artists.*
LP: OSV 21653
MC: OSVC 21653
LPPD: OSVP 21653

ROCKY HORROR SHOW (Original Roxy Cast) (Various artists).
Tracks: / Science fiction: *Various artists* / Double feature: *Various artists* / Dammit Janet: *Various artists*/ Over at the Frankenstein place: *Various artists* / Sweet transvestite: *Various artists* / Time warp: *Various* artists / Sword of Damocles, The: *Various artists* / Charles Atlas song (plus reprise): *Various artists* / What ever happened to Saturday night: *Various artists* / Touch-a, touch-a, touch me: *Various artists* / Once in a while: *Various artists* / Eddie's teddy: *Various artists* / Planet Schmanet Janet: *Various artists*/ Rose tint my world: *Various artists* / I'm going home: *Various artists* / Super heroes: *Various artists.*
LP: ODE 9009
MC: ODEC 9009

ROCKY HORROR SHOW (London Cast) (Various artists).
Tracks: / Time warp: *Various artists* / Sweet transvestite: *Various artists* / Dammit Janet: *Various artists*/ Science fiction: *Various artists* / Rocky's birth: *Various artists* / Wise up Janet Weiss: *Various artists.*
LP: CHR 1811
MC: ZCHR 1811

ROCKY HORROR SHOW (Original London Cast) (Various artists).
Tracks: / Science fiction-double feature: *Various artists* / Dammit Janet: *Various artists* / Over at the Frankenstein place: *Various artists* / Sweet transvestite: *Various artists* / Time warp: *Various artists* / Sword of damocles: *Various artists* / Hot patootie: *Various artists* / Touch-a-touch-a-touch-a-touch-me: *Various artists*/ Once in a while: *Various artists* / Rose tint my world: *Various artists* / I'm going home: *Various artists*/ Superheroes: *Various artists* / Science fiction-double feature (reprise): *Various artists.*
LP: DOJOLP 54
MC: DOJOTC 54

ROCKY HORROR..AUDIENCE PARTICIPATION (Various artists).
LP: ODE 1032
MC: ODEC 1032

SWEET TRANSVESTITE (See Under Head, Anthony) (Head, Anthony).

Rocky Mountain..

ROCKY MOUNTAIN HIGH (Various artists).
MC: VCA 101

Rockytops

LIFE CAN BE BEAUTIFUL.
Tracks: / Virginia / Together again / Love me tonight / Life can be beautiful / She can't read my writing / Bandy the rodeo clown / Fire on the mountain / Amazing grace / Love couldn't be any better / Entertainer, The / Silver wings / Moving on.
LP: FE 015

Roden, Jess

JESS RODEN.
MC: ICM 9286

STONE CHASER.
LP: ILPS 9531

Rodger, Mart

GIVE US A STOMPER KID (Rodger, Mart & Manchester Jazz).
Tracks: / Copenhagen / I can't say / Georgia on my mind / Dusty rag / Bogalusa strut / Papa dip / Saturday night function / Sweet Sue just you / Wild man blues / Fidgety feet.
LP: OWSLP 2601

JAZZ TALE OF TWO CITIES (Rodger, Mart & Manchester Jazz).
LP: GHB 224

Rodgers, Clodagh

CLODAGH RODGERS.
LP: SF 8033

Rodgers, Dick

ENTERS THE POLKA HALL OF FAME.
2LP: PC 376

Rodgers, Gene

PIANO SOLOS WITH RHYTHMS.
LP: 88 UR 007

Rodgers & Hammerstein

CAROUSEL (Various artists).
LP: MCG 6028
MC: MCGC 6028

RODGERS AND HAMMERSTEIN'S GREATEST HITS (Various artists).
Tracks: / June is bustin' out all over: *Various artists* / Oh what a beautiful mornin': *Various artists* / Surrey with the fringe on top, The: *Various artists* / Bali Ha'i: *Various artists* / You'll never walk alone: *Various* artists / Do-re-mi: *Various artists* / Hello, young lovers: *Various artists* / People will say we're in love: *Various artists* / This nearly was mine: *Various artists* / My favourite things: *Various artists* / Sound of music, The: *Various artists* / Happy talk: *Various artists* / Some enchanted evening: *Various artists*/ Getting to know you: *Various artists* / Wonderful guy, A: *Various artists* / Edelweiss: *Various artists*/ I whistle a happy tune: *Various artists* / If I loved you: *Various artists* / There is nothin' like a dame: *Various* artists / Shall we dance: *Various artists* / Climb every mountain: *Various artists* / Oklahoma: *Various artists*.
LP: . . . . . **WW 2048**
MC: . . . . . **WW 20484**

Rodgers & Hart

BOYS FROM SYRACUSE (Various artists).
Tracks: / Ladies of the evening: *Various artists* / Falling in love with love: *Various artists* / Shortest day of the year: *Various artists* / Oh diogenes: *Various artists* / I had twins: *Various artists* / He and she: *Various artists* / What can you do with a man?: *Various artists* / Dear old Syracuse: *Various artists*/ This can't be love: *Various artists* / You have cast your shadow on the sea: *Various artists* / Come with me: *Various artists* / Sing for your supper: *Various artists*.
LP: . . . . . **DS 15016**

EASY TO REMEMBER (Various artists).
LP: . . . . . **SH 355**

IT'S SMOOTH,IT'S SMART-IT'S RODGERS,IT'S HART (Various artists).
LP: . . . . . **MES 7069**

RODGERS & HART IN LONDON (Various artists).
LP: . . . . . **SH 183**

SONG IS...RICHARD RODGERS AND LORENZ HART (Various artists).
Tracks: / We'll be the same: *Arden, Victor/Phil Ohman Orchestras* / My heart stood still: *Matthews, Jessie* / Blue room: *Savoy Orpheans* / Little things you do, The: *'Hutch'* / Little birdie told me so, A: *Wolfe, Roger* Kahn Orchestra / Why do you suppose?: *Ross & Sargent* / Maybe it's me: *Hylton, Jack & His Orchestra* / Girl friend: *Light Opera Company* / Mountain greenery: *Light Opera Company* / Step on the blues: *Light Opera Company*/ Whats the use of talking: *Light Opera Company* / Thou swell: *Beiderbecke, Bix & His Gang* / Its easy to remember: *Crosby, Bing* / Yours sincerely: *Reisman, Leo Orch.* / Dancing on the ceiling: *Matthews, Jessie* / Blue Moon: *Trumbauer, Frankie* / Hello: *Light Opera Company* / Where's that rainbow?: *Light Opera Company*/ Tree in the park, A: *Hart, Lorenz & Richard Rogers* / Give her a kiss: *Coslow, Sam* / With a Song in my heart: *'Hutch'*.
LP: . . . . . **AJA 5041**
MC: . . . . . **ZC AJA 5041**

Rodgers, Jimmie (1)

20 OF THE BEST: JIMMIE RODGERS.
Tracks: / Blue yodel no. 1 (T for Texas) / Soldier's sweetheart, The / Blue yodel no. 9 (Standing on the corner) / Blue yodel no. 2 (My lovin' gal Lucille) / Blue yodel no. 3 / Blue yodel no. 4 (California blues) / Waiting for a train / Blue yodel no. 5 / Blue yodel no. 6 / Hobo Bill's last ride / Anniversary blue yodel (No. 7) / Blue yodel no. 8 (mule skinner blues) / Brakeman's blues, The / T B blues / Blue yodel no. 10 / Blue yodel no. 11 / Blue yodel no. 12 / In the jailhouse now no. 2 / Jimmie Rodgers' last blue yodel.
LP: . . . . . **NL 89370**
MC: . . . . . **NK 89370**

LEGENDARY PERFORMER, A.
Tracks: / Sleep, baby, sleep / Blue yodel no. 1 (T for Texas) / In the jailhouse now / Ben Dewberry's final run / You and my old guitar / Whippin' that old TB / TB blues / Mule skinner blues (Blue yodel No. 8) / Old love letters (bring memories of you) / Home call.
LP: . . . . . **PL 12504**
MC: . . . . . **PK 12504**

MY OLD PAL.
Tracks: / Blue yodel no.1 (T for Texas) / Away out on the mountain / Frankie and Johnny / Gambling bar room blues / When the cactus is in bloom / Sleep, baby, sleep / My old pal / Daddy and home / My Carolina sunshine girl / Why there's a tear in my eye / We miss him when the evening shadows fall / Never no mo' blues / Blue yodel no. 3 / I'm sorry we met / Blue yodel no. 5 / Any old time / Lullaby yodel / Looking for a new mama.
LP: . . . . . **AJA 5058**
MC: . . . . . **ZC AJA 5058**

MY ROUGH AND ROWDY WAYS.
LP: . . . . . **HAT 3091**
MC: . . . . . **HATC 3091**

NEVER NO MO' BLUES.
Tracks: / Never no mo' blues / Daddy and home / Blue yodel no. 4 (California blues) / Waiting for a train / You and my old guitar / Prairie lullaby / Blue yodel no. 6 / Dear old sunny south by the sea / Jimmie's mean mama blues / Pistol packin' papa / Old pal of my heart / My little lady.
LP: . . . . . **NL 90009**
MC: . . . . . **NK 90009**

TRAIN WHISTLE BLUES.
Tracks: / Jimmie's mean mama blues / Southern Cannonball, The / Jimmie the kid / Travellin' blues / Mystery of number 5, The / Memphis yodel / Blue yodel no. 4 (California blues) / Hobo Bill's last ride / Waiting for a train / Ben Dewberry's final run / My rough and rowdy ways / Blue yodel no. 7 (Anniversary blue yodel) / Brakeman's blues, The / Let me be your side track / Hobo's meditation, The / Train whistle blues.
LP: . . . . . **AJA 5042**
MC: . . . . . **ZC AJA 5042**

Rodgers, Jimmie (2)

BEST OF JIMMIE RODGERS, THE.
Tracks: / Honeycomb / Kisses sweeter than wine / Oh-oh I'm falling in love again / Long hot summer, The / Secretly / Make me a miracle / Are you really mine / Wizard, The (CD only.) / Bimbombey / I'm never gonna tell (CD only.) / Ring-a-ling-a-lario / Wonderful you / Tucumcari / T.L.C. Tender love and care / Waltzing Matilda / Woman from Liberia / English country garden / Soldier won't you marry me / We can't go wrong (LP version) (12" only.) / Love mission (12" only.).
LP: . . . . . **ROU 5005**
MC: . . . . . **TCROU 5005**
MC: **790 767 4**

KISSES SWEETER THAN WINE.
MC: . . . . . **HSC 3403**

YOU AND MY OLD GUITAR.
MC: . . . . . **RR 300**

Rodgers, Nile

ADVENTURES IN THE LAND OF THE GOOD GROOVE.
Tracks: / It's all in your hands / My love song for you / Rock bottom / Most down / Kand of the good groove / Yum yum / Beet / Get her crazy.
LP: . . . . . **B 0073**

B MOVIE MATINEE.
Tracks: / Groove master / Let's go out tonight / Stay out of the light / Same wavelength / Plan number 9 / State your mind / Face in the window / Doll squad.
LP: **925290 1**

Rodgers, Paul

CUT LOOSE.
Tracks: / Fragile / Cut loose / Live in peace / Sweet sensation / Rising sun / Boogie mama / Morning after the night before / Northwinds / Superstar woman / Talking guitar blues.
LP: **780 121-1**
MC: **780 121-4**

Rodgers, Richard

RICHARD RODGERS BALLET MUSIC.
Tracks: / Ghost town / Slaughter on 10th Avenue / Princess Zenobia ballet.
LP: . . . . . **TER 1114**
MC: . . . . . **ZCTER 1114**

RICHARD RODGERS & N.Y. PHILHARMONIC (Rodgers, Richard/ N.Y.Philharmonic).
Tracks: / Slaughter on tenth avenue / Victory / Lover / Most beautiful girl in the world / Falling in love with love / Oh, what a beautiful morning / March of the Siamese Children / Carousel waltz.
LP: . . . . . **CBS 61895**

Roditi, Claudio

CLAUDIO.
LP: . . . . . **UP 27 27**

Rodney's Glory

RODNEY'S GLORY.
MC: . . . . . **GTDC 095**

Rodrigues, Amalia

BEST OF AMALIA RODRIGUES.
LP: **1A 022 58067**

GOSTAVA DE SER QUEM ERA.
LP: **2C 068 40533**

Rodriguez, Alfred

PATATO-TOTICO.
LP: . . . . . **ESP 8407**

Rodriguez, Johnny

JOHNNY RODRIGUEZ.
Tracks: / Down on the Rio Grande / Don't be afraid to say goodbye / When the honeymoon ends / Fools for each other / Driftin' away / Mexico holiday / Paid vacation / Street walker / Hand on my shoulder / I give my life a second look.
LP: . . . . . **EPC 83731**

THROUGH MY EYES.
Tracks: / What'll I tell Virginia / One sided love affair / One affair later / Where did it go / I'll go back to her / One, two, three / You've lost that lovin' feeling / Feeling / Whatever gets me through the night / Love, look at us no / Welcome to love.
LP: . . . . . **EPC 84196**

Rodriguez, Maria

LA TREMENDA.
LP: . . . . . **WCB 001**

Rodriguez, Silvio

DIAS Y FLORES.
LP: . . . . . **HNBL 1322**
MC: . . . . . **HNBC 1322**

Rodriguez, Willie

FLATJACKS.
Tracks: / Moliendo cafe / Nanigo soul / Brasileira / Flatjacks / After words / El sueno de Frances / Serenata / Mr. Yoss / It happened in Monterey / Seafood Wally / Tasty.
LP: . . . . . **RSLP 469**

Rodrique, Gene

BAYOU CAJUN MUSIC OF GENE RODRIQUE, THE.
LP: **6062**
MC: . . . . . **6062 TC**

Rods

HEAVIER THAN THOU.
Tracks: / Heavier than thou / Make me a believer / Angels never run / Crossfire / I'm gonna rock / She's trouble / Born to rock / Chains of love / Communication breakdown / Fool for your love / Cold sweat and love / Music man.
LP: . . . . . **ZEB 9**

LET THEM EAT METAL.
LP: . . . . . **MFN 29**

RODS LIVE, THE.
LP: . . . . . **MFN 16**
MC: . . . . . **TMFN 16**

RODS, THE.
Tracks: / Power lover / Crank it up / Hungry for some love / Music man / Woman / Nothing going on in the city / Get ready to rock 'n' roll / Ace in the hole / Rock hard / Roll with the night.
LP: . . . . . **SPART 1182**

WILD DOGS.
Tracks: / Too hot to stop / Waiting for tomorrow / Violation / Burned by love / Wild dogs / You keep me hangin' on / Rockin' 'n' rollin' again / End of the line / No sweet talk / Honey / Night lives to rock, The.
LP: . . . . . **SPART 1196**
MC: . . . . . **TCART 1196**

Rodska, Christian

KING IN LOVE, A (see under King in Love (bk)).

MAN CALLED KYRIL, THE (See also John Trenhaile).

PRINCE & THE PEKINGESE, THE (see under Prince & the Pekingese (bk)).

Rodwell, Bryan

PROJECTED SOUNDS OF BRYAN RODWELL, THE.
Tracks: / Entry of the Queen of Sheba / Autumn leaves / Buttons and bows / All the things you are / Four brothers / Alpine ride / Autumn too soon / Jeanie with the light brown hair / Atlantic drive / Over the rainbow / Soho strut.
LP: . . . . . **PRZ 001**
MC: . . . . . **CPRZ 001**

PURELY FOR PLEASURE (Eminent F 225 Organ).
Tracks: / Dues blues / Moonlight serenade / But not for me / Gone with the wind / Lover come back to me / Take the 'A' train / Nightingale sang in Berkely Square / Sweet Georgia Brown / Patty / Tangerine / Bandology.
LP: . . . . . **GRS 1125**

Roe, Tommy

20 GREATEST HITS: TOMMY ROE.
LP: **2236212**
MC: **2236214**

GOLDEN GREATS: TOMMY ROE.
Tracks: / Sheila / Susie darlin' / Folk singer, The / Everybody / Come on / Carol / Party girl / Sweet pea / Hooray for Hazel / It's now a Winter's day / Sing along with me / Little Miss Sunshine / Dizzy / Heather Honey / Jack and Jill / Jam up jelly tight.
LP: . . . . . **MCM 5021**
MC: . . . . . **MCMC 5021**

HITS AND RARITIES.
LP: . . . . . **JUDD 75100**

Roedelius

JARDIN AU FOU.
Tracks: / Fou fou / Toujours / Rue fortune / Balsam / Cafe central / Le jardin / Gloria Dolores / Etoiles / Schone welt.
LP: **90 291**

Roedelius, Eno M.

AFTER THE HEAT.
LP: . . . . . **SKY 021**

AUF LEISEN SOHLEN.
LP: . . . . . **SKY 94**

DURCH DIE WUSTE.
LP: . . . . . **SKY 014**

Roedelius, Hans

BASTIONEN DER LIEBRE (Fortress of Love).
LP: . . . . . **VE 42**
MC: . . . . . **TCVE 42**

GESCHENK DES AUGENBLICKS.
Tracks: / Gesckenk des Augenblicks (gift of the moment) / Adieu Quichotte / Troubadour / Kleine blume irgendwo (little flower somewhere) / Ohn' unterlass (continuously) / Gefundene zeit (time regained) / Sehnsucht ich will dich lassen (to be free and yearning) / Das sanfte (mellowness) / Tag fur tag (day by day) / Zu fussen der berge am ufer des sees / Wurzeln des glucks (roots of joy).
LP: . . . . . **EGED 34**

MOMENTI FELICI.
Tracks: / Im Frubtau / Leicht zu fub / Anima mundi / Uber den wolken / Aufgewacht / Capriccio / Guten morgen / Am weiber / Pas de deux.
LP: . . . . . **VE 4**
MC: . . . . . **TCVE 4**

Roessler, Paul

ABOMINABLE.
LP: . . . . . **SST 196**
MC: . . . . . **SSTC 196**

Roethke, Theodore

THEODORE ROETHKE READS.
MC: **1351**

Roger

MANY FACETS OF ....
Tracks: / I heard it through the grapevine / So ruff so tuff / Chunk of sugar / Do it Roger / Maxx axe / Blue.
LP: . . . . . **K 56960**

SAGA CONTINUES, THE.
Tracks: / In the mix / Play your guitar, brother roger / Break song / I keep trying / Midnight hour / Bucket of blood / TC song / Girl, cut it out.
LP: **9239751**

UNLIMITED.
Tracks: / I want to be your man / Night and day / Been this way before / Composition to commemorate / Papa's got a brand new bag / Thrill seekers / Tender moments / If you're serious / Private lover / I really want to be your man.
LP: . . . . . **K 925496 1**
MC: . . . . . **K 925496 4**

Roger, Aldus

KING OF FRENCH ACCORDION.
LP: **114**

PLAYS FRENCH MUSIC.
LP: **107**
MC: . . . . . **107 TC**

PLAYS THE CAJUN FRENCH CLASSICS.
LP: **122**

Rogers, Anton

PHANTOM OF THE OPERA (See also Gaston Leroux).

Rogers, Billie

ONE NIGHT STAND...WOMENS LIB IN 1944.
LP: . . . . . **JLP 1018**

Rogers, Carol

ALTERNATIVES TO MARRIAGE (See under Alternatives to...).

Rogers, Cece

CECE ROGERS.
Tracks: / Forever / Lonely girl / Love will make you do that / I wanna be / Someday / I found someone / I think I love you / I need you / Why me.
LP: . . . . . **K 781 202 1**
MC: . . . . . **K 781 202 4**

Rogers, D.J.

LOVE, MUSIC AND LIFE.
Tracks: / Love will make it better / Hold out for love / Love is on the way / She has eyes for me / Saved by love / Beauty and the beast / No need to say goodbye / No price / Love is all I need / You against you.
LP: PL 12218

ON THE ROAD AGAIN.
Tracks: / On the road again / One more day / Love can be found / Let my life shine / Secret lady / Holding on to love / Girl I love you / Only while it lasts / Say you love me one more time.
LP: PL 42021

Rogers, Evan

LOVE GAMES.
Tracks: / Hold on / Private joy / Full time lover / Sweet 16 / Don't jump to conclusions / One track mind / I'll break the rules for you / Be mine tonight.
LP: PL 89573

Rogers, Gamble

SORRY IS AS SORRY DOES.
LP: FF 362

Rogers, Ginger

FRED ASTAIRE AND GINGER ROGERS STORY, THE (See under Astaire, Fred) (Rogers, Ginger/Fred Astaire).

GINGER ROGERS.
LP: CC 100/21

GINGER ROGERS COLLECTION (20 Golden Greats).
Tracks: / Let's face the music and dance / We can't get along / Dear Sir / Used to be you / Music makes me / Shake your powder puff / Out for no good / Out of sight out of mind / Girl of the moment / I got a new lease of life / Don't mention love to me / I'll string along with you / Eeny meeny miney mo / You'll be reminded of me / Yam, The / My ship / Piccolino, The / Weekend in the country, A / You'll never know / Before the parade passes by.
LP: DVLP 2058
MC: DVMC 2058
LP: BRP 2027

MISS GINGER ROGERS.
Tracks: / Embraceable you / I used to be colour blind / Isn't this a lovely day / But not for me / I'll string along with you / They can't take that away from me / Night and day / Did you ever see a dream walking? / They all laughed / We're in the money / Fine romance, A / Let's call the whole thing off / I'm putting all my eggs in one basket.
LP: ODN 1002

RARE RECORDINGS 1930-1972.
LP: SH 2042

STORY OF VERNON & IRENE CASTLE (See under Astaire, Fred) (Rogers, Ginger/Fred Astaire).

Rogers, Harlan

COLOURS OF PRAISE (Rogers, Harlan/Smitty Price).
LP: MM R 0189
MC: MM C 0189

COLOURS OF PRAISE II (Rogers, Harlan/Smitty Price).
LP: MM R 0224
MC: MM C 0224

TIMELESS COLOURS.
LP: MM R 0161
MC: MM C 0161

Rogers, Jimmy

CHESS MASTERS.
Tracks: / Left me with a broken heart / Blues all day long / Today today blues / World's in a tangle,The / She loves another man / Hard working man / Chance to love / My little machine / Mistreated baby / What's the matter / You're the one / If it ain't me / One kiss / I can't believe / What have I done / My baby don't love me no more / Crying shame / Give love another chance / This has never been / Rock this house / My last meal / You don't know / Can't keep from worrying.
2LP: GCH 2-6027
MCSET: GCHK 2-6027
2LP: CXMD 4008

CHICAGO BAND.
LP: BRP 2027

CHICAGO BLUES (Rogers, Jimmy & Left Hand Frank).
LP: JSP 1008

CHICAGO GOLDEN YEARS.
2LP: 427012

DIRTY DOZENS (Rogers, Jimmy & Left Hand Frank).
Tracks: / Take a walk / You're sweet / Mean red spider / Fishing in my pond / Crazy woman blues / Information, please / Dirty dozens / Oh baby / Honky tonk / One-room country shack / Cleo's gone / Baby please.
LP: JSP 1090

FEELIN' GOOD.
LP: MB 1006

LIVE: JIMMY ROGERS (Rogers, Jimmy & Left Hand Frank).
Tracks: / Ioppy drunk / I can't keep from worrying / Frank's blues / Linda Lu / Blues for Freddy / That's alright / Brown skinned woman.
LP: JSP 1043

LUDELLA.
LP: BEDLP 13

Rogers, Kenny

20 GOLDEN HITS: KENNY ROGERS.
LP: MA 29284
MC: MAMC 929284
LP: 1A 222 929284

20 GREATEST HITS: KENNY ROGERS.
MC: 2630214

ANTHOLOGY - KENNY ROGERS.
Tracks: / But I know I love you / Ruby (Don't take your love to town) / Something's burning / Tell it all brother / Lucille / Day time friends,night time lovers / Just dropped in / Gambler, The / She believes in me / You decorated my life / Coward of the county / Don't fall in love with a dreamer / Love the world away / We've got tonight / Buried treasure / This woman / Eyes that see in the dark / What about me / Crazy / Tomb of the unknown love / Make no mistake, she's mine.
2LP: VSOPLP 148
MC: VSOPMC 148
MC: 911 151
2LP: 911 144

AT HIS BEST: KENNY ROGERS.
Tracks: / Ruby, don't take your love to town / Me and Bobby McGee / Reuben James.
LP: FUN 9035
MC: FUNC 9035

BEST OF KENNY ROGERS.
LP: BWY 100

CHRISTMAS (KENNY ROGERS).
Tracks: / But I know... / Christmas everyday / Kentucky homemade Christmas / Carol of the bells / Kids / Sweet little Jesus boy / Christmas is my favourite time of the year / White Christmas / My favourite things / O' holy night / When a child is born.
LP: ED 2607201
MC: ED 2607204
LP: MFP 5796
MC: TCMFP 5796

CLASSICS (Rogers, Kenny & Dottie West).
Tracks: / All I ever need is you / Till I can make it on my own / Just the way you are / You needed me / Let it be me / Together again / Midnight flyer / You've lost that lovin' feeling / Let's take the long way round the world / Another somebody done somebody wrong song.
LP: MFP 5601
MC: TCMFP 5601
MC: 4XLL 9535
LP: UAG 30235

COLLECTION.
LP: 1A 022 58094

COLLECTION: KENNY ROGERS.
Tracks: / Trying just as hard / Ruby don't take your love to town / Heed the call / We all got to help each other / Ticket to nowhere / Conditions (just dropped in) / She even woke me up to say goodbye / Where does Rosie go / Sunshine / Reuben James / Loser / Church without a name / My Washington woman / Run thru your mind / I just wanna give my love to you / Last few threads of love / Tell it all brother / I'm gonna sing you a sad song Susie / What am I gonna do / Sleep comes easy / After all (I live my life) / For the good times / Lay it down / Me and Bobby McGee / Always leaving always gone / Calico silver / Way it used to be, The / Something's burning / Hurry up love.
2LP: CCSLP 111
MC: CCSMC 111

COUNTRY DOUBLE (Rogers, Kenny & Conway Twitty).
MCSET: M 10164

COUNTRY STORE: KENNY ROGERS.
Tracks: / Love lifted me / Abraham, Martin and John / Precious moments / I would like to see you again / Runaway girl / World needs a melody, The / You gotta be tired / Home made love / While the feeling's good / Heavenly sunshine / There's an old man in our town.
LP: CST 34
MC: CSTK 34
MC: CSTK 46

DAYTIME FRIENDS (ALBUM).
Tracks: / Daytime friends / Desperado / Rock and roll man / Living again / I'll just write my music and sing my songs / My world begins and ends with you / Sweet music man / Am I too late / We don't make love anymore / Ghost of another man / Let me sing for you.
LP: UAS 30119

EVERY TIME TWO FOOLS COLLIDE (Rogers, Kenny & Dottie West).
Tracks: / Everytime two fools collide / You and me / What's wrong with us today / Beautiful lies / That's the way it could have been / Why don't we go somewhere and love / Baby I'm a want you / Anyone who isn't me tonight / Loving gift, The / We love each other.
LP: UAS 30170

EYES THAT SEE IN THE DARK.
Tracks: / This woman / You and I / Buried treasure / Islands in the stream / Living with you / Evening star / Hold me / Midsummer night / I will always love you / Eyes that see in the dark.
LP: NL 90084
MC: NK 90084
LP: RCALP 6088

FABULOUS KENNY ROGERS,THE.
Tracks: / Ruby don't take your love to town / Tulsa turnaround / Where does Rosie go / Love woman / Reuben James / I'm gonna sing you a sad song Susie / Me & Bobby McGee / Molly / Something's burning / Elvira / Tell it all brother / King of Oak Street, The / For the good times.
LP: SHM 3228
MC: HSC 3228

FOR THE GOOD TIMES (Rogers, Kenny & The First Edition).
Tracks: / For the good times / It's gonna be better / Home made lies / Sleep comes easy / But you know I love you / Something's burning / Shine on Ruby mountain / Run thru your mind / My Washington woman / She even woke me up to say goodbye / Elvira / Stranger in my place, A / Hurry up love / Ticket to nowhere / After all I live my life / Me and Bobby McGee / It's raining in my mind / Just dropped in (to see what condition my condition is in) / Shadow in the corner of your mind / Reuben James.
LP: ARA 1001
MC: ARAC 1001

GAMBLER,THE.
Tracks: / Gambler, The / I wish that I could hurt that way again / King of Oak Street, The / Making music for money / Hoodooin of Miss Fannie Deberry / She believes in me / Tennessee bottle / Sleep tight, goodnight man / Little more like me / San Francisco Mabel Joy / Morgana Jones.
LP: UAG 30220
MC: TCK 30220

GIDEON.
Tracks: / Goin' home to the rock / Gideon Tanner / No good Texas rounder / Don't fall in love with a dreamer / Buckeroos / You were a good friend / Call me up (and I'll come calling on you) / These chains / Somebody help me / One place in the night / Sayin' goodbye.
LP: UAK 30303

GOLDEN GREATS: KENNY ROGERS (Rogers, Kenny & The First Edition).
Tracks: / Ruby, don't take your love to town / Tulsa turn around / Elvira / Reuben James / King of Oak Street, The / Me and Bobby McGee / Just dropped in (to see what condition my condition is in) / For the good times / Something's burning / Tell it all brother / Sunshine / Poem for my little lady / She even woke me up to say goodbye / Heed the call / I believe in music.
LP: MCM 5018
MC: MCMC 5018

GREATEST HITS: KENNY ROGERS.
Tracks: / Gambler, The / Lady / Don't fall in love with a dreamer / Ruby don't take your love to town / She believes in me / Coward of the county / Lucille / You decorated my life / Reuben James / Love the world away / Every time two fools collide / Long arm of the law.
LP: 2230215
MC: 2130215

HEART OF THE MATTER.
Tracks: / Don't wanna have to worry / You made me feel love / Morning desire / Heart of the matter / Don't look in my eyes / Best of me, The / Tomb of the unknown love / People in love / I can't believe your eyes / Our perfect song.
LP: PL 87023
MC: PK 87023

I PREFER THE MOONLIGHT.
Tracks: / I prefer the moonlight / Now and forever / We're doin' alright / Make no mistake, she's mine / One more day / She's ready for someone to love her / I don't call him daddy / Factory / We fell in love anyway / You can't say (you don't love me anymore).
LP: PL 86484
MC: PK 86484

KENNY.
Tracks: / You turn the light on / You decorated my life / She's a mystery / Goodbye Marie / Tulsa turnaround / I want to make you smile / Santiago midnight moonlight / One man's woman / In and out of your heart / Old folks / Coward of the county.
LP: UAG 30273

KENNY ROGERS.
Tracks: / Laura (what's he got that I ain't got) / I wasn't man enough / Mother country music / Why don't we go somewhere and love / Green green grass of home / Till I get it right / Lucille / Son of Hickory Holler's tramp, The / Lay down beside me / Puttin' in overtime at home / While I play the fiddle.
LP: UAS 30046

KENNY ROGERS STORY, THE (20 Golden Greats).
Tracks: / Lucille / Lady / Long arm of the law / You decorated my life / Sweet music man / Ruby don't take your love to town / Love or something like it / Through the years / You are so beautiful / Don't fall in love with a dreamer (with Kim Carnes) / Gambler, The / Daytime friends / We've got tonight (With Sheena Easton) / Love lifted me / Coward of the county / Reuben James / Desperado / She believes in me / Something's burning / Blaze of glory.
LP: EMTV 39
MC: TC EMTV 39
MC: EJ 360669 4
LP: EJ 360669 1

LADIES AND OUTLAWS.
LP: PLAT 4901
MC: PLAC 4901

LADY (Rogers,Kenny with Kim Carnes & Dottie West).
Tracks: / Lady / Don't fall in love with a dreamer / Lucille / She believes in me / You decorated my life / Coward of the county / Goodbye Marie / Every time two fools collide / Sail away / Gambler, The / Love the world away / Long arm of the law.
LP: LBG 30334
MC: TCLBG 30334

LOVE LIFTED ME.
Tracks: / Love lifted me / Abraham, Martin and John / Precious memories / I would like to see you again / Runaway girl / World needs a melody / You gotta be tired / Home-made love / While the feeling's good / Heavenly sunshine / There's an old man in our town.
LP: LBR 1015

LOVE OR SOMETHING LIKE IT (ALBUM).
Tracks: / Love or something like it / There's a lot of that going around / Buried treasure / Something about your song / Momma's waiting / We could have been the closest of friends / I could be so good for you / Sail away / Even a fool would let go / Highway flyer / Starting again.
LP: UAS 30194

LOVE SONGS: KENNY ROGERS.
Tracks: / Lady / Ruby don't take your love to town / Lucille / She believes in me / Together again / Don't fall in love with a dreamer / You decorated my life / Every time two fools collide / All I ever need is you / You needed me / Why don't we go somewhere and love / Love or something like it / Another somebody done somebody wrong song / My world begins and ends with you / You and me / We love each other / You've lost that loving feeling (CD only.) / But you know I love you (CD only.) / Love lifted me (CD only.) / Just the way you are.
MC: TCMFP 5880

LOVE SONGS: KENNY ROGERS.
Tracks: / Always leavin' always alone / What am I gonna do / Girl get a hold of yourself / I found a reason / It's gonna be better / She even woke me up to say goodbye / I just wanna give my love to you / Last few threads of love / Way it used to be, The / I'm gonna sing you a sad song Susie / But you know I love you / Shadow in the corner of your mind / Stranger in my place, A / Sunshine / Once again she's all alone / My Washington woman / Hurry up love / Home made lies / Poem for my little lady.
MC: HSC 3278

LOVE WILL TURN YOU AROUND.
Tracks: / Love will turn you around / Love song / Fighting fire with fire / Maybe you should know / Somewhere between lovers and friends / Take this heart / If you can lie a little bit / I'll take care of you / Fool in me / I want a son.

LP: .... LBG 30350

LUCILLE.
Tracks: / Laura (What's he got that I ain't got) / I wasn't man enough / Mother country music / Why don't we go somewhere and love / Green green grass of home / Till I get it right / Lucille / Son of Hickory Holler's tramp, The / Lay down beside me / Puttin' in overtime at home / While I play the fiddle.
LP: .... MFP 5764
MC: .... TCMFP 5764

ONCE UPON A CHRISTMAS (see under Parton, Dolly) (Rogers, Kenny & Dolly Parton).

RUBY, DON'T TAKE YOUR LOVE TO TOWN.
Tracks: / Ruby, don't take your love to town / Green green grass of home / Sweet music man / Love or something like it / You and me / King of Oak Street, The / Reuben James / Puttin' in overtime at home / Daytime friends / Let it be me / Buried treasure / Son of Hickory Holler's tramp, The / I wasn't man enough (CD only) / Mother country music (CD only) / Lay down beside me (CD only) / Lucille (CD only).
LP: .... MFP 50514
MC: .... TCMFP 50514

RUBY DON'T TAKE YOUR LOVE TO TOWN.
Tracks: / Ticket to nowhere / Conditions (Just dropped in) / She even woke me up to say goodbye / My Washington woman / Run thru your mind / Sleep comes easy / After all (I live my life) / For the good times / Something's burning / Hurry up. Love / Trying just as hard / Ruby don't take your love to town / Heed the call / we all got to help each other / Poem for my little lady / Where does Rosie go / Sunshine / Ruben James / Loser / Church without a name / Green green grass of home / Sweet music man / Daytime friends.
LP: .... SHLP 117
MC: .... SHTC 117

SHARE YOUR LOVE.
Tracks: / Share your love / Blaze of glory / I don't need you / Good life / Makes me wonder if I ever said goodbye / Through the years / So in love with you / Goin' back to Alabama / Without you in my life / Grey beard.
LP: .... LBG 30339
MC: .... TC LBG 30339

SHINE ON.
Tracks: / Something's burning / Just remember you're my sunshine / Tell it all, brother / Ruby don't take your love to town / Stranger in my place / I'm gonna sing you a sad song Susie / She even woke me to say goodbye / Shine on Ruby Mountain / Me and Bobby McGee / Molly / Then I miss you / Sunshine / Someone who cares / Elvira.
LP: .... K 24037

SINGLES ALBUM: KENNY ROGERS.
Tracks: / Ruby don't take your love to town / Reuben James / But you know I love you / Something's burning / Just dropped in / Lucille / Daytime friends / While the feeling's good / Love lifted me / Today I started loving you again / Love or something like it / Sail away / Gambler, The / She believes in me.
LP: .... UAK 30263
MC: .... TCK 30263

SOMETHING INSIDE SO STRONG.
Tracks: / Planet Texas / If I knew what I know now / There lies the difference / When you put your heart in it / Maybe (Something inside) so strong / One night / If I ever fall in love again / Vows go unbroken (always true to you) / Love the way you do.
LP: .... K 9257921
MC: .... K 9257924

SOMETHING'S BURNING.
Tracks: / For the good times / It's gonna be better / Home made lies / Sleep comes easy / But you know I love you / Something's burning / Shine on ruby mountain / Run thru your mind / My Washington woman / She even woke me up to say Goodbye / Elvira / Stranger in my place, A / Hurry up, love / Ticket to nowhere / After all, I live my life / Me and Bobby McGee / It's raining in my mind / Conditions (just dropped in) / Shadow in the corner of your mind / Reuben James.
2LP: .... PPD 2004
MC: .... PPK 2004

THEY DON'T MAKE 'EM LIKE THEY USED TO.
Tracks: / This love we share / If I could hold on to love / You're my love / Time for love, A / They don't make 'em like they used to / Life is good, love is better / Just the thought of losing you / Anything at all / After all this time / Twenty years ago.
LP: .... PL 85633
MC: .... PK 85633

VERY BEST OF KENNY ROGERS, THE.
Tracks: / What I did for love / Ruby don't take your love to town / Don't fall in love with a dreamer / Gambler, The / Daytime friends / Love is strange / She believes in me / Lucille / Lady / Coward of the county / You decorated my life / Love lifted me / Something's burning / Islands in the stream.
LP: 7599264571
MC: 7599264574

WE'VE GOT TONIGHT.
Tracks: / We've got tonight / Scarlet fever / Farther I go / No dreams / Bad enough / All my life / How long / Love, love, love / What I learned from loving you / You are so beautiful.
MC: .... TC-LBG 30357
LP: .... LBG 30357

WE'VE GOT TONIGHT (see under Easton, Sheena) (Rogers, Kenny & Sheena Easton).

WHAT ABOUT ME.
Tracks: / Didn't we / Somebody took my love / Crazy / Stranger / Heart to heart / What about me / Night goes on / Dream dancin' / Two hearts one love / I don't want to know.
LP: .... PL 85043
MC: .... PK 85043

Rogers, Kenny Jr

YES - NO, MAYBE.
LP: .... YL 0132

Rogers, Kim

SOUNDTRACK OF MY LIFE.
LP: .... ILPS 9966
MC: .... ICT 9966
LP: 842 796 1
MC: 842 796 4

Rogers, Nigel

SONGS FOR TENOR AND LUTE BY JOHN DOWLAND (Rogers, Nigel & Paul O'dette).
Tracks: / Come away, come sweet love / Come heavy sleep / Wilt thou unkind thus reave me? / If my complaints could passions move / My thoughts are winged with hopes / Awake sweet love / Sorrow stay / Fine knacks for ladies / Flow my tears / Shall I sue / I saw my lady weep / When Pheobus first did Daphne love / Say, love, if ever thou did'st find / Fie on this feigning / Weep you no more sad fountains / Love those beams / Sweet stay awhile / To ask for all thy love / Were every thought an eye / Shall I strive with words to move?.
MC: .... VC 7907261
LP: .... VC 7907264

Rogers, Richard

CAN'T STOP.
Tracks: / Spread a little love / Can't stop loving you / Sweet essence / Bed of roses / Anything you want / (I'll be your) dream lover / Take care of you / Crazy in love.
LP: .... BCM 460 LP
MC: .... BCM 460 MC

Rogers, Ron

DON'T PLAY WITH MY EMOTIONS.
LP: .... IRSP 30

Rogers, Roy

COUNTRY SIDE OF..., THE.
LP: .... HAT 3116
MC: .... HATC 3116

GOOD LIFE (Rogers,Roy/Dale Evans).
LP: .... SAC 5095

KING OF THE COWBOYS (Rogers, Roy/Sons of the Pioneers).
Tracks: / Hawaiian cowboy / Hasta la vista / There'll never be another Pecos Bill / I'm gonna gallop, gallop to gallup, New Mexico / Stampede / With a sweep of my sombrero / Saddle serenade / Make believe cowboy / Horseshoe moon / Church music / Cowboy heaven / Ride, son ride / Don't ever leave me (Previously unissued.) / Buck-eye cowboy / Four legged friend, A.
LP: .... BFX 15124

ROLL ON TEXAS MOON.
Tracks: / Yellow rose of Texas / Don't fence me in / Gay ranchero, A / Roll on Texas moon / I met a miss in Texas / On the old Spanish trail / May the good Lord take a likin' to ya / San Fernando Valley / I'm a rollin' / Little hula honey / California Rose / Home in Oklahoma / Rock me to sleep in my saddle / Old fashioned cowboy / There's a cloud to the valley of sunshine / Along the Navajo Trail.
LPPD: .... BDP 15203

ROY ROGERS & THE SONS OF THE PIONEERS (The Republic Years) (Rogers, Roy/Sons of the Pioneers).
LP: .... STV 81212
MC: .... CTV 81212

SLIDEWINDER.
LP: BP-2687

SWEET HOUR OF PRAYER (Rogers,Roy/Dale Evans).
Tracks: / What a friend / Light of the world is Jesus / Near to the heart of God / Sweet hour of prayer / Where he leads me / Since Jesus came into my heart / In the garden / Old rugged cross, The / Near the cross / I love to tell the story / He is so precious to me / Love lifted me.
LP: .... HAT 3088
MC: .... HATC 3088

Rogers, Sally

CLOSING THE DISTANCE (Rogers, Sally & Claudia Schmidt).
LP: .... FF 425

GENERATIONS.
LP: .... FF 493

IN THE CIRCLE OF THE SUN.
LP: .... FF 413

LOVE WILL GUIDE US.
LP: .... FF 365

SATISFIED CUSTOMERS.
LP: .... FF 381

UNCLAIMED PINT, THE.
LP: .... FF 409

Rogers, Shorty

BACK AGAIN- LIVE AT THE CONCORDE CLUB.
Tracks: / Shorty / Deep roots / Down home / Evolving / Full circle / Lift off / Warm valley / My romance.
LP: .... VL 1

BLUES EXPRESS.
LP: .... NL 89502

CLICKIN' WITH CLAX.
Tracks: / Toyland / Adam in New York / I dig Ed / Clickin' with Clax / Put the goodies on / Our song / Pete's meat / Mike's peak.
LP: .... K 50481

COLLABORATION (Rogers, Shorty/ Andre Previn).
LP: .... NL 89308

GREATEST HITS: SHORTY ROGERS.
Tracks: / Short stop / Blues for Brando / Goof and I, The / Sweetheart of Sigmund Freud / Gigi... / Martian's lullaby / Doggin' around / Morpo / Bunny / Blues express / Tickle toe / Red dog play.
LP: .... CL 89807
MC: .... CK 89807

JAZZ WALTZ (Rogers, Shorty Big Band).
Tracks: / Greensleeves / Witchcraft / Taste of honey, A.
LP: .... DS 843

LIVE FROM THE RENDEZVOUS BALLROOM 1953 (Rogers, Shorty Big Band).
LP: .... SC 801

MARTIANS STAY AT HOME.
Tracks: / Loaded / Martians stay home / Lady in red, The / Amber leaves / Bill / Barbaro / Peals / 12th Street rag / Easy.
LP: .... K 50714

MODERN SOUNDS (Rogers, Shorty/ Gerry Mulligan).
Tracks: / Popo / Didi / Four others / Over the rainbow / Apropos / Sam and the lady / Westwood walk / Ballad, A / Walking shoes / Rocker / Taking a chance on love / Flash / Simbah / Ontet.
LP: .... AFF 158
MC: .... TCAFF 158

RETURN TO RIO (Rogers, Shorty & His Giants).
LP: .... DS 899
MC: .... DSC 899

SHORT STOPS (Rogers, Shorty with His Orchestra & The Giants).
Tracks: / Powder puff / Pesky serpent, The / Bunny / Pirouette / Morpo / Diablo's dance / Mambo del crow / Indian club / Coop de graas / Infinity promenade / Short stop / Boar jibu / Contours / Tale of an African lobster / Chiquito loco / Sweetheart of Sigmund Freud / Blues for Brando / Chino / Wild one / Windswept / Topsy / Basie eyes / It's sand, man / Doggin' around / Jump for me / Over and out / Down for double / Swingin' the blues / H and J / Tickle toe / Taps Miller / Walk, don't run.
LP: .... NL 85917
MC: .... NK 85917

SHORTY ROGERS AND HIS GIANTS VOL.1 (Rogers, Shorty & His Giants).
2LP: .... PM 43549

SHORTY ROGERS SWINGS.
LP: .... NL 83012
MC: .... NK 83012

WEST COAST JAZZ.
Tracks: / Isn't it romantic? / Tricky diddler / Oh play that thing / Not really the blues / Martians go home / My heart stood still / Michele's meditation / That's what I'm talking about.
LP: .... ATL 50247

WHEREVER THE FIVE WINDS BLOW (Rogers, Shorty Quintet).
LP: .... FS 19

YESTERDAY, TODAY AND FOREVER.
Tracks: / Budo / Blood count / Yesterday, today and forever / T.N.T / Wagon wheels / Lotus bud / Have you hugged a Martian today?.
LP: .... CJ 223

Rogers, Sydney

MIRACLE WORKER.
LP: .... ETH 22145

TIPPIN' IN.
LP: .... ETH 22225

Rogerson, Jerome

SING IN THE SPIRIT (Rogerson, Jerome & Prayz).
Tracks: / Only what you do for Christ / Oh magnify the Lord / Any day now / Remember me / God is able / Sing in the Spirit / Great is Thy faithfulness / Just another day.
LP: .... WIL 3004
MC: .... ZCWIL 3004

Rogie, S.E.

PALM WINE GUITAR MUSIC.
Tracks: / Twist with the mouningstars / Please go easy with me / Do me justice / I wish I was a cowboy / She caught me red hot / Time in my life, A / My lovely Elizabeth / Advice to schoolgirls / Baby lef marah / Nyalima nyapoi / Easy baby / Man stupid being.
LP: .... COOK 010
MC: .... COOKC 010

PALM WINE SOUNDS OF S.E. ROGIE.
LP: .... PLAY 009

Rogue

FALLEN ANGELS.
LP: .... EPC 69235

LET IT GO.
LP: .... EPC 81987

WOULD YOU LET YOUR DAUGHTER.
Tracks: / My lady / Borderline / Run brother run / Completely / One to one / Bright eyes / Sad cafe / Somewhere down the line / Sixteen summers / My friend.
LP: .... ARL 5028

Rogue Male

ANIMAL MAN.
Tracks: / Progress / L.U.S.T. / Take no shit / You're on fire / Real me,The / Animal man,The / Belfast / Job centre / Low rider / Passing,The.
LP: .... MFN 68

FIRST VISIT.
LP: .... MFN 40

Rogues Gallery

ROGUES GALLERY.
LP: .... FESTIVAL 3
MC: .... FESTIVAL 3C

Roicoco

14 GREAT ALL-TIME JIVERS, VOL 3 (Various artists).
LP: .... JIVIN 184

WEEKEND AT TAHITI (Roicoco & His Music Of The Isles).
LP: .... DEE 251
MC: .... MF 251

Roidinger, Adelhard

SCHATTSEITE.
LP: .... ECM 1221

Roko

ROKO.
MC: 843 353 4
LP: 843 353 1

Rokotto

ROKOTTO.
Tracks: / Boogie on up / Tell me / Jungle fever / Shack up / Moonlight / Dancin' / For the broken hearted / Get on down / Six million dollar baby / You better / Brick house.
LP: .... ETAT 15

Roland And Oliver

ROLAND AND OLIVER (Various artists).
Tracks: / Roland and Oliver / Bell of Atri, The: *Various artists* / King Robert and the Angel: *Various artists*/ Sir Huon the brave.
MC: .... ANV 645

Roland, Gene

BAND THAT NEVER WAS, THE (See Parker, Charlie) (Roland, Gene Orchestra & Charlie Parker).

Roland, Ken

TWO SIDES OF KEN ROLAND.
LP: .... NEVLP 104

Roland, Paul

BURNT ORCHIDS.
LP: . . . . SCOOP 2

CABINET FULL OF CURIOSITIES, A.
Tracks: / Mad house / Wyndham Hill / Jumbee / Gary Gilmore's eyes / Burn / Stranger than strange / Walter the occultist / Demon in a glass case / Green glass violins (Extra track on CD only) / Berlin (Extra track on CD only) / Cairo (Extra track on CD only) / Happy families (Extra track on CD only) / Gabrielle (Extra track on CD only) / Madame Guillotine (Extra track on CD only) / Mad Elaine (Extra track on CD only).
LP: . . . . ROSE 135

DANSE MACABRE.
Tracks: / Witchfinder General / Madame Guillotine / Great Edwardian air raid, The / Hanging judge, The / Still falls the snow / Matilda mother / Gabrielle / Requiem / Buccaneers / In the opium den / Twilight of the rock.
LP: . . . . KIRI 052
LP: . . . . FC 062

DUEL.
LP: . . . . ROSE 178

HAPPY FAMILIES.
LP: . . . . ROSE 163

MASQUE.
LP: . . . . ROSE 231

Roland Rat

ALBUM OF THE CASSETTE, THE.
LP: . . . . RATL 1001

CASSETTE OF THE ALBUM, THE.
MC: . . . . ZCRAT 1001

LIVING LEGEND - THE ALBUM.
LP: . . . . REB 614
MC: . . . . ZCF 614

Roland, Walter

LUCILLE BOGAN & WALTER ROLAND (See under Bogan, Lucille).

WALTER ROLAND 1933-35 (The Remaining Sides).
LP: . . . . DLP 530

Rolfe, Nigel

ISLAND STORIES.
Tracks: / African flower / Going Boeing / Three monkeys / Made in Japan / Heartbeat drumbeat / Ostrich, The / Amerikaye / Breast mound bowl.
LP: . . . . RKLP 4
MC: . . . . RKMC 4

Rolie, Gregg

GREGG ROLIE.
Tracks: / Young love / Close my eyes / I wanna go back / Let me out / Over & over / Don't talk / Zap me / Marianne / It's only make believe / Deep blue sea.
LP: . . . . CBS 26636
MC: 40 26636

Rolinson, Chris

ELECTRIC PRAISE.
LP: . . . . DAY R 4017
MC: . . . . TC DAY 4017

ELECTRIC PRAISE VOL. 2.
LP: . . . . PR R 7501
MC: . . . . PR C 7501

Roll Along Prairie

ROLL ALONG PRAIRIE MOON (Various artists).
LP: . . . . SH 304
MC: . . . . TC SH 304

Roll On

ROLL ON (Various artists).
LP: . . . . REDTV 1

Rollens, Audley

ALL I WANT.
Tracks: / All I want / Sounds cool killer.
LP: . . . . W 1990

ROLE MODE.
LP: . . . . W 2396

Rollerball (film)

ROLLERBALL (Original soundtrack) (Various artists).
LP: . . . . LN 10291
MC: L4N 10291

ROLLERBALL (Original Soundtrack) (Various artists).
LP: 1831831
MC: 1831834

Rollercoaster

WONDERIN'.
Tracks: / I wish / Reggae woman / Higher ground / Superstition / Mr. W / Living for the city.
LP: . . . . CABLP 1006
LP: . . . . N 136

Rollers

RICOCHET.
Tracks: / Doors, bars, metal / Life on the radio / No doubt about it / Roxy lady / Ricochet / Won't you come home with me / Ride / Lay your love on the line / That's where the boys are / Set the fashion / This is your life.
LP: . . . . EPC 85004

Rollin' Sixties

ROLLIN' SIXTIES (Various artists).
Tracks: / Letter, The: *Box Tops* / Baby, let me take you home: *Animals* / Let's work together: *Canned Heat* / Billie Jo: *Rodgers, Clodagh* / Listen to the band: *Monkees* / Snoopy v the Red Baron: *Royal Guardsmen* / Baby, please don't go: *Them* / Rise and fall of Flingel Bunt, The: *Shadows* / Eleanore: *Turtles* / Everything's alright: *Mojos* / Google eye: *Nashville Teens* / Mighty Quinn: *Manfred Mann* / Days of Pearly Spencer: *McWilliams, David* / Thank U very much: *Scaffold* / In crowd, The: *Gray, Dobie* / Pictures of matchstick men: *Status Quo.*
LP: . . . . BOOMER 111
MC: . . . . BOOMER C 111

Rolling Stones

12 X 5.
Tracks: / Around and around / Confessin' the blues / Empty heart / Time is on my side / Good times, bad times / It's all over now / 2120 South Michigan Avenue / Under the boardwalk / Congratulations / Grown up wrong / If you need me / Suzie Q.
LP: . . . . LKD 5335
MC: . . . . LSLDC 5335

1965/70.
Tracks: / I can't get no satisfaction / Get off my cloud / As tears go by / 19th nervous breakdown / Out of time / Lady Jane / Let's spend the night together / Paint it black / Ruby Tuesday / Yesterday's papers / Jumpin' Jack Flash / Sympathy for the devil / Honky tonk women / Gimme shelter.
LP: 6495098
MC: 7195098

AFTERMATH.
Tracks: / Mother's little helper / Stupid girl / Lady Jane / Under my thumb / Doncha brother me / Going home / Flight 505 / High and dry / Out of time (long version) / It's not easy / I am waiting / Take it or leave it / Think / What to do.
LP: . . . . SKDL 4786
LP: . . . . LK 4786

BEGGARS BANQUET.
Tracks: / Sympathy for the devil / No expectations / Dear Doctor / Parachute woman / Jigsaw puzzle / Street fighting man / Prodigal son / Stray cat blues / Factory girl / Salt of the earth.
LP: . . . . SKDL 4955
MC: . . . . KSKC 4955
LP: . . . . SKL 49955

BETWEEN THE BUTTONS.
Tracks: / Let's spend the night together / Yesterday's papers / Ruby Tuesday / Connection / She smiled sweetly / Cool calm and collected / All sold out / My obsession / Who's been sleeping here / Complicated / Miss Amanda Jones / Something happened to me yesterday.
LP: . . . . SKL 4852

BIG HITS (HIGH TIDE AND GREEN GRASS).
Tracks: / Have you seen your mother, baby, standing in the shadow / Paint it black / It's all over now / Last time, The / Heart of stone / Not fade away / Come on / Satisfaction / Get off my cloud / As tears go by / 19th nervous breakdown / Lady Jane / Time is on my side / Little red rooster.
LP: . . . . TXS 101
MC: . . . . KTXCS 101

BIG HITS VOL.2 (Through the past darkly).
LP: . . . . SKL 5019

BLACK AND BLUE.
Tracks: / Hot stuff / Hand of fate, The / Cherry oh baby / Memory motel / Hey Negrita melody / Fool to cry / Crazy mama.
LP: 4502031
MC: 4502034
LP: . . . . COC 59106
LP: . . . . CUN 59106

DECEMBER'S CHILDREN (AND EVERYBODY'S).
Tracks: / She said yeah / Talkin' bout you / You better move on / Look what you've done / Singer not the song, The / Route 66 / Get off my cloud / I'm free / As tears go by / Gotta get away / Blue turns to grey / I'm moving on (live).
LP: 6.24314

DIRTY WORK.
Tracks: / One hit / Fight / Harlem shuffle / Hold back / Too rude / Winning ugly / Back to zero / Dirty work / Had it with you / Sleep tonight.
LP: . . . . CBS 86321
MC: 40 86321
LP: . . . . CUN 86321
LP: 4659531
MC: 4659534

EMOTIONAL RESCUE.
Tracks: / Summer romance / Send it to me / Let me go / Indian girl / Where the boys go / Down in the hole / Emotional rescue / She's so cold / All about you.
LP: . . . . CUN 39111
LP: 4502061
MC: 4502064

EXILE ON MAIN STREET.
Tracks: / Rocks off / Rip this joint / Casino boogie / Tumbling dice / Sweet Virginia / Torn and frayed / Sweet black angel / Loving cup / Shake your hips.
LP: 4501961
MC: 4501964
LP: . . . . COC 69100
2LP: . . . . CUNSP 69100

FIRST EIGHT ALBUMS.
LPS: . . . . ROLL 1

FLASHPOINT.
Tracks: / Intro (continental drift) / Start me up / Sad sad sad / Miss you / Ruby Tuesday / You can't always get what you want / Factory girl / Little red rooster / Paint it black / Sympathy for the devil / Brown sugar / Jumpin' Jack Flash / Satisfaction / High wire / Sex drive / Rock and a hard place (Only on MC and CD.) / Can't be seen (Only on MC and CD.).
LP: 4681351
MC: 4681354

GET STONED.
2LP: . . . . ADEP 32

GET YER YA-YA'S OUT (Rolling Stones live in concert).
Tracks: / Jumpin' Jack Flash / Carol / Stray cat blues / Love in vain / Midnight rambler / Sympathy for the devil / Live with me / Little Queenie / Honky tonk women / Street fighting man.
LP: . . . . SKL 5065

GIMME SHELTER.
Tracks: / Jumpin' Jack Flash / Love in vain / Honky tonk women / Street fighting man / Sympathy for the Devil / Gimme shelter / Under my thumb / Time is on my side / I've been loving you too long / Fortune teller / Lady Jane / Satisfaction.
MC: . . . . KSKC 5101
LP: . . . . SKL 5101

GOATS HEAD SOUP.
Tracks: / Dancing with Mr. D / 100 years ago / Coming down again / Doo doo doo doo (Heartbreaker) / Angie / Silver train / Hide your love / Winter / Can you hear the music / Star star.
LP: 4502071
MC: 4502074
LP: . . . . COC 59101
LP: . . . . CUN 59101

HOT ROCKS 1964-1971.
Tracks: / (I can't get no) satisfaction / Get off my cloud / Paint it black / Under my thumb / Ruby Tuesday / Let's spend the night together / Jumpin' Jack Flash / Sympathy for the devil / Honky tonk women / Gimme shelter / You can't always get what you want / Brown sugar / Time is on my side / Heart of stone / Play with fire / As tears go by / Mother's little helper / 19th nervous breakdown / Street fighting man / Midnight rambler / Wild horses.
MCSET: 8201404
2LP: 8201401

(I CAN'T GET NO) SATISFACTION (LP).
Tracks: / (I can't get no) satisfaction / Tell me / It's all over now / Lady Jane / Let's spend the night together / Have you seen your mother, baby, standing in the shadow / Time is on my side / We love you / Honky tonk women / 19th nervous breakdown / Paint it black / Street fighting man / As tears go by / Last time, The / Get off my cloud / Jumpin' Jack Flash.
LP: 8101711
MC: 8101714

IT'S ONLY ROCK 'N' ROLL.
Tracks: / If you can't rock me / Ain't too proud to beg / It's only rock 'n' roll / Till the next goodbye / Luxury / Time waits for no one / Dance little sister / If you really want to / Short and curlies / Fingerprint file.
LP: 4502021
MC: 4502024
LP: . . . . COC 59103
LP: . . . . CUN 59103

LET IT BLEED.
Tracks: / Gimmi shelter / Love in vain / Country honk / Live with me / Let it bleed / Midnight rambler / You got the silver / Monkey man / You can't always get what you want.
LP: . . . . SKL 5025
MC: . . . . KSKC 5025

LOVE YOU LIVE.
Tracks: / Fanfare for the common man / Honky tonk women / If you can't rock me / Get off my cloud / Happy / Hot stuff / Star star / Tumbling dice / Fingerprint file / You gotta move / You can't always get what you want.
LP: 4502081
MC: 4502084
LP: . . . . COC 89101
2LP: . . . . CUNSP 69101

MADE IN THE SHADE.
Tracks: / Brown sugar / Tumbling dice / Happy / Dance little sister / Wild horses / Angie / Bitch / It's only rock 'n' roll / Doo doo doo doo (heartbreaker) / Rip this joint.
LP: 4502011
MC: 4502014

METAMORPHOSIS.
LP: . . . . SKL 5212

MILESTONES.
LP: . . . . SKL 5098

MORE HOT ROCKS (Big hits and fazed cookies).
Tracks: / Tell me / Not fade away / Last time, The / It's all over now / Good times, bad times / I'm free / Out of time / Lady Jane / Sittin' on a fence / Have you seen your mother, baby, standing in the shadow / Dandelion / We love you / She's a rainbow / 2000 light years from home / Child of the moon / No expectations / Let it bleed / What to do / Money / Come on / Fortune teller / Poison ivy / Bye bye Johnny / I can't be satisfied / Long long while.
2LP: 8201431
MC: 8201434

MUSIC AND MEDIA INTERVIEW PICTURE DISC.
LPPD: . . . . RS 2023

MUSIC FOR THE MILLIONS.
Tracks: / Route 66 / I just want to make love to you / Honest I do / I need you, baby / Now I've got a witness / Little by little / I'm a king bee / Carol / Tell me / Can I get a witness? / You can make it if you try / Walking the dog.
LP: 6495 108
MC: 7195 108

OUT OF OUR HEADS.
Tracks: / She said 'yeah' / Mercy mercy / Hitch hike / That's how strong my love is / Good times / Gotta get away / Talkin bout you / Cry to me / Oh baby / Heart of stone / Under assistant west coast promotion man, The / I'm free.
LP: . . . . LKD 5336
MC: . . . . LSLDC 5336
LP: . . . . LK 4733

PRECIOUS STONES.
LPPD: . . . . PD 10005

REWIND (1971-1984) (Best of the Rolling Stones).
Tracks: / Brown sugar / Undercover of the night / Start me up / Tumbling dice / It's only rock n roll / She's so cold / Hang fire / Miss you / Beast of burden / Fool to cry / Waiting on a friend / Angie / Emotional rescue.
LP: . . . . CUN 1
LP: . . . . EJ 2601061
MC: 4501994
LP: 4501991

ROCK 'N' ROLLING STONES.
LP: . . . . SKL 5149

ROLLED GOLD.
Tracks: / Come on / I wanna be your man / Not fade away / Carol / It's all over now / Little red rooster / Time is on my side / Last time, The / Satisfaction / Get off my cloud / 19th nervous breakdown / As tears go by / Under my thumb / Lady Jane / Out of time / Paint it black / Have you seen your mother, baby, standing in the shadow / Let's spend the night together / Ruby Tuesday / Yesterday's papers / We love you / She's a rainbow / Jumpin' Jack Flash / Honky tonk women / Sympathy for the devil / Street fighting man / Midnight rambler / Gimme shelter.
2LP: . . . . ROST 1/2
MCSET: K2R 26

ROLLING STONES.
Tracks: / Route 66 / I just want to make love to you / Honest I do / I need you baby / Now i've got a witness / Little by little / I'm a king bee / Carol / Tell me (you're coming back) / Can I get a witness / You can make it if you try / Walking the dog.
LP: . . . . LKD 4605
MC: . . . . KSDC 4605
LP: . . . . LK 4605
MC: 8200474
LP: 8200471

ROLLING STONES IN CONCERT.
Tracks: / Under my thumb / Get off my cloud / Lady Jane / Not fade away / Last time, The / 19th nervous breakdown.
2LP: DT6 28565

MCSET: CS4 28565
LP: 6640037

ROLLING STONES: INTERVIEW PICTURE DISC.
LPPD: BAK 2109

ROLLING STONES PICTURE DISC.
Tracks: / Honky tonk women / Get off my cloud / Little Queenie / Jumpin' Jack Flash / Satisfaction / Under my thumb / Last time, The / Sympathy for the devil / Let's spend the night together / Carol.
LP: 361 30010

ROLLING STONES, VOL 2.
Tracks: / Everybody needs somebody to love / Down home girl / You can't catch me / Time is on my side / What a shame / Grown up wrong / Down the road apiece / Under the boardwalk / I can't be satisfied / Pain in my heart / Off the hook / Suzie Q.
LP: SKL 3661
MC: KSKC 4661
LP: LK 4661

SINGLES COLLECTION: THE LONDON YEARS.
Tracks: / Come on / I want to be loved / I wanna be your man / Stoned / Not fade away / Little by little / It's all over now / Good times, bad times / Tell me / I just want to make love to you / Time is on my side / Congratulations / Little red rooster / Off the hook / Heart of stone / What a shame / Last time, The / Play with fire / (I can't get no) satisfaction / Under assistant West coast promotion man / Spider and the fly / Get off my cloud / I'm free / Singer not the song, The / As tears go by / Gotta get away / 19th nervous breakdown / Sad day / Paint it black / Stupid girl / Long long while / Mother's little helper / Lady Jane / Have you seen your mother, baby, standing in the shadow / Who's driving your plane / Let's spend the night together / Ruby Tuesday / We love you / Dandelion / She's a rainbow / 2000 light years from home / In another land / Lantern, The / Jumpin' Jack flash / Child of the moon / Street fighting man / No expectations / Surprise, surprise / Honky tonk women / You can't always get what you want / Memo from Turner / Brown sugar / Wild horses / I don't know why / Try a little harder / Out of time / Jiving sister Fanny / Sympathy for the devil.
LPS: 8209001
MCSET: 8209004

SLOW ROLLERS.
Tracks: / You can't always get what you want / Take it or leave it / You better move on / Time is on my side / Pain in my heart / Dear doctor / As tears go by / Ruby Tuesday / Play with fire / Lady Jane / Sittin' on the fence / Backstreet girl / Under the boardwalk / Heart of stone.
LP: TAB 30
MC: KTBC 30

SOLID ROCK.
Tracks: / Carol / Route 66 / Fortune teller / I wanna be your man / Poison Ivy / Not fade away / Satisfaction / Get off my cloud / Jumpin' Jack Flash / Connection / All sold out / Citadel / Parachute woman / Live with me / Honky tonk women.
LP: TAB 1
MC: KTBC 1

SOME GIRLS.
Tracks: / Miss you / When the whip comes down / Just my imagination / Some girls / Lies / Faraway eyes / Respectable / Before they make me run / Beast of burden / Shattered.
LP: 4501971
MC: 4501974
LP: CUN 39108

STEEL WHEELS.
Tracks: / Sad, sad, sad / Mixed emotions / Terrifying / Hold on to your hat / Hearts for sale / Blinded by love / Rock and a hard place / Can't be seen / Almost hear you sigh / Continental drift / Break the spell / Slipping away.
LP: 4657521
MC: 4657524

STICKY FINGERS.
Tracks: / Brown sugar / Sway / Wild horses / Can't you hear me knocking? / You gotta move / Bitch / I got the blues / Sister morphine / Dead flowers / Moonlight mile.
LP: 4501951
MC: 4501954
LP: COC 59100
LP: CUN 59100

STILL LIFE (American Concert 1981).
Tracks: / Under my thumb / Let's spend the night together / Shattered / Twenty flight rock / Let me go / Time is on my side / Just my imagination / Start me up / Satisfaction / Take the A train / Star spangled banner.
LP: CUN 39115
LP: 4502041
MC: 4502044

STONE AGE.
LP: SKL 5084

STONED ALCHEMY (See under Stoned Alchemy) (Various artists).

STONES STORY VOL.1.
Tracks: / Come one / I wanna be your man / Not fade away / Carol / It's all over now / Little red rooster / Time is on my side / Last time, The / Satisfaction / Get off my cloud / 19th nervous breakdown / As tears go by / Under my thumb / Lady Jane / Out of time / Paint it black / Have you seen your mother, baby, standing in the shadow / Let's spend the night together / Ruby Tuesday / Yesterday's papers / We love you / She's my rainbow / Jumpin' Jack Flash / Honky tonk women / Sympathy for the devil / Street fighting man / Midnight rambler / Gimme shelter.
2LP: 6645407
MCSET: 7582102

STONES STORY VOL.2.
Tracks: / Tell me / Everybody needs somebody / Play with fire / Mother's little helper / Heart of stone / No expectations / Surprise surprise / High and dry / Something happened to me yesterday / Sittin' on the fence / 2000 light years from home / She smiled sweetly / Sing this all together / Take it or leave it / Dandelion / I just want to make love to you / Off the hook / Stray cat blues / Connection / Cool calm and collected / I am waiting / Dear doctor / Flight 505 / Under assistant west coast promotion man, The / Under assistant West Coast promotion man / All sold out / You can't always get what you want.
2LP: 6640030
MCSET: 7540030

STONES STORY VOL.3.
Tracks: / Stupid girl / M 6 obsession / Under the boardwalk / Stoned / Pain in my heart / Ride on baby / Backstreet girl / Miss Amanda Jones / Route 66 / Empty heart / She said yeah / Doncha bother me / Fortune teller / Going home / Complicated / Think / 2120 South Michigan Avenue / My girl / It's not easy / Can I get a witness / What to do / Around and around / Poison ivy / Who's been sleeping here / Please go home / Blue turns to grey / One more try / Cry to me / You better move on / Spider and the fly, The.
MCSET: 7540041
2LP: 6640041

STORY OF THE STONES.
Tracks: / Jumpin' Jack Flash / Route 66 / I wanna be your man / Mothers little helper / You can't always get what you want / Get off my cloud / Carol / Satisfaction / It's all over now / Time is on my side / Play with fire / Off the hook / Little red rooster / Let it bleed / Standing in the shadows / Let's spend the night together / 19th nervous breakdown / Not fade away / Walking the dog / Heart of stone / Ruby Tuesday / Street fighting man / Paint it black / Last time, The / We love you / You better move on / Over my shoulder / Come on / I wanna make love to you / Honky tonk women.
LP: NE 1201
MC: CE 2201

SUCKING IN THE SEVENTIES.
Tracks: / Shattered / Everything is turning to gold / Hot stuff / Time waits for no one / Fool to cry / Mannish boy / When the whip comes down / If I was a dancer / Crazy mama / Beast of burden.
LP: CUNS 39112
LP: 4502051
MC: 4502054

TATTOO YOU.
Tracks: / Start me up / Hang fire / Slave / Little T. & A. / Black limousine / No use in crying / Neighbours / Worried about you / Tops / Heaven / Waiting for a friend.
LP: CUNS 39114
LP: 4501981
MC: 4501984

THEIR SATANIC MAJESTIES REQUEST.
Tracks: / Citadel / In another land / Sing this all together (see what happens) / She's a rainbow / Lantern, The / Gomper / 2,000 light years from home / On with the show / 2,000 man.
LP: TXS 103
MC: 8201294
LP: 8201291

TIME WAITS FOR NO-ONE (Anthology 1971-1977).
Tracks: / Time waits for no-one / Bitch / All down the line / Dancing with Mr. D / Angie / Star star / If you can't rock me / Get off my cloud / Hand of fate, The / Crazy mama / Fool to try.
LP: COC 59107

TWENTY SUPER HITS.
Tracks: / Dandelion / Heart of stone / Talkin' 'bout you / Little by little / Bye bye Johnny / Something happened to me yesterday / You better move on / My girl / If you need me / Child of the moon / Under assistant west coast promotion man, The / I just wanna make love to you / Walking the dog / Under the boardwalk / Honest I do.
LP: 6.23502

UNDER COVER.
Tracks: / Too much blood / Pretty beat up / Too tough / All the way down / It must be hell / Undercover of the night / She was hot / Tie you up (The pain of love) / Wanna hold you / Feel on baby.
LP: ATAK 61
MC: TCATAK 61
LP: 4502001
MC: 4502004
LP: CUN 1654361

Rollini, Adrian

1938-40 (Rollini, Adrian His Quintet His Trio).
LP: M 8036

Rollins Band

TURNED ON - LIVE IN VIENNA, AUSTRIA.
LP: EFA 16178401

Rollins, Henry

DO IT (Rollins, Henry Band).
LP: SERVM 004

HARD VOLUME.
LP: SERV 010LP

HOT ANIMAL MACHINE.
LP: SAVE 024

LIFETIME (Rollins, Henry Band).
Tracks: / Burned beyond recognition / What am I doing here? / 1,000 times beyond / Lovely / Wreckage / Gun in mouth blues / You look at you / If you're alive / Turned out.
LP: SAVE 065

LIVE- HENRY ROLLINS AND GORE (Rollins, Henry & Gore).
LP: EKSAKT 034

READINGS - SWITZERLAND.
MC: ACTIONK 001

SWEAT BOX.
LPS: TXH 015

Rollins, Sonny

ALFIE.
LP: MCA 39107
MC: MCAC 39107

ALL THE THINGS YOU ARE.
Tracks: / Yesterdays / Summertime / Lover man / 'Round midnight / Afternoon in Paris / It could happen to you / All the things you are / Just friends / At McKies / Now's the time / My one and only love / Trav'lin light.
LP: NL 82179
MC: NK 82179

ALTERNATE TAKES.
Tracks: / I'm an old cowhand / Come, gone / Way out west / Song is you / You / I've found a new baby.
LP: COP 034

ALTERNATIVE ROLLINS, THE (With Herbie Hancock, Ron Carter, Jim Hall).
Tracks: / Now is the time / Django / Fifty Second Street theme / I remember Clifford / St. Thomas / Afternoon in Paris / Trav'lin' light / Winter in wonderland / Four / When you wish upon a star.
2LP: PL 43268

BEST OF SONNY ROLLINS.
Tracks: / Decision / Poor butterfly / Why don't I (CD only.) / Misterioso / Tune up / How are things in Glocca Morra / Sonnymoon for two / Softly as in a morning sunrise (CD only.) / Striver's row (CD only.).
LP: B1 93203
LP: 793 203 1

BRASS AND TRIO.
Tracks: / Who cares / Love is a simple thing / Grand street / Far out East / What's my name? / If you were the only girl in the world / Manhattan / Body and soul.
LP: 2304 192

CONTEMPORARY LEADERS (Rollins, Sonny/Barney Kessel).
LP: COP 018

DANCING IN THE DARK.
Tracks: / Just Once / O T Y O G / Promise, The / I'll String Along With You / Allison.
LP: MX 9155
MC: MXC 9155

DON'T STOP THE CARNIVAL.
Tracks: / Don't stop the carnival / Silver city / Autumn nocturne / Camel / Nobody else but me / Non cents / Child's prayer, A / President Hayes / Sais.
2LP: M 55005

EAST BROADWAY RUN DOWN.
Tracks: / East Broadway run down / Blessings in diguise / We kiss in a shadow.
LP: JAS 69

FREEDOM SUITE.
Tracks: / Some day I'll find you / Till there was you / Will you still be mine / Shadow waltz.
LP: RLP 258
MC: RLPC 258

GRAZ CONCERT 1963 (see under Roach, Max) (Rollins, Sonny Trio & Max Roach Quintet).

IN EUROPE 1963, VOL. 1.
Tracks: / On Green Dolphin Street / Introduction / Without a song / Oleo / Sonny's tune / Sonny's tune (second version).
LP: UJ 29

IN SWEDEN 1959.
Tracks: / Another me, another you / I've told every little star / Stay as good as you are / Oleo / It don't mean a thing / Paul's pal / Love letters.
LP: INGO 9

ISLAND LADY.
LP: LPPS 111 07

LIVE IN AIX EN PROVENCE 1959.
Tracks: / Woddin' you / But not for me / Ladybird.
LP: RJ 502

LIVE IN EUROPE.
LP: UJ 22

LIVE IN JAPAN.
LP: GSS 4

LOVE AT FIRST SIGHT.
Tracks: / Little lulu / Dream that we fell out of / Strode rode / Very thought of you, The / Caress / Double feature.
LP: M 9098

MASTERS OF JAZZ.
LP: CL 42874

NEWK'S TIME.
Tracks: / Tune up / Asiatic races / Wonderful wonderful / Surrey with the fringe on top / Blues for Philly Joe / Namely you.
LP: BST 84001
LP: BNS 40011

NIGHT AT THE VILLAGE VANGUARD.
Tracks: / Old devil moon / Sonnymoon for two / Night in Tunisia / Softly as in a morning sunrise / Strivers Row / I can't get started.
LP: BST 81581
MC: 4BN 81581

NIGHT AT THE VILLAGE VANGUARD VOL.1.
Tracks: / Night in Tunisia / I've got you under my skin / Softly as in a morning sunrise / Four / Woody 'n' you / Old devil moon.
LP: BNS 40010

NO PROBLEM.
Tracks: / No problem / Here you come again / Jo Jo / Coconut bread / Penny saved / Illusions / Joyous lake.
LP: M 9104

ON IMPULSE.
Tracks: / On Green Dolphin Street / Everything happens to me / Hold 'em Joe / Blue room / Three little words.
LP: JAS 2
MC: JAS C2

ON THE OUTSIDE.
LP: NL 82496
MC: NK 82496

PRESTIGE YEARS VOL. 1 (1949-53).
Tracks: / Elysee (alternate take) / Elysee / Opus 5 / Hi-lo (alternate take) / Fox hunt, The / Morpheus / Down / Blue room / Whispering / I know / My old flame / It's only a paper moon / Time on my hands / Mambo bounce / This love of mine / Shadrack / Slow boat to China / With a song in my heart / Scoops / Newk's fadeaway / Compulsion / Serpent's tooth / Serpent's tooth (alternate take) / Round midnight / In a sentimental mood / Stopper, The / Almost like being in love / No moe / Let's call this / Think of one / Think of one (alternate take) / Friday the 13th.
LP: PRE 4001

PRESTIGE YEARS VOL. 2 (1954-56).
Tracks: / Soft shoe / Confab in tempo / I'll take romance / Airegin / Oleo / But not for me / But not for me (alternate take) / Doxy / Movin' out / Swingin' for Bumsy / Silk 'n' satin / Solid / I want to be happy / Way you look tonight / More than you know / There's no business like show business / Paradox / Raincheck / There are such things / It's alright with me / In your own sweet way / No line /

Weird blues / I feel a song coming on / Pent-up house / Valse hot / Kiss and run / Count your blessings.
LP: . . . . **PRE 4002**

PRESTIGE YEARS VOL. 3 (1956).
Tracks: / My reverie / Most beautiful girl in the world, The / Paul's pal / When your lover has gone / Tenor madness / You don't know what love is / St. Thomas / Strode rode / Blue seven / Moritat / I've grown accustomed to her face / Kids know / House I love in, The / Bird medley / I remember you / Melancholy baby / Old folks / They can't take that away from me / Just friends / My little suede shoes / Star eyes / B swift / My ideal / Sonny boy / Two different worlds / Ee-ah / B quick.
LP: . . . . **PRE 4003**

QUARTET, THE.
Tracks: / God bless the child / John S. / You do something to me / Where are you / Without a song / Bridge, The / If ever I would leave you / Brown skin gal / Don't stop the carnival / Night has a thousand eyes, The / My ship / Love letters / Long ago (and far away) (Featuring Jim Hall, guitar.).
LP: . . . . **PL 85634**
MC: . . . . **PK 85634**

ROLLINS PLAYS FOR BIRD (Rollins, Sonny Quintet).
LP: . . . . **OJC 214**

SAXOPHONE COLOSSUS AND MORE.
Tracks: / Moritat / Blue seven / Strode rode / St. Thomas / You don't know what love is / Kids know / House I live in, The / I've grown accustomed to her face / Star eyes / I feel a song coming on / Pent up house / Kiss and run.
2LP: . . . . **PR 24050**

SOLO ALBUM, THE.
Tracks: / Soloscope (Part 1) / Sonny Rollins' tenor saxophone / Soloscope (Part 2).
LP: . . . . **M 9137**

SONNY ROLLINS AND THAD JONES QUINTETS (Rollins, Sonny & Thad Jones Quintets).
LP: . . . . **ZET 704**

SONNY ROLLINS IN STOCKHOLM 1959.
LP: . . . . **DRLP 73**

SONNY ROLLINS PLUS FOUR (Rollins, Sonny/Clifford Brown).
LP: . . . . **OJC 243**

SONNY ROLLINS QUINTET/ THAD JONES AND HIS ORCHESTRA.
LP: . . . . **FS 261**

SONNY ROLLINS VOL.1.
Tracks: / Decision / Bluesnote / How are things in Glocca Morra / Plain Jane / Sonnysphere.
LP: . . . . **BST 81542**
MC: . . . . **TCBST 81542**
LP: . . . . **BLP 1542**

SONNY ROLLINS VOL.2.
Tracks: / Why don't I / Wail march / Misterioso / Reflections / You stepped out of a dream / Poor butterfly.
MC: **4BN 81558**
LP: . . . . **BST 81558**
LP: . . . . **BLP 1558**

SOUND OF SONNY, THE.
Tracks: / Last time I saw Paris, The / Toot toot tootsie / Dearly beloved / Cutie / Mangoes / Just in time / What is there to say / Every time we say goodbye / It could happen to you.
LP: . . . . **RLP 241**

STUTTGART 1963 CONCERT.
LP: . . . . **JC 106**

TOUR DE FORCE.
LP: . . . . **OJC 095**

WAY OUT WEST.
Tracks: / I'm an old cowhand / Solitude / Come gone / Wagon wheels / There is no greater love / Way out West.
LP: . . . . **COP 006**

Rollin'Thunder

HOWL.
Tracks: / Atlantic to Pacific / B.A.R.B. / Pink and greens / Going South / Bloodstained legends / Shadow fall / Immortal soul / Street of lost causes / Once.
LP: . . . . **SHARP 039**

LONESOME.
LP: . . . . **NICK 002**

Romaine, Anne

GETTIN' ON COUNTRY.
LP: . . . . **ROUNDER 3009**

TAKE A STAND.
LP: . . . . **FF 323**

Roman Grey

EDGE OF THE SHADOW.
LP: . . . . **EM 9516 1**

Roman Holliday

COOKIN' ON THE ROOF.
Tracks: / Don't try to stop it / Motor mania / Stand by / Cookin' on the roof / Serious situation / Jive dive.
LP: . . . . **HIP 9**
MC: . . . . **HIPC 9**

Roman, Lyn

WANTED.
Tracks: / Faith / Billy The Kid / Love slave / Different kind of sweet, A / Born to live / We belong together / Don't look back.
LP: . . . . **ICH 1015**

Roman Scandals

ROMAN SCANDALS (see under Cantor, Eddie) (Cantor, Eddie).

Romance, Romance

ROMANCE, ROMANCE (Original Broadway Cast) (Various artists).
Tracks: / Little comedy, The: *Various artists* / Goodbye Emily: *Various artists* / I'll always remember the song: *Various artists* / Night it had to end, The: *Various artists* / Think of the odds: *Various artists* / Let's not talk about it: *Various artists* / Through a window: *Various artists* / Small craft warnings: *Various* artists / So glad I married her: *Various artists* / Letters: *Various artists* / It's not too late: *Various* artists / Oh what a performance: *Various artists* / Women on Vienna: *Various artists* / Summer share: *Various* artists / Plans A & B: *Various artists* / Words he doesn't say: *Various artists* / Romantic notions: *Various artists* / Romance romance: *Various artists.*
LP: . . . . **TER 1161**
MC: . . . . **ZCTER 1161**

Romancers

ROMANCERS (Saki) read by Hugh Burden) (Various artists).
MC: . . . . **SA 5**

Romanian Virtuosi

CONCERT DES VIRTUOSES ROUMAINS.
LP: . . . . **CELLIER 006**

Romano, Joe

AND FINALLY ROMANO.
Tracks: / Chance It / Love Nest, The / Dance of the Infidels / U.M.M.G. / Joe Cheeze / Daydreams / Like blues.
LP: . . . . **FS 311**

Romanos, Carlos

LATIN-THE MODERN WAY (Romanos, Carlos & his orchestra).
LP: . . . . **DS 033**

TIJUANA FEVER (Romanos, Carlos & Latin Magic).
LP: . . . . **SAV 135**

Romans

LAST DAYS AT THE RANGE.
LP: **2156 1**

TRIGGER HAPPY.
LP: . . . . **GRP 006**

Romantic...

ROMANTIC YEARS, THE (Various artists).
LP: . . . . **RLP 776**

Romantics

NATIONAL BREAKOUT.
Tracks: / Tomboy / Forever yours / Stone pony / New cover story / Night like this, A / National breakout / 21 and over / I can't tell you anything / Take me out of the rain / Friday at the hideout / Poor little rich girl.
LP: . . . . **EPC 84716**

ROMANTICS.
Tracks: / When I look in your eyes / Tell it to Carrie / First in line / Keep in touch / Girl next door / What I like about you / She's got everything / Till I see you again / Hung on you / Little white lies / Gimme one more chance.
LP: . . . . **EPC 84095**

Romantique Orchestra

BEAUTIFUL LOVE SONGS COLLECTION, THE.
Tracks: / Do that to me one more time / Ebony and ivory / Just when I needed you most / If you leave me now / Lately / What a fool believes / Your song / When I need you / Nights in white satin / Lyin' eyes / She's out of my life / One day in your life / My simple heart / Mandy / I only want to be with you / I made it through the rain / She's gone / Hopelessly devoted to you / After the love is gone / One day I'll fly away / Evergreen / Sometimes when we touch / Three times a lady / 50 ways to leave your lover.
2LP: . . . . **CR 092**
MCSET: . . . . **CRT 092**

BEAUTIFUL WALTZ COLLECTION, THE.
2LP: . . . . **CR 097**
MCSET: . . . . **CRT 097**

Romany tales

ROMANY TALES (Various artists).
Tracks: / Romany tales: *Various artists* / Carrot top: *Various artists* / Black lopez: *Various artists*/ Mayfly, The: *Various artists* / Magic peg-basket, The: *Various artists* / Bird-woman, The: *Various artists*/ Romany who talked to animals, The: *Various artists.*
MC: . . . . **ANV 639**

Rome, Harold

TOUCH OF ROME, A.
LP: . . . . **MRS 907**

Rome Symphony

BEN HUR (See under Ben Hur).

Romeo & Juliet

ROMEO AND JULIET (See under Royal Ballet) (Royal Ballet).

ROMEO AND JULIET (See under Shakespeare, William) (Marlowe Dramatic Society).

ROMEO & JULIET (VIDEO) (see under Prokofiev (composer)) (Bolshoi Ballet).

Romeo & Juliet (bk)

ROMEO AND JULIET (see under Shakespeare, William) (Various artists).

Romeo & Juliet (film)

ROMEO AND JULIET (ZEFFIRELLI PRODUCTION) (Rota, Nino).
MC: **92057.4**

Romeo, Max

HOLDING OUT MY LOVE TO YOU.
LP: . . . . **ABL 10044**
LP: . . . . **SHAN 43002**

I LOVE MY MUSIC.
LP: . . . . **SGL 106**

OWEN GRAY MEETS MAX ROMEO (see Gray, Owen) (Romeo, Max & Owen Gray).

WAR IN A BABYLON.
Tracks: / One step forward / Uptown babies / Chase the devil / War ina Babylon / Norman / Stealin' / Tan and see / Smokey room / Smile out of style.
LP: . . . . **ILPS 9392**
MC: . . . . **RRCT 23**

Romeo Void

BENEFACTOR.
Tracks: / Never say never / Wrap it up / Flashflood / Undercover kept / Ventilation / Chinatown / Orange / Shake the hands of time / SOS.
LP: . . . . **CBS 85929**

INSTINCTS.
Tracks: / Out on my own / Just too easy / Billy's birthday / Going to neon / Six days and one / Girl in trouble (is a temporary thing), A / Say no / Your life is a lie / Instincts.
LP: . . . . **CBS 25969**

Romeo's Daughter

ROMEO'S DAUGHTER.
Tracks: / Heaven in the back seat / I cry myself to sleep at night / Hymn (look through golden eyes) / Inside out / Colour you a smile / Don't break my heart / Wild child / Velvet tongue / I like what I see.
LP: . . . . **HIP 69**
MC: . . . . **HIPC 69**

Romero, Celedonio

PROGRAM OF SPANISH GUITAR MUSIC, A (Romero, Celedonio & His Son Celin Romero).
Tracks: / Serenata Esponola / Mazurka / Minuetto / Leyenda / Fantasia / Zapateado classico / Pavana and Danza / Sarabanda and Bouree / Rumores de la caleta / Estudio in B minor / El noi de la mere / El testamento de amelia.
LP: **1008 502**

Romero, Pepe

FLAMENCO.
Tracks: / Noche en malaga / Seguiri yas / Medias Granadinas / Fandangos de Huelva / Alegrias por Rosas / Bulerias / Soleares / Alegrias por fiesta / Farrucas / Zapateado del Perchel.
LP: **1009 004**

Romero, Raoul

MUSIC OF RR LAS VEGAS JAZZ ORCHESTRA.
LP: . . . . **SB 2031**

Romiosini

PICTURES OF CRETE.
LP: . . . . **EULP 1049**
MC: . . . . **EUMC 1049**

SONG AND DANCES FROM GREECE.
LP: . . . . **EULP 1005**

Romney, Erick

LUMIERE L'ANMOU.
LP: . . . . **KL 053**

Ronald, Terry

ROMA.
LP: . . . . **MCA 10241**
MC: . . . . **MCAC 10241**

Ronalde, Ronnie

HAPPY WHISTLER, THE.
Tracks: / Mockin' Bird Hill / I miss my Swiss / Yodeling whistler / Bells across the meadow / MacNamara's band / Dream of Olwen / If I were a blackbird / On wings of song / Skater's waltz / Happy whistler, The / Il Bacio / Yodelling waltz / Song of the mountains / Pleasant peasant / Tritsch tratsch polka / When you were sweet sixteen / I left my heart in an English garden / Ave Maria.
LP: . . . . **SH 395**
MC: . . . . **TC SH 395**

Ronda Dos Quatro

PORTUGAL - CHANTS ET DANSES.
Tracks: / Chula velha / Idanha-a-nova / Gota / O segador / O sapatinho me aperta / Maragato / Lib'ra nos e domine / Minha rua e um jardim / Saias / Romance mineta / Chula batida / Milho grosso / Quando o menino nasceu / Entrudo.
LP: . . . . **ARN 33793**
MC: . . . . **ARN 433793**

Rondat, Patrick

JUST FOR FUN.
LP: . . . . **GRUB 16**
MC: . . . . **TGRUB 16**

RAPE OF THE EARTH.
Tracks: / Rape of the earth.
LP: . . . . **GRUB 20**
MC: . . . . **TGRUB 20**

Rondo Veneziano

GENIUS OF VENICE.
LP: . . . . **RON 2**
MC: . . . . **ZCRON 2**

NOT QUITE JERUSALEM (FILM) (See under Not Quite Jerusalem).

ODISSEA.
LP: . . . . **RON 3**
MC: . . . . **ZCRON 3**

VENICE IN PERIL.
LP: . . . . **RON 1**
MC: . . . . **ZCRON 1**

Ronettes

COLPIX YEARS 1961-63, THE.
LP: **000156**

FROSTY THE SNOWMAN (see under Phil Spector EP).

RONETTES SING THEIR GREATEST HITS.
LP: **2307 003**

Ronk, Dave Van

SOMEBODY ELSE NOT ME.
LP: . . . . **PH 1065**
MC: . . . . **PH 1065C**

Ronmar Accordion...

SOUNDS ACCORDION (Ronmar Accordion Orchestra).
Tracks: / Thunderer march, The / Bonanza two-step / Carnival of Venice / Sea shanty fantasy / Clarinet polka / Sorgenfrei / Carmen vorspiel / Cole Porter medley / Mrs. Mary Printy / Ische suite / Dambusters march.
MC: . . . . **Unknown**

Ronmar Concert

CHRISTMAS TIME.
LP: . . . . **AFA 882**
MC: . . . . **AFAC 882**

ROCK 'N' ROMANCE (ACCORDING TO RONMAR).
Tracks: / My fair lady / Nina polka / Cha cha time / Fritzi waltz / Circassian circle / Tamboo / Jealousie / Rock around the clock / Kindermarsch / Blackthorn stick quadrille / Tico tico / Glenn Miller story / Il treno / Colonel Bogey.
LP: . . . . **AFA 862**
MC: . . . . **ZAFA 862**
MC: . . . . **AFAC 862**

Ronnie & Carl

DOWN BY THE RIVER.
LP: . . . . **PC 868**

Ronnie & The Jitters

ROLL OVER.
LP: . . . . **NERD 014**

Ronson, Mick

AMERICAN MUSIC (See under Hunter-Ronson) (Ronson, Mick & Ian Hunter).

PLAY DON'T WORRY.
Tracks: / Billy Porter / Angel No. 9 / This is for you / White light / Play don't worry /

Hazy days / Girl can't help it, The / Empty bed (Io me ne andrei) / Woman.
LP: APL1 0681

SLAUGHTER ON TENTH AVENUE.
Tracks: / Love me tender / Growing up and I'm fine / Only after dark / Music is lethal / I'm the one / Pleasure man (medley) / Slaughter on 10th Avenue.
LP: APL1 0353

Ronstadt, Linda

CANCIONES DE MI PADRE.
Tracks: / Por un amor / Los laureles / Hay unos ojos / La cigarra / Tu solo tu / Y andale / Rogaciano el huapanguero / La charreada / Dos arbolitos / Corrido de cannea / La barca de guaymas / La calandria / El sol que tu eres.
LP: 960 765-1
MC: 960 765-4

CRY LIKE A RAINSTORM, HOWL LIKE THE WIND.
Tracks: / Still within the sound of my voice / Cry like a rainstorm / All my life / Don't know much / Adios / Trouble again / I keep it hid / So right, so wrong / Shattered / When something is wrong with my baby / Goodbye my friend.
LP: EKT 76
MC: EKT 76C

DON'T CRY NOW.
Tracks: / I can almost see it / Love has no pride / Silver threads and golden needles / Desperado / Don't cry now / Sail away / Colorado / Fast one / Everybody loves a winner / I believe in you.
LP: K 43002

FOR SENTIMENTAL REASONS.
Tracks: / When you wish upon a star / Bewitched / You go to my head / But not for me / My funny valentine / I get along without you very well / Am I blue / I love you for sentimental reasons / Straighten up and fly right / Little girl blue / Round midnight.
LP: 960 474-1
MC: 960 474-4

GET CLOSER.
Tracks: / Get closer / Moon is a harsh mistress, The / I knew you when / Easy for you to say / People gonna talk / Talk to me of Mendocino / I think it's gonna work out fine / Mr. Radio / Lies / Tell him / Sometimes you can't win / My blue tears.
LP: E 0185
MC: E 01854
LP: 9601851

GREATEST HITS: LINDA RONSTADT.
Tracks: / You're no good / Silver threads and golden / Desperado / Love is a rose / That'll be the day / Long long time / Different drum / When will I be loved? / Love has no pride / Heatwave / It doesn't matter anymore / Tracks of my tears.
LP: K 53055
MC: K4 53055

GREATEST HITS: LINDA RONSTADT, VOL 2.
Tracks: / It's so easy / I can't let go / Hurt so bad / Blue bayou / How do I make you? / Back in the USA / Ooh baby baby / Poor, poor, pitiful me / Tumbling dice / Just one look / Someone to lay down beside me.
MC: K4 52255
LP: K 52255

HASTEN DOWN THE WIND.
Tracks: / Lose again / Tattler / If he's ever near / That'll be the day / Lo siento me vida / Hasten down the wind / Rivers of Babylon / Give one heart / Try me again / Crazy / Down so low / Someone to lay down beside me.
LP: K 53045

HEART LIKE A WHEEL.
Tracks: / You're no good / It doesn't matter anymore / Faithless love / Dark end of the street / Heart like a wheel / When will I be loved / I can't help it (if I'm still in love with you) / Keep me from blowing away / You can close your eyes.
LP: 3C 054 81823
MC: 3C 254 81823
LP: IC 038 81823

LINDA RONSTADT.
Tracks: / Rock me on the water / Crazy arms / I won't be hangin' around / I still miss someone / In my reply / I fall to pieces / Ramblin' round / Birds / Faithful / Rescue me.
LP: FA 3015
MC: TCFA 3015
LP: GO 2013

LINDA RONSTADT & FRIENDS.
LP: 1A 028 81072

LIVING IN THE USA.
Tracks: / Back in the U.S.A. / When I grow too old to dream / Just one look / Alison / White rhythm and blues / All that you dream / Ooh baby baby / Mohammed's radio / Blowing away / Love me tender.
LP: K 53085

LUSH LIFE.
Tracks: / When I fall in love / Skylark / It never entered my mind / Mean to me / When your lover has gone / I'm a fool to want you / You took advantage of me / Sophisticated lady / Can't we be friends / My old flame / Falling in love again / Lush life.
LP: 960 387-1
MC: 960 387-4

MAD LOVE.
LP: K 52210

PRISONER IN DISGUISE.
Tracks: / Love is a rose / Hey mister, that's me upon the jukebox / Roll um easy / Tracks of my tears / Prisoner in disguise / Heatwave / Many rivers to cross / Sweetest gift, The / You tell me that I'm falling down / I will always love you / Silver blue.
LP: K 53015

RETROSPECTIVE.
2LP: 5C 138 85170

SIMPLE DREAMS.
Tracks: / It's so easy / Carmelita / Simple man, simple dreams / Sorrow lives here / I never will marry / Blue bayou / Poor poor pitiful me / Maybe I'm right / Tumbling dice / Old paint.
LP: K 53065

TO KNOW HIM IS TO LOVE HIM (see under Parton, Dolly) (Ronstadt, Linda/ Dolly Parton/Emmylou Harris).

TWO ORIGINALS OF LINDA RONSTADT.
Tracks: / I fall to pieces / Crazy arms / I still miss someone.
2LP: IC 134 52760/61

WHAT'S NEW.
Tracks: / Skylark / Mean to me / My old flame / What's new / Lush life / Love man / Goodbye / For sentimental reasons / Crazy he calls me / When I fall in love.
LP: 960 489-1
MC: 960 489-4
LP: 9602601
MC: 960 260-4

Roogalator

PLAY IT BY EAR.
LP: RIDE 1

Rooke, Fred

BALLADS OF BAWLENGRO (VOL 1).
Tracks: / Barham Gur and the Luri / Charlie Fox / Gipsy nailsmith / Paraffin man / Gipsy's dream / Gipsy brothers / Prize fighters / Wandering fellow / Piglets / Archie Mead / Gipsy fiddler / Gipsy and the farmer / Uncle Awram / Didikai caravan / Liquid gold / She whistled for the weasel / Scrap metal man / I know a wood / Sapling, The.
MC: 60-045

BALLADS OF BAWLENGRO (VOL 2).
Tracks: / Pilgrims / Hooky pin / Jobie Lee / Holly and the ivy, The / Birth of the fiddle / Creation of man / Lo Lamkin / Loverin' Lovell / Sammy / Never kill the bees / Jack goes to bed / J. in the sack / 'appy Bos'ell's lurcher / Uncle Wallace / Liny Silk's cockfight / What are the worms for / Merchant's daughter / Ring, The / M's. D. & the robbers / Man in the moon, The.
MC: 60-046

RABBIT PIE.
Tracks: / Git you home / Joseph talk to the dicky / Cheese for the bitch / Rat in the hedgerow / Take me poachin' / Blazen window / If you would grow the barley / Swallow and trout / Wrong train / Fen men, The / Night-soil men, The / Tommy Gray / Ruddy ole cow / Farmer Brown / What, you on holiday / Little bit of string / Robin, the / Copeman's billy-goat / Bumper crop / Cock-doves / To be a pig-man / View, the / Jack Roberts / Tic beans / Animal cards / Blade of grass / Pregnant Sally / Your barrer wants some ile.
MC: 60-044

Room

CLEAR.
LP: RFB 26

IN EVIL HOUR.
LP: RFA 42
MC: CRFA 42

NEMESIS.
LP: RF 47

Room Nine

VOICES OF A SUMMER'S DAY.
LP: CLM 002

Room With A View

ROOM WITH A VIEW, A (Film Soundtrack) (Various artists).
Tracks: / O mio babbino caro: *Various artists* (From Gianni Scicchi by Puccini. Vocal-Kiri Te Kanawa.) / Pensione Bertollini, The: *Various artists* / Lucy, Charlotte and Miss Lavish see the city: *Various artists* / In the piazza signoria: *Various artists* / Embankment, The: *Various artists* / Phaethon: *Various artists* / Hi il bel sogno di doretta: *Various artists* (From La Rondine, Act One by Puccini. Vocal-Kiri Te Kanawa) / Storm, The: *Various artists*/ Home and the betrothal: *Various artists* / Sacred lake: *Various artists* / Allan sisters, The: *Various artists*/ In the National Gallery: *Various artists* / Windy corner: *Various artists* / Habanera: *Various artists*/ Broken engagement: *Various artists* / Return to Florence: *Various artists* / End title: *Various artists.*
LP: MOMENT 101
MC: MOMENTC 101

ROOM WITH A VIEW, A (see under Forster, E.M.) (Dench, Judi).

Roomful Of Blues

DRESSED UP TO GET MESSED UP.
Tracks: / Money talks / What happened to the sugar / Let's ride / Yes indeed! / Albi's boogie / Last time, The / Oh oh / Dressed up to get messed up / He knows the rules / Whiplash.
LP: FIEND 37
LP: VR 018
MC: VR 018C

HOT LITTLE MAMA.
Tracks: / Hot little mama / Big question, The / New Orleans shuffle / Sufferin' mind / Caravan / Loan me a helping hand / Long distance operator / Something to remember you by / Two bones and a pick / Little fine healthy thing / Sugar coated love / Jeep's blues.
LP: CH 39
LP: V 021
MC: VRC 021

LIVE AT LUPO'S HEARTBREAK HOTEL.
Tracks: / Gator's groove / Welcome to Lupo's / Coconut milk / Three hours past midnight / Three hundred pounds / House of joy / Pink champagne / Please don't leave me / Zydeco boogaloo.
LP: REU 1024

Rooney, Jim

BRAND NEW TENNESSEE WALTZ.
Tracks: / Brand new Tennessee waltz / Be my friend tonight / Amanda / Heaven become a woman / We must believe in magic / Fish and whistle / Dreaming my dreams / Six white horses / Satisfied mind.
LP: AP 012

COLLECTION: JIM ROONEY & BILL KEITH (see Keith, Bill) (Rooney, Jim & Bill Keith).

ONE DAY AT A TIME.
LP: ROUNDER 3008

READY FOR THE TIMES TO GET BETTER.
Tracks: / In it for the long run / Only the best / I recall a gypsy woman / Broided orange / Ready for the times to get better / South in New Orleans / Tennessee blues / Interest on the loan / Girl at the end of the hall / No expectations.
LP: AP 004

Roosters

I NONE GOT OVER (see under Brown, Nappy/The Roosters) (Roosters (The)/ Nappy Brown).

Root Boy Slim

DON'T LET THIS HAPPEN TO YOU.
LP: BEDLP 1

LEFT FOR DEAD (Root Boy Slim & The Sex Change Band).
LP: BEDLP 4

ZOOM (Root Boy Slim & The Sex Change Band).
LP: ILP 004

Root, Charlie

THIS PARTY IS IT (See under Rudder, David) (Root, Charlie/David Rudder).

Roots

AFRICAN IMAGE.
Tracks: / Fly machine / War cry / Way I feel / Uneasy playboy / From the roots / African beer.
LP: GR 8306
MC: GRC 8306

Roots, Desi

GOOD THING GOING (see Minott,Sugar/Desi Roots) (Roots, Desi/ Sugar Minott).

Roots Of..

ROOTS OF ROCK (Various artists).
LP: L 1063

Roots Of David

ROOTS OF DAVID (Various artists).
LP: TWLP 1021

Roots Of Inflation

ROOTS OF INFLATION (See under UNESCO reports).

Roots of Reggae

ROOTS OF REGGAE, THE (See under Reggae ...) (Various artists).

Roots Of Rock

ROOTS OF ROCK (Various artists).
LP: YAZOO 1063

Roots Radics

FOREVER EVER BACKWARDS.
LP: HB 69

FREELANCE.
Tracks: / Earsay / Rainbow / I'm not a king / Too much fuss / Party time / Everywhere Natty go / Dance with me / Midnight / Mash it up / Reggae on Broadway.
LP: KVL 9021

RADICAL DUB SESSION.
LP: SGL 102

SCIENTIST AND JAMMY STRIKE BACK.
Tracks: / Storming the death star / Mission impossible / Alien aborts / Buck Rogers in the Black Hole / Death of Mr. Spock / Princess takes her revenge / Crushing of the Stormtroopers / Flash Gordon meets Luke Skywalker / Son of Darth Vader / C3PO + R2D2 = The force.
LP: TRLS 210

Roots Rockers

REGGAE MASTERPIECES.
LP: VSLP 4005
MC: VSMC 009

REGGAE MASTERPIECES, VOL 2.
LP: VSLP 4056

Roots To Roots

SOUL TO SOUL, VOL 1.
LP: VSLP 2008

SOUL TO SOUL, VOL 2.
LP: VSLP 2009

Rootsman

MR MUSIC MAN.
LP: LPL 006

SOCA AMBASSADOR.
LP: LPL 010

Roper, Skid

ROOT HOG OR DIE (See under Nixon, Mojo) (Roper, Skid & Mojo Nixon).

Roques, Andre

CA C'EST DE L'ACCORDEON.
Tracks: / Chantons sarlot / Miss Karting / Sabor ami / Bal du Samedi soir / A la canaro / Don Pepito / Les filles du Quercy / Brise cadurcienne / Douce reverie / L'auberge des routiers / Je ne veux plus revoir tes yeux / Senor Manuello / Notre Quercy.
LP: ILD 42043
MC: Unknown

LE QUERCY (Roques, Andre & His Orchestra).
Tracks: / Quercy mon beau pays / Vin de cahors / Filles de montbauban / Quercy querla / Bourree quercynoise / La capalleto / Mon canal du midi / Grand pere / Auvergne et Quercy / Aio de rosta / Chez la mere Antoine a pas legers / A pas legers / Polka piquee.
LP: ILD 42058
MC: Unknown

Ros, Edmundo

DANCE AGAIN.
LP: PFS 4016

EARLY YEARS.
Tracks: / No can do / Chico chico / Tia Maria / Manana / Chi bim bam bom / Rumba royal / El toreador / Bunch of bananas / Another night like this / El Armadillo / It was never like this / Jamaica farewell / After you've gone.
2LP: DPA 3059/60

EDMUNDO ROS TODAY.
LP: PFS 4421

LATIN FAVOURITES.
Tracks: / La cucaracha / One note samba / Girl from Ipanema / Valencia / Blame it on the bossa nova / La paloma / La golondrina / Mexico / Meditation / Spanish gypsy dance / Jet flight / Vaya con dios.
LP: DGS 12

LATIN SONG AND DANCE MEN (Ros, Edmundo & Victor Sylvester Orch).
Tracks: / Brazil / Coffee song, The / Perhaps, perhaps, perhaps / Green eyes / Perfidia / Frenesi / Quiet nights of quiet stars / Lady of Spain / Wedding samba / Cuanto lagusta / Come closer to me /

Amapola / Guantanamera / South of the border / Meditation / Y Viva Espana.
LP: NSPL 18614

LATINO (see Heath, Ted) (Ros, Edmundo & Ted Heath).

MUSIC FOR THE MILLIONS.
Tracks: / La cucaracha / One note samba / Girl from Ipanema / Valencia / Blame it on the bossa nova / La Paloma / La golondrina / Mexico / Meditation / Spanish gypsy dance / Jet flight / Vaya con dios.
LP: 8101201
MC: 8101204

ROS REMEMBERS.
MC: KDKC 28033

THIS IS MY WORLD.
LP: PFS 4263

Ros, Patrick

SPECIAL FEELINGS.
LP: MAGIC LP 1
MC: MAGIC C 1

Rosaleen

IRISH MELODIES (Rosaleen & The Ramblers).
MC: GTDC 096

Rosario, Ralphi

I WANT YOUR LOVE.
Tracks: / I want your love.
LP: SUN 2783

Rosary Murders

ROSARY MURDERS, THE (Original Soundtrack) (Various artists).
Tracks: / In your eyes: *Various artists* / Jogging: *Various artists* / Phone company: *Various artists*/ Marble orchard, The: *Various artists* / Second story priest: *Various artists* / Pull yourself together: *Various artists* / Scratch father steel: *Various artists* / Sister blabbermouth: *Various artists* / Confessional call: *Various artists* / Father Koesler and Pat take a walk: *Various artists* / Fint the obituary: *Various artists*/ Sister Ann's last bath: *Various artists.*
LP: EDL 2505.1

Rosbif

BOURREE A SIX.
Tracks: / Bourree a six / Amour et printemps / Italian rant, An / Les filles de mons pays / Rondeau / Buisson fleuri / Spaniard, The / Two mazurkas / Suite no.2 / La soufflette.
LP: FSLP 5

TRADITIONAL DANCE MUSIC FROM CENTRAL FRANCE.
Tracks: / Waltz / March of the Cabrettaires / Suite of 3 bourrees in two time / Waltzes / Les enfants / Les enfants du pauvre homme / La tricotadda / Bouree / Au vist lou lomp / Bouree de cusset / J'm' en vas chantant riant / Le fountaine verte / Souvenir de Myrelingue / Fil et Bobine / Scottische 1 / Scottische 2 / Plante un chou / Polka piquee / 2 versions of Taitou / Pincou / Mazurka D'Auvergne / Waltz / Valse a Eric / Garcons de la Montagne / La Louise / Mazurka Gasconne / Mazurka de Lapleau.
LP: FSLP 3

TRADITIONAL DANCE MUSIC FROM S. FRANCE.
LP: HR 1

Rose, Al

AL ROSE PRESENTS - JOURNEYS INTO JAZZ.
LP: GHB 66

Rose Among Thorns

ROSE AMONG THORNS.
Tracks: / Prologue, The / Journey, The / Keep me warm / Dancing drum / Lady of Hay / Heart and Soul / So much to tell / Losers 'n' Dreamers / Lunar love / Hold on / Sail away / Take me home.
MC: HTDMC 6

Rose, Betsy

WINGS AGAINST THE SKY.
LP: F 31
MC: C 31

Rose Brothers

EVERYTHING'S COMING UP ROSES.
Tracks: / Personal touch / Easy love / Jealous / Celebrate / I get a rush / Fast lane / Just within reach / I wanna be your lover.
LP: MAL 0011

IN THE MIX.
LP: XS 2204

ROSE BROTHERS.
LP: MSS 2201

Rose, David

16 ORIGINAL HITS.
MC: MC 1626

VERY THOUGHT OF YOU.
Tracks: / When I fall in love / Ain't misbehavin' / When you're with me / Very thought of you, The / Tony's theme / Every time we say goodbye / Smoke gets in your eyes / Embraceable you / Kings road / How high the moon / Misty / I've got a crush on you.
LP: MOIR 102
MC: CMOIR 102

Rose (Film)

ROSE, THE (See under Midler, Bette) (Midler, Bette).

Rose, John

FORWARD OF SHORT LEG.
LP: ST 7529

Rose, Jon

JON ROSE & SHELLEY HIRSCH (See also Hersch, Shelley) (Rose, Jon/Shelley Hirsch).
LP: HOT 1019

Rose, Judy

GIRL NOBODY KNOWS.
LP: WRS 127

Rose, Kristi

SOME PEOPLE (Rose, Kristi & The Midnight Walkers).
LP: ROUNDER 9002
MC: ROUNDER 9002C

Rose Marie

COLLECTION: ROSE MARIE.
MC: CCSMC 277
2LP: CCSLP 277

LOOKING FOR LOVE.
LP: A1 LP 1001
MC: A1C 1001

ROSE MARIE PARTY ALBUM, THE.
Tracks: / Make the world go away / Hurt / Old rugged cross, The / When your old wedding ring was new / Answer to everything, The / This is my mother's day / Legend in my time, A / When I leave the world behind / Pal of my cradle days / You'll never know / I apologise / Sunshine of your smile / If I had my life to live over / Cry / My mother's eyes / Let the rest of the world go by.
LP: STAR 2374
MC: STAC 2374

ROSE MARIE SINGS JUST FOR YOU.
Tracks: / Make the world go away / Hurt / Old rugged cross, The / When your old wedding ring was new / Answer to everything, The / This is my mother's day / Legend in my time, A / When I leave the world behind / Pal of my cradle days / You'll never know / I apologise / Sunshine of your smile / If I had my life to live over / Cry / My mother's eyes / Let the rest of the world go by.
LP: ROSE 001
LP: RMTV 1
MC: RMTVC 1
MC: CLAMC 229

SENTIMENTALLY YOURS.
Tracks: / I don't know why I love you / Let me call you sweetheart / Who's sorry now / Good luck, good health, God bless you / What do you want to make those eyes at me for / Jerusalem / At the end of the day / Just one more chance / You're nobody till somebody loves you / Please don't go / Have you ever been lonely / Crazy / Beautiful dreamer / Love letters in the sand / Anniversary waltz / I'll be seeing you.
LP: STAR 2302
MC: STAC 2302

SO LUCKY.
Tracks: / Is it too late? / Anniversary song / Let bygones be bygones / You're breaking my heart / My world keeps getting smaller / Everyday / Harbour lights / So lucky / Sweet sixteen / St. Therese of the roses / All the love in the world.
MC: RMLC 2
LP: RMLP 2
MC: CLAMC 228

TAKE IT TO THE LIMIT.
Tracks: / Take it to the limit / It must be him / When I leave the world behind / Danny boy.
MC: HSC 3236
LP: SHM 3236

TEARDROPS AND ROMANCE.
Tracks: / Wheel of fortune / After all these years / Dear daddy / Pal must be a pal forever, A / Just for the old times sake / Wekking, The / Little one / Danny boy / Mistakes / Child of mine / When I grow too old to dream / Ave Maria / I fall to pieces / I'll never fall in love again / Now is the hour / We'll meet again.
LP: RMLP 3
MC: RMC 3
MC: CLAMC 230

TOGETHER AGAIN.
Tracks: / Way old friends are, The / Among my souvenirs / I'll be your sweetheart / So deep is the night / Strollin' underneath the arches / Behind the footlights / Nobody's child / Abide with me / Mama / You always hurt the one you love / Just out of reach / Someday / I'm sorry / Love is all / Last waltz, The.
LP: STAR 2333
MC: STAC 2333

Rose Marie (Film)

ROSE MARIE (Original Soundtrack) (Various artists).
LP: MCA 25009
MC: MCAC 25009

Rose, Mike

SKA VILLE, THE (Rose, Mike & Vin Gordon).
LP: STLP 006

SOUL AND SAX.
Tracks: / You close the door / Can't be with you tonight / Turn back the time / Mr. Dream maker / That night we met / My heart is yearning / I was such a fool / You spend your life loving me.
LP: OLP 025

SOUL AND SAX VOL. II.
Tracks: / Because I love you / I'll choose you / Rolling on / From my heart / My love is true / Special kind of love / I found love / Closer to me.
LP: OLP 028

Rose, Mykal

FREE YOURSELF.
Tracks: / Mother and child reunion / Hot pop / Buzz you / Promised land / Richie the rich / Eyes / Demonstration / Invasion / Just do it / Proud / Don's party.
LP: PL 74809
MC: PK 74809

Rose Of Avalanche

ALWAYS THERE.
LP: FIRELP 7
LP: EM 9633

FIRST AVALANCHE.
Tracks: / Stick in the works / Rise to the groove / Thousand landscapes, A / Conceal me / Goddess / American girls / Gimme some lovin' / L.A. rain.
LP: REFIRELP 4
LP: LILLP 003

IN ROCK.
Tracks: / Dreamland / Not another day / Height of the clouds (part 1) / Height of the clouds (part 2) / Darkorjan / Yesterday once more.
LP: FIRELP 12

LIVE AT THE TOWN AND COUNTRY.
Tracks: / Stick in the works / Just like yesterday / Mainline man / Velveteen / 1000 landscapes / Waiting for the sun / Always there / Dreamland / Too many castles / Gimme some lovin'.
LP: CONTE 104
MC: CONTAPE 104

NEVER ANOTHER SUNSET.
Tracks: / What's going down / Nowhere to run / You don't belong / Devils embrace, The / Never another sunset / Delusions / Her fatal charm / Don't fly too high / Romantic vision, A.
LP: AVELP 001
MC: AVEC 001

STRING A BEADS.
LP: AVELP 002

Rose Of Sharon

SINCE JESUS PASSED BY.
LP: PC 331

Rose Of Tralee

ROSE OF TRALEE (2) (10 original hits from home).
MC: CHR 07

Rose Of Washington ...

ROSE OF WASHINGTON SQUARE, THE Original soundtrack (Various artists).
LP: SH 2074

Rose, Pam

PAM ROSE SINGS.
LP: LKLP 6547

Rose, Patrick

SPECIAL (LP).
LP: SVLP 001

Rose, Pete

PETE ROSE JAZZ BAND.
Tracks: / Stevedore stomp / La mooche / Honeysuckle rose / Scrapple from the apple / Sheik of Araby, The / Mama don't allow.
LP: FBJ 1849

Rose Rose

MOSH OF ASS.
LP: FACE 2

SPLIT ALBUM (See under Sic) (Rose Rose/ Sic).

Rose Royce

BEST OF CAR WASH.
Tracks: / Car wash / Zig zag / Water / Doin' what comes naturally / I'm going down / Put your money where your mouth is / I wanna get next to you / Daddy rich / Yo yo / Sunrise.
LP: MCL 1609
MC: MCLC 1609
LP: MCF 2799

CAR WASH (LP).
LP: FA 3043

CHIC & ROSE ROYCE GREATEST HITS (See under Chic for details) (Rose Royce & Chic).

FRESH CUT.
Tracks: / Doesn't have to be this way / Lonely road / Mask doll / I found someone / Listen up / If walls could talk / Just my imagination / For my peace of mind / Fighting chance / I know I'm in the mood.
LP: CAL 227
MC: CAC 227

GOLDEN TOUCH.
Tracks: / And you wish for yesterday / I wanna make it with you / Funkin' around / Golden touch / Love is in the air / You're a winner / Would you please be mine / Help yourself.
LP: K 56881
MC: K4 56881

GREATEST HITS: ROSE ROYCE.
Tracks: / Love don't live here anymore / Wishing on a star / I wanna get next to you / Angel in the sky / I'm in love (and I love the feeling) / I wonder where you are tonight / You're on my mind / Is it love you're after / Car wash / It makes you feel like dancin' / Do your dance / First come, first served / Put your money where your mouth is / Ooh boy.
LP: RRTV 1
MC: RRTV 41

IN FULL BLOOM.
Tracks: / Wishing you a star / You can't please everybody / Ooh boy / Do your dance / You're my world girl.
LP: K 56394
MC: K 456394

IS IT LOVE YOU'RE AFTER.
Tracks: / Car wash / Is it love you're after / Wishing on a star / Love don't live here anymore / Magic touch / Do your dance / It makes you feel like dancin' / I wanna get next to you / Put your money where your mouth is / I'm going down.
LP: BLATLP 9
MC: BLATMC 9

JUMP STREET.
Tracks: / Jump street / Illusions / R.R. express / Famous last words / Tell me that I'm dreaming / Please return your love to me / Fight it.
LP: K 56958

MUSIC MAGIC.
LP: MKL 2

PERFECT LOVER.
Tracks: / Perfect lover.
LP: 781 944-1

RAINBOW CONNECTION IV.
Tracks: / I wonder where you are tonight / Is it love you're after / Shine your light / What are you waiting for? / Bad mother funker / You can't run from yourself / Lock it down / Pazzaz.
LP: K 56714
MC: K4 56714

SHOW MUST GO ON, THE.
LP: MKLH H5
MC: ZCMK 5

STRIKES AGAIN.
Tracks: / Get up off your fat / Do it, do it / I'm in love (and I love the feeling) / First come, first served / Love don't live here anymore / Angel in the sky / Help / Let me be the first to know / That's what's wrong with me.
LP: K 56557

STRONGER THAN EVER.
Tracks: / Dance with me / Sometimes lady / Best love / Still in love / You blew it / Somehow we made it through the rain / Fire in the funk / Talk to me.
LP: EPC 85634
MC: 40 85634

THEIR GREATEST HITS (Side By Side) (Rose Royce & Chic).
MC: DINMC 23
LP: DINTV 23

Rose, Samantha

IN PERSON.
LP: EMPLP 902

TOGETHER IN LOVE.
LP: WIR 12L 701

Rose Tattoo

ASSAULT AND BATTERY.
Tracks: / Out of this place / All the lessons / Let it go / Assault and battery / Magnum maid / Rock 'n' roll is king / Manzil madness / Chinese Dunkirk / Sidewalk Sally / Suicide city.
LP: CAL 127
MC: CAC 127
LP: STRLP 003

ROCK 'N' ROLL OUTLAWS.
Tracks: / Rock 'n' roll outlaw / Nice boys / Butcher and fast Eddy, The / One of the boys / Remedy / Bad boy for love / T.V. / Stuck on you / Tramp / Astra wally.
LP: CAL 125
MC: CAC 125
LP: STRLP 002
MC: STRMC 002

SCARRED FOR LIFE.
Tracks: / Scarred for life / We can't be beaten / Juice on the loose / Who's got the cash / Branded Texas / It's gonna work itself out / Sydney girls / Dead set / Revenge.
LP: CAL 144
MC: CAC 144
LP: STRLP 004
MC: STRMC 004

SOUTHERN STARS.
LP: STRLP 005

Rose, Tim

I'VE GOT A MESSAGE TO YOU.
LP: SEE 213

MORNING DEW.
Tracks: / I got a loneliness / I'm gonna be strong / I've gotta do things my way / Fare thee well / Eat drink and be merry / Morning dew / Where was 17 / You're slipping away from me / Long time man / Come away Melinda.
LP: ED 267

Rose, Tony

ON THE BANK OF GREEN WILLOW.
LP: LER 2101

POOR FELLOWS.
LP: DIN 324

SONGS OF A CHANGING WORLD (see Raven, Jon/Nic Jones/Tony Rose) (Rose, Tony/Nic Jones/Jon Raven).

UNDER THE GREENWOOD TREE.
Tracks: / Jockie to the fair / Just as the tide was flowing / Lark in the morning, The / Searching for lambs / Basket of eggs / John Blunt / Grand conversation on Napoleon / Sheath and knife / Trees they do grow high, The.
LP: LER 2024

YOUNG HUNTING.
LP: LER 2013

Rose, T.T.

MELLOW MOODS.
LP: TKJRLP 21

Rose, Wally

REVISITED.
LP: SOS 1057

YERBA BUENA DAYS (Rose, Wally/Lu Watters/Benny Strickler).
LP: DC 12003

Rosebud

ROSEBUD.
Tracks: / My baby, your baby / Landslide / Eye of the hurricane / Fire / Fool for a broken heart / Dynamite / Too late now / Hot'n'heavy / Love you till the day I die.
LP: MMT 3304

Rosebury, Arthur

ARTHUR ROSEBURY AND HIS KIT-CAT DANCE BAND (Rosebury,Arthur and his Kit-cat dance band).
Tracks: / Mississippi melody / I'm crazy over you / Bluegrass / If I had you / Nobody's fault but your own / Spread a little happiness / I'm a one man girl / Looking at you / What is this thing called love / Do something / Breakaway / Big city blues / Broadway / Sing a little love song / Sitting on the cold wet grass / Little things you do, The / With a song in my heart.
LP: SH 310

Rosehip String Band

ROSEHIP STRING BAND.
LP: FF 013

Roselli, Jimmy

COME INTO MY LIFE.
Tracks: / When your old wedding ring was new / Come into my life / Laugh it off / Right from the heart / Why don't we do this more often / Dancing has ended, The / There, I've said it again / Broken hearts belong to yesterday / You are mine / Rage to live / Could this be me / Million dreams ago, A.
LP: SCENE 8
MC: SCENEC 8

DADDY'S LITTLE GIRL.
LP: C 1026
MC: CA 1026

HEART AND SOUL OF JIMMY ROSELLI.
MC: JRC 105

LET ME SING AND I'M HAPPY.
Tracks: / Let me sing and I'm happy / Sonny boy / All by myself / Swanee / Toot toot tootsie / Back in your own back yard / April showers / Anniversary song / Lisa / My mammy / Ma blushin' Rosie / After you've gone.
LP: C 1018
MC: CA 1018
LP: C 1019
MC: CA 1019
LP: JR 100
MC: JRC 100

MORE I SEE IN YOU, THE.
LP: SCENE 6
MC: SCENEC 6

ROCKABYE YOUR BABY.
Tracks: / Rockabye your baby with a Dixie melody / Somewhere along the way / Little pal / Ida / Cry / Because you're mine / I surrender dear / You make me feel so young / My mother's eyes / I apologise / Sweet Lorraine / That's my desire / Prisoner of love.
LP: C 1009
MC: CA 1009

SALOON SONGS.
Tracks: / Carolina in the morning / Daddy you've been a mother / Bye bye blues / Heart of my heart / Who's sorry now / Down by the old mill stream / I'm sorry I made you cry / Margie / Daddy's little girl / That old gang of mine / If I had my way / Ace in the hole, The / When I lost you / I want a girl (Just like the girl..).
LP: C 1007
MC: CA1007

SALOON SONGS VOL2.
Tracks: / Please don't talk about me / When your old wedding ring was new / Baby face / Lager saga of Al. K. Hall, The / Five foot two, eyes of blue / When Irish eyes are smiling / My gal Sal / Somebody stole my gal / My melancholy baby / Nobody's sweetheart / Maybe / Yes sir, that's my baby / Medley: Dear old girl / I don't wanna go home.
LP: C 1008
MC: CA 1008
MC: JRC 103

SALOON SONGS VOL4.
LP: C 1001
MC: CA 1001

THERE MUST BE A WAY.
LP: C 1014
MC: CA 1014

WHEN YOUR OLD WEDDING RING WAS NEW.
LP: A1 LP 1000
MC: A1C 1000

Rosemary's Baby

ROSEMARY'S BABY (Original Soundtrack) (Various artists).
LP: 254891.1

Rosemary's Children

KINGS AND PRINCES.
Tracks: / Kings and princes / Visiting a house / W.W. 1 / Round and round / Lighthouse song.
LP: BRED 77

Rosenbaum, Art

FIVE STRING BANJO.
Tracks: / Sally Goodin / Had a little fight in Mexico / Liberty goin' cross the sea / Old Reuben / Got a little home to go to / Grub spring / Texas rangers / Dry and dusty: turkey in the straw / Water bound / Grey eagle / Muskrat / Make me a pallet down on your floor / John Henry.
LP: SNKF 101

Rosengarden, Bobby

BY REQUEST.
LP: SLP 8079
MC: SC 8079

Rosengren, Bernt

SUMMIT MEETING (See also Sandstrom, Nisse) (Rosengren, Bernt/ Nisse Sandstrom Quintet).
LP: PHONT 7560

TENTET - LIVE!.
LP: DRLP 55

Rosenthal & Old Dog

INDIAN SUMMER.
LP: FF 078

Rosie & The Originals

ANGEL BABY (See under Young, Karen).

Rosier, Pier

CAREMENT NEWS (Rosier, Pier & Gazoline).
LP: GP 4008

Rosnes, Renee

RENEE ROSNES.
Tracks: / Storyteller, The / Playground for the birds / Bright Mississippi / Diana / I.A. blues / Punjab / Everything I love / Fleur-de-lis.
LP: B1 93561
LP: 793 561 1

Rosolino, Frank

CONNECTION.
Tracks: / I may be wrong / Things we did last summer / Frieda / Doxy / My de luxe / Flamingo.
LP: AFF 111

FRANK ROSOLINO QUINTET (Rosolino, Frank Quintet).
LP: VSOP 16

FRANK ROSOLINO SEXTET (Rosolino, Frank Sextet).
LP: AFF 61

FRANKLY SPEAKING (Rosolino, Frank Quintet).
Tracks: / Frenesi / Rhythm rascals / Moonlight in Vermont / Missus, The / There's no you / Our delight / Now I lay me down (to dream of you) / Taps miller / Slan / Stairway to the stars / King fish.
LP: AFF 69

THINKING ABOUT YOU.
LP: 2014

TROMBOMANIA (see under Winding, Kai) (Rosolino, Frank/Jay Jay Johnson/ Kai Winding).

ZOOT SIMS AND FRANK ROSOLINO (See under Sims, Zoot) (Sims, Zoot/ Frank Rosolino).

Ross

SWINGERS, THE (see under Lambert) (Ross/Lambert/Hendricks).

Ross, Alan

ARE YOU FREE ON SATURDAY?.
Tracks: / Are you free on Saturday? / What you gonna do about it / Man with the white glove / Mystified / Get the gun / Nothing gets in my way / Baby ... please / Punishment Park / Love is love.
LP: EBY 1000

RESTLESS NIGHTS.
Tracks: / Restless nights / Ain't it a shame / Kamina / I will be alright / Angel / Joe Henry / Land of the snows / Salvation / Don't back away.
LP: EBY 1003
MC: EBK 1003

Ross, Andy

ANDY ROSS ORCHESTRA PLAY BILL & BOBBIE FAVOURITE (Ross, Andy Orchestra).
LP: DS 007

COME DANCE TO BILL AND BOBBY IRVINES (Ross, Andy Orchestra).
MC: TDS 007

DANCE PARTY (Ross, Andy Orchestra).
Tracks: / New York, New York / Can't buy me love / Cornet carillon / Killing me softly with his song / Amparita roca / Hill Street / Disco medley / Li'l darlin' / Hoe down / Praterleben / Salsa medley.
LP: DS 055

DANCING FEET (Ross, Andy Orchestra).
Tracks: / Dancing feet / I can't get started / Toujours l'amour toujours / It don't mean a thing / Railway children, The / Spinning wheel / Embraceable you / How lucky you are / Thou swell / Portrait of you / Teach me tonight / Rock around the clock / Time after time / May each day / Sing sing sing / White rose of Athens / Opportunity.
LP: PTLS 1107
MC: PTLC 1107

IT'S KNEES UP TIME, JOIN IN & SING WITH ANDY ROSS & HIS PALS (Ross, Andy Orchestra).
Tracks: / More we are together, The / Swanee / Yes sir that's my baby / Round her neck she wore a golden locket / Underneath the arches / We'll meet again / I'll see you in my dreams / Honeysuckle and the bee, The / Pretty baby / All by yourself in the moonlight / Hold your hand out you naughty boy / You naughty boy / Let's all go down the Strand / Jolly good company / Bye bye blackbird / Row row row / On mother Kelly's doorstep / I used to sigh for the silvery moon / Me and my shadow / Lambeth walk / Cokey cokey / Conga, The (I came, I saw I conga'd) / For he's a jolly good fellow / Auld lang syne / Goodnight sweetheart.
LP: CBS 31505

SING 'N' SWING.
Tracks: / California here I come / Baby face / Won't you come home Bill Bailey / Daddy wouldn't buy me a bow-wow / Strollin' in the park / Lily of Laguna / Boomps a daisy / Ballin the Jack / Gay gordons / Marie's wedding / Loch Lomond / Will ye no come back again / Y viva espana / By the light of the silvery moon / You made me love you / Amen / Joshua fit de battle of Jerico / Michael row the boat ashore / Got the whole world in his hands / Amen reprise / Down by the riverside / Polly wolly doodle / Camptown races / Meet me in St. Louis / Joshua / Early bird / Daisy bell / Danny boy / She'll be coming round the mountain / There's a tavern in the town / Rain, rain, rain / Scotland the brave / If you're Irish / We'll keep a welcome / Maybe it's because I'm a Londoner / Land of hope and glory.
LP: PKL 5570

Ross, Annie

ANNIE ROSS SINGS A SONG WITH MULLIGAN (Ross, Annie/Gerry Mulligan).
Tracks: / I feel pretty / I've grown accustomed to your face / All of you / Give me the simple life / This is always (alternative version) / It don't mean a thing / Lady's in love with you, The / You turned the tables on me / I've grown accustomed to your face (alternative version) / This is always / My old flame / This time the dream's on me / Let there be love / Between the devil and the deep blue sea / How about you? / I guess I'll have to change my plan.
LP: FS 27

DRIP DROP (See under Fame, Georgie) (Fame, Georgie/Annie Ross).

HONG KONG BLUES (See under Fame, Georgie).

IN HOAGLAND 81 (Ross, Annie & Georgie Fame).
LP: BELP 181

KING PLEASURE SINGS/ANNIE ROSS SINGS (see King Pleasure) (Ross, Annie/King Pleasure).

LIKE SOMEONE IN LOVE (Ross, Annie/Johnny Spence & His Orchestra).
Tracks: / Lot of livin' to do, A / Let me love you / All the things you are / I'm gonna go fishin' / Like someone in love / Limehouse blues / Handful of songs / All of you / Fly me to the moon / Nature boy / What's new / Love for sale.
LP: BDL 1049

SELECTION OF STANDARDS... (see under Fame, Georgie) (Fame, Georgie, Hoagy Carmichael & Annie Ross).

SING A SONG OF BASIE (See under Lambert, Hendricks) (Ross, Annie & Hendricks Lambert).

SINGS A HANDFUL OF SONGS.
LP: FS 221

Ross, Billy

MISTY MOUNTAIN (see Jackson, Billy) (Ross, Billy & Billy Jackson).

Ross, David

LET THE SUNSHINE IN (Ross, Diana & The Supremes).
LP: ML 5305

POET'S GOLD.
MC: 1741

Ross, Diana

20 GOLDEN GREATS: DIANA ROSS.
Tracks: / Do you know where you're going to / Touch me in the morning / Stop, look, listen (to your heart) / No one gets the prize / Ain't no mountain high enough / Love hangover / All of my life / I'm still waiting / Lovin', livin' and givin' / Boss, The / Remember me / Surrender / Reach out and touch (somebody's hand) / Gettin' ready for love / Doobedood'ndoobe, doobedood'ndoobe / I thought it took a little time (but today I fell in love).
LP: EMTV 21
MC: CMTV 21
LP: ZL 72008
MC: ZK 72008

20 GOLDEN GREATS: DIANA ROSS & SUPREMES.
Tracks: / Where did our love go? / Baby love / Come see about me / Stop in the name of love / Back in my arms again / I hear a symphony / My world is empty without you / Love is like an itching in my heart / You can't hurry love / You keep me hangin' on / Love is here and now you're gone / Happening, The / Reflections / In and out of love / Forever came today / Some things you never get used to / Love child / I'm livin' in shame / No matter what sign you are / Someday we'll be together.
LP: ZL 72009
MC: ZK 72009
LP: EMTV 5

25TH ANNIVERSARY: DIANA ROSS (Ross, Diana & The Supremes).

Tracks: / Where did our love go / Come see about me / Stop in the name of love / Back in my arms again / You can't hurry love / Love is here and now you're gone / Happening, The / Someday we'll be together / I'm gonna make you love me / When the lovelight starts shining through his eyes / Nothing but heartaches / My world is empty without you / Love is like an itching in my heart / I'm livin' in shame / Forever came today / Some things you never get used to / Composer, The / No matter what sign you are / Blue room / Manhattan / Who can I turn to (when nobody needs me) / Some day my prince will come / Sleepwalk / Treat me nice John Henry / Come on and see me / It's all your fault / Ooh wee baby / Come on boy / Heigh-ho / Those D.J. shows / Sincerely / Surfer boy / Beach ball / Heaven must have sent you / Just a little misunderstanding / Coca cola commercial (1) (Special lyrics to 'When the lovelight starts shining through his eyes') / Coca cola commercial (2) (Special lyrics to 'Baby love') / Supremes - interview / Baby love / I hear a symphony / Reflections / You keep me hangin on / Love child / In and out of love / If I ruled the world / When you wish upon a star / Are you sure love is the name of this game / Penny pincher / Send me no flowers / We couldn't get along without you.
LP: . . . . **WL 72436**
MC: . . . . **WK 72436**

AIN'T NO MOUNTAIN HIGH ENOUGH.
Tracks: / Reach out and touch (somebody's hand) / Now that there's you / You're all I need to get by / These things will keep me loving you / Ain't no mountain high enough / Something on my mind / I wouldn't change the man he is / Keep an eye / Where there was darkness / Can't it wait until tomorrow / Dark side of the world.
MC: . . . . **WK 72733**

ALL THE GREAT HITS.
Tracks: / It's my turn / Theme from Mahogany / Reach out and touch / Touch me in the morning / I'm still waiting / All of my life / Surrender / Remember me / Upside down / I'm coming out / Tenderness / My old piano / Boss, The / It's my house / Love hangover / Ain't no mountain high enough.
LP: . . . . **ZL 72016**
MC: . . . . **ZK 72016**

ALL THE GREATEST HITS: DIANA ROSS.
Tracks: / It's my turn / Do you know where you're going to / Reach out and touch (somebody's hand) / Touch me in the morning / I'm still waiting / All of my life / Surrender / Remember me / Upside down / I'm coming out / Tenderness / My old piano / Boss, The / It's my house / Love hangover / Ain't no mountain high enough.
LP: . . . . **STMA 8036**
MC: . . . . **CSTMA 8036**

ANTHOLOGY - DIANA ROSS & THE SUPREMES (See under Supremes) (Ross, Diana & The Supremes).

BABY IT'S ME.
Tracks: / Gettin' ready for love / You got it / Baby it's me / Too shy to say / Your love is so good for me / Top of the world / All night lover / Confide in me / Same love that made me laugh, The / Come in from the rain.
LP: . . . . **STMS 5097**
MC: . . . . **CSTMS 5097**

BOSS, THE.
Tracks: / No one gets the prize / I ain't been licked / All for one / Boss, The / Once in the morning / It's my house / Sparkle / I'm in the world.
LP: . . . . **STMS 5049**
MC: . . . . **CSTMS 5049**
LP: . . . . **STML 12118**
LP: . . . . **WL 72095**

CAPTURED LIVE ON STAGE (Ross, Diana & The Supremes).
Tracks: / T.C.B. / Medley (1) (Stop! in the name of love/Come see about me/My world is empty without yo) / Medley (2) (The lady is a tramp/Let's get away from it all.) / Monologue - Diana Ross (1) / Love is here and now you're gone / I'm gonna make you love me / Monologue - Mary Wilson / Can't take my eyes off you / Monologue - Diana Ross & Mary Wilson / Reflections / My man / Didn't we / It's alright with me / Big spender / Falling in love with love / Love child / Dialogue - Diana Ross / Aquarius / Monologue -Diana Ross (2) / Impossible dream, The / Monologue - Diana Ross (3) / Someday we'll be together / Closing dialogue - Diana Ross & the Supremes.
2LP: . . . . **WL 72438**
MC: . . . . **WK 72438**

DIANA.
Tracks: / Upside down / Tenderness / Friend to friend / I'm coming out / Have fun (again) / My old piano / Now that you're gone / Give up.
LP: . . . . **STMA 8033**
MC: . . . . **CSTMA 8033**
LP: . . . . **WL 72430**
MC: . . . . **WK 72430**

DIANA & MARVIN (See Gaye, Marvin) (Ross, Diana & Marvin Gaye).

DIANA ROSS (2).
Tracks: / Do you know where you're going to / I thought it took a little time (but today I feel in love) / You're good my child / One love in my lifetime / Ain't nothin' but a maybe / After you / Smile / Love hangover / Kiss me now.
LP: . . . . **WL 72375**
MC: . . . . **WK 72375**

DIANA ROSS (3).
LP: . . . . **STML 12022**

DIANA ROSS (ORIGINALLY 1970).
Tracks: / Reach out and touch (somebody's hand) / Now that there's you / You're all I need to get by / These things will keep me loving you / Ain't no mountain high enough / Something on my mind / I wouldn't change the man he is / Keep an eye / Where there was darkness / Can't it wait until tomorrow? / Dark side of the world.
LP: . . . . **STMS 5017**
MC: . . . . **CSTMS 5017**
LP: . . . . **SFTML 11159**

DIANA ROSS & THE SUPREMES: 20 GOLDEN GREATS (Ross, Diana & The Supremes).
Tracks: / Where did our love go? / Baby love / Come see about me / Stop, in the name of love / Back in my arms again / I hear a symphony / My world is empty without you / Love is like an itching in my heart / You can't hurry love / You keep me hangin' on / Love is here and now you're gone / Happening, The / Reflections / In and out of love / Forever came today / Some things you never get used to / Love child / I'm livin' in shame / No matter what sign you are / Someday we'll be together.
LP: . . . . **MTV 5**
MC: . . . . **CMTV 5**

DIANA ROSS & THE SUPREMES WITH THE TEMPTATIONS (Ross, Diana & The Supremes & The Temptations).
Tracks: / I'm gonna make you love me / My guy / My girl / Uptight / Sweet inspiration / I'll try something new / Ain't no mountain high enough / I second that emotion / Why must we fall in love? / For better or worse / Weight, The / I'll be doggone / Stubborn kind of fellow.
LP: . . . . **TMS 3513**
MC: . . . . **TMC 3513**
LPS: . . . . **ALBUM 67**
MCSET: . . . . **CASSETTE 67**
LP: . . . . **STML 11096**
LP: . . . . **STMS 5015**

DIANA (TV SPECIAL).
Tracks: / Don't rain on my parade / Long to be (close to you) / Remember me / Ain't no mountain high enough / I love you (call me) / Love story / Bill Cosby entertains / Danny Thomas entertains.
LP: . . . . **STMS 5048**
MC: . . . . **CSTMS 5048**
LP: . . . . **SHM 3203**
MC: . . . . **HSC 3203**

DIANA'S DUETS (Ross, Diana & various artists).
Tracks: / Endless love / I'm gonna make you love me / My mistake (was to love you) / I'll try something new / You're a special part of me / I second that emotion / I'll keep my light in my window / Try it, baby / Stop, look and listen / Pops, we love you / Uptight / You are everything / Stubborn kind of fellow / Ain't nothing like the real thing.
LP: . . . . **STML 12163**
MC: . . . . **CSTML 12163**

DYNAMIC DIANA (Ross, Diana & The Supremes).
Tracks: / Baby love / Stop, in the name of love / Shake me, wake me / Mother dear / Ask any girl / Heatwave / I'm so glad / Who could ever doubt my love / Any girl in love (knows what I'm going through) / I'm in love again / Honey boy / Get ready / Always in my heart / Everything is good about you.
LP: . . . . **TMS 3505**
MC: . . . . **TMC 3505**

EARLY YEARS 1961-1964 (Ross, Diana & The Supremes).
Tracks: / Where did our love go / Come see about me / Run run run / Long gone lover / Standing at the crossroads of love / Who's loving you? / When the lovelight starts shining thru his eyes / Baby love / You've really got a hold on me / Time changes things / You bring back memories / Buttered popcorn / I want a guy / Do you love me / Let me go the right way / Breathtaking guy.
LP: . . . . **STMR 9008**
MC: . . . . **CSTMR 9008**

EASE ON DOWN THE ROAD (See under Jackson, Michael) (Ross, Diana & Michael Jackson).

EATEN ALIVE.
Tracks: / Eaten alive / Oh teacher / Experience / Chain reaction / More and more / I'm watching you / Love on the line / I love being in love with you / Crime of passion / Don't give up on each other / Eaten alive (extended remix).
LP: . . . . **ROSS 2**
MC: . . . . **TCROSS 2**
LP: . . . . **EJ 2404081**
MC: . . . . **EJ 2404084**

EVENING WITH....
Tracks: / Overture / Here I am / I wouldn't change a thing / Lady is a tramp, The / Touch me in the morning / Smile / Send in the clowns / Love hangover / I want you back / Motown story: Motown overture / Money (that's what I want) / Please Mr. Postman / Fingertips / Reach out and touch (somebody's hand) / You keep me hangin' on / Baby love / Someday we'll be together / Stop in the name of love / You can't hurry love / Reflections / My world is empty without you / I hear a symphony / Girls / Point (everything's got 'em), The / Me and my arrow / Lifeline / Everything's got 'em (reprise) / Working girls / Lady sings the blues / T'aint nobody's business if I do / I cried for you / Aux lies Hawaii / Stormy weather / Jump in the pot (and let's get hot) / I need a little sugar in my bowl / My man / One giant step / Chorus line, A / Music in the mirror, The / What I did for love / Improvisations / Dance / Ten looks three / Do you know where you're going to / Ain't no mountain high enough.
2LP: . . . . **TMSP 6005**
MCSET: . . . . **CTMSP 6005**
2LP: . . . . **WL 72268**
MC: . . . . **WK 72268**

EVERY GREAT NO 1 HIT (See under Supremes) (Ross, Diana & The Supremes).

EVERYTHING IS EVERYTHING.
Tracks: / My place / Ain't no sad song / Everything is everything / Baby it's love / I'm still waiting / Doobedood'ndoobe, doobedood'ndoobe / Come together / Long and winding road, The / I love you (call me) / How about you? / Close to you.
LP: . . . . **STMS 5047**
MC: . . . . **CSTMS 5047**
LP: . . . . **STML 11178**

FORCE BEHIND THE POWER.
Tracks: / Change of heart / When you tell me that you love me / Battlefield / Blame it on the sun / You're gonna love it / Heavy weather / Force behind the power, The / Heart (don't change my mind) / Waiting in the wings / You and I / One shining moment / If we hold on together / No matter what you do (Only on CD single).
MC: . . . . **TCEMD 1023**

GREATEST HITS: DIANA ROSS.
Tracks: / Remember me / Didn't you know (you'd have to cry sometime) / Doobedood'ndoobe, doobedood'ndoobe / Surrender / And if you see him / Ain't no mountain high enough / How about you / Reach out and touch (somebody's hand) / These things will keep me loving you / Reach out I'll be there / Close to you / I'm still waiting.
LP: . . . . **STMA 8006**
LP: . . . . **WL 72478**
MC: . . . . **WK 72478**

GREATEST HITS: DIANA ROSS VOL.1 & 2 (See under Supremes) (Ross, Diana & The Supremes).

GREATEST HITS: DIANA ROSS VOL.2.
Tracks: / Touch me in the morning / Love hangover / Sorry doesn't always make it right / Imagine / Last time I saw him / All of my life / Do you know where you're going to? / I won't last a day without you / Behind closed doors / Love me / Good morning heartache / I thought it took a little time (but today I fell in love).
LP: . . . . **STML 12036**
MC: . . . . **CSTML 12036**
LP: . . . . **ZL 72028**

GREATEST HITS LIVE, THE.
Tracks: / Intro - Dirty Diana / I'm coming out / Upside down / What can one person do / Missing you / Mirror, mirror / Chain reaction / Muscles / Dirty looks / Love hangover / Man I love, The / Do you know where you're going to / Ain't no mountain high enough / Paradise / This house / Workin' overtime / Stop in the name of love / You keep me hangin' on / You can't hurry love / Where did our love go? / Baby love / Why do fools fall in love / Endless love / Reach out and touch somebody's hand.
2LP: . . . . **EMDC 1001**
MC: . . . . **TCEMDC 1001**

I'M STILL WAITING.
Tracks: / I'm still waiting / Surrender / I can't give back the love I feel for you / Remember me / And if you see him / Reach out I'll be there / Didn't you know (you'd have to cry sometime)? / Simple thing like cry, A / Did you read the morning paper? / I'll settle for you / I'm a winner / All the befores.
LP: . . . . **WL 72082**
MC: . . . . **WK 72082**
LP: . . . . **STML 11193**
LP: . . . . **STMS 5031**

I'M STILL WAITING & ALL THE GREAT HITS.
Tracks: / I'm still waiting (1990 remix) / Upside down / My old piano / Tenderness / Boss, The / It's my turn / Touch me in the morning / Endless love / Love hangover (PWL remix) / Do you know where you're going to? / Remember me / Reach out and touch (somebody's hand) / I'm coming out / It's my house / All of my life / Surrender / Ain't no mountain high enough.
LP: . . . . **ZL 72716**
MC: . . . . **ZK 72716**

LADY SINGS THE BLUES (Film soundtrack).
Tracks: / Lady sings the blues / Baltimore brothel / Billie sneaks into Dean and Dean's / Swinging uptown / T'aint nobody's business if I do / Big Ben / C.C. rider / All of me / Man I love, The / Them there eyes / Gardenias from Louis / Cafe Manhattan / Had you been around / Love theme / Country tune / I cried for you / Billy and Harry / Mean to me / Fine and mellow / What a little moonlight can do / Louis visits Billie on tour / Persuasion / Agent's office / Love is here to stay / Lover man oh where can you be? / You've changed / Gimme a pigfoot and a bottle of beer / Good morning heartache / My man / Don't explain / Strange fruit / God bless the child / Closing theme.
2LP: . . . . **TMSP 1131**
MCSET: . . . . **CTMSP 1131**
2LP: . . . . **ZL 72129**
MC: . . . . **ZK 72129**

LAST TIME I SAW HIM.
Tracks: / Last time I saw him / No one's gonna be a fool for ever / Love me / Sleepin' / You / Turn around / When will I come home to you? / I heard a song / Stone liberty / Behind closed doors.
LP: . . . . **STMS 5071**
MC: . . . . **CSTMS 5071**
LP: . . . . **STML 11255**

LET THE SUN SHINE IN/CREAM OF THE CROP (See Under Supremes) (Ross, Diana & The Supremes).

LIVE AT CAESAR'S PALACE.
Tracks: / Overture / Don't rain on my parade / Big Mabel Murphy / Reach out and touch (somebody's hand) / Stop, in the name of love / My world is empty without you / Baby love / I hear a symphony / Ain't no mountain high enough / Corner of the sky / Being green / I loves you, Porgy / Lady sings the blues / God bless the child / Good morning heartache / T'aint nobody's business if I do / Lady is a tramp, The / My man.
LP: . . . . **STMS 5019**
MC: . . . . **CSTMS 5019**

LIVE AT LONDON'S TALK OF THE TOWN (21 titles) (Ross, Diana & The Supremes).
Tracks: / Michelle / Yesterday / Baby love / More / Happening, The / Mame / Reflections / Lady is a tramp, The / Without a song / Stop in the name of love / Second hand Rose / In and out of love.
LP: . . . . **MFP 50447**

LIVE: DIANA ROSS.
LP: . . . . **WL 72075**
MC: . . . . **WK 72075**
LP: . . . . **STML 11248**

LOVE CHILD (Ross, Diana & The Supremes).
Tracks: / Love child / Keep an eye / How long has that evening train been gone? / Does your mama know about me? / Honey bee (keep on stinging me) / Some things you never get used to / He's my sunny boy / You've been so wonderful to me / Don't break these chains of love / You ain't livin' till you're lovin' / I'll set you free / Can't shake it loose.
LP: . . . . **STMS 5070**
MC: . . . . **CSTMS 5070**
LP: . . . . **STML 11095**

LOVE SONGS: DIANA ROSS.
Tracks: / Do you know where you're going to / Endless love / Love me / Sorry doesn't always make it right / Crying my

heart out for you / I thought it took a little time (but today I fell in love) / These things will keep me loving you / It's my turn / Sparkle / Touch me in the morning / I'm still waiting / All night lover / You're all I need to get by / All of my life.
LP: . . . . **NE 1200**
MC: . . . . **CE 2200**

LOVE SONGS: DIANA ROSS & MICHAEL JACKSON (Ross, Diana & Michael Jackson).
Tracks: / I'm still waiting / Touch me in the morning / All of my life / Love hangover / Ain't no mountain high enough / Endless love / Reach out and touch (somebody's hand) / Do you know where you're going to / Got to be there / Ain't no sunshine / Farewell my Summer love / Ben / One day in your life / I'll be there / Girl you're so fine / Never can say goodbye.
LP: . . . . **STAR 2298**
MC: . . . . **STAC 2298**

LOVE SONGS: MICHAEL JACKSON & DIANA ROSS (See under Michael Jackson for details) (Ross, Diana & Michael Jackson).

LOVE SUPREME (See Under Supremes) (Ross, Diana & The Supremes).

MAHOGANY (See under Mahogany) (Film soundtrack) (Various artists).

NEVER-BEFORE-RELEASED MASTERS (See under Supremes) (Ross, Diana & The Supremes).

PORTRAIT VOLS. 1 & 2.
Tracks: / Where did our love go / Baby love / Stop in the name of love / You can't hurry love / You keep me hangin on / Happening, The / Reflections / Love child / I'm gonna make you love me / I second that emotion / Someday we'll be together / Doobedood'ndoobe, doobedood'ndoobe / Ain't no mountain high enough / Remember me / Surrender / Love hangover / I'm still waiting / Reach out and touch (somebody's hand) / All of my life / Sorry doesn't always make it right / Do you know where your going to / Touch me in the morning / Upside down / It's my house / Boss, The / My old piano / I'm coming out / It's my turn / Endless love.
LP: . . . . **STAR 2238**
MCSET: . . . . **STAC 2238**

RED HOT RHYTHM 'N' BLUES.
Tracks: / Dirty looks / Stranger in paradise / Shine / Shockwaves / Selfish one / Mr. Lee / Tell mama / There goes my baby / Summertime / Cross my heart / It's hard for me to say (Produced by Luther Vandross) / Tell me again.
LP: . . . . **EMC 3532**
MC: . . . . **TCEMC 3532**

REFLECTIONS (Ross, Diana & The Supremes).
Tracks: / Reflections / I'm gonna make it / Forever came today / I can't make it alone / In and out of love / Bah-bah-bah / What the world needs now is love / Up, up and away / Love makes me do foolish things / Then / Misery makes its home in my heart / Ode to Billy Joe.
LP: . . . . **WL 72368**
MC: . . . . **WK 72368**
LP: . . . . **STML 11073**

ROSS.
LP: . . . . **EST 1867051**

SILK ELECTRIC.
Tracks: / Muscles / So close / Still in love / Fool for your love / Turn me over / Who / Love's lies / In your arms / Anywhere you run to / I am me.
LP: . . . . **FA 3184**
MC: . . . . **TCFA 3184**
LP: . . . . **EST 27313**
MC: . . . . **TC EST 27313**

SWEPT AWAY.
Tracks: / Missing you / Touch by touch / Rescue me / It's your move / Swept away (Spoken introduction written by Diana Ross.) / Telephone / Nobody makes me crazy like you do / All of you / We are the children of the world / Forever young.
LP: . . . . **ROSS 1**
MC: . . . . **TCROSS 1**
LP: . . . . **FA 3200**
MC: . . . . **TCFA 3200**

T.C.B. - THE ORIGINAL SOUNDTRACK (Ross, Diana & The Supremes with The Temptations).
Tracks: / T.C.B. / Stop, in the name of love / You keep me hangin' on / Get ready / Way you do the things you do, The / Taste of honey, A / Eleanor Rigby / Do you know the way to San Jose? / Mrs. Robinson / Respect / Somewhere / Ain't too proud to beg / Hello, young lovers / For once in my life / I know I'm losing you / With a song in my heart / Without a song / Come see about me / My world is empty without you / Baby love / I hear a symphony / Impossible dream, The.
LP: . . . . **STMS 5048**
MC: . . . . **CSTMS 5048**
LP: . . . . **STML 11110**

THEIR VERY BEST - BACK TO BACK (Ross, Diana/Michael Jackson/Gladys Knight/Stevie Wonder).
LP: . . . . **PTVR 2**
MC: . . . . **PTVT 2**

TO LOVE AGAIN.
Tracks: / It's my turn / Stay with me / One more chance / Crying my heart out for you / Do you know where you're going to? / I thought it took a little time (but today I fell in love) / To love again / No one's gonna be a fool for ever / Touch me in the morning.
LP: . . . . **STML 12152**
MC: . . . . **CSTML 12152**

TOGETHER (Ross, Diana & The Supremes with The Temptations).
LP: . . . . **STML 11122**

TOUCH ME IN THE MORNING.
Tracks: / Touch me in the morning / All of my life / We need you / Leave a little room / I won't last a day without you / Little girl blue / My baby / Imagine / Brown baby / Save the children.
LP: . . . . **WL 72074**
MC: . . . . **WK 72074**
LP: . . . . **STML 11239**

VERY BEST OF DIANA ROSS.
Tracks: / Reach out and touch (somebody's hand) / Ain't no mountain high enough / Reach out and touch (somebody's hand) / Now that there's you / Remember me / My place / I'm still waiting / Reach out I'll be there / And if you see him / Touch me in the morning / Good morning heartache / Love is here to stay / Lover man / Baby, I love your way / Young mothers / Imagine / Too shy to say / Do you know where you're going to? / Love hangover / Don't knock my love / Last time I saw him / Sleepin' / Same love that made me laugh, The / Smile / Together / My mistake (was to love you) / Gettin' ready for love / Lovin', livin' and givin' / No one gets the prize / Boss, The / Now that you're gone / Upside down / Crying my heart out for you / It's my turn / Endless love.
2LP: . . . . **TMSP 6017**
MCSET: . . . . **CTMSP 6017**
2LP: . . . . **WL 72135**
MCSET: . . . . **WK 72135**

WHY DO FOOLS FALL IN LOVE?.
Tracks: / Why do fools fall in love / Sweet surrender / Mirror mirror / Endless love / It's never too late / Think I'm in love / Sweet nothin's / Two can make it / Work that body.
MC: . . . . **TCFA 3186**
LP: . . . . **FA 3186**
LP: . . . . **EST 26733**

WORKIN' OVERTIME (ALBUM).
Tracks: / Workin' overtime / Say we can / Take the bitter with the sweet / Bottom line / This house / Paradise / Keep on dancing / What can one person do / Going through the motions / We stand together.
LP: . . . . **EMD 1009**
MC: . . . . **TCEMD 1009**

Ross, Doctor Isiah

HARMONICA BLUES, THE (See also Terry, Sonny/Sonny Boy Williamson) (Ross, Doctor/ Sonny Boy Williams/ Sonny Terry).

HARMONICA BOSS (Doctor Ross).
LP: . . . . **BRP 2013**

HARMONICA MAN, THE.
Tracks: / Boogie disease / Baby please don't go / Harmonica boogie / Decoration day / How much more long / Don't worry 'bout the bear / That's alright mama / Blue in the night / Do the boogie woogie / Rockin' after midnight / Ethel Mae / San Francisco breakdown.
LP: . . . . **BEAR 2**

HIS FIRST RECORDINGS.
LP: . . . . **ARHOOLIE 1065**

JIVIN' THE BLUES.
LP: . . . . **BEAR 15**

ONE MAN BAND.
Tracks: / Doctor Ross's rock / My little woman / Mama's blues / Thirty two twenty / Chicago breakdown / Good morning little schoolgirl / Hobo blues / Fox chase, The / Going down slow / Boogie woogie, The.
LP: . . . . **SNTF 862**

Ross, Dwight

ROSS 1.
LP: . . . . **ICH 1017**
MC: . . . . **ZCICH 1017**

Ross, Jackie

FULL BLOOM.
Tracks: / Selfish one / Everything but love / Wasting time / I had to walk with my man / Be sure you know / Summertime / I've got the skill / Change your ways / Don't take my love / Haste makes waste / From you (I wanna hear it) / Misty.
LP: . . . . **GCH 8095**
MC: . . . . **GCHK 78095**

Ross, Kevin

RAW MATERIAL (see Wallen,Per Henrik) (Ross, Kevin/Steve Reid/Per Henrik Wallen).

Ross, Lindsay...

GREAT SCOTTISH DANCE BANDS VOL 1 (Ross, Lindsay & His Scottish Dance Band).
Tracks: / Miss Mary Douglas (jig) / Barbara bane of new deer / Miss Kirsty batchelor / Flowers of Edinburgh / Sing tae me the auld scots songs / My he'rt is sair / Ca' the ewes / Annie Laurie / Kiss me quick / Donald Iain Rankine / Tam's hunting horn / Wind that shakes the piggery, The / Stein song, The / Whistler's song, The / Silver wedding (jig), The / St. Bernards waltz / Gold and silver / Crossing the Alps / MacDonald of the Isles (march to Harlaw) / MacDonald's awa' tae the war / Lady Louisa MacDonald's strathspey / Abercairney highlanders.
LP: **2384 088**

LINDSAY ROSS AND HIS SCOTTISH DANCE BAND (Ross, Lindsay & His Scottish Dance Band).
LP: . . . . **WGR 056**
MC: . . . . **CWGR 056**

Ross, Steven

MIDNIGHT DRIVE.
LP: . . . . **RR 92891**
MC: . . . . **RR 92894**

Rosselson, Leon

BRINGING THE NEWS FROM NOWHERE.
LP: . . . . **CF 390**

FOR THE GOOD OF THE NATION.
LP: . . . . **CF 381**

I DIDN'T MEAN IT.
LP: . . . . **CF 392**

PALACES OF GOLD.
LP: . . . . **CF 249**

ROSSELSONGS.
MC: . . . . **CFC 1**

TEMPORARY LOSS OF VISION.
LP: . . . . **CF 384**

THAT'S NOT THE WAY IT'S GOT TO BE (Rosselson, Leon/Roy Bailey).
LP: . . . . **CF 251**

WORD IS HUGGA MUGGA, THE.
LP: . . . . **LER 3015**

Rossendale Male Voice

VALLEY OF SONG, THE (Rossendale Male Voice Choir).
Tracks: / Ma belle marguerite / Donkey serenade, The / I gave my love a cherry / Phil the fluter's ball / Down in the valley / What shall we do with the drunken sailor / Hippopotamus song, The / Muss I denn / There is nothin' like a dame / I will give my love an apple / Ghost's high noon, The / Yesterday / Mad dogs and Englishmen / Cease thy affections / Lighthouse keeper and the mermaid, The / Blow the wind southerly / Old superb, The.
LP: . . . . **LBR 003**
MC: . . . . **LBT 003**

Rosser & Davis

FRIENDS.
LP: . . . . **LEG 25**
MC: . . . . **LEGC 25**

WISH I COULD PLAY LIKE THAT.
LP: . . . . **LEG 26**
MC: . . . . **LEGC 26**

Rossi, Manuel

CLASSICAL DREAMS.
LP: **6 26211**
MC: **4 26211**

Rossi, Tino

DISQUE D'OR.
Tracks: / Une rose / Le pinzuto / Solenzara / Le soueil ne se couche jamais / Parle plus bas / Ajaccio / J'avais vingt ans / Mon pays / Ah, le petit vin blanc / Love story / Le reve passe / O Corse, ile d'amour / Vieni vieni / Tant qu'il y aura des etoiles / Chanson pour Nina / Le plus beau tango du monde / Marinella / Tchi-tchi.
LP: **2C 070 72008**

TINO ROSSI.
Tracks: / O Corse ile d'amour / Vieni vieni / J'ai reve d'une fleur / L'amour est une etoile / Chanson pour Nina / J'aime les femmes, c'est ma folie / Marinella / Tchi-tchi / Bella Ragazzina / Loin des guitares / Tarentelle / Ecoutez les mandolines / Seranade de Lena / Laissez-moi vous aimer / Pescadore / Quand on est marinier / Tant qu'il y aura des etoiles / Tango d'un soir / Chanson pour ma brune / Mia piccolina / Apres toi je n'aurai plus d'amour / Credo / Rien qu'un chant d'amour / Je vous aime sans espoir.
2LP: **1568523**
MCSET: **1568529**

TOP SIXTEEN.
MC: . . . . **PM 1562554**

Rossington Collins

ANYTIME, ANYPLACE, ANYWHERE.
Tracks: / Prime time / Three times as bad / Don't misunderstand me / One good man / Opportunity / Getaway / Winners and losers / Misery loves company / Sometimes you can put it out.
LP: . . . . **MCL 1748**
MC: . . . . **MCLC 1748**

THIS IS THE WAY.
Tracks: / Tashauna / Gonna miss it when it's gone / Don't stop me now.
LP: . . . . **MCF 4018**

Rossington, Norman

ADVENTURES OF PORTLAND BILL (See under Adventures of...).

Rossini (composer)

ARIAS FROM L'ITALIANA IN ALGERI ETC. (Various artists).
MC: **4254304**

CENERENTOLA/BARBIERE HIGHLIGHTS (Various artists).
MC: **4277144**

LA CENERENTOLA/BARBIERE DI SIVIGLIA-HIGHLIGHTS (Various artists).
MC: . . . . **MC 4277144 GW**

LE COMTE ORY (Orchestra Et Choeur De L'Opera Lyon).
MC: **422 406-4**

L'ITALIANA IN ALGERI (See under Vienna Philharmonic Orchestra) (Vienna Philharmonic Orchestra).

ROSSINI (Various artists).
MC: . . . . **DLCMC 207**

SEVEN GREAT OVERTURES (Vienna State Opera Orchestra).
MC: . . . . **VETC 6525**

Rosslyn Mountain Boys

ROSSLYN MOUNTAIN BOYS.
LP: . . . . **AD 2010**

Rosso, Nini

GRAFFITI COLLECTION.
MC: . . . . **GRMC 19**

GREATEST HITS: NINI ROSSO.
MC: **260 901 4**

Rostal & Schaefer

MELODIES WITH MEMORIES.
LP: . . . . **EMC 3104**

WITH RON GOODWIN & THE ROYAL LIVERPOOL PHILHARMONIC ORCH..
Tracks: / Beatles concerto / She loves you / Eleanor Rigby / Yesterday / All my loving / Hey Jude / Here, there and everywhere / Something / Can't buy me love / Long and winding road, The / Fool on the hill / Lucy in the sky with diamonds / Michelle / Maxwell's silver hammer / Here comes the sun / Hard day's night, A.
LP: . . . . **PAS 10014**

Rostand, Edmund

CYRANO DE BERGERAC (Various artists).
MCSET: **0306**

Rostock Vampires

TRANSYLVANIAN DISEASE.
LP: . . . . **NB 014**

Rosy Vista

YOU BETTER BELIEVE IT.
MLP: . . . . **N 0033**

Rot (label)

END OF AN ERA (Best of Rot) (Various artists).
LP: . . . . **ASS 100**

Rota, Nino

CINEMA ITALIANO (See under Mancini, Henry) (Rota, Nino & Ennio Morricone).

NINO ROTA MOVIES, THE (see under films) (Various artists).

Rotary Connection

PEACE.
Tracks: / Opening round / Silent night / Christmas love / Last call for peace / Shopping bag menagerie / Silent night / Christmas child / Peace at last / Santa's

little helpers / Sidewalk Santa / If peace was all we had / Silent chant.
LP: GCH 8102

Roth, Arlen

GUITARIST.
LP: ROUNDER 3022
MC: ROUNDER 3022C

HOT PICKUPS.
Tracks: / Kids on the block / Not her usual man / Poor side of town / When a man loves a woman / Restless age / Treat her right / North Sea / On a cold dark night / August nights.
LP: SNTF 845
LP: ROUNDER 3044
MC: ROUNDER 3044C

LONELY ST..
LP: FF 363

PAINT JOB.
LP: BR 1225

Roth, David Lee

CRAZY FROM THE HEAT.
Tracks: / Easy Street / Just a gigolo / I ain't got nobody / California girls / Coconut grove.
LP: 925222 1
MC: 925222 4

EAT 'EM AND SMILE.
Tracks: / Yankee rose / Shy boy / I'm easy / Ladies' nite in Buffalo? / Goin' crazy / Tobacco Road / Elephant gun / Big trouble / Bump and grind / That's life.
LP: WX 56
MC: WX 56 C

LITTLE AIN'T ENOUGH, A.
LP: WX 403
MC: WX 403 C

SKYSCRAPER.
Tracks: / Hot dog and a shake / Stand up / Hina / Perfect timing / Two fools a minute / Knucklebones / Just like paradise / Bottom line / Skyscraper / Damn good / California girls (Only on re-released issue.) / Just a gigolo (Only on re-released issue.).
LP: WX 140
MC: WX 140 C
LP: WX 236
MC: WX 236 C

Roth, Philip

ZUCKERMAN BOUND.
MC: 1768

Roth, Uli John

BEYOND THE ASTRAL SKIES (Roth, Uli John & Electric Sun).
Tracks: / Night the master comes, The / What is love? / Why? / I'll be there / Return / Ice breaker / I'm a river / Angel of peace / Eleison / Son of sky / Homesick blues / East of Mississippi.
LP: ROTH 1
MC: TC ROTH 1

Rothenberg, Ned

OPPOSITES ATTRACT (See Under Dresher, Paul) (Rothenberg, Ned & Paul Dresher).

Rothensmear, Pat

PAT ROTHENSMEAR.
Tracks: / Sahara Hotel / Golden boys / Odenora / Princes / Magic candle tragic canary / Area of the circle, the / Xmas song / I heart / Gentle axe, A.
LP: SST 154
MC: SSTC 154

Rother, Michael

SUSSHERZ UND TIEFENSCHARFE.
LP: 825 619-1

Rotherfield, Jane

ATLANTIC BRIDGE (Rotherfield, Jane & Allan Carr).
LP: SIF 1080
MC: CSIF 1080

THERE AND BACK (Rotherfield, Jane & Allan Carr).
LP: TP 011

Rots

RETURN OF THE SEVEN.
Tracks: / Straight line / Can't take it no more / Is it you / Affairs / Crazy for you / Spin art / Lucy's head / Suicide / Behave yourself / Bach on the track.
LP: HR 011

Rotzkotz

MUCH FUNNY.
LP: 083 612

Rouen

YOUNG FOR A DAY.
Tracks: / Young for a day / Hold me / Wheels are turning / Don't take them away / Guilt / Let it all out / Lying all the time / Shot in the morning light / Ordinary life / Splash / Shake.
LP: EGLP 72
MC: EGMC 72

Rouge

FRISE ET ACIDE.
LP: LR 170

Rough Cutt

ROUGH CUTT.
Tracks: / Take her / Piece of my heart / Never gonna die / Dreamin' again / Cutt your heart out / Black widow / You keep breaking my heart / Kids will rock / Dressed to kill / She's too hot.
LP: 9252681

WANTS YOU.
Tracks: / Rock the USA / Bad reputation / Don't settle for less / Hot and heavy / Take a chance / We like it loud / Double trouble / You wanna be a star / Let em' talk / Night cries out, The.
LP: 925484 1
MC: 925484 4

Rough Trade

O TEMPORA! (O mores!).
LP: WKFMLP 65

ROUGHEST TRADE.
Tracks: / Crimes of passion / All touch / Lie back and let me do everything / Weapons / Birds of a feather / Grade B movie / Baptism of fire / High school confidential / Shaking the foundations / Territorial, The / America bad and beautiful.
LP: WKFMLP 43
MC: WKFMMC 43

SHAKING THE FOUNDATIONS.
Tracks: / Crimes of passion / Endless nights / Shaking the foundations / Vertigo / Numero fatale / All touch / America / Bad and beautiful / I want to live / Kiss me deadly / Fire down below / Beg for it.
LP: CBS 25412
MC: 40 25412

Roughhouse

ROUGHHOUSE.
LP: FC 44178

Roulettes

RUSS, BOB, PETE AND MOD.
Tracks: / Soon you'll be leaving me / Tell tale tit / Bad time / Can you go? / I'll remember tonight / You don't love me / Stubborn kind of fellow / Mebody / I hope he breaks your heart / Find out the truth / This little girl / What you gonna do? / Long cigarette, The / Junk / Tracks of my tears / I can't stop.
LP: ED 113

Round Midnight

ROUND MIDNIGHT.
MC: LCS 14124
LP: LOP 14124

Round Midnight (Film)

ROUND MIDNIGHT (Film Soundtrack) (Various artists).
Tracks: / Round midnight: *Various artists* / Body and soul: *Various artists* / Berangere's nightmare: *Various* artists / Fair weather: *Various artists* / Una noche con Francis: *Various artists* / Peacocks, The: *Various* artists / How long has this been going on?: *Various artists* / Rhythm-a-ning: *Various artists* / Still time: *Various artists* / Minuit aux champselysees: *Various artists* / Chan's song: *Various artists* / Now's the time: *Various artists* / Autumn in New York: *Various artists* / Encore: *Various artists* / April in Paris: *Various artists* / Parisienne thorotare: *Various artists.*
LP: 4500791
MC: 4500794
LP: CBS 70300
MC: 40 70300

Round, Thomas

LILAC TIME (See under 'Bronhill, June' for details) (Round, Thomas/June Bronhill).

Roundheads & Cavaliers

MUSIC OF THE ROUNDHEADS AND CAVALIERS (See under St. George's Canzona).

Roundtown Boys

DEADHEADS AND SUCKERS.
LP: 2001

Roundtree

ROLLER DISCO.
Tracks: / Get on up / Tonight's the night / Manhattan fever / Discocide / Manhattan / Lightning striking twice.
LP: ILPS 9527

Rouse, Charlie

CHASE IS ON, THE (Rouse, Charlie/ Paul Quinichette).
Tracks: / Chase is on, The / When the blues come on / This can't be love / Last time for love / You're cheating yourself / Knittin' / Tender trap, The / Things I love, The.
MC: TCAFF 154
LP: AFF 154

EPISTROPHY.
Tracks: / Nutty / Blue monk / Epistrophy / Ruby, my dear / 'Round midnight.
LP: LLP 1521

HOWARD MCGHEE JAZZ BROTHERS & CHARLIE ROUSE (see under McGhee, Howard).

JORDAN, ROUSE, TAYLOR - LES LIAISONS DANGEREUSES (see Jordan, Duke) (Rouse, Charlie/Duke Jordan).

MOMENTS NOTICE (Rouse, Charlie Quartet).
LP: SLP 4079

PLAYIN' IN THE YARD (Rouse, Charlie & Stan Tracey).
Tracks: / Playin' in the yard / In a sentimental mood / I've found a new baby / Li'l ol' Pottsville / Li'l Sherrie / Wee.
LP: SJ 116

SOCIAL CALL (Rouse, Charlie/Red Rodney).
LP: UP 27.18

Rouse, Mikel

COLORADO SUITE (see Reininger, Blaine) (Rouse, Mikel/Blaine Reininger).

WALK IN THE WOODS (Rouse, Mikel/ Broken Consort).
LP: MTM 6

Rouska's Dollar

ROUSKA'S DOLLAR CACOPHONY (Various artists).
Tracks: / Wonderland: *Cassandra Complex* / Cash crop: *Third Circle* / 21st century bible: *Son Of Sam* / View from Eden: *Good Shepherds* / Onassis: *WMTID.*
LP: UGRA 1

Roussos, Demis

25 WORLD HITS.
Tracks: / Happy to be on an island in the sun / Can't say how much I love you / For ever and ever / So dreamy / My friend the wind.
2LP: 6686 051
MCSET: 7523 051

DEMIS.
Tracks: / Lament / We're shining / Take me sailing / Song without end / Song for the free / Gypsy lady / Need to forget / Race to the end / Where are they now?.
LP: POLS 1061
MC: POLSC 1061

DEMIS ROUSSOS.
Tracks: / Forever and ever / Schones madchen aus arcadia / We shall dance / Lay it down / Mara / Perdoname / Sing an ode to love / Say you love me / So dreamy / Mauela / My reason / Someday, somewhere / Velvet mornings / Goodbye my love goodbye / Die neachte von athen / My friend the wind / When forever is gone / Can't say how much I love you / Kyrila / From souvenirs to souvenirs / Mourir aupres don amour / My only fascination / White wings / Sister Emilyne / Die bouzouki, die nacht und der wein / When I'm a kid.
2LP: 818 401 1
MCSET: 818 401 4

FOREVER AND EVER.
Tracks: / Forever and ever / My friend the wind / My reason / Lay it down / Lovely sunny days / Lost in a dream / Velvet mornings / Rebecca / When I'm a kid / Goodbye my love goodbye.
LP: PRICE 33
MC: PRIMC 33
LP: 6325 021
LP: 6395196

GREATER LOVE.
LP: BRLP 98
MC: BRMC 98

GREATEST HITS: DEMIS ROUSSOS.
Tracks: / We shall dance / My reason / Forever and ever / Goodbye my love goodbye / My friend the wind / Velvet mornings / Lovely lady of Arcadia / Someday, somewhere / My only fascination / Sing an ode to love / Perdoname / From souvenirs to souvenirs / Happy to be on an island in the sun / Mourir aupres de mon amour / Ainsi soitil / Lost in love.
LP: ADAH 436
MC: ADAHC 436

GREEK SONGS (see Leandros, Vicky) (Roussos, Demis/Vicky Leandros/Nana Mouskouri).

HAPPY TO BE.
LP: 9101 027

LIFE AND LOVE.
LP: 9199 873

LIVE!.
LP: BRLP 44
MC: BRMC 44

MAGIC.
Tracks: / Happy to be on an island in the sun / I love you / When forever has gone / May be forever / Margarita / Time and tide / Let it happen / Day O (Banana boat song) / Before the storm / My face in the rain / Because / Sister Emilyne.
LP: CN 2042
MC: CN4 2042
LP: 9101131

MAN OF THE WORLD.
Tracks: / Man of the world / Lost in love / Miss you nights / Little girl / I need you / I'd give my life / Sorry / How glad I am you came / San Pedro's children / Wedding song / Love it away / We're over.
LP: 6302 018

MUSIC OF DEMIS ROUSSOS VOL.1 1974/75.
MC: 7206 079

MY FRIEND THE WIND.
Tracks: / Rain and tears / We shall dance / Forever and ever (and ever) / My friend the wind / My reason / Goodbye my love goodbye / Follow me / Summer wine / Marie Jolie / Summer in her eyes / Greater love / Tropicana bay / Island of love / Lovely lady of Arcadia / I found you (CD only.) / Spring Summer Winter and Fall (CD only.) / I want to live (CD only.) / End of the world (CD only.).
LP: MFP 5871
MC: TCMFP 5871

MY ONLY FASCINATION.
LP: 6325 094

REFLECTION.
LP: DEMIS 1
MC: ZCDEM 1

SOUVENIRS.
LP: 6325 201

VELVET MORNINGS.
Tracks: / My only fascination / I'll be your friend / Names / Happy to be on an island in the sun / O my friends you've been untrue to me / Lovely lady of Arcadia / Forever and ever / My friend the wind / White wings / Velvet mornings / Mountains beyond / Goodbye my love goodbye.
LP: 6395074

Routledge, Keith

WORSHIP HIS MAJESTY.
LP: SOP R 2011
MC: SOP C 2011

Routledge, Patricia

ALICE IN WONDERLAND (see under Carroll, Lewis (aut)).

FORTY YEARS ON/A WOMAN OF NO IMPORTANCE (see under Forty Years On (bk)) (Gielgud, Sir John/Patricia Routledge (nars)).

WUTHERING HEIGHTS (see under Wuthering Heights (bk)).

Roux, Jose

DANSES D'AUVERGNE - BOURREES, VALSES, SCOTTISCH (Roux, Jose & L'Auvernha Tournidjaire).
Tracks: / Lo bouoli lo Marianno / Ent'anara garda / L'Aurillacoise / Paro lou loup, petiote / Regret d'Auvergne / Tiro l'auto / Lou diziou be pierrou / De delai lou ribotel / L'aiguo de rotzo / Lo codretto / La Louise / Mariez-moi ma mere / Garcons de la montagne / O Cahla, pauvre Cahla / La grande / Ai vist lou loup.
LP: ARN 33495
MC: ARN 433495

Rover

ROVER, THE (L'AVVENTURIERO) (Original Soundtrack) (Various artists).
LP: SP 8022

Rovers

NO MORE BREAD AND BUTTER.
LP: LAT 1118

ROVERS, THE.
LP: LAT 1095

Roving journeyman

ROVING JOURNEYMAN Songs of the travellers (Various artists).
Tracks: / Roving journey man, The: *Various artists* / Atching tan song: *Various artists* / Beggar wench: *Various* artists / Berryfields o'Blair, The: *Various artists* / Bogie's bonnie belle: *Various artists* / Choring song: *Various artists* / Hush little baby: *Various artists* / I binged avree: *Various artists* / Beggarman, The: *Various artists* / Little gypsy girl: *Various artists* / Lost lady found, The: *Various artists* / McPherson's rant: *Various artists* / Mandi went ti poov the grys: *Various artists* / Moss o' Burreldale, The: *Various* artists / Next pudden Ken: *Various artists* / Row-dow-dow: *Various artists* / Squire and the gipsy: *Various* artists / Blooming lavender: *Various artists* / Tramps and hawkers: *Various*

artists / Travelling candyman: *Various artists* / Flash girls: *Various artists*.
MC: 60-031

Rowan, Chris

LIVIN' THE LIFE (Rowan, Chris & Lorin).
LP: . . . . AP 011

Rowan, Keith

ROWAN, KEITH & ROONEY (Rowan, Keith & Rooney).
Tracks: / Blue Ridge Mountain blues / Riding high in Texas / Outlaw love / Texican badman / Caravan / Midnight moonlight / Sleep with one eye open / Flint hill special / Tennessee blues / Auld lang syne.
LP: . . . . WF 016

Rowan, Neil

AMAZING SOUNDS OF NEIL ROWAN, THE.
Tracks: / Horse of the year theme / Loch Lomond / Nothern lights / Westering home / Toccata / Erinskay love song / Sky boat song / Quando, quando, quando / Chattanooga choo choo / American patrol / In the mood / Dark island / I got rhythm.
LP: . . . . AFA 841
MC: . . . . AFAC 841

NEIL ROWAN.
Tracks: / Jigs / Bluebell polka / March/ Strathspey/Reel / Waltzes / Reels / Road to the isles medley / Amazing Grace / Sweet Georgia Brown / Czardas.
LP: . . . . AFA 832
MC: . . . . AFAC 832

Rowan, Peter

ALL ON A RISING DAY.
MC: . . . . SPDC 1044

DUST BOWL CHILDREN.
Tracks: / Dust bowl children / Before the streets were paved / Electric blanket / Little mother / Barefoot country road / Seeds my daddy sowed / Tumbleweed / Dream of a home / Rainmaker.
LP: . . . . SH 3781
MC: . . . . ZCSH 3781

FIRST WHIPPERWILL, THE.
Tracks: / I'm on my way back to the old home / I'm just a used to be / I believed in you darling / Sweetheart you done me wrong / When the golden leaves begin to fall / I was left on the street / Goodbye old pal / When you are lonely / First whipperwill, The / Sitting alone in the moonlight / Boat of love / It's mighty dark to travel.
LP: . . . . SH 3749
MC: . . . . ZCSH 3749

MEDICINE TRAIL.
Tracks: / Riding high in Texas / My foolish pride / River of stone / Revelation / Lying on the line / Medicine trail / Blues come bother me / Dreaming I love you / Maui momma / Prairie lullabye.
LP: . . . . FF 205

NEW MOON RISING (Rowan, Peter & The Nashville Bluegrass Band).
Tracks: / That high lonesome sound / Trail of tears / Memories of you / Moth to a flame, A / I'm gonna love you / One way / New moon rising / Jesus made the wine / Cabin of love / Meadow green.
LP: . . . . SPD 1014
MC: . . . . SPDC 1014

OLD AND IN THE WAY (see Garcia, Jerry) (Rowan, Peter/Jerry Garcia/David Grisman).

PETER ROWAN.
Tracks: / Outlaw love / Break my heart again / Woman in love, A / When I was a cowboy / Land of the Navajo / Free Mexican Airforce, The / Panama red / Midnite moonlite / Gypsy King's farewell, The.
LP: . . . . SPD 1005
MC: . . . . SPDC 1005
LP: . . . . FF 071

PETER ROWAN AND RED HOT PICKERS.
Tracks: / Hobo song, The / Old old house / Willow garden / Jimmy Brown the Newsboy / Wild Billy Jones / Hiroshima mon amour / Come ye tender hearted / Oh Susanna / Rosalie McFall / Good woman's love, A.
LP: . . . . SH 3733
MC: . . . . ZCSH 3733

PETER ROWAN AND THE WILD STALLIONS (Rowan, Peter & The Wild Stallions).
Tracks: / I can't get mellow / Hotter she burns, The / Fool myself again / Baby let's play house / Call it love / Woman in love, A / Cries of love / Refugee / Sheila rendezvous / Primavera dell' amore.
LP: . . . . AP 016

REVELRY.
Tracks: / Holly wells of Ireland, The / Maelstrom / Sitting on the top of the world / Rising o' the bones / Lovesick blues / Talkin' bluegrass / Black mountain juice / Mansion on the hill / When I was a cowboy / No place like home.
LP: . . . . WF 012

TEXICAN BAD MAN.
Tracks: / Sweet Melinda / Four corners / Vacant sea, A / I can't help it / Squeeze box man / Texican badman / What of Alicia / While the ocean roars / Awake my love / On the blue horizon.
LP: . . . . AP 010

WALLS OF TIME.
Tracks: / Roving gambler / Lone pilgrim / Raglan Road / Going up the mountain / Casey's last ride / Moonshiner / Thirsty in the rain / Walls of time / Plains of waterloo.
LP: . . . . SH 3722
MC: . . . . ZCSH 3722

WILD STALLIONS.
LP: . . . . AP 016

WITH THE RED HOT PICKERS.
LP: . . . . SPIN 108
MC: . . . . SPIC 108

Rowans Three

TRAVELLING NORTH.
Tracks: / Unicorn / Couter's candy / When the wind blows / Bango blues / Ian gun cuaich / Peggy Gordan / Leis an lurgainn / Musgravt / Westlin winds.
MC: . . . . NOR 1

Rowe, Alan

ORGAN RECITAL.
Tracks: / Grand jeu / Nun bitten wir der heiligen geist / Vive le roi / O Dulcissima maria / Intermedes du ve ton / Now let the men of Suffolk sing / Voluntary in a minor / How beautiful are the feet / Let the bright seraphim / Organ concerto / Who would true valour see.
MC: . . . . BH 8810

Rowe, John (aut)

BIT OF A DO, A (see under Bit Of A Do (bk)).

Rowland, Kevin

KEVIN ROWLAND & DEXYS MIDNIGHT RUNNERS (VIDEO) (see under Dexys Midnight Runners) (Rowland, Kevin & Dexy's Midnight Runners).

WANDERER, THE.
Tracks: / Young man / Walk away / You'll be the one for me / Heartaches by the number / I am a wanderer / Tonight / When you walk alone / Age can't wither you / I want / Remember me.
LP: . . . . MERH 121
MC: . . . . MERHC 121

Rowland, Mike

FAIRY WING, THE.
MC: . . . . C 500

SILVER WINGS.
MC: . . . . C 502

TITANIA - THE FAIRY QUEEN.
MC: . . . . C 504

Rowles, Jimmy

FIORELLE UPTOWN/ MARY SUNSHINE DOWNTOWN.
LP: . . . . FS 267

IF I'M LUCKY (see Sims, Zoot) (Rowles, Jimmy & Zoot Sims).

ISFAHAN.
Tracks: / Marjo / Black butterfly / It might as well be spring / How deep is the ocean / Voices deep within me / Yesterdays / Button up your overcoat / This is a night for love / Isfahan.
LP: . . . . SNTF 790
MC: . . . . ZCSN 790

LET'S GET ACQUAINTED WITH JAZZ (Rowles, Jimmy Sextet).
LP: . . . . VSOP 11

MUSIC'S THE ONLY THING THAT'S ON MY MY MIND (Rowles, Jimmy & George Mraz).
LP: . . . . AP 188

PEACOCKS (Rowles, Jimmy & Michael Hashim).
LP: . . . . ST 227

REMEMBER WHEN.
MC: . . . . CHEMC 11

TRIO (Rowles, Jimmy, Red Mitchell & Donald Bailey).
MC: 740094

WARM TENOR (see Sims, Zoot) (Rowles, Jimmy & Zoot Sims).

WEATHER IN A JAZZ VANE (Rowles, Jimmy Septet).
LP: . . . . VSOP 48

Rowles, Stacy

TELL IT LIKE IT IS.
Tracks: / Most like Lee / Old folks / Alabamy home / Mighty like the blues / Tell it like it is / There is no greater love / Devils' island / Lotus blossom.
LP: . . . . CJ 249

Rowsome, Leo

CLASSICS OF IRISH PIPING VOL.1.
LP: 12T 259

CLASSICS OF IRISH PIPING VOL.3.
LP: 12T 322

KING OF PIPERS.
LP: . . . . CC 1
MC: 4CC 1

Rox

VIOLENT BREED.
LP: . . . . MFN 11

Roxanne

ROXANNE.
LP: . . . . POLD 5226
MC: . . . . POLDC 5226

Roxanne (Film)

ROXANNE (Film Soundtrack) (Various artists).
Tracks: / Roxanne: *Various artists* / Starry sky: *Various artists* / Just honest - we did it: *Various artists*/ Roxanne's theme: *Various artists* / Game, set and match: *Various artists* / Panache, The: *Various artists*/ Roxanne's eyes: *Various artists* / Blue Danube: *Various artists* / Written in the wind: *Various artists*/ Roxanne (end title): *Various artists*.
LP: . . . . FILM 023
MC: . . . . FILMC 023

Roxette

JOYRIDE (ALBUM).
Tracks: / Joyride / Hotblooded / Fading like a flower (every time you leave) / Knockin' on every door / Spending my time / I remember you (Not on album) / Watercolours in the rain / Big L, The / Soul deep (Not on album) / (Do you get) excited? / Church of your heart (Not on album) / Small talk / Physical fascination / Things will never be the same / Perfect day.
LP: . . . . EMD 1019
MC: . . . . TCEMD 1019

LOOK SHARP.
Tracks: / Look, The / Dressed for success / Sleeping single / Paint / Dance away / Cry / Chances / Dangerous / Half a woman, half a shadow / View from a hill / I could never give you up (CD only.) / Shadow of a doubt / Listen to your heart.
LP: . . . . EMC 3557
MC: . . . . TCEMC 3557

Roxx Gang

THINGS YOU'VE NEVER DONE BEFORE.
Tracks: / Scratch my back / No easy way out / Race with the devil / Red rose / Live fast die young / Too cool for school / Ball'n'chain / Fastest gun in town / Nine lives / Need your sex.
LP: . . . . VUSLP 4
MC: . . . . VUSMC 4

Roxy Music

ATLANTIC YEARS 1973-1980.
Tracks: / Dance away / Angel eyes / Over you / Love is the drug / Oh yeah / My only love / In the midnight hour / Ain't that so / Still falls the rain / Do the Strand.
LP: . . . . EGLP 54
MC: . . . . EGMC 54

AVALON.
Tracks: / More than this / Space between, The / India / While my heart is still beating / Main thing / Take a chance with me / Avalon / To turn you on / True to life / Tara.
LP: . . . . EGLP 50
MC: . . . . EGMC 50
LP: . . . . EGHP 50

COUNTRY LIFE.
Tracks: / Thrill of it all / Three and nine / All I want is you / Out of the blue / If it takes all night / Bittersweet / Triptych / Casanova / Really good time, A / Prairie rose.
LP: . . . . EGLP 16
MC: . . . . EGMC 16
LP: . . . . ILPS 9303

FIRST SEVEN ALBUMS, THE.
LPS: . . . . EGBS 1

FLESH AND BLOOD.
Tracks: / In the midnight hour / Oh yeah / Same old scene / Flesh and blood / My only love / Over you / Eight miles high / Rain, rain, rain / Running wild / No strange delight.
LP: . . . . EGLP 46
MC: . . . . EGMC 46
LP: . . . . POLH 002

FOR YOUR PLEASURE.
Tracks: / Do the Strand / Beauty Queen / Strictly confidential / Editions of you / In every dream home a heartache / Bogus man, The / Grey lagoons / For your pleasure.
LP: . . . . EGLP 8
MC: . . . . EGMC 8
LP: . . . . ILPS 9232

GREATEST HITS: ROXY MUSIC.
Tracks: / Virginia plain / Do the Strand / All I want is you / Out of the blue / Pyjamarama / Editions of you / Love is the drug / Mother of pearl / Song for Europe / Thrill of it all / Street life.
LP: 2302 073
LP: . . . . EGLP 31

HEART STILL BEATING (LIVE).
LP: . . . . EGLP 77
MC: . . . . EGMC 77

HIGH ROAD, THE.
Tracks: / Can't let go / My only love / Like a hurricane / Jealous guy.
LP: . . . . EGMLP 1
MC: . . . . EGMMC 1

MANIFESTO.
Tracks: / Ain't that so / Cry cry cry / Dance away / Manifesto / My little girl / Spin me round / Still falls the rain / Trash / Stronger through the years.
LP: . . . . EGLP 38
MC: . . . . EGMC 38
LP: . . . . POLH 001

ROXY MUSIC.
Tracks: / Bitters end / Bob, The / Chance meeting / If there is something / Ladytron / Re-make/Re-model / 2HB / Would you believe? / Sea breezes.
LP: . . . . EGLP 6
MC: . . . . EGMC 6
LP: . . . . ILPS 9200

ROXY MUSIC EARLY YEARS BOX SET (Roxy Music/For your pleasure/ Stranded).
MC: . . . . EGBM 3

ROXY MUSIC LATER YEARS BOX SET.
MC: . . . . EGBM 4

SIREN.
Tracks: / Love is the drug / End of the line / Sentimental fool / Whirlwind / She sells / Could it happen to me? / Both ends burning / Nightingale / Just another high.
LP: . . . . EGLP 20
MC: . . . . EGMC 20
LP: . . . . ILPS 9344

STRANDED.
Tracks: / Street life / Just like you / Amazon / Psalm / Serenade / Song for Europe / Mother of pearl / Sunset.
LP: . . . . EGLP 10
MC: . . . . EGMC 10
LP: . . . . ILPS 9252

VIVA ROXY MUSIC.
Tracks: / Out of the blue / Pyjamarama / Bogus man, The / Chance meeting / If there is something / In every dream home a heartache / Do the Strand / Can't let go / My only love / Like a hurricane / Jealous guy.
LP: 2302 053
MC: 3100 353
LP: . . . . ILPS 9400
LP: . . . . EGLP 25
MC: . . . . EGMC 25

Roy, Alan

FORGOTTEN DREAMS.
Tracks: / Forgotten dreams / Scotch on the rocks / Strangers on the shore / Spanish flea / Windmills of your mind / Dambusters march / Sabre dance / Amazing grace / Walk in the Black Forest, A / Moulin Rouge / Oh mein papa / Black bear, The.
LP: . . . . NA 122
MC: . . . . NC 122

HAPPY ACCORDION OF ALAN ROY.
Tracks: / Accordion club march / Cuckoo waltz / Isla neuk / Swiss polka / Wild mountain tyme / Savoy American medley / Dave and Daisy / Polka des as / Jane Findlay's farewell to home / March hare / Dashing white sergeant / Mon Paris selection.
LP: . . . . LILP 5101

Roy, Alvin

JAZZ IN PARK ROYAL (Roy, Alvin Star Sound).
LP: . . . . ZR 1012

Roy, Freddie

TO LOVE SOMEBODY.
MC: . . . . FJ 3301C
LP: . . . . FJ 3301

Roy, Harry

ARE YOU LISTENING? (Roy, Harry & His Orchestra).
2LP: . . . . SH 187/8

BUGLE CALL RAG (Roy, Harry & His Orchestra).
Tracks: / Bugle call rag / It had to be you / Darktown strutter's ball / I've found a new baby / You made a plaything out of my heart / Blues in mayfair / Guilty / Cuban moonlight / Lover man / Leicester Square rag / Imaginez / Temptation rag / Old gal's got that new look / Park Lane blues / You're my baby / Canadian capers / After you get what you want, you don't want it / Picadilly rag.
LP: . . . . **RFL 20**

EVERYBODY'S SWINGIN' IT NOW (Roy, Harry & His Tiger Ragamuffins).
Tracks: / Jazz me blues / You gotta know how to dance / Someday, sweetheart / Everybody's swingin' it now / Hot lips / Jealous / Whispering / Poor butterfly / Ev'ry time I look at you / Swing / Scat singers, The / Shine / That's a plenty / Eeny meeny miney mo / Memories of you / Rain / Goodbye blues / I heard a song in a taxi / I'm a ding dong daddy / Farewell blues / You rascal you / Muddy waters / Bugle call rag / Tiger rag / St. Louis blues.
LP: . . . . **AJA 5050**
MC: . . . . **ZC AJA 5050**

GOLDEN AGE OF HARRY ROY AND HIS ORCHESTRA, THE (Roy, Harry & His Orchestra).
Tracks: / Bugle call rag / Roy rag, The (Roy) / Alexander's ragtime band / Canadian capers / She had to go and lose it at the Astor / Emaline / Mood indigo / Jubilation rag / Tiger rag / Somebody stole my gal / Twelfth St. rag / Nobody's sweetheart / Porcupine rag / Temptation rag / What a difference a day made / Heatwave.
LP: . . . . **GX 2508**
MC: . . . . **TCGX 2508**

HARRY ROY AND HIS ORCHESTRA (Roy, Harry & His Orchestra).
Tracks: / Truckin' on down / No moon,no stars, just you / London on a rainy night / Troublesome trumpet / Smoke gets in your eyes / Beat o'my heart (The) / Gertie the girl with the gong / Object of my affection, The / Cowboy in Manhatten / Let's have a jubilee / Louisiana lullaby / We're gonna have smooth sailing / Love and a dime / Words are in my heart, The / My hat's on the side of my head / Was in the mood (I) / Hurricane Harry / Stars over Devon / You've got me crying again / Swingly little thingy.
LP: . . . . **OLD 8**
MC: . . . . **COLD 8**

HE'S TERRIFIC!.
Tracks: / Three little fishes / Limehouse blues / Mama, that moon is here again / Clarinet marmalade / I'm on a see saw / Shut-eye / O, O, O, O, O, Oh-Boom! / No name rag / She's tall, she's tan, she's terrific / Lady likes to move, The / Maple leaf rag / Milenberg joys / On the outside looking in / There's a ranch in the rockies / Down home rag / And the angels sing.
MC: . . . . **CMOIR 304**

HOT-CHA-MA-CHA-CHA (Roy, Harry & His Orchestra).
Tracks: / Rock and roll / There's a new day coming / Twelfth Street rag (Bowman) / When a St. Louis woman comes down to New Orleans / Stay out of the south / Canadian capers / Roy rag, The (Roy) / Let's call it a day / Troublesome trumpet / Eadie was a lady / Bugle call rag / Mama dont want no peas 'n' rice 'n' coconut oil / Lover / Build a little home / My pet / Black panther.
LP: . . . . **AJA 5035**
MC: . . . . **ZC AJA 5035**

LET'S SWING IT.
Tracks: / Let's swing it / There's a small hotel / Life is empty without love / Cubalero, The / Remember me / Sentimental fool / Here comes the sandman / Goodnight my love / There's that look in your eyes again / Speaking of the weather / I feel like a feather in the breeze / With plenty of money and you / Love bug will bite you, The / Lookin' around corners for you / What will I tell my heart / Let's put our heads together / Boo-hoo / All's fair in love and war.
LP: . . . . **BUR 013**
MC: . . . . **4 BUR 013**

MAYFAIR NIGHTS (Roy, Harry & His Orchestra).
Tracks: / There's a new day comin' / Lou'siana lullaby / Build a little home / Keep young and beautiful / Lonely feet / Beat o' my heart / Ridin' around in the rain / When you climb those golden stairs / Ill wind (you're blowin' me no good) / Dreamy serenade / Like taking candy from a baby / Say it / Casa Loma stomp / What are you going to do (when love comes)? / La cucaracha / Stay as sweet as you are / Continental, The / Love is just around the corner / June in January / Rock and roll.
LP: . . . . **SVL 171**

MILENBERG JOYS.
LP: . . . . **HQ 3022**

RAGGIN' THE RAGS (Roy, Harry & The Hotcha Boys).
Tracks: / Tiger rag / Leave it to Eddie / Harry's rag / Leicester Square rag / Love is / Uncle Wilbur / Sweet Georgia Brown / 12th Street rag.
LP: . . . . **JOY 131**

THERE GOES THAT SONG AGAIN (Roy, Harry & His Band).
Tracks: / Drummer boy / That's the moon, my son / Missouri scrambler / My heart tells me / Pennsylvania polka / Infatuation / You are my sunshine / There goes that song again / Kindergarten conga / Two pairs of shoes / You're wrong / Tzigane swing / I've got a gal in Kalamazoo / Sweetheart it's you / Victory roll rag / Our back street is Broadway / Sailor with the navy blue eyes, The / Swinging with Rig.
LP: . . . . **PLE 501**
MC: . . . . **TC-PLE 501**

TRUCKIN' ON DOWN (Roy, Harry & His Orchestra).
Tracks: / What a little moonlight can do / I wish I were twins / Jungle fever / Dr. Heckle and Mr.Jibe / Valentina rumba / Easter parade / You and the night and the music / Blue moon / Stars over Devon / Truckin' on down / Piano madness / My girl's a rhythm fan / Heart of gold / Man of my dreams, The / Way you look tonight, The / Fine romance, A / Boo-hoo / Rita, the rumba queen / Broken hearted clown / Why can't we make love?.
LP: . . . . **SVL 191**
MC: . . . . **CSVL 191**

Roy, I.

LYRICS MAN, THE.
LP: . . . . **MMLP 0016**

Roy, William

WHEN I SING ALONE.
LP: . . . . **AP 213**

Royal Air Force

70 YEARS (RAF Central Band).
Tracks: / Brave defenders / Royal Air Force march past / Spitfire preluge and fugue / Lawrence of Arabia / Four caballeros / TV sports themes / Oor Wullie / Fanfare on the RAF call / March and dance of the comedians / Little light music, A / Viva musica / Introduction and march from the Battle Of Britain / Those magnificent men in their flying machines / Concert march- Cockleshell heroes / Elegy / March- Uxbridge.
LP: . . . . **BND 1039**
MC: . . . . **ZC BND 1039**

BEST OF THE CENTRAL BAND OF THE RAF (RAF Central Band).
Tracks: / Salute to the Royal Air Force / Colditz march / Slide kicks / Forsyte saga / Pentagon / Reach for the sky / Poll's dance finale and 2nd suite / March of the King's men / Jumping bean / British Empire / Carousel waltz / Slavonic waltz no. 7 / Battle of Britain.
LP: . . . . **OU 2225**
LP: . . . . **OU 2090**

BRITISH MUSIC FOR CONCERT BAND (RAF Central Band).
LP: . . . . **EL 2700934**

BRITISH MUSIC FOR CONCERT BAND VOL. 2 (RAF Central Band).
LP: . . . . **EL 2704671**
MC: . . . . **EL 2704674**

CAVALRY OF THE CLOUDS AND OTHER MARCHES (RAF Central Band).
Tracks: / Royal Air Force march past / Cavalry of the clouds / New colonial, The / Bless 'em all / Out of the blue / Ballad of Sulaiman, The / Officer of the day / Old Panama / Prelude spitfire / 633 squadron / Airborne divsion / King o' the clouds / Those magnificent men in their flying machines / R.A.F. anniversary march / Dambusters / Crown imperial.
LP: . . . . **ESD 1078001**
MC: . . . . **TCESD 1078004**

DANKE SCHON (Band of the RAF Germany).
Tracks: / Stage centre / Avengers, The / Walk in the Black Forest, A / Swinging safari / Beer barrel polka / Danke schon / War of the worlds / Wonderland by night / Old comrades / Country gardens / Skyrider / Colonel Bogey / Elizabethan serenade / Carmina burana.
LP: . . . . **PRM 107D**
MC: . . . . **CPRM 107D**

DIAMONDS IN THE SKY (RAF Central Band).
LP: . . . . **TWOX 1076**

HIGHER AND HIGHER (Central Band of the RAF).
LP: . . . . **DS 028**

I COULD HAVE DANCED ALL NIGHT (RAF Central Band).
LP: . . . . **DS 045**

KEEPERS OF THE PEACE (RAF Band of Germany).
Tracks: / Berliner luft / Royal Air Force march past / Squadron / Holyrood / Always ready / Keepers of the peace / Tornado / Skywatch / Skywriter, The / Ein festburg (A firm fortress) / Vallis vesperis (Ramparts of the west) / Imner bereit (Always ready) / To seek and strike.
LP: . . . . **BND 1017**
MC: . . . . **ZC BND 1017**

MAGNIFICENT MEN (RAF Regiment Band).
Tracks: / Those magnificent men in their flying machines / Royal Air Force association march / Fox covert / Battle of Britain / Zealous in support / Dambusters march / Walls are men, The / Holyrood / Raiders of the lost ark / Early one morning / Sounds familiar / Pavane / Beguine festival / My name is Bond.
MC: . . . . **ZC BND 1027**
LP: . . . . **BND 1027**

MARCHING WITH THE RAF (RAF Central Band).
LP: . . . . **OU 2188**

R.A.F. BRIZE NORTON SINGERS.
Tracks: / Sing we can and chant it / As torrnets in Summer / Elijah rock / Lennon & McCartney / Lona boat song / Feelings / Homing / All in the April evening / Eagle high / Unbounded grace / Fairest evening / Angels rolled the stone away.
LP: . . . . **MM 0593**

RAF TUNES OF GLORY.
MC: . . . . **AM 21**

ROYAL AIRFORCE.
LP: . . . . **EV 100**

SALUTE TO HEROES (50th Anniversary Album) (RAF Central Band).
Tracks: / Royal Air Force march past / Pathfinder's march, The / Dambusters / Those magnificent men in their flying machines / Reach for the sky / Out of the blue / Crown imperial / 633 squadron / Colditz march / Cavalry of the clouds / Secret army / Aces high / Spitfire prelude / Battle of Britain / We'll meet again / Valiant years, The (CD only.) / White cliffs of Dover (CD only.) / Run, rabbit, run (CD only.).
LP: . . . . **RAF 1**
MC: . . . . **TCRAF 1**

STRIKE UP THE BAND (RAF Central Band).
Tracks: / Strike up the band / Hora staccato / Marche lorraine / Stardust / Stage centre / Autumn leaves / Mozart rondo / Arromanches / Prelude:richard III / British / Prince of wales march / Festive overture / March from little suite / Procession of nobles / Festmusik der stadt wien.
LP: . . . . **EL 270 590 1**
MC: . . . . **EL 270 590 4**

Royal Artillery...

IT'S MUSIC EVERYWHERE (Royal Artillery Orchestra).
Tracks: / Watching the wheat / Fiddle faddle / Shy serenade / Harry Lime theme / Cafe Mozart waltz / Souveneir d'Ukraine / Serenade for a gondolier / Intermezzo 'Manon Lescaut' / Intermezzo from Cavalleria Rusticana.
LP: **15-57**

MARCHING STRINGS (Royal Artillery Orchestra).
Tracks: / Royal artillery slow march / Marching strings / Stars and stripes forever / Skye boat song / Knot's Landing / El Capitan / March of the toys / Seventy-six trombones / Semper fedilis / Trap, The / Entry of the boyards / Marching folk / Allies, The / Ob-la-di Ob-la-da / Winged dagger, The.
MC: . . . . **ZC BND 1031**
LP: . . . . **BND 1031**

Royal Assassins

ROYAL ASSASSINS, THE.
Tracks: / Open up the rivers / Second breath / Feels so good / High wire / Ju ju man / Quiet sun / Brave new world / Song of a bullet / Let's partake.
LP: . . . . **FIRELP 13**

Royal, Billy Joe

ROYAL TREATMENT, THE.
Tracks: / I'll pin a note on your pillow / Give 'em my number / He'll have to go / Look what you've done to my heart / Let it rain / It's who's in your heart / Out of sight and on my mind / It keeps right on a-hurtin' / She don't cry like she used to / Place for the heartache, A.
LP: . . . . **K 790 658 1**
MC: . . . . **K 790 658 4**

Royal College of Music

CAROLS FOR CHRISTMAS (see under Jones, Aled) (Royal College of Music ChamberChoir/AledJones/ DavidWillcocks).

Royal Corps (1)

GILBERT AND SULLIVAN ON PARADE (Royal Corps of Transport Band).
Tracks: / Pirates of Penzance / Savoy soldiers, The / Sullivan's law / Overture / Yeoman of the guard, The / Sullivan at sea / March of the peers / Poet's march, The.
LP: . . . . **BND 1008**
MC: . . . . **ZC BND 1008**

IN CONCERT (Royal Corps of Transport Band).
Tracks: / Marche Americane / Trumpet volutary / Romance / Allegretto from Irish symphony / Duet from the Pearl Fishers / El rancho grande / Pentagon / March bombasto / Overture- Gypsy Baron / Allegro spiritoso / Hejre Kate / O solo mio / Sing sing sing / Wait for the wagon.
LP: . . . . **BND 1042**
MC: . . . . **ZC BND 1042**

MUSIC FROM THE HORSE OF THE YEAR SHOW (TV theme) (Royal Corps of Transport Band).
Tracks: / Musical joke, A / Fanfare for the Horse Of The Year show / Man's man for a' that / Greensleeves / Policeman's holiday / King Cotton.
LP: . . . . **BND 1001**
MC: . . . . **ZC BND 1001**

SALUTE TO ABBA (Royal Corps of Transport Band).
Tracks: / March - Waterloo / Name of the game / I have a dream / Gimme gimme gimme / S.O.S. / Dancing queen / Fernando / Overture -Arrival / Arrival / Dum dum diddle / Tiger / My love my life / Why did it have to be me / Chiquitita / Money money money / Hasta manana / Mama mia / Thank you for the music.
LP: . . . . **PRD 2015**
MC: . . . . **PHD 4 2015**

SOUSA THE MARCH KING (Royal Corps of Transport Band).
LP: . . . . **DR 17**

WAIT FOR THE WAGON (Royal Corps of Transport Band).
LP: . . . . **DR 5**

Royal Corps (2)

ICE TIME (Royal Corps of Signals).
MC: . . . . **ZCM 330**

WINTER SPORTS (Royal Corps Signals Concert Band).
Tracks: / Alpen tanz / Ski slope for beginners / Toboggan / Les patineurs / Tyrolean tubas / Winter carnival / Austrian dance / Sleigh ride / Snow flakes / Tyrolean tavern / Troika / Clarinet polka / Snow coach / March of the Swiss alpine club.
LP: . . . . **REC 268**

Royal Counts

ACAPPELLA SOUL.
LP: . . . . **CATA 904**

Royal Court Of China

GEARED AND PRIMED.
Tracks: / Geared and primed / Half the truth / It came crashing down the staircase / Six empty bottles / Mr. Indecision / Tijuana go / Dragon park / So yer love is true / This time around / Take me down.
LP: . . . . **AMA 5234**
MC: . . . . **AMC 5234**

Royal Doulton Band

BRASS ARIA.
LP: . . . . **TBX 3014**

BRASS BAND COUNTRY.
Tracks: / Dixie / Your cheatin' heart / Take me home country roads / Don't it make my brown eyes blue / One day at a time / Country and western / Rocky top / All I have to do is dream / Burlington, Quincy and Cincinatti express / For the good times / I love my love / Battle hymn of the republic.
LP: . . . . **BNB 2010**
MC: . . . . **ZC BNB 2010**

BRASS SHOWCASE.
MC: . . . . **PRD 42013**
LP: . . . . **PRD 2013**

CHRISTMAS CELEBRATION FOR BRASS BAND.
Tracks: / Prelude to Christmas / Sleigh ride / When a child is born / Cornet carillon / Lullaby for Christmas / White Christmas / Joyful occasion, A / Silent night / Three carols for brass / Mary's boy child / Hark the herald angels sing / Coventry carol / We wish you a merry Christmas.
LP: . . . . **BNB 2001**

MC: . . . . ZC BNB 2001

CLAYHANGER.
Tracks: / Clayhanger / Falcons, The / To a wild rose / Trumpets wild / March of the toys / Instant concert / Pendine march / Rosary, The / Entertainer, The / Work song / Paint your wagon selection.
LP: . . . . TBX 3005

FESTIVAL FANFARE.
Tracks: / Festival fanfare / Floral dance / My love is like a red red rose / Tiptoe through the tulips / Pastorale / Watching the wheat / Beautiful garden's march / National garden festival theme / To a wild rose / Clog dance / Serenade to peace / Merry old gardener, The / Heritage of the potteries / Country gardens / Tranquility.
LP: . . . . BNB 2009
MC: . . . . ZC BNB 2009

HYMNS FOR BAND.
Tracks: / Praise my soul the king of heaven / Onward christian soldiers / King of love my shepherd is, The / Day thou gavest lord is ended, The / All things bright and beautiful / Lord's my shepherd, The / Amazing grace / Immortal invisible God only wise / Holy city, The / Now the day is over / He who would valiant be / All people that on earth do dwell / Old rugged cross, The / Now thank we all our God / Ave Maria / O praise ye the lord / Let us with a gladsome mind / Abide with me / Jerusalem / How sweet the name of Jesus sounds.
LP: . . . . BNB 2006
MC: . . . . ZC BNB 2006

IMAGES IN BRASS.
LP: . . . . BNB 2007
MC: . . . . ZC BND 2007

STANDARD OF ST GEORGE.
Tracks: / Star wars / Who pays the ferryman / Sunshine of your smile, The / Devil's gallop / Smoke gets in your eyes / French comedy overture / Standard of St. George, The / Bassomatic / Snowy white polka / My old Kentucky home.
LP: . . . . TB 3015

Royal Engineers Band

GOLDEN HOUR OF NATIONAL ANTHEMS AND INTERNATIONAL.
Tracks: / God save the queen / Soldier's song, The / Advance Australia fair / God defend New Zealand / O Canada / Star spangled banner, The / Hail to the chief / Russian national anthem / Hope / La brabanconne / Wilhelmus van Nassouwe / Ons hemecht / La Marseillaise / Deutschland lied / Schwelsenpsalon / In di mameli / God save the Queen (half version) / Maame - our land / Du gamla du fria / King Kristian / Yes we love with fond devotion / Commonwealth marches / Waltzing Matilda / Maple leaf forever / Rule Britannia / America the beautiful / March Militaire / Racozy march / Radetzky march / Figaro / Soldiers' marches / Soldiers in the park / There's someting about a soldier / Scottish soldier, A / Soldiers' chorus / Soldiers of the Queen.
LP: . . . . GH 611

MELODY ON THE MOVE.
LP: . . . . TP 302
MC: . . . . TK 302

UBIQUE.
Tracks: / Triumph of right / Marche la ronde / Royal standard / Invincible eagle, The / Florentier march / Carnival day / Engeland vaarders / Cavalry of the steppes / Friedlander marsch / Aida grand march / Bullfighters / Waltzing Matilda / Hurrah for the C.R.E. / Wings.
LP: . . . . MM 0585

Royal Family

STRAIGHT FROM THE UNDERGROUND.
LP: . . . . SPOCK 2
MC: . . . . SPOCK 2C

Royal Family & The

IN THE SEA OF E.
LP: . . . . PHASE 003

LIVE: ROYAL FAMILY & THE POOR.
LP: . . . . LOOSE 13

PROJECT THE.
LP: . . . . FACT 140

Royal Guardsmen

SNOOPY AND HIS FRIENDS THE ROYAL GUARDSMEN.
LP: . . . . HDY 1913
MC: . . . . ZCHDY 1913

Royal House

CAN YOU PARTY ? (RE-ISSUE).
LP: . . . . CHAMP 1017
MC: . . . . CHAMPK 1017

Royal Liverpool...

RULE BRITANNIA (Royal Liverpool Philharmonic Orchestra).
Tracks: / Pomp and circumstance march 1 / Pomp and circumstance march 4 / British grenadiers, The / Dambusters march / RAF march past / On the quarter deck / Hornpipe / Rule Britannia.
MC: . . . . TCCFP 4567

SYMPHONY NO.4/SERENADE FOR STRINGS (see under Tchaikovsky) (Royal Liverpool Philharmonic Orch./St. John's Smith Sq Orch.).

SYMPHONY NO.8 (DVORAK) (see under Dvorak) (Royal Liverpool Philharmonic Orchestra/London Philharmonic O).

Royal Marines...

AND THE BAND PLAYED ON... (Royal Marines Commando Forces Band).
Tracks: / San carlos march / 'Drake 400' suite / Fanfare and melody / Sailing / Commando general (J.J.) / Warship / Shadow of your smile / Cancberra march / Battle of Trafalgar.
LP: . . . . EMC 3434
MC: . . . . TCEMC 3434

BEST OF THE ROYAL MARINES.
LP: 2384 126
MC: 3192 684

BEST OF THE ROYAL MARINES (2) (Band Of H.M. Royal Marines).
Tracks: / Marche Lorraine / Pomp and circumstance march no.1 / El Capitan / Solid men to the front / Thunderer, The / King Cotton / Army and Marine / Le pere la Victoire / National emblem / Hands across the sea / Invincible eagle, The / Old comrades / Under the double eagle / L'entente cordiale / Semper fidelis / Bugler's holiday / Anchors aweigh / Colonel Bogey / On the quarterdeck / Derby day / Old Panama / Contemptibles, The.
MC: . . . . EG 769 935 4

BY LAND AND SEA (Band Of H.M. Royal Marines).
Tracks: / National emblem / Preobrakensky march / Top malo / Concert march- Cockleshell heroes / Captain general, The / President elect, The / By land and sea / Anchors aweigh / Post horn gallop / Picconautical / In party mood / Falcon crest / Overture- Monte Carlo or bust / Barwick green / Elizabeth Tudor.
MC: . . . . ZC BND 1030
LP: . . . . BND 1030

CHRISTMAS CELEBRATION (Chichester Cath. Choir & Marines).
Tracks: / Joy to the world / Virgin Mary, The / Gift carol, The / How far is it to Bethlehem / Sleigh ride / Child is born, A / Make we merry on this festival / Yuletide souffle / Ding dong merrily on high / Our joyful feast / Love came down at Christmas / I come from the highest heaven / Troika / Joseph dearest / Rise up shepherd / Silent night.
LP: . . . . BND 1045
MC: . . . . ZC BND 1045

COLDITZ MARCH (Band Of H.M. Royal Marines).
MC: . . . . TCIDL 4

FOCUS ON THE ROYAL MARINES BAND (Royal Marines Band).
Tracks: / Steadfast and true / English dances Nos. 2 and 4 / Seascape / Love of three oranges / Floral dance / Largo / Florentiner / Thunderer / Plymouth Hoe / Edinburgh Castle / Sentry's song / Thin red line / Trumpetino / Under the Padstow lifeboat / Oliver selection / Nibelungen march / Spartacus (love theme) / Prelude from Richard III / Colonel Bogey / Drake's drum / Life on the ocean wave, A / Britanic salute / General salute / Rule Britannia / Land of hope and glory.
2LP: . . . . FOS 61/62

GLOBE AND LAUREL (Band Of H.M. Royal Marines).
Tracks: / On parade / Globe and laurel / Officer of the day / Cavalry of the Steppes / Uncle Sammy / Dad's army march / Belphegor / Advance guard, The / My regiment / Brass buttons / Gladiator's farewell / Punjab / Contemptibles, The / Voice of the guns / Robinson's grand entree / Dunedin / Vimy ridge / On the square.
MC: . . . . BND 61057

GRAND NIGHT FOR SINGING, A.
LP: . . . . TWOX 1049

HANDS ACROSS THE SEA.
Tracks: / Hands across the sea / Royal Welsh Fusiliers, The / Legionaires, The / Daughters of Texas / Gallant seventh, The / Golden jubilee / Pride of the wolverines / Hail to the spirit of liberty / From Maine to Oregon / Diplomat / Powhatan's daughter / Kansas wildcats / Sound off / Thunderer, The.
LP: . . . . EL 2701521
MC: . . . . EL 2701524

HERE COMES THE BAND (Royal Marines Band).
Tracks: / Life on the ocean wave, A / Vedette / Old comrades / Comtemptibles / Sarie Marais / Viscount Nelson / Belle of Chicago / Gladiator / Cavalry of the Steppes / Barcelona / Country gardens / Here comes the band / Pomp and circumstance march no.1 / March (Holst) / English folk song suite.
LP: . . . . ESD 7190
MC: . . . . TCESD 7190

IMPERIAL ECHOES (Royal Marines Band).
Tracks: / Imperial echoes / High School cadets / Royal salute / New Colonial march / Action front / Col. J. Ward / Sailing / Luftwaffe march / Nibelungen march / Marching sergeants / Glorious years / Washington Post / Scottish emblem / Officer of the day / Mountbatten march / Blaze away.
LP: . . . . TWOX 1079

MARCH ON (Band Of H.M. Royal Marines).
Tracks: / Liberty bell / Light of foot / With sword and lance / Thunderbirds / Sons of the brave / On the square / Two imps, The / Galloping home / Liberators, The / Eye level / Fantasia on British sea songs / Rule Britannia / Entry of the gladiators / H.M. Jollies / Le reve passe / Little bugler, The / Marche Lorraine / Sussex by the sea / When the saints go marching in / On the track (Xylophone solo: Band Corporal Alan Webb.) / Birdcage walk / Huntsmen, The (Posthorn Solo: Staff Bandmastger Sydney Rose, LRAM, LGSM.) / March of the toys / Fanfare / Sunset.
MC: . . . . TCEMS 1345

MARCHING WITH THE MARINES.
MC: . . . . TC-EXE 59

MEN OF ACTION.
Tracks: / Life on the ocean wave, A / On the quarter deck / Overture, the marriage of Figaro / Salute to James Last / Jesu joy of man's dersiring / Slavonic rhapsody / State occasion / Greensleeves / Purple pageant, The / Chimes of liberty / Flying eagle / Men of action / Nobilmente / General Mitchell / Heralds of victory / Marche vanier / Barnum and Bailey's favourite / Trombone king, The.
LP: . . . . BNC 1010
MC: . . . . ZC BNC 1010

OLD COMRADES - NEW COMRADES.
Tracks: / Old comrades / In the Bristol fashion / Lichfield / Cairo Road / Ventis secundis / Sea shanties / Parade of brass / Blue devil / New comrades / H.M. jollies / Broadlands / Little swiss piece / HMY Britannia / Nation, The / Up periscope / Glorious victory.
LP: . . . . GRALP 1
MC: . . . . GRTC 1

ON PARADE (Band Of H.M. Royal Marines).
Tracks: / Colonel Bogey / Crown Imperial / Life on the ocean wave, A.
2LP: . . . . MFP 1015
MCSET: . . . . TC MFP 1015
2LP: . . . . DL 1015
MC: . . . . TCDL 1015

PLYMOUTH'S OWN (Royal Marines Commando Forces Band).
Tracks: / Sarie Marais / Vanished army, The / Smithy, The / Post horn pandemonium / Solitude / Two imps, The / March of the cobblers / Up periscope / Old superb, The / Yankee doodle dandy / Fantasia on British sea songs / Hootenanny.
LP: . . . . GRALP 4
MC: . . . . GRTC 4

PORTSMOUTH (Band Of H.M. Royal Marines).
Tracks: / Heart of oak / Portsmouth / Warship / Splice the mainbrace / Nelson touch, The / Trafalgar / Viscount Nelson / Hands across the sea / Under the white ensign / Sea songs / Victory / Salute to the sovreign / Bugle fanfare / Drum display / Evening hymn / Sunset / Fantasia on British sea songs / Land of hope and glory.
LP: . . . . BND 1050
MC: . . . . ZC BND 1050

SOLID MEN TO THE FRONT Favourite marches vol. 3 (Band Of H.M. Royal Marines).
LP: . . . . EL 2705871
MC: . . . . EL 2705874

SOMETHING DIFFERENT.
Tracks: / Rocky theme / Return of the Saint / Coronation scot / Send in the clowns / Stardust / Parade of the charioteers / Manhattan skyline / Once upon a time / Green berets, The.
LP: . . . . FBR 0848
MC: . . . . FBC 0848

SPECTACULAR ROYAL MARINES (Royal Marines Band).
Tracks: / 1812 overture / Troika / Slaughter on 10th Avenue / Alla Marcia / Grand march / Jupiter / Crown imperial.
LP: . . . . NTS 225

SPECTACULAR SOUNDS OF, THE (Royal Marines & Argyll & Sutherland Highlanders).
Tracks: / Fanfare royal occasion / Life on the ocean wave, A / Hielan laddie / Famous songs of the British Isles medley / Fine old English gentleman, A / To be a farmers boy / Here's a health unto His Majesty / British Grenadiers, The / Minstral boy, The / Annie Laurie / Men of Harlech / Pipe selection / Gordon boy (lang) / Barren rocks of Aden / Brown haired maiden, The / Marie's wedding / Major A C S Boswell / Captain D P Thomson / Lieutenant Colonel H. L. Clark / Sea shanties medley / Horn pipe / What shall we do with the drunken sailor / Portsmouth / Rovin', A / Hornpipe / Highland fling / Dornoch links, The / Marquis of Huntly, The / Man's a man for a' that, A / Arrival / Black bear, The / Fanfare no.1 / Royal salute / Drum beatings "Maranatha" / Time off / Argyll broadswords, The / Glendaurel highlanders / O'er the bows to Ballindalloch / Miss Ada Crawford / Because he was a bonny lad / Piper o'Drummond / Sleepy Maggie / All the blue bonnets are over the mountain / Soldiers return / Chariots of fire / Crown imperial / Day thou gavest, Lord is ended, The / Sunset / Rule Britannia / Auld lang syne / Scotland the brave / Campbells are coming, The.
LP: . . . . MFP 5833
MC: . . . . TCMFP 5833

STARS AND STRIPES FOREVER John Philip Famous Marches (Band Of H.M. Royal Marines).
Tracks: / King Cotton / Gladiator / Belle of Chicago / Semper fidelis / Invincible eagle, The / Manhattan beach / El capitan / Washington post / Crusader / Black troop / Fairest of the fair, The / High school cadets / Stars and stripes forever.
LP: . . . . ASD 1651461
MC: . . . . TCASD 1651464

THIS IS THE ROYAL MARINES BAND.
Tracks: / Warship / Eye level / Washington post / Huntsmen, The / Cavalry of the Steppes / On the track / Piper in the meadow / Evening breeze / Bridge too far, A / Imperial echoes / Penny whistle song, The / High school cadets / Alfie / Novelty march / March of the cobblers / Troika / Guns of Navarone / Blaze away.
LP: . . . . THIS 5
MC: . . . . TCTHIS 5

VERY BEST OF: BAND OF HM ROYAL MARINES.
LP: . . . . TWOX 1063
MC: . . . . TC - TWOX 1063

VERY BEST OF THE ROYAL MARINES BAND (Band Of H.M. Royal Marines).
Tracks: / Colonel Bogey / Standard of St. George, The / Great little army / El abanico / National Emblem / Anchors Aweigh / Semper Fidelis / Cockershell heroes / Espana / Life on the ocean wave, A / Warship / On the square / This guy's in love with you / Sutherland's law theme / Shadow of your smile / Troika / Eye level / What the world needs now is love / On the track / When the saints go marching in.
LP: . . . . MFP 5789
MC: . . . . TCMFP 5789

Royal, Marshal

LIVE A THE 1990 CONCORD JAZZ FESTIVAL (See Under Wess, Frank) (Royal, Marshal & Frank Wess & Rick Wilkins).

SNOOKY AND MARSHAL'S ALBUM (See under Young, Snooky (Young, Snooky & Marshal Royal).

Royal Opera House

SWAN LAKE (VIDEO) (see under Tchaikovsky (composer) (Various artists).

Royal Philharmonic

20 FILMHARMONIC GREATS.
Tracks: / Hawaii / Walk on the wild side / Man with the golden arm / Tara's theme / Spellbound / To kill a mockingbird / Exodus / Magnificent seven, The / Charade / Born free / Pink panther / Lara's theme / Barsalino / Love story / Lawrence of Arabia / Baby elephant walk / Raindrops keep falling on my head / Gigi / Shadow of your smile / Alfie.
LP: . . . . PLE 7009
MC: . . . . PLC 7009

ARRESTED (Royal Philharmonic Orchestra & friends).
Tracks: / Overture / De, do, do, do, de, da, da, da / Released / Every little thing

she does is magic / Roxanne / Truth hits everybody / Arrested / Message in a bottle / Invisible sun / Walking on the moon / Don't stand so close to me / Finale.
LP: . . . . BLEND 4
MC: . . . . ZCBLEND 4
LP: . . . . RCALP 8001

AS TIME GOES BY.
LP: . . . . STAR 2240
MC: . . . . STAC 2240

ASHKENAZY - LIVE IN MOSCOW.
Tracks: / Khovanshchina prelude / Piano concerto No. 3 (Beethoven) / Daphnis et Chloe - Suite No. 2 (Ravel) / Nutrcracker suite (Tchaikovsky) / Waltz of the Flowers.
LP: . . . . RPO 8021

BALLET MUSIC FROM SPARTACUS
Onedin Line theme music.
LP: . . . . EL 2701091
MC: . . . . EL 2701094

BEST OF HOOKED ON CLASSICS (Clark, Louis & Royal Philharmonic Orchestra).
Tracks: / Hooked on classics (1 and 2) / Can't stop the classics / Night at the opera, A / Hooked on America / Symphonies of the seas / Hooked on a can can / Also sprach Zarathustra / Journey through the classics / Hooked on Tchaikovsky / Hooked on romance (opus 3) / Tales of the Vienna waltz / If you knew Sousa / If you knew Sousa (and friends) / Scotland the brave (Hookery Jiggery Jock).
LP: . . . . ONE 1266
MC: . . . . OCE 2266

BIZET: ORCHESTRAL WORKS 1 (see under Bizet (composer)).

BIZET: ORCHESTRAL WORKS 2 (see under Bizet (composer)).

BIZET: ORCHESTRAL WORKS 3 (see under Bizet, composer).

CLASSIC GOLD VOL.2.
2LP: RTD4 2032

CLASSIC THEMES (Royal Philharmonic Orchestra & friends).
LP: . . . . NML 1001
MC: . . . . ZCNML 1001

CLASSICAL SPECTACULAR (Live at the Royal Albert Hall).
Tracks: / William Tell overture (Rossini) / Stars and stripes forever / Chorus of the Hebrew slaves / Pomp and circumstance march no.1 (Elgar) (Land of hope and glory) / Bolero / Blue Danube / Polovtsian dances (from Prince Igor - Borodin) / 1812 overture.
LP: . . . . RPO 8019
MC: . . . . ZC RPO 8019

CLASSICS OF LOVE.
Tracks: / Three times a lady / If you leave me now / Up where we belong / You don't bring me flowers / Imagine / Weekend in New England / Miss you nights / One day I'll fly away / Memory / With you I'm born again / One day in your life / Sun ain't gonna shine anymore, The.
LP: . . . . MFP 5792
MC: . . . . TCMFP 5792

COLOURS.
Tracks: / Ochre / Red / Green / Sienna / Black / Mauve / Gold / Azure / Yellow / Grey.
LP: . . . . PL 25123

DVORAK NEW WORLD SYMPHONY (see under Dvorak (composer))(Brahms Academic Fe.

ELGAR CELLO CONCERTO (see under Elgar (composer)).

EVENING WITH RPO ON THEIR 50TH ANNIVERSARY.
LPS: . . . . DMT 101
MC: . . . . DMTC 101

FAVOURITE CLASSICS (Clark, Louis & Royal Philharmonic Orchestra).
LP: . . . . LCLP 2
MC: . . . . LCMC 2

FIESTA.
Tracks: / La torre del oro / El tambor de granderos / El ano pasado por agua / Ensenanza libre / La corte del faraon / Azucrillos y Aguardiente / La calesesa / El husped del Sevillano / La grand via / Luisa Fernanda / Dona Francisquita / Ague / Bohemios / La roveltasa / La rosa del Azafran / Alma de dios / La Leyenda del Beso / Jardines de Granada / Las Leandras / El pobre Valbuena / El rey que rabio / La Alegria da la Huerta / El Bateo / Los Favilanes / La Parranda / La boda de Luis Alonso / El Barbarillo de Azafran / El Baile de Luis Alonso / El trust de los Tenorois.
LP: 25083

FROM THIS MOMENT ON (See under Ewing, Maria) (Ewing, Maria & The Royal Philharmonic Orchestra).

GERSHWIN (see under Vakarelis, Janis) (Royal Philharmonic Orchestra/Janis Vakerelis/Henry Lewis).

GERSHWIN GOLD (Gershwin 50th Anniversary Tribute) (Royal Philharmonic Orchestra/Andrew Litton).
Tracks: / Rhapsody in blue / Swanee / Nobody but you / Do it again / Clap yo' hands / Who cares? / Strike up the band / Sweet and low down / Somebody loves me / Bidin' my time / 'S wonderful / That certain feeling / Do do do / Lady be good / Man I love, The / I'll build a stairway to paradise / Embraceable you / Fascinating rhythm / My one and only / Liza / I got rhythm.
LP: . . . . RPO 8008
MC: . . . . ZC RPO 8008
MC: . . . . ZCPRD 9002

GREAT HITS FROM HOOKED ON CLASSICS (Clark, Louis & Royal Philharmonic Orchestra).
LP: . . . . SHM 3158
MC: . . . . HSC 3158

GREAT LOVE SONGS OF JULIO.
Tracks: / Het / Me olvide de vivir / Trentay tres anos / Preguntale / Abrazame / Un dia tu / Un dia yo / No me vuelvo a enamorar / De nina a mujer / Momentos.
LP: . . . . FM 39209
MC: . . . . FMT 39209

HOOKED ON CLASSICS (Clark, Louis & Royal Philharmonic Orchestra).
Tracks: / Hooked on classics / Hooked on romance / Hooked on Bach / Hooked on Tchaikovsky / Hooked on a song / Hooked on Mozart / Hooked on a can can / Hooked on Mendelssohn.
LP: . . . . ONE 1146
MC: . . . . OCE 2146
MC: . . . . PWKMC 4017

HOOKED ON CLASSICS 2 (Can't Stop the Classics) (Clark, Louis & Royal Philharmonic Orchestra).
LP: . . . . ONE 1173
MC: . . . . OCE 2173

HOOKED ON CLASSICS 3 (Journey Through the Classics) (Clark, Louis & Royal Philharmonic Orchestra).
Tracks: / Also sprach Zarathustra / Journey through the classics / Hooked on romance / Viva Vivaldi / Dance of the furies / Scotland the brave / Journey through the classics part 2 / Journey through America / Hooked on marching / Symphony on the seas / Hooked on Rodgers and Hammerstein.
LP: . . . . ONE 1226
MC: . . . . OCE 1226

HOOKED ON CLASSICS, THE ULTIMATE COLLECTION.
Tracks: / Symphony of the seas / Hooked on Mendelssohn / Hooked on classics parts 1 & 2 / Dance of the furies / Hooked on romance / Hooked on classics (3) / Hooked on Rodgers and Hammerstein / Night at the opera / Also sprach Zarathustra / Hooked on Bach / Journey through the classics / Scotland the brave / Tales of the Vienna woods / Can't stop the classics II / Hooked on romance (part 2) / Hooked on baroque.
MC: . . . . MCTC 003

ISLAND IN THE SUN (Songs of Harry Belafonte).
Tracks: / Jamaica farewell / Banana boat song / Island in the sun / Yellow bird / I do adore her / Haiti cherie / Hosanna / Come back, Liza / Angelique-o / Dolly dawn.
LP: . . . . PIPLP 709
MC: . . . . ZCPIP 709

LAST NIGHT OF THE PROMS.
Tracks: / Land of hope and glory / Rule Britannia / Jerusalem / Trumpet concerto / Cockaigne overture / Elizabeth of Glamis / Crown imperial / Fantasia on British sea songs / God save the queen.
LP: . . . . CTVLP 501
MC: . . . . CTVMC 501

LOVE CLASSICS.
Tracks: / More than words can say / Weekend in New England / Fanfare / Miss you nights / One day I'll fly away / Memory / With you I'm born again / One day in your life / Sun ain't gonna shine anymore, The / Three times a lady / If you leave me now / Up where we belong / You don't bring me flowers / Imagine.
LP: . . . . NML 1003
MC: . . . . ZCNML 1003

MAHLER - SYMPHONY NO.4 (conducted by Michiyoshi Inoue).
MC: . . . . ZCRPO 8017
LP: . . . . RPO 8017

MOUNTBATTEN (TV soundtrack).
Tracks: / Mountbatten / Homeless / Mob violence / New viceroy, The / Nehru / Jinnah and the Muslim day of action / Banquet, A / Refugee camp / 10,000 patans / Tryst with destiny, A / Independence day / Teachings of Gandhi / Horror train / Upheaval of nature / Rape of a village / Column, The / Assassination of Gandhi / Farewell dinner / Goodbye India / Last viceroy (end titles), The.
LP: . . . . TER 1113
MC: . . . . ZCTER 1113

MUSIC FOR FILMS (See under Bax (composer)).

ORCHESTRAL TUBULAR BELLS.
LP: . . . . V 2026

PETER AND THE WOLF/CARNIVAL OF THE ANIMALS, THE (Royal Philharmonic Orchestra/Angela Rippon).
Tracks: / Peter and the wolf / Carnival of the animals, The.
MC: . . . . ZC QS 6017

PIANO CONCERTI NO.19/24 (see under Mozart) (Royal Philharmonic Orchestra/Jorge Federico Osorico).

PLAYS THE BEST OF THE ALAN PARSONS PROJECT (See under Parsons, Alan Project) (Philharmonic Orchestra/Andrew Powell).

PORTRAIT OF JULIO IGLESIAS.
LP: . . . . PREC 5008
MC: . . . . ZPREC 5008

RHYTHM AND CLASSICS (Clark, Louis & Royal Philharmonic Orchestra).
Tracks: / Symphony No. 5 / Phantom of the opera / Canon / Ode to joy / Aranjuez mon amour / Toccata and fugue in D minor / William Tell / In the hall of the mountain king / Flight of the bumble bee / Arrival of the Queen of Sheba, The / Post horn galop.
LP: . . . . STAR 2344
MC: . . . . STAC 2344

RITE OF SPRING/FIREBIRD (STRAVINSKY) (see under Stravinsky).

RPO PLAYS THE QUEEN COLLECTION.
Tracks: / Flash / Play the game / We are the champions / Don't stop me now / Love of my life / Killer queen / You're my best friend / Teo torriate (let us cling together) / Under pressure / Crazy little thing called love / Bohemian rhapsody.
LP: . . . . MFP 41 5673 1
MC: . . . . MFP 41 5673 4
LP: . . . . SHM 3158
LP: . . . . EMTV 33

SCREEN THEMES.
Tracks: / Die hard / Big / Roger Rabbit / Milagro, The / Beanfield war / Beetlejuice.
LP: . . . . VS 5208
MC: . . . . VSC 5208

SIR CHARLES GROVES: AN ENGLISH CELEBRATION.
Tracks: / Serenade for strings (Elgar) / Variations on a theme of Frank Bridge (Britten) / Fantasia on a theme by Thomas Tallis (Vaughan Williams) / Fantasia concertante on a theme of Corelli (Tippett).
LP: . . . . RPO 8020
MC: . . . . ZC RPO 8020

SONGS OF JOHN DENVER.
Tracks: / Annie's song / Leaving on a jet plane / Perhaps love / Take me home country roads / Rocky mountain high / How can i leave you again / Sunshine on my shoulders / Fly away / Follow me / Singing skies and dancing waters.
LP: . . . . PIPLP 708
MC: . . . . ZCPIP 708

SORCERER'S APPRENTICE, THE (see under Mexican State) (Royal Philharmonic Orchestra/Mexican State Symphony Orch.).

STAGE AND SCREEN FAVOURITES (Conducted by Vic Lewis).
Tracks: / Don't cry for me Argentina / M.A.S.H. (theme from) / Serenade for strings / Coco / Always Madamoiselle / Hannie Caulder / 49th Parallel / So much you loved me / Louise / Escape me never / My ship / Little Prince.
MC: . . . . HSC 3299

STILL LIFE (Clark, Louis & Royal Philharmonic Orchestra).
LP: . . . . LC TV 1
MC: . . . . LC TVC 1

SUPERSTAR SYMPHONY.
Tracks: / Abbature / Dancing queen / Fernando / Waterloo / S.O.S. / Mama Mia / Eagle / I have a dream / Does your mother know / Money money money / Knowing me, knowing you / Gimme gimme gimme / Chiquitita / Name of the game / Summertime City / Thank you for the music / Take a chance on me / You don't bring me flowers / Beautiful noise / Solitary noise / Holly holy / Solitary man / Cracklin' rosie / Brother Love's travelling salvation show / Play me / Forever in blue jeans / Sweet Caroline / September morn / I am ... I said / You don't bring me flowers / Song sung blue / Shilo / Kentucky woman.
MCSET: . . . . CRT 025

SYMPHONY NO.6 (GLAZUNOV) (see under Glazunov (composer)) (London Symphony Orchestra/Royal Philharmonic Orchestra).

SYMPHONY NO.31/NO.36 (see under Mozart) (Royal Philharmonic Orchestra/ London Philharmonic Orchestra).

VERY BEST OF 'HOOKED ON CLASSICS' (Clark, Louis & Royal Philharmonic Orchestra).
Tracks: / Hooked on classics (parts 1 & 2) / Hooked on Tchaikovsky / Hooked on a can can / Journey through the classics / Hooked on Haydn / If you knew sousa / Can't stop the classics / Hooked on romance opus 3 / Hooked on romance / Hooked on a song / Hooked on Mozart / Journey through the classics (part 2).
MC: . . . . PWKMCS 4017

Royal Rasses

HUMANITY.
Tracks: / San Salvador / They know not jah / Old time friends / Unconventional people / Humanity / Mr. Kissinger / Kingston II.
LP: . . . . UAG 30227

Royal Romance

ROYAL ROMANCE (Various artists).
LP: . . . . WIN 001
MC: 4CWIN 001

Royal Scots Dragoon...

AMAZING SOUND OF..., THE (Royal Scots Dragoon Guards).
Tracks: / Heykens serenade / Earl of Mansfield / Black bear, The / Il sienzio / Wooden heart / Scottish soldier / Pipe band selection / Banjo breakdown / Circassian circle / Gruagach / O'er the bows to Ballindalloch / Day is ended / Let's have a Ceilidh / Fairy dance, The / Lord of the dance / Scottish waltz / Campbeltown Loch / Now is the hour.
LP: . . . . NL 70121
MC: . . . . NK 70121
LP: . . . . INTS 5250
LP: . . . . SF 8310
MC: . . . . PK 11632

FAREWELL TO THE GREYS (Royal Scots Dragoon Guards).
Tracks: / Fanfare, trot and canter / Keel row, The / My love she's but a lassie yet / Cornet carillon / Duck / Scotland the brave / Man of harlech / Garb of old Gaul / Dancing feet / Going home / Abide with me / Reveille / Highland laddie / Amazing grace.
LP: . . . . NL 70123
MC: . . . . NK 70123
LP: . . . . INTS 5243
LP: . . . . NL 25212

GOLDEN SOUNDS OF THE ROYAL SCOTS DRAGOON GUARDS (Royal Scots Dragoon Guards).
Tracks: / Heykens serenade / Abide with em / Day is ended / Road to the isles / Water is wide / Second to none / Blackthorn stick / Kilworth Hills / Amazing grace / my home / Scotland the brave / Wooden heart / Going home / Now is the hour.
LP: . . . . NL 70275
MC: . . . . NK 70275
LP: . . . . INTS 5248
LP: . . . . PL 25087
MC: . . . . PK 25087

IN THE FINEST TRADITION (Royal Scots Dragoon Guards Pipes & Drums).
LP: . . . . BND 1049
MC: . . . . ZC BND 1049

INTO THE EIGHTIES (Royal Scots Dragoon Guards).
Tracks: / Scottish selections / Carillon / Bright eyes / Moorhouse memories / Drummer's call / March, strathspey and reel / Shepherd's song / Yorkshire bells / Hazel's dream / 4/4 marches / Piper's dance.
LP: . . . . TRS 101

LEGENDARY AMAZING GRACE, THE (Royal Scots Dragoon Guards).
Tracks: / Amazing grace / Rocksticks / Una paloma blanca / 6/8 marches / MacNeils of Ugadale / Crossing the Rhine / Dovecote park / Rock'n'roll march / Largo / Turn on the sun / Flower o'Scotland / Mingulay boat song.
LP: . . . . PKL 5550

MAGIC MOMENTS (Royal Scots Dragoon Guards).
Tracks: / Jubilant / Back o' Bennachie, The / Drunken piper, The / 72nd's farewell to Aberdeen, The / Corriechollie's welcome / My love she's but a lassie yet / Rantin' rovin' Robin / Cornet carillon / Leaving Rhu Vaternish / Nameless / Duck, The / Eleanor's / Drummer's salute, The / Amazing grace / Russian imperial anthem / Garb of old gaul / Men of harlech / Achany glen /

Craig a Bhodaich / MacFarlane's reels / Dancing feet / Dr. Ross welcome to the Argyllshire gathering / Going home / Keel row, The / Bonnie Dundee / Abide with me / Scotland the breave / Highland laddie / Road to the Isles, The / Trumpeter's holiday / Schone maid / Ode to joy / Drummer's call / Little drummer boy / Dark island / Pour un flirt / Bunessan / Abanda / Hills of Alva, The / Donald Willie and his dog / Second to none / Miss Girdle / Donald and his smuggled drappie, The / Earl of Airlie / Blackthorn stick / Kilworth hills.
MC: . . . . **NK 71023**

ORIGINAL VERSION OF AMAZING GRACE (Scots Dragoon Guards).
Tracks: / Amazing grace / Trumpeter's holiday / Little drummer boy / Dark island / Bunessan / Road to the isles.
LP: . . . . **CDS 1157**
MC: . . . . **CAM 471**

ROYAL SCOTS DRAGOON GUARDS (Royal Scots Dragoon Guards).
Tracks: / Amazing grace / Gallowa hills / Lili Marlene / Skye boat song / Black Watch polka / Battle of the Somme / Highland wedding / Mill in the Glen / Hills of home / Crossing the Rhine / Dovecote Park.
LP: . . . . **GH 673**

ROYAL SCOTS DRAGOON GUARDS (Royal Scots Dragoon Guards).
Tracks: / Dark Island / Intercontinental gathering, An / Mingulay boat song / Borodin, bongos and brass / Staffordshire knot / Sung sung blue / William Allan / Brauch Lonach / Shoals of herring / Lark in clear air / Rustic bridge / Highland cradle song / Road to the Isles / Queensman / Way old friends do / Sweet Caroline / Misty / Auld hoose, The / Bind / Angus Mackinnon.
LP: . . . . **WK 30175**
MC: . . . . **WKC 192**
MC: . . . . **ASK 771**

SCOTTISH SALUTE (Royal Scots Dragoon Guards).
MC: . . . . **KITV 455**

SPOTLIGHT ON THE ROYAL SCOTS (Royal Scots Dragoon Guards).
Tracks: / Amazing grace / Rocksticks / Arrival / Theme in glory / Retreat airs / 6/8 marches / Floral dance / Turn on the sun / Rockout / Mingulay boat song.
2LP: . . . . **SPOT 6803**
MCSET: . . . . **ZCSPT 6803**

Royal Showband

ROYAL SHOWBAND STORY.
LP: . . . . **STAL 1046**

Royal Teens

BELIEVE ME.
LP: . . . . **DEMAND 0010**

SHORT SHORTS (See under Bennett, Joe 'Black slacks').

Royal Tunbridge

50 YEARS OF SONG (Orpheus Choir & R.A. Brass).
LP: . . . . **BND 1046**
MC: . . . . **ZC BND 1046**

Royal Wedding

ROYAL WEDDING ANDREW & SARAH (H.R.H. The Prince Andrew and Miss Sarah Ferguso (Various artists).
LP: . . . . **REP 596**
MC: . . . . **ZCH 596**

ROYAL WEDDING CHARLES & DIANA (Various artists).
LP: . . . . **REP 413**
MC: . . . . **ZCH 413**

Royal Wedding (Film)

ROYAL WEDDING (In The Good Old Summertime) (Various artists).
Tracks: / Too late now: *Various artists* / Ev'ry night at seven: *Various artists* / Happiest day of my life, The: *Various artists* / I left my hat in Haiti: *Various artists* / You're all the world to me: *Various artists*/ How could you believe me when I said I loved you...: *Various artists* / I don't care: *Various artists* / Meet me tonight in dreamland: *Various artists* / Pay that barber shop chord: *Various artists* / Last night when we were young: *Various artists* / Put your arms around me honey: *Various artists* / Merry Christmas: *Various artists*.
LP: **4502301**
MC: **4502304**

ROYAL WEDDING (See Under Nacy Goes To Rio) (Various artists).

Royal Welch Fusiliers

TO THE BEAT OF A DRUM (Royal Welch Fusiliers/Blaenavon Male Voice Choir).
Tracks: / Fanfare - the 300th / Men of Glamorgan / Lilliburlero / Grenadiers slow march / How stands the glass around / Quick march of the 23rd regiment / Marquis of Granby / Sospan fach / My Lord what a morning / Girl I left behind me, The / Lass of Richmond Hill / Calon lan / Soldiers of the Queen / Goodbye Dolly Gray / U.S. Marine Corps hymn / Myfymwy / We'll keep a welcome / Vive la Canadienne / Keep the home fires burning / It's a long way to Tipperary / March of the Grenadiers / Royal Welch Fusiliers / Wish me luck as you wave me goodbye / Rachie / Cwm Rhondda / That astonishing infantry / British Grenadiers, The / Men of Harlech / Land of my fathers / God save the Queen.
MC: . . . . **BND 61058**

Royal, Willie

SKYLINE.
LP: . . . . **ICH 1011**
MC: . . . . **ZCICH 1011**

Royalle Delite

SPEND A LITTLE TIME WITH ME.
Tracks: / Send a little time with me.
MC: . . . . **ZCMK 60**

Royals

ISRAEL BE WISE.
Tracks: / Israel be wise / Come let's hold hands / If you want good / Happy time / Lonely lover / Never be a tomorrow before today / I cried / Everything's so nice / New generation / Same old story.
LP: . . . . **UAG 30206**

MOVING ON.
Tracks: / It's real / Facts of life / Rising sun / Malnutrition / Familiar music / Moving on / Vanity crazy / Swing low.
LP: . . . . **KVL 9006**

PICK UP THE PIECES.
LP: . . . . **LBR 1010**

ROYALS COLLECTION.
Tracks: / Pick up the pieces / Ghetto man / Jah Jah knows / Sufferer of the ghetto / If I were you / When you are wrong / Promised land / Only for a time / Blacker black / Peace and love / My sweat turns to blood / Come a long way / Stand and give praise / Freedom fighters / Israel be wise / If you want good / Happy time / Never be a tomorrow before today.
LP: . . . . **TRLS 219**

Royce, Kenneth

BONES IN THE SAND.
MC: . . . . **CAT 4035**

Roys

KICKED OFF THE TRAIN.
LP: . . . . **SEEZ 61**

Royston

I'VE BEEN LOVING YOU SO LONG.
Tracks: / I've been loving you so long / I've got no reason to quit / This is my year for Mexico / Cool water / Piroque Joe / Never miss a real good thing / Just between you and me / Today I started loving you again / Heaven is my woman's love / Silver threads among the gold / Streets of Baltimore / Lonesome fugitive.
LP: . . . . **FHR 098**

Roza, Lita

LOVE SONGS FOR NIGHT PEOPLE.
Tracks: / How did he look / Trust in me / This is no laughing matter / Misty / I'll close my eyes / Paradise / Wild is the wind / My heart belongs to Daddy / But beautiful / Tenderly / Wee small hours / They say.
LP: . . . . **BDL 1048**

SOMEWHERE, SOMEHOW, SOMEDAY.
Tracks: / That's the beginning of the end / I've got my eyes on you / Oh dear what can the matter be / But beautiful / I'll never say 'never again' / End of a love affair, The / Not mine / As children do / There's nothing better than love / Allentown jail / Once in a while / Nel blu di pinto di blu / This is my town / Maybe you'll be there / Sorry, sorry, sorry / I could have danced all night / All alone / Other woman, The / Love can change the stars.
LP: **C5-552**
MC: **C5K-552**

UNCHAINED MELODIES - FOUR STARS OF THE 50'S (see under Unchained Melodies) (Roza, Lita/Dickie Valentine/Joan Regan/Jimmy Young).

YOU'RE DRIVING ME CRAZY (Roza, Lita with Billy Munn's All Stars).
Tracks: / Between the Devil and the deep blue sea / Willow weep for me / Little white lies / Moon song (That wasn't meant for me) / Wrap your troubles in dreams / I only have eyes for you / You turned the tables on me / I cover the waterfront / You're driving me crazy / Moonglow / You took advantage of me / No moon at all / My one and only love.
LP: . . . . **PLE 509**
MC: . . . . **TC-PLE 509**

Rozsa, Miklos

BEN-HUR (See under Ben Hur).

CLASSIC FILM SCORES BY MIKLOS ROZSA (see under Films) (Various artists).

CLASSIC MIKLOS ROZSA, THE (see under Films) (Nuremberg Symphony Orchestra).

IMMORTAL FILM MUSIC OF MIKLOS ROZSA (see under Films).

MIKLOS ROZSA: SPELLBOUND CONCERTO (Utah Symphony Orchestra).
Tracks: / New England Sinfonette / Because of him / World, the flesh & the devil, The.
LP: **704 260**
MC: **C704 260**

THIEF OF BAGHDAD/JUNGLE BOOK (see under Films) (Nuremberg Symphony Orchestra).

R.T.B.F.

FRENCH SONGS VOL 1 (see under Farley, Carole) (Orchestre Symphonique de la RTBF/Carole Farley/ Ens.d.Bruxell).

FRENCH SONGS VOL 2 (see under Farley, Carole) (Orchestre Symphonique de la RTBF/Carole Farley).

RTE Radio Orchestra

GREATEST THEMES.
LP: . . . . **RTE 109C**

MISE EIRE.
LP: . . . . **CEFTV 134**

Rubalcaba, Gonzalo

GIRALDILLA.
Tracks: / Rumbero / Proyecto latino / Giraldilla / Campo finda / Encuentro / Presidente / Comienzo.
2LP: **158011**

LIVE IN HAVANA VOL 1.
Tracks: / Nueva cubana / Concatenacion heroica / On green dolphin street.
LP: **115954**

LIVE IN HAVANA VOL 2.
LP: **115956**

MI GRAN PASION.
LP: **15998**

Rubber Ducks

POP CLUB CONVOY.
Tracks: / Pop club convoy / Pop club shuffle.
LP: . . . . **DPMC 101**

Rubber Rodeo

SCENIC VIEWS.
LP: . . . . **MUNCH 1**
MC: . . . . **MUNCC 1**

Rubella Ballet

AT THE END OF THE RAINBOW.
LP: . . . . **BND 2LP**

BALLET BAG.
MC: . . . . **XN 2004**
MC: . . . . **ZN 2004**

COCKTAIL MIX.
LP: . . . . **DAYGLO 005**

IF.
LP: . . . . **DAYGLO 004**

RUBELLA BALLET BIRTHDAY BOX, THE.
Tracks: / Ballet dance / Love life / Slant and life / Trial 13 / Tangled web / 42+ / Money talks / Death train / Arctic flowers / False flowers / Let us out / Plastic life / 'T' / Thugs / It'll never happen to me / Animal house / Rainbow love.
2LP: . . . . **DAYGLO 006**

Rubettes

BEST OF THE RUBETTES.
Tracks: / Sugar baby love / Tonight / Under one roof / Judy run run / I'm just dreaming / I can do it / Jukebox jive / Little darlin' / Julia / Foe dee oh dee / You're the reason why / Sha na na song.
LP: **2384 111**
MC: **843 896 4**

GREATESTS HITS:RUBETTES.
Tracks: / Sugar baby love / I can do it / Foe dee oh dee / Let's be used to be / Stuck on you / Jukebox jive / Tonight / Breakdown / Making love in the rain.
MC: . . . . **DSK 121**

IMPACT.
Tracks: / Juke box jive / I can do it / Little darlin' / Under one roof / Beggarman, The / Sha na na song / Put the beat to that music / Allez oop / Judy run run / My Buddy Holly days / Julia / Ooh la la.
LP: **6886 562**
MC: **7486 560**

STILL UNWINDING.
Tracks: / Movin' / No no cherie / Still unwinding / New York Tower / St. Andreas / Goodbye Dolly Gray / Truth of the matter / When Hays was young / Do you ever think of me / Does it gotta be rock'n'roll.
LP: **2383520**

WE CAN DO IT.
LP: . . . . **ETAT 001**

Rubin, Joel

BRAVE OLD WORLD (Rubin, Joel Klezmer Band).
MC: . . . . **GVMMC 122**

Rubinel, Ronald

ZOULOU.
LP: . . . . **GD 033**

Rubini, Michael

HUNGER, THE/YEAR OF LIVING DANGEROUSLY (See under Hunger).

Rubinoos

BACK TO THE DRAWING BOARD.
Tracks: / Falling in love / I wanna be your boyfriend / Promise me / Hold me / Ronnie / Drivin' music / Operator / Jennifer / Arcade queen / Lightning love affair / 1 2 3 forever.
LP: . . . . **BSERK 018**

RUBINOOS.
Tracks: / I think we're alone now / Leave my heart alone / Hard to get / Peek-a-boo / Rock and roll is dead / Memories / Nothing a little love won't cure / Wouldn't it be nice / Make it easy / I never thought it would happen.
LP: . . . . **BSERK 10**

RUBINOOS IN WAX.
Tracks: / Falling in love / I wanna be your boyfriend / Promise me / hold me / Ronnie / Drivin' music / Operator / jennifer / Arcade Queen / Lightning love affair / 1,2,3 forever.
LP: . . . . **BSERK 18**

Rubovia

RUBOVIA (Various artists).
LP: . . . . **REC 282**

Ruby Blue

DOWN FROM ABOVE.
LP: **8425681**
MC: **8425684**

GLANCES ASKANCES.
Tracks: / Give us our flag back / Quiet mind, The / Just relax / So unlike me / Walking home / Meaning of life, The / Wintery day / Sitting in a cafe / Bless you.
LP: . . . . **RF 53**
MC: . . . . **RFC 2**

Ruby & The Romantics

OUR DAY WILL COME.
Tracks: / Our day will come / When you're young and in love / Nobody but my baby / How deep is the ocean? / Does he really care for me? / I'm sorry / By the way / End of the world / Moonlight and music / Baby come home / I cry alone / Your baby doesn't love you anymore / Hey there, lonely boy / What a difference a day made / I'm much better off than I've ever been / Young wings can fly.
LP: . . . . **CRM 2030**

Rucker, Ellyn

ELLYN.
Tracks: / In your own way / One morning in May / Close enough for love / Nadine's waltz / Blues for big scotia / Round midnight / Night has a thousand eyes.
LP: . . . . **CAP 10187**
MC: . . . . **CS 10187**

THIS HEART OF MINE.
Tracks: / I never get enough of you / Sweet Lorraine (ball and chain) / At long last love / Waltz for Debby / Get out of town / Born to be blue / Stompin' at the Savoy / All this and heaven too / Gee baby, ain't I good to you / Turn out the stars / This heart of mine.
MC: **74010-4**

Rucker, James Sparky

DRIVE BACK THE NIGHT.
LP: . . . . **LR 42.062**

Rudd, Roswell

INSIDE JOB.
Tracks: / Sacred song / Mysterioso / Inside job.
LP: . . . . **FLP 41029**

Rudder, David

1990.
Tracks: / Calypso rising / Just a carnival / One more officer / Down at the shebeen / 1990 / Dark secret / Johannesburg woman / Working on the join / Victory is certain / There is a land.
MC: **828 215 4**
LP: **828 215 1**

HAITI (Rudder, David & Charlie Root).

Tracks: / Bacchanal lady / Panama / Engine room / This party is it / Rally round the West Indies / Haiti / Front line / One love.
LP: . . . . LONLP 60
MC: . . . . LONC 60

POWER AND THE GLORY, THE.
LP: . . . . CR 010

Ruddigore

RUDDIGORE (see under Gilbert & Sullivan).

Rude Girls

AWAKENING.
LP: . . . . FF 424

Rudimentary Peni

CACOPHONY.
LP: . . . . BOOB 002
MC: . . . . BOOB 002C

DEATH CHURCH.
LP: . . . . CHRIST 6

EXTENDED PLAYS (EP's of RP).
LP: . . . . CHRIST 15

Rudolf

RUDOLF (Various artists).
MC: . . . . STC 310A

Ruefrex

FLOWERS FOR ALL OCCASIONS.
LP: . . . . KAT LP 1

PLAYING CARDS WITH DEAD MEN.
LP: . . . . BLUNT 041

Rufaro

RUFARO.
LP: . . . . PC 432

Ruff, Michael

ONCE IN A LIFETIME.
LP: 925159 1

Ruff Ruff & Ready

WORD OF MOUTH.
LP: . . . . SIGH 16
MC: . . . . SIGH 46

Ruffelle, Frances

ON MY OWN.
MC: . . . . SCOREC 2

Ruffians

RUFFIANS.
LP: 601 878

Ruffin, Jimmy

20 GOLDEN CLASSICS: JIMMY RUFFIN.
Tracks: / What becomes of the broken hearted / Don't you miss me a little bit baby / As long as there is love love / I'll stay forever my love / Baby I've got it / I've passed this way before / Sad and lonesome feeling / Don't let him take your love from me / World so wild / Nowhere to hide (from your heart) / This guy's in love with you / Gonna give her all the love I've got / Let's say goodbye tomorrow / It's wonderful / Gonna keep on tryin' till I win your love / Farewell is a lonely sound / Living in a world I created for myself / On the way out (on the way in) / Maria (you were the only one) / Stand by me / Halfway to paradise.
LP: . . . . STMR 9012
MC: . . . . CSTMR 9012

GREATEST HITS: JIMMY RUFFIN.
LP: . . . . STML 11259

GREATEST MOTOWN HITS.
Tracks: / What becomes of the brokenhearted / Baby I've got it / I've passed this way before / Gonna give her all the love I've got / World so wide, nowhere to hide / Don't you miss me a little bit baby / Everybody needs love / It's wonderful (to be loved by you) / Gonna keep on tryin' till I win your love / This guy's in love with you / Farewell is a lonely sound / Stand by me / As long as there is l-o-v-e love / Sad and lonesome feeling / I'll say forever my love / Don't let him take your love from me / Maria (you were the only one) / Living in a world I created for myself / Let's say goodbye tomorrow / He ain't heavy, he's my brother.
LP: . . . . WL 72654
MC: . . . . WK 72654

JIMMY RUFFIN WAY.
LP: . . . . STML 11048

SUNRISE.
Tracks: / Hold on / Forever / Night of love / Searchin' / Changin' me / Where do I go / Two people / Jealousy / Songbird.
LP: 2394 258

Ruffin & Kendricks

RUFFIN & KENDRICKS (Ruffin, David & Eddie Kendricks).
Tracks: / I couldn't believe it / Ordinary girl / One more for the lonely hearts club / Whatever you got / Don't know why you're dreaming / Family affair / One last kiss / You only get what you put out / Goodnight pillow.
LP: . . . . PL 86765
MC: . . . . PK 86765

Ruffy & Tuffy

CLIMAX.
LP: . . . . STAR 3

Rufty Tufty

RUFTY TUFTY (Various artists).
Tracks: / Rufty tufty: *Various artists* / Water kelpie, The: *Various artists* / Hare and the hedgehog: *Various artists* / King thrush-beard: *Various artists* / Span of life, The: *Various artists* / Six swans, The: *Various artists.*
MC: . . . . ANV 620

Rufus

MASTERJAM (Rufus & Chaka Khan).
Tracks: / Do you love what you feel.
LP: . . . . MCG 4007

NUMBERS.
LP: . . . . ABCL 5263

PARTY TIL YOU'RE BROKE.
LP: . . . . MCF 3108

RUFUSIZED.
LP: . . . . ABCL 5063

STOMPIN' AT THE SAVOY (Rufus & Chaka Khan).
2LP: 923679 1
MC: 923679 4

Rugg, Louisa

ICARUS (see Cripps,Geoff/Louisa Rugg) (Rugg, Louisa/Geoff Cripps).

Rugolo, Pete

INTRODUCING PETE RUGOLO.
LP: . . . . FS 165

JACK THE RIPPER (see McHugh, Jimmy) (Rugolo, Pete/ Jimmy McHugh).

RUGOLOMANIA.
LP: . . . . FS 166

Ruins

STONEHENGE.
LP: . . . . SHIMMY 037

Ruiz, Hilton

CROSS CURRENTS.
LP: . . . . ST 248

DOIN' IT RIGHT.
LP: . . . . PL 83085
MC: . . . . PK 83085

EL CAMINO (THE ROAD).
Tracks: / West side blues / Come dance with me / Sometimes I / El camino (the road) / Message from the chief / Eastern vibrations.
LP: . . . . PL 83024

FANTASIA.
LP: . . . . YX 7548

SOMETHING GRAND (Ruiz, Hilton Ensemble).
Tracks: / Home cookin' / Puerto Rican children / Four west / Something grand / Sunrise over Madarao / One step ahead.
LP: . . . . PL 83011
MC: . . . . PK 83011

STRUT.
Tracks: / Sidewinder, The / Going back to New Orleans / Bluz / Aged in soul / All my love is yours / Soca serenade / Why don't you steal my blues / Lush life (Only on CD.).
LP: . . . . PL 83053
MC: . . . . PK 83053

Ruiz, Pedro

LE SALTERIO MEXICAIN.
Tracks: / Serenata huasteca / Las bicicletas / La zandunga / La llonora / Las perlitas / La bikina / Guadalajara / La negra / Alejandra / El sinaloense / Los chiapanecas / Sobre las olas / La bamba / Jarabe tapatio.
LP: . . . . ARN 30133

Rumania

RUMANIAN 'DOINA', THE with Gheorghe Zamfir (Various artists).
LP: . . . . CEL 001
MC: . . . . MCCEL 001

TZIGANE... TZIGANE (Various artists).
Tracks: / Hategana: *Various artists* / Balada lui, corbea si hora: *Various artists* / Csardas rominesc: *Various artists* / Foaie verde de aluna: *Various artists* / Cintec de pahar: *Various artists* / Chansons styriques: *Various artists* / Hora - lautareasca: *Various artists* / Visegrad: *Various artists* / Csardas: *Various* artists / Noce tzigane a la roumaine: *Various artists* / Ciocirlia: *Various artists* / Am iubit si-am sa lubesc: *Various artists.*
LP: . . . . ARN 30080
MC: . . . . ARN 430080

Rumanian Angel Appeal

NOBODYS CHILD (Various artists).
LP: . . . . WX 353
MC: . . . . WX 353 C

Rumbas & Sambas

RUMBAS AND SAMBAS (Various artists).
MC: . . . . CPK 2

Rumble chillen

RUMBLE CHILLEN (Various artists).
Tracks: / Rhumba chillen: *Williams, Albert* / I'm gonna shake it: *Gordon, Roscoe* / Tuckered out: *Brenston, Jackie* / Love my baby: *Little Junior Parker & The Blue Flames* / Left job boogie: *Doctor Ross* / Don't say tomorrow: *Prisonaires* / Walked all night: *Booker, Charlie* / Ugly woman: *O'Neal, Johnny* / Wolf call boogie: *Hot Shot Love* / Everybody's in the mood: *Howlin' Wolf* / I feel so worried: *Lewis, Sammy & Willie Johnson* / Shim-sham-shimmy: *Emerson, Billy 'The Kid'* / Gee I wish: *Love, Billy* / Hold me in your arms: *Cotton, James* / Terra mae: *Doctor Ross* / Gotta let you go: *Louis, Joe Hill.*
LP: . . . . CRM 2033

Rumble Fish (film)

RUMBLE FISH (FILM SOUNDTRACK) (See under Copeland, Stewart) (Copeland, Stewart).

Rumble Militia

ENNOMBRE DEL LEY.
2LP: . . . . ATOMH 005

FU OFF COMMERCIAL.**
LP: . . . . ATOMH 002

Rumillajta

CITY OF STONE.
LP: . . . . TUMI 001

HOJA DE COCA.
LP: . . . . CA 84
MC: . . . . CCA 84

PACHAMAMA.
LP: . . . . TUMI R003

TIERRA MESTIZA.
Tracks: / Palomita laicu laicu / Jacku / Carnaval del valle / Corti poncho / Tierra aymara / Tierra mestiza / Cacharpaya del exilio / Linda Potosina / Wasi ponguito / Guambrita / Como un grito de lucha.
LP: . . . . RUM 1891
MC: . . . . RUM 1891C

WIRACOCHA.
LP: . . . . RUM 1871

Rummel, Jack

BACK TO RAGTIME.
LP: . . . . SOS 1118

Rumour

PURITY OF ESSENCE.
Tracks: / My little red book / I don't want the night to end / Have you seen my baby / Falling in love with a dream / Tula / Writing in the water / Houston / It's gonna work out fine / More than she will say / Pyramids / That's the way the ball rolls.
LP: . . . . SEEZ 27

RUMOUR.
Tracks: / Frogs / Sprouts / Clogs / Krauts.
LP: . . . . SEEZ 13

Rumpelstiltskin

RUMPELSTILTSKIN (Ogilvy, Ian).
MC: . . . . LP 208

RUMPELSTILTSKIN (well loved tales up to age 9).
MC: . . . . PLB 96

RUMPELSTILTSKIN (Various artists).
MC: . . . . STC 306B

RUMPELSTILTSKIN: THE FLYING TRUNK (See under Grimm Brothers).

Rumpf, Inga

INGA.
Tracks: / It's only love / City jungle / Ice cold / Love potion / Grade B movie / I know who I am / Roxanne / I'm a woman / Pain in my heart / Breakdown.
LP: . . . . PL 13499

Rumpole Of The Bailey

RUMPOLE OF THE BAILEY (By John Mortimer) (Mckern, Leo).
MCSET: . . . . TC-LFP 7110

Rumsey, Howard

JAZZ ROLLS ROYCE (Rumsey, Howard Lighthouse All Stars).
LP: . . . . FS 136

MUSIC FOR LIGHTHOUSEKEEPING (Rumsey, Howard Lighthouse All Stars).
LP: 1007 528

Run D.M.C.

BACK FROM HELL.
Tracks: / Sucker D.J's / What's it all about / Faces / Pause / Back from hell / Groove to the sound / Naughty / Not just another groove / Ave, The / Bob your head / Kick the frama lama lama / Word is born / Don't stop / P upon a tree / Livin' the city / Party time.
LP: . . . . FILER 401
MC: . . . . FILECT 401

KING OF ROCK.
Tracks: / Rock the house / King of rock / You talk too much / Jam-master jammin' / Roots, rap, reggae / Can you rock it like this / You're blind / It's not funny / Daryl and Joe.
LP: . . . . BRLP 504
MC: . . . . BRCA 504
LPPD: . . . . PBRLP 504
MC: . . . . ICM 2044
MC: 842 741 4
LP: . . . . FILER 205

RAISING HELL.
Tracks: / Peter Piper / It's tricky / My Adidas / Walk this way / Is it live / Perfection / Hit it run / Raising hell / You be illin' / Dumb girl / Son of Byford / Proud to be black.
LP: . . . . LONLP 21
MC: . . . . LONC 21

RUN D.M.C..
Tracks: / Hard times / Rock box / Jam-master Jay / Hollis crew (Krush groove 2) / Sucker M.C.S. (Krush groove 1) / It's like that / Wake up / 30 days / Jay's game.
LP: . . . . BRLP 506
MC: . . . . BRCA 506
MC: . . . . ICM 2045
MC: 846 561 4
LP: . . . . FILER 202
MC: . . . . FILERCT 202

RUN D.M.C: INTERVIEW PICTURE DISC.
LPPD: . . . . BAK 2069

TOUGHER THAN LEATHER (Film Soundtrack).
Tracks: / Run's house / Mary, Mary / They call us Run D.M.C. / Beats to the rhyme / Radio station / Papa crazy / Tougher than leather / I'm not going out like that / How'd ya do it, Dee? / Miss Elaine / Soul to rock 'n' roll / Ragtime.
LP: . . . . LONLP 38
MC: . . . . LONC 38

TOUGHER THAN LEATHER (VIDEO) (See under Tougher Than Leather) (Various artists).

Run Of The Arrow

RUN OF THE ARROW (Original Soundtrack) (Various artists).
LP: . . . . AEI 3102

Run Westy Run

GREEN CAT ISLAND.
Tracks: / Johnny John / Elektrick go / Kiss the night / Keep out / Starlight / Last swallow / Could ya would ya / Cardinal drive / Hate in the morning / Whada / Get on / So long.
LP: . . . . TTR 89199-1

HARDLY, NOT EVEN.
LP: . . . . SST 192

RUN WESTY RUN Original Sound Track (Various artists).
LP: . . . . SST 199
MC: . . . . SST 199 C

Runaway

RUNAWAY (Original Soundtrack) (Various artists).
LP: . . . . STV 81234
MC: . . . . CTV 81234

Runaway Train

RUNAWAY TRAIN (Original Soundtrack) (Various artists).
Tracks: / Jailbreak: *Various artists* / Moving on: *Various artists* / Destination unknown: *Various artists*/ Clear the track: *Various artists* / Reflections: *Various artists* / Runaway train: *Various artists*/ Prison memories: *Various artists* / Yellow rose of Texas: *Various artists* / Collision course: *Various artists*/ Past, present and future: *Various artists* / Red for danger: *Various artists* / Gloria: *Various artists*/ End of the line: *Various artists.*
LP: . . . . A 267
MC: . . . . C 267

Runaways

AND NOW...THE RUNAWAYS.
Tracks: / Saturday night special / Eight days a week / Mama weer all crazee now / I'm a million / Right now / Take over / My buddy and me / Little lost girls / Black leather.
LP: . . . . ARED 3
MC: . . . . CARED 3

FLAMING SCHOOLGIRLS (Runaways & Cherie Currie).
Tracks: / Introduction / Strawberry fields forever / C'mon / Hollywood cruisin' / Blackmail / Is it day or night? / Here comes the sun / Hollywood dream / Don't abuse me / I love playin' with fire / Secrets.

LP: BRED 9

LIVE IN JAPAN.
LP: 6338 833

QUEENS OF NOISE.
LP: 9100 032

RUNAWAYS.
Tracks: / School days / Wait for me / Wasted / Don't go away / Waiting for the night / Blackmail / You drive me wild / I love playin' with fire / Born to be bad / Take it or leave it.
LP: MERB 12
MC: MERBC 12

WAITIN' FOR THE NIGHT.
LP: 9100 047

YOUNG AND FAST.
LP: ST 72866

Rundgren, Todd

ACAPPELLA.
Tracks: / Blue orpheus / Johnee jingo / Pretending to care / Hodja / Lost horizons / Something to fall back on / Miracle in the bazaar / Lockjaw / Honest work / Mighty love.
LP: 925128 1
MC: 925128 4

ADVENTURES IN UTOPIA.
LP: BRIC 6991

ANOTHER LIFE.
Tracks: / Another life / Wheel, The / Seven rays, The / (Intro) Mister Trisuits / Something's coming / Heavy metal kids / Do ya / Just one victory.
LP: K 55508

ANTHOLOGY : TODD RUNDGREN.
Tracks: / Can we still be friends / All the children sing / Too far gone / Sweet memories / It wouldn't have made any difference / Hell it's me / I saw the light / Just one victory / Love of the common man / Verb "to love", The / Sometimes I don't know what to feel / Couldn't I just tell you / Tiny demons / Initiation / Real man / Long time a long way to go, A / Long flowing robe / Compassion / We gotta get you a woman / Dream goes on forever, A / Last ride, The / Don't you ever learn? / Bang the drum all day / Zen archer.
LP: RAWLP 035
MC: RAWTC 035

BACK TO THE BARS.
Tracks: / Real man / Love of the common man / Verb to love, The / Love in action / Dream goes on forever, A / Sometimes I don't know what to think / Range wars, The / Black and white / Last ride, The / Cliches / Don't you ever learn / Never never land / Black Maria / Zen Archer / I'm so proud / Oh baby baby / La la means I love you / I saw the light / It wouldn't have made any difference / Eastern intrigues / Initiation / Couldn't I just tell you / Hello it's me.
2LP: K 68511

EVER POPULAR TORTURED ARTIST EFFECT, THE.
LP: LMGLP 2000
MC: ZC LMG 2000

FAITHFUL.
Tracks: / Happenings ten years time ago / Good vibrations / Rain / Most likely you'll go your way and I'll go mine / If six was nine / Strawberry Fields forever / Black and white / Love of the common man / When I pray / Cliches / Verb 'to love', The / Boogies (hamburger hell).
LP: K 55510

HEALING.
Tracks: / Healer / Pulse / Flesh / Golden goose, The / Compassion / Shine / Healing (pt 1) / Healing (pt 3) / Healing (pt 2).
LP: AALP 3522
MC: BHS 3522
LP: ILPS 9657

HERMIT OF MINK HOLLOW.
Tracks: / All the children sing / Can we still be friends / Hurting for you / Too far gone / Onomatopoeia / Determination / Bread / Rag lady / You cried wolf / Lucky guy / Out of control.
LP: K 55521

INITIATION, THE.
Tracks: / Real man / Born to synthesize / Death of rock and roll, The / Eastern intrigues / Initiation / Fair warning / Treatise on cosmic fire, A / Fire of mind or solar fire, The / Fire of spirit or electric fire, The / Internal fire or fire by friction, The.
LP: K 55504

NEARLY HUMAN.
Tracks: / Want of a nail, The / Parallel lines / Fidelity / Hawking / Unloved children / Waiting game, The / Can't stop running / Feel it / I love my life.
LP: K 9258811
MC: K 9258814

OOPS SORRY WRONG PLANET.
Tracks: / Trapped / Windows / Love in action / Martyr, The / Abandon city / Gangreen / Crazy lady blue / Back on the street / Marriage of heaven and hell / Mt. angel / Rape of the young / Love is the answer.
LP: K 55517

P.O.V (Rundgren, Todd/Utopia).
LP: GRUB 5

RUNT/HERMIT OF MINK HOLLOW.
Tracks: / Broke down and busted / Believe in me / We gotta get you a woman / Who's that man / Once burned / Devil's bite / I'm in the clique / There are no words / Baby let's swing / Last thing you said, The / Don't tie my hands / Birthday cards / All the children sing / Can we still be friends / Hurting for you / Too far gone / Onomatopoeia / Determination / Bread / Bag lady / You cried wolf / Lucky guy / Out of control / Fade away.
MC: TFOMC 3
2LP: TFOLP 3

SECOND WIND.
MC: 7599264784

SOMETHING ANYTHING.
Tracks: / I saw the light / I wouldn't have made any difference / Wolfman Jack / Cold morning light / It takes two to tango / Sweeter memories / Intro / Breathless / Night the carousel burned down, The / Saving grace / Marlene / Song of the viking / I went to the mirror / Black Maria / One more day (no word) / Couldn't I just tell you / Torch song, The / Little red lights / Overture / Money: messin' with the kid / Dust in the wind / Piss Aaron / Hello it's me / Some folks is even whiter than me / You left me sore / Slut.
2LP: K 65501
2LP: ESDLP 007
MCSET: ESDMC 007

SWING TO THE RIGHT (Rundgren, Todd/Utopia).
LP: BRK 3666
MC: ZCBRK 3666

TODD.
Tracks: / How about a little fanfare / I think you know / Spark of life / Elpee's worth of toons, An / Dream goes on forever, A / Lord Chancellor's nightmare, The / Drunken blue rooster / Last number 1 lowest common denomination, The / Useless begging / Sidewalk cafe / Izzat love / Heavy metal kids / In and out of the chakras we go / Don't you ever learn / Sons of 1984.
LP: K 85501
LP: CLALP 177
MC: CLAMC 177

UTOPIA.
Tracks: / Utopia theme / Freak parade / Freedom fighters / Ikon, The.
LP: K 55501

UTOPIA RA.
Tracks: / Hiroshima / Singring and the glass guitar / Jealousy / Eternal love / Sunburst finish.
LP: K 55514

WIZARD, A TRUE STAR, A.
Tracks: / International feel / Never never land / Tic tick tick it wears off / You / Need your head / Rock and roll / Pussy / Dogfight giggle / You don't have to camp around / Flamingo / Zen Archer / Just another onionhead / Da da dali / When the shit hits the fan / Sunset Boulevard / Le feel internacionale / Sometimes I don't know what to feel / Does anybody love you / I'm so proud / Ooh baby baby / La la means I love you / Cool jerk / Hungry for love / I don't want to tie you down / Is it my name / Just one victory.
LP: CLALP 134
LP: K 45513
MC: CLAMC 134
LP: IRSP 10

Rundle, Bob

BUTTON AND BLOWS.
MC: 60-124

Runestaff

RUNESTAFF.
Tracks: / Do it / Whatever you want from me / Time's running out / Road to ruin / Runestaff / Last time, The / Games you play / Last chances.
LP: HMRLP 26
MC: HMRMC 26

Running Blind (bk)

RUNNING BLIND (Desmond Bagley) (Jarvis, Martin (nar)).
MCSET: LFP 7232
MCSET: LFP 417 232 5

Running Loose

RUNNING LOOSE (TV Soundtrack) (Various artists).
LP: RUNLP 1
MC: ZCRUN 1

Running Man

RUNNING MAN, THE (Original Soundtrack) (Various artists).
LP: TER 1158
MC: ZCTER 1158

Running Scared

RUNNING SCARED (Original soundtrack) (Various artists).
Tracks: / Sweet freedom: *McDonald, Michael* / Man size love: *Klymaxx* / I just wanna be loved: *Ready For* The World / Running scared: *Waybill, Fee* / Once in a lifetime: *New Edition* / I know what I want: *Labelle*, Patti / Say you really want me: *Wilde, Kim* / El Chase: *Temperton, Rod* / Never too late to start: *Temperton, Rod.*
LP: MCG 6012
MC: MCGC 6012

Running Wild

BLAZIN' STONE.
LP: NO 1711
MC: NO 1714

BRANDED AND EXILED.
LP: N 0030
LP: NUK 030

DEATH OR GLORY.
Tracks: / Riding the storm / Renegade / Evilution / Running blood / Highland glory (the eternal flight) / Marooned / Bad to the bone / Tortuga bay / Death or glory / Battle of Waterloo / March on (CD only.).
LP: EMC 3568
MC: TCEMC 3568

GATES TO PURGATORY.
LP: N 0012
LP: NUK 012

PORT ROYAL.
LP: NUK 122
MC: ZCNUK 122
LP: N 0122 1
MC: N 0122 2

READY FOR BOARDING.
LP: N 0108
MC: N 0108-2
LP: NUK 108
MC: ZCNUK 108

UNDER JOLLY ROGER.
LP: N 0062
LP: NUK 062
MC: ZCNUK 062
MC: N 0063

Runrig

BIG WHEEL, THE.
Tracks: / Headlights / Healer in your heart / Abyhainn an t-sluaigh/The crowded river / Always the winner / This beautiful pain / An cuibhle mor/The big wheel / Edge of the world / Hearthammer / I'll keep coming home / Flower of the west.
MC: ZCHR 1858
LP: CHR 1858

CUTTER AND THE CLAN, THE.
Tracks: / Alba / Cutter, The / Hearts of olden glory / Pride of the summer / Worker for the wind / Rocket to the moon / Only rose, The / Protect and survive / Our earth was once green / Aubhal as airds, An.
LP: RR 008
MC: RRC 008
LP: CHR 1669
MC: ZCHR 1669

HEARTLAND.
LP: RR 005
MC: RRC 005

HIGHLAND CONNECTION, THE.
MC: RRC 001
LP: RR 001

ONCE IN A LIFETIME.
Tracks: / Dance called America / Protect and survive / Chiu mi'n geamradh / Rocket to the moon / Going home / Cnoc na feille / Nightfall on Marsco / S to mo leannan / Skye / Loch Lomond.
LP: CHR 1695
MC: ZCHR 1695

PLAY GAELIC.
Tracks: / Dusig mo run / Sguaban arbhair / Tillidh mi / Criogal cridhe / Nach neonach neisd a tha e / Sunndach / Air an traigh / De ni mi and puirt / An ros / Ceol an dannsa / Chiu mi'n geamradh / Cum 'ur n'aire.
LP: NA 105
MC: NC 105
LP: LILP 5182
MC: LICS 5182

RECOVERY.
LP: RR 002
MC: RRC 002

SEARCHLIGHT.
Tracks: / News from Heaven / Every river / City of lights / Eirinn / Tir a'mhurain / World appeal / Tear down these walls / Only the brave / Siol ghoraidh / That final mile / Smalltown / Precious years.
LP: CHR 1713
MC: ZCHR 1713

Runswick, Daryl

NO SURRENDER (Film soundtrack) (See under No Surrender).

Rupert Bear (bk)

ADVENTURES OF RUPERT BEAR (Rupert Bear).
MCSET: DTO 10540

FAVOURITE RUPERT STORIES (Bennett, Judy (nar)).
MC: 00 1034588

RUPERT AND THE CHOCOLATE BUTTONS GANG (Unknown narrator(s)).
MC: 0 00 102125 7

RUPERT AND THE FROG SONG (for ages 5-10) (Unknown narrator(s)).
MC: PLBR 212

RUPERT AND THE MAGIC SEEDS (Unknown narrator(s)).
MC: PLBR 280

RUPERT AND THE NUTWOOD STAGE.
MC: 0 00 102128 1

RUPERT AND THE OLD HAT (Unknown narrator(s)).
MC: PLBR 281

RUPERT AND THE WOBBLY WITCH (Unknown narrator(s)).
MC: 0 00 102127 3

RUPERT AND THE YELLOW ELEPHANT (Unknown narrator(s)).
MC: 0 00 102126 5

RUPERT BEAR (Nutwood Chums).
LP: CMAE 1
MC: CMAEC 1

RUPERT BEAR AND THE HIDDEN LAKE (Bennett, Judy (nar)).
MC: TTS 9811

RUPERT BEAR AND THE LONELY BIRD (Bennett, Judy (nar)).
MC: TTS 9810

RUPERT BEAR AND THE MUDDLED MAGIC (Bennett, Judy (nar)).
MC: TTS 9812

RUPERT BEAR AND THE YOUNG DRAGON (Bennett, Judy (nar)).
MC: TTS 9801

RUPERT BEAR - STORIES FROM THE 1982 ANNUAL.
MC: PTB 636

RUPERT BEAR'S NEW ADVENTURES.
MC: 00 104 132 0

SINGS A GOLDEN HOUR OF NURSERY RHYMES.
LP: SPR 8524
MC: SPC 8524

STORIES OF RUPERT BEAR VOL.1 (Unknown narrator(s)).
MCSET: DTO 10519

STORIES OF RUPERT BEAR VOL.2 (Unknown narrator(s)).
MCSET: DTO 10525

Rupkina, Yanka

KALIMENKO DENKO.
LP: HNBL 1334
MC: HNBC 1334

Rural Blues

SACRED TRADITION, THE.
LP: HER 206

Rusca, Mario

RECREATIONS (Rusca, Mario, Group).
LP: J 0130

Rush

2112.
Tracks: / Lessons / Passage to Bangkok, A / Something for nothing / Tears / Twilight zone / 2112 overture / Temples of syrinx, The / Discover / Presentation / Oracle, The / Dream, The / Soliloquy / Grand finale.
LP: PRICE 79
MC: PRIMC 79

ALL THE WORLD'S A STAGE.
Tracks: / Anthem / Bastille day / By Tor and the snow dog / At the tobes of Hades / Across the styx / Of the battle / Epilogue / Fly by night / In the mood / In the end / Lakeside park / Something for nothing / 2112 overture / Temples of syrinx, The / Presentation / Soliloquy / Grand finale / What you're doing / Working man / Finding my way.
2LP: PRID 1
MCSET: PRIDC 1

CARESS OF STEEL.
Tracks: / Bastille day / Fountain of Lamneth / In the valley / Didacts and

narpets / No one at the bridge / Panacea / Bacchus plateau / Fountain, The / I think I'm going bald / Lakeside park / Necromancer, The / Into the darkness / Under the shadow / Return of the Prince.
LP: . . . . **PRICE 20**
MC: . . . . **PRIMC 20**

CHRONICLES.
Tracks: / Finding my way / Fly by night / Bastille day / 2112 overture / Temples of syrinx / Farewell to kings, A / Trees, The / Freewill / Tom Sawyer / Limelight / Subvisions / Distant early warning / Big money, The / Force ten / Mystic rhythms (live) / Working man / Anthem / Lakeside Park / What you're doing (live) / Closer to the heart / La villa strangiato / Spirit of radio, The / Red Barchetta / Passage to Bangkok, A / New world man / Red sector A / Manhattan Project / Time stand still / Show don't tell.
LPS: **8389361**
MCSET: **8389364**

EXIT....STAGE LEFT.
Tracks: / Spirit of radio / Red barchetta / YYZ / Passage to Bangkok, A / Closer to the heart / Beneath, between and behind / Jacob's ladder / Broon's bane / Trees / Xanadu / Freewill / Tom Sawyer / La villa strangiato.
2LP: **6619 053**
MCSET: **7558 053**

FAREWELL TO KINGS.
LP: **9100 042**
LP: . . . . **PRICE 92**
MC: . . . . **PRIMC 92**

FLY BY NIGHT.
Tracks: / Anthem / Beneath, between and behind / Best I can / By Tor and the snow dog / At the tobes of hades / Across the styx / Of the battle / Epilogue / Fly by night / In the end / Making memories / Rivendell.
LP: . . . . **PRICE 19**
MC: . . . . **PRIMC 19**

GRACE UNDER PRESSURE.
Tracks: / Distant early warning / After image / Red sector, A / Enemy within, An / Body electric / Kid gloves / Red lenses / Between the wheels.
LP: . . . . **VERH 12**
MC: . . . . **VERHC 12**

HEMISPHERES.
LP: . . . . **GR 8303**
LP: **9100 059**
LP: . . . . **PRICE 118**
MC: . . . . **PRIMC 118**

HOLD YOUR FIRE.
Tracks: / Force team / Time stands still / Open secrets / Prime mover / Lock and key / Tai Shan / High water.
LP: **8324641Q1**
LP: **832 464 1**
LP: . . . . **VERH 47**
MC: . . . . **VERHC 47**

MOVING PICTURES.
Tracks: / Tom Sawyer / Red Barchetta / YYZ / Limelight / Camera, The / Witch hunt / (Part III of Fear) / Vital signs.
LP: **6337 160**
MC: **7141 160**

PERMANENT WAVES.
LP: **9100 071**
MC: **7142 720**

POWER WINDOWS.
Tracks: / Big money, The / Grand design / Manhattan Project / Marathon / Territories / Middletown dreams / Emotion detector / Mystic rhythms.
LP: . . . . **VERH 31**
MC: . . . . **VERHC 31**

PRESTO.
LP: . . . . **WX 327**
MC: . . . . **WX 327 C**

ROLL THE BONES.
MC: . . . . **WX 436 C**
LP: . . . . **WX 436**

RUSH.
Tracks: / Before and after / Finding my way / Here again / In the mood / Need some love / Take a friend / What you're doing / Working man.
LP: . . . . **PRICE 18**
MC: . . . . **PRIMC 18**

RUSH ARCHIVES.
2LP: **6641 799**
MC: **7649 103**

RUSH: INTERVIEW PICTURE DISC.
LPPD: . . . . **BAK 2083**

RUSH THROUGH TIME.
LP: **6337 171**
MC: **7141 171**

SHOW OF HANDS, A.
Tracks: / Big money, The / Subdivisions / Marathon / Turn the page / Manhattan project / Mission / Distant early warning / Mystic rhythms / Witch hunt / Rhythm method (Neil Peart drum solo.) / Force ten / Time stands still / Red sector, A / Closer to the heart.
2LP: **836 346-1**
MC: **836 346-4**

SIGNALS.
Tracks: / Subdivisions / Analog kid, The / Chemistry / Digital man / Weapon, The / New world man / Losing it / Countdown.
LP: **6337 243**
MC: **7141 243**

Rush, Bobby

RUSH HOUR.
Tracks: / I wanna do the do (extended version) / I can't find my keys / Let's do it together / Intermission / Nickname / Evil is / No axe ta grind / Hey western union man.
LP: . . . . **CRB 1196**
MC: . . . . **TCCRB 1196**

Rush, Jennifer

HEART OVER MIND.
Tracks: / I come undone / Down to you / Heart over mind / Search the sky / Flames of Paradise (Duet with Elton John.) / Love of a stranger / Heart wars / Stronghold / Sidekick / Call my name.
LP: **4504701**
MC: **4504704**

JENNIFER RUSH.
Tracks: / Madonna's eyes / 25 lovers / Come give me your hand / Nobody move / Never gonna turn back again / Ring of ice / Into my dreams / I see a shadow (not a fantasy) / Surrender / Power of love, The.
LP: . . . . **CBS 26488**
MC: **40 26488**
LP: **4609471**
MC: **4609474**

MOVIN'.
Tracks: / Destiny / Live wire / Silent killer / Automatic / If you're ever gonna lose my love / Ave Maria (survivors of a different kind) / Testify with my heart / Yester-me, yester-you, yesterday / Right time has come now / Hero of a fool.
LP: . . . . **CBS 26710**
MC: **40 26710**

PASSION.
Tracks: / Love get ready / You're my one and only / Falling in love / When I look in your eyes / Remind my heart / Keep all the fires burning bright / Same heart / My heart is still young / You don't know what you've got / Rain coming down on me / Now that it's over.
LP: **4629681**
MC: **4629684**

TILL I LOVED YOU (see under 'Domingo, Placido') (Rush, Jennifer & Placido Domingo).

WINGS OF DESIRE.
Tracks: / Wings of desire / Pleasure / Midnight mirage / Angel / Higher ground / Love is a wild thing / For all that / Love is the language (of the heart) / Cry / Walk away.
LP: **4660001**
MC: **4660004**

Rush, Otis

CLASSIC RECORDINGS.
Tracks: / All your love / Three times a fool / She's a good 'un / It takes time / Double trouble / My love will never die / My baby is a good 'un / Checking on my baby / Jump sister Bessie / I can't quit you baby / If you were mine / Groaning the blues / Keep on loving me baby / Sit down baby / Love that woman / Violent love / So many roads, so many trains / I'm satisfied / So close / All your love / You know my love / I can't stop baby.
MC: . . . . **TCCRB 1107**
LP: . . . . **CRB 1107**

COLD DAY IN HELL.
LP: . . . . **DL 638**

DOOR TO DOOR (see under King, Albert) (Rush, Otis/Albert King).

FINAL TAKES, THE (Rush, Otis & Buddy Guy).
LP: . . . . **FLY 594**

GROANING THE BLUES.
LP: . . . . **FLY 560**

LIVE AT THE CHICAGO BLUES FESTIVAL (Rush, Otis & Little Walter).
LP: . . . . **CL 291283**
MC: . . . . **CLMC 9291283**

LOST IN THE BLUES.
Tracks: / Hold that train / You've been an angel / Little red rooster / Trouble, trouble / Please love me / You don't have to go / Got to be some changes made / You got me running / I miss you so.
MC: . . . . **ZCSN 1045**

OTHER TAKES, THE (1956-58) (Rush, Otis/Magic Sam).
LP: . . . . **FLY 562**

OTIS RUSH.
Tracks: / Double trouble / Jump sister Bessie / She's a good 'un (take A) / Checking on my baby / Sit down baby / Love that woman / Keep on loving me baby (Take B) / Keep on loving me baby (Take A) / My baby is a good 'un / If you were mine / I can't quit you baby / All your love / Groaning the blues / It takes time / Violent love / Three times a fool / My love will never die / She's a good 'un (take B).
LP: . . . . **FLY 650**

RIGHT PLACE, WRONG TIME.
Tracks: / Right place, wrong time / Easy go / Three times a fool / Rainy night in Georgia / Natural ball / I wonder why / Your turn to cry / Lonely man / Take a look behind.
LP: . . . . **ED 220**
LP: . . . . **BULLFROG 301**

SO MANY ROADS/LIVE IN CONCERT.
LP: . . . . **DL 643**

TOPS.
Tracks: / Right place, wrong time / Crosscut saw / Tops / Feels so bad / Gambler's blues / Keep on loving me baby / I wonder why.
LP: . . . . **FIEND 143**

TROUBLES TROUBLES.
LP: . . . . **SNTF 756**

VINTAGE BLUES (See under King, Albert for details) (Rush, Otis/Albert King).

WINDY CITY BLUES (see under Little Walter) (Little Walter/Otis Rush).

Rush, Tom

CLASSIC RUSH.
Tracks: / On the road again / Cuckoo, The / Who do you love / Joshua gone Barbados / Shadow dream song / Urge for going / Galveston slood / Love made a fool of you / No regrets / Rockport Sunday / Something in the way she moves / Circle game.
LP: . . . . **K 42073**

LATE NIGHT RADIO.
LP: . . . . **HS 48011**

Rushen, Patrice

LET THERE BE FUNK.
Tracks: / Let your heart be free / Let there be funk / What's the story / Shout it out / Yolon / Traverse / Hump / Roll with the punches / Steppin' stones / Sojourn.
LP: . . . . **PR 10110**

MUSIC OF THE EARTH.
Tracks: / Music of the earth / When I found you / Changes / Wishful thinking / Let's sing a song of love / Hang it up / Cha cha / It's just a natural thing / Didn't you know / Play.
LP: . . . . **K 52104**

NOW.
LP: **9603601**
MC: **9603604**

POSH.
Tracks: / Never gonna give you up / Don't blame me / Look up / I need your love / Time will tell / Dream / Funk won't let you know / This is all I really know.
LP: **6E 302**

SHOUT IT OUT.
Tracks: / Hump, The / Shout it out / Stepping stones / Let your heart be free / Roll with the punches / Let there be funk / Yolon / Sojourn.
LP: . . . . **PR 10101**

STRAIGHT FROM THE HEART.
Tracks: / Forget me nots / I was tired of being alone / All we need / Number one / Where there is love / Breakout / If only / Remind me / She will take you down to love.
LP: . . . . **K 52532**

WATCH OUT!.
Tracks: / Watch out! / Breakin' all the rules / Long time coming / All my love / Somewhere / Anything can happen / Burnin' / Till she's out of your mind / Come back to me / Tender lovin'.
LP: **207831**
MC: **407831**

Rushing, Jimmy

BIG BAND BLUES 1949-52.
LP: . . . . **KK 814**

BLUESWAY SESSIONS/BLUES YEARS.
Tracks: / Baby don't tell on me / Berkely campus blues / Blues in the dark / Everyday I have the blues / Evil blues / Keep the faith baby / Sent for you yesterday / I left my baby / Sonny boy blues / Bad loser / You can't run around / Tell me I'm not too late / Crying blues / Undecided blues / Take me back baby / We remember Pres.
2LP: . . . . **CDX 13**

ESSENTIAL JIMMY RUSHING, THE.
Tracks: / I may be wrong / See see rider / Sent for you yesterday / How long how long blues / I can't understand / How you want lovin' done? / My friend Mister Blues / Sometimes I think I do / Goin' to Chicago / Everyday / Rock and roll / Good morning blues / Evenin' / Take me back, baby / Take me with you, baby / If this ain't the blues.
2LP: . . . . **VJD 556**

GOOD MORNIN' BLUES (see under Basie, Count) (Rushing, Jimmy & The Count Basie Band).

I-WANT-A-LITTLE-GIRL.
Tracks: / My baby's business / Jimmy's round the clock blues / Thursday blues / Good mornin' blues / I've got to have you, that's all / I-want-a-little-girl / I'm so lonely / Go get some more you fool / Hi-ho Sylvester / Way I feel, The / In the moonlight / She's mine, she's yours / Where were you? / Somebody's spoiling these women / My last affair / Baby, don't tell on me.
LP: . . . . **OFF 3020**

JAZZ ODYSSEY OF JIMMY RUSHING.
LP: . . . . **FS 270**

JIMMY WITHERSPOON/JIMMY RUSHING (See under Rushing, Jimmy) (Rushing, Jimmy/Jimmy Witherspoon).

RUSHING LULLABIES.
LP: . . . . **FS 271**

SMITH GIRLS, THE.
LP: . . . . **FS 273**

YOU AND ME THAT USED TO BE, THE.
Tracks: / You and me that used to be, The / Fine and mellow / When I grow too old to dream / I surrender dear / Linger awhile / Bei mir bist du schon / My last affair / All God's chillun got rhythm / More than you know / Home / Thanks a million.
LP: . . . . **NL 86460**
MC: . . . . **NK 86460**

Rushton, Willie (nar)

COMIC RHYMES (Rushton, Willie & Sheila Steafel).
MC: **0600560899**

TALE OF ALE, THE.
2LP: . . . . **FRRD 023/24**

Ruskin

KING OF THE GOLDEN RIVER.
LP: . . . . **KPM 7007**

Russco

FACE THE WORLDS Folksongs for today.
MC: **60-094**

Russeil, Linda

COLONAL CHRISTMAS, A (Russeil, Linda & companie).
LP: . . . . **FF 402**

Russell, Arthur

INSTRUMENTALS.
LP: . . . . **SIDE 8401**

WORLD OF ECHO.
Tracks: / Soon to be innocent fun / Tone bone kone / Answers me / Being it / Place I know / She's the star / I take this time / Treehouse / See-through / Hiding your present from you / Wax divan / All-boy all-girl / Lucky cloud / Let's go swimming / Tower of meaning (rabbit's ear).
LP: . . . . **ROUGH 114**

Russell, Bill

FROM OLD LEAVES.
LP: . . . . **FR 111**

Russell, Brenda

BRENDA RUSSELL.
Tracks: / So good so right / In the thick of it / If only for one night / Way back when / Little bit of love, A / You're free / Think it over / God bless you.
LP: . . . . **AMA 3174**
MC: . . . . **AMC 3174**
LP: . . . . **AMLJ 739**

GET HERE.
Tracks: / Gravity / Just a believer / Piano in the dark / This time I need you / Make my day / Le restaurant / Midnight eyes / Get here.
LP: . . . . **AMA 5178**
MC: . . . . **AMC 5178**

KISS ME WITH THE WIND.
Tracks: / Kiss me with the wind / All American / Waiting for you / Dinner with Gershwin / Night train to Leningrad / On your side / Stupid love / Stop running away / Justice in truth / Good for love / Drive my car ('til sunset).
LP: **3952711**
MC: **3952714**

Russell, Calvin

CRACK IN TIME, A.
Tracks: / Crack in time, A / Big brother / Nothin' / Behind the eight ball / Automated / North Austin slim / One step ahead / Living at the end of a gun / I should have been home / My way / This

is my life / Little stars / Moments / Wagon to stars.
LP: ROSE 209

Russell, Dan

LET SLEEPING DOGS LIE (see under Reid, Junior's "movie star").

Russell, Devon

MONEY SEX AND VIOLENCE.
LP: RNLP 0010
MC: RNC 0010

PRISON LIFE.
LP: TWLP 1008

Russell Family

RUSSELL FAMILY OF DOOLIN, CO. CLARE, THE.
LP: 12TS 251

Russell, George

AFRICAN GAME, THE.
Tracks: / Event I: Organic life on earth begins / Event II: The Paleolithic game / Event III: Consciousness / Event IV: The survival game / Event V: The human sensing of unity with great / Event VI: African Empires / Event VII: Cartesian man / Event VIII: The mega-minimalist age / Event IX: The future.
LP: BT 85103
MC: TCBT 85103

ELECTRONIC SONATA FOR SOULS LOVED BY NATURE - 1968.
Tracks: / Part 1 / Part 2.
LP: SN 1034

JAZZ IN THE SPACE AGE (Russell, George & His Orchestra).
Tracks: / Chromatic Universe-Part 1 / Dimensions / Chromatic Universe-Part 2 / Lydiot, The / Waltz from outer space / Chromatic Universe-Part 3.
LP: AFF 152

SO WHAT.
Tracks: / So what / Rhymes / War gewessen / Time spiral.
LP: BT 85132

STRATUSPHUNK (Russell, George Sextet).
LP: OJC 232

TRIP TO PRILLARGURI (Russell, George Sextet).
Tracks: / Theme / Souls / Event III: Consciousness / VIPs / Stratusphink / Esoteric / Circle / Man on the moon.
LP: SN 1029

Russell, Janet

GATHERING THE FRAGMENTS.
LP: HAR 003
MC: HARC 003

JANET RUSSELL AND CHRISTINE KYDD (Russell, Janet/Christine Kydd).
Tracks: / Buy broom besoms / Dainty Davie / Up wi' the Carls o'Dysart / De'ils awa' with the exciseman, the / Deja mal Mariee / Bonnie at morn / Children of Africa / My Donald / Ode to big blue / Tae the weavers gin ye gang / Old and strong / Mountain song / Do you love an apple / Last carol / Stand up fight for your rights / Everyone 'neath a vine and fig tree.
MC: CTRAX 011

Russell, John

HOME COOKING (see Coldman,Richard & John Russell) (Russell, John & Richard Coldman).

Russell, Johnny

COUNTRY STORE: JOHNNY RUSSELL.
Tracks: / Act naturally / Rednecks, white socks and blue ribbon beer / Making plans / Good hearted woman / Busted / Kaw-liga / Working man blues / Catfish John / All I have to offer you is me / Blue eyes crying in the rain / Luckenbach, Texas / Jambalaya / Today I started loving you again / King of the road.
LP: CST 44
MC: CSTK 44

MR. ENTERTAINER.
Tracks: / Nobody touches my baby / Our marriage was a failure / Some day I'll sober up / Too late to turn back now / She goes walking through my mind / Over Georgia / She burnt the little roadside tavern down / Finer things in life, The / Queen of my heart / Remembering / Some kind of a woman / Leona / I'm staying / Your fool / This man and woman thing / What a price.
LP: NL 90000
MC: NK 90000

Russell, Leon

AMERICANA.
LP: K 56534

BEST OF LEON RUSSELL.
Tracks: / Shoot out at the plantation / Delta lady / Hummingbird / Song for you / Tightrope / Stranger in a strange land.
LP: ISA 5013

LEON RUSSELL AND THE SHELTER PEOPLE.
Tracks: / Stranger in a strange land / Of thee I sing / Hard rains a-gonna fall / Crystal closet queen / Home sweet Oklahoma / Alcatraz / Ballad of mad dogs and Englishmen, The / It takes a lot to laugh, it takes a train to cry / She smiles like a river / Sweet Emily / Beware of darkness / It's all over now, baby blue / Love minus zero / No limit / She belongs to me.
LP: AMLS 65003

LIVE ALBUM: LEON RUSSELL (Russell, Leon & New Grass Revival).
Tracks: / Over the rainbow / I've just seen a face / One more love song / Pilgrim land / Georgia blues / I believe to my soul / Prince of peace / Rollin' in my sweet baby's arms / Stranger in a strange land / I want to be at the meeting / Wild horses / Jambalaya / Caribbean / Jumpin' Jack Flash.
LP: K 56891

Russell, Luis

1926-30 (Russell, Luis & His Orchestra).
Tracks: / 29th and dearborn / Sweet Mumtaz / Plantation joys / Please don't turn me down / Dolly mine / Savoy shout / Call of the freaks, The / It's tight like that / New call of the freaks, The / Feeling the spirit / Jersey lightning / Way he loves is just too bad, The / Jersey lightning / Broadway rhythm / Doctor blues / Saratoga shout / Song of the Swanee / Louisiana swing / Poor li'l me / On revival day.
LP: VLP 54

1930-1934.
Tracks: / Give me your telephone number / Higginbotham blues / Muggin' lightly / Panama / High tension / I got rhythm / Saratoga drag / Ease on down / Honey, that reminds me / You rascal, you / Goin' to town / Say the word / Freakish blues / Darktown strutters' ball / My blue Heaven / Ghost of the freaks / Hokus pokus / Primitive / Ol' man river.
LP: VLP 57

LUIS RUSSELL AND ORCHESTRA (1929-30) (Russell, Luis & His Orchestra).
LP: S 828

Russell, Micho

LIMESTONE ROCK, THE.
MC: GTDC 104

MICHO RUSSELL.
LP: TRL 1009
MC: TRC 1009

TRADITIONAL MUSIC OF COUNTY CLARE.
LP: FRR 004

Russell, Pee Wee

CHRONOLOGICAL REMEMBRANCE, A.
LP: IAJRC 28

COLLEGE CONCERT, THE (Russell, Pee Wee & Red Allen).
Tracks: / Blue Monk / I want a little girl / Body and soul / Pee Wee's blues / Two degrees east, three degrees west / Graduation blues.
LP: JAS 78

HOT LIQUORISH (Russell, Pee Wee & His Rhythm Cats).
LP: HD 6614

INDIVIDUALISM OF..., THE.
Tracks: / Love is just around the corner / Squeeze me / Ballin' the Jack / I'd do most anything for you / California here I come / St. James infirmary / Baby won't you please come home / Lady's in love with you, The / Struttin' with some barbecue / St. Louis blues / Sweet Lorraine / Sentimental journey / If I had you / Coquette / Lady is a tramp, The.
2LP: SJL 2228

JAM SESSION IN SWINGVILLE (Russell, Pee Wee & Coleman Hawkins).
Tracks: / Jammin' in Swingville / Cool sunrise / Spring's swing / Love me or leave me / I want to be happy / Phoenix / So glad / Things ain't what they used to be / I may be wrong / Vic's spot / Years ago.
2LP: PR 24051

JAZZ REUNION (Russell, Pee Wee & Coleman Hawkins).
Tracks: / If I could be with you one hour tonight / Tin tin deo / Mariooch / All too soon / 29th and 8th / What am I here for?.
LP: CS 9020

MUGGSY SPANIER AND PEE WEE RUSSELL (see Spanier, Muggsy) (Russell, Pee Wee/Muggsy Spanier).

OVER THE RAINBOW.
LP: XAN 192

PEE WEE RUSSELL AND THE RHYTHM CATS.
LP: SS 109

PIED PIPER OF JAZZ THREE DEUCES AND HOT FOUR, THE.
Tracks: / Jig walk / Deuces wild / Last time I saw Chicago / About face / Take me to the land of jazz / Rose of Washington Square / Keepin' out of mischief now / D. A. blues.
LP: 6.25490

WE'RE IN THE MONEY.
LP: BLP 60909

Russell, Ray

WHY NOT NOW.
Tracks: / Outland / Prelude 1 / Pour me a fish / Blue shoes ... no dance / Lundy Island / Pan piper / Cildscape / If only ... / Murmers in reverse / Sketches of Gil.
LP: TET 3
MC: CTET 3

Russell, Stephen

FIRST ORBIT (a taoist meditation).
MC: C 160

SUNDANCER.
Tracks: / Sundancer / First popular symphony in D sharp / Song of the steps / Tales from the womb.
LP: TET 1
MC: CTET 1

Russell, Tom

POOR MANS DREAMS.
Tracks: / Blue wing / Heart of a working man, The / Veteran's day / Walking on the moon / Outbound plane / Navajo rug / Spanish burgundy / Gallo de Cielo / La Frontera / Under the gun / Bergenfield.
LP: RUSS LP 2

ROAD TO BAYAMON (Russell, Tom Band).
LP: PH 1116
MC: PH 1116C
LP: ROUNDER 1116

Russia

AKVARELLI AND TCHARIVINI GITARY (Various artists).
MC: SM 00386

ALEXSANDROU SONG AND DANCE ENSEMBLE (Various artists).
MC: SM 00126

COIL MUSIC FROM USSR (Various artists).
MC: T33.8

DANCES & FOLK DANCES BY RUSSIAN COMP. (Various artists).
MC: M 00241

ESTONIAN FOLK MUSIC (Various artists).
MC: SM 00395

FESTIVAL OF RUSSIAN FOLK SONGS (Various artists).
LP: HQS 1409

FROM OLD RUSSIA (Russian Dance Music) (Various artists).
MC: M 00133

IVANOV KRAMSKOY (Russian Guitar Music) (Various artists).
MC: SM 00431

LES BALALAIKAS DES TZIGANES RUSSES (Various artists).
Tracks: / Les yeux verts: *Various artists* / Boublitchki: *Various artists* / Ne sois pas jaloux, ne sois pas Fache: *Various artists* / Mon bohemien: *Various artists* / Ne pars pas: *Various artists* / Plaine, ma plaine: *Various artists* / Le sarafan rouge: *Various artists* / Kalinka: *Various artists* / Tzigane et samovar: *Various artists* / L'amour s'est enfui: *Various artists* / Le vieux Tzigane: *Various artists* / Kalinka: *Various artists* / Vradanka: *Various artists* / Pourquoi m'astu aime: *Various artists.*
LP: ARN 33724
MC: ARN 433724

MEMORIES OF MOSCOW (Russian melodies & rhythms) (Various artists).
LP: ALP 110

MERRY MELODIES (Russian Popular Music) (Various artists).
MC: SM 00253

MOSCOW RADIO RUSSIAN FOLK INSTRUMENTS (Various artists).
LP: C 01737-8

NORTHERN RUSSIAN FOLK CHORUS FOLK SONGS (Various artists).
LP: C 01671-2

OLD RUSSIAN FOLK SONGS (Various artists).
MC: SM 00246

OMSK STATE RUSSIAN FOLK CHOIR FOLK SONGS (Various artists).
LP: CM 02071-2

OSIPOV RUSSIAN FOLK ORCHESTRA VOL.2 (Traditional Music) (Various artists).
LP: CM 04385-6

OSIPOV RUSSIAN FOLK ORCHESTRA VOL.1 (Traditional Music) (Various artists).
LP: CM 02541-2

PETRUSHKA (Russian Vocal Quartet) (Various artists).
MC: SM 00244

PIATNITSKY STATE ACADEMIC FOLK CHORUS (Various artists).
MC: SM 00079

PYATNITSKY STATE RUSSIAN FOLK CHOIR, VOL. 3 (Various artists).
LP: CM 02801-2

PYATNITSKY STATE RUSSIAN FOLK CHOIR, VOL. 4 (Various artists).
LP: C 01871-2

PYATNITSKY STATE RUSSIAN FOLK CHOIR, VOL. 2 (Various artists).
LP: CM 02135-6

RUSSIAN (see under Language Courses).

RUSSIAN ACCORDEON MUSIC (Various artists).
MC: SM 00267

RUSSIAN DANCE MUSIC (Various artists).
MC: M 00132

RUSSIAN FAVOURITES (Various artists).
MC: HR 8156

RUSSIAN FOLK FESTIVAL, A (Various artists).
LP: ASD 3550

RUSSIAN FOLK INSTRUMENTS ENSEMBLE (Various artists).
LP: CM 03225-6

RUSSIAN OLD MARCHES & WALTZES (Various artists).
MC: SM 00154

RUSSIAN ORTHODOX CHURCH MUSIC (VOLUME 19) (Various artists).
MCSET: CIKO 20D

RUSSIAN ORTHODOX CHURCH MUSIC (VOLUME 11) (Christmas Vigil) (Various artists).
LP: IKO 12
MC: CIKO 12

RUSSIAN ORTHODOX CHURCH MUSIC (VOLUME 12) (Various artists).
LP: IKO 13
MC: CIKO 13

RUSSIAN ORTHODOX CHURCH MUSIC (VOLUME 13) (Liturgy of St.John Chrysostom, The) (Various artists).
LP: IKO 14
MC: CIKO 14

RUSSIAN ORTHODOX CHURCH MUSIC (VOLUME 1) (Various artists).
LP: IKO 1
MC: CIKO 1

RUSSIAN ORTHODOX CHURCH MUSIC (VOLUME 18) (Various artists).
MC: CIKO 19

RUSSIAN ORTHODOX CHURCH MUSIC (VOLUME 3) (Various artists).
LP: IKO 4F

RUSSIAN ORTHODOX CHURCH MUSIC (VOLUME 8) (Vespers of Good Friday) (Various artists).
LP: IKO 9
MC: CIKO 9

RUSSIAN ORTHODOX CHURCH MUSIC (VOLUME 9) (Various artists).
LP: IKO 10
MC: CIKO 10

RUSSIAN ORTHODOX CHURCH MUSIC (VOLUME 10) (Various artists).
LP: IKO 11
MC: CIKO 11

RUSSIAN ORTHODOX CHURCH MUSIC (VOLUME 2) (Various artists).
LP: IKO 2
MC: CIKO 2

RUSSIAN ORTHODOX CHURCH MUSIC (VOLUME 4) (Various artists).
LP: IKO 5
MC: CIKO 5

RUSSIAN ORTHODOX CHURCH MUSIC (VOLUME 5) (Various artists).
LP: IKO 6
MC: CIKO 6

RUSSIAN ORTHODOX CHURCH MUSIC (VOLUME 6) (Various artists).
LP: IKO 7
MC: CIKO 7

RUSSIAN ORTHODOX CHURCH MUSIC (VOLUME 17) (Various artists).
MC: CIKO 18

RUSSIAN ROMANCES (Various artists).
MC: SM 00268

RYATNITSKY STATE RUSSIAN FOLK CHOIR, VOL. 1 (Various artists).
LP: . . . . CM 02139 4

SKALDS (Russian Ensemble) (Various artists).
MC: . . . . SM 00139

SONGS OF TOURISTS (Various artists).
MC: . . . . M 00152

SOUL OF RUSSIA (Various artists).
LP: . . . . ADL 501
MC: . . . . ADK 501

SPRING VOICES (Various artists).
MC: . . . . Sm 00122

TOP MELODY '72 (Various artists).
MC: . . . . M 00196

TRADITIONAL RUSSIAN SONGS VOL.2 (Red Army Ensemble).
LP: . . . . CM 02137 8

TRADITIONAL RUSSIAN SONGS VOL.1 (Red Army Ensemble).
LP: . . . . CM 02873 4

TRADITIONAL RUSSIAN SONGS VOL.3 (Red Army Ensemble).
LP: . . . . C 05661 2

TRIO ROMEN (Various artists).
MC: . . . . SM 00451

UKRAINIAN FOLK SONGS (Various artists).
MC: . . . . M 00135

Russian Balalaika

FOLKSONGS.
LP: . . . . CM 04141-2

Russian Jazz Group

WING GROUP-HELMUT ORUSAAR.
MC: . . . . SM 00393

Russian Radio Ensemble

LIGHT JAZZ.
MC: . . . . M 00177

Russkies

RUSSKIES (Original Soundtrack) (Various artists).
LP: . . . . STV 81335

Russo, Mike

HIS GUITAR AND PIANO.
LP: . . . . ARHOOLIE 4003

Russo, Rafa

PETRIFIED FOREST, A.
LP: . . . . CPCY 93

Rustic Hinge

REPLICAS.
Tracks: / T on the lawn for three / Excitation wavelength / Litmus transformation / Ocus pocus / Crystallized petard / Kinesis / But that was then that was but / Last time, The / High tide play Rustic Hinge / Rumanian folk dance No. 1 / Macedonia / Radio Kabul / Rumanian folk dance No.2 / Mastadon.
LP: . . . . RECK 3

Rustic Parts

DON'T YOU WISH YOU WERE.
Tracks: / Shores of Old Blighty, The / City of New Orleans / Beachcomber / Cock o' the north / Peggy Gordon / Sailor Jack McCoy / Lovely like me / Musician, The / D'Arcy Farrow / Mrs. Canatelli's / Early morning rain / Dirty old man.
LP: . . . . SFA 075

Rustler Presents

WARWICK TAPES, THE (Various artists).
LP: . . . . BUNNER 1

Rusty, Daddy

ACID (See under Irie, Tipper) (Rusty, Daddy & Tipper Irie).

Rusty Dusty

RUSTY DUSTY (Various artists).
LP: . . . . LP 379

Rutherford, Mike

ACTING VERY STRANGE.
Tracks: / Acting very strange / Day to remember / Maxine / Halfway there / Who's fooling who / Couldn't get arrested / I don't wanna know / Hideaway.
LP: . . . . K 99249

MIKE & THE MECHANICS.
LP: 252496 1
MC: 252496 4

SMALLCREEPS DAY.
Tracks: / Between the tick and the tock / Working in line / After hours / Cats and rats in this neighbourhood / Smallcreep alone / Out into the daylight / At the end of the day / Moonshine / Time and time again / Romani / Every road / Overnight job.
LP: . . . . CHC 53
LP: . . . . CAS 1149
MC: . . . . CHCMC 53

Rutherford, Paul (1)

HOLYWELL CONCERT, THE (See under Coxhill, Lol) (Coxhill, Lol/Haslam/Rutherford/Riley).

OH WORLD.
MC: . . . . BRCA 533
LP: . . . . BRLP 533

Rutherford, Paul (2)

ISKRA 1903 (Rutherford, Paul/Derek Bailey/Barry Guy).
2LP: . . . . INCUS 3/4

LIVE - MOERS (SOLO TROMBONE 1976).
LP: . . . . RING 01014

NEUPH.
Tracks: / Yep / Realign / Three levels / Paunch and Judies / Chefor / Phase 2 / Neuph.
LP: . . . . SFA 092

Ruthless Blues

RUTHLESS BLUES.
Tracks: / Fine, fine, fine / Better things to do / Never told me why / Too many drivers / Solid gold mustang / Tie me up / Maintenance man / Tightrope blues / Ain't no love (in the heart of the city).
LP: . . . . PTLS 1102
MC: . . . . PTLC 1102

Ruthless People

RUTHLESS PEOPLE (Original Soundtrack) (Various artists).
Tracks: / Ruthless people: *Jagger, Mick* / Give me the reason: *Vandross, Luther* / Modern woman: *Joel, Billy* / Wherever I lay my hat: *Young, Paul* / No say in it: *Machinations* / Waiting to see you: *Hartman, Dan* / Dance champion: *Kool & The Gang* / Neighbourhood watch: *Colombier, Michael* / Stand on it: *Springsteen, Bruce* / Don't you want my love: *Nicole*.
LP: . . . . EPC 70299
MC: 40 70299

Ruthless Rap Assassins

KILLER ALBUM.
Tracks: / Crew from the north / Law of the jungle, The / And it wasn't a dream / Go wild / Just mellow / Here today...here tomorrow / Justice (just us) / Posse strong / Jealous MC / That's my nigger / To the other MC's / Yakety yak / B-Line / Three the hard way.
LP: . . . . SYLP 6005
LP: 794 424 1
MC: . . . . TCSYLP 6005
MC: 794 424 4

THINK - IT AIN'T ILLEGAL YET.
Tracks: / What did you say your name was? / Listen to the hit / Why me? / Think / Hard and direct / I got no time / Radio / Down and dirty / No tale, no twist / Pick up the pace / (I try to) flow it out / Less mellow.
LP: . . . . EMC 3604
MC: . . . . TCEMC 3604

Rutland, Brian

UNDECIDED (Rutland, Brian Band).
LP: . . . . FLY 213

Rutles

RUTLES, THE.
Tracks: / Hold my hand / Number one / With a girl like you / I must be in love / Ouch! / Living in hope / Love life / Nevertheless / Good times roll / Doubleback alley / Cheese and onions / Another day / Piggy in the middle / Let's be natural.
LP: . . . . K 56459
MC: K4 56459

Rutles Highway...

RUTLES HIGHWAY REVISITED (Various artists).
LP: . . . . SHIMMY 041

Rutman, Neil

PIANO CONCERTI NO.12/22 (see under Mozart) (Rutman, Neil/Academy of London).

Ruts

BABYLON'S BURNING (See under XTC).

CRACK, THE.
Tracks: / Babylon's burning / Dope for guns / S.U.S. / Something that I said / You're just a... / It was cold / Savage circle / Jah war / Criminal mind / Backwater / Out of order / Human punk.
LP: . . . . OVED 80
LP: . . . . V 2132
MC: . . . . OVEDC 80

GRIN AND BEAR IT.
Tracks: / West one (shine on me) / Staring at the rude boys / Demolition dancing / Secret soldier / H eyes / In a rut / Love in vain / S.U.S. / Babylon's burning / Society.
LP: . . . . OVED 57
LP: . . . . V 2188
MC: . . . . OVEDC 57

LIVE AND LOUD.
LP: . . . . LINK LP 013

LIVE: RUTS.
Tracks: / Sus / Dope for guns / It was cold / In a rut / Society / Jah war / Babylon's burning / You're just a / Love song / Criminal mind / Demolition dancing.
LP: . . . . DOJOLP 52

PEEL SESSIONS: RUTS (Complete Sessions 1979-81).
LP: . . . . SFRLP 109
MC: . . . . SFRC 109

Ruts D.C

ANIMAL NOW.
LP: . . . . V 2193

RHYTHM COLLISION.
Tracks: / Whatever we do / Militant / Push yourself - make it work / Accusation / Rhythm collision.
LP: . . . . BOLP 4

RHYTHM COLLISION DUB VOL.1 (Ruts D.C & Mad Professor).
MC: . . . . A 151

Rutter, John

MUSIC FOR CHRISTMAS.
LP: . . . . WST R 9624
MC: . . . . WST C 9624

RVT Ljubljana Big Band

INVITATION TO DANCE.
LP: . . . . DS 076

Ryan, Barry

ELOISE.
Tracks: / Kitsch / It is written / We did it together / My mama / Who puts the lights out / Hurt, The / Eloise / Colour of my love / Today / Follow me / Where have you been / Red man.
LP: 2872 109
MC: 3472 109

Ryan, Bill

MIDNIGHT IN THE MORNING.
LP: . . . . HPE 637

Ryan, Jimmy

COMMODORE CLASSICS (Ryan, Jimmy/Edmond Hall/Wilbur De Paris).
LP: AG6 24096

JIMMY RYANS & THE UPTOWN CAFE SOCIETY... (Ryan, Jimmy, Deparis Brothers, Edmond Hall).
Tracks: / I've found a new baby / I've found a new baby (alternative choice) (Previously unissued) / (What did I do to be so) black and blue / (What did I do to be so) black and blue (alter (Previously unissued) / Change o' key boogie / Change o' key boogie (alternative choice) / Sheik of Araby, The / Sheik of Araby, The (alternative choice) (Previously unissued) / Man I love, The / Man I love, The (alternative choice) (Previously unissued) / Downtown cafe boogie / Downtown cafe boogie (alternative choice) (Previously unissued) / Uptown cafe blues / Coquette.
LP: AG6 24296

Ryan, John

CAPTAIN PUGWASH (Hawkins, Peter).
MCSET: CC/041

Ryan, Lloyd

CIRCULAR STORM.
Tracks: / Dervish / Smiffy / I feel pretty / Rio / Self portrait / Norwegian wood / Midnight / Festival.
LP: . . . . LRLP 002

NEW DIRECTIONS (Ryan, Lloyd Jazz Four).
LP: . . . . LRLP 0001

Ryan, Mick

FAIR WAS THE CITY (Ryan, Mick/Jon Burge).
LP: . . . . LTRA 506

Ryan, Pat

DISTANT APPLAUSE.
MC: . . . . RIV 089

LEABOY'S LASSIE.
Tracks: / Shipyard apprentice, The / Snows they melt the soonest, The / Ploughman lads / Cock o' the north / Cathy Shaw / False love won back / Miner's lad, The / Flowers of the town / Village fool / Bonnie light horseman, The / Man of the earth / Leaboy's lassie.
LP: . . . . FHR 094

MOVING ON (Ryan, Pat/Chris Pollington/Chris Parkinson).
LP: . . . . TSR 043

TIME TO RETURN, A.
MC: . . . . RIV 067

Ryan, Phil

ARDOURS OF THE LOST RAKE (See under Brown, Pete (Lyricist)) (Ryan, Phil & Pete Brown).

Ryan, Richard

RAVENSWOOD POEMS.
LP: . . . . CCT 17

Ryan, Ron

NASSINGTON FLYER (see Duffy Brothers) (Ryan, Ron & Duffy Brothers).

Ryan, Sean

TAKE THE AIR.
LP: . . . . CEF 142
MC: . . . . CEFC 142

Ryan's Daughter

RYAN'S DAUGHTER (Film Soundtrack) (Various artists).
Tracks: / Main title: *Various artists* / Where was I when the parade went by: *Various artists* / You don't want me then: *Various artists* / Michael's theme: *Various artists* / Ride through the woods: *Various artists* / Obsession: *Various artists* / Overture: *Various artists* / Shakes based on Michael's theme: *Various artists* / Rosy and the schoolmaster: *Various artists* / Michael shows Randolph his strange treasure: *Various artists* / It was a good time (Rosy's theme): *Various artists*.
LP: 2315 028

RYAN'S DAUGHTER (Original Soundtrack) (Various artists).
LP: . . . . MCA 25142
MC: . . . . MCAC 25142

Rydell, Bobby

18 GOLDEN HITS.
LP: . . . . CAMEO 2001

ALL THE HITS.
LP: . . . . LSP 1058

GOOD TIME WITH BOBBY RYDELL.
LP: . . . . CLP 8025

JINGLE BELL ROCK (See under Checker, Chubby) (Rydell, Bobby & Chubby Checker).

WILD ONE.
Tracks: / Dream lover / Stagger Lee / This magic moment / Tossin' and turnin' (all night) / Wild one / Wildwood days / Forget him / Then you can tell me goodbye / Kissin' time U.S.A. / Volare.
LP: . . . . PRCV 130

Ryder, Kris

KRIS RYDER.
Tracks: / Lonely room / All in one night / Can't keep a good man down / Ordinary girl, ordinary guy / We're alive / Born loser / Lost in a strange vibration / Zoom in on me / I don't wanna fuss / Own up, you're crazy.
LP: . . . . SKLR 5312

Ryder, Mitch

DETROIT WITH MITCH RYDER (See under Detroit) (Ryder, Mitch & Detroit).

NEVER KICK A SLEEPING DOG.
LP: . . . . TOWLP 5
MC: . . . . ZCTOW 5

REV UP - THE BEST OF MITCH RYDER AND THE DETROIT WHEELS (Ryder, Mitch & The Detroit Wheels).
Tracks: / Jenny take a ride / Little Latin lupe lu / Shakin' with Linda / I like it like that / I had it made / Breakout / Shake a tail feather / Takin' all I can get (CD only.) / You get your kicks (CD only.) / Sticks and stones (CD only.) / Baby Jane (Mo-mo Jane) (CD only.) / Joy (CD only.) / Devil with a blue dress on / Good golly Miss Molly / Sock it to me baby / Too many fish in the sea / Three little fishes / I'd rather go to jail / Ooh papa doo / I hope / I never had it better.
LP: . . . . ROU 5003
LP: 793 632 1
MC: . . . . TCROU 5003
MC: 793 632 4

WHEELS OF STEEL (Ryder, Mitch/Detroit Wheels).
Tracks: / Jenny take a ride / Sock it to me baby / Little Latin lupe lu / You get your kicks / Devil with the blue dress / Good golly Miss Molly / Breakout / Shake a tail feather / Too many fish in the sea / Three little fishes.
LP: . . . . DOW 5
MC: . . . . ZCDOW 5

Rye Whiskey Road Band

I DREAMED OF HIGHWAYS.
Tracks: / No use running / I dreamed of highways / My elusive dreams / Help yourself to me / Catfish John / How much time does it take? / I know you've never been this far before / I recall a gypsy woman / Good to be back home again / Millers cave / Loving arms / I'm taking my love to my baby.
LP: . . . . FHR 072

RUNNING KIND, THE.
Tracks: / Running kind, The / When my blue moon turns to gold again / Please Mr., please / Hurt so bad / Some broken hearts never mend / Does Fort Worth ever cross your mind / Sunshine / I've got a couple of more years on you babe / Feelings / Mexican girl / Down and out blues / What have you got planned tonight Diana.
LP: . . . . **FHR 107**

Ryerson, Ali

CHARLES LOOS AND ALI RYERSON
(See under Loos, Charles) (Ryerson, Ali & Charles Loos).

Ryerson, Alim

WONDERLAND (Ryerson, Alim/Roy Williams/Mick Pyne Trio).
LP: . . . . **WONDER 1**

Rypdal, Terje

AFRIC PEPPERBIRD (Rypdal, Terje, Jan Garbarek & Anderson).
Tracks: / Sharabee / Mahjong / Beast of Kommodo / Blow away zone / MYB / Concentus / Afric pepperbird / Blupp.
LP: . . . . **ECM 1007**

AFTER THE RAIN.
LP: . . . . **ECM 1083**

BLUE (Rypdal, Terje/Chasers).
Tracks: / Curse, The / Kompet Gar / I disremember quite well / Og hva synes vi om det / Last nite / Blue / Tanga / Om bare.
LP: . . . . **ECM 1346**

CHASER.
Tracks: / Ambiguity / Once upon a time / Geysir / Closer look, A / Orion / Chaser / Transition / Imagi (theme).
LP: . . . . **ECM 1303**

EOS (Rypdal, Terje/David Darling).
Tracks: / Laster / Eos / Bedtime story / Light years / Melody / Mirage / Adagietto.
LP: . . . . **ECM 1263**

ODYSSEY.
2LP: . . . . **ECM 1067/68**

SART (Rypdal, Terje/Stenson/Jan Garbarek).
LP: . . . . **ECM 1015**

SINGLES COLLECTION, THE.
LP: . . . . **ECM 1383**
MC: **8377494**

SUNRISE.
MC: **7104655**

TERJE RYPDAL (Rypdal, Terje/Fintl/Jan Garbarek).
LP: . . . . **ECM 1016**

TO BE CONTINUED.
LP: . . . . **ECM 1192**

UNDISONUS.
LP: . . . . **ECM 1389**

WAVES.
Tracks: / Per ulv / Karusell / Stenskoven / Waves / Dain curse, The / Charisma.
LP: . . . . **ECM 1110**

WHAT COMES AFTER.
LP: . . . . **ECM 1031**

WHENEVER I SEEM TO BE AWAY.
LP: . . . . **ECM 1045**

WORKS: TERJE RYPDAL.
Tracks: / Waves / Den forste sne / Hung, The / Better off without you / Innseiling / Rainbow / Topplue, vooter & skjerf / Descendre.
LP: **8254281**

Rythm Syndicate

RYTHM SYNDICATE.
Tracks: / Hey Donna / P.A.S.S.I.O.N. / Suite / Anatomy of a love affair / Baby talk / Blinded by love / All she wants is everything / Sometimes love is not enough / Pass it on / You really rock me / Love is the reason / You'll never walk alone / Shoulder to cry on, A / Tearin' down the walls.
LP: . . . . **EMC 3598**
MC: . . . . **TCEMC 3598**

S

S. Express

INTERCOURSE.
LP: LP 14
MC: CA 14
LP: 4685671
MC: 4685674

ORIGINAL SOUNDTRACK.
Tracks: / S Express / Superfly guy / Hey music lover.
LP: LEFT LP 8
MC: LEFT C 8
LPPD: LEFT LP D8

SA 42

PRO PATRIA.
Tracks: / Over the sea / You are / Instr Robert / Pro Patria / Secret garden / Why not? / Submarine dance / Carnaval / Right thing / Voice of hell / Autopsy / Pleasure and crime.
LP: LD 8929

Sa, Sandra

SANDRA SA.
LP: BR 4002
MC: BRC 4002

Saalstrom & Sandstrom

FIDDLE MUSIC FROM UPPLAND.
LP: PH 2017

Saatchi, Phil

STRIPPED.
Tracks: / Little in love, A / When we dream / King of another country / Build a bridge / Love is a mission / No one gonna love you (like I do) / Wheel of fortune / Poor man's paradise / White flag / People of the New World.
LP: AMA 5152
MC: AMC 5152

Sabbat

DREAMWEAVER.
LP: NUK 132
MC: ZCNUK 132
LP: N 0132 1
MC: N 0132 4

HISTORY OF A TIME TO COME.
Tracks: / Cautionary tale, A / Hosanna in excelsis / Behind the crooked cross / Horned is the hunter / For an eye / For those who died / Dead man's robe, A / Church bizarre, The.
MC: N 0099
LP: NUK 098
MC: ZCNUK 098
LP: N 0098

MOURNING HAS BROKEN.
Tracks: / Demise of history, The / Paint the world black / Voice of time, The / Without a trace / Theological void / Dumbstruck / Dreamscape / Mourning has broken.
LP: NO 1621
MC: NO 1624

Sabia

LIVE IN CULVER CITY.
LP: FF 494

PORTAVOZ.
LP: FF 412

Sabien, Randy

IN A FOG (Sabien, Randy Jazz Quintet).
LP: FF 297

Sablon, Jean

1933/1936.
Tracks: / Le meme coup / Je suis sexappeal / Le jour ou je te vis / Prenez garde au grand mechant loup / Je sais que vous etes jolie / Par correspondance / Continental / Moss Otis rigrets / Un baiser / La derniere bergere / Un amour comme le notre / Le petite ile / Cette chanson est pour vous / Rendezvous sous la pluie / Un seul couvert, please James / Si tu m'aimes.
LP: SH 368

JEAN SABLON.
2LP: 2C 178 15428/29

POUR TOI - 'LE CHANTEUR DE CHARME'.
Tracks: / Ces petites choses / Seul / Continental, The / J'm'en fous, car je l'aime / Depuis que je suis a Paris / Si j'aime Suzy / Rendezvous sous la pluie / Je sais que vous etes jolie / Duo des aveux / Vous qui passez sans me voir / Il ne faut pas briser un reve / Puisque vous partez en voyage / Le jour ou je te vis / Les pieds dans l'eau / La chanson des rues / Parce que je vous aime / Quand je te parle d'amour / Cette chanson est pour vous.
LP: CHD 134
MC: MCHD 134

Sabotage

BEHIND ENEMY LINES.
LP: TE 2001

SABOTAGE.
LP: TE 2002

Sabotee Sancerroise

DANSES DU PAYS DE SANCERRE.
Tracks: / Bourree au pe duret / Bourree droite de sancerre / Bourree de feux / Hardi l'gars d'maimbray / Bourree des quatre peteux / Valse / Suite de polkas / La chieuvre en judgement / Sont noirs, sont pas gris / Bourree a deux temps a Jean Rameau / Le garcon marinier / La bergere aux champs / La valse au p'tit Louis / La valse a fleuret / Mon cotillon / La petite polka / Mazurka / Les crapiaudes / Bourre des conscrits de Sancerre.
LP: ARN 33543

Sabri Brothers

QAWWALI SUFI MUSIC FROM PAKISTAN (Sabri Brothers & Ensemble).
Tracks: / Aliah hoo / Allah hoo / Dama dum must Qalandar / Dai halima / Tu Rehnaward shoq hai.
LP: H 72080

YAH HABIB.
Tracks: / Saqia aur pila / Ya sahib ul jamal / Allah hi allah tan mein tar / Kal kamaliya wale.
LP: RWLP 12
MC: RWMC 12

Sabrina

SABRINA.
LP: IBILP 1
MC: IBIMC 1
LP: 835 295 1

SABRINA: INTERVIEW PICTURE DISC.
LPPD: BAK 2115

Sabu

HEARTBREAK.
LP: HMUSA 36
MC: HMAMC 36

Sacbe

AZTLAN.
Tracks: / Mijo / Central axis / Sleeping lady / Son / Don't tell me, I know / Soulmates / Aztlan / If I lose my life.
LP: TR 521
MC: TRC 521

STREET CORNER.
Tracks: / Curuba / Coyoacan / Street corner / Hermanos / Soledad compartida / Sunset at sunset / El mago / Bob Marley / Papemoe / Mongu.
LP: DS 864

Sacco & Vanzetti

SACCO & VANZETTI (Film Soundtrack) (Various artists).
LP: NL 70231

Sacharine Trust

WORLDBROKEN.
LP: SST 046

Sache, Die

WHY I HATE AMERICA.
Tracks: / Why I hate America / My mind / Around and around / Bleakness weakness / Going wild in the country / Selling poverty / Come closer.
LP: FABML 014

Sachs, Aaron

JAZZVILLE VOL.3 (See under Smith, Charlie for details) (Sachs, Aaron Sextet/ Charlie Smith Trio).

Sachse, Joe

BERLIN TANGO (Sachse, Joe/David Moss).
LP: ITM 1448

Sackville All Stars

SACKVILLE ALL STARS CHRISTMAS RECORD.
LP: 3038

TRIBUTE TO LOUIS ARMSTRONG.
MC: MC 3042

Sackville Folk

IRISH SONGS OF FREEDOM, VOL.1.
LP: 824 669 4

IRISH SONGS OF FREEDOM, VOL.2.
LP: 824 670 4

Sacred Arias

SACRED ARIAS.
LP: CFP 4532
MC: TCCFP 4532

Sacred Chaos

SACRED CHAOS.
LP: AAARRG 020

Sacred Child

SACRED CHILD.
LP: BD 034

Sacred Cowboys

SACRED COWBOYS.
LP: ROSE 37

TROUBLE FROM PROVIDENCE.
LP: CGAS 806

Sacred Denial

EXHUMED.
LP: 102 942

EXTRA STRENGTH.
LP: 102 941

NORTH OF THE ORDER.
LP: SD003

SIFTING THROUGH THE WRECKAGE.
Tracks: / Sifting through the wreckage / When I sleep / Brothers inventions / Some curiosity / Conquer / No way / Take a look around / Violent affection.
LP: NB 101
LP: 872 943
LP: NB 010

Sacred Reich

ALIVE AT THE DYNAMO.
LP: RO 94311

AMERICAN WAY, THE.
Tracks: / Love ..... hate / Crimes against humanity / I don't know / State of emergency / American way, The / Way it is, The / Flavors.
LP: RO 93921
MC: RO 93924

IGNORANCE.
Tracks: / Death squad / Victim of demise / Layed to rest / Ignorance / No believers / Violent solutions / Rest in peace / Sacred Reich / Administrative decisions.
LP: RR 9578
LP: ZORRO 30
MC: TZORRO 30

IGNORANCE/SURF NICARAGUA.
MC: RR 95784

SURF NICARAGUA.
LP: RR 9512 1

Sacred Rite

IS NOTHING SACRED.
LP: MEGATON 0018

RITUAL, THE.
LP: MEGATON 0014

Sacred Songs

CLASSIC YEARS IN DIGITAL STEREO (see under Classic Years...) (Various artists).

Sacred Warrior

REBELLION.
LP: SS R 8116
MC: SS C 8116

Sacrifice

FORWARD TO TERMINATION.
LP: RR 9595

TORMENT IN FIRE.
LP: RR 9697

Sacrilege

BEYOND THE REALMS OF MADNESS.
Tracks: / Lifeline / At death's door / Sacred / Out of sight, out of mind.
LP: GURT 4

TURN BACK TRILOBITE.
LP: FLAG 29

WITHIN THE PROPHECY.
LP: FLAG 15
MC: TFLAG 15

Sacrilege B.C.

PARTY WITH GOD.
LP: VM 102
MC: VM 102C

TOO COOL TO PRAY.
LP: GWLP 47

Sad Cafe

BEST OF SAD CAFE.
LP: NL 70253
MC: NK 70253

FACADES.
Tracks: / Take me to the future / Nothing left Toulouse / Everyday hurts / Strange little girl / Crazy oyster / Emptiness / Cottage love / Angel / Get me outta here / My oh my.
LP: RCALP 3033
MC: RCAK 3033
LP: PL 25249

FANX-TA-RA.
Tracks: / Babylon / Shellshock / Hungry eyes / Shadow on the wall / Black rose / Further adventures of mad Alan, The / Fanx, ta-ra / Flingus holiday / Immortal / Sail on / Clumbidextrous / I believe (love will survive).
LP: INTS 5132
MC: INTK 5132
LP: PL 25101
MC: PK 25101

LIVE: SAD CAFE.
Tracks: / On with the show / Emptiness / Strange little girl / Hungry eyes / La-di-da / What am I gonna do / Keeping it from the troops / Everyday hurts / Take me to the future / Feel like dying / Immortal / Restless / My oh my / Black rose / Bell end.
LP: SADLP 5

MISPLACED IDEALS.
Tracks: / Restless / Here come the clowns / Run home, girl / Let love speak for itself / No place to go / Mario / Relax / Feel like dying / On with the show / Black rose / Babylon.
LP: INTS 5133
MC: INTK 5133
LP: PL 25133
MC: PK 25133

OLE.
LP: POLD 5045

POLITICS OF EXISTING, THE.
LP: CAF ELP 1
MC: CAF ELK 1

SAD CAFE.
Tracks: / La di da / Digital daydream blues / What am I gonna do / Keeping it from the troops / I'm in love again / Losin' you / Dreamin' / No favours, no way / Love today.
LP: SADLP 4

WHATEVER IT TAKES.
Tracks: / Whatever it takes / This heart's on fire / Stay with me tonight / Back to zero / So cold / Take me / Don't give up on love / Blood on the sand.
LP: LLP 119
MC: LLK 119

Sad Lovers & Giants

EPIC GARDEN MUSIC.
LP: CHIME 0001

FEEDING THE FLAME.
LP: CHIME 0003

HEADLAND.
LP: CHIME 110

IN THE BREEZE.
LP: 0007 M

LES ANNES VERTES.
LP: CHIME 40 S

TOTAL SOUND.
LP: CHIME 0022

Sadane, Mark

EXCITING.
LP: BSK 3675

ONE WAY LOVE AFFAIR.
Tracks: / One way love affair / You're the one for me / Fool in me / Never gonna stop this heart of mine / Standing in the shadows of love / Sit up / Girl come on / Love can't wait / Midnight love dance / Make up your mind.
LP: K 56895

Saddlebottom

SADDLEBOTTOM (See under King-Smith, Dick) (King-Smith, Dick).

Saddleworth

IN CELEBRATION (Saddleworth Male Voice Choir).
LP: . . . . LKLP 8002

Sade

DIAMOND LIFE.
Tracks: / Smooth operator / Your love is king / Hang on to your love / When am I gonna make a living / Frankie's first affair / Cherry pie / Sally / I will be your friend / Why can't we live together.
LP: . . . . EPC 26044
MC: 40 26044

PROMISE.
Tracks: / Is it a crime? / Sweetest taboo, The / War of the hearts / Jezebel / Mr. Wrong / Never as good as the first time / Fear / Tar baby / Maureen / You're not the man (Track on cassette only) / Punch drunk (On cassette only.).
LP: . . . . EPC 86318
MC: 40 86318
LP: 4655751
MC: 4655754

STRONGER THAN PRIDE.
Tracks: / Love is stronger than pride / Paradise / Nothing can come between us / Haunt me / Turn my back on you / Keep looking / Clean heart / Give it up / I never thought I'd see the day / Siempre hay esperanza.
LP: 4604971
MC: 4604974

Sadler, Sgt. Barry

SONGS OF OUR FIGHTING MEN.
Tracks: / I'm a lucky one / Letter from Vietnam / Badge of courage / Saigon / Salute of the nurses / I'm watching the raindrops fall / Garet trooper / Soldier has come home, The / Lullaby / Trooper's lament / Bamiba / Ballad of the Green Berets.
LP: . . . . NL 83547
MC: . . . . NK 83547

S.A.D.O.

CIRCLE OF FRIENDS.
LP: . . . . N 0091
LP: . . . . NUK 091
MC: . . . . ZCNUK 091
MC: . . . . N 0092

DIRTY FANTASY.
LP: . . . . NUK 115
LP: . . . . N 0115 1
MC: . . . . ZCNUK 115
MC: . . . . N 0115 2

SENSITIVE.
Tracks: / Talk about me / Just married / Women and whiskey / Dear Miss J / Every time / Bad lovin / Time out / Love lies / Run baby run.
LP: . . . . NUK 147
MC: . . . . ZCNUK 147

Sadonians

DISAPPOINTMENTS (see also Clint Eastwood) (Sadonians & Clint Eastwood).

Sadowitz, Jerry

GOBSHITE.
LP: . . . . GOBSHITE 01

Sadus

SWALLOWED IN BLACK.
LP: . . . . RO 93681
MC: . . . . RO 93684

Safe Soul

SAFE SOUL (See under Soul) (Various artists).

Saffire

HOT FLASH (Saffire The Uppity Blues Woman).
Tracks: / Two in the bush is better than one in the hand / Sloppy drunk / One good man / Dirty sheets / Tom cat blues / Learn to settle for less / You'll never get me out of your mind / (Mr Insurance man) take out that thing / Hopin' it'll be alright / Little bit of your loving goes a very long way / Shopping for love / Elevator man / Torch song / Torch song (part 2) / Why don't you do right / Prove me wrong / (No need) Pissin' on a skunk.
MC: . . . . AC 4796

UPPITY BLUES WOMAN, THE.
LP: . . . . AL 4780

Sa-Fire

SA-FIRE.
Tracks: / Boy, I've been told / Thinking of you / It's a crime / Gonna make it / Together / Love is on her mind / I wanna make you mine / You said you loved me / Better be the only one / Love at first sight.
LP: 834922-1
MC: 834922.4

Safranski, Eddie

THREE KENTON'S BE BOPPERS GROUPS 1947-50 (see Ferguson,Maynard/Vido Musso/Eddie Safranski) (Safranski, Eddie, Maynard Ferguson, Vido Musso).

Saga

BEHAVIOUR.
Tracks: / Listen to your heart / Take a chance / What do I know? / Misbehaviour / Nine lives of Miss Midi / You and the night / Out of the shadows / Easy way out / Promises / Here I am (goodbye) / Once upon a time.
LP: . . . . PRT 26579
MC: 40 26579

HEADS OR TAILS.
Tracks: / Flyer / Catwalk / Sound of strangers / Writing / Intermission / Social orphan / Vendetta / Scratching the surface / Pitchman.
LP: . . . . PRT 25740

IMAGES AT TWILIGHT.
Tracks: / It's time / See them smile / Slow motion / You're not alone / Take it or leave it / Images / Hot to cold / Mouse in a maze.
LP: 2391 437

SILENT KNIGHT.
Tracks: / Don't be late / What's it gonna be / Time to go / Compromise / Too much to lose / Help me out / Someone should / Careful where you step.
LP: 237 416 6

WILDEST DREAMS.
LP: 817941

WORLDS APART.
Tracks: / On the loose / Wind him up / Amnesia / Framed / Time's up / Interview / No regrets / Conversations / No stranger.
LP: . . . . PRT 25054

Sagar, Lois

REGAL LADY.
Tracks: / Wonderful one / Charmaine / Stranger on the shore / Mardi gras / Loveliest night of the year / Don't be cross / Till / Certain smile, A / Memory / Seventy-six trombones / Tie a yellow ribbon / Mr. Sandman / Moonlight serenade.
MC: . . . . AC 197

STEPPING OUT WITH LOIS SAGAR.
Tracks: / Wonderful one / Snowbird / I may be wrong / April in Portugal / Lady is a tramp, The / Tears / Mistakes / Vaya con dios / Brazil / Quando, quando, quando / Manana / Only you / Affair to remember, An / Alone / Gettin' sentimental over you / Loveliest night of the year / Merry widow / Love will find a way / Ari verdeci roma / Strangers in the night / Bunch of Thyme / Hurt / Una paloma blanca / Y viva espana / Can't help falling in love / Are you lonesome tonight / Unless / Hello Dolly / Who's sorry now / Ma he's making eyes at me / Blue moon / Again / I'm in the mood for love / Wheels / Never on a Sunday / In a little Spanish town / You're sixteen / Singing the blues / Raining in my heart / Side by side / Until it's time for you to go.
MC: . . . . AC 179

Sagittarius Electric

DRIVING RHYTHMS.
Tracks: / Night ride / Driving home to you / Day trip / Highland road, The / Regency road / Travelling / High ride / Driving the light fantastic / Nostalgic journey / Heaven and earth.
MC: SAG/CAS/1
LP: SAG/LPR/1

Sahara Eternel

SAHARA ETERNEL (Various artists).
Tracks: / Metilli-des-chaambas: *Various artists* / Fantasia: *Various artists* / Sous la tente Saharienne: *Various artists* / La haddra du desert: *Various artists* / Timimoun: *Various artists* / Chant des baroudeurs: *Various artists* / Karkabous, les chants de la nuit: *Various artists.*
LP: . . . . ARN 33371

Sahara (film)

SAHARA (Film Soundtrack) (Various artists).
LP: . . . . STV 81211

Sahib, Sahib

ALL STAR SEXTETS.
2LP: . . . . SJL 2245

Sahl, Mort

WATERGATE.
LP: . . . . GNPS 2070

Sahm, Doug

BACK TO THE'DILLO (Sahm, Doug/ Augie Meyers).
Tracks: / Same ole story / Don't fight it / I pity the fool / Think / Oh Carol / Crazy arms / Buevo Laredo / Purple haze / Jazzer.
LP: . . . . SNTF 890

DOUG SAHM & BAND (Sahm, Doug & Band).
Tracks: / Is anybody going to San Antone / It's gonna be easy / Your friends / Poison love / Wallflower / Dealer's blues / Faded love / Blues stay away from me / Papa ain't salty / Me and Paul / Don't turn around / I get off.
LP: . . . . ED 154

FINALLY IN LIGHTS (see Meyers, Augie) (Sahm, Doug/Augie Meyers).

HELL OF A SPELL.
Tracks: / Tunnel vision / Ain't into lettin' you go / All the way to nothing / Hanging on a thread / I'll take care of you / Things I used to do / I don't mind at all / Nothin' but the blues / Hell of a spell / Can't fake it / Next time you see me.
LP: . . . . CHR 1249

JUKE BOX MUSIC.
Tracks: / I won't cry / Crazy baby / Hey little girl / Money over love / You're mine tonight / It hurts to love someone / Buzz buzz buzz / She put the hurt on me / I don't believe / Chicken and the bop (Available on CD only) / Goodnight my love (Available on CD only) / My dearest darling / What's your name / Golly gee (Available on CD only) / Talk to me, talk to me.
LP: . . . . CH 278

LIVE: DOUG SAHM.
Tracks: / Turn on your lovelight / Stagger Lee / Things I used to do, The / Papa ain't salty / He don't love you like I love you / Next time you see me / Mr. Pitiful / James Brown Medley / Think / Please please please / Night train.
LP: . . . . TOP 172
MC: . . . . KTOP 172

SIR DOUGLAS - HIS FIRST RECORDING.
Tracks: / Just a moment / Sapphire / Why why why / Whirlaway / Baby tell me / More and more / Slow down / If you ever need me / Crazy Daisy / Can't believe you wanna leave.
LP: . . . . CR 30188

SIR DOUGLAS-WAY BACK WHEN HE WAS JUST DOUG SAHM.
LP: . . . . LP 8001

SIR DOUG'S RECORDING TRIP (Sahm, Doug & The Sir Douglas Quintet).
Tracks: / Are inlaws really outlaws / Sell a song / I'm glad for your sake (but I'm sorry for mine) / Whole lotta peace of mind / You never get too big and you sure don't get too heavy... / I wanna be your mama again / Mendocino / If you really want me to I'll go / And it didn't even bring me down / Lawd I'm just a country boy in this great big... / Texas me / Nuevo laredo / Revolutionary ways / Be real / Catch the man on the rise / She's huggin' you, but she's lookin' at me / Keep your soul / Me and my destiny / Wasted days, wasted nights / Gypsy, The / Stoned faces don't lie / Michoacan / Sir Doug's recording trip / Sixty minutes of your love / In the dark / Dynamite woman / Linda Lou / Too many docile minds / You're doin' it too hard / Westside blues again.
2LP: . . . . DED 255

TEXAS ROAD RUNNER.
LP: . . . . BLP 701

Sahotas

AAJA.
LP: . . . . MUT 1102
MC: . . . . CMUT 1102

Sailor

DRESSED FOR DROWNING.
Tracks: / Danger on the Titanic / Don't send flowers / Private eye / Don't look a gift horse / Runaway / Hat check girl / Pearl Harbour / Starlight / Who will stop the rain.
LP: . . . . CRB 84534
MC: 40 84534

TROUBLE.
LP: . . . . EPC 69192

Sailor 2

SAILOR 2 (TV Soundtrack) (Various artists).
Tracks: / To the limit and beyond: *Various artists* / Why all the nice girls: *Various artists* / Mission wolf rock: *Various artists* / Man o'war: *Various artists* / Tribute: *Various artists* / Immortal memory: *Various artists.*
LP: . . . . REH 411
MC: . . . . ZCR 411

Sailor's Horse

SAILOR'S HORSE, THE (May Day: Minehead documentary of Somerset).
MC: 60-216

Sain, Oliver

BLUE MAX.
Tracks: / Party hearty (get up and hustle) / She's a disco queen / London express / Apricot splash (the prayer) / Have you ever been mellow (you are beautiful) / Just a lonely man / Hey butterfly.
LP: . . . . CLP 532

BUS STOP.
Tracks: / Bus stop / Goin' back to Memphis / Laid back / Sporty Mae / Nightime / Double bump, The / California sunset / Libra's dream / Blowing for love / Soul serenade.
LP: . . . . CLP 518

CONDITION YOUR HEARTS (See also Turner, Ike) (Sain, Oliver/ Ike Turner/ Clayton Love).

Saint & Greavsie

FUNNY OLD GAME.
LP: . . . . WERA 1
MC: . . . . WERC 1

Saint Joan

SAINT JOAN (Various artists).
MCSET: . . . . ARGO 1253

Saint-Eloi, P

A LA DEMANDE.
LP: . . . . GD 020

Sainte-Marie, Buffy

BEST OF BUFFY.
Tracks: / Soulful shade of blues / Summer boy / Universal soldier / Better to find out for yourself / Cod'ine / He's a keeper of the fire / Until it's time for you to go / Rolling log blues / God is alive, magic is afoot / Guess who I saw in Paris / Piney wood hills / Now that the buffalo's gone / Take my hand for a while / Ground hog / Circle game / My country 'tis of thy people / You're dying / Many a mile / Cripple creek / I'm gonna be a country girl again / Vampire / Little wheel spin and spin / Winter boy / Los pescadores / Sometimes when I got to thinkin'.
2LP: . . . . VSD 3

BEST OF BUFFY SAINTE-MARIE VOL 1.
LP: . . . . VMLP 5309
MC: . . . . VMTC 6309

SPOTLIGHT ON BUFFY SAINTE-MARIE.
Tracks: / Soldier blue / Universal soldier / My country 'tis of thy people / You're dying / Co'dine / Suffer the little children / She used to wanna be a ballerina / I'm gonna be a country girl again / Little wheel spin and spin / Cripple creek / Many a mile / Ground hog song to a seagull / Smackwater Jack / It's my way / Bells / Sweet September morning / Poppies / Moonshot / Until it's time for you to go / Los Pescadores / Now that the buffalo's gone / Piney wood hills / Song of the French partisan / Take my hand for a while.
2LP: . . . . SPOT 1018
MCSET: . . . . ZCSPT 1018

Saints

ALL FOOLS DAY.
LP: . . . . POLD 5203
MC: . . . . POLDC 5203

BEGINNING TO LOVE YOU.
LP: . . . . CL 2007

BEST OF SAINTS.
LP: . . . . RAZ 21

ETERNALLY YOURS.
LP: . . . . FC 035

LITTLE MADNESS TO BE FREE, A.
LP: . . . . ROSE 38

LIVE IN A MUD HUT.
LP: . . . . ROSE 55

MONKEY PUZZLE.
LP: . . . . ROSE 1
MC: . . . . ROSE 1C

NEW ROSE YEARS, THE (Greatest hits).
LP: . . . . FC 060
MC: . . . . FC 060 C

OUT IN THE JUNGLE.
LP: . . . . ROSE 11

PREHISTORIC SOUNDS.
LP: . . . . FC 036

PRODIGAL SON.
LP: . . . . MRILP 001
MC: . . . . MRIMC 001

SAINTS MEET THE SINNERS, THE.
Tracks: / Since my best girl turned me down / Way down yonder in New Orleans / It's a sin to tell a lie / Where did you stay last night / Tin roof blues / Washington and Lee swing / Clarinet marmalade / Nobody knows you when you're down and out / 'S wonderful / What did I do to be so black and blue /

Make me a pallet on the floor / As long as I live.
LP: C5-512
MC: C5K-512

Saint-Saens (composer)

CARNIVAL OF THE ANIMALS (See under Mussorgsky (composer)) (Jones, Philip Brass Ensemble).

PETER AND THE WOLF/CARNIVAL OF THE ANIMALS (see under Royal Philharmonic) (Royal Philharmonic Orchestra).

SAINT SAENS (Various artists).
MC: .... DLCMC 221

SAINT-SAENS MUSIC FOR ORGAN (Phillips, Margaret).
Tracks: / Three rhapsodies on Breton themes / Fantaisie in D flat Op. 101 / Prelude and fugue in G Op. 109 No. 2 / Prelude and fugue in C Op. 109 No. 3 / Prelude and fugue in D Op. 109 No. 1 / Fantaisie in C Op. 157 / Fantaisie in E flat.
MC: .... YORKMC 110

Saisse, Philippe

VALERIAN.
Tracks: / Land of the morning calm / Valerian / Chihuahua pearl / God son Paris / Ma muse / Rameau's nephew / Glamorous Glennis / In memoriam faure / Aztec ace / Tiahuanaco.
LP: 371 073-1
MC: 371 073-4

Sakamoto, Ryuichi

B-2 UNIT.
LP: .... ILPS 9656

BEAUTY.
Tracks: / You do me (edited version) / Calling from Tokyo / Rose, A / Asadoya yunta / Futique (Only on MC and CD) / Amore / We love you (remix) / Diabaram / Pile of time, A (Only on MC and CD) / Romance (Only on MC and CD) / Chinsagu no hana.
LP: .... VUSLP 14
MC: .... VUSMC 14
MC: .... OVEDC 382

FORBIDDEN COLOURS (see under Sylvian, David) (Sakamoto, Ryuichi & David Sylvian).

LAST EMPEROR (OST) (See under 'Last Emperor') (Sakamoto, Ryuichi & David Byrne).

LEFT HANDED DREAM.
Tracks: / Just about enough / Left band / Slat dance / Saru to Yuki to Gomi No Kodomo / Kachakuchanee / Arrangement / Once in a lifetime / Garden of poppies / Boku no kakera.
LP: .... EPC 25109

MERRY CHRISTMAS MR. LAWRENCE (See Merry Christmas Mr. Lawrence).

MUSICAL ENCYCLOPEDIA.
Tracks: / Field work (Featuring Thomas Dolby) / Etude / Paradise lost / M.A.Y. in the backyard / Steppin' into Asia / Tibetan dance / Zen-gun / In a forest of feathers.
LP: .... DIX 34
MC: .... CDIX 34

NEO GEO.
Tracks: / Before long / Neo geo / Risky / Free trading / Shogunade / Parata / Okinawa song / After all.
LP: 4600951
MC: 4600954

Sakata, Akira

DANCE (Sakata, Akira Trio).
LP: .... ENJA 4002

MOOKO.
Tracks: / Nitchimo satchimo / Hieyashi bushi / Wann kann ich sie wiedersehen / Hitsujikai no bansan / Kibaminzoku no odori / Mooko.
MC: .... TCVE 46
LP: .... VE 46

Sakhile

AFRICAN ECHOES.
Tracks: / Maluti / Mshandira phamwe / Crossroads / Song for bra zakes / Phambili / Mantenga falls / Same time next year / Tears of joy.
MC: .... KAZ MC 17

NEW LIFE.
LP: .... HIP 13
MC: .... HIPC 13

Saki (author)

BROGUE (see under Brogue) (Burden, Hugh (nar)).

OPEN WINDOW, THE.
Tracks: / Open window, The / Romancers, The / Sredni Vashtar / Seventh pullet, The / Lumber room, The.
MC: .... ANV 659

QUAIL SEED.
Tracks: / Quail seed / She-wolf, The / Story teller / Schartz-Metterklume method, The / Talking out of Tarrington.
MC: .... ANV 660

SAKI 1 By H.H. Munro (Burden, Hugh (nar)).
MC: .... TTC/SA 01

SAKI 2 By H.H. Munro (Burden, Hugh (nar)).
MC: .... TTC/SA 02

SAKI 3 By H.H. Munro (Burden, Hugh (nar)).
MC: .... TTC/SA 03

SAKI 4 By H.H. Munro (Burden, Hugh (nar)).
MC: .... TTC/SA 04

SAKI 5 By H.H. Munro (Burden, Hugh (nar)).
MC: .... TTC/SA 05

SAKI 6 By H.H. Munro (Burden, Hugh (nar)).
MC: .... TTC/SA 06

SHE WOLF & OTHERS (see under She Wolf (bk) (Burden, Hugh (nar)).

TOBERMORY & OTHER STORIES (Newth, Jonathan).
MCSET: .... COL 2015

Sakuma, Masahide

LISA.
LP: .... NEWLP 102
MC: .... NEWMC 102

Salad From Atlantis

SEA GREEN SPIRAL.
LP: .... COX 011

Salamander

LIVE: NORTH SEA JAZZ FESTIVAL.
LP: .... DRLP 31

Salas Humara, Walter

LAGARTIJA.
LP: .... ROUGH 144
MC: .... ROUGHC 144

Salas, Patricia

FESTIVAL LATINO.
LP: .... EULP 1062
MC: .... EUMC 1062
LP: .... EULP 1074
MC: .... EUMC 1074

Salas, Steve

HARDER THEY COME, THE (Salas,Steve Colourcode).
Tracks: / Stand up / Caught in the middle of it / Two bullets and a gun / Over and over again / Indian chief / Blind / Just like that / Harder they come, The / Baby walk on / Cover me.
LP: .... ILPS 9963
MC: .... ICT 9963

Saleh, Kumbi

BE A GOOD SAMARITAN.
Tracks: / Che che kule / Be a good samaritan / Te ona / Eku eghemi / Ohia / Ke eye miing aahu.
LP: 88066

Salem 66

DOWN THE PRIMROSE PATH.
LP: .... HMS 152

FREQUENCY AND URGENCY.
Tracks: / Postcard / Holiday / Bad news / Grunzella daze / Wanderlust / Broken bottles / People express / Blue / Desk clerk / Widow's walk.
LP: .... HMS 078

Sales, Tony

FREEDOM (see Convoy, Dave) (Sales, Tony & Dave Convoy).

Salim, Abdel Gadir

NUJUM AL-LAIL - STARS OF THE NIGHT.
Tracks: / Gidraishinna / Al-lemoni / Nujum al-lail / Nitlaga nitlaga / Jeenaki / A'abir sikkah.
LP: .... ORB 039

SOUNDS OF SUDAN VOL. 1 (Songs from Kordofan).
LP: .... WCB 002

Salisbury Cathedral

CAROLS FROM SALISBURY (Various artists).
Tracks: / Sans Day carol: *Salisbury Cathedral* / Three kings, The: *Salisbury Cathedral* / I sing of a maiden: *Salisbury Cathedral* / Holly and the ivy, The: *Salisbury Cathedral* / In the bleak mid winter: *Salisbury Cathedral*/ O little town of Bethlehem: *Salisbury Cathedral* / Shepherd's pipe carol: *Salisbury Cathedral* / Gabriel's message: *Salisbury Cathedral* / Cherry tree carol, The: *Salisbury Cathedral* / I wonder as I wander: *Salisbury Cathedral*/ God rest ye merry gentlemen: *Salisbury Cathedral* / In dulci jubilo: *Salisbury Cathedral*.
LP: .... E 77068

CHOIR OF SALISBURY CATHEDRAL (Various artists).
LP: .... SAGA 5225

MUSIC FROM SALISBURY CATHEDRAL (Various artists).
LP: .... REC 323
MC: .... ZCM 323

Sallyangie

CHILDREN OF THE SUN.
Tracks: / Strangers / Lady Mary / Children of the sun / Lover for all seasons / River song / Banquet on the water / Balloons / Midsummer night's happening / Love in ice crystals / Changing colours / Chameleon / Milk bottle / Murder of the children in San Francisco.
LP: .... TRA 176

Salma & Sabina

SING THE HITS OF ABBA IN HINDI.
LP: .... MUT 1006

Salman, Shukur

OUD RECITAL.
LP: .... HEAD 16

Salmontails

SALMONTAILS.
Tracks: / Jolly beggar, The / Rounding of Cape Horn / Admiral Benbow / April morning / Andy's gone with cattle / Rosabella / Captain Ward and the rainbow / Pipe on the hob / Chevy chase / Mallorca / Here's the tender coming / Lord Gregory / Sunny banks, The.
LP: .... OBL 001

Salomon String...

MOZART PIANO QUARTETS (See under Richard Burnett) (Salomon String Quartet).

Salon Bombay

SALON BOMBAY (Various artists).
LP: .... SBL 12595
MC: .... SBLC 12595

Salonisti, Saestetto

LOVE LETTER, A.
Tracks: / Love letter, A / Chanson triste / Ideale / Melody in F / Letzter fruhling / Du bist die welt fur mich / Spiel auf deiner geige / Du sollst der Kaiser / Meiner seele sein / Wien, wien nur du Allein / Mors et Vita.
LP: .... IM 004

Salsa

BEST OF SALSA (Various artists).
LP: 520 222

DEMASIADO CALENTE HOT (Various artists).
LP: .... CLP 168

SALSA GREATS, VOL 1 (Various artists).
LP: .... SLP 495

Salsa (film)

SALSA (Original Soundtrack) (Various artists).
LP: .... IMCA 6232
MC: .... IMCAC 6232

Salsaya Big Band

LIVE IN LUXOR.
LP: .... SJP 209

Salsoul Orchestra

HOW HIGH.
Tracks: / I'll keep you warm / Resorts international / Stop and think / Have a good time / My number's up / How high.
LP: .... SSLP 1518

Salt

BEYOND A SONG.
LP: .... PC 11

Salt 'N' Pepa

BLACK'S MAGIC.
Tracks: / Expression / Doper than dope / Negro wit' and ego' / You showed me / Do you want me / Swift / I like to party / Black's magic / Start the party / Let's talk about sex / I don't know / Live and let die / Independent / Expression (Brixton bass mix) (Only on CD or cassette).
LP: 8281641
MC: 8281644

BLITZ OF SALT 'N' PEPA HITS, A.
Tracks: / Push it (US remix) / Expression (Brixton bass edit) / Independant (remix) / Shake your thang (it's your thing) / Twist and shout / Tramp / Do you want me (remix) / My mike sounds nice / I'll take your man.
LP: 828249-1
MC: 828249-4

HOT COOL VICIOUS.
Tracks: / Beauty and the beat / Tramp / I'll take your man / It's all right / Chick on the side / I desire / Showstopper, The / My mike sounds nice.
LP: .... CHAMP 1007
MC: .... CHAMPK 1007

SALT 'N' PEPA: INTERVIEW PICTURE DISC.
LPPD: .... BAK 2119

SALT WITH A DEADLY PEPA.
Tracks: / Intro jam / Salt with a deadly pepa, A / I like it like that / Solo power (Lets get paid) / Shake your thang / I gotcha / Let the rhythm run (remix) / Everybody get up / Spinderella's not a fella / Solo power (Syncopated soul) / Twist and shout / Hyped on the mic / Push it.
LP: .... FFRLP 3
MC: .... FFRMC 3

Salten, Felix (aut)

BAMBI.
MC: .... TS 338

BAMBI (See under Bambi (bk)) (Kendall, Felicity (nar)).

Saltmine Band

ROYAL PRAISE (see under Pope, Dave) (Saltmine Band/Dave Pope).

Salty Dog

EVERY DOG HAS IT'S DAY.
LP: 7599242701
MC: 7599242704
MC: .... GEFC 24270

Salty Dogs Jazzband

ACE IN THE HOLE.
LP: .... GHB 207

Salu Salu Band

EFRE EOPAS STRING BANDS.
LP: .... VP 421

Saluzzi, Dino

KULTRUM.
LP: .... ECM 1251

ONCE UPON A TIME - FAR AWAY IN THE SOUTH.
Tracks: / Jose, Valeria and Matias / And the Father said... / Revelation, The / Silence / And he loved his brother, till the end / Far away in the south... / We are the children.
LP: .... ECM 1309

SOLO BANDONEON (Saluzzi, Dino & Andina).
LP: .... ECM 1375

VOLVER (See under Rava, Enrico) (Saluzzi, Dino Quintet & Enrico Rava).

Salvador, Sal

BERNIES TUNES.
LP: .... ST 251

BOO BOO BE DOOP.
LP: .... AFF 68

IN OUR OWN SWEET WAY.
Tracks: / I'm afraid the masquerade is over / Breezeway / Anthropology / Blue monk / Parallelogram / Mr. P.C. / Somewhere over the rainbow / In your own sweet way.
LP: .... ST 224

STOP SMOKING OR ELSE BLUES (Salvador, Sal Quartet).
LP: .... FS 227

TRIBUTE TO THE GREATS.
LP: .... FS 207

WORLD'S GREATEST JAZZ STANDARDS (Salvador, Sal Quartet).
LP: .... ST 234

Salvation

DIAMONDS ARE FOREVER.
LP: .... CALCLP 022

SASS.
Tracks: / (Clearing out the) Debris / Leavy by day / Johnny B serious / Innocent, The / Tumbleweed / Bamboo / Paint it rose / Very go round / To high heaven / Ravishing.
LP: .... EIRSA 1033

Salvation Army

BY REQUEST.
LP: .... WW 5038
LP: .... WRD R 3022
MC: .... WRD C 3022

CHRISTMAS WITH THE SALVATION ARMY V2 (Salvation Army Hendon Corps).
Tracks: / Joy to the world / Holly and the ivy, The / Hark the herald angel sing / While shepherds watched.
LP: .... WST R 9704
MC: .... WST C 9704

CHRISTMAS WITH THE SALVATION ARMY INTERNATIONAL STAFF BAND (Salvation Army International Staff Band, (The)).
Tracks: / O come all ye faithful / We three kings of Orient are / While shepherds watched their flocks by night / Away in a manger.
LP: .... WRD R 3026
MC: .... WRD C 3026

PEACE IN OUR TIME (Salvation Army Band).
Tracks: / Peace in our time / To God be the glory / Jehovah is our strength / Simply trusting / Christ is all / Lord and Father of mankind, The / Yield not to temptation / Rock of ages / There is a wideness in God's mercy / Kingdom triumphant / Who is on the Lord's side / My home is in Heaven / Stand up, stand up for Jesus / Peace perfect peace / When He cometh / Immortal love forever full / When I survey the wondrous Cross / Have you been to Jesus / Thou art the way / Set forth within the sacred Word.
LP: WST 9638
MC: WC 9638

Salvation (film)

SALVATION (Original soundtrack) (Various artists).
Tracks: / Salvation: *New Order* / Twanky party: *Cabaret Voltaire* / Play the beat: *Dominique* / Let's go: *New Order* / Salvation have you said: *Hood* / Jesus saves: *Cabaret Voltaire* / Destroy all evil: *Dominique*/ Touched by the hand of god: *New Order* / You can blackmail Jesus: *Jumpin' Jesus* / Nightmare: *Hood*/ Come on: *Baker, Arthur* / Sputnik: *New Order* / Skullcrusher: *Various artists*.
LP: TWI 774
MC: TWIC 774

Sam Brothers 5

LAFAYETTE ZYDECO.
LP: ARHOOLIE 1081

Sam & Dave

18 GREATEST HITS: SAM & DAVE.
LP: MA 26287
MC: MAMC 926287

20 GREATEST HITS: SAM & DAVE (2).
Tracks: / Soul man / Hold on I'm comin' / Can't you find another way of doing it / Bring it on home to me / Summertime / Wonderful world / Another Saturday night / You got me / Can't find another way / You got me hummin' / I thank you / Soul sister, brown sugar / Sittin' on the dock of the bay / You send me / Don't pull your love / Cupid / Gimme some lovin' / Said I wasn't gonna tell nobody / Soothe me.
LP: 226 224 5
MC: 216 224 5

BEST OF SAM AND DAVE.
Tracks: / Soul man / I thank you / You don't know what you mean to me / Soul sister brown sugar / Hold on I'm coming / Can't you find another way of doing it / Everybody's got to believe in somebody / May I baby / I take what I want / You don't know like I know / When something is wrong with my baby / Soothe me.
LP: 881202 1

CAN'T STAND UP FOR FALLING DOWN.
Tracks: / Baby baby don't stop now / I can't stand up for falling down / Born again / My reason for living / This is your world / Holdin' on / Come on in / When you steal from me / I'm not an indian giver / Get it / Ooh ooh ooh / Don't pull your love / Knock it out the park / You easily excite me / One part love, two part pain / Jody Ryder got killed.
LP: ED 133

DOUBLE DYNAMITE.
LP: 589003

GREATEST HITS: SAM AND DAVE.
LP: SHLP 119
MC: SHTC 119

HOLD ON I'M COMING.
LP: PLP 5
MC: PMC 5
LP: 588 045

HOLD ON, I'M COMING (OLD GOLD) (See under Eddie Floyd - Knock On Wood).

SOUL MAN.
LP: 589 015
LP: 589003

SOUL SISTER.
LP: PLP 16
MC: PMC 16

SWEET SOUL MUSIC.
Tracks: / Hold on I'm coming / 634-5789 / Respect / Funky street / How sweet it is to be loved by you / I thank you / Soul sister brown sugar / I'll be doggone / Satisfaction / Land of a thousand dances / Funky broadway / Sweet soul music.
LP: TOP 163
MC: KTOP 163

Sam The Sham

BEST OF SAM THE SHAM & THE PHARAOHS (Sam The Sham & The Pharaohs).
LP: SPELP 103
MC: SPEMC 103

PHARAOHIZATION (Sam The Sham & The Pharaohs).
LP: RNLP 122

Samandar, Bijan

MUSIC OF IRAN-THE TAR VOL. 1.
LP: LLST 7220

MUSIC OF IRAN-THE TAR VOL. 2.
LP: LLST 7201

Samba Con Salsa

LATIN MUSIC FROM THE BASS CLEF.
LP: WAVE LP 31

Sambora, Richie

STRANGER IN THIS TOWN.
Tracks: / Rest in peace / Church of desire / Stranger in this town / Ballad of youth / One light burning / Mr Bluesman / Rosie / River of love / Father time / Answer, The.
LP: 8488951
MC: 8488984

Samhain

NOVEMBER-COMING-FIRE.
Tracks: / Diabolos '88 / In my grip / Mother of mercy / Birthright / To walk the night / Let the day begin / Halloween II / November's fire / Kiss of steel / Unbridled / Human pony girl.
LP: REVLP 82

Sammes, Mike

MIKADO THE/IOLANTHE (Sammes, Mike Singers).
MCSET: DTO 10244

SING-A-LONG PARTY HITS (See under Big Ben Banjo Sing-a-Long Party Hits) (Sammes, Mike Singers).

SONGS WE LOVE, THE (Sammes, Mike Singers).
MCSET: DTO 10074

Samms, Mike

ON EVERY HIGHWAY.
MC: PSP 002

Sammy & Rosy...

MY BEAUTIFUL LAUNDERETTE/ SAMMY & ROSY GET LAID/W (See under My Beautiful Laundrette) (Various artists).

Sample, Joe

ASHES TO ASHES.
LP: 7599263181
MC: 7599263184

CARMEL.
LP: CRP 16001
LP: ABCL 5266

CARMEL/RAINBOW SEEKER.
Tracks: / Carmel / Painting / Cannery row / Rainy day in Monterey, A / Sunrise / Midnight and mist / More beautiful each day / Rainbow seeker / In all my wildest dreams / There are many stops along the way / Melodies of love / Fly with wings of love / As long as it lasts / Islands in the rain / Together we'll find a way.
MCSET: MCA 2 113

FANCY DANCE.
Tracks: / Children's song / Fancy dance / All the lonely years / Another blues / Svenska flicka / Old town.
LP: SNTF 788

HUNTER, THE.
Tracks: / Hunter, The / Blue ballet / Beauty and the beast / Wings of fire / Just a little higher / Night flight.
LP: MCF 3164
MC: MCFC 3164

OASIS.
Tracks: / Oasis / New places / New faces / Teardrops / Asian eyes / Survivor / Love's paradise / Wonderland / Mirage.
LP: MCF 3289
MC: MCFC 3289

RAINBOW SEEKER.
Tracks: / Rainbow seeker / In all my wildest dreams / There are many stops along the way / Melodies of love / Fly with wings of love / As long as it lasts / Islands in the rain / Together we'll find a way.
LP: MCL 1624
MC: MCLC 1624

ROLES.
Tracks: / Woman you're drivin' me mad / Gifted, The / Friends and lovers / Ego mania mambo / Fortune hunter / Ship of fools / Passionist.
LP: MCF 3371
MC: MCFC 3371

SPELLBOUND.
Tracks: / Seven years of good luck / Spellbound / Somehow our love survives / All God's children / Leading me back to you / U turn / Bones jive / Luna en New York / Sermonized / Looking glass.
LP: 925781 1
MC: 925781 4

SWING STREET CAFE (Sample, Joe & David T.Walker).
Tracks: / Hallelujah, I love her so / Rock house / Honest I do / Next time U see me / Woke up this morning / C.C. rider / Honky tonk / After hours.
LP: ICRP 5785
MC: ICRPC 5785
LP: CRP 16004

VOICES IN THE RAIN.
Tracks: / Voices in the rain / Burnin' up the carnival / Greener grass / Eye of the hurricane / Dreams of dreams / Shadows / Sonata in solitude.
LP: MCL 1765
MC: MCLC 1765
LP: MCG 4016

Sample, Nick

WHY DON'T YOU PLAY HOUND DOG? (see under Presley, Elvis).

Sampler..

TRADITIONAL MUSIC ON ROUNDER (Various artists).
LP: ROUNDER 0145

Sampson, Colin

ONLY YOU.
LP: GGLP 001

THAT GOOD LOVING.
LP: GGLP 004

Sampson, Deryck

BOOGIE EXPRESS.
Tracks: / Boogie in C / Basin street boogie / Steady time special / Kansas City boogie woogie / Homeless on the range / Monday's wash / Blackberry jam / Table top boogie / Boogie serenade / Hen house boogie / Canal street boogie woogie / Boogie express / Flash in de pan / Boogie de concerto.
LP: HQ 2006

Sampson, Edgar

SWING SOFTLY SWEET SAMPSON.
Tracks: / Lullaby in rhythm / Hoopdee whodee / If dreams come true / Stompin' at the Savoy / I'll be back for more / Happy and satisfied / Cool and groovy / Blue Lou / Blues made me feel this way. The / Light and sweet / Sweetness of you, The / Don't be that way.
LP: JASM 1020

Sam's Bumper Jumper

SAM'S BUMPER JUMPER (See under Fireman Sam) (Alderton, John (nar)).

Sam's Night Watch

SAM'S NIGHT WATCH (See under Fireman Sam) (Alderton, John (nar)).

Sam's Rabbit Rescue

SAM'S RABBIT RESCUE (See under Fireman Sam) (Alderton, John (nar)).

Samson

AND THERE IT IS.
LP: METALPM 126

BEFORE THE STORM.
Tracks: / Danger zone / Stealing away / Red skies / I'll be round / Test of time / Life on the run / Turn out the lights / Losing my grip / Young idea.
LP: POLS 1077

DON'T GET MAD GET EVEN.
Tracks: / Are you ready / Love hungry / Burning up / Fight goes on / Don't get mad get even / Into the valley / Bite on the bullet / Doctor ice / Front page news / Leaving love (behind).
LP: POLD 5132

HEAD ON.
Tracks: / Hard times / Take it like a man / Vice versa / Manwatcher / Too close to rock / Thunderburst / Hammerhead / Hunted / Take me to your leader / Walking out on you.
LP: GEMLP 108

HEAD TACTICS (Samson (featuring Bruce Dickinson)).
Tracks: / Vice versa / Earth mother / Losing my grip / Take it like a man / Once bitten / Go to hell / Hard times / Nice girl / Too close to rock / Walking out on you.
LP: EST 2006
MC: TCEST 2006

LAST RITES.
Tracks: / Mr. Rock and Roll / Big brother / Koz / Leavin' you / It's not easy as it seems / Telephone / Wrong side of time / Primrose shuffle / I wish I was the saddle of a schoolgirl's bike / Inside out.
LP: THBL 015

LIVE AT READING '81.
LP: FRSLP 001
MC: FRSMC 001

PILLARS OF ROCK.
Tracks: / Danger zone / Stealing away / Red skies / Losing my grip / Running out of time / Drivin' with zz / Young idea / Test of time / Leaving love (behind) / Fight goes on / Don't get mad get even / Doctor Ice / Front page news / Bite on the bullet / Into the valley / Tomorrow or yesterday / Mr. Rock and roll / Love hungry.
LP: VSOPLP 151
MC: VSOPMC 151

REFUGEE.
Tracks: / Good to see you / Turn on the lights / Room 109 / Look to the future / Too late / Silver screen, The / Can't live without your love / Love this time / State of emergency / Someone to turn to / Samurai sunset.
LP: GMGLP 001
MC: GMGMC 001

SHOCK TACTICS.
LP: RCALP 5031
MC: RCAK 5031

SURVIVORS.
Tracks: / It's not as easy as it seems / I wish I was the saddle of a school girl / Big brother / Tomorrow or yesterday / Koz / Six foot under / Wrong side of time / Mr. Rock and Roll / Primrose shuffle / Telephone / Leavin' you.
LP: THBL 001
MC: THBC 001

THANK YOU AND GOODNIGHT.
LP: METALP 102

Samson Et Dalila

SAMSON ET DALILA (VIDEO) (see under Saint-Saens, Camille) (Various artists).

Samson, Paul

JOINT FORCES.
Tracks: / Burning emotion / No turning back / Russians / Tales of the fury / Reach out to love / Chosen few / Tramp / Power of love, The / Tell me.
LP: RAWLP 018
MC: RAWTC 018

Samson, Sam

SWING IN THE SPRING 1939/42 (Samson, Sam Och Hans Orkester).
LP: DRLP 19

Samuels

SKYLIGHT (see under Lande) (Samuels/ Lande/McCandless).

Samuels, Arthur

REPOSSESSION, THE/THE TELLTALE HEART (Various artists).
MC: NF 1

Samuels, Dave

TEN DEGREES NORTH.
Tracks: / White Nile / Ten degrees north / Real world / Para pastorius / Rendezvous / Ivory coast / Walking on the moon / Freetown / Angel falls / Footpath.
LP: MCA 6328

Samurai

FIRES OF HELL.
Tracks: / Fires of hell / Dreams of the world.
LP: EBON 25

SACRED BLADE.
LP: EBON 24

San Francisco Bay

SAN FRANCISCO BAY GOSPEL (see under Gospel).

San Francisco Blues

EAGLE OF THE USA, THE.
LP: MMRC 107

San Francisco Mime

ALBUM, THE.
LP: FF 316

STEELTOWN.
LP: FF 347

San Francisco Symphony

DVORAK SYMPHONY NO.9 (See under Dvorak (Composer)).

San Jose

HARD TO HANDLE.
LP: SANC 7901

Sanborn, David

ANOTHER HAND.
MC: 7559610884

AS WE SPEAK.
LP: BSK 3650
LP: K 56975

BACKSTREET.
Tracks: / I told U so / When you smile at me / Believer / Backstreet / Tear for crystal, A / Bums cathedral / Blue beach / Neither one of us.
LP: 923906 1
MC: 923906 4

CHANGE OF HEART, A.
Tracks: / Chicago song / Imogene / High roller / Tin tin / Breaking point / Change of heart, A / Summer / Dream, The.
LP: 925479 1

MC: 925479 4

CLOSE UP.
Tracks: / Slam / J.T. / Leslie Ann / Goodbye / Same girl / Pyramid / Tough / So far away / You are everything.
LP: . . . . K 925715 1
MC: . . . . K 925715 4

DOUBLE VISION (See under James, Bob/David Sanborn) (Sanborn, David & Bob James).

HIDEAWAY.
Tracks: / Hideaway / Carly's song / Anything you want / Seduction, The / Lisa / If you would be mine / Creeper / Again and again.
LP: . . . . BSK 3379

LET IT SPEAK.
LP: . . . . K 56975

STRAIGHT TO THE HEART.
Tracks: / Hideaway / Straight to the heart / Run for cover / Smile / Lisa / Love and happiness / Lotus blossom / One hundred ways.
LP: 925150 1

VOYEUR.
Tracks: / Let's just say goodbye / It's you / Wake me when it's over / One in a million / Run for cover / All I need is you / Just for you.
LP: . . . . K 56900
MC: D4 56900

Sanchez

IN FINE STYLE.
LP: . . . . CRLP 3

LONELINESS.
Tracks: / Loneliness leave me alone / I love you / Ben / Tell it like it is / Nine to five / Hard times / Please return your love / Falling in love / Lost my lover / Trains and boats and planes.
LP: . . . . WRLP 17
MC: . . . . WRLC 17

MI LOVE MI GIRL BAD (See under Flourgan) (Sanchez & Flourgan).

NUMBER ONE.
Tracks: / Place mash up / Behind the wall / Here I am / Mexican divorce / Praise jah dub / Mash up dub / Wall of dub / Come to rule / Baby can I hold you / Can't hold on to it / Praise jah / Can I hold you dub / Ruling dub.
MC: . . . . MCT 1012
LP: . . . . MLPS 1012

OVER YOU (See under Griffiths, Marcia) (Griffiths, Marcia and Sanchez).

SANCHEZ.
Tracks: / Sanchez.
LP: . . . . VALP 1

SWEETEST GIRL, THE.
LP: . . . . RMM 1419
LP: . . . . RRTG 7708
MC: . . . . RRTGC 7708

WAYNE WONDER AND SANCHEZ PT. 2 (See under Wonder, Wayne) (Wonder, Wayne & Sanchez).

WILD SANCHEZ.
Tracks: / Wild Sanchez / My guy / Muriel (April) / One in a million / All at once / Wild frontier / Loner, The / Strangers in the dark / Johnny boy.
LP: . . . . GREL 122

Sanchez, Poncho

BIEN SABROSO.
Tracks: / Ahora / Bien sabroso / Nancy / Keeper of the flame / Brisa / Sin timbal / Una mas / Half and half / I can.
LP: . . . . CJP 239

CAMBIOS (CHANGES).
Tracks: / Yesterdays / El sabroson / Cambios / My foolish heart / Hey Bud / Insight / In a sentimental mood / Pique / Sky dive / Chanko.
MC: . . . . CJP 439 C

CHILE CON SOUL.
Tracks: / Song for Cal / Night in London, A / Mama guela / Soul burst / Will you still be mine / Lover come back to me / Chile con soul / Nueva charanga (CD only.) / Quieto / Commigo (CD only.) / Ti-pon-pa / Cold sweat / Funky broadway.
MC: . . . . CJP 406C

EL CONGUERO.
Tracks: / Siempre me va bien / Mi negra / Shiny stockings / Si no hay amor / Yumbambo / Agua dulce / Night walk / Tin tin deo / Cuidado.
LP: . . . . CJP 286

FUERTE - STRONG.
Tracks: / Fuerte! / Baila mi gente / It could happen to you / Lo llores, mi corazon / Ixtapa / Co co my my / Siempre te amare / Alafia / Daahoud.
LP: . . . . CJP 340
MC: . . . . CJPC 340

LA FAMILIA.
LP: . . . . CJP 369
MC: . . . . CJP 369 C

NIGHT AT KIMBALL'S EAST, A.
Tracks: / Jumpin' with Symphony Sid / Co co may may / Cinderella / James Brown medley / Baila mi gente / Yumbamba / Night in Tunisia, A / Se acabo lo que se daba/Domitila.
MC: . . . . CJP 472C

PAPA GATO.
Tracks: / Quindembo / Papa Gato / Serenidade / Jumpin' with Symphony Sid / Baila baila / Pan dulce / Tania / Senor blues / Manteca.
LP: . . . . CJP 310

PONCHO.
Tracks: / Baila Mi Gente / Morning / Mama Guela / Gaviota.
LP: . . . . DS 799

SONANDO.
Tracks: / Night in Tunisia, A / Sonando / Summer knows / Con tres tambores bata / Almendra / Sueno / Cals pals / Peruchin / Este san.
LP: . . . . CJP 201
MC: CJPC201

STRAIGHT AHEAD.
Tracks: / Pensativa / I remember spring / Once again.
LP: . . . . DS 813

Sancious, David

BRIDGE, THE.
LP: . . . . K 52403
LP: . . . . SPART 1162

TRUE STORIES.
Tracks: / Sound of love / Move on / Prelude 3 / On the inside / Fade away / Ever the same / Interlude / Matter of time.
LP: . . . . SPART 1082

Sanctified Soul

SANCTIFIED SOUL (See under Soul) (Various artists).

Sanctuary

INTO THE MIRROR BLACK.
Tracks: / Future tense / Taste revenge / Long since dark / Epitaph / Eden lies obscured / Mirror black, The / Seasons of destruction / One more murder / Communion.
LP: 4658761
MC: 4658764

PRICE TO PAY.
MC: . . . . SANC 1

REFUGE DENIED.
Tracks: / Battle angels / Termination force / Die for my sins / Soldiers of steel / Sanctuary / White rabbit / Ascension to destiny / Third war, The / Veil of disguise.
LP: 4608111
MC: 4608114

Sandberg, Paul

HIDING PLACE HE.
LP: . . . . PC 758

LATELY HAVE YOU SEEN THE SUN.
LP: . . . . PC 3

WELCOME TO THE FAMILY.
LP: . . . . PC 791

Sandburg Sound Book

SANDBURG SOUND BOOK FOR CHILDREN (Various artists).
LPS: . . . . SBC 113

Sandeman, Mary

INTRODUCING MARY SANDEMAN.
Tracks: / Song for a winter's night / Dumbarton's drums / Massacre of Glencoe / Fond kiss, A / Cherubino's song / My love, my life / Lady singer, The / Song of the sea / Alasdair Mhiccolla / Love of seasons.
LP: . . . . REL 468
MC: . . . . REC 468

MARY SANDEMAN'S REQUESTS.
LP: . . . . RELS 477
MC: . . . . RECS 477

Sanders, Billy

JA SO NE PARTY.
Tracks: / Jackety Jack / Lass sein / That's love / Mein Dixieland / Muss es denn immer so sein / Weit ist der weg nach Rio / Italien fieber / Ja so'ne party / Di di Dinah / Ich bin kein schoner mann / Du hast soviel sex appeal / In Brooklyn ist was los / Daisy, du musst schlafen geh'n / Doch du lasst mich nie allein.
LP: . . . . BFX 15038

Sanders, Coon

NIGHTHAWK BLUES Vol. 1.
LP: . . . . BR 144

Sanders, Irene

BLUE LADIES VOL. 1.
LP: . . . . DLP 579

Sanders, Joe

VICTORY PARADE (Sanders, Joe & His Orchestra/Henry King & His Orch.).
LP: . . . . AIRCHECK 7

Sanders, Pharoah

AFRICA.
Tracks: / You've got to have freedom / Naima / Origin / Speak low / After the morning / Africa.
LP: . . . . SJP 253

BLACK UNITY.
LP: . . . . AS 9026

JOURNEY TO THE ONE.
Tracks: / Greetings to Idris / Doktor Pitt / Kazuko (peace child) / After the rain / Soledad / You've got to have freedom / Yemenja / Easy to remember / Think about the one / Bedria.
LP: . . . . TR 108

KARMA.
Tracks: / Creator has a master plan, The / Creater has a master plan, The (part 2) / Colors.
LP: . . . . MCA 39122

MOONCHILD.
Tracks: / Moon child / Moon rays / Night has a thousand eyes, The / All or nothing at all / Soon / Mananberg.
LP: . . . . SJP 326

PHAROAH SANDERS LIVE.
LP: . . . . TR 116

PRAYER BEFORE DAWN, A.
Tracks: / Light at the edge of the world, The / Dedication to James W Clark / Softly for Shyla / After the rain / Greatest love of all, The / Midnight at Yoshi's / Living space / In your own sweet way / Christmas song, The.
LP: . . . . TR 127

REJOICE.
LP: . . . . TR 112

TAUHID.
LP: . . . . AS 9138

TEMBI.
Tracks: / Astral travelling / Red black and green / Thembi / Love / Morning prayer / Bailophone dance.
LP: . . . . JAS 53
MC: . . . . JAS C53

WELCOME TO LOVE.
Tracks: / You don't know what love is / Nearness of you, The / My one and only love / I want to talk about you / Soul eyes / Nancy / Polka dots and moonbeans / Say it (over and over again) / Lament / Bird song, The.
MC: . . . . MCSJP 358

Sanders, Teddy

SUE BLUE (Sanders, Teddy Sextet).
LP: . . . . DS 809

Sanderson, Tommy

KEEP ON DANCING (Sanderson, Tommy & His Orchestra).
LP: . . . . MTS 2

THERE GOES THAT SONG AGAIN (See Wilce, Malcolm) (Sanderson, Tommy/ Malcom Wilce).

Sandi & The Sunsetz

HEAT SCALE.
Tracks: / Heat scale / Great wall / Bongazuna / Tohmei ningen / El puzzlo / Alive / Eve of Adam / An antenna / Zoot kook / Kingdoms without corners / Shyana Pura.
LP: . . . . ALF 85642

IMMIGRANTS.
Tracks: / Dreams of immigrants / Open sesame / Living on the front line / Mirrors of eyes / You get what you need / Jinjirogeh / Chunk of funk / Perfect strangers / Illusion wanted / Where the fire still burns.
LP: 250 004 1

Sandke, Jordan

RHYTHM IS OUR BUSINESS (Sandke, Jordan & Jaki Byard & Co.).
LP: . . . . ST 259

Sandke, Randy

NEW YORK STORIES.
LP: . . . . ST 264

Sandler, Albert

GOLDEN AGE OF ALBERT SANDLER.
Tracks: / Pomone waltz / From the land of the sky blue water / Bird songs at eventide / Chanson hindoue / Shy serenade / Serenade les millions d'arlequin / Phantom melody, The / Serenade (staendchen) / Demande et reponse / Thais-meditation / In an 18th century drawing room / Old violin, An / Dreaming - waltz / On wings of song / Largo.
LP: . . . . GX 41 2546 1
MC: . . . . GX 41 2546 4

SERENADES.
Tracks: / Pomone waltz / From the land of the sky blue water / Bird songs at eventide / Chanson hindoue / Shy serenade / Les millions d'arlequin / Chanson / Phantom melody / Serenade / Demande et response / Thais / In an 18th century drawing room / Old violin, An / Dreaming waltz / On the wings of song / Handels largo.
LP: . . . . SH 255

Sandmen

WESTERN BLOOD.
Tracks: / Western blood / I'm accusing you / House in the country / Say yes / Heart of steel / 500% / Bellman, The / Hello it's me again / It's alright / Hate your ways / I met a girl.
LP: . . . . AMA 5239
MC: . . . . AMC 5239
LP: . . . . GARD 4

Sandor Deki

DIGITAL GIPSY MUSIC SOUND.
LP: . . . . SLPD 10178
MC: . . . . MK 10178

Sandoval, Arturo

FLIGHT TO FREEDOM.
Tracks: / Flight to freedom / Last time I saw you / Caribeno / Samba de amore / Psalm / Rene's song / Body and soul / Tanga / Caprichosos de la habana / Marianela.
LP: . . . . GRP 96341
MC: . . . . GRP 96344

JUST MUSIC.
Tracks: / El misterioso / Sambeando / Georgia on my mind / Libertao carnaval / Saving all my love / Al chicoy / My love.
LP: . . . . JHR 008

NO PROBLEM.
Tracks: / Nuestro blues / Los elefantes / Donna Lee / Rimsky / Campana / Fiesta mojo.
LP: . . . . JHR 001
MC: . . . . JHC 001

REUNION (see under D'Rivera, Paquito) (D'Rivera, Paquito & Arturo Sandoval).

STRAIGHT AHEAD (Sandoval, Arturo & Chucho Valdes).
LP: . . . . JHR 007

TUMBAITO.
LP: 15973

Sandpebbles

SANDPEBBLES (Film soundtrack) (Various artists).
LP: . . . . FILM 048
MC: . . . . FILMC 048

Sandpipers

GUANTANAMERA.
MCSET: . . . . DTO 10079

LATIN LOVE AFFAIR.
MCSET: . . . . DTO 10079

OVERDUE.
Tracks: / Hang on sloopy / I'll never love anyone anymore / Broken slumber / Island / Skidrow Joe / Living is the lovin' thing / Life is a song worth singing / Crying in the rain / Moonlight / Love in your heart / You're a great way to fly / Last time, The.
LP: . . . . SATL 4006

Sandra

EVERLASTING LOVE.
LP: . . . . SRNLP 18
MC: . . . . SRNMC 18

LONG PLAY, THE.
Tracks: / In the heat of the night / On the tray (seven years) / Little girl / You and I / I'll never be Maria Magdalena / Heartbeat (that's emotion) / Sisters and brothers / Change your mind.
LP: . . . . DIX 40
MC: . . . . CDIX 40

PAINTINGS IN YELLOW.
LP: . . . . V 2636
MC: . . . . TCV 2636

Sands, Evie

SUSPENDED ANIMATION.
Tracks: / Lady of the night / Keep my lovelight burning / Take a little love / I can't wait for you / As we fall in love once more / Get up / You sho' look good to me / You can do it / I don't want to let go / Brain damage.
LP: . . . . PL 12943

Sands Family

AFTER THE MORNING.
LP: . . . . LEAF 7012

NOW AND THEN.
LP: . . . . SLP 1008

REAL IRISH FOLK.
Tracks: / Here I am amongst you / O'Reilly from County Caven / Trip to Rathlin / There'll have to be some changes / No man's land / I'm terrible man / Bonnie Kellswater / Three jigs / 26th May, The / Tenpenny bit, The / Jacksons morning brush / Johnny my man / Misty mourne shore.
LP: . . . . GES 1201
MC: . . . . KGEC 1201

YOU'LL BE WELL LOOKED AFTER.
LP: LEAF 7005

Sands, Tommy

BLUE RIBBON BABY.
LP: REV 3001

DOWN BY BENDY'S LANE.
LP: SIF 1085
MC: CSIF 1085

SANDS STORM.
Tracks: / Maybellene / Hearts of stone / Since I met you baby / Oop shoop / Warm your heart / Tweedle Dee / Such a night / Honey love / Blue velvet / Little mama / Chicken and the hawk.
LP: JAS 302
MC: JAS C302

SINGING OF THE TIMES.
LP: SLP 1005

Sandstrom, Nisse

HOME COOKING (See under Flanagan, Tommy) (Sandstrom, Nisse/Red Mitchell/Tommy Flanagan).

SUMMIT MEETING (see under Rosengren, Bernt) (Sandstrom, Nisse/ Bernt Rosengren).

YOUNG FOREVER (Sandstrom, Nisse/ Horace Parlan/Red Mitchell).
LP: PHONT 7562

Sandvik Big Band

SANDVIK BIG BAND.
LP: DRLP 26

Sandy, Tam

AMANG THE NEEPS AND BARLEY WITH (Sandy, Tam & Geordie).
MC: CWGR 067

Sandy's Fancy

SANDY'S FANCY (Various artists).
LP: FF 260

Sandy's Sidemen

PLAYING COMPOSITIONS....
Tracks: / Nobody met the train / Stay / Swiss Kriss / High time / Look the other way / Candy stripes / Mouseparty / My neck of the woods.
LP: JASM 2014

Saneam

YEAR 2000, THE.
MC: CMUT 1076

Sang, Samantha

FROM DANCE TO LOVE.
Tracks: / From dance to love / It's the falling in love / In the midnight hour / Moments / I'll never get enough of you.
LP: UAG 30274

Sangare, Oumou

MOUSSOLOU.
Tracks: / Djama kaissoumou / Diaraby nene / Woula bara diagna / Moussolou / Diya gneba / Ah ndiya.
LP: WCB 021
MC: WCC 021

Sangeet, Apna

APNA SANGEET.
LP: IND 1158

BHANGRE DA RAJA.
MC: CMUT 1110

CHAKK DE PHATTAY.
LP: MUT 1071
MC: CMUT 1071

Sangeet, Betaab

CHALLA CHALLA.
MC: BIP 405

Sangeeta

BREATH OF FRESH BHANGRA, A.
LP: KEDAL 4
MC: KEDA 4

Sangha, Sukhdez Singh

BHANGRA FOR THE YOUNG ONES.
LP: SSRLP 5104

Sangster, John

DOUBLE VIBES HOBBIT.
LP: S 1376

FOR LEON BISMARCK.
LP: S 1379

HOBBIT SUITE, THE.
LP: S 1340

Sanity Plexus

DEVILS DECEPTION.
Tracks: / Top / Masculine mask / Stains / Squalor / Boy can get scared, A / Service with a smile.
LP: MTW1 GOO 1

Sankey, Katie

I DON'T KNOW WHY.
Tracks: / I need thee every hour / Where are you going / He touched me / Thats how much / I don't know why / All you need is god / Till shiloh comes / God made me.
LP: KEY 4007
MC: KEYMC 4007

Sankomota

DREAMS DO COME TRUE.
LP: BUSH 1

SANKOMOTA.
LP: ELP 2007

Sanna

SANNA.
MC: MR 1014

Sansch, Bert

SKETCHES.
LP: TP 035
MC: CTP 035

Sansone, Jumpin'

MR. GOOD THING (Sansone, Jumpin' Johnny & The Blues Party).
Tracks: / Trouble / She wants money / Dishrag / Goodbye to love / Don't cry baby / Midnight til morning / Mr. Good Thing / Way down the line / Running from trouble / Johnny and Janie.
LP: KIN 4039
MC: KIN 4039MC

Santa Claus Blues

SANTA CLAUS BLUES (Various artists).
LP: JASS 8

Santa Claus: The Movie

SANTA CLAUS: THE MOVIE (Film Soundtrack) (Various artists).
Tracks: / Main title: *Jones, Aled* / Arrival of the elves: *Various artists* / Making toys: *Ambrosian Children's Choir* / Christmas rhapsody: *Various artists* / It's Christmas again: *Ambrosian Children's Choir* / March of the elves: *Various artists* / Patch,natch!: *Ambrosian Children's Choir* / It's Christmas all over the world: *Easton, Sheena* / Shouldn't do that: *Kajagoogoo* / Sleigh ride over Manhattan: *Various artists* / Sad patch: *Various artists* / Patch versus Santa: *Various artists* / Thank you Santa: *Ambrosian Children's Choir.*
LP: AML 3101
MC: TCAML 3101

Santa Sangre (film)

SANTA SANGRE (Film Soundtrack) (Various artists).
Tracks: / Fin del mundo: *Boswell, Simon* / Alma: *Boswell, Simon* / Alejandra: *Circus Orgo* / Triste: *Boswell, Simon* / Besame mucho: *Silver Hombre* / Acid revenge: *Boswell, Simon* / Herbage: *Boswell,* Simon / Truck: *Boswell, Simon* / Dejame llorar: *Concha Y Fenix* / Holy guitar: *Boswell, Simon* / Grave business: *Boswell, Simon* / Heart: *Boswell, Simon* / Kids' theme: *Boswell, Simon* / Wingbeat: *Boswell, Simon* / Church tattoo: *Boswell, Simon* / Sweet dreams: *Boswell, Simon* / Karnival: *Boswell, Simon.*
LP: PTLS 1104
MC: PTLC 1104

Santamaria, Mongo

HAPPY AS A FAT RAT.
LP: VS 61

IMAGES: MONGO SANTAMARIA.
LP: VS 92

LIVE AT JAZZ ALLEY.
Tracks: / Home / Bonita / Philadelphia / Para II (Only on CD) / Manteca / Ponce / Come Candela / Iblano (Only on CD) / Juan Jose (Only on CD) / Afro blue.
MC: CJPC 427

MONGO MAGIC.
LP: 520 319

MONGO'S GROOVE.
Tracks: / Manteca / Pachanga twist / Dot dot dot / Para ti / Conga pa gozar / Watermelon man / Sweet tater pie / Este mambo / Happy now / Nothing for nothing.
LP: BGP 1001
MC: BGPC 1001

OLE OLA.
LP: CJP 387
MC: CJPC 387

RED HOT.
Tracks: / Watermelon man / A mi no me enganan / Jai alai / Jamaican sunrise / Afro-Cuban fantasy / Sambita.
LP: CBS 83340

SOCA ME NICE.
Tracks: / Con mi ritmo / Cookie / Cu-bop alert / Day tripper / Kathy's waltz / Quiet fire / Soca me nice / Tropical breeze.
LP: CJP 362
MC: CJP 362 C

SOY YO.
Tracks: / La manzana (the apple) / Sweet love / Soy yo (that's me) / Salazar / Mayeya / Oasis / Smooth operator / Un dia de playa (a day at the beach).
LP: CJP 327
MC: CJPC 327

SUMMERTIME (see Gillespie, Dizzy) (Santamaria, Mongo & Dizzy Gillespie).

WATERMELON MAN.
Tracks: / Watermelon man / Funny money / Cut that cane / Get the money / Boogie cha-cha blues / Don't bother me no more / Love oh love / Yeh-yeh / Peanut vendor / Go git it / Bayou roots / Sauvito / El toro / Fat back / Mongo's groove / Creole / Para ti / Jungle bit / My sound / Morning after / Nothing for nothing.
LP: M 47012

YAMBU (Santamaria, Mongo Y Sus Ritmos Afro Cubanos).
Tracks: / Yeye / Congobel / Macunsere / Timbales & bongo / Yambu / Bricamo / Longoito / Conga pa gozar / Mi guaguanco / Columbia.
LP: ORB 036

Santana

ABRAXAS.
Tracks: / Singing winds / Crying beasts / Black magic woman / Gypsy queen / Oye como va / Incident at Neshabur / Se a cabo / Mother's daughter / Samba pa ti / Hope you're feeling better / El nicoya.
LP: CBS 32032
MC: 40 32032
LP: CBS 64087

AMIGOS.
Tracks: / Let me / Tell me are you tired? / Europa / Let it shine / Gitano / Dance sister dance / Take me with you.
LP: CBS 86005
LP: CBS 32476

BEYOND APPEARANCES.
Tracks: / Breaking out / Written in sand / How long / Brotherhood / Spirit / Say it again / Who loves you / I'm the one who loves you / Touch-down raiders / Right now.
LP: CBS 86307
MC: 40 86307
LP: CBS 241

BORBOLETTA.
Tracks: / Spring manifestations / Cantos de los flores / Life is anew / Give and take / One with the sun / Aspirations / Practice what you preach / Mirage / Here and now / Flor de canela / Promise of a fisherman / Borboletta.
LP: CBS 32157
LP: CBS 69084

CARAVANSERAI.
Tracks: / Eternal caravan of reincarnation / Waves within / Look up (to see what's coming down) / Just in time to see the sun / Song of the wind / All the love of the universe / Future primitive / Stone flower / La fuente del ritmo / Every step of the way.
LP: CBS 32060
MC: 40 32060
LP: CBS 65299

FESTIVAL.
LP: CBS 86020
MC: 40 86020

FREEDOM.
Tracks: / Veracruz / She can't let go / Once it's gotcha / Love is you / Songs of freedom / Deeper, dig deeper / Praise / Mandela / Before we go / Victim of circumstance.
LP: 4503941
MC: 4503944

GREATEST HITS: SANTANA.
Tracks: / Evil ways / Jin-go-lo-ba / Hope you're feeling better / Samba pa ti / Persuasion / Black magic woman / Oye como va / Everything's coming up roses / Se a cabo / Everybody's everything.
LP: 32386
MC: 40 32386
LP: CBS 69081

INNER SECRETS.
LP: CBS 86075

LATIN TROPICAL.
Tracks: / Soul sacrifice / Fried neckbones and home fries / Santana jam / Latin tropical / Let's get ourselves together.
LP: THBL 079

LOTUS.
Tracks: / Meditation / Going home / A-1 funk / Every step of the way / Black magic woman / Gypsy queen / Oye como va / Yours is the light / Batukada / Xibaba (she-ba-ba) / Stone flower / Waiting / Castillos de arena / Se a cabo / Samba pa ti / Savor / Toussaint l'overture / Incident at Neshabur / Lotus.
LPS: CBS 66325
MCSET: 4679434

MARATHON.
Tracks: / Marathon / Lightning in the sky / Aqua marine / You know that I love you / All I ever wanted / Stand up / Runnin' / Summer lady / Love / Stay (beside me) / Hard times.
LP: CBS 86098
MC: 40 86098

MOONFLOWER.
Tracks: / Dawn-go within / Carnaval / Let the children play / Jugando / I'll be waiting / Zulu / She's not there / Bahia / Black magic woman / Gypsy queen / Dance sister dance / Europa / Flor d'luna / Soul sacrifice / El Morocco / Transcendance / Savor / Toussaint l'overture.
2LP: CBS 22180
MC: 40 22180
LP: CBS 88272

ONENESS- SILVER DREAMS GOLDEN REALITY.
Tracks: / Chosen hour / Arise awake / Light versus darkness / Jim Jeannie / Transformation day / Victory / Silver dreams golden smiles / Cry of the wilderness / Guru's song / Oneness / Life is just a passing parade / Golden dawn / Free as the morning sun / I am free / Song for Devadip.
LP: CBS 86037

PERSUASION.
Tracks: / Jingo / El corazon manda / La puesta del sol / Persuasion / As the years go by.
LP: OR 0058
LP: THBL 071

SANTANA.
LP: CBS 63815
LP: CBS 32003

SANTANA 3.
Tracks: / Batukada / No one to depend on / Taboo / Toussaint l'overture / Everything's everything / Guajira / Jungle strut / Everything's coming our way / Para los rumberos.
LP: CBS 69015

SHANGO.
Tracks: / Nile / Hold on / Night hunting time / Nowhere to run / Neuva York / Oxun / Body surfing / What does it take (to win your love) / Let me inside / Warrior / Shango.
LP: CBS 85914

SPIRITS DANCING IN THE FLESH.
Tracks: / Let there be light / Spirits dancing in the flesh / Gypsy woman / It's a jungle out there / Soweto (Africa libre) / Choose / Peace on Earth / Mother Earth / Third stone / Full moon / That lady / Jin-go-lo-ba / Goodness and mercy.
LP: 4669131
MC: 4669134

SWINGS OF DELIGHT, THE.
2LP: CBS 22057

THIRD ALBUM.
LP: CBS 32058

VIVA SANTANA - LIVE.
Tracks: / Everybody's everything / Black magic woman/Gypsy queen / Guajira / Jungle strut / Jingo / Ballin' / Bambara / Angel negro / Incident at Neshabur / Just let the music speak / Super boogie/Hong Kong blues / Song of the wind / Abi cama / Vilato / Paris finale / Brotherhood / Open invitation / Aqua marine / Dance sister dance / Europa / Peraza 1 / She's not there / Bambele / Evil ways / Daughter of the night / Peraza II / Black magic woman/ Gypsy queen (live Montreal) / Oye como va / Persuasion / Soul sacrifice.
LPS: 4625001
MC: 4625004

VIVA SANTANA (THE VERY BEST OF SANTANA).
Tracks: / She's not there / Well alright / Oye como va / Let the music set you free / I'll be waiting / What does it take (to win your love) / Black magic woman/Gypsy queen / Samba pa ti / Carnaval / Let the children play / Dance sister dance / Se a cabo / Everythings coming our way / Jin-go-lo-ba.
LP: NE 1338
MC: CE 2338

ZEBOP.
Tracks: / Changes / E papa re / Primera invasion / Searchin' / Over and over / Winning / Tales of Kilimanjaro / Sensitive kind / American gypsy / I love you too much / Brightest star / Hannibal.
LP: CBS 84946

Santana, Carlos

BLUES FOR SALVADOR.
Tracks: / Bailando / Aquatic park / I'm gone / Bella / Trane / Deeper, dig deeper / Mingus / Now that you know / Hannibal / Blues for Salvador.
LP: 4602581
MC: 4602584

HAVANA MOON.
Tracks: / Watch your step / Lightnin' / Who do you love / Mudbone / One with you / Equador / Tales of kilmanjaro / Havana moon / Daughter of the night /

They all went to Mexico / Vereda tropical.
LP: . . . . **CBS 25350**

ILLUMINATIONS (Santana, Carlos & Alice Coltrane).
LP: . . . . **CBS 69063**

LOVE DEVOTION SURRENDER (Santana, Carlos & John McLaughlin).
LP: . . . . **CBS 69037**

SWING OF DELIGHT, THE.
Tracks: / Swapan tari / Spartacus love theme / Phuler matan / Song for my brother, A / Jharna Kala / Gardenia in llave / Golden hours / Shere Khan / Tiger, The.
2LP: . . . . **CBS 22075**
MCSET: **40 22075**

THEY ALL WENT TO MEXICO (see Nelson, Willie) (Santana, Carlos & Willie Nelson).

WELCOME Carlos Santana & Buddy Miles live (Santana, Carlos & Buddy Miles).
Tracks: / Going home / Love, demotion and surrender / Samba de Sausalito / When I look in your eyes / Yours is the light / Mother Africa / Light of life, The / Flame-sky / Welcome / Marbles / Lava / Evil ways / Faith interlude / Them changes / Free from funkafide filth.
MC: . . . . **TFOMC 14**
2LP: . . . . **TFOLP 14**
2LP: . . . . **CBS 69040**
2LP: . . . . **CBS 65142**

Santers

GUITAR ALLEY.
LP: . . . . **HMUSA 3**

RACING TIME.
Tracks: / Mistreatin' heart / Mystical eyes / Still I am / Dog without a home / Road to Morocco, The / Two against the world / Backstreets / Winter freeze / Hard time lovin' you / Racing time.
LP: . . . . **HMILP 4**

SANTE FE.
LP: . . . . **BSS 326**

Santing, Mathilde

BEAST AND BOW.
LP: . . . . **MD 7890**

MATHILDE SANTING.
LP: **2409511**

OUT OF THIS DREAM.
Tracks: / Love of the common man / Town without pity / Wanting things / One day as a lion / Broken bicycle / Tempted / Is there any way out of this dream? / Twenty tambourines / She needs me / Kings and queens / Too close for comfort / Sheep in fog.
LP: . . . . **WX 96**
MC: . . . . **WX 96C**

WATER UNDER THE BRIDGE.
Tracks: / Too much / Our days / Turn your heart / All the fun / Sweet nothin's / I'm not mending broken hearts / It may not always be so / Maggie and Millie and Mollie and May / Water under the bridge / Boat trip.
LP: . . . . **WX 18**
MC: . . . . **WX 18C**

Santos, Moacir

OPUS 3, NO.1.
LP: . . . . **DS 795**

Santrra

OXYD.
LP: . . . . **OXYD 01**

Sapp, Jane

JANE SAPP.
LP: . . . . **FF 265**

Sapphires

SAPPHIRES.
Tracks: / Dead man's grave / Telling lies / Green umbrella / Crystal ball / Temptation / Restless / No way out / World of confusion / No exception / In your mirror / Rockin' chair.
LP: . . . . **SWN 001**

Saqqara Dogs

WORLD CRUNCH.
LP: . . . . **PRAY 006**

Saraband

CLOSE TO IT ALL.
Tracks: / Close to it all / Winter song / This moment / Retrospect / I'm your man / Black Jack Davy / Peace will come / River / Herbie / Richmond.
LP: . . . . **FHR 050**

Saracen

CHANGE OF HEART.
Tracks: / We have arrived / Love on sight / Julie / Seabird / Meet me at midnight / Jekyll and Hyde / Cheating / Face in the crowd / Hot love / Bridge of tears.
LP: . . . . **NEAT 1016**

HEROES, SAINTS AND FOOLS.
Tracks: / Crusader / Rock of ages / No more lonely nights / Horsemen of the Apocalypse / Heroes, saints and fools / Dolphin ride / Ready to fly.
LP: . . . . **MPRGR 492**

Sarafina

SARAFINA (Featuring Hugh Masakela) (Various artists).
LP: . . . . **SHAN 43052**
LP: . . . . **BMG 9304.1**
MC: . . . . **BMG 9304.4**
MC: . . . . **RK 89307**
MC: . . . . **SHANC 43052**
LP: . . . . **RL 89307**

Saraya

SARAYA.
Tracks: / Love has taken it's toll / Healing touch / Get U ready / Gypsy child / One night away / Alsace Lorraine / Runnin' out of time / Back to the bullet / Fire to burn / St. Christopher medal / Drop the bomb.
LP: **837 764-1**
MC: **837 764-4**

WHEN THE BLACKBIRD SINGS.
LP: **8490871**
MC: **8490874**

Sarbib, Saheb

IT COULDN'T HAPPEN WITHOUT YOU.
Tracks: / Conjunctions / It couldn't happen without you / Watchmacallit / You don't know what love is / East 11th Street / Sasa's groove / Crescent.
LP: . . . . **SN 1098**

Sarde, Cliff

DREAMS OUT LOUD.
LP: . . . . **PJ 88034**
MC: . . . . **PJC 88034**

Sarde, Philippe

ENNEMIS INTIMES (See under Ennemis Intimes) (Various artists).

PIRATES (FILM) (See under Pirates (film) (Various artists).

QUI C'EST CE GARCON (See under Qui C'est Ce Garcon) (Various artists).

Sardines

HOT DIGGETY DOG BAND.
Tracks: / Yes I will / Drinking / Touch wood / Big mouth shut / Where do we go from here / Hold me closely / Little things / Motormouth / Don't look so sad / Roots.
LP: . . . . **PF 001**

Sardinia

CATALOGNE ETERNELLE (Various artists).
Tracks: / Coversa animada: *Various artists* / El menut de la casa: *Various artists* / El saltiro de la Cardina: *Various artists* / Girona lievantina: *Various artists* / Amont l avall: *Various artists* / La placa de Montseny: *Various artists* / El llac per joguina: *Various artists* / Bona festa: *Various artists* / Els non presoners: *Various artists* / Llevantina: *Various artists* / L'amic Roura: *Various artists* / Devotes de la morereta: *Various artists*.
LP: . . . . **ARN 30151**
MC: . . . . **ARN 430151**

Sargeant, Will

THEMES FOR GRIND.
LP: . . . . **HAPLP 001**

Sargent

LIVING IN THE FAST LANE.
LP: . . . . **AMP 10**

SGT.
LP: . . . . **SKULL 8367**

Sarony, Leslie

ROY HUDD PRESENTS LESLIE SARONY.
Tracks: / 14 rollicking sailors / I lift up my finger and I say tweet tweet / Sweet Fanny Adams / Gorgonzola / Wheezy Anna / Yer gotta get aht / When the guards are on parade / Rhymes / Shut the gate / Umpa umpa / Old sow / I like riding on a choo-choo-choo / Strolling down the Strand / Jollity farm.
LP: . . . . **RTRS 101**

Sarstedt, Clive

ASIA MINOR (see under Sarstedt, Peter) (Sarstedt, Clive & Peter).

Sarstedt, Peter

ASIA MINOR (Sarstedt, Peter & Clive).
Tracks: / Dream pilot / Teradactyl walk / Glider / India / River, The / Corigador / Vaguely connected.
LP: . . . . **KNEWL 01**
MC: . . . . **KNEWMC 01**

NEVER SAY GOODBYE.
Tracks: / Suzanne / Katerina / Nothing personal / Friends / Roma / Hemingway / Camera / Don Quixote / Stress / Why would anybody.
LP: . . . . **PETER 1**
MC: . . . . **PETMC 1**

PETER SARSTEDT.
LP: . . . . **SULP 1219**

P.S..
Tracks: / You'll never be alone again / Hollywood sign / Mulberry dawn / Beirut / I'll be your baby tonight / I am no longer / Another day / Muscle twitch / Waitress in the whiskey / St. Louis blues.
LP: . . . . **AHAL 8006**

UP DATE.
LP: . . . . **STELP 12**

Sarstedt, Robin

MY RESISTANCE IS LOW (OLD GOLD) (See under Becaud, Gilbert/Little love & ...).

Sartana

SARTANA/LONG DAY OF VENGEANCE,THE (Various artists).
LP: . . . . **INGM 003**

Sartre, Jean-Paul

NO EXIT (Various artists).
MCSET: **327**

Sash, Leon

I REMEMBER NEWPORT.
LP: . . . . **DL 416**

Sashay, Scion

SUCCESS.
LP: . . . . **JLLP 019**

Satan

COURT IN THE ACT.
Tracks: / Into the fire / Trial by fire / Blades of steel / No turning back / Broken treaties / Break free / Hunt you down / Ritual, The / Dark side of innocence / Alone in the dock.
LP: . . . . **NEAT 1012**

INTO THE FUTURE.
2LP: **601 898**

SUSPENDED SENTENCE.
LP: **081 837**

Satan Defloration Inc.

SATAN DEFLORATION INCORPORATED (Satan Defloration Incorporated).
Tracks: / Quasimodo / Panic in Wehrmacht / Wanker / Absolute banger / Young blood / You're wrong / Chainsaw / Massacre / I don't care / Take off your hands / I wanna f**k ya / Bullshit / Disappointment / Bloodsucker.
LP: **805 035**

Satanic Malfunctions

HELLBOUND.
LP: . . . . **TEA 002**

Satanic Rites

NO USE CRYING.
LP: . . . . **CHUB 002**

Satan's Revenge

SATAN'S REVENGE (Various artists).
LP: . . . . **GWD 90536**
MC: . . . . **GWC 90536**

Satchell, David

EXPERIENCE, THE.
MC: . . . . **C 144**

IMAGES: DAVID SATCHELL.
MC: . . . . **C 126**

Satchmo Legacy Band

SALUTE TO POPS VOL. 1.
LP: **121116-1**

Satchmo, Pluggy

BATTLE OF THE GIANTS, ROUND 1 (see Gray, Owen) (Satchmo, Pluggy & Owen Gray).

Satellites Four

EARTHLESS.
LP: . . . . **WR 1887**
MC: . . . . **WRC 1887**

Sater, Almir

ALMIR SATER INSTRUMENTAL.
Tracks: / Corumba / Minas Gerais / Vinnta do capeta / Luzeiro / Benzinho / O rio de piracicaba / Na piratininga: de jeep / Doma / Viola de buruti / De Minas Pra Riba.
LP: . . . . **RRPL 004**

Satie (composer)

HOMAGE TO ERIK SATIE, VOL.1 His original works for orchestra (Utah Symphony Orchestra).
MC: . . . . **VETC 6527**

SATIE: PARADE; MERCURE; RELACHE (New London Orchestra).
MC: . . . . **KA 66365**

SEPT TABLEAUX PHONIQUES (Various artists).
Tracks: / Trois bonbons de York pour Erik Satie: *Satie (composer)* / Budapest subway: *Satie (composer)* / Welcome: *Satie (composer)* / Moving things from A to B: *Satie (composer)* / Falz waltz: *Satie (composer)* / For memories of an amnesiac: *Satie (composer)* / Allair meets: *Satie (composer)* / Faction de Satie (I can't get no): *Satie (composer)*.
LP: . . . . **NATO 59**

TROIS SARABANDES ET SIX GNOSSIENNES (Various artists).
Tracks: / Trois sarabandes et six gnossiennes: *Satie (composer)*.
LP: . . . . **NATO 410**

Sato, Masahiko

TRINITY.
LP: . . . . **ENJA 2008**

Sato, Shinobu

RED DRAGONFLY.
LP: . . . . **FF 476**

Sator Codex

WANNA START A FIRE.
LP: . . . . **CALCLP 007**

Satriani, Joe

FLYING IN A BLUE DREAM.
Tracks: / Flying in a blue dream / Mystical potato head groove thing, The / Can't slow down / Headless / Strange / I believe / One big rush / Big bad moon / Feeling, The / Phone call, The / Day at the beach / Back to Shalla-bal / Ride / Forgotten, The (Part one) / Forgotten, The (Part two) / Bells of Lal, The (Part one) / Bells of Lal, The (Part two) / Into the light.
LP: . . . . **GRUB 14**
MC: . . . . **TGRUB 14**

NOT OF THIS EARTH.
Tracks: / Not of this Earth / Snake, The / Rubina / Memories / Brother John / Enigmatic, The / Driving at night / Hords of locusts / New day / Headless horseman.
LP: . . . . **GRUB 7**
MC: . . . . **TGRUB 7**

SURFING WITH THE ALIEN.
Tracks: / Surfing with the alien / Ice 9 / Crushing day / Always with you, always with me / Satch boogie / Hill of the skull / Circles / Lords of Karma / Midnight / Echo.
LP: . . . . **GRUB 8**
MC: . . . . **TGRUB 8**

Satta

SATTA.
Tracks: / Declaration of rights / Good Lord / Forward on a yard / Know Jah today / Abendigo / Timasgan / Black man strain / African race / I'n'I / Satta (the best).
LP: . . . . **AZ 2000**

Sattelites

HERE IS TODAY'S NEWS.
LP: . . . . **BYLP 1**

Satton, Lon

INSPIRATIONS.
Tracks: / Up where we belong / How great thou art / Take my hand precious Lord / Amazing grace / You'll never walk alone / He / Love of God, The / Oh happy day / Every time I feel the Spirit / People get ready.
LP: . . . . **REB 701**
MC: . . . . **ZCF 701**

Saturday Night Fever

SATURDAY NIGHT FEVER (Film Soundtrack) (Various artists).
Tracks: / Stayin' alive: *Bee Gees* / How deep is your love: *Bee Gees* / Night fever: *Bee Gees* / More than a woman: *Bee Gees* / Jive talkin': *Bee Gees* / You should be dancing: *Bee Gees* / More than a woman: *Tavares* / Calypso breakdown: *Donaldson, Ralph* / If I can't have you: *Elliman, Yvonne* / Fifth of Beethoven, A: *Murphy, Walter* / Open sesame: *Kool & The Gang* / Boogie shoes: *K.C. & The Sunshine Band* / M.F.S.B.: *K.C. & The Sunshine Band* / K. Jee: *K.C. & The Sunshine Band* / Disco inferno: *Tramps* / Manhattan skyline: *Tramps* / Night on disco mountain: *Tramps* / Salsation: *Tramps*.
MCSET: **351 701-4**
2LP: . . . . **SPDLP 5**
2LP: **2658 123**

Satyricon

SATYRICON (Original Film Score) (Various artists).
Tracks: / Teatrino di vernacchio: *Various artists* / Il giardino delle delizie: *Various artists* / Notturni nella suburra: *Various artists* / La schiavetta imnamorata: *Various artists* / La cena de trimalcione: *Various artists* / Madeja - perimadeja: *Various artists* / Mio amato gitone: *Various artists* / Il cena de trimalcione: *Various artists* / Tema di gitone: *Various artists* / Il trionfo del nuovo Cesare: *Various artists* / Encolpio e ascito prigionier: *Various artists* / Sulla nave di lica: *Various artists* / Le nozze

sul mare: *Various artists*/ Il fuoco delle vestali: *Various artists* / L'oracolo salmodiante: *Various artists* / Mi ascolti gitone: *Various* artists / Storia della matrona de efeso: *Various artists* / Encolpio ha perduto la sua spada: *Various artists*/ Il minotauro: *Various artists* / La danse des singes: *Various artists* / La nuova isola: *Various artists*.
LP: . . . . UAS 29118

Saucy Songs

CLASSIC YEARS IN DIGITAL STEREO
(see under Classic Years...) (Various artists).

Saulsberry, Rodney

RODNEY SAULSBERRY.
Tracks: / Look watcha done now / I wonder / Poor little rich girl / Hey girl / You gotta hold on to your love / Second chance / Her song / Time is on our side.
LP: . . . . ALE 5605
MC: . . . . ZCALE 5605

Saunders, Camilia

TIME CHANGES.
LP: . . . . RRA 006
MC: . . . . RRA MC 006

Saunders, Jesse

JESSE.
LP: . . . . SAUND 1
MC: . . . . ZCSSAUND 1

Saunders, Ric

WHENEVER.
LP: . . . . WF 020
MC: . . . . WF 020C

Sauter, Eddie

DIRECTIONS IN MUSIC (Sauter, Eddie/ Bill Finegan).
Tracks: / Doodletown fifers / Azure te / When hearts are young / April in Paris / Moonlight sleighride / Nina never knew / Love is a simple thing / Foggy day, A / How about choo (how about you?) / Autumn leaves / Two bats in a cave / Over the rainbow / Wild wings in the woods / These foolish things / Horseplay / Dream play / Clarinet a la King / Old folks / Thundisbreak, The (the thunderer).
LP: . . . . NL 86468
MC: . . . . NK 86468

RETURN OF THE DOODLETOWN FIFERS, THE (Sauter, Eddie/Bill Finegan).
Tracks: / Doodletown fifers / April in Paris / Churchmouse / When hearts are young / One is a lonely number / Doodletown races / Midnight sleighride / Moonlight on the ganges / Foggy day, A / Rain / Thursday's child / Darn that dream.
LP: . . . . ED 2607691
MC: . . . . ED 2607694

Savage

HYPERACTIVE.
Tracks: / We got the edge / Eye for an eye / Hard on your heels / Blind hunger / Gonna tear ya heart out / Runnin' scared / Stevie's vengeance / Cardiac / All set to sing / Keep it on ice / She don't need you.
LP: . . . . ZEB 4
MC: . . . . CZEB 4

LOOSE 'N' LETHAL.
LP: . . . . EBON 12

Savage, Edna

SENTIMENTAL JOURNEY, A (See under Holliday, Michael) (Savage, Edna & Michael Holiday).

Savage Interlude (bk)

SAVAGE INTERLUDE (Carole Mortimer) (Boyd, Carole (nar)).
MC: . . . . PMB 003

Savage, Johnny

JOHNNY SAVAGE ALBUM, THE.
Tracks: / Love is in the air / If / Sometimes when we touch / I (who have nothing) / Bridge over troubled water / So deep is the night / Love me tonight / Till / Love on the rocks / Rhondda, The / Help me make it through the night / My way.
LP: . . . . LOCO 1014

Savage Pencil

ANGEL DUST (Music for movie bikers).
LPPD: . . . . FU 3

HALLOWEEN 2 ENGRAVED (see Sonic Youth) (Savage Pencil/Sonic Youth).

Savage Progress

CELEBRATION.
LP: . . . . DIX 6

Savage Republic

CEREMONIAL.
LP: . . . . SAVE 022

CUSTOMS.
LP: . . . . SAVE 071

JAMAHIRIYA.
Tracks: / So it is written / Spice fields / Viva la rock 'n' roll / Tabula rasa / Il papa sympatico / Pios den mila yia ti lambri / Lethal musk / Lebanon 2000 / Moujahadeen / Jamahiriya.
LP: . . . . SAVE 061

LIVE IN EUROPE.
LP: . . . . SAVE 087

TRAGIC FIGURES.
Tracks: / When all else fails / Ivory Coast / Exodus / Machinery / Real men / Film noir / Attempted coup / Next to nothing / On the prowl / Zulu zulu / Flesh that walks / Tragic figures.
LP: . . . . SAVE 021
LP: . . . . SSLP 001

TREK.
MC: . . . . WEBOY 002C

TREK 86.
2LP: . . . . SAVE 042/043

TRUDGE.
MLP: . . . . BIAS 011

Savage Steel

BEGINS WITH A NIGHTMARE.
LP: . . . . NRR 17
MC: . . . . NRC 17

Savage, Tony

40 GOLDEN OLDIES.
Tracks: / I do like to be beside the seaside / Make it a party / Sing as we go / Songs of the sea / All the nice girls love a sailor / Stein song, The / Sunshine of your smile, The / Following in my father's footsteps / Somewhere my love / This is my song / Roll along covered wagon / Sunset trail, The / Old faithful / Don't fence me in / Horsey horsey / Lili Marlene / Happy days are here again / Ferry Boat Inn, The / On the crest of a wave / Keep your sunny side up / White cliffs of Dover, The / Quartermaster's song, The / Paper doll / I'll be seeing you / Red sails in the sunset / We'll meet again / Bless 'em all / And the band played on / Goodnight Irene / My bonne / Harbour lights / Always in my heart / On Donna Clara / Washing on the siegfried line, The / Goodbye Sally / Run rabbit run / Hey little hen / Kiss me goodnight Sergeant Major / Roll out the barrel / If I had my way / When they sound the last all clear / Russian rose / Now is the hour.
LP: . . . . NO. 10

GOLDEN OLDIES.
Tracks: / Roses of Picardy (Request time:) / One day at a time (Request time:) / Old rugged cross, The (Request time:) / If I can help somebody (Request time:) / Amazing grace (Reques time:) / Please release me (Request time:) / I love you because (Request time:) / Please (Request time:) / Pennies from Heaven (Request time:) / It had to be me (Request time:) / Among my souvenirs (Request time:) / Deed I do (Request time:) / Tangerine (Request time:) / Quick step (Chicago swing) (Sing-along-dance time:) / Chicago (Sing-along-dance time:) / Five foot two eyes of blue (Sing-along-dance time:) / When the red, red robin comes bob, bob, bobbin' along (Sing-along-dance time:) / I've got sixpence (Sing-along-dance time:) / Foxtrot (break away blues) (Sing-along-dance time:) / All of me (Sing-along-dance time:) / I don't want to set the world on fire (Sing-along-dance time:) / You need hands (Sing-along-dance time:) / Paper roses (Rhumba (Royal). Sing-along-dance time:) / Amapola (Sing-along-dance time:) / Arrivederci (Sing-along-dance time:) / And I love you so (Sing-along-dance time:) / Spanish eyes (Novelty dance. Sing-along-dance time:) / Birdie song, The (Last waltz (modern waltz). Sing-along-dance time:) / Edelweiss (Sing-along-dance time:) / Charmaine (Sing-along-dance time:) / Wonderful world of the young (Sing-along-dance time:) / Who's taking you home tonight (Sing-along-dance time:).
LP: NO.5

GOOD OLD SONGS IN DANCETIME, THE.
Tracks: / If your face wants to laugh well let it (Quickstep (Mayfair)) / Gilbert and Filbert (Quickstep (Mayfair)) / Has anybody here seen Kelly? (Quickstep (Mayfair)) / Coal black Mammy of mine (Quickstep (Mayfair)) / I've got rings on my fingers (Quickstep (Mayfair)) / Broadway melody (Quickstep (Mayfair)) / Alice blue gown (Modern waltz) / If those lips could only speak (Modern waltz) / Sally (Modern waltz) / If I had my life to live over (Modern waltz) / La cumparsita (Square tango) / At the balalaika (Square tango) / She was one of the early birds (Old Tyme waltz (Lilac)) / Bird in a gilded cage (Old Tyme waltz (Lilac)) / Cruising down the river (Old Tyme waltz (Lilac)) / Eton boating song (Old Tyme waltz (Lilac)) / Harry Lime theme (Harry Lime foxtrot) / You were meant for me (Harry Lime foxtrot) / Here we are, here we are (Military two step) / Fall and follow me (Military two step) / Man who broke the bank at Monte Carlo (Military two step) / Let's all go down the Strand (Military two step) / Take me back to dear old blighty (Military two step) / Till the boys come home (Military two step) / Pack up your troubles in your old kit bag (Military two step) / Goodbye-ee (Military two step) / Anniversary waltz (Anniversary waltz selection) / My old dutch (Anniversary waltz selection) / In apple blossom time (Anniversary waltz selection) / Memories (Anniversary waltz selection) / You belong to my heart (Rhumba Royal) / How wonderful to know (Rhumba Royal) / I can't begin to tell you (Rhumba Royal) / Green eyes (Rhumba Royal) / Underneath the arches (Breakaway blues) / Home town (Breakaway blues) / Maybe it's because I'm a Londoner (Breakaway blues) / Show me the way to go home (Breakaway blues) / Lambeth walk (Breakaway blues) / If you were the only girl in the world (Old Tyme twist) / Broken doll (Old Tyme twist) / Let's have another one (Old Tyme twist).
LP: NO.9

KEEP YOUR SUNNY SIDE UP.
LP: NO.11

MORE SING-ALONG-DANCE TIME.
Tracks: / I wanna say hello (Mayfair) / Whispering (Mayfair) / Is it true what they say about Dixie? (Mayfair) / Give my regards to Broadway (Mayfair) / Lonesome and sorry (Mayfair) / Ain't she sweet (Mayfair) / Are you lonesome tonight (Modern waltz) / When I grow too old to dream (Modern waltz) / Ramona (Modern waltz) / Till we meet again (Modern waltz) / In a shady nook (Foxtrot (Breakaway blues)) / Glory of love (Foxtrot (Breakaway blues)) / Rockabye your baby with a Dixie melody (Foxtrot (Breakaway blues)) / Happy days and lonely days (Foxtrot (Breakaway blues)) / I can't give you anything but love baby (Foxtrot (Breakaway blues)) / Happy days and lonely nights (Foxtrot (Breakaway blues)) / Red sails in the sunset (Cha cha cha) / South of the border (Cha cha cha) / Somebody stole my gal (Quickstep) / Who's sorry now (Quickstep) / Blue skies (Quickstep) / When you're smiling (Quickstep) / She's a lassie from Lancashire (Lilac waltz) / Meet me tonight in dreamland (Lilac waltz) / Two little girls in blue (Lilac waltz) / By the side of the Zuyder Zee (Lilac waltz) / Joshu-ah (Lilac waltz) / Marie Elena (Rhumba (Royal)) / Strangers in the night (Rhumba (Royal)) / Something stupid (Rhumba (Royal)) / Marta (Rhumba (Royal)) / Cock o' the north (Gay Gordon's) / Wi' a hundred pipers (Gay Gordon's) / Annie Laurie (Gay Gordon's) / Loch Lomond (Gay Gordon's) / Bluebells of Scotland (Gay Gordon's).
LP: NO.4

SING-ALONG-DANCE TIME.
Tracks: / California here I come (Quickstep Medley (Mayfair)) / Who were you with last night (Quickstep Medley (Mayfair)) / Who's sorry now (Quickstep Medley (Mayfair)) / Four leaf clover (Quickstep Medley (Mayfair)) / Maggie (Quickstep Medley (Mayfair)) / Wait till the sun shines Nellie (Quickstep Medley (Mayfair)) / I wonder who's kissing her now (Modern Waltz Medley) / It's a sin to tell a lie (Modern Waltz Medley) / Let the rest of the world go by (Modern Waltz Medley) / Hello hello who's your lady friend (Barn Dance Medley) / Pack up your troubles in your old kit bag (Barn Dance Medley) / Just like the ivy (Barn Dance Medley) / Daddy wouldn't buy me a bow-wow (Barn Dance Medley) / I'm Henry the eighth I am (Barn Dance Medley) / Lily of Laguna (Barn Dance Medley) / I do like to be beside the seaside (Barn Dance Medley) / St. Bernards waltz (St Bernards waltz medley) / I belong to Glasgow (St Bernards waltz medley) / Two lovely black eyes (St Bernards waltz medley) / Meet me tonight in dreamland (St Bernards waltz medley) / Down at the old Bull and Bush (St Bernards waltz medley) / Let's twist again (Twist medley) / I love a lassie (Twist medley) / My old man said follow the van (Twist medley) / When the saints go marching in (Twist medley) / Tea for two cha cha / Wheels cha cha cha (Cha cha cha medley) / On the sunny side of the street (Slow foxtrot medley (Break away blues)) / Me and my shadow (Slow foxtrot medley (Break away blues)) / Moonlight and roses (Slow foxtrot medley (Break away blues)) / Come back to Erin (Pride of Erin waltz medley) / My wild Irish rose (Pride of Erin waltz medley) / After the ball (Pride of Erin waltz medley) / Daisy bell (Pride of Erin waltz medley) / She was one of the early birds (Pride of Erin waltz medley) / Jealousy (Square tango medley) / Isle of Capri (Square tango medley) / Heart of my heart (The Slosh Novelty Dance medley) / Bye bye blackbird (The Slosh Novelty Dance medley) / Carolina in the morning (The Slosh Novelty Dance medley) / You made me love you (The Slosh Novelty Dance medley) / For me and my gal (The Slosh Novelty Dance medley) / We'll meet again (The Slosh Novelty Dance medley).
LP: NO.3

TONY AND HIS SON DOMINIC PLAY THE ORGAN.
Tracks: / Here we are again (Request time:) / I do like to be beside the seaside (Request time:) / Spanish eyes (Request time:) / Edelweiss (Request time:) / Blaydon races (Request time:) / Whispering grass (Request time:) / I love you because (Request time:) / Amazing grace (Request time:) / Keep right on to the end of the road / Aniversary waltz (Request time:) / Men of Harlech (Request time:) / We'll keep a welcome (Request time:) / Tie a yellow ribbon (Request time:) / Viva Espana (Request time:) / 12th Street rag (Request time:) / When the saints go marching in (Request time:) / We'll meet again (Request time:) / Merry widow waltz (Dance time: Valeta Medley) / Little Annie Rooney (Dance time: Valeta Medley) / In the shade of the old apple tree (Dance time: Valeta Medley) / Give me a little cosy corner (Barn dance medley) / Roaming in the gloaming (Barn dance medley) / I wouldn't leave my little wooden hut (Barn dance medley) / Happy wanderer, The (Barn dance medley) / Honeysuckle and the bee, The (Barn dance medley) / Soldiers of the queen (Barn dance medley) / Softly softly (Modern waltz medley) / Don't bring Lulu (Quick step medley) / Ma he's making eyes at me (Quick step medley) / I want a girl just like the girl who married dear old dad (Quick step medley) / When you're smiling (Quick step medley) / St. Bernard's medley (St Bernard's waltz medley) / Oh oh Antonio (St Bernard's waltz medley) / In the good old summertime (St Bernard's waltz medley) / I'll be your sweetheart (St Bernard's waltz medley) / Side by side (Slow foxtrot medley) / On a slow boat to China (Slow foxtrot medley) / Strollin' (Slow foxtrot medley) / Farmer's wife, The (Traditional medley) / Kaiser Bill's batman (Traditional medley).
LP: NO.1

Savalas, Telly

TELLY.
LP: . . . . MCF 2699

Savannah Jazzband

WITH TRADITIONAL STYLE (Savannah Jazzband/Mary Asquith).
LP: . . . . TSR 029

Savatage

DUNGEONS ARE CALLING, THE.
LP: . . . . MFN 42

FIGHT FOR THE ROCK.
Tracks: / Fight for the rock / Out on the streets / Crying for love / Day after day / Edge of midnight, The / Hyde / Lady in disguise / She's only rock 'n' roll / Wishing well / Red light paradise.
LP: 781 634-1
MC: 781 634-4

GUTTER BALLET.
Tracks: / Of rage and war / Temptation revelation / Silk and steel / Hounds / Mentally yours / Gutter ballet / When the crowds are gone / She's in love / Unholy, The / Summer's rain.
LP: . . . . K 782 008 1
MC: . . . . K 782 008 4

HALL OF THE MOUNTAIN KING.
Tracks: / 24 hours ago / Beyond the doors of dark / Legion / Strange wings / Prelude to madness / Hall of the mountain king / Price you pay, The / White witch / Last down, The / Devastation.
LP: . . . . K 781 775 1
MC: . . . . K 781 775 4

POWER OF THE NIGHT.
Tracks: / Power of the night / Unusual / Warriors / Necrophilia / Washed out / Hard for love / Fountain of youth / Skull session / Stuck on you / In the dream.
LP: 781 247-1

SIRENS.
Tracks: / Sirens / Holocaust / I believe / Rage / On the run / Twisted little sister / Living for the night / Scream murder / Out on the streets.
LP: . . . . MFN 48

Save The Children...

CHRISTMAS CAROLS AND FESTIVE SONGS (See under Christmas) (Various artists).

Savery, Finn

WAVEFORM (Savery, Finn Trio).
LP: . . . . **MLP 15641**

Savitt, Jan

FUTURISTIC SHUFFLE 1938 - 41 (Savitt, Jan & His Orchestra).
LP: . . . . **BS 7113**
MC: . . . . **BS 7113C**

IN DISCO ORDER VOLUME 1.
LP: . . . . **AJAX 113**

JAN SAVITT - 1938 VOLUME 2.
LP: . . . . **AJAX 152**

JAN SAVITT - 1938 VOLUME 3.
LP: . . . . **AJAX 162**

JAN SAVITT AND THE TOP HATTERS (Savitt, Jan & The Top Hatters).
LP: . . . . **GELP 15096**

Savoy Brown

BEST OF SAVOY BROWN.
Tracks: / Train to nowhere / Mr. Downchild / Stay with me baby / Shake 'em on down / Leavin' again / Needle and spoon / Hellbound train / Coming your way / Made up my mind / Let it rock / Highway blues.
LP: **C5-504**
LP: . . . . **TAB 39**
MC: **C5K-504**

BLUES ROOTS (Savoy Brown Blues Band).
Tracks: / Train to nowhere / Louisiana blues / I'm tired / Needle and spoon / Hard way to go / Tell mama / Hellbound train / Wang dang doodle.
LP: . . . . **ROOTS 7**

GETTING TO THE POINT (Savoy Brown Blues Band).
Tracks: / Flood in Houston / Stay with me, baby / Incredible gnome meets jaxman / Give me a penny / Downchild / Getting to the point / Big city lights / You need love.
LP: . . . . **SKL 4935**

HARDWAY TO GO, A.
LP: . . . . **PLP 6**
MC: . . . . **PMC 6**

HIGHWAY BLUES.
Tracks: / Train to nowhere / Mr. Downchild / Stay with me, baby / Shake 'em on down / Leavin' again / Needle and spoon / Hellbound train / Coming down your way / Made up my mind / Let it rock / Highway blues.
LP: . . . . **SEE 45**

LOOKING IN.
Tracks: / Gypsy / Poor girl / Money can't save your soul / Sunday night / Looking in / Take it easy / Sitting an' thinking / Leavin' again / Romanoff.
LP: . . . . **SKL 5066**

MAKE ME SWEAT.
LP: . . . . **SNTF 1001**
LP: . . . . **GNPS 2193**
MC: **GNP5 2193**

SHAKE DOWN (Savoy Brown Blues Band).
Tracks: / Ain't superstitious / Let me love you, baby / Black night / High rise / Rock me, baby / Oh pretty woman / Little girl / Dormouse rides the rails, The / It's all my fault / Shake 'em on down.
LP: . . . . **SKL 4883**

Savoy Havana Band

CHARLESTON (Savoy Havana Band/ Savoy Orpheans/Sylvians).
Tracks: / Charleston / Headin' for Louisville / Blue room / Where'd you get those eyes? / Hard hearted Hannah / Five foot two eyes of blue / Fascinating rhythm / You're in Kentucky sure as you're born / Side by side / Masculine women, feminine men / Pasadena / Dinah / Turkish towel Charleston / San Francisco / Crazy words, crazy tune / She don't wanna / Baby face / I love my chili bom-bom / Someone to watch over me / Whisper song, The.
LP: . . . . **CHD 160**
MC: . . . . **MCHD 160**

Savoy Hotel Orpheans

BODY AND SOUL (see Gibbons, Carroll) (Gibbons, Carroll & Savoy Hotel Orpheans).

STOMP OFF,LET'S GO.
Tracks: / Eccentric / Oh Eva / Hard hearted Hannah / Copenhagen / Come on over / Blue evening blues / Oh that sweet in suite 16 / Stomp off, let's go / Dinah / Static strut / Jig walk / Hop skip / I'm telling the birds / Back beats / Little brown baby / Vladivostock / Ain't that too bad? / That's my hap-hap-happiness.
LP: . . . . **HDL 111**
MC: . . . . **CHDL 111**

Savoy Jazzmen

JUBILEE.
LP: . . . . **BURL 018**

ONCE MORE FOR LUCK.
LP: . . . . **BURL 024**

SAVOY RAG.
Tracks: / Button up your overcoat / Savoy rag / Porter's love song to a chambermaid, A / Cake walkin' babies from home / Mabel / Chant / Heebie jeebies / Summertime / Buddy's habits / Black and blue / Too busy / Going home.
LP: . . . . **BURL 010**

YOU'VE GOT THE RIGHT KEY.
Tracks: / 1919 march / Papa Dip / Petite Fleur / Shout 'em Aunt Tillie / Jenny's ball / Jeep's blues / Dapper Dan / You've got the right key.
LP: . . . . **BURL 001**

Savoy, Marc

OH WHAT A NIGHT.
LP: . . . . **ARHOOLIE 5023**
MC: . . . . **C 5023**

Savoy-Doucet Cajun

LES HARIAS.
LP: . . . . **ARHOOLIE 5029**
MC: . . . . **C 5029**

WITH SPIRITS.
LP: . . . . **ARHOOLIE 5037**
MC: . . . . **C 5037**

Saw Doctors

IF THIS IS ROCK AND ROLL....
MC: . . . . **ROCC 7**
LP: . . . . **ROCK 7**

Saw Throat

INDESTROY.
LP: . . . . **ACHE 19**

Saw Thunder

MANOEUVRES.
LP: . . . . **BULB 5**

Sax, Rias

LAST DANCE (Sax, Rias & Brass Section/Christian Pittius).
LP: . . . . **ISST 194**

Sax Shop

MANUEL LANDY.
LP: . . . . **ISST 143**

Saxon

ANTHOLOGY: SAXON.
Tracks: / Rockin' again / Rock 'n' roll gypsy / Stallions of the highway / Battle cry / Party 'til you puke / Backs to the wall / Sixth form girls / Heavy metal thunder / Midnight rider / Out of control / Power and the glory / Warrior / Just let me rock / Rock city / Machine gun / Freeway mad / Wheels of steel / Midas touch / Suzie hold up / Still fit to boogie.
2LP: . . . . **RAWLP 038**
MC: . . . . **RAWTC 038**

BACK ON THE STREETS.
Tracks: / Power and the glory / Backs to the wall / Watching the sky / Midnight rider / Never surrender / Princess of the night / Motorcycle man / 747 (Strangers in the night) / Wheels of steel / Nightmare / Back on the streets / Rock 'n' roll gypsy / Broken heroes / Devil rides out / Party 'til you puke / Rock the nations / Waiting for the night / Ride like the wind / I can't wait anymore / We are the strong.
2LP: . . . . **VSOPLP 147**
MC: . . . . **VSOPMC 147**

BEST OF SAXON.
Tracks: / Eagle has landed, The / Ride like the wind / Crusader / Rainbow theme/Frozen rainbow / Midas touch / Denim and leather / Broken heroes / Dallas 1 p.m. / 747 (strangers in the night) (live) / Princess of the night (live) / And the band played on (CD only.) / Never surrender (CD only.) / This town rocks (CD only.) / Strong arm of the law (live) (CD only.) / Heavy metal thunder (live) (CD only.).
LP: . . . . **EMS 1390**
MC: . . . . **TCEMS 1390**

BIG TEASER.
Tracks: / Big teaser.
LP: . . . . **CAL 200**
MC: . . . . **CAC 200**
LP: . . . . **ATAK 59**
MC: . . . . **TCATAK 59**

CRUSADER.
Tracks: / Crusader prelude, The / Crusader / Little bit of what you fancy, A / Sailing to America / Set me free / Just let me rock / Bad boys (like to rock 'n' roll) / Do it all for you / Rock city / Run for your lives.
LP: . . . . **EMS 1168**
MC: . . . . **TCEMS 1168**
LP: . . . . **ATAK 76**
MC: . . . . **TCATAK 76**

DENIM AND LEATHER.
Tracks: / Princess of the night / Never surrender / Out of control / Rough and ready / Play it loud / And the bands played on / Midnight rider / Fire in the sky / Denim and leather.
LP: . . . . **FA 3175**
MC: . . . . **TCFA 3175**
LP: . . . . **CAL 128**
LP: . . . . **EMS 1163**

DESTINY.
Tracks: / Ride like the wind / Where the lightning strikes / I can't wait anymore / Calm before the storm / S.O.S. / Song for Emma / For whom the bell tolls / We are strong / Jericho siren / Red alert.
LP: . . . . **EMC 3543**
MC: . . . . **TCEMC 3543**

EAGLE HAS LANDED, THE.
Tracks: / 747 (Strangers in the night) / Princess of the night / Strong arm of the law / Heavy metal thunder / 20,000 ft / Wheels of steel / Never surrender / Fire in the sky / Machine gun / Rock the nations / Motorcycle man.
LP: . . . . **EMS 1166**
MC: . . . . **TCEMS 1166**
LP: . . . . **ATAK 74**
MC: . . . . **TCATAK 74**
LP: . . . . **CAL 137**

FLIPHITS (4 TRACK CASSETTE EP).
Tracks: / 47 (Strangers in the night) / And the bands played on / Never surrender / Princess of the night.
MC: . . . . **RCXK 013**

GREATEST HITS LIVE: SAXON.
Tracks: / Opening theme / Heavy metal thunder / Rock & roll gypsy / And the bands played on / Twenty thousand feet / Ride like the wind / Motor cycle man / 747 (Strangers in the night) / See the light shinin' / Frozen rainbow / Princess of the night / Wheels of steel / Denim & leather / Crusader / Rockin' again / Back on the streets again.
2LP: . . . . **ESDLP 132**
MCSET: . . . . **ESDMC 132**

INNOCENCE IS NO EXCUSE.
Tracks: / Rockin' again / Call of the wild / Back on the streets / Devil rides out / Rock 'n' roll gypsy / Broken heroes / Gonna shout / Everybody up / Raise some hell / Give it everything you've got.
LP: . . . . **SAXON 2**
MC: . . . . **TCSAXON 2**
LPPD: . . . . **SAXONP 2**

MUSIC AND MEDIA INTERVIEW PICTURE DISC.
LPPD: . . . . **MM 1243**

POWER AND THE GLORY.
Tracks: / Power and the glory / Redline / Warrior / Nightmare / This town rocks / Watching the sky / Midas touch / Eagle has landed, The.
LP: . . . . **EMS 1167**
MC: . . . . **TCEMS 1167**
LP: . . . . **CAL 147**
MC: . . . . **CAC 147**
LP: . . . . **ATAK 75**
MC: . . . . **TCATAK 75**

ROCK 'N' ROLL GYPSIES.
Tracks: / Power and the glory / And the bands played on / Rock the nations / Dallas, 1 p.m. / Broken heroes / Battle cry / Rock'n'roll gypsies / Northern lady / I can't wait anymore / This town rocks / Eagle has landed, The (Only on CD.) / Just let me rock (Only on CD.).
LP: . . . . **RR 94161**
MC: . . . . **RR 94164**
LP: . . . . **ENVLP 535**
MC: . . . . **TCENV 535**

ROCK THE NATIONS.
Tracks: / Rock the nations / Battle cry / Waiting for the night / We came here to rock / You ain't no angel / Running hot / Party 'til you puke / Empty promises / Motorcycle man / Northern lady.
LP: . . . . **EMC 3515**
MC: . . . . **TCEMC 3515**
LP: . . . . **ATAK 128**
MC: . . . . **TCATAK 128**

SAXON.
Tracks: / Rainbow theme / Frozen rainbow / Big teaser / Judgement day / Stallions of the highway / Backs to the wall / Still fit to boogie / Millie Guard.
LP: . . . . **ATAK 57**
MC: . . . . **TCATAK 57**
LP: . . . . **EMS 1161**
MC: . . . . **TCEMS 1161**
LP: . . . . **CAL 110**

SOLID BALL OF ROCK, A.
LP: . . . . **LPVIR 4**
MC: . . . . **MCVIR 4**

STRONG ARM METAL.
LP: . . . . **CAL 212**
MC: . . . . **CAC 212**
LP: . . . . **ATAK 58**
MC: . . . . **TCTAK 58**

STRONG ARM OF THE LAW.
Tracks: / Heavy metal thunder / To hell and back again / Strong arm of the law / Taking your chances / 20,000 Ft. / Hungry years / Sixth form girls / Dallas 1 p.m..
LP: . . . . **FA 3176**
MC: . . . . **TCFA 3176**
LP: . . . . **CAL 120**
LP: . . . . **EMS 1162**

WHEELS OF STEEL.
Tracks: / Motorcycle man / Stand up and be counted / 747 (strangers in the night) / Freeway mad / See the light shining / Fighting gang / Suzi hold on / Machine gun / Wheels of steel.
LP: . . . . **FA 41 3143 1**
MC: . . . . **FA 41 3143 4**
LP: . . . . **CAL 115**

Saxon, Sky

FIRE WALL.
LP: . . . . **ROSE 93**

FULL SPOON OF SEEDY BLUES, A (Saxon, Sky Blues Band).
LP: . . . . **SMB 152**

IN SEARCH OF BRIGHTER COLORS (Saxon, Sky & Fire Wall).
Tracks: / I hear the mountains crash / Lightning lightning / Put something sweet between your lips / Barbie doll look / Big screen, The / Baby baby / Come on pretty girl / Kick kick / Paisley rocker / Come a here right now.
LP: . . . . **ROSE 155**

MASTERS OF PYSCHEDELIA.
LP: . . . . **ROSE 36**

TAKES ON GLORY (Saxon, Sky 'Sunlight').
LP: **400 291**

Saxophone

SAXOPHONE (See under Jazz) (Various artists).

Say It With Music

SAY IT WITH MUSIC (1923-1933) (Various artists).
2LP: . . . . **MES 7084/5**

Sayama, Masahiro

PLAY ME A LITTLE MUSIC.
MC: . . . . **JC 3305**

Sayer, Cynthia

CYNTHIA SAYER'S BANJO.
Tracks: / Doin' the new low down / When I leave the world behind / Swing 42 / Georgia rainbow / Give me liberty or give me love / Chinatown my chinatown / Pastime rag no.4 / Once in a while / What'll I do / Blues my naughty sweetie gives to me / Oh baby don't say no / Digga digga doo.
LP: . . . . **J 008**

JAZZ BANJO (see also under Wellstood, Dick) (Sayer, Cynthia / Dick Wellstood).
MC: . . . . **J MC 010**

Sayer, Eddy

WATERGLASS (See under Tassano, Simon) (Sayer, Eddy & Simon Tassano).

Sayer, Leo

ANOTHER YEAR.
LP: . . . . **CHR 1087**

COLLECTION: LEO SAYER.
MC: . . . . **CCSMC 295**

COOL TOUCH (ALBUM).
Tracks: / Cool touch / Rely on me / Young and in love / Paper back town / Going home / My favourite / I can't stop / Heaven knows / Agents of the heart / Suki's missing.
LP: . . . . **EMC 3578**
MC: . . . . **TCEMC 3578**

ENDLESS FLIGHT.
LP: . . . . **CHR 1125**

FANTASY.
MCSET: . . . . **ZCDP 106**

HAVE YOU EVER BEEN IN LOVE.
Tracks: / Till you come back to me / Sea of heartbreak / More than I can say / Darlin / Don't wait until tomorrow / How beautiful you are / Orchard road / Aviation / Heart (Stop beating in time) / Your love still brings me to my knees / Have you ever been in love / Wounded heart / Love games / Never has a dream come true.
LP: . . . . **LEO TV 1**
MC: . . . . **ZCLEQ 1**

HERE.
Tracks: / World has changed, The / When the money runs out / End, The / Lost control / Englishman in the USA, An / Who will the next fool be? / Work / Oh girl / Ghosts / Takin' the easy way out.
LP: . . . . **CDL 1240**
MC: . . . . **ZCDL 1240**

JUST A BOY.
Tracks: / Telepathy / Train / Bells of St. Mary's / One man band / In my life /

When I came home this morning / Long tall glasses / Another time / Solo / Giving it all away.
LP: . . . . **CHR 1068**
MC: . . . . **ZCHR 1068**

LEO.
Tracks: / One man band / More than I can say / Show must go on / When I need you / Long tall glasses / Why is everybody going home? / Moonlighting / I can't stop loving you / You make me feel like dancing / Giving it all away / Let it be / Oh wot a life.
LP: . . . . **MFP 41 5663 1**
MC: . . . . **MFP 41 5663 4**

LEO SAYER.
Tracks: / Show must go on / Bells of St. Mary's / Only dreaming / Silver bird / On the old dirt road / Moonlighting / Giving it all away / Bedsitter land / Another year / Oh what a life / One man band / Why is everybody going home? / Long tall glasses / Train / I will not stop fighting / Streets of your town / Last gig of Johnny B. Goode / Unlucky in love / When I came home this morning / Innocent bystanders / Dancer / Don't say it's over / Telepathy / Drop back.
2LP: . . . . **SSD 8030**
MCSET: . . . . **SSDC 8030**

LEO SAYER (CHRYSALIS).
LP: . . . . **CDL 1198**
MC: . . . . **ZCDL 1198**

LIVING IN A FANTASY.
Tracks: / Time ran out on you / Where did we go wrong / You win - I lose / More than I can say / Millionaire / Once in a while / Living in a fantasy / She's not coming back / Let me know / Only foolin'.
LP: . . . . **CDL 1297**
MC: . . . . **ZCDL 1297**

SHOW MUST GO ON, THE.
Tracks: / Moonlighting / Giving it all away / One man band / Silver bird / Show must go on, The / Another year / On the old dirt road / Oh what a life / Only dreaming / Bells of St. Mary's / Why is everybody going home / Bedsitter land.
LP: . . . . **SHM 3035**
MC: . . . . **HSC 3035**

SILVERBIRD.
Tracks: / Innocent bystanders / Goodnight old friend / Drop back / Silver bird / Show must go on / Dancer / Tomorrow / Don't say it's over / Slow motion / Oh wot a life / Why is everybody going home?.
LP: . . . . **CHR 1050**

THUNDER IN MY HEART.
Tracks: / Thunder in my heart / Easy to love / Leave well enough alone / I want you back / It's over / Fool for your love / There isn't anything / World keeps on turning / Everything I've got / We can start all over again.
LP: . . . . **CDL 1154**
MC: . . . . **ZCDL 1154**

VERY BEST OF LEO SAYER.
Tracks: / You make me feel like dancing / Raining in my heart / How much love / Dancing the night away / Thunder in my heart / I can't stop loving you / One man band / Giving it all away / Train / Let it be / Long tall glasses / Moonlighting / Show must go on / When I need you.
LP: . . . . **CDL 1222**
MC: . . . . **ZCDL 1222**

WHEN I NEED YOU (ALBUM).
Tracks: / You make me feel like dancing / Hold on to my love / I hear the laughter / Thunder in my heart / Magdalena / No business like love business / When I need you / Reflections / How much love? / Raining in my heart / I think we fell in love too fast / Endless flight.
LP: . . . . **SHM 3118**
MC: . . . . **HSC 3118**

WORLD RADIO.
Tracks: / Heart (stop beating in time) / Paris dies in the morning / Have you ever been in love / Rumours / Heroes / Till you let your heart win / End of the game, The / Wondering where the lions are / We've got ourselves in love / World radio.
LP: . . . . **CDL 1345**
MC: . . . . **ZCDL 1345**

Sayer, Lyell

TWO-UP (Sayer, Lyell & Clem Parkinson).
LP: . . . . **LRF 109**

VICTORIA STREET.
LP: . . . . **LRF 146**

Sayers, Dorothy L.

MURDER MUST ADVERTISE (Carmichael, Ian).
MCSET: . . . . **ZBBC 1124**

NINE TAILORS, THE (Various artists).
MCSET: . . . . **ZBBC 1056**

Sayers, Pete

CY-CLONE.
LP: . . . . **DBWLP 1006**

WATERMELON SUMMER.
Tracks: / Watermelon summer / Raining in my heart / Dark hollow / Rawhide / Through the bottom of the glass / Turn your radio on / Fire on the mountain / Doin' my time / Chariots of fire / All I have to do is dream / Total stranger / Ukelele lady / Radio voices.
LP: . . . . **XTRA 1168**

Sayle, Alexei

CAK.
LP: . . . . **CAK 1**
MC: . . . . **ZCAK 1**

FISH PEOPLE TAPES,THE.
Tracks: / Metro at the disco / It ain't hard to be an animal / Twenty Tom Waits and a box of swans / That's a Milton Springsteen / Song of the revolutionary stool pigeon / Ullo John got a new motor.
MC: . . . . **IMC 9**

PANIC.
Tracks: / Meanwhile / Panic / Story of little Woo / Play that funky music Jewish boy / Romford bypass / Didn't you kill my brother / Further story of little Woo / Word association / Further story of little Woo / Do dis do dat / Gospel.
LP: . . . . **CBS 26767**
MC: **40 26767**

Saylor, David

AIN'T NO STOPPING US NOW (See Starr, Edwin) (Saylor, David & Edwin Starr).

Sayonara

SAYONARA Film soundtrack (Various artists).
LP: . . . . **ERS 6513**

Scab Cadillac

TAGGED AND NUMBERED.
Tracks: / Now the party's starting / Explain this / Fool for Wall Street / In the mind / Stupid flu / Home of the what / Driver / Down in the shit / Gaza stripteaze / Crigine II / Fashion fall out.
LP: . . . . **RAVE 004**

Scabs

ROCKERY.
LP: . . . . **SMASH 001**

ROYALTY IN EXILE.
Tracks: / Crime wave / Little lady / You don't need a woman / Hard times / Lucky star / Come on / Live it up / Barkeep / I need you / Time / Medicine man.
LP: . . . . **BIAS 160**

SKINTIGHT.
LP: . . . . **BIAS 102**

Scaffold

SINGLES A'S & B'S.
Tracks: / 2 day's Monday / Goodbat nightman / Thank u very much / Do you remember / 1 2 3 / Lily the pink / Charity bubbles / Gin gan goolie / Liver birds / Bus dreams / Liverpool Lou / Blind jellyfish / Ide B. the first / Carry on krow / Today / Buttons of your mind / Goose / All the way up / Please sorry / Ten years after on / Commercial break / Do the Albert / 3 blind jellyfish / Strawberry jam.
LP: . . . . **CM 114**

Scaggs, Boz

BOZ SCAGGS.
Tracks: / I'm easy / I'll be long gone / Another day (another letter) / Now you're gone / Finding her / Look what I've got / Waiting for a train / Loan me a dime / Sweet release.
LP: . . . . **K 40419**

BOZ SCAGGS AND BAND.
Tracks: / Monkey time / Runnin' blue / Up to you / Love anyway / Flames of love / Here to stay / Nothing will take your place / Why why why / You're so good.
LP: . . . . **CBS 31848**
MC: **40 31848**

DOWN TWO THEN LEFT.
Tracks: / Still falling for you / Hard times / Clue, A / Whatcha gonna tell your man / We're waiting / Hollywood / Then she walked away / Gimme the goods / 1993 / Tomorrow never came / Tomorrow never came(reprise).
LP: . . . . **CBS 86028**
MC: **40 86028**

HITS.
Tracks: / Lowdown / You make it so hard (to say no) / Miss Sun / Lido shuffle / We're all alone / Breakdown dead ahead / Look what you've done to me / What can I say / Dinah Flo / You can have me anytime.
LP: . . . . **CBS 84706**
MC: **40 84706**

MIDDLE MAN.
Tracks: / You can have me anytime / Breakdown dead ahead / Jojo / Simone / Middleman / Do like you do in New York / Angel you / Isn't it time / You got some imagination.
LP: . . . . **CBS 86094**
MC: **40 86094**

OTHER ROADS.
Tracks: / What's number one / Claudia / Heart of mine / Right out of my head / I don't hear you / Mental shakedown / Crimes of passion / Funny / Cool running / Night of Van Gough, The.
LP: **4611121**
MC: **4611124**

SILK DEGREES.
Tracks: / What can I say / Georgia / Jump street / What do you want the girl to do? / Harbour lights / Lowdown / It's over / Love me tomorrow / Lido shuffle / We're all alone.
LP: . . . . **CBS 81193**
LP: **32036**

SLOW DANCER.
Tracks: / Slow dancer / Angel lady come just in time / There is someone / Hercules / Pain of love / Sail on / White moon / Let it happen / I got your number / Take it for granted.
LP: . . . . **CBS 32072**
MC: **40 32072**

Scala, Primo

PRIMO SCALA & HIS ACCORDION BAND (Scala, Primo & His Accordion Band).
Tracks: / May I / Goodnight lovely little lady / Love thy neighbour / When the poppies bloom again / Shoe shine boy / Home town / It looks like rain in Cherry Blossom Lane / For all that I care / Lullaby of the Volga / I want to hear those old time melodies again / Yours / You and I / There's a home in Wyomin' / Heaven in the pines / Isle of Capri / Donkey serenade, The / One night in Napoli / You don't have to tell me / Side by side / Wheel of the wagon is broken, The / At the close of a long long day.
LP: . . . . **RFL 6**

SHOE SHINE BOY (Scala, Primo & His Accordion Band).
Tracks: / Shoe shine boy / Let us be sweethearts over again / I dream of San Marino / Dinner for one please, James / Poor little Angeline / When did you leave Heaven? / Little old lady / It looks like rain in Cherry Blossom Lane / Lady of Madrid / On Treasure Island / Oh they're tough, mighty tough, in the west / It's the talk of the town / Goodnight to you all.
LP: . . . . **JOYD 295**

STRIKE UP THE BAND (Scala, Primo & His Accordion Band).
Tracks: / Strike up the band / I won't tell a soul / Love walked in / September in the rain / Girl in the Alice blue gown / I'll never make the same mistake again / Learn to croon / Moon song / Oh Joanna / I cover the waterfront / Boo-hoo / Where are you? / When shall we meet again? / Lady of Madrid / Jeepers creepers / I have eyes / Home at sundown / When my dream boat comes home / Beer barrel polka.
LP: . . . . **RFL 33**

Scales, Arthur

ARTHUR SCALES.
LP: . . . . **IAM R 3800**
MC: . . . . **IAM C 3800**

Scales, Prunella (nar)

AFTER HENRY (See under After Henry) (Various artists).

CANTERBURY TALES, THE (see under Chaucer, Geoffrey (aut)) (Scales, Prunella (nar) & Martin Starkie (nar)).

COLD COMFORT FARM (see under Cold Comfort Farm (bk)).

EMMA (See under Austen, Jane).

MAPP AND LUCIA (see under Mapp and Lucia (bk)).

PERSUASION (See under Austen, Jane).

WIFE OF BATH'S TALE (see under Chaucer, Geoffrey (aut)) (Scales, Prunella (nar) & Richard Bebb (nar)).

Scalphunters

SCALPHUNTERS, THE (Film Soundtrack) (Various artists).
LP: . . . . **MCA 25042**
MC: . . . . **MCAC 25042**

SCALPHUNTERS/HANG 'EM HIGH/ THE WAY WEST (Various artists).
Tracks: / Scalphunters - prologue: *Various artists* / Square dance for loco horses: *Various artists* / Scalphunters theme: *Various artists* / Forced march: *Various artists* / Moving on: *Various artists* / Hang 'em high: *Various artists* / Rachel (love theme): *Various artists* / Tumbleweed wagon: *Various artists* / I'll get 'em myself: *Various artists* / Rachel (love theme): *Various artists* / It's no deal: *Various artists*/ Hang 'em high: *Various artists* / Way west, The: *Serendipity Singers* / Way west, The - overture (main title): *Various artists* / Lige celebrates: *Various artists* / We're crossing first: *Various artists* / Flowers for Mr. Mack: *Various artists* / Water and Billy's death: *Various artists* / Mercy McBee: *Serendipity Singers*/ Buffaloes and indians: *Various artists* / Becky's theme: *Various artists* / One to Crystal city - Tadlock's end: *Various artists* / Reluctant mercy: *Various artists* / Way west, The - finale: *Various artists*.
LP: . . . . **LPMGM 27**
LP: **794 946 1**
MC: . . . . **TCMGM 27**
MC: **794 946 4**

Scam

SCAM.
LP: . . . . **ROCK 5**

Scan Tester

I NEVER PLAYED TO MANY POSH DANCES.
2LP: **2/12T455/6**

Scandal

WARRIOR.
Tracks: / Warrior / Beat of a heart / Hands tied / Less than half / Only the young / All i want / Talk to me / Say what you will / Tonight / Maybe we went to far.
LP: . . . . **CBS 25860**

Scandalous John

SCANDALOUS JOHN (Film Soundtrack) (Various artists).
Tracks: / Pastures green: *Various artists* / Iris and Fido: *Various artists* / Pastures green: *Various artists*/ Desert lullaby: *Various artists* / Train to Quivira: *Various artists* / Touch and go: *Various artists*/ Scandalous John: *Various artists* / Warbag: *Various artists* / McCanless country: *Various artists* / Paco the brave: *Various artists* / Amanda: *Various artists* / Maripsas D'Amora: *Various artists* / Tribes: *Various artists* / Conquistador/ Quivira/ City of gold: *Various artists* / Paco the great engineer: *Various artists* / Pastures green: *Various artists*.
LP: . . . . **BVS 5004**

Scanjazz

SCANJAZZ-VOLUME 3.
LP: . . . . **SOS 1056**

SUNSET CAFE STOMP.
LP: . . . . **SOS 1038**

Scanlon, Pat

SONGS FOR FUTURE GENERATIONS (Scanlon, Pat & Black Water String Band).
LP: . . . . **ROUNDER 4016**
MC: . . . . **ROUNDER 4016C**

Scanner

HYPERTRACE.
LP: . . . . **N 0111**
MC: . . . . **N 0111-2**
LP: . . . . **NUK 111**
MC: . . . . **ZCNUK 111**

TERMINAL EARTH.
Tracks: / Law, The / Not alone / Wonder / Buy or die / Touch the light / Terminal earth / From the dust of ages / Challenge, The.
LP: . . . . **NUK 141**
MC: . . . . **ZCNUK 141**

Scanner Darkly

THIS IS THE WAY.
Tracks: / This is the way / It's been a happy death / One more step / Take it all away / Reptiles tears, A / Burn baby burn / Cigarette in the rain / Just for today / Miriam / Blue ocean sand.
LP: . . . . **SUB 33010-14**

Scapa Flow

GUIDE, THE.
LP: **081117**

Scarface (film)

SCARFACE (Film Soundtrack) (Various artists).
LP: . . . . **MCF 3198**

Scarlatti, A

TWO CANTATAS & 'LA FOLIA' VARIATIONS (Dawson, Lynne & Purcell Quartet, The).
MC: . . . . **KA 66254**

Scarlet Fantastic

TWENTY FOUR HOURS.
Tracks: / Rhythm of resistance / No memory / Belle rose / Follow that star / Hang on (to that inspiration) / Silver bullet / Lucky seven / Stay / Film star kiss / Exterminating angel / No memory (no technology) (Extra track on CD only.) / Plug me in (Extra track on CD only.) / I blame thee not (Extra track on CD only.).
LP: **208994**
MC: **408994**

Scarlet Pimpernel (bk)

SCARLET PIMPERNEL, THE (Orczy Baroness) (Powell, Robert (nar)).
MC: . . . . **LFP 7469**

Scarlet Riviera

JOURNEY WITH AN ANGEL.
LP: . . . . **TET 8**
MC: . . . . **CTET 8**

Scarlet & The Black

SCARLET & THE BLACK, THE (Film Soundtrack) (Various artists).
LP: . . . . **C'BUS 120**

Scarlett & Black

SCARLETT & BLACK.
Tracks: / You don't know / Let yourself go-go / Dream out loud / Someday / What is love / Miracle or mirage / Yesterday's gone / Real love / If it's all the same to you / City of dreams.
LP: . . . . **V 2518**
MC: . . . . **TCV 2518**

Scarr, Geoff

CUMALOT (Bawdy Ballads Vol. 1).
LP: . . . . **BB 00 10**

Scars

AUTHOR AUTHOR.
Tracks: / Leave me in Autumn / Fear of the dark / Aquarama / David / Silver dream / Obsessions / Everywhere I go / Lady in the car with the glasses on and a gun / She's alive / Je t'aime, c'est la morte / Your attention please / All about you.
LP: . . . . **PREX 5**
MC: . . . . **PRICS 5**

Scartaglen

MIDDLE PATH, THE.
Tracks: / Siuil arun / John Doolan / Broken down squatter, The / Gander in the pratie hole / Toss the feathers / Jezaig / Cantiga / Valencia harbor / D.G. Lynch's reel / Niely Cleere's / As I walked out upon the ice / Maids of Amargh / Jolly journeyman / Castle Island / Jack broke da prison door / Stoneking / Vinland reel / Bonnie James Campbell / Miss Lillian Williams.
LP: . . . . **CIR 001**
MC: . . . . **CIR 001C**

Scary Thieves

SCARY THIEVES.
Tracks: / Inside the night / Game of love / Tell me, girl / Waiting game, The / Halloween / Live in another day / Dying in vain / Only fascination / Somebody, somewhere / Thieves of virtue.
LP: . . . . **SCARY 1**
MC: . . . . **TCSCARY 1**

Scat Opera

ABOUT TIME.
LP: . . . . **MFN 111**
MC: . . . . **TMFN 111**

Scatter, Peter

STRICTLY FOR DANCING (See under Charlton, George) (Scatter, Peter & George Charlton).

STRICTLY PETER SCATTER (Scatter, Peter & His Music).
Tracks: / On top of the world / Last thing on my mind / Sugartime / Around the corner / Story of my life / Peyton Place / Always / Tammy / Where the blue of the night / How can you buy Killarney? / Flett from flotta / Earl of Dalhousie's march / Sweet maid of Mull, The / Mobile / La mer / Your cheatin' heart / I love you because / Somewhere over the rainbow / Perfidia / Quando, quando, quando / El cumbanchero / Buona sera / Pickin' a chicken / Yellow bird.
LP: . . . . **MWM 1026**

Scatterbrain

MOUNTAINS GO RHYTHMIC.
LP: . . . . **IRMG 11**

Scattered Order

CAREER OF THE SILLY THING.
LP: . . . . **INK 17**

Scene is Now

TOTAL JIVE.
LP: . . . . **SR 0587**

Scene Of The Crime

SCENE OF THE CRIME (Various artists).
LP: . . . . **SUS 3**

Scent Of Oleander

SCENT OF OLEANDER, A (See under Lea, Constance) (Lea, Constance).

Schaechter, Lifshe

WIDMAN AZ DI FURST AVEK.
MC: . . . . **GVMMC 111**

Schaefer, Hal

EXTRAORDINARY JAZZ PIANIST, THE.
Tracks: / You are too beautiful / Yesterdays / You stepped out of a dream / I'll take romance / I can't get started / Tangerine.
LP: . . . . **DS 781**

RCA JAZZ WORKSHOP, THE.
LP: . . . . **FS 82**

Schaffer, Janne

CHINESE, THE.
Tracks: / Halkans affair / Air mattress / Mignon / Filet / Daniel sover / Harvest machine / Chinese, The / Titus / Marbles / No registration.
LP: . . . . **BUTT 006**

EARMEAL.
Tracks: / Hot days and summer nights / Happy feet / To a beautiful painter / Bromma express / Shrimp / Shrimp a la carte / It's never too late / Oriental sign / Frederick's place.
LP: . . . . **CBS 83002**

ELECTRIC GRAFFITI.
Tracks: / Berzellii Park / Ellipse / Silent running / Pipeline / Via Danielli / Dorothee's farewell / Indigo / Electric graffiti / Time.
LP: . . . . **VBRLP 27**
MC: . . . . **VBRMC 27**

TRAFFIC.
Tracks: / Emerald city / Flight 05 / Like a new born child / Cats' eyes / Rose tango / September / Traffic / Windshift / Springfire / Belongings.
LP: . . . . **HAI 108**

Schaffner, Karl

MANY LIVES AGO (Metaphysical Music).
MC: . . . . **C 307**

Schaubroeck, Armand

ARMAND SCHAUBROECK LIVE AT THE.... (Schaubroeck, Armand Steals).
2LP: . . . . **MIRROR 4**

I CAME TO VISIT, BUT DECIDED TO STAY (Schaubroeck, Armand Steals).
LP: . . . . **MIRROR 3**

I SHOT MY GUARDIAN ANGEL (Schaubroeck, Armand Steals).
LP: . . . . **MIRROR 8**

LOT OF PEOPLE WOULD LIKE TO SEE, A (Schaubroeck, Armand Steals).
LPS: . . . . **MIRROR 0**

RATF..... (Schaubroeck, Armand Steals).
LP: . . . . **MIRROR 7**

SHAKIN'SHAKIN' (Schaubroeck, Armand Steals).
LP: . . . . **MIRROR 5**

Scheer Music

RAPPIN' IT UP.
LP: . . . . **PA 8025**

Scheètz, Jeff

WOODPECKER STOMP.
MC: . . . . **RR 00014**

Scheid, Elmer

ELMER SCHEID STORY, THE (see under Elmer Scheid story) (Various artists).

Schell, Daniel & Kara

IF WINDOWS THEY HAVE.
Tracks: / Un celte / Remi sace an lacis dore / Vienna Carmen / Moustiquaries / If windows they have / Bigna zomer en ik loop altjid / Listen to short wave: Je suis dans / Tapi la nuit / Buches/logs/holz.
LP: . . . . **MTM 13**

Scheme

BLACK AND THE WHITES.
LP: . . . . **SCHEME 001**
MC: . . . . **SCHEME C001**

Schenker, Michael

ASSAULT ATTACK (Schenker, Michael Group).
Tracks: / Assault attack / Rock you to the ground / Dancer / Samurai / Desert song, The / Broken promises / Searching for a reason / Ulcer.
LP: . . . . **CHR 1393**
MC: . . . . **ZCHR 1393**

BUILT TO DESTROY (Schenker, Michael Group).
Tracks: / Rock my nights away / I'm gonna make you mine / Dogs of war / Systems failing / Captain Nemo / Still love that little devil / Red sky / Time waits for no one / Walk the stage.
LP: . . . . **CHR 1441**
MC: . . . . **ZCHR 1441**
LPPD: . . . . **CHRP 1441**

COLLECTION: M.S.G. (Schenker, Michael Group).
MC: . . . . **CCSMC 294**

MICHAEL SCHENKER GROUP (Schenker, Michael Group).
Tracks: / Armed and ready / Cry from the nations / Victim of illusion / Bijou pleasurette / Feels like a good thing / Into the arena / Looking out from nowhere / Tales of mystery / Lost horizons.
LP: **41 3105 1**
MC: **41 3105 4**
LP: . . . . **CHR 1302**
MC: . . . . **ZCHR 1302**

MSG (Schenker, Michael Group).
Tracks: / Ready to rock / Attack of the mad axeman / On and on / Let sleeping dogs lie / I want more / Never trust a stranger / Looking for love / Secondary motion.
LP: . . . . **CHR 1336**
MC: . . . . **ZCHR 1336**

ONE NIGHT AT BUDOKAN (Schenker, Michael Group).
Tracks: / Armed and ready / Cry from the nations / Attack of the mad axeman / Axeman / But I want more / Victim of illusion / Into the arena / On and on / Never trust a stranger / Let sleeping dogs lie / Courvoisier concerto / Lost horizons / Doctor doctor / Are you ready to rock?.
2LP: . . . . **CTY 1375**
MCSET: . . . . **ZCTY 1375**

PERFECT TIMING (Schenker, Michael Group).
Tracks: / Gimme your love / Here today / Don't stop me now / No time for losers / Follow the night / Get out / Love is not a game / Time / I don't wanna lose / Rock 'till you're crazy.
LP: . . . . **EMC 3539**
MC: . . . . **TCEMC 3539**

PORTFOLIO.
Tracks: / Doctor doctor / Rock bottom / Rock will never die / Armed and ready / Ready to rock / Assault attack / Ulcer / Attack of the mad axeman / I'm a loser / Reasons to love / Too hot to handle / Only you can rock me / Lights out / Arbory hill / Love drive / Searching for a reason / Rock my nights away / Captain Nemo.
LP: . . . . **CNW 1**
MC: . . . . **ZCNW 1**

ROCK WILL NEVER DIE (Schenker, Michael Group).
Tracks: / Captain Nemo / Rock my nights away / Are you ready to rock? / Attack of the mad axeman / Into the arena / Rock will never die / Desert song, The / I'm gonna make you mine / Doctor doctor.
LP: . . . . **CUX 1470**
MC: . . . . **ZCUX 1470**

SAVE YOURSELF (Schenker, Michael Group).
Tracks: / Save yourself / Bad boys / Anytime / Get down to bizness / Shadow of the night / What we need / I am your radio / There has to be another way (instrumental) / This is my heart / Destiny / Take me back (Not on album.).
LP: . . . . **EMC 3567**
MC: . . . . **TCEMC 3567**

Scherr, Louis

BEST THING FOR YOU, THE.
LP: . . . . **AP 226**

Schickert, Gunther

SAMTVOGEL.
Tracks: / Apricot brandy / Kriegsmaschinen / Fahrt zur Holle / Wald.
LP: **0040 176**

Schifrin, Lalo

ANNO DOMINI (Film soundtrack).
Tracks: / Golgatha / Valerius and Sarah / King Herod's march / Eternal land,The / Fisherman, The / Peter and Thomas trek / Roman celebration / Road to Damascus,The / New love / Gladiator school / Majesty of Rome, The / Corina and Caleb / Roman legion / Wedding procession / Nero the lover / Martyrdom / Exalted love.
LP: . . . . **REB 561**
MC: . . . . **ZCF 561**

CAT STRIKES AGAIN, THE (See under Smith, Jimmy) (Schifrin, Lalo & Jimmy Smith).

Schiller, Allan

FUR ELISE 19 popular piano pieces.
Tracks: / Fur Elise (Beethoven) / Noontide nocturne (Field) / Mazurkas op.7/1 (Chopin) / Waltz op.34/2 (Chopin) / Fantaisie-inpromptu op.66 (Chopin) / Venetian gondola song op.19 (Mendelssohn) (Song without words) / Bees' wedding, The (Song without words) / Consolation No.3 / Music box, The (de Severac) / Clair de lune / Arabesque No.2 / Girl with the flaxen hair, The / Wedding day at Troldhaugen (Grieg) / March of the dwarfs / Granada / Tango (Albeniz) / Asturias.
MC: . . . . **ZC QS 6032**

Schipa, Tito

TITO SCHIPA.
LP: . . . . **GVC 505**
MC: . . . . **GK 87969**

TITO SCHIPA (VICTOR) (Mozart, Massenet, Handel).
MC: . . . . **GK 87969**

Schizophrenia

SCHIZOPHRENIA - A VIEWPOINT (Laing, R.D.).
MC: . . . . **PT 34**

Schlager, Een

EEN SCHLAGER GAT OP STAP 1934-9.
LP: . . . . **H 2010**

Schlager Parade

SCHLAGER PARADE (Various artists).
LP: **022-58233**
MC: **222-58233**

Schlippenbach,

PAYAN (Schlippenbach, Alexander Von).
LP: . . . . **ENJA 2012**

Schloss, Cynthia

COUNTRY REGGAE.
LP: . . . . **SLP 003**

NOT AS HAPPY (See under McGregor, Freddie) (Schloss, Cynthia & Freddie McGregor).

REGGAE EXPERIENCE, A.
LP: . . . . **WKSLP 010**
MC: . . . . **WKSC 010**
LP: . . . . **CRLP 2**

Schmeltztiegel

ALLE MEINE LEIBETAGE.
LP: . . . . **EULP 1020**

FOLKLORE FROM THE OSTSEE.
LP: . . . . **EULP 1008**

Schmidt, Claudia

CLAUDIA SCHMIDT.
LP: . . . . **FF 066**

MIDWESTERN HEART.
LP: . . . . **FF 241**

NEW GOODBYES, OLD HELLOES.
LP: . . . . **FF 305**

OUT OF THE DARK.
LP: . . . . **FF 361**

Schmidt, Irmin

FILM MUSIK - VOL.3/4.
2LP: . . . . **SPOON 18/19**

TOY PLANET.
Tracks: / Seven game, The / Toy planet / Two dolphins go dancing / Yom tov / Springlight rite / Rapido de noir / When the waters came to life.
LP: . . . . **VE 48**
MC: . . . . **TCVE 48**

Schmidt, Joey

JOEY, LAWRENCE AND MYRON.
LP: . . . . **R 8202**

Schmitt, Georges

JOY TO THE WORLD (Schmitt, Georges/Bernard Struber).
Tracks: / O Sanctissima / Silent night / O Christmas tree / Jesu, joy of man's desiring / Rudolph the red nosed reindeer / O gentle little Jesus / Come on shepherds / Ave Maria / Wake up, all you shepherds / Joy to the world / Jingle bells / On the Christmas tree / Come along children / First Noel, The / Dance of the Santons / O joyful day / Ring sleigh bells / Angels from the realms of glory / Song of Christmas / Holy child is born, The.
LP: . . . . **SDL 357**
MC: . . . . **CSDL 357**

Schmitt, Timothy B

PLAYIN' IT COOL.
LP: **960 3591**

Schmoelling, Johannes

WUIVEND RIET.
LP: . . . . **IRS 949 160**

ZOO OF TRANQUILITY.
Tracks: / Anteater, The / Woodpecker, The / Wedding cake, The / Rise of the smooth automation, The / Zoo of tranquility, The / Lawnmower, The / Zoo and Jonas, The.
LP: . . . . **TET 5**
MC: . . . . **CTET 5**

Schneebiegl, Rolf

ICH BIN SO GERN DAHEIM (see under Scholz, Walter) (Schneebiegl, Rolf/his orig Black Forest Mus'ns/Walter Scholz).

Schneider, Helen

EXPOSED.
Tracks: / Hot summer nights / Shout / Piece of my heart / Weekend / Pessimism / Out for the night / Fight and

never love / Valerie / The pro / Illusion / Rock n roll gypsy.
LP: . . . . K 58480

LET IT BE NOW.
Tracks: / Let it be now / Every step of the way / Someday / Time / Until now / Loneliness / Love me / Am I too late / Valentino tango / Caress me babe.
LP: . . . . FL 12710
MC: . . . . FK 12710

SCHNEIDER WITH A KICK.
Tracks: / Rock 'n' roll gypsy / You really got me / Shadows of the night / Turn me on / Don't let me be misunderstood / Let me touch you / Tinker tailor / Angry times / I'd like to be a child again / Not a day goes by.
LP: . . . . K 58294

SO CLOSE.
Tracks: / So close / Trying to say goodbye / All the time / Sad eyes / Cuddle up / Why don't we live together / Darlin' / Your mind is on vacation / How I miss you / I never meant to hurt you.
LP: . . . . FL 12037

Schneider, John

MEMORY LIKE YOU, A.
Tracks: / What's a memory like you (doin' in a love like this) / You're the last thing I needed tonight / Who cares / Somebody's gonna love her / Old rainbow jukebox and you, An / If we can't have forever (let's take tonight) / One more night / He finally made up her mind / One who got away, The / Welcome home.
LP: . . . . IMCA 5668

TAKE THE LONG WAY HOME.
Tracks: / At the sound of the tone / Broken promised land / She's ready for someone to love her / Sounds like something I would say / Better class of losers / Gettin'even / Auction, The / This time / Just when / Take the long way home.
LP: . . . . MCF 3348
MC: . . . . MCFC 3348

YOU AIN'T SEEN THE LAST OF ME.
Tracks: / I lost my head last night / So good / When the right one comes along / Angelena / If it was anyone but you / Hillbilly boy with the rock 'n' roll blues / Credit / Gunfighter, The / Redneck is the backbone of America, A / Love, you ain't seen the last of me.
LP: . . . . MCF 3375
MC: . . . . MCFC 3375

Schnell Fenster

SOUND OF TREES, THE.
LP: 9031711571
MC: 9031711574

Schnitter, David

GLOWING.
LP: . . . . MR 5222

GOLIATH.
Tracks: / Swing thing / Goliath / My funny valentine / Memories / Night and day.
LP: . . . . MR 5153

INVITATION.
Tracks: / Invitation / Blue Monk / Body and soul / Donna Lee / Fat Face Fenner's saloon.
LP: . . . . MR 5108

THUNDERING.
Tracks: / Thundering / Stardust / Flying cloud / Caa purange / Herb's blues / There goes the ball game.
LP: . . . . MR 5197

Schnitzler, Conrad

CONAL.
LP: . . . . U 002

Schoenberg, Eric

ACCOUSTIC GUITAR.
LP: . . . . ROUNDER 3017

STEEL STRINGS.
LP: . . . . ROUNDER 3041

Schoenberg, Loren

LOREN SCHOENBERG ORCHESTRA.
LP: . . . . AVIVA 6005

SOLID GROUND.
Tracks: / Midriff / They say it's wonderful / Solid ground / Coquette / After all / Maid with the flaccid air, The / Bulgar and other balkan-type inventions), The / You are / Only trust your heart / This one's for Basie / I double dare you / Blue monk.
LP: . . . . CIJD 40186H

Schoener, Eberhard

EVENTS.
LP: . . . . IC 064 45879

VIDEO FLASHBACK.
Tracks: / Trans am / Only the wind / Speech behind speech / Koan / Octagon / Frame of mind / Signs of emotions / Code word Elvis / Video magic.
LP: . . . . UNKNOWN

Schoenfeld, Philip

BEST OF SCOTT JOPLIN.
Tracks: / Easy winners / Maple leaf rag / Entertainer, The.
LP: . . . . SDS 613

Schofield, Philip

ADVENTUROUS FOUR, THE (see under Blyton, Enid (aut)).

Scholars

WHEN WINDS BREATHE SOFT.
Tracks: / Let me careless / When the winds breathe soft / You gave me your heart / Battishill-amidst the myrtles / Deh, dove / In paper case / Callcott o santch me swift / Nightingale, The / Music all powerful / Humble tenant, The / To all...the scholars.
LP: . . . . DSLO 33

Scholfield, Stan

CHAMPIONS ENTERTAIN (Scholfield, Stan Accordion Band).
LP: . . . . WS 205

Schonberger, Heinz

HOLIDAY.
LP: . . . . MWM 006

Schonherz & Scott

ONE NIGHT IN VIENNA.
Tracks: / Wishing well / Windows of the world / Carnival / Peace of mind / One night in Vienna / Bayangume / Cairo / Sentimental walk (Theme from "Diva".).
LP: 371060-1
MC: 371060-4

Schoof, Manfred

DISTANT THUNDER.
LP: . . . . ENJA 2066

School Daze

SCHOOL DAZE (Soundtrack) (Various artists).
LP: . . . . MTL 1031
MC: . . . . TCMTL 1031

School Of Violence

WE ARE THE PEOPLE.
LP: . . . . RR 95021

Schoolly D

AM I BLACK ENOUGH FOR YOU.
LP: . . . . HIP 85
MC: . . . . HIPC 85

SATURDAY NIGHT (LP).
LP: . . . . MELTLP 2
MC: . . . . MELT TC 2

SCHOOLY-D.
LP: . . . . MELT LP 1

SMOKE, SOME KILL.
LP: . . . . HIP 64
MC: . . . . HIPC 64

School-Rebels

HAPPY SONG (see Farrell, Bobby) (School-Rebels & Bobby Farrell).

Schopfer, Klaus

MEET ME (Schopfer, Klaus Peter).
LP: . . . . ISST 182

Schreeching Weasal

SCHREECHING WEASAL LP.
Tracks: / Dingbat / Zombie / This ain't Hawaii / We skate / Runaway / Police insanity / Stupid over you / I hate Led Zeppelin / My right / Nicaragua / Sunshine / I wanna be naked / Boogada / Ashtray / American suicide / Psychiatrist / Mad at the paper boy / I love to hate / More problems / Supermarket fantasy / Holy hardcore / Professional distribution / Used cars / Hunter / I believe in UFOs / Hey suburbia.
LP: . . . . WEASALP

Schreier, Peter

SYMPHONY NO.2 (MENDELSSOHN) (see under Mendelssohn (Composer)) (Schreier, Peter/Leipzig Gewandhaus Orch/Leipzig Radio Chor.).

Schroeder, Robert

BRAIN VOYAGER.
LP: . . . . RRK 715030
MC: . . . . RRKC 715030

COMPUTER VOICE.
LP: . . . . RRK 15025

PARADISE.
Tracks: / In memory of paradise / Moments / Deep dream / Balance / Future memories / Skywalker / Time machine / Timeless.
LP: . . . . RRK 15.024

TIMEWAVES.
Tracks: / Turn of a dream, The / Waveshape attack / Waveshape decay / Love and emotion / Message, The / Imagine.
LP: 15.033

Schubert, Adrian

ADRIAN SCHUBERT & HIS SALON ORCHESTRA (Schubert, Adran & His Salon Orchestra/I.Kaufman/H.Lambert).
LP: . . . . CI 012

Schubert (composer)

FRANZ SCHUBERT: WANDERER FANTASY (Leonskaja, Elisabeth).
Tracks: / Wanderer fantasy (Schubert) / Piano sonata no.18 op.78 D894 (in G major).
MC: 244 189-4

IMPROMPTUS OP 90 - IMPROMPTUS OP 142 (Brendel).
MC: 422 237 4
LP: 422 237 1

LIEDER (SCHUBERT) (Mathis, Edith).
Tracks: / Fruhlingsgraube (Spring faith) / An die untergehende Sonne (To the setting Sun) / Die rose (The rose) / Suleika I & II / Wonne der wehmuth (Bliss in sadness) / Gott im Fruhling (The Lord in Spring) / An die nachtigall (To the nightingale) / Lachen und weinen (Laughing and crying) / Die forelle (The trout) / Der hirt auf dem felsen (The shepherd on the rock) (With Kurt Weber (clarinet).) / Am grabe Anselmos (At Anselmo's grave) / Mignon I & II / Erster verluss (First loss) / Rastlose liebe (Restless love) / Gretchen am spinnrade (Gretchen at the spinning-wheel) / Das madchen (the young girl) / Wiegenlied (Lullaby).
LP: 150 026-1
MC: 150 026-4

PIANO QUINTET 'THE TROUT'/ STRING TRIOS (Various artists).
MC: 422 838-4

PIANO SONATAS IN G AND IN C (Brendel).
MC: 422 340-4
LP: 422 340-1

PIANO TRIO NO 1/NOTTURNO D897 (Beaux Arts Trio).
MC: 422 836-4

ROSAMUNDE (Various artists).
MC: 4278174

SCHUBERT (Various artists).
MC: . . . . DLCMC 208

SCHUBERT STRING QUARTETS (D804, D810) (Melos Quartet).
Tracks: / String quartet no.13 in A minor D804 (Schubert) / String quartet no.14 in D minor D804 (Schubert) ('Death and the maiden').
LP: 150 058-1
MC: 150 058-4

SONG CYCLES VOL 1 (Luxon, Benjamin & David Willison).
LP: . . . . ABRD 1361
MC: . . . . ABTD 1361

STRING QUINTET (Various artists).
MC: 4277254

STRING QUINTET IN C MAJOR (Various artists).
MC: . . . . MC 4277254 GW

SYMPHONY NO.8/NO.3 (SCHUBERT) (Philharmonia Orchestra/Los Angeles Philharmonic Orchestra).
MC: 4278184

SYMPHONY NO.9 (SCHUBERT) (Great) (Philharmonia Orchestra).
MC: . . . . ZC QS 6029

SYMPHONY NO. 8 IN B MINOR 'UNFINISHED' (See Solti, Sir George) (Vienna Philharmonic Orchestra).

TROUT QUINTET (ETC) (SCHUBERT) (Prometheus Ensemble).
Tracks: / Trout quintet (Schubert).
LP: . . . . DCA 694
MC: . . . . ZC DCA 694

WINTERREISE... (Various artists).
MC: 4277244

WINTERREISE (Various artists).
MC: . . . . MC 4277244 GW

Schulman, Ira

BLOWIN' WITH THE WIND.
Tracks: / Let's talk / But not for me / Fascinating rhythm / Nightcap / This can't be love / Broadway / Woodwind nocturne / Polka dots and moonbeams / Scarlatti / Conversation piece / Toccata in F.
LP: . . . . TR 535

Schultze, Kristian

EXPEDITION EXTRA.
LP: 625627

Schulze, Klaus

ANGST (Film soundtrack).
Tracks: / Freeze / Pain / Memory / Surrender / Beyond.
LP: . . . . THBL 2.027
MC: . . . . THBC 2.027

APHRICA (Schulze, Klaus / Rainer Bloss).
LP: . . . . INT 200001

BABEL.
Tracks: / Nebuchadnezzar's dream / Foundation / Tower raises, The / First clouds / Communication problems / Gap of alienation, The / Immuring insanity / Heaven under feet / Deserted stones / Facing abandoned tools / Vanishing memories / Sinking into oblivion / Far from earth.
LP: . . . . VE 5
MC: . . . . TCVE 5

BLACK DANCE.
Tracks: / Waves of changes / Some velvet phasing / Voices of syn.
LP: . . . . OVED 23

CYBORG.
2LP: . . . . ISADORA 9005/6

DIG IT.
Tracks: / Death of an analogue / Weird caravan / Looper isn't a hooker / Synthasy.
LP: 0060 353

DREAMS.
Tracks: / Classical move, A / Five to four / Dreams / Klaustrophony.
LP: . . . . THBL 039

DRESDEN PERFORMANCE/ DRESDEN IMAGINARY SCENES.
LP: . . . . VED 903
MC: . . . . TCVED 903

DRIVE INN (Schulze, Klaus / Rainer Bloss).
Tracks: / Drive Inn / Sightseeing / Truckin' / Highway / Racing / Road to clear / Drive out.
LP: . . . . INT 200002
LP: . . . . THBL 2.028

DUNE.
Tracks: / Dune / Shadows of ignorance.
LP: 0060 225

EN - TRANCE.
Tracks: / En=trance / A=numerique / Fm delight / Velvet system.
LP: . . . . THBL 2.061
LP: . . . . MCF 3110

IRRLICHT.
LP: . . . . ISADORA 9004

MEDITERREAN PADS.
Tracks: / Decent changes / Mediterranean pads / Percussion planante.
LP: . . . . THBL 081

MIRAGE.
Tracks: / Aeronef / Eclipse / Exvasion / Lucidinterspace / Destination void / Xylotones / Cromwaves / Willowdreams / Liquidmirrors / Springdance.
LP: . . . . THBL 033
MC: . . . . THBC 033
LP: 0060 040

MOONDAWN.
Tracks: / Floating / Mindphaser.
LP: 0001 088
LP: . . . . ISADORA 9007

TIMEWIND.
Tracks: / Bayreuth return / Wahnfried 1883.
LP: . . . . OVED 24

TIMEWIND (AMBIENT BOX SET) (See under Ambient).

Schuman, Tom

EXTREMITIES.
Tracks: / Extremities / Mood swing / Palisades Parkway / Loving you / Skywriter / To B.E. / Crystal lane / Front seat reservation.
LP: . . . . GRP 96251
MC: . . . . GRP 96254

Schumann, Aaron

HONKY TONK COWBOY.
LP: . . . . BCLP 2

Schumann (composer)

CHOPIN/SCHUMANN PIANO CONCERTI (see under Vasary, Tamas) (Vasary, Tamas/Northern Sinfonia of England).

PIANO CONCERTO - CELLO CONCERTO With Franz, Maisky & Bernstein (Vienna Philharmonic Orchestra).
MC: 4278194

SCHUMANN (Various artists).
MC: . . . . DLCMC 209

Schumann, Theo

TANZ IN THEO'S BEAT BAR (Schumann, Theo Formation).
LP: 855 561

Schutz, Dieter

COMET, THE.
LP: . . . . SKY 112

SYMPHONIAE SACRAE.
MCSET: . . . . RK 77910

VOYAGE.
LP: SKY 102

Schuur, Diane

DEEDLES.
LP: GRP 91010
MC: GRPM 91010

DEEDLES & BASIE (Schuur, Diane & Count Basie Orchestra).
LP: GRP 91039
MC: GRPM 91039
DAT: GRT 9550

DIANE SCHUUR COLLECTION.
LP: GRP 95911
MC: GRP 95914

SCHUUR THING.
Tracks: / Needle in a haystack / By design / Love dance / Love you back / Someday / Someday we'll all be free / It don't mean a thing / American wedding song / Take me to the river / Make a plan / Sure thing.
LP: GRP 91022
MC: GRPM 91022

TALKIN' 'BOUT YOU.
LP: GR 9567
MC: GRC 9567

TIMELESS.
Tracks: / How long has this been going on? / Easy to love / Come rain or come shine / How about me / Do nothing till you hear from me / Time for love, A / I can't believe that you're in love with me / Please send me someone to love / Impossible / Don't like goodbyes.
LP: GRP 91030
MC: GRPM 91030

Schwab, Siegfried

GUITARISSIMO CONFIANCA (See under Horton, Peter) (Schwab, Siegfried/ Peter Horton).

Schwaller, Roman

SCHWALLER SCHWALLER (Schwaller, Roman Quartet).
LP: FLC 5049

Schwartz, Abe

MASTER OF KLEZMER MUSIC, VOL.1.
MC: GVMMC 126

Schwartz, Arthur

FROM THE PEN OF....
Tracks: / Love is a dancing thing / You and the night and the music / Rainy night in Rio, A / If there's someone lovelier than you / Rhode Island is famous for you / Alone together / That's entertainment / Dancing in the dark / Gal in Calico, A / Shine on your shoes / I guess I'll have to change my plan / Triplets / Something to remember you by / By myself.
LP: NL 70495
MC: NK 70495
LP: RS 1029

Schwartz, Eddie

NO REFUGE.
Tracks: / No refuge / Spirit of the night / Tonight / Good with your love / Heart on fire / Over the line / Auction block / All our tomorrows.
LP: K 50847

Schwarz, Tracey

HOME AMONG THE HILLS (Schwarz, Tracey & Eloise).
Tracks: / Home among the hills / Wild Bill Jones / Wayworn traveller, The / Green valley waltz / Keep my skillet good and greasy / I'll never forsake you / Where the soul of man never dies / Uncle Henry / Meet me tonight in the moonlight / Blind child, The / John Henry / When the bees are in the goldenrod / How beautiful Heaven must be / Fly around my pretty little miss.
LP: BF 15007

Schwarzkopf, Elisabeth

CHRISTMAS ALBUM, THE.
LP: EG 763 574 2

Schwarzwalder

UNSER HAUMEISTER.
MC: SLOB 001

Schwingungen

SCHWINGUNGEN (Various artists).
2LP: SKY 2/103/4

Science Fiction

CLASSIC SCIENCE FICTION STORIES (Henson, Nicky (nar)).
MCSET: TTDMC 406

SCIENCE FICTION ADVENTURES 1.
MCSET: DTO 10556

SCIENCE FICTION ADVENTURES VOL. 2.
MCSET: DTO 10557

SCIENCE FICTION SOUNDBOOK (Shatner, William & Leonard Nimoy).
LPS: SBR 104
MCSET: SBC 104

Science Looks...

SCIENCE LOOKS AT SPEECH (Fry, Dr. D.B.).
MC: SS 105

Scientific Americans

LOAD AND GO.
MC: A 111

Scientific Approach...

SCIENTIFIC APPROACH TO RELIGION (Hardy, Sir Alister).
MC: SS 114

Scientific View...

SCIENTIFIC VIEW OF MEDITATION (Ornstein, Professor Robert).
MC: SS 123

Scientist

1999 DUB (Scientist/Peter Chemist).
LP: HB 27
MC: HBC 27

BIG SHOWDOWN 1980, THE (Scientist & Prince Jammy).
Tracks: / Round 1 / Round 2 / Round 3 / Round 4 / Round 5 / Round 6 / Round 7 / Round 8 / Round 9 / Round 10.
LP: GREL 10

CRUCIAL CUTS.
Tracks: / Burning sun dub / 18 Drumalie Avenue / Gad man the prophet / Rise with him dub / Next door dub / Mass murder and corruption / King Tubby's hi-fi / Raw dub / Jack Ruby's hi power.
LP: KVC 6004

CRUCIAL CUTS VOL.II.
Tracks: / 13 Bread Lane dub / 11 Guava Road dub / Ethiopian high priest / President, The / Forgive them oh jah / Everlasting version / Knockout version / King Sturgav / People's choice, the lion / Dub the daughter.
LP: KVC 6005

DUB DUEL AT KING TUBBY'S (Scientist V The Professor).
Tracks: / Creation mix / Raw dub - choice of dub / Dub the daughter / Cultural vibes / Collie weed and dub / Cool profile style / Pride of the dread / Turn corn meal and fresh milk / Feel good.
LP: KVL 9015

HEAVYWEIGHT DUB CHAMPION.
Tracks: / Seconds away / Straight left / Upper cut / Kidney punch / Saved by the bell / Right across / Jab / One-two / Below the belt / Knock out.
LP: GREL 13

HIGH PRIEST OF DUB.
Tracks: / Hail him in dub / Gad man the prophet / Reuben first born / Ethiopian high priest / Repatriation is a must / Their hands in blood / Vatican, The / President, The / Forgive them, oh Jah / Mass murder and corruption.
LP: KVL 9011

IN THE KINGDOM OF DUB.
Tracks: / 18 Drumalie Avenue dub / Next door dub / 305 Spanish Town Road dub / 13 Bread Lane dub / 14 gross quit glade dub / 11 Guava Road dub / Kingdom dub / Chariot dub / Thunder and lightning (dub) / Disciple dub / Jerusalem dub / Burning sun dub.
LP: KVL 9004

PEOPLE'S CHOICE, THE.
Tracks: / Everlasting version / Version forever / Piece more version, A / Knock out version / King Tubby's hi-fi / Jack Ruby's hi power / Jah love of twelve tribe / King Sturgav / People's choice, the lion.
LP: KVL 9014

SCIENTIST ENCOUNTERS PAC-MAN.
Tracks: / Under surveillance / Price's wrath / Space invaders re-group / World cup squad lick their wounds / Vampire initiative / Malicious intent / Dark secret of the box, The / S.O.S. / Man trap / Look out - behind you.
LP: GREL 46

SCIENTIST MEETS THE SPACE INVADERS.
Tracks: / Beam down / Red shift / Time warp / Cloning process / Pulsar / Laser attack / Dematerialise / Fission / Supernova explosion / Quasar.
LP: GREL 19
MC: GREEN 19

SCIENTIST RIDS THE WORLD OF THE EVIL CURSE OF THE VAMPIRES.
Tracks: / Voodoo curse, The / Dance of the vampires / Blood on his lips / Cry of the werewolf / Mummy's shroud, The / Corpse rises, The / Night of the living dead / Your teeth in my neck / Ghost of Frankenstein / Plague of zombies.
LP: GREL 25
MC: GREEN 25

SCIENTIST WINS THE WORLD CUP.
Tracks: / Five dangerous matches Pt. 1 / Five dangerous matches Pt. 2.
LP: GREL 37

Scientist &...

SCIENTISTS AND RESPONSIBILITY (Pauling, Proffessor Linus).
MC: SS 127

Scientists

ATOM BOMB BABY.
LP: ANDA 37

BLOOD RED RIVER.
Tracks: / When fate deals its mortal blow / Spin, The / Rev head / Burnout / Set it on fire / Blood red river.
LP: ANDA 27

HEADING FOR A TRAUMA.
LP: ANDA 39

HUMAN JUKEBOX, THE.
Tracks: / Human jukebox, The / Shine / Distortion / Place called bad / Hungry eyes / Brain dead / It must be nice.
LP: KAR 105 L

THIS HEART DOESN'T RUN ON BLOOD.
LP: ANDA 32

WEIRD LOVE.
LP: KAR 103L

YOU GET WHAT YOU DESERVE.
LP: KAR 101L

Sci-Fi Music Festival

SCI - FI MUSIC FESTIVAL VOL 2 (Various artists).
Tracks: / Red Sonja: *Various artists* / Lifeforce: *Various artists* / Close Encounters of the Third Kind suite: *Various artists* / Halloween: *Various artists.*
LP: A 268
MC: C 268

Scion Sashay Success

IN THE BALANCE.
LP: HCF 002 LP

Sclavis, Louis

AD AUGUSTA PER AUGUSTIA.
Tracks: / La signification des choix musicaux / Musique pour une ceremonie / Jour plus tard / Per angustia / Le pardon / Levo levo / Vitesses / A.D. augusta.
LP: NATO 14

RECONTRES.
Tracks: / Weekend du lundi / L'Echappe / To meet / Les brumes / Simili / Advantage / La russe / Pour memoire.
LP: NATO 500

Scobey, Bob

ALEXANDER'S JAZZ BAND (Scobey, Bob, Alexander's Jazz Band).
LP: DC 12004

Scofield, John

BAR TALK.
LP: AN 3022

BLUE MATTER.
Tracks: / Blue matter / Trim / Heaven hill / So you say / Now she's blonde / Make me / Nag, The / Time marches on.
LP: SNTF 985
MC: 188702 4

EAST MEETS WEST.
LP: BKH 533

ELECTRIC OUTLET.
Tracks: / Big break, The / Best Western / Pick hits / Filibustero / Thanks again / King for a day / Phone home / Just my luck.
LP: GR 8405
MC: GRC 8405

FLAT OUT.
LP: 188903 1
MC: 188903 4

JOHN SCOFIELD - LIVE.
LP: ENJA 3013

LOUD JAZZ.
LP: 1888011
MC: 1888014

PICK HITS LIVE.
Tracks: / Picks and pans / Heaven will / Blue matter / Trim / Make me / Pick hits / Protocol / Thanks again / Georgia on my mind.
LP: 1888051
MC: 1888054

ROUGH HOUSE.
LP: ENJA 3033

SHINOLA.
LP: ENJA 4004

SOLAR (See Abercrombie, John) (Scofield, John/John Abercrombie).
LP: PA 8031

STILL WARM.
Tracks: / Techno / Still warm / High and mighty / Protocol / Rule of thumb / Picks and pans / Gil b 643.
LP: SNTF 980
LP: GR 8508
MC: GR 85084

TIME ON MY HANDS.
Tracks: / Wabash III / Since you asked / So sue me / Let's say we did / Flower power / Stranger to the light / Nocturnal mission / Farmacology / Time and tide (CD only.) / Be hear now (CD only.) / Fat lip (CD only.).
LP: B1 92894
LP: 792 894 1

WHO'S WHO.
Tracks: / Looks like meringue / Cassidae / Beatles, The / Spoons / Who's who / How the west was won / Beckon call / New strings attached / How to marry a millionaire / Fat dancer.
LP: NL 83071
MC: NK 83071

Scofield, Paul (nar)

HEART OF DARKNESS (see under Heart Of Darkness (bk)).

NAPOLEON OF NOTTINGHILL, THE (see under Napoleon of...(bk)).

QUIVER FULL OF ARROWS (See under Archer, Jeffrey (aut)).

Scooby

MONEY HONEY (See under Irie, Sweetie).

Scooby Doo

GHOSTLY APACHE.
MC: LL 41 8044 4

HORROR AT HANGWOOD HALL.
MC: LL 41 8045 4

PHANTOM PARROT, THE.
MC: LL 41 8043

Scoop (bk)

SCOOP (Evelyn Waugh) (Cadell, Simon).
MCSET: CC/023

Scorcher

WAKE UP THE PARTY.
LP: CNT 019

Scorpions

ACTION.
Tracks: / I'm goin' mad / It all depends / Leave me / In search of the peace mind / Inheritance / Action / Lonesome crow.
LP: 0040 150

ANIMAL MAGNETISM.
Tracks: / Make it real / Don't make no promises (your body can't keep) / Hold me tight / 20th century man / Lady starlight / Falling in love / Only a man / Zoo, The / Animal magnetism.
LP: ATAK 48
MC: TCATAK 48
LP: FA 3217
MC: TCFA 3217
MC: TCSHSP 4113
LP: SHSP 4113

BEST OF THE SCORPIONS.
Tracks: / Steam rock fever / Pictured life / Robot man / Back stage queen / Speedy's coming / Hellcat / He's a woman she's a man / In trance / Dark lady / Sails of Charon, The / Virgin killer.
LP: RCALP 3035
MC: RCAK 3035
LP: NL 74006
MC: NK 74006

BEST OF THE SCORPIONS VOL.2.
Tracks: / Top of the bill / They need a million / Longing for fire / Catch your train / Speedy's coming (live) / Crying days / All night long (live) / This is my song / Sun in my hand / Well burn the sky (live).
LP: NL 74517
MC: NK 74517

BLACKOUT.
Tracks: / Blackout / Can't live without you / You give me all I need / Now / Dynamite / Arizona / China white / When the smoke is going down.
LP: FA 41 3126 1
MC: FA 41 3126 4
LP: FA 3126
MC: TCFA 3126
LP: SHVL 823

CRAZY WORLD.
Tracks: / Tease me please me / To be with you in heaven / Restless night / Kicks after six / Money and fame / Don't believe her / Wind of change / Lust or love / Hit between the eyes / Send me an angel.
LP: 846908 1
MC: 846908 4

FLY TO THE RAINBOW.
Tracks: / Speedy's coming / They need a million / Drifting sun / Fly, people fly / This is my song / Fly away / Fly to the rainbow.
LP: NL 70084
MC: NK 70084
LP: RS 1023

GOLD BALLADS.
Tracks: / Still loving you / Holiday / Always somewhere / When the smoke is going down / Lady starlight.
MLP: **2603361**

GOLD ROCK.
LP: **0040 016**

HURRICANE ROCK.
Tracks: / Fly to the rainbow / Speedy's coming / In trance / Robot man / Polar nights / We'll burn the sky / Steamrock fever / He's a woman, she's a man / Another piece of meat / Coast to coast / Love drive / Zoo, The / Blackout / Can't live without you / When the smoke is going down / Dynamite / Rock you like a hurricane / Still loving you / Coming home / Rhythm of love.
LP: . . . . **VSOPLP 156**
MC: . . . . **VSOPMC 156**

IN TRANCE.
Tracks: / Dark lady / In trance / Life's like a river / Top of the bill / Living and dying / Robot man / Evening wind / Sun in my hand / Longing for fire / Night lights.
LP: . . . . **NL 70028**
MC: . . . . **NK 70028**
LP: . . . . **INTS 5251**
LP: . . . . **RS 1039**

LONESOME CROW.
LP: . . . . **METALPS 114**
LP: . . . . **HMILP 2**
MC: . . . . **HMIMC 2**
LPPD: . . . . **HMIPD 2**

LOVE AT FIRST STING.
Tracks: / Bad boys running wild / Rock you like a hurricane / I'm leaving you / Coming home / Same thrill, The / Big city nights / As soon as the good times roll / Crossfire / Still loving you.
LP: . . . . **ATAK 69**
MC: . . . . **TCATAK 69**
LP: . . . . **SHSP 2400071**
LP: . . . . **FA 3224**
MC: . . . . **TCFA 3224**

LOVEDRIVE.
Tracks: / Loving you Sunday morning / Another piece of meat / Always somewhere / Coast to coast / Can't get enough / Is there anybody there? / Lovedrive / Holiday.
LP: . . . . **FA 4130801**
MC: . . . . **TCFA 41 30804**
LP: . . . . **FA 3080**
MC: . . . . **TCFA 3080**
LP: . . . . **SHSP 4097**
MC: . . . . **TCSHSP 4097**

ROCK GALAXY.
Tracks: / Speedy's coming / They need a million / Drifting sun / Fly people fly / This is my song / Far away / Fly to the rainbow / Dark lady / In trance / Life's like a river / Top of the bill / Living and dying / Robot man / Evening wind / Sun in my hand / Longing for fire / Night lights.
LP: . . . . **CL 28390**

ROCKERS 'N' BALLADS.
Tracks: / Rock you like a hurricane / Can't explain / Rhythm of love / Big city nights / Lovedrive / Is there anybody there / Holiday / Still loving you / No one like you / Blackout / Another piece of meat / You give me all I need / Hey you / Zoo, The / China white.
LP: . . . . **EMD 1014**
MC: . . . . **TCEMD 1014**

SAVAGE AMUSEMENT.
Tracks: / Don't stop at the top / Rhythm of love / Passion rules the game / Media overkill / Walking on the edge / We let it rock (you let it roll) / Every minute everyday / Love on the run / Believe in love.
LP: . . . . **SHSP 4125**
MC: . . . . **TCSHSP 4125**

SCORPIONS: INTERVIEW PICTURE DISC.
LPPD: . . . . **BAK 2101**

STILL LOVING YOU (ALBUM).
Tracks: / Believe in love / Born to touch your feelings / Lady Starlight / Is there anybody there / Walking on the edge / When the smoke is going down / Always somewhere / Holiday / Still loving you.
LP: . . . . **EMC 3586**
MC: . . . . **TCEMC 3586**

TAKE OFF.
LP: . . . . **NL 28486**

TAKEN BY FORCE.
Tracks: / Steamrock fever / We'll burn the sky / I've got to be free / Riot of your time, The / Sails of Charon, The / Your light / He's a woman, She's a man / Born to touch your feelings.
LP: . . . . **RCALP 3024**
MC: . . . . **RCAK 3024**
LP: . . . . **NL 70081**
MC: . . . . **NK 70081**
LP: . . . . **PL 28309**
MC: . . . . **PK 28309**

TOKYO TAPES.
Tracks: / All night long / Pictured life / Backstage queen / Polar nights / In trance / We'll burn the sky / Suspender love / In search of the peace of the mind / Fly to the rainbow.
2LP: . . . . **NL 70008**
MCSET: . . . . **NK 70008**
2LP: . . . . **NL 28331**

VIRGIN KILLER.
Tracks: / Pictured life / Catch your train / Backstage Queen / Virgin killer / Hell cat / Crying days / Polar nights / Yellow raven.
LP: . . . . **PPL 14225**
LP: . . . . **NL 70031**
LP: **2621820**

WORLD WIDE LIVE.
Tracks: / Countdown / Coming home / Blackout / Bad boys running wild / Loving you sunday morning / Make it real / Big city nights / Coast to coast / Holiday / Still loving you / Rock you like a hurricane / Can't live without you / Zoo, The / No-one like you / Dynamite.
2LP: . . . . **SCORP 1**
MCSET: . . . . **TCSCORP 1**
2LP: . . . . **EN 2403433**
MCSET: . . . . **EN 2403435**

Scot, Stevenson

GRIM TALES FROM THE SCOTS (Sheddon, John).
MCSET: . . . . **COL 4004**

Scotch Measure

SCOTCH MEASURE.
LP: **12TS 436**

Scotdisc Premiere...

GO COUNTRY WESTERN (Scotdisc Premiere Accordion Band).
LP: . . . . **ITV 420**
MC: . . . . **KITV 420**

Scotland

24 GREAT CELTIC SONGS (Various artists).
LP: . . . . **CDULP 8**

100 MINUTES OF SCOTTISH FAVOURITES (Various artists).
MC: . . . . **ZCTON 124**
MC: . . . . **ZCTON 126**

ALL SCOTLAND ACCORDION FESTIVAL (See under Accordion ...) (Various artists).

ALL THE BEST FROM SCOTLAND-VOL 1 (Various artists).
Tracks: / Rowan tree: *Various artists* / Scotland again: *Various artists* / Dark Lochnagar: *Various artists*/ Aye ready: *Various artists* / Ae fond kiss: *Various artists* / Work of the weavers: *Various artists*/ Caledonia: *Various artists* / Skye boat song: *Various artists* / Amazing grace: *Various artists* / Contentment: *Various artists* / Lords my shepherd: *Various artists* / Man'a man: *Various artists* / Ye banks and braes: *Various artists* / Massacre of Glencoe: *Various artists* / Auld lang syne: *Various artists.*
LP: . . . . **LILP 5100**
MC: . . . . **LICS 5100**
LP: . . . . **KMLP 305**

ALL THE BEST FROM SCOTLAND-VOL 2 (Various artists).
Tracks: / Bonnie Aberdeen: *Various artists* / Highland bridge depot: *Various artists* / Major J. McGillvary: *Various* artists / My ain folk: *Various artists* / Loch Lomond: *Various artists* / Dark island: *Various artists*/ Sweet afton: *Various artists* / Bonnie lass o' Fyvie: *Various artists* / Jessie's hornpipe: *Various artists*/ Kirk's hornpipe: *Various artists* / Drumlees: *Various artists* / Island spinning song: *Various artists*/ Banjo breakdown: *Various artists* / Fiddlers choice: *Various artists* / Scotland your a lady: *Various artists*/ Flowers of Edinburgh: *Various artists* / Wee dug Tim, The: *Various artists* / Lucky Scaup: *Various artists*/ Rose of Allandale: *Various artists* / Skye boat song: *Various artists* / Morag of Dunvegan: *Various artists*/ When you and I were young Maggie: *Various artists* / Twa racruiting sergeants: *Various artists.*
LP: . . . . **LOCLP 1006**
MC: . . . . **ZCLOC 1006**

BAGPIPE IN ITALY (Various artists).
LP: . . . . **LLST 7343**

BEST OF DANCE BANDS & DANCES OF SCOTLAND (Various artists).
LP: . . . . **LILP 5116**
MC: . . . . **LICS 5116**

BEST OF SCOTTISH DANCE BANDS, THE (Various artists).
MC: . . . . **HR 8196**

BONNIE SCOTLAND (Various artists).
MCSET: . . . . **DTO 10238**

BONNIE SCOTLAND SHOW (Various artists).
LP: . . . . **LILP 5069**
MC: . . . . **LIMC 5069**

BONNY LASS COME O'ER THE BURN (Various artists).
Tracks: / Twa corbies: *Fisher, Ray* / Fil uo ro hu-o: *MacLennan, Dolina* / Gypsie laddie: *Gray, Robin*/ Beggarman, The: *Kent, Enoch* / Hug o ran o ru: *MacLennan, Dolina* / Donal Don: *Kent, Enoch* / Kilbogie: *Fisher, Ray & Archie* / Night visiting song: *Fisher, Ray & Archie* / Bonnie lass come o'er the burn: *Kent,* Enoch / Far over the Forth: *Fisher, Ray* / Butcher boy: *Kent, Enoch* / Puirt a beul: *MacLennan, Dolina*/ Erin go bragh: *Kent, Enoch* / Bratach bana: *MacLennan, Dolina.*
LP: **12T 128**

CALEDONIA (Various artists).
LP: . . . . **H 72006**

CALEDONIAN COMPANION (Instrumental Music from Scotland) (Various artists).
Tracks: / Lady Madeline Sinclair: *Caledonian Companion* / High road to Linton: *Caledonian Companion* / White cockade, The: *Caledonian Companion* / Neil Gow's farewell to whiskey: *Caledonian Companion* / Miss Jean Milligan: *Caledonian* Companion / Muckin' o' Geordie's byre: *Caledonian Companion* / Kinnegad slashers: *Caledonian Companion* / Bugle horn, The: *Caledonian Companion* / Brig o'Perth: *Caledonian Companion* / Reel of Tulloch, The: *Caledonian* Companion / Forbes Morrison: *Caledonian Companion* / Ten pound fiddle, The: *Caledonian Companion* / Smith's gallant fireman, The: *Caledonian Companion* / Jenny dang the weaver: *Caledonian Companion* / Bonnie Dundee: *Caledonian* Companion / Hot punch: *Caledonian Companion* / Kenmore's up and awa': *Caledonian Companion* / J.B. Milne: *Caledonian Companion* / Lovat scouts, The: *Caledonian Companion* / Breakdown, The: *Caledonian Companion*/ Caddam Woods: *Caledonian Companion* / Polka: *Caledonian Companion* / Smith's a gallant fireman, The: *Caledonian* Companion / Soldiers joy: *Caledonian Companion* / Kirrie debbuck, The: *Caledonian Companion* / Sir David Davidson of Cantray: *Caledonian Companion* / Tam Bain's lum: *Caledonian Companion* / Blue bonnets o'er the border: *Caledonian* Companion / Far frae Scotia's shores: *Caledonian Companion* / Alley crocker: *Caledonian Companion* / Orange and blue: *Caledonian Companion* / Mrs. MacLeod of Raasay: *Caledonian Companion* / Highland wedding: *Caledonian* Companion / Doctor MacDonald: *Caledonian Companion* / Lady Charlotte Campbell: *Caledonian Companion* / High road to Linton: *Caledonian Companion* / Mason's apron: *Caledonian Companion* / Timour the tartar: *Caledonian Companion.*
LP: **12TS 266**

CAMERON MEN (Classic Scots fiddle recordings from the thirti (Various artists).
Tracks: / Abercairney highlanders: *Various artists* / Ballochmyle: *Various* artists / Speed the plough: *Various* artists / Miss Drummond of Perth: *Various artists* / Maggie Cameron: *Various artists* / Favourite, The: *Various* artists / Loch Katrine: *Various artists* / Miss Lyall: *Various artists* / Loch Leven: *Various artists*/ Earl Dalhouse: *Various artists* / Lady Mary Ramsay: *Various artists* / Soldier's joy: *Various artists*/ Dashing white sergeant: *Various artists* / My love she's but a lassie yet: *Various artists* / Rose tree, The: *Various artists* / Original Brechin bridge: *Various artists* / Victoria hornpipe: *Various artists* / Bonnie Anne: *Various artists* / Bob Johnston: *Various artists* / Auld lichties, The: *Various artists* / John MacFadyen of Melfort: *Various artists* / Brig o'Perth: *Various artists* / Earl of Crawford's reel, The: *Various* artists / Rock and wee pickle tow, The: *Various artists* / Blackthorn stick: *Various artists* / Teviot Brig: *Various artists* / Humours of Donnybrook: *Various artists* / Rossity ends: *Various artists* / Smith's a gallant fireman: *Various artists* / Pretty Peggy: *Various artists* / Cumberland reel: *Various artists*/ Father O'Flynn: *Various artists* / Auld brig o Ayr: *Various artists* / Wind that shakes the barley, The: *Various* artists / Rakes of Kildare, The: *Various artists* / Swallow tail: *Various artists* / Queen's welcome to Deeside, The: *Various artists* / Drummer, The: *Various artists* / Farewell to gartly: *Various artists* / Stirling castle: *Various artists* / Highland queen: *Various artists* / Forth brig: *Various artists* / Banks of Allan, The: *Various artists* / Craigellachie brig: *Various artists* / Lasses O' Stewarton: *Various artists.*
LP: **12T 321**

CARILLONS OF SCOTLAND (Various).
Tracks: / Scotch on the rocks / Oak and the ash, The / Charlie is my darling / Mariner's hymn / Esterlitta / Estudio 5 for guitar / See the conquering hero / Round o' / Sailor's song / Tambourin / Sarabande / Harp that once through Tara's hall, The / Martyrs / Ellers / Sandgate dandling.
LP: . . . . **SDL 341**
MC: . . . . **CSDL 341**

CELEBRATION OF SCOTTISH MUSIC, A (Various artists).
LP: . . . . **TP 028**
MC: . . . . **CTP 028**

CEUD MILE FAILTE (Gaelic ceilidh) (Various artists).
Tracks: / Seaforth lullaby, The: *Various artists* / Sleeps the noon: *Various artists* / St. Kilda bird song: *Various artists* / Cronan bleodhainn: *Various artists* / Posadh piuthar Iain Bhain: *Various artists* / Am falbh thu learn a ribhinn og: *Various artists* / Mor a cheannaich: *Various artists* / Balaich an lasgaich: *Various artists*/ Duanag an t-seoladair: *Various artists* / Gaol nan cruinneag: *Various artists* / Crodh chailein: *Various* artists / An t-eilean aluinn: *Various artists* / Fhlaesgaich oig as ceanalta: *Various artists* / Birlinn ghoraidh chrobhain: *Various artists.*
LP: . . . . **LILP 5006**

COME AWA BEN THE HOOSE (Various artists).
Tracks: / Mary Milnes Banchory Junior: *Various artists* / Doon at the mains-memories: *Various artists* / Alex Green: *Various artists* / Sheena Blackhall: *Various artists* / Rebecca Hunter: *Various artists* / John Mearn's favourite: *Various artists* / David Davidson: *Various artists* / Fiddle trio: *Various artists.*
MC: . . . . **CWGR 110**

COME TO THE HIGHLANDS - VOL 1 (Various artists).
MC: . . . . **CWGR 015**

COME TO THE HIGHLANDS - VOL 2 (Various artists).
MC: . . . . **CWGR 016**

COME TO THE HIGHLANDS - VOL 3 (Various artists).
MC: . . . . **CWGR 017**

COMPETING HIGHLAND DANCER PLAYED BY... (Various artists).
MC: . . . . **KITV 516**

CONTROVERSY OF PIPERS, A (Various artists).
LP: . . . . **TP 008**

COORSE AND FINE SONGS AND BALLADS OF DUNDEE (Various artists).
LP: . . . . **SPR 1017**
MC: . . . . **SPRC 1017**

DANCING STRINGS OF SCOTLAND (Various artists).
Tracks: / Reel of the 51st division, The: *Various artists* / Linton ploughman: *Various artists* / Scottish waltz: *Various artists* / Hamilton house: *Various artists* / Dashing white sergeant: *Various artists* / Duke of Perth: *Various artists* / Strip the willow: *Various artists* / Gay Gordons: *Various artists* / Petronella: *Various artists* / Highland schottische: *Various artists* / Circassian circle: *Various artists.*
LP: . . . . **LILP 5175**
MC: . . . . **LICS 5175**

DISCOVER SCOTLAND VOL.1 (Various artists).
Tracks: / Original: *Carmichael, John & His Band* / Kathleen's reel: *Carmichael, John & His Band* / Bauaria: *Carmichael,* John & His Band / Dixie: *Carmichael, John & His Band* / Do you think you could love me again: *MacLeod, Jim & His* Band / Skye boat song: *Scott, Tommy Strings of Scot* / Richmora: *Oakbank Sound* / Pomander jig, The: *Oakbank* Sound / Wee sergeant, The: *Oakbank Sound* / Rab Smillies J.G: *Oakbank Sound* / Maggie: *Gillies, Alasdair*/ Silver darlin': *Marlettes* / Marie's wedding: *Garden, Bill & His Highland Fiddle Orchestra* / Vist tramping songs: *Garden, Bill & His Highland Fiddle Orchestra* / Marquis of Huntly, The: *Garden, Bill & His Highland Fiddle Orchestra*/ Roxburgh Castle: *Garden, Bill & His Highland Fiddle Orchestra* / Scotland the brave: *Garden, Bill & His Highland* Fiddle Orchestra / From Scotland with love: *Scott, Tommy Strings of Scot* / Wild mountain thyme: *Marlettes*/ Marching through the heather: *Frazer, Grant* / Johnny lad: *Frazer, Grant* / Flower of Scotland:

Frazer, Grant / Jigtime: Garden, Bill & His Highland Fiddle Orchestra / McFlannels: Garden, Bill & His Highland Fiddle Orchestra / Para Handy: Garden, Bill & His Highland Fiddle Orchestra / Man's a man for a' that, A: Harper, Addie & The Wick Trio / Scots wha' hae: Harper, Addie & The Wick Trio / Auld lang syne: Harper, Addie & The Wick Trio/ I love a lassie: Anderson, Stuart / Roaming in the gloaming: Anderson, Stuart / Wee Deoch an' Doris: Anderson, Stuart / Stop your ticklin' Jock: Anderson, Stuart / Keep right on to the end of the road: Anderson, Stuart/ Denny & Dunipace Pipe Band, The: Denny & Dunipace Pipe Band / Major Bobby: Denny & Dunipace Pipe Band / Muckin' o' Geordie's byre: Denny & Dunipace Pipe Band / Glendurel highlander: Denny & Dunipace Pipe Band / Bonnie Dundee: Denny & Dunipace Pipe Band.
MC: . . . . KITV 428

DISCOVER SCOTLAND VOL.2 (Various artists).
Tracks: / Dovecote Park: MacLeod, Jim & His Band / Glendaurel highlanders: MacLeod, Jim & His Band / These are my mountains: MacLeod, Jim / Great Glen, The: Scott, Tommy / Scotland my home: Gillies, Alasdair / Whistle and I'll dance: Cameron, Mary / Morag of Dunvegan: Scott, Tommy / Reals and jigs: Garden, Bill Fiddle Orchestra / Black Watch polka: Denny & Dunipace... / Touch of Gaelic, A: Gonnella, Ron / I belong to Glasgow: Grant, Lou / Crags of Tumbledown Mountain: Harper, Addie & Wick Band / Lament: Denny & Dunipace....
MC: . . . . KITV 449

DOUBLE SCOTCH (SCOTTISH PUB SING-ALONG) (Various artists).
LP: . . . . PHL 496

FIDDLER'S RALLY 76 (Various artists).
LP: . . . . REC 262

FLOWER OF SCOTLAND (Various artists).
MCSET: . . . . WW 6044

FORTH BRIDGE CENTENARY (Music of Scotland) (Various artists).
MC: . . . . KITV 520

GLASGOW HORIZONS (Various artists).
Tracks: / Riverside jig: Scotia / Cholesterol: McNaughtan, Adam / Sunrise in South Africa: McMorland, Alison/ Wee white rose of Scotland: Laurie, Tom / Glasgow Peggy: Laurie, Cy / Inveroran: McIntyre, Geordie/ Lament of a working class heroes wife: McMorland, Alison & Kirsty / Glasgow councillor, The: McNaughtan, Adam/ Out by the Isle: McMorland, Alison / In praise of Lochcarron: Beaton, Murdo / Another Valley: Laurie, Tom / Leaving song, The: McIntyre, Geordie / Time wears awa': McMorland, Alison / Braemar wall, The: Scotia.
LP: . . . . LIFL 7018
MC: . . . . LFC 7018

GOLDEN HOUR OF SCOTTISH DANCE BANDS (Various artists).
LP: . . . . GH 657

GOLDEN HOUR OF SCOTTISH FAVOURITES (Various artists).
Tracks: / Tartan, The: Stuart, Colin / Maid I adore, The: Alexander Brothers / They found Donald's troosers: Kennedy, Calum / Forty shades of green: MacLeod, Jim & His Band / Bonnie wee Jeannie McCall: Stuart, Colin/ Loch Maree islands: Kennedy, Calum / We're no awa' tae bide awa': Daly, Glen / Waggle o' the kilt, The: Stuart, Colin / Sing us a song of Bonnie Scotland: Daly, Glen / Muckin' o' Geordie's byre: Houliston, Max & his Scottish Band / Dark Lochnagar: Kennedy, Calum / Come to Fiona's wedding: MacLeod, Jim & His Band / Campbeltown Loch: Alexander Brothers / Dark island: Starr, Will / When I leave old Glasgow behind: Daly, Glen / Mairi's wedding: Alexander Brothers / Scottish trilogy: Martell, Lena / McGinty's meal and ale: Alexander Brothers.
LP: . . . . GH 596
MC: . . . . KGHMC 144

GREAT SONGS OF SCOTLAND (Various artists).
Tracks: / Bonnie Earl O'Moray, The: Various artists / O whistle: Various artists / Afton water: Various artists / Durisdeer: Various artists / Scots wha' hae: Various artists / Annie Laurie: Various artists/ Gae bring tae me a pint o'wine: Various artists / Wee cooper o' Fife, The: Various artists / Ye banks and braes: Various artists / Birks o Aberfeldy, The: Various artists / Ca the yowes: Various artists / Sleeps the noon: Various artists / I'll ay ca' in by yon toun: Various artists / This is no my plaid: Various artists/ Loch Lomond: Various artists / Auld lang syne: Various artists.
LP: . . . . ALM 4009
MC: . . . . ZC ALM 4009

GREATEST CEILIDH BAND YOU EVER SAW (Various artists).
LP: . . . . MILP 1001

HOW ARE THINGS IN AUCHTERTURRA? (Various artists).
LP: . . . . STW 86
MC: . . . . STW 86C

I WAS BORN IN GLASGOW (Various artists).
LP: . . . . GAL 102
MC: . . . . GAL 102C

INTERNATIONAL GATHERING OF THE CLANS (Various artists).
LP: . . . . EMA 783

INVERARAY CASTLE CEILIDH (Various artists).
Tracks: / Iona's wedding: Various artists / Glendaurel highlanders: Various artists / Birlinn ghoraidh chrobhain: Various artists / Fhir a' bhata: Various artists / Maili dhonn, bhoidheach dhonn: Various artists / Failte dhat is shante lest: Various artists / Ho ro mo nighean donn bhoid heach: Various artists / Hi o ro eile: Various artists / Langavall: Various artists / Heights of Dargai, The: Various artists / Blackberry bush: Various artists / Leanabh an aigh: Various artists / Cathair a chulchinn: Various artists / An t-eilean aluinn: Various artists / Hills of Lorne, (The): Various artists / David Ross: Various artists/ Thug mi mo lamh do'n eileanach: Various artists / Si mo leannan an te ur: Various artists / Oran do reidemeid earr-ghaidheal: Various artists.
LP: . . . . NEVLP 106
MC: . . . . NEVC 106

IRELAND, SCOTLAND, BRITTANY AND GALICIA (Various artists).
LP: . . . . LLST 7327

LOCHABER TO DONEGAL (Various artists).
LP: . . . . HEB 2

LOCHAN (Various artists).
LP: . . . . CM 018

MORE GRAMPIAN GEMS (Various artists).
LP: . . . . MOR 4020

MULL FIDDLERS (Various artists).
MC: . . . . MR 1003

MUM AND ME VISIT CAMPBELL'S COUNTRY (Various artists).
LP: . . . . LKLP 6039

MUSIC AND SONG OF SCOTLAND (A Greentrax Showcase) (Various artists).
Tracks: / Scotland the brave: Lothian & Borders Police Band / Bonnie Galloway: Lothian & Borders Police Band/ Rowan tree, The: Lothian & Borders Police Band / Highland laddie: Lothian & Borders Police Band / Dumbarton's drums: Redpath, Jean / Rolling hills of the borders, The: McCalmans / Burke and Hare: Laing, Robin/ Bonnie moorhen: Heywood, Heather / Old bean waltz: Hardie, Ian / Hospital wood: Hardie, Ian / Auchope cairn: Hardie, Ian / Glasgow that I used to know, The: McNaughtan, Adam / Bleacher lass o' Kelvinhaugh: Paterson, Rod / If wishes were fishes: Bogle, Eric / Yonder banks: Fisher, Archie / Shipyard apprentice: Fisher, Archie / Carls o'Dysart: Russell, Janet/ Christine Kydd / De'ils awa' wi' the exciseman, The: Russell, Janet/ Christine Kydd / Farm auction, The: MacKintosh, Iain / Donald McLean's farewell to Oban: Bain, Aly/Cunningham, Phil/ Sands of Burness, The: Bain, Aly/ Cunningham, Phil / Miller's reel: Bain, Aly/Cunningham, Phil / Maid of Islay: MacDonald, Iain / Canan nan gaidheal: MacPhee, Catherine-Ann / Birnie bouzie: Beck, Jack / Fife and a' the lands about it: Heritage / Freedom come all ye: Porteous, Lindsay and friends.
MC: . . . . CTRAX 030

NEW VOICES FROM SCOTLAND (Various artists).
LP: 12T 133

NIMBLE FINGERS (Various artists).
Tracks: / Rebecca Hunter: Various artists / Alex Green: Various artists / Bruce Lindsay: Various artists/ Gordon Duncan: Various artists.
MC: . . . . CWGR 114

OVER HEATHER MOORLAND (Various artists).
Tracks: / Loch Maree Islands: Miller, Ina / Barrowburn reel, The: Harper, Addie & The Wick Band / Walking on the moon: Harper, Addie & The Wick Band / Elliot's fancy: Harper, Addie & The Wick Band / Rose of Allendale: Duffus, George / Jacqueline waltz: Geddes, Graham & His Band / Roses of Prince Charlie: Miller, Ina/ Allstair of the Den: Shand, Jimmy Jnr. & His Band / Highland Donald: Shand, Jimmy Jnr. & His Band / Hopeful lover: Shand, Jimmy Jnr. & His Band / Mingulay boat song, The: McCalmans / Leaving Lismore: Nicolson, Eann & The Wick Scottish Dance Band / I left my dearie: Nicolson, Eann & The Wick Scottish Dance Band / Crovan's galley: Nicolson, Eann & The Wick Scottish Dance Band / Morag of Dunvegan: Nicolson, Eann & The Wick Scottish Dance Band/ Crags of Tumbledown mountain: Regimental Band Of The Scots / Bluebell polka: Geddes, Graham & His Band / Farewell to Nova Scotia: Miller, Ina / MacFarlane o' the sprots o' Burnieboozie: Pattullo, Gordon / Barnyards o' Delgaty: Pattullo, Gordon / Bonnie lass o 'Fyvie: Pattullo, Gordon / Pair o' Nicky Tams, A: Pattullo, Gordon/ Gin I were where the gaudie rins: Pattullo, Gordon / Muckin o' Geordie's Byre, The: Neeps & The Barley Band/ Teviot brig: Neeps & The Barley Band / Love me a laddie: Neeps & The Barley Band / Kirkwall Bay: Miller, Ina / Hen's march: Nicolson, Eann & The Wick Scottish Dance Band / Waters of Kyleaku, The: Dawson, Sandy/ Pibroach MacKenzie's farewell: Nicolson, Eann & The Wick Scottish Dance Band / Heights of Dargai, The: Nicolson, Eann & The Wick Scottish Dance Band / Battle of the Somme: Nicolson, Eann & The Wick Scottish Dance Band / Happy we've been a'thegither: Miller, Ina / Shiftin' bobbins: Geddes, Graham & His Band / Caddam Woods: Geddes, Graham & His Band / Bill Sutherland: Geddes, Graham & His Band / Kinclaven brig: Geddes, Graham & His Band.
MC: . . . . CWGR 135

PATTER - THE ALBUM, THE (Various artists).
Tracks: / Glasgow that I used to know, The: Various artists / Wee walkies, The: Various artists / Daphne Broon: Various artists / Oor Hamlet: Various artists / Bargain hunter, The: Various artists / Remembering: Various artists / Peoples palace, The: Various artists / Effen bee, The: Various artists / Glasgow rap: Various artists / Sam the skull: Various artists / Lost dinner ticket, The: Various artists / Jelly piece song, The: Various artists / Pawning the flute: Various artists / Summertime: Various artists/ Hooked on granny: Various artists / Sick visitor, The: Various artists.
LP: . . . . LIDL 6020
MC: . . . . LIDC 6020

POPULAR SONGS OF SCOTLAND (sung in Gaelic) (Various artists).
Tracks: / Dark island: Solley, David / Shoals of herring: Lochies / Lewis sailing song: MacDonald Sisters/ Song of home: Govan Gaelic Choir / Old rugged cross: Sound Of Mull / My sweet auburn maid: Lochies/ Carloway: Na Siaraich / Air and traig: Run Rig / Road to Ness, The: MacDonald, Donald / Whisky's my delight: Na Siaraich / Will ye no come back again?: Lochies / Puirt-a-beul: MacLean, Norman / Dancing on the sands: MacDonald Sisters / I once loved a lass: Lochies / Isle of my heart: Marshall, Billy (Uilleam)/ Thistle of Scotland, The: MacRae, Donald.
LP: . . . . LILP 5117
MC: . . . . LICS 5117

ROUND AT CALUM'S (Various artists).
MC: . . . . ZCSMPS 8926

SCOTLAND FOREVER (Various artists).
LP: . . . . WGR 075
MC: . . . . CWGR 075

SCOTLAND IN SONG (Various artists).
Tracks: / These are my mountains: Sutherland, Alex / Old Scottish waltz: Stewart, Andy / Man's a man for a' that, A: Caern folk / Piper o'Dundee, The: Caern folk / Wee Kirkcudbright centipede, The: MacDonald, Alistair/ Water is wide, the: McBennett, Helen / Auld Lang Syne: Stewart, Andy / Raggle taggle...: MacDonald, Kathleen/ Go away from: MacDonald, Kathleen / All around...: MacDonald Sisters / Highland lullaby: MacDonald, Alistair/ Farewell my love: McBennett, Helen / Sailing...: Alex Sutherland Singers.
MC: . . . . 4 HOM 011

SCOTLAND - THE DANCES AND THE DANCE BANDS (Various artists).
Tracks: / Eightsome reel: Holmes, Ian & Scottish Dance Band / Strip the willow: Johnstone, Jim & His Band / West Highland waltz: MacDonald, Fergie & Highland / Dashing white Sergeant: MacPhail, Ian & His Scottish Dance Band/ Danadian barn dance: Johnstone, Jim & His Band / Waltz country dance: Keith, Lex & His Scottish Band / Irish jiggery: MacDonald, Fergie & Highland / Grand march: Wilson, Calum / Jig strathspey and reel: Lothian Scottish Dance Band / St. Bernard's waltz: Johnstone, Jim & His Band / Boston Two Step: Ellis, John & His Highland Country Band / Reel (hoop her and gird her): Glendaruel Scottish Dance Band / Pride o' erin waltz: MacLeod, Bobby & His Music / Gay Gordons: Campbell, Colin & his Highland Band / Two highland schottissches: Ellis, John & His Highland Country Band / Military two step: Johnstone, Jim & His Band / Lothian lads: Lothian Scottish Dance Band(Only on CD) / Palais glyde, The: Johnstone, Jim (Only on CD) / Hebridean waltz: Carmichael, John (Only on CD) / Irish military two step: MacDonald, Fergie (Only on CD).
LP: . . . . LILP 5163
MC: . . . . LICS 5163

SCOTLAND - THE MUSIC OF A NATION (Various artists).
Tracks: / Caddam Woods: Golden Fiddle Orchestra / Strathspeys and reel: Burgess, John D / Bonnie lass o' Bon Accord: Ford, Tommy / Medley: Gonnella, Ron / 4/4 marches: Dysart & Dundonald Pipe Band / Slow air and marches: MacKay, Rhona / Mrs Hamilton of Pencaitland: Glasgow Caledonian Strathspey & Reel Society / Gay Gordons: Ellis, John & His Highland Country Band / Free and easy: Hunter, Karen / Petronella: Brock, Robin & His Dance Band / March Strathspey and reel: MacFadyen, Iain / Hangman's reel, The: MacLean, Calum / Waltzes: Dysart & Dundonald Pipe Band / Reels: Currie Brothers / Cro cheann T Saile: MacKay, Rhona / Marches: Glasgow Caledonian Strathspey & Reel Society / Dumbarton's drum: Gaelforce Orchestra (Only on CD) / Mary of Argyll: Gaelforce Orchestra (Only on CD) / Trilogy: Gaelforce Orchestra (Only on CD).
LP: . . . . LILP 5164
MC: . . . . LICS 5164

SCOTLAND - THE PIPES AND DRUMS (Various artists).
Tracks: / Scotland the brave: St. Andrews Pipe Band / Highland laddie: St. Andrews Pipe Band / Brigadier snow: Polkemmet Grorud Pipe Band / Flowers of the forest, The: P.M. Angus MacDonald / Muldron Glen: Fraser, Simon University Pipe Band / Black Watch polka: Strathclyde Police Pipe Band / Colin's cattle: Shotts & Dykehead Caledonia Pipe Band / Amazing grace: Toyota Pipes & Drums / Drum fanfare: Strathclyde Police Pipe Band / Mason's apron: 78th Fraser Highlanders Pipe Band / Earl of Mansfield, The: MacLeod, P.M. Donald / Rowan tree: Shotts & Dykehead Caledonia Pipe Band / Flower of Scotland, The: Pipes/Drums/Military Band of Scottish Div.School of Music/ Conundrum, The: Dysart & Dundonald Pipe Band / Waltzing Matilda: Queensland Irish Association Pipe Band / We're no 'awa bide awa': Queensland Irish Association Pipe Band / Selection: 78th Fraser Highlanders (Only on CD) / Irish airs and reels: Polkemmet Grorud Pipe Band (Only on CD) / Medley: Triumph Street Pipe Band (Only on CD) / Highland Cathedral: Pipes/Drums/ Military Band of Scottish Div.School of Music (Only on CD).
LP: . . . . LILP 5161
MC: . . . . LICS 5161

SCOTLAND - THE SINGERS AND THE SONGS (Various artists).
Tracks: / Hail Caledonia: Nicol, James / Scotland my home: Campbell, Shona / Thistle of Scotland, The: Morrison, Peter / Ballad of Glencoe: Duffus, George / Rumour, The: Stewart, Andy / Royal mile, The: Stuart, Colin/ Teuchter music: Alexander Brothers / Of A the airts: McCue, Bill / Saturday dance, The: McKellar, Kenneth/ Culloden: Morrison, Peter / Loch Lomond: Solley, David / Four Mairies, The: Bernadette / Wee room, The: Clydesiders / Broadsword of Scotland, The: Alexander Brothers / Ba m'eudail ban: MacLeod, Donnie/ Kinloch Rannoch lullabye: Jacobites / Abide with me: Hughes, Clifford / Scotland yet: Tartan Lads/ Medley: McKellar, Kenneth (Only on CD) / Flower of Scotland: Nicol, James (Only on CD) / Dark Lochnagar: Alexander Brothers (Only on CD) / Scotland the brave: Morrison, Peter (Only on CD).
LP: . . . . LILP 5162
MC: . . . . LICS 5162

SCOTS SONG AND MUSIC - LIVE AT KINROSS FESTIVAL (Various artists).
Tracks: / Millbank cottage: Various artists / Barley mow, The: Various artists / Hash of Bennagoak: Various artists / Unst bride's march: Various artists / Cameron Highlanders, The: Various artists / False false hae ye been: Various artists / Coolie's reel: Various artists / Bonnie Galloway: Various artists / Soldier's joy: Various artists / Green grows the laurel: Various artists /

Morag's starthspey - the ale is dear: *Various artists* / Harvest home: *Various artists* / Muckle Friday fair: *Various artists* / John Spence of Uyeasound: *Various artists* / Devil he cam tae the man at the ploo, The: *Various artists* / Craw dang pussie: *Various artists* / Bonnie Banchory: *Various artists.*
LP: . . . . **SPR 1003**

SCOTS SONG AND MUSIC, VOLUME 1 (Various artists).
Tracks: / Da burn o weindalittle: *Various artists* / Laird of Drumblair, The: *Various artists* / Bonnie laddie ye gang by me: *Various artists* / Major D. Manson: *Various artists* / Oliver Jack - Willaford: *Various artists*/ Hame drunk cam I: *Various artists* / Winter is past, The: *Various artists* / Barmaid, The - carpenters reel: *Various artists* / When I wis just but sweet sixteen: *Various artists* / Humours of Bandon: *Various artists*/ Mile rarbhaisg air a ghaoil: *Various artists* / Cro cheann T Saile: *Various artists* / Crossing the minch: *Various artists* / Clatterin o the Cylde's waters: *Various artists* / Da peerie hoose ahint da burn: *Various artists.*
LP: . . . . **SPR 1001**
MC: . . . . **SPRC 1001**

SCOTTISH 2 (Golden hour of) (Various artists).
MC: . . . . **KGHMC 156**

SCOTTISH ACCORDION MAGIC (Various artists).
MC: . . . . **CAR 001**

SCOTTISH AND IRISH FOLK SONGS (Various artists).
LP: **CFP4 14497 1**

SCOTTISH FAVOURITES (Various artists).
Tracks: / Scotland the brave: *Various artists* / Travellin home: *Various artists* / These are my mountains: *Various* artists / De'il amang the tailors: *Various artists* / Dancing in Kyle: *Various artists* / Here's to the Gordons: *Various artists* / Dark Lochnagar: *Various artists* / My ain folk: *Various artists* / Scottish soldier, A: *Various artists* / Loch Maree: *Various artists* / I belong to Glasgow: *Various artists* / Down in the glen: *Various artists* / Calum's ceilidh: *Various artists* / Dark island: *Various artists* / Dashing white sergeant: *Various artists* / Cock o the north: *Various artists* / Auld scots mither o' mine: *Various artists*/ Skye boat song: *Various artists* / Five lovely lassies from Bannion: *Various artists* / Scottish working man, The: *Various artists* / Roamin in the gloamin: *Various artists* / I love a lassie: *Various artists* / She is ma daisy: *Various artists* / Stop your ticklin Jock: *Various artists* / Granny's heilan' hame: *Various artists* / Black bear, The: *Various artists.*
LP: . . . . **LBLP 2001**
MC: . . . . **ZCLBP 2001**
MC: . . . . **TGSMC 109**

SCOTTISH FAVOURITES (Various artists).
Tracks: / Mairi's wedding (reel medley): *Shand, Jimmy* / My ain folk: *Anderson, Moira* / End of the road: *Lauder,* Sir Harry / Hamilton rant medley: *Powrie, Ian Band* / Scotland the brave: *Wilson, Robert* / Haymakers, The: *Wick Scottish Dance Band* / Donald, where's yer troosers: *Stewart, Andy* / I belong to Glasgow: *Fyfe, Will*/ Pride of Scotland (waltz medley): *Wick Fiddlers* / Roamin' in the gloamin': *Logan, Jimmy* / Road and the miles to Dundee, The: *Tartan Lads* / Sound the pibroch: *Corries* / Gay gordons medley: *MacLeod, Jim & His Band*/ Rowan tree: *McKellar, Kenneth* / Amazing grace: *First Battalion Scots Guards* / Scottish soldier, A: *Stewart, Andy* / I love a lassie: *Lauder, Sir Harry* / Auld lang syne: *Glasgow Phoenix Choir.*
MC: . . . . **HR 8158**

SCOTTISH PIPE BAND FAVOURITES (Hour of internationally acclaimed trad. hits) (Various artists).
Tracks: / Amazing grace: *Various artists* / Oft in the stilly night: *Various artists* / Devil in the kitchen: *Various artists* / MacAllister's dirk: *Various artists* / Day has ended, The: *Various artists* / We're no awa' tae bide awa': *Various artists* / Flower of Scotland: *Various artists* / Scotland the brave: *Various artists* / Skye boat song: *Various artists* / Highland laddie: *Various artists.*
LP: . . . . **OCN 2025WL**
MC: . . . . **OCN 2025WK**

SCOTTISH SAMPLER (Various artists).
Tracks: / Andy Stewart medley: *Various artists* / Gaelic waltz medley: *Various artists* / Reel medley: *Various artists* / Jig medley: *Various artists* / Popular song medley: *Various artists* / Burns reel medley: *Various* artists / Burns waltz medley: *Various artists* / Strathspey medley: *Various artists* / Harry Lauder medley (Gay Gordons Tempo): *Various artists.*
LP: . . . . **REC 125**
MC: . . . . **MRMC 019**

SCOTTISH TRADITION Waulking songs from Barra (Various artists).
LP: . . . . **TNGM 111**

SCOTTISH TRADITION VOL.1 Bothy ballads-music from the N.E (Various artists).
LP: . . . . **TNGM 109**

SCOTTISH TRADITION VOL.2 Music from the Western Isles (Various artists).
LP: . . . . **TNGM 110**

SCOTTISH TRADITION VOL.4 Shetland fiddle music (Various artists).
LP: . . . . **TNGM 117**

SCOTTISH TRADITION VOL.5 Muckle sangs-Classic Scots ballads (Various artists).
2LP: . . . . **TNGM 119/D**

SCOTTISH TRADITION VOL.6 Gaelic psalms from Lewis (Various artists).
LP: . . . . **TNGM 120**

SCOTTISH TRADITION VOL.8 James Campbell of Kintail (Various artists).
MC: . . . . **TNGM 140**

SONGS OF SCOTLAND VOL.1 (Various artists).
LP: . . . . **LOCLP 1021**
MC: . . . . **XCLOC 1021**

SONGS OF SCOTLAND VOL.2 (Various artists).
MC: . . . . **ZCLOC 1027**
LP: . . . . **LOCLP 1027**

SONGS OF SCOTLAND VOL.3 (Various artists).
Tracks: / Bonnie lass O'Ballochmyle: *Various artists* / Jock O'Hazeldean: *Various artists* / Wild mountain thyme: *Clydesiders* / Will you walk: *Douglas, John* / Thistle of Scotland: *Tartan Lads* / Will ye no come back again: *Dunbar, Valerie* / Glencoe: *Gillies, Anne Lorne* / Green oak tree: *Tartan Lads* / Sweet afton: *Mallan, Peter* / Soft lowland tongue o' the borders: *Dunbar, Valerie* / Road and the miles to Dundee, The: *Douglas, John* / Land I have left, The: *Clydesiders.*
LP: . . . . **LOCLP 1032**
MC: . . . . **ZCLOC 1032**

SONGS OF SCOTLAND VOL.4 (Various artists).
Tracks: / Home to the Kyles: *Clydesiders* / Auld meal mill, The: *Gordon, Joe & Sally Logan* / Bonnie Galloway: *Mallan, Peter* / Misty islands of the highlands: *Dunbar, Valerie* / Wee sprig o'heather, A: *Tartan Lads*/ Our ain fireside: *Gillies, Anne Lorne* / Loch Lomond: *Dunbar, Valerie* / Island of Arran: *Clydesiders*/ Rowan tree: *Gillies, Anne Lorne* / Inverary Inn: *Mallan, Peter* / Old rustic bridge: *Gordon, Joe & Sally Logan* / Home that I love: *Beggars Mantle.*
LP: . . . . **LOCLP 1038**
MC: . . . . **ZCLOC 1038**

SOUNDS OF SCOTLAND (Various artists).
LP: . . . . **LIBS 4001**
MC: . . . . **LIBC 4001**

SOUNDS OF THE WEST (Various artists).
Tracks: / Welcome to my life: *Various artists* / Praise the Lord: *Various artists* / Bonnie Galloway: *Various* artists / Road to Leirinmore: *Various artists* / Waltz medley: *Various artists* / Tiny bubbles: *Various* artists / Burns medley: *Various artists* / Mother's way: *Various artists* / Rothesay Bay: *Various artists*/ Tears: *Various artists* / Somewhere between: *Various artists* / Going home: *Various artists.*
LP: . . . . **ITV 389**
MC: . . . . **KITV 389**

SPECTACULAR PIPES OF SCOTLAND (Various artists).
MC: . . . . **4 HOM 010**

SPIRIT OF SCOTLAND (Various artists).
LP: . . . . **REL 473**
MC: . . . . **REC 473**

TARTAN ALBUM (Various artists).
LP: . . . . **RELP 466**

TASTE OF TARTAN, A (Various artists).
LP: . . . . **MFP 50479**
MC: . . . . **TCMFP 50479**

THIS IS SCOTLAND (Various artists).
MC: . . . . **TCTHIS 3**

THIS IS SCOTLAND (Various artists).
Tracks: / Hundred thousand welcomes, A: *Various artists* / Amazing grace: *Various artists* / Come to the Ceilidah-John Worth's jig: *Various artists* / Dancing in Kyle: *Various artists* / Abide with me: *Various artists* / Massacre of Glencoe: *Various artists* / Jaqueline waltz: *Various artists* / Always Argyll: *Various artists*/ Punch bowl reel: *Various artists* / Archaracle midgie: *Various artists* / Bonnie Mary of Argyle: *Various artists* / Skyline of Skye: *Various artists* / Reels / 4/4 marches: *Various artists.*
MC: . . . . **KITV 354**

THIS IS SCOTLAND (EMI) (Various artists).
LP: . . . . **THIS 3**

THIS IS SCOTLAND (RCA) (Various artists).
Tracks: / Scotland the brave: *Various artists* / Killiecrankie: *Various artists* / Swingalong reels: *Various* artists / Island dance: *Various artists* / Piper's refuge: *Various artists* / Peat fire flame: *Various* artists / Marches: *Various artists* / Mingulay boat song: *Various artists* / Amazing grace: *Various artists*/ Lights in Lochindaal: *Various artists* / Set of 4 x 32 bar reels: *Various artists* / My home: *Various artists*/ Tailor, The: *Various artists* / Dashing white sergeant: *Various artists* / Singalong section: *Various artists.*
LP: . . . . **LSA 3098**
LP: . . . . **NL 25180**

THIS IS SCOTLAND VOLUME II (Various artists).
Tracks: / Bluebell polka: *McLeod, Jim & His Band* / Come by the hills: *McLeod, Jim & His Band* / Barren rocks of Aden: *Denny & Dunipace Pipe Band* / Highland laddie: *Denny & Dunipace Pipe Band* / Mhairi's wedding: *Denny* & Dunipace Pipe Band / Black bear, The: *Denny & Dunipace Pipe Band* / Take me home: *Gillies, Alasdair* / Jans dance: *Garden, Bill & His Highland Fiddle Orchestra* / Mathematician, The: *Garden, Bill & His Highland Fiddle Orchestra*/ High level, The: *Garden, Bill & His Highland Fiddle Orchestra* / Dark Island: *Anderson, Stuart* / Scotland again: *Marlettes* / Annie Laurie: *Scott, Tommy's Pipes & Strings of Scotland* / Addie Harper Jig, The: *Harper, Addie* & The Wick Trio / Garstairs dream: *Harper, Addie & The Wick Trio* / Unshackled Lord of the hills: *Harper, Addie* & The Wick Trio / Mull of Kintyre: *Scott, Tommy's Pipes & Strings of Scotland* / Yer mither: *Grant, Lou* / Ice on the road: *Oakbank Sound* / John Gillespie's dog: *Oakbank Sound* / Bird bone, The: *Oakbank Sound*/ Oor wullie: *Oakbank Sound* / Wild mountain thyme: *Ray, Barbara* / Cowal gathering: *Carmichael, John & His Band* / Eleanor: *Carmichael, John & His Band.*
MC: . . . . **KITV 427**

TILT O' THE KILT (Various artists).
2LP: . . . . **COMP 2**
MCSET: . . . . **ZCCOM 2**

TILT O' THE KILT VOL 2 (Various artists).
Tracks: / Song of the Clyde: *Various artists* / I want a bonnie lassie: *Various artists* / March medley: *Various* artists / Bonnie wee thing: *Various artists* / Lonely Scapa Flow: *Various artists* / Scottish waltz: *Various* artists / Bonnie Oban Bay: *Various artists* / Gordon Scottishe: *Various artists* / Campbeltown Loch: *Various artists* / Duke and Duchess of Edinburgh: *Various artists* / Hiking song medley: *Various artists* / By the lochside: *Various artists* / Friendly folk o' the border: *Various artists* / Waggle o' the kilt: *Various artists*/ Gay Gordons: *Various artists* / Scottish working man: *Various artists* / All along Loch Long: *Various artists*/ Legend of Scotland: *Various artists* / My lagan love: *Various artists* / Marching home: *Various artists.*
LP: . . . . **COMP 6**
MC: . . . . **ZCCOM 6**

TREASURES OF SCOTLAND (Various artists).
Tracks: / Killiecrankie: *Various artists* / St Kilda bird song: *Various artists* / Of a the airts: *Various* artists / Roseacre: *Various artists* / Scots wha ha'e: *Various artists* / Gallowa' hills, The: *Various* artists / Massacre of Glencoe: *Various artists* / Johnny Cope: *Various artists* / Road to the isles, The: *Various artists* / Dancing in Kyle: *Various artists* / Isle of Arran: *Various artists* / Goodwife admit the wanderer: *Various artists* / Ca the ewes: *Various artists* / Loch Maree Islands: *Various artists*/ Dunkeld volunteers, The: *Various artists.*
LP: . . . . **LILP 5113**
MC: . . . . **LICS 5113**

TRIBUTE IN SONG TO ROBERT BURNS (Various artists).
Tracks: / There was a man: *Various artists* / Bonnie lass O'Ballochmyle: *Various artists* / John Anderson my Jo: *Various artists* / There was a lad: *Various artists* / Ae fond kiss: *Various artists* / My love is like a red red rose: *Various artists* / Man's a man, A: *Various artists* / Ye banks and braes: *Various artists*/ Ca' the Yowes: *Various artists* / Corn rigs: *Various artists* / Aye waukin' O: *Various artists* / Sweet afton: *Various artists* / Lea rig, The: *Various artists* / Star o' Rabbie Burns, The: *Various artists.*
LP: . . . . **LOCLP 1039**
MC: . . . . **ZCLOC 1039**

VOICE OF SCOTLAND (Various artists).
LP: . . . . **ONCR 525**
MC: . . . . **TC ONCR 525**

WELCOME TO SCOTLAND (Various artists).
Tracks: / Scotland the brave: *Various artists* (4/4 and 2/4 marches) / Highland laddie: *Various artists* (4/4 and 2/4 marches) / Earl of Mansfield: *Various artists* (4/4 and 2/4 marches) / Barren rocks of Aden: *Various artists*/ Northern lights of old Aberdeen: *Various artists* (Medley) / Rothesay bay: *Various artists* (Medley) / I belong to Glasgow: *Various artists* (Medley) / Tommy darling: *Various artists* (Gay Gordon) / Horo my nut brown maiden: *Various artists* (Gay Gordon) / Jeannie's bawbee: *Various artists* (Gay Gordon) / Piper o'Dundee, The: *Various* artists (Gay Gordon) / Mull of Kintyre: *Various artists* (Gay Gordon) / De'ils awa' with the exciseman, The: *Various* artists (The De'ils conundrum) / Conundrum (The): *Various artists* (The De'ils Conundrum) / Devil among the tailors: *Various artists* (The De'ils Conundrum) / Maggie: *Various artists* (The De'ils Conundrum) / Up in the morning early: *Various artists* (6/8 marches) / O'er the water to Charlie: *Various artists* (6/8 marches) / Cam ye by Atholl: *Various artists* (6/8 marches) / Haggis song: *Various artists* (6/8 marches) / Dark island: *Various artists*(Slow airs with organ accompaniment) / Mist covered mountains The: *Various artists* (Slow airs with organ accompaniment) / Roxburgh castle: *Various artists* (Border reel) / Hamilton rant: *Various artists* (Border reel) / Miss Jane of Violetbank: *Various artists* (Border reel) / Moving cloud: *Various artists* (Border reel) / Song of the Clyde: *Various artists* (Border reel) / Isle of Mull: *Various artists* (Slow air 3/4 march, 2/4 march) / Kilworth hills: *Various artists* (Slow air 3/4 march, 2/4 march) / Scotch on the rocks: *Various artists* (Slow air 3/4 march, 2/4 march) / Scots wha' hae: *Various artists* (Rabbie Burns marches) / Duncan Gray: *Various artists* (Rabbie Burns marches) / We kirkcudbright centipede: *Various artists* (Rabbie Burns marches) / Scottish soldier, A: *Various artists*(Andy Stewart favourites) / Road and the miles to Dundee, The: *Various artists* (Andy Stewart favourites) / Take me back: *Various artists* (Andy Stewart favourites) / Campbeltown Loch: *Various artists* / Muckin' o' Geordie's byre: *Various* artists (Andy Stewart favourites) / Donald, where's yer troosers: *Various artists* (Andy Stewart favourites) / Wild rover: *Various artists* (Andy Stewart favourites) / Farewell my love: *Various artists* (Andy Stewart favourites) / Stop your ticklin' Jock: *Various artists* (Hooked on Scotch) / Loch Lomond: *Various artists* (Hooked on Scotch) / Flowers of Scotland: *Various artists* (Hooked on Scotch) / Will ye come back again: *Various artists* (Hooked on Scotch) / We're no awa' tae bide awa': *Various artists* (Hooked on Scotch) / Auld lang syne: *Various artists*(Hooked on Scotch) / Nut brown: *Various artists* / Flowers of Edinburgh: *Various artists* / Lass o' paties mill: *Various artists* / Davy nick nack: *Various artists* / Highland road, The: *Various artists* / He's aye a kissing me: *Various artists* / Mhic Iarla na bratach bana: *Various artists* / Annie Laurie: *Various artists*/ Piper o'Dundee, The: *Various artists* / Cam ye by Atholl: *Various artists* / Cameron men, The: *Various artists*/ Bluebells of Scotland: *Various artists* / Peat fire flame: *Various artists* / De'il amang the tailors (medley): *Various artists* / Willie's gane tae Melville Castle: *Various artists* / Mairi's wedding: *Various artists*/ West country barn dance Abercairney highlanders: *Various artists* / Man's a man, A: *Various artists* / Jim Bais wedding march: *Various artists* / 72nd highlanders, The: *Various artists* / Farewell to Aberdeen: *Various artists* / Scotland is my ain hame: *Various artists* / Dornoch links, The: *Various artists.*
LP: . . . . **BER 019**
MC: . . . . **KBER 019**
MC: . . . . **KGEC 1226**

WELCOME TO SCOTLAND Musical tour in song and dance (Various artists).
LP: **GLNA501**

WELCOME TO THE HIGHLANDS (Various artists).
LP: . . . . **WGR 074**

MC: . . . . CWGR 074

WHITE HEATHER CLUB, THE (Various artists).
MC: . . . . HR 8195

WORLD OF SCOTLAND (Various artists).
LP: . . . . SPA 41
MC: . . . . KCSP 41

WORLD OF SCOTLAND VOL.2 (Various artists).
LP: . . . . SPA 420
MC: . . . . KCSP 420

YELLOW ON THE BROOM, THE (Various artists).
Tracks: / Yellow on the broom, The: *Lovie, Robert* / Oor fairm toon: *Murray, Duncan* / Drumdelgie: *Dawson*, Sandy / Buchan Bobby, The: *Duncan, John* / It's lonely in the bothy: *Hepburn, Geordie* / Bonnie briar bush, The: *Various artists* / Ploughboy, The: *Various artists* / Kitchie deem, The: *Various artists* / Neeps tae pluck: *Various artists* / Wedding of McGinnis, The: *Various artists* / Orraman's lament: *Various artists*/ North east shore, The: *Various artists* / Barnyards of Delgaty, The: *Various artists* / MacFarlane O'the sprots O burniboozie: *Various artists* / Buchan ploorman, The: *Various artists*.
MC: . . . . CWGR 122

Scotland World Cup

EASY EASY (LP).
LP: 2383 282

SCOTLAND WORLD CUP SQUAD Argentina 1978.
LP: . . . . KLP 08

Scotrail Vale Of ...

BOTH SIDES OF THE TRACKS (Scotrail Vale Of Atholl Pipe Band).
LP: . . . . LAP 115
MC: . . . . LAP 115C

NO RESERVATIONS (Scotrail Vale Of Atholl Pipe Band).
Tracks: / Zito the bubbleman / Marjorie Lowe / Gallowglass, The / Jig (4th horn concerto - Mozart) / House in St. Peter's, The / Monymusk / Mrs. Stewart of Grandtully / Miss Monaghan's / Maggie's pancakes / Hawk, The / March/Strathspey/Reel / John McDonald of Glencoe / Atholl cummers, The / John Morrison of Assynt House / Isobel Blackley / Sweeny's Reel / Molly Rankine's / Hogties' reel / Kenny the Sparrowman / Boys of Ballmote, The / Double Rise, The / Brest St. Mark jig / Hag at the churn, The / Smeceno Horo / Moutains of Pomeroy, The / Thomas Maxwell of Briarsbush / Garba Chriochan / Snug in the blanket / Congress reel, The / John Keith Laing / Hills of Kowloon, The / L.L. Wade's Welcome to Inverness / Lyndhurst / Killoran Bay / St. Jean-des-Vignes / Summertime / Big parcel, The / Jim Blakeley / Mrs. Macleod of Raasay / Galician jigs.
LP: . . . . LAP 122
MC: . . . . LAP 122C

SALUTATIONS (Scotrail Vale Of Atholl Pipe Band).
MC: . . . . DUNCAS 005

Scots Country Comfort

STILL ROLLIN'.
LP: . . . . WGR 043
MC: . . . . CWGR 043

Scots Guards...

AMAZING GRACE (Scottish Division, Pipe & Drums).
Tracks: / Amazing grace / Cock o' the north / Bluebells of Scotland / Scotland the brave / Kumbaya / Auld lang syne.
LP: . . . . CDS 1116

BAND OF THE SCOTS GUARDS.
LP: . . . . SFXL 54

CLASSICAL SPECTACULAR (live at the Royal Albert Hall)(see under Royal Philharmonic (Scots Guards/Welsh Guards bands/Royal Philharmonic Orchestra).

PIPES AND DRUMS (Scots Guards Pipes & Drums Band).
Tracks: / March medley / March medley / March, strathspey and reel medley / Solo pipes / March medley / Slow march medley / March medley / Drum display / March medley / March, strathspey and reel medley / Solo pipes / March medley / March medley / March medley / Regimental quick march.
LP: . . . . BND 1043
MC: . . . . ZC BND 1043

SCOTS GUARDS SALUTE TO THE COMMONWEALTH, THE.
Tracks: / Spirit of pageantry / Irish washerwoman, The / Highland gathering / Waltzing Matilda / Welsh rhapsody / Swinging safari / Falklands, The / Highland rose / Carnival from 'Caribbean cameo' / Wellington waltz / Alouette / English suite.
LP: . . . . PRM 108D
MC: . . . . CPRM 108D

Scott, Bobby

COMPOSTIONS OF BOBBY SCOTT, THE.
LP: . . . . FS 208

Scott, Bon

EARLY YEARS (Scott, Bon & Valentinos).
Tracks: / To know you is to love you / She said / Everyday I have to cry / I can't dance with you / Peculiar hole in the sky / Love makes sweet music / I can hear raindrops / Why me / Sooky Sooky.
LP: C5-520
MC: C5K-520

SEASONS OF CHANGE 1968-72.
LP: . . . . RVLP 33

Scott, Elfrida

BURNS SONGS IN GAELIC.
Tracks: / Soraidh mhic a' phearsain / Se an duin am fear get tha sin / Sheumasaich do n ainm, A / Tha mo chridhe sa ghaidhealtachd / Fhathast na mo dhuisg / Truis na h'oisgean / Bruaichean abhainn duin / Ruith socair shruth ach duinn / Cruachan arbhair / Mac Anndrais mo ghradh / Feuch sa a ghraidh cia gorm a choill / Uilleam thog e peice braich.
MC: . . . . CTRAX 042

BY YON CASTLE WA'.
Tracks: / Lovely Argyll / Caledonia / I know a lad / Let him go let him tarry.
MC: . . . . CWGR 101

Scott, Ellie

LOOK FOR ME.
Tracks: / Look for me / Heart over mind / Together again / Dog like that / I wouldn't want to live / In my Tennessee mountain home / Come on Ellie / My grandfather's clock / Almost persuaded / Before I met you / Little green valley / Without knowing.
LP: . . . . BSS 310

Scott, Isaac

BIG TIME BLUES MAN.
Tracks: / Help / Listen to the blues / Standing on the outside / Seattle blues / Moonbelly / Don't let my baby ride / Let my mind run back / Feast goin' on / On the road again.
LP: . . . . RL 046

ISAAC SCOTT BLUES BAND (Scott, Isaac Blues Band).
Tracks: / There's gotta be a change / Ice cold / Same old blues / You send me / Rock me / Going back to Oakland / Blues at midnight / Steal away / Honky tonk.
LP: . . . . RL 023

Scott, Jack

BURNING BRIDGES.
Tracks: / What in the world's come over you / Burning bridges / Oh, little one / Cool water / Patsy / Is there something on your mind / My dream come true / Steps one and two / All I see is blue / Laugh and the world laughs with you / It only happened yesterday / Little feeling called love, A.
LP: . . . . JAS 305
MC: . . . . JAS C305

GREASEBALL.
Tracks: / Greaseball ((Previously unissued)) / Lonesome Mary ((Previously unissued)) / Cryin' in my beer ((Previously unissued)) / Troubles brewin' ((Previously unissued)) / True love is blind ((Previously unissued)) / Precious Lord ((Previously unissued)) / Baby baby / Good deal Lucille / You can bet your bottom dollar / I'm satisfied with you / Bella / Baby Marie.
LP: . . . . DJLP 2050
LP: . . . . BB 2050

GRIZZILY BEAR.
Tracks: / Two timin' woman / Baby she's gone / You can bet your bottom dollar / Baby baby / Found a woman / Oh little one / Patsy / Cruel world / Good deal Lucille / What in the world's come over you / Burning bridges / It only happened yesterday / Now that I / Steps one and two / Little feeling called love, A / Strange desire / My dream come true / One of these days / Grizzly bear / Cry cry cry / You only see what you wanna see / Part where I cry, The / Strangers / Laugh and the world laughs with you / Meo myo / Sad story / I can't hold your letters / If only / Green green valley / Before the bird flies / May you never be alone / Insance / Face to the wall / You're just getting better / As you take a walk through my mind.
2LP: . . . . CDX 12

I REMEMBER HANK WILLIAMS.
LP: . . . . BUY 034

JACK SCOTT.
Tracks: / Baby she's gone / Two timin' woman / What am I living for / Go wild / Little Sadie / There comes a time / I never felt like this / With your love / Leroy / Geraldine / Way I walk, The / Midgie / My true love / Save my soul / Goodbye baby.
LP: . . . . BB 2022
LPPD: . . . . BB 2035

JACK SCOTT (16 TRACKS).
LP: . . . . KK 794

LEGENDARY, THE.
LP: . . . . BBR 1003
MLP: . . . . BBR 0024

SCOTT ON GROOVE.
Tracks: / Flakey John / Jingle bell slide / There's trouble brewin / Tall tales / Wiggle on out / I knew you first / Blue skies (moving in on me) / I prayed for an angel / Separation's now granted / Thou shalt not steal / Road keeps winding, The ((Previously unissued)) / Let's learn to live and love again / Don't hush the laughter / This is where I came in ((Previously unissued)) / Looking for Linda / I hope, I think, I wish / Standing on the outside looking in ((Previously unissued)) / Gone again ((Previously unissued)) / I don't believe in tealeaves / What a wonderful night out.
LP: . . . . BFX 15005

SPIRIT MOVES ME, THE.
LP: . . . . RM 348

WHAT IN THE WORLD'S COME OVER YOU (LP).
LP: . . . . BUY 024

Scott, John

SOUTHWARK CATHEDRAL ORGAN.
LP: . . . . ACA 507

Scott, Mabel

FINE FINE BABY.
Tracks: / Elevator boogie / Give me a man / Don't cry baby / Baseball boogie / Have you ever watched love die / Subway blues / Catch 'em young, treat 'em rough, tell 'em nothin' / Boogie woogie choo choo train / No more cryin' the blues / Disgusted / Somebody goofed / Wailin' daddy / Yes! / Mr. Fine / Mabel blues.
LP: . . . . JB 606

Scott, Margaretta

ALICE IN WONDERLAND & THROUGH THE LOOKING GLASS (See under Carroll, Lewis) (Scott, Margaretta & Jane Asher).

Scott, Marilyn

I GOT WHAT DADDY LIKE (Scott, Marilyn/Mary Deloatch).
LP: . . . . KM 710

Scott, Millie

I CAN MAKE IT GOOD FOR YOU.
Tracks: / I can make it good for you / Maybe tonight / It's my life / Keep it to yourself / I wanna be yours / To the letter / Love of your own, A / Heaven / Key, The / Falling in love.
MC: . . . . BRCA 522
LP: . . . . BRLP 522

LOVE ME RIGHT.
Tracks: / 2 hot 2 handle / Every little bit / One stop lover / Don't take your love / Love me right / Let's talk it over / Can't stand the heat / Automatic / Prisoner of love.
LP: . . . . BRLP 511
MC: . . . . BRCA 511

Scott, Ossie

MY WAY.
LP: . . . . TDWD 9

REGGAE EXPOSURE WITH SAX.
Tracks: / It's not too late to dance / Only time will tell / Moods and magic / Bless you / I just want to be your everything / Easy loving / Time is the master / Julia.
LP: . . . . LDLP 006
LP: . . . . HM 114

SUPREME SOUNDS OF OSSIE SCOTT, THE.
Tracks: / Secret love / Honey / Now is the hour.
LP: . . . . VSLP 4013

WONDERFUL SOUND OF OSSIE SCOTT.
LP: . . . . TDWD 14

WONDERFUL SOUNDS OF OSSIE SCOTT, THE.
LP: . . . . WER/LP 115

Scott, Peggy

LOVERS' HOLIDAY (see Benson, Jo Jo) (Scott, Peggy & Jo Jo Benson).

SOUL SHAKE (Scott, Peggy & Jo Jo Benson).
Tracks: / Lover's holiday / Picking wild mountain berries / Love will come breaking up on you / Pure love and pleasure / Magic fingers / I want to love you baby / It's the only way / Big city blues / Soul shake / Doing our thing / Over the hill underground / True soul lovin' / Money don't satisfy / We got our bag / Every little bit hurts / You can never get something for nothing.
LP: . . . . CRB 1122

Scott, Pete

DON'T PANIC.
Tracks: / Misty / Remembered by / One of these days / Peeping Tom / Where do I go from here? / Too late to say that now / Cat wants a kipper / Twilight is the time / Down among the dead men / Mrs. Hayes / Little Boy Blue / Winter train / Someone else's dreams.
LP: . . . . RUB 003

JIMMY THE MOONLIGHT.
Tracks: / Too much to lose / Baby stay / Look at the rain / All come back on you / Old-fashioned girl / Suzy's song / Home on a cloud / Keramoti / Houseboat song.
LP: . . . . RUB 020

Scott, Ray

REAL MEMPHIS SOUND VOLUME 2, THE.
Tracks: / Boppin' wigwam Willie / Tonight will be the last time / Boy meets girl / I just don't figure / Loving wanting you / Whispering winds / Fool he used to be / Say anything but not goodbye / Train's done gone, the / Just behind your smile / You drive me crazy / San Antone / My life's desire / I'll never be dreamer / Wedding bells / So long I'm gone.
LP: . . . . WLP 8913

Scott, Raymond

BUSINESS MAN'S BOUNCE.
LP: . . . . GELP 15029

POPULAR MUSIC.
LP: . . . . SWH 31

RAYMOND SCOTT AND ORCHESTRA, VOL. 2 1944 (Scott, Raymond & Orchestra).
LP: . . . . HSR 211

Scott, Rena

LOVE ZONE.
LP: . . . . SDI 7511

Scott, Rhoda

RHODA SCOTT IN NEW YORK.
LP: 920417

Scott, Ronnie

BATTLE ROYAL (Scott, Ronnie & Kenny Graham).
Tracks: / Not so fast / Battle royal / Fast / Twins' bed / Smoke gets in your eyes / Scott's expedition / Avalon / Love me or leave me / Nemo / Troubled air / Eureka / Seven eleven / All the things you are.
LP: . . . . ESQ 311

BOP AT CLUB 11 (See under Dankworth, Johnnie) (Scott, Ronnie/ Johnnie Dankworth).

GREAT SCOTT VOLUME 1.
LP: . . . . ESQ 303

LIVE AT THE JAZZ CLUB, VOLUME 1 (Scott, Ronnie & His Orchestra).
Tracks: / Popo / Pantagrulian / Mullenium / Nearness of you, The / Nemo / All the things you are / Champ, The / Daydream / On the alamo / What's new / I may be wrong.
LP: . . . . ESQ 328

MUSIC FROM RONNIE'S.
2LP: 11PP 603

SERIOUS GOLD.
Tracks: / Invitation / Lazy afternoon / Forty colours / Hey-oke sweet ballad / Send in the clowns / Interfusion.
LP: . . . . NSPL 18542
MC: . . . . ZCP 18542

Scott, Russell

FRIENDS AND NEIGHBOURS.
Tracks: / Friends & neighbours / Autumn concerto / I'll see you again / Love / Lucky day / My prayer / How soon / Dream / Autumn leaves / Anniversary song.
LP: . . . . DS 048

MUSIC AND DANCING WITH RUSSELL SCOTT.
Tracks: / Baby face / Congratulations / Mountain greenery / True love / Edelweiss / Cara mia / C'est si bon / Fine romance, A / As time goes by / Gipsy / Dearly beloved / Maria Elena / Please / I'm everybody's fool.
LP: . . . . DS 036
MC: . . . . TDS 036

Scott, Shirley

BLUE FLAMES (Scott, Shirley/Stanley Turrentine).
Tracks: / Funky fox, The / Hip knees and legs / Five spot after dark / Grand Street / Flamingo.
LP: . . . . PR 7338

MC: . . . . PRC 7338

Scott, Sir Walter

IVANHOE (Pigott-Smith, Tim (nar)).
MCSET: **418 000-4**
MCSET: . . . . **ARGO 1076**

Scott, Sonny

COMPLETE CHRONOLOGICAL (1933).
LP: . . . . **BD 2020**

Scott, Tim

HIGH LONESOME SOUND,THE.
Tracks: / Sound of thunder, The / I could be anything / Great escape, The / Easy time / Release / Low ride / Fire down / In this world / High hopes / Under a new heaven / Hey sister.
LP: . . . . **K 9241371**
MC: . . . . **K 9241374**

Scott, Tom

BEST OF TOM SCOTT.
Tracks: / New York connection / Spindrift / Breezin' easy / Dirty old man / Nite creatures / Shadows / Rock island rocket / Time and love / Tom cat / Gotcha.
LP: . . . . **CBS 84347**

BLOW IT OUT.
Tracks: / Blow it out.
MC: **4678964**

DESIRE.
Tracks: / Desire / Sure enough / Only one, The / Stride / Johnny B. Badd / Meet somebody / Maybe I'm amazed / Chunk of funk.
LP: . . . . **K 52411**

FLASHPOINT.
LP: . . . . **GRPA 9571-1**
MC: . . . . **GRPM 9571-4**

INTIMATE STRANGERS.
Tracks: / Intimate strangers / Sudden attractions / Hi steppers / Day and nite out together / Getaway / Nite creatures / Loving and leaving / Lost inside the love of you / Do you feel me now / Breezin' easy / You're so good to me / Puttin' the bite on you / Beautiful music.
LP: . . . . **CBS 83309**

KEEP THIS LOVE ALIVE.
Tracks: / If you're not the one for me (Vocals: Brenda Russell and Bill Champlin) / Miz thang (instrumental) / Keep this love alive (Vocals: David Pack) / Kilimanjaro (instrumental) / Reason for the rain (Vocal: Bill Champlin) / Givin' our best (instrumental) / Only a heartbeat away (Vocal: Will Lee) / You mean everything to me / Whenever you dream of me (Vocal: Diane Schuur.).
LP: . . . . **GRP 96461**
MC: . . . . **GRP 96464**

STREAMLINES.
LP: . . . . **GRP 91044**
MC: . . . . **GRPM 91044**

THEM CHANGES.
Tracks: / Zoot suit / Pick up the pieces / Chester and Bruce / Desire / Them changes / Too hot / Serpentine fire / Dahomey dance / We belong together (Only on CD.).
LP: . . . . **GRP 96131**
MC: . . . . **GRP 96134**

Scott, Tommy

PIPES AND STRINGS OF SCOTLAND.
Tracks: / Pride of bonnie Scotland, The / Ode to joy / Abide with me / Scottish banner, The / 'Tis a gift (to be simple) / Bonnie Mary of Argyle / Send in the clowns / Jesu, joy of man's desiring / Rose of Kelvingrove, The / Song of the wind / Scott's choice / Light of the morning / Little drummer boy / Carnival is over, The.
LP: . . . . **ITV 394**
LP: . . . . **ITV 456**
MC: . . . . **KITV 456**

PIPES AND STRINGS OF SCOTLAND VOL.2.
Tracks: / From Scotland with love / Sailing / Scotland forever / Marching home / Mull of Kintyre / Plaisir D'amour / Going home / Sands of time / Amazing Grace / Home of mine / Il Silenzio / McWhinnie's salute / Rememberance / Auld lang syne / Loch Lomond / Skye boat song.
LP: . . . . **ITV 362**
MC: . . . . **KITV 362**

TOMMY SCOTT AND HIS PIPES AND DIXIE BANDS.
MC: . . . . **KITV 521**

TOMMY SCOTT COLLECTION.
Tracks: / Scotland forever / My ain folk / Going home / Old Scots mother mine / Glencoe / Rowan tree / Abide with me / Road to Dundee, The / Amazing Grace / Flower of Scotland / Bonnie Mary of Argyle / Auld lang syne.
LP: . . . . **ITV 431**
MC: . . . . **KITV 431**

TOMMY SCOTT'S HOPSCOTCH CEILIDH PARTY.
LP: . . . . **ITV 528**
MC: . . . . **KITV 528**

TOMMY SCOTT'S ROYALE HIGHLAND SHOWBAND (Scott, Tommy's Royale Highland Showband).
Tracks: / Red river rose / March march march all the way / Morag of Dunvegan / Mingulay boat song / Maggie may / Day is ended / P.K.'s salute / Pigeon on the gate / Pipes o' Drummond / De'il among the tailors / Kilt is my delight, The / Pipers patrol / Mount Fuji / Water is wide, The / Flute salad / Dark island / May kway o'may kway / High road to Linton.
LP: . . . . **ITV 426**
MC: . . . . **KITV 426**

TOMMY SCOTT'S SCOTLAND.
Tracks: / Annie Laurie / Dark Lochnagar / Great Glen, The / Skye boat song / Amazing Grace / Flower of Scotland / Will ye no come back again / Scotland forever / My love is like a red red rose / Flowers of the forest / Rowan tree / Green trees of Tyrol / My Ain folk / Auld lang syne.
LP: . . . . **ITV 411**
MC: . . . . **KITV 411**

Scott, Toni

CHIEF, THE.
LP: . . . . **CHAMP 1022**
MC: . . . . **CHAMPK 1022**

Scott, Tony

52ND STREET SCENE.
Tracks: / Blues for the street / Love is just around the corner / Body and soul / Mop mop / Lester leaps in / Lover man (oh where can you be) / Woody 'n' you / Round midnight / Ornithology.
LP: . . . . **JASM 1011**

AFRICAN BIRD.
Tracks: / African bird (suite) / Spirits return / Spirits dance / Come back Mother Africa / African bird / Requiem for lost spirits.
LP: . . . . **SN 1083**

BOTH SIDES OF TONY SCOTT (Scott, Tony Quartet).
Tracks: / Cry me a river / My funny Valentine / Star dust / More than you know / Everything happens to me / Counterpoint pleasant / East coast, west side / You and I.
LP: . . . . **FS 335**

MODERN ART OF JAZZ, THE.
LP: . . . . **FS 238**

MUSIC FOR ZEN MEDITATION.
Tracks: / Is not all one? / Murmuring sound of the mountain / Quivering leaf, ask the wind / After the snow the fragrance / To drift like clouds / Za-zan (meditation) / Prajina paramita hridya sutra / Sanzan (moment of truth) / Satori (enlightenment).
LP: **2304 138**

SUNG HEROES.
Tracks: / Misery (to lady day) / Portrait of Anne Frank / Remembrance of Art Tatum / Requiem for 'Hot Lips' Page / Blues for an African friend / For Stefan Wolpe / Israel / Memory of my father / Lament to manolete.
LP: . . . . **SSC 1015**

TONY SCOTT PLAYS GYPSY.
LP: . . . . **FS 248**

Scott, Willie

SHEPHERD'S SONG, THE.
Tracks: / Shepherd's song / Piper MacNeil / Kielder hunt, The / Jamie Raeburn / Bonnie wee trampin' lass / Bloody Waterloo / Jock geddes / Dowie dens of Yarrow, The / Herd laddie o' the glen / Lads that were reared among heather, The.
LP: **12T 183**

Scott-Heron, Gil

1980 (Scott-Heron, Gil & Brian Jackson).
Tracks: / Shut 'um down / Alien (hold on to your dream) / Willing / Corners / 1980 / Push comes to shove / Shah Mot / Late last night.
LP: **201733**

BEST OF GIL SCOTT-HERON.
Tracks: / Revolution will not be televised, The / Bottle, The / Winter in America / Ain't no such thing as Superman / Re-Ron / Shut 'um down / Angel dust / B movie.
LP: **206618**
MC: **406618**

GLORY (The Gil Scott Heron Collection).
Tracks: / Johannesburg / Revolution will not be televised, The / Blue collar / New York City / Hello Sunday hello road / We almost lost Detroit / Angel dust / Bottle, The / Winter in America / Delta man / South Carolina (Barnwell) / Inner city blues / Show bizness / B Movie / Lady Day and John Coltrane / I think I'll call it morning / You can depend on (the train from Washington) / Shut 'um down / Ain't no such thing as superman / Klan, The / Fast lane / Race track in France / Storm music / Save the children / Song for Bobby Smith / Beginnings / Legend in his own mind.
2LP: **303913**
MCSET: **503913**

MOVING TARGET.
Tracks: / Fast lane / Washington DC / No exit / Blue collar / Explanations / Ready or not / Black history of the world.
LP: **204921**

REFLECTIONS.
Tracks: / Storm music / Grandma's hands / Is that jazz? / Morning thoughts / Inner city blues / Siege of New Orleans / Gun / B movie.
LP: . . . . **SPART 1180**

REVOLUTION WILL NOT BE TELEVISED, THE.
Tracks: / Revolution will not be televised, The / Sex education - ghetto style / Get out of the ghetto blues, The / No knock / Lady Day and John Coltrane / Pieces of a man / Home is where the hatred is / Brother / Save the children / Whitey on the moon / Did you hear what they said? / When you are who you are / I think I'll call it morning / Sign of the ages, A / Or down you fall / Needle's eye, The / Prisoner, The.
LP: . . . . **NL 86994**
MC: . . . . **NK 86994**

TALES OF GIL.
Tracks: / Washington D.C / Save the children / Angel dust / Gun / Blue collar / Alien (hold on to your dream) / Three miles down / Bottle, The / Winter in America / Is that jazz / 'B' Movie.
2LP: . . . . **ESDLP 021**
MCSET: . . . . **ESDMC 021**

Scottish

BEST IN SCOTTISH DANCE MUSIC, THE VOL.1 (Various artists).
Tracks: / Hamilton House: *Various artists* / MacPhail's reels: *Various artists* / Polka: *Various artists* / Duke of Perth: *Various artists* / Scottish waltz: *Various artists* / Scottish reform: *Various artists* / Marching with Robin: *Various artists* / Bagpipe medley: *Various artists* / Highland laddie: *Various artists* / Lea rig, The: *Various artists* / Hesitation waltz, The: *Various artists* / Isle of Skye: *Various artists* / Maxwell's rant: *Various artists* / Dunoon barn dance: *Various artists.*
LP: . . . . **C 1004**
MC: . . . . **TC 1004**

BEST IN SCOTTISH DANCE MUSIC, THE VOL.2 (Various artists).
Tracks: / Highland laddie: *Various artists* / Blue bonnets o'er the border: *Various artists* / Reels: *Various artists* / Waltz: *Various artists* / Duncan barn dance: *Various artists* / Scottish ramble: *Various artists* / Trip to Bavaria: *Various artists* / Eva three step: *Various artists* / Dundee whaler: *Various artists* / Waltzes: *Various artists* / Two and two: *Various artists* / Polka: *Various artists* / New Ashludie rant: *Various artists* / Scottish waltz selection: *Various artists.*
LP: . . . . **C 1005**
MC: . . . . **TC 1005**

NATIONAL FESTIVAL OF POPULAR SCOTTISH MUSIC (Various artists).
Tracks: / Roses of Prince Charlie: *Morrison, Peter* / Bonnie lass o' Bon Accord: *MacLeod, Jim & His Band* / Gallant forty twa: *Dunbar, Valerie* / Granny's heilan' hame: *Dunbar, Valerie* / Schiehallion: *Gaberlunzie* / Rowan tree: *Gonnella, Ron* / Rap tap tap: *Mallan, Peter* / Johnnie Cope: *Glasgow Phoenix Choir* / Hame of mine: *McCue, Bill* / Take me back: *Stewart, Andy* / We'd better bide a wee: *Gordon, Joe & Sally Logan* / Flower of Scotland: *Shotts & Dykehead...* / Troy's wedding: *Shotts & Dykehead...* / Crossing the minch: *Shotts & Dykehead...* / Kismuils galley: *McDonald, Alastair* / Burnie boozie: *Tartan Lads* / Rustic brig, The: *Tartan Lads* / Aye waukin' o: *Caledonia choir* / Laird of Drumblair, The: *Pattullo, Gordon* / Mason's apron: *Pattullo, Gordon* / Ae fond kiss: *Dunbar, Valerie* / Broad sword of Scotland, The: *McCue, Bill* / Jacqueline waltz: *Carmichael, John & His Band* / Bonnie Dundee: *McDonald, Alastair* / Rose of Allandale: *Logan, Sally & Gordon* / Green oak tree: *Tartan Lads* / Mary of Argyll: *Mallan, Peter* / Rowan tree: *Various artists* / A loo nae a ladie but ane: *Various artists* / Bonnie Prince Charlie: *Various artists* / Up in the morning early: *Various artists* / Rustic brig: *Shotts & Dykehead Caledonia Pipe Band* / Andy where's your kilt: *Stewart, Andy* / Isle of Mull: *Various artists* / Atholl and Breadalbane gathering: *Various artists* / Lady Madeline Sinclair: *Various artists* / High road to Linton: *Gonnella, Ron* / Muckin' o' Geordie's byre: *Morrison, Peter* / Dunblane: *MacLeod, Jim & His Band* / Old folks: *Gaberlunzie.*
2LP: . . . . **KLPD 4001**

Scottish Chamber

AN OLD FASHIONED CHRISTMAS.
Tracks: / Let's have an old-fashioned Christmas / O little town of Bethlehem / Away in a manger / Twelve days of Christmas, The / Benedicamus domino / Deck the hall / We three kings of Orient are / Hawaiian lullaby / Child in a manger / Shepherd's farewell, The (Berlioz) / Hark the herald angels sing / In dulci jubilo / Stille nacht / Mary's boy child / Little drummer boy / Rudolf the red-nosed reindeer / I saw mummy kissing Santa Claus / Tomorrow shall be my dancing day / Ding dong merrily on high / O come all ye faithful.
MC: . . . . **MVPC 829**
LP: . . . . **MVP 829**

ROSSINI OVERTURES (See under Rossini for full details).

SCOTTISH AND ITALIAN SYMPHONIES (See under Mendelssohn (composer)).

SCOTTISH AND ITALIAN SYMPHONIES (MENDELSSOHN) (see under Mendelssohn (composer)).

SERENADE FOR STRINGS IN E (See under Dvorak (Composer)).

SULLIVAN OVERTURES (See under Gilbert and Sullivan).

VIOLIN CONCERTOS 4 & 5 (See under Mozart).

Scottish Dance Band...

ACCORDION CLUB NIGHT (Scottish Dance Band & Solo Instrumentalists).
LP: . . . . **LILP 5013**

Scottish Fiddle Orch.

FIDDLER'S PARTY, THE.
MCSET: . . . . **RECD 485**

FIDDLERS RALLY VOL 1 (KELVIN HALL).
LP: . . . . **REL 454**
MC: . . . . **REC 454**

FIDDLERS RALLY VOL 2 (KELVIN HALL).
LP: . . . . **REL 455**
MC: . . . . **REC 455**

FIDDLERS TO THE FORE.
2LP: . . . . **RELD 472**
MCSET: . . . . **RECD 472**

GREAT PERFORMANCES (Scottish Fiddle Orchestra & John Mason).
LP: . . . . **SFO 2**
MC: . . . . **ZCSFO 2**

PRINCE OF THE MISTS.
LP: . . . . **RELS 484**
MC: . . . . **RECS 484**

SCOTTISH FIDDLE ORCHESTRA AT THE ROYAL ALBERT HALL, THE.
2LP: . . . . **RELD 464**
MCSET: . . . . **RECD 464**

SCOTTISH FIDDLERS PROM.
2LP: . . . . **RELD 470**
MCSET: . . . . **RECD 470**

TAM O'SHANTER AND CUTTY-SARK OVERTURE, THE.
LP: . . . . **REL 475**
MC: . . . . **REC 475**

Scottish Folk...

FREEDOM COME ALL YE (Scottish Folk Singers For Ethiopia).
LP: . . . . **WHR 001**

Scottish Gas...

SCOTTISH GAS CALEDONIA PIPE BAND (Scottish Gas Caledonia Pipe Band).
LP: . . . . **LAP 121**

Scottish & Irish ..

TUNES OF GLORY (Scottish & Irish Imports Pipe Band).
Tracks: / Medley / 3/4 marches / Tunes of glory / Amazing grace / 6/8 marches / March strathspey and reel / Breton set / Medley (2).
LP: . . . . **LILP 5167**
MC: . . . . **LICS 5167**

Scottish National...

CHRISTMAS CAROLS Cond. John Currie (Scottish National Orchestra/ Chorus).
Tracks: / I saw three ships / Still the night / Past 3 o'clock / Dans cette etable / Wassail / Little Jesus, sweetly sleep / It came upon a midnight clear / Seven joys of Mary, The / Fum fum fum / Es ist ein ros entsprungen / Tomorrow shall be my dancing day / Cradle, The / Holly and the ivy, The / Child in a manger / Hodie,

Christus natus est / Love came down at Christmas / O come all ye faithful.
LP: ACM 2043
MC: ZC ACM 2043

FIDDLER'S RALLY (Scottish National Mod 1975).
Tracks: / Marches / Reels / March and strathspey and 2 reels / Gaelic airs / Slow air, march, strathspey and reel / Dance tunes / Kate Dalrymple.
LP: REC 231
MC: MRMC 043

Scottish Philharmonic

SCOTTISH PHILHARMONIC SINGERS.
Tracks: / In praise of Islay / Rosebud by my early walk, A / Johnnie Cope / Fairy lullaby, A / Scots wha hae / Island herdsmaid, The / Duncan Gray / Iona boat song / Ossianic processional / Flow gently sweet Afton / Charlie is my darling / Sky boat song, The / Fife fisher song, A / Ye banks and braes / Ca' the Yowes / Loch Lomond / Island sheiling song / Eriskay love lilt / Flowers o' the forest, The / Donald Ewan's wedding.
MC: LIDC 6033

Scottish Tradition

FIDDLER AND HIS ART.
LP: TNGM 141

SCOTTISH TRADITION VOL.7 (sung by Calum Ruadh) (Various artists).
LP: TNGM 128

Scrambled Feet

SCRAMBLED FEET (Original Broadway cast) (Various artists).
MC: DRGC 6105

Scratch Acid

BERSERKER.
LP: HOLY 002

JUST KEEP EATING.
LP: SAVE 012

SCRATCH ACID.
LP: HOLY 001

Scratch Band

FEATURING DANNY FLOWERS.
LP: MCF 3136

SCRATCH BAND.
Tracks: / When we dance / Wonder / Don't go no further / Prisoner of romance / Last song, The / Rock'n'roll love letter / Make it better / Danny and Laura / One night / I only want to be with you.
LP: SHY 8529

Scratch & Upsetters

SUPER APE.
Tracks: / Zion's blood / Croaking lizard / Black vest / Underground / Curly dub / Dread lion / Three in one / Patience / Dub along / Super ape.
LP: ILPS 9417
MC: RRCT 13

Scrawl

HE'S DRUNK.
Tracks: / 1 green beer ready / For your sister / I feel your pain / Small day / Major, minor / Breaker breaker / Believe / Let it all hang out / Rocky top.
LP: ROUGH 138

SMALLTOOTH.
LP: ROUGH 150
MC: ROUGHC 150

Scream

BANGING THE DRUM.
LP: DISCHORD 25
MC: DISCHORD 25C

LIVE IN EUROPE (At Van Hall, Amsterdam).
LP: K 001/113

NO MORE CENSORSHIP.
LP: RAS 4001

STILL SCREAMING.
LP: DISCHORD 9

THIS SIDE UP.
LP: DISCHORD 155

Scream for Help (film)

SCREAM FOR HELP (See under Jones, John-Paul) (Jones, John Paul).

Scream Your ...

SCREAM YOUR BRAINS OUT (Various artists).
LP: UNKNOWN

Screaming Believes

REFUGEES FROM THE LOVE GENERATION.
LP: MD 7921

Screaming Blue

BIKINI RED.
Tracks: / Sweet water pools / Bikini red / Too much love / I can speak American / Big brother muscle / I wanna be a Flintstone / Jesus Chrysler drives a Dodge / Lie detector / 55 the law / All shook down / Waltz.
LP: WX 117
MC: WX 117 C

GOOD AND GONE.
Tracks: / Someone to talk to / I want up / Good and gone / You're gonna change / Happy home / Tracking the dog.
LP: WX 16
MC: WX 16C
LP: NED 7

GUNSHY.
Tracks: / Wild blue yonder / Holiday head / Smash the market place / Just for fun / Let's go down to the woods / Talking doll / Twin Cadillac valentine / President Kennedy's mile / Clear view / Killer born man.
LP: WX 41
MC: WX 41C

TOTALLY RELIGIOUS.
LP: K 9608591
MC: K 9608594

Screaming Jets

ALL FOR ONE.
Tracks: / C'mon / No point / Better / Needle / Shine on / Starting out / Stop the world / Blue sashes / Sister tease / F.R.C.
LP: 8484111
MC: 8484414

Screaming Target

HOMETOWN HI-FI.
MC: ICT 9979
LP: ILPS 9979

Screaming Trees

BUZZ FACTORY.
Tracks: / Black sun morning / Flower web / End of the universe.
LP: SST 248
MC: SST 248 C

EVEN IF AND ESPECIALLY WHEN.
Tracks: / Transfiguration / Straight out to any place / World painted / Don't look down / Girl behind the mask / Flying / Cold rain / Other days and different planets / Pathway, The / You know where it's at / Back together / In the forest.
LP: SST 132

FRACTURE IN TIME, A.
Tracks: / Asylum / Understand / Balance / Coliseum / Big hitter / M 1 1 3 s / Don't afraid / Fractured time.
LP: NTVLP 29
MC: NTVC 29

INVISIBLE LANTERN.
LP: SST 188
MC: SSTC 188

POLLY PEREGRIN (See Beat Happening) (Screaming Trees & Beat Happening).

Screaming Tribesman

BONES AND FLOWERS.
LP: 4601201

Screams

SCREAMS.
LP: INS 2007

Screeching Weasel

BOOGADA BOOGADA BOOGADA.
LP: WETLP 5

Screen Idols

FOLLOW YOUR HEART.
Tracks: / Soul searching / Zingaro / Devil in me, The / Full moon love / Follow your heart / Little beast of youth / Let it all go / Misunderstood / Word, the.
LP: MOMENT 118
MC: MOMENTC 118

PREMIERE.
Tracks: / Troublemaker / Blind man / Living in a jar / We just can't go on / You slayed me / It's only love / Paris fashions / Hit me where it hurts / Do what you do well / Screen idols.
LP: CBR 1001

Screwdriver

NO MAMA.
Tracks: / No mama / Dance hall vibes / Mandela / Singerman / Woman / Give me your love / Bills / Marcia.
LP: DSR 8701

Scriabin (composer)

GRAND SONATA (TCHAIKOVSKY)/ SCRIABIN (see under Petcherski, Alma) (Petcherski, Alma).

Scritti Politti

CUPID AND PSYCHE '85.
Tracks: / Word girl, The / Small talk / Absolute / Little knowledge, A / Don't work that hard / Perfect way / Lover to fall / Wood beez (pray like Aretha Franklin) / Hypnotize / Flesh and blood (CD & cassette only) / Absolute (version) (CD & Cassette only) / Hypnotize (version) (CD & cassette only) / Wood Beez (version) (CD & Cassette).
LP: V 2350
MC: TCV 2350
LP: OVED 294
MC: OVEDC 294

PROVISION.
Tracks: / Boom, there she was / Overnite / First boy in this town (Lovesick) / All that we are / Best thing ever / Oh Patti (don't feel sorry for loverboy) / Bam salute / Sugar and spice / Philosophy now / Oh Patti (don't feel sorry for loverboy) (extended) (CD & Cassette only) / Boom-there she was (dub) (CD & Cassette only).
LP: V 2515
MC: TCV 2515
MC: OVEDC 368

SONGS TO REMEMBER.
Tracks: / Asylums in Jerusalem / Slow soul, A / Jacques Derrida / Lions after slumber / Faithless / Sex / Rock a boy blue / Gettin', havin' and holdin' / Sweetest girl, The.
LP: ROUGH 20
MC: ROUGHC 20

Scrivenor, Gove

COCONUT GOVE.
LP: FF 084

SHADY GOVE.
LP: FF 048

Scrodd, Crystal Belle

BELLE DE JOUR.
LP: UD 021

INEVITABLE CRYSTAL BELLE SCRODD RECORD.
LP: UD 017

Scrooged

SCROOGED (Original Soundtrack) (Various artists).
Tracks: / Put a little love in your heart: *Lennox, Annie & Al Green* / Wonderful life: *Lennon, Julian* / Sweetest thing: *New Voices Of Freedom* / Love you take, The: *Hartman, Dan/Denise Lopez* / Get up'n'dance: *Kool Moe Dee* / We three kings of Orient are: *Davis, Miles/Larry Carlton* / Christmas must be tonight: *Robertson, Robbie*/ Brown eyed girl: *Poindexter, Buster* / Christmas song, The: *Cole, Natalie*.
LP: AMA 3921
MC: AMC 3921

Scruffy The Cat

HIGH OCTANE REVIVAL.
LP: 88561-8115-1

TINY DAYS.
LP: 88561-8158-1

Scruggs, Earl

FOGGY MOUNTAIN BREAKDOWN (See under Flatt, Lester) (Scruggs, Earl & Lester Flatt).

LESTER FLATT AND EARL SCRUGGS (see under Flatt, Lester) (Scruggs, Earl & Lester Flatt).

TOP OF THE WORLD.
Tracks: / Sittin' on top of the world / We'll meet again / Sweetheart / Could you love me one more time / Love gone cold / Lindsey / Carolina star / Till the end of the world rolls round / Paradise / Lay me down in Dixie / Rollercoaster.
LP: CBS 25097

Scrunter

PARTY LOVER.
LP: JN 001

Scullion

BALANCE AND CONTROL.
LP: K 58205
MC: K4 58205

SCULLION.
LP: LUN 037

Scum

BORN TOO SOON.
Tracks: / Have away from home / Ain't no you / American mould / Double cross / Bunker life / Go to war / Junkhead / Beer can nightmare / Pyramid mail blues / Pool hunt / Exit death / No hope for religion / So m.u.c.h. hate.
LP: GURT 18

Scum Boys

VAMP ATTACK.
Tracks: / Vamp attack.
LP: RUMBLE 008

Scum Rats

LET ME BE BAD.
Tracks: / Let me be bad.
LP: RUMBLE 005

S.D.I.

SATANS DEFLORATION.
LP: 805035

Sea Hags

SEA HAGS, THE.
LP: CHR 1655
MC: ZCHR 1655

Sea Hawk

SEA HAWK (Film Soundtrack) (Various artists).
LP: 704.300
MC: C 704.300

Sea Level

BALL ROOM.
Tracks: / La di da / Digital daydream blues / What am I gonna do / Keeping it from the troops / I'm in love again / Losin' you / Dreamin' / No favours, no way / Love today.
LP: SPART 1145

ON THE EDGE.
Tracks: / Fifty four / King grand / Living in a dream / Lotta colada / This could be the worst / Uptown downtown / Electron cold / On the wong.
LP: 242 917 7

Sea of Love

SEA OF LOVE (Film Soundtrack) (Various artists).
Tracks: / Sea of love: *Various artists* / Poetic killing: *Various artists* / Cocktails and fingerprints: *Various artists* / Fear and passion: *Various artists* / Helen's 45: *Various artists* / Is she or isn't she: *Various artists* / Sea of love Reprise: *Various artists*.
LP: 842 170 1
MC: 842 170 4

Sea Shanties

SEA SHANTIES (Various artists).
LP: 12TS 234

SEA SHANTIES (Various artists).
LP: SODE 237
MC: SODET 237

SEA SONGS & SHANTIES (Various artists).
LP: TPS 205

SEA SONGS VOL.1 (Various artists).
MC: 60-512

Sea Train

BEST OF SEA TRAIN & MARBLED MESSENGER,THE.
Tracks: / Oh my love / Sally Goodin / Creepin' midnight / I'm willin' / Song of job / Home to you / 13 questions / Marbleheaded messenger / London songs / Gramercy / State of Georgia's mind / Losing all the years / Mississippi moon / How sweet thy song.
LP: SEE 96

SEA TRAIN.
Tracks: / Sea train / Let the duchess know / Pudding street / Portrait of the lady as a young artist / As I lay here losing / Rondo / Sweet creek's suite / Outwear the hills.
LP: ED 196

Sea Wolf

SEA WOLF (see London, Jack) (Boland, Arthur).

Sea Wolves

SEA WOLVES (Film soundtrack) (National Philharmonic Orchestra).
LP: EMC 3340
MC: TCEMC 3340

Seaford College...

CAROLS FOR THE FAMILY (Seaford College Chapel Choir).
MC: MCFRC 522

HYMN FOR EVERYMAN, A (Seaford College Chapel Choir).
Tracks: / Praise my soul, the King of heaven / Guide me o thou great Redeemer / Once in Royal David's city / Lord's my shepherd, The / O praise ye the Lord / Praise to the holiest / Lord of all hopefulness / Mine eyes have seen the glory / Day thou gavest, Lord is ended, The / Soldiers of Christ / Lead us heavenly Father, lead us / Amazing Grace / Child in a manger / O brother man / Lord of our life / O bless us and guide us / Fight the good fight / There is a green hill / Abide with me.
LP: GRALP 29
MC: GRTC 29

MY COUNTRY (Seaford College Chapel Choir).
Tracks: / Jerusalem / Pie Jesu / My song is love unknown / Be still my soul / Chorale / Litany of the passion / How great the harvest is / I would be true / Let thy merciful ears O Lord / God that made earth and heaven / I vow to thee my country / Kyrie / King of love my shepherd is, The / Nunc Dimittis / Sanctus / Dear Lord and Father of mankind / Jesu, joy of man's desiring / Ave verum corpus / Love Divine.
LP: GRALP 14
MC: GRTC 14

ROYAL CAROL CONCERT, A (Seaford College Chapel Choir).
Tracks: / Sound of angels, A / Once in royal David's city / Tender shoot, A / Angel Gabriel, The / While shepherds watched their flocks by night / Shepherds in the field abiding / Ding dong merrily on high / Away in a manger / Schlaf, mein kindlein / Infant holy / Shepherds' farewell, The / Susser die glocken nie klingen / In the bleak mid winter / Once as I remember.
LP: .... **LPB 825**
MC: .... **LPBC 825**

Seal

SEAL.
LP: .... **ZTT 9**
MC: .... **ZTT 9C**

Seal Boy

SEAL BOY, THE (Various artists).
Tracks: / Seal boy, The: *Various artists* / Advice merchant, The: *Various artists* / Boy who knew where the winds came from: *Various artists* / Reindeer fur coat, The: *Various artists* / Blacksmith's son, The: *Various artists*/ Footsteps and the three reindeer: *Various artists.*
MC: .... **ANV 648**

Sealed Knot

CLASSICAL SPECTACULAR (live at the Royal Albert Hall)(see under Royal Philharmonic (Sealed Knot musketeers/ Royal Philharmonic Orchestra).

Seals & Crofts

GET CLOSER.
Tracks: / Sweet green fields / Get closer / Red long ago / Goodbye old buddies / Baby blue / Million dollar horse / Don't fall / Passing thing.
LP: .... **K 56209**

GREATEST HITS: SEALS & CROFTS.
Tracks: / When I meet them / Diamond girl / Hummingbird / Castles in the sand / East of Ginger trees / I'll play for you / Ruby Jean and Billie Lee / King of nothing / Summer breeze / We may never pass this way (again).
LP: .... **K 56176**

ONE ON ONE.
Tracks: / Love theme (my fair share), The / This day belongs to me / Janet's theme / John Wayne / Pincic / Flying / Reflections / Love conquers all / It'll be alright / Hustle / Time out / Party, The / Basketball game, The / This day belongs to me (reprise).
LP: .... **K 56402**

Seals, Dan

BEST OF DAN SEALS, THE.
Tracks: / Three time loser / God must be a cowboy / My baby's got good timing / You still move me / Bop / Everything that glitters (is not gold) / Meet me in Montana / You bring out the wild of me / My old yellow car / I will be there (remix) / One friend.
LP: .... **EST 2049**
MC: .... **TCEST 2049**

ON ARRIVAL.
Tracks: / Good times / Made for lovin' you / Wood / She flew the coupe / Bordertown / Water under the bridge / Love on arrival / Heart in search of love, A / Lonestar / Game of love.
MC: **C4 91782**
MC: **791 782 4**

ON THE FRONT LINE.
Tracks: / On the front line / Three time loser / Fewer threads than these / Gonna be easy now / Guitar man out of control / I will be there / You still move me / While I'm here / I'm still strung out on you / Lullaby.
LP: .... **AML 3114**
MC: .... **TCAML 3114**

RAGE ON.
Tracks: / Big wheels in the moonlight / They rage on / Five generations of rock county Wilsons / Twenty four hour love / Factory town / Addicted / Heartache just around the bend, A / Maybe I'm missing you now / Fool me once, fool me twice / Long Long Island nights / Those.
LP: .... **EST 2070**
MC: .... **TCEST 2070**

Seals, Son

BAD AXE.
Tracks: / Don't pick me for your fool / Going home (where women got meat on their bones) / Just about to lose your clown / Friday again / Cold blood / Out of my way / I think you're fooling me / I can count on my blues / Can't stand to see her cry / Person to person.
LP: .... **SNTF 927**

CHICAGO FIRE.
Tracks: / Buzzard luck / I'm not tired / Leaving home / Landlord at my door / Gentleman from the windy city / Goodbye little girl / Watching every move you make / Crying time again / Nobody wants a loser.
LP: .... **SNTF 838**

LIVE 'N' BURNING.
LP: .... **SNTF 782**

LIVING IN THE DANGER ZONE.
Tracks: / Frigidaire woman / I can't lose the blues / Woman in black / Tell it to another fool / Ain't that some shame / Arkansas woman / Danger zone, The / Last four nickels / My time now / Bad axe / My life.
MC: .... **AC 4798**

MIDNIGHT SON.
Tracks: / I believe (you're trying to make a fool out of me) / No, no, baby / Four full seasons of love / Telephone angel / Don't bother me / On my knees / Don't fool with my baby / Strung-out woman / Going back home.
LP: .... **SNTF 728**

SON SEALS BLUES BAND (Seals, Son Blues Band).
Tracks: / Mother-in-law blues / Sitting at my window / Look now, baby / Your love is a cancer / All you love / Cotton pickin' blues / Hot sauce / How could she leave me? / Going home tomorrow / Now that I'm down.
LP: .... **SNTF 679**

Sealy, Joe

CLEAR VISION (Sealy, Joe Trio).
LP: **4007**

LIVE AT ERROLS (Sealy, Joe & Friends).
LP: .... **JC 0004**

Seamen, Phil

PHIL ON DRUMS.
LP: .... **77 SEU 12/53**

PHIL ON DRUMS.
LP: .... **HEP 2037**

Seance

BLUE DOLPHIN BLUE.
LP: .... **150 BPM**

Seannachie

TAKE NOTE.
LP: .... **RR 002**
MC: .... **RRC 002**

WITHIN THE FIRE.
LP: .... **RR 001**
MC: .... **RRC 001**

Search

SEARCH.
Tracks: / Like the way you funk with me / Is it love (for now) / Peanut butter and jam / Get up off your assets / Do you love me still? / Missing you / Song for Carrie.
LP: .... **PWLP 1001**

Search For Paradise

SEARCH FOR PARADISE (Film Soundtrack) (Various artists).
LP: .... **LOC 1034**

Searchers

100 MINUTES OF THE SEARCHERS.
MC: .... **ZCTON 103**

BEST OF THE SEARCHERS 1963-1964, THE.
Tracks: / Sweets for my sweet / Stand by me / Love potion No. 9 / Some other guy / Where have all the flowers gone / Money (that's what I want) / I'll be missing you / Sugar and spice / Needles and pins / It's in her kiss / When you walk in the room / Saints and searchers / What have they done to the rain? / Someday we're gonna love again / All my sorrows / Don't throw your love away.
MC: .... **PWKMC 4076**

C90 COLLECTOR SERIES.
LP: .... **C 904**

COLLECTION: SEARCHERS.
2LP: .... **CCSLP 208**
MC: .... **CCSMC 208**

EP COLLECTION, THE: SEARCHERS.
Tracks: / When you walk in the room / (I'll be) missing you / Oh my lover / This empty place / No one else could love me / What have they done to the rain / Goodbye my love / 'Til I met you / Can't help forgiving you / I don't want to go on without you / 'Til you say you'll be mine / Sweets for my sweet / Since you broke my heart / Too many miles / Take me for what I'm worth / Take it or leave it / Someday we're gonna love again / Bumble bee / System, The / Love potion number nine / Money / Alright / Ain't that just like me (Available on CD only) / Everything you do (Available on CD only) / If I could find someone (Available on CD only) / It's all been a dream (Available on CD only) / Hungry for love (Available on CD only) / Sea of heartbreak (Available on CD only) / Ain't gonna kiss ya (Available on CD only) / Don't cha know (Available on CD only).
LP: .... **SEE 275**
MC: .... **SEEK 275**

GOLDEN HOUR OF THE SEARCHERS.
MC: .... **KGHMC 101**

GOLDEN HOUR OF THE SEARCHERS, VOL 2.
Tracks: / Bumble bee / Does she really care for me / Second hand dealer / Ain't gonna kiss ya / Magic potion / Stand by me / Livin' lovin' wreck / Be my baby / Something you got baby / Western union / Don't ya know / I'm ready / Everybody come and clap your hands / Your hands / Crazy dreams / Too many miles / Goodnight baby / Some other guy / If I could find someone / Each time / When I get home / Let the good times roll / I'll be doggone / Listen to me / Can't help forgiving you / Hi-heel sneakers.
MC: .... **KGHMC 132**

GOLDEN HOUR: SEARCHERS.
Tracks: / Needles and pins / When you walk in the room / I don't want to go on without you / He's got no love / What have they done to the rain? / Farmer John / I count the tears / Someday we're gonna love again / Goodbye my love / All my sorrows / Have you ever loved somebody? / Sugar and spice / Sweets for my sweet / Take me for what I'm worth / Four strong winds / Love potion No 9 / Hungry for love / Till I met you / Don't throw your love away / You wanna make her happy / Saints and searchers / Sea of heartbreak / This feeling inside / Take it or leave it.
MC: .... **ZCGH 541**
LP: .... **GH 541**

GREATEST HITS: SEARCHERS.
Tracks: / Love Potion No.9 / When you walk in the room / Needles and pins / Sugar and spice / Sweets for my sweet / Magic potion / It's in her kiss / Don't throw your love away / Shimmy shimmy / High heel sneakers / Da doo ron ron / Twist and shout / Stand by me / What have they done to the rain.
LP: .... **SHLP 135**
MC: .... **SHTC 135**
LP: .... **RNLP 162**

HIT COLLECTION.
Tracks: / Sweets for my sweet / Sugar and spice / Needles and pins / Don't throw your love away / Someday we're gonna love again / When you walk in the room / Love potion No.9 / What have they done to the rain? / Goodbye my love / Bumble bee / He's got no love / When I get home / Take me for what I'm worth / Take it or leave it / Have you ever loved somebody?.
LP: .... **PYL 4002**
MC: .... **PYM 4002**

HUNGRY HEARTS.
Tracks: / Forever in love (near to heaven) / Love lies bleeding / Lonely weekend / Somebody told me / Every little tear / Sweets for my sweet (1988 version) / No other love / This boy's in love / Fooled myself once again / Baby, I do / Push, push / Needles and pins.
LP: **209459**
MC: **409459**

IT'S THE SEARCHERS.
Tracks: / Sea of heartbreak / Glad all over / It's in her kiss / Livin' lovin' wreck / Where have you been? / Shimmy shimmy / Needles and pins / This empty place / Gonna send you back to Georgia / I count the tears / High heel sneakers / Can't help forgiving you / Sho' know a lot about love / Don't throw your love away.
LP: .... **PYL 6016**
MC: .... **PYM 6016**
LP: .... **NPL 18092**

LOVE LIES BLEEDING.
Tracks: / Needles and pins / Someday we're gonna love again / Sugar and spice / When you walk in the room / Goodbye my love / Don't throw your love away / He's got no love.
LP: .... **DOW 11**
MC: .... **ZCDOW 11**

MEET THE SEARCHERS.
Tracks: / Sweets for my sweet / Alright / Love potion No.9 / Farmer John / Stand by me / Money / Da doo ron ron / Ain't gonna kiss ya / Since you broke my heart / Tricky Dicky / Where have all the flowers gone? / Twist and shout.
LP: .... **PYL 6014**
MC: .... **PYM 6014**
LP: .... **NPL 18086**

NEEDLES AND PINS.
LP: **26 21358**

NEEDLES AND PINS.
MCSET: .... **DTO 10225**

PLAY FOR TODAY.
Tracks: / Another night / September girls / Murder in my heart / She made a fool of you / Silver / Sick and tired / Radio romance / Infatuation / Almost Saturday night / Everything but a heartbeat / Little bit of heaven, A / New day.
LP: .... **SRK 3533**

SEARCHERS.
Tracks: / Heart's in her eyes / Switchboard Susan / Feeling fine / Back to the war / This kind of love affair / Lost in your eyes / It's too late / Love's melody / No dancing / Love's gonna be strong / Don't hang on.
LP: .... **SRK 6086**

SEARCHERS PLAY THE SYSTEM (Rarities, oddities and flipsides).
Tracks: / It's all been a dream / Saturday night out / I pretend I'm with you / No-one else could love me / I'll be missing you / This feeling inside / Till I met you / So far away / I'm never coming back / Don't hide it away / It's just the way (love will come and go) / Popcorn double feature / Lovers / Western Union / I'll cry tomorrow / Secondhand dealer / Crazy dreams / System, The.
LP: .... **PYL 6019**
MC: .... **PYM 6019**

SEARCHERS, THE.
MC: **C90 2**

SILVER SEARCHERS.
Tracks: / Sweets for my sweet / Don't throw our love away / Someday we're gonna love again / What have they done to the rain / Goodbye my love / He's got no love / System, The / Needles and pins / Take me for what I'm worth / Take it or leave it / Have you ever loved somebody / Each time / Till you say you'll be mine / Sugar and spice / Everybody come and clap your hands / When I get home / Till I met you / I don't want to go on without you / Everything you do / When you walk in the room / Western union / Popcorn double feature / Bumble bee / Four strong winds / Too many miles.
LP: .... **NRT 2**
MC: .... **ZCNRT 2**

SOUNDS LIKE THE SEARCHERS.
Tracks: / Everybody come and clap your hands / If I could find someone / Magic potion / I don't want to go on without you / Bumble bee / Something you got baby / Let the good times roll / Tear fell, A / Till you say you'll be mine / You wanna make her happy / Everything you do / Goodnight baby.
LP: .... **PYL 6017**
MC: .... **PYM 6017**
LP: .... **NPL 18111**

SPOTLIGHT ON THE SEARCHERS.
Tracks: / Sweets for my sweet / Sugar and spice / Da doo ron ron / Money / Twist and shout / Farmer John / Needles and pins / System, The / Love potion No 9 / Hungry for love / Have you ever loved somebody? / Someday we're gonna love again / Don't throw your love away / Each time / When I get home / Sea of heartbreak / It's in her kiss / Be my baby / When you walk in the room / He's got no love / Take it or leave it / Goodbye my love / What have they done to the rain? / Take me for what I'm worth.
2LP: .... **SPOT 1014**
MC: .... **ZCSPT 1014**

SUGAR AND SPICE.
Tracks: / Sugar and spice / Don't cha know? / Some other guy / One of these days / Listen to me / Unhappy girls / Ain't that just like me? / Oh my lover / Saints and searchers / Cherry stones / All my sorrows / Hungry for love.
LP: .... **PYL 6015**
MC: .... **PYM 6015**
LP: .... **NPL 18089**

SWEETS FOR MY SWEET.
Tracks: / Sweets for my sweet / He's got no love / Take me for what I'm worth / What have they done to the rain? / Someday we're gonna love again / Take it or leave it / Needles and pins / Have you ever loved somebody / Don't throw your love away / When you walk in the room / Sugar and spice / Goodbye my love.
LP: .... **FBLP 8084**
MC: .... **ZCFBL 8084**

TAKE ME FOR WHAT I'M WORTH.
Tracks: / I'm ready / I'll be doggone / Does she really care for me / It's time / Too many miles / You can't lie to a liar / Don't you know why / I'm your loving man / Each time / Be my baby / Four strong winds / Take me for what I'm worth.
LP: .... **PYL 6018**
MC: .... **PYM 6018**
LP: .... **NSPL 18120**

ULTIMATE COLLECTION.
Tracks: / Needles and pins / Sweets for my sweet / When you walk in the room.
2LP: .... **CTVLP 003**
MC: .... **CTVMC 003**

WHEN YOU WALK IN THE ROOM.
Tracks: / When you walk in the room / Needles and pins / Twist and shout / Da

doo ron ron / Saturday night out / Money / Love potion No. 9 / Some day we're gonna love again / System / When I get home / Sweets for my sweet / Don't throw your love away / Oh my lover / Stand by me / Each time / Goodbye my love / He's got no love / Sugar and spice / What have they done to the rain / Take me for what I'm worth.
LP: . . . . **NSPL 18617**
MC: . . . . **ZCP 18617**

Searchlight

SEARCHLIGHT.
Tracks: / Fight, The / Lord, you are worthy / If my people / If the world believed / Perfect love / Hurry up, it's night / Gaze into your eyes / He'll never let you go / On the rock / Thank you Jesus.
LP: . . . . **MIR 5012**
MC: . . . . **ZCMIR 5012**

Sears

IF ONLY....
LP: . . . . **FISH 9**

Sease, Marvin

BREAKFAST.
Tracks: / Love is a game / Same old woman / I belong to you / Lately / I can't forget you girl / Condom on your tongue / I ate you for my breakfast / Tell me.
LP: . . . . **LONLP 65**
MC: . . . . **LONC 65**

MARVIN SEASE.
Tracks: / Double crosser / Let's get married today / Love me or leave me / Ghetto man / You're number one / Dreaming / Candy licker.
LP: . . . . **LONLP 33**
MC: . . . . **LONC 33**

Seaside Special

SEASIDE SPECIAL (THEME FROM) (See under Batt, Mike 'Summertime City').

Seasons

SEASONS Various artists (Various artists).
LP: . . . . **NE 1060**
MC: . . . . **CE 2060**

Seaton, B. B.

EVERYDAY PEOPLE.
Tracks: / Now I know / Good to me / Just a little more time / Private lessons / Everyday people / Gimme little love / Tell me if you're ready / Still look sexy / Some day I'll be free / Photographs and souvenirs.
LP: . . . . **CRX 9**

REGGAE COUNTRY CLASSICS.
LP: . . . . **PILP 90**

THIN LINE BETWEEN LOVE AND HATE.
LP: . . . . **TRLS 59**

Seaton, Johnny

REACTION.
LP: . . . . **ROUNDER 9004**
MC: . . . . **ROUNDER 9004C**

UPTOWN.
LP: . . . . **LPL 8403**

Seaward, Lesley

AN IRRESISTIBLE FORCE (Charlton, Ann).
MC: . . . . **PMB 019**

COMING HOME.
MC: **0263 11505 1**

FLAME OF DIABLO (See under Sara Craven).

PASSIONATE DECEPTION.
MC: **0263 11503 8**

Seawind

SEAWIND.
Tracks: / What cha doin' / Two of us / Love him, love her / Everything needs love / Shout / Still in love / Pra vose / I need your love / Long, long time.
LP: . . . . **AMLH 64824**

Sebadoh

FREED MAN, THE.
LP: . . . . **HMS 145**

Sebastian, John

WELCOME BACK.
Tracks: / Hideaway / She's funny / You go your way and I'll go mine / Didn't want to have to do it / One step forward, two steps back / Welcome back (I needed her most when I told) / Song a day in Nashville, A / Warm baby / Let this be out time to get along.
LP: . . . . **K 54074**

Sebastian, John B

JOHN B SEBASTIAN.
Tracks: / Red-eye express / She's a lady / What she thinks about / Magical connection / You're a big boy / Rainbows all over your blues / How have you been / Baby, don't ya get crazy / Room nobody lives in, The / Fa-fana-fa / I had a dream.
LP: . . . . **ED 304**

Sebesky, Don

FULL CYCLE.
Tracks: / Naima / Django / Intrepid fox / Waltz for Debbie / All blues / Un poco loco.
LP: . . . . **N 6551**
LP: . . . . **GNPS 2164**
MC: **GNP5 2164**

MOVING LINES (Arrangers' workshop).
LP: . . . . **ASLP 811**
MC: . . . . **ZCAS 811**

Sebestyen, Marta

MARTA SEBESTYEN AND MUZIKAS (Sebestyen, Marta with Muzikas).
LP: . . . . **HNBL 1330**
MC: . . . . **HNBC 1330**

MARTA SEBESTYEN SINGS.
LP: . . . . **SLPX 18118**

Sebo, Ferenc

HUNGARIAN FOLK MUSIC (Sebo, Ferenc Ensemble).
LP: . . . . **ROUNDER 5005**

MUSIC AND DANCES OF HUNGARY (Sebo, Ferenc Ensemble).
Tracks: / Lassie Magyar / A Tunder / Katonakiseru es - pontoro / Dunantuli ugros Dallamok / A Bekakiraly / En Laemberkent / Rejjelmek / A Hetedik / Dorombi Muzsika / Janos gacsi dudaljon kend / Sverelem Sverelem / Dudan / Ugrotanc.
LP: . . . . **ARN 33444**
MC: . . . . **ARN 433444**

Sebresky, Don

SYMPHONIC SONDHEIM.
LP: . . . . **WX 357**
MC: . . . . **WX 357C**

Secession

DARK ENCHANTMENT, A.
Tracks: / Eventide / Promise, The / Love lies bleeding / Sneakyville / Winifred / Box that holds a secret, The / Ocean blue / Radioland / Magician / Love lies bleeding (reprise) / Wolf, The.
LP: . . . . **SRNLP 11**
MC: . . . . **SRNMC 11**

Seck, Phione

LE POUVOIR D'UN COEUR PUR.
LP: . . . . **STERNS 1023**

Secombe, Harry

BLESS THIS HOUSE.
LP: . . . . **WW 5052**
MC: . . . . **WW 4 5052**

FAVOURITE CHRISTMAS CAROLS (Secombe, Harry With The Westminster City Choir).
Tracks: / O come all ye faithful / Once in Royal David's city / Silent night / Away in a manger.
LP: . . . . **SHM 3250**
MC: . . . . **HSC 3250**

GOLDEN MEMORIES (See Anderson, Moira) (Secombe, Harry & Moira Anderson).

HARRY SECOMBE COLLECTION.
Tracks: / If I ruled the world / Ah sweet mystery of life / Vienna, city of my dreams / This is my song / Catari catari / Falling in love with love.
2LP: . . . . **PDA 020**
MCSET: . . . . **PDC 020**

HARRY SECOMBE'S HIGHWAY OF SONG.
LP: . . . . **HWAY 1**
MC: . . . . **ZCWAY 1**

HARRY'S CHOICE.
Tracks: / Moonlight and roses / Take me to your heart again / You'll never walk alone / When you wish upon a star / Story of a starry night / Younger than Springtime / Wonderful Copenhagen / Stranger in Paradise / Three coins in the fountain / One day when we were young / Keep the home fires burning / Eternally.
LP: . . . . **SPR 8537**
MC: . . . . **SPC 8537**

HIGHWAY COMPANION, THE.
Tracks: / Highway theme / Remember / Abide with me / Death is nothing at all / As long as this exists / In Heavenly love abiding / Final judgement / Everything I had hoped for / Cover me with love / On charity / Love divine / Gift of friends / Diary of a church mouse / Nativity, The / I would be true / Something good can emerge / Answer me, world / O God, our help in ages past / Walking away / Rock of ages / Ruth / Our little fella / We will not weep / When you look back on your life / Lord's my shepherd, The / Acceptable year of the Lord, The / Prayer of the Iona community / He was so young / St. Francis of Assisi's prayers / St. Patrick's breastplate / Prayer / Onward Christian soldiers / Irish blessing, An.
LP: . . . . **WRD R 3033**
MC: . . . . **WRD C 3033**

HIGHWAY OF LIFE.
LP: . . . . **STAR 2289**
MC: . . . . **STAC 2289**

HOW GREAT THOU ART.
Tracks: / Onward Christian soldiers / It is no secret / Swing low, sweet chariot / Beautiful isle of somewhere / All things bright and beautiful / How great Thou art (end s1) / Battle hymn of the republic / Desiderata / Whispering hope / Lord's my shepherd, The / Perfect day / God be in my head.
LP: . . . . **CBR 1017**
MC: . . . . **KCBR 1017**

IF I RULED THE WORLD.
Tracks: / Be my love / Bless this house / Falling in love with love / I believe in love / If I ruled the world / Mama / O Sole Mio / Speak to me of love / This is my song / Younger than Springtime.
LP: . . . . **TIME 14**
MC: . . . . **TIMEC 14**
LP: . . . . **CN 2001**
MC: **CN4 2001**
LP: **6870 501**

IF I RULED THE WORLD.
MCSET: . . . . **DTOL 10212**

KEEP LOVE ALIVE (see Loussier, Jacques) (Secombe, Harry & Jacques Loussier).

MUSICAL WORLD OF HARRY SECOMBE, THE.
Tracks: / Day by day / Send in the clowns / I've grown accustomed to her face / If ever I would leave you / Au rond du Temple Saint / On the street where you live / Where is love / Gigi / Speak softly love / Mimi tu piu non torni / Battle hymn of the Republic / Desiderata / Whispering hope / Lord's my shepherd, The / Perfect day / God be in my head / Onward christian soldiers / It is no secret / Swing low sweet chariot / Beautiful Isle of Somewhere / All things bright and beautiful / How great thou art.
2LP: . . . . **CR 075**
MCSET: . . . . **CRT 075**

ONWARD CHRISTIAN SOLDIERS.
Tracks: / Onward Christian soldiers / Count your blessings / How sweet the name of Jesus sounds / Faith can move mountains / Jerusalem / Old rugged cross, The / How great Thou art / Wonderful words of life / Guide me o thou great Jehovah / I'll walk with God / When I survey the wondrous cross / Lord's prayer, The.
LP: . . . . **WRD R 3031**
MC: . . . . **WRD C 3031**

ONWARD CHRISTIAN SOLDIERS (SINGLE).
Tracks: / Onward Christian soldiers / Battle hymn of the Republic.
LP: . . . . **SAMMY TWO**

SACRED SONGS.
LP: . . . . **TIME 13**
MC: . . . . **TIMEC 13**
LP: . . . . **RBL 7501**

SECOMBE'S PERSONAL CHOICE.
LP: . . . . **BETS 707**

SIR HARRY SECOMBE SINGS THE ALL TIME GREAT SONGS.
Tracks: / Where do I begin / I have dreamed / I believe / Somewhere my love / What a wonderful world / You'll never walk alone / What kind of fool am I / With a song in my heart / Somewhere / Amazing grace / Edelweiss / Stranger in paradise / Some enchanted evening / September song / Moon river / Ave Maria / Smile / Climb every mountain / Bless this house / Impossible dream, The / Lover come back to me / Tonight / Abide with me.
MCSET: . . . . **DTO 10296**

SONG AND A PRAYER, A.
Tracks: / Onward Christian soldiers / It is no secret / Swing low, sweet chariot / Beautiful Isle of somewhere / All things bright and beautiful / How great thou art / Battle hymn of the Republic / Whispering hope / Lord's my shepherd, The / Perfect day / God be in my head.
LP: . . . . **ACLP 013**
MC: . . . . **ACK 013**

SONGS OF MY HOMELAND.
Tracks: / God bless the Prince of Wales / Myfanwy / Gwenith Gwyn / Calon lan / All through the night / Land of my fathers / Men of Harlech / David of the white rock / ospan fach / Aberystwyth / We'll keep a welcome / Ash Grove, The.
LP: **9109232**

SONGS OF PRAISE.
MC: . . . . **ASK 761**

THESE ARE MY SONGS.
Tracks: / On the street where you live / Where is love / Gigi / Speak softly love / O mimi tu piu non torni (from La Boheme) / Day by day / Send in the clowns / I've grown accustomed to her face / If ever I would leave you / Au fond du temple saint.
LP: . . . . **ACLP 003**
MC: . . . . **ACK 003**

TOGETHER (SECOMBE/TREORCHY) (Secombe, Harry & Treorchy Male Choir).
LP: . . . . **WST R 9698**
MC: . . . . **WST C 9698**

Second Chapter Of Acts

ENCORES.
Tracks: / Which way the wind blows / Easter song / Last day of my life / Psalm 63 (as morning breaks) / Prince song, The / Hey, watcha say? / Yaweh / Morning comes when you call / Love, peace, joy / He loves me / Son comes over the hill, The.
LP: . . . . **MYR 1103**
MC: . . . . **MC 1103**

FARAWAY PLACES.
LP: . . . . **OAK R 3009**
MC: . . . . **OAK C 3009**

HOW THE WEST WAS ONE.
Tracks: / Concert introduction / Hey, watcha say / Song introduction / Change / Now that I belong to you / Phil's introduction / What a day / Love broke thru / Take me closer / My life / Another try / Rejoice / Just the same / Hallelujah / Time / Easter song / Dance with you / Something tells me / Yaweh / Psalm 61 / Grinding stone / Receive.
2LP: . . . . **MYD 1061**
MCSET: **MC2D 1061**

HYMNS.
LP: . . . . **OAK R 3007**
MC: . . . . **OAK C 3007**

HYMNS II.
MC: . . . . **OAK C 3012**
LP: . . . . **OAK R 3012**

IN THE VOLUME OF THE BOOK.
Tracks: / Start every day with a smile / Yaweh / Something tells me / Grey song, The / Now that I belong to you / Psalm 63 (as morning breaks) / Prince song, The / Morning comes when you call / Borrowed time / Last day of my life / Hey, watcha say / Keep on shinin' / I can't get near you.
LP: . . . . **MYR 1026**
MC: . . . . **MC 1026**
MCSET: . . . . **TWIN C 103**
2LP: . . . . **OAK R 0016**
MCSET: . . . . **OAK C 0016**

MANSION BUILDER.
Tracks: / Rod and staff / Mansion builder / Psalm 63 (as morning breaks) / Gold in the clouds / I'll live my life away / Rainbow / Well, haven't you heard / Lightning flash / Starlight, starbright / Make my life a prayer to you / Daydreamer.
LP: . . . . **BIRD 114**
MC: . . . . **TC BIRD 114**

NIGHT LIGHT.
LP: . . . . **OAK 3003**
MC: . . . . **OAK C 3003**

REJOICE.
Tracks: / Rejoice / Bread of life / Nobody can take my life / Here I go / Rise up and take a bow / I've got a break in my heart / Don't understand / Heaven came to Earth / Will you remember me / Mountain tops.
LP: . . . . **BIRD 130**
MC: . . . . **TC BIRD 130**

ROAR OF LOVE, THE.
MC: . . . . **OAK C 0015**

WITH FOOTNOTES.
Tracks: / Which way the wind blows / Going home / With Jesus / Devil's lost again, The / Love, peace, joy / I don't wanna go home / Easter song / He loves me / Good news / I fall in love / Change / Son comes over the hill, The.
LP: . . . . **MYR 1011**
MC: . . . . **MC 1011**

Second Chorus

SECOND CHORUS (Film Soundtrack) (Various artists).
LP: . . . . **HS 404**

Second Communication

MY CHROMOSOMAL FRIEND.
LP: . . . . **KK 044**

Second House Saturday

SONGS OF SCOTTISH MUSIC HALL.
LP: . . . . **LILP 5084**
MC: . . . . **LICS 5084**

Second Image

SECOND IMAGE.
Tracks: / Can't keep holding on '83 / Special lady / All been said and done / Life is what you make it / Is it me? /

Better take time / Star / Love turns me upside down / What's happening.
LP: . . . . POLS 1081

STRANGE REFLECTIONS.
LP: . . . . MCF 3255

Second Layer

SECOND LAYER.
2LP: . . . . LD 8711

WORLD OF RUBBER.
Tracks: / Definition of honour / In bits / Fixation / Save our souls / Distortion / Underneath the gloss / Zero / Japanese headset / Black flowers.
LP: . . . . BRED 14

Second Time Around

SECOND TIME AROUND (Various artists).
2LP: . . . . CR 5160
MCSET: . . . . CRT 5160

SECOND TIME AROUND DANCEBAND: 30'S, 40'S MUSIC (Second Time Around Danceband).
LP: . . . . STA 1

SECOND TIME AROUND DANCEBAND: SENIORS GOLD (Second Time Around Danceband).
LP: . . . . STA 3

SECOND TIME AROUND DANCEBAND: SENIOR PROM (Second Time Around Danceband).
LP: . . . . STA 2

Secrecy

ART IN MOTION.
MC: . . . . ZCNUK 157
LP: . . . . NUK 157

Secret

SECRET.
Tracks: / Satellite / Going down again / Hotel Caribineros / What is wrong / Sick and tired / I don't wanna go out there / Modern art / Night after night / Fallen for an angel / Another cold night in Germany / I'm alive / Lucky lizard.
LP: . . . . AMLH 68504

Secret Affair

BEHIND CLOSED DOORS.
Tracks: / What did you expect / I'm a bullet / Only madmen laugh / When the show's over / My world / Sound of confusion / Life's a movie too / Looking through my eyes / Live for today / Streetlife parade.
LP: . . . . I-SPY 2

BUSINESS AS USUAL.
Tracks: / Lost in the night / Follow the leader / Do you know / Hide and seek / I could be you / Somewhere in the city / She's on fire / Three wise monkeys / One voice in the darkness / Dance master / Big beat, The / One day (in your life).
LP: . . . . I-SPY 3
MC: . . . . TCSPY 3

GLORY BOYS.
Tracks: / Glory boys / Shake & shout / Going to a go go / Time for action / New dance / Days of change / Don't look down / One way world / Let your heart dance / I'm not free (but I'm cheap).
LP: . . . . I-SPY 1

Secret Agent

SECRET AGENT, THE (see under Conrad, Joseph) (Pigott-Smith, Tim (nar)).

Secret Diary of...

SECRET DIARY OF ADRIAN MOLE, THE (See under Adrian Mole).

Secret Garden (bk)

SECRET GARDEN, THE (Bloom, Claire (nar)).
MC: 1463

SECRET GARDEN, THE (Watford, Gwen (nar)).
MCSET: . . . . LFP 7314

SECRET GARDEN, THE (Gordon, Hannah (nar)).
MC: . . . . P 90027

SECRET GARDEN, THE (Jackson, Glenda).
MCSET: . . . . SAY 51

SECRET GARDEN, THE.
MCSET: . . . . DTO 10574

SECRET GARDEN, THE (Richardson, Miranda (nar)).
MC: 0600560597

SECRET GARDEN, THE (Children's Classics).
MC: . . . . PLBC 76

Secret Island (bk)

SECRET ISLAND, THE (see under Blyton, Enid (aut) (Francis, Jan (nar)).

Secret of Abbey Place

SECRET OF ABBEY PLACE (See under Young, Rose) (Young, Rose).

Secret of Kelly's...

SECRET OF KELLY'S MILL, THE (Zena Carus) (Greaves, Nigel (nar)).
MCSET: 086 222 042-3

Secret of Nimh (film)

SECRET OF NIMH (Original soundtrack) (Various artists).
LP: . . . . TER 1026

Secret Of Santa

SECRET OF SANTA VITTORIA (Film Score) (Various artists).
Tracks: / Song of Secret of Santa Vittoria (stay): *Various artists* / Big fool Bombolini: *Various artists* / Swastika: *Various artists* / Hiding the wine: *Various artists* / Love and tears: *Various artists* / Con lo zigo zigo zza: *Various artists* / Viva Bombolini: *Various artists* / Streets of Santa Vittoria: *Various artists*/ Search: *Various artists* / Bei Kerzenlicht: *Various artists* / Celebration: *Various artists*.
LP: . . . . UAS 29053

SECRET OF SANTA VITTORIA (Original Soundtrack) (Various artists).
LP: . . . . MCA 25034
MC: . . . . MCAC 25034

Secret Of The Glen

SECRET OF THE GLEN (Cathy Charles) (Craig, Karen (nar)).
MCSET: . . . . MRC 1041

Secret Of The Sahara

SECRET OF THE SAHARA (Original Soundtrack) (Various artists).
LP: . . . . BL 71559
MC: . . . . BK 71559

Secret Places

SECRET PLACES (Original Soundtrack) (Various artists).
LP: . . . . V 2312

Secret Service

OH SUSIE.
Tracks: / Ten o'clock postman / Darlin' you're my girl / Why don't you try to phone / She wants me / Family delight / Angel on wheels.
LP: . . . . SNTF 823

Secret Seven (bk)

ALL RECORDINGS (see under Blyton, Enid (aut).

Secret Sorrow (bk)

SECRET SORROW, A (See Van der Zee, Karen) (Seaward, Lesley).

Secret Staircase (bk)

SECRET STAIRCASE, THE/THE HIGH HILLS (See under Brambly Hedge (bks)).

Secret Syde

HIDDEN SECRETS.
LP: . . . . HH 001

Sect

SOFT LIGHTS AND LOUD GUITARS (Sect, The/Red Letter Day).
Tracks: / It's cold outside / American dream / War starts at midnight, The / Fade away / Fall apart / Barely alive / Shades / Less I see the more I think of you, The / Whole world gets me down, The / Unclean.
LP: . . . . REM 001

VOICE OF REASON, THE.
Tracks: / Far away / This tinsel town / Night child / Drugsville / Never go / Battlefield / Voice of reason, The / George / Underground rockers / Waiting for the night / Ripped and torn / Merrydown blues.
LP: . . . . RAZ 27

Section 5

FOR THE LOVE OF OI.
LP: . . . . LINK LP 08

WAY WE WERE, THE.
LP: . . . . LINKLP 119

WE WON'T CHANGE.
LP: . . . . OIR 002

Section 25

ALWAYS NOW.
Tracks: / Friendly fires / Dirty disco / C.P. / Loose talk costs lives / Inside out / Melt close / Hit / Babies in the Bardo / Be brave / New horizon.
LP: . . . . FACT 45
MC: . . . . FACT 45 C

FROM THE HIP.
LP: . . . . FACT 90

LOVE AND HATE.
LP: . . . . FACT 160
MC: . . . . FACTC 160

Sector 27

SECTOR 27.
Tracks: / Invitation / Not ready / Mary Lynne / Looking at you / 525 / Total recall / Where can we go tonight? / Take it or leave it / One fine day / Bitterly disappointed.
LP: 6359039

Sedaka, Neil

3 GREAT GUYS (see under Cooke, Sam) (Sedaka, Neil/Paul Anka/Sam Cooke).

20 GOLDEN PIECES: NEIL SEDAKA.
Tracks: / Silent movies / Dimbo / Express yourself / Little song / What have they done? / Home / Gone with the morning / Carousel / Better days are coming / Adventures of a boy child wonder / Cardboard California / Anywhere you're gonna be / That's when the music takes me / Solitaire / I'm a song, sing me / Rosemary blue / Beautiful you / God bless Joanna / Don't let it mess your mind / One more mountain to climb.
LP: . . . . BDL 2030
MC: . . . . AJKL 2030

ALL YOU NEED IS THE MUSIC.
Tracks: / All you need is the music / Candy kisses / Should've never let her go / Sad, sad story / Tillie the twirler / Love keeps getting stronger everyday / Born to be bad / What a surprise / You can hear the love / City boy.
LP: . . . . POLS 1003

BACKTRACKIN'.
2LP: . . . . TRACK 2
MCSET: . . . . TRACK K 2

BEST OF NEIL SEDAKA.
Tracks: / Breaking up is hard to do / Happy birthday sweet sixteen / Diary, The / Sweet little you / You mean everything to me / Next door to an angel / Oh Carol / King of clowns / Stairway to heaven / Run Samson run / Calendar girl.
MC: . . . . PMPK 1009
LP: . . . . PMP 1009
LP: . . . . CBR 1010

COME SEE ABOUT ME.
Tracks: / Come see about me / Your precious love / Rhythm of the rain / Tears on my pillow / It's all in the game / New Orleans / Searchin' / Earth angel / Cathy's clown / Stagger Lee.
LP: . . . . MCF 3211
MC: . . . . MCFC 3211

FABULOUS NEIL SEDAKA,THE.
Tracks: / Little devil / I must be dreaming / Sweet little you / Happy birthday sweet sixteen / Oh Carol / Breaking up is hard to do / As long as I live / I go ape / King of clowns / Stairway to Heaven / Run, Samson, run / You mean everything to me / Calendar girl / Diary, The / Next door to an angel / Answer to my prayer / Girl for me, The / Going home to Mary Lou / You gotta learn your rhythm 'n' blues / World through a tear / Alice in Wonderland / Let's go steady again / Dreamer, The / Bad girl / Sunny / Same old fool.
2LP: . . . . CR 060
MCSET: . . . . CRT 060

GOOD TIMES.
Tracks: / Love made me feel this way / Sweet dreams / Let me walk with you again / Rosarita / Hungry years / Wonderful world of love / Good times / Paint me again / Tomorrow never came.
LP: . . . . N 6558
MC: . . . . ZCN 6558

GREATEST HITS: NEIL SEDAKA.
Tracks: / I go ape / Oh Carol / Stairway to heaven / Run Sampson run / You mean everything to me / Calendar girl / I must be dreaming / Little devil / Happy birthday sweet sixteen / Next door to an angel / Let's go steady again.
LP: . . . . INTS 5023

HIS GREATEST HITS OF THE 60'S.
Tracks: / Oh Carol / Little devil / I go ape / Happy birthday sweet sixteen / Breaking up is hard to do / Calendar girl / Stairway to heaven / Next door to an angel / King of clowns / You mean everything to me / One way ticket (to the blues) / Sweet little you.
LP: . . . . MFP 5819
MC: . . . . TCMFP 5819

I'M A SONG.
MC: . . . . ORC 012

IN THE POCKET.
Tracks: / Do it like you done it when you meant it / Junky for your love / Letting go / You better leave that girl alone / My friend / It's good to be alive again / You / Should've never let you go / You're so good for me / What a difference a day made.
LP: . . . . POLS 1022

LAUGHTER AND TEARS.
Tracks: / Standing on the outside / Love will keep us together / Solitaire / Other side of me, The / Little loving, A / Lonely nights / Brighton / I'm a song, sing me / Breaking up is hard to do / Laughter in the rain / Cardboard California / Bad blood / Queen of 1964 / Hungry years / Betty Grable / Beautiful you / That's when the music takes me / Our last song together.
LP: . . . . SPELP 108
MC: . . . . SPEMC 108
LP: 2383 399
MC: 3170 399

LAUGHTER IN THE RAIN.
LP: 2383 265

LIVE AT THE ROYAL FESTIVAL HALL.
LP: 2383 299

MAGIC MOMENTS.
Tracks: / I go ape / Oh Carol / Stairway to Heaven / Run, Samson, run / You mean everything to me / Calendar girl / I must be dreaming / Little devil / Happy birthday sweet sixteen / King of clowns / As long as I live / Breaking up is hard to do / Next door to an angel / Let's go steady again / Bad girl / Diary, The / Wait till you see my baby / I belong to you / Don't lead me on / Circulate / Forty winks away / Walk with me / You've gotta learn your rhythm 'n' blues / Sweet little you / We can make it if we try / Dreamer, The / I hope he breaks your heart / Let the people talk / Alice in Wonderland.
MC: . . . . NK 89403

NEIL SEDAKA LIVE AT THE ROYAL FESTIVAL HALL/STEPPIN' OUT.
Tracks: / I'm a song, sing me / Other side of me, The / Solitaire / For the good of the cause / Let daddy know / Laughter in the rain / Our last song together / Oh Carol / Stairway to Heaven / Little devil / Happy birthday sweet sixteen / Breaking up is hard to do / Next door to an angel / Calendar girl / Going nowhere / That's when the music takes me / Sing me / You gotta make your own sunshine / Perfect strangers / Steppin' out / Love in the shadows / Cardboard California / Here we are, falling in love again / I let you walk away / Good times, good music, good friends / No. 1 with a heartache / Bad and beautiful / Summer nights.
MCSET: . . . . TWOMC 5
LP: . . . . SPELP 65

NEIL SEDAKA'S GREATEST HITS.
Tracks: / I go ape / Oh Carol / As long as I live / Stairway to Heaven / Run, Samson, run / You mean everything to me / Calendar girl / I must be dreaming / Little devil / Happy birthday sweet sixteen / King of clowns / Breaking up is hard to do / Next door to an angel / Let's go steady again.
LP: . . . . NL 89171
MC: . . . . NK 89171

NOW.
Tracks: / Losing you / What have they done to my town / Pictures from the past / Since you've been gone / On the road again / Summertime madness / My world keeps slipping away / Love is spreading over the world / Bring me down slow / Big parade.
LP: . . . . POLS 1027

OH CAROL.
Tracks: / Oh Carol / One way ticket / Happy birthday sweet sixteen / Calendar girl / Breaking up is hard to do.
LP: . . . . CDS 1147
MC: . . . . CAM 479
LP: 26 21200
MC: 24 21200

OVERNIGHT SUCCESS.
LP: 2442 131

PRELUDE.
Tracks: / Little song / Superbird / Rosemary blue / Cardboard California / Silent movies / What have they done to the moon? / God bless Joanna / Prelude / One more mountain to climb / Is anybody gonna miss you?.
LP: . . . . MTLP 1001

SOUNDS OF SEDAKA.
Tracks: / Puppet man / Johnny Walker, Old Grandad, Jack Daniels & you / Ebony angel / Wheeling West Virginia / You with darkness on your mind / Love of a woman / Workin' on a groovy thing / World I threw away / Don't look over your shoulder / Cellophane disguise / Girl I left behind / Summer symphony.
LP: . . . . MCF 2780

STAIRWAY TO HEAVEN (LP).
LP: . . . . PFP 1007
MC: . . . . PFC 1007

TRA-LA DAYS ARE OVER, THE.
LP: 2315 248

TRA-LA DAYS ARE OVER, THE (2).

Tracks: / Little brother / Standing on the inside / Alone in New York in the rain / Caribbean rainbow / Let daddy know / Suspicions / Love will keep us together / Other side of me / Rock & roll wedding day / For peace and love / Our last song together.
LP: 2459 315

Seddiki, Sidi

SHOUFI.
MC: . . . . ORBC 063

Seducer

CAUGHT IN THE ACT (SEDUCER).
Tracks: / Don't fall in love (rock'n'roll) / Do you believe? / Creeper, The / Wednesday / Remember (walking in the sand) / Call your name / Take you home / Halloween / Rollercoaster / Blizzard / On the run.
LP: . . . . THBL 016

'EADS DOWN - SEE YOU AT THE END.
LP: . . . . STUDLP 2

TOO MUCH AIN'T ENOUGH.
LP: . . . . ILP 027

Seduction (Group)

NOTHING MATTERS WITHOUT LOVE.
LP: . . . . AMA 5280
MC: . . . . AMC 5280

Seeds (Group)

EVIL HOODOO.
Tracks: / March of the flower children / Wind blows your hair, The / Tripmaker / Try to understand / Evil hoodoo / Chocolate river / Pushing too hard / Falling off the edge / Mr. Farmer / Up in her room / Can't seem to make you mine / Pictures and designs / Flower lady and her assistant / Rollin' machine / Out of the question / Satisfy you.
LP: . . . . KIRI 082
LPPD: . . . . STRANGEP 1

FALLING OFF THE EDGE.
Tracks: / Wind blows your hair, The / Other place, The / She's wrong / Nobody spoil my fun / Falling off the edge / Pretty girl / Moth and the flame / I'll help you / Cry wolf / Plain spoken.
LP: . . . . SMB 158
LP: . . . . GNPS 2107
MC: GNP5 2107

FUTURE.
LP: . . . . GNPS 2038

LEGENDARY MASTER RECORDINGS.
Tracks: / Can't seem to make you mine / No escape / Lose your mind / Evil hoodoo / Girl I want you / Pushin' too hard / Try to understand / Nobody spoil my fun / It's a hard life / You can't be trusted / Excuse, excuse / Falling in love.
LP: . . . . SNTF 746

RAW AND ALIVE.
LP: . . . . GNPS 2043
MC: GNP5 2043

SEEDS BLUES BAND.
LP: . . . . GNPS 2040
MC: GNP5 2040

SEEDS, THE.
LP: . . . . GNPS 2023
MC: GNP5 2023
LP: . . . . LLP 5021

WEB OF SOUND, A.
LP: . . . . OLLP 5024
LP: . . . . GNPS 2033
MC: GNP5 2033

Seefelder

HEADWINDS.
LP: . . . . ISST 180

Seeger, Mike

FRESH OLD TIME MUSIC.
LP: . . . . ROUNDER 0262
MC: . . . . ROUNDER 0262C

Seeger, Peggy

AMERICAN FOLK SONGS FOR CHILDREN (Seeger, Peggy & Mike).
LPS: . . . . ROU 8001/2/3
MCSET: . . . . ROU 8001/2/3C

AMERICAN FOLK SONGS FOR CHRISTMAS (Seeger, Peggy & Mike).
2LP: . . . . R 0268/69
MC: . . . . R 0268/69C

AT THE PRESENT MOMENT (Seeger, Peggy & Ewan MacColl).
LP: . . . . ROUNDER 4003

BLOOD AND ROSES 1 (Seeger, Peggy & Ewan MacColl).
LP: . . . . ESB 79

BLOOD AND ROSES 2 (Seeger, Peggy & Ewan MacColl).
LP: . . . . ESB 80

BLOOD AND ROSES 3 (Seeger, Peggy & Ewan MacColl).
LP: . . . . ESB 81

BLOOD AND ROSES 4 (Seeger, Peggy & Ewan MacColl).
LP: . . . . ESB 82

BLOOD AND ROSES 5 (Seeger, Peggy & Ewan MacColl).
LP: . . . . ESB 83

COLD SNAP (see MacColl,Ewen) (Seeger, Peggy & Ewan MacColl).

DIFFERENT THEREFORE EQUAL.
LP: . . . . BR 1061

HOT BLAST (see MacColl, Ewen) (Seeger, Peggy & Ewan MacColl).

KILROY WAS HERE (see under MacColl, Ewen) (Seeger, Peggy & Ewan MacColl).

NAMING OF NAMES (See under MacColl, Ewan) (Seeger, Peggy & Ewan MacColl).

PENELOPE ISN'T WAITING ANY MORE.
LP: . . . . ROUNDER 4011

SATURDAY NIGHT AT THE BULL AND MOUTH (see MacColl, Ewen) (Seeger, Peggy & Ewan MacColl).

Seeger, Pete

ARLO GUTHRIE & PETE SEEGER IN CONCERT (see Guthrie, Arlo).

CAN'T YOU SEE THIS SYSTEM'S ROTTEN THROUGH AND THROUGH.
LP: . . . . GVR 234

GREATEST HITS: PETE SEEGER.
Tracks: / Little boxes / Wimoweh / Where have all the flowers gone? / Abi Yoko / Talking union / Bells of Rhymney / Turn, turn, turn (to everything there is a season) / Which side are you on? / We shall overcome / Living in the country / Darling Corey / Guantanamera.
LP: . . . . EMB 31642

PEACE AND FREEDOM IN SOUTH AMERICA (Seeger, Pete & Illapu).
LP: . . . . GVR 228

PETE SEEGER.
LP: . . . . SM 4040-2

PETE SEEGER, VOL. 1.
LP: . . . . SM 4038
MC: . . . . MC 4038

PETE SEEGER, VOL. 2.
LP: . . . . SM 4039

PETE SEEGER WITH ILLAPU.
LP: . . . . GVR 233

Seekers

BEST OF THE SEEKERS.
LP: 1A 022 58091
LP: . . . . SCX 6268

COME THE DAY.
LP: . . . . SX 6093

LIVE AT THE TALK OF THE TOWN.
LP: . . . . SCX 6278

ONE AND ONLY.
Tracks: / Morningtime ride / Danny boy / Waltzing Matilda / Blowin' in the wind / Lemon tree / What have they done to the rain.
2LP: . . . . MFP 1002

SEEKERS GREATEST HITS, THE.
Tracks: / Georgy girl / I'll never find another you / Morningtown ride / World of our own, A / Love is kind, love is wine / Turn, turn, turn! / Carnival is over, The / When the good apples fall / Times they are a-changin'.
MC: 4XL 9397

SEEKERS, THE.
Tracks: / I'll never find another you / World of our own, A / Carnival is over, The / Some day one day / Walk with me / Morningtown ride / Georgy girl / When will the good apples fall / Emerald City / We shall not be moved / Island of dreams / Open up them pearly gates / Kumbaya / Blowin' in the wind / Wreck of the old '97 / Lemon tree / Whisky in the jar / Five hundred miles / Gypsy Rover, The / South Australia / Danny boy / Waltzing Matilda / Water is wide, The.
MC: . . . . HR 8164

SEEKERS, THE (EMI).
Tracks: / Morningtown ride / 59th Street Bridge song / Well, well, well / Island of dreams / Red rubber ball / Yesterday (CD only.) / Turn, turn, turn (CD only.) / Leaving of Liverpool, The / Times they are a-changin', The / Louisiana man / Emerald city / World of our own, A / Georgy girl / This land is your land / Music of the world a turnin', The / Come the day / Open up them pearly gates / All over the world / We shall not be moved / Love is kind, love is wine / Sinner man / Walk with me / You can tell the world (CD only.) / Carnival is over, The / When will the good apples fall / Someday one day / California dreamin' (CD only.) / I'll never find another you.
MC: . . . . TCIDL 107
MC: 790 370 4

SEEKERS-SEEN IN GREEN.
LP: . . . . SCX 6193

SEEKERS,THE.
LPS: . . . . ALBUM 18
MCSET: . . . . CASSETTE 18
LP: 1A 052 05819
LP: . . . . LK 4694

SEEKERS,THE(I'LL NEVER FIND ANOTHER YOU).
MC: . . . . TCIDL 12

THIS IS THE SEEKERS.
Tracks: / Georgy girl / Walk with me / Kumbaya / Colours of my life / Louisiana man / When will the good apples fall? / Five hundred miles / Music of the world a-turnin' / Sinner man / Come the day / You can tell the world / We shall not be moved / All over the world / Just a closer walk with thee / On the other side / Emerald City / Some day one day / I'll never find another you.
LP: . . . . THIS 19
MC: . . . . TCTHIS 19

VERY BEST OF THE SEEKERS.
Tracks: / Island of dreams / Blowin' in the wind / World of our own, A / This land is your land / I'll never find another you / California dreamin' / Kumbaya / Times they are a-changin' / Colours of my life / Some day one day / Morningtown ride / Five hundred miles / Love is kind, love is wine / Allentown Jail / Music of the world a-turnin' / Just a closer walk with thee / Cottonfields / We're moving on / Leaving of Liverpool / Carnival is over, The.
LP: . . . . EMC 3026
MC: . . . . TCEMC 3026

WORLD OF OUR OWN, A.
LP: 33SX 1722

Seely, Jeannie

GREATEST HITS: JACK GREENE & JEANNIE SEELY (see under Greene, Jack) (Seely, Jeannie/Jack Greene).

Seema, Puseletso

HE O OE OE Music from Lesotho (Seema, Puseletso & Tau Ea Linare).
Tracks: / He o oe oe / Leshano / Vatse halenone / Ha motsoane / Mathabo / Tsetala / Linare / Thaba tsepe / Katla ka sotleha / Bajoetse saki / Kesetse mahiomolenu.
LP: . . . . ORB 003

Seers

PSYCH OUT.
Tracks: / Wildman / Rub me out / One summer / Welcome to deadtown / I'll be there / You keep me praying / Walk / Sun is in the sky / Fly away / Breathless / Freedom trip / (All late nite) tequila drinking blues / Magic potion / Lightning strikes.
MC: . . . . CBRED 86
LP: . . . . BRED 86

Seesaw

SEESAW (Original Broadway Cast) (Various artists).
Tracks: / Nobody does it like me: *Various artists* / Welcome to Holiday Inn: *Various artists* / It's not where you start: *Various artists*.
LP: . . . . X 15563
MC: . . . . XT 15563

Sefton, Catherine

EMER'S GHOST.
MC: 2CCA 3065

Segal, Charles

COME FLY WITH ME (Segal, Charles His Piano & Orchestra).
MC: . . . . VCA 070

SINATRA SONGBOOK,THE (Segal, Charles Orchestra).
MC: 44 540

SLEEPY SHORES(MIDNIGHT STRINGS) (Segal, Charles His Piano & Orchestra).
MC: . . . . VCA 076

Segal, Erich

LOVE STORY.
MC: 2093

Segami, Y

LATIN PERCUSSION.
Tracks: / Historia de un amor / La virgen de la Macarena / Tico tico / Besame mucho / Guantanamera / La bamba / Babalu / Anna / Maria Elena / Adios Mariquita Linda.
LP: . . . . SX 7003

Segarini, Bob

GOODBYE L.A..
Tracks: / This city / I like the beatles / I hardly know her name / Odd couples / Day and night / Nervous breakdown / Teenage love / Please please please / Rock n roll moment / Who's loving you / Demographics / Title track / Airhead.
LP: . . . . EPC 84086

GOTTA HAVE POP.
Tracks: / Gotta have pop / Hide away / Afraid of the ocean / I don't wanna lose you / Don't believe a word I say / Livin' in the movies / Steady Eddie / Dressed in the dark / When the lights are out / Love story.
LP: . . . . EPC 83806

Seger, Bob

AGAINST THE WIND (Seger, Bob & The Silver Bullet Band).
Tracks: / Horizontal bop, The / You'll accompany me / Her strut / No man's land / Long man's land / Long twin silver line / Against the wind / Good for me / Betty Lou's gettin' out tonight / Fire lake / Shinin' brightly.
LP: . . . . EAST 12041
MC: . . . . TCEAST 12041

BEAUTIFUL LOSER.
Tracks: / Beautiful loser / Black night / Katmandu / Jody girl / Travelin' man / Momma / Nutbush city limits / Sailing nights / Fine memory.
LP: . . . . EST 11378
LP: . . . . FA 41 31171

DISTANCE, THE (Seger, Bob & The Silver Bullet Band).
Tracks: / Even now / Makin' Thunderbirds / Boomtown blues / Shame on the moon / Love's the last to know / Roll me away / House behind a house / Comin' home / Little victories.
LP: . . . . EST 12254
MC: . . . . TCEST 12254

FIRE INSIDE, THE (Seger, Bob & The Silver Bullet Band).
Tracks: / Take a chance / Real love, The / Sightseeing / Always in my heart / Fire inside, The / Real at the time / Which way / Mountain, The / Blind love / She can't do anything wrong.
LP: . . . . EST 2149
MC: . . . . TCEST 2149

LIKE A ROCK (Seger, Bob & The Silver Bullet Band).
Tracks: / American storm / Like a rock / Miami / Ring, The / Tightrope / Aftermath / Sometimes / It's you / Somewhere tonight / Living inside my heart / Katmandu.
LP: . . . . EST 2011
MC: . . . . TCEST 2011

LIVE BULLET.
Tracks: / Nutbush City limits / Travellin' man / Beautiful loser / Jody girl / Looking back / Get out of Denver / Let it rock / I've been working / Turn the page / U.M.C. / Bo Diddley / Ramblin' gamblin' man / Heavy music / Katmandu.
2LP: . . . . ESTSP 16
MCSET: . . . . TC2 ESTSP 16

MONGREL.
Tracks: / Song to Rufus / Evil Edna / Highway child / Big river / Mongrel / Lucifer / Teachin' blues / Leanin' on my dream / Mongrel too / River deep, mountain high.
LP: . . . . FA 3072
MC: . . . . TCFA 3072
LP: . . . . GO 2022

NIGHT MOVES.
Tracks: / Rock and roll never forgets / Night moves / Fire down below / Sunburst / Sunspot baby / Mainstreet / Come to poppa / Ship of fools / Mary Lou.
LP: . . . . FA 3022
MC: . . . . TCFA 3022
LP: . . . . EAST 11557
MC: . . . . TCEAST 11557
MC: . . . . TCEST 2160

NINE TONIGHT.
Tracks: / Nine tonight / Trying to live my life without you / You'll accompany me / Hollywood nights / Night moves / Rock 'n' roll never forgets / Let it rock / Old time rock'n'roll / Mainstreet / Against the wind / Fire down below / Her strut / Feel like a number / Fire lake / Betty Lou's gettin' out tonight / We've got tonight.
2LP: . . . . ESTSP 23
MCSET: TC2ESTSP 23

RAMBLIN' GAMBLIN' MAN.
Tracks: / Ramblin' gamblin' man / Tales of Lucy blue / Ivory / Gone / Down home / Train man / White wall / Black eyed girl / 2+2=2 / Doctor fine / Last song, The.
LP: . . . . GO 2018

REAL LOVE, THE.
Tracks: / Real love, The / Which way / Mountain, The (Only on 12" and CD Single.) / Hollywood nights (Only on CD Single.).
MC: . . . . TCCL 628

SEVEN (Seger, Bob & The Silver Bullet Band).
Tracks: / Get out of Denver / Long song comin' / Need ya / School teacher / Cross of gold / U.M.C. (upper middle class) / Seen a lot of floors / 20 years from now / All your love.

LP: . . . . GO 2006
MC: . . . . TC GO 2006

SMOKIN O.P.'S.
Tracks: / Bo diddley / Love the one you're with / If i were a carpenter / Hummingbird / Let it rock / Turn on your lovelight / Jesse james / Someday / Heavy music.
LP: . . . . IC 064 85348
MC: . . . . IC 264 85348

STRANGER IN TOWN.
Tracks: / Hollywood nights / Still the same / Old time rock'n'roll / Till it shines / Feel like a number / Ain't got no money / We've got tonite / Brave strangers / Famous final scene, The.
LP: . . . . EAST 11698
MC: . . . . TCEAST 11698

Segovia, Andres

PORTRAIT OF ANDRES SEGOVIA, A.
Tracks: / Recuerdos de la Alhambra / Tonadilla / Estudio X en la mayor / XV en sol mayor / XIX en si menor / VI en la mayor / Romanza / Sevilla / Granada / Zambra granadina / Capricho diabouco.
LP: . . . . SMR 734
MC: . . . . SMC 734

Seicright, Floyd Lloyd

PAINTED FACES.
LP: . . . . PPC 0024

Seiko

SEIKO.
Tracks: / All the way to heaven / He's so good to me / Leave it up to fate / Right combination, The / Goodbye my baby / Who's that baby / With your love / Everything feels alright / Halfway to heaven / Try getting over you.
LP: 4665571
MC: 4665574

Seiler, Peter

SENSITIVE TOUCH.
Tracks: / Still the same sun / Reef moods / Journey to nowhere / I'm on my way / Mountain peaks / Her song / Sensitive touch.
LP: . . . . THBL 2.052

Seivewright, Andrew

JUBILEE FANFARES.
Tracks: / Fanfare for organ (Cook) / Adagio / Song of sunshine / Suite Gothique (Opus 25) / Fanfare and processional (Wagner) / Wondrous love (Variations on a shape-note hymn) / Variations on "America"(1891) for organ / Weeping willow.
LP: . . . . APS 361

Seixas (composer)

CARLOS SEIXAS HARPSICHORD SONATAS (Woolley, Robert).
Tracks: / Sonata in D minor (7/25) (Seixas) / Sonata in D minor (27/80) (Seixas) / Sonata in A major (57/80) (Seixas) / Sonata in F sharp minor (14/25) (Seixas) / Sonata in E major (34/80) (Seixas) / Sonata in C minor (12/80) (Seixas) / Sonata in G major (47/80) (Seixas) / Sonata in D minor (24/80) (Seixas) / Sonata in B flat major (78/80) (Seixas) / Sonata in E flat major (32/80) (Seixas) / Sonata in G minor (50/80) (Seixas).
MC: . . . . CSAR 43

Seizure

SERIOUSLY DELIRIOUS.
LP: . . . . BOXLP 004

Seka

LOVES HYMN.
LP: . . . . TG 92971

Selassie I Rockers

30 PIECES OF DUB.
LP: . . . . JLLP 801

Selby, Hubert

BACK HOME.
Tracks: / Opera off the cuff / Love everlasting / Dambusters march / No business like show business / My funny valentine / September in the rain / Lullaby of Birdland / Tico Tico / Tea for two / Post horn galop / Twelfth St. rag.
MC: . . . . AC 171

MR. PRESIDENT ENTERTAINS.
Tracks: / Shadow of your smile / Paloma, (La) / On a slow boat to China / 'S wonderful / You are my lucky star / Because you're mine / Be my love / Here's that rainy day / Her name is Mary / Ting a ling / Jealousy / If you knew Susie / I'll always be in love with you / You're the cream in my coffee.
LP: . . . . AML 308
MC: . . . . AC 200

Seldom Scene

ACT 3.
Tracks: / Chim chim cheree / Little Georgia Rose / Another lonely day / Willie boy / Faded love / Rider / Muddy water / Sing me back home / Hail to the redskins / Don't bother me with white satin / Heaven.
LP: . . . . REB 1528
MC: . . . . REBMC 1528

ACT 4.
LP: . . . . SH 3709
MC: . . . . ZCSH 3709

AFTER MIDNIGHT.
LP: . . . . SH 3721
MC: . . . . ZCSH 3721

AT THE SCENE.
LP: . . . . SH 3736

BAPTIZING.
Tracks: / By the side of the road / Brother John / Dreaming of a little cabin / Fallen leaves / He took your place / Take him in / Hobo on a freight train to heaven / Will you be ready to go home / Were you there / Walk with you again / Gospel medley.
LP: . . . . SAVE 035
MC: . . . . REBMC 1573
LP: . . . . REB 1573

CHANGE IN SCENERY, A.
Tracks: / Breaking new ground / Casting a shadow in the road / Settin' me up / Alabama clay / I'll be a stranger there / West Texas wind / Satan's choir / In despair / What goes on / One way rider.
LP: . . . . SH 3763
MC: . . . . ZCSH 3763

LIVE AT THE CELLAR DOOR.
Tracks: / Doing my time / California cottonfield's / Panhandle country / Muddy waters / Rawhide / Baby blue / City of New Orleans / Grandfather's clock / Fields have turned brown, The / Hit parade of love / Will the circle be unbroken / Pickaway / Dark hollow / Small exception of me / If I were a carpenter / Old gray bonnet / C & O canal / Georgia rose / Colorado turnaround / He rode all the way to Texas / White line / Rider.
2LP: . . . . REB 1547/48
MCSET: . . . . REBC 1547/48

LIVE: CELEBRATION 15TH ANNIVERSARY.
Tracks: / Sitting on top of the world / Big train from Memphis / Lorena / Dark as a dungeon / Blue Ridge / Raised by the railroad line / Don't know my mind / Drifting too far from the shore / Those memories of you / Keep me from blowing away / Wheels / Carolyn at the broken wheel inn / If I needed you / Rose of old Kentucky / I couldn't find my walkin' shoes / Workin' on a building / Say you lied / High on a hilltop / Sweetest gift, The / Take me on your life boat.
LP: . . . . SH 2202
MC: . . . . ZCSH 2202

NEW SELDOM SCENE ALBUM, THE.
LP: . . . . REB 1561
MC: . . . . REBMC 1561

OLD TRAIN.
LP: . . . . REB 1536
MC: . . . . REBMC 1536

SCENIC ROOTS.
Tracks: / If you ever change your mind / Lost in your memory / Wrath of God, The / Before I met you / Red Georgia Clay / I've cried my last tear / Not in my arms / Highway of heartache / Long black veil / Last call to glory / Distant train / How mountain girls can love.
LP: . . . . SH 3785
MC: . . . . ZCSH 3785

SELDOM SCENE VOL. 1.
LP: . . . . REB 1511
MC: . . . . REBMC 1511

SELDOM SCENE VOL. 2.
LP: . . . . REB 1520
MC: . . . . REBMC 1520

Selecter

CELEBRATE THE BULLET.
Tracks: / (Who likes) facing situations / Deep water / Red reflections / Tell me what's wrong / Bomb scare / Washed up and left for dead / Celebrate the bullet / Selling out your future / Cool blue lady / Their dream goes on / Bristol and Miami.
LP: . . . . CHR 1306
MC: . . . . ZCHR 1306

TOO MUCH PRESSURE.
Tracks: / Three minute hero / Time hard / They make me mad / Missing words / Danger / Street feeling / My collie (not a dog) / Too much pressure / Murder / Out on the streets / Carry go bring come / Black and blue / James Bond.
LP: . . . . CDLTT 5 002
MC: . . . . ZCDL TT 5 002

Self Control

BROKEN UP.
LP: . . . . DS 5X 1

Self, Jim

CHILDREN AT PLAY (Self, Jim Quintet).
Tracks: / Children at play / Jitterbug waltz / Waltz samba / Peacocks, The / Peggy's blue skylight / Secrets.
LP: . . . . DS 886

TRICKY LIX.
Tracks: / Tricky Lix / Take the stairs / 'Round midnight / Night lights / Another time / Somebody's samba / Heather on the hill / I love you / My funny valentine / Farewell burn, The.
MC: . . . . CJ 430 C

Self, Ronnie

RONNIE SELF.
LP: . . . . COLDE 2014

Selfish Gene

SELFISH GENE Dawkins, Richard.
MC: . . . . PT 22

Seliga, Frank

ON THE ROCKS - IN STRICT TEMPO RHYTHM (Seliga, Frank & His Dance Orchestra).
LP: . . . . ORC 76012

Sellers Engineering...

REFLECTIONS.
MC: . . . . SRC 311

Sellers, John

LET PRAISE ARISE.
LP: . . . . WING 525
MC: . . . . TC WING 525

Sellers, Peter

BEST OF SELLERS.
Tracks: / Trumpet volunteer, The / Auntie Rotter / All the things you are / We need the money / I'm so ashamed / Party political speech / Balham, gateway to the south / Suddenly it's folk song.
LP: . . . . MRS 5157
LP: . . . . PMD 1069

COLLECTION, THE (see under EMI Comedy Classics).

HE'S INNOCENT OF WATERGATE (Sellers, Peter & Spike Milligan).
LP: . . . . SKL 5194

PARKINSON INTERVIEW, THE.
LP: . . . . REH 402
MC: . . . . ZCR 402

PETER & SOPHIA (Sellers, Peter/ Sophia Loren).
Tracks: / Goodness gracious me / Smith / Zoo be zoo be zoo / Ukelele lady / Setting fire to the policeman / Bangers and mash / Oh lady be good / To keep my love alive / Why worry / Grandpa's grave / I fell in love with an Englishman / Africa today / Fare thee well.
LP: . . . . PMC 1131
LP: . . . . OU 2233

SELLERS MARKET.
Tracks: / All-England George Formby finals / Complete guide to accents of the British Isles.
LP: . . . . UAG 30266

SONGS FOR SWINGIN' SELLERS.
Tracks: / You keep me swingin' / So little time / Contemporary scene 1 and 2 / My old dutch / Puttin' on the smile / Common entrance / I haven't told her, she hasn't told me / Shadows on the grass / Wouldn't it be loverly / We'll let you know / Peter Sellers sings George Gershwin.
LP: . . . . NTS 212
LP: . . . . PMC 1111

SONGS OF SELLERS, THE.
Tracks: / Goodness gracious me / Hard day's night, A / Boiled bananas and carrots / She loves you / My old dutch / Lady be good / Any old iron / Putting on the smile / Bangers and mash / Help / They're removing grandpa's grave to build a sewer / Peter Sellers sings George Gershwin.
LP: . . . . MFP 5640
MC: . . . . TCMFP 5640
LP: . . . . MFP 4156401

Selley, Graham

SENSATIONAL SOUND OF SELLEY, THE.
LP: . . . . SUS 525
MC: . . . . CSUS 525

Selvin, Ben

CHEERFUL LITTLE EARFUL (Selvin, Ben/his orchestra).
Tracks: / You were meant for me / Broadway melody / Miss you / Am I blue? / Let me sing and I'm happy / It's easy to fall in love / Cheerful little earful / Me / This is the missus / Now's the time to fall in love / You're getting to be a habit with me / Young and healthy.
LP: . . . . SVL 165

Selvon, Samuel

CONTEMPORARY LITERATURE READINGS (See Under Nichols, Grace) (Selvon, Samuel & Grace Nichols).

Sema

THREE SEASONS ONLY (see under Haigh, Robert) (Sema & Robert Haigh).

Semantics

BWANA JUNCTION.
LP: 400 246

Sembello, Michael

BOSSA NOVA HOTEL.
Tracks: / Maniac / Superman / Talk / First time / Cowboy / Cadillac / It's over / Automatic man / Lay back / Godzilla.
LP: 9239201

Seminal Rats

OMNIPOTENT.
LP: . . . . GOES ON 10

Semprini

GOLDEN CLASSICS.
Tracks: / Gold and silver waltz / La golondrina / Rakoczy march / Serenade (Schubert) / Polonaise Op. 40 No. 1 in A Major / On wings of song / Barcarolle / Skaters walts (Waldteufel) / Waltz in C Sharp minor Opus 64 No. 2 (Chopin) / Trepak / Meditation from "Thais" (Massenet) / Swan lake waltz / Hungarian fantasy / Solveig's song / March of the dwarfs.
MC: . . . . TCEMS 1298

GOLDEN MOMENTS, THE.
Tracks: / Gold and silver waltz / Traumerei / Chanson de matin / Sonata in C sharp minor Opus 27 no.2 (Beethoven) / Chanson hindoue / Prelude in C sharp minor / La mer / Symphony / Introduction and rondo capriccioso / Misty Montmartre / To the spring / My devotion / Sheep may safely graze / Rustle of Spring / Skater's waltz / Clair de lune / La golondrina / Cradle song / Meditation / Rooftop rhapsody / Liebestraum / Viva navarra / Tristesse / Chopin from 'Carnival' / Avant de mourir.
2LP: . . . . MFP 1031
MCSET: . . . . TCMFP 1031

MOTORWAY SERENADE.
MC: . . . . TC MMC 5003

SEMPRINI CLASSICAL PIECES.
MC: . . . . TCIDL 3

Semuta

SEMUTA.
Tracks: / No face, no name / Blue pearl / By no means beautiful / Bopso / Little angels / Danielle / La fayette / Losers.
LP: . . . . LAM 101

Senator, Asher

ASHER SENATOR V JOHNNY RINGO (Senator, Asher & Johnny Ringo).
LP: . . . . FADLP 002

BORN TO CHAT.
LP: . . . . FADLP 004

Senator Flux

CRIMINAL SPECIAL, THE.
LP: . . . . EM 93641
MC: . . . . EM 93644

SHOTGUN FOR COSMO.
Tracks: / New age alchemy / Zeno's half-step / Nomadology / Crystal flux / Just another thing / Distance, The / Black road / Jenny had a boyfriend / Highway times / Three rings of Ballantine.
LP: . . . . R 33/8711

SPECTACLES, TESTICLES, WALLET AND WATCH.
LP: . . . . R 33-8817

STORYKNIFE.
LP: . . . . EM 92631

Senators

HOPES AND BODIES.
Tracks: / Deceit / Crying wolf, A / I'm always sorry now / Brown eyed girl / Monday's coming / Naked with you / Ordinary heartbreak / Good morning world / Little things, The / Just like me / For asking.
MC: . . . . TCV 2616
LP: . . . . V 2616

WELCOME TO OUR WORLD.
Tracks: / One more chance / Everything's fine / I don't care about the past / Man's gonna win again / Quiet life / I cared / Man no more / My special prayer / In my heart and in my house / Love and small talk / Little Italy / Strange (CD & Cassette only) / Don't mess around with me (CD & Cassette only).
LP: . . . . V 2552
MC: . . . . TCV 2552

Sendak, Maurice

HIGGLETY PIGGLETY POP (or There must be more to life) (Grimes, Tammy (nar)).
MC: 1519

HORNBOOK FOR WITCHES, A (Price, Vincent).
MC: 1497

SENDAK SOUNDBOOK, THE (Grimes, Tammy (nar)).
LPS: . . . . SBC 124

Senegal

CHANTS, PERCUSSIONS ET RYTHMES DU SENEGAL (Various artists).
Tracks: / Yesu Kristo: *Various artists* / Karibum faita: *Various artists* / Sanctus: *Various artists*/ Jesus est ne: *Various artists* / Notre pere: *Various artists* / Agnus dei: *Various artists* / Noel diola: *Various artists* / Ni robo ganagen: *Various artists* / Noel a la balendine: *Various artists*.
LP: . . . . ARN 33689

CHANTS & RYTHMES DE CASAMANCE (Various artists).
Tracks: / U tyinoral bu sindo ol: *Various artists* / Atau deyi: *Various artists* / Yanve u dyanten oli: *Various* artists / Litanie des saints: *Various artists* / Messe diola: *Various artists* / Marie, usenom kagnen: *Various artists*.
LP: . . . . ARN 33695
MC: . . . . ARN 433695

KORA, BALAFON ET PERCUSSIONS DU SENEGAL (Various artists).
Tracks: / Introduction a la fete: *Various artists* / Danse Peul: *Various artists* / Danse le fete: *Various* artists / Tambours senegalais: *Various artists* / Zamba: *Various artists* / L'oiseau chasseur: *Various artists* / Improvisation a la kora: *Various artists* / La griot malinke: *Various artists*.
LP: . . . . ARN 33602

MESSE ET CHANTS AU MONASTERE DE KEUR MOUSSA (Various artists).
Tracks: / Tatyu len: *Various artists* / Borombi: *Various artists* / Gloire a dieu: *Various artists* / If la rog: *Various artists* / Meditation pour Saint Luc: *Various artists* / Suma fit: *Various artists*/ Mburtum yalla: *Various artists* / Gon la rog: *Various artists* / Sur tes remparts: *Various artists*.
LP: . . . . ARN 33576
MC: . . . . ARN 433576

PERCUSSION OF SENEGAL (Various artists).
LP: . . . . PS 33508

Sensation Jazz Band

OCEAN QUEEN.
LP: WRC1 1919

Sensational

CHURCH, LET'S GET READY FOR THE RESURRECTION.
LP: . . . . MAL 04401

HYMNS (See under Jackson Southernaires).

I SURRENDER ALL.
LP: . . . . MAL 04391

SONGS OF PRAISE.
LP: . . . . MCA 28001

VICTORY IS MINE.
LP: . . . . MAL 4427
MC: . . . . MALC 4427

Sense

HOLD ON.
LP: . . . . CAL 202

Sense of Beauty

SENSE OF BEAUTY VOL. 2 (Various artists).
LP: . . . . U 028
MC: . . . . U 0284

Sense & Sensibility

SENSE AND SENSIBILITY (See under Austen, Jane) (Bloom, Claire (nar)).

SENSE AND SENSIBILITY (See under Austen, Jane) (Badel, Sarah (nar)).

Senseless Things

POSTCARD CV.
LP: . . . . WC 004

UP AND COMING.
LP: . . . . WC 006

Senslis Killin

CHAINSAW BOOGIE.
LP: . . . . ARENA 1012

Senter, Boyd

SOLOS AND SENTERPEDES-VOL.1-1927-28.
Tracks: / Down-hearted blues / Boss of the stomps / Grind out, The / I ain't got nobody / T'aint clean / Eniale blues / Just so-so / Prickly heat / Sister Kate / Mobile blues / No more / Original stack o'lee blues / Original Chinese blues / Somebody's wrong.
LP: . . . . HQ 2044

Sentimental Journey

SENTIMENTAL JOURNEY (see under Sterne, Laurence) (Sinden, Donald).

Sentinel Beast

DEPTHS OF DEATH.
LP: . . . . RR 9694

Seow, Yitkin

ROMANTIC CELLO, THE (see under Lloyd-Webber, Julian) (Seow, Yitkin/ Julian Lloyd-Webber).

Sepia

WHAT THE HELL IS HAPPENING.
LP: . . . . ISST 138

Seppuku

TAXI GIRL.
Tracks: / Les armees de la nuit / N'importe quel soir / Musee tong / Les damnes (chant des enfants morts) / Les armees de la nuit (instrumental) / Armies of the night / Scarlet woman / Tong museum / Viviane vog / Avenue du crime / John Doe 85 / Treizime section / La femme ecarlate / On any evening / Avenue of crime.
LP: . . . . FC 047
MC: . . . . FC 047 C

Septic Death

NOW THAT I HAVE THE ATTEN..
LP: 0012-01D

Sepultura

ARISE.
LP: . . . . RO 93281
MC: . . . . RO 93284
LPPD: . . . . RO 93288

BENEATH THE REMAINS.
LP: . . . . RO 9511-1
MC: . . . . RO 95114

MORBID VISIONS.
LP: . . . . SHARK 4
LP: . . . . RO 92761
MC: . . . . RO 92764

SCHIZOPHRENIA.
LP: . . . . SHARK 006
LP: . . . . RO 93601
MC: . . . . RO 93604

SCHIZOPHRENIA/ MORBID VISIONS.
MC: . . . . SHARKMC 017

Sepulveda, Charlie

NEW ARRIVAL, THE.
MC: . . . . ANC 8767

Sequence

SEQUENCE.
Tracks: / Simon says / Times we're alone, The / We don't rap the rap / Funk a doodle rock jam / And you know that / Funky sound (Tear the roof off) / Come on let's boogie.
LP: . . . . SHLP 1003
MC: . . . . ZCSH 1003

Serafina

STORY OF A WHALE, THE (Various artists).
LP: . . . . MFP 5593
MC: . . . . TCMFP 5593

Seratt, Kenny

GIVE ME A TITLE AND I'LL WRITE YOU A SONG.
Tracks: / Give me a title and I'll write you a song / Always chasing rainbows / Hide me / What do you do when it's over / There's just one way / Too many bar rooms / Nothing good in goodbye / That silver haired daddy of mine / Don't put Grandma in a rest home / Jesus makes the sunshine in my life.
LP: . . . . BRA 1005
MC: . . . . BRC 1005

RIDIN' THE BIG A.
Tracks: / Ridin' the big A / Queen of the road / It ain't no good to love a truck drivin' man / Diesel devil / I'm truckin' my way to glory / Jody's on the run / I've got a truck / No longer mine / Six days on the road / White blind fever / Snow on the mountain.
LP: . . . . BRA 1007
MC: . . . . BRC 1007

SATURDAY NIGHT IN DALLAS.
Tracks: / Saturday night in Dallas / Bitter end, The / Most wanted woman / Sidewalks are grey / Damn good drinking song / Honky tonk nights / We made memories / Never gonna be a country star / Giving up easy / Hung over on love.
LP: . . . . BRA 1002
MC: . . . . BRC 1002

Serenade For Strings

SERENADE FOR STRINGS (Various artists).
MC: TC2MOM 108

Serious Drinking

HITS, THE MISSES AND OWN GOALS, THE.
LP: . . . . PLAYLP 14

REVOLUTION STARTS AT CLOSING TIME.
Tracks: / Revolution starts at closing time, The / Winters over / Spirit of 66' / Love on the terraces / Bobby Moore was innocent / Hangover / Countdown to Bilko / Really good bloke / 12XU / Am I coming over to yours.
LP: . . . . UPLP 3

THEY MAY BE DRINKERS ROBIN, BUT THEY'RE ALSO HUMAN BEINGS.
LP: . . . . UPLP 7

Serpent & The Rainbow

SERPENT & THE RAINBOW (Film Soundtrack) (Various artists).
LP: . . . . STV 81362
MC: . . . . CTV 81362

Serra, Eric

NIKITA (FILM SOUNDTRACK) (See under Nikita).

Sertl, Doug

GROOVIN' (Sertl, Doug Big Band).
Tracks: / Eternal triangle, The / Invitation / Groovin' on Uranus / Airegin / Triste / Guess who I saw today / Falling in love with love.
LP: . . . . DS 920

UPTOWN EXPRESS.
LP: . . . . PA 8048

Servant

LIGHT MANOEUEVRES.
LP: . . . . MYR 1182
MC: . . . . MC 1182

SWIMMING IN A HUMAN OCEAN.
LP: . . . . MYRR 6829
MC: . . . . MYRC 6829

Servants

DISINTERESTED.
Tracks: / Move out / Restless / Thin skinned / Hush now / Hey, Mrs John / Big future / Power of woman, The / Third wheel / Self destruction / They should make a statue / Look like a girl / Afterglow.
LP: . . . . PAPLP 005

Session 57

SESSION 57.
LP: . . . . ROCK 9006

Sestetto Swing..

FIVE CONTINENTS (Sestetto Swing de Roma).
LP: . . . . IJC 003

Sesto, Camilo

CAMILO.
Tracks: / Can't change your mind / Too deep in love / There I go again / Who better than I / Shoulder to shoulder / Boats against the current / Next best thing to love / Here, there and everywhere / It's the way you do it.
LP: 205073
MC: 405073

Set The Tone

SHIFTIN' AIR AFFAIR.
Tracks: / Rap your love / All tied up / Prove it / Skin me / Start the bus / Grind.
LP: . . . . ILPS 9736

Sete, Bola

OCEAN.
LP: . . . . SNTF 695

Setzer, Brian

KNIFE FEELS LIKE JUSTICE, THE.
Tracks: / Knife feels like justice, The / Barbwire fence / Haunted river / Boulevard of broken dreams / Bobby's back / Radiation ranch / Chains around your heart / Maria / Three guys / Aztec / Breath of life.
LP: . . . . AML 3102
MC: . . . . TCAML 3102

LIVE NUDE GUITARS.
Tracks: / Red lightning blues / Rockability / Rebelene / Nervous breakdown / Every tear that falls / Temper sure is rising / When the sky comes tumblin' down / She thinks I'm trash / Love is repaid by love alone / Rosie in the middle / So young so bad so what / Rain washed away everything.
LP: . . . . MTL 1025
MC: . . . . TCMTL 1025
LP: . . . . AML 3127
MC: . . . . TCAML 3127
LP: 7469631
MC: 7469634

Sevelle, Taja

TAJA SEVELLE.
Tracks: / Love is contagious / Wouldn't you love to love me? / Popular / How could you do me so bad? / Take me for a ride / If I could get your attention / Infatuation / Baby's got a lover / Mama 16 / Fly for your painted rainbow.
LP: 925546 1
MC: 925546 4

Seven A 3

COOLIN' IN CALIFORNIA.
Tracks: / Coolin' in Cali / That's how we're livin' / Everybody gets loose / Man's gotta do what a man's gotta do, A / Freestyle '88 / Express the mind / Hit 'em again / Drums of steel / Goes like dis / Half bouldin / Other half ince, The / Lucifer.
LP: 9242091
MC: 9242094

Seven Brides For Seven

SEVEN BRIDES FOR SEVEN BROTHERS (Original London Cast) (Various artists).
Tracks: / June bride: *Various artists* / When you're in love: *Various artists* / Overture: *Various artists*/ Bless your beautiful hide: *Various artists* / Wonderful wonderful day: *Various artists* / One man: *Various* artists / Goin' co'rtin': *Various artists* / Love never goes away: *Various artists* / Sobbin' women: *Various* artists / Townsfolk's lament, The: *Various artists* / Woman ought to know her place, A: *Various artists* / We gotta make it through the winter: *Various artists* / Lonesome polecat: *Various artists* / Spring spring spring: *Various artists* / Glad that you were born: *Various artists* / Wedding dance: *Various artists* / Finale: *Various artists*.
LP: 4502321
MC: 4502324
LP: . . . . CAST 2
MC: . . . . CASTC 2

SEVEN BRIDES FOR SEVEN BROTHERS (Film Soundtrack) (Various artists).
LP: . . . . MCA 25021
MC: . . . . MCAC 25021

SEVEN BRIDES FOR SEVEN BROTHERS (ORIGINAL ISSUE) (Film soundtrack) (Various artists).
LP: . . . . MGM C 853

SEVEN BRIDES FOR SEVEN BROTHERS/ANNIE GET YOUR GUN (Film soundtracks) (Various artists).
Tracks: / Bless your beautiful hide: *Various artists* / Wonderful, wonderful day: *Various artists* / Lonesome polecat: *Various artists* / Goin' co'tin': *Various artists* / Sobbin' women: *Various artists* / June bride: *Various artists* / Spring Spring Spring: *Various artists* / When your in love: *Various artists* / I got the sun in the morning: *Various artists* / They say it's wonderful: *Various artists* / You can't get a man with a gun: *Various artists* / My defences are down: *Various artists* / Doin' what comes natur'lly: *Various artists*/ Girl that I marry, The: *Various artists* / Anything you can do: *Various artists* / There's no business like show business: *Various artists*.
LP: 2353 032
MC: 3110 038

SEVEN BRIDES FOR SEVEN BROTHERS/LILI (Film soundtrack) (Various artists).
Tracks: / Bless your beautiful hide: *Keel, Howard* (Seven Brides For Seven Brothers) / Wonderful, wonderful day: *Powell*, Jane (Seven Brides For Seven Brothers) / Lonesome polecat: *Lee, Bill & Brothers* (Seven Brides For Seven Brothers) / Goin' co'tin': *Powell, Jane & Brothers* (Seven Brides For Seven Brothers) / Sobbin' women: *Keel, Howard & Brothers*(Seven Brides For Seven Brothers) / June bride: *Gibson, Virginia & Girls* (Seven Brides For Seven Brothers) / Spring, spring, spring: *Various artists* (Seven Brides For Seven Brothers) / When you're in love: *Keel, Howard, Jane Powell* (Seven Brides For Seven Brothers) / Adoration: *Various artists* (Lili) / Hi lili hi lo: *Caron, Leslie & Mel Ferrer* (Lili) / Lili & the puppets, Part I: *Various artists* (Lili) / Lili & the puppets, Part II: *Various artists* (Lili).
LP: . . . . LPMGM 9
MC: . . . . TCMGM 9
LP: 793 305 1
MC: 793 305 4

Seven Deadly Sins

SEVEN DEADLY SINS (Original Broadway Cast) (Various artists).
LP: . . . . AKL 5175

Seven Samurai

7 SAMURAI/RASHOMON (See under Rashomon) (Various artists).

Seven Seconds

CREW, THE.
LP: . . . . BYO 5
MC: . . . . BYO 5C

NEW WIND.

LP: BYO 14
MC: BYO 14C

OURSELVES.
LP: GWLP 49

WALK TOGETHER ROCK TOGETHER.
LP: BYO 10
MC: BYO 10C

Seven Stars

SEVEN STARS.
Tracks: / Avalon / Old lads / Stardust / World is waiting for the sunrise, The / Satin doll / Someone to watch over me / I wanna go home.
LP: CJ 217
MC: CJC 217

Seven Stories

JUDGES AND BAGMEN.
Tracks: / Gift horse / Sleeping through another war / Walk through Babylon / Stripped down man / Paralysed / Harbour me / Couldn't get arrested / Declare yourself / Kicking against the bricks / Everything that rises.
LP: 4667471
MC: 4667474

Seven Suffolk Singers

KNIFE IN THE WINDOW, THE.
Tracks: / Sailor boy / House of ill fame, The / 'Scarboro' number one / William and Polly / Dark-eyed sailor / Old couple in the wood / Stand you up steady-o / Molecatcher / Burlington Fair (rambleaway) / Poor little soldier's boy / Bold General Wolfe / Highwayman outwitted / Ship that never returned, The / Knife in the window, The / Light dragoon, The / Barbara Allen / Nonsense song / I'll be level wiv her / Jealousy / Poor smuggler's boy / Scarboro' number two / Faithful plough, The / Foggy dew, The / Loss of the Ramillies, The / Muddley barracks (recruiting song).
MC: 60-099

Seventeen

CAPTURED IN ICE.
LP: LOLITA 5051

Seventh Angel

TORMENT, THE.
LP: FLAG 51

Seventh Sign

SEVENTH SIGN (Original Soundtrack) (Various artists).
Tracks: / Opening, fish, desert, wrath, 1st seal: *Various artists* / Nightmare, The: *Various artists* / David's apartment: *Various artists* / Abby follows David to the synagogue: *Various artists* / World in trouble: *Various* artists / Parchment 2.29: *Various artists* / Stabbing, The: *Various artists* / Attempted suicide: *Various* artists / Lucci revealed: *Various artists* / Last martyr, The: *Various artists* / Walk to the gas chamber: *Various artists* / Birth: *Various artists* / Abby's death: *Various artists* / End credits: *Various artists.*
LP: EDL 2506.1

Seventh Voyage Of

SEVENTH VOYAGE OF SINBAD (Film Soundtrack) (Various artists).
LP: STV 81135

Seventh Wave

PSI-FI.
Tracks: / Return to foreverland / Roads to rome / Manifestations / Loved by you / Only the beginning / Aether anthem / Astral animal / El tuto / Camera obscura / Star palace of the Sombre Warrior.
LP: GULP 1010

THINGS TO COME.
Tracks: / Sky scraper / Metropolis / Intercity water rat / Escalator / Old dog song / Smog, fog and sunset / Fail to see / Premonition / Festival / Ever so lightly / Communication skyways / Things to come / 1999 / Dance of the Eloi.
LP: GULP 1001

Seventh Wonder

WORDS DON'T SAY ENOUGH.
LP: RRL 2004

Severed Heads

BAD MOOD GUY.
Tracks: / Hot with fleas / Nation / Unleash your sword / Jet lag / Contempt / Bad mood guy / Dressed in air / Rabbi Nardoo Flagoon / Heaven in what heaven eats / Mad dad mangles a strad.
LP: VOLT 10
LP: UNKNOWN
LP: NET 005

BIG BIGOT, THE.
LP: VOLT 7

BULKHEAD.
Tracks: / Dead eyes opened / Greater reward / Hot with fleas / Goodbye tonsils / Twenty deadly diseases / Propellor / Petrol.
LP: NET 005
LP: NTL 30018

CITY SLAB HORROR.
LP: INK 9

CLIFFORD DARLING Please don't live in the past.
2LP: INK 16 D

COME VISIT THE BIG BIGOT.
LP: NTL 30003
MC: NTLC 30003

MEDIA JINGLES.
MC: MFM 42

ROTUND FOR SUCCESS.
LP: NET 14

SIDE 2.
MC: MFM 41

SINCE THE ACCIDENT.
LP: INK 002

Sewell, Anna (aut)

BLACK BEAUTY (see under Black Beauty (bk)).

Sewer Zombies

REACH OUT AND....
LP: UNKNOWN

Sex Clark Five

STRUM AND DRUM.
LP: SUBORG 007

Sex Gang Children

BEASTS.
Tracks: / Beasts / Cannibal queen / Who on earth can that be / Sense of elation / Into the abyss / Dieche / Salvation / Mocnoglia / Times of our lives.
LP: DOJOLP 30
LP: JAMS 34

ECSTASY AND VENDETTA OVER NEW YORK.
MC: A 127

LIVE London and Glasgow, 1983.
LP: SEX 2

NIGHTLAND USA, 1983.
LP: AHLP 1001

RE-ENTER THE ABYSS.
Tracks: / State of mind / Killer K / Shout and scream / Sebastian / Beasts / Into the abyss / Deiche / Times of our lives / Draconian dream.
LP: DOJOLP 13
MC: DOJOTC 13

SEX AND LEGEND.
LP: JAMS 666

SONG AND LEGEND.
Tracks: / Crack up, The / German nun / State of mind / Sebastian / Draconian dream / Shout and scream / Killer K / Cannibal queen / Kill machine / Song and legend.
LP: DOJOLP 16

Sex Pistols

10TH ANNIVERSARY.
LP: JOCK LP 3

BEST OF AND THE REST OF, THE.
Tracks: / Anarchy in the UK / I wanna be me / I'm a lazy sod / Dolls (new york) / Don't give me no lip child / Substitute / Liar / No feelings / No fun / Pretty vacant / Problems.
MC: ARLC 1008

BEST OF...AND WE DON'T CARE.
LP: YX 7247

BETTER LIVE THAN DEAD.
Tracks: / Substitute / No fun / Pretty vacant / Anarchy in the UK.
LP: 722 551

FILTH AND THE FURY, THE Six-album box set.
LPS: JOCK BOX 1

FLOGGING A DEAD HORSE.
Tracks: / Anarchy in the UK / I wanna be me / God save the Queen / Do you no wrong / Pretty vacant / Holidays in the sun / No fun / My way / Something else / Silly thing / C'mon everybody / I'm not your stepping stone / Great rock'n'roll swindle, The / No one is innocent.
LP: V 2142
MC: TCV 2142
LP: OVED 165
MC: OVEDC 165

GREAT ROCK'N'ROLL SWINDLE, THE (Film Soundtrack - Single Album).
Tracks: / God save the Queen (Symphony) / Great rock'n'roll swindle, The / You need hands / Silly thing / Lonely boy / Something else / Rock around the clock / C'mon everybody / Who killed Bambi / No one is innocent / L'anarchie pour le UK / My way.
LP: V 2168
MC: TCV 2168
LP: OVED 234
MC: OVEDC 234

GREAT ROCK'N'ROLL SWINDLE, THE (Film soundtrack-Double Album).
Tracks: / God save the Queen (Symphony) / Johnny B. Goode / Road runner / Anarchy in the UK / Don't give me no lip, child / I'm not your stepping stone / L'anarchie pour le UK / Silly thing / My way / I wanna be me / Something else / Rock around the clock / Lonely boy / EMI (orch) / Great rock'n'roll swindle, The / Friggin' in the riggin' / You need hands / Who killed Bambi? / Belsen was a gas / Black arabs / Substitute / No one is innocent / C'mon everybody.
2LP: VD 2510
MC: TCVD 2510

IT SEEMED TO BE THE END UNTIL THE NEXT BEGINNING.
LP: JOCKLP 12

LAST SHOW ON EARTH.
LP: JOCK LP 1

LIVE AND LOUD.
MC: LINKMC 063
LP: LINKLP 063

LIVE WORLDWIDE.
LP: KOMA 788017

MINI LP, THE.
MLP: APOCA 3
MLP: MINI 1

MUSIC AND MEDIA INTERVIEW PICTURE DISCS.
LPPD: SP 1001

NEVER MIND THE BOLLOCKS-HERE'S THE SEX PISTOLS.
Tracks: / Holidays in the sun / Bodies / No feelings / Liar / God save the Queen / Problems / Seventeen / Anarchy in the UK / Submission / Pretty vacant / New York / EMI.
LP: V 2086
MC: TCV 2086
LP: OVED 136
MC: OVEDC 136

NO FUTURE U.K.?.
LP: RRLP 117
MC: RRLC 117

ORIGINAL PISTOLS.
LP: APKPD 13
LP: FA 4131491
LP: RRLP 101
MC: RRLC 101

ORIGINAL PISTOLS LIVE.
Tracks: / No feelings / Anarchy in the U.K. / I'm a lazy sod / Liar / Dolls (New York) / Don't give me no lip child / Substitute / Pretty Vacant / I wanna be me / Problems / Submission / No fun.
MC: DOJOTC 45
LP: FA 3149
MC: TCFA 3149
LP: FA 313 149 1
MC: FA 313 149 4
LP: DOJOLP 45

PRETTY VACANT.
2LP: RRLD 004

SOME PRODUCT - CARRI ON SEX PISTOLS.
Tracks: / Very name "Sex Pistols", The / From beyond the grave / Big tits across America / Complex world of John Rotten, The / Sex Pistols will play / Is the Queen a moron? / F**king rotter, The.
LP: VR 2

Sexteto ...

SONES CUBANOS, VOL.2 (Sexteto Habanera).
LP: FL 9054
MC: C 9054

SONES CUBANOS VOL. 1 (Sexteto Bolona).
LP: FL 9053
MC: C 9053

Sexteto Tango

MAGIA PORTENA: ORIGINAL TANGOS FROM ARGENTINA.
LP: NL 70339

Sexton, Ann

LOVE TRIALS.
Tracks: / I want to be loved / I'm his wife, you're just a friend / Who's gonna love you? / I had a fight with love (and I lost) / Be serious / Colour my world blue / You've been doing me wrong for so long / Have a little mercy / Loving you, loving me / Love, love, love / Come back home / Keep on holding on / You're letting me down / You're gonna miss me.
LP: CRB 1143

Sexton, Charlie

PICTURES FOR PLEASURE.
Tracks: / Impressed / Beat's so lonely / Restless / Hold me / Pictures for pleasure / Tell me / Attraction / You don't belong / Space.
LP: MCG 6002
MC: MCGC 6002

Sexton, Michael

TASTE OF TRADITIONAL IRISH MUSIC & SONG, A (Sexton, Michael & P.J.Murphy).
MC: GTDC 084

Seychelles

LES ILES SEYCHELLES.
Tracks: / Zerenion / Zoli fleu / Sega moutia / Mariana marche / Pas pleurer / Marie / Contre-danse / Sega Marie en essai.
LP: ARN 33364
MC: ARN 433364

Seymour Orchestra

18 FAVOURITE FILM THEMES (Seymour Studio Orchestra).
Tracks: / Star trek / Star wars / 2001 / Superman / Rocky, theme from / Chariots of fire / Cavatina / Diamonds are forever / E.T., Theme from / Close Encounters of the Third Kind suite / Good, the bad and the ugly, The / Bright eyes / Do you know where you're going to (Theme from Mahogany) / Godfather, The / I just called to say I love you / Axel F / Evergreen / Pink panther.
LP: SHLP 154
MC: SHTC 154

ENDLESS LOVE SONGS (Seymour Symphony Orchestra).
Tracks: / Careless whisper / Move closer / Endless Love / Ebony and ivory / For your eyes only / Arthur's theme / Hello again / I love a rainy night / Hopelessly devoted to you / I only want to be with you / I'd rather leave while I'm in love / Mandy / I write the songs / Nights in white satin / Suddenly / Over the rainbow / With you I'm born again / Could it be I'm falling in love.
LP: SHLP 152
MC: SHTC 152

Seymour, Phil

PHIL SEYMOUR.
Tracks: / Precious to me / I found a love / Love you so much / Baby it's you / Let her dance / Then we go up / Don't blow your life away / We don't get along / Trying to get to you / I really love you / Won't finish here.
LP: EPC 85000

Seymour, Terry

TERRY SEYMOUR BIG BAND (Seymour, Terry Big Band).
LP: WAVE LP 15

SFF

SUNBURST.
LP: 0060 068

SYMPHONIC PICTURES.
LP: 0060 010

TICKET TO EVERYWHERE.
Tracks: / Open doors / Song from India / Ticket to everywhere / Spain span Spanish / Here and now / Slow motion / Folk 'n' roll.
LP: 0060 173

S.G.M.

AGGRESSION.
LP: GWLP 48

Sgt. Cribb Mystery

ABRACADAVER - A SERGEANT CRIBB MYSTERY (See under Abracadaver... (bk) (Lovesey, Peter).

Sgt. Pepper

JUDGEMENT DAY.
LP: ARILP 006

SHAKA MEETS PEPPER (see under Shaka, Jah) (Sgt. Pepper & Jah Shaka).

Sha Na Na

20 GOLDEN HITS: SHA NA NA.
LP: MA 25685

20 GREATEST HITS: SHA NA NA.
LP: 2636521
MC: 2636524

GOLDEN HOUR OF ROCK AND ROLL REVIVAL, A.
Tracks: / Rock and roll is here to stay / Come go with me / Silhouettes / Yakety yak / Tell Laura I love her / Heartbreak Hotel / At the hop / In the still of the night / Sea cruise / Sixteen candles / Earth angel / High school confidential / Rock around the clock / Little darlin' / Wanderer, The / Remember then / Great balls of fire / Maybe I'm old fashioned / Sh-boom (life could be a dream) / Get a job / So fine, you're so fine / Splish splash / Easier said than done / Long tall Sally.
MC: KGHMC 133

SHA NA NA IS HERE TO STAY.
Tracks: / Sixteen candles / Earth angel / Just like Romeo and Juliet / Great balls of fire / Breaking up is hard to do / Young love / At the hop / Silhouettes / Come go with me / Rock 'n' roll is here to stay.
LP: 252 209 1

MC: 252 209 4

Shaan

DANCE AND ROMANCE.
MC: SC 5102

Shabazz, Lakim

PURE RIGHTEOUSNESS.
LP: TUFLP 5557
LP: SDLP 1
MC: SDLC 1

Shack

ZILCH.
Tracks: / Emergency / Someone's knocking / Joh Kline / I need you / Realization / High rise low life / Who killed Clayton Square / Who'd believe it / What's it like... / Believers, The.
LP: GHETT 1
MC: GHETTC1

Shackle

SHACKLE.
Tracks: / I'm getting good at missing you / Roll in my sweet baby's arms / Help me make it through the night / Tennessee flat top box / Husbands and wives / Detours / I heard the Blue Birds sing / Kiss an angel good mornin' / For the good times / Swinging doors / Ladies love outlaws / Battle of New Orleans.
LP: DUD 8

Shade, Will

FRIENDS, 1961 (Shade, Will & Gus Cannon).
LP: DLP 561

Shades

ACE OF SHADES.
Tracks: / Hi ho silver / Linda T / See you in dreamland / Dinner with Drac / Lynch mob / Rockin' Redwing / Beeza Bill's boogie / You look like a woman / Georgina / Sweet girl to me / Miss Minnie Mouse / Cruel sea / Rally round the flag.
MC: MFM 010
LP: MFLP 005

Shades Of...

SHADES OF NEW ORLEANS (Various artists).
LP: GHB 140

Shades of Rhythm

SHADES OF RHYTHM.
LP: ZTT 8
MC: ZTT8C

Shadow

HIGH TENSION.
LP: GS 2279

PRESSURE POINT.
LP: GS 2296
MC: GSC 2296

RAW ENERGY.
Tracks: / Janette / Pandora / If I wine / Tabakna / Way way out.
LP: HVLP 004

SHADOW, THE.
Tracks: / Death to the shadow / Terror at Wolf's Head Knoll, The.
LP: TOTEM 1038

SHADOWS IN THE STREETS.
Tracks: / Born to hustle / Best lady / Piece a cake / Party in the streets / Shadows in the street / Sinister way / Clouds / Tennis shoes.
LP: K 52311

Shadow the Sheepdog

SHADOW THE SHEEPDOG (see under Blyton, Enid (aut)) (Timothy, Christopher (nar)).

Shadowfax

DREAMS OF CHILDREN,THE.
LP: TAC 1038

FOLKSONGS FOR A NUCLEAR VILLAGE.
Tracks: / Firewalker, The / We used to laugh / Solar wind / Behind green eyes / Lucky mud / Madagascar cafe / Against the grain / No society / Elephant ego / Folksong for a nuclear village.
LP: EST 2057
MC: TCEST 2057

ODD GET EVEN, THE.
Tracks: / Oassis / One winter morning / 1001 nights / Pause in the rain, A / Her dress hang there / Changing of the guard / Boomerang / Odd get even, The / Sujata / One heart.
LP: 210708
MC: 410708

SHADOWDANCE.
Tracks: / New electric India / Watercourse way / Ghost bird / Distant voices / Shadowdance / Brown rice/ Karmapa chenno / Song for my brother, A.
LP: 371029-1
MC: 371029-4

SHADOWFAX.
Tracks: / Angel's flight / Vajra / Wheel of dreams / Oriental eyes / Move the clouds / Thousand teardrops, A / Ariki (hummingbird spirit) / Marie.
LP: 371022-1
MC: 371022-4

TOO FAR TO WHISPER.
Tracks: / Too far to whisper / What goes around / China blue / Orang-utan gang, The / Road to Hanna / Street noise / Slim limbs akimbo / Tsunami / Maceo / Ritual.
LP: 371051-1
MC: 371051-4
LP: WHA 1051

WHAT GOES AROUND (THE BEST OF SHADOWFAX).
Tracks: / Angel's flight / Vajra / Thousand teardrops, A / New electric india / Shadowdance / Brown rice/ Karmapa chenno / Another country / Dreams of children, The / Shaman song / What goes around / Orangutan gang (strikes back), The / Road to Hanna.
LP: WT 1104

Shadowland

BEAUTY OF ESCAPING.
LP: 7599242861
MC: 7599242864

Shadows

20 GOLDEN GREATS: SHADOWS.
Tracks: / Apache / Frightened city / Guitar tango / Kon-tiki (From the film "Summer Holiday".) / Genie with the light brown lamp / Warlord, The / Place in the sun, A / Atlantis / Wonderful land / F.B.I. / Savage, The (From the film "The Young Ones".) / Geronimo / Shindig / Stingray / Theme for young lovers (From the film "Wonderful Life".) / Rise and fall of Flingel Bunt, The / Maroc 7 / Dance on / Rise and fall of Flingel Bunt, The / Man of mystery / Foot tapper.
LP: EMTV 3
MC: TCEMTV 3

20 ROCK'N'ROLL HITS: SHADOWS.
Tracks: / Feeling fine / Don't be a fool / Driftin' / Jet black / Saturday dance / Lonesome fella / Chinchilla / Stranger, The / Quartermaster's stores / Be bop a lula / Apache / Man of mystery / F.B.I. / 36-24-36 / Savage, The / Shadoogie / Baby my heart / Rumble / Round and round / Dance on.
LP: 1A 062Z 07146

ANOTHER STRING OF HOT HITS AND MORE.
Tracks: / Wonderful land / Atlantis / Black is black / Goodbye yellow brick road / River deep, mountain high / Rise and fall of Flingel Bunt, The / Midnight cowboy / Pinball wizard / See me, feel me / Apache / God only knows / Stardust / Walk, don't run / Most beautiful girl, The / Good vibrations / Something / Superstar / Trains and boats and planes / Honky tonk women / F.B.I. / Kon-Tiki.
LP: MFP 5630
MC: TCMFP 5630
LP: MFP 4156301
MC: TCMFP 4156304
LP: EMC 3339

APACHE.
LP: 1A 028 07098
MC: 2C 008 04700

AT THEIR VERY BEST.
Tracks: / Apache / Man of mystery / Shindig / Wonderful land / Rise and fall of flingel bunt / Deer hunter, Theme from / Boys, The / Frightened city, The / Theme for young lovers / Dance on / Savage, The / F.B.I. / Guitar tango / Genie with the light brown lamp / Atlantis / Foot tapper / Don't cry for me Argentina / Kon-Tiki / Geronimo / Stranger, The.
MC: 841 520 4
LP: 841 520 1

BEST OF THE SHADOWS.
Tracks: / Foot tapper / Main theme / I met a girl / Maroc 7 / I wish I could shimmy like my sister Arthur / Dreams I dream, The / Quartermaster's stores / My grandfather's clock / I can't forget / Bombay duck / Late night set / Dear old Mrs Bell / Rumble / It's been a blue day / Running out of world / Chu chi / Back home / Will you be there? / Place in the sun, A / Somewhere / This hammer / Tomorrow's cancelled / It's a man's world / Slaughter on Tenth Avenue.
2LP: 4C 128 52615/17
LP: C148 04859/860

CHANGE OF ADDRESS.
Tracks: / Mozart forte / Midnight creepin' / Change of address / Just the way you are / Indigo / Arty's party / Outdigo / Hello Mr. W.A.M. / Temptation / Albatross / If you leave me now / Equinoxe part 5.
LP: 2442 179
LP: SPELP 8

COLLECTION: SHADOWS.
Tracks: / Just the way you are / Turning point / Midnight creepin' / Shady lady, The / Thing me jig / Johnny Stacatto / Stack it / If you leave me now / Equinoxe (part V) / Change of address / Fender bender / Temptation / Fourth man, The / Summer love '59 / Mozart forte / Albatross.
LP: CN 2104
MC: CN4 2104

DANCE ON WITH THE SHADOWS.
LP: 1A 022 1583431
MC: 1A 222 1583434

DANCE WITH THE SHADOWS.
Tracks: / Chattanooga choo-choo / Blue shadows / Fandango / Tonight / That's the way it goes / Big 'B' / In the mood / Lonely bull, The (El solo toro) / Dakota / French dressing / High and mighty / Don't it make you feel good / Zambesi / Temptation.
LP: 33SX 1619

DANCE WITH THE SHADOWS/SOUND OF THE SHADOWS.
Tracks: / Chattanooga choo choo / Blue shadows / Tonight (From West Side Story.) / That's the way it goes / Big "B" / In the mood / Lonely bull, The / Dakota / French dressing / High and mighty / Don't it make you feel good / Zambesi / Temptation / Brazil / Lost city, The / Little bitty tear, A / Blue sky, blue sea, blue me / Bossa roo / Five hundred miles / Cotton pickin / Deep purple / Santa Ana / Windjammer / Dean's theme / Breakthru / Let it be me / National provincial samba / Fandango.
2LP: DL 1092
MC: TCDL 1092
2LP: EDP 1546323

DANCING IN THE DARK.
Tracks: / Dancing in the dark / Life in the jungle / Queen of hearts / Cat 'n' mouse / I will return / Shoba / No dancing / High noon / Telstar / More than I can say / Outdigo / Spot the ball / Time is tight / Elevenis / Mountains of the moon / Whiter shade of pale, A.
MC: PWKMC 4031P

DIAMONDS.
Tracks: / Diamonds / Imagine/Woman / Missing (Theme from) / You rescue me / Hats off to Wally / Nut rocker / I'm gonna be your guardian angel / Up where we belong / This ole house / Africa / Arty's party / Can't play your game / Old romantics, The / Our Albert / Cowboy cafe / We don't talk anymore.
LP: PWKLPS 4018P
MC: PWKMCS 4018P

DISQUE D'OR.
Tracks: / Apache / Kon-tiki / Nivram / Shadoogie / Shazam / Driftin / Geronimo / F.B.I. / Perfidia / Little 'B' / Jet black / Guitar tango / Frightened city / Quartermaster's stores.
LP: 2C 070 05278

DRIFTIN'.
LPPD: AR 30086

EP COLLECTION, THE: SHADOWS.
Tracks: / Perfidia / 36-24-36 / All day / My grandfather's clock / Lady Penelope / Zero 'x' theme / Thunderbird / Finders keepers / Mustang / Shane (theme from) / Giant (theme from) / Shotgun / Las tres carabelas / Adios muchachos / Valencia / Granada / Tonight / Fandango / Little princess / Gonzales / Jet black (live) / Driftin' (live).
LP: SEE 246
MC: SEEK 246

EP COLLECTION, THE: SHADOWS VOL 2.
Tracks: / Omoide no nagisa / Londonderry air / Theme from the boys / Foot tapper / Les girls / Shazam / Sleepwalk / Bongo blues / Flyder and the spy, The / Chinchilla / Gin iro no michi / Kimi to itsumademo / Boys, The / Round and round / Friends / Guitar boogie / F.B.I. / Ranka chank / Autumn / Walkin'.
MC: SEEK 296
LP: SEE 296

EST.1958 (Shadows/Cliff Richard).
Tracks: / Voyage to the bottom of the bath / Arranged life of a daily man, The / Banana man / Magical Mrs. Clamps, The / Here I go again loving you / Maggie's samba / Don't forget to catch me / Not the way that it should be / Somewhere by the sea / Girl on the bus / Ooh la la / What's behind the eyes of Mary / Dreams I dream, The.
LP: SCX 6282

FROM HANK, BRIAN, BRUCE AND JOHN.
Tracks: / Snap, crackle and how's your dad / Thing of beauty, A / Letter, The / Wild roses, The / Holy cow / Last train to Clarksville / Day I met Marie, The / Evening glow / Naughty nippon lights / San Francisco / Tokaido line, The / Alentjo / Let me take you there / Better man than I, A.
LP: BGOLP 20

GREATEST HITS: SHADOWS.
Tracks: / Apache / Man of mystery / F.B.I. / Midnight / Frightened city / Kon-tiki / 36-24-36 / Savage, The / Peace pipe / Wonderful land / Stars fell on Stockton / Guitar tango / Boys, The / Dance on / Stranger, The.
LP: ATAK 44
MC: TCATAK 44
LP: SCX 1522
MC: TCSCX 1522
LP: 33SX 1522

GUARDIAN ANGEL.
Tracks: / How do I love thee / Hammerhead / Saturday Western, The / Look back on love (from the film Terminal Choice) / Johnny Staccato / I will return / I'm gonna be your guardian angel / Can't play your game / On a night like this / Turning point / Our Albert.
LP: POLD 5169

HITS OF THE SHADOWS VOL 1.
MC: VCA 016

HITS RIGHT UP YOUR STREET.
Tracks: / Telstar / Chi mai / We don't talk anymore / Imagine / Woman / Hats off to Wally / One day I'll fly away / Summer love '59 / Misty / This ole house / Winner takes all / Sailing / Thing-me-jig / More than I can say / Cowboy cafe / Third man, Theme from / Nut rocker.
LP: SPELP 78
MC: SPEMC 78
LP: POLD 5046

HOUR OF THE SHADOWS, AN.
Tracks: / Foot tapper / Friday on my mind / Winchester Cathedral / Maria Elena / Semi-detached suburban Mr. James / Jigsaw / Stardust / Trains and boats and planes / Ranka-chank / What a lovely tune / Little B / Shindig / Shazam / Rhythm and greens / Genie with the light brown lamp / Walkin' / All my sorrows / I wish I could shimmy like my sister Arthur / Frightened city / Mustang / Alice in Sunderland / Slaughter on Tenth Avenue.
MC: HR 4181234
MC: HR 8123

IMAGES OF ....
MC: KNMC 16014

JIGSAW.
Tracks: / Jigsaw / Prelude in E major / Cathy's clown / Friday on my mind / Chelsea boot / With a hmm hmm on my knee / Tennessee waltz / Stardust / Semi detached suburban / Winchester cathedral / Maria Elena / Green eyes.
LP: SCX 6148
LP: BGOLP 66
MC: BGOMC 66

LIFE IN THE JUNGLE.
Tracks: / Life in the jungle / High noon / Treat me nice / Cat 'n' mouse / Chariots of fire / No dancing / Riders of the range / Old romantics, The / You rescue me / Lili Marlene / Raunchy.
LP: SPELP 88
MC: SPEMC 88

LIFE IN THE JUNGLE/THE SHADOWS 'LIVE' AT ABBEY ROAD.
Tracks: / Life in the jungle / High noon / Missing, The, theme from / Treat me nice / Cat 'n' mouse / Chariots of fire / No dancing / Riders of the range / Old romantics, The / You rescue me / Lili Marlene / Raunchy / Third man, Theme from / Thing me jig / Runaway / All I have to do is dream / It doesn't matter anymore / Johnny B. Goode / Over in a flash / Summer love 59 / Oh boy / Crying in the rain / Arty's party.
2LP: SHADS 1
MCSET: SHADC 1

LIVE: SHADOWS.
Tracks: / Shazam! / Dance on / Nivram / Apache / Exodus / Foot tapper / Little bitty tear, A / Putting on the style / Slaughter on Tenth Avenue / Don't make my baby blue / Rise and fall of Flingel Bunt, The / Somewhere / Little 'B' / F.B.I..
2LP: MFP 1018

MOONLIGHT SHADOWS.
Tracks: / Moonlight shadow / Walk of life / I just called to say I love you / Every breath you take / Nights in white satin / Hello / Power of love (The) / Three times a lady / Against all odds / Hey Jude / Dancing in the dark / I know him so well / Memory / Imagine / Sailing / Whiter shade of pale, A.
LP: PROLP 8
MC: PROMC 8

MORE HITS.
Tracks: / Foot tapper / Atlantis / Shindig / Theme for young lovers / Geronimo / Shazam! / Rise and fall of Flingel Bunt, The / Genie with the light brown lamp / Mary-Anne / Stingray / Rhythm and

greens / Don't make my baby blue / Lute number / Drum number.
LP: ATAK 55
MC: TCATAK 55
LP: SCX 3578
MC: TCSCX 3578

ORIGINAL CHART HITS 1960-1980, THE.
Tracks: / Apache / Man of mystery / Stranger, The / F.B.I. / Midnight / Frightened city, The / Kon-tiki / Savage, The / Peace pipe / Shadoogie / Wonderful land / Sleepwalk / Guitar tango / Boys, The / Dance on / Foot tapper / Atlantis / Shindig / Geronimo / Theme for young lovers / Perfidia (CD only.) / Mustang (CD only.) / Cosy (CD only.) / Nivram (CD only.) / Little B (CD only.) / Rise and fall of Flingel Bunt / Rhythm and greens / Genie with the light brown lamp / Mary-Anne / Stringray / Don't make my baby blue / Warlord / I met a girl / Place in the sun, A / Dreams I dream, The / Maroc 7 / Bombay duck / Tomorrow's cancelled / Dear old Mrs Bell / Slaughter on 10th Avenue / Turn around and touch me / Let me be the one / Don't cry for me Argentina / Deer hunter, Theme from / Riders in the sky (CD only.) / Thunderbirds theme (CD only.) / Little princess (CD only.) / Tonight (CD only.) / Flyder and the spy (CD only.) / Chatta nooka choo choo (CD only.).
2LP: EM 1354
MCSET: TCEM 1354

OUT OF THE SHADOWS.
Tracks: / Rumble / Bandit, The / Cosy / 1861 / Perfidia / Little b / Bo Diddley / South of the border / Spring is nearly here / Are they all like you / Tales of a raggy tramline / Some are lonely / Kinda cool.
LP: AWM 9001
MC: AWMC 9001
LP: 33SX 1458

RARITIES.
LP: NUT 2

REFLECTION.
Tracks: / Eye of the tiger / Crockett's theme / Right here waiting / Every little thing she does is magic / Sealed with a kiss / Uptown girl / Strawberry Fields forever / Riders in the sky '90 / Flashdance / Something's gotten hold of my heart / Love changes everything / Nothing's gonna stop us now / Bilitis / You'll never walk alone / Always on my mind.
MC: 847 120 4
LP: 847 120 1

ROCK ON WITH THE SHADOWS.
Tracks: / Apache / Man of mystery / F.B.I. / Frightened city / Shazam / Savage.
LP: MFP 50468
MC: TCMFP 50468

ROCKIN' WITH CURLY LEADS.
LP: EMA 762
LP: BGOLP 84

SHADES OF ROCK.
LP: SCX 6420

SHADOOGIE.
Tracks: / Apache / Quartermaster's stores / Mustang / Shotgun / Man of mystery / Stranger, The / Lonesome fella / F.B.I. / Frightened city / Midnight / Kon-Tiki / 36-24-36 / Peace pipe / Savage, The / Shadoogie / Nivram / Stand up and say that / Gonzales / Wonderful land / Stars fell on Stockton / Boys, The / Guitar tango / Dance on / Perfidia / Rumble / Little 'B' / Atlantis / Foot tapper / Shazam! / Round and round / Shindig / Sleepwalk / Rise and fall of Flingel Bunt, The / Little princess / Stingray / Alice in Sunderland / Dakota / Late night set / Lucille / Rockin' with Curly Leads / Honourable puff puff / Let me be the one.
2LP: 5C 154 06129/31
2LP: PM 1551503

SHADOW MUSIC.
LP: SCX 6041

SHADOWS DOUBLE ALBUM.
Tracks: / Apache / Savage, The / This hammer / Foot tapper / Shadoogie / Perfidia / Kon-tiki / Man of mystery / Theme for young lovers / Alice in Sunderland / Rumble / Quartermasters stores / Dakota / Deep purple / Nivram / Mustang / Guitar tango / Dance on / F.B.I. / Lost city, The / Lonesome fella / Frightened city / Brazil / Lonely bull, The.
LP: 1568103
MC: 1568109

SHADOWS IN THE 60'S, THE.
Tracks: / Dance on / Foot tapper / Guitar tango / Man of mystery / Stranger, The / Midnight / 36-24-36 / Peace pipe / Stars fell on Stockton / Boys, The / Mary Anne / Don't make my baby blue / Frightened city / Savage, The / Shindig / Breeze and I / All day / What a lovely tune / Bo Diddley / Quartermaster's stores / Bandit, The (CD only.) / Little B (CD only.) / South of the border (CD only.) / Shazam (CD only.).
LP: MFP 5873
MC: TCMFP 5873
LP: MFP 6076

SHADOWS STORY VOLUME 2.
LP: 5c 052 04502

SHADOWS STORY,THE.
Tracks: / Apache / F.B.I. / 36-24-36 / Little 'B' / Mustang / Foot tapper / Day I met Marie, The / Shadoogie / Sleepwalk / Winchester Cathedral / River deep, mountain high.
LP: 5C 052 04831

SHADOWS, THE.
Tracks: / F.B.I. / Apache / Savage, The / This hammer / Perfidia / Kon-tiki / Man of mystery / Theme for young lovers / Rumble / Quarter master's lovers / Dakota / Deep purple / Guitar tango / Dance on / Lost city, The / Lonesome fella / Brazil / Lonely bull, The.
LP: 33SX 1374
LP: FA 4061

SHADOWS VOCALS,THE.
Tracks: / Bandit, The / Saturday dance / Feeling fine / Don't be a (with love) / Baby my heart / Lonesome fella / All my sorrows / Mary Ann / My way / Will you be there / Little bitty tear, A / Me oh my / That's the way it goes / Stay around / One way to love / Day I met Marie, The / Dreams I dream, The / Don't make my baby blue / This hammer / Be bop a lula (Live).
LP: EG 2600751
MC: EG 2600754

SIMPLY SHADOWS.
Tracks: / I know you were waiting (for me) / We don't need another hero / Walking in the air / Careless whisper / Don't give up / I guess that's why they call it the blues / Heart will break tonight, A / Lady in red / Pulaski / Take my breath away / Eastenders / I want to know what love is / Skye boat song / Jealous guy / Chain reaction / Howard's Way.
LP: SHAD 1
MC: SHADC 1

SOUND OF THE SHADOWS.
LP: 33SX 1736

SPECS APPEAL.
LP: EMC 3066

STEPPIN' TO THE SHADOWS.
Tracks: / You win again / I wanna dance with somebody (who loves me) / He ain't heavy he's my brother / Candle in the wind / Farewell my lovely / Mountains of the moon / Nothings gonna change my love for you / Heaven is a place on earth / When the going gets tough / Alone / All I ask of you / Stack it / Shoba / You keep me hangin' on / Some people / One moment in time.
LP: SHAD 30
MC: SHADC 30

STRING OF HITS.
Tracks: / Riders in the sky / Parisienne walkways / Classical gas / Deer Hunter (Cavatina), Theme from / Bridge over troubled water / You're the one that I want / Heart of glass / Don't cry for me Argentina / Song for Duke / Bright eyes / Rodrigo's guitar concerto de aranjuez / Baker Street.
LP: 1A 024 1583791
MC: 1A 224 1583794
LP: MFP 41 5724 1
LP: MFP 5724
MC: TCMFP 5724
MC: MFP 41 5724 4
LP: EMC 3310

TOGETHER (see under Richard, Cliff) (Shadows/Cliff Richard).

XXV.
Tracks: / Africa / Going home / Up where we belong / You don't have to say you love me / Modern way / Diamonds / Time is tight / Memory / Liverpool days / Queen of hearts / Whiter shade of pale.
LP: POLD 5120

Shadows Of Knight

GEE-EL-O-ARE-I-AY (GLORIA).
Tracks: / Gloria / Light bulb blues / I got my Mojo working / Dark side / Let it rock / Oh yeah / It always happens that way / You can't judge a book by the cover / I just wanna make love to you / Bad little woman / Gospel zone / Hey Joe / I'll make you sorry / Peepin' and hidin' / Tomorrow's gonna be another day / Spoonful.
LP: ED 157
LP: RAD 11

Shadowy Men

ON A SHADOWY PLANET.
LP: GLALP 031

Shady Grove Band

ON THE LINE.
LP: FF 462

Shafer, Ted

SAN FRANCISCO JAZZ (Shafer, Ted Jelly Roll Jazz Band).
LP: GHB 165

TED SHAFERS JELLY ROLL JAZZ BAND VOL 1 (Shafer, Ted Jelly Roll Jazz Band).
LP: MMRC 101

TED SHAFERS JELLY ROLL JAZZ BAND VOL 2 (Shafer, Ted Jelly Roll Jazz Band).
LP: MMRC 102

TED SHAFERS JELLY ROLL JAZZ BAND VOL 3 (Shafer, Ted Jelly Roll Jazz Band).
LP: MMRC 104

Shafer, Whitey

MEMPHIS MEMORY.
Tracks: / Honey bees and tulips / Down by the railroad tracks / Who's a fool (Previously unissued.) / I'm so lonesome when I'm busted / Love don't live here anymore / Bottle your memory and me, The / Touching home / I'll break out again tonight / Lullaby mountain (Previously unissued.) / Outskirts of somehwere, The / Big big show on wheels / Between Winston, Salem and Nashville Tennesee.
LP: BFX 15148

MY HOUSE IS YOUR HONKY TONK.
Tracks: / My house is your honky tonk / I need someone like me to hold on to / I'm tired of 'puttin' up with puttin' on / Warm red wine / Love inflation / Please don't do that anymore / It's all over town (Previously unissued.) / What did you expect me to do / Ole' drug store (Previously unissued.) / It's much too late to start quittin' now / Love always makes me cry / Let's love it over again.
LP: BFX 15149

Shaffer, Doreen

WONDERFUL SOUND.
LP: REV 008

Shaft (film)

SHAFT (Film Soundtrack) (Various artists).
2LP: 68.701
MC: 78.701

SHAFT (ORIGINAL SOUNDTRACK) (See under Hayes, Isaac) (Hayes, Isaac).

Shaftesbury

LULL BEFORE THE STORM, THE.
LP: OKA 001

WE ARE THE BOYS.
LP: OKA 002

Shag

SHAG (Film Soundtrack) (Various artists).
Tracks: / Surrender: *Goffin, Louise* / Shag: *Page, Tommy* / Saved: *Baker, Laverne* / Diddley daddy: *Isaak, Chris* / Seven lonely days: *Lang, K.D.* / Shaggin' on the grandstand: *Ballard, Hank* / Oh what a night: *Moonliters* / I'm in love again: *Newman, Randy* / I'm leaving it all up to you: *Baker, Laverne/Ben E.King* / Our day will come: *Lang, K.D.* / Cat fight: *Paley, Andy* / Lonely boy: *Kamen, Nick.*
LP: WX 208
MC: WX 208 C

Shaggs

PHILOSOPHY OF THE WORLD.
LP: ROUNDER 3032
MC: ROUNDER 3032C

SHAGGS' OWN THING.
LP: ROUNDER 3056
MC: ROUNDER 3056C

Shah

BEWARE.
Tracks: / Total devastation / Coward / Save the human race / Threshold of pain / Beware / Bloodbrothers / Age of dismay / Say hi to Anthrax.
LP: ATOMH 009

Shah, Idries

FRAMEWORK FOR NEW KNOWLEDGE.
MC: SS 101

Shail, Mike

NO HOLES BARD & EEZUM SQUUEZUM.
MC: 45 127

Shaka, Jah

BRIMSTONE AND FIRE.
LP: SHAKA 831

COMMANDMENTS OF DUB.
LP: ROUGH 50

COMMANDMENTS OF DUB CHAPTER 1.
LP: SHAKA 824

COMMANDMENTS OF DUB CHAPTER 2.
LP: SHAKA 841

COMMANDMENTS OF DUB CHAPTER 3.
LP: SHAKA 847 LP

COMMANDMENTS OF DUB CHAPTER 4.
LP: SHAKA 851 LP

COMMANDMENTS OF DUB CHAPTER 5.
LP: SHAKA 856

COMMANDMENTS OF DUB CHAPTER 6.
LP: SHAKA 860 LP

COMMANDMENTS OF DUB CHAPTER 8.
LP: SHAKA 868 LP

COMMANDMENTS OF DUB CHAPTER 10.
LP: SHAKA 916

DELIVERANCE (PART 6).
LP: SHAKA 860

DISCIPLES, THE.
LP: SHAKA 871

DUB SYMPHONY.
Tracks: / Black steel / Dub symphony / Sound clinic dub / True independence / Immortal dub / Dance wicked / Come and get dub / Cryptic dub / Mystic dub / Earth rightful dub.
LP: MLPS 1044
MC: MCT 1044
LP: 846 272 1
MC: 846 272 4

KING'S MUSIC.
LP: SHAKA 845

MUSIC MESSAGE, THE.
Tracks: / Know yourself / Do the right thing / Be like a lion / All things / Giver of life / No dub / Right dub / Lion dub / Positive dub / Life (dub).
LP: SHAKA 777 LP

MY PRAYER.
LP: SHAKA 873

REVALATION SONGS.
Tracks: / Preachers dub / Prophet dub / Vision (dub) / Judgement Dub / Lightning (dub) / Powerful dub / Thunderous (dub) / Seven seas dub.
LP: SHAKA 833 LP

SHAKA MEETS PEPPER (Shaka, Jah & Sgt. Pepper).
LP: SHAKA 849

WARRIOR.
Tracks: / Dependant dub / Life dub / Nyha dub / Nioni dub / Tiumphant dub / Majesty dub / Praise in dub / Feleh dub / School of dub / Rainbow dub.
LP: SHAKA 867 LP

Shakatak

BITTER SWEET.
LP: 8479101
MC: 8479104

COOLEST CUTS, THE.
Tracks: / Down on the street / Invitations / Living in the UK / Slip way / Stranger / Steppin' (live) / Brazilian dawn / Easier said than done / Night birds / Streetwalkin' / Dark is the night / City rhythm / Walk the walk / Rio nights / Mr. Manic & Sister Cool.
LP: NE 1422
MC: CE 2422

DAY BY DAY.
Tracks: / Day by day / Once upon a time / Secret / Physical attraction / City rhythm / I must be dreaming / Africa / Goodbye / Mickey mouse / Vive la fantasy.
LP: POLH 24
MC: POLHC 24

DOWN ON THE STREET.
Tracks: / Down on the street / Holding on / Summer sky / Hypnotised / Watching you / Don't blame it on love / Photograph / Fire dance / Lady (to Billie Holiday).
LP: SPELP 109
MC: POLDC 5148
MC: SPEMC 109

DRIVING HARD.
Tracks: / Livin' in the UK / Into the night / Toot the shoot / Lumiere / Late night flight / Waves / Steppin' / Covina / You never know / Brazilian dawn.
LP: POLS 1030

DRIVING HARD/NIGHTBIRDS.
Tracks: / Into the night / Toot the shoot / Lumiere / Late night flight / Waves / Covina / You never know / Brazilian dawn / Living in the UK / Steppin (Live) / Steppin' / Night birds / Streetwalkin' / Rio nights / Fly the wind / Easier said

than done / Bitch to the boys / Light of my life / Taking off.
LP: SPELP 100
MC: SPEMC 100
MC: 3574 136

GREATEST GROOVES.
Tracks: / Down on the street / Dr Dr / Photograph / Invitations / Holding on / Streetwalkin' / Feels like the right time / Takin' off / Africa / City rhythm / Watching you / Dark is the night / Physical attraction / Walk the walk / I must be dreaming / Day by day / Nightbirds / Covina / Lady / Love of all time / Fly like the wind / Easier said than done.
2LP: VSOPLP 142
MC: VSOPMC 142

INVITATIONS.
Tracks: / Lose myself / Lonely afternoon / Steppin out / Stranger / Invitations / Usual situation / Sol fuego / In shadows.
LP: SPELP 86
MC: SPEMC 86
LP: POLD 5068

LIVE IN JAPAN.
Tracks: / Dark is the night / Streetwalkin / Watching you / Invitations / Nightbirds / Don't blame it on love / Easier said than done / Down on the street.
MC: POLHC 21
LP: POLH 21

MANIC AND COOL.
Tracks: / Mr. Manic & Sister Cool / Slow dancing / Time of my life, The / M.O.N.E.Y / Nobody holds me (quite the way you do) / Doctor doctor / Walk the walk / Releasin' the feeling / Something special / Stop / Love of all time / Orient express.
LP: POLD 5222
MC: POLDC 5222

NIGHTBIRDS.
Tracks: / Taking off / Lisa / Go for it / Rio nights / Nightbirds / Fly the wing / Easier said than done / Bitch to the boys / Light of my life.
LP: POLS 1059
MC: POLSC 1059

OUT OF THIS WORLD.
Tracks: / Dark is the night / Don't say that again / Slip away / On nights like tonight / Out of this world / Let's get together / If you can see me now / Sanur.
LP: POLD 5115

TURN THE MUSIC UP (ALBUM).
Tracks: / Turn the music up / Better believe it.
LP: 841 077 1
MC: 841 077 4

Shake, Jump, Shout

SHAKE, JUMP, SHOUT (Various artists).
Tracks: / Hold me back (remix): *West Bam* / Callas: *Vox Mystica* / Heavy mental: *Heavy Mental* / Saxophone (Dick's mix): *West Bam* / Exzess: *Dick* / Alarm clock: *West Bam* / Time: *Beat In Time* / On a mission: *Dick* / Hell or heaven: *L.U.P.O* / Dreams: *Darling, Grace* / Is it raw enough?: *Heavy Mental* / Aka aka: *Eastbam.*
LP: YOBLP 1
MC: YOBMC 1

Shake Shake Shake

SHAKE SHAKE SHAKE IT BABY (Various artists).
LP: SIN ALLEY 3

Shake'N'Jive

SHAKE'N'JIVE (Various artists).
Tracks: / Shakin' all over: *Various artists* / Willie and the hand jive: *Various artists* / Rock and roll is here to stay: *Various artists* / Let's twist again: *Various artists* / Finger poppin' time: *Various artists* / Bristol stomp: *Various artists* / Sh'boom: *Various artists* / Chicka boom: *Various artists* / Come and get it: *Various artists* / High times: *Various artists* / Bend me shape me: *Various artists* / I don't know why but I do: *Various artists.*
LP: SPR 8529
MC: SPC 8529

Shakers & Cobras

THIS STUFF'S GONNA BUST YOUR BRAINS OUT.
Tracks: / Medicine train / Stop breaking down / Prisoner of love / How did you know / GI's twist / Fanfoogie / Driftin' / Bentley / Blonde de luxe / Scalp / Spring theme.
LP: ARE 001

Shakespeare, Mark

PERCHANCE TO DREAM.
LP: GRS 1183

SPOTLIGHT ON SHAKESPEARE.
Tracks: / Bohm symphony / Music / Memory / Tocca tocca / Classica (arr.) / Jetzt geht die party los / Kreuzberger nachte / Y viva Espana / Tico tico / Thunder and lightning / Schneewalzer klarinetten muckel / Trompeten echo / Hey, Das ist music / What I did for love / Good, the bad and the ugly, The / Ghost riders in the sky / Yellow rose of Texas / Farmer and the cowman / Amor amor / Brazil.
LP: GRS 1191
MC: KGRS 1191

Shakespeare, William

ALL'S WELL THAT ENDS WELL (Marlowe Dramatic Society).
MCSET: ARGO 1271

ALL'S WELL THAT ENDS WELL (Various artists).
MCSET: SAY 105

ALL'S WELL THAT ENDS WELL (Various artists).
MCSET: 212

ANTONY AND CLEOPATRA (Various artists).
MCSET: SAY 63

ANTONY AND CLEOPATRA (Various artists).
MCSET: 235

AS YOU LIKE IT (Marlowe Dramatic Society).
MCSET: ARGO 1028

AS YOU LIKE IT (Various artists).
MCSET: 210

AS YOU LIKE IT (Suzman, Janet & John Stride).
MCSET: SAY 22

COMEDY OF ERRORS, THE A lover's complaint (Marlowe Dramatic Society).
MCSET: 417 943-4
MCSET: ARGO 1106

COMEDY OF ERRORS, THE (Various artists).
MCSET: 205

CORIOLANUS (Various artists).
MCSET: 417 946-4

CORIOLANUS (Various artists).
MCSET: 0226

CYMBELINE (Various artists).
MCSET: 417 949-4

HAMLET (Old Vic Company).
MCSET: SAY 35
MCSET: TC LFP 7021
MCSET: ARGO 1127

HAMLET (Old Vic company / Gielgud, John).
MCSET: LFP 41 7218 5
MCSET: LFP 7218

HAMLET (Various artists).
MCSET: ZBBC 1004

HAMLET (Various artists).
MCSET: 232

HAMLET (Jacobi, Derek & The Old Vic Company).
LPS: D 158 D 3

HENRY IV PART 1 (Various artists).
MCSET: SAY 88

HENRY IV - PART 1 (Various artists).
MCSET: 217

HENRY IV - PART 2 (Various artists).
MCSET: 218

HENRY IV PART II (Various artists).
MCSET: SAY 89

HENRY V (Various artists).
MCSET: 219

HENRY V (Various artists).
MCSET: SAY 103

HENRY VI, PART 1 (Various artists).
MCSET: 418 027-4

HENRY VI, PART 2 (Various artists).
MCSET: 418 030-4

HENRY VI, PART 3 (Various artists).
MCSET: 418 033-4

HOW PLEASANT TO KNOW MR LEAR (Unknown narrator(s)).
MC: THE 604

JULIUS CAESAR with Marlowe Dramatic Society (Holm, Ian/Richard Johnson/William Squire).
MCSET: SAY 40
MCSET: ARGO 1043

JULIUS CAESAR (Various artists).
MCSET: 0230

KING HENRY VIII (Various artists).
MCSET: 418 036-4

KING JOHN (Various artists).
MCSET: 414 742-4

KING LEAR (Various artists).
MCSET: 0233
MCSET: ZBBC 1002

KING LEAR (Various artists).
MCSET: SAY 67

KING LEAR/DUCHESS OF MALFI (Thomas, Dylan).
MC: 1158

LOVE'S LABOUR'S LOST (Various artists).
MCSET: SAY 106

LOVE'S LABOUR'S LOST (Various artists).
MCSET: 207

MACBETH (Marlowe Dramatic Society).
MCSET: SAY 21
MCSET: ARGO 1025

MACBETH (Guinness, Sir Alec / Old Vic company).
MC: LFP 41 7228 5
MCSET: LFP 7228

MACBETH (Various artists).
MCSET: ZBBC 1005

MACBETH (Marlowe Dramatic Society).
MCSET: 231

MEASURE FOR MEASURE (Various artists).
MCSET: 418 051-4

MEASURE FOR MEASURE (Various artists).
MCSET: 204

MERCHANT OF VENICE, THE (Marlowe Dramatic Society).
MCSET: SAY 83
MCSET: ARGO 1199

MERCHANT OF VENICE, THE (Various artists).
MCSET: 209

MERRY WIVES OF WINDSOR, THE (Various artists).
MCSET: 203

MERRY WIVES OF WINDSOR, THE (Various artists).
MCSET: 414 733-4
MCSET: ARGO 1211

MIDSUMMER NIGHT'S DREAM, A (Various artists).
MCSET: SAY 38
MCSET: ARGO 1040

MIDSUMMER NIGHT'S DREAM, A (Scales, Prunella/Ian McKellen).
MCSET: 208

MIDSUMMER NIGHT'S DREAM, A (Old Vic company / Robert Helpman).
MCSET: LFP 7266

MUCH ADO ABOUT NOTHING (Marlowe Dramatic Society).
MCSET: 206

MUCH ADO ABOUT NOTHING (Various artists).
MCSET: SAY 36
MCSET: ARGO 1034

OTHELLO (Various artists).
MCSET: ZBBC 1003

OTHELLO (Marlowe Dramatic Society).
MCSET: SAY 64
MCSET: ARGO 1157

OTHELLO (Various artists).
MCSET: 0225

PERICLES (Various artists).
MCSET: 418 039-4

RICHARD II (Various artists).
MCSET: SAY 66

RICHARD II (Various artists).
MCSET: 216

RICHARD III (Various artists).
MCSET: SAY 94

RICHARD III (Various artists).
MCSET: 0223

ROMEO AND JULIET (Marlowe Dramatic Society).
MCSET: ARGO 1229

ROMEO AND JULIET (Various artists).
MCSET: 0228

ROMEO & JULIET (Various artists).
MCSET: SAY 37

ROMEO & JULIET (Various artists).
MCSET: LFP 7296

SONNETS (Pasco, Richard (nar)).
MCSET: SAY 114

SONNETS (Various artists).
MCSET: 241

SONNETS-WILLIAM SHAKESPEARE (See under Geilgud, William).

TAMING OF THE SHREW (Various artists).
MCSET: 211

TAMING OF THE SHREW, THE (Marlowe Dramatic Society).
MCSET: SAY 65
MCSET: ARGO 1160

TEMPEST, THE (Marlowe Dramatic Society).
MCSET: SAY 69
MCSET: ARGO 1103

TEMPEST, THE (Various artists).
MCSET: 201

THESE ARE WOMAN.
MC: 243

TIMON OF ATHENS (Various artists).
MCSET: 414 739-4

TITUS ANDRONICUS (Various artists).
MCSET: 414 703-4

TRAGEDY OF RICHARD III, THE (Marlowe Dramatic Society).
MCSET: ARGO 1262

TROILUS & CRESSIDA (Various artists).
MCSET: 417 937-4

TWELFTH NIGHT (Various artists).
MCSET: 213

TWELFTH NIGHT (Old Vic Company).
MCSET: SAY 39
MCSET: ARGO 1130

TWO GENTLEMEN OF VERONA (Various artists).
MCSET: 417 940-4

VENUS AND ADONIS/ RAPE OF LUCRECE, THE (Various artists).
MCSET: 414 745-4

WINTER'S TALE, THE (Various artists).
MCSET: 214

WINTER'S TALE, THE (Marlowe Dramatic Society).
MCSET: SAY 81
MCSET: ARGO 1193

WORLD OF SHAKESPEARE, THE (Various artists).
Tracks: / Richard II (excerpt): *Various artists* / Henry IV (excerpt): *Various artists* / Henry V (excerpt): *Various artists* / Julius Caeser (excerpt): *Various artists* / MacBeth (excerpt): *Various artists* / Twelfth night (excerpt): *Various artists* / King Lear (excerpt): *Various artists* / Othello (excerpt): *Various artists*/ Anthony and Cleopatra (excerpt): *Various artists* / Tempest (excerpt): *Various artists* / Sonnets (excerpt): *Various artists.*
MCSET: SAY 41
LP: SPA 558

Shakespear's Sister

SACRED HEART.
Tracks: / Heroine / Run silent / Run deep / Dirty mind / Sacred heart / Heaven in your arms / You're history / Break my heart / Red rocket / Electric moon / Primitive love / Could you be loved / Twist the knife (Only on CD.) / You made me come to this (Only on CD.).
LP: 828 131-1
MC: 828 131-4

Shakey Jake

KEY WON'T FIT, THE.
LP: MB 1002

MOUTH HARP BLUES.
Tracks: / Mouth harp blues / Love you baby / Jake's cha cha / Gimme a smile / My broken heart / Angry love / Things is alright / Easy baby / Things are different baby / It won't happen again.
LP: CH 236

Shakin' Pyramids

CELTS & COBRAS.
LP: V 2216

SKIN 'EM UP.
Tracks: / Take a trip / Tennessee rock'n'roll / Let's go / Teenage boogie / Tired'n'sleepy / Wild little Willie / Cry cry kitten / Sixteen chicks / Pretty bad blues / I got a baby / Sunset of my tears / Hellbent on rockin'.
LP: OVED 52
LP: V 2199

Shakin' Street

SHAKIN' STREET.
Tracks: / No compromise / Solid as a rock / No time to lose / Soul dealer / Susie Wong / Every man, every woman is a star / Generation X / So fine / I want to box you.
LP: 84115

Shaking Down ...

SHAKING DOWN THE ACORNS (Shaking Down The Acorns).
LP: ROUNDER 0018

Shakti

DEMONIC FORCES.
MLP: SUB 002

Shalamar

BEST OF SHALAMAR.
Tracks: / Night to remember, A / Make that move / Take that to the bank / Uptown festival (part 1) / I can make you feel good / Friends / Amnesia / Second time around, The / I owe you one / Over and over / There it is / Disappearing act / Dead giveaway / My girl loves me.

LP: MCG 6080
MC: MCGC 6080

BIG FUN.
Tracks: / Right time for us / Take me to the river / Right in the socket / Second time around / I owe you one / Let's find the time for love / Girl.
LP: FL 13479

CIRCUMSTANTIAL EVIDENCE.
Tracks: / Circumstantial evidence / Games / Love's grown deep / Plaything / Female / Born to love / Worth waitin' for / Imaginary love.
LP: MCF 3387
MC: MCFC 3387

FRIENDS.
Tracks: / Night to remember / Don't try to change me / Help me / On top of the world / I don't wanna be the last to know / Friends / Playing to win / I just stopped by because I had to / There it is / I can make you feel good.
LP: K 52345

GO FOR IT.
Tracks: / Go for it / Appeal / Final analysis / You've got me running / Sweeter as the days go by / Talk to me / Good feelings / Rocker.
LP: SOLA 10
MC: SOLC 10

GREATEST HITS: SHALAMAR.
Tracks: / Attention my baby / Second time around / Make that move / This is for the lover in you / Full of fire / Take that to the bank / I owe you one / Sweeter as the days go by / Somewhere there's a love / Right in the socket.
LP: SOLA 3001
MC: SOLC 3001

GREATEST HITS: SHALAMAR.
Tracks: / Over and over / Night to remember, A / Uptown festival (part 1) / There it is / I can make you feel good / Disappearing act / Dead giveaway / Friends / Amnesia / My girls love me / Make that move / Second time around / Take that to the bank / I owe you one.
LP: SMR 8615
MC: SMC 8615

HEARTBREAK.
Tracks: / Amnesia / Dancing in the street / Whenever you need me / Heartbreak / Don't get stopped in Beverly Hills / My girl loves me / Melody (an erotic affair) / Deceiver.
LP: MCL 1850
MC: MCLC 1850
LP: MCF 3242

LOOK.
Tracks: / Closer / Dead giveaway / You can count on me / Right here / No limits / Disappearing act / Over and over / You're the one for me / You won't miss love / Look.
LP: K 960239-1

THREE FOR LOVE.
Tracks: / Full of fire / Attention to my baby / Somewhere there's a love / Some things never change / Make that move / This is for the lover in you / Work it out / Pop along kid.
LP: SOLA 8
MC: SOLC 8

UPTOWN FESTIVAL (ALBUM).
Tracks: / Inky dinky wang dang doo / Beautiful night, The / Uptown festival / Going to a go go / I can't help myself / Uptight (everything's alright) / Stop in the name of love / It's the same old song / Tears of a clown, The / Love is like an itching in my heart / This old heart of mine is weak for you / Baby love / He was really saying something / High on life / Ooh baby, baby / You know / Forever came today.
LP: FL 12289

WAKE UP.
Tracks: / Caution / This love is hot / Wake up / Why lead me on / Groove talk / All I wanna do / Come together / For sure / I'll give U love / I want U / Pink box.
LP: 4671191
MC: 4671194

Shalawambe

SAMORA MACHEL.
LP: MON 002

Shaljean, Bonnie

FAREWELL TO LOUGH NEAGH.
Tracks: / Roslyn Castle / Captain O'Neill / Colonel O'Hara / Sir Festus Birke / Foweles in the frith / Edi beo thu hevene quene / Summer is icumen in / Clocks back reel / Kilburn jig / Diarmuid's well / Wild Irishman, The / Her mantle so green / Planxty Drew / Mary O'Neill / Maid of Derry, The.
MC: CSDL 372

ROUNDTOWER (See under Bryne, Packie) (Shaljean, Bonnie & Packie Byrne).

Shall We Dance?

SHALL WE DANCE? (Various artists).
2LP: COX 005/6

SHALL WE DANCE/SWINGTIME Original soundtracks (Various artists).
LP: SH 2028
MC: CSH 2028

Sham 69

ADVENTURES OF THE HERSHAM BOYS, THE.
Tracks: / Money / Fly dark angel / Joey's on the street again / Cold blue in the night / Mister you're a better man than I / Lost on highway 46 / Voices / Questions and answers / What have we got.
LP: POLD 5025

ANGELS WITH DIRTY FACES.
LP: RRLP 104
MC: RRLC 104

BEST OF THE REST OF SHAM 69, THE.
Tracks: / Red London / Angels with dirty faces / That's life / Everybody's different / They don't understand / Hersham boys / White riot / What have we got / Voices / Questions and answers / Borstal breakout / Joey's on the street again / Tell us the truth / James Dean / If the kids are united.
LP: RRLP 112

COMPLETE LIVE.
Tracks: / Hurry up Harry / I don't wanna / If the kids are united / Borstal breakout / Angels with dirty faces / They don't understand / Rip and tear / Day tripper / That's life / Poor cow / Give a dog a bone / Questions and answers / Tell us the truth / Hersham boys / Vision and the power / White riot.
LP: CLALP 153
MC: CLAMC 153

FIRST, THE BEST AND THE LAST.
Tracks: / Borstal breakout / Hey little rich boy / Angels with dirty faces / Cockney kids are innocent / If the kids are united / Sunday morning nightmare / Hurry up Harry / Questions and answers / Give the dog a bone / Hersham boys / Tell the children / Unite & win.
LP: 2383 596

GAME.
Tracks: / Game, The / Lord of the flies / In and out / Human zoo / Give a dog a bone / Tell the children / Spray it on the wall / Simon / Poor cow / Dead or alive / Deja Vu / Run wild run free.
LP: RRLD 002
LP: POLD 5033

LIVE AND LOUD.
LP: LINK LP 04

LIVE AND LOUD VOL 2.
LP: LINK LP 025

LIVE AT THE ROXY.
LP: RRLP 133
MC: RRLC 133

SHAM 69 LIVE.
MC: ARLC 1011

TELL US THE TRUTH.
LP: RRD 001
LP: 2383 491

THAT'S LIFE.
Tracks: / Hersham boys / Angels with dirty faces / Hurry up Harry / If the kids are united / Borstal breakout.
LP: SHAMX 1
LP: POLD 5010

VOLUNTEER.
LP: LLP 117
MC: LLK 117

Shambleau

SHAMBLEAU Moore, C.L. (Moore, Catherine).
MC: CP 1667

Shamen

DROP.
Tracks: / Something about you / Passing away / Young 'til yesterday / World theatre / Through with you / Where do you go / Do what you will / Happy days / Through my window / Velvet box / I dont like the way the world is / Other side, The / Four letter girl.
LP: SOMALP 1
MC: SOMAC 1

EN-TACT.
LP: TPLP 22
MC: TPLP 22C
LPPD: TPLP 22SP

IN GORBACHEV WE TRUST.
Tracks: / Synergy / Raspberry infundibulum / Adam strange / Transcendental / Raptyouare / Sweet young thing / War prayer / Jesus loves Amerika / Misinformation / In Gorbachev we trust.
LP: FIEND 666
MC: FIENDC 666

PHORWARD.
LP: SOMALP 3
MC: SOMAC 3

PROGENY.
LP: TRPLP 32
MC: TRPC 32

STRANGE DAY DREAMS.
Tracks: / Do what you will / It's all around / Grim reaper of love / Long gone / Something about you / Strange day dreams / Golden hair / CM says a lot / Fire engine / Knature of a girl (Submission).
LP: MASO 33041
MC: MASO 33041C

Shamrock Band

EARLY US (See under Sullivan, Dan).

Shamrock Shore

CUCHULAINN.
MC: GTDC 029

Shamrock Singers

IRISH SINGALONG.
LP: HALP 155
MC: HACS 7055
MC: SMAC 9015

Shanahan, Bernie

BERNIE SHANAHAN.
LP: K 781934-1
MC: K 781934-4

Shanahan, John

DANCE OF FLIES (see Gordon, Steve) (Shanahan, John & Steve Gordon).

Shand Family

THREE GENERATIONS OF SHAND Family album, The.
Tracks: / Bonnie Kirkwall Bay / Gay Gordons / Way down south / Karlstad valsen / Polka / Dream valley of Glendaruel, The / Battle of the Somme / Molly Lee / Harveston castle / Plougboy, The / Bridal path, The / Scottish waltzes / Jigs / Irish hornpipes / Battle is o'er, The / Castle dangerous / Green hills of Tyrol / MacNamara's band / Hot asphalt / Garden where the praties grow / Irish washerwoman, The / Now is the hour / Aloha land.
LP: BER 006
MC: KBER 006

Shand, Jimmy

AT THE END OF A PERFECT DAY.
LP: WGRTV 3
MC: CWGRTV 3

AUCHTERMUCHTY CEILIDH (Shand, Jimmy & His Band).
LP: WGR 042
MC: CWGR 042

BONNIE SCOTLAND (Shand, Jimmy & His Band).
MC: CWGR 049
LP: WGR 049

ECHOES IN THE GLEN (Shand, Jimmy & His Band).
MC: CWGRTV 1
LP: WGRTV 1

FAMILY ALBUM (Shand, Jimmy, Jimmy Shand Jnr & Diane Shand).
LP: GES 1214
MC: KGEC 1214

FIFTY YEARS ON (Shand, Jimmy & His Band).
LP: WGR 062
MC: CWGR 062

FOCUS ON JIMMY SHAND (Shand, Jimmy & His Band).
Tracks: / Balmoral Highlanders, The / Jessie Smith / Rachel Rae / Arthur's seat / Eugene Stratton / Bonnie lass o' Bon Accord / Rory o' More / Dublin jig / Blackthorn stick / Thistle, The / Yodelling waltz / Shand's special scotch / Logie o' Buchan / Robin Adair / Up in the morning / Caul kail het again / Australian ladies / South of the Grampians / Roll her on the hill / Gift for gaff / Millbank cottage / Stumpic / Kate Dalrymple / Happy to meet / 74th farewell to Edinburgh, The / Rik-ma-ree / Colonel Robertson / Cold wind from Ben Wyvis / Hillbilly roundup, A / Ole faithful / Empty saddles / St. Valery / Victoria hornpipe / Storrers, The / Henshine, The / My home / Highland cradle song / Rowan tree / Gay Gordons / Cameron Highlanders, The / Bonnie Banchory / Pooer oot / Highland wedding / Kenmore's up and awa' / Peterie-kick / Irish jig / Irish girl, The / Kinnegad slashers / Ploughman's love / Oh gin I were a baron's heir / Memories / Kirkconnel Lea / Ye banks and braes / Douce Dundee / Duchess of Edinburgh / Sandy Cameron / Raigmore House / Bonnie Bon Accord / Duke of Roxburgh / Highland brigade at Tel-el-Kebir, The / Mrs. Dorothy Tulloch / 72nd Highlanders farewell to Edinburgh, The / Crackaboot / Why I left my hame / There was a lad / Man's a man for a' that, A / O a' the airts / Mason's apron / Breakdown, The / Circassian circle / When I look at bonnie Aberdeen / Kate Dalrymple / Donnybrook boy / Humours of Donnybrook / Paddy o'Rafferty / Lad wi' the plaidie, The / Smith's a gallant fireman, The / Duncan Davidson / Ash grove, The / Jenny Jones / Rocky mountain medley / Chicken reel / Turkey in the straw / Athole Highlanders, The / MacDuff castle / Speed and plough.
2LP: FOS 27/28
MCSET: KFOC 28070

GOLDEN YEARS OF JIMMY SHAND (Shand, Jimmy & His Band).
Tracks: / Bluebell polka / Wee rock and pickle tow / Quaker, The / Dancing dustman, The / Jimmy Shand waltz / O gub I were a barons heir / Come let us dance and sing / 72nd Highlanders' farewell to Edinburgh / Circassian circle / George Harrison's reel / Davy Nick Nack / Carey Alexander's jig / Newhaven jig.
LP: GLN 1001
MC: TCGLN 1001

GUID LUCK GO WI' YE (Shand, Jimmy & His Band).
Tracks: / Miss Bennett's jig / John Mearn's favourite / Balcomie house / Braes of Breadalbane, The / Auld lucky / Neil Gows' second wife / Jimmy Shand's compliments to Miss Jean Milligan / Lass o' paties mill / Harveston castle / Deveron reel, the / Bonnie Dundee / Logie o' Buchan / Scots wha' hae / Leezie Lindsay / Honeymoon, the / Pat Cushnie's fancy / Jean MacKinnon's jig / Queen's bridge / Calton Hill reel / Hopeful lover / Lamb skinnet jig / John Grumlie / I lo'ed nae a lassie but ane / Brinkie braes / Neidpath castle / Doctor and Mrs.Green / Tom's highland fling / Scotch mist / Light and airy jig / Carey Alexander's jig / Guid luck go wi' ye' / Newhaven jig / Elliot's fancy strathspey and reel / Linton ploughman / Muckin' o' Geordie's byre / Lady Nellie Wemyss / Baidley's house / Major Mackie.
LP: GRALP 26
MC: GRTC 26

HAPPY HOURS WITH JIMMY SHAND.
Tracks: / Happy hours / Macdonald of Sleat / De'il amang the tailors / Lucky Scaup / Masons apron / Lassie / Lord Lovat's Lament / Meeting of the waters / St. Andrews parade / Harveston castle / Breadalbane reel / Bobby Watson / Auld hoose, The / Rothesay Bay / Bonnie Galloway / Lass from Braco, The / Para Handy / White leather club, The / Bonnie Isle of Gletness / Sunset over Foula / Rona's voe / Scotland the brave / We're no awa' tae bide awa' / Maggie and Jock / Roll along Kentucky moon / Omaha / Missouri waltz, The / Whispering pines of Nevada, The / New Scotland Strathspey, The / Miss Drummond of Perth / Miss Nancy frowns / Lady Charlotte Murray's favourite / Stobhall / Howard Lockhart polka.
LP: MFP 41 5751 1
MC: MFP 41 5751 4
LP: MFP 5751
MC: TCMFP 5751

JIMMY SHAND.
Tracks: / Bluebell polka / Glendaurel highlanders / White heather jig - six twenty twostep / Veleta (set dance).
MC: TCIDL 109
MC: 795 437 4

LAST TEN YEARS, THE (Shand, Jimmy & His Band).
Tracks: / Georgina Catherine MacDonald fancy / Lord Randall's bride / Calton Hill reel / Lady Elgin of Broomhall / Lord Elgin of Broomhall / Green glens of Antrim / Come back to Erin / Bryce Laing's welcome to Auchtermuchty / John and Mary's Young's golden wedding anniversary / Threave Castle polka / Major Norman Orr Ewing / Crossing the new Forth Bridge / 72nd Highlanders' farewell to Aberdeen / Jimmy Shand's 80th year / Now is the hour / At the end of a perfect day / MacKenzie highlanders / Glengarry quickstep, The / Teribus / Sweet maid of Glendaruel / Francis Wright's waltz / Suptd. Ian Thompson's farewell to the Fife police / Jimmy Shand's compliments to Willie Laird / Guardians of the Gulf / Royal Guard Regiment of H.M. Sultan Of Oman / Heather mixture twostep / Badge of Scotland / 51st Highland Division / Hills of Alva, The / MacNeils of Ugadale / John D. Burgess / Hugh MacPherson / Piper's weird, The / Flower o' the Quern / Cradle song / Lochanside / Bill Dickman of Stonehouse / Woodlands polka / Scottish horse / Bugle horn, The / McDonald's awa' tae the war / Gentle maiden, The / Believe me if all those endearing young charms / Come back

Paddy Reilly to Bally / James Duff / Rose of Tralee / Ian Powrie's welcome to Dunblane / Jimmy Shand's compliments to Ian Powrie / Whitley chapel barn dance, The / Miss Elder / John MacDonald of Glencoe / Maresland twostep, The.
MC: CWGRTV 13

LEGENDARY JIMMY SHAND.
Tracks: / Linton ploughman / Marching with Jimmy Shand / Gaelic waltz selection / Gay Gordons / When you and I were young Maggie / Bluebell polka / Irish two step / Royal Scots polka / I'll take you home agin Kathleen / Highland schottische / Swilcan / Northern lights of Aberdeen / Black dance, The.
LP: MFP 50477
MC: TCMFP 50477

LEGENDARY JIMMY SHAND, THE.
Tracks: / Muckin' o' Geordie's byre / Lady Nellie Wemyss / Braidley's house / Major Mackie / Scotland the brave / Thistle of Scotland / We're no awa' tae bide awa' / Cailin mo ruin-sa / Leaving barra / Morag of Dunvegan / Cock o' the north / Jeannie King / Bluebell polka / If you're Irish / With my shillelagh under me arm / Royal Scots polka / Lord Lyndoch / Duke of Gordon / Laird o' Thrums, The / Lady Anne Hope / Gordon B. Cosh / Kinkell braes / Ythan bar / Northern lights of Aberdeen / Black dance, The / Thurso wedding, The / Wandering drummer, The / Breadalbane reel / Miss Bennetts jig / John Mearn's favourite / Balcomie House / Threave castle polka / Mrs. Cholmondely's reel / Lass o' paties mill / O Harveston Castle / Deveron reel, The / Blow the wind southerly / O hey ya seen the roses blow / Cushie butterfield / Cullercoats fish lass / Peter's peerie boat / Boonie doon / Jeanie's blue e'en / Neidpath castle / Tom's highland fling / Scotch mist / Lamb skinnet / John Grumlie / I lo'ed nae a lassie but Ane / Brinkie braes / Aunice Gillie's farewell to Loch Gilphead / John Bain Mackenzie / Galloway house reel / Georgina Catherine McDonald's fancy.
MC: HR 8177

LEGENDS OF SCOTLAND (Shand, Jimmy & His Band).
Tracks: / Muckin' o' Geordie's byre / Lady Nellie Wemyss / Braidley's house / Major Mackie / Cock o' the north / Jeannie King / Lord Lyndoch / Duke of Gordon / Laird o' Thrums, The / Lady Anne Hope / If you're Irish / With my shillelagh under me arm / Royal Scots polka / Swilcan, The / Gordon B Cosh / Kinkell braes / Ithan bar / Northern lights of old Aberdeen / Scotland the brave / Thistle of the north, The / We're no awa' tae bide awa' / Cailin mo ruin-sa / Leaving Barra / Morag of Dunvegan / When you and I were young Maggie / Bluebell polka / I'll take you home again Kathleen / Black dance, The / Wedding / Wandering drummer, The / Breadalbane reel.
MC: ZCLLS 705

MAGIC SHAND.
MC: TCMFP 5613

MAGIC SOUNDS OF SHAND, THE (Shand, Jimmy & His Band).
Tracks: / Waves of Tory, The / Buchan waltz, The / Heather mixture rant / Grosvenor House strathspey / Country dance waltz / Queens bridge / Cumberland reel / Balmoral circle dance / Schottische / Pipe marches / Old tyme waltz / Hornpipe selection / Miss Hadden's reel.
LP: MFP 5613

NEW SOUND OF JIMMY SHAND & HIS BAND (Shand, Jimmy & His Band).
Tracks: / Gay Gordons / Waltzes / Marches / Pipe marches / Irish waltz selection / West Country barn dance / Lowland waltz.
LP: GLN 1012

SCOTLAND MY HOME (Shand, Jimmy & His Band).
Tracks: / Marie MacLean's wedding march / Kirkwall Bay / Memories of Buckhaven / Doctor A.W. Forbes Catto ERD-OLT / Helen Black of Inveran / Jimmy Shand MBE / Leaving Stornoway / Tocherless lass, The / Oh how I love thee maiden fair / Mull of the cool high bens / Uist my love / Kirriemuir polka / Mrs. Cruickshanks of Wester Coul / Kilberry ball / Pat Shaw's tradition / Pat Shaw's rant / Jimmy Shand's compliments to Jim Crawford / Ella Crawford's fancy / My home / Alexander Blue of Dunning (Perthshire) / Slow air (Melodeon solo.) / Margaret Ann Robinson / Eva three step / Kaly Shaw / Queenie of Larkhill / Bessie Lee / Memories of Orkney / 1938 Canadian three step / Clan MacFarlane / St. Catherine's pipe band / Ontario, Canada / Minty of Ellenbrook Estate / Perth, Western Australia / Hearken my love / Denham's march / Dundee.
LP: GLN 1028
MC: TCGLN 1028

SCOTLAND'S OWN (Shand, Jimmy & His Band).
Tracks: / Highland laddie / Jimmy Shand's jig / Royal salute / Kendall's hornpipe / Heather mixture jig / Howard Lockhart polka / Lassies O'Dunse / Mason's apron / Express, The / La tempete / Marie's wedding / Road to the isles / Waverley.
LP: GRALP 5
MC: GRTC 5

SCOTTISH FANCY, A (Shand, Jimmy & His Band).
Tracks: / White heather jig / Grosvenor House strathspey / Campbells are coming, The / Balmoral strathspey / Miss Hadden's reel / Quiet & snug strathspey / Hooper's jig / Waltz country dance / Galloway House reel / Express, The (CD only.) / La tempete (CD only.) / Marie's wedding (CD only.) / Road to the isles, The (CD only.) / Waverley (CD only.).
LP: GRALP 37
MC: GRTC 37

TRIBUTE TO JIMMY SHAND - THE FIRST 46 YEARS (Shand, Jimmy & His Band).
Tracks: / Rakes of Kildare, The / Teviot Brig / Bottom of the punchbowl / My love she's but a lassie yet / Fair maid of Perth / Liberton pipe band polka / Roxburgh Castle / Lady MacKenzie of Coull / Dromleys / Bluebell polka / Happy hours / Shuffling Samuel / Moonstruck / Swanee / Stein song, The / Take me back to dear old Blighty / Welcome Christmas morning / Geordie Watson's co-worker of Whitehills / Blind boys / Haymakers jig / Lincolnshire poacher / Pop goes the weasel / Somebody stole my gal / Bye bye, blackbird / Oh Johnny, oh Johnny oh / 79th farewell to Gibraltar / Brydie's polka / Welcome home fisher lads / Gowna Hill / Margaret Cook's fancy / Anster fisherman, The / Standchen-serenade / Gay Gordons / Gavin Stoddart / Meeting of the waters, The.
LP: GLN 1017
MC: TCGLN 1017

Shand, Jimmy Jnr.

COME TO THE DANCE (Shand, Jimmy Jnr. & His Band).
Tracks: / Flowers of Edinburgh / Lass o' paties mill / Davy Nick Nack / Alyth Burn / Original tune (jig) / Maid of Bellevue, The / Stobhall / John Peel / Geordie hinny / Blaydon races / British Grenadiers, The / Wearing of the green, The / Over the sea to Skye / Forty shades of green / Edzell waltz, The / Abercairney Highlanders / Glens of Angus, The / Glenlogie / Mrs. Margaret Shand / Diane's favourite / Black bear, The / Muckin' o' Geordie's byre / Dance with Polly / Pride of Erin waltz / Homes of Donegal / Boys from County Armagh / Rose of Arranmore / Wild rover / Blow the man down / I'm a rover / Oh dear, what can the matter be?.
LP: GES 1018
MC: KGEC 1018

MAGIC OF JIMMY SHAND JNR & HIS BAND (Shand, Jimmy Jnr. & His Band).
Tracks: / Auchtermuchty gala march, The / Lass from Glasgow town / Badenoch polka / Gay Gordons / Shamrock waltz / Reels / Rabbie burns marches / Trip to Bavaria / Singalong waltz / Jigs / Medley / Eva three step.
LP: GES 1207

MIST COVERED MOUNTAINS.
MC: CWGR 104

PRIDE OF SCOTLAND.
Tracks: / Auchtermuchty gala march, The / Badenoch polka / Ring family two-step / Trip to Bavaria / Welcome Christmas morning / Lass from Glasgow town / Singalong waltz / Morning has broken / Eva three step / Lord of the dance.
MC: 4 HOM 012

Shandi

SHANDI.
Tracks: / Walk the streets / Show down / Heartbeat / Tuff baby / Bottom line / Mine / Don't sweat it / I yi yi yi / Nobody loves you better / Boy crazy.
LP: 2394267

Shane, Mark

BLUEBERRY RHYME With Dave Shapiro.
LP: JCE 91

Shanghai

SHANGHAI.
Tracks: / S.O.S. / Always a rebel / X-ray vision / I need your love / Talk to me / Born to rock / Brand new boy / All of my tears / On video / Girl who likes to cry.
LP: CHR 1389
MC: ZCHR 1389

Shango

SHANGO FUNK THEOLOGY.
LP: CAL 207

Shangri-Las

20 GREATEST HITS: SHANGRI-LAS.
LP: MA 21285
MC: MAMC 921285

65!.
Tracks: / Right now & not later / Never again / Give us your blessing / Sophisticated boom boom / I'm blue / Heaven only knows / Train from Kansas city / Out in the street / What's a girl supposed to do / Dum dum ditty / You cheated you lied / Boy.
LP: CRM 2029

DIXIE CUPS MEET THE SHANGRI-LAS (See under Dixie Cups).

GOLDEN HITS: THE SHANGRI-LAS.
Tracks: / Leader of the pack / Train from Kansas city / Heaven only knows / Remember (walking in the sand) / I can never go home anymore / What is love / Past, present and future / Out in the street / Give him a great big kiss / Long live our love / Give us your blessing / Sophisticated boom boom.
LP: 6430 154

LEADER OF THE PACK (ALBUM).
Tracks: / Give him a great big kiss / Leader of the pack / Bull dog / It's easier to cry / What is love / Remember (walking in the sand) / Twist and shout / Maybe / So much in love / Shout / Goodnight my love / You can't sit down.
LP: CRM 2028
LP: TOP 100
MC: KTOP 100
LP: 20097
MC: 40097

LEADER OF THE PACK (ALBUM) (2).
LP: RMB 5633

REMEMBER.
Tracks: / Leader of the pack / Give him a great big kiss / Maybe / Out in the streets / Give us your blessing / Right now and not later / Remember (walkin' in the sand) / I can never go home anymore / Long live our love / Past present and future / Train from Kansas City / Shout / Twist and shout / I'm blue / You cheated, you lied / So much in love.
LP: INS 5021
MC: TCINS 5021

TEEN ANGUISH VOL.2.
LP: CRM 2005

Shani

SHANI (THE SOUND OF ZAMBIA).
LP: WOMAD 009
MC: WOMCAS 009

Shank, Bud

BUD SHANK PLAYS CONCERTO FOR ALTO SAX AND ORCHESTRA (Shank, Bud & The Royal Philharmonic Orchestra).
Tracks: / Here's that rainy day / Body and soul / Concerto for jazz alto saxophone and orchestra.
LP: MOLE 12

BUD SHANK PLAYS TENOR (see under (Pacific Jazz II collection).

LIVE AT THE HAIG.
Tracks: / How about you / Lover man / Ambassador blues / I heard you cried last night / Out of this world / Miles sign off / Set ends.
LP: VL 02

PLAYS TALES OF THE PILOT.
MC: 740254

REEDS AND WOODWINDS VOL 1 (1956/7).
LP: INGO 17

REEDS AND WOODWINDS VOL 2 (Shank, Bud/Bob Cooper).
LP: INGO 18

SELECTED CLASSICAL WORKS FOR GUITAR AND FLUTE (see Almeida, Laurendo) (Shank, Bud & Laurendo Almeida).

THAT OLD FEELING (Shank, Bud Quartet).
Tracks: / Whisper not / Dream dancing / Cabin in the sky / El wacko / No Moe / I've told every little star / As time goes by / That old feeling.
LP: COP 035

THIS BUD'S FOR YOU.
Tracks: / I'll be seeing you / Nica's dream / Never never land / Space maker / Visa / Cotton blossom / Bouncing with Bud.
LP: MR 5309

Shankar

M.R.C.S..
Tracks: / Adagio / March / All I care / Reasons / Back again / Al's hallucinations / Sally / White buffalo / Ocean waves.
LP: ECM 1403
MC: 8416424

Shankar, Ravi

GENESIS (Film Soundtrack).
Tracks: / Genesis theme / Woman reminiscing / Fair / Return from the film / Passion / Jealousy and fighting / Variation on Genesis theme / Bounty full of crops / Song in the fair / Swing / Camel / Genesis: Title.
LP: A 287
MC: C 287

GENIUS OF RAVI SHANKAR, THE.
2LP: 67269

INSIDE THE KREMLIN.
Tracks: / Prarambh / Shanti-mantra / Three ragas in D minor / Sandhya / Tarana / Bahu-rang.
LP: 209620
MC: 409620

LIVE AT CARNEGIE HALL (Shankar, Ravi & A A Khan).
LP: DS 7920
MC: TC 7920

MORNING AND EVENING RAGAS.
LP: EASD 1356

MUSIC FROM INDIA.
MC: TC 7153

NOBODY TOLD ME.
Tracks: / Chittham irangaayo / Chodhanai thanthu / Nadru dri dhom - tillana.
LP: ECM 1397

PANCHA NADAI PALLAVI (Shankar Group).
Tracks: / Ragam tanam pallavi / Ragam: Sankarabharanam / Ragam tanam pallavi / Talam mahalakshmi tala / 9/12 beats / Pancha nadai pallavi.
LP: ECM 1407

PANDIT RAVI SHANKAR.
MC: 4558 674

PASSAGES (See under Glass, Philip) (Glass, Philip & Ravi Shankar).

PATHER PANCHALI/ RAGA RAGESHRI.
MC: TCS 7156

PORTRAIT OF A GENIUS.
LP: BGOLP 99

RAVI SHANKAR IN CONCERT.
MC: TCS 7155

RGS. KAMSHWARI/GANGSHWARI.
LP: EASD 1502

RGS. S KALYAN/S SARANG.
LP: EASD 1519

SONG FOR EVERYONE (Shankar).
LP: ECM 1286

TANA MANA (Shankar, Ravi Project).
Tracks: / Chase, The / Tana mana / Village dance / Seven and 10 1/2 / Friar park / Romantic voyage / Memory of Uday / West eats meat / Reunion / Supplication.
LP: 209.962
MC: 409.962

VISION.
Tracks: / All for you / Vision / Astral projection / Psychic elephant / Message, The.
LP: ECM 1261

WEST MEETS EAST (Shankar, Ravi & Y Menuhin).
LP: ECSD 2536

WHO'S TO KNOW.
Tracks: / Ragam tanam pallavi / Ananda nadamaadum tillai sankara.
LP: ECM 1195

Shankly, Bill

SHANKLY ON SOCCER VOLUME 1.
LP: TECLP 001

SO YOU THINK YOU KNOW ABOUT FOOTBALL.
LP: PPLP 001
MC: PPMC 001

Shanks

MASTERBAIT.
Tracks: / Not too much / Pink f**k / Headspin / Masterbait / My personal landslide / That's how / Snakepit / Lazy chair / Bus / Muscles / Chemical beach / I got out of her system.
LP: SCHEMER 8907

Shannon

DO YOU WANNA GET AWAY.
Tracks: / Do you wanna get away / Doin' what you're doin' / Stop the noise / Stronger together / Urgent / Why can't

we pretend / Let me see your body move / Bedroom eyes.
LP: JABH 10

LET THE MUSIC PLAY.
Tracks: / Let the music play / Sweet somebody / Someone waiting home / Give me tonight / My hearts divided / It's you / One man.
LP: JABL 1
MC: JABLC 1

LOVE GOES ALL THE WAY.
Tracks: / Prove me right / Love goes all the way / Dancin' / Sabotage my heart / You put a spark in my life / Right track / Faces in the crowd / You blew.
LP: JABH 24
MC: JABHC 24

Shannon Castle Singers

MUSIC FROM A MEDIAEVAL BANQUET IN IRELAND.
MC: RGMC 2

Shannon, Del

20 ROCK'N'ROLL HITS: DEL SHANNON.
Tracks: / Keep searchin' / Hats off to Larry / Handy man / Red rubber ball / When you walk in the room / Oh pretty woman / Swiss maid / Hey little girl / Little town flirt / Crying / Runaway / Big hurt, The / Under my thumb / Two kinds of teardrops / Summer in the city / Where were you when I needed you? / Everybody loves a clown / Kicks / Pied piper / Action.
LP: IC 064 82752

DEL SHANNON.
Tracks: / Hats off to Larry / Lightning strikes / Little town flirt / Sunny / Summer in the city / Pied piper / She / Handy man / Swiss maid / Hey little girl / Crying / Two kinds of teardrops / Keep searchin' / What's a matter baby / Runaway.
LP: MFP 41 5746 1
MC: MFP 41 5746 4
MC: TCMFP 5746

DEL SHANNON.
Tracks: / Runaway / Keep searchin' / Little town flirt / I ran all the way home / Runaround Sue / Stranger in town / Hats off to Larry (Available on CD single only.) / Swiss maid / Two kinds of teardrops / So long, baby / Hey little girl / Handy man.
LP: COUNT 8
MC: ZC CNT 8

DROP DOWN AND GET ME.
Tracks: / Sea of love / Life without you / Out of time / Sucker for your love / To love someone / Cheap love / Drop down and get me / Maybe tomorrow / Liar / Never stop tryin' / Midnight train.
LP: FIEND 8

GREATEST HITS: DEL SHANNON.
LP: 34044
MC: 64044

GREATEST HITS: DEL SHANNON.
LP: BRLP 51
MC: BRMC 51

HATS OFF TO DEL SHANNON.
LP: HAX 8071

HIT PARADE.
Tracks: / Runaway / Keep searchin' / So long baby / Breakup / From me to you / Handy man / Do you want to dance / Two silhouettes / Little town flirt / Hats off to Larry / Sue's gotta be mine / Two kinds of teardrops / Stranger in town / Dream baby / Mary Jane / Cry myself to sleep / I go to pieces / Kelly / Swiss maid / Hey, little girl.
LP: HAR 8545

I GO TO PIECES.
Tracks: / Misery / Wide wide world / Ginny in the mirror / You never talked about me / Don't gild the lily, Lily / I won't be there / Dream baby / She thinks I still care / From me to you / Broken promises / Why don't you tell him / Do you wanna dance / I go to pieces / Break up / Mary Jane / That's the way love is.
LP: ED 174

LITTLE TOWN FLIRT.
LP: HAX 8091

LIVE IN ENGLAND.
Tracks: / Hats off to Larry / Handy man / Swiss maid / Hey little girl / Little town flirt / Kelly / Crying / Two kinds of teardrops / Coopersville yodel / Answer to everything, The / Keep searchin' / What's a matter baby? / So long, baby / Runaway.
LP: FA 3020
MC: TCFA 3020

LOOKING BACK.
MC: VSOPMC 161

ROCK ON.
LP: ORELP 514
MC: OREMC 514

RUNAWAY HITS.
Tracks: / Little town flirt / Runaway / Jody / Hats off to Larry / So long baby / Swiss maid / Answer to everything, The / Hey little girl / Cry myself to sleep / Two kinds of tear drops / Kelly / Handy man / Two silouettes / Sue's gotta be mine / Keep searchin' / Stranger in town.
LP: XED 121

VERY BEST OF DEL SHANNON.
Tracks: / Runaway / Swiss maid / Two kinds of teardrops / His latest flame / From me to you / I don't care anymore / Hey little girl / Hats off to Larry / Little town flirt / Kelly / Broken promises / I wake up crying / Jody / Answer to everything, The / Handy man / Keep searchin' / Wamboo, The / Stranger in town / Don't gild the lily Lily / This is all I have to give / You never talked about me / Misery / Sue's gotta be mine / Do you wanna dance / Move it on over / Two silhouettes / Mary Jane / Why don't you tell him / Break up / So long baby.
LP: CRMD 1001

Shannon, Dick

PECK KELLEY JAM - VOL 1 (see Kelley, Peck) (Shannon, Dick Quartet/ Peck Kelley).

PECK KELLEY JAM - VOL 2 (see Kelley, Peck) (Shannon, Dick Quartet/ Peck Kelley).

Shannon, Hugh

SALOON SINGER.
2LP: AP 171/2

TRUE BLUE HUGH.
LP: AP 140

Shannon, Ronald

MAN DANCE (Shannon Jackson, Ronald & The Decoding Society).
LP: AN 1008

TABOO (Shannon Jackson, Ronald & The Decoding Society).
Tracks: / Mental holiday / Vacating the body / Ain't supposed to be / No routines / Forgive me / Be back shortly / Taboo / Mothers and sons / Challenge to manhood / Little things that count.
LP: VE 47
MC: TCVE 47

Shannon, Seamus

IRISH ACCORDION MUSIC.
LP: CBRL 4056

TRADITIONAL IRISH ACCORDION.
LP: SOLP 1037
MC: COX 1037

Shante, Roxanne

BAD SISTER.
Tracks: / Bad sister / Live on stage / Independent woman / Knockin' hiney / My groove gets better / Feeling kinda horny / Gotta get paid / Let's rock y'all / Fatal attraction / Wack it / Skeezer / What's on your mind / Go on girl / Have a nice day.
LP: AMA 9013
MC: AMC 9013

Shantung Music Society

MUSIC OF CONFUCIOUS' HOMELAND.
LP: LLST 7112

Shanty Crew

LET THE WIND BLOW FREE.
LP: ESSAR 014

SHANTY CREW.
Tracks: / Let the wind blow free / Royal Artillery man / Haul away for Rosie / Mobile Bay / Flash frigate / Hog eye / 24th of February / La houla t'chalez / Roll the woodpile down / Haul 'er away / Rolling down to old Maui / Shake her Johnnie / Fire maringo / Is the big fella gone / Cheerly man / Six feet of mud / Haul on the bowline / Coal black Rose / Eddystone light / Emma Emma let me be / Minuglay boat song.
LP: 014
MC: Unknown

Shape Up & Dance

SHAPE UP AND DANCE, VOL 1 (Kendal, Felicity).
LP: LEG 1
MC: LEGC 1

SHAPE UP AND DANCE, VOL 2 (Rippon, Angela (nar)).
Tracks: / Slow hand / Hands up / Land of make believe / Physical / Turn your love around / It's a love thing.
LP: LEG 2
MC: LEGC 2

SHAPE UP AND DANCE, VOL 3 (St. Clair, Isla (nar)).
LP: LEG 3
MC: LEGC 3

SHAPE UP AND DANCE, VOL 4 (Danielle, Suzanne).
LP: LEG 7
MC: LEGC 7

SHAPE UP AND DANCE, VOL 5 (Brookes, Christina).
LP: LEG 8
MC: LEGC 8

SHAPE UP AND DANCE, VOL 6 (Lulu).
LP: LEG 19
MC: LEGC 19

SHAPE UP AND DANCE, VOL 7 (Aston, Jay).
Tracks: / I do it all for you / Piece of the action / What a feeling / She works hard for the money / Every breath you take / If you can't stand the heat.
LP: LEG 20
MC: LEGC 20

SHAPE UP AND DANCE, VOL 8 (Dando, Suzanne).
Tracks: / Karma chameleon / Walking in the rain / Down under / Save a prayer.
LP: LEG 21
MC: LEGC 21

SHAPE UP AND DANCE, VOL 9 (Best, George & Mary Stavin).
LP: LEG 22
MC: LEGC 22

SHAPE UP AND DANCE, VOL 10 (Boulaye, Patti).
Tracks: / Wherever I lay my hat / Red red wine / Do you really want to hurt me / Tahiti / It's late.
LP: LEG 23
MC: LEGC 23

Shapiro, Helen

25TH ANNIVERSARY ALBUM: HELEN SHAPIRO.
Tracks: / Walkin' back to happiness / Keep away from other girls / Basin Street blues / Don't treat me like a child / It's my party / Little Miss Lonely / She needs company / Stop and you will become aware / Something wonderful / Tell me what he said / Fever / You don't know / Look who it is / St. Louis blues / In my calendar / Let's talk about love / Woe is me / Queen for tonight / Here in your arms / Birth of the blues.
LP: MFP 41 5741 1
MC: MFP 41 5741 4

BEST OF THE EMI YEARS: HELEN SHAPIRO.
Tracks: / Tip toe through the tulips / Don't treat me like a child / You don't know / Walkin' back to happiness / Birth of the blues / Tell me what he said / Little Miss Lonely / St. Louis blues / Teenager in love, A / Keep away from other girls / Let's talk about love / Lipstick on your collar / Little devil / Queen for tonight / I want to be happy / Look who it is / Woe is me / All alone am I / Fever / Walk on by.
MC: TCEMS 1398
LP: 1A 022 58031

EP COLLECTION, THE: HELEN SHAPIRO.
Tracks: / Little devil / I don't care / Don't treat me like a child / You don't know / Teenager in love, A / Lipstick on your collar / Beyond the sea / Little Miss Lonely / Day the rains came, The / Tell me what he said / Walking back to happiness / I apologise / Let's talk about love / When I'm with you / Because they're young / St. Louis blues / Goody goody / Birth of the blues / Keep away from other girls / After you've gone.
LP: SEE 272
MC: SEEK 272

HELEN IN NASHVILLE.
Tracks: / Not responsible / I cried myself to sleep last night / Young stranger / Here today and gone tomorrow / It's my party / No trespassing / I'm tickled pink / I walked right in (with my eyes wide open) / Sweeter than sweet / You'd think he didn't know me / When you hurt me / I cry / Woe is me.
LP: C5-545

HELEN SHAPIRO.
Tracks: / Don't treat me like a child / You don't know / Walkin' back to happiness / Tell me what he said / Let's talk about love / Little Miss Lonely / Keep away from other girls / Queen for tonight / Woe is me / Look who it is / Fever / Look over your shoulder / Tomorrow is another day / Shop around / I wish I'd never loved you / When I'm with you / Marvellous lie / Kiss 'n' run / I apologise / Sometime yesterday / I don't care / Cry my heart out / Daddy couldn't get me one of those / Walking in my dreams / Ole Father Time / He knows how to love me / I walked right in (with my eyes wide open) (Available on CD only.) / You won't come home (Available on CD only.) / I was only kidding (Available on CD only.) / It's so funny I could cry (Available on CD only.).
MC: HR 8192

QUALITY OF MERCER, THE.
Tracks: / Out of breath / Goody goody / I thought about you / I'm building up to an awful letdown / Midnight sun / Jubilation t-cornpone / When a man loves a woman / Fools rush in / I'm old fashioned / G.I. jive / Tangerine / Laura / Jeepers creepers / Satin doll / Autumn leaves / I wanna be around / Skylark / Cinderella / You go your way / Johnny Mercer medley / Scared to death.
LP: CLGLP 014
MC: ZCLG 014

STRAIGHTEN UP AND FLY RIGHT.
Tracks: / Straighten up and fly right / Cry me a river / Let yourself go.
LP: OVLP 507

TOPS WITH ME.
LP: 33SX 1397

TOPS WITH ME & HELEN HITS OUT.
Tracks: / Little devil / Will you love me tomorrow / Because they're young / Day the rains came, The / Are you lonesome tonight? / Teenager in love / Lipstick on your collar / La mer / Sweet nothin's / You mean everything to me / I love you / You got what it takes / My guy / All alone am I / He's a rebel / Move over, darling / Keep your hands off my baby / Remember me / Shop around / Walk on by / End of the world / It might as well rain until September / Baby it's you / Please Mr. Postman / It's in his kiss / Stay.
2LP: EDP 1546343
MCSET: TC2 EDP 1546349

Sharif, Omar

TALES OF THE DESERT.
LP: TC 1590
MC: CDL 51590

Sharing The House..

STATIC NATION (Sharing The House With Mother).
MC: ZCAIC 2

Shark Island

LAW OF THE ORDER.
Tracks: / Paris calling / Shake for me / Somebody's falling / Bad for each other / Passion to ashes / Spellbound / Get some strange / Why should I believe / Ready or not / Chain, The.
LP: 4659561
MC: 4659564

Shark Taboo

BLACK ROCK SANDS.
LP: PLASLP 021

EVERYONE'S A FREAK.
Tracks: / Everyone's a freak / Drowning / Woman to woman / Rose of romance / Silent majority / Call this peace.
LP: NED 14

Shark Vegas

YOU HURT ME.
LP: V 2360
MC: TCV 2360

Sharkey

SHARKEY & HIS KINGS OF DIXIELAND (see under Bonano, Sharkey) (Sharkey & His Kings of Dixieland).

Sharkey, Feargal

FEARGAL SHARKEY.
Tracks: / Good heart, A / You little thief / Ghost train / Ashes and diamond / Made to measure / Someone to somebody / Don't leave it to nature / Love and hate / Bitter man / It's all over now.
LP: OVED 218
MC: OVEDC 218

SONGS FROM THE MARDI GRAS.
LP: V 2642

WISH.
Tracks: / Cold cold streets / More love / Full confession / Please don't believe in me / Out of my system / Strangest girl in paradise / Let me be / Blue days / If this is love / Safe to touch.
LP: V 2500
MC: TCV 2500
LP: OVED 304
MC: OVEDC 304

Sharkeys Machine

SHARKEYS MACHINE (Original Soundtrack) (Various artists).
LP: BSK 3653

Sharks

FROM THE BEGINNING TO THE END.
LP: NERD 046

PHANTOM ROCKERS.
LP: NERD 008

Sharky's Machine

LET'S BE FRIENDS.
Tracks: / Collide collide / Chevy van blues / Lover / Red goose shoes / Lock and dam / Route killdozer / Stray cat blues / Road hang / Postscientific strut, The / Blue moon / Lear jet song / Mando

the midget / Big boss man / Motor city madhouse.
LP: SR 7087
LP: SHIMMY 004

Sharma, Shivkumar

CLASSICAL AND FOLK MELODIES.
LP: ECSD 2729

MELODIES OF ROMANCE.
LP: ECSD 2947
MC: TC 3997

RGS. MADHUVANTI/JOG.
LP: ECSD 2457
MC: TC 5172

Sharman, Dave

1990.
LP: NUK 152
MC: ZCNUK 152

Sharon

SHARON IN SONG.
LP: TSLP 89

Sharon, Ralph

MAGIC OF COLE PORTER (Sharon, Ralph Trio).
Tracks: / You're the top / All through the night / Easy to love / Get out of town / You'd be so nice to come home to / I concentrate on you / I've got you under my skin / Down in the depths on the 90th floor / So in love / Anything goes / Let's do it / From this moment on / What is this thing called love / Do I love you / Night & day / I love Paris / Love for sale / I love you / It's alright by me / All of you / I get a kick out of you / Why should I / Just one of those things / Long last love / Begin the beguine / Sorta Porter.
MC: CSIV 1123

MAGIC OF GEORGE GERSHWIN, THE (Sharon, Ralph Trio).
Tracks: / Fascinating rhythm / They all laughed / Somebody loves me / S'wonderful s'marvellous / But not for me / Soon / I loves you Porgy / I got rhythm / They can't take that away from me / Someone to watch over me / Man I love, The / Love is here to stay / There's a boat dat's leavin' soon for New York / Rhapsody in blue / Foggy day, A / Embraceable you / Liza (all the cloud'll roll away) / How long has this been going on / Swanee / Love walked in (Golden Follies) / Oh lady be good.
MC: CSIV 116

MR & MRS JAZZ (Sharon, Ralph & Sue).
LP: FS 243

Sharp

SHARP.
Tracks: / Playboy / Second to none / Love or money / Tomorrow each day / Can't get enough / Can't take my eyes off you / Double your pleasure / Available.
LP: 9607801
MC: 9607804

Sharp, Brian

BRIAN SHARP IN JAPAN.
Tracks: / Love is the sweetest thing / Music / Mexican shuffle, The / Three times a lady / Die entfuhring aus dem serail / Aria / Isn't she lovely / Dream of Olwen.
LP: GRS 1082

MAGIC OF BRIAN SHARP, THE.
Tracks: / Undecided / All of me / What a difference a day made / When lights are low / Dance ballerina dance / I saw stars / Gypsy in my soul / Hallelujah I love her so / Let's face the music and dance / You stepped out of a dream / I've got the world on a string / After you've gone / When you wore a tulip / Moon was yellow, The / More than you know / Sapphire / Bon sante.
LP: GRS 1093

NIGHTHAWK.
Tracks: / Morning glory / Love letters / My foolish heart / Janine / Opus one / In the mood / Johnson rag / Chattanooga choo choo / Take the 'A' train / Skyliner / Song that I sing, The / Begin the beguine.
LP: GRS 1129
MC: KGRS 1129

ORCHESTRAL KEYBOARDS.
LP: GRS 1175

ORCHESTRAL SOUNDS OF BRIAN SHARP.
Tracks: / All creatures great and small / Fifth of Beethoven, A / Je voudrais tant que tu comprennes / Manhattan skyline / Concerto pour une voix / House of dreams / Salsation / Bewitched, bothered and bewildered / When I fall in love / We're all alone / Badinerie / All by myself / Besame mucho / I can't make it on my own / Love is a many splendoured thing.
LP: GRS 1073

ORCHESTRALLY YOURS.
LP: GRS 1120

ORGAN FIESTA VOL.1 (Sharp, Brian & The Riha Orchestra).
MC: VCA 049

ORGAN FIESTA VOL.2 (Sharp, Brian & The Riha Orchestra).
MC: VCA 082

ORGAN FIESTA VOL.3 (Sharp, Brian & The Riha Orchestra).
MC: VCA 089

PERSONAL SELECTION FOR YOU, A.
Tracks: / I can see clearly now / What a difference a day made / Bewitched bothered and bewildered / When I fall in love / Satin doll / Manhattan skyline / Aria / House of dreams / My Cherie Amour / Bon Sante / Mexican shuffle, The / Ghetto child / Sapphire / What I did for love / Die entfuhring aus dem serail / Solitaire / Give me the simple life / Laughter in the rain.
MC: KGRS 1105

PLAYS MAINLY HAMMOND.
Tracks: / Give me the simple life / Girl talk / Till / More / Lullaby of the leaves / Superstar / Here, there and everywhere / Satin doll / For all we know / Sleepy shores / So nice / Mozart Symphony No.40 / Don't dream of anybody but me (li'l darlin') / Aquarius.
LP: GRS 1012

WURLITZER WONDERLAND.
Tracks: / Rag-a-de-rag / In a little Spanish town / Radetzky march / Morning has broken / Moonlight serenade / Bagatelle / Charleston medley / Blumen-corso / El bimbo / Poet and peasant / Manhattan / Carousel.
LP: GRS 1047

Sharp Cuts

SHARP CUTS (Various artists).
Tracks: / I like girls: *Various artists* / I'm gonna follow you: *Various artists* / Black haired girl: *Various* artists / Last supper, The: *Various artists* / Live among the dancers: *Various artists* / Keep it tight: *Various* artists / She's illegal: *Various artists* / Unable: *Various artists* / Soul kiss: *Various artists*/ Kids just wanna dance: *Various artists.*
LP: K 52222

Sharp, Dave

HARD TRAVELLIN'.
Tracks: / In the city / It ain't long for the day / Wonderful world / Long black night / Last smilin' villain from the south / New age Eden / Hard travellin' / In the dead of night / Big road blue / Joey the jone / Homeless child.
LP: EIRSLP 1059
MC: EIRSTC 1059

Sharp Edges

SLICE OF LIFE.
LP: PRL 70192

Sharp, Elliott

CARBON.
LP: ST 3003

FRUCTAL.
LP: ST 7515

HAMMER, ANVIL, STIRRUP (Sharp, Elliott & The Soldier String Quartet).
2LP: SST 232

IN NEW YORK (See under Attar, Bachir) (Attar, Bachir & Elliot Sharp).

IN THE LAND OF THE YAHOOS.
LP: ST 7536

MARCO POLO'S ARGALI.
LP: ST 7508

MONSTOR CURVE.
LP: SST 208

NOTS.
LP: GLALP 020

TESSALATION ROW Land of the Yahoos, The.
LP: SST 128

VIRTUAL STANCE.
Tracks: / Virtual stance / Bean / War Mongers / Onebigone / No remorse / One little one / Wrap it up.
LP: ST 7526

Sharp, Rebby

IN ONE MOUTH AND OUT THE OTHER.
Tracks: / Some men / Up jumped chair legs / Hard acid rain / These venetian eyes / Just in time / I'm so hard / Crater creek / Gimme back my fifteen dollars / Goin' to the roof / Sittin' on top of the john / Let the piper call the tune / Hesitation blues / Tar baskets / Holding forth / He leadeth me / Walk by the fire.
LP: SHIMMY 032

Sharpe, Barrie K

BLIND FAITH (See also Brown, Diana) (Sharpe, Barrie K & Diana Brown).

LOVE OR NOTHING (see under Brown, Diana) (Sharpe, Barrie K & Diana Brown).

SUN WORSHIPPERS (See under Brown, Diana) (Sharpe, Barrie K & Diana Brown).

Sharpe, Bill

FAMOUS PEOPLE.
Tracks: / Famous people (US remix) / Shuffle, The / Remix, remake, remodel / Silhouettes / Peach / Change your mind / Catching a train / Fools in a world of fire / Washed away / Fair weather girl.
LP: POLH 20
MC: POLHC 20

Sharpe, Boogsie

STEEL & BRASS EQUALS GOLD.
Tracks: / Bacchanal lady / This party is it / Happy / Drive it / Wet me down.
LP: GS 2287

Sharpe, Cecil

AN HOUR WITH... (Sharpe, Cecil / Ashley Hutchings).
LP: DAM 014

Sharpe, Dee Dee

CAMEO PARKWAY SESSIONS.
Tracks: / Mashed potato time / Set my heart at ease / Gravy / Baby cakes / Ride / Night / Do the bird / Lover boy / Rock me in the cradle of love / You'll never be mine / Wild / Why doncha ask me / Where did I go wrong? / Willyam Willyam / Never pick a pretty boy / He's no ordinary guy / Remember you're mine / To know him is to love him / I really love you / Standing in the need of love.
LP: HAU 8514

Sharpe, Jack

CATALYST Tribute to Tubby Hayes (Sharpe, Jack Big Band).
Tracks: / Milestones / You know I care / Sharpe edge / Suddenly last Tuesday / Keith / Souriya / Allisamba.
LP: FRG 716

Sharpe & Numan

AUTOMATIC.
LP: 839 520 1
MC: 839 520 4

Sharpe, Ray

LIVE AT THE BLUEBIRD VOLUME I.
LP: FH 6507

RAY SHARPE.
LP: JLP 331959

Sharpe, Rocky

LET'S GO (Sharpe, Rocky & The Replays).
Tracks: / Shout shout / Whole lotta loving / She don't want me now / Alright okay you win / Heart / You were made for me / Too much monkey business / Come on let's go / Get a job / Never be anyone else but you / Tick tock / Can't stand it anymore / Love love love / Looking for an echo.
LP: CWK 3019

ROCK IT TO MARS.
Tracks: / Buzz buzz buzz / Heartaches / Teenager in love / Dream lover / Only one / Masquerade is over / You're the one / Love bug / Little darlin' / Mr.Lonely / I will follow him / Donna the prima donna / Martian hop / Choo-choo valentine.
LP: CWK 3013

SHOUT SHOUT (Sharpe, Rocky & The Replays).
Tracks: / Come on, let's go / Get a job / Never be anyone else but you / Tick tock / Can't stand it anymore / Love, love, love / Looking for an echo / Shout shout (knock yourself out) / Whole lotta loving / She don't want me now / Alright, OK you win / Heart / You were made for me / Too much monkey business.
LP: TOSS 1

STOP PLEASE STOP (ALBUM) (Sharpe, Rocky & The Replays).
Tracks: / Quarter to three / Heart and soul / 9,999,999 tears / Dynamo twist / First crush / Baby I'm sorry / It will stand / Let's twist again / Heart beat / If you wanna be happy / Stop, please stop / Little dab'll do ya, A / La bamba.
LP: POLD 5102

Sharpe, Tom (aut)

PORTERHOUSE BLUE (Rhys Jones, Griff).
MCSET: CAB 269

PORTERHOUSE BLUE (Jason, David).
MCSET: 060055855X

Sharpe-Gamble, Dee Dee

WHAT COLOUR IS LOVE.
Tracks: / I believe in love / Just as long as I know you're mine / Tryin' to get the feeling again / I wanna be your woman / Flashback / Nobody could take your place / What color is love? / I'd really love to see you tonight / Hang your portrait / What color is love?.
LP: PIR 82433

Sharples, Bob

WORLD OF ALBERT KETELBEY (Sharples, Bob/New Symphony Orchestra).
LP: SPA 187

Sharriff, Imam Omar

IMAM OMAR SHARRIFF.
MC: C 207

Sharrock, Sonny

ASK THE AGES.
MC: AXCT 3006
LP: AXLPS 3006

GUITAR.
LP: EMY 102

HIGHLIFE (Sharrock, Sonny Band).
LP: EMY 119 LP

MONKEY POCKIE BOO.
LP: AFF 35

SONNY SHARROCK: LIVE IN NEW YORK.
LP: EMY 108

Shaskeen

BACK TO THE GLEN.
Tracks: / Shaskeen, The / Lady Ann Montgomery / Morrison's reel / Eileen Curran / Tommy Mulhamir's jig.
LP: HPE 643
MC: HPC 643

DAWN, THE.
LP: XHRL 5003
MC: CXHRL 5003

GALWAY'S OWN SHASKEEN.
LP: SOLP 1038

IRISH TRADITIONAL MUSIC.
MC: COX 1038

JOYS OF LIFE, THE.
MC: GTDC 018
MC: CFA 3502

MY LOVE IS IN AMERICA.
MC: GTDC 072

SHASKEEN.
Tracks: / Reels, jigs, hornpipes / Bunch of Thyme / Day of the clipper, The / Cathy's fling / Anything for John Joe.
LP: HPE 679
MC: HPC 679
LP: CBRL 4053

S-Haters

COME.
LP: CHIME 00 04 M

Shatner, William (nar)

FOUNDATION - PSYCHOHISTORIANS (See under Foundation - Psychohistorians).

MIMSY WERE THE BOROGOVES.
LP: TC 1509
MC: CDL 51509

Shava Shava

AAJA PARDESIA.
Tracks: / Jhan jhraan de bol / Bhabhi nach le / Aaja pardesia / Nagri nagri lavan hoki / Nahin pyaar nabhinde / Laal soot utte / Tere vich band.
LP: MUT 1052
MC: CMUT 1052

BACHKE RAHEYO.
LP: MUT 1067
MC: CMUT 1067

HEARTBEAT.
LP: MUT 1130
MC: CMUT 1130

Shaved Pigs

BREAKFAST IS SERVED.
LP: 3825 U
LP: SR 0787

Shaver, Billy Joe

HELL RAISERS (I love country) (Shaver, Billy Joe & Johnny Paycheck).
Tracks: / I'm just an old chunk of coal / Old five and dimers like me / Fit to kill and going out in style / When the word was thunderbird / AMTRAK (and ain't coming back) / Oklahoma wind / Saturday night / I been to Georgia on a fast train / Take this job and shove it / She's all I got / Drinkin' and drivin' / I'm the only hell (mama ever raised) / Fifteen beers ago / Turnin' off a memory / You better move on / Outlaw's prayer, The.
LP: 4504331

Shavers, Charlie

ART FORD'S JAZZY PARTY July 1958.
LP: AFJP 2

CHARLIE SHAVERS.
Tracks: / Deuce-a-rini / Summertime / Echoes of Harlem / Amor / Rose room / She's funny that way / On the spot / Bye bye blackbird / Nature boy / Avalon / St. Louis blues / I want a little girl / I

concentrate on you / What is this thing called love? / Pennies from Heaven / I'm forever blowing bubbles / My funny valentine / But beautiful / Bei mir bist du schon.
LP: **LP 21**
LP: **HEP 23**

JAZZ OFF THE AIR Volume 7 (Shavers, Charlie Quartet).
Tracks: / Undecided / St Louis blues / What is this thing called love / My funny valentine / I'm forever blowing bubbles / Rose room / Pennies from Heaven / Tisket a tasket, A / Over the rainbow / Bernies tune.
LP: **SPJ 154**

LIVE: CHARLIE SHAVERS.
LP: **33302**

MAN AND HIS MUSIC, A (see Hodges, Johnny) (Shavers, Charlie / Johnny Hodges).

NOVEMBER 1961 & MARCH 1962 (Shavers, Charlie Quartet).
Tracks: / Old apple tree / You got nothin' / Snow in Lovers' Lane / My old Kentucky home / Love gave me you / In the good old summertime / Give my regards to Broadway / Ain't gonna get fooled again / Carry me back to old Virginny / She's only a bird in a gilded cage / My wild Irish rose / Tetched in the head.
LP: **JV 106**

SWING ALONG.
LP: **500070**
LP: **JL 70**

SWING WITH CHARLIE.
LP: **500084**

TRUMPET MAN.
Tracks: / Deuce-a-rini / Summertime / Echoes of Harlem / Amor / Rose room / She's funny that way / On the spot / Bye bye blackbird / Nature boy / Avalon.
LP: **LP 21**
LP: **PHOENIX 21**

Shaw, Artie

22 ORIGINAL BIG BAND RECORDINGS (Shaw, Artie & His Orchestra).
LP: **HSR 401**

1938 BAND IN HI-FI, THE.
Tracks: / Sobbin' blues / I can't believe that you're in love with me / It had to be you / My reverie / Sweet Adeline / Who blew out the flame? / Copenhagen / Begin the beguine / You're a sweet little headache / What is this thing called love? / Jungle drums.
LP: **FANFARE 28 128**
LP: **JASM 2522**
MC: **JASMC 2522**

1949, VOL 1 (Shaw, Artie & His Orchestra).
Tracks: / Stardust / Tea for two / They can't take that away from me / Things are looking up / Softly as in a morning sunrise / He's funny that way / I only have eyes for you / Let's fall in love / So in love / You do something to me / I get a kick out of you / Begin the beguine / I concentrate on you / 'S wonderful / Orinoco / Carnival / Nightmare.
LP: **SOL 508**

1949, VOL 2 (Shaw, Artie & His Orchestra).
Tracks: / Comes love / I cover the waterfront / Krazy kat / Love walked in / Moonglow / So easy / Innuendo / Gue le le / Summit ridge drive / Grabtown grapple, The / Smoke gets in your eyes / Pied piper / Cross your heart / Cool daddy.
LP: **SOL 509**

1937-38 VOL.3 (Shaw, Artie/Rhythm Makers).
LP: **SWDM 7005/6**

1937-39 VOL.1 (Shaw, Artie/Rhythm Makers).
LP: **SWDM 7001/2**

1949-50 VOL.3 (Shaw, Artie & His Orchestra).
Tracks: / Minesota / Smooth and easy / Don't take your love from me / Exactly like you / How deep is the ocean / Together / Too marvellous for words / Very thought of you, The / Love is the sweetest thing / Bedford drive / Love of my life / Fred's delight / Love for sale / Similau / Time on my hands.
LP: **SOL 510**

1937-1938 VOL.2 (Shaw, Artie/Rhythm Makers).
LP: **SWDM 7003/4**
MC: **CAWE 26**

ARTIE SHAW.
LP: **BO 708**
LP: **LPJT 6**

ARTIE SHAW AND ORCHESTRA VOL. 4 1939 (Shaw, Artie & His Orchestra).
Tracks: / Nightmare (opening theme) / You're mine, you / You're a lucky guy / I'm coming Virginia / Table in a corner, A / Yesterdays / Melancholy lullaby / I'm sorry for myself / Traffic jam / Last two weeks in July / My heart stood still / Lilacs in the rain / Man from Mars.
LP: **HSR 149**

ARTIE SHAW AND ORCHESTRA VOL. 3 1939 (Shaw, Artie & His Orchestra).
Tracks: / Nightmare / Rose room / Go fly a kite / Comes love / Moonray / Don't worry 'bout me / Carioca / Nightmare (closing theme) / Nightmare (opening theme) / Out of nowhere / Put that down in writing / Many dreams ago / Day in, day out / One foot in the groove / St. Louis blues.
LP: **HSR 148**

ARTIE SHAW AND ORCHESTRA VOL. 3 (1938-39) (Shaw, Artie & His Orchestra).
Tracks: / Softly as in a morning sunrise / I won't tell a soul / Back bay shuffle / If I had you / Thanks for everything / I used to be colour blind / Together / Stardust / Who blew out the flame / Between a kiss and a sigh / Just you, just me / Let's stop the clock / In the mood / Deep in a dream / Diga diga doo.
LP: **HSR 140**

ARTIE SHAW AND THE RHYTHMAKERS 1937-38 (Shaw, Artie/ Rhythm Makers).
LPS: **SWING 7005-4**

ARTIE SHAW COLLECTION (20 golden greats).
Tracks: / Begin the beguine / Indian love call / Jungle drums / Carioca / Traffic jam / Frenesi / Summit Ridge Drive / Temptation / Stardust / Smoke gets in your eyes / Dancing in the dark / My blue Heaven / It had to be you / Accentuate the positive / 'S wonderful / September song / Summertime / Foggy day, A / These foolish things / They can't take that away from me.
LP: **DVLP 2013**
MC: **DVMC 2013**

ARTIE SHAW & HIS MUSICIANS 1949.
Tracks: / Minesota / Smooth and easy / Don't take your love from me.
LP: **FH 6**

ARTIE SHAW & HIS ORCHESTRA (Shaw, Artie & His Orchestra).
Tracks: / 'S wonderful / Man and his dream, A / April in Paris / Summertime / I cover the waterfront / Blues (end s1) / I could write a book / Don't take your love from me / Beyond the blue horizon / Maid with the flaccid air, The / Time on my hands / Deep purple / Prelude in C major.
LP: **CBR 1013**
MC: **KCBR 1013**

ARTIE SHAW & HIS ORCHESTRA 1938 VOL.2 (Shaw, Artie & His Orchestra).
Tracks: / Deep in a dream / Nightmare / Softly as in a morning sunrise / I won't tell a soul / If I had you / Thanks for everything / I used to be colour blind / Together / Stardust / Who blew out the flame / Between a kiss and a sigh / Just you, just me / Let's stop the clock / In the mood / Diga diga doo.
LP: **HMA 5066**

ARTIE SHAW & HIS ORCHESTRA 1938 VOL.1 (Shaw, Artie & His Orchestra).
Tracks: / Nightmare / April in my heart / Night over Shanghai / Small fry / What is this thing called love / Just a kid named Joe / When I go a-dreamin' / Leapin' at the Lincoln / Lambeth walk / They say / Shine on harvest moon / Out of nowhere / Simple and sweet / Blue interlude / I'll be with you in apple blossom time.
LP: **HMA 5065**

ARTIE SHAW ON THE AIR.
Tracks: / Shoot the likker to me John boy / One night stand / I ain't comin' / Chant / Serenade to a savage / Carioca / I'm comin', Virginia / Man from Mars / Donkey serenade, The / Lamp is low, The / Octoroon / Them there eyes / Along the Santa Fe trail / Looking for yesterday / Everything's jumpin'.
LP: **AIRCHECK 11**
LP: **SH 2016**

ARTIE SHAW, VOL. 1, 1938.
Tracks: / April in my heart / Night in Shanghai / Small fry / Just a kid named Joe / When I go a-dreamin' / Leapin' at the Lincoln / What is this thing called love / Lambeth walk / They say / Shine on harvest moon / Out of nowhere / Simple and sweet / Blue interlude / Apple blossom time / Deep in a dream.
LP: **HSR 139**

ARTIE SHAW VOL 5 1938-39.
Tracks: / Sweet Adeline / Monday morning / Lover come back to me / Two sleepy people / I cover the waterfront / This can't be love / I can't believe that your in love with me / Sweet Sue / Oh you crazy moon / I'm yours / What's new / I can't give you anything but love / Over the rainbow / Everything's jumpin'.
LP: **HSR 176**

BEGIN THE BEGUINE (Shaw, Artie & His Orchestra).
Tracks: / Nightmare / Softly as in a morning sunrise / Gue le le / He's funny that way / Cool daddy / Grabtown grapple, The / You do something to me / Cross your heart / Minnesota / Smooth and easy / Tea for two / I only have eyes for you / Carnival / So in love / Things are looking up / Krazy kat / Innuendo / Bedford drive / Pied piper / 'S wonderful / Let's fall in love / Stardust / Begin the beguine.
LP: **DBD 07**
MC: **DBDC 07**

BEGIN THE BEGUINE, VOL.1 (Shaw, Artie & His Orchestra).
Tracks: / Love of my life / Ghost of a chance / How deep is the ocean? / I got the sun in the morning / You do something to me / In the still of the night / My heart belongs to Daddy / Night and day.
LP: **MVS 503**

BEGINNING, THE (Shaw, Artie & His Orchestra).
LP: **HEP 1024**

BENNY GOODMAN & HIS ORCHESTRA 1935 (Artie Shaw & his new music).
MC: **UMK 99006**

BEST OF ARTIE SHAW.
Tracks: / Nightmare / Black bay shuffle / Any old time / Stardust / Blues in the night / Carioca / Concerto for clarinet in A / Begin the beguine / Traffic jam / Frenesi.
LP: **NL 89104**
MC: **NK 89104**

BEST OF ARTIE SHAW & HIS ORCHESTRA (Shaw, Artie & His Orchestra).
Tracks: / Nightmare / Back Bay shuffle / Any old time / Stardust / Blues in the night / Carioca / Concerto for clarinet in A / Deep purple / Begin the beguine / Traffic jam / Frenesi.
LP: **INTS 5022**

BEST OF ARTIE SHAW (STARCALL) (Shaw, Artie & His Orchestra).
Tracks: / Frenesi / Stardust / Moonglow / Oh lady be good / All the things you are / Temptation / Begin the beguine / Serenade to a savage / Indian love call / Traffic jam / Nightmare / Dancing in the dark.
LP: **NL 11089**

BEST OF BIG BANDS.
MC: **4669594**

BLUE INTERLUDE.
Tracks: / Shine on harvest moon / Blue interlude / April in my heart.
LP: **2M 056 64855**
MC: **2M 256 64855**

BLUES IN THE NIGHT.
Tracks: / Blues in the night / Just kiddin' around / Take your shoes off, baby / St. James Infirmary (part 1) / St. James Infirmary (part 2) (takes 1/2) / Suite no.8 / Two in one blues / Lady Day / Little jazz / Summertime / Foggy day, A / Lucky number / Soon / Natch / They didn't believe me / Just floatin' along.
LP: **NL 82432**
MC: **NK 82432**

BORN TO SWING (Shaw, Artie & His Orchestra).
Tracks: / Milenburg joys / Stealin' apples / Born to swing / Call of the freaks, The / Posin' / Hold your hat / Someday, sweetheart / Lost in the shuffle / Wake up and live / Azure / I'd rather be right / I'll never let you cry / Meade Lux special / There'll be some changes made.
LP: **BLJ 8020**

COMPLETE ARTIE SHAW & RHYTHMAKERS Vol. 5 (Shaw, Artie/ Rhythm Makers).
LP: **SWDM 7005**

COMPLETE ARTIE SHAW & RHYTHMAKERS Vol. 2 1937-8 (Shaw, Artie/Rhythm Makers).
LP: **SWDM 7001**

COMPLETE GRAMERCY FIVE SESSIONS, THE (Shaw, Artie & His Gramercy Five).
Tracks: / Special delivery stomp / Summit Ridge Drive / Keepin' myself for you / Cross your heart / Dr. Livingstone, I presume / When the quail come back to San Quentin / My blue Heaven / Smoke gets in your eyes / Grabtown grapple, The / Sad sack, The / Scuttlebutt / Gentle drifter, The / Mysterioso (take 1) / Mysterioso (take 2) / Hop, skip and jump.
LP: **NL 87637**
MC: **NK 87637**

CONCERTO FOR CLARINET (Shaw, Artie & His Orchestra).
Tracks: / Nightmare / Back bay shuffle / Any old time / Yesterdays / Copenhagen / My heart stood still / Deep purple / Begin the beguine / One night stand / I'm comin' / Virginia / Pastel blue / Carioca / One foot in the groove / I surrender, dear / Oh, lady be good / Traffic jam / Frenesi / Adios mariquita linda / Chantez les bas / April in Paris / Stardust / I'm confessin' (that I love you) / Blues (parts 1 and 2) / Concerto for clarinet in A / Blues in the night / Solid Sam / Deuces wild / Sometimes I feel like a mother-less child / Bedford drive / Little jazz.
2LP: **DPM 2028**

DEUX GRANDES ANNEES (1938-39).
Tracks: / Begin the beguine / Indian love call / Comin' on / Back bay shuffle / Any old time / I can't believe that you're in love with me / Non-stop flight / What is this thing called love? / Copenhagen / Softly as in a morning sunrise / It had to be you / My heart stood still / Rosalie / Rose room / This is it / Deep purple / Prosschai / I'm coming, Virginia / Snug as a bug in a rug / One foot in the groove / Out of nowhere / I can't afford to dream / Serenade to a savage / You're a lucky guy / Nightmare / Sobbin' blues / Together / Carioca on you / Sweet Sue / St. Louis blues.
2LP: **PM 43175**

HOLLYWOOD PALLADIUM.
Tracks: / Whispers in the night / Canto carbli / There I go / Prelude in C major / Doctor Livingstone, I presume / Nobody knows the trouble I've seen / There'll be some changes made / Time was / Do you know why? / Frenesi / Looking for yesterday / Along the Santa Fe trail / Everything's jumpin'.
LP: **HEP 19**

I CAN'T GET STARTED (Shaw, Artie & His Gramercy Five).
LP: **2304 208**

INDISPENSABLE ARTIE SHAW VOLS.1/2 1938-39 (Shaw, Artie & His Orchestra).
Tracks: / Begin the beguine / Indian love call / Comin' on / Back bay shuffle / Any old time / I can't believe that you're in love with me / Non-stop flight / What is this thing called love / Copenhagen / Softly as in a morning sunrise / It had to be you / My heart stood still / Rosalie / Rose room / This is it / Deep purple / Prosschai / I'm coming, Virginia / Snug as a bug in a rug / One foot in the groove / Out of nowhere / I can't afford to dream / Serenade to a savage / You're the lucky guy / Nightmare / Sobbin' blues / Together / Carioca / At sundown / I've got my eyes on you / Sweet Sue / St. Louis blues.
2LP: **NL 89820**
MCSET: **NK 89820**

INDISPENSABLE ARTIE SHAW VOLS.5/6 1944-45 (Shaw, Artie & His Orchestra).
Tracks: / Lady Day / Jumpin' on the merry-go-round / I'll never be the same / 'S wonderful / Bedford drive / Grabtown grapple, The / Sad sack, The / Little jazz / Tea for two / Summertime / Time on my hands / Foggy day, A / Man I love, The / I could write a book / Thrill of a lifetime / Lucky number / Love walked on / Soon / Natch / They can't take that away from me / Someone to watch over me / Things are looking up / Maid with the flaccid air, The / No one but you / Dancing on the ceiling / I can't get started with you / Just floatin' along / I can't escape from you / Scuttlebutt / Gentle drifter, The / Mysterioso / Hop, skip and jump.
2LP: **NL 89914**
MC: **NK 89914**

INDISPENSABLE ARTIE SHAW VOLS.3/4 1940-42 (Shaw, Artie & His Orchestra).
Tracks: / Frenesi / King for a day / Special delivery stomp / Summit Ridge Drive / Chantez les bas / Stardust / Blues (parts 1 and 2) / What is there to say? / Who's excited? / Prelude in C major / When the quail comes back to San Quentin / Concerto for a clarinet (parts 1 & 2) / Moonglow / Confessin' / Love me a little / Beyond the blue horizon / Blues in the night / Rockin' chair / Take your shoes off, baby / Solid Sam / Just kiddin' around / St. James Infirmary / Deuces wild / Someone's rocking my dreamboat / Carnival / Needlenose / Two in one blues / Sometimes I feel like a motherless child.
2LP: **NL 89774**
MC: **NK 89774**

MELODY & MADNESS, VOL 1 (Shaw, Artie & His Orchestra).
Tracks: / Yam, The / Non-stop flight / Who blew out the flame? / Shoot the

rhythm to me, John boy / Back bay shuffle / Yesterdays / What is this thing called love? / Copenhagen / It had to be you / Simple and sweet / Rockin' the state / You got me / In the mood / Shine on harvest moon.
LP: . . . . **NOST 7609**

MELODY & MADNESS, VOL 2 (Shaw, Artie & His Orchestra).
Tracks: / Hold your hat / Jeepers creepers / Saving myself for you / Indian love call / Time out / Serenade to a savage / Softly as in a morning sunrise / Diga diga doo / Begin the beguine / My heart belongs to daddy / Prosschai / Rose room / My own / At sundown.
LP: . . . . **NOST 7613**
MC: . . . . **NOST 8613**

MELODY & MADNESS, VOL 3 (Shaw, Artie & His Orchestra).
Tracks: / Zigeuner / I have eyes / Carioca / My heart stood still / I'm comin', Virginia / Deep purple / Diga diga doo / Shoot the rhythm to me, John boy / Together / I cried for you / Back bay shuffle / I want my share of love / Jungle drums / Rosalie.
LP: . . . . **NOST 7627**
MC: . . . . **NOST 8627**

MELODY & MADNESS, VOL 4 (Shaw, Artie & His Orchestra).
Tracks: / Non-stop flight / My heart belongs to daddy / Chant / Double mellow / Better than average girl / Gang busters / Pastel blue / It's all yours / Prosschai / Nightmare / I'm coming, Virginia / I'm in love with the Honourable Mr. So and So / One foot in the groove.
LP: . . . . **NOST 7628**

MELODY & MADNESS, VOL 5 (Shaw, Artie & His Orchestra).
Tracks: / Serenade to a savage / Rosalie / You're so indiff'rent / Copenhagen / At sundown / Supper time / Snug as a bug in a rug / Diga diga doo / Begin the beguine / Shoot the rhythm to me, John boy / Carioca / It had to be you / Traffic jam.
LP: . . . . **NOST 7637**

ORIGINAL SOUNDS OF THE SWING ERA, VOL 7.
LP: . . . . **CL 05517**

PIED PIPER, THE (Shaw, Artie & His Orchestra).
LP: . . . . **FH 1005**

SONG OF INDIA (see Dorsey, Tommy) (Shaw, Artie/Tommy Dorsey).

SWING GOES ON VOL 3.
Tracks: / Traffic jam / Begin the beguine / Lover come back to me / Zigeuner / What is this thing called love? / It had to be you / Softly as in a morning sunrise / Octoroon / Nightmare / Back bay shuffle / Jungle drums / Copenhagen.
LP: . . . . **IC 054 52712**

SWINGING BIG BANDS, 1938-40, VOL 2.
Tracks: / Begin the beguine / Indian love call / Nightmare / Jungle drums / Carioca / Man I love, The / Donkey serenade, The / Lady be good / I surrender, dear / All the things you are / I didn't know what time it was / Summit Ridge Drive.
LP: . . . . **SM 3621**

SWINGING BIG BANDS, 1938-45, VOL 1.
Tracks: / Yesterdays / Rosalie / Love come back to me / Diga diga doo / Stardust / Serenade to a savage / Moonglow / Grabtown grapple, The / Summertime / Temptation / Frenesi / Zigeuner.
LP: . . . . **SM 3620**

THIS IS ARTIE SHAW.
Tracks: / Begin the beguine / Indian love call / Any old time / Back bay shuffle / Deep in a dream / It had to be you / Jungle drums / Donkey serenade, The / Deep purple / All the things you are / Frenesi / Cross your heart / Summit ridge drive / Temptation / Star dust / My blue Heaven / Smoke gets in your eyes / Moonglow / Dancing in the dark.
LP: . . . . **NL 89411**
MC: . . . . **NK 89411**
2LP: **26 28034**

THOU SWELL (Shaw, Artie & His Orchestra).
Tracks: / Shoot the likker to me John boy / All alone / I'll be with you in apple blossom time / Blue skies / Sweet Lorraine / Same old line, The / Blues, The / It's a long way to Tipperary / Because I love you / Chant / My blue Heaven / Streamline / Sugar foot stomp / Thou swell / Pretty girl is like a melody, A / Japanese sandman.
LP: . . . . **AJA 5056**
MC: . . . . **ZC AJA 5056**

TRAFFIC JAM.
Tracks: / Man I love, The / Muchodenada / Love is the sweetest thing / Love walked in / You're mine / Oh you crazy moon / Serenade to a savage / Sweet little headache / What is this thing called love? / Thanks for everything / Mood in question / Orinoco / Traffic jam / I'm comin', Virginia / Last two weeks in July / Lilacs in the rain.
LP: **20135**
MC: **40135**

UNCOLLECTED, THE (Shaw, Artie & His Orchestra).
Tracks: / Sweet Adeline / Monday morning / Lover come back to me / Two sleepy people / I cover the waterfront / This can't be love / I can't believe that you're in love with me / Sweet Sue / Oh you crazy moon / I'm yours / What's new? / I can't give you anything but love / Over the rainbow / Everything jumping.
LP: . . . . **HUK 176**

WITH STRINGS, VOL.2 (Shaw, Artie & His Orchestra).
Tracks: / What is this thing called love / I believe / Love for sale / I've got you under my skin / Get out of town / Anniversary song.
LP: . . . . **MVS 507**

Shaw, Charles "Bobo"

BUGLE BOY BOP (Shaw, Charles "Bobo" & Lester Bowie).
LP: . . . . **MR 5268**

CHARLES 'BOBO' SHAW.
LP: . . . . **MR 5232**

Shaw, Donald

BAILTEAN (VILLAGES).
MC: . . . . **MR 1018**

Shaw, Eddie

KING OF THE ROAD.
LP: . . . . **R 7608**

Shaw, Gene

DEBUT IN BLUES (Shaw, Gene Sextet).
Tracks: / Debut in blues / Karachi / Gentle princess, The / When sunny gets blue / Thieves carnival / Not too cool / Who knows? / Travelog.
LP: . . . . **ARC 501**

Shaw, George Bernard

ARMS & THE MAN A play in three acts (Various artists).
MC: . . . . **TTC/GBS 1**

CAESAR & CLEOPATRA (Various artists).
MCSET: **0304**

HEARTBREAK HOUSE (Various artists).
MCSET: **0335**

JOHN BULL'S OTHER ISLAND (Various artists).
MCSET: **0346**

MAJOR BARBARA (Various artists).
MCSET: **0319**

MISALLIANCE (Various artists).
MCSET: **0365**

PYGMALION (McCowen, Alec & Diana Rigg).
MCSET: . . . . **SAY 28**

PYGMALION (Various artists).
MCSET: **0354**

SAINT JOAN (See under Saint Joan) (Various artists).

ST. JOAN (Various artists).
MCSET: **0311**
MCSET: . . . . **SAY 42**

Shaw, Gerald

HOME AND AWAY.
Tracks: / Gremlins in the galley / That's all / Harlem / Sentimental journey / Sweet Sue / Kerry dance, The / Always / I know why / Ain't misbehavin' / Rickshaw ride / Lullaby of Birdland / Hot dog / Whisky galore.
MC: . . . . **AC 178**

STATE VISIT.
Tracks: / All the things you are / Very thought of you, The / Espana selection / Richard Rodgers selection.
MC: . . . . **AC 169**

Shaw, Graham

I AM THE MINSTREL.
LP: . . . . **TSR 030**

Shaw, Mark

ALMOST.
Tracks: / Under your spell / Run while you can / Happy families / Love so bright / Mrs Wonderful / Home / Sometimes insane / Tidal wave / My kind of love / The one that got away.
LP: . . . . **EMC 3602**
MC: . . . . **TCEMC 3602**

Shaw, Marlena

IT IS LOVE.
LP: **831 438-1**
MC: **831 438-4**

LOVE IS IN FLIGHT.
Tracks: / Before you know it / I want to know / I'll remember you / This time / Love is in flight / Loving you / I must be in love / With you.
LP: **837 312-1**
MC: **837 312-4**

TAKE A BITE.
Tracks: / It was a very good year / I'm a foster child / Love dancin' / I thank you / Touch me in the morning / Shaw biz / Suddenly it's how I like to feel / No one yet / Haven't we been in love before / I'll be your friend.
LP: . . . . **CBS 83216**

Shaw, Milt

PRECIOUS LITTLE THING CALLED LOVE, A (Shaw, Milt & His Orch./Moe Baer & His Wardman Park Orch.).
LP: . . . . **CI 018**

Shaw, Phillipe

HOVIS BISCUITS, THE (Shaw, Phillipe & The Fotokopies).
LP: . . . . **G 250**

Shaw, Robert

TEXAS BARRELHOUSE PIANO.
LP: . . . . **ARHOOLIE 1010**

Shaw, Roland

JAMES BOND 007 (Shaw, Roland Orchestra).
Tracks: / You Only Live Twice / Goldfinger / From Russia With Love / On Her Majesty's Secret Service / Diamonds Are Forever / Thunderball / Underneath the mango tree / Pussy Galore's flying circus / Look of love, The / Dawn raid on Fort Knox / Bond below disco volante / 007 Theme.
MC: **4178544**

LARCANGE PLAYS TRENET (see Larcange,Maurice) (Shaw, Roland / Maurice Larcange).

Shaw, Sandie

20 GOLDEN PIECES: SANDIE SHAW.
Tracks: / One note samba / Yes my darling daughter / Ne me quitte pas (If you go away) / Every time we say goodbye / I get a kick out of you / Time after time / You've not changed / Today / Show me / Those were the days / Reviewing the situation / Mama roux / Maybe I'm amazed / Rose garden / Monsieur Dupont / Anytime, anywhere / Think it all over / What now my love / Scarborough fair / Tonight in Tokyo.
LP: . . . . **BDL 2051**
MC: . . . . **BDC 2051**

BEST OF SANDIE SHAW, THE.
Tracks: / (There's) always something there to remind me / Puppet on a string / Girl don't come / Message understood / Tomorrow / Nothing comes easy / I don't need anything / Think sometimes about me / Run / Long live love / I'll stop at nothing / How can you tell / Don't you know / You can't blame him / (It's a pity) the ship is sinking / Stop before you start / Gotta see my baby every day / Talk about love.
MC: . . . . **TCMFP 5918**

CHOSE LIFE.
LP: . . . . **PR 2002**

COLLECTION: SANDIE SHAW.
Tracks: / Puppet on a string / Everybody loves a lover / I'll stop at nothing / As long as you're happy baby / If you ever need me / Tomorrow / Long live love / Nothing comes easy / I'd be far better off without you / Lemon tree / You don't love me no more / Think sometimes about me / No moon / Message understood / Had a dream last night / Tell the boys / Run / Girl don't come / Gotta see my baby everyday / How can you tell / Stop feeling sorry for yourself / I don't need anything / You won't forget me / There's always something there to remind me.
MC: . . . . **CCSMC 251**

EP COLLECTION, THE: SANDIE SHAW.
LP: . . . . **SEE 305**
MC: . . . . **SEEK 305**

GOLDEN HOUR OF SANDIE SHAW, A.
Tracks: / Puppet on a string / Nothing comes easy / Long live love / Hide all emotion / You won't forget me / I'll stop at nothing / Tell the boys / No moon / Think sometimes about me / I don't think you want me anymore / Stop before you start / Message understood / Had a dream last night / Stop feeling sorry for yourself / Tomorrow / Keep in touch / (There's) always something there to remind me / I'd be far better off without you / Girl don't come / Long walk home / More / How can you tell if ever you need me.
MC: . . . . **KGHMC 108**

GOLDEN HOUR OF SANDIE SHAW, A (2).
MC: . . . . **KGHMC 145**

GREATEST HITS: SANDIE SHAW.
Tracks: / Puppet on a string / Message understood / Nothing comes easy / Had a dream last night / Long live love / Stop feeling sorry for yourself / Hide all emotion / Tomorrow / You won't forget me / Keep in touch / I'll stop at nothing / There's always something there to remind me / Tell the boys / I'd be far better off without you / No moon / Girl don't come / Think sometimes about me / Long walk home / Don't you count on it / I don't think you want me anymore / Stop before you start / How can you tell / If ever you need me.
LP: . . . . **GH 533**

HELLO ANGEL.
Tracks: / Hello angel.
LP: . . . . **ROUGH 110**
MC: . . . . **ROUGHC 110**

REMINDING YOU.
Tracks: / Always something there to remind me / Girl don't come / Message understood / I'll stop at nothing / Puppet on a string / Long live love / Tomorrow / Nothing comes easy.
LP: . . . . **DOW 8**
MC: . . . . **ZCDOW 8**

SANDIE.
LP: . . . . **NPL 18110**

Shaw, Thomas

BORN IN TEXAS.
LP: . . . . **ADVENT 2801**

Shaw, Tommy

AMBITION.
Tracks: / No such thing / Dangerous games / Weight of the world / Ambition / Ever since the world began / Are you ready for me / Somewhere in the night / Love you too much / Outsider, The / Lay them down.
LP: . . . . **K 781 798 1**
MC: . . . . **K 781 798 4**

GIRLS WITH GUNS.
Tracks: / Girls with guns / Come in and explain / Lonely school / Heads up / Kiss me hello / Fading away / Little girl world / Outside in the rain / Free to love you / Race is on, The.
LP: . . . . **AMA 5020**
MC: . . . . **AMC 5020**

Shaw, Woody

CONCERT ENSEMBLE.
Tracks: / Hello to the wind / Obsequious / Jean Marie / In the land of the blacks.
LP: . . . . **MR 5139**

IN MY OWN SWEET WAY.
LP: **7003 A1**

IN MY OWN WAY.
LP: **70031**

IRON MEN, THE.
Tracks: / Iron man / Jitterbug waltz / Symmetry / Diversion one / Song of songs / Diversion two.
LP: . . . . **MR 5160**

LITTLE RED'S FANTASY.
Tracks: / Jean Marie / Sashianova / In case you haven't heard / Little Red's fantasy / Tomorrow's destiny.
LP: . . . . **MR 5103**

LOTUS FLOWER.
LP: . . . . **ENJA 4018**

LOVE DANCE.
Tracks: / Love dance / Obsequious / Sunbath / Soulfully I love you / Zoltan.
LP: . . . . **MR 5074**

MOONTRANE, THE.
Tracks: / Moontrane / Are they only dreams? / Tapscott's blues / Sanyas / Katrina ballerina.
LP: . . . . **MR 5058**

NIGHT MUSIC.
Tracks: / Orange cresent / To kill a brick / All the things you are / Apex.
LP: **9602991**

SETTING STANDARDS.
Tracks: / There is no greater love / All the way / Spiderman blues / Touch of your lips, The / What's new / When lore is new.
LP: . . . . **MR 5318**

Shay's Rebellion

DANIEL SHAY'S REBELLION.
LP: . . . . **FF 427**

Sh-Boom

SH-BOOM (Various artists).
LP: . . . . **OCN 2042WL**
MC: . . . . **OCN 2042WK**

She Devil (film)

LIFE AND LOVES OF A SHE DEVIL (See under Life & Loves) (TV soundtrack) (Various artists).

She Loves Me...

SHE LOVES ME (Original Broadway Cast) (Various artists).
LP: . . . . **DS 215008**

MC: DS2C 15008

She Rockers

ROCKERS FROM LONDON.
LP: . . . . HIP 105
MC: . . . . HIPC 105

She Stoops to Conquer

SHE STOOPS TO CONQUER Oliver Goldsmith.
MCSET: 309

She Wolf (bk)

SHE WOLF & OTHERS (Saki) (Burden, Hugh (nar)).
MC: . . . . SA 2

Shea, George Beverly

BILLY GRAHAM'S FAVOURITES.
Tracks: / Touch of his hand on mine / Lord's my shepherd, (The) / Standing on the promises / He giveth more grace / I've tried in vain / Cross is not greater, The / And can it be? / Follow, I will follow Thee / King of all kings, The / But this one thing I know / When I get to the end of the way / To God be the glory.
LP: . . . . NL 89265
MC: . . . . NK 89265

GEORGE BEVERLY SHEA AND FRIENDS (Shea, George Beverly & Friends).
LP: . . . . WST R 9679
MC: . . . . WST C 9679

HYMNS YOU KNOW & LOVE.
Tracks: / Holy, holy, holy / Stand up, stand up for Jesus / Amazing grace / O come, o come Emmanuel / Abide with me / Rock of ages / Bless this house / Old rugged cross, The / Peace in the valley / How great Thou art / Lord's my shepherd, The / Lord's prayer, The.
LP: . . . . INTS 5077
MC: . . . . INTK 5077

MY FAVOURITE SONGS.
MC: . . . . TC WRD 3007

OLD RUGGED CROSS, THE.
Tracks: / I have come from the darkness / Blood will never lose its power, The / Leaning on the everlasting arms / Amazing grace / Glory / What am I worth? / Learning to lean / Old rugged cross, The / I'd rather have Jesus / Let us break bread together.
LP: . . . . WST 9589
MC: . . . . WC 9589

SINGS 20 BEST LOVED HYMNS.
Tracks: / Sunshine / Blessed assurance / He the pearly gates will open / There is a balm in Gilead / Jesus is the sweetest name I know / Yes, He did / So this is life / That old-fashioned home / When I met my Saviour / God leads us along / Roll, Jordan, roll / Lead me gently home, Father / Under His wings / I'd rather have Jesus / Love of God, The / Ninety and nine, The / If we could see beyond today / Softly and tenderly / In the garden / Yes, there is comfort.
LP: . . . . PC 310
LP: . . . . NL 89265
MC: . . . . NK 89265

Sheahan, John

IN OUR OWN TIME (Sheahan, John & Michael Howard).
LP: . . . . HM 039

Shear, Jules

DEMO-ITIS.
LP: 3244 1

Shearer, John

CHILDREN'S PARTY TIME.
LP: . . . . BGC 233

Shearer, Moira (nar)

BALLET SHOES (See under Ballet Shoes).

Shearer's Nightmare

BURNING SLEEPERS.
LP: . . . . LRF 149

Shearing, George

500 MILES HIGH.
LP: . . . . MPS 68 219

ALONE TOGETHER (Shearing, George & Marian McPartland).
Tracks: / O grande amor / To Bill Evans / All through the night / Born to be blue / They say it's Spring / Alone together / There'll be other times / Nobody else but me / Chasing shadows / Improvisation on a theme.
LP: . . . . CJ 171
MC: . . . . CJ 171 C

BEAUTY AND THE BEAT (see under Lee, Peggy) (Shearing, George & Peggy Lee).

BEST OF GEORGE SHEARING.
Tracks: / Roses of Picardy / Early Autumn / East of the sun / Honeysuckle rose / Lullaby of Birdland / September in the rain / Little white lies / You don't know what love is / You stepped out of a dream / September song / Jumpin' with symphony Syd.
LP: . . . . MFP 5608

CAPITOL YEARS.
Tracks: / Baubles, bangles and beads / Young and foolish / Kinda cute / Stardust / One note samba / Early Autumn / Lullaby of Birdland / Lovewise / Samba da borboleta / East of the sun / September in the rain / East of the sun / Come rain or come shine / Continental, The / Call me irresponsible / I'll be around / Bluesette / When your lover has gone / Breeze and I, The / Days of wine and roses / Pick yourself up.
MC: . . . . TCEMS 1414

CHAMPAGNE EVENING (Shearing, George & Mel Torme).
Tracks: / All God's children / Born to be blue / Simple life / Good morning heartache / Manhattan hoedown / Love / You'd be so nice to come home to / It might as well be Spring / Nightingale sang in Berkeley Square, A / Lullaby of Birdland.
LP: . . . . CJ 190
MC: . . . . CJC 190

DEXTERITY.
Tracks: / Dexterity / You must believe in Spring / Sakura sakura / Long ago and far away / Can't we be friends / As long as I live / Please send me someone to love / Duke Ellington medley.
LP: . . . . CJ 346
MC: . . . . CJ 346 C

ELEGANT EVENING, AN (Shearing, George & Mel Torme).
Tracks: / I'll be seeing you / Love and the moon / Oh, you crazy moon / No moon at all / After the waltz is over / This time the dream's on me / Last night, when we were young / You changed my life / I had the craziest dream / Darn that dream / Brigg fair / My foolish heart / You're driving me crazy.
LP: . . . . CJ 294
MC: . . . . CJC 294

EVENING AT CHARLIE'S, AN (Shearing, George & Mel Torme).
Tracks: / Just one of those things / On Green Dolphin Street / Dream dancing / I'm hip / Then I'll be tired of you / Caught in the middle of my years / Welcome to the club / Nica's dream / Chase me Charlie / Love is just around the corner.
LP: . . . . CJ 248
MC: . . . . CJC 248

FIRST EDITION (Shearing, George & Jim Hall).
Tracks: / Street of dreams / To Antonio Carlos Jobim / Careful / I see nothing to laugh about / Without words / I hear a rhapsody / To Tommy Flanagan / Emily.
LP: . . . . CJ 177
MC: . . . . CJC 177

GEORGE SHEARING Compact/ Walkman jazz.
Tracks: / Lullaby of Birdland / Time after time / How deep is the ocean? / G and G after you've gone / Con alma / Yesterdays / This can't be love / Too close for comfort / Entertainer, The / Love walked in / When I fall in love / Cheryl / It don't mean a thing.
MC: 833 284-4

GEORGE SHEARING IN DIXIELAND (Shearing, George/Dixie Six).
Tracks: / Clap your hands / Truckin' / New Orleans / Take five / Blue Monk / Alice in Dixieland / Mighty like the blues / Destination Moon / Soon / Lullaby of Birdland / Desafinado.
LP: . . . . CJ 388
MC: . . . . CJ 388C

GETTING IN THE SWING OF THINGS (Shearing, George Trio).
LP: . . . . MPS 68 253

GRAND PIANO.
Tracks: / When a woman loves a man / It never entered my mind / Mack the knife / Nobody else but me / Imitations / Taking a chance on love / If I had you / How insensitive / Easy to love / While we're young.
LP: . . . . CJ 281
MC: . . . . CJC 281

IN CONCERT AT THE PAVILION (Shearing, George & Brian Torff).
LP: . . . . CJ 132

IT'S EASY TO REMEMBER.
Tracks: / It's easy to remember / Nearness of you, The / Wednesday night hop / Poinciana / Consternation / Fourth deuce / Blue moon / Missouri scrambler / Man from Minton's, The / Overnight hop / Someone to watch over me / To be or not to bop.
LP: . . . . JASM 2009

JAZZ CONCERT.
Tracks: / Walkin' / Love is just around the corner / I cover the waterfront / Love walked in / There with you / Bel Aire.
LP: . . . . EMS 1157
MC: . . . . TCEMS 1157

LIGHT, AIRY AND SWINGING.
LP: . . . . MPS 68 094

LIVE AT THE CAFE CARLYLE (Shearing, George & Don Thompson).
Tracks: / Pent-up house / Shadow of your smile / Teach me tonight / Cheryl / Blues for breakfast / P.S. I love you / I cover the waterfront / Tell me a bedtime story / Stratford stomp / Inside.
LP: . . . . CJ 246
MC: . . . . CJC 246

MANY FACETS OF GEORGE SHEARING, THE.
LP: . . . . MPS 68 177

MORE GRAND PIANO (solo piano).
Tracks: / My silent love / Change partners / My favourite things / You don't know what love is / Ramona / People / East of the sun / I can't get started / Dream / Wind in the willows.
LP: . . . . CJ 318
MC: . . . . CJC 318

MUSIC OF COLE PORTER, THE (Shearing, George / Barry Tuckwell).
Tracks: / I concentrate on you / Everything I love / I've got you under my skin / Easy to love / In the still of the night / Every time we say goodbye / But in the morning, no / So in love / After you / All through the night / Do I love you?.
LP: . . . . CC 2010
MC: . . . . CCMC 2010

MY SHIP.
LP: . . . . MPS 68 096

NAT KING COLE WITH GEORGE SHEARING (see under Cole, Nat King/ George Shearing) (Shearing, George & Nat King Cole).

ON TARGET (Shearing, George Trio).
Tracks: / Fjaerlins vingot / Last night when we were young / Amaryllis / Strange enchantment / Look at that face / Songbird / This is all I ask / Portrait of Jennie / Nightingale sang in Berkeley Square.
LP: 15551
MC: . . . . CMOIR 133

PERFECT MATCH, A (Shearing, George/Ernestine Anderson).
LP: . . . . CJ 357
MC: . . . . CJ 357 C

PIANO.
Tracks: / It had to be you / Daisy / Thinking of you / Sweet and lovely / It's you or no one / Wendy / Am I blue? (CD only.) / Miss Invisible (CD only.) / You're my everything / John O'Groats / Waltz for Claudia / For you / Children's waltz / Happiness is a thing called Joe.
LP: . . . . CJ 400
MC: . . . . CJ 400C

REUNION, THE (see under Grappelli, Stephane) (Shearing, George & Stephane Grappelli).

SHEARING ON STAGE.
Tracks: / September in the rain / On the street where you live / Roses of Picardy / Little Niles / Caravan / I'll remember April / Little white lies / East of the sun / Nothing be de best / Love is just around the corner / Walkin' / I cover the waterfront / Love walked in / Bel-Air.
LP: . . . . REN 004

SPIRIT OF 176, THE (see under Jones, Hank) (Shearing, George & Hank Jones).

TOP DRAWER (Shearing, George & Mel Torme).
Tracks: / Smoke gets in your eyes / Hi-fly / Shine on your shoes / Stardust / Away in a manger / Here's to my lady / What's this? / Oleo / How do you say auf wiedersehen?.
LP: . . . . CJ 219
MC: . . . . CJC 219

VINTAGE YEAR (see under Torme, Mel) (Shearing, George & Mel Torme).

WINDOW.
LP: . . . . MPS 68 200

YOUNG GEORGE SHEARING, THE 1939 - 1944.
Tracks: / Pretty girl is like a melody, A / Guilty / Can't we be friends? / Rosetta / I don't stand a ghost of a chance / How come you do me like you do? / Coquette / Sweet Lorraine / Stomp in F / More than you know / Time on my hands / Afraid of you.
LP: . . . . JASM 2008

Shearston, Gary

SPRINGTIME, THE.
LP: . . . . LRF 022

Shebeen

COME WEST ALONG THE ROAD.
MC: . . . . GTDC 041

Sheehan, Stephen

EYES OF THE WILDERNESS.
LP: . . . . ROSE 199

Sheen, Stevie

ALMOST LIVE AT THE VENUE, TOKYO JOE'S CAN PASTILLA.
Tracks: / For the love of Norma / San Miguel Danny / Terry is a wanker / Bosch em / Take your time - do it right / Half a days gone and Carl hasn't earnt a peseta / How much - too much / 100% pure beef hamburger / "18-30's" Where are you? / Pepo / Eh Dickhead / Where's Co-Co / Hello Julie ...get your gear off....
LP: . . . . SH 007

Sheena...

SHEENA: QUEEN OF THE JUNGLE (Film Soundtrack) (Various artists).
LP: . . . . ACH 017
LP: . . . . STV 81225
MC: . . . . CTV 81225

Sheer Melodrama

SHEER MELODRAMA & OTHER STORIES FROM.. (see under Wallace, Edgar) (Spoken Word (Group)).

Sheerin, Danny

INTRODUCING DANNY SHEERIN AND SILVERWINGS (Sheerin, Danny & Silverwings).
LP: . . . . FRC 013

Sheets Of Silence

CHANGING THE TIDE.
MC: . . . . DHC 26

Sheffer, Jonathan

PURE LUCK.
LP: . . . . VS 5330
MC: . . . . VSC 5330

Shegui

AROUND THE WORLD FOR SPORT.
LP: . . . . CM 005

IN THE WIND.
LP: . . . . SHP 106

Sheila E

GLAMOROUS LIFE, THE.
Tracks: / Belle of St.Mark, The / Shortberry strawcake / Noon rendezvous / Oliver's house / Next time wipe the lipstick off your collar / Glamorous life, The.
LP: 925107 1
MC: 925107 4

ROMANCE 1600.
Tracks: / Sister fate / Dear Michael Angelo / Love bizarre, A / Toy box / Yellow / Romance 1600 / Merci for the speed of a mad clown in Summer / Bedtime story.
LP: 9253171
MC: 9253174

SEX CYMBAL.
LP: 7599262551
MC: 7599262554

SHEILA E.
Tracks: / One day (I'm gonna make you mine) / Wednesday like a river / Touch me / Faded photographs / Koo koo / Pride and passion / Boy's club / Soul salsa / Hon E. man / Love on a blue train.
LP: . . . . WX 63
MC: . . . . WX 63 C

Sheldon, Jack

BLUES IN THE NIGHT (Sheldon, Jack & The Swedish All Stars).
LP: . . . . PHONT 7569

HOLLYWOOD HEROES (Sheldon, Jack Quintet).
Tracks: / Joint is jumpin', The / Pardon my southern accent / Poor butterfly / Lover / Rosetta / I thought about you / I want to be happy.
LP: . . . . CJ 339
MC: . . . . CJC 339

JACK SHELDON & HIS EXCITING BIG BAND.
LP: . . . . GNPS 9036

JACK SHELDON QUARTET, THE.
Tracks: / I love you / Daydream / Cherry / Don't get around much anymore / Bye bye Blackbird / I'm getting sentimental over you / Shadow of your smile / Get out of town / Ours / Poor butterfly / Very thought of you, The.
LP: . . . . CJ 228

Sheller, William

QUARTUORS.
LP: . . . . SIDE 8415

Shelley, Anne

INTRODUCING.. (Shelley, Anne & The Marines).
LP: . . . . TSLP 87

Shelley, Percy Bysshe

TREASURY.
MC: 8026

Shelley, Pete

HEAVEN AND THE SEA.
Tracks: / Waiting for love / On your own / They're coming for you / I surrender / Life without reason / Need a minit / Never again / My dreams / Blue eyes / You can't take that away / No moon....
LP: MERH 90
MC: MERHC 90
LP: INLP 400234

HOMOSAPIEN.
LP: ILPS 9676

XL-1.
LP: XL 1

Shelley, Peter

BEST OF PETER SHELLEY.
LP: MAG 4003

Shelleyan Orphan

CENTURY FLOWER.
LP: ROUGH 137
MC: ROUGHC 137

HELLEBORINE.
LP: ROUGH 97
MC: ROUGHC 97

Sheltering Sky (film)

SHELTERING SKY, THE (Film Soundtrack) (Various artists).
MC: TCV 2652
LP: V 2652

Shelton, Allen

DARKNESS ON THE DELTA (See under Baker, Kenny) (Baker, Kenny & Bob Hicks).

SHELTON SPECIAL WITH MCREYNOLD.
LP: ROUNDER 0088
MC: ROUNDER 0088C

Shelton, Anne

ANNE SHELTON SINGS WITH AMBROSE & HIS ORCHESTRA.
Tracks: / Lady who didn't believe in love, The / Taking a chance on love / Rhyme with everything that's beautiful / Dance with a dolly / It can't be wrong / Daddy / I never mention your name / I'll walk alone / My Yiddishe momma / I know why (and so do you) / So long, Sarah Jane / Where's my love? / Journey's end / All or nothing at all / If you please / Robin Hood / Anywhere / Wedding waltz.
LP: RFL 41
MC: KRFLC 41

ANNE SHELTON'S SENTIMENTAL JOURNEY.
Tracks: / Sentimental journey / Tangerine / Nightingale sang in Berkeley Square, A / Don't fence me in / I'll walk alone / Run rabbit run / When the lights go on again / White cliffs of Dover, The / You'll never know / After all / Don't sit under the apple tree / I left my heart at the stage door canteen / Roll out the barrel / I'll get by / Boogie woogie bugle boy / I'll be seeing you / Chattanooga choo choo / Lili Marlene / Just look around.
LP: PRX 21

COLLECTION: ANNE SHELTON.
Tracks: / Cross over the bridge / Song of the trees / Answer me / If I give my heart to you / I remember mama / Crystal ball / If you've never been in love / Song of the barefoot Contessa / If we all said a prayer / Arrivederci, darling / Bridge of sighs / Why does it have to be me / For you, for me / Goodnight, well it's time to go / Tobermory Bay / Book / What have they told you / Teach me tonight / Oh baby mine, I get so lonely / Don't say goodbye.
LP: ONCM 521

EMI YEARS, THE: ANNE SHELTON.
Tracks: / Cross over the bridge / Answer me / If I give my heart to you / I remember mama / Song of the barefoot contessa / Arriverderci darling / Bridge of sighs / Tobermory bay / Book, The / Teach me tonight / Don't say goodbye / Kissing tree, The / Don't leave me now / I get so lonely / Goodnight, well it's time to go / If we all said a prayer.
LP: EMS 1368
MC: TCEMS 1368

I'LL BE SEEING YOU.
Tracks: / I'll be seeing you / I'll be with you in apple blossom time / Nightingale sang in Berkeley Square, A / Pair of silver wings / At last / Last time I saw Paris, The / I'll never smile again / Fools rush in / Kiss the boys goodbye / Amapola / Blues in the night / Where or when / You'd be so nice to come home to / I never mention your name / How deep is the ocean? / Anniversary song.
LP: DVL 2
MC: KDVC 2

MAGIC OF ANNE SHELTON, THE.
Tracks: / Arrivederci darling / Cross over the bridge / Song of the trees / Answer me / Crystal ball / We all said a prayer / Kissing tree, The / If I give my heart to you / I remember mama / If you've never been in love / Song of the barefoot contessa / Jukebox rag / Ay ay ay baio / Bridge of sighs / Why does it have to be me? / For you, for me / Goodnight, well it's time to go / Tobermory Bay / Don't leave me now / Book, The / What have they told you? / Teach me tonight / Oh baby mine, I get so lonely / Don't say goodbye / Love him so much I could scream.
2LP: 41 1048 3
MCSET: 41 1048 9

SING IT AGAIN, ANNE.
Tracks: / Tangerine / Smoke gets in your eyes / Taking a chance on love / I remember you / How green was my valley / I'll never smile again / How did he look? / Village of St. Bernadette / My Yiddishe momma / Lay down your arms / I got it bad and that ain't good / Perfidia / Happiness is a thing called Joe / There's a lull in my life / Let there be love / Souvenir d'Italie / Let's face the music and dance / Man that got away, The.
LP: PLE 510
MC: TC-PLE 510

Shelton, Roscoe

STRAIN ON YOUR HEART.
Tracks: / Roll with the punch / I can't help myself / I'm still the man / I want to keep you if you want to stay / Question / I have some crying to do / My best friend / Worry / Mastermind / There's a heart break somewhere / Running for my life / Keep your mind on me / Strain on my heart / Easy going fellow / Man's love, A / Blind man / You're the dream.
LP: CRB 1151

Shenandoah (show)

SHENANDOAH (Original Broadway cast) (Various artists).
LP: AGL 1 3763
MC: AGK 1 3763
MC: GK 83763

Shepard, James

RED SKY AT NIGHT (Shepard, James Versatile Brass).
LP: LKLP 6600

Shepard, Jean

I'M A BELIEVER.
Tracks: / I'm a believer / It keeps right on a-hurtin' / Another somebody done somebody wrong song / I think I'll wait till tomorrow / Good nights make good mornings / Another neon night / Blanket on the ground / He loves everything he gets his hand on / We had some good times / It doesn't hurt to ask.
LP: MFP 50513
MC: TCMFP 50513

LONESOME LOVE.
Tracks: / Thief in the night, A / I'll hold you in my heart / Weak and the strong, The / You'd better go / Sweet temptation / I'll never be free / You win again / I hate myself / You're telling me sweet lies again / Memory / You can't break the chains of love / I love you because.
LP: HAT 3072
MC: HATC 3072

SONGS OF A LOVE AFFAIR.
Tracks: / Passing love affair, A / Shadows on the wall / Girls in disgrace / Over and over / Hello old broken heart / Mysteries of life, The / Tell me what I want to hear / I'll thank you all my life / Sad singin' and slow ridin' / Did I turn down a better deal / I married you for love / It's hard to tell the married from the free.
LP: HAT 3042
MC: HATC 3042

THIS IS JEAN SHEPARD.
LP: HAT 3131
MC: HATC 3131

VERY BEST OF JEAN SHEPARD, THE.
Tracks: / Slippin' away / Mercy / I'll do anything it takes to stay with you / Ain't love good? / Tip of my fingers, The / Poor sweet baby / Another neon night / Come on phone / Would you lay with me (in a field of stone)? / It keeps right on a-hurtin' / At the time / Wife of a hard-working man / Think I'll go somewhere and cry myself to sleep / Namedropper / Let me be there / He loves everything he gets his hands on / Silver threads and golden needles / He thinks I still care / City lights / Bright lights and country music.
LP: LBR 1003
MC: TCR 1003

Shepard, Ollie

SHEPARD, OLLIE & HIS KENTUCKY BOYS (Shepard, Ollie & His Kentucky Boys).
LP: OT 1210

Shepard, Vonda

VONDA SHEPARD.
Tracks: / Don't cry Ilene / He ain't with me / Baby, don't you break my heart slow / Hold out / Looking for something / I shy away / I've been here before / New Marilyn, A / La journee / Jam karet (time is elastic).
LP: 925 718-1
MC: 925 718-4

Shepherd, Dave

AIRMAIL SPECIAL (Shepherd, Dave Quintet).
MC: CHV 313

SHEPHERD'S DELIGHT (Shepherd, Dave Quintet).
LP: 77LEU 12/35

Shepherd, David

CINEMA ORGAN ENCORES.
LP: DEROY 1352

DAVID SHEPHERD IN AUSTRALIA.
LP: DEROY 1440

GOODBYE (see Blackmore, George) (Shepherd, David & George Blackmore).
2LP: CF 273/4

MELODY ON THE MOVE.
Tracks: / On the quarterdeck / When day is done / Demande et reponse / Boyfriend Sel / Buffoon / Misty / Tunes from the shows / I don't know how to love Him / You, the night, and the music.
MC: AC 187

STRATFORD SOUND, THE.
Tracks: / Castles in Spain / Legend / It happened in Monterey / Charleston / Stranger in Paradise / Cole Porter medley / Manhattan / So do I / Embraceable you.
MC: AC 186

THAT GOLDEN AGE.
Tracks: / ABC march, The / Serenade from the ballet Les Millions d'Arlequin / Torch song parade of 1937 / Shooting star / Selection / Pennies from Heaven / Rodeo march / Newrad / Dreaming / Serenade in the night / Deep purple / High heels / Serenade / Skyscraper fantasy, Theme from.
LP: GRS 1119

THEATRELAND.
Tracks: / Theatreland / Destiny / Blue moon / Besame mucho / Meditation / Love story theme / My heart and I / In love for the very first time / I wish you love / Taking a chance on love / Notturno Opus 54 No. 4 / Passepied from "Le roi s'amuse" / Can't take my eyes off you / Jerome Kern favourites.
LP: GRS 1116

Shepherd, Don

ADNAMS ALE.
Tracks: / Adnams ale / Rambleaway / Jolly Waggoners / Blow the candle out / Rocks of Bawn / Tailor's breeches, The / Come a' ye tramps and hawkers / Ploughman, The / Furze field / Lincolnshire wedding song / Gentleman soldier, The / Parting glass, The.
LP: SFA 093

SUN AND THE MOON, THE.
Tracks: / Old fid / Farmers toast, The / Harvest home / Hunt is up, The / Cutty Wren, The / Sun and the moon, The / Lagan love / Rambling sailor / Broom besoms / Rigs of London / Black crow / Farmer and the fence, The / Nobody loves you when you're down and out.
LP: SFA 013

Shepherd, James

COLNE VALLEY MVC.
LP: LKLP 6343

JAMES SHEPHERD VERSATILE BRASS, THE (Shepherd, James Versatile Brass).
Tracks: / Impact / My favourite things / Mexican hat dance / Three dance miniatures / Varied mood / Bye, bye blues / Cossack ride and slavonic dance / (They long to be) close to you / Good bye to love / We've only just begun / Sing / Chanson suisse / By the time I get to Phoenix / Prelude and escapede / Trouble with the tuba is..., The / Conversations in brass (third movement).
LP: SB 331
MC: KBSC 331

POPULAR CONTRASTS (Shepherd, James Versatile Brass).
Tracks: / Cushie butterfield / Londonderry Air / Annie's song / Rondeau from Abdalazer / Feelings / Trumpet fiesta / Trumpet triplets / Solitaire / She's out of my life / Badinerie / Lord's prayer, The / Way we were, The / Basque, La / Speak softly love / At the sign of the swingin' cymbals.
LP: LKLP 7000

RHYTHM AND BLUES (Shepherd, James Versatile Brass).
Tracks: / Arrival of the Queen of Sheba, The / Moonlight in Vermont / Long John's hornpipe / Lazybone blues / Three English dances / Rhythm and blues / Little white donkey, The / Fantasy and vibrations / Three miniatures.
LP: PRL 035D
MC: CPRL 035D

SIMPLY VERSATILE (Shepherd, James Versatile Brass).
Tracks: / Virtuosity / Chansonerie / Typewriter, The / Three dance episodes / Kraken / Pavane pour une infante defunte / Rule Britannia / Three dances from 'Threepenny opera'.
LP: PRL 019
MC: CPRL 019

STRIKE UP THE BAND (Shepherd, James Versatile Brass).
Tracks: / Strike up the band / Cavatina / Czardas / Gymnopedie No.1 / Finale from violin concerto / Harmonious brass men / Sabre dance / Send in the clowns / Rondeau / Humoresque / Caprice / Portrait of Gershwin.
LP: SB 337
MC: KBSC 337

Shepherd, Robbie

ROBBIE SHEPHERD READS DUFTON SCOTT.
Tracks: / Auction sale / Old bellman, The / Selling sewing machines / Hugh McCurrie's marriage / My communicative friend / Rural drive, A / Out of his element / Sandy on sousa / Examination of a witness / Drama in a barn.
MC: ACLMC 4

STORY OF TURRIFF SHOW.
MC: CWGR 002

Shepherd, Vic

MOTTY DOWN, A (Shepherd, Vic & John Bowden).
LP: BURL 015

Shepley, Tom

HOW DO YOU DO (Shepley, Tom Band).
LP: TSR 031

Shepp, Archie

ARCHIE SHEPP/THE NEW YORK CONTEMPORARY FIVE VOL.2 (Shepp, Archie & New York Contemporary Five).
LP: SLP 1009

BIRD FIRE.
LP: WW 006

BLASE.
Tracks: / My angel / There is a balm in Gilead / Sophisticated lady / Touareg / Blase.
LP: AFF 7

DOWN HOME NEW YORK.
Tracks: / Down home New York / Round midnight / May 16th / Fourth world / Straight Street.
LP: SN 1102

DUET (Shepp, Archie & Dollar Brand).
Tracks: / Fortunato / Barefoot boy form Queens Town / Left alone / Proof of the man / Ubu suku / Moniebah.
LP: YX 7532

FIFTH OF MAY (Shepp, Archie & Jasper Van't Hof).
LP: LR 45.004

FIRE MUSIC.
Tracks: / Hambone / Malcolm, Malcolm Semper Malcolm / Los Olvidados.
LP: AS 86
LP: MCA 39121
MC: ASC 86

FORCE (Shepp, Archie & Max Roach).
Tracks: / Sweet Mao / Suid Afrika, 76.
2LP: UNI 28976

FOUR FOR TRANE.
Tracks: / Syeeda's song flute / Mr. Syms / Cousin Mary / Niema / Rufus.
LP: JAS 31
MC: JAS C31

GOIN' HOME.
LP: SCS 1079

GOOD LIFE, THE.
LP: VR 005
MC: VR 005C

HOUSE I LIVE IN, THE (Shepp, Archie Quintet).
LP: SCC 6013

IN MEMORY OF ARCHIE SHEPP (Shepp, Archie & Chet Baker).
LP: LR 45.006
MC: LR 65.006

INDOMITABLE.
Tracks: / One for the trane (part 1) / One for the trane (part 2).
LP: 5C 064 61177

LADYBIRD.

Tracks: / Donna Lee / Relaxin' at Camarillo / Now's the time / Ladybird / Flamingo.
LP: . . . . YX 7543

LIVE AT THE PAN AFRICAN FESTIVAL.
LP: . . . . AFF 41

LIVE IN SAN FRANCISCO.
Tracks: / Keep your heart right / Lady sings the blues / In a sentimental mood / Sylvia / Wedding / Wherever June bugs go.
LP: . . . . JAS 75

LIVE IN TOKYO (Shepp, Archie Quartet).
Tracks: / Caravan / In a sentimental mood / Steam / Straight Street.
LP: . . . . YX 7538

LOOKING AT BIRD.
LP: . . . . SCS 1149

LOVER MAN.
LP: . . . . SJP 287

MAMA ROSE.
LP: . . . . SCS 1169

MAMA TOO TIGHT.
Tracks: / Portait of Robert Thompson, A / Prelude to a kiss / Break strain, The / Dem basses / Mama too tight / Theme for Ernie / Basher.
LP: . . . . JAS 18
MC: . . . . JAS C18

MONTREUX 1.
Tracks: / Lush life / U-jamaa / Crucificado / Miss Toni.
LP: . . . . FLP 41027

MONTREUX 2.
Tracks: / Steam / Along came Betty / Blues for Donald Duck.
LP: . . . . FLP 41034

NEW THING AT NEWPORT (see Coltrane, John) (Shepp, Archie & John Coltrane).

ON GREEN DOLPHIN STREET.
Tracks: / On Green Dolphin Street / Enough / Scene is clean, The / In a mellow blues / I thought about you.
LP: . . . . YX 7524

ON THIS NIGHT.
Tracks: / Mac man / In a sentimental mood / Gingerbread boy / On this night / Original Mr. Sonny Boy Williamson / Pickaninny.
LP: . . . . JAS 46
MC: . . . . JAS C46

PARLAN DUO REUNION (Shepp, Archie & Horace Parlan).
LP: . . . . LR 45.003

PASSPORT TO PARADISE Archie Shepp plays Sydney Bechet.
LP: . . . . WW 002

POEM FOR MALCOLM.
Tracks: / Mamarose / Poem for Malcolm / Rain forest / Oleo.
LP: . . . . AFF 78

SEA OF FACES, A.
LP: . . . . BSR 002

SOUL SONG.
LP: . . . . ENJA 4050

SPLASHES (Shepp, Archie Quartet).
Tracks: / Arrival / Reflexions / Groovin high / Steam / Manhattan.
LP: . . . . LR 45.005

STEAM.
LP: . . . . ENJA 2076

THERE'S A TRUMPET IN MY SOUL.
Tracks: / There's a trumpet in my soul suite (part 1) / Samba da rua / Zaid (part 1) / Down in Brazil / There's a trumpet in my soul suite (part 2) / Zaid (part 2) / It is the year of the rabbit / Zaid (part 3).
LP: . . . . FLP 41016

THREE FOR A QUARTER ONE FOR A DIME.
LP: . . . . JAS 68

TRAY OF SILVER.
Tracks: / No smokin' / If you could see me now / Nica's dream / Cookin' at the Continental.
LP: . . . . YX 7806

TROUBLE IN MIND (Shepp, Archie & Horace Parlan).
LP: . . . . SCS 1139

YASMINIA / POEM FOR MALCOLM.
Tracks: / Yasmina - a black woman / Sonny's back / Body and soul / Rain Forest / Oleo / Mamarose / Poem for Malcolm.
LP: . . . . AFF 21

Sheppard, Andy

ANDY SHEPPARD.
Tracks: / Java jive / Esme / Twee / Sol / Coming second / Want a toffee? / Liquid.
LP: . . . . AN 8720
MC: . . . . ANC 8720
MC: . . . . ICM 2048
LP: . . . . ILPM 2048

IN-CO-MOTION.
MC: . . . . ANC 8766
LP: . . . . AN 8766

INTRODUCTIONS IN THE DARK.
Tracks: / Romantic / Rebecca's / Optics / Conversations / Forbidden fruit.
MC: . . . . ANC 8742
LP: . . . . AN 8742
MC: . . . . ICM 2054
LP: . . . . ILPM 2054

SOFT ON THE INSIDE.
MC: . . . . ANC 8751
LP: . . . . AN 8751

Sheppard, Bob

TELL TALE SIGNS.
Tracks: / Hidden agenda / Might as well be / Once removed / Tell tale signs / Point of departure / Shifting sands / Echoes / You betta' off / A.J. / How deep is the ocean.
MC: . . . . WT 0129

Sheppard, Craig

TWO VIOLIN SONATAS, THE (see under Prokofiev) (Sheppard, Craig/ Mayumi Fujikawa).

Sheppard, Doug

ETHEL THE FROG (Sheppard, Doug & Terry Hopkinson).
Tracks: / Eleanor Rigby / Apple of your eye / Staying on my mind / You need wheels / Bleeding heart / Fight back / Don't do it / Why don't you ask / Whatever happened to love / Fire bird.
LP: . . . . EMC 3329

Sheppard, T.G.

FINALLY.
Tracks: / Only one you / Crazy in the dark / Wasn't it a short forever / All my cloudy days are gone / In another minute / We're walking on thin ice / You're the first to last this song / She's got everything it takes to make me stay / I wish you could have turned my head....
LP: . . . . K 56978

I LOVE 'EM ALL.
Tracks: / We belong in love tonight / What's forever for / Party time / Silence on the line / Touch me all over again / I loved 'em every one / You waltzed yourself right into my life / Face the night alone / Troubled waters / State of our union, The.
LP: . . . . K 56941

Sheppard-Missett, Judi

JAZZERCISE.
Tracks: / Squeeze me / Which way is up / Rockford files / Boogie woogie bugle boy / Animal house / Teach me tonight / Baretta's theme / Sweet nothin's / Car wash / T'aint nobody's business if I do / Girl from Ipanema / Don't pull your love.
LP: . . . . MCF 3144
MC: . . . . MCFC 3144

Shep's Banjo Boys

BANJO SINGALONG.
Tracks: / Baby face / I'm looking over a four leaf clover / After you've gone / Lover come back to me / Home in Pasedena / Nobody's sweetheart / Bill Bailey won't you please come home / Tea for two / Me and my shadow / Margie / Some of these days / If you knew Susie / Roll out the barrel / Deed I do / Let me call you sweetheart / Five foot two eyes of blue / Who.
LP: . . . . SPR 8527
MC: . . . . SPC 8527

BIG BAND FAVOURITES.
MCSET: . . . . DTO 10084

SHEP'S BANJO BOYS.
LP: . . . . NEVLP 113

She-Ra

CATRA'S ICE PALACE (for ages 5-10) (Unknown artist(s)).
MC: . . . . PLBS 200

SECRET OF THE SWORD, THE (for ages 5-10) (Unknown artist(s)).
MC: . . . . PLBS 173

SHADOW WEAVER'S MAGIC MIRROR (for ages 5-10) (Unknown artist(s)).
MC: . . . . PLBS 172

SHE-RA & THE DARK POOL (for ages 5-10) (Unknown artist(s)).
MC: . . . . PLBS 171

SHE-RA & THE GOLDEN GOOSE (for ages 5-10) (Unknown artist(s)).
MC: . . . . PLBS 199

SHE-RA & THE SURPRISE PARTY (for ages 5-10) (Unknown artist(s)).
MC: . . . . PLBS 182

SPIRIT IS KIDNAPPED (for ages 5-10) (Unknown artist(s)).
MC: . . . . PLBS 181

Sherbourne, Janet

SLOWER THAN MOLASSES (Sherbourne, Janet & Mark Lockett).
Tracks: / Heavy set / All you can eat / Tree sequence / Slower than molasses / China / My lovesick hours / Click / 19 to the dozen / Sirian air / Luna.
LP: . . . . PRACTICAL 3

Sherbs

SKILL, THE.
Tracks: / I have the skill / Back to zero / Cindy is waiting / Crazy in the night / I'll be faster / Never surrender / No turning back / Love you to death / Into the heat / I'm OK / Juliet and me / Parallel bars.
LP: . . . . K 50783

Sheridan

RIVALS, THE (Various artists).
MCSET: 2020

Sheridan, Mike

BIRMINGHAM BEAT (Sheridan, Mike & The Nightriders).
Tracks: / No other guy / Tell me what you're gonna do / Please Mr. Postman / In love / Brand new cadillac / Thing of the past, A / What a sweet thing that was / Fabulous / Here I stand / Lonely weekends / Take my hand / Make them understand / Stop, look and listen / Don't turn your back on me.
LP: . . . . ED 120

Sheridan, Sue (nar)

FUN FOR THE SECRET SEVEN (see under Blyton, Enid (aut)) (Sheridan, Sue (nar) & Nigel Anthony (nar)).

GOOD WORK SECRET SEVEN (see under Blyton, Enid (aut)) (Sheridan, Sue (nar) & Nigel Anthony (nar)).

SECRET SEVEN WIN THROUGH (see under Blyton, Enid (aut)) (Sheridan, Sue (nar) & Nigel Anthony (nar)).

THREE CHEERS SECRET SEVEN (see under Blyton, Enid (aut)) (Sheridan, Sue (nar) & Nigel Anthony (nar)).

Sheridan, Tony

HAMBURG 1961 (See under Beatles) (Sheridan, Tony & The Beatles).
LP: . . . . TOP 108
MC: . . . . KTOP 108

ICH LIEB'DICH SO.
Tracks: / Ich lieb'dich so / Der kiss me song / Arme kleine Lilly / Eyrst wenn man treu sein kann / Madison kid / Veedeboom slop slop / Wolgalied / Let's slop tonight / Alles nur arus liebe / Ich will bei dir bleiben / Ich las dich nie mehr wieder gehn' / Hey ba ba re bop / Vive l'armour / Ya Ya,Parts 1&2 / La bamba / Malagueña (Spanisch).
LP: . . . . BFX 15249

JUST A LITTLE BIT OF TONY SHERIDAN.
Tracks: / Just a little bit / Kansas City / Save the last dance for me / Unchained melody / Get on the right track baby / You'd better move on / Skinny Minnie / Jambalaya / Mary Ann / Will you love me tomorrow / My babe / Sweet Georgia Brown / I got a woman.
LP: 831 998-1
MC: 831 998-4

MEET THE BEAT.
Tracks: / Jailhouse rock / Let's dance / Ruby baby / Sweet Georgia Brown / Hey ba ba re bop / Do-re-mi / Shake it some more / My bonnie / Shake, rattle and roll / Just you and me / Creep, The / Fever / Skinny Minnie / What'd I say?.
LP: 819 826-1
MC: 819 826-4

Sheriff, Dave

FILL MY HAT WITH SILVER.
Tracks: / Lonesome me / You're my best friend / I can make it with you / Little ol' wine drinker me / For the good times / Rhinestone cowboy / She's mine / Silver wings / Door is always open, The / Ruby / I should have known better / Not fade away / Leaving of Liverpool.
LP: . . . . BSS 302

I'LL BE ALONE TONIGHT.
LP: . . . . BSS 201

WITH FOUR CARD EXPRESS.
LP: . . . . BSS 154

Sheriff, Jack

LAUGH YOURSELF AWAKE.
LP: . . . . CHIME 0021

Sherlock Holmes

SHERLOCK HOLMES (TV soundtrack) (Various artists).
LP: . . . . TER 1136
MC: . . . . ZCTER 1136

SHERLOCK HOLMES (Original London cast) (Various artists).
Tracks: / Sherlock Holmes: *Various artists* / Without him, there can be no me: *Various artists* / London is London: *Various artists* / Vendetta: *Various artists* / Anything you want to know: *Various artists* / Her face: *Various artists* / Men like you: *Various artists* / Lousy life, A: *Various artists* / I shall find her: *Various artists* / No reason: *Various artists* / Halcyon days: *Various artists* / Without him, there can be no me (reprise): *Various artists* / Down the apples 'n' pears: *Various artists* / He's back: *Various artists*/ Million years ago or was it yesterday, A: *Various artists* / Best of you, the best of me, The: *Various artists*/ Sherlock Holmes (reprise): *Various artists.*
LP: . . . . BL 74145
MC: . . . . BK 74145

SHERLOCK HOLMES' ADVENTURES (Wood, John (nar)).
MCSET: 2097

Sherlock Holmes...

ADVENTURES OF SHERLOCK HOLMES, THE (See under Adventures of...) (Hardy, Robert (nar)).

ADVENTURES OF SHERLOCK HOLMES, THE (Sir Arthur Conan Doyle) (Pickering, Donald).
MC: . . . . PTB 601

ADVENTURES OF SHERLOCK HOLMES, THE (Sir Arthur Conan Doyle) (Hardy, Robert (nar)).
Tracks: / Resident patient, The / Case of identity, The / Adventure of the Blue Carbuncle, The / Five orange pips, The.
MCSET: 418 141-4

ADVENTURES OF SHERLOCK HOLMES VOL.1 (Various artists).
MCSET: . . . . ZBBC 1200

ADVENTURES OF SHERLOCK HOLMES VOL.3 (Various artists).
MCSET: . . . . ZBBC 1202

ADVENTURES OF SHERLOCK HOLMES VOL.2 (Various artists).
MCSET: . . . . ZBBC 1201

CASE BOOK OF SHERLOCK HOLMES, THE (Sir Arthur Conan Doyle) (Hardy, Robert (nar)).
Tracks: / Adventure of the three garridebs / Adventure of the lion's mane, The / Adventure of the retired colourman, The.
MCSET: 414 748-4

FOUR SHERLOCK HOLMES STORIES (Sir Arthur Conan Doyle) (Hardy, Robert (nar)).
Tracks: / Adventure of the three students, The / Greek interpreter, The / Adventure of the Sussex vampire, The / Adventure of Charles Augustus Milverton, The.
MCSET: . . . . SAY 2
MCSET: . . . . ARGO 1004

HOUND OF THE BASKERVILLES (Sir Arthur Conan Doyle).
MC: . . . . PLBC 82

HOUND OF THE BASKERVILLES, THE (Sir Arthur Conan Doyle) (Burden, Hugh (nar)).
MCSET: . . . . LFP 7212
MC: 001042424
MCSET: . . . . LFP 417 212 5

HOUND OF THE BASKERVILLES, THE (Sir Arthur Conan Doyle) (Williamson, Nicol (nar)).
MCSET: 505

MEMOIRS OF SHERLOCK HOLMES (Sir Arthur Conan Doyle) (Hardy, Robert (nar)).
Tracks: / Yellow face, The / Stockbroker's clerk, The / "Gloria Scott", The / Final problem, The.
MCSET: . . . . SAY 108

MORE SHERLOCK HOLMES STORIES (Sir Arthur Conan Doyle) (Hardy, Robert (nar)).
Tracks: / Adventure of the dying detective / Adventure of Shoscombe Old Place / Musgrave ritual / Crooked man.
MCSET: . . . . SAY 98
MCSET: . . . . ARGO 1202

RETURN OF SHERLOCK HOLMES, THE (Sir Arthur Conan Doyle) (Hardy, Robert (nar)).
Tracks: / Adventure of the empty house, The / Adventure of the solitary cyclist, The / Adventure of the red cycle, The / Adventure of the Mazarin Stone, The.
MCSET: . . . . SAY 109

SHERLOCK HOLMES (Sir Arthur Holmes).
MCSET: . . . . ZBBC 1091

SHERLOCK HOLMES (Sir Arthur Conan Doyle).
MCSET: . . . . ZBBC 1031

SHERLOCK HOLMES 3 (Sir Arthur Conan Doyle).
Tracks: / Musgrave ritual, The / Black Peter / Bruce Partington plus / Dancing men.

MCSET: .... ZBBC 1123

SHERLOCK HOLMES SOUNDBOOK (Sir Arthur Conan Doyle).
MC: .... SBC 107

SHERLOCK HOLMES STORIES, VOL 1 (Sir Arthur Conan Doyle) (Rathbone, Basil (nar)).
MC: .... CDL 51172

SHERLOCK HOLMES STORIES, VOL 2 (Sir Arthur Conan Doyle) (Rathbone, Basil (nar)).
MC: .... CDL 51208

SHERLOCK HOLMES STORIES, VOL 3 (Sir Arthur Conan Doyle) (Rathbone, Basil (nar)).
MC: .... CDL 51220

SHERLOCK HOLMES STORIES, VOL 4 (Sir Arthur Conan Doyle) (Rathbone, Basil (nar)).
MC: .... CDL 51240

SHOSCOMBE OLD PLACE (Sir Arthur Conan Doyle).
Tracks: / Shoscombe Old Place / Illustrious client, The.
MC: .... ANV 644

STUDY IN SCARLET, A (Sir Arthur Conan Doyle) (Powell, Robert (nar)).
MC: .... ZCF 501

Sherman, Allan

GIFT OF LAUGHTER, A Best of Allan Sherman.
LP: .... RNLP 70818

VERY BEST OF ALLAN SHERMAN, THE.
Tracks: / That old back scratcher / Your mother's here to stay / Sarah Jackman / Shine on Harvey Bloom / Painless dentist song, The / Second hand nose / Hello Muddah, hello faddah / Twelve gifts of Christmas / Mexican hat dance / My Zelda / Waste of money, A / Bye bye blumberg.
LP: .... K 56056

Sherman, Ben

CHRISTMAS BELLS.
LP: .... BSS 317

Sherman, Bim

ACROSS THE RED SEA.
LP: .... ONULP 17

AFRICAN RUBADUB (Sherman, Bim & Allstars).
LP: .... RDL 800

CENTURY (Sherman, Bim & The Voluntary).
LP: .... CENTURY 100
LP: .... CENTURY 001

DANGER.
LP: .... CENTURY 200

EXPLOITATION.
LP: .... RDL 1100

HAUNTING GROUND.
LP: .... RDL 600

LOVERS LEAP.
LP: .... RDL 700

MEETS HORACE ANDY AND U BLACK.
LP: .... OMLP 13

Sherman, Daryl

SHE'S A GREAT,GREAT GIRL..
LP: TJ1001

Sherman, Morton

BEAT THE BOX (Sherman, Morton & Belluci).
Tracks: / Sucks the beat / Beat professor / Crisis situation / Musical / Spirit of Bulgaria / Blow up the DJ / Agreppo / Robbin' and stealin' / MC Call / Not afraid of dance / Hmm hmm / Freak to the beat / Move your ass / Lala / Shake your hips / Secrets of Africa / Zeitgeist / Collecting the money.
2LP: .... SUB 50

Sherrick

SHERRICK.
Tracks: / Tell me what it is / Just call / Baby I'm for real / This must be love / Do you baby / All because of you / Let's be lovers tonight / Lady you are / Send for me.
LP: .... WX 118
MC: .... WX 118 C

Sherriff Jack

WHAT LOVE.
LP: .... CHIME 34

Sherrill, Pappy

33 YEARS OF P&P (Sherrill, Pappy & Snuffy Jenkins).
LP: .... ROUNDER 0005

CRAZY WATER (Sherrill, Pappy & Snuffy Jenkins).
LP: .... ROUNDER 0059

WILEY ZEKE & HOMER (Sherrill, Pappy & The Morris Brothers).
LP: .... ROUNDER 0022

Sherwood, Bobby

1944: BOBBY SHERWOOD (Sherwood, Bobby & His Orchestra).
LP: .... CLP 28

1944-46 (Sherwood, Bobby & His Orchestra).
LP: .... CLP 115

ONE NIGHT STAND - 1946.
LP: .... JLP 1028

POLITELY.
LP: .... GELP 15018

SHERWOOD SWINGS.
LP: .... SWH 35

VICTORY PARADE OF SPOTLIGHT BANDS 1945 (Sherwood, Bobby & His Orchestra).
Tracks: / Girlfriend / Floating / New world jumps, The / I don't want to love you / Swingin' at the semloh / Elk's parade, The / Lover, come back to me / Song of the wanderer / Don't you know I care / I dream of you / Accentuate the positive.
LP: .... AIRCHECK 3

Sherwood Rise

FROM THE WOOD.
LP: .... DIN 321

She's Gotta Have it

SHE'S GOTTA HAVE IT (Film Soundtrack) (Various artists).
Tracks: / She's gotta have it (Opening credits): *Various artists* / Brooklyn Bridge: *Various artists* / He's on it: *Various artists* / Thought: *Various artists* / Nola: *Various artists* / Ferrybank restaurant: *Various* artists / Work montage: *Various artists* / Who will be the one: *Various artists* / Nola-instrumental: *Various* artists / Thought, A (reprise): *Various artists* / Nola cleans up: *Various artists* / Opal: *Various artists*/ Final confession: *Various artists* / Ind line: *Various artists* / She's walkin': *Various artists* / Opal (reprise): *Various artists* / Hawk, The: *Various artists* / Nola - piano: *Various artists* / End credits: *Various artists.*
LP: .... AN 8713
MC: .... ANC 8713

She's Out of Control

SHE'S OUT OF CONTROL (Film Soundtrack) (Various artists).
Tracks: / Where's the fire: *Hinton, Troy* / You should be loving me: *Starr, Brenda.K.* / Concentration: *Thornally, Phil* / Loneliest heart, The: *Boy's Club* / Hunger of love: *Faltermeyer, Harold* / Khe Fm radio sweeper: *Ladd, Jim* / Winning side: *Oingo Boingo* / Daddy's little girl: *Wilson, Brian* / Venus: *Avalon, Frankie*/ You really got me: *Kinks* / Feel the shake: *Jet Boy.*
LP: .... MCA 6281
MC: .... MCAC 6281

Sheshwe

SHESHWE: SOUNDS OF THE MINES (Various artists).
LP: .... ROUNDER 5031
MC: .... ROUNDER 5031C

Shetland...

DA MERRIE BOYS Shetland fiddle music (Various artists).
Tracks: / Aandowing at da bow: *Various artists* / Da muckle reel o Finnigirt: *Various artists* / Back reel: *Various* artists / Loddie: *Various artists* / Da whenna burn: *Various artists* / Trowie burn: *Various artists*/ Jack is yet alive: *Various artists* / Waterman's hornpipe: *Various artists* / Doon da rooth: *Various artists*/ Da aald hill grinnd: *Various artists* / Fram apon 'im: *Various artists* / Garstairs dream: *Various artists*/ Da craw dang da pussy: *Various artists* / Da forfit o'da ship: *Various artists* / Merry boys o'Greenland: *Various* artists / Da wattle: *Various artists* / Bonnie isle of Whalsay: *Various artists* / Antarctic ice: *Various* artists / Da de'il i'da kitchen: *Various artists* / Scollay's reel: *Various artists* / Da accident o'voe: *Various artists* / Lucky, can you link ony: *Various artists* / I lo'ed nae a lassie but ane: *Various artists*/ Da aald stuir back agin: *Various artists* / Cuckoo's nest, The: *Various artists* / Mind what you do: *Various* artists / Winyadepla: *Various artists* / Uncle Freddy's tune: *Various artists* / Da blue yow: *Various* artists / Da south end: *Various artists* / Hen's march: *Various artists* / Bride's march: *Various artists*/ Da farder ben da wylkomer: *Various artists* / Gosabrough waltz: *Various artists* / Da bride is a boanie ting: *Various artists* / More grog's coming: *Various artists* / Sail her owre de raftrees: *Various artists*/ Be nort da daeks o' voe: *Various artists* / Da brig: *Various artists* / Lerwick lasses: *Various artists*/ Scalloway lasses: *Various artists* / Underhill: *Various artists* / Square da mizzen: *Various artists*/ Shetland Isles hornpipe: *Various artists* / Taste da green: *Various artists* / Mrs. McLeod's reel: *Various* artists / Du's been long awa: *Various artists* / Da guizer's reel: *Various artists* / Cross reel: *Various* artists / Stumpie: *Various artists* / Da nippin' grund: *Various artists* / Norwegian waltz: *Various artists*/ Aald swaara: *Various artists* / Kiss her and clap her: *Various artists* / Shaalds o foula: *Various artists*/ Vallafield: *Various artists* / Foula reel: *Various artists.*
MC: 60-068

SHETLAND FIDDLERS (Various artists).
LP: .... LEA 2052

Shifnal Male Voice

CLOSE THINE EYES.
LP: .... MMLP 1029

Shift

SHIFT (Various artists).
LP: .... SHIFT 1

Shih, Patricia

LEAP OF FAITH.
LP: .... FF 485

Shilton, Peter

SIDE BY SIDE (see under Clemence, Ray) (Clemence, Ray/Peter Shilton).

Shimizu, Yasuki

MUSIC FOR COMMERCIALS.
LP: .... MTM 12

Shine, Brendan

AT HOME.
LP: .... PLAY 1020
MC: .... CPLAY 1020

BEST OF BRENDAN SHINE.
LP: .... PLAY 1001

BLUE MISTY EYES.
LP: .... PLAY 1016
MC: .... CPLAY 1016

BRENDAN SHINE COLLECTION.
LP: .... PLAYTV 1
MC: .... CPLAYTV 1

CATCH ME IF YOU CAN.
LP: .... PLAY 1015
MC: .... CPLALP 1015

CEILI HOUSE.
LP: .... PLAY 1007 B
MC: .... CPLAY 1007

COUNTRY AND IRISH.
LP: .... PLAY 1011

IRISH SIDE OF BRENDAN SHINE.
Tracks: / Ballinasloe fair / Coastline of Mayo / Ou' bally moe / Ballymena hat / Where my Eileen is waiting / If you ever go to Ireland.
LP: .... HPE 616

IRISH STARTIME.
LP: .... IST 4447

LIVE AT THE THATCH.
LP: .... THATCH 1
MC: THATCHC1

MAGIC MOMENTS.
LP: .... SMR 991
MC: .... SMRC 991

MEMORIES.
Tracks: / Danny boy / If I were a blackbird / Old bog road / Dublin in the rare oul times / Mountains of Mourne / Banks of my own lovely Lee, The.
LP: .... PLAYTV 3
MC: .... CPLAYTV 3

MOONSHINE.
LP: .... PLAY 1018

MY OLD COUNTRY HOME.
LP: .... PLAY 1017

NEW ROADS.
LP: .... PLAY 1012
MC: .... CPLAY 1012

NICE AND EASY.
LP: .... PLAY 1013
MC: .... CPLAY 1013

PICTURE OF MY WORLD, A.
LP: .... PLAY 1022
MC: .... CPLAY 1022

SHINE ON 21.
MC: .... CPLAY 1026

SIMPLE LOVE SONGS.
LP: .... PLAY 1014

THIS IS BRENDAN SHINE.
LP: .... PLAY 1009
MC: .... CPLAY 1009

WITH LOVE.
LP: .... PLAY TV 2
MC: .... PLAY TCV 2

Shine on Harvey Moon

SHINE ON HARVEY MOON (Various artists).
Tracks: / Shine on Harvey Moon: *Various artists* / Sentimental journey: *Various artists* / As time goes by: *Various artists* / It had to be you: *Various artists* / In the mood: *Various artists* / So nice to come home to: *Various* artists / Gonna get along without you now: *Various artists* / We'll gather lilacs: *Various artists* / Stardust: *Various artists.*
LP: .... IMG 0003
MC: IMG4 0003

Shine, Ralph

RALPH SHINES BLUES BAND, THE (Shine, Ralph Blues Band).
LP: .... BR 102

Shinehead

REAL ROCK, THE.
Tracks: / Real rock, The / World of the video game / Good things / Dance down the road / Till I kissed you / Musical madness / Family affair / Potential / Strive / Love and marrage rap / Cigarette breath.
LP: .... EKT 75
MC: .... EKT 75C

UNITY.
LP: .... EKT 53
MC: .... EKT 53C

Shines, Johnny

COUNTRY BLUES (Shines, Johnny & Blind Will Dukes).
Tracks: / Rambling blues / Maggie Lee blues / You're the one that I love / Sweet home Chicago / Shake 'em on down / Moanin' and groanin' the blues / Terraplane blues / Dead shrimp blues / Steady rollin man / Me andthe devil / Mean hearted woman / Ramblin' blues / Hobo blues / Milk cow blues / Mistreated so long / Sail on little woman / Hoodoo man.
LP: .... JSP 1079

DUST MY BROOM Job series vol1 (Shines, Johnny/Robert Lockwood).
LP: .... FLY 563

HEY BA-BA-RE-BOP.
LP: .... ROUNDER 2020
MC: .... ROUNDER 2020C

JOHNNY SHINES' BAND WITH BIG WALTER HORTON (Shines, Johnny Band & Walter Horton).
LP: .... T 2217

JOHNNY SHINES & COMPANY.
Tracks: / Little wolf / Mr. Cover / Shaker / Shotgun whupin' / Lost love letter blues / Stand by me / Blood ran like wind / Chief Tiscaloosa / I'm getting old / Mother's place / Jim string.
LP: .... BMLP 1065

LIVE IN ST LOUIS, 1974.
LP: .... WOLF 120 914

Shining (Film)

SHINING, THE (Original Soundtrack) (Various artists).
Tracks: / Shining, The: *Shining* / Rocky mountains: *Shining* / Lontano: *Shining* / Music for strings, percussion and celesta: *Shining* / Utrenja: *Shining* / Awakening of Jacob: *Shining* / De natura sonoris No.2: *Shining* / Home: *Shining.*
LP: .... K 56827

Shiny Men

SHINY MEN.
LP: .... EX 002

Ship Ahoy

SHIP AHOY/LAS VEGAS NIGHTS (Original Soundtracks) (Various artists).
LP: .... HS 5011

Ship of Adventure (bk)

SHIP OF ADVENTURE, THE (see under Blyton, Enid (aut)) (Blake, Roger (nar) & Elizabeth Lindsay (nar)).

Shipley, Ellen

BREAKING THROUGH THE ICE.
Tracks: / Heart to heart / Fotogenic / Jamie / This little girl / Talk don't shout solo / Lost without your love / Promise to keep / Living for the tenderness.
LP: .... PL 12626

ELLEN SHIPLEY.
Tracks: / I surrender / Man of the world / Catch the cobra / Heroes of yesterday / Good thing going / I'm jumping out of my skin / Little sister / Last tears / Stray dog / Over the edge.
LP: .... FL 13428

Shirati Jazz

BENGA BEAT.
LP: .... WCB 003
LP: .... CGLP 4433
MC: .... CGC 4433

MY LIFE AND LOVES.
LP: .... AFRILP 04

Shirelles

BEST OF THE SHIRELLES.
MC: 16-15

COLLECTION: SHIRELLES.
MC: . . . . **CCSMC 238**

GREATEST HITS.
Tracks: / Dedicated to the one I love / Tonight's the night / Will you love me tomorrow / Mama said / Thing of the past, A / What a sweet thing that was / Big John / Baby it's you / Soldier boy / Welcome home / Stop the music / It's love that really counts / Everybody loves a lover / Foolish little girl / Don't say goodnight and mean goodbye / What does a girl do? / Sha-la-la / Thank you baby / Maybe tonight / Don't go home (my little darling) / Boys (Available on CD only) / Abracadabra (Available on CD only).
LP: . . . . **ACT 011**

JUKE BOX GIANTS.
Tracks: / Soldier boy / Dedicated to the one I love / Foolish little girl / What a sweet thing that was / Everybody loves a lover / Don't say goodnight and mean goodbye / Big John / Baby it's you / It's love that really counts / Stop the music / Will you love me tomorrow / Mama said / I met him on a Sunday / Boys / Thing of the past, A / Thank you baby / Welcome home / Tonight's the night / Blue holiday / Things I want to hear, The.
LP: . . . . **AFEMP 1008**

LOST & FOUND.
Tracks: / Good good time / Long day, short night / You'll know when the right boy.... / Rocky / Go tell her / Remember me / For my sake / Celebrate your victory / Hands off, he's mine / Crossroads in your heart / He's the only guy I'll ever love / One of the flower people / I'm feeling it too / If I had you / There goes my heart / Shh, I'm watching the movie.
LP: . . . . **ACT 010**

MAMA SAID.
Tracks: / Mama said / Will you love me tomorrow / Tonights the night / Foolish little girl / Everybody loves a lover / Thank you baby / Soldier boy / Dedicated to the one I love / Baby it's you / I met him on a Sunday / Welcome home / Boys.
LP: . . . . **TOP 127**
MC: . . . . **KTOP 127**

SHA LA LA LA LA.
Tracks: / Will you love me tomorrow / Mama said / Dedicated to the one I love / Boys / Tonight's the night / Look-a-here baby / Soldier boy / Mama, here comes the bride / Maybe tonight / You're under arrest / Foolish little girl / Welcome home / Tonight you're gonna fall in love with me / Putty in your hands / Sha-la-la-la / It's love that really counts.
LP: . . . . **ACT 003**

SOLDIER BOY.
LP: . . . . **RMB 5610**

SOULFULLY YOURS.
Tracks: / Last minute miracle / No doubt about it / Shades of blue / Wait till I give the signal / Till my baby comes home / Love that man / Don't say goodnight and mean goodbye / Too much of a good thing / March (you'll be sorry) / Bright shiny colours / Don't go home, my little darling / His lips get in the way / Doom's day / Stop the music / Baby it's you.
LP: . . . . **KENT 032**

WILL YOU LOVE ME TOMORROW.
Tracks: / Dedicated to the one I love / Tonight's the night / Will you love me tomorrow / Boys / Mama said / Thing of the past, A / What a sweet thing that was / Big John / Baby it's you / Soldier boy / Welcome home baby / Stop the music / It's love that really counts / Everybody loves a lover / Foolish little girl / Don't say goodnight and mean goodbye / What does a girl do? / Sha-la-la / Thank you baby / Maybe tonight.
LP: . . . . **CRM 2037**
MC: . . . . **TCCRM 2037**

Shirley & Lee

BEST OF SHIRLEY & LEE vol 1.
Tracks: / Let the good times roll / Rock all night / Feel so good / I'm gone / Lee's dream / That's what I'll do / Don't you know I love you / Everybody's rockin' / Why did I / I feel good / Baby / T'll thrill you.
LP: . . . . **CH 47**

HAPPY DAYS.
Tracks: / Bewildered / Good for nothing baby / Everybody needs somebody / Lovers mistake / Your day is coming / I'll never be free / Shirley come back / After last night.
LP: . . . . **MAN 5025**

RESPECTFULLY YOURS.
Tracks: / After last night / Two peas in a pod / Let's live it up / Ya moves me / Everybody / Lover's mistake / Your day is coming / I'll never.
LP: . . . . **MAN 5040**
LP: . . . . **MAN 5040**

Shirley Valentine

SHIRLEY VALENTINE (Film Soundtrack) (Various artists).
Tracks: / Girl who used to be me, The: *Austin, Patti* / Shirley Valentine, Theme from: *Various artists* / Affection: *Various artists* / Crumbling resolve: *Various artists* / Dreams: *Various artists* / Costas: *Various* artists / Coming to Greece: *Various artists* / Nocturne: *Various artists* / Arrivalin mykonos: *Various artists.*
LP: . . . . **FILM 062**
MC: . . . . **FILMC 062**

Shirra, Tom

MOOD INDIGO (Shirra, Tom & His Friends).
Tracks: / Tribute to Glenn Miller / Just in time / Can't buy my love / Skye boat song / Mood indigo / Feelings / All the things you are / Ae fond kiss / Stardust / Days of wine and roses / My ain folk / Moonlight serenade / Roamin' in the gloamin' / Auld lang syne.
LP: . . . . **LILP 5055**

Shirts

INNER SLEEVE.
Tracks: / I'm not one of those / One last chance / Can't get it through my head / I've had it / I don't wanna know / Pleasure is the pain / As long as the laughter lasts / Too much trouble / Hanging around / Small talk.
LP: . . . . **EST 12085**

STREETLIGHT SHINE.
Tracks: / Laugh and walk away / Love is a fiction / Don't you hesitate / Milton at the Savoy / Ground zero / Triangulum / Out on the ropes / I feel so nervous / Starts with a handshake / Can't cry anymore / Outside the cathedral door / Kensington Gardens.
LP: . . . . **SHSP 4104**

Shisler, Geoffrey

CANTORIAL MELODIES (Shisler, Cantor Geoffrey).
Tracks: / Rabbi Chanaya Ben Akashya / Ki Keshimcha / Uvedivrei kodshecha / Veshamru / Sephirat haomer / Ahavat r'ayah / Sim Shalom / Brich shemei / Eitz chayim / Magen avot / Chanukah berachot / Haneirot halalu / Cantor Geoffrey Shisler / Stephen Robins.
MC: . . . . **L 006 161C**

Shiv & Hari

YUGAL BANDI.
Tracks: / Raga jhinjhoti / Raga msihra piloco.
LP: . . . . **SNTF 655**

Shiva

FIREDANCE.
Tracks: / How can I? / En cachent / Wild machine / Borderline / Stranger lands / Angel of monz / Rendezvous with death / User / Call me in the morning / Shiva.
LP: . . . . **HMRLP 6**

Shiva Burlesque

MERCURY BLUES.
LP: . . . . **SAVE 091**

SHIVA BURLESQUE.
Tracks: / Indian Summer / Two suns / Lonesome death of Shadow Morton, The / Black ship, The / Morning / Work the rat / Water lilies / Train mystery / Marysupermarket.
LP: . . . . **WEEAT 005**

Shiva's Headband

KALEIOSCOPTIC.
LP: . . . . **TOCK 012**

Shoc Corridor

TRAIN OF EVENTS.
LP: . . . . **QLP 5**

Shock Headed Peters

FEAR ENGINE.
LP: . . . . **PKLP 0020**

Shock Tactics...

SHOCK TACTICS & OTHER STORIES (see under Munro, H.H.) (Various artists).

Shock Therapy

CANCER.
LP: . . . . **SAVE 085**

MY UNSHAKEABLE BELIEF.
LP: . . . . **SAVE 045**

SHOCK THERAPY.
2LP: . . . . **HOLY 003**

TOUCH ME AND DIE.
LP: . . . . **SAVE 070**

Shock Treatment

SHOCK TREATMENT (Original Soundtrack) (Various artists).
LP: . . . . **K 56957**

Shockabilly

COLOSSEUM.
LP: . . . . **ROUGH 68**

EARTH VS SHOCKABILLY.
LP: . . . . **ROUGH 48**
LP: . . . . **SHIMMY 017**

JUST BEAUTIFUL - LIVE.
Tracks: / Intro / Georgia in a jug / Eight miles high / Plunger routine / Are you experienced / Burma shave / Rake / Birdcage routine / Outro / Oh Yoko / Dang me / Luicifer Sam / Nobody's place / Heartful of soul / Good girl's gonna go bad / Psychotic reaction / Hard day's night, A / Train kept a rolling.
LP: . . . . **SDE 8914**

SHOCKABILLY HEAVEN.
LP: . . . . **SAVE 008**

VIETNAM.
LP: . . . . **SAVE 001**

Shocked, Michelle

CAPTAIN SWING.
Tracks: / Ged is a real estate developer / On the greener side / Silent ways / Sleep keeps me awake / Cement lament, The / (Don't you mess around with) my little sister / Looks like Mona Lisa / Too little too late / Street corner ambassador / Must be luff.
LP: . . . . **CVLP 2**
MC: . . . . **CVMC 2**
LP: **838 878 1**
MC: **838 878 4**

SHORT SHARP SHOCKED.
Tracks: / When I grow up / Hello Hopeville / Memories of East Texas / Making the run to Gladewater / Graffiti limbo / If love was a train / Anchorage / L and N don't stop here anymore, The / VX FX DX / Black widow.
LP: . . . . **CVLP 1**
MC: . . . . **CVMC 1**

TEXAS CAMPFIRE TAPES.
Tracks: / 5 a.m. in Amsterdam / Secret admirer, The / Incomplete image, The / Who cares? / Down on Thomas St. Fogtown / Steppin' out / Hep cat, The / Necktie / (Don't you mess around with) my little sister / Ballad of patched eye and Meg, The / Secret to a long life, The / Chain smoker, The (CD only) / Stranded in a limousine (CD only) / Goodnight Irene (CD only).
LP: . . . . **COOK 002**
MC: . . . . **COOKC 002**

Shocker

SHOCKER (Film Soundtrack) (Various artists).
Tracks: / Shocker: *Dudes Of Wrath* / Love transfusion: *Pop, Iggy* / No more Mr. Nice Guy: *Megadeth* / Sword and stone: *Bonfire* / Timeless love: *Saraya* / Shockdance: *Dudes Of Wrath* / Demon bell (The ballad of Horace Pinker): *Dangerous Toys* / Awakening, The: *Voodoo X* / Different breed: *Dead On* / Shocker (reprise): *Dudes Of Wrath.*
LP: . . . . **SBKLP 3**
LP: **793 233 1**
MC: . . . . **SBKTC 3**
MC: **793 233 4**

SHOCKER (FILM BACKGROUND MUSIC) (Goldstein,William).
LP: . . . . **VS 5247**
MC: . . . . **VSC 5247**

Shocking Miss Pilgrim

MOTHER WORE TIGHTS/THE SHOCKING MISS PILGRIM (see Mother wore tights) (Various artists).

Shoe People

PC BOOT TAKES CHARGE (Narrated by Philip Whitchurch) (Whitchurch, Philip).
MC: **00 1021869**

TRAMPY'S RAINBOW SURPRISE (Narrated by Philip Whitchurch) (Whitchurch, Philip).
MC: **00 1021850**

Shoemake, Charlie

AWAY FROM THE CROWD (Shoemake, Charlie Sextet).
Tracks: / Dandi's smile / He needs me / Away from the crowd / Evening run / Small talk / Gentle man / Sometime yesterday / Young and foolish.
LP: . . . . **DS 856**

BLUE SHOE.
Tracks: / Blue shoe / Dream, The / Rainbows / Cure for the common chord / Why, someone tell me, why?.
LP: . . . . **MR 5221**

CROSS ROADS (Shoemake, Charlie Sextet).
Tracks: / Say it isn't so / Child in me / Fleeting resemblance / Cross roads / Recondite / Dunbar's pace / Christmas bells.
LP: . . . . **DS 878**

INCANDESCENT (Shoemake, Charlie Sextet).
LP: . . . . **DS 904**

PLAYS THE MUSIC OF DAVID RAKSIN (Shoemake, Charlie Sextet).
Tracks: / Too late blues / Mirror, mirror, mirror / Bad and the beautiful / Striver, The.
LP: . . . . **DS 894**

SUNSTROKE.
Tracks: / This happy madness / That's Earl's brother / Sunstroke / You'll love New York / 42nd Street / We'll be together again.
LP: . . . . **MR 5193**

Shoemake, Sandi

SLOWLY.
Tracks: / Yardbird suite / You're blase / Flamingo / I wish I knew.
LP: . . . . **DS 889**

Shoenfelt, Phil

BACKWOODS CRUCIFIXION.
Tracks: / Garden of Eden / Light that surrounds you, The / Devil's hole / Walkaway / Marianne, I'm falling / Psyche / Hateful heart / Salvation Hotel.
LP: . . . . **PAPLP 002**
MC: . . . . **PAPMC 002**

Shoes For Industry

TALK LIKE A WALK.
LP: . . . . **FRY 1**

Shoes (group)

BLACK VINYL SHOES.
Tracks: / Boys don't lie / Do you wanna get lucky / She'll disappear / Tragedy / Writing a postcard / Not me / Someone finer / Capital gain / Fatal running start / Okay it really hurts / Fire for a while / If you'd stay / Nowhere so fast.
LP: . . . . **SRK 6075**

BOOMERANG.
Tracks: / In her shadow / Curiosity / Mayday / Too soon / Double talk / Summer rain / Under the gun / Tube, The / What love means / Bound to be a reason / Shake it away / Tested charms.
LP: . . . . **FC 028**

PRESENT TENSE.
Tracks: / Tomorrow night / Too late / Hangin' around with you / Your very eyes / In my arms again / Somebody has what I had / Now and then / Every girl / I don't miss you / Cruel you / Three times: See me, say it, listen / I don't wanna hear it.
LP: . . . . **K 52187**

SILHOUETTE.
Tracks: / Get my message / Will you spin for me / When push comes to shove / Shining / It's only you / Twist and bend it / I wanna give it to you / Turn around / Running wild / Oh, Angeline / Bound to fade / Suspicion.
LP: . . . . **FIEND 19**

SILHOUETTE.
LP: . . . . **ROSE 44**
MC: . . . . **ROSE 44C**

STOLEN WISHES.
LP: . . . . **ROSE 202**

TONGUE TWISTER.
Tracks: / Your imagination / Burned out love / Things you do, The / Only in my sleep / Karen / Satisfies, The / Girls of today / Hopin' shes the one / When it hits / Yes or no / Found a girl / Hate to run.
LP: . . . . **K 52261**

Shoes Of The Fisherman

SHOES OF THE FISHERMAN, THE (Original Soundtrack) (Various artists).
LP: . . . . **MCA 25130**
MC: . . . . **MCAC 25130**

Shoes Were For Sunday

SHOES WERE FOR SUNDAY (Weir, Molly).
MC: . . . . **CAB 001**

Shogun

HIGH IN THE SKY.
Tracks: / High in the sky.
LP: . . . . **ATA 913**

Shogun (Film)

SHOGUN (Original Soundtrack) (Various artists).
Tracks: / Shogun: *Shogun* / Japans, The: *Shogun* / Tea and jealousy: *Shogun* / Nocturne: *Shogun*/ Toranga: *Shogun* / To the galley: *Shogun* / Miriko: *Shogun* / Ceremonial: *Shogun* / Despair and madness: *Shogun* / Anjiro: *Shogun* / Blackthorne: *Shogun* / Escape from Osaka: *Shogun* / Finale: *Shogun* / Cloak and dagger: *Shogun* / Shock to the heart: *Shogun* / Voices from the heart: *Shogun*/ You are what you are: *Shogun* / Love is a game: *Shogun* / Cold truth: *Shogun* / If tomorrow comes: *Shogun*/ Can't live without your love: *Shogun* / First time: *Shogun* / Out of love again: *Shogun.*

LP: ATA 006
LP: 2394 283
MC: 3216 283
LP: JETLP 248
MC: JETCA 248

Shojitabuchi

SHOJITABUCHI FIDDLES AND SINGS.
LP: JIN 4008

Shok Paris

STEEL AND STARLIGHT.
LP: ILP 020
MC: ILPC 020

Sholle, Jon

CATFISH FOR SUPPER (Sholle, Jon & Grisman Bromberg).
LP: ROUNDER 3026
MC: ROUNDER 3026C

Shondell, Troy

MANY SIDES OF TROY SHONDELL.
LP: LPBR 5602

Shondells

SHORT SHARP SHOTS (see under James, Tommy) (Shondells/Tommy James).

Shook, Robert L.

PERFECT SALES PRESENTATION, THE (Secrets of Success series).
MC: 0600560643

Shooting From...

SHOOTING FROM THE HIP (Various artists).
LP: GILP 999

Shooting Party (film)

SHOOTING PARTY, THE (Original soundtrack) (Royal Philharmonic Orchestra).
LP: STV 81235

Shooting Star

HANG ON FOR YOUR LIFE.
LP: V 2221

III WISHES.
LP: V 2235

SHOOTING STAR.
LP: V 2130

SILENT SCREAM.
LP: V 2358
MC: TCV 2358

Shooting Times

SHOOTING TIMES (Random shots) (Eddington, Paul).
MCSET: ZBBC 1159

Shop Assistants

WILL ANYTHING HAPPEN.
Tracks: / I don't wanna be friends with you / All day long / Before I wake / Caledonian Road / All that ever mattered / Fixed grin / Somewhere in China / Train from Kansas City / Home again / Seems to be / After dark / All of the time / What a way to die / Nature lover.
LP: AZLP 2
MC: ZAZLP 2

Shopping Trolley

SHOPPING TROLLEY.
LP: HNBL 1349
MC: HNBC 1349

Shore, Dinah

BEST OF DINAH SHORE.
Tracks: / Sentimental journey / Chantez, chantez / Hi-lili hi-lo / Blue canary / Sweet violets / What can I say after I say I'm sorry / Blues in the night / Memphis blues / Come rain or come shine / I got it bad and that ain't good / Deep purple / I concentrate on you.
LP: INTS 5062

BING AND DINAH SHORE (See under Crosby, Bing) (Shore, Dinah/Bing Crosby).

CAPITOL YEARS, THE: DINAH SHORE (Best Of).
Tracks: / I'm old fashioned / I only have eyes for you / Mississippi mud / It's so nice to have a man around the house / Our love is here to stay / Way down yonder in New Orleans / I hadn't anyone till you / Where or when / Easy to love / They can't take that away from me / It's easy to remember / South / Gipsy, The / Somebody loves me / I'm coming Virginia / Laughing on the outside (crying on the inside) / Buttons and bows / Sentimental journey.
LP: EMS 1342
MC: TCEMS 1342

'DEED I DO 1942-52.
Tracks: / Deed I do / On the sunny side of the street / Tess's torch song / Time on my hands / How high the moon / Sugar blues / At last / Until the real thing comes along / Night and day / I'm gonna love that guy / I've got the world on a string / Someone like you / It isn't fair / I feel a song coming on / Way you look tonight / Put 'em in a box, tie 'em with ribbon / You do something to me / Beat me daddy, eight to the bar / This can't be love / My guy's come back.
LP: HEP 30

DINAH SHORES GREATEST HITS.
Tracks: / I'll walk alone / Buttons and bows / Gypsy, The / Blues in the night / Laughing on the outside (crying on the inside) / Jim / Dear hearts and gentle people / It's so nice to have a man around the house / Chantez, chantez.
MC: 4XL 9447

DINAH SINGS, PREVIN PLAYS (Shore, Dinah & Andre Previn).
Tracks: / Man I love, The / April in Paris / That old feeling / I've got you under my skin / Then I'll be tired of you / Sleepy time gal / My melancholy baby / My funny valentine / It had to be you / I'll be seeing you / If I had you.
LP: CAPS 2600081
MC: TC CAPS 2600084

DINAH SINGS SOME BLUES WITH RED (Shore, Dinah & The Red Norvo Quintet).
Tracks: / Bye bye blues / I can't face the music / Someday, sweetheart / It's funny to everyone but me / Who / I can't believe that you're in love with me / I ain't got nothin' but the blues / Lucky in love / Do nothing till you hear from me / It's alright with me / Skylark / Lover, come back to me.
LP: EG 2606091
MC: EG 2606094

DINAH, YES INDEED!.
Tracks: / It all depends on you / Falling in love with love / Where or when / Easy to love / Get out of town / They can't take that away from me / Sentimental journey / One I love belongs to somebody else, The / I'm old fashioned / Love is here to stay / Taking a chance on love / Yes indeed.
LP: MFP 5606
MC: TCMFP 5606
LP: 2C 068 85290

HOLDING HANDS AT MIDNIGHT.
Tracks: / Nice work if you can get it / Easy to love / Come rain or come shine / Once in a while / It had to be you / You're driving me crazy / That great come and get it day / Moanin' in the mornin' / Under a blanket of blue / Taking a chance on love / I concentrate on you / Yesterdays.
LP: NL 89467
MC: NK 89467

LAVENDER BLUE.
Tracks: / They didn't believe me / They can't take that away from me / I may be wrong (but I think you're wonderful) / Gypsy, The / Anniversary song / It's easy to remember / Come rain or come shine / It all depends on you / Little white lies / Golden earrings / I'll be seeing you / Lavender blue / Laughing on the outside (crying on the inside) / I get along without you very well.
LP: MOIR 122
MC: CMOIR 122

MOMENTS LIKE THESE.
Tracks: / Deep purple / When the world was young / Moments like this / I'll remember April / These foolish things / I fall in love too easily / What's new? / I can dream, can't I / Now I know / How long as this been going on? / Something wonderful.
LP: NL 90042
MC: NK 90042

Short Dogs Grow

MATT DILLON.
LP: ROUGHUS 037

Short, J.D.

EARLY RECORDINGS 1930-33.
LP: WSE 118

LEGACY OF THE BLUES VOL. 8 (See under Legacy of the Blues).

Short, Luke

MAN COULD GET KILLED, A (Clancy, Jack).
MCSET: CAB 258

Short, Memphis

I'M JUST ME...COUNTRY STYLE.
LP: BSS 354

Shorter, Wayne

ADAM'S APPLE.
Tracks: / Adam's apple / 502 blues (drinkin' and drivin') / El gaucho / Footprints / Teru / Chief Crazy Horse / Collector, The.
LP: BST 84232
MC: 4BN 84232

ATLANTIS.
Tracks: / Endangered species / Three Marias, The / Last silk hat, The / When you dream / Who goes there? / Atlantis / Shere Khan / Criancas / On the eve of departure.
LP: CBS 26669
MC: 40 26669

BEST OF WAYNE SHORTER (Blue Note Years).
Tracks: / Speak no evil / Infant eyes / Tom Thumb (CD only.) / Lost / Adam's apple / Footprints / Virgo (CD only.) / Ju ju (CD only.) / Water babies (CD only.).
LP: B1 91141

BLUES A LA CARTE.
Tracks: / Blues a la carte / Harry's last stand / Down in the depths / Pug nose / Black diamond / Mack the knife.
LP: AFF 144

ETCETERA.
Tracks: / Etcetera / Penelope / Toy tune / Barracudas / Indian song.
LP: LBR 1037

JOY RYDER.
Tracks: / Someplace called 'where' / Joy ryder / Cathay / Over Shadow Hill way / Anthem / Causeways / Daredevil.
LP: 4606781
MC: 4606784

JU JU.
Tracks: / Ju ju / Deluge / House of jade / Mahjong / Yes and no / Twelve more bars to go.
LP: BST 84182
MC: 4BN 84182

NATIVE DANCER.
MC: 4670954

PHANTOM NAVIGATOR.
Tracks: / Condition red / Mahogany bird / Remote control / Ya manja / Forbidden, plan-it! / Flagships.
LP: 4503651
MC: 4503654

POWER OF THREE (VIDEO) (See under Petrucciani, Michel) (Petrucciani, Michel/Wayne Shorter/Jim Hall).

SECOND GENESIS.
Tracks: / Ruby and the pearl / Pay as you go / Second Genesis / Mister chairman / Tenderfoot / Albatross / Getting to know you / I didn't know what time it was.
LP: AFF 114

SOOTHSAYER, THE (IMPORT).
Tracks: / Lost / Angola / Angola (alt. take) / Big push, The / Soothsayer, The / Lady Day / Valse triste.
LP: LBR 1021

SPEAK NO EVIL.
Tracks: / Fee fi fo fum / Dance cadaverous / Speak no evil / Infant eyes / Wild flower / Out to lunch / Straight up and down / Witch hunt.
LP: BST 84194

SUPER NOVA.
Tracks: / Super nova / Swee-pee / Dindi (pronounced "Jin-jee") / Water babies / Capricorn / More than human.
LP: B1 84332

WAYNE SHORTER.
2LP: GNPS 2-2075

WAYNING MOMENTS.
Tracks: / Black Orpheus / Devils' Island / Moon of Manakoora / Dead end / Wayning moments / Powder keg / All or nothing at all / Callaway went that-a-way.
LP: AFF 126

Shorthouse, Bert

DANCE AWAY (Shorthouse, Bert & The Glenlomond Scottish Band).
Tracks: / Jessie's hornpipe / Eva three step / Strip to the willow / Gay Gordons / Flowers of Edinburgh / West Coast barn dance / Slosh, The (A la Scottish).
LP: LOCLP 1003
MC: ZCLOC 1003

MERRY CHRISTMAS AND A HAPPY NEW YEAR, A (Shorthouse, Bert/Swingalongs).
Tracks: / Jingle bells / Silent night / O little town of Bethlehem / Hark the herald angels sing / God rest ye merry gentlemen / Holly and the ivy, The / While shepherds watched their flocks by night / See, amid the winter's snow / Once in Royal David's city / Ding dong merrily on high / We three kings of Orient are / I saw three ships / Away in a manger.
2LP: DL 41 1068 3
MC: DL 41 1068 9
2LP: DL 1068
MC: TCDL 1068

...WITH FRIENDS (Shorthouse, Bert & The Glenlomond Scottish Band).
Tracks: / Lass o'bon accord, The / Conundrum, The / New rigged ship, The / Tam Bains lum / Lum / Jean / Gay Gordons / Dashing white sergeant / Bonnie Tiree / Singalong medley / Isle of Mull / Green glens of Antrim / Train journey, The / North / Kinross two-step, The.
MC: ZCLOC 1017
LP: LOCLP 1017

Shortwave Band

GREATEST HITS: SHORTWAVE BAND.
Tracks: / Fistful of fiddles / Spatter the dew / Drunken sailor / King of the fairies, The / Down the hill / Irish wolfhound / Clog dance / Girl who broke my heart / Delvinside / Merrily kissed the Quaker.
LP: AVA 107

Shorty The President

PRESENTING SHORTY.
LP: CTLP 118

Shoscombe Old Place

SHOSCOMBE OLD PLACE (see under Sherlock Holmes).

Shostakovich

BALLET SUITES 1-3 (Scottish National Orchestra/ Harvi).
LP: ABRD 1376
MC: ABTD 1376

END GAMES (see under Brodsky Quartet) (Brodsky Quartet).

STRING QUARTET (See under Medici String Quartet for details) (Medici String Quartet).

STRING QUARTETS NO.7-9 (SHOSTAKOVICH) (Brodsky Quartet).
Tracks: / String quartet no.7 (Shostakovich) / String quartet no.8 (Shostakovich) / String quartet no.9 (Shostakovich).
MC: 244 919-4

SYMPHONIES NOS. 1 & 6 (Jarvi, Neeme).
LP: ABRD 1148
MC: ABTD 1148

SYMPHONY NO.5 /BALLET SUITE NO.5 (Jarvi, Neeme).
LP: ABRD 1336
MC: ABTD 1336

SYMPHONY NO.7 (SHOSTAKOVICH) (Jarvi, Neeme).
LP: ABRD 1312
MC: ABTD 1312

SYMPHONY NO.9 (SHOSTAKOVICH) (Jarvi, Neeme/Scottish National Orch.).
LP: ABRD 1279
MC: ABTD 1279

SYMPHONY NO.10 (SHOSTAKOVICH) (Scottish National Orchestra).
LP: ABRD 1319
MC: ABTD 1319

Shot Black & White

UNDERSTAND.
Tracks: / I believe / Underprivileged race / Far off / End of days / Man look around / Day in / Put down the arms / Understand / Freedom.
LP: SKAR 007

Shot In The Dark

SHOT IN THE DARK.
Tracks: / Playing with lightning / I want the moon / All my life / Turn around / Just as well / Shot in the dark / Make up my mind / Speak my language / Angry songs / Some towns.
LP: 2394297

Shotgun

BORN TO ROCK.
LP: LPL 8210

TENNESSEE ROCKIN'.
Tracks: / Cadillac 55 / Jubal cane / Tennessee rockin' / Hillbilly shuffle / Save me pretty baby / Saturday night rockin' / Boogie woogie feeling / Rockabilly rebel / Grey coat boy / Rock 'n' roll hotel / Pontiac 59 / Billygoat rock.
LP: MFLP 002

Shotgun Brides

NOTHIN' VENTURED.
Tracks: / Nothing ventured / Can't upset you / Why why why / Do what I do / Promises / Rock Hudson / So far away / Restless / Shakin' / Stop looking / My time.
LP: NEAT 1045

Shotgun Messiah

SHOTGUN MESSIAH.
Tracks: / Bop city / Shout it out / Explorer, The / Dirt talk / Nervous / Don't care 'bout nothin' / Squeezin' teazin' / Nowhere fast / I'm your love.
LP: MFN 105
MC: TMFN 105

Shotts & Dykehead...

CHAMPION OF CHAMPIONS (Shotts & Dykehead Caledonia Pipe Band).
LP: LILP 5111
MC: LICS 5111

SHORES OF LOCH KATRINE (Shotts & Dykehead Caledonia Pipe Band).

Tracks: / Shores of Loch Katrine, The / Colonel Robertson / Dream valley of Glendaruel, The / Killiecrankie / Colonel Craig Brown / Archie McKinlay / Glendaurel highlanders / Loch Katrine / Glasgow week in Hamburg.
LP: LILP 5009
MC: LICS 5009

SHOTTS & DYKEHEAD CALEDONIA PIPE BAND (Shotts & Dykehead Caledonia Pipe Band).
Tracks: / Cullen Bay / Mrs. Flora Duncan / Dr. Cam Stewart / Ariston castle / Dolina MacKay / Carradale Bay / Isle of Man highland games / Caver Hill / MacNeill's farewell toBarra / Major Nickerson's fancy / Judge's dilemma, The / P/M Wm. Gray's farewell to Glasgow Police / Royal Scottish pipers' society, The / Brig. Gen. Ronald Cheape of Tiroran / P/M Donald McLean of Lewis / Tug argan gap / Argyllshire gathering, The / Conundrum, The / John Macdonald of Glencoe / Colin's cattle / Shoal's herring / Lewis A. Turrell's unnamed tune / Balmoral / Paddy's leather breeches / Donald Cameron's powder horn / Lucy Cassidy / Children of Tarbert / Scots Guards farewell to Toronto, The / Dhorlin, The / Dundee city police pipe band / J.A. Burgess.
LP: LILP 5038
MC: LICS 5038

Shout

IN YOUR FACE.
Tracks: / Borderline / Give me an answer / Getting ready / Getting on with life / Ain't givin' up / When the love is gone / Faith hope and love / In your face / Moonlight sonata / Waiting on you.
LP: MFN 92
MC: TMFN 92

IT WON'T BE LONG.
LP: MFN 88
MC: TMFN 88

Show Boat

SHOW BOAT (Original soundtrack) (Various artists).
Tracks: / Make believe: *Various artists* / Bill: *Various artists* / Can't help lovin' dat man: *Various artists*/ Life upon the wicked stage: *Various artists* / You are love: *Various artists* / I might fall back on you: *Various artists* / Why do I love you: *Various artists* / Ol' man river: *Various artists.*
LP: CBS 70281
MC: 40 70281

SHOW BOAT (HMV) (Various artists).
LPS: RIVER 1
MCSET: TCRIVER 1
2LP: EX 7491081
MCSET: EX 7491084

SHOW BOAT (ORIGINAL ISSUE) (Studio cast recording) (Various artists).
LP: CLP 1310

SHOW BOAT - THE BROADWAY ALBUM (Highlights) (Various artists).
Tracks: / Show Boat overture: *Various artists* / Cotton blossom: *Various artists* / Where's the mate for me: *Various* artists / Make believe: *Various artists* / Ol' man river: *Various artists* / Can't help lovin' dat man: *Various* artists / Life on the wicked stage: *Various artists* / Till good luck comes my way: *Various artists* / I might fall back on you: *Various artists* / Queenie's ballyhoo: *Various artists* / You are love: *Various artists*/ Show Boat Finale Act 1: *Various artists* / At the fair: *Various artists* / Why do I love you: *Various artists*/ Bill: *Various artists* / Goodbye my Lady love: *Various artists* / After the ball: *Various artists* / Hey, feller: *Various artists* / Finale ultimo: *Various artists.*
LP: EL 7498471
MC: EL 7498474

SHOWBOAT (Original Broadway Cast) (Various artists).
LP: AC 55
MC: BT 55

SHOWBOAT (Original London cast) (Various artists).
LP: OCR 1
MC: OCRC 1

SHOWBOAT (Original 1971 London Cast) (Various artists).
Tracks: / Cotton blossom: *Various artists* / Where's the mate for me: *Various artists* / Make believe: *Various* artists / Can't help lovin' dat man: *Various artists* / I might fall back on you: *Various artists* / Ol' man river: *Various artists* / How'd you like to spoon with me: *Various artists* / You are love: *Various artists*/ Queenie's ballyhoo: *Various artists* / Nobody else but me: *Various artists* / At the fair: *Various artists*/ Bill: *Various artists* / Dance away the night: *Various artists* / Why do I love you?: *Various artists*/ Finale: *Various artists.*
LP: TER 1057
MC: ZCTER 1057

SHOWBOAT (1962) (1962 Revival Cast With Barbara Cook) (Various artists).
LP: PS 02220
MC: PST 02220

SHOWBOAT/BANDWAGON (Film Soundtracks) (Various artists).
Tracks: / Ol' man river: *Warfield, William* (Showboat) / Make believe: *Keel, Howard/Kathryn Grayson* (Showboat) / I might fall back on you: *Champion, Gower & Marge* (Showboat) / Can't help lovin' dat man: *Gardner, Ava* (Showboat) / Why do I love you: *Keel, Howard/ Kathryn Grayson* (Showboat) / Bill: *Gardner, Ava* (Showboat) / Life upon the wicked stage: *Champion, Gower & Marge* (Showboat) / You are love: *Keel, Howard/Kathryn Grayson* (Showboat) / Ol' man river (reprise): *Warfield, William* (Showboat) / Shine on your shoes, A: *Astaire, Fred* (Band Wagon) / By myself: *Astaire, Fred* (Band Wagon) / Dancing in the dark: *Various artists* (Band Wagon) / Triplets: *Astaire, Fred/Nanette Fabray*/ Jack Buchanan (Band Wagon) / New sun in the sky: *Various artists* (Band Wagon) / I guess I'll have to change my plans: *Adams, India* (Band Wagon) / Louisiana hayride: *Fabray, Nanette* (Band Wagon) / I love Louisa: *Astaire, Fred* (Band Wagon) / That's entertainment: *Astaire, Fred/Nanette Fabray/Jack Buchanan* (Band Wagon).
LP: LPMGM 10
MC: TCMGM 10

Show Of Hands

SHOW OF HANDS.
Tracks: / Time passes / Another war / Live animals / Real love / Contagious / Hard lines / Retribution / Far away / God made the world / What have we done / Think again.
LP: EIRSA 1009
MC: EIRSAC 1009

Show Side Of David

SHOW SIDE OF DAVID JACOBS (see under Jacobs, David) (Jacobs, David with various artists).

Show Stoppers

SHOWSTOPPERS (Various artists).
LP: ADL 513
MC: ADK 513

Showaddywaddy

BEST STEPS TO HEAVEN, THE.
Tracks: / Hey rock 'n' roll / Sweet music / Three steps to heaven / Trocadero / Rock and roll lady / Heartbeat / When / Under the moon of love / You got what it takes / Dancin' party / I wonder why / Little bit of soap, A / Pretty little angel eyes / Why do lovers break each other's hearts? / Blue moon / Why?.
LP: SHTV 1
MC: SHMC 1

BRIGHT LIGHTS.
MC: SHOTC 6
LP: SHOLP 6
LP: SPART 1142

CREPES & DRAPES.
Tracks: / Sweet little rock'n'roller / Sea cruise / Just a country boy / Lost / That's rock'n'roll / Twist and shout / Night at Daddy Gees / Come on let's go / That's alright with me / I appreciate the job / Win your heart / Remember then.
MC: SHOTC 5
LP: SHOLP 5
LP: ARTV 3

GOOD TIMES.
MC: SHOTC 7
LP: SHOLP 7
LP: BELLS 271

GREATEST HITS: SHOWADDYWADDY.
Tracks: / Hey rock'n'roll / Rock'n'roll lady / Sweet music / Chain gang / King of the jive / Trocadero / Three steps to heaven / Heartbeat / Heavenly / Johnny remember me / Under the moon of love / Hey Mr. Christmas.
LP: GENIELP 1
MC: GENIELC 1
LP: ARTY 145
LP: ARTV 1

JUMP, BOOGIE AND JIVE.
LP: PTLS 1112
MC: PTLC 1112

LIVING LEGENDS.
Tracks: / Who put the bomp / It's so easy / I don't want to dream anymore / Fooling around with my heart / Things / You're my soul and inspiration / Little ole wine drinker me / Goody goody / Don't bring me down / Sorry (I ran all the way) / Mona Lisa / Run for your life / Hey little girl.
LP: RCALP 6069
MC: RCAK 6069
MC: SHOTC 8
LP: SHOLP 8

RED STAR.
MC: SHOTC 4
LP: SHOLP 4
LP: SPARTY 1023

ROCK ON WITH SHOWADDYWADDY.
Tracks: / Hey rock'n'roll / Sweet music / King of the jive / Lookin' back / Trocadero / Under the moon of love / Pretty little angel eyes / You got what it takes / Rollercoaster / Don't turn your back on me baby / Superstar / When.
LP: MFP 50504
MC: TCMFP 50504

SHOWADDYWADDY.
Tracks: / Hey rock 'n' roll / Heartbeat / Rock and roll lady / In above your head / Windows / Sweet little rock 'n' roller / You've got personality / Teen canteen / Smiling eyes / Hey Mr. Christmas / Heavenly / I wonder why.
LP: SHM 3105
MC: HSC 3105
MC: SHOTC 1
LP: SHOLP 1
LP: BELLS 248

STEP TWO.
MC: SHOTC 2
LP: SHOLP 2
LP: BELLS 256

TROCADERO.
MC: SHOTC 3
LP: SHOLP 3
LP: SYBEL 8003

UNDER THE MOON OF LOVE.
Tracks: / Under the moon of love / Rock and roll lady / When (Extra track available on 12" version only.) / Heartbeat (Extra track available on 12" version only.) / Sweet music / Trocadero / Remember then / Blue moon / Come on let's go / Something else / Dancin' party / Night at Daddy Gee's, A / Footsteps / Sea Cruise / King of the jive / Temptation / Little bit of soap, A.
LP: MFP 41 5703 1
MC: MFP 41 5703 4

VERY BEST OF SHOWADDYWADDY.
LP: SPART 1178

Showcase 883

MUSIC WORKS.
LP: 2001

Showmen

SOME FOLKS DON'T UNDERSTAND IT.
Tracks: / It will stand / Country fool / This misery / Wrong girl, The / Fate planned it this way / For you my darling / Valley of love / Owl sees you, The / Swish fish / I'm coming home / Strange girl / I love you, can't you see / Let her feel it in your kiss / True fine mama / 39-21-40 shape / It will stand.
LP: CRB 1165
MC: TCCRB 1165

Showpieces For...

SHOWPIECES FOR ORCHESTRA (Various artists).
MC: TC2MOM 109

Shows

50 FAVOURITE SHOWSTOPPERS (Various artists).
MCSET: TR 4115455
MCSET: TR 1545

70, GIRLS, 70 (Original London Cast) (Various artists).
MC: ZCTER 1186

ANNIE GET YOUR GUN (Berlin, Irving).
MC: TCANNIE 1

ARE YOU LONESOME TONIGHT (Original London cast) (Various artists).
Tracks: / Peace in the valley: *Various artists* / Heartbreak hotel: *Various artists* / That's alright mama: *Various* artists / I don't care if the sun don't shine: *Various artists* / Loving you: *Various artists* / Blue suede shoes: *Various artists* / Hound dog: *Various artists* / If I can dream: *Various artists* / All my trials: *Various artists* / NBC-TV special (1988): *Various artists* / You gave me a mountain: *Various artists*/ I was the one: *Various artists* / If we never meet again: *Various artists* / Are you lonesome tonight: *Various artists.*
LP: CAST 1
MC: CASTC 1

BLITZ (Original London cast) (Various artists).
Tracks: / Our hotel: *Various artists* / Tell him, Tell her: *Various artists* / I want to whisper something: *Various* artists / We're going to the country: *Various artists* / Day after tomorrow, The: *Various artists* / Another morning: *Various artists* / Who's this geezer Hitler?: *Various artists* / Be what you wanna be: *Various artists*/ Opposities: *Various artists* / Entr'acte: *Various artists* / Far away: *Various artists* / Down the Lane: *Various artists* / Petticoat Lane(On a Saturday ain't so nice): *Various artists* / So tell me: *Various artists*/ Mums and Dads: *Various artists* / Who wants to settle down?: *Various artists* / Is this gonna be a wedding?: *Various artists* / Duty calls: *Various artists* / Blitz(finale): *Various artists.*
LP: TER 1056
MC: ZCTER 1056
LP: AEI 1117

BLOOD BROTHERS (1988 London Cast recording) (Various artists).
LP: CAST 17
MC: CASTC 17

BROADWAY MAGIC, VOL.2 (Various artists).
Tracks: / I'm always chasing rainbows: *Various artists* / Rain in Spain: *Various artists* / Miss Marmelstein: *Various artists* / Dream drummin': *Various artists* / Soft music: *Various artists* / Bosom buddies: *Various* artists / What do the simple folk do?: *Various artists* / Put on a happy face: *Various artists* / You'll never get away from me: *Various artists* / Two by two: *Various artists* / I want to be happy: *Various artists.*
LP: CBS 31845

BUDDY (Original London Cast Recording) (Various artists).
LP: QUEUE 1
MC: QUEUE C1

CARD, THE (Original London cast) (Various artists).
LP: AEI 1124
MC: OCRC 5

DAYS OF HOPE (Original London Cast) (Various artists).
MC: ZCTER 1183

GOLDEN SONGS OF STAGE AND SCREEN (See under Films...) (Various artists).

GRAND NIGHT FOR SINGING (Various artists).
Tracks: / It's a grand night for singing: *Various artists* / Heather on the hill: *Various artists* / On a clear day: *Various artists* / Oklahoma: *Various artists* / If I loved you: *Various artists* / Seventy-six trombones: *Various artists* / Look to the rainbow: *Various artists* / There but for you go I: *Various artists* / My favourite things: *Various artists* / Welcome home: *Various artists.*
LP: CBS 73867
MC: 40 73867

GREATEST RECORDINGS OF THE BROADWAY MUSICAL THEA (Archive collection) (Various artists).
LPS: UNKNOWN

JOSEPH & AMAZING TECHNICOLOR DREAMCOAT (Original Cast) (Various artists).
Tracks: / Jacob and sons: *Various artists* / Joseph's dreams: *Various artists* / Poor, poor Joseph: *Various* artists / One more angel in heaven: *Various artists* / Potiphar: *Various artists* / Close every door: *Various* artists / Go go go Joseph: *Various artists* / Pharaoh story: *Various artists* / Poor poor Pharoah: *Various* artists / Pharoah's dreams explained: *Various artists* / Brothers come to Egypt, The: *Various artists* / Benjamin calypso: *Various artists* / Joseph all the time: *Various artists* / Jacob in Egypt: *Various artists* / Stone the crows: *Various artists* / Those Canaan days: *Various artists* / Any dream will do: *Various artists*/ Grovel grovel: *Various artists* / Song of the King: *Various artists* / Who's the thief?: *Various artists.*
LP: SPELP 6
MC: SPEMC 6
LP: MFP 50455
LP: 2394 102
MC: 3216 003
MC: HR 8200

JOSEPH & THE AMAZING TECHNICOLOR DREAMCOAT (Various artists).
LP: 5111301
MC: 5111304

LES MISERABLES (Original London cast) (Various artists).
Tracks: / At the end of the day: *Various artists* / I dreamed a dream: *Various artists* / Lovely ladies: *Various artists* / Who am I?: *Various artists* / Come to me: *Various artists* / Confrontation: *Various artists*/ Castle on a cloud: *Various artists* / Master of the house: *Various artists* / Stars: *Various artists*/ Look down: *Various artists* / Little people: *Various artists* / Red and black: *Various artists* / Do you hear the people sing?: *Various artists*/ I saw him once in my life: *Various artists* / Heart full of love, A: *Various artists* / One day more: *Various artists* / On my own: *Various artists* / Attack, The: *Various* artists / Little fall of rain, A: *Various artists* / Drink with me: *Various*

artists / Bring him home: *Various* artists / Dog eat dog: *Various artists* / Soliloquy: *Various artists* / Empty chairs at empty tables: *Various* artists / Wedding chorale: *Various artists* / Beggars at the feast: *Various artists* / Finale: *Various artists*.
LP: ENCORE 1
MC: ENCOREC 1

LES MISERABLES (HIGHLIGHTS) (International recording) (Various artists).
MC: CASTC 20

LYRICS BY LERNER (Various artists).
LP: MRS 903

MISS SAIGON (Various artists).
LP: ENCORE 5
MC: ENCORE C5

OFF THE WALL (Various artists).
MC: SCENEC 20

OLIVER (All Star Cast) (Various artists).
MC: ZCTER 1184

PAL JOEY (Original London Cast) (Various artists).
MC: ZCTER 1005

PIRATES OF PENZANCE, THE (D'Oyly Carte Opera Company's 1989 Production) (Various artists).
MCSET: ZCTER2 1177

SALAD DAYS (Revival London cast) (Various artists).
Tracks: / Things that are done by a Don, The: *Various artists* / We said we wouldn't look back: *Various artists*/ Find yourself something to do: *Various artists* / I sit in the sun: *Various artists* / Oh, look at me: *Various* artists / Hush-hush: *Various artists* / Out of breath: *Various artists* / Cleopatra: *Various artists*/ Sand in my eyes: *Various artists* / It's easy to sing: *Various artists* / We're looking for a piano: *Various* artists / Time of my life, The: *Various artists* / Saucer song, The: *Various artists* / We don't understand our children: *Various artists*.
LP: TER 1018
MC: ZCTER 1018

STREET SCENE (Original London Cast) (Various artists).
MCSET: ZCTER2 1185

Shox Lumania

LIVE AT THE PEPPERMINT LOUNGE.
MC: A 105

Shrapnel

SHRAPNEL.
Tracks: / Didn't know I loved you / Nations / Master of my destiny / Hope for us all / It's a crime.
LP: 9602811

Shreeve, Mark

ASSASSIN.
Tracks: / Assassin / Angel of fire / Tyrant / System six.
LP: U 021
LP: HIP 21
MC: HIPC 21

CARE.
LP: YLP 502
MC: YK 502

CRASH HEAD.
Tracks: / Crash head / Darkness comes / Edge of darkness / Dead zone, The / Shrine / Angels of death / It / Night church / Hellraiser.
LP: HIP 42
MC: HIPC 42

LEGION.
Tracks: / Legion / Storm column / Flags / Sybex factor / Domain 7 / Con / Stand, The.
LP: HIP 28
MC: HIPC 28

THOUGHTS OF WAR.
LP: U 001

Shrew Kings

10 X OVER.
MC: CRUST 15

SAD BUT TRUE.
LP: SLICE 10

Shriekback

BEST OF SHRIEKBACK, THE.
MC: ICT 9960
LP: ILPS 9960

BEST OF SHRIEKBACK VOLUME 2.
Tracks: / Nemesis / Fish below the ice / Hand on my heart / New home / Despite dense weed / Midnight maps / Mercy dash / Malaria / Under the lights / My careful hands / Nerve / Lines from the library.
LP: KAZ LP 5
MC: KAZ MC 5

BIG NIGHT MUSIC.
Tracks: / Underwaterboys / Exquisite / Reptiles and I, The / Sticky jazz / Cradle song / Black light trap / Gunning for the Buddha / Running on the rocks / Shining path / Pretty little thing.
LP: ILPS 9849
MC: ICT 9849

GO BANG.
Tracks: / Intoxication / Shark-walk / Nighttown / Dust and shadow / Go bang / New man / Big fun.
LP: ILPS 9910
MC: ICT 9910

INFINITE, THE.
Tracks: / Lined up / Clear trails / Accretions / Sway / Madness into method / My spine (is the bass line) / Mothloop / Sexthinkone / Evaporation / Kind of fascination, A / Working on the ground.
LP: KAZ LP 1
MC: KAZ MC 1

JAM SCIENCE.
Tracks: / Hand on my heart / Newhome / Achtung / Party line / Midnight maps / Mercy dash / Under the lights / My careful hands / Suck / Hubris.
LP: 206416
MC: 406416

OIL AND GOLD.
Tracks: / Malaria / Everything that rises must converge / Fish below the ice / This big hush / Faded flowers / Nemesis / Only thing that shines / Health and knowledge and wealth and power / Hammerhead / Coelocanth.
LP: 207206
MC: 407206

Shrieve, Michael

BIG PICTURE, THE (Shrieve, Michael & David Beal).
LP: LPFOR 17060-1
MC: MCFOR 17060-4

STILETTO.
Tracks: / Scratch / Moon over you / Las Vegas tango / Gauguin's regret / Stilleto / Four winds / Bella coola.
LP: PL 83050
MC: PK 83050

TRANSFER STATION BLUE.
LP: LPFOR 23
MC: MCFOR 23

Shrieve & Roach

LEAVING TIME, THE.
Tracks: / Leaving time, The / March of honor / San Diego / Theme from the far away / Tribes / Big sky / Edge runner.
LP: PL 83032
MC: PK 83032

Shropshire Lad

SHROPSHIRE LAD, A (Various artists).
Tracks: / Shropshire lad, A: *Various artists* / Far in a western brookland & tis time: *Various artists* / I think: *Various artists* / By Wenlock Town: *Various artists* / When the lad for longing sighs & Reveille & in: *Various* artists / Along the field: *Various artists* / Lent Lily, The: *Various artists* / Oh when I was in love with you: *Various artists* / Ludlow town: *Various artists* / When I was one and twenty: *Various artists* / Far in a western playtown: *Various artists*.
2LP: E 77031 2
MCSET: KE 77031 2

Shrubs

VESSELS OF THE HEART.
LP: DOM 2

Shtokolov, Boris

RUSSIAN SONGS & ROMANCES (BORIS SHTOKOLOV).
MC: SM 00051

Shucks

HILLBILLY SWING.
Tracks: / Gonna romp and stomp / San Antonio rose / Lowdown blues / Kinfolks in Carolina / Honey just allow me one more chance / Rainy night in Georgia / Mystery train / Blues stay away from me / Shotfun boogie / She came from the mountains / Unreal / Heartbreak mountain.
LP: SFA 072

TWO DAYS TWO TRACKS.
Tracks: / My shoes keep walking back to you / Two days two tracks / I'm gonna buy me a jukebox / Wabash cannonball / Mississippi river blues / Blue moon of Kentucky / Tennesse local / You win again / North to Alaska / What do I care / California blues / I won't go huntin' with you Jake.
LP: SFA 052

Shuffle The...(bk)

SHUFFLE THE SHOEMAKER.
MCSET: DTO 10552

Shulzhenko, K

FOLK SONGS.
MC: SM 00170

Shumsky, Oscar

MUSIC FOR VIOLIN & PIANO VOL. 4 (Shumsky, Oscar/William Wolfram).
Tracks: / Tambourin Chinois / Tchaikovsky: Andante Cantabille, Humoresque / Londonderry Air / Molly on the shore / Works in style of Chanson Louis XIII et Pavane / Scherzo (Dittersdorf) / Andantino (Martini) / Tambourin / Minuett.
LP: ALH 971
MC: ZC ALH 971

Shunters

SINCE MORNING.
LP: NC 002

Shusha

DURABLE FIRE Songs by English poets.
Tracks: / Ariel's song / Durable fire / True love doth pass away / Thomas the rhymer's song / Ophelia's song / So we'll go no more a roving / Lake Isle of Innisfree, The / Be not too hard / South of the great sea / Queen of love / Song of the wondering Angus / With silent melancholy / Sonet - shall I compare thee / Love and lass.
LP: LIN 1

FROM EAST TO WEST.
Tracks: / Tall girl / Sun is shining, The / Girl from Shiraz / I swear to God I love you / Wheat flower, The / Girl with little mouth / Stars in heaven / Oh Leyli / Violet, The.
MC: TGSMC 138
LP: TGS 138

HERE I LOVE YOU.
Tracks: / Here I love you / Pity the children / You can always feel it / Brief / Poet and the gypsy / Lola / Sunset on persepolis / King of hearts / Refugee / Idol, The.
LP: RHAP 2

PERSIAN LOVE SONGS & MYSTIC CHANTS.
LP: TNGS 108

SONG OF LONG-TIME LOVERS.
LP: TGS 114

Shut Up & Dance

DANCE BEFORE THE POLICE COME.
LP: SUADLP 001
MC: SUADC 001

Shute, Nevil (aut)

ON THE BEACH (Neill, Sam).
MCSET: LFP 7220

TOWN LIKE ALICE, A (McKern, Leo).
MCSET: LFP 7330

TOWN LIKE ALICE, A (Bailey, Robin (nar)).
MC: CAB 339

Shuur, Diane

PURE SHUUR.
Tracks: / Nobody does me / All caught up / Deed I do / What a difference a day makes / Touch / Baby, you got what it takes / Unforgettable / I could get used to this / You don't remember me / Hold out / We can only try.
LP: GRP 96281
MC: GRP 96284

Shy

BRAVE THE STORM.
Tracks: / Hold on / My apollo / Reflections / Keep the fires burning / Hunter, The / Shy / Brave the storm / Wild wild woman / Caught in the act / Was I wrong.
LP: PL 70605
MC: PK 70605

EXCESS ALL AREAS.
Tracks: / Emergency / Can't fight the nights / Young heart / Just love me / Break down the walls / Under fire / Devil woman / Talk to me / When the love is over / Telephone.
MC: PK 71221
LP: PL 71221

MISSPENT YOUTH.
LP: MCG 6069
MC: MCGC 6069

ONCE BITTEN TWICE SHY.
LP: EBON 15

Shy, Jean

TOUGH ENOUGH (Shy, Jean & Hannsjorg Scheid).
Tracks: / Are you tough enough / Maze (I just wanna escape) / How can you say that you're the one? / Rock my body tonight / Some day I'll go to Africa / Ricky tick / I wish I could find the way / Then you came.
LP: SOHOLP 7

Shy People (film)

SHY PEOPLE (Film Soundtrack) (Tangerine Dream).
Tracks: / Shy people / Joe's place / Harbour, The / Nightfall / Dancing on a white moon / Civilized illusions / Swamp voices / Transparent days / Shy people (reprise).
LP: FILM 027
MC: FILMC 027

Shy Reptiles

SHY REPTILES.
LP: 838701 1
MC: 838 701 4

Siam

FAREWELL.
Tracks: / Lovers / Phone for contact / Survivor / Hello / Runner, The / Daydream.
LP: VMA 001

Sibbles, Leroy

ALL FOR ONE,ONE FOR ALL (see Brown, Dennis/Leroy Sibble) (Sibbles, Leroy & Dennis Brown).

FRANKIE PAUL V LEROY SIBBLES (see under Paul, Frankie) (Sibbles, Leroy & Frankie Paul).

Sibelius (composer)

KALEVALA, THE (excerpts) (Richardson, Ian).
MC: CDL 51688

SYMPHONY NO. 1 IN E MINOR, OP 39 (Philharmonia Orchestra).
MC: 4250284

VIOLIN CONCERTI (see under Brodski, Vadim) (Brodsky, Vadim/Polish Radio National Symphony Orchestra).

Siberian Folk Choir

SIBERIAN STATE FOLK CHOIR.
LP: CM 02141-2

Siberian Four

HOMO LIBER.
LP: LR 114

Siberry, Jane

BOUND BY THE BEAUTY.
LP: WX 293
MC: WX 293C

SPECKLESS SKY, THE.
Tracks: / One more colour / Seven steps to the wall / Very large hat, The / Mien bitte / Vladimir - Vladimir / Mimi on the beach / Map of the world / Empty city, The / Taxi ride, The.
LP: 925578 1
MC: 925578 4

WALKING, THE.
Tracks: / White tent the raft, The / Red high heels / Goodbye / Ingrid / Lena is a white table / Walking, The / Lobby, The / Bird in the gravel, The.
LP: 925678 1
MC: 925678 4

Siburn, Innes

THATS WHAT THE BLUES.
LP: MFF 001

Sic

SPLIT ALBUM (Sic/ Rose Rose).
LP: DYL 2

Sic Boy Federation

EXPLODING BABY.
Tracks: / Sic boys / Exploding baby / British troops in Cyprus / Hanging out of the window / Lorry drivers song / Big windows in Tokyo / 10 Rillington Place / World disasters / Desperate to survive.
LP: MLP 2

Sic 'Em Dogs On

SIC 'EM DOGS ON (Various artists).
LP: HER 201

Sicilian (film)

SICILIAN, THE (Film Soundtrack) (Various artists).
Tracks: / Sicilian, The: *Hungarian State Symphony Orchestra* / Camilla returns from riding: *Hungarian State Symphony* Orchestra / Stealing grain: *Hungarian State Symphony Orchestra* / Camilla's horses: *Hungarian State Symphony Orchestra*/ On the stairs: *Hungarian State Symphony Orchestra* / Monastery ride: *Hungarian State Symphony Orchestra* / I'm not leaving...yet: *Hungarian State Symphony Orchestra* / Off to Palermo: *Hungarian State Symphony Orchestra* / Giuliano recovered: *Hungarian State Symphony Orchestra* / Monastery, The: *Hungarian State Symphony Orchestra* / Fire from heaven: *Hungarian State Symphony Orchestra* / Terranova: *Hungarian State Symphony Orchestra* / They join him: *Hungarian State Symphony Orchestra* / Little Guiliano: *Hungarian State Symphony Orchestra* / Don Massino in Rome: *Hungarian State Symphony Orchestra* / Jewel robbery, The: *Hungarian State Symphony Orchestra* / With this ring: *Hungarian State Symphony Orchestra* / Silvio's blessing: *Hungarian State Symphony Orchestra* / To Frisella's: *Hungarian State*

Symphony Orchestra / Confession, The: *Hungarian State Symphony Orchestra* / That's life, gentlemen: *Hungarian State Symphony Orchestra* / Meeting ends, The: *Hungarian State Symphony Orchestra* / Ginestra massacre: *Hungarian State Symphony Orchestra* / Giuliano's funeral: *Hungarian State Symphony Orchestra* / End title: *Hungarian State Symphony Orchestra*.
LP: . . . . . **V 2487**
MC: . . . . . **TCV 2487**

Sicily

FOLK MUSIC & SONGS OF SICILY (Various artists).
Tracks: / Peasant songs: *Various artists* / Songs of the salt workers: *Various artists* / Songs of the cart drivers: *Various artists* / Songs of the tuna fishers: *Various artists*.
LP: . . . . . **LLST 7333**

SICILIAN TRADITIONAL SONGS AND MUSIC (see under Carini, Baronessa De) (Carini, Baronessa De).

Sick Rose

FACES.
LP: . . . . . **EELP 006**

Sickler, Don

MUSIC OF KENNY DORHAM (Sickler, Don/Jimmy Heath/Cedar Walton).
LP: . . . . . **UP 27.17**

Sickness Of Snake

NIGHTMARE CULTURE (See under Current 93) (Sickness Of Snake/Current 93).

Sicroff, Elan

JOURNEY TO INACCESSIBLE PLACES.
Tracks: / Journey to inaccessible places / Hymns from a great temple (No 10) / Bokharian dervish, hadji asvatz-troov, The / Hymn for Easter Thursday / Hymns from a great temple (No 1) / Initiation of the priestess, The.
LP: . . . . . **EGED 45**
MC: . . . . . **EGEDC 45**

Sid & Nancy

SID AND NANCY - LOVE KILLS (Film Soundtrack) (Various artists).
Tracks: / Love kills: *Strummer, Joe* / Haunted: *Pogues* / Pleasure and pain: *Jones, Steve* / Chinese choppers: *Pray For Rain* / She never took no for an answer: *Cale, John* / Love kills: *Circle Jerks* / Off the boat: *Pray For Rain* / Dum dum club: *Strummer, Joe* / Burning room: *Pray For Rain* / Junk theme: *Pogues* / I wanna be your dog: *Oldman, Gary* / Taxi to heaven: *Pray For Rain*.
LP: . . . . . **MCG 6011**
MC: . . . . . **MCGC 6011**

Side By Side

SIDE BY SIDE (Various artists).
Tracks: / I'll say it's true: *Various artists* / On my knees: *Various artists* / Let's go down together: *Various* artists / When the saints go marching in: *Various artists* / Lily Dale: *Various artists* / I want to: *Various* artists / Would you lay with me: *Various artists* / Side by side: *Various artists* / I'll know you're gone: *Various artists* / Bye bye love: *Various artists* / Jo and the cowboy: *Various artists* / I hate the way I love it: *Various artists* / Sick, sober & sorry: *Various artists* / Love got in the way: *Various artists*/ No charge: *Various artists* / Lover boy please: *Various artists*.
LP: . . . . . **CBS 31812**
MC: **40 31812**

Side By Side By

SIDE BY SIDE BY SONDHEIM (Original London cast) (Various artists).
Tracks: / Comedy tonight: *Various artists* / Love is in the air: *Various artists* / Little things you do together, The: *Various artists* / You must meet my wife: *Various artists* / Getting married today: *Various artists*/ I remember: *Various artists* / Can that boy foxtrot: *Various artists* / Too many mornings: *Various artists*/ Company: *Various artists* / Another hundred people: *Various artists* / Barcelona: *Various artists* / Being alive: *Various artists* / I never do anything twice (Madam's song): *Various artists* / Bring on the girls: *Various artists* / Ah, Paree: *Various artists* / Buddy's blues: *Various artists* / Broadway baby: *Various* artists / You could drive a person crazy: *Various artists* / Everybody says don't: *Various artists* / There won't be trumpets: *Various artists* / Anyone can whistle: *Various artists* / Send in the clowns: *Various artists*/ Pretty lady: *Various artists* / We're gonna be alright: *Various artists* / Boy like that, A: *Various artists*/ Boy from ..., The: *Various artists* / If momma was married: *Various artists* / Losing my mind: *Various artists*/ Could I leave you: *Various artists* / I'm still here: *Various artists* / Side by side by side: *Various artists*.
2LP: . . . . . **BL 81851**
2LP: **CBL2 1851**
MC: . . . . . **DPMK 1037**
MC: . . . . . **GK 81851**

Side Effect

ALL ABOARD.
LP: . . . . . **E 160049**

PORTRAITS.
Tracks: / I can't play / Do it / Make you mine / Midnight lover / It's got to be love / Reggae dancin' / If you believe / Loveliest men in the town, The / Lords prayer, The.
LP: . . . . . **K 52295**

Side Effects

SIDE EFFECTS, THE.
LP: . . . . . **DB 58**

Sidebottom, Frank

5.9.88.
LP: . . . . . **IT 058**
MC: . . . . . **ITC 058**

13.9.88.
MC: . . . . . **IT 060**

Sidewalk

NON STOP HIT MIX.
Tracks: / Tragedy / I'm alive / I close my eyes and count to ten / I heard it through the grapevine / I feel love / One-two-three / Rescue me / Y.M.C.A. / High energy / Dancing in the street / Funkytown / Locomotion, The / Lay all your love on me / Lost in music / Everlasting love / Flashdance (what a feeling).
LP: . . . . . **SHM 3281**
MC: . . . . . **HSC 3281**

Sideway Look

SIDEWAY LOOK.
Tracks: / Spring again / Can't talk anymore / Till the bitter end / Just for the weekend / Knowing you from today / Freetown / Tell me tonight / Is this tomorrow? / One for you / Heartache.
LP: . . . . . **V 2323**
MC: . . . . . **TCV 2323**

Sidewinder

ALL WOUND UP.
LP: . . . . . **BSS 332**

CUACHA.
Tracks: / I can wait / Clock strikes twelve / Bell jar / I guess it doesn't matter anymore / More than that / Blood on our hands / Magazine / Inside / I'll go home / Hole in my head / What she said.
LP: . . . . . **SORC 1**

Sidhu, Amarjit

AHO.
LP: . . . . . **MUT 1044**
MC: . . . . . **CMUT 1044**

MELA.
LP: . . . . . **BHANGRA 8LP**
MC: . . . . . **BHANGRA 8MC**

NACHO METE NAL.
LP: . . . . . **MUT 1032**
MC: . . . . . **CMUT 1032**

SCHOOLE NAHI JANA.
LP: . . . . . **MUT 1113**
MC: . . . . . **CMUT 1113**

SHONKAN BHANGRE DEE.
MC: . . . . . **CMUT 1149**

Sidman, David

SPEAK OF THE SUN hard bop jazz (Sidman, David Quartet).
MC: . . . . . **GVMMC 401**

Sidney, Anthony

ANTHOLOGY - ANTHONY SIDNEY.
Tracks: / St. Patrick's Day / Snail stepper / Prologo / My classic soul / Changing shadow / April / Line of women in white, A / Wonder world / Peru / Little David.
LP: . . . . . **CONTE 149**

Sidney, Margaret

FIVE LITTLE PEPPERS, THE (Harris, Julie).
LP: . . . . . **TC 1533**
MC: . . . . . **CDL 1533**

Sidran, Ben

OLD SONGS FOR THE NEW DEPRESSION.
Tracks: / Easy Street / Piano players.
LP: . . . . . **AN 1004**

ON THE LIVE SIDE.
Tracks: / Doctor's blues, The / Piano players / Good travel agent, A / Mitsubishi boy / On the cool side / Space cowboy / Last dance.
LP: **370206-1**
MC: **370206-4**

TOO HOT TO TOUCH.
Tracks: / Shine a light on me / Enivre d'amour / Everything happens to me / Freedom jazz dance / On the sunny side / Critics / Too hot to touch / I wanna be a / Pepper / Longing for Bahia.
LP: **370108-1**
MC: **370108-4**

Siebel, Paul

LIVE WITH DAVID BROMBERG & GARY WHITE.
Tracks: / Lonesome house / Women make a fool out of me / I'm in the jailhouse now / If I could stay / You are my sunshine / I'm so lonesome I could cry / Pinto pony / It's a long way to Nashville / Louise / Honest Sam.
LP: . . . . . **RAG 1006**

Siegal Schwall

SIEGAL SCHWALL REUNION CONCERT, THE.
Tracks: / You don't love me like that / Devil / Leaving / Hey, Billie Jean / I wanna love ya / I think it was the wine / I don't want you to be my girl / When I've been drinking / Hush, hush.
LP: . . . . . **AL 4760**

Siege Of Troy

SIEGE OF TROY, THE (Various artists).
Tracks: / Siege of Troy: *Various artists* / Perseus and the gorgon: *Various artists* / Theseus: *Various artists*.
MC: . . . . . **ANV 646**

Siegel, Janis

AT HOME: JANIS SEIGEL.
Tracks: / Trouble man / Small day tomorrow / Million dollar secret, The / Night trane / Bob White / (If I had) rhythm in my nursery rhymes / Black coffee / From Vienna with love / Cruel master of my dreams, The.
LP: **781 748-1**
MC: **781 748-4**

EXPERIMENT IN WHITE.
Tracks: / Back to the islands / All the love in the world / Lovin' eyes / Hammer and nails / How high the moon / Don't get scared / Guess who I saw today? / To be with you / Jackie.
LP: . . . . . **K 50903**

Sierra Leone Music

SIERRA LEONE MUSIC (Various artists).
LP: . . . . . **ZS 41**

Siesta (film)

SIESTA (see under Davis, Miles) (Davis, Miles/Marcus Miller).

Siffre, Labi

CRYING, LAUGHING, LOVING, LYING.
LP: . . . . . **NSPL 28163**

LABI SIFFRE COLLECTION, THE.
Tracks: / Make my day / Too late / Watch me / My song / For the children / It must be love / Prayer / Crying, laughing, loving, lying / Nothing in the world like love / If you have faith / Some say / Fool me a good night / Just a little more line / Give love.
LP: . . . . . **CFRC 506**
MC: . . . . . **MCFRC 506**

MAKE MY DAY.
Tracks: / Make my day / Watch me / For the children / Prayer / Nothing in the world like love / Some say / Just a little more line / Words / Maybe tomorrow / I love you / Maybe / Talk about / Too late / My song / It must be love / Crying, laughing, loving, lying / If you have faith / Fool me a good night / Give love / Something on my mind / I don't know what's happened to ... / Bless the telephone / Who do you see / Cannock Chase.
2LP: . . . . . **VSOPLP 137**
MC: . . . . . **VSOPMC 137**

MAN OF REASON.
LP: . . . . . **WOL 1015**
MC: . . . . . **WOLMC 1015**

SINGER AND THE SONG.
LP: . . . . . **NSPL 28147**

SO STRONG.
Tracks: / Listen to the voices / Nothin's gonna change / I will always love you / All I wanna do / And the wind blows / (Something inside) So strong / Lovers / Hard road / I'm all right / When you're lonely.
LP: . . . . . **WOL 9**
MC: . . . . . **ZWOL 9**

Siger Band

HEALING.
LP: . . . . . **SPJ 533**

LIVE IN HUNGARY.
LP: . . . . . **SPJ 526**

Sigerson, Davitt

DAVITT SIGERSON.
Tracks: / You're a lover now / Praying at your alter / I never fall in love / Still obsession with you / Cry for love / Mood piece / Twist / Ain't it ever thus / Break my heart.
LP: . . . . . **ILPS 7011**

FALLING IN LOVE AGAIN.
LP: . . . . . **ILPS 7025**
MC: . . . . . **ICT 7025**

Sigler, Bunny

I'VE ALWAYS WANTED TO SING.
Tracks: / By the way you dance / I'm funkin' you tonight / Crying my eyes out / It's simple things you do / Half a man / Let's get freaky now / Glad to be your lover.
LP: . . . . . **SSLP 1512**

MY MUSIC.
Tracks: / I'm the bunny / My music / Thank you baby for last night / Come on and dance, dance, dance / Ladies man / Calling me back / Somebody loves you / Woman, woman / Just let me love you tonight / Can't believe that you love me.
LP: . . . . . **PIR 18765**

Siglo XX

BABIES ON A BATTLEFIELD.
Tracks: / Studio-sides.
2LP: . . . . . **ANT 0311**

FEAR AND DESIRE.
Tracks: / Fear and desire / Everything is on fire / Lost in violence / Sorrow and pain / 35 poems / On the third day / My sister called silence / Pain came, The.
LP: . . . . . **BIAS 87**

FLOWERS FOR THE REBELS.
Tracks: / Sister in the rain / Fear / No one is innocent / Afraid to tell / Sister suicide / Till the act is done / Shadows / Flesh and blood / Ride.
LP: . . . . . **BIAS 051**

LIVE SIDES.
Tracks: / Life-sides.
LP: . . . . . **ANT 0312**

SIGLO XX.
MLP: . . . . . **ANT 013**

UNDER A PURPLE SKY.
LP: . . . . . **BIAS 145**

Sigmund...

INNATE (Sigmund Und Sein Freund).
MLP: . . . . . **ANT 093**

LOVE LUST HATE (Sigmund Und Sein Freund).
LP: . . . . . **ANT 113**

Sigmund, Al

GUITAR MAGIC.
LP: . . . . . **ISST 144**

Sign

SIGN 2.
LP: . . . . . **POW 5504**

Sign Language

MONTREUX.
LP: **371058-1**
MC: **371058-4**

Signa, Tony

GRIDLOCK.
LP: . . . . . **SLP 8075**

STRAIGHT FROM THE TOP (See under DeAngelis, Jim) (Signa, Tony/Jim DeAngelis).

Signal To Noise Set

SIGNAL TO NOISE SET (Various artists).
LP: . . . . . **ONLY 2**

Signalman...

SIGNALMAN, THE/TO BE READ AT DUSK (see under Dickens, Charles) (Various artists).

Signorelli, Frank

1946-49 (See Napoleon, Phil) (Signorelli, Frank/ Phil Napoleon).

Sigue Sigue Sputnik

DRESS FOR EXCESS.
Tracks: / Albinoni Vs Star Wars (Pts. 1&2) / Boom boom satellite / Hey Jayne Mansfield superstar / Super crook blues / Rio rocks / Success / Dancerama / Orgasm / M.A.D. (mutual assured destruction) / Is this the future.
LP: . . . . . **PCS 7328**
MC: . . . . . **TCPCS 7328**

FIRST GENERATION.
LP: . . . . . **FREUD 35**

FLAUNT IT.
Tracks: / Love missile F1-11 / Sex bomb boogie / Atari baby / Rocket Miss U.S.A. / 21st Century boy / Massive retaliation / Teenage thunder / She's my man.
LP: . . . . . **PCS 7305**
MC: . . . . . **TCPCS 7305**
LPS: . . . . . **PCSS 7305**
MCSET: . . . . . **TCPCSS 7305**

MUSIC AND MEDIA INTERVIEW PICTURE DISC.
LPPD: . . . . . **MM 1204**

Silas Marner (bk)

SILAS MARNER (see under George, Eliot) (Dench, Judi).

Sileas

BEATING HARPS.
Tracks: / Pipers, The / Silver Whistle / Oh wee white rose of Scotland / Solos, The / Puirt a beul / Shore of Gruinard, The / Ca' The Yowes / Dogs, The / Beating harps.
MC: CSIF 1089
LP: SIF 1089

DELIGHTED WITH HARPS.
Tracks: / Brigs, The / Cadal chan fhaigh mi (I can get no sleep) / Reels / Eppie morrie / Air and reel / Da day dawn / Little cascade, The / Tha mulad / S coltach mi ri craobh gun duilleag / John Anderson my Jo / Judges dilemma / Inverness gathering, The.
LP: LAP 113
MC: LAP 113C

Silence

IN THE GARDEN OF EDEN.
LP: AUL 734

Silencers

BLUES FOR BUDDHA.
Tracks: / Answer me / Scottish rain / Real McCoy, The / Blues for Buddha, A / Walk with the night / Razor blades of love / Skin games / Wayfaring stranger / Sacred child / Sand and stars / My love is like a wave.
LP: PL 71859
MC: PK 71859

DANCE TO THE HOLY MAN.
Tracks: / Singing ginger / Robinson Crusoe in New York / Bulletproof heart / Art of self deception, The / I want you / One inch of heaven / Hey Mr. Bank Manager / This is serious/ John the revelator / Afraid to love / Rosanne / Electric storm / When the night comes down / Robinson rap / Just can't be bothered (Track on cassette/ CD only.) / Cameras and colliseums (Track on cassette/ CD only.).
LP: PL 74924
MC: PK 74924

LETTER FROM ST.PAUL, A.
Tracks: / Painted moon / I can't cry / Bullets and blue eyes / God's gift / I see red / I ought to know / Letter from St. Paul, A / Blue desire / Possessed.
MC: PK 71336
LP: PL 71336

Silent Guests

IN MY SECRET GARDEN.
LP: PROP 1

Silent Running

DEEP.
Tracks: / Deep in the heart of nowhere / Angel of mercy / When will I learn / Sunshine in the rain / Deliverance / Everything your heart desires / Strength of our love / Flame of love / Local hero / Something so wrong.
LP: 782 006-1
MC: 782 006-4

SHADES OF LIBERTY.
Tracks: / Home is where the heart is / Emotional warfare / One in a million day / Sticks and stones / That's life / Shades of liberty / Crimson days / young hearts / Go for the heart.
LP: PCS 2401171

WALK ON FIRE.
Tracks: / Sanctuary / Heartland / Hunger, The / Heartbreak city / Walk on fire / Winds of war / Under your skin / Till tomorrow comes.
LP: 781 797-1
MC: 781 797-4

Silent Running (film)

SILENT RUNNING (Film soundtrack) (Various artists).
LP: VC 81072
LP: STV 81072

Silent Witness

SILENT WITNESS, THE (Film soundtrack) (Various artists).
LP: GULP 1030
MC: ZCGUL 1030

Silhouettes

AIN'T SHE SWEET.
LP: VA 4

GO LATIN.
LP: VA 2

Silicon Chips

SILICON CHIPS - THEIR IMPACT (See under UNESCO reports).

SILICON CHIPS - THEIR USES (See under UNESCO reports).

Silicon Teens

MUSIC FOR PARTIES.
LP: STUMM 2

Silje

TELL ME WHERE YOU'RE GOING (ALBUM).
Tracks: / Tell me where you're going / Fall / Roundabout / Middle of love, The / Move along Ruby / Meter's running, The / Welcome to another day / Faces / Louie come back / For tomorrow / Tell me where you're going / Marlena (Not on album.) / Waltz for you (Not on album.).
LP: LPLIF 1001
LP: 794 487 1
MC: TCLIF 1001
MC: 794 487 4

Silk, J.M.

HOLD ON TO YOUR DREAM.
Tracks: / Intro mix in E-flat minor / I can't turn around / On the rebound / Let the music take control / Jack your body / She's so far away / Lucky to be loved / Shadows of your love / Cry of the lonely / Heart of passion.
LP: PL 86249
MC: PK 86249

Silk Stockings

SILK STOCKINGS (Film soundtrack) (Various artists).
Tracks: / Too bad: *Various artists* / Paris loves lovers: *Various artists* / Stereophonic sound: *Various artists* / It's a chemical reaction: *Various artists* / That's all of you: *Various artists* / Satin and silk: *Various artists* / Silk stockings: *Various artists* / Without love: *Various artists* / Fated to be mated: *Various artists* / Josephine: *Various artists* / Siberia: *Various artists* / Red blues..: *Various artists* / Ritz roll and rock: *Various artists*.
LP: CBS 70290
MC: 40 70290
LP: MCA 39074
MC: MCAC 39074

SILK STOCKINGS/LES GIRLS (Various artists).
Tracks: / Too bad: *Astaire, Fred/Peter Lorre/Joseph Buloff/Jules Munshin* (Silk Stockings.) / Paris loves lovers: *Astaire, Fred/Cyd Charisse/Carol Richards* (Silk Stockings.) / Stereophonic sound: *Astaire, Fred/Janis Paige* (Silk Stockings.) / It's a chemical reaction, that's all/All of you: *Astaire, Fred/Cyd Charisse/Carol Richards* (Silk Stockings.) / Satin and silk: *Paige, Janis* (Silk Stockings.) / Without love: *Astaire, Fred/Cyd Charisse/Carol Richards* (Silk Stockings.) / Fated to be mated: *Astaire, Fred/Cyd Charisse/Carol Richards* (Silk Stockings.) / Josephine: *Paige, Janis* (Silk Stockings.) / Siberia: *Lorre, Peter/ Joseph Buloof/Jules Munshin* (Silk Stockings.) / Red blues: *Russians* (Silk Stockings.) / Ritz roll and rock, The: *Astaire, Fred* (Silk Stockings.) / Too bad: *Charisse, Cyd/Peter Lorre/Joseph Buloff/Jules Munshin* (Silk Stockings.) / Les girls: *Kelly, Gene/Kendall, Kay/Mitzi Gaynor/Tania Elg* (Les Girls.) / You're just too too: *Kelly, Gene/Kay Kendall* (Les Girls.) / Ca, c'est l'amour: *Elg, Tania* (Les Girls.) / Ladies in waiting: *Gaynor, Mitzi/ Kay Kendall/Taina Elg* (Les Girls.) / Why am I so gone (about that gal): *Kelly, Gene*(Les Girls.).
LP: LPMGM 16
LP: 794 251 1
MC: TCMGM 16
MC: 794 251 4

Silk & Suede

HITS OF THE 70'S.
MC: ZCFPA 1020

Silk Touch

DREAMING OF BLONDIE.
MC: ZCFPA 1021

Silkwood

SILKWOOD (Film soundtrack) (Various artists).
LP: DRG 6107
MC: DRGC 6107
LP: NFP 5501

Silly Sisters

NO MORE TO THE DANCE.
Tracks: / Blood and gold / Cake and ale / Fine horseman / How shall I / Hedger and ditcher / Agincourt Carol / Barring of the door, The / What'll we do / Almost every circumstance / Old miner, The.
LP: 12TS 450
MC: KTSC 450

Silly Wizzard

BEST OF SILLY WIZZARD.
LP: SHAN 79048

CALEDONIAS HARDY SONS.
LP: SHY 7004
LP: SHAN 79015

FIRST ALBUM.
LP: SHY 7022

GLINT OF SILVER, A.
LP: SIF 1070
MC: CSIF 1070

GOLDEN,GOLDEN.
LP: RELS 478
MC: RECS 478

KISS THE TEARS AWAY.
Tracks: / Queen of Argyl / Golden golden / Finlay M Macrae / Banks of the Lee / Sweet Dublin Bay / Mo nighean donn / Gradh mo chroidhe / Banks of the Bann / Greenfields of Glentown / Galtee reel / Bobby Casey's number two / Wing commander Donald MacKenzie's reel / Loch Tay boat song.
LP: SHY 7025
MC: SHC 7025
LP: SHAN 79037

LIVE IN AMERICA.
LP: RELS 476
MC: RECS 476

SO MANY PARTINGS.
LP: SHY 7010
LP: SHAN 79016

WILD AND BEAUTIFUL.
LP: SHY 7016
LP: SHAN 79028

WINTERFOLK 80 (see Battlefield Band).

Silos

ABOUT HER STEPS.
LP: RC21
LP: DMC 020

CUBA.
LP: CALCLP 021

Silva, Marcos

HERE WE GO (Silva, Marcos & Intersection).
Tracks: / Peeling onions / Pra joaninha (For ladybug) / Baiao do povo (Dance of the people) / Manuzelita / Fancy talk / Brasilian people / Rose coloured glasses / Maxiranda / Waltz in E - flat / Groovin' in the closet.
LP: CR 5004
MC: CRC 5004

WHITE AND BLACK (Silva, Marcos & Intersection).
LP: CR 5006
MC: CR 5006C

Silver

I CRY A RIVER.
LP: AFFLP 001

Silver Bullet

BRING DOWN THE WALLS NO LIMIT SQUAD RETURNS.
Tracks: / 20 seconds to comply / Raw deal / Attitude academy / Undercover anarchist / Ruff karnage / Bring forth the guillotine / Guns of mind alone / Legions of the damned / He spins around / Bring down the walls.
LP: PCS 7350
MC: TCPCS 7350

Silver Bullet (Film)

SILVER BULLET (FILM) (Film soundtrack) (Various artists).
LP: STV 81264

Silver Condor

SILVER CONDOR.
Tracks: / For the sake of survival / Angel eyes / Sayin' goodbye / Carolina (nobody's right nobody's wrong) / One you left behind, The / We're in love / You could take my heart away / It's over / Standing in the rain / Goin' for broke.
LP: CBS 85026
MC: 40 85026

Silver Convention

DISCOTHEQUE VOL 2.
LP: MAG 5011

GREATEST HITS: SILVER CONVENTION.
LP: MAG 6001

Silver, Dave

SPARKLING SOUND OF.. (Silver, Dave & His Band).
LP: BBR 141

Silver Fox

UP AGAINST THE BEAST (See under Brother D).

Silver, Horace

BEST OF HORACE SILVER (Blue Note years).
Tracks: / Opus de funk / Doodlin' / Room 608 (CD only.) / Preacher, The / Senor Blues / Cool eyes (CD only.) / Home cookin' / Soulville (CD only.) / Cookin' at the continental / Peace / Sister Sadie / Blowin' the blues away (CD only.).
LP: B1 91143

BEST OF HORACE SILVER - VOL. 2.
Tracks: / Song for my father / Que pasa / Pretty eyes / Cape Verdean blues, The / Nutville (CD only.) / Mexican hip dance (CD only.) / Gregory is here / Jody grind, The / Serenade to a soul sister.
LP: B1 93206
LP: 793 206 1

BLOWIN' THE BLUES AWAY.
Tracks: / Blowin' the blues away / St. Vitus dance, The / Break city / Peace / Sister Sadie / Baghdad, The / Melancholy mood / How did it happen?.
LP: BST 84017
MC: 4BN 84017

DOIN' THE THING (AT THE VILLAGE GATE).
Tracks: / Filthy McNasty / Doin' the thing / Cool eyes (alt. take) / It ain't s'posed to be like that / Kiss me right / Gringo.
LP: B1 84076

FINGER POPPIN' WITH THE HORACE SILVER QUINTET (Silver, Horace Quintet).
Tracks: / Finger poppin' / Juicy Lucy / Swingin' the samba / Sweet stuff / Cookin' at the Continental / Come on home / You happened my way / Mellow D.
LP: BST 84008

HORACE SILVER & THE JAZZ MESSENGERS (Silver, Horace & The Jazz Messengers).
Tracks: / Room 608 / Creepin' in / Stop time / To whom it may concern / Hippy / Preachers, The / Hankerin' / Doodlin'.
MC: 4BN 81518
LP: BST 81518
LP: 781 518 1
LP: BLP 1518

HORACE SILVER TRIO.
Tracks: / Safari / Ecaroh / Prelude to a kiss / Message from Kenya / Horoscope / Yeah / How about you / I remember you / Opus de funk / Nothing but the soul / Silverware / Day in, day out / Thou swell (CD only.) / Quicksilver (CD only.) / Knowledge box (CD only.) / Buhaina (CD only.).
LP: B1 81520
LP: BLP 1520

SERENADE TO A SOUL SISTER.
Tracks: / Psychedelic Sally / Serenade to a soul sister / Rain dance / Jungle juice / Kindred spirit / Next time I fall in love.
LP: BST 84277

SIX PIECES OF SILVER.
Tracks: / Cool eyes / Shirl / Camouflage / Enchantment / Senor blues / Senor blues (45 version) / Virgo / For heaven's sake / Tippin' / Senor blues (vocal version).
LP: BLP 1539
LP: B1 81539

SONG FOR MY FATHER (Silver, Horace Quintet).
Tracks: / Song for my father / Natives are restless tonight, The / Calcutta cutie / Que pasa / Kicker / Lonely woman / Sanctimonious Sam (CD only.) / Sighin' and cryin' (CD only.) / Silver threads among the soul (CD only.).
LP: BST 84185
MC: TCBST 84185

Silver, Jimmy

RIGHT OLD KNEES UP, A (Silver, Jimmy & His Music).
Tracks: / California here I come / Bye bye blackbird / Enjoy yourself / Give my regards to Broadway / I'm looking over a four leaf clover / Toot toot tootsie / Swanee / How ya gonna keep 'em down on the farm? / Margie / Don't dilly dally on the way / Hello, hello, who's your lady friend? / Who were you with last night? / It's a long way to Tipperary / Take me back to dear old Blighty / I've got a lovely bunch of coconuts / Carolina in the morning / Pretty baby / Rockabye your baby with a Dixie melody / You made me love you / If you were the only girl in the world / That old feeling / In a shanty in old Shantytown / Dinah / Some of these days / That gang that sang 'heart of my heart' / Lily of Laguna / Oh you beautiful doll / I belong to Glasgow / When Irish eyes are smiling.
LP: DVL 4

Silver, Mike

FREE.
Tracks: / Down south / Niago and Irvana / Not that easy / Old fashioned saturday night / Mine for ever more / Easy way out / Sailors all / Blues run the game / First flight / free.
LP: SR 0184
MC: SC 0184

MIDNIGHT TRAIN.
Tracks: / Do I miss the love look / Some way out / When the song is over / Kleine Weinig / Los Angeles / Midnight train / Maybe it's just love / Children of tomorrow.
LP: BIG 001

NO MACHINE.

Tracks: / Sunshine city woman / No machine / Certain something / Pia's painting / N.A.S.A / Circle of stones / Good friday / Let it be so / Heatwave.
LP: **SR 0286**
MC: **SC 0286**

ROADWORKS (LIVE).
Tracks: / Too many lies / Angel in deep shadow / Pretoria / Heatwave / Somebody's angel / Old fashioned Saturday night / Where would you rather be tonight / Let it be so / Not that easy / N.A.S.A. / Down South / Circle of stones / Nothing to do with me (Not on album) / Sailors all (Not on album) / Certain something (Only on CD) / Time for leaving (Only on CD) / Mine for ever more (Only on CD).
LP: **SRO 190**
MC: **SRO 190C**

Silver Screen

ITV CHILDREN'S THEMES (See under ITV Children's Themes.

Silver Skates (bk)

SILVER SKATES, THE (Mary M Dodge) (Bloom, Claire (nar)).
MC: **1493**

Silvera, Jeanette

WHEN I NEED YOU.
LP: **LP 281**

Silverado

SILVERADO (Film soundtrack) (Various artists).
LP: **GEF 70268**
MC: **4070268**

Silverfish

FAT AXL.
LP: **WIJ 6**
MC: **WIJ 6C**

Silverhawks

SILVERHAWKS: THE ORIGIN.
MC: **0 00 109012 7**

SILVERHAWKS: THE PLANET EATER.
MC: **0 00 109013 5**

Silverhead

16 AND SAVAGED.
LP: **PURL 701**

SILVERHEAD.
LP: **PURL 700**

Silvers, Colonel Jim

COLONEL JIM SILVERS.
Tracks: / Julie / Cash on the barrelhead / For your own good / I ate the whole damn hog / Call me a cab / Blue night / Crying my heart out over you / Ain't it strange / Last to get the news / Music-making mama / Losing you may be the best thing yet / Scrap of paper and a 20 cent pen.
LP: **ABOUT 1009**

Silverspoon, Dooley

UNDER THE INFLUENCE.
Tracks: / As long as you know (who you are) / Building my world around you / Believe in me / Bump me baby (parts 1&2) / Let me be the number one / Game players / Right under your nose.
LP: **SEL 1**

Silverstein, Deborah

AROUND THE NEXT BEND.
LP: **FF 429**

Silverstein, Shel

FREAKING AT THE FREAKERS' BALL.
Tracks: / Thumb sucker / I got stoned and I missed it / Sarah, Cynthia, Sylvia Stout would not take the garbage out / Stacy Brown got two / Polly in a pomy / Freakin' at the freakers' ball / All about you / Don't give a dose to the one you love most / Peace proposal, The / Masochistic baby / Liberated lady / Man who got no sign, The.
LP: **CBS 31766**
MC: **40 31766**

GREAT CONCH TRAIN ROBBERY, THE.
LP: **FF 211**

Silvertone Steel...

SILVERTONE STEEL ORCHESTRA (Silvertone Steel Orchestra).
Tracks: / Silvertone jump / Bari a dotti wan o die / Yankee dollar / Sole / Rosalin / Cha cha maleba / Limbo rock / Put the wood on the fire / Happy feelin's / Brown beans and rice / Dona / Coffee road / Archie / When the saints go marching in.
LP: **JOYS 242**

Silvertones

ONE CHANCE WITH YOU.
LP: **STING 009**

SILVER BULLETS.
Tracks: / I'll take you home / Early in the morning / Sugar sugar / Souvenir of Mexico / Rejoice, Jah Jah children / Rejoicing skank / That's when it hurts / Soul sister / Rock me in your soul / Sweet and loving baby / He'll break your heart / Are you sure?.
LP: **TRLS 69**

Silvertones Choir

SO DEEP IS THE NIGHT.
LP: **POL 806**

Silverwind

BY HIS SPIRIT.
LP: **BIRD 166**
MC: **TC BIRD 166**

SET APART.
LP: **BIRD R 186**
MC: **BIRD C 186**

SILVERWIND.
Tracks: / Taking the narrow street / When I looked into your eyes / Your love / Give him your heart, child / I don't worry / I am in love / Ode to a lost innocence / Never had a reason / Walking this road / I will bless the Lord.
LP: **BIRD 128**
MC: **TC BIRD 128**

Silverwing

ALIVE AND KICKING.
Tracks: / Teenage love affair / That's entertainment / Flashbomb fever / Adolescent sex / Everything happens at night / Rock and roll are four-letter words / Soldier girl.
LP: **BULP 1**

Silvester, Victor

60 YEARS ON.
Tracks: / Cheek to cheek / Hello dolly / Blue moon / Blue star / Chi mai / Nothing can last forever / Luna rossa / Easy to love / You do something to me / Love walked in / Love is here to stay / Diane / Rose in the bud / Emperor waltz.
LP: **DS 052**

100 MINUTES OF VICTOR SILVESTER.
MC: **ZCTON 111**

CELEBRATION PARTY DANCES.
Tracks: / Anniversary waltz / Hokey cokey / Sucu sucu / Valeta, The / Darktown strutters' ball / Poor little Angeline / Ten pretty girls / Rock around the clock / Spanish gypsy dance / Happy birthday to you / I'm 21 today / La conga / St. Bernard's waltz / Gay Gordons / In a little Spanish town / Cha-cha-cha / Charleston / Boomps a daisy / Everybody's doing it now / Jive / Lambeth walk / Knees up Mother Brown / Auld lang syne / I left my heart in San Francisco (CD only.) / Fascinating rhythm (CD only.) / Amparita roca (CD only.) / Washington post (CD only.) / Tequila (CD only.) / Do you ken John Peel (CD only.) / Mambo jambo.
LP: **OU 2062**
MC: **TCOU 2062**
MC: **TCIDL 102**
MC: **795 428 4**

GET RHYTHM IN YOUR FEET.
Tracks: / Get rhythm in your feet / Lambeth walk / Did you go down Lambeth way / Little lady make believe / Music, maestro, please / Florianopolis / I shall always remember you smiling / Why do I lie to myself about you / Straighten up and fly right / Moonlight Avenue / Don't ever pass me by / Begin the beguine / On the sunny side of the street / I'll pray for you / How deep is the ocean / I hum a waltz / South of pago pago / Sweet Georgia Brown / Accentuate the positive / If I should fall in love again / Don't say goodbye.
LP: **EG 2606271**
MC: **EG 2606274**

GOLDEN HOUR OF STRICT TEMPO DANCING VOL. 4 (Silvester, Victor & His Ballroom Orchestra).
Tracks: / Save your kisses for me / Tie a yellow ribbon / Whispering / Cabaret / Yes sir, that's my baby / Lullaby of Broadway / Red roses for a blue lady / From this moment on / Stella by starlight / As time goes by / Someone to watch over me / Way we were, The / Stars fell on Alabama / (They long to be) close to you / Poor butterfly / Always / Glamorous night / Indiscreet / Liebestraum / Remember (you forgot to remember) / What'll I do / All alone / Look to the rainbow.
MC: **KGHMC 135**

GOLDEN HOUR OF VICTOR SILVESTER, A.
Tracks: / You're dancing on my heart / Born free / Stars in my eyes / Look of love, The / Call me / Love me tonight / Whistler and his dog, The / I'd rather charleston / Glamorous nights / Rio Rita / Joanna / Tijuana taxi / I double dare you / Second time around / Lovely lady / South of the border / Guantanamera / Petita / Skirl o the the pipes / Eton boating song / Ob la di ob la da / In the Summertime / Acapulco 1922 / Yeh yeh.
MC: **KGHMC 106**

HOLLYWOOD HERITAGE.
Tracks: / My foolish heart / It can't be wrong / Broadway melody / Foggy day / Boy next door, The / Around the world / At the Balalaika / Hernando's hideaway / You stepped out of a dream / Gigi / Que sera sera / Wonderful wonderful day / Gal in calico, A / Days of wine and roses / Moon river / Charade.
LP: **NSLP 18612**
MC: **ZCP 18612**

I'LL GO WHERE THE MUSIC TAKES ME.
Tracks: / Musktrat ramble / You go to my head / One / Feelings / Copacabana / Send in the clowns / You'll never know / Dearly beloved / One I love / La cumparsita / Ja da / My blue heaven / Carnival / Y.M.C.A..
2LP: **VSP 2**
MCSET: **ZCVSP 2**

IN STRICT TEMPO.
Tracks: / Supposing / You're in Kentucky sure as you're born / Green eyes / So rare / At dusk / Sleep tight / It's a sin to tell a lie / Paul Jones / You're here, you're there / Will you remember / Can I forget you / Carelessly / You needn't have kept it a secret / House beautiful / Maria, my own / Goodnight to you all / Don't say goodbye.
LP: **BUR 006**
MC: **4 BUR 006**

JUST THE WAY YOU ARE.
Tracks: / Just the way you are / Some enchanted evening / They all laughed / Mountain greenery / Cavatina / Kiss in your eyes, The / Jealousy / Alabama jubilee / Too close for comfort / Lady's in love with you, The / Call me irresponsible / You're my everything / Amore baciami / I give my heart / Belle of the ball / Gotta be this or that / My foolish heart / It can't be wrong / Broadway melody / Foggy day, A / Boy next door, The / Around the world / At the balalaika / Hernando's hideaway / You stepped out of a dream / Gigi / Que sera sera / Wonderful, wonderful day / Girl in Calico, A / Days of wine and roses / Moon river / Charade.
2LP: **VSPA 3**

LET'S DANCE (Silvester, Victor & His Ballroom Orchestra).
Tracks: / On your toes / My blue heaven / Very thought of you, The / If I had you / It happened in Monterey / One night of love / I once had a heart Margarita / You know it all smarty / Kiss the boys goodbye / June in January / September song / Roses of Picardy / Ramona / Could be / Gotta be this or that / Apple for teacher, An / Time on my hands / Stella by starlight / Love is my reason / Love everlasting (l'amour, toujours, l'amour) / Nice work if you can get it / Moonlight and roses / You couldn't be cuter / Deep purple / Once in a while / Luna rossa (Blushing moon) / Goody goody / Zing went the strings of my heart.
2LP: **DL 1197**
MC: **TCDL 1197**

LET'S HAVE A PARTY.
Tracks: / Paul Jones / Let me call you sweetheart / Wedding samba, The / If you knew Susie / You made me love you / After the ball / Waiting for the Robert E. Lee / Cha cha cha - tea for two / See me dance the polka / St. Bernards waltz / Jolly brothers, The / Samba-mambo, jambo / Fascinating rhythm / Pasodoble-Amparito roca / Joey's song / Washington Post / Black bottom / When Irish eyes are smiling / Por eavor / Tequila / Viennese waltz / Blue Danube / I left my heart in San Francisco / Honeysuckle and the bee, The / Lily of Laguna / Goodbye-ee / I feel fine / Blaze away / Do you ken John Peel / Our waltz.
LP: **ONCR 526**

MORE DANCING FAVOURITES.
Tracks: / Fine romance, A / Sing my heart / How deep is the ocean? / September song / One love for you / Spurs of the gaucho / Embraceable you / That certain feeling / Love letters / Our day will come / This nearly was mine / Stompin' at the Savoy / Undecided / Mull of Kintyre / When I fall in love / More.
2LP: **VSP 1**
MCSET: **ZCVSP 1**

QUICK, QUICK, SLOW.
Tracks: / You're dancing on my heart / Lonesome and sorry / April in Paris / Love walked in / Amor amor / Charleston / It happened in Monterey / Three o'clock in the morning / Whispering (medley) / I'll see you in my dreams / Avalon / Marie / Tea for two / It's the talk of the town / Media luz, A / That certain feeling / Wonderful one / Always.
LP: **SH 420**
MC: **TCSH 420**

SILVESTER DANCETIME.
Tracks: / Walk in the Black Forest, A / Gentle on my mind / Witchcraft / Honey / Best of everything, The / Valentine shadow waltz / Desert song, The / Poem / Goin' out of my head / Spinning wheel / Knees up mother Brown / Sugar sugar / Young gifted and black / Gimme dat ding / Quando, quando, quando / How insensitive / Coffee song, The / Be in / Flor del alma / So what's new / Mexican shuffle / Baby face / Five foot two, eyes of blue / March of the mods.
LP: **GH 605**

SLOW, SLOW, QUICK, QUICK, SLOW.
Tracks: / In the still of the night / Dancing in the dark / I've got my love to keep me warm / They can't take that away from me / Love letters / Stars fell on Alabama / Kiss in your eyes, The / Liebestraum / If I should fall in love again / Hernando's hideaway / Spurs of the gaucho / Wonderful, wonderful day / Ja da / Tea for two / Frenesi / At the Copa - Copacabana / Green cockatoo, The / Brazil / Carnival / Watch what happens / Green eyes / My Cherie amour / Makin' whoopee / Viva Espana.
2LP: **PYL 7005**
MC: **PYM 7005**

SONG AND DANCE MEN (See under Bygraves, Max) (Silvester, Victor & Max Bygraves).

SPOTLIGHT ON VICTOR SILVESTER.
Tracks: / Save your kisses for me / I'm in a dancing mood / Put on a happy face / Mistral / Media luz, A / Mi amigo / Teach me tonight / Guantanamera / Eye level / Tequila / Tijuana taxi / So what's new? / Way we were, The / I only have eyes for you / Chanson d'amour / Mull of Kintyre / Edelweiss / One love / Begin the beguine / More / Strangers in the night / Copacabana / La Bamba / One-note samba.
2LP: **SPOT 1013**
MCSET: **ZCSPT 1013**

SPOTLIGHT ON VICTOR SILVESTER, VOL 2.
Tracks: / Fascination / Always / Andante / Jealousy / Santa Catarinea / Upstairs downstairs / As time goes by / It can't be wrong / Once in a while / At the Jazz Band Ball / Skyliner / Jazz me blues / Girl from Ipanema / Side by side / It had to be you / Brazil / Up, up and away / Ma que nada / Laura / More than you know / Our day will come / Spanish gypsy dance / Undecided / Cerveza.
2LP: **SPOT 6800**
MCSET: **ZCSPT 6800**

STRICT TEMPO.
LP: **KGHLP 200**

VERY THOUGHT OF YOU, THE.
Tracks: / Way you look tonight / Wishing (will make it so) / Lovely to look at / Love is a many splendoured thing / Love is my reason / Music in May / Lonesome and sorry / Ecstacy / Very thought of you, The / I hadn't anyone till you / This year's kisses / Thou swell / Tell me I'm forgiven / Will you remember / One kiss / Do something / Mearness of you, The / Say it isn't so / In the still of the night / Lot of livin' to do, A / Kiss in the dark / One love / Most beautiful girl in the world, The / I once had a heart Margarita / I still get jealous / Trumpet cha cha / Romantica / I wish you love / Tico tico / Green cockatoo, The / Swinging on a star / Way down yonder in New Orleans.
2LP: **VSP 4**

VICTOR SILVESTER (Collector's Series).
MC: **C 906**

VICTOR SILVESTER'S JIVE BAND.
Tracks: / Stompin' at The Savoy / Way down yonder in New Orleans / Pardon me pretty baby / I'm coming, Virginia / Poor butterfly / I wish I were twins / You took advantage of me / How am I to know? / Ida, sweet as apple cider / Blue Lou / Please do it again / My melancholy baby / How come you do me like you do? / One I love belongs to somebody else, The / Love me or leave me / Undecided / Boston bounce / There's honey on the moon tonight / Coquette.
LP: **EG 2605801**
MC: **EG 2605804**

WALTZES, TANGOS AND MODERN BEAT.
Tracks: / Indiscreet / Stars in my eyes / Mi amigo / Flor del alma / When you're away / Lovely lady / Aquarius / Young, gifted and black / Poem / Shadow waltz / Sugar sugar / Ob la di ob la da.
LP: **NSPL 18351**

Silvo, Johnny

IN THE SPOTLIGHT.
LP: **SFA 114**

TIME ENOUGH TO SPARE.

Tracks: / Gypsy woman / Southbound train / Gotta get a hold of Hazel / Time / This train / Teach your children / Backwater blues / First time ever I saw your face, The / Glory of love / Cassey's last ride / Black girl.
LP: PLR 003

Simak, Clifford (nar)

AESOP FABLES (See under Aesop...).

Simeone, Harry

LITTLE DRUMMER BOY (Simeone, Harry Chorale).
Tracks: / Sing we now of Christmas / Angels we have heard on high / Away in a manger / What child is this / Joy to the world / Go tell it on the mountain / It came upon a midnight clear / Good King Wenceslas / We three kings of Orient are / Villancico / Hark the herald angels sing / Bring back a torch / Isabella / Lo how a rose e'er blooming / Deck the halls / Christmas man / Rejoice / Master in the hall / O tannenbaum / O holy night / Little drummer boy / Coventry carol / Rise up shepherds / God rest ye merry gentlemen / O little town of Bethlehem / O come little children / Ding dong / While shepherds watched their flocks by night / First noel, The / Friendly beasts, The / Silent night / Christmas greeting, A.
LP: HDY 1925
MC: ZCHDY 1925
LP: T 580
LP: AFEMP 1029

Simmons, Carl

HELLO ROCK AND ROLL.
LP: TOSHLP 001

Simmons, David

HEAR ME OUT.
Tracks: / Will they miss me / Once in a while / Yesterday's song / Success / Taxi Greyhound Station / I'll be what you want / Hard and heavy / Then you can tell me goodbye / It's a shame.
LP: FT 553

Simmons, Desmond

ALONE ON PENGUIN ISLAND.
LP: DOM 331

Simmons, Gene

GOIN' BACK TO MEMPHIS (Simmons, Jumpin' Gene).
Tracks: / Goin' back to Memphis / Shape you left me in / Haunted house / Hey, hey little girl / I'm coming down with love / You can have her / Hotel happiness / I'm a ramblin man / Skinny Minnie / Mattie Rea / Folsom Prison blues / Down in the alley / Come on over, put some love on me / Bossy boss / Go on shoes / Keep that meat in the pan.
LP: HIUKLP 416

HAUNTED HOUSE.
Tracks: / Catahoula cur dog / You pulled the plug / Five o'clock happy hour / It's so hard to believe / River rat / Haunted house / Wy didn't I think of that / Way down yonder in Baton Rouge / Patchwork quilt / Kings and queens / I'm tired of sharin' Sharon / Next to nothing / I remember loving you / Will the circle be unbroken / 86 more miles to go / In Memphis / J.C. and J.C. / Troubled land over there.
LP: MFLP 059

I DONE TOLD YOU.
Tracks: / I done told you / Drinkin' scotch / Money money money / Juicy fruit / You can't break the chains of love / Crazy woman / Drinkin' wine / I don't love you baby / Pop and mama / Blues at midnight / Down on the border / If I'm not wanted / Guitar boogie / Shake, rattle and roll.
LP: SUNLP 1008

Simmons, Gene (Kiss)

GENE SIMMONS SOLO ALBUM.
LP: 6399084

Simmons, Leroy

THINGS AND TIME.
LP: ARILP 057

Simmons, Norman

I'M THE BLUES (Simmons, Norman Quintet).
Tracks: / I'm the blues, part 1 / I'm the blues, part 2 / Juicy Lucy / I ain't got nothin' but the blues / Good humour / Los milagros pequenos / Why try to change me now?.
LP: MJP 1002

MIDNIGHT CREEPER.
Tracks: / Some day my prince will come / Midnight creeper / Confirmation / Blackout / Send in the clowns / Emily.
LP: MJP 1001

RAMIRA THE DANCER (Simmons, Norman Quartet).
Tracks: / Ramira / Oleo / Stairway to the stars / Blue juice / My shining hour / Where is my lady? / How insensitive / Four.
LP: SPJ LP 13

Simmons, Patrick

ARCADE.
Tracks: / Out on the streets / So wrong / Don't make me do it / Why you givin' up / Too long / Knocking at your door / If you want a little love / Have you seen her / Sue sad / Dream about me.
LP: E 0225

Simmons, Sonny

MANHATTAN EGOS.
LP: ARHOOLIE 8003

Simon & Bard

ENORMOUS RADIO, THE.
LP: FF 321

MUSAIC.
LP: FF 243

TEAR IT UP.
LP: FF 262

Simon, Carly

ANOTHER PASSENGER.
Tracks: / Half a chance / It keeps you runnin' / Fairweather father / Cow town / He likes to roll / In times when my head / One love stand / Riverboat gambler / Darkness 'til dawn / Dishonest modesty / Libby / Be with me.
LP: K 52036

ANTICIPATION.
Tracks: / Anticipation / Legend in your own time / Our first day together / Girl you think you see, The / Summer's coming around again / Share the end / Garden, The / Three days / Julie through the glasses / I've got to have you.
MC: K 462042
LP: K 42101

BEST OF CARLY SIMON.
Tracks: / That's the way I've always heard / Right thing to do / Mockingbird / Legend in your own time / Haven't got time for the pain / You're so vain / No secrets / Night owl / Anticipation / Attitude dancing.
LP: K 52025
MC: K 452025

BEST OF CARLY SIMON (1991).
LP: EKT 86
MC: EKT 86C

BOYS IN THE TREES.
Tracks: / You belong to me / Boys in the trees / Back down to Earth / Devoted to you / De bat (fly in my face) / Haunting / Tranquillo (melt my heart) / You're the one / In a small moment / One man woman / For old times sake.
LP: K 52066

COME UPSTAIRS.
Tracks: / Come upstairs / Stardust / Them / Jesse / James / In pain / Three of us in the dark / Take me as I am / Dessert.
LP: K 56828

COMING AROUND AGAIN.
Tracks: / Itsy bitsy spider / If it wasn't love / Coming around again / Give me all night / As time goes by / Do the walls come down / It should have been me / Stuff that dreams are made of, The / Two hot girls / You have to hurt / All I want is you / Hold what you've got.
LP: 208140
MC: 408140
MC: 411038

GREATEST HITS LIVE: CARLY SIMON.
Tracks: / You're so vain / Nobody does it better / Coming around again / It happens every day / Anticipation / Right thing to do / Do the walls come down / You belong to me / Two hot girls / All I want is you / Never been gone.
LP: 209196
MC: 409196

HAVE YOU SEEN ME LATELY.
Tracks: / Better not tell her / Didn't I / Have you seen me lately? / Life is eternal / Waiting at the gate / Happy birthday / Holding me tonight / It's not like him / Don't wrap it up / Fisherman's song / We just got here.
LP: 211044
MC: 411044

HELLO BIG MAN.
Tracks: / You know what to do / Menemsha / Damn, you get to me / Is this love / Orpheus / It happens every day / Such a good day / Hello big man / You don't feel the same / Floundering.
LP: 923886 1

HOT CAKES.
Tracks: / Safe and sound / Mind on my man / Think I'm gonna have a baby / Older sister / Just not true / Hot cakes / Misfit / Forever my love / Mockingbird / Grown up / Haven't got time for the pain.
LP: K 52005

MY ROMANCE.
Tracks: / My romance / By myself / I see your face / When your lover is gone / In the wee small hours of the morning / My funny valentine / Something wonderful / Little girl blue / He was good to me / What has she got / Bewitched / Danny boy / Time after time.
LP: 210602
MC: 410602

NO SECRETS.
Tracks: / Right thing to do / Carter family / You're so vain / His friends are more than fond of Robin / We have no secrets / Embrace me, you child / It was so easy / Waited so long / Night owl / When you close your eyes.
LP: K 42127
MC: K 442127

PLAYING POSSUM.
Tracks: / After the storm / Love out in the street / Look me in the eyes / More and more / Slave attitude / Dancing / Sons of Summer / Waterfall / Are you ticklish / Playing possum.
LP: K 52020

SPOILED GIRL.
Tracks: / My new boyfriend / Come back home / Tonight and forever / Spoiled girl / Tired of being blonde / Wives are in Connecticut / Anyone but me / Make me feel something / Can't give up / Black honeymoon.
LP: 4506221
MC: 40 26376
MC: 4506224

SPY.
Tracks: / Vengeance / We're so close / Just like you do / Coming to get you / Never been gone / Pure sin / Love you by heart / Spy / Memorial day.
LP: K 52147
MC: K 452147

TORCH.
Tracks: / Blue of blue / I'll be around / I got it bad and that ain't good / I get along without you very well / Body and soul / Hurt / From the heart / Spring is here / Pretty strange / What shall we do with the child / Not a day goes by.
LP: K 56935

YOU'RE SO VAIN.
Tracks: / You're so vain / Best thing / Reunions / Alone / One more time / That's the way I've always heard / It should be / Anticipation / Rolling down the hills / Dan, my fling / Just a sinner / Another door / Love's still growing.
LP: SHM 3062
MC: HSC 3062

Simon, F.

GUN CONTROL.
Tracks: / Baby doll love / Breathless / Hungry life / Perfect world / Phones / Million miles from happiness / Mad man drum / Hold the bunker / Doctor Christie / Here comes my laugh.
LP: CHR 1496
MC: ZCHR 1496

Simon & Garfunkel

BOOKENDS.
Tracks: / Bookends / Save the life of my child / America / Overs / Voice of old people / Old friends / Fakin' it / Punky's dilemma / Hazy shade of winter / At the zoo / Mrs. Robinson.
LP: CBS 32073
MC: 40 32073

BRIDGE OVER TROUBLED WATER.
Tracks: / Bridge over troubled water / El condor pasa / Cecilia / Keep the customer satisfied / So long, Frank Lloyd Wright / Boxer, The / Baby driver / Only living boy in New York, The / Why don't you write me / Bye bye love / Song for the asking.
LP: CBS 63699
MC: 40 63699

CONCERT IN CENTRAL PARK.
Tracks: / Mrs. Robinson / Homeward bound / America / Me and Julio down by the schoolyard / Scarborough Fair / April come she will / Wake up little Susie / Still crazy after all these years / American tune / Late in the evening / Slip slidin' away / Heart in New York, A / Kodachrome / Maybellene / Bridge over troubled water / Fifty ways to leave your lover / Boxer, The / Old friends / Feeling groovy / Sound of silence, The.
MC: 4096008
LP: 96008
LP: GEF 96008

GRADUATE, THE (Film soundtrack).
Tracks: / Sound of silence, The / Jungleman party foxtrot / Mrs. Robinson / Sunporch cha-cha / Scarborough Fair / On the strip / April come she will / Great effect / Big bright green pleasure machine.
LP: CBS 32359
MC: 40 32359
LP: CBS 70042

GREATEST HITS: SIMON & GARFUNKEL.
Tracks: / Mrs. Robinson / For Emily, whenever I may find her / Boxer, The / Feeling groovy / Sound of silence, The / I am a rock / Scarborough fair / Canticle / Homeward bound / Bridge over troubled water / America / Kathy's song / If I could / Bookends / Cecilia.
LP: CBS 69003
MC: 40 69003

PARSLEY, SAGE, ROSEMARY AND THYME.
Tracks: / Scarborough Fair / Patterns / Cloudy / Big bright green pleasure machine, The / 59th Street Bridge song / Dangling conversation, The / Flowers never bend with the rainfall / Simple desultory philippic / For Emily, whenever I may find her / Poem on an underground wall, A / Seven o'clock news / Silent night.
LP: CBS 32031
MC: 40 32031
LP: CBS 62860

SIMON & GARFUNKEL COLLECTION, THE.
Tracks: / I am a rock / Homeward bound / America / 59th Street Bridge song / Wednesday morning 3 a.m. / El condor pasa / At the zoo / Scarborough Fair / Boxer, The / Sound of silence, The / Mrs. Robinson / Keep the customer satisfied / Song for the asking / Hazy shade of Winter / Cecilia / Old friends / Bookends / Bridge over troubled water.
LP: CBS 10029
MC: 40 10029

SOUND OF SILENCE.
Tracks: / Sound of silence, The / Leaves that are green, The / Blessed / Somewhere they can't find me / Kathy's song / Homeward bound / Most peculiar man / I am a rock / Richard Cory / April come she will.
LP: CBS 32020
MC: 40 32020
LP: CBS 62690

WEDNESDAY MORNING, 3AM.
Tracks: / You can tell the world / Last night I had the strangest dream / Bleecker Street / Sparrow, The / Benedictus / Peggy-O / He was my brother / Sound of silence, The / Go tell it on the mountain / Sun is burning, The / Times they are a-changin' / Wednesday morning 3am.
LP: CBS 32575
MC: 40 32575
LP: CBS 63370

Simon, Joe

DROWNING IN THE SEA OF LOVE.
Tracks: / Glad to be your lover / Something you can do today / I found my dad / Mirror don't lie, The / Ole night owl / You are everything / If / Let me be the one (the one who loves you) / Pool of bad luck.
LP: SEW 021
MC: SEWC 021

GET DOWN.
Tracks: / Get down, get down (get on the floor) / Fire burning / It be's that way sometimes / Music in my bones / You don't want to believe it (my man) / In my baby's arms / Still at the mercy of your love / It's crying time in Memphis.
LP: SEW 013
MC: SEWC 013

LOOKING BACK (Best of Joe Simon).
Tracks: / Chokin' kind, The / My special prayer / No sad songs / San Francisco is a lonely town / Message from Maria / Looking back / Baby don't be looking in my mind / Teenagers' prayer / Nine pound steel / (You keep me) hangin' on / Put your trust in me / It's hard to get along / Misty blue / Farther on down the road / Yours love / That's the way I want our love.
LP: CRB 1202
MC: TCCRB 1202

LOVE VIBRATIONS.
Tracks: / Love vibrations / Can we come and share in love / Going through these changes / I can't stand a liar / Somebody for everybody / To get to you / If you got the time / It must be love / I.O.U..
LP: 2391375

MR. RIGHT.
LP: CLTLP 354
MC: ZCCLT 354

SOUL NEIGHBOURS (See Hughes, Jimmy) (Simon, Joe & Jimmy Hughes).

Simon, Paul

BLUES, THE (See under Newman, Randy) (Simon, Paul/Randy Newman).

GRACELAND.
Tracks: / Boy in the bubble, The / Graceland / I know what I know / Gumboots / Diamonds on the soles of

her shoes / You can call me Al / Under African skies / Homeless / Crazy love Vol 2 / All around the world or the myth of fingerprints.
LP: . . . . WX 52
MC: . . . . WX 52C

GREATEST HITS:PAUL SIMON.
Tracks: / Something so right / Fifty ways to leave your lover / Kodachrome / Me and Julio down by the schoolyard / American tune / Gone at last / Still crazy after all these years / My little town / Mother and child reunion / Loves me like a rock / Stranded in a limousine / Slip slidin' away / Mardi gras.
LP: . . . . CBS 10007
MC: 4010007
LP: 4501661
MC: 4501664

HEARTS AND BONES.
Tracks: / Think too much / Train in the distance / Cars are cars / Late great Johnny Ace, The / Allergies / Hearts and bones / When numbers get serious / Song about the moon / Rene and Georgette Magritte with their dog after the war.
LP: 923942 1
MC: 923942 4

LIVE RHYMIN' - IN CONCERT.
Tracks: / Me and Julio down by the schoolyard / Homeward bound / American tune / El condor pasa / Duncan / Boxer, The / Mother and child reunion / Sound of silence, The / Jesus is the answer / Bridge over troubled water / Loves me like a rock / America.
LP: . . . . CBS 69059
LP: 925590 1
MC: 925590 4

MAGIC OF PAUL SIMON, THE.
MC: . . . . VENUMC 5

NEGOTIATIONS AND LOVE SONGS (1971-1986).
Tracks: / Mother and child reunion / Me and Julio down by the schoolyard / Something so right / St. Judy's comet / Loves me like a rock / Have a good time / Fifty ways to leave your lover / Still crazy after all these years / Late in the evening / Slip slidin' away / Hearts and bones / Train in the distance / Rene and Georgette Magritte with their dog after the war / Diamonds on the soles of her shoes / You can call me Al / Graceland (Only on LP.) / Kodachrome.
LP: . . . . WX 223
MC: . . . . WX 223 C

ONE-TRICK PONY (Film soundtrack).
Tracks: / Late in the evening / That's why God made the movies / One-trick pony / How the heart approaches what it yearns / Oh Marion / Ace in the hole / Nobody / Jonah / God bless the absentee / Long long day.
LP: . . . . K 56846
MC: K4 56846

PAUL SIMON.
Tracks: / Mother and child reunion / Duncan / Everything put together falls apart / Run that body down / Armistice Day / Me and Julio down by the schoolyard / Peace like a river / Papa hobo / Hobo blues / Paranoia blues / Congratulations.
LP: . . . . CBS 69007
MC: 40 69007
LP: 925588 1
MC: 925588 4

PAUL SIMON: INTERVIEW PICTURE DISC.
LPPD: . . . . BAK 2153

RHYTHM OF THE SAINTS.
LP: . . . . WX 340
MC: . . . . WX 340 C

STILL CRAZY AFTER ALL THESE YEARS.
Tracks: / Still crazy after all these years / My little town / I do it for your love / 50 ways to leave your lover / Night game / Gone at last / Some folk's lives roll easy / Have a good time / You're kind / Silent eyes.
LP: . . . . CBS 86001
MC: 40 86001
LP: 925591 1
MC: 925591 4

THERE GOES RHYMIN' SIMON.
LP: 925589 1
MC: 925589 4
LP: . . . . CBS 69035

Simon, Ralph

TIME BEING.
LP: . . . . GR 8002

Simon, Tito

FEELING HIGH.
Tracks: / When you touch me I'm feeling high / My happiness / Wild world / I'm depending on you / Tonight is the night sweet darling / Running around in circles / Children of Africa / Wait and see / Let's have a night out / 6345789 / 6345789 that's my number / Kingston fourteen wailing souls / Kingston 14.
LP: . . . . TITO 01

HEAT IS ON, THE.
LP: . . . . TILP 001

I CRIED A TEAR.
Tracks: / I cried a tear / Every beat of my heart / I would rather go blind / River of tears / That's where it's at / Tell it like it is / After loving you / Hold on to what you've got.
LP: . . . . FELP 10

MONDAY MORNING FEELING.
Tracks: / Build it up / How many times? / You can't be serious / I'll be true to you / Oh what a feeling / Easy come, easy go / Count the hours / This Monday morning feeling / Read the news / She ain't nothing but the real thing / Valley of love / Jump hallelujah / I'm standing by / Oh Patricia.
LP: . . . . TRLS 108

NEVER LET ME GO.
LP: . . . . KRILP 007

WE MEET AGAIN.
LP: . . . . NULP 001

Simona, Tiziana

GIGOLO (Simona, Tiziana/Kenny Wheeler).
LP: . . . . ITM 0014

Simone, Nina

AMAZING NINA SIMONE, THE.
Tracks: / Blue prelude / Children go where I send you / Tomorrow / Stompin' at the Savoy / It might as well be Spring / You've been gone too long / That's him over there / Chilly winds don't blow / Middle of the Night, Theme from / Can't get out of this mood / Willow weep for me.
LP: . . . . OFF 6002
MC: . . . . OFF 46002

ARTISTRY OF NINA SIMONE, THE.
Tracks: / Mr. Bojangles / I shall be released / Do what you gotta do / Since I fell for you / I want a little sugar in my bowl / I can't see nobody / Ain't got no....I got life / To love somebody / Turn me on / Seems I'm never tired lovin' you / Romance in the dark / My man's gone now / How long must I wander? / Blues for Mama.
LP: . . . . NL 89018
MC: . . . . NK 89018
LP: . . . . INTS 5193

BACKLASH.
LP: . . . . SJAZZ 6
MC: . . . . SJAZZC 6

BALTIMORE.
Tracks: / Baltimore / Everything must change / Family, The / My father / Music for lovers / Rich girl / That's all I want from you / Forget / Balm in gilead / If you pray right.
LP: . . . . CTI 9010

BALTIMORE (RE-ISSUE).
LP: 4607301
MC: 4607304

BEST OF NINA SIMONE.
Tracks: / In the morning / I shall be released / Day and night / It be's that way sometimes / I want a little sugar in my bowl / My man's gone now / Why? (the king of love is dead) / Compensation / I wish I knew how it would feel to be free / Go to hell / Do what you gotta do / Suzanne.
LP: . . . . NL 90376
MC: . . . . NK 90376

BEST OF NINA SIMONE (2).
Tracks: / I love you Porgy / Break down and let it all out / Four women / Pirate Jenny / Sinner man / Don't let me be misunderstood / I put a spell on you.
LP: . . . . TIME 10
MC: . . . . TIMEC 10

BLACK SOUL.
Tracks: / Here comes the sun / Mr. Bojangles / I think it's going to rain today.
LP: . . . . CL 42220
MC: . . . . CK 42220

BLUES, THE.
Tracks: / Do I move you ? / Day and night / In the dark / Real real / My man's gone now / Backlash blues / I want a little sugar in my bowl / Buck / Since I fell for you / House of the rising sun, The / Blues for Mama / Pusher, The / Turn me on / Nobody's fault but mine / Go to hell / I shall be released / Gin house blues.
MC: . . . . NK 83101

COLLECTION: NINA SIMONE.
LP: . . . . MA 16185
MC: . . . . MAMC 916185

CRY BEFORE I GO.
Tracks: / Trouble in mind / After you've gone / Nobody / Hard walkin' Hannah / Cry before I go / Can't stand to leave / Big legged woman / Funky funky soul.
LP: . . . . MAN 5039

DON'T LET ME BE MISUNDERSTOOD.
Tracks: / Don't let me be misunderstood / Last rose of summer / Ne me quitte pas / Work song / Little girl blue / Trouble in mind / Strange fruit / Love me or leave me / Come ye / I put a spell on you / Don't explain / Wild is the wind / What more can I say / Nobody knows you (when you're down and out) / I loves you, Porgy (live) / Mississippi goddam (live).
LP: 834081
MC: 834084

FINE AND MELLOW.
Tracks: / Fine and mellow / Rags and old iron / Satin doll / Memphis in June / Twelfth of never / I got it bad and that ain't good / Return home, The / Sayonara / It don't mean a thing / Just say I love him / I'll look around / Do nothing till you hear from me / I love to love / Will I find my love? / Black swan.
LP: . . . . GH 607

FODDER ON HER WINGS.
Tracks: / I sing just to know that I'm alive / Fodder on her wings / Vous etes seuls, mais je desire etre / Avec vous / Il y a un baume a gilhead / Heaven belongs to you / Liberian calypso / Thandewye / I was just a stupid dog to them / Colour is a beautiful thing / There is no returning.
LP: 1067 885

GIN HOUSE BLUES.
Tracks: / Ain't no use / I want a little sugar in my bowl / Gin House blues / Backlash blues / Assignment song / Young gifted and black.
LP: . . . . MAN 5031

HERE COMES THE SUN.
Tracks: / Here comes the sun / Just like a woman / Oh child / Mr. Bojangles / New world coming / Angel of the morning / How long must I wander? / My way.
LP: . . . . INTS 5025
MC: . . . . INTK 5025
LP: . . . . NL 89421

I PUT A SPELL ON YOU.
LP: . . . . BL 7671

I WANT A LITTLE SUGAR IN MY BOWL.
Tracks: / Ain't no use / I want a little sugar in my bowl / Gin house blues / Ain't got no....I got life / Four women / No opportunity necessary.
LP: . . . . MAN 5007

LADY MIDNIGHT.
Tracks: / I put a spell on you / Nobody knows you (when you're down and out) / Trouble in mind / Mood indigo / Feeling good / Pirate Jenny(live) / I loves you porgy / Wild is the wind / For myself / Beautiful land / This years kisses / Plain gold ring / Don't let me be misunderstood / One September day / Little girl blue / Keep on breaking my heart / Love me or leave me / Ballad of Hollis Brown, The / Strange fruit / Something wonderful (from The King And I) / Don't explain / Last rose of summer / What more can I say? / Mississippi goddam / For 'roar of the grease.
2LP: . . . . VSOPLP 106
MC: . . . . VSOPMC 106

LIVE AND KICKIN'.
LP: . . . . FREUD 32
MC: . . . . FREUDC 32

LIVE AT RONNIE SCOTT'S.
Tracks: / God, God, God / If you knew / Mr. Smith / Fodder on her wings / Be my husband / I love you, Porgy / Other woman, The / Mississippi goddam / For a while / See live woman / I sing just to know I'm alive / My baby just cares for me.
MC: . . . . ESMMC 013

LIVE AT VINE STREET.
LP: 831 437-1
MC: 831 437-4

MAGIC MOMENTS.
Tracks: / Ain't got no....I got life / Backlash blues / Gin house blues / I loves you Porgy / Suzanne / To love somebody / I can't see nobody / I shall be released / Just like Tom Thumb's blues / Revolution (part 1) / Revolution (part 2) / Young gifted, and black / Here comes the sun / Just like a woman / Mr. Bojangles / Nobody's fault but mine / Everyone's gone to the moon / Another Spring / I get along without you very well / Who am I? / Poppies / Let it be me / I want a little sugar in my bowl.
MC: . . . . NK 89896

MAGIC OF NINA SIMONE, THE.
Tracks: / Work song / You can have him / Little Liza Jane / Fine and mellow / Porgy / Angel of the morning / Lovin' woman / My way / Nina's blues / Here comes the sun.
MC: . . . . VENUMC 2

MUSIC FOR THE MILLIONS.
Tracks: / I put a spell on you / Mississippi / Goddam / Don't let me be misunderstood / Trouble in mind / Laziest girl in town / I loves you, Porgy / Ne me quitte pas / Gimme some / Nobody knows you (when you're down and out) / Strange fruit / Take care of business / Don't take all night.
LP: 8123 781
MC: 8123 784

MY BABY JUST CARES FOR ME.
Tracks: / My baby just cares for me / Don't smoke in bed / Mood indigo / He needs me / Love me or leave me / I loves you Porgy / You'll never walk alone / Good bait / Central Park blues / Plain gold ring / Little girl blue / My baby just cares for me (extended version) / My baby just cares for me (ext. smooch time) / Love me or leave me.
LP: . . . . CR 30217
MC: . . . . TCCR 30217

NE ME QUITTE PAS.
2LP: 406502

NINA AT TOWN HALL.
Tracks: / Black is the colour of my true love's hair / Exactly like you / Other woman, The / Under the lowest / You can have him / Summertime / Cotton eyed Joe / Return home / Wild is the wind / Fine and mellow.
LP: . . . . OFF 6012
MC: . . . . OFF 46012

NINA SIMONE AT NEWPORT.
Tracks: / Trouble in mind / Porgy / Little Liza Jane / You'd be so nice to come home to / Flo me la / Nina's blues / In the evening by the moonlight.
LP: . . . . OFF 6014
MC: . . . . OFF 46014

NINA SIMONE COLLECTION (Her Golden Greats).
Tracks: / House of the Rising Sun / Gin House blues / Don't let me be misunderstood / He was too good to me / When I was a young girl / Brown baby / Just in time / Zungo / Way I love you, The / Backlash blues / Please read me / Seeline woman / If he changed my name.
LP: . . . . DVLP 2104
MC: . . . . DVMC 2104

NINA SIMONE (DAKOTA LABEL).
Tracks: / House of the Rising Sun / Gin house blues / Ne me quitte pas / When I was a young girl / Devil's workshop / Just in time / Don't let me be misunderstood / Backlash blues / To love somebody / Ain't got no....I got life / Sealine woman / Please read me.
LP: . . . . COUNT 9
MC: . . . . ZC CNT 9

NINA SIMONE (MERCURY LABEL).
Tracks: / My baby just cares for me / Feeling good / He ain't coming home no more / Brown eyed handsome man / If I should lose you / Black is the colour of my true loves hair / Gal from Joe's, The / Don't explain / Keeper of the flame / Mood indigo / Tell me more and more and then some more / Strange fruit / Chilly winds don't blow / I'm going back home / I put a spell on you / Sinnerman.
MC: 838 007-4

NINA SIMONE (RCA).
MC: 495055

NINA SIMONE SINGS THE BLUES.
Tracks: / Do I move you? / Day and night / In the dark / Real real / My man's gone now / Backlash blues / I want a little sugar in my bowl / Buck / Since I fell for you / House of the Rising Sun / Blues for Mama.
LP: . . . . NL 89365
MC: . . . . NK 89365
LP: 26 21230

NINA SIMONE STORY, THE.
Tracks: / When I was a young girl / Just in time / He was too good to me / House of the rising sun / Life / To love somebody / Don't let me be misunderstood / Devil's workshop / Seeline woman / Gin house blues / Brown baby / I'm gonna say / Promises / Children go where I send you / Zungo / If he changed my name / Backlash blues.
MCSET: . . . . DVREMC 15

NINA'S BACK.
LP: . . . . FREUD 28
MC: . . . . FREUDC 28
LP: . . . . VPI 1007
MC: . . . . VPIC 1007

'NUFF SAID.
LP: . . . . SF 7979

OUR LOVE.
Tracks: / Don't let me be misunderstood / How can I make him love me? / I am blessed / Our love / Laziest girl in town / Nobody / Night song / Don't take all night.

LP: . . . . B 90118
MC: . . . . MB 990118

PORTRAIT OF A SONG STYLIST.
MC: . . . . HARMC 112

PORTRAIT OF NINA SIMONE.
Tracks: / Four women / Nobody wants you / Assignment song / No opportunity necessary / I love my baby / Strange fruit / I love to love / Ding song / Sinner man / I want a little sugar in my bowl.
2LP: . . . . ALB 189

REPLAY ON NINA SIMONE.
LP: . . . . FEDB 5021
MC: . . . . CFEDB 5021

RIGHT ON.
LP: 509108

VERY RARE EVENING WITH NINA SIMONE, A.
LP: . . . . PM 018

Simonelli, Dante

MEMORIES OF ITALY.
Tracks: / Tatantella suite / La dosolina / Il grillo e la formica / A retu a la Pizzulu / Reginella campagnola / Vola vola vola / Una gita a li castelli / La danza / Return to Surriento / Santa Lucia / Funiculi funicula.
LP: . . . . VP 460

Simple, Lee J.

PHANTOM OF THE SOAP OPERA.
Tracks: / Phantom of the soap opera.
LP: . . . . RIV 89001

Simple Man

SIMPLE MAN, A (Various artists).
Tracks: / White on white: *Various artists* / Characters appear, The: *Various artists* / Organ grinder, An: *Various* artists / Sitting: *Various artists* / Death of mother: *Various artists* / Going to work: *Various artists*/ Coming from the hill: *Various artists* / Waiting: *Various artists* / Golden room, The: *Various artists*/ Three Anns: *Various artists* / Seascape: *Various artists* / Man with red eyes: *Various artists* / Clogs: *Various artists* / Homage: *Various artists*.
MC: . . . . SCENEC 16

Simple Minds

CELEBRATION.
Tracks: / Life in a day / Chelsea girl / Premonition / Factory / Calling your name / I travel / Changeling / Celebrate / Thirty frames a second / Kaleidoscope.
LP: . . . . V 2248
MC: . . . . TCV 2248
LP: . . . . SPART 1183
LP: . . . . OVED 275
MC: . . . . OVEDC 275

EMPIRES AND DANCE.
Tracks: / I travel / Today I died again / This fear of Gods / Celebrate / Constantinople line / Twist, run, repulsion / Thirty frames a second / Kant-kino / Room / Capital city.
LP: . . . . OVED 211
MC: . . . . OVEDC 211
LP: . . . . SPART 1140

EMPIRES AND DANCE (See under Simple Minds CD Box Set).

LIFE IN A DAY (See under Simple Minds CD Box Set).

LIFE IN A DAY.
Tracks: / Someone / Life in a day / Sad affair / All for you / Pleasantly disturbed / No cure / Chelsea girl / Wasteland / Destiny / Murder story.
LP: . . . . OVED 95
MC: . . . . OVEDC 95
LP: . . . . VM 6
LP: . . . . ZULP 1

LIVE-IN THE CITY OF LIGHT.
Tracks: / Ghostdancing / Big sleep / Waterfront / Promised you a miracle / Someone, somewhere in summertime / Oh jungleland / Alive and kicking / Don't you (forget about me) / Once upon a time / Book of brilliant things / East at Easter / Sanctify yourself / Love song / Sun city / Dance to the music / New gold dream.
MCSET: . . . . SMDCX 1
2LP: . . . . SMDLX 1

NEW GOLD DREAM (81-82-83-84).
Tracks: / Someone, somewhere in summertime / Colours fly and catherine wheel / Promised you a miracle / Big sleep / Somebody up there likes you / New gold dream / Glittering prize / Hunter and the hunted / King is white and in the crowd.
LP: . . . . V 2230
MC: . . . . TCV 2230

ONCE UPON A TIME.
Tracks: / Once upon a time / All the things she said / Ghostdancing / Alive and kicking / Oh jungleland / I wish you were here / Sanctify yourself / Come a long way.
LP: . . . . V 2364
MC: . . . . TCV 2364

REAL LIFE.
LP: . . . . V 2660
MC: . . . . TCV 2660

REEL TO REAL CACOPHONY.
Tracks: / Real to real / Naked eye / Citizen (dance of youth) / Veldt / Carnival (shelter in a suitcase) / Factory / Cacophony / Premonition / Changeling / Film theme / Calling your name / Scar.
LP: . . . . OVED 124
MC: . . . . OVEDC 124
LP: . . . . V 2246
LP: . . . . SPART 1109

REEL TO REAL CACOPHONY (See under Simple Minds CD Box Set).

SIMPLE MINDS: BOX SET.
MCSET: . . . . SMBXC 1

SIMPLE MINDS: INTERVIEW PICTURE DISC.
LPPD: . . . . BAK 2070

SISTER FEELINGS CALL.
Tracks: / Theme for great cities / American, The / 20th century promised land / Wonderful in young life / League of nations / Careful in career / Sound in 70 cities.
MC: . . . . OVEDC 2
LP: . . . . OVED 2

SONS AND FASCINATION.
Tracks: / In trance as mission / Sweat in bullet / 70 cities as love brings the fall / Boys from Brazil / Love song / This earth that you walk upon / Sons and fascination / Seeing out the angel / Theme for great cities (CD & Cassette only) / American, The (CD & Cassette only) / 20th century promised land (CD & cassette only) / Wonderful in young life (CD & cassette only) / Careful in career (CD & Cassette only).
LP: . . . . V 2207
MC: . . . . TCV 2207
LP: . . . . OVED 292
MC: . . . . OVEDC 292

SPARKLE IN THE RAIN.
Tracks: / Up on the catwalk / Book of brilliant things / Speed your love to me / Waterfront / East at Easter / Street hassle / White hot day / C moon / Kick inside of me, The / Shake off the ghosts / Cry like a baby.
LP: . . . . V 2300
MC: . . . . TCV 2300
MC: . . . . OVEDC 346
LP: . . . . OVED 346

STREET FIGHTING YEARS.
Tracks: / Street fighting years / Wall of love / Take a step back / Let it all come down / Belfast child / Soul crying out / This is your land / Kick it in / Mandela day / Biko.
LP: . . . . MINDS 1
MC: . . . . MINDC 1

Simple Pip

JAMES REEVES.
MC: . . . . TTC/K 04

Simple Simon

REGGAE MOVE.
LP: . . . . VSLP 4067

Simplicity

INTRODUCING SIMPLICITY.
Tracks: / Little green apples / Listen to the ocean / Banks of the Ohio / Coming home / Shame and scandal / Malaguena / Tom Dooley / Guantanamera / Catch a train / St.Louis blues / Summertime / Plaiser d'amour.
LP: . . . . SRTZ CUS059

Simply Red

MEN AND WOMEN.
Tracks: / Right thing, The / Infidelity / Suffer / I won't feel bad / Every time we say goodbye / Let me have it all / Love fire / Move on out / Shine / Maybe someday.
LP: . . . . WX 85
MC: . . . . WX 85C

NEW FLAME, A.
Tracks: / It's only love / New flame, A / You've got it / To be with you / More / Turn it up / Love lays it's tune / She'll have to go / If you don't know me by now / Enough / I asked for water (10" and 12" only) / Write me your... (10" and 12" only) / Funk on out (instumental) (10" only).
LP: . . . . WX 242
MC: . . . . WX 242C

PICTURE BOOK.
Tracks: / Come to my aid / Sad old red / Look at you now / Heaven / Jericho / Money's too tight to mention / Holding back the years / Open up the red box / No direction / Picture book.
LPPD: . . . . EKT 27P
LP: . . . . EKT 27
MC: . . . . EKT 27C

SIMPLY RED: INTERVIEW PICTURE DISC.
LPPD: . . . . TT 1001
LPPD: . . . . BAK 2044

Simpson, Carole

ALL ABOUT CAROLE.
Tracks: / You make me feel so young / Listen little girl / You forgot your gloves / Sure thing / Gentleman friend / Your name is love / Everytime / Oh look at me now / Time / I'll be around / There will be another you / Just because we're kids.
LP: . . . . JAS 309
MC: . . . . JAS C309

Simpson, Eddie

TWO SOUL CHIEFS (Simpson, Eddie/ Marcell Strong).
LP: . . . . RL 039

Simpson, Martin

GOLDEN VANITY.
LP: . . . . LER 2099

GRINNING IN YOUR FACE.
Tracks: / It doesn't matter anymore / Little birdie / First cut is the deepest / Roving gambler / This way may last you for years / Master of war / Green linnet / Grinning in your face / Reuben's train / Your cheatin' heart / Handsome Molly / Townships Biko / Moonshine.
LP: 12TS 430

LEAVES OF LIFE.
LP: . . . . SHAN 97008

NOBODY'S FAULT BUT MINE.
LP: . . . . DAM 013

SAD OR HIGH KICKING.
LP: 12TS 438

SPECIAL AGENT.
LP: . . . . WF 008
MC: . . . . WF 008C

TRUE DARE OR PROMISE (Simpson, Martin & Jessica).
Tracks: / Past caring / Not the whisky talking / Young man / Bedlam boys / Wholly in my keeping / Rising of the woman, The / Man smart (woman smarter) / Essequibo river / Keel row, The.
LP: 12TS 446

Simpson, Paul

ONE.
LP: . . . . CHR 1721
MC: . . . . ZCHR 1721

SIMPSON STREET.
LP: . . . . EASYLP 2
MC: . . . . EASYMC 2

Simpson, Red

20 GREAT TRUCK HITS: RED SIMPSON.
Tracks: / Truck drivin' man / Nitro express / Give me 40 acres / Motivatin' man / Big Mack / 6 days on the road / Sleeper, 5 by 2 / Take me home / Tombstone every mile / Born to be a trucker / Diesel smoke, dangerous curves / Truck drivin' fool / Hold on ma'm / Truckin' on down the road / Fur coats and fancy clothes / Country western truck drivin' singer / I'm a truck / Milesaver man / Awful lot to learn about truck drivin' / If the world ran out of diesel.
LP: 7C 062 85895

ROLL, TRUCK, ROLL.
LP: . . . . HAT 3074
MC: . . . . HATC 3074

Simpson, Ted

FIDDLING PETE & THE CROSS EYED BULL.
LP: . . . . LRF 105

Simpsons

SIMPSONS SING THE BLUES, THE.
LP: 7599243081
MC: 7599243084
LP: . . . . GEF 24308
MC: . . . . GEFC 24308

Sims, Frankie Lee

WALKING WITH FRANKIE (1960).
Tracks: / Woman why'd you break my heart? / Short-haired woman / My home ain't here / Lucy Mae blues / Jelly Roll Baker / Come back baby - 1 & 2 / Send my soul to the devil / As long as I live / Walking with Frankie / Don't be mad with me / Going back to Dallas / Going to the river / Frankie Lee boogie.
LP: . . . . KK 7428

Sims, Joyce

ALL ABOUT LOVE.
Tracks: / Looking for a love / Take caution with my heart / Natural woman / You mean the world to me / All about love / Don't let this feeling die / I surrender / Crazy love / Here we go again / I love you more.
LP: 828 129 1
MC: 828 129 4

COME INTO MY LIFE.
Tracks: / Come into my life / Love makes a woman / It wasn't easy / All and all / Lifetime love / Change in you, A / Walk away / All and all (the UK remix) / All and all (Megamix) (Track only on CD.).
LP: . . . . LONLP 47
MC: . . . . LONC 47

Sims, Zoot

AL & ZOOT (See under Cohn, Al) (Sims, Zoot & Al Cohn).

BASIE & ZOOT (see Basie,Count) (Sims, Zoot & Count Basie).

BEST OF ZOOT SIMS.
Tracks: / Willow weep for me / Blues for Louise / Someday, sweetheart / Wrap up / Girl from Ipanema / More than you know / Main stem / I got it bad and that ain't good.
LP: 23 10 850
MC: K10 850

BIG STAMPEDE, THE.
Tracks: / You're my girl / Purple cow, The / Ill wind / Big stampede, The / Too close for comfort / Jerry's jaunt / How now blues / Bye ya.
LP: . . . . MTLP 017

BLUES FOR TWO (Sims, Zoot & Joe Pass).
Tracks: / Blues for two / Dindi / Remember / Poor butterfly / Black and blue / Pennies from Heaven / I hadn't anyone till you / Take off.
LP: . . . . D 2310 879
MC: . . . . D 10 879

BODY AND SOUL (See under Cohn, Al) (Sims, Zoot & Al Cohn).

BROTHER IN SWING.
LP: 500077
LP: . . . . JL 77

CHET BAKER AND STRINGS: FEATURING ZOOT SIMS (See under Baker, Chet) (Baker, Chet & Zoot Sims).

DOWN HOME (Sims, Zoot Quartet).
Tracks: / Jive at five / Doggin' around / Ascap / Avalon / I cried for you / Bill Bailey won't you please come home / Goodnight sweetheart / There'll be some changes made / I've heard that blues before.
LP: . . . . AFF 87

EITHER WAY (see Cohn,Al & Zoot Sims) (Sims, Zoot & Al Cohn).

FROM A TO Z (see Cohn, Al & Zoot Sims Sextet).

GASSER, A (see under Ross, Annie) (Sims, Zoot & Annie Ross).

HAPPY OVER HOAGY (Sims, Zoot & Al Cohn Septet).
LP: . . . . JASS 12

HAWTHORNE NIGHTS.
Tracks: / Hawthorne nights / Main stem / More than you know / Only a rose / Girl from Ipanema / I got it bad and that ain't good / Fillings / Dark clouds.
LP: 2310 783
MC: K10 783

I WISH I WERE TWINS.
Tracks: / I wish I were twins / Georgia / Changes / Touch of your lips, The / Fish horn, The / Come closer to me / You go your way.
LP: 2310 868
MC: K10 868

IF I'M LUCKY (Sims, Zoot & Jimmy Rowles).
Tracks: / Where our love has gone / Legs / If I'm lucky / Shadow waltz / You're my everything / It's alright with me / Gypsy sweetheart / I hear a rhapsody.
LP: 231 0803
MC: K10 803

IN A SENTIMENTAL MOOD.
LP: . . . . SNTF 932

IN PARIS - 1956.
LP: . . . . SW 8417

INNOCENT YEARS, THE (Sims, Zoot Four).
Tracks: / Pomme au four / I hear a rhapsody / Over the rainbow / Very thought of you, The / If you were mine / Indian Summer.
LP: 2310 872
MC: K10 872

JOE & ZOOT (Sims, Zoot & Joe Venuti).
2LP: . . . . VJD 523

JUST FRIENDS (Sims, John Haley/ Harry Sweets Edison).
Tracks: / Nature boy / How deep is the ocean / My heart belongs to daddy / I understand / Just friends / Blue skies / Until tonight / Little tutu, A.
LP: 231 0841
MC: K10 841

MOTHER - MOTHER (See under Terry, Clark) (Sims, Zoot & Clark Terry).

NASHVILLE (Sims, Zoot & Dick Nash).
Tracks: / Way you look tonight / Nashville / You don't know what love is / Compatability.
LP: ZMS 2004

ON CAMPUS (See under Charles, Teddy) (Sims, Zoot and Teddy Charles).

ONE TO BLOW ON.
Tracks: / September in the rain / Down at the loft / Ghost of a chance / Not so deep / Them there eyes / Our pad / Dark clouds / One to blow on.
LP: MTLP 012

PASSION FLOWER.
Tracks: / It don't mean a thing / In a mellow tone / I got it bad and that ain't good / I let a song go out of my heart / Black butterfly / Do nothing till you hear from me / Your love has faded / Bojangles / Passion flower.
LP: 2312 120
MC: K 12 120

QUIETLY THERE - ZOOT SIMS PLAYS JOHNNY MANDEL.
Tracks: / Rissy / Time for love / Cinnamon and cloves / Low life / Zoot / Emily / Quietly there.
LP: 2310 903
MC: K10 903

SOMEBODY LOVES ME.
Tracks: / Summerset / Honeysuckle rose / Summer thing, A / Somebody loves me / Gee baby / Ain't I good to you / Nirvana / Indiana / Memories of you / Come rain or come shine / Up a lazy river / Send in the clowns / Airmail special / Ham hock blues / Ring dem bells.
MC: MC 8514

STRETCHING OUT (Sims, Zoot & Bob Brookmeyer).
Tracks: / Stretching out / Now will you be good / Pennies from Heaven / King Porter / Ain't misbehavin' / Bee Kay.
LP: FS 44

SWEETEST SOUNDS, THE (see Gustafsson, Rune) (Simms, Zoot & Rune Gustafsson).

SWINGER, THE.
Tracks: / Moon is low, The / Now I lay me down to dream of you / On the Alamo / Danielle / Mr. J.R. blues / Jeep is jumpin' / She's funny that way / Dream of you.
LP: 23210 861
MC: K10 861

TENOR CONTRASTS VOLUME 2 (Sims, Zoot/Al Cohn/James Moody).
LP: ESQ 320

TONITE'S MUSIC TODAY (Sims, Zoot & Bob Brookmeyer).
LP: BLP 60907

WAITING GAME.
Tracks: / Old folks / I wish I knew / Once we loved / It's a blue world / September song / Over the rainbow / Stella by starlight / One I could have loved / You go to my head / Does the sun really shine on the moon?.
LP: JAS 62

WARM TENOR (Sims, Zoot & Jimmy Rowles).
Tracks: / Dream dancing / Old devil moon / Blues for Louise / Jitterbug waltz / You go to my head / Blue prelude / Comes love / You're my thrill.
LP: 231 0831
MC: K10 831

ZOOT! (Sims, Zoot Quartet).
LP: OJC 228

ZOOT PLAYS SOPRANO.
Tracks: / Someday, sweetheart / Moonlight in Vermont / Wrap your troubles in dreams / Blues for Louise / Willow weep for me / Wrap up / Ghost of a chance / Baubles, bangles and beads.
LP: 2310 770
MC: K10 770

ZOOT SIMS.
LP: OJC 242
LP: JR 156

ZOOT SIMS AND BOB BROOKMEYER (Sims, Zoot & Bob Brookmeyer).
Tracks: / King, The / Lullaby of the leaves / I can't get started / Snake eyes / Morning fun / Whooeeeeee / Someone to watch over me / My old flame / Box cars.
LP: BLP 60914

ZOOT SIMS/ DICK NASH (Sims, Zoot & Dick Nash).
Tracks: / Way you look tonight / Nashville / You don't know what love is / Compatability.
LP: ZM 1008

ZOOT SIMS & THE GERSHWIN BROTHERS.
Tracks: / Man I love, The / How long has this been going on? / Lady be good / I've got a crush on you / I got rhythm / Embraceable you / 'S wonderful / Someone to watch over me / Isn't it a pity? / Summertime.
LP: 2310 744
MC: K10 744

ZOOT SIMS WITH THE BOB BROOKMEYER QUINTET (Sims, Zoot & The Bob Brookmeyer Quintet).
LP: PUMPKIN 108

ZOOTCASE.
Tracks: / My silent love / Jane O / Dancing in the dark / Memories of you / Trotting / I wonder who / It had to be / Zoot sings the blues / Zoot sings the blues (take 2) / East of the sun (and west of the moon) / Morning fun / Tangerine / Zootcase / Red door, The / Howdy podner / (American idyll) Indian summer, An / Toot number two / What's new?.
2LP: PR 24061

Simukonda, Ackim

LADY SUNSHINE.
LP: LD 5012

Sin Alley

SIN ALLEY, VOL 4 (Various artists).
LP: 5562

Sinatra, Frank

16 HITS (See under Dorsey, Tommy).

20 CLASSIC TRACKS: FRANK SINATRA.
Tracks: / Come fly with me / Around the world / French Foreign Legion / Moonlight in Vermont / Autumn in New York / Let's get away from it all / April in Paris / London by night / It's nice to go travellin' / Come dance with me / Something's gotta give / Just in time / Dancing in the dark / Too close for comfort / I could have danced all night / Saturday night is the loneliest night of the week / Cheek to cheek / Baubles, bangles and beads / Day in, day out.
LP: MFP 50530
MC: TCMFP 50530

20 GOLDEN CLASSICS, VOL 1.
LP: 20035

20 GOLDEN GREATS: FRANK SINATRA.
Tracks: / That old black magic / Love and marriage / Fools rush in / Lady is a tramp, The / Swingin' down the lane / All the way / Witchcraft / It happened in Monterey / You make me feel so young / Nice 'n' easy / Come fly with me / High hopes / I've got you under my skin / Chicago / Three coins in the fountain / It's nice to go travellin' / Young at heart / In the wee small hours of the morning / Tender trap, The / Let's do it.
LP: EMTV 10
MC: TCEMTV 10

20 GOLDEN PIECES: FRANK SINATRA.
Tracks: / Now is the hour / Don't forget tonight tomorrow / Haunted heart / My shining hour / Hair of gold, eyes of blue / Lady from 29 palms / Little white lies / Suddenly it's spring / It only happens when I dance with you / Very thought of you, The / One hundred years from today / Golden earrings / I'm in the mood for love / You're the top / Right kind of love, The / Let me love you tonight / My happiness / I'll get by / Tenderly / Speak low.
LP: BDL 2046
MC: BDC 2046

1938-1940 (See Under Dorsey, Tommy) (Sinatra, Frank & Tommy Dorsey).

ADVENTURES OF THE HEART.
Tracks: / I guess I'll have to dream the rest / If only she looked my way / Love me / Nevertheless / We kiss in a shadow / I am loved / Take my love / I could write a book / Mad about you / Sorry / Stromboli / It's only a paper moon.
LP: 32319

ALL THE WAY.
Tracks: / All the way / High hopes / Talk to me / French Foreign Legion / To love and be loved / River stay 'way from my door / Witchcraft / It's over / Old MacDonald had a farm / This was my love / All my tomorrows / Sleep warm.
LP: ED 2601791
MC: ED 2601794

BEST OF FRANK SINATRA.
Tracks: / Chicago / Witchcraft / Lady is a tramp, The / Nice and easy.
LP: 1A 022 58137
MC: 1A 222 58137
LP: ST 21140

BEST OF FRANK SINATRA AND TOMMY DORSEY (Sinatra, Frank & Tommy Dorsey).
Tracks: / Stardust / I think of you / There are such things / How about you / I'll never smile again / I'll be seeing you / Without a song / Street of dreams / Poor you / April played the fiddle / This love of mine / One I love, The / I guess I'll have to dream the rest / We three.
LP: 107 4063
MC: 770 4063

BEST OF OL' BLUE EYES.
Tracks: / I've got you under my skin / I have dreamed / Witchcraft / In the wee small hours of the morning / Girl from Ipanema / Last night when we were young / Let me try again / Fly me to the moon / Come rain or come shine / How insensitive / All or nothing at all / Something.
LP: K 54042
MC: K4 54042

BROADWAY KICK/ ADVENTURES OF THE HEART.
Tracks: / There's no business like show business / They say it's wonderful / Some enchanted evening / You're my girl / Lost in the stars / Why can't you behave? / I whistle a happy tune / Girl that I marry, The / Can't you just see yourself? / There but for you go I / Bali Ha'i / Where is my Bess? / I guess I'll have to dream the rest / If only she'd looked my way / Love me / Nevertheless (I'm in love with you) / We kiss in a shadow / I am loved / Take my love / I could write a book / Mad about you / Sorry / On the island of Stromboli / It's only a paper moon.
LP: CBS 22182
MC: 40 22182

CAPITOL COLLECTORS SERIES: FRANK SINATRA.
Tracks: / I'm walking behind you / I've got the world on a string / From here to eternity / South of the border / Young at heart / Don't worry 'bout me / Three coins in the fountain / Melody of love / Learnin' the blues / Same old Saturday night / Love and marriage / Love is the tender trap / How little it matters how little we know / Hey jealous lover / Can I steal a little love / All the way / Chicago / Witchcraft / High hopes / Nice 'n' easy.
MC: C4 92160
MC: 792 160 4

CAPITOL YEARS, THE: FRANK SINATRA.
Tracks: / I've got the world on a string / Lean baby / I love you / South of the border / From here to eternity / They can't take that away from me / I get a kick out of you / Young at heart / Three coins in the fountain / All of me / Taking a chance on love / Someone to watch over me / What is this thing called love / In the wee small hours of the morning / Learnin' the blues / Our town / Love and marriage / Love is the tender trap / Weep they will / I thought about you / You make me feel so young / Memories of you / I've got you under my skin / Too marvelous for words / Don't like goodbyes / How little it matters how little we know / Your sensational (single version) / Hey jealous lover / Close to you / Stars fell on Alabama / I got plenty o' nuttin' / I wish I were in love again / Lady is a tramp, The / Night and day / Lonesome road / If I had you / Where are you? / I'm a fool to want you / Witchcraft / Something wonderful happens in summer / All the way / Chicago / Let's get away from it all / Autumn in New York / Come fly with me / Everybody loves somebody / It's the same old dream / Put your dreams away / Here goes / Angel eyes / Guess I'll hang my tears out to dry / Ebb tide / Only the lonely / One for my baby (and one more for the road) / To love and be loved (single version) / I couldn't care less / Song is you, The / Just in time / Saturday night (is the loneliest night of the week) / Come dance with me / French foreign legion / One I love (belongs to somebody else), The / Here's that rainy day / High hopes / When no one cares / I'll never smile again / I've got a crush on you / Embraceable you / Nice 'n' easy / I can't believe that you're in love with me / On the sunny side of the street / I've heard that song before / Almost like being in love / I'll be seeing you / I gotta right to sing the blues.
LPS: C1 94777
LPS: 794 777 1

CAPITOL YEARS, THE: FRANK SINATRA.
LPS: SINATRA 20
MCSET: TCSINATRA 20

CLOSE TO YOU.
Tracks: / Close to you / P.S. I love you / Love locked out / Everything happens to me / It's easy to remember / Don't like goodbyes / With every breath I take / Blame it on my youth / It could happen to you / I've had my moments / I couldn't sleep a wink last night / End of a love affair, The / If it's the last thing I do / There's a flaw in my flute / Wait till you see her.
LP: ED 2601381
MC: ED 2601384

LP: 2C 068 54579

COLLECTION: FRANK SINATRA.
2LP: CCSLP 122
MC: CCSMC 122

COLLECTION: FRANK SINATRA.
Tracks: / Come fly with me / April in Paris / Bewitched / Lady is a tramp, The / I've got you under my skin / When your lover has gone / I get a kick out of you / Where or when / All the way / You make me feel so young / Somebody loves me / They say its wonderful / You do something to me / I don't stand a ghost of a chance with you / Music stopped, The / I've got my love to keep me warm / People will say we're in love / Lover / Night and day / That old black magic.
LP: DVLP 2015
MC: DVMC 2015

COLLECTION: FRANK SINATRA (The Love Songs).
Tracks: / Tell her you love her / You go to my head / One for my baby / Don't worry 'bout me / Wrap your troubles in dreams / I'll string along with you / Half as lovely / If I had you / Violets for your furs / It all depends on you / Someone to watch over me / When I stop loving you / Out of nowhere / Like someone in love / One I love, The / You are too beautiful / Our love is here to stay / Taking a chance on love / It worries me / It only happens when I dance with you.
MC: DVMC 2101
LP: DVLP 2101

COME BACK TO SORRENTO.
LP: TFL 5082

COME DANCE WITH ME.
Tracks: / Come dance with me / Something's gotta give / Just in time / Dancing in the dark / Too close for comfort / I could have danced all night / Saturday night is the loneliest night of the week / Day in, day out / Cheek to cheek / Baubles, bangles and beads / Song is you, The / Last dance.
LP: ED 2600801
MC: ED 2600804
LP: LCT 6179

COME FLY WITH ME.
Tracks: / Come fly with me / Around the world / Isle of Capri / Moonlight in Vermont / Autumn in New York / On the road to Mandalay / Let's get away from it all / April in Paris / London by night / Brazil / Blue Hawaii / It's nice to go travellin'.
LP: ED 2600951
MC: ED 2600954
MC: 4XL 9190
LP: LCT 6154

COME SWING WITH ME.
Tracks: / Day by day / Sentimental journey / Almost like being in love / Five minutes more / American beauty rose / Yes indeed / On the sunny side of the street / Don't take your love from me / That old black magic / Lover / Paper doll / I've heard that song before / I love you (CD only.) / Why should I cry over you (CD only.) / How could you do a thing like that to me (CD only.) / River stay 'way from my door (CD only.) / I gotta right to sing the blues (CD only.).
LP: ED 2601801
MC: ED 2601804
LP: W 1594

CONCERT SINATRA.
LP: R 1009

CYCLES.
Tracks: / Rain in my heart / Both sides now / Little green apples / Pretty colours / Cycles / Wandering / By the time I get to Phoenix / Moody river / My way of life / Gentle on my mind.
LP: K 44013

DAYS OF WINE AND ROSES.
Tracks: / Days of wine and roses / Moon river / Way you look tonight / Three coins in the fountain / In the cool cool cool of the evening / Secret love / Swinging on a star / It might as well be Spring / Continental, The / Love is a many splendoured thing / All the way.
LP: K 44003

DORSEY-SINATRA SESSIONS, 1940-42 (see Dorsey, Tommy) (Sinatra, Frank & Tommy Dorsey).

DUETS.
LP: PJ 001

EARLY YEARS, THE.
Tracks: / Night and day / Blue skies / Stardust / Night we called it a day, The.
LP: 26 21726

FABULOUS FORTIES, THE.
LP: SM 4194
MC: MC 4194

FRANCIS ALBERT SINATRA.
Tracks: / Girl from Ipanema / Dindi / Change partners / Quiet night of quiet stars / Meditation / If you never come to

me / How insensitive / Concentrate on you / Baubles, bangles and beads / Once I loved.
LP: K 44008

FRANK.
Tracks: / I hadn't anyone till you / Night and day / Misty / Stardust / Come rain or come shine / It might as well be Spring / Prisoner of love / That's all or nothing at all / Yesterday / I'm getting sentimental over you / Imagination / There are such things / East of the sun (and west of the moon) / Daybreak / Without a song / I'll be seeing you / Take me / It's almost you / Polka dots and moonbeams / It started all over again / One I love belongs to somebody else, The / I'm getting sentimental over you (reprise).
LP: K 64016

FRANK SINATRA & BING CROSBY (Sinatra, Frank & Bing Crosby).
Tracks: / Granada / Someone lovelier than you / Imagination / Wanted / Take a change / Young at heart / 'Til we meet again / Among my souvenirs / September song / As time goes by / Meet me tonight in dreamland / It's a long, long trail.
LP: SM 3612
MC: MC 3612

FRANK SINATRA CHRISTMAS COLLECTION (Frank's Christmas greats).
Tracks: / Christmas song, The / White Christmas / O little town of Bethlehem / Adeste fideles / It came upon a midnight clear / Santa Claus is coming to town / Jingle bells / Silent night / Christmas dreaming / Have yourself a merry little Christmas / Hark the herald angels sing.
LP: DVLP 2079
MC: DVMC 2079

FRANK SINATRA COLLECTION, THE.
Tracks: / Nice 'n' easy / Cheek to cheek / I'm gonna sit right down and write myself a letter / As time goes by / Witchcraft / I've got you under my skin / You make me feel so young / I can't get started / I get a kick out of you / Chicago / Come fly with me / Lady is a tramp, The / Tender trap, The / My funny valentine / Night and day / You'd be so nice to come home to / Dancing in the dark / Let's get away from it all / Nice work if you can get it / One for my baby.
LP: EMTV 41
MC: TCEMTV 41

FRANK SINATRA (ENTERTAINERS LABEL).
LP: ENT LP 13001
MC: ENT MC 13001

FRANK SINATRA IN CONCERT.
Tracks: / Come fly with me / I've got a crush on you / I've got you under my skin / Shadow of your smile / Street of dreams / One for my baby / Fly me to the moon / One o'clock jump / You make me feel so young / All of me / September of my years / Get me to the church on time / It was a very good year / Don't worry 'bout me / Makin' whoopee / Where or when / Angel eyes / My kind of town.
2LP: K 64002

FRANK SINATRA IN ITALIA.
MC: 24-1072-1

FRANK SINATRA & LENA HORNE (Sinatra, Frank & Lena Horne).
LP: 20037
MC: 40037

FRANK SINATRA (REPRISE LABEL).
Tracks: / World we knew (over and over), The / Something stupid / This is my love / Born free / Don't sleep in the subway / This town / This is my song, you are there / Drinking again / Some enchanted evening.
LP: K 44009

FRANK SINATRA SINGS THE SELECT COLE PORTER.
Tracks: / I've got you under my skin / I concentrate on you / What is this thing called love? / You do something to me / At long last love / Anything goes / Night and day / Just one of those things / I get a kick out of you / You'd be so nice to come home to / I love Paris / From this moment on / C'est magnifique / It's alright with me / Mind if I make love to you / You're sensational.
MC: C4 96611

FRANK SINATRA STORY.
LP: TFL 5030

FRANK SINATRA & TOMMY DORSEY (Sinatra, Frank & Tommy Dorsey).
LP: BLJ 8019

FRANK SINATRA, VOL. 2.
LP: SM 3631

FRANK SINATRA, VOL. 3.
LP: SM 3632

FRANK SINATRA, VOL. 4.
LP: SM 3633

FRANK SINATRA, VOL. 5.
LP: SM 3634

FRANK SINATRA (WORLD RECORDS).
LPS: ALBUM 47
MCSET: CASSETTE 47

GOT THE WORLD ON A STRING.
Tracks: / I've got the world on a string / Them there eyes / If I could be with you / Under a blanket of blue / Just you, just me / Let's fall in love / Hands across the table / You must have been a beautiful baby / Someone to watch over me / I'll string along with you / Thou swell / You took advantage of me / Where or when / This can't be love / Try a little tenderness / Platinum blues / I'm confessin' / Sometimes I'm happy / My funny valentine / That old black magic.
LP: SMT 007
MC: SMTC 007

GREAT FILMS AND SHOWS.
Tracks: / Night and day / I wish I were in love again / I got plenty o' nuttin' / I guess I'll have to change my plan / Nice work if you can get it / I won't dance / You'd be so nice to come home to / I got it bad and that ain't good (CD only.) / From this moment on / Blue moon / September in the rain / It's only a paper moon / You do something to me / Taking a chance on love / Get happy / Just one of those things / I love Paris / Chicago / High hopes / I believe / Lady is a tramp, The / Let's do it (With Shirley MacLaine.) / C'est magnifique / Tender trap, The / Three coins in the fountain / Young at heart / Girl next door, The / They can't take that away from me / Someone to watch over me / Little girl blue / Like someone in love / Foggy day, A / I get a kick out of you / My funny valentine / Embraceable you / That old feeling / I've got a crush on you / Dream / September song / I'll see you again / As time goes by / There will never be another you / I'll remember April / Stormy weather / I can't get started / Around the world / Something's gotta give / Just in time / Dancing in the dark / Too close for comfort / I could have danced all night / Cheek to cheek / Song is you, The / Baubles, bangles and beads / Almost like being in love / Lover / On the sunny side of the street / That old black magic / I've heard that song before / You make me feel so young / Too marvellous for words / It happened in Monterey / I've got you under my skin / How about you / Pennies from Heaven / You're getting to be a habit with me / You brought a new kind of love to me / Love is here to stay / Old devil moon / Makin' whoopee / Anything goes / What is this thing called love / Glad to be unhappy / I get along without you very well / Dancing on the ceiling / Can't we be friends / All the way / To love and be loved / All my tomorrows / I couldn't sleep a wink last night / Spring is here / One for my baby / Time after time / It's alright with me / It's the same old dream / Johnny Concho theme (wait for me) / Wait till you see her / Where are you / Lonely town / Where or when / I concentrate on you / Love and marriage.
LPS: FS 1

GREAT SONGS FROM GREAT BRITAIN.
LP: R 1006

GREATEST HITS: FRANK SINATRA (The Early Years).
Tracks: / I've got a crush on you / If you are but a dream / Nancy (with the laughing face) / Girl that I marry, The / House that I live in, The / Dream / Saturday night is the loneliest night of the week / Five minutes more / Coffee song, The / Sunday, Monday or always / Put your dreams away.
LP: CBS 31677
MC: 40 31677
LP: RSLP 1025

GREATEST HITS: FRANK SINATRA.
Tracks: / Foggy day, A / I get a kick out of you / My funny valentine / You make me feel so young / I've got you under my skin / I've got the world on a string / Pennies from Heaven / Blue moon / One for my baby / Day in, day out / Cheek to cheek / Nice 'n' easy / It's only a paper moon / Young at heart / Lady is a tramp, The / Night and day / Brazil / Come fly with me / Only the lonely / I love Paris / Always / All the way / That old black magic / Chicago.
2LP: 5C 180 82263/4
MCSET: 923954 4

GREATEST HITS: FRANK SINATRA, VOL.2.
Tracks: / Shadow of your smile / Yesterday / Blue lace / For once in my life / Born free / My way / Little green apples / Both sides now / Mrs. Robinson / Call me irresponsible / Gentle on my mind / Love's been good to me.
LP: K 44018
MC: K4 44018
LP: RSLP 1032

GREATEST HITS: FRANK SINATRA, VOL.1.
Tracks: / Strangers in the night / Summer wind / It was a very good year / Somewhere in your heart / Forget Domani / Something stupid / That's life / Tell her / World we knew, The / When somebody loves you / This town / Softly as I leave you.
LP: K 44011
MC: K4 44011

HAVE YOURSELF A MERRY LITTLE CHRISTMAS.
Tracks: / White Christmas / Jingle bells / O little town of Bethlehem / Have yourself a merry little Christmas / Christmas dreaming / Silent night, holy night / It came upon a midnight clear / Adeste fideles / Santa Claus is coming to town.
LP: 4604641
MC: 4604644

HELLO YOUNG LOVERS.
MC: 4601664

I REMEMBER TOMMY.
LP: R 1003

IN THE BEGINNING.
Tracks: / I've got a crush on you / If you are but a dream / Nancy / Girl that I marry, The / House that I live in, The / Mean to me / I have but one heart / Moon was yellow, The / Full moon and empty arms / Put your dreams away / Day by day / I couldn't sleep a wink last night / Ol' man river / Time after time / I'm a fool to want you / Saturday night is the loneliest night of the week / Five minutes more / Sunday, Monday or always / Coffee song, The / Dream.
2LP: CBS 22108
MC: 40 22108

IN THE WEE SMALL HOURS.
Tracks: / In the wee small hours of the morning / Glad to be unhappy / I get along without you very well / Deep in a dream / I see your face before me / Can't we be friends / When your lover has gone / What is this thing called love / I'll be around / Ill wind / It never entered my mind / I'll never be the same / This love of mine / Last night when we were young / Dancing on the ceiling.
LP: CAPS 1008
MC: TCCAPS 1008

IT MIGHT AS WELL BE SWING (Sinatra, Frank/Count Basie).
Tracks: / In other words / I wish you love / I believe in you / More / I can't stop loving you / Hello Dolly / I wanna be around / Best is yet to come, The / Good life / Wives and lovers.
LP: CBS 44004
LP: K 44004
LP: R 1012

I'VE GOT YOU UNDER MY SKIN.
LP: ENT LP 13035
MC: ENT MC 13035

KISSES AND TEARS.
Tracks: / So they tell me / Help yourself to my heart / If you please / You'll know when it happens / All through the day / There's something missing / Kisses and tears / Meet me at the Copa / My love for you.
LP: MTM 023

L.A. IS MY LADY.
Tracks: / L.A. is my lady / Best of everything, The / How do you keep the music playing? / Teach me tonight / It's all right / Mack the knife / Until the real thing comes along / Stormy weather / If I should lose you / Hundred years from today / After you've gone.
LP: 925145 1
MC: 925145 4

LEGENDARY CONCERTS VOL. 1.
LP: 39014
MC: 69014

LEGENDARY CONCERTS VOL. 2.
LP: 39015
MC: 69015

LEGENDARY CONCERTS VOL 3.
LP: 39016
MC: 69016

LEGENDARY, THE.
MC: MRT 40040

LIVE AT MONTECARLO SPORTING CLUB (June 14, 1958).
LP: LOP 14 019

LONG AGO AND FAR AWAY.
Tracks: / Little white lies / Suddenly / It's Spring / This can't be love / Long ago and far away / One hundred years from today / I'm in the mood for love / Tenderly / Speak low / My happiness / I'll get by / Now is the hour / I found a new baby / You can't be true dear.
LP: TOP 121
MC: KTOP 121

LOOK TO YOUR HEART.
Tracks: / Look to your heart / Any time, anywhere / Not as a stranger / Our town / You, my love / Same old Saturday night / Fairytale / Impatient years, The / I could have told you / When I stop loving you / If I had three wishes / I'm gonna live 'til I die.
LP: ED 2601401
MC: ED 2601404
LP: LCT 6181

LOVE IS A KICK.
Tracks: / You do something to me / Bim bam baby / My blue Heaven / When you're smiling / Saturday night is the loneliest night of the week / Bye bye baby / Continental, The / Deep night / Should I / American beauty rose / Five minutes more / Farewell farewell to love.
LP: CBS 32736
MC: 40 32736

MAIN EVENT, THE.
Tracks: / Overture / It was a very good year / All the way / My kind of town / Lady is a tramp, The / I get a kick out of you / Let me try again / Autumn in New York / I've got you under my skin / Bad bad Leroy Brown / Angel eyes / You are the sunshine of my life / House I live in, The / My kind of town / My way.
LP: K 54031

MAN ALONE, A.
Tracks: / Man alone, A / Night / I've been to town / From promise to promise / Single man, The / Beautiful strangers / Lonesome cities / Love's been good to me / Empty is / Out beyond the window / Some travelling music.
LP: K 44016
LP: RSLP 1030

MAN AND HIS MUSIC, A.
LP: R 1016

MOONLIGHT SINATRA.
LP: R 1018

MOST BEAUTIFUL SONGS, THE.
Tracks: / Strangers in the night / Cycles / Swinging on a star / Summer wind / Fine romance, A / Baubles, bangles and beads / My way / Goody goody / Moonlight serenade / It was a very good year / Days of wine and roses / Ring a ding ding / Moon river / Call me irresponsible / Somethin' stupid / Shadow of your smile, the / September song / That's life / Girl from Ipanema / Ol' man river / Stardust / Come fly with me / What now my love / More.
LP: K 64011

MUSICAL MONTAGE, A.
LP: AR 105

MY BEST YEARS, VOL 1.
Tracks: / Pistol packin' mama / I found a new baby / You can't be true, dear / I'm in the mood for love / Love is blue / I'll dance at your wedding / Long ago and far away / My shining hour.
LP: DO 90063

MY BEST YEARS, VOL 2.
Tracks: / This can't be love / My happiness / I'll get by / Lili Bolero / Hair of gold, eyes of blue / I wonder who's kissing her now / Long ago and far away / Tenderly / Little white lies / Haunted house / I'll string along with you / How soon?.
LP: DO 90064

MY WAY.
Tracks: / Watch what happens / Hallelujah, I love her so / Yesterday all my tomorrows / My Way / For once in my life / If you go away / Mrs. Robinson / Didn't we? / Day in the life of a fool, A.
LP: K 44015
MC: K4 44015
LP: RSLP 1029

NEW YORK, NEW YORK (His Greatest Hits).
Tracks: / I get a kick out of you / Something stupid / Moon river / What now my love / Summer wind / Mrs. Robinson / My way / Strangers in the night / For once in my life / Yesterday / That's life / Girl from Ipanema / Lady is a tramp, The / Bad, bad Leroy Brown / Ol' man river.
LP: WX 32
MC: WX 32 C

NICE 'N' EASY.
Tracks: / Nice 'n' easy / That old feeling / How deep is the ocean / I've got a crush on you / You go to my head / Fools rush in / Nevertheless (I'm in love with you) / She's funny that way / Try a little tenderness / Embraceable you / Mam'selle / Dream.
LP: ED 2601421
MC: ED 2601424
LP: W 1417

NO ONE CARES.

Tracks: / When no one cares / Cottage for sale / Stormy weather / Where do you go? / I don't stand a ghost of a chance / Here's that rainy day / I can't get started / Why try to change me now? / Just friends / One I love belongs to somebody else, The.
LP: . . . . **ED 2601411**
MC: . . . . **ED 2601414**

NOW IS THE HOUR.
Tracks: / I wonder who's kissing her now / I wish I didn't love you so / How soon / Lady from 29 Palms / You do / Serenade of the bells / Golden earrings / Dance ballerina dance / I'll dance at your wedding / Lili Bolero / Little white lies / Tree in the meadow, A / My happiness / You call everybody darling / Now is the hour.
LP: . . . . **SHLP 106**
MC: . . . . **SHTC 106**
LP: **20034**
MC: **40034**

NOW IS THE HOUR (METEOR).
Tracks: / Now is the hour / Don't forget tonight tomorrow / Haunted heart / My shining hour / Hair of gold, eyes of blue / Lady from 29 palms / Little white lies / Suddenly it's spring / It only happens when I dance with you / Very thought of you, The.
LP: . . . . **MTM 003**

OFF THE RECORD WITH FRANK SINATRA.
Tracks: / I wonder who's kissing her now / Let me love you tonight / I'll get by / This can't be love / I heard you cried last night / Long ago and far away / My happiness / I wish I didn't love you so / Some other time / I'm in the mood for love / Pistol packin' mama / Golden earrings / Serenade of the bells / Lady from 29 palms / After I say I'm sorry / Lover is blue, A / Hair of gold, eyes of blue / Little white lies / Wing and a prayer / Little Bolero / Don't forget tonight tomorrow / I found a new baby / One hundred years from today.
2LP: . . . . **FEDD 1011**
MCSET: . . . . **CFEDD 1011**

OL' BLUE EYES.
Tracks: / Witchcraft / Come fly with me / Young at heart / Tender trap, The / All the way.
LPPD: . . . . **AR 30080**

OL' BLUE EYES IS BACK.
Tracks: / You will be my music / Winners theme (From Maurice.) / Nobody wins / Send in the clowns / Dream away / Let me try again / There used to be a ball park / Noah / You're so right (for what's wrong in my life).
LP: . . . . **K 44249**

ONE NIGHT STAND WITH FRANK SINATRA.
LP: . . . . **JOYCE 1121**

ORIGINAL RECORDINGS 1939-42.
Tracks: / All or nothing at all / Too romantic / Hear my song, Violetta / Yours is my heart alone / I'll never smile again / Whispering / Oh, look at me now / Blue skies / Sinner kissed an angel, A / Somewhere a voice is calling / There are such things / I'll take Tallulah.
LP: . . . . **SM 3055**
MC: . . . . **MC 3055**

ORIGINAL SESSIONS, VOL 1.
Tracks: / Night and day / Somebody loves me / You make me feel so young / Just one of those things / Nevertheless / On the sunny side of the street / Love me or leave me / You are love / They didn't believe me / Out of nowhere / I've got my love to keep me warm / For you.
LP: . . . . **MTM 007**

ORIGINAL SESSIONS, VOL 2.
Tracks: / Blue skies / They say it's wonderful / 'S wonderful / Begin the beguine / Ol' man river / Don't blame me / Laura / It all depends on you / I fall in love with you every day / Music stopped, The / I don't stand a ghost of a chance / You do something to me.
LP: . . . . **MTM 004**

POINT OF NO RETURN.
Tracks: / When the world was young / I'll remember April / September song / Million dreams ago, A / I'll see you again / There will never be another you / Somewhere along the way / It's a blue world / These foolish things / As time goes by / I'll be seeing you / Memories of you.
LP: . . . . **ED 2601771**
MC: . . . . **ED 2601774**

PORTRAIT OF SINATRA.
Tracks: / Let's face the music and dance / Nancy (with the laughing face) / I've got you under my skin / Let me try again / Fly me to the moon / All or nothing at all / For once in my life / Bonita / My kind of town / Call me irresponsible / All the way / Strangers in the night / Didn't we? / Come fly with me / Second time around / In the wee small hours of the morning / Bad, bad Leroy Brown / Softly as I leave you / Cycles / Send in the clowns / That's life / Little green apples / Song of the Sabia / Goody goody / Empty tables / I believe I'm gonna love you / Stargazer / I sing the songs / I write the songs / You are the sunshine of my life / It was a very good year / Something stupid / Young at heart / You make me feel so young / Yesterday / Pennies from Heaven / Something / If / Star / Love's been good to me / My way.
2LP: . . . . **K 64039**
MCSET: **K4 64039**

RADIO DAYS.
MCSET: . . . . **DTO 10304**

RARE RECORDINGS 1935 - 1970.
LP: . . . . **SH 2040**
MC: . . . . **CSH 2040**

RARE SINATRA, THE.
Tracks: / Don't make a beggar of me / Ya better stop / Day in, day out / Memories of you / If it's the last thing I do / I couldn't care less / Take a chance / There's a flaw in my flute / Song is you, The / Where or when / It all depends on you / One I love belongs to somebody else, The.
LP: . . . . **ATAK 66**
MC: . . . . **TCATAK 66**
LP: . . . . **EST 24311**
MC: . . . . **TCEST 24311**
LP: . . . . **MFP 5856**
MC: . . . . **TCMFP 5856**
MC: . . . . **TCESTK 24311**

RARITIES.
Tracks: / Why shouldn't I? / Two hearts are better than one / Girl that I marry, The / Could 'ja? / Things we did last summer, The / Stella by starlight / So far / It only happens when I dance with you / When is sometime? / Where is the one / Nature boy / Bop goes my heart / It happens every Spring / Accidents will happen / London by night / Bim bam baby.
LP: **4651651**
MC: **4651654**

REPLAY ON FRANK SINATRA VOL.1.
LP: . . . . **FEDB 5001**
MC: . . . . **CFEDB 5001**

REPLAY ON FRANK SINATRA VOL.2.
LP: . . . . **FEDB 5029**
MC: . . . . **CFEDB 5029**

REPRISE YEARS, THE.
Tracks: / In the still of the night / Granada / I'm getting sentimental over you / Without a song / I get a kick out of you / Night and day / Come rain or come shine / All or nothing at all / Nightingale sang in Berkeley Square / All alone / I won't dance / Ol' man river / I've got you under my skin / In the wee small hours of the morning / Nancy / Way you look tonight / Fly me to the moon / All the way / Luck be a lady / I only miss her when I think of her / September of my years / This is all I ask / It was a very good year / Strangers in the night / Call me irresponsible / Moon love / Don't worry / One for my baby / My kind of town / Poor butterfly / How insensitive / Dindi / By the time I get to Phoenix / Cycles / Didn't we / Something stupid / Love's been good to me / Man alone, A / Goin' out of my head / Something / Train / Lady Day / Drinking angels / Send in the clowns / Let me try again / What are you doing the rest of your life / If / Put your dreams my way.
LPS: . . . . **K 94003**
LPS: **7599265011**
MC: **7599265014**

RING-A-DING-DING.
LP: . . . . **R 1001**

SALOON SONGS.
Tracks: / One for my baby / I should care / These foolish things / I guess I'll have to dream the rest / It never entered my mind / When your lover has gone / Body and soul / That old feeling / Ghost of a chance / There's no you / Guess I'll hang my tears out to dry / Why try to change me now.
LP: **4600181**
MC: **4600184**

SALUTE TO SINATRA (See Under Salute To Sinatra) (Various artists).

SCREEN SINATRA.
Tracks: / From here to eternity / Three coins in the fountain / Young at heart / Just one of those things / Someone to watch over me / Not as a stranger / Tender trap, The / Wait for me (Johnny Concho theme) / All the way / Chicago / Monique-Song from Kings Go Forth / They came to Cordura / To love and be loved / High hopes / All my tomorrows / It's alright with me / C'est magnifique / Dream.
LP: . . . . **CAPS 1038**
MC: . . . . **TCCAPS 1038**
LP: . . . . **MFP 5835**
MC: . . . . **TCMFP 5835**

SEPTEMBER OF MY YEARS.
Tracks: / September of my years / How old am I / Don't wait too long / It gets lonely early / This is all I ask / Last night when we were young / Man in the looking glass, The / It was a very good year / When the wind was green / Hello young lovers / I see it now / Once upon a time / September song.
LP: . . . . **K 44005**

SEXY, SWINGING SINATRA.
Tracks: / Blue moon / These foolish things / Autumn leaves.
LPS: . . . . **PM 155 177 3**

SHE SHOT ME DOWN.
Tracks: / Good thing going / Hey look, no crying / Thanks for the memory / Long night / Bang bang / Monday morning quarterback / South to a warmer place / I loved her / Gal that got away / It never entered my mind.
LP: . . . . **L 54117**

SINATRA.
2LP: . . . . **SM 3762/2**
MC: **4XL 8345**

SINATRA AND COMPANY.
LP: . . . . **RSLP 1033**

SINATRA AND STRINGS.
LP: . . . . **R 1004**

SINATRA AT THE SANDS (Sinatra, Frank/Count Basie).
MC: . . . . **REP 64002**
LP: . . . . **RLP 1019**

SINATRA CHRISTMAS ALBUM, THE.
Tracks: / Jingle bells / Christmas song, The / Mistletoe and holly / I'll be home for Christmas / Have yourself a merry little Christmas / Christmas waltz / First Noel, The / Hark the herald angels sing / O little town of Bethlehem / Adeste fideles / It came upon a midnight clear / Silent night / White Christmas (CD only) / Christmas waltz (alternate).
LP: . . . . **CAPS 1809871**
MC: . . . . **TC CAPS 1809874**
LP: . . . . **MFP 5797**
MC: . . . . **TCMFP 5797**

SINATRA FOR THE SINATRAPHILE.
LP: . . . . **AX 6**

SINATRA LOVE SONGS.
Tracks: / Nearness of you / If I had you / Nevertheless / You go to my head / My melancholy baby / How deep is the ocean / Embraceable you / She's funny that way / For every man there's a woman / I don't know why (I just do) / Someone to watch over me / Love me.
LP: **4600161**
MC: **4600164**

SINATRA PLUS.
LP: . . . . **SET 303**

SINATRA SCREEN.
Tracks: / Continental, The / It's the same old dream / Laura / Stormy weather / I've got a crush on you / House I live in, The / All through the day / I couldn't sleep a wink last night / Time after time / But beautiful / I fall in love too easily / Brooklyn Bridge.
LP: **4600151**
MC: **4600154**

SINATRA SINGS RODGERS & HART.
LP: . . . . **SRS 5083**

SINATRA SINGS SONGS FOR PLEASURE.
LP: . . . . **MFP 1120**

SINATRA SINGS...OF LOVE AND THINGS.
Tracks: / Nearness of you, The / Hidden persuasion / Moon was yellow, The / I love Paris / Monique / Chicago / Love looks so well on you / Sentimental baby / Mr. Success / They came to Cordura / I gotta right to sing the blues / Something wonderful happens in summer.
LP: . . . . **ED 2601781**
MC: . . . . **ED 2601784**

SINATRA SOUVENIR.
LP: . . . . **TFL 5138**

SINATRA STAGE.
Tracks: / There's no business like show business / Song is you, The / September song / Oh what a beautiful morning / They say it's wonderful / Bess, oh where's my Bess? / Where or when / I could write a book / Why was I born? / Lost in the stars / All the things you are / Ol' man river.
LP: **4600141**
MC: **4600144**

SINATRA STANDARDS.
Tracks: / Saturday night is the loneliest night in the week / Poinciana / Try a little tenderness / Autumn in New York / April in Paris / Dream / Nancy (with the laughing face) / Put your dreams away / I'm glad there is you / Day by day / Close to you / I'm a fool to want you.
LP: **4600171**
MC: **4600174**

SINATRA SWINGS.
Tracks: / Should I / Birth of the blues / Mean to me / It all depends on you / Deep night / Sweet Lorraine / Castle rock / Why can't you behave / My blue Heaven / S'posin' / You can take my word for it baby / Blue skies.
LP: **4600131**
MC: **4600134**
LP: . . . . **R 1002**

SINATRA: THE CONCERTS (20 Live Greats).
Tracks: / At long last love / I could have danced all night / Imagination / Moon was yellow, The / Embraceable you / Dancing in the dark / Road to Mandalay, The / Just one of those things / Willow weep for me / Angel eyes / My funny valentine / My blue Heaven / Come fly with me / I get a kick out of you / I've got you under my skin / April in Paris / All the way / Bewitched / Lady is a tramp, The / Night and day.
LP: . . . . **DVLP 2061**
MC: . . . . **DVMC 2061**

SINATRA: THE DUETS.
Tracks: / Little learning is a dangerous business / Kisses and tears / Love means love / Mama will bark / Good man is hard to find, A / Love me tender / Tea for two / Exactly like you / Camptown races / When you're smiling / Me and my shadow / Take me out to the ball game / Gotta be this or that / How about you / Birth of the blues / Down by the old mill stream / Yes sir / Some enchanted evening / Them there eyes / Beautiful dreamer / Witchcraft / Come fly with me / I begged her / Downtown / These boots are made for walking.
LP: . . . . **DVLP 2051**
MC: . . . . **DVMC 2051**

SINATRA: THE RADIO YEARS 1939-55.
Tracks: / All or nothing at all / After all / I've got my eyes on you / Polka dots and moonbeams / Deep night / Whispering / Sky fell down, The / On the isle of may / It's a blue world / Fable of the rose / Marie / Lover is blue, A / Careless / I'll never smile again / Our love affair / East of the sun / One I love, The / Shadows on the sand / That's how it goes / I get a kick out of you / Let's get lost / Embraceable you / Night and day / Close to you / I couldn't sleep a wink last night / Falling in love with you / Music stopped, The / My ideal / Speak low / People will say we're in love / Long ago and far away / I'll get by / Sweet Lorraine / Swinging on a star / These foolish things / Very thought of you, The / All the things you are / My melancholy baby / Homesick that's all / Till the end of time / What makes the sunset? / I fall in love too easily / I begged her / Don't forget tonight tomorrow / That's for me / I found a new baby / I'm always chasing rainbows / Aren't you glad you're you? / It might as well be spring / Lilly belle / If I loved you / Slowly / Great day / I only have eyes for you / Oh,what it seemed to be / Full moon and empty arms / Exactly like you / I fall in love with you every day / It's a good day / My sugar is so refined / Ole buttermilk sky / Lullaby of broadway / I won't dance / Touch of your hand, The / Why was I born? / All through the day / Make believe / Song is you, The / All the things you are / You can't see the sun when you're crying / Anniversary song / You do / Let it snow, let it snow, let it snow / I wish I didn't love you so / Wrap your troubles in dreams / Nature boy / My haunted heart / Little white lies / A tree in the meadow / It only happens when I dance with you / My happiness / O sole mio / I found a new baby / It isn't fair / Body and soul / When you're smiling / I've got a crush on you / My foolish heart / Best things in life are free, The / I love you / Why remind me? / Just you, just me / Somebody loves me / Polka dots and moonbeams / Sorry / Young at heart / Among my souvenirs / September song / As time goes by / Take a chance / Till we meet again / Meet me in dreamland / There's a long long trail / Don't blame me / 'S wonderful / It all depends on you / Night and day / Somebody loves you / Nevertheless / On the sunny side of the street / Love me or leave me / Try a little tenderness / Out of nowhere / I've got my love to keep me warm / What can I say? / Between the devil and the deep blue sea / One hundred years from today / I'm in the mood for love / Tenderly / Hello young lovers / She's funny that way / I don't know why / Come rain or come shine.
LPS: . . . . **MTBS 001**

SINATRA: THE UNOBTAINABLE (20 rare greats).

Tracks: / Old school teacher / If you please / You'll know when it happens / So they tell me / It's all up to you / My love for you / All through the day / Life is so peculiar / There's something missing / Meet me at the Copa / Home on the range / Lilly Belle / Help yourself to my heart / Bop goes my heart / My cousin Louella / Cantana / Chattanooga shoeshine boy / Old master painter, The / Fella with an umbrella, A / Shine.
LP: . . . . DVLP 2071
MC: . . . . DVMC 2071

SINATRA WITH SWINGING BRASS.
LP: . . . . R 1005

SINATRA-BASIE (Sinatra, Frank/Count Basie).
LP: . . . . R 1008

SINATRA'S GOLD.
Tracks: / Lady is a tramp, The / Young at heart / My funny valentine / 3 coins in the fountain.
MC: 4XL 8346

SINATRA'S SINATRA.
Tracks: / I've got you under my skin / In the wee small hours of the morning / Second time around / Nancy / Witchcraft / Young at heart / All the way / How little we know / Pocketful of miracles / Oh what it seemed to be / Call me irresponsible / Put your dreams away.
LP: . . . . K 44002
LP: . . . . R 1010

SINATRA'S SWINGIN' SESSION.
Tracks: / When you're smiling / Blue moon / S'posin' / It all depends on you / It's only a paper moon / My blue Heaven / Should I / September in the rain / Always / I can't believe you're in love with me / I concentrate on you / You do something to me / Sentimental baby / Ol' MacDonald / Hidden persuasion.
LP: . . . . ED 2602461
MC: . . . . ED 2602464
LP: . . . . W 1491

...SINGS FOR ONLY THE LONELY.
Tracks: / Only the lonely / Angel eyes / What's new / It's a lonesome old town / Willow weep for me / Goodbye / Blues in the night / Guess i'll hang my tears out to dry / Ebb tide / Spring is here / Gone with the wind / One for my baby / Sleep warm (CD only.) / Where or when (CD only.).
LP: . . . . ED 2601391
MC: . . . . ED 2601394
LP: . . . . LCT 6168

SOFTLY AS I LEAVE YOU.
LP: . . . . R 1013

SOME NICE THINGS I'VE MISSED.
Tracks: / You turned my world around / Sweet Caroline / Summer knows, The / Tie a yellow ribbon / Satisfy me one more time / If / What are you doing the rest of your life? / Bad bad Leroy Brown / You are the sunshine of my life.
LP: . . . . K 54020

SOMETHIN' STUPID (see under Sinatra, Nancy).

SONGS BY SINATRA.
Tracks: / I won't dance (A) / Touch of your hand, The (A) / Who (A) / Smoke gets in your eyes (A) / Kern medley (A) / All through the day (A) / Make believe (A) / Song is you, The (A) / All the things you are (A) / What makes the sunset (B) / In the middle of May (B) / Scene from 'Anchors Aweigh' (B) / I fall in love too easily (B) / I begged her (B) / Charm of you, The (B).
LP: . . . . AX 7
LP: . . . . PJ 003

SONGS FOR SWINGIN' LOVERS.
Tracks: / Too marvellous for words / Old devil moon / Pennies from Heaven / Love is here to stay / I've got you under my skin / I thought about you / We'll be together again / Makin' whoopee / Swingin' down the lane / Anything goes / How about you / You make me feel so young / It happened in Monterey / You're getting to be a habit with me / You brought a new kind of love to me.
LP: . . . . SLCT 6106
MC: . . . . TCSLCT 6106
LP: . . . . LCT 6106

SONGS FOR YOUNG LOVERS.
Tracks: / Girl next door, The / They can't take that away from me / Violets for your furs / Someone to watch over me / My one and only / Little girl blue / Like someone in love / Foggy day, A / It worries me / I can read between the lines / I get a kick out of you / My funny valentine.
LP: . . . . ED 2600741
MC: . . . . ED 2600744

STRANGERS IN THE NIGHT.
Tracks: / Strangers in the night / Summer wind / All or nothing at all / Call me / You're driving me crazy / On a clear day / My baby just cares for me / Downtown / Yes sir, that's my baby / Most beautiful girl in the world, The.
LP: . . . . K 44006
LP: . . . . R 1017

STRING ALONG.
Tracks: / I'll string along with you / How soon? / Mimi / After I say I'm sorry / Lover is blue, A / Speak low / Dance ballerina dance / Serenade of the bells / Devil and the deep blue sea / My heart tells me / I wonder who's kissing her now? / Long ago and far away.
LP: . . . . MTM 014

SUDDENLY IT'S SPRING.
Tracks: / I wish I didn't love you so / Lili Bolero / Suddenly it's spring / You're the top / Lilly belle / Wing and a prayer / It's all up to you / Some other time / You've got a hold on me / Right kind of love, The.
LP: . . . . MTM 018

SUNNY SIDE OF THE STREET.
MC: 510423.8

SUPERGOLD.
2LP: . . . . IC 134 81333/4

SWING EASY.
Tracks: / Jeepers creepers / Taking a chance on love / Wrap your troubles in dreams / Lean baby / I love you / I'm gonna sit right down and write myself a letter / Get happy / All of me / How could you do a thing like that to me / Why should I cry over you / Sunday / Just one of those things.
LP: . . . . ED 2600811
MC: . . . . ED 2600814
LP: . . . . W 587

SWINGIN' AFFAIR, A.
Tracks: / Night and day / I wish I were in love again / I got plenty o' nuttin' / I guess I'll have to change my plan / Nice work if you can get it / Stars fell on Alabama / No one ever tells you / I won't dance / Lonesome road / At long last love / You'd be so nice to come home to / I got it bad and that ain't good / From this moment on / If I had you / Oh, look at me now.
LP: . . . . CAPS 2600171
MC: . . . . TCCAPS 2600174

SWINGING, SEXY SINATRA.
Tracks: / Autumn leaves / April in Paris / Blues in the night / Ebb tide / One for my baby / Gone with the wind / Stormy weather / That old feeling / How deep is the ocean? / Fools rush in / Try a little tenderness / Embraceable you / September song / I'll see you again / These foolish things / As time goes by / I'll be seeing you / My funny valentine / Come fly with me / Come dance with me / Just in time / I could have danced all night / Baubles, bangles and beads / Dancing in the dark / Cheek to cheek / Something's gotta give / When you're smiling / It's only a paper moon / September in the rain / My blue Heaven / Always / You do something to me / Blue moon / That old black magic / Jeepers creepers / All of me.
2LP: 2C 152 81700/2

TENDERLY.
Tracks: / One hundred years from today / Golden earrings / I'm in the mood for love / You're the top / Right kind of love / Let me love you tonight / My happiness / I'll get by / Tenderly / Speak low.
LP: . . . . MTM 001

THAT'S LIFE.
LP: . . . . RSLP 1020

THIS IS SINATRA VOL.1.
Tracks: / I've got the world on a string / Three coins in the fountain / Love and marriage / From here to eternity / South of the border / Rain (falling from the skies) / Gal that got away / Young at heart / Learnin' the blues / My one and only love / Tender trap, The / Don't worry 'bout me.
LP: . . . . EMS 1237
MC: . . . . TCEMS 1237
LP: . . . . ED 2606981
MC: . . . . ED 2606984

THIS IS SINATRA VOL.2.
Tracks: / Hey jealous lover / Everybody loves somebody / Something wonderful happens in summer / Half as lovely / You're cheatin' yourself (if you're cheatin' on me) / You'll always be the one I love / You forgot all the words / How little we know (how little it matters) / Time after time / Crazy love / Johnny Concho theme (wait for me) / If you are but a dream / So long, my love / It's the same old dream / I believe / Put all your dreams away (for another day).
LP: . . . . EMS 1238
MC: . . . . TCEMS 1238
LP: . . . . ED 2606991
MC: . . . . ED 2606994

THIS LOVE OF MINE.
MC: 4XL 9052

TRIBUTE TO FRANK SINATRA, A (See under Wunderlich, Klaus) (Wunderlich, Klaus).

TRILOGY.
Tracks: / Song is you, The / But not for me / I had the craziest dream / It had to be you / Let's face the music and dance / Street of dreams / My shining hour / All of you / More than you know / They all laughed / You and me (we wanted it all) / Just the way you are / Something / MacArthur Park / New York, New York / Summer me, winter me / Song sung blue / For the good times / Love me tender / That's what God looks like / What time does the next miracle leave? / World war none / Future, The / I've been there / Song without words / Before the music ends (finale).
LPS: . . . . K 64042

V-DISC RECORDINGS, VOL 1.
LP: . . . . AX 1

VOICE 1942-1952, THE (The Columbia Years).
Tracks: / One for my baby / I should care / These foolish things / I guess I'll have to dream the rest / It never entered my mind / When your lover has gone / Body and soul / That old feeling / Ghost of a chance / There's no you / Guess I'll hang my tears out to dry / Why try to change me now / Nearness of you, The / If I had you / Never the less / You go to my head / My melancholy baby / How deep is the ocean / Embraceable you / She's funny that way / For every man there's a woman / I don't know why (I just do) / Someone to watch over me / Love me / Saturday night is the loneliest night in the week / Poinciana / Try a little tenderness / Autumn in New York / April in Paris / Dream / Nancy (with the laughing face) / Put your dreams away / I'm glad there is you / Day by day / Close to you / I'm a fool to want you / Should I / Birth of the blues / Mean to me / It all depends on you / Deep night / Sweet Lorraine / Castle rock / Why can't you behave / My blue Heaven / S'posin / You can take my word for it baby / Blue skies / Continental, The / It's the same old dream / Laura / Stormy weather / I've got a crush on you / House I live in, The / All through the day / I couldn't sleep a wink last night / Time after time / But beautiful / I fall in love too easily / Brooklyn Bridge / There's no business like show business / Song is you, The / September song / Oh what a beautiful morning / They say it's wonderful / Bess, oh where's my Bess? / Where or when / I could write a book / Why was I born / Lost in the stars / All the things you are / Ol' man river.
2LP: 4502221

VOICE, THE.
Tracks: / I don't know why / Try a little tenderness / Ghost of a chance / Paradise / These foolish things / Laura / She's funny that way / Fools rush in / Over the rainbow / That old black magic / Spring is here / Lover.
LP: . . . . CBS 32520
MC: 40 32520

WATERTOWN.
LP: . . . . RSLP 1031

WHEN YOUR LOVER HAS GONE.
LP: . . . . ENC 101

WHERE ARE YOU?.
Tracks: / Where are you? / Night we called it a day, The / I cover the waterfront / Maybe you'll be there / Laura / Lonely town / Autumn leaves / I'm a fool to want you / I think of you / Where is the one / There's no you / Baby, won't you please come home / I can read between the lines (CD only.) / It worries me (CD only.) / Rain (falling from the skies) (CD only) / Don't worry 'bout me (CD only).
LP: . . . . CAPS 2600181
MC: . . . . TCCAPS 2600184

WITH TOMMY DORSEY AND HIS ORCHESTRA (See under Dorsey, Tommy).

YOU MAKE ME FEEL SO YOUNG.
Tracks: / Night and day / Laura / Somebody loves me / Little white lies / This can't be love / You make me feel so young / Speak low / You do something to me / Begin the beguine / Tenderly / On the sunny side of the street / Love me or leave me / They didn't believe me / Out of nowhere / I've got my love to keep me warm / For you.
LP: . . . . ENT LP 13024
MC: . . . . ENT MC 13024

YOUNG, THE 1940-42.
LP: . . . . SM 4012

Sinatra, Nancy

ALL TIME HITS.
Tracks: / These boots are made for walking / So long, babe / How does that grab you, darlin'? / Last of the secret agents, The / Friday's child / Sugar town / Love eyes / Something stupid / You only live twice / Lightning's girl / Tony Rome / 100 years / Good time girl / Hook and ladder.
LP: . . . . RNLP 70227
MC: . . . . RNC 70227

BOOTS.
LP: . . . . R 6202

DID YOU EVER (Sinatra, Nancy & Lee Hazelwood).
Tracks: / Did you ever / Tippy toe / Back on the road / Arkansas coal (suite) / Congratulations / Down from Dover / Friendship train / Paris summer / Big red balloon / Got it together.
LP: . . . . SF 8240

GREATEST HITS: NANCY SINATRA (Featuring Frank Sinatra & Lee Hazlewood).
Tracks: / Storybook children / These boots are made for walking / Sugar town / Something stupid / How does that grab you, darlin'? / Summer wine / Sundown sundown / I've been down so long / Sand / Oh lonesome me / Ladybird / Jackson / You've lost that lovin' feeling / Some velvet morning / Did you ever / Elusive dreams / Greenwich Village folk song man / So long babe / Jackson.
LP: . . . . PLAT 3903
MC: . . . . PLAC 3903

HOW DOES THAT GRAB YOU DARLIN'.
LP: . . . . R 6207

NANCY AND LEE (Sinatra, Nancy & Lee Hazelwood).
LP: . . . . RSLP 6273
LP: . . . . K 44126

NANCY'S GREATEST HITS.
LP: . . . . RSLP 6409

Sinatras

BETRAYAL.
LP: . . . . SBR 3LP

Sinbad the Sailor

SINBAD THE SAILOR (Various artists).
Tracks: / Sinbad the sailor: *Various artists* / Maruf the cobbler: *Various artists* / Lives of Sultan Mahmud, The: *Various artists.*
MC: . . . . ANV 663

SINBAD THE SAILOR (Lee, Dennis (nar)).
MC: 1245

VOYAGES OF SINBAD I TO III (Jones, Terry (nar)).
MC: . . . . LPMC 212

VOYAGES OF SINBAD IV TO VI (Jones, Terry (nar)).
MC: . . . . LPMC 213

Sinceros

PET ROCK.
Tracks: / Dissapearing / Memory Lane / Socially / Down down / Barcelona / Falling in and out of love / Sleight of hand / Nothing changes / Girl I realise / As the world turns / Midsong.
LP: . . . . EPC 85003

SOUND OF SUNBATHING.
Tracks: / I still miss you / Quick, quick, slow / My little letter / Hanging on too long / World's apart / Take me to your leader / Little white lie / Break her heart / So they know / Good luck.
LP: . . . . EPC 83632

Sindecut

CHANGING THE SCENERY.
Tracks: / Demanding cycle of a word bound / Live the life / Too rough / Tell my why / Crack business / Having / Won't change / Braincell / Slowdown / To the heart.
LP: . . . . V 2635
MC: . . . . TCV 2635

Sinden, Jeremy (nar)

CRUEL COUNT, THE (See under Cruel Count).

LITTLE WHITE DOVES OF LOVE (see under Little White Doves... (bk)).

WALTZ OF HEARTS, THE (see under Waltz of Hearts (bk)).

Sinden, Leon (nar)

RIDDLE OF THE SANDS, THE (see under Riddle Of The...(bk)).

Sinful

GONNA RAISE HELL.
LP: . . . . SHADE 3

Sing

SING (Film Soundtrack) (Various artists).
Tracks: / Sing: *Thomas, Mickey* / Birthday suit: *Kemp, Johnny* / Romance (love theme): *Carrack, Paul & Terri Nunn* / You don't have to ask me twice: *Peeples, Nia* / One more time: *Bolton, Michael* / Somethin' to believe in: *Champlin, Bill* / Total concentration:

...atti / (Everybody's gotta) face ...ic: *Cronin, Kevin*/ What's the matter with love: *Wilkerson, Laurnea* / We'll never say goodbye: *Garfunkel, Art.*
LP: 4634551
MC: 4634554

Sing Out!

SING OUT (TV Theme) (Various artists).
LP: TMB 115
MC: TMBC 115

Singana, Margaret

WE ARE GROWING.
Tracks: / We are growing / Music for Africa / At the zoo / Many rivers to cross / Where is the love / Why did you do it / We are growing (Shaka Zulu mix) / Reach out to the children / My name is Margaret / Man gave names to all the animals / Stand by your man / I never loved a man / Have you ever seen the rain / Hamba bikele.
LP: MOMENT 114
MC: MOMENTC 114
LP: PVBL 1003
MC: PVBLC 1003

Singelton, Charlie

MODERN MAN.
Tracks: / Make your move on me baby.
LP: 207462

Singer, Hal

SWING ON IT.
LP: JSP 1028

Singer, James

RAGGA YUPPING TRAIN (See under Family Love) (Singer, James & Family Love).

Singers & Players

LEAPS AND BOUNDS.
LP: BRED 58

REVENGE OF THE UNDERDOG.
LP: ONULP 11

STAGGERING HEIGHTS.
Tracks: / African blood / Shipers in the streets / School days / Socca / Bedward the flying preacher / Matter of time, A / Autobio / This assembly.
LP: ONULP 23

VACUUM PUMPING.
LP: ONULP 39
MC: ONULP 39C

WAR OF WORDS.
LP: ONULP 5

Singers Unlimited

ACAPELLA I.
Tracks: / Both sides now / London by night / Here, there and everywhere / Lullaby / Michell / Fool on the hill / Emily / Since you asked / More I cannot wish you / Try to remember.
LP: 815 671-1
MC: 815 671-4

ACAPELLA II.
Tracks: / Clair / Killin' me softly with his song / Yesterday / My romance / Lost in the stars / April in Paris / Girl talk / Nature boy / I don't know where I stand / Autumn in New York / Like someone in love / Indian Summer.
LP: 8218601

ACAPELLA III.
Tracks: / Anything goes / Way we were, The / One more time, Chick Corea / Sweet Lorraine / Jeanie with the light brown hair / Someone to light up my life / Love is here to stay / Entertainer, The / All the things you are / Sometimes I feel like a motherless child / I wish you love.
LP: 8218821

CHRISTMAS (SINGERS UNLIMITED).
Tracks: / Deck the halls / Ah bleak and chill the wintry wind / Bright, bright the hollly berries / Nigh Bethlehem / While by my sheep / It came upon a midnight clear / Silent night / Joy to the world / Wassailing song carol of the Russian children / Good King Wenceslas / O come all ye faithful / Coventry carol / Have yourself a merry little Christmas.
LP: MPS 68 105

EVENTIDE.
Tracks: / Deep purple / Air from suite in D / Put your dreams away / I loved you / In the still of the night / Mona Lisa / Feelings / Gymnopedie / Yours truly Rosa / Marlies / How beautiful is night / Eventide.
LP: 8218721

FEELING FREE.
Tracks: / You are the sunshine of my life / Time for love, A / Green Dolphin Street / So many stars / Feeling free with Patrick B / Ja da / Skylark / On a clear day / I'm shadowing you / Where is the love.
LP: 8218581

FOUR OF US.
LP: MPS 68 106

FRIENDS.
LP: MPS 68 150

IN TUNE.
LP: MPS 68 085

INVITATION.
LP: MPS 68 107

JUST IN TIME.
LP: MPS 68 179

SENTIMENTAL JOURNEY.
Tracks: / More I see you, The / Sleepy time gal / I get along without you very well / Angel eyes / As time goes by / I'll remember April / If I didn't care / Sentimental journey.
LP: 8218571

SINGERS UNLIMITED.
MC: 831 373-4

SPECIAL BLEND, A.
LP: MPS 68 101

WITH ROB MCCONNELL AND THE BOSS BRASS.
Tracks: / Tangerine / Laura / Lullaby of the leaves / You are my sunshine / Sophisticated lady / Beautiful friendship, A / It might as well be spring / Chelsea morning / Dindi / Pieces of dreams.
LP: 817 486-1

Singh, Gurdev

RAGS, MALKAUNS AND MEGH (see under India) (Jasani,Viram # Gurdev Singh # Ustad Latif Ahmed Khan).

Singh, Jasjit & Chitra

SOMEONE, SOMEWHERE.
MC: TCS 40235

Singie, Singe

TWO UPRISING STARS (Singie, Singie/ Bobby Melody).
LP: MROLP 185

Singin' in the Rain

SINGIN' IN THE RAIN (Original London Cast) (Various artists).
Tracks: / Singin' in the rain (overture): *Various artists* / Fit as a fiddle: *Various artists* / Temptation: *Various* artists / I can't give you anything but love: *Various artists* / Be a clown: *Various artists* / Too marvellous for words: *Various artists* / You are my lucky star: *Various artists* / Moses: *Various artists* / Golod morning: *Various artists* / Singin' in the rain: *Various artists* / Would you: *Various artists* / Fascinating rhythm: *Various artists* / Singin' in the rain (finale): *Various artists.*
LP: RAIN 1
MC: RAINC 1

SINGIN' IN THE RAIN (Original London Cast) (Various artists).
Tracks: / Singin' in the rain: *Various artists* / You are my lucky star: *Various artists* / Moses: *Various* artists / Good morning: *Various artists* / Fit as a fiddle: *Various artists* / All I do is dream of you: *Various* artists / Make 'em laugh: *Various artists* / You were meant for me: *Various artists* / Broadway ballet: *Various artists.*
LP: CBS 70282
MC: 40 70282

SINGIN' IN THE RAIN/EASTER PARADE (Various artists).
Tracks: / Singin' in the rain: *Kelly, Gene* (Singin' In The Rain) / Fit as a fiddle: *Kelly, Gene/Donald O'Connor*(Singin' In The Rain) / All I do is dream of you: *Reynolds, Debbie/Girly Chorus* (Singin' In The Rain) / Make 'em laugh: *O'Connor, Donald* (Singin' In The Rain) / You were meant for me: *Kelly, Gene* (Singin' In The Rain) / Good morning: *Reynolds, Debbie with Gene Kelly & Donald O'Connor* (Singin' In The Rain) / All I do is dream of you: *Kelly, Gene*(Singin' In The Rain) / Moses: *Kelly, Gene/Donald O'Connor* (Singin' In The Rain) / Broadway ballet: *Kelly, Gene*(Singin' In The Rain) / You are my lucky star: *Kelly, Gene/Debbie Reynolds* (Singin' In The Rain) / Steppin' out with my baby: *Astaire, Fred* (Easter Parade) / Fella with an umbrella, A: *Garland, Judy/ Peter Lawford* (Easter Parade) / Shaking the blues away: *Miller, Ann* (Easter Parade) / I love a piano: *Various artists* (Easter Parade) / Snooky Ookums: *Various artists* (Easter Parade) / When the midnight choo choo leaves for Alabam': *Various artists* (Easter Parade) / Couple of swells, A: *Garland, Judy & Fred Astaire* (Easter Parade) / It only happens when I dance with you: *Astaire,* Fred (Easter Parade) / Better luck next time: *Garland, Judy* (Easter Parade) / Easter parade: *Garland, Judy & Fred Astaire* (Easter Parade).
LP: LPMGM 4
MC: TCMGM 4
LP: 793 300 1
MC: 793 300 4

SINGING IN THE RAIN (Various artists).
Tracks: / Singing in the rain: *Kelly, Gene* / 'S wonderful: *Kelly, Gene* / Rose Marie: *Keel, Howard*/ I remember it well: *Chevalier, Maurice & Hermione Gingold* / Wunderbar: *Keel, Howard/Kathryn Grayson* / Over the rainbow: *Garland, Judy* / Stranger in paradise: *Blyth, Ann/ Vic Damone* / Ol man river: *Warfield, William*/ You are my lucky star: *Various artists* / Indian love call: *Various artists* / Anything you can do: *Various artists* / There's no business like show business: *Various artists.*
LP: 6878 134
MC: 7413 134

Singing Francine

DEDICATION.
LP: GS 2295

Singing Kettle

SCOTCH BROTH.
LP: KOP 18
MC: KOP 18C

Singing Loins

SONGS FOR THE ORGAN.
LP: HANG 044 UP

Singing Sex Symbols

SINGING SEX SYMBOLS OF THE AIR WAVES (Radio Vocalists of the 1930's) (Various artists).
LP: SH 2058

Singing Stones

SINGING STONES, THE (Various artists).
Tracks: / Singing stones, The: *Various artists* / Yellow bird and the pipe of peace: *Various artists* / Pontiac and the sixty chiefs: *Various artists* / Dog and the bear, The: *Various artists* / Fair Mohican, The: *Various artists* / Trail to the west, The: *Various artists.*
MC: ANV 636

Single Gun Theory

EXORCISE THIS WASTELAND.
LP: NTL 30010
MC: NTLC 30010

Singleton, Charlie

NOTHING VENTURED NOTHING GAINED.
Tracks: / I wanna be with you / Nothing ventured nothing gained / Thank you / Spending money / Over my head / Love machine / Vain / Too busy thinking about my baby / Almost over you.
LP: 4605841
MC: 4605844

Singleton, Valerie

STORY OF AJEEB & THE 40 LOVELY GIRLS.
MC: BS 45

STORY OF AJEEB & THE 40 LOVELY GIRLS & STORY OF SHAHRAZ.
MC: BS 50

STORY OF SINBAD THE SAILOR THE STORY OF THE LITTLE HUNCHBACK.
MC: BS 52

STORY OF THE FISHERMAN & STORY OF MA'ARUF THE COBBLER.
2LP: BS 51

STORY OF THE FISHERMAN & THE JINNEE.
MC: BS 43

Singspiration Trio

SONGS FOR CHILDREN NO. 1.
Tracks: / Welcome song / There's a welcome here / Birds upon the treetop / Praise Him, praise Him / Stop look and listen for Jesus / Mustard seed a faith, A / Wise man and the foolish man, The / Whisper a prayer / Happy Day express, The / On the faith line / What do I have / Deep and wide / Wide, wide as the ocean / I'm living by faith / One door and only one / I am the door / Put a little sunshine in your smile / Climb climb up sunshine mountain.
LP: PC 781

SONGS FOR CHILDREN NO. 2.
Tracks: / Jesus bids us shine / Bring them in / All through the night / Day after day / There's not a day that passes / Life begins / Jesus is a never-failing friend / I have the joy / Fishers of men / Fishing, I'm fishing / Lord is watching over me, (The) / I don't have to wait / Saviour, like a shepherd lead us / Jesus loves even me / Jewels / You can smile / Carry a smile in your heart / Smile, only smile / Smile it down / Sing and smile a prayer / What am I doing for Jesus? / Do, Lord / Little helpers for Jesus / Everybody ought to love Jesus / Jesus loves the little children / Everybody ought to love him / Jesus loves the little ones / Jesus loves me.
LP: PC 782

Sinitta

SINITTA.
LP: BOYLP 1
MC: ZCBOY 1

WICKED.
LP: FARE 2
MC: FAREC 2

Sink

ANOTHER LOVE TRIANGLE.
LP: DYL 6

Sinking Of The

SINKING OF THE LUSITANIA (1915 Spoken Word) (Various artists).
MC: GE 001

Sinner

DANGEROUS CHARM.
LP: N 0101 1
MC: N 0101 2

TOUCH OF SIN.
LP: N 0026

Sins

SINS (TV soundtrack) (Various artists).
Tracks: / It's hard to be tender: *Simon, Carly* / Love and passion: *Various artists* / Oath, The: *Various* artists / Arrival in Paris: *Various artists* / Venezia anziana: *Various artists* / Face to face with the mirror: *Various artists* / At Susumos: *Various artists* / Concerto for Helen: *Various artists* / Hubert: *Various* artists / Despair: *Various artists* / Happy moments: *Various artists* / Golden ball: *Various artists*/ Jeanne death: *Various artists* / Remembering: *Various artists* / Holland concertino: *Various artists*/ Roofs of Paris: *Various artists.*
LP: 826 720 1
MC: 826 720 4

Sins Of The Flesh

FIRST COMMUNION.
LP: PLASLP 026

Siobhan & Pride

SINGING COUNTRY.
Tracks: / Daddy Frank / You'll never miss the water / Silver threads and golden needles / If I didn't shed a tear / Sing me an old fashioned song / Give an Irish boy to me / That's a no no / She burned the roadside tavern down / Wait a little longer please Jesus / Things are gonna be alright / What I've got in mind / Down the wrong road again / Once around the dance floor / Three leaf shamrock.
LP: HRL 182
MC: CHRL 182

Sioux

SIOUX.
Tracks: / So you say you lost your baby / Here without you / Ooh Las Vegas / Hickory wind / Renaissance fair / In my hour of darkness / Amarillo / Colorado / Feel a whole lot better / God's own singer / Time between.
LP: ANCL 2019

Sioux, Tammi

ACT NATURALLY.
Tracks: / Put your hand in the hand / Crystal chandeliers / Act naturally / Your cheatin' heart / Today I started loving you again / Me and Bobby McGee / Crying time / Okie from Muskogee / Country girl / Is anybody going to San Antone / Honey / Dear God.
LP: SFA 037

Siouxsie & Banshees

HYENA.
Tracks: / Take me back / Running town / Pointing bone / Blow the house down / Dazzle / We hunger / Belladonna / Swimming horses / Bring me the head of the preacher man.
LP: SHEHP 1
MC: SHEHC 1
LP: POLR 2002

JOIN HANDS.
Tracks: / Poppy day / Regal zone / Placebo effect / Icon / Premature burial / Playground twist / Mother / On mein papa / Lords prayer.
LP: POLD 5024

JU JU.
Tracks: / Spellbound / Into the light / Arabian knights / Halloween / Monitor night shift / Sin in my heart / Head cut / Voodoo dolly.
LP: POLS 1034
MC: POLDC 1034

KALEIDOSCOPE.
Tracks: / Happy house / Tenant / Trophy / Hybrid / Clockface / Lunar camel / Christine / Desert kisses / Red light / Paradise place / Skin.
LP: 244 217 7
MC: 318 414 6

KISS IN THE DREAMHOUSE, A.
Tracks: / Cascade / Green fingers / Obsession / She's a carnival / Circle / Melt / Painted bird / Cacoon / Slowdive.
LP: POLD 5064
MC: POLDC 5064

NOCTURNE.
Tracks: / Intro - The rite of spring / Israel / Dear Prudence / Paradise place / Melt / Cascade / Pulled to bits / Nightshift / Sin in my heart / Slowdive / Painted bird / Happy house / Switch / Spellbound / Helter skelter / Eve white eve black / Voodoo dolly.
LP: . . . . **SHAH 1**
MC: . . . . **SHAHC 1**

ONCE UPON A TIME 'THE SINGLES'.
Tracks: / Hong Kong garden / Mirage / Staircase, The (mystery) / Playground twist / Happy house / Christine / Israel / Spellbound / Arabian knights / Fire works.
LP: . . . . **POLS 1056**
MC: . . . . **POLSC 1056**

PEEP SHOW.
Tracks: / Peek-a-boo / Killing jar / Scarecrow / Carousel / Burn-up / Ornaments of gold / Turn to stone / Rawhead and bloody bones / Last beat of my heart / Rhapsody.
LP: . . . . **SHELP 5**
MC: . . . . **SHEMC 5**

POW WOW (INTERVIEW 1984).
LP: . . . . **PEEK-A-TWO**

SCREAM, THE.
Tracks: / Pure / Jigsaw feeling / Overground / Carcass / Helter skelter / Mirage / Metal postcard / Nicotine stain / Surburban relapse / Switch.
LP: . . . . **POLD 5009**
MC: . . . . **POLDC 5009**

SIOUXSIE & BANSHEES: INTERVIEW PICTURE DISC.
LPPD: . . . . **BAK 2089**

SUPERSTITION.
LP: **8477311**
MC: **8477314**

THROUGH THE LOOKING GLASS.
Tracks: / Hall of mirrors / Trust in me / This wheels on fire / Strange fruit / This town ain't big enough for the both of us / You're lost little girl / Passenger, The / Gun / Little Johnny Jewel.
LP: . . . . **SHELP 4**
MC: . . . . **SHEMC 4**

TINDERBOX.
LP: . . . . **SHELP 3**
MC: . . . . **SHEMC 3**

Siozade, Raymond

PIANO AT BRETELLES, THE.
LP: **42065**

Sir Douglas Quintet

BORDER WAVE.
Tracks: / Who'll be next in line / It was fun while it lasted / Down on the border / I keep wishing for you / Revolutionary wars / Old habits die hard / You're gonna miss me / Sheila tequila / Tonite / Border wave.
LP: . . . . **CHR 1330**

COLLECTION: SIR DOUGLAS QUINTET.
Tracks: / Mendocino / And it didn't even bring me down / At the crossroads / Nuevo laredo / Wasted days and wasted nights / She's about a mover / Old habits die hard / You're gonna miss me / Sheila tequila / Tonite tonite / Border wave / Who'll be next in line / It was fun while it lasted / Down on the border / I keep wishing for you / Revolutionary ways / Dynamite woman / Stoned faces don't lie / Texas me / Magic illusion / Song of everything / You never too big and....
2LP: . . . . **CCSLP 133**
MC: . . . . **CCSMC 133**

LOVE YA, EUROPE.
LP: . . . . **SNTF 936**

MENDOCINO.
LP: **9279 125**
MC: **7259 125**

MIDNIGHT SUN.
Tracks: / Let's don't waste a minute / This time / High high bye bye / One more time / Someday / Carol Jane / Meet me in Stockholm / Charisma face / Be real / Little Georgie baker / Sugar bee.
LP: . . . . **SNTF 897**

QUINTESSENCE.
Tracks: / Who were you thinking of / Down to saying goodbye / Adios Mexico / Village girl / Wicked wicked woman / I know you / If this ain't love / Velma from Selma / Got it bad for you / Tomorrow just might change / Rollen blues.
LP: . . . . **SNTF 881**
LP: . . . . **VR 004**
LP: . . . . **V 004**
MC: . . . . **V 004C**

RIO MEDINA.
Tracks: / San Antonio boogie / In the zone alone / Viking girl / Never be a Saint / Every breath you take / Everybody gets lonely sometimes / Can't go back to Austin / Que Pasa / Anymore / Tejano / Sleepwalk.
LP: . . . . **SNTF 912**

VERY MUCH ALIVE.
Tracks: / Dynamite woman / One way, crash course love affair / My girl / Drivin' wheel / Starry eyes / Emotional goner / Henrietta / Glad for your sake / Knock on wood.
LP: . . . . **SNTF 804**

Sir Francis Drake

SIR FRANCIS DRAKE (history for ages 8+) (Unknown narrator(s)).
MC: . . . . **PLBH 105**

Sir George

SIR GEORGE PRESENTS PARTY MUSIC (Various artists).
LP: . . . . **SGLP 002**

Sir Gibbie

SIR GIBBIE (see MacDonald, George) (Fleming, Tom).

Sir Lancelot

TRINIDAD IS CHANGING 1940's/ 1950's.
Tracks: / Century of the common man, The / Trinidad is changing / Donkey City / Neighbour neighbour leave me door / Night in Central Park, A / Ugly woman / Scandal in the family / Young girls today, The / Oken karange / Sweet like a honey bee / Pan American way / Gimme crab and callaloo / Mary Ann / Take me take me (to San Pedro) / Matilda, Matilda / West Indian families.
LP: . . . . **HT 321**

Sir Smasham Uppe

SIR SMASHAM UPPE (Various artists).
MC: . . . . **ANV 611**

Siravo & Joseph

RODGERS & HART MEET COLE PORTER (Siravo & Joseph Orchestras).
Tracks: / Where or when / My funny valentine / Blue moon / Bewitched, bothered and bewildered / Falling in love with love / I married an angel / Spring is here / Most beautiful girl in the world, The / Lady is a tramp, The / You are too beautiful / I didn't know what time it was / My heart stood still / Begin the beguine / Night and day / Anything goes / Easy to love / I've got you under my skin / In the still of the night / You're the top / You'd be so nice to come home to / It's de-lovely / Get out of town.
LP: . . . . **CBR 1001**
MC: . . . . **KCBR 1001**

Sirdar Wakefield...

ACCORDEON ORCHESTRA (Sirdar Wakefield Brass Band).
Tracks: / Espana cani / Intermezzo aus 100 nacht / Rio plata / Grosstadt-melodien / Melodie, melodie u. rhythmus / Nibelungen march / Moonlight on the Alster / Air from suite in D / Overture die felsenmuhle tyrolean tubas.
LP: . . . . **LK LP 6260**

Sirens Of 7th Avenue

SIRENS OF 7TH AVENUE, THE.
LP: . . . . **ROSE 92**

Sirkel & Co.

SIRKEL & COMPANY WITH MICK TAYLOR.
Tracks: / Stop it I'm green / Living in the laid back / Snow fields / Low tide / Riff a bit / I haven't got to much time / East coast rocker / Bathroom swimmer / Got a passion / Nothing to say / Up on your cloud / Sunday night / Get your roll up.
LP: . . . . **AFF 1**

Sirocco

VOYAGE.
LP: . . . . **LRF 184**

Sissay, Lemn

BLACKVIBE.
Tracks: / Mother Thatcher / Whitworth park / Discovered bi / City sigh / NF is / Gatting v Pakistan / Wake up niggers / Petty black bourgeoisie / Gill Scott heron shines / I have a dream / Nursery rhyme / Rhythms / Arts council criteria / Crime pays / Wilberforce / Over the top and underground / Gold from the stone / Mancnoids / Ace under my sleeve / Tense, tattered, tortured, tried.
MC: . . . . **BIP 305**

Sissle, Noble

SISSIE AND HIS SIZZLING SYNCOPATORS (With Tommy Ladnier & Sydney Bechet) (Sissle, Noble/Tommy Ladnier/Sidney Bechet).
LP: . . . . **CJM 22**

Sista Ruby

WOMAN DJ.
LP: . . . . **KM 011**

Sister Breeze

RYDDIM RAVINGS.
MC: . . . . **A 153**

Sister Candy

BLACK CULTURE.
LP: . . . . **VSLP 4026**

Sister Carol

BLACK CINDERELLA.
LP: . . . . **JLLP 017**

JAH DISCIPLE.
MC: . . . . **MCT 1033**
LP: . . . . **MLPS 1033**

Sister Charmaine

DEBI DEBI GIRL (see under Metro, Peter) (Sister Charmaine/Peter Metro).

JUNE RANKS MEETS SISTER CHARMAINE (Sister Charmaine/June Ranks).
LP: . . . . **TECHLP 01**

Sister Double

SISTER DOUBLE HAPPINESS.
LP: . . . . **SST 162**

Sister March's Secret

SISTER MARCH'S SECRET (see Lester, Jane) (Guthrie, Gwyneth).

Sister Rain

SISTER RAIN.
LP: . . . . **VOW 004**

WATER IN TIDE.
LP: . . . . **VOW 09**
MC: . . . . **VOW 09C**

Sister Ray

NO WAY TO EXPRESS.
LP: . . . . **R 33-8816**

RANDOM VIOLENCE.
Tracks: / Release / Feelings / Way to go / I've just seen your face / This girl / That's what friends are for / Madman's laugh, the / There is sound / Die young / Random violence / Moral, the / Face, the / Modern mama / See me / Hate / She wants to have Bob's baby.
LP: . . . . **R 33/8706**

TO SPITE MY FACE.
LP: . . . . **RES 339025**

Sister Sledge

ALL AMERICAN GIRLS (ALBUM).
Tracks: / All American girls / He's just a runaway / If you really want me / Next time you'll know / Happy feeling / Ooh you caught my heart / Make a move / Don't you let me lose it / Music makes me feel good / I don't want to say goodbye.
LP: . . . . **K 50774**

FREAK OUT (see under Chic) (Sister Sledge & Chic).

GREATEST HITS: SISTER SLEDGE.
Tracks: / Frankie / Mama never told me / All American girls / Dancing on the jagged edge / When the boys meet the girls / Smile / Lost in music / Thinking of you / He's the greatest dancer / We are family.
LP: . . . . **WX 26**
MC: . . . . **WX 26 C**

LOVE SOMEBODY TODAY.
Tracks: / Got to love somebody / You fooled around / I'm a good girl / Easy street / Reach your peak / Pretty baby / How to love / Let's go on a vacation.
LP: . . . . **K 50693**
MC: **K4 50693**

SISTERS, THE.
Tracks: / Super bad sisters / My guy / Lightfootin' / My special way / Grandma / Get you in our love / Il Macquillage Lady / Everybody's friend / All the man I need / Jackie's theme / There's no stopping us.
LP: . . . . **K 50853**

WE ARE FAMILY.
Tracks: / He's the greatest dancer / Lost in music / Somebody loves me / Thinking of you / We are family / Easier to love / You're a friend to me / One more time.
LP: . . . . **K 50587**
MC: **K4 50587**

WHEN THE BOYS MEET THE GIRLS.
Tracks: / When the boys meet the girls / Boys most likely, The / Dancing on the jagged edge / Frankie / You're fine / Hold out poppy / Boy most likely, The / You need me / Following the leader / Peer pressure.
LP: **781 255-1**
MC: **781 255-4**

Sisterhood

GIFT.
Tracks: / Jihad / Colours / Giving ground / Finland red, Egypt white / Rain from heaven.
LP: . . . . **SIS 020**
MC: . . . . **SIS 020C**

Sisters Of Mercy

FIRST, LAST AND ALWAYS.
Tracks: / Black planet / Walk away / No time to cry / Rock and a hard place, A / Marian (version) / First and last and always / Possession / Nine while nine / Amphetamine logic / Some kind of stranger.
LP: . . . . **MR 337L**
MC: . . . . **MR 337C**

FLOODLAND.
Tracks: / Dominion/Mother Russia / Flood I / Lucretia my reflection / 1959 / This corrosion / Flood II / Driven like the snow / Never land / Torch (Cassette and CD only) / Colours (CD only).
LP: . . . . **MR 441L**
MC: . . . . **MR 441C**

SISTERS OF MERCY: INTERVIEW PICTURE DISC.
LPPD: . . . . **BAK 2082**

VISION THING, THE.
LP: . . . . **MR 449L**
MC: . . . . **MR 449 C**

Sittaford Mystery (bk)

SITTAFORD MYSTERY, THE (Agatha Christie).
MCSET: . . . . **ZBBC 1126**

Sitwell, Dame Edith

DYLAN THOMAS & EDITH SITWELL READ HER POEMS (Sitwell, Edith & Dylan Thomas).
MC: **1343**

EDITH SITWELL READING HER POEMS.
MC: **1016**

Sivuca

GUITARS UNLIMITED.
LP: . . . . **SNTF 978**

SIVUCA.
LP: . . . . **VSD 79337**

Six Hands In Tempo

ALL IN GOOD TIME.
Tracks: / Tain't no sin to take off your skin / Dinner for one please, James / Take a step / Layla / Gloria / Shanghai Lil / Hello bluebird / Any little fish / Blue room / Minnie the moocher / Kicking the gong around / Friday on my mind / Triplets / Great westerns / To keep my love alive.
LP: . . . . **BURL 006**

DESPERATE DIGITS.
LP: . . . . **PLR 054**

Six Strings

SIX STRINGS SAMPLER.
LP: . . . . **SAPLP 100**
MC: . . . . **SAPMC 100**

Six Swingers

SIX SWINGERS VOL 2 1935-1936.
Tracks: / Weather man / Swingin' the lead / Hot pie medley £3 / Black coffee / Lulu's back in town / Dere's jazz in them there horns / Georgia rockin' chair / Truckin' on down.
MC: . . . . **NEO 954**

Six & Violence

LETTUCE PRAY.
LP: . . . . **FR 1069**

Sixteen, Earl

JULIA.
LP: . . . . **TWLP 1003**
MC: . . . . **TWDV 1003**

SHINING STAR.
LP: . . . . **VSLP 4023**

SONGS FOR A REASON.
LP: . . . . **VS 2011**

SONGS OF LOVE AND HARDSHIP.
Tracks: / Ok my love / When will I get pay / Take it to the bossman / Love me baby / When the rent man comes / Special request to everybody / Going to the studio / Stay at home / Black star liner / Too much confusion.
LP: . . . . **KVL 9019**

SPECIAL REQUEST.
LP: . . . . **TWLP 1016**

Sixth Comm

ASYLUM.
LP: . . . . **EYAS 013**

COMING OF SEVEN, THE.
LP: . . . . **EYAS 007**

FRUITS OF YGGDRASIL, THE (See also Aswyn, Freya) (Sixth Comm/ Freya Aswyn).

LEAVES OF YGGDRASILL (See Aswyn, Freya) (Sixth Comm/ Freya Aswyn).

MAMMON (Sixth Comm/Concrete Temple).
LP: . . . . **EYAS 053**

MORTHOGENESIS.
LP: . . . . **EYAS 059**

NOTHING LIFE, A.
MC: . . . . **EYAS 003**

SEETHING.
LP: . . . . **CENAS 156**

...HE WHEEL.
LP: . . . . EYAS 002

WINTER SADNESS.
LPS: . . . . EYAS 001

Sjako

L'AMOUR QUI FAIT BOUM.
LP: . . . . COL 269502

Sjoren, Irene

SWEET SUPRISE (Sjoren, Irene Quintet).
LP: . . . . DRLP 109

Sjosten, Lars

BELLS, BLUES AND BROTHERHOOD (Sjosten, Lars Trio).
Tracks: / 24th of April / May it do some good / One certain lady / Monologue and dialogue about the blues / Triad / It's from Lester actually / I thought the roof was falling down / Inner voice, The / Bells, blues and brotherhood.
LP: . . . . DRLP 46

ROOTS AND RELATIONS (Sjosten, Lars Quartet).
LP: . . . . DRLP 164

Ska

BIRTH OF SKA, THE (Various artists).
LP: . . . . TRLS 274
MC: . . . . ZCTRL 274

BLUEBEAT YEARS (Birth of a Music) (Various artists).
LP: . . . . IRSP 5

CLUB SKA 67 (Various artists).
Tracks: / Guns of Navarone: *Skatalites* / Phoenix city: *Alphonso, Roland* / Shanty town: *Dekker, Desmond* / Broadway jungle: *Flames* / Contact: *Richards, Roy* / Guns fever: *Brooks, Baba* / Rub up, push up: *Hines,* Justin / Dancing mood: *Wilson, Delroy* / Stop making love: *Gaylads* / Pied piper: *Marley, Rita* / Lawless Street: *Soul Brothers* / Ska-ing West: *Sir Lord Comic* / Copasetic: *Rulers.*
MC: . . . . ZCIRSP 4
MC: . . . . MCT 1008
LP: . . . . MLPS 1008
MC: . . . . ICM 2058
MC: 846 603 4

DOUBLE BARREL SKA (Various artists).
LP: . . . . PHZD 45

ELEMENTALS UK (Various artists).
LP: . . . . BBSLP 007
MC: . . . . BBSMC 007

GEMS FROM TREASURE ISLE (Various artists).
LP: . . . . TRLS 206

I COULD'A BEEN A CONTENDER (Various artists).
LP: . . . . RUDELP 004

INTENSIFIED (Various artists).
Tracks: / El pussy cat: *Alphonso, Roland* / James Bond: *Morris, Eric* / Solomon Grundie: *Morris, Eric* / Penny reel: *Brooks, Baba* / Teenage ska: *Brooks, Baba* / Duck soup: *Charms* / Carry, go, bring come: *Charms* / Rukumbine: *Duffus, Shenley* / University goes ska: *Drummond, Don & Drumbago* / Stampede: *Drummond,* Don & Drumbago / Independent anniversary ska: *Skatalites* / John and James: *Maytals* / Rocket ship: *McCrook,* Tommy / We are rolling: *Stranger Cole* / Housewives choice: *Derrick & Patsy* / Higher the monkey climbs, The: *Hines, Justin.*
LP: . . . . IRSP 2
LP: . . . . MLPS 1006
MC: . . . . MCT 1006
MC: . . . . ICM 2062
MC: 846 001 4

INTENSIFIED, VOL. 2 (Various artists).
Tracks: / Six and seven books of Moses: *Maytals* / Doctor Kildare: *Skatalites* / Congo war: *Lord Brynner* And The Shieks / Woman come: *Marguerita* / Man in the street: *Drummond, Don* / What a man doeth: *Morris,* Eric / Lucky seven: *Skatalites* / Miss Ska-culation: *Alphonso, Roland And The Soul Brothers* / Doctor ring-a-ding: *Alphonso, Roland And The Soul Brothers* / Run Joe: *Stranger Cole* / Sucu-sucu: *Skatalites* / Great wuga wuga, The: *Sir Lord Comic* / Dick Tracy: *Skatalites* / Mount Zion: *Dekker, Desmond & The Aces* / Marcus Junior: *Soul Brothers* / Train to Skaville: *Ethiopians.*
MC: . . . . MCT 1007
LP: . . . . MLPS 1007
MC: . . . . ICM 2061
MC: 846 002 4

LET'S SKA AGAIN (Various artists).
Tracks: / Let's dance again: *Ska Boys* / Hoot to Skaville: *Ska Boys* / I'm a natural man: *Ska Boys* / You got to move: *Ska Boys* / Struggling man: *Maroons* / Scorcher, The: *Prophets* / Kung Fu fighting: *Cimarons* / Skaing South: *Des All Stars* / Hat trick: *V Roy* / I'll take you there: *Deltones* / Reggae woman: *Rohden, Pat* / Night food: *Notes, Freddie* / Do it: *Ranks, Dizzy* / It's too late: *Aitken, Laurel.*
LP: . . . . NC 007
MC: . . . . TCNC 007

MAN ABOUT SKA TOWN (Various artists).
LP: . . . . KELP 004

MAX THE DOG SAYS... DO THE SKANK (Various artists).
LP: . . . . PCRLP 001

MORE INTENSIFIED (Various artists).
Tracks: / Six and seven books of Moses: *Maytals* / Dr. Kildare: *Skatalites* / Congo war: *Lord Brynner And The Shieks* / Woman come: *Marguerita* / Man in the street: *Drummond, Don* / What a man doeth: *Morris,* Eric / Lucky seven: *Skatalites* / Miss Sca-culation: *Soul Brothers* / Dr. ring-a-ding: *Soul Brothers* / Run Joe: *Stranger Cole* / Sucu-sucu: *Skatalites* / Great Wuga Wuga, The: *Sir Lord Comic* / Dick Tracy: *Skatalites* / Mount Zion: *Dekker, Desmond* / Marcus Junior: *Soul Brothers* / Train to Skaville: *Ethiopians.*
MC: . . . . ZCIRSP 3
LP: . . . . IRSP 3

MUSIC IS MY OCCUPATION Ska instrumentals 1962-75 (Various artists).
Tracks: / Magic: *McCook, Tommy* / Green island: *Drummond, Don* / Musical store room: *Drummond, Don* / Vitamin A: *Brooks, Baba* / Strolling in: *McCook, Tommy* / River bank parts 1 & 2: *Brooks, Baba* / Silver dollar: *McCook, Tommy & The Skatalites* / Doctor Decker: *Brooks, Baba/Don Drummond* / Eastern standard time: *Drummond,* Don / Yard broom: *McCook, Tommy* / Music is my occupation: *McCook, Tommy/Don Drummond* / Apanga: *McCook,* Tommy / Don de lion: *McCook, Tommy/Don Drummond* / Guns fever: *Brooks, Baba* / Twelve minutes to go: *McCook, Tommy.*
LP: . . . . TRLS 259
MC: . . . . ZCTRL 259
LP: . . . . TRLP 259

ORIGINAL SKA EXPLOSION VOL.1 (Various artists).
Tracks: / Best things in life: *Clarke, Lloyd* / Summer time: *Clarke, Lloyd* / Redeem: *Clarke, Lloyd* / Power: *Beckford, T* / Bismark special: *Skatalites* / Kiss for my love: *Angles* / Back biter: *Beckford, T* / Three men went to hunt: *Clarke, Lloyd* / Yes I know: *Beckford, T.*
LP: . . . . CGLP 012

PLANET SKA (Various artists).
LP: . . . . PHZA 57

RUDE AWAKENING (Various artists).
LP: . . . . WAKE 1
MC: . . . . WAKE 1MC

RUDE AWAKENING VOL.2, THE (Various artists).
LP: . . . . AWAKE 2
MC: . . . . AWAKE 2MC

SKA BA DIP ESSENTIAL KING EDWARDS (Various artists).
LP: . . . . KELP 002

SKA BEATS 1 (Various artists).
Tracks: / Mental ska (the rap): *Longsy D* / Just keep rockin' (house mix): *Double Trouble Feat. Rebel MC* / Force ten from Navarone: *Roughneck* / Musical scorcha (kung fu mix): *Rackit Allstar* / Resolution '99: *Maroon Town* / Rock to dis (house mix): *Jamaica Mean Time* / We play ska (the trojan horse mix): *Children Of The Night* / This is ska (Buster's original ska mix): *Longsy D & Buster Bloodvessel* / Skanking with the toreadors: *Ministry Of Ska* / Rude boy shuffle, The: *Rude Boys* / Swingin' thing, The (swing to dis mix): *Flowers Ltd & BMG.*
LP: . . . . SKACID 001
MC: . . . . SKACID 001MC

SKA EXPLOSION (Various artists).
LP: . . . . RUDELP 2

SKA LUTATIONS FROM KING EDWARDS (Various artists).
LP: . . . . KELP 003

SKA REVIVAL, VOL.1 (Various artists).
LP: . . . . LUDLP 1

SKA SCANDAL (Various artists).
Tracks: / Scandal: *Drummond, Don* / Judge not: *Marley, Robert* / Honour your mother and father: *Dekker, Desmond* / Miss Jamaica: *Cliff, Jimmy* / Love me baby: *Aitken, Laurel* / Turn down date: *Campbell, Cornell* / Exodus: *Ranglin, Ernest* / We'll meet: *Roy & Millie* / Mr. Kruschev: *Skitter* / Russian roulette: *King Edwards* / Now that you're dead: *Beckford, Theophilus* / Girls rush: *Clark, Lloyd* / Japanese girl: *Clark, Lloyd* / Beyond: *Patrick, Kentrick* / Christine Keeler: *Alphonso, Roland* / Get on the ball: *Gabbidon, Basil.*
MC: . . . . ICT 9929
LP: . . . . ILPS 9929

SKA STARS OF THE 80'S (Various artists).
LP: . . . . GAZLP 006

SKA STRICTLY FOR YOU (Various artists).
LP: . . . . CSD 301

SKANDAL (Various artists).
LP: . . . . PHZA 46

SKANKIN' ROUND THE WORLD VOL.1 (Various artists).
LP: . . . . PHZA 21
MC: . . . . PHZC 21

SKANKIN' ROUND THE WORLD VOL.2 (Various artists).
LP: . . . . PHZA 33

SKANKIN' ROUND THE WORLD VOL.3 (Various artists).
LP: . . . . PHZA 070

SKAVILLE USA VOL.1 (Various artists).
LP: . . . . SKAR 001

SKA-VILLE USA VOL.3 (Various artists).
LP: . . . . SKAR 006

SKA-VILLE USA VOL.4 (Various artists).
LP: . . . . SKAR 010

SKA-VILLE USA VOL 2 (Various artists).
LP: . . . . SKAR 003

SKAVOLUTION (Various artists).
LP: . . . . KELP 001

THIS ARE TWO TONE (Various artists).
Tracks: / Gangsters: *Specials* / Madness: *Madness* / On my radio: *Selector* / Tears of a clown: *Beat* / Rudi a message to you: *Specials* / Too much pressure: *Selector* / Too experienced: *Bodysnatchers* / Ranking full stop: *Various artists* / Too much too young: *Specials* / Selecter, The: *Selecter* / Stereotype: *Specials* / Mantovani: *Swinging Cats* / Do nothing Rico: *Specials* / Boiler, The: *Rhoda Dakar* / Ghost town: *Specials* / Jungle music: *Specials.*
LP: . . . . CHR TT 5007
MC: . . . . ZCHRT 5007
MC: . . . . CCD 5007

THIS IS SKA (Various artists).
LP: . . . . STAR 2366
MC: . . . . STAC 2366

TWELVE INCHES OF PURE SKA (Various artists).
LP: . . . . RUDELP 005

UNICORN 3 - INTO THE LIGHT (Various artists).
LP: . . . . PHZA 23

VIVE LE SKA (Various artists).
LP: . . . . PHZA 44

Ska Flames

SKA FEVER (LP).
LP: . . . . GAZLP 004

Ska-Dows

SKA'D FOR LIFE.
Tracks: / Ska'd for life / Twice / Grooving power / Mr. Walker / I wish you were mine / We gotta get out of this place / Yes, yes, yes / Monster reggae / Bang bang Lulu / Man of mystery / Rhapsody in Buh / Apache / Shocking.
LP: . . . . SKATE 3

Skagarack

SKAGARACK.
Tracks: / Move it in the night / I'm alone / Saying / Damned woman / Don't turn me upside down / Lies / Victim of the system / City child / Double crossed.
LP: 8294 461
MC: 8294 464

Skaggs, Ricky

COMIN' HOME TO STAY.
Tracks: / I'm tired / Hold what you've got / (Angel on my mind) that's why I'm walking / Home is wherever you are / If you don't believe the bible / San Antonio rose / Lord, she sure is good at lovin' me / Old kind of love / Thanks again / Woman you won't break mine.
LP: 4606921
MC: 4606924

COUNTRY BOY.
Tracks: / Wheel hoss / Country boy / Something in my heart / Patiently waiting / Two highways / Rendezvous / Brand new me / Window up / Above / Baby, I'm in love with you / I'm ready to go.
LP: . . . . EPC 26170
MC: 40 26170

COUNTRY GENTLEMAN.
LP: . . . . VNP 5319
MC: . . . . VNP 6319

COUNTRY STORE: RICKY SKAGGS.
Tracks: / Don't get above your raising / Crying my heart out over you / Sweet temptation / Heartbroken / You may see me walkin' / Don't let your sweet love die / One way rider / Uncle Pen / I don't care / Wound time can't erase, A / Low and lonely / Don't cheat in your home town / I wouldn't change you if I could / So round, so firm, so fully packed.
LP: . . . . CST 37
MC: . . . . CSTK 37

DON'T CHEAT IN OUR HOME TOWN.
Tracks: / Don't cheat in your home town / Honey (open that door) / Wound time can't erase, A / Vision of mother, A / Uncle Pen / I'm head over heel in love / Don't step over an old love / She's more to be pitied / Keep a memory / Children go where I send thee.
LP: . . . . EPC 25654
MC: 40 25654

FAMILY AND FRIENDS.
Tracks: / Lost and I'll never find the way / Two different worlds / River of memory / Talk about sufferin' / Think of what you've done / Toy heart / Hallelujah I'm ready / Say / Won't you be mine / Won't it be wonderful there / River of Jordan.
LP: . . . . SDLP 015
MC: . . . . SDC 015
LP: . . . . ROUNDER 0151
MC: . . . . ROUNDER 0151C

FAVOURITE COUNTRY SONGS.
Tracks: / If that's the way you feel / Sweet temptation / I'll take the blame / Waitin' for the sun to shine / You may see me walkin' / Can't you hear me callin' / Your old love letters / Lost to a stranger / Wound time can't erase, A / Nothing can hurt you.
LP: . . . . EPC 26433
MC: 40 26433

GOLDEN MEMORIES.
MC: 2630034

HIGHWAYS AND HEARTACHES.
Tracks: / Heartbroke / You've got a lover / Don't think I'll cry / Don't let your sweet love die / Nothing can hurt you / I wouldn't change you if I could / Can't you hear me callin / Highway 40 blues / Let's love the bad times away / One way rider.
LP: . . . . EPC 85715

KENTUCKY THUNDER.
Tracks: / Hummingbird / Lovin' only me / Fields of home, The / Heartbreak hurricane / Let it be you / Lonesome for you / Kentucky thunder.
LP: 4651441
MC: 4651444

LIVE IN LONDON: RICKY SKAGGS.
Tracks: / Uncle Pen / Heartbroke / She didn't say why / Cajun moon / Country boy / I've got a new heartache / You make me feel like a man / Rockin' the boat / Honey (open that door) / Don't get above your raising.
LP: . . . . EPC 22618
MC: 40 22618
LP: . . . . SHM 3252
MC: . . . . HSC 3252

LOVES GONNA GET YA!.
Tracks: / Hard row to hoe, A / Love's gonna get you someday / I'm beside myself / I wonder if I care as much / Don't stop gypsy / I won't let you down / Walkin' in Jerusalem / Artificial heart / Love can't ever get better than this / Daddy was a hard working honest man / Raisin' the Dickens / New star shining.
LP: . . . . EPC 57095
MC: 40 57095

PERSONAL CHOICE (I love country).
Tracks: / Heartbroke / If that's the way you feel / Sweet temptation / I'll take the blame / Waitin' for the sun to shine / You may see me walkin' / Window up above / Uncle Pen / Highway 40 blues / I don't care / Can't you hear me callin' / Your old love letters / Lost to a stranger / Wound time can't erase, A / Country boy / Love's gonna get you someday.
LP: 4510061
MC: 4510064

RICKY SKAGGS & TONY RICE (See under Rice, Tony) (Skaggs, Ricky & Tony Rice).

SECOND GENERATION BLUEGRASS (Skaggs, Ricky/K. Whitley).
Tracks: / Don't cheat in your home town / Dream of a miner's child / Memories of mother / Poor Monroe / Daybreak in Dixie / All I ever loved was you / My deceitful heart / Son of Hobert / Sea of regret / Those two blue eyes / Wildwood flower / This weary heart.
LP: . . . . SDLP 043
LP: . . . . SDLP 043
MC: . . . . SDC 043
LP: . . . . REBEL 1504

SKAGGS & RICE (Skaggs, Ricky & Tony Rice).
Tracks: / Bury me beneath the willow / Mansions for me / There's more pretty

girls than one / Memories of mother and dad / Where the soul of man never dies / Talk about sufferin' / Will the roses bloom / Tennessee blues / Old crossroads, The / Have you someone in heaven waiting.
LP: . . . . SDLP 054
LP: . . . . SH 3711
MC: . . . . ZCSH 3711

SWEET TEMPTATION.
Tracks: / I'll take the blame / Cabin home on the hill / Baby I'm in love with you / I'll stay around / Could you love me one more time / Sweet temptation / Put it off until tomorrow / Baby girl / Forgive me / I know what it means to be lonesome.
LP: . . . . RITZLP 0030
MC: . . . . RITZLC 0030
LP: . . . . SH 3706
MC: . . . . ZCSH 3706

THAT'S IT.
Tracks: / Red apple rag / Darktown strutters' ball / Florida blues / Bubble gum song, The / Whitesburg / Meetn' house branch / Sweet Georgia Town / Hook and line / Southern moon / 21 fiddle salute / That's it / Evergreen shore, The.
LP: . . . . SLP 1550
LP: . . . . SDLP 040
MC: . . . . SDC 040

WAITIN' FOR THE SUN TO SHINE.
Tracks: / If that's the way you feel / Don't get above your raising / Your old love letters / Low and lonely / Waitin' for the sun to shine / You may see me walkin' / Crying my heart out over you / Lost to a stranger / I don't care / So round, so firm, so fully packed.
LP: . . . . EPC 84986

Skaos

BEWARE.
LP: . . . . PHZA 24

CATCH THIS BEAT.
LP: . . . . PHZA 56

Skara Brae

SKARA BRAE.
LP: . . . . SHAN 79034

Skarbek, Charlie

OLYMPIC THEMES.
MC: . . . . OLYM 1 MC

Skatalites

CELEBRATION TIME.
LP: . . . . SOLPO 01101

LIVE AT REGGAE SUNSPLASH.
LP: . . . . SYNC 02

RETURN OF THE BIG GUNS.
LP: . . . . ILPS 9775

SCATTERED LIGHT.
Tracks: / China clipper / Marcus junior / Dahil Sayo / Determination / Shot in the dark / Confucius / Re-burial / Scattered lights / Ringo / Ska-ta-shot / Non-stop / Lawless Street.
LP: . . . . CDB 1000B
LP: . . . . AL 9309

SKATALITES WITH SLY & ROBBIE & THE TAXI GANG.
LP: . . . . VSLP 4055

STRETCHING OUT.
MC: . . . . A 141
LP: . . . . DANLP 045

Skate To Hell

SKATE TO HELL VOL 1 (Various artists).
LP: . . . . SKATE 001

Skateboard

SKATEBOARD Film soundtrack (Various artists).
Tracks: / Skate out: *Various artists* / Good morning LA: *Various artists* / Sweet rider: *Various artists*/ Randi loves Jason: *Various artists* / Empty swing in the playground: *Various artists* / Competition boogie: *Various* artists / Riding high: *Various artists* / Fast buck: *Various artists* / Freddie: *Various artists*/ Dogtown double cross: *Various artists* / My heart is just a retread in that tire sale: *Various artists* / Jason's theme: *Various artists* / Take me higher: *Various artists* / Ten gs on the downhill: *Various artists*/ Gotta be on top: *Various artists* / Skateboard theme: *Various artists*.
LP: . . . . BL 12769
MC: . . . . BK 12769

Skatemaster Tate

DO THE SKATE.
MC: . . . . BRCA 576
LP: . . . . BRLP 576

Ska-ville

SKA FANTASTIC.
LP: . . . . STUDIO 16

Skeelbred, Ray

STOMPIN' 'EM DOWN.
LP: . . . . SOS 1124

Skeezicks

SELLING OUT.
Tracks: / Get straight / Slam brigade / Nazi youth / Stay awake / Sauerkrauts / Trapped in labels / Join our crew / Nothing lasts forever / Fast and loud / Growing up / Selling out / H.M. sucks / Lee got VD / Consequences / What you are / Seasick.
LP: . . . . HH 008

Skeletal Family

BURNING OIL.
LP: . . . . REDLP 44

FUTILE COMBAT.
LP: . . . . REDLP 57

GHOSTS.
LP: . . . . ONS 1

TOGETHER - BURNING OIL/FUTILE COMBAT.
MC: . . . . REDC 59

Skeletons

IN THE FLESH.
Tracks: / Outta my way / Older guys / Laugh at me / Waitin' for a slow dance / Meaning of the blues / I'm little but I'm loud / Thirty days in the workhouse / I play the drums / Primitive / For every heart.
LP: . . . . FIEND 178
LP: . . . . NBT 3302

ROCKIN' BONES.
Tracks: / Trans am / Tell her I'm gone / Very last day / Blood surfin' / Sour snow / Gas money / She drives me out of my mind / B gas accord / Crazy country hop.
LP: . . . . NBT 3301
LP: . . . . FIEND 177

Skellern, Peter

AIN'T LIFE SOMETHING?.
Tracks: / Still magic / Abdul Abulbul Amir / Rockin' chair / Now I've seen the light / Big-time chief / Winter song / Rock on / You're a lady / Ain't life something? / Sad affair / Lean back (and let it happen) / Song of the critics / Don't it matter anymore? / That is the end of the news.
LP: . . . . TAB 79
MC: . . . . KTBC 79

ASTAIRE.
Tracks: / Cheek to cheek / Continental / Isn't this a lovely day / No strings / Let's call the whole thing off / Night and day / Puttin' on the Ritz / They can't take that away from me / Top hat / Way you look tonight.
LP: . . . . TIME 15
MC: . . . . TIMEC 15
LP: . . . . MERH 111
MC: . . . . MERHC 111
LP: 9102 702
MC: 410.341

BEST OF PETER SKELLERN.
Tracks: / Still magic / Too much, I'm in love / My lonely room / Up for the shoot / Now I've seen the light / Big-time chief / And so it passes / Abdul Abulbul Amir / Tattooed lady, The / Winter song / Manifesto / Roll away / Somebody call me tonight / Lean back (and let it happen) / You're a lady / Hold on to love / Society ladies / Send my heart to San Francisco / Rockin' chair / Piano rag / Lie safely there / That is the end of the news / Our Jackie's getting married / Hymn song / Keep in your own backyard / Rock on / End of the show.
2LP: . . . . DPA 5007
MCSET: . . . . KMC 25007

BUSY LINE (See under Murphy, Rose 'Busy line') (Skellern, Peter/Rose Murphy).

HAPPY ENDINGS.
Tracks: / Lancashire lullaby / Oh boy, Harold / Curses / Unexpected visitation (from the BBC) / Socrates / I'll love you 'til I die / Another sinner on his way / Jerusalem the golden / Changed / Municipal melody / Don't look with pity / Hello, is that you? / Daphne's catastrophe / Life / Someday soon / Birdman of B flight / Slowdown / Dogfight.
LP: . . . . REP 430
MC: . . . . ZCH 430

INTRODUCING...RIGHT FROM THE START.
Tracks: / You're a lady / And so it passes / My lonely room / Our Jackie's getting married / Streaker, The / Manifesto / Too much, I'm in love / Hold on to love / Lie safely there / Make it easy for me / Keep in your own backyard / She had to go and lose it at the Astor / All last night / End of the show.
LP: . . . . TAB 9
MC: . . . . KTAB 9

LOVELIGHT.
Tracks: / How loved you are / One in the eye for the moon / These foolish things / What are you doing the rest of your life / All the things you are / What love I've found in you / Folks who live on the hill, The / Not a day too soon / When you wish upon a star / September song.
LP: . . . . SNTF 987

PETER SKELLERN.
Tracks: / You're a lady / Sad affair / Keep in your own backyard / Ain't life something? / Don't it matter anymore? / Manifesto / Now I've seen the light / Apollo II / Our Jackie's getting married / Every home should have one / Rock on / Roll on Rhoda / All last night / My lonely room / Goodnight / Symphonion.
LP: . . . . SKL 5151
MC: . . . . KSKC 5151

RIGHT FROM THE START.
Tracks: / You're a lady / And so it passes / My lonely room / Our Jackies getting married / Streaker / Manifesto / Too much / I'm in love / Hold on to love / Lie safely there / Make it easy for me / Keep in your own backyard / She had to go and lose it at the Astor / All last night / End of the show.
MC: . . . . KTBC 9
LP: . . . . TAB 9

SKELLERN.
Tracks: / Big G / All 'cause of you / Love is the sweetest thing / Put out the flame / Sweet words / When I got you / When somebody thinks you're wonderful / Where do we go from here? / While I'm away / You and I.
LP: . . . . PRICE 47
MC: . . . . PRIMC 47
LP: 9109 701
MC: 410490

STILL MAGIC.
Tracks: / Raining in my heart / Two sleepy people / Is you is or is you ain't my baby / Skylark / Deep purple / Too much, I'm in love / Cold feet / Still magic.
LP: . . . . PRICE 80
MC: . . . . PRIMC 80
LP: 6359036
MC: 410491

STRING OF PEARLS, A.
Tracks: / Busy line / Clouds will soon roll by, The / Tell me that that ain't wrong / Deep Henderson / I'll string along with you / They all laughed / About a quarter to nine / All or nothing at all / Stormy weather / Symphony in riffs.
LP: . . . . MERL 10
MC: . . . . MERLC 10
MC: 410.342

WHO PLAYS WINS (Original London cast) (Skellern, Peter & Richard Stilgoe).
Tracks: / Two pals in harmony / C5 / James Galway / Love is the sweetest thing / Hi-me-roo / Ramblers song, The / Chant / Curate and the priest, The / SAS / Red eyes, The / By God we're good now / Mr. James / Packed lunch / Laugh at the lover / Piano repair man/Black and white rag / This is the ladies / You're a lady / Show stopper.
LP: . . . . SCENE 1
MC: . . . . SCENEC 1

YOU'RE A LADY.
Tracks: / You're a lady / Sad affair / Keep in your own backyard / Ain't life something / Don't it matter anymore / Manifesto / Now I've seen the light / Apollo II / Our Jackie's getting married / Every home should have one / Rock on / Roll on Rhoda / All last night / My lonely room / I don't know / Roll away / Somebody call me tonight / Sleep guitar / Goodnight / Symphonion.
LP: . . . . CN 2079
MC: CN4 2079

Skelmanthorpe

MOVIN' ON (Skelmanthorpe Male Voice Choir).
Tracks: / By Babylon's wave / Close thine eyes / Festing I watch / Mrs. Worthington / Movin' on / Long day closes, The / Vive l'amour / Autumn leaves / Pirates of Penzance (selection) / Rustics and fishermen / I only have eyes for you / Morte Christe.
LP: . . . . LKLP 6335
MC: . . . . LK 6335

Skeptik

SO THE YOUTH.
Tracks: / Born to lose / Stop it while you can / Traitor / Alternative Ulster.
LP: . . . . RRR 17

Skeptix

SNALLYGASTER.
Tracks: / Haunted host / Three miles to the exit / Idle time / World of your own / Expanding and contracting / Dating, dancing and death / White falcon / Oreo / Jesus said / Forget it / Ghost of Abraham Lincoln / Woman / Close to you / Grisly remains.
LP: . . . . R 33/8603

Skerry Ramblers

RETURN TO THE SHAMROCK SHORE.
Tracks: / Nancy Spain / Green fields of France / Lark in the morning, The / Last rose of summer / Dublin reel / Carrickfergus / Rambles of spring / Long before your time / Logan's lament / Nora / Stack of wheat / Speed the plough / Paddy's green shamrock shore.
LP: . . . . HRL 194
MC: . . . . CHRL 194

Sketch

COLOUR BLIND.
Tracks: / Wanting you / Cool for love / Out the door / Heroes / Wot can you do? / Family ties / Don't tell me your name / Rio / Burning up / Read between the lines.
LP: . . . . ZAT 3

HEART BEAT.
LP: . . . . ZAT 5

SECONDS COUNT.
Tracks: / Feels so good / Fever / Fine and mellow / Heroes / Stormy Monday / Crazy Sunday / Was it something you said? / Cool for love.
LP: . . . . ZAT 2

Skid Row

SKID ROW.
Tracks: / Big guns / Sweet little sister / Can't stand the heartache / Piece of me / 18 and life / Rattlesnake shake / Youth gone wild / Here I am / Makin' a mess / I remember you / Midnight tornado.
LP: . . . . K 781 936 1
MC: . . . . K 781 936 4

SLAVE TO THE GRIND.
MC: . . . . WX 423C
LP: . . . . WX 423

Skid Row (Gary Moore)

GARY MOORE, BRUSH SHIELS AND NOEL BRIDGEMAN.
LP: . . . . ESSLP 025
MC: . . . . ESSMC 025

SKID ROW.
LP: 450 263 1
MC: 4502634

Skidmore, Alan

S.O.H. (Skidmore, Alan, Tony Oxley & Ali Haurand).
LP: . . . . EGO 4011

TRIBUTE TO 'TRANE (Skidmore, Alan Quartet).
Tracks: / Resolution / Lonnie's lament / Bessie's blues / Crescent / Dear Lord / Naima / Mr P.C..
LP: . . . . MM 075

Skids

ABSOLUTE GAME.
Tracks: / Circus games / Out of town / Goodbye civilian / Children saw the shame, The / Woman in winter, A / Hurry on boys / Happy to be with you / Devils decade, The / One decree / Arena.
LP: . . . . OVED 43
MC: . . . . OVEDC 43
LP: . . . . V 2174

DAYS IN EUROPE.
Tracks: / Animation / Charade / Dulce et decorum est (pro patria mor) / Olympian, The / Home of the saved / Working for the Yankee dollar / Thanatos / Masquerade / Day in Europa, A / Peaceful times.
LP: . . . . OVED 42
MC: . . . . OVEDC 42
LP: . . . . V 2138

FANFARE.
Tracks: / Into the valley / Working for the yankee dollar / Sweet suburbia / Woman in winter, A / Masquerade / Saints are coming, The / Animation / Out of town / T.V. stars / Of one skin / Charade / Circus games.
LP: . . . . VM 2
MC: . . . . VMC 2

JOY.
Tracks: / Blood and soil / Challenge, the wanderer, A / Men of mercy / Memory, A / Iona / In fear of fire / Brothers / And the band played Waltzing Matilda / Men of the fall, The / Sound of retreat, The (instrumental) / Fields.
LP: . . . . V 2217
MC: . . . . TCV 2217
LP: . . . . OVED 200
MC: . . . . OVEDC 200

SCARED TO DANCE.
Tracks: / Into the valley / Scared to dance / Of one skin / Dossier (of fallibility) / Melancholy soldiers / Hope and glory / Saints are coming, The / Six times / Calling the tune / Integral plot / Scale / Charles.
LP: . . . . OVED 41
MC: . . . . OVEDC 41
LP: . . . . V 2116

Skiff Skats

SKIFF SKAT STUFF.
LP: SPIN 204

Skiffle

KINGS OF SKIFFLE (Various artists).
2LP: DS 3212/12

SKIFFLE (Various artists).
LP: TAB 56

Skin

BLOOD/SHAME.
2LP: PROD 33025

SHAME, HUMILITY, REVENGE.
LP: 33PROD 11

WORLD OF SKIN.
LP: YGLP 002

Skin & Bone

LET IT BE ME.
Tracks: / Summertime blues / Only you / Rhythm of the rain / Have I the right / Singing the blues.
MC: CWGR 103

SKIN & BONE (Various artists).
MC: SB 01

Skin & Bones

NOT A PRETTY SIGHT.
LP: EQNLP 2
MC: EQNMC 2

Skin Chamber

WOUNDED.
LP: RC 92741
MC: RC 92744

Skin Deep

MORE THAN SKIN DEEP.
LP: SKANK 103

Skin Games

BLOODRUSH, THE.
Tracks: / Brilliant shining / Heaven blessed / Tirade / Cowboy Joe / Big me / Your luck's changed / Where the wild things are / No criminal mind / Money talks / Dancing on.
LP: 4632851
MC: 4632854

Skin Lagoon

ADVENTURES IN THE LOVE TRADE.
LP: UNKNOWN
MC: UNKNOWN

Skin Talk

SKIN TALK (Various artists).
LP: INTEL 3

Skin The Peeler

SKIN THE PEELER.
LP: STP 1

Skin the Piper

BEYOND THE PALE.
Tracks: / Paddy's green shamrock shore / Cottage in the grove / Maid behind the bar, The / Now I'm easy / Boulavogue / As I roved out / Beyond the pale / Bishop's loft, The / Jamie Foyers / Sheey's jig / Creel, (The) / Raglan Road / Pipe on the hob / Freedom come all ye.
MC: FS 1

Skin Yard

FIST SIZED CHUNKS.
LP: CRZ 009
MC: CRZC 009

Skinbeat

SKINBEAT - THE FIRST TOUCH.
LP: SKINL 101
MC: SKINC 101

Skinhead

ROUGH AND RUGGED.
LP: ALMPL 001

Skinner, Barry

ABROAD AS I WAS WORKING.
LP: MU 7417

BUSHES AND BRIARS (see under Lakeman, Geoff) (Skinner, Barry/Geoff Lakeman).

Skinner, Bob

ME AND MY GUITAR.
LP: C 2021

Skinner Box

SKINNER BOX.
Tracks: / Drowning Street / Field of holes / Slide of glass / Grenadine / Low bird, A / Turn around / Proud flesh / Filed under R / Born to be ice / At the portal.
LP: SAVE 064

Skinner, Jimmy

ANOTHER SATURDAY NIGHT.
Tracks: / Lonesome at your table / Where do we go from here / We've got things in common / Married to a friend / Just ramblin' on / No fault of mine / Hafta do somethin' about it / Another Saturday night / Please don't send Cecil away / Reasons to live / Big city / Walkin' my blues away / Two squares away / Temptation smiles / John Wesley Hardin / I found my girl in the USA.
LP: BFX 15266

NO.1 IN BLUEGRASS.
LP: SLP 988
MC: GT 5988

SONGS THAT MAKE THE JUKEBOX PLAY.
LP: HAT 3126

Skinner, Scott

STRATHSPEY KING, THE.
Tracks: / President - air and variations, The / Lucania polka / Freebooter, The / Tullochgorum / East neuk of Fife / Allegory / Miller o'hirn, The / MacKenzie fraser / Auld wheel, The / Bagpipe marches / Cameron Highlanders, The / Inverness gathering, The / Celebrated hornpipes / Eugene Stratton / Banks, The / Highland reels Laird o'thrums / Gavin McMillan / Laird of Drumblair, The / Gladstone's reel / Bonnie lass o' Bon Accord / Marquis of Huntly's farewell / Ten pound fiddle, The / Highland Schottische / No. 2 Sandy Cameron Miller o'hirn / Glenlivet, The / Triumph country dance / Triumph / Timour the tartar / Left handed fiddler, The / Speed the plough / De'il among the tailors / Home sweet home / Iron man Strathspey, The / Bungalow reel, The / Cradle song / Braes o' Auchtertyre, The / Athole highlanders, The / Glengrant / Tulchan Lodge / Parrot, The / Humorous pizzicato / Mrs. Scott Skinner / MacKenzie hay / Devil's elbow, The.
LP: 12T 280

Skinny Boys

SKINNY AND PROUD.
Tracks: / Skinny around / I wanna be like / Rip the cut, part II / Caves of the city / Cool Johnny / Something from the past / This record is hell / I won't stop / Poison this place.
LP: 10771J
LP: 10791J
LP: HIP 55
MC: HIPC 55

THEY CAN'T GET ENOUGH.
LP: HIP 73
MC: HIPC 73

Skinny Puppy

BITE.
LP: FACE 15

CHAINSAW.
Tracks: / Chainsaw.
MC: NTMC 6305

CLEANSE, FOLD AND MANIPULATE.
Tracks: / First aid / Addiction / Shadow cast / Draining faces / Mourn, The / Second touch / Tear or beat / Trauma hounds / Anger / Epilogue.
LP: NTL 30011
LP: EST 2052
MC: TCEST 2052
MC: NTLC 30011

MIND: THE PERPETUAL INTERCOURSE.
Tracks: / One time one place / Gods gift / Three blind mice / Love / Stairs and flowers / Antagonism / 200 years / Dig it / Burnt with water.
LP: EST 2028
LP: BIAS 43
MC: TCEST 2028

RABIES.
LP: NET 023

REMISSION AND BITES.
LP: MFACE 010

SKINNY PUPPY.
LP: FACE 10

VIVISECT VI.
Tracks: / Dogsh*t / VS gas attack / Harsh stone white / Human disease (S.K.U.M.M.) / Who's laughing now? / Testure? / State aid / Hospital waste / Fritter (Stella's home).
LP: EST 2079
MC: TCEST 2079

Skip

FUNK (Skip & Exciting Illusions).
MC: A 132

Skipsey, Barry

N.T. ROAD.
LP: LRF 140

Skipworth & Turner

HARLEM NIGHTS.
MC: BRCA 539
LP: BRLP 539
MC: ICM 2046
MC: 842 399 4

SKIPWORTH & TURNER.
Tracks: / Thinking about your love / Nepenthe / Let me down easy / Hot pursuit / Street parade / This is the night / Could not get over you.
MC: BRCA 508
LP: BRLP 508

Skitzo

SKITZO MANIA.
Tracks: / Skitzo mania / Doctor Death / Shipwreck Island / Witching hour / Lonesome train / Possessed / I'm going Skitzo / Caledonia / Poltergeist / Your cheatin' heart / Under pressure / House of the rising sun.
LP: NERD 028

Skizzo

NEW KIND OF DANCE, A.
LP: BB 010

Skjelbred, Ray

RAY SKJELBRED & HAL SMITH (Skjelbred, Ray & Hal Smith).
LP: SOS 1097

SOLO JAZZ PIANO 1973/1974.
LP: BR 2

Skopelitis, Nicky

NEXT TO NOTHING.
Tracks: / Bad blood / Black eyes / Shotgun mews / Altai / Ta magika / Second skin / Omens.
LP: VE 41
MC: TCVE 41

Skull

NO BONES ABOUT IT.
Tracks: / No bones about it.
LP: MFN 117
MC: TMFN 117

Skullflower

FORM DESTROYER.
LP: BVP 10

Skunk

LAST AMERICAN VIRGIN.
LP: TTR 891561

Sky

CADMIUM.
Tracks: / Troika / Fayre / Girl in winter, A / Mother Russia / Telex from Peru / Boy from Dundee, The / Night / Then and now / Return to me / Son of Hotta.
LP: 205.885
MC: 405.885

CLASSIC SKY.
Tracks: / Toccata / Gymnopedie No.1 / Meheeco / Dance of the little fairies / Grace, The / Chiropodie No. 2 / Westway / El cielo / Fool on the hill / Troika / Then and now / Moonroof / Carrillon.
MC: 410.361

FORTHCOMING (SKY 4).
Tracks: / Masquerade / Ride of the Valkyries / March to the scaffold / To yelasto pedi (Theme from 'Z') / Waltz no.2 from Valses Nobles et Sentimentales / Fantasy / My Giselle / Xango / Fantasia / Skylark.
LP: ASKY 4
MC: ZCASK 4

GREAT BALLOON RACE, THE.
Tracks: / Desperate for your love / Allegro / Land, The / Peter's wedding / Great balloon race, The / Lady and the imp, The / Caldando / Roley-Stone / Night sky.
LP: EPC 26419
MC: 40 26419

MASTERPIECES-THE VERY BEST OF SKY.
Tracks: / Toccata / Westway / Fool on the hill / Gymnopedie / Vivaldi / Skylark / Troika / Hotta / Masquerade / Girl in winter, A / Dance of the little fairies / Chiropodie no.1 / Keep me safe and keep me warm.
LP: STAR 2241
MC: STAC 2241

MOZART.
LP: MERH 116
MC: MERHC 116

SKY.
Tracks: / Westway / Carrillon / Danza / Gymnopedie No.1 / Cannonball / Where opposites meet.
LP: ARLH 5022
MC: ACARH 5022

SKY 1.
Tracks: / Westway / Carillon / Danza / Gymnopedie no.1 / Cannonball / Where opposites meet-Part 1 / Where opposites meet-Part 2 / Where opposites meet-Part 3 / Where opposites meet-Part 4 / Where opposites meet-Part 5.
LP: FA 3162
MC: TCFA 3162
LP: ARL 5022

SKY 2.
Tracks: / Hotta / Dance of the little fairies / Sahara / Fifo / Vivaloi / Tuba smarties / Ballet -volta / Gavotte and variations / Andante / Tristan's magic garden / El cielo / Scipio (part 1 & 2) / Toccata.
LP: ADSKY 2
MC: ZCSKY 2

SKY 3.
Tracks: / Grace / Chiropodie no.1 / Westwind / Sarabande / Connecting rooms / Moonroof / Sister Rose / Hello / Dance of the big fairies / Meheeco / Keep me safe and keep me warm / Shelter me from darkness.
LP: ASKY 3
MC: ZCSKY 3
MC: ZCASK 3

SKY 5 LIVE.
Tracks: / Antigua / Animals, The (parts 1,2,3,4,5) / Bathroom song / KP 11 / Dance of the little fairies / KP 1 / Love duet.
LP: 302171
MC: 502171

SKY (BOX SET).
Tracks: / Westway / Carrillon / Danza / Gymnopedie no.1 / Cannonball / Where opposites meet (pts 1,2,3,4,5) / Hotta / Dance of the little fairies / Sahara / Fifo / Vivaldi / Tuba smarties / Ballet-volta / Gavotte and variations / Andante / Tristan's magic garden / El cielo / Scipio / Toccata / Grace / Chiropodie No.1 / Westwind / Sarabande / Connecting rooms / Moonroof / Sister Rose / Hello / Dance of the big fairies / Meheeco / Keep me safe and keep me warm / Shelter me from darkness.
LPS: SKYBX 1
MCSET: ZCSBX 1

SONGS THAT MADE AMERICA FAMOUS.
LP: AD 4101

Sky Cries Mary

DON'T EAT THE DIRT.
LP: ARTY 026

Sky High

THUNDER ON THE MOUNTAIN (Sky High & The Mau Mau).
LP: SK 1816

Sky High (film)

SKY HIGH (Film soundtrack) (De Shannon, Jackie).
MC: ZCATX 8

Sky Over Berlin

SKY OVER BERLIN (WINGS OF DESIRE), THE (Film Soundtrack) (Various artists).
LP: A 316
MC: C 316

Skybandits

SKYBANDITS (Film soundtrack) (Various artists).
LP: STV 81297

Skyboat

SHIP IN DISTRESS.
LP: PLR 035

Skyclad

WAYWARD SONS OF....
LP: NO 1631
MC: NO 1634

Skyhooks

GUILTY UNTIL PROVEN INSANE.
Tracks: / Women in uniform / Life in the modern world / Trouble with the computer / B.B.B. boogie / Twisted innocence / Hotel hell / Point in the distance / Meglomania / Why don'tcha all get *ucked.
LP: UAG 30241

Skylarks

ALL OF IT.
LP: CC 49
MC: 4CC 49

Skyline

LATE TO WORK.
LP: FF 261

Skyliners

ONCE UPON A TIME.
Tracks: / Once upon a time / That's my world / What's your plan / Dry your eyes / Always something there to remind me / Yesterday, today and tomorrow / Maybe I could have loved you better / Put a little love in your heart / Thought of yesterday, The / Make mine as good as yours / And so it goes.
LP: CH 268

SINCE I DON'T HAVE YOU.
Tracks: / Since I don't have you / This I swear / I'll be seeing you / Lonely way to be / If I loved you / Warm / When I fall in love / Tired of me / Pennies from Heaven / It happened today / Zing went the strings of my heart / One night, one night / Tomorrow / Lorraine from Spain / I can dream, can't I.
LP: CH 78

Skymasters

BIG BAND FAVOURITES.
Tracks: / Skyliner / Begin the beguine / Trumpet blues and cantabile / I'm getting

sentimental over you / Pink panther theme / One o'clock jump / Opus one / Moonlight serenade / Take the 'A' train / Love / Lean baby / Sing, sing, sing.
LP: 830 301 1
MC: 830 301 4

Skynard, Lynard

VERY BEST OF LYNARD SKYNARD.
2LP: . . . . MCLD 624
MCSET: . . . . MCLDC 624

Skyrockets

DANCE BAND YEARS - THE 1940'S (see under Geraldo & His Orchestra) (Skyrockets & Geraldo & His Orchestra).

SKYY

INNER CITY.
Tracks: / Because of you / Two hearts / Dancin' to be dancin' / Pay up / Passion in the night / I got your number / Love is blind / Slow motion / It's my life.
LP: FL84161

SKYY.
Tracks: / This groove is bad / First time around / Let's turn it out / Fallin' in love again / Stand by me / Disco dancin' / Let's get up.
LP: . . . . SSLP 1516

Slab!

DECENSION.
LP: . . . . INK 32

MUSIC FROM THE IRON LUNG.
Tracks: / Mars on ice / Painting the Forth Bridge / Oedipus / Big mac / Paralax Avenue / Yukon / Flirt.
LP: . . . . MINK 25

SANITY ALLERGY.
LP: . . . . INK 37

Slack, Freddie

BOOGIE WOOGIE.
LP: . . . . OL 2829

BOOGIE WOOGIE ON THE 88.
Tracks: / Rockin' the boogie / Cow cow boogie / Humoresquire / Down the road a piece / After sours / Between 18th and 19th on Chestnut Street / Rhum boogie / Bolero / Pig foot Pete / Rain drops / Beat me daddy, eight to the bar / Beating with chopsticks.
LP: . . . . OFF 12000

Slade

ALIVE.
Tracks: / Get on up / Take me back 'ome / My baby left me / Be / Mama weer all crazee now / Burnin' in the heat of love / Everyday / Gudbuy t'Jane / One eye Jacks / Cum on feel the noize / Hear me calling / In like a shot from my gun / Darling be home soon / Know who you are / Keep on rocking / Get down with it / Born to be wild.
2LP: 2669060

AMAZING KAMIKAZE SYNDROME, THE.
Tracks: / My oh my / Run runaway / C'est la vie / Slam the hammer down / Cocky rock boys / In the doghouse / Ready to explode / Razzle dazzle man / Cheap 'n' nasty love / High and dry.
LP: . . . . PL 70116
MC: . . . . PK 70116

BEGINNINGS (See Under Ambrose Slade).

COZ I LUV YOU.
Tracks: / Coz I luv you / Dapple rose / My life is natural / Angelina / Candidate / Sweet box / Look wot you dun / Could I / Raven / Gospel according to Rasputin / Shape of things to come / Get down and get with it.
LP: 2872 107
MC: 3472 107

CRACKERS' -THE CHRISTMAS PARTY ALBUM.
Tracks: / Let's dance / Santa Claus is coming to town / Hi ho silver lining / We'll bring the house down / Cum on feel the noize / All join hands / Okey cokey / Merry Christmas everybody / Do you believe in miracles / Let's have a party / Get down and get with it / My oh my / Run runaway / Here's to ..(the New Year) / Do they know it's Christmas / Auld lang syne / You'll never walk alone.
LP: . . . . STAR 2271
MC: . . . . STAC 2271

NOBODY'S FOOL.
LP: 2383 377

OLD, NEW, BORROWED AND BLUE.
LP: 2383 261

ON STAGE.
Tracks: / Rock and roll preacher / When I'm dancin' I ain't fighting / Take me bak 'ome / Everyday / Lock up your daughters / We'll bring the house down / Night to remember, A / Gudbuy t'Jane / Mama weer all crazee now / You'll never walk alone.
LP: . . . . PL 70080
MC: . . . . PK 70080
LP: . . . . RCALP 3107

PLAY IT LOUD.
MC: 8491784

ROGUES GALLERY.
LP: . . . . PL 70604
MC: . . . . PK 70604

SLADE ALIVE.
Tracks: / Hear me calling / In like a shot from my gun / Darling be home soon / Know who you are / Keep on rocking / Get down with it / Born to be wild.
LP: . . . . SPELP 84
MC: . . . . SPEMC 84
LP: 2383 101
MC: 8411144

SLADE COLLECTION 81-87, THE.
Tracks: / Run runaway / Everyday (live) / We'll bring the house down / Ruby red / (And now the waltz) C'est la vie / Do you believe in miracles / Still the same / My oh my / All join hands / Wheels ain't coming down / 7 year bitch / Myzterious Mizter Jones / Lock up your daughters / Me and the boys / Gudbuy t'Jane (live) / Mama weer all crazee now (Live) / Love is like a rock (Bonus track on CD only.).
LP: . . . . NL 74926
MC: . . . . NK 74926

SLADE IN FLAME (Film soundtrack).
Tracks: / How does it feel / Them kinda monkeys can't swing / So far so good / Summer song / OK yesterday was yesterday / Far far away / This girl / Lay it down / Heaven knows / Standing on the corner.
LP: 2485 233
MC: 3201 741
LP: . . . . RE 1000
LP: 2442 126

SLADE SMASHES.
LP: . . . . POLTV 13

SLADES GREATS.
Tracks: / Cum on feel the noize / My friend Stan / Far far away / Coz I luv you / Everyday / Thanks for the memory / Bangin' man / Skweeze me, pleeze me / Mama weer all crazee now / Look wot you dun / Take me bak 'ome / Let's call it quits / Merry Xmas everybody / How does it feel / Get down with it / Gudbuy T'Jane.
LP: . . . . SLAD 1
MC: . . . . SLADC 1

SLADEST.
LP: 2442 119

SLAYED ?.
LP: 2383 163

STORY OF: SLADE.
2LP: 2689 001
MCSET: 3539 101

TILL DEAF DO US PART.
Tracks: / Rock and roll preacher / Lock up your daughters / Till deaf do us part / Ruby red / She brings out the devil in me / Night to remember, A / M'hat m'coat / It's your body not your mind / Let the rock roll out of control / That was no lady that was my wife / Knuckle sandwich Nancy / Till deaf resurrected.
LP: . . . . RCALP 6021
MC: . . . . RCAK 6021

WE'LL BRING THE HOUSE DOWN.
Tracks: / We'll bring the house down / Night starvation / Wheel's ain't coming down / Hold on to your hats / My baby's got it / When I'm dancin' I ain't fighting / Dizzy mama / Nuts, bolts and screw / Lemme love into ya / I'm a rocker.
LP: . . . . NL 71149
MC: . . . . NK 71149
LP: . . . . SKATE 1
MC: . . . . KAT 1

YOU BOYZ MAKE BIG NOIZE.
Tracks: / Love is like a rock / That's what friends are for / Still the same / Fools go grazy / She's heavy / We won't give in / Won't you rock with me / Ooh la la in L.A. / Me and the boys / Sing shout (knock yourself out) / Roaring silence, The / It's hard having fun nowadays / You boyz make big noize / Boyz (inst).
LP: . . . . PL 71260
MC: . . . . PK 71260

Slade, Stanley

MR. STORMALONG (Sea Shanties).
MC: 30 207

Slaithwaite Band

MERRYDALE (Brass & Reed).
LP: . . . . LKLP 6028

Slam

I WANNA SMELL YOU.
LP: . . . . WB 8810

Slam Dance

SLAM DANCE (Film Soundtrack) (Various artists).
LP: . . . . ISTA 15
MC: . . . . ICT 15

Slam Slam

FREE YOUR FEELINGS.
LP: . . . . MCA 10147
MC: . . . . MCAC 10147

Slamm Syndicate

IT'S OUR TURN.
Tracks: / Bump, The / What's going on / Say it loud / Ohio / It's our turn / Lonely now / Knowledge reigns supreme / Sorry / It can be done.
LP: . . . . ICH 1058
MC: . . . . ICH 1058MC

Slammer

NIGHTMARE SCENARIO.
LP: . . . . HMRLP 170
MC: . . . . HMRMC 170

WORK OF IDLE HANDS.
Tracks: / Fenement zone / If thine eye / Johnny's home / Razor's edge / Hellbound / Hunt you down / God's prey / Fight or fall / No excuses / Born for war (Only on CD.).
LP: . . . . WX 273
MC: . . . . WX 273C

Slammin Watusis

SLAMMIN WATUSIS, THE.
Tracks: / Won't sell out / Watusi war / Bitter pill / It just ain't right / Walking on knives / King of cha-cha / U want it, U got it / Some sex / Let it out / Skt, Skt, Skt / It's alright to show you care / Run too fast / Be a man.
LP: 4607541
MC: 4607544

Slap, Robert

ATLANTIS: CRYSTAL CHAMBER (Inner Harmony New Age Music).
MC: . . . . C 318

Slapp Happy

SORT OF.
LP: . . . . RRS 5

Slapshot

STEP ON IT.
LP: . . . . TAANG 028

SUDDEN DEATH OVERTIME.
LP: . . . . EM 93751

Slapstick Of Another

SLAPSTICK OF ANOTHER KIND Original soundtrack (Various artists).
LP: . . . . STV 81163

Slater, Jim (aut)

AMAZING MONSTERS (See under Amazing Monsters) (Jarvis, Martin (nar)).

Slater, Les

LES SLATER.
Tracks: / Twelfth St. rag / Who were you with last night / Ma he's making eyes at me / Roll out the barrel / Somebody stole my gal / Glad rag doll / I'm gonna sit right down and write myself a letter / For me and my gal / When I'm sixty four / I wonder who's kissing her now / Are you lonesome tonight / Amazing grace / If you knew Susie / Bill Bailey won't you please come home / Baby face / You are my sunshine / Memories / I'm forever blowing bubbles / Now is the hour / Old piano rag / Music music music / Darktown strutters' ball / Side by side / Shine on harvest moon / You made me love you / Maybe it's because I'm a Londoner / Daisy Bell / When Irish eyes are smiling / I belong to Glasgow / Crusing down the river / She's a lassie from Lancashire / If you were the only girl in the world / Always / Alice blue gown / Oh Johnny / Ain't she sweet / Waiting for the Robert E. Lee / Five foot two / Who's sorry now / Oh you beautiful doll / Happy days and lonely nights / Show me the way to go home / I'm getting sentimental over you / We'll meet again.
LP: . . . . GRS 1095

Slater, Mike

JOLLY GOOD COMPANY.
LP: . . . . GRS 1153

Slatkin, Leonard

CLASSIC MARCHES (Slatkin, Leonard/ Saint Louis Symphony Orchestra).
Tracks: / Damnation de faust / Ruins of Athens / Le prophete / Midsummer night's dream / Caucasian sketches - procession of Sardar / Radetzky march / Cydalise et le Chevre-pied / Nutcracker ballet suite / Pomp and circumstance march no.1 / Aida / Gounod - funeral march of a marionette / Love for three oranges / Karelia suite / Empire strikes back, The / Babes in toyland (march of the toys) / Ganz - Saint Louis symphony march / Stars and stripes forever.
MC: . . . . RK 87716

Slaughter

STICK IT TO YA.
LP: . . . . CHR 1702
MC: . . . . ZCHR 1702

Slaughter House

SLAUGHTER HOUSE.
LP: . . . . ZORRO 11

Slaughter, Joe

ALL AROUND MY HOBBY HORSES'S HEAD.
LP: . . . . KSLP 003
MC: . . . . KSC 003

PIED PIPER OF FEEDBACK.
LP: . . . . CRELP 084

Slaughter, Johnny

MURDER (see Toyan) (Slaughter, Johnny/Toyan/Tipper Lee).

Slaughter & the Dogs

DO IT DOG STYLE.
LP: . . . . FNARRLP 002

LIVE AT THE FACTORY.
LP: . . . . RRLP 114

RABID DOGS.
Tracks: / You're a bone / Johnny T / We don't care / Victims of the vampire / I'm mad / Mystery girls / Where have all the bootboys gone / Waiting for the man / Boston babies / We don't care (reprise).
LP: . . . . RRLP 109

SLAUGHTERHOUSE TAPES.
LP: . . . . LINKLP 092

WAY WE WERE, THE.
LP: . . . . THRUSHLP 1

Slaughtered...

SLAUGHTERED BOX SET (Various artists).
LPS: . . . . LTS 30B

Slaughterhoff

LA LUNA.
LP: . . . . TORSO 33054

Slave

JUST A TOUCH OF LOVE (LP).
Tracks: / Just a touch of love / Are you ready for love / Funky lady / Roots / Painted pictures / Thank you / Shine / Warning.
LP: . . . . K 50684

MAKE BELIEVE.
Tracks: / Juicy-o / Chillin' / You (got the power to say no) / You take my breath away / Flashdance... what a feeling / Holiday / I like your style / Lonely girl.
LP: . . . . ICH 1009
MC: . . . . ZCICH 1009

NEW PLATEAU.
Tracks: / Jungle dance / Ez lovin' U / K.O.G. / Ooohh / Word is out, The / Share your love / Forever mine / Motorway.
LP: 7902381

REBIRTH.
Tracks: / Are you ready / Way you dance, The / My everything / Everybody's talkin' / Thrill me / Victim of circumstance / I love you / Andy's ways / Behind closed doors / How is this love.
LP: . . . . ICH 1055
MC: . . . . ICH 1055 MC

SHOWTIME.
Tracks: / Snap shot / Party lites / Spice of life / Smokin' / Wait for me / Steal your heart / For the love of U / Funken town.
LP: . . . . K 50831

SLAVE '88'.
LP: . . . . ICH 1030
MC: . . . . ZCICH 1030

STONE JAM.
Tracks: / Stone jam / Let's spend some time together / Feel my love / Starting over / Sizzlin' hot / Watching you / Dreamin' / Never get away.
LP: . . . . SD 5224

UNCHAINED AT LAST.
Tracks: / Jazzy Lady / I'd like to get you / Don't u be afraid / All we need is time / Thrill me / Don't waste my time / It's my heart that's breakin' / Babe show me.
LP: . . . . LPACERT 1
LP: . . . . ICH 1002

Slave Dance

DEFENDER OF THE LIE.
LP: . . . . PCE 1

Slave Raider

TAKE THE WORLD BY STORM.
Tracks: / Take the world by storm / Back stabbing / Make some noise / Burning too hot / Long way from home / Survival of the fittest / Devil comes out in me, The / Black hole.
LP: . . . . HIP 60
MC: . . . . HIPC 60

WHAT DO YOU KNOW ABOUT ROCK 'N' ROLL?.
Tracks: / Is there rock'n'roll in Heaven / Bye bye baby / Sin city social / High priest of good times, The / What do you know about rock'n'roll / Iron bar motel / Jailbreak / Youngblood / Keep on

pushing / Roller coaster / Magistrate, The / Guilty / Wreckin' machine.
LP: 11411 J
LP: HIP 68
MC: HIPC 68

Slaves of New York

SLAVES OF NEW YORK (Film Soundtrack) (Various artists).
Tracks: / Good life: *Inner City* / Tumblin' down: *Marley, Ziggy & The Melody Makers* / Buffalo stance: *Cherry,* Neneh / Some guys have all the luck: *Priest, Maxi* / Girlfriend: *Boy George* / Warrior: *Public Image* Ltd (PIL) / Admit it: *Ambitious Lovers* / Fall in love with me: *Pop, Iggy* / Love overlap: *Ambitious Lovers* / Tongue dance: *Les Rita Mitsouko.*
LP: V 2597
MC: TCV 2597

Slaves To Rock

SLAVES TO ROCK (Various artists).
LP: IW 1018

Slayer

HELL AWAITS.
Tracks: / Hell awaits / At dawn they sleep / Praise of death / Captor of sin / Hardening of the arteries / Kill again / Haunting the chapel / Necrophiliac / Crypts of eternity.
LP: RR 979 51
MC: RR 979 54
LP: ZORRO 8
MC: TZORRO 8

LIVE UNDEAD.
LPPD: 720151
LP: RR 9574
MC: RR 957 44
LP: ZORRO 29
MC: TZORRO 29

REIGN IN BLOOD.
Tracks: / Angel of death / Piece by piece / Necrophobic / Altar of sacrifice / Jesus saves / Criminally insane / Reborn / Epidemic / Postmortem / Raining blood.
LP: LONLP 34
MC: LONC 34
LPPD: LONPP 34

SEASONS IN THE ABYSS.
LP: 84968711
MC: 84968714

SHOW NO MERCY.
Tracks: / Evil has no boundaries / Die by the sword / Metal storm / Black magic / Final command, The / Show no mercy / Antichrist, The / Fight till death / Aggressive perfector / Tormentor / Crionics / Face the Slayer.
LP: RR 9868
LPPD: 722141
MC: RR 986 84
LP: ZORRO 7
MC: TZORRO 7

SLAYER: INTERVIEW PICTURE DISC.
LPPD: BAK 2046

SOUTH OF HEAVEN.
Tracks: / South of heaven / Silent scream / Live undead / Behind the crooked cross / Mandatory suicide / Ghosts of war / Read between the lies / Cleanse the soul / Dissident aggressor / Spill the blood.
LP: LONLP 63
MC: LONC 63

Sledge, Percy

ANY DAY NOW.
Tracks: / When a man loves a woman / Warm and tender love / Tears me up / Baby help me / Left field / I had a talk with my woman / Dark end of the street / Cover me / Take time to know her / Sudden stop / Any day now / Angels listened in, The / True love travels on a gravel road / Stop the world tonight / Help me make it through the night / Sunshine.
LP: CRB 1078
MC: TCCRB 1078

BEST OF PERCY SLEDGE (ATLANTIC).
Tracks: / When a man loves a woman / Out of left field / Take time to know her / Warm and tender / Just out of reach (of my two empty arms) / Dark end of the street / Cover me / Sudden stop / Baby help me / It tears me up / My special prayer / You're all around me.
LP: K 40026
LP: WX 89
MC: WX 89C

GREATEST HITS: PERCY SLEDGE.
LP: B 80040
MC: MB 980040
LP: 226 2212
MC: 216 2212

GREATEST HITS: PERCY SLEDGE.
MC: GM 0204

HEART AND SOUL.
MC: KNMC 12061

HIS TOP HITS.
MC: 810

IF LOVING YOU IS WRONG.
Tracks: / If loving you is wrong I don't want to be right / When a man loves a woman / Take time to know her / Warm and tender love / It tears me up / Behind closed doors / Try a little tenderness / (Sittin' on) the dock of the bay / Tell it like it is / You send me / Bring it on home to me / My special prayer / I've been loving you too long / Cover me.
LP: CRB 1138

OUT OF LEFT FIELD.
Tracks: / My adorable one / Take time to know her / My special prayer / Thief in the night / Out of left field / It tears me up / When a man loves a woman / You're pouring water on a drowning man / Just out of reach (of my tow empty arms) / Cover me / Warm and tender love.
LP: BDL 3007

PERCY.
Tracks: / Bring your lovin' to me / You had to be there / All night train / She's too pretty to cry / I still miss someone / Faithful kind, The / Home type thing / Personality / I'd put angels around you / Hard lovin' woman / When a man loves a woman.
LP: CRB 1152
MC: TCCRB 1152

SOUL SENSATION (See under Aretha Franklin) (Sledge, Percy/ Aretha Franklin).

ULTIMATE COLLECTION, THE.
LP: WX 95
MC: WX 95C

WANTED AGAIN.
Tracks: / Keep the fire burning / Kiss an angel good morning / If you've got the money honey / Today I started loving you again / Wabash cannonball / Wanted again / Hey good lookin' / He'll have to go / She thinks I still care / For the good times.
LP: FIEND 140

WARM AND TENDER LOVE.
Tracks: / Make it good and make it last / When a man loves a woman / Walkin' in the sun / Warm and tender love / God love / Out of left field / Behind closed doors / Jst out of reach / I believe in you / Take time to know her.
LP: BMM 006

WHEN A MAN LOVES A WOMAN (1).
Tracks: / I'll be your everything / If this is the last time / Hard to be friends / Blue water / Love away people / Take time to know her / Out of left field / Warm and tender love / It tears me up / When a man loves a woman / Walkin' in the sun / Behind closed doors / Make it good and make it last / Good love, The / I believe in you / My special prayer.
LP: TOP 113
MC: KTOP 113

WHEN A MAN LOVES A WOMAN (2).
Tracks: / When a man loves a woman / Warm and tender love / Just out of reach / Dark end of the street / Cover me / My special prayer / Sudden stop / You're all around me / It tears me up / Out of left field / Take time to know her / Baby help me.
LPPD: AR 30065
LP: SHM 3064
MC: HSC 3064
MC: HSC 3287

WHEN A MAN LOVES A WOMAN (3).
MC: 510439.4

Sledgehammer

BLOOD ON THEIR HANDS.
LP: JAMS 32

Sleep Chamber

SINS OF OBSESSION.
LP: EFA 4531

Sleep Gently In The

SLEEP GENTLY IN THE WOMB (Various artists).
LP: BORN 3
MC: BORNC 3

Sleeping Beauty

SLEEPING BEAUTY (Hampshire, Susan).
MC: 3600

SLEEPING BEAUTY..
MC: TS 303

SLEEPING BEAUTY (Various artists).
MC: STC 302B

SLEEPING BEAUTY.
MC: DIS 004

SLEEPING BEAUTY (Bryer, Denise).
MC: BKK 405

SLEEPING BEAUTY & PUSS IN BOOTS (Bryan, Dora).
MC: LP 302
MC: LPMC 302

SLEEPING BEAUTY, THE (well loved tales up to age 9) (Unknown narrator(s)).
MC: PLB 110

SLEEPING BEAUTY, THE (Various artists).
Tracks: / Sleeping Beauty: *Various artists* / Dumpling: *Various artists* / Giant with the three golden hairs, The: *Various artists* / Faithful John: *Various artists* / Golden key: *Various artists.*
MC: ANV 614
MLP: D 301
MC: D 9DC

SLEEPING BEAUTY, THE (See under Tschaikowsky) (Tschaikowsky).

Sleeping Dogs Wake

THRENODY.
LP: TPLP 27

UNDERSTANDING.
LP: TPLP 11

Sleeping With The ...

SLEEPING WITH THE ENEMY (Original Soundtrack) (Various artists).
Tracks: / Morning on the beach: *Various artists* / Funeral, The: *Various artists* / Brown eyed girl: *Morrison,* Van / Thanks Mom: *Various artists* / Spring cleaning: *Various artists* / Ring, The: *Various artists*/ Brave girl, A: *Various artists* / Fears: *Various artists* / What did he do?: *Various artists* / Storm, The: *Various artists* / Carnival, The: *Various artists* / Remember this: *Various artists.*
MC: 4681264
LP: 4681261

Sleepy Time Helpers

BABY BIRDIE BOMBER (Various artists).
MC: MM C 0231

BLOOPER'S BLOOPERS (Various artists).
MC: MM C 0230

CAPER AT THE CASTLE (Various artists).
MC: MM C 0227

FEARFIGHTIN' FARLEY (Various artists).
MC: MM C 0233

KIDS' PRAISE PARADE (Various artists).
MC: MM C 0229

ROUGH RIDIN' RODEO (Various artists).
MC: MM C 0228

UH-OH ART PROJECTS (Various artists).
MC: MM C 0232

Sleeze Bees

SCREWED, BLUED AND TATTOOED.
Tracks: / Rockin' the western world / House is on fire / Screwed, blued and tattooed / Stranger than paradise / Damned if we do, damned if we don't / Heroes die young / This time / When the brains go down to the balls / Don't talk about roses / Girls girls, nasty nasty.
LP: 7567820691
MC: 7567820694

Slepian, Don

SONIC PERFUME.
LP: SYN 312
MC: SYNC 312

Slevin, Jimi

FREE FLIGHT.
LP: CCF 7

Slice of ...

SLICE OF A SATURDAY NIGHT (Original Soundtrack) (Various artists).
LP: QUEUE 2
MC: QUEUEC 2

Slick

SPACE BASS (ALBUM).
Tracks: / Space bass / Feeling good / Sexy cream / Put your pants on / Whole world is dancing.
LP: FT 560

Slick, Earl

IN YOUR FACE.
LP: ZORRO 34
MC: TZORRO 34

Slick, Grace

BARON VON TOLLBOOTH.
LP: 26 21350

BARON VON TOLLBOOTH AND THE CHROME NUN (See under Freiberg, David).

CONSPICUOUS ONLY BY IT'S ABSENCE (See under Great Society) (Slick,Grace & The Great Society).

DREAMS.
Tracks: / Dreams / El diablo / Face to the wind / Angel of night / Seasons / Do it the hard way / Full moon man / Let it go / Garden of man.
LP: RCALP 3040
MC: RCAK 3040
LP: PL 13544
LP: PIPLP 030
MC: PIPMC 030

MANHOLE.
Tracks: / Jay / Manhole (theme from) / Come again / Toucan / It's only music / Better lying down / Epic (No. 38).
LP: 26 21351
LP: BFL1 0347

SOFTWARE.
Tracks: / Call it right call it wrong / Me and me / All the machines / Fox face / Thru' the window / It just won't stop / Habits / Rearrange my face / Bikini Atoll.
LP: PL 84791
MC: PK 84791

SUNFIGHTER (See Kantner, Paul) (Slick,Grace/Paul Kantner).

WELCOME TO THE WRECKING BALL.
Tracks: / Mistreater / Shot in the dark / Wrecking ball / Round and round / Shooting star / Just a little love / Sea of love / No more heroes.
LP: RCALP 5007
LP: PIPLP 029
MC: PIPMC 029

Slick Rick

GREAT ADVENTURES OF SLICK RICK.
Tracks: / Treat her like a prostitute / Ruler's back / Children's story / Moment I feared, The / Let's get crazy / Indian girl / Teenage love / Mona Lisa / Kit (what's the scoop) / Hey young world / Teacher teacher / Lick the balls.
LP: 4632021
MC: 4632024

Slickaphonics

CHECK YOUR HEAD AT THE DOOR.
Tracks: / Going going gone / Never say never / Dig my way to China / That's it / Jungle in my heart / It's you again / Writing on the wall / Gettin' crazy.
LP: 626387

Slickee Boys

CYBERNETICS DREAMS OF PI.
LP: ROSE 33

FASHIONABLE LATE.
LP: ROSE 147

LIVE AT LAST.
Tracks: / Gotta tell my why / Dream lovers / Missing part / Sleepless nights / Disconnected / Droppin' off to sleep / Brain that refused to die, The / Death lane / Life of the party / Pictures of matchstick men / When I go to the beach / Jailbait Janet / This party sucks / Here to stay.
LP: ROSE 169

UH OH...NO BREAKS.
LP: ROSE 57

Slide

DOWN SO LONG.
LP: 838 964 1
MC: 838 964 4

Slik

SLIK.
LP: SYBEL 8004

Slim & Bam

MCVOUTY.
Tracks: / Vouteroone / Operatic aria / Hey stop that dancing up there / September in the rain / Sonny boy / Avocado seed soup symphony (parts 1 & 2) / Yep roc / Heresay / Gaillard special / Matzoh balls.
LP: HEP 6

SON OF MCVOUTY.
Tracks: / Cement mixer / Chicken rhythm / Fried chicken / Who's goin' steady with who / African jive / Rough idea / B 19 / Yep roc / Ya ha ha / Tutti frutti / Train / C jam.
LP: HEP 11

Slim, Bumble Bee

BUMBLE BEE SLIM 1931-37.
LP: DLP 506

BUMBLE BEE SLIM 1934-37.
LP: BOB 9

BUMBLE BEE SLIM VOL. 1 (1932-34).
LP: BD 2085

EVERYBODY'S FISHING.
LP: PY 1808

Slim, Magic

CHICAGO BLUES SESSIONS 10 (Slim, Magic/Nick Holt).
LP: WOLF 120 856

Slim & Slam

SLIM & SLAM.
LP: TAX 8043

SLIM & SLAM VOL.3.
LP: TAX 8044

VOUT, JAM AND JIVE LIVE.
LP: MERITT 503

Slim, Tarheel

LOCK ME IN YOUR HEART (Slim, Tarheel/Little Ann Slim).
Tracks: / Lock me in your heart / Don't ever leave me / Forever I'll be yours / It's too late / Wild cat tamer / You gonna reap / Too much competition / Security / Number nine train / Much too late / Anything for you / Can't stay away Pt.1 / You make me so good / My kinda woman / Got to keep on lovin' you / Can't stay away from you.
LP: CRB 1213

NUMBER 9 TRAIN (See under Big Mac 'Rough dried woman').

TOO MUCH COMPETITION.
LP: CG 709-10
LP: SG 709-10

WILDCAT TAMER (Slim, Tarheel/Little Ann Slim).
Tracks: / Wildcat tamer / Number 9 train / Guy with the '45' / My flight / Too much competition / My kinda woman / Little sidecar / I'm gonna throw you out / Lock me in your heart / Don't ever leave me / Security / Anything for you / Forever I'll be yours / Can't stay away from you / Got to keep on lovin' you / You make me feel so good.
LP: KK 7430

Slimehunters

HOT IN HERE.
LP: STING 008

Slinger, Cees

CEES SLINGER AND FRIENDS (Slinger, Cees/Philly Joe Jones/Clifford Jordan/Isla Eckinger).
LP: SJP 225

Slint

TWEEZE.
LP: JHR 136

Slipper & The Rose

SLIPPER & THE ROSE, THE (Film soundtrack) (Various artists).
LP: MCA 1540
MC: MCAC 1540

Slits

BOOTLEG.
Tracks: / Bootleg / Retrospective.
LP: Y 3

CUT.
Tracks: / Instant hit / So tough / Spend spend spend / Shoplifting / FM / Ping pong affair / Newtown / Love and romance / Typical girls / Adventures close to home.
LP: ILPS 9573

PEEL SESSIONS:SLITS (2).
LP: SFPMA 207

RETURN OF THE GIANT SLITS.
Tracks: / Earthbeat / Or what it is / Face place / Walkabout / Difficult fun / Animal space / Improperly dressed / Life on earth.
LP: CBS 85269

Sloan, P.F.

SONGS OF OTHER TIMES (Sloan, P.F./Grass Roots).
Tracks: / Sins of A Family, The / Take Me For What I'm Worth / Karma - A study of divinations / You Baby / Where Were You When I Needed You / I get out of breath / Let Me Be / Halloween Mary / I Found A Girl / Only When You're Lonely / This precious time / You Never Had It So Good / This morning / Here's where you belong / This is what I was made for / What am I doing here with you / You baby / Where were you when I needed you / Only when you're lonely / You never had it so good / This is what I was made for.
LP: WIK 73

Sloan, William F

MAX BRAND'S BEST WESTERN STORIES (see under Brand, Max (aut)) (Brand, Max (aut)).

Sloane, Carol

CAROL SINGS.
Tracks: / Cheek to cheek / Morning star / Older man is like an elegant wind, An / Frasier (the sensuous lion) / If dreams come true / Don't be that way / Prelude to a kiss / Looking back / Checkered hat / My leopard.
LP: Unknown
LP: AP 211

DON'T GO AWAY.
LP: AP 212

SOPHISTICATED LADY.
LP: AP 195

Sloane, Jackson

OLD ANGEL MIDNIGHT.
Tracks: / Devil may care / So many times / Old angel midnight / One and all blues / We'll be together again / Jack Kerouac said / Spiderman / Caravan / Bernie's tune / Walk on the wild side.
LP: PRIMA 001

Sloane, Sally

GARLAND FOR SALLY, A (1894-1982).
LP: LRF 136

Sloman, John

DISAPPEARANCES CAN BE DECEPTIVE.
Tracks: / Foolin' myself / Breathless / Jealous / In too deep / Save us / Now you say goodbye / Perfect strangers / She talks about you / Parting you / Hooked on a dream.
LP: WKFMLP 114
MC: WKFMMC 114

Slovak Philharmonic

WATER GOBLIN/WITCH AND TC (See under Dvorak (Composer)).

Slovenly

RIPOSTE.
Tracks: / Way untruths are, The / Old / new / On the surface / Prejudice / Emma / Enormous critics / Myer's dark / Not mobile / As if it always happens / Little resolve, A.
LP: SST 089

WE SHOOT FOR THE MOON.
LP: SST 209
MC: SST 209 C

Slow Children

SLOW CHILDREN.
Tracks: / Brazilian magazines / I got a good mind / Talk about horses / Malicious / She's like America / President am I (hard time) / Too weak to eat / Home life / Staring at the ceiling / Ticket to France / Stuck in transit.
LP: ENVY 501
MC: ENCAS 501

Slow Down Zone

WORKING FIELDS.
Tracks: / Answer me / Daydream blues / Trouble / Big screen, The / Teach me / Tombstone / East to west / Crazy / Don't leave me tonight / Working fields, The.
LP: EGS 1

Slow Jam

CRAB APPLE.
Tracks: / Square peg / Fat, drunk and... / Couch potato / Crabapple / Big heavy metal fan / Expresso / Boomerang / Shoulder tab / 6.14 / Sad sack.
LP: STR 001

Slowburner

AN EMOTIONAL BUSINESS.
LP: BURNLP 001

Slowdive

JUST FOR A DAY.
LP: CRELP 094
MC: CCRELP 094

Slug The Night ...

SLUG THE NIGHT WATCHMAN (Slug The Night Watchman).
Tracks: / Slap my face / Jesus and Mary / British steel / Don't build my up / Drinking my whisky / Holyman / Consuela / Happening thing / Sweet Louise / Texas information / Can't stop it (Only on CD.) / Sell my soul (Only on CD.) / L.U.R.V.E. (Only on CD.).
LP: LLP 131
MC: LLK 131

Sluggers

OVER THE FENCE.
Tracks: / Over the fence / Perfect man, The / Written in the wind / Live wire / As we believe / I can't help myself / Jack in the box / Storm of love / In that magic moment / City lights.
LP: 207816
MC: 407816

Sluggy

JUST CALL SLUGGY.
LP: MMLP 0013

SETTLE SLUGGY.
LP: PH 0013

Slumbers

SCREAM AND SHOUT.
Tracks: / Scream and shout.
LP: ANT 057

Slurpy Gloop

I HEARD IT IN A BATH IN OHIO.
LP: SG 1

Slutt

MODEL YOUTH.
Tracks: / Angel / Breaking all the rules / Twisted / Women of the night / Revolution / Atomic envelope / T.K.O. / Thrill me / Shooting for love / Through the fire / Too far to run / Model youth / Blue suede shoes.
LP: NEAT 1043

Sly Fox

LET'S GO ALL THE WAY.
Tracks: / Let's go all the way / Don't play with fire / I still remember / Won't let you go (A wedding song) / Stay true / If push comes to a shove / Merry go round / Come to te llama? (what is your name?) (Reduced remix).
LP: EST 2015
MC: TCEST 2015

Sly & Revolutionaries

SENSI DUB.
Tracks: / Burn pipe dub / Sensi dub / Sellers dub / Weed base dub / Stone dub / Smokers dub / Sly challenge dub / Planters dub / Legal (dub).
LP: RDL 1000

TRENCH TOWN DUB.
LP: OMLP 12

Sly & Robbie

DJ RIOT.
LP: MLPD 1051
MC: MCT 1051
LP: 846 346 1
MC: 846 346 4

DUB EXTRAVAGANZA.
Tracks: / Eden dub / Mystic mix / His imperial majesty / Weeping willow / Tonight is the night / Firehouse special / African culture / Crisis dub / Sound man style.
LP: CSAP 100X
MC: ZCSAP 100X

HARDCORE DUB (Sly & Robbie With The Revolutionaires).
LP: OMLP 0010

LANGUAGE BARRIER.
Tracks: / Make 'em move / Get to this, get to that / No name on the bullet / Miles(black satin) / Bass & trouble / Language barrier, The.
LP: ILPS 9831
LP: ILPM 9831
MC: 826 195 4

MEET KING TUBBY.
Tracks: / Disgraceful / Dread dread / African roots / Playful / Forever / War / Everybody's / Passion / Peace / Conference.
LP: VSLP 5014

PRESENT TAXI.
MC: ICT 9662
LP: ILPS 9662

REGGAE GREATS (A dub experience).
Tracks: / Destination unknown / Assault on Station 5 / Joy ride / Demolition city / Computer malfunction / Jailbreak / Skull and crossbones / Back to base.
LP: IRG 7
MC: IRGC 7
MC: RRCT 29

RHYTHM KILLERS.
LP: BRLP 512
MC: BRCA 512
MC: ICM 2047
MC: 842 785 4

SENSI DUB VOL.4.
Tracks: / Rizla dub / Gummie dub / Sensi dub (part 4) / Sniffer dog dub / Ital spliff dub / Chalice man dub / Red up dub / Ninnie dub / Gully bank dub / Jailhouse dub.
LP: OMLP 0018

SILENT ASSASSIN.
Tracks: / Rebel / Woman for the job / Steppin' / No one can top this boy / Party together / Come again / Ride the riddin' / Adventures of a bullet / Man on a mission / Under arrest / Dance hall / Living a lie / Letters to the president / It's me.
MC: BRCA 537
LP: BRLP 537

SLY AND ROBBIE PRESENTS....
LP: ILPS 9908

SOUND OF TAXI, VOL.1 (Sly & Robbie with various artists).
LP: Unknown

SOUND OF TAXI VOL.2 (Sly & Robbie with various artists).
LP: TAXI LP 005

STING, THE.
LP: TAXI LP 006

SUMMIT, THE.
Tracks: / All aboard / Super cool / My turf / Rice & peas / Spy VS spy / First light / Free at last / Here and beyond.
LP: RAS 3032
MC: RASC 3032

TAXI FARE.
LP: HB 39
MC: HBC 39

TAXIGANG V PURPLEMAN.
LP: TRLS 240

UHURU IN DUB.
Tracks: / Eden dub / Mystic mix / His imperial majesty / Weeping willow / Bad girls dub / Tonight is the night / Firehouse special / African culture / Crisis dub / Sound man style.
LP: CSLP 2
MC: ZCSLC 02

Sly & the Family Stone

AIN'T BUT THE ONE WAY.
LP: K 923700 1

ANTHOLOGY - SLY & THE FAMILY STONE.
2LP: EPC 22119

ANTHOLOGY - SLY & THE FAMILY STONE (2).
Tracks: / Dance to the music / M'lady / Life / Fun / Sing a simple song / Everyday people / Stand / I want to take you higher / Don't call me nigger, whitey / You can make it if you try / Hot fun in the summertime / Thank you (falletinme be mice elf agin) / Everybody is a star / Family affair / Runnin' away / You caught me smilin' / Thank you for talking to me Africa / Babies makin' babies / If you want me to stay / Que sera sera.
LP: 4601751
MC: 4601754

BACK ON THE RIGHT TRACK.
Tracks: / Remember who you are / Back on the right track / If it's not addin' up / Same thing / It takes all kinds / Who's to say? / Sheer energy.
LP: K 56640

DANCE TO THE MUSIC.
Tracks: / You're my only love / Heavenly angel / Oh what a night / You've forgotten me / Yellow moon / Honest / Nerves / Help me with my broken heart / Long time alone / Uncle Sam needs you my friend.
LP: THBL 1.029

FRESH.
Tracks: / In time / If you want me to stay / Let me have it all / Frisky / Thankful 'n' thoughtful / Skin I'm in / I don't know / Keep on dancing / Que sera sera / If it were left up to me / Babies makin' blues.
LP: XED 232
MC: CED 232

GREATEST HITS: SLY & THE FAMILY STONE.
Tracks: / I want to take you higher / Everybody is a star / Stand / Life / Fun / You can make it if you try / Dance to the music / Everyday people / Hot fun in the summertime / M'lady / Sing a simple song / Thank you.
LP: CBS 32029
MC: 40 32029
LP: 4625241
MC: 4625244

TEN YEARS TOO SOON.
Tracks: / Dance to the music / Sing a simple song / I get high on you / Everyday people / You can make it if you try / Stand / This is love.
LP: EPC 83640

THERE'S A RIOT GOING ON.
Tracks: / Luv'n'Haight / Just like a baby / Poet, The / Family affair / Africa talks to you - 'The Asphalt Jungle' / There's a riot goin' on / Brave and strong / (You caught me) smilin' / Time / Spaced cowboy / Runnin' away / Thank you for talking to me Africa.
LP: XED 165
MC: CED 165
LP: EPC 64613
LP: ED 165

SM Group

BEST OF MCCARTNEY.
Tracks: / My love / Jet / Band on the run / Letting go / Uncle Albert/Admiral Halsey / Hi hi hi / Another day / Listen to what the man said / Live and let die.
LP: BE 601

Smack

LIVE DESIRE.
LP: HD 026

Smack My Crack

SMACK MY CRACK (Various artists).
LP: GPS 030
MC: GPS 030 C

Smackee

PARTY LIGHTS.
LP: BSS 320

Small Assassin (bk)

SMALL ASSASSIN, THE (Ray Bradbury).
MC: CDL 51677

Small Faces

AUTUMN STONE.
Tracks: / Here comes the nice / Autumn stone / Collibosher / All or nothing / Red balloon / Lazy Sunday / Call it something

nice / I can't make it / Afterglow of your love / Sha-la-la-la-lee / Universal / Rollin' over / If I were a carpenter / Every little bit hurts / My mind's eye / Tin soldier / Just passing / Itchycoo park / Hey girl / Wide eyed girl on the wall / Whacha gonna do about it / Wam bam thank you mam.
LP: . . . . CLALP 114
MC: . . . . CLAMC 114
LP: . . . . IMLD 01

BIG HITS.
LP: . . . . V 2166
MC: . . . . TCV 2166

COLLECTION: SMALL FACES.
Tracks: / Lazy Sunday / Rollin' over / If I were a carpenter / Every little bit hurts / All or nothing / Itchycoo Park / My minds eye / Sha-la-la-la-lee / Watcha gonna do about it / Afterglow of your love / Here comes the nice / I feel much better / Don't burst my bubble / Autumn stone / Universal / Tin soldier / Hey girl / Tell me have you ever seen me / I can't make it.
2LP: . . . . CCSLP 108
MC: . . . . CCSMC 108

FOR YOUR DELIGHT, THE DARLINGS OF....
LP: . . . . V 2178

FROM THE BEGINNING.
Tracks: / Runaway / My mind's eye / Yesterday, today and tomorrow / That man / My way of giving / Hey girl / Tell me, have you ever seen me? / Come back and take this hurt off me / All or nothing / Baby don't do it / Plum Nellie / Sha-la-la-la-lee / You really got a hold on me / Whatcha gonna do about it?.
LP: . . . . DOA 2
MC: . . . . KDOAC 2
LP: . . . . LK 4879

GOLDEN HITS: SMALL FACES.
LP: 20049
MC: 40049

GREATEST HITS: SMALL FACES.
LP: . . . . CLALP 146
MC: . . . . CLAMC 146

NIGHTRIDING: SMALL FACES.
Tracks: / Itchycoo Park / Tin soldier / Lazy Sunday / Here comes the nice / Red balloon / Afterglow of your love / Long ago and worlds apart / Rollin' over / Sha-la-la-la-lee / If I were a carpenter / Hey girl / Watcha gonna do about it.
MC: . . . . KNMC 10007
LP: . . . . KNLP 10007

OGDEN'S NUT GONE...FLAKE.
Tracks: / Ogden's nut gone flake / Afterglow of your love / Long agos and worlds apart / Rene / Son of a baker / Lazy Sunday / Happiness Stan / Rollin' over / Hungry intruder, The / Journey, The / Mad John / Happy days toy town / Tin soldier (live).
LP: . . . . CLALP 116
MC: . . . . CLAMC 116
LP: . . . . V 2159
LP: . . . . IMLP 012

OGDEN'S NUT GONE...FLAKE(IMPORT).
LP: . . . . OLLP 5217

QUITE NATURALLY.
Tracks: / Rollin' over (March '68) / Song of a baker (May '68) / I feel much better (December '67) / Talk to you (June '67) / Tin soldier (December '67) / Autumn stone (March'69) / Become like you (June'67) / I can't make it (March'67) / Donkey rides, a penny, a glass (July '68) / Rene (May'68) / I'm only dreaming (August'67) / Hungry intruder, The (June'68) / Red balloon (March'69) / Just passing (March'67).
LP: . . . . SHLP 145
MC: . . . . SHTC 145

ROCK ROOTS.
Tracks: / What'cha gonna do about it / What's a matter baby / I've got mine / It's too late / Sha-la-la-la-lee / Grow your own / Hey girl / Almost grown / All or nothing / Understanding / My mind's eye / I can't dance with you / I can't make it / Just passing / Patterns / E to D.
LP: . . . . ROOTS 5

SHA LA LA LA LEE.
Tracks: / Sha-la-la-la-lee / My mind's eye / Grow your own / You better believe it / Sorry she's mine / Own up time / Patterns / What'cha gonna do about it / Understanding / It's too late / Come on children / I've got mine / Hey girl / All or nothing.
LP: . . . . TAB 16
MC: . . . . KTBC 16

SINGLES A'S AND B'S, THE.
Tracks: / Watcha gonna do about it / Hey girl / My mind's eye / E to D / Itchycoo Park / Lazy Sunday / Wham bam thank you man / I'm only dreaming / I can't dance with you / Sha la la la lee / All or nothing / I can't make it / Here comes the nice / Tin soldier / Afterglow of your love / Talk to you / Donkey rides, a penny a glass / It's too late.
LP: . . . . SEE 293
MC: . . . . SEEK 293

SMALL FACES.
Tracks: / Shake / Come on children / You better believe it / It's too late / One night stand / What'cha gonna do about it / Sorry she's mine / Own up time / You need loving / Don't stop what you are doing / E to D / Sha-la-la-la-lee / What's a matter baby (CD only) / I've got mine (CD only.) / Grow your own (CD only.) / Almost grown. (CD only.).
LP: . . . . LK 4790
LP: . . . . IMSP 008

SMALL FACES (GERMAN IMPORT).
LP: . . . . OLLP 5251

SMALL FACES GREATEST HITS.
Tracks: / Itchycoo Park / Wham bam thank you mam / Universal / Son of a baker / Rene / Here comes the nice / Tin soldier / Autumn stone / Afterglow of your love / Red balloon / All or nothing / Lazy Sunday.
LP: . . . . IML 2008
MC: . . . . ZCIM 2008

SMALL FACES, THE.
Tracks: / You'd better believe it / Sorry she's mine / Own up time / I've got mine / Understanding / What's the matter baby / Runaway / That man / My way of giving / Tell me have you ever seen me / Come back and take this hurt off me / Baby don't do it.
LP: . . . . NW 6000

SORRY SHE'S MINE.
LP: . . . . PLP 29
MC: . . . . PMC 29

ULTIMATE COLLECTION.
Tracks: / All or nothing / Lazy Sunday / Tin soldier.
2LP: . . . . CTVLP 004
MC: . . . . CTVMC 004

Small, Fred

HEART OF THE APPALOOSA.
LP: . . . . ROUNDER 4014
MC: . . . . ROUNDER 4014C

I WILL STAND FAST.
LP: . . . . FF 491

NO LIMIT.
LP: . . . . ROUNDER 4018
MC: . . . . ROUNDER 4018C

Small, Freddie

MEDLEY REGGAE COLLECTION (PART 2).
LP: . . . . PILP 028

Small, Judy

HOME FRONT.
LP: . . . . RR 8808

Small, Michael

MOBSTERS.
LP: . . . . VS 5334
MC: . . . . VSC 5334

Small Woman (bk)

SMALL WOMAN, THE (Alan Burgess) (Bergman, Ingrid (nar)).
MCSET: . . . . SAY 17

Smart, Charles

ORGAN & CHIMES CHRISTMAS ALBUM (Smart, Charles & James Blades).
LP: . . . . ECS 2052

Smart, Leroy

BACK TO BACK (see Reid,Junior/Leroy Smart) (Smart, Leroy/Junior Reid).

BANK ACCOUNT.
LP: . . . . Unknown

DREAD HOT IN AFRICA.
LP: . . . . BSLP 1004

GIVE ME LOVING (see under Radicals' rumtree).

IMPRESSIONS OF LEROY SMART.
LP: . . . . BSLP 1005

JAH LOVES EVERYONE.
LP: . . . . BSLP 1008

LEROY SMART.
Tracks: / She love to dance / I want your love / Release the chain / Me nah leave you / Come a me / Number one / Badminded people / Collie man / Worries tonight / Fisherman.
MC: SKDCT-010

LIVE UP ROOTS CHILDREN.
LP: . . . . BLP 6

MUSICAL DON.
Tracks: / She loves to dance / I want your love / Release / Ma nah leave you / Number one / Badminded people / Collie man / Worries tonight / Fisherman.
LP: . . . . SKDLP 010

PROPAGANDA.
LP: . . . . BSLP 1009

ROCKERS AWARD WINNERS (See under Minott, Sugar).

SHE JUST A DRAW CARD.
LP: . . . . Unknown

SHE LOVE IT IN THE MORNING.
LP: . . . . GGLP 0031

SHOWCASE.
LP: . . . . FSLP 001

SOUL AND INSPIRATION (see under Osbourne, Johnny "Get cracking").

TEMPTATIONS.
LP: . . . . CR 001

WITH ROOTS RADIX & FRIENDS.
LP: . . . . VSLP 4022

Smart Pils

NO GOOD, NO EVIL.
LP: . . . . FISH 17

Smarties

OPERATION THUNDERBUNNY.
LP: 089 313

Smash Palace

SMASH PALACE.
Tracks: / Living on the borderline / Count the days / Love will find a way / Never say no again / Juliet to me / No love lost / Night to remember, A / Pieces of my heart / Night of a thousand faces.
LP: . . . . EPC 26577
MC: 40 26577

Smashed Gladys

SMASHED GLADYS.
LP: . . . . USA 49
MC: . . . . HMAMC 49

SOCIAL INTERCOURSE.
Tracks: / Lick it into shape / 17 goin' on crazy / Play dirty / Dive in the dark / Eye of the storm / Hard to swallow / Legs up / Eye for an eye / Cast of nasties / Sermonette.
LP: . . . . K 9607761
MC: . . . . K 9607764

Smeck, Roy

PLAYS HAWAIIAN GUITAR ETC.
LP: . . . . L 1052

WIZARD OF THE STRINGS.
LP: 7002

Smegma

NATTERING NAYBOBS OF NEGATIVITY.
Tracks: / Pile / Happy baby rhumba / Spring flowers / Freakish high / Limp dynamics / Thru the warty evening / Innermost cravings / Porky section / Eu vont / Mouthful of rubber.
LP: . . . . DMC 012

Smell Funky Beast

BURNIN'.
LP: . . . . NTVLP 050

Smersh

BEAT FROM 20,000 FATHOMS, THE.
LP: . . . . RRR 008

EMMANUELLE GOES TO BANGKOK.
Tracks: / Touch of Venus / Great Ceasar's ghost / Burn / Titanic fantastic / Blonde devil / You remind me of summer / Armoured man / Under your hoop / Brown out / Riding with the Pharoahs / Discotes.
LP: . . . . KK 47

GREATEST STORY EVER DISTORTED, THE.
Tracks: / Licorice rope / Jack your metal / Japanese princess / Bootie heaven / Spook house.
LP: . . . . KK 019

HAVING A WET DOWN.
LP: . . . . DMC 027

PART OF THE ANIMAL THAT PEOPLE DON'T LIKE, THE.
LP: . . . . DMC 009

Smetana (composer)

SMETANA (Various artists).
MC: . . . . DLCMC 214

Smike (show)

SMIKE (Original cast recording) (Various artists).
Tracks: / Doing things by numbers: *Various artists* / Here I am: *Various artists* / We'll find our day: *Various artists* / In the warm light of a brand new day: *Various artists* / Brimstone and treacle: *Various artists.*
2LP: . . . . SMIKE 1
MCSET: . . . . SMIKE C1

SMIKE! (Original London cast) (Various artists).
Tracks: / Overture - daily test: *Various artists* / Here I am (looking for my name): *Various artists* / Stop and just think who you could be: *Various artists* / Transition music: *Various artists* / Dotheboys hall: *Various* artists / We've got the youngsters' interests at heart: *Various artists* / Don't let life get you down: *Various* artists / In the warm light of a brand new day: *Various artists* / Brimstone and treacle: *Various artists*/ We'll find our day: *Various artists* / Reprise: *Various artists* / Dotheboys rock: *Various artists.*
LP: . . . . FBLP 8085
MC: . . . . ZCFBL 8085

Smiles, Kenny

MAGIC.
LP: . . . . BM 31

Smiley, Billy

NEW NIGHT.
LP: . . . . MLR 7009
MC: . . . . MLC 7010

Smiley's People

SMILEY'S PEOPLE (John Le Carre).
MCSET: . . . . TC LFP 7106

SMILEY'S PEOPLE (Music from the television soundtrack) (Various artists).
LP: . . . . REP 439
MC: . . . . ZCH 439

SMILEY'S PEOPLE (Various artists).
MCSET: . . . . ZBBC 1131

Smith, Al

HEAR MY BLUES.
LP: . . . . OBC 514

Smith, Arlene

ARLENE SMITH & THE CHANTELS (Smith, Arlene & The Chantels).
LPS: 000385

Smith, Arthur

ARTHUR "GUITAR" SMITH & VOICES (Smith, Arthur "Guitar Boogie").
LP: . . . . HAT 3025
MC: . . . . HATC 3025

JUMPIN' GUITAR (Smith, Arthur "Guitar Boogie").
LP: . . . . RR 425

MISTER GUITAR (Smith, Arthur "Guitar Boogie").
LP: . . . . SLP 173
MC: . . . . GT 5173

Smith, Bessie

ANY WOMAN'S BLUES.
Tracks: / Jailhouse blues / St. Louis gal / Sam Jones blues / Cemetery blues / Far away blues / I'm going back to my used to be / Whoa, Tillie / Take your time / My sweetie went away / Any woman's blues / Chicago bound blues / Mistreating Daddy / Frosty morning blues / Haunted house blues / Eavesdropper's blues / Easy come, easy go / Graveyard dream blues / I'm wild about that thing / You've got to give me some / Kitchen man / I got what it takes / Nobody knows you (when you're down and out) / Take it right back / He's got me goin' / It makes my love come down / Wasted life blues / Dirty nogooder's blues / Blue spirit blues / Worn out papa blues / You don't understand / Don't cry baby / Keep it to yourself / New Orleans hop slop blues.
LP: . . . . CBS 66262

BESSIE SMITH COLLECTION (20 Golden Greats).
Tracks: / Alexander's ragtime band / Gin House blues / Careless love blues / Nobody's blues but mine / What's the matter now? / Baby doll / Hard time blues / After you've gone / At the Christmas ball / Young woman's blues / Florida bound blues / I've been mistreated and I don't like it / Jazzbo Brown from Memphis Town / My man blues / I want ev'ry bit of it / New Gulf Coast blues / Squeeze me / Hard-driving papa / Lonesome desert blues / St. Louis blues.
LP: . . . . DVLP 2008
MC: . . . . DVMC 2008

BESSIE SMITH STORY, THE.
Tracks: / Careless love blues / J.C. Holmes blues / He's gone blues / Nobody's blues but mine / I ain't got nobody / My man blues / New Gulf Coast blues / I've been mistreated and I don't like it / Lonesome desert blues / Squeeze me / What's the matter now? / I want every bit of it / Jazzbo Brown from Memphis Town / Gin house blues / Money blues / Baby doll / Hard driving papa / Lost your head blues / Hard time blues / One and two blues / Young woman's blues / Preachin' the blues / Backwater blues / After you've gone / Alexander's ragtime band.
MCSET: . . . . DVREMC 11

CLASSICS VOL.1 (1925-26).
MC: . . . . NEO 702

CLASSICS - VOL.3 - 1928/31.
MC: . . . . NEO 751

COLLECTION: BESSIE SMITH.
LP: 4633391
MC: 4633394

COMPLETE COLLECTION VOL.1, THE.
MC: 4678954

EMPRESS OF THE BLUES.
LP: . . . . LPJT 36

EMPRESS, THE (Including C.Hawkins,F.Henderson,L.Armstrong).
Tracks: / Sing Sing Prison blues / Follow the deal on down / Sinful blues / Woman trouble blues / Love me daddy blues / Dying gambler's blues / St. Louis blues / Reckless blues / Sobbin' hearted blues / Cold in hand blues / You've been a good ole wagon / Cake walkin' babies from home / Yellow dog blues / Soft pedal blues / Dixie flyers blues / Nashville woman's blues / Muddy water / There'll be a hot time in the old town tonight / Trombone cholly / Send me to the 'lectric chair / Them's graveyard words / Hot springs blues / Lock and key / Mean old bedbug blues / Good man is hard to find, A / Homeless blues / Looking for my man blues / Dyin' by the hour / Foolish man blues / Thinking blues / Pickpocket blues.
2LP: B2VL 082

JAZZ CLASSICS IN DIGITAL STEREO (Bessie Smith 1925-1933).
Tracks: / Empty bed blues / Alexander's Ragtime Band / Preachin' the blues / Keep it to yourself / Trombone Cholly / At the Christmas Ball / Kitchen man / You've got to give me some / He's got me goin' / Devil's gonna git you / Send me to the 'lectric chair / Baby doll / Take me for a buggy ride / Young woman's blues.
LP: . . . . REB 602
MC: . . . . ZCF 602

L'ART VOCAL VOLUME 3: LA SELECTION 1923-1933 (See Under L'Art Vocal).

NOBODY'S BLUES BUT MINE.
Tracks: / Careless love blues / J.C. Holmes blues / I ain't goin' to play no second fiddle / He's gone blues / Nobody's blues but mine / I ain't got nobody / My man blues / New Gulf Coast blues / Florida bound blues / At the Christmas ball / I've been mistreated and I don't like it / Red mountain blues / Golden rule blues / Lonesome desert blues / Them has been blues / Squeeze me / What's the matter now? / I want ev'ry bit of it / Jazzbo Brown from Memphis town / Gin house blues / Money blues / Baby doll / Hard-driving papa / Lost your head blues / Hard time blues / Honey man blues / One and two blues / Young woman's blues / Preachin' the blues / Backwater blues / After you've gone / Alexander's ragtime band.
LPS: . . . . CBS 67232

ST. LOUIS BLUES (Smith, Bessie & Various artists).
Tracks: / I cover the waterfront / Somebody loves me / Do that thing / I don't know, I don't care blues / Freight train blues / Sorrowful blues / Don't shake it no more / Praying blues.
LP: . . . . BLJ 8001

WHOLE ST. LOUIS BLUES SOUNDTRACK.
LP: . . . . BLJ 8025

WORLDS GREATEST BLUES SINGER.
Tracks: / Down hearted blues / Gulf coast blues / Aggravatin' papa / Beale Street mama / Baby won't you please come home? / Oh daddy (you won't have no mama at all) / T'aint nobody's business if I do / Keeps on a rainin' (Papa, he can't make no time) / Mama's got the blues / Outside of that / Bleeding hearted blues / Yodelling blues / If you don't know who will / Nobody in town can bake a sweet jelly roll like mine / See if I care / Baby have pity on me / On revival day / Moan, you moaners / Hustlin' Dan / Black mountain blues / In the house blues / Long old road / Blue blue / Shipwreck blues / Need a little sugar in my bowl / Safety mama / Do your duty / Gimme a pigfoot and a bottle of beer / Take me for a buggy ride / Down in the dumps.
2LP: . . . . CBS 66258

Smith, Bessie Mae

ST.LOUIS BESSIE 1927-30.
LP: . . . . MSE 223

Smith, Bill

AUSTRALIAN STORIES (Smith, Bill & Friends).
LP: . . . . ARF 177

BILL SMITH ENSEMBLE (Smith, Bill Ensemble).
LP: 4008

CONVERSATION PIECES (Smith, Bill/ Stuart Broomer).
Tracks: / Configuration, A / Outline of miniature potted trees, An / First jump / Imagine a (short) monument / Briefly inquire after its whereabouts.
LP: . . . . SERIES 002
LP: . . . . ONARI 002

PICK A NUMBER.
Tracks: / Up (a love song for Captain Robot) / Little Boo / Bones and giggles / Interludes.
LP: . . . . ONARI 004

Smith, Bob

BETTER THAN AN ORCHESTRA (Smith, Bob Ideal Band).
Tracks: / Ideal one step / Empress tango / Red flag, The / Wull's wireless wails (parts 1 & 2) / Ideal lancers 1st, 5th fig, The / Why worry / Middy march, The / Medley of Irish waltzes / Dulcimer tuner from an old national half favourite (1 & 2) / I still love you / Call of the pipes.
LP: 12T 320

IDEAL MUSIC (Smith, Bob Ideal Band).
Tracks: / Eightsome reel (part 1) / Argyle and Sutherland highlanders / International, The / Canal cruise (parts 1&2), The / Big reason blues / Boston two step / March: Horse guards blue / Barn dance: Woodland voices / Eightsome reel (part 2) / Ashcroft's reel / Londonderry air / Breakdown / Liverpool and Highlevel hornpipes / Medley of popular waltzes / La varsovienne / Happy hours.
LP: 12T 319

JAZZ AT THE APOLLO.
Tracks: / Tippin' in / Station break / After hours / Bess boogie / Dash hound boogie / Blue keys / Flip a coin / Cinder bottom / Buffalo nickel / Desert night / Danny boy / Skippin' and hoppin' / Night watch / Tread lightly / Lightfoot / Don't shake those hips at me.
LP: . . . . OFF 3045

Smith, Bobby

SMOKIN' BLUEGRASS (Smith, Bobby & Boys From Shiloh).
Tracks: / Let your love flow / Don't let the smokey mountain smoke / Fifteen miles from Birmingham / Shig-a-dig / Down on the corner / Bluer than midnight / Shiloh march / Packing up and leaving / Fall, The / Jamboree / Gretna Green / Dinner bell.
LP: . . . . CMH 6225

Smith, Bryan

AN INVITATION TO BRYAN SMITH'S PARTY.
LP: . . . . DS 025

AT THE ROYAL ALBERT HALL (see Irvine, Bill & Boggie).

BACK IN YOUR OWN BACKYARD.
LP: . . . . DS 018
MC: . . . . TDS 018

BANJO TIME (Smith, Bryan & The Boys).
LP: . . . . DS 054

BRYAN SMITH AND HIS HAPPY PIANO.
LP: . . . . DTL 3013

BRYAN SMITH AND HIS OLD TIME ORCHESTRA.
LP: . . . . MTS 27

CLASSICALLY YOURS (Smith, Bryan & His Concert Orchestra).
Tracks: / Swiss guard march / Deutschmeister Regimentsmarsch / Wiener burger / Waltzing with Lehar / True love gavotte / Stephanie gavotte / Carmen tango / Girls were made to love and kiss / Melody in F / I'm always chasing rainbows / Coppelia waltz / Nocturne waltz.
LP: . . . . DS 035

COUNTRY AND WESTERN.
LP: . . . . DS 032
MC: . . . . TDS 032

DANCING FOR PLEASURE (Smith, Bryan & His Festival Orchestra).
Tracks: / Horse guards blue / Stella d'Italia (Star of Italy) / Closer / Once in a while / Edwardians, The / Sobre las olas (Over the waves) / I'll never say 'never again' again / That's a plenty / Blue Tahitian moon / Just for a while / Suzy / Tango 65 / Egerland march / Bandstand march / Make believe / It looks like rain in Cherry Blossom Lane / Kind regards / Pink Colombine / Rags and tatters / Stumbling / Student Prince waltz / Any time's kissing time / Tango hacienda / Tango sombrero.
2LP: . . . . DL 41 1062 3
MC: . . . . DL 41 1062 9

ENTERTAINER, THE.
LP: . . . . DTL 3008

EVERYBODY DANCE.
LP: . . . . DS 002

GOES TO TOWN WITH HIS HAPPY PIANO.
Tracks: / Johnson rag / Love / Forgotten dreams / Serenade / Words / Lady be good / Side by side / Enjoy yourself / Just one more chance / In San Francisco / Temptation rag.
LP: . . . . DS 059

GREATEST HITS OF FLANAGAN & ALLEN (Smith, Bryan/Monty Pierce & Roy Hudd).
LP: . . . . BTS 1012

HAPPY PIANO OF BRYAN SMITH IN SEQUENCE TIME , THE.
LP: . . . . DS 003

HAWAIIAN PARADISE.
LP: . . . . DS 024
MC: . . . . TDS 024

I WANT TO BE HAPPY.
LP: . . . . MTS 26

LET'S BE HAPPY (Smith, Bryan And Riverboat Band).
LP: . . . . DS 058

MUSIC MUSIC MUSIC (Smith, Bryan & His Happy Band).
Tracks: / Music-music-music / Stumbling / Crazy otto rag / Careless hands / Song of my life / Cuban love song / El cubanchero.
LP: . . . . DS 064

PIANO MAN, THE.
LP: . . . . BTS 1010

PLAY IT AGAIN.
LP: . . . . DS 047

RIVERBOAT SHUFFLE.
LP: . . . . DS 039
MC: . . . . TDS 039

ROBIN'S RETURN (Smith, Bryan & His Piano).
LP: . . . . BTS 1007

SEQUENCE TIME AT THE RADIO 2 BALLROOM VOLUME 3 (Smith, Bryan & His Festival Orchestra).
Tracks: / Festivity / Frivolry / Portland Bill / In Grinzing / Thomas and Sarah / Freshman's folly / Do something / Undecided / Story of a starry night / My heart cries for you / La vendetta d'amour / When violins are playing.
LP: . . . . REC 358
MC: . . . . ZCM 358

SEQUENCE TIME AT THE RADIO 2 BALLROOM (Smith, Bryan & His Festival Orchestra).
Tracks: / Sky high / Fire on the horizon / Thrills / Dollar Princess / Dorfkinder waltz / How wonderful to know / Love walked in / Wings / Chivalry / Here, there and everywhere / Spanish eyes / Our secret / Bye and bye sweetheart / When forever has gone / Lonesome and sorry / Congratulations / Hear my song Violetta / Isle of Capri.
LP: . . . . REC 285
MC: . . . . ZCM 285

SEQUENCE TIME AT THE RADIO 2 BALLROOM VOLUME 2 (Smith, Bryan & His Festival Orchestra).
Tracks: / Light horse march, The / Tolzer schutzenmarsch / Carnival children / Flattery / Glad days / Armalita / Walk right back / Melody you will never forget, A / Jubilee waltz, The / Whisper while you waltz / I'll close my eyes / Gardybylaten maqqidudiog jeg.
LP: . . . . REC 336
MC: . . . . ZCM 336

SIDE BY SIDE WITH TWO BRYANS (see under Dee, Brian) (Smith, Bryan/ Brian Dee).

TWO'S COMPANY.
LP: . . . . DS 029

UGLY BUG BALL.
LP: . . . . BTS 1013

VERY BEST OF BRYAN SMITH & HIS HAPPY PIANO, THE.
Tracks: / Robin's return / Last order's please / Keep your seats please / Chinese laundry blues / Shades of gold / One of those songs / Let's fall in love / Too young / Around the world / It happened in Monterey / I wonder who's kissing her now / I'll always love you / When I grow too old to dream / Sway / Deed I do / Popsie / You're just in love / Waiting for the Robert E. Lee / Alabama jubilee / Good morning / When my dreamboat comes in / Should I / Brasilia / Don't dilly dally on the way / Bye bye blackbird / When the red, red robin comes bob, bob, bobbin' along / Underneath the arches / Strollin' / Down forget-me-not lane / Miss you / How wonderful to know / On a slow boat to China / C'est magnifique / Anything goes / Turkey in the straw.
LP: . . . . PLAT 20
MC: . . . . PLAC 20

YOUR RADIO REQUESTS (Smith, Bryan & His Festival Orchestra).
Tracks: / Spring romance / Old timers march / Summer walk / Rastus on parade / Song of the sea shore / Golden waltz medley / Scarlet ribbons / Dreamy eyes / La vendetta d'amour / Solitaire.
LP: . . . . DS 056

YOUR SEQUENCE REQUESTS.
LP: . . . . DTL 3012

Smith, Byther

TELL ME HOW YOU LIKE IT.
Tracks: / Tell me how you like it / I don't like to travel / Cut you loose / Walked all night long / Close to you / Come on in this house / 33 Pounds of joy / Hold that train / You ought to be ashamed / What my mama told me / This little voice.
LP: . . . . RL 061

Smith, Carl

CARL SMITH'S GREATEST HITS: VOL 1.
LP: . . . . GT 0058

OLD LONESOME TIMES 1951-56.
LP: . . . . SS 25
MC: . . . . CSS 25

Smith, Carrie

FINE AND MELLOW.
LP: . . . . AP 164

Smith, Charlie

JAZZVILLE VOL.3 (Smith, Charlie Trio/ Aaron Sachs Sextet).
LP: . . . . FS 244

TESTIFYIN' (Smith,Charles/Chuck Armstrong/Ted Ford).
Tracks: / My great loss (ashes to ashes) / Glad to be home / I'm useless / Why can't I cry / Only time you say you love me, The / Stand up and take it like a man / Pull me out of the water / Two pillows / Why does it hurt so bad / How sweet it is to be loved by you / I'm gonna forget about you / Keep your mind on me / She's gonna come back / Pretty girls everywhere / Please give me another chance / You're gonna need me.
LP: . . . . CRB 1153

WASSIT GOTTA DEW WI YEW.
Tracks: / Little children / Jeans song / Chimbley sweep / Norfick dumplin' / Wassit gotta dew wi yew bor / Muck spreadin' time / My hat wot a beautiful view / jubilee baby / young barber / My God wont we poor / Larst weeks news / Sum muthers dew have em / Fule of the family / Shud down the yard, The.
LP: . . . . SFA 097

Smith, Clara

CLARA SMITH VOL.1 (1923).
LP: . . . . VLP 15
LP: . . . . DLP 566

CLARA SMITH VOL.2 (1923-24).
LP: . . . . VLP 16
LP: . . . . DLP 567

CLARA SMITH VOL.3 (1924).
LP: . . . . VLP 17
LP: . . . . DLP 568

CLARA SMITH VOL.4 (1925-26).
LP: . . . . DLP 569

CLARA SMITH VOL.5 (1926-28).
LP: . . . . DLP 570

CLARA SMITH VOL.6 (1928-30).
LP: . . . . DLP 571

CLARA SMITH VOL.7 (1930-32).
LP: . . . . DLP 572

Smith, Clarence

COMPILATION (1929-30).
LP: . . . . OL 2831

COMPILATION 1928-29-30 (Smith, Clarence 'Pinetop' & Romeo Nelson).
LP: . . . . OL 2330

Smith, Connie

20 OF THE BEST: CONNIE SMITH.
Tracks: / Once a day / Then and only then / I can't remember / If I talk to him / Nobody but a fool / Ain't had no lovin' / Hurtin' all over / I'll come running / Cincinnati, Ohio / Burning a hole in my mind / Baby's back again / Run away, little tears / Ribbon of darkness / You and your sweet love / I never once stopped loving you / Where is my castle? / Just one time / Just for what I am / If it ain't love / Love is the look you're lookin' for.
LP: . . . . NL 89523
MC: . . . . NK 89523

BACK IN BABY'S ARMS.
Tracks: / Back in baby's arms / Long black limousine / I can't get used to being lonely / Fool No. 1 / Gone too far / Wedding cake, The / Too many rivers / How great Thou art / Call, The / Now / What would I do without you.
LP: . . . . LSA 3129

BEST OF CONNIE SMITH, THE.
Tracks: / Once a day / I can't remember / Tiny blue transistor radio / I'll come running / I saw a man / If I talk to him / Then and only then / Ain't had no lovin' / Darling, are you ever coming home /

Hurtin's all over, The / Cincinnati, Ohio / Nobody but a fool (would love you).
LP: . . . . LSA 3055

BESTS OF THE SMITH GIRL.
Tracks: / Other side of you, The / Hinges on the door / Once a day / Then and only then / It's just my luck / I don't love you anymore / Tiny blue transistor radio / Don't forget (I still love you) / Darling, are you ever coming home / Threshold / I'm ashamed of you / Tell another lie.
LP: . . . . HAT 3089
MC: . . . . HATC 3089

FAMOUS COUNTRY MUSIC MAKERS - CONNIE SMITH.
Tracks: / There goes my everything / I love Charley Brown / I don't want your memories / How sweet it is / Sundown of my mind / Dream painter / Love has a mind of its own / If you won't tell / Ain't nothin' shakin' (but the leaves) / It's gonna rain today / Ain't we havin' us a good time / Thank you for loving me / Back in my baby's arms again / Run away little tears / I'm sorry if my love got in your way / Sunshine of my world, The / Today I started loving you again / It's such a pretty world today / Only mama that'll walk the line / It's now or never / Gentle on my mind / Just one time / My heart has a mind of its own / Pas souvent (once a day) / Wait for the light to shine / If God is diead (who's that living in my soul) / Too much to gain to lose / Gathering flowers for the masters bouquet / Amazing grace / That's all this old world needs / Don't let me walk too far from Calvary / Family bible.
2LP: . . . . PL 42000

GREATEST HITS: CONNIE SMITH VOL 1.
Tracks: / Just one time / Hurtin's all over, The / Just for what I am / Once a day / Cincinnati, Ohio / Ribbon of darkness / Where is my castle / I'll come running / Baby's back again / Run away little tears.
LP: APL1 0275

WHERE IS MY CASTLE?.
LP: . . . . HAT 3112
MC: . . . . HATC 3112

Smith, Dallas

PETALS (see Allen, Marcus) (Smith, Dallas/ Allen Marcus).

SUMMER SUITE (see Bell, Teja) (Smith, Dallas/ Teja Bell).

Smith, Darden

ALL I WANT IS EVERYTHING (See under Hewerdine, Boo) (Hewerdine, Boo & Darden Smith).

DARDEN SMITH.
Tracks: / Two dollar novels / Want you by my side / Love me like a soldier / Little Maggie / Day after tomorrow / God's will / Talk to me / Coldest winter / Place in time / Driving rain.
LP: 4608751
MC: 4608754

NATIVE SOIL.
LP: . . . . RM 001

TROUBLE NO MORE.
Tracks: / Midnight train / Frankie and Sue / All the king's horses / 2000 years / Ashes to ashes / Fall apart at the seams / Trouble no more / Long way home / Listen to my own voice / Johnny was a lucky one / Bottom of a deep well.
LP: 4671231
MC: 4671234

Smith, Dave

OUT OF THIS WORLD.
Tracks: / Airborne / Last post / Dambusters / 633 squadron / I love you because / Misty / Chattanooga choo choo / Fly me to the moon / Bergvagabunden / Anything goes / American trilogy / Under the sign of the double eagle / I can see clearly now / House of the Rising Sun / Stardust / Camptown races / Oh Susannah / She'll be coming round the mountain / In a mellow tone / Toccata and Fugue / Music.
LP: . . . . GRS 1118

Smith, Derek

DARK EYES (Smith, Derek Trio).
LP: . . . . EWIND 711

DEREK SMITH PLAYS THE MUSIC OF JEROME KERN.
Tracks: / Ol' man river / Fine romance, A / Folks who live on the hill, The / I'm old fashioned / Long ago and far away / Way you look tonight / I won't dance.
LP: . . . . PRO 7055

LOVE FOR SALE (Smith, Derek Trio).
Tracks: / Love for sale / Summertime / Tristesse / Too close for comfort / One to warm up on / Autumn leaves / Sweet Lorraine / Day in the life of a fool, A.
LP: . . . . PRO 7002

MAN I LOVE, THE (Smith, Derek Quartet).
Tracks: / Man I love, The / Yesterdays / Topsy / There's a small hotel / These foolish things / Between the Devil and the deep blue sea / I'm in the mood for love.
LP: . . . . PRO 7035

Smith, Dick King

SHEEP-PIG, THE (Thorne, Stephen).
MCSET: CC/030

Smith, Dodie

ONE HUNDRED AND ONE DALMATIANS (Lumley, Joanna).
MCSET: . . . . LFP 7132

Smith, Ernie

MR. SMITH'S CLASSICS.
Tracks: / Key card / Bend down low / You won't see me / All for Jesus / Pitta patta / Life is just for living / Reggae reggae / One man same man / We the people / Duppy gunman.
LP: . . . . KRLP 3002
MC: . . . . KRK 3002

Smith, 'Fast' Eddie

CAN U DANCE (See under Jason, Kenny 'Jammin').

CAN YOU DANCE ? (See under Jason, Kenny "Jammin") (Smith, 'Fast' Eddie & Kenny Jammin Jason).

Smith, Fenton

WOMAN AS NICE, A.
Tracks: / Woman as nice, A / Nice instrumental.
LP: . . . . SGLP 28

Smith, Frederick E

633 SQUADRON (Ward, Simon).
MCSET: . . . . LFP 41 7144 5

Smith, Funny Papa

ORIGINAL HOWLING WOLF, THE.
LP: . . . . L 1031

Smith, George

HOME TO THE WESTERN ISLES (Smith, George & The Hebrideans).
Tracks: / Barn dance / Gaelic waltz / Racing along / Fiddler's fancy / Shottische / Willie's Hebrides / Strauss waltzes / Peurt a beul / Gay Gordons / To Scandinavia / Piper's call.
MC: . . . . HEB 1

Smith, George

ARKANSAS TRAP.
LP: . . . . BC 002

BOOGIE'N WITH GEORGE.
LP: . . . . MB 1001

...OF THE BLUES.
LP: . . . . CCR 1015

Smith, Gordon

DOWN ON MEAN STREET.
LP: . . . . AP 005

LONG OVERDUE.
LP: . . . . OLLP 5296

TAKIN' TIME.
LP: . . . . AP 002

Smith, Gregg

MONEY TALKS.
Tracks: / Low down / Blues in my blood / Money talks / Party warrior / Stick and stay / Stuck on you / You men don't get the blues / You are / Crying in the chapel.
LP: . . . . ULT 4024
MC: . . . . ULTMC 4024

Smith, Hal

BUTCH THOMPSON AND HAL SMITH (See under Thompson, Butch) (Smith, Hal & Butch Thompson).

HAL SMITH TRIO (Smith, Hal Trio).
LP: . . . . J 156

HAL SMITH'S CREOLE SUNSHINE ORCHESTRA (Smith, Hal & his Creole Sunshine Orchestra).
LP: . . . . SOS 1077

HAL SMITH'S RHYTHMAKERS (Smith, Hal & Butch Thompson).
LP: . . . . J 136

MILENBERG JOYS (see Thompson, Butch) (Smith, Hal/Butch Thompson/ Charlie Devore).

RAY SKJELBRED & HAL SMITH (See under Skjelbred Ray) (Smith, Hal/Ray Skjelbred).

Smith, Hobart

OLD TIMEY RAP, THE.
Tracks: / Soldier's joy / Peg and awl / Great Titanic, The / Banjo group 1 / Black Annie / Sally Ann / Chinquapin pie / Last chance / John Greer's tune / Short life of trouble / Devil and the farmer's wife, The / Sitting on top of the world / Stormy rose the ocean / Bonaparte's retreat / Cuckoo bird / Columbus stockade blues / Banjo group II / Cindy / Girl I left behind me, The / John Hardy / Meet me in rose time / Rosie / Uncloudy day.
LP: 12T 187

Smith, Huey

IMPERIAL SIDES 1960/61, THE (Smith, Huey & The Clowns).
LP: . . . . PM 1546731

PITTA PATTIN' (Smith, Huey "Piano" & Friends).
Tracks: / Rockin' pneumonia and the boogie woogie flu / Through fooling around / It do me good / Don't you just know it / I'll never forget / Coo coo over you / Smile for me / You got to / We like mambo / Bury me dead / (I do thing's come) naturally / Whatcha bet / I've got everything / Baby you hurt me / Blues '67 / High blood pressure.
LP: . . . . CRB 1164
MC: . . . . TCCRB 1164

ROCKIN' & JIVIN' (Smith, Huey "Piano").
Tracks: / Witchaway to go / Young blood / Rockin' pneumonia and the boogie woogie flu / Jambalaya / Foreday in the morning / Don't you just know it / I'm so blue / Little chicken wah wah / I think you're jiving me / Hip little monkee.
LP: . . . . CRM 2020

ROCKIN' PNEUMONIA AND BOOGIE WOOGIE FLU (Smith, Huey "Piano").
Tracks: / Little chicken wah wah / Little Liza Jane / Just a lonely clown / Hush your mouth / Don't you know yockomo / High blood pressure / Don't you just know it / Well I'll be John Brown / Tu-ber-cu-lucas and sinus blues / Dearest darling / She got low down / Second line.
LP: . . . . CH 9

SOMEWHERE THERE'S HONEY FOR THE GRIZZLY (Smith, Huey & The Clowns).
Tracks: / Somewhere / Rockin' behind the Iron Curtain / Somebody put a tack (in the cotton-pickin' chair) / Doing the beatnik twist / Suzie Q / Every once in a while / I tried / Scald dog / Would you believe it / Talk to me, baby / At the Mardi Gras / Genevieve / Havin' a good time / We like Birdland.
LP: . . . . CH 100

'TWAS THE NIGHT BEFORE CHRISTMAS (Smith, Huey & The Clowns).
LP: . . . . ACE 1027

Smith, Ian

GOLDEN GRATES (Smith, Ian (The Vagabond King)).
Tracks: / All night cafe / Short nosed 44 / Ignorance is bliss / Windy City blues / Danger in love / Cry o beloved country / Tonight I'll sleep alone / Richard's dream / Check on your baby / If you change your mind / Furs and diamonds.
LP: . . . . COLDLP 4

Smith, Jabbo

JABBO SMITH VOL 1 1928/29.
Tracks: / Willow tree / 'Sippi / Thou swell / Perisian rug / Got butter on it / Ready hokum / Jazz battle / Little Willie blues / Sleepy time blues / Take your time / Sweet'n'low blues / Take me to the river / Ace of rhythm.
LP: . . . . FJ 130

JABBO SMITH VOL 2 1929-1938.
Tracks: / Let's get together / Sau-sha stomp / Michigander blues / Dectaur street tutti / Till times get better / Lina blues / Wierd and blue / Croonin' the blues / I got the stinger / Boston skuffle / Tangay blues / Moanful blues / Band box stomp / Rhythm in Spain / Absolutely / More rain more rest / How can cupid be so stupid.
LP: . . . . FJ 131

SWEET 'N' LOW DOWN (Smith, Jabbo & His Rhythm Aces).
Tracks: / Black and tan fantasy / Take me to the river / What more can a poor fellow do? / Sweet and low down / Sleepytime blues / Jazz battle / Little willie blues / Take your time / Sau sha stomp / Let's get together / Michigander blues / Decatur street tutti / Till times get better / Ace of rhythm.
LP: . . . . AFS 1029
MC: . . . . TCAFS 1029

Smith, Jack

ROCKABILLY PLANET.
LP: . . . . FF 510

WHISPERING BARITONE.
Tracks: / My blue Heaven / Song is ended, The / Miss Annabelle Lee / When day is done / Sunshine / Whispering / I never dreamt you'd fall in love with me / Afraid of you / 'S wonderful / Funny face / My one and only / Crazy rhythm / If I had you / That's my weakness now / Song I love, The / Peace of mind / Sally of my dreams / I faw down an' go boom / Encore / I'll be getting along / Lily of Laguna / It all depends on you / Blue skies / Possibly / Birth of the blues / There's always a way into trouble / Half a moon / I kiss your hand / Madame Ramona.
LP: . . . . SHB 31
MC: . . . . TC2 SHB 31

Smith, Jimmy (UK)

BIG BAND STYLE.
Tracks: / Volare / Goody, goody / 9 to 5 / Chanson d'amour / Red sails in the sunset / Silly little song / Happy days are here again / Shanty in old shanty town.
MC: . . . . CSU 588

HAMMOND BY NIGHT.
Tracks: / At my time in life / One morning in May / Sunday, Monday, or always / Only you / That's all I ask of you / London by night / So tired / That old feeling / In the wee small hours of the morning / Please be kind / Love me as though there were no tomorrow / I can't get started / Ebb tide.
MC: . . . . CSUS 003

I PLAY PIANO.
Tracks: / Can't get enough of you / Cherry / You'll never know / Manhattan / I will wait for you / Corcovado (Quiet nights) / Blue eyes / Lollipops and roses / I'm confessin' / This one's for you / Pieces of dreams / In the still of the night.
LP: . . . . SUP 308

JIMMY SMITH AT THE ORGAN.
Tracks: / Stranger In Paradise / It's A Sin To Tell A Lie / Night Winds / You Go To My Head / Sleepwalk 9 / Lost in lonliness / Dancing On The Ceiling / Blue mist / Jungle bunny / Mr. Jim.
LP: . . . . XELLP 102
MC: . . . . XELMC 102

JUST ORGAN...JUST FOR YOU.
Tracks: / Lady is a tramp, The / Girl from Ipanema / Foggy day, A / April in Paris / Like someone in love / Just for you / This could be the start of something big / Misty / You're nobody till somebody loves you / Hello, misty eyes / If I ruled the world / Jukata jive.
LP: . . . . SUJ 001

LIL' DARLIN'.
Tracks: / I just called to say I love you / Day my heart caught fire, The / Li'l darlin' / Most beautiful girl, The / Most beautiful girl, The / Senorita de Islas.
LP: . . . . SUJ 002

LOVELY WAY TO SPEND AN EVENING, A.
Tracks: / Lovely way to spend an evening, A / Don't blame me / You light up my life / Shadow of your smile / This guy's in love with you / For all we know / We have all the time in the world / I've grown accustomed to her face / Moonlight in Vermont / You're sensational / You needed me / I've never been in love before / It only takes a moment / Let me try again.
LP: . . . . SU 101
MC: . . . . CSU 101

MUSIC TO MOTOR BY.
Tracks: / Flying down to Rio / Southern nights / Silly little song / I wonder who's kissing her now / After you've gone / Mister sandman / Sheik of Araby, The / I love Paris / Hello, young lovers / Sweet Sue / Honeysuckle rose / Button up your overcoat / Pennies from Heaven / Music to drive by / Sailing / Hey Jude / Green green grass of home / Dream / What I did for love / Lonely shepherd / Whiter shade of pale, A / When the saints go marching in / Mack the knife / Blue J blues.
MC: . . . . CSM 1

ON DAYS LIKE THESE.
Tracks: / How high the moon / Do that to me one more time / I've got my love to keep me warm / New York, New York / Please don't talk about me when I'm gone / Blue moon / I should have known / On a clear day / Easy to love / On days like these / Stay / Desafinado / Strike up the band / For the good times.
MC: . . . . CSU 106
LP: . . . . SU 106

ON THE RIVIERA.
Tracks: / Day that my heart caught fire / Things we did last summer, The / What a difference a day made / What are you doing the rest of your life? / For once in my life / Rachmaninov piano concerto No 2, Op 18 / On the Riviera / Windmills of your mind / C'est si bon / Come in from the rain / Tie a yellow ribbon / I'll survive / Can't smile without you / Could it be magic? / Stargazer / If I never sing another song.
LP: . . . . GRS 1079

ORCHESTRAL MAGIC OF JIMMY SMITH, THE.
LP: . . . . SUS 526

PARTY SIDE OF JIMMY SMITH, THE.

Tracks: / More I see you, The / There will never be another you / Very thought of you, The / All of me / When you're smiling / Who's sorry now? / So what's new? / Oh baby / I believe in music / Just in time / I can't get over getting over you / I don't want to walk without you / Sing / We can sing in the sunshine / When you smile / Rise / Gonna get along without you now / I love to love (but my baby loves to dance) / Your love / It all depends on you / Get a little sand between your toes / I can't give you anything but love / Delilah / Night and day / Dancing in the dark / My heart belongs to daddy / I'm in the mood for dancing.
LP: . . . . GRS 1084

SO REAL, SO BEAUTIFUL.
Tracks: / So real, so beautiful / Trust in me / Charade / You and me against the world / Consuelo's love theme (From the film "Children Of Sanchez".) / Time after time / Here's that rainy day / Fly me to the moon / I've got you under my skin / For once in my life / Lover / All of me / Have you met Miss Jones? / Begin the beguine.
MC: . . . . CSU 105
LP: . . . . SU 105

SWING AND SING ALONG IN THE BIG BAND STYLE.
Tracks: / Volare / Goody goody / Always / Happy days are here again / Nine to five / Those were the days / Something stupid / Chanson d'amour / Old fashioned way, The / Mame / Lulu's back in town / Alexander's ragtime band / Red sails in the sunset / In a shanty in old Shantytown / Silly little song / Out of nowhere / If I had my way / Smoke gets in your eyes / Slow boat to China / Little on the lonely side, A / I'll get by / We'll meet again / If I should fall in love again / Are you lonesome tonight?.
LP: . . . . SUF 588
MC: . . . . CSUF 588

TALKING HANDS.
Tracks: / Opus one / Crazy rhythm / Isn't she lovely? / At seventeen / But beautiful / Wave / They can't take that away from me / Teddy bears' picnic / Even now / Walk in love (talking hands) / 'S wonderful / Go (before you break my heart) / Lover come back to me / One / Bye bye blues / This is all I ask / I'm not in love.
LP: . . . . GRS 1080

TO WAIT FOR LOVE.
Tracks: / Il coraggio di dire ti amo / My foolish heart / Music maestro please / If you were the only girl in the world / I'm in the mood for love / Chi mai / World is waiting for the sunrise, The / Nothing in the world to do with me / To wait for love / L.O.V.E. / If he walked into my life.
LP: . . . . SU 102

TWO SIDES OF JIMMY SMITH.
Tracks: / Fools rush in / Mind if I make love to you? / Lady is a tramp, The / Just the way you are / I've never been a woman before / At the Copa - Copacabana / Southern nights / Flying down to Rio / As time goes by / Way we were, The / Baubles, bangles and beads / Don't cry out loud / At long last love / Tangerine / Please don't talk about me when I'm gone / Vienna, city of my dreams / It had to be you.
LP: . . . . GRS 1072

Smith, Jimmy (USA)

BACK AT THE CHICKEN SHACK.
Tracks: / Back at the Chicken Shack / When I grow too old to dream / Minor chant / Messy Bessie / On the sunny side of the street.
LP: . . . . BST 84117
MC: 4BN 84117

BEST OF JIMMY SMITH (Blue Note Years).
Tracks: / Sermon / Fungii mama (CD only.) / When Johnny comes marching home / Jumpin' the blues / Back at the chicken shack / Champ, The (CD only.) / All day long (CD only.).
LP: B1-91140

CAT, THE.
Tracks: / Joy house theme / Basin Street blues / Cat, The / Carpetbagger's theme / St. Louis blues / Chicago serenade / Delon's blues / Blues in the night / Love cage theme.
MC: 1912 205
LP: 810 046 1
MC: 810 046 4
LP: 2304 153

CHAMP, THE.
LP: . . . . BLP 1514

CRAZY BABY.
Tracks: / When Johnny comes marching home / Makin' whoopee / Night in Tunisia / Sonnymoon for two / Mack the knife / What's new / Alfredo.
LP: . . . . BST 84030

GO FOR WHATCHA KNOW.
Tracks: / Fungii mama / Go for what you know / Bass face / She's out of my life / We can make it work / No substitute.
LP: . . . . BT 85125

GOT MY MOJO WORKING.
Tracks: / High heel sneakers / Satisfaction / One two three / Mustard greens / Got my mojo working / Johnny come lately / C jam blues / Hobson's hop.
LP: 2304 191
LP: . . . . VLP 912

HOME COOKIN'.
LP: . . . . BST 84050

HOUSE PARTY.
Tracks: / J.O.S. / What is this thing called love / Just friends / Cherokee / Blues after all / Au privave / Lover man.
MC: 4BN 84002
LP: . . . . BST 84002

JIMMY SMITH PLAYS THE BLUES (Compact/Walkman Jazz).
MC: 829 537-4

KEEP ON COMIN'.
Tracks: / Keep on comin' / Be yourself / No problem / Summertime / Yesterdays / Callitwhachawanna / Piano medley.
LP: 960301-1

MIDNIGHT SPECIAL.
Tracks: / Midnight special / Subtle one, A / Jumpin' the blues / Why was I born / One o'clock jump.
LP: . . . . BST 84978
MC: . . . . BSC 84978
LP: . . . . BST 84078

MR.JIM.
Tracks: / Stranger in paradise / It's a sin to tell a lie / Night winds / You go to my head / Tenderly / Caravan / Bongo rock / Cherokee.
LP: . . . . MAN 5038

OFF THE TOP.
Tracks: / I'll drink to that / M-A-S-H, Theme from / Ain't misbehavin' / Jimmy Smith rap / Endless love / Mimosa / Off the top.
LP: . . . . K 52418

PRAYER MEETING.
Tracks: / Prayer meeting / I almost lost my mind / Stone cold dead / In the market / When the saints go marching in / Red top / Picnicking.
LP: . . . . BST 84164
MC: . . . . TCBST 84164

SERMON, THE.
Tracks: / Sermon / You came a long way from St. Louis / Ape woman / Georgia on my mind / G'won train / Any number can win / What'd I say / Ruby / Tubs / Blues for C.A..
MC: 4BN 84011
LP: . . . . BST 84011
LP: 2332085

UNPREDICTABLE JIMMY SMITH, THE (Bashin') (Smith, Jimmy & Big Big Band).
Tracks: / Walk on the wild side / Ol' man river / In a mellow tone / Step right up / Beggar for the blues / Bashin' / I'm an old cowhand.
LP: 823 308-1
MC: 823 308-4
LP: 230 448 1

Smith, Johnny

FOURSOME VOL.2.
LP: . . . . FS 126

MOONLIGHT IN VERMONT (Smith, Johnny Quintet).
Tracks: / Where or when / Tabu / Moonlight in Vermont / Jaguar / Ghost of a chance, A / Vilia / My funny valentine / Sometimes I'm happy / Stars fell on Alabama / Nice work if you can get it / Tenderly / Cavu / I'll be around / Yesterdays / Cherokee / What's new / I'll remember april / Lullaby of birdland.
LP: . . . . FS 92

NEW QUARTET, THE.
LP: . . . . FS 127

Smith & Jones

ALAS SMITH AND JONES (From the TV series) (Smith, Mel & Griff Rhys-Jones).
LP: . . . . REB 527
MC: . . . . ZCF 527

BITTER AND TWISTED (Smith, Mel & Griff Rhys-Jones).
Tracks: / Bits we managed to get on side 1 / Rest, The.
LP: . . . . DIX 79
MC: . . . . CDIX 79

Smith, Keely

CAPITOL YEARS, THE: KEELY SMITH (Best of).
Tracks: / Sweet and lovely / Cocktails for two / Song is you, The / I'll get by / Lullaby of the leaves / On the sunny side of the street / I can't get started / I'll never smile again / S'posin' / East of the sun / All the way / I never knew / I wish you love / You go to my head / When your lover has gone / Fools rush in / Don't take your love from me / Imagination.
LP: . . . . EMS 1359
LP: 794 311 1
MC: . . . . TCEMS 1359
MC: 794 311 4

HEY BOY, HEY GIRL (see Prima, Louis) (Smith, Keely & Louis Prima).

LENNON & MCCARTNEY SONGBOOK.
LP: . . . . R 6142

POLITELY.
Tracks: / Sweet and lovely / Cocktails for two / Song is you, The / I'll get by / Lullaby of the leaves / On the sunny side of the street / I can't get started / I'll never smile again / S'posin' / East of the sun (and west of the moon) / All the way / I never knew (I could love anybody).
LP: . . . . T 1073

SWINGIN' PRETTY.
Tracks: / It's magic / It's been a long, long time / Stormy weather / Indian love call / Nearness of you, The / What is this thing called love? / Man I love, The / You're driving me crazy / Stardust / There will never be another you / Someone to watch over me / What can I say, after I say I'm sorry?.
LP: . . . . ED 2604231
MC: . . . . ED 2604234

WILDEST SHOW AT TAHOE, THE (see Prima, Louis) (Smith, Keely & Louis Prima).

Smith, Keith

BALL OF FIRE (Smith, Keith & Vic Dickenson).
Tracks: / Medi two / You're a lucky guy / I've got a feeling / After you've gone / Cherry Red rides again / Gee baby / Ball of fire / This one's for you, Lennie.
LP: . . . . HJ 103

GEORGE CHISHOLM/KEITH SMITH/ HEFTY JAZZ (see under Chisholm, George) (Smith, Keith/George Chisholm/ Hefty Jazz).

KEITH SMITH & ALTON PURNELL LIVE (Smith, Keith Band & Alton Purnell).
LP: . . . . 77 LEU 12/13

KEITH SMITH'S AMERICAN ALL-STARS IN EUROPE, 1966 (Smith, Keith & His American All-Stars).
Tracks: / Struttin' with some barbecue / Beale Street blues / Bugle boy / Melancholy blues / Panama rag / Royal Garden blues / See you kidder / Hindustan / Preaching / Shake it don't break it.
LP: . . . . HJ 102

KEITH SMITH'S HEFTY JAZZ.
LP: . . . . J 145

UP JUMPED THE BLUES (Smith, Keith, Chosen Five & Benny Waters).
LP: . . . . HJ 105

WAY DOWN YONDER IN NEW ORLEANS (Smith, Keith & Sammy Rimmington).
Tracks: / Down in the jungle town / Put a shine on your shoes / Black and blue / Way down yonder in New Orleans / Snag it / Ting a ling / Someday you'll be sorry / Memphis blues / Hymn for George / Struttin' with some barbecue.
LP: . . . . HJ 101

Smith, Kendell

NIGHTMARE ON DOWNING STREET.
LP: . . . . ARILP 047

TIME RUNNING OUT.
Tracks: / Blues get raid / Hustle / Unkonto we sizwe / It is time / Dry land tourist / Say what you like / Time running out.
LP: . . . . ARILP 036

Smith, Lacy

SIDELINES.
LP: . . . . IAI 37.38.47

Smith, Leo

CLASSIC COLE (see DeGaetani, Jan) (Smith, Leo & Jan DeGaetani).

DIVINE LOVE.
LP: . . . . ECM 1143

HUMAN RIGHTS.
LP: . . . . GRAMM 24

SPIRIT CATCHER.
LP: . . . . N 19

Smith, Little George

OOPIN' DOOPIN' DOOPIN'.
Tracks: / Telephone blues / Blues in the dark / Blues stay away / Rockin' / California blues / Oopin' doopin' doopin' / Cross-eyed Suzie Lee / You don't love me / Down in New Orleans / I found my baby / Love life / Have myself a ball.
LP: . . . . CH 60

Smith, Lonnie Liston

BEST OF LONNIE LISTON SMITH.
Tracks: / Quiet moments / Space princess / In the park / Give peace a chance / Fruit music / Gift of love / Journey into love.
LP: . . . . CBS 84348
MC: 40 84348

BEST OF LONNIE LISTON SMITH, THE.
Tracks: / Expansions / Love beams / Song of love / Meditations / Voodoo woman / Space lady / Starlight and you starbeams.
LP: . . . . PL 12897

DREAMS OF TOMORROW.
Tracks: / Lonely way to be / Mystic woman / Love I see in your eyes, The / Dreams of tomorrow / Never too late / Rainbows of love / Divine light / Garden of peace.
LP: . . . . ASLP 1000
MC: . . . . ZCAS 1000

EXPANSIONS (ALBUM).
Tracks: / Expansions / Dessert nights / Summer days / Voodoo woman / Peace / Shadows / My love.
LP: . . . . NL 80934
MC: . . . . NK 80934

GOTCHA.
Tracks: / Sweet honey wine / I need your love / What's done is done / Do it / Journey to within / My Latin sky.
LP: . . . . TKR 83356

LOVE GODDESS.
Tracks: / Love goddess / Obsession / Heaven / Monk's mood / Star flower / Giving you the best that I've got / Don't write cheques that your body can't cash / Dance floor / I'm your melody (Only on cassette and CD.) / Blue in green (Only on cassette and CD.) / Blue Bossa (Only on cassette and CD.) / Child is born, A (Only on cassette and CD.).
LP: . . . . STA 4021
MC: . . . . STAMC 4021

LOVE IS THE ANSWER.
Tracks: / In the park / Love is the answer / Speak about it / Bridge through time / On the real side / Enchantress / Give peace a chance / Free and easy.
LP: . . . . CBS 84365

LOVELAND.
Tracks: / Sunburst / Journey into love / Floating through space / Bright moments / We can dream / Springtime magic / Loveland / Explorations.
LP: 82837

REJUVENATION.
LP: . . . . ASLP 810
MC: . . . . ZCAS 810

RENAISSANCE.
Tracks: / Space lady / Mardi gras / Starlight and you / Mongotee / Song of love / Between here and there / Renaissance.
LP: . . . . PL 11822

SILHOUETTES.
Tracks: / Warm / If you take care of me I'll take care of you / Silhouettes / Summer afternoon / Enlightenment / City of lights / Once again love / Just us two.
LP: . . . . ASLP 805
MC: . . . . ZCAS 805

SONG FOR THE CHILDREN.
Tracks: / Song for the children / Lover's dream / Aquarian cycle / Street festival / Midsummer magic / Nightlife / Gift of love / Fruit music.
LP: 83809

THINK.
Tracks: / Son of Ice Bag / Call of the wild / Think / Three blind mice / Slouchin'.
LP: . . . . BST 84290
LP: 784 290 1

Smith, Louis

LOUIS SMITH QUINTET (Smith, Louis Quintet).
LP: . . . . SCS 1096

PRANCIN'.
LP: . . . . SCS 1121

Smith, Mack Allen

GOTTA ROCK TONIGHT.
Tracks: / Gotta rock tonight / You got me running / My baby left me / Shake your moneymaker / Hobo man / Skeleton fight / Mean old Frisco / Treat me nice / If I could only get one hit / Hey Clyde / Tulsa time / Who the heck is Bob Willis? / Memphis / You ain't nothin' but the best / Ain't got no business doin' business today / Rag mama / Flip flop and fly.
LP: . . . . CR 30201

SOUND OF MACK ALLEN SMITH.
LP: . . . . REDITA 105

Smith, Mamie

CRAZY BLUES.
Tracks: / That thing called love / You can't keep a good man down / Crazy blues / It's right here for you / Fare thee honey blues / Road is rocky, The / Mem'ries of you mammy / If you don't want me blues / Don't care blues / Lovin' Sam from Alabam / Jazzbo Ball / What have I done / Frankie blues / "U" need some loving blues / Dangerous blues / Daddy, your mama is lonesome for you.
LP: . . . . **OFF 6037**

GOIN' CRAZY WITH THE BLUES.
LP: . . . . **DLP 555**

MAMIE SMITH VOL.1 (Crazy blues).
LP: . . . . **DLP 551**

MAMIE SMITH VOL.2 (Get hot).
LP: . . . . **DLP 552**

MAMIE SMITH VOL.3 (Mamie Smith blues 1922).
LP: . . . . **DLP 553**

MAMIE SMITH VOL.4 (First lady of the blues).
LP: . . . . **DLP 554**

Smith, Mandy

MANDY.
LP: . . . . **HF 2**
MC: . . . . **HFC 2**

Smith, Margo

BEST OF THE TENNESSEE YODELLER.
Tracks: / Way it used to be, The / Take my breath away / Cowboy yodel song / Lovesick blues / Waitin' and Needin' (drives me crazy) / Hand clappin' foot stompin' country / Tenessee yodellers / My weakness / Chime bells / Indian love call / Ridin' high / Wedding bells / I want to be our cowboy sweetheart.
LP: . . . . **MCL 1838**
MC: . . . . **CLC 1838**

MARGO SMITH.
Tracks: / Don't break my heart that loves you / Still a woman / Love's explosion / If I give my heart to you / It only hurts for a little while / Little things mean a lot / Paper lovin' / Shuffle song / There I said it / Save your kisses for me.
LP: . . . . **IMCA 39048**

Smith, Marvin

KEEPER OF THE DRUMS.
Tracks: / Just have fun / Miss Ann / Love will find a way / Song of joy / Creeper, The / Now I know / Thinking of you / Simple samba song, A.
LP: . . . . **CJ 325**
MC: . . . . **CJC 325**

ROAD LESS TRAVELLED, THE (Smith, Marvin 'Smitty').
Tracks: / Neighbourhood, The / Wish you were here with me part 1 / Gothic 17 / Road less travelled, The / I'll love you always / Salsa blue / Concerto in B.G. / Wish you were here with me part 2.
LP: . . . . **CJ 379**
MC: . . . . **CJ 379C**

Smith, Mel

SCRATCH 'N' SNIFF (Smith, Mel & Griff Rhys-Jones).
Tracks: / I spy / Antiques roadshow / Hooligans / Drugs / Video nasties / Meryl Streep / Autumn / Richard Branson / Christmas / Bob Geldof / V.D. / Mia Farrow / Aids / Taboos / Perverts / Animals / Senior citizens / Rigor mortis / Marvellous marvellous / Sex.
LP: . . . . **DIX 51**
MC: . . . . **CDIX 51**

Smith, Michael

AUSTIN STREAM (Smith, Michael Quartet).
LP: . . . . **SAJ 09**

LA MUSIQUE BLANCHE.
LP: . . . . **LDY 74601**

LOVE STORIES.
LP: . . . . **FF 461**

MI CYAAN BELIEVE IT.
LP: . . . . **ILPS 9717**
MC: . . . . **ICT 9717**

REFLECTION ON PROGRESS.
LP: . . . . **SLP 1006**
LP: . . . . **SLP 4014**

Smith, Michael W

BIG PICTURE.
LP: . . . . **RRA R 0009**
MC: . . . . **RRA C 0009**

CHRISTMAS (Smith, Michael W/ Hollywood Presby. Choir/American Boys Choir).
Tracks: / Sing, choirs of angels / Lux venit (The Light comes) / Arise, shine, for your light has come / Anthem for Christmas / First snowfall (instrumental) / Christ the Messiah / No eye had seen / All is well / Memoirs (instrumental: The voice/Good King Wenceslas/Hark, the Herald Angels sing) / Gloria (rock version of Angels we have heard on high) / Silent night.
LP: . . . . **RRA R 0052**
MC: . . . . **RRA C 0052**

GO WEST YOUNG MAN.
LP: . . . . **RRAR 0063**
MC: . . . . **RRAC 0063**

SING UNTO HIM.
Tracks: / How majestic is your name / Friends / Jude doxology / Great is the Lord / Hosanna / Stubborn love.
LP: . . . . **WST R 8978**
MC: . . . . **WST C 8978**

Smith, Mike

IT'S ONLY ROCK'N'ROLL.
LP: . . . . **RNR 100**

Smith, O.C

COLLECTION: O.C. SMITH.
Tracks: / Honey / That's life / Son of Hickory Holler's tramp / Moody / Me and you / Together / Simple life / Primrose Lane / Pretending / Love song / Empty hearts / Little green apples / You and I / Sweet loveliness.
2LP: . . . . **PDA 068**

HICKORY HOLLER REVISITED.
LP: . . . . **CBS 63362**

Smith, Patti

DREAM OF MY LIFE.
Tracks: / People have the power / Going under / Up there, down there / Paths that cross / Dream of life / Where duty calls / Looking for you (I was) / Jackson song, The.
LP: **209172**
MC: **409172**

EASTER.
Tracks: / Till victory / Space monkey / Because the night / Ghost dance / Babelogue / Rock 'n' roll nigger / Privilege / We three / 25th floor / Easter / Break it up / High on rebellion.
LP: . . . . **FA 3058**
MC: . . . . **TCFA 3058**
LP: . . . . **SPART 1043**

HORSES.
Tracks: / Gloria / Redondo beach / Birdland / Free money / Break it up / Land / Elegie / Kimberely / Land-horses / Land of a thousand dances / La mer.
LP: . . . . **ARTY 122**
LP: **201 112**
MC: **401 112**

NEVER ENOUGH.
Tracks: / Never enough / Downtown train / Give it time / Call to heaven / River cried, The / Isn't it enough / Sue Lee / Tough love / Heartache heard round the world.
LP: **4500751**
MC: **4500754**

RADIO ETHIOPIA.
Tracks: / Ask the angels / Ain't it strange / Poppies / Pissing in the river / Pumping (my heart) / Distant fingers / Radio Ethiopia / Abyssinia.
LP: . . . . **SPARTY 1001**
MC: . . . . **TCSPARTY 1001**
LP: **201117**
MC: **401 117**

WAVE.
Tracks: / Frederick / Dancing barefoot / Citizen ship / Hymn revenge / Seven ways of going / Broken flag / Wave / So you want to be a rock 'n' roll star.
LP: . . . . **SPART 1086**
MC: . . . . **TCART 1086**
LP: **201 139**
MC: **401 139**

Smith, Paul

ART TATUM TOUCH, VOL.1, THE.
Tracks: / Yesterdays / Baubles and beads / Humoresque / Blue skies / Over the rainbow / Nice work if you can get it / Poor butterfly / Tangerine / I only have eyes for you / You and the night and the music.
MC: . . . . **OUTSTANDING 4**

AT HOME.
Tracks: / Girl from Ipanema, The / Bernie's tune / Cheek to cheek / Wave / I'm beginning to see the light / Cherokee.
MC: . . . . **OUTSTANDING 22**

BALLAD TOUCH, THE.
Tracks: / Marguerite / Nadia's theme / There will never be another you / My funny Valentine / Brian's song / Misty / I write the songs / Evergreen / Body and soul.
MC: . . . . **OUTSTANDING 3**

GARNERING THE BLUES.
Tracks: / Darktown stutters' ball / Blue moon / I got rhythm / Mood indigo / St. Louis blues / You are the sunshine of my life / Mack the knife / Honeysuckle rose / Swanee River.
MC: . . . . **OUTSTANDING 51**

HEAVY JAZZ, VOL. 1.
Tracks: / Lover / You are too beautiful / Pick yourself up / I got rhythm / 'S wonderful / Foggy day, A / What is this thing called love.
MC: . . . . **OUTSTANDING 9**

HEAVY JAZZ, VOL. 3.
Tracks: / Love for sale / Samba de Orfeo / Cute / I'll remember April / Take the 'A' train / Lady is a tramp / Tenderly.
MC: . . . . **OUTSTANDING 11**

INTROSPECTIVE.
Tracks: / How long has this been going on / You'd be so nice to come home to / Slow blues / Artie Shaw's moonray / Jeepers creepers / Little girl blue / I remember you / Huntington beach / Give me the simple life / Beecher boogie.
MC: . . . . **OUTSTANDING 52**

LIVE AND LEARN.
LP: . . . . **DAY R 4039**
MC: . . . . **DAY C 4039**

LIVE JAM SESSIONS AT THE HAIG (Smith, Paul & Various Artists).
LP: . . . . **JAM 102**

MASTER TOUCH, THE.
Tracks: / On Green Dolphin Street / Around the world in eighty days / I could have danced all night / Fourth way, The / Here's that rainy day / Alone together / Get me to the Church on time / Lullabye of the leaves / Black Orpheus / Waltz of the time / When the world was young / All the things you are.
MC: . . . . **OUTSTANDING 2**

MYSTERIOUS BARRICADES.
LP: . . . . **FF 264**

NO FRILLS.
LP: . . . . **DAY R 4157**
MC: . . . . **DAY C 4157**

PHANTOM MEETS THE WIZARD, THE (Golden Anniversary Album).
Tracks: / Over the rainbow / Angel of music / Ding dong the witch is dead / Think of me / Phantom of the Opera / Merry old land of Oz / Music of the night / If I only had a brain / Point of no return / We're off the see the wizard / Prima Donna / All I ask of you.
MC: . . . . **OUTSTANDING 50**

SOFTLY BABY (Smith, Paul Quartet).
Tracks: / Softly / Taking a chance on love / Easy to love / Long live Phineas / I didn't know what time it was / I'll remember April / Invitation / I got rhythm / Man I love, The / Blues a la' P.T.
LP: . . . . **JAS 311**
MC: . . . . **JAS C311**

THIS ONE COOKS.
Tracks: / Laura / How high the moon / Meditation / Soon / It's only a paper moon / Cumana / Love come back to me / Autumn leaves.
MC: . . . . **OUTSTANDING 12**

Smith, Phoebe

I AM A ROMANY (Smith, Phoebe & Family).
Tracks: / Blackberry fold / Young Ellender / Captain Thunderbolt / Moll Varden / Oxford girl / Blacksmith courted me, A / Riddle song / Higher Germanie / Step dance tunes / Hopping song, the / Jolly herring.
MC: **60-100**

ONCE I HAD A TRUE LOVE.
Tracks: / Once I had a true love / Blacksmith courted me, A / Young Ellender / Molly Vaughan / Tanyard side, The / Yellow handkerchief, The / Wexport girl, The / Poor little maiden, The.
LP: **12T 193**

Smith, Ray

COUNTRY SIDE, THE.
Tracks: / It wasn't easy / Thank you love / Lucille / Without you / Oh Danny boy / Light the candles / How's his memory doing today / Walking into your life / One hand on the bottle and one foot in the grave / She's pulling me back again / Kaw-liga.
LP: . . . . **CR 30175**

I'M RIGHT BEHIND YOU BABY.
Tracks: / Break up / So young / Right behind you baby / Life is the flower / You made a hit / Forever yours / Little girl / Shake around / Why why why / Willing and ready / I want to be free / Sail away / Two pennies and a string / Rockin' bandit.
LP: . . . . **SUNLP 1009**

IT'S GREAT, IT'S RAY SMITH.
LP: **75.002**

RARE ITEM THE ROCKIN' BANDITS.
LP: . . . . **REV 3004**

ROCKIN' IN GERMANY.
LP: . . . . **RLP 003**

SOUTH SIDE STRUT - A TRIBUTE TO DON EWELL.
LP: . . . . **SOS 1162**

Smith, Rex

CAMOUFLAGE.
Tracks: / Camouflage / New Romeo / In the heat of the night / Don't talk / Get it right / Love with a perfect stranger / Real love / Tears / Two hearts / Roll me.
LP: . . . . **CBS 25343**
MC: **40 25343**

EVERLASTING LOVE.
Tracks: / Love will always make you cry / Still thinking of you / Everlasting love / Rock me slowly / What becomes of the brokenhearted / Remember the love songs / Don't go believin' / Oh girl.
LP: . . . . **CBS 85223**

SOONER OR LATER.
Tracks: / You take my breath away / Sooner or later / Simply Jessie / Love street / Better than it's ever been before / Never gonna give you up / Sway / Oh what a night for romance / Ain't that peculiar / If you think you know how to love me.
LP: . . . . **CBS 83688**

Smith, Richard

PREMIUM BLUES (Smith, Richard Band).
Tracks: / Boat of brass / Doctor Seuss (genius) / Wild Bill Hickock / Pick turned blue / Paper flies / Pick a pocket / Funny G-1 / Middle aged man.
LP: . . . . **BSL 1201**

Smith, Richard Jon

RICHARD JON SMITH.
Tracks: / Stay with me tonight / Don't go walking out that door / Baby's got another.
LP: . . . . **HIP 5**
MC: . . . . **HIPC 5**

Smith, Ronald

BEETHOVEN ON ORIGINAL INSTRUMENTS (See under Beethoven for full details).

Smith, Russell

BOY NEXT DOOR.
LP: **1A 064 24015 1**

Smith Sisters

BLUEBIRD.
LP: . . . . **FF 328**

MOCKINGBIRD.
LP: . . . . **FF 370**

Smith, Slim

DANCE HALL CONNECTION.
LP: . . . . **WENLP 3021**

EVERYBODY NEEDS LOVE (LP).
LP: . . . . **PMLP 3228**

JUST A DREAM.
LP: . . . . **PMLP 3242**

MEMORIAL.
Tracks: / Sitting in the park / Beatitude, The / My conversation / Time has come, The / Will you still love me?.
LP: . . . . **TBL 198**

TIME HAS COME THE.
LP: . . . . **PMLP 3240**

Smith St Society

TAKE ME TO THE LAND OF JAZZ.
LP: . . . . **GHB 208**

Smith, Steve

VITALIVE.
LP: . . . . **VBR 20511**
MC: . . . . **VBR 20514**

Smith, Steven

STEVEN SMITH & FATHER & 16 GREAT SONGS (Smith, Steven & Father).
LP: . . . . **SKL 5128**

Smith, Stuff

DESERT SANDS.
Tracks: / Desert sands / Soft winds / Things ain't what they used to be / It don't mean a thing / Time and again / I know that you know.
LP: **2304 536**

LIVE AT MONTMARTRE.
LP: . . . . **SLP 4142**

LIVE IN PARIS 1965.
LP: . . . . **FC 120**

STUFF SMITH & ONYX CLUB ORCHESTRA (Smith, Stuff & His Onyx Club Orchestra).
LP: . . . . **CC 12**

STUFF SMITH TRIO 1943 (Smith, Stuff Trio).
LP: . . . . **CLP 132**

SWINGIN' STUFF (Smith, Stuff Quartet).
Tracks: / Bugle blues / Only time will tell / C jam blues / One o'clock jump / My blue Heaven / Blues for Timmy.
LP: . . . . **SLP 4087**

TOWN HALL CONCERT 1945 (See Coleman, Bill) (Smith, Stuff & Bill Coleman).

VARSITY SESSION THE VOLUME 2 (Smith, Stuff & His Orchestra).
LP: SLP 703

VIOLINS NO END (see Grappelli, Stephane) (Smith, Stuff & Stephane Grappelli).

Smith, Sydney Goodsir

DEVIL'S WALTZ, THE.
LP: CCA 8

Smith, Tab

I DON'T WANT TO PLAY IN YOUR KITCHEN.
LP: BP 503

JOY AT THE SAVOY.
LP: BP 509

WORLD'S GREATEST ALTOIST - THESE FOOLISH THINGS.
Tracks: / I can't believe that you're in love with me / It's no sin / Spider rock / My baby / Cherry / Slow and easy / Seven up / Moondream / These foolish things / T.G. blues / Love is a wonderful thing / Can't we take a chance / You belong to me / Ace high / Cottage for sale / All my life.
LP: BP 511

Smith, Terry

BRITISH JAZZ ARTISTS 2 (See under Lee, Tony) (Smith, Terry/ Tony Lee).

Smith, Tommy

GIANT STRIDES.
LP: GFM LP8001

PEEPING TOM.
Tracks: / New road, The / Follow your heart / Merry go round / Slip of the tongue / Interval time (CD only.) / Simple pleasures (CD only.) / Peeping Tom / Quiet picnic (CD only.) / Affairs, please / Harlequin / Boats and boxes (CD only.) / Biting at the apple / Baked air (CD only.).
LP: BLT 1002
LP: 794 335 1
MC: TCBLT 1002
MC: 794 335 4

STANDARDS.
Tracks: / Star eyes / Speak low / Sky lark / September song / Blacken blue / Mil dew / You've changed / My secret love / Night and day / My old flame / Julia / lover / Dream scapes (part 1) (CD and cassette only.) / Silent but deadly (Dream scapes part 4) (CD and cassette only.).
LP: BLT 1003
MC: TCBLT 1003

STEP BY STEP.
Tracks: / Ally the wallygator / Step by step / Ghosts / Pillowtalk / Time piece / Springtime / Freetime (CD only.) / Ever never land (CD only.).
LP: BLT 1001
MC: TCBLT 1001

Smith, Trixie

ST. LOUIS BLUES (see Smith, Bessie).

TRIXIE SMITH AND IDA COX (1924-26) (Smith, Trixie and Ida Cox).
MC: NEO 705

Smith, T.V.

CHANNEL FIVE.
Tracks: / Token of my love / Burning rain / Suit, The / Beautiful bomb.
LP: EXIT 5

LAST WORDS OF THE GREAT EXPLORER (Smith, T.V.'s Explorers).
Tracks: / I live for everything / Servant / Have fun / Walk away / Last words of the great explorer / Imagination / Easy way / Unwelcome guest / Perfect life.
LP: KRL 85087

Smith, W

TUBA TRIO VOL 1 (see under Rivers, Sam) (Smith, W & J Daley & Sam Rivers).

TUBA TRIO VOL 2 (See under Rivers, Sam) (Smith, W & J Daley & Sam Rivers).

TUBA TRIO VOL 3 (See under Rivers, Sam) (Smith, W & J Daley & Sam Rivers).

Smith, Warren

LAST DETAIL, THE.
Tracks: / Red cadillac and a black moustache / Book of broken hearts / That's why I sing in a honky tonk / Heartaches by the number / Blue suede shoes / I don't believe I'll fall in love today / Between the Devil and the deep blue sea / Rock 'n' roll Ruby / Ubangi stomp / Folsom Prison blues / Roll over Beethoven / Movin' on / Golden rocket medley / That's alright mama / Rhumba boogie.
LP: CRM 2026

LEGENDARY SUN PERFORMERS.
Tracks: / Red cadillac and a black moustache / Rock 'n' roll Ruby / Ubangi stomp / Miss Froggie / Got love if you want it / So long, I'm gone / Uranium rock / Dear John / Golden rocket / I like your kinda love / Sweet sweet girl / Tonight will be the last night / Who / I'd rather be safe than sorry / Black Jack David / Goodbye Mr. Love.
LP: CR 30132

MEMORIAL ALBUM.
Tracks: / Rock 'n' roll Ruby / Roll over Beethoven / Folsom Prison blues / Book of broken hearts / Movin' on / Rhumba boogie / Golden rocket / Ubangi stomp / Blue suede shoes / Between the Devil and the deep blue sea / Red cadillac and a black moustache / That's alright mama.
LP: MFM 001

REAL MEMPHIS ROCK & ROLL.
Tracks: / Rock 'n' roll Ruby / I'd rather be safe than sorry / Black Jack David / Ubangi stomp / So long I'm gone / Miss froggie / Got love if you want it / I fell in love / Goodbye Mr. Love / Sweet sweet girl / Tell me who / Tonight will be the last night / Darkest cloud, The / Who took my baby / Hank Snow medley / I couldn't take the chance / Dear John / Red cadillac and a black moustache / Stop the world / Do I love you / Uranium rock / I like your kind of love.
2LP: CDX 23

WARREN SMITH.
Tracks: / Who took my baby / Rock 'n' roll Ruby / Ubangi stomp / I got love if you want it / Uranium rock / Miss Froggie / Red cadillac and a black moustache / Black Jack David / Do I love you / I like your kinda love / Stop the world I'll jump off / So long I'm gone / Tell me who / Goodbye Mr. Love.
LP: SUNLP 1048

Smith, Wayne

SLENG TENG.
Tracks: / Under me sleng teng / In thing / Love don't love me / My Lord my God / Icky all over / E20 / Like a dragon / Hard to believe / Leave her for you / Walk like granny.
LP: GREL 91

SMOKERS SUPPER.
LP: UNKNOWN

WICKED IN A DANCE HALL.
MC: RRTGC 7785

YOUTHMAN SKANKING.
LP: DH 2005

Smith, Wilbur

BURNING SHORE, THE (Drake, Gabrielle).
MCSET: LFP 7310

DARK OF THE SUN, THE.
MCSET: CAB 301

GOLDEN FOX (See under Golden Fox) (Valentine, Anthony).

LEOPARD HUNTS IN DARKNESS, THE (Woodward, Edward).
MCSET: LFP 7194
MCSET: LFP 4171945

POWER OF THE SWORD (Drake, Gabrielle).
MCSET: LFP 7316

RAGE (Drake, Gabrielle).
MCSET: LFP 7332

TIME TO DIE, A (Valentine, Anthony).
MCSET: LFP 7496

Smith, Willie

TEA FOR TWO.
Tracks: / Morning after / I had a premonition / My heart is a heartless ring / I'm a heck of a guy / Flight of the jitterbug / St. Louis blues / I got it bad and that ain't good / Blue skies / How high the moon / Tea for two / Moon child.
LP: BLJ 8040

Smith, Willie the Lion

GRAND PIANO (DUETS) (Smith, Willie the Lion & Don Ewell).
Tracks: / I've found a new baby / Porter's love song, A / I would do anything for you / Some of these days / Just you, just me / Everybody loves my baby / Can't we be friends / You took advantage of me / Keepin' out of mischief now / Sweet Georgia Brown.
LP: 2004
LP: S 1228

HARLEM PIANO (Smith, Willie the Lion & Luckey Roberts).
LP: 1010 035

MEMOIRS OF WILLIE 'THE LION'.
Tracks: / Relaxin' / Sand dune / Alexander's ragtime band / Shine / That barbershop chord / Redhead / Where's my red red rose? / Blue skies / Nagasaki / Running wild / Diga diga doo / Got everything but you / Doin' the new low down / Love will find a way / I'm just wild about Harry / Memories of you / Porter's love song to a chambermaid, A / Old-fashioned love / Carolina shout / Keepin' out of mischief now / Sophisticated lady / Solitude / Portrait of the Duke / Satin doll / When it's sleepy time down South / Sheik of Araby, The / Keep your temper / Bring on the band / Old stamping ground / Harlem joys / Love remembers / I'm all out of breath / Tango a la Caprice / Sneakaway.
2LP: PL 43171

MEMORIAL.
2LP: 400021

ORIGINAL 14 PLUS TWO.
Tracks: / Morning air / Echoes of spring / Concentrating / Fading star / Passionette / Rippling waters / Sneakaway / Finger buster / What is there to say? / Between the Devil and the deep blue sea / Boy in the boat / Tea for two / I'll follow you / Stormy weather / Three keyboards / Lion and the lamb.
LP: 624591
LP: 6.25491

PORK AND BEANS.
Tracks: / Pork and beans / Moonlight cocktail / Spanish Venus / Junk man rag / Squeeze me / Love will find a way / I'm just wild about Harry / Memories of you / Alexander's ragtime band / All of me / Ain't misbehavin' / Man I love, The / Summertime / Ain't she sweet.
LP: BLP 30123

WILLIE 'THE LION' SMITH.
LP: GNPS 9011

WILLIE 'THE LION' SMITH VOL 1.
Tracks: / Echo of spring / Here comes the band / Relaxin' / Contrary motions / Zig zag / Twelfth Street rag / Late hours / Portrait of the Duke / Dardanella / Quand Madelon / Cuttin' out / Charleston / Carolina shout / I'm gonna ride the rest of the way.
LP: JR 113

WILLIE 'THE LION' SMITH VOL 2.
Tracks: / Darktown strutters' ball / Stormy weather / Get together blues / Nagasaki / Can you hear me? / Trains and planes / Pretty baby / Conversation on Park Avenue / Sweet Sue.
LP: JR 132

Smithereens

BEAUTY AND SADNESS.
LP: ENVLP 519

BLOW UP.
Tracks: / Top of the pops / Too much passion / Tell me when did things go so wrong / Evening dress / Get a hold of my heart / Indigo blues / Now and then / Girl in room 12 / Anywhere you are / Over and over again / It's alright / If you want the sun to shine.
LP: EST 2151
MC: TCEST 2151

ESPECIALLY FOR YOU.
LP: 32081 1
LPPD: SEAX 73258

GREEN THOUGHTS.
Tracks: / Only a memory / House we used to live in / Something new / World we know, The / Especially for you / Drown in my own tears / Deep black / Elaine / Spellbound / If the sun doesn't shine / Green thoughts.
LP: 3375 1
MC: 3375 4
LP: ENVLP 504
MC: TCENV 504

SMITHEREENS 11.
Tracks: / Girl like you, A / Blues before and after / Blue period / Baby be good / Room without a view / Yesterday girl / Cut flowers / William Wilson / Maria Elena / Kiss your tears away.
LP: ENVLP 1000
LP: 791 194 1
MC: TCENV 1000
MC: 791 194 4

Smiths

CASUAL (Interview Picture Disc).
LPPD: BAK 6015
MC: MBAK 6015

HATFUL OF HOLLOW.
Tracks: / William, it was really nothing / What difference does it make? / These things take time / This charming man / How soon is now? / Handsome devil / Hand in glove / Still ill / Heaven knows I'm miserable now / This night has opened my eyes / You've got everything now / Accept yourself / Girl afraid / Back to the old house / Reel around the fountain / Please, please, please let me get what I want.
LP: ROUGH 76
MC: ROUGHC 76

LOUDER THAN BOMBS.
Tracks: / Is it really so strange? / Sheila take a bow / Shoplifters of the world unite / Sweet and tender hooligan / Half a person / London / Panic / Girl afraid / Shakespeare's sister / William, it was really nothing / You just haven't earned it yet,baby / Heaven knows I'm miserable now / Ask / Golden light (Featuring Kirsty MacColl).
2LP: ROUGH 255
MC: ROUGHC 255
2LP: 925569 1

MEAT IS MURDER.
Tracks: / Headmaster ritual, The / Barbarism begins at home / Rusholme ruffians / I want the one I can't have / What she said / Nowhere fast / That joke isn't funny anymore / Well I wonder / Meat is murder.
LP: ROUGH 81
MC: ROUGHC 81

MUSIC AND MEDIA INTERVIEW PICTURE DISC.
LPPD: MM 1207

QUEEN IS DEAD, THE.
Tracks: / Frankly, Mr. Shankly / I Know it's over / Never had no one ever / Cemetery gates / Big mouth strikes again / Vicar in a tutu / There is a light that never goes out / Some girls are bigger than others / Queen is dead, The / Boy with the thorn in his side, The.
LP: ROUGH 96
MC: ROUGHC 96

RANK (Live LP, The).
Tracks: / Queen is dead, The / Panic / Vicar in a tutu / Ask / Rusholme ruffians / Marie's the side / What she said / Cemetery gates / London / Bigmouth strikes again / Draize.
LP: ROUGH 126
MC: ROUGHC 126

SMITHS: INTERVIEW PICTURE DISC.
LPPD: BAK 2013

SMITHS, THE.
LP: ROUGH 61
MC: ROUGHC 61
LP: 250651

STRANGEWAYS HERE WE COME.
LP: ROUGH 106
MC: ROUGHC 106

WORLD WON'T LISTEN, THE.
Tracks: / Panic / Ask / London / Big mouth strikes again / Shakespeare's sister / There is a light that never goes out / Shoplifters of the world unite / Boy with the thorn in his side, The / Asleep / Unloveable / Half a person / Stretch out and wait / That joke isn't funny anymore / You haven't earned it yet baby / Rubber ring / Oscillate wildly / Money changes everything(cassette only).
MC: ROUGHC 101
LP: ROUGH 101
LP: 4509781

Smoke

MY FRIEND JACK.
LP: MBT 5001

Smokehouse

LET'S SWAMP AWHILE.
Tracks: / It's goin' on / Braggin' 'bout your baby / Big mistake / Fork in the road / Sweet little woman / I didn't know / Poontang blues / Evil woman / Skin is back / Day Jack Frost killed Parson Brown, The.
LP: ICH 9003
MC: ICH 9003 MC

Smoken, Lauren

LAUREN SMOKEN.
Tracks: / Haven't I had enough / Rockabye baby / Smile / Gonna give love one more try / I need the money / Licence to love / Come to me / Cry wolf / Little boy dreams / Never learn to say goodbye.
LP: LOPL 502
MC: LOPC 502

Smokey Babe

HOTTEST BRAND GOIN'.
Tracks: / Now your man done gone / Something wrong with my machine / Long way from home / Melvanie blues / Ocean blues / Coon hunt / Hottest brand goin' / Insect blues / I'm goin' back to Mississippi / Locomotive blues / Boogy woogy rag / Cold, cold snow.
LP: CH 261

Smokey Joe

STEP IT UP & GO (Smokey Joe and Red Hadley).
LP: REDITA 130

Smokey & The Bandit

SMOKEY & THE BANDIT (Original Soundtrack) (Various artists).
LP: MCA 1673
MC: MCAC 1673

SMOKEY & THE BANDIT 2 (Original Soundtrack) (Various artists).
LP: MCA 37161

Smokey Valley Boys

SMOKEY VALLEY BOYS.
LP: ROUNDER 0029

Smokie

ALL FIRED UP.
LP: WAGLP 1
MC: WAGMC 1

BEST OF SMOKIE.
LP: STAR 2455
MC: STAC 2455

BOULEVARD OF BROKEN DREAMS.
Tracks: / Boulevard of broken dreams / Think about the night / Love take me away / Young hearts / Angelina / Falling apart / Sometimes you cry / Moving mountains / Stop rewind / Northern soul.
LP: WAGLP 2
MC: WAGMC 2

BRIGHT LIGHTS & BACK ALLEYS.
Tracks: / It's your life / I can't stay here tonight / Sunshine Avenue / Think of me / In the heat of the night / Needles and pins / No one could ever love you more / Dancer / Baby it's you / Walk right back.
LP: SRAK 530
MC: TC SRAK 530

CHANGING ALL THE TIME.
Tracks: / Don't play your rock 'n' roll to me / If you think you know how to love me / It's natural / Give it to me / We're flying high / Changing all the time / Julie / Take me in / Umbrella day / Back to Bradford.
MC: 411029

GREATEST HITS LIVE: SMOKIE.
LP: WAGLP 3
MC: WAGMC 3

MONTREUX ALBUM, THE.
LP: SRAK 6757

OTHER SIDE OF THE ROAD.
Tracks: / Other side of the road / Do to me / Belinda / Big fat mama / Don't take your love away this time / London is burning / Babe it's up to you / You don't care / All alone / I can't stop loving you / Too many pennies in hell / Samantha Elizabeth / San Francisco Bay.
LP: SRAK 539

SMOKIE/CHANGING ALL THE TIME.
LP: SRAK 517

SMOKIE'S GREATEST HITS.
Tracks: / If you think you know how to love me / Don't play your rock 'n' roll to me / Something's been making me blue / Wild wild angels / Baby it's you / I'll meet you at midnight / Living next door to Alice / Lay back in the arms of someone / It's your life / Needles and pins / For a few dollars more / Oh Carol / Mexican girl / Changing all the time.
LP: FA 41 3114 1
MC: FA 41 3114 4
LP: FA 3114
MC: TCFA 3114

SMOKIE'S HITS.
Tracks: / If you think you know how to love me / Don't play your rock'n'roll to me / Something's been making me blue / Wild wild angels / I'll meet you at midnight / Living next door to Alice / Lay back in the arms of someone / It's your life / Needles and pins / For a few dollars more / Oh Carol / Mexican girl / Take good care of my baby.
LP: SRAK 540

SOLID GROUND.
Tracks: / Jet lagged / I'm in love with you / Everything a man could need / My woman don't like rock'n'roll / Take good care of my baby / Rock'n'roll woman / Your love is so good for me / Long time coming / Melody goes on.
LP: SRAK 545

STRANGERS IN PARADISE.
Tracks: / Introduction / Love remains a stranger / Falling for you / Yesterday's dreams / Come on home / Can you feel my heartbeat / Two strangers falling / You'll be lonely tonight / Mirror mirror / Now it's too late / Long way from home / Strangers in paradise.
LP: SRAK 546

Smokin' Beats

SMOKIN' BEATS VOL.2A (Various artists).
LP: BLUELP 2

Smoky Babe

HOT BLUES.
LP: ARHOOLIE 2019

Smooth & Co

HALF STEPPIN'.
LP: MS 8

Smooth, Joe

PROMISED LAND.
Tracks: / Promised land / Oh so true / Inside my mind / Purple haze / Going down / Can't fake the feeling / He's all I need / I try / Perfect world.
LP: DJART 903
MC: ZCART 903

REJOICE.
LP: 466385 1
MC: 466385 4

Smooth Sax:

SMOOTH SAX: LATE NIGHT FAVOURITES Various artists (Various artists).
2LP: CR 5156
MCSET: CRT 5156

Smotherman, Michael

MICHAEL SMOTHERMAN.
Tracks: / Crazy in love / Green eyes / Magic wishes / Matter of time / Cold burn / If you think you're hurtin' me / Do I ever cross your mind / Fais do do / All the way down / Freedom's legacy.
LP: EPC 85010

Smothers, Smoky

SMOKY SMOTHERS 1960-1962.
Tracks: / I can't judge nobody / Come on rock little girl / Honey I ain't teasin' / You're gonna be sorry / Give it back / Smokey's lovesick blues / I ain't gonna be no monkey man no more / Midnight and day / I've been drinking muddy water / Crying tears / What am I going to do / Blind and dumb man blues / Way up in the mountains of kentucky / Case is closed / Hello little schoolgirl.
LP: KK 7406

Smurfs

MERRY CHRISTMAS WITH THE SMURFS.
LP: DULP 2
MC: ZCDUL 2

SMURF SONG, THE (see under Father Abraham) (Father Abraham).

SMURFING SING SONG.
Tracks: / You're a pink toothbrush / Smurfin' cowboy / Merry go round / Silly little song / Summertime / Smurf baby / Smurfing land / Smurf hop / When the smurfs / Little smurf boat / Come to the party / Smurf lullaby.
LP: SMURF R2
MC: KSMUC R2

SMURFS PARTY TIME.
LP: DULP 1
MC: ZCDUL 1

Smyth, Gilli

FAIRY TALES.
Tracks: / Wassilissa (Stories) / Three tongues (stories), The / Pied piper.
LP: CRL 5018

MOTHER.
Tracks: / I am a fool / Back to the womb / Mother / Shakti yone / Keep the children free / Prostitute poem (street version) / O.K. man this your world / Next time ragtime / Time of the goddess / Taliesin.
LP: CRL 5007

Snafu

IF YOU SWEAR, YOU'LL CATCH NO FISH.
LP: BYO 017

NO ONE ELSE WANTED TO PLAY.
LP: BYO 9

Snail

FLOW.
Tracks: / I've got a lady / Here with you / Love should flow / Threw it away / Letting go / Tonight / Rollin' in your love / Forever / Your bird can sing / Broke up, broke down.
LP: HLP 6005

Snake Corps

FLESH ON FLESH.
LP: CHIME 14

MORE THAN THE OCEAN.
LP: CHIME 112

SMOTHER EARTH.
LP: CHIME 0052

Snake Finger

AGAINST THE GRAIN.
LP: SN 8353

CHEWING HIDES THE SOUND.
LP: TORSO 40008
LP: V 2140

GREENER POSTURES.
LP: RIDE 5
LP: TORSO 40009

MANUEL OF ERRORS.
LP: TORSO 40010

NIGHT OF DESIRABLE OBJECTS.
LP: REDLP 78
MC: REDC 78

Snakepit Rebels

SNAKEPIT REBELS.
Tracks: / Snakepit rebels.
LP: FLC 5114

Snakes Of Shake

GRACELANDS AND THE NATURAL WOOD.
LP: SPRAY 106
MC: CSPRAY 106

SOUTHERN CROSS (ALBUM).
LP: TOBL 1

Snakeshead

KARATE MOVES.
LP: GNPS 2176
MC: GNP5 2176

Snap

WORLD POWER.
Tracks: / Power, The / Cult of snap / I'm gonna get you (to whom it may concern) / Mary had a little boy / Ooops up / Believe the hype / Witness the strength / Blase blase.
LP: 210789
MC: 410789

Snapdragons

DAWN RAIDS ON MORALITY.
Tracks: / Dole boys on futons / Silent world, The / Dead, The / No expectations / Life's a crack / Dreamtime / Man of her dreams, The / Dawn raids on morality / Closer / Hole in the stars, The.
LP: NTVLP 042
MC: NTVC 42

ETERNAL IN A MOMENT.
LP: NTVLP 054

Snapes, Martyn

MISSING FROM HOME.
Tracks: / Jimmy Jones / Vision on / Missing from home / Digging up the dirt / Eye to eye / Say it with passion / Hard luck story / Get out clause, The / HMV / Class of '99, The / Wasting kind, The.
LP: SLRZ 1050
MC: TCSLRZ 1050
LP: 794 626 1
MC: 794 626 4

Snapper

SHOTGUN BLOSSOM.
Tracks: / Shotgun blossom.
LP: ONLYLP 010
MC: ONLYMC 010

Snatch

SNATCH.
LP: WITCH 1

Snatch & The Poontangs

SNATCH AND THE POONTANGS.
LP: SNATCH 101

Sneakers

MOVIE STAR.
Tracks: / Movie star / Changes.
LP: LP 6

SNEAKER.
Tracks: / Don't let me in / More than just the two of us / One by one / Jaymes / In time / Get up, get out / Looking for someone like you / Millionaire / No more lonely days.
LP: HSLP 1

Sneaks Noyse

CHRISTMAS NOW IS DRAWING NEAR (See under Christmas Carols).

Sneaky Feelings

HARD LOVE STORIES.
LP: FNE 26

SENTIMENTAL EDUCATION.
LP: FNE 14

WAITING FOR TOUCHDOWN.
Tracks: / Better than before / Waiting for touchdown / Someone else's eyes / Strangers again / Wouldn't cry / Not to take sides / Throwing stones / Major Barbara / Strange and conflicting feelings... / Husband house / Won't change.
LP: FNUK 2

Sneetches

LIGHTS OUT WITH THE SNEETCHES.
Tracks: / I need someone / In my car / Lonelei / 54 hours / I don't expect her for you / Home again / No one knows / Only for a moment.
LP: KSLP 007

SOMETIMES THAT'S ALL WE HAVE.
LP: CRELP 43

Snell, Adrian

ALPHA & OMEGA (Film soundtrack) (See under Alpha & Omega) (Various artists).

LISTEN TO THE PEACE.
LP: DOVE 51

SOMETHING NEW UNDER THE SUN.
LP: DOVE 63

Snell, David

PURE GENIUS.
Tracks: / Secret love / All the things you are / I'm old fashioned / I want to be happy / Tea for two / More / Gone with the wind / Stella by starlight / Girls are made to love and kiss / Speak love / Here's that rainy day / Fiona.
LP: SIV 1109
MC: CSIV 1109

Snell, Nigel (author)

DAVIDS FIRST DAY AT SCHOOL.
MC: LL 41 8039 4

KATE VISITS THE DOCTOR.
MC: LL 41 8038 4

SUE LEARNS TO CROSS THE ROAD.
MC: LL 41 8041 4

Snidero, Jim

MIXED BAG (Snidero, Jim Quintet).
LP: CRISS 1032

Sniff 'N' The Tears

BEST OF SNIFF 'N' THE TEARS, A.
MC: WIKC 102

FICKLE HEART.
Tracks: / Driver's seat / New lines on love / Carve your name on my door / This side of the blue horizon / Sing / Rock and roll music / Fight for love / Thrill of it all / Slide away / Last dance / Looking for you.
LP: SNIP 1
LP: WIKM 9

GAMES UP, THE.
Tracks: / Game's up, The / Moment of weakness / What can daddy do / Night life / If I knew then / One love / Five & zero / Poison pen mail / Rodeo drive.
LP: SNIP 2

LOVE/ACTION.
Tracks: / Driving beat, The / Put your money where your mouth is / Snow white / For what they promise / Without love / Steal my heart / That final love / Don't frighten me / Love action / Shame.
LP: SNIP 3

RETROSPECTIVE.
Tracks: / Drivers seat / Hungry eyes / Shame / One love / Bagatelle / New lines on love / Ride blue divide / Snow white / Poison pen mail / Love / Action / Rodeo drive.
LP: TONE 1

RIDE BLUE DIVIDE.
Tracks: / Hand of fate, The / Hungry eyes / Roll the weight away / Like wildfire / Trouble is my business / You may find your heart / Gold / Ride blue divide / Company man.
LP: TOSS 3

Snipers

ALLIGATOR.
LP: ROSE 77

BIS.
LP: ROSE 29

OPEN THE ATTACK.
LP: MEGATON 0013

QUICK AND DEAD.
LP: MEGATON 0012

Snips

LA ROCCA.
Tracks: / Police car / Happy sometimes / Tight shoes / Work / Telepathy / What is pop / Nine o'clock / La Rocca / Skies of England / Rain / Dark outside / Backs of millions.
LP: EMC 3359

Snitchnose Switch

SNITCHNOSE SWITCH (See under Bangers & Mash).

Snoopy

SNOOPY (Original New York cast) (Various artists).
LP: DRG 6103

SNOOPY (Original London cast) (Various artists).
Tracks: / Snooper (Overture): *Various artists* / World according to Snoopy, The: *Various artists* / Snoopy's song: *Various artists* / Woodstock's theme: *Various artists* / Hurry up face: *Various artists* / Edgar Allan Poe: *Various artists* / Mothers day: *Various artists* / I know now: *Various artists* / Vigil, The: *Various* artists / Clouds: *Various artists* / Where did that little dog go?: *Various artists* / Dime a dozen: *Various* artists / Daisy hill: *Various artists* / When do the good things happen: *Various artists* / Great writer, The: *Various artists* / Poor sweet baby: *Various artists* / Don't be anything less than everything you can: *Various* artists / Big bow-wow, The: *Various artists* / Just one person: *Various artists* / Snoopy (Finale): *Various artists*.
LP: TER 1073
MC: ZCTER 1073

Snow, Hank

20 OF THE BEST: HANK SNOW.
Tracks: / I'm movin' on / Golden rocket / Rhumba boogie / Music makin' Mama from Memphis / Gold rush is over, The / Lady's man / Gal who invented kissin',

The / Fool such as I, A / Spanish fireball / When Mexican Joe met Jole Blon / I don't hurt anymore / Let me go lover / Would you mind / Last ride, The / Miller's cave / Beggar to a king / I've been everywhere / Man who robbed the bank at Santa Fe, The / Ninety miles an hour / Hello love.
LP: . . . . **NL 89422**
MC: . . . . **NK 89422**
LP: . . . . **INTS 5213**

AWARD WINNERS.
Tracks: / Sunday mornin' comin' down / I threw away the rose / Ribbon of darkness / No one will ever know / Just bidin' my time / Snowbird / (The seashores of) Old Mexico / Me and Bobby McGee / For the good times / Gypsy feet.
LP: . . . . **LSA 3057**

BEST OF HANK SNOW.
Tracks: / I'm movin' on / Rhumba boogie, The / Let me go, lover / With this ring, I thee wed / Music makin' mama from Memphis / Millers' Cave / I don't hurt anymore / Golden rocket / Bluebird Island / I've been everywhere / (Now and then, there's) a fool such as I / Ninety miles an hour (down a dead end street).
LP: . . . . **LSA 3022**

COUNTRY CLASSICS.
LP: . . . . **HAT 3084**
MC: . . . . **HATC 3084**

COUNTRY MUSIC HALL OF FAME.
Tracks: / Nobody's child / Beggar to a king / Governor's hand / Get on my love train / My Filipino rose / Gloryland march, The / Somewhere someone is waiting for you / Friend / You're wondering why / Blind boy / What more can I say / Tears in the trade winds / He dropped the world in my hands / Poor little Jimmie / Down at the pawnshop / What then / Crashing rolling thunder in my mind / Wild flower / Listen / Who's been here since I've been gone.
LP: . . . . **PL 43349**

FAMOUS COUNTRY MUSIC MAKERS - HANK SNOW.
Tracks: / Letter edged in black / Old Shep / Prisoner's prayer, The / Drunkard's child, A / Don't make me go to bed and I'll be good / Convict and the rose, The / Put my little shoes away / Little buddy / There's a little box of pine on the 7.29 / Nobody's child / I'm here to get my baby out of jail / Prisoner's song, The / Colour song, The / Answer to Little Blossom, The / There's a star spangled banner waving / Walking the last mile / Old Rover / Prisoner's dream, The / Put your arms around me / Your little band of gold / Rocking alone in an old rocking chair / Mother I thank you for the Bible you gave / Little Joe.
2LP: . . . . **DPS 2023**

FAMOUS COUNTRY MUSIC MAKERS - HANK SNOW (Volume 2).
Tracks: / I'm movin' on / I've forgotten you / Honeymoon on a rocketship / In an 18th century drawing room / It's only you (only you, that I love) / I just telephone upstairs / Jimmie the kid / Why did you give me your love / When Jimmie Rodgers said goodbye / Ben Dewberry's final run / Mystery of number five, The / Golden rocket / How to play the guitar / Let's pretend / No longer a prisoner / On that old Hawaiian shore with you / Silver bells / Goldrush is over, The / First nighters, The / Old spinning wheel, The / Star spangled waltz / Gal who invented kissin', The / I never will marry / Down the trail of aching hearts.
LP: . . . . **DPS 2057**

HITS OF HANK SNOW.
Tracks: / North to Chicago / Come the morning / Hijack / That's you and me / Merry go round of love / Easy to love / I just wanted to know (how the wind was) / Name of the game was love, The / Late and great love (of my heart), The / Colorado country morning / Vanishing breed / Rome wasn't built in a day / Hello love / Who will answer (Aleluya No. 1).
LP: . . . . **PL 42175**
MC: . . . . **PK 42175**

HITS OF HANK SNOW.
LP: **26 21718**
MC: **2421718**

JUST KEEP A-MOVIN'.
Tracks: / Just keep a-movin' / Music makin' mama from Memphis / Bill is falling due, The / Can't have you blues / Scale to measure love, A / Cryin', prayin', waitin', hopin' / I can't control my heart / Love's game of let's pretend / My Arabian baby / Blue sea blues / Caribbean / Blossoms in the springtime / Chattin' with a chick in Chattanooga / I'm glad I got to see you once again / Cuba rhumba / Owl and I, The.
LP: . . . . **DT 33004**

OLD DOC BROWN AND OTHER NARRATIONS.
Tracks: / Old Doc Brown / That pioneer mother of mine / Blind boy / What is a father / Horse's prayer, the / Lazybones / How to play the guitar / Little britches / First nighters, the / Trouble, trouble, trouble / What do I know today.
LP: . . . . **HAT 3066**
MC: . . . . **HATC 3066**

RAILROAD MAN.
Tracks: / Waiting for a train / Big wheels / Last ride, The / Streamlined canon ball, The / Ghost trains / Pan American / Southbound / 'Way out there / Chattanooga choo choo / Wreck of the number nine, The / Lonesome whistle / Crazy engineer, The.
LP: . . . . **NL 90003**
MC: . . . . **NK 90003**

Snow Mountain

SNOW MOUNTAIN (see Gavin, Catherine) (Hood, Morag).

Snow, Phoebe

AGAINST THE GRAIN.
Tracks: / Every night / Do right woman, dor right man / He's not just another man / Random time / In my life / You have not won / Mama don't break down / Oh L.A. / Married men / Keep a watch on the shoreline.
LP: . . . . **CBS 82915**

BEST OF PHOEBE SNOW.
Tracks: / Two fisted love / All over / Poetry man / Teach me tonight / Don't let me down / Shaky ground / Love makes a woman / Never letting go / Every night / Harpo's blues.
LP: . . . . **CBS 32643**
MC: **40 32643**
LP: . . . . **CBS 84909**

IT LOOKS LIKE SNOW.
Tracks: / Autobiography / Teach me tonight / Stand up on the rock / In my girlish days / Mercy on those / Don't let me down / Drink up the melody / Fat chance / My faith is blind / Shakey ground.
LP: . . . . **CBS 81714**

ROCK AWAY.
Tracks: / Cheap thrills / Baby please / Gasoline Alley / Rock away / Mercy, mercy, mercy / Games / Down in the basement / Shoo-rah-shoo-rah / Something good / I believe in you / Two fisted love / All over / Poetry man / Teach me tonight / Don't let me down / Shakey ground / Love makes a woman / Never letting go / Every night / Harpo's blues.
LP: . . . . **K 50780**
MC: **K4 50780**

SOMETHING REAL.
Tracks: / Mr. Wondering / Touch your soul / I'm your girl / Soothin' / Cardiac arrest / Something real / We might never feel this way / If I can just get through the night / Best of my love.
LP: . . . . **EKT 56**
MC: . . . . **EKT 56 C**

SOMETIMES LOVE FORGETS (See under Goodman, Steve) (Goodman, Steve & Phoebe Snow).

Snow Queen (bk)

SNOW QUEEN (Various artists).
MC: . . . . **TS 313**

SNOW QUEEN (Film Soundtrack) (Various artists).
LP: . . . . **FA 920**

SNOW QUEEN (Matthew, Pamela).
LP: . . . . **TMP 9004**
MC: **TMP4 9004**

SNOW QUEEN, THE (see Andersen, Hans Christian) (Andersen, Hans Christian).

SNOW QUEEN, THE (A fairy tale) (Makarova, Natalia).
MC: **13491 6004 4**

SNOW QUEEN, THE (well loved tales up to age 9) (Unknown narrator(s)).
MC: . . . . **PLB 111**

SNOW QUEEN, THE (Nesbitt, Cathleen).
MC: **1229**

Snow Spider (bk)

SNOW SPIDER, THE (See also Jenny Nimmo) (Asher, Jane (nar)).

Snow Tiger (bk)

SNOW TIGER, THE (Desmond Bagley) (Davenport, Nigel (nar)).
MCSET: . . . . **CAB 302**

Snow White (bk)

SNOW WHITE (Various artists).
MC: . . . . **ANV 619**

SNOW WHITE AND ROSE RED (well loved tales age up to 9).
MC: . . . . **PLB 71**

SNOW WHITE AND THE SEVEN DWARFS (Original Soundtrack) (Various artists).
LP: . . . . **WD 001**
MC: . . . . **WDC 001**

SNOW WHITE AND THE SEVEN DWARFS (Film Soundtrack) (Various artists).
Tracks: / Overture: *Various artists* / I'm wishing: *Various artists* / One song: *Various artists* / With a smile and a song: *Various artists* / Whistle while you work: *Various artists* / Heigh ho: *Various artists*/ Buddle-uddle-ud-dum: *Various artists* / Silly song: *Various artists* / Some day my prince will come: *Various artists* / Finale: *Various artists.*
LP: . . . . **REC 539**
MC: . . . . **ZCM 539**

SNOW WHITE AND THE SEVEN DWARFS (well loved tales age up to 9).
Tracks: / Snow White and the seven dwarfs / Water of life, The / Little people / Goose girl, The / King wren.
MC: . . . . **TS 316**
MC: . . . . **PLB 72**
LP: . . . . **D 3906**
LPPD: . . . . **D 3101**
MLP: . . . . **D 310**
MC: . . . . **D 1DC**

SNOW WHITE AND THE SEVEN DWARFS.
MC: . . . . **DIS 001**

SNOW WHITE AND THE SEVEN DWARFS.
MC: . . . . **STK 001**

SNOW WHITE & OTHER FAIRY TALES (Brothers Grimm) (Bloom, Claire (nar)).
MC: **1266**

Snowboy

DECARGO MAMBIT.
LP: . . . . **JAZIDLP 040**

RITMO SNOWBOY (LP).
LP: . . . . **JAZIDLP 19**

Snowden, Elmer

JAZZ COLLECTION VOL. 12.
LP: . . . . **IAJRC 12**

Snowden, Jean

DAY OF MIRACLES (Snowden, Jean & Les).
Tracks: / Day of miracles / Nothing is impossible / One yielded life / Hiding place / Happiness is the Lord / Moment of truth, The / Give him your heart / Lovely is his name / Cross every ocean / Oh, he's so wonderful / Thirty pieces of silver / Worthy is the lamb.
LP: . . . . **PC 799**

Snowman

SNOWMAN, THE (Film Soundtrack & Story) (Cribbins, Bernard (nar)).
LP: . . . . **CBS 71116**
MC: **40 71116**

Snowmen

HOKEY COKEY THE ALBUM.
Tracks: / Superman / Agadoo / Birdie song, The / Let's twist again / Rock around the clock / Hokey cokey / Snowball / Ice dance / Walkin' with my angel / What do you want to make those eyes at me for / Simple Simon / March of the Mods / Can-can.
LP: . . . . **SGLP 1**
MC: . . . . **SGC 1**

Snowy Red

BEAT IS OVER, THE.
LP: . . . . **ANT 116**

COMPILATION, THE 1980-4.
LP: . . . . **ANT 098**

SNOWY RED.
LP: . . . . **DIRTY DANCE 12002**

VISION.
LP: . . . . **SW 12003**

Snuff

SNUFF SAID.
LP: . . . . **PLAYLP 10**
MC: . . . . **PLAYMC 10**

Snyder, Bill

BEWITCHING HOUR.
LP: . . . . **MOIR 118**
MC: . . . . **CMOIR 118**

MAGIC TOUCH, THE (Snyder, Bill & Orchestra).
LP: . . . . **MOIR 209**
MC: . . . . **CMOIR 209**

Snyder, John

PIECES OF LIGHT (See McPhee, John) (Snyder, John & John McPhee).

So

HORSESHOE IN THE GLOVE.
Tracks: / Are you sure / Dreaming / Burning bush / Horseshoe in the glove / Capitol Hill / Tips on crime / Villains / Would you die for me / Are you sure (12" mix) (CD only) / First of May (CD only) / Dreaming (cocktail mix) (CD only).
LP: . . . . **PCS 7316**
MC: . . . . **TCPCS 7316**

So Hot So Sweet

SO HOT SO SWEET Various Artists (Various artists).
LP: . . . . **HVLP 005**

So Long & Thanks...

SO LONG, AND THANKS FOR ALL THE FISH (Douglas Adams) (Moore, Stephen (nar)).
MCSET: . . . . **LFP 7208**
MCSET: . . . . **LFP 4172085**

S.O.B.

THRASH NIGHT.
LP: . . . . **RISE 002**

WHAT'S THE TRUTH.
LP: . . . . **RISE 4**
MC: . . . . **RISE 4 MC**

Sobule, Jill

THINGS HERE ARE DIFFERENT.
Tracks: / Living colour / Too cool to fall in love / Pilar / So kind / Disinformation / Gifted child, The / Sad beauty / Life goes on without you / Evian / Tell me your dreams / Golden cage.
LP: . . . . **MCG 6102**
MC: . . . . **MCGC 6102**

Soca...

HOT HOT SOCA (Various artists).
LP: . . . . **RRTG 7706**
MC: . . . . **RRTGC 7706**

SOCA INVASION VOL.2 (Various artists).
LP: . . . . **JWLP 005**

SOCA TRAIN (Various artists).
Tracks: / Hot hot hot: *Arrow* / Don't back back: *Sparrow* / Soca train: *Various artists* / Boots: *Gabby*/ Notting Hill: *Explainer* / Soca Tarzan: *Carzy* / Sugar bum bum: *Kitchener* / Tide is low, The: *Wildfire.*
LP: . . . . **LONLP 2**
MC: . . . . **LONC 2**

STREET SOCA (Various artists).
LP: . . . . **SOCA 1**
MC: . . . . **ZCSOC 1**

THIS IS SOCA 2 (Various artists).
Tracks: / Neighbour, neighbour: *Sousy* / Bend down and rock: *Jacobs, Carl & Carol* / Bahia girl: *Gyal*/ I don't mind: *Soso, Winston* / Party people rock: *Arrow* / Hammer (The): *Roots, Charlie* / To young to soca: *Montano, Machel* / We want more grynner: *Grynner, Mighty* / Miss Barbados: *Gabby* / Pan rising: *Sharp, Boogsie* (Featuring Denys Plummer).
LP: . . . . **LONLP 20**
MC: . . . . **LONC 20**

THIS IS SOCA 3 (Various artists).
Tracks: / Calypso music: *Various artists* / Jourvert music: *Various artists* / Madness: *Various artists*/ Yes darling: *Various artists* / Bahia girl: *Various artists* / Kojak: *Various artists* / Dedication: *Various artists* / Permission to mash up the place: *Various artists* / Tabanka: *Various artists* / One day: *Various artists* / Sing ram bam: *Various artists* / Say say: *Various artists* / Thunder: *Various* artists / Doctor, doctor: *Various artists* / Spring garden on fire: *Various artists* / Burn dem: *Various artists.*
2LP: . . . . **LONDP 43**
MCSET: . . . . **LONDC 43**

THIS IS SOCA (1984) (Various artists).
Tracks: / Hot hot hot: *Arrows* / Feeling nice: *Designer* / Lorraine: *Explainer* / Keep fit man: *All Rounder* / Lucy: *Blue Boy* / Ain't boung for yoh: *Crazy* / You ask for it: *Black Stalin.*
LP: . . . . **OVLP 512**

Soccio, Gino

CLOSER.
Tracks: / Try it out / Street talk / It's been too long / Hold tight / Love is / Closer.
LP: . . . . **K 50790**

OUTLINE.
Tracks: / Dancer / So lonely / Visitors, The / Dance to dance / There's a woman.
LP: . . . . **K 56620**

SOCIAL HARP.
LP: . . . . **ROUNDER 0094**

Social Distortion

PRISON BOUND.
LP: . . . . **GWLP 43**

Social Kaos

FREE STYLE.
Tracks: / Rain dance / Future shock / Tellin Mel / Free style / Soul me / Tellin Mel (remix).
LP: . . . . **SCAM 005**

SABOTAGE.

Tracks: / Raindance / Tellin me / Soul me / Future shock / Free style / Tellin' me (remix).
LP: . . . . SCAM 006
MC: . . . . SCAM 006C

Social Unrest

BEFORE THE FALL.
LP: . . . . K 001 106

NOW & FOREVER.
LP: . . . . K 001 117

Societe Detimides

A LA PARADE DES GISEAUX.
Tracks: / Idol / Composition aux 2 colleurs / Le 14 eme / Merci / Asaphum / Rouge et bleu / Decompte / Boun de la tete / Non / Idol 2 / Le femme autravail / S.I.X..
LP: . . . . KK 32

Society's Rejects

SKINS 'N' PUNKS VOL 1 (Society's Rejects/Last Rough....).
LP: . . . . OIR 007

Socolow, Frank

SOUNDS BY SOCOLOW.
LP: . . . . FS 148

Sodom

AGENT ORANGE.
Tracks: / Agent orange / Tired and red / Incest / Remember the fallen / Magic dragon / Exhibition bout / Ausgebombt / Baptism of fire.
LP: 08-7596

BETTER OFF DEAD.
Tracks: / Eye for an eye / Saw is the law, The / Capture the flag / Never healing wound / Resurrection / Shellfire defense / Turn your head around / Bloodtrials / Better off dead / Stalinorgel.
LP: 0876261
MC: 0876264

IN THE SIGN OF EVIL.
Tracks: / Outbreak of evil / Blasphemer / Burst command 'til war / Sepulchral voice / Witching metal.
LP: 602 120

OBSESSED BY CRUELTY.
LP: . . . . SH 0040
LP: 082 121

PERSECUTION MANIA.
LP: 087 507
MC: 085 708

THIS MORTAL WAY OF LIFE.
LP: 807 575

Sodom & Gomorrah

SODOM & GOMORRAH (Film soundtrack) (Various artists).
2LP: . . . . DLD 1/2
LP: . . . . NL 42755

Sods

MINUTES TO GO.
LP: . . . . SFLP 3

Sofa Head

WHAT A PREDICAMENT.
LP: . . . . COX 026

Soft Boys

CAN OF BEES.
LP: . . . . AUL 709
LP: . . . . CLAW 1001

LIVE AT THE PORTLAND ARMS.
Tracks: / Give it to the soft boys / Sandra's having her brain out / Give me a spanner, Ralph / My Eveline / Human music / I like bananas because they have no bones / Horns large horns / Book of love / Wish I had my baby / White shoe blues / In the mood / That's when your heartaches begin / Have a heart, Betty (I'm not fireproof) / Duke of squeeze, The / All shook up.
LP: . . . . MOIST 4

TWO HALVES FOR THE PRICE OF ONE.
LP: . . . . BYE 1

UNDERWATER MOONLIGHT.
Tracks: / I wanna destroy you / Kingdom of love / Positive vibrations / I got the hob / Insanely jealous / Tonight / You'll have to go sideways / I'm an old pervert / Queen of eyes / Underwater moonlight.
LP: . . . . ARM 1

WADING THRU A VENTILATOR.
LP: . . . . SOFT 1
LPPD: . . . . SOFT 1P

Soft Cell

ART OF FALLING APART.
Tracks: / Forever the same / Where the heart is / Numbers / Heat / Kitchen sink drama / Baby doll / Loving you hating me / Art of falling apart.
LP: . . . . BIZL 3
MC: . . . . BIZLC 3
LP: . . . . SOD 2

IN YOUR BED (see under Almond, Marc).

LAST NIGHT IN SODOM, THE.
Tracks: / Mr. Self destruct / Slave to this / Little rough rhinestone / Meet murder my angel / Best way to kill The / L'esqualita / Down in the subway / Surrender (to a stranger) / Soul inside / Where was your heart (when you needed it most).
LP: . . . . BIZL 6

MEMORABILIA - THE SINGLES (Soft Cell & Marc Almond).
Tracks: / Memorabilia (remix) / Tainted love / Bedsitter / Say hello wave goodbye (remix) / What / Torch / Soul inside / Where the heart is / I feel love / Tears run rings / Lover spurned, A / Something's gotten hold of my heart.
LP: 8485121
MC: 8485124

NON STOP ECSTATIC DANCING.
Tracks: / Memorabilia / Where did our love go / What! / Man could get lost / Chips on my shoulder / Sex dwarf.
LP: . . . . BZX 1012
MC: . . . . BZM 1012

NON STOP EROTIC CABARET.
Tracks: / Frustration / Tainted love / Seedy films / Youth / Sex dwarf / Entertain me / Chips on my shoulder / Bedsitter / Say hello / Secret life / Wave goodbye.
LP: . . . . BZLP 2
MC: . . . . BZMC 2
MC: 800 061 4
LP: 800 061 1

SINGLES 1981-1985, THE.
Tracks: / Memorabilia / Tainted love / Bedsitter / Say hello, wave goodbye / Torch / What / Where the heart is / Numbers / Soul inside / Down in the subway.
LP: . . . . BZLP 3
MC: . . . . BZMC 3

Soft Heap

SOFT HEAP.
Tracks: / Terranova / Awol / Circle line / Petit 3's / Short hand / Para.
LP: . . . . CRL 5014

Soft Machine

ALIVE AND WELL AND LIVING IN PARIS.
Tracks: / White kite / Eos / Odds bullets and blades, pt I / Odds bullets and blades, pt II / Song of the sunbird / Puffin / Huffin / Number three / Nodder, The / Surrounding silence / Soft space.
LP: . . . . IC 064 60438
LP: . . . . SEE 290

AS IF.
Tracks: / Facelift / Slightly all the time / Kings and Queens / Drop / Chloe and the pirates / As if.
MC: . . . . ELITE 006 MC

AT THE BEGINNING.
Tracks: / That's how much I need you now / Save yourself / Jet propelled photograph / I should've known / When I don't want you / Memories / She's gone / You don't remember / I'd rather be with you.
LP: . . . . CR 30196

BUNDLES.
Tracks: / Hazard profile part 1 / Hazard profile part 2 / Hazard profile part 3 / Hazard profile part 4 / Hazard profile part 5 / Gone sailing / Bundles / Land of the bag snake / Man who waved at trains, The / Peff / Four gongs two drums / Floating world, The.
LP: . . . . SEE 283

COMPLETE PEEL SESSIONS: SOFT MACHINE.
LP: . . . . SFRLP 201
MC: . . . . SFRMC 201

COMPLETE, THE/ THIRD (See Under Blossom Toes) (Soft Machine/ Blossom Toes).

FIFTH.
Tracks: / All white / Drop / M.C. / As if / L B O / Pigling bland / Bone.
LP: . . . . CBS 31748

FOURTH.
LP: . . . . CBS 64280

JET PROPELLED PHOTOGRAPHS.
Tracks: / That's how much I need you now / Save yourself / I should've known / Jet propelled photograph / When I don't want you / Memories / You don't remember / She's gone / I'd rather be with you.
LP: . . . . LIK 36
MC: . . . . TCLIK 36

LAND OF COCKAYNE.
Tracks: / Over 'n' above / Lotus groves / Isle of the blessed / Panoramania / Behind the crystal curtain / Palace of glass / Hot biscuit slim / Velvet mountain / Lot of what you fancy.
LP: . . . . EMC 3348

LIVE AT THE PROMS.
Tracks: / Out-rageous / Facelift / Esther's nosejob / Pig / Orange skin food / Door opens and closes, A / Pigling bland / Ten-thirty returns to the bedroom.
LP: . . . . RECK 5

SOFT MACHINE.
Tracks: / Hope for happiness / Joy of a toy / Why am I so short / So boot if at all / Certain kind, A / Save yourself / Priscilla / Lullaby letter / We did it again / Plus belle u'une poubelle / Why are we sleeping / Box 25/4.
LP: . . . . WIKA 57
MC: . . . . WIKC 57

SOFT MACHINE VOL.2.
Tracks: / Pataphysical introduction Part 1 / Concise British alphabet Part 1, A / Hibou, anemone and bear / Hulloder / Dada was here / Thank you Pierrot Luniere / Have you ever bean green / Pataphysical introduction Part 2 / Out of tunes / Concise British alphabet Part 2, A / As long as he lies perfectly still / Dedicated to you but you weren't listening / Fire engine passing with bells clanging / Pigs / Orange skin food / Door opens and closes, A / 10.30 returns to the bedroom.
LP: . . . . WIKA 58
MC: . . . . WIKC 58

SOFTS.
Tracks: / Aubade / Tale of taliesin, The / Ban ban caliban / Song of Aeolus / Out of season / Second bundle / Kayoo / Camden tandem, The / Nexus / One over the eight / Etika.
LP: . . . . SEE 285

THIRD.
Tracks: / Facelift / Slightly all the time / Moon in June / Out bloody rageous.
2LP: . . . . LIKD 35
MCSET: . . . . TCLIKD 35
2LP: . . . . CBS 66246

UNTOUCHABLE, THE.
Tracks: / Hazard profile part 1 / Hazard profile part 2 / Hazard profile part 3 / Hazard profile part 4 / Hazard profile part 5 / Man who waved at trains, The / Peff / Four gongs two drums / Ban ban caliban / Song of Aeolus / Aubade / Second bundle / Kayoo / Camden tandem, The / Nexus / One over the eight / Etika / Puffin / Huffin / Nodder, The / Soft space.
2LP: . . . . CCSLP 281
MC: . . . . CCSMC 281

Soft Side Of...

SOFT SIDE OF HARD ROCK, THE (See under Hard Rock) (Various artists).

Soft Verdict

FOR AMUSEMENT ONLY.
LP: . . . . TWI 049

Software

DIGITAL DANCE.
Tracks: / Oceans breath / Magnificent shore / Waking voice / Island sunrise / Magic beach / Seagulls audience / Digital dance.
LP: . . . . THBL 2.051

ELECTRONIC UNIVERSE.
2LP: . . . . KS 80055/56

Soho (dance)

GODDESS.
LP: . . . . SAVLP 1
MC: . . . . SAVMC 1

NOISE.
Tracks: / Spend some time / Little girl (Only on CD) / Be my love (Only on CD) / Sweet thing / Burning houses / Who killed the president? / Said I want you / Message from my baby / Piece of you / I'm a receiver / (You won't) Hold me down / John Wayne said.
LP: . . . . HEDLP 1
MC: . . . . HEDMC 1

Soki Vangu

ZIZINA BIS.
LP: 425.005

Sokolow, Fred

BLUEGRASS BANJO INVENTIONS.
Tracks: / Straw dog / Muddy roads / Dog house blues / Harland stomp / Cotton-eyed Joe / Life's too short / Hell among the yearlings / Sullivan's hornpipe / Bach's two-part invention / Deep elem blues / Demonstration rag / Bonaparte's retreat / Learning to let go of you / Gamelan medley / Windy mountain / Sugar in the gourd / Let me fall.
LP: . . . . SNKF 131

Sol Invictus

AGAINST THE MODERN WORLD.
LP: . . . . LAY 024

Sol Paradise

SLOW PASSION (see under Paradise, Sol).

Solal, Martial

BIG A BAND.
LP: 733617

SOLAL '56.
LP: 500110

SOLO SOLAL.
LP: . . . . MPS 68 221

SUITE FOR TRIO.
LP: . . . . MPS 68 002

WHEN A SOPRANO MEETS A PIANO (See Bechet, Sidney) (Solal, Martil & Sidney Bechet).

Solar Enemy

DIRTY VS UNIVERSE.
LP: . . . . TM 92681

Sold Out

SOULED - THE MAGIC OF....
Tracks: / Souled - the magic of....
LP: 4678081
MC: 4678084

Soldier's Tale

SOLDIER'S TALE, THE (See under Stravinsky for details) (Various artists).

Solid Air

IT AIN'T GONNA HAPPEN.
Tracks: / Face of love / Promises, promises / Man across the road / Way I am, The / It ain't gonna happen.
MC: . . . . PCN 107

PRIDE AND PAIN.
MC: . . . . PCN 126

WAY PAST BEDTIME.
Tracks: / Anti anti / Now that I've found your love / Living in a real world / Stranger to myself / All of my dreams / Intro / What's missing / Artifical heart / Borrowed love / Stop me from starting this feeling / Breathless / Don't let love let you down / Never to much / Roses / Passion from a woman / Dial my number / Falling in love / Hold on / What about me / Amityville / Outro.
MC: . . . . PCN 117
LP: 4501101
MC: 4501104

Solid Gold...

SOLID GOLD MILLION SELLERS (Various artists).
MC: . . . . AM 23

Solid Senders

SOLID SENDERS (see under Johnson, Wilco).

Solid Soul

SOLID SOUL (See under Soul) (Various artists).

Solis, Sebastian

EL GAUCHO, EL INKA.
LP: . . . . EULP 1033
MC: . . . . EUMC 1033

FROM CUBA TO TIERRA DEL FUEGO.
LP: . . . . EULP 1066
MC: . . . . EUMC 1066

Solitaire Orchestra

ROMANTIC NIGHTS.
Tracks: / Magic / She's gone / 50 ways to leave your lover / Time passages / Nights in white satin / Baker street / After the love has gone / Just when I needed you most / Ebony and ivory / I only want to be with you / I'd rather leave when I'm in love / Lyin' eyes / I made it through the rain / One day in your life / My simple heart (Not available on CD.) / When I need you / Hopelessly devoted to you (Not available on CD.) / Your song (Not available on CD.) / Castles in the air / She's out of my life (Not available on CD.) / I believe in you (Not available on CD.) / Lately (Not available on CD.) / Mandy (Not available on CD.) / If you leave me now / Oh babe what would you say (Not available on CD.) / What a fool believes / Miles away (Not available on CD.).
2LP: . . . . STDLP 27
MC: . . . . STDMC 27

Solitude Aeturnus

INTO THE DEPTHS OF SORROW.
LP: . . . . RO 92651
MC: . . . . RO 92654

Solley, David

DARK ISLAND, THE.
Tracks: / An T-Eilean Dorcha / Mi'n seo 'nam onar / Theid mi cuide riut / An ataireachd ard / Fail oro bho'n dh'fhag sinn / Mo run geal dileas / An T-Eilean mu thuath / Puirt a beul / An teid thu leam a mhairi? / Mo nighean chruinn donn / Alasdair an duin / Mo mhathair.
MC: . . . . LICS 5001
LP: . . . . LILP 5001

GREAT SONGS OF SCOTLAND.
Tracks: / Lass o'bon accord, The / Skye boat song / Harry Lauder medley / Roamin' in the gloamin' / Loch Lomond /

Scotland the brave / Ye banks and braes / Westering home / Old Scots mother mine / Rowan tree / Uist tramping song / Granny's heilan' hame / We're no awa' tae bide awa'.
LP: . . . . LILP 5076
MC: . . . . LICS 5076

HIGHLANDS AND ISLANDS.
Tracks: / Te bhan / Sine chaluim bhain / Leis an lurgainn / Island sheiling song / Mo nighear bhan / Mo ghleannan / Oran mor mhichleoid / Puirt a beul / Cuir a chinn dilis / Leaving Barra / Eileen fraoich.
LP: . . . . LILP 5008
MC: . . . . LICS 5008

Sollo, Jake

JAKE SOLLO.
Tracks: / Father time, mother nature / Say no more / Weebo me weebo / Pas du tout / Five o five / African gypsy / Show me how / Greetings.
LP: . . . . N 102

Sollscher,Goran

CAVATINA.
Tracks: / Granada / Portrait / Sakura / Georgia on my mind / Romance d'amour.
LP: 4137201
MC: 4137204

Solna Brass

SWEDISH CHAMPIONS.
Tracks: / Marcia / Norwegian dance No. 2 / Maple leaf rag / Valse triste / Spanish gypsy dance / Old fabodpsalm from Dalcarlia / Under the blue and yellow flag / Trombone concerto / Mock morris / Swedish rhapsody.
LP: . . . . PL 25147
MC: . . . . PK 25147

Solo, David

SOLO MUSIC (In the quiet of the evening & other songs).
Tracks: / I will be your mountain / Captivated by the melody / In the quiet of the evening / Morning is another lonely day / You're my inspiration / That old love song / Girl with the smile in her eyes, The / Cotton country music / Dance to the rhythm (Included in medley with "Goodbye") / Goodbye (Included in medley with "Dance to the rhythm").
LP: . . . . SREC 001

Solo, Jim Kahr

BLUES & LOVE SONGS- (My guitar & I have travelled).
LP: . . . . LR 42.064

Solo, Napoleon

HOW TO STEAL THE WORLD.
LP: . . . . PHZA 29

SHOT.
LP: . . . . BBSLP 006
MC: . . . . BBSMC 006

Solo, Sal

HEART AND SOUL.
Tracks: / Heart beat / Poland your spirit won't die / Shout shout / Music and you / Contact / Go now / Forever be.
LP: . . . . MCF 3288
MC: . . . . MCFC 3288

Solo (T.V. series)

SOLO (Various artists).
MC: . . . . HBTD 1406

Soloff, Lew

BUT BEAUTIFUL.
LP: . . . . K 28P 6468

HANALEI BAY.
Tracks: / Salazar / My buddy / Hanalei bay / Feliciade, A / La toalla / Emily / Well you needn't.
LP: K28P 6365

YESTERDAYS.
LP: . . . . K 28P 6448

Soloists of the

RUSSIAN OLD ROMANCES.
MC: . . . . M 00415

Soloman Grundy

SOLOMAN GRUNDY.
LP: . . . . NAR 043LP
MC: . . . . NAR 043MC

Solomon, Diane

IF YOU WERE MY LADY (see Campbell, Glen) (Solomon, Diane & Glen Campbell).

LIVE ON TOUR.
Tracks: / It's all wrong but it's all right / Love me tonight / He's out of my life / You're my best friend / City of New Orleans / Queen of the silver dollar / Why have you left the one you left for me / All this time / Della and the dealer / You can do it / Standing room only / That's what friends are for / Help me make it through the night.
LP: . . . . BDL 3000
MC: . . . . AJKL 3000

TAKE TWO.
LP: 6308 236

Solomon & Geiseking

SOLOMON & GEISEKING (Various artists).
LP: . . . . REH 718
MC: . . . . ZCR 718

Solomon Islands

SOLOMON ISLANDS - FATALEKE & BAEGU MUSIC (Various artists).
MC: . . . . AUD 58027

Solomon & Sheba

SOLOMON & SHEBA (Film soundtrack) (Various artists).
LP: . . . . MCA 1425
MC: . . . . MCAC 1425

Solstice

NEW LIFE/ PEACE FOR THE NEW AGE.
MC: . . . . RO 001C

SILENT DANCE.
LP: . . . . EQRLP 001

Solti, Sir George

ALSO SPRACH ZARATHUSTRA (Solti Collection) (Chicago Symphony Orchestra).
MC: 4304454

BOLERO (RAVEL) (Solti Collection) (Chicago Symphony Orchestra).
MC: 4304444

FLYING DUTCHMAN, THE - OVERTURE (Solti Collection) (Chicago Symphony Orchestra).
MC: 4304484

ORCHESTRA! (Music from the Channel 4 TV series) (Solti, Sir George/Dudley Moore).
MC: 4308384
LP: 4308381

PICTURES AT AN EXHIBITION (Solti Collection) (Chicago Symphony Orchestra).
MC: 4304464

PLANETS, THE (HOLST) (Solti Collection) (London Philharmonic Orchestra).
MC: 4304474

SYMPHONIE FANTASTIQUE (BERLIOZ) (Solti Collection) (Chicago Symphony Orchestra).
MC: 4304414

SYMPHONY NO. 4 IN E MINOR (BRAHMS) (Solti Collection) (Chicago Symphony Orchestra).
MC: 4304404

SYMPHONY NO. 5 IN C SHARP MINOR (MAHLER) (Solti Collection) (Chicago Symphony Orchestra).
MC: 4304434

SYMPHONY NO. 6 IN B MINOR, 'PATHETIQUE' (Solti Collection) (Chicago Symphony Orchestra).
MC: 4304424

SYMPHONY NO. 8 IN B MINOR 'UNFINISHED' (SCHUBERT) (Solti Collection) (Vienna Philharmonic Orchestra).
MC: 4304394

SYMPHONY NO. 9 'CHORAL' (BEETHOVEN) (Solti Collection) (Chicago Symphony Orchestra).
MC: 4304384

SYMPHONY NO. 40 IN G MINOR (MOZART) (Solti Collection) (Chamber Orchestra of Europe).
MC: 4304374

Solution

HOW TO SOLVE THE RUBIK CUBE.
MC: . . . . NEVC 96

Solvarmt

OLLE ORRJE.
LP: . . . . DRLP 103

Solyom, Janos

JANOS SOLYOM PLAYS BEETHOVEN.
LP: . . . . ARTE 7108

Some, Belouis

BELOUIS SOME.
Tracks: / Let it be with you / Stranger than fiction / Some girls / Passion play / Animal magic / Dream girl / My body / Wind of change / What I see.
LP: . . . . PCS 7310
MC: . . . . TCPCSX 7310

SOME PEOPLE.
Tracks: / Some people / Stand down / Imagination / Walk away / Aware of you / Target practice / Have you ever been in love / Tail lights / Jerusalem.
LP: . . . . EJ 2403181
MC: . . . . EJ 2403184
LP: . . . . FA 3197
MC: . . . . TCFA 3197

Some Guys Have ...

SOME GUYS HAVE ALL THE LUCK (See under Reggae) (Various artists).

Some Have Fins

BUBBLE DISEASE.
Tracks: / Well hell / Be your bride / Derailed / Douche bag fever / Cindy can't breathe / So I bow / Bubble disease / Princess is best / No / Burst.
LP: . . . . AAAH LP 1

Some Like It Hot

SOME LIKE IT HOT (Film soundtrack) (Various artists).
Tracks: / Runnin' wild: *Monroe, Marilyn* / Sugar blues: *Deutsch, Adolph & His Orchestra* / Runnin' wild: *Deutsch,* Adolph & His Orchestra / Down among the sheltering palms: *Society Syncopators* / Randolph Street rag: *Deutsch,* Adolph & His Orchestra / I wanna be loved by you: *Monroe, Marilyn* / Park Avenue fantasy: *Deutsch, Adolph & His Orchestra* / Down among the sheltering palms: *Monroe, Marilyn* / La Cumparsita: *Various artists* / I wanna be loved by you: *Monroe, Marilyn* / I'm through with love: *Monroe, Marilyn* / Sugar blues: *Deutsch, Adolph* & His Orchestra / Tell the whole darn world: *Deutsch, Adolph & His Orchestra* / Play it again Charlie: *Deutsch,* Adolph & His Orchestra / Sweet Georgia Brown: *Malneck, Matty & His Orchestra* / By the beautiful sea: *Society Syncopators* / Some like it hot: *Malneck, Matty & His Orchestra.*
LPPD: . . . . UASP 30226
LP: . . . . UAS 30226
LP: 1C 064 82894

Some Other Guys

SOME OTHER GUYS (See under 60's) (Various artists).

Somebody Famous

GIFT, THE.
LP: . . . . RD 001

Somers, Debroy

DEBROY SOMERS & HIS BAND (1927-32) (Somers, Debroy & His Band).
Tracks: / Savoy sea songs medley / Masquerade / Red roofed chalet, A / Laughing Marionette / Roses for remembrance / In a little Spanish town / Slipping round the corner / Going home / Night time brings dreams of you / So blue / Night when love was born, The / You're just the one girl for me / Rag doll / Sunset down in Somerset / Good news selection / Just imagine / Best things in life are free, The / Lucky in love / Varsity drag.
LP: . . . . JOY'D 282
MC: . . . . TC JOY'D 282

Somerville, Jimmy

GREATEST HITS: JIMMY SOMERVILLE.
Tracks: / Smalltown boy / Don't leave me this way / It ain't necessarily so / Comment te dire adieu / Never can say goodbye / Why ? / You are my world / For a friend / I feel love / There's more to love / So cold the night / Mighty real / To love somebody / Run from love / Tomorrow (Available on CD and cassette.) / Disenchanted (Available on CD and cassette.) / Read my lips.
LP: 828 226 1
MC: 828 226 4

READ MY LIPS.
Tracks: / Comment te dire adieu / You make me feel (mighty real) / Perfect day / Heaven here on earth (with your love) / Don't know what to do (without you) / Read my lips (enough is enough) / My heart is in your hands / Control / And you never thought this could happen to you / Rain.
LP: 828 166 1
MC: 828 166 4

SINGLES COLLECTION, THE.
MC: 8282684
LP: 8282681

Something Against You

SOMETHING AGAINST YOU (Various artists).
LP: . . . . PS 014

Something Fierce

COMPLETELY UNGLUED.
LP: . . . . URINAL 1

Something For The ...

SOMETHING FOR THE BOYS (Original Broadway Cast) (Various artists).
LP: . . . . AEI 1157

Something Happens

BEEN THERE, SEEN THAT, DONE THAT.
Tracks: / Beach / Incoming / Take this with you / Forget Georgia / Way I feel, The / Both men crying / Burn clear / Give it away / Tall girls club / Shoulder high / Here comes the only one again / Be my love / Promised (CD only) / Seven days 'til 4 a.m. (CD only) / Free and easy (CD only).
LP: . . . . V 2561
MC: . . . . TCV 2561

I KNOW RAY HARMAN (Live album).
Tracks: / Beach / Incoming / Seven days 'til 4 a.m. / Free & easy / Take this with you / Promised.
LP: . . . . V 2535
MC: . . . . TCV 2535

STUCK TOGETHER WITH GOD'S GLUE.
Tracks: / What now / Hello hello hello hello hello (petrol) / Parachute / Esmerelda / I had a feeling / Kill the roses / Brand new God / Room 29 / Patience business, The / Devil in Miss Jones / Good time coming / Feel good / Skyrockets.
LP: . . . . V 2628
MC: . . . . TCV 2628

Something Pretty..

SOMETHING PRETTY BEAUTIFUL (Something Pretty Beautiful).
LP: . . . . CRELP 075

Something Shocking

PINK.
LP: . . . . F 3015

Something Stirs

SOMETHING STIRS various artists (Various artists).
MC: . . . . ARR 013

Something To Believe

SOMETHING TO BELIEVE.
LP: . . . . BYO 4

Something To Remember

SOMETHING TO REMEMBER (Various artists).
LP: . . . . F 3009

Something Wicked

SOMETHING WICKED THIS WAY COMES (see under Enid).

Something Wild

SOMETHING WILD (Film Soundtrack) (Various artists).
Tracks: / Loco de amor: *David Y Celia* / Ever fallen in love (with someone you shouldn't've): *Fine Young Cannibals*/ Zero zero seven Charlie: *UB40* / Not my slave: *Oingo Boingo* / You don't have to cry: *Cliff, Jimmy*/ With or without you: *Jones, Steve* / High life: *Okossun, Sonny* / Man with a gun: *Harrison, Jerry* / Temptation: *New Order* / Wild thing: *Sister Carol.*
LP: . . . . MCF 3355
MC: . . . . MCFC 3355

Sometimes...

SOMETIMES A GREAT NOTION (Various artists).
LP: . . . . TOPCAT 1

Somewhere A Voice

LOVE LOGIC & EGO.
LP: . . . . PEY 001

Somewhere In A

SOMEWHERE IN A SKELETON (Various artists).
LP: . . . . BR 7006

Sommer,Gunter

ASCENSUER POUR LE 28 (Sommer,Gunter et Trois Vieux Amis).
Tracks: / Nelly et Sylvain / Daniel und sein volvo / Makoko apercoit / Toute pour raoul / Jiair und J.E. / Isabel.
LP: . . . . NATO 329

HORMUSIK ZWEI.
Tracks: / Chatenay / Villedieu / Isabelle icebox.
LP: . . . . NATO 49

Sommers, Joanie

DREAM (Sommers, Joanie & Bob Florence).
Tracks: / More I see you, The / Too close for comfort / Man that got away, The / I'm old fashioned / Guiding star / They can't take that away from me / I wish you love / One-note samba / House is not a home, A / Dream.
LP: . . . . DS 887

Sommers, Patti

LAST NIGHT, THE.
Tracks: / Step right into the sunshine / Everything I touch turns to tears / Never can say goodbye / Hungry years / One singular sensation / Last night / On a clear day / What I did for love / How high the moon / Sing a rainbow / Only have eyes for you / Sweet life.
LP: . . . . BNLP 1002

Somo Somo

PARIS.
LP: . . . . STERNS 1014

SOMO SOMO'(ZAIRE/UK).

Tracks: / Mosese 2000 / Masikiki ya mola / Jamy jamy / Mele / Cheko.
LP: STERNS 1007

Son Of Acido!

SON OF ACIDO!.
LP: ACIDLP 801

Son Of Ind

DELIRIOUS.
LP: REACT 1

Son Of Oi!

SON OF OI (Various artists).
LP: LINK LP 030

Son Of Sam

RICH AND FAMOUS.
Tracks: / Starch / Millenium beat per minute / Goodbye junkie Jim / Cuts 'n' bruises / Nature's made a mistake / Moan bloody moan / She weeps / Cain.
LP: CONCORD 027

Sona Diabate

SONS DE LA SAVANE.
LP: SLP 77

Sondergaard, Jens

NO COAST.
LP: SLP 4126

Sondheim

COLLECTORS SONDHEIM, A (Various artists).
Tracks: / Anyone can whistle: *Various artists* / Follies: *Various artists* / Evening primrose: *Various artists* / Little night music, A: *Various artists* / Pacific overtures: *Various artists* / Company: *Various artists.*
LPS: CRL 4 5359
MCSET: CRK 4 5359

Sonerien Du

WINTERFOLK 80 (see Battlefield Band).

Sones Jarochos

MUSIC OF MEXICO - VOL.1.
LP: ARHOOLIE 3008

Song & Dance

SONG AND DANCE (1984 London cast) (Various artists).
Tracks: / Song and dance (overture): *Various artists* / Take that look off your face: *Various artists* / Let me finish: *Various artists* / It's not the end of the world: *Various artists* / Letter home: *Various artists*/ Sheldon Bloom: *Various artists* / Capped teeth and Caesar salad: *Various artists* / Exit: *Various artists*/ Second letter home: *Various artists* / Unexpected song: *Various artists* / Come back with the same look in your eyes: *Various artists* / Let's talk about you: *Various artists* / Tell me on a Sunday: *Various artists*/ Married man: *Various artists* / Third letter home: *Various artists* / Nothing like you've ever known: *Various* artists / Song and dance (finale): *Various artists* / When you want to fall in love: *Various artists* / Dance: *Various artists.*
2LP: BL 70480
MCSET: BK 70480

SONG AND DANCE (Original London cast) (Various artists).
Tracks: / Song and dance (overture): *Various artists* / Let me finish: *Various artists* / It's not the end of the world: *Various artists* / You made me think you were in love: *Various artists* / Letter home: *Various* artists / Sheldon Bloom: *Various artists* / Capped teeth and Caesar salad: *Various artists* / Second letter home: *Various artists* / Last man in my life, The: *Various artists* / Come back with the same look in your eyes: *Various artists* / Take that look off your face: *Various artists* / Tell me on a Sunday: *Various artists*/ I love New York: *Various artists* / Married man: *Various artists* / I'm very you, you're very me: *Various* artists / Let's talk about you: *Various artists* / Nothing like you've ever known: *Various artists* / Song and dance (finale): *Various artists* / When you want to fall in love: *Various artists* / Dance: *Various artists.*
2LP: PODV 4
MCSET: PODVC 4

SONG AND DANCE (Original Broadway Cast) (Various artists).
LP: CBL1 7162
MC: CBK1 7162

Song Is You

SONG IS YOU Great British dance bands play Jerome Kern (Various artists).
LP: SHB 73

Song Of Bernadette

SONG OF BERNADETTE, THE/ ISLAND IN THE SKY (Original Soundtrack) (Various artists).
LP: STV 81116

Song Of Norway

SONG OF NORWAY, THE (Original Broadway Cast) (Various artists).
LP: MCA 1524
MC: MCAC 1524

Song Of The Chanter

SONG OF THE CHANTER (Various artists).
MC: COX 1028

Song Remains The ...

SONG REMAINS THE SAME, THE (Film soundtrack) (See under Led Zeppelin) (Led Zeppelin).

Song Without End

SONG WITHOUT END (Film soundtrack) (Various artists).
LP: GGL 30169

Songbook

SONGBOOK (Original London cast) (Various artists).
Tracks: / Songbook: *Various artists* / East river rhapsody: *Various artists* / Talking picture show: *Various* artists / Mr. Destiny: *Various artists* / Your time is defferent to mine: *Various artists* / Pretty face: *Various artists* / Je vous aime milady: *Various artists* / Les halles: *Various artists* / Olympics song 1936: *Various artists* / Nazi party pooper: *Various artists* / I'm gonna take him home to momma: *Various artists*/ Bumpity bump: *Various artists* / Girl in the window: *Various artists* / Victory V: *Various artists*/ April in Wisconsin: *Various artists* / Happy hickory: *Various artists* / Lovely Sunday morning: *Various* artists / Rusty's dream ballet: *Various artists* / torm on my heart: *Various artists* / Pokenhatchit: *Various* artists / Public protest committee: *Various artists* / I accuse: *Various artists* / Messages: *Various* artists / I found love: *Various artists* / Don't play the love song any more: *Various artists* / Golden oldie: *Various artists* / Climbin': *Various artists* / Nostalgia: *Various artists.*
LP: NSPL 18609

Songs For New Lovers

SONGS FOR NEW LOVERS (Dardanelle Vocal) (Various artists).
LP: ST 202

Songs For Tomorrow

SONGS FOR TOMORROW Various artists (Various artists).
Tracks: / Rise and shine: *Various artists* / Campfire welcome: *Various artists* / Cuckoo clock, The: *Various* artists / Wild mountain thyme: *Various artists* / Indian prayer: *Various artists* / Yellow bird: *Various* artists / Tails: *Various artists* / Jungle mammy song: *Various artists* / Coconut tree: *Various artists*/ Bees of paradise: *Various artists* / Light a little candle: *Various artists* / One day: *Various artists*/ Colours of Christmas, The: *Various artists* / Sing along song: *Various artists* / Me he manu rere: *Various* artists / Su-ta-ra-dah-dey: *Various artists* / Come and go with me: *Various artists* / Bantu echo song: *Various* artists / Himalayan lullaby: *Various artists* / Breton fisherman's prayer: *Various artists* / Song of the child: *Various artists* / Babylon: *Various artists* / Hebrew peace round: *Various artists* / Hawaiian fisherman's song: *Various artists.*
LP: REC 389
MC: ZCM 389

Songs From the Boss

SONGS FROM THE NEW INTERNATIONAL various artists (Various artists).
LP: LOOSE 012

Songs Of...

SONGS OF GEBIRTIG AND WARSHAVSKY (Various artists).
MC: GVMMC 133

SONGS OF INDIA (See under India) (Various artists).

SONGS OF IRELAND (See under Ireland...) (Various artists).

SONGS OF LOVE,LUCK, ANIMALS & MAGIC (Various artists).
Tracks: / Love Song: *Douglas, Frank A* / Grizzly bear war song: *Douglas, Frank A* / Rabbit song: *Douglas, Frank A* / Gambling songs: *Douglas, Frank A* / Love Song: *Figuerosa, Aileen* (Music of the Yurok(Indian)) / Basket song: *Figuerosa, Aileen* / Brush dance: *Figuerosa, Aileen* / Brush dance song: *Figuerosa, Aileen* / Love Song: *Ella Norris* / Seagull song: *Ella Norris* / Song to stop the Rain: *Ella Norris* / Hunting Song: *Florence Shaughnessy* / Brush dance: *Douglas, Frank A* / Brush dance: *Simms, Hector* / Gambling songs: *Lopez, Sam & Lauren Bommelyn* / Pelican song: *Loren Bommelyn* / Gambling songs: *Various artists*/ Gambling songs: *Various artists* / Ceremonial dance: *Various artists* / Ending ceremonial dance: *Various artists.*
LP: NW 297

SONGS OF OLD IRELAND (See under Ireland...) (Various artists).

SONGS OF THE CIVIL WAR (See under America) (Various artists).

Songs Of Fellowship

SONGS OF FELLOWSHIP VOL.1 A new song (Various artists).
LP: DOVE 47

SONGS OF FELLOWSHIP VOL.2 City of God (Various artists).
LP: DOVE 53

Songs Of Home

SONGS OF HOME (Various artists).
LP: TT 2

SONGS OF HOME (Various artists).
LP: FRC 002

Songs of Life

SONGS OF LIFE (Music from Mission '89) (Various artists).
MC: WST C 9710

Songwriters

NO.1 WITH A BULLET.
LP: YL 0112

Sonia

BOY I LOVE, THE (see under McCarlos,Don "Sweet Africa").

EVERYBODY KNOWS.
Tracks: / You'll never stop me from loving you / Everybody knows / Listen to your heart / Someone like you / Counting every minute / Can't forget you / Now I'm without you / Can't help the way that I feel / Climb to the top of a mountain / End of the world.
LP: CHR 1734
MC: ZCHR 1734

YOU'VE GOT A FRIEND (See under Big Fun for media details) (Sonia & Big Fun).

Sonic Boom

SPECTRUM.
Tracks: / Help me please / Angel / You're the one / If I should die / Lonely Avenue / Rock'n'roll / Pretty baby.
LP: ORELP 506
MC: OREMC 506

Sonic Violence

CASKET CASE.
LP: VILE 023

JAGD.
LP: VILE 020
MC: VILE 020 MC

Sonic Youth

BAD MOON RISING.
LP: BFFP 1

CONFUSION IS SEX.
Tracks: / Inhuman / World looks red, The / Confusion is sex / Making the nature scene / Lee is free / She's in a bad mood / Protect me you / Freezer burn I wanna be your dog / Shaking hell.
LP: ND 02
LP: SST 096

DAYDREAM NATION.
LP: BFFP 34
MC: BFFP 34C

DIRTY BOOTS EP.
Tracks: / Dirty boots (edit) / White kross (live) / Eric's trip (live) / Cinderella's big score (live) / Dirty boots (live) / Bedroom, The (live).
MLP: DGC 21634
MC: DGCC 21634

E.V.O.L.
LP: BFFP 4
MC: BFFP 4C

GOO.
Tracks: / Dirty boots / Tunic (song for Karen) / Mary-Christ / Kool thing / Mote / My friend Goo / Disappearer / Mildred Pierce / Cinderella's big score / Scooter and Jinx / Titanium expose.
LP: 7599242971
MC: 7599242974
LP: DGC 24297
MC: DGCC 24297

I'M GONNA FUCK YOUR MOTHER.
2LP: KAR 006

KILL YOUR IDOLS.
LP: ZS 010
LP: ZENSOR 10

SISTER.
LP: BFFP 20
MC: BFFP 20C

SONIC YOUTH.
LP: ND 001
LP: ND 01
LP: SST 097

Sonics

BOOM.
LP: FC 020

FULL FORCE (Best of the Sonics).
LP: LILP 400387

HERE ARE THE SONICS.
LP: FC 017

LIVE FANZ ONLY.
LP: FC 033

PSYCHO.
LP: KIRI 104

Sonn, Larry

SOUND OF SONN, THE (Sonn, Larry & His Orchestra).
Tracks: / Frank but earnest / Close cover before striking / Sonn also rises, The / We three / Zanzy / Nutty / It looks like rain in Cherry Blossom Lane / Lemon twist / From A to Z / Flat cap, The / Ida bridges falling down / O'dem bums.
LP: JASM 1007

Sonnets

SONNETS (see under Shakespeare, William).

Sonnier, Jo El

CAJUN LIFE.
Tracks: / Cajun life / Tes yeux bleu / Allons a lafayette / Bayou teche / Les flames d'enfer / Lacassine special / Chere Alice / Louisiana blues / Les grande bois / Perrodin two-step.
LP: SNTF 839
MC: ROUNDER 3049C
LP: ROUNDER 3049

COME ON JOE.
Tracks: / Baby hold on / Paid the price / So long baby goodbye / No more one more time / Come on Joe / Rainin' in my heart / Louisiana 1927 / Tear stained letter / I've slipped her mind.
LP: PL 86374
MC: PK 86374

HAVE A LITTLE FAITH.
Tracks: / Scene of the crime, The / If your heart should ever roll this way again / Ooh ooh ooh / Have a little faith in me / I'll never get over you / Hurt in my heart, The / Solid gold plated fool / Walls / Evangeline special.
LP: PL 90453
MC: PK 90453

Sonnier, Lee

FAIS DO DO BREAKDOWN (Sonnier, Lee & Happy Fats(1940's)).
Tracks: / Setre chandelle / Allons dance colinda / Dans les grande meche / Chere Catan / Fais do do breakdown / Dans la platin / Chere eci et cher laba / Along the river / Cankton two step / War widow waltz / La valse de hadocol / Crowley two step / La blues de Cajin / Acadian all star special.
LP: FLY 609

Sonny

LOVE A LITTLE LATIN (Sonny and the 'Boys from LA').
Tracks: / Cuban love song / From Russia with love / Maria elena / Solitaire / If I had a hammer / He's a tramp / Dream a little dream / Sueno que estou junto a ti / That tat cat jive / Girl from Ipanema / Desafinado / Meditation / Tell me when (quando quando) / Singin' in the rain / O meu violao / I'm not in love.
LP: SUS 518

Sonny & Cher

ALL I EVER NEED IS YOU (OLD GOLD) (See under Cher/Gypsies, tramps and thieves).

LOOK AT US.
LP: ATL 5036

SONNY & CHER COLLECTION.
LP: 9548301521
MC: 9548301524

VERY BEST OF SONNY & CHER.
Tracks: / I got you, babe / Just you / But you're mine / Sing c'est la vie / Beautiful story / What now my love? / Beat goes on / Let it be me / Living for you / Laugh at me / It's the little things / Little man.
LP: SHM 3063
MC: HSC 3063

WONDEROUS WORLD OF SONNY & CHER.
LP: 587 006

Sonny & Jed

SONNY & JED/THE CANNIBALS Original soundtracks (Various artists).
LP: C'BUS 111

Sonoko

LA DEBUTANTE.
LP: CRAM 056

Sonora Matancer

ISMAEL MIRANDA.
LP: JM 632

Sons & Lovers (bk)

SONS AND LOVERS (see under Lawrence, D.H.) (McKellan, Ian).

Sons Of Angels

SONS OF ANGELS.
LP: 7567821011
MC: 7567821014

Sons Of Arqa

ARQA.
LP: . . . . ARKA 007

ARQA OLOGY.
LP: . . . . ONE G 2L

EARTHLING.
MC: . . . . BIP 302

Sons Of Bix

OSTRICH WALK.
LP: . . . . J 59

Sons Of Champlin

MARIN COUNTY SUNSHINE 1968-1971.
Tracks: / 1982-A / Black and blue rainbow / Hello sunlight / Everywhere / Don't fight it, do it / Jesus is coming / It's time / Love a woman / Terry's tune / Headway / Follow your heart.
LP: . . . . LIK 21

Sons Of Freedom

SONS OF FREEDOM.
Tracks: / Super cool wagon / Criminal / Mona Lisa / Dead dog on the highway / Holy rollers, The / Judy come home / Is it love / F**k the system / This is TAO / Alice Henderson.
LP: 828 123-1
MC: 828 123-4

Sons Of Heroes

SONS OF HEROES.
Tracks: / Living outside your love / Lost in wonderland / Don't make it so hard / Love insight / Hot kiss / Strange eyes / Dream machines / Start of the human race / All broke up.
LP: . . . . MCF 3193

Sons of Ishmael

PARIAH MARTYR DEMANDS A SACRIFICE.
LP: . . . . OTT 1202
LP: . . . . ACHE 10

Sons Of Jah

URBAN GUERRILLA.
LP: . . . . NCLP 005

Sons Of Jobs..

SONS OF JOBS FOR THE BOYS (Various artists).
LP: . . . . LIE 2

Sons Of Katie Elder

SONS OF KATIE ELDER, THE (Original Soundtrack) (Various artists).
LP: . . . . LAALP 001

Sons Of Sam

GOLDEN AGE OF DISCO, THE.
LP: . . . . FM 009

Sons Of The Arqua

ARQ OF THE ARQUANS.
LP: . . . . FACE 11

Sons Of The Dolls

SONS OF THE DOLLS.
LP: . . . . FC 002

Sons Of The Pioneers

20 OF THE BEST: SONS OF THE PIONEERS.
Tracks: / Riders in the sky / Don't fence me in / Red river valley / Carry me back to the lone prairie / One more ride / Way out there / Song of the bandit / Room full of roses / Ringo twilight on the trail / Room full of roses / Cool water / My adobe hacienda / Along the Navajo trail / El Paso / Song of the pioneers / Shifting, whispering sands / Ragtime cowboy Joe / Mystery of his way / Tumbling tumbleweeds / Last round-up, The.
LP: . . . . NL 89525
MC: . . . . NK 89525

1940.
LP: . . . . JEMF 102

COWBOY COUNTRY.
Tracks: / One more ride / Yaller yaller gold / Graveyard filler of the west / King of the river / All the way (Previously unissued.) / No rodeo dough / Lie low little doggies (The cowboy's prayer) / Little doggies (the cowboy's prayer) / Old pioneer / Bar none ranch, The / Out in pioneer town / Serenade to a coyote (Previously unissued.) / Wagon train.
LP: . . . . BFX 15071

EDITION 1 (Cool Water 1945/46).
Tracks: / Cool water / Timber trail / You'll be sorry when I'm gone / Forgive and forget / Gold star mother with silvery hair / You're getting tired of me / Columbus stockade blues / Cowboy camp meetin' / I wear your memory in my heart / Tumbling tumbleweeds / No one to cry to / Everlasting hills of Oklahoma, The / Grievin' my heart out for you / Out California way / Stars and stripes on Iwo Jima (Isle).
LP: . . . . BFX 15202

EDITION 2 (Teardrops In My Heart 1946/47).
Tracks: / Teardrops in my heart / Chant of the wanderer, The / Let's pretend / Will there be sagebrush in Heaven? / Penny for your thoughts / Baby doll / Letter marked unclaimed, The / Trees / Cigarettes, whisky and wild, wild women / You don't know what lonesome is / Too high too wide too low / You'll never miss the water / Have I told you lately that I love you / My best to you / Blue prairie / Lead me gently home father.
LP: . . . . BFX 15252

EDITION 3 (Hundred And Sixty Acres 1946/47).
Tracks: / Hundred and sixty acres, A / Calico apron and gingham gown / Whiffenpoof song, The / Wind / Where are you / Out in pioneer town / Two eyes two lips but no heart / Cowboy country / Power in the blood / Let me share your name / Happy birthday polka / Read the Bible every day / Sea walker, The / Old rugged cross, The / Last round-up, The / Bar-none ranch (in the sky), The.
LP: . . . . BFX 15253

EDITION 4 (Riders In The Sky 1947/49).
Tracks: / Santa Fe, New Mexico / Down where the Rio flows / I still do / Serenade to a coyote / Red River valley / Riders in the sky / Sentimental, worried and blue / The Missouri is a devil of a woman / My feet take me away / Room full of roses / Let's go west again / Lie low little doggies(The cowboy's prayer) / No rodeo dough / Touch of God's hand / Little grey home in the west / Rounded up in glory.
LP: . . . . BFX 15254

EDITION 5 (Land Beyond The Sun 1949/50).
Tracks: / Land beyond the sun / Wagon's west / Outlaws / Rollin' dust / Song of the wagonmaster / Wind / Love at the country fair / Wedding dolls (from your wedding cake) / Old man atom / I told them about you / Chuckawalla swing / What this country needs / Eagle's heart, The / Baby, I ain't gonna cry no more / Little white cross / Roses.
LP: . . . . BFX 15255

EDITION 6 (And Friends 1950/51).
LP: . . . . BFX 15282

EDITION 7 (There's a Goldmine In 1951/52).
Tracks: / Empty saddles / There's a goldmine in the sky / I still do / Old pioneer / Home on the range / Heartbreak hill / Outlaw / Wind / Diesel smoke x 2 / Waltz of the roses / Ho le o / Almost / Resurrectus / Wondrous word / Lord's prayer, The.
LP: . . . . BFX 15283

FAVOURITE COWBOY SONGS.
Tracks: / Tumbling tumbleweeds / Press along to the big coral / Wind / Bunkhouse bugle boy / Home on the range / La Borachita / Timber trail / Happy cowboy / Cowboy lament / Pajarillo Barrenquero / So long to the Red River Valley / Come and get it / Cool water / Curly Joe from Idaho / Cowboy's dream / Along the Santa Fe trail / Last round-up, The / Far away stomp / Red River Valley / Carry me back to the lone prairie / Sweet Betsy from pike / Slow moving cattle / Texas stomp / Yellow rose of Texas / Everlasting hills of Oklahoma, The.
LP: . . . . HAT 3069
MC: . . . . HATC 3069

LUCKY U RANCH RADIO.
2LP: . . . . JEMF 2201

RADIO TRANSCRIPTIONS VOL.1.
Tracks: / 1849 blues / It's a great day / Lord, you made the cowboy happy / Believe me if all those endearing young charms / One more river to cross / Move on, you lazy cattle / That pioneer mother of mine / Sagebush symphony / Tumbleweed trail / Hi filootin' Newton / Yippi yi yippi yo / Yellow rose of Texas / It's a cowboy's life for me / Lazy / Waitin' for the sun to say good... / Old black mountain trail, The / Mexicali rose / Texas polka / Home again in Wyoming / Song of the San Juan Joaquin.
MC: . . . . CSR 7C

RADIO TRANSCRIPTIONS VOL.2.
Tracks: / Yodel your troubles away / So long to the Red River Valley / Termite's love song, The / Far away stomp / Slim / I follow the stream / Too high too wide too low / Hi ho little doggies / Rose of ol' Santa Fe / Cattle call rondolet / Westward Ho / Prairie revenge / Santa Fe trail / Jubilation jamboree / Timber trail / Round-up in the sky / Whoopie ti yi yo / Cowboy's serenade, The / Well, well, well / Hard times come again no more.
MC: . . . . CSR 8C

RADIO TRANSCRIPTIONS VOL.3.
Tracks: / Wagon wheels / Don Juan / Riding down the canyon / Biscuit blues / Cowpoke / Cornflower / Silent trails / Graveyard filler of the west / Song of the bandit / Sky ball paint / West is my soul, The / Cowboy camp meetin' / Following the sun all day / Whispering wind / Trail dreaming / Redwood tree.
MC: . . . . CSR 9C

RADIO TRANSCRIPTIONS VOL.4.
Tracks: / Pecos Bill / Carry me back to the lone prairie / I follow the stream / Love song of the waterfall / Cherokee strip, The / Cowboy jubilee / Stars of the west / Night falls on the prairie / Lord you made the cowboy happy / Round / Up in the sky / Buffalo / Lillies grow high, The / Too high, too wide, too low / Round up / Time is over / He's ridin' home / Touch of God's hand.
MC: . . . . CSR 10C

SONS OF THE PIONEERS.
Tracks: / Song of the bandit / At the rainbows end / Hold that critter down / When the golden train comes down / Cajun stomp / You must come in at the door / Devil's great grandson / Cowboy night herd song / Send him home to me / Touch of God's hand.
LP: . . . . CBS 25015

STANDARD RADIO TRANSCRIPTIONS 1934/35, VOL.2, THE.
Tracks: / Put on your old grey bonnet / Dear old girl / Gospel train / Dese bones gwine to rise again / Lone star trail, The / Little red barn / Hills of old Kentucky / Little Annie Rooney / Jim crack corn / Rufus Rastas Johnson Brown / Jordan am a hard road to travel / Threw it out of the window.
MC: . . . . CSR 6C

STANDARD RADIO TRANSCRIPTIONS 1934/35, THE.
Tracks: / Swiss yodel / When round-up is over / Hear dem bells / Giddyap Napoleon / Ain't we crazy / Side walk waltz / Bells of Baltimore / White mule of mine / Sweet Betsy from Pike / She came rollin' down the mountain / Grandfather's clock / Little brown jug.
MC: . . . . CSR 5C

Sophie

SOPHIE U.S. Cast (Various artists).
LP: . . . . AEI 1130

Sophie's Choice

SOPHIE'S CHOICE (Film Soundtrack) (Various artists).
Tracks: / Sophie's Choice love theme: *Various artists* / Train ride to Brooklyn: *Various artists* / Returning the tray: *Various artists* / Coney Island fun: *Various artists* / Songs without words: *Various artists*/ Op 30, no 1: *Various artists* / Emily Dickenson: *Various artists* / Aren't all women like you?: *Various* artists / Rite on the Brooklyn Bridge: *Various artists* / Stingo; Polish lullaby: *Various artists* / Nathan returns: *Various artists* / Southern plantation: *Various artists* / I'll never leave you: *Various artists*/ Stingo and Sophie together: *Various artists* / Ample make this bed: *Various artists* / Sophies Choice end credits: *Various artists.*
LP: . . . . N 5016
LP: . . . . SCRS 1002

Sophocles

ANTIGONE (Various artists).
MCSET: 0320

OEDIPUS REX (Various artists).
MCSET: 2012

Soprano Summit

LIVE AT BIGHORN JAZZ FESTIVAL.
LP: . . . . J 56

Sopwith Camel

FRANTIC DESOLATION.
LP: . . . . ED 185

MIRACULOUS HUMP RETURNS FROM THE MOON.
Tracks: / Fazon / Coke, suede and waterbeds / Dancin' wizard / Sleazy street / Orange peel / Oriental fantasy / Sneaky Smith / Monkeys on the moon / Astronaut food / Brief symptoms.
LP: . . . . XED 205

Sorbye, Lief

SPRINGDANCE.
LP: . . . . EULP 1056
MC: . . . . EUMC 1056

Sorcerer

SORCERER (Film soundtrack) (See under Tangerine Dream) (Tangerine Dream).

Sorcerer's

SORCERER'S APPRENTICE, THE (well loved tales up to age 9) (Unknown narrator(s)).
MC: . . . . PLB 97

Sore Throat

DISGRACE TO THE CORPSE OF SID.
LP: . . . . MOSH 10

NEVER MIND THE NAPALM HERE'S SORE THROAT.
Tracks: / Intro (rapists die) / D.T.C.H.C. / Vac head / Process of elimination / S.S.A. (part 2) / R.O.T. / Only the dead / War system / Sacrilege / Pesticide death / Trenchfoot / Satans radish / Funicidal tendencies / Bomb The Whitehouse.
LP: . . . . EARLP 001

SOONER THAN YOU THINK.
Tracks: / Wonder drug / 7th heaven / Flak jacket / Routine patrol / British subject / Mr. Right / Off the hook / Crackdrown / Sooner than you think.
LP: . . . . FLAK 101

UNHINDERED BY TALENT.
LP: . . . . COX 012

Soria Moria Castle

SORIA MORIA CASTLE (Various artists).
Tracks: / Soria Moria castle: *Various artists* / Changeling: *Various artists* / Peter and the troll: *Various artists* / Troll and Smoky Joe, The: *Various artists* / Dapplegrim: *Various artists.*
MC: . . . . ANV 640

Sorkness, Bjorn

BEARBURGER, THE.
MC: . . . . U 018 MC

Sorokus

SOROKUS.
Tracks: / It's going on / Think about it / Cruizin' / Brown eyes / Where would I be / One more lady / Take me to your place / Gentle touch, The.
LP: . . . . TRLP 122
LP: . . . . TRPL 122

Sorrels, Rosalie

ALWAYS A LADY.
LP: . . . . PH 1029

MOMENTS OF HAPPINESS.
LP: . . . . PH 1033

Sorrows

PINK, PURPLE, YELLOW & RED.
Tracks: / Take a heart / Pink purple yellow and red / I don't wanna be free / Don't sing no sad songs for me / My gal / Baby / No, no, no, no / Cara-lin / You've got what I want / Let the live live / Let me in / Come with me / How love used to be / Teenage letter / We should get along fine / She's got the action.
LP: . . . . KIRI 089

TEENAGE HEARTBREAK.
Tracks: / Teenage heartbreak / I don' like it like that / Bad times good times / I don't like that / I want you tonight / Lonely girl / She comes and goes / Can't go back / All you gotta say / I want you so bad / Can't you tell a lie / Second chance / Television.
LP: . . . . EPC 84265

Sorry

THAT WAY IT IS.
LP: . . . . HMS 039

Sorry Bamba

LE TONNERE DU DOGON.
LP: . . . . PB 15

S.O.S. Band

12" TAPE: S.O.S. BAND.
Tracks: / Just be good to me / Just the way you like it / Weekend girl / Finest, The / Borrowed Love.
MC: 4501324

DIAMOND IN THE RAW.
LP: 4607351
MC: 4607354

HIT MIXES, THE.
Tracks: / Just be good to me (vocal remix) / Borrowed love (extended version) / Just the way you like it (long version) / Finest, The (extended version) / No lies (special version) / No lies (dub mix) / Take your time (do it right).
LP: 460597 1
MC: 460597 4

JUST BE GOOD TO ME (OLD GOLD) (See under Mtume 'Juicy fruit' (Old Gold)).

JUST BE GOOD TO ME/WEEKEND GIRL (OLD GOLD) (See under Mtume/ Juicy fruit).

JUST THE WAY YOU LIKE IT.
Tracks: / No one's gonna love you / Weekend girl / Just the way you like it / Breakup / Feeling / I don't want nobody else / Body break.

LP: . . . . **TBU 26058**
MC: **40 26058**
LP: **467 016 1**
MC: **467 016 4**

ON THE RISE.
Tracks: / Tell me if you still care / Just be good to me / For your love / I'm not runnin' / If you want my love / On the rise / Who's making love? / Steppin' the stones.
LP: **4501651**
MC: **4501654**
LP: . . . . **TBU 25476**

ONE OF MANY NIGHTS.
LP: **364003 1**
MC: **364003 4**

SANDS OF TIME.
Tracks: / Even when you sleep / Sands of time / Borrowed love / Nothing but the best / Finest, The / No lies / Two time lover / Do you still want to? / Sands of time (reprise).
LP: . . . . **TBU 26863**
MC: **40 26863**
LP: **460946 1**
MC: **460946 4**

S.O.S.
Tracks: / S.O.S. (Dit, dit, dit, dash, dash, dash, dit, dit, dit) / What's wrong with our love affair / Open letter / Love won't wait for love / Take your time (do it right) / I'm in love / Take love where you find it / S.O.S. (reprise).
LP: . . . . **TBU 32541**
MC: **40 32541**
LP: . . . . **TBU 84445**

SOS BAND, THE.
Tracks: / Can't get enough / High hopes / Have it your way / Your love / Good and plenty / Looking for you / These are the things / You shake me up / Groovin'.
LP: . . . . **TBU 25078**

WEEKEND GIRL (OLD GOLD) (See under O'Jays - Put our heads together).

Soskin, Mark

RHYTHMIC VISION.
Tracks: / Colossus / Mambo mio / Walk tall / Caribbean party / Stomp / That's what friends are for / Opening / Bolinas.
LP: . . . . **PR 10109**

Soso, Winston

AH CAN'T HELP IT.
LP: . . . . **GS 2307**
MC: . . . . **GSC 2307**

OUT ON THE EDGE.
LP: . . . . **GS 2290**

Souchon, Doc

DOC SOUCHON AND HIS MILENBURG BOYS.
LP: . . . . **GHB 131**

Soul

20 GREAT "UNKNOWN" SOUL CLASSICS OF THE 60'S AND (Various artists).
Tracks: / And the rains came: *Various artists* / Ain't that soul?: *Millionaires* / Hey stoney face: *Love, Mary* / Dance, children, dance: *Various artists* / Think it over baby: *Love, Mary* / Slow and easy: *Various* artists / If I could turn back the hands of time: *Garett, Vernon* / Get lost: *King, Al* / Sweet temptation: *Watson, Cressa* / You just cheat and lie: *Hill, Z.Z.* / If I could do it all over again: *Hill, Z.Z.* / You are my sunshine: *Shane, Jackie* / Let freedom ring: *Turner, Frank* / I've got a right to lose my mind: *Various* artists / I'm not ashamed: *Various artists* / With all my heart: *White, Margo* / You know it ain't right: *Lil' Bob & The Lollipops* / Blue on blue: *Ikettes* / Woman needs a man, A: *Baker, Yvonne* / It's raining: *Thomas, Irma*.
LP: . . . . **DROP 1013**
MC: . . . . **CROP 1013**

60'S SOUL (Various artists).
LP: . . . . **KNLP 15006**
MC: . . . . **KNMC 15006**

60'S SOUL CLUB (Various artists).
Tracks: / Summertime: *Stewart, Billy* / Farther on up the road: *Simon, Joe* / Show me: *Tex, Joe* / How I miss you baby: *Womack, Bobby* / Barefootin': *Parker, Robert* / Getting mighty crowded: *Everett, Betty*/ Get on up: *Esquires* / Rescue me: *Bass, Fontella* / Come on sock it to me: *Johnson, Syl* / Land of a thousand dances: *Kenner, Chris* / Ride your pony: *Dorsey, Lee* / Selfish one: *Ross, Jackie* / Lover's holiday: *Scott, Peggy & Jo Jo Benson* / Nothing can stop me: *Chandler, Gene*.
LP: . . . . **INS 5005**
MC: . . . . **TCINS 5005**

100 MINUTES OF SOUL GREATS (Various artists).
MC: . . . . **ZCTON 121**

1320 SOUTH LAUDARDALE AVENUE (Various artists).
Tracks: / Listen (take 1): *Green, Al* / Get back baby: *Green, Al* / Starting over again: *Green, Al* / Everything to me: *Green, Al* / Sweet song: *Green, Al* / Listen (take 2): *Green, Al* / Nothing impossible with love: *Green, Al* / Fool can't see the light, A: *Wright, O.V.* / I'm gonna be a big man some day: *Wright, O.V.* / Did you ever have the blues: *Bryant, Don* / With your hand: *Bryant, Don* / Run to me: *Bryant, Don* / It ain't easy: *Bryant, Don* / Coming on strong: *Bryant, Don*.
LP: . . . . **HIUKLP 430**

AMERICAN SOUL 1966-72 (Various artists).
LP: . . . . **CGB 1003**

BEST OF CHESS, CHECKER, CADET SOUL (Various artists).
LP: . . . . **CXMP 2003**

BEST OF OKEH VOL.1 (Various artists).
LP: **81224**

BEST OF OKEH VOL.2 (Various artists).
LP: **81532**

BEST OF RARE, THE (Various artists).
Tracks: / Expansions: *Liston Smith, Lonnie* / Oops here I go again: *Wright, Edna* / Till you take me love: *Mason,* Harvey / Never (gonna let you go): *Charme* / Miss Cheryl: *Banda Black Rio* / Delerium: *McGhee, Fancine*/ Stick by me: *Serenade* / Haboglabotribin: *Wright, Bernard* / Holding you loving you: *Blackman, Donald*/ Work to do: *Main Ingredient* / Action speaks louder than words: *Chocolate Milk* / Love me like this: *Real To Reel* / Close Encounters of the Third Kind: *Page, Gene* / Mr. Business: *Browne, Tom*.
LP: **211083**
MC: **411083**

BIG CITY SOUL SOUND (Various artists).
LP: . . . . **KENT 061**

BLACK MUSIC IS OUR BUSINESS (Galaxy of soul, A) (Various artists).
Tracks: / Drifting: *Huey, Claude "Baby"* / Why would you blow it: *Huey, Claude "Baby"* / Zig zag lightning: *Taylor,* Little Johnny / Big blue diamonds: *Taylor, Little Johnny* / I finally got wise: *Keen, Billy* / I got to tell somebody: *Everett, Betty* / Man don't cry: *Witherspoon, Jimmy* / Love me right: *Witherspoon, Jimmy* / Why do you have to lie?: *Right Kind* / She's looking good: *Collins, Rodger* / Lover set me free: *Grier, Roosevelt*/ Thompin': *Merced Blue Notes* / When you find a fool bump his head: *Coday, Bill* / How can I forget you?: *Williams, Lenny* / My babe: *McCoy, Freddie* / Doing the best I can (with what I got): *Williams, Larry & The ATS Express*.
LP: . . . . **KENT 085**

BLACK SATIN (Various artists).
Tracks: / When a man loves a woman: *Sledge, Percy* / Hold on I'm coming: *Sam & Dave* / Heatwave: *Reeves,* Martha (1) / Knock on wood: *Floyd, Eddie* / Up on the roof: *Drifters* / Rescue me: *Bass, Fontella*/ Do the funky chicken: *Thomas, Rufus* / Hey there lonely girl: *Holman, Eddie* / Everlasting love: *Knight,* Robert / Jimmy Mack: *Reeves, Martha (1)* / If loving you is wrong I don't want to be right: *Sledge, Percy*/ Hey girl don't bother me: *Tams* / B.A.B.Y.: *Thomas, Carla* / Patches: *Carter, Clarence* / I heard it through the grapevine: *Reeves, Martha (1)* / (Sittin' on) the dock of the bay: *Sledge, Percy* / Harlem shuffle: *Bob & Earl* / Lover's concerto: *Toys* / Best thing that ever happened to me, The: *Knight, Gladys & The Pips*/ Under the boardwalk: *Drifters* / Softly whispering I love you: *New Congregation* / Da doo ron ron: *Crystals*/ Midnight train to Georgia: *Knight, Gladys & The Pips* / Try a little tenderness: *Sledge, Percy* / My guy: *Wells,* Mary / You little trust maker: *Tymes* / Soul man: *Sam & Dave* / Quicksand: *Reeves, Martha (1)* / Then he kissed me: *Crystals* / Tighten up: *Bell, Archie & The Drells*.
MCSET: . . . . **CRT 022**

BLACK SOUL (Various artists).
Tracks: / Dancing in the street: *Reeves, Martha (1)* / Hold on: *Sam & Dave* / Harlem shuffle: *Bob & Earl*/ Every beat of my heart: *Knight, Gladys* / He's so fine: *Chiffons* / Walking the dog: *Thomas, Rufus*/ My guy: *Wells, Mary* / Save the last dance for me: *Drifters* / Love on a mountain top: *Knight, Robert*/ Da doo ron ron: *Crystals* / Something old, something new: *Fantastics* / Knock on wood: *Floyd, Eddie*/ Do the funky chicken: *Thomas, Rufus* / B.A.B.Y.: *Thomas, Carla* / Heatwave: *Reeves, Martha (1)* / Will you love me tomorrow: *Shirelles* / Rescue me: *Bass, Fontella* / Soul man: *Sam & Dave* / Sweet talking guy: *Chiffons* / Saturday night at the movies: *Drifters*.
LP: . . . . **PAST 2**

BLUES AND SOUL POWER (See under Blues) (Various artists).

BORN ON THE BAYOU (Various artists).
Tracks: / Born on the bayou: *Bad Habits* / Knock on wood: *Fred, John & The Playboys* / 96 tears: *Stampley,* Joe and the Uniques / Summertime blues: *Tom and the Cats* / Nadine: *Rogue Show* / You really got a hold on me: *5 x 5* / I don't want to discuss it: *Bad Habits* / Boogie chillun: *Fred, John & The Playboys* / Soul man: *5 x 5* / Out of sight: *Fred, John & The Playboys* / Good good lovin': *Tom and the Cats* / Sugar bee: *Stampley, Joe and the Uniques* / Harlem shuffle: *In Crowd (group)* / I've been lovin' you too long: *Fred, John & The Playboys* / Treat her right: *Stampley, Joe and the Uniques* / Night owl: *Bad Habits*.
LP: . . . . **CR 30212**

CAPITOL CLASSICS VOL. 2 (Various artists).
Tracks: / Be thankful for what you've got: *Devaughan, William* / Hard to get around: *B B & Q Band* / Before you break my heart: *Dunlap, Gene* / Call on me: *Maze* / Work that sucker to death: *Xavier* / Really, really love you: *Parker, Cecil* / There ain't nothin' (like your lovin'): *Laurence, Paul* / Promise me: *Dayton*/ It's just the way I feel: *Dunlap, Gene & The Ridgeways* / Annie Mae: *Cole, Natalie*.
LP: . . . . **EMS 1338**
MC: . . . . **TCEMS 1338**

CHESS SISTERS OF SOUL (Various artists).
Tracks: / Wang dang doodle: *Taylor, Koko* / Selfish one: *Ross, Jackie* / Mama didn't lie: *Bradley, Jan*/ Two sides (to every story): *James, Etta* / Take me for a little while: *Ross, Jackie* / Rescue me: *Bass,* Fontella / Only time will tell: *James, Etta* / I had a talk with my man: *Collier, Mitty* / Lovin' you more every day: *James, Etta*.
LP: . . . . **CXMP 2052**
MC: . . . . **ZCCXMP 2052**

CHICAGO SOUL UPRISING (The Real Sound of Chicago 1967-1975) (Various artists).
Tracks: / Since you showed me how to be happy: *Wilson, Jackie* / I love you: *Leavill, Otis* / Give it away: *Chi-lites*/ Girl don't care, The: *Chandler, Gene* / Am I the same girl: *Acklin, Barbara* / Sly slick and wicked: *Lost*Generation / I'll be right there: *Davis, Tyrone* / Funky chicken: *Henderson, Willie* / Follow the leader: *Major Lance* / Love uprising: *Leavill, Otis* / Let me be the man my daddy was: *Chi-lites* / Could I forget you: *Davis, Tyrone* / Got to find me a lover: *Franklin, Erma* / Girl I need you: *Artistics* / Wait a minute: *Lost Generation* / Don't burn no bridges: *Wilson, Jackie & The Chi-Lites*.
LP: . . . . **CRB 1160**
MC: . . . . **TCCRB 1160**

CHRISTMAS SOUL SPECIAL (See under Christmas...) (Various artists).

CLASSIC MELLOW MASTERCUTS VOL. 1 (Various artists).
Tracks: / She's so good to me: *Vandross, Luther* / Risin' to the top: *Burke, Keni* / Outstanding: *Gap Band*/ Joy and pain: *Maze* / Give me the sunshine: *Leo's Sunshipp* / Hold me tighter in the rain: *Griffin, Billy*/ I'm out of your life: *Arnie's Love* / You'll never know: *Hi-Gloss* / What you won't do for love: *Caldwell,* Bobby / I'm back for more: *Johnson, Al & Jean Carn* / Fruit song, The: *Reynolds, Jeannie* / Mellow mellow right on: *Lowrell*.
LP: . . . . **CUTSLP 3**
MC: . . . . **CUTSMC 3**

CLASSIC SOUL YEARS SERIES 1964 (Various artists).
Tracks: / Hey girl don't bother me: *Tams* / Lovers always forgive: *Knight, Gladys & The Pips* / It's in his kiss: *Everett, Betty* / Chapel of love: *Dixie Cups* / Gonna send you back to Georgia: *Shaw, Timmy* / I just don't know what to do with myself: *Hunt, Tommy* / Do wah diddy: *Exciters* / Loving you more everyday: *James,* Etta / I had a talk with my man: *Collier, Mitty* / Sha-la-la: *Shirelles* / Let it be me: *Everett, Betty* & Jerry Butler / Soulville: *Franklin, Aretha* / Um, um, um, um, um, um: *Lance, Major* / Soul serenade: *Curtis,* King / Selfish one: *Ross, Jackie* / Hurt by love: *Foxx, Inez & Charlie* / Quiet place, A: *Mimms, Garnet*/ Beg me: *Jackson, Chuck* / So far away: *Jacobs, Hank* / Keep on pushing: *Impressions* / I can't stand it: *Soul Sisters* / Time is on my side: *Thomas, Irma*.
2LP: . . . . **CSYR LP 64**
MC: . . . . **CSYR MC 64**

CLASSIC SOUL YEARS SERIES 1965 (Various artists).
Tracks: / Rescue me: *Fontella Bass* / Duck, The: *Lee, Jackie* / Sitting in the park: *Stewart, Billy*/ Who's that lady: *Isley Brothers* / Lipstick traces (on a cigarette): *O'Jays* / Getting mighty crowded: *Everett, Betty* / Come tomorrow: *Knight, Marie* / Goin' out of my head: *Little Anthony* / Birds and the bees: *Akens,* Jewel / Baby I'm yours: *Lewis, Barbara* / If you gotta make a fool: *Brown, Maxine* / Boy from New York City: *Ad Libs* / Gee baby: *3 Degrees* / We're gonna make it: *Little Milton* / In crowd, The: *Ramsey, Lewis* Trio / Misty: *Vibrations* / Jerk, The: *Larks* / Iko iko: *Dixie Cups* / It was easier to hurt her: *Mimms, Garnet* / Hold what you've got: *Tex, Joe* / I can't work no longer: *Butler, Billy* / I don't know what ...: *Little Richard* / You're gonna make me cry: *Wright, O.V.* / Stay in my corner: *Dells*.
LP: . . . . **CSYRLP 65**
MC: . . . . **CSYRMC 65**

CLASSIC SOUL YEARS SERIES 1966 (Various artists).
Tracks: / Barefootin': *Parker, Robert* / I spy for the F.B.I.: *Thomas, Jamo* / Lot of love, A: *Banks, Homer*/ Holy cow: *Dorsey, Lee* / Karate: *Emperors* / I'm gonna make you love me: *Warwick, Dee Dee* / I'm your puppet: *Purify, James & Bobby* / Love is a hurting thing: *Rawls, Lou* / When a woman loves a man: *Lester,* Ketty / Sweet talking guy: *Chiffons* / Searching for my love: *Moore, Bob* / Summertime: *Stewart, Billy*/ Sunny: *Herb, Bobby* / Maybe: *3 Degrees* / Tell it like it is: *Neville, Aaron* / I fooled you this time: *Chandler, Gene* / No man is an island: *Van Dykes* / Soul at sunrise: *Juggy* / What did I do wrong: *Harris,* Betty / Bad mouthin': *Mighty Sam* / It's a man's man's man's world: *Brown, James* / There's something on my mind: *Baby Ray* / Hurt: *Little Anthony* / For you precious love: *Butler, Jerry*.
LP: . . . . **CSYR LP 66**
MC: . . . . **CSYR MC 66**

CLASSIC SOUL YEARS SERIES 1967 (Various artists).
Tracks: / Dance to the music: *Sly & the Family Stone* / O - O - I love you: *Dells* / Dirty man: *Lee, Laura*/ Gimme little sign: *Wood, Brenton* / River of soul: *Capel, Larry* / For your precious love: *Toney, Oscar Jr* / Show me: *Tex, Joe* / Never let me go: *Dykes, Van* / No more tears: *Jive Five* / Everlasting love: *Knight, Robert* / Do what you gotta do: *Wilson, Al* / I believe in you: *Baker, Sam* / My ship is coming in: *Jackson, Walter* / Girl from Texas, The: *Lewis, Jimmy* / When she touches me: *Mighty Sam* / Can't last much longer: *Harris, Betty* / Working on your case: *O'Jays* / Hunk of funk: *Dozier, Gene* / Nothing takes the place of ...: *McCall, Toussaint* / Money: *Little Richard* / Rough dried woman: *Big Mac*/ Everybody needs help: *Holiday, Jimmy* / 60 minutes of your love: *Banks, Homer* / Get on up: *Esquires*.
LP: . . . . **CSYR LP67**
MC: . . . . **CSYR MC67**

CLASSIC SOUL YEARS SERIES 1968 (Various artists).
Tracks: / Nothing can stop me: *Chandler, Gene* / Without love: *Toney, Oscar Jr* / Cry baby cry: *Van & Titus*/ Cowboys to girls: *Intruders* / Uptight good man: *Lee, Laura* / Please don't change me now: *Dells* / Yesterday has gone: *Little Anthony* / Good to me: *Thomas, Irma* / Snake, The: *Wilson, Al* / At the dark end of the tunnel: *Little Milton* / Baby you got it: *Wood, Brenton* / Look over your shoulder: *O'Jays*/ I'd rather go blind: *James, Etta* / We got a good thing going: *King, Clydie* / I've got love for my baby: *Young Hearts* / Where is my baby: *Neville, Aaron* / Baby make your own sweet music: *Johnson, Johnny* / And black is beautiful: *Lee, Nickie* / When a man cries: *Robinson, Johnny* / Gonna get that boat (part 1): *Lytle, Johnny*/ Lover's holiday: *Scott, Peggy* / I'm glad it's over: *Mack, Oscar* / Love that never grows: *Tig, J & L*.
LP: . . . . **CSYR LP68**
MC: . . . . **CSYR MC68**

CLASSICS AND RARITIES (Various artists).
LP: **2429193**

CLUB CLASSICS (Various artists).
Tracks: / Soul city walk: *Bell, Archie & The Drells* / Love is lost, The: *Melvin, Harold & The Bluenotes* / I don't love you anymore: *Pendergrass, Teddy* / It ain't reggae (but its funky): *Instant Funk* / Life on Mars: *Wansel,* Dexter / I'll always love my mama: *Intruders* / Do it anyway you wanna: *People's Choice* / You'll never find another love like mine: *Rawls, Lou* / If you wanna go back: *Carn, Jean* / Come go with me: *Pockets*.
LP: . . . . **VAULT 1**
MC: . . . . **VAULT 401**

CLUB CLASSICS II (Various artists).

Tracks: / Family affair: *Sly & the Family Stone* / Let's groove: *Bell, Archie & The Drells* / Harvest for the world: *Isley Brothers* / Jam, jam, jam: *People's Choice* / Let's clean up the ghetto: *Philadelphia All Stars*/ Always there: *Bobo, Willie* / Barbara Ann: *Lewis, Webster* / Was that all it was: *Carn, Jean* / Sweetest pain, The: *Dexter, Wansell*.
LP: . . . . **VAULT 2**
MC: . . . . **VAULT 402**

CRY CRY CRYING (Various artists).
Tracks: / From a whisper to a scream: *Toussaint, Allen* / I just don't know what to do with myself: *Jackson, Chuck*/ Invitation: *Copeland, Johnny* / Girl you turned your back on my love: *Charles, Lee* / Cry me a river: *Knight*, Marie / Put yourself in my place: *Big Maybelle* / Human: *Hunt, Tommy* / Love ain't what it used to be: *Diplomats*/ It hurts so good: *Love, Katie & The Four Shades Of Black* / You're in love: *Brown, Maxine* / Saving my love for you: *Franklin, Erma* / Loser again: *Moore, (Miss) Jackie* / Don't say goodnight and mean goodbye: *Shirelles*/ Have you seen her: *Chi-lites* / It's all over: *Independents*.
LP: . . . . **KENT 030**

DANCE FLOOR DISASTER (Various artists).
Tracks: / Hard working man: *Nitzsche, Jack Orchestra* (Featuring Captain Beefheart on vocals.) / You can do it: *Hudson*, Al & The Partners / Blue moon: *Bland, Bobby* / Shoo doo fu fu ooh: *Williams, Lenny* / Heart breakers: *King*, B.B. / Soul perception: *Johnson, Harold* / Sting me baby: *Garrett, Jo Ann* / Y K W: *Verdell, Jackie*/ Puffin' on down the track: *Masekela, Hugh* / Hard work: *Handy, John* / Screaming please: *Ace, Buddy*/ Chose it: *Smoke* / Hound dog: *Williams, Jeanette* / That's why I'm always crying: *Parker, Junior* / Don't put me down: *El Chicano* / You've got to learn: *Jones, Buster*.
LP: . . . . **KENT 076**

DEEP SOUL COLLECTION, THE (Various artists).
LPS: . . . . **BOX 251**
MCSET: . . . . **TCBOX 251**

DEEP SOUTH, THE (Various artists).
Tracks: / Cheaters never win: *Borders Tony* / I can't make it by myself: *Gardner, Stu* / Afflicted: *Wright*, O.V. / Gonna try: *Mike & The Censations* / Everyday will be like a holiday: *Haywood, Leon* / Something reminds me: *Carter, Melvin* / Everyday of my life: *Augustine Twins, The* / I Wake Up Crying: *Leroy & The Drivers*/ Ain't much of a home: *James, Jesse* / Bring It Down: *Jon-Lee Group* / I feel like crying: *Sam & Bill*/ Thanks for yesterday: *Eddie & Ernie* / Will my baby: *Little Mr Lee and The Cherokees* / These Arms of Mine: *Matt & Robert* / In return for your love: *Tolliver, Kim* / Keep on loving me: *Bland, Bobby*.
LP: . . . . **KENT 075**

DETROIT GOLD VOL. 1 (Various artists).
LP: . . . . **SS 8021**

DETROIT GOLD VOL. 2 (Various artists).
LP: . . . . **SS 8022**

DISCONNECTIONS (Various artists).
Tracks: / I like what you're doing to me: *Young & Company* / Here's to you: *New York Skyy* / Double Dutch: *Smith*, Frankie / Chill out: *Free Expression* / I wish: *Rollercoaster* / Lock it up: *Leprechaun* / Feels like I'm in love: *Marie, Kelly* / Love (is gonna be on your side): *Firefly* / Strut your sexy stuff lady: *Young & Company* / Stretch: *B.T.Express* / Just a groove: *Adams, Glen Affair* / Wide receiver: *Henderson, Michael*/ Rappers delight: *Sugarhill Gang* / We got the groove: *Players Association* / Give up the funk: *B.T.Express*/ In the forest: *Baby O* / No time like now: *Philly Cream* / By all means: *Mouzon, Alphonse* / We got the funk: *Positive Force* / She's a groovy freak: *Real Thing* / Keep in touch: *Freeez* / Pata pata: *Osibisa*/ Get down mellow mellow sound, The: *Players Association* / Can you feel the force: *Real Thing*.
2LP: . . . . **COMP 1**
MC: . . . . **ZCCOM 1**

DOWN TO THE LAST HEARTBREAK (Various artists).
Tracks: / Hello heartbreaker: *Little Charles & The Sidewinders* / He's the kind of guy: *Clay, Judy* / One more time: *Scott, Benny* / Not now but later: *Johnson, Walter* / I'm down to my last heartbreak: *Pickett, Wilson*/ Big mistake: *Parker, John* / It sho' ain't me: *Turner, Ike & Tina* / Can't get enough: *Thomas, Irma*/ Don't stop loving me this time: *Preyer, Marvin* / I'm really thankful: *Troy, J B* / Love makes good things unwise: *Various artists* / Lonesome guy: *Robinson, Roscoe* / Strange lips start old memories: *Traits* / Every man needs a woman: *Troy, J B* / You're gonna reap what you sow: *Copeland, Johnny*.
LP: . . . . **KENT 084**

EBONY (Various artists).
Tracks: / I don't wanna dance: *Grant, Eddy* / Deja vu: *Warwick, Dionne* / Ms. Grace: *Tymes* / You to me are everything: *Real Thing* / Stand by me: *King, Ben E.* / Ebony: *Williams, George* / Me and Mrs. Jones: *Paul, Billy* / Letter, The: *Warwick, Dionne* / I wanna get next to you: *Rose Royce* / Hurt: *Manhattans*/ Tears on my pillow / Make it with you: *Williams, Esther* / Sad sweet dreamer: *Sweet Sensation* / Midnight train to Georgia: *Knight, Gladys* / Lady love: *Rawls, Lou* / My simple heart: *3 Degrees* / Love is: *Brothers* Johnson / I'm stone in love with you: *Mathis, Johnny* / One in a million (girl): *O'Jays* / Don't make me over: *Houston, Thelma* / One hundred ways: *Jones, Quincy* / Float on: *Floaters* / Circles: *Atlantic Starr*/ Free: *Williams, Deniece* / Drift away: *Various artists* / Hey girl, don't bother me: *Tams* / Rescue me: *Bass, Fontella* / If you don't know me by now: *Melvin, Harold & The Bluenotes*.
2LP: . . . . **STD 6**
MCSET: . . . . **STDK 6**

ESSENTIAL SOUL (Various artists).
MC: **2462**

ESSENTIAL SOUL (Various artists).
Tracks: / Make it easy on yourself: *Butler, Jerry* / Land of a thousand dances: *Kenner, Chris* / Release me: *Phillips*, Esther / You're no good: *Everett, Betty* / You can make it if you try: *Allison, G* / Soulful dress: *Sugar* Pie Desanto / Here comes the judge: *Markham, Pigmeat* / In crowd, The: *Ramsey, Lewis Trio* / Moon river: *Butler*, Jerry / I like it like that: *Kenner, Chris* / Raindrops: *Clark, Dee* / Get out of my life woman: *Dorsey, Lee* / Down home girl: *Robinson, Alvin* / Rescue me: *Fontella Bass*.
LP: . . . . **KNLP 15003**
MC: . . . . **KNMC 15003**

ESSENTIAL SOUL WEEKENDER (Various artists).
2LP: . . . . **LPSD 151**

FANTASISED SOUL (Various artists).
LP: . . . . **K 2417031**
MC: . . . . **K 2417034**

FAST, FUNKY & FANTASTIC (70's soul from fantasy) (Various artists).
Tracks: / Will they miss me: *Simmons, David* / Always there: *Side Effect* / I need you girl: *Three Pieces*/ Motown review: *Philly Cream* / Get your lies straight: *Coday, Bill* / Evil Ways: *Tjader, Cal* / Mr Weatherman: *Water & Power* / Walking in rhythm: *Blackbyrds* / Take all the time you need: *Checkmates Ltd* / S-A-T-I-S-F-A-C-T-I-O-N: *Lee, Laura* / I told you so: *Janice* / It's music: *Harris, Damon* / I don't want to be a Lone Ranger: *Watson, Johnny 'Guitar'* / Danger: *Everett, Betty*.
LP: . . . . **KENT 082**

GARAGE GROOVES OF DETROIT (Various artists).
LP: . . . . **CDMOTCLP 52**

GIRLS WITH SOUL (Various artists).
Tracks: / Woman to woman: *Brown, Shirley* / It ain't long enough: *Clay, Judy* / Keep on searching: *Alexander*, Margie / Wishes and dishes: *Sweet Inspirations* / Punish me: *Joseph, Margie* / You just don't know: *Weston*, Kim / Short stopping: *Brown, Veda* / Funny: *Hot Sauce* / Mr. Big Stuff: *Knight, Jean* / I like what you're doing to me: *Thomas, Carla* / Don't start lovin' me (if you're gonna stop): *Brown, Veda* / Circuits overloaded: *Foxx, Inez & Charlie* / Stop in the name of love: *Joseph, Margie* / I have learned to do without you: *Staples, Mavis* / It's time to pay for the fun (we've had): *Jeanne & The Darlings* / So I can love you: *Emotions (group)*.
LP: . . . . **STAXL 5003**
MC: . . . . **STAXK 5003**

GOLDEN AGE OF BLACK MUSIC 1970-1975 (Various artists).
Tracks: / Don't play that song: *Franklin, Aretha* / Groove me: *King Floyd* / Precious precious: *Moore, Jackie*/ Don't let the green grass fool you: *Pickett, Wilson* / Don't knock my love (part 1): *Pickett, Wilson* / First time ever I saw your face, The: *Flack, Roberta* / Daydreaming: *Franklin, Aretha* / Could it be I'm falling in love: *Detroit Spinners* / Killing me softly with his song: *Flack, Roberta* / Until you come back to me: *Franklin*, Aretha / Then came you: *Warwick, Dionne/Spinners (USA)* / Sideshow: *Blue Magic* / Feel like makin' love: *Flack, Roberta* / They just can't stop it (games people play): *Detroit Spinners*.
LP: **781 912-1**
MC: **781 912-4**

GOLDEN AGE OF BLACK MUSIC 1977-1988 (Various artists).
Tracks: / Dance, dance, dance: *Chic* / Closer I get to you, The: *Flack, Roberta & Donny Hathaway* / Le freak: *Chic* / We are family: *Sister Sledge* / Good times: *Chic* / You are in my system: *System* / (Pop pop pop) goes my mind: *Levert* / Don't disturb this groove: *System* / Come share my love: *Howard, Miki*/ Casanova: *Levert* / So amazing: *Albright, Gerald*.
LP: . . . . **K 781 913 1**
MC: . . . . **K 781 913 4**

GOLDEN AGE OF BLACK MUSIC 1960-1970 (Various artists).
Tracks: / Stand by me: *King, Ben E.* / When a man loves a woman: *Sledge, Percy* / I never loved a man (the way I love you): *Franklin, Aretha* / Sweet soul music: *Conley, Arthur* / Respect: *Franklin, Aretha* / Soul man: *Sam & Dave* / Baby I love you: *Franklin, Aretha* / (Sittin' on) The dock of the bay: *Redding, Otis*/ Chain of fools: *Franklin, Aretha* / Slip away: *Carter, Clarence* / Since you've been gone (sweet sweet baby): *Franklin, Aretha* / Too weak to fight: *Carter, Clarence* / Think: *Franklin, Aretha* / Can I change my mind: *Davis, Tyrone* / I say a little prayer: *Franklin, Aretha* / Rainy night in Georgia: *Benton, Brook*.
LP: . . . . **K 781 911 1**
MC: . . . . **K 781 911 4**

GOLDEN LADIES OF SOUL (Various artists).
MC: . . . . **SSC 3077**

GOLDEN SOUL (Various artists).
LP: . . . . **K 50332**
MC: . . . . **AMP 021**

GOLDEN SOUL OF THE 60'S (Various artists).
LP: . . . . **FUN 9007**
MC: . . . . **FUNC 9007**

GOOD TIMES (Various artists).
Tracks: / Memphis train: *Thomas, Rufus* / Some kind of wonderful: *Soul Brothers Six* / Memphis soul stew: *King Curtis* / Somebody (somewhere): *Turner, Ike & Tina* / Keep looking: *Burke, Solomon* / Things get better: *Floyd*, Eddie / Three time loser: *Pickett, Wilson* / Let the good times roll: *Charles, Ray* / Looking for a fox: *Carter*, Clarence / Sweet sweet baby: *Franklin, Aretha* / Good lovin': *Olympics* / Philly dog: *Mann, Herbie*/ I can't stop: *Conley, Arthur* / But it's alright: *Jackson, J.J.* / Help me: *Sharpe, Ray* / One way love: *Drifters*.
LP: . . . . **KENT 094**

GOT TO GET YOUR OWN (Some rare grooves, Vol 1) (Various artists).
Tracks: / Got to get your own: *Wilson, Reuben* / Black water gold: *African Music Machine* / Goo bah: *Continental Showstoppers* / Funky song: *Ripple* / Moon walk: *Ellis, Pee Wee* / Tropical: *African Music Machine*/ You're losing me: *Sexton, Ann* / I don't know what it is but it sure is funky: *Ripple* / So much trouble in my mind: *Quatermain, Joe* / That thang: *Ellis, Pee Wee* / Dapp, The: *African Music Machine* / I don't dig no phony, part 2: *Scott, Moody* / Brother man, sister Ann: *Smith, Clemon*.
LP: . . . . **CRM 2032**
MC: . . . . **TCCRM 2032**

GREAT SIXTIES SOUL GROUPS (Various artists).
Tracks: / Sly, the slick, and the wicked, The: *Lost Generation* / Woman: *Esquires* / Think twice before you walk away: *Porgy & The Monarchs* / Afraid of love: *Maestro, Johnny & The Crests* / Until you came along: *Visitors*/ There's still a tomorrow: *Diplomats* / Kiss and make up: *Inspirations* / Can't understand it: *Independents*/ You never loved me: *Chancellors* / Lonely old world: *Artistics* / Why do you wanna make me blue: *Platters*/ You have no time to lose: *Four Pennies* / Sugar (don't take away my candy): *Jive Five* / I got my own thing going: *Little Charles & The Sidewinders* / You're my one and only baby: *Intruders* / Another time, another place: *Persuaders*.
LP: . . . . **KENT 083**

GROOVE LINE, THE - SOUL HITS '72-82 (Various artists).
Tracks: / Lady Marmalade: *Labelle* / Boogie nights: *Heatwave* / I thought it was you: *Hancock, Herbie*/ She's a winner: *Intruders* / Harvest for the world: *Isley Brothers* / (You said) you'd gimme some more: *K.C.* & The Sunshine Band / Play that funky music: *Wild Cherry* / Summer of '42, Theme from: *Biddu Orchestra* / I love to love: *Charles, Tina* / Groove line, The: *Heatwave* / You bet your love: *Hancock, Herbie* / Best of my love: *Emotions* / T.S.O.P.: *MFSB* / That lady: *Isley Brothers* / Kiss & say goodbye: *Manhattans*/ Back Stabbers: *O'Jays* / Dr Love: *Charles, Tina* / Take good care of yourself: *3 Degrees*.
MC: . . . . **PWKMC 4062**

GUYS WITH SOUL (Various artists).
Tracks: / Who's making love: *Taylor, Johnnie* / I forgot to be your lover: *Bell, William* / I've never found a girl: *Floyd, Eddie* / Stop half loving these woman: *Lewis, Jimmy* / In the rain: *Dramatics* / Starting all over again: *Mel & Tim* / Packed up and took my mind: *Little Milton* / I like everything about you: *Hughes*, Jimmy / Knock on wood: *Floyd, Eddie* / I've been lonely for so long: *Knight, Frederick* / Cheaper to keep her: *Taylor, Johnnie* / Nothing takes the place of you: *Hayes, Isaac* / Nearer: *Johnson, Lou* / Lovin' on borrowed time: *Bell, William* / What I don't know won't hurt me: *Thompson, Paul*.
LP: . . . . **STAXL 5006**
MC: . . . . **STAXK 5006**

HEART AND SOUL II - BODY AND SOUL (18 classic soul cuts) (Various artists).
Tracks: / Miss you like crazy: *Cole, Natalie* / What's love got to do with it: *Turner, Tina* / Running with the night: *Richie, Lionel* / I say a little prayer: *Franklin, Aretha* / All of my life: *Ross, Diana* / Reach out, I'll be there: *Four Tops* / My one temptation: *Paris, Mica* / I really didn't mean it: *Vandross, Luther*/ If only I could: *Youngblood, Sydney* / Sexual healing: *Gaye, Marvin* / Being with you: *Robinson, Smokey*/ (Sittin' on) the dock of the bay: *Redding, Otis* / Where is the love: *Paris, Mica & Will Downing* / Tonight I celebrate my love: *Flack, Roberta & Peabo Bryson* / With you I'm born again: *Preston, Billy & Syreeta* / Best thing that ever happened to me: *Knight, Gladys & The Pips* / One day I'll fly away: *Crawford, Randy* / In your eyes: *Benson, George*.
LP: **840 776 1**
MC: **840 776 4**

HEART AND SOUL III (Various artists).
Tracks: / Sign your name: *D'arby, Terence Trent* / Easy: *Commodores* / Love don't live here anymore: *Rose* Royce / Private dancer: *Turner, Tina* / I live for your love: *Cole, Natalie* / Tracks of my tears: *Robinson*, Smokey & The Miracles / Respect: *Franklin, Aretha* / Lovers, The: *O'Neal, Alexander* / Come into my life: *Sims, Joyce* / Papa was a rollin' stone: *Temptations* / My girl: *Redding, Otis* / When a man loves a woman: *Sledge, Percy* / Tired of being alone: *Green, Al* / Touch me in the morning: *Ross, Diana* / My cherie amour: *Wonder, Stevie* / Farewell my summer love: *Jackson, Michael* / Way we were, The: *Knight, Gladys*/ Loving you: *Riperton, Minnie*.
LP: **845 009 1**
MC: **845 009 4**

I'LL TAKE YOU THERE (Second Rosco show) (Various artists).
LP: . . . . **K 40542**

IN CROWD, THE (It's in his kiss) (Various artists).
Tracks: / In crowd, The: *Gray, Dobie* / Gee wizz (look at his eyes): *Thomas, Carla* / Love on a mountain top: *Knight, Robert* / Ya ya: *Dorsey, Lee* / Only the strong survive: *Butler, Jerry* / Two lovers: *Wells, Mary* / Heatwave: *Reeves, Martha (1)* / Harlem shuffle: *Bob & Earl*.
LP: . . . . **OCN 2014WL**
MC: . . . . **OCN 2014WK**

IN LOVE WITH SOUL (Various artists).
Tracks: / Slow hand: *Pointer Sisters* / Friends: *Stewart, Amii* / Dreaming: *Goldsmith, Glen* / Risin' to the top: *Burke, Keni* / You'll never know: *Hi-Gloss* / Somewhere: *Rushen, Patrice* / If you're lookin' for a way out: *Odyssey* / Body talk: *Imagination* / This time I'll be sweeter: *Bofill, Angela* / Jack and Jill: *Raydio* / You know how to love: *Hyman, Phyllis* / Just don't want to be lonely: *Main Ingredient*/ Didn't I blow your mind this time: *Delfonics* / Greatest love of all, The: *Benson, George*.
MC: **410 471**
LP: **210 471**

IN LOVE WITH SOUL (See Under In Love With...) (Various artists).

IN LOVE WITH SOUL II (The Quiet Storm) (Various artists).
Tracks: / Do what you do: *Jackson, Jermaine* / Stay the night: *Parker, Ray Jnr.* / Can't we fall in love again: *Hyman, Phyllis & Michael Henderson* / Love all the hurt away: *Franklin, Aretha & George Michael* / I'm in love: *Pointer Sisters* / This time: *Kiara/Shanice Wilson* / Closer than close: *Carne, Jean* / Love changes: *Kashif* / If ever a love there was: *Four Tops/Aretha Franklin* / I just wanna be your girl: *Chapter Eight/Anita* Baker / Girl blue: *Main Ingredient* / It will be alright: *Odyssey* / Tonight I give in: *Bofill, Angela*/ How many times can we say

goodbye: *Warwick, Dionne & Luther Vandross* / Georgy Porgy: *Charme/ Luther Van Dross.*
MC: **411469**

IT'S ALL PLATINUM (Various artists).
LP: **6830 200**

JUKE BOX STORY (Various artists).
LP: . . . . **PER 33 8606**
MC: . . . . **PER 733 8606**

JUST A LITTLE OVERCOME - STAX VOCAL GROUPS (Various artists).
Tracks: / No strings attached: *Mad Lads* / These old memories: *Mad Lads* / I'm so glad I fell in love with you: *Mad Lads* / Highway to Heaven: *Dramatics* / Since I've been in love: *Dramatics* / Mannish boy: *Newcomers*/ Girl this boy loves you: *Newcomers* / Just a little overcome: *Nightingales* / Baby, don't do it: *Nightingales*/ I'm with you: *Nightingales* / Whole bit of love, A: *Temprees* / Your love (is all I need): *Temprees*/ I refuse to be lonely: *Stingers* / Showered with love: *Ollie & The Nightingales* / Mellow way (you treat your man): *Ollie & The Nightingales* / All because of you: *Limitations* / Echo, The: *Epsilons* / Make this young lady mine: *Mad Lads* (Available on CD only) / Your love was strange: *Dramatics* (Available on CD only) / Open up your heart (let me come in): *Newcomers* (Available on CD only) / Anyone can: *Leaders* (Available on CD only) / Love's creeping up on me: *United Image* (Available on CD only).
LP: . . . . **SXD 019**

KENT 50 (Various artists).
Tracks: / Doctor Love: *Sheen, Bobby* / Determination: *Parrish, Dean* / Hand it over: *Jackson, Chuck*/ Baby without you: *Monday, Danny* / La rue, The: *Edmund Jr., Lada* / It's torture (instrumental): *Brown,* Maxine Band / Wrong girl, The: *Showmen* / Homework: *Rush, Otis* / I've lost you: *Wilson, Jackie*/ Music to my heart: *Austin, Patti* / I can't believe what you say: *Turner, Ike & Tina* / Wack wack: *Young* Holt Unlimited / Work song: *Hunt, Tommy* / I love you (yeah): *Impressions* / I'll never forget you: *O'Jays*/ Time is on my side: *Thomas, Irma.*
LP: . . . . **KENT 050**

KENT STOP DANCING (Various artists).
Tracks: / Louie Louie: *Kingsmen* / 99th floor: *Moving Sidewalks* / Sha-la-la: *Various artists* / Killer Joe: *Rocky Fellers* / Twist and shout: *Isley Brothers* / Just a little bit: *Head, Roy* / Turn on your lovelight: *Gordon, Benny* / Oh no not my baby: *Brown, Maxine* / Washed ashore (on a lonely island in the sea): *Platters* / Your love keeps lifting me higher and higher: *Wilson, Jackie* / That's enough: *Robinson, Roscoe*/ Love makes a woman: *Acklin, Barbara* / Get on up: *Esquires* / I keep forgettin': *Jackson, Chuck* / Wack wack: *Young Holt Trio* / I'm gonna miss you: *Artistics.*
LP: . . . . **KENT 029**

KENT STOP DANCING - THE SEQUEL (Various artists).
Tracks: / Ski storm: *Snowmen* / Every night a new surprise: *Moving Sidewalks* / Can you help me: *Knickerbockers*/ Shake a tail feather: *Turner, Ike & Tina* / Baby workout: *Wilson, Jackie* / Humphrey stomp: *Harrison, Earl*/ Gonna send you back to Georgia: *Shaw, Timmy* / Cooking gear: *Arnold, Gear* / With this ring: *Platters*/ Nothing can stop me: *Chandler, Gene* / Follow the leader: *Major Lance* / Just a little misunderstanding: *Williams,* Johnny / (Your love keeps lifting me) higher and higher: *Wilson, Jackie* / Ain't no soul: *Milsap, Ronnie*/ Come see about me: *Dodds, Nella* / Am I the same girl: *Acklin, Barbara.*
LP: . . . . **KENT 066**

KENTSTAX (Various artists).
Tracks: / Sweet Sherry: *Barnes, J.J.* / Love's creeping up on me: *United Image* / Just keep on lovin' me: *Mancha,* Steve / I'm the one who loves you: *Banks, Darrell* / Little by little and bit by bit: *Weston, Kim* / You made me a woman: *Lewis, Barbara* / One more chance: *Joseph, Margie* / It makes me wanna cry: *Staples, Mavis*/ Give 'em love: *Soul Children* / Losing boy: *Giles, Eddie* / Bet you I win: *Little Milton* / Chains of love: *Barnes, J.J.* / Since I lost my baby's love: *Major Lance* / I don't wanna lose you: *Mancha, Steve*/ It's all up to you: *Hughes, Jimmy* / Wade in the water: *Little Sonny.*
LP: . . . . **KENT 095**

LIBERTY BELLES (Various artists).
Tracks: / We got a good thing going: *King, Clydie* / It ain't right (lovin' to be lovin'): *Turner, Tina* / Take a look: *Thomas, Irma* / One part, two part: *King, Clydie* / Proud Mary: *Turner, Tina* / I'm on the outside looking in: *Washington, Baby* / I'm movin' on: *Yuro, Timi* / I'm moving on (part two): *Yuro, Timi* / Time is on my side: *Thomas, Irma* / Ooh poo pah doo: *Turner, Tina* / All around the world: *Washington, Baby*/ Gotta travel on: *Yuro, Timi* / Wish someone would care: *Thomas, Irma* / It's all over but the crying: *Washington, Baby* / I'll never stop loving you: *King, Clydie* / I want to take you higher: *Turner, Tina.*
LP: . . . . **EG 2604831**
MC: . . . . **EG 2604834**

LOST SOUL (Various artists).
2LP: . . . . **EPC 22153**

LOUISIANA SOUTHERN SOUL (Various artists).
LP: . . . . **KK 791**

LOVE TRAIN-THE BEST OF PHILADELPHIA (Various artists).
LP: . . . . **PIR 25316**
MC: **40 25316**

MAJOR BILL'S TEXAS SOUL (Various artists).
Tracks: / Action: *Hobbs, Willie* / Dead: *Robin, Ede* / My baby's back: *Duncan, James* / Monkey time: *Mills, Billy* / One woman lover: *Hobbs, Willie* / Mr. Pitiful: *Robert & Matt* / Man without a woman, A: *Brown, Matt* / It's me: *Copeland, Johnny* / Woman is a nice thing, A: *Hobbs, Willie* / Soul of a man: *Thomas, Robert* / These arms of mine: *Matt & Robert* / Under the pines: *Mills, Billy* / Cry cry cry: *Hobbs,* Willie / All these things: *Mills, Billy* / Evening in Paris: *Milburn, Amos Jr.* / Soul symphony: *Sons of Moses.*
LP: . . . . **CRB 1167**

MECCA MAGIC (Various artists).
LP: . . . . **KENT 090**

MEMPHIS GOLD:THE VERY BEST OF STAX (Various artists).
LP: . . . . **STAXL 5014**
MC: . . . . **STAXK 5014**

MIDNIGHT LOVE AFFAIR (Various artists).
LP: . . . . **SHM 3114**

MODERN SOUL STORY (Various artists).
2LP: . . . . **LPSD 120**
MC: . . . . **CPSD 120**

MODERN SOUL STORY 2 (Various artists).
Tracks: / Let's spend some time together: *Houston, Larry* / Ain't nothing wrong with that baby: *Jones, Jimmy (singer)*/ Don't you worry baby: *Banks, F.E* / You can win: *Bileo* / Over the top: *Dawson, Roy* / 100 South of..: *Philadelphia society* / Have some sympathy: *Wilson, Dustin* / Thankful for this life: *Feale, Marvin* / No rebate on love: *Dramatics* / Only way is up, The: *Clay, Otis* / I'm so happy: *Lord C.M* / Let the people talk: *Steptonen* / I need you: *Jenkins, Dianne* / You have to lose love...: *Randolph, Jimmy.*
2LP: . . . . **LPSD 122**

MODERN SOUL STORY VOL 3 (Various artists).
2LP: . . . . **LPSD 133**

MODERN TIMES, THE (Various artists).
LP: . . . . **LPSS 105**

MOMENTS IN SOUL (Various artists).
LP: . . . . **SMR 023**
MC: . . . . **SMC 023**

MOMENTS IN SOUL (Various artists).
Tracks: / If you were here tonight: *O'Neal, Alexander* / I knew you were waiting: *Michael, George and Aretha Franklin* / I still haven't found what I'm looking for: *Chimes* / I need lovin': *Williams, Alison* / Give me the reason: *Vandross, Luther* / Keep on movin': *Soul II Soul* / Don't be a fool: *Loose Ends* / If you don't know me by now: *Simply Red* / State of independence: *Summer, Donna* / Ain't nobody: *Khan, Chaka* / Fantasy: *Black* Box / What did I do to you: *Stansfield, Lisa* / Get here: *Adams, Oleta* / Thinking about your love: *Thomas,* Kenny / Beautiful love: *Adeva* / Something in red: *Kaset, Angela* / Carrying a torch: *Jones, Tom*/ Matter of fact, A: *Innocence.*
LP: . . . . **ADD 25**
MC: . . . . **ZDD 25**

MOONLIGHTING (Various artists).
Tracks: / Divine emotions: *Narada* / Casanova: *Levert* / I want her: *Sweat, Keith* / Rain, The: *Jones,* Oran "Juice" / Love is contagious: *Seville, Taja* / Gotta get you home tonight: *Wilde, Eugene* / Nite and day: *Sure, Al B.* / Wishing on a star: *Various artists* / Sexual healing: *Gaye, Marvin* / I want to be your man: *Roger* / Lovers, The: *O'Neal, Alexander* / Feel so real: *Arrington, Steve* / Baby come to me: *Austin, Patti & James Ingram* / Moonlighting: *Jarreau, Al* / Caught up in the rapture (remix): *Baker, Anita*/ Tender love: *Force M.D.'s.*
LP: . . . . **WX 202**
MC: . . . . **WX 202C**

MOTOR CITY MAGIC, VOL 1 (Various artists).
Tracks: / Honey baby (be mine): *Innervision* / I'm a fool, I must love you: *Falcons* / Plain brown wrapper: *Rice,* Larry / Walk right on it: *Motor City Runners* / You must have been a warlock: *Third Chapter* / That's all she wrote: *King Diamond* / Message to the black women, A: *King Diamond* / I just want to love you: *Innervision*/ God must have created love: *Bursey, Flery* / I can't help it, I'm falling: *Falcons* / I'm in love again: *Innervision.*
LP: . . . . **CRM 2035**

MOTOR CITY MAGIC, VOL 2 (Various artists).
Tracks: / Standing on guard: *Falcons* / Over you: *Capreez* / Second time around: *Innervision* / Watch your step now: *Motor City Runners* / I'm tempted: *Falcons* / Wait a minute: *Tim Tam & The Turn Ons* / How to make a sad man glad: *Capreez* / You got the power baby: *Falcons* / You must have been a warlock: *Motor* City Runners / Love, look what you made me do: *Falcons* / Detroit getdown: *New Breed* / Gotta find a way to get back home: *Innervision.*
LP: . . . . **CRM 2036**

MOVE INTO SOUL EP (Various artists).
LP: . . . . **MVLP 4**

MOVE INTO SOUL PART 2 (Various artists).
LP: . . . . **MVLP 5**

MOVE INTO SOUL PART 3 (Various artists).
LP: . . . . **MVLP 7**

MOVE INTO SOUL PART 4 (Various artists).
LP: . . . . **MVLP 9**

MOVE INTO SOUL PART 6 (Various artists).
LP: . . . . **MVLP 13**

MOVING ON UP (Various artists).
Tracks: / I get what I want: *Lasalle, Denise* / Choosing you: *Williams, Lenny* / Please don't run from me: *Clinton,* George / My life is so wonderful (when you're around): *Dells* / Ooh baby: *Porter, Nolan* / I got a bone to pick with you: *Andrews, Ruby* / It's all over: *Mann, Charles* / I'll be your forever more: *Love Unlimited*/ I only get this feeling: *Jackson, Chuck* / I thought you were mine: *Natural Four* / Just can't get you out of my mind: *Four Tops* / Fish ain't bitin': *Dozier, Lamont* / When the bottom falls out: *Perkins, Ike* / Where have you been?: *Carlton, Carl.*
LP: . . . . **KENT 013**

MUSIC CITY SOUL (SUN RECORDINGS) (Various artists).
LP: . . . . **CR 30107**

NEW YORK CITY SOUL (Various artists).
Tracks: / I'm on my way: *Parrish, Dean* / Friends and lovers: *Lands, Hoagy* / Next in line, The: *Lands, Hoagy*/ Detroit sounds: *Megatons* / You're the love of my life: *Jones, Brenda Lee* / I've gotta hear it from you: *Jackson* Brothers / I'm gone: *Sharae, Billy* / Beachcomber: *Gibson, Johnny* / Keep the boy happy: *Chiffons*/ Yes I love you baby: *Dynamics* / Cover girl: *Spencer, Carl* / Beautiful music: *Fields, Lily & Hoagy Lands*/ When I'm in your arms: *Casualeers* / Call on me: *Law, Johnny Four* / Silly little girl: *Dean & Jean*/ Proud soul heritage: *Hebb, Bobby.*
LP: . . . . **KENT 043**

NITEFLITE (Various artists).
Tracks: / Shiver: *Benson, George* / Shake you down: *Abbott, Gregory* / Always: *Atlantic Starr* / Sweet love: *Baker, Anita* / If you were here tonight: *O'Neal, Alexander* / Almaz: *Crawford, Randy* / Loving you: *Various artists* / Give me the reason: *Vandross, Luther* / Criticize: *O'Neal, Alexander* / Weekend Girl: *S.O.S. Band* / So amazing: *Vandross, Luther* / How 'bout us: *Champaign* / Rock with you: *Jackson,* Michael / Show Me The Way: *Bell, Regina* / Secret Lovers: *Atlantic Starr* / One More Chance: *Jacksons, The.*
LP: . . . . **MOOD 4**
MC: . . . . **MOODC 4**

NITEFLITE 2 (Various artists).
Tracks: / Roses are red: *Mac Band* / Saturday love: *Cherrelle & Alexander O'Neal* / Any love: *Vandross, Luther*/ Come into my life: *Sims, Joyce* / Just the way you like it: *S.O.S. Band* / Ain't no sunshine: *Withers, Bill*/ Can't stay away from you: *Estefan, Gloria* / Rock me tonight (for old time's sake): *Jackson, Freddie* / Stop to love: *Vandross, Luther* / Wishing on a star: *Rose Royce* / After the love has gone: *Earth, Wind & Fire*/ Never knew love like this: *O'Neal, Alexander* / Piano in the dark: *Russell, Brenda* / Why (can't we live together): *Sade* / Tonight I celebrate my love: *Flack, Roberta & Peabo Bryson* / Sexual healing: *Gaye, Marvin.*
LP: . . . . **MOOD 8**
MC: . . . . **MOOD C8**

NITEFLITE/NITEFLITE 2 (Twofer) (Various artists).
2LP: **4662531**
MC: **4662534**

OKEH SOUL (Various artists).
2LP: . . . . **EPC 22126**
MC: **40 22126**

ON THE SOUL SIDE (Various artists).
Tracks: / Love and desire: *Holloway, Patrice* / Gonna fix you good (every time you're bad): *Little Anthony & The Imperials*/ Doctor Love: *Sheen, Bobby* / Ready, willing and able: *Holiday, Jimmy & Clydie King* / Lot of love, A: *Banks,* Homer / Lipstick traces (on a cigarette): *O'Jays* / Record, The: *Barnum, H.B.* / It was easier to hurt her: *Mimms, Garnet* / Fortune teller: *Spellman, Benny* / It will stand: *Showmen* / Boy watcher: *Thompson,* Ginger / Do wah diddy: *Exciters* / I want you to be my baby: *Greenwich, Ellie* / Point of no return: *McDaniels, Gene* / Baby, I love you: *Holiday, Jimmy* / What's a matter, baby?: *Yuro, Timi.*
LP: . . . . **KENT 006**

ON THE UP BEAT (Various artists).
Tracks: / Serious: *Allen, Donna* / Fake: *O'Neal, Alexander* / No lies: *S.O.S. Band* / See me: *Vandross,* Luther / Thigh ride: *Tawatha* / Shake you down: *Abbott, Gregory* / Happy: *Surface* / After loving you: *Juicy* / Rain, The: *Jones, Oran "Juice"* / My favourite person: *O'Jays.*
LP: . . . . **ONUP 1**
MC: . . . . **ONUP C1**

ONE MINIT AT A TIME (Various artists).
Tracks: / Well: *Jimmie & Vella* / Lot of love, A: *Banks, Homer* / Take me: *Womack, Bobby* / I'm gonna do all I can to do right by my man: *Turner, Ike & Tina* / Girls from Texas, The: *Lewis, Jimmy* / Working on your case: *O'Jays* / Party in the woods: *Persuasions* / Funky Broadway: *Dozier, Gene* / Gonna get that boat: *Turner, Ike & Tina* / I wanna be free: *Players* / Give me your love: *Holiday, Jimmy* / I know you know I know: *Banks, Homer* / Hunk of funk, A: *Dozier, Gene* / I can't stand the pain: *Irwin, Dee* / Shing a ling: *King, Clydie.*
LP: . . . . **SSL 6002**
MC: . . . . **TCSSL 6002**

PHILADELPHIA CLASSICS (Various artists).
Tracks: / Love is the message: *MFSB* / Sound of Philadelphia, The: *MFSB & Three Degrees* / Dirty ol' man: *3* Degrees / I love music: *O'Jays* / Don't leave me this way: *Melvin, Harold & The Bluenotes* / Love train: *O'Jays*/ I'll always love my mama: *Intruders* / Bad luck: *Melvin, Harold & The Bluenotes.*
2LP: . . . . **PIR 88274**

PHILADELPHIA YEARS VOL.1, THE (Various artists).
Tracks: / You're the reason why: *Ebonys* / I miss you: *Melvin, Harold & The Bluenotes* / Backstabbers: *O'Jays*/ Win, place or show: *Intruders* / If you: *Melvin, Harold & The Bluenotes* / Me and Mrs Jones: *Paul, Billy*/ 992 arguments: *O'Jays* / Love train: *O'Jays* / Tossin' and turnin': *Sigler, Bunny* / Yesterday: *Melvin,* Harold & The Bluenotes / Am I black enough for you: *Paul, Billy* / It's forever: *Ebonys* / I'll always love my mama: *Intruders* / Time to get down: *O'Jays* / Love I lost: *Melvin, Harold & The Bluenotes* / Dirty ol' man: *3 Degrees* / I wanna know your name: *Intruders* / Put your hands together: *O'Jays* / Love epidemic: *Trammps* / Thanks for saving my life: *Paul, Billy* / T.S.O.P.: *MFSB* / Year of decision: *3 Degrees*/ Satisfaction: *Melvin, Harold & The Bluenotes* / I believe: *Ebonys* / For the love of money: *O'Jays*/ Where do we go from here?: *Trammps* / Love train Part 1: *Sigler, Bunny* / When will I see you again: *3 Degrees*/ Love is the message: *MFSB* / Get your love back: *3 Degrees* / You bring out: *Derek & Cyndi* / Where are...: *Melvin, Harold & The Bluenotes* / Sunshine: *O'Jays* / Be truthful to me: *Paul, Billy* / I didn't know: *3 Degrees* / Bad luck: *Melvin, Harold & The Bluenotes* / Give the people what: *O'Jays* / Sexy: *MFSB*/ Hope that we can be together soon: *Melvin, Harold & The Bluenotes* / City of brotherly love: *Soul Survivors*/ I could dance all night: *Bell, Archie & The Drells* / Take good care: *3 Degrees* / Do it any way you wanna: *People's Choice* / Long lost forever: *3 Degrees* / Let me make love to you: *O'Jays* / Wake up: *Melvin, Harold &* The Bluenotes / I love music: *O'Jays* / Zip,

The: MFSB / Nursery rhymes: People's Choice / Soul City walk: Bell, Archie & The Drells / Let's make a baby: Paul, Billy / Let's groove: Bell, Archie & The Drells / Tell the: Melvin, Harold & The Bluenotes / Livin' for the weekend: O'Jays / I'm not in love...: Sharp, Dee / You'll never find another...: Rawls, Lou.
LPS: KNLP 42001
MCSET: KNMC 42001

PHILADELPHIA YEARS VOL.1, THE (See under Philadelphia...) (Various artists).

PHILADELPHIA YEARS VOL 2, THE (See under Philadelphia...) (Various artists).

PHILADELPHIA YEARS VOL 2, THE (Various artists).
LPS: KNLP 42002
MCSET: KNMC 42002

PHILLYBUSTERS VOL.IV (Various artists).
Tracks: / I love music: O'Jays / Soul city walk: Bell, Archie / Love is everywhere: Unknown artist(s)/ I'm not in love: Unknown artist(s) / Wake up everybody: Melvin, Harold & The Bluenotes / Philadelphia freedom: Unknown artist(s) / Let's make a baby: Paul, Billy / You'll never find another love like mine: Rawls, Lou/ No tell motel: Unknown artist(s) / Float like a butterfly: Unknown artist(s) / Round 1: Unknown artist(s)/ Love epidemic: Unknown artist(s) / Summertime and I'm feeling mellow: Unknown artist(s) / Here we go again: People's Choice / Message in our music: O'Jays.
LP: PIR 81658

PLATFORM SOUL (Various artists).
LP: CE 2456

PURE SOUL (Various artists).
Tracks: / I got caught: Carter, Clarence / Ask me 'bout nothing (but the blues): Bland, Bobby / Mirror, mirror on the wall: Saints / Doomed by jealousy: Montre El, Jackie / No cookies in my bag: Britton, Aldora/ You played on a player: Green, Garland / Check my tears: Trends / Mr. Soft touch: Williams, Jeanette/ Court of love: Unifics / Drop by my place: Carlton, Little Carl / This time will be different: Blue Notes/ Mr. Independent: Soul Twins / Do you love me: Rayons / I still love you: Stanback, Jean / Your baby doesn't love you anymore: Ruby & The Romantics.
LP: KENT 019

RAINBOW ROAD - SOUTH CAMP (Various artists).
Tracks: / Tearstained face: Varner, Don / When it's over: Varner, Don / Let me be a woman: Varner, Brenda/ You made your bed: Bradford, Eddie / Self preservation: Brandon, Bill / What kind of spell: Borders Tony/ You ain't woman enough (to take my man): Lynn, Loretta / You better believe it: Borders Tony / Masquerade: Varner, Don / Home just ain't home at suppertime: Hill, Z.Z. / Strangest feeling: Brandon, Bill / Cheaters never win: Borders Tony / Heaven help me (I'm falling in love): Edwards, June / All I need is you: Brandon, Bill / It's a mans world: Causey, Buddy / It sure was fun: Bradford, Eddie / One woman man: Varner, Don / Rainbow road: Brandon, Bill / You left the water running: Varner, Don / Think I'll go somewhere and cry myself to sleep: Perkins, Joe / Love and a friend: Borders Tony / I'll be your baby tonight: Brandon, Bill / Movin' in the groove: Brandon, Bill / Don't give up on me: Varner, Brenda / Your big chance: Brandon, Bill / Close to me: Various artists / Sugar makes everything sweeter: Sledge, Percy Jnr.
LP: CRB 1225

RARE (Various artists).
Tracks: / Action speaks louder than words: Chocolate Milk / Ain't no change: New Birth / If you've got it ...: Headhunters / Turn off the lights: Larry Young's Fuel / Haboglabotribin': Wright, Bernard / Walk that walk: Irvine, Weldon / 2 win u back: Jones Girls / Let it go: Broom, Bobby / Elevate our minds: Williams, Linda / Looking up for you: Wycoff, Michael / I love you: Irvine, Weldon / Holding you, loving you: Blackman, Donald / How about love: Chocolate Milk.
LP: NL 90070
MC: NK 90070

RARE 2 (Various artists).
Tracks: / Pop: Limit / Spoiled: Main Ingredient, featuring Cuba Golding / April lady: Wax / Will you take my love?: Mason, Harvey / How's your love life, baby?: Perry, Greg / Since I found you: Bowman, Candy/ I've quit running the streets: Green, Garland / Tropical love: Bofill, Angela / When and if I fall in love: Wax / We've got the love: Plush / Evening of love: Main Ingredient, featuring Cuba Golding / I've got to see you right away: Perry, Jeff / Never (gonna let you go): Charme.
LP: PL 71681
MC: PK 71681
LP: NL 74704
MC: NK 74704

RARE 3 (Various artists).
Tracks: / Ain't no time for nothing: Various artists / I'm always dancin' to the music: Golson, Benny / Rough out there: Modulations / Miss Cheryl: Banda Black Rio / We're getting down: Irvine, Weldon / Shake it up: Vibrations / Passion play: Sugarhill Gang / Love me like this: Real To Reel / Work to do: Main Ingredient / Yellow sunshine: Yellow Sunshine / Am I cold, am I hot: Harris, Bill.
LP: 209.498
MC: 409.498
LP: 210935
MC: 410935

RARE 4 (Various artists).
Tracks: / Sweet power your embrace: Mason, James (nar) / Evil vibrations: Mighty Riders / Grand theft: Chocolate Milk / All that matters: Michigan Avenue / La la for love: Serenade / Let me be your pacifier: Green, Garland / Oops here I go again: Wright, Edna / Renaissance: Smith, Lonnie Liston / Under the skin: Brothers/ Stick by me: Serenade / Dance the night away: Kruz.
LP: 210.007
MC: 410.007
LP: 210936
MC: 410936

RARE 5 (Various artists).
LP: 210928
MC: 410928

RARE GROOVE 2 (Various artists).
Tracks: / It's all right now: Harris, Eddie / London express: Sain, Oliver / I wouldn't change a thing: Escovedo, Coke / Atmosphere strut: Cloud One / Four play: Wesley/Horny Horns / Funky music is the...: Dynamic Corvettes / Get me back on time: Pickett, Wilson / Bus stop: Sain, Oliver / Bye bye baby: Bay City Rollers / Bump, The: Kenny / Baker Street: Rafferty, Gerry / Love is in the air: Young, John Paul/ Tiger feet: Mud / My Sharona: Knack / Now is the time: James, Jimmy / Jack in the box: Moments (group) / Heaven must be missing an angel: Tavares / You're my first....: White, Barry / I love America: Juvet, Patrick / Girls: Moments & Whatnauts / Rock the boat: Hues Corporation / You sexy thing: Hot Chocolate.
LP: RARELP 2
MC: ZCRARE 2

RARE GROOVES (Various artists).
LP: CHILLP 1
MC: ZCCHIL 1

RARE PRELUDES VOL.1 (Various artists).
Tracks: / C'mon stop: Black Gold / Your love: Satin, Silk & Lace / Music got me, The: Visual / I don't wanna hear it: Adams, Gayle / You are the one: Pilot / On a journey (I sing the funk electric): Electrik Funk / Some how some way: Visual / All I need is you: Starshine / Don't stop my love: Passion.
LP: 210.008
MC: 410.008

RETURN OF SUPERBAD (Various artists).
LP: NE 1421
MC: CE 2421

RHYTHM IN SOUL (Various artists).
MC: ASK 782

RHYTHM IN SOUL - VOL.2 (Various artists).
MC: ASK 793

RHYTHM OF THE NIGHT (Various artists).
Tracks: / Single life: Cameo / Freeway of love: Franklin, Aretha / Nightshift: Commodores / If you were here tonight: O'Neal, Alexander / Gotta get you home tonight: Wilde, Eugene / Treat her like a lady: Temptations/ Love can't turn around: Farley "Jackmaster" Funk / Pull up to the bumper: Jones, Grace / Finest (The): S.O.S. Band / Mine all mine: Cashflow / Cherish: Kool & The Gang / Your love is king: Sade / Ain't nothin' goin' on but the rent: Guthrie, Gwen / Rhythm of the night: DeBarge.
LP: NE 1348
MC: CE 2348

SAFE SOUL VOL.1 (Various artists).
Tracks: / Just loving you: Green, Garland / Once you fall in love: McLoyd, Eddie / I'll see you in hell first: Mitchell, Phillip / Rising cost of love: Jackson, Millie / It takes both of us: Act One / If I can't have your love: Brown, Jocelyn / Plenty of love: C-Brand / Stay with me: Martin, Daltrey / Still in love with you: Bailey, J R / My shining star: Fatback (Band) / Sweet music, soft lights and you: Jackson, Millie & Isaac Hayes / I'll see you in hell first (alternative take): Mitchell, Phillip (Available on CD only) / Feed me your love: Fatback (Band) (Available on CD only).
LP: SEW 020

SAFE SOUL VOL.2 (Various artists).
LP: SEWD 022

SALSOUL 1 (Various artists).
Tracks: / All of my lovin': Williams, Jimmy / Are you single?: Aurra / All about the paper: Holloway, Loletta/ Can you see where I'm coming from?: Instant Funk / Ten per cent: Double Exposure / Take some time: Salsoul Orchestra / Step out of my dream: Stranglers / Falling in love: Surface.
LP: LIPS 1
MC: TCLIPS 1

SANCTIFIED SOUL (Various artists).
LP: 241 703 1
MC: 241 703 4

SEXUAL HEALING (Various artists).
Tracks: / Sexual healing: Gaye, Marvin / Never too much: Vandross, Luther / There's nothing like this: Omar/ Baby come to me: Austin, Patti & James Ingram / Get here: Adams, Oleta / If you were here tonight: O'Neal, Alexander / Joy and pain: Maze featuring Frankie Beverly / When a man loves a woman: Sledge, Percy / If you don't know me by now: Melvin, Harold & The Bluenotes / Rock me tonight (for old times sake): Jackson, Freddie/ Solid: Ashford & Simpson / Rock your baby: Macrae, George / Hang on in there baby: Bristol, Johnny/ I want your sex: Michael, George / I'm gonna love you just a little more babe: White, Barry / Love won't let me wait: Harris, Major / Tonight I celebrate my love: Flack, Roberta & Peabo Bryson / I want to wake up with you: Gardiner, Boris.
LP: EMTV 60
MC: TCEMTV 60

SHEER ECSTASY (Various artists).
Tracks: / Doctor's orders: Maegan / I've got you where I want you, babe: Stereo Fun Inc. / Trouble in Paradise: Sylvester / Dancing through the night: Alikia / Love me real: Gaynor, Gloria / Ready or not: Miller, Cat / Pillow talk: Lusst / My man must be American: Simone / Too late: Sylvester / Go go gorilla: Gazuzu.
LP: XTLP 4
MC: XTCC 4

SHEER ECSTASY (VOL. 2) (Various artists).
Tracks: / Rhythm of your love (Re-mix): Roberts, Isabel / Living for the city: Sylvester / Sizzlin': Mitchell, Brenda / With you I could have it all: Houston, Cissy / I don't wanna fall in love again: Silver, Karen/ AM-FM: King, Natasha / So shy: Mac Mac - Jammolott kingdom / Love is like an itching in my heart: Cijay/ Big time operator: Coulson, Julie / Spotlite of love: Juice.
LP: XTLP 5
MC: XTCC 5

SHOVE IT (Various artists).
Tracks: / My man, a sweet man: Jackson, Millie / Night fever: Fatback (Band) / Can you get to that: Funkadelic/ Pain: Ohio Players / Baby let me take you (in my arms): Detroit Emeralds / Man size job, A: Lasalle, Denise/ Keep on stepping: Fatback (Band) / Get down, get down (get on the floor): Simon, Joe / Pleasure: Ohio Players / It's all over but the shouting: Jackson, Millie / Funky dollar bill: Funkadelic.
LP: SEWX 015
MC: SEWCX 015

SILKY SOUL HITS OF THE 70'S (OLD GOLD) (Various artists).
LP: OG 1004
MC: OG 2004

SIXTIES SOUL STARS (Various artists).
LPS: BOX 253
MCSET: TCBOX 253

SLIPPIN' AROUND (Various artists).
LP: HDH LP 010

SLOW 'N' MOODY, BLACK 'N' BLUESY (Various artists).
Tracks: / Nothing can change this love: Hill, Z.Z. / You messed up my mind: Hammond, Clay / I can't stand it: Holiday, Jimmy / Directly from my heart: Little Richard / I don't need: Turner, Ike & Tina / Let's get together: Arthur & Mary / Darling I'm standing by you: Jones, Jeanette / Baby i'll come right away: Love, Mary / If i'd lose you: Day, Jackie / I don't wanna lose you: Young, Tami / (Baby) come to me: Little Henry & The Shamrocks / Ain't nobody's business: King, B.B. / Every dog has his day: Copeland, Johnny / Baby what you want me to do: Little Richard.
LP: KENT 003

SOLAR GALAXY OF STARS Various artists (Various artists).
Tracks: / Lady: Whispers / Song for Donnie: Whispers / And the beat goes on: Whispers / Right in the socket: Shalamar / I owe you one: Shalamar / Take that to the bank: Shalamar / Second time around: Shalamar / Givin' in to love: Lakeside / All the way live: Lakeside / Rock, The: Dynasty/ I've just begun to love you: Dynasty / I don't wanna be a freak: Dynasty.
2LP: SOLA 4
MCSET: SOLC 4

SOLAR SYSTEM, THE (Various artists).
Tracks: / Midas touch: Midnight Star / And the beat goes on: Whispers / Take that to the bank: Shalamar/ Romeo where's Juliet: Collage / Wet my whistle: Midnight Star / It's a love thing: Whispers / There it is: Shalamar / Get in touch with me: Collage / Headlines: Midnight Star / Night to remember, A: Shalamar / Sweet sensation: Whispers / Operator (edited version): Midnight Star / Over and over: Shalamar/ Some kinda lover: Whispers.
LP: MCG 3338
MC: MCGC 3338

SOLID SOUL (2) (Various artists).
Tracks: / You're the first, the last, my everything: White, Barry / Hang on in there girl: Bristol, Johnny / Wonderful world: Cooke, Sam / Don't leave me this way: Melvin, Harold & The Bluenotes / Papa was a rollin' stone: Temptations / Family affair: Sly & the Family Stone / Didn't I blow your mind: Delfonics / Working in a coalmine: Dorsey, Lee / Harlem shuffle: Bob & Earl / You make me feel brand new: Stylistics / Tired of being alone: Green, Al / I heard it through the grapevine: Gaye, Marvin / How sweet it is to be loved by you: Walker, Junior & The All Stars / Papa's got a brand new bag: Brown, James / Barefootin': Parker, Robert / Love train: O'Jays / Reet petite: Wilson, Jackie.
LP: STAR 2304
MC: STAC 2304

SOME 'MODERN' SOUL (The Buddah Collection) (Various artists).
Tracks: / Oh lovin' you: Paragons / Dance and free your mind Pt. 1: Sins of Satan / Sharing: Vitamin E/ Midnight lady: Morris, David Jnr. / Deeper and deeper: Wilson, Bobby / Makin' love ain't no fun (without the one you love): Ebonys / I wanna make love to you: Norman,Jimmy / I can't fight your love: Modulations/ You and I: Anderson, Joe / Everybody stand and clap your hands (for the entertainer): Black Satin & Fred Parris.
2LP: NEXLP 154

SOUL AFFAIR (Various artists).
Tracks: / What becomes of the broken hearted?: Ruffin, Jimmy / Hey girl don't bother me: Tams / If you don't know me by now: Melvin, Harold / Everlasting love: Knight, Robert / Hey there lonely girl: Holman, Eddie/ Save the last dance for me: Drifters / Stand by me: King, Ben E. / I will: Winters, Ruby / When a man loves a woman: Sledge, Percy / Do it anyway you wanna: Peoples Choice / Backfield in motion: Mel & Tim/ Love on a mountain top: Knight, Robert / Mr. Big Stuff: Carne, Jean / Love I lost, The: Melvin, Harold & The Bluenotes / Knock on wood: Floyd, Eddie / Show and tell: Wilson, Al / I've passed this way before: Ruffin, Jimmy / Something old, something new: Fantastics / Tighten up: Bell, Archie / Harlem shuffle: Bob & Earl.
LP: CRX 14
MC: CRXC 14

S.O.U.L. AGENTS (Various artists).
Tracks: / I don't want to lose you: Wilson, Jackie / Girl I need you: Artistics / Everything's wrong: Cooperettes/ I'm the one to do it: Baker, Laverne / After you: Acklin, Barbara / Keep your chin up: Ross, Jackie/ Love ain't nothin' but pain: Smith, Marvin / Ain't there something money can't buy: Young Holt Trio / I get the sweetest feeling: Franklin, Erma / One monkey don't stop no show: Baker, Laverne / From the teacher to the preacher: Chandler, Gene & Barbara Acklin / Thank you baby: Butler, Billy / There goes the lover: Chandler, Gene / That's what you are to me: Robbins, Tracie / To change my love: Chi-lites / You left me: Artistics.
LP: KENT 025

SOUL AND THEN SOME (Various artists).
LP: BLUE LP 1

SOUL BY THE SEA (Various artists).
LP: REB 857
MC: ZCF 857

SOUL CITIES (Various artists).

Tracks: / Stop shovin' me around: Delicates / First date: Doods, Nella / Why why why: Leavill, Otis/ Hang up the phone: Wyatt, Johnny / She broke his heart: Just Brothers / I refuse to give up: Reid, Clarence/ Look my way: Williams, Maurice / One who really loves you, The: Sugar Pie Desanto / Get a hold of yourself: Platters / Midsummer night in Harlem: Thomas, Charlie / Send my baby back: Hughes, Freddie / Dedicated to the greatest: Copeland, Johnny / Fall guy: Cautions / Gonna give her all the love I've got: Gordon, Benny/ My arms aren't strong enough: Clay, Judy / I've got love for you: Intruders.
LP: . . . . **KENT 089**

SOUL CLASSICS (Various artists).
Tracks: / When a man loves a woman: Sledge, Percy / Saturday night at the movies: Drifters / Walking the dog: Thomas, Rufus / Just one look: Troy, Doris / Tonight's the night: Burke, Solomon / Knock on wood: Floyd, Eddie / Under the boardwalk: Drifters / If you need me: Burke, Solomon / Patches: Carter, Clarence/ Stand by me: King, Ben E. / Hold on I'm coming: Sam & Dave / Soul man: Sam & Dave / Dance to the music: Sly & the Family Stone / Baby I'm yours: Lewis, Barbara / Warm and tender love: Sledge, Percy/ Save the last dance for me: Drifters.
LP: . . . . **OCN 2002WL**
MC: . . . . **OCN 2002WK**

SOUL CLASSICS - CHESS MASTERS (Various artists).
LP: . . . . **CHXL 106**
MC: . . . . **CHXT 106**

SOUL COLLECTION VOL 1 (Various artists).
2LP: **303792**
MCSET: **503792**

SOUL COLLECTION VOL 2 (Various artists).
2LP: **303838**
MCSET: **503838**

SOUL DECADE (Various artists).
LP: **240807 1**
MC: **240807 4**

SOUL DECADE - THE 60'S (Various artists).
MCSET: . . . . **ZK 74816**
2LP: . . . . **ZL 74816**

SOUL GALORE Various artists (Various artists).
LP: . . . . **SINLP 1**

SOUL JEWELS VOL.1 (Let's Do It Over) (Various artists).
Tracks: / Our love: Powell, Bobby / How do you walk away from fear: Taylor, Ted / I can't stand to see you go: Valentine, Joe / I stayed away too long: Wallace Brothers / In time: Powell, Bobby / To be free: Bass, Fontella / Strangest feeling: Taylor, Ted / Nothing takes the place of you: McCall, Toussaint / Woman's love, A: Valentine, Joe / I'm not going to cry over spilt milk: Powell, Bobby / I want everyone to know: Bass, Fontella / Friendship only goes so far: Taylor, Ted / Hold my hand: Powell, Bobby / My baby's gone: Wallace Brothers / Let's do it over: McCall, Toussaint.
MC: . . . . **TCCRB 192**
LP: . . . . **CRB 1192**

SOUL JEWELS VOL.3 (Various artists).
Tracks: / I need some lovin': Taylor, Little Johnny / Take time to know the truth: Patterson, Bobby / I had my heart set on you: Young, Billy Joe / I'm asking forgiveness: Ridgley, Tommy / Something strange is going on in my house: Taylor, Ted / Until you were gone: Perkins, Joe / What would I do without you: Taylor, Little Johnny / I pledge: Lonnie & Floyd / One ounce of prevention: Patterson, Bobby / Let's call the whole thing off: Taylor, Ted / I'm not going to leave: Perkins, Joe / I ask myself a question: Taylor, Little Johnny/ Give this fool another chance: Young, Billy Joe / I'm in the wrong: Patterson, Bobby / I want to be a part of you: Taylor, Ted / How are you fixed for love: Taylor, Little Johnny.
LP: . . . . **CRB 1194**

SOUL JUKE BOX HITS (Various artists).
2LP: . . . . **DLP 2064**
MCSET: . . . . **DMC 4064**

SOUL MINING (Various artists).
Tracks: / Soul Man: Sam & Dave / Knock on Wood: Floyd, Eddie / Patches: Carter, Clarence / Walking the dog: Thomas, Rufus / Rescue Me: Bass, Fontella / In crowd, The: Various artists / Love wont let me wait: Harris, Major / Duck, The: Lee, Jacky / Western movies: Olympics / I Know: George, Barbara/ Rainy night in Georgia: Various artists / Get on up: Esquires.
LP: . . . . **TOP 149**
MC: . . . . **KTOP 149**

SOUL OF A MAN (Various artists).
LP: . . . . **KENT 038**

SOUL OF DETROIT (See under Northern Soul) (Various artists).

SOUL OF NEW YORK (Various artists).
LP: . . . . **BLUETTLP 1**

SOUL PASSION (Various artists).
LP: . . . . **CN 2055**
MC: **CN4 2055**

SOUL REFLECTION (Various artists).
Tracks: / Three times a lady: Commodores / I don't wanna lose you: Turner, Tina / Have you seen her: M.C. Hammer / Stop to love: Vandross, Luther / Criticize: O'Neal, Alexander / Yah mo B there: Ingram, James/Michael McDonald / There'll be sad songs (to make you cry): Ocean, Billy / Almaz: Crawford, Randy / If you don't know me by now: Melvin, Harold & The Bluenotes / Just my imagination (running away with me): Temptations / I second that emotion: Robinson, Smokey & The Miracles / Too busy thinking about my baby: Gaye, Marvin / Hold back the night: Trammps / Just the way you are: White, Barry / You sexy thing: Hot Chocolate / Always: Atlantic Starr / Baby, come to me: Austin, Patti & James Ingram.
MC: **845 334 4**
LP: **845 334 1**

SOUL & REGGAE FAVOURITES Various artists (Various artists).
MC: . . . . **ASK 795**

SOUL SEARCHING VOL. 1 (Various artists).
Tracks: / Show me: Jones, Glenn / Imitation of love: Jackson, Millie / Give a little more: Butler, Jonathan/ Hurting inside: Turner, Ruby / Children of the ghetto: Real Thing / I'm in love: Turner, Ruby / I need to be by myself: Jackson, Millie / It's never too late to try: Ocean, Billy / Letter, The: Wilson, Precious / Don't turn your back: Bell Armstrong, Vanessa.
LP: . . . . **HOP 216**
MC: . . . . **HOPC 216**

SOUL SEARCHING VOL. 2 (Various artists).
LP: . . . . **HOP 218**
MC: . . . . **HOPC 218**

SOUL SENSATION (Various artists).
MC: . . . . **DY 17**
MC: . . . . **AM 19**

SOUL SHOTS VOL.1 We got more soul (dance party) (Various artists).
Tracks: / But it's alright: Jackson, J.J. / Two for the price of one: Williams, Larry & Johnny Watson / Your love keeps lifting me higher and higher: Wilson, Jackie / Ain't nothing but a house party: Show Stoppers / Duck, The: Lee, Jacky / I take what I want: Purify, James & Bobby / Harlem shuffle: Bob & Earl / Funky broadway (part 1): Dyke & The Blazers / Boogaloo down Broadway: Fantastic Johnny C / Barefootin': Parker, Robert/ I got you (I feel good): Brown, James & The Famous Flames / We got more soul: Dyke & The Blazers / Summertime: Stewart, Billy.
LP: . . . . **RNLP 70037**
MC: . . . . **RNC 70037**

SOUL SHOTS VOL.2 In crowd (sweet soul), The (Various artists).
Tracks: / Get on up: Esquires / It's got to be mellow: Haywood, Leon / Love makes the world go round: Jackson, Deon / Sunny: Hebb, Bobby / Cowboys to girls: Intruders / Gimme little sign: Wood, Brenton / Black pearl: Checkmates Ltd / In crowd, The: Various artists / My pledge of love: Jeffrey, Joe Group / Backfield in motion: Mel & Tim / She shot a hole in my soul: Curry, Clifford / Jerk, The: Larks / Oogum boogum song, The: Wood, Brenton / Mercy, mercy, mercy: Williams, Larry & Johnny Watson.
LP: . . . . **RNLP 70038**
MC: . . . . **RNC 70038**

SOUL SHOTS VOL.3 Soul twist (soul instrumentals) (Various artists).
Tracks: / Night train: Brown, James & The Famous Flames / Last night: Mar Keys / Soul twist: Curtis, King & The Noble Knights / Groovin': Booker T & The MGs / Wack wack: Young Holt Trio / Grazing in the grass: Masekela, Hugh / Soul serenade: King Curtis / Twine time: Cash, Alvin & The Crawlers / Time is tight: Booker T & The MGs / In crowd, The: Lewis, Ramsey / Soul finger: Barkays / Horse, The: Nobles, Cliff & Co. / Soulful strut: Young Holt Unlimited / Harlem nocturne: Viscounts.
LP: . . . . **RNLP 70039**
MC: . . . . **RNC 70039**

SOUL SHOTS VOL.4 Tell mama (screamin' soul sisters) (Various artists).
Tracks: / Nitty gritty: Ellis, Shirley / Tell mama: James, Etta / Hard to handle: Drew, Patti / Bold soul sister: Ike & Tina Turner / Lee Cross: Franklin, Aretha / Heartbeat: Jones, Gloria / Stay with me: Ellison, Lorraine / Wang dang doodle: Taylor, Koko / I know (you don't love me no more): George, Barbara/ Rescue me: Fontella Bass / Hypnotized: Jones, Linda / Why (am I treated so bad): Sweet Inspiration/ Ask me: Brown, Maxine / You send me: Franklin, Aretha.
LP: . . . . **RNLP 70040**
MC: . . . . **RNC 70040**

SOUL SHOTS VOL.5 La la means I love you (soul ballads) (Various artists).
Tracks: / Tell it like it is: Neville, Aaron / Sitting in the park: Stewart, Billy / Hey there lonely girl: Holman, Eddie / La la means I love you: Delfonics / That's all: Midniters / Yes I'm ready: Mason, Barbara / Oh what a night: Dells / I do love you: Stewart, Billy / I'm your puppet: James & Bobby Purify/ Funny: Hinton, Joe / Love is a hurtin' thing: Rawls, Lou / Cry baby: Mimms, Garnet/Enchanters / Dark end of the street: Carr, James / People get ready: Impressions (group).
LP: . . . . **RNLP 70041**
MC: . . . . **RNC 70041**

SOUL SOLDIERS (Various artists).
Tracks: / I'm the one who loves you: Banks, Darrell / No one blinder (than a man who won't see): Banks, Darrell/ Just because your love has gone: Banks, Darrell / Only the strong survive: Banks, Darrell / Got to get rid of you: Barnes, J.J. / Snowflakes: Barnes, J.J. / I like everything about you: Hughes, Jimmy / I'm so glad: Hughes, Jimmy / Did you forget: Hughes, Jimmy / Chains of love: Hughes, Jimmy / Just ain't strong as I used to be: Hughes, Jimmy / Since I lost my baby's love: Major Lance / I wanna make up (before we break up): Major Lance / That's the story of my life: Major Lance / Girl come on home: Major Lance/ Ain't no sweat: Major Lance / Beautiful feeling: Banks, Darrell (Available on CD only) / When a man loves a woman: Banks, Darrell (Available on CD only) / Let 'em down baby: Hughes, Jimmy (Available on CD only).
LP: . . . . **SX 012**
MC: . . . . **SXC 012**

SOUL SOURCE (See under 60's) (Various artists).

SOUL SOUVENIRS (Various artists).
Tracks: / I'm in need of love: Courtney, Lou / Hip to your ways: Ujima / Love is here: Messina, Jimmy/ Just a kiss away: Miles, Buddy / You make me a believer: Dozier, Lamont / Good life: Humphrey, Bobbi/ Loves to hot to hide: Coulter, Clifford / Crazy: Gaines, Rosie / I'm back for more (album version): Johnson, Al / How can I be sure: Jackson, Randy / Look at me, look at you (we're flying): Shaw, Marlena / You know you want to be loved: Barrow, Keith.
LP: **4678781**
MC: **4678784**

SOUL STARTRACKS (Various artists).
Tracks: / Living a little laughing a little: Detroit Spinners / I say a little prayer: Franklin, Aretha / Killing me softly with his song: Flack, Roberta / When a man loves a woman: Sledge, Percy / In the midnight hour: Pickett, Wilson / Saturday night at the movies: Drifters / I've been loving you too long: Redding, Otis / Dark end of the street: Carter, Clarence / Show must go on: Dees, Sam / Move on up: Mayfield, Curtis / New York City life: Wilson, Tony / Ghetto, The: Hathaway, Donny / What am I going to do about you girl: Dozier, Lamont/ Star in the ghetto: Average White Band / 634 5789: Pickett, Wilson / Try a little tenderness: Redding, Otis / Sweet soul music: Conley, Arthur / Knock on wood: Floyd, Eddie / Hold on I'm coming: Sam & Dave/ Green onions: Booker T & The MGs.
LP: **K4 58042**

SOUL SURVIVORS (Various artists).
Tracks: / Troglodyte: Soul Survivors / Snake, The: Various artists / Girl watcher: Various artists/ Got to get you off my mind: Various artists / Only the strong survive: Various artists / Slipaway: Various artists / Tonights the night: Various artists / Show and tell: Various artists / Supernatural thing: Various artists / Looking for a love: Various artists / Can I change my mind: Various artists / Groovy situation: Various artists.
LP: . . . . **TOP 151**

SOUL TIME (Various artists).
Tracks: / Happy hippie: Womack, Bobby / If you need me: Burke, Solomon / Too weak to fight: Carter, Clarence/ Turn back the hands of time: Davis, Tyrone / Bring it on home: Floyd, Eddie / I've never found a girl: Floyd, Eddie / B A B Y: Thomas, Carla / Do the funky chicken: Thomas, Rufus / Last night: Mar Keys / Hey there lonely girl: Holman, Eddie / Love on a mountain top: Knight, Robert / Trapped by a thing called love: Lasalle, Denise.
LP: . . . . **TOP 157**
MC: . . . . **KTOP 157**

SOUL TO SOUL (Various artists).
Tracks: / You make me feel brand new: Stylistics / You're the first, the last, my everything: White, Barry / More: Gaye, Marvin / Reunited: Peaches & Herb / One and only: Knight, Gladys & The Pips / Hang on in there baby: Bristol, Johnny / Crazy about your love: Manhattans / Stop me from starting this feeling: Rawls, Lou / Day by day: Shakatak / Never can say goodbye: Gaynor, Gloria / Without you: 3 Degrees / Nightlife: Stewart, Verdi / Hustle, The: McCoy, Van & Soul City Symphony / Native New Yorker: Odyssey/ Sex machine: Brown, James (Only available on CD.) / Hold on to my love: Ruffin, Jimmy (Only available on CD.) / Part time lover: Helms, Jimmy (Only available on CD.) / Can't give you anything but my love: Stylistics (Only available on CD.) / Make it with you: Williams, Esther (Only available on CD.) / Help me make it through the night: Knight, Gladys & The Pips (Only available on CD.) / Close the door: Pendergrass, Teddy / Best of my love: Emotions (group)/ All the love in the world: Warwick, Dionne / Kiss and say goodbye: Manhattans (Not available on CD.) / Love train: O'Jays / Never knew love like this before: Mills, Stephanie / Living inside your love: Hyman, Phyllis (Not available on CD.) / If you don't know me by now: Melvin, Harold.
2LP: . . . . **STDLP 21**
MC: . . . . **STDMC 21**

SOUL TO SOUL VOL.1 (Various artists).
MC: . . . . **SSC 1**

SOUL TRAIN (Various artists).
Tracks: / Do the whoopee: Desanto, Sugar Pie / Soul poppin': Jones, Johnny & The King Casuals / Soul bossa nova: Sattin, Lonnie / 3 days, 1 hour, 30 minutes: Wilson, Jackie / Watermelon man: Sattin, Lonnie / Batman to the rescue: Baker, Laverne / Little girl lost: Brown, Maxine / So fine: Turner, Ike & Tina & The Ikettes/ We need an understanding: Turner, Ike & Tina & The Ikettes / Bad night: Ambrose, Sammy / Damelo baby: Aztecs/ Jerkin' time: Diplomats / Soul train: Little Richard / Smokey Joe's: Candy & The Kisses / Come see about me: Dodds, Nella / Just a little bit of your soul: Jackson, Chuck Orchestra.
LP: . . . . **KENT 080**

SOUL UPRISING (Various artists).
LP: . . . . **KENT 034**

SOUL YEARS 1970, THE (Various artists).
MC: . . . . **KNMC 22070**

SOUL YEARS 1971, THE (Various artists).
MC: . . . . **KNMC 22071**

SOUL YEARS 1972, THE (Various artists).
MC: . . . . **KNMC 22072**

SOUL YEARS 1973, THE (Various artists).
MC: . . . . **KNMC 22073**

SOUL YEARS 1974, THE (Various artists).
MC: . . . . **KNMC 22074**

SOUL YEARS 1975, THE (Various artists).
Tracks: / Can't give you anything but my love: Stylistics / Right back where we started from: Nightingale, Maxine/ Walkin' in rhythm: Blackbyrds / Hold back the night: Trammps / What am I gonna do with you: White, Barry/ This will be: Cole, Natalie / Can I take you home little girl: Drifters / What a diff'rence a day makes: Phillips, Esther / Take good care: 3 Degrees / Ride a wild horse: Clark, Dee / Do it anyway you wanna: People's Choice / Swing your daddy: Gilstrap, Jim / Reach out: Gaynor, Gloria / Girls: Moments & Whatnauts/ There goes my first love: Drifters / I love music: O'Jays / Lady Marmalade: Labelle / Try to remember: Knight, Gladys & The Pips / Shining star: Earth, Wind & Fire / Wake up everybody: Melvin, Harold & The Bluenotes/ You sexy thing: Hot Chocolate / Pick up the pieces: Average White Band / Fire: Ohio Players / Hustle, The: McCoy, Van / That's the way I like it: K.C. & The Sunshine Band / I wanna dance: Disco Tex & The Sexolettes/ (Are you ready) do the bus stop: Fatback (Band) / Loving you: Riperton, Minnie.
2LP: . . . . **KNLP 22075**
MCSET: . . . . **KNMC 22075**

SOUL YEARS 1976, THE (Various artists).
Tracks: / Love really hurts (without you): *Ocean, Billy* / Midnight train to Georgia: *Knight, Gladys & The Pips*/ I'm your puppet: *Purify, James & Bobby* / Hurt: *Manhattans* / Misty blue: *Moore, Dorothy* / Get up offa that thing: *Brown, James* / Don't stop it now: *Hot Chocolate* / You'll never find: *Rawls, Lou* / Sophisticated lady: *Cole, Natalie* / Love ballad: *L.T.D.* / This is it: *Moore, Melba* / Kiss and say goodbye: *Manhattans*/ Movin': *Brass Construction* / Play that funky music: *Wild Cherry* / You see the trouble: *White, Barry*/ Shake your booty: *K.C. & The Sunshine Band* / Spanish hustle: *Fatback (Band)* / Can't help falling in love: *Stylistics*/ I'll be good to you: *Brothers Johnson* / Who'd she coo: *Ohio Players* / Harvest for the world: *Isley Brothers*/ Now is the time: *James, Jimmy & The Vagabonds* / Disco lady: *Taylor, Johnnie* / Funky weekend: *Stylistics*/ You to me are everything: *Real Thing* / Darlin' darlin' baby: *O'Jays* / Soul city walk: *Bell, Archie*/ Heaven must be missing an angel: *Tavares*.
2LP: . . . . **KNLP 22076**
MCSET: . . . . **KNMC 22076**

SOUL YEARS 1977, THE (Various artists).
Tracks: / Show you the way to go: *Jacksons* / Baby don't change your mind: *Knight, Gladys & The Pips* / I believe you: *Moore, Dorothy* / Lovely day: *Withers, Bill* / Free: *Williams, Deniece* / Strawberry letter 23: *Brothers* Johnson / It's ecstasy when you lay down next to me: *White, Barry* / Boogie nights: *Heatwave* / Love hit me: *Nightingale, Maxine* / Saturday nite: *Earth, Wind & Fire* / Shuffle, The: *McCoy, Van* / That's what friends are for: *Williams, Deniece* / Baby come back: *Player* / Too hot to handle: *Heatwave* / Red light spells danger: *Ocean, Billy* / Whodunnit: *Tavares* / Greatest love of all, The: *Benson, George* / So you win again: *Hot Chocolate* / Keep it comin' love: *K.C. & The Sunshine Band* / Everytime I turn around: *L.T.D.*/ Ain't gonna bump no more: *Tex, Joe* / Best of my love: *Emotions* / Let's clean up the ghetto: *Philadelphia* All Stars / I will: *Winters, Ruby* / Don't leave me this way: *Melvin, Harold & The Bluenotes* / Jack and Jill: *Parker, Ray Jnr.& Raydio* / Real mother: *Watson, Johnny 'Guitar'* / Native New Yorker: *Odyssey*.
2LP: . . . . **KNLP 22077**
MCSET: . . . . **KNMC 22077**

SOUL YEARS 1978, THE (Various artists).
Tracks: / September: *Earth, Wind & Fire* / I thought it was you: *Hancock, Herbie* / Shame: *King, Evelyn "Champagne"*/ Blame it on the boogie: *Jacksons* / More than a woman: *Tavares* / Dance (disco heat): *Sylvester* / If I can't have you: *Elliman, Yvonne* / Boogie oogie oogie: *Taste Of Honey* / Is this a love thing: *Parker, Ray* Jnr.& Raydio / Holding on (when love): *L.T.D.* / Used to be my girl: *O'Jays* / Fantasy: *Earth, Wind & Fire* / Our love: *Cole, Natalie* / Get down: *Chandler, Gene* / Always and forever: *Heatwave* / Close the door: *Pendergrass, Teddy* / Whenever you want my love: *Real Thing* / Too much too little too late: *Mathis*, Johnny & Deniece Williams / Shake and dance with me: *Con Funk Shun* / Don't hold back: *Chanson* / Stuff like that: *Jones, Quincy* / Every one's a winner: *Hot Chocolate* / Come back and finish what you started: *Knight*, Gladys & The Pips / Come to me: *Winters, Ruby* / You make me feel: *Sylvester* / Your sweetness is my ...: *White, Barry* / Flashlight: *Parliament* / Givin' up, givin' in: *3 Degrees*.
2LP: . . . . **KNLP 22078**
MCSET: . . . . **KNMC 22078**

SOUL YEARS 1979, THE (Various artists).
Tracks: / After the love has gone: *Earth, Wind & Fire* / I will survive: *Gaynor, Gloria* / Ladies night: *Kool* & The Gang / Ain't no stoppin' us now: *McFadden & Whitehead* / H.A.P.P.Y. radio: *Starr, Edwin* / Ring my bell: *Ward, Anita* / Reunited: *Peaches & Herb* / My simple heart: *3 Degrees*.
2LP: . . . . **KNLP 22079**
MCSET: . . . . **KNMC 22079**

SOUL YEARS 1980 (Various artists).
MC: . . . . **KNMC 22080**

SOUL YEARS 1981 (Various artists).
MC: . . . . **KNMC 22081**

SOUL YEARS 1982 (Various artists).
MC: . . . . **KNMC 22082**

SOUL YEARS 1983 (Various artists).
MC: . . . . **KNMC 22083**

SOUL YEARS 1984 (Various artists).
MC: . . . . **KNMC 22084**

SOUL YEARS OF MINIT RECORDS (Struttin' & Flirtin' 1966-1969) (Various artists).
Tracks: / What is this: *Womack, Bobby* / 60 minutes of your love: *Banks, Homer* / Working on your case: *O'Jays*/ Hunk of funk, A: *Dozier, Gene & The Brotherhood* / Baby I love you: *Holiday, Jimmy* / I know you don't want me no more: *Jones, Gloria* / Fly me to the moon: *Womack, Bobby* / How I miss you baby: *Womack, Bobby & D. Carter*/ Get right: *Players* / I wish it would rain: *Turner, Ike & Tina* / Worried life blues: *Parker, Little Junior*/ My heart is in danger: *Ray, Alder* / I've got love for my baby: *Young Hearts* / I'm gonna do all I can to do right by my man: *Turner, Ike & Tina*.
LP: . . . . **SSL 6028**
MC: . . . . **TCSSL 6028**

SOULED OUT - THE BEST OF CHELSEA (Various artists).
LP: . . . . **CHELV 1007**
MC: . . . . **CHELC 1007**

SOULFUL LOVE (Various artists).
Tracks: / Misty blue: *Simon, Joe* / If you don't want my love (give it back): *Womack, Bobby* / I do love you: *Stewart, Billy* / Tell it like it is: *Neville, Aaron* / Nothing takes the place of you: *McCall, Toussaint*/ I had a talk with my man: *Collier, Mitty* / Stand by me: *Little Milton* / Love is blue: *Dells* / Release me: *Phillips, Esther* / When a man loves a woman: *Sledge, Percy* / At last: *James, Etta* / Sweet woman like you, A: *Tex, Joe* / Ruler of my heart: *Thomas, Irma* / Sitting in the park: *Stewart, Billy*.
MC: . . . . **TCINS 5006**
LP: . . . . **INS 5006**

SOULFUL STUFF (Various artists).
Tracks: / Am I the same girl: *Acklin, Barbara* / Love makes a woman: *Acklin, Barbara* / Oh no not my baby: *Brown, Maxine* / Since I found you: *Brown, Maxine* / Baby it's you: *Shirelles* / I'm gonna miss you: *Artistics*/ Saving my love for you: *Franklin, Erma* / Just don't know what to do with myself: *Hunt, Tommy* / Just as long as you need me: *Independents* / Love uprising: *Leavill, Otis* / I'm the one to do it: *Baker, Laverne*/ I keep forgettin': *Jackson, Chuck* / Any day now: *Jackson, Chuck* / Turn back the hands of time: *Davis*, Tyrone / Lonely teardrops: *Wilson, Jackie* / Can't get enough: *Thomas, Irma* / Can't get you off my mind: *Diplomats* / Put yourself in my place: *Big Maybelle* / Make the night a little longer: *Hunt, Tommy* / Girl don't care, The: *Chandler, Gene* / Have you seen her: *Chi-lites* / Sly, the slick and the wicked, The: *Lost Generation* / Soulful strut: *Young Holt Unlimited*.
MC: . . . . **KENC 919**

SOULIN' VOL.4 (Various artists).
LP: . . . . **BLP 504**

SOULIN' VOL 1 (Various artists).
LP: . . . . **BLP 501**

SOULIN' VOL 2 (Various artists).
LP: . . . . **BLP 502**

SOULIN' VOL 3 (Various artists).
LP: . . . . **BLP 503**

SOULMATES (Various artists).
Tracks: / Rainy night in Georgia, A: *Benton, Brook* / Knock on wood: *Floyd, Eddie* / Tighten up: *Bell, Archie* / Tonight's the night: *Various artists* / Soul man: *Sam & Dave* / Walking the dog: *Thomas, Rufus* / Warm and tender love: *Various artists* / Patches: *Carter, Clarence* / Stand by me: *King, Ben E.* / Hold on I'm coming: *Sam & Dave* / Goin' out of my head: *Little Anthony* / Shoop shoop song: *Everett, Betty*.
LP: . . . . **SPR 8526**
MC: . . . . **SPC 8526**

SOUND OF ALABAMA SOUL (Various artists).
Tracks: / My love looks good: *Knight, Frederick* / I'm falling in love: *Knight, Frederick* / My love is real: *Controllers* / When did you stop: *Various artists* / Its only a matter of time: *True Image* / Fool and his money, A: *True Image* / Take another look: *Saunders, Frankie* / I won't stop loving you: *Ward, Anita*/ I'm ready for your love: *Ward, Anita* / It ain't fair: *True Image*.
LP: . . . . **TRLP 113**
LP: . . . . **TRPL 113**

SOUND OF NEW ORLEANS, THE (Various artists).
LPS: . . . . **BOX 254**
MCSET: . . . . **TCBOX 254**

SOUND OF PHILADELPHIA (Various artists).
Tracks: / Me and Mrs Jones: *Paul, Billy* / I love music: *O'Jays* / Don't leave me this way: *Melvin, Harold* & The Bluenotes / Nights over Egypt: *Jones Girls* / Year of decision: *3 Degrees* / Love train: *O'Jays*/ Love TKO: *Pendergrass, Teddy* / When will I see you again: *3 Degrees* / Show me the way to go: *Jacksons*/ If you don't know me by now: *Melvin, Harold & The Bluenotes* / Backstabbers: *O'Jays* / You'll never find another love like mine: *Rawls, Lou* / Wake up everybody: *Melvin, Harold & The Bluenotes* / TSOP: *MFSB* / Soul City walk: *Bell, Archie & The Drells* / Love I lost, The: *Melvin, Harold & The Bluenotes*.
LP: . . . . **SHM 3309**
MC: . . . . **HSC 3309**

SOUND OF ST. LOUIS SOUL (Various artists).
Tracks: / Got to forget you: *Beverley, Charles* / Good women go bad: *Carr, Barbara* / Taking a chance: *Beverley*, Charles / You've been doing wrong: *Carr, Barbara* / Hollywood: *Beverley, Charles* / Sweet loving baby: *Dee*, Dave / Don't you wanna man: *Hunter/Ross* / Good times are gone, The: *Hunter/Ross* / I'd love you tomorrow: *Hunter/Ross* / Rose bush: *Hunter/Ross*.
LP: . . . . **TRLP 108**
LP: . . . . **TRPL 108**

SOUND STAGE 7 STORY, THE (Various artists).
Tracks: / Easy going fellow: *Shelton, Roscoe* / Hymn no. 5: *Gaines, Earl* / I'm his wife, you're just a friend: *Sexton, Ann* / I love you: *Baker, Sam* / Only time you say you love me, The: *Smith, Charles* / (You keep me) hangin' on: *Simon, Joe* / Whole lot of man, A: *Davis, Geator* / All the time: *Washington, Ella* / Sometimes you have to cry: *Baker, Sam* / Chokin' kind, The: *Simon, Joe* / He called me baby: *Washington, Ella*/ Your heart is so cold: *Davis, Geator* / Strain on my heart: *Shelton, Roscoe* / You're gonna miss me: *Sexton*, Ann / I'll take care of you: *Gaines, Earl* / I'm not through loving you: *Brown, Lattimore* / I don't care who knows: *Church, Jimmy* / Soon as darkness falls: *Shelton, Roscoe* / What made you change your mind: *King*, Bobby / Human: *Brief Encounter (film)* / Judge of hearts: *Hobbs, Willie* / Someone bigger than you or me: *Baker, Sam* / We've got to save it: *Scott, Moody* / Let me come on home: *King, Bobby* / I'm ready to love you now: *Shelton, Roscoe* / Just a glance away: *Baker, Sam* / Try something new: *Billups, Eddie* / Ooh I love you: *Cashmeres* / I got love: *Byrd, Leon* / Woman's touch, A: *Scott, Moody* / My faith in you: *Church, Jimmy* / I know your heart has been broken: *Shelton, Roscoe*.
2LP: . . . . **CDX 45**

SOUTHERN SOUL BELLES (Various artists).
Tracks: / Love of my man, The: *West, Barbara* / I'm in love: *Lavette, Betty* / That's all a part of lovin' him: *Young, Tommie* / Every little bit hurts: *Scott, Peggy* / Fight fire with fire: *Holiday, Shay* / Easier to say (than do): *Lavette, Betty* / Do you still feel the same: *Young, Tommie* / Shell of a woman, A: *Allen*, Doris / Nearer to you: *Lavette, Betty* / Anyone but you: *West, Barbara* / Giving up: *Ad Libs* / Gonna make a change: *Montgomery, Carolyn* / Hanging heavy in my mind: *Allen, Doris* / You brought it all on yourself: *Young, Tommie* / Let me down easy: *Lavette, Betty* / Give me back the man I love: *West, Barbara*.
LP: . . . . **CRB 1035**
LP: . . . . **INS 5018**
MC: . . . . **TCINS 5018**

SOUTHERN SOUL BROTHERS (Various artists).
Tracks: / Easy going fellow: *Mills, Billy* / Just the touch of your hand: *Vann, Paul* / One of these days: *Brown*, Piney / Wife you save (maybe your own), The: *Little Richie* / Loving her was easier: *Gaines, Earl* / I'll find my sunshine: *Scott, Moody* / Hey girl: *Beavers, Jackie* / Mojo blues: *John R* / You made your bed so hard: *Davis, Geator* / That's all I want from you: *Baker, Sam* / Sad memories: *Mills, Billy* / I wish I was a baby: *Little Richie* / Wedding cake, The: *Shelton, Roscoe* / Nashville women: *Brown, Piney* / Woman's touch, A: *Scott, Moody* / V.C. blues: *Orange, Allen*.
LP: . . . . **CRB 1156**

SOUTHERN SOUL SISTERS (Various artists).
Tracks: / Somebody else is gonna plough your field: *Hendrix, Margie* / I can't afford to lose him: *Washington, Ella*/ You can't win: *Sexton, Ann* / You don't need him: *Jordan, Vivalore* / Put your trust in me: *Black, Alder* Ray / Do right baby: *Hendrix, Margie* / If time could stand still: *Washington, Ella* / You got to use what you got: *Sexton, Ann* / I've got mama's recipe: *Hendrix, Margie* / Maybe: *Jordan, Vivalore* / Just because the package has been opened: *Black, Alder Ray* / If I work my thing on you: *Sexton, Ann* / Don't destroy me: *Hendrix*, Margie / I don't care about the past: *Washington, Ella* / Sugar daddy: *Sexton, Ann* / Jim Dandy: *Hendrix, Margie*.
LP: . . . . **CRB 1153**

SPOTLIGHT ON SOUL (Various artists).
LP: . . . . **SPOT 1031**
MC: . . . . **ZCSPT 1031**

SSS SOUL SURVEY (Various artists).
Tracks: / Cryin' in the streets: *Perkins, George* / Lonely room: *Murray, Mickey* / Game of love: *Hobbs, Willie*/ I have no one: *Hamilton, Big John* / Action speaks louder than words: *Bell, Reuben* / That's how strong my love is: *Giles, Eddie* / How much can a man take: *Hamilton, Big John* / Them changes: *Hamilton, Big John & Doris* Allen / Baby you got it: *Murray, Clarence* / One way love affair: *White, Danny* / Lift me up: *Hamilton*, Big John / If I could see you one more time: *Adams, Johnny* / Lonely man: *Soul, Johnny* / Too late: *Bell, Reuben* / Some leaving alone: *Bush, Tommy* / Take this hurt off me: *Hamilton, Big John*.
LP: . . . . **CRB 1034**

STAN'S SOUL SHOP (Various artists).
Tracks: / No more ghettos in America: *Winston, Stanley* / Man in love, A: *Perkins, George* / Losing boy: *Giles*, Eddie / What was I supposed to do: *Carter, Clarence* / You're gonna miss me: *Bell, Reuben* / You got me tamed: *Hammond, Clay* / Lord will make a way, The: *Robinson, Roscoe* / That's enough: *Robinson, Roscoe* / Prelude to a heartbreak: *Montclairs, The* / I wake up crying: *Camille, Bob* / Cry to me: *Powell, Bobby* / I get my groove from you: *Patterson, Bobby* / Stand by me: *Soul Stirrers* / I still love you: *Steele, Eddie*/ Good thing: *Jones, Casey* / Going home to Georgia: *Gilliam, Johnny*.
LP: . . . . **CRB 1033**

STAX 20 GOLDEN GREATS (Various artists).
Tracks: / Shaft: *Various artists* / Private number: *Various artists* / Respect yourself: *Various artists*/ Who's making love: *Various artists* / Starting all over again: *Various artists* / Soul limbo: *Various artists*/ Shortstopping: *Various artists* / I've been lonely for so long: *Various artists* / I'll be the other woman: *Various artists* / Dedicated to the one I love: *Various artists* / Time is tight: *Various artists* / I'll take you there: *Various artists* / My baby specializes: *Various artists* / Knock on wood: *Various artists* / Woman to woman: *Various artists* / In the rain: *Various artists*.
LP: . . . . **STX 3013**

STAX SIRENS AND VOLT VAMPS (Various artists).
Tracks: / Try a little tenderness: *Sweet Inspirations* / I've got to go on without you: *Brown, Shirley* / Take it off her (and put it on me): *Brown, Veda* / Love slave: *Alexander, Margie* / Shouldn't I love him: *John*, Mable / Got to be the man: *Emotions* / Save the last kiss for me: *Knight, Jean* / Nobody: *Joseph, Margie*/ Who could be loving you: *Ross, Jackie* / Standing in the need of your love: *Jeanne & The Darlings* / I'll never grow old: *Charmells* / Give love to save love: *Clay, Judy* / You hurt me for the last time: *Foxx, Inez & Charlie*/ I like what you're doing (to me): *Thomas, Carla* / If I had it my way: *Weston, Kim* / How can you mistreat the one you love: *Love, Katie* (Available on CD only) / Love changes: *Charlene & The Soul Serenaders* (Available on CD only) / What happened to our good thing: *Haywood, Kitty* (Available on CD only) / Where would you be today: *Ilana*(Available on CD only).
LP: . . . . **SX 013**
MC: . . . . **SXC 013**

STAX TRAX: 18 CLASSIC SOUL HITS (Various artists).
Tracks: / I'll take you there: *Staple Singers* / Time is tight: *Booker T & The MGs* / Knock on wood: *Floyd, Eddie* / Stay with me, baby: *Brown, Shirley* / I've been lonely for so long: *Knight, Frederick* / Private number: *Clay, Judy & William Bell* / Long walk to D.C.: *Staple Singers* / Sixty minutes man: *Thomas, Rufus* / Why I keep living these memories: *Knight, Jean* (end s1) / Shaft, Theme from: *Hayes, Isaac* / Bring it on home to me: *Floyd, Eddie* / Woman to woman: *Brown, Shirley* / Respect yourself: *Staple Singers* / Soul limbo: *Booker T & The MGs* / Mr. Big Stuff: *Knight, Jean* / My girl: *Floyd, Eddie* / (Sittin' on) the dock of the bay: *Staple Singers* / Funky chicken: *Thomas, Rufus*.
LP: . . . . **CBR 1023**
MC: . . . . **KCBR 1023**

STAX/VOLT REVUE, VOL 1: LIVE IN LONDON (Various artists).
LP: **SD7721**

STAX/VOLT REVUE, VOL 2: LIVE IN PARIS (Various artists).
LP: SD7722

SUNSET SOUND OF LA (Various artists).
Tracks: / Roses are red: Mac Band / Don't be cruel: Brown, Bobby (1) / If it isn't love: New Edition/ Sleepless weekend: Huntsberry, Howard / You're puttin' a rush on me: Mills, S / Middles of the night: Body/ I'm the one: Perri / I'll give you love: Sue Ann / Girlfriend: Pebbles (Singer) / Some kind of lover: Watley, Jody / Lovin' on next to nothin': Knight, Gladys / Passion and pain: McClain, Janice / Intimacy: St. Paul / Slow starter: Hall, Randy / One track mind: Pettus, Giorge.
LP: DEAL 1
MC: DEALC 1

SWAMPLAND SOUL (Various artists).
LP: GRLP 7754

SWEET BLACK MUSIC (Various artists).
Tracks: / This magic moment: Various artists / Warm and tender love: Various artists / We need understanding: Various artists / Sweet lovin' woman: Various artists / You broke your promise: Various artists / Smoke gets in your eyes: Various artists / Beautiful world outside: Various artists / Stand by me: Various artists/ Shake a tail feather: Various artists / Win your love for me: Various artists / He's so fine: Various artists / Love really hurts without you: Various artists.
MC: 510479.3

SWEET SOUL MUSIC (Various artists).
Tracks: / Time is tight: Booker T & The MGs / Private number: Clay, Judy & William Bell / I'll take you there: Staple Singers / Shoutin' out love: Emotions (group) / To the push and pull (Part 1): Thomas, Rufus/ Come tomorrow: Joseph, Margie / Lonely for your love: Bell, William / Shaft, Theme from: Hayes, Isaac/ Watcha see is watcha get: Dramatics / I had a talk with my man: Foxx, Inez & Charlie / Take care of your homework: Taylor, Johnnie / Why is the wine sweeter: Floyd, Eddie / Holy cow: Anderson, Stephan / Mr. Big Stuff: Knight, Jean / Soul clap '69: Booker T & The MGs / I've been lonely for so long: Knight, Frederick/ Slipped, tripped and fell in love: Sweet Inspirations / Baby that's a no no: Lewis, Barbara / Starting all over again: Mel & Tim / Son of Shaft: Bar-Kays / Dedicated to the one I love: Temprees / Respect yourself: Staple Singers / When something is wrong with my baby: Weston, Kim / I wake up wanting you: Thomas, Carla/ Who's making love: Taylor, Johnnie / I've never found a girl: Floyd, Eddie / Sweeter he is, The: Soul Children / Pin the tail on the donkey: Newcomers, The.
2LP: CR 049
MCSET: CRT 049

SWEET SOUL MUSIC (2) (Various artists).
Tracks: / If you don't know me by now: Melvin, Harold / Dancing in the street: Reeves, Martha (1) / What becomes of the broken hearted?: Ruffin, Jimmy / My guy: Wells, Mary / Rescue me: Bass, Fontella / Rock your baby: McCrae, George / Spanish harlem: King, Ben E. / Sweet soul music: Sam & Dave.
LP: OCN 2001WL
MC: OCN 2001WK

SWEET SOULFUL CHICAGO (Various artists).
Tracks: / Wrapped, tied and tangled: Baker, Laverne / Love song: Artistics / Help yourself: Butler, Billy/ I'm in danger: Visitors / Feeling's gone, The: Esquires / Hold on: Smith, Marvin / It's all over between us: Charles, Lee / Getting nowhere fast: Smith, Floyd / I love you: Leavill, Otis / It could have been me: Franklin, Erma / Fool, fool, fool (look in the mirror): Acklin, Barbara / Sweeter as the days go by: Major Lance / No easy way down: Jackson, Walter / You can't keep a good man down: Davis, Tyrone/ My baby's gone: Chandler, Gene / You got me walking: Blake, Cicero.
LP: KENT 070

TEAR STAINED SOUL (The Quinvy Broadway sound Vol 1) (Various artists).
Tracks: / Tearstained face: Varner, Don / Push Mr.Pride aside: Bradford, Eddie / Mojo mama: Varner, Don/ Hand shaking: Braswell, Jimmy / Little bit of love, A: Bradford, Eddie / When it's over: Varner, Don/ You made your bed: Bradford, Eddie / Bless your sweet little soul: Johnson, Al / Meet me in church: Varner, Don / Home for the summer: Braswell, Jimmy / Don't give up on me: Varner, Brenda / Love waits for no man: Johnson, Al / Down in Texas: Varner, Don / Let me be a woman: Varner, Brenda.
LP: CRB 1219

TEARS IN MY EYES (Various artists).
Tracks: / Should I let him go: Parker, Paulette / I don't want to go: Little Mr Lee and The Cherokees / I ain't myself anymore: Bland, Bobby / He made woman for man: Wright, O.V. / It's private tonight: Adams, Arthur/ First love: Mirettes / I wanna make you happy: Mandolph, Magaret / Beginning of my end, The: Unifics/ Shopping for love: Mike and The Censations / I need your love to comfort me: Sam & Bill / Let me hear it from you: McLean, Chuck / Inside story, The: Ace, Buddy / Long walk on a short pier, A: Davis, Rhonda / Thrill is gone (The): King, B.B. / Tears in my eyes: Fascinations / This must end: Impressions (group).
LP: KENT 045

THIS IS CHARLY SOUL (See under Charly (label)) (Various artists).

THIS IS SOUL (Various artists).
Tracks: / Mustang Sally: Pickett, Wilson / B-A-B-Y: Thomas, Carla / Sweet soul music: Conley, Arthur/ When a man loves a woman: Sledge, Percy / I got everything I need: Sam & Dave / What is soul: King, Ben E. / Fa fa fa fa fa (sad song): Redding, Otis / Knock on wood: Floyd, Eddie / Keep looking: Burke, Solomon / I never loved a man (the way I loved you): Franklin, Aretha / Warm and tender love: Sledge, Percy/ Land of a thousand dances: Pickett, Wilson.
LP: K 20023

THIS IS SOUL (Various artists).
LP: SOUL 1
MC: SOULK 1
LP: 780 168-1
MC: 780 168-4

THIS IS SOUL (See under This Is Soul) (Various artists).

TOO GOOD TO BE FORGOTTEN MORE SOUL CLASSICS (Various artists).
Tracks: / Whispers: Wilson, Jackie / Oh no not my baby: Various artists / Have you seen her: Chi-lites/ There was a time: Chandler, Gene / I just don't know what to do with myself: Hunt, Tommy / Love of my man, The: Kilgore, Theola / Washed ashore (on a lonely island in the sun): Platters / Hook and sling: Bo, Eddie/ No pity (in the naked city): Wilson, Jackie / To good to be forgotten: Chi-lites / Love makes a woman: Acklin, Barbara / I'm gonna miss you: Artistics / Tell him I'm not home: Jackson, Chuck / Long after tonight is all over: Radcliffe, Jimmy / With this ring: Platters / Midsummer night in Harlem: Thomas, Charlie & The Drifters.
LP: CRB 1161
MC: TCCRB 1161

TOTAL EXPERIENCE (Various artists).
Tracks: / Big fun: Gap Band / Don't waste your time: Yarbrough & Peoples / Keeping secrets: Switch/ Change your wicked ways: Ford, Pennye / Ready or not: Goodie / Billy and Baby Gap: Billy & Baby Gap/ Guilty: Yarbrough & Peoples / Best friends: Towns, Eddie / Backed up against the wall: King, Will/ Sexual therapy: Paul, Billy / Confess it baby: Prime Time.
LP: TOTELP 2
MC: ZCTOTE 2

TRACKS OF MY TEARS (The best of Smokey Robinson) (Various artists).
LP: DINTV 17
MC: DINMC 17

TRACKS OF MY TEARS (Various artists).
Tracks: / Tracks of my tears: Robinson, Smokey & The Temptations / I'm not in love / Jealous guy: Roxy Music/ (I just) died in your arms: Cutting Crew / See the day: Lee, Dee C / After the love has gone: Earth, Wind & Fire / Farewell is a lonely sound: Ruffin, Jimmy / Desperado: Eagles / Can't be with you tonight: Boucher, Judy / I guess thats why they call it the blues: John, Elton / All cried out: Moyet, Alison / Only when you leave: Spandau Ballet / Love dont live here anymore: Rose Royce / On my own: Labelle, Patti & Michael McDonald / I'm still waiting: Ross, Diana / Hold me now: Logan, Johnny.
LP: STAR 2295
MC: STAC 2295

TRIPPIN' ON YOUR SOUL (Various artists).
Tracks: / Special kind of woman: Thompson, Paul / I may not be what you want: Mel & Tim / Sea shells: Charmels/ Did my baby call: Bad Lads / Whole world's a picture show: Newcomers / Yes Sir Brother: Brown, Shirley/ Come what may: Williams, John Gary / I've been born again: Taylor, Johnny / Blind Alley: Emotions/ Baby that's a no no: Lewis, Barbara / Trippin' on your love: Staple Singers / If it's love that you want: Brown, Randy / Taking all the love I can: Joseph, Margie / Ain't no need ...: Allen, Rance Group.
LP: KENT 096

T.S.O.P.: THE SOUND OF PHILADELPHIA (See under Philadelphia...) (Various artists).

T.S.O.P.: THE SOUND OF PHILADELPHIA (Various artists).
Tracks: / T.S.O.P: MFSB / I love music: O'Jays / Love I lost, The: Melvin, Harold & The Bluenotes/ Let 'em in: Paul, Billy / You'll never find another love like mine: Rawls, Lou / I'll always love my mama: Intruders / Show you the way to go: Jacksons / Ain't no stoppin' us now: McFadden & Whitehead / Let's groove: Bell, Archie & The Drells / What's your name?: Stylistics / Love train: O'Jays / Lady love: Rawls, Lou / Whole town's laughing at me, The: Pendergrass, Teddy / If you don't know me by now: Melvin, Harold & The Bluenotes / Me & Mrs. Jones: Paul, Billy / Love TKO: Pendergrass, Teddy / Holdin' on: Wansel, Dexter / Nights over Egypt: Jones Girls / Was that all it was: Carne, Jean / Turn off the lights: Pendergrass, Teddy / Wake up everybody: Melvin, Harold & The Bluenotes / Backstabbers: O'Jays / Life on Mars: Wansel, Dexter / Sexy: MFSB / When will I see you again?: 3 Degrees / Close the door: Pendergrass, Teddy/ See you when I get there: Rawls, Lou / Let's clean up the ghetto: Philadelphia All Stars.
2LP: NE 1406
MCSET: CE 2406

UNDER THE STREETLAMP (Various artists).
Tracks: / Stop hiding in the closet / Under the streetlamp: Various artists / Dearest one: C-Quents / Lost in a city: Majors / You're the beat of my heart: Freddy and the Sounds Of Soul / I'll be hangin' on: Parris, Fred & the Restless Hearts / Baby I need you: Ambers / Beware, beware.: Compliments / Someone: Metros/ Just remember me: Creations / Looking for a love of my own: Classics / Running wild: Ex Saveyons/ There'll still be a sweet tomorrow: Ethnics / Cryin' bitter tears: Steelers / All the way: Dandeliers/ Weeping baby all the time: Grier Brothers.
LP: LPSS 109

UP ALL NIGHT (See Under Up All Night) (Various artists).

URBAN CLASSICS (Various artists).
Tracks: / Cross the track (we better go back): Maceo & The Macks / I believe in miracles: Jackson Sisters / I know you got soul: Byrd, Bobby.
LP: URBLP 4
MC: URBMC 4

URBAN CLASSICS VOL 2 (Various artists).
Tracks: / She's the one: Brown, James / You're the song I've always wanted to sing: Thomas, Timmy / Soul, soul, soul, (somebody): Wild Magnolias / Pass the peas: J.B.'s / Funky stuff: Kool & The Gang / Misdemeanor: Sylvers, Foster / Never get enough: Byrd, Bobby / Mr. Big Stuff: Collins, Lyn / I dig everything about you: Mob / Brother green: Ayers, Roy / Yes, it's you: Sweet Charles.
LP: URBLP 5
MC: URBMC 5

URBAN CLASSICS VOL 3 (Various artists).
Tracks: / Making my daydream real: We Are The People / You and I: Bristol, Johnny / I have learned to do without you: Taylor, Debbie / Funky luvah: Creative Source / Shake her loose: Jackson Sisters / Let me in your life: Cofield, Pat / Power of love: McClain, Alton & Destiny / Tell me what you want: Ruffin, Jimmy/ Grandma's hands: Blossoms / You're hardly gone: Thomas, Tyrone / Moonlight lovin': Hayes, Isaac.
LP: 841 515 1
MC: 841 515 4

VOLUME 2 (Various artists).
Tracks: / Have pity on me: Young,Billy / Left the water running: Young,Billy / Can you be a one man woman: Dees, Sam / Put you back in your place: Dees, Sam / Maryanna: Dees, Sam / Love starvation: Dees, Sam/ I'm gonna start a war: Barbara & The Browns / I don't want to have to wait: Barbara & The Browns / Plenty of room: Barbara & The Browns / To know I can't touch: Barbara & The Browns / Too much: Entertainers... / I tried to tell you: Entertainers... / Tell him tonight: Bollinger,William / You can lead your woman to the altar: Bollinger,William.
LP: GCH 8118

WALKING THE BACK STREETS AND CRYING (Various artists).
Tracks: / Tin Pan Alley: Various artists / Don't ask me no questions: Various artists / Big legged woman: Various artists / Part time love: Various artists / Can't you see what you're doing to me: Various artists / Walking the back streets and crying: Various artists / At the drive in: Various artists / Left hand woman: Various artists / Hello sundown: Various artists / Open the door to your heart: Various artists / It's hard going up: Various artists.
LP: STM 7004

WE FUNK THE BEST (Various artists).
Tracks: / First time around: Various artists / We funk the best: Various artists / Love thang: Various artists / Sing sing: Various artists / Burning spear: Various artists / Got my mind made up: Various artists / Showdown: Various artists / I'm funkin' you tonight: Various artists / Jingo: Various artists/ Ice cold love: Various artists.
LP: SSLM 4002

WHAT'S HAPPENING...STATESIDE (Various artists).
Tracks: / Ready, willing and able: Holiday, Jimmy & Clydie King / Dead end street: Rawls, Lou / Working on your case: O'Jays / Lookin' for a love: Womack, Bobby / Girls from Texas, The: Lewis, Jimmy / As long as I have you: Mimms, Garnet / I'm waitin' at the station: Neville, Aaron / Tell it like it is: Swan, Bettye/ Nutbush city limits: Turner, Ike & Tina / Better use your head: Little Anthony & The Imperials / Mockingbird: Foxx, Inez & Charlie / Who's that lady: Isley Brothers / Mardi gras in: Professor Longhair / Ain't nothing you can do: Hill, Z.Z. / Lot of love, A: Banks, Homer.
LP: SSLX 1
MC: TCSSLX 1

WHEN A MAN LOVES A WOMAN (SOUL) (16 Classic Soul Hits) (Various artists).
LP: PFP 1001
MC: PFC 1001

WINDY CITY SOUL (Various artists).
Tracks: / Lay it on me: Maurice & Mac / Lean on me: Maurice & Mac / You left the water running: Maurice & Mac / So much love: Maurice & Mac / Temptation: Brothers,Knight / 'Bout to get me: Brothers,Knight/ Sinkin' low: Brothers,Knight / She's A1: Brothers,Knight / Searchin' for my love: Moore,Bobby & The Rhythm Aces / How can you do it baby: Moore,Bobby & The Rhythm Aces / Hey Mr DJ: Moore,Bobby & The Rhythm Aces/ Promise is a promise, A: Lasalle, Denise / Love reputation, A: Lasalle, Denise / Countdown: Lasalle, Denise/ Love is a five letter word: Phelps,James / Wasting time: Phelps,James / Oh what a feeling: Phelps,James.
LP: GCH 8117

YOU BETTER BELIEVE IT (Various artists).
Tracks: / You better believe it: Borders Tony / I think I'd do it: Hill, Z.Z. / Since I fell for you: Brandon, Bill / Living high on the hog: Borders Tony / He kept on talking: Varner, Don / Faithful and true: Hill, Z.Z. / Cornbread woman: Borders Tony / Masquerade: Varner, Don / When you get what you want: Brandon, Bill / Cheaters never win: Borders Tony / Handshaking: Varner, Don / Home just ain't home (at suppertime): Hill, Z.Z. / Lonely weekends: Borders Tony / Strangest feeling: Brandon, Bill / I'm still in love with you: Varner, Don / It's a hang up baby: Hill, Z.Z..
LP: CRB 1223

YOU FOUND THE VOCAL GROUP SOUND PART 3 (Various artists).
LP: SS 8033

YOU FOUND THE VOCAL GROUP SOUND PART 1 (Various artists).
LP: SS 8031

YOU FOUND THE VOCAL GROUP SOUND PART 2 (Various artists).
LP: SS 8032

Soul Affair Orchestra

SOUL AFFAIR.
LP: CRLP 506

Soul Asylum

AND THE HORSE THEY RODE IN ON.
LP: 3953181
MC: 3953184

CLAM DIP & OTHER DELIGHTS.
LP: GOES ON 22

HANG TIME.
Tracks: / Down on up to me / Little too clean / Sometime to return / Cartoon / Beggars and choosers / Endless farewell / Standing in the doorway / Marionette / Ode / Jack of all trades / Twiddly dee / Heavy rotation.

LP: . . . . AMA 5197
MC: . . . . AMC 5197

MADE TO BE BROKEN.
LP: . . . . ROUGH 102

WHILE YOU WERE OUT.
LP: . . . . GOES ON 16

Soul Brothers

JIVE EXPLOSION (South African Township Music).
Tracks: / Akabongi (Don't say thanks) / Buya mama wami (Come back mother) / Phuma layikhaya (get out of this house) / Ngihamba nawe (I'm going with you) / Inhlalayenza (usual thing) / Isilingo (Temptations) / Uthando (Love) / Shesh ungazise (Hurry up) / Isicelo (Proposal) / Isikhwele (Jealous) / Sivikele baba (Protect us, Lord) / Isithembiso (Promises) / Ukhaliswa yini (CD only).
LP: . . . . EWV 8
MC: . . . . TCEWV 8

SWINGIN' THE BLUES (Soul Brothers at Home).
LP: . . . . PHONT 7570

Soul City USA

SOUL CITY USA (Various artists).
LP: . . . . BLUESTLP 1

Soul, David

BAND OF FRIENDS.
Tracks: / Troubador / Beechwood blues / Surrender to me / Dancin Jones / Goodbye Gatsby / Fools for each other / Can't change my heart / You're a woman now / Piper / Count and the temptress, The / Fool for love.
LP: . . . . NRGL 5000
MC: . . . . NRGC 5000

BEST DAYS OF MY LIFE.
Tracks: / Simple man / Waking up alone / Carlito / Dreamers / I can't afford that feeling anymore / That's enough for me / Maybe we can work it out / How can you tell you got it / Dutchman, The / Distant shore / Best days of my life.
LP: . . . . NRGL 5001
MC: . . . . NRGC 5001

BEST OF DAVID SOUL.
Tracks: / Silver lady / Going in with my eyes open / Topanga / Nobody but a fool or a preacher / Landlord / One more mountain to climb / Bird on a wire / Tattler / 1927 Kansas city / It sure brings out the love in your eyes / Don't give up on us / Let's have a quiet night in / I wish I was / Seem to miss so much (coalminers song).
LP: . . . . CSAPLP 104
MC: . . . . CSAPMC 104

DAVID SOUL.
LP: . . . . PVLP 1012

PLAYING TO AN AUDIENCE OF ONE.
LP: . . . . PVLP 1026

Soul daze/Soul nites

SOUL DAZE/SOUL NITES (Various artists).
2LP: . . . . RTL 2080 AB

Soul Fever

SOUL FEVER (Various artists).
MC: . . . . GM 0216

Soul Hunters

JUST IN THE NICK OF TIME.
LP: . . . . CONTE 135

Soul II Soul

CLUB CLASSICS VOL.1.
Tracks: / Keep on movin' / Back to life (however do you want me) / Feel free / Live rap / Dance / Jazzie's groove / Fairplay / Happiness / Holdin' on Bambelea / African dance / Acapella.
LP: . . . . DIX 82
MC: . . . . CDIX 82

VOLUME II - 1990 A NEW DECADE.
Tracks: / Get a life / Jazzie B / Daddae Harvey / Love comes through / People / Missing you / Courtney blows / 1990 a new decade / Dreams a dream, A / Time (untitled) / In the heat of the night / Our time has now come / Nomsa caluza / Sonti mndebele.
LP: . . . . DIX 90
MC: . . . . CDIX 90

Soul Man (film)

SOUL MAN (Film Soundtrack) (Various artists).
Tracks: / Soul man: *Moore, Sam & Lou Reed* / Outside: *Nu Shooz* / Bang, bang, bang (who's on the phone)?: *Ricky*/ Totally academic: *Russell, Brenda* / Suddenly it's magic: *Williams, Vesta* / Sweet Sarah: *Scott, Tom*/ Black girls: *Chong, Rae Dawn* / Models: *Evolution* / Love and affection: *Davis, Martha & Sly Stone*/ Eek-ah-bo-static automatic: *Stone, Sly*.
LP: . . . . AMA 3903
MC: . . . . AMC 3903

Soul Of The Machine

SOUL OF THE MACHINE (Various artists).
Tracks: / Rizzo: *Various artists* / Time and the river: *Various artists* / Water trade: *Various artists*/ Ayers rock: *Various artists* / Peace of mind: *Various artists* / Land of the morning calm: *Various artists*/ Cityscape: *Various artists* / Chorale: *Various artists* / In the age of steam: *Various artists* / Lure of silence, The: *Various artists*.
LP: 371 700-1
MC: 371 700-4

Soul On Sound

SOUL ON SOUND NO 33 (Various artists).
MC: . . . . SOSS 032

Soul Shakin'

SOUL SHAKIN' (Various artists).
LP: . . . . SHM 3108
MC: . . . . HSC 3108

Soul Sisters

DAZZLE.
LP: . . . . CHILLP 7
MC: . . . . ZCCHIL 7

Soul Sonic Force

RENEGADES OF FUNK (See under Bambaataa, Afrika) (Soul Sonic Force & Afrika Bambaata).

Soul Stirrers

GOD SAID IT.
LP: . . . . SL 14569

I CAN SEE THE LIGHT SHINING.
LP: . . . . SL 14635

I'VE GOT SO MUCH TO BE THANKFUL FOR.
LP: . . . . SL 14611

LIVE IN CONCERT.
Tracks: / Introduction / He's my friend / Be with me, Jesus / I'm travelling on / Wade in the water / God is able / Lord, remember me / When the gates swing open / Touch the hem of his garment / If you love Jesus / Raise your hand / Amazing grace / I will trust in the Lord.
LP: . . . . MIR 5025
MC: . . . . MIR 5025MC

SHE'S GONE ON HOME.
LP: . . . . SL 14530

STAND BY ME FATHER.
Tracks: / Put a little love in your heart / Stand by me Father / He's my guide / Without God in my life / Set me free / In Heaven with him / Glory bound train / Amazing Grace.
LP: . . . . MIR 5013
MC: . . . . ZCMIR 5013

WILL THE REAL SOUL STIRRERS PLEASE STAND UP.
Tracks: / If you love Jesus raise your hand / Nobody's child / Hey brother / Are you holding on / Until then / Touch the hem of His garment / He'll welcome us / They crucified Him / Walk along with me / Stop on board and follow me.
LP: . . . . MIR 5006
MC: . . . . ZCMIR 5006

Soul Train

JAZZ ISVERIGE '86.
LP: . . . . CAP 1335

Souled American

AROUND THE HORN.
LP: . . . . ROUGH 151

FLUBBER.
LP: . . . . ROUGH 141
MC: . . . . ROUGHC 141

Soulside

HOT BODI-GRAM.
LP: . . . . DISCHORD 38

TRIGGER.
MC: . . . . DISCHORD 29 C
LP: . . . . DISCHORD 29

Sound...

SOUND OF APPLAUSE VOL.1 Various artists (Various artists).
LP: . . . . NE 1219
MC: . . . . CE 2220

SOUND OF APPLAUSE VOL.2 Various artists (Various artists).
LP: . . . . NE 1220
MC: . . . . CE 2219

Sound (band)

ALL FALL DOWN.
Tracks: / All fall down / Party of the mind / Monument / In suspense / Where the love is / Song and dance / Calling the new tune / Red paint / Glass and smoke / We could go far.
LP: 240019 1

FROM THE LION'S MOUTH.
Tracks: / Winning / Sense of purpose / Contact the fact / Skeletons / Judgement / Fatal flaw / Possession / Fire / Silent air / New dark age.
LP: . . . . KODE 5

HEADS AND HEARTS.
Tracks: / Whirlpool (Album only) / Total recall / Under you / Burning part of me / Love is not a ghost (Album only) / Wildest dreams / One thousand reasons (Album only) / Restless time (Album only) / Mining for heart (Album only) / World as it is (Album only) / Temperature drop / Counting the days (CD only) / Winning (CD only) / Dreams then plans (CD only) / Longest days (CD only) / Under you (CD only) / Golden soldiers (CD only) / Silent air (CD only) / Sense of purpose (CD only) / New way of life (CD only) / Heartland (CD only) / Missiles (CD only).
LP: . . . . STAT LP 24
MC: . . . . STATC 24

IN THE HOTHOUSE.
LP: . . . . STAT D LP 1

JEOPARDY.
Tracks: / I can't escape myself / Heartland / Hour of need / Words fail me / Missiles / Heyday / Jeopardy / Night versus day / Resistance / Unwritten law / Desire.
LP: . . . . KODE 2

SHOCK OF DAYLIGHT.
LP: . . . . STAB 1
MC: . . . . STAB C 1

SOUND, THE.
LP: . . . . STATLP 24
MC: . . . . STATC 24

THUNDER UP.
LP: . . . . BIAS 053

Sound Barrier

SUBURBIA SUITE, THE.
LP: . . . . PACT 10

Sound Effects

ESSENTIAL SOUND EFFECTS (Various artists).
Tracks: / Water: *Various artists* / Horses: *Various artists* / Farmyard: *Various artists* / Sports: *Various* artists / Space: *Various artists* / Zoo: *Various artists* / Air travel: *Various artists* / Trains: *Various artists* / Motor traffic: *Various artists* / Boats: *Various artists* / Disaster: *Various* artists / Weather: *Various artists* / Interior atmospheres: *Various artists* / Bells: *Various artists*/ Music for silent movies: *Various artists*.
LP: . . . . REFX 448

ESSENTIAL SOUND EFFECTS (2) (Various artists).
MC: . . . . ZCF 792

MUSIC AND SOUND LIBRARY VOLS.1 & 2 (Various).
2LP: . . . . MSL 12

SOUND EFFECTS AND LINDRUM FILLS.
Tracks: / Drum fills and cowbell tracks / Scratching / Satellite signals / Asteroids / Lazer gun / Earthquake / Explosion / Space invaders.
LP: . . . . XTLP 2

SOUND EFFECTS NO.1 (Various artists).
LP: . . . . RED 47
MC: . . . . ZCM 47

SOUND EFFECTS NO.2 (Various artists).
LP: . . . . RED 76
MC: . . . . ZCM 76

SOUND EFFECTS NO.3 (Various artists).
LP: . . . . RED 102
MC: . . . . ZCM 102

SOUND EFFECTS NO.4 (Various artists).
LP: . . . . RED 104
MC: . . . . ZCM 104

SOUND EFFECTS NO.5 (Various artists).
LP: . . . . RED 105
MC: . . . . ZCM 105

SOUND EFFECTS NO.6 (Various artists).
LP: . . . . RED 106
MC: . . . . ZCM 106

SOUND EFFECTS NO.7 (Various artists).
LP: . . . . RED 113
MC: . . . . ZCM 113

SOUND EFFECTS NO.8 (Various artists).
LP: . . . . RED 126
MC: . . . . ZCM 126

SOUND EFFECTS NO.9 (Various artists).
LP: . . . . RED 164
MC: . . . . ZCM 164

SOUND EFFECTS NO.10 (Music and effects for home movies) (Various artists).
LP: . . . . RED 120
MC: . . . . ZCM 120

SOUND EFFECTS NO.11 (Off beat sound effects) (Various artists).
LP: . . . . REC 198
MC: . . . . RMC 4013

SOUND EFFECTS NO.12 (Out of this world) (Various artists).
LP: . . . . REC 225
MC: . . . . MRMC 040

SOUND EFFECTS NO.13 (Death and horror) (Various artists).
LP: . . . . REC 269
MC: . . . . ZCM 269

SOUND EFFECTS NO.14 (Steam trains in stereo) (Various artists).
LP: . . . . REC 220

SOUND EFFECTS NO.15 (Vanishing sounds in Britain) (Various artists).
LP: . . . . REC 227
MC: . . . . MRMC 041

SOUND EFFECTS NO.16 (Disasters) (Various artists).
LP: . . . . REC 295
MC: . . . . ZCM 295

SOUND EFFECTS NO.17 (Birds and other sounds of the countryside) (Various artists).
LP: . . . . REC 299
MC: . . . . ZCM 299

SOUND EFFECTS NO.18 (Holiday sound effects) (Various artists).
LP: . . . . REC 301
MC: . . . . ZCM 301

SOUND EFFECTS NO.19 (Doctor Who sound effects from TV series) (Various artists).
LP: . . . . REC 316
MC: . . . . ZCM 316

SOUND EFFECTS NO.20 (Sporting sound effects) (Various artists).
LP: . . . . REC 322
MC: . . . . ZCM 322

SOUND EFFECTS NO.21 (Death and horror Vol.2) (Various artists).
LP: . . . . REC 340
MC: . . . . ZCM 340

SOUND EFFECTS NO.22 (Music for silent movies) (Various artists).
LP: . . . . REC 347
MC: . . . . ZCM 347

SOUND EFFECTS NO.23 (Relaxing sounds) (Various artists).
Tracks: / Country stream: *Various artists* / Ariel currents: *Various artists* / Garden in springtime: *Various artists* / Seashore: *Various artists* / Forest adagio: *Various artists* / Rain: *Various artists*.
LP: . . . . REC 360
MC: . . . . ZCM 360

SOUND EFFECTS NO.24 (Combat) (Various artists).
LP: . . . . REC 383
MC: . . . . ZCM 383

SOUND EFFECTS NO.25 (Sounds of speed) (Various artists).
LP: . . . . REC 390
MC: . . . . ZCM 390

SOUND EFFECTS NO.26 (Science fiction) (Various artists).
LP: . . . . REC 420
MC: . . . . ZCM 420
MC: . . . . ZCM 420

SOUND EFFECTS NO.27 (Even more death and horror) (Various artists).
Tracks: / Staking a vampire - three mallet blows: *Various artists* (Band 1 - Intentional death) / Two throat cuts: *Various* artists (Band 1 - Intentional death) / Gas chamber (cyanide tablets into acid): *Various artists* (Band 1 - Intentional death) / Wrists cut - the blood drips into the bucket: *Various artists* (Band 1 - Intentional death) / Assorted stabbing: *Various artists* (Band 1 - Intentional death) / Drilling into the head - enough said: *Various artists* (Band 1 - Intentional death) / Body put into the acid bath: *Various artists* (Band 1 - Intentional death) / Self immolation: *Various* artists (Band 1 - Intentional death) / Silencer (pistol): *Various artists* (Band 1 - Intentional death Vocal, Synth, Mechanical) / Electric fire thrown into the bath: *Various artists* (Band 1 - Intentional death) / Boiling oil - poured off the castle wall: *Various artists* (Band 1 - Intentional death) / Tongue pulled out: *Various artists* (Band 2 -Torture) / Fingernails pulled out: *Various artists* (Band 2 - Torture) / Fingers chopped off: *Various artists*(Band 2 - Torture) / Trial by ordeal (picking ring from deep pot of: *Various artists* (Band 2 - Torture contd - if burns healed quickly then innocent - some c) / Whipping: *Various artists* (Band 2 - Torture) / Torture lab AD 2500: *Various* artists (Band 2 - Torture) / Lift falling (with passengers): *Various artists* (Band

3 - Accidental? death) / Female falling from a height (ladies first!): *Various artists* (Band 3 - Accidental? death) / Male falling from a height: *Various* artists (Band 3 - Accidental? death) / Reaction (to previous sounds): *Various artists* (Band 4) / Werewolf - transformation from human to beast: *Various artists* (Side 2 - Nasty animals and birds) / Giant killer bees (no honey from these): *Various* artists (Side 2 - Nasty animals and birds) / Sleeping dragon - don't wake it up: *Various artists* (Side 2 - Nasty animals and birds) / Dragon moving through bushes - occasional flam: *Various artists* (Side 2 - Nasty animals and birds) / Dragon kill - the death of the monster: *Various artists* (Side 2 - Nasty animals and birds) / Pterodactyl flying - with squawks: *Various artists* (Side 2 - Nasty animals and birds) / Vultures feeding - if you lie around long enou: *Various artists*(Side 2 - Nasty animals and birds) / Piranha fish feeding - don't go for a swim: *Various artists* (Side 2 - Nasty animals and birds) / Birds attack a feed: *Various artists* (Side 2 - Nasty animals and birds) / Triffids - sting, talking: *Various artists* (Side 2 - Nasty animals and birds).
LP: . . . . **REC 452**
MC: . . . . **ZCM 452**

SOUND EFFECTS NO.28 (Comedy) (Various artists).
Tracks: / Human: *Various artists* / Fights: *Various artists* / Footsteps: *Various artists* / Crashes: *Various artists* / Laughter and applause: *Various artists* / Animals: *Various artists* / Bizarre: *Various artists* / Birds: *Various artists* / Impacts: *Various artists* / Space age: *Various artists*.
LP: . . . . **REC 478**
MC: . . . . **ZCM 478**

SOUND EFFECTS NO.29 (Hi-Tech FX) (Various artists).
Tracks: / Computer bleeps: *Various artists* / Disk drive: *Various artists* / Drive activity: *Various artists*/ Printers: *Various artists* / Video games: *Various artists* / Stings: *Various artists* / Heavier stings: *Various artists* / Whooshes and zings: *Various artists* / Computer background fax: *Various artists* / Singularly Simon: *Various artists* / Computer rant: *Various artists* / Computer waltz: *Various artists*/ Invaders rock: *Various artists* / Arcadea: *Various artists* / JDC background: *Various artists* / Fanfares: *Various artists* / Purple space and white coronas: *Various artists* / Ascending asteroids: *Various artists*/ Pulsar patterns: *Various artists* / Through the black hole: *Various artists* / Force of the universe: *Various artists* / "43": *Various artists*.
LP: . . . . **REC 531**
MC: . . . . **ZCM 531**

SPECTACULAR SOUND EFFECTS VOL. 1 (Various artists).
LP: . . . . **THIS 34**
MC: . . . . **TCTHIS 34**

SPECTACULAR SOUND EFFECTS VOL. II (Various artists).
LP: . . . . **THIS 35**
MC: . . . . **TCTHIS 35**

Sound Garden

BADMOTORFINGER.
LP: **395374 1**
MC: **395374 4**

LOUDER THAN LOVE.
LP: . . . . **AMA 5252**
MC: . . . . **AMC 5252**

ULTRAMEGA OK.
LP: . . . . **SST 201**
MC: . . . . **SSTC 201**

Sound In Brass

HANDBELLS IN HARMONY (Sound in Brass Handbells).
Tracks: / Black and white rag / Syncopated clock / Girl with the flaxen hair, (The).
LP: . . . . **SDL 289**
MC: . . . . **CSDL 289**

MUSIC BY SOUND IN BRASS HANDBELLS (Sound in Brass Handbells).
Tracks: / Whistling Rufus / On wings of song / Washington Post march / Wiegenlied / Stephen Foster selection / Life let us cherish / Quicksilver polka / Nola / Parade of the tin soldiers / Ash Grove, The / Original rags / Tales from the Vienna woods / I've heard it before medley.
LP: . . . . **SDL 274**
MC: . . . . **CSDL 274**

Sound Iration

IN DUB.
LP: . . . . **MOWLP 1**

Sound Of Europe

SOUND OF EUROPE (Various artists).
Tracks: / Dei Lorelei: *Various artists* / Oompah polka: *Various artists* / Hans and Liesel: *Various artists*/ Trudies waltz: *Various artists* / Eine kleine biermusik: *Various artists* / Muss I denn: *Various artists*/ Chez Michel: *Various artists* / Mon amour: *Various artists* / Madame Sophie: *Various artists* / Promenade au montmartre: *Various artists* / Ma petite: *Various artists* / Les matelots: *Various artists* / Pommes frites: *Various artists* / D'accord: *Various artists*.
MC: . . . . **OAK C 104**

Sound Of Music

SOUND OF MUSIC (1981 London Revival Cast) (Various artists).
Tracks: / Sound of music, The: *Various artists* / Overture and preludium: *Various artists* / Morning hymn and allelulia: *Various artists* / I have confidence in me: *Various artists* / Sixteen going on seventeen: *Various artists* / My favourite things: *Various artists* / Climb every mountain: *Various artists* / Lonely goatherd, The: *Various artists* / Sound of music, The: *Various artists* / Do-re-mi: *Various artists* / Something good: *Various artists* / Processional and Maria: *Various artists* / Edelweiss: *Various artists* / Climb every mountain: *Various artists*.
LP: . . . . **EPC 70212**
LP: . . . . **SB 6616**
MC: . . . . **VCS 67257**
MC: **40 32670**

SOUND OF MUSIC (Film Soundtrack) (Various artists).
Tracks: / Prelude: *Andrews, Julie* / Overture and Preludium: *Nuns Chorus* / Morning hymn and Alleluia: *Nuns* Chorus / Maria: *Nuns Chorus* / I have confidence in me: *Andrews, Julie* / Sixteen going on seventeen: *Truhitte*, Dan & Charmain Carr / My favourite things: *Andrews, Julie* / Climb every mountain: *Wood, Peggy* / Lonely goatherd, The: *Andrews, Julie, Charmaine Carr & the children* / Do-re-mi: *Andrews, Julie, Charmaine Carr & the children*/ Something good: *Andrews, Julie & Christopher Plummer* / Processional and Maria: *Nuns Chorus* / Climb every mountain: *Andrews, Julie/ Christopher Plummer/Charmain Carr/ Children* / Edelweiss: *Plummer, Christopher/Julie Andrews* ....
LP: . . . . **PL 82005**
MC: . . . . **PK 82005**
LP: . . . . **NL 90368**
MC: . . . . **NK 90368**
LP: . . . . **RB 16616**

SOUND OF MUSIC (Original London Cast) (Various artists).
Tracks: / Preludium: *Various artists* / Sound of music, The: *Various artists* / Maria: *Various artists*/ Bell is no bell, A: *Various artists* / I have confidence in me: *Various artists* / Do-re-mi: *Various artists*/ Sixteen going on seventeen: *Various artists* / My favourite things: *Various artists* / Lonely goatherd, The: *Various artists* / How can love survive: *Various artists* / So long, farewell: *Various artists* / Climb every mountain: *Various artists* / Something good: *Various artists* / Wedding sequence: *Various artists*/ Maria (Reprise): *Various artists* / Concert do-re-mi (reprise): *Various artists* / Edelweiss: *Various artists*/ So long, farewell (reprise): *Various artists* / Climb every mountain (reprise): *Various artists*.
LP: . . . . **CBS 32670**
MC: **40 32670**
LP: . . . . **OCR 2**
MC: . . . . **OCRC 2**

SOUND OF MUSIC (Original Broadway Cast) (Various artists).
MC: . . . . **PST 32601**

SOUND OF MUSIC (ORIGINAL ISSUE) (London cast) (Various artists).
LP: . . . . **CLP 1453**

SOUND OF MUSIC (ORIGINAL ISSUE) (Broadway cast) (Various artists).
LP: . . . . **ABL 3370**

SOUND OF MUSIC (RE-ISSUE) (Film soundtrack) (Various artists).
LP: . . . . **INTS 5134**

Sound Of New Orleans

SOUND OF NEW ORLEANS, THE (See under Soul) (Various artists).

Sound Of Philadelphia

SOUND OF PHILADELPHIA (See under Soul) (Various artists).

Sound Of Picante

SOUND OF PICANTE (Various artists).
Tracks: / Bye bye blues: *Various artists* / Summer knows, The: *Various artists* / Fiz a cama na varanda: *Various artists* / Rainfall: *Various artists* / Tango allegra: *Various artists* / Don't cry for me Argentina: *Various artists* / Maria Cervantes: *Various artists* / Happy lypso: *Various artists* / Sin Timbal: *Various artists*.
LP: . . . . **CJP 295**
MC: . . . . **CJPC 295**

Sound Of St. Louis

SOUND OF ST. LOUIS (See under Soul) (Various artists).

Sound Sensation

ROUND AND ROUND.
MC: . . . . **CHV 333**

TOP HITS OF THE YEAR.
MC: . . . . **CHV 328**

Sound Syndicate

SOUND SYNDICATE (Various artists).
LP: **1431**
MC: **2431**

Sounds For Wargames

SOUNDS FOR WARGAMES (Various artists).
MC: . . . . **AC 114**

Sounds Incorporated

SOUNDS INCORPORATED.
Tracks: / Spartans, The / Detroit / Rinky dink / My little red book / Hall of the mountain king / One mint julep / Last night / Crane / Emily / Mogambo / Bullets / Spanish Harlem / Little bird / If we lived on top of a mountain / Old and the new, The / Grab this thing / Boil over / I'm comin' through / Fingertips / I'm in love again.
LP: . . . . **CM 116**

Sounds Jamaica

REGGAE FROM SUNSET TO DAWN.
MC: . . . . **CHV 342**

Sounds Like Music

SOUNDS LIKE MAGIC Various artists (Various artists).
LP: . . . . **SHM 3188**
MC: . . . . **HSC 3188**

Sounds of Ampleforth

SOUNDS OF AMPLEFORTH (Various artists).
Tracks: / Kyrie and Angus Dei from the Missa Choralis: *Various artists* / Christmas and Easter plainsong: *Various* artists / Piece heroique: *Various artists* / God be in my head: *Various artists* / Cantata No. 86 (Jesu, joy of man's desiring): *Various artists*.
MC: . . . . **HAC 801**

Sounds Of Blackness

EVOLUTION OF GOSPEL.
LP: **3953611**
MC: **3953614**

Sounds of Christmas

SOUNDS OF CHRISTMAS (Various artists).
MC: . . . . **TC 040**

Sounds of Living World

SOUNDS OF LIVING WORLD (Various artists).
LP: . . . . **REC 321**
MC: . . . . **ZCM 321**

Sounds of Scotland

SOUNDS OF SCOTLAND, THE (Various artists).
Tracks: / Scottish soldier, A: *Stewart, Andy* / Amazing grace: *Pipes & Drums, 1st Bat Scot Guards* / 6.20, The: *Shand, Jimmy* (Signature tune of White Heather Club.) / Auld scots sangs, The: *Anderson, Moira* / Down in the glen: *Wilson, Robert* / Wild rover: *Tartan Lads* / Isle of Skye: *Corries* / I love a lassie: *Logan, Jimmy*/ Miss Elspeth Campbell: *Various artists* / Inverary Castle: *Argyll & Sutherland Highlanders* / Mrs. McPherson of Inveran: *Argyll & Sutherland Highlanders* / Scotland the brave: *Wilson, Robert* / My ain house: *Anderson*, Moira / Campbeltown Loch: *Various artists* / Sky is bluer in Scotland, The: *Tartan Lads* / Drunken piper: *Pipes & Drums, 1st Bat Blackwatch* / Highland laddie: *Pipes & Drums, 1st Bat Blackwatch* / Black bear, The: *Pipes &* Drums, 1st Bat Blackwatch / Road to the Isles: *Stewart, Andy* / Victory polkas: *Drums & Pipes, 1st Bat Gordon* Highlanders / Willie the woodcutter: *MacLeod, Jim* / Tom Clements reel: *MacLeod, Jim* / Trumpet hornpipe: *MacLeod, Jim* / Bonnie Galloway: *Various artists* / Here's to scotch whiskey: *Tartan Lads* / Bonnie Dundee: *Corries* / Liberton pipe band polka: *Wick Scottish Dance Band & Wick Fiddlers* / Heather bells will bloom again: *Stewart, Andy* / My ain folk: *Anderson, Moira* / Rothesay Bay: *Anderson, Moira* / When you and I were young Maggie: *Tartan Lads* / Gathering of the clans: *Wilson, Robert* / Hills O' the Clyde: *Wilson, Robert*/ Gay gordons: *Johnstone, Jim & His Band* / 51st Highland division: *Johnstone, Jim & His Band* / Far o'er: *Johnstone, Jim & His Band*.
2LP: . . . . **DL 1122**
MC: . . . . **TCDL 1122**

Sounds of the Screen

TV GIANTS (Various artists).
Tracks: / Taxi: *Sounds of the Screen* / M.A.S.H.: *Sounds of the Screen* / Minder (I could be so good for you): *Sounds of the Screen* / Star trek: *Sounds of the Screen* / Rockford files, The: *Sounds of the Screen*/ Dynasty: *Sounds of the Screen* / Jewel in the crown: *Sounds of the Screen* / Emmerdale Farm: *Sounds of the* Screen / A Team: *Sounds of the Screen* / Knight rider: *Sounds of the Screen* / Hill Street Blues: *Sounds of the* Screen / Dallas: *Sounds of the Screen* / Fame: *Sounds of the Screen* / Thorn Birds, The: *Sounds of the Screen*.
LP: . . . . **VCLP 8**
MC: . . . . **ZCVCL 8**

Sounds Orchestral

CAST YOUR FATE TO THE WIND.
LP: . . . . **PYL 4011**
MC: . . . . **PYM 4011**
LP: . . . . **NPL 38041**

DREAMS.
Tracks: / Words / Me, the peaceful heart / Love is blue / Jennifer Juniper / Soul coaxing / Green tambourine / Step inside, love / What a wonderful world / I can take or leave your loving / Do you know the way to San Jose? / Simon Smith and the amazing dancing bear / Simon says / Classical gas / Scarborough fair / Sleepy shores / Canadian sunset / Clouds / Downtown / Bridge over troubled water / Cast your fate to the wind / Stranger on the shore / Without you / Handel's largo / April in Portugal.
2LP: . . . . **COMP 9**
MC: . . . . **ZCCOM 9**

IMAGES: SOUNDS ORCHESTRAL.
Tracks: / He ain't heavy he's my brother / Your song / Scarborough fair / Bridge over troubled waters / Wichita lineman / Michelle / Here, there and everywhere / Cast your fate to the wind / Jennifer juniper / Je t'aime... / Classical gas / Sleepy shores / Close to you (they long to be) / If you could read my mind.
MC: . . . . **KNMC 16010**

LOVE IS EVERYTHING.
MCSET: . . . . **DTO 10049**

Sounds Sensations

POP CONCERT-VOLUME 2.
Tracks: / Atomic / Another brick in the wall / Riders in the sky / Chosen few / Whatever you want / Silver dream machine / Video killed the radio star / Chiquitita / Going underground / Duke of Earl / Nightboat to Cairo / Star wars.
LP: . . . . **TMP 9015**
MC: **TMP4 9015**

Sounds Tzigane

SOUNDS TZIGANE (Various artists).
LP: . . . . **MOR 24**

Soup Dragons

CROTCH DEEP TRASH (ALBUM).
LP: . . . . **RTVLP 001**
MC: . . . . **RTVMC 001**

LOVEGOD.
LP: . . . . **SOUPLP 2R**
MC: . . . . **SOUPMC 2R**

THIS IS OUR ART.
Tracks: / Kingdon chairs / Great empty space / Majestic head / Turning stone / Vacate my space / On overhead walkways / Passion protein / King of the castle / Soft as your face / Family ways / Another dreamticket.
LP: . . . . **WX 169**
MC: . . . . **WX 169C**
LP: . . . . **K 925702 1**
MC: . . . . **K 925702 4**

Sources Of Energy

SOURCES OF ENERGY (See under UNESCO reports).

Sourswet (film)

SOURSWEET (Film soundtrack) (Hartley, Richard).
LP: . . . . **MOMENT 119**
MC: . . . . **MOMENTC 119**

Sousa & Pryor Bands

SOUSA & PRYOR BANDS, THE Original Recordings- 1901-1926.
Tracks: / Patriot, The (Track 4 The Sousa Band) / Pasquinade (Track 5 The Sousa Band) / Glory of the yankee navy (Track 6 The Sousa Band) / Trombone sneeze (Track 7 The Sousa Band) / Musical joke on "Bedilia", A (Track 8 The Sousa Band) / Ben Hur (Track 9 The Sousa Band) / General Pershing march (Track 10 The Pryor Band) / General mix-up march (Track 11 The Pryor Band) / March Shannon (Track 12 The Pryor

Band) / Battleship Conneticut shuffle (Track 13 The Pryor Band) / Alagazam march (Track 14 The Pryor Band) / Yankee shuffle (Track 15 The Pryor Band) / Teddy bears' picnic (Track 16 The Pryor Band) / Down the field march (Track 17 The Pryor Band) / Falcon march (Track 18 The Pryor Band) / Repasz band march (Track 19 The Pryor Band) / Federal march (Track 1 The Sousa Band) / Creole belles (Track 2 The Sousa Band) / At a Georgia camp meeting (Track 3 The Sousa Band).
LP: . . . . NW 282

South America

MUSIC OF THE RAIN FOREST PYGMIES (Various artists).
LP: . . . . LLST 7157
MC: . . . . LLCT 7157

South Bank Orchestra

LILLIE.
LP: . . . . MOR 516

South, Eddie

TOGETHER (see Reinhardt, Django) (South, Eddie/Django Reinhardt/ Stephane Grappelli).

WITH DJANGO REINHARDT, STEPHANE GRAPPELLI ETC (South, Eddie & others).
LP: . . . . SW 8405
MC: . . . . SWC 8405

South Frisco Jazz Band

BROKEN PROMISES.
LP: . . . . SOS 1180

IN SEARCH OF THE FAMOUS GROUSE.
LP: . . . . SOS 1143

SAN FRANCISCO JAZZ.
LP: . . . . MMRC 113

SOUTH FISCO JAZZ BAND-VOLUME 3.
LP: . . . . SOS 1103

South India

MUSIC OF SOUTH INDIA Kerela and Tamil Nadu (Various artists).
LP: . . . . LLST 7358

South, Joe

INTROSPECT.
Tracks: / All my hard times / Rose garden / Mirror of your mind / Redneck / Don't throw your love to the wind / Greatest love, The / Games people play / These are not my people / Don't you be ashamed / Birds of a feather / Gabriel.
LP: . . . . SEE 69

South Louisiana...

ROCK 'N' ROLL BEAT (South Louisiana Rockers).
Tracks: / Do baby do / Me and my baby / Mickey Lee / Oh baby what can I do / On the corner of the street / All by myself / Plant you know / Jump and shout / Big boy blues / Girls girls girls / Rock and roll beat / Rock me mama / My baby's cheatin / Eeny meeny miney mo.
LP: . . . . FLY 598

South Memphis Jug Band

SOUTH MEMPHIS JUG BAND.
LP: . . . . FLY 113

South Of...

SOUTH OF THE BORDER (Various artists).
LP: . . . . ADL 505
MC: . . . . ADK 505

South Pacific

SOUTH PACIFIC (Original Broadway Cast) (Various artists).
LP: . . . . CBS 32264
MC: . . . . PST 32604

SOUTH PACIFIC (Various artists).
LP: . . . . SB 2011
MC: . . . . VCS 67259

SOUTH PACIFIC (1986 Studio Recording) (Various artists).
Tracks: / South Pacific overture: *Various artists* / Dites moi: *Various artists* / Cock-eyed optimist: *Various* artists / Twin soliloquies: *Various artists* / Some enchanted evening: *Various artists* / Bloody Mary: *Various* artists / There is nothin' like a dame: *Various artists* / Bali Ha'i: *Various artists* / I'm gonna wash that man right outa my hair: *Various artists* / Wonderful guy, A: *Various artists* / Younger than Springtime: *Various* artists / This is how it feels: *Various artists* / Entr'acte: *Various artists* / Happy talk: *Various* artists / Honey bun: *Various artists* / You've got to be carefully taught: *Various artists* / This nearly was mine: *Various artists* / March, The: *Various artists* / Take off, The: *Various artists* / Communications established: *Various artists* / Finale ultimo: *Various artists*.
MC: . . . . SMT 42205
LP: . . . . SM 42205

SOUTH PACIFIC (Film Soundtrack) (Various artists).
Tracks: / South Pacific overture: *South Pacific* / Dites-moi: *South Pacific* / Cock-eyed optimist: *South Pacific* / Twin soliloquies: *South Pacific* / Some enchanted evening: *South Pacific* / Bloody Mary: *South* Pacific / My girl back home: *South* Pacific / There is nothin' like a dame: *South Pacific* / Bali Ha'i: *South* Pacific / I'm gonna wash that man right outa my hair: *South Pacific* / I'm in love with a wonderful guy: *South* Pacific / Younger than Springtime: *South Pacific* / Happy talk: *South Pacific* / Honey bun: *South Pacific*/ Carefully taught: *South Pacific* / This nearly was mine: *South Pacific* / Finale: *South Pacific*.
LP: . . . . NL 83681
MC: . . . . NK 83681

SOUTH PACIFIC (1988 London Cast) (Various artists).
LP: . . . . CAST 11
MC: . . . . CASTC 11

SOUTH PACIFIC (ORIGINAL ISSUE) (Various artists).
LP: . . . . RB 16065

South Pacific Isles

SOUTH PACIFIC ISLAND MUSIC (Various artists).
LP: . . . . H 72088

South West Wind

MUSIC FROM COUNTY CLARE.
LP: . . . . CC 47
MC: 4CC 47

Southampton All Stars

TRIBUTE TO GLENN MILLER (Southampton All Stars Orchestra).
MC: . . . . VOL 2

Southbound

TRACKS.
LP: . . . . WRS 133

Southend Connection

SOUTHEND CONNECTION, THE (Various artists).
LP: . . . . WF 045

Souther, J.D.

YOU'RE ONLY LONELY.
Tracks: / You're only lonely / If you don't want my love / Last in love / White rhythm and blues / 'Til the bars burn down / Moon just turned blue / Songs of love / Fifteen bucks / Trouble in paradise.
LP: 83753

Souther, Richard

HEIRBORNE.
LP: . . . . ML R 7004
MC: . . . . ML C 7004

INNERMISSION.
MC: . . . . ML C 7012

Southern...

SOUTHERN SANCTIFIED SINGERS (Various artists).
LP: . . . . RL 328

Southern Death Cult

SOUTHERN DEATH CULT.
Tracks: / All glory / Fat man / Today / False faces / Crypt, The / Crow / Faith / Vivisection / Apache / Moya.
LP: . . . . BBL 46
MC: . . . . BBLC 46
LP: . . . . BEGA 46

Southern Eagle...

THAT NASTY SWING (Southern Eagle String Band).
Tracks: / Second class hotel / Spinning room blues / N.R.A. blues / Mexican rag / Charles Guiteau / Cole Younger / Do' round my Lindy / There ain't no bugs on me / Bile the cabbage down / Snowdrop / Cotton mill colic / That nasty swing / Willie Moore / Alimony woman / Kansas City blues / Walkin' blues, The.
LP: . . . . BF 15010

Southern Filmharmonic

SOUND OF MOVIES (Southern Filmharmonic Orchestra).
MC: . . . . ZCFPA 1012

Southern Jazz Group

SOUTHERN JAZZ GROUP, 1950.
LP: . . . . S 1415

SOUTHERN JAZZ GROUP-VOL.2-1946-1950.
LP: . . . . DC 12022

SOUTHERN JAZZ GROUP-VOL.3-1946-1950.
LP: . . . . DC 12023

SOUTHERN JAZZ GROUP-VOL.4-1946-1950.
LP: . . . . DC 12024

SOUTHERN JAZZGROUP-VOL.1-1946-1950.
LP: . . . . DC 12021

Southern, Jeri

COFFEE, CIGARETTES AND MEMORIES.
LP: . . . . FS 255

JERI SOUTHERN MEETS COLE PORTER.
Tracks: / I concentrate on you / Don't look at me that way / Get out of town / It's alright with me / Let's fly away / Why shouldn't I / It's bad for me / You're the top.
LP: . . . . PM 1553011
MC: . . . . PM 1553014

JERI SOUTHERN MEETS JOHNNY SMITH.
LP: . . . . FS 156

LIVE AT THE CRESCENDO.
Tracks: / I thought of you last night / I get a kick out of you / Dancing on the ceiling / Blame it on my youth / Remind me / You better go now / I'm just a woman / Something I dreamed last night / Nice work if you can get it / When I fall in love.
LP: . . . . T 1278

SOUTHERN BREEZE.
LP: . . . . FS 123

WHEN I FALL IN LOVE.
Tracks: / When I fall in love / Fire down below / You better go now / I thought of you last night / Occasional man, An / Where walks my true love / Candlelight conversation / Just in time / I'm in love with the honourable Mr. So and So / Autumn in New York / You make me feel so young / All in fun / Little girl blue / Someone to watch over me / Cabin / Every time we say goodbye.
LP: . . . . MCL 1791
MC: . . . . MCLC 1791

YOU BETTER GO NOW.
Tracks: / You better go now / Give me time / Something I dreamed last night / Man that got away, The / When I fall in love / Just got to have him around / Dancing on the ceiling / Speak softly to me / What good am I without you / I though of you last night / That ole devil called love / Remind me.
LP: . . . . OFF 12007

Southern Lighting

DOWN THE ROAD.
LP: . . . . MLCR 103

Southern Mountain Boys

LOVE SICK AND SORROW (see Lundy, Ted) (Southern Mountain Boys/Ted Lundy/Bob Paisley).

Southern Pacific

SOUTHERN PACIFIC.
Tracks: / First one to go / Someone's gonna love me tonight / Thing about you / Perfect stranger / Send me somebody to love / Reno bound / Blaster / Luanne / Heroes / Bluebird wine.
LP: 9252011

ZUMA.
Tracks: / Midnight highway / Honey I dare you / New shade of blue / Dream on / Invisible man, The / Wheels on the line / Just hang on / All is lost / Bail out / Trail of tears.
LP: 925609 1
MC: 925609 4

Southern, Sheila

25 NURSERY RHYMES (Southern, Sheila with Mike Sammes).
Tracks: / Boys and girls come out to play / Hickory dickory dock / Old King Cole / Hot cross buns / Three blind mice / Pop goes the weasel / London Bridge / Baa baa black sheep / Little Polly Flinders / Bobby Shaftoe / Little Miss Muffet / Old Mother Hubbard / Oranges and lemons / Sing a song of sixpence / Polly put the kettle on / Ride a cock horse / Here we go round the mulberry bush / Humpty Dumpty / Pussy cat, pussy cat / Jack and Jill / Hey diddle diddle / My little nut tree / What are little boys made of / Horsey horsey / Hush-a-bye.
LP: . . . . DMT 2003
MC: . . . . DMTK 2003

FOUR CLASSIC STORIES AND 20 POPULAR NURSERY RHYMES.
Tracks: / Boys and girls come out to play / Cock-a-doodle-doo / Pata cake pata cake / Tom Thumb (story) / Hey diddle dumplin' / Little Jack Horner / One two buckle my shoe / Three blind mice / Goldilocks & the three bears / What are little boys made of / Peter Piper / Owl & the pussy cat / Old woman in a shoe / Frog he would a wooin' go, A / Dance to your daddy / Little Red Riding Hood (story) / Doctor Foster / Tom Thumb the pipers son / Twinkle twinkle little star / Little Bo Peep / Dick Whittington (story) / Ride a cock horse / Pussy cat where have you been / Horsey horsey / Hush a bye baby / Boys and girls come out to play.
LP: . . . . HN 3100
MC: . . . . CHN 3100

SINGS THE BACHARACH & DAVID SONGBOOK.
LP: . . . . OAK R 136

WITH LOVE (Southern, Sheila/Royal Philharmonic Orchestra).
Tracks: / What are you doing the rest of your life / My funny valentine / My coloring book / How beautiful is night / Nearness of you / Losing my mind / Country girl / My one and only love / Memory / Touch me in the morning / She's out of my life.
MC: . . . . CSIV 1107

Southern Soul Belles

SOUTHERN SOUL BELLES (See under Soul) (Various artists).

Southern Stompers

FASCINATING RHYTHM (Southern Stompers 1974).
LP: . . . . LC 22S

I'VE GOT FORD ENGINE 1969-72 (see under Lane, Steve) (Southern Stompers/ Steve Lane).

SOUTHERN STOMPERS IN CONCERT (see under Lane, Steve) (Southern Stompers/Steve Lane/Michele).

STEVE LANE'S JUBILEE RECORD (Southern Stompers 1950-75).
LP: . . . . SLC 26

Southern String...

SOUTHERN STRING BANDS (Various artists).
MC: . . . . C 220

Southern Swing

SOUTHERN SWING (Various artists).
MC: . . . . VOL 3

Southon, Sonny

FALLING THROUGH A CLOUD.
Tracks: / Two worlds / Don't hold back / I don't come any other way / What would I do? / Falling through a cloud / Girl who wouldn't cry / So proudly / Too much love / Another day / Say goodbye.
LP: . . . . SRNLP 29
MC: . . . . SRNMC 29

Southroad Connection

AIN'T NO TIME TO SIT DOWN.
LP: . . . . UAG 30288

POSITIVE ENERGY.
Tracks: / Something special / Positive energy / Just let me know / Southroad funktation / We came to funk me out / I can't say no, if you ask me / It's got to be good / Right thing to do.
LP: . . . . UAG 30316

Southside Johnny

AT LEAST WE GOT SHOES (Southside & The Asbury Jukes).
Tracks: / Hard to find / Tell me (that our love's still strong) / Walk away Renee / Take my love / You can count on me / Till the end of the night / I only want to be with you / Lorraine / I can't wait / Under the sun.
LP: . . . . PL 71049
MC: . . . . PK 71049

BETTER DAYS (Southside Johnny & The Asbury Jukes).
Tracks: / Coming back / All I needed was you / It's been a long time / Soul's on fire / Better days / I've been working too hard / Ride the night away / Right to walk away, The / All night long / All the way home / Shake 'em down.
LP: . . . . EMC 3607
MC: . . . . TCEMC 3607

HAVIN' A PARTY (Southside Johnny & The Asbury Jukes).
Tracks: / I don't want to go home / Broke down piece of man / Talk to me / Love on the wrong side of town / Fever / Trapped again / Without love / When you dance / This time it's for real / Havin' a party.
LP: 31772

HEARTS OF STONE (Southside Johnny & The Asbury Jukes).
Tracks: / Got to be a better way home / This time baby's gone for good / I played the fool / Take it inside / Hearts of stone / Talk to me / Next to you / Trapped again / Light don't shine.
LP: . . . . EPC 82994

I DON'T WANT TO GO HOME.
LP: . . . . EPC 32079

IN THE HEAT (Southside Johnny & The Jukes).
Tracks: / Love goes to war / New Romeo / Love is the drug / Captured / I can't live without love / Over my head / Don't look back / Tell me lies / Action speaks louder than words / New coat of paint.

LP: 823 747-1
MC: 823 747-4

JUKES (Southside Johnny & The Asbury Jukes).
Tracks: / All I want is everything / I'm so anxious / Paris / Security / Living in the real world / Your reply / Time / I remember last night / Wait in vain / Vertigo.
LP: 9100067

SLOW DANCE.
Tracks: / On the air tonight / Sirens of the night / Ain't that peculiar / Little Calcutta / Act of love / Slow dance / Your precious love / No secret / When the moment is right / Walking through midnight.
LP: . . . . PL 71794
MC: . . . . PK 71794

Southwark Cathedral

SOUTHWARK CATHEDRAL CHOIR (Southwark Cathedral Choir).
Tracks: / O Emmanuel (Advent antiphon - plainsong.) / Wilderness / Lullay my liking / In manus Tuas / Benedictus / Mass in G (Schubert) / Exultimus et laetemur (Plainsong.) / Christ being raised from the dead / Coelos ascendit hodie / Dum complerentur / Ave Maria / Beati quorum / For He shall give His angels.
LP: . . . . ACA 506
MC: . . . . CACA 506
LP: . . . . ACA 542
MC: . . . . CACA 542

Southwest F.O.B.

SMELL OF INCENSE.
Tracks: / Smell of incense / Tomorrow / You're looking so fine / Downtown woman / Green skies / Monday's world / Bells of Baytown/And another thing / I'm comin' / On my mind / All one big game / Independent me / Beggarman, The / As I look at you.
LP: . . . . WIK 81

Southwood Martin

I'VE BEEN THERE.
MC: . . . . AMC 23001

Souvenir Big Band

LOVE SONGS COLLECTION, THE (Souvenir Big Band & The Ritz Romantic Strings).
MCSET: . . . . DTO 10328

Souvenir De Paris

SOUVENIR DE PARIS (See under France) (Various artists).

Souvenir in Sound

SOUVENIR IN SOUND (100 Golden Years of the Gramaphone) (Various artists).
Tracks: / Vesti la giubba: *Caruso, Enrico* / I hear you calling me: *McCormack, John* / Liebeslied: *Kreisler*, Fritz / Etude in A flat: *Cortot, Alfred* / Prelude from cello suite no.1 in G: *Casals, Pablo* / Song of the flea: *Chaliapin, Feodor* / Recuerdos de la Alhambra: *Segovia, Andres* / Overture - The silken ladder: *Toscanini*, Arturo / Mattinata: *Gigli, Benjamino* / Adagio sostenuto: *Schnabel, Artur* (From the Moonlight Sonata.) / Soave sia il vento: *Schwarzkopf, Elisabeth* (from Cosi fan tutte.) / Hora staccato: *Heifetz, Jascha* / Vissi d'arte: *Callas, Maria* (from Tosca) / Rondo: *Brain, Dennis* (from Horn Concerto No. 4 in E flat K 495.) / Ave Maria: *Menuhin*, Yehudi / Prelude in C sharp minor: *Rubinstein, Artur* / Habanera: *De Los Angeles, Victoria* / Swan, The: *Du* Pre, Jacqueline / Prelude to Act 3 of Lohengrin: *Boult/NPO* / Celeste Aida: *Domingo, Placido* / Summertime: *Te Kanawa, Kiri* (from Porgy and Bess.) / O fortuna: *Previn, Andre and the London Symphony Orchestra* (from Carmina Burana.).
LP: . . . . EH 7630181
MC: . . . . EH 7630184

Souvenirs

SOUVENIRS (BEST OF BROADWAY AND HOLLYWOOD) (Various artists).
LP: . . . . CL 42081

Sovereign

BURIED TREASURE.
LP: . . . . TAB 104LP
MC: . . . . TAB 104CAS

Sovereign's Parade

SOUNDS OF SOUNDHURST (Various artists).
LP: . . . . LR 102

Sovetsko Foto

THE ART OF BEAUTIFUL BUTLING.
LP: 089323

Soviet Army...

SOVIET ARMY CHORUS AND BAND (Soviet Army Chorus And Band).
Tracks: / Song of youth / Birch tree in a field did stand / Far away / Volga boat song / You are always beautiful / Along Peter's street / Tipperary / Ah lovely night / Kamarinskaya / Annie Laurie / Song of the plains / Kalinka / Bandura / Oh no, John / Snow flakes / Ukrainian poem / Soldiers chorus (From the Decembrists.).
LP: . . . . SXLP 30062
MC: . . . . TCEXE 155

Soviet France

ASSAULT AND MIRAGE.
LP: . . . . REDLP 68A

ELSTRE.
LP: . . . . REDLP 45

FLOCK OF ROTATIONS, A.
LP: . . . . REDLP 68

GARISTA.
MC: . . . . GARISTA 001

GESTURE SIGNAL THREAT.
LP: . . . . REDLP 067A

LOOK INTO ME.
LP: . . . . CHARRMLP 014

MISFITS LOONEY TUNES AND SQUALID CRIMINALS.
LP: . . . . REDLP 068

MOHNOMISCHE.
LP: . . . . REDLP 040

NORSCHE.
LP: . . . . REDLP 023

POPULAR SOVIET SONGS AND YOUTH CULTURE.
MC: . . . . REDC 58
LP: . . . . REDLP 58

SHOUTING AT THE GROUND.
Tracks: / Smocking erde / Palace of ignitions / Come to the edge / Revenue of fire / Dybbuk / Camino real / Stocc blainers / Fickle whistle / Carole the breed bate / Marrch dynamic / Wind thief / Shamany enfluence / Death of trees, The.
LP: . . . . REDLP 91

Sovine, Red

16 ALL TIME FAVOURITES.
LP: . . . . SLP 3010
MC: . . . . GT 53010

16 GREATEST HITS: RED SOVINE.
LP: . . . . SLP 991
MC: . . . . GT 5991

16 NEW GOSPEL SONGS.
LP: . . . . GT 0013

BEST OF RED SOVINE.
LP: . . . . SLP 952
MC: . . . . GT 5952

CLASSIC NARRATIONS.
LP: . . . . SLP 436

GIDDY-UP-GO.
LP: . . . . GT 0073

LITTLE ROSA.
Tracks: / If Jesus came to your house / Are you mine / Hold everything / Why baby why / Outlaw / Best years of my life, The / Little Rosa / Best years of my life, The / I'm so glad / You are mine (blue moon of Kentucky).
LP: . . . . BDL 1028

ONE AND ONLY, THE.
Tracks: / No money in this deal / One is a lonely number / Invitation to the blues / If I could come back / Brand new low / Hold everything / Little Rosa / Why baby why / Color of the blues / Heart of a man, A / Long time to forget / More from habit than desire.
LP: . . . . OFF 9005

PHANTOM 309.
LP: . . . . GT 0072

SUNDAY WITH SOVINE.
LP: . . . . SLP 427
MC: . . . . GT 5427

SUPER COLLECTION - BEST OF RED SOVINE.
2LP: . . . . GTV 111

TEDDY BEAR.
Tracks: / Teddy bear / Little Rosa / It ain't no big thing (but it's growing) / Last mile on the way, The / Bootlegger king / Daddy / Love is / 1460 Elder Street / Does steppin' out mean daddy took a walk / Eighteen wheels hummin' home sweet home / Sad violins.
LP: . . . . GT 0071
LP: . . . . SD 968X
MC: . . . . SDC 968
LP: . . . . LSA 3286

Soyka, Ray

ACCORDEON POLONAIS - DANSES (Soyka, Ray & Al & Orchestra).
Tracks: / Salcia / Amigo / Serce moje walc / Dalej powedrowal / Na ferme / Lakeview / Helena / Mamus moja / Nie mam nic walc / Squeegee / Na niedziele / Polske wesele.
LP: . . . . ARN 33729
MC: . . . . ARN 433729

Space

DEEPER ZONE.
Tracks: / Deeper zone / Inner voices / Space media / Mixed up / One the air / Love starring you and me.
LP: . . . . N 5011

JUST BLUE.
Tracks: / Just blue / Final signal / Secret dreams / Symphony / Save your love for me / Blue tears / My love is magic.
LP: . . . . NSPH 28275

LE MEILLEUR DE SPACE.
Tracks: / Magic fly / Save your love for me / Air force / Inner voices / Space media / Tender force / Robots / My love is music / Just blue / On the air.
LP: . . . . N 5013

MAGIC FLY (LP).
LP: . . . . NSPL 28232

SPACE.
LP: . . . . SPACELP 1

VERY BEST OF SPACE, THE.
LP: . . . . SOHOLP 6

Space Boat (bk)

SPACE BOAT, THE (Childrens story book) (Unknown narrator(s)).
MC: . . . . RWM 004

Space Maggots

LEAVE IT.
LP: . . . . SOL 6

Space Negros

PINK NOISE.
LP: . . . . GLALP 013

Spaceballs The Movie

SPACEBALLS - THE MOVIE (Film soundtrack) (Various artists).
Tracks: / Spaceballs: *Spaceballs The Movie* / My heart has a mind of its own: *Spaceballs The Movie* / Heartstrings: *Various artists* / Spaceballs love theme instrumental: *Various artists* / Winnebago crashes, The (Spaceballs build mega-maid): *Various artists* / Spaceballs: *Various artists* / Hot together: *Various artists* / Good enough: *Various artists* / Wanna be loved by you: *Various artists*.
LP: . . . . K 255193 1
MC: . . . . K 255193 4

Spacecamp

SPACE CAMP (Film soundtrack) (Various artists).
LP: . . . . BL 85856
MC: . . . . BK 85856

Spacek, Sissy

HANGIN' UP MY HEART.
Tracks: / Hangin' up my heart / Have I told you lately that I love you / He don't know me / Lonely but only for you / This time I'm gonna beat you to the truck / Honky tonkin' / Old home town / Smooth talkin' daddy / If you could only see me now / If I can just get through tonight.
LP: 790 100-1

Spacelings

2,000 MEGA TONS OF LOVE.
LP: . . . . VOW 006

GROUNDED.
Tracks: / Hit, The / Change, The / Boy vs. girl / Chime, The.
LP: . . . . MED 003

Spaceman & King Arthur

SPACEMAN AND KING ARTHUR, THE (see Drake 400) (Various artists).

Spacemen 3

PERFECT PRESCRIPTIONS.
Tracks: / Take me to the other side / Walking with Jesus / Ode to street hassle / Ecstasy symphony / Transparent radiation / Feel so good / Things'll never be the same / Come down easy / Call the doctor.
LP: . . . . GLALP 026
MC: . . . . GLAMC 026
LP: . . . . REFIRELP 6
MC: . . . . REFIRE MC 6

PERFORMANCE.
Tracks: / Mary Anne / Come together / Things'll never be the same / Take me to the other side / Rollercoaster / Starship / Walkin' with Jesus.
LP: . . . . GLALP 030

PLAYING WITH FIRE.
LP: . . . . FIRELP 16
MC: . . . . FIREMC 16

RECURRING.
Tracks: / Big City / Just to see you smile (Orchestral mix) / I love you / Set me free/I've got the key / Set me free (reprise) / Why couldn't I see / Just to see you smile (instrumental) / When tomorrow hits / Feel so sad (reprise) / Hypnotized / Sometimes / Feeling just fine (head full of shit) / Billy Whizz/Blue 1 / Drive/Feel so sad / Feeling just fine (alternative mix).
LP: . . . . FIRELP 23
MC: . . . . FIREMC 23

SOUND OF CONFUSION.
LP: . . . . GLALP 018
LP: . . . . REFIRELP 5
MC: . . . . REFIREMC 5

Spaelimenninir

A FERD (Spaelimenninir I Hoydolum).
LP: . . . . SHD 6

GLUGGAMYND (Spaelimenninir I Hoydolum).
LP: . . . . SHD 5

HINVEGIN.
LP: . . . . SHD 10
MC: . . . . SHD 10MC

REKAVIDUR (Spaelimenninir I Hoydolum).
LP: . . . . SHD 7

SPAELIMENNINIR I HOYDOLUM (Spaelimenninir I Hoydolum).
LP: . . . . SHD 1

SYNG BARA VID (Spaelimenninir I Hoydolum).
LP: . . . . SHD 8

UMAFTUR (Spaelimenninir I Hoydolum).
LP: . . . . SHD 2

Spagna

DEDICATED TO THE MOON.
Tracks: / Call me / Dedicated to the moon / So easy / Power of money, The / Easy lady / Dance, dance, dance / Why can't I say (I love you babe) / Baby blue / Girl, it's not the end of the world.
LP: 4506461
MC: 4506464

YOU ARE MY ENERGY.
Tracks: / I wanna be your wife / This generation / Let me (say I love you) / Me and you / You are my energy / Why don't we talk anymore / Every girl and boy / Woman in love / 10 March 1959 (memories of the taste of freedom).
LP: 4630721
MC: 4630724

Spain...

CHANT PROFOND DU PAYS BASQUE (Various artists).
Tracks: / Boga boga: *Various artists* / Adios ene maitia: *Various artists* / Olhette: *Various artists*/ Goiseko izarra: *Various artists* / Ama: *Various artists* / Berceuse basque: *Various artists* / Agur yainkoaren ama: *Various artists* / Maritxu: *Various artists* / Elurra teilatuan: *Various artists* / Mendian zoin den eder: *Various artists* / Jeiki jeiki: *Various artists* / Uholde baten pare: *Various artists*/ Agur jaunak: *Various artists* / Xo xo mariano: *Various artists* / Oi mirakulu guziz: *Various artists*/ Gernikako arbola: *Various artists* / Bestarat: *Various artists*.
LP: . . . . ARN 33376
MC: . . . . ARN 433376

ESPAGNE ETERNELLE (Various artists).
Tracks: / Ronda festiva: *Various artists* / Alborada de gaita: *Various artists* / Foliada de Bagueixos: *Various artists* / Que si, que si: *Various artists* / Amoroso: *Various artists* / Minera: *Various artists*/ El alba del rocio: *Various artists* / Bolero: *Various artists* / El mariner: *Various artists* / Jota de Baile: *Various artists* / Bolero: *Various artists* / El Pericote: *Various artists* / Baile de pandereta: *Various artists* / Picayos de Viernoles: *Various artists* / La entradilla: *Various artists*.
LP: . . . . ARN 33305

LA FOILE DE LA SPAGNA (See under Music de Madrid) (Various artists).

MAGIC OF SPAIN (Various artists).
Tracks: / Y viva Espana: *Various artists* / Sevillanas: *Various artists* / Mi talisman: *Various artists*/ El porompompero: *Various artists* / Entre dos aguas: *Various artists* / Fiesta: *Various artists* / Taka-takata: *Various artists* / Charly: *Various artists* / Espana cani: *Various artists* / Valencia: *Various artists*/ Granada: *Various artists* / La felicidad: *Various artists* / Pepita y Juanita: *Various artists* / Rumba flamenca: *Various artists* / Maria Isabel: *Various artists* / Costa Brava: *Various artists* / La paloma: *Various artists* / La chevecha: *Various artists* / Fin de Semana: *Various artists* / El Gato Montes: *Various artists*.
LP: . . . . NTS 210
MC: . . . . TCNTS 210

SOUL OF SPAIN (Various artists).
2LP: . . . . ADL 520
MCSET: . . . . ADK 520

SOUL OF SPAIN (Various artists).
LP: . . . . GGL 0017

SOUNDS OF SPAIN (Various artists).
Tracks: / Historia de un amor: *Ostberg, Max* (From Love Story.) / Diego

sacromonte & su conjunto flamenco-malaguenas: *Ostberg*, Max / Cantqar y cantar: *Los Diablos* / Mi catapum: *Chacho* / Que sera: *Acuarius* / Rosy: *Santamaria*, Lorenzo / Pena, tristeza y dolor: *Gitanos, Peret & Sus* / Que nadie sepa mi sufrir: *Gitanos, Peret & Sus*/ Un rayo de sol: *Los Diablos* (from Fernando.) / Oh, oh, July: *Los Diablos* / Cu-cu-rru-cu-cu-paloma: *De Ypacarai, Felix & Sus Paraguayos* / Si vas a calatayud: *Gran Orchestra De Profesores Solistas* / La la la: *Chacho*/ Alguien canto (The music played): *Monro, Matt* / Y viva Espana: *Marina, Imca* / Sevillanas: *Sacromonte*, Diego & Su conjunto Flamenco / Mi talisman: *Los Diablos* / El porompompero: *Los Javaloyas* / Taka-takata: *De Luis, Luis* / Charly: *Santabarbara* / Espana cani: *Gran Orchestra De Profesores Solistas* / Granada: *Gran Orchestra De Profesores Solistas* / La Paloma: *Gran Orchestra De Profesores Solistas* / La felicidad: *Grupo 15* / Costa Brava: *De Ypacarai, Felix & Sus Paraguayos* / Fin de Semana: *Los Diablos*.
2LP: . . . . DL 1149
MC: . . . . TCDL 1149

SPAIN: CANTE FLAMENCO (Various artists).
LP: . . . . LLST 7363

SPAIN: SOUL OF SPANISH FLAMENCO (Various artists).
LP: . . . . H 72002

SPAIN: SPANISH ARMADA (Various artists).
MC: . . . . GH 005

VIVA ESPANA (Various artists).
Tracks: / Danza no.5 de Granados: *Various artists* / Jotas: *Various artists* / Calor de Espana: *Various artists*/ La charra: *Various artists* / Eres alta: *Various artists* / Ocairi acaira: *Various artists* / Ines: *Various artists* / Romance anonyme: *Various artists* / Riau chibiribiri: *Various artists* / Los cuatros muleros: *Various artists* / Tiruriru: *Various artists* / Sitio de Zaragoza: *Various artists*.
LP: . . . . ARN 33653

Spand, Charlie

CHARLIE SPAND 1929-40.
LP: . . . . BD 2035

Spandau Ballet

BEST OF SPANDAU BALLET, THE.
Tracks: / To cut a long story short / Freeze, The / Musclebound / Chant No. 1 (I don't need this pressure on) / Paint me down / She loved like diamond / Instinction / Lifeline / True / Gold / Only when you leave / I'll fly for you / Highly strung / Round and round / Fight for ourselves / Through the barricades / How many lies / Raw / Be free with your love.
LP: . . . . CHR 1894
MC: . . . . ZCHR 1894

DIAMOND.
Tracks: / Chant no.1 (I don't need this pressure) / Instinction / Paint me down / Coffee club / Diamond / Pharaoh / Innocence and science / Missionary.
LP: . . . . CHR 1353
MC: . . . . ZCHR 1353
LPS: . . . . C BOX 1353

GREATEST HITS: SPANDAU BALLET.
Tracks: / True / Chant no.1 (I don't need this pressure) / Gold / Lifeline / To cut a long story short / Only when you leave.
MC: . . . . THPA 1232

HEART LIKE A SKY.
Tracks: / Be free with your love / Crashed into love / Big feeling / Matter of time, A / Motivator / Raw / Empty spaces / Windy town / Handful of dust, A.
LP: 4633181
MC: 4633184

JOURNEYS TO GLORY.
Tracks: / To cut a long story short / Reformation / Mandolin / Muscle bound / Ages of blows / Freeze, The / Confused / Toys.
LP: . . . . CHR 1331
MC: . . . . ZCHR 1331
MCSET: . . . . ZCDP 103

PARADE.
Tracks: / Only when you leave / Highly strung / I'll fly for you / Nature of the beast / Revenge for love / Always in the back of my mind / With the pride / Round and round.
LP: . . . . CDL 1473
MC: . . . . ZCDL 1473

SINGLES COLLECTION, THE.
Tracks: / Gold / Lifeline / Round and around / Only when you leave / Instinction / Highly strung / True / Communication / I'll fly for you / To cut a long story short / Chant no.1 (I don't need this pressure) / She loved like diamond / Paint me down / Freeze / Musclebound.
LP: . . . . SBTV 1
MC: . . . . ZSBTV 1

THROUGH THE BARRICADES.
Tracks: / Barricades - introduction / Cross the line / Man in chains / How many lies / Virgin / Fight for ourselves / Swept / Snakes and lovers / Through the barricades / With pride.
LP: 4502591
MC: 4502594

TRUE.
Tracks: / Gold / Pleasure / Communication / Code of love / Lifeline / Heaven is a secret / Foundation / True.
LP: . . . . CDL 1403
MC: . . . . ZCDL 1403

TWELVE INCH MIXES.
Tracks: / Gold / Lifeline / Round and round / Only when you leave / Instinction / Highly restrung / True / Communication / I'll fly for you / To cut a long story short / Chant no.1 (I don't need this pressure) / She loved like diamond / Paint me down / Freeze, The / Musclebound.
LP: SBD1
MC: ZSBD1

Spaniels

GREAT GOOGLEY MOO.
LP: . . . . CRB 1021

SPANIELS, THE.
LP: . . . . JOY 197

STORMY WEATHER.
Tracks: / Lovey dovey / Tree little words / People will say we're in love / I'll be waiting / Stormy weather / Why I love you / Baby come along with me / I owe you / Bounce / Red snails in the sunset / Please don't tease / You painted pictures / Baby sweets / One hundred years from today / Stranger in love, A / Let's make up.
LP: . . . . CRB 1114

Spanier, Muggsy

1924-1928.
LP: . . . . FJ 108

AFTER YOU'VE GONE (see Hines ,Earl).

AT CLUB HANGOVER.
LP: . . . . SLP 249

CLASSIC SMALL GROUPS Vol. 2.
LP: . . . . MERITT 7

FRANCIS JOSEPH MUGGSY SPANIER (1926-9).
LP: . . . . GAPS 150

GREAT SIXTEEN, THE.
Tracks: / Big butter and egg man / Someday sweetheart / Black and blue / Riverboat shuffle / Livery stable blues.
MC: . . . . NEO 854

HESITATIN' BLUES.
Tracks: / Hesitatin blues / Little David play your harp / Judy / American patrol / Chicago / Baby brown / When my dreamboat comes home / Wreck of the old '97 / No lovers allowed / Careless love / More than you know / Can't we be friends / My wild Irish rose / Oh Dr Ochsner / Since we fell out of love / Washington and Lee swing / Two o'clock jump.
MC: . . . . TCAFS 1030
LP: . . . . AFS 1030

HOT HORN.
LP: . . . . SLP 4053

HOT HORN 1944 (Spanier, Muggsy & His Ragtimers).
LP: 6.26167

JAZZ CLASSICS IN DIGITAL STEREO.
LP: . . . . REB 687
MC: . . . . ZCF 687

MUGGSY SPANIER AND PEE WEE RUSSELL (Spanier, Muggsy & Pee Wee Russell).
MC: . . . . HM 06

MUGGSY SPANIER COLLECTION (20 golden greats).
Tracks: / I can't give you anything but love / Sugar / Tin roof blues / Indiana / Sweet Lorraine / Three little words / Dixieland one-step / I ain't gonna give nobody none of my jelly roll / Fidgety feet / Alice blue gown / St. Louis blues / Angry / Lucky to me / Livery stable blues / Relaxing at the Touro / I'm sorry I made you cry / Bugle call rag / Dippermouth blues / Muskrat ramble / Lady be good.
LP: . . . . DVLP 2090
MC: . . . . DVMC 2090

MUGGSY SPANIER & FRANK TESCHEMAKER (Spanier, Muggsy & Frank Teschemaker).
Tracks: / Buddy's habits / Chicago blues / Mobile blues / Really a pain / Hot mittens / Everybody loves my baby / Why couldn't it be me / Why couldn't it be poor little me / China boy / Bull frog blues / Nobody's sweetheart / Sister Kate / Jazz me blues / Darktown strutters' ball / Whoopee stomp.
LP: . . . . SM 3088

MUGGSY SPANIER & HIS ALL STARS.
Tracks: / Jazz me blues / Pat's blues / Squeeze me / Pee Wee speaks / At the jazz band ball / Relaxin' at the Touro / You are lucky to me / Tin roof blues / Cherry / That's a plenty.
LP: . . . . SM 3575

MUGGSY SPANIER & HIS RAGTIME BAND, VOL 1.
Tracks: / Big butter and egg man / Someday, sweetheart / Eccentric / That da da strain / At the Jazz Band Ball / Sister Kate / Dippermouth blues / Livery stable blues / Riverboat shuffle / Relaxin' at the Touro / At sundown / Bluin' the blues / Lonesome road / Dinah / Black and blue / Mandy make up your mind.
LP: . . . . SM 3574
MC: . . . . MC 3574

MUGGSY SPANIER, MIFF MOLE & LOU MCGARITY (Spanier, Muggsy, Miff Mole & Lou McGarity).
LP: . . . . SLP 4020

MUGGSY SPANIER (WITH EDDIE CONDON ETC.).
LP: . . . . LPJT 16

MUGGSY SPANIER WITH G BRUNIES AND A NICHOLAS (Spanier, Muggsy, G Brunies and A Nicholas).
LP: . . . . J 33

MUGGSY SPANIER-VOL 2 (Spanier, Muggsy & His Dixieland All Stars).
LP: . . . . SLP 4056

NICK'S - NEW YORK.
Tracks: / Angry / Weary blues / Snag it / Alice blue gown / Sweet Lorraine / Oh, lady be good / Sugar / September rain.
LP: 6.25494

ON V-DISC 1944-45.
LP: E-1020

ONE OF A KIND.
LP: . . . . GL 6024

RARE CUSTOM 45'S.
LP: . . . . IAJRC 42

RELAXIN' AT THE TOURO (1952).
LP: . . . . J 115

RICHMOND AND CHICAGO DAYS, 1924-28.
Tracks: / Steady roll blues / Mobile blues / Really a pain / Chicago blues / Hot mittens / Buddy's habits / Someday, sweetheart / Why can't it be poor little me? / Everybody loves my baby / Bullfrog blues / China boy / Jazz me blues / Sister Kate / Nobody's sweetheart / Friars Point shuffle / Darktown strutters' ball.
MC: . . . . CFJ 108
LP: . . . . S 806

SIDNEY BECHET & MUGGSY SPANIER BIG FOUR (see Bechet,Sidney & Muggsy Spanier etc.) (Spanier, Muggsy & Sidney Bechet).

SPANIER IN CHICAGO, 1954.
LP: . . . . LC 2

TIN ROOF BLUES (Spanier, Muggsy & Earl Hines).
Tracks: / Deep forest / Tiger rag / Tin roof blues / Limehouse blues / Memphis blues / High society / Boogie woogie on St. Louis blues / Struttin' with some barbecue / Ugly chile / Bugle call rag / Wang wang blues / Rosetta / Bill Bailey won't you please come home / St. James' infirmary / Wolverine blues / Lazy river / That's a plenty / If I could be with you one hour tonight / Royal Garden blues.
2LP: . . . . VJD 549

Spanks

HOT FOR YOUR LOVE.
LP: . . . . PETC 014

LUCILLE.
Tracks: / Lucille.
LP: . . . . TORSO 008

SCREAM THE BLUES.
Tracks: / Scream the blues / Take a trip / (I wish you) Goodbye / Forget about you / Teenage head.
LP: . . . . PETC 011

Spann, Otis

BLUES IS WHERE IT'S AT, THE.
LP: . . . . CCR 1016

BLUES NEVER DIE.
Tracks: / Blues never die / I got a feeling / One more mile to go / Feeling good / After while / Dust my broom / Straighten up baby / Come on / Must have been the Devil / Lightning / I'm ready.
LP: . . . . CH 231

BLUES OF OTIS SPANN.
Tracks: / Rock me, mama / I came from Clarksdale / Keep your hand out of my pocket / Spann's boogie / Sarah Street / Blues don't like nobody / Country boy / Pretty girls everywhere / Meet me in the bottom / Lost sheep in the fold / I got a feeling / Jangle boogie / Natural days / You're gonna need my help / Stirs me up.
LP: . . . . SEE 54

BOSSES OF THE BLUES VOL 2 (Spann, Otis & Eddie 'Cleanhead' Vinson).
Tracks: / Cleanhead blues / Pass out / Alimony blues / Cleanhead is back / Juice head baby / Old maid boogie / I needs to be be'd wid / Got my mojo workin' / Sellin' my thing / Moon blues / I'm a dues payin' man / Make a way.
LP: . . . . NL 88312
MC: . . . . NK 88312

BOTTOM OF THE BLUES, THE.
LP: . . . . BGOLP 92
MC: . . . . BGOMC 92

CANDID SPANN, VOL 1.
Tracks: / Hard way, The / Take a little walk with me / Otis in the dark / Baby child / Little boy blue / Country boy / Beat up team / My daily wish / Great Northern stomp / I got rambling on my mind / No. 2 / Worried life blues / Instrumental boogie / Captain's apprentice, The / Knocker upper man / Fine time / Joe Hill / Cape May / Fine time / Harvest has been taken in, The / Tottie poem / We got married on Sunday / Greenland whale fisheries / Harry Eddom / Moon was a warning, The.
LP: . . . . CCR 1003

CANDID SPANN, VOL 2.
Tracks: / It must have been the devil / Otis' blues / Going down slow / Half ain't been told / Monkey face women / This is the blues / Strange woman / Evil ways / Come day go day / Walking the blues / When things go wrong / Bad condition / My home in the delta.
LP: . . . . CCR 1004

CRYIN' TIME.
Tracks: / Home to Mississippi / Blues is a botheration / You said you'd be on time / Crying time / Blind man / Someday / Twisted snake / Green flowers / New boogaloo, The / Mule kicking in my stall.
LP: . . . . VSD 6514

HALF AIN'T BEEN TOLD.
LP: . . . . BC 001

NOBODY KNOWS CHICAGO LIKE I DO.
Tracks: / Popcorn man / Brand new house / Nobody knows Chicago like I do / Steel mill blues / Down on Sarah street / T'aint nobody's bizness if I do / Chicago blues / My home is on the delta / Spann blues.
LP: . . . . CRB 1062

OTIS SPANN IS THE BLUES.
Tracks: / Hard way, The / Take a little walk with me / Otis in the dark / Little boy blue / Country boy / Beat-up team / My daily wish / Great Northern stomp / I got rambling on my mind / Worried life blues.
LP: . . . . CS 9001
LP: . . . . CCR 1003

RAREST.
LP: . . . . JSP 1070

TAKE ME BACK HOME.
LP: . . . . BM 9004

WALKING THE BLUES.
Tracks: / It must have been the devil / Otis blues / Going down slow / Half ain't been told / Monkey face woman / This is the blues / Evil ways / Come day go day / Walkin' the blues.
LP: . . . . CS 9025

Spanner Thru' Ma

SPANNER THRU' MA BEATBOX.
LP: . . . . EARTH 003

Spark Gap Wonder Boys

CLUCK OLD HEN.
LP: . . . . ROUNDER 0002

Spark, Muriel

PRIME OF MISS JEAN BRODIE/GIRLS OF SLENDER MEANS.
MC: . . . . IAB 88062

Sparks

ANTS IN MY PANTS.
Tracks: / I predict / Sextown USA / Sherlock Holmes / Nicotina / Mickey Mouse / Moustache / Instant weight loss / Tarzan & Jane / Decline & fall of me / Eaten by the monster of love.
LP: . . . . K 50888

INDISCREET.
LP: . . . . ILPS 9345

INTERIOR DESIGN.
LP: . . . . CAL 230
MC: . . . . CAC 230

KIMONO MY HOUSE.
LP: ILPS 9272

MAEL INTUITION - THE BEST OF SPARKS 1974-76 (It's a Mael, Mael, Mael World).
Tracks: / This town ain't big enough for the both of us / Hasta manana monsieur / Tearing the place apart / At home, at work, at play / Never turn your back on Mother Earth / Get in the swing / Amateur hour / Looks, looks, looks / Thanks but no thanks / Gone with the wind / Something for the girl with everything / Thank God it's not Christmas.
LP: ILPS 9493
MC: ZCI 9493

MUSIC THAT YOU CAN DANCE TO.
Tracks: / Music that you can dance to.
LP: TOONLP 2
MC: TOONC 2

NUMBER ONE IN HEAVEN.
Tracks: / Tryouts for the human race / Academy award performance / La dolce vita / Beat the clock / My other voice / Number one song in heaven, The.
LP: OVED 137
MC: OVEDC 137
LP: V 2115
LP: FA 3035

PROPAGANDA.
LP: ILPS 9312

SPARKS IN OUTER SPACE.
Tracks: / Cool places / Popularity / Prayin' for a party / All you ever think about is sex / Please baby please / Rockin' girls / I wish I looked a little better / Lucky me lucky you / Fun bunch of guys from outer space / Dance godammit.
LP: 780 055-1

TERMINAL JIVE.
LP: V 2137

WHOMP THAT SUCKER.
LP: WHO 1
MC: WHOK 1

Sparks, J.J.

BRIXTON BLUE BEAT (Sparks, J.J. & The City Gents).
LP: STLP 1004

Sparks, Larry

BEST OF LARRY SPARKS.
LP: REBEL 1609
MC: REBEL 1609C

BLUE SPARKS.
LP: REBEL 1618
MC: REBEL 1618C

DARK HALLOW.
LP: REBEL 1597

GONNA BE MOVIN'.
LP: REBEL 1664
MC: REBEL 1664C

JOHN DEERE TRACTOR.
LP: REBEL 1588
MC: REBEL 1588C

LARRY SPARKS SINGS HANK WILLIAMS.
Tracks: / No one will ever know / Dixie cannonball / Someday you'll call my name / I'm so lonesome I could cry / Battle of Armegeddon / Waltz of the wind / Singing waterfall / Mind your own business / My heart would know / I saw the light / Mansion on the hill / Blue love.
LP: CO 759

LONESOME GUITAR (Sparks, Larry & The Lonsesome Ramblers).
Tracks: / Chittlin' cookin' time in Cheatum County / Faded love / Old spinning wheel, The / Ramblin' guitar / In the garden / Florida blues / Carroll County blues / Time changes everything / Buffalo girls / Farewell blues / Under the double eagle / Low and lonely.
LP: REBEL 1633
MC: REBEL 1633C

RAMBLIN' BLUEGRASS (Sparks, Larry & The Lonsesome Ramblers).
LP: GT 0010

TESTING TIMES, THE.
LP: REBEL 1611
MC: REBEL 1611C

Sparks, Melvin

SPARKLING.
LP: MR 5248

Sparks, Trevor

COOL OUT.
Tracks: / Cool out / Count the tears / My lover's calling me / Respect baby mother / I love you / Wings of love / Bye bye love / Tell my girl / I'm in love with a beautiful woman.
LP: LALP 24

DEVOTED TO YOU (LP).
LP: BTLP 040

SPARKS.
LP: BTRLP 006

SPEAK SOFTLY (See Junior Wilson) (Sparks, Trevor/Mystic man/Junior Wilson).

Sparrow

SPARROW VS THE REST.
Tracks: / How you jammin' / Music and rhythm / Saltfish / Witch doctor / My woman / Fat man / Statue, The / Pan jam fete / We kinda music / It's all wrong but it's all right.
LP: DYLP 3001

SWEETER THAN EVER.
LP: DY 3429

Sparrow, Johnny

SPARROW'S FLIGHT.
Tracks: / Boudoir boogie / When your lover has gone / Paradise rock / What's new / Serenade to Satchmo / Always / Indiana / Jump steady / Sparrow's flight no.2 / Sparrow in the barrel / I'll see you in my dreams / Yesterdays / Am I blue.
LP: KK 832

Sparrow's Young

RISING STARS.
LP: MANDM 0015

Spartacus

SPARTACUS (Film Soundtrack) (Various artists).
LP: MODEM 1012
MC: MODEMC 1012
LP: MCA 1534
MC: MCAC 1534

SPARTACUS (VIDEO) (See under Bolshoi Ballet) (Bolshoi Ballet).

Spartacus R

AFRICA I SEE.
LP: ZMRLP 2
MC: ZMRC 2

FREEDOM FIRST.
LP: ZMRLP 4
MC: ZMRC 4

THIRD WORLD WAR.
LP: ZMRLP 3

Spartan Warriors

STEEL N CHAINS.
LP: GRC 2164

Spasmodique

HAVEN.
LP: SCH 9014

NORTH.
LP: SCHEMER 8902

START TO BELIEVE.
LP: M 8801

Spaulding, James

PLAYS THE LEGACY OF DUKE ELLINGTON.
LP: SLP 4034
LP: SLP 1019

Spazz

NIGHT ON THE TOWN, A.
LP: GVM 404

Spazztic Blurr

SPAZZTIC BLURR.
Tracks: / Blurr hogs / Images / ABC's / Spazztic puke / Fuck yeah / Bouge jonzin / Call in sick / Bedrock blurr / He nota home / Unless.. / Let there be blurr / Ace / Def metal / Miexicalli.
LP: MOSH 5

Spear Of Destiny

EPIC YEARS, THE.
Tracks: / Wheel, The / Rainmaker / Prisoner of love / Playground of the rich / Young men / Up all night / Come back / All my love (ask nothing) / Mickey / Liberator.
LP: 4634011
MC: 4634014
LP: TBLP 1019
LP: 4508721
MC: 4508724

GRAPES OF WRATH.
Tracks: / Wheel, The / Flying Scotsman / Roof of the world / Aria / Solution / Murder of love / Preacher, The / Man who tunes the drums, The / Grapes of wrath / Omen of the times.
LP: EPC 32779
MC: 40 32779

ONE-EYED JACKS.
Tracks: / Rainmaker / Young men / Everything you've ever wanted / Don't turn away / Liberator / Prisoner of love / Playground of the rich / Forbidden planet / Attica / These days are gone.
LP: 4508861
MC: 4508864
LP: EPC 25836

OUTLANDS.
Tracks: / Outlands / Land of shame / Traveller, The / Was that you? / Strangers in our town / Whole world's waiting, The / Tonight / Miami Vice / Never take me alive / Pumpkin man (CD & Cassette only) / Land of shame (12" version) (CD & Cassette) / Traveller, The (dub version) (CD & Cassette only) / Time of our lives (original version) (CD & Cassette only) / Strangers in our town (extended version) (CD & Cassette only).
LP: DIX 59
MC: CDIX 59
LP: 905791
MC: OVEDC 361
LP: OVED 361

PRICE YOU PAY, THE.
Tracks: / So in love with you / Tinsel Town / Price, The / I remember / Dreamtime / Radio radio / If the guns / View from a tree / Junkman / Soldier, soldier (CD only) / Brave new world (CD only).
LP: V 2549
MC: TCV 2549
MC: OVEDC 362
LP: OVED 362

WORLD SERVICE.
Tracks: / Rocket ship / Up all night / Come back / World service / I can see / All my love (ask nothing) / Mickey / Somewhere in the East / Once in her lifetime / Harlan county.
LP: EPC 26514
MC: 40 26514

Spears, Billie Jo

16 COUNTRY FAVOURITES.
Tracks: / You're my man / One more chance / Cheatin' kind, The / I'll take a melody / Look what they've done to my song Ma / If it ain't love / Ease the want in me / Dallas / It makes no difference now.
MC: HSC 3277

17 GOLDEN PIECES OF BILLIE JO SPEARS.
Tracks: / Look what they've done to my song, Ma / It makes no difference now / He's on the run again / Danny / I'm so lonesome I could cry / Fever / You're my man / Ease the want in me / Dallas / Sunshine / Come on home / Which way are you going / I stayed long enough / I'll never be free / Step child / Souvenirs and Californian memories / It coulda been me.
LP: BDL 2033

BEST OF BILLIE JO SPEARS.
Tracks: / Mr. Walker / It's all over / Blanket on the ground / '57 Chevrolet / Misty blue / Rainy days & stormy nights / What I've got in mind / Never did like whiskey / Standing tall / Your good girl's gonna go bad.
MCSET: 4XLL-9282

BILLIE JO SPEARS.
LP: RITZLP 0016
MC: RITZC 0016

BLANKET ON THE GROUND.
Tracks: / Blanket on the ground / I can only judge your future by his past / Then give him back to me / Permanently lonely / Since I fell for you / Come on home / All I want is you / Before your time / I've never loved anyone more.
LP: GO 2010

COUNTRY COLLECTION.
MC: KNMC 13055

COUNTRY GIRL.
LP: WW 5109

FEVER.
Tracks: / Look what they've done to my song, Ma / It makes no difference now / He's on the run again / Danny boy / I'm so lonesome I could cry / Fever / You're my man / Ease the want in me / Dallas / Sunshine.
LP: CBR 1005
MC: KCBR 1005

FOR THE GOOD TIMES.
Tracks: / For the good times / I love you because / Games people play / Yours love / What a love I have in you / Your old love letters / Breakaway / Help me make it through the night / True love / I'll share my world with you / Put a little love in your heart / Marty Gray / Today I started loving you again / Snowbird.
LP: MFP 50515
MC: TCMFP 50515

GREATEST HITS OF BILLE JO SPEARS.
LP: U 3018-2

I WILL SURVIVE.
Tracks: / I will survive / Angel in your arms / Everyday I have to cry / It should have been easy / I'm good at what I do / Livin' our love together / I think I'll go home / You / Happy ever after / Rainy days and stormy nights.
LP: UAG 30249

IF YOU WANT ME (ALBUM).
Tracks: / If you want me / Never did like whiskey / Too far gone / Heartbreak Hotel / Here comes those lies again / I'm not easy / Seeing is believing / Here comes my baby back again / Every word I write / That's what friends are for / No other man.
LP: GO 2024

IT COULD HAVE BEEN ME.
Tracks: / He's on the run again / Danny (baby ruby) / Come on home / Which way you gone Billy / You're my man / I'll never be free / Step child / Souvenirs and Californian memories / It coulda been me.
LP: SHLP 104
MC: SHTC 104

MIDNIGHT BLUE.
Tracks: / Midnight love / Can't change my heart / Love dies hard / Baby on my mind / Settin' me up / Blowing away / Midnight blue / We just came apart at the dreams / C'est la vie / Too far gone / Sweet dreams / Ain't no money.
LP: PMP 1007
MC: PMPK 1007

ODE TO BILLIE JO.
Tracks: / Ode to Billy Joe / Take me to your world / Livin' in a house full of love / Softly and tenderly / Pittsburgh General / Faded love / You and your sweet love / I stayed long enough / I don't wanna play house / Big stick of dynamite / Stand by your man / Tips and tables / Till something better comes along / Get behind me, Satan, and push / When you hurt me (more than I love you) / Apartment No.9 / It coulda been me / Souvenirs and Californian memories / He's got more love in his little finger / Mr. Walker, it's all over.
LP: EG 2605281
MC: EG 2605284

SINGLES ALBUM: BILLIE JO SPEARS.
LP: UAK 30231

SINGLES: BILLIE JO SPEARS.
Tracks: / Blanket on the ground / Silver wings and golden rings / Another somebody done somebody wrong song / What I've got in mind / Sing me an old fashioned song / Every time two fools collide / If you want me / Every time I sing a love song / Misty blue / Never did like whiskey / I've got to go / Lonely hearts club / '57 Chevrolet / Love ain't gonna wait for us.
MC: TCK 30231
LP: UCK 30231

SINGS THE COUNTRY GREATS.
Tracks: / 57 Chevrolet / Loving him was easier / Another somebody done somebody wrong..(Hey won't you play) / Till something better comes along / Sing me an old fashioned song / Every time I sing a love song / See the funny little clown / That's what friends are for / Blanket on the ground / Ode to Billy Joe / Misty blue / I don't wanna play house / Hurt / Stand by your man / He's got more love in his little finger / Take me to your world.
LP: MFP 5784
MC: TCMFP 5784

SPECIAL SONGS.
Tracks: / What the world needs now is love / Snowbird / Lay down beside me / Broken lady / Everything is beautiful / Heartbreak hotel / Desperado / Your good girl's gonna go bad / I fall to pieces / Rose garden / Bridge over troubled water / Loving him was easier.
LP: LBG 30333

TWENTY COUNTRY GREATS.
Tracks: / Queen of the silver dollar / Crying time / I'll never love like this again / All I have to do is dream / Tenessee waltz / What I've got in mind / Just the way you are / This ole house / Rocky top / Blue bayou / For the good times / Fire and rain / Crystal chandeliers / It's a heartache / Silver threads and golden needles / Fifty seven Chevrolet / I'm gonna be a country girl again / Here you come again / Blue blue day / Blanket on the ground.
MC: WW 22010

VOICE OF BJS, THE.
LP: HAT 3106
MC: HATC 3106

WE JUST CAME APART AT THE DREAMS.
Tracks: / Can't change my heart / Blowing away / Sweet dreams / Love dies hard / C'est la vie / We just came apart at the dreams / Settin' me up / Too far gone / Ain't no money / Baby on my mind.
LP: PREM 101
MC: PREMK 101

WHAT I'VE GOT IN MIND (ALBUM).
Tracks: / You could know as much about a stranger / I've never loved anyone more / I can only judge your future by his past / Too much is not enough / Yesterday / What the world needs now is love / I fall to pieces /

Blanket on the ground / What I've got in mind / There's more to a tear than meets the eye / Everyday I have to cry / Sweet music man / Husbands and wives / Here come's my baby / Slow movin' outlaw / 57 Chevrolet.
LP: . . . . **EMS 1312**
MC: . . . . **TCEMS 1312**
LP: . . . . **UAS 29955**

Special AKA

IN THE STUDIO.
Tracks: / Bright lights / Lonely crowd, The / Housebound / What I like most about you is your girlfriend / Night on the tiles / Nelson Mandela / War crimes / Racist friend / Alcohol / Break down the door.
LP: . . . . **CHRTT 5008**
MC: . . . . **ZCHRT 5008**

JUNGLE MUSIC (see under Rico) (Special AKA & Rico).

Special Binaural

ADVENTURE IN BINAURAL.
LP: . . . . **VBN 1**

Special Ed

LEGAL.
LP: . . . . **FILER 297**
MC: . . . . **FILERCT 297**

YOUNGEST IN CHARGE.
LP: . . . . **FILER 280**
MC: . . . . **FILERCT 280**

Special EFX

CONFIDENTIAL.
LP: . . . . **GRP 95811**
MC: . . . . **GRP 95814**

DOUBLE FEATURE.
Tracks: / Lady and the sea, The / Jamaica, Jamaica / Passages / Golden days / Sunflower / Mirrors / Just a little time / Search for a rainbow / Thy kingdom come / Northern light (Bonus track on CD only.) / Oasis (Bonus track on CD only.).
LP: . . . . **GRP 91048**
MC: . . . . **GRPM 91048**

JUST LIKE MAGIC.
Tracks: / Ballerina / Jazz lambada / Lovely Michelle / One day / Pastoral / Greenpeace / On-screen romance / Looking for seventh heaven / Free the forest.
LP: . . . . **GRP 96091**
MC: . . . . **GRP 96094**

MODERN MANNERS.
Tracks: / Fountain of you / Fun in the sun / Modern manners / After one empty step / Toy shop, The / Mystical remedies / Buttermilk falls / Greenway North / High society.
LP: . . . . **GRPA 1014**
MC: . . . . **GRPC 1014**
MC: . . . . **GRPM 91014**
LP: . . . . **GRP 91014**

MYSTIQUE.
Tracks: / Hands of the healer / Rainy Sunday / Udu voodoo / Pleasance / Noel / Islands / Sidestreet paradise, A / When the earth was flat / Sleeping tiger, The / Dreamer of dreams (Bonus track on CD only) / Ritual (Bonus track on CD only).
LP: . . . . **GRP 91033**
MC: . . . . **GRPM 91033**

PEACE OF THE WORLD.
Tracks: / Festival / Dancing with a ghost / Summer's end / Quiet beauty / Lady from Rio / Jungle talk / Gianluca / Lullaby for Julia / Peace of the world.
LP: . . . . **GRP 96401**
MC: . . . . **GRP 96404**

SLICE OF LIFE.
LP: . . . . **GRP 91025**
MC: . . . . **GRPM 91025**

SPECIAL EFX.
LP: . . . . **A 1007**
MC: . . . . **C 1007**

Special Forces

SPECIAL FORCES.
Tracks: / Into the scene / Poor little rocker / Fool with my money / Hard day / Win or lose / Give me rock / Don't run / Black beauty / Far side of midnight / Darkness.
LP: . . . . **ERC 1825-1**

Special Olympics

VERY SPECIAL CHRISTMAS, A (See under Christmas) (Various artists).

Special Request

SPECIAL REQUEST AND POPULAR DEMAND (Various artists).
LP: . . . . **HB 05**

Speciality Records

SPECIALITY ROCK'N'ROLL (See under Rock 'n' Roll) (Various artists).

Specials

BEST OF SPECIALS, THE.
Tracks: / Gangsters / Message to you Rudi, A / Nite club / Too much too young / Guns of Navarone / Rat race / Rude boys outta jail / Stereotype / Internation jet set / Do nothing / Ghost town / Why? / Friday night / Saturday morning / Racist friend / Free Nelson Mandela / What I like most about you is your girlfriend.
LP: . . . . **CHRTT 5010**
MC: . . . . **ZCHRT 5010**

GANGSTERS (See under Special AKA).

MORE SPECIALS.
Tracks: / Enjoy yourself (it's later than you think) / Man at C & A / Hey little rich girl / Do nothing / Pearl's cafe / Sock it to 'em JB / Stereotype / Stereotype (part 2) / Holiday fortnight / I can't stand it / International jet set / Enjoy yourself (reprise).
LP: . . . . **CHR TT 5003**
MC: . . . . **ZCHR T 5003**

SPECIALS,THE.
Tracks: / Message to you Rudy, A / Do the dog / It's up to you / Nite klub / Doesn't make it alright / Concrete jungle / Too hot / Monkey man / (Dawning of a) New era / Blank expression / Stupid marriage / Too much too young / Little bitch / You're wondering now.
LP: . . . . **FA 41 3116 1**
MC: . . . . **FA 41 3116 4**
MCSET: . . . . **ZCDP 104**
LP: . . . . **CDLTT 5001**
MC: . . . . **ZCDLT 5001**

Speckled Band

SPECKLED BAND, THE (Various artists).
Tracks: / Speckled band, The: *Various artists* / Blue carbuncle, The: *Various artists*.
MC: . . . . **ANV 641**

Speckled Red

1929-38.
LP: . . . . **WSE 113**

SPECKLED RED IN LONDON, 1960.
Tracks: / Woke up this morning / Dirty mistreater / I've had my fun / Caledonia / It feels so good / Oh red / Milk cow blues / Bugle call stomp / Early in the morning / Blu-Della boogie / Dad's piece / Tain't nobody's bizness if I do.
LP: . . . . **LC 11**

Spector, Phil

GREATEST HITS / CHRISTMAS ALBUM (Various artists).
Tracks: / River deep, mountain high: *Turner, Ike & Tina* / Be my baby: *Ronettes* / Proud Mary: *Checkmates Ltd* / Zip-a-dee-doo-dah: *Soxx, Bob B. & The Blue Jeans* / You've lost that lovin' feeling: *Righteous Brothers*/ Da doo ron ron: *Crystals* / He's a rebel: *Crystals* / Baby I love you: *Ronettes* / White Christmas: *Love, Darlene* / Frosty the snowman: *Ronettes* / Santa Claus is coming to town: *Crystals* / Sleigh ride: *Ronettes* / Rudolph the red nosed reindeer: *Crystals* / Winter wonderland: *Love, Darlene* / Here comes Santa Claus: *Soxx, Bob B. & The Blue Jeans* / Silent night: *Spector, Phil & Artists*.
2LP: . . . . **PSLP 1/2**
MCSET: . . . . **PSLK 1**

PHIL SPECTOR: EARLY PRODUCTIONS '58-61 (Various artists).
LP: . . . . **RNDF 203**

PHIL SPECTOR: ECHOES OF THE SIXTIES (Various artists).
Tracks: / River deep, mountain high: *Turner, Ike & Tina* / Then he kissed me: *Crystals* / Be my baby: *Ronettes*/ Why do lovers break each others hearts: *Soxx, Bob B. & The Blue Jeans* / Proud Mary: *Checkmates Ltd* / Today I met the boy I'm gonna marry: *Love, Darlene* / Zip-a-dee-doo-dah: *Soxx, Bob B. & The Blue Jeans* / Best part of breaking up: *Ronettes* / You've lost that lovin' feeling: *Righteous Brothers* / Da doo ron ron: *Crystals*/ He's a rebel: *Crystals* / Not too young to get married: *Soxx, Bob B. & The Blue Jeans* / Uptown: *Crystal*, The / Unchained melody: *Righteous Brothers* / Walking in the rain: *Ronettes* / He's sure the boy I love: *Crystals*/ Ebb tide: *Righteous Brothers* / Wait till my Bobby gets home: *Love, Darlene* / Baby I love you: *Ronettes*.
LP: **2307 013**
MC: **3107 013**

PHIL SPECTOR WALL OF SOUND, VOL.3 (see under Crystals) (Crystals).

PHIL SPECTOR'S CHRISTMAS ALBUM.
Tracks: / White Christmas / Frosty the snowman / Bells of St. Mary's / Santa Claus is coming to town / Sleigh ride / Marshmallow world / I saw mommy kissing Santa Claus / Rudolph the red nosed reindeer / Winter wonderland / Parade of the wooden soldiers / Christmas (baby please come home) / Here comes Santa Claus.
LP: **2307 005**
MC: **3107 005**
LP: . . . . **SAPCOR 24**
LP: . . . . **CDL 1625**
MC: . . . . **ZCDL 1625**

WALL OF SOUND (Various artists).
Tracks: / You've lost that lovin' feeling: *Righteous Brothers* / White cliffs of Dover, The: *Righteous Brothers*/ Georgia on my mind: *Righteous Brothers* / I love you for sentimental reasons: *Righteous Brothers* / You'll never walk alone: *Righteous Brothers* / Just once in my life: *Righteous Brothers* / Unchained melody: *Righteous Brothers* / You're my soul and inspiration: *Righteous Brothers* / Ebb tide: *Righteous Brothers* / Guess who: *Righteous Brothers* / Hung on you: *Righteous Brothers* / Great pretender, The: *Righteous Brothers* / River deep, mountain high: *Turner, Ike & Tina* / Baby, let's stick together: *Dion* / Torpedo Rock: *Spector, Phil* Wall of Sound Orchestra / Home of the brave: *Bonnie & The Treasures* / Why can't a boy and girl just stay in love?: *Stevens, April* / This could be the night: *Modern Folk Orchestra* / Puddin' 'n' tain: *Alley Cats* / Act naturally: *Willis, Betty* / But you don't love me: *Soxx, Bob B. & The Blue Jeans* / Hold me tight: *Treasures*/ Walk, The: *Soxx, Bob B. & The Blue Jeans* / If I had a hammer: *Willis, Betty* / All grown up: *Crystals*/ Little boy: *Crystals* / Run, run, run, runaway: *Love, Darlene* / He's a quiet guy: *Love, Darlene* / Stumble and fall: *Love, Darlene* / Strange love: *Love, Darlene* / Take it from me: *Love, Darlene* / Long way to be happy: *Love, Darlene* / Playing for keeps: *Love, Darlene* / Johnny baby please come home: *Love, Darlene* / Today I met the boy I'm gonna marry: *Love, Darlene* / Fine fine boy: *Love, Darlene* / Wait till my Bobby gets home: *Love, Darlene* / Lord, if you're a woman: *Love, Darlene* / I love him like I love my very life: *Love, Darlene* / Not too young to get married: *Soxx, Bob B. & The Blue Jeans* / Why do lovers break each other's hearts?: *Soxx, Bob B. & The Blue Jeans* / Let the good times roll: *Soxx, Bob B. & The Blue Jeans* / My heart beats a little faster: *Soxx, Bob B. & The Blue Jeans* / Baby I love you: *Soxx, Bob B. & The Blue Jeans* / Doctor Kaplan's office: *Soxx, Bob B. & The Blue Jeans* / Zip-a-dee-doo-dah: *Soxx, Bob B. & The Blue Jeans* / White cliffs of Dover, The: *Soxx, Bob B. & The Blue Jeans* / This land is your land: *Soxx, Bob B. & The Blue Jeans* / Here come's my baby: *Soxx, Bob B. & The Blue Jeans* / I shook the world: *Soxx, Bob B. & The Blue Jeans* / Everything's gonna be alright: *Soxx, Bob B. & The Blue Jeans* / Walking in the rain: *Ronettes* / Do I love you?: *Ronettes* / So young: *Ronettes* / Best part of breaking up: *Ronettes* / I wonder: *Ronettes* / What'd I say?: *Ronettes*/ Be my baby: *Ronettes* / You baby: *Ronettes* / Baby I love you: *Ronettes* / How does it feel?: *Ronettes*/ When I saw you: *Ronettes* / Chapel of love: *Ronettes* / I can hear music: *Ronettes* / Is this what I get for loving you?: *Ronettes* / Born to be together: *Ronettes* / Paradise: *Ronettes* / Soldier baby: *Ronettes* / Woman in love: *Ronettes* / Everything under the sun: *Ronettes* / I wish I never saw the sunshine: *Ronettes* / Keep on dancing: *Ronettes* / Here I sit: *Ronettes* / Why don't they let us fall in love?: *Ronettes* / Lovers: *Ronettes* / Born to be with you: *Dion* / Make the woman love me: *Dion* / Your own backyard: *Dion* / He's got the whole world in His hands: *Dion* / Only you know: *Dion* / New York City song: *Dion* / In and out of showers: *Dion* / Good lovin' man: *Dion* / He's a rebel: *Crystals*/ Uptown: *Crystals* / There's no other: *Crystals* / Oh yeah, maybe baby: *Crystals* / Please hurt me: *Crystals*/ Mashed potato time: *Crystals* / Another country, another world: *Crystals* / He's sure the boy I love: *Crystals*/ Then he kissed me: *Crystals* / On Broadway: *Crystals* / What a nice way to turn seventeen: *Crystals*/ He hit me (and it felt like a kiss): *Crystals* / I love you, Eddie: *Crystals* / Look in my eyes: *Crystals*/ No one ever tells you: *Crystals* / Da doo ron ron: *Crystals* / White Christmas: *Love, Darlene* / Frosty the snowman: *Ronettes* / Bells of St. Mary's: *Soxx, Bob B. & The Blue Jeans* / Santa Claus is coming to town: *Crystals*/ Sleigh ride: *Ronettes* / Marshmallow world: *Love, Darlene* / I saw mommy kissing Santa Claus: *Ronettes*/ Rudolph the red nosed reindeer: *Crystals* / Christmas (baby please come home): *Love, Darlene* / Here comes Santa Claus: *Soxx, Bob B. & The Blue Jeans* / Silent night: *Spector, Phil*.
LPS: . . . . **WOS 1**

Spector, Ronnie

UNFINISHED BUSINESS.
Tracks: / Who can sleep / Love on a rooftop / Dangerous / Burning love / Unfinished business / (If I could) walk away / Heart song / True to you / When we danced / Good love is hard to find.
LP: **4508561**
MC: **4508564**

Spectrum

IT'S TOO HOT FOR WORDS.
LP: . . . . **ROUNDER 0161**
MC: . . . . **ROUNDER 0161C**

LIVE IN JAPAN.
Tracks: / Cabin in Caroline / Blue umbrella / Smoke the cigarette / Hickory wind / Sea of heartbreak / Driving nails / Pig in the pen / Roll Buddy / Until you come back home again / Ain't misbehavin' / Don't get around much anymore / Rabbit in a log / End of the line (sukiyaki).
LP: . . . . **ROUNDER 0184**
MC: . . . . **ROUNDER 0184C**

OPENING ROLL.
LP: . . . . **ROUNDER 0136**
MC: . . . . **ROUNDER 0136C**

TRIBUTE TO THELONIOUS MONK.
LP: . . . . **SWLP 1001**

Spedding, Chris

CAFE DAYS.
LP: . . . . **ROSE 216**

CHRIS SPEDDING.
Tracks: / Jump in my car / Hungry man / Motor biking / Catch that train / Nervous / Boogie City / New girl in the neighbourhood / School days / Sweet disposition / Bedsit girl / Guitar jamboree.
LP: . . . . **SRAK 519**

ENEMY WITHIN.
LP: . . . . **ROSE 94**
MC: . . . . **ROSE 94C**

GUITAR GRAFITTI.
Tracks: / Video life / Radio times / Time warp / Midnight boys / Bored, bored / Walking / Breakout / Frontal lobotomy / Hey Miss Betty / More lobotomy.
LP: . . . . **SRAK 534**
MC: . . . . **TC SRAK 534 81**
LP: . . . . **FC 054**

HURT.
Tracks: / Wild in the street / Silver bullet / Lone rider / Woman trouble / Ain't superstitious / Wild wild women / Road runner / Stay dumb / Get outa my pagoda / Hurt by love.
LP: . . . . **SRAK 529**

I'M NOT LIKE EVERYBODY ELSE.
Tracks: / I'm not like everybody else / Box number / I got a feeling / Crying game, The / Depravity / Musical press / Contract / Counterfeit / Shot of rhythm and blues, A / Mama coco.
LP: . . . . **SRAK 542**
LP: . . . . **FC 055**

MEAN'N'MOODY.
Tracks: / For what we are about to hear / Backwood progression / Only lick I know, The / Listen while I sing my song / Saw you yesterday / Hill, The / Don't leave me / White lady / She's my friend / London town / Dark end of the street / Please Mrs. Henery / Never carry anymore than you can eat / Words don't come / Backwood theme.
LP: . . . . **SEE 40**

MOTOR BIKIN' (Best of Chris Spedding).
Tracks: / Motor bikin' / New girl in the neighbourhood / Nervous / Jump in my car / Running around / Pogo dancing / The pose / Wild in the street / Silver bullet / Roadrunner / Get outa my padoda / Hurt by love / Bored, bored / Hey Miss Betty / Walking / Breakout / Gun fight / Evil / I'm not like everybody else / Box number / Crying game, The / I got a feeling / Shot of rhythm 'n' blues, A / Guitar jamboree.
MC: . . . . **TCEMS 1425**

Speed Kills

SPEED KILLS (See under Heavy Metal) (Various artists).

Speed Limit

FIRST OFFENCE.
Tracks: / One in a crowd / Vino / Watching T.V. / Down the boozer / Motorbike / Kid / Speed limit / Hard way, The / Down at the Ritz / Doing time / Monday morning / Teabreak.
LP: . . . . **SATL 4011**

Speed O Metors

DAY IN THE LIGHTS.
Tracks: / Day in the lights / Out on the streets / Work / Lenny / Streetwalkers / Hit the highway / Tonight tonight / Can't eat / You said / Tired of living.
LP: . . . . **ACRO 5**

Speed Reading

SPEED READING (see under 'Sutphen, Dick').

Speed Trials

SPEED TRIALS, THE (Various artists).
LP: . . . . HMS 011

Speedstars

JOEY HARRIS & THE SPEEDSTARS (see Harris, Joey) (Speedstars/Joey Harris).

Speedy West

STEEL GUITAR FROM OUTER SPACE.
Tracks: / Steel guitar rag / Hub cap roll / Roadside rag / Crackerjack / Skiddle dee boo / Bustin' through / Yankee clover / Shuffleboard rag / Sand canyon swing / Shawnee trot / On the Alamo / Water baby blues / Space man in orbit / Sunset at Waikiki / Lazy summer evening / Totem pole dance / Afternoon of a swan / Speedy's special / Double or nothing / Slow and easy / Reflections from the moon / Tulsa twist / Rippling waters / Wild and woolly west.
LP: . . . . SEE 249

Spellbound

BREAKING THE SPELL.
LP: . . . . SNTF 934

ROCKIN' RECKLESS.
Tracks: / Rockin' reckless.
LP: . . . . SNTF 952

Spellbound (film)

SPELLBOUND (Film Soundtrack) (Utah Symphony Orchestra).
LP: . . . . DUN 116
LP: 704.260

Spelleogenesis

SPELLEOGENESIS (Original Soundtrack) (Various artists).
LP: . . . . NOMLP 001

Spellman, Benny

CALLING ALL CARS.
LP: . . . . BANDY 70018

FORTUNE TELLER (LP).
Tracks: / Fortune teller / Stickin' wit cha baby / In the night / Every now and then / T'aint it the truth / Life is too short / You don't love me no more / Talk about love / I feel good / Liptsick traces (on a cigarette) / I'll never leave you / It's for you / Word game, The / You got to get it / Anywhere you go / 10-4 (calling all cars).
LP: . . . . CRB 1168
MC: . . . . TCCRB 1168

Spence, Alexander Skip

OAR.
Tracks: / Little hands / Cripple creek / Diana / Margaret - tiger rug / Weighted down (the prison song) / War in peace / Broken heart / All come to meet her / Books of Moses / Dixie peach promenade / Lawrence of Euphoria / Grey / Afro.
LP: . . . . ED 282

Spence, Barrington

SPEAK SOFTLY.
LP: . . . . TRLS 117

Spence, Brian

BROTHERS.
LP: . . . . POLD 5195
MC: . . . . POLDC 5195

REPUTATION.
Tracks: / Reputation / Come back home / Without your love / There you go / You got the whip / Hand in hand / See the boy / Sliding down / Will she be home again / My arms are strong.
LP: . . . . POLD 5225
MC: . . . . POLDC 5225

Spence, Joseph

BAHAMAN GUITARIST.
LP: . . . . ARHOOLIE 1061

HAPPY ALL THE TIME.
LP: . . . . CGLP 4419

LIVING ON THE HALLELUJAH SIDE.
LP: . . . . ROUNDER 2021
MC: . . . . ROUNDER 2021C

Spence, Judson

JUDSON SPENCE.
Tracks: / Yeah yeah yeah / If you don't like it / Everything she do / Love dies in slow motion / Attitude / Hot and sweaty / Down in the village / Dance with me / Higher / Forever me, forever you.
LP: . . . . WX 227
MC: . . . . WX 227 C

Spence, Sonya

IN THE DARK.
MC: . . . . SKYCAS 10
LP: . . . . SKYLP 10

Spencer, Don

SINGS THE SONGS OF PLAY SCHOOL.
LP: . . . . NEVLP 127

Spencer, Earle

BIG BAND PIONEER.
LP: . . . . IAJRC 41

EARLE SPENCER & HIS NEW BAND SENSATION OF 1946.
LP: . . . . FH 16

Spencer, Jeremy

FLEE.
Tracks: / Deeper / Sunshine / Love our way outta here / Flee / Cool breeze / You've got the right / Travellin'.
LP: . . . . K 50624

Spencer, John

LAST LP, THE (Spencer, John Louts).
Tracks: / Can't buy my soul / Mary-Lou and the sunshine boy / Crazy for my lady / That's as meam as meam can get to be / What you do to my heart / My old lady (she's got the meanest face in town) / Cuba libre / Sweet sensation / Natural man / Can't mean it / No expectations.
LP: . . . . BEGA 3

TRYING TO MATTER.
Tracks: / Trying to matter / Jukebox Cinderella / I'll have to say I love you in a song / Too many do-goods / Ballad of Easy Anna / Far beyond / Holding on / Ode to the road / Losers and fools / Prisoner's last letter.
LP: . . . . BSS 308

Spencer, John B.

BREAK AND ENTRY.
Tracks: / Chained to the love of a son / Judea / Break and entry / Too much of a woman (to take it like) / Only dancing / My Thai bride / One way flight / Poor man on the cross / Ca ne fait rien / Whiteboy.
LP: . . . . JBSLP 1
MC: . . . . JBSMC 1

OUT WITH A BANG.
Tracks: / Out with a bang / Funny honey / Gingham white and blue / Acceptable losses / Plaisir d'amour / Forgotten the blues / Hold on to your heartache / Cry baby cry / Flesh and blood / Chris is in love again / One more whiskey / Sad reunion / Answer only with your eyes.
LP: 12TS 444

PARLOUR GAMES.
Tracks: / Parlour games / Billy / Slow beers / Sweet Lucinda / Poor little rich boy / Drive in movies / Behold the king is dead / Dead man's shoes / Alone together / Left hand of love / Count ten / London I knew, The / Going down South / Quiet nights.
LP: . . . . RTMLP 23
MC: . . . . RTMMC 23

Spencer, Johnny

ALL MY CLOUDY DAYS ARE GONE.
MC: . . . . IRBC 2004

Spencer, Tarney

RUN FOR YOUR LIFE (Spencer, Tarney Band).
Tracks: / No time to lose / Race is almost run / Won'tcha tell me / Live again / Run for your life / Don't / Far better man / Lies / Heart will break tonight, A / I'm alive.
LP: . . . . AMLH 64757

Spendel, Christoph

READY FOR TAKE OFF.
Tracks: / Salsito / Carly / Ready for take off / Monday in July / Rain / Queen's plaza / Downtown / Tapsi strikes again.
LP: . . . . LR 45010

SPENDEL.
Tracks: / White cars / New York P.M. / Mr. Cameo / Midnight / Columbus circle / Byton funk / Banana republic / Eilat / Otto's magic bus / Hugo update, The / Suite 11F / Piano graffity / Manhattan candlelight.
LP: . . . . LR 45014

Spender, Stephen

FOUR TWENTIETH CENTURY POETS (see under Lewis, C. Day).

STEPHEN SPENDER READING HIS POETRY.
MC: 1084

Spenser, Edmund

FAERIE QUEEN & EPITHALAMION (MacLiammoir, Micheal).
MC: 1126

Spermbirds

COMMON THREAD.
LP: . . . . FULL 002

NOTHING IS EASY.
LP: . . . . WEBITE 31
LP: 081 263

SOMETHING TO PROVE.
LP: . . . . ACHE 06
LP: 081 227

Sphere

FLIGHT PATH.
Tracks: / If I should lose you / Pumpkin's delight / Played twice / El Sueno / Christina / Flight path.
LP: 960 313 1

FOUR FOR ALL.
LP: 831674-1
MC: 831674-4

FOUR IN ONE.
Tracks: / Four in one / Light blue / Monk's dream / Evidence / Reflections / Eronel.
LP: . . . . K 52415

PRESENT TENSE.
LP: . . . . SGC 1012

SPHERE.
LP: . . . . SGC 1010

Sphinx

BURNING LIGHTS.
LP: . . . . SKULL 8389

Spicer, George

BLACKBERRY FOLD.
Tracks: / Blackberry fold / Cutaway Mike / Oyster girl, The / Faithful sailor boy, The / Three jolly boys / Irish hop pole puller, The / Cunning cobbler, The / Folkestone murder, The / German clockmender / Henry my son / Coming home late / I wish there was no prisons / Searching for young lambs / Old militia drum, The.
LP: 12T 235

Spicher, Buddy

AMERICAN SAMPLER.
LP: . . . . FF 021

BUDDIES (Spicher, Buddy & Buddy Emmons).
Tracks: / Autumn fling / Little darlin' / Uncle Pen / Magic swing / Watch what happens / Joy spring / Broken down in tiny pieces.
LP: . . . . SNTF 741
LP: . . . . FF 041

FIDDLE CLASSICS.
LP: . . . . FF 278

ME AND MY HEROES.
LP: . . . . FF 065
MC: . . . . FF 065C

PLATINUM FIDDLE.
Tracks: / Orange blossom special / Black mountain rag / Touch my heart / Norwegian wood / Rocky top / Bobby's rainbow / Twinkle twinkle little star / Haste to the wedding / Eighth of January / Shannon waltz / Fire on the mountain / Snowflake breakdown.
LP: . . . . PRCV 105

Spider

ROCK 'N' ROLL GYPSIES.
Tracks: / A.W.O.L. / Talkin' bout rock 'n' roll / Part of the legend / Did ya like it baby / Them that start the fightin' (don't fight) / What you're doing to me / Lady (I'm dyin' for you) / Till I'm certain / Rock 'n' roll forever will last / All the time.
LP: . . . . RCALP 3101
MC: . . . . RCAK 3101

ROUGH JUSTICE.
Tracks: / Here we go rock 'n' roll / Moring after the night before / Rock 'n' roll gypsies / Martyred / Time to go now / Death row / Minstrel / You make me offers / Midsummer morning.
LP: . . . . AMLX 68563

SPIDER.
Tracks: / New romance / Burning love / Shady lady / Everything is alright / Crossfire / Little darlin' / Brotherly love / What's going on / Don't waste your time / Zero.
LP: 2394 260

Spider & The Fly

SPIDER & THE FLY, THE Victorian & Edwardian songs & duets (Various artists).
LP: . . . . A 66063

Spiderman

SPIDERMAN IN MACHINES & MONSTERS (Various artists).
MC: 41 5715 4

SPIDERMAN IN THE RETURN OF DR.OCTOPUS.
MC: 41 5713 4

SPIDERMAN IN THE SCORPION TAKES A BRIDE (Various artists).
MC: 41 5710 4

Spiders

BEST OF THE SPIDERS VOL.2.
Tracks: / That's enough / Don't knock / Sukey, Sukey, Sukey / Mmm mmm baby / I'm searching / Am I the one / Witchcraft / You're the one / I'm slippin' in / True you dont love me / She keeps me wondering / I did'nt want to do it / Walking around in circles.
LP: . . . . KC 106

BEST OF THE SPIDERS VOL 1.
Tracks: / Don't pity me / Bells in my heart / I'll stop crying / Real thing, The / Honey bee / How I feel / Goodbye / For a thrill / Dear Mary / Thats the way to win my heart / Tears began to flow / Lost and bewildered / You played the part / All in my heart.
LP: . . . . KC 105

Spiderz

PRESSURE.
Tracks: / Do you feel the pressure / Not sensitive / I wanna be used for love / I want to believe / Shake your head / Fall / Birthday / At night I call your name / Let's stick to dancing / I'm yours tonight / She's a teaser.
LP: . . . . FLAK 103

Spiegelman, Joel

NEW AGE BACH (The Goldberg Variations).
Tracks: / Aria / Variations 1-15 / Variations 16-30 / Aria da Capo.
LP: . . . . K 790 927 1
MC: . . . . K 790 927 4

Spies Like Us

SPIES LIKE US (Film Soundtrack) (Various artists).
Tracks: / Ace tomato company, The: *Various artists* / Off to spy: *Various artists* / Russians in the desert: *Various artists* / Pass in the tent: *Various artists* / Escape: *Various artists* / To the bus: *Various artists*/ Road to Russia, The: *Various artists* / Rally 'round: *Various artists* / W.A.M.P.: *Various artists*/ Martian act: *Various artists* / Arrest: *Various artists* / Recall: *Various artists* / Winners: *Various artists.*
LP: . . . . TER 1110
MC: . . . . CTV 81270

Spikes

COLOUR IN A BLACK FORREST.
Tracks: / River of love / French bible / Leningrad / She's melting / Spy in my house / Katrina / This is Australia / Dreamtime / So damn cold / Meaning of life, The / Give me everything.
LP: . . . . ZINLP 1

SIX SHARP CUTS.
LP: . . . . RIB 2

Spillane, Davy

ATLANTIC BRIDGE.
Tracks: / Atlantic Bridge / Davie's reels / Daire's dream / Tribute to Johnny Doran / O'Neill's statement / Sliverish / By the river of gems / Pigeon on the gate / In my life / Lansdowne blues.
LP: . . . . COOK 009
MC: . . . . COOKC 009
MC: 4TA 3019
LP: . . . . TA 3019

OUT OF THE AIR.
Tracks: / Atlantic bridge / Daire's dream / Mystic seacliffs / Litton Lane / River of gems / Storm, The / Road to Ballyalla, The / One for Phil.
LP: . . . . COOK 016
MC: . . . . COOKC 016
LP: . . . . TA 2017

SHADOW HUNTER, THE.
Tracks: / Lucy's tune / Indiana drones / Carron streams / Watching the clock / Walker of the snow / Hidden ground / White crow, The / Moyasta junction / Journeys of a dreamer / One day in June / Equinox / Host of the air, The.
LP: . . . . COOK 030
MC: . . . . COOKC 030

Spinal Tap

THIS IS SPINAL TAP (Tour Soundtrack).
Tracks: / Hell hole / Tonight I'm gonna rock you / Heavy duty / Rock'n'roll creation / America / Cups and cakes / Big bottom / Sex farm / Stonehenge / Gimme some money / Flower people.
LP: 817 846-1
MC: 817 846-4
LP: . . . . LUSLP 2
MC: . . . . LUSMC 2

Spinetti, Victor

VERY PRIVATE DIARY, A.
MC: . . . . SCENEC 14

Spink, Arthur

COUNTRY BOX.
Tracks: / Dixie / Gypsy woman / Three bells / Texas in my heart / Don't it make my brown eyes blue / San Antonio Rose / Sweet surrender / You're the only good thing / There goes my everything / Sittin' alone in an old rockin' chair / Battle hymn of the republic / Island of dreams / Duelling banjos / Last farewell, The.
LP: . . . . GES 1210

HAPPY ACCORDION.
LP: . . . . GES 1197

Spinners

18 GOLDEN FAVOURITES.
Tracks: / Love is teasin' / Blaydon races / Aunt Maggie's remedy / Last thing on my mind / Lamorna / Poverty knock / D-day dodgers / Lord of the dance / Everybody loves Saturday night / All day singing / Keep your feet still Geordie Hinney / Sing out, shout with joy / Banks of the Ohio / Amazing grace / Water o' Tyne, The / John Barleycorn / We shall not be moved / So long it's been good to know you.
LP: . . . . NTS 165
MC: . . . . TCNTS 165

20 GOLDEN FOLK SONGS.
Tracks: / Moonshiner / Guantanamera / Foggy dew / Seventeen come Sunday / Tom Brown / Shepherd lad / Jamaica farewell / Dance the flora / Colliers' rant, The / To be a farmer's boy / Deep blue sea / To hear the nightingale / Derby ram / Castles in the air / Parting glass.
LP: . . . . NTS 193

AROUND THE WORLD...AND BACK AGAIN.
LP: . . . . DID 712

BLAYDON RACES.
MC: . . . . TCIDL 7

BY ARRANGEMENT.
MC: . . . . TCEMC 3009

CARIBBEAN SUNSHINE HITS.
Tracks: / Jamaica farewell / Zombie jamboree / Guantanamera / Everybody loves Saturday night / Deep blue sea / Tom Brown / Mary Ann / Mek me hold / Fan me soldier man / Little boy / Dip and fall back / Lime juice ship.
LP: . . . . OU 2235

FINAL FLING.
Tracks: / Blues my naughty sweetie gives to me / Marques, The / Thirty pieces of silver / Three score and ten / Old pubs, The / Old Johnny Booker / Redemption song / Blow ye winds in the morning / Michael row the boat ashore / Carrickfergus / Coal, coal for Manchester / Practice up your courtesy / Calton Weaver, The / Pratty flowers / Fairlie duplex engine, The / Stormy weather boys / Castles in the air (single version) / To be a farmer's boy / Zombie jamboree / When I first came to this land / Derby ram, The / Come landlord fill the flowing bowl / Jamaica farewell / Mary Ann / Greensleeves / Asi-K-Atali / Dance the Flora / Go slow / Fan me soldier man / Brigg Fair/Harvest home / Will ye go lassie go / Maggie May / Seventeen come Sunday / Foggy dew, The / Villikins and his Dinah / Black and white / Lovely Joan.
2LP: . . . . EN 5007
MCSET: . . . . TCEN 5007

FOLK AT THE PHIL!.
Tracks: / Aram sa-sa / Colon man / 'Enery my son / Fried bread and brandy oh / Here's to Cheshire / I wish I was back in Liverpool / Irish rover, The / John Peel / Little Matty Groves / Lord Randal / Maggie May / Mermaid, The / Outlandish knight, The / Silver in the stubble / Woman sweeter than man.
LP: . . . . SPR 8571
MC: . . . . SPC 8571

GOLDEN HOUR OF THE SPINNERS, A.
Tracks: / Liverpool Lou / Tom Dooley / Morning has broken / Granny's old armchair / Freight train / Dirty old town / Imagine / Family of man / Going to the zoo / Leaving of Liverpool / Black and white / Wild rover / Beth Davey (whiskey on a Sunday) / Football crazy / Yellow bird / Little boxes / Matchstalk men and matchstalk cats and dogs / Scarborough Fair / Island in the sun / Bring a little water Sylvie / Good night Irene.
MC: . . . . KGHMC 138

HERE'S TO THE SPINNERS.
Tracks: / Here's to the couple / Zombie Jamboree / Any complaints / Chevalier de la table ronde / Colliers' rant, The / Last thing on my mind / Come Landlord fill the flowing bowl / Foggy dew, The / Keep your feet still Geordie Hinney / Guantanamera / Derby Ram, The / Castles in the air / Blaydon races / Tom Brown / Jamaica farewell / To be a farmers boy / Will ye go lassie go / Bucket of the mountain dew / D-Day dodgers / Dip and fall back / Perry merry Dixie / When I first came to this land / So long, it's been good to know you.
2LP: . . . . MFP 1038
MCSET: . . . . TCMFP 1038

HERE'S TO YOU...FROM THE SPINNERS.
Tracks: / Football crazy / Island in the sun / Messing about on the river / Dirty old town / London roving Jack / Liverpool Lou / Here's to you sweet England / Black and white / Eros / Kumbaya / Morning has broken / Going to the zoo / Seth Davey (whiskey on a Sunday) / Malaika / Sweet Thames flow softly / Leaving of Liverpool.
LP: . . . . N 145
MC: . . . . ZCN 145
LP: . . . . PYL 10
MC: . . . . PYM 10

IN MY LIVERPOOL HOME.
Tracks: / Maggie May / Island in the sun / Rukumbine / Johnny Todd / Creeping Jane / Roving navvy / Lure of the mines / Home, boys, home / Scarborough fair / Wor Geordie's lost his penka / Dingle regatta / Barnyards of Delgaty / Family of man / Wild rover / South Australia / Tom's gone to Hilo / Haul on the bowline / Stockholm tar / Peace round / Heavy rain / Matty rag / Imagine / Worried man / Midnight special / Pick a bale of cotton / In my Liverpool home / Matchstalk men / Black and white.
2LP: . . . . SPN 1
MCSET: . . . . ZCSPN 1
LP: . . . . PYL 5001
MC: . . . . PYM 5001

LAST NIGHT WE HAD A DO.
Tracks: / Whisky in the jar / Granny's old armchair / Yellow bird / Little boxes / Rock Island line / Bring a little water, Sylvie / Cushie butterfield / Pub with no beer, A / Midnight special / Judy drowned / Freight train / Car song, The / Frankie and Johnny / Tom Dooley / Strangest dream / Goodnight, Irene.
LP: . . . . N 6553
MC: . . . . ZCN 6553
LP: . . . . PYL 11
MC: . . . . PYM 11

LOVE IS TEASING.
LP: . . . . SCX 6493

MUSIC OF THE SPINNERS, 1968 - 1971.
Tracks: / Adam in the garden / Barbara Allen / Black and white / Dirty old town / Ellen Vannin tragedy / Family of man / I wish I was back in Liverpool / In my Liverpool home / John Peel / Minstrel boy / She moved through the fair / Woman sweeter than man.
MC: 7215 040

SAINTS MEET THE SPINNERS, THE (see under Saints) (Spinners/The Saints).

SINGING CITY, THE.
Tracks: / Orange and the green, The / Leaving of Liverpool / In my Liverpool home / Dirty old town / Maggie May / Marco Polo / Liverpool lullaby / Manchester rambler, The / Liverpool Judies / Jug of punch / Drunken sailor / Three jolly boys.
LP: . . . . PRICE 63
MC: . . . . PRIMC 63

SONGS OF THE TALL SHIPS.
Tracks: / Santa Ana / Whisky Johnny / Spanish ladies / Clear the track / Portsmouth / Lowlands away / Do let me go / Roll Alabama roll / Stormy along / New York gals / Little Sally Rackett / Paddy lay back / Donkey riding / Old Swansea Town / Blow, boys, blow / Liverpool hornpipe / Jackie Brown / Lime juice ship / Blow the man down / Ebeneezer, The / Shenandoah.
LP: . . . . EG 2602101
MC: . . . . EG 2602104

SPINNERS.
Tracks: / Black and white / William Brown / Asi K atali / Auntie Maggie's remedy / Love is teasing / All day singing / Dance the flora / Calico printers clerk / Rovin', A / Go slow / Moonshiner / Lover and his lass / Maggie May / Poverty knock / Lord of the dance / Everybody loves Saturday night.
LP: . . . . EMS 1077791

SPINNERS ARE IN TOWN, THE.
LP: 6309014

SPINNERS IN CONCERT, THE.
Tracks: / All day singing / Moonshiner / William Brown / Bleacher lass o' Kelvinhaugh / Jane and Louisa / Tom Brown / Castles in the air / Calico printer's clerk / Guantanamera / Deep blue sea / Poverty knock / Lamorna / Cobbler's song, The / Ring of iron, The / Waltzing Matilda / Little boy / Mule skinner blues / So long, it's been good to know you.
MC: . . . . HR 8141

SPINNERS LIVE PERFORMANCE.
LP: 6870 502

SPINNERS, THE.
Tracks: / Fried bread and brandy oh / Family of man / In my Liverpool home / Liverpool barrer boy / Dirty old town / Maggie May / Liverpool lullaby / Leaving of Liverpool / Black and white island woman / Wimoweh / Asi-K-Atali / Hosanna / Evening of roses / Philimorioojay / Skye boat song / Jug of punch / Manchester rambler, The / Mechanical blackbird / Sunshine / I wish I was back in Liverpool / Lincolnshire poacher / Fireship, The / Why oh why / John Peel / Shortness of sight / A-roving / Here's to Cheshire / Strangest dream.
MCSET: . . . . DTOL 10068

SPUN GOLD.
Tracks: / Liverpool Lou / Tom Dooley / Morning has broken / Granny's old armchair / Freight train / Dirty old town / Imagine / Family of man / Going to the zoo / Black and white / Wild Rover / Yellow bird / Little boxes / Matchstalk men and matchstalk cats and dogs / Scarborough fair / Island in the sun / Bring a little water Sylvie / Goodnight Irene.
MC: . . . . ZCN 6560
LP: . . . . N 6560
LP: . . . . PYL 12
MC: . . . . PYM 12

SWINGING CITY, THE.
LP: 6382 002

THIS IS THE SPINNERS.
Tracks: / Lord of the dance / Guantanamera / All day singing / Love is teasing / Liverpool hornpipe / Come landlord fill the flowing bowl / We shall not be moved / John Barleycorn / Paddy lay back / Dance the flora / Last thing on my mind / Castles in the air / Calico printer's clerk / Twanky Dillo / Auntie Maggie's remedy / Soldier's cloak / Deep blue sea / Sussex carol.
LP: . . . . THIS 7

YOUR 20 FAVOURITE CHRISTMAS CAROLS.
Tracks: / Hark the herald angels sing / While shepherds watched their flocks by night / Silent night / Good King Wenceslas / In dulci jubilo / I saw three ships / In the bleak mid winter / Deck the hall / O little town of Bethlehem / First Noel, The / Sussex carol, The / Wassailing song, The / Once in Royal David's city / Ding dong merrily on high / We three kings of Orient are / Away in a manger / O come all ye faithful / Rocking carol, The / Holly and the ivy, The / God rest ye merry gentlemen.
LP: . . . . ED 2607471
MC: . . . . ED 2607474

Spiral Jetty

DOGSTAR.
Tracks: / Dogstar.
LP: . . . . ILLUSION 018

Spirit

BEST OF SPIRIT, THE.
Tracks: / Fresh garbage / Uncle Jack / Mechanical world / Taurus / Girl in your eyes / Straight arrow / Topango windows / Gramophone man / Water woman / Great canyon fire in general, The / Elijah.
LP: . . . . CBS 31693

BEST OF SPIRIT VOL.2.
Tracks: / 1984 / Mechanical world / Nature's way / Animal zoo / Fresh garbage / I got a line on you / Prelude, nothin' to hide / Uncle Jack / Morning will come / Dark eyed woman.
LP: . . . . EPC 32516

CLEAR.
Tracks: / Dark eyed woman / Apple orchard / So little time to fly / Ground hog / Policeman's ball / Ice / Give a life take a life / I'm truckin' / Clear / Caught / New dope in town / Cold wind.
LP: . . . . ED 268

FAMILY THAT PLAYS TOGETHER, THE.
Tracks: / I got a line on you / It shall be / Poor Richard / Sikly Sam / Drunkard, The / Darlin' if / All the same / Jewish / Dream within a dream / She smiled / Aren't you glad.
LP: . . . . XED 162
MC: . . . . CED 162

FUTURE GAMES.
Tracks: / CB talk / Stars of love / Kahauna dream / Buried in my brain / Bionic unit / So happy now / All along the watchtower / Would you believe / Jack Bond / Star Trek dreaming / Interlude XM / China doll / Hawaiian times / Gorn attack / Interlude 2001 / Detroit city / Freakout frog / Romulan experience, The / Monkey see monkey do / Mr. Olympus / Journey of Nomad, The / Ending.
LP: . . . . PIPLP 003
MC: . . . . PIPMC 003

JOURNEY TO POTATOLAND.
LP: . . . . BEGA 23

LIVE: SPIRIT.
LP: . . . . ILP 001

POTATOLAND.
Tracks: / We've got a lot to learn / Potatoland / Open up your hand / Information suite / Mash potatoes / Midnight train / Oil slick / Million years.
LP: . . . . CHORD 010
MC: . . . . CHORDTC 010

RAPTURE IN THE CHAMBERS.
Tracks: / Hard love / Love tonight / Thinking of / Rapture in the chambers / Mojo man / Contact / Prisoner, The / One track / Mind / Enchanted forest / Human sexuality / Shera princess of power / End suite.
LP: . . . . EIRSA 1014
MC: . . . . EIRSAC 1014

ROCK GIANTS.
LP: 544 37

SON OF SPIRIT.
LP: . . . . PIPLP 002
MC: . . . . PIPMC 002

SPIRIT.
Tracks: / Fresh garbage / Uncle Jack / Mechanical world / Taurus / Girl in your eyes / Straight arrow / Topanga windows / Gramophone man / Water woman / Great canyon fire in general, The / Elijah.
LP: . . . . ED 311

SPIRIT OF '76.
Tracks: / America, the beautiful / Times they are a-changin' / Victim of society / Lady o' the lakes / Tampa jam (pt.1) / Maunaloa / What do I have / Sunrise / Walking the dog / Tampa jam (pt.2) / Joker on the run / When? / Like a rolling stone / Once again / Feeling in time / Happy / Jack Bond / My road / Tampa jam (pt.3) / Thank you Lord / Urantia / Guide me / Veruska / Hey Joe / Jack Bond (pt.2) / Star spangled banner, The.
2LP: . . . . DED 251

THIRTEENTH DREAM, THE.
Tracks: / Black satin nights / Mr. Skin / Mechanical World / Pick it up / All over the world / 1984 / Uncle Jack / Natures way / Fresh garbage / I got a line on you.
LP: . . . . MERL 35

TWELVE DREAMS OF DR. SARDONICUS.
Tracks: / Nothin' to hide / Nature's way / Animal zoo / Love has found a way / Why can't I be free / Mr. Skin / Space child / When I touch you / Street worm / Life has just begun / Morning will come / Soldier / We've got a lot to learn / Potatoland (theme) / Open up your heart / Morning light / Potatoland (prelude) / Potatoland (introduction) / Turn to the right / Donut house / Fish fry road / Information / My friend.
LP: . . . . CBS 32006
MC: 40 32006
LP: . . . . ED 313

Spirit Level

MICE IN THE WALLET.
Tracks: / Bristol blues / Too late, too late / Orinoco / All heaven in a rage / Peggy's blue skylight / Fifty years in a factory.
LP: . . . . SPJ 522

SPIRIT LEVEL.
LP: . . . . SPJ 528

Spirit Of Praise

EXPRESSION OF PRAISE (Spirit of Praise Orchestra/Choir).
Tracks: / For I'm building a people of power / Jesus, we enthrone You / Father, we love You / I will enter His gates / Majesty / Our God reigns / For this purpose / I love You, Lord / You are the King of Glory / Reign in me / We bring a sacrifice of praise / Jesus, name above all names / When I feel the touch / He is Lord / Jesus, take me as I am / Rejoice, rejoice / Shine, Jesus, shine / Hosanna / There is a Redeemer / Father God, I wonder.
LP: . . . . SOP R 2029
MC: . . . . SOP C 2029

Spirit Of St Louis

SPIRIT OF ST. LOUIS (Film Soundtrack) (Various artists).
LP: . . . . ERS 6507
MC: . . . . VSC 5212

Spirit Of The Day

LABOUR DAY.
Tracks: / Darkhouse / Profiteers / Run boy / Expensive/Cinema of pain / Take it from the source / Political / Hounds that wait outside your door / Drinking man / Gottingen street.
LP: . . . . FBLP 400617
MC: . . . . FBMC 700617

Spirit Of The West

SAVE THIS HOUSE.
LP: 9031709711
MC: 9031709714

TRIPPING UP THE STAIRS.
LP: . . . . PH 1113
MC: . . . . PH 113C

Spirit Of Vienna

SPIRIT OF VIENNA (Various artists).
MC: TC2MOM 102

Spirits Of Rhythm

RHYTHM PERSONIFIED (1933/4).
LP: . . . . JSP 1088

SPIRITS OF RHYTHM.
LP: . . . . GARDENIA 4009

Spisar Party

SPISAR PARTY (Various artists).
LP: 33.5001

Spitballs

SPITBALLS.
Tracks: / I can only give you everything / Gino is a coward / Over and over / Bad moon rising / Life's too short / Let her dance / I want her so bad / Telstar / Way over there / Chapel of love / Knock on wood / Just like me / Boris the spider / Feel too good / Batman.
LP: . . . . BSERK 15

Spitfire Band

FLIGHT III.
Tracks: / Airmail special / Back Bay shuffle / Cherokee / South Rampart street parade / You made me love you / I'll never smile again / For all we know / Bugle call rag / Don't be that way / Accentuate the positive / On the Atchison, Topeka and Santa Fe / Stompin' at the Savoy / No more dancing.
LP: . . . . CBS 26163

SPITFIRE BAND FLIES AGAIN, THE.
LP: . . . . MLAT 1237

SPITFIRE BAND FLIGHT II, THE.
LP: . . . . MLAT 1238

SPITFIRE BAND SWINGS DOWN BROADWAY, THE.
LP: . . . . LAT 1230

SPITFIRE BAND SWINGS THE MOVIES, THE.
LP: . . . . LAT 1234

Spitting Image

SPIT IN YOUR EAR (TV Soundtrack)(Spitting Image Caste) (Various artists).
Tracks: / Spitting Image sig tune: *Various artists* / Ronnie and Maggie goodbye: *Various artists* / Royal singalong: *Various artists* / Weather forecast: *Various artists* / Coleman peaks: *Various artists* / We've got beards: *Various artists* (ZZ Top) / Second coming: *Various artists* / Someone famous has died: *Various artists*/ Tea at Johnnies: *Various artists* / Trendy Kinnock: *Various artists* / Do do run Ron: *Various artists*/ Ronnie's birthday: *Various artists*/ One man and his bitch: *Various artists* / Special relationship: *Various* artists / Clean rugby songs: *Various artists* / O'Toole's night out: *Various artists* / Spock the actor: *Various* artists / Line of celebrities: *Various artists* / Price is right, The: *Various artists* / Botha tells the truth: *Various artists* / I've never met a nice South African: *Various artists* / End announcement: *Various* artists / Andy and Fergie: *Various artists* / Pete Townsend appeals: *Various artists* / Our generation (The Who): *Various artists* / Three Davids, The: *Various artists* / Party system, The: *Various artists* / Hello you must be going: *Various artists* / Naming the Royal baby: *Various artists* / Bruno and Ruthless: *Various* artists / South Bank show on Ronnie Hazelhurst: *Various artists* / Bernard Manning newsflash: *Various artists*/ Juan Carlos meets the Queen: *Various artists* / Chicken song, The (celebrity megamix): *Various artists* / Lawson goes bonkers: *Various artists* / Talk bollocks: *Various artists* / Snooker games: *Various artists* / Good old British bloke: *Various artists* / Black moustache: *Various artists* (Prince.) / Uranus: *Various artists*/ Dennis Thatcher's pacemaker: *Various artists* / John And Tatum - the young marrieds: *Various artists* / We're scared of Bob: *Various artists* / Trooping the colour: *Various artists* / Night thoughts: *Various artists.*
LP: . . . . OVED 227
MC: . . . . OVEDC 227
LP: . . . . V 2403
MC: . . . . TCV 2403
MC: . . . . VVIPC 110

Spittle, Dusty

COUNTRY WORLD OF....
MC: . . . . SPVP 172C

Spivak, Charlie

1942: CHARLIE SPIVAK (Spivak, Charlie & His Orchestra).
LP: . . . . SLP 16

1946 (Spivak, Charlie & His Orchestra).
LP: . . . . CLP 80

CHARLIE SPIVAK 1941, VOL 2.
Tracks: / Slow and easy / Comin' thro' the rye / Everything happens to me / Combination solid / This love of mine / Let's go home / Don't take your love from me / Hop, skip and jump / It's always you / After I say I'm sorry / I understand / Charlie's horse.
LP: . . . . HSR 188

CHARLIE SPIVAK AND HIS ORCHESTRA 1943-46 (Spivak, Charlie & His Orchestra).
Tracks: / Stardreams / Mean to me / Seranade in blue / I used to love you / Cuddle up a little closer / Blue Lou / Laura / More than you know / Stardust / Accentuate the positive / Solitude / Travelin' light / Blue champagne / Let's go home / It's the same old dream / Saturday night.
LP: . . . . HMP 5044
LP: . . . . HSR 105

CHARLIE SPIVAK & JIMMY JOY 1945 (Spivak, Charlie & His Orchestra).
Tracks: / Star dreams / Into each life some rain must fall / Wonderful winter / Every time we say goodbye / If you were but a dream / Right as rain / Even Steven / Shine on harvest moon / Blue skies / I dream of you / Savoy is jumpin', The / How many hearts have you broken? / Green eyes / Don't ever change / Dark eyes.
LP: . . . . AIRCHECK 6

HOP SKIP AND JUMP.
Tracks: / Slow and easy / This love of mine / Mean to me / Stardust / Blue champagne / Comin' thro' the rye / Let's go home / Charlie's horse / Everything happens to me / I understand / Cuddle up / Travelin' light / Got the moon in my pocket / Combination solid / Hop skip and jump / Serenade in blue.
MC: 40181
LP: 20181

NOW 1981 (Spivak, Charlie & His Orchestra).
LP: . . . . SLP 17

ONE WAY PASSAGE.
LP: . . . . FH 28

STAR DREAMS (Spivak, Charlie Orchestra & Dubby Spivak).
LP: . . . . CLP 100

Spivak, Dubby

IT'S SO PEACEFUL IN THE COUNTRY.
LP: . . . . AP 146

SWINGS LIGHTLY.
LP: . . . . AP 189

Spivey, Victoria

EASY RIDERS JAZZ BAND, THE.
LP: . . . . GHB 17

VICTORIA SPIVEY (1926-37).
LP: . . . . BD 2079

Spizzles

SPIKEY DREAM FLOWERS.
Tracks: / Brain washing time / Five year mission / Dangers of living / Robots holiday / Soldier soldier / Downtown / Risk / Central Park / Scared / Melancholy.
LP: . . . . AMLE 68523

SPK

AT THE CRYPT.
MC: . . . . SRC 004

AUTO-DA-FE.
LP: . . . . WULP 002

DIGITALIS AMBIGUA, GOLD AND POISON.
LP: . . . . NTL 30017
MC: . . . . NTLC 30017

FROM SCIENCE TO RITUAL.
LP: . . . . PLASMA 004

INFORMATION OVERLOAD.
LP: . . . . NORMAL 09

MACHINE AGE VOODOO.
Tracks: / Junk funk / With love from china / High tension / One world / Flesh and steel / Metropolis / Metal dance / Thin ice / Crime of passion.
LP: . . . . WX 10

OCEANIA.
Tracks: / Oceania / Doctrine of eternal ice, The / Breathless / Mouth to mouth / Kambuja / Crack / Seduction, The / Dies irae.
LP: . . . . SER 11

ZAMIA LEHMANNI.
LP: . . . . SER 09

Splash (film)

SPLASH (Film soundtrack) (Various artists).
LP: . . . . PIPLP 710
MC: . . . . ZCPIP 710

Splash Of Colour

SPLASH OF COLOUR.
LP: . . . . K 58415

Splatcats

RIGHT ON.
LP: . . . . PRL 70091

Splendour Of Strings

SPLENDOUR OF STRINGS (Various artists).
Tracks: / Cherokee: *Various artists* / Harbour lights: *Various artists* / End of a love affair, The: *Various* artists / Estrelita: *Various artists* / Catch a falling star: *Various artists* / One I love: *Various* artists / Lady of Spain: *Various artists* / La vie en rose: *Various artists* / I'll never smile again: *Various* artists / By the waters of Minnetonka: *Various artists* / All in the golden afternoon: *Various artists* / World is waiting for sunrise: *Various artists* / Breeze and I: *Various artists* / Someday: *Various artists*/ Green leaves of summer: *Various artists* / Splendour of strings: *Various artists* / Summer place: *Various* artists / Dance ballerina dance: *Various artists* / Granada: *Various artists* / Story of a starry night: *Various* artists / Intermezzo: *Various artists* / Cottage for sale: *Various artists* / How high the moon: *Various artists* / Baby won't you please come home: *Various artists.*
2LP: . . . . DPA 3069/70

Spliff

85555.
Tracks: / Deja vu / Tonite / Emergency exit / Carbonara / Computers are stupid / Kill / Passion play / Jerusalem / In those days.
LP: . . . . CBS 85739

SPLIFF RADIO SHOW.
Tracks: / Spliff / Jungle / Sweet as radio / Gravy / Disco / Kaine / Stoned airlines (jingle) / Cheap chicks / Wysocki College (jingle) / Deep in the city / Producers / Keep your feet on the ground (jingle) / Jet set star / Rock is a drug.
LP: . . . . CBS 84555

Spliffy, Herbert

EASY SQUEEZE (See Donaldson, Eric) (Spliffy, Herbert & Eric Donaldson).

Splinter

SPLINTER.
Tracks: / Innocent / Plane leaving Tokyo / Another time another place / Too far down the line / Take it or leave it / Passing through / Touch yet never feel / Don't leave me now / All that love / Sailaway.
LP: . . . . BPLP 002

Splintered Sword

SPLINTERED SWORD (see Treece, H) (Sheddon, John).

Split Beaver

WHEN HELL WON'T HAVE YOU.
Tracks: / Savage / Going straight / Gimme head / Cruisin / Levington gardens / Hounds of hell / Likewise / Living in and out / Get out, stay out / Bailiff, The.
LP: . . . . HMRLP 3

Split Crow

ROCKSTORM.
LP: . . . . GRC 2167

Split Enz

BEGINNING OF THE ENZ.
Tracks: / My mistake / Crosswords / Bold as brass / Another great divide / Charley / Late last night / Stranger than fiction / Time for a change / Walking down a road.
LP: . . . . CHR 1329
MC: . . . . ZCHR 1329

COLLECTION 1973-1984 (BEST OF).
2LP: . . . . CCQ 050

CONFLICTING EMOTIONS.
Tracks: / Stait old line / Bullet brain and cactus head / Message to my girl / Working up an appetite / Our day / No mischief / Devil you know / I wake up every night / Conflicting emotions / Bon voyage.
LP: . . . . AMLX 64963

DIZRYTHMIA.
Tracks: / Bold as brass / My mistake / Parrot fashion love / Sugar and spice / Without a doubt / Crosswords / Charley / Nice to know / Jamboree.
LP: . . . . CHR 1145
MC: . . . . ZCHR 1145

MENTAL NOTES.
Tracks: / Late last night / Walking down a road / Titus / Lovey dovey / Sweet dreams / Stranger than fiction / Time for a change / Matinee idyll / Woman who loves you, The / Mentalnotes.
LP: . . . . CHR 1131
MC: . . . . ZCHR 1131

TIME AND TIDE.
Tracks: / Dirty creature / Giant heartbeat / Hello Sandy Allen / Never ceases to amaze me / Lost for words / Small world / Take a walk / Pioneer / Six months in a leaky boat / Haul away / Log cabin fever / Make sense of it.
LP: . . . . AMLH 64894
MC: . . . . CAM 64894

TRUE COLOURS.
Tracks: / Shark attack / I got you / Whats the matter with you / Double happy / I wouldn't dream of it / I hope I never / Nobody takes me seriously / Missing person / Poor boy / How can I resist her / Choral sea.
LP: . . . . AMHL 64822
MC: . . . . CAM 64822

WAIATA.
Tracks: / Hard act to follow / One step ahead / I don't wanna dance / Iris / Whale / Clumsy / History never repeats / Walking through the ruins / Ships / Ghost girl / Albert of India.
LP: . . . . AMLH 64848
MC: . . . . CAM 64848

Split Level

SONS OF LIBERTY.
LP: . . . . WHAR 1238
MC: . . . . WHAC 1238

Split Second

BALLISTIC STATUES.
Tracks: / Wriggle mortis / Drinking sand / Neuro beat / Close combat / Check it out / Cybernetics and Pavlovian warfare / Ballistic statues.
LP: . . . . ANT 054

FROM THE INSIDE.
LP: . . . . ANT 088LP

LAY BACK AND JOIN.
LP: . . . . AS 5025
MC: . . . . AS 5025C

MUSCLE MACHINE/COLLOSEUM CRASH (See under Colloseum crash/ Muscle machine).

SPLIT SECOND, A.
LP: . . . . WAX 050

Splodge

IN SEARCH OF THE SEVEN GOLDEN GUSSETS.
LP: . . . . RAZ 1

Splodgenessabounds

SPLODGENESSABOUNDS.
Tracks: / Malcolm opera (Course you can, Malcolm etc) / Whimsy zoom zoom / It's that sound / I fell in love with a female plumber from Harlesden, NW10 / Anarchy chaos Stanley Ogden / Blow away like a fart in a thunderstorm / Poison babies vs batman / Two little boys / Rolf / I've got lots of famous people living under the floorboard.. / Porky scratchins / Simon Templar / Desert Island Joe / What's that funny noise / Wiffy smells / Two pints (dub).
LP: . . . . SML 1121
MC: . . . . KSCM 1121

Spoilt Brats

TRACTOR OF DESIRE.
LP: . . . . BLOB 3

Spoken Word (Group)

NO MORE COCOONS.
2LP: . . . . VIRUS 59

Spongehead

POTTED MEAT SPREAD.
Tracks: / Share our hate / No picnic / Jerzy gurl / Mail it off to China / Rollin' vengince / Amerikkka / I am a vacuum / Maybe / Supersonic plane / Theoretical paradigm of chaos, The / Walking uphill / Thought for a day / Dead inside.
LP: . . . . SHIMMY 016

Spontaneous Music

BIOSYSTEM.
LP: . . . . INCUS 24

LIVE AT NOTRE DAME HALL.
LP: . . . . SFA 112

SO WHAT DO YOU THINK.
LP: . . . . TGS 118

SOURCE, THE.
LP: . . . . TNGS 107

SPONTANEOUS MUSIC ENSEMBLE.
LP: . . . . AFF 81

Spook & The Ghouls

WHITECHAPEL MURDERS, THE.
Tracks: / Reaper grim / Vampira / Love me so / Twisted kind / Werewolf in our town / Bela Lugosi's dead / Death ride / Demon barber of Fleet Street / Nightmares from beyond / Let 'em swing / Gallows are awaiting / Dead flesh creeping / Live and raw / Rocker.
LP: . . . . NERD 043

Spoons

ARIAS AND SYMPHONIES.
LP: . . . . AMLH 64920

Sport Of Kings

PARADE.
LP: . . . . **P 2002**
LP: . . . . **P 2008**

Sport & Politics

SPORT AND POLITICS (See under UNESCO reports).

Sports

DON'T THROW STONES.
Tracks: / Suspicious minds / Live work and play / Don't throw stones / Thru the window / Who listens to the radio / Tired of me / Wedding ring / Reckless / Step by step / Mailed it to your sister / You ain't home yet / Big sleep.
LP: . . . . **SRUK 6001**

Spot The Dog

SPOT THE DOG (See Hill, Eric) (Nicholas, Paul).

Spotlight On.....

SPOTLIGHT ON CREST RECORDS (Various artists).
LP: . . . . **RSRLP 1011**

SPOTLIGHT ON DANCE (Various artists).
LP: . . . . **SPOT 1032**
MC: . . . . **ZCSPT 1032**

Spotnicks

BEST OF THE SPOTNICKS.
Tracks: / Amapola / I'm coming home / Karelia / Hava nagila / Happy guitar / Moonshot / How can you leave me like that / Recado / Cape Kennedy / Green eyes / In the mood.
LP: **2459365**

BEST OF THE SPOTNICKS (2).
Tracks: / Telstar / Hava nagila / Petite fleur / Happy mandolin / Ol'e faithful / Orange blossom special / Johnny guitar / Rocket man / Spotnicks theme / Amapola / Pony express / Carelia / Moonshot / Drina / Goofus / Last space train.
LP: . . . . **CHR 1171**
MC: . . . . **ZCHR 1171**

HIGHWAY BOOGIE.
Tracks: / Highway boogie / Lost property / Could it be love? / Mighty bump / Love is a symphony / Truck driver's dream / Just another boy / Dolly H. / Let it roll roll roll / Besame mucho.
LP: . . . . **MFLP 036**

IN THE MIDDLE OF THE UNIVERSE.
Tracks: / Drop me in the middle of the universe / Time is tight / Still the one / Boat on the river / My love will never change / Space truck / Spanish eyes / Don't stop / Gina Lola breakdown / Help me make it through the night / Sign radio / No such like.
LP: . . . . **MILL 5019**
LP: **20109**
MC: **40109**
LP: . . . . **MFLP 032**

LOVE IS BLUE.
Tracks: / Happy guitar / Nikita / Love me tender / Misty / Loving you / Blue bayou / Breeze and I / Albatross / Amazing grace / Greensleeves / It's over / Entertainer, The.
MC: **510463.7**

MUSIC FOR THE MILLIONS.
Tracks: / Johnny Guitar / Spotnicks theme / Orange blossom special / Rocket man, The / Galloping guitars / Amapola / Ghost riders in the sky / Dark eyes / Joey's song / La rosita / Space party.
LP: **810 228-1**
MC: **3201761**
LP: **2482584**

OUT-A-SPACE.
LP: . . . . **PS 40036**

RARITIES.
LP: **33 8028**

ROCKING GUITAR SOUNDS.
LP: **33.8025**

SPOTNICKS RARITIES.
LP: **33.8028**

SPOTNICKS, THE.
Tracks: / Orange blossom special / Spotnicks' theme / Ghost riders in the sky / Galloping guitars / Old spinning wheel / Thundernest / She she, little Sheila / Amapola / Hava nagila / Moonshot / Rocket man / What did I say? / Hey good lookin' / Spanish gypsy dance.
LP: **831 999-1**
MC: **831 999-4**

Spotts, Roger Hamilton

ROGER HAMILTON SPOTTS' BIG BAND (Spotts, Roger Hamilton & his Big Band).
LP: . . . . **SB 5004**

Sprague, Billy

WHAT A WAY TO GO.
LP: . . . . **RRA R 0008**
MC: . . . . **RRA C 0008**

Sprague, Carl T.

COWBOY SONGS FROM TEXAS.
Tracks: / Gold mine in the sky / Boston burglar / Orphan girl, The / Utah Carol / Just break the news to mother / Chicken / When you come to the end of the day / Pal that I love, The / Ole faithful / Cowman's prayer / Sarah Jane / My Carrie Lee / Zebra Dun / Mormon cowboy, The / Cowboy's meditation / Kicking mule, The.
LP: . . . . **BF 15006**

FIRST POPULAR SINGING COWBOY,THE.
Tracks: / Home on the range / It is no secret / Following the cowtrail / Girl I loved in sunny Tennessee, The / When the work's all done this fall / Kissing / Club meeting, The / Bad companions / Rounded up in glory / Red river valley / Roll on little dogies / Last round-up, The / Last fierce charge, The / Gambler, The.
LP: . . . . **BF 15002**

Sprague, Peter

BRID RAGA (Peter Sprague, Bill Mays, Sam Most).
LP: . . . . **XAN 184**

MESSAGE SENT ON THE WIND, THE.
LP: . . . . **XAN 193**

MUSICA DEL MAR.
Tracks: / I hear a rhapsody / My folk's song / Just one of those things / You stepped out of a dream / Chick's tune / Musica del mar / I thought about you / Invention in D / Chanting with Charles.
LP: . . . . **CJ 237**

NA PALI COAST.
Tracks: / Japanese waltz / Magic Mizz Melissa / Children's song No 6 / Na pali coast / I could write a book / If I should lose you / I didn't know about you / Coltrane.
LP: . . . . **CJ 277**
LP: . . . . **SPR 1013**

Sprangeen

SPRANGEEN.
LP: . . . . **SPR 1013**
MC: . . . . **SPRC 1013**

Spread Eagle

SPREAD EAGLE.
Tracks: / Broken city / Back on the bitch / Switchblade serenade / Hot sex / Suzy suicide / Dead of winter / Scratch like a cat / Thru these eyes / Spread eagle / 42nd street / Shotgun kiss.
LP: . . . . **MCG 6092**
MC: . . . . **MCGC 6092**

Spredthick

EMPTY POCKET BLUES.
Tracks: / Nottingham poachers / Weeping willow blues / Peggy and the soldier / Trumpet hornpipe / They all laughed / Andrew Lammie / I had a dream last night / Hello Mary Lou / Cuttin' out / If only / Lovely Joan / Satisfied / Sonatina in C / Fighting the jug / Buy broom besoms / Darktown strutters' ball / William Taylor.
MC: **45-089**

MIXED BREW.
MC: **45 089**

SPREDTHICK.
LP: . . . . **ACT 3**

Spring Harvest

LIGHTS TO THE WORLD.
Tracks: / Lights to the world / God is good / In moments like these / For this purpose / You are the king of glory / I just want to praise you / We are here to praise you.
LP: . . . . **SOR P 2001**
MC: . . . . **SOR C 2001**

Spring Sampler '87

SPRING SAMPLER '87 (MCA Master Series) (Various artists).
Tracks: / Mr. Chow: *Acoustic Alchemy* / Solving a dream: *Jarvis, John* / Dreams of flight: *Meyer, Edgar*/ Stone circle: *Acoustic Alchemy* / Wunjo: *Reaves, Giles* / Southern hospitality: *Jarvis, John* / Sowelu: *Reaves, Giles* / Allegro vivace: *Meyer, Edgar*.
LP: . . . . **IMCA 5959**
MC: . . . . **IMCAC 5959**

Springer, Mark

PIANO.
LP: . . . . **JAMS 46**

SWANS AND TURTLES (Springer,Mark & Sarah Sarhandi).
LP: . . . . **VE 902**
MC: . . . . **TCVE 902**

Springfield

GREAT GUNS.
Tracks: / Sea shores of old Mexico / All the world is lonely now / I'd rather be sorry / You only want me when you're lonely / Amazing Grace / Waiting for a train / Jesus walked today / Ramblin' fever / Lady's man / El Paso / Once or twice a day / Legend in my time, A / Wedding bells.
MC: . . . . **LK 6363**

Springfield, Dusty

DUSTY SONGBOOK.
Tracks: / I close my eyes and count to ten / I start counting / Summer is over / Your hurtin' kinda love / Who gets your love / Where am I going / Son of a preacher man / Am I the same girl / What's it gonna be / Morning please don't come / Yesterday when I was young / Breakfast in bed / Magic garden / Give me time / Spooky / I will come to you / Brand new me / I'll try anything / Colour of your eyes, The / Learn to say goodbye.
LP: . . . . **CN 2107**
MC: **CN4 2107**

DUSTY - THE SILVER COLLECTION.
Tracks: / I only want to be with you / Stay awhile / I just don't know what to do with myself / Wishin' and hopin' / Losing you / Give me time / 24 hours from Tulsa / If you go away / Just one smile / Son of a preacher man / All I see is you / You don't have to say you love me / I close my eyes and count to ten / Some of your lovin' / In the middle of nowhere / Little by little / How can I be sure / Look of love, The / My colouring book / Brand new me, A / I'll try anything / Goin' back / Anyone who had a heart (CD only) / Am I the same girl (CD only).
LP: . . . . **DUSTV 1**
MC: . . . . **DUSTC 1**

DUSTY...DEFINITELY.
LP: . . . . **SBL 7864**
MC: **846 049 4**

DUSTY'S SOUNDS OF THE 70'S (double cassette).
MCSET: . . . . **DTOL 10275**

EVERYTHING'S COMING UP DUSTY.
LP: . . . . **RBL 1002**
LP: . . . . **BGOLP 74**
MC: . . . . **BGOMC 74**

FROM DUSTY WITH LOVE.
LP: . . . . **SBL 7927**

GIRL CALLED DUSTY, A.
Tracks: / Mama said / Do-re-mi / My colouring book / Twenty four hours from Tulsa / You don't own me / When the lovelight starts shining in his eyes / Mockingbird / Nothing / Anyone who had a heart / Wishin' and hopin' / Will you love me tomorrow / Don't you know.
LP: . . . . **BL 7594**
MC: **842 699 4**

GOLDEN HITS: DUSTY SPRINGFIELD.
LP: . . . . **BL 7737**

GREATEST HITS: DUSTY SPRINGFIELD.
Tracks: / All I see is you / Am I the same girl / Don't forget about me / Give me time / Goin' back / How can I be sure / I close my eyes and count to ten / I just don't know what to do with myself / I only want to be with you / I'll try anything / In the middle of nowhere / Little by little / Look of love, The / Losing you / Some of your lovin' / Son of a preacher man / Stay awhile / Wishin' and hopin' / You don't have to say you love me / Your hurtin' kind of love.
LP: **9279 305**
MC: **7259 305**
LP: . . . . **PRICE 45**
MC: . . . . **PRIMC 45**
LP: **9109629**

IN MEMPHIS PLUS.
Tracks: / Breakfast in bed / Don't forget about me / Haunted / I believe in you / I can't make it alone / I don't want to hear it anymore / I want to be a free girl / In the land of make believe / Just a little lovin' / Just one smile / No easy way down / So much love / Son of a preacher man / What do you do when love dies / Windmills of your mind.
LP: . . . . **PRICE 83**
MC: . . . . **PRIMC 83**

IT BEGINS AGAIN.
LP: **9109 607**

LIVING WITHOUT YOUR LOVE.
Tracks: / Be somebody / Closet man / Dream on / Get yourself to love / I just fall in love again / I'm coming home again / Living without your love / Save me, save me / You can do it / You've really got a hold on me.
LP: **910 961 7**

LOVE SONGS: DUSTY SPRINGFIELD.
Tracks: / You don't have to say you love me / I've been wrong before / I can't make it alone / Come back to me / Let's talk it over / This girl's in love with you / Some of your lovin' / Don't let me lose this dream / Broken blossoms / It was easier to hurt him / That's how heartaches are made / All I see is you / I just don't know what to do with myself / Who (will take my place) / So much love / I can't give back the love I feel for you / Never love again / Losing you / Look of love, The / My colouring book / I think it's gonna rain today / Just a little lovin' / How can I be sure / If you go away.
MCSET: . . . . **DTO 10255**

MEMPHIS PLUS.
Tracks: / Just a little lovin' / So much love / Breakfast in bed / Son of a preacher man / I don't want to hear it anymore / Don't forget about me / Just one smile / Windmills of your mind / In the land of make believe / No easy way down / I can't make it alone / I want to be a free girl / I believe in you / What do you do when love dies.
LP: **6381023**

REPUTATION (ALBUM).
Tracks: / Reputation / Send it to me / Arrested by you / Time waits for no one / I was born this way / In private / Daydreaming / Nothing has been proved / I want to stay here / Occupy your mind.
LP: . . . . **PCSD 111**
LP: **794 401 1**
MC: . . . . **TCPCSD 111**
MC: **794 401 4**

SON OF A PREACHER MAN.
Tracks: / Son of a preacher man / You don't own me / Mockingbird / Everyday I have to cry / When the lovelight starts shining thru his eyes / 24 hours from tulsa / Anyone who had a heart / Sunny / Don't you know / Do-re-mi / Nothing / If you go away.
LP: . . . . **SPR 8539**
MC: . . . . **SPC 8539**

VERY BEST OF DUSTY SPRINGFIELD.
LP: . . . . **NE 1139**
MC: . . . . **CE 2139**

WHERE AM I GOING.
LP: . . . . **SBL 7820**
MC: **846 050 4**

Springfield, Rick

BEAUTIFUL FEELINGS.
Tracks: / Bruce / Just one look / Solitary one, The / Spanish eyes / Everybody's cheating / Looking for the one / Cold feet / Brand new feeling / Beautiful feelings / Guenevere.
LP: **824 107 1**
MC: **824 107 4**

GREATEST HITS: RICK SPRINGFIELD.
Tracks: / Jessie's girl / I've done everything for you / Love is alright tonight / Don't talk to strangers / What kind of fool am I / Affair of the heart / Human touch / Love somebody / Bop 'till you drop / Celebrate youth / State of the heart / Rock of life.
LP: . . . . **PL 90394**
MC: . . . . **PK 90394**

HARD TO HOLD (Film Soundtrack).
Tracks: / Love somebody / Don't walk away / Bop 'till you drop / Taxi dancings / S.F.O. / Stand up / When the lights go down / Great lost art of conversation, The / Go swimming.
LP: . . . . **BL 84935**
MC: . . . . **BK 84935**

JESSIE'S GIRL.
LP: . . . . **UNKNOWN**
MC: . . . . **UNKNOWN**

LIVING IN OZ.
Tracks: / Human Touch / Alyson / Affair of the heart / Living in Oz / Me and Johnny / Motel eyes / Tiger by the tail / Souls / I can't stop hurting you / Like Father like son / I can't stop hurting you.
LP: . . . . **PL 84660**
MC: . . . . **PK 84660**
LP: . . . . **NL 90309**
MC: . . . . **NK 90309**
LP: . . . . **RCALP 6076**

ROCK OF LIFE.
Tracks: / Language of love / Rock of life / Honeymoon in Beirut / World start turning / One reason (to believe) / Soul to soul / Tear it all down / Woman / Dream in colour / Hold on to your dream / If you think you're groovy.
LP: . . . . **PL 86220**
MC: . . . . **PK 86220**

SUCCESS HASN'T SPOILED ME YET.
Tracks: / Calling all girls / I get excited / What kind of fool am I / Kristina / Tonight / Black is black / Don't talk to strangers / How do you talk to girls / Still crazy for you / American girl, The / Just one kiss / April 24,1981.

LP: . . . . RCALP 6033
MC: . . . . RCAK 6033
LP: . . . . NL 84767

TAO.
Tracks: / Dance this world away / Celebrate youth / State of the heart / Written in rock / Power of love, The / Tao of heaven, The / Walking on the edge / Stranger in the house / My fathers chair / Walk like a man.
LP: . . . . PL 85370
MC: . . . . PK 85370

WORKING CLASS DOG.
Tracks: / Everybody's girl / Daddy's pearl / Red hot and blue love / Inside Silvia / Love is alright tonight / Jessie's girl / Hole in my heart / Carry me away / I've done everything for you / Light of love.
LP: . . . . NL 84766
MC: . . . . NK 84766
LP: . . . . RCALP 6014

Springs, Helena

NEW LOVE.
Tracks: / I need the night / Midnight lady / I want you / Love satisfaction / Laugh in my face / A.D. / Paper money / New love / Black stockings (Live) / Be soft with me tonight / Other side of the world.
LP: 208119
MC: 408119

Springsteen, Bruce

BORN IN THE U.S.A..
Tracks: / Cover Me / Born in the U.S.A. / Darlington country / Working on the highway / Downbound train / I'm on fire / No surrender / Bobby Jean / I'm goin' down / Glory days / Dancing in the dark / My hometown.
LP: . . . . CBS 86304
MC: 40 86304

BORN TO RUN.
Tracks: / Johnny 99 / Spirit in the night (In box set) / Because the night (In box set) / Tenth Avenue freeze-out / Thunder road / Born to run / Night Back streets / She's the one / Meeting across the river / Jungleland.
LPS: . . . . BRUCE B2
LP: . . . . CBS 69170
MC: 40 69170

BOXED SET OF FOUR 12" SINGLES.
LPS: . . . . BRUCE 1

BRUCE SPRINGSTEEN.
LPS: . . . . CBS 66353

DARKNESS ON THE EDGE OF TOWN.
Tracks: / Badlands / Adam raised a Cain / Something in the night / Candy's room / Racing in the street / Promised land / Factory / Streets of fire / Prove it all / Darkness on the edge of town.
LP: . . . . CBS 32542
MC: 40 32542
LP: . . . . CBS 86061

GREETINGS FROM ASBURY PARK,N.J..
Tracks: / Blinded by the light / Growing up / Mary Queen of Arkansas / Does this bus stop at 82nd Street? / Lost in the flood / Angel for you / Spirit in the night / Its hard to be a saint in the city.
LP: . . . . CBS 32210
MC: 40 32210

LIVE 1975-1985.
Tracks: / Thunder road / Adam raised a Cain / Spirit in the night / 4th of July / Asbury park (Sandy) / Paradise by the 'c' / Fire / Growing up / It's hard to be a saint in the city / Backstreets / Rosalita / Raise your hand / Hungry heart / Two hearts / Cadillac ranch / You can look (but you'd better not touch) / Independence day / Badlands / Because the night / Candy's room / Darkness on the edge of town / Racing in the street / This land is your land / Nebraska / Johnny 99 / Reason to believe / Born in the U.S.A. / Seeds / River, The / War / Darlington country / Working on the highway / Promised land / Cover me / I'm on fire / Bobby Jean / My home town / Born to run / No surrender / Tenth Avenue freeze-out / Jersey girl.
MC: 4502274
LP: 4502271

MUSIC AND MEDIA INTERVIEW PICTURE DISC.
LPPD: . . . . BS 1012

NEBRASKA.
Tracks: / Nebraska / Atlantic City / Mansion on the hill / Johnny / Highway patrolman / State trooper / Used cars / Open all night / My fathers house / Reason to believe.
LP: . . . . CBS 25100
MC: 40 25100
LP: 4633601
MC: 4633604

RIVER, THE.
Tracks: / Ties that bind, The / Sherry darling / Jackson Cage / Two hearts / Independence day / Hungry Heart / Out in the street / Crush on you / You can look (but you'd better not touch) / I wanna marry you / River, The / Point blank / Cadillac Ranch / I'm a rocker / Fade away / Stolen car / Ramrod / Price you pay, The / Wreck on the highway.
2LP: . . . . CBS 88510
MCSET: 40 88510

SONGS FROM THE BOSS (See under Songs From..) (Various artists).

TUNNEL OF LOVE.
Tracks: / Ain't got you / Tougher than the rest / All that heaven will allow / Spare parts / Cautious man / Walk like a man / Tunnel of love / Two faces / Brilliant disguise / One step up / When you're alone / Valentine's day.
LP: 4602701
MC: 4602704
LPPD: 4602700

WILD, THE INNOCENT AND THE E.STREET SHUFFLE, THE.
Tracks: / E. Street shuffle, The / 4th of July / Asbury Park (Sandy) / Kitty's back / Wild Billy's circus / Incident on 57th Street / Rosalita / New York City serenade.
LP: . . . . CBS 32363
MC: 40 32363

Springtime In The ...

SPRINGTIME IN THE ROCKIES/ SWEET ROSIE O'GRADY (Original Soundtracks) (Various artists).
LP: . . . . SH 2090

Sproule, Daithi

IRONMAN, THE (See under Peoples, Tommy) (Sproule, Daithi with Tommy Peoples).

Sprouse, Blaine

BLAINE SPROUSE.
LP: . . . . ROUNDER 0117

BRILLIANCY.
Tracks: / Don't let your deal go down / Florida rag / Fireball express / Miss the Mississippi / Brilliancy / Did you ever see the devil, Uncle Joe / Cherokee Maggie / Mist on the moor, The / Tennessee hayride / Paula's waltz / Old Ebenezer.
LP: . . . . ROUNDER 0209
MC: . . . . ROUNDER 0209C

INDIAN SPRINGS (Sprouse, Blaine & Kenny Baker).
Tracks: / Oh demi slippers / Molly darlin' / Owensboro / Avalon / September waltz / Three days in Dublin / Coker creek / K and W waltz / Cottontown breakdown / Indian springs.
LP: . . . . ROUNDER 0259
MC: . . . . ROUNDER 0259C

SUMMERTIME.
LP: . . . . ROUNDER 0155
MC: . . . . ROUNDER 0155C

Sprout Head Uprising

EARLY SPRING.
LP: . . . . MICKL 02

SONS OF ARQA.
MC: . . . . BIP 403

Spruill, Wild Jimmy

HARD GRINDIN' BLUESMAN, THE.
LP: . . . . KK 7429

Spud

SMOKING ON THE BOG.
Tracks: / Tickle your fancy / Anna Livia / Nothing's gonna stop us tonight / Farmer's cursed wife, The / Scarlett / Nine points of roguery, The / Full-scale love / Gusty frolics / Waves rise and fall / For shame of doing wrong / Fool for you again.
LP: . . . . SNTF 742

Spur, Silver

COME TO ME (See under Newton, Juice) (Spur,Silver & Juice Newton).

Spy Eye

HOT PURSUITS.
LP: . . . . PHZA 076

Spy V. Spy

XENOPHOBIA (WHY).
LP: 2553491
MC: 2553494

Spy Who Came Of Age

SPY WHO CAME OF AGE (Book Two of The Secret Pilgrim) (Le Carre, John).
MCSET: . . . . LFP 7523

Spy Who Loved Me

SPY WHO LOVED ME (Film soundtrack) (Various artists).
Tracks: / Nobody does it better: *Simon, Carly* / Bond '77: *Various artists* / Ride to Atlantis: *Various artists*/ Mojave club: *Various artists* / Nobody does it better: *Various artists* / Anya: *Various artists* / Tanker, The: *Various artists* / Pyramids, The: *Various artists* / Eastern lights: *Various artists* / Conclusion: *Various artists* / Spy who loved me, The (end titles): *Various artists.*
LP: . . . . UAG 30098
MC: . . . . TCK 30098
LP: 5C 062 99370

Spy With The

SPY WITH THE PLATINUM HEART, THE (Original Soundtrack) (Various artists).
Tracks: / Opening titles-masquerade: *Various artists* / Fly by night: *Various artists* / Chinatown: *Various* artists / Passion's killer: *Various artists* / Body in the bay: *Various artists* / Wheelspin: *Various* artists / Adams takes a trip: *Various artists* / S.P.Y.D.A.'s web: *Various artists* / Night with Nuki, A: *Various artists* / Frisco disco: *Various artists* / Tuxedo tussle: *Various artists* / Operation 'H': *Various artists* / End title: *Various artists.*
LP: . . . . DN 2001

Spyri, Johanna

HEIDI (Bloom, Claire (nar)).
MC: 1292

HEIDI (Dench, Judi).
MCSET: . . . . SAY 11

HEIDI.
MC: . . . . TS 325

Spyro Gyra

ACCESS ALL AREAS.
2LP: . . . . MCSP 310

ALTERNATIVE CURRENT.
Tracks: / Shakedown / Taking the plunge / PG / I believe in you / Binky's dream no. 6 / Sunflurry / Heartbeat / Mardi gras / Alternating currents.
LP: . . . . MCF 3288

BREAKOUT.
Tracks: / Bob goes to the store / Freefall / Doubletake / Breakout / Body wave / Whirlwind / Swept away / Guiltless.
LP: . . . . MCF 3334
MC: . . . . MCFC 3334

CARNAVAL.
Tracks: / Cafe amore / Dizzy / Awakening / Cashaca / Foxtrot / Sweet 'n' savvy / Bittersweet / Carnaval.
LP: . . . . MCL 1711
MC: . . . . MCLC 1711
LP: . . . . MCF 3087

CATCHING THE SUN.
Tracks: / Catching the sun / Cockatoo / Autumn of our love / Laser material / Percolator / Philly / Lovin' you (interlude) lovin' you / Here again / Safari.
LP: . . . . MCL 1763
MC: . . . . MCLC 1763
LP: . . . . MCG 4009

CITY KIDS.
Tracks: / City kids / Serpent in Paradise / Ballad, A / Nightlife / Islands in the sky / Conversations / Silver lining / Haverstraw road.
LP: . . . . MCF 3178
MC: . . . . MCFC 3178

COLLECTION.
Tracks: / You can count on me / What exit / Nu sungo / Unknown soldier, The / Morning dance / Old San Juan / Shakedown / Mallet ballet / Catching the sun / Para ti latino / Incognito / Harbour nights / Limelight / Breakout.
LP: . . . . GR 9642
MC: . . . . GRC 9642

FAST FORWARD.
Tracks: / Bright lights / Para ti latino / Alexandra / Ocean parkway / Speak easy / Futurephobia / 4MD / Shadow play / Escape hatch / Tower of Babel.
LP: . . . . GR 9608
MC: . . . . GRC 9608

FREETIME.
Tracks: / Freetime / Telluride / Summer strut / Elegy for 'Trane / Pacific sunrise / Amber dream / String soup.
LP: . . . . MCF 3119

INCOGNITO.
LP: . . . . MCF 3151

MORNING DANCE.
Tracks: / Morning dance / Jubilee / Rasul / Song for Lorraine / Starburst / It does'nt matter / Little Linda / End of Romanticism / Heliopolis.
LP: . . . . MCL 1788
MC: . . . . MCLC 1788
LP: . . . . INS 2003

MORNING DANCE/CATCHING THE SUN.
Tracks: / Catching the sun / Cockatoo / Autumn of our love / Laser material / Percolator / Philly / Loving you / Here again / Safari / Morning dance / Jubilee / Rasul / Song for Lorraine / Starburst / Heliopolis / It doesn't matter / Little Linda / End of romanticism.
MCSET: . . . . MCA 2 100

POINT OF VIEW.
LP: . . . . MCA 6309
MC: . . . . MCAC 6309

SPYRO GYRA.
Tracks: / Shaker song / Opus O'opus / Mallet ballet / Pygmy funk / Cascade / Leticia / Mead / Paula / Paw prints / Galadriel / Cafe Amore / Dizzy / Awakening / Cashaca / Foxtrot / Sweet and savvy / Bittersweet / Carnival.
LP: . . . . MCL 1626
MC: . . . . MCLC 1626
LP: . . . . FA 3047
LP: . . . . INS 2008

SPYRO GYRA/ CARNAVAL.
Tracks: / Shaker song / Opus d'opus / Mallet ballet / Pygmy funk / Cascade / Leticia / Mead / Paula/paw prints / Galadriel / Cafe amore / Dizzy / Awakening / Cashaca / Foxtrot / Sweet and savvy / Bittersweet / Carnaval.
MCSET: . . . . MCA 2110

STORIES WITHOUT WORDS.
Tracks: / Cayo Hueso / Serpentine shelly / Del corazon / Early light / Nu sungo / Chrysalis / Joy ride / Pyramid.
LP: . . . . MCF 3390
MC: . . . . MCFC 3390

Squadronaires

BIG BAND SPECTACULAR (RAF Squadronaires Band).
Tracks: / There's something in the air / Lover / Splanky / John Brown's other body / Stardust / Doin' Basies' thing / Autumn leaves / Sweet Georgia Brown / Glenn Miller Medley, The / In the mood / Little brown jug / String of pearls / Moonlight serenade / St. Louis blues march / Song of India / All the things you are / Captiva sound / That warm feeling / South Rampart Street parade / Switch in time / Pennsylvania 6 5000 / Scott's place / Basie straight ahead / Bedtime for drums / Sounds familiar.
MC: . . . . ZC BND 1037
LP: . . . . BND 1037

FLYING HOME.
Tracks: / Rhapsody for reeds / Boogie woogie bugle boy / No love no nothing / My blue Heaven / This is always / Sally water / I may be wrong but I think you're wonderful / Blues in the night / One-zy two-zy / Shoo shoo baby / Pennsylvania polka / Doctor, lawyer, Indian chief / Concerto for drums / Five minutes more / Drummin' man / Flying home / There's something in the air.
LP: . . . . RFL 19

Squandered Message

LIFE.
LP: . . . . EFA 5146

Square Crows

SQUARE CROWS.
LP: . . . . DIN 330

Squealer

HUMAN TRACES.
LP: 601755

Squeeze

ARGY BARGY.
Tracks: / Pulling mussels (from the shell) / Another nail in my heart / Separate beds / Misadventure / I think I'm go-go / Farfisa beat / Here comes that feeling / Vicky verky / If I didn't love you / Wrong side of the moon / There at the top.
LP: . . . . AMLH 64802
MC: . . . . CAM 64802

BABYLON AND ON.
Tracks: / Hourglass / Footprints / Tough love / Prisoner, The / 853 5937 / In today's room / Trust me to open my mouth / Striking matches / Cigarette of a single man / Who are you? / Waiting game, The / Some Americans / Splitting into three / Wedding bells.
LP: . . . . AMA 5161
MC: . . . . AMC 5161

COOL FOR CATS.
Tracks: / Slap and tickle / Revue / Touching me touching you / It's not cricket / Its so dirty / Hop skip and jump / Up the junction / Hard to find / Slightly drunk / Goodbye girl / Cool for cats / Up the junction (live).
LP: . . . . AMLH 68503
MC: . . . . CAM 68503

COSI FAN TUTTI FRUTTI.
Tracks: / Big beng / By your side / I won't ever go drinking again / Hits of the year / Heartbreaking world / No place like home / Last time forever / I learnt how to pray / King George Street.
LP: . . . . AMA 5085
MC: . . . . AMC 5085

EAST SIDE STORY.
Tracks: / In quintessence / Someone else's heart / Tempted / Piccadilly / There's no tomorrow / Woman's world, A / Is that Love / F-hole / Labelled with love / Someone else's bell / Mumbo Jumbo / Vanity fair / Messed around.
LP: . . . . AMLH 64854
MC: . . . . CAM 64854

FRANK.
Tracks: / Frank / If it's love / Peyton place / Rose I said / Slaughtered, gutted and heartbroken / (This could be) the last time / She doesn't have to shave / Love circles / Melody motel / Can of worms / Doctor Jazz / It's too late.
LP: . . . . AMA 5278
MC: . . . . AMC 5278

PLAY.
MC: . . . . WX 428C
LP: . . . . WX 428

ROUND AND A BOUT, A.
Tracks: / Footprints / Pulling mussels (from the shell) / Black coffee in bed / She doesn't have to shave / Is that love / Doctor Jazz / Up the junction / Slaughtered / Gutted and heartbroken / Is it too late? / Cool for cats / Take me I'm yours / If it's love / Hourglass / Labelled with love / Annie get your gun / Boogie woogie country girl / Tempted.
LP: . . . . DFCLP 1
MC: . . . . DFCC 1

SINGLES 45 AND UNDER / BABYLON AND ON.
Tracks: / Take me I'm yours / Up the junction / Another nail in my heart / Hourglass / Prisoner, The / Trust me to open my mouth / Cigarette of a single man / Some Americans / Goodbye girl / Slap and tickle / Pulling mussels / Footprints / Splitting into three / Striking matches / Who are you?.
MC: . . . . AMC 24111

SINGLES 45'S AND UNDER.
Tracks: / Take me I'm yours / Goodbye girl / Cool for cats / Up the Junction / Slap and tickle / Another nail in my heart / Pulling mussels (from the shell) / Is that love / Tempted / Labelled with love / Black coffee in bed / Annie get your gun.
LP: . . . . AMLH 68552
MC: . . . . CAM 68552

SQUEEZE.
Tracks: / Sex master / Bang bang / Strong in reason / Wild sewerage tickles Brazil / Out of control / Take me I'm yours / Call, The / Model / Remember what / First thing wrong / Hesitation / Get smart.
LP: . . . . AMID 122
MC: . . . . CMID 122

SQUEEZE: INTERVIEW PICTURE DISC.
LPPD: . . . . BAK 2074

SWEETS FROM A STRANGER.
Tracks: / Out of touch / I can't hold on / Point of view / Stranger than the stranger on the shore / Onto the dance floor / When the hangover strikes / Black coffee in bed / I've returned / Tongue like a knife / His house, her home / Very first dance, The / Elephant ride, The.
LP: . . . . AMLH 64899
MC: . . . . CAM 64899

Squier, Billy

DON'T SAY NO.
Tracks: / In the dark / Stroke / My kinda lover / You know what I like / Too daze gone / Lonely is the night / Whadda you want from me / Nobody knows / I need you / Don't say no.
LP: . . . . EST 12146

ENOUGH IS ENOUGH.
Tracks: / Shot of love / Love is the hero / Lady with a tenor sax / All we have to give / Come home / Break the silence / Powerhouse / Lonely one, The / Till its over / Wink of an eye.
LP: . . . . EST 2024
MC: . . . . TCEST 2024

HOTTEST NIGHT OF THE YEAR, THE.
Tracks: / Everybody wants you / Emotions in motion / Learn how to live / In your eyes / Keep me satisfied / It keeps you rocking / One good woman / She's a runner / Catch 22 / Listen to the heartbeat.
LP: . . . . EST 12217
MC: . . . . TC EST 12217
LP: . . . . EST 12225

SIGNS OF LIFE.
Tracks: / All night long / Rock me tonite / Eye on you / Take a look behind ya / Reach for the sky / 1984, (Another) / Fall for love / Can't get next to you / Hand me downs / Sweet release.
LP: . . . . EJ 2401921

TALE OF THE TAPE.
Tracks: / Big beat, The / Calley oh / Rich kid / Like I'm lovin' you / Who knows what a love can do / You should be high love / Who's your boyfriend / Music's all right / Young girls.
LP: . . . . EST 12062

Squire

GET SMART.
LP: . . . . LO 2

HITS FROM 3,000 YEARS AGO (See under Meynell, Anthony) (Meynell, Anthony & Squire).

SINGLES ALBUM: SQUIRE.
LP: . . . . LO 3

Squire, Chris

FISH OUT OF WATER.
Tracks: / Hold out your hand / You by my side / Silently falling / Lucky seven / Safe (canon song).
LP: . . . . K 50203

Squires

GOING ALL THE WAY WITH THE SQUIRES.
LP: . . . . LP 008

Squires, Audrey

AUDREY SQUIRES IN CONCERT.
Tracks: / Answer me / I write the songs / One day at a time / Sometimes when we touch / I can see clearly now / So deep is the night / You needed me / Your good girl gonna go bad / Love is all / It's a miracle / Just the way you are / Can't smile without you.
LP: . . . . KMLP 303
MC: . . . . ZCMLP 303

Squires, Dorothy

EMI YEARS, THE.
Tracks: / Gypsy, The / I'll close my eyes / It's a pity to say goodnight / Danger ahead / Tree in the meadow, A / Mother's day / Reflections on the water / Yes, I'll be there / Roses of Picardy / Say it with flowers / Blue snowfall / Whoever / How deep is the ocean? / Are you? / Moonlight and roses / Bless your heart my darling / Once upon a time / Look around / Someone other than me / Call of spring, The.
MC: . . . . TCEMS 1420

SAY IT WITH FLOWERS.
Tracks: / Mothers day / So tired / Roses of Picardy / I'd give the world (to you sweetheart) / Say it with flowers / Our love story / Say goodnight but not goodbye / On the sunny side of the street / Do I worry / Halfway to Ireland (you're halfway to heaven) / Yes I'll be here / Once in a while / Baby come home / Life's desire / My resistance is low / I'll never know why / Bewitched (from 'Pal Joey".) / Secret that's never been told, A / Little white cloud that cried, The / Maid of the valley / Faith / Be anything / To be worthy of you / Mistakes / Unforgettable / At the end of the day / Any time / I don't care / Tree in the meadow, A / Gypsy, The / I'll close my eyes.
2LP: . . . . DL 1158
MC: . . . . TCDL 1158
2LP: 411 158 1
MC: 411 158 4

THREE BEAUTIFUL WORDS OF LOVE.
MC: . . . . MCFRC 521
LP: . . . . CFRC 521

WE CLOWNS.
LP: . . . . ES 001

WITH ALL MY HEART.
Tracks: / Look around / Tammy tell me true / Point of no return / Where can I go? / Your flowers arrived too late / Seasons of / Summer place / For once in my life / I wish you love / Say it with flowers / We'll gather lilacs / Honeysuckle rose / Tulips from Amsterdam / Red the rose.
2LP: . . . . DPA 3073/4

Squires, Rosemary

MY ONE AND ONLY.
Tracks: / If I had you / What a little moonlight can do / Street of dreams / Get out of town / Lullaby of the leaves / All you want to do is dance / Crazy he calls me / Smoky eyes / All too soon / Winter wonderland / Day in, day out / I poured my heart into a song / I'm in love for the very first time / Carioca / Have you met Miss Jones / Tess's torch song / I lost my sugar in Salt Lake City / Junior and Julie / My one and only / Mr. Snow.
LP: C5-543
MC: C5K-543

Squirrel Bait

SKAG HEAVEN.
Tracks: / Kid dynamite / Virgil's return / Black light poster child / Choose your poison / Short straw wins / Short straw wins / Too close to the fire / Slake train coming / Rose Island Road / Tape to California.
LP: . . . . HMS 072

SQUIRREL BAIT.
LP: . . . . HMS 028

Squirrel of Wirral

SQUIRREL OF WIRRAL (Unknown narrator(s)).
MC: . . . . STC 305

SRC

REVENGE OF THE QUACKENBUSH BROTHERS.
Tracks: / Daystar / Midnight fever / Across the land of light / I remember your face / Marionette / By way of you / Exile / New crusader / Black sheep / Never before now.
LP: . . . . KIRI 054

Sreaming Trees

WORLD CRASH.
LP: . . . . NTVLP 065

Sridhar, K.

SHRINGAR (Sridhar, K. & K Shivakumar).
Tracks: / Raga bageshri / Raga bageshri (continued) / Raga bageshri (live).
LP: . . . . RWLP 7
MC: . . . . RWMC 7

St. Austell Band

ST AUSTELL SALUTES GOFF RICHARDS.
Tracks: / Stage centre / Sweet nightingale / Flying fingers / Aeronauts, The / Trailblaze / Folks who live on the hill, The / Jaguar / May dance / Songs of the quay.
LP: . . . . PRL 012
MC: . . . . CPRL 012

St. Brendan's Voyage

ST. BRENDAN'S VOYAGE (Various artists).
Tracks: / St. Brendans voyage: *Various artists* / Legend of the cross, The: *Various artists.*
MC: . . . . ANV 625

St. Christopher

BACHARACH.
Tracks: / Prayer for the sea, A / And I wonder / She can wait forever / Love of a sister, The / Thrill of the year, The / Almost December / Who's next on cupid's hit list / Gabriel.
LP: . . . . SARAH 403

St. Clair, Carl

GREETINGS TO YOU VOL.2.
LP: . . . . TUR 005

IT MUST BE YOU (LP).
LP: . . . . KAL 009

St. Clair, Isla (nar)

CHANT VILLAGE STORIES (see under Chant Village Stories (bk)).

ISLA.
Tracks: / Mary's boy child / Green is the holly / Little drummer boy / First Noel, The / Nativity / Isn't it a goodly thing / Christmas song, The / Silent night / Ding dong merrily on high / Winter wonderland / Child in a manger / Mid-winter song.
LP: . . . . SKL 5317

SINGS TRADITIONAL SCOTTISH SONGS.
LP: . . . . TGS 112
MC: . . . . TGSMC 112

SONG AND THE STORY, THE.
Tracks: / Sovay / Adieu ye streams / Smuggler's song, A / Shooting Goshcen's cock ups / Plooman laddie, The / Three score and ten / Machiner's song, The / Fisherman's wife, The / Trimdon Grange explosion, The / Bold English navvy, The / Blackleg miner / Weaver and the factory maid, The / Gallant frigate Amphitite, The / Yellow handkerchief, The / Curragh of Kildare, The / Goodbye to the thirty foot trailer / Copshawholme fair.
LP: . . . . ISLA 1

St. Clair, Mick

MEET THE SAINT.
LP: . . . . SSRLP 5112
MC: . . . . SC 5112

St. Claire, Bette

AT BASIN STREET EAST.
LP: . . . . FS 222

St. Clement Danes

MUSIC FROM ST. CLEMENT DANES (St. Clement Danes Choir, organ, bells and chimes).
Tracks: / Psalm 23 (the Lord is my shepherd) / How shall I fitly meet Thee? / O magnum mysterium / Stille nacht / I saw three ships / When to the temple Mary went / Adoramus te / Ye now are sorrowful / This joyful Eastertide / Coelos ascendit hodie / Let the bright seraphim / Greater love / Oranges and lemons / Toccata in B minor (Gigout).
MC: . . . . CSDL 356

St. Columba's

CHRISTMAS MUSIC FROM ST. COLUMBA'S CHURCH, SUTTON COLDFIELD (St. Columba's, Sutton Coldfield).
Tracks: / On Christmas night / O little town of Bethlehem / Sans Day carol / Mary's lullaby / Der tag der ist so freudenreich / Joys seven / Once in Royal David's city (end s1) / Maiden most gentle, A / Cherry tree carol, The / Little donkey / Little road to Bethlehem, The / Silent night / In dulci jubilo / Ding dong merrily on high / O come all ye faithful.
LP: . . . . APS 360
MC: . . . . CAPS 360

St. Cyr, Johnny

PAUL BARBARIN AND JAZZBAND ON SOUTHLAND (St. Cyr, Johnny & Hot Five).
LP: . . . . GHB 112

St. Davids Cathedral

ST. DAVID'S CATHEDRAL CHOIR.
LP: . . . . APR 301

St. Edmund, Roundhay

CHORAL MUSIC FROM YORKSHIRE (St. Edmund, Roundhay/David Pickering).
Tracks: / Let the bright Seraphim (From "Samson") / Let their celestial concerts (From "Samson") / Benedictus (From Missa Brevis "Sancti Joannis de Deo") / Trout, The / Pie Jesu (From the Requiem Mass) / Litany to Mary / Magnificat (From Service in G (end s1)) / Zadok the priest / Lord, let me know mine end / Madonna and child / He shall feed His flock (From The Messiah) / I saw the Lord.
LP: . . . . APS 359

St. Elmo's Fire

ST. ELMO'S FIRE (Film soundtrack) (Various artists).
Tracks: / St Elmo's fire (man in motion): *Parr, John* / Shake down: *Squier, Billy* / Young and innocent: *Elefante*/ This time it was really right: *Anderson, Jon* / Saved my life: *Waybill, Fee* / Love theme: *Foster, David*/ Georgetown: *Foster, David* / If I turn you away: *Moss, Vikki* / Stressed out (Close to the edge): *Airplay.*
LP: 781 261-1
MC: 781 261-4

St. George's Canzona

MUSIC OF THE ROUNDHEADS AND CAVALIERS.
Tracks: / Prince Rupert's march / Goddesses/Parson's farewell/ Nonesuch / Hey then, up we go / Daphne / When the King enjoys his own again / Fancy / North-country maid, The / Sad pavan for these distracted times, A / Vive le Roy / Rupert's retreat / Verse for double organ / King's last farewell, The / Coffin for King Charles and a pit for the people, A / Royal lament for the King's come home in peace (End of Cavalier music, start of Roundhead music.) / Bannockburn air / Gather your rosebuds / Kemp's jig (Medley) / French tuckato / Woodycock / Whitelocke's coranto / Daphne / Batali / Great boobee, The / Digger's song, The / Rufty Tufty Medley (Consists of: Rufty Tufty/Newcastle/ Once I loved a maiden/Argeers) / Scots march / Can she excuse my wrongs? / Coranto and sarabande / Bransle of war / Voluntary for double organ / Owl, The.
2LP: . . . . ACD 253

TAPESTRY OF MUSIC FOR ROBIN HOOD AND HIS KING, A.
Tracks: / English estampie, The / Robin and Marion / Fanfare / Je nuns hons pris / Tristan's lament / Two voiced estampie / Alla fontanella / Quant je plus / Redit aetas aurea / Maid in the Moon, The / Ah, Robin / Sally's fancy/The maiden's blush / Bonnie, sweet Robin / Now Robin / Robin Hood and the tanner / Parson's farewell, The/Goddesses / Nutting girl, The / Stingo / Shepherds hey / My Robin / Greenwood/Dargason.
LP: . . . . ACM 2017

St. George's Chapel

20 CHRISTMAS CAROLS.
Tracks: / Once in Royal David's city / Hark the herald angels sing / God rest ye merry, gentlemen / Holly and the ivy, The / Gabriel's message / It came upon a midnight clear / People look East / There is no rose of such virtue (Joubert) / Away in a manger / Stable in Bethlehem, A (P. Taylor) / First nowell, The / O come, all ye faithful / On Christmas night (The Sussex carol) / Silent night / Jesus Christ the apple tree / In the bleak mid winter / While shepherds watched their flocks / Ding dong merrily on high / In dulci jubilo / O little town of Bethlehem.
MC: . . . . MVPC 827
LP: . . . . MVP 827

St. Hellier

TERRA FIRMA.
LP: . . . . GILP 888

St. James, Phyllis

AIN'T NO TURNING BACK.
Tracks: / Candlelight afternoon / Ain't no turnin' back / Ruler of the hunt / Phonemate / This time / If you believe / Livin' on the border / Sweet rhythm / Back in the race.
LP: . . . . **ZL 72298**

St. Joan

ST. JOAN (Film Soundtrack) (Various artists).
LP: . . . . **LCT 6134**

St. John Smith Square

ON HEARING THE FIRST CUCKOO IN SPRING (and 9 other great classical melodies) (St. John Smith Square Orchestra).
Tracks: / On hearing the first cuckoo in Spring / Fantasia on Greensleeves / Morning (Grieg) / Pavane (Ravel) / Rosamunde ballet music (Schubert).
MC: . . . . **ZC QS 6007**

St. Johns...

HOSANNA (St. John the Divine Cathedral Choir).
LP: . . . . **GR 1002**

St. John's Cambridge

CHRISTMAS AT ST. JOHNS (St. John's College Cambridge Choir).
LP: . . . . **ZRG 782**

CHRISTMAS CAROLS (St. John's College Cambridge Choir).
Tracks: / God rest ye merry gentlemen / Ding dong merrily on high / O little town of Bethlehem / Unto us a boy is born / Good King Wenceslas / Holly and the ivy, The / I sing of a maiden / Two Welsh carols / Silent night / Hark the herald angels sing / Jesus Christ the apple tree / In the bleak mid winter / O come all ye faithful / Shepherd's pipe carol / On Christmas night / Away in a manger / There is no rose / Balulalow.
LP: . . . . **ABRD 1201**
MC: . . . . **ABTD 1201**

WORLD OF ST. JOHN'S (St. John's College Cambridge Choir).
LP: . . . . **SPA 300**

WORLD OF XMAS VOL 2 (St. John's College Cambridge Choir).
Tracks: / Ceremony of carols, A / Torches / Adam lay y-bounden / There is no rose / My dancing day / Up good Christian folk / Rockin' / Balulalow / Seven joys of Mary, The / Cherry tree carol, The / Ding dong merrily on high / Adeste fideles.
LP: . . . . **SPA 164**
MC: . . . . **KCSP 164**

St. John's Portsmouth

ST. JOHNS RC CATHEDRAL PORTSMOUTH BOYS CHOIR (St. John's RC Cathedral Portsmouth Boys Choir).
LP: . . . . **LPB 767**

St. John's Smith Sq.

BABAR THE LITTLE ELEPHANT (see under Rippon, Angela) (St. John's Smith Sq. Orchestra/Angela Rippon/David Parkhouse).

SYMPHONY NO.3/NO.4 (MENDELSSOHN) (see under Mendelssohn (composer)) (St. John's Smith Sq. Orchestra).

SYMPHONY NO.4/SERENADE FOR STRINGS (see under Tchaikovsky) (St. John's Smith Sq. Orchestra/Royal Liverpool Philh'm. Orch).

VIRTUOSO VIOLIN (See under Hasson, Maurice) (St. John's Smith Sq. Orchestra/Maurice Hasson/Ian Brown).

St. Joseph's...

BEAUTY OF MAORI SONG (St. Joseph's Maori Girls Choir).
Tracks: / Te wero / Taku ripene pai / He wawata / Rona / Ho pono koia / Te upoko / Kalahi ti.
LP: . . . . **SLC 122**
MC: . . . . **TC SLC 122**

HYMNS AND SONGS FOR CHILDREN VOL.1 (St. Joseph's School Choir, Colwyn Bay.).
Tracks: / Morning has broken / All creatures of our God and King / Dare to be a Daniel / Go tell it on the mountain / Lord of the Dance / Jesus loves me / Put your hand in the hand / Immortal, invisible, God only wise / Holy, holy, holy / Kumbaya / I think when I read / Seek ye first / Oh Jesus, I have promised / God make my life a little light.
LP: . . . . **WRD R 3020**
MC: . . . . **WRD C 3020**

HYMNS AND SONGS FOR CHILDREN VOL.2 (St. Joseph's School Choir, Colwyn Bay.).
LP: . . . . **WRD R 3021**
MC: . . . . **WRD C 3021**

St. Lewis, Cliff

VINTAGE POINT VOL.1 (St. Lewis, Cliff & Rhythm Ryders).
LP: . . . . **UNKNOWN**

St. Louis...

RHYTHM & BLUES SHOWTIME WITH... (St. Louis King Of Rhythm).
2LP: . . . . **SJP 231/232**

ST LOUIS TOWN 1929-33.
LP: . . . . **L 1003**

St. Louis Ragtimers

SHOWBOAT ERA.
LP: . . . . **AP 122**

ST. LOUIS RAGTIMERS, VOL. 1, THE.
LP: . . . . **AP 75**

ST. LOUIS RAGTIMERS, VOL. 2, THE.
LP: . . . . **AP 81**

ST. LOUIS RAGTIMERS, VOL. 4, THE.
LP: . . . . **AP 116**

St. Louis Symphony...

BERNSTEIN (St. Louis Symphony Orchestra).
Tracks: / Candide (overture) / Fancy free / Facsimile / On the town (Three dance episodes).
MC: . . . . **EL 7639054**

GERSHWIN IN THE MOVIES 1/2 (St. Louis Symphony Orchestra).
2LP: . . . . **A 249/250**
MCSET: . . . . **C 249/250**

GERSHWIN IN THE MOVIES VOL.1 (1931-1945) (St. Louis Symphony Orchestra).
Tracks: / Embraceable you / They all laughed / Love is here to stay / Strike up the band / Fascinating rhythm / But not for me / Rhapsody in blue / Man I love, The / Seconde rhapsodie.
LP: . . . . **A 249**
MC: . . . . **C 249**

GERSHWIN IN THE MOVIES VOL.2 (1951-1959) (St. Louis Symphony Orchestra).
Tracks: / I'll build a stairway to paradise / Somebody loves me / American in Paris, An / Someone to watch over me / 'S wonderful / Introduction / Porgy sings / Fugue / Ouragan / Bonjour free.
LP: . . . . **A 250**
MC: . . . . **C 250**

St. Louise's...

ST. LOUISE'S COLLEGE CHOIR, BELFAST (St. Louise's College Choir, Belfast).
Tracks: / Though the mountains may fall / Greatest thing, The / All good gifts / Son of David / One bread, one body / Sing my soul / Bridges / Turn to me / To you Yahueeh I lift up my soul / O the word of my lord / Peace / Celebration song.
LP: . . . . **HRL 212**
MC: . . . . **CHRL 212**

St. Magnus...

CHOIR AND ORGAN OF ST. MAGNUS CATHEDRAL (St. Magnus Cathedral Choir).
Tracks: / O sing a new song to the Lord / Ave verum corpus / Sleepers wake for the nights in flying / Blessing and honour / Declare his honour / O come let us sing to the Lord / In the bleak mid winter / O give thanks unto the Lord / Carillon / Jerusalem.
LP: . . . . **LILP 5033**

ST. MAGNUS CATHEDRAL CHOIR, KIRKWALL, ORKNEY (St. Magnus Cathedral Choir).
Tracks: / O send thy light forth and thy truth (Psalm 43 vv 3-5: tune - Martyrs) / Te Deum laudamus (in B flat) / Christ hath a garden / From the rising of the sun / Drop, drop slow tears / View me, Lord, as a work of Thine / Lift up your heads, o ye gates / Benedictus / Jubilate Deo (in B flat) / Psalm prelude (set 2 no 3) (Howells) (end s1) / Nobilis, humilis (13th century hymn to St. Magnus) / Ave Maria, hail blessed flower / Variations on mein junges leben hat ein end / Exsultate justi / All creatures of our God and King / O Thou, the Central Orb / Gabriel's message / Psallite unigenito / Old hundredth.
LP: . . . . **APS 364**

St. Martin...

SERENADE (See under Reilly, Tommy) (St. Martin-in-the-Field/Tommy Reilly).

St. Mary....

AVE MARIE (St. Mary & St. Anne's Choir, Abbots Bromley).
LP: . . . . **APS 315**
MC: . . . . **CAPS 315**

POPULAR CHRISTMAS CAROLS (St. Mary's Choir, Warwick).
Tracks: / While shepherds watched their flocks by night / Away in a manger / First noel, The / Silent night / God rest ye merry gentlemen / O little town of Bethlehem / O come all ye faithful / Once in royal David's city / Holly and the ivy, The / As with gladness men of old / Good King Wenceslas / Ding dong merrily on high / Little drummer boy / Rockin' / In the bleak mid winter / Hark the herald angels sing.
LP: . . . . **XMS 666**
MC: . . . . **XMSC 666**

St. Michael-le-Belfry

BEHOLD THE MAN (St. Michael-Le-Belfry (York) Choir).
LP: . . . . **MSR 004**
MC: . . . . **MSC 004**

MY SPIRIT WILL COME (St. Michael-Le-Belfry (York) Choir).
Tracks: / This man Jesus / Create in us / My spirit will come / Do what is good / Breathe on me / Holy Lord / Hosanna / Siya hamba / Seeing You daily with wonders and signs / I will build / In your name / Jesus, You're with me / Keep movin' on / Shalom.
LP: . . . . **WST R 9686**
MC: . . . . **WST C 9686**

St. Michaels College

CHOIR OF ST. MICHAELS, THE.
LP: . . . . **APR 303**

TORCHES (Favourite Christmas carols).
LP: **CFP4 14473 1**
MC: **CFP4 14473 4**

St. Paradise

ST. PARADISE.
Tracks: / Straight to you / Gamblin' man / Jackie / Miami slide / Hades / Live it up / Jesse James / Tighten the knot / Beside the sea.
LP: . . . . **K 56689**

St. Paul's...

CAROLLING AT CHRISTMAS (St. Paul's Cathedral Choir).
MC: . . . . **AMP 022**

CHRISTMAS MUSIC FROM ST PAULS CATHEDRAL (St. Paul's Cathedral School Choir).
Tracks: / Bidding bell / Come, Thou Redeemer of the earth / Gabriel's message / Truth from above, The / Noble stem of Jess, The / Organ chorale: Es ist ein Ros'entsprungen / People look east / Cherry tree carol, The / Maiden most gentle, A / Lo He comes with clouds descending / Cathedral bells / O come all ye faithful / Up good Christian folk / In the bleak mid winter / Once in Royal David's city / Ding dong merrily on high / Sans day carol / In dulci jubilo / Hark the herald angels sing.
LP: . . . . **PRDS 2521**
MC: . . . . **PRCS 2521**
LP: **8833157**

PRAISE TO THE LORD (St. Paul's Cathedral Choir).
MC: . . . . **KH 88036**

REJOICE (St. Paul's Boy's Choir).
LP: . . . . **NE 1064**

St. Philips Choir

SING FOREVER.
LP: . . . . **REB 692**
MC: . . . . **ZCF 692**

St. Preux

CONCERTO FOR ONE VOICE.
Tracks: / Concerto pour une voix / Andante pour piano / Divertissement / Sonate vendeene / Harmonies / Prelude pour piano / Adagio pour trompette / Variations / Allegro / Impromptu.
LP: **114891**

St. Prix, Dede

MI SE SA.
Tracks: / Mi Se Sa / Katchopine / Ponssey / Haiti / Roule / Demele / Ton Krab-La / Thalemon.
LP: . . . . **ILPS 9875**
MC: . . . . **ICT 9875**

St. Richard's....

BIBLE, THE (The amazing book0 (St. Richard's with St. Andrew's Junior School Choir).
MC: . . . . **SP C 1145**

SING TO GOD VOL.1 (St. Richard's with St. Andrew's Junior School Choir).
LP: . . . . **SAC 5093**
MC: . . . . **WC 5093**

SING TO GOD VOL.2 (St. Richard's with St. Andrew's Junior School Choir).
LP: . . . . **SAC 5097**

St. Stithians Band

PAVILION BRASS.
MC: . . . . **SENC 1083**

St. Stithians Male...

SING WITH SHANKEY (St. Stithians Male Voice Choir).
MC: . . . . **SENC 505**

St. Tropez

BELLE DE JOUR.
Tracks: / Fill my love with your love / One more minute / Hold on to love / Think I'm gonna fall in love with you / Belle de jour / Most of all / When you are gone / Je t'aime / Violation / On a rien a perdre / La symphonie Africaine / Coeur a coeur.
LP: . . . . **CDL 1242**

St. Val, Tanya

TAMBOO.
LP: . . . . **HDD 2436**

St. Vitus

HALLOWS VICTIM.
LP: . . . . **SST 052**

LIVE.
LP: **086873**

MOURNFUL CRIES.
LP: . . . . **SST 161**
MC: . . . . **SSTC 161**

ST. VITUS.
LP: . . . . **SST 022**

V.
Tracks: / Living backwards / When emotion dies / Ice monkey / Angry man / I bleed black / Patra / Jack Frost / Mind food.
LP: **086 806**

St. Vitus Dance

HELLO MRS MERCURY, IS FREDDIE COMING OUT?.
LP: . . . . **UNKNOWN**

LOVE ME LOVE MY DOGMA.
Tracks: / Silence / Have no fear / Contemptible / Horse sense / Perish the thought / Napoleons noise / Inequality street / Meet Mohammed / Dancing class / Fish on a Friday.
LP: . . . . **PROBE 10**

St. Winifred's...

20 ALL TIME CHILDRENS FAVOURITES (St. Winifred's School Choir).
Tracks: / Nick nack paddy wack / Nellie the elephant / Poppa piccolino / My brudda Sylveste / Little white bull / Yellow submarine / Little Sir Echo / Scarlet ribbons / Grandfather's clock / Do-re-mi / Three little fishes / Simon says / Half way down the stairs / Postman Pat / You're a pink toothbrush / Swinging on a star / Sparrow, The / Ugly duckling, The / Sing a rainbow / Over the rainbow.
LP: . . . . **MFP 41 5732 1**
MC: . . . . **MFP 41 5732 4**
MC: . . . . **TCMFP 5732**

AND THE CHILDREN SING (St. Winifred's School Choir).
Tracks: / Top of the world / And all the world sang / Bread and fishes / Matchstalk men and matchstalk cats and dogs / Bright eyes / Evensong / Everyday / Colour of my world / Pinocchio / Mull of Kintyre / I saw the grass / Any dream will do.
LP: . . . . **MFP 50470**
MC: . . . . **TCMFP 50470**

CHILDRENS' PARTY TIME (St. Winifred's School Choir).
Tracks: / If you're happy and you know it / Farmer's in his den, The / Oranges and lemons / Here we go round the mulberry bush / Old MacDonald had a farm / London Bridge / Dancing queen / Brown girl in the ring / Yellow submarine / Rivers of Babylon / Waterloo / Simon says / Matchstalk men and matchstalk cats and dogs / Bright eyes / When you wish upon a star.
MC: . . . . **HR 8112**
MC: . . . . **HR 4181124**

CHRISTMAS FOR EVERYONE (St. Winifred's School Choir).
Tracks: / When a child is born / Away in a manger / Calypso carol / Once in royal David's city / Little donkey / White Christmas / Christmas for everyone / Mary's boy child / We three kings of Orient are / O little town of Bethlehem / Silent night / Little drummer boy / In a lowly stable / Have yourself a merry little christmas.
LP: . . . . **MFP 5591**
MC: . . . . **TCMFP 5591**

GRANDAD (See under Dunn, Clive).

IT'S A SMALL WORLD (St. Winifred's School Choir).
Tracks: / It's a small world / Chim chim cheree / Little April showers / Never smile at a crocodile / Zip-a-dee-doo-dah / Who's afraid of the big bad wolf / Bibbidi bobbidi boo / Heigh ho / Whistle while you work / Candle on the water / He's a tramp / Let's go fly a kite / Ugly bug ball, The / Give a little whistle / When you wish upon a star.
LP: . . . . **MFP 415633 1**
MC: . . . . **TCMFP 415633 4**

MY VERY OWN PARTY RECORD (St. Winifred's School Choir).
Tracks: / Who's afraid of the big bad wolf / Nellie the elephant / Runaway train / Teddy bear's picnic / Hooray hooray it's a holi holiday / Brown girl in the ring / Dancing queen / If you're happy and you know it / Paloma blanca / Yellow submarine / Rivers of Babylon / Simon says / Waterloo / Continental soldiers / Grand old Duke of York, The / One finger one thumb / Wind my bobbin / Head and shoulders, knees and toes / Farmer's in his den / In a cottage / Oranges and lemons / Here we go round the mulberry bush / Old McDonald / London Bridge.
LP: . . . . MFP 50505
MC: . . . . TCMFP 50505

Stabbins, Ashley

FIRE WITHOUT BRICKS (Stabbins, Ashley, Duo).
LP: . . . . BEAD 4

Staber, Dick

LISTEN TO MY SONG.
LP: . . . . FR 149

PICKIN' AROUND THE COOKSTOVE (WITH FRIENDS).
LP: . . . . ROUNDER 0040

Stabilizers

TYRANNY.
Tracks: / I don't need the pain / Now I hear you / One simple thing / Underground / Does your love lie open / You pull me down / Tyranny / Place to hide, A / (If I) found Rome.
LP: . . . . CBS 26854
MC: 40 26854

Staccato

STACCATO (TV soundtrack) (Bernstein, Elmer).
LP: . . . . TER 1021

Stack-A-Records

STACK-A-RECORDS Various artists (Various artists).
LP: . . . . LP 8308

STACK-A-RECORDS Various artists (Various artists).
LP: . . . . NERD 007

Stackridge

STACKRIDGE.
LP: . . . . BGOLP 65

Stacy, Clive

ROCKIN' AROUND.
LP: . . . . BLK 7707

Stacy, Jess

BLUE NOTION.
LP: . . . . JCE 90

JESS STACY AND FRIENDS.
LP: 6.24298

JESS STACY ON THE AIR.
Tracks: / Someone to watch over me / Lady be good / Cherry / Rosetta / Honeysuckle rose / Keepin' out of mischief now / Three little words / Jumpin' with Jess / DA blues / After you've gone / Sweet Lorraine / I wish I could shimmy like my sister Kate / China boy / You're driving me crazy.
LP: . . . . AIRCHECK 26

PIANO JAZZ 1935-39.
Tracks: / In the dark / Flashes / Barrelhouse / World is waiting to the sunrise, The / Sugar / Down to steamboat Tennesse / Sell out, The / Ramblin' / Complainin' / Ain't goin' nowhere.
MC: . . . . NEO 849

PIANO SOLOS (1935-56).
LP: . . . . S 1248

STACY 'N' SUTTON (Stacy, Jess/Ralph Sutton).
Tracks: / Fascinating rhythm / You took advantage of / Indiana / Oh baby / Stars fell on Alabama / If I could be with you / I want to be happy / I can't get started / Jeepers creepers / I'll dance at your wedding / Fussin' / Eye opener, The / T'aint nobody's business if I do / Sneakaway / I got rhythm.
LP: . . . . AFS 1020

TWO GOOD MEN (See Wilson, Teddy) (Stacy, Jess & Teddy Wilson).

WITH LEE WILEY, SPECS POWELL & SOLOS - 1938 & 1944.
Tracks: / Ramblin' / Candlelights / Complainin' / Ain't goin' nowhere / She's funny that way / You're driving me crazy / Sell out, The / Ec-stacy / Down to Steamboat Tennessee / Sugar / After you've gone / Blues fives u.a..
LP: AG6 24298

Staddlecombe

STADDLECOMBE (see Winchester, Kay) (Thomson, Hilary).

Stadium Dogs

WHAT'S NEXT.
LP: . . . . MAG 5025
MC: . . . . ZCMAG 5025

Stafford, Jo

BROADWAY REVISITED (Romantic ballads from the theatre).
Tracks: / My romance / Something to remember you by / They say it's wonderful / I'm always chasing rainbows / Make the man love me / Dancing in the dark / September song / Spring is here / If I were a bell / Mountain high, valley low / I'm your girl / Night and day.
LP: . . . . COR 118

CAPITOL YEARS, THE: JO STAFFORD.
Tracks: / Best things in life are free, The / Long ago and far away / On the sunny side of the street / Boy next door, The / I'll be with you in appleblossom time / Ragtime cowboy Joe / There's no you / Diamonds are a girls best friend / (Play a) simple melody / Let's take the long way home / Stanley Steamer / You belong to me / Shrimp boats / Georgia on my mind / Jambalaya / Come rain or come shine / Day by day / Gentleman is a dope, The / I'll be seeing you / Trolley song, The.
LP: . . . . EMS 1371
LP: 795 756 1
MC: . . . . TCEMS 1371
MC: 795 756 4

DOWN MEMORY LANE (Stafford, Jo & Gordon MacRae).
Tracks: / Wunderbar / Where are you going to be / When the moon shines / Tea for two / Need you / Thought in my heart, A / Monday, Tuesday, Wednesday / Dearie / Neapolitan nights / Bibbidi bobbidi boo / 'A' you're adorable / I'll string along with you / To think you've chosen me / Say something sweet to your sweetheart / My darling, my darling / Girls were made to take care of boys / Down the lane.
MC: . . . . CMOIR 402

G.I. JO (Jo Stafford sings songs of World War II).
Tracks: / I'll walk alone / I left my heart at the stage door canteen / No love / Do nothing / We mustn't say goodbye / You'll never know / I'll remember April / It could happen to you / I don't want to walk without you / I fall in love too easily / I'll be seeing you.
LP: . . . . COR 105

GREATEST HITS: JO STAFFORD.
MC: 4XL 9399

HITS OF JO STAFFORD, THE.
Tracks: / You belong to me / Shrimp boats / Yesterdays / Make love to me / Georgia on my mind / Jambalaya / Come rain or come shine / No other love / Day by day / Gentleman is a dope, The / I'll be seeing you / Trolley song, The.
LP: . . . . MFP 41 5668-1
MC: . . . . MFP 41 5668-4

INTRODUCING JO STAFFORD.
Tracks: / Begin the beguine / Congratulations / Why can't you behave? / Scarlet ribbons / Too marvellous for words / Over the rainbow / Just reminiscing / Walkin' my baby back home / I remember you / Happy times / Baby, won't you please come home / Smoke dreams / Roses of Picardy / If I ever love again / Sometime / Always true to you in my fashion.
LP: . . . . EMS 1273
MC: . . . . TCEMS 1273

JO PLUS BLUES (The best of the blues).
Tracks: / Blues is an old old story, The / John Henry / Sometimes I feel like a motherless child / Nobody knows the trouble I've seen / Blues is a tale of trouble, The / Kansas City blues / Memphis blues / Blues is a travelling thing, The / He's gone away / Every night when the sun goes in / Seems like when it comes in the morning / Times change / Lover man / Blues in the night.
LP: . . . . COR 114

JO PLUS BROADWAY (A swinging album of Broadway hits).
Tracks: / Love for sale / Happiness is a thing called Joe / How high the moon / Speak low / It never entered my mind / Taking a chance on love / Anything goes / Gentleman is a dope, The / I got it bad and that ain't good / Old devil moon / Any place I hang my hat is home / Tomorrow mountain.
LP: . . . . COR 112

JO PLUS JAZZ.
Tracks: / Just squeeze me / For you / Midnight sun / You'd be so nice to come home to / Folks who live on the hill, The / I didn't know about you / What can I say, after I say I'm sorry? / Dream of you / Imagination / S'posin' / Daydream / I've got the world on a string.
LP: . . . . COR 108

JO STAFFORD: BY REQUEST (Fan favourites through the years).
Tracks: / As I love you / Early Autumn / September in the rain / I cover the waterfront / Don't worry 'bout me / Blue skies / Young and foolish / Easy come, easy go / Sleepy time down south / Dancing on the ceiling / If / King of Paris, The.
LP: . . . . COR 119

JO STAFFORD: INTERNATIONAL HITS (Continental requests and US hits).
Tracks: / Little man with a candy cigar / Come rain or come shine / Allentown Jail / Long ago and far away / September song / Around the corner / Stardust / Keep it a secret / Symphony / On London Bridge / No other love / Teach me tonight.
LP: . . . . COR 115

JO STAFFORD SINGS AMERICAN FOLK SONGS (The famous Capitol album).
Tracks: / Shenandoah / Black is the colour / Old Joe Clark / Poor wayfaring stranger / Barbara Allen / Single girl / Red Rosey Bush / I wonder as I wander / Cripple Creek / Nightingale, The / Johnny has gone for a soldier / Sourwood Mountain.
LP: . . . . COR 110

JO STAFFORD'S GREATEST HITS (Stafford's best on Columbia).
Tracks: / You belong to me / Yesterdays / Jambalaya / I should care / Gentleman is a dope, The / Make love to me / Embraceable you / Shrimp boats / All the things you are / St. Louis blues.
LP: . . . . COR 106
MC: . . . . COR 106C

MUSIC OF MY LIFE (America's most versatile singing star).
Tracks: / Night we called it a day, The / Georgia on my mind / Day by day / Candy / If it takes me all my life / One I love, The / I'll never smile again / Tennessee waltz / On the Alamo / Sunday kind of love, A / All the things you are / Whatcha know, Joe?.
MC: . . . . COR 123C
LP: . . . . COR 123

OLD RUGGED CROSS (Stafford, Jo & Gordon MacRae).
Tracks: / Whispering hope / Abide with me / In the garden / Beyond the sunset / Beautiful Isle of somewhere / It is no secret / I found a friend / Old rugged cross, The / Rock of ages / Star of hope / Now the day is over / Perfect day.
LP: . . . . MFP 5798
MC: . . . . TCMFP 5798

SKI TRAILS (Winter favourites for the fireside).
Tracks: / Baby, it's cold outside / Moonlight in Vermont / Let it snow, let it snow, let it snow / By the fireside / Winter weather / It happened in Sun Valley / I've got my love to keep me warm / Nearness of you, The / Winter wonderland / June in January / Whiffenpoof song, The / Sleigh ride.
LP: . . . . COR 113

SONGS OF FAITH, HOPE AND LOVE (Whispering hope and the best of religious songs.
Tracks: / Whispering hope / It is no secret / Beautiful Isle of somewhere / I found a friend / Suddenly there's a valley / Lord's my shepherd, The / Beautiful garden of prayer, The / He bought my soul at Calvary / Each step of the way / Star of hope / Lord, keep Your hand on me / Peace in the valley.
LP: . . . . COR 111

STARRING JO STAFFORD.
Tracks: / Serenade of the bells / On the Alamo / No other love / Red river valley / Ivy / Fools rush in / Sunday kind of love, A / Gentleman is a dope, The / Symphony / Tumbling tumbleweeds / You keep coming back like a song / Day by day.
LP: . . . . ED 2604291
MC: . . . . ED 2604294

STARS OF THE 50'S.
LP: 5C 050 81048

YOU'LL NEVER WALK ALONE (Stafford, Jo & Gordon MacRae).
MC: 4XL 9536
LP: . . . . WRD R 3024

Stafford, Joe

SINGS SONGS OF SCOTLAND.
LP: 203.678
MC: 403.678

THANK YOU FOR CALLING.
LP: 204.060
MC: 404.060

Stafford, Johnny

TWENTY HARMONICA GREATS.
LP: . . . . MFP 41 5660-1
MC: . . . . MFP 41 5660-4

Stafford, Terry

SUSPICION.
Tracks: / Suspicion / Margarita / Playing with fire / Invitation to a kiss / Slowly but surely / For you my love / Follow the rainbow / Are you a fool like me / Judy / She wishes I were you / Pocket full of rainbows / Everything I need / I'll touch a star / Everybody loves somebody / Til love comes to you / Kiss me quick.
LP: . . . . CH 213
LP: . . . . CLP 1001

Staffordshire Regiment

MUSIC BY THE BAND OF....
Tracks: / Rule Britannia / Grandioso / Pop looks Bach / Luftwaffe march / Rock 'n' roll march / Holiday in spain / Tambourin / Regimental quick march / Romaika / Medley.
LP: . . . . MM 0573
MC: . . . . MMC 0573

Stage

SHOW CLASSICS (Various artists).
2LP: . . . . STAR 2010
MCSET: . . . . STAC 2010

Stage Dolls

STAGE DOLLS.
Tracks: / Still in love / Wings of steel / Lorraine / Waitin' for you / Love cries / Mystery / Don't stop believin' / Hanoi waters / Ammunition.
LP: 841 259 1
MC: 841 259 4

Stage Door Canteen

STAGE DOOR CANTEEN/ HOLLYWOOD CANTEEN (Film soundtrack) (Various artists).
2LP: . . . . CC 100-11/12

Stages In Life

STAGES IN LIFE (Various artists).
LP: . . . . ATLP 001

Stained Glass

OPEN ROAD.
Tracks: / Wild and free / Winter traveller / Just a day / Black Jack David / Kiss the day goodbye / City song / Poll miles / Jolly beggar, The / Lord Franklin / White House blues.
LP: . . . . SFA 019

Staines, Bill

REDBIRD'S WING.
LP: . . . . PH 1118
MC: . . . . PH 1118C

RODEO ROSE.
LP: . . . . PH 1079

WILD WILD HEART.
LP: . . . . PH 1100
MC: . . . . PH 1100C

Stainsby, Trevor

RHYTHM OF RETURN, THE.
LP: . . . . HWYL 003

Stairway

AQUAMARINE.
MC: . . . . C 143

MOONSTONE.
MC: . . . . C 168

Stairway To The Stars

STAIRWAY TO THE STARS (Original London Cast) (Various artists).
Tracks: / That's dancing: *Various artists* / Who's sorry now: *Various artists* / You stepped out of a dream: *Various* artists / Fine romance, A: *Various artists* / Three little words: *Various artists* / Bye bye baby: *Various* artists / Chattanooga choo choo: *Various artists* / Rose's turn: *Various artists* / Finale, hooray for Hollywood: *Various artists* / Ma belle Marguerite: *Various artists* / S'wonderful: *Various artists* / Not even nominated: *Various artists* / Life upon the wicked stage: *Various artists* / Buttons and bows: *Various artists* / I got a girl in Kalamazoo: *Various artists* / Lucky numbers: *Various artists* / Bosom buddies: *Various artists*.
LP: . . . . CAST 21
MC: . . . . CASTC 21

Stalag 17

STALAG NO. 17 SUPERVISION EXCURSION (Various artists).
LP: . . . . Unknown

WE WILL BE FREE (See under Asylum) (Stalag 17/ Asylum/ Toxic Waste).

YOU ARE NOT ALONE(EP) (see under Hex) (Hex/ Oi Polloi/ Stalag 17/ Symbol Of Freedom).

Stalker, John

STALKER.
MCSET: . . . . LFP 7352

Stamey, Chris

IN THE WINTER OF LOVE (LP).
LP: . . . . PA 8022

IT'S ALRIGHT.

LP: SP 65180

Stamm, Marvin

STAMMPEDE.
MC: PAC 8022

Stampede

HURRICANE TOWN.
Tracks: / I've been told / Love letters / Casino junkie / Other side / Turning in circles / Hurricane town / Girl / Runner / Mexico.
LP: POLS 1083

OFFICIAL BOOTLEG.
Tracks: / Missing you / Moving on / Days of wine and roses / Hurrican town / Shadows of the night / Baby driver / Runner / There and back.
LP: ROCK 1

Stampfel, Peter

PETER STAMPFEL & THE BOTTLECAPS (Stampfel, Peter & The Bottlecaps).
LP: ROUNDER 9003
MC: ROUNDER 9003C
LP: REU 1016

PETER STAMPFEL & THE BOTTLECAPS (Stampfel, Peter & The Bottlecaps).
Tracks: / Drink American / Surfer angel / Random violence / Lonely junkie / Screaming industrial breakdown / Everything must go / Oh what a night for love / Impossible groove / Funny the fist time / Trials / Troubles / Tribulations / Paraphernalia / Press on.
LP: REU 1016

Stampfel & Weber

GOING NOWHERE FAST.
LP: ROUNDER 3051

Stampley, Joe

20 GREATEST HITS: JOE STAMPLEY.
LP: 20096
MC: 40096

GOOD OL' BOYS - ALIVE AND WELL, THE (See under Bandy, Moe) (Stampley, Joe and Moe Bandy).

GREATEST HITS: JOE STAMPLEY.
Tracks: / Roll on big mama / Billy, get me a woman / Whiskey talkin' / What a night / Sheik of Chicago / Dear woman / There she goes again / Everyday I have to cry some / Hey baby / Take me back.
LP: EPC 83487

HEY JOE, HEY MOE (See under Bandy, Moe) (Bandy, Moe & Joe Stampley).

JOE STAMPLEY.
MC: ZCGAS 709

JUST GOOD OL' BOYS (See under Bandy, Moe) (Bandy, Moe & Joe Stampley).

LIVE FROM BAD BOB'S (See under Bandy, Moe) (Stampley, Joe/Moe Bandy).

WHERE'S THE DRESS? (see Bandy, Moe) (Stampley, Joe and Moe Bandy).

Stana La Vita

STANA LA VITA/DOMANI ACCADRA (See under Domani accadra) (Various artists).

Stanbrook Abbey

CHRISTMAS CHANT (see under Prinknash Abbey) (Stanbrook Abbey Nuns/Prinknash Abbey Monks).

O GIVE THANKS TO THE LORD (see under Prinknash Abbey) (Stanbrook Abbey Nuns/Prinknash Abbey Monks).

WELLSPRINGS (Stanbrook Abbey Nuns).
LP: SDL 363
MC: CSDL 363

Stand

DAPHNE WILL BE BORN AGAIN.
LP: ST 7534

Stand By Me

STAND BY ME (Film Soundtrack) (Various artists).
Tracks: / Everyday: *Holly, Buddy* / Let the good times roll: *Shirley & Lee* / Come go with me: *Del-Vikings/* Whispering bells: *Del-Vikings* / Get a job: *Silhouettes* / Lollipop: *Chordettes* / Yakety yak: *Coasters/* Great balls of fire: *Lewis, Jerry Lee* / Mr. Lee: *Bobbettes* / Stand by me: *King, Ben E.*.
LP: WX 92
MC: WX 92 C

Stand & Deliver

STAND AND DELIVER (Film Soundtrack) (Various artists).
LP: 704.590
MC: C 704.590

Stand In For Love

STAND IN FOR LOVE (Various artists).
Tracks: / It's starting to get to me now: *Thomas, Irma* / Underneath my make up: *Thrills* / No, no, I can't help you: *McKay, Beverley* / I'm through trying to prove my love for you: *Womack, Bobby* / I found a new love: *Holiday, Jimmy* / Let's live: *Neville, Aaron* / Get out of my life: *Little Anthony/Imperials/101 Strings* / Quiet place, A: *Mimms, Garnet/Enchanters* / I can't wait until I see my baby's face: *Washington/King* / Missin' my baby: *King, Clydie* / Anyone who knows what love is (will understand): *Thomas, Irma* / That's how much I love you: *Houston, Eddie* / Everyday: *Neville, Aaron* / Workin' on a groovy thing: *Drew, Patti.*
LP: KENT 056

Standing Stones

STANDING STONES (Various artists).
LP: NAGE 5
MC: NAGEC 5

Stanley Brothers

16 GREATEST HITS: STANLEY BROTHERS.
LP: SLP 3003
MC: GT 53003
LP: SD 3003

20 BLUEGRASS ORIGINALS.
LP: SLP 5026
MC: GT 55026

83 COLLECTORS EDITION VOL 1.
LP: GT 0103

83 COLLECTORS EDITION VOL 2.
LP: GT 0104

83 COLLECTORS EDITION VOL 3.
LP: GT 0105

83 COLLECTORS EDITION VOL 4.
LP: GT 0106

83 COLLECTORS EDITION VOL 5.
LP: GT 0107

83 COLLECTORS EDITION VOL 6.
LP: GT 0108

BANJO IN THE HILLS.
LP: KLP 872
MC: GT 5872

BEST OF THE STANLEY BROTHERS.
LP: SLP 953
MC: GT 5953

COUNTRY PICKIN' AND SINGIN'.
LP: HAT 3125

FOLK CONCERT.
LP: KLP 834
MC: GT 5834

FOLK SONG FESTIVAL.
LP: SLP 791
MC: GT 5791

LITTLE OLD COUNTRY CHURCH HOUSE, THE.
Tracks: / That old country church / Nobody answered me / Shake my mother's hand for me / I heard my mother call my name in prayer / Mother's only sleeping / Shake hands with mother again / Hide in the blood / Give me your hand / Where we'll never grow old / Leaning on the everlasting arms / Angel band / Farther along.
LP: CO 738

LONG JOURNEY HOME.
Tracks: / Long journey home / Will you miss me / I'll be true to the one I love / No letter in the mail today / Pretty Polly / Wildwood flower / Two more years and I'll be free / Ramshackle shack on the hill / East Virginia blues / Pig in the pen / Your saddle is empty old pal / Nine pound hammer / Cluck old hen / Wild and reckless hobo / Rabbit in a log / Mountain pickin'.
LP: CO 739

ON THE RADIO, VOLUME 1.
Tracks: / Roll in sweet baby's arms / Few more seasons, A / Love me darlin' just tonight / Black mountain blues / My Lord's gonna set me free / How mountain girls can love / Mississippi sawyer / Orange blossom special / Daniel prayed / Shenandoah waltz / How far to Little Rock / Mother's footsteps guide me on / Pig in a pen / Cripple creek.
LP: CO 780
MC: CO 780MC

ON THE RADIO, VOLUME 2.
Tracks: / Uncle Pen / Little glass of wine / Midnight ramble / Heaven / Don't go out tonight / Fire on the mountain / Mother no longer waits at home / He will set your fields on fire / Big Tilda / If we never meet again / Whoa mule.
LP: CO 781
MC: CO 781MC

ON WCYB FARM AND FUNTIME.
LP: REB 855

RECORDED LIVE VOL. 2.
LP: REB 1495

SONGS THEY LIKE THE BEST.
LP: KLP 772
MC: GT 5772

STANLEY BROTHERS.
Tracks: / Long journey home / Will you miss me / I'll be true to the one that I love / No letter in the mail today / Pretty Polly / Wildwood flower / Two more years and I'll be free / East Virginia blues / Pig in a pen / Your saddle is empty old pal / Nine pound hammer / Cluck old hen / Wild and reckless hobo / Rabbit in a cog / Mountain pickin'.
LP: SAVE 040

STANLEY BROTHERS OF WEST VIRGINIA (Volume 4).
Tracks: / Hold to God's unchanging hand / When I lay my burdens down / In Heaven we'll never grow old / Somebody touched me / Lord I'm coming home / Give me the roses while I live / Swing low sweet chariot / Paul and Silas / Gathering flowers for the masters bouquet / Old country church / Will you miss me.
LP: CO 754
MC: CO 754 MC

STANLEY BROTHERS (REBEL).
LP: REB 1487
MC: REBMC 1487

STANLEY BROTHERS SING BLUEGRASS FOR YOU.
LP: OHCS 323

STANLEY BROTHERS & THE CLINCH MOUNTAIN BOYS (Stanley Brothers & The Clinch Mountain Boys).
LP: KLP 615
MC: GT 5615

STANLEY BROTHERS VOL.1, THE (Columbia Sessions 1949-50).
Tracks: / Vision of mother / White dove / Gathering flowers for the master's bouquet / Angels are singing in heaven tonight, The / It's never too late / Have you someone (in heaven waiting).
LP: SS 09

STANLEY BROTHERS VOL.2, THE.
Tracks: / Old home, The / Drunkard's hell, The / Fields have turned brown, The / Hey hey hey / Lonesome river, The / I'm a man of constant sorrow / Pretty Polly / Life of sorrow, A / Sweetest love, The / Wandering boy, The / Let's part.
LP: SS 10

THAT LITTLE OLD COUNTRY.
LP: SAVE 027

TOGETHER FOR THE LAST TIME.
LP: REB 1512

UNCLOUDY DAY (Volume 3).
LP: CO 753
MC: CO 753 MC

Stanley, Chris

INCREDIBLE.
LP: MS 003

Stanley, Chuck

FINER THINGS IN LIFE,THE.
Tracks: / Day by day / Love toy / Never gonna let you go / Burning up / Make you mine tonight / Jammin' to the bells / All and all / Real soon / When it all falls down.
LP: 4504831
MC: 4504834

Stanley, Finton

FINTON STANLEY ON TOUR.
Tracks: / Happy hours polka / Pigalle / St. Patricks day medley / Quando, quando, quando / Don't you forget it / Irish reels / Freight train / West's awake / I love Paris / High level reel / Somewhere my love / Black and white rag / Scottish selection.
LP: 811 869-1
MC: 811 869-4

FINTON STANLEY ON TOUR VOL.2.
Tracks: / She taught me how to yodel / Greensleeves / French waltz / My Lagan love / Scottish island breeze / Medley / Irish reels / Derry air / Hungarian dance no. 5 / In the mood / Retour des hirondelles / Viva Espana / Reels / Souveneir musette / Tico tico / Brazil.
LP: 811 870-1
MC: Unknown

Stanley & Iris

STANLEY AND IRIS (Film Soundtrack) (Various artists).
Tracks: / Stanley and Iris: *Various artists* / Bicycle, The: *Various artists* / Finding a family: *Various artists* / Putting it all together: *Various artists* / Letters: *Various artists* / Reading lessons: *Various artists* / Factory work: *Various artists* / Stanley at work: *Various artists* / Stanley and Iris end credits: *Various artists* / Stanley's invention: *Various artists.*
LP: VS 5255
MC: VSC 5255

Stanley, Michael

HEARTLAND (Stanley, Michael Band).
Tracks: / I'll never need anyone more / Lover / Don't stop the music / He can't love you / Working again / All I ever wanted / Say goodbye / Hearts on fire / Voodoo / Carolyn / Save a little piece for me.
LP: AML 3015

Stanley, Paul

PAUL STANLEY SOLO ALBUM.
LP: 6399085

Stanley, Ralph

CHILD OF A KING.
LP: REB 1616
MC: REBMC 1616

CLINCH MOUNTAIN GOSPEL.
LP: REB 1571
MC: REBMC 1571

CRY FROM THE CROSS.
LP: REB 1499
MC: REBMC 1499

DOWN WHERE THE RIVER BENDS.
LP: REB 1579
MC: REBMC 1579

HILLS OF HOME.
LP: KLP 1069
MC: GT 51069

I CAN TELL YOU THE TIME.
LP: REB 1637
MC: REBMC 1637

I WANT TO PREACH GOSPEL.
LP: REB 1522
MC: REBMC 1522

I WEAR A WHITE ROSE.
LP: REB 1590
MC: REBMC 1590

I'LL ANSWER THE CALL.
LP: REB 1657
MC: REBMC 1657

LET ME REST ON A PEACEFUL MOUNTAIN.
LP: REB 1544
MC: REBMC 1544

'LIVE' AT THE OLD PLACE.
LP: REB 1627
MC: REBMC 1627

LIVE IN JAPAN (Stanley, Ralph & The Clinch Mountain Boys).
2LP: REB 2202

LONESOME AND BLUE.
LP: REB 1648
MC: REBMC 1648

MAN AND HIS MUSIC, A.
LP: REB 1530
MC: REBMC 1530

MEMORY OF YOUR SMILE, A.
LP: REB 1606
MC: REBMC 1606

OLD COUNTRY CHURCH.
LP: REB 1508
MC: REBMC 1508

OLD HOME PLACE.
LP: REB 1562
MC: REBMC 1562

ON AND ON.
LP: CO 776
MC: CO 776 C

SNOW COVERED MOUND.
LP: REB 1613
MC: REBMC 1613

SOMETHING OLD, SOMETHING NEW.
LP: REB 1503

STANLEY SOUND TODAY.
LP: REB 1601

Stano

CONTENT TO WRITE I DINE.
LP: DTLP 025

ONLY.
MC: MMUMC 891
LP: MMUML 891

SEDUCING DECADENCE.
LP: ST 7517

Stansfield, Lisa

AFFECTION.
Tracks: / This is the right time / Mighty love / Sincerity / Love in me, The / All around the world / What did I do to you? / Live together / You can't deny it / Poison / When are you coming back? / Affection / Wake up baby (Only on cassette and CD.) / Way you want it, The.
LP: 210379
MC: 410379

Stanshall, Vivian

HENRY AT NDIDIS KRAAL.
LP: VERB 1

SIR HENRY AT RAWLINSON END.
Tracks: / Aunt Florrie's walk / Interlewd / Wheelbarrow / Socks / Rub, The /

Nice'n'tidy / Pigs 'ere purse / 6/8 hoodoo / Smeeton / Fool and bladder endroar / Jungle bunny / Beasht inshide, The / Rawlinsons and Maynards / Papadumb.
LP: .... CAS 1139
LP: .... CHC 83
MC: .... CHCMC 83

SIR HENRY AT RAWLINSON END (See under Sir Henry At... (Various artists)).

TEDDY BOYS DON'T KNIT.
Tracks: / King Kripple / Slave valse / Gums / Biwilderbeeste / Calypso to calapso / Tube, The / Ginger geezer / Cracks are showing, The / Flung a dummy / Possibly an arm chair / Fresh faced boys / Terry keeps his clips on / Bass Macaw and broken bottles / Nose hymn / Everyday I have the blues / Smoke signals at night / Nouveau riffe.
LP: .... CAS 1153
MC: 7144 121

Staple Singers

AT THEIR BEST.
MC: 2651214

BE ALTITUDE: RESPECT YOURSELF.
Tracks: / This world / Respect yourself / Name the missing word / I'll take you there / This old town / We the people / Are you sure / Who do you think you are / I'm just another soldier / Who.
LP: .... SXE 001

BRAND NEW DAY.
Tracks: / Brand new day / Child's life / Come out of your shell / If it wasn't for a woman / He / Garden party / I believe in music / Which way did it go / This time around / You've got to make an effort / Unity.
LP: .... STM 7009

HOLD ON TO YOUR DREAM.
Tracks: / Ride it on out / There's got to be rain in your life / Message in our music / Cold and windy nights / Stupid Louie / Hold on to your dream / Show off the real you / Old flames / Love came knocking.
LP: .... T 636
MC: .... C 636

PRAY ON.
Tracks: / Pray on / Don't drive me away / Downward road / Will the circle be unbroken / Stand by me / Ain't that good news / If I could hear my mother / Going away / Don't knock / Uncloudy day / I know I got religion / Somebody save me / Let's go home / This may be the last time / I had a dream / Calling me.
LP: .... GNC 1002

RESPECT YOURSELF - THE BEST OF.
Tracks: / Heavy makes you happy / Long walk to DC / This world / Respect yourself / I see it / We'll get over / Take you there / Oh la de da / Are you sure / If you're ready (come go with me) / Touch a hand, make a friend / City in the sky / People come out of your shell / You've got to earn it (Available on CD only) / Love is plentiful (Available on CD only) / Got to be some changes (Available on CD only) / Be what you are (Available on CD only) / This old town (Available on CD only) / Slow train (Available on CD only) / My main man (Available on CD only).
LP: .... SX 006
MC: .... SXC 006

STAND BY ME.
Tracks: / Stand by me / If I could hear my mother pray / God's wonderful love / Calling me / Uncloudy day / I know I've got religion / Swing low sweet chariot / On my way to heaven / I'm coming home / I had a dream / Help me Jesus / Love is the way / Let's go home / This may be the last time / I'm leaning / Going away / Downward road / Pray on / Good news / Day is passed and gone / Don't knock / Will the circle be unbroken / Born in Bethlehem / I've been scorned / Sit down servant / Two wings.
2LP: .... DJD 28028

STAPLE SINGERS.
Tracks: / Are you ready? / Life during wartime / Nobody can make it on there own / Back to the war / Reason to love / We stand (together, forever) / Start walking / Love works in strange ways.
LP: .... EPC 26537
MC: 40 26537

STAPLE SINGERS AT THEIR BEST.
Tracks: / If you're ready (come go with me) / Respect yourself / This world / You're gonna make me cry / Touch a hand, make a friend / City in the sky / I'll take you there / You've got to earn it / Oh la de da / Heavy makes you happy / Be what you are / My main man / Long walk to DC.
LP: .... STAXL 5004
MC: .... STAXK 5004

STAPLE SINGERS, THE.
MC: .... ZCGAS 745

STAPLES SINGERS, THE.
LP: .... SX 001

TURNING POINT.
Tracks: / This is our night / Slippery people / Bridges instead of walls / Turning point / Right decision / H-a-t-e / On my own again / That's what friends are for.
LP: .... EPC 26212

WE'LL GET OVER.
Tracks: / Give a damn / Everyday people / End of the road / Tend to your own business / Solon Bushi (Japanese folk song) / Challenge, The / God bless the children / Games people play / Wednesday in your garden, A / Gardener, The / When do I get paid.
LP: .... MPS 8532
MC: .... MPS 585532

Staples, Mavis

DON'T CHANGE ME NOW.
Tracks: / Ready for the heartbreak / Sweet things you do / Chokin' kind, The / House is not a home, A / Security / Good to me / You send me / I'm tired / Why can't it be like it used to be (Available on CD only) / You're the fool (Available on CD only) / You're all I need / I have learned to do without you / How many times / Endlessly / Since I fell for you / Since you became a part of my life / Don't change me now / You're driving me (to the arms of a stranger) (Available on CD only) / Pick up the pieces (Available on CD only) / Chains of love (Available on CD only) / What happened to the real me (Available on CD only).
LP: .... SX 014
MC: .... SXC 014

TIME WAITS FOR NO-ONE.
LP: .... K 925798-1
MC: .... K 925798-4

Staples, Pop

JAMMED TOGETHER (See under Cropper, Steve) (Staples, Pop/ Steve Cropper/ Albert King).

Stapleton, Cyril

GOLDEN HOUR OF STRICT TEMPO DANCING VOL 3 (Stapleton, Cyril & His Show Band).
MC: .... DLCMC 126

Stapleton, Maureen

SUMMER PEOPLE, THE.
LP: .... TC 1498
MC: .... CDL 51498

Stapleton, Robin

GOLD AND SILVER (Stapleton, Robin & His Orchestra).
Tracks: / Gold and silver / By the waters of Minnetonka / Fantasia on Greensleeves / Neopolitan nights / Over the waves / Skaters' waltz / Maiden's prayer / Caprice Viennoise / Menuet / Dance of the hours / Zigeunerweisen / Cygne / Swan Lake scene / In a Persian market / Sinfonia / Jewels of the Madonna / Le cinquantaine / Fur Elise / Liebestraum / Kammenoi-Ostrov.
2LP: .... MFP 1003

Star

STAR (Film soundtrack) (Various artists).
LP: .... SSL 10233

Star Accordion Band

ALL TIME FAVOURITES.
LP: .... KSLP 607
MC: .... ZCSLP 607

COUNTRY FAVOURITES.
Tracks: / Things / Release me / Jambalaya / Oh lonesome me / Country roads / Dear God / Old rugged cross, The / For the good times / Your cheatin' heart / Banks of the Ohio / Let me be there.
LP: .... KSLP 601
MC: .... ZCSLP 601

COUNTRY FAVOURITES - VOL.2.
Tracks: / Wabash cannonball / Tiny bubbles / Heartaches by the number / Queen of the silver dollar / North to Alaska / He'll have to go / Adios amigo / I can't stop loving you / Don't let me cross over / Lucille / Silver threads and golden needles / Please help me, I'm falling / Jealous heart / Gentle on my mind / Snowbird / Send me the pillow that you dream on / Okie from Muskogee / Last thing on my mind / American trilogy.
LP: .... KSLP 604
MC: .... ZCSLP 604

INSPIRATIONAL FAVOURITES.
MC: .... ZCSLP 616

IRISH FAVOURITES.
Tracks: / Galway bay / Mother machree / Paddy mcginty's goat / Wild colonial boy / Black velvet band / Wild rover / Minstrel boy / My wild irish rose / Danny boy / Irish lullaby / Whisky in the jar / When irish eyes are smiling / Cockels and muscles / Dear old donegal / Green glens of antrim / Old house.
LP: KLP603

PARTY FAVOURITES.
Tracks: / Beautiful Sunday / Paloma blanca / Who were you with last night / Venus in blue jeans / Birdie dance / Rock around the clock / Guantanamera / Daisy bell / Pack up your troubles in your old kit bag / Blue suede shoes / Pretty woman / In the mood / Chattanooga choo choo / Moon river.
LP: .... KSLP 605
MC: .... ZCSLP 605

SCOTTISH DANCE FAVOURITES.
Tracks: / Dashing white sergeant / Breakdown / Highland cradle song / Snow in Summer / Canadian jig / Drunken piper / Mrs. Macleod / Duke of Perth / Staten island / Victoria hornpipe / Hot punch / Petronella / Sporty boys / Louden's bonnie woods / Fairy dance, The / My home / Keel row, The / Bonnie Dundee / Cock o the north / Bonnie lass.
LP: .... KSLP 608
MC: .... ZCSLP 608

SCOTTISH FAVOURITES.
Tracks: / I belong to Glasgow / Amazing grace / Roamin' in the gloamin' / Star o' Rabbie Burns, The / Rowan tree / Westering home / Mairi's wedding / Ye banks and braes / Loch Lomond / Scotland again / Auld lang syne.
LP: .... KSLP 602
MC: .... ZCSLP 602

SCOTTISH FAVOURITES VOL.2.
Tracks: / These are my mountains / Song of the Clyde / Dancing in Kyle / Sottish soldier / Donald, where's yer troosers / Crooked bawbee / There was a lad.
LP: .... KSLP 606
MC: .... ZCSLP 606

SENTIMENTAL FAVOURITES.
LP: .... KSLP 611
MC: .... ZCSLP 611

Star Child

STAR CHILD (Wilde, Oscar (author)).
MC: .... BKK 415

Star Club Show

STAR CLUB SHOW (Various artists).
LP: 6498 192
MC: 7133 192

Star Inc.

JAMES BOND FILM THEMES.
LP: 26008
MC: 46008

SYNTHESIZER GREATEST.
LP: .... ARC 938101
MC: .... ARC 938104

Star Is Born

STAR IS BORN, A (Film soundtrack) (Various artists).
LP: .... CBS 86021
MC: 40 86021
LP: .... ACS 8740
MC: .... BT 8740

STAR IS BORN, A (Remastered Soundtrack) (Various artists).
MC: .... JST 44389

Star, Orrin

FUN SONGS AND FANCY PICKIN'.
LP: .... FF 456

NO FRETS BARRED.
LP: .... FF 267

PREMIUM BLEND (Star, Orrin & Gary Mehalick).
LP: .... FF 234

Star Parade

STAR PARADE VOL 1 (Various artists).
Tracks: / Love letters in the sand: *Boone, Pat* / Just out of reach: *Cline, Patsy* / Day O (banana boat song): *Belafonte, Harry* / Only you: *Various artists* / Trains and boats and planes: *Warwick, Dionne* / Mystery train / Stand by your man: *Turner, Tina* / Tampico: *Christy, June* / I left my heart in San Francisco: *Bennett, Tony* / I've got my love to keep me warm: *Starr, Kay* / Come on-a my house: *Clooney, Rosemary* / Jezebel: *Laine, Frankie* / Johnny guitar: *Lee, Peggy* / Raindrops keep falling on my head: *Thomas, B.J.* / Over the rainbow: *Garland, Judy* / Foggy day, A: *Smith, Keely.*
MC: .... LCS 14145
LP: .... LOP 14 145

STAR PARADE VOL 2 (Various artists).
Tracks: / Learnin' the blues: *Sinatra, Frank* / Tenderly: *Holiday, Billie* / Que sera sera: *Day, Doris*/ Smile: *Various artists* / Summertime: *Vaughan, Sarah* / And her tears flowed like wine: *O'Day, Anita*/ I love you Samantha: *Crosby, Bing* / Nobody knows the trouble I've seen: *Jackson, Mahalia* / That old black magic: *Fitzgerald, Ella* / Georgia on my mind: *Charles, Ray* / Careless love: *Wiley, Lee* / My old flame: *Washington, Dinah* / Jeepers creepers: *Connor, Chris* / I can't give you anything but love: *Various artists* / Vaya con Dios: *Ford, Mary* / What's new: *Eckstine, Billy.*
MC: .... LCS 14146
LP: .... LOP 14 146

STAR PARADE VOL 3 (Various artists).
Tracks: / That's amore: *Martin, Dean* / Softly as in a morning sunrise: *Christy, June* / Angelina/ Zooma zooma: *Prima, Louis* / Swinging on a star: *Polk, Lucy Ann* / Cry: *Ray, Johnnie* / Waltzing Matilda: *Ives, Burl* / One o'clock jump: *Lambert, Hendricks...* / Caldonia: *Jordan, Louis* / Lulu's back in town: *Torme, Mel* / When your lover has gone: *London, Julie* / Up a lazy river: *Mills Brothers with Bing Crosby* / Sing, sing, sing: *Andrew Sisters, The* / Tom Dooley: *Kingston Trio, The* / Day by day: *Stafford, Jo* / Keep on churnin (till the butter comes): *Harris, Wynonie* / Detour ahead: *McCall, Mary Ann.*
MC: .... LCS 14148
LP: .... LOP 14 148

Star, Sandy

MAN A PREPS (See under Ninja Man) (Star, Sandy & Ninja Man).

Star Signs..

AQUARIUS Linda Goodman star signs (Goodman, Linda).
MC: 0600559769

ARIES Linda Goodman star signs (Goodman, Linda).
MC: 0600559742

CANCER Linda Goodman star signs (Goodman, Linda).
MC: 0600559661

CAPRICORN Linda Goodmans star signs (Goodman, Linda).
MC: 060055967X

GEMINI Linda Goodman star signs (Goodman, Linda).
MC: 060055970X

LEO Linda Goodman star signs (Goodman, Linda).
MC: 0600559688

LIBRA Linda Goodman star signs (Goodman, Linda).
MC: 0600559750

PISCES Linda Goodmans star signs (Goodman, Linda).
MC: 0600559769

SAGITTARIUS Linda Goodman star signs (Goodman, Linda).
MC: 0600559718

SCORPIO Linda Goodman star signs (Goodman, Linda).
MC: 0600559726

TAURUS Linda Goodman star signs (Goodman, Linda).
MC: 0600559696

VIRGO Linda Goodman star signs (Goodman, Linda).
MC: 0600559734

Star Sisters

STARS ON 45.
Tracks: / Boogie woogie bugle boy / South American way / Bei mir bist du schon / In the mood / Rum and coca cola / Tico tico / Say si si / Pennsylvania 6-5000 / Joseph Joseph / Ti-Pi-Tin / String of pearls / Hold tight / Beer barrel polka / Don't sit under the apple tree / Moonlight serenade / Oh Ma-Mal / Tuxedo Junction / Pistol packin' mama / Pennsylvania polka / Yes / My darling daughter / Happy days are here again / American patrol / Chattanooga choo choo / Double Dutch jive / Stars serenade / Plaza - 7900.
LP: .... CBS 25588
MC: 40 25588

Star Spangled Rhythm

STAR SPANGLED RHYTHM (Original Soundtrack) (Various artists).
LP: .... SH 2045

STAR SPANGLED RHYTHM (Various artists).
LP: .... CC 100/20

Star Spangled

COLLECTORS ITEM, A.
LP: .... FF 031

Star Trek

INSIDE STAR TREK (Various artists).
Tracks: / Asimov's world of science fiction: *Various artists* / William Shatner meets Captain Kirk: *Various artists*/ Origin of Spock: *Various artists* / Letter from a network censor: *Various artists* / Star Trek philosophy: *Various artists.*
LP: .... CBS 31765
MC: 40 31765

STAR TREK Storyteller Little L.P. (Various artists).
LP: .... D 461

MC: . . . . D 461 DC

STAR TREK (TV Soundtrack) (Various artists).
LP: . . . . NCP 706
MC: . . . . ZCNCP 706

STAR TREK Television soundtrack (Various artists).
LP: . . . . PYL 6041
MC: . . . . PYM 6041

STAR TREK II - THE WRATH OF KHAN (Various artists).
Tracks: / Star Trek (main theme): *Various artists* / Star Trek (closing theme): *Various artists* / Black ship tension: *Various artists* / By any other name: *Various artists* / Vian lab: *Various artists* / Time grows short: *Various artists* / Mirror, mirror: *Various artists* / Trouble with Tribbles, The: *Various artists*/ Empath, The: *Various artists* / Help him: *Various artists* / Vian's farewell: *Various artists*.
LP: . . . . D 462
MC: . . . . D 462 DC
LP: . . . . K 50905

STAR TREK III - THE SEARCH FOR SPOCK (Film Soundtrack) (Various artists).
Tracks: / Star Trek III prologue and main title: *Various artists* / Klingons: *Various artists* / Stealing the Enterprise: *Various artists* / Mind meid, The: *Various artists* / Bird of prey decloaks: *Various artists*/ Returning to Vulcan: *Various artists* / Katra ritual, The: *Various artists* / Star Trek III (end titles): *Various artists*.
LP: . . . . TREK 1
MC: . . . . TCTREK 1
LP: . . . . SKBK 12360
LP: . . . . EJ 2401771

STAR TREK IV- THE VOYAGE HOME (Film soundtrack) (Various artists).
Tracks: / Main title: *Various artists* / Whaler, The: *Various artists* / Market street: *Various artists*/ Crash-whale fugue: *Various artists* / Ballad of the whale: *Various artists* / Gillian seeks Kirk: *Various* artists / Chekhov's run: *Various artists* / Time travel: *Various artists* / Hospital chase: *Various artists*/ Probe, The: *Various artists* / Home again: end credits: *Various artists*.
LP: . . . . IMCA 6195
MC: . . . . IMCAC 6195

STAR TREK - ORIGINAL TV SOUNDTRACK (Original Soundtrack) (Royal Philharmonic Orchestra).
Tracks: / Cage, The / Where no man has gone before.
LP: . . . . GNPS 8006
MC: GNP5 8006

STAR TREK - SOUND EFFECTS: THE TV SERIES (Various artists).
LP: . . . . GNPS 8010
MC: GNP5 8010

STAR TREK: THE MOTION PICTURE (Film Soundtrack) (Various artists).
Tracks: / Star trek: *Various artists* / Klingon battle: *Various artists* / Leaving drydock: *Various artists*/ Cloud, The: *Various artists* / Enterprise, The: *Various artists* / Ilia's theme: *Various artists* / Vefur flyover: *Various artists* / Meld, The: *Various artists* / Spock walk: *Various artists* / End title: *Various artists*.
LP: . . . . CBS 70174
MC: 40 70174
LP: . . . . PS 36334
MC: . . . . PST 36334

STAR TREK: THE NEXT GENERATION (Various artists).
LP: . . . . GNPS 8012
MC: GNP5 8012

STAR TREK - TV SERIES VOL. 2 (Various artists).
MC: . . . . CTV 704300

STAR TREK V - THE FINAL FRONTIER (Film Soundtrack) (Various artists).
Tracks: / Mountain, The: *Various artists* / Barrier, The: *Various artists* / Without help: *Various artists*/ Busy man, A: *Various artists* / Open the gates: *Various artists* / Moon's a window to heaven, The: *Various* artists / Angry god, An: *Various artists* / Let's get out of here: *Various artists* / Free minds: *Various artists* / Life is a dream: *Various artists*.
LP: 4659251
MC: 4659254

STAR TREK VOL.1 - THE TV SERIES (TV Soundtrack) (Royal Philharmonic Orchestra).
Tracks: / Is there in truth no beauty / Paradise syndrome.
LP: . . . . LXDR 703
MC: . . . . LXDC 703

STAR TREK VOL.2 - THE TV SERIES (TV Soundtrack) (Royal Philharmonic Orchestra).
Tracks: / Conscience of the king / Spectre of the gun / Enemy within / I, mudd.
LP: . . . . LXDR 704
MC: . . . . LXDC 704

STAR TREK VOL 3 - THE TV SERIES (TV Soundtrack) (Royal Philharmonic Orchestra).
LP: 704.270
MC: . . . . C 704.270

STARTREK - THEME (See under Roddenberry, Gene) (Roddenberry, Gene).

Star Turn

ARE YOU AFFILIATED.
LP: . . . . TURNLP 1
MC: . . . . TURNMC 1

Star Wars

STAR WARS (Film Soundtrack) (London Symphony Orchestra).
Tracks: / Star Wars main title / Imperial attack / Princess Leia's theme / Desert and the robot auction, The / Last battle, The / Ben's death and the fighter attack / Little people work, The / Rescue of the princess / Inner city / Cantina band / Land of the sandpeople, The / Return home, The / Walls converge, The / Princess appears / Throne room and end title, The.
LP: 2679 092
MC: 3528 033
LP: . . . . BTD 541
2LP: 2658 151
2LP: 2T 541
MCSET: C2 2T 541

STAR WARS (Various artists).
MC: . . . . D 150DC

STAR WARS (London Philharmonic Orchestra).
Tracks: / Main title / Imperial attack / Princess Leia's theme / Ben's death and the fighter attack / Land of the sandpeople, The / Return home, The / End title / 2001 / Battle of the planets (Mars) / Mercury / Venus / Space tumble.
LP: . . . . DMT 2001

STAR WARS TRILOGY (Music From the Films) (Various artists).
Tracks: / Star Wars main title: *Various artists* / Princess Leia's theme: *Various artists* / Here they come: *Various* artists / Asteroid field, The: *Various artists* / Yoda's theme: *Various artists* / Imperial march: *Various* artists / Parade of the Ewoks: *Various artists* / Luke and Leia: *Various artists* / Fight with tie fighters: *Various artists* / Jabba the Hutt: *Various artists* / Darth Vader's death: *Various artists* / Forest battle, The: *Various artists* / Star Wars finale: *Various artists*.
LP: . . . . TER 1067
MC: . . . . ZCTER 1067

STAR WARS/CLOSE ENCOUNTERS OF THE THIRD KIND (See under Close Encounters...) (Various artists).

STORY OF STAR WARS (Various artists).
LP: . . . . D 62101

Starburst

STARBURST (Various artists).
LP: . . . . SHM 3190
MC: . . . . HSC 3190

Starcastle

REAL TO REEL.
Tracks: / Half a mind to leave ya / Whatcha gonna do / We did it / Nobody's fool / Song for Alaya / So here we are / She / Stars are out tonight / When the sun shines at midnight.
LP: . . . . CBS 82916

Starcher, Buddy

COUNTRY LOVE SONGS.
Tracks: / Beautiful blue-eyed blonde / West Virginia hills, The / Let's / Song of the waterwheel, The / Those brown eyes / I'll still write your name in the sand / Wildwood flower / Foggy mountain top / Too late to worry / My shadow grows tall / We'll be sweethearts when we're old / Midnight special / Todays joy today.
LP: . . . . BF 15017

Stardust

MUSIC OF HOAGY CARMICHAEL.
LP: . . . . MOR 532

Stardust, Alvin

6 TRACK HITS: ALVIN STARDUST.
Tracks: / My coo ca choo / Guitar star / Red dress / You, you, you / Dreambreaker / You're my everything.
MC: 7SC 5030

ALVIN STARDUST.
LP: . . . . MAG 5004

GREATEST HITS: ALVIN STARDUST.
LP: . . . . MAG 4002
MC: . . . . ZCMAG 4002
LP: 1A 022 58201
MC: 1A 222 58201

GREATEST HITS OF ALVIN STARDUST.
Tracks: / Jealous mind / Good love can never die / Heartbreak / Pretend / Sweet cheatin' Rita / Shake on little roller / Guitar star / Red dress / I feel like Buddy Holly / Tell me why / My coo ca choo / I won't run away / You you you / Weekend.
LP: . . . . CSALP 105
MC: . . . . CSAMC 105

I FEEL LIKE...ALVIN STARDUST.
Tracks: / Pink bedroom / Give it a little time / America / Morning after, The / I won't run away / I feel like Buddy Holly / Got my money on you / I do so love you now / She's so young / In the morning / Save the children / Hurt by love / So near to Christmas.
LP: . . . . CHR 1489
MC: . . . . ZCHR 1489

JAILHOUSE ROCK.
LP: . . . . PL 42792

ROCK ON WITH ALVIN STARDUST.
Tracks: / My co cachoo / Jealous mind / Red dress / You you you / Tell me why / Heartbeat.
LP: . . . . MFP 50464

ROCK WITH ALVIN.
LP: . . . . MAG 5007

UNTOUCHABLE, THE.
LP: . . . . MAG 5001

Stardust (film)

STARDUST (Film soundtrack) (Various artists).
2LP: . . . . RG 2009/10

Starfighters

POWER CRAZY.
LP: . . . . HOP 200
MC: . . . . HOPC 200

Stargard

BACK 2 BACK.
Tracks: / You're the one / Here comes love / Just one love / Back to the funk / High on the boogie / Cat and me, The / It's your love that I'm missing / Diary.
LP: . . . . K 56854

WHICH WAY IS UP (OLD GOLD) (See under Rose Royce/Car wash).

WHICH WAY IS UP (THEME FROM) (See under Rose Royce/Car wash).

Stargazers

BACK IN ORBIT.
LP: . . . . CH 312

WATCH THIS SPACE.
Tracks: / Tossin' 'n' turnin' / Hey Marie / Swingin' aye / Marcelle mania / Walking the chalk line / Hey there you / Perdido/ Caravan / Groove baby groove / Follow your heart / Pretty senorita / Spin that 45 / True love / Rocketship to the moon.
LP: . . . . EPC 25053

Starita, Ray

RHAPSODY IN RHYTHM (Starita, Ray & His Ambassadors).
Tracks: / Rhapsody in rhythm / Crazy rhythm / Love lies / Every little moment / Spread a little happiness / That's what I call keen / Through / Blues hills of Pasedena / Un-tcha-am-tcha-da-da-da / There's somebody new / Blue days are over / Come on baby / Blue river / My dream memory / Gee it must be love / Dancing in your sleep / Sunshine of Marseilles / If I had three wishes / It's not you / There's always tomorrow.
LP: . . . . SVL 155

Starjets

STARJETS.
Tracks: / Schooldays / Any danger love / Ten years / Run with the pack / What a life / Smart boys / It's a shame / I'm so glad / War is over / War stones / Sitting on top of the world.
LP: . . . . EPC 83534

Stark

COMMUNICATING BALANCE.
MC: . . . . DHC 7

FOND ADIEU.
MC: . . . . DHC 9

INSANITY IS ONLY A HAIRBREADTH AWAY.
MC: . . . . DHC 1

SINGLE,THE.
MC: . . . . DHC 5

Stark Raving Mad

AMERIKA.
LP: . . . . NB 8

SOCIAL SICKNESS.
LP: . . . . NB 017

Stark,Bengt

PUPILS AND TEACHERS.
Tracks: / Up jumped spring / Line for lyons / Dallab / Spain / Doxy / Farmer's waltz / Scratcher, The.
LP: . . . . PHONT 7516

Starkey, Zak

WIND IN THE WILLOWS (See under Hardin, Eddie) (Starkey, Zak & Eddie Hardin).

Starkie, Martin (nar)

CANTERBURY TALES, THE (see under Chaucer, Geoffrey (aut)) (Scales, Prunella (nar) & Martin Starkie (nar)).

Starkman

......AND OTHER VOICES (Leah And The Starkman).
MC: . . . . DHC 16

BEACH FATIGUE REVUE.
MC: . . . . DHC 25

BENEFITS OF BALANCE.
MC: . . . . DHC 24

LAST RESORT.
MC: . . . . DHC 20

SCANTILY SCULPTURED.
MC: . . . . DHC 15

STARK CONTRAST.
MC: . . . . DHC 18

WAKE UP/VIBETHING (It's Krats/ Vibething).
MC: . . . . DHC 11

WEIRD STRATEGY.
MC: . . . . DHC 12

Starlight Express

STARLIGHT EXPRESS (Original London Cast) (Various artists).
Tracks: / Starlight Express overture: *Various artists* / Rolling stock: *Various artists* / Call me Rusty: *Various* artists / Lotta locomotion, A: *Various artists* / Pumping iron: *Various artists* / Freight: *Various artists*/ AC/DC: *Various artists* / Hitching and switching: *Various artists* / He whistled at me: *Various artists*/ Race-heat one: *Various artists* / There's me: *Various artists* / Blues, The: *Various artists* / Belle: *Various artists* / Race-heat two: *Various artists* / Race-heat three: *Various artists* / Starlight Express: *Various artists* / Rap, The: *Various artists* / Uncoupled: *Various artists* / Rolling stock (reprise): *Various artists* / C.B.: *Various artists* / Race-uphill final: *Various artists* / Right place, right time: *Various artists* / Race-downhill final: *Various artists* / No comeback: *Various artists* / One rock 'n' roll too many: *Various artists* / Only He: *Various artists* / Only you: *Various artists* / Light at the end of the tunnel: *Various artists*.
2LP: . . . . LNER 1
MCSET: . . . . LNERC 1

Starlight Rider

STARLIGHT RIDER (See under Haycox, Ernest) (Haycox, Ernest).

Starling, John

LONG TIME GONE.
Tracks: / Long time gone / Turned you to stone / Half a man / Jordan / White line / Hobo on a freight train to heaven / Last thing I needed / Brother juke box / Carolyn at the Broken Wheel Inn / He rode all the way to Texas / Drifting too far from the shore / Dark hollow (Only on CD) / Lonesome whistle (Only on CD) / Roads and other reasons (Only on CD) / Sin City (Only on CD).
LP: . . . . SH 3714
MC: . . . . ZCSH 3714

WAITIN' ON A SOUTHERN TRAIN.
Tracks: / New Delhi freight train / We know better / Carolina star / Other side of life, The / Waitin' on a southern train / Heart trouble / Homestead in my heart / Hey bottle of whisky / Those memories of you / Slow movin' freight train.
LP: . . . . SH 3724
MC: . . . . ZCSH 3724

Starman

STARMAN (Original Soundtrack) (Various artists).
LP: . . . . TER 1097
MC: . . . . VC 81233
MC: . . . . ZCTER 1097
LP: . . . . CST 8004

Starpoint

HAVE YOU GOT WHAT IT TAKES.
LP: . . . . EKT 71
MC: . . . . EKT 71 C

HOT TO TOUCH.
Tracks: / Fresh start / Tough act to follow / Hot to the touch / After all is said and done / Park it / One step closer to your love / Say you will / Swept away / Heart attack.
LP: . . . . K 960810 1
MC: . . . . K 960810 4

RESTLESS.
Tracks: / What you been missing / One more night / Restless / See the light / Till the end of time / Don't take your love away / Emotions / Objects of my desire.

LP: . . . . EKT 11

SENSATIONAL.
Tracks: / He wants my body / D.Y.B.O. / Prove it tonight / Sensational / Another night / More we love, The / Touch of your love / Second chance.
LP: . . . . K 960722 1
MC: . . . . K 960722 4

Starpower

STARPOWER (Various artists).
2LP: . . . . SSD 8036

Starr, Edwin

20 GREATEST MOTOWN HITS.
Tracks: / Stop her on sight (S.O.S.) / 25 miles / Headline news / Agent double o soul / Backstreet / I want my baby back / Funky music sho nuff turns me on / Soul master / You've got my soul on fire / Who's right or wrong / War / Stop the war now / Way over there / Take me clear from here / Cloud nine / There you go / Gonna keep on tryin' till I win your love / Time / My weakness is you / Harlem.
MC: . . . . WK 72429
LP: . . . . WL 72429

AFTERNOON SUNSHINE.
Tracks: / Overture to afternoon sunshine / Pretty girl / Ruby Begonia / Eavesdropper / I just wanna do my thing / Mr. Davenport and Mr. James / Not having you / Accident / Everybody needs love / Edge of insanity.
LP: . . . . GTLP 19

CLEAN.
Tracks: / I'm so into you / Jealous / Contact / Storm clouds on the way / Don't waste your time / Music brings out the beast in me / Working song.
LP: . . . . BT 559

STONGER THAN YOU THINK I AM.
Tracks: / Never turn my back on you / Tell a star / Sweet / Upside down / Bigger and better / Stronger than you think I am / Get up whirlpool / Bop bop song.
LP: . . . . T 615

Starr, Freddie

AFTER THE LAUGHTER.
Tracks: / It's only make believe / Fever / I don't want to talk about it / Love hurts / Halfway to paradise / You got it / I will / Sun ain't gonna shine anymore, The / Teddy bear / I love how you love me / Run to my loving arms / I'm lost without you.
LP: . . . . CHR 1739
MC: . . . . ZCHR 1739
LP: . . . . ADD 10
MC: . . . . ZDD 10
MC: . . . . TCMFP 5909

IT'S ME.
LP: . . . . OZONE 101
MC: . . . . ZCZONE 101

SPIRIT OF ELVIS, THE.
LP: . . . . KAM 002

WANDERER, THE.
Tracks: / Wanderer, The / You don't have to say you love me / Maybe tomorrow / Little sister / Nights in white satin / True love ways / Vincent / Needles and pins / You've lost that lovin' feeling / Running scared / She's mine / Somebody else's girl / Just for you / Till I can't take it anymore.
LP: . . . . ADD 17
MC: . . . . ZDD 17

Starr, Jack

BLAZE OF GLORY.
LP: . . . . US 8

BURNING STARR.
LP: . . . . US 16

OUT OF THE DARKNESS.
LP: . . . . MFN 34

ROCK THE AMERICAN WAY.
LP: . . . . PBL 101

Starr, Kay

1947: KAY STARR.
LP: . . . . HUK 214

BACK TO THE ROOTS.
LP: . . . . GNPS 2090
MC: GNP5 2090

BLUE STARR.
Tracks: / It's a lonesome old town / You're driving me crazy / House is haunted, The / We three / I really don't want to know / Blue Starr / Wedding bells / It's funny to everyone but me / Little white lies / Just like a butterfly (that's caught in the rain) / Blue and sentimental.
LP: . . . . NL 90045
MC: . . . . NK 90045

FABULOUS FAVOURITES.
Tracks: / Wheel of fortune / Rock and roll waltz / Side by side / Comes a-long-a-love / Bonapartes retreat / Half a photograph / Mississippi / So tired / I'm the lonesomest gal in town / Hoop dee doo / Allez-vous-en, go away / Foolin' around.
LP: . . . . MFP 5603

IN A BLUE MOOD.
Tracks: / After you've gone / Woman likes to be told, A / Maybe you'll be there / I'm waiting for ships that never come in / What will I tell my heart? / Evenin' / He's funny that way / I got the spring fever blues / Don't tell him what happened to me / I got it bad and that ain't good / Everybody's somebody's fool / Until the real thing comes along.
LP: . . . . EG 2606101
MC: . . . . EG 2606104

IN THE 40'S.
LP: . . . . HSR 214

JAZZ SINGER.
Tracks: / I never knew / My man / Breezin' along with the wind / All by myself / Hard hearted Hannah / Me too / Happy days and lonely nights / I only want a buddy, not a sweetheart / Hummin' to myself / My honey's arms / Sunday / Anything for you.
LP: . . . . CAPS 1867481
MC: . . . . TC CAPS 1867484

JUST PLAIN COUNTRY.
Tracks: / Pins and needles in my heart / Crazy / Four walls / My last date (with you) / Blues stay away from me / Walk on by / Oh, lonesome me / I can't help it (if I'm still in love with you) / I really don't want to know / Singing the blues / Don't worry.
LP: . . . . HAT 3049
MC: . . . . HATC 3049

KAY STARR COUNTRY.
LP: . . . . GNPS 2083
MC: GNP5 2083

KAY STARR STYLE,THE.
Tracks: / Side by side / Someday sweetheart / What can I say after I say I'm sorry.
LP: . . . . PM 1552961
MC: . . . . PM 1552964

MOVIN'.
LP: . . . . T 1254

MOVIN' (REISSUE).
Tracks: / On a slow boat to China / I cover the waterfront / Around the world / Sentimental journey / Night train / Riders in the sky / Goin' to Chicago blues / Indiana / Song of the wanderer / Swingin' down the lane / Lazy river / Movin'.
LP: . . . . JAS 307
MC: . . . . JAS C307

PURE GOLD: KAY STARR.
Tracks: / Rock and roll waltz / Rockin' chair / Georgia on my mind / My heart reminds me / Oh, how I miss you tonight / It's a lonesome old town / Dry bones / Fit as a fiddle / You're driving me crazy / Wrap your troubles in dreams / I'll never say "never again" again / Only love me.
LP: . . . . INTS 5090
MC: . . . . INTK 5090

WHEEL OF FORTUNE AND OTHER HITS.
MC: 4XL-9286

Starr, Ringo

BLAST FROM YOUR PAST.
Tracks: / You're sixteen / No no song / It don't come easy / Photograph / Back off boogaloo / Only you (and you alone) / Beacoups of blues / Oh my my / Early 1970 / I'm the greatest.
LP: . . . . MFP 50524

GOODNIGHT VIENNA.
Tracks: / Goodnight Vienna / Occapella / Oo-wee / Husbands and wives / Snookeroo / All by myself / Call me / No no song / Only you / Easy for me.
LP: . . . . IC 062 05762
LP: . . . . PMC 7168

RINGO.
Tracks: / I'm the greatest / Have you seen my baby / Photograph / Down and out / Sunshine life for me (Sail away Raymond) / You're sixteen (you're beautiful and you're mine) / Oh my my / Step lightly / Six o'clock / Devil woman / You and me (babe) / It don't come easy / Early 1970.
LP: . . . . PCTC 252
LP: . . . . EMS 1386
MC: . . . . TCEMS 1386

RINGO STARR.
Tracks: / I'm the greatest / Have you seen my baby / Photograph / Sunshine life for me / You're sixteen, you're beautiful / Oh my my / Step lightly / Six o'clock / Devil woman / You and me.
LP: . . . . MFP 50508

RINGO STARR AND HIS ALL-STARR BAND (Starr, Ringo & His All-Starr Band).
Tracks: / It don't come easy / No-no song, The / Iko iko / Weight, The / Shine silently / Honey don't / You're sixteen, you're beautiful and you're mine / Quarter to three / Raining in my heart / Will it go round in circles / Photograph.
LP: . . . . EMS 1375
MC: . . . . TCEMS 1375

ROTOGRAVURE.
Tracks: / Dose of rock 'n' roll, A / Hey baby / Pure gold / Crying / You don't know me at all / Cookin' / I'll still love you / Could this be called a song? / Las brisas / Lady Gaye.
LP: 2485 235
MC: 3201 743

SENTIMENTAL JOURNEY.
LP: . . . . PCS 7101

STOP AND SMELL THE ROSES.
Tracks: / Private property / Wrack my brain / Drumming is my madness / Attention / Stop and take the time to smell the roses / Dead giveaway / You belong to me / Sure to fall / Nice way / Back off Boogaloo.
LP: . . . . RCALP 6022
MC: . . . . RCAK 6022

Starr, Stella

STELLA'S STARR HITS.
LP: . . . . PELICAN 21

Starr, Will

THIS IS WILL STARR IN STARR TIME.
Tracks: / Jacqueline waltz / Frank Jamieson two step / Plaisance / Dark island / Woodland flowers / Auteuil-Langchamp / Amazing grace / Household Brigade two-step.
MC: . . . . ZCSMPS 8935

THIS IS WILL STARR MUSIC WITH A KICK.
Tracks: / Dancing fingers / Gordon Scottishe / Swiss polka / Oslo waltz / Irish hornpipes (medley) / Circassian circle medley / Looking for a partner / Para Handy / Pipe marches medley / Scottish waltz / Scottish waltz medley Scot / March hare / Strathspey and reel medley.
MC: . . . . ZCSMPS 8923

THIS IS WILL STARR - THE DADDY OF THEM ALL.
Tracks: / Tushkar reel, The / Ian Duncan / New high level / Calum Donaldson / Cuckoo waltz / Royal Scots polka / John Stephen of Chance Inn / Margaret's fancy / Sidlaw Hills / Bandboys / Kenmore's up and awa' / Charlie Hunter / Drunken parson, The / A. M. Shinnie / Shetland two-step / Gracieuse / Tap wood polka / Johnstone hornpipe / Banks hornpipe / High level hornpipe / Life in the Finland woods / Rock in the wee pickle tow, The / Dovecote Park / Highland lilt / Big Barney.
LP: . . . . PKL 5511
MC: . . . . ZCMA 1460

Starry Ride

STARRY RIDE (Various artists).
LP: . . . . PSYCHO 29

Stars

STARS VOL.1.
LP: . . . . VDL 1005

STARS VOL.2.
LP: . . . . VDL 1006

STARS VOL.2 (Various artists).
LP: . . . . VDL 1013

Stars For...

STARS FOR UNICEF (Various artists).
LP: 233 526 2

Stars of...

STARS OF THE STREETS ENCORE (Various artists).
LP: . . . . CA 125

Stars Of Faith

OF BLACK NATIVITY.
Tracks: / My sweet Lord / I'm glad about it / This joy / Hard way, The / I'm a soldier / My hope is built / We shall be changed / Come over here / Get away Jordan / Too late.
2LP: . . . . ALB 161

Stars Of Heaven

SACRED HEART HOTEL.
Tracks: / Sacred heart hotel / Talk about it now / Moonstruck / So you know / You only say what anyone could say / Folksong / Man without a shadow.
LP: . . . . RTM 73

SPEAK SLOWLY.
LP: . . . . ROUGH 131
MC: . . . . ROUGHC 131

Starship

GREATEST HITS (TEN YEARS AND CHANGE 1979-1991).
Tracks: / Jane / Find your way back / Stranger / No way out / Laying it on the line / Don't lose any sleep / We built this city / Sara / Nothing's gonna stop us now / It's not over ('til it's over) / It's not enough / Good enough.
LP: . . . . PL 82423
MC: . . . . PK 82423

KNEE DEEP IN HOOPLA.
Tracks: / We built this city / Sara / Tomorrow doesn't matter tonight / Rock myself to sleep / Desperate heart / Private room / Before I go / Hearts of the world will understand / Love rusts.
LP: . . . . FL 85488
MC: . . . . FK 85488
LP: . . . . NL 90367
MC: . . . . NK 90367

LOVE AMONG THE CANNIBALS.
Tracks: / Burn, The / It's not enough / Trouble in mind / I didn't mean to stay all night / Send a message / Wild again (CD only.) / Love among the cannibals / We dream in color / Healing waters / Blaze of love / I'll be there.
LP: . . . . PL 90387
MC: . . . . PK 90387

NO PROTECTION.
Tracks: / Beat patrol / Nothing's gonna stop us now / It's not over ('til it's over) / Girls like you / Wings of a lie / Children, The / I don't know why / Transatlantic / Babylon / Set the night to music.
LP: . . . . FL 86413
MC: . . . . FK 86413

Starship Orchestra

CELESTIAL SKY.
Tracks: / You're a star / New York, New York / Waiting game, The / Aquelas coisas todas / Genie / Celestial sky / Yesterday / Serious business / Give me some skin.
LP: . . . . CBS 84558

NEW YORK, NEW YORK (OLD GOLD)
(See under Shaw, Marlena/Yuma).

Starshooter

MODE.
LP: . . . . FC 042

STARSHOOTER.
LP: . . . . FC 039
MC: . . . . FC 039C

Starsound

STARS MEDLEY.
Tracks: / Greatest rock and roll band in the world / Stars on steve / Stars on jingle / It's not a wonder, it's a miracle.
LP: . . . . CBS 85651
MC: 40 85651

STARS ON 45.
Tracks: / Do you want to know a secret / Nowhere man / Eight days a week / My sweet lord / Hard day's night, A / Video killed the radio star / Cathy's clown / Bird dog / Sherry / Buona sera / At the hop.
LP: . . . . MFP 5799
MC: . . . . TCMFP 5799
LP: . . . . CBS 86132

STARS ON 45 (OLD GOLD).
LP: . . . . OG 1600
MC: . . . . OG 2600

STARS ON 45 VOL.2.
LP: . . . . CBS 85181

Starstruck

THRU TO YOU.
LP: . . . . SKULL 8396

Starting Here...

STARTING HERE STARTING NOW (Broadway Cast) (Various artists).
MC: . . . . GK 82360

Starting School

STARTING SCHOOL (Unknown narrator(s)).
MC: . . . . PLB 257

Startled Insects

CURSE OF PHEROMONES.
Tracks: / Creatures / Igor's horn / Underworld / Shrimps in love / Fastest claw / Lost at sea / Big wheel / Loco / Glass mountain / Moho.
MC: . . . . ANC 8708
LP: . . . . AN 8708

LIFEPULSE.
LP: . . . . SIGH 1-9
MC: . . . . SIGH 4-9

STARTLED INSECTS.
LP: . . . . ML 1

Startrax

REGGAES GREATEST HITS.
LP: . . . . SHM 3084
MC: . . . . HSC 3084

STARTRAX CLUB DISCO.
LP: . . . . KSYA 1001

Starvation Army

MERCENARY POSITION.
LP: . . . . RAVE 017

Starvin' Marvin

STARVIN MARVIN.
Tracks: / Starvin Marvin.

LP: . . . . ANT 033

Starz

BRIGHTEST STARZ.
Tracks: / Rock six times / Cherry baby / Pull the plug / So young, so bad / Violation / Subway terror / Sing it shout it / She / Coliseum rock / Boy's in action.
LP: . . . . HMUSA 8
MC: . . . . HMAMC 8

COLLOSEUM ROCK.
Tracks: / So young, so bad / Take me / No regrets / My sweet child / Don't stop now / Outfit / Last night I wrote a letter / Coliseum rock / It's a riot / Where will it end.
LP: . . . . EST 11861

LIVE IN ACTION.
Tracks: / (She's just a) fallen angel / Tear it down / Live wire / Monkey business / Detroit girls / She / Rock six times / Subway terror / Cool one / X ray specs / Cherry baby / Waiting on you / Greatest riffs of all time / Coliseum rock / Pull the plug / Boys in action / Johnny all alone.
2LP: . . . . RO 94271

LIVE IN CANADA.
LP: . . . . HMUSA 46
MC: . . . . HMAMC 46

PISS PARTY.
LP: . . . . HMASP 50

State Academic Choir

STATE ACADEMIC RUSSIAN CHOIR.
LP: . . . . CM 01961-2

State Funeral Of...

STATE FUNERAL OF SIR WINSTON CHURCHILL,K.G.,OM,C (Spoken Word (Group)).
2LP: . . . . WCF 101

State Northern Chorus

RUSSIAN FOLK SONGS (STATE NORTHERN FOLK CHORUS).
MC: . . . . SM 00068

State Of Mickey

UNDERGROUND.
LP: . . . . ANTAR 9

State Of Play

BALANCING THE SCALES.
Tracks: / Naked as the day you were born / Natural colour (remix) / Rockabye baby / Workman / Human kind / Winds of change / We go under / Take me to the king / Lost souls / Rescue (CD only) / Trout, The (Cassette & CD only) / Strange air (Cassette & CD only).
LP: . . . . V 2382
MC: . . . . TCV 2382

State Omsk Folk Chorus

RUSSIAN FOLK SONGS (STATE OMSK FOLK CHORUS).
MC: . . . . SM 00039

State Russian Chorus

RUSSIAN FOLK SONGS (STATE RUSSIAN CHORUS).
MC: . . . . SM 00040

State Street Aces

OLD FOLKS SHUFFLE VOL.3.
LP: . . . . SOS 1106

PASS OUT LIGHTLY.
LP: . . . . SOS 1041

State Street Ramblers

STATE STREET RAMBLERS 1931 Vol. 2.
LP: . . . . HERWIN 105

State Street

STATE STREET SWINGERS & CHICAGO BLACK SWANS.
LP: . . . . BD 2047

States

STATES, THE.
LP: . . . . CHR 1229

Stateside Smashes

STATESIDE SMASHES (Various artists).
MC: . . . . PLAC 345

Statetrooper

STATETROOPER.
Tracks: / Shape of things to come / Set fire to the night / Dreams of the faithful / Stand me up / Veni vidi vici / Last stop to heaven / She got the look / Too late / Armed and ready.
LP: . . . . WKFMLP 91
MC: . . . . WKFMMC 91

Static Seekers

BODY AUTOMATIC.
LP: . . . . AXS 007

Statler Brothers

ATLANTA BLUE.
Tracks: / Atlanta blue / If it makes a difference / Let's just take one night at a time / Angel in her face / Hollywood / One takes the blame / Give it your best / No love lost / One size fits all / My only love.
LP: . . . . MERL 40

CHRISTMAS PRESENT.
LP: 824 785-1
MC: 824 785-4

COUNTRY STORE: STATLER BROTHERS.
Tracks: / Bed of roses / Do you remember these / Flowers on the wall / I'll go to my grave loving you / Thank you world / Susan when she tried / Whatever happened to Randolph Scott / Carry me back / Class of 57, The / Pictures / New York city.
LP: . . . . CST 14
MC: . . . . CSTK 14

FOUR FOR THE SHOW.
Tracks: / Count on me / You oughta be here with me / We got the memories / I don't dream anymore / Forever / Only you / For cryin' out loud / Will you be there / I believe I'll live for him / More like daddy than me.
LP: . . . . MERH 91
MC: . . . . MERHC 91

MAPLE STREET MEMORIES.
Tracks: / Our street / Tell me why / Maple Street memories / Deja vu / Am I crazy? / Best I know how, The / I'll be the one / Beyond romance / I lost my heart to you / Jesus showed me so.
LP: . . . . MERH 112
MC: . . . . MERHC 112

PARDNERS IN RHYME.
Tracks: / Hello Mary Lou / Sweeter and sweeter / Memory lane / Remembering you / Too much on my heart / I'm sorry you had to be the one / Her heart of mine / You don't wear blue so well / Autumn leaves / Amazing grace.
LP: . . . . MERH 71
MC: . . . . MERHC 71

TODAY.
Tracks: / Oh baby mine (I get so lonely) / Some memories last forever / Promise, The / I'm dyin' a little each day / There is you / Guilty / Elizabeth / Right on the money / I never want to kiss you goodbye / Sweet by and by.
LP: . . . . MERL 25
MC: . . . . MERLC 25

YEARS AGO.
Tracks: / Don't wait on me / Today I went back / In the garden / Chet Atkin's hand / You'll be back / Years ago / Love was all we had / We ain't even started yet / Dad / Memories are made of this.
LP: 6337 177

Statman, Andy

FLATBUSH WALTZ.
LP: . . . . ROUNDER 0116

NASHVILLE MORNINGS, NEW YORK NIGHTS.
LP: . . . . ROUNDER 0174
MC: . . . . ROUNDER 0174C

Staton, Candi

CANDI STATON.
Tracks: / Looking for love / Halfway to heaven / One more try / If you feel the need / Hunter gets captured by the game, The / It's real / Betcha I'm gonna get ya.
LP: . . . . K 56803

CHANCE.
Tracks: / I ain't got nowhere to go / When you wake up / Rock / Chance / I live / Me and my music.
LP: . . . . K 56641

HOUSE OF LOVE.
Tracks: / Victim / Honest I do love you / Yesterday evening / I wonder will I ever get over it / I'm gonna make you love me / So blue / Take my hand.
LP: . . . . K 56510

MAKE ME AN INSTRUMENT.
Tracks: / Sin doesn't live here anymore / God can make something out of nothing / Let go and tell God / Make me an instrument / He is no farther than a thought away / Oh how He must love me / God specialises / Nothing can separate me (from your love).
LP: . . . . MYR 1180
MC: . . . . MC 1180

MUSIC SPEAKS LOUDER THAN WORDS.
Tracks: / Nights on Broadway / You are / Dreamer of a dream, A / Music speaks louder than words / Cotton Candi / Listen to the music / When you want love / One more chance / On love / Main thing / Before the next teardrop falls / Music speaks louder than words (reprise).
LP: . . . . K 56360

STAND UP AND BE A WITNESS.
Tracks: / Stand up / I'm depending on you / You don't know / He's always there / Advance / God's got an answer / Until you make it through / Glory of Jesus / Hallel.
LP: . . . . BMLP 077

SUSPICIOUS MINDS.
Tracks: / Love and be free / Suspicious minds / In the still of the night / Sunshine of our love, The / Hurry sundown / Tender hooks / Count on me.
LP: . . . . SHLP 1005
MC: . . . . ZCSH 1005

TELL IT LIKE IT IS (Staton, Candi/ Bettye Swann).
Tracks: / Someone you use / I'd rather be an old man's sweetheart (Full title: I'd rtather be an old man's sweetheart (than a young man's) / Evidence / Sweet feeling / I'm just a prisoner (of your good lovin') / Do your duty / Get it when I want it / Tell it like it is / These arms of mine / No faith, no love / Cover me / Don't you ever get tired (of hurtin' me) / You're up to your same old tricks again / Today I started loving you again / Willie and Laura Mac Jones.
LP: . . . . SSL 6003
MC: . . . . TCSSL 6003

YOUNG HEARTS RUN FREE.
Tracks: / Run to me / Destiny / What a feeling / You bet your sweet / Sweet love / Young hearts run free / Living for you / Summer time with you / I know.
LP: . . . . K 56259

Staton, Dakota

CRAZY HE CALLS ME.
Tracks: / Crazy he calls me / Idaho / Invitation / Can't live without him anymore / I never dreamt / Party's over, The / Angel eyes / No moon at all / What do you know about love / Morning, noon or night / How does it feel? / How high the moon.
LP: . . . . JAS 303
MC: . . . . JAS C303

LATE LATE SHOW.
Tracks: / Broadway / Trust in me / Summertime / Misty / Foggy day, A / What do you see in her? / Late late show, The / My funny valentine / Give me the simple life / You showed me the way / Moonray / Ain't no use.
LP: . . . . CAPS 2600101
MC: . . . . TC CAPS 260 010-4

LET ME OFF UPTOWN.
Tracks: / When lights are low / Willow weep for me / But not for me / You don't know what love is / Best thing for you, The / Song is you, The / Avalon / Until the real things come along / If I should lose you / Gone with the wind / Let me off uptown / Anything goes / When sunny gets blue / They all laughed / Too close for comfort / Cherokee / September in the rain / East of the sun / It's you or no one / Song is ended, The / Goodbye / Love walked in.
LP: . . . . REN 005

Stator

STATOR (Various artists).
2LP: . . . . INNR 001

Status Quid

BORING SONGS (see under Hee Bee Gee Bees).

Status Quo

100 MINUTES OF STATUS QUO.
MC: . . . . ZCTON 101

1982.
Tracks: / She don't fool me / Young pretender / Get out and walk / Jealousy / I love rock 'n' roll / Resurrection / Dear John / Doesn't matter / I want the world to know / I should have known / Big man.
LP: 6302 169

AIN'T COMPLAINING.
LP: . . . . VERH 58
MC: . . . . VERHC 58

B SIDES AND RARITIES.
Tracks: / I (who have nothing) / Neighbour neighbour / Hurdy gurdy man / Laticia / (We ain't got) nothin' yet / I want it / Almost but not quite there / Wait just a minute / Gentleman Joe's sidewalk cafe / To be free / When my mind is not alive / Make me stay a little bit longer / Auntie Nellie / Price of love, The / Little Miss Nothing / Down the dustpipe / Face without a soul / In my chair / Gerdundula / Tune to the music / Good thinking Batman / Time to fly / Do you live in fire / Josie.
2LP: . . . . CCSLP 271
MC: . . . . CCSMC 271

BACK TO BACK.
Tracks: / Mess of the blues / Ol' rag blues / Can't be done / Too close to the ground / No contract / Win or lose / Margerita time / Your kind of love / Stay the night / Gin down town tonight.
LP: . . . . VERH 10
MC: . . . . VERHC 10

BEST OF STATUS QUO (The Early Years).
Tracks: / Down the dustpipe / Gerdundula / In my chair / Umleitung / Lakky lady / Daughter / Railroad / Tune to the music / April, Spring, Summer and Wednesdays / Mean girl / Spinning wheel blues.
LP: . . . . NSPL 18402
MC: . . . . ZCP 18402

BLUE FOR YOU.
Tracks: / Is there a better way / Mad about the boy / Ring of a change / Blue for you / Rain / Rollin' home / That's a fact / Ease your mind.
LP: 9102 006
LP: . . . . PRICE 55

C.90 COLLECTOR.
Tracks: / Down the dustpipe / Mean girl / Lakky lady / Spinning wheel blues / Railroad / Race without a soul / Ice in the sun / Sheila / Antique Angelique / Mr. Mind detector / Price of love, The / Technicolour dreams / Spicks and specks / In my chair / Gerdundula / Na na na / Need your love / Umleitung / Pictures of matchstick men / Are you growing tired of my love / Green tambourine / Black veils of melancholy / Poor old man / So ends another life / Clown, The.
MC: . . . . C 903

CAN'T STAND THE HEAT.
LP: 9102 027

CAN'T STAND THE HEAT/ 1982.
MC: 8480904

COLLECTION: STATUS QUO.
Tracks: / Pictures of matchstick men / Green tambourine / Technicolour dreams / Sunny cellophane skies / Paradise flat / Clown, The / Antique Angelique.
2LP: . . . . PDA 046
MCSET: . . . . PDC 046

COLLECTION: STATUS QUO.
Tracks: / Ice in the sun / Lakky lady / Is it really me / Gerdundula / Neighbour neighbour / Paradise flat / Pictures of matchstick men / Mean girl / Down the dustpipe / Josie / Good thinking Batman / Lazy poker blues / Are you growing tired of my love / Antique Angelique / Umleitung / Something's going on in my head / Shy fly / Little Miss Nothing / Sunny cellophane skies / Clown, The / Nothing at all / Technicolour dreams / Spinning wheel blues / To be free.
2LP: . . . . CCSLP 114
MC: . . . . CCSMC 114

DOG OF TWO HEAD.
Tracks: / Umleitung / Na na na / Something's going on in my head / Railroad / Gerdundula / Mean girl / Someone's learning.
LP: . . . . NSPL 18371
LP: . . . . PYL 6023
MC: . . . . PYM 6023
LP: . . . . CLALP 206
MC: . . . . CLAMC 206

DOUBLE GOLD DISC.
LP: . . . . VG 416006

EARLY WORKS, THE.
Tracks: / I (who have nothing) / Neighbour, neighbour / Hurdy gurdy man / Laticia / (We ain't got) nothin' yet / I want it / Almost but not quite there / Wait just a minute / Pictures of matchstick men / Gentleman Joe's sidewalk cafe / Black veils of melancholy / To be free / Ice in the sun / When my mind is not live / Elizabeth dreams / Paradise flat / Technicolour dreams / Spicks and specks / Sheila / Sunny cellophane skies / Green tambourine / Make me stay a little bit longer / Auntie Nellie / Are you growing tired of my love / So ends another life / Price of love, The / Face without a soul / You're just what I was looking for today / Antique Angelique / Poor old man / Mr Mind Detector / Clown, The / Velvet curtains / Little Miss Nothing / When I awake / Nothing at all / Josie / Down the dustpipe / Time to fly / Do you live in fire / (April), Spring, Summer and Wednesdays / Daughter / Everything / Lazy poker blues / Is it really me? / Gotta go home / Junior's waiting / Shy fly / Lakky lady / Need your love / Spinning wheel blue / In my chair / Gerdundula (original version) / Tune to the music / Good thinking batman / Umleitung / Nanana / Something going on in my head / Mean girl / Railroad / Someone's learning / Nanana (2) / Nanana (3) / Gerdundula.
LPS: . . . . ESBLP 136

FRESH QUOTA.
Tracks: / Do you live in fire / Time to fly / Josie / Good thinking Batman / Neighbour neighbour / Hey little woman.
LP: . . . . DOW 2
MC: . . . . ZCDOW 2

FROM THE BEGINNING.
LPPD: . . . . PYX 4007
MC: . . . . PYM 4007
LP: . . . . PYZ 4007

FROM THE MAKERS OF....
Tracks: / Pictures of matchstick men / Ice in the sun / Down the dustpipe / In my chair / Junior's wailing / Mean girl / Gerdundula / Paper plane / Big fat mama / Roadhouse blues / Break the rules / Down down / Bye bye Johnny / Rain / Mystery song / Blue for you / Is there a better way / Again and again / Accident prone / Wild side of life / Living on an island / What you're proposing / Lies / Rock and roll / Something 'bout you baby / Dear John / Caroline / Roll over lay down / Backwater / Little lady / Don't drive my car / Whatever you want / Hold you back / Rockin' all over the world / Don't waste my time.
LPS: . . . . **PRO LP 1**
MCSET: . . . . **PRO MC 1**
LPS: . . . . **PRO BX 1**

GOLDEN HOUR OF STATUS QUO VOL. 1.
Tracks: / Pictures of matchstick men / Mr. Mind Detector / You're just what I was looking for today / Clown, The / When I awake / Ice in the sun / Spicks and specks / Poor old man / Gentleman Joe's sidewalk cafe / Sheila / Black veils of Melancholy / Price of love, The / Paradise flat / When my mind is not live / Elizabeth dreams / Are you growing tired of my love / So ends another life / Velvet curtains / Sunny cellophane skies / Face without a soul / Green tambourine.
LP: . . . . **GH 556**
MC: . . . . **ZCGH 556**
MC: . . . . **KGHMC 110**

GOLDEN HOUR OF STATUS QUO VOL. 2.
LP: . . . . **GH 604**
MC: . . . . **ZCGH 604**

HELLO.
Tracks: / And it's better now / Blue eyed lady / Caroline / Claudie / Forty five hundred times / Reason for living / Roll over lay down / Softer ride.
LP: . . . . **PRICE 16**
MC: . . . . **PRIMC 16**
LP: **6360 098**
MC: **8481724**

IN THE ARMY NOW.
LP: . . . . **VERH 36**
MC: . . . . **VERHC 36**

INTROSPECTIVE: STATUS QUO.
LP: . . . . **LINT 5003**
MC: . . . . **MINT 5003**

JUST FOR THE RECORD.
Tracks: / In my chair / Something's going on in my head / Umleitung / Railroad / Lakky lady / Nanana / Mean girl / Someone's learning / Gotta go home / Spinning wheel blues / Down the dustpipe / Gerdundula.
LP: . . . . **NSPL 18607**
MC: . . . . **ZCP 18607**

JUST SUPPOSIN'.
Tracks: / What you're proposing / Run to mummy / Don't drive my car / Lies / Over the edge / Wild ones / Name of the game / Coming and going / Rock 'n' roll.
LP: **6302 057**

LIVE AT THE N.E.C..
Tracks: / Caroline / Roll over lay down / Backwater / Little lady / Don't drive my car / Whatever you want / Hold you back / Rockin' all over the world / Over the edge / Don't waste my time.
LP: **818 947 1**
MC: **818 947 4**

LIVE: STATUS QUO.
Tracks: / Backwater / Big fat mama / Bye bye Johnny / Caroline / Don't waste my time / Forty five hundred times / In the chair / Is there a better way / Junior's wailing / Just take me / Little Lady / Most of the time / Rain / Roudhose blues / Roll over lay down.
2LP: . . . . **PRID 5**
MCSET: . . . . **PRIDC 5**
LP: **6641 580**

MA KELLY'S GREASY SPOON.
Tracks: / Spinning wheel blues / Daughter / Everything / Shy fly / Junior's wailing / Lakky lady / Need your love / Lazy poker blues / Is it really me? / Gotta go home / April, Spring, Summer and Wednesdays.
LP: . . . . **NSPL 18344**
LP: . . . . **PYL 6022**
MC: . . . . **PYM 6022**

MUSIC AND MEDIA INTERVIEW PICTURE DISC.
LPPD: . . . . **MM 1221**

MUSIC OF STATUS QUO, THE (1972-1974).
Tracks: / All the reasons / Backwater / Big fat mama / Blue eyed lady / Break the rules / Caroline / Drifting away / Just take me / Paper plane / Reason for living / Roll over lay down / Softer ride.
LP: **9279 314**
MC: **7215 038**

NA NA NA.
Tracks: / Pictures of matchstick men / Ice in the sun / In my chair / Railroad / Umleitung / Daughter / Down the dustpipe / Shy fly / Mean girl / Na na na / Gerdundula / Lakky lady.
LP: . . . . **FBLP 8082**
MC: . . . . **ZCFBL 8082**

NEVER TOO LATE.
Tracks: / Something 'bout you baby I like / Take me away / Never too late / Falling in, falling out / Carol / Long ago / Mountain lady / Don't stop me now / Enough is enough / Riverside.
LP: **6302 104**

NEVER TOO LATE/ BACK TO BACK.
MC: **8480884**

NIGHTRIDING: STATUS QUO.
Tracks: / Pictures of matchstick men / Gerdundula / Are you growing tired of my love / Black veils of melancholy / Green tambourine / Mean girl / Ice in the sun / Down the dustpipe / Poor old man / Spicks and specks / In my chair / Technicolour dreams / Gotta go home / Sunny cellophane skies.
MC: . . . . **KNMC 10018**

ON THE LEVEL.
Tracks: / Broken man / Bye bye Johnny / Down, down / I saw the light / Most of the time / Night ride / Over and one / What to do / Where am I?.
LP: . . . . **PRICE 39**
MC: . . . . **PRIMC 39**
LP: **9102 002**
MC: **8481744**

PERFECT REMEDY.
LP: **842 098 1**
MC: **842 098 4**

PICTURESQUE MATCHSTICKABLE MESSAGES FROM THE STATUS QUO.
Tracks: / Black veils of melancholy / When my mind is not alive / Ice in the sun / Elizabeth dreams / Gentleman Joe's sidewalk cafe / Paradise flat / Technicolour dreams / Spicks and specks / Sheila / Sunny cellophane skies / Green tambourine / Pictures of matchstick men.
LP: . . . . **PYL 6020**
MC: . . . . **PYM 6020**

PILEDRIVER.
Tracks: / All the reasons / Big fat mama / Don't waste my time / O baby / Paper plane / Roadhouse blues / Unspoken words / Year, A.
LP: . . . . **PRICE 17**
MC: . . . . **PRIMC 17**
LP: **6360 082**
MC: **8481714**

PORTRAIT: STATUS QUO.
LP: . . . . **BRLP 54**
MC: . . . . **BRMC 54**

QUO.
Tracks: / Backwater / Break the rules / Don't think it matters / Drifting away / Fine, fine, fine / Just take me / Lonely man / Slow train.
LP: . . . . **PRICE 38**
MC: . . . . **PRIMC 38**
LP: **9102 001**

QUO/ BLUE FOR YOU.
MC: **8480894**

QUOTATIONS VOL. 1 The Early Years.
Tracks: / I (who have nothing) / Neighbour neighbour / Hurdy gurdy man / Laticia / (We ain't got) nothin' yet / I want it / Almost but not quite there / Wait just a minute.
LP: . . . . **PYL 6024**
MC: . . . . **PYM 6024**

QUOTATIONS VOL 2 (Alternatives).
Tracks: / To be free / Make me stay a little bit longer / Auntie Nellie / Price of love, The / Down the dustpipe / In my chair / Gerdundula / Tune to the music / Good thinking Batman / Time to fly / Do you live in fire / Jose.
LP: . . . . **PYL 6025**
MC: . . . . **PYM 6025**

REST OF STATUS QUO, THE.
LP: . . . . **PKL 5546**
MC: . . . . **ZCPKB 5546**

ROCK TIL YOU DROP.
Tracks: / Like a zombie / All we really wanna do (Polly) / Fakin' the blues / One man band / Rock 'til you drop / Can't give you more / Warning whot / Let's work together / Bring it on home / No problems / Good sign / Tommy / Nothing comes easy / Fame or money / Price of love / Forty five hundred times.
LP: **5103411**
MC: **5103414**

ROCKIN' ALL OVER THE WORLD.
Tracks: / Baby boy / Can't give you more / Dirty water / For you / Hard time / Hold you back / Let's ride / Rockin' all over the world / Too far gone / Who am I? / You don't own me / Rockers rollin'.
LP: . . . . **PRICE 87**
MC: . . . . **PRIMC 87**

ROCKING ALL OVER THE YEARS.
Tracks: / Pictures of matchstick men / Ice in the sun / Paper plane / Caroline / Break the rules / Down down / Roll over lay down / Rain / Wild side of life / Rockin' all over the world / Whatever you want / What you're proposin' / Something 'bout you baby I like / Rock'n'roll / Dear John / Ol' rag blues / Marguerita time / Wanderer, The / Rollin' home / In the army now / Burning bridges (on and off and on again) / Anniversary waltz (part 1).
2LP: **846 797 1**
MCSET: **846 797 2**
MC: **846 797 4**

SPARE PARTS.
Tracks: / Face without a soul / You're just what I was looking for today / Are you growing tired of my love / Antique Angelique / So ends another life / Poor old man / Mr. Mind detector / Clown, The / Velvet curtains / Little Miss Nothing / When I awake / Nothing at all.
LP: . . . . **PYL 6021**
MC: . . . . **PYM 6021**
LP: . . . . **CLALP 205**
MC: . . . . **CLAMC 205**

SPOTLIGHT ON STATUS QUO.
Tracks: / Pictures of matchstick men / Ice in the sun / Spicks and specks / Antique Angelique / Are you growing tired of my love / Black veils of melancholy / Down the dustpipe / Spinning wheel blues / Umleitung / Someone's learning / Daughter / Lakky lady / In my chair / Mean girl / Railroad / Junior's wailing / Is it really me / Gotta go home / Tune to the music / Everything / Something's going on in my head / Shy fly / Lazy poker blues / Na na na / Gerdundula.
2LP: . . . . **SPOT 1010**
MCSET: . . . . **ZCSPT 1010**

SPOTLIGHT ON STATUS QUO VOLUME 2.
Tracks: / Need your love / Face without a soul / To be free / Sheila / Green tambourine / Price of love / Spring, summer and Wednesdays / Gentleman Joe's sidewalk cafe / When my mind is not live / So ends another life / Mr. Mind Detector / Poor old man / Little Miss Nothing / When I awake / Sunny cellophane skies / Paradise flat / Velvet curtains / Clown / Nothing at all / Jose / Make me stay a little bit longer / Technicolour dreams / You're just what I was looking for today / Elizabeth dreams.
LP: . . . . **SPOT 1028**
MC: . . . . **ZCSPT 1028**

STATUS QUO (1).
Tracks: / Sunny cellophane skies / Paradise / Mr. Mind detector / Clown, The / When my mind is not alive / Antique Angelique.
LP: . . . . **HMA 260**
MC: . . . . **HSC 322**

STATUS QUO (2).
Tracks: / Down the dustpipe / Lakky lady / Spinning wheel blues / Shy fly / Gerdundula / Daughter / Railroad / Umleitung / Mean girl / Everything / Little Miss Nothing / Junior's wailing / Tune to the music / In my chair / When I awake / So ends another life / Nothing at all / Something on in my head / Someone's learning / Sheila / Price of love, The / Ice in the sun / Got to go home / Na na na.
2LP: . . . . **SSD 8035**
MCSET: . . . . **SSDC 8035**

STATUS QUO: INTERVIEW PICTURE DISC.
LPPD: . . . . **BAK 2110**

TO BE OR NOT TO BE.
Tracks: / Drifting away / Let me fly / Night ride / Softer ride / Lonely nights / Too far gone / Runaway / Don't drive my car / Hard ride / Backwater / Ring of a change / All through the night.
LP: . . . . **CN 2062**
MC: **CN4 2062**

TWELVE GOLD BARS VOL.1.
Tracks: / Rockin' all over the world / Down down / Caroline / Paper plane / Break the rules / Again and again / Mystery song / Roll over lay down / Rain / Wild side of life / Whatever you want / Living on an island.
LP: . . . . **QUOTV 1**

TWELVE GOLD BARS VOLS. 1 & 2.
Tracks: / Rockin' all over the world / Down down / Caroline / Paper plane / Break the rules / Again and again / Mystery song / Roll over lay down / Rain / Wild side of life / Whatever you want / Living in an island / What you're proposing / Lies / Something 'bout you baby I like / Don't drive my car / Dear John / Rock and roll / Ol' rag blues / Mess of the blues / Marguerita time / Going down town tonight / Wanderer.
2LP: . . . . **QUOTV 2**
MC: . . . . **QUOMC 2**

WHATEVER YOU WANT.
Tracks: / Breaking away / Come rock with me / High flyer / Living on an island / Rockin' on / Runaway / Shady lady / Whatever you want / Who asked you / Your smiling face.
LP: **9102 037**

WHATEVER YOU WANT/ JUST SUPPOSIN'.
MC: **8480874**

WORKS: STATUS QUO.
Tracks: / Pictures of matchstick men / Ice in the sun / Black veils of melancholy / Are you growing tired of my love? / Down the dustpipe / In my chair / Mean girl / Lakky lady.
LP: . . . . **DOW 10**
MC: . . . . **ZCDOW 10**

Stavin, Mary

IT TAKES TWO (see Best, George & Mary Stavin) (Stavin, Mary & George Best).

Stavis, George

MORNING MOOD.
Tracks: / Sunlight / Full moon / Morning mood / Finland / Goblins / Kingpins / Carnival / Mistral / Hall of the Mountain King.
LP: . . . . **APN 30201**

Stayin' Alive

STAYIN' ALIVE (Film Soundtrack) (Various artists).
Tracks: / Woman in you: *Bee Gees* / Love you too much: *Bee Gees* / Breakout: *Bee Gees* / Someone belonging to someone: *Bee Gees* / Life goes on: *Bee Gees* / Stayin' alive: *Bee Gees* / Far from over: *Stallone, Frank* / Look out for number one: *Stallone, Frank* / Finding out the hard way: *Various artists* / Moody girl: *Various artists* / (We dance) so close to the fire: *Various artists* / I'm never gonna give you up: *Various artists*.
LP: . . . . **RSBG 3**
MC: . . . . **TRSBG 3**

Stayrcase

STAYRCASE.
LP: . . . . **MR 451**

Stead, Joe

BAKER'S SCORE, A.
LP: . . . . **GVR 230**

HARVEST HAS BEEN TAKEN IN, THE.
LP: . . . . **SFA 120**

LIVE AT THE WHITTLEBURY FOLK CLUB.
Tracks: / Then I took out assurance upon her / Sailor Jack McCoy / Whittlebury buses / Standing behind Richard Burton / I missed the last bus with you / Cold night in Heathrow, A / Irish jokes / Tottie poem / Wife jokes / Goodbye again / Trip to the dentist, A / I didn't care / Terrible saga of the Tamworth man, The / Sister Josephine / All about coming home late / Loneliness of the long distance folk singer, The.
LP: . . . . **SFA 007**

OBSCENITIES.
Tracks: / Mary Baker city mix / Lag's song, The / Sunday supplement world / Advice to fellas (about these things called women) / Hop hop hop / Ting a ling a loo / Old Fid / Proper man, A / No free lunch / These are more enlightened days / Twice shy / Stoned on Red Leb / Daniel in the lions den (he locked the lion's jaw).
LP: . . . . **SFA 100**

Steady B

BRING THE BEAT BACK.
Tracks: / Bring the beat back / Get physical / Suprise / Cheating girl / Do the fila / Stupid Fresh / Hit me / Nothin' but the bass / Yo mutha.
LP: . . . . **HIP 45**
MC: . . . . **HIPC 45**

GOING STEADY.
Tracks: / Analogy of a black man / Stone cold hustler / Attitude problem / Anyway U want it / Going steady / Ego trippin' / Nasty girls / Mac Daddy / Purple haze.
LP: . . . . **HIP 90**
MC: . . . . **HIPC 90**

LET THE HUSTLERS PLAY.
Tracks: / Let the hustlers play.
LP: . . . . **HIP 71**
MC: . . . . **HIPC 71**

STEADY B V.
LP: . . . . **HIP 110**
MC: . . . . **HIPC 110**

WHAT'S MY NAME.
Tracks: / Gangster rockin' / My Benz / Hold it now / Rockin music / Introduction / Hilltop, The / Rong ho'le / Believe me

das bad / What's my name / Don't disturb the groove.
LP: 10601 J
LP: HIP 54
MC: HIPC 54

Steady, Freddie

LUCKY 7.
Tracks: / Say you'll go / What I got / Night time / Love you tonight / High lonesome country soul / I like whiskey / I hear neon angels sing / You can't judge a book by the cover / I've been framed / Ride through wild country.
LP: HLD 005

Steafel, Sheila

COMIC RHYMES (See under Rushton, William) (Steafel, Sheila & William Rushton).

Steagall, Rod

COWBOY FAVOURITES.
Tracks: / Horses and wars / When the work's all done this fall / Navajo train / Smokey / Tennessee stud / Red headed stranger / Riding down the canyon / Little Joe the wrangler / Strawberry roan / My heroes have always been cowboys / Bandito gold / Dawson legate / Two pairs of Levis and a pair of Justin boots / Night the Copenhagen saved the day, The / Tight levis and yellow ribbons / Tyin' knots in the devils tails / Willie the wondering gypsy and me / I was born to be a cowboy / Running out of sunsets / One empty cot in the bunkhouse.
2LP: Delta 1166

Stealers Wheel

BEST OF STEALERS WHEEL (Featuring Gerry Rafferty).
Tracks: / Stuck in the middle with you / Nothing's gonna to change my mind / Star / This morning / Steamboat row / Next to me / Right or wrong / Go as you please / Benediction / Waltz / Blind faith / Late again / Wheelin' / Jose.
LP: CSAP 106
MC: CSAPMC 106

Stealing Heaven

STEALING HEAVEN (Film Soundtrack) (Various artists).
LP: TER 1166
MC: ZCTER 1166

Steam...

STEAM AND HARNESS (Various).
LP: SDL 284
MC: CSDL 284

Steam (group)

NA NA HEY HEY KISS HIM GOODBYE (OLD GOLD) (See under Bobby Hebb - Sunny).

Steam Jenny

GLEN COE.
Tracks: / Glencoe / Whisky in the jar / Loch Lomond / Mingulay boat song / Ae fond kiss / Kelty clippie / Wild mountain thyme / Gipsy rover / Coulters candy / Gallowa' hills / Bunch of thyme / Rose of Allandale / What you meant to me.
MC: ZCLBP 2008

Steampacket

FIRST SUPERGROUP, THE.
Tracks: / Can I get a witness? / In crowd, The / Baby take me / Baby baby / Back at the chicken shack / Cry me a river / Oh baby, don't you do it / Holy smoke / Lord remember me.
LP: LIK 14

Stecher, Jody

RASA (Stecher, Jody & Krishna Bhatt).
LP: CCF 2

SONG THAT WILL LINGER (Stecher, Jody & Kate Brislin).
LP: ROUNDER 0274

Steding, Walter

DANCING IN HEAVEN.
Tracks: / You got it / All the way / Dancing in heaven / My room / Joke, The / Crusade / Lexington / Secret spy / White house / Flip flop / Bee's, The.
LP: CHR 1413
MC: ZCHR 1413

Steel Angels

AND THE ANGELS WERE MADE OF STEEL.
LP: MAD 2016

Steel Band

CARNIVAL OF ANTIGUA VOL.2.
Tracks: / Pusch (steelband) / Keep the pace (chant) / Tune for Pan (steelband) / Lynch scratch band / Brass band / Sugar cane (chant) / Supa stars (steelband) / Farmers (band) / Explosion.
LP: PSTZ 2008

HEART OF TRINIDAD.
LP: GNPS 82

PANORAMA.
MC: CS 4015

STEELBANDS FROM TRINIDAD AND TOBAGO (Various artists).
MC: CS 4017

Steel Crazy

STEEL CRAZY.
LP: AABT 200

Steel, Ivy

REINCARNATION (Steel, Ivy & friends).
LP: JC 0001

Steel Pole Bath Tub

LURCH.
Tracks: / Christina / Hey you / Paranoid / I am Sam I am / Bee sting / Swerve / Heaven on dirt / Lime away / River, The / Time to die / Welcome aboard it's love / Hey Bo Diddley / Thru the windshield of love / Tear it apart.
LP: TUPLP 16

Steel Pulse

BABYLON THE BANDIT.
Tracks: / Save black music / Not King James version / School boy's crush / Sugar daddy / Kick that habit / Blessed is the man / Love walks out / Don't be afraid / Babylon the bandit.
LP: EKT 30
MC: EKT 30 C

CAUGHT YOU.
Tracks: / Drug squad / Harassment / Reggae fever / Shining / Heart of stone / Rumours / Caught you dancing / Burning flame / Higher than high / Nyabinghi voyage.
LP: ILPS 9613

EARTH CRISIS.
LP: WMDLP 002
MC: WMDC 002

HANDSWORTH REVOLUTION.
Tracks: / Handsworth revolution / Bad man / Soldiers / Sound check / Prodigal / Ku klux klan / Prediction / Macka splaff.
LP: ILPS 9502
MC: ICT 9502
MC: RRCT 24

REGGAE GREATS.
Tracks: / Sound system / Babylon makes the rules / Don't give in / Soldier / Prodigal son / Ku klux klan / Macka splaff / Drug squad / Reggae fever / Handsworth revolution.
LP: IRG 3
MC: IRGC 3
LP: ICM 2049
MC: 842 719 4

STATE OF EMERGENCY.
Tracks: / State of emergency / Dead end circuit / Steal a kiss / Hijacking / Push / Love this reggae music / Reaching out / Said you was an angel / Melting pot / Disco dropping out.
LP: MCA 42192
LP: MCF 3427
MC: MCFC 3427

TRIBUTE TO THE MARTYRS.
Tracks: / Unseen guest / Sound system / Jah Pickney / Biko's kindred lament / Tribute to the martyrs / Babylon makes the rules / Uncle George / Blasphemy.
LP: ILPS 9568
MC: RRCT 17

TRUE DEMOCRACY.
LP: WMDLP 001
MC: WMDC 001

VICTIMS.
LP: MCA 10172
MC: MCAC 10172

Steel, Rusti

MORE DOLLARS THAN SENSE (Steel, Rusti & The Tin Tax).
LP: NERD 051

Steele, Chrissy

MAGNET TO STEELE.
Tracks: / Love you till it hurts / Armed and dangerous / Move over / Love don't last forever / Try me / Two bodies / Murder in the first degree / King of hearts / Magnet to Steele / Two lips (don't make a kiss) / Cry myself to sleep.
LP: CHR 1843
MC: ZCHR 1843

Steele, Davy

LONG TIME GETTING HERE.
LP: BKN 1001

Steele, Jan

VOICES AND INSTRUMENTS (Steele,Jan/John Cage).
LP: EGED 25

Steele, Jo Ann

COUNTRY GIRL.
Tracks: / Loving you, loving me / Bits and pieces / Beginning of goodbye / If I were you babe / Fool in you (ain't foolin' me), The / My want - your fever's going down / I feel the cheater is you / I cry a lot in school / One too many times / Picking up the pieces / I dreamed it was over / Unless you stop hurting me / Love on borrowed time / Children of my mind / I can't keep my hands off you.
LP: BDL 1053

Steele, Joan

LONESOME NO MORE (Steele, Joan/John Magaldi).
LP: AP 156

LOOKING BACK - EARL BROWN COMPOSITIONS.
LP: AP 239

'ROUND MIDNIGHT.
LP: AP 94

Steele, Maureen

NATURE OF THE BEAST.
Tracks: / Nature of the beast / Physical therapy / Save the night for me / Sneak preview / Rock my heart / Bad girls do it better / Do you like it when I hurt you / Sidetracked / My shy lover / Boys will be boys.
LP: ZL 72372
MC: ZK 72372

Steele, Sandra

SANDRA STEELE.
Tracks: / Your love still brings me to my knees / I'm hung up on you / Love we share, The / Why can't you do it with me / Better than ever / Make me your lover / I'm afraid to fall in love with you / Person to person / I'll wait you out / Half the way.
LP: UAG 30301

Steele, Terry

KING OF HEARTS.
Tracks: / Prisoner of love / If I told you once / Delicious / Tonight's the night / Get that love / Anyway you want it / What cha' tryin' to do / You fixed the wound / Forever yours / My prayer.
LP: K1 94101
LP: 794 101 1
MC: K4 94101
MC: 794 101 4

Steele, Tommy

20 GREATEST HITS: TOMMY STEELE.
Tracks: / Singing the blues / Rock with the caveman / Butterfingers / Come on, let's go / Water water / Only man on the island, The / Marriage type love / Light up the sky / Elevator rock / Little white bull / Handful of songs / It's all happening / Happy guitar / Shiralee / Knee deep in the blues / Nairobi / Tallahassee lassie / She's too far above me / What a mouth / Flash, bang, wallop.
LP: SPR 8531
MC: SPC 8531

FOCUS ON TOMMY STEELE.
Tracks: / Little white bull / Butterfingers / Rebel rock / Georgia on my mind / Cannibal pot / Kookaburra / Knee deep in the blues / Where have all the flowers gone / Flash bang wallop / Giddy up a ding dong / Hiawatha / Come on, let's go / She's too far above me / What a mouth.
2LP: FOS 21/22

REBEL ROCK.
Tracks: / Rock with the caveman / Nairobi / Butterfingers / Singing the blues / Little Darlin' / Hollerin' and screamin' / Come on let's go / Hey you / Grandad's rock / Shout / It's all happening / Put a ring on her finger / Boys and girls / Doomsday rock / Rock around the town / Razzle dazzle / Young love / Knee deep in the blues.
MCSET: DTO 10287

ROCK 'N' ROLL YEARS, THE (Steele, Tommy & The Steelemen).
Tracks: / Rock with the caveman / C'mon let's go / Butterfly / Give give give / Elevator rock / Rebel rock / You gotta go / Build up / Put a ring on her finger / You were mine / Swallertail coat / Singing the blues / Doomsday rock / Knee deep in the blues / Two eyes / Take me back baby / Writing on the wall / Hey you / Teenage party / Plant a kiss / Rock around the town / Drunken guitar / Tallahassee lassie.
LP: SEE 203

TOMMY STEELE STAGE SHOW (Steele, Tommy & The Steelemen).
Tracks: / Giddy up a ding dong / Treasure of love / Honky tonk blues / Razzle dazzle / Kaw-liga / Teenage party / Wedding bells / What is this thing called love / On the move / Rock with the cavemen.
LP: LFT 1287

TOMMY STEELE STORY (Steele, Tommy & The Steelemen).
Tracks: / Take me back baby / I like / Butterfingers / Handful of songs / You gotta go / Water water / Cannibal pot / Will it be you / Two eyes / Build up / Time to kill / Elevator rock / Teenage party / Doomsday rock.
LP: LFT 1288

VERY BEST OF TOMMY STEELE.
Tracks: / Nairobi / Tallahassie Lassie / Kookaburra / Flash, bang, wallop / She's too far above me / Happy guitar / Young love / Butterfingers / Green eye / Where have all the flowers gone? / Handful of songs / Marriage type love / Georgia on my mind / Come on let's go / Sweet Georgia Brown / It's all happening / Only man on the island, The / Princess / Writing on the wall, The / What a mouth (what a North and South).
MC: PWKMC 4071P

Steeler

RULIN' THE EARTH.
LP: ES 4009

STEELER.
LP: ES 4001
LP: SH 1007

STRIKE BACK.
LP: 081 890

UNDERCOVER.
LP: 087 510
MC: 087 511

Steeleye Span

ADAM CATCHED EVE.
LP: BD 3004

ALL AROUND MY HAT.
LP: 41 5706 1
MC: 41 5706 4
LP: CHR 1091
MC: ZCHR 1091
LP: SH 79059 CD

BACK IN LINE.
LP: FLUT 2
LP: SHAN 79063

BELOW THE SALT.
Tracks: / Spotted cow / Rosebuds in June / Jigs / Sheepcrook and black dog / Royal forester / King Henry / Gaudete / John Barleycorn / Saucy sailor.
LP: CHR 1008
MC: ZCHR 1008
LP: SHAN 79039

BEST OF AND THE REST OF.
MC: ARLC 1012

BEST OF STEELEYE SPAN.
Tracks: / Gaudete / All around my hat / Thomas the rhymer / Alison Gross / Little Sir Hugh / Cam ye o'er frae France / Long lankin / Gone to America / Let her go down / Black Jack Davy / Bach goes to Limerick.
LP: CHR 1467
MC: ZCHR 1467

COLLECTION: STEELEYE SPAN.
MC: CCSMC 292

COMMONERS CROWN.
Tracks: / Little Sir Hugh / Bach goes to Limerick / Long lankin / Dogs and ferrets / Galtee farmer / Demon lover, The / Elf call / Weary cutters / New York girls.
LP: CHR 1071
MC: ZCHR 1071

EARLY YEARS, THE.
Tracks: / Blacksmith / Marrowbones / Westron wynde / All things are quite silent / Lovely on the water / Boys of Bedlam / My Johnny was a shoemaker / Cold haily windy night / Horn of the hunter / Lark in the morning, The / Prince Charlie Stuart / Reels / Dark-eyed sailor / Rave on / Brisk young butcher, The / Wee weaver, The / When I was on horseback / Female drummer / Skewball.
2LP: VSOPLP 132
MC: VSOPMC 132

FOLK ELECTRIC FOLK Original field recordings.
MC: 60-123

HARK THE VILLAGE WAIT.
Tracks: / Calling-on song, A / Blacksmith / Fisherman's wife, The / Blackleg miner / Dark-eyed sailor / Copshawholme fair / All things are quite silent / Hills of Greenmore / My Johnny was a shoemaker / Lowlands of Holland, The / Twa corbies / One night as I lay on my bed.
LP: CREST 22
MC: ZCEST 22
LP: SHAN 79052
LP: CREST 003
MC: CRESTMC 003

LIVE AT LAST.
Tracks: / Athole highlanders, The / Walter Bulwer's polka / Saucy sailor / Black freighter / Maid and the palmer / Hunting the wren / Montrose / Bonnets so blue / False knight on the road.
LP: CHR 1199
MC: ZCHR 1199

NOW WE ARE SIX.
Tracks: / Seven hundred elves / Edwin / Drink down the moon / Now we are six / Thomas the rhymer / Mooncoin jig, The / Long-a-growing / Two magicians / Twinkle, twinkle little star / To know him is to love him.

LP: . . . . CHR 1053
MC: . . . . ZCHR 1053
LP: . . . . SH 79060 CD

ORIGINAL MASTERS.
Tracks: / Sir James the rose / Black Jack Davy / All around my hat / Wife of Usher's well, The / Fighting for strangers / Thomas the rhymer / Seven hundred elves / Long lankin / Elf call / Cam ye o'er frae France / Bonnie moorhen, The / Alison Gross / Mooncoin jig, The / Drink down the moon / Stewball / Lovely on the water / Jigs / Brides favourite, The / Tansey's fancy / One misty moisty morning / Saucy sailor / Gaudete.
2LP: . . . . CJT 3
MC: . . . . ZCJTD 3

PARCEL OF ROGUES.
Tracks: / One misty moisty morning / Alison Gross / Bold poachers, The / Ups and down, The / Robbery with violins / Wee wee man, The / Weaver and the factory maid, The / Rogues in a nation / Can ye o'er frae France / Hares on the mountain.
LP: . . . . CHR 1046
MC: . . . . ZCHR 1046
LP: . . . . SHAN 79045

PLEASE TO SEE THE KING.
Tracks: / Blacksmith / Cold, haily, windy night / Bryan O'Lynn / Hag with the money, The / Prince Charlie Stuart / Boys of Bedlam / False knight on the road / Lark in the morning, The / Female drummer / King, The / Rave on (Bonus track on the 3/91 releases.).
LP: . . . . CREST 8
MC: . . . . ZCEST 8
LP: . . . . CAS 1029
LP: . . . . CREST 005
MC: . . . . CRESTMC 005

PORTFOLIO.
LP: . . . . CHR 1647
MC: . . . . ZCHR 1647

ROCKET COTTAGE.
Tracks: / London / Bosnian hornpipes, The / Ofreo / Nathan's reel / Twelve witches / Brown girl, The / Fighting for strangers / Silgo maid / Sir James the Rose / Drunkard, The.
LP: . . . . CHR 1123
MC: . . . . ZCHR 1123

ROCKET COTTAGE (CASSETTE SET).
MCSET: . . . . ZCDP 110

SAILS OF SILVER.
Tracks: / Sails of silver / My love / Barnet Fair / Senior service / Gone to America / Where are they now / Let her go down / Longbone / Marigold/harvest home / Tell me why.
LP: . . . . CHR 1304

STEELEYE SPAN.
Tracks: / Bryan O'Lynn / Skewball / Dancing at Whitsun / Paddy Clancy's jig / Gower wassail / Wee weaver, The / Dowd's favourite / Four knights drunk / General Taylor / Lowlands of Holland, The.
LP: . . . . SHM 3040
MC: . . . . HSC 3040

STEELEYE SPAN (2LP).
2LP: . . . . CR 5154
MCSET: . . . . CRT 5154

STORM FORCE TEN.
Tracks: / Awake awake / Sweep chimney sweep / Wife of the soldier, The / Victory, The / Black freighter / Some rival / Treadmill song, The / Seventeen come Sunday.
LP: . . . . CHR 1151
MC: . . . . ZCHR 1151

SUMMER SOLSTICE.
LP: . . . . SHAN 79046

TEMPTED AND TRIED.
2LP: . . . . ADD 9
MC: . . . . ZDD 9

TEN MAN MOP (..Or Mr Reservoir Rides Again).
Tracks: / Gower wassail / Jigs / Four nights drunk / When I was on horseback / Marrowbones / Captain Coulston / Reel: Wee weave / Skewball.
LP: . . . . CREST 9
MC: . . . . ZCEST 9
LP: . . . . SHAN 79049
MC: . . . . SHANC 79049
LP: . . . . CREST 009
MC: . . . . CRESTMC 009

TIME SPAN.
2LP: . . . . CRD 1

Steelheart

STEELHEART.
Tracks: / Love ain't easy / Can't stop me lovin' you / Like never before / I'll never let you go / Everybody loves Eileen / Shelia / Gimme gimme / Rock 'n' roll (I just wanna) / She's gone / Down 'n' dirty.
LP: . . . . MCG 6118
MC: . . . . MCGC 6118

Steelover

GLOVE ME.
LP: . . . . SKULL 8361

Steely & Cleevie

AT THE TOP.
LP: . . . . RMM 1653

PRESENT SOUNDBOY CLASH.
LP: . . . . FILER 292
MC: . . . . FILERCT 292

REAL ROCK STYLE.
Tracks: / Now mi come / Rich and switch / Homely girl / Row your love / Real version / Love me / Shake them down / Shock out / Live good / Rock version.
LP: . . . . VPRL 1047

Steely Dan

AJA.
Tracks: / Black cow / Aja / Deacon blues / Peg / Home at last / I got the news / Josie.
LP: . . . . MCL 1745
MC: . . . . MCLC 1745
LP: . . . . ABCL 5225

BEST OF STEELY DAN (Do It Again).
Tracks: / Rikki don't lose that number / Reelin' in the years / Kid charlemagne / Doctor WU / FM / My old school / Fez, The / Do it again / Pretzel logic / Any major dude will tell you / Black Friday / Showbiz kids / Peg / Haitian divorce.
LP: . . . . STAR 2297
MC: . . . . STAC 2297

CAN'T BUY A THRILL.
Tracks: / Do it again / Dirty work / Kings / Midnite cruiser / Only a fool / Reelin' in the years / Fire in the hole / Brooklyn (owes the charmer and me) / Change of the guard / Turn that heartbeat over again.
LP: . . . . MCL 1769
MC: . . . . MCLC 1769
LP: . . . . ABCL 5024

CAN'T BUY A THRILL/AJA.
Tracks: / Do it again / Dirty work / Kings / Midnite cruiser / Only a fool / Reelin' in the years / Fire in the hole / Brook Lyn (owes the charmer and me) / Change of the guard / Turn that heartbeat over again / Black cow / AJA / Deacon blues / Peg / Home at last / I got the news / Josie.
MCSET: . . . . MCA 2 101

COUNTDOWN TO ECSTASY.
Tracks: / Bodhisattva / Razor boy / Boston rag / Your gold teeth / Show biz kid / My old school / Pearl of the quarter / King of the world.
LP: . . . . MCL 1654
MC: . . . . MCLC 1654
LP: . . . . FA 3069
MC: . . . . TCFA 3069

GAUCHO.
Tracks: / Babylon sisters / Hey nineteen / Glamour profession / Gaucho / Time out of mind / My rival / Third world man.
LP: . . . . MCF 3090
MC: . . . . MCFC 3090
LP: . . . . MCL 1814
MC: . . . . MCLC 1814

GOLD.
Tracks: / Hey nineteen / Green earring / Deacon blues / Chain lightning / FM / Black cow / King of the world / Babylon sisters.
LP: . . . . MCF 3145
MC: . . . . MCFC 3145
LP: . . . . MCA 10387
MC: . . . . MCAC 10387

GREATEST HITS: STEELY DAN.
LP: . . . . ABCD 616
2LP: . . . . MCLD 608

GREATEST HITS: STEELY DAN.
Tracks: / Do it again / Reeling in the years / My old school / Bodhisattva / Show biz kids / East St. Louis toodle-oo / Rikki don't lose that number / Pretzel logic / Any major dude will tell you / Here at the western world / Black Friday / Bad sneakers / Doctor Wu / Haitian divorce / Fez, The / Kid Charlemagne / Peg / Josie.
LP: . . . . ABCD 616

KATHY LIED.
Tracks: / Black Friday / Bad sneakers / Rose darling / Daddy don't live in that New York City no more / Doctor Wu / Everyone's gone to the movies / Your gold teeth II / Chain lightning / Any world (that I'm welcome to) / Throw back the little ones.
LP: . . . . MCL 1800
MC: . . . . MCLC 1800
LP: . . . . ABLC 5094

KATY LIED/ROYAL SCAM.
Tracks: / Black Friday / Bad sneakers / Rose darling / Daddy don't live in that New York City no more / Doctor Wu / Everyone's gone to the movies / Your gold teeth II / Chain lightning / Any world (that I'm welcome to) / Throw back the little ones / Kid Charlemagne / Caves of Altmira / Don't take me alive / Sign in stranger / Fez, The / Green earring / Haitian divorce / Everything you did / Royal scam, The.
MCSET: . . . . MCA 2 109

OLD REGIME.
Tracks: / Brain tap shuffle / Came back baby / Don't let me in / Old regime / Brooklyn / Mock turtle song / Soul rain / I can't function / Yellow peril / Let george do it.
LP: . . . . THBL 040
MC: . . . . THBC 040

PRETZEL LOGIC.
Tracks: / Rikki don't lose that number / Night by night / Any major dude will tell you / Barrytown / East St. Louis toodle-oo / Parker's band / Thru with buzz / Pretzel logic / With a gun / Charlie freak / Monkey in your soul.
LP: . . . . MCL 1781
MC: . . . . MCLC 1781
LP: . . . . SPBA 6282

PRETZEL LOGIC/COUNTDOWN TO ECSTACY.
Tracks: / Rikki don't lose that number / Night by night / Any major dude will tell you / Barrytown / East St. Louis toodle-oo / Parkers band / Thru with buzz / Pretzel logic / With a gun / Charlie freak / Monkey in your soul / Bodhisattva / Razor boy / Boston rag / Your gold teeth / Show biz kid / My old school / Pearl of the quarter / King of the world.
MCSET: . . . . MCA 2 115

REELIN' IN THE YEARS.
Tracks: / Do it again / Reelin' in the years / My old school / Bodhisattva / Show biz kid / Rikki don't lose that number / Pretzel logic / Black Friday / Bad sneakers / Doctor Wu / Haitian divorce / Kid Charlemagne / Fez, The / Peg / Josie / Deacon blues / Hey nineteen / Babylon sisters.
LP: . . . . DANTV 1
MC: . . . . DANTC 1

ROYAL SCAM, THE.
Tracks: / Kid Charlemagne / Sign in stranger / Fez, The / Caves of Altmira / Don't take me alive / Green earring / Haitian divorce / Everything you did / Royal scam, The.
LP: . . . . MCL 1708
MC: . . . . MCLC 1708
LP: . . . . ABCL 5161
LP: . . . . DIDX 370

STONE PIANO.
Tracks: / Android warehouse / Horse in town, A / More to come / Parkers band / Ida lee / Stone piano / Any world / Take it out on me / This seat's been taken / Barrytown.
LP: . . . . THBL 054

SUN MOUNTAIN.
Tracks: / Berry town / Android warehouse / More to come / Sun mountain / Ida Lee / Any world (that I'm welcome to) / Stone piano / Caves of Altmira / Horse in town, A / Roaring of the lamb / Parker's band / Oh, wow it's you / You go where I go / This seat's been taken / Little with sugar, A / Take it out on me.
MC: . . . . SHTC 128

Steen Vigs Jazz

STEEN VIGS JAZZ ORCHESTRA.
LP: . . . . SLP 608

Steenhuis, Wout

HAWAIIAN COUNTRY.
Tracks: / Just good ol' boys / Good year for the roses, A / Hawaiian country / I can hear Kentucky calling me / For the good times / Banks of the Ohio / Sweet dreams / Rocky top / Cool and green and shady eclipse / Love's been good to me / Vaya con dios.
LP: . . . . VAL 8052
MC: . . . . VAL 68052

HAWAIIAN MEMORIES (see Kontikis feat.Wout Steenhuis) (Steenhuis, Wout & The Kontikis).

HAWAIIAN PARADISE/CHRISTMAS.
LP: . . . . WW 5106

MAGIC OF HAWAII (Steenhuis, Wout & The Kontikis).
Tracks: / Hawaiian wedding song / Trade winds / Bali Ha'i / Lovely hula hands / Pearly shell / Halekaluni / Sweet leilani / Song of the islands / Harbour lights / Beyond the reef / Drifting and dreaming / Blue Hawaii / Taboo / Hawaiian war chant / On a little bamboo bridge / Malikini hula / On the beach at Waikiki / Farewell Hawaii.
LP: . . . . WW 2012
MC: . . . . WW 20124

WOUT STEENHUIS.
Tracks: / Treasure island / Kontika hula / Catamaran / Moonglow / Jungle sleep / Beyond the reef / Tahiti nui / Trade winds / Pacific blues / Girl Friday / Nina bobo / In the wee small hours of the morning / Summertime / Makin' whoopee / She's leaving home / Bach plays Wout / My funny valentine / Bossa esplendida / I love her / Body and soul / Gentle rain, The / One who walks by the sea / Malindi / Grains of sand.
2LP: 2668019

Steeple Jack

SERENA MABOOSE.
LP: . . . . EES 016

Steig, Jeremy

OUTLAWS.
LP: . . . . ENJA 2098

SOMETHING ELSE (Steig, Jeremy/Jan Hammer).
Tracks: / Home / Cakes / Swamp carol / Down stretch / Give me some / Come with me / Dance of the mind / Up tempo thing / Elephant hump / Rock No.6 / Slow blues in G / Rock No.9 / Something else.
MC: . . . . MC 8512

Steig, William

DOCTOR DE SOTO AND OTHER STORIES.
MC: 1751

DOMINIC (CHAPTERS 1-7).
MC: 1738

ROLAND, THE MINSTREL PIG & OTHER STORIES (Channing, Carol).
MC: 1305

Stein, Andy

GOIN' PLACES (Stein, Andy & Friends).
LP: . . . . SOS 1146

Stein, Chris

WILD STYLE THEME RAP 1 (see Grandmaster Caz&Chris Stein) (Stein, Chris & Grandmaster Caz).

Stein, Ira

ELEMENTS (Stein,Ira/Russel Walder).
LP: C-1020

Stein, Lou

LOU STEIN & FRIENDS (Stein, Lou & Friends).
Tracks: / Honeysuckle rose / I'll be seeing you / Sweetest sounds, The / Dancing in the dark / Fine romance, A / Foggy day, A / All the things you are / What is this thing called love / Georgia / I'll remember April / Younger than Spring time / Let's face the music and dance.
LP: . . . . WJLPS 17

LOU STEIN TRIO (Stein, Lou Trio).
Tracks: / Take the 'A' train / No man alone / Li'l darlin' / My funny valentine / Shadow of your smile / Glad / Jumpin' at the keyboard / Hello little friend / Ballade, The / Something / Yesterday.
LP: . . . . J 0128

SOLO PIANO.
LP: . . . . AP 198

Steinbeck, John

GRAPES OF WRATH (See Under Grapes Of Wrath (book)).

SNAKE AND JOHNNY BEAR, THE.
MC: 1750

Steiner, Max

CLASSIC FILM SCORES BY MAX STEINER (see under Films) (Various artists).

REVISITED.
LP: . . . . CT MS 7

Steinman, Jim

BAD FOR GOOD.
Tracks: / Bad for good / Lost boys and golden girls / Love and death and an American guitar / Stark raving love / Out of the frying pan (and into the fire) / Surf's up / Dance in my pants / Left in the dark.
LP: . . . . EPC 32791
MC: 40 32791
LP: . . . . EPC 84361

Steinman, Lydia

TOUCH ME IN THE MORNING.
LP: . . . . UNKNOWN
MC: . . . . UNKNOWN

Stelin, Tena

WICKED INVENTION.
LP: . . . . MOWLP 002
MC: . . . . MOWCS 002

Stella

IF YOU DO LIKE MY MUSIC.
Tracks: / Si tu aimes ma musique / No girl like me / I remember you / Got to have you back / Ten miles west of Heaven / Solitaire / If you do like my music / Mr. Tattooed Man / Baby it's up to you / Renegade / Yo yo.
LP: . . . . PTLS 1074

Stems

AT FIRST SIGHT.
LP: . . . . L 38735

Stenberg, Berdien

RONDO RUSSO.
Tracks: / Moldau / Rondo Russo / Gymnopedie no.1 / Schertzo / Tambourin / Anitra's dance / Allegro / Morning moon / Merry we will be.
LP: . . . . LEG 18
MC: . . . . LEGC 18

Stenson

SART (see under Rypdal) (Stenson/Rypdal/Garbarek).

Stenson, Bobo

TRIPLE PLAY JAZZ PIANO (see Werner, Lasse) (Stenson, Bobo/Lasse Werner/Jan Wallgren).

VERY EARLY (Stenson.Bobo Trio).
LP: . . . . DRLP 148

WITCHI-TAI-TO (See under Garbarek) (Stenson,Bobo/J.Garbarek).

Stent, Malcolm

GO AND PLAY UP YOUR OWN END.
LP: . . . . SWL 2002

LOAD OF BULL,A.
LP: . . . . SHY 7003

Step Lively

STEP LIVELY (Film soundtrack) (Various artists).
LP: . . . . HS 412

Step Stone

STEP STONE (Various artists).
LP: . . . . FF 480

Step This Way

STEP THIS WAY (Presented by Peggy Spencer) (Various artists).
Tracks: / Disco: *Various artists* / Music: *Various artists* / Samba: *Various artists* / Cha cha cha: *Various artists* / Jive and rock'n'roll: *Various artists* / Social foxtrot: *Various artists* / Social quickstep: *Various artists.*
LP: . . . . REC 374

Stephanie

LIVE YOUR LIFE.
Tracks: / Live your life / I'm waiting for you / Dance with me / Le sega Mauricien / Young ones everywhere / One love to give / How can it be / Irresistible / Besoin.
LP: . . . . CAL 224
MC: . . . . CAC 224

Stephens, Greg

BEGGAR BOY OF THE NORTH (Stephens, Greg/Crookfinger Jack).
Tracks: / Canny Cumberland / Yorkshire lasses / One-horned sheep, The / Never love thee more / Cumberland Nelly / John Peel / Lonsdale hornpipe / Northern lass, The / Liverpool hornpipe / Keswick bonny lassies / Willow tree / Corn rigs / Nanny O / Old Lancaster hornpipe / Chester waits / Farewell Manchester / Beggar boy of the north / Bishop of Chester's jig / Andrew Carey / Drops of brandy / Mad Molly / Jenny my blithest maid / Glory of the North, The / Northern nanny / Cantsfield polka, The.
LP: . . . . FE 014

Stephens, Richie

ON BROADWAY.
LP: . . . . BMLP 044

Stephens, Sam

PRETTY PLOUGHBOY, THE (See under Lennox-Martin, Anne) (Stephens, Sam and Anne Lennox-Martin).

TURN THE MUSIC ON (Stephens, Sam and Anne Lennox-Martin).
LP: . . . . DIN 328

Stephens,Bruce

WATCH THAT FIRST STEP.
LP: . . . . SRLP 104

Stephenson, Martin

BOAT TO BOLIVIA (Stephenson, Martin & The Daintees).
Tracks: / Colleen / Little red bottle / Tribute to the late Reverend Gary Davis / Running water / Candle in the middle / Piece of the cake / Look down, look down / Slow lovin' / Caroline / Rain / Crocodile crier / Boat to Bolivia / Slaughter man / Wholly humble heart.
LP: . . . . KWLP 5
MC: . . . . KWC 5

GLADSOME, HUMOUR & BLUE (Stephenson, Martin & The Daintees).
Tracks: / There comes a time / Slaughterman / Wait, The / Old church is still standing, The / I can see / Even the night / Wholly humble heart / Me and Mathew / Nancy / Goodbye John / I pray.
LP: . . . . KWLP 8
MC: . . . . KWMC 8

SALUTATION ROAD (Stephenson, Martin & The Daintees).
Tracks: / Left us to burn / Endurance / In the heat of the night / Big North lights / Long hard road / Heart of the city / Too much in love / We are storm / Migrants / Morning time / Salutation Road.
LP: 8281981
MC: 8281984

Stephenson, Van

RIGHTEOUS ANGER.
Tracks: / Modern day Delilah / I know who you are (and I saw what you did) / What the big girls do / Don't do that / Others only dream / Righteous anger / Cure will kill you, The / You've been lied to before / Heart over mind / All american boy.
LP: . . . . MCL 1854
MC: . . . . MCLC 1854
LP: . . . . MCF 3229

SUSPICIOUS HEART.
LP: . . . . MCF 3336
MC: . . . . MCFC 3336

Step'in Out

ANOTHER HAPPY CUSTOMER.
Tracks: / One more star / Arethas' song / If it could change / Just because / Another happy customer / Once every blue funk / I'll try it again / Get your troubles on the run.
LP: . . . . MON LP 031

Steppenwolf

BORN TO BE WILD (See under McGuire, Barry/Eve of destruction).

BORN TO BE WILD (OLD GOLD) (2) (see under McGuire, Barry - Eve of Destruction.

GOLD.
Tracks: / Magic carpet ride / Pusher, The / Born to be wild / Sookie sookie / It's never too late / Rock me / Hey lawdy mama / Move over / Who needs you? / Jupiter child / Screaming night hog.
LP: . . . . FA 3052
MC: . . . . TCFA 3052
LP: . . . . MCL 1619
MC: . . . . MCLC 1619
LP: . . . . MCL 1502

GOLDEN GREATS: STEPPENWOLF.
Tracks: / Born to be wild / Magic carpet ride / Rock me / Move over / Hey lawdy mama / It's never too late / Who needs you? / Monster / Snow blind friend / Pusher, The / Sookie sookie / Jupiter's child / Screaming dog night / Ride with me / For ladies only / Tenderness.
LP: . . . . MCM 5002
MC: . . . . MCMC 5002

MONSTER.
LP: . . . . SSL 5021

NIGHTRIDING: STEPPENWOLF.
MC: . . . . KNMC 10022

RISE AND SHINE.
Tracks: / Let's do it all / Do or die / Wall, The / Keep rockin' / Sign on the line / Time out / Rise and shine / Daily blues, The / Rock'n'roll war / We like it, we love it.
LP: . . . . EIRSA 1037

STEPPENWOLF.
Tracks: / Sookie Sookie / Everybody's next one / Berry rides again / Hoochie coochie man / Born to be wild / Your wall's too high / Desperation / Pusher, The / Girl I knew, A / Take what you need / Ostrich, The.
LP: . . . . MCL 1857
MC: . . . . MCLC 1857
LP: . . . . SSL 5020

STEPPENWOLF LIVE.
LP: . . . . SSL 5029

Steppes

DROP OF THE CREATOR.
LP: . . . . VOXX 200044

ENQUIRE WITHIN.
LP: . . . . VOXX 200.058

HARPS AND HAMMERS.
LP: . . . . VOXX 200064

INQUIRE WITHIN.
LP: . . . . VOXX 200058

TOURISTS FROM TIMENOTYET.
Tracks: / Bigger than life / Somebody waits / Make us bleed / Holding up well / More than this / See you around / Prayer for you / Lonely girl / Living so dead / Lazy old son / We make dreams come true.
LP: . . . . KIRI 103

Steps Ahead

MAGNETIC.
Tracks: / Trains / Beirut / In a sentimental mood / Magnetic love / Sumo / All the tea in China / Something I said / Reprise.
LP: 9604411
MC: 9604414

MODERN TIMES.
LP: 9603511

N.Y.C..
Tracks: / Well in that case / Lust for life / Red neon, go or give / Charanga / Get it / N.Y.C. / Stick jam / Absolutely maybe / Festival paradiso.
LP: . . . . INTU 1
MC: . . . . TCINTU 1
LP: . . . . INT 30071
MC: . . . . INT 30074

STEPS AHEAD.
Tracks: / Pools / Islands / Loxodrome / Both sides of the coin / Skyward bound / Northern cross / Trio / Steps ahead.
LP: 9601681

Stereo MC's

33-45-78.
Tracks: / On 33 / Use it / Gee street / Neighbourhood / Toe to toe / What is soul? / Use it (part 2) / Outta touch / Sunday 19th March / This ain't a love song / Ancient concept / On the mike / Back to the future.
MC: . . . . BRCA 532
LP: . . . . BRLP 532
MC: . . . . ICM 2072
LP: . . . . ILPM 2072

SUPERNATURAL.
LP: . . . . BRLP 556
MC: . . . . BRCA 556

SUPERNATURAL/ULTIMATUM BREAKS.
2LP: . . . . BRLPX 556

Stereo One...

STEREO 1 ALL STARS (Various artists).
LP: . . . . DSR 2908

STEREO ONE ALL STAR (Various artists).
LP: . . . . DSR 2909

Stereotaxic Device

STEREOTAXIC DEVICE.
LP: . . . . KK 046

Sterhli, Angela

DREAMS COME TRUE (See Under Barton, Lou Ann) (Sterhli, Angela, Lou Ann Barton & Marcia Ball).

Sterling Cooke Force

FULL FORCE.
LP: . . . . EBON 20

Sterling, Dave

PUTTIN' IN OVERTIME AT HOME.
LP: . . . . BSS 218

Sterling Void

IT'S ALL RIGHT.
Tracks: / It's all right / Runaway / Got to get close / Summertime / Living in the last days / Someday / Set me free / Do you wanna dance / Serve it up / Loving you.
LP: 466 146 1
MC: 466 146 4

Stern, Leni

NEXT DAY, THE.
LP: . . . . PJ 88035
MC: . . . . PJC 88036

Stern, Mike

JIGSAW.
Tracks: / Another way around / To let you know / Rhyme or reason / Loose ends / Jigsaw / Kwirk.
LP: . . . . K 782 027 1
MC: . . . . K 782 027 4

TIME IN PLACE.
LP: . . . . K 781 840 1
MC: . . . . K 781 840 4

Sterne, Laurence

SENTIMENTAL JOURNEY (Sinden, Donald).
MCSET: . . . . SAY 14
MCSET: . . . . ARGO 1019

Stetsasonic

IN FULL GEAR.
Tracks: / This is it, y'all (go stetsa II) / Sally / It's in my song / Odad, The / Rollin' wit rush / Miami bass / In full gear / D B C let the music play / Float on / Pen and paper / Stet troop '881.
LP: . . . . AMA 9001
MC: . . . . AMC 9001

Steven, Steve

STEVE STEVEN.
LP: . . . . WX 261
MC: . . . . WX 261C

Stevens, April

ALONE.
LP: . . . . SAM 1
MC: . . . . SAMC 1

WHAT KIND OF FOOL AM I (See under Tempo, Nino) (Stevens, April & Nino Tempo).

Stevens, Cat

BUDDAH AND THE CHOCOLATE BOX.
LP: . . . . ILPS 9274

CAT STEVENS.
MC: . . . . SPC 8574

CATCH BULL AT FOUR.
Tracks: / Sitting / Boy with a moon and star on his head / Angelsea / Silent sunlight / Can't keep it in / 18th Avenue (Kansas City nightmare) / Freezing steel / O'Caritas / Sweet scarlet / Ruins.
LP: . . . . ILPS 9206
MC: . . . . ICT 9206

COLLECTION: CAT STEVENS.
Tracks: / First cut is the deepest / School is out / Lovely city / Hummingbird / Granny / I love my dog / Kitty / Baby get your head screwed on / Lady / Here comes my wife / Matthew and son / Tramp / Come on baby (shift that log) / Blackness of the night / Portobello Road / Here come's my baby / Come on and dance / Northern wind / I've found a love / I'm gonna be king.
2LP: . . . . CCSLP 127
MC: . . . . CCSMC 127

FOREIGNER.
LP: . . . . ILPS 9240

GREATEST HITS: CAT STEVENS.
Tracks: / Wild world / Oh very young / Can't keep it in / Hard headed woman / Moonshadow / Two fine people / Peace train / Ready / Father and son / Sitting / Morning has broken / Another Saturday night.
LP: . . . . ILPS 9310
MC: . . . . ICT 9310

IZITSO.
LP: . . . . ILPS 9451

MATTHEW AND SON.
Tracks: / Matthew and son / I love my dog / Here come's my baby / Bring another bottle baby / Portobello Road / I've found a love / I see a road / Baby get your head screwed on / Granny / When I speak to the flowers / Tramp / Come on and dance / Hummingbird / Lady / School is out (CD only) / I'm gonna get me a gun (CD only).
LP: . . . . SML 1004

MONA BONE JAKON.
Tracks: / Lady D'Arbanville / Maybe you're / Pop star / I think I see the light / Trouble / Mona bone jakon / I wish I wish / Katmandu / Fill my eyes / Timer / Time / Lillywhite.
LP: . . . . ILPS 9118
MC: . . . . ICT 9118

MUSIC FOR THE MILLIONS.
Tracks: / Matthew and son / Here come's my baby / Lovely city / I love my dog / Here comes my wife / Granny / I'm gonna get me a gun / Kitty / First cut is the deepest / Bad night, A / School is out / Where are you.
LP: 8200041
MC: 8200044

NEW MASTERS.
Tracks: / Kitty / I'm so sleepy / Northern wind / Laughing apple / Smash your heart / Moonstone / First cut is the deepest / I'm gonna be king / Ceylon city / Blackness of the night / Come on baby (shift that log) / I love them all.
LP: . . . . DOA 5

TEA FOR THE TILLERMAN.
Tracks: / Where do the children play / Hard headed woman / Wild world / Sad Lisa / Miles from nowhere / But I might die tonight / Longer boats / Into white / On the road to find out / Father and son / Tea for the tillerman.
LP: . . . . ILPM 9135
MC: . . . . ICM 9135
LP: . . . . MFQR 1-035
MC: 842 352 4

TEASER AND THE FIRECAT.
Tracks: / Wind, The / Ruby love / If I laugh / Changes IV / How can I tell you? / Tuesday's dead / Morning has broken / Bitter blue / Moon shadow / Peace train.
LP: . . . . ILPM 9154
MC: . . . . ICM 9154
LP: . . . . ILPS 9154
MC: 842 350 4

VERY BEST OF CAT STEVENS, THE.
Tracks: / Where do the children play / Wild world / Tuesday's dead / Lady D'Arbanville / First cut is the deepest / Oh very young / Ruby love / Morning has broken / Moonshadow / Matthew and son / Father and son / Can't keep it in / Hard headed woman / Old school yard / I love my dog / Another Saturday night / Sad Lisa / Peace train.
MC: . . . . CATVC 1
LP: . . . . CATV 1

VIEW FROM THE TOP.
2LP: . . . . DPA 3019/20
MC: . . . . KDPC 28028

Stevens, Clive

ATMOSPHERES (Stevens, Clive & Friends).
LP: . . . . ST 11263

VOYAGE TO URANUS (Stevens, Clive & Friends).
LP: . . . . SM 11676

Stevens, Dane

FOR A RAINY DAY.
LP: . . . . BSS 162

Stevens, Flo

FLO' GENTLY, SWEET COUNTRY.
LP: . . . . BGC 238
MC: . . . . KBGC 238

ROCK 'N' ROLL WALTZ.
LP: . . . . BGC 309

SWEET DREAMS.
LP: . . . . NA 107
MC: . . . . NC 107

Stevens, Gary

MY TYPE OF COUNTRY.
LP: . . . . BSS 224

Stevens, John

APPLICATION, INTERACTION AND... (Stevens, John/Trevor Watts/Barry Guy).
LP: . . . . SPJ 513

ENDGAME (see Guy, Barry) (Stevens, John & Barry Guy & Howard Riley & Trevor Watts).

FREEBOP.
Tracks: / Blue line / Rhythm is / Take care / Okko / Kook.
LP: . . . . AFF 101

LIFE OF RILEY, THE (Solkus).
LP: . . . . AFF 130

LONGEST NIGHT, VOL 1 (Stevens, John & Evan Parker).
LP: . . . . OG 120

LONGEST NIGHT, VOL 2 (Stevens, John & Evan Parker).
LP: . . . . OG 420

NO FEAR (Stevens, John/Trevor Watts/ Barry Guy).
LP: . . . . SPJ 508

Stevens, Jonathan

CREATIONLAND.
LP: . . . . FF 443

Stevens, Kenni

BLUE MOODS.
LP: . . . . KENILLP 1
MC: . . . . ZKEN 1

LIVING ON THE EDGE.
Tracks: / Living on the edge / Love takes over the dance / Gonna take time / Sailing / Living on the edge (reprise) / I know how / You're a sin / Someone / After all.
LP: . . . . DBLP 505
MC: . . . . ZCDB 505

YOU.
Tracks: / Who's been loving you / Hurt this way / Never gonna give you up / 24-7-365 / You don't know / I bleed for you / You / Didn't mean to hurt you / Work me up (Extra track on cassette & CD.) / Anne (Extra track on cassette & CD.).
LP: . . . . DBLP 502
MC: . . . . ZCDB 502

Stevens, Lamona

SONGS OF DONNA SUMMER.
MC: . . . . ZCFPA 1022

Stevens, Leith

JAZZ THEMES FROM 'PRIVATE HELL' (Stevens, Leith & His Orchestra).
LP: . . . . FS 232

Stevens, Meic

GITAR YNY TWLLDAN STAR.
LP: . . . . SAIN 1273M

NOS DU NOS DA.
LP: . . . . SAIN 1239M

Stevens, Mike

LIGHT UP THE NIGHT.
Tracks: / Time with you / C'est l'affaire / Looks like rain / Sao Paulo / Tapestry / Joy and pain / Light up the night / My funny valentine / Into the heat / Easy way out.
LP: . . . . PL 71641
MC: . . . . PK 71641
LP: . . . . CGILLP 3
MC: . . . . ZCCHIL 3

SET THE SPIRIT FREE.
Tracks: / Cool with your love / Set the spirit free / Sunset trip / Love TKO / Tell her / I'm a romantic / Ride the bullet train / Precious / Latinesque / Finest one, The / Roxanne (Only on CD.) / Living groove, The (Only on CD.) / Sparkle (in your eyes).
LP: . . . . CHILLP 9
MC: . . . . ZCCHIL 9

Stevens, Ray

6 TRACK HITS.
Tracks: / Misty / Everything is beautiful / Streak, The / Bridget the midget / Along came Jones / Ahab the Arab.
MC: 7SC 5008

BESIDE MYSELF.
Tracks: / I saw Elvis in a UFO.
LP: . . . . MCA 42303
MC: . . . . MCAC 42303

BOTH SIDES OF RAY STEVENS.
Tracks: / Gitarzan / Moonlight special / Mr. Business man / Bridget the midget / Streak, The / Freddie Feelgood / Misty / Everything is beautiful / Young love / Sunshine / All my trials / Turn your radio on.
LP: . . . . GEM 007
MC: . . . . GEMC 007

DON'T LAUGH NOW.
Tracks: / Such a night / Written down in my heart / Take that girl away / Always there / Where the sun don't shine / Oh Leo lady / Don't laugh now / This old piano / Country boy country club girl / Why don't we go somewhere and love.
LP: . . . . RCALP 3054

EVERYTHING IS BEAUTIFUL.
LP: . . . . CBS 64074

GREATEST HITS: RAY STEVENS.
Tracks: / Streak, The / Shriner's convention / It's me again Margaret / Turn your radio on / Misty / Mississippi Squirrel revival, / Gitarzan / Ahab the Arab / Along came Jones / Everything is beautiful.
LP: . . . . IMCA 5918
MC: . . . . IMCAC 5918

HE THINKS HE'S RAY STEVENS.
LP: . . . . MCF 3265

ME.
Tracks: / Love will beat your brains out / Mary Lou nights / Special anniversary / Piedmont Park / Me / My Dad / Yolanda / Piece of paradise called Tennessee / Kings and Queens / Game show love.
LP: 8127 801

MISTY.
LP: 9109 401

RAY STEVENS GREATEST HITS COLLECTION, THE.
Tracks: / Everything is beautiful / Nashville / Mr. Business man / Little Egypt / Sir thanks a lot / Turn your radio on / Misty / Don't boogie woogie / Gitarzan / Moonlight special / Sunshine / Ahab the arab / Bridget the midget / Isn't it lonely together / Unwind / You've got the music inside / Just so proud to be there / Along came Jones / Streak, The / All my trials / Have a little talk with myself / Sunday morning comin' down / Freddie Feelgood / Lady of Spain.
2LP: . . . . PDA 061

SHRINER'S CONVENTION.
Tracks: / Shriner's convention / Last laugh / Rita's letter / Watch song / Dooright family / Hey there / Put it in your ear / You're never goin' to Tampa with me / Coin machine.
LP: . . . . PL 13574

VERY BEST OF RAY STEVENS.
Tracks: / Misty / Streak, The / Along came Jones / Ahab the Arab / Bridget the midget / Have a little talk with myself / Everything is beautiful / Turn your radio on / Mr. Business man / Sunday morning coming down / Isn't it lonely together / Gitarzan.
LP: . . . . SPR 8554
MC: . . . . SPC 8554

Stevens, Ronnie

STORYTIME TOP TEN - VOL.4.
MC: . . . . VCA 058

STORYTIME TOP TEN - VOL.8 (Stevens, Ronnie & Toddy).
MC: . . . . VCA 062

STORYTIME TOP TIME - VOL.5.
MC: . . . . VCA 059

Stevens, Shakin'

20 ROCKABILLY HITS.
Tracks: / You mostest girl / Sexy ways / Honey hush / Evil hearted / Jungle rock / My baby died / Reet petite / Monkey's uncle / Silver wings / Memphis earthquake / Rock around with Ollie Vee / Story of the rockers / Frantic / Baby blue / Ready Teddy / Tear it up / Justine / Oakie boogie / Wine, wine, wine / Blue swingin' mama.
LP: . . . . SMT 004
MC: . . . . SMS 004
MC: . . . . SMTC 004

AT THE ROCKHOUSE.
Tracks: / Honey hush / My bucket's got a hole in it / Evil hearted / Wine, wine, wine / Rock around with Ollie Vee / Oakie boogie / Blue swingin' mama / Baby blue / You mostest girl / Sexy ways / Reet petite / Memphis earthquake.
LP: . . . . MFM 009
MC: . . . . MFMC 009
LP: . . . . MFLP 004

BOP WON'T STOP.
Tracks: / Bop won't stop / Why do you treat me this way / Diddle I / Don't be two faced / Livin' lovin' wreck / Rockin' good way, A / Brand new man / I cry just a little bit / As long as / Love worth waiting for, A / Love me tonight / It's late.
LP: . . . . EPC 86301

CLASSICS (Shakin' Stevens/Sunsets).
Tracks: / Justine / Jungle rock / True love / My baby died / Story of the rockers / Frantic / Ready teddy / Monkey's uncle / Tear it up / Silver wings / Rockabilly rock / Red flag rock.
LP: . . . . MFM 019

C'MON MEMPHIS.
LP: . . . . R&C 1005

COLLECTION: SHAKIN' STEVENS.
LP: . . . . IC 028 64535

COLLECTION: SHAKIN' STEVENS PT. 1 & 2.
Tracks: / Sweet little sixteen / Monkey's uncle / Tear it up / Silver wings / Ready Teddy / Reet petite / Outlaw man / Queen of the hop / Lady lizard / Story of the rockers / Jungle rock / Justine / You mostest girl / Girl in red / Rock around with Ollie Vee / Blue swingin' mama / Sugaree / I don't care / Tiger / Frantic.
2LP: . . . . CCSLP 153
MC: . . . . CCSMC 153

EXTRA.
Tracks: / Blue moon of Kentucky / Outlaw man / I told you so / Buzz buzz buzz / Train kept a rollin' / Spirit of Woodstock / Tallahassee lassie / Alan Freed / Riot in cell block 9 / Like a teenager / Manhattan melodrama / Me and Bobby McGhee.
LP: LF6 25539
MC: PF6 25539

GIVE ME YOUR HEART.
Tracks: / Josephine / Give me your heart / Sapphire / Oh Julie / I'll be satisfied / Vanessa / Boppity bop / Don't tell me we're through / Shirley / You never talked about me / Too too much / You're evil / Que sera, sera.
LP: . . . . EPC 10035

GREATEST HITS: SHAKIN' STEVENS.
Tracks: / This ole house / You drive me crazy / Letter to you, A / It's raining / Green door / Hot dog / Teardrops / Breaking up my heart / Oh Julie / Marie, Marie / Love worth waiting for, A / It's late / Give me your heart tonight / Shirley / Blue Christmas / Cry just a little bit / Rockin' good way, A / I'll be satisfied.
LP: . . . . EPC 10047
MC: 40 10047
LP: 4669931
MC: 4669934

HOT DOG.
LP: . . . . EPC 32126
MC: 40 32126

LET'S BOOGIE.
Tracks: / Come see about me / Forever you / Little boogie woogie (in the back of my mind), A / Because I love you / What do you want to make those eyes at me for / Hits keep coming medley, The / Cry just a little bit / You drive me crazy / Rockin' good way, A / Give me your heart tonight / Love worth waiting for, A / Green door / I'll be satisfied / Letter to you, A / Oh Julie / It's late / Marie, Marie / It's raining / Hot dog / Teardrops / This ole house.
LP: 4601261
MC: 4601264

LIPSTICK, POWDER AND PAINT.
Tracks: / Lipstick, powder and paint / Bad reputation / Don't lie to me / I'm leaving you / Shape I'm in, The / Don't knock upon my door / Turning away / Love you out loud / As long as I have you / With my heart / Ain't it a shame (you win again) / So long baby goodbye.
LP: . . . . EPC 26646
MC: 40 26646

MANHATTAN MELODRAMA.
Tracks: / Manhattan melodrama / Blue moon of Kentucky / Alan Freed / California cowboy / Lady lizard / Punk / Outlaw man / Riot in cell block 9 / I told you so / Tallahassee lassie / Longer stronger love / Like a teenager / Don't jive me no more / Holy roller / No other baby / Get back John.
LP: . . . . WW 2003
MC: . . . . WW 20034
LP: . . . . JULEP 19
MC: . . . . KJULEP 19

MARIE MARIE.
Tracks: / Hey Mae / Baby if we touch / Marie Marie / Lonely boy blue / Make it right tonight / Move / Slippin' and slidin' / Shooting gallery / Revenue man / Make me know you're mine / Two hearts / Nobody.
LP: . . . . EPC 84547

ORIGINAL SHAKIN' STEVENS AND THE SUNSET - VOL.2.
MC: . . . . CHV 339

ORIGINAL SHAKIN' STEVENS, THE.
MC: . . . . CHV 239

PLATINUM HIGH SCHOOL (See under Johnny Storm) (Stevens, Shakin', Jets & Jonny Storm).

PROFILE: SHAKIN' STEVENS.
Tracks: / It came out of the sky / Lady Lizard / Tallahassee lassie / Buzz buzz buzz / Outlaw man / Riot in cell block 9 / I told you so / Longer, stronger love / Train kept a rollin' / Like a teenager / Get back John / Don't jive me no more / Cast iron arm.
LP: 6.25051
MC: CL4 25051

ROCK 'N' ROLL.
MC: . . . . STAC 2454
LP: . . . . STAR 2454

ROCK ON WITH A LEGEND.
Tracks: / Leroy / Flying saucers / Please Mr. Mayor / Lights out / I'll try / Down yonder we go balling / Hawkins mood / Down on the farm / Lonesome train / I believe what you say / Train kept a rollin' / Spirit of Woodstock / I hear you knocking / Thirty days / School days.
LP: . . . . MFP 50544
MC: . . . . TCMFP 50544

ROCKIN' AND SHAKIN'.
LP: . . . . SHM 3149
MC: . . . . HSC 3149

ROCKIN' SHAKY.
LPPD: . . . . PD 40001

SEXY WAYS.
Tracks: / Honey hush / Evil hearted / Drinkin' wine spo-dee-o-dee / Blue swingin' mama / Rockabilly earthquake / Rock around with Ollie Vee / Sexy ways / You mostest girl / My bucket's got a hole in it / Baby blue.
LP: . . . . RD 3001

SHAKE IT UP.
Tracks: / Frantic / Monkey's uncle / Tear it up / Justine / Ready Teddy / Reet petite / Story of the rockers / Okie boogie / Jungle rock / My baby died.
LP: . . . . RD 3000

SHAKIN' ALL OVER (Stevens, Shakin'/ Sunsets).
MCSET: . . . . DTO 10242

SHAKIN' STEVENS.
Tracks: / Roll over Beethoven / White lightning / One night with you / High heel sneakers / Tallahassee lassie / Yakety yak / Maybellene / Hearts made of stone / Good rockin' tonight / At the hop / Walking on the water / Rip it up / Saturday night rock.
LP: . . . . CN 2046
MC: CN4 2046

SHAKIN' STEVENS (2).
Tracks: / Sugaree / This time / Peggy Sue / Nut rocker / Lazy lizard / Tiger / Outlaw man / Donna / Jungle rock / Red flag rock / Queen of the hop / Girl in red / Wee wee hours.
2LP: . . . . BCBR 1001

SHAKIN' STEVENS (ASTAN).
LPPD: . . . . AR 30008

SHAKIN' STEVENS (POLYDOR).
Tracks: / You can't sit down / I'm ready / So glad you're mine / Let's dance / Till I waltz again with you / Such a night / Justine / Baby blue / Wait and see / Can't believe you wanna leave / Whole lotta shakin' goin' on / Jenny Jenny / Tutti frutti.
LP: 2384 114
LP: . . . . SPELP 43

SHAKIN' STEVENS (PREMIER/ EVEREST DOUBLE).
Tracks: / Sugaree / This time / Baby I don't care / Wee wee hours / Hey good lookin' / Lonesome town (end s1) / Peggy Sue / Two hearts, two kisses / Queen of the hop / Nut rocker / Smokin' a long cigarette (shewn in Premier catalogue as 'Californian cowboy') / Lady lizard (end s2) / Tiger / Girl in red / Outlaw man / Manhattan melodrama / Don't rip me off / Sweet little sixteen (end s3) / Jungle rock / Donna / Red flag rock / Get back John / Silver wings / Give me a break.
2LP: . . . . BCBR 1001
2LP: . . . . PPD 2003
MC: . . . . PPK 2003

SHAKIN' STEVENS & THE SUNSETS (Stevens, Shakin'/Sunsets).
Tracks: / Cast iron arm / Leroy / Flying saucers / Please Mr. Mayor / Lights out / I'll try / Down yonder we go balling / Hawkin's mood / Down on the farm /

Lonesome train / I believe what you say / Train kept a rollin' / Spirit of Woodstock / I hear you knocking / Thirty days / Schooldays.
LP: . . . . **NUT 25**

SHAKIN' STEVENS & THE SUNSETS.
Tracks: / Come along with me / Right string baby / Rock and roll singer / Girl please stay / Honey don't / Little Queenie / Sea cruise / Sea of heartbreak / Superstar / That is rock 'n'roll.
LP: . . . . **SHM 3065**
MC: . . . . **HSC 3065**

SHAKIN' STEVENS (WARWICK) (Stevens, Shakin'/Sunsets).
MCSET: . . . . **WW 6049**

SHAKY.
Tracks: / Mona Lisa / You drive me crazy / Baby I'm knockin' / It's raining / Don't she look good? / Green door / Don't bug me, baby / Don't tell me your troubles / I'm gonna sit right down and write myself a letter / This time, baby / You're a child / Don't turn your back / Let me show you how / I'm lookin'.
LP: **4506241**
MC: **4506244**
LP: . . . . **EPC 10027**

SILVER WINGS.
LP: **20003**
MC: **40003**

TAKE ONE.
Tracks: / Lovestruct / Hot dog / Is a bluebird blue / That's alright / Without love / Shame shame shame / Shotgun boogie / I got burned / I guess I was just a fool / Ah poor little baby / Little pigeon / Do what you did.
LP: . . . . **EPC 83978**
MC: **40 83978**

THIS OLE HOUSE (ALBUM).
MC: **40 32572**
LP: . . . . **EPC 84985**

TIGER (Stevens, Shakin'/Sunsets).
Tracks: / Tiger / Girl in red / Outlaw man / Manhattan melodrama / Don't rip me off / Sweet little sixteen (end s1) / Jungle rock / Donna / Red flag rock / Get back John / Silver wings / Give me a break.
LP: . . . . **CBR 1000**
MC: . . . . **KCBR 1000**

TRACK YEARS, THE.
Tracks: / Somebody touched me / Just walking in the rain / Mountain of love / Rebound / You always hurt the one you love / No other baby / Way down yonder in New Orleans / Keep a knockin' / Gotta lotta livin' to do / Ruby baby / Never / Tossin' and turnin' / Hound dog.
LP: . . . . **MFP 5760**
MC: . . . . **TCMFP 5760**
LP: . . . . **MEDIA 3**
MC: . . . . **MEDIAC 3**

ULTIMATE ROCK 'N' ROLLER, THE.
LP: . . . . **BBR 1018**

WHOLE LOTTA SHAKY, A.
Tracks: / What do you want to make those eyes at me for / How many tears can you hide / Jezebel / Sea of love / True love / Just one look / Oh Julie / Do you really love me too / I'm gonna sit right down and write myself a letter / Hello Josephine / Woman (what have you done to me) / Heartbeat / Tired of toein' the line / Mona Lisa.
LP: . . . . **MOOD 5**
MC: . . . . **MOODC 5**

Stevens, Stu

COMMAND PERFORMANCE.
MC: . . . . **VCA 108**

EMMA AND I.
Tracks: / Mind painter / When I dream / That old brown dog / Loving arms / Emma and I / My woman my wife / Sunday morning coming down / Got my guitar / Room for a boy / Lady lay down / Bridge over troubled water / Hard to be humble / Three kinds of flowers.
LP: . . . . **EGL 012**

FUNNY FACE.
Tracks: / Funny face / Chokin' kind, The / Four strong winds / I don't want to cry / Tree in the meadow, A / Revelation / Mexico City / Good hearted woman / Derby's castle / Love me tender / Colorado / Yours love / Streets I have walked.
MC: . . . . **ASH 109 C**

LONER, THE.
Tracks: / Lady luck / Riverboat / America you are my woman / Love of the common people / West side of Texas / Miami sunset / Wrap my arms around the world / Rain / Had to run / Every night when I cry myself to sleep.
LP: . . . . **EGL 002**

MAN AND HIS MUSIC, THE.
Tracks: / Rose, The / Dry your eyes / Little boy genius / Three times a lady / Nancy Lee / My heroes have always been cowboys / Always on my mind / Dream it back / Imagine / Suspicious minds / While the feelings good / Girl you love, The.
MC: . . . . **ASH 020 C**

MAN FROM OUTER SPACE (ALBUM).
LP: . . . . **MCF 3041**

OLD RUGGED CROSS.
Tracks: / Eltigre / I can't keep my hands off you / Winter world away / Red cloud's day / Cowboys and daddies / Biff / Beautiful noise / Lady oh / American trilogy / Old rugged cross, The / Eyes of my child.
LP: . . . . **ASH C101**

SONGS THAT MADE STU STEVENS (THE VOICE), THE.
Tracks: / I'm from outer space / Hello pretty baby / When I dream / Woman woman my wife / Lion in the winter / Save the last dance for me / Streets of London / One red rose / West side of Texas / Winter world away / If I can't touch her at all / Remember me at sunrise / Looking for a place to sleep / God forsaken land / If I heard you call my name / Hudson bay.
LP: . . . . **YB LP 123**

STU STEVENS.
MC: . . . . **VCA 092**

TOGETHER AGAIN.
Tracks: / Together again / I am ... I said / Lucille / Queen of the silver dollar / What have you got planned tonight Diana / Big house / Legend in my time, A / Broken lady / We had it all / Teach your children / Trying to matter.
LP: . . . . **EGL 001**

Stevens, Tony

WAY LOVE'S SUPPOSED TO BE.
LP: . . . . **RITZLP 0034**
MC: . . . . **RITZLC 0034**

Stevens, Wallace

WALLACE STEVENS READING.
MC: **1068**

Stevenson, Doug

STEEL ON MY MIND.
LP: . . . . **BGC 222**
MC: . . . . **KBGC 222**

Stevenson, Robert

BODY SNATCHER, THE (Sheddon, John).
MCSET: . . . . **COL 2009**

BODY SNATCHERS, THE (See under Graham, John - Love and the lonely) (Various artists).

CHILD'S GARDEN OF VERSES, A (Anderson, Dame Judith).
MC: **1077**

KIDNAPPED (Fairbanks, Douglas Jnr (nar)).
LP: . . . . **TC 1636**
MC: . . . . **CDL 51636**

KIDNAPPED (children's classics) (Kidnapped).
MC: . . . . **PLBC 176**

MASTER OF BALLANTRAE (Watson, Tom).
MCSET: . . . . **COL 4005**

STRANGE CASE OF DR. JEKYLL AND MR. HYDE (horror classics for ages 7-12).
MC: . . . . **PLBC 196**

STRANGE CASE OF DR. JEKYLL AND MR. HYDE (Quayle, Anthony (nar)).
MC: **1283**

STRANGE CASE OF DR. JEKYLL AND MR. HYDE (Baker, Tom).
MCSET: . . . . **SAY 12**
MCSET: . . . . **ARGO 1013**
2LP: . . . . **ZDSW 722/3**

STRANGE CASE OF DR. JEKYLL AND MR. HYDE (Hurt, John).
MC: . . . . **PTB 619**

TREASURE ISLAND (Richardson, Ian).
MCSET: **2075**

TREASURE ISLAND (Treasure Island).
MCSET: . . . . **DTO 10576**

TREASURE ISLAND (children's classics) (Unknown narrator(s)).
MC: . . . . **PLBC 74**

TREASURE ISLAND (Bate, Anthony).
MCSET: . . . . **TC LFP 7018**
MCSET: . . . . **LFP 7170**
MC: . . . . **LFP 417 170 5**

TREASURE ISLAND (Buck, David).
MC: . . . . **LFP 41 7170-5**
MCSET: **CC/013**

Stevenson, Savourna

TICKLED PINK.
LP: . . . . **SPR 1016**
MC: . . . . **SPRC 1016**

TWEED JOURNEY.
MC: . . . . **ECL 9001TC**

Stevie

STEVIE (Film Soundtrack) (Various artists).
LP: . . . . **CBS 70165**
MC: . . . . **CBS 43 70165**

Stevie B

LOVE AND EMOTION.
MC: **8490124**
LP: **8490121**

Stevie V

ALL RECORDINGS (See under Adventures of Stevie V).

Stewart, Al

24 CARAT.
Tracks: / Running man / Midnight rocks / Constantinople / Merlin's time / Mondo sinistro / Murmansk run/Ellis Island / Rocks in the ocean / Paint by numbers / Optical illusion.
MC: . . . . **PK 25306**
LP: . . . . **PL 25306**

BEST OF AL STEWART.
Tracks: / Year of the cat / On the border / If it doesn't come naturally leave it / Time passages / Almost Lucky / Merlin's time / Valentina way / Running man / Roads to Moscow / Here in Angola / Rumours of war.
LP: . . . . **PL 70715**
MC: . . . . **PK 70715**

CAROL.
Tracks: / Carol / Next time.
LP: . . . . **CBS 32524**

CHRONICLES - THE BEST OF AL STEWART.
Tracks: / Year of the cat / On the border / If it doesn't come naturally, leave it / Time passages / Almost Lucy / Song on the radio (Not on album) / Running man (Not on album) / Merlin's time / In Brooklyn / Soho (needless to say) (live) (Not on album) / Small fruit song, A / Manuscript / Roads to Moscow (live) / Nostradamus - Pt. 1 / World goes to Riyadh (live) (Nostradamus - Pt. 2).
LP: . . . . **EMC 3590**
MC: . . . . **TCEMC 3590**

EARLY YEARS, THE.
Tracks: / Bedsitter images / In Brooklyn / Electric Los Angeles sunset / Clifton in the rain / You should have listened to Al / Manuscript / Small fruit song / Life and life only / Love chronicles.
LP: . . . . **PL 25131**
LP: . . . . **FA 3165**
MC: . . . . **TCFA 3165**

INDIAN SUMMER/LIVE.
Tracks: / Here in Angola / Pandora / Indian Summer / Delia's gone / Princess Olivia / Running man / Time passages / Merlin's time / If it doesn't come naturally leave it / Roads to Moscow / Nostradamus / World goes to Riyadh / Nostadamus part two / Soho (needless to say) / On the border / Valentina way / Clarence frogman / Henry 1 / Year of the cat.
2LP: . . . . **PL 70257**
MC: . . . . **PK 70257**
2LP: . . . . **RCALP 9001**

LAST DAYS OF THE CENTURY.
Tracks: / Last days of the century / Real and unreal / King of Portugal / Where are they now / License to steal / Josephine Baker / Antarctica / Ghostly horses of the plain / Red toupee / Bad reputation / Fields of France.
LP: . . . . **ENVLP 505**
MC: . . . . **TCENV 505**
LP: . . . . **ENVLP 1007**
MC: . . . . **TCENV 1007**

LOVE CHRONICLES.
Tracks: / In Brooklyn / Old Compton street blues / Ballad of Mary Foster / Life and life only / You should have listened to Al / Love chronicles.
LP: . . . . **INTS 5120**
MC: . . . . **INTK 5120**
LP: . . . . **NL 70271**
MC: . . . . **NK 70271**

MODERN TIMES.
LP: . . . . **CBS 32019**

ORANGE.
LP: . . . . **CBS 32061**

PAST PRESENT AND FUTURE.
LP: . . . . **CBS 32036**

RUSSIANS AND AMERICANS.
Tracks: / Lori don't go right now / Don't go right now / Gypsy and the rose, The / Accident on 3rd street / Strange girl / Russians & Americans / Cafe society / 1-2-3 / Candidate.
LP: . . . . **PL 70307**
MC: . . . . **PK 70307**

TIME PASSAGES.
Tracks: / Valentina way / Life in dark water / Man for all seasons / Almost lucky / Time passages / Palace of Versailles / Timeless skies / End of the day / Song on the radio.
LP: . . . . **PL 70274**
MC: . . . . **PK 70274**
LP: . . . . **PL 25173**

YEAR OF THE CAT.
Tracks: / Lord Grenville / On the border / Midas shadow / Sand in your shoes / If it doesn't come naturally, leave it / Flying sorcery / Broadway hotel / One stage before / Year of the cat.
LP: . . . . **PL 70005**
MC: . . . . **PK 70005**
LP: . . . . **NL 71493**
MC: . . . . **NK 71493**
LP: . . . . **RS 1082**
MC: . . . . **PK 11749**
LP: . . . . **FA 3253**
MC: . . . . **TCFA 3253**

YEAR OF THE CAT (OLD GOLD) (See under Climax Blues Band - Couldn't Get It).

ZERO SHE FLIES.
Tracks: / My enemies have sweet voices / Small fruit song / Gethsemane again / Burbling / Electric Los Angeles sunset / Manuscript / Black Hill / Anna / Room of roots / Zero she flies.
LP: . . . . **NL 70874**
MC: . . . . **NK 70874**
LP: . . . . **CBS 63848**

Stewart, Amii

AMII.
Tracks: / Time is tight / Power play / Easy on your love / Love's in disguise / Lover to lover / Break these chains / Love ain't no toy / Mystery of love / Conspiracy / This generation.
LP: . . . . **PL 70112**
MC: . . . . **PK 70112**

AMII STEWART.
Tracks: / Knock on wood / You really touched my heart / Light my fire / 137 disco heaven / Bring it on back to me / Closest thing to heaven / Am I losing you / Get your love back / Only a child in your eyes.
LP: . . . . **K 50593**
MC: **K4 50593**

BEST OF AND THE REST OF, THE.
Tracks: / Knock on wood / You really touch my heart / 137 disco heaven / Paradise bird / My guy, my girl / Light my fire / Only a child in your eyes / Step into the love line / Ash 48 / Jealousy.
MC: . . . . **ARLC 1023**

HITS, THE.
Tracks: / Knock on wood / Ash 48 / Light my fire / 137 disco heaven / You really touch my heart.
LP: . . . . **SED 9000**
MC: . . . . **ZCSED 9000**

PARADISE BIRD.
Tracks: / Letter, The / Paradise bird / He's a burglar / Jealousy / Right place, wrong time / Step into the love line / Paradise found.
LP: . . . . **K 50673**
MC: **K4 50673**

Stewart, Andy

20 GOLDEN SCOTTISH FAVOURITES.
Tracks: / Scottish soldier / By the Lochside / Donald where's yer troosers / Road and miles to Dundee / Courtin' in the kitchen / Wee hoose amang the heather / Lassie come and dance with me / Campbeltown Loch / Fou the noo / Tunes of glory / Doctor Finlay / Highlandman's umbrella, The / Muckin' o Georgie's byre / Heather bells will bloom again / I love to wear the kilt / Tobermory treasure / Going down the water / Wee too clerk / Dancing in Kyle / Battles o'er, The.
LP: . . . . **GLN 1014**

20 SCOTTISH FAVOURITES-COLLECTION.
Tracks: / Scottish soldier, A / Doctor Finlay / Campbeltown Loch / Battles o'er, The / Highlandman's umbrella, The / I'm off to bonnie Scotland / Road to the Isles / Scotland yet / Farewell 51st farewell / Muckin' o' Geordie's byre / Donald, where's yer troosers / Girl from Glasgow town / Horo my nut brown maiden / Tunes of glory / Wild rover / Road and the miles to Dundee, The / Gourtin' in the kitchen / Lassie come and dance with me / I love to wear the kilt / Going doon the water.
LP: . . . . **MFP 41 5700 1**
MC: . . . . **MFP 41 5700 4**
MC: . . . . **TCMFP 5700**

ANDY STEWART.
LP: **35 116**

ANDY STEWART (2).
Tracks: / Donald where's your troosers? / Cock o' the North / Wild rover / I love to wear the kilt / I'm going courtin' / Highland gentleman, A / D'ye mind lang syne / Blow blow my kilt awa' / Scottish soldier, A / Campbeltown loch / Mary

Mack / Dr. Finlay / End of the road / Battle's o'er, The / Tobermory / Tunes of glory / Girl from Glasgow town, The / Muckin' o' Geordie's byre.
LP: IDL 100
MC: TCIDL 100

ANDY STEWART'S GREATEST HITS.
Tracks: / Campbeltown Loch / Road to Dundee, The / Donald, where's yer troosers / Barren rocks, The / Battle is o'er, The / Dancing in Kyle / Callin' mo ruin-sa / Morag of Dunvegan / By the Lochside / Tunes of glory / D'ye mind lang syne.
LP: PKL 5561
MC: ZCPKB 5561

BACK IN THE BOTHY.
Tracks: / Nicky Tams / Road and the miles to Dundee, The / Barnyards of Delgaty / Sunday painter / Auld maid in a garret, An / Maggie / Muckin' o' Geordie's byre / MacFarlane o' the Sproats / Bonnie lass o' Fyvie / Kissing in the dark / My ain lass / Daunder through the town, A / Aikey brae / De ye mind lang syne / McGinty's meal and ale.
LP: LIDL 6021
MC: LIDC 6021

BEST OF ANDY STEWART.
Tracks: / Andy where's your kilt / Heart of Midlothian / Maggie / I belong to Glasgow / Sailing up the Clyde / We've got a baby in the house / Ninety-four this morning / Country dance / Country roads / Rumour, The / Song of the Clyde / Northern lights of old Aberdeen / Rothesay Bay / Old Scottish waltz / I will go / Granny's heilan' hame / Will ye no come back again / Skye boat song / Come over the stream Charlie.
MC: KGEC 1237
LP: GES 1237

BRAND NEW FROM ANDY (Stewart, Andy & Jimmy Blue Band).
LP: PKL 5524
MC: ZCHPKB 5524
MC: ZCPKB 5524

COME IN COME IN.
Tracks: / Come in, come in / Dark island / Corn rigs / Rumour, The / I'm Dan your man / Amazing grace / Lassie come and dance with me / They're playin' country music / Together again / Lads o'bonnie Scotland / Ra wee cock sparra / Danny boy / Scotland yet / Girl from Glasgow town.
LP: LIDL 6008
MC: LIDC 6008

COUNTRY BOY (Stewart Andy with Ann Williams).
Tracks: / Act naturally / Crying time / Help me make it through the night / Once a day / It takes people like you to make people like me / My heart skips a beat / I'm gonna be a country boy again / Country song / Together again / Little girl / It keeps right on a-hurtin' / Take me back into your heart / Me and Bobby McGee.
LP: PKL 5532
MC: ZCRKB 5532

DUBLIN LADY (Stewart, Andy/Manus Lunny).
Tracks: / Take her in your arms / Where are you / Dublin Lady / Freedom is like gold / Bogie's bonnie belle / Dinny the piper / Heart of the home / Humours of whiskey / Tak' it man tak' it.
LP: SIF 1083
MC: CSIF 1083

FOR AULD LANG SYNE.
Tracks: / Andy, where's your kilt? / We're no awa' tae bide awa' / Take me home country roads / Farewell, 51st, farewell / Country dance, The / Toast to the lassies / Lassies o' hame / My ain lass / Farewell, and joy be with you all / Y'all come / Northern lights of old Aberdeen / Rothesay Bay / I belong to Glasgow / Gallant forty twa / Maggie / My hameland / Old Scottish waltz / Auld lang syne.
LP: GES 1217
MC: KGEC 1217

LEGENDS OF SCOTLAND.
Tracks: / Campbeltown loch / Battle is o'er, The / Take me back / Donald, where's yer troosers / Muckin' o' Geordie's byre / Scottish soldier, A / Barren rocks of Aden / Road to Dundee, The / Dancing in Kyle / Cailin mo ruin-sa / Morag of Dunvegan / By the lochside / Tunes of glory / D'ye mind lang syne.
MC: ZCLLS 702

MY SCOTLAND.
Tracks: / I belong to Glasgow / Tillietudlem castle / I love a lassie / Donald, where's yer troosers / Star o' Rabbie Burns, The / Stop your ticklin' Jock / Bee baw babbity / Dashing white sergeant / Scotland the brave / Waggle o' the kilt, The / Wil ye no come back again / Granny's heilan' hame.
MC: 4 HOM 008

SCOTLAND IS ANDY STEWART.
Tracks: / Girl from Glasgow town / Fair maid of Perth / Gallowa' hills / Rumour, The / Lassie o' Dundee / I will go / Heart of Midlothian / Song of Inverness / Bonnie Strathyre / Song of the Clyde / Kelso collie / Granny's heilan' hame / Big Kilmarnock bonnet.
LP: GES 1196
MC: KGEC 1196

Stewart, Andy M.

BY THE HUSH.
LP: SHY 7018

FIRE IN THE GLEN (Stewart, Andy M/ Phil Cunningham/Manus Lunny).
LP: 12TS 443

Stewart, Belle

QUEEN AMONG THE HEATHER.
Tracks: / Queen among the heather / Here's a health to all true lovers / Betsy Belle / Berryfields o'Blair, The / Soft country chiel (the toon o'dalry) / Whistlin' at the ploo / Bonnie wee lassie frae Gourock, The / Overgate, The / Blooming Caroline o' Edinburgh / Busk busk, bonnie lassie / Late last night / Twa brothers, The / Leezie Lindsay.
LP: 12TS 307

STEWARTS O'BLAIR (Stewart, Belle & family).
Tracks: / Come a' you jolly Ploomen / Lakes of Shillin / Bonnie hoose o' Airlie / Moving on song / Nobleman, A / Jock Stewart / Inverness-shire / Banks of the Lee / Betsy belle / Dawning of the day / My dog and gun / Berryfields o'Blair, The / I'm no coming oot the noo / Mickey's warning / Hatton woods / Parting song / Canntaireachd.
LP: LIFL 7010
MC: LIFC 7010

Stewart, Billy

BILLY STEWART TEACHES OLD STANDARDS NEW TRICKS.
Tracks: / Temptation / Exodus / Fly me to the moon / Let's fall in love / Somewhere / Ol' man river / Every day I have the blues / Who can I turn to / Moonlight in Vermont / Secret love / When I fall in love / It's alright with me.
LP: GCH 8089
MC: GCHK 78089

ONE MORE TIME.
Tracks: / Billy's blues part 2 / Fat boy / Reap what you sow / Sugar and spice / Strange Feeling / Count me out / Keep lovin' / I do love you / Sitting in the park / Love me / Summertime / How nice it is / Because I love you / Over the rainbow / Everyday I have the blues / Secret love / Temptaion 'bout to get me / Why do I love you so / Cross my heart / Golly golly gee / One more time / Tell me the truth / I'm in love (oh yes I am) / We'll always be together.
LP: LPM 7004

Stewart, Bob

GOIN' HOME (Stewart, Bob - First Line Band).
Tracks: / Subi la nas alturas / Art deco / Bell and ponce / Tunk / Sugar finger / Sweet Georgia Brown / Priestess.
LP: 8344271

IN A SENTIMENTAL MOOD.
LP: ST 266

UP LIKE THE SWALLOW (See under Crowley, Jimmy) (Stewart, Bob/Jimmy Crowley).

Stewart, Dave

BIG IDEA, THE (Stewart, Dave & Barbara Gaskin).
Tracks: / Levi Stubb's tears / My scene / Grey skies / Subterranean homesick blues / Heatwave / Crying game, The / Deep underground / Shadowland / Mr. Theremin / New Jerusalem.
MC: RACS 0172

DAVE STEWART AND THE SPIRITUAL COWBOYS (Stewart, David A. & The Spiritual Cowboys).
Tracks: / Soul years / King of the hypocrites / Diamond Avenue / This little town / On fire / Heaven and earth / Love shines / Party town / Mr Reed / Fashion bomb / Jack talking / Hey Johnny / Devil's just been using you, The / Spiritual love.
LP: PL 74710
MC: PK 74710

LILY WAS HERE (See under 'Lily Was Here') (Stewart, David A & Candy Dulfer).

SHORES OF THE NORTH (see Watt, John) (Stewart, Davey/John Watt).

Stewart, David A.

HONEST (Stewart, David A. & The Spiritual Cowboys).
MC: PK 75081
LP: PL 75081

Stewart, Davie

DAVIE STEWART.
Tracks: / MacPherson's rant / Jolly beggar, The / Cantering: the 74th highlander's farewell to Edinburgh / Pipers bonnet, The / Mrs. MacLeod of Raasay / I'm often drunk and I'm seldom sober / Taghter Jack Walsh / Connaught man's rambles, The / Overgate, The / Merchant's son, The / Daft piper, The / Boolavogue / Harvest home, The / Dowie dens of Yarrow, The.
LP: 12T 293

LIFE TRAVELLING ROADS.
MC: 60-462

SCOTS BALLADS (ACC).
MC: 60-180

TWO SCOTS TINKER TALES.
MC: 30 461

Stewart, Eric

FROOTY ROOTIES.
Tracks: / Ritual, The / Make the pieces fit / Never say "I told you so" / Night and day / All my loving following you / Rockin' my troubles away / Doris the florist (the bouquet that nobody caught) / Guitaaaaaarghs (rooties) / Strictly business.
LP: MERS 9
MC: MERSC 9

GIRLS.
Tracks: / Girls opening music / Girls / Disco grindin' / Switch le bitch / Disco bumpin' / Aural exciter / Warm, warm, warm / Tonight / Snatch the gas / Your tough is soft / Trouble shared / Discollapse / Make the pieces fit.
LP: POLD 5032

Stewart Family

STEWARTS OF BLAIR, THE.
Tracks: / Huntingtower / Caroline of Edinburgh Town / In London's fair city / Queen amang the heather / Dowie dens of Yarrow, The / Lakes of Shillin / Ower yon hills there lives a lassie / Convict's song / Young Jamie Foyers / Corncake amang the whinney knowes, The / Busk busk, bonnie lassie / Fagail liosmor / 74th farewell to Edinburgh, The / Shepherd's crook / Miss Proud.
LP: 12T 138
LP: LILP 7010

TRAVELLING STEWARTS THE.
Tracks: / Johnnie my man / Willie's fatal visit / Battle is o'er, The / Scotland the brave / 51st division in Egypt, The / Bogie's bonnie belle / McGinty's meal and ale / My bonnie Tammy / McPherson's lament / Drunken piper / Brig o'Perth / Reel of Tulloch, The / Loch Dhui / Dawning of the day / Donald's return to Glencoe.
LP: 12T 179

Stewart, Gary

20 OF THE BEST: GARY STEWART.
Tracks: / Drinkin' thing / Ramblin' man / She's acting single (I'm drinkin' doubles) / Mazelle / Oh, sweet temptations / Quits / Whisky trip / Cactus and the rose / She's got a drink problem / Brotherly love / Out of hand / Flat natural norn good timin' man / In some room above the street / Your place or mine / Ten years of this / Single again / Stone wall (around your heart) / Are we dreamin' the same dream / Let's forget that we're married / She sings amazing grace.
LP: NL 89372
MC: NK 89372

GARY.
Tracks: / Mazelle / Shady streets / Next thing you know / Everything a good little girl needs / Same man / Blues don't care who's got 'em / I've just seen the rock of ages / Walkaway / Lost highway / One more.
LP: PL 13288

YOUR PLACE OR MINE.
Tracks: / Your place or mine / Rachel Lea / Drinking again / Blue ribbon blues / Pretend I never happened / I had to get drunk last night / I ain't living long like this / Broken hearted people / Ten years of this.
LP: PL 12199

Stewart, Jermaine

FRANTIC ROMANTIC.
Tracks: / We don't have to take our clothes off / Versatile / Moonlight carnival / Don't ever leave me / Dance floor / Jody / Give your love to me / Out to punish / Frantic romantic / Word is out, The / Word is out, The (West mix-ext. version) (CD & Cassette only) / We don't have to take our clothes off (spec (CD & Cassette only).
LP: DIX 26
MC: CDIX 26

SAY IT AGAIN.
Tracks: / Don't talk dirty to me / Say it again / Get lucky / Got to be love / Dress it up / Don't have sex with your ex / Is it really love? / Call it a miracle / Eyes / My house / She's a teaser / My body.
LP: SRNLP 14
MC: SRNMC 14

WHAT BECOMES A LEGEND MOST.
Tracks: / Tren de amor / Set me free / State of my heart / I'd rather be with you / Every woman wants to / Lies / One lover / Call me before you come / Gourmet love / Please say you will / Betty Blue / Holes in my jeans.
LP: DIX 88
MC: DIXC 88

WORD IS OUT.
Tracks: / Word is out, The / I like it / In love again / Debbie / Reasons why / Get over it / Month of Mondays / You / Spies / Brilliance.
LP: XID 4
MC: CXID 4

Stewart, Jimmy

TOUCH, THE.
Tracks: / Gipsy 86 / Dreams / Jim's tune / Touch, The / Rainbow / Tune for Bill and Jim, A / Wes / Personal touch.
LP: BKH 50301

Stewart, John

BOMBS AWAY DREAM BABIES.
Tracks: / Gold / Lost her in the sun / Runaway fool of love / Somewhere down the line / Midnight wind / Over the hill / Hand your heart to the wind / Spinnin' of the world / Comin' out of nowhere / Heart of the dream.
LP: RSS 6

CALIFORNIA BLOODLINES PLUS.
Tracks: / California bloodlines / Razor back woman / She believes in me / Omaha rainbow / Pirates of Stone County Road,The / Shackles and chains / Heart full of woman and a bellyful of Tenness / Willard / Big Joe / Mother country / Lonesome picker / You can't look back / Missouri birds / July, you're a woman / Never goin' back / Friend of Jesus / Marshall wind.
LP: SEE 87

DREAM BABIES GO HOLLYWOOD.
Tracks: / Hollywood dreams / Wind on the river / Wheels of thunder / Monterey / Spirit of the water / Lady of fame / Raven / Love has tied my wings / Nightman / Moonlight rider.
LP: RSD 5007

FORGOTTEN SONGS OF SOME OLD YESTERDAY.
Tracks: / All time woman / Anna on a memory / Armstrong / Cannons in the rain / Road away / Wheatfield lady / You can't look back / July, you're a woman / Let the big horse run / Cody / California bloodlines / Mother country / Hung on the heart / Rodeo Mary.
LP: PL 43155

MEET JOHN STEWART.
Tracks: / Mr. Lucky / My heart and I / September affair / Li'l darlin' / Alley cat / Dream acres suite / I'm grinzing.
MC: AC 181

MEMORIES OF JOHN STEWART.
Tracks: / My heart and I / Alley cat / Body and soul / Lady is a tramp, The / I got rhythm / It's foolish but it's fun / If I'm lucky / Misty / Showboat selection / Li'l darlin' / Chloe.
MC: AC 167

PHOENIX CONCERTS, THE.
LP: CL 43254

TRANCAS.
Tracks: / It ain't the gold / Reasons to rise / Pilots in blue / Chasing down the rain / Till the lights come home / Bringing down the moon / All the lights / Rocky top / American way, The / Chosen, The.
LP: SSAD 01
LP: FEDL 102
MC: CFEDL 102

Stewart & Kyle

ISN'T IT STRANGE.
LP: PC 112

YOURS FOREVER.
LP: PC 837

Stewart, Louis

ACOUSTIC GUITAR DUETS (Stewart, Louis & Martin Taylor).
Tracks: / Pick yourself up / Morning of the carnival / Jive at five / Comin' thro' the rye / Cherokee / Stompin' at the Savoy / Darn that dream / Farewell to Erin.
LP: LRLP 7
MC: LRCS 7

ALONE TOGETHER (Live at The Peacock) (Stewart, Louis & Brian Dunning).
Tracks: / There will never be another you / Windows / Definitely doctored / Inner urge / Israel / Alone together / Triste / Donna Lee.

LP: . . . . LRLP 5

BAUBLES, BANGLES AND BEADS (Stewart Louis & Peter Ind).
LP: . . . . WAVE LP 12

DRUMS AND FRIENDS (See Under Wadham, John) (Stewart, Louis & John Wadham).

GOOD NEWS.
LP: . . . . VILLA 001

I THOUGHT ABOUT YOU.
Tracks: / I thought about you / Litha / Smiling Billy / Unit 7 / November girl / Straight no chaser.
LP: . . . . LAM 103

OUT ON HIS OWN.
Tracks: / Blue bossa / Windows / Darn that dream / Wave / She moved through the fair / Make someone happy / I'm all smiles / Stella by starlight / Lazy afternoon / Invitation / I'm old fashioned / General Mojo's well laid plan / What's new ?.
LP: . . . . LRLP 1
MC: . . . . LRCS 1

Stewart, Lucy

TRADITIONAL SINGER FROM ABERDEENSHIRE VOL. 1.
Tracks: / Battle of O'Harlaw / Two pretty boys / Tifty's Annie / Laird o' drum, The / Doon by the greenwood sidie O / Beggar king, The / Bonnie hoose o' Airlie / Barbara Allen / Swan swims so bonnie O, The.
MC: . . . . CTRAX 031

Stewart, Mark

AS THE VENEER OF DEMOCRACY STARTS TO FADE.
LP: . . . . STUMM 24

LEARNING TO COPE WITH COWARDICE.
LP: . . . . ONULP 24

MARK STEWART.
Tracks: / Survival / Survivalist / Anger / Hell is empty / Stranger / Forbidden colour / Forbidden (dub) / Fatal / Attraction.
LP: . . . . STUMM 43

METATRON.
LP: . . . . STUMM 62
MC: . . . . CSTUMM 62

Stewart, Mary

THUNDER ON THE RIGHT.
MC: . . . . CAB 318

Stewart, Norman

MUSIC AND SONG FROM SCOTLAND.
LP: . . . . CM 003

Stewart, Rex

ART FORD'S JAZZ PARTY September 1958.
LP: . . . . AFJP 6

BIG JAZZ 1940 (Stewart, Rex & Jack Teagarden).
LP: E-1010

HOLLYWOOD JAM (Stewart, Rex All Stars Band).
Tracks: / Blues jam / Someday, sweetheart / Muskrat ramble / Mood indigo / Sheik of Araby, The.
LP: . . . . D 1017

RENDEZVOUS WITH REX.
Tracks: / Tillie's twist / Pretty ditty / Tell me more / Trade winds / My kind of gal / Blue echo.
LP: . . . . AFF 165

Stewart, Rod

ABSOLUTELY LIVE.
Tracks: / Stripper, The / Tonight I'm yours / Sweet little rock 'n' roller / Hot legs / Tonight's the night / Great pretender, The / Passion / She won't dance with me / Little Queenie / You're in my heart / Rock my plimsoul / Young Turks / Guess I'll always love you / Gasoline Alley / Maggie May / Tear it up / Do ya think I'm sexy? / Sailing / I don't want to talk about it / Stay with me.
2LP: 923743 1
MC: 923743 4
LP: . . . . RVLP 17

ATLANTIC CROSSING.
Tracks: / Three times a loser / Alright for an hour / All in the name of rock'n'roll / Drift away / Stone cold sober / I don't want to talk about it / It's not the spotlight / This old heart of mine / Still love you / Sailing.
LP: . . . . K 56151
MC: K4 56151
LP: . . . . RVLP 4
LP: . . . . K 56151
MC: K4 56151

ATLANTIC CROSSING/A NIGHT ON THE TOWN.
MC: 923955 4

AUTUMN STONE.
Tracks: / Just a little misunderstood / Baby come home / Collie bosker, A / Fly, The (instrumental) / Anything (instrumental) / Sparky rides / Wide eyed girl / Red balloon / Autumn storm.
LP: 2215245
MC: 2115245

BEST OF ROD (1985) (Full title: Best of Rod Stewart).
Tracks: / Maggie May / Cut across Shorty / Let you down / I know I'm losing you / Handbags and gladrags / It's all over now / Street fighting man / Gasoline Alley / Every picture tells a story / What made Milwaukee famous / Oh no, not my baby / Jodie / You wear it well / Let me be your car / Pinball wizard / Sailor / Angel / Mine for me.
2LP: . . . . PRID 10
MCSET: . . . . PRIDC 10

BEST OF ROD STEWART (1977).
Tracks: / Angel / Cut across Shorty / Every picture tells a story / Gasoline Alley / Handbags and gladrags / I'm losing you / It's all over now / Jodie / Let me be your car / Maggie May / Mine for me / Oh no, not my baby / Old raincoat won't ever let you down, An / Pinball wizard / Sailor / Street fighting man / What made Milwaukee famous / You wear it well.
2LP: 6643 030
MCSET: 7599 141

BEST OF THE BEST.
LP: 9279 135

BLONDES HAVE MORE FUN.
Tracks: / Do ya think I'm sexy? / Dirty weekend / Ain't love a bitch? / Best days of my life / Is that the thanks I get? / Attractive female wanted / Blondes have more fun / Last summer / Standing in the shadows of love / Scarred and scared.
LP: . . . . K 56572
MC: K4 56572
LP: . . . . RVLP 8

BODY WISHES.
Tracks: / Dancin' alone / Baby Jane / Move me / Body wishes / Sweet surrender / What am I gonna do / Ghetto blaster / Ready now / Strangers / Again / Satisfied.
LP: 9238771
MC: 9238774

CAMOUFLAGE.
Tracks: / Infatuation / All right now / Some guys have all the luck / Can we still be friends? / Bad for you / Heart is on the line / Camouflage / Trouble.
LP: 925095 1
MC: 925095 4

CAN I GET A WITNESS.
LP: 20119
MC: 40119

EARLY STEWART.
Tracks: / Maggie May / Mandolin wind / Gasoline Alley / Every picture tells a story / Reason to believe / Tomorrow is such a long time (Only on CD.) / Angel (Only on CD.).
LP: 840 241
MC: 840 244

EVERY BEAT OF MY HEART.
Tracks: / Who's gonna take me home / Another heartache / Night like this, A / Red hot in black / Here to eternity / Love touch / In my own crazy way / Every beat of my heart / Ten days of rain / In my life / Trouble.
LP: . . . . WX 53
MC: . . . . WX 53 C

EVERY PICTURE TELLS A STORY.
Tracks: / True blue / You wear it well / I don't want to discuss it / You're my girl / Sweet little rock 'n' roller / Sailor / Dixie toot / Street fighting man / Every picture tells a story / Seems like a long time / That's alright / Amazing grace / Tomorrow is such a long time / Henry / Maggie May / Mandolin wind / I'm losing you / Reason to believe.
LP: . . . . PRICE 15
MC: . . . . PRIMC 15
LP: 6338 063
LP: 8426361

FACES FEATURING ROD STEWART (see Faces & Rod Stewart) (Stewart, Rod & Faces).

FOOLISH BEHAVIOUR.
LP: . . . . RVLP 11

FOOTLOOSE AND FANCY FREE.
Tracks: / Hot legs / You're insane / You're in my heart / Born loose / You keep me hangin' on / If loving you is wrong I don't want to be right / You gotta nerve / I was only joking.
LP: . . . . K 56423
MC: K4 56423
LP: . . . . RVLP 5

GASOLINE ALLEY.
Tracks: / Gasoline alley / It's all over now / Only a hobo / My way of giving / Country comfort / Cut across shorty / Lady Day / Jo's lament / I don't want to discuss it.
LP: 6360 500
LP: 6336 546
LP: . . . . PRICE 28

GASOLINE ALLEY/ SMILE.
MC: 8469884

GREATEST HITS: ROD STEWART.
Tracks: / Hot legs / Maggie May / Do ya think I'm sexy / You're in my heart / Sailing / I don't want to talk about it / Tonight's the night / Killing of Georgie, The / First cut is the deepest / I was only joking.
LP: . . . . ROD TV 1
MC: . . . . ROD TV 41

GREATEST HITS: ROD STEWART VOL.1.
Tracks: / First cut is the deepest / I was only joking / You're in my heart / Tonight's the night / Hot legs / Killing of Georgie, The / Maggie May / Do ya think I'm sexy? / Sailing / I don't want to talk about it.
LP: . . . . K 56744
MC: K4 56744

HITS OF ROD STEWART, THE.
LP: . . . . CN 2077
MC: CN4 2077

HOT RODS.
Tracks: / Let me be your car / Los Paraguayos / Twisting the night away / Mandolin wind / Streetfighting man / You wear it well / Italian girls / Sailor / Pinball wizard / Mine for me / Jodie / Maggie May.
LP: 6463061

I'VE BEEN DRINKING (See under Beck, Jeff) (Stewart, Rod & Jeff Beck).

JUKE BOX HEAVEN (14 rock'n'roll greats).
Tracks: / Sweet little rock 'n' roller / Bring it on home to me / I wish it would rain / Mama you been on my mind / Jealous guy / Twistin the night away / Pinball wizard / Handbags and gladrags / Angel / Mine for me / Street fighting man / Girl from the north country / Oh no not my baby / I'd rather go blind.
LP: . . . . CN 2082
MC: CN4 2082

MAGGIE MAY.
Tracks: / Maggie May / Sailing / Oh no, not my baby / Street fighting man / It's all over now / Mandolin wind / Man of constant sorrow / Reason to believe / Twistin' the night away / Angel / Girl from the north country / Sweet little rock 'n' roller.
LP: . . . . CN 2045
MC: CN4 2045

MAGIC OF ROD STEWART, THE.
Tracks: / Why does it go on / Shake / Just a little misunderstood / Ain't that loving you baby / Sparky rides / Day will come, The / Bright lights big city / Keep your hands off her / Mopper's blues / Red ballroom.
MC: . . . . VENUMC 3

MUSIC OF 1970-71.
Tracks: / Blind prayer / Country comfort / Cut across Shorty / Every picture tells a story / Gasoline Alley / Handbags and gladrags / I'm losing you / Man of constant sorrow / Mandolin wind / Old raincoat won't ever let you down, An / Reason to believe / Street fighting man.
MC: 7145 069

NEVER A DULL MOMENT.
Tracks: / True blue / Los Paraguayos / Mama you been on my mind / Italian girls / Angel / Interludings / You wear it well / I'd rather go blind / Twistin' the night away.
LP: 6499 153

NIGHT ON THE TOWN, A.
Tracks: / Ball trap / Pretty flamingo / Big bayou / Wild side of life / Trade winds / Tonight's the night / First cut is the deepest / Fool for you, A / Killing of Georgie, The.
LP: . . . . K 56234
MC: K4 56234
LP: . . . . RVLP 1

NIGHTRIDING: ROD STEWART.
Tracks: / Every picture tells a story / Seems like a long time / That's alright / Amazing Grace / Tomorrow is a long time / Angel / Old raincoat won't ever let you down, An / Henry / Maggie May / Mandolin wind / (I know) I'm losing you / Reason to believe / Lady Day / I'd rather go blind.
MC: . . . . KNMC 10002
LP: . . . . KNLP 10002

OH NO NOT MY BABY.
LP: RJ7 376

OLD RAINCOAT WON'T LET YOU DOWN, AN.
Tracks: / Street fighting man / Man of constant sorrow / Blind prayer / Handbags and gladrags / Old raincoat won't ever let you down, An / I wouldn't ever change a thing / Cindy's lament / Dirty old town.
LP: . . . . PRICE 27
MC: . . . . PRIMC 27
LP: 633 661 0

ORIGINAL FACE, THE.
LP: . . . . THBL 085

OUT OF ORDER.
Tracks: / Lost in you / Wild horse, The / Lethal dose of love / Forever young / My heart can't tell you no / Dynamite / Nobody knows you (when you're down and out) / Crazy about her / Try a little tenderness / When I was your man.
LP: . . . . WX 152
MC: . . . . WX 152 C

OVERTURE AND BEGINNERS (Stewart, Rod & Faces).
LP: 9100 001

REASON TO BELIEVE (See under the recording Maggie May).

RIDIN' HIGH Vol. 1.
LP: . . . . SM 3985

ROCK ALBUM,THE.
LP: 830 784 1
MC: 830 784 4

ROD STEWART.
Tracks: / You wear it well / Gasoline Alley / I know I'm losing you / Pinball wizard / Every picture tells a story / Amazing grace / I'd rather go blind / I don't want to discuss it / That's alright / Old raincoat won't ever let you down, An / What made Milwaukee famous / Handbags and gladrags.
LP: . . . . CN 2059
MC: CN4 2059
LP: 824 319 1

ROD STEWART (CAMBRA).
Tracks: / Maggie May / Pinball wizard / Every picture tells a story / Gasoline Alley / Bring it on home to me / You send me / Angel / Street fighting man / Mandolin wind / Old raincoat won't ever let you down, An / Farewell / Sweet little rock 'n' roller / What made Milwaukee famous / Country comfort / Handbags and gladrags / It's all over now / You wear it well / Reason to believe / Mine for me / That's alright / Oh no, not my baby / Twistin' the night away.
MCSET: . . . . CRT 026

ROD STEWART COLLECTION, THE (Best of Rod Stewart).
LP: . . . . WX 314
MC: . . . . WX 314C

ROD STEWART (MERCURY).
Tracks: / Reason to believe / You wear it well / Mandolin wind / Country comfort / Maggie May / Handbags and gladrags / Street fighting man / Twistin' the night away / Los Paraguayos / Im losing you / Pinball wizard / Gasoline Alley.
LP: 824 319 1
MC: 824 319 4

SHAKE.
LP: . . . . XELLP 109
MC: . . . . XELMC 109

SING IT AGAIN ROD.
LP: 6499 484

SMILER.
Tracks: / Sweet little rock 'n' roller / Lochnagar / Farewell / Sailor / Bring it on home to me / Let me be your car / (You make me feel) a natural man / Dixie toot / Hard road / I've grown accustomed to her face / Girl from the north country / Mine for me.
LP: 9104 011

SOMEDAY.
LP: . . . . PLP 24
MC: . . . . PMC 24

STORYTELLER (Complete Anthology 1964-1990).
LPS: 9259871
MCSET: 9259874

TONIGHT I'M YOURS.
Tracks: / Tonight I'm yours / How long? / Tora tora tora / Tear it up / Only a boy / Just like a woman / Jealous / Sonny / Young Turks / Never give up on a dream.
LP: . . . . K 56951
MC: K4 56951
LP: . . . . RVLP 14

TWO GREAT POP CLASSICS.
Tracks: / Maggie May / Reason to believe / Only a hobo / Tomorrow is a long time / It's all over now.
2LP: 8301881

WERELDSUCCESSEN SERIES.
Tracks: / Reason to believe / Maggie May / You wear it well / Angel / What made Milwaukee famous / Oh no, not my baby / Farewell / Bring it on home to me / You send me.
2LP: 6619 054
MCSET: 7558 061

WIDE EYED GIRL.
LP: PLP 10
MC: PMC 10

Stewart, Roman

LOSE RESPECT (See under Levy, Barrington for details) (Stewart, Roman/ Trinity/Barrington Levy).

RULING AND CONTROLLING.
LP: PHLP 010

Stewart, Sandy

SINGS THE SONGS OF JEROME KERN.
LP: AP 205

Stewart, Slam

DIALOGUE (Stewart, Slam & Bucky Pizzarelli).
Tracks: / Slam blow / It's only a paper moon / That's my kick / Very thought of you, The / Jersey bounce / Night wind / Masquerade / B and S blues / I got rhythm.
LP: SNTF 811
LP: ST 201

NEW YORK, NEW YORK.
LP: ST 204

Stewart, Tinga

KEY TO YOUR HEART.
LP: LDLP 003

NO DRUGS.
LP: LALP 25

RESPECT ME.
LP: PICKLP 7

Stewart, Wayne

ASPEN SKYLINE (Stewart Wayne & Friends).
LP: SBR 4207

Stewart, Wynn

CHALLENGE YEARS, THE 1958-1963.
Tracks: / Wishful thinking / Heartaches for a dime / Open up my heart / Three cheers for the losers / Rain rain / I sold the farm / Slightly used / Falling for you / I'd rather have America / Yankee go home (Duet with Jan Howard) / Come on (fast take) / Uncle Tom got caught / Never out of my heart / Long black limousine / School bus love affair / She just tears me up / Big big love / Donna on my mind / How the other half lives (Duet with Jan Howard) / With this ring / Another day, another dollar / Wrong company (Duet with Jan Howard) / Judy / We'll never love again / Wall to wall heartaches / I'm not the man I used to be / Couples only / Loversville / Don't look back / I don't feel at home / I done done it / Above and beyond / Come on / Wishful thinking (version 2) / Big city / If you see my baby / Playboy / Girl in white / One more memory / Searching for another you / One way to go / Hungry heart.
2LP: BFD 15261

SONGS OF WS, THE.
LP: HAT 3110
MC: HATC 3110

Stezo

CRAZY NOISE.
LP: SBUKLP 7
MC: SBUKMC 7

Stickdog

HUMAN.
LP: VIRUS 64

Sticky Fingers

STICKY FINGERS.
Tracks: / Wastin' my love / Takin' a chance on you / Night time / Party song.
LP: EPC 83612

Stidham, Arbee

MY HEART BELONGS TO YOU.
Tracks: / My heart belongs to you / You'll be sorry / I found out for myself / Any time you ring my bell / Stidham jumps / So tired of dreaming / I've got so many worries / Let my dreams come true / Barbeque lounge / Feel like I'm losing you / Sixty minutes to wait / Bad dream blues / Don't set your cap for me / I stayed away too long / I don't play / Look me straight in the eyes.
LP: IG 404

Stiff Little Fingers

ALL THE BEST.
Tracks: / Suspect device / Wasted life / Alternative Ulster / 78 rpm / Gotta get away / Bloody Sunday / Straw dogs / You can't say crap on the radio / At the edge / Running bear / White Christmas / Nobody's hero / Tin soldiers / Back to front / Mr. Fire coal man / Just fade away / Go for it / Doesn't make it alright / Silver lining / Safe as houses / Sad eyed people / Two guitars clash / Listen / That's when your blood bumps / Good for nothing / Talkback / Stands to reason / Bits of kids / Touch and go / Price of admission, The.
2LP: CTY 1414
MCSET: ZCTY 1414
MCSET: TCEM 1428

GO FOR IT.
Tracks: / Just fade away / Go for it / Only one, The / Hit and misses / Kicking up a racket / Safe as houses / Gate 49 / Silver lining / Piccadilly Circus / Back to front (Extra track on Fame release.).
LP: CHR 1339
MC: ZCHR 1339
LP: FA 3216
MC: TCFA 3216

HANX.
Tracks: / Nobody's hero / Gotta getaway / Wait and see / Barbed wire love / Fly the flag / Alternative Ulster / Johnny was / At the edge / Wasted life / Tin soldiers / Suspect device.
MC: ZCHR 1300
LP: CHR 1300
LP: FA 3215
MC: TCFA 3215

INFLAMMABLE MATERIAL.
Tracks: / Suspect device / State of emergency / Here we are nowhere / Wasted life / No more of that / Barbed wire love / White noise / Breakout / Law and order / Johnny was / Alternative Ulster / Closed groove.
LP: ROUGH 1
LP: EMC 3554
MC: TCEMC 3554

LIVE AND LOUD.
2LP: LINK LP 026

NO SLEEP TIL BELFAST.
Tracks: / Alternative Ulster / Roots radicals rockers and reggae / Silver lining / Wait and see / Gotta getaway / Just fade away / Wasted life / Only one, The / Nobodys heroes / At the edge / Listen / Barbed wire love / Fly the flag / Tin soldiers / Suspect device / Johnny was.
MCSET: KAZ MC 6

NOBODY'S HEROES.
Tracks: / Gotta getaway / Wait and see / Fly the flag / At the edge / Nobody's hero / Bloody dub / Doesn't make it alright / I don't like you / No change / Suspect device / Tin soldiers.
LP: CHR 1270
MC: ZCHR 1270
LP: EMC 3555
MC: TCEMC 3555

NOW THEN.
Tracks: / Falling down / Won't be told / Love of the common people / Price of admission, The / Touch and go / Bits of kids / Welcome to the whole week / Big city nights / Talkback / Is that what you fought the war for.
LP: CHR 1400
MC: ZCHR 1400

PEEL SESSIONS: STIFF LITTLE FINGERS (2).
Tracks: / Johnny was / Law and order / Barbed wire love / Suspect device / Wait and see / At the edge / Nobody's hero / Straw dogs / No change / I don't like you / Fly the flag / Doesn't make it all right.
LP: SFRLP 106
MC: SFRMC 106

SEE YOU UP THERE.
Tracks: / Alternative Ulster / Common people / Just fade away / Wasted life / At the edge / Barbed wire love / Tin soldiers / Suspect device / Silver lining / Gotta getaway / Piccadilly Circus / Gate 49 / Listen / Fly the flag / Wild rover / Johnny was.
2LP: VGD 3515
MC: VGDC 3515

STIFF LITTLE FINGERS.
LP: SFRLP 1
MC: SFRMC 1

Stikky

WHERE'S MY LUNCH PAIL?.
LP: ACHE 15

Stiletto

BLAME IT ON YOUTH.
LP: A 28

Stilgoe, Richard

BODYWORK (Musical Light Opera 88).
LP: CAST 15
MC: CASTC 15

WHO PLAYS WINS (See Skellern, Peter) (Stilgoe, Richard & Peter Skellern).

Still Waters

I RESERVE THE RIGHT.
Tracks: / I reserve the right / Women / Keeping myself alive / Kalifornia kool / Sometimes sunshine / Fair warning / Alone on a Saturday night / Ain't we a pair.
LP: 242 917 6

LES ILES SEYCHELLES (See under Seychelles).

LIFE'S RAILROAD (Still Waters Trio).
LP: PC 330

Stills

LONG MAY YOU RUN.
Tracks: / Long may you run / Make love to you / Midnight on the bay / Black coral / Ocean girl / Let it shine / 12/8 blues / Fontaine bleau / Guardian angel.
LP: K 54081

Stills, Stephen

BEST OF STEPHEN STILLS.
Tracks: / Love the one you're with / It doesn't matter / We are not helpless / Marianne / Bound to fall / Isn't it about time / Change partners / Go back home / Johnny's garden / Rock and roll crazies / Cuban bluegrass / Sit yourself down.
LP: K 50327

DOWN THE ROAD (Stills, Stephen Manassas).
LP: K 40440

ILLEGAL STILLS.
LP: CBS 81330

MANASSAS (Stills, Stephen Manassas).
LP: K 60021

RIGHT BY YOU.
Tracks: / 50/50 / Stranger / Flaming heart / Love again / Can't let go / No problem / Grey to green / Only love can break your heart / No hiding place / Right by you.
LP: 780 177-1

STEPHEN STILLS.
Tracks: / Love the one you're with / Do for the others / Church (part of someone) / Old times, good times / Go back home / Sit yourself down / To a flame / Black Queen / Cherokee / We are not helpless.
LP: K 40341
LP: 2401 004

STEPHEN STILLS VOL.2.
LP: 2401 013

STILLS.
LP: CBS 69146

TWO ORIGINALS OF STEPHEN STILLS (Stephen Stills and Stephen Stills 2).
Tracks: / Love the one you're with / Do for the others / Church (part of someone) / Old times, good times / Go back home / Sit yourself down / To a flame / Black Queen / Cherokee / We are not helpless / Change partners / Nothin' to do but today / Fishes & scorpions / Sugar babe / Know you got to run / Open secret / Relaxing town / Singin' call / Ecology song / World game / Marianne / Bluebird revisited.
2LP: K 60063

Stimulators

LOUD, FAST RULES.
MC: A 109

Sting

BRING ON THE NIGHT.
Tracks: / Bring on the night / Consider me gone / Low life / We work the black seam / Driven to tears / Dream of the blue turtles, The / Demolition man / One world / Love is seventh wave / Moon over Bourbon Street / I burn for you / Another day / Children's crusade / Down so long / Tea in the Sahara.
2LP: BRING 1
MCSET: BRINC 1

DREAM OF THE BLUE TURTLES / NOTHING LIKE THE SUN.
MC: AMC 24110

DREAM OF THE BLUE TURTLES, THE.
Tracks: / If you love somebody set them free / Love is the seventh wave / We work the black seam / Russians / Children's crusade / Shadows in the rain / Consider me gone / Dream of the blue turtles, The / Moon over Bourbon Street / Fortress around your heart.
LP: DREAM 1
MC: DREMC 1
LPPD: DREMP 1

...NADA COMO EL SOL.
LP: 393 295 0

NOTHING LIKE THE SUN.
Tracks: / Lazarus heart, The / Be still my beating heart / Englishman in New York / History will teach us nothing / They dance alone / Fragile / We'll be together / Straight to my heart / Rock steady / Sister moon / Little wing / Secret marriage, The.
LP: AMA 6402
MC: AMC 6402

SOLDIER TALE, THE (Igor Stravinsky) (Sting/Vanessa Redgrave).
LP: 461048 1
MC: 461048 4

SOUL CAGES, THE.
LP: 396 405 1
MC: 396 405 4

Stingrays

CRYPTIC AND COFFEE TIME.
LP: KSLP 001

DINOSAURS.
Tracks: / Soul sale / Just can't help myself / Blue girl / On the rocks / You got a hard time comin' / Drive-in movie / Standing in line / Strangelove / My flash on you / Joe Strummer's wallet / Puppet, The / Ah what?.
LP: WIKM 16

ESSENTIAL STING-RAYS, THE.
Tracks: / Math of trend / I want my woman / Soul sale / You got a hard time comin' / Standing in line / Joe Strummer's wallet / Puppet, The / Crusher, The / Escalator / Come on kid / Pretence / Don't break down / Image / Go ask Alice / Satisfy you / Down on me.
LP: WIK 61

GOODBYE TO ALL THAT LIVE VOL 2.
Tracks: / Perverted justice / Save the tiger / Militant tendency / Behind the beyond / Hopelessness / Burden of dreams, The / June rhyme / Elvis, Gladys and the Guru / Go ask Alice / Don't sell yourself / From the kitchen sink / Y'know sometimes love is an awful bore.
LP: MB 18

LIVE RETALIATION.
LP: MB 1

STINGRAYS STORY.
LP: MB 2

Stinit, Dane

ORIGINAL SUN RECORDINGS.
Tracks: / Don't knock what you don't understand (take 1) / Always on the go / Don't knock what you don't understand (take 7) / Kilgore jail / Mean eyed cat / Ghost of Mary Lou, The / Flip top flipper / Sweet country girl / Muddy ole river (near Memphis Tennessee) / Heartache catches up with me (take 10) / Windy City / Heartache catches with me (take 15) / Shot out of the saddle / I'm a rounder.
LP: BFX 15337

Stirling, Leigh

IN THE WINGS.
Tracks: / Standing in the wings / Ain't that strange / It's only a simple song / Rock'n'roll yee-haw man / Listening to the moonlight / Little bit of what you fancy, A / Five star taxi / Road to Damascus / My life on earth / Until I come home.
LP: WKR 1001

Stitched Back Foot

MANIC & GLOBAL.
Tracks: / Dirty's happened, The / Hold that dream / Need not profit / Wheel of life / Daily rack / Careful balance / Pianos in the lake / Doc OC / It hurts me / Frog march / Big mess / Pine / She'll invent the world / Marie Celeste / Big fat life / Down to earth.
LP: IT 061

SEVEN EGG TIMING GREATS.
Tracks: / Why (am I this way) / Watery song / Pressure's building / More power / Through these days / Fashion scum / Say you care / Pete pick.
LP: EAT 9
LP: IT 057

Stitt, Sonny

AT THE D.J. LOUNGE.
Tracks: / McKie's / It all depends on you / Blue moon / I'm in the mood for love / Free love.
LP: GCH 8085
MC: GCHK 78085

BOP SESSION, THE (See under Gillespie, Dizzy) (Stitt, Sonny/Dizzy Gillespie/John Lewis/Max Roach).

BOSS TENORS (See under Ammons, Gene) (Stitt, Sonny & Gene Ammons).

CHAMP, THE.
Tracks: / Champ, The / Sweet and lovely / Midgets, The / Eternal triangle, The / All the things you are / Walkin'.
LP: MR 5023

CONSTELLATION.
Tracks: / Constellation / I don't stand a ghost of a chance / Webb city / By accident / Ray's idea / Casbah / It's magic / Topsy.
LP: MR 5323

EVERY DAY I HAVE THE BLUES (see under Crayton, Pee Wee) (Stitt, Sonny, Joe Turner and Pee Wee Crayton).

FEATURING HOWARD MCGHEE.
LP: 2273242
MC: 2173242

FOR MUSICIANS ONLY (See under Getz, Stan) (Stitt, Sonny/Stan Getz/ Dizzy Gillespie).

GOOD LIFE (Stitt, Sonny & Hank Jones).
LP: BKH 528

IN WALKED SONNY (Stitt, Sonny/Art Blakey & The Jazz Messengers).
Tracks: / Blues march / It might as well be Spring / Birdlike / I can't get started / Ronnie's a dynamite lady / In walked Sonny.
LP: **SNTF 691**
MC: **ZCSN 691**

JAWS 'N' STITT AT BIRDLAND (See under Davis, Eddie Lockjaw) (Stitt, Sonny & Eddie Lockjaw Davis).

JUG & SONNY (See under Ammons, Gene) (Stitt, Sonny & Gene Ammons).

JUST FRIENDS (Stitt, Sonny & Red Holloway).
Tracks: / Way you look tonight / Forecast / You don't know what love is / Getting sentimental over you / Lester leaps in / Just friends / All God's chillun got rhythm.
LP: **AFF 181**

LAST STITT SESSION, THE.
Tracks: / Steamroller / I'll be seeing you / Out of nowhere / Sweet Georgia Brown / Keepin' it / This is always / Makin' it / Angel eyes.
LP: **MR 5269**

LAST STITT SESSIONS Vol. 2.
LP: **MR 5280**

LOOSE WALK (see Jackson, Milt) (Stitt, Sonny & Milt Jackson).

LOVERMAN (Stitt, Sonny & The Giants).
Tracks: / Night work / Matter horns / Loverman / Satin doll / Don't blame me / Hello.
LP: **BLM 52009**

MADE FOR EACH OTHER.
LP: **DS 426**

MOONLIGHT IN VERMONT.
Tracks: / West 46th Street / Who can I turn to? / Moonlight in Vermont / Flight cap blues / It might as well be Spring / Constellation / Blues for PCM.
LP: **YX 7530**

MY BUDDY (Sonny Stitt plays G.Ammons).
LP: **MR 5091**

NIGHT WORK (Stitt, Sonny & The Giants).
Tracks: / Night work / Matter horns / Lover man / Satin doll / Don't blame me / Hello.
LP: **BLP 30154**

NOW.
Tracks: / Surfin' / Lester leaps in / Estrellita / Please don't talk about me when I'm gone / Touchy / Never / Sh / My mother's eyes / Getting sentimental over you.
LP: **JAS 25**
MC: **JAS C25**

SALT AND PEPPER (Stitt, Sonny & Paul Gonsalves).
Tracks: / Salt and pepper / S'posin (I should fall in love with you) / Lord of the flies (theme from) / Perdido / Stardust.
MC: **JAS C26**
LP: **JAS 26**

SONNY.
LP: **500074**

SONNY STITT.
Tracks: / Stardust / Cherokee / Autumn in New York / Gypsy, The / Loverman / Matterhorns / Hello / Nightwork.
LP: **BLP 60130**

SONNY STITT MEETS SADIK HAKIM (Stitt, Sonny & Sadik Hakim).
Tracks: / Christopher Street jump / Little girl blue / Easy to love / You are the sunshine of my life / South Georgia blues / All God's chillun got rhythm / Round midnight / Fine and dandy.
LP: **PRO 7034**

SONNY STITT WITH THE NEW YORKERS (Stitt, Sonny/The New Yorkers).
LP: **FS 274**

SONNY, SWEETS & JAWS (Stitt, Sonny/Sweets Edison/Eddie Lockjaw Davis).
Tracks: / Lady be good / What's new? / There is no greater love / Chef, The / I can't get started / Lester leaps in.
LP: **GATE 7007**
MC: **CGATE 7007**

SONNY'S BACK.
Tracks: / Canadian sunset / Sonny's bounce / Soon / Dodge City / It might as well be spring / Constellation / Street of dreams.
LP: **MR 5204**

SONNY'S BUBBA'S SESSIONS.
Tracks: / Sonny's blues / Old folks / Lax / Yesterdays / What's new? / Four.
LP: **GATE 7012**
MC: **CGATE 7012**

SUPER STITT.
Tracks: / How high the moon / Body and soul / Pennies from Heaven / Every tub / Thou swell / Baritone blues / Blue and sentimental.
LP: **LP 15**

SUPER STITT, VOL 2.
Tracks: / Sweet Georgia Brown / I'm in the mood for love / Tri-horn blues / If I should lose you / Indiana / Wigmen / Melancholy baby / Flyin' home.
LP: **LP 23**

TENOR BATTLES (Stitt, Sonny & Eddie Lockjaw Davis).
Tracks: / Rollercoaster / Don't blame me / Whoops / All the things you are.
LP: **LP 19**

Stivell, Alan

ALAN STIVELL.
LP: **6886 168**

CELTIC SYMPHONY.
MC: **R 3088/89C**

CHIMINS DE TERRE.
LP: **9279038**
MC: **7259038**

HARPES DU NOUVEL AGE.
LP: **ROUNDER 3094**
MC: **ROUNDER 3094C**

JOURNEE A LA MAISON.
LP: **ROUNDER 3062**
MC: **ROUNDER 3062C**

RENAISSANCE OF THE CELTIC HARP.
Tracks: / Airde Cuan / Eliz Iza / Gaelic waltz / Gaeltacht / Caitlin trial / Herman Dubh / Little cascade, The / Manx melody / Mary Pontkalleg / Na reubairean / Penily manuscript of harp music / Ap Huw - Penilyn / Port an deorai / Port ui Mhuirgheasa / Struan Robertson.
LP: **PRICE 51**
MC: **PRIMC 51**
LP: **ROUNDER 3067**
MC: **ROUNDER 3067C**

Stobart, Kathy

ARDERIA (Featuring Marion Williams Vocal).
Tracks: / Arbeia / Detour ahead / Pieces of dreams / As is / 2HS / If I thought you'd ever change your mind / Enchanted into cry of triumph.
LP: **SPJ 509**

SAXPLOITATION (Stobart, Kathy/Joe Temperley 5).
Tracks: / Softly as in a morning sunrise / My funny valentine / Tickle toe / Drop me off in Harlem / In a sentimental mood / Blues in the closet / Crazy he calls me / Cottontail.
LP: **SPJ 503**

Stockhausen, Karlheinz

CEYLON.
Tracks: / Ceylon / Bird of passage.
LP: **CHR 1110**
MC: **ZCHR 1110**

Stockhausen, Markus

APARIS (Stockhausen, Markus Trio).
Tracks: / Aparis / Poseidon / Carnaval / High ride / Rejoice / Peach.
LP: **ECM 1404**

COSI LONTANO...QUASI DENTRO (So Far Almost Inside).
LP: **ECM 1371**

Stockholm Monsters

ALMER MATER.
LP: **FACT 80**

Stockholm Philharmonic

PAAVO BERGLUND AND STOCKHOLM PHILHARMONIC ORCH (See under Berglund, Paavo) (Berglund, Paavo/Stockholm Philharmonic Orchestra).

Stockholm Police Choir

POLISKOREN.
Tracks: / Down our way / I left my heart in San Francisco / Summertime / Sentimental journey / E en gronmalad bat / Nocturne / Kullerullvisan / Kersti lill sov gott / Afrikansk bon / Vallat fran Alvdalen / Brudmarsch fran jarna / Leksands klockor / Tryggare kan ingen vara / I himmelen I himmelen / O store gud.
LP: **PHONT 7522**

Stockton's Wing

AMERICAN SPECIAL.
LP: **TA 4001**
MC: **4TA 4001**

CELTIC ROOTS REVIVAL.
Tracks: / Slipside / Clamdiggers / You always will be mine / Polkas / Southern Cross / No worries / Feasta na fienne / Woody Island, The / Stone grey pier / Se mo croi.
LP: **RGLP 6**
MC: **RGMC 6**

FULL FLIGHT.
Tracks: / Over the moors / So many miles / Dancing in the dark / Full flight / Why wait until tomorrow / Hey Marsha / New Clare revival / Avondale / Fox's hasp.
LP: **831 183-1**
MC: **831 183-4**

LIGHT IN THE WESTERN SKY.
MC: **4TA 3009**
LP: **TA 3009**

STOCKTON'S WING.
LP: **TA 2004**
MC: **4TA 2004**

TAKE A CHANCE.
LP: **TA 3004**
MC: **4TA 3004**

TAKE ONE LIVE.
LP: **REVL 2**

Stoddart, Pipe Major

PIPERS OF DISTINCTION (Stoddart, Pipe Major GNM).
MC: **ZCMON 806**

Stoke Original Theatre

SOUVENIR FROM STOKE.
LP: **SDL 296**

Stoker, Bram (author)

DRACULA (Various artists).
MCSET: **SAY 104**
MCSET: **ARGO 1223**

DRACULA (Valentine, Anthony).
MC: **PTB 631**

DRACULA (McCallum, David / Carole Shelley).
MC: **1468**

DRACULA (Horden, Sir Michael).
MC: **0600560554**

DRACULA (horror classics for ages 7-12).
MC: **PLB 120**

Stoker, Richard

FINE AND MELLOW (see Fazarro, Susan) (Stoker, Richard & Susan Fazarro).

Stokes, Doris

WELCOME TO MY WORLD.
LP: **BLIPP DS 001**
MC: **DSC 001**

Stokes, Frank

1927-29 THE REMAINING TITLES.
Tracks: / Half cup of tea / Ain't gonna be like I used to be / Hunting blues / Rockin' on the hill / Filling in blues (parts 1 & 2) / South Memphis blues / Bunker Hill blues / Right now blues / Shiney town blues / Downtown blues / Bedtime blues / What's the matter blues / It won't be long now / I got mine / T'aint nobody's business if I do (Parts 1 & 2) / Take me back / How long / Frank Stoke's dream.
LP: **MSE 1002**

CREATOR OF THE MEMPHIS BLUES.
LP: **L 1056**

FRANK STOKES.
LP: **RL 308**

FRANK STOKES DREAM (Memphis blues anthology).
LP: **L 1008**

Stoltzman

COPLAND - CORIGLIANO.
MC: **RK 87762**

Stomach Mouths

WILD TRIP.
LP: **VOXX 200040**

Stone Alliance

HEAD UP.
LP: **PMR 20**

Stone Book

STONE BOOK (Garner, Alan (nar)).
LP: **ZDSW 724**

Stone By Stone

I PASS FOR HUMAN.
LP: **SST 247**
MC: **SSTC 247**

Stone City Band

BOYS ARE BACK.
Tracks: / All day and all of the night / Feel good 'bout yourself / Keep love happy / Ganja / Freaky / Funky reggae / Lovin' you is easy / Tin soldier.
LP: **STML 12150**

OUT FROM THE SHADOW.
LP: **STML 12190**
MC: **CSTML 12190**

Stone Fury

BURNS LIKE A STAR.
LP: **MCF 3249**
MC: **MCFC 3249**

Stone, Jah

BABY LOVE (see Sensations) (Stone, Jah & Sensations).

Stone, Lew

10.30 TUESDAY NIGHT (Stone, Lew & His Band).
LP: **ACL 1147**

COFFEE IN THE MORNING (Stone, Lew & His Band).
Tracks: / Coffee in the morning / Riptide / Looking for a little bit of blue / Emaline / Because it's love / White jazz / I hate myself / Josephine / Rollin' home / What a little moonlight can do / My song for you / Love in bloom / Freckle face you're wonderful / Wagon wheels / Blue jazz / Out for no good / With my eyes wide open, I'm dreaming / Mauna loa.
LP: **PLE 505**
MC: **TC-PLE 505**

ECHO OF A SONG, THE (Stone, Lew & His Band).
Tracks: / All of me / Save the last dance for me / One more kiss / By the fireside / Was that the human thing to do / Now that you're gone / Goodnight, Vienna / My sweet Virginia / Can't we talk it over / Just humming alone / Auf wiedersehen my dear / Rain on the roof / It ain't no fault of mine / Echo of a song, The.
LP: **HAL 12**

GET HAPPY.
Tracks: / Beale Street blues / Transatlantic lullaby / Farewell blues / In Santa Lucia / Speakeasy / Who'll buy an old gold ring / Nine pins in the sky / P.S. I love you / Let it snow, let it snow, let it snow / Get happy / Weep no more my baby / My wubba dolly / Two cigarettes in the dark / Wednesday night hop / Lonely feet / Papa tree-top tall / At the Jazz Band Ball / Little drummer boy.
LP: **RFL 7**

GOLDEN AGE OF LEW STONE (Stone, Lew & His Band).
LP: **GX 41 2534 1**
MC: **GX 41 2534 4**

POP GOES YOUR HEART (Stone, Lew & His Band).
Tracks: / Long may we love / He didn't even say goodbye / Continental, The / Caranga / June in January / Winter wonderland / I ain't got nobody / Pop goes your heart / Beauty must be loved / Because of once upon a time / Maybe I'm wrong again / I was lucky / Seein' is believin' / Anything goes / I get a kick out of you / Lovely to look at / She's a Latin from Manhattan / East of the sun and west of the moon / Cheek to cheek / Isn't this a lovely day?.
LP: **SVL 196**
MC: **CSVL 196**

PRESENTING LEW STONE 1934-35 (Stone, Lew & His Band).
2LP: **SH 177/8**

SING ME A SWING SONG.
Tracks: / Stone favourites - part one / He didn't even say goodbye / My old dog / Wanderer / Tina / Where is the sun / Stars fell on Alabama / So close to the forest / Long may we love / Girl with the dreamy eyes / Sing me a swing song / Two trumpet toot / House hop / You never looked so beautiful / What are we gonna do with baby / Carelessly / Ebony shadows / Stone favourites - part two.
LP: **BUR 014**
MC: **4 BUR 014**

WITH AL BOWLLY.
MC: **CHAL 14**

Stone, R & J

WE DO IT (ALBUM).
Tracks: / We do it / I never had it so good / Live life / Man like me with a woman like you, A / Oh baby you / One chance / Here you are / Dancing Jones / I know I love him / This will be (an everlasting love) / There's no other way.
LP: **RS 1052**

Stone Roses

ALBUMS.
Tracks: / I wanna be adored / She bangs the drum / Waterfall / Don't stop / Bye bye bad man / Elizabeth my dear / (Song for my) sugar sponge sister / Made of stone / Shoot you down / This is the one / I am the resurrection.
LP: **ORELP 502**
MC: **OREC 502**

STONE ROSES.
LP: **OREZLP 502**
MC: **OREZC 502**

WHAT A TRIP.
LP: **BAK 6016**
MC: **MBAK 6016**

Stone, Rosetta

EYE FOR THE MAIN CHANCE, AN.
LP: **EXPAL 12**
MC: **EXPALMC 12**

Stone, Sly

FAMILY AFFAIR (ALBUM).
Tracks: / My woman's head / New breed, The / As I get older / Somethin' bad / Fire in my heart / She's my baby / Free as a bird / Girl won't you go / Everything I need / Why can't you stay / Off the hook / Dance your pants off / Under the influence of love / Crazy love song / Seventh son.
MC: . . . . **THBC 119**

Stone The Crows

CONTINUOUS PERFORMANCE.
LP: **2391 043**

STONE THE CROWS.
Tracks: / Big Jim Salter / Love 74 / Touch of your loving hand / Sad Mary / Good time girl / On the highway / Mr. Wizard / Sunset cowboy / Raining in your heart / Seven lakes.
LP: . . . . **THBL 070**

Stone, Tony

FOR A LIFETIME.
Tracks: / This is serious / Can't say bye / Heartbreak in the making / For a lifetime / Life after romance / Love don't come no stronger / Instant love / Why does living / My good friend James / Something about your....
LP: . . . . **CHR 1614**
MC: . . . . **ZCHR 1614**

Stonebolt

KEEP IT ALIVE.
Tracks: / Keep it alive / Nights like tonight / Price of love / Don't ya hide it / Keep me company / Tryin' to hide / Love struck / Don't worry boys / Let it all go / New lease on love.
LP: . . . . **PL 10357**

STONEBOLT.
Tracks: / Was it you / I still love you / One man's heartache / Sail on / Shadow, The / Do it right / Singin' in the streets / Queen of the night / Stay in line.
LP: . . . . **RRL 2006**

Stonebridge McGuinness

CORPORATE MADNESS.
Tracks: / Heartbeat / Love on the street / Small town days / Leading with my heart / I wish it was summer / Corporate madness / Heart to heart / Oh eeh baby / Are you ready Ruby / New friends.
LP: . . . . **PL 25275**

Stoneham, Ernest V.

ERNEST V. STONEHAM AND BLUE RIDGE CORN SHUCKERS (Stoneham, Ernest V./Blue Ridge Corn Shuckers).
LP: . . . . **ROUNDER 1008**

Stoneham, Harry

BY MYSELF.
MC: . . . . **DJH 42066**

IN THE STILL OF THE NIGHT.
LP: . . . . **DJM 22078**

SOLID GOLD HAMMOND.
2LP: . . . . **MFP 1010**
MCSET: . . . . **TCMFP 1010**

Stonehill, Randy

BETWEEN THE GLORY & THE FLAME.
Tracks: / Glory and the flame, The / Die young / Fifth Avenue breakdown / Grandfather's song / Find your way to me / Christine / Rainbow / Givin' it up for love / Letter to my family / Farther on.
LP: . . . . **MYR 1108**
MC: . . . . **MC 1108**

CELEBRATE THIS HEARTBEAT.
LP: . . . . **MYR 1166**
MC: . . . . **MC 1166**

SKY IS FALLING.
Tracks: / One true love / Bad fruit / Jamey's got the blues / Through the glass darkly / Great American cure / Venezuela / Sweet emily's / Trouble coming.
LP: . . . . **SRA 2005**

STONEHILL.
LP: . . . . **XSTLP 1**

WILD FRONTIER,THE.
LP: . . . . **MYR R 1230**
MC: . . . . **MYR C 1230**

Stoneman, Scotty

LIVE IN L.A. (Stoneman, Scotty & Kentucky Colonels).
LP: . . . . **SBR 4206**

Stooges

LIVE AT THE WHISKEY A GO-GO.
LP: . . . . **MIG 7**

NO FUN (Featuring Iggy Pop).
Tracks: / 1969 / Real cool time / No fun / Dirt / Down on the street / Loose / T.V. eye / I wanna be your dog / I feel alright.
LP: . . . . **K 52234**

RUBBER LEGS.
LP: . . . . **FC 037**

Stookey, Noel Paul

BAND & BODYWORKS.
Tracks: / I wanna testify / Then the quail came / Lay me down / Every flower / Juice / Garden song / Love all around / Means are the end, The / How can I keep from singing / Know Jesus / Sandman theme, The.
LP: . . . . **MYR 1087**
MC: . . . . **MC 1087**

Stop Smoking

YOUR LAST CIGARETTE - NO EXCEPTIONS (see under 'Sutphen, Dick') (Sutphen, Dick).

Stop The World

STOP THE WORLD I WANT TO GET OFF (Original London Cast) (Various artists).
Tracks: / ABC: *Various artists* / I wanna be rich: *Various artists* / Typically English: *Various artists*/ Lumbered: *Various artists* / Gonna build a mountain: *Various artists* / Glorious Russia: *Various artists*/ Mellinki Meilchick: *Various artists* / Typiache Deutsche: *Various artists* / Nag nag nag: *Various artists*/ All-American: *Various artists* / Once in a lifetime: *Various artists* / Mumbo jumbo: *Various artists*/ Someone nice like you: *Various artists* / What kind of fool am I?: *Various artists.*
LP: . . . . **TER 1082**
MC: . . . . **ZCTER 1082**

STOP THE WORLD I WANT TO GET OFF (ORIG ISSUE) (London cast) (Various artists).
LP: . . . . **LK 4408**

STOP THE WORLD I WANT TO GET OFF (See under Newley, Anthony) (Newley, Anthony).

Stopak, Bernie

REMEMBER ME.
LP: . . . . **ST 274**

Stoppard, Tom (author)

DOG IT WAS THAT DIED.
MC: . . . . **ZCF 503**

ROSENCRANTZ AND GUILDSTERN ARE DEAD (Various artists).
MCSET: . . . . **ZBBC 1058**

Storey, Charlie

CHARLIE STOREY AND HIS ALL STARS (Storey, Charlie & His All Stars).
MC: . . . . **GVMMC 210**

Storey, Liz

PART OF FORTUNE.
Tracks: / Toy soldiers / Elephant trainer, The / Teased hair / Myth America / Part of fortune / Reconciliation / Duende / Ana / Ubi caritas.
LP: . . . . **PL 83001**

SOLID COLORS.
Tracks: / Wedding rain / Pacheco pass / Without you / Hymn / Things with wings / Solid colours / Bradley's dream / Water caves / Peace piece.
LP: **C-1023**

SPEECHLESS.
Tracks: / Forgiveness / Frog park / Welcome home / Hermes dance / Speechless / Back porch / Vigil.
LP: . . . . **PL 83037**
MC: . . . . **PK 83037**

UNACCOUNTABLE EFFECT.
LP: . . . . **TAC 1034**

Storeyville Jazz Band

STOREYVILLE JAZZ BAND.
LP: . . . . **LD 5010**

Stories..

STORIES FOR A RAINY DAY (Craig, Wendy (nar)).
LP: . . . . **STMP 9025**
MC: **STMP4 9025**

STORIES FROM PIPPI LONGSTOCKING (See under Lindgren, Astrid).

WORLD OF STORIES (Hepburn, Katherine).
MCSET: . . . . **LFP 7180**

Stories (band)

WALK AWAY FROM THE LEFT BANKE.
Tracks: / Hello people / I'm coming home / Nice to have you here / High and low / Darlin' / Love is in motion / Hey France / Please please / Believe me / Words / Top of the city / What comes after / Brother Louie / Bridges / If it feels good do it / Mammy blue / Soft rain (Only on CD.) / I can't understand it (Only on CD.) / Step back (Only on CD.) / Kathleen (Only on CD.).
LP: . . . . **SEE 238**

Stories For Children

STORIES FOR CHILDREN (see under Wilde, Oscar) (Morley, Robert).

Storm

STORM, THE.
LP: **91741-1**
MC: **91741-4**

Storm, Gale

GALE STORM HITS.
Tracks: / On Treasure Island / Now is the hour / Lucky lips / Never leave me / Teen age prayer, A / Why do fools fall in love / I walk alone / Tell me why / Memories are made of this / Orange blossoms / I hear you knocking / Ivory tower / My heart belongs to you / Dark moon.
LP: . . . . **CH 102**

SENTIMENTAL ME.
LP: . . . . **JASM 1047**

Storm, Johnny

FLAME ON!.
Tracks: / Excuses, excuses / So they say / Sweet baby goodbye / Change your ways / Liza Jane / My baby just won't let me / Fast Eddie / Sunrise / Earthquake / How many hearts / Don't let me be the last to know / Loving man.
LP: . . . . **MFLP 003**
LP: . . . . **MFM 008**

FOR GREASY KIDS ONLY (Storm, Johnny & The Sunsets).
Tracks: / Only thing, The / Ain't giving up nothing / Out of sight / He's old enough to know better / Lend me your heart / Rockin' behind the iron curtain / Just a little too much / With this ring / I can really rock'n'roll / Your line was busy / Forgive me / Hydro electric damn / Cool baby / Good hard rock.
LP: . . . . **MFLP 014**

PLATINUM HIGH SCHOOL (Storm, Johnny/Shakin' Stevens & The Jets).
Tracks: / Justine / Hey baby / Hydro electric damn / Sleep rock'n'roll / Forgive me / Jungle rock / Rockabilly baby / Out of sight / Only thing, The / James Dean / My baby died / Story of the rockers.
LP: . . . . **MFM 013**
LP: . . . . **MFLP 017**

Storm Warning

SPIRIT LEVEL.
LP: . . . . **ZK 1002**

STORM WARNING (see Higgins, Jack) (Goring, Marius).

Storm, Warren

BOPPIN' TONIGHT (Storm, Warren/ Al Ferrier).
LP: . . . . **FLY 525**

MAMA MAMA MAMA.
LP: . . . . **FLY 603**

Stormbringer

STORMBRINGER.
LP: . . . . **SKULL 8391**

Stormtroopers Of Death

SPEAK ENGLISH OR DIE.
LP: . . . . **RR 9725**
MC: . . . . **RR 97254**

Stormwitch

BEAUTY AND THE BEAST.
Tracks: / Call of the wicked / Beauty and the beast / Just for one night / Emerald eyes / Tears by the firelight / Tigers of the sea / Russia's on fire / Cheyenne / Welcome to Bedlam.
LP: . . . . **GAMA 880763**
LP: **805528**

STRONGER THAN HEAVEN.
LP: **941 312**

Stormy Monday (film)

STORMY MONDAY (Film Soundtrack) (King, B.B. & Mike Figgis).
Tracks: / Stormy monday / Kate and Brendan / Weegee / Thrill is gone, The / On the quay / Dawn and the Tyne / Road to Poland, The / Finney makes a point / Star-spangled banner, The / Carrie / Just a closer walk with thee / Krakow dawn / Niezapomne ciebe (I won't forget you) / Train across the river / Muzac for lovers.
LP: . . . . **V 2537**
MC: . . . . **TCV 2537**

Stormy Weather

PULSE.
LP: . . . . **SPJ 535**

Stormy Weather (film)

STORMY WEATHER (Film Soundtrack) (Various artists).
LP: . . . . **SH 2037**
MC: . . . . **CSH 2037**

Storr, Catherine

CLEVER POLLY AND THE STUPID WOLF (See under Griffiths, Derek) (Griffiths, Derek).
MCSET: **CC/024**

Storrs, David

CHANNEL FOR THE LIGHT.
MC: . . . . **C 319**

MANIFESTATION OF THE PYRAMIDS (inspiring progressive new age music).
MC: . . . . **C 324**

Story, Carl

16 GREATEST HITS: CARL STORY.
LP: . . . . **SLP 3004**
MC: . . . . **GT 53004**

BLUEGRASS GOSPEL COLLECTION (Story, Carl & His Rambling Mountaineers).
Tracks: / Somebody touched me / We shall meet again someday / Fourth man, The / Will you miss me / Million years in glory / Will there be a traffic light / Sweetest gift / Heaven bound train / When the angels carry me home / My loved ones are waiting for me / Shout and shine / Family reunion / Are you afraid to die / You can't believe everything you hear / Angel band / Thank the Lord for everything / Always be kind to mother / Angels rock me to sleep / I'm going home.
LP: . . . . **CMH 9005**
MC: . . . . **CMH 9005C**

GOSPEL QUARTET FAVOURITES.
LP: . . . . **HAT 3128**

GOSPEL REVIVAL.
LP: . . . . **SLP 127**
MC: . . . . **GT 5127**

Story, Little Bob

LIGHT OF MY TOWN.
Tracks: / Light of my town / Switchblade Julie / Golden jail / Rockin' down my street / Women on my side / Steely blue morning / Bus stop / Game we are playing here / Go boy / Song for the blind.
LP: . . . . **PL 37412**

Story, Liz

ESCAPE OF THE CIRCUS PONIES.
Tracks: / Broken arrow drive / Inside out / Escape of the circus ponies / Church of tress / Sounding joy, The / Another shore / Incision / Worth winning / Empty forest, The.
MC: . . . . **WT 1099**

Story Of....

STORY OF BACH (Hart, Derek & London Theatre Players).
MC: . . . . **BKK 412**

STORY OF BEETHOVEN (Devlin, William & London Theatre Players).
MC: . . . . **BKK 410**

STORY OF CHOPIN (Hardy, Robert & London Theatre Players).
MC: . . . . **BKK 411**

STORY OF MOZART (McCowan, Alex & London Theatre Players).
MC: . . . . **BKK 409**

STORY OF SIR GALAHAD (Richardson, Ian).
LP: . . . . **TC 1625**
MC: . . . . **CDL 51625**

STORY OF STAR WARS (Film Soundtrack Adaptation) (Various artists).
LP: . . . . **T 550**
MC: . . . . **C 550**

STORY OF SWAN LAKE adapted by Ward Botsford (Various artists).
MC: . . . . **CDL 51673**

STORY OF THE TAJ MAHAL, THE (Various artists).
Tracks: / Story of the Taj Mahal, The: *Various artists* / Man who made gold, The: *Various artists* / Young ant, The: *Various artists* / Miser and the generous man, The: *Various artists* / Koh-i-noor, The: *Various artists*/ King who had everything, The: *Various artists* / Meatballs' fate, The: *Various artists* / Emerald scorpion, The: *Various artists.*
MC: . . . . **ANV 637**

STORY OF THE THREE KINGS John of Hildeshem (Rose, George (nar)).
MC: . . . . **CDL 51724**

Story Of Electricity

STORY OF ELECTRICITY, THE (Sprung aus denwolken).
LP: . . . . **DSA 54009**

Story of Hatim Tai

STORY OF HATIM TAI, THE (Various artists).
Tracks: / Story of Hatim Tai, The: *Various artists* / Princess, the Vizier and the Ape, The: *Various artists*/ Deaf brother and the blind brother, The: *Various artists* / Sultan's emissary and the leopard, The: *Various artists*/ Faithful gazelle, The: *Various artists.*
MC: . . . . **ANV 601**

Story So Far

STORY SO FAR, THE (Various artists).
LP: SZMLP 1

Story, Tim

IN ANOTHER COUNTRY.
LP: U 009

THREE FEET FROM THE MOON.
LP: U 027
MC: U 0274

UNTITLED.
LP: U 024

Storytime For ...

STORYTIME FOR 2 YEAR OLDS.
MC: PLB 284

STORYTIME FOR 3 YEAR OLDS.
MC: PLB 253

STORYTIME FOR 4 YEAR OLDS.
MC: PLB 267

STORYTIME FOR 5 YEAR OLDS.
MC: PLB 254

STORYTIME FOR 6 YEAR OLDS.
MC: PLB 268

Storytime Top Ten

STORYTIME TOP TEN VOL.7 (Various artists).
MC: VCA 061

STORYTIME TOP TEN VOL 3 (Briers, Richard).
MC: VCA 057

Stovall, Babe

1958-1964.
Tracks: / Careless love / Big road blues / C.C. Rider / Going away to wear you off my mind / Don't want you to go / Good morning blues / Salty dog / Going to New Orleans / Woman blues / I ain't gonna be your dog no more / Time is winding up.
LP: FLY 625

Stover, Don

THINGS IN LIFE.
LP: ROUNDER 0014

WITH THE WHITE OAK MOUNTAIN BOYS.
LP: ROUNDER 0039

Strachan, John

GLENLOGIE.
Tracks: / Lang Johnnie More (This track lasts thirteen minutes.) / Royal forester / Robin Hood and Little John / Bonnie lass o' Fyvie / Beggarman, The / McPherson's rant / Binnorie-o / Johnny-O'Breadislie / Clydes waterside / Laird O' drum, The.
MC: 60-065

TINKER'S WEDDING.
Tracks: / Plooman laddie, The / Guise o'tough, The / Bonnie Udny / O gin I were where the gadie rins / Hairsts o'rettie / Mormond braes / Beggar wench / Ball o' Kirriemuir / Twa'n twa / Cuckoo's nest, The / Jock the bog-head crew / Rhynie / List, bonny laddie / Jolly miller / Erin go bragh.
MC: 60-066

Stradivari

STRADIVARI (Soundtrack From The Film) (Various artists).
LP: LP 422 8491 PH
MC: MC 422 8494 PH

Straight Down The ...

STRAIGHT DOWN THE MIDDLE (Great moments in golf) (Various artists).
LP: HAV 1025
MC: HAVC1025

Straight Eight

NO NOISE FROM HERE.
LP: ERPR 001

SHUFFLE'N'CUT.
Tracks: / I'm sorry / I can't stop / Power cut / Tonite / When I'm alone with you / Tombstone / On the rebound / Christine / Will you love me / Don't turn your back / Satisfied / Only you.
LP: FLUSH 1

STRAIGHT EIGHT (Various artists).
LP: SNTF 1012

STRAIGHT TO THE HEART.
Tracks: / Faded stars / Tomorrow / Desperation / You are what you are / Walls can't keep us apart / Straight to the heart / One more chance / I don't need your lovin' / Only the truth hurts / Next time.
LP: LOGO 1032

Straight & Gay

STRAIGHT & GAY (Various artists).
LP: ST 118

Straight Shooter

MOVIN' OUTSIDE MOVIN' INSIDE.
LP: SKY 088

Straight To Hell

STRAIGHT TO HELL (Film Soundtrack) (Various artists).
Tracks: / Good, the bad and the ugly, The: *Pogues* / Rake at the gates of hell, The: *Pogues* / If I should fall from grace with God: *Pogues* / Rabinga: *Pogues* / Danny boy: *Pogues* / Evil darling: *Strummer, Joe* / Ambush or mystery rock: *Strummer, Joe* / Money guns and coffee: *Pray For Rain* / Killers: *Pray For Rain* / Salsa y ketchup: *Zander Schloss* / Big nothing: *Macmanus gang, The.*
LP: DIABLO 1
MC: ZDIABLO 1

Strait, George

BEYOND THE BLUE MOON.
Tracks: / Beyond the blue moon / Overnight success / Leavin' been comin' / What's going on in your world / Too much of too little / Hollywood squares / Ace in the hole / Baby's gotten good at goodbye / Angel, Angeline / Oh me oh my sweet baby.
LP: MCA 42266
MC: MCAC 42266

CHILL OF AN EARLY FALL.
LP: MCA 10204
MC: MCAC 10204

DOES FORT WORTH EVER CROSS YOUR MIND.
Tracks: / Does Fort Worth ever cross your mind / Any old time / I need someone like me / You're dancin' this dance all wrong / Honky tonk Saturday night / I should have watched that first step / Love comes from the other side of town / Cowboy rides away, The / What did you expect me to do / Fireman.
LP: MCF 3272
MC: MCFC 3272

GEORGE STRAIT.
MC: MCGC 6082

GREAT STRAIT (The Essential Collection).
Tracks: / Ocean front property / You're something special to me / Marina Del Ray / Fool hearted memory / Baby's gotten good at goodbye / Does Fort Worth ever cross your mind / Nobody in his right mind would've left her / Deep water / If you're thinking you want a stranger / Let's fall to pieces together / Baby blue / All my ex's live in Texas / Beyond the blue neon / Famous last words of a fool / Chair, The (Only on CD.) / Dance time in Texas (Only on CD.) / Amarillo by morning (Only on CD.).
LP: MCG 6082
MC: MCGC 6082

GREATEST HITS: GEORGE STRAIT.
Tracks: / Unwound / Down and out / If you're thinking you want a stranger... / Fool hearted memory / Marina del ray / Amarillo by morning / Fire I can't put out, A / You look so good in love / Right or wrong / Let's fall to pieces together.
LP: IMCA 5567
MC: IMCAC 5567

GREATEST HITS: GEORGE STRAIT VOL 2.
Tracks: / Does Fort Worth ever cross your mind / Cowboy rides away, The / Fireman / Chair, The / You're something special to me / Nobody in his right mind would've left her / It ain't cool to be crazy about you / Ocean front property / All my ex's live in Texas / Am I blue.
LP: MCF 3400
MC: MCFC 3400

IF YOU AIN'T LOVIN' YOU AIN'T LIVIN'.
LP: MCA 42114
MC: MCAC 42114

LIVIN' IT UP.
Tracks: / Someone had to teach you / Heaven must be wondering where you are / I've come to expect it from you / Lonesome rodeo cowboy / When you're a man on your own / Drinking champagne / We're supposed to do that now and then / She loves me (she don't love me) / Love without end, Amen / Stranger in my arms.
LP: MCG 6115
MC: MCGC 6115

NUMBER 7.
Tracks: / Deep water / Nobody in his right mind would've left her / Rhythm of the road / I'm never gonna let you go / You still get to me / Stranger things have happened / It ain't cool to be crazy about you / Why'd you go and break my heart? / My old flame is burnin' another honky tonk down / Cow town.
MC: MCFC 3332
LP: MCF 3332

OCEAN FRONT PROPERTY.
Tracks: / All my ex's live in Texas / Someone's walkin' around upstairs / Am I blue / Ocean front property / Hot burning flames / Without you here / My heart won't wander very far from you / Second chances / You can't buy your way out of the blues / I'm all behind you now / Someone's walkin' around upstairs.
LP: MCF 3358
MC: MCFC 3358

RIGHT OR WRONG.
Tracks: / You look so good in love / Right or wrong / Little heaven's rubbing off on me, A / 80 proof bottle of tear stopper / Every time it rains (Lord don't it pour) / You're the cloud I'm on (when I'm high) / Let's fall to pieces together / I'm satisfied with you / Our paths may never cross / Fifteen years going up (and one night coming down).
LP: IMCA 5450

SOMETHING SPECIAL.
Tracks: / You're something special to me / Last time the first time / Haven't you heard / In too deep / Blue is not a word / You sure got this ol' redneck feelin blue / Chair, The / Dance time in Texas / Lefty's gone / I've seen that look on me(a thousand times).
LP: MCF 3306
MC: MCFC 3306

STRAIT COUNTRY.
Tracks: / Unwound / Honky tonk downstairs / Blame it on Mexico / If you're thinking you want a stranger... / I get along with you / Down and out / Friday night fever / Everytime you throw dirt on her (you lose a little ground) / She's playing hell trying to get me to heaven / Her goodbye hit me in the heart.
LP: IMCA 270 92

STRAIT FROM THE HEART.
Tracks: / Fool hearted memory / Honky tonk crazy / Only thing I have left / Steal of the night, The / I can't see Texas from here / Marina del ray / Lover in disguise / Heartbroke / Amarillo by morning / Fire I can't put out, A.
LP: IMCA 5320

Straitjacket Fits

HAIL.
LP: ROUGH 147
MC: ROUGHC 147

Straker, Nick

NICK STRAKER.
LP: FLAME LP 3
MC: FLAME C3

WALK IN THE PARK, A.
Tracks: / Walk in the park, A / Don't come back / Another night in jail / Sleeping alone / Leaving on the midnight train / Little bit of jazz, A / Last goodbye / Come over / Modern music / Magazine.
LP: CBS 84608
MC: 40 84608

Straker, Peter

REAL NATURAL MAN.
Tracks: / Late night taxi dancer / Nasty / Possessed / It ain't easy / They've got you dancing / Wappem bappem / Illusions confusions / Melancholy / Mrs.Warren / Real natural man.
LP: TRAIN 12

Stramash

MCGINN OF THE CARLTON (The songs and stories of Matt McGinn).
Tracks: / Magic shadow show, The / Dundee ghost, The / Rob Roy MacGreegor-o / Benny has been / Pill, The / Janetta / Foreman O'Rourke, The / Get up get out / If it wisnae for the Union / Can o' tea / I'm looking for a job / Three nights and a Sunday / We'll have a May-day / Magic shadow show, The (instrumental) / Jeannie Gallacher / Red yo-yo, The / Coorie Doon / Gallowgate calypso, The / Troubled waters in my soul / Bingo Bella / I owe you / Manura manya / Depth of my ego / Skin.
MC: CTRAX 034

Strand

STRAND.
Tracks: / Rock it tonight / Long hot summer / I like it like that / Just a little more time / Prisoners in paradise / Stay away from me girl / Frustration / Children of the night / Dirty little girl / Can't look back.
LP: ILPS 9594

Strandberg, Goran

PIANO - DAWN.
LP: DRLP 141

SILENT TRACES.
LP: DRLP 39

Strange Advance

DISTANCE BETWEEN, THE.
Tracks: / Till the stars fall / Love becomes electric / Who lives next door? / Love is strange / This island earth / Hold you / Crying in the ocean / Wild blue / Rock and whirl / Ultimate angels / Alien time.
LP: PTLS 1094
MC: PTLC 1094

Strange, Billy

BEST OF BILLY STRANGE.
LP: GNPS 2037

DYN-O-MITE GUITAR.
LP: GNPS 2094

GREAT WESTERN THEMES.
LP: GNPS 2046
MC: GNP5 2046

RAILROAD MAN.
LP: GNPS 2041

Strange Creek Singers

STRANGE CREEK SINGERS.
LP: ARHOOLIE 4004

Strange Cruise

STRANGE CRUISE.
Tracks: / Hit and run / Beat goes on / Rebel blue rocker / Communication / This old town / Animal call / Heart is a lonely runner / Love addiction / Where were their hearts / 12 miles high.
LP: EMC 3513

Strange Folk

UNHAND ME YOU BEARDED LOON.
Tracks: / Jolly hangman / Shoot the hippy / Badger and the bird, The / Meg Murphy's sons / Midnight in Preston / Pottingshed polka / Polka Piquee / Rats of the 40, The / Bitts park polka / Frozen ponds / Langdale gang / Upland geese / Benbecula hornpipe / Fields of the glen, The / Whitewater dash / Face the day / Wynass jig.
LP: FE 069
MC: FE 069C

Strange Fruit

DEBUT.
Tracks: / Whelk / New horizons / Song for Jude / Night time / Night / White City / Moonchild.
LP: PTLS 1073

Strange Rapture

STRANGE RAPTURE (see Robins, Denise) (Guthrie, Gwyneth).

Strange, Richard

GOING GONE (Strange, Richard & The Engine Room).
LP: NISHI 205

PHENOMENAL RISE OF RICHARD STRANGE, THE.
LP: V 2203

Strange Riders (bk)

STRANGE RIDERS AT BLACK PONY INN.
MCSET: DTO 10523

Strangeloves

I WANT CANDY.
LP: OLLP 5231

Stranger Than Paradise

STRANGER THAN PARADISE (See under Lurie, John) (Lurie, John).

Strangers At Black...

STRANGER RIDERS AT BLACK PONY INN.
MC: PTB 633

Strangeways

NATIVE SONGS.
Tracks: / Dance with somebody / Only a fool / So far away / Where do we go from here? / Goodnight LA / Empty street / Stand up and shout / Shake the seven / Never gonna lose it / Face to face.
LP: 208579
MC: 408579

STRANGE WAYS.
LP: 207648
MC: 407648

Stranglers

10.
Tracks: / Sweet smell of success / Someone like you / 96 tears / In this place / Let's celebrate / Man of the earth / Too many teardrops / Where I live / Out of my mind / Never to look back.
LP: 4664831
MC: 4664834
LPPD: 4664830

ALL LIVE AND ALL OF THE NIGHT.
Tracks: / Was it you / Down in the sewer / Always the sun / Golden brown / North winds / European female / Strange little girl / Nice 'n' sleazy / Toiler on the sea / Spain / London lady / All day and all of the night / No more heroes.
LP: 4602591
MC: 4602594

AURAL SCULPTURE.
Tracks: / Ice queen / Skin deep / Let me down easy / No mercy / North winds / Uptown / Punch and Judy / Spain / Laughing / Souls / Mad hatter.
LP: 4504881
MC: 4504484
LP: EPC 26220

BLACK AND WHITE.
Tracks: / Tank / Nice 'n' sleazy / Outside Tokyo / Mean to me / Sweden (all quiet on the eastern front) / Hey (rise of the robots) / Toiler on the sea / Curfew / Threatened / Do you wanna / In the shadows / Enough time / Death and night and blood (Yukio) (Extra track available on CD only) / Tits (Extra track available on CD only) / Walk on by.
LP: . . . . **EPC 26439**
MC: **40 26439**
LP: . . . . **ATAK 29**
MC: . . . . **TCATAK 29**
LP: . . . . **UAK 30222**
MC: . . . . **TCK 30222**

COLLECTION, THE (1977-82).
Tracks: / Get a grip on yourself / Peaches / Hanging around / No more heroes / Duchess / Walk on by / Waltzinblack / Something better change / Nice 'n' sleazy / Bear cage / Who wants the world / Golden brown / Strange little girl / La folie / Bear cage.
LP: . . . . **LBG 30353**
MC: . . . . **TCLBG 30353**
LP: . . . . **FA 3230**
MC: . . . . **TCFA 3230**
LP: . . . . **LBS 30353**

DREAMTIME.
Tracks: / Always the sun / Dreamtime / Was it you / You'll always reap what you sow / Ghost train / Nice in Nice / Big in America / Shakin' like a leaf / Mayan skies / Too precious.
LP: . . . . **EPC 26648**
MC: **40 26648**
LP: **4633661**
MC: **4633664**
LPPD: **11 26648**

FELINE.
Tracks: / Midnight summer dream / It's a small world / Ships that pass in the night / European female / Let's tango in Paris / Paradise / All roads lead to Rome / Blue sister / Never say goodbye.
LP: . . . . **EPC 32711**
MC: **40 32711**
LP: . . . . **EPC 25237**

GREATEST HITS: STRANGLERS.
Tracks: / Peaches / Something better change / No more heroes / Walk on by / Duchess / Golden brown / Strange little girl / European female / Skin deep / Nice in Nice / Always the sun / Big in America / All day and all of the night / 96 tears / No mercy (Available on cassette and CD format only.).
LP: **4675411**
MC: **4675414**

LA FOLIE.
Tracks: / Non stop / Everybody loves you when you're dead / Tramp / Let me introduce you to the family / Ain't nothin' to it / Love to hate / Pin up / Two to tango / Golden brown / How to find true love and happiness in the present day / La folie.
LP: . . . . **FA 41 3083 1**
MC: . . . . **FA 41 3083 4**
LP: . . . . **FA 3083**
MC: . . . . **TCFA 3083**
LP: . . . . **LBG 30342**

LIVE (X-CERT).
Tracks: / Get a grip on yourself / Dagenham Dave / Burning up time / Dead ringer / Hanging around / Feel like a wog / Straight out / Do you wanna - death and night and blood / Five minutes / Go buddy go / Peasant in the big shitty (CD only) / In the shadows (CD only).
LP: . . . . **ATAK 33**
MC: . . . . **TCATAK 33**
LP: . . . . **UAG 30224**
MC: . . . . **TCK 30224**

MENINBLACK.
Tracks: / Waltzinblack / Just like nothing on earth / Second coming / Waiting for the meninblack / Turn the centuries turn / Two sunspots / Four horsemen / Thrown away / Manna machine / Hallo to our men / Top secret (Extra track available on Compact Disc only).
LP: . . . . **ATAK 34**
MC: . . . . **TCATAK 34**
LP: . . . . **FA 3208**
MC: . . . . **TCFA 3208**
LP: . . . . **LBG 30313**
MC: . . . . **TCLBG 30313**

MUSIC AND MEDIA INTERVIEW PICTURE DISC.
LPPD: . . . . **STRANG 1001**

NO MORE HEROES.
Tracks: / I feel like a wog / Bitching / Dead ringer / Dagenham Dave / Bring on the nubiles / Something better change / No more heroes / Peasant in the big shitty / Burning up time / English towns / School mam / In the shadows.
LP: . . . . **ATAK 32**
MC: . . . . **TCATAK 32**
LP: . . . . **FA 3190**
MC: . . . . **TCFA 3190**
LP: . . . . **UAG 30200**

OFF THE BEATEN TRACK.
Tracks: / Go buddy go / Top secret / Old codger / Man in white / Rock it to the moon / Love 30 / Shut up / Walk on by(full length version) / Vietnamerica / Mean to me / Cruel garden / Yellowcake UF6 / 5 Minutes.
LP: . . . . **LBG 5001**
MC: . . . . **TCLBG 5001**

ORAL SCULPTURE.
LP: **4504481**

RARITIES.
Tracks: / Choosey Susie / Peaches / No more heroes / Walk on by / Sverige / N'emmenes pas Harry / Fools rush out / Bear cage / Shah shah a go go / Meninblack, The / Tomorrow was the hereafter / Rok it to the moon (CD only.) / Shut up (CD only.) / Old codger (CD only.) / Yellowcake UF6 (CD only.) / Vietnamerica (CD only.) / Love 30 (CD only.) / Mony mony / Mean to me.
LP: . . . . **EMS 1306**
MC: . . . . **TCEMS 1306**

RATTUS NORVEGICUS (Stranglers IV).
Tracks: / Sometimes / Goodbye Toulouse / London lady / Princess of the streets / Hanging around / Peaches / Get a grip on yourself / Ugly / Down in the sewer: Falling / Down in the sewer: Trying to get out again / Rats rally.
MC: . . . . **TCFA 3001**
LP: . . . . **FA 3001**
LP: . . . . **UAG 30045**

RAVEN, THE.
Tracks: / Longships / Raven, The / Dead loss Angeles / Ice / Baroque / Bordello / Nuclear device / Shah shah a go go / Don't bring Harry / Duchess / Meninback / Genetix / Bear cage.
LP: . . . . **FA 41 3131 1**
MC: . . . . **FA 41 3131 4**
LP: . . . . **UAG 30262**
LP: . . . . **ATAK 30**
MC: . . . . **TCATAK 30**
LP: . . . . **FA 3131**
MC: . . . . **TCFA 3131**

SINGLES (THE UA YEARS).
Tracks: / (Get a) grip (on yourself) / Peaches / Go buddy go / Something better change / Straighten out / No more heroes / Five minutes / Nice 'n' sleazy / Walk on by / Duchess / Nuclear device / Don't bring Harry / Bear cage / Who wants the world / Thrown away / Just like nothing on earth / Let me introduce you to the family / Golden brown / La folie / Strange little girl.
2LP: . . . . **EM 1314**
MC: . . . . **TC-EM 1314**

STRANGLERS: INTERVIEW PICTURE DISC.
LPPD: . . . . **BAK 2033**

Straps

STRAPS.
Tracks: / House of the rising sun / Brixton / Ex directory / Police news / Lies / New age / Pox kid / What's on the box.
LP: . . . . **CYC 2**

Strasser, Hugo

BEST OF HUGO STRASSER.
LP: **1A 022 58064**

DANCE HITS 1983.
LP: . . . . **IC 088 46650**

DANCE INTO '81 WITH HUGO STRASSER.
Tracks: / Theater / Josefine / Maria Celina / Galaball / Moonlight and shadows / Jogging / Funky town / Weekend / Sun of Jamaica / What's another year / It's a real good feeling / Jive '81 / Rockabilly rebel / I see a boat on the river / Aloha oe.
LP: . . . . **DS 038**
MC: . . . . **TDS 038**

DANCE INTO 1982.
Tracks: / Agadou / Leib mich ein Letztes / Samba morena / Marie-marie / Lorley / Hands up / Making your mind up / Paper music / This ole house / Sukiyaki / Ariane / San Jose / Cafe Musette / Shaddup you face / Archibald / Dance little birdie.
LP: . . . . **DS 050**

DANCE INTO THE EIGHTIES WITH....
LP: . . . . **DS 026**
MC: . . . . **TDS 026**

DANCE RECORD '81.
LP: . . . . **IC 066 46095**

DANCE RECORD OF THE YEAR.
LP: . . . . **HSO 756**

DANCING CLARINET, THE.
LP: . . . . **IC 6062 29493**
LP: . . . . **DS 019**

DER GOLDENE TANZSCHUH.
LP: . . . . **HSO 751**

DIE TANNZPLATTE.
LP: . . . . **IC 066 45692**

DIE TANZPLATTE DES JAHRES '78.
LP: . . . . **HSO 757**

DIE TANZPLATTE DES JAHRES '86.
LP: **066 147080**

DIE TANZPLATTE DES JAHRES 75/76.
LP: . . . . **HSO 753**

HIT PARTY.
LP: . . . . **IC 066 45694**

HIT PARTY OF THE YEAR VOL.2.
LP: . . . . **HSO 754**

HUGO STRASSER'S DANCE PARTY (Strasser, Hugo & His Dance Orchestra).
Tracks: / Crazy rhythm / Congratulations / Love Story theme / I could have danced all night / Fascination / Ramona / Maria from Bahia / Samba cielito / Reet petite / Red roses for a blue lady / Moonlight and roses / Undecided / Frenesi / La cumparsita / Kiss of fire / Spanish gypsy dance / Y viva Espana / Wunderbar.
LP: . . . . **GRALP 38**
MC: . . . . **GRTC 38**

ROMANTIC CLARINET.
LP: . . . . **IC 066 45946**

SUPERGOLD.
LP: . . . . **IC 134 45490/91**

TANGO-ERFOLGE MIT HUGO STRASSER.
LP: . . . . **HSO 752**

TANGOS.
LP: **066 1469191**

TANZ GALA INTERNATIONAL VOL. 2.
LP: **066 147032**

TANZ MAL WIEDER.
LP: **1A 022 58064**

TANZ MIT..VOL.1.
LP: . . . . **IC 134 30089/90**

TANZ MIT...VOL.2.
LP: . . . . **IC 134H 30091/92**

TANZPLATTE '87.
LP: **066 1471971**

TANZPLATTE 1985.
LP: **066 1469201**

UND SEIN TANZORCHESTER.
LP: . . . . **IC 066 32456**

Strata Institute

CIPHER SYNTAX.
Tracks: / Slang / Bed stuy / Turn of events / Decrepidus / Ihgnat down / Micro-move / Wild / Humantic / Abacus / Ihgnat.
LP: **8344251**

Stratas, Teresa

STRATAS SINGS WEILL.
Tracks: / I'm a stranger here myself / Havanna lied / Surabaya Johnny / Foolish heart / Ich bin eine arme verwanute / One life to live / J'attende un navire / Das lied von der harten nuss / Lonely house / Le roir d'aquitaine / Denn wie man sich bettete / Le train du ciel / Das lied von der Unzulanglichkeit / It never was you / Der kleine leutenant des liben gottes.
LP: **9791311**
MC: **9791314**

Strathclyde Police

CHAMPION OF CHAMPIONS (Champions of The World).
LP: . . . . **LILP 5129**
MC: . . . . **LICS 5129**

SIX IN A ROW.
Tracks: / March strathspey & reel / Marches / Slow air - Jigs and hornpipe / 9/8 marches / 2/4 marches / Solo pipe selection / Drum salute / Slow air, hornpipe and jigs / March strathspey & reel (2) / Slow air, hornpipe and jigs (2) / March strathspey & reel (3).
LP: . . . . **LILP 5165**
MC: . . . . **LICS 5165**

Strathspey, Elgin

ELGIN STRATHSPEY & REEL SOCIETY (Strathspey, Elgin Reel Society).
LP: . . . . **BGC 291**
MC: . . . . **KBGC 291**

Stratus

THROWING SHAPES.
LP: . . . . **STEEL 31001**
MC: . . . . **STEELC 31001**

Strauss, J. (composer)

BLUE DANUBE, THE (Vienna Philharmonic Orchestra).
MC: **4254254**

CHAMPAGNE & LAUGHTER (Various artists).
Tracks: / Blue Danube: *Various artists* / Nun's chorus: *Various artists* / Emperor, The: *Various artists*/ Bruderlein: *Various artists* / Die Fledermaus ovt.: *Various artists* / Chacun a song gout: *Various artists*/ Laughing song, The: *Various artists* / Radestsky march: *Various artists* / Tritsch-tratsch polka: *Various* artists / Thunder and lightning: *Various artists* / Perpetuum mobile: *Various artists* / Champagne polka: *Various artists*.
LP: . . . . **CFP 4499**
LP: . . . . **CFP 4144991**
MC: . . . . **CFP 4144994**
MC: . . . . **TCCFP 4499**

EMPEROR WALTZ/THE BLUE DANUBE/TALES FROM THE VIENNA WOODS (Vienna Philharmonic Orchestra).
MC: **4278204**

ROSES FROM THE SOUTH (Vienna Philharmonic Orchestra).
MC: **4254294**

STRAUSS (Various artists).
MC: . . . . **DLCMC 219**

STRAUSS WALTZES (Various artists).
MCSET: . . . . **DTO 10028**

STRAUSS'S GREATEST HITS (Various artists).
MC: **40 79026**

TALES FROM THE VIENNA WOODS (Vienna Philharmonic Orchestra).
MC: **4254264**

VIENNA BLOOD (Vienna Philharmonic Orchestra).
MC: **4254284**

VIENNA DANCES (see under London Symphony...) (London Symphony Orchestra).

WINE, WOMEN AND SONG (Vienna Philharmonic Orchestra).
MC: **4254274**

Strauss, R. (composer)

ALSO SPRACH ZARATHUSTRA (See under Solti, Sir George) (Chicago Symphony Orchestra).

AUS ITALIEN, 4 SONGS (Various artists).
LP: . . . . **ABRD 1383**
MC: . . . . **ABTD 1383**

MACBETH/ALSO SPRACH ZARATHUSTRA (Vienna Philharmonic Orchestra).
MC: **4278214**

RICHARD STRAUSS: DON JUAN (ETC) (Philharmonia).
Tracks: / Don Juan / Tod und verklarung (Death and transfiguration) / Horn concerto no.1 (Frank Lloyd on horn).
MC: . . . . **ZC DCA 697**

STRING QUARTETS (See under Medici String Quartet for details) (Medici String Quartet).

Stravinsky (composer)

PETRUSHKA (Vienna Philharmonic Orchestra).
MC: **4250264**

RITE OF SPRING/FIREBIRD (STRAVINSKY) (National Youth Orchestra of G.B./Royal Philharmonic Orch.).
Tracks: / Rite of Spring, The (Stravinsky) / Firebird suite.
MC: . . . . **ZC QS 6031**

SOLDIER'S TALE, THE (Featuring Sting/Vanessa Redgrave, Ian McKellen) (Various artists).
Tracks: / Soldier's march, The: *Various artists* / Soldiers march (reprise): *Various artists* / Pastorale: *Various* artists / Airs by a stream: *Various artists* / Royal march: *Various artists* / Little concert: *Various* artists / Three dances: *Various artists* / Devil's dance: *Various artists* / Little chorale: *Various artists* / Great chorale: *Various artists* / Triumphal march of the devil: *Various artists*.
LP: **4610481**
MC: **461 048 4**

VIOLIN CONCERTO (See under London Philharmonic Orch.) (London Philharmonic Orchestra).

Straw Dogs

YELLOW AND BLUE ATTACK.
LP: **2181 1**

Straw, Syd

SURPRISE.
Tracks: / Think too hard / Heart of darkness / Chasing vapor trails (his turn to cry) / Almost magic / Crazy American / Hard times / Future 40's (string of pearls) / Unanswered question, The / Sphinx / Racing the ruins / Golden dreams.
LP: . . . . **VUSLP 6**
MC: . . . . **VUSMC 6**

Strawberry Alarm Clock

STRAWBERRIES MEAN LOVE.
Tracks: / Incense and peppermints / Rainy day mushroom pillow / Sit with the

guru / Tomorrow / Black butter - present / Love me again / Pretty song from psych out, The / World's on fire, The / Birds in my tree / Birdman of Alkatrash, The / Small package / They saw the fat one coming / Strawberries mean love.
MC: . . . . **WIKC 56**
LP: . . . . **WIK 56**

Strawberry Statement

STRAWBERRY STATEMENT, THE (Various artists).
Tracks: / Circle game: *Sainte-Marie, Buffy* / Market basket: *MGM Studio Orchestra/Ian Freebairn* / Down by the river: *Young, Neil* / Long time gone: *Crosby, Stills & Nash* / Cyclatron: *MGM Studio Orchestra/Ian Freebairn*/ Something in the air: *Thunderclap Newman* / Also Sprach Zarthustra: *Berlin Philharmonic Orchestra* / Loner, The: *Young, Neil* / Coit tower: *MGM Studio Orchestra/Ian Freebairn* / Fishin' blues: *Red Mountain Jug Band*/ Concerto in D minor: *MGM Studio Orchestra/Ian Freebairn* / Helpless: *Crosby, Stills, Nash & Young* / Pocket band: *MGM Studio Orchestra/Ian Freebairn* / Give peace a chance: *Various artists*.
LP: . . . . **LPMGM 19**
LP: **794 290 1**
MC: . . . . **TCMGM 19**
MC: **794 290 4**

Strawberry Switchblade

STRAWBERRY SWITCHBLADE.
Tracks: / Since yesterday / Deep water / Another day / Little river / 10 James Orr Street / Let her go / Who knows what love is / Go away / Secrets / Being cold.
LP: . . . . **KODE 11**
MC: . . . . **CODE 11**

Strawbs

BEST OF THE STRAWBS.
Tracks: / Hero and heroine / Tears and pavan / Glimpse of heaven, A / Round and round / New world / Benedictus / Shine on silver sun / To be free / Where do you go (when you need a hole to crawl in) / Autumn / Heroine's theme / Deep summer's sleep / Winter long, The / Don't try to change me / Little sleepy / Part of the union / Song of a sad little girl / Down by the sea / Lay down / Heavy disguise / Lemon pie / Blue angel / Divided / Half worlds apart / At rest.
2LP: . . . . **AMLM 66005**

BURSTING AT THE SEAMS.
LP: . . . . **AMLH 68144**

DON'T SAY GOODBYE.
Tracks: / Boy and his dog, A / Let it rain / We can make it together / Tina Del Fada / Big brother / Something for nothing / Evergreen / That's when the crying starts / Beat the retreat.
LP: . . . . **STRAWBS 1**
MC: . . . . **STRAWBC 1**
LP: . . . . **TOOTS 3**
MC: . . . . **TOOTS 3C**

FROM THE WITCHWOOD.
LP: . . . . **AMLH 64304**

GRAVE NEW WORLD.
LP: . . . . **AMLH 68078**

HERO & HEROINE.
LP: . . . . **AMLH 63607**

JUST A COLLECTION OF ANTIQUES & CURIOS.
LP: . . . . **AMLS 994**

Strawhead

FAREWELL MUSKET, PIKE & DRUM.
LP: . . . . **TSR 026**

FORTUNES OF WAR.
LP: . . . . **TSR 032**

GENTLEMEN OF FORTUNE (FOLK).
LP: . . . . **TSR 045**

LAW LIES BLEEDING.
LP: . . . . **DRGN 872**

NEW VINTAGE, A.
MC: . . . . **DRGNMC 892**

SEDGEMOOR.
LP: . . . . **DRGN 851**

SONGS FROM THE BOOK OF ENGLAND.
2LP: . . . . **DRGN 8735/6**

THROUGH SMOKE & FIRE.
LP: . . . . **TSR 040**

TIFFIN.
LP: . . . . **DRGN 902**

Stray

LIVE AT THE MARQUEE.
LP: . . . . **GULP 1039**
MC: . . . . **ZCGUL 1039**

SATURDAY MORNING PICTURES.
Tracks: / Our song / After the storm / Sister Mary / Move that wigwam / Leave it out / How could I forget you / Mr Hobo / Queen of the sea.
LP: . . . . **TRS 110**

Stray Cats

BACK TO THE ALLEY (The Best Of The Stray Cats).
Tracks: / Stray cat strut / Rock this town / Rebels rule / Built for speed / Little Miss Prissy / Too hip gotta go / My one desire / I won't stand in your way (Only on CD) / C'mon everybody (live) / Fishnet stockings / Runaway boys / (She's) Sexy and 17 / Baby blue eyes / Jeannie, Jeannie, Jeannie / You don't believe me / Ubangi stomp (Only on CD) / Double takin' baby / Storm the embassy / Rumble in Brighton / Gonna ball.
LP: **210963**
MC: **410963**

BLAST OFF.
Tracks: / Blast off / Gina / Everybody needs rock 'n' roll / Gene and Eddie / Rockabilly rules / Bring it back again / Slip, slip, slippin' in / Rockabilly world / Rockin' all over the place / Nine lives.
LP: . . . . **MTL 1040**
MC: . . . . **TCMTL 1040**

GONNA BALL.
Tracks: / Baby blue eyes / Little Miss Prissy / Wasn't that good / Crying shame / She'll stay just one more day / You don't believe me / Wicked whisky / Rev it up and go / Lonely summer nights / Crazy mixed up kid.
LP: . . . . **STRAY 2**
MC: . . . . **TCAT 2**

RACE IS ON, THE (See under Edmunds, Dave) (Stray Cats & Dave Edmunds).

RANT 'N' RAVE WITH THE STRAY CATS.
Tracks: / Rebels rule / Too hip, gotta go / Look at that cadillac / Something's wrong with my radio / 18 miles to Memphis / (She's) sexy and 17 / Dig dirty doggie / I won't stand in your way / Hotrod gang / How long you wanna live / Anyway.
LP: . . . . **STRAY 3**
MC: . . . . **TCAT 3**

STRAY CATS.
Tracks: / Runaway boys / Fishnet stockings / Ubangi stomp / Jeannie, Jeannie, Jeannie / Storm the embassy / Rock this town / Rumble in Brighton / Stray cat strut / Crawl up and die / Double talkin' baby / My one desire / Wild saxophone.
LP: . . . . **STRAY 1**
MC: . . . . **TCAT 1**

STRAY CATS/GONNA BALL.
Tracks: / Runaway boys / Fishnet stockings / Ubangi stomp / Jeannie, Jeannie, Jeannie / Storm the embassy / Rock this town / Rumble in Brighton / Stray Cat strut / Crawl up and die / Double talkin' baby / My one desire / That mellow saxophone / Baby blue eyes / Little Miss Prissy / Wasn't that good / Crying shame / (She'll stay just) one more day / You won't believe me / Gonna ball / Wicked whisky / Rev it up and go / Lonely summer nights / Crazy mixed up kid.
MC: . . . . **XTWO 21**

Strayhorn, Billy

BILLY STRAYHORN & ELLINGTON ORCHESTRA (Strayhorn, Billy & Ellington Orchestra).
LP: **2MJP 1055**

CUE FOR SAXOPHONE (Strayhorn, Billy Septet).
Tracks: / Cue's blue now / Gone with the wind / Cherry / Watch your cue / You brought a new kind of love to me / When I dream of you / Rose room.
LP: . . . . **AFF 166**

Strazzeri, Frank

KAT DANCIN'.
Tracks: / Speak low / Remember / Trees / Moment to moment / Soultrane.
LP: . . . . **DS 933**

MAKE ME RAINBOWS.
LP: . . . . **FS 312**

RELAXIN'.
LP: . . . . **SB 1007**

Streatfeild, Noel

BALLET SHOES (See under Ballet Shoes).

Street Ducks

TARRED AND FEATHERED.
LP: . . . . **ABR 018**

Street Fleet

STREET FLEET (Film Soundtrack) (Various artists).
LP: . . . . **MCF 3204**

Street Level

STREET LEVEL (Various artists).
LP: . . . . **RTL 2048**
MC: . . . . **4 CRTL 2048**

Street, Maxwell

CHICAGO BLUES SESSIONS 11 (Street, Maxwell/Jimmy Davis).
LP: . . . . **WOLF 120 857**

Street, Pamela

MILL RACE, THE.
MC: . . . . **SOUND 36**

Street, Patrick

IRISH TIMES.
LP: . . . . **SPD 1033**
MC: . . . . **SPDC 1033**

NO. 2 PATRICK STREET.
LP: . . . . **SIF 1088**
MC: . . . . **CSIF 1088**

Street Scene

STREET SCENE (Kurt Weill show) (Various artists).
LP: . . . . **COL 4139**

Street Survivors

STREET SURVIVORS (Various artists).
Tracks: / Down to the wire: *Various artists* / Devil in you, The: *Various artists* / Love injection: *Various* artists / Let it ride: *Various artists* / Never run: *Various artists* / Walk in the woods: *Various artists*/ Too late: *Various artists* / Come on: *Various artists* / You belong to me: *Various artists* / Triangle: *Various artists* / Little Caesar: *Various artists* / Black cherry: *Various artists* / Bang tango: *Various* artists / NRG: *Various artists* / Fire: *Various artists* / Tomorrow's child: *Various artists* / Sphinx in Cairo: *Various artists* / Rain on fire: *Various artists* / Lunatic fringe: *Various artists* / Believe it or not: *Various artists*.
LP: . . . . **RO 94791**

Street To Street

STREET TO STREET, VOL 1 (Various artists).
LP: . . . . **OELP 501**

STREET TO STREET, VOL 2 (Various artists).
Tracks: / Days on edge: *Egypt for Now* / Thesis: *Cooling Towers* / Total recall: *Systems* / Eden: *Chinese* Religion / Unrest in the real world: *Games* / Song, The: *Games* / Glare of lights: *Systems* / Make this day end soon: *Cooling Towers* / Soldiers: *Egypt for Now* / Chambers: *Chinese Religion*.
LP: . . . . **OELP 502**

Streetband

DILEMMA.
Tracks: / Mirror star / It's no problem / Picture book / Starry eyed / Dilemma / One good reason / Here comes that man / Call me soon / Slaughterhouse 5.
LP: . . . . **LOGO 1017**

LONDON.
Tracks: / You're all I need / Happy families / Truth without lies / Things are never quite what they seem / It takes a thief / One more step / Any decisions / Mystery / His finest hour / Love sign / Loud music.
LP: . . . . **LOGO 1012**

STREETBAND (Streetband with Paul Young).
Tracks: / Happy families / Toast / One more step / Mystery / Love sign / Loud music / Mirror star / Picture book / Starry eyed / One good reason / Dilemma / Call me soon / Any decisions / Here comes that man.
2LP: . . . . **CR 140**
MCSET: . . . . **CRT 140**

Streetbeat

STREET BEAT (Various artists).
LP: . . . . **SHM 3116**

Streetmark

DREAMS.
LP: . . . . **SKY 101**

Streets (group)

CRIMES IN MIND.
Tracks: / Don't look back / Nightmare begins / Broken glass / Hit n run / Crimes in mind / I can't wait / Gun runner / Desiree / Hate race / Turn my head.
LP: **781 246-1**

Streets Of Blairgowrie

STREETS OF BLAIRGOWRIE.
MC: **60-182**

Streetwalkers

BEST OF THE STREETWALKERS.
LP: **846 661 1**
MC: **846 661 4**

RED CARD.
LP: **9102 010**

Strehli, Angela

SOUL SHAKE (Strehli, Angela Band).
LP: . . . . **AN 006**

Streisand, Barbra

BARBRA JOAN STREISAND.
LP: . . . . **CBS 32236**
MC: **40 32236**

BARBRA STREISAND ALBUM, THE.
Tracks: / Cry me a river / My honey's loving arms / I'll tell the man in the street / Taste of honey, A / Who's afraid of the big bad wolf / Soon it's gonna rain / Happy days are here again / Keepin' out of mischief now / Much more / Come to the supermarket / Sleeping bee.
LP: . . . . **CBS 32010**
MC: **40 32010**
LP: **902196 1**
MC: **902196 4**

BROADWAY ALBUM.
Tracks: / Putting it together / If I love you / Something's coming / Not while I'm around / Being alive / I have dreamed / We kiss in a shadow / Something wonderful / Send in the clowns / Pretty women / Ladies who lunch, The / Can't help lovin' dat man / I loves you Porgy / Porgy, I's your woman now / Somewhere.
LP: . . . . **CBS 86322**
MC: **40 86322**

CHRISTMAS ALBUM.
Tracks: / Christmas song, The / Jingle bells / Have yourself a merry little Christmas / Christmas song, The / White Christmas / My favourite things / Best of gifts / Sleep in heavenly peace (Silent night) / Gounod's Ave Maria / O little town of Bethlehem / I wonder as I wander / Lord's prayer, The.
LP: . . . . **CBS 31850**
MC: **40 31850**

CLASSICAL BARBRA.
Tracks: / Debussy / Beau soir / Canteloupe / Brezairola / Faure / Pavanne / Apres un reve / Orff / Carmina burana / In trutina / Rinaldo / Lascia chio pianga / Dank sei dir, Herr Ogerman.
LP: . . . . **CBS 73484**
MC: **40 73484**

COLLECTION OF GREATEST HITS AND MORE.
Tracks: / We're not makin' love any more / Woman in love / All I ask of you / Comin' in and out of your life / What kind of fool / Main event/Fight, The / Someone that I used to love / By the way / Guilty / Memory / Way he makes me feel, The / Somewhere.
LP: **4658451**
MC: **4658454**

COLOUR ME BARBRA.
Tracks: / Yesterdays / One kiss / Minute waltz, The / Gotta move / Non c'est bien / Where or when / C'est si bon / Where am I going / Starting here, starting now.
LP: . . . . **CBS 32128**

EMOTION.
Tracks: / Emotion / Make no mistake / He's mine / Time machine / Best I could / Left in the dark / Heart don't change my mind / When I dream you're a step in the right direction / Clear sailing / Here we are at last.
LP: . . . . **CBS 86309**
MC: **40 86309**

GOLDEN HIGHLIGHTS OF ... (XMAS).
LP: **54734**
MC: **40 54734**

GREATEST HITS: BARBRA STREISAND.
Tracks: / People / Second hand Rose / Why did I choose you / He touched me / Free again / Don't rain on my parade / My colouring book / Sam / You made the pants too long / My man (Mon homme) / Gotta move / Happy days are here again.
LP: . . . . **CBS 63921**
MC: **40 63921**

GREATEST HITS: BARBRA STREISAND VOL.2.
Tracks: / Evergreen / Prisoner, The / My heart belongs to me / Songbird / You don't bring me flowers ((With Neil Diamond)) / Way we were, The / Sweet inspiration / Where you lead / All in love is fair / Superman / Stoney end.
LP: . . . . **CBS 10012**
MC: **40 10012**

GREATEST HITS VOL 1.
LP: . . . . **CBS 66349**

GUILTY.
Tracks: / Guilty / Woman in love / Run wild / Promises / Love inside / What kind of fool / Life story / Never give up / Make it like a memory.
LP: . . . . **CBS 86122**
MC: **40 86122**
LP: . . . . **H 86122**

JE M'APPELLE BARBRA.
Tracks: / What now my love / Autumn leaves / Speak to me of love / Once upon a time / I wish you love / Clopin clopant / Ma premiere chanson.

LP: 32317

LOVE SONGS: BARBRA STREISAND.
Tracks: / Memory / You don't bring me flowers / My heart belongs to me / Wet / New York state of mind / Man I loved, A / No more tears / Comin' in and out of your life / Evergreen / I don't break easily / Kiss me in the rain / Lost inside of you / Way we were, The / Love inside.
LP: . . . . CBS 10031
MC: 40 10031

MY NAME IS BARBRA, VOL. 2.
LP: . . . . BPG 62603
MC: 4687844

NO MORE TEARS (See under Summer, Donna) (Streisand, Barbra & Don Johnson).

NUTS (Film soundtrack).
MLP: 6513796

ONE VOICE.
Tracks: / Somewhere / Evergreen (Love theme from "A Star Is Born".) / Something's coming / People / Over the rainbow / Guilty / What kind of fool / Papa, can you hear me / Way we were, The / It's a new world / Happy days are here again / America, the beautiful.
LP: 4508911
MC: 4508914

SECOND BARBRA STREISAND ALBUM, THE.
LP: . . . . CBS 32022
MC: 40 32022

SONG BIRD.
LP: . . . . CBS 86060

STONEY END.
Tracks: / I don't know where I stand / Hands off the man / If you could read my mind / Just a little lovin' / Let me go / Stoney end / No easy way down / Time and love / Maybe / Free the people / I'll be home.
LP: . . . . CBS 32562
MC: 40 32562
LP: . . . . CBS 64269
MC: 4659124

SUPERMAN.
Tracks: / Superman / Don't believe what you read / Baby me baby / I found you love / Answer me / My heart belongs to me / Cabin fever / Love comes from unexpected places / New York State of mind / Lullaby for myself.
LP: . . . . CBS 86030

THIRD ALBUM.
Tracks: / My melancholy baby / Just in time / Take a chance on love / Bewitched, bothered and bewildered / Never will I marry / As time goes by / Draw me a circle / It had to be you / Make believe / I had myself a true love.
LP: . . . . CBS 32041
MC: 40 32041

TILL I LOVED YOU.
Tracks: / Places you find love, The / On my way to you / Till I loved you / Love light / All I ask of you / You and me for always / Why let it go / Two people / What were you thinking of / Some good things never last / One more time around.
LP: 4629431
MC: 4629434

WAY WE WERE, THE (Original soundtrack).
Tracks: / Being at war with each other / Something so right / Best thing you've ever done / Way we were, The / All in love is fair / What are you doing the rest of your life / Summer me winter me / Pieces of dreams / I've never been a woman before / My buddy / How about me.
LP: . . . . CBS 69057
MC: 40 69057

WET.
Tracks: / Wet / Come rain or come shine / Splish splash / On rainy afternoons / After the rain / No more tears (enough is enough) (with Donna Summer.) / Niagara / I ain't gonna cry tonight / Kiss me in the rain.
LP: . . . . CBS 86104
MC: 40 86104

YENTL (Original soundtrack).
Tracks: / Where is it written / Papa can you hear me / This is one of those moments / No wonder the way he makes me feel / No matter what happens.
LP: . . . . CBS 86302
MC: 40 86302

Stren, Patti

HUG ME.
MC: . . . . CDL 51715

Stress

BIG WHEEL, THE.
MC: . . . . ARR 014

PINK OBOE.
LP: . . . . WX 368
MC: . . . . WX 368C

REALITY SYNDROME, THE.
MC: . . . . HOOT CR 1

RESTRAINT.
MC: . . . . ARR 010

Stress (Label)

D-STRESS (Various artists).
LP: . . . . SS 2
MC: . . . . SSC 2

Stretcheads

FIVE FINGERS, FOUR THINGIES..... (A thumb, a facelift and a new identity).
LP: . . . . SOMALP 2

PISH IN YOUR SLEAZEBAG.
LP: . . . . BFFP 058

Strevens, Eddie

TAKING A CHANCE ON LOVE.
LP: . . . . HAL 15
LP: . . . . SHAL 15

Stribling, Neville

SACRAMENTO CONNECTION.
LP: . . . . S 1408

Strictly Instrumental

STRICTLY INSTRUMENTAL (Various artists).
Tracks: / Mustang: *Rocking R's* / Heat: *Rocking R's* / Haunted trains: *Millionaires* / Scandal: *King* Rock / Band stand: *Rockaways* / Vibrations: *Royal Jokers* / Beatnik: *Royal Jokers* / Wierd: *Rhythm* Rockers / Wibcee: *Crowns* / Go tune, The: *Crowns* / Midnight express: *Willy Treamain's Thunderbirds* / Impact: *Rambling Ramblers* / Spit fire: *Glynn Hipp's Jokers* / Rocket city rock: *Rocket City Rockettes.*
LP: . . . . BB 2002

Stride, John (aut)

AS YOU LIKE IT (See under Shakespear, William).

Stride, Pete

NEW GUITARS IN TOWN (Stride, Pete & John Plain).
Tracks: / Laugh at me / School girls / Cold old night / He'll have to go / Just like a clown / Half the time / New guitars in town / Cure for love / Restless king / You better move on / Pick me up.
LP: . . . . BEGA 17

Strife

RUSH.
Tracks: / Backstreets of heaven / Man of the wilderness / Magic of the dawn / Indian dream / Life is easy / Better than I / Rush.
LP: . . . . CHR 1063
MC: . . . . ZCHR 1063

Strike

STRIKE.
LP: . . . . SWORDLP 002

WORKERS SPEAK TO THEIR SLAVE MASTER.
Tracks: / New approach to workers / Bad management / Better working conditions / More opportunity / More power to the workers / Management attitude to workers / Union and management / Stop victimisation.
LP: . . . . WE 001

Strike Up The Band

STRIKE UP THE BAND (Film soundtrack) (Various artists).
LP: . . . . HS 5009

String Bands

STRING BANDS 1927-29 (Various artists).
LP: . . . . HK 4009

STRING BANDS, THE (Various artists).
LP: . . . . OT 100

STRING BANDS VOL.2, THE (Various artists).
LP: . . . . OT 101

String Of Pearls

DANCE GREATS OF THE WAR YEARS (String Of Pearls Orchestra).
MC: . . . . ZPRST 818

String Ragtime

STRING RAGTIME To do this you gotta know how (Various artists).
LP: . . . . L 1045

String Trio Of New

FIRST STRING.
LP: . . . . BSR 0031

STRING TRIO OF NEW YORK & JAY CLAYTON (String Trio of New York & Jay Clayton).
LP: . . . . WW 008

Stringbean

SALUTE TO UNCLE DAVE MACON (Stringbean & His Banjo).
LP: . . . . SLP 215
MC: . . . . GT 5215

Stringdusters

STRINGDUSTERS, THE.
Tracks: / Ten degrees and getting colder / Good time Charlie's got the blues / Streets of Baltimore / Tried so hard / Peaceful easy feeling / Shackles and chains / Woman turn around / Morning / Nashville again / I sure like your smile / Letter to a lady / Early morning rain / Butchie's tune.
LP: . . . . FHR 069

Strings For Pleasure

BEST OF BACHARACH.
LP: . . . . MFP 1334

Strinholm, Jan

WHY DO YOU PLAY SO LONG?.
LP: . . . . DRLP 154

Stritch, Elaine

EASY STREET.
LP: . . . . MRS 908

Stroe, Corneliu

TRANSYLVANIAN SUITE (See under Tavitian, Harry) (Stroe, Corneliu/Harry Tavitian).

Strollers

FIVE CATS DOWN....BOPPIN AND STROLLIN.
Tracks: / Bop 'n' stroll / Love my baby / I've got your letter / 10 cats down / Oh baby babe / Eyes wide open / Roll on big mama / Hoy hoy hoy / Worrying kind, The / Down the line / Eeny meeny / Trying to get to you / Baby you're using me / You're so fine.
LP: . . . . MFLP 009

LONDON PRIDE.
Tracks: / Long blonde hair / Oh baby babe / Ten cats down / Eeny meeny / Your baby blue eyes / Good love / Who do you love? / Too many / I've got your letter / Bop'n'stroll / Trying to get to you / Rockabye boogie / Drugstore rock'n'roll / I ain't never / We say yeah! / Tear it up / Lost rockers return / Strolers shuffle / Love me / You're so fine.
LP: . . . . MFM 016

Strong, Barrett

LOVE IS YOU.
Tracks: / You are my one and only love / All I wanna do is be with you / I'm so in love with you / You're a mighty good love / You turn me on / You make me feel the way I do / Love is you / When you're truly in love.
LP: . . . . TRLP 101
LP: . . . . TRPL 101

Strong, Benny

THAT CERTAIN PARTY.
LP: . . . . GNPS 9013

Strong, Bob

BOB STRONG AND ORCHESTRA 1944-45 (Strong, Bob & His Orchestra).
LP: . . . . CLP 129

BOB STRONG ON THE AIR (Strong, Bob & His Orchestra).
Tracks: / What is this thing called love? / Strange music / London bridge is falling down / Her tears flowed like wine / I don't want to love you / Embraceable you / Hittin' the silk / And the angels sing / Allah's holiday / Hang your heart on a hickory limb / Pagan love song / Comes love / Little man who wasn't there, The / Sunday / Apple for teacher, An.
LP: . . . . AIRCHECK 23

ONE NIGHT STAND.
LP: . . . . JLP 1027

TONE COLOR SERENADE.
LP: . . . . GELP 15024

Strong, Patience

PATIENCE STRONG.
Tracks: / Quiet corner / Through the year with Patience Strong.
LP: . . . . M 44001

QUIET CORNER WITH GAVIN DEARD.
MC: . . . . KM 44001

Stroud, Ken

PUT ANOTHER NICKEL IN.
LP: . . . . GRS 1164

Strozier, Frank

REMEMBER ME (Strozier, Frank Sextet).
LP: . . . . SCS 1066

WALTZ OF THE DEMONS.
Tracks: / W K Blues / Waltz of the demons / Starlings theme / I don't know / Runnin' / Off shore.
LP: . . . . ATS 5
MC: . . . . KATS 5
LP: . . . . AFF 49

WHAT'S GOING ON? (Direct Cut album) (Strozier, Frank Quintet).
LP: . . . . SDC 17001

Struber, Bernard

JOY TO THE WORLD (see under Schmitt, Georges) (Struber, Bernard/Georges Schmitt).

Strummer, Joe

EARTHQUAKE WEATHER.
Tracks: / Gangsterville / King of the bayou / Island hopping / Slant six / Dizzy's goatee / Shouting street / Boogie with your children / Leopardskin limousines / Sikorsky parts / Jewellers and bums / Highway one zero street / Ride your donkey / Passport to Detroit / Sleepwalk.
LP: 4653471
MC: 4653474

WALKER (see under Walker).

Strummin' Mental

STRUMMIN' MENTAL, VOL 1 1957-65 (Various artists).
LP: . . . . LR 1

STRUMMIN' MENTAL, VOL 2 1957-65 (Various artists).
LP: . . . . LR 2

STRUMMIN' MENTAL, VOL 3 1957-65 (Various artists).
LP: . . . . LR 3

STRUMMIN' MENTAL, VOL 4 1957-65 (Various artists).
LP: . . . . LR 4

STRUMMIN' MENTAL, VOL 5 (Various artists).
LP: . . . . LR 5

Strunz & Farah

GUITARRAS (Strunz, Jorge & Adeshir Farah).
Tracks: / Curandero / Chumash / Suenos (Part 1) / Suenos (Part 2) / Zambalera / Tropico / Talisman, The / Feathered serpent, The / Mirage.
LP: . . . . M 9136

Strutt, Nick

LAST TRAIN SOUTH (See Golbey, Brian) (Strutt, Nick & Brian Golbey).

Strutters, Harry

BORNEO (Strutters, Harry Hot Rhythm Orchestra).
Tracks: / Borneo / Black Beauty / Barnacle Bill / Rockin' in rhythm / Doodlin' blue / Wherever there's love / Zonky / Symphonic raps / St. James infirmary blues / Froggie Moore / Nagasaki / East St. Louis toodle-oo / Everybody stomp.
LP: . . . . BLM 51108

HARRY STRUTTERS' HOT RHYTHM ORCHESTRA (Strutters, Harry Hot Rhythm Orchestra).
Tracks: / Rhythm king / Charleston / Am I blue / Copenhagen / Take your tomorrows / Ice cream / How could Red Riding Hood? / Sugar foot strut / Jazz me blues / Mooche / Chili bom bom / Candy lips.
LP: . . . . BLP 12130

TOTUS PORCUS.
LP: . . . . BLP 12196

Struttin' & Flirtin'

STRUTTIN' AND FLIRTIN' (Various artists).
LP: 3970631
MC: 3970634

Strutting...

STRUTTING AT THE BRONZE PEACOCK (Various artists).
LP: . . . . CHD 223

Stryper

AGAINST THE LAW.
Tracks: / Against the law / Two time woman / Rock the people / Two bodies (one mind, one soul) / Not that kind of guy / Shining star / Ordinary man / Lady / Caught in the middle / All for one / Rock the hell out of you.
LP: . . . . ENVLP 1010
MC: . . . . TCENV 1010
MC: 773 527 4

IN GOD WE TRUST.
Tracks: / In God we trust / Always there for you / Keep the fire burning / I believe in you / Writing on the wall / It's up 2 U / World of you and I, The / Come to the everlife / Lonely / Reign, The.
LP: . . . . MYRR 1252
MC: . . . . MYRC 1252
LP: . . . . ENVLP 501
MC: . . . . TCENV 501
LPPD: . . . . PENVLP 501
LP: . . . . ENVLP 1008
MC: . . . . TCENV 1008

SOLDIERS UNDER COMMAND.
LP: . . . . MYR R 1228
MC: . . . . MYR C 1228
LP: . . . . MFN 72

STRYPER: INTERVIEW PICTURE DISC.

LPPD: . . . . BAK 2052

TO HELL WITH THE DEVIL.
Tracks: / Abyss (to hell with the devil) / To hell with the devil / Calling on you / Free / Honestly / Way, The / Sing along song / Rockin' the world / All of me / More than a man.
LP: . . . . MFN 70
LP: . . . . MYR R 1129
MC: . . . . MYR C 1229
MC: . . . . TMFN 70
LP: . . . . ENVLP 1009

YELLOW AND BLACK ATTACK, THE.
Tracks: / Loud 'n' clear / My love I'll always show / You know what to do / Common rock / You won't be lonely / Loving you / Reasons for the season.
LP: . . . . MFN 74

STS 8 Mission

MYSTERY OF TIME.
Tracks: / Mighty call / Calling in the dark / Lost command / Desperate child / None of your business / Always lying / I'll never loose my way / Mystery of time.
LP: . . . . ATOMH 011

Stuart, Alice

ALL THE GOOD TIMES.
LP: . . . . ARHOOLIE 4002

Stuart, Colin

TOURING SCOTLAND.
Tracks: / Hiking song, The / Scottish waltz medley / Lass o'leven vale, The / Bonnie Balmaha / Misty Islands / Dancing in Kyle / Skye boat song / Heart of Scotland, The / Royal Deeside / Royal mile / Banks of the Forth, The / Harry Lauder medley.
LP: . . . . LILP 5110
MC: . . . . LICS 5110

Stuart, Francis

ALTERNATIVE GOVERNMENT.
MC: 4CCT 18
LP: . . . . CCT 18

Stuart, Gene

AT HOME.
MCSET: . . . . HTC 8015

DARLIN' THINK OF ME.
LP: . . . . CBRL 4067
LP: . . . . BRL 4067

FIRST CLASS COUNTRY.
Tracks: / Day the blizzard hit our town, The / Picture of your mother / Word or two to Mary / End of everything / I'm not mixed up anymore / My son calls another man daddy / Your old love letters / Down the road I go / Darling think of me / You're no longer a sweetheart of mine / Wreck of the number nine, The / What things money can't buy.
LP: . . . . PHL 413
MC: . . . . CPHL 413

GREATEST HITS: GENE STUART.
LP: . . . . HALP 120

GREATEST HITS: GENE STUART VOL.2.
LP: . . . . SHARP 2
MC: . . . . SHARP 2 (TC)

JUST FOR WHAT I AM.
LP: . . . . BRL 4099

ME AND THE BOYS.
LP: . . . . RBA 128
LP: . . . . DRL 2014

ONCE AGAIN.
LP: . . . . RBA 104

PRECIOUS MEMORIES.
LP: . . . . BRL 4089
MC: . . . . CBRL 4089

REMEMBER YOU'RE MINE (Stuart, Gene & The Homesteaders).
Tracks: / Remember you're mine / Veil of white lace / Foolin' around / Forever and ever / Excuse me I think I've got a heartache / Heartaches by the number / Jealous heart / Careless darling / Leona / Oh lonesome me / Old woman from Wexford / Bold O'Donaghue / Home boy's home / You can't make a heel toe the mark / Out of my mind over you / Where is my Nora.
MC: . . . . CHRL 188

SINCERELY IRISH.
LP: . . . . RBA 134

TWILIGHT COUNTRY.
LP: . . . . RBA 123

Stuart, Jerry

ROCKY RUN.
Tracks: / Rocky run / Black still waters / Misty mountain / Deliverence will come / Stuart's march / Land of the dead / Shining path, The / Bicycle song / Must I go / Galaxy.
LP: . . . . CO 767

Stuart, Marty

BUSY BEE CAFE.
Tracks: / One more ride / Blue railroad train / I don't love nobody / Watson's blues / Busy bee cafe / Down the road / Hey porter / Boogie for Clarence / Get in line brother / Soldier's joy / Long train gone.
LP: . . . . SH 3726
MC: . . . . SH 3726C

MARTY.
Tracks: / Precious memories / Hard hearted / Rawhide / Dock of the bay / Crazy creek blues / Just a little talk with Jesus / Love grown cold / Mystery train / Tiger man / Kansas City / Big boss man / Little help from my friends, A / My Sally Goodin.
LP: 0013

Stubblefield

COUNTIN' ON THE BLUES.
Tracks: / Remembrance / For those you didn't know / Going home / Montauk / My ideal / Countin' the blues.
LP: . . . . ENJA 5051

Stubblefield,John

PRELUDE.
LP: . . . . SLP 4011

Stubbs, Tish

ENGLISH FOLKSINGER, (THE) (see under Richards, Sam) (Stubbs, Tish & Sam Richards).

INVITATION TO NORTH AMERICA (Stubbs, Tish & Sam Richards).
LP: . . . . SDL 280

Stubbs, Una (nar)

ADVENTURES OF CREAMCAKE AND COMPANY (See under Adventures of ...).

Stuck

DENNIS STAR PRESENTS "STUCK", VOL. 1 (Various artists).
Tracks: / Stuck: *Early Black* / I found love: *Pliers & Bernie Don* / Dance and spread out: *General Trees*/ Evil doers: *Flourgan* / Artical love: *Don, Beenie* / Didn't mean to turn you on: *Melody, Mikey* / Let the good times roll: *Pliers* / Guide me o Jah: *Chaplin, Charlie (Reggae)* / Them a come: *Honey & Spice*/ Stuck version: *Firehouse Crew*.
LP: . . . . GREL 126
MC: . . . . GREEN 126

Stud

STUD, THE (Film Soundtrack) (Various artists).
LP: . . . . RTD 2029

STUD (THEME FROM) (See under Biddu Orchestra).

Student Prince (film)

STUDENT PRINCE (FILM) (See under Lanza, Mario) (Lanza, Mario).

Students Choir Utrecht

OFFICIUM TENEBRARUM.
MC: . . . . MCCEL 022

Studio London

E. MORRICONE.
LP: 26006
MC: 46006

FEELINGS.
LP: 26002
MC: 46002

Studio Two Selection

STUDIO TWO SELECTION.
Tracks: / Magnificent seven, The / Barcarolle (From Tales of Hoffman.) / La danza / Sleepy shores (Theme from Owen MD.) / Eso beso / Musetta's waltz song (From La Boheme.) / Trepak / Stranger on the shore / U.S. Marine Corps hymn / Dance little bird / This ole house / Making your mind up / Rondo (eine kleine nachtmusik) / Gold and silver waltz / Trap / April in Portugal / Guantanamera / Super trouper / My old piano / Feels like I'm in love / Yellow bird / One furtive tear / Carmen overture / Onedin line theme / Oklahoma / Oh, what a beautiful morning / E.T., Theme from.
MC: . . . . TCSTR 2

Study In Scarlet

STUDY IN SCARLET, A (see under Sherlock Holmes) (Various artists).

Stuermer, Daryl

STEPPIN' OUT.
LP: . . . . GRPA 9573-1
MC: . . . . GRPM 9573-4

Stuff

STUFF.
Tracks: / Foots / My sweetness / Do you want some of this / Looking for the juice / Reflections on divine love / How long will it last / Sun song / Happy farms / Dixie up on the roof.
LP: . . . . K 56305

Stump

FIERCE PANCAKE, A.
Tracks: / Lying it down / In the green / Roll the bodies over / Bone / Eager bereaver / Chaos / Alcohol / Charlton Heston / Heartache / Visit to the doctor, A / Fierce pancake, A / Boggy home.
LP: . . . . CHEN 9
MC: . . . . ZCHEN 9

QUIRK OUT.
MC: . . . . STUFF CU 2

Stunning

PARADISE IN THE PICTUREHOUSE.
LP: . . . . ROCK 005
MC: . . . . ROCC 005

Stunt Man

STUNT MAN (Film soundtrack) (Various artists).
LP: . . . . T 626

Stupids

JESUS MEETS THE STUPIDS.
LP: . . . . SOL 7

PERUVIAN VACATION.
LP: . . . . GURT 9

RETARD PICNIC.
LP: . . . . GURT 15

VAN STUPID.
MLP: . . . . SOL 2

Stur, King

LIVE AT FOUR PATHS, CLARENDON (Stur, King/Gav Sounds).
LP: . . . . DHS 4

Sturm Group

CENTURY HO.
LP: . . . . GS 157

Stutz Bear Cats

ACADEMY AWARD WINNERS & NOMINATIONS.
Tracks: / Chattanooga choo choo / How about you / I'll never stop loving you / Trolley song, The / What are you doing the rest of your life / Gonna fly now / Shadow of your smile / That old feeling / I fall in love too easily / Nobody does it better / Over the rainbow / Talk to the animals.
LP: . . . . SIV 1112
MC: . . . . CSIV 1112

SONGS WE SING.
Tracks: / Ain't what you do it's the way that you do it / I should care / Knock me a kiss / Twelth street rag / Sentimental journey / Tuxedo junction / Jumpin live / Song that I sing / Is you is or is you ain't my baby / All the things you are / All the things you are / Boogie woogie bugle boy / Night in Tunisia.
LP: . . . . MMT LP 112
MC: . . . . MMT TC 112

Style Council

CAFE BLEU.
Tracks: / Mick's blessing / Me ship came in / Blue cafe / Paris match, The / My ever changing moods / Dropping bombs on the whitehouse / Gospel / Strength of your nature / You're the best thing / Here's one that got away / Headstart for happiness / Council meeting.
LP: . . . . TSCLP 1
MC: . . . . TSCMC 1

CONFESSIONS OF A POP GROUP.
Tracks: / It's a very deep sea / Story of someone's show, The / Changing of the Guard / Little boy in a castle, The / Dove flew down from the elephant, A / Gardener of Eden, The (A three piece suite) / Life at a top peoples' health farm / Why I went missing / I was a dole dad's toy boy / How she threw it all away / Confessions 1, 2 & 3 / Confessions of a pop group.
LP: . . . . TSCLP 5
MC: . . . . TSCMC 5
LP: 835 785 1
MC: 835 785 4

COST OF LIVING.
Tracks: / It didn't matter / Right to go / Heavens above / Fairytales / Angel / Walking the night / Waiting / Cost of living, The / Woman's song, A.
LP: . . . . TSCLP 4
MC: . . . . TSCMC 4
LP: 831 443-1
MC: 831 443-4

HOME AND ABROAD (LIVE).
LP: . . . . TSCLP 3
MC: . . . . TSCMC 3
LP: 829 143-1
MC: 829 143-4

OUR FAVOURITE SHOP.
Tracks: / Homebreaker / All gone away / Come to Milton Keynes / Internationalist / Stones throw away, A / Stand up comics instructions, The / Boy who cried wolf / Man of great promise, A / Down in the Seine / Lodgers, The / Luck / With everything to lose / Our favourite shop / Walls come tumbling down / Shout to the top.
LP: 825 700-1
MC: 825 700-4
LP: . . . . TSCLP 2
MC: . . . . TSCMC 2

SINGULAR ADVENTURES OF THE STYLE COUNCIL, THE (Greatest hits vol 1).
Tracks: / You're the best thing / Have you ever had it blue / Money go round / My ever changing moods / Long hot summer / Lodgers, The / Walls come tumbling down / Shout to the top / Wanted / It didn't matter / Speak like a child / Solid bond in your heart, A / Life at a top peoples health farm / Promised land / How she threw it all away (Only on cassette and CD) / Waiting (Only on cassette and CD) / Have you ever had it blue (12" version) (CD only) / My ever changing moods (12" only) / Long hot summer (12" version) (CD only).
LP: . . . . TSCTV 1
MC: . . . . TSCTC 1

STYLE COUNCIL: INTERVIEW PICTURE DISC.
LPPD: . . . . BAK 2032

Styles, Vibes &

STYLES, VIBES AND HARMONY (A Tribute to Brian Wilson) (Various artists).
LP: . . . . DM 004
MC: . . . . DM 004 MC

Stylistics

1982.
Tracks: / We should be lovers / United / Call on you / My heart / Always something there to remind me / You're leaving / Don't come telling me lies / Lighten up.
LP: . . . . PIR 85791

ALL ABOUT LOVE.
Tracks: / Can't give you anything but my love / Na na is the saddest word / Jenny / Honky tonk cafe, A / I will love you always / I plead guilty / Can't help falling in love / Let's put it all together / You are beautiful / Funky weekend.
LP: . . . . CN 2044
MC: CN4 2044

BEST OF THE STYLISTICS.
LP: 9109 003

BEST OF THE STYLISTICS (1990).
MC: . . . . PRIMC 23
LP: . . . . PRICE 23

BEST OF THE STYLISTICS VOL.2.
LP: 9109 010

BLACK SATIN.
Tracks: / Could this be the end / Country living / Doin' the streets / I won't give up / It's too late / Keeping my fingers crossed / Let them work it out / Love comes easy / Make it last / Only for the children / Pay back is a dog / Point of no return / Satin doll / There's no reason / You'll never get to heaven / You're as right as rain.
LP: 9198230

CLOSER THAN CLOSE.
Tracks: / What's your name / I've got this feeling / Mine all mine / Habit / Searchin' / It's only love / Closer than close / Almost there.
LP: . . . . PIR 85159

FABULOUS.
LP: 9109 008

FROM THE MOUNTAIN.
LP: 9109 002

GREAT LOVE HITS, THE.
Tracks: / Rock 'n' roll baby / You make me feel brand new / I'm stone in love with you / Hey girl, come and get it / We can make it happen again / Peek-a-boo / You are everything / You'll never get to heaven / I will love you always / Love comes easy / Betcha by golly wow / If you are there / Break up to make up / People make the world go round.
LP: . . . . CN 2063
MC: CN4 2063

GREATEST HITS: STYLISTICS.
LP: . . . . BRLP 43
MC: . . . . BRMC 43

HITS, THE.
Tracks: / Betcha by golly wow / Break up to make up / I can't give you anything but love / Can't help falling in love / Funky weekend / I'm stone in love with you / Let's put it all together / Na na is the saddest word / Peek a boo / Rockin' roll baby / 7000 dollars and you / Sing baby sing / Sixteen bars / Star on a TV show / You make me feel brand new / You'll never get to heaven.
LP: 6467650

HURRY UP THIS WAY AGAIN.
Tracks: / Driving me wild / It started out / And I'll see you no more / Found a love

you couldn't handle / Maybe it's love this time / Hurry up this way again / It started out / I have you, you have me / Is there something on your mind.
LP: . . . . PIR 84323
MC: 40 84323

LET'S PUT IT ALL TOGETHER.
LP: 6466 013

ROCKIN' ROLL BABY.
LP: 6466 012

SOME THINGS NEVER CHANGE.
Tracks: / Some things never change / Give a little love for love / Don't change / Girl in yellow, The / Row your love / Love is not the answer / Hooked on your lovin' / When will I learn / Just the two of us.
MC: . . . . OVEDC 186
LP: . . . . OVED 186

THANK YOU BABY.
LP: 9109 005

VERY BEST OF THE STYLISTICS.
Tracks: / Can't give you anything but my love / Let's put it all together / I'm stone in love with you / You make me feel brand new / Sing baby sing / Na na is the saddest word / Sixteen bars / Betcha by golly wow / Rock 'n' roll baby / Star on a TV show / Funky weekend / Break up to make up / Can't help falling in love / Peek-a-boo / 7000 dollars and you / You'll never get to heaven.
LP: . . . . PRICE 23
MC: . . . . PRIMC 23

YOU ARE BEAUTIFUL.
LP: 9109 006

Stylus

STYLUS.
Tracks: / Discover your life / Bush walkin' / Look at me / Sweetness / Work out fine / Funky music / Got to be / Kissin' / Natural feeling / Hangin'.
LP: . . . . PDL 2011

Styx

BEST OF STYX.
Tracks: / You need love / Lady / I'm gonna make you feel it / What has come between us / Southern woman / Rock and roll feeling / Winner takes all / Best thing / Witch wolf / Grove of Eglantine, The / Man of miracles.
LP: . . . . PL 13116
MC: . . . . PK 13116

CAUGHT IN THE ACT.
Tracks: / Music time / Too much time on my hands / Babe / Snow blind / Best of times, The / Suite madame blue / Rockin' the paradise / Blue collar man / Miss America / Don't let it end / Fooling yourself / Crystal ball / Come sail away / Mr. Roboto.
2LP: . . . . AMLM 66704

CORNERSTONE.
Tracks: / Lights / Why me / Babe / Never say never / Boat on the river / Borrowed time / First time / Eddie / Love in the moonlight.
LP: . . . . AMLK 63711
MC: . . . . CKM 63711

EDGE OF THE CENTURY.
Tracks: / Love is the ritual / Show me the way / Edge of the century / Love at first sight / All in a days work / Not dead yet / World tonite / Carrie Ann / Homewrecker / Back to Chicago.
LP: 395327 1
MC: 395327 4

EQUINOX.
Tracks: / Light up / Lorelei / Mother dear / Lonely child / Midnight ride / Born for adventure / Prelude 12 / Suite Madame blue.
LP: . . . . AMLH 64559

GRAND ILLUSION, THE.
Tracks: / Grand illusion / Fooling yourself / Superstars / Come sail away / Miss America / Man in the wilderness / Castle walls / Grand finale.
LP: . . . . AMLH 64637
MC: . . . . CAM 64637

KILROY WAS HERE.
Tracks: / Mr. Roboto / Cold war / Don't let it end / High time / Heavy metal poisoning / Just get through this night / Double life / Haven't we been here before.
LP: . . . . AMLX 63734

LADY.
Tracks: / You need love / Lady / Day, A / You better ask / Little fugue in 'G' / Father O.S.A. / Earl of Roseland / I'm gonna make you feel it.
LP: . . . . PL 13594

MAN OF MIRACLES.
LP: . . . . FL 13115

PARADISE THEATRE.
Tracks: / A.D. 1928 / Rockin in paradise / Too much time on my hands / Nothing ever goes as planned / Best of times, The / Lonely people / She cares / Snowblind / Halfpenny, two penny / A.D. 1958 / State street Sadie.
LP: . . . . AMLH 63719
MC: . . . . CKM 63719
LP: . . . . AMLK 63719

PIECES OF EIGHT.
Tracks: / I'm OK / Great white hope / Sing for the day / Message, The / Lords of the ring / Blue collar man / Queen of spades / Renegade / Pieces of eight / Aku-aku.
LP: . . . . AMLH 64724
MC: . . . . CAM 64724

ROCK GALAXY.
Tracks: / Movement for the common man / Children of the land / Street college / Fanfare for the common man / Mother nature's matinee / Right away / What has come between us / Best thing / Quick is the beat of my heart / After you leave me / You need love / Lady / Day, A / You better ask / Little fugue in G / Father O S A / Earl of Roseland / I'm gonna make you feel it.
2LP: . . . . CL 43215
MC: . . . . PK 43215

SERPENT IS RISING, THE.
LP: . . . . FL 13112

STYX.
Tracks: / Movement for the common man / Right away / What has come between us / Best thing / Quick is the beat of my heart / After you leave me.
LP: . . . . FL 13110
LP: . . . . PL 13593

Sub Pop 200

SUB POP 200 (Various artists).
LP: . . . . GR 0052

Sub Rosa

INTERIOR DESIGN.
LP: . . . . EXPAL 2

Subdudes

SUBDUDES, THE.
LP: . . . . K 782 015 1
MC: . . . . K 782 015 4

Subhumans

29-29 SPLIT VISION.
LP: . . . . FISH 16

DAY THE COUNTRY DIED.
LP: . . . . SDL 9
LP: . . . . XLP 1
MC: . . . . XLP 1C

EPLP.
LP: . . . . FISH 14
MC: . . . . FISH 14C

FROM THE CRADLE TO THE GRAVE.
LP: . . . . FISH 8

INCORRECT THOUGHTS.
LP: . . . . CD 036

WORLDS APART.
LP: . . . . FISH 12

Sublime

HONEY AND WINE.
MC: . . . . SUB 3

PARTY.
MC: . . . . SUB 2

SUBLIME.
MC: . . . . SUB 1

Sublime Harmonie

SUBLIME HARMONIE (Victorian Musical Boxes and Polyphons) (Various).
Tracks: / March of the Toreadors / Hallelujah Chorus / Ave Maria / War march of the priests / Lost chord, The / Waltz from Faust (Gounod) / Largo (Handel) / Wedding song, The (Wagner) / Wedding march (Mendelssohn) / I have a song to sing (Sullivan) / Behold the Lord High Executioner (Sullivan) / Valse des fees.
LP: . . . . SDL 303
MC: . . . . CSDL 303

Subliminal Aura

EASE THE PRESSURE.
Tracks: / Ease the pressure.
LP: . . . . XLT 8

Submit To The Beat

SUBMIT TO THE BEAT (Various artists).
LP: . . . . SUBL 01

Subramaniam, Dr. L

BLOSSOM.
Tracks: / Time is right / Inner peace / What's happening / Blossom / Dancing dolls / Roots / Prayer.
LP: . . . . CRP 16003

FANTASY WITHOUT LIMITS.
Tracks: / Fantasy without limits / Feeling lonely / Mani talks / 5-3/4 / Frenzy.
LP: . . . . TR 524
MC: . . . . TRC 524

GARLAND.
LP: . . . . SLP 4075

INDIAN CLASSICAL MUSIC.
LP: . . . . DS 202

SOUTH INDIAN STRINGS (The art of Dr. L. Subraniam).
LP: . . . . LLST 7350
MC: . . . . LLCT 7350

Subsonic Bleeps

SUBSONIC BLEEPS (Various artists).
LP: . . . . BLEEPSLP 1
MC: . . . . BLEEPSMC 1

Subtle Plague

INHERITANCE.
LP: . . . . HEY 014 1
MC: . . . . HEY 014 4

Subulakshmi, M.S.

CLASSICAL MUSIC OF INDIA.
LP: . . . . PMAE 501

SUPRABATHAMS.
LP: . . . . CDPMLP 5048

Suburban Rebels

SUBURBAN REBELS (Various artists).
LP: . . . . SEC 11

Subverse/Desecration

SPLIT.
LP: . . . . ACHE 08

Subway

SUBWAY (Film Soundtrack) (Various artists).
Tracks: / Subway: *Various artists* / Guns and people: *Various artists* / Burglary: *Various artists* / Masquerade: *Various artists* / Childhood drama: *Various artists* / Man Y: *Various artists* / Congabass: *Various artists* / Song to Xavier: *Various artists* / Speedway: *Various artists* / It's only mystery: *Various artists* / Drumskate: *Various artists* / Dolphin dance: *Various artists* / Racked animal: *Various artists* / Pretext: *Various artists* / Dark passage II: *Various artists.*
LP: . . . . OVED 223
MC: . . . . OVEDC 223
LP: . . . . GM 9702
MC: . . . . GMK 9702
LP: V2371

Subway Surfers

SUBWAY SURFERS.
LP: . . . . EFA 4478

Success-n-Effect

BACK-N-EFFECT.
Tracks: / Angel dust / Blueprint / Robo's housin' / 7'g's I'll flow / Slick the slick / Real deal (Holyfield) / Nuthin' but success (so use it) / Mack of the year / Jump 2 it (house from the South) / Slow flow / So many faces / Nuthin' but success (so use it) (Miami style) / 360.
LP: . . . . ICH 1108
MC: . . . . ICH 1108 MC

Such, Ernst

APHRICA (see Schulze, Klaus) (Such, Ernst/Klaus Schulze/Rainier Bloss).

Such Men...

SUCH MEN ARE DANGEROUS (See under Graham, Vanessa) (Graham, Vanessa).

Suchet, David (nar)

POIROT INVESTIGATES VOL. 1 (see under Poirot ...(bk)).

POIROT INVESTIGATES VOL. 2 (see under Poirot ...(bk)).

Suchy, Chuck

DAKOTA BREEZES.
LP: . . . . FF 453

MUCH TO SHARE.
LP: . . . . FF 382

Suck

SUCK Various artists (Various artists).
LP: . . . . INST 4

Suckers

GET SUCKED.
MC: . . . . SUCKERS 1

Suckspeed

DAY OF LIGHT, THE.
LP: . . . . FH 12017

Sudden Afternoon

DANCING SHOES.
LP: . . . . CHIME 16

Sudden & Howard

KISS YOU KIDNAPPED CHARABANC.
LP: . . . . CRELP 022

Sudden Impact...

SUDDEN IMPACT AND THE BEST OF DIRTY HARRY (Film soundtrack) (Various artists).
LP: 923990 1
MC: 923990 4

Sudden, Nikki

BACK TO THE COAST.
LP: . . . . CRELP 083

BIBLE BELT,THE.
LP: . . . . SHARP 110

DEAD MEN TELL NO TALES.
Tracks: / When I cross the line / Before I leave you / Dog latin / Wooden leg / Dog rose / How many lies / Cup full of change / Kiss at dawn.
LP: . . . . CRELP 016

GROOVE CREATION (Sudden, Nikki & The French Revolution).
2LP: . . . . CRELP 041D

JACOBITES (Sudden, Nikki & Dave Kusworth).
LP: . . . . GLALP 008

LAST BANDITS IN THE WORLD, THE (See under Fean, Johnny) (Sudden, Nikki/Fean, Johnny/Carmody,Simon).

TEXAS (Sudden, Nikki & The Jacobites).
LP: . . . . CRELP 012

WAITING ON EGYPT.
LP: . . . . ABT 003

Sudden Sway

76 KIDS FOREVER.
LP: . . . . ROUGH 133

KO-OPERA.
LP: . . . . ROUGH 142

SUDDEN SWAY.
LP: . . . . BYN 8

Sudhalter, Dick

FRIENDS WITH PLEASURE.
LP: . . . . AP 159

Sudquist, Ragnar....

SUDQUIST, RAGNAR HYLEN SVEN (Various artists).
LP: . . . . KLPS 117

Sue Records...

BEAT IS ON (Sue instrumentals 1959-67) (Various artists).
Tracks: / I got a woman: *McGriff, Jimmy* / Going home: *Turner, Ike* / Fat back: *Doggett, Bill* / June's blues: *Commandos* / So far away: *Jacobs, Hank* / Stick shift: *Duals* / Good time tonight: *Doggett, Bill* / New breed, The (pt.1): *Turner, Ike & The Kings of Rhythm* / Chicken scratch: *Commandos* / Monkey hips and rice: *Jacobs, Hank* / Soul at sunrise: *Juggy* / All about my girl: *McGriff, Jimmy* / New breed, The (pt.2): *Turner, Ike & The Kings of Rhythm* / M.G. blues: *McGriff, Jimmy.*
LP: . . . . SSL 6029
MC: . . . . TCSSL 6029

SUE RECORDS-MAXIMUM R&B (Various artists).
MC: . . . . ENSUC 3

SUE STORY,THE (Various artists).
LP: . . . . OLLP 8022

Sueno

SUENO - THE ESSENTIAL MEDIATERREAN DANCE TRAX (Various artists).
LP: . . . . BCM 333LP
MC: . . . . BCM 333MC

Sueno Columbiano

SUENO COLUMBIANO (Various artists).
MC: . . . . MCTM 1029
LP: . . . . MLPM 1029

Sufferers Choice

SUFFERERS CHOICE (See under Reggae...) (Various artists).

Suffocation

EFFIGY OF THE FORGOTTEN.
LP: . . . . RC 92751
MC: . . . . RC 92754

HUMAN WASTE.
LP: . . . . NB 051

Sugar Babies

SUGAR BABIES - THE BURLESQUE MUSICAL (Broadway Cast Recording) (Various artists).
Tracks: / Sugar babies overture: *Various artists* / Good old burlesque show, A: *Various artists* / Intro: Welcome to the Gaiety: *Various artists* (Spoken words only.) / Let me be your sugar baby: *Various artists* / In Louisiana: *Various artists* / I feel a song coming on: *Various artists* / Going back to New Orleans: *Various artists*/ Broken Arms Hotel, The: *Various artists* (Cassette & CD only.) / Sally: *Various artists* / Don't blame me: *Various* artists / Immigration rose: *Various artists* / Little red house: *Various artists* (Cassette & CD only.) / Sugar baby bounce: *Various artists* (Cassette & CD only.) / Introduction Mme Rentz: *Various artists* (Spoken words only.) / Down at the Gaiety Burlesque: *Various artists* / Mr. Banjo man: *Various*

artists / When my sugar walks down the street: *Various artists* / Candy butcher: *Various artists* (Spoken words only.) / Entr'Acte: *Various artists* / I'm keeping myself available for you: *Various artists* / Exactly like you: *Various artists* / I'm in the mood for love: *Various artists* / I'm just a song & dance man: *Various artists* / Warm and willing: *Various* artists / Father dear, father dear: *Various artists* (Cassette & CD only.) / Boss upstairs, The: *Various artists*(Cassette & CD only.) / Cuban love song: *Various artists* (Cassette & CD only.) / Every week another town: *Various* artists (McHugh Medley.) / I can't give you anything but love: *Various artists* (McHugh Medley.) / I'm shooting high: *Various artists* / When you and I were young Maggie blues: *Various artists* / On the sunny side of the street: *Various artists* / You can't blame your Uncle Sammy: *Various artists*.
LP: . . . . **SCX 6714**
MC: . . . . **TCSCX 6714**

Sugar Blue

CROSSROADS.
LP: . . . . **TOL 1**

LOUISIANA RED AND SUGAR BLUE (see under Louisiana Red) (Sugar Blue/ Louisiana Red).

Sugar Creek

SUGAR CREEK.
LP: . . . . **MFN 55**

Sugar Ray

KNOCKOUT (Sugar Ray & The Blue Tones).
LP: . . . . **SPD 1021**
LP: . . . . **CDVR 037**

Sugarcubes

HERE TODAY, TOMORROW, NEXT WEEK.
LP: **TPLP15L**
MC: **TPC15L**

ILLUR ARFUR.
LP: . . . . **TPLP 16CL**
MC: . . . . **TPLP 16C**

LIFE'S TOO GOOD.
LP: . . . . **TPLP 5**
MC: . . . . **TPC 5**
DAT: . . . . **DTPLP 5**

SUGARCUBES: INTERVIEW PICTURE DISC.
LPPD: . . . . **BAK 2129**

Sugarhill

SUGARHILL:- THE 12" REMIXES (Various artists).
MC: . . . . **ESSMC 027**
LP: . . . . **ESSLP 027**

Sugarhill Gang

8TH WONDER.
Tracks: / Funk box / On the money / 8th wonder / Showdown / Gigolo / Hot hot summer day.
LP: . . . . **SHLP 1001**
MC: . . . . **ZCSH 1001**

Suicidal Tendencies

CONTROLLED BY HATRED/FEEL LIKE SHIT...DEJA-VU.
Tracks: / Master of no mercy / How will I laugh tomorrow / Just another love song / Waking the dead / Controlled by hatred / Choosing my own way of life / Feel like shit...deja vu / It's not easy / How will I laugh tomorrow (heavy emotion ver.).
LP: **4653991**
MC: **4653994**

FIRST ALBUM.
Tracks: / Suicide's an alternative/You'll be sorry / I shot the devil / Won't fall in love today / Memories of tomorrow / I saw your mommy... / I want more / Two sided politics / Subliminal / Institutionalised / Possessed / Fascist pig / Suicidal failure / Possessed to skate (CD only) / Human guinea pig (CD only) / Two wrongs don't make a right (but they make me feel better) (CD only).
LP: **FLP1011**
LP: . . . . **V 2495**
MC: . . . . **TCV 2495**

HOW WILL I LAUGH TOMORROW WHEN I CAN'T EVEN SMILE TODAY.
Tracks: / Trip at the brain / Hearing voices / Pledge your allegiance / How will I laugh tomorrow / Miracle, The / Surf and slam / If I don't wake up / Sorry? / One too many times / Feeling's back, The / Suicyco mania (CD only).
LP: . . . . **V 2551**
MC: . . . . **TCV 2551**

JOIN THE ARMY.
Tracks: / Suicidal maniac / Join the army / You got, I want / Little each day, A / Prisoner, The / War inside my head / I feel your pain and I survive / Human guinea pig (CD only) / Possessed to skate / No name, no words / Cyco / Two wrongs don't make a right (but they make me feel better) / Looking in your eyes.
LP: . . . . **V 2424**
MC: . . . . **TCV 2424**
LP: . . . . **OVED 307**
MC: . . . . **OVEDC 307**

LIGHTS...CAMERA...REVOLUTION!.
Tracks: / You can't bring me down / Lost again / Alone / Lovely / Give it revolution / Get whacked / Send me your money / Emotion No. 13 / Disco's out / Murder's in / Go'n breakdown.
LP: **4665691**
MC: **4665694**

Suicide

CHEREE.
Tracks: / Ghost rider / Rocker USA / Cheree / Johnny / Girl / Frankie teardrop / Che.
LP: . . . . **FIEND 74**

GHOST RIDERS.
MC: . . . . **A 145**

HALF-ALIVE.
MC: . . . . **A 103**

PICTURES.
Tracks: / Suicide Romeo / Grey / Snapshot / Treble chord / Modern romance / Vision / Pictures / Ching chang / Needles in the camels eye.
LP: . . . . **ILPS 7010**

SUICIDE.
Tracks: / Diamonds, furcoat, champagne / Mr.Ray / Sweetheart / Fast money music / Touch me / Harlem / Be bop kid / Las Vegas man / Shadazz / Dance.
LP: . . . . **ILPS 7007**

WAY OF LIFE, A.
Tracks: / Wild in blue / Surrender / Jukebox baby 96 / Rain of ruin / Sufferin' in vain / Dominic Christ / Love so lovely / Devastation / Heartbeat.
LP: . . . . **CHAPLP 35**

Suicide Squad

LIVE IT WHILE YOU CAN.
Tracks: / Live it while you can / Can't use ya / No solution / Bad boy blues.
LP: . . . . **MFN 85 M**

Suicide Twins

SILVER MISSILES AND HAND GRENADES.
LP: . . . . **LICLP 9**
MC: . . . . **LICK 9**

Suilleabhain, Michael

OILEAN/ISLAND.
Tracks: / Heartwork / Ah, sweet dancer / Idir eatarthu / Between worlds / Carolan's farewell to music / Oilean/ island / 1st movement / 2nd movement / 3rd movement / Ah, sweet dancer (version).
LP: . . . . **VE 40**
MC: . . . . **TCVE 40**

Sukay

HUAYRASAN - MUSIC OF THE ANDES.
LP: . . . . **FF 501**

INSTRUMENTAL, THE.
LP: . . . . **FF 108**

MAMA LUNA.
LP: . . . . **FF 433**

SOCAVON (Traditional music of The Andes).
LP: . . . . **FF 351**

TUTAYAY.
LP: . . . . **FF 374**

Suleyman..

SULEYMAN THE MAGNIFICENT (Film Soundtrack) (Various artists).
LP: . . . . **LPCEL 023**
MC: . . . . **MCCEL 023**

Sulivan, Frank

FIRST IMPRESSIONS.
Tracks: / Minority / Been too long / Beautiful love / Lush life / Ladybird / Alone together / Israel / Round midnight / I could write a book / Something for Sam / All of you.
LP: . . . . **REV 34**

Sullivan, Dan

DAN SULLIVAN'S SHAMROCK BAND.
Tracks: / Dan Sullivan's hornpipe / Tickling Mary Jane / Rabbit catcher / Londonderry hornpipe / Miller's reel / Duffy the dancer / Bantry bay / Billy Hanafin's reel / Green grow the rushes-o / Versouviana dance / Boil the kettle early / Groves hornpipe / Johnny will you marry me / Blackberry blossom / Bonnie Kate / I'm leaving Tepperary / Silver slipper / Jerry Daly's hornpipe.
LP: **12TS 366**

EARLY US (Sullivan, Dan & Shamrock Band).
LP: **12T 366**

Sullivan, Ira

BIRD LIVES (Sullivan, Ira & Chicago Jazz Quintet).
Tracks: / Klactoveesedstein / In other words / Shaw 'nuff / Perhaps / Love letters / Mohawk.
LP: . . . . **AFF 71**

DOES IT ALL.
LP: . . . . **MR 5242**

HORIZONS.
Tracks: / E flat tuba G / Norwegian wood / Everything happens to me / Adah / Horizon / Oh gee / Nineveh.
LP: . . . . **DS 873**

INCREDIBLE IRA SULLIVAN PLAYS VARIOUS INSTRUMENTS.
Tracks: / Lonely moments / Our delight / Bernie's tune / Kim's lament / Can't get out of this mood / On the seventh day / Satin doll.
LP: . . . . **ST 208**

IRA SULLIVAN.
LP: . . . . **FF 075**

IRA SULLIVAN QUARTET.
LP: . . . . **DL 402**

NICKY'S TUNE.
LP: . . . . **DS 422**

Sullivan, Jim

ROCK AND ROLL WRECKS (Sullivan, Jim Band).
LP: . . . . **STLP 011**

Sullivan, Joe

AND THE ALLSTARS.
Tracks: / Jazz me blues / Save it pretty mama / Memphis blues / Coquette / Basin Street blues / That da da strain.
LP: . . . . **SS 114**

AT THE PIANO.
LP: . . . . **SS 104**

GIN MILL.
LP: . . . . **PUMPKIN 112**

PIANO MAN (1935/40).
LP: . . . . **T 1005**

Sullivan, Maxine

CLOSE AS PAGES IN A BOOK (Sullivan, Maxine & Bob Wilber).
Tracks: / As long as I live / Gone with the wind / Rockin' rhythm / Darn that dream / Every time / Harlem butterfly / Loch Lomond / Too many tears / Jeepers creepers / Restless / You're driving me crazy / Close as pages in a book.
LP: . . . . **MES 6919**
LP: . . . . **AP 203**

GOOD MORNING LIFE.
LP: . . . . **AP 193**

GREAT SONGS OF THE COTTON CLUB, THE.
Tracks: / Happy as the day is long / You gave me ev'rything but love / As long as I live / Raisin' the rent / 'Neath the pale Cuban moon / Ill wind / Between the devil and the deep blue sea / I love a parade / Harlem holiday / Get yourself a new broom / Stormy weather / In the silence of the night / That's what I hate about love / Primitive prima donna / I've got the world on a string.
LP: . . . . **A 270**
MC: . . . . **C 270**

I LOVE TO BE IN LOVE (See also under Hyman, Dick) (Sullivan, Maxine / Dick Hyman).
LP: **TDJ101**

IT WAS GREAT FUN.
LP: . . . . **AP 185**

MAXINE (Sullivan, Maxine & Ted Easton's Jazzband).
LP: . . . . **AP 167**

MAXINE SULLIVAN & IKE ISAACS QUARTET (Sullivan, Maxine & Ike Isaacs Quartet).
LP: . . . . **AP 154**

MAXINE SULLIVAN WITH ELLIS LARKINS 1944-48 (see also under Larkins, Ellis) (Sullivan, Maxine & Ellis Larkins).
LP: **TJ6001**

MAXINE SULLIVAN WITH THE BOB HAGGART QUINTET... (Sullivan, Maxine with The Bob Haggart Quintet).
LP: . . . . **AP 210**

MUSIC OF HOAGY CARMICHAEL (see under Wilber, Bob) (Sullivan, Maxine & Bob Wilber).

QUEEN, THE (VOL.1).
LP: . . . . **KS 2052**

QUEEN, THE (VOL.2).
LP: . . . . **KS 2053**

QUEEN, THE (VOL.3).
LP: . . . . **KS 2054**

QUEEN, THE (VOL.4).
LP: . . . . **KS 2055**

SINGS THE MUSIC OF BURTON LANE.
LP: . . . . **ST 257**

SINGS THE MUSIC OF JULES STYNE (Sullivan, Maxine/Keith Ingram Sextet).
MC: **817 834**
LP: **817 831**

SULLIVAN - SHAKESPEARE - HYMAN.
Tracks: / When I was as a tiny little boy / O mistress mine / Winter and spring / It was a lover and his lass / Take, oh, those lips away / Blow, blow, thou winter wind / Under the greenwood tree / Sigh no more, ladies / Come away, come away / Death / When daffodils begin to peer / Lawn as white as driven snow / Take, oh, take / There's never been a time / Where do I go from here? / Storybook children / Take my hand for a while.
LP: . . . . **MES 7038**

UPTOWN (Sullivan, Maxine with the Scott Hamilton Quintet).
Tracks: / You were meant for me / I thought about you / Goody goody / Something to remember you by / Wrap your troubles in dreams / You're a lucky guy / Georgia on my mind / By myself / I got the right to sing the blues / Just one of those things.
LP: . . . . **CJ 288**
MC: . . . . **CJC 288**

WE JUST COULDN'T SAY GOODBYE (Sullivan, Maxine & Art Hodes' Band).
LP: . . . . **AP 128**

Sullivan, Rocky

ILLEGAL ENTRY.
Tracks: / Everybody's got a price / Leave it at that / You / Jacknife lover / Who's kiddin' who / Whatcha get / Bring back the night / Back up girl / Bigelow 6-5000 / Roxy / Fever dreams.
LP: . . . . **RAG 1010**

Sullivan, Tony

SULLY'S FANCY-TRADITIONAL IRISH BANJO.
LP: . . . . **HM 301**

Sultan, Kenny

BLOODSHOT EYES (See under Ball, Tom) (Sultan, Kenny/Tom Ball).

Sultana, Parweens

INNOVATION MEETS TRADITION.
MC: . . . . **TCS 7364**

MEGH ALAYA.
LP: . . . . **ECSD 2910**

Sultry Soul Sisters

SULTRY SOUL SISTERS -WONNDER WOMAN VOL.3 (Various artists).
LP: . . . . **RNLP 065**

Sulzmann, Stan

EVERYBODY'S SONG BUT MY OWN (Sulzmann, Stan & John Taylor).
Tracks: / Introduction to no particular song / Little fella, The / Old ballad / My old man / Everybody's song but my own / Gigolo / Sea lady / Gnu suite (part 1) / Sweet Yakity Waltz / In the mood.
LP: . . . . **LTLP 004**
MC: . . . . **LTMC 004**

KRARK (With Tony Hymas).
LP: . . . . **GCM 792**

ON LOAN WITH GRATITUDE.
LP: . . . . **GCM 772**

Sumac, Yma

FUEGO DEL ANDE.
Tracks: / La molina (the mill song) / Flor de canela (cinnamon flower) / Gallito Caliente (the hot rooster) / La pampa y la puna (the plains and the mountain) / Dale que dale / Llora corazon (crying heart) / Huanchina (enchanted lake) / La perla de chira (the pear) / Mi palomita / Virgenes del sol / Gallito ciego (one eyed rooster) / Clamour (I won't forget you).
LP: . . . . **T 1169**

LEGEND OF THE JIVARO.
LP: . . . . **PM 1552981**
MC: . . . . **PM 1552984**

VOICE OF XTABY.
LP: . . . . **PM 1565611**
MC: . . . . **PM 1565614**

Sumlin, Hubert

BLUES ANYTIME.
LP: . . . . **LR 42 004**

FUNKY ROOTS.
LP: **512503**

GAMBLIN' WOMEN (Sumlin, Hubert & Carey Bell).
LP: . . . . **LR 42.008**

HUBERT SUMLIN'S BLUES PARTY.
Tracks: / Hidden charms / West side soul / Soul that's been abused, The / Letter to my girlfriend / How can you leave me, little girl / Blue guitar / Down in

the bottom / Poor me, pour me another drink / Living the blues.
LP: FIEND 94
LP: BT 1036
MC: BT 1036C

Summer Breeze

SUMMER BREEZE, VOLS 1 & 2 (Various artists).
Tracks: / Breakaway: *Gallagher & Lyle* / Wide eyed and legless: *Fairweather-Low, Andy* / Mr. Tambourine man: *Byrds*/ Float on: *Floaters* / You bet your love: *Hancock, Herbie* / All over the world: *Hardy, Francoise* / They shoot horses don't they?: *Racing Cars* / Summer of '42: *Biddu* / Fantastic day: *Haircut 100* / Sunday girl: *Blondie* / Escape: *Holmes, Rupert* / Wonderful world, beautiful people: *Cliff, Jimmy* / Seasons in the sun: *Jacks, Terry* / Oh Lori: *Alessi* / Fantasy Island: *Tight Fit* / Barbados: *Typically Tropical*/ Summer breeze: *Isley Brothers* / All out of love: *Unknown* / Lovely day: *Withers, Bill* / Dedicated to the one I love: *Mamas & Papas* / Suicide is painless: *M.A.S.H.* / Daydream believer: *Monkees* / Summer of my life: *May, Simon* / I can see clearly now: *Various artists* / Love is in the air: *Young, John Paul*/ Woodstock: *Matthews Southern Comfort* / San Francisco: *McKenzie, Scott* / Lazy Sunday: *Small Faces*/ Sunny afternoon: *Kinks* / No answers: *Aimee, Debbie* / Daydream: *Lovin' Spoonful* / In the Summertime: *Mungo Jerry*.
2LP: STAR 2231
MCSET: STAC 2231

Summer Chart Party

SUMMER CHART PARTY (Various artists).
Tracks: / I should be so lucky: *Minogue, Kylie* / Blue savannah: *Erasure* / Use it up and wear it out: *Pat 'n' Mick* / Perfect: *Fairground Attraction* / Ride on time: *Black Box* / All around the world: *Stansfield, Lisa* / Got to get: *Rob 'N' Raz featuring Leila K* / Never gonna give you up: *Astley, Rick* / Right back where we started from: *Sinitta* / Too many broken hearts: *Donovan, Jason* / Time warp: *Damien* / Give a little love back to the world / Happenin' all over again: *Gordon, Lonnie* / Only way is up, The: *Yazz* / Strawberry fields forever: *Candy Flip* / Don't it make you feel: *Dennis, Stefan* / That's what I like: *Jive Bunny* / Venus: *Don Pablo's Animals*.
LP: BWTX 1
MC: BWTXC 1

Summer, Donna

ALL SYSTEMS GO.
Tracks: / All systems go / Bad reputation / Love shock / Jeremy / Only the fool survives / Dinner with Gershwin / Fascination / Voices cryin' out / Thinkin' bout my baby.
LP: WX 130
MC: WX 130 C

ANOTHER PLACE AND TIME.
Tracks: / This time I know it's for real / I don't wanna get hurt / In another place and time / Whatever your heart desires / If it makes you feel good / When love takes over you / Only one, The / Sentimental / Breakaway / Love's about to change my heart.
LP: WX 219
MC: WX 219 C

BAD GIRLS.
Tracks: / Hot stuff / Bad girls / Love will always find you / Walk away / Dim all the lights / Journey to the centre of your heart / One night in a lifetime / Can't get to sleep at night / On my honour / There will always be you / All through the night / My baby understands / One love / Lucky / Sunset people.
2LP: 6685031
MCSET: 7599 493
LP: CALD 5007

BEST OF DONNA SUMMER, THE.
LP: WX 397
MC: WX 397C

CATS WITHOUT CLAWS.
Tracks: / Supernatural love / It's not the way / There goes my baby / Suzanna / Cats without claws / Oh Billy please / Eyes / Maybe it's over / I'm free / Forgive me.
LP: 2508061
MC: 2508064

COLD LOVE.
Tracks: / Love is in control / Mystery of love / Woman in me / State of independence / Live in America / Protection / (If it) hurts just a little / Love is just a breath away / Lush life.
LP: K 99163
MC: K4 99163

DONNA SUMMER.
Tracks: / Love is in control / Mystery of love / Woman in me, The / State of independence / Living in America / Protection / If it hurts just a little / Love is just a breath away / Lush life.
LP: K 99124

FOUR SEASONS OF LOVE.
Tracks: / Spring affair / Summer fever / Autumn changes / Winter melody / Spring reprise.
LP: PRICE 4

GREATEST HITS: DONNA SUMMER VOL.1.
Tracks: / Love to love you baby / I feel love / I remember yesterday / I love you / Heaven knows / Last dance.
LP: 9128 032
MC: 7268 023
LP: GTLP 028

GREATEST HITS: DONNA SUMMER VOL.2.
Tracks: / MacArthur Park / Hot stuff / Bad girls / Dim all the lights / Sunset people / No more tears / On the radio.
LP: 9128 033
MC: 7268 024

I LOVE TO DANCE.
LP: PER 33 8601
MC: PER 733 8601

I REMEMBER YESTERDAY.
Tracks: / I remember yesterday / Love's unkind / Back in love again / Black lady / Take me / Can't we just sit down and talk it over? / I feel love.
LP: PRICE 3
MC: PRIMC 3
LP: GTLP 025
LP: CBS 31718

LIVE AND MORE.
Tracks: / Once upon a time / Fairytale high / Faster and faster to nowhere / Spring affair / Rumour has it / I love you / Only one man / I remember yesterday / Love's unkind / Man I love, The / I got it bad and that ain't good / Some of these days / Way we were, The / Mimi's song / Try me, I know we can make it / Love to love you, baby / I feel love / Last dance / MacArthur Park / One of a kind / Heaven knows.
2LP: 6685 030
MCSET: 7599 492
2LP: CALD 5006

LOVE TO LOVE YOU BABY.
Tracks: / Love to love you baby / Virgin Mary / Need-a-man blues / Whispering waves / Pandora's boy / Full of emptiness.
LP: GTLP 008
LP: PRICE 21

LOVE TRILOGY.
Tracks: / Try me I know we can make it better / Could it be magic / Wasted / Prelude to love / Come with me.
LP: PRICE 22

LOVE TRILOGY, A.
LP: GTLP 010

ON THE RADIO.
Tracks: / On the radio / Love to love you baby / Try me, I know we can make it / I feel love / Our love / I remember yesterday / I love you / Heaven knows / Last dance / MacArthur Park / Hot stuff / Bad girls / Dim all the lights / Sunset people / No more tears / Niagra / I ain't gonna cry tonight / Kiss me in the rain.
LP: CALD 5008

ONCE UPON A TIME.
LP: CALD 5003

SHE WORKS HARD FOR THE MONEY.
Tracks: / She works hard for the money / Stop, look and listen / He's a rebel / Woman / Unconditional love / Love has a mind of it's own / Tokyo / People people / I do believe (I fell in love).
LP: MERL 21

SHOUT IT OUT.
LP: BMLP 078

SUMMER COLLECTION, THE.
Tracks: / She works hard for the money / Bad girls / On the radio / Stop, look and listen / Last dance / MacArthur Park / Heaven knows / Unconditional love / I love you / Enough is enough (no more tears).
LP: MERH 84
MC: MERHC 84

WALK AWAY.
Tracks: / Bad girls / Hot stuff / On the radio / I feel love / Walk away / Last dance / Sunset people / MacArthur park.
LP: 6302 070
MC: 7144 070
LP: NBLP 7244

WANDERER, THE.
Tracks: / Cold love / Who do you think you're foolin' / Night life / Stop me / I believe in Jesus / Looking up / Wanderer / Grand illusion / Breakdown / Running for cover.
LP: K 99124

Summer, Henry Lee

I'VE GOT EVERYTHING.
Tracks: / Treat her like a lady / Roll me / My turn train / Hey baby / My Louisa / Louie Louie Louie / Don't leave / Something is missing / Got no money / Close enough to me / What's a poor boy to do.
LP: 4650141
MC: 4650144

Summer Lease

SUMMER LEASE (see Chameleon for details) (Chameleon).

Summer Lightning

SUMMER LIGHTNING (see Wodehouse, P.G.) (Carmichael, Ian).

Summer Means Fun

SUMMER MEANS FUN (Various artists).
Tracks: / Summer means fun: *Bruce and Terry* / Surf city: *Rip Chords* / Pipeline: *Flash Cadillac & The Continental* Kids / Surfin' USA, surfin' Safari, Miser Lou: *Hot Doggers* / Custom machine: *Bruce & Terry* / Jersey: *Johnson,* Bruce / Hey little cobra: *Various artists* / This little woodie surfin' craze: *Rip Chords* / Hamptons, The: *Johnson, Bruce* / Three window coupe: *Rip Chords* / Trophy machine: *Rip Chords* / Like summer rain: *Jan & Dean* / Help me Rhonda: *Rivers, Johnny* / Hot rod USA beach girl summer USA: *Rip Chords*.
LP: 22139
MC: 40 22139

Summer Memories

SUMMER MEMORIES (Various artists).
LP: BRLP 59
MC: BRMC 59

Summer Of 42

SUMMER OF '42 (Film Soundtrack) (Various artists).
LP: 46098

Summer Of Love

SUMMER OF LOVE (Various artists).
LP: RNDA 71106
LP: SHIMMY 001

SUMMER OF LOVE (DINO LABEL) (See under 60's) (Various artists).

Summer, Ray

STARLIGHT SOUNDS OF SUMMER.
Tracks: / May each day of the year be a good one / When the blue of the night / I don't want to set the world on fire / You're nobody till somebody loves you / Someone to watch over me / Isn't she lovely? / Those lazy, hazy, crazy days of summer / People will say we're in love / If I were a rich man / Just for you / I just called to say I love you / Unforgettable / Teach me tonight / Misty / Makin' whoopee / I'm just wild about Harry / When day is done / Long ago and far away.
LP: SUS 505

YOURS.
Tracks: / When I fall in love / Whiffenpoof song, The / Poor butterfly / But beautiful / I'd like to teach the world to sing / Bye bye blues / After the ball / 'S wonderful / Yours / Two lovers / That would be so nice / Moonlight lady / Gentle on my mind / Southern nights / Amor / April showers.
LP: SUS 508

Summer & Smoke

SUMMER & SMOKE (Film Soundtrack) (Various artists).
LP: ERS 6519

Summer Story (film)

SUMMER STORY, A (Film Soundtrack) (Delerue, Georges).
Tracks: / Love in the loft / Summer poem / We meet Megan / Sheep shearing / Ashton arrives / Waiting for Megan / Abandoned / Flashback and rescue / Gentle maiden, The (instrumental) / Return to the hill / At the beach / Megan leaves forever / Missed the train / Megan at work / Night meeting / Megan in the field / Thinking of Ashton / Ashton's son (theme from "A Summer Story") / Falling in love / Coming to town.
LP: V 2562
MC: TCV 2562
LP: 790961.1
MC: 790961.4

Summer Wine... (bk)

SUMMER WINE CHRONICLES - GALA WEEK (Roy Clarke).
MCSET: CAB 298

Summerfield, Saffron

FANCY MEETING YOU HERE.
LP: MUM 1202

SALISBURY PLAIN.
LP: MUM 1001

Summerhill

I WANT YOU.
LP: HUCS 102

LOW DOWN.
Tracks: / Rosebud / I'll keep you in mind / Lately / Knew I would return / Hold back the heartache / It's gonna be alright / I can't stay / Say goodbye.
LP: SORCM 4

WEST OF HERE.
Tracks: / Don't let it die / If you hold a gun / I've found a friend / Somehow, somewhere / I have a reason / Here I am / Ballad of Summerhill, The / If I knew you better / Lately / Last to find out.
LP: 843 130 1
MC: 843 130 4

Summerlands Tapes

BIBLE TRUTH SERIES.
MC: UNKNOWN

CURRENT EVENTS & PROPHECY SERIES.
MC: UNKNOWN

HEALING,PRAYER,SPIRITUAL GIFTS ETC..
MC: UNKNOWN

SCIECE OF THE SPIRIT SERIES (Summer Means Fun).
MC: UNKNOWN

SUCCESSFUL LIVING SERIES.
MC: UNKNOWN

Summers, Andy

BEWITCHED (Summers, Andy & Robert Fripp).
Tracks: / Parade / What kind of man reads Playboy? / Begin the day / Train / Bewitched / Maquillage / Guide / Forgotten steps / Image and likeness.
LP: AMLX 68569
MC: CXM 68569

CHARMING SNAKES.
Tracks: / Mexico 1920 / Charming snakes / Big thing / Rainmaker / Charis / Mickey goes to Africa / Innocence falls prey / Passion of the shadow / Monk gets ripped / Easy on the ice / Strong and the beautiful, The.
LP: 210712
MC: 410712

GOLDEN WIRE, THE.
Tracks: / Piece of time, A / Golden wire, The / Earthly pleasures / Imagine you / Vigango / Blues for snake / Island of silk, The / Journey through blue regions / Piya tose / Rain forest in Manhatten / Thousand stones, A.
LP: 209 784
MC: 409 784

I ADVANCE MASKED (Summers, Andy & Robert Fripp).
Tracks: / I advance masked / Under bridges of silence / China, yellow leader / In the cloud forest / New Marimba / Girl on a swing / Hardy country / Truth of skies / Painting and dance / Still point / Lakeland, Aquarelle / Steven on seven / Stultified.
LP: AMLH 64913
MC: CAM 64913
LP: EGLP 52

MYSTERIOUS BARRICADE.
LP: 20 9966
MC: 40 9966

X.Y.Z..
Tracks: / Love is the strangest way / How many days / Almost there / Eyes of a stranger / Change, The / Scary voices / Nowhere / X.Y.Z. / Only road, The / Hold me.
LP: MCF 3382
MC: MCFC 3382

Summers, Bill

ON SUNSHINE.
Tracks: / Walking on sunshine / You've got me lovin' again / She's gone / Musicland / Dancin' lady / Love's all we need / Feel the heat / Learn to live as one / Samba de Oakland.
LP: PR 10107

Summers, Bob

INSIDE OUT (Summers, Bob Quintet).
Tracks: / Autumn leaves / There will never be another you / For Heaven's sake.
LP: DS 897

Summers, Dave

SUMMERS IN CLEVELAND.
LP: SBOL 4022

Summers, Gene

DANCE DANCE DANCE.
LP: CRM 2027

EARLY ROCKING RECORDINGS.
Tracks: / School of rock and roll / Floppin' / Nervous / Alabama shake / Loco cat / Turnip greens / Trying to get to you / Straight skirt / Hey, my baby /

Gotta lotta that / I'll never be lonely / Twixteen / Suzie Q / Be bop a lula.
LP: . . . . WLP 8826

GENE SUMMERS IN NASHVILLE.
Tracks: / Mystery train / I will rock and roll with you / Put your cat clothes on / Blue Monday / Walk on by / Singing the blues / Big river / Tennessee Saturday night / Today I started loving you again / I still miss someone.
LP: . . . . MFM 002

LIVE IN SCANDINAVIA.
Tracks: / Rip it up / Back in the USA / Rockabilly rebel / Almost 12 O'Clock / Rockin' daddy / School of rock'n'roll / Hoy hoy hoy / Be bop a lula / Let's play house / High school confidential / Boppin' the blues.
LP: . . . . SJLP 841

TEXAN REBEL ROCK A BOOGIE SHAKE, THE.
LP: 33.8011

Summers, J.B.

J.B. & THE BLUES SHOUTERS (Summers,J.B & Blues Shouters).
LP: . . . . KK 833

Summers, John

COMPROMISE KID.
LP: . . . . LRF 079

INDIANA FIDDLER.
LP: . . . . ROUNDER 0194

Summers, Lorraine

COME TO ME.
Tracks: / End of the world / Just when I needed you most / Words / I'll never fall in love again / Torn between two lovers / Just out of reach / Sometimes when we touch / It's a heartache / Lay down beside me / If this is love / Bright eyes / Come to me.
LP: . . . . KLP 23
MC: . . . . ZCKLP 23

Summertime On Icarus

SUMMERTIME ON ICARUS/ INTO THE COMET (Clarke, Arthur C.) (Mower, Patrick).
MC: . . . . PTB 621

Summertime Serenade

SUMMERTIME SERENADE (The famous Dubbledick Carl Frei street organ) (Various artists).
LP: . . . . AFL 103
MC: . . . . KAFL 103

Sun

DESTINATION SUN.
Tracks: / Radiation level / Pure fire / I wanna be with you / Disco down / Light of the universe / Deep rooted feeling / Baby I confess / Hallelujah feeling.
LP: . . . . EST 11941

Sun Also Rises

SUN ALSO RISES, THE (Film Soundtrack) (Various artists).
LP: . . . . AEI 3109

Sun, David

DEEP ENCHANTMENT.
MC: . . . . C 209

HARMONY.
MC: . . . . C 210

ISLAND CALLED PARADISE, AN.
MC: . . . . C 206

PEACE.
MC: . . . . C 203

SECRET GARDEN, THE.
MC: . . . . C 205

SERENITY.
MC: . . . . C 202

SUNRISE.
MC: . . . . C 207

SUNSET.
MC: . . . . C 208

TRANQUILITY.
MC: . . . . C 204

Sun Dial

OTHER WAY OUT.
LP: . . . . UFO 1LP
MC: . . . . UFO 1MC

Sun Islanders

SOUNDS STEEL BAND (Sun Islanders Steel Orchestra).
Tracks: / Marianne / Island in the sun / Perhaps / Zombie jamboree / Saturday night / Shame and scandal in the family / Yellow bird / Queen of the bands / Interlude / Mas in Toronto.
LP: . . . . MORR 21

Sun, Joe

HANK BOGART STILL LIVES.
LP: . . . . DFG 8418

I AIN'T HONKY TONKIN' NO MORE.
Tracks: / I ain't honky tonkin' no more / Slow movin' freight train / Stepping out blues / Fraulein / Will the circle be unbroken / Gimme some lovin' / Take the time to fall / Livin' outside of the law / Holed up in some honky tonk / Boys in the back of the bus.
LP: . . . . K 52327

OLD FLAMES.
Tracks: / Old flames / Blue ribbon blues / I came on business for the king / Born too late / Ozark Mountain lullaby / Midnight train of memories / High and dry / This body that I call my home / That evil child / Long black veil.
LP: . . . . OV 1734

OUT OF YOUR MIND.
Tracks: / Out among the stars / Shotgun rider / Out of your mind / I'll find it where I can / Little bit of push / I'd rather go on hurtin' / Mysteries of life / Why you been gone so long / I'm still crazy about you / One timers.
LP: . . . . OV 1743

SUN NEVER SETS, THE (Sun, Joe & The Solar System).
LP: . . . . SNTF 922

TWILIGHT ZONE.
LP: . . . . DFG 8403

Sun Life Stanshawe

AVONDALE.
MC: . . . . GRTC 41

CARNIVAL.
Tracks: / Roman carnival overture / Burlesque from Carnival / Carnival of the animals suite / Carnival in Seville / Lisbon Carnival / Carnival (overture).
LP: . . . . BBR 1005
MC: . . . . BBT 1005

CONDUCTOR'S SHOWCASE.
Tracks: / Yodelling brass / Hungarian dance / Leviathan / Shepherd's song / Cranberry Corner USA / Ave verum corpus / When the boat comes in / Night flight to Madrid / Stars and stripes / Fugue in E flat / Alborado del gracioso / Bone idyll / Promenade.
LP: . . . . SDL 328
MC: . . . . CSDL 328

SPECTRUM.
Tracks: / Spectrum (Gilbert Vinter) / Variations on a ninth (Gilbert Vinter) / Academic Festival overture / Suite Gothique.
LP: . . . . SDLB 262
MC: . . . . CSDLB 262

Sun Power

SUN POWER, VOLUME 1 (Various artists).
LP: . . . . BFMLP 108

Sun Ra

BLUE DELIGHT.
LP: . . . . AMA 5260
MC: . . . . AMC 5260

COSMOS.
LP: . . . . COB 37001

COSMOS SUN CONNECTION.
LP: . . . . SRRRD 1

DANCING SHADOWS.
Tracks: / Dancing shadows / Imagination / Exotic forest / Sun Ra and his band from outer space / Shadow world / Theme of the stargazers / Outer spaceways incorporated / Next stop Mars.
LP: . . . . B 90130

HELIOCENTRIC WORLDS OF SUN RA.
Tracks: / Sun myth, The / House of beauty / Cosmic chaos.
LP: . . . . ESP 1017

HELIOCENTRIC WORLDS OF SUN RA Vol. 1.
LP: . . . . ESP 1014

LOVE IN OUTER SPACE (Sun Ra & His Arkestra).
LP: . . . . LR 154

NIGHT IN EAST BERLIN, A (Sun Ra & His Cosmo Discipline Arkestra).
LP: . . . . LR 149

NOTHING IS....
LP: . . . . ESP 1045

NUCLEAR WAR.
LP: . . . . Unknown

OTHER WORLDS.
Tracks: / Heliocentric / Outer nothingness / Other worlds / Cosmos, The / Of heavenly things / Nebulae dancing in the sun.
LP: . . . . B 90131

OUT THERE A MINUTE.
LP: . . . . BFFP 42
MC: . . . . BFFP 42C

PICTURES OF INFINITY (Sun Ra & His Arkestra).
Tracks: / Saturn / Song of the sparer / Spontaneous simplicity / Somewhere there / Outer spaceways incorporated.
LP: . . . . BLP 30103

PURPLE NIGHTS.
MC: 395 324 4
LP: 395 324 1

SOLAR-MYTH APPROACH, VOL 1.
Tracks: / Spectrum / Realm of lightning / Satellites are spinning, The / Legend / Seen III, took 4 / They'll come back / Adventures of Bugs Hunter.
LP: . . . . AFF 10

SOLAR-MYTH APPROACH, VOL 2.
Tracks: / Utter nots, The / Outer spaceways (inc. scene 1 take 1) / Pyramids / Interpretation / Ancient Ethiopia / Strange worlds.
LP: . . . . AFF 76

SOLO PIANO, VOL 1.
LP: . . . . IAI 3738 50

SOLO PIANO, VOL 2.
LP: . . . . IAI 3738 58

SOUND OF JOY.
LP: . . . . DS 414

STRANGE CELESTIAL ROAD.
LP: . . . . ROUNDER 3035
MC: . . . . ROUNDER 3035C
LP: . . . . Y19 LP

SUN MYTH, THE.
Tracks: / Sun myth / House of beauty / Cosmic choas.
LP: . . . . B 90132

SUN RA.
Tracks: / For the sunrise / Of the other tomorrow / From out where others dwell / On sound infinity spheres / House of eternal being, The / Gods of the thunder rain / Lights on a satellite / Take the 'A' train / Prelude / El is the sound of joy / Encore 1 / Encore 2 / We travel the spaceways.
LP: . . . . IC 1039

SUN RA ARKESTRA NEETS SALAH RAGAB IN EGYPT.
LP: . . . . CM 106

SUN SONG.
LP: . . . . DL 411

VISIONS (See also Dickerson, Walt) (Sun Ra & Walt Dickerson).

Sun Records

BEST OF SUN ROCKABILLY VOL 1 (See Under Rockabilly) (Various artists).

BEST OF SUN ROCKABILLY VOL 2 (See Under Rockabilly) (Various artists).

LEGENDARY SUN SOUND, THE (Various artists).
LPS: . . . . BOX 255
MCSET: . . . . TCBOX 255

MEMPHIS BEAT (Various artists).
Tracks: / Sorry I lied: *Thomas, Cliff* / Treat me right: *Thomas, Cliff* / I'm on my way home: *Thomas, Cliff*/ Stairway to nowhere: *Barton, Ernie* / Raining the blues: *Barton, Ernie* / Trouble in my mind: *Adams, Billy*/ Betty and Dupree: *Adams, Billy* / Got my mojo working: *Adams, Billy* / There won't be anymore: *Rich, Charlie*/ Bobaloo: *Johnson, Bill* / Honey bee: *Hinton, Don* / Fire: *Vel-tones* / I'm getting better all the time: *Pitman, Barbara* / I ain't never: *Stuart, Jeb* / Uncle Jonah's place: *Dorman, Harold* / Rockin' bandit: *Smith, Ray.*
LP: . . . . CR 30149

SOUND OF SUN, THE (Various artists).
Tracks: / Bear cat: *Thomas, Rufus* / Just walkin' in the rain: *Prisonaires* / Feeling good: *Parker, Little* Junior & The Blue Flames / Drinkin' wine spo-dee-o-dee: *Yelvington, Malcolm* / Boogie disease: *Doctor Ross*/ Red hot: *Emerson, Billy 'The Kid'* / Blue suede shoes: *Perkins, Carl* / Rock 'n' roll ruby: *Smith, Warren*/ I walk the line: *Cash, Johnny* / Ooby dooby: *Orbison, Roy/Teen Kings* / Red headed woman: *Burgess, Sonny*/ Flyin' saucers rock 'n' roll: *Riley, Billy Lee And The Little Green Men* / Whole lotta shakin' goin' on: *Lewis, Jerry* Lee / Raunchy: *Justis, Bill & His Orchestra* / Pretend: *Mann, Carl* / Lonely weekends: *Rich, Charlie*/ Tiger man: *Thomas, Rufus* / Mystery train: *Little Junior's Blue Flames* / Boppin' the blues: *Perkins, Carl*/ Come on little mama: *Harris, Ray* / Great balls of fire: *Lewis, Jerry Lee* / Right behind you baby: *Smith, Ray.*
LP: . . . . SAM 3
MC: . . . . TCSAM 3

SUN BLUES ARCHIVES, VOL.1 (Blue Guitar) (Various artists).
Tracks: / Hucklebuck, The: *Hooker, Earl* / Mexicali hip shake: *Hooker, Earl* / Drive, The: *Hooker, Earl*/ Razorback: *Hooker, Earl* / Blue guitar: *Hooker, Earl* / Red river variations: *Hooker, Earl* / Move on down the line: *Hooker, Earl* / Guitar rag: *Hooker, Earl* / Charlie Booker: *Hooker, Earl* / Walked all night: *Hooker, Earl* / Pinetop's boogie woogie: *Perkins, Pinetop* / Baby tell me your name (feel so worried): *Combo,* Lewis Johnson / Harping on it: *Coy Love & Pat Hare* / Wolf call boogie: *Coy Love & Pat Hare* / Flypaper boogie: *Lawson, L.B.* / Missing in action: *Lawson, L.B.* / Scott's boogie: *Lawson, M J.*
LP: . . . . SUNLP 1060

SUN BLUES ARCHIVES, VOL.2 (Bootin' Boogie) (Various artists).
Tracks: / I don't like it: *Gordon, Roscoe* / Don't take it out on me: *Gordon, Roscoe* / If you want your woman: *Gordon, Roscoe* / You been cheatin' on me: *Gordon, Roscoe* / Hey hey girl: *Gordon, Roscoe* / Mean woman: *Gordon, Roscoe* / Real pretty mama: *Gordon, Roscoe* / Shoobie oobie: *Gordon, Roscoe* / Sally Jo: *Gordon,* Roscoe / Go ahead on: *Red Guitars* / Baby please don't go: *Red Guitars* / Love my baby: *Parker, Junior*/ Sittin' at the bar: *Parker, Junior* / Feeling bad: *Parker, Junior* / Mean mean woman: *Snow, Eddie/Elven Parr* / Skin and bone - 1: *Snow, Eddie/ Elven Parr* / Skin and bone - 2: *Snow, Eddie/Elven Parr.*
LP: . . . . SUNLP 1061

SUN BLUES ARCHIVES, VOL.3 (Deep Harmony) (Various artists).
Tracks: / I wonder why: *Hunki-Dori* / I'd like to be there: *Hunki-Dori* / Why don't you use your head: *Hunki-Dori*/ Baby don't leave me: *Hunki-Dori* / This misery: *Hunki-Dori* / Workin' on a building: *Hunki-Dori* / I hear the saviour calling: *Hunki-Dori* / Old time religion: *Hunki-Dori* / Down home: *Hunki-Dori* / Fire: *Vel-tones* / Did you: *Vel-tones* / Blessed be the name: *Southern Belles* / What do you do next: *Prisonaires*/ There is love in you: *Prisonaires* / Dreaming of you: *Prisonaires* / Friends call me a fool: *Prisonaires*/ I wish: *Prisonaires.*
LP: . . . . SUNLP 1062

SUN BOX, THE (Various artists).
Tracks: / Rocket 88: *Brenston, Jackie* (with the Delta Cats) / T-Model Boogie: *Gordon, Roscoe* / Howlin' for my baby: *Howlin' Wolf* / Mr. Highwayman: *Howlin' Wolf* / Treat me mean and evil: *Louis, Joe Hill* / Tiger man: *Louis, Joe Hill* / Prison bound blues: *Nix, Willie* / My baby left me: *Hill, Raymond* / Sweet home Chicago: *Williams, Albert* / Easy: *Jimmy & Walter* / Bear cat: *Thomas, Rufus* / Just walking in the rain: *Prisonaires* / Feeling good: *Parker, Little Junior & The Blue Flames* / Mystery train: *Little Junior's Blue Flames* / Cotton crop blues: *Cotton, James* / Boogie disease: *Doctor Ross* / When it rain it really pours: *Emerson, Billy 'The Kid'* / So long baby goodbye: *Lewis, Sammy & Willie Johnson* / Rockin' chair daddy: *Harmonica* Frank / My kind of carryin' on: *Poindexter, Doug & The Starlite Wranglers* / Cry cry cry: *Cash, Johnny* / Let the juke box keep on playing: *Perkins, Carl* / Defrost your heart: *Feathers, Charlie* / Rock 'n' roll Ruby: *Smith, Warren* / Slow down: *Earls, Jack & The Jimbos* / It's me baby: *Yelvington, Malcolm* / Feeling low: *Chaffin, Ernie* / Folsom prison blues: *Cash, Johnny & The Tennessee Two* / I walk the line: *Cash, Johnny &* The Tennessee Two / Home of the blues: *Cash, Johnny & The Tennessee Two* / Ballad of a teenage queen: *Cash, Johnny* & The Tennessee Two / Way of a woman in love, The: *Cash, Johnny & The Tennessee Two* / Boppin' the blues: *Perkins,* Carl / Dixie fried: *Perkins, Carl* / Breathless: *Lewis, Jerry Lee* / Come on little mama: *Harris, Ray*/ Flyin' saucers rock 'n' roll: *Riley, Billy Lee And The Little Green Men* / Ain't got a thing: *Burgess, Sonny*/ Put your cat clothes on: *Perkins, Carl* / Rock baby rock it: *Carroll, Johnny* / Love me baby: *Thompson,* Hayden / Milkshake mademoiselle: *Lewis, Jerry Lee* / Red cadillac and a black moustache: *Smith, Warren* / Blue suede shoes: *Perkins, Carl* / Ooby dooby: *Orbison, Roy/Teen Kings* / Whole lot of shakin' going on: *Lewis,* Jerry Lee / So long I'm gone: *Smith, Warren* / Raunchy: *Justis, Bill & His Orchestra* / Great balls of fire: *Lewis, Jerry Lee* / Guess things happen that way: *Cash, Johnny & The Tennessee Two* / Mona Lisa: *Mann, Carl*/ Lonely weekends: *Rich, Charlie.*
LPS: . . . . SUN BOX 100

SUN COUNTRY BOX (11 record set) (Various artists).
Tracks: / Slim Rhodes show: *Rhodes, Slim* / Skunk hollow boogie: *Rhodes, Slim* / Save a little love for me: *Rhodes, Slim* / Memphis bounce: *Rhodes, Slim* / Sixty days: *Rhodes, Slim* / Hotfoot rag: *Rhodes, Slim* / Time marches on: *Rhodes, Slim* / Ozark boogie: *Rhodes, Slim* / Red white & blue: *Rhodes, Slim* / Don't believe: *Rhodes, Slim* / Uncertain love: *Rhodes, Slim* / House of sin, The: *Rhodes, Slim* / Are you ashamed of me: *Rhodes, Slim* / Bad girl: *Rhodes, Slim* / Gonna romp and stomp: *Rhodes, Slim* /

Take and give: Rhodes, Slim / Do what I do: Rhodes, Slim / I've never been so blue: Rhodes, Slim / Swamp root: Floyd, Harmonica Frank / Goin' away walkin': Floyd, Harmonica Frank / Step it up: Floyd, Harmonica Frank / Tomcat: Floyd, Harmonica Frank / She done moved: Floyd, Harmonica Frank / Howlin' tomcat (2): Floyd, Harmonica Frank / Grand medical menagerist: Floyd, Harmonica Frank / Rockin' chair money: Floyd, Harmonica Frank / How can it be: Price, Bob / Sticks and stones: Price, Bob / Tennessee drag: Hadley, Red / If I had as much money (as I have time): Hadley, Red / Boogie ramble: Hadley, Red / Blues waltz: Ripley Cotton Choppers / Silver bell roses and sunshine: Ripley Cotton Choppers / In the dark: Peterson, Earl / Nothing to lose but my heart: Peterson, Earl / I'm leaving my heart up to you: Peterson, Earl / Make room in the lifeboat for me: Seratt, Howard / Jesus means all to me: Seratt, Howard / Troublesome waters: Serrat, Howard / I must be saved: Seratt, Howard / Now she cares no more for me: Poindexter, Doug / My kind of carryin' on: Poindexter, Doug / How do you think I feel: Moore, Scotty With Elvis Presley / Honky tonk gal: Perkins, Carl / Gone gone gone: Perkins, Carl / Dixie bop: Perkins, Carl / Sure to fall: Perkins, Carl / Tennessee: Perkins, Carl / Everyone's tryin' to be my baby: Perkins, Carl / Forever yours: Perkins, Carl / Breaking my heart: Perkins, Carl/ Drinkin' wine spo-dee-o-dee: Yelvington, Malcolm / Just rolling along: Yelvington, Malcolm / Yakety yak: Yelvington, Malcolm / Way down blues: Yelvington, Malcolm / Rockin' with my baby: Yelvington, Malcolm / It's me baby: Yelvington, Malcolm / Goodbye Marie: Yelvington, Malcolm / Mr. Blues: Yelvington, Malcolm / First and last love: Yelvington, Malcolm / Did I ask you to stay: Yelvington, Malcolm / Trumpet goin' to sea: Yelvington, Malcolm / Lonely sweetheart: Taylor, Bill / Split personality: Taylor, Bill & Smokey Joe / Hula bop: Baugh, Smokey Joe / She's a woman: Baugh, Smokey Joe / Story of Paul Revere: Baugh, Smokey Joe / Listen to me: Baugh, Smokey Joe / Signifying monkey, The: Baugh, Smokey Joe / Girl with green eyes and red hair: Enlow, Thurman / Runnin' around: Feathers, Charlie / I've been deceived: Feathers, Charlie / Peepin' eyes: Feathers, Charlie / I've been deceived: Feathers, Charlie / We're getting closer to being apart: Various artists / Defrost your heart: Feathers, Charlie / Wedding gown of white: Feathers, Charlie / Bottle to the baby: Feathers, Charlie / Man in love, A: Feathers, Charlie / How long: Wimberly, Maggie Sue / Daydreams come true: Wimberly, Maggie Sue / They who condemn: Wimberly, Maggie Sue / Call me anything but call me: Wimberly, Maggie Sue/ Rock and roll cinnamon free: Wimberly, Maggie Sue / No more: Haggett, Jimmy / They call our love a sin: Haggett, Jimmy / How come you do me: Haggett, Jimmy / Rhythm called rock and roll: Haggett, Jimmy / Rock me baby: Haggett, Jimmy / Rabbit action: Haggett, Jimmy / Someday you will pay: Miller Sisters / You didn't think I would: Miller Sisters / Look what you've done to my heart: Miller Sisters / I know I can't forget you (but I'll try): Miller Sisters / There's no right way to do me wrong: Miller Sisters / You can tell me: Miller Sisters / Woody: Miller Sisters / Finders keepers: Miller Sisters / My Isle of Golden dreams: Miller Sisters / Ten cats down: Miller Sisters / It only hurts for a little while: Miller Sisters / Got you on my mind: Miller Sisters / Chains of love: Miller Sisters / I can't find time to pray: Miller Sisters & Cast Kind / When you stop lovin' me: King, Cast / Like a weed in a garden: King, Cast / Satisfied with me: King, Cast / Please believe me: King, Cast / Round and round: King, Cast / Destiny: King, Cast / Baby doll: King, Cast / Rock 'n' roll Ruby: Smith, Warren / I'd rather be safe than sorry: Smith, Warren/ Black Jack David: Smith, Warren / Ubangi stomp: Smith, Warren / Tonight will be the last night: Smith, Warren / Tell me who: Smith, Warren / I couldn't take the chance: Smith, Warren / Darkest cloud, The: Smith, Warren / So long I'm gone (1): Smith, Warren / So long I'm gone (2): Smith, Warren / So long I'm gone (3): Smith, Warren / Who took my baby: Smith, Warren / Miss Froggie: Smith, Warren / Stop the world: Smith, Warren / Red cadillac and a black moustache: Smith, Warren / Got love if you want it: Smith, Warren / I fell in love: Smith, Warren / Hank Snow medley: Smith, Warren / Do I love you: Smith, Warren / I like your kind of love: Smith, Warren / Uranium rock: Smith, Warren / Goodbye Mr. Love (1): Smith, Warren/ Sweet sweet girl: Smith, Warren / Dear John: Smith, Warren / Goodbye Mr. Love (2): Smith, Warren/ Feeling low: Chaffin, Ernie / Lonesome for my baby: Chaffin, Ernie / I'm lonesome: Chaffin, Ernie/ Laughin' and jokin': Chaffin, Ernie / Linda: Chaffin, Ernie / Heart of me: Chaffin, Ernie / I'll walk alone: Chaffin, Ernie / Be faithful to me: Chaffin, Ernie / Got you on my mind: Chaffin, Ernie/ Born to lose: Chaffin, Ernie / Nothing can change my love for you: Chaffin, Ernie / Miracle of you: Chaffin, Ernie / Please don't ever leave me: Chaffin, Ernie / Easy to love: Self, Mack / Goin' crazy: Self, Mack / Everyday: Self, Mack / Easy to love (2): Self, Mack / Mad at you: Self, Mack / Vibrate: Self, Mack / Little one: Self, Mack / Lovin' memories: Self, Mack / Willie Brown: Self, Mack/ I'm feeling sorry: Lewis, Jerry Lee / I'm feelin' sorry (2): Lewis, Jerry Lee / I'm the guilty one: Lewis, Jerry Lee / Jump right out of this jukebox: Wheeler, Onie / Walking shoes: Wheeler, Onie / That's all: Wheeler, Onie / Tell 'em off: Wheeler, Onie / Jump right out of this jukebox (2): Wheeler, Onie / Bonaparte's retreat: Wheeler, Onie / Train of love: Cash, Johnny / Home of the blues: Cash, Johnny / Ballad of a broken heart: Blake, Tommy / Story of a broken heart, The: Cash, Johnny / Ballad of a teenage queen: Clement, Jack/ Ballad of a teenage queen: Cash, Johnny / Quench my thirst: Clement, Jack / Ten years: Clement, Jack/ Your lover boy: Clement, Jack / Black haired man: Clement, Jack / Wrong: Clement, Jack / Alimony blues: Steele, Gene / Daisy bread boogie: Steele, Gene / Try doin' right: Mississippi Slim / Fallen angel: Gunter, Hardrock / Gonna dance all night: Gunter, Hardrock / Jukebox: Rhythm Rockers / Help me find my baby: Rhythm Rockers / Fiddle bop: Rhythm Rockers / Honky tonk gal: Ballman, Wanda / I'm gonna find her: Dixieland Drifters / Maybe tomorrow: Dixieland Drifters.
LPS: . . . . BFX 15211/11

Sun Rhythm Section

OLD TIME ROCK 'N' ROLL.
Tracks: / Old time rock 'n' roll / Red hot / That's alright mama / Let it roll / Still rockin' / Don't send me no more drinks / You're a heartbreaker / Tutti frutti / Love my baby.
LP: . . . . MFLP 2073

OLD TIME ROCK 'N' ROLL.
LP: . . . . FF 445

Sun Tso-Liang

CHINESE DRUMS & GONGS.
LP: . . . . LLST 7102
MC: . . . . LLCT 7102

Sunbeams

WE'VE GOT A LOVELY BUNCH OF COCONUTS.
LP: 33.8021

Sunburn (film)

SUNBURN (Film soundtrack) (Various artists).
LP: . . . . RTL 2044

Sunbury Junior Singers

CHRISTMAS SONGS & CAROLS (Sunbury Junior Singers of the Salvation Army).
LP: . . . . SAC 5066
MC: . . . . WC 5066

GOSPEL SONGS & SPIRITUALS (Sunbury Junior Singers of the Salvation Army).
LP: . . . . SAC 5031
MC: . . . . WC 5031

MORNING HAS BROKEN (Sunbury Junior Singers of the Salvation Army).
LP: . . . . BAB 3522
MC: . . . . TC BAB 3522

Suncats

JAILHOUSE ROCKABILLY.
LP: . . . . LP 8702

Sunday In The Country

SUNDAY IN THE COUNTRY (Film soundtrack) (Various artists).
LP: . . . . STV 81227

Sunday In The Park

SUNDAY IN THE PARK WITH GEORGE (Original Broadway Cast) (Various artists).
LP: HBC1 5042
MC: HBE1 5042

Sundays

READING, WRITING, ARITHMETIC.
LP: . . . . ROUGH 148
MC: . . . . ROUGHC 148

Sundholm, Roy

CHINESE METHOD.
Tracks: / Back in the neighbourhood / Robbed / Go zero / Way the story ended / Place in the world / Girls are out now / Waiting for the night / Did you ever have a heart / Every minute / Should I wait for you.
LP: . . . . ENVY 10

EAST TO WEST.
Tracks: / Bridge across the river / East to west / Terminal / Me and my mercedes / Doing what comes natural / Good girls don't wear white / My hearts on fire / Don't bring it down / I can't sleep at night / Ain't looking to replace you.
LP: . . . . ENVY 503
MC: . . . . ENCAS 503

Sundogs

UNLEASHED.
LP: . . . . F 40
MC: . . . . C 40

Sundown

ALL ALONE TOGETHER.
Tracks: / Rose of Cimarron / Hard hearted / Blue eyes crying in the rain / Carmen / Ride me down easy / Living in the west / Country Joe and Mickey Finn / 'Till I gain control again / Cotton Jenny / Turn out the light (love me tonight) / Back home again / All alone together.
LP: . . . . FHR 105

HAPPY STATE OF MIND.
LP: . . . . BSS 142

Sundown (Film)

SUNDOWN (Film Soundtrack) (Various artists).
LP: . . . . FILM 044
MC: . . . . FILMC 044

Sundown Playboys

SATURDAY NIGHT CAJUN MUSIC.
LP: 6072
MC: . . . . 6072 TC

Sunfire

SUNFIRE.
Tracks: / Shake your body / Step in the light / Feet / Givin' away my heart / Keep rockin' my love / Millionaire / Sexy lady / Young, free and single.
LP: . . . . W 3730

Sunglasses After Dark

UNTAMED CULTURE.
LP: . . . . GRAM 19

Sunkel, Phil

EVERY MORNING I LISTEN TO ... (Sunkel, Phil And His Jazz Band).
LP: . . . . FS 74

Sunny & Mel

HERE'S A LITTLE SUNSHINE.
Tracks: / Here's a little sunshine / Aba daba honeymoon / Lodi / Ballade pour Adeleine / Cottonfields / Easy winners / Hold me / Y solo tu / Baby baby don't get hooked on me / Gambler, The / Railway children, Theme from / Another somebody done somebody wrong song / Something stupid.
LP: . . . . DL 001
MC: . . . . DT 001

Sunny & Showboat

SUNNY & SHOWBOAT (Original London Casts) (Various artists).
LP: . . . . SH 240

Sunnyland Slim

DECORATION BLUES (Sunnyland Slim Blues Band).
LP: . . . . LR 42.015

DEVIL IS A BUSY MAN.
Tracks: / Ain't nothin' but a child / Brown skinned woman / Hit the road again / Gin drinkin' baby / Goin' back to Memphis / Devil is a busy man / Shake it baby / Bassology / I want my baby / Blue baby / Jivin' boogie / My heavy load / Keep your hands out of my money / Mud kickin' woman / Every time I get to drinking.
LP: . . . . OFF 6043

LEGACY OF THE BLUES VOL. 11 (See under Legacy of the Blues).

LITTLE BROTHER MONTGOMERY & SUNNYLAND SLIM (See under Montgomery, Little Brother) (Sunnyland Slim & Little Brother Montgomery).

SAD AND LONESOME BLUES (BLUES ROOTS VOL.9) (see Blues Roots Vol.9).

SUNNYLAND SPECIAL (Job series vol.4).
LP: . . . . FLY 566

Suns Of Arqa

ECLECTICISM.
MC: . . . . ONEG 001

INDIA.
LP: . . . . ONEG 001L

JAGGERNAUT.
LP: . . . . ANT 104

REVENGE OF THE MOZABITES.
Tracks: / Acid tablas / World peace - a dream / Skullys reel / Bali citra / Skullys jig / Piece of the world / Acid tablas dub / Nanta snake dance, A / Return of he Mozabites / Sanaiscara Saturn / Paintings of a cave.
LP: . . . . MICKL 01

WADADA MAGIC.
LP: . . . . ANT 024

Sunset

STILL SEARCHING.
Tracks: / Still searching / Answer to everything, The / Cracklin' Rosie / Lyin' eyes / Born again / Please stay / Cover of The Rolling Stone / Everybody's making it big / Don't forget to remember me / Sing unto the lord / It is no secret.
LP: . . . . KT 001

Sunset All Stars

JAMMIN' AT SUNSET, VOL 1.
Tracks: / I found a new baby / I surrender, dear / Tea for two / Skylark / California clipper / Ventura jump / Windjammer / I don't stand a ghost of a chance with you / All the things you are / Experiment perilous.
LP: . . . . BLP 30112

JAMMIN' AT SUNSET, VOL 2.
Tracks: / Get happy / Blues in my heart / Sweets / It was meant to be / Jefferson jump / Nothin' from nothin' / I found a new baby / I never knew / These foolish things / My blue Heaven / I cover the waterfront / Messin' on Melrose.
LP: . . . . BLP 30113

Sunset Dance Orchestra

DANCING YEARS OF BING CROSBY, THE.
Tracks: / Swinging on a star / Wrap your troubles in dreams / Where the blue of the night / White Christmas / Pennies from Heaven / Don't fence me in / Moonlight becomes you / Cool, cool, cool of the evening / Sunshine cake / Home on the range / Bells of St. Mary's / Blue skies.
LP: . . . . SLS 50423
MC: . . . . TCT 50423

Sunset Gun

IN AN IDEAL WORLD.
Tracks: / Sister / Paint the town red / On the right side / Company / Stop / How can you mend a broken heart / Stay with me / Tongue tied and twisted / Life of the free man / Face up to what is true.
LP: . . . . CBS 26584
MC: 40 26584

Sunsets

TIGER (see under Stevens, Shakin') (Sunsets/Shakin' Stevens).

Sunshine

SUNSHINE (Film Soundtrack) (Various artists).
LP: . . . . MCF 2566

Sunshine Boys

SUNSHINE BOYS 1929-31.
LP: . . . . FV 206
LP: . . . . FJ 206

Sunshine Mix

SUNSHINE MIX (See under Reggae) (Various artists).

Sunshine, Monty

CRANE RIVER JAZZ BAND, 1950-53 (See under Crane River Jazz Band) (Sunshine, Monty & The Crane River Jazz Band).

MONTY SUNSHINE'S JAZZ BAND (Sunshine, Monty Jazz Band).
LP: . . . . SOS 1110

ON SUNDAY.
LP: . . . . WAM/O No.10

PORTRAIT VOL 2.
LP: . . . . WAM/O No.12

SUNSHINE IN LONDON.
Tracks: / St. Phillip Street breakdown / Dusty road / Just a closer walk with thee / Careless love / C jam blues / You rascal you / Burgundy Street blues / East coast trot / When you and I were young, Maggie / High society.
LP: . . . . BLP 12135

Sunsonic

MELTING DOWN ON MOTOR ANGEL.
LP: 8435381
MC: 8435384

Sunwind

SUN BELOW, THE.
Tracks: / Under the trees / Two ladies / Happy tune / Sun below, The (rising) / Sun below, The / Mr. Yang.
LP: . . . . MMC 005
MC: . . . . TCMMC 1005

Suonatori

EIV' VUSTU U LUVVU (Suonatori Delle Quattro Province).
LP: . . . . RD 011

Suonsaari, Klaus

REFLECTING TIMES (Suonsaari, Klaus Quintet).

LP: . . . . SLP 4125

Super Biton De Segou

AFRO JAZZ DU MALI.
LP: . . . . BP 13

Super Cat

SWEETS FOR MY SWEET.
LP: . . . . WALP 001

Super Diamono De Dakar

BOROM DAAROU.
MC: . . . . BP 8308

MAM.
LP: 8011

PEOPLE.
LP: . . . . ENC 139

Super Horns

SUPER HORNS (See under Jazz (Various artists).

Super Lover Cee

GIRLS - I GOT 'EM LICKED (Super Lover Cee & Casanova Rud).
LP: 960807 1
MC: 960807 4

Super Maxi's

SUPER MAXI'S VOL 2 (Various artists).
Tracks: / After the love has gone: *Princess* / Sayonara (don't stop): *Marrow, Lee* / Ocean of crime (we're movin' on): *Prime Time* / Cenerentola: *Cinderella (Group)* / Heaven I need, The: *3 Degrees* / Call my name (the final disco remix): *Creative Connection* / Front line: *Hanselmann, David* / Boat, The: *Bolland* / Eye to eye: *TMF* / Mary is a clerk: *Gaznevada* / Rock & rock: *Rock & rock gang* / Step by step: *Silver Pozzoli*.
LP: 6 26280
MC: 4 26280

Super Rail Band

NEW DIMENSIONS IN RAIL CULTURE (Super Rail Band of the Buffet de la Gare de Bamako, Mali).
Tracks: / Foliba / Bedianamogo / Tallassa / Konowale / Mali yo.
LP: . . . . ORB 001

Super Sax

SUPER SAX (See under Jazz) (Various artists).

Super Sounds

SUPER SOUNDS (Various artists).
Tracks: / I know him so well: *Various artists* / Every breath you take: *Various artists* / Oh lady be good: *Various* artists / Manana: *Various artists* / Diamonds are a girl's best friend: *Various artists* / Mambo jambo: *Various* artists / Certain smile, A: *Various artists* / Aquarius: *Various artists* / Love letters in the sand: *Various* artists / Jersey bounce: *Various artists* / Dance to the music: *Various artists* / Crazy rhythm: *Various* artists / Something's gotta give: *Various artists* / When I fall in love: *Various artists* / Why do I love you: *Various artists* / Take me home country roads: *Various artists* / Have you ever been lonely: *Various artists* / That old funky rolls: *Various artists* / S'posin': *Various artists*.
MC: . . . . CSUS 33

Super Stocks

SURFIN' INSTRUMENTALS.
LP: . . . . ENC 9563

Superblue

SUPERBLUE.
Tracks: / Open sesame / Summertime / Marvelous Marvin / Time off / I remember Clifford / Conservation / Once forgotten / M and M.
LP: B1 91731
LP: 791 731 1

Supercats

BOOPS DEH.
LP: . . . . Unknown

Supercharge

BODY RHYTHMS.
LP: . . . . V 2118

Superfly

SUPERFLY (See under Mayfield, Curtis) (Mayfield, Curtis).

Supergirl

SUPERGIRL (Film Soundtrack) (Various artists).
LP: . . . . CST 8001
LP: . . . . STV 81231
MC: . . . . CTV 81231

Supergran

SUPER GRAN (See Billy Connolly for details) (Connolly, Billy).

Supergrass

SUPERGRASS, THE (Film soundtrack) (Various artists).
Tracks: / Slave to the rhythm: *Jones, Grace* / Gotta get you home tonight: *Wilde, Eugene* / Drop the bomb: *Trouble Funk* / Tequila: *No Way Jose* / Two tribes: *Frankie Goes To...* / Arrival at the Royal Hotel: *Tippett*, Keith / No woman no cry / Love theme: *Tippett, Keith* / Move closer: *Nelson, Phyllis* / Harvey's theme: *Tippett, Keith* / Ultimo ballo: *Maimone, Angele* / Supergrass: *Arnold, P.P.*.
LP: . . . . ISTA 11
MC: . . . . ICT 11

Superman

DOUBLE TROUBLE (Unknown narrator(s)).
MC: . . . . PLBS 278

SUPERMAN (Studio cast of the 1966 show) (Various artists).
LP: . . . . AKOS 2970

SUPERMAN (Film Soundtrack) (Various artists).
Tracks: / Superman (main title): *Various artists* / Planet Krypton, The: *Various artists* / Destruction of Krypton: *Various artists* / Trip to earth, The: *Various artists* / Growing up: *Various artists* / Superman love theme: *Various artists* / Leaving home: *Various artists* / Fortress of solitude, The: *Various artists*/ Flying sequence (can you mind), The: *Various artists* / Super rescues: *Various artists* / Lex Luther's lair: *Various artists* / Superfeats: *Various artists* / March of the villains, The: *Various artists* / Chasing rockets: *Various artists* / Turning back the world: *Various artists* / End title: *Various artists*.
2LP: . . . . K 66084
MC: . . . . K 4 66084

SUPERMAN 2 (Original soundtrack) (Various artists).
LP: . . . . K 56892
MC: K4 56892

SUPERMAN III (Film Soundtrack) (Superman III).
LP: 923879 1

SUPERMAN IN DEATH FROM A DISTANT GALAXY (Super Heroes series) (Various artists).
MC: 41 5711 4

SUPERMAN & THE NEUTRON NIGHTMARE (Super Heroes series) (Various artists).
MC: 41 5712 4

SUPERMAN - THE STORY (Various artists).
MC: . . . . PLBS 277

SUPERMAN THEME (see Williams, John) (Film soundtrack).

Superman & Spiderman

SUPERMAN AND SPIDERMAN.
Tracks: / One look / Baby mother / Plan your family / Superman & spiderman / Reggae rock / Murder / Reality / Road block / Sencemina posse / I blood and bone.
LP: . . . . KVL 9025
MC: . . . . KVC 9025

Supermax

WORLD OF TODAY.
Tracks: / World of today / Love machine / Reality / Music express / Camillo / Be what you are / I wanna be free.
LP: . . . . K 50423

Supernatural Stories

EXORCISM OF BROTHER SIMEON (Various artists).
MCSET: . . . . BS 18/21

MONSTERS OF THE EARTH (Various artists).
MC: . . . . BS 19

NOSTRADAMUS (Various artists).
MC: . . . . BS 22

TRUE STORIES OF THE SUPERNATURAL (Dyall, Valentine).
MCSET: . . . . BS 17/20

UFO'S/ THE PYRAMID MYSTERY (Various artists).
MC: . . . . BS 17/20

Supersax

EMBRACEABLE YOU.
LP: 25604
MC: 40 25604

STRAIGHTEN UP AND FLY RIGHT.
Tracks: / Koko / Super sax / Bamboo / Chi chi / Country / Straighten up and fly right / April in Paris / Some day my prince will come / Laura.
LP: 4503841
MC: 4503844

SUPERSAX & L.A. VOICES VOL.2.
LP: 26324
MC: 40 26324

Superstar Session

SUPERSTAR SESSION (Various artists).
LP: 20026
MC: 40026

Superted

SUPERTED: SUPERTED & BULK'S STORY (Hawkins, Peter).
MC: 0 00 109011 9

SUPERTED: SUPERTED IN SUPERTED'S DREAM (Hawkins, Peter).
MC: 0 00 109010 0

SUPERTED: SUPERTED & THE LUMBERJACKS (Hawkins, Peter).
MC: 0 00 109009 7

SUPERTED: SUPERTED & THE POTHOLE RESCUE (Hawkins, Peter).
MC: 0 00 109008 9

Supertramp

AUTOBIOGRAPHY OF SUPERTRAMP, THE.
Tracks: / Goodbye stranger / Logical song, The / Bloody well right / Breakfast in America / Take the long way home / Crime of the century / Dreamer / From now on / Give a little bit / It's raining again / Cannonball / Ain't nobody but me / Hide in your shell / Rudy.
LP: . . . . TRAMP 1
MC: . . . . TRAMC 1

BREAKFAST IN AMERICA.
Tracks: / Gone Hollywood / Logical song, The / Goodbye stranger / Breakfast in America / Oh darling / Take the long way home / Lord is it mine / Just another nervous wreck / Casual conversation / Child of vision.
LP: . . . . AMLK 63708
MC: . . . . CKM 63708

BREAKFAST IN AMERICA/CRIME OF THE CENTURY (see under Crime of the century).

BROTHER WHERE YOU BOUND.
Tracks: / Cannonball / Still in love / No inbetween / Better days / Brother where you bound / Ever open door.
LP: . . . . AMA 5014
MC: . . . . AMC 5014

CRIME OF THE CENTURY.
Tracks: / School / Bloody well right / Hide in your shell / Asylum / Dreamer / Rudy / If everyone was listening / Crime of the century.
LP: . . . . AMLS 68258
MC: . . . . CAM 68258

CRIME OF THE CENTURY/ BREAKFAST IN AMERICA.
Tracks: / School / Bloody well right / Asylum / If everyone was listening / Gone Hollywood / Goodbye stranger / Oh darling / Lord is it mine / Casual conversations / Bloody well right / Hide in your shell / Rudy / Crime of the century / Logical song, The / Breakfast in America / Take the long way home / Just another nervous wreck / Child of vision.
MC: . . . . AMC 24104

CRISIS ? WHAT CRISIS ?.
Tracks: / Easy does it / Sister moonshine / Ain't nobody but me / Soapbox opera, A / Another man's woman / Lady / Poor boy / Just a normal day / Meaning, The / Two of us, The.
LP: . . . . AMLH 68347
MC: . . . . CAM 68347

CRISIS WHAT CRISIS/ EVEN IN THE QUIETEST MOMENTS.
MCSET: . . . . CAM CR 7

EVEN IN THE QUIETEST MOMENTS.
Tracks: / Give a little bit / Loverboy / Even in the quietest moments / Downstream / Babaji / From now on / Fool's overture.
LP: . . . . AMLK 64634
MC: . . . . CAM 64634

FAMOUS LAST WORDS.
Tracks: / Crazy / Put on your old brown shoes / It's raining again / Bonnie / Know who you are / My kind of lady / C'est le bon / Waiting so long / Don't leave me now.
LP: . . . . AMLK 63732
MC: . . . . CKM 63732

FREE AS A BIRD.
Tracks: / It's alright / Not the moment / It doesn't matter / Where I stand / Free as a bird / You never can tell with friends / Thing for you / Awful thing to waste, An / I'm begging you.
LP: . . . . AMA 5181
MC: . . . . AMC 5181

INDELIBLY STAMPED.
Tracks: / Your poppa don't mind / Travelled / Rosie had everything planned / Remember / Forever / Potter / Coming home to see you / Times have changed / Friend in need / Aries.
LP: . . . . AMLH 64306
MC: . . . . CAM 64306

PARIS (LIVE DOUBLE).
Tracks: / School / Ain't nobody but me / Logical song, The / Bloody well right / Breakfast in America / You started laughing / Hide in your shell / From now on / Dreamer / Rudy / Soapbox opera, A / Asylum / Take the long way home / Fool's overture / Two of us, The / Crime of the century.
2LP: . . . . AMLM 66702
MCSET: . . . . CLM 66702

SUPERTRAMP.
Tracks: / It's a long road / Aubade / And I am not like other birds of prey / Words unspoken / Maybe I'm a beggar / Home again / Nothing to show / Shadow song / Try again / Surely.
LP: . . . . SHM 3139
MC: . . . . HSC 3139
LP: . . . . AMID 123
MC: . . . . CMID 123

SUPERTRAMP (LIVE 88).
Tracks: / You started laughing / It's alright / Not the moment / Breakfast in America / From now on / Oh darling / Just another nervous wreck / Logical song, The / I'm your hoochie coochie man / Crime of the century / Don't you lie to me.
LP: . . . . AMA 3923
MC: . . . . AMC 3923

Suppe (composer)

OVERTURES (See under Dvorak (Composer) (Ljubljana Symphony Orchestra/ Nanut).

Supper Club

SUPPER CLUB SINGERS (Various artists).
LP: . . . . DUN 110

Supply Demand & Curve

SUPPLY DEMAND & CURVE.
LP: . . . . LUN 009

Supreme Cool Beings

SURVIVAL OF THE COOLEST.
MC: . . . . KC 007

Supremes

ANTHOLOGY - DIANA ROSS & THE SUPREMES (Ross, Diana & The Supremes).
Tracks: / Let me go the right way / Breath-taking guy, A / When the lovelight starts shining thru' his eyes / Standing at the crossroads of love / Run, run, run / Where did our love go / Baby love / Ask any girl / I'm livin' in shame / Composer, The / No matter what sign you are / Someday we'll be together / Come see about me / Stop in the name of love / Back in my arms again / Nothing but heartaches / I hear a symphony / My world is empty without you / Love is like an itching in my heart / You can't hurry love / You keep me hangin' on / Love is here and now you're gone / Happening, The / Reflections / In and out of love / Forever came today / Some things you never get used to / Love child / I'm gonna make you love me / I'll try something new / Uptight (everything's alright) / I second that emotion.
2LP: . . . . ZL 72130

AT THE COPA.
Tracks: / Put on a happy face / I am woman / Baby love / Stop in the name of love / Boy from Ipanema, The / Make someone happy / Come see about me / Rockabye your baby with a Dixie melody / Queen of the house / Group introduction / Somewhere / Back in my arms again / You're nobody loves you.
LP: . . . . STMS 5045
MC: . . . . CSTMS 5045

GREATEST HITS: SUPREMES.
Tracks: / Up the ladder to the roof / Bad weather / Nathan Jones / Everybody's got the right to love / Automatically sunshine / Touch / I guess I'll miss the man / Stoned love / River deep, mountain high / Floy Joy / Together we can make such sweet music / Your wonderful sweet sweet love / You gotta have love in your heart / Bill, when are you coming back / Reach out and touch (somebody's hand).
LP: . . . . STMS 5098
MC: . . . . CSTMS 5098
LP: . . . . WL 72124
MC: . . . . WK 72124
LP: . . . . STML 11063
LP: . . . . STMR 9010

I HEAR A SYMPHONY.
Tracks: / Stranger in Paradise / Yesterday / I hear a symphony / Unchained melody / With a song in my heart / Without a song / My world is empty without you / Lover's concerto / Any girl in love (knows what I'm going through) / Wonderful, wonderful / Everything is good about you / He's all I got.
LP: . . . . STMS 5012
MC: . . . . CSTMS 5012

LIVE AT THE TALK OF THE TOWN.
LP: . . . . STML 11070

LOVE CHILD/SUPREMES A GO GO (See under Ross, Diana) (Ross, Diana & The Supremes).

LOVE SUPREME (Ross, Diana & The Supremes).
Tracks: / You can't hurry love / Baby love / Happening, The / Automatically sunshine / Up the ladder to the roof / Stoned love / Where did our love go? / Love is here and now you're gone / Reflections / In and out of love / Stop in the name of love / Come see about me / I'm gonna make you love me / Love child / I'm living in shame / Floy joy / You keep me hangin' on / I second that emotion / Nathan Jones / Someday we'll be together.
LP: . . . . **ZL 72701**
MC: . . . . **ZK 72701**

MAGNIFICENT 7, THE (Supremes & Four Tops).
Tracks: / Knock on my door / For your love / Without the one you love / Reach out and touch (somebody's hand) / Stoned soul picnic / Baby (you've got what it takes) / River deep, mountain high / Ain't nothing like the real thing / Everyday people / It's got to be a miracle (this thing called love) / Taste of honey, A / Together we can make such sweet music.
LP: . . . . **STMS 5016**
MC: . . . . **CSTMS 5016**
LP: . . . . **STML 11179**

MEET THE SUPREMES.
LP: . . . . **SL 10109**

MERRY CHRISTMAS.
Tracks: / White Christmas / Silver bells / Born of Mary / Children's Christmas song / Little drummer boy / My Christmas tree / Rudolph the red nosed reindeer / Santa Claus is coming to town / My favourite things / Twinkle twinkle little me / Little bright star / Joy to the world.
LP: . . . . **STMS 5084**
MC: . . . . **CSTMS 5084**
LP: . . . . **WL 72113**
MC: . . . . **WK 72113**

MORE HITS BY THE SUPREMES.
Tracks: / Ask any girl / Nothing but heartaches / Mother dear / Honey boy / Back in my arms again / Whisper you love me, boy / Only time I'm happy, The / He holds his own / Who could ever doubt my love? / Heartaches don't last always / I'm in love again.
LP: . . . . **STMR 9006**
MC: . . . . **CSTMR 9006**
LP: . . . . **WL 72117**
MC: . . . . **WK 72117**

MOTOWN SPECIAL.
Tracks: / You keep me hangin' on / This old heart of mine / Stop, in the name of love / Mother, you smother you / Put yourself in my place / There's no stopping us now / Baby love / Come and get these memories / Baby, I need your loving / I guess I'll always love you / I can't help myself / Love is in our hearts.
LP: . . . . **STMX 6001**
MC: . . . . **CSTMX 6001**

RODGERS & HART COLLECTION (See under Ross, Diana) (Ross, Diana & The Supremes).

STONED LOVE.
LP: . . . . **MFP 50421**

SUPREMES A GO GO (Ross, Diana & The Supremes).
Tracks: / Love is like an itching in my heart / This old heart of mine / You can't hurry love / Shake me, wake me / Baby, I need your loving / These boots are made for walking / I can't help myself / Get ready / Put yourself in my place / Money (that's what I want) / Come and get these memories / Hang on, Sloopy.
LP: . . . . **STMS 5013**
MC: . . . . **CSTMS 5013**
LP: . . . . **WL 72072**
LP: . . . . **STML 11039**

SUPREMES SING MOTOWN (Ross, Diana & The Supremes).
Tracks: / You keep me hangin' on / You're gone, but always in my heart / Love is here and now you're gone / Mother, you smother you / I guess I'll always love you / I'll turn to stone / It's the same old song / Going down for the third time / Love is in our hearts / Remove the doubt / There's no stopping us now / Heatwave.
LP: . . . . **STMS 5014**
MC: . . . . **CSTMS 5014**
LP: . . . . **STML 11047**

SUPREMES SING RODGERS & HART.
LP: . . . . **STML 11054**

TOUCH.
Tracks: / This is the story / Nathan Jones / Here comes the sunrise / Love it came to me this time / Johnny Raven / Have I lost you / Time and love / Touch / Happy (is a bumpy road) / It's so hard for me to say goodbye.
LP: . . . . **STML 11189**
MC: . . . . **WK 72742**

WE REMEMBER SAM COOKE (Ross, Diana & The Supremes).
LP: . . . . **WL 72445**
MC: . . . . **WK 72445**

WHERE DID OUR LOVE GO (ALBUM).
Tracks: / Where did our love go / Run, run, run / Baby love / When the lovelight starts shining through his eyes / Come see about me / Long gone lover / I'm giving you your freedom / Breathtaking guy / He means the world to me / Standing at the crossroads of love / Your kiss of fire / Ask any girl.
MC: . . . . **WK 72735**

WHERE DID OUR LOVE GO/I HEAR A SYMPHONY (See under Ross, Diana) (Ross, Diana & The Supremes).

Sure, Al B.

IN EFFECT MODE.
Tracks: / Nite and day / Oooh, this love is so / Killing me softly with her song / Naturally mine / If I'm not your lover / Off on your own / Rescue me.
LP: . . . . **WX 173**
MC: . . . . **WX 173 C**

PRIVATE TIMES..AND THE WHOLE 9.
Tracks: / Hotel California / Touch you / So special / I want to know / No matter what you do / Shades of grey / Private times / Missunderstanding / Channel J / Had enuff? / Just for the moment / Sure thang.
LP: . . . . **WX 395**
MC: . . . . **WX 395C**

Sureshots

FOUR TO THE BAR.
LP: . . . . **NOSE 16**

Surf M.C.'s

SURF OR DIE.
Tracks: / Surf or die / Big wednesday / This surf is live / Can't get a tan / Gotta get air / Rock that beach / That's call for ya / Boomin' it / You will be served.
LP: . . . . **PRO 1235**

Surf Punks

MY BEACH.
Tracks: / My beach / My wave / Teenage girls / Shoulder hopper / Dummies, The / Beer-can beach / Surfer's nitemare / I live for the sun / Meet me at the beach / Big top / Somebody ripped my stick / Letter from Hawaii / Surfmen, The / Can't get a tan / Surf instructor, The / Punch out at Malibu / Bird bathroom.
LP: . . . . **EPC 84346**

Surf Rats

STRAIGHT BETWEEN THE EYES.
LP: . . . . **LMLP 069**

TROUBLE.
LP: . . . . **LM LP 015**

Surface

2ND WAVE.
Tracks: / Shower me with your love / Closer than friends / Can we spend some time / You are my everything / I missed / Black shades / Hold on to love / Where's that girl.
LP: **4629801**
MC: **4629804**

3 DEEP.
Tracks: / First time / Give her love / Rainbow (reprise) / All I want is you / Tomorrow / You're the one / We don't have to say goodbye / Never gonna let you down / "10" / Don't wanna turn you off / Kid stuff (young love) (interlude) / When it comes to love / Echoes / Ain't givin' up / Love x trust / Kid stuff (believe in yourself).
LP: **4673381**
MC: **4673384**

HAPPY (OLD GOLD) (See under Jones, Oran Juice/The rain).

RACE THE NIGHT.
Tracks: / Intro / Someday / Race the night / Take the morning / Paris / It's no good / Night creature / Don't try / Hideaway / Bad girls / Story teller.
LP: . . . . **KILP 4002**

SURFACE.
Tracks: / Let's try again / Happy / We're all searching / Lately / Gotta make love tonight / Who loves you / You're fine / Lady wants a man / Girls were made to love and kiss / Feels so good.
LP: **4500991**
MC: **4500994**

Surfadelics

BAD LITTLE GIRL.
LP: . . . . **MB 12**

Surfaris

SINGLES 1963-1967.
LP: . . . . **MCL 1842**
MC: . . . . **MCLC 1842**

WIPE OUT (OLD GOLD) (see under Chantays -Pipeline(Old Gold)).

Surfin' Dave

IN SEARCH OF A DECENT HAIRCUT (Surfin' Dave & The Absent Legends).
LP: . . . . **CRAM 041**

Surfin' Lungs

BIGGEST WAVE.
LP: . . . . **BEAT 1**

COWABUNGA.
Tracks: / Pray for sun / Hey muscles / Last beach party / 389 / Waroaint / Rockin' in rameses tomb / Surf taboo / Down at the 'b' club / Quasimodo a go go / Surfin' chinese.
MC: . . . . **WIK 41**

Surfin' Wombatz

LAGER LOUTS.
LP: . . . . **NERD 045**

Surfing

CALIFORNIA SURF MUSIC 1962-74 (Various artists).
LP: . . . . **CGB 1009**

ORIGINAL SURFIN' HITS (Various artists).
LP: . . . . **GNPS 84**
MC: **GNP5 84**

SURF CITY DRAG CITY (Various artists).
Tracks: / Surfin' USA: *Beach Boys* / Surf city: *Jan & Dean* / Surf route 101: *Super Stocks* / Shoot the curl: *Honeys* / I live for the sun: *Sunrays* / Be true to your school: *Knights* / Summer means fun: *Fantastic* Baggys / Warmth of the sun: *Wilson, Murry* / Hot rod USA beach girl summer USA: *Knights* / Drag city: *Jan & Dean* / Repossession blues: *Hot Rod Rally* / Little Honda: *Super Stocks* / I get around: *Knights*/ Don't worry baby: *Beach Boys* / Beach blanket bingo: *Loren, Donna* / Ride the wild surf: *Jan & Dean*.
LP: . . . . **EMS 1180**
MC: . . . . **TCEMS 1180**

SURF WAR (Various artists).
LP: . . . . **SURF 13002**

SURFER'S STOMP (Various artists).
Tracks: / Heart and soul: *Jan & Dean* / R.P.M.: *Four Speeds* / Chug a lug: *Sunsets* / Something a little bit different: *Jan & Dean* / Powershift: *Usher, Gary* / Muscle bustle: *Loren, Donna* / Ski storm: *Snowmen*/ Four on the floor: *Four Speeds* / C.C. cinder: *Sunsets* / Burnin' rubber: *Moles, Gene/Softwinds* / Rendezvous stomp: *Rhythm Rockers* / Lonely surfer boy: *Sunsets* / Cheater slicks: *Four Speeds* / Cannon ball: *Soul Surfers* / Twin pipes: *Moles, Gene/ Softwinds* / Surfin' Sally: *Petticoats* / Midsummer night's dream, A: *Jan & Dean* / Mag wheels: *Usher, Gary* / My sting ray: *Four Wheels* / Wanted, one girl: *Jan & Dean*.
LP: . . . . **LIK 39**

SURFIN' GERMANY (Various artists).
Tracks: / Barbara Ann: *Tories* / Summer in Hawaii: *Blue Brothers* / Lass dir zeit: *Crazy Girls* / Der knuller mausi muller: *Michael & The Firebirds* / Achterbahn 8: *Magnets* / Ganz allein: *Beach Boys* / Hey little blondie: *Steff* / California sun: *Quick, Benny* / Ein reise nach New York: *Mama Betty's Band* / Wir wollen nach haus: *Peter & Alex* / Holiday city: *Club Gerry Freidrich* / Kleine kiddio: *Williams, Gene*/ Olympic nights: *Wuerges, Paul*.
LP: . . . . **BFX 15250**

SURFIN' IN THE SUBWAY (Various artists).
LP: . . . . **SUBORG 004**

SURFIN' OLDIES (Various artists).
LP: . . . . **SURF 1005**

SURFIN' USA (Various artists).
LP: . . . . **SHM 974**
MC: . . . . **HSC 357**

Surgeon's Affair (bk)

SURGEON'S AFFAIR (Elizabeth Harrison) (Boyd, Carole (nar)).
MC: . . . . **PMB 009**

Surgery

NATIONWIDE.
LP: . . . . **ARR 89201**
MC: . . . . **ARR 89201MC**

Surgin

WHEN MIDNIGHT COMES.
LP: . . . . **MFN 58**

Surinam

FROM SLAVERY TO FREEDOM (Various artists).
LP: . . . . **LLST 7354**

Surman, John

AMAZING ADVENTURES OF SIMON SIMON.
Tracks: / Nestor's saga (the tale of the ancient) / Buccaneers / Kentish hunting (Lady Margaret's air) / Pilgrim's way (to the seventeenth walls) / Within the halls of Neptune / Phoenix and the fire / Fide et amore (by faith and love) / Merry pranks (the jester's song) / Fitting epitaph, A.
LP: . . . . **ECM 1193**

MIROSLAV VITOUS GROUP (see under Vitous) (Surman/Vitous/Kirkland/ Christensen).

PRIVATE CITY.
LP: . . . . **ECM 1366**

ROAD TO SAINT IVES.
Tracks: / Polperro / Tintagel / Trethevy quoit / Rame head / Mevagissey / Lostwithiel / Perranporth / Bodmin moor / Kelly Bray / Piperspool / Marazion / Bedruthan steps.
LP: . . . . **ECM 1418**
MC: **8438494**

SONATINAS.
LP: . . . . **SJ 106**

S.O.S.
LP: . . . . **OG 400**

SUCH WINTERS OF MEMORY (see Krog,Karin/John Surman).

SURMAN FOR ALL SAINTS.
Tracks: / Round the round / Twelve alone / Electric plunger / Cascadence / Walls / Satisfied air / Matador / Saints alive / Bari-carolle.
LP: . . . . **OG 529**
LP: . . . . **ECM 1295**

UPON REFLECTION.
Tracks: / Edges of illusion / Filigree / Caithness to Kerry / Beyond a shadow / Prelude and rustic dance / Lampfighter / Following behind / Constellation.
LP: . . . . **ECM 1148**

Surprise Surprise

SURPRISE SURPRISE (THEME FROM) (See under Black, Cilla).

Surprize

IN MOVIMENTO.
LP: . . . . **FBN 26**

Surrender

SURRENDER (Film soundtrack) (Various artists).
LP: . . . . **STV 81348**
MC: . . . . **CTV 81348**

Survivor

CAUGHT IN THE GAME.
Tracks: / Caught in the game / Jackie don't go / I never stopped loving you / It doesn't have to be this way / Ready for the real thing / Half life / What do you really think? / Slander / Santa Ana winds.
LP: . . . . **SCT 25575**
MC: **40 25575**

EYE OF THE TIGER.
Tracks: / Hesitation dance / One that really matters / I'm not that man anymore / Children of the night / Ever since the world began / American heartbeat / Silver girl / Feels like love / Eye of the tiger / Take you on a Sunday.
LP: . . . . **SCT 32537**
MC: **40 32537**
LP: . . . . **SCT 85845**
LP: . . . . **EPC 32537**

PREMONITION.
Tracks: / Chevy nights / Summer nights / Poor man's son / Runaway lights / Take you on a Saturday / Light of a thousand smiles / Love is on my side / Heart's a lonely hunter.
LP: . . . . **SCT 85289**

SURVIVOR.
Tracks: / Somewhere in America / Can't getcha offa my mind / Let it be now / As soon as love finds me / Youngblood / Love has got me / Whole town's talking, The / 20/20 / Freeland / Nothing can shake me (from your love) / Whatever it takes.
LP: . . . . **K 50698**

TOO HOT TO SLEEP.
Tracks: / She's a star / Too hot to sleep / Rhythm of the city / Across the miles / Can't give it up / Desperate dreams / Didn't know it was love / Here comes desire / Tell me I'm the one / Burning bridges.
LP: **836 589-1**
MC: **836 589-4**

VITAL SIGNS.
Tracks: / I can't hold back / High on you / First night / Search is over, The / Broken promises / Popular girl / Everlasting / It's the singer not the song / I see you in everyone / Moment of truth (Extra track available on cassette only.).
LP: . . . . **SCT 26126**
MC: **4026126**

WHEN SECONDS COUNT.

Tracks: / How much love / Keep it right here / This love / Man against the world / Rebel son / Oceans / When seconds count / Backstreet love affair / In good faith / Can't let you go.
LP: 4501361
MC: 450136 4

Survivors

SURVIVORS.
Tracks: / Get rhythm / I forgot to remember to forget / Goin' down the road feeling bad / That silver haired daddy of mine / Matchbox / I'll fly away / Whole lotta shakin' goin' on / Rockin' my life away / Blue suede shoes / There will be peace in the valley for me / Will the circle be unbroken / I saw the light.
LP: 85609

Susan

GIRL CAN'T HELP IT.
Tracks: / You're my number one / Koi seyo otome / Training / Blow up / I need your love / I only come out at night / Go go / Nuit de Saint-Germain / Tokyo Sue / My love.
LP: . . . . EPC 85394

Suskind, Patrick (nar)

PERFUME - THE STORY OF A MURDERER (See under Perfume - The Story ...).

Suso

SUSO.
LP: . . . . CAL 209

Suso, Foday 'Musa

HAND POWER.
LP: . . . . FF 318

MANSA BENDUNG BRILLIANT KORA.
LP: . . . . FF 380

Suso, Jali Nyama

SONGS OF THE GAMBIA.
LP: . . . . SNTF 729

Suspect

SUSPECT (Film Soundtrack) (Various artists).
LP: 704.390
MC: . . . . C 704.390

Suspects (bk)

SUSPECTS (William J Canitz).
MCSET: 0600558584

Sussex Harvest

COLLECTION OF TRADITIONAL SONGS FROM SUSSEX, A.
LP: 12T 258

Sutch, Screaming Lord

ALIVE AND WELL.
Tracks: / I'm a hog for you baby / Travers blues / Bye bye Johnny / Bony Moronie.
LP: . . . . B. 80010
MC: MB.80010

JACK THE RIPPER.
LP: . . . . KOMA 788018

ROCK AND HORROR.
Tracks: / Screem and screem / All black and hairy / Jack the ripper / Monster rock / Rock and shock / Murder in the graveyard / London rocker / Penny penny / Rock a billy madman / Oh well / Loonabilly / Go Berry go.
LP: . . . . CH 65

SCREAMING LORD SUTCH.
LP: . . . . MAD 1
LP: . . . . RGM 7777

SCREAMING LORD SUTCH AND THE SAVAGES.
Tracks: / 'Til the following night / Jack the ripper / She's fallen in love with the monsterman / Dracula's daughter / Monster in black tights / Purple people eater / All black and hairy / Murder in the graveyard / Loony rock / Good golly Miss Molly / Don't you just know it / I'm a hog for you / Come back baby / Train kept a rollin', The / Honey hush / Bye bye baby / You don't care / London rocker.
MC: . . . . TCEMS 1433

Sutcliff, Bobby

ANOTHER COMPLETE MESS.
LP: . . . . URINAL 2D

ONLY GHOSTS REMAIN.
LP: . . . . PVC 8957
MC: . . . . PVCC 8957

Sutcliffe, Irene (nar)

PRIDE AND PREJUDICE (See under Austen, Jane).

Suter Blind Date

FIRST RENDEZ-VOUS.
LP: . . . . JUNGLE 65071

Suter, Sylvie

NI JALOUISIE DANS L'AIR (See under Jacquet, Georgie) (Suter, Sylvie & Georgie Jacquet).

Sutherland, Alex

22 SCOTTISH SINGALONG FAVOURITES VOL 3 (Sutherland, Alex Band).
Tracks: / Sing us a song of bonnie Scotland / Bluebells of Scotland / Dundee weaver / Soft lowland tongue of the Borders / Scotch on the rocks o / Wee kirkcudbright centipede / Loch maree islands / Brass o'Killiecrankie / Misty islands of the Highlands / Never kissed a bonnie lass before / Will ye no come back again.
LP: . . . . GES 1212

Sutherland Brothers

REACH FOR THE SKY (Sutherland Brothers & Quiver).
Tracks: / When the train comes / Dirty city / Arms of Mary / Something special / Love on the moon / Ain't too proud / Doctor Dancer / Reach for the sky / Moonlight lady / Mad trail.
LP: . . . . CBS 32655
MC: 40 32655
LP: . . . . CBS 69191

SLIPSTREAM (Sutherland Brothers & Quiver).
LP: . . . . CBS 81593

WHEN THE NIGHT COMES DOWN.
Tracks: / Natural thing / Have you ever been hurt? / First love / Easy come, easy go / As long as I've got you / I'm going home / When the night comes down / Dreams of you / Cruisin' / On the rocks / Crazy town.
LP: . . . . CBS 83427

Sutherland, Iain

MIXED EMOTIONS.
LP: . . . . AVAL 4

Sutherland, Isabel

LICHT BOB'S LASSIE.
Tracks: / S'Ann an ile / False bride, The / Roving ploughboy, The / Laird o' the Denty Doon / Two brothers, the / Old maid in a garret / Greenwood side / Lord Lovat / I'm a young bonnie lassie / Beggarman, The / Overgate, the / Lang a-growing / Bleacher lassie, The / Tullochgorum / I lost my love and I care not / Moon shined on my bed last night, the / O love is teasin' / 4 Maries.
MC: 60-062

VAGRANT SONGS OF SCOTLAND.
LP: 12T 151

Sutherland, Joan

JOAN SUTHERLAND SINGS HANDEL.
LP: . . . . GRV 1

WORLD OF JOAN SUTHERLAND, THE.
LP: . . . . SPA 100
MC: . . . . KCSP 100

Sutherland, Mackie

LITTLE MISS BLUE EYES.
LP: . . . . WGR 086
MC: . . . . CWGR 086

Sutherland, Nadine

UNTIL.
LP: . . . . ABL 110068
LP: . . . . DSR 5992

Sutherland, Pete

POOR MAN'S DREAM.
LP: . . . . FF 336

Sutherland, Willie

LIVE AT THE TOWER HOTEL,ELGIN (Sutherland,Willie & Frankie Coutts).
Tracks: / Po' folks / I'll be a bachelor till I die / When two worlds collide / Jackson / Blue side of lonesome / Railroad bum / My love is like a red red rose / My heart skips a beat / Listen to me / Blow the wind southerly / Snowflake / Old shep / Take me back / Night watch, The.
MC: . . . . CTN 001

Sutphen, Dick

ACCELERATED (HIGH-SPEED) LEARNING.
MC: . . . . RX 105

ATTRACTING PERFECT LOVE.
MC: . . . . RX 102

BANISH PAIN - MIND POWER AND PAIN RELIEF.
MC: . . . . RX 121

BECOME A NEW PERSON.
MC: . . . . RX 114

CALM AND PEACEFUL MIND, A.
MC: . . . . RX 103

CHARISMA - DRAWING PEOPLE TO YOU.
MC: . . . . RX 134

CONCENTRATION - POWER PLUS.
MC: . . . . RX 126

CREATE WEALTH - POWER PROGRAMMING.
MC: . . . . RX 115

DO MORE IN LESS TIME.
MC: . . . . RX 135

DREAM SOLUTIONS-FIND YOUR ANSWERS IN YOUR DREAMS.
MC: . . . . RX 106

FEEL SECURE NOW.
MC: . . . . RX 119

GOOD LIFE, THE - HEALTH, WEALTH AND HAPPINESS.
MC: . . . . RX 104

GREAT MEMORY, A.
MC: . . . . RX 131

HEALING FORCE - USING YOUR MIND TO HELP HEAL.
MC: . . . . RX 117

HOW TO DECIDE EXACTLY WHAT YOU WANT.
MC: . . . . RX 125

INCREDIBLE SELF-CONFIDENCE.
MC: . . . . RX 127

INTENSIFY CREATIVE ABILITY.
MC: . . . . RX 128

LOVE MYSELF - SELF-ESTEEM PROGRAMMING.
MC: . . . . RX 122

PERFECT WEIGHT - PERFECT BODY.
MC: . . . . RX 111

POWER AND SUCCESS - GET IT, KEEP IT, USE IT.
MC: . . . . RX 132

POWER OF PERSISTENCE, THE.
MC: . . . . RX 129

POWERFUL PERSON - PROGRAMMING.
MC: . . . . RX 101

RADIANT HEALTH AND A STRONG IMMUNE SYSTEM.
MC: . . . . RX 116

RIGHT-BRAIN SOLUTIONS (Programming to find creative answers within).
MC: . . . . RX 118

SATISFACTION AND HAPPINESS.
MC: . . . . RX 110

SLEEP LIKE A BABY.
MC: . . . . RX 112

SPEAK UP - SAY WHAT YOU WANT TO SAY.
MC: . . . . RX 123

SPEED READING.
MC: . . . . RX 133

SUCCESS AND EXCELLENCE (high performance and goal accomplishment).
MC: . . . . RX 107

SUCCESSFUL INDEPENDENT LIFESTYLE.
MC: . . . . RX 120

TAKE CONTROL OF YOUR LIFE.
MC: . . . . RX 109

TENNIS: CONCENTRATION,TIMING,STROKES & STRATEGY.
MC: . . . . RX 130

ULTIMATE RELAXATION.
MC: . . . . RX 136

UPPER HAND, THE (quick thinking and fast action).
MC: . . . . RX 113

WEIGHT LOST.
MC: . . . . RX 124

YOUR LAST CIGARETTE - NO EXCEPTIONS!
MC: . . . . RX 108

Sutter, Art

ART OF COUNTRY, THE.
Tracks: / Fool such as I / That'll be the day / Only love / You were always on my mind / Evening star / I fall to pieces / Dreams of the everyday housewife / Still / Me and Bobby McGee / Send me the pillow that you dream on / You never can tell / Your cheating heart / Wolverton Mountain / Please help me I'm falling.
LP: . . . . LIDL 6014
MC: . . . . LIDC 6014

ART OF LOVE.
Tracks: / When I fall in love / I love you because / When your old wedding ring was new / As time goes by / Anniversary waltz / Wedding song, The / Our house / I only have eyes for you / Those endearing young charms / And I love you so / If / Song for you, A / Looking through the eyes of love / Best days of my life.
LP: . . . . LIDL 6013
MC: . . . . LIDC 6013

Sutton, Chris

CHRIS SUTTON.
Tracks: / Trouble / Tell it like this / Prince of justice / Voices / (You just can't)tear it from a heart / Don't get me wrong / You worry me / Know it all / That one love / Don't push your love / Money ain't worth it.
LP: . . . . POLD 5193
MC: . . . . POLDC 5193

Sutton, Lee

BEST OF LEE SUTTON: UNCENSORED.
LP: . . . . NTS 163

Sutton, Ralph

ALLIGATOR CRAWL.
LP: . . . . JCE 92

BIX BEIDERBECKE SUITE.
Tracks: / In the dark / Flashes / Candlelights / In a mist.
LP: AG6.25525

FEB 7, 8 1982 Great piano solos (Sutton, Ralph & Cosenza Jazz Workshop).
LP: . . . . FDC 3003

LIVE: RALPH SUTTON.
LP: . . . . FLY 204

OFF THE CUFF Live.
LP: . . . . AP 163

ON SUNNIE'S SIDE OF THE STREET (see Braff, Ruby) (Sutton, Ralph & Ruby Braff).

PARTNERS IN CRIME (Sutton, Ralph & Bob & Len Barnard).
Tracks: / Swing that music / One morning in May / Old folks / Rain / I never knew / Slow boat to China / It's wonderful / How can you face me? / West End avenue blues / Diga diga doo.
LP: . . . . SVL 505
MC: . . . . SVC 505

PIANO SOLOS.
LP: 2012

PIANO SOLOS.
LP: . . . . 88 UR 004
LP: 2012

RAGTIME PIANO.
LP: . . . . VG 500871

RALPH SUTTON QUARTET.
LP: . . . . SLP 275
LP: . . . . SLP 4013

RALPH SUTTON & THE ALL STARS (Sutton, Ralph & The All Stars).
LP: . . . . JA 45

STACY 'N' SUTTON (See Stacy, Jess) (Sutton, Ralph/Jeff Stacy).

Suzie

DIE GROSSEN ERFOLGE.
Tracks: / Johnny komm (Johnny loves me) / Du, du, du gehst vorbei (When my love passes by) / Da doo ron ron / Wenn ich mich einmal verliebe / Max und Moritz / Wenn du nicht weiss (the things that I feel) / Ich will immer nur dich (Don't let it happen again) / Ich war allein (Wonderin') / Ich hab noch zeit (J'ai le temps) / Adios amor / Was du heut nicht lernst / Wiedersehn ist wunderschon.
LP: . . . . LB 212 002

Suzman, Janet (aut)

AS YOU LIKE IT (See under Shakespeare, William).

Suzuki, Yoshio Chin

MORNING PICTURE.
LP: . . . . NEWLP 103
MC: . . . . NEWMC 103
MC: . . . . JC 3306

Sven, Deejay

HOLIDAY RAP (see M.C. Miker G) (Sven, Deejay & M.C. Miker G).

Svirka

WOMEN'S BALKAN CHORUS.
MC: . . . . GVMMC 802

SWA

WINTER.
LP: . . . . SST 238
MC: . . . . SST 238 C

YOUR FUTURE (IF YOU HAVE ONE).
LP: . . . . SST 053

Swainson, Neil

FORTY NINTH PARALLEL (Swainson, Neil Quintet).
Tracks: / Forty ninth parallel / Port of Spain / Southern exposure / On the lam / Don't hurt yourself / Homestretch.
MC: . . . . CJ 396C

Swalk

WAY WE WERE..., THE.
LP: . . . . DISLP 004

Swallow

HIT MAN, THE.
LP: . . . . SCR 6857

ON THE STREETS OF BROOKLYN.
LP: . . . . SCR 3129
MC: . . . . SCRC 3129

SWALLOW.
LP: . . . . TUPLP 001

Swallow, Steve

CARLA (Swallow, Steve Sextet).
Tracks: / Deep trouble / Crab alley / Fred and Ethel / Read my lips / Afterglow / Hold it against me / Count the ways / Last night.
LP: . . . . XW 2

DUETS (See under Bley, Carla).

Swallow Tongue

STAIN UPON THE SILENCE, A.
LP: . . . . BRED 55

Swamp Blues

SWAMP BLUES, VOL 2.
Tracks: / Coolin' aboard / Storm in Texas / Gray's bounce / Hoo doo blues / Worries life blues / I want some body / I don't know why / Honey bee blues / Baton rouge breakdown / Showers of rain / Number ten at the station and number twelve is on the road / Baby please don't go.
LP: . . . . SNTF 774

Swamp Dogg

I CALLED FOR A ROPE....
Tracks: / I'd lie to you for your love / Come to L.A. / We need a revolution / Kiss me / Myocardial infarction (heartbreak) / Shut your mouth / Happy dog day / Let the good times roll / 1958 / Touch me.
LP: . . . . SDE 4003
MC: . . . . SDE 4003MC
LP: . . . . SNTF 1027

I'M NOT SELLING OUT, I'M BUYING IN.
Tracks: / Swamping salutations / Wine, women & rock'n'roll / Just a little time left / Love we got ain't worth two dead flies / Low friends in high places / Hundred & ... / Total destruction to your mind once again / California is drowning and I live down by the river / Sexy sexy sexy number 3.
LP: . . . . SNTF 875

UNCUT AND CLASSIFIED 1A.
Tracks: / Buzzard luck / Don't you try to be my man / Forever hold your peace / Creeping away / Remember I said tomorrow / Mama's baby, daddy's maybe / Ebony and jet / Swamprapp one / Synthetic world.
LP: . . . . CRB 1026

UNMUZZLED.
Tracks: / Gazelle (part 1) / What my woman can't do for me / I lay awake / Wonder how I got here / Baby is mine, The / I've never been to Africa / Barney's beanery / Paradoxical (no bugles) / I should never have written this song / Eat the goose (before the goose eats you) / Call me nigger / Gazelle (part 2).
LP: . . . . CRB 1045

Swamp Rats

UNRELATED SEGMENTS.
LP: . . . . EVA 12058

Swamp Terrorists

GRIM STROKE DISEASE.
Tracks: / Truth or dare / Nightmare / So sweet - it's painful / I spit on you / Stoneblind / Baron blood / Ostracize / Alka-dig / Deranged / Torso (God told me to) / Mortal greyhound.
LP: MA3-1
MC: MA3-4

Swamp Thing

SWAMP THING (Film Soundtrack) (Various artists).
LP: . . . . STV 81154

Swampsurfers

VARIED FOOD FOR LOST MINDS.
Tracks: / In memory / Virgin with the hookers experience, The / This is America / Train thundering through my brain / What makes a man / No affairs (part 1) / Stand up / Pyscho metal / You've changed / No affairs (part 2) / Dawn of the new gods / Zanibo.
LP: . . . . HH 010

Swamptrash

IT DON'T MAKE NO NEVER MIND.
LP: . . . . DISPLP 12
MC: . . . . DISPC 12
LP: . . . . FFUS 3301
MC: . . . . FFUS 3301C

MYSTERY GIRLS.
LP: . . . . KICKASS 2

Swamstrom, Kenneth

PUMPIN' PIANO.
LP: 33.8015

Swan Arcade

DIVING FOR PEARLS.
Tracks: / Raise your banner / Black seam / Donibristle mine disaster / Bitch fox / Four green fields / Dwelling in Beaulahland / Hounds of the Meynall / Shipbuilding / Weary whaling grounds / Brilliant mistake / Peat bog soldiers, The / Only remembered.
LP: . . . . FE 054

FULL CIRCLE.
MC: . . . . SY 02

MATCHLESS.
LP: . . . . MU 7428

SWAN ARCADE.
LP: . . . . LER 2032

TOGETHER FOREVER.
Tracks: / For the sake of days gone by / Georgie on a spree / Dives and Lazarus / Paperback writer / Goodnight loving trail / Mighty rocky road / Go from my window / Together forever / Lola / Boomer's story / Keep in faith.
LP: . . . . FE 037

Swan Down Gloves

SWAN DOWN GLOVES (Original London cast) (Various artists).
Tracks: / Overture: *Various artists* / With the sun arise: *Various artists* / Everything's going to be fine: *Various artists* / Catastrophe: *Various artists* / Let's be friends: *Various artists* / Make your own world: *Various* artists / How's the way: *Various artists* / Going into town: *Various artists* / Stuck in a muddle: *Various* artists / Best foot forward: *Various artists* / Demewer but dangerous: *Various artists* / Muck: *Various artists* / Any old rose: *Various artists* / Firedown: *Various artists* / Finale: *Various artists.*
LP: . . . . TER 1017
MC: . . . . ZCTER 1017

Swan Esther

SWAN ESTHER (Various artists).
LP: . . . . MCF 3166

Swan (Film)

SWAN, THE (Film Soundtrack) (Various artists).
LP: . . . . MCA 25086
MC: . . . . MCAC 25086

Swan Lake

SWAN LAKE (VIDEO) (see under Tchaikovsky (composer)) (Various artists).

Swan Silvertones

DAY BY DAY.
LP: . . . . SL 14555

GET IT RIGHT WITH THE SWAN SILVERTONES.
LP: . . . . RNLP 70081

GET YOUR SOUL RIGHT.
Tracks: / Is God satisfied with me / At the cross / I'll search heaven / What about you? / Great day in September / Seek, seek / Singin' in my soul / Sinner man / Sign of the judgement / Oh Mary don't you weep / Lady called mother, A / Get your soul right / Move somewhere / Stand up and testify / He saved my soul / Brighter day ahead.
LP: . . . . GNC 1003

I SEE THE SIGN OF JUDGEMENT.
LP: . . . . SL 14604

Swanerud, Thore

MORE THAN YOU KNOW.
LP: . . . . DRLP 85

STAR DUST.
LP: . . . . DRLP 100

Swann, Bettye

MAKE ME YOURS.
Tracks: / Make me yours / Fall in love with me / Don't look back / Don't wait too long / Don't take my mind / I can't stop loving you / I think I'm falling in love / Heartache is gone / I will not cry / What is my life coming to / Change is gonna come, A.
LP: . . . . CLP 541

Swann, Donald

EVENING IN CRETE.
MC: . . . . TC WRS 1006

REQUIEM FOR THE LIVING (See also C.Day Lewis) (Swann, Donald & C. Day Lewis).

SWANN WITH TOPPING (Swann, Donald & Frank Topping).
Tracks: / Gossip gossip whisper chat / I love you / Abraham and Sarah / Owl song / Eye of my mind / How did we get this far / May every day / Battersea-on-thames / It's a great life / Heroes with hearing aids / Time and tide / Walls of Jericho / Rose / Salmon and the trout / God made all the little creatures.
LP: . . . . MMT LP 110

Swann In Love

SWANN IN LOVE (Film Soundtrack) (Various artists).
LP: . . . . STV 81224
LP: . . . . A 240

Swans

BURNING WORLD, THE.
LP: . . . . MCG 6047
MC: . . . . MCGC 6047

CHILDREN OF GOD.
Tracks: / New mind / In my garden / Sex God sex / Blood and honey / Like a drug / You're not real, girl / Beautiful child / Blackmail / Trust me / Real love / Blind love / Children of God.
LP: . . . . 33 PROD 17
MC: . . . . CPROD 17

COP.
LP: . . . . KCC 001

FEEL GOOD NOW.
LP: . . . . LOVE ONE

FILTH.
LP: NDO3
LP: . . . . YGLP 1
MC: . . . . YGMC 1

GREED.
LP: . . . . KCC 2

HOLY MONEY.
LP: . . . . KCC 003

WHITE LIGHT FROM THE MOUTH OF INFINITY.
LP: . . . . YGLP 3
MC: . . . . YGMC 3

Swansway

FUGITIVE KIND, THE.
Tracks: / Soul train / Keeping it strong / Club secrets / In trance / Je joue / Blade, The / Anchor / When the wild calls / Stay / Illuminations.
LP: . . . . SWAN 1

Swarbrick, Dave

BUT TWO CAME BY (See under Carthy, Martin for details) (Swarbrick, Dave/ Martin Carthy).

CEILIDH ALBUM.
LP: . . . . SNTF 764

CLOSE TO THE WIND (see Nicol,Simon/Dave Swarbrick) (Swarbrick, Dave/Simon Nicol).

FLITTIN'.
LP: . . . . SPIN 101

LIFE AND LIMB (See under Carthy, Martin) (Swarbrick, Dave/Martin Carthy).

LIFT THE LID AND LISTEN.
Tracks: / Queen's jig / Dick's maggot / Fanny Power / Three sea captains / Kate Dalrymple / Miss Monaghan / Hares foot / Sally gardens / Lark in the clear air / Banbury Bill / Maid of the mill / Highland Mary / Flitter dance / Peter O'Tavey (manx wedding dance) / Mona's delight / Hunt the wren / Lift the lid and listen / Princess Royal / French ambassador, The / Nonsuch / Our ship she sailed / Dargason.
LP: . . . . SNTF 763

LIVE AT THE WHITE BEAR.
LP: . . . . WHITE BEAR 01

PRINCE HEATHEN (See under Carthy, Martin) (Swarbrick, Dave/Martin Carthy).

SMIDDYBURN.
Tracks: / Wat ye wha I met the streen / Ribbons of the redheaded girl, The / Ril gan ainm / Sir Charles Coote / Smiths / I have a wife of my own / Lady Mary Haye's Scotch measure / Wishing / Victor's return, The / Gravel walk / When the battle is over / Sword dance / Young black cow, The / Sean O'Dwyar of the glen / Hag with the money, The / Sleepy Maggie / It suits me well.
LP: . . . . LOGO 1029
MC: . . . . KLOGO 1029
LP: . . . . GOL 1029

SWARBRICK.
Tracks: / Heilanman, The / Drowsy Maggie / Cathy's march / White cockade, The / Doc Boyd's jig / Durham rangers / My singing bird / Nightingale, The / Once I loved a maiden fair / Killarney boys of pleasure / Lady in the boat / Rosin the Bow / Timour the Tartar / Byker Hill / Ace and deuce of pipering, The / Hole in the wall / Ben Dorain / Hullichans / Chorous jig / 79th farewell to Gilbratar / Arthur McBride / Snug in the blanket.
LP: . . . . TRS 118
MC: . . . . KTRS 118

WHEN THE BATTLE IS OVER.
Tracks: / It suits me well / My singing bird / Once I loved a maiden fair / Bonaparte's retreat / Nightingale, The / Wishing / Kallarney boys of pleasure, The / Shepherd's hey / When the battle is over / Ace and deuce of pipering, The / Rocky road to Dublin / Coulin.
LP: . . . . CFRC 528
MC: . . . . MCFRC 528

Swarbriggs

SWARBRIGGS GREATEST HITS.
LP: . . . . SP LEAF 7013

Swartz, Harvey

IT'S ABOUT TIME (Swartz, Harvey & Urban Earth).
LP: 1390111
MC: 1390114

OLD TIME FEELING (see Jordan, Sheila) (Swartz, Harvey/Sheila Jordan).

UNDERNEATH IT ALL.
Tracks: / Rainbow / Beauty within the beat / Firewalk / Underneath it all / Leaving.
LP: . . . . GR 8202

URBAN EARTH.
LP: . . . . GR 8503

Swayne, Giles

CRY.
Tracks: / Void / Light / Darkness / Sky / Sea / Dryland / Vegetation / Sun / Moon / Stars / Creatures of the air and water / Creatures of the dry land / Rest.
2LP: . . . . REF 550
MC: . . . . ZCD 550

SWE Stars

PAPS - ITALIENISCHE NACHT.
Tracks: / Italienische nacht / Paps (Puff the magic dragon) / Bingel bangel boy / Das gluck kommt vom treusein / Ein schiff fuhr nach Santiago de Chile / Wenn wir zwei uns wiederseh'n / Sag nur auf wiedersehen / Wann kommst du wieder? / Wer nicht kommt zur rechten zeit / Frauen sind doch nur frauen / Nepomuk (foolin' around) / Wenn du weinst (like a child) / Immer am sonntag / Vergessen ist schwer..
LP: . . . . LB 213 003

Sweat

NO MORE RUNNING.
Tracks: / No more running / Isn't anything sacred anymore / Here comes another lonely night / I can hardly wait / Can't help myself / I must be crazy / Do you wanna break my heart / Please don't say you love me / Why'd you have to lie / How much longer.
LP: . . . . DDLP 2

Sweat, Keith

I'LL GIVE YOU ALL MY LOVE.
LP: . . . . EKT 60
MC: . . . . EKT 60 C

MAKE IT LAST FOREVER.
Tracks: / Something just ain't right / Right and a wrong way / Tell me it's me you want / I want her / Make it last forever / In the rain / How deep is your love / Don't stop your love.
LP: 9607631
MC: 9607634

Swedish All Stars

BLUES IN THE NIGHT (see Sheldon, Jack / the Swedish All Stars) (Swedish All Stars, (The) / Jack Sheldon).

Swedish Evergreens

SVENSKA EVERGREENS.
2LP: . . . . PHONT 7408/09
MCSET: . . . . PHONT 8408/09

Swedish Jazz Kings

AFTER TONIGHT, VOL. 2.
LP: . . . . SOS 1188

TRIBUTE TO CLARENCE WILLIAMS, A.
LP: . . . . SOS 1122

Swedish Radio Jazz

RAINBOW SKETCHES.
LP: . . . . FLC 5906

Swedish Spelmans Trio

AMERICAN SWEDISH SPELMANS TRIO.
LP: . . . . ROUNDER 6004

Sweeney, Birdy

LAUGH WITH THE REST OF THE LEPRECHAUNS.
MC: . . . . CT 111

Sweeney Todd

SWEENEY TODD (Original Broadway cast) (Various artists).
Tracks: / Ballad of Sweeney Todd: *Various artists* / No place like London: *Various artists* / Barber and his wife: *Various artists* / Worst pies in London: *Various artists* / Poor thing: *Various artists* / My friends: *Various artists* / Attend the tale of Sweeney Todd: *Various artists* / Lift your razor high: *Various artists*/ Sweeny Green finch and linnet bird: *Various artists* / Ah Miss Johanna: *Various artists* / Pireli's miracle elixir: *Various artists* / Contest: *Various artists* / Wait: *Various artists* / Sweeney pondered and Sweeney planned: *Various artists* / His hands were quick his fingers strong: *Various artists* / Johanna kiss me: *Various artists*/ Ladies in their sensitivites: *Various artists* / Pretty women: *Various artists* / God, that's good: *Various* artists

/ Epiphany: *Various artists* / Little priest: *Various artists* / Johanna: *Various artists*/ By the sea: *Various artists* / Wigmaker sequence: *Various artists* / Sweeney'd waited too long before: *Various artists* / Letter: *Various artists* / Not while I'm around: *Various artists* / Parlour song: *Various artists*.
2LP: CBL 2
MC: CBK 2
2LP: CBL2 03379
MCSET: CBK2 3379

Sweeney's Men

LEGEND OF SWEENEY'S MEN, THE.
Tracks: / Rattlin' roarin' Willie / Sullivan's John / Sally Brown / Exile's jig / Dicey Riley / Tom Dooley / Willie o' Winsbury / Pipe on the hob / Johnston / Dreams for me / Brain jam / Mistake no doubt, A / Go by Brooks / When you don't care for me / After thoughts / My dearest dear / Hall of mirrors.
LP: TRANDEM 4

TRACKS OF THE SWEENEY.
Tracks: / Dreams for me / Pipe on the hob / Brain jam / Pretty Polly / Standing on the shore / Mistake no doubt / Go by brooks / When you don't care for me / Hiram Hubbard / Hall of mirrors.
LP: TRA SAM40

Sweet

BLOCKBUSTERS.
Tracks: / Ballroom blitz / Hellraiser / New York connection / Little Willy / Burning / Need a lot of lovin' / Wig wam bam / Blockbuster / Rock and roll disgrace / Chop chop / Alexander Graham Bell / Poppa Joe / Co Co / Funny funny.
LP: NL 74313
MC: NK 74313

COLLECTION: SWEET.
Tracks: / Teenage rampage / Rebel rouser / Solid gold brass / Stairway to the stars / Turn it down / Sixteens, The / Into the night / No you don't / Fever of love / Lies in your eyes / Fox on the run / Restless / Set me free / AC#DC / Sweet f.a. / Action / Peppermint twist / Heartbreak today / Lost angels / Lady Starlight.
2LP: CCSLP 230
MC: CCSMC 230

CUT ABOVE THE REST.
Tracks: / Call me / Play all night / Big apple waltz / Dorian Gray / Discophony / Eye games / Mother Earth / Hold me / Stay with me.
LP: POLD 5022

DESOLATION BOULEVARD.
Tracks: / Ballroom blitz / Six-teens, The / No you don't / A.C.D.C. / I wanna be committed / Sweet F.A. / Fox on the run / Set me free / Into the night / Solid gold brass.
LP: 26 21430
LP: CLALP 170
MC: CLAMC 170

HARD CENTRES (The rock years).
Tracks: / Set me free / Sweet F A / Restless / Yesterday's rain / White mice / Cockroach / Keep it in / Live for today / Windy City / Midnight to daylight.
LP: ZEB 11
MC: CZEB 11

IDENTITY CRISIS.
LP: 2311 179

OFF THE RECORD.
Tracks: / Fever of love / Lost angels / Midnight to daylight / Windy city / Live for today / She gimme lovin' / Laura Lee / Hard times / Funk it up.
LP: PL 25072

STARKE ZEITEN.
LP: 208867
MC: 408867

STRUNG UP.
Tracks: / Hellraiser / Burning / Someone else will / Rock'n'roll disgrace / Need a lot of lovin' / Done me wrong alright / You're not wrong for loving me / Man with the golden arm, The / Action / Fox on the run / Set me free / Miss Demeanour / Ballroom blitz / Burn on the flame / Solid gold brass / Sixteen, The / I wanna be committed / Blockbuster.
2LP: 26 28124
2LP: SPC 001
MC: SPK 0001

SWEET FANNY ADAMS.
LP: 26 21325
LP: LPK 15038

SWEET SIXTEEN.
Tracks: / Alexander Graham Bell / Poppa Joe / Little Willy / Wigwam bam / Blockbuster / Hellraiser / Ballroom blitz / Teenage rampage / Rebel rouser / Sixteens / Fox on the run / Action / Lies in your eyes / Stairway to the stars / Lost angels / Love is like oxygen / Sweet sixteen.
LP: GRAM 16
MC: CGRAM 16

SWEET'S BIGGEST HITS.
Tracks: / Wig wam bam / Little Willy / Done me wrong alright / Poppa Joe / Funny funny / Co co / Alexander Graham Bell / Chop chop / You're not wrong for loving me / Jeannie / Spotlight.
LP: SF 8316
LP: 2621127

SWEETS GOLDEN GREATS.
Tracks: / Blockbuster / Hellraiser / Ballroom blitz / Teenage rampage / Sixteens / Turn it down / Fox on the run / Action / Lost angels / Lies in your eyes / Fever of love / Stairway to the stars.
LP: PL 25111

WATER'S EDGE.
Tracks: / Sixties man / Getting in the mood for love / Tell the truth / Own up / Too much talking / Thank you for loving me / At midnight / Water's edge / Hot shot gambler / Give the lady some respect.
LP: POLS 1021

Sweet Charity

SWEET CHARITY (Original Broadway cast) (Various artists).
LP: CBS 32662
MC: 40 32662

SWEET CHARITY 1987 Revival of the original Broadway cast (Various artists).
LP: SV 17179
MC: 4 XS 17179

SWEET CHARITY (Film soundtrack) (Various artists).
Tracks: / Overture: *Various artists* / You should see yourself: *Various artists* / Big spender: *Various artists*/ Charity's soliloquy: *Various artists* / Rich man's frug: *Various artists* / If my friends could see me now: *Various* artists / Too many tomorrows: *Various artists* / There's gotta be something better than this: *Various artists*/ Charity's theme: *Various artists* / I'm the bravest individual: *Various artists* / Rhythm of life: *Various* artists / Baby dream your dream: *Various artists* / Sweet charity: *Various artists* / Where am I going?: *Various* artists / I love to cry at weddings: *Various artists* / I'm a brass band: *Various artists* / Finale: *Various artists*.
LP: MOIR 203
MC: CMOIR 203

Sweet Charles

FOR SWEET PEOPLE FROM SWEET CHARLES.
LP: URBLP 9
MC: URBMC 9

Sweet Comfort Band

BREAKIN' THE ICE.
Tracks: / Got to believe / Breakin' the ice / Young girl / Melody / Harmony / I need your love again / Good feeling / Searchin' for love / Lord is calling, The / I love you with my life.
LP: LSX 7053
MC: LC 7053

HEARTS OF FIRE.
Tracks: / Isabel / You can make it / They just go on / Road, The / Feel like singin' / Now or never / Can you help me / Contender, The / Just like me / You need a reason / Visions of Africa / Future walking / Floating down the river Richan / Synthetica / Dea Mediterranea / Ancient city / From the album / Atlantic / Dance of the neutrinos / Eldila / Mercury's / Voyager.
LP: LS 7062
MC: LC 7062

HOLD ON TIGHT.
Tracks: / Hold on tight / Take it, save it / Falling star / You're the one / Angel / Chasing the wind / Don't tell me you love me / Undecided / Carry me / More than you need / Find your way.
LP: LS 7057
MC: LC 7057

Sweet Dreams (film)

SWEET DREAMS (Life And Times Of Patsy Cline) (Cline, Patsy).
Tracks: / San Antonio rose / Seven lonely days / Your cheatin' heart / Lovesick blues / Walking after midnight / Foolin' around / Half as much / I fall to pieces / Crazy / Blue moon of Kentucky / She's got you / Sweet dreams.
LP: MCG 6003
MC: MCGC 6003

SWEET DREAMS (VIDEO) (see under Cline, Patsy) (Various artists).

Sweet Exorcist

CLONKS COMING.
LP: WARPLP 1

Sweet FA

STICK TO YOUR GUNS.
Tracks: / Prince of the city / Rhythm of action / Daily grind / Whiskey river / Breakin' the law / Devil's road / Nothin' for nothin' / Do a little drivin' / Stick to your guns / I love women / Heart of gold / Southern comfort.
LP: MCG 6093
MC: MCGC 6093

Sweet Honey in the

BREATHS (Best of Sweet Honey in the Rock).
Tracks: / Breaths / Stranger blues / Joanne little / Ella's song / More than a paycheck / Mandiacapella / Study war no more / Waters of Babylon (Rivers of Babylon) / Oughta be a woman / On children / Chile your waters run red through Soweto / Azanian freedom song.
LP: COOK 008
MC: COOKC 008

FEEL SOMETHING DRAWING ME ON.
LP: SPIN 124
LP: FF 375

GOOD NEWS.
Tracks: / Breaths / Chile your waters run red through Soweto / Good news / If you had lived / On children / Alla that's all right, but / Echo / Oh death / Biko / Oughta be a woman / Time on my hands / Sometime.
LP: FF 245
LP: COOK 027
MC: COOKC 027

LIVE AT CARNEGIE HALL.
Tracks: / Beautitudes / Where are the keys to the kingdom / Emergency / Are my hands clean / Peace / My lament / Run run mourner run / Letter to Dr. Martin Luther King / Ode to the international debt / Your worries ain' like mine / Song of the exile / Denko / Drinking of the wine / Wade in the water (CD only.) / Our side won (CD only.).
MC: COOKC 012
LP: COOK 012
LP: FF 106
LP: BAKE 003
MC: BAKEC 003

OTHER SIDE, THE.
LP: SPIN 123
LP: FF 366

WE ALL...EVERYONE OF US.
LP: SPIN 106
MC: SPIC 106
LP: FF 317

Sweet Inspirations

HOT BUTTERFLY.
Tracks: / Hot fun / Face to face / That's when you know / Hot butterfly / It's the simple things you do / Do it right.
LP: RSS 12

Sweet Lies

SWEET LIES (Film soundtrack) (Various artists).
Tracks: / Riptide: *Palmer, Robert* / Want you more: *Palmer, Robert* / A.I.E.: *La Compagnie Creole* / La ville de lumiere: *Gold* / Monogamy: *Palmer, Robert* / Wamba: *Salif Keita* / Rue Galande: *Jones, Trevor* / Zouk-la-se sel medikamen nou ni: *Desvarieux, Jacob F & Georges Decimus* / Sweet lies (club version): *Desvarieux, Jacob F & Georges Decimus* / Sweet lies: *Palmer, Robert* / La compagnie creole: *A I E* / La vile de lumiere: *Gold* / Peter's theme: *Jones, Trevor* / Woke up laughing: *Palmer, Robert* / Robert Montgomery: *Palmer, Robert*.
LP: ISTA 16
MC: ICT 16

Sweet People

MUSIC FOR THE MILLIONS.
Tracks: / Lake Como / Elodie / Santa Barbara / Nuits blanche / Perce / Aria pour notre amour / L'estrie / Ballade pour tsi-co tsi-co / Et les chantaient / Santorin.
LP: 815203 1
MC: 815203 4

SWEET PEOPLE.
Tracks: / Lake Como / Elodie / Santa Barbara / Nuits blanche / Perce / Birds were singing / L'estrie / Ballade pour tsi-co tsi-co / Aria pour notre amour / Santorin.
LP: 231 100 8

Sweet, Phil

MEMPHIS BLUE STREAK.
Tracks: / Memphis blue streak / Shake, rattle and roll / Breakin' daylight / Reba Faye / Red cadillac and a black moustache / My baby left me / Good rockin' tonight / My baby's long gone / It's love baby / Mystery train / Blue yodel no. 10 / Still rockin' after all these years.
LP: CR 30206

Sweet, Rachel

...AND THEN HE KISSED ME.
Tracks: / Shadows of the night / Then he kissed me / Be my baby / Billy and the gun / Party girl / Two hearts full of love / Little darlin' / Fool's story / Everlasting love / Streetheart.
LP: CBS 85006
MC: 40 85006

BLAME IT ON LOVE.
Tracks: / Blame it on love / Voo doo / Paralysed / Sticks and stones / American girl / Heart is a lonely hunter / Hearts on the line / Cruisin' love / Baby love / Cool heart.
LP: CBS 250 37

EVERLASTING LOVE (see under "Smith, Rex") (Sweet, Rachel & Rex Smith).

PROTECT THE INNOCENT.
Tracks: / Tonight / Jealous / I've got a reason / New age / Baby let's play house / New rose / Fools gold / Take good care of me / Spellbound / Lovers lane / Foul play / Tonight Ricky.
LP: SEEZ 18

THEN HE KISSED ME.
Tracks: / Shadows of the night / Then he kissed me / Be my baby now / Billy and the gun / Party girl / Two hearts full of love / Little darlin' / Fool's story / Everlasting love / Streetheart.
LP: CBS 85223

Sweet Rosemary (bk)

SWEET ROSEMARY (Fay Chandos) (Andrews, June (nar)).
MCSET: CLT 1008

Sweet Soul Music

SWEET SOUL MUSIC (See under Soul) (Various artists).

Sweet Substitute

SOPHISTICATED LADIES.
Tracks: / Lullaby of Broadway / Sophisticated lady / Tiger blues / Sleepy Suzie / Take me to the Mardi Gras / I got an uncle in Harlem / Good morning heartache / Dear Mr.Berkeley / Sweet misery / Do you know what it means to miss New Orleans? / Satin doll.
LP: BLM 51010

TEN CENTS A DANCE.
LP: SKL 5276
MC: KSKC 5276

Sweet Talking Oldies

SWEET TALKING OLDIES (See under 60's) (Various artists).

Sweet Tee

IT'S TEE TIME.
LP: FILER 269
MC: FILERCT 269

Sweet Tooth

SOFT WHITE UNDERBELLY.
MLP: MOSH 26
MC: MOSH 26 MC

Sweetenlo

NOT TO BE TOOKEN LIGHTLY.
Tracks: / Back for the payback / No to be tooken lightly / Original tramp, The (radio version) / Keepin' it smooth / I'll make you dance / You wanna dance / Just rolling / Original tramp, The / Burger the bed, The / That's sweetenlo / I'm that type of nigga / You can't stop the hip hop.
LP: ICH 1069
MC: ICH 1069MC

Sweethearts (film)

SWEETHEARTS (Film Soundtrack) (Various artists).
LP: SH 2025
MC: CSH 2025

Sweethearts Of The...

SWEETHEARTS OF THE RADIO (Various artists).
LP: EXLP 001

Sweethearts Of.(Group)

ONE TIME, ONE NIGHT (Sweethearts Of The Rodeo).
Tracks: / Satisfy you / Blue to the bone / We won't let that river come between us / So sad (to watch good love go bad) / Don't look down / One time, one night / You never talk sweet / I feel fine / If I never see midnight again / Gone again / Until I stop dancing.
LP: 4607791
MC: 4607794

SWEETHEARTS OF THE RODEO (Sweethearts Of The Rodeo).
Tracks: / Midnight girl / Hey doll baby / Since I found you / Gotta get away (12" version only) / Chains of gold (12" version only) / Chosen few / Everywhere I turn / I can't resist.
LP: 4605311
MC: 4605314

Sweetie Irie

DJ OF THE FUTURE.
LP: MLPS 1068
MC: MCT 1068

Sweetmouth

GOODBYE TO SONGTOWN.
MC: PK 74971
LP: PL 74971

Sweets For My Baby

SWEETS FOR MY BABY (Various artists).
LP: GALP 009
MC: GALC 009

Swell Maps

COLLISION TIME.
LP: ROUGH 41

JANE FROM OCCUPIED EUROPE.
LP: MAPS 002
LP: TROY 2

TRAIN OUT OF IT.
LP: ANTAR 4

TRIP TO MARINEVILLE, A.
LP: MAPS 001
LP: TROY 1

WHATEVER HAPPENS NEXT.
LP: TROY 3

Swenson, May

POETRY AND VOICE OF MAY SWENSON.
LP: TC 1500

Swervedriver

RAISE.
LP: CRELP 093
MC: CCRELP 093

Swift, Duncan

OUT LOOKING FOR THE LION.
LP: BEAR 28
MC: BEARMC 28

Swift Jewel Cowboys

CHUCK WAGON SWING.
Tracks: / Chuck wagon swing / My untrue cowgirl / Raggi-n' the rails / Memphis blues / Coney Island washboard / Fan it / Little Willie Green / Memphis oomph / Willie the weeper / Swingin' at the Circle S / Dill pickle rag / Rose room / Bug scuffle / You gotta ho de ho.
LP: STR 806

Swift, Jonathan

GULLIVER'S TRAVELS.
MC: TS 320

GULLIVER'S TRAVELS (children's classics).
MC: PLBC 80

GULLIVER'S TRAVELS (Horden, Sir Michael).
MCSET: 414 730-4

GULLIVER'S TRAVELS (Hart, Derek).
MC: BKK 404

GULLIVER'S TRAVELS (Rodgers, Anton).
MCSET: LFP 7451

MODEST PROPOSAL, THE (Magee, Patrick).
MC: 1383

Swift, Tufty

HOW TO MAKE A BAKEWELL TART (See under Harris, Sue).

Swig The Swing

SWIG THE SWING.
LP: SWIG 1

Swim

SUNDRIVE ROAD.
LP: MCG 6099
MC: MCGC 6099

Swimming Pool Queues

DEEP END, THE.
Tracks: / Little misfit / Big fat tractor / Stick in my hand / A-bomb woke me up, The / Rat bait / Restless youth / Stock car sin / Walk like a chicken / Black bus / Overheated / I like to take orders from you.
LP: ARM 12

SWIMMING POOL Q'S, THE.
Tracks: / Bells ring, The / Pull back my spring / Purple spring / Knave, The / Some new highway / Just property / Silver slipper / She's bringing down the poison / Celestion / Sacrificial altar.
LP: AMA 5012
MC: AMC 5012

Swimming With Sharks

SWIMMING WITH SHARKS.
Tracks: / Careless love / Idiot / No longer friends / Conspiracy / Sweet sadness / Four winds / Don't spoil my day / Duet alone / Holy Johnny / Swimming with sharks.
LP: WX 182
MC: WX 182 C

Swinburne, Algernon..

SELECTED POETRY OF SWINBURNE (Swinburne, Algernon Charles).
LP: TC 1560
MC: CDL 1560

Swindells, Steve

FRESH BLOOD.
Tracks: / Turn it on, turn it off / Fresh blood / I feel alive / Low life Joe / Bitter and twisted / I don't wait on the stairs / Is it over now / Down on love street / Figures of authority / Shot down in the night.
LP: K 50738

Swinfield, Ray

ANGEL EYES.
LP: WAVE LP 23

RAIN CURTAIN.
LP: N 132

Swing

GREAT SWING JAM SESSIONS VOL.2 (Various artists).
Tracks: / China boy: *Various artists* / Body and soul: *Various artists* / Honeysuckle rose: *Various artists*/ Stardust: *Various artists* / Intermezzo: *Various artists* / Song of the islands: *Various artists* / Flying home: *Various artists* / Tempo and swing: *Various artists* / With a twist of the wrist: *Various artists*/ Lower register: *Various artists* / Jazz me blues: *Various artists* / Floyd's guitar blues: *Various artists.*
LP: SM 3115

SWING.
Tracks: / Big bucks / Right idea, The / Serenade in blue / Tweedlee dee / Caravan / Mirage / Let the good times roll / Dancing in the dark / Closer I get to you, The / Tocadero ballroom / Crazy he calls me / Make love to me baby.
LP: K 52329
MC: K4 52329

Swing Collection

MUSIC GOES ROUND AND ROUND THE 30'S, THE.
LP: HO 510

Swing For A Crime

SWING FOR A CRIME (Various artists).
LP: GMG 75031

Swing Out Sister

IT'S BETTER TO TRAVEL.
LP: OUT LP 1
MC: OUT MC 1

KALEIDOSCOPE WORLD.
Tracks: / You on my mind / Where in the world? / Forever blue / Heart for fire / Tainted / Waiting game, The / Precious game / Masquerade / Between strangers / Kaleidoscope affair, The.
LP: 838 293 1
MC: 838 293 4

Swinging Blue Jeans

ALL THE HITS PLUS MORE.
LP: PRST 003
MC: ZPRST 003

BLUE JEANS ARE SWINGING.
Tracks: / Ol' man Mose / That's the way it goes / It's all over now / Lawdy Miss Clawdy / It's so right / All I want is you / Save the last dance for me / Around and around / Long tall Sally / Some sweet day / Don't it make you feel good / Tutti frutti.
LP: BGOLP 55

BRAND NEW AND FADED.
Tracks: / Dancing / Rainbow morning / Sweet Louise / Baby mine / Ring ring / Boomerang / Hippy hippy shake (introduction) / Long Tall Sally / Good golly Miss Molly / Cottonfields / Don't make me over / You're no good / Hippy hippy shake.
LP: BULL 1001

DANCIN'.
MC: ASK 778

LIVE SHARIN'.
Tracks: / Tulane / My life / Again and again / Good golly Miss Molly / Don't stop / I saw her standing there / She loves you / Caroline / You're no good / Heatwave / Shakin' all over / It's so easy / When will I be loved / Hard day's night, A / Hippy hippy shake.
LP: PRST 502
MC: ZPRST 502

SHAKE: THE BEST OF THE SWINGING BLUE JEANS.
Tracks: / Hippy hippy shake / Don't make me over / Good golly Miss Molly / Do you know / Long tall Sally / You're no good / Tutti frutti / It isn't there / Shakin' all over / Make me know you're mine / Shake, rattle and roll / Save the last dance for me / Lawdy Miss Clawdy / It's too late now / Good lovin' / Tremblin' / Around and around / Rumours, gossip, words, untrue / That's the way it goes / Some sweet day.
LP: EMS 1123
MC: TCEMS 1123
LP: NUT 15

SWINGING BLUE JEANS.
LP: 1A 052 06794

Swingle

SKYLINER.
Tracks: / Sunny side of the street / Mood indigo / Chattanooga choo choo / Back Bay shuffle / Opus No. 1 / Li'l darlin' / Fascinating rhythm / Serenade in blue / Us.
LP: SCX 6617

Swingle II

NO TIME TO TALK.
LP: CBS 83458

Swingle Singers

BEST OF THE SWINGLE SINGERS
Compact/Walkman jazz.
Tracks: / Le marche de limoges / Little David's fugue / Andante / Ricercare A6 / Romance Espagnole / Alexander's fugue / Little prelude and fugue.
MC: 830701-4

COMPACT JAZZ: SWINGLE SINGERS.
Tracks: / Air for G String / Etude Op.25 no.2 / Aranjuez mon amour.
MC: 831 701-4

FOLIO.
Tracks: / Flight of the bumble bee / Reverie / Sonata / Clair de lune / Prelude / Minuet / Intermezzo / Pavanne / Rondo / La fille aux cheveux de lin / Fur elise / Swan.
LP: SCX 6631

JAZZ SEBASTIAN BACH.
Tracks: / Choral prelude / Aria / Prelude in F / Bourre / Sinfonia / Canon / Invention in C / Fuges in D & D minor.
LP: 824 544 1
MC: 824 544 4
LP: BL 7572

NOTHING BUT BLUE SKIES.
MC: MODEMC 1009
LP: MODEM 1009

PLACE VENDOME (Swingle Singers & MJQ).
Tracks: / Little David's fugue / When I am laid in earth / Vendome / Ricercare A6 / Air for G String / Alexander's fugue / Three windows.
LP: 824 545 1
MC: 824 545 4

SWINGLE SINGERS CHRISTMAS ALBUM.
Tracks: / Jingle bells / God rest ye merry gentlemen / White christmas / O Tannenbaum / We three kings.
LP: 6570 220

Swingles

CHRISTMAS (SWINGLES).
Tracks: / Rudolph the red nosed reindeer / O tannenbaum / Little drummer boy / Santa Claus is coming to town / Jingle bells / Silent night / Ave Maria.
LP: POLD 5206
MC: POLHC 5206

INSTRUMENTALS.
LP: POLD 5205
MC: POLDC 5205

REFLECTIONS.
LP: ULT 33 1806
MC: PER 733 1806

Swinson, Antonia

MORE ADVENTURES OF MY LITTLE PONY (See Jennifer Zabel).

MY LITTLE PONY: GUSTY AND GENIE (See Jennifer Zabel).

MY LITTLE PONY: THE GRAND PONY PARADE (See Jennifer Zabel).

Swiss Family Robinson

SWISS FAMILY ROBINSON (see Wyss, Johann).

Switch

AM I STILL YOUR BOYFRIEND?.
Tracks: / Treason / Am I still your boyfriend / Just can't pull away / I won't give up / Spend my life with you / Forever my love / I'm so satisfied / Switch it baby / It's all up to you / Lovers don't hold back / Keeping secrets.
LP: FL 89407

REACHING FOR TOMORROW.
Tracks: / Power to dance / My friend in the sky / Don't take my love away / Keep movin' on / Brighter tomorrow / Reaching for tomorrow / I finally found someone new / Honey I love you / Get back with you.
LP: STML 12135

SWITH II.
Tracks: / You're the one for me / Next to you / Best beat in town / Calling on all girls / Go on doin' what you feel / Fallin' / I call your name.
LP: STML 12112

Switzerland...

SWITZERLAND - YODELS OF APPENZELL (Various artists).
LP: AUD 58026

Swope, Earl

LOST SESSION, THE (Swope, Earl Sextet & Lennie Tristano).
Tracks: / Tea for two / Tea for two (version 2) / Blue Lou / These foolish things / These foolish things (version 2) / Talk of the town / Talk of the town (version 2) / Yesterdays / What is this thing called love / Don't blame me / I found a new baby / I can't get started / Night in Tunisia.
LP: NOST 7635

Sword

METALIZED.
LP: GWLP 10

SWEET DREAMS.
LP: GWLP 45
MC: GWTC 45
LP: RO 9476 1
MC: RO 9476 4

Sword of Jah Mouth

INVASION.
LP: PBLP 01

Sword & The Sorcerer

SWORD & THE SORCERER (Film Soundtrack) (Various artists).
LP: TER 1023

SXL

SXL.
LP: EMY 106

Syar

DEATH BEFORE DISHONOUR.
LP: SKULL 8308
MC: TAPE 78308

Sybil

INDEPENDENT (See under Salt N Pepa) (Sybil & Salt N Pepa).

LET YOURSELF GO.
Tracks: / Falling in love (remix) / Let yourself go (inst) / Let yourself go / Don't make me over / My love is guaranteed / U and me 2 nite / Falling in love / Walkin' in the moonlight / All through the night / On our way to love.
LP: CHAMP 1009
MC: CHAMPK 1009
LP: CHAMPX 1009
MC: CHAMXK 1009

SYBIL (IMPORT).
MC: STM 1018

SYBILIZATION.
LP: HF 17
MC: HFC 17

WALK ON BY.
MC: HFMC 10
LP: HF 10

Sydney Salvation Army

DANIEL (Sydney Salvation Army Band).
LP: KLO 43

Sye

TURN ON THE FIRE.
LP: RR 9781

Sykes, Roosevelt

BLUES FROM BOTTOMS.
LP: 77LEU 12/50

BOOGIE HONKEY (Sykes, Roosevelt & The Original Honeydrippers).
LP: OL 2818

COUNTRY BLUES PIANO ACE.
LP: L 1033

DIRTY MOTHER FOR YOU.
LP: BT 2008

FEEL LIKE BLOWING MY HORN.
LP: DS 632
LP: DL 632

HONEYDRIPPER'S DUKE'S MIXTURE (VOLUME 4), THE.
Tracks: / Rock me / Going down slow / Ice cream freezer / Lost my boogie / Sweet Georgia Brown / St. James infirmary / Honeysuckle rose / Basin Street blues / Woman is in demand, A / Dirty mother for you.
LP: 80604

ORIGINAL HONEYDRIPPER, THE.
Tracks: / Cow cow blues / Drivin' wheel / What'd I say / Viper song / Early morning blues / Dirty mother for you / I'm a nut / Running the boogie / Honeysuckle rose / Too smart too soon / Sweet home Chicago / I like what you did / Please don't talk about me when I'm gone.
LP: BP-005
LP: BMLP 068

RAINING IN MY HEART (Uniteds).
LP: DL 642

ROCK IT 1946-54.

LP: WBJ 004

ROOSEVELT SYKES 1929-34.
LP: MSE 1011

ROOSEVELT SYKES (Live at Webster College, St. Louis, Feb. 1974).
LP: DLP 526

ROOSEVELT SYKES 1929-41.
LP: BD 2013

ROOSEVELT SYKES 1929-1942.
LP: BOB 3

WEST HELENA BLUES - 1945-57.
LP: WBJ 005

Sylane Singers

REFLECTIONS OF IRELAND (Sylane Singers & Friends).
MC: GTDC 047

Sylla, M'Mah

SAHEL (see under Diaeate, Son/M'Mah Sylla) (Sylla, M'Mah & Son Diaeate).

Sylum

SYLUM.
LP: WKFMLP 44

Sylva, Mynus

REGGAE DOWN CARNIVAL SHOWCASE '84.
LP: CSLP 0014

Sylvain, Sylvain

SYLVAIN SYLVAIN.
Tracks: / Teenage news / What's that got to do with rock 'n' roll / I'm so sorry / Emily / Without you / Every boy and every girl / 14th Street beat / Deeper and deeper / Ain't got no home / Tonight.
LP: PL 13475

Sylvan, Rikki

SILENT HOURS.
Tracks: / Billy / Cigarette / Black needles / Soft core / I am a video / What's that sound? / Thin white line / Nighthawk / Underground / Into the void.
LP: KRL 85198

Sylvers

BIZARRE.
Tracks: / Tension / Bottom line / Falling for your love / Boomerang / Bizzare / In one love and out the other / Got to be crazy / You turn me on / Let my love shine in / Something's gotta give.
LP: GEF 26019

CONCEPT.
Tracks: / Heart repair man / Come back lover, come back / P.S. / Just when I thought it was over / I'm gettin' over / Take it to the top / Reach out / There's a place / Taking over.
LP: K 52307

DISCO FEVER.
Tracks: / Mahogany / Is everybody happy / Come and stay all night / Dancing right now / Gimme gimme your lovin' / I feel so good tonight / Hoochie coochie dancin' / Forever.
LP: CAL 2050

FOREVER YOURS.
Tracks: / Don't stop, get off / Love changes / Forever yours / Swept for you baby / Play this one last record / Come dance with me / Come on down to my house / Diamonds are rare / Love won't let me go / Just a little bit longer.
LP: CAL 2045

Sylvers, Leon F.III

LEON SYLVERS III.
Tracks: / Make it count / Gotta find a way / Time machine / Help me find love / So hung up on you / Safe and sound / Living life at the maximum / All or nothing / Let's go thru it / When love moves in / Make it count (12" version) (Only on CD.).
LP: ZL 72681
MC: ZK 72681

Sylvester

CALL ME.
Tracks: / Trouble in paradise / Call me / Good feeling / He'll understand / One night only / Too late / Power of love, The / Band of gold.
LP: XTLP 3
MC: XTCC 3

GREATEST HITS: SYLVESTER.
LP: XL 89106
MC: XK 89106

LIVING PROOF.
Tracks: / Overture / Blackbird / This could be magic / Song for you, A / Happiness / Loverman / You are my friend / Can't stop dancing / In my fantasy.
LP: FT 573

M1015.
Tracks: / Rock the box / Sex / I don't wanna think about it / Taking love into my own hands / Take me to heaven / How do you like your love / Lovin' is really my game / Shadow of a heart.
LP: CHR 1492

MIGHTY REAL.
Tracks: / Stars / Body strong / Down down down / You make me feel mighty real / I / I need somebody to love tonight / Over and over / Dance.
LP: FTA 3009

MUTUAL ATTRACTION.
Tracks: / Someone like you / Living for the city / Summertime / Mutual attraction / Talk to me / Cool of the evening / Sooner or later / Anything can happen.
LP: 925527 1
MC: 925527 4

SELL MY SOUL.
Tracks: / I need you / I'll dance to that / Change up / Sell my soul / Doin' it for the real thing / Cry me a river / My life is loving you / Fever.
LP: F 9601

STAR - BEST OF SYLVESTER.
Tracks: / Stars (everybody is one) / Dance (disco heat) / Down, down, down / I need somebody to love tonight / I (who have nothing) / You make me feel (mighty real) / My life is loving you / Can't stop dancing / Body strong (Available on CD and cassette only) / Over and over (Available on CD and cassette only) / Disco international (Available on CD and cassette only).
LP: SEW 007
MC: SEWC 007

STARS (ALBUM).
Tracks: / Stars / Body strong / I / I need somebody to love tonight.
LP: FT 556

SYLVESTER: GREATEST HITS.
Tracks: / Do you wanna funk / Dance (disco heat) / You make me feel (mighty real) / I need somebody to love / 'Stars' intro / Can't stop dancing / Stars.
LP: 8170441

SYLVESTER & GRIFFIN (Sylvester & Griffin).
Tracks: / Please come into my life / Till midnight / Rozanne / Never alone / Wolf river / Light that shone / You go your way / Girl be here tonight / If you give your love to me / Did you hear the news today.
LP: POLD 5063

TOO HOT TO SLEEP.
Tracks: / New beginnings / Thinking right / Can't forget the love / Too hot to sleep / Give it up / Here is my love / Can't you see / Oooh baby baby / I can't believe I'm in love.
LP: F 9607

Sylvester, Victor

LATIN SONG AND DANCE MEN (See also Ros, Edmundo) (Sylvester, Victor & Edmundo Ros).
MC: ZCP 18614

Sylvia

SOMEBODY LOVES YOU.
LP: SNTF 723

Sylvia (country)

ONE STEP CLOSER.
Tracks: / Falling in love / One step closer / Breakin' it / Cry just a little bit / I can't help the way I don't feel / Read all about it / Only the shadows know / I love you my heart / True blue / Eyes like mine.
LP: PL 85413
MC: PK 85413

SWEET YESTERDAY.
Tracks: / Nobody / Mirage / Sweet yesterday / You're a legend in your own mind / Cry baby cry / You can't go back home / Like nothing ever happened / It won't hurt to dream / Not tonight / I feel cheated / Missin' you / Mill, The / I'll make it right with you.
LP: RCALP 3108
MC: RCAK 3108

Sylvia (soul)

PILLOW TALK (OLD GOLD) (See Sylvia & Company - Shame Shame Shame).

Sylvian, David

ALCHEMY (An index of possibilities).
Tracks: / Ancient evening / Incantation (part 2 of words with the Sharman) / Awakening (part 3 of words with the Sharman) / Preparations for a journey / Steel cathedrals.
MC: SYL 1

BRILLIANT TREES.
Tracks: / Pulling punches / Ink in the well, The / Nostalgia / Red guitar / Weathered wall / Back waters / Brilliant trees.
LP: V 2290
MC: TCV 2290
LP: OVED 239
MC: OVEDC 239

FLUX AND MUTABILITY.
Tracks: / Flux (a big bright colour world) / Mutability (a new beginning in the offing).
LP: VE 43
MC: TCVE 43

GONE TO EARTH.
Tracks: / Taking the veil / Laughter and forgetting / Before the bullfight / Gone to Earth / Wave / River man / Silver moon / Healing place, The / Answered prayers / Where the railroad meets the sea / Wooden cross, The / Silver moon over sleeping steeples / Campfire coyote country / Bird of prey vanishes into a bright blue, A / Home / Sunlight seen through towering trees / Upon this earth.
LP: VDL 1
MC: TCVDL 1

PLIGHT AND PREMONITION (Sylvian, David & Holger Czukay).
Tracks: / Plight (the spiralling of winter ghosts) / Premonition.
LP: VE 11
MC: TCVE 11

SECRETS OF THE BEEHIVE.
Tracks: / September / Boy with the gun, The / Maria / Orpheus / Devil's own, The / When poets dreamed of angels / Mother and child / Let the happiness in / Waterfront / Forbidden colours (CD only).
LP: V 2471
MC: TCV 2471
MC: OVEDC 349
LP: OVED 349

Symarip

SKINHEAD MOONSTOMP.
Tracks: / Skinhead moonstomp / Phoenix city / Skinhead girl / Try me best / Skinhead jamboree / Chicken merry / These boots are made for walking / Must catch a train / Skin flint / Stay with him / Fung shu / You're mine.
LP: TRLS 187

Symbol of Freedom

YOU ARE NOT ALONE(EP) (see under Hex) (Hex/ Oi Polloi/ Stalag 17/ Symbol Of Freedom).

Symbols From The ...

SYMBOLS FROM THE MAGIC DRUM (See under Eno, Brian) (Eno, Brian).

Symons, Julian

GIGANTIC SHADOW, THE (Ball, Nicholas).
MC: CAT 4036

Symphonion

SYMPHONION MUSIC BOX (Eroica three disc, The) (Various artists).
Tracks: / Tales of Hoffman: *Various artists* / Aida march: *Various artists* / Bells of Corneville: *Various artists* / Stephanie Gavotte: *Various artists* / Mockingbird, The: *Various artists* / Estudiantina waltz: *Various artists* / Von Hummel: *Various artists* / Old hundred: *Various artists* / Spin, spin: *Various artists*/ Symphonion march: *Various artists* / Cavalleria rusticana: *Various artists* / Miserere troubadour: *Various artists* / La paloma: *Various artists* / Stabat mater: *Various artists* / Silent night: *Various artists*/ Come all ye children: *Various artists* / Freischutz prayer: *Various artists* / Ave Maria: *Various artists*/ Verlassen, verlassen: *Various artists* / Wedding march: *Various artists* / Skater's waltz: *Various artists*/ Wine, women and song: *Various artists* / Poet and peasant: *Various artists* / Monastery bells: *Various artists*.
LP: RCB 7
MC: RCB C7

Symphony Of The Body

SYMPHONY OF THE BODY (Smith, Anthony).
LP: REC 367

Syndicate

KEEP.
Tracks: / Name, The / Baby's gone / If they don't come / Underground / I love Hollywood / Word, The / Heaven / Here comes the day / All the people / They shine bright.
LP: EMC 3559
MC: TCEMC 3559

Synergy

AUDION.
Tracks: / Orbit five / Revolt at L-5 / Terminal Hotel / Electric blue / Ancestors / After the earthquake / Falcons and eagles / Flight of the looking glass / Shibolet / End to history, An / Somebody loves you / Charlie Brown / Our loving will grow / Somebody knows / O'oh leh leh / Our anniversary / Yesterday once more / Ciao ciao bambina / Hasta la vista / You're nobody till somebody loves you / Who do you think you are / Vo bate pa tu / Think about the good times / Was a sunny day.
LP: PB 6005
MC: PBC 6005

COMPUTER EXPERIMENTS VOL.1.
LP: SYN 104
MC: SYNC 104

CORDS.
LP: PB 6000
MC: PBC 6000

ELECTRONIC REALISATIONS FOR ROCK ORCHESTRA.
LP: PB 6001
MC: PBC 6001

GAMES.
LP: PB 6003
MC: PBC 6003

JUPITER MENACE (Film soundtrack).
Tracks: / Alignment, The / Alien Earth / Rampage of the elements (the Jupiter menace) / Pueblo bonito / Prophecy - the prophecy fullfilled - warriors, The / Earth in space / Ancient gods / Plunge solar observatory, The / Survivalists / Cities on the brink / Mystery of Piri Reis, The / Final alignment, The / Closing theme.
LP: HAI 105

METROPOLITAN SUITE.
LP: SYN 204
MC: SYNC 204

SEMI-CONDUCTOR.
LP: PB 11002
MC: PBC 11002

SHINE ON US.
Tracks: / Orbit five / Revolt at L-5 / Terminal hotel / Electric blue / Ancestors / After the earthquake / Falcons and eagles / Fight of the looking glass / Shibolet / End of history.
LP: LOGO 1033

Synethia

SYNETHIA.
Tracks: / Really good lovin' / I've got the love you've been missing / It be's that way sometimes / Come back into my life / Ladies, men get lonely too / Whatever, whenever, whomever / In my arms / You were doing bad when I met cha / What a feeling.
LP: JSX 4025
MC: JSX 4025 MC

Synge, John

PLAYBOY OF THE WESTERN WORLD, THE (Various artists).
MCSET: 0348

Synger, Liller

BUCKET SUCCESSOR.
LP: SLP 431

LILLER SYNGER.
LP: SLP 606

Synthphonic Variations

SEASONS.
Tracks: / Moonlight sonata / Move closer / One more night / Greatest love of all, The / Snowman, The / One day I'll fly away / Pictures of winter / Careless whisper / Cover me / Fur Elise / Holding back the years / On my own / Seasons / Don't give up / Pachebel canon / Your love is King / Power of love, The / Raining in my heart.
LP: 4501491
MC: 4501494

Syreeta

BEST OF SYREETA.
Tracks: / With you I'm born again / He's gone / To know you is to love you / Go for it / Just a little piece of you / I can't give you back the love I feel for you / One more time for love / Something on my mind / Harm our love / Spinnin' and spinnin' / Your kiss is sweet / Let's make a deal / Love fire / She's leaving home / Keep him like he is / I like every little thing about you / I'm going left / It will come.
LP: STMR 9014
MC: CSTMR 9014

GO FOR IT (See under Preston, Billy) (Preston, Billy & Syreeta).

IT WILL COME IN TIME (See under Preston, Billy) (Preston, Billy & Syreeta).

PLEASE STAY (See under Preston, Billy for details).

SET MY LOVE IN MOTION.
Tracks: / Quick slick / Move it do it / You set my love in motion / There's nothing like a woman in love / Can't shake your love / I must be in love / Wish upon a star / Out the box / I know the way to your heart / I love you.
LP: STML 12162
MC: CSTML 12162

STEVIE WONDER PRESENTS.
Tracks: / I'm going left / Spinnin' and spinnin' / Your kiss is sweet / Come and get this stuff / Heavy day / Cause we've ended as lovers / Just a little piece of you / Waiting for the postman / When your daddy's not around / I wanna be by your side / Universal sound of the world.
LP: STMS 5079
MC: CSTMS 5079

SYREETA.
Tracks: / Blame it on the sun / Let me be the one you need / You bring out the love in me / Please stay / He's gone / Love fire / Here's my love / Signed, sealed, delivered, I'm yours / Dance for me children / One more time for love.
LP: . . . . **STML 12137**
MC: . . . . **CSTML 12137**

WITH YOU I'M BORN AGAIN (See under Preston, Billy for details).

Syron Danes

BRINGER OF EVIL.
LP: . . . . **EBON 23**

System

DON'T DISTURB THIS GROOVE.
Tracks: / Don't disturb this groove / Come as you are (Superstar) / Save me / Heart beat of the city / Groove / Nightmare lover / House of rhythm / Didn't I blow your mind / Soul boy / Modern girl.
LP: . . . . **K 781 691-1**
MC: . . . . **K 781 691-4**

PLEASURE SEEKERS, THE.
Tracks: / Pleasure seekers / It takes two / Big city beat / Love won't wait for lovin' / This is for you / My radio rocks / Did in by a friend / I don't run from danger.
LP: . . . . **POLD 5182**
MC: . . . . **POLDC 5182**

RHYTHM AND ROMANCE.
LP: . . . . **K 781896-1**
MC: . . . . **K 781896-4**

Szabo, Gabor

BELSTA RIVER.
LP: . . . . **FLC 5030**

FEMME FATALE (See under Corea, Chick) (Corea, Chick & Garbor Szabo).

HIGH CONTRAST (Szabo, Gabor & Bobby Womack).
Tracks: / Breezin' / Amazon / Fingers / Azure blue / Just a little communication / If you don't want my love, give it back / I remember when.
LP: . . . . **AFF 193**
MC: . . . . **TCAFF 193**

SMALL WORLD.
LP: . . . . **FLC 6001**

Szabo, Sandor

RITUAL OF A SPIRITUAL COMMUNITY.
LP: . . . . **LR 157**

SANCTIFIED LAND.
Tracks: / Arrivers / Our presence and thirtyness / Equation of the existence / Ferdinandus / Miramare / Sikonda / Sanctified land / Departers.
LP: . . . . **HWYL 6**
MC: . . . . **HWYLA 6**

Szajner, Bernard

BRUTE REASON.
LP: . . . . **ILPS 9735**
MC: . . . . **ICT 9735**

SOME DEATHS TAKE FOREVER.
LP: . . . . **IRC 005**

SUPERFICIAL MUSIC.
LP: . . . . **IRC 008**

Szakcsi

MYSTIC DREAMS.
LP: . . . . **GRP 95771**

SA-CHI.
Tracks: / Peace for Pastorius / Dark beauty / Still dreaming / One morning / Ria / Orange and black / Pure passion / Broken English / Arabesque / Good times / Old times / Song K (Extra track on CD.).
LP: . . . . **GRP 91045**
MC: . . . . **GRPM 91045**

Szemzo, Tibor

SNAPSHOT FROM THE ISLAND.
LP: . . . . **LR 151**

T

T LA Rock

LYRICAL KING.
Tracks: / Lyrical king (from the boogie down bronx) / Tudy fruity Judy / This beat kicks / It's time to chill / Back to burn / Breakin' bells / Big beat in London / Live drummin' with the Country Boy / Three minutes of beat box / Bust these lyrics.
LP: DIX 52
MC: CDIX 52

ON A WARPATH.
LP: SBUKLP 9
MC: SBUKMC 9

T. Rex

18 GREATEST HITS: T. REX.
LP: FUN 9029

BEARD OF STARS.
Tracks: / Prelude / Day laye, A / Woodland bop, A / First heart might dawn dart / Pavilions of sun / Organ blues / By the light of the magical moon / Wind cheetah / Beard of stars / Great horse / Dragon's ear / Lofty skies / Dove / Elemental child.
LP: SLRZ 1013
LP: FEDB 5035
MC: CFEDB 5035

BEARD OF STARS/UNICORN.
Tracks: / Prelude: a day laye / Woodland bop, The / First heart might dawn dart / Pavilions of sun / Organ blues / By the light of the magical moon / Wind cheetah / Beard of stars / Great horse / Dragon's ear / Dove / Elemental child / Chariots of silk / 'Pon a hill / Seal of seasons, The / Throat of winter, The / Cat black (the wizard's hat) / Stones for Avalon / She was born to be my unicorn / Like a white star / Tangled and far / Tulip that's what you are / Warlord of the royal crocodiles / Evenings of Damask / Sea beasts / Iscariot / Nijinsky hind / Pilgrim's tale / Misty coast of Albany, romany soup.
2LP: TFOLP 15
MC: TFOMC 15
2LP: TOOFA 9/10

BEST OF T.REX.
LP: TON 2

BOLAN BOOGIE.
Tracks: / Get it on / Beltane walk / King of the mountain cometh / Jewel / She was born to be my unicorn / Dove / Woodland rock / Ride a white swan / Raw ramp / Jeepster / Fist heart mighty dawn dart / By the light of the magical moon / Summertime blues / Hot love.
LP: HIFLY 8
MC: ZCFLY 8
LP: CLALP 145
MC: CLAMC 145

COLLECTION: T. REX.
Tracks: / Hot rod mama / Strange orchestras / Chateau in Virginia Waters / Mustang Ford / Graceful fat Sheba / Deborah / Stacey Grove / Salamanda Palaganda / Travelling tragition, The / Chariots of silk / Seal of seasons, The / Cat black (the wizard's hat) / She was born to be my unicorn / Warlord of the royal crocodiles / Woodland bop, The / Dove / Beard of stars / Elemental child / One inch rock / Seagull woman / Mambo Sun / Life's a gas / Ride a white swan / Jeepster.
2LP: CCSLP 136
MC: CCSMC 136

COLLECTION: T-REX (PICKWICK).
Tracks: / Ride a white swan / Mustang Ford / Salamanda Palaganda / Get it on / Deborah / Jeepster / Hot love.
2LP: PDA 044
MCSET: PDC 044

ELECTRIC WARRIOR.
Tracks: / Mambo sun / Cosmic dancer / Jeepster / Monolith / Lean woman blues / Get it on / Planet Queen / Girl / Motivator, The / Life's a gas / Rip off.
LP: HIFLY 6
MC: ZCFLY 6
MC: CLAMC 180

FUTURISTIC DRAGON.
Tracks: / Futuristic dragon / Jupiter liar / Chrome sitar / All alone / New York City / My little baby / Calling all destroyers / Theme for a dragon / Sensation boulevard / Ride my wheels / Dreamy lady / Dawn storm / Casual agent.
LP: RAP 507
MC: RAPC 507
LPPD: RAPD 507
LP: BLN 5004
LP: MARCL 507
MC: MARCK 507

GET IT ON.
Tracks: / Get it on / Ride a white swan / Jeepster / One inch rock / King of the rumbling spires / Cosmic dancer / Jewel / Telegram Sam / Metal guru / Solid gold easy action / 20th century boy / Groover, The / Truck on (tyke) / I love to boogie.
LP: FA 3154
MC: TCFA 3154

GREATEST HITS: T. REX.
LP: PLP 50
MC: PMC 50
LP: BLN 5003

MAIN MAN.
Tracks: / Telegram Sam / Metal guru / Children of the revolution.
2LP: CR 5161
MCSET: CRT 5161

MY PEOPLE WERE FAIR AND HAD SKY IN....
Tracks: / My people were fair and had sky in... (Full title: My people were fair and had sky in their hair but now they'r) / Red hot mama / Scene scol / Strange orchestras / Dwarfish trumpet blues / Mustang Ford / Afghan woman / Knight / Graceful fat Sheba / Wielder of words / Frowning atahuallpa (my Inca love).
LP: FEDB 5013
MC: CFEDB 5013
LP: SLRZ 1003

NIGHTRIDING: T. REX.
Tracks: / Ride a white swan / Hot love / Get it on / Deborah / Consuela / Children of Rarn / One inch rock / Cosmic dancer / Raw ramp / Summertime blues / She was born to be my unicorn / Knight.
MC: KNMC 10003
LP: KNLP 10003

OFF THE RECORD WITH T. REX.
2LP: FEDD 1000
MCSET: CFEDD 1000

PLATINUM COLLECTION.
Tracks: / Get it on / Ride a white swan / By the light of the magical moon / Beltane walk / King of the rumbling spires / Lean woman blues / Hot love / Motivator, the / Is it love / Woodland rock / Seagull woman / Deborah / One inch rock / Salamanda palaganda / Mustang Ford / Stacey grove / She was born to be my unicorn / Jeepster / Summertime blues / Cosmic dancer / Raw ramp / Life's a gas / Hot rod mama.
2LP: PLAT 1002
MCSET: ZCPLT 1002

PROPHETS, SEERS AND SAGES.
Tracks: / Debora / Stacey Grove / Wind quartets / Conesuala / Trelawny lawn / Aznageel the mage / Friends, The / Salamanda palaganda / Our wonderful brownskin man / O Harley (the saltimbanques) / Eastern spell / Travelling tragition, The / Juniper suction / Scenes of dynasty.
LP: FEDB 5022
MC: CFEDB 5022

PROPHETS, SEERS AND SAGES, ANGELS OF THE AGES.
Tracks: / Prophets, seers and sages / Angels of the ages, The / Deborah / Stacey Grove / Wind quartets / Conesuala / Trelawny lawn / Aznageel the mage / Friends, The / Salamanda palaganda / Our wonderful brownskin man / O Harley (the saltimbanques) / Eastern spell / Travelling tragition, The / Juniper suction / Scenes of dynasty / My people were fair and had sky in their hair.... / Red hot mama / Scenes of child star / Strange orchestras / Chateau in Virginia Waters / Dwarfish trumpet blues / Mustang Ford / Afghan woman / Knight / Graceful fat Sheba / Wielder of words / Frowning atahuallpa (my inca love).
2LP: TOOFA 3
MCSET: ZCTOF 3

PROPHETS, SEERS.../MY PEOPLE WERE FAIR....
Tracks: / Deborah / Stacey Grove / Wind quartets / Conesuala / Trelawny lawn / Aznageel the mage / Friends, The / Salamanda palaganda / Our wonderful brown skin man / O Harley (the saltimbanques) / Eastern spell / Travelling Tragition, The / Juniper suction / Scenes of Dynasty / Hot rod Mama / Scenescof / Child star / Strange orchestras / Chateau in Virginia Waters / Dwarfish trumpet blues / Mustang Ford / Afghan woman / Knight / Graceful fat Sheba / Wielder of words / Frowning atahuallpa (my inca love).
MC: TFOMC 6
2LP: TFOLP 6
2LP: TOOFA 3/4

REPLAY ON T. REX: BOLAN BOOGIE.
LP: FEDB 5006
MC: CFEDB 5006

REPLAY ON T. REX: ELECTRIC WARRIOR.
LP: FEDB 5004
MC: CFEDB 5004

SINGLES COLLECTION VOL 1.
Tracks: / Deborah / Child star / One inch rock / Salamanda palaganda / Pewter suitor / Warlord of the royal crocodiles / King of the rambling spires / Do you remember / By the light of the magical moon / Find a little wood / Groover, The / Midnight / Black Jack / Squint eye mangle / Truck on (tyke) / Sitting here / Teenage dream / Satisfaction pony / Light of love / Explosive mouth / Zip gun boogie / Space boss / New York city / Chrome star / Dreamy lady / Ride a white swan / Is it love / Summertime blues / Hot love / Woodland rock / King of the mountain cometh / Get it on / Do you wanna dance / (Sittin' on the) dock of the bay / London boys / Solid baby / I love to boogie / Baby boomerang / Laser love / Life's an elevator / To know you is to love you / City port / There was a time / Jeepster / Life's a gas / Telegram Sam / Cadillac / Baby strange / Metal Guru / Thunderwing / Lady / Children of the revolution / Jitterbug love / Sunken rags / Solid gold easy action / Born to boogie / 20th century boy / Free angel / Soul of my suit, The / All alone / Dandy in the underworld / Groove a little / Tame my tiger / Celebrate summer / Ride my wheels / Crimson moon / Jason B Sad.
LPS: MARCL 510
MCSET: MARCK 510

SOLID GOLD T. REX.
Tracks: / 20th Century boy / Groover, The / New York City / I love to boogie / Mystic lady / Children of the revolution / Dreamy lady / Metal guru / Telegram Sam / Truck on (Tyke) / Light of love / Laser love / Dandy in the underworld / Soul of my suit, The / London boys / Solid gold easy action.
LP: FA 3005
MC: TCFA 3005

T. REX.
LP: HIFLY 2

T. REX IN CONCERT.
Tracks: / Ride a white swan / Deborah / Hot love / Get it on / One inch rock / Telegram Sam / Metal guru / Summertime blues.
LP: A BOLAN 1

T. REX (SIERRA).
Tracks: / Get it on / Summertime blues / Beltane walk / Mustang Ford / Woodland rock / Life's a gas / Hot love / Jeepster / Motivator, The / Cosmic dancer / Hot rod mama / Is it love / Children of Rarn / Jewel / Visit, The / Childe / Time of love is now / Diamond meadows / Root of star / One inch rock / Summer deep / Seagull woman / Sun eye / Wizard, The.
LP: COUNT 11
MC: ZC CNT 11
LP: FEDB 5010
MC: CFEDB 5010

TEENAGE DREAM.
LP: SHM 3217
MC: HSC 3217

T.REX FOUR LP PICTURE DISC BOX SET.
LPS: WARRIOR 14

UNICORN.
Tracks: / Unicorn / Chariots of silk / 'Pon a hill / Seal of seasons, The / Throat of winter, The / Cat black (the wizard's hat) / Stones for Avalon / She was born to be my unicorn / Like a white star, tangled and far / Tulip, that's what you are / Warlord of the royal crocodiles / Evenings of Damask / Sea beasts / Iscariot / Nijinsky hind / Pilgrim's tale, The / Misty coast of Albany, The / Romany soup.
LP: FEDB 5024
MC: CFEDB 5024
LP: SLPZ 1007

UNOBTAINABLE T. REX, THE.
Tracks: / Celebrate summer / Sunken rags / Tame my tiger / City port / Thunderwing / Satisfaction pony / Midnight / Jitterbug love / To know him is to love him / Do you wanna dance / Dock of the bay / Cadillac / Free angel / Life's an elevator / Sitting here / Lady.
LP: NUT 28
MC: TC NUT 28

ZIP GUN BOOGIE.
Tracks: / Light of love / Solid baby / Precious star / Token of my love / Till dawn / Girl in the thunderbolt suit / I really love you babe / Golden belt / Zip gun boogie.
LP: RAP 506
LPPD: RAPD 506
MC: RAPC 506

T T Quick

METAL OF HONOUR.
Tracks: / Metal of honour / Front burner / Hard as rock / Child of sin / Asleep at the wheel / Come beat the band / Hell to pay queen of the scene / Glad all over / Siren song.
LP: ILPS 9847
MC: ICT 9847

Tabackin, Lew

COLLECTION (See Under Akiyoshi, Toshiko) (Tabackin, Lew & Toshiko Akiyoshi).

DESERT LADY (Tabackin, Lew Quartet).
Tracks: / Hot house / Pyramid / Chelsea Bridge (Only on CD.) / Johnny come lately / Desert lady / Bit byas'd, A / You'll never know (Only on CD.) / Yesterdays / You leave me breathless / Serenade to Sweden.
MC: CJ 411 C

INSIGHTS (see Akiyoshi, Toshiko) (Tabackin, Lew & Toshiko Akiyoshi).

Tabak

FEMME.
LP: HDD 2434

Tabane, Philip

MALOMBO.
LP: BIG 002

UNH.
LP: 9792251
MC: 9792254

Taboola Rasa

WORLDBEAT.
LP: BASLP 002

Tabor, June

ABYSSINIANS.
Tracks: / Month of January / Scarecrow / One night as I lay on my bed / She moves among men / Lay this body down / Smiling shore / Bonnie boy / I never thought my love would leave me / Bonnie Hind / Fiddle and the drum, The.
LP: 12TS 432
MC: 5 SH 79038

AIRS AND GRACES.
Tracks: / While gamekeepers lie sleeping / Plains of Waterloo / Bonnie May / Reynardine / Band played waltzing Matilda, The / Young waters / Waly waly / Merchant's son, The / Queen among the heather / Pull down the lads.
LP: 12TS 298
MC: 5 SH 79055

AQABA.
Tracks: / Old man's song / Searching For Lambs / Banks of Red Roses, The / Where Are You Tonight / Verdi Cries / Grazier's daughter / Seven summers / Mayn Rue Plats.
LP: 12TS 449
MC: KTSC 449

ASHES AND DIAMONDS.
Tracks: / Reynard the fox / Devil and bailiff McGlynn, The / Streets of forbes / Lord Maxwell's last goodnight / Now I'm easy / Clerk saunders / Earl of Aboyne, The / Lisbon / Easter tree, The / Cold and raw / No man's land / Flowers of the forest.
LP: 12TS 360

BEES ON HORSEBACK (See under Davenport, Bob) (Tabor, June & Bob Davenport).

CUT ABOVE (Tabor, June & Martin Simpson).

Tracks: / Admiral Benbow / Davy Lowston / Flash company / Number two top seam / Strange affair / Heather down the moor / Joe Peel / Le roi Renaud / Riding down to Portsmouth / Unicorns.
LP: **12TS 410**

FREEDOM AND RAIN (Tabor, June & The Oyster Band).
Tracks: / Mississippi summer / Lullaby of London / Night comes in / Valentine's day is over / All tomorrow's parties / Dives and Lazarus / Dark eyed sailor / Pain or paradise / Susie Clelland / Finisterre.
LP: . . . . **COOK 031**
MC: . . . . **COOKC 031**

SOME OTHER TIME.
LP: . . . . **HNBL 1346**
MC: . . . . **HNBC 1346**

Tabor, Laszlo

ECHOES OF ITALY (See under Mantovani) (Tabor, Laszlo/Mantovani).

WORLD OF GYPSY ROMANCE.
Tracks: / Hungarian gypsy dance / Gypsy tears / Two guitars / Gypsy airs / Czardas / Bohemian dance / Dark eyes / Play gypsies, dance gypsies / Romany violin / Gypsy dance.
LP: . . . . **SPA 117**
MC: . . . . **KCSP 117**

Tabu Ley

AFRICA SELECTION (ZAIRE).
Tracks: / Amilo / Camarade de sous / Sanza misato / Ebeze.
LP: . . . . **STERNS 1011**

BABETI SOUKOUS.
Tracks: / Presentation / Kinshasa / Soroza / Linga ngai / Moto akokufa / Nairobi / Seli ja / I need you / Amour nala / Tu as dit que / Sentimenta / Pitie / Mosola.
LP: . . . . **RWLP 5**
MC: . . . . **RWMC 5**

HAFI DEO.
LP: . . . . **GEN 117**

IN AMERICA AND CANADA.
LP: . . . . **GEN 109**
MC: . . . . **C 2006**

KING SA.
MC: . . . . **C 2004**

LOYENGHE (Tabu Ley & M Bell).
2LP: . . . . **GEN 107/8**
MC: . . . . **C 2005**

SACRAMENTO (Tabu Ley & Nyboma).
LP: . . . . **GEN 119**

SARAH.
LP: . . . . **GEN 113**
MC: . . . . **C 2008**

Tackhead

STRANGE THINGS.
Tracks: / Nobody to somebody / Wolf in sheeps clothing / Class rock / Dangerous sex / Strange things / Take a stroll (CD only.) / Hyperspace (CD only.) / Super stupid / See the fire burning / Re-entry (CD only.) / For this I sing / Change / Steaming (CD only.) / Positive suggestion / Fix the machine (CD only.).
LP: . . . . **SBKLP 1003**
LP: **795 193 1**
MC: . . . . **SBKTC 1003**
MC: **795 193 4**

TACKHEAD SOUND SYSTEM.
LP: . . . . **TACKLP 001**

TACKHEAD TAPE TIME.
Tracks: / Mind at the end of tether / Half cut again / Reality / M.O.V.E. / Hard left / Get this / Man in a suitcase / What's my mission now? (fight the devil).
LP: . . . . **NTL 30015**
LP: . . . . **TACKLP 1**
LP: . . . . **EFA 4529**
MC: . . . . **NTLC 30015**

Taco

AFTER EIGHT.
Tracks: / Singin' in the rain / Tribute to Tino / Puttin' on the Ritz / I should care / Carmella / La vie en rose / Cheek to cheek / After eight / Livin' in my dreamworld / Encore / Thanks a million.
LP: . . . . **PL 28520**
MC: . . . . **PK 28520**

Tacticos, Manos

MUSIC FROM THE GREEK ISLANDS (Tacticos, Manos & his Bouzoukis).
Tracks: / O Andonis (theme from 'Z') / Lefteris / Delfini - Delfinaki / Natane to Ikosiena / San sfiriksis tries fores / Nostalgia / Athena / Vrehi O Theos / Epipoleos (impulsive) / Tist' anathema in 'afto / Ela agapi mou / Stou kosmou tin aniforia / Strose to stroma sou yia thio / Afto to agori (that boy) / Siko horepse kouli mou / Siko horepse sirtaki / Faliriotissa / Laikos horos / Ta pedia tou pirea / Pai-pai / Ftochologia / Varka sto yialo / Ta thakria mou eene kafta.
2LP: . . . . **MFP 1029**
MCSET: . . . . **TCMFP 1029**

Tactics

BLUE AND WHITE FUTURE WHALE.
LP: . . . . **RF 58**

BONES OF BARRY HARRISON, THE.
LP: . . . . **LRF 113**

GLEBE.
LP: . . . . **LRF 094**

HOLDEN INTERVIEW.
Tracks: / Fat man / Hard hat nine iron / Committee of love / Know what I know / Coat tails / Hole in my life / Shark bed rally.
LP: . . . . **RFM 055**

MY HOUDINI.
LP: . . . . **LRF 064**

Tacuma, Jamaaladeen

MUSIC WORLD.
Tracks: / Kimono queen / Tokyo cosmopolitaan / Matsuru / Rouge / Kismet / Creator has a master plan, The / Jamila's theme / One more night.
LP: . . . . **SNTF 979**

RENAISSANCE MAN.
Tracks: / Renaissance man / Flash back / Let's have a good time / Next stop, The / Dancing in your head / There he stood / Battle of images, The / Sparkle.
LP: . . . . **GR 83081**
MC: . . . . **GR 83084**

SHOW STOPPER.
Tracks: / Sunk in the funk / Rhythm box / From me to you / Animated creation / Bird of paradise / Show stopper / From the land of sand / Sophisticated us.
LP: . . . . **GR 8301**

Tad

GOD'S BALLS.
LP: . . . . **GR 0051**

SALT LICK.
LP: . . . . **GR 0076**

Tadley Band

AT THE LAKESIDE.
Tracks: / Rosslyn / Overture from the Royal Fireworks / Trombone trio / Clowns, The / Gymnopedie no.1 / Come back to Sorrento / Prelude and fugue / Festival prelude, A / Believe me / If all those endearing young charms / Feelings / Rockford files, The / Cossack patrol / Cavalry of the Steppes / Star wars.
LP: . . . . **BBR 701**

Taff, Russ

MEDALS.
LP: . . . . **MYR 1173**
MC: . . . . **MC 1173**

RUSS TAFF.
LP: . . . . **MYR R 1247**
MC: . . . . **MYR C 1247**

Taffetas

TAFFETAS, THE (Original off-Broadway cast) (Various artists).
Tracks: / Sh'boom: *Various artists* / Mr. Sandman: *Various artists* / Three bells, The: *Various artists* / I'm sorry: *Various artists* / Ricochet: *Various artists* / I cried: *Various artists* / Cry: *Various* artists / Smile: *Various artists* / Achoo cha-cha: *Various artists* / Mockin' Bird Hill: *Various artists* / Tonight you belong to me: *Various artists* / Happy wanderer, The: *Various artists* / Constantinople: *Various* artists / My little grass shack: *Various artists* / C'est si bon: *Various artists* / Sweet song of India: *Various artists* / Arrivederci Roma: *Various artists* / See the USA in your Chevrolet: *Various artists* / Allegheny moon: *Various artists* / Tennessee waltz: *Various artists* / Old Cape Cod: *Various artists* / Fly me to the moon: *Various artists* / Nel blue de pinto di blue: *Various artists* / Around the world: *Various* artists / Music! Music! Music!: *Various artists* / You're just in love: *Various artists* / Love letters in the sand: *Various artists* / L-O-V-E: *Various artists* / I-M-4-U: *Various artists* / Rag mop: *Various* artists / You, you, you: *Various artists* / Puppy love: *Various artists* / How much is that doggie in the window: *Various artists* / Hot canary, The: *Various artists* / Tweedlee dee: *Various artists* / Lollipop: *Various artists* / Sincerely: *Various artists* / Johnny Angel: *Various artists* / Mr. Lee: *Various* artists / Dedicated to the one I love: *Various artists* / Where the boys are: *Various artists* / I'll think of you: *Various artists* / Little darlin': *Various artists* / Spotlight on the music: *Various artists*.
LP: . . . . **TER 1167**
MC: . . . . **ZCTER 1167**

Tafolla, Joey

OUT OF THE SUN.
LP: . . . . **RR 9573**

T.A.G.G.

DELIVERY.
LP: . . . . **ST 3006**

Taggart, Blind Joe

1926-1934.
LP: . . . . **WSE 122**

BLIND JOE TAGGART 1927-31.
LP: . . . . **HER 204**

GUITAR EVANGELIST, A 1926-31.
LP: . . . . **HERWIN 204**

Tahiti

TAHITI ET BORA-BORA (le juillet polynesien) (Various artists).
Tracks: / Otea: *Various artists* / Ute: *Various artists* / Otea Aparima: *Various artists* / Ua Hiti o te ra: *Various artists* / Himene Tama'i: *Various artists* / Apamai ia'u: *Various artists* / Tahiti here: *Various artists* / To rima rarie: *Various artists* / La orana: *Various artists* / Pikoe moe ana: *Various* artists / Marama e tura ma: *Various artists* / Himene tarava: *Various artists* / Moanapoiri: *Various artists* / Pao'a: *Various artists* / Bora bora: *Various artists*.
LP: . . . . **ARN 30153**
MC: . . . . **ARN 430153**

Tai Pan

TAI PAN (Film Soundtrack) (Various artists).
LP: . . . . **STV 81293**
MC: . . . . **CTV 81293**

Tailgate Ramblers

PAUSE AND RECORD.
LP: . . . . **J 32**

Tailgators

HIDE YOUR EYES.
LP: . . . . **LS 93961**

MUMBO JUMBO.
Tracks: / Mumbo jumbo / Little girl blue / I need love / Thank you baby / Allon's rock 'n' roll / Chase the devil / Maria Elena / Yard dog / Behind the wheel / Tail shaker / Colinda.
LP: . . . . **ZONG 010**
LP: . . . . **WR 986**
MC: . . . . **WRC 986**

OK, LET'S GO.
LP: . . . . **LS 94461**

SWAMP ROCK.
LP: . . . . **GRUB 6**

TORE UP.
LP: . . . . **WR 1987**
MC: . . . . **WRC 1987**

Taiwan

PEUPLES ABORIGENES DE TAIWAN (chants de travail et d'amour) (Various artists).
Tracks: / Chants de fauchage: *Various artists* / L'ouverture d'un chantier de construction: *Various artists* / Chant de la cueillette du the: *Various artists* / Chant du bouvier: *Various artists* / Chant de la bouviere: *Various* artists / Chant du retour au port: *Various artists* / Chant de la peche en mer: *Various artists* / Chant du pillage du millet: *Various artists*.
LP: . . . . **ARN 33785**

Taj Mahal

BIG BLUES (Live at Ronnie Scott's).
Tracks: / Big Blues / Mail box blues / Stagger Lee / Come on in my kitchen / Local local girl / Soothin' / Fishin' blues / Statesboro' blues / Everybody is somebody.
MC: . . . . **ESMMC 002**

BRER RABBIT (See under Brer Rabbit) (Glover, Danny & Taj Mahal).

COLLECTION: TAJ MAHAL.
Tracks: / Fishin' blues / Leaving trunk / Six days on the road / Dust my broom / Going up the country / Candy man / Stagger Lee / Diving duck blues / Clara (St. Kitts woman) / Statesboro blues / Lot of love, A / Take a giant step / Further down the road / Little red hen / E-Z rider / Texas woman blues / Free song, A / Oh mama, don't you know / Railroad bill / Everybody's got to change sometime.
MC: . . . . **CCSMC 180**
2LP: . . . . **CCSLP 180**

GIANT STEP.
Tracks: / Linin' Track / Country blues no.1 / Wild ox man / Little Rain Blues / Little soulful tune, A / Candy Man / Cluck Old Hen / Colored Aristocracy / Blind boy rag / Stagger Lee / Cajun tune / Fishin' Blues / Annie's lover.
2LP: . . . . **DED 264**

GOING HOME.
Tracks: / Stateboro blues / Dust my broom / You don't miss your water / Good morning Miss Brown / Six days on the road / Sweet home Chicago / Little red hen / Frankie and Albert / Johnny too bad / New E-Z rider blues / Black jack David / Black Jack David / Satisfied and tickled too / Brown eyed handsome man / Clara (St Kitts woman).
LP: . . . . **CBS 31844**
MC: **40 31844**

LIKE NEVER BEFORE.
Tracks: / Don't call us / River of love / Scattered / Ev'ry wind (in the river) / Blues with a feeling / Squat that rabbit / Take all the time you need / Love up / Cakewalk into town / Big legged mommas are back in style / Take a giant step.
MC: **411679**

LIVE AND DIRECT.
Tracks: / Jorge Ben / Reggae no. 1 / You're gonna need somebody / Little brown dog / Take a giant step / L-O-V-E love / And who / Suva serenade / Airplay.
MC: . . . . **THBC 121**

NATCH'L BLUES, THE.
Tracks: / Good morning Miss Brown / Corina, Corina / I ain't gonna let nobody steal my mail... / Done changed my way of living / She caught the Katy / Cuckoo, The / You don't miss your water / Lot of love, A.
LP: . . . . **ED 231**

TAJ.
Tracks: / Everybody is somebody / Paradise / Do I love her / Light of the Pacific / Deed I do / Soothin' / Pillow talk / Local local girl / Kauai Kalypso / French letter.
LP: . . . . **SNTF 975**

TAJ MAHAL.
Tracks: / Leaving trunk / Statesboro blues / Checkin' up on my baby / Everybody's got to change sometime / EZ rider / Dust my broom / Diving duck blues / Celebrated walkin' blues.
LP: . . . . **ED 166**
MC: . . . . **CED 166**

TAKE A GIANT STEP.
Tracks: / Jorge Ben / Reggae number one / You're gonna need somebody on your bond / Little brown dog / Take a giant step / Airplay / L-O-V-E love / And who / Suya serenade.
LP: . . . . **MAGL 5035**
MC: . . . . **ZCMAG 5035**

Takahashi, Tatsuya

TATSUYA TAKAHASHI PLAYS MILES AND GIL.
LP: **K28P 6492**

Takahashi, Yukihiro

BEATNIKS.
LP: . . . . **STATLP 13**

NEUROMANTIC.
Tracks: / Glass / Grand espoir / Connection / New (red) roses / Extraordinary / Drip dry eyes / Curtains / Charge / Something in the air.
LP: . . . . **ALF 85393**
MC: **40 85393**

WHAT...ME WORRY.
Tracks: / What...me worry / It's gonna work out / Sayonara / This strange obsession / Flashback / Real you / Disposable love / My highland home in Thailand / All you got to do / It's all too much.
LP: . . . . **ALF 85954**

WILD AND MOODY.
Tracks: / Wild and moody / Stranger things have happened / Kill that thermostat / Helpless / Price to pay / Bounds of reason, bonds of love / Walking to the beat.
LP: . . . . **JCS 11**

Takanaka, Masayoshi

SAUDADE.
Tracks: / Fair wind, A / Saudade / Eana / Breakin' loose / Ride 'em high / Chill me out / New York strut / Forest of my heart, The / Manifestation.
LP: **810 506-1**
MC: **810 506-4**

Takase, Aki

SONG FOR HOPE (Takase, Aki Trio).
LP: . . . . **ENJA 4012**

Takatina, He Toa

AUTHENTIC MAORI SONGS.
MC: . . . . **SODET 007**

Take 5

TAKE 5 (Various artists).
LP: . . . . **SHELTER 4**

Take 6

SO MUCH 2 SAY.
LP: **7599258921**
MC: **7599258924**

TAKE 6.
Tracks: / Gold mine / If we ever / Mary / Get away Jordan / Milky-white way / Spread love / Quiet place, A / David and Goliath / He never sleeps / Let the words.

LP: K 925670 1
MC: K 925670 4

Take 7 Schizzo

TAKE 7 SCHIZZO (Various artists).
LP: DO 310
MC: DO 310 MC

Take Me Out To ...

TAKE ME OUT TO THE BALL PARK (Film soundtrack) (Various artists).
LP: CC 100.18

Take Your Head ...

TAKE YOUR HEAD OFF AND LISTEN (Various artists).
LP: LP 001

Taken By Force

TAKEN BY FORCE (Various artists).
LP: F 3004

Talas

SINK YOUR TEETH INTO THAT.
Tracks: / Sink your teeth into that / Hit and run / NV 443345 / High speed on ice / Shy boy / King of the world / Outside lookin' in / Never see my cry / Smart lady / Hick town.
LP: GRUB 1

TALAS.
LP: ZORRO 32

Talbert, Tom

THINGS AS THEY ARE (Talbert, Tom Septet).
LP: SB 2038

Talbot, Jamie

ALTITUDE.
LP: MVLP 21

Talbot, Jeffrey

GOLDEN TENOR.
LP: EL 2705171
MC: EL 2705174

Talbot, John Michael

BE EXALTED.
LP: WING R 529
MC: WING C 529

COME TO THE QUIET.
Tracks: / Gloria / Sparrow song / World artist corp / Psalm 95 (Come worship the Lord) / Psalm 63 (as morning breaks) / Psalm 51 / Psalm 86 / Psalm 23 (the Lord is my shepherd) / Peace prayer (St. Francis) / Peter's canticle (1 Peter 2:21-25; 3:8-9, 13-22) / Philippians canticle (Philippians 2:1-11) / Psalm 62 / Psalm 91 / Psalm 131 (Come to the quiet).
LP: WING 512
MC: TC WING 512

EMPTY CANVAS.
LP: ML R 7015
MC: ML C 7015

FOR THE BRIDE.
Tracks: / Psalm 45: Ode of the bridegroom / Wedding dance / Ode of the bride / Holy is his name / Annunciation, The: Dance of the heavens / Gabriel's song / Song of songs: Canticle of the bride / Celebration dance / Canticle of the groom.
LP: WING 508
MC: TC WING 508

GOD OF LIFE.
LP: WING 524
MC: TC WING 524

HEART OF THE SHEPHERD.
LP: WING R 531
MC: WING C 531

LIGHT ETERNAL.
MC: TC WING 518

LORD'S SUPPER, THE.
Tracks: / Prelude / We shall stand forgiven / Glory to God in the high / Creed 1 / Creed 2 / Holy holy holy / Communion song / Lord's prayer, The / Lamb of God.
LP: WING 510
MC: TC WING 510

LOVER AND THE BELOVED, THE.
LP: SP R 1193
MC: SP C 1193

NEW EARTH, THE.
Tracks: / Greatest 'tis love, The / Shiloh; King of kings / Dance with him / Last trumpet, The / Prepare ye the way / Cast down your cares / Coming, The / New earth, The / Let the people sing amen.
LP: BIRD 108
MC: TC BIRD 108

PAINTER, THE (Talbot, John Michael & Terry).
Tracks: / Greeting / Wonderful counselor / Advent suite part 1 &2 / Behold the new kingdom / Create in me a clean heart / Paint my life / Mystery / Jesus has come / Empty canvas, The.
LP: BIRD 124
MC: TC BIRD 124

QUIET REFLECTIONS.
MC: SP C 1150

QUIET, THE.
LP: ML R 7001
MC: ML C 7001

REGATHERING, THE.
LP: SP R 1153
MC: SP C 1153

SONGS FOR WORSHIP.
MC: TC WING 521

SONGS FOR WORSHIP.
MC: TC WING 521

SONGS FOR WORSHIP 2.
LP: WING R 527
MC: WING C 527

TROUBADOUR OF THE GREAT KING.
Tracks: / Sunrise / Dance of creation / Alleluia / How many and wonderful / Brother Sun and Sister Moon / Sing a new song / Hymn to the praises of God / Pleiades and Orion, The / Lilies of the field, The / Prayer for guidance / Rebuild my temple / Without guile / Praises of the virtues, The / Let us adore the Lord / My God and my all / Mount Alverna / Troubadour / Prayer before the Cross.
LP: WING 514
MC: TC WING 514

Talbot, Terry

TERRY TALBOT.
LP: OAK R 3011
MC: OAK C 3011

TIME TO LAUGH, A TIME TO SING, A.
Tracks: / Down to the well / Bible land / Lamplighter / Angels sing hallelujah / Pleasin' you pleases me / Never let yesterday / Hollywood lies / Takin' the time / Father.
LP: BIRD 119
MC: TC BIRD 119

Tale Of Ale

STORY OF THE ENGLISHMAN AND HIS BEER.
2LP: FRR 023/024

Tale of Scheherezade

TALE OF SCHEHEREZADE (Lee, Dennis (nar)).
MC: 1373

Tale Of Two Cities

TALE OF TWO CITIES (see Dickens, Charles) (Pasco, Richard (nar)).

TALE OF TWO CITIES, A (see under Dickens, Charles) (Gielgud, Sir John (nar)).

TALE OF TWO CITIES VOLUME 1, A (See under Dickens, Charles) (Dance, Charles).

TALE OF TWO CITIES VOLUME 2, A (See under Dickens, Charles) (Dance, Charles).

Talent Showcase

TALENT SHOWCASE (Various artists).
LP: NT 0012

Tales...

TALES OF WITCHES, GHOSTS AND GOBLINS (Price, Vincent).
MC: 1393

Tales from...

TALES FROM THE ARABIAN NIGHTS (Various artists).
Tracks: / Tales from the Arabian nights: *Various artists* / Three sisters: *Various artists* / Three dervishes' tales, The: *Various artists* / Dib-dib, The: *Various artists.*
MC: ANV 655

Tales From A Long Room

TALES FROM A LONG ROOM (See also Peter Tinniswood).

Tales Of Beatrix

TALES OF BEATRIX POTTER (Film Soundtrack) (Various artists).
LP: CSD 3690

Tales Of Narnia...

TALES OF NARNIA (see under Lewis, C. S.).

Tales of Terror

TALES OF TERROR.
LP: CD 015

Tales Of Toad (bk)

TALES OF TOAD.
MCSET: DTO 10551

Talila

OTT AZOI (Talila & Kol Aviv Ensemble).
Tracks: / Lomar zich iberbeten / Der rebbe elimeylech / Die mame is gegangen / Kinder yorn / Belz / Yiddish mame / Reizele / Liedele.
LP: ARN 34360
MC: ARN 434360

YIDDISH SONGS - VOL.2 (Talila & Kol Aviv Ensemble).
Tracks: / Die grine kuzine / Die zun vet arunter / Lomir zingen und tanzen / Malkala / Papir is dokh weiss / Ya-bo-bom / H'ayale / Unter a klein beimale.
LP: ARN 34477
MC: ARN 434477

Talion

KILLING THE WORLD.
LP: WADES 001

Talisman

TAKIN THE STRAIN.
LP: CELA 1 T

TALISMAN.
Tracks: / Snowbird / Sailing / Leaving on a jet plane / Morning town ride / Our last song together / Help me make it through the night / That'll be the day / To love somebody / All around my hat / Jolene / Streets of London / I'm a song.
LP: SRTZ 76371

Talk Radio

TALK RADIO/WALL STREET (Film Soundtrack) (Various artists).
Tracks: / Unpredictable: *Kent* / We know where you live: *Tick* / He has a heart: *Trend* / Bud's scam: *Copeland, Stewart* / Trading begins: *Copeland, Stewart* / Break up: *Copeland, Stewart* / End title: *Copeland,* Stewart / Just come right in here please: *Dietz* / We feel too much: *Tick* / Are you with me: *Copeland, Stewart* / Tall weeds, The: *Copeland, Stewart* / Anacott steel: *Copeland, Stewart.*
LP: VS 5215
MC: VSC 5215

Talk Talk

COLOUR OF SPRING, THE.
Tracks: / Happiness is easy / I don't believe in you / Life's what you make it / April 15th / Living in another world / Give it up / Chameleon day / Time it's time.
LP: EMC 3506
MC: TCEMC 3506
LP: ATAK 145
MC: TCATAK 145

HISTORY REVISITED (The Remixes).
Tracks: / Living in another world - '91 / Such a shame / Happiness is easy (dub) / Today / Dum dum girl / Life's what you make it / Talk Talk / It's my life / Living in another world (Curious world dub mix).
LP: PCS 7349
MC: TCPCS 7349

IT'S MY LIFE.
Tracks: / Dum dum girl / Such a shame / Renee / It's my life / Tomorrow / Started / Last time, The / Call in the night boys / Does Caroline know / It's you.
LP: EMC 2400021
MC: TCEMC 2400024
LP: ATAK 116
MC: TCATAK 116

IT'S MY MIX.
Tracks: / Why is it so hard / Talk talk / My foolish friend / It's my life / Dum dum girl / Such a shame.
LP: ST 6542
MC: 4 XT 6542

NATURAL HISTORY (Very Best of Talk Talk).
Tracks: / Today / Talk talk / My foolish friend / Such a shame / Dum dum girl / It's my life / Give it up / Living in another world / Life's what you make it / Happiness is easy / I believe in you / Desire.
LP: PCSD 109
LP: 793 976 1
MC: TCPCSD 109
MC: 793 976 4

PARTY'S OVER, THE.
Tracks: / Talk talk / It's so serious / Today / Party's over, The / Hate / Have you heard the news / Mirror man / Another word / Candy.
LP: ATAK 65
MC: TCATAK 65
LP: FA 3187
MC: TCFA 3187
LP: EMC 3413

SPIRIT OF EDEN.
Tracks: / Rainbow, The / Eden / Desire / Inheritance / I believe in you / Wealth.
LP: PCSD 105
MC: TCPCSD 105
LP: PCS 7319
MC: TCPCS 7319
LP: ATAK 156
MC: TCATAK 156

Talkin' Loud...

TALKIN' LOUD SAMPLER (Various artists).
LP: 8467921
MC: 8467924

Talking Bird

TALKING BIRD, THE (Various artists).
Tracks: / Talking bird, The: *Various artists* / Little dwarf, The: *Various artists* / Zaid the roper: *Various* artists / Barber and the dyer, The: *Various artists* / Inescapable shoes, The: *Various artists* / Olives and gold: *Various artists.*
MC: ANV 664

Talking Drums

REASSEMBLY.
LP: STICKY 012
LP: GUM 011
MC: GUM 011C

Talking Heads

FEAR OF MUSIC.
Tracks: / I Zimbra / Mind / Cities / Paper / Life during wartime / Memories can't wait / Air / Heaven / Animals / Electric guitar / Drugs.
LP: SRK 6076

LITTLE CREATURES.
Tracks: / And she was / Give me back my name / Creatures of love / Lady don't mind / Perfect world / Stay up late / Walk it down / Television man / Road to nowhere.
LP: TAH 2
MC: TAHTC 2
LP: EJ 2403521
MC: EJ 2403524
LPPD: EJ 2403520
LP: ATAK 146
MC: TCATAK 146

MORE SONGS ABOUT BUILDINGS AND FOOD.
Tracks: / Thank you for sending me an angel / With our love / Good thing / Warning sigh / Girls want to be with the girls, The / Found a job / Artists only / I'm not in love / Stay hungry / Take me to the river / Big country.
LP: K 56531
MC: K4 56531

NAKED.
Tracks: / Blind / Mr. Jones / Totally nude / Ruby dear / Nothing but flowers / Democratic circus / Facts of life / Mommy, daddy / Big daddy / Cool water / Bill* (*Extra track on cassette & CD only.).
LP: EMD 1005
MC: TCEMD 1005
LP: EMC 790156
LP: ATAK 158
MC: TCATAK 158

NAME OF THIS BAND IS TALKING HEADS, THE.
Tracks: / New feeling / Clean break, A / Don't worry about the government / Pulled up / Psycho killer / I zimbra / Drugs / Houses in motion / Artists only / Stay hungry / Air / Building on fire / Memories (can't wait) / Great curve, The / Cross-eyed and painless / Take me to the river.
2LP: SRK 23590
MCSET: SRC 23590

REMAIN IN LIGHT.
Tracks: / Great curve, The / Cross-eyed and painless / Born under punches (heat goes on) / Houses in motion / Once in a lifetime / Listening wind / Seen and not seen / Overload.
LP: SRK 6095
MC: SRC 6095

SPEAKING IN TONGUES.
Tracks: / Burning down the house / Making flippy floppy / Swamp / Girlfriend is better / Slippery people / I get wild / Pull up the roots / Moon rocks / This must be the place.
LP: 923883 1
MC: 923883 4

STOP MAKING SENSE (Film Soundtrack).
Tracks: / Psycho Killer / Swamp / Slippery people / Burning down the house / Girl friend is better / Once in a lifetime / What a day that was / Life during wartime / Take me to the river.
LP: TAH 1
MC: TAHTC 1
LP: EJ 2402431
MC: EJ 2402434
LP: ATAK 147
MC: TCATAK 147

TALKING HEADS '77.
Tracks: / Uh-oh, love comes to town / New feeling / Tentative decisions / Happy day / Who is it? / No compassion / Book I read / Don't worry about the government / First week / Last week....carefree / Psycho killer / Pulled up.
LP: 9103 328
MC: SRC 23591

TALKING HEADS: INTERVIEW PICTURE DISC.
LPPD: BAK 2017

TRUE STORIES.
Tracks: / Love for sale / Puzzlin' evidence / Hey now / Papa Legba / Wild wild life / Radio head / Dream operator / People like us / City of dreams / Wild wild life (Long E.T. mix) (CD only.).
LP: EU 3511

MC: . . . . TCEU 3511
LP: . . . . EMC 3511
MC: . . . . TCEMC 3511
LP: . . . . FA 3231
MC: . . . . TCFA 3231

Talking To God

TALKING TO GOD (Various artists).
LP: . . . . **LPLTD 006**
MC: . . . . **MS LTD 006**

Talking With...(bk)

TALKING WITH THE ONE MINUTE MANAGER (Kenneth Blanchard) (Blanchard, Kenneth (nar) & Spencer Johnson (nar)).
MC: **0600560651**

Tall Boys

WEDNESDAY ADDAMS' BOYFRIEND.
Tracks: / Wednesday Addams' boyfriend / Feel it / Star / Baron, The / Through a glass / Beast on the moor.
LP: . . . . **NED 8**

Tall Dwarfs

GOODBYE CRUEL WORLD.
Tracks: / Phil's disease (day one) / Songs of the silents / Maybe / Paul's place / Nothing's going to happen / Pictures on the floor / Clover / Luck or loveliness / Phil's disease (day four) / Beauty / Walking home/This room is wrong.
LP: . . . . **FNE 15**

Tall Tales & True

SHIVER.
Tracks: / Trust / Tinytown / Bridge, The / Song for when I'm gone / Hold on / Heart / Stranger on the stair / Think of yourself / Passing out the chains / April.
LP: **838 209 1**
MC: **838 209 4**

Tall, Tom

HOT ROD IS HER NAME.
Tracks: / Goldie Jo Mahome / Underway / Give me a chance / If you knew what I know / Please be careful / Are you mine / Out of line / Boom boom boomerang / Will this dream of mine come true / Hot rod is her name / Whose pidgeon are you / Don't you know, don't you know / I want to walk with you / Come with me / Remembering you / You loved another one better than me / Why must I wonder / I gave my heart to two people.
LP: . . . . **BFX 15189**

Talley, James

AMERICAN ORIGINALS.
Tracks: / Find somebody and love them / Bury me in New Orleans / Baby she loves a rocker / Whiskey on the side / Are they gonna make us outlaws again / Way to say I love you / New York town / Open all night / Montana song / Ready to please / We're all one family.
LP: . . . . **BFX 15182**

Tallis Scholars

BYRD. GREAT SERVICE.
LP: **1585 11**
MC: **1585T 11**

CHRISTMAS CAROLS AND MOTETS.
Tracks: / Angelus ad virginem / Nowell sing we / There is no rose / Nowell / Dieu vous garde / Lullay I saw / Lully, lulla thou tiny little child / Lullaby (William Byrd).
LP: **1585-10**
MC: **1585T-10**

PANGE LINGUA (JOSHQUIN).
LP: **1585-09**
MC: **1585T-09**

Tallis, Thomas

LAMENTATIONS OF JEREMIAH, THE.
MC: **8333084**

Talon

NEVER LOOK BACK.
LP: . . . . **SH 009**

Talulah Gosh

ROCK LEGENDS, VOL.69.
LP: . . . . **CON 00026**
LP: . . . . **AGAS 004**

THEY'VE SCOFFED THE LOT.
LP: . . . . **SARAH 064**

Talyllyn Non Stop

TALYLLYN NON STOP - ENGINE NO.4 (Thomas, Edward).
LP: . . . . **RESM 016**

Tamblyn, William

HOSANNA IN EXCELSIS!.
LP: . . . . **AS 1003**

Tamil Nadu

TAMIL NADU (Various artists).
LP: . . . . **VPA 8483**

Taming Of The Shrew

TAMING OF THE SHREW, THE (see under Shakespeare, William) (Various artists).

Tamlins

I'LL BE WAITING.
LP: . . . . **LLLP 027**
MC: . . . . **LLC 27**

LOVE DIVINE.
LP: . . . . **SKDLP 008**

Tammles

EMBARQUEMENT IMMEDIAT.
LP: . . . . **BUR 813**

SANS BAGAGE.
LP: . . . . **BUR 832**

TAMMLES.
LP: . . . . **BUR 810**

Tampa Red

1921-31 (Tampa Red & Georgia Tom).
LP: . . . . **DLP 585**

1928-1946.
LP: . . . . **BOB 15**

BOTTLENECK GUITAR 1928-37.
LP: . . . . **L 1039**

CRAZY WITH THE BLUES.
LP: . . . . **OL 8001**

DON'T TAMPA WITH THE BLUES.
LP: . . . . **OBC 516**

GUITAR WIZARD, THE 1935-42.
LP: . . . . **OT 1201**

GUITAR WIZARD, THE 1935-53.
LP: . . . . **BC 25**

KEEP ON JUMPING 1946-52.
LP: . . . . **WBJ 001**

MIDNIGHT BLUES.
LP: . . . . **BT 2003**

TAMPA RED 1928-41.
LP: . . . . **BD 2001**

TAMPA RED WITH JOHNNY JONES (Tampa Red & Johnny Jones).
Tracks: / It's a brand new boogie / Corrine blues / New bad luck blues / Come on if you're coming / Poor stranger blues / Sure enough I do / Put your money where your mouth is / Looka there looka there / Sugar baby / New deal blues / I'll never let you go / Don't blame Shorty for that / Too late, too late / 1950 blues / I'm gonna put you down / Got a mind to leave this town.
LP: . . . . **KK 7411**

YOU CAN'T GET THAT STUFF NO MORE.
LP: . . . . **OL 2816**

Tams

18 GREATEST HITS.
MC: **2636054**

ATLANTA SOUL CONNECTION.
Tracks: / Hey girl don't bother me / It's alright / You lied to your daddy / What kind of fool / Untie me / What do you do / LAugh it off / Don't you just know it / Concrete jungle / Shelter / There's a great big change in me / Trouble maker / Standing in / Anna / It's better to have loved a little / Be young, be foolish, be happy.
LP: . . . . **CRB 1064**

BEACH MUSIC FROM...THE TAMS.
Tracks: / There ain't nothin' like shaggin' / Thank you John / Making true love / Showtime / Get a job / My baby sure can shag.
LP: . . . . **CLTLB 6500**

THERE AIN'T NOTHING LIKE SHAGGIN'.
Tracks: / There ain't nothing like shaggin' / Hey girl, don't bother me / Making true love / Thank you John / Get a job / Be young, be foolish, be happy / Showtime / Weep little girl / What kind of fool (do you think I am) / My baby sure can shag.
LP: . . . . **V 2499**
MC: . . . . **TCV 2499**
LP: . . . . **OVED 303**
MC: . . . . **OVEDC 303**

Tamson, Jock Bairns

JOCK TAMSON'S BAIRNS.
LP: . . . . **TP 002**

LASSES FASHION, THE.
Tracks: / Lasses fashion / Robin, The / Merry nicht under the tummel brig / Braes o'Balquhidder, The / Greig's strathspey / Miss Wharton Duff / Lady Keith's Lament / Gates of Edinburgh, The / O'er bogie / Mrs. Gordon's reel / Tibbie Fowler / Strathspey-The Shetland fiddlers society / Grant's reel / Gladstone's reel / Laird O' drum, The / Kempy kaye / Donald, Willy & his dog / Peter Mackintosh of Skeabost.
LP: **12TS 424**

Tan, Melvyn

I'VE GOT TO GET TO INDIANA.
Tracks: / I've got to get to Indiana / Early morning light / It looks like love / Six wheel boogie / Phoenix / If I said you had a beautiful body / Some day soon / Lucille / Country roads.
LP: . . . . **WDL 501**

Tan Tan

MUSICAL NOSTALGIA TODAY.
LP: . . . . **RAINBOW 01**

Tandy, Gilles

LA COLERE MONTE.
LP: . . . . **ROSE 95**

Tandy, Napper

AWAY WE GO.
LP: . . . . **FRC 008**

WILL IT EVER BE FRIDAY.
MC: . . . . **CMCS 1026**

Tandy-Morgan

EARTH RISE (Tandy-Morgan Band).
Tracks: / Earth rise / Under the blue / Asteroid / Suddenly / Escape from the citadel / Caesar of the galaxy / One thousand worlds / Spaceship Earth / Zero zero / Third planet, The / Ria / Princeton / Pictures in my pillow / Secret, (The).
LP: . . . . **WKFMLP 68**
MC: . . . . **WKFMMC 68**

Tanega, Norma

WALKING MY CAT NAMED DOG (OLD GOLD) (See Toys - Lovers Concerto for details).

Tanganyika

TANGANYIKA Modern AfroAmerican jazz (Various artists).
LP: . . . . **VSOP 20**

Tangerine

TANGERINE.
LP: . . . . **CRELP 061**
MC: . . . . **CCRELP 061**

Tangerine Dream

ALPHA CENTAURI/ ATEM.
Tracks: / Sunrise in the third system / Fly and collision of the comas sola / Alpha centauri / Atem / Fauni-gena / Circulation of events / Wahn.
LP: . . . . **VD 2504**
LP: **86561-8069-1**

BEST OF TANGERINE DREAM.
Tracks: / Central Park (New York) / Livemiles (part 2) (extract) / Song of the whale (part 1 - from Dawn) / Le parc (L.A. - Streethawk) / Poland (extract) / Wahn / Ashes to ashes / Tyger / Dolphin dance / Song of the whale (part 2 - from dusk) / Yellowstone Park (Rocky mountains) / Astral voyager / Sunrise in the third system / Zelt.
LP: . . . . **HIP 75**
MC: . . . . **HIPC 75**

CANYON DREAMS (see under Canyon Dreams).

COLLECTION: TANGERINE DREAM.
Tracks: / Genesis / Circulation of events / Fauni-gena / Alpha centauri / Fly and collision of comas sola / Journey through a burning brain / Birth of liquid plejades / White clouds.
2LP: . . . . **CCSLP 161**
MC: . . . . **CCSMC 161**

CYCLONE.
Tracks: / Bent cold sidewalk / Rising runner missed by endless sender / Madrigal meridian.
LP: . . . . **OVED 71**
MC: . . . . **TCV 2097**
MC: . . . . **OVEDC 71**
LP: . . . . **V 2097**

DREAM SEQUENCE ("Best of" Compilation).
Tracks: / Dream is always the same, The / Phaedra / Rubicon (part 1 - excerpt) / Stratosfear (excerpt) / Choronzon / Cherokee Lane (live) / Cinnamon Road / Kiew mission / Ricochet part 2 / Cloudburst flight / Force majeure (excerpt) / Tangram (part 1) / Beach stone / Logos (parts 1 & 2- live) / White eagle / Dominion / Love on a real train.
LPS: . . . . **TDLP 1**
MCSET: . . . . **TDC 1**

ENCORE (Tangerine Dream live).
Tracks: / Cherokee Lane / Monolight / Coldwater canyon / Desert dream.
2LP: . . . . **VD 2506**
MC: . . . . **TCVD 2506**

EXIT.
Tracks: / Kiew mission / Pilots of purple twilight / Choronzon / Exit / Network 23 / Remote viewing.
LP: . . . . **V 2212**
MC: . . . . **TCV 2212**
MC: . . . . **OVEDC 166**
LP: . . . . **OVED 166**

FIRESTARTER (See under Firestarter for details).

FLASHPOINT (1985 Film Soundtrack).
Tracks: / Going West / Afternoon in the desert / Plane ride / Mystery tracks / Lost in the dunes / Highway patrol / Love phantasy / Madcap story / Dirty cross roads / Flashpoint.
LP: . . . . **HMILP 29**
MC: . . . . **HMIMC 29**

FORCE MAJEURE.
Tracks: / Force Majeure / Cloudburst flight / Thru Metamorphic rocks.
LP: . . . . **V 2111**
MC: . . . . **TCV 2111**
LP: . . . . **OVED 111**
MC: . . . . **OVEDC 111**

FROM DAWN TILL DUSK - 1973-88.
MC: . . . . **MCTC 034**

GREEN DESERT.
LP: **88561-8072-1**
LP: . . . . **HOP 226**
MC: . . . . **HOPC 226**

HYPERBOREA.
Tracks: / No mans land / Hyperborea / Cinnamon road / Sphinx lightning.
LP: . . . . **V 2292**
MC: . . . . **TCV 2292**
LP: . . . . **OVED 175**
MC: . . . . **OVEDC 175**

IN THE BEGINNING.
LPS: . . . . **TANG 1**

LE PARC.
LP: . . . . **HIP 26**
MC: . . . . **HIPC 26**

LILY ON THE BEACH.
Tracks: / Too hot for my chinchilla / Lily on the beach / Alaskan summer / Desert drive / Mount Shasta / Crystal curfew / Paradise cove / Twenty nine palms / Valley of the kings / Radio city / Blue Mango Cafe / Gecko / Long island sunset.
LP: **210.103**
MC: **410.103**

LIVE MILES.
LP: . . . . **HIP 62**
MC: . . . . **HIPC 62**

LOGOS (Live at the Dominion-London-1982).
LP: . . . . **OVED 167**
MC: . . . . **OVEDC 167**
LP: . . . . **V 2257**

MELROSE.
Tracks: / Melrose / 3 bikes in the sky / Dolls in the shadow / Yucatan / Electric lion / Rolling down Cahuenga / Art of vision / Desert train / Cool at heart.
LP: **211185**
MC: **411185**

MIRACLE MILE.
Tracks: / Teetering scales / One for the book / After the call / On the spur of the moment / All of a dither / Final statement.
LP: **210.887**
MC: **410.887**

MUSIC FROM THE 21ST CENTURY (Tangerine Dream/Neil Norman).
Tracks: / Tangram.
LP: . . . . **GNPS 2146**
MC: **GNP5 2146**

NEAR DARK (Film Soundtrack).
Tracks: / Caleb's blues / Pick up at high noon / Rain in the third house / Bus station / Goodtimes / She's my sister / Mae comes back / Father and son / Severin dies / Flight at dawn / Mae's transformation.
LP: . . . . **FILM 026**
MC: . . . . **FILMC 026**

OPTICAL RACE.
Tracks: / Marakesh / Atlas eyes / Mothers of rain / Twin soul tribe / Optical race / Cat scan / Sun gate / Turning of the wheel / Midnight trail, The / Ghazal (Love song).
LP: **2042-1-P**
MC: **2042-4-P**
LP: **209557**
MC: **409557**

PHAEDRA (See under Tangerine Dream CD Box Set).

PHAEDRA.
Tracks: / Phaedra / Mysterious semblance at the strand of nightmares / Movements of a visionary / Sequent C.
LP: . . . . **OVED 25**
MC: . . . . **OVEDC 25**
LP: . . . . **V 2010**

POLAND.
LP: . . . . **HIP 22**
MC: . . . . **HIPC 22**
LPPD: . . . . **HIPX 22**

RICOCHET.
Tracks: / Ricochet part 1 / Ricochet part 2.
LP: . . . . **OVED 26**
MC: . . . . **OVEDC 26**
LP: . . . . **V 2044**

RICOCHET (See under Tangerine Dream CD Box Set).

RUBYCON (See under Tangerine Dream CD Box Set).

RUBYCON.
Tracks: / Rubycon part 1 / Rubycon part 2.
LP: . . . . **OVED 27**
MC: . . . . **OVEDC 27**
LP: . . . . **V 2025**

SHY PEOPLE (see under Shy People).

SORCERER (Original Soundtrack).
Tracks: / Search / Call, The / Creation / Vengeance / Journey, The / Grind / Rain forest / Abyss / Mountain road, The / Impressions of sorcerer / Betrayal.
LP: . . . . **MCL 1646**
MC: . . . . **MCLC 1646**
LP: . . . . **MCF 2806**

STRATOSFEAR.
Tracks: / Stratosfear / Big sleep in search of Hades, The / 3 a.m. at the border of the marsh / Invisible limits.
LP: . . . . **V 2068**
MC: . . . . **TCV 2068**
MC: . . . . **OVEDC 70**
LP: . . . . **OVED 70**

TANGRAM.
Tracks: / Tangram set (part 1 & 2).
LP: . . . . **OVED 112**
MC: . . . . **OVEDC 112**
LP: . . . . **V 2147**

THIEF (Film Soundtrack).
Tracks: / Beach theme / Doctor Destructo / Diamond diary / Burning bar / Beach scene / Scrap yard / Trap feeling / Igneous.
LP: . . . . **OVED 72**
MC: . . . . **OVEDC 72**
LP: . . . . **V 2198**

TYGER.
Tracks: / Tyger / London / Alchemy of the heart / Smile.
LP: . . . . **HIP 47**
MC: . . . . **HIPC 47**

UNDERWATER SUNLIGHT.
Tracks: / Song of the whale / Song of the whale: from dawn... / ...to dusk / Dolphin dance / Ride on the Ray / Scuba Scuba / Underwater twilight.
LP: . . . . **HIP 40**
MC: . . . . **HIPC 40**

WAVELENGTH (Film soundtrack) (See under Wavelength).

WHITE EAGLE.
Tracks: / Mojave-plan / Midnight in Tula / Convention of the 24 / White Eagle.
LP: . . . . **V 2226**
MC: . . . . **TCV 2226**
LP: . . . . **OVED 150**
MC: . . . . **OVEDC 150**

ZEIT.
Tracks: / Birth of liquid plejades / Nebulous dawn / Origin of supernatural possibilities / Zeit.
2LP: . . . . **VC 2503**
2LP: **88561-80670-1**

Tangier

FOUR WINDS.
LP: **979125 1**
MC: **979125 4**

STRANDED.
LP: **7567916031**
MC: **7567916034**

Tanglewood

RISE AND SHINE.
Tracks: / Destruction road / Reggae music sweet / Charles Manson / Bless be the tides / Cold Europe / Rise and shine / My people's needs / Let's live life / Run run come / Man in the jungle.
LP: . . . . **CRX 10**

TANGO

TANGO (Various artists).
Tracks: / Adios muchachos: *Various artists* / Jalousie: *Various artists* / La paloma: *Various artists*/ Le plus beau tango du monde: *Various artists* / La cumparsita: *Various artists* / Violetta: *Various artists*/ Caminito: *Various artists* / Tomo y obligo: *Various artists* / Cueta a bajo: *Various artists* / Poema: *Various artists* / Adios pampa mia: *Various artists* / Silencio: *Various artists.*
LP: . . . . **IMS 8161681**

Tango Fran Argentina

TANGO FRAN ARGENTINA (A dazzling musical adventure) (Various artists).
LP: . . . . **PHONT 7547**

Tangos

TANGOS - THE EXILE OF GARDEL (Film Soundtrack) (Various artists).
LP: . . . . **A 280**

Tank

ARMOURED PLATED.
Tracks: / Don't walk away / Power of the hunter / Run Like Hell / Filth hounds of Hades / (He fell in love with a) storm trooper / Red Skull Rock / Snake, The / Who needs love songs / Stepping on a Land mine / Turn your head around / Crazy horses / Some came running / Hammer on / Shellshock / T.W.D.A.M.O. / Biting and scratching / Used leather (hanging loose) / Blood, guts and beer / Filth bitch boogie / T.A.N.K..
LP: . . . . **RAWLP 009**
MC: . . . . **RAWTC 009**

FILTH HOUNDS OF HADES.
Tracks: / Shellshock / Struck by lightning / Run like hell / Blood, guts and beer / That's what dreams are made of / Turn your head around / Heavy artillery / Who needs love songs / Filth hounds of Hades / Stormtrooper.
LP: . . . . **KAM L1**

HONOUR AND BLOOD.
LP: . . . . **MFN 26**

TANK.
Tracks: / Reign of thunder / With your life / Enemy below, the / Suffer / March on, sons of nippon / None but the brave / Lost / It fell from the sky.
LP: . . . . **GWLP 23**
MC: . . . . **GWTC 23**

THIS MEANS WAR.
LP: . . . . **MFN 3**
LPPD: . . . . **MFN 3P**
MC: . . . . **TMFN 3**

Tank of Danzig

DON'T STOP THE MUSIC.
LP: . . . . **ANT 030**

Tankard

ALIEN.
MLP: . . . . **NUK 131**
MLP: . . . . **N 0131 5**

CHEMICAL INVASION.
LPPD: . . . . **N 0109**
LP: . . . . **N 0096**
LP: . . . . **NUK 096**
MC: . . . . **ZCNUK 096**
MC: . . . . **N 0097**

FAT, UGLY, LIVE.
LP: . . . . **NO 1661**
MC: . . . . **NO 1664**

HAIR OF THE DOG.
LP: . . . . **NUK 150**
MC: . . . . **ZCNUK 150**

MEANING OF LIFE, THE.
Tracks: / Open all night / We are us / Dancing on our grave / Mechanical man / Beermuda / Meaning of life, The / Space beer / Always them / Wheel of rebirth / Barfly.
LP: . . . . **NUK 156**
MC: . . . . **ZCNUK 156**

MORNING AFTER, THE.
LP: . . . . **NUK 123**
MC: . . . . **ZCNUK 123**
LP: . . . . **N 0123 1**
MC: . . . . **N 0123 2**

ZOMBIE ATTACK.
LP: . . . . **NUK 046**
LP: . . . . **N 0046**

Tannahill Weavers

ARE YE SLEEPING, MAGGIE.
Tracks: / Are ye sleeping, Maggie / Ferrickside / Galley of Lorne / Birnie bouzle / Cam ye by Atholl / Hugaibh oirbh / Gypsy laddie, The / My love's in Germany / Overgate, The / Can the yowes.
LP: . . . . **PLR 001**

DANCING FEET.
Tracks: / Turf lodge / Tranent Muir / Isabeaux S'y Promene / Fisher row / Wild mountain Thyme / Maggie's pancakes / Mary Morrison / Campbeltown kiltie ball / Final trawl, The.
LP: . . . . **SIF 1081**
MC: . . . . **CSIF 1081**

LAND OF LIGHT.
Tracks: / Lucy Cassidy / Scottish settlers lament, The / Ronald Maclean's farewell to Oban / Dunrobin castle / Rovin' heilandman, The / Yellow haired laddie / Land of light / Queen amang the heather/Mairi Anne... / Bustles and bonnets / American stranger, The / Conon Bridge.
LP: . . . . **SIF 1067**
MC: . . . . **CSIF 1067**

OLD WOMAN'S DANCE, THE.
Tracks: / Gloomy winter's now awa / Wha'll dance wi Wattie / Traditional pipe major Gorge Allan / McGregors, The / Bonnie was yon Rosie Briar / Laird of Cockpen, The / Irish washerwoman, The / Cook in the kitchen, The / Miss Girdle.
LP: . . . . **PLR 010**

TANNAHILL WEAVERS.
Tracks: / Geese in the bog, The / Jig of slurs, The / Jock Stewart / Tae the weavers gin ye gang / Blackberry bush / Willie Cummings / Red speckled hen, The / Dalena McKay / Merchant's son, The / Doctor Ross' 50th welcome to the Argyllshire gathering / Ned of the hills / Gypsy laddie, The / Lady Mary / De'ils awa' with the exciseman, The / Cam ye o'er frae france / Cameron McFadgen / Humours of Cork, The / Skyeman's jig, The.
LP: . . . . **PLR 017**

TANNAHILL WEAVERS, 4.
Tracks: / Johnnie Cope / Athole highlanders, The / Trooper and the maid, The / Sound of sleat, The / I once loved a lass / Paddy o'Rafferty / Sandy Duff / Auld lang syne / Captain Carswell / Susan MacLeod / Caberfeidh / Gaberlunzie man, The / Mrs. MacLeod of Raasay / Terror time, The / Birkin tree, The / Lieutenant Maguire / Donald MacLean.
LP: . . . . **PLR 028**

Tanned Leather

SADDLE SOAP.
Tracks: / You blew it if you do it / Country boy / Hard road back to Georgia, A / Alright, it's alright / Donna, do you wanna? (a summer song) / Greyhound, take me home to San Francisco / Please come home forever / Calvin Jones / St. John's river / Frosty morning / Sheep shell corn by the rattle of his horn / Soldier and the lady, The / Prince William / Pant Corlan yr wyn / Jack o' diamonds / Muddy roads / Cuffey / Conversation with Beth / Hallelujah - I'm a bum / Little rabbit, A / Rolling of the stones / Shall I sue / Butterfly / Polly Vaughan / Young Collins.
LP: . . . . **RESP 013**

Tannehill, Frank

FRANK TANNEHILL 1932-41.
LP: . . . . **BD 2027**

Tannen, Holly

FROSTY MORNING (Tannen, Holly & Pete Cooper).
LP: . . . . **PLR 015**

Tanner, Gid

HEAR THESE NEW SOUTHERN FIDDLE AND GUITAR RECORDS.
LP: . . . . **ROUNDER 1005**
MC: . . . . **ROUNDER 1005C**

KICKAPOO MEDICINE SHOW (Tanner, Gid & His Skillet Lickers).
Tracks: / Nancy rollin' / Farmer's daughter, The / I ain't no better now / Never seen the likes since gettin' upstairs / Arkansas sheik, The / You got to stop drinking shine / You got to stop kickin' my dog around / Cumberland gap / On a buckin' mule / Paddy won't you drink some cider / Don't you hear Jerusalem moan / Prettiest little girl in the county / Kikapoo medicine show parts 1 & 2 / Rake and the rambling boy / New Dixie / Mississippi Sawyer.
LP: . . . . **ROUNDER 1023**
MC: . . . . **ROUNDER 1023C**

Tanner, Phil

GREAT MAN OF GOWER (Tanner, Phil & F.A.Bracey).
Tracks: / Gower reel (mouth-music) / Oyster girl, The / Sweet primroses / Bold Henry Martin / Dark-eyed sailor / Lass of Swansea town / Barbara Allen / Parson and the clerk, The / Bonnie bunch of roses, The / Pottery canal song / Young Roger esq. / Over the hills to glory / Gower wassail.
MC: **60-057**

Tansey, Seamus

IRISH TRADITIONAL MUSIC.
LP: . . . . **OLP 1007**

JIGS, REELS AND AIRS.
MC: . . . . **HSMC 028**

SEAMUS TANSEY.
LP: . . . . **LEA 2005**

SLIGO CEILI (Tansey, Seamus & Group).
LP: . . . . **SOLP 1022**

TRADITIONAL IRISH MUSIC.
MC: . . . . **COX 1007**

Tansey's Fancy

TANSEY'S FANCY.
LP: . . . . **PLR 065**

Tansley School

OUR FAMILY ALBUM (Children Of Tansley School).
Tracks: / Our family / My grandfather's clock / That doggie in the window / We're all going to a birthday party / Uncles and aunts / No one quite like Grandma / What would we do without dad / My two cousins / Ginger Tom / Grandma's feather bed / My brudda Sylvest / My mum is one in a million.
LP: . . . . **NTS 232**

Tantrum

RATHER BE ROCKIN'.
Tracks: / Rather be rockin' / Don't turn me off / You are my world / Sammy and Susie / Runnin' / How long / You need me / Take a look / Applaud the winner / Search for a reason.
LP: . . . . **OV 1247**

Tanza, Steven

CONUNDRUM.
Tracks: / Brittania / Blockade / Bloodbath / Facelift / Deadbeat / Downtown / To work / State hate / Earmark / Red card / One way / This England / In the city / Look and learn / Order / Watch and ward / State of emergency / Hammer and fist / Song for Pip, A.
LP: . . . . **ST 7540**

Tanzania Sound

TANZANIA SOUND.
MC: . . . . **OMA 106C**

Tap Dance Kid

TAP DANCE KID (Original Broadway Cast) (Various artists).
Tracks: / Overture: *Various artists* / Another day: *Various artists* / Four strikes against me: *Various artists*/ Class act: *Various artists* / They never hear what I say: *Various artists* / Dancing is everything: *Various* artists / Fabulous feet: *Various artists* / I could get used to him: *Various artists* / Man in the moon, The: *Various artists* / Like him: *Various artists* / My luck is changing: *Various artists* / Someday: *Various* artists / I remember how it was: *Various artists* / Tap tap: *Various artists* / Dance if it makes you happy: *Various artists* / Williams song: *Various artists* / Finale: *Various artists.*
LP: . . . . **TER 1096**
MC: . . . . **ZCTER 1096**

Tap (Film)

TAP (Film Soundtrack) (Various artists).
Tracks: / Bad boy: *Various artists* / All I want is forever: *Various artists* / Baby what you want me to do: *Various* artists / Strong as steel: *Various artists* / Forget the girl: *Various artists* / Can't escape the rhythm: *Various artists* / Lover's intuition: *Various artists* / Somebody like you: *Various artists* / Max's theme (instrumental): *Various artists* / Free: *Various artists.*
LP: **4650811**
MC: **4650814**

Tapscott, Horace

IN NEW YORK.
LP: . . . . **IP 7724**

SONG OF THE UNSUNG.
LP: . . . . **IP 7714**

Tar

HANDSOME.
LP: . . . . **ARR 1**

Tar Babies

FRIED MILK.
LP: . . . . **SST 101**

HONEY BUBBLE.
LP: . . . . **SST 236**
MC: . . . . **SSTC 236**

NO CONTEST.
LP: . . . . **SST 169**
MC: . . . . **SSTC 169**

Tara

BELFAST CITY BY THE LAGAN SIDE.
Tracks: / City by the Lagan side / Nancy Spain / Lough Sheelin eviction, The / Rambles of spring / Shipyard slips / Catch me if you can / Fields of Athenry / Farewell to the Rhonda / Rathlin island / Lonesome boatman, The (Instrumental on tin whistle.) / Rose of Mooncoin / Four pounds a day / My Lagan flows softly / Ringsend rose.
LP: . . . . **PHL 472**
MC: . . . . **CPHL 472**

BOYS IN THE LANE.
LP: . . . . **EULP 1019**

FOLK BALLADS FROM IRELAND.
Tracks: / Home by the Lee / This land we love / Right says she / Any Tipperary Town / German clockwinder, The / Slievegallion Braes / John O'Dreams / Shane O'Neil / Juice of the Barley, The / Lovely Leitrim / Mary Mac / Rose of Allendale / Take me back to Castlebar / Carrickfergus.
LP: . . . . **DHL 708**
MC: . . . . **CDHL 708**

RIGS OF THE TIME.
LP: . . . . **EULP 1006**
MC: . . . . **EUMC 1006**

Taramis

QUEEN OF THIEVES.
LP: . . . . **RR 9526 1**

Tarbuck, Jimmy

JIMMY TARBUCK.
Tracks: / I Should be so lucky / More I see you, The / Never gonna give you up / Together forever / There's a kind of hush / Over and over / Yesterday man / Hands

up / Follow the fairway / Una paloma blanca / Viva Espana / Lucky fella / Locomotion, The / Concerto in U / Atmosphere / Again / Whole lotta shakin' goin' on / Great balls of fire / It's only rock 'n' roll / Sweet little sixteen / Johnny B. Goode / Good golly Miss Molly / Gonna rip it up / Sha-la-la-la-lee / Blue suede shoes / All shook up / Gentle on my mind / Everybody's talkin' / He'll have to go / Wonderful tonight / Release me / Your cheatin' heart.
LP: . . . . TARBY 1
MC: . . . . TARBYC 1

Targe

TARGE.
LP: . . . . BSS 386

Target

MASTER PROJECT GENESIS.
LP: . . . . AAARRG 016

MISSION EXECUTED.
LP: . . . . AAARRG 007

Tari Singers

PARTY SING-A-LONG.
MC: . . . . ZCSLP 612

SCOTTISH SINGALONG.
MC: . . . . ZCSLP 614

Tarka The Otter

TARKA THE OTTER (Film Soundtrack) (Various artists).
LP: . . . . ZSW 613
MC: . . . . KZSWC 613

Tarleton's Jig

FIT OF MIRTH FOR A GROAT, A.
Tracks: / Selenger's round / Dragon of Wantley, The / Tombeau de Mezangeau / Tunbridge Doctors of physic, The / Over the hills and far away / Joan's placket is torn/Childgrove / Hide-Park frolic, The / Parson's farewell / Courtiers, courtiers / Toccata arpeggiata / Mr. George Tollitt's Division upon a ground / Cheshire round/The West Country jig.
MC: . . . . NMP 1522

FOR KING AND PARLIAMENT !.
Tracks: / Prince Rupert's march / French report / Vive le Roy / Battle of Worcester / Gather your rosebuds / Halfe Hannikin / We be soldiers three / Cuckold's all in a row / Sir Thomas Fairfax:his march / Psalm CXVII / Scots march / Drive the cold winter away / Lord of Carnavans jegg / When cannons are roaring / Clean contrary way / King / Millfield / Rump song.
LP: . . . . NMP 1521

Tarnfarbe

HEROES OF TODAY.
LP: . . . . NB 016

Tartan Brass

OUR SCOTLAND.
Tracks: / Amazing grace / Ye banks and braes / Loch Lomond / Lord of the dance / Skye boat song / Annie Laurie / Johnny Cope / Mhari's wedding / My love is like a red red rose / Wee cooper o' Fife, The / Aye waukin o' / Mull of the cool bens / Auld lang syne.
LP: . . . . LILP 5152
MC: . . . . LICS 5152

Tartan Lads

BY THE LOCHSIDE.
Tracks: / By the lochside / Lovely glens of Angus, The / Bandboys / Granny's heilan' hame / Bonnie lass o' Fyvie / Dark island / Tartan, The / Back o' Reries Hill / Johnny lad / Sing us a song of Bonnie Scotland / It's a long way to Tipperary / Pack up your troubles in your old kit bag / Keep right on to the end of the road / Morag's fairy glen / Lochcote / Royal Belfast / Trumpet hornpipe / High level hornpipe / Flower of Scotland / My bonnie Shirley Ann / Gracieuse / Farmer's boy.
LP: . . . . LILP 5027
MC: . . . . LICS 5027

EVENING WITH THE TARTAN LADS.
LP: . . . . REL 463
MC: . . . . REC 463

LEGENDS OF SCOTLAND.
Tracks: / Lammas tide, The / Martelette Polka / Auld meal mill, The / Wee sprig o'heather, A / Bonnie lass o' Bon Accord / O a' the airts / Man's a man, A / Corn rigs / Scotland the brave / Green oak tree / Captain Carswell / Thistle of Scotland / Over the drills / Rowan tree / Jock O'Hazeldean / Old maid in a garret / Under freedom's flag / Burnie boozie / Rustic brig, The / Barnyards of Delgaty.
MC: . . . . ZCCLS 711

MEMORIES OF SCOTLAND.
LP: . . . . LOCLP 1029
MC: . . . . ZCLOC 1029

SCOTLAND THE BRAVE.
Tracks: / Take me back / Wild mountain thyme / Sons of the brave / Always Argyll / Our island home / My Florence / Kissing in the dark / Bonnie wee Jeannie McCall / Gallant forty twa / Lammas tide, The / Road and the miles to Dundee, The / Back to bonnie Scotland / O'er the hills to Ardentinny / Accordion polka / Danny boy / Scotland the brave / Bonnie lass o' Bon Accord / Star o' Rabbie Burns, The.
LP: . . . . LOCLP 1020
MC: . . . . ZCLOC 1020

SCOTLAND YET.
Tracks: / Loch Maree islands / Dark neuve chapel / Jacqueline waltz / Aye ready / My mother's land / Dugald McColl's farewell to France / Mrs. H.L.MacDonald of Dunach / Gala braes / Lads of bonnie Scotland, The / Scotland yet / Killiecrankie / Pipe Major Sam Scott / Kirkhill / Angus MacKinnon / Top of Ben Lomond, The / Ballad of Glencoe / Gordon for me, (A) / Jock MacKay / I belong to Glasgow / Pigmies polka / Bonnie Banchory.
LP: . . . . LILP 5049
MC: . . . . LICS 5049

SCOTLAND'S OWN TARTAN LADS.
Tracks: / Rose of Allandale / Burnie boozie / Rustic brig, (The) / Barnyards of Delgaty / Martelette polka / Green oak tree / Roses of Prince Charlie / Bluebell polka / Four ways of love / Bonnie Aberdeen / Bonnie wells o' Wearie / Over the drills / Heather bells will bloom again / King George V's army / Campbells' farewell to Redcastle / Murray's welcome / Burning bridges / Northern lights / Loch Lomond / Auld Scots mither o' mine.
LP: . . . . LOCLP 1004
MC: . . . . ZCLOC 1004

SCOTTISH COUNTRY ROADS.
Tracks: / Summer road / Bonnie / Strathyre / Clarinet polka / You're my best friend / Lights in Lochindaal / Bluebells of Scotland / Anna Marie / Mull of Kintyre / San Antonio rose / Scottish selection / Bonnie naver bay / My own land / Annie's song / One day at a time.
LP: . . . . REL 465
MC: . . . . REC 465

SEASONS.
Tracks: / Rowan tree / Jock O'Hazeldean / Auld man in the garret / These hands / Captain Carswell / Flower of Scotland / Doctor Sandy Lang of Bathgate / Doctor Ross's 50th welcome / Mr. & Mrs. Alex Ross / Song of the Clyde / Seasons / Thistle of Scotland / Cuckoo waltz / Lovely glens of Angus, The / Bonnie lass o' Scotland / Farewell and joy / Sharpshooters march / McLaughlin's ceilidh.
LP: . . . . LOCLP 1009
MC: . . . . ZCLOC 1009

WELCOME TO OUR MUSIC.
Tracks: / Lucille / Almost persuaded / Son of the scottish soldier / Lay down beside me / Medley of mist covered mountains / Over the sea to Skye / Bonnie lass o'Dundee.
LP: . . . . REL 469
MC: . . . . REC 469

Tartar People

MUSIC OF THE TARTAR PEOPLE (Various artists).
LP: . . . . TGM 129

Tarzen

TARZEN.
Tracks: / Taboo / Pack rules / Running with the wrong guys / Love you wild / Shout that name / Tarzen / Hills have eyes, The / Drum talk / Jungle muscle / Tribal man.
LP: 790277 1

Tasby, Finis

BLUES MECHANIC.
Tracks: / Find somethin' else to do / Midnight train / Don't listen to a friend / Too many people / Rather trust a stranger / Drinkin' bad whiskey / Get drunk and be somebody / Walking the highway / Travellin' band.
LP: . . . . CH 122

Tashan

CHASING A DREAM.
Tracks: / Read the dream / Strung out on you / If words can express / Thank you father / Love is / I don't ever / So much in love / Read my mind / Ooh wee baby / Chasing a dream / Got the right attitude.
LP: 4501581
MC: 4501584

ON THE HORIZON.
Tracks: / Black man / Howya livin' / Keep movin' on / Save the family / Heaven / Tears of joy / Think about you all the time / Do you wanna know / Lovin' great feelin' / Changes / On the horizon / This one's for James.
LP: 465 521 1
MC: 465 521 4

Tashian, Barry

TRUST IN ME (Tashian, Barry & Holly).
Tracks: / Trust in me / Home / Blue eyes / Ramona / Making a change / You're running wild / Party doll / My favourite memory / Poor woman's epitaph / Look both ways / Boy who cried love, The / I can't dance.
LP: . . . . RR 302
MC: . . . . MCRR 302

Task Force

FORBIDDEN FRUIT.
Tracks: / Forbidden fruit / Remember these eyes / Cry baby cry / You'll never leave me / I got something for you / Tobacco Road.
LP: . . . . THBM 001

Tassano, Simon

WATERGLASS (Tassano, Simon & Eddy Sayer).
MC: . . . . CO 1

Taste

ON THE BOARDS.
LP: 2459 338
LP: 583 083

TASTE.
LP: 583 042
LP: 2459 327

TASTE LIVE AT THE ISLE OF WIGHT.
LP: 2383 120

Taste Of Honey

LADIES OF THE EIGHTIES.
Tracks: / Sayonara / We've got the groove / I'll try something new / Lies / Diamond real / Never go wrong / Midnight snack / Leavin' tomorrow.
LP: . . . . EST 12173

TWICE AS SWEET.
Tracks: / Ain't nothin' but a party / Rescue me / Goodbye baby / I'm talkin' 'bout you / Superstar superman / She's a dancer / Sukiyaki / Don't you lead me on / Say that you'll stay.
LP: . . . . EST 12089

Taste Of Sugar

TUUUT.
LP: . . . . SD 4009

Taste Of Summer

TASTE OF SUMMER (Various artists).
LP: . . . . AELP 1
MC: . . . . AEMC 1

Taste Test

TASTE TEST (Various artists).
LP: . . . . NAR 045LP
MC: . . . . NAR 045MC

Taster

TASTER, A (Various artists).
LP: . . . . R 101

Tasty Licks

ANCHORED TO THE SHORE.
LP: . . . . ROUNDER 0120

TASTY LICKS.
LP: . . . . ROUNDER 0106
MC: . . . . ROUNDER 0106C

Tate, Buddy

BALLAD ARTISTRY OF BUDDY TATE, THE.
LP: 3034

BUDDY TATE AND THE MUSE ALL STARS.
Tracks: / Jumpin' at the Woodside / Blue creek / Candy / Tangerine / She's got it.
LP: . . . . MR 5198

CRAZY LEGS AND FRIDAY STRUT (see McShann, Jay) (Tate, Buddy & Jay McShann).

GREAT BUDDY TATE, THE.
LP: . . . . CJ 163

INSTRUMENTAL FOR DANCING (Tate, Buddy & Frank Culley).
LP: . . . . KK 784

JUMPIN' ON THE WEST COAST.
Tracks: / Tate's a jumpin' / Blue and sentimental / Vine Street breakdown / Ballin' from day to day / Six foor two blues / Kansas City local / Things you done for me, baby, The / Early morning blues / Good morning judge.
LP: . . . . BLP 30128

JUST JAZZ (Tate, Buddy & Al Grey).
LP: . . . . UP 27 21

KANSAS CITY JOYS (Tate, Buddy/Paul Quinichette/Jay McShann).
LP: . . . . SNTF 716
MC: . . . . ZCSN 716

KANSAS CITY WOMAN.
Tracks: / Kansas City woman / One for me, The / Pamela / Candyville / Outswinger / Steevos / Clarinet lemonade / Swinging Scorpio.
LP: . . . . BLP 30163

LONG TALL TENOR (Tate, Buddy & Humphrey Lyttelton).
Tracks: / I cover the waterfront / Sweetie / Rompin' with Buck / Buddy Tate from Texas State / Rock a bye Basie / Buddy's bit / I cried for you.
LP: . . . . CLGLP 008

QUARTET.
Tracks: / June night / If you could see me now / Alone together / Bye bye blackbird / Georgia on my mind / Someday, sweetheart / I remember April.
LP: 3027

SHERMAN SHUFFLE.
Tracks: / Curtains of the night / Back in your own back yard / Have you met Miss Jones / Sherman shuffle / Best things in life are free, The / Lover man / Body and soul / Warm valley / Potentate.
LP: 3017

SWINGING LIKE....TATE (Tate, Buddy & His Orchestra).
Tracks: / Bottle it / Walk that walk / Miss Sadie Brown / Moon eyes / Rockin' Steve / Rompin' with Buck.
LP: . . . . AFF 171

TATE A TETE AT LA FONTAIN (Tate, Buddy & Tete Montoliu).
LP: . . . . SLP 4030
LP: . . . . SLP 267

TEXAS TWISTER, THE.
LP: . . . . NW 352

TOUR DE FORCE (see Cohn,Al/Scott Hamilton/Buddy Tate).

Tate, Grady

AIN'T BUT A FEW OF US LEFT (see Jackson, Milt) (Tate, Grady/ Milt Jackson/ Oscar Peterson/ Ray Brown).

Tate, Howard

GET IT WHILE YOU CAN.
Tracks: / Ain't nobody home / Part time love / Glad I knew better / How blue can you get / Get it while you can / baby I love you / I learnd it all the hard way / Everyday I have the blues / How come my bull dog don't bark / Look at granny run run.
LP: . . . . POLD 5096

Tate, Snuky

BABYLON UNDER PRESSURE.
Tracks: / My girl / Mommy / Babylon under pressure / Back to Africa / Afreakmas / Light my fire / I don't know samba / Won't be around / Faulty machinery.
LP: . . . . CHR 1421
MC: . . . . ZCHR 1421

Tate, Tommy

TOMMY TATE.
Tracks: / For the dollar bill / On the real side / Listen to the children / Castles in the sky / This train / I just don't know / Let me entertain you / We don't.
LP: . . . . MS 3
LP: . . . . TRLP 107
LP: . . . . TRPL 107

Tate, Troy

LIBERTY.
Tracks: / Sorrow / Girl on a ferry / Merry go round / High altitude / Liberty / All in a row / Tomorrow i'll be gone / Round and round / God's puppet / Airport of silence.
LP: 925 312 1

TICKET TO THE DARK.
Tracks: / Party / Thomas / Love is / Winning team / All the way up / Whip crack away / Safety net / House of the new breed / Lifeline / I'm not your toy.
LP: 925 160 1

Tatiana & Zouti

GOUME LEKOL.
LP: . . . . HDD 2452

Tattoo

BLOOD RED.
LP: . . . . RR 94961

TATTOO.
Tracks: / What did he do / Give it to ya easy / Send a ship / I still want you / Absolutely love / It's cold outside / Yer stale / Lonely Saturday night / This is your city / Highway calls my name.
LP: . . . . PDL 2003

Tattooed Love Boys

BLEEDING HEARTS.
LP: . . . . LUSLP 1
MC: . . . . LUSMC 1

NO TIME FOR NURSERY RHYMES.
LP: . . . . LUSLP 7
MC: . . . . LUSMC 7

Tatum, Art

20TH CENTURY PIANO GENIUS.
2LP: 8261291

1945: ART TATUM.
Tracks: / Body and soul / I guess I'll have to change my plan / What is this

thing called love? / Crazy rhythm / Sweet Georgia Brown / Can't we be friends? / Limehouse blues / Among my souvenirs / I'm gonna sit right down and write myself a letter / Stay as sweet as you are / Sugar foot stomp / You took advantage of me.
LP: . . . . SM 3117

ART OF TATUM, THE.
LP: 2673751
MC: 2673754

ART TATUM.
LP: . . . . LPJT 63

ART TATUM 1940-44.
LP: . . . . LPJT 1

ART TATUM AND ERROLL GARNER (Tatum, Art & Erroll Garner).
LP: . . . . FS 306

ART TATUM AT THE CRESCENDO VOL.1.
LP: . . . . GNPS 9025

ART TATUM AT THE CRESCENDO VOL.2.
LP: . . . . GNPS 9026

ART TATUM COLLECTION (20 golden greats).
Tracks: / Smoke gets in your eyes / Willow weep for me / Somebody loves me / Blue skies / Sweet Lorraine / Someone to watch over me / I cover the waterfront / I won't dance / On the sunny side of the street / My heart stood still / Japanese sandman / What does it take (to win your love) / Nice work if you can get it / She's funny that way / Don't blame me / Taboo / Dardanella / It's the talk of the town / Dancing in the dark / I gotta right to sing the blues.
LP: . . . . DVLP 2064
MC: . . . . DVMC 2064

ART TATUM ON THE AIR.
Tracks: / Tiger rag / Young and healthy / Morning, noon and night / When day is done / Stardust / Chinatown, my Chinatown / Lulu's back in town / Humoresque / I know that you know / Sweet Lorraine / How high the moon / Ain't misbehavin' / Song of the vagabonds / Smoke gets in your eyes.
LP: . . . . AIRCHECK 21

ART TATUM, VOLS 1 & 2.
Tracks: / It's only a paper moon / Just a gigolo / Three little words / I gotta right to sing the blues / On the sunny side of the street / Somebody loves me / Why was I born? / If I could be with you one hour tonight / Mean to me / You took advantage of me / Body and soul / I guess I'll have to change my plan / Can't we be friends? / Among my souvenirs / I'm gonna sit right down and write myself a letter / Stay as sweet as you are / Fine and dandy / I've got the world on a string / What is this thing called love? / Crazy rhythm / Limehouse blues / All God's chillun got rhythm / I gotta right to sing the blues / I'm coming, Virginia.
2LP: . . . . VJD 511

ARTISTRY OF TATUM, THE.
2LP: 400031

BEST OF ART TATUM.
Tracks: / Night and day / Willow weep for me / Blues in my heart / Caravan / Foggy day, A / Hallelujah / Can't we be friends? / Have you met Miss Jones? / Elegy / Love for sale.
LP: 2310 887

COMPLETE CAPITOL RECORDINGS, THE.
Tracks: / Willow weep for me / I cover the waterfront / Aunt Hagar's blues / Nice work if you can get it / Someone to watch over me / Dardanella / Time on my hands / Sweet Lorraine / Somebody loves me / Don't blame me / My heart stood still / You took advantage of me / I gotta right to sing the blues / How high the moon / Makin' whoopee / Going home / Blue skies / It's the talk of the town / Dancing in the dark / Tenderly / Melody in F / September song / Would you like to take a walk / Tea for two / Out of nowhere / Lover / Just one of those things / Indiana.
2LP: . . . . AFFD 191
MCSET: . . . . TCAFFD 191

COMPLETE TRIO SESSIONS VOL.1 (Featuring Tiny Grimes & Slam Stewart).
Tracks: / I got rhythm / Cocktails for two / I ain't got nobody / After you've gone / Moonglow / Deep purple / I would do anything for you / Liza / Tea for two / Honeysuckle Rose / Man I love, The / Dark eyes / Body and soul / I know that you know.
LP: . . . . OFF 3001

COMPLETE TRIO SESSIONS VOL.2 (Featuring Tiny Grimes & Slam Stewart).
Tracks: / On the sunny side of the street / Flying home / Boogie / Topsy / If I had you / Soft winds / Long, long ago / Variations on a theme by Flotow / If I had you / Warm up with sandman / Thou swell 1 / Thou swell 2 / Thou swell 3.
LP: . . . . OFF 3002

ERROLL GARNER & ART TATUM, VOL 1 (see Garner, Erroll) (Tatum, Art & Erroll Garner).

FIRST RECORDINGS (In concert).
Tracks: / Tiger Rag / Tea for two / St. Louis blues / Tiger rag / Sophisticated lady / How High the moon / Humouresque / Tatum-pole boogie / Someone to watch over me / Yesterdays / I know that you Know / Willow weep for me / Man I love, The / Kerry dance, the.
LP: . . . . CBS 26550
MC: 40 26550

GENIUS, THE.
Tracks: / Fifty second street theme / Midnight melody / Gang o'notes / Just before dawn / Between midnight and dawn / Apollo boogie / Hallelujah / Song of the vagabonds / Runnin' wild / Memories of you / Poor butterfly / Kerry dance, The.
LP: . . . . BLP 30124

GET HAPPY.
Tracks: / Happy feet / Royal Garden blues / Ain't misbehavin' / Stardust / In a sentimental mood / Man I love, The / Running wild / I can't get started / Get happy / Begin the beguine / It had to be you / Humoresque / Hallelujah / Lullaby in rhythm / Oh, you crazy moon / Over the rainbow.
LP: . . . . BLP 30194

KEYSTONE SESSIONS.
LP: . . . . VS 81021

MASTERS OF JAZZ VOL.8.
LP: . . . . SLP 4108

MOODS.
Tracks: / It had to be you / Oh, you crazy moon / Over the rainbow / Day in, day out / Exactly like you / Hallelujah, Hallelujah / Memories of you / Yesterdays / Jitterbug waltz / I cover the waterfront / Love for sale / Just like a butterfly / Sweet Lorraine.
LP: . . . . OFF 3042

PIANO MASTERY.
Tracks: / Humoresque / It had to be you / Begin the beguine / Where or when / Night and day / Poor butterfly / Don't blame me / Man I love, The / Ja da / I found a new baby / Somebody loves me / Exactly like you.
LP: . . . . SS 105

PIANO SOLO.
LP: 2M 056 80800
MC: 2M 256 80800

PIANO SOLO (ZETA).
LP: . . . . ZET 708

PIANO SOLOS.
LP: . . . . JP 5005

PURE GENIUS (Cleveland Ohio Broadcast 1934, L.A. 1945, NYC 1945).
Tracks: / Young and Healthy / Morning noon and night / When day is done / Stardust / Chinatown my Chinatown / Man I love, The / Taboo / Somebody loves Me / Why was I born / If I could be with you one hour tonight / Tea for two / Mean to me / It's only a paper Moon / Just a gigolo / Three little Words / I Gotta right to sing the blues.
LP: . . . . ATS 3
MC: . . . . TCATS 3

PURE GENIUS.
Tracks: / Gone with the wind / Stormy weather / Tea for two / Elegy / Humoresque / Sweet Lorraine / Get happy / Lullaby of the leaves / Tiger rag / Emaline / Love me / St. Louis blues / Begin the beguine / Rosetta / Indiana / Wee baby blues / Stompin' at The Savoy / Last goodbye blues / Battery bounce / Lucille / Rock me, mama / Corina Corina / Lonesome graveyard / I got rhythm / Cocktails for two / After you've gone / Moonglow / Deep purple / I would do anything for you / Honeysuckle rose.
2LP: . . . . AFFD 118

REMARKABLE ART OF TATUM, THE (Tatum, Art Trio).
LP: . . . . AP 88

SONG OF THE VAGABONDS.
Tracks: / Tea for two / Poor butterfly / I've got a right to sing the blues / Taboo / Ain't misbehavin' / Royal Garden blues / I got rhythm / Hallelujah / Song of the vagabonds / Lover / Memories of you / Running wild / Yesterdays / Kerry dance, The.
LP: . . . . BLP 30166

STRANGE AS IT SEEMS.
LP: . . . . CI 011

TATUM GROUP MASTERPIECES VOL.1.
Tracks: / What is this thing called love? / I'll never be the same / Makin' whoopee / Hallelujah / Perdido / More than you know / How high the moon.
LP: 2310 720
MC: K10 720

TATUM GROUP MASTERPIECES VOL.2.
Tracks: / Verve blues / Plaid / Somebody loves me / September song / Deep purple.
LP: 2310 731
MC: K10 731

TATUM GROUP MASTERPIECES VOL.3.
Tracks: / Blues in C / Undecided / Under a blanket of blue / Blues in B flat / Foggy day, A / Street of dreams / 'S wonderful.
LP: 2310 732
MC: K10 732

TATUM GROUP MASTERPIECES VOL.4.
Tracks: / Old-fashioned love / Blues in my heart / My blue Heaven / Hands across the table / You're mine / You / Idaho.
LP: 2310 733

TATUM GROUP MASTERPIECES VOL.5.
Tracks: / Night and day / I won't dance / In a sentimental mood / Moon is low, The / Moon song / You took advantage of me / This can't be love / I surrender, dear.
MC: K10 734

TATUM GROUP MASTERPIECES VOL.6.
Tracks: / Just one of those things / More than you know / Some other spring / If / Blue Lou / Love for sale / Isn't it romantic? / I'll never be the same / I guess I'll have to change my plan / Trio blues.
LP: 2310 735
MC: K10 735

TATUM GROUP MASTERPIECES VOL.7.
Tracks: / Deep night / This can't be love / Memories of you / Once in a while / Foggy day, A / Lover man / You're mine / You / Makin' whoopee.
LP: 2310 736
MC: K10 736

TATUM GROUP MASTERPIECES VOL.8.
Tracks: / Gone with the wind / All the things you are / Have you met Miss Jones? / My one and only love / Night and day / My ideal / Where or when.
LP: 2310 737
MC: K10 737

TATUM GROUP MASTERPIECES VOL.9.
Tracks: / This can't be love / Stars fell on Alabama / Lover man / Prisoner of love / Love for sale / Body and soul / Please be kind.
LP: 2310 775
MC: K10 775

TATUM SOLO MASTERPIECES VOL.1.
Tracks: / Moonglow / Love for sale / Body and soul / Just a sittin and a rockin / Paper moon / Have you met Miss Jones? / Stay as sweet as you are / My last affair / Willow weep for me.
LP: 2310 723
MC: K10 723

TATUM SOLO MASTERPIECES VOL.2.
Tracks: / Elegy / This can't be love / There will never be another you / Gone with the wind / Ghost of a chance / Lover come back to me / I'll see you in my dreams / Heatwave / September song.
LP: 2310 729
MC: K10 729

TATUM SOLO MASTERPIECES VOL.3.
Tracks: / Yesterdays / Tenderly / Jitterbug waltz / Love me or leave me / Deep purple / Begin the beguine / Dixieland band / All the things you are / Crazy rhythm / Prisoner of love.
LP: 2310 730
MC: K10 730

TATUM SOLO MASTERPIECES VOL.4.
Tracks: / Aunt Hagar's blues / Isn't this a lovely day / Ill wind / I've got the world on a string / Stardust / Man I love, The / What's new? / They can't take that away from me.
LP: 2310 789
MC: K10 789

TATUM SOLO MASTERPIECES VOL.5.
Tracks: / Makin' whoopee / Don't worry 'bout me / That old feeling / Louise / Fine and dandy / Stompin' at The Savoy / Blue moon / I cover the waterfront / Stars fell on Alabama / You're driving me crazy.
LP: 2310 790
MC: K10 790

TATUM SOLO MASTERPIECES VOL.6.
Tracks: / I've got a crush on you / There's a small hotel / Night and day / Way you look tonight / Cherokee / I'm coming, Virginia / Do nothing till you hear from me / You're blase / Ain't misbehavin'.
LP: 2310 791
MC: K10 791

TATUM SOLO MASTERPIECES VOL.7.
Tracks: / Mighty like a rose / What does it take (to win your love) / Taboo / Humoresque / Smoke gets in your eyes / Moon song / Dancing in the dark / Japanese sandman / So beats my heart for you.
LP: 2310 792
MC: K10 792

TATUM SOLO MASTERPIECES VOL.8.
Tracks: / In a sentimental mood / Blue skies / These foolish things / She's funny that way / Sweet Lorraine / Sunny side of the street / I won't dance / You go to my head / Talk of the town.
LP: 2310 793
MC: K10 793

TATUM SOLO MASTERPIECES VOL.9.
Tracks: / Too marvellous for words / You took advantage of me / Sophisticated lady / I'm in the mood for love / Everything I have is yours / Blue Lou / Embraceable you / I didn't know what time it was / Tea for two / Come rain or come shine.
LP: 2310 835
MC: K10 835

TATUM SOLO MASTERPIECES VOL.10.
Tracks: / After you've gone / When your lover has gone / Very thought of you, The / Please be kind / Indiana / I surrender, dear / Blues in my heart / Would you like to take a walk? / I can't give you anything but love.
LP: 2310 862
MC: K10 862

TATUM SOLO MASTERPIECES VOL.11.
Tracks: / I only have eyes for you / If you hadn't gone away / Without a song / I gotta right to sing the blues / I hadn't anyone till you / S'posin' / Mean to me / You're mine, you / I'll see you again / Moon is low, The.
LP: 2310 864
MC: K10 864

TATUM SOLO MASTERPIECES VOL.12.
Tracks: / Lullaby in rhythm / Boulevard of broken dreams / Judy / Someone to watch over me / Danny boy / Happy feet / Out of nowhere / Over the rainbow / Just like a butterfly (that's caught in the rain) / Memories of you.
MC: K10 870
LP: 2310 870

V-DISCS, THE.
LP: . . . . BLP 60114

Tau Ea Lesotho

NYATSI TIOHA PELA'KA.
LP: . . . . BIG 003

Tauber, Richard

CLASSIC YEARS.
MC: . . . . ZCRP 858

GOLDEN AGE OF RICHARD TAUBER.
Tracks: / We'll gather lilacs / One alone / English rose / Lover come back to me / One day when we were young / Long ago (and far away) / Sympathy / Dearly beloved / Can I forget you / Waltz song / Pedro, the fisherman / I knew that you must care / Love serenade / Sylvia / Largo (ombra maifu) / At the Balalaika / For this I pray / Serenade / Ave Maria / Serenade - Farewell my love - Farewell.
LP: . . . . GX 2504
MC: . . . . TCGX 2504
LP: . . . . MFP 5830
MC: . . . . TCMFP 5830

GOLDEN MELODIES.
Tracks: / Asleep in the deep / Viennese and italian songs / Land without music / Lockende ziel.
LP: . . . . GEMM 263

GOODNIGHT SWEETHEART.
LP: . . . . GEMM 231

GREAT VOICES OF THE CENTURY.
Tracks: / Prize song / Am stillen herd / Selig sind / Ach so fromm / Solo profugo / Ewig will lehdir gehoeren / Non plangere liu / Nessun dorma / Lug dursel lug / Addio fiorito asil / Lenski's aria / Adieu mignon / Di rigori armato / Flower song / Recondita armonia / Lucevan le stelle.
LP: . . . . GVC 502

OLD CHELSEA - A MUSICAL ROMANCE.
LP: SR 5007

PARADISE LOST, A (Tauber, Richard & Dajos Bela).
LP: REH 754
MC: ZCR 754

SONGS AND DUETS.
Tracks: / Love never comes too late / Nobody could love you more / Lovely as a night in June / Free and young (Frie un jung da bie) / Much has been written of love / Cup of tea with you, A / Love what has given you this magic power / Gianniana mia / Fascination / Rose Marie / Indian love call / Serenade / Will you remember / Waltz of my heart / Sweethearts.
LP: EG 2601861
MC: EG 2601864

THIS WAS RICHARD TAUBER.
LP: SRS 5065
MC: TCEXE 54

VOICE OF ROMANCE, THE.
LPS: ALBUM 43
MCSET: CASSETTE 43

Taupin, Bernie

HE WHO RIDES THE TIGER.
Tracks: / Monkey on my back / Born on the 4th July / Venezuela / Approaching Armageddon / Lover's cross / Blitz babies / Valley nights / Love / Whores of Paris.
LP: K 52220

TRIBE.
Tracks: / Friend of the flag / Corrugated iron / Citizen Jane / Hold back the night / She sends shivers / Billy Fury / I still can't believe that you're gone / Conquistador / New Lone Ranger, The / Desperation train.
LP: PL 85922
MC: PK 85922

Tavagna

INCONTRU (See under Juame, Andre Quartet/Tavagna) (Tavagna & Andre Juame Quartet).

Tavares

BEST OF TAVARES.
Tracks: / Heaven must be missing an angel / She's gone / Mighty power of love / Check it out / One step away / I wanna see you soon / Whodunnit / Bein' with you / It only takes a minute / Love I never had, The / My ship / Don't take away the music.
LP: FA 3026
MC: TCFA 3026
MC: 4XL 9401
LP: EST 11701

CHECK IT OUT.
Tracks: / If that's the way you want it / Strangers in dark corners / That's the sound that lonely makes / Check it out / Wish you were with me Mary / I'll never say never again / Little girl / Let's make the best of what we've got / I'm in love / Mama's little girl.
LP: EST 11258

HEART AND SOUL OF TAVARES.
Tracks: / Heaven must be missing an angel / Bein' with you / Love uprising / She's gone / Never had love like this before / That's the sound that lonely makes.
MC: KNMC 12054

HEAVEN MUST BE MISSING AN ANGEL (See Taste of Honey - Boogie oogie oogie).

LOVE UPRISING.
Tracks: / Only one I need to love / Break down for love / Love uprising / Loneliness / Knock the wall down / Hot love / Don't wanna say goodnight / Do you believe in love / She can wait forever / In this lovely world / Lifetime of love.
LP: EST 12117

MADAME BUTTERFLY.
Tracks: / Straight from your heart / Games, games / Madame Butterfly / Let me heal the bruises / Never had a love like this before / One telephone call away / My love calls / Positive forces / I'm back for more.
LP: EA ST 11874

NEW DIRECTIONS.
Tracks: / Penny for your thoughts / I hope you'll be very unhappy without me / Got to find my way back to you / Mystery lady / Maybe we'll fall in love again / Abracadabra love you too / Skin you're in / Wanna be close to you.
LP: RCALP 3103
MC: RCAK 3103

SKY HIGH.
LP: EST 11533

VERY BEST OF TAVARES, THE.
Tracks: / Heaven must be missing an angel (remixed 12" v angel mix) / She's gone / Mighty power of love / Check it out / One step away / I wanna see you soon / More than a woman (remixed version) / Whodunnit (remixed 12" version) / Bein' with you / It only takes a minute / Love I never had, the / My ship / Don't take away the music (remixed 12" version.
LP: EMS 1165
MC: TCEMS 1165

WORDS & MUSIC.
Tracks: / Ten to one / Deeper in love / Caught short / My all in all / Words and music / Baby I want you back / I really miss you baby / Don't play so hard to get / Us and love.
LP: PL 84700

Tavener, John

PANIKHIDA (Various artists).
MC: CIKO 21

RUSSIAN ORTHODOX CHURCH MUSIC (VOLUME 7) Liturgy of St.John Chrysostom Opus 32, The (Europa Singers).
LP: IKO 8
MC: CIKO 8

Taverner

MISSA CORONA SPINEA (Crown of Thorns Mass) (Sixteen, The).
MC: KA 66360

MISSA CORONA SPINEA Crown of Thorns Mass (Christ Church Cathedral, Oxford Choir).
Tracks: / Missa Corona Spinea (Taverner) / Votive antiphon (Taverner).
LP: GAU 115
MC: ZC GAU 115

Taverners

BLOWING SANDS.
LP: LER 2080

LAZY AFTERNOON.
Tracks: / Loser can be winners / Rose of Allandale / Sit you down / New St. George, The / Railway hotel / George's bar / Price of coal, The / Lazy afternoon / John Blunt / Merrily kissed the quaker's wife / I could not take my eyes off her / Name and number / Buddy, can you spare a dime.
LP: FHR 112

SAME OLD FRIENDS.
Tracks: / I'm looking out for number one / Friends / Back again / Take me back to Eastbourne / Hills of Shiloh, The / Sinking of the Reuben James, The / Bells of Rhymney / Down by the Sally gardens / Banks of the Bann / Jock Stewart / Spencer the rover / Same old friends.
LP: FHR 101

Tavitian, Harry

TRANSYLVANIAN SUITE (Tavitian, Harry/Corneliu Stroe).
LP: LR 132

Tawatha

WELCOME TO MY DREAM.
Tracks: / Thigh ride / Did I dream you / Love shine / Love goes higher / Welcome to my dream / Are you serious / More than before / Waiting's over, The / No more tears.
LP: 4509351
MC: 4509354

Tawney, Cyril

BETWEEN DECKS.
Tracks: / Lean and unwashed tiffy / Ship came sailing, A / Chicken on a raft / Grey funnel line / Man at the Nore, The / Sally free and easy / Stanley the rat / Pull the string / Six feet of mud / Oggy man's no more, the / Sailor cut down / Nobby hall / Diesel and shale.
MC: 45-092

DOWN AMONGST THE BARLEY STRAW.
LP: LER 2095

IN THE NAVAL SPIRIT.
Tracks: / That's what it's like in the navy / I was walking through the dockyard in a panic / 23rd flotilla song / You'll be happy little sweetheart in the spring / Gosport Nancy / Jenny Wren bride / Matelot and a pongo, A / Stripey and Blondie / A.A. gunner lay dying, An / Corrosion has set in / Waiting for the day / Mary was a three badge wren / A25 song / Sinking of H.M.S. Hood, The.
MC: NEP 000

ROUND THE BUOY.
Tracks: / Bell bottom trousers / Shotley stew / Sailor's wives / S.B.A.'s song / Jervis Bay, The / I was only seventeen / Dockyard matey's sons / Sod 'em all / Pilot's prayer, The / Four-funnel medley / Noble eight of December, The / Onward Christian sailors / Brothers St. John, The / Hospital ship song / Russian convoy escort's song / Stocker's lament, The / Raleigh song, The / Can a dockyard matey run ? / Oggie song, The / Matelot's song, The.
MC: NEP 001

SAILOR'S DELIGHT (Songs about seafarers and the fairer sex).
Tracks: / New York girls / Venezuela / Yarmouth town / Mary Ann / Chinese maiden's lament / Lowlands away / Short jacket and white trousers / Cruisin' round Yarmouth / Jack Tarr on the shore / Lady Franklin's lament / Man at the Nore, The / Cupid's garden / Gosport Nancy / Sailor cut down in his prime, The / Maggie May.
MC: NEP 003

SALLY FREE AND EASY.
Tracks: / Cheering the Queen / Sally free and easy / Nobby Hall / Grey funnel line / Lean and unwashed tiffy / Six feet of mud / Ballad of Sammy's bar, The / Diesel and shale / Drunken sailor, The / Suit of grey, The / Chicken on a raft / Oggie man, The / Stanley the rat / Reunion.
MC: NEP 002

Tax Loss

HEY MISTER RECORD MAN.
Tracks: / Hey Mister record man / Car 67 / My crazy friend / Folk like us / If you were going my way / Headlights / Waltz / It's the pits / Sad people / Running out of reasons / Spare me the sad eyes / Last guided tour / There is no conspiracy / Goodbye you stupid turkeys.
LP: LOGO 1015

Taxi Gang

ELECTRO REGGAE-VOL.1.
Tracks: / Triplet Interpolating don't go / Peter Gunn / Pastor dub / Pumping iron / Twilight Zone / Taxi connection / Sting, The / Watertbed.
LP: ISSP 4012
MC: ICT 4012

SIXTIES SEVENTIES AND EIGHTIES (Sly & Robbie).
LP: ILPS 9668

Taxi Girl

CHERCHEZ LE GARCON.
LP: FC 040
MC: FC 040C

COMPILATION.
LP: FC 049
MC: FC 049C

QUELQUE PART DANS PARIS.
LP: FC 071

SEPPUKU.
LP: OVED 11

Taxi (TV Series)

TAXI (THEME) (See under James, Bob) (James, Bob).

Taxman

EVERYTHING (See under Kicking Back) (Kicking Back & Taxman).

Taylor, Alex

DANCING WITH THE DEVIL.
Tracks: / House of cards / Can't break the habit / Let the big dog eat / Birds of a feather / Change in me, A / Dancing with the devil / No life at all / Practice what you preach / Black sheep.
LP: ICH 9007
MC: ICH 9007MC

Taylor, Allan

CIRCLE ROUND AGAIN.
Tracks: / Simple song / Back again / Morning lies heavy, The / My father's room / Proud and noble savage, The / Mistress music / Lavinia Forsythe-Jones / Story, The / Misty on the water / Old Joe.
LP: CRO 205
MC: CROC 205

LINES.
LP: T 002
MC: T 002 C

ROLL ON THE DAY.
Tracks: / Looking for you / Time / Give a hand / For an old friend / Madman / Standing at the door / Driving down to St Tropez / Ballad for the unknown soldier / Hard to tell / Taking it one day at a time / Roll on the day.
LP: RUB 040
MC: RUBC 040

TRAVELLER, THE.
Tracks: / Homestate / It's your way / Running in a crowded city / Traveller, The / Lone pilgrim / Land of the north wind / Cold hard town / Ladies are the loving kind, The / Lady take your time / Good to see you.
LP: RUB 026
MC: RUBC 026

WIN OR LOSE.
LP: T 001

Taylor, Alpheus

STRUGGLIN'.
LP: BLACKANT 1

Taylor, Andy

DANGEROUS.
Tracks: / Don't believe a word / Feel like makin' love / Space station No. 5 / Mustang Sally / Cocaine / Stone cold sober / Lola / Sympathy for the devil / Violence / Live wire.
LP: 395338 1
MC: 395338 4

THUNDER.
Tracks: / I might lie / Don't let me die young / Life goes on / Thunder / Night train / Tremblin' / Bringin' me down / Broken window / French guitar.
LP: MCG 6018
MC: MCGC 6018

Taylor, Art

A.T'S DELIGHT.
Tracks: / Syeeda's song flute / Epistrophy / Move / High seas / Kookoo & fungi / Blue interlude.
LP: BST 84047

TAYLOR'S WAILERS.
LP: OJC 094

Taylor, Billy

CROSS SECTION.
Tracks: / Eddie's theme / Lullaby of Birdland / Tune for Tex / Billy's beat / I love to mambo / Early morning mambo / Mood for Mendes / Goodbye / Moonlight in Vermont / I'll be around / Candido / Mambo azul.
LP: PR 7071

WHERE'VE YOU BEEN (Taylor, Billy Quartet).
Tracks: / Where've you been?.
LP: CJ 145

Taylor, Bobby

FIND MY WAY BACK (Taylor, Bobby & The Vancouvers).
LP: MOTCLP 46

Taylor, Bram

BIDE A WHILE.
Tracks: / Valley of Strathmore, The / Mind, hussy, what you do / Fields of Athenry / Sally Wheatley / I'll lay you down / Brookland roads / On board the Kangaroo / Miner's wife's lament, The / Red is the rose / Mary from Dungloe / Little husband, The / Bide awhile.
LP: FE 041

DREAMS AND SONGS TO SING.
Tracks: / Lady of beauty / Cry wild bird / How can I keep from singing / Annan water / April morning / Dancing at whitsun / Ferrybank piper, The / Sally gardens / Wheel the perambulator / Together at heart / Hard times / Wheel of fortune.
LP: FE 057

TAYLOR MADE.
Tracks: / Time and trouble / Too far from she / Withered and died / Man in the moon, The / Asikatali / Ears of Marches' daughter, The / Lessons of time / Bonnie blue eyed Nancy / Broom o'the Cowdenknowes / Flowers of Lancashire, The / Albert's pretty flowers / From a distance.
LP: FE 075
MC: FE 075C

Taylor, Cecil

3 PHASIS.
LP: NW 303

AIR.
LP: ENJA 3005

CECIL TAYLOR QUARTET IN EUROPE (Taylor, Cecil Quartet).
LP: JC 111

CECIL TAYLOR UNIT.
Tracks: / Idut / Serdab / Holiday en masque.
LP: NW 201

CELL WALK FOR CELESTE.
LP: CS 9034

CHINAMPAS.
LP: LR 153

CONQUISTADOR.
Tracks: / Conquistador / With (exit).
LP: BST 84260
LP: B1 84260

DARK TO THEMSELVES (Taylor, Cecil Unit).
LP: ENJA 2084

EMBRACED (See under Williams, Mary Lou) (Taylor, Cecil/Mary Lou Williams).

HISTORIC CONCERTS (See under Roach, Max) (Taylor, Cecil & Max Roach).

IN FLUORESCENCE.
MC: 395 323 4

INDENT.
Tracks: / Indent: first layer / Indent: second layer (part 1) / Indent: second layer (part 2) / Indent: third layer.

LP: FLP 41038

INNOVATIONS.
LP: 28 422

JUMPIN' PUMPKINS.
LP: CS 9013

LIVE IN BOLOGNA (Taylor, Cecil Unit).
2LP: LR 404/405

LIVE IN THE BLACK FOREST.
LP: MPS 68 220

LIVE IN VIENNA (Taylor, Cecil Unit).
2LP: LR 408/9

LOOKING AHEAD.
Tracks: / Luyah, the glorious step / African violets / Of what / Wallering / Toll / Excursion on a wobbly rail.
LP: COP 030

NEFERTITI-BEAUTIFUL ONE.
2LP: FLP 41095/2

NEW YORK CITY RHYTHM AND BLUES (Taylor, Cecil & Buell Neidlinger).
Tracks: / OP / Cell walk for Celeste / Cindy's main mood / Things ain't what they used to be.
LP: CS 9017

PRAXIS.
2LP: CM 104/105

SILENT TONGUES.
Tracks: / Abyss / Petals and filaments / Jitney / Taylor crossing part one / Crossing part two / After all / Jitney No. 2 / After all No. 2.
LP: FLP 41005

STUDENT STUDIES.
Tracks: / Amplitude / Niggle feuigle / Student studies part 1 / Student studies part 2.
2LP: AFFD 74

TZOTZIL MUMMERS TZOTZIL.
LP: LR 162

UNIT STRUCTURES.
Tracks: / Steps / Enter, evening (soft line structure) / Enter, evening (alt. take) / Unit structure / As of now / Section / Tales (8 whisps).
LP: BST 84237
LP: BNS 40023

WHAT'S NEW?.
Tracks: / What's new? / Nefertiti, the beautiful one, has come (first variation) / Lena (second variation) / Nefertiti, the beautiful one, has come (second variation).
LP: FLP 40124

WORLD OF CECIL TAYLOR, THE.
LP: CS 9006

Taylor, Charlie

FILLIN IN THE BLUES (1928/30).
LP: HERWIN 205
LP: HER 205

Taylor, Chip

LAST CHANCE.
Tracks: / (I want) the real thing / Son of a rotten gambler / I read it in a Rolling Stone / (The coal fields of) Shickshinny / I wasn't born in Tennessee / (Likes of) Louise, The / It's still the same / IOU in cash box / Family of one / Clean your own tables / Last chance.
LP: K 56036

Taylor, Christopher

QUIET NIGHTS.
MC: KGRS 1172

STEPPING OUT.
LP: GPR 18

THEME FOR 1983.
Tracks: / Theme for 1983.
LP: GRS 1128

Taylor, C.P

AND A NIGHTINGALE SANG.
MC: SOUND 20

Taylor, Dave

BIG 'N' BOUNCY.
LP: LP 8709

CADILLACS AND MOONLIGHT.
LP: PYL 14
MC: PYM 14

MIDNIGHT ROCK.
LP: NERD 009

STEPPIN' OUTTA LINE.
LP: MLP 8606

Taylor, Derek

MY KIND OF JOLSON.
LP: OKLP 3008
MC: ZCOK 3008

Taylor, Earl

BLUE GRASS TAYLOR MADE.
LP: HAT 3094
MC: HATC 3094

Taylor, Eddie

BIG TOWN PLAYBOY.
Tracks: / Bad boy / E.T. blues / Ride em on down / Big town playboy / You'll always have a home / Don't knock at my door / Bongo beat / I'm gonna love you / Lookin' for trouble / Find my baby / Stroll out west / Trainfare / Leave this neighbourhood / I'm sittin' here / Do you want me to cry.
LP: CRB 1015

I FEEL SO BAD.
LP: ADVENT 2802

MY HEART IS BLEEDING (Taylor, Eddie Blues Band).
LP: LR 42.009

READY FOR EDDIE (Taylor, Eddie Playboy).
Tracks: / I'm a country boy / Seems like a million years / Gamblin' man / After hours / Sloppy drunk / Ready for Eddie / You don't love me / Too late to cry / You'll always have a home / Playboy boogie / My little machine / Cross-cut saw.
LP: BEAR 6
LP: BRP 2032

RIDE 'EM ON DOWN (See under Reed, Jimmy) (Taylor, Eddie/Jimmy Reed).

STILL NOT READY FOR EDDIE.
LP: AN 005

Taylor, Eva

EVA TAYLOR 1925-26 (Taylor, Eva & Clarence Williams).
LP: FJ 121

LEGENDARY EVA TAYLOR AND MAGGIES BLUE 5, THE.
LP: KS 2042

Taylor, Felice

I FEEL LOVE COMIN' ON (OLD GOLD) (see under Mel & Tim -Backfield in motion).

Taylor, Gary

COMPASSION.
Tracks: / Compassion / Tease me / Lonely heart / Easier said than done / Love you to the limit / Don't ask my neighbour / I won't stop / I'll always be / Follow (CD & Cassette only).
LP: DIX 77
MC: CDIX 77

TAKE CONTROL.
LP: EXLP 05

Taylor, Greg Fingers

HARPOON MAN.
LP: RL 058

Taylor, Hound Dog

BEWARE OF THE DOG (Taylor, Hound Dog & The House Rockers).
Tracks: / Give me back my wig / Sun is shining, The / Kitchen sink boogie / Dust my broom / Comin' around the mountain / Let's get funky / Rock me / It's alright / Freddie's blues.
LP: SNTF 701

GENUINE HOUSEROCKING MUSIC (Taylor, Hound Dog & The House Rockers).
Tracks: / Ain't got nobody / Gonna send you back to Georgia / Fender bender / My baby's coming home / Blue guitar / Sun is shining / Phillips goes bananas / What'd I say / Kansas City / Crossroads.
LP: SNTF 879
LP: SNTF 879

HOUND DOG TAYLOR AND THE HOUSE ROCKERS (Taylor, Hound Dog & The House Rockers).
Tracks: / She's gone / Walking the ceiling / Held my baby last night / Taylor's rock / It's alright / Phillip's theme / Wild about you baby / I just can't make it / It hurts me too / 44 blues / Give me back my wig / 55th Street boogie.
LP: SNTF 676
MC: AC 4701

HOUSE ROCKIN' BOOGIE.
Tracks: / Ships on the ocean / Rockin' with the dog / Everyday I have the blues / No hair / Walking the ceiling / Mother in law blues / Stinging the blues / Rockin' boogie.
LP: JSP 1049

KINGS OF THE SLIDE GUITAR (Taylor, Hound Dog/Johnny Littlejohn).
Tracks: / Watch out, hound dog / Scrappin' / Sittin' here alone / Downhome special / What in the world / Can't be still / Bloody tears / I had a dream / When I think about my baby / Keep on running / She's too much.
LP: JSP 1074

NATURAL BOOGIE (Taylor, Hound Dog & The House Rockers).
Tracks: / Take five / Hawaiian boogie / See me in the evening / You can't sit down / Sitting at home alone / One more time / Roll your moneymaker / Buster's boogie / Sadie / Talk to my baby / Goodnight boogie.
LP: SNTF 678
MC: AC 4704

Taylor, James

CLASSIC SONGS (Best of James Taylor).
Tracks: / Fire and rain / Mexico / You've got a friend / How sweet it is to be loved by you / Carolina on my mind / Something in the way she moves / Shower the people / Sweet baby James / That's why I'm there / Everyday / Up on the roof / Your smiling face / Her town too / Handy man / Don't let me be lonely tonight / Only a dream in Rio.
LP: JTV 1
MC: JTV 1C

DAD LOVES HIS WORK.
Tracks: / Hard times / Her town too / Hour that the morning comes / I will follow / Believe it or not / Stand and fight / Only for me / Summer's here / Sugar trade / London Town / That lonesome road.
LP: CBS 86131
MC: 40 86131

FLAG.
Tracks: / Company man / Johnnie come back / Day tripper / I will not lie for you / Brother trucker / Is that the way you look? / B.S.U.R. / Rainy day man / Millworker / Up on the roof / Chanson Francais / Sleep come free me.
LP: CBS 32220
MC: 40 32220
LP: CBS 86091
MC: 40 86091

GORILLA.
Tracks: / Mexico / Music / How sweet it is (to be loved by you) / Wandering / Gorilla / You make it easy / I was a fool to care / Lighthouse / Angry blues / Love songs / Sarah Maria.
LP: K 56137

GREATEST HITS: JAMES TAYLOR.
Tracks: / Something in the way she moves / Carolina on my mind / Fire and rain / Sweet baby James / Country roads / You've got a friend / Don't let me be lonely tonight / Walking man / How sweet it is to be loved by you / Mexico / Shower the people / Steamroller.
LP: K 56309
MC: K4 56309

IN THE POCKET.
Tracks: / Shower the people / Junkie's lament, A / Money machine / Slow burning love / Everybody has the blues / Daddy's all gone / Woman's gotta have it / Captain Jim's drunken dream / Don't be sad 'cause your sun is down / Nothing like a hundred miles / Family man / Golden moments.
LP: K 56197

JAMES TAYLOR.
Tracks: / Don't talk now / Something's wrong / Knockin' round the zoo / Sunshine sunshine / Taking it in / Something in the way she moves / Carolina in my mind / Brighten your night with my day / Night owl / Rainy day man / Circle 'round the sun / Blues is just a bad dream, The.
LP: SAPCOR 3
MC: TCSAPCOR 3

J.T..
Tracks: / Your smiling face / There we are / Honey don't leave L.A. / Another grey morning / Bartender's blues / Secret o'life / Handy man / I was only telling a lie / Looking for love on Broadway / Terra nova / If I keep my heart out of sight / Traffic jam.
LP: CBS 32162
MC: 40 32162

MOCKINGBIRD (see under "Simon, Carly") (Taylor, James and Carly Simon).

MUD SLIDE SLIM AND THE BLUE HORIZON.
Tracks: / Love has brought me around / You got a friend / Places in my past / Riding on a railroad / Soldiers / Mud slide slim / Hey Mister, that's me / Upon the jukebox / You can close your eyes / Machine gun Kelly / Long ago and far away / Let me ride / Highway song / Isn't it nice to be home again.
LP: WS 2561
LP: K 46085
MC: K4 46085

NEVER DIE YOUNG.
Tracks: / Never die young / T-Bone / Baby boom baby / Runaway boy / Valentine's day / Sun on the moon / Sweet potato pie / Home by another way / Letter in the mail / First of May.
LP: 4604341
MC: 4604344

ONE MAN DOG.
LP: K 46185

SWEET BABY JAMES.
Tracks: / Sweet baby James / Lo and behold / Sunny skies / Steam Roller / Country roads / Oh Susannah / Fire and rain blossom / Anywhere like heaven / Oh baby don't you lose your lip on me / Suite for 20G / Love has brought me around / You've got a friend / Places in my past / Riding on a railroad / Soldiers / Mud slide slim / Hey mister, that's me upon the jukebox / You can close your eyes / Machine gun Kelly / Long ago and far away / Let me ride / Highway song / Isn't it nice to be home again.
LP: K 46043
MC: K4 46043

THAT'S WHY I'M HERE.
Tracks: / That's why I'm here / Song for you far away / Only a dream in Rio / Turn away / Going around one more time / Everyday / Limousine driver / Only one, The / Mona / Man who shot Liberty Valance, The / That's why I'm here (reprise).
LP: CBS 25547
MC: 40 25547

TWO ORIGINALS: SWEET BABY JAMES & MUD SLIDE SLIM.
Tracks: / Sweet baby James / Lo and behold / Sunny skies / Steamroller / Country roads / Oh Susannah / Fire and rain / Blossom / Anywhere like Heaven / Oh baby don't you lose your lip on me / Suite for 20G / Love has brought me around / You've got a friend / Places in my past / Riding on a railroad / Soldiers / Mud Slide Slim / Hey mister, that's me upon the jukebox / You can close your eyes / Machine Gun Kelly / Long ago and far away / Let me ride / Highway song / Isn't it nice to be home again.
2LP: K 66029

YOU'VE GOT A FRIEND.
LP: MOOD 10

Taylor, Jeremy

DONE IN A FLASH.
LP: SFA 073

LIVE AT THE YOUNG VIC.
LP: JT 1

Taylor, Jesse 'Guitar'

LAST NIGHT.
LP: BEDLP 14

Taylor, Jim

PHELAN'S MAGIC PICTURE SHOW.
LP: LRF 131

Taylor, John

AS TIME GOES BY VOL.1 (See also under Howard Beaumont).

AS TIME GOES BY VOL.2 (see Beaumont, Howard) (Taylor, John & Howard Beaumont).

AZIMUTH (Taylor, John/N. Winstone/K. Wheeler).
LP: ECM 1099

IT TAKES TWO TO TEMPO (See also Beaumont, Howard) (Taylor, John & Howard Beaumont).

Taylor, Johnnie

CRAZY 'BOUT YOU.
LP: MALP 7452
MC: MALC 7452

DISCO LADY (OLD GOLD) (See under Emotions/Best of my life).

EVER READY.
Tracks: / Hey Mr. Melody / Ever ready / Keep on dancing / I gotta keep groovin' / You / Soul fillet / Bittersweet love / I love to make love / When it's raining / Give me my baby.
LP: CBS 82776

IN CONTROL.
LP: MAL 7446
MC: MALC 7446

JUST AIN'T GOOD ENOUGH.
LP: BG 10001
MC: BGCX 10001

LOVERBOY.
Tracks: / Don't make me late / Loverboy / Lately / You can't win / Something is going wrong / If I lose your love / Girl of my dreams / Nothing like a lady / Happy times / Universal lady.
LP: MALP 012
MC: MALC 7440

SOMEBODY'S GETTIN' IT.
Tracks: / Disco lady / Somebody's gettin' it / Pick up the pieces / Running out of lines / Did he make love to you / Your love is rated X / I'm just a shoulder to cry on / Love is better in the a.m. / Just a happy song / Right now.
LP: CRB 1216
MC: TCCRB 1216

THIS IS YOUR NIGHT.
LP: MAL 7421
MC: MALC 7421

WALL TO WALL.
LP: MAL 7431

LP: MALP 003
MC: MALC 7431

WHO'S MAKING LOVE?.
Tracks: / Who's making love / I'm not the same person / Hold on this time / Woman across the river / Can't trust your neighbour / Take care of your homework / I'm trying / Poor make believer / Payback hurts / Mr Nobody is somebody now / Rather drink muddy water.
LP: SXE 004
LP: SX 004

Taylor, Joseph

UNTO BRIGG FAIR.
Tracks: / Sprig of thyme / Died for love / White hare, The / Lord Bateman / Rufford Park poachers / Gipsy's wedding day / Worcester City / Creeping Jane / Murder of Maria Marten / Bold Robin Hood / T'owd yowe wi' one horn / Sheffield apprentice, The.
LP: LEA 4050

Taylor, Joyce

SING ALONG HAMMOND STYLE.
Tracks: / Music, music, music / Five foot two, eyes of blue / Bow bells / Ma, he's making eyes at me / You are my sunshine / I never see Maggie alone / Maybe / Say it every day / Shine on, harvest moon / Only you and you alone / If you were the only girl in the world / Wine, women and song / Gold and silver / Blue Danube / Rosenkavalier waltz / Let's all go down the Strand / On the prom prom promenade / All the nice girls love a sailor / McDougal, McNab and McKay / I've got a lovely bunch of coconuts / Baby face / Who were you with last night? / If you knew Susie / Row, row, row your boat / Put your arms around me, honey / Toot toot tootsie, goodbye / You made me love you / On Mother Kelly's doorstep / Gang that sang heart of my heart / With these hands / Friends and neighbours / I wonder who's kissing her now / Whispering waltz / Three o'clock in the morning / Every step towards Killarney / Alice blue gown.
LP: JOY 139

Taylor, J.T

FEEL THE NEED.
LP: MCA 10306
MC: MCAC 10306

Taylor, Kevin

IRISH TRADITIONAL MUSIC.
LP: INC 7418

PIANO AND PIANO ACCORDIAN.
LP: SHAN 7418

Taylor, Koko

AUDIENCE WITH THE QUEEN, AN (Live from Chicago).
Tracks: / Let the good times roll / I'm a woman / Going back to IUKA / Devil's gonna have a field day, The / Come to Mama / I'd rather go blind / Let me love you / Wang dang doodle.
LP: SNTF 988

BLUES IN HEAVEN.
Tracks: / I got what it takes / What kind of man is this / Wang dang doodle / Separate or integrate / Good advice / Egg or the hen / Just love me / Insane asylum / Tell me the truth / Nitty gritty / Blues heaven / I got all you need.
LP: 515042
MC: 715042

EARTH SHAKER.
LP: SNTF 775

FROM THE HEART OF A WOMAN.
Tracks: / Something strange is going on / I'd rather go blind / Keep your hands off him / Thanks but no thanks / If you got a heartache / Never trust a man / Sure had a wonderful time last night / Blow top blues / If walls could talk / It took a long time.
LP: SNTF 868

I GOT WHAT IT TAKES.
Tracks: / Trying to make a living / I got what it takes / Mama / Voodoo woman / Be what you want to be / Honky tonky / Big boss man / Blues never die / Find a fool / Happy home / What's what I'm crying.
LP: SNTF 687
MC: AC 4706

JUMP FOR JOY.
LP: AL 4784
MC: AC 4784

KOKO TAYLOR.
Tracks: / I love you like a woman / I love a lover like you / Don't mess with the messer / I don't care who knows / Wang dang doodle / I'm a little mixed up / Nitty gritty / Fire / Whatever I am,you made me / Twenty-nine ways / Insane asylum / Yes / It's good for you.
LP: GCH 8039
MC: GCHK 78039

LP: CH 9263

QUEEN OF THE BLUES.
LP: SNTF 941

Taylor, Linda

TAYLOR MADE.
LP: GPLP 31

Taylor, Little Johnny

I SHOULDA BEEN A PREACHER.
Tracks: / Somebody's got to pay / Help yourself / Things I used to do, The / Driving wheel / True love / I smell trouble / Double or nothing / Sometimey woman / All I want is you / You'll need another favour / First class love / If you love me / My heart is filled with pain / Since I found a new love / Please come home for Christmas.
LP: RL 030

PART-TIME LOVE.
Tracks: / You're the one / As quick as I can / What you need is a ball / You gotta go on / She tried to understand / Since I found a new love / Darling, believe me / She's yours, she's mine / Stay sweet / Somewhere down the line / Part time love.
LP: CRB 1012
LP: CH 229

STUCK IN THE MUD.
Tracks: / Stuck in the mud / Full Time Love / I will give it all / Back To You / First Class Love / There Is Something On Your Mind / Everybody Knows About My Good Thing / You can help yourself / Your fade is further on down the road.
LP: ICH 1022
MC: ZCICH 1022

UGLY MAN.
Tracks: / Have you ever been to Kansas City / Never be lonely and blue / LJT / Ugly man / It's my fault, darlin' / I enjoy you / How can a broke man survive / King-size souvenir / Have you ever been to Kansas City (Reprise).
LP: ICH 1042
MC: ZCICH 1042

Taylor, Martin

ACCOUSTIC GUITAR DUETS (see under Stewart, Louis) (Taylor, Martin & Louis Stewart).

DON'T FRET.
Tracks: / I love you / Blue in green / I'm old fashioned / Laverne Walk / Moonlight in Vermont / Mugavero / Don't fret / You know it's true.
LP: AKH 014
MC: AKC 014

MATTER OF TIME, A (See under Giltrap, Gordon) (Taylor, Martin & Gordon Giltrap).

SARABANDA.
LP: 1390181
MC: 1390184

SKYE BOAT.
Tracks: / Mouse's spinney / Check it out / St. Thomas / Falling in love with love / Body and soul / Billie's bounce / Stompin' at the Savoy.
LP: CJ 184

TAYLOR MADE (Martin Taylor, John Richardson, Peter Ind).
LP: WAVE LP 17

TRIBUTE TO ART TATUM.
LP: HEP 2032

TRIPLE LIBRA (Taylor, Martin & Peter Ind).
LP: WAVE LP 24

Taylor, Mick

MICK TAYLOR.
Tracks: / Leather jacket / Alabama / Slow blues / Baby I want you / Broken hands / Giddy up / S.W.5.
LP: CBS 82600

STRANGER IN THIS TOWN.
LP: 084 649

Taylor, Montana

MONTANA'S BLUES.
LP: OL 2815

Taylor, Paddy

BOY IN THE GAP, THE.
LP: CC 8

SLOW AIRS AND DANCES.
MC: 60-171

Taylor, Rod

WHERE IS YOUR LOVE MANKIND.
LP: GREL 17

Taylor, Roger

FUN IN SPACE.
Tracks: / Fun in space / No violins / Laugh or cry / Let's get crazy / Future management / My country / Good times are now / Magic is loose / Interlude in Constantinople / Airheads.
LP: EMC 3369

STRANGE FRONTIER.
Tracks: / Strange frontier / Beautiful dreams / Man on fire / Racing in the street / Masters of war / Killing time / Abandonfire / Young love / It's an illusion / I cry for you.
LP: RTA 1
MC: TC RTA 1
LP: EJ 240 137 1

Taylor, Rusty

GIVE ME A CALL (Taylor, Rusty & Jazz Makers).
LP: SOS 1082

GOOD OLD BAD OLD DAYS.
LP: SOS 1028

RUSTY TAYLOR'S JAZZ REVIEW.
LP: SOS 1186

Taylor, Steve

BEST WE COULD FIND, THE.
LP: SP R 1180
MC: SP C 1180

I PREDICT 1990.
LP: MYR R 1246
MC: MYR C 1246

LIMELIGHT (live at Greenbelt).
Tracks: / This disco / I want to be a clone / You don't owe me nothing / On the fritz / We don't need no colour code / Whatever happened to sin? / Meltdown / Not gonna fall away.
LP: BIRD R 176
MC: BIRD C 176

MELTDOWN.
MC: TC BIRD 154

ON THE FRITZ.
LP: BIRD 158
MC: TC BIRD 158

Taylor, Ted

KEEP WALKING ON.
LP: CRB 1011

SOMEBODY'S ALWAYS TRYING (1958-66).
LP: RB 1005

TED TAYLOR 1976.
Tracks: / Somebody's getting it / Steal away / Stick by me / Standing in the wings of a heartache / Caught up in a good woman's love / I'm gonna hate myself in the morning / It takes a fool to be a fool again / You make loving easy / High heel sneakers.
LP: CLP 538

Taylor, Tim

ANITA & TIM (see under Perras, Anita) (Perras, Anita & Tim Taylor).

Taylor, Tot

BOX OFFICE POISON.
Tracks: / Australian / Arise Sir Tot / I was frank / Spoil her / Mr. Strings / Nevermore / Ballad of Jackie and Ivy, The / People will talk / I never rome / Babysitting / Mr. String's come back / My independant heart.
LP: TOTAL 3

INSIDE STORY, THE.
LP: TOTAL 2

JUMBLE SOUL.
Tracks: / Living in lego land / Crimson challenge, The / Offbeat / Pop town / Man with the gong / Spoil her.
LP: TOTAL 4

MENSWEAR.
LP: TOTAL 6

MY BLUE PERIOD.
Tracks: / Wrong idea, The / It must have been a craze / It's good for you / It's all a blur / Wild scene / I'll wait / Compromising life, The / Young world / I'll miss the lads / It's not a bad old place / Girl did this, A.
LP: TOTAL 5

PLAYTIME.
LP: TOTAL 1

SCRAPBOOK.
LPS: TOTAL 7

Taylor, Trevor

ACCORDION GOLDS.
Tracks: / Hot points / Petite waltz / Bel viso / Canadian capers / Free and easy / Clarinet polka / Cubanola / Waltz accordia / Bourrasque / Comedians gallop / Tico, tico / Jolly caballero / Ragging the minor / Accordion polka / Carnival of Venice.
LP: E 500

Taylor, Tut

FRIAR TUT.
LP: ROUNDER 0011

OLD POST OFFICE, THE.
Tracks: / Granny Grass's push cart / Old post office, The / Tennessee Dulcimer works / Golden slippers / Pickin' flat / Wayfaring stranger / Monkey wrench / Kentucky long rifle / Alla Lee / Resophonic guitar / Copycat / Bad Blake's blues / Autry's peach orchid / Many anniversaries.
LP: FF 008

Taylor, Tyrone

COTTAGE IN NEGRIL.
Tracks: / Cottage in Negril.
LP: DCLP 01
LP: DSR 6533

JAMMING IN THE HILLS.
LP: WENLP 3033

Taylor, Vera

I FOUND OUT (Taylor, Vera & Eddie 'Big Town Playboy').
LP: WOLF 120.711

Taylor, Vic

YOUR PRECIOUS LOVE.
LP: J.C. 002

Taylor-Good, Karen

GOOD.
LP: DFG 8401

T.Bones

DEM BONES (see under Farr, Gary) (T.Bones/Gary Farr).

LONDON 1964-1965 (see Farr, Gary) (T.Bones/Gary Farr).

TC Matic

CHOCO.
LP: FC 068

L'APACHE.
LP: FC 067

T.C.B.

T.C.B. (See under Ross, Diana).

Tchaikovsky Ballet

TCHAIKOVSKY BALLET (Various artists).
LP: ADL 515
MC: ADK 515

Tchaikovsky, Bram

FUNLAND.
Tracks: / Stand and deliver / Shall we dance / Heart of stone / Breaking down the walls of heartache / Model girl / Why does my mother phone me / Used to be my used to be / Together my love / Soul surrender / Miracle cure / Egyptian mummies.
LP: SPART 1164

STRANGE MAN, CHANGED MAN.
Tracks: / Robber / Strange man, changed man / Lonely dancer / I'm the one that's leaving / Girl of my dreams / Bloodline / Nobody knows / Lady from the USA / I'm a believer / Sarah smiles / Turn on the light.
LP: RAD 17

Tchaikovsky (composer)

1812 OVERTURE (Mexico City Philharmonic Orchestra).
Tracks: / 1812 Overture / Swan Lake (Act 1 waltz) / Romeo and Juliet Fantasy Overture / Marche slave.
MC: ZC QS 6008

GRAND SONATA (TCHAIKOVSKY)/ SCRIABIN (see under Petcherski, Alma) (Petchersky, Alma).

NUTCRACKER, THE (Israel Philharmonic Orchestra).
MC: 4255094

SYMPHONY NO.4/CAPRICCIO ITALIEN (Berlin Philharmonic Orchestra).
MC: 4273544
LP: 4273541

SYMPHONY NO.4/SERENADE FOR STRINGS (Royal Liverpool Philharmonic Orch./St. John's Smith Sq Orch.).
Tracks: / Symphony no.4 op.36 (Tchaikovsky) (cond. Enrique Batiz.) / Serenade for strings op.48 (Tchaikovsky) (cond. John Lubbock.).
MC: ZC QS 6027

SYMPHONY NO.5 (TCHAIKOVSKY) (London Symphony Orchestra).
MC: 4278224

SYMPHONY NO.6 IN B MINOR (Pathetique) (Vienna State Opera Orchestra).
MC: VETC 6501

SYMPHONY NO.6 (TCHAIKOVSKY) Pathetique (Los Angeles Philharmonic Orchestra).
MC: 4278234

SYMPHONY NO 5 (TCHAIKOVSKY) (London Symphony Orchestra).
MC: 426 065-4

SYMPHONY NO. 6 IN B MINOR, 'PATHETIQUE' (See under Solti, Sir George) (Chicago Symphony Orchestra).

TCHAIKOVSKY (Various artists).
MC: DLCMC 213

TCHAIKOVSKY Hamlet/Romeo & Juliet/Francesca da Rimini (London Philharmonic Orchestra).
Tracks: / Hamlet (Tchaikovsky) / Romeo and Juliet (Tchaikovsky) / Francesca da Rimini (Tchaikovsky).
MC: . . . . **ZC DCA 670**

TCHAIKOVSKY'S GREATEST HITS (Various artists).
MC: **40 79018**

VARIATIONS ON A ROCOCO THEME, OP 33 (See under Dvorak (composer)) (Various artists).

VIOLIN CONCERTI (see under Brodski, Vadim) (Brodsky, Vadim/Polish Radio National Symphony Orchestra).

VIOLIN CONCERTO (See under London Philharmonic Orch.) (London Philharmonic Orchestra).

Tchicai, John

CONTINENT (Tchicai, John & Hartmut Gerkin).
LP: . . . . **CM 102**

DARKTOWN HIGHLIGHTS (Tchicai,John & Strange Brothers).
LP: . . . . **SLP 1015**

LIVE IN ATHENS.
LP: . . . . **CM 101**

PUT UP THE FIGHT (Tchicai,John Group).
LP: . . . . **SLP 4141**

Tchico

DINAMIC AFRO SOUKOUS.
LP: . . . . **AR 1000**

FULL STEAM AHEAD (Tchico & Les officers of African Music).
Tracks: / Nostagie d'Afrique / Veronica-Linda / Au revoir Adely / Detty loveinda / Sane-mamadou.
LP: . . . . **ORB 007**

T-Connection

FUNKANNECTION.
Tracks: / Funkannection / Coming back for more / Funky lady / Don't stop the music / Saturday night / At midnight / Midnight train / Love supreme.
LP: . . . . **TKR 82546**

PURE AND NATURAL.
Tracks: / Girl watching / Party night / Little more love / Slippin' away / Might as well dance / Rushing through the crowd / Best of my love / Groombay time.
LP: . . . . **EST 12191**

Te Kanawa, Kiri

60 MINUTES OF MUSIC.
Tracks: / O divine redeemer / Laudate dominum / Jesus que ma joie demeure / Sanctus / Panis angelicus / Ave Maria / Exsultate jubilate / Let the bright seraphim / Let their celestial concerts / Trumpet tune.
MC: **4169104**

BLUE SKIES (Te Kanawa, Kiri/Nelson Riddle Orchestra).
Tracks: / Blue skies / Speak low / It might as well be spring / I didn't know what time it was / Here's that rainy day / Yesterdays / So in love / How high the moon / True love / Gone with the wind / When I grow too old to dream / Folks who live on the hill, The.
LP: . . . . **KTKT 1**
MC: . . . . **KTKC 1**

CHANTS D'AUVERGNE VOL 1.
LP: . . . . **SXDL 7604**

CHRISTMAS WITH KIRI.
LP: . . . . **PROLP 12**

COME TO THE FAIR (Folk Songs and Ballads).
LP: . . . . **EL 2700401**
MC: . . . . **EL 2700404**
MC: . . . . **TCASD 2700404**

KIRI.
Tracks: / O mio bambino caro / E strano-ah, fors' e'lui / Mi tradi / Le manoir de Rosemonde / La vie anterieure / Muttertandelei op.43 / Daphne / Old Sir Faulk / Vissi d'arte / Ah fuggi il traditor / She is far from the land / Chanson triste / Befreit op.9 no.4 / Apres un reve / Through gilded trellises / Come to the fair.
LP: . . . . **NE 1424**
MC: . . . . **CE 2424**

KIRI SINGS GERSHWIN.
Tracks: / Somebody loves me / Things are looking up / Someone to watch over me / Summertime / Man I love, The / I got rhythm / Boy wanted / Love walked in / Love is here to stay / But not for me / Soon / Meadow serenade / Nice work if you can get it / By Strauss / Embraceable you.
LP: . . . . **EL 2705741**
MC: . . . . **EL 2705744**
MC: . . . . **EL 7474544**

LITTLE CHRISTMAS MUSIC, A (see under King's Singers) (Te Kanawa, Kiri/ King's Singers/City of London Sinfonia).

MY FAVOURITE THINGS.
LP: . . . . **SHM 3218**
MC: . . . . **HSC 3218**

PUCCINI ARIAS.
LP: . . . . **CBS 37298**
MC: **40-37298**

RAINBOW IN THE SKY.
Tracks: / On a clear day / Time for us / Both sides now / Shadow of your smile / All the way / Impossible dream, The / It's getting better / When the world was young / This is my song / Yesterday / Little green apples / Day in the life of a fool, A.
LP: . . . . **SLC 96**

RAVEL SCHEHERAZADE.
MC: . . . . **EL 2701354**

ROYAL OCCASION, A (Te Kanawa, Kiri with National Youth Choir of New Zealand).
Tracks: / National anthem / Standchen / All my trials / Now sleeps the crimson petal / She is far from the land / Do not go my love / Hymne / Hine e hine / Whakarongo mai / Pokarekareana / New Zealand anthem.
LP: . . . . **TRL 025**
MC: . . . . **TCTRL 025**

Te Track

LET'S GET STARTED.
Tracks: / Only Jah Jah know / Look within yourself / Couldn't walk away / It's up to you / Simple things / Let's get started / Isn't it time / Judge and jury / We don't get along / Let's get started (version).
LP: . . . . **GREL 121**

Tea Pad Songs

TEA PAD SONGS VOL.1 (Various artists).
LP: . . . . **ST 103**

TEA PAD SONGS VOL.2 (Various artists).
LP: . . . . **ST 104**

Teachers

TEACHERS (Film soundtrack) (Various artists).
Tracks: / Teacher teacher: *38 Special* / One foot back in your door: *Roman Holliday* / Edge of a dream (Theme fron "Teacher"): *Cocker, Joe* / Interstate love affair: *Night Ranger* / Fooling around: *Mercury, Freddie*/ Cheap sunglasses: *ZZ Top* / Understanding: *Seger, Bob & The Silver Bullet Band* / I can't stop the fire: *Martin, Eric* / In the jungle: *Motels* / I'm the teacher: *Hunter, Ian.*
LP: . . . . **EJ 2402471**
MC: . . . . **EJ 2402474**

Teagarden, Jack

1939: JACK TEAGARDEN (Teagarden, Jack & His Orchestra).
LP: . . . . **M 8024**

1943.
Tracks: / Wolverine blues / Clarinet marmalade / All or nothing at all / Chinatown, my Chinatown / Somewhere a voice is calling / Night and day / Aunt Hagar's blues / Dark eyes / Octoroon / Swinging on a garden gate / Nobody knows the trouble I've seen / Rhythm hymn / Baby won't you please come home / Fort Knox jump / Ah sweet mystery of life.
LP: . . . . **QU 040**
LP: . . . . **QUEEN 040**

BIG BAND GEMS.
LP: . . . . **T 5003**

BIG JAZZ 1940 (See Stewart, Rex) (Teagarden, Jack & Stewart, Rex).

BIG T AND MIGHTY MAX (Teagarden, Jack & Max Kaminsky).
LP: **6.24060**

BIG T AND THE CONDON GANG.
LP: . . . . **PUMPKIN 106**

BIRTH OF A BAND.
LP: . . . . **GOJ 1038**
MC: . . . . **GOJC 1038**

DIXIELAND BIG BAND ALL STARS.
Tracks: / Introduction / South Rampart Street parade / My inspiration / Basin street blues / That naughty waltz / Milenberg Joys / Barcarolle / High society / Pagan love song / Paducah parade / South Rampart Street parade No 2 / Dixieland, The / Riverboat shuffle / Honeysuckle rose.
LP: . . . . **JASM 2510**
MC: . . . . **JASMC 2510**

HOLLYWOOD BOWL CONCERT, 1963 (Teagarden, Jack & Bobby Hackett).
Tracks: / Sweet Georgia Brown / St. James' Infirmary / Fidgety feet / My funny valentine / Struttin' with some barbecue / When it's sleepy time down South / Muskrat ramble.
LP: . . . . **SS 102**

HUNDRED YEARS FROM TODAY, A.
Tracks: / You rascal you / That's what I like about you / Chances are / I got the Ritz from the one I love / I've got it / Plantation moods / Shake your hips / Somebody stole Gabriel's horn / Love me / Blue river / Hundred years from today, A / I just couldn't take it baby / Fare thee well / Ol pappy / Junk man / Stars fell on Alabama / Your guess is just as good as mine.
LP: . . . . **CHD 153**
MC: . . . . **MCHD 153**

I GOTTA RIGHT TO SING THE BLUES.
Tracks: / That's a serious thing / I'm gonna stomp Mr. Henry Lee / Dinah / Never had a reason to believe in you / Tailspin blues / Dancing with tears in my eyes / Sheik of Araby, The / Basin Street blues / You rascal you / Two tickets to Georgia / I gotta right to sing the blues / Ain't cha glad? / Texas tea party / Hundred years from today / Fare thee well to Harlem / Christmas night in Harlem / Davenport blues.
LP: . . . . **AJA 5059**
MC: . . . . **ZC AJA 5059**

JACK TEAGARDEN.
Tracks: / I gotta right to sing the blues / Somebody loves me / Two sleepy people / That's right, I'm wrong / Washboard blues / Lazybones / Small fry / Rockin' chair / Stardust / Off to the races / Deep river / Harlem jump / Well of course / Shine / Basin Street blues / Sheik of Araby, The / St. James' Infirmary / Baby won't you please come home? / Bad actin' woman.
LP: . . . . **QU 027**
LP: . . . . **QU 012**

JACK TEAGARDEN.. In San Francisco.
Tracks: / That's a plenty / Tin roof blues / Struttin' with some barbecue / Maple leaf rag / Shine / I gotta right to sing the blues / Jazz me blues / Tin roof blues / I'm gonna stomp mr. Henry Lee / Handful of keys / Royal Garden blues.
LP: . . . . **RARITIES 39**

JACK TEAGARDEN (2) (Teagarden, Jack & Max Kaminsky).
Tracks: / Chinatown / Big T blues / Rockin' chair / Pitchin' a bit short / Love nest / Everybody loves my baby / Eccentric / Guess who's in town.
LP: **AG6 24060**

JACK TEAGARDEN (3) (See under Frankie Trumbauber TNT) (Teagarden, Jack & Trumbauber, Frankie).

JACK TEAGARDEN ALLSTARS (Hangover Club, San Francisco, 1954) (Teagarden, Jack Allstars).
LP: . . . . **FDC 1026**

JACK TEAGARDEN AND EARL HINES (Teagarden, Jack & Earl Hines).
LP: . . . . **AWE 20**

JACK TEAGARDEN AND MAX KAMINSKY (See under Kaminsky, Max) (Teagarden, Jack & Max Kaminsky).

JACK TEAGARDEN AND RED NICHOLS (1929-31) (Teagarden, Jack & Red Nichols).
LP: . . . . **GAPS 180**

JACK TEAGARDEN AND THE CONDON GANG 1944 (Teagarden, Jack & Condon Gang).
LP: . . . . **PUMPKIN 104**

JACK TEAGARDEN & BOBBY HACKETT ALL STARS 1963 (see Hackett, Bobby) (Teagarden, Jack & Bobby Hackett).

JACK TEAGARDEN IN CONCERT.
LP: . . . . **SOUNDS 1203**

JACK TEAGARDEN / LOUIS ARMSTRONG (See also under Armstrong, Louis) (Teagarden, Jack & Louis Armstrong).

JAZZ ORIGINAL.
Tracks: / King Porter stomp / Eccentric / Davenport blues / Original dixieland one-step / Bad actin' woman / Mis'ry and the blues / High society / Music to love by / Meet me where they play the blues / Riverboat shuffle / Milenberg joys / Blue funk.
LP: . . . . **AFF 141**

JAZZ ULTIMATE (see Hackett, Bobby & Jack Teagarden) (Teagarden, Jack & Bobby Hackett).

LESTER MEETS MILES (See MJQ & Jack Teagarden AllStars) (Teagarden, Jack all stars & M.J.Q).

LIVE: MODERN JAZZ ROOM, OHIO 1958 (Teagarden, Jack Sextet & Don Ewell).
LP: . . . . **PUMPKIN 121**

LOUIS ARMSTRONG AND JACK TEAGARDEN (See under Armstrong, Louis) (Teagarden, Jack & Louis Armstrong).

MASTERS OF JAZZ VOL.10.
LP: . . . . **SLP 4110**

MEMORIAL.
LP: . . . . **CV 1073**

ON OKINAWA (Teagarden, Jack Allstars).
LP: . . . . **IAJRC 33**

ON THE AIR 1936-38.
Tracks: / Music goes round and around, The / Announcer's blues / Got a 'bran new suit / St Louis blues / I hope Gabriel likes my music / Alexander's ragtime band / I'm comin', Virginia / Flat foot floogie / Small fry / Aunt Hagar's blues / FDR Jones / Mutiny in the nursery / Jeepers creepers / Christmas night in Harlem / John Peel.
LP: . . . . **AIRCHECK 24**

SHINE (Teagarden, Jack & Pee Wee Russell).
Tracks: / Shine / St. James' Infirmary / World is waiting for the sunrise, The / Big eight blues / Baby won't you please come home? / Dinah / Zutty's hootie blues / There'll be some changes made / I've found a new baby / Everybody loves my baby.
LP: . . . . **SM 3096**

SINCERELY.
LP: . . . . **IAJRC 19**

STANDARD LIBRARY OF JAZZ VOL 2.
LP: . . . . **SLP 704**

STARS FELL ON ALABAMA.
LP: . . . . **LPJT 77**
MC: . . . . **MCJT 77**

SWINGING GATE,THE.
LP: . . . . **GOJ 1026**

THAT'S A SERIOUS THING.
Tracks: / I'm gonna stomp Mr. Henry Lee / That's a serious thing / She's a great great girl / My kinda love / Tailspin blues / Never had a reason to believe in you / Ridin' but walkin' / Fare thee well to Harlem / Nobody's sweetheart / Blue Lou / Blues, The (take 1) / St. Louis blues / St. James infirmary / Jack Armstrong blues / I cover the waterfront / There'll be some changes made.
LP: . . . . **NL 90440**
MC: . . . . **NK 90440**

TROMBONE T FROM TEXAS.
Tracks: / I gotta right to sing the blues / Love me or leave me / Jeepers creepers / Basin street blues / Blues to the lonely / Beale street blues / Someday, sweetheart / After you've gone / Nobody knows the trouble I've seen / Body and soul / Riverboat shuffle / Love me / Prelude to the blues / Farewell blues / Aunt Hagar's blues / Somebody loves me.
LP: . . . . **AFS 1015**
MC: . . . . **TCAFS 1015**

UNFORGETTABLE JACK TEAGARDEN, THE.
LP: . . . . **HDL 104**

V DISC ALL STARS,THE (See under Armstrong, Louis) (Teagarden, Jack & Louis Armstrong).

VARSITY SIDES.
Tracks: / If I could be with you one hour tonight / My melancholy baby / Can't we talk it over / Blues, The / Love for sale / Moon and the willow tree, The / Wham / Devil may care / Night on the Shalimar / I hear bluebirds / Fatima's drummer boy / Now I lay me down(to dream of you) / Wait till I catch you in my dreams / And so do I / River home.
LP: . . . . **WL 70827**
MC: . . . . **WK 70827**

Teal Joy

MOOD IN MINK.
LP: . . . . **FS 322**

Teamwork

BEST OF YOUR FAMILY REQUESTS.
Tracks: / Baby blue / My lagan flows softly / Give an Irish girl to me / Back hills of Dakota / Ring your mother wore / Silver sandals / Is there anyone can tell me / Two little orphans / Everybody's reaching out for someone / Newry town / Tiny bubbles / Que sera sera.
LP: . . . . **PHL 479**
MC: . . . . **CPHL 479**

SING ME AN OLD FASHIONED SONG.
Tracks: / Sing me an old fashioned song / Be nobody's darling but mine / Turn out the lights (love me tonight) / Mothers love's a blessing, A / We stood at the altar / Heart into heart / Sunset years of life, The / Bunch of thyme / This world is not my home / I'll forgive and I'll try to forget / Jeannie's afraid of the dark / World of our own, A.

LP: PHL 457
MC: CPHL 457

Tear Garden

TIRED EYES SLOWLY BURNING.
Tracks: / Deja vu / Room with a view / Coma / Valium / You and me and rainbows (parts one to six) / Ooh ee oo ee.
MC: NTLC 30019
LP: NTL 30019

Tear, Robert

BRITTEN FOLK SONGS.
MC: ED 2903524

FOLK SONGS (Tear, Robert & Phillip Ledger).
Tracks: / Captain's apprentice, The / As I walked out / Bushes and briars / Geordie / On board a 98 / Ploughman, The / Brewer, The / Rolling in the dew / Truth sent from above, The / Joseph and Mary / Saviour's love, The / Reveillez-vous / Piccarz / Chanson de Quete / Ballads de Jesus Christ / She's like the swallow / Morning dew, The / Maiden's lament, The / Cuckoo, The / Lawyer, The / Searching for lambs / How cold the wind doth blow.
LP: HQS 1412

I DREAM OF JEANNIE.
Tracks: / I hear you calling me / Passing by / Christopher Robin is saying his prayers / Angels guard thee / Homing / First mercy / Silent noon / Vale / Cherry hung with snow / If I can help somebody / Cuckoo / Big lady moon / Ora pro nobis / Little road to Bethlehem, The / I dream of Jeannie with the light brown hair / Serengata / When song is sweet.
LP: ZK 76

Teardrop Explodes

EVERYBODY WANTS TO SHAG...THE TEARDROP EXPLODES.
Tracks: / Ouch monkeys / Serious danger / Metranil Vavin / Count to ten and run for cover / In-psychopedia / Soft enough for you / You disappear from view / Challenger, The / Not my only friend / Sex / Terrorist / Strange house in the snow.
LP: 842 439 1
MC: 842 439 4

KILIMANJARO.
Tracks: / Ha ha I'm drowning / Sleeping gas / Treason / Second head / Reward poppies / Went crazy / Brave boys keep their promises / Bouncing babies / Books / Thief of Baghdad, The / When I dream.
LP: PRICE 59
MC: PRIMC 59
LP: 6359 035
LP: 836 897-1
MC: 836 897-4

PIANO.
LP: DLP 004
MC: DMC 004

WILDER.
Tracks: / Bent out of shape / Colours fly away / Seven views of Jerusalem / Pure joy / Falling down around me / Culture bunker / Tiny children / Passionate friend / Like Leila Khaled said / Great dominions.
LP: 6359 056
MC: 7150 056
LP: PRICE 112
MC: PRIMC 112
LP: 836 896 1

Teardrop Time

TEARDROP TIME (Various artists).
MC: GM 0203

Tears For Fears

HURTING, THE.
Tracks: / Mad world / Pale shelter / Ideas as opiates / Memories fade / Suffer the children / Hurting / Watch me bleed / Change / Prisoner, The / Start of the breakdown.
LP: MERS 17
MC: MERSC 17

SEEDS OF LOVE, THE.
Tracks: / Badman's song / Sowing the seeds of love / Advice for the young at heart / Standing on the corner of the third world / Swords and knives / Famous last words / Woman in black.
LP: 8387301
MC: 8387304

SONGS FROM THE BIG CHAIR.
Tracks: / Shout / Working hour, The / Everybody wants to rule the world / Mother's talk / I believe / Broken / Head over heels / Broken (live) / Listen.
LP: MERH 58
MC: MERHC 58
LP: VBK 13353

TEARS FOR FEARS: INTERVIEW PICTURE DISC.
LPPD: BAK 2158

Tease

TEASE.
Tracks: / Note, The / Better wild (than mild) / Firestarter / Body heat / Total control / Soft music / Baby be mine / I wish you were here.
LP: EPC 26963
MC: 40 26963

Teaze

ONE NIGHT STANDS.
Tracks: / Back in action / Young and reckless / Heartless world / Red hot ready / Through the years / Reach out / Loose change / Touch the wind.
LP: HMUSA 30

TASTE OF TEAZE.
LP: HMUSA 4

Tebbet, Admiral

LEAVE PEOPLE BUSINESS.
LP: WRLP 13

Techniques

TECHNIQUES, THE CLASSICS.
Tracks: / You don't care / My girl / Travelling man / Wish it would rain / Queen Majesty / Love is not a gamble / There comes a time / I am in love / Little did he know / I'm in the mood.
LP: WRLP 18

Techno Animal

GHOSTS.
LP: PATH 006

Techno Orchestra

CASUAL TEASE.
LP: STLP 003

Techno Twins

TECHNOSTALGIA.
Tracks: / I wanna be loved by you / Swing together / Beautiful women in Bermuda shorts / Gone with the wind / Hi tech / Donald and Julie go boating / I got you babe / Falling in love again / Romantic night / Kings and queens of pleasure / Can't help falling in love (long version) / Angels of mercy.
LP: TECH 1
MC: ZCTEC 1

Technofunk

MIRADA ROCK (see Griffin, Reggie & Technofunk) (Technofunk & Reggie Griffin).

Technology...

TECHNOLOGY TWO EDGED SWORD (King, Dr. Alexander) (King, Dr. Alexander).
MC: SS 112

Technos

FOREIGN LAND.
LP: TECH 7700

Technotronic

BODY TO BODY.
Tracks: / Move that body / Work / Release yourself / Cold chillin' / Voices / Money makes the world go round / Body to body / Get it started / Yeh yeh / Gimme the one (Only on CD) / Bogarts breakfast (Only on CD).
LP: 4683421
MC: 4683424

PUMP UP THE JAM.
Tracks: / Pump up the jam / Get up (before the night is over) / Tough / Take it slow / Come on / This beat is Technotronic / Move this / Come back / Rockin' over the beat / Raw / Wave / String.
LP: SYRLP 1
MC: SYRMC 1

TECHNOTRONIC.
MC: STAC 2461
LP: STAR 2461

Ted

BLUE VIRGIN ISLES.
Tracks: / Satellite / Blue virgin isles / 505 to Casablanca / Take me back to Hollywood / Wanna live, got to give / Love, you're makin' all the fools / Baby blue eyes / Back in the business / Puddle of pain / Love lies free / Just for the money.
LP: EPC 83653

Ted & The Tall Tops

CRAZY DATE.
Tracks: / Crazy date / Honky tonic ramblin man / Bad boy / Trouble maker / Lose your money / Gulp coast Saturday night.
LP: ROSE 122

Tedder, Dr. Richard

AIDS - THE FACTS (See under Aids).

Tedder, Mike

CHOOSE LIFE (see also under Markee, Dave).

Teddy Bear

TEDDY BEAR (Various artists).
MC: TRUC 2

TEDDY BEAR TRUK 2 (Various artists).
MC: VCA 620

Teddy Bears

MY LITTLE PET.
LP: TREY 20207

Teddy Bear's Picnic

TEDDY BEAR'S PICNIC, THE (Various artists).
MC: STC 017
MC: STC 309A

Teddy Ruxpin

FUN AT THE FAIR.
MC: PLBX 279

SURPRISE VISITOR, A.
MC: PLBX 278

TEDDY'S DREAM.
MC: STK 007

TO THE RESCUE.
MC: STK 008

Teddy & The Tigers

TEAR IT UP.
LP: LP 8009

Tedesco, Tommy

ALONE AT LAST.
Tracks: / Child is born, A / Dreamsville / Nature boy / Trees.
LP: TR 517

AUTUMN.
Tracks: / Dolphin dance / Bag's groove / Song is you, The / Manha De Carnaval.
LP: TR 514

HOLLYWOOD GYPSY, A (Tedesco, Tommy Trio).
Tracks: / Impressions of Hollywood Boulevard / Cavatina / Gypsy fade, A / My man Shelly / BLT / Body and soul / Stella by starlight / Our waltz / All the things you are.
LP: DS 928

LIVE IN CONCERT AT THE MUSICIAN'S INSTITUTE (Tedesco, Tommy Trio).
LP: TR 534
MC: TRC 534

MY DESIREE (Tedesco, Tommy Quintet).
LP: DS 851
MC: DSC 851

WHEN DO WE START (Tedesco, Tommy Quintet).
LP: DS 789
MC: DSC 789

Tee, Richard

BOTTOM LINE.
Tracks: / If you want it / What can I say / Bottom line / Nippon lights / Rhapsody in blue / Miss-Understanding / Spring is you / No real way / Moving on.
LP: K 28P 6364

NATURAL INGREDIENTS.
Tracks: / What a woman really means / Now / Nut's off the screw / Tell it like it is / Us / Back door man / Spinning song.
LP: CBS 84194

STROKIN'.
Tracks: / First love / Everyday / Strokin' / I wanted it too / Virginia Sunday / Jesus children of America / Take the 'A' train.
LP: CBS 83339

Tee-Jay, Abdul

KANKA KURU (Tee-Jay, Abdul Rokoto).
LP: FMSL 2018
MC: FMSC 3018

Teen Beat

TEEN BEAT (Various artists).
LP: CGB 1002
MC: TC CGB 1002

Teen Dream

GAMES.
LP: MSS 2206

Teen Queens

ROCK EVERYBODY.
Tracks: / Rock everybody / Red top / Eddie my love / Zig zag / All my love / Baby mine / Riding the boogie / Just goofed / Love sweet love / So all alone / My heart's desire / Teenage gold / Let's make up / Billy Boy.
LP: CH 186

Teen Wolf

TEEN WOLF (Film soundtrack) (Various artists).
Tracks: / Flesh on fire: *House, James* / Big bad wolf: *Wolf sisters, The* / Win in the end: *Safan, Mark*/ Shootin' for the moon: *Holland, Amy* / Silhouette: *Palmer, David* / Way to go: *Viena, Mark* / Good news: *Morgan,David* / Transformation: *Teen Wolf* / Boof: *Teen Wolf.*

LP: SCRS 1010
MC: SCRSC 1010

Teenage....

TEENAGE MEETING (Various artists).
Tracks: / Teenage meeting (we're gonna rock it up right tonight): *Various artists* / Story of love: *Various artists*/ Dream on: *Various artists* / Lazy Joe: *Various artists* / You're gonna see: *Various artists* / Blue mood: *Various artists* / Send my love (special delivery): *Various artists* / Count to three: *Various artists*/ Don't waste your time: *Various artists* / Bongo gully: *Various artists* / Teacher crush: *Various artists*/ Tom Tom: *Various artists* / Don't believe them: *Various artists* / Bitterness: *Various artists* / I wish that we were married: *Various artists* / It's their world: *Various artists.*
LP: SEL 5

Teenage Cruisers

TEENAGE CRUISERS (Film soundtrack) (Various artists).
LP: RNLP 016

Teenage Dance Party

TEENAGE DANCE PARTY (Various artists).
LP: BLK 7705

Teenage Fan Club

CATHOLIC EDUCATION, A.
Tracks: / Heavy metal / Catholic education / Don't need a drum / Heavy metal II / Eternal light / Everybody's fool / Everthing flows / Too involved / Critical mass / Catholic education II / Every picture I paint.
LP: PAPLP 004
MC: PAPMC 004

KING, THE.
LP: CRELP 096

Teenage Head

FRANTIC CITY.
LP: LAT 1081

Teencats

TEDDY BOP.
LP: LP 8710

Tees-side Fettlers

RING OF IRON.
LP: TSR 016

TRAVELLING THE TEES.
LP: TSR 021

Teeze

TEEZE.
LP: RR 9741

Teezy

WANTED BY THE MASSIVE.
LP: TWLP 1006

Teitelbaum, Richard

TIME ZONES (Teitelbaum, Richard/ Anthony Braxton).
Tracks: / Crossing / Behemoth dreams.
LP: FLP 41037

Tek 9

O.G. KINGDOM OF DUB.
Tracks: / O.G. kingdom of dub.
LP: RIV 1205

Telemann (Composer)

MUSIQUE DE TABLE (King's Consort).
MC: KA 66278

PARIS QUARTETS - AMERICAN BAROQUE (Various artists).
MC: CSAR 39

Telephone...

CHATTERBOX CLASSICS 1 (Various).
MC: CBX 102

CHATTERBOX HUMOUR 1 (Various).
MC: CBX 103

CHATTERBOX MIXED BAG 1 (Various).
MC: CBX 104

CHATTERBOX POPS 1 (Various).
MC: CBX 101

Telephone Bill

MANHATTAN DOLL (Telephone Bill/ Smooth Operators).
LP: DID 713

Telephone (group)

AU COEUR DE LA NUIT.
LP: V 2195

CRACHE TON VENIN.
Tracks: / Crache ton venin / Fait divers / J'suis parti de chez mes parents / Facile / La bambe humaine / J'sais pas quoi faire / Ne me regardes pas / Regardes moi / Un peu de ton amour / Tu vas me manquer.
LP: PMLP 1001

TELEPHONE.
LP: OVED 10

UN AUTRE MONDE.

LP: V 2316

Telescopes

TASTE.
LP: GOES ON 32
LP: CHEREE 009LP

Television

20 BBC DRAMA THEMES (Various artists).
Tracks: / Cleopatras: *Various artists* / Squadron: *Various artists* / Shoestring: *Various artists* / Chinese detective, The: *Various artists* / Telford's change: *Various artists* / Blake's 7: *Various artists*/ Aphrodite inheritance: *Various artists* / We the accused: *Various artists* / Scorpion: *Various artists*/ Who pays the ferryman: *Various artists* / Chi Mai: *Various artists* / Smiley's people: *Various artists*/ Poldark: *Various artists* / Penmarric: *Various artists* / Mackenzie: *Various artists* / Horseman riding by: *Various artists* / Nancy Astor: *Various artists* / Nanny: *Various artists* / To serve them all my day's: *Various artists* / Palisers: *Various artists.*
LP: REH 464
MC: ZCR 464

20 GREAT TV THEMES (Various artists).
Tracks: / Vanity fair: *Various artists* / One game, The: *Various artists* / Square deal: *Various artists*/ Match eye, The: *Various artists* / Witness: *Various artists* / Doctor Who: *Various artists* / Campion: *Various artists* / Ruth Rendell mysteries: *Various artists* / Agatha Christie's Poirot: *Various artists*/ Me and my girl: *Various artists* / World cup: *Various artists* / Wish me luck: *Various artists* / Inspector Morse: *Various artists* / Forever Green: *Various artists* / 7 faces of woman: *Various artists* / Tales of the unexpected: *Various artists* / To have and to hold: *Various artists* / Two of us, The: *Various artists*/ Professionals, The: *Various artists* / Upstairs, downstairs: *Various artists.*
LP: WEEKLP 2
MC: WEEKMC 2

ALL YOUR FAVOURITE TV THEMES (Various artists).
MC: AIM 39

'ALLO 'ALLO (The War Diaries of Rene Artois) (Various artists).
MCSET: ZBBC 1094

AMERICAN TELEVISION THEMES (The Prime Time Collection volume 1) (Various artists).
Tracks: / Midnight caller: *Various artists* / L.A. Law: *Various artists* / Twin peaks: *Various artists*/ Star Trek: the next generation: *Various artists* / North and South: *Various artists* / Hooperman: *Various* artists / Murder, she wrote: *Various artists* / Spenser for hire: *Various artists* / 21 Jump Street: *Various* artists / Newhart: *Various artists* / Hunter: *Various artists* / Bronx zoo, The: *Various artists*/ Sonny Spoon: *Various artists.*
MC: TVPMC 400

AMERICAN TELEVISION THEMES (2) (The Primetime Collection volume 2) (Various artists).
Tracks: / Thirty something: *Various artists* / Falcon Crest: *Various artists* / Doogie Howser M.D.: *Various* artists / Highway To Heaven: *Various artists* / Quantum Leap: *Various artists* / Macgyver: *Various artists*/ Slap Maxwell Story: *Various artists* / Head Of The Class: *Various artists* / Alf: *Various artists* / Wiseguy: *Various artists* / Nutt House, The: *Various artists* / Remington Steele: *Various artists* / Men: *Various artists* / Bring 'em back alive: *Various artists.*
MC: TVPMC 401

BBC CHILDREN'S TV THEMES (See under BBC...) (T.V.Themes).

BBC CHILDREN'S TV THEMES (Various artists).
Tracks: / Doctor Who theme: *Various artists* / Captain Zep: *Various artists* / Magic roundabout: *Various* artists / Paddington bear: *Various artists* / Animal magic: *Various artists* / Dukes of Hazzard: *Various* artists / Watch: *Various artists* / Trumpton: *Various artists* / Monkey: *Various artists* / Heads and tails: *Various artists* / Saturday Superstore: *Various artists* / Blue Peter: *Various artists* / Willo the wisp: *Various artists* / Grange hill: *Various artists* / Pink panther: *Various artists* / Swap shop: *Various artists* / Take Hart: *Various artists* / Monkee's theme, The: *Various artists* / Mr. Men: *Various artists* / Think again: *Various artists* / Playschool: *Various artists.*
LP: REH 486
MC: ZCR 486

BBC COMEDY THEMES (Various artists).
Tracks: / Goodies theme: *Various artists* / Fawlty Towers: *Various artists* / Likely lads: *Various artists*/ Some mothers do 'av 'em: *Various artists* / Q.8: *Various artists* / Steptoe and son: *Various artists*/ Monty Python: *Various artists* / Mash: *Various artists* / Dad's army: *Various artists* / Going straight: *Various artists* / Last of the Summer wine: *Various artists* / Liver birds: *Various artists* / Rise and fall of Reginald Perrin: *Various artists* / It ain't half hot Mum: *Various artists.*
LP: REH 387

BBC SPACE THEMES (Various artists).
Tracks: / Apollo: *Various artists* / Also sprach Zarathustra: *Various artists* / Moonbase 3: *Various artists*/ A for Andromeda: *Various artists* / Sky at night: *Various artists* / Fanfare for the common man: *Various* artists / Journey into space: *Various artists* / Astronauts: *Various artists* / Blake's 7: *Various artists*/ Star trek: *Various artists* / Mars: *Various artists* / Tomorrow's world: *Various artists* / Dr. Who: *Various artists.*
LP: REH 324

BBC SPORTING THEMES (Various artists).
Tracks: / Grandstand: *Various artists* / Wimbledon: *Various artists* / Match of the day: *Various artists*/ Ski Sunday (pop goes Bach): *Various artists* / Test cricket: *Various artists* / Snooker: *Various artists*/ Rugby special: *Various artists* / Sportsnight: *Various artists* / Question of sport: *Various artists*/ Darts: *Various artists* / Commonwealth games: *Various artists* / World Cup: *Various artists* / Rugby: *Various artists* / Sport on Two: *Various artists* / Athletics: *Various artists* / Bowls: *Various artists.*
MC: HSC 648

BEST AMERICAN TV THEMES, THE (Various artists).
Tracks: / Magnum: *Various artists* / P.I.: *Various artists* / Airwolf: *Various artists* / Cosby show, The: *Various artists* / Mike Hammer: *Various artists* / Lou Grant: *Various artists* / Cheers: *Various* artists / Hill Street blues: *Various artists* / Hollywood wives: *Various artists* / Cagney and Lacey: *Various* artists / St. Elsewhere: *Various artists* / Touch of scandal: *Various artists* / Taxi: *Various artists*/ Simon and Simon: *Various artists* / Rockford files: *Various artists.*
LP: USTP 7777
MC: USTC 7777

BEST OF THE TEST (Various artists).
2LP: OGWTLP 1
MCSET: OGWTMC 1

CLASSIC TV THEMES (Various artists).
LP: SPA 580

DARLING BUDS OF MAY (Featuring Music from the TV Series) (English Light Concert Orchestra & Barry Guard).
Tracks: / Perfick / Home farm / Pop's Rolls Royce / Strawberry time / In a party mood / Pufin' Billy / Breath of french air, A / Dinner in the shade / Gore court match / On the river / Hop picker's hop, The / Calling all workers / Devil's gallop / Girl in yellow, The / Gymkhana, The / Darling buds of May, The.
MC: TCEMC 3612
LP: EMC 3612

DIGITAL THEMES SPECTACULAR (See under Films) (Various artists).

DIGITAL THEMES SPECTACULAR VOL. 2 (See under Film Music) (Various artists).

DREAMS & THEMES (Various artists).
LP: RONLP 10
MC: CRON 10

EIGHTEEN TV/FILM THEMES (see under Films) (Various artists).

ITV CHILDREN'S THEMES (Various artists).
Tracks: / Super gran: *Various artists* / Knight rider: *Various artists* / Joe 90: *Various artists* / Captain Scarlet: *Various artists* / Fall guy, The: *Various artists* / Sooty show theme, The: *Various artists*/ Dangermouse: *Various artists* / Fraggle rock: *Various artists* / Stingray: *Various artists* / Ghostbusters: *Various artists* / A Team: *Various artists* / Batman theme: *Various artists* / Black Beauty: *Various* artists / Thunderbird: *Various artists* / Dogtanian: *Various artists* / Handful of songs: *Various artists*/ Blockbusters, Theme from: *Various artists* / Follyfoot farm: *Various artists.*
MC: HSC 3263

MAGNUM P.I. (The American TV hits album) (Various artists).
Tracks: / Mike Hammer: *Caine, Daniel Orchestra* / Lou Grant: *Caine, Daniel Orchestra* / Cagney and Lacey: *Caine,* Daniel Orchestra / Rockford files, The: *Caine, Daniel Orchestra* / Taxi: *Caine, Daniel Orchestra* / Bill Cosby show: *Caine, Daniel Orchestra* / Cheers: *Caine, Daniel Orchestra* / Hill Street blues: *Caine, Daniel Orchestra*/ Hollywood wives: *Caine, Daniel Orchestra* / St. Elsewhere: *Caine, Daniel Orchestra* / Simon and simon: *Caine, Daniel Orchestra.*
LP: ATVP 5555
MC: ATVC 5555

MAGNUM P.I. AND OTHER THEMES (Various artists).
MC: FILMC 703

MASTER OF THE GAME (Television Soundtrack) (Various artists).
LP: REB 521

MIAMI VICE II (TV soundtrack) (Various artists).
Tracks: / Mercy: *Jones, Steve* / Last unbroken heart, The: *Labelle, Patti* / Crockett's theme: *Hammer, Jan*/ Lives in the balance: *Browne, Jackson* / Original Miami Vice theme, The: *Hammer, Jan* / Send it to me: *Knight, Gladys & The Pips* / When the rain comes down: *Taylor, Andy* / Lover: *Roxy Music* / In dulce decorum: *Damned.*
LP: MCG 6019
MC: MCGC 6019

MIAMI VICE III (TV Soundtrack) (Various artists).
LP: MCG 6033
MC: MCGC 6033

MICHAEL STROGOFF (Various artists).
LP: HIFLY 30
MC: ZCFLY 30

MUPPET BABIES (Various artists).
Tracks: / Muppet babies theme, The: *Various artists* / Merry go round: *Various artists* / Sleep rockin': *Various* artists / Dream for you inspiration: *Various artists* / Good things happen in the dark: *Various artists* / Camilla: *Various artists* / Rocket to the stars: *Various artists* / Practice makes perfect: *Various artists*/ It's up to you: *Various artists* / I can't help being a star: *Various artists.*
LP: REH 613
MC: ZCR 613

ORANGES ARE NOT THE ONLY FRUIT (Various artists).
MCSET: ZBBC 1152

ORIGINAL TV HITS OF THE SIXTIES (Various artists).
Tracks: / Route 66: *Riddle, Nelson* / Doctor Kildare theme: *Spence, Johnny* / Human jungle, The: *Barry, John*/ Saint, The: *Fahey, Brian* / Danger man theme: *Fahey, Brian* / Man from uncle, The: *Fahey, Brian* / Avengers, The: *Various artists* / Baron, The: *Various artists* / Thunderbirds: *Various artists* / Dept. S: *Stapleton, Cyril & Orchestra* / Prisoner, The: *Grainer, Ron.*
LP: MOMENT 105
MC: MOMENTC 105

PARADISE CLUB, THE (Various artists).
Tracks: / This boy: *Best Way To Walk* / Mercenary man: *Pride* / For KC: *Davis, Snake & The Charmers*/ Wrong side of the river: *Lawson,Dave* / Feather fin and limb: *Tracey, Stan Big Band* / Circles: *Carmel*/ Vegas throat: *Jack Rubies* / Roadrunner: *Gigantic Rock & Blues Band* / Rumour has it, rumour is...: *Lawson,Dave*/ Paradise club, The - opening: *Lawson,Dave* / Bye bye Mr Blues: *Catastrophy* / Unbelievable: *Best Way To Walk* / Ma's funeral: *Lawson,Dave* / Oh boy: *Gigantic Rock & Blues Band* / Paradise club, The - end titles: *Tracey, Stan Big Band* / Body talk: *Junction* / Try a little tenderness: *Lotis, Dennis/Laurie Holloway*/ Great crane robbery: *Lawson,Dave* / Paradise club, The: *Lawson,Dave.*
LP: REB 764
MC: ZCF 764

PERSUADERS, THE & OTHER THEMES BY JOHN BARRY (Various artists).
LP: CBS 64816

PETER GUNN (TV Soundtrack) (Various artists).
MC: 1956.4

PETER THE GREAT (TV soundtrack) (Various artists).
Tracks: / Main title: *Various artists* / Cathedral: *Various artists* / Alexander: *Various artists* / Tartars, The: *Various artists* / Two living tears: *Various artists* / His first sail: *Various artists*/ Foreign colony, The: *Various artists* / Eudoxia: *Various artists* / Peter's wedding: *Various artists*/ Tsar and Tsaritsa: *Various artists* / New Tsarevich, The: *Various artists* / Death of Natalyda - The slap: *Various* artists / Great embassy, The: *Various artists* / Gopak: *Various artists* / Alexis and Danilo: *Various* artists / Battle of Poltova: *Various artists* / Sophia and Alexis - Ordeal - Martyrdom: *Various artists* / Requiem: *Various artists* / Peter's theme: *Various artists.*
LP: FILM 006
MC: FILMC 006

REILLY - ACE OF THEMES (Various artists).
Tracks: / Reilly: *Various artists* / To serve them all my days: *Various artists* / Bouquet of barbed wire: *Various* artists / Onedin line: *Various artists* / Flame trees of thika: *Various artists* / O agatha: *Various* artists / Jennie: *Various artists* / Skorpion: *Various artists* / On the line: *Various artists* / Cavatina: *Various artists* / Walk on: *Various artists* / Who pays the ferryman: *Various artists* / Upstairs downstairs: *Various artists* / Black beauty: *Various artists* / Tales of the unexpected: *Various artists*/ Winds of war: *Various artists* / Hollywood: *Various artists* / Chi mai: *Various artists.*
LP: BUSLP 1004
MC: BUSK 1004

ROLL OVER BEETHOVEN (Tv theme) (Various artists).
LP: TVLP 2
MC: ZCTV 2

SESAME STREET FEVER (Various artists).
Tracks: / Sesame Street fever: *Various artists* / Doin' the pigeon: *Various artists* / Rubber duckie: *Various* artists / Trash: *Various artists* / C is for cookie: *Various artists* / Has anybody seen my dog?: *Various artists.*
LP: 2310637

SIX WIVES OF HENRY VIII (Various artists).
Tracks: / Fanfare: *Various artists* / Passomezzo du Roy: *Various artists* / Gaillarde d'Ecosse: *Various artists*/ Mille ducats: *Various artists* / Larocque gaillarde: *Various artists* / Allemande: *Various artists*/ La mourisque: *Various artists* (Wedding march) / If love now reigned: *Various artists* / Pourquoi - ronde: *Various artists.*
LP: RESL 1

SOAP OPERA THEMES (Various artists).
LP: GNPS 2200
MC: GNP5 2200

SOUNDS VISUAL (Original TV themes) (Various artists).
Tracks: / Television march, The (BBC tv theme): *London Symphony Orchestra* / ITN news (non-stop): *John Malcolm Orchestra*/ Mainly for women (jockey on the carousel): *Melodi Light Orchestra* / Potter's wheel, The (from the BBC interlude): *Melodi* Light Orchestra / Saturday night out: *Melodi Light Orchestra* / Picture parade: *Queen's Hall Light Orchestra*/ Farming (a quiet stroll): *Queen's Hall Light Orchestra* / Big night out (all sports march): *Melodi Light Orchestra*/ ITV soccer theme (fanfare in beat): *Johnny Hawksworth Orchestra* / Compact (city movement): *Roger Roger & His Orchestra*/ Animal magic (Las Vegas): *Laurie Johnson Orchestra* / BBC 2 service information theme (walk and talk): *Syd Dale Orchestra*/ Owen M.D. (Sleepy Shores): *Johnny Pearson & His Orchestra* / News at ten (The awakening): *Group 50 Orchestra*/ Mastermind (Approaching menace): *Neil Richardson Orchestra* / This is your life: *Laurie Johnson Orchestra.*
MC: YRS 603

SPACE INVADED - BBC SPACE THEMES (Various artists).
Tracks: / Dr Who: *Various artists* / Blake's 7: *Various artists* / Sky at night: *Various artists* / Fanfare for the common man: *Various artists* / Cosmos: *Various artists* / Tomorrow's world: *Various artists* / K-9 and Co.: *Various artists* / Leisure hive, The: *Various artists* / Comet is coming: *Various artists*/ Hitch hiker's guide to the galaxy: *Various artists.*
LP: REH 442
MC: ZCR 442

STARS FROM STARS & GARTERS (TV soundtrack) (Various artists).
LP: GGL 0252

STEPTOE AND SON (Original TV Soundtrack) (Various artists).
MCSET: ZBBC 1145

TELEVISION'S GREATEST HITS VOL.2 (65 themes from the 50's and 60's) (Various artists).
Tracks: / Looney tunes: *Various artists* / Peanuts: *Various artists* / Odd couple, The: *Various artists*/ Bewitched: *Various artists* / Monkees: *Various artists* / Time tunnel, The: *Various artists* / Rawhide: *Various artists* / Daktari: *Various artists* / Virginian, The: *Various artists* / Peter Gunn: *Various* artists / Saint, The: *Various artists* / I spy: *Various artists* / Avengers, The: *Various artists* / Monty Python: *Various artists* / Road runner:

Various artists / Merrie melodies: *Various artists* / Huckleberry hound: *Various artists* / Mighty mouse: *Various artists* / Pink panther: *Various artists*/ Spiderman: *Various artists* / Partridge family: *Various artists* / Car 54 where are you: *Various artists*/ Voyage to the bottom of the sea: *Various artists* / Maverick: *Various artists* / Wagon train: *Various artists*/ Route 66: *Various artists* / Outer limits: *Various artists.*
2LP: . . . . **FILM 034 D**
MC: . . . . **FILMC 034**

TELEVISION'S GREATEST HITS VOL.1 (65 themes from the 50's and 60's) (Various artists).
Tracks: / Flintstones, The: *Various artists* / Popeye: *Various artists* / Yogi bear: *Various artists*/ Fireball XL5: *Various artists* / Beverly hillbillies: *Various artists* / Addams family, The: *Various artists*/ Star Trek: *Various artists* / Batman theme: *Various artists* / Flipper: *Various artists* / Mission impossible: *Various artists* / Perry Mason (theme from): *Various artists* / Munsters, The: *Various artists* / Ironside: *Various artists* / Bugs bunny: *Various artists* / Felix the cat: *Various artists* / Top cat: *Various* artists / Jetsons, The: *Various artists* / Mr. Ed: *Various artists* / I love Lucy: *Various artists*/ Lost in space: *Various artists* / Twilight zone: *Various artists* / Bonanza: *Various artists* / Man from Uncle, The: *Various artists* / Get smart: *Various artists* / Dragnet: *Various artists* / Secret agent man: *Various artists* / F.B.I.: *Various artists* / Hawaii five-O: *Various artists* / 77 Sunset Strip: *Various artists.*
LP: . . . . **TVT 1100**
MC: . . . . **TVTC 1100**
2LP: . . . . **FILM 024 D**
MC: . . . . **FILMC 024**

TELEVISION'S GREATEST HITS VOL 3 (65 Favourite Themes from the 70's & 80's) (Various artists).
Tracks: / Muppet show, The: *Various artists* / Mr. Magoo: *Various artists* / Dastardly and Mutley: *Various* artists / Scooby Doo: *Various artists* / Cheers: *Various artists* / Taxi: *Various artists* / Happy days: *Various artists* / L.A. law: *Various artists* / St. Elsewhere: *Various artists* / M*A*S*H: *Various* artists / Hart to Hart: *Various artists* / A Team: *Various artists* / Miami vice: *Various artists*/ Hill Street blues: *Various artists* / Dallas: *Various artists* / Dynasty: *Various artists* / Love boat: *Various artists* / Sesame street: *Various artists* / Inspector Gadget: *Various artists* / Archies, The: *Various artists* / Barney Miller: *Various artists* / All in the family: *Various artists* / Knots Landing: *Various artists* / Waltons - theme: *Various artists* / Little house on the prairie: *Various artists* / Wonder woman: *Various artists* / Streets of San Francisco: *Various artists* / Starsky and Hutch, Theme from: *Various artists* / Kojak: *Various artists* / Magnum: *Various artists* / Rockford files: *Various artists.*
2LP: . . . . **FILM 035 D**
MC: . . . . **FILMC 035**

TELLY HITS (Various artists).
Tracks: / Cagney and Lacey: *Various artists* / Howards way: *Various artists* / Eastenders: *Various artists*/ Dallas: *Various artists* / Big deal: *Various artists* / Edge of darkness: *Various artists* / Tomorrows world: *Various artists* / Front line, The: *Various artists* / Whickers world: *Various artists* / Tripods, The: *Various artists* / Bergerac: *Various artists* / Miss Marple: *Various artists* / Voyage of the heroes: *Various artists* / Tender is the night: *Various artists* / In search of the Trojan War: *Various artists*/ Snooker: *Various artists.*
2LP: . . . . **BBSR 508**
MCSET: . . . . **BBSC 508**

TELLY HITS VOLUME 2 (Various TV themes) (Various artists).
Tracks: / World cup '86: *Various artists* / Bread: *Various artists* / Marriage, The: *Various artists*/ Miami vice: *Various artists* / Lovejoy: *Various artists* / Mastermind: *Various artists* / Hideaway: *Various artists* / Film '86: *Various artists* / Dead head: *Various artists* / I, Claudius: *Various* artists / Ski Sunday: *Various artists* / Hold the back page: *Various artists* / A.D. - Anno domini: *Various artists* / Strike it rich: *Various artists.*
MC: . . . . **BBSC 616**
LP: . . . . **BBSR 616**

THAT WAS THE WEEK THAT WAS (TV soundtrack) (Various artists).
LP: . . . . **PMC 1197**

THEMES (Various TV and Film themes) (Various artists).
Tracks: / Onedin line theme, The: *Various artists* / Diamonds are forever: *Various artists* / Love story: *Various* artists / Madly: *Various artists* / Summer knows, The: *Various artists* / Time for us, A: *Various artists*/ Sleepy shores: *Various artists* / Rosy's theme: *Various artists* / For all we know: *Various artists*/ Red tent, The: *Various artists* / Death in Venice theme: *Various artists* / Look around and you'll find me there: *Various artists* / Sunrise, sunset: *Various artists.*
MC: . . . . **SPC 8572**

THEMES (Various artists).
Tracks: / Chi mai: *Morricone, Ennio* / Cavatina: *Williams, John* / Light of experience: *Belmonde, Pierre*/ Cavalleria rusticana - Intermezzo: *Various artists* / Bilitis: *Lai, Francis* / Canon suite from Ordinary People: *Various artists* / Ballade pour Adeline: *Clayderman, Richard* / Air on a G string: *Williams, John* / Don't cry for me Argentina: *Belmonde, Pierre* / Concierto de Aranjuez: *Brett, Paul* / Sleepy shores: *Sounds Orchestral*/ Largo from 'New World Symphony': *National Brass Band* / Sailing / Onedine line, Theme: *Keating John/London Symphony Orchestra.*
LP: . . . . **NE 1122**
MC: . . . . **CE 2122**

THEMES AND DREAMS (Various artists).
Tracks: / Anna of the five towns: *London Film Orchestra* / Lillie: *South Bank Orchestra* / Thorn birds - love theme: *Martin, Juan & Royal Philharmonic Orchestra* / Mapp and Lucia: *South Bank Orchestra* / Reilly, ace of spies - theme: *Olympic Orchestra* / Bouquet of barbed wire: *South Bank Orchestra* / Waltons - theme: *Giltrap, Gordon*/ Sahara: *Morricone, Ennio* / Married man, A: *South Bank Orchestra* / Woman of substance, A: *London Film Orchestra*/ Cavatina: *Williams, John* / Onedin line, The: *Keating John/London Symphony Orchestra* / Drummonds: *South* Bank Orchestra / Song of freedom: *Mansell Chorale* / Make peace not war: *South Bank Orchestra* / Atlantis: *London Film Orchestra* / Love for Lydia: *South Bank Orchestra* / Upstairs downstairs: *South Bank Orchestra.*
LP: . . . . **FEDL 101**
MC: . . . . **CFEDL 101**

THEMES AND DREAMS (TRAX) (Various artists).
Tracks: / All I ask of you: *Brightman, Sarah & Cliff Richard* / I want to know what love is: *Foreigner* / Rose, The: *Midler, Bette* / Albatross: *Fleetwood Mac* / Rockliffe's folly (theme from): *Various artists* / Howard's way: *May, Simon Orchestra* / Cacharpaya: *Incantation* / Mission, The: *Various artists* / St. Elmo's fire: *Parr, John* / Emma's war: *Various artists* / Chariots of fire: *Vangelis* / Pachelbel canon: *Various* artists / Oa: *Various artists* / Oxygene: *Jarre, Jean Michel* / Brideshead revisited: *Various artists*/ Love story: *Various artists* / Take my breath away: *Berlin* / Gymnopedie no.1: *Various artists* / Imagine: *Lennon, John* / Close Encounters of the Third Kind suite: *Williams, John (Composer).*
2LP: . . . . **MODEM 1020**
MC: . . . . **MODEMC 1020**

THEMES FROM THE 60'S (Various artists).
Tracks: / Avengers, The: *Various artists* / To sir with love: *Various artists* / On her majesty's secret service: *Various artists* / Man in a suitcase: *Various artists* / Prisoner: *Various artists* / Up the junction: *Various artists* / Captain Zeppos: *Various artists* / Man from UNCLE, The: *Various artists* / Mission impossible: *Various artists* / 4 x 4: *Various artists* / You only live twice: *Various artists* / Batman theme: *Various artists.*
LP: . . . . **WSR 002**

THIRTYSOMETHING (TV Soundtrack) (Various artists).
LP: . . . . **GEF 24413**
MC: . . . . **GEFC 14413**

THORN BIRDS AND OTHER BBC TV THEMES (Various artists).
Tracks: / Thorn birds: *Various artists* / By the sword divided: *Various artists* / District nurse: *Various* artists / Living planet: *Various artists* / To serve them all my days: *Various artists* / News week: *Various* artists / Threshold: *Various artists* / Cold wind: *Various artists* / Russell Harty theme: *Various artists*/ Diana: *Various artists* / Just good friends: *Various artists* / Mayfair concert: *Various artists* / History man: *Various artists* / Dark side of the sun: *Various artists* / Johnny Jarvis: *Various artists*/ Flight of the Condor: *Various artists.*
LP: . . . . **REH 524**
MC: . . . . **ZCR 524**

TINKER TAILOR SOLDIER SPY (Various artists).
MCSET: . . . . **ZBBC 1071**

TOP 20 TV THEMES (Various artists).
MC: . . . . **WEEKMC 3**

TOP BBC TV THEMES VOL.2 (Various artists).
Tracks: / Onedin line: *Various artists* / All creatures great and small: *Various artists* / Empire Road: *Various* artists / Great egg race: *Various artists* / Blake's 7: *Various artists* / Sexton Blake: *Various artists*/ Last farewell, The: *Various artists* / Telford's change: *Various artists* / Two up, two down: *Various artists*/ Aphrodite inheritance: *Various artists* / My son, my son: *Various artists* / Horseman riding by: *Various artists* / Mastermind: *Various artists* / Don't forget to write: *Various artists.*
LP: . . . . **REH 365**

TOP BBC TV THEMES VOL.3 (Various artists).
Tracks: / Dallas: *Various artists* / Tinker, tailor, soldier, spy: *Various artists* / Tomorrow's world: *Various* artists / Pride and prejudice: *Various artists* / Shoestring: *Various artists* / Body in question: *Various* artists / Man alive: *Various artists* / Holiday 80/81: *Various artists* / Parkinson: *Various artists*/ Penmarric: *Various artists* / Knots Landing: *Various artists* / Six wives of Henry VIII: *Various artists*/ Breakaway: *Various artists* / Enigma files: *Various artists.*
LP: . . . . **REH 391**

TOP BBC TV THEMES-VOL. 4 (Various artists).
Tracks: / Juliet Bravo: *Various artists* / Maybury: *Various artists* / Chinese detective, The: *Various artists*/ Hi de hi: *Various artists* / Not the nine o'clock news: *Various artists* / Speak for yourself: *Various artists*/ Cosmos: *Various artists* / Chi mai: *Various artists* / MacKenzie: *Various artists* / Nanny: *Various* artists / We the accused: *Various artists* / Poldark: *Various artists* / I Claudius: *Various artists*/ Goodbye darling: *Various artists.*
LP: . . . . **REH 424**

TOP T.V. THEMES (Various artists).
Tracks: / Lillie: *Various artists* / Who pays the ferryman?: *Various artists* / Crossroads: *Various artists*/ Prince Regent: *Various artists* / Monty Python's flying circus: *Various artists* / Van der Valk theme: *Various* artists / Match of the day: *Various artists* / Horse of the year theme: *Various artists* / Soap: *Various* artists / Kojak theme: *Various artists* / Sky at night theme: *Various artists* / Nationwide: *Various artists* / Emmerdale farm: *Various artists* / Hawaii five-o: *Various artists.*
LP: . . . . **TAB 18**

TRAINER (Music from the TV Series) (Various artists).
Tracks: / More to life: *Richard, Cliff* / Grass roots: *May, Simon Orchestra* / Bookies, The: *May, Simon Orchestra*/ Mo's theme: *May, Simon Orchestra* / Country life: *May, Simon Orchestra* / Arkenfield: *May, Simon Orchestra*/ Heaven's gate (trainer romantic variation): *May, Simon Orchestra* / Woman of the world: *Mazelle, Kym* / Intuition: *May, Simon Orchestra* / Racer: *May, Simon Orchestra* / Superstud: *May, Simon Orchestra* / Shades of grey: *May, Simon Orchestra* / Trainer (opening titles) (extended version): *May, Simon Orchestra.*
LP: . . . . **EMC 3601**
MC: . . . . **TCEMC 3601**

TRIAL OF MRS MAYBRICK (1889) & MRS MERRIFIELD (1 (Various artists).
MC: . . . . **BS 1/2 DB**

TUBE, THE (TV soundtrack) (Various artists).
LP: . . . . **NE 1261**

T.V HITS ALBUM (Various artists).
Tracks: / Miami vice: *Various artists* / Connie: *Various artists* / Minder: *Various artists* / In sickness and in health: *Various artists* / Auf wiedersehen pet: *Various artists* / Eastenders: *Various artists*/ Travelling man: *Various artists* / Roll over beethoven: *Various artists* / Dempsey and makepeace: *Various* artists / Lakeland rock: *Various artists* / Shine on harvey moon: *Various artists* / Bill: *Various artists*/ Smugglers blues: *Various artists* / Nog: *Various artists* / Sons and daughters: *Various artists* / Blott on the landscape: *Various artists.*
LP: . . . . **TVLP 3**
MC: . . . . **ZCTV 3**

T.V. HITS VOL.2 (Various artists).
LP: . . . . **TVLP 10**
MC: . . . . **ZCTV 10**

TV THEME SINGALONG ALBUM (Various artists).
LP: . . . . **RNIN 703**

TV THEMES AMERICA (Various artists).
Tracks: / Dallas: *Various artists* / Perfect strangers: *Various artists* / Knot's Landing: *Various artists*/ Midnight caller: *Various artists* / Head of the class: *Various artists* / Mission: Impossible: *Various* artists / McGyver: *Various artists* / Cagney and Lacey: *Various artists* / Dynasty: *Various artists*/ Odd couple, The: *Various artists* / High chaparral: *Various artists* / Mash: *Various artists* / Bonanza: *Various artists* / Taxi: *Various artists* / Rockford files, The: *Various artists* / Doctor Kildare: *Various artists.*
LP: . . . . **REB 763**
MC: . . . . **ZCF 763**

TV TUNES (Various artists).
Tracks: / Neighbours: *Various artists* / Prisoner cell block H: *Various artists* / LA Law: *Various artists*/ Hill Street blues: *Various artists* / Dynasty: *Various artists* / Cheers: *Various artists* / Taxi: *Various* artists / St. Elsewhere: *Various artists* / Peter Gunn: *Various artists* / A Team: *Various artists*/ Streets of San Francisco: *Various artists* / Hart to Hart: *Various artists* / Sons and daughters: *Various* artists / Young doctors: *Various artists* / WKRP in Cincinnati: *Various artists* / Greatest American hero: *Various artists* / Welcome back Kotter: *Various artists* / Starsky and Hutch: *Various artists* / Mission impossible: *Various artists* / Country practice, A: *Various artists* / Waltons: *Various artists* / Monkees: *Various artists* / Odd couple: *Various artists* / Addams family, The: *Various artists* / Monty Python's flying circus: *Various artists* / Happy days: *Various artists* / Laverne and Shirley: *Various artists*/ Flintstones: *Various artists* / Yogi bear: *Various artists* / Top cat: *Various artists* / Jetsons, The: *Various artists* / Woody Woodpecker show: *Various artists* / Sesame Street: *Various artists* / Scooby Doo: *Various artists* / Inspector Gadget: *Various artists* / Mr. Magoo: *Various artists* / Popeye: *Various artists* / Road Runner: *Various artists* / Bugs bunny: *Various artists* / Dastardly and Mutley: *Various* artists / My three sons: *Various artists* / Mr Ed: *Various artists* / Beverly Hillbillies: *Various artists*/ Get smart: *Various artists* / Hogan's heroes: *Various artists* / Car 54 where are you: *Various artists*/ Green acres: *Various artists* / Rawhide: *Various artists* / Dallas: *Various artists* / Batman theme: *Various artists.*
LP: . . . . **NE 3429**
MC: . . . . **CE 3429**

TWILIGHT ZONE (1) - MUSIC FROM THE TV SERIES (TV Soundtrack) (Various artists).
Tracks: / Invaders, The: *Various artists* / Where is everybody: *Various artists* / I sing the body electric: *Various artists* / Jazz themes: *Various artists* / Nervous man in a four dollar room: *Various artists* / Walking distance: *Various artists* / Main title: *Various artists* / End title: *Various artists.*
LP: . . . . **STV 81171**

TWILIGHT ZONE (2) - MUSIC FROM THE TV SERIES (TV Soundtrack) (Various artists).
Tracks: / Main theme: *Various artists* / Back there: *Various artists* / And when the sky was opened: *Various artists* / Passerby, The: *Various artists* / Lonely, The: *Various artists* / Two: *Various artists*/ End theme, The: *Various artists.*
LP: . . . . **STV 81178**

TWILIGHT ZONE (3) - MUSIC FROM THE TV SERIES (TV soundtrack) (Various artists).
LP: . . . . **STV 81185**

TWILIGHT ZONE (4) - MUSIC FROM THE TV SERIES (TV soundtrack) (Various artists).
LP: . . . . **STV 81192**

TWILIGHT ZONE (5) - MUSIC FROM THE TV SERIES (TV soundtrack) (Various artists).
MC: . . . . **STV 81205**

VARIOUS RECORDINGS (see under Power Pack Orchestra) (Various artists).

VISIONS (Various artists).
Tracks: / Flying (theme from ET): *Various artists* / Harry's game (theme from): *Various artists* / M.A.S.H., Theme from: *Various artists* / Hill Street blues: *Various artists* / Chariots of Fire: *Various artists* / Brideshead Revisited: *Various artists* / Arthur's theme: *Various artists* / I don't know how to love him: *Various artists*/ Don't cry for me Argentina: *Various artists* / Eve of the war, (The): *Various artists* / Star wars: *Various* artists / Fame: *Various artists* / For your eyes only: *Various artists* / Dallas: *Various artists*/ Shoestring: *Various artists* / Chain, The: *Various artists* / Angela: *Various artists* / Take that look off your face: *Various artists.*
LP: . . . . **NE 1199**
MC: . . . . **CE 2199**

WONDER YEARS (Various artists).
LP: . . . . . K 7820321
MC: . . . . . K 7820324

WORLD OF BBC TV THEMES, THE (Various artists).
Tracks: / Shadow of the noose: *Various artists* / Eagle's eye view: *Various artists* / Supersense: *Various artists* / Franchise affair, The: *Various artists* / Top of the pops: *Various artists* / Atlantic realm: *Various artists* / Christabel: *Various artists* / Doctor Who: *Various artists* / South of the border: *Various artists* / Rockcliffe's folly: *Various artists* / Celts, The: *Various artists* / Bread: *Various artists*/ Great rift, The: *Various artists* / Rockcliffe's babies: *Various artists* / Blind justice: *Various artists*/ Victorian kitchen garden: *Various artists* / Pulaski: *Various artists* / Champion: *Various artists*/ Chelworth: *Various artists* / Thunder dragons: *Various artists* / First born: *Various artists* / Animal squad: *Various artists*.
LP: . . . . . REB 705
MC: . . . . . ZCF 705

WORLD OF TV THEMES (Various artists).
LP: . . . . . SPA 217
MC: . . . . . KCSP 217

Television (Band)

ADVENTURE (Television).
Tracks: / Glory / Days / Foxhole / Careful / Carried away / Fire, The / Ain't that nothin' / Dream's dream, The.
LP: . . . . . K 52072

BLOW UP, THE.
MC: . . . . . A 114

MARQUEE MOON.
Tracks: / See no evil / Venus / Friction / Marquee moon / Elevation / Guiding light / Prove it / Torn curtain.
LP: . . . . . K 52046
MC: . . . . . K 452046

Telex

LOOKING FOR ST. TROPEZ.
Tracks: / Moskow diskow / Pakmovast / Cafe de la jungle / Ca plane pour moi / Some day - un jour / Something to say / Rock around the clock / Victime de la societe / Twist a Saint Tropez.
LP: . . . . . SRK 6072

LOONY TUNES.
Tracks: / I don't like music / Spike Jones / Dingo bells / Baby, when? / Rendezvous dans l'espace / Temporary children / Beautiful life / I want your brain / Happy end / Peanuts.
LP: . . . . . K 781914-1
MC: . . . . . K 781914-4

NEUROVISION.
Tracks: / We are all getting old / My time / Tour de France / Plus de distance / Euro-vision / Dance to the music / Realite / Cliche / A/B / En route vers de nouvelles aventures / Finale.
LP: . . . . . SRK 6090

REMIXES.
LP: . . . . . LD 8943

Telfer, John

RUBADUB-POP GOES THE NURSERY RHYMES (see Bell, Madelaine) (Telfer, John/Madelaine Bell).

Telham Tinkers

HOT IN ALICE SPRINGS.
LP: . . . . . ERON 031

Tell Me You ...

TELL ME YOU LOVE ME (Various artists).
LP: . . . . . ULP 2

Tell Tale Hearts

NOW SOUNDS OF THE TELL TALE HEARTS, THE.
LP: . . . . . VOXX 200036

TELLTALE HEARTS.
LP: . . . . . LOLITA 5045
LP: . . . . . VOXX 200027

Tella, Sylvia

SPELL.
LP: . . . . . SRL 1005

WILL YOU STILL WANT ME.
LP: . . . . . SYLVIA 01

Tellulive

TELLULIVE.
LP: . . . . . FF 224

Tellybugs

TELLYBUGS (Various artists).
MC: . . . . . CBUG 100

Temiz, Okay

DERVISH SERVICE (Temiz, Okay Trio).
LP: . . . . . SNTF 1020

ORIENTAL WIND.
Tracks: / Oriental wind / Karasar zeybegi / Estergon kalesi / Kabak / Jula kara nayni / Cokertime.
LP: . . . . . SNTF 737
LP: . . . . . SNTF 809

TURKISH FOLK JAZZ (Temiz, Okay Trio).
Tracks: / Taksim / Introduction / Batum / Ulah-Balkan / Doktur / Kurt Havasi / Madimak / Uskudar / Anadolu Havasi / Trabzon karsilamasi.
LP: . . . . . SNTF 668

Tempchin, Jack

JACK TEMPCHIN.
LP: . . . . . SPART 1078

Temper Temper

TEMPER TEMPER.
LP: . . . . . DIX 97
MC: . . . . . CDIX 97

Temperance Seven

33 NOT OUT.
MC: . . . . . URMC 103

HOT TEMPERANCE SEVEN.
LP: . . . . . WAM/O No.5

TEA FOR EIGHT.
MC: . . . . . URMC 101

TEMPERANCE SEVEN 1961.
LP: . . . . . PMC 1152

TEMPERANCE SEVEN PLUS ONE.
LP: . . . . . RG 11

Temperley, Joe

JUST FRIENDS (Temperley, Joe/Jimmy Knepper).
Tracks: / John's bunch / Stella by starlight / Just in time / Poor butterfly / Just friends / Yardbird suite / Aristocracy / Sophisticated lady / Lester leaps in.
LP: . . . . . HEP 2003

SAXPLOITATION (See under Stobart, Kathy) (Temperley, Joe & Kathy Stobart).

Tempest

BOOTLEG.
MC: . . . . . HEY 026CS

FIVE AGAINST THE HOUSE.
Tracks: / Montezuma / Lady left this / Ice cold in / Which one? / Better and better / Big black Cadillac / Clara Bow / Miss deep freeze / Eat the wall / At a low ebb / Blame it on the breeze.
LP: . . . . . GRAM 15

TEMPEST, THE.
Tracks: / Lazy Sunday / Tonight / Diane / Tempest, The / Bluebell / Didn't we have a nice Michael Sheerin time / Don't you realise / Leave the boy alone / Always the same / This is the world.
LP: . . . . . PESTL 7001

TEMPEST, THE (see under Shakespeare, William) (Various artists).

Templar, Whistling Vic

TEA AND BACCY (See under Rocking Richard) (Templar, Whistling Vic & Rocking Richard).

Temple Church Choir

CHRISTMAS CAROLS.
LP: . . . . . CLP 1309

FAVOURITE HYMNS.
MC: . . . . . TCESD 7136

TEMPLE TRADITION.
LP: . . . . . ABY 817

Temple Gates

TEMPLE GATES.
LP: . . . . . MMLP 012

Temple, Johnny

JOHNNY TEMPLE 1935-39.
LP: . . . . . DLP 511

JOHNNY TEMPLE: 1936-40.
LP: . . . . . BD 2067

Temple, Paul and...

PAUL TEMPLE AND THE HARKDALE ROBBERY Durbridge, Francis (Durbridge, Francis).
MC: . . . . . PTB 613

Temple, Shirley

LITTLE MISS WONDERFUL.
Tracks: / On the good ship Lollipop / Baby take a bow / When I'm with you / Laugh, you son of a gun / At the codfish ball / Love's young dream / On accounta I love you / Goodnight my love / But definitely / In our little wooden shoes / Picture me without you / Git on board, li'l chilun / Animal crackers in my soup / That's what I want for Christmas / You've got to S-M-I-L-E (to be H-A double P-Y) / Early bird / He was a dandy / Right somebody to love, The / Hey, what did the blue jay say? / Believe me if all those endearing young charms / When I grow up / Oh my goodness / World owes me a living, The / Dixie-Anna / Toy trumpet, The / Polly Wolly Doodle.
LP: . . . . . CHD 141
MC: . . . . . MCHD 141

SHIRLEY TEMPLE.
MC: . . . . . MRT 40038

Templemore Band

CONCERT BRASS.
Tracks: / Girl I left behind me, The / Amazing grace / 633 Squadron / Easter hymn / Wellington march / Greensleeves / Birdie song, The / Londonderry air / Twelfth St. rag / Elvira Madigan / Can-can / Sousa on parade.
LP: . . . . . PHL 453

Templemore Male Voice

BUILDING FOR TIME AND ETERNITY.
Tracks: / What a friend we have in Jesus / What a day that will be.
LP: . . . . . SGOL 110

Templeton, Luke

SONGS FROM OVER THERE.
Tracks: / I'm putting all my eggs in one basket / St. Louis blues / Slumming on Park Avenue / Dinah / Bicycle built for two / You're the top / Boom! / Little Sir Echo / Onward christian soldiers / Lady Winterbottoms song.
MC: . . . . . K 1008

Tempo...

TEMPO DE BAHIA (Various artists).
LP: . . . . . BM 123
MC: . . . . . BMC 123

Temptation

TEMPTATION (Various artists).
LP: . . . . . MODEM 1042

Temptations

20 GOLDEN GREATS: TEMPTATIONS.
Tracks: / Just my imagination (running away with me) / I wish it would rain / I second that emotion / Beauty is only skin deep / I'm losing you / Cloud nine / Take a look around / Superstar / Papa was a rollin' stone / Power / I'm gonna make you love me / My girl / You're my everything / I can't get next to you / Get ready / Ain't too proud to beg / I could never love another (after loving you) / Ball of confusion / Psychedelic shack / Law of the land.
LP: . . . . . STML 12140
MC: . . . . . CSTML 12140
LP: . . . . . ZL 72160

25TH ANNIVERSARY: TEMPTATIONS.
Tracks: / I want a love I can see / So much joy / It don't have to be this way / Further you look the less you see / My girl / Since I lost my baby / I can't get next to you / Cloud nine / Just my imagination (running away with me) / Come to me / Soulmate / Tear from a woman's eyes / Wherever I lay my hat / Don't look back / Get ready / Ain't too proud to beg / Truly yours / Papa was a rollin' stone / Thanks to you / Glasshouse / Power / Treat her like a lady.
LP: . . . . . WL 72435
MC: . . . . . WK 72435

ALL DIRECTIONS.
Tracks: / Funky music sho nuff turns me on / Run Charlie run / Papa was a rollin' stone / Love woke me up this morning / I ain't got nothin' / First time ever I saw your face, The / Mother nature / Do your thing.
LP: . . . . . STMS 5052
MC: . . . . . CSTMS 5052
LP: . . . . . WL 72321
LP: . . . . . STML 11218

ANTHOLOGY - TEMPTATIONS (Volumes 1 & 2).
Tracks: / Way you do the things you do, The / I'll be in trouble / Girl's alright with me, The / Girl (why you wanna make me blue) / My girl / It's growing / Since I lost my baby / My baby / Don't look back / Get ready / Ain't too proud to beg / Beauty is only skin deep / I'm losing you / All I need / You're my everything / It's you that I need (loneliness made me realise) / I wish it would rain / I truly, truly believe / I could never love another (after loving you) / Runaway child, running wild / Ol' man river / Try to remember / Impossible dream, The / I'm gonna make you love me (with Diana Ross & The Supremes.) / Please return your love to me / Cloud nine / Don't let the Joneses get you down / I can't get next to you / Psychedelic shack / Ball of confusion / Funky music sho nuff turns me on / I ain't got nothin' / Just my imagination (running away with me) / Superstar (remember how you got where you are) / Mother nature / Love woke me up this morning / Papa was a rollin' stone / Masterpiece / Shakey ground / Power / Sail away / Treat her like a lady.
2LP: . . . . . TMSP 6003
MCSET: . . . . . CTMSP 6003
2LP: . . . . . ZL 72178

BACK TO BASICS.
Tracks: / Miss busy body (get your body busy) / Sail away / Outlaw / Stop the world right here (I wanna get off) / Battle song, The (I'm the one) / Hollywood / Isn't the night fantastic / Make me believe in love again.
LP: . . . . . STML 12196
MC: . . . . . CSTML 12196

BEST OF THE TEMPTATIONS.
LP: . . . . . STAR 2281
MC: . . . . . STAC 2281

CLOUD NINE.
Tracks: / Cloud nine / I heard it through the grapevine / Runaway child running wild / Love is a hurtin' thing / Hey girl (I like your style) / Why did she have to leave me (why did she have to go?) / I need your lovin' / Don't let him take your love from me / I gotta find a way (to get you back) / Gonna keep on tryin' till I win your love.
LP: . . . . . STMS 5020
MC: . . . . . CSTMS 5020
LP: . . . . . STML 11109

DIANA ROSS JOINS THE TEMPTATIONS/TOGETHER (See under Ross, Diana) (Temptations/Diana Ross).

GET READY.
Tracks: / You're the one I need / Too busy thinking about my baby / I gotta know now / Just another lonely night / Say you / Fading away / It's a lonely world without your love / Get ready / Everybody needs love / Born to love you / You'll lose a precious love / You've got to earn it.
LP: . . . . . TMS 3507
MC: . . . . . TMC 3507

GETTING READY.
LP: . . . . . STML 11035

GIVE LOVE AT CHRISTMAS.
Tracks: / Give love on Christmas day / Christmas song, The / Love comes with Christmas / Everything for Christmas / Christmas everyday / Silent night.
LP: . . . . . STMS 5085
MC: . . . . . CSTMS 5085
LP: . . . . . WL 72356
MC: . . . . . WK 72356

GREATEST HITS: TEMPTATIONS.
LP: . . . . . WL 72646
MC: . . . . . WK 72646

GREATEST HITS, VOL 2: TEMPTATIONS.
LP: . . . . . WL 72647
MC: . . . . . WK 72647
LP: . . . . . STML 11170

I'M GONNA MAKE YOU LOVE ME (See under Ross, Diana) (Temptations/Diana Ross).

LEGEND (See under Ross, Diana) (Temptations with Diana Ross & The Supremes).

MASTERPIECE.
LP: . . . . . STMS 5021
MC: . . . . . CSTMS 5021
MC: . . . . . WK 72076
LP: . . . . . WL 72076
LP: . . . . . STML 11229

NITE AT THE APOLLO LIVE, A (see also Daryl Hall, John Oates) (Daryl Hall & John Oates with The temptations).

POWER.
Tracks: / Power / Struck by lightning twice / Isn't the night fantastic / How can I resist your love / Can't you see sweet thing / Go for it / I'm coming home.
LP: . . . . . STML 12136

PSYCHEDELIC SHACK.
LP: . . . . . STMS 5051
MC: . . . . . CSTMS 5051
LP: . . . . . STML 11147

PUZZLE PEOPLE.
Tracks: / I can't get next to you / Hey, Jude / Don't let the Joneses get you down / Message from a black man / It's your thing / Little green apples / You don't love me no more / Since I've lost you / Running away (ain't gonna help you) / That's the way love is / Slave.
LP: . . . . . STMS 5050
MC: . . . . . CSTMS 5050
LP: . . . . . STML 11133

SKY'S THE LIMIT.
Tracks: / Gonna keep on tryin' till I win your love / Just my imagination (running away with me) / I'm the exception to the rule / Smiling faces sometimes / Man / Throw a farewell kiss / Ungena za ulimwengu (unite the world) / Love can be anything (can't nothing be love but love).
MC: . . . . . WK 72743

SOLID ROCK.
LP: . . . . . STML 11202

SPECIAL.
Tracks: / Friends / Special / All I want from you / She's better than money /

One step at a time / Fill me up / Go ahead / Loveline / Soul to soul / O.A.O. lover (CD only.).
LP: ZL 72667
MC: ZK 72667

SURFACE THRILLS.
Tracks: / Surface thrills / Love on my mind / Tonight / One man woman / Show me your love / Seeker, (The) / What a way to put it / Bring your body here (exercise chant) / Made in America.
LP: STML 12182
MC: CSTML 12182

T.C.B.-THE ORIGINAL SOUNTRACK (See under Ross, Diana) (Temptations with Diana Ross & The Supremes).

TEMPTATION'S GREATEST HITS.
LP: STML 11042

TEMPTATIONS LIVE.
LP: STML 11053

TEMPTATIONS SING SMOKEY.
Tracks: / Way you do the things you do, The / Baby baby I need you / My girl / What love has joined together / You'll lose a precious love / Who's lovin' you? / It's growing / What's so good about goodbye.
LP: STMR 9005
MC: CSTMR 9005

TEMPTATIONS, THE.
Tracks: / Aiming at your heart / Evil woman (gonna take your love) / Best of both worlds / Ready willing and able / Open their eyes / Oh what a night / Life of a cowboy,The / Just ain't havin' fun / What else / Your lovin' is magic.
LP: STML 12159
MC: CSTML 12159

TEMPTATIONS WITH A LOT OF SOUL.
LP: STML 11057

TEMPTATIONS XMAS CARD.
LP: SHM 3202
MC: HSC 3202

TO BE CONTINUED....
Tracks: / Lady soul / Message to the world / To be continued / Put us together again / Someone / Girls (they like it) / More love, your love / Fine mess, A (from 'A Fine Mess'.) / You're the one / Love me right.
LP: ZL 72515
MC: ZK 72515

TOGETHER AGAIN.
Tracks: / I got your number / Look what you started / I wonder who she's seeing now / 10 x 10 / Do you wanna go with me / Little things / Every time I close my eyes / Lucky / Put your foot down.
LP: ZL 72616
MC: ZK 72616

TOUCH ME.
Tracks: / Magic / Give her some attention / Deeper than love / I'm fascinated / Touch me / Don't break your promise to me / She got tired of loving me / Do you really love your baby / Oh lover.
LP: ZL 72413
MC: ZK 72413

TRULY FOR YOU.
Tracks: / Running / Treat her like a lady / How can you say that it's over / My love is true / Memories / Just to keep you in my life / Set your love right / I'll keep my light in my window.
LP: ZL 72342
MC: ZK 72342
LP: WL 76244
MC: WK 76244

Tems, Mick

GOWERTON FAIR.
Tracks: / Carmarthen bells / Margam bando boys / Soap, starch and candles / Cutty Wren, The / Blwyddyn Newydd Dda / Pendine calennig / Glory song, The / Gowerton Fair / Ty coch caerdydd / Pant Corlan yr wyn / Get up a New Years morning / Swansea hornpipe / Will Griffy's music / Miner's life is like a sailor's, A / Montevideo.
LP: SFA 074

Ten City

FOUNDATION.
Tracks: / That's the way love is / Where do we go / Suspicious / Close and slow / One kiss will make it better / Devotion / Satisfaction / You must be the one / For you / Foundation.
LP: WX 249
MC: WX 249 C

STATE OF MIND.
LP: WX 393
MC: WX 393C

Ten Commandments

TEN COMMANDMENTS, THE (Film soundtrack) (Various artists).
Tracks: / Prelude: *Various artists* / In the bulrushes: *Various artists* / Bitter life, The: *Various artists*/ Love and ambition: *Various artists* / Hard bondage, The: *Various artists* / Egyptian dance: *Various artists*/ Crucible of God, The: *Various artists* / And Moses watered Jethro's flock: *Various artists* / Bedouin dance: *Various artists* / I am that I am: *Various artists* / Overture: *Various artists* / Thus says the lord: *Various artists* / Plagues, The: *Various artists* / Exodus: *Various artists* / Pillar of fire, The: *Various* artists / Red sea: *Various artists* / Ten commandments: *Various artists* / Go, proclaim liberty: *Various artists.*
LP: MODEM 1010
MC: MODEMC 1010

Ten Ten

WALK ON.
Tracks: / When it rains / There goes everything / Rags / This one in you / Where the flowers grow / One life / Beyond me / Walk on / Million miles away / Silver heaven.
LP: CHR 1532
MC: ZCHR 1532

Ten To Midnight

10 TO MIDNIGHT (Film Soundtrack) (Various artists).
LP: STV 81172

Ten To One...

TEN TO ONE SUPPER HITS,VOL. 1 (Various artists).
LP: Unknown

Ten Years After

10 YEARS AFTER THE GOLDRUSH (Various artists).
LP: CON 00020

ABOUT TIME.
LP: CHR 1722
MC: ZCHR 1722

ALVIN LEE & COMPANY.
LP: SML 1096
MC: KSCM 1096

CLASSIC PERFORMANCES OF TEN YEARS AFTER.
Tracks: / I'm going home / One of these days / I'd love to change the world / Tomorrow I'll be out of town / Good morning little schoolgirl / Baby won't you let me rock 'n' roll you / Rock & roll music to the world / It's getting harder / Positive vibrations / Choo choo Mama.
LP: CHR 1134
MC: ZCHR 1134

COLLECTION: TEN YEARS AFTER.
Tracks: / Hear me calling / No title / Spoonful / I can't keep from crying sometimes / Standing at the crossroads / Portable people / Rock your mama / Love like a man (long version) / I want to know / Speed kills / Boogie on / I may be wrong but I won't be wrong always / At the woodchopper's ball / Spider in your web / Summertime / Shantung cabbage / I'm going home.
2LP: CCSLP 115
MC: CCSMC 115
MC: CCSMC 293

CRICKLEWOOD GREEN.
Tracks: / Sugar the road / Working on the road / 50,000 miles beneath my brain / Year 3,000 blues / Me and my baby / Love like a man / Circles / As the sun still burns away.
LP: CHR 1084
MC: ZCHR 1084
LP: SML 1065

GOIN' HOME.
Tracks: / Hear me calling / Going to try / Love like a man / No title / I woke up this morning / Woodchoppers' ball / I'm going home.
LP: CHR 1077
MC: ZCHR 1077

GREATEST HITS: TEN YEARS AFTER VOL.1.
MC: CP4 22436

HEAR ME CALLING.
Tracks: / Hear me calling / Feel it for me / Help me / Spoonful / I want to know / No title / I'm going.
LP: TAB 12

LIVE AT READING '83.
LP: FRSLP 003
MC: FRSMC 003

LOVE LIKE A MAN (OLD GOLD) (See under Them - Here comes the night).

ORIGINAL RECORDINGS VOL.1.
Tracks: / I'm going home / Feel it for me / Portable people / Love until I die / Speed kills / Help me / Going to try / Hear me calling / Don't want you Woman / Spider in your web (Live) / Sounds / Losing the dogs.
LP: SEE 80

ORIGINAL RECORDINGS VOL.2.
Tracks: / One of these days / Over the hill / Two time mama / Stoned woman / Good morning little schoolgirl / Fifty thousand miles beneath my brain / If you should love me / My baby left me / Think about the times / Working on the road / Love like a man.
LP: SEE 90

PORTFOLIO.
2LP: CHR 1639
MC: ZCHR 1639

POSITIVE VIBRATIONS.
Tracks: / Nowhere to run / Positive vibrations / Stone me / Without you / Going back to Birmingham / It's getting harder / You're driving me crazy / Look into my life / Look me straight in the eyes / I wanted to boogie.
LP: CHR 1060
MC: ZCHR 1060

RECORDED LIVE.
Tracks: / One of these days / You give me loving / Good morning little schoolgirl / Hobbitt / Help me / Classical things / Scat thing / I can't keep from crying sometimes / Sometimes / Sometimes / Silly thing / Slow blues in 'C' / I'm going home / Choo choo Mama.
2LP: CTY 1049
MCSET: ZCTY 1049

ROCK 'N' ROLL MUSIC TO THE WORLD.
Tracks: / You give me loving / Convention prevention / Turned off TV blues / Standing at the station / You can't win them all / Religion / Choo choo mama / Tomorrow I'll be out of town / Rock & roll music to the world.
LP: CHR 1009
MC: ZCHR 1009

SPACE IN TIME, A.
Tracks: / One of these days / Here they come / I'd love to change the world / Over the hill / Baby won't you let me rock 'n' roll you / Once there was a time / Let the sky fall / Hard monkeys / I've been there too / Uncle Jam.
LP: CHR 1001
MC: ZCHR 1001

SSSH.
Tracks: / Bad scene / Two time Mama / Stoned woman / Good morning little schoolgirl / If you should love me / I don't know that you don't know my name / Stomp, The / I woke up this morning.
LP: CHR 1083
MC: ZCHR 1083
LP: SML 1052

STONEDHENGE.
Tracks: / I can't live without you, Lydia / Woman trouble / Skoobly-oobly-doo-bob / Hear me calling / Sad song / Three blind mice / No title / Faro / Speed kills.
LP: SML 1029
MC: KSCM 1029
LP: 8295342

TEN YEARS AFTER.. (Various artists).
LP: CON 00022

TEN YEARS AFTER.
Tracks: / Baby won't you let me rock 'n' roll you / Good morning little schoolgirl / Rock'n'roll music to the world / Tomorrow I'll be out of town / I woke up this morning / Working on the road / One of these days / Hear me calling / Me and my baby / Gonna run.
LP: SHM 3038
MC: HSC 3038
LP: SHM 3038

UNDEAD.
Tracks: / I may be wrong / At the woodchoppers' ball / Spider in your web / Summertime - Shantung cabbage / I'm going home.
LP: SML 1023
MC: KSCM 1023

WATT.
Tracks: / I'm coming on / My baby left me / Think about the times / Band with no name, The / Gonna run / She lies in the morning / Sweet little sixteen.
LP: SML 1078

Ten Years With Maggie

TEN YEARS WITH MAGGIE (Various artists).
MCSET: ZBBC 1102

Tenants

TENANTS, THE.
Tracks: / Look the other way / Schoolgirl / I love romance / Sheriff / Winner, The / How do you sleep at night / You don't know what I've been thru / Connect the dots / What's in it for me? / Forget about forgetting.
LP: EPC 25541

Tender Is The Night

TENDER IS THE NIGHT (Various artists).
Tracks: / Tender is the night: *Various artists* / Rosemary's waltz: *Various artists* / I'm forever blowing bubbles: *Various artists* / Nicole and Tommy: *Various artists* / Jovial Joe: *Various artists* / Hindustan: *Various* artists / Poor butterfly: *Various artists* / I ain't gonna give nobody none of my jelly roll: *Various artists*/ Clap hands here comes Charlie: *Various artists* / Tea for two: *Various artists* / Wedding of the painted doll, The: *Various artists* / Let's misbehave: *Various artists* / Fascinating rhythm: *Various artists* / Painting the clouds with sunshine: *Various artists* / Harlems Araby: *Various artists* / Ain't she sweet: *Various artists*/ Keep your temper: *Various artists* / Thank your father: *Various artists.*
LP: REB 582
MC: ZCF 582

Tender Lugers

JOHNNY ORGY.
LP: KIK 1

Tender Mercies

TENDER MERCIES (Film Soundtrack) (Various artists).
LP: LBG 7511471

Tenebrae (film)

TENEBRAE (Film soundtrack) (Goblin).
LP: TER 1064

Tenko

DISAPPEARANCE.
LP: REC 016
LP: RECREC 16

Tennessee Three

LET THE GOOD TIMES ROLL.
LP: CRIMLP 138

Tennessee Tooters

1924-1926 (Tennessee Tooters & The Hottentots).
2LP: DFJ 117

TENNESSEE TOOTERS 1924-25.
MC: NEO 711

TENNESSEE TOOTERS AND THE HOTTENTOTS (Tennessee Tooters & The Hottentots).
LP: FJ 117

Tenney, Gerry

SING A YIDDISH SONG (Tenney, Gerry & Betty Albert Schreck).
MC: GVMMC 134

Tennille, Toni

DO IT AGAIN (Tennille,Toni & Big Band).
Tracks: / Do it again / Close your eyes / Can't help lovin' dat man / Our love is here to stay / Let's do it / Day dream / Do nothing til you hear from me / More than you know / I got it bad and that ain't good / I'll only miss him when I think of him / Someone to watch over me / I thought about you / Guess who I saw today / But not for me.
LP: USA 596
LP: PREC 5006
MC: ZPREC 5006

MORE THAN YOU KNOW.
LP: UNKNOWN

Tennis

TENNIS (see under Sutphen, Dick) (Sutphen, Dick).

Tennors, Clive

RIDE YOU DONKEY.
LP: LALP 008

Tenor Fly

WICKEDEST SOUND (See Under Rebel MC) (Tenor Fly & Rebel MC).

Tenor Saw

CLASH (Tenor Saw & Don Angelo).
LP: BM 003

FEVER.
LP: BMLP 013

GOLDEN HEN, THE (Tenor Saw & Don Angelo).
LP: UTLP 004

POWER HOUSE PRESENTS (Tenor Saw & Nitty Gritty).
LP: DSR 6630

Tenors Anyone

TENORS ANYONE (Various artists).
Tracks: / Skull buster: *Various artists* / It's the talk of the town: *Various artists* / Ante room: *Various* artists / Pennies from Heaven: *Various artists* / In a pinch: *Various artists* / Poop deck: *Various artists*/ These foolish things: *Various artists* / Blues for the month of May: *Various artists* / I should care: *Various artists* / Along about this time of year: *Various artists.*
LP: MTLP 013

Tenpole Tudor

EDDIE, OLD BOB, DICK & GARY.
Tracks: / Swords of a thousand men / Go wilder / I wish / Header now / There are boys / Wunderbar / Tell me more / Judy annual / I can't sleep / Anticipation / What else can I do / Confessions.
LP: SEEZ 31

MC: .... ZSEEZ 31

LET THE FOUR WINDS BLOW.
Tracks: / Let the four winds blow / Throwing my baby out with the bath water / Trumpeters / It's easy to see / What you doing in Bombay / Local animal / Her fruit is forbidden / Tonight is the night / Unpaid debt, The / King of Siam / Sea of thunder.
LP: .... SEEZ 42
MC: .... ZSEEZ 42

Tension

BREAKING POINT.
Tracks: / One nation / Wrecking crew / Reach for your sword / Angels from the past / W O C / Shock treatment.
LP: .... RR 9599

Tent

SIX EMPTY PLACES.
Tracks: / Seven years part 1 (No thought) / Seven years part 2 (Abundance) / Parachuting in Bolivia / Intellectual stance / No way of knowing / Dockland lullaby / She's waiting to be looked at / Shiny black FBI shoes, up and down the stair / I thought things were ironed out.
LP: .... BRED 17

Tepepa

TEPEPA (Film Soundtrack) (Various artists).
LP: .... C'BUS 106

Tequila Sunrise

TEQUILA SUNRISE (Film soundtrack) (Various artists).
Tracks: / Surrender to me: *Wilson, Ann/ Robin Zander* / Do you believe in shame?: *Duran Duran* / Recurring dream: *Crowded House* / Give a little love: *Marley, Ziggy & The Melody Makers* / Don't worry baby: *Everly Bros. & Beach Boys* / Dead on the money: *Taylor, Andy* / Unsubstantiated: *Church* / Beyond the sea: *Darin, Bobby*/ Tequila dreams: *Gruisin, Dave/Lee Ritenour* / Jo Ann's song: *Gruisin, Dave/David Sanborn.*
LP: .... C 11 H 91185
MC: .... C 41 H 91185
LP: .... EST 2086
MC: .... TCEST 2086

Terkel, Studs

HARD TIMES (The story of the Depression).
MCSET: 2048

Terminal Cheesecake

ANGELS IN PIG-TAILS.
LP: .... PATH 003
MC: .... PATH 003 MC

JOHNNY TOWN MOUSE.
LP: .... WIIJLP 1

VCL.
LP: .... UNKNOWN

Terminal City...

TERMINAL CITY RICHOCHET (Original Soundtrack) (Various artists).
LP: .... VIRUS 075

Terminal Tower

ARCHIVAL COLLECTION (See under Pere Ubu) (Terminal Tower/Pere Ubu).

Terminator

TERMINATOR, THE (Film soundtrack) (Various artists).
LP: .... ENG 72000.1
MC: .... ENG 72000.4

Terminator X

TERMINATOR X AND THE VALLEY OF THE JEEP BEETS.
Tracks: / Vendetta ... the big getback / Buck whylin' / Homey don't play dat / Juvenile delinquintz / Blues, The / Back to the scene of the bass / Can't take my style / Wanna be dancin' / DJ is the selector / Run that go / Power thang / No further / High priest of turbulence / Ain't got nuthin'.
LP: 4684211
MC: 4684214

Terms Of Endearment

TERMS OF ENDEARMENT (Film soundtrack) (Various artists).
LP: .... EST 2401221

Ternent, Billy

AT THE INTERNATIONAL DANCE CHAMPIONSHIP (Ternent, Billy & His Orchestra).
LP: 15-60

SHE'S MY LOVELY (Ternent, Billy & His Orchestra).
Tracks: / She's my lovely / Mississippi dreamboat / Stormy weather / You're the rainbow / Where are you now? / I've got a heart filled with love / I have a vision / Roundabout still goes round, The / Walkin' by the river / When they ask about you / I wonder why / Say a little prayer for the boys over there / Dear little isle I love / I like riding on a choo choo.
LP: .... PLE 503
MC: .... TC-PLE 503

TERNENT SOUND, THE (Ternent, Billy and His Orchestra).
Tracks: / She's my lovely / How about you / Mr. Wonderful / Unforgettable / Hold my hand / Gipsy in my soul, The / Zing went the strings of my heart / Certain smile (A) / Pretty girl is like a melody (A) / Happy days and lonely nights / Tammy / I'll be with you in apple blossom time.
LP: .... PLE 518

THAT UNMISTAKABLE SOUND (Ternent, Billy & His Orchestra).
Tracks: / Avalon / Can't take my eyes off you / You forgot to remember / Dream a little dream of me / Those were the days / Always / Three little words / It's the natural thing to do / I've got a pocketful of dreams / One, two, button your shoe / Don't blame me / Hold me / Try a little tenderness / I left my heart in San Francisco / Lonesome road / If I had you / By the fireside / Goodnight sweetheart / If my friends could see me now.
LP: .... JASM 2020

Terraplane

MOVING TARGET.
Tracks: / Moving target / When I sleep alone / I survive (live) / I can't live without your love (live) / If that's what it takes / Good things going / Promised land / Moving target / Hostage to fortune / Heartburn / Hearts on fire / I will come out fighting / Nothing on but the radio.
LP: 4601571
MC: 4601574

Terrell, Tammi

2 CLASSIC ALBUMS : GREATEST HITS (See under Gaye, Marvin) (Gaye, Marvin, Diana Ross, Tammi Terrell).

EASY (See under Gaye, Marvin).

GREATEST HITS: TAMMI TERRELL (See under Gaye, Marvin for details) (Terrell, Tammi & Marvin Gaye).

ONION SONG (see Gaye, Marvin) (Terrell, Tammi & Marvin Gaye).

TWO CAN HAVE A PARTY (see Gaye, Marvin) (Terrell, Tammi & Marvin Gaye).

UNITED (see under Gaye, Marvin) (Terrell, Tammi & Marvin Gaye).

YOU'RE ALL I NEED (see under Gaye, Marvin) (Terrell, Tammi & Marvin Gaye).

Territories...

TERRITORIES - VOL.1 (Various artists).
LP: .... ARCADIA 2006

TERRITORIES- VOL.2 (Various artists).
LP: .... ARCADIA 2007

TERRITORIES - VOL.3 THE SOUTH (Various artists).
LP: .... ARCADIA 2010

Terror Vision

TERROR VISION (Film soundtrack) (Various artists).
LP: .... ENG 2120.1

Terrorizer

WORLD DOWNFALL.
Tracks: / After world obliteration / Tear of napalm / Corporation pull in / Resurrection / Need to live / Dead shall rise / Injustice / Storm of stress / Human prey / Condemned system / Enslaved by propaganda / Whirlwind struggle / World downfall / Ripped to shreds.
MC: .... MOSH 16 MC
LP: .... MOSH 16

Terry

SILVERADO TRAIL (Terry & The Pirates).
Tracks: / Wish I was your river / Sweet emotions / I can't dance / Heartbeatin' away / Silverado trail / Follow her around / Risin' of the moon / Mustang ride / Gun metal blues / Inlaws and outlaws / Nighthawkin' the dawn.
LP: .... WIK 89

Terry, Al

AL TERRY & JIM NEWMAN (Terry, Al/ Jim Newman).
LP: .... FLY 573

GOOD DEAL, LUCILLE.
Tracks: / Good deal, Lucille (2nd recording) / Roughneck blues / Coconut girl / Bring some rain / Follow me / It's better late than never / Because I'm yours / Am I seeing things / Watch dog / My baby knows / What a fool I was to fall (Previously unissued.) / Last date / What are you to me / Passing the blues around / Your sweet lies / Lesson of love.
LP: .... BFX 15107

Terry, Alistair

YOUNG AT HEART.
LP: .... WKFMLP 51

Terry, Clark

AIN'T MISBEHAVIN'.
Tracks: / Jitterbug waltz / Your feets too big / Honeysuckle rose / Mean to me / It's a sin to tell a lie / Ain't misbehavin' / Squeeze me / Handful of keys / Black and blue / I can't give you anything but love / Joint is jumpin', The.
LP: 2312 105
MC: .... K 12 105

ALTERNATE BLUES (Terry, Clark/ Freddie Hubbard/Dizzy Gillespie/Oscar Peterson).
Tracks: / Alternate one / Alternate two / Alternate three / Alternate four / Wrap your troubles in dreams / Here's that rainy day / Gypsy / If I should lose you.
LP: 2312 136
MC: .... K 12 136

BIG B-A-D BAND LIVE AT BUDDY'S PLACE.
Tracks: / Modus operandi / Come Sunday / Gap sealer / Jeep's blues / Swiss Air / Big bad blues / Sugar cubes.
LP: .... VSD 79373

CLARK TERRY AND HIS JOLLY GIANTS (Terry, Clark & His Jolly Giants).
LP: .... VHD 79365

COLOUR CHANGES.
LP: .... CS 9009

DUKE WITH A DIFFERENCE.
LP: .... OJC 229

EFFERVESCENT.
Tracks: / Perdido / On the trail / Jazzhouse blues / In der Heimat gibt's ein Widerseh'n / Straight no chaser / Wham / Take the 'A' train.
LP: 5C 064 61175

FUNK DUMPLIN'S (Terry, Clark Quintet).
LP: .... MTX 1002

HAPPY HORNS OF CLARK TERRY.
Tracks: / Rockin' in rhythm / In a mist / Return to Swahili / Ellington rides again / Impulsive / Do nothing till you hear from me / Jazz conversations / High towers.
LP: .... JAS 28
MC: .... JAS C28

IN PARIS 1960.
LP: .... SW 8406

IT'S WHAT'S HAPPENIN'.
Tracks: / Electric mumbles / Secret love / Take me back to Elkhart / Take the 'A' train / Tee pee time / On the trail.
LP: .... JAS 43
MC: .... JAS C43

LIVE ON 57TH STREET (Terry, Clark Big Bad Band).
Tracks: / Dirty old man / On the trail / Fading fleur / Hymn for Kim / Take the 'A' train / Shell game / Here's that rainy day / Rock skipping at the Blue Note.
LP: .... BEAR 13

MEMORIES OF DUKE.
Tracks: / Passion flower / Happy-go-lucky local / Echoes of Harlem / Sophisticated lady / Things ain't what they used to be / I let a song go out of my heart / Cottontail / Everything but you / Come Sunday.
LP: 2312 118
MC: .... K 12 118

MOTHER - MOTHER (Terry, Clark & Zoot Sims).
Tracks: / First movement / Jubilation (second movement) / Exultation (third movement) / Revelation (fourth movement).
LP: 2312 115
MC: .... K 12 115

OSCAR PETERSON AND CLARK TERRY (see Peterson, Oscar) (Terry, Clark & Oscar Peterson).

PAYNE, TERRY, GREEN - THE CONNECTION (See Green, Bennie) (Terry, Clark/Bennie Green/Cecil Payne).

PORTRAITS.
Tracks: / Pennies from Heaven / Sugar blues / Autumn leaves / Finger filibuster / Little jazz / When it's sleepy time down south / Live at five / Ciribiribin / OW / I can't get started / I don't wanna be kissed.
LP: .... JR 2

SERENADE TO A BUS SEAT (Terry, Clark Quintet).
LP: .... OJC 066

TOP AND BOTTOM BRASS.
LP: .... RSLP 295

TRIBUTE TO FROG (See under Thilo, Jesper) (Terry, Clark Quintet/Jesper Thilo).

YES, THE BLUES.
Tracks: / Diddlin' / Railroad porter blues / Swingin' the blues / Marina Bay rednecks / Quicksand / Snapper / Kidney stew.
LP: .... D 2312 127
MC: .... K 12 127

Terry & Gerry

FROM LUBBOCK AND CLINTWOOD EAST.
LP: .... IT 022
MC: .... IT 022C

Terry, Helen

BLUE NOTES.
Tracks: / Act of mercy / Come on and find me / Love, money and sex / Right in front of you / Forbidden fruit / All night makes it right / Perfect kiss, The / Feeling your heart / Close watch / Stuttering.
LP: .... OVED 219
MC: .... OVEDC 219

Terry, Mike

30 PIANO FAVOURITES.
Tracks: / Sweet Georgia Brown / Chicago / Who's sorry now / Portrait of my love / Danger ahead beware / With these hands / I never see Maggie alone / Let him go, let him tarry / Let's do it again / Your flowers arrived too late / Our garden / Point of no return / Roll out the barrel / Bye bye blackbird / If you knew Susie / Carolina in the morning / California here I come / My Mammy / Bobby's girl / Well respected man, A / Pepe / Jane Street / Portrait painter of Paree / Gilly gilly ossenfeffer katzenellenbogen by the sea / How lucky you are / What is the reason / When Irish eyes are smiling / Darktown strutters' ball / Bill Bailey won't you please come home / When the saints go marching in.
LP: .... PRX 19

CLACKERS.
Tracks: / I'll be with you in apple blossom time / Honeysuckle and the bee, The / Moonlight and roses / Scotland the brave / I love a lassie / Roaming in the gloaming / I can't give you anything but love baby / Side by side / Happy days and lonely nights / Always / My wonderful one / I'm forever blowing bubbles / Conkers / When the red, red robin comes bob, bob, bobbin' along / I wonder where my baby is tonight / Five foot two, eyes of blue / Bless your heart my darling / Game of chance / Sally / For me and my gal / Oh you beautiful doll / Toot toot tootsie goodbye / Rockabye your baby with a Dixie melody / I'm looking over a four leaf clover / You made me love you / Clackers.
LP: .... JOYS 233

LIVE AT THE PAVILION THEATRE, GLASGOW, VOL 1.
Tracks: / Play on music / Nobody does it like me / Bumble boogie / Amazing grace / Sabre dance / All the nice girls love a sailor / Hello hello / Mademoiselle from Armentiers / I do like to be beside the seaside / I've got a lovely bunch of coconuts / John Brown's boogie / Lara's theme / Black and white rag / Rhapsody in blue / My way.
LP: .... PRX 4

LIVE AT THE PAVILION THEATRE, GLASGOW, VOL 2.
Tracks: / Clackers / Ave Maria / Hey Jude / In the mood / Hi lili hi lo / I wonder who's kissing her now / When Irish eyes are smiling / Bicycle built for two / I belong to Glasgow / Warsaw concerto tiger rag / Love is blue / If you knew Susie / Roll out the barrel / Knees up mother Brown / My old man / Swanee / Sorba's dance / Dark Lochnagar.
LP: .... PRX 5

QUEEN OF CLUBS.
Tracks: / Big Ben boogie / Disc jockey rag / Black and white rag / Jane Street / Five foot two eyes of blue / Honky tonk train blues / Sentimental journey / Victoria roll / Sabre dance / La Paloma / Lara's theme / Exodus.
LP: .... PRX 13

TRIBUTE TO WINIFRED ATTWELL.
Tracks: / I'll be with you in apple blossom time / Shine on Harvest moon / Blue skies / I'll never say never again again / I'll see you in my dreams / Poor people of Paris, The / Coronation rag / Tiger rag / Music, music, music / This ole house / Heartbreaker / Woody woodpecker song, The / Last train to San Fernando / Bring a little water Sylvie / Putting on the style / Don't you rock me daddy-o / Black and white rag / Flirtation waltz / Jubilee rag / Charleston / Singing the blues / Green door / See you later alligator / Shake, rattle and roll / Rock around the clock / Razzle dazzle.
LP: .... PRX 26
MC: .... TC PRX 26

Terry, Pat

ALL JAZZED UP.
LP: .... CLP 54

Terry, Ruby

CHAPTER ONE.
LP: MALP 4433
MC: MALC 4433

Terry, Sonny

BROWNIE MCGHEE & SONNY TERRY WITH EARL HOOKER (See under McGhee, Brownie) (Terry, Sonny & Brownie McGee with Earl Hooker).

BROWNIE & SONNY'S BLUES (Terry, Sonny & Brownie McGee with Earl Hooker).
LP: 512505

HARMONICA BLUES (Terry, Sonny/Dr. Ross/Hammie Nixon).
LP: SLP 4008

HARMONICA BLUES, THE (See under Ross, Doctor) (Terry, Sonny/ Doctor Ross/ Sonny Boy Williams).

SONNY IS KING.
LP: OBC 521

SONNY TERRY 1938-55 (Terry, Sonny/ Brownie McGhee/Woody Guthrie).
LP: DLP 536

SONNY TERRY 1952.
Tracks: / Wine head woman / Four o'clock blues / Baby let's have some fun / Bad luck blues / Lonesome room / News for you baby / No love blues.
LP: KK 807

SONNY TERRY AND BROWNIE MCGHEE (Terry, Sonny & Brownie McGhee).
LP: BGOLP 75

SONNY'S STORY.
Tracks: / I ain't gonna be your dog no more / My baby done gone / Worried blues / High powered woman / Pepperheaded woman / Sonny's story / I'm gonna get on my feet after a while / Four o'clock blues / Telephone blues / Great tall engine.
LP: OBC 503

SPORTING LIFE BLUES (Terry, Sonny & Brownie McGhee).
LP: JSP 1110
MC: JSP CC 1110

TOUGHEST TERRY AND BADDEST BROWN (Terry, Sonny & Buster Brown).
LP: CG 709-11

WALK ON (Terry, Sonny & Brownie McGhee).
Tracks: / Gonna lay my body down / Drinking in the blues / Po' boy / Just rode in your town / Sun's gonna shine / Everybody's blues / Trouble in mind / I'm a stranger here myself / Down by the riverside / Walk on / Blues for the lowlands / Right on that shore / Blowin' the fuses.
LP: 20051
MC: 40051
LP: BDL 1018
MC: BDC 1018

WHOOPIN' (Terry, Sonny/Johnny Winter/ Willie Dixon).
LP: SNTF 915

WHOOPIN' THE BLUES.
Tracks: / Whoopin' the blues / All alone blues / Worried man blues / Leaving blues / Scream' and cryin' blues / Riff and harmonica jump / Crow Jane blues / Beer garden blues / Hot headed woman / Custard pie blues / Early morning blues / Harmonica rag / Dirty mistreater don't you know / Telephone blues.
LP: CRB 1120

WIZARD OF THE HARMONICA.
LP: SLP 218

YOU HEAR ME TALKIN' (Terry, Sonny & Brownie McGhee).
Tracks: / You hear me talkin' / Going down slow / Raise a ruckus tonight / C.C. rider / Cindy Cindy / Right now / Worried life blues / John Henry / Crawdad hole / Ain't gonna study war no more / Take this hammer / That good old jelly roll.
LP: B 90081

Terry, Todd

TO THE BATMOBILE, LET'S GO.
MC: CSRE 82009
LP: SBUKLP 2

Terry, Tony

FOREVER YOURS.
Tracks: / Forever yours / Lovey dovey / Fulltime girl / Daydreaming / Here with me / She's fly / Wassup wit u / Up and down love / Young love / What would it take / Forever yours (late night version) / Lovey dovey (remix).
LP: 4605041
MC: 4605044

TONY TERRY.
Tracks: / Head over heels / Bad girl / Baby love / Friends and lovers / With you / Come home with me / That kind of guy / Tongue tied / Let me love you / Read my mind / Everlasting love.
LP: 4658281
MC: 4658284

Terzis, Michalis

NOSTIMON IMAR.
LP: EULP 1076
MC: EUMC 1076

Teschemaker, Frank

MUGGSY SPANIER & FRANK TESCHEMAKER (see Spanier, Muggsy) (Teschemaker, Frank & Muggsy Spanier).

Tesh, John

TOUR DE FRANCE/ THE EARLY YEARS.
LP: 210713
MC: 410713

Tesla

FIVE MAN ACOUSTICAL JAM.
LP: GEF 24311
MC: GEFC 24311

GREAT RADIO CONTROVERSY.
Tracks: / Hang tough / Lady luck / Heaven's trail / Be a man / Lazy days, crazy nights / Did it for the money / Yesterdaze gone / Making magic / Way it is, The / Flight to nowhere / Love song / Paradise / Party's over, The.
LP: WX 244
MC: WX 244 C
MC: GEFC 24224
LP: GEF 24224

MECHANICAL RESONANCE.
Tracks: / Ez come ez go / Cumin' atcha live / Gettin' better / 2 late 4 love / Rock me to the top / We're no good together / Modern day cowboy / Changes / Little Suzie's on the up / Love me / Cover queen / Before my eyes.
LP: 924120 1
MC: 924120 4
MC: GEFC 24120
LP: GEF 24120

PSYCHOTIC SUPPER.
LP: GEF 24424
MC: GEFC 24424

Tess

TESS (Film soundtrack) (Various artists).
LP: 9101 279
LP: MCA 1543
MC: MCAC 1543

Tess Of The...

TESS OF THE D'URBERVILLES (see under Hardy, Thomas) (Shearer, Moira (nar)).

Test Department

BEATING THE RETREAT.
Tracks: / Fall from light, The / Kick to kill / Sweet sedation / Spring into action / Beating the retreat / Total state machine / Plastic / Inheritance / Cold witness.
LP: TEST 2-3
MC: TESTC 2-3
LP: TEST 12
MC: TESTC 13
LP: TEST 33

GODODDIN.
LP: MOP 4

GOODNIGHT OUT, A.
LP: MOP 003

PAX BRITANNICA.
LP: MOP 6

SECOND EDITION BOXED SET.
LP: TEST 23

SHOULDER TO SHOULDER.
LP: MOP 1

TERRA FIRMA.
Tracks: / Nadka / Siege / Current affairs / Dark eyes / Terra firma.
LP: SUB 33009-12
MC: BIASCS 1010

UNACCEPTABLE FACE OF FREEDOM.
LP: MOP 2

Testament

LEGACY,THE.
Tracks: / Over the wall / Haunting,The / Burnt offerings / Raging waters / Curse of the legions of death / First strike is deadly / Do or die / Alone in the dark / Apocalyptic city.
LP: 781 741-1
MC: 781 741-4

LIVE IN EINDHOVEN.
Tracks: / Over the wall / Burnt offerings / Do or die / Apocalyptic city / Reign of terror.
LP: 780 226-1
MC: 780 226-4

NEW ORDER, THE.
Tracks: / Eerie inhabitants / New order, The / Trial by fire / Into the pit / Hypnosis / Disciples of the watch / Preacher, The / Day of reckoning, A / Musical death (a dirge).
LP: K 781 849 1
MC: K 781 849 4

PRACTICE WHAT YOU PREACH.
Tracks: / Practice what you preach / Perilous nation / Envy time / Time is coming / Blessed in contempt / Greenhouse effect / Sins of omission / Ballad, The (A song of hope) / Nightmare (coming back to you) / Confusion fusion.
LP: WX 297
MC: WX 297C

SOULS OF BLACK.
LP: 7567821431
MC: 7567821434

Tester, Lewis

MAN IN THE MOON.
Tracks: / Waltzes / Schottische / Jenny Lind polka / Schott number 2 / Heel and toe polka / Schott number 3 / Waltz number 3 / Step waltz / Broom dance / Country steps numbers 1 and 2 / Barbary bell / Lancers / S: Poison in a glass of wine / False bride, The / Lakes of Coolfin.
MC: 45-085

Testimony

TESTIMONY (Film soundtrack) (Various artists).
Tracks: / Lady Macbeth: *Various artists* / 2nd piano concerto No. 2 (2nd movement): *Various artists* / 11th symphony (1st movement): *Various artists* / 5th symphony (1st movement): *Various artists* / 11th symphony (1st movement): *Various artists* / 8th string quartet (3rd movement): *Various artists* / 7th symphony (excerpt) (1st movement): *Various artists* / 5th symphony (1st movement): *Various artists* / Violin concerto No. 1 (Passacag Lia): *Various artists* / 13th symphony (excerpt) (1st movement): *Various artists* / 2nd piano concerto No. 2 (2nd movement): *Various artists*.
LP: V 2536
MC: TCV 2536

Tetes Noires

CLAY FOOT GODS.
LP: ROUNDER 9008
MC: ROUNDER 9008C

Teugels, Walem

MORTIER ORGAN VOL.1.
LP: JOYS 221

MORTIER ORGAN VOL.2.
LP: JOYS 239

Teupen, Johnny

JUST FRIENDS (See Thielemans, Toots) (Teupen, Johnny/Toots Thielemans/Paul Kuhn).

Tew, Alan

YOU ARE THE SUNSHINE OF MY LIFE (Tew, Alan Orchestra).
LP: GH 642
MC: ZCGH 642

Tewkesbury Abbey

CHAPEL HOUR - BLUE COAT SCHOOL, BIRMINGHAM.
LP: LPB 766

Tex, Joe

AIN'T I A MESS.
Tracks: / All I could do was cry (parts 1 and 2) / You keep her / Ain't I a mess / Baby you're right / Sit yourself down / Don't play / Get closer together / I'll never break your heart pts 1+2.
LP: GCH 8120

BEST OF JOE TEX.
Tracks: / Sysljfm (the letter song) / Hold what you've got / One monkey don't stop no show / You better get it / You got what it takes / I believe I'm gonna make it / Show me / Papa was too / Woman can change a man, A / Love you save, The / Build your love / I've got to do a little bit better.
LP: 780 173-1
MC: 780 173-4

DIFFERENT STROKES.
Tracks: / Have you ever / My neighbours got the gimmes / Mrs Wiggles / Baby it's rainin' / Under your powerful love / Don't play with me / Same things it took to get me, The / All a man needs is his woman's love / When a woman stops loving a man / I can see everybody's baby / She said yeah / Time brings about a change / I don't want you to love me / I'm gonna try love again / This time we'll make it all the way / It's ridiculous / We're killing ourselves / Back off / Does it run in your family / Living in the last days / I've seen enough.
2LP: CDX 41
MC: TCCDX 41

STONE SOUL COUNTRY.
Tracks: / Just out of reach / Detroit city / Set me free / Heartbreak Hotel / Together again / King of the road / At the dark end of the street / I'll never do you wrong / Make the world go away / Funny how time slips away / Ode to Billy Joe / Release me / Skip a rope / Engine engine / Honey / By the time I get to Phoenix / Green green grass of home / Papa's dreams.
LP: CRB 1215
MC: TCCRB 1215

VERY BEST OF JOE TEX, THE.
Tracks: / Hold what you've got / One monkey don't stop no show / Woman (can change a man), A / I want (do everything for you) / Don't make your children pay (for your mistakes) / Sweet woman like you, A / Love you save, The / You better believe it baby / I've got to do a little bit better / S.Y.S.L.J.F.M. (The letter song) / I believe I'm gonna make it / Woman sees a hard time (when her man is gone), A / Watch the one (that brings the bad news) / Papa was too / Truest woman in the world, The / Show me / Woman like that, yeah / Woman's hands, A / Skinny legs and all / Men are getting scarce / I'll never do you wrong / Keep the one you've got / You need me, baby / Buying a book / It ain't sanitary / You're right, Ray Charles / I gotcha.
2LP: CDX 29
MC: TCCDX 29

Tex, John

GUESS WHO'S A SUCKER FOR YOU (see under Ivan, Ranking's "Education").

Tex Mex

HISTORIC CORRIDOS (Various artists).
MC: C 211

TEX-MEX VOL. 1 (An introduction) (Various artists).
LP: FL 9003

TEX-MEX VOL. 2 (Corridos - part 1) (Various artists).
LP: FL 9004

TEX-MEX VOL. 3 (Corridos - Part II) (Various artists).
LP: FL 9005

TEX-MEX VOL. 4 (Norteno accordion I) (Various artists).
LP: FL 9006

TEX-MEX VOL. 5 (Early string bands) (Various artists).
LP: FL 9007

TEX-MEX VOL. 6 (Cancioneros de Ayer I) (Various artists).
LP: FL 9011

TEX-MEX VOL. 7 (Cancioneros de Ayer II) (Various artists).
LP: FL 9012

TEX-MEX VOL. 8 (Cancioneros de Ayer III) (Various artists).
LP: FL 9013

TEX-MEX VOL. 9 (C1ancioneros de Ayer IV) (Various artists).
LP: FL 9016

TEX-MEX VOL. 10 (Narciso Martinez) (Various artists).
LP: FL 9017

TEX-MEX VOL. 11 (El Ciego Melquiades) (Various artists).
LP: FL 9018

TEX-MEX VOL. 12 (Norteno accordion II) (Various artists).
LP: FL 9019

TEX-MEX VOL. 13 (Norteno accordion III) (Various artists).
LP: FL 9020

TEX-MEX VOL. 14 (Chicano experience, The) (Various artists).
LP: FL 9021

TEX-MEX VOL 15 (Lydia Mendoza vol 1) (Various artists).
LP: FL 9023

TEX-MEX VOL 16 (Lydia Mendoza vol 2) (Various artists).
LP: FL 9024

TEX-MEX VOL 17 (Hermanas Padilla, Hermanas Mendoza etc.) (Various artists).
LP: FL 9035

TEX-MEX VOL. 18 (Los Madrugadores) (Various artists).
LP: FL 9036

TEX-MEX VOL. 19 (Los Hermanos Chavarria) (Various artists).
LP: FL 9037

TEX-MEX VOL. 24 (Texas-Mexican Conjunto) (Various artists).
LP: FL 9049

Tex & The Horseheads

LIFE IS COOL.
LP: 2062 1

LIVE: TEX & THE HORSEHEADS.
LP: ENIGMA 21351

TOT ZIENS LIVE IN HOLLAND.
LP: 213351

Texana Dames

TEXANA DAMES.
LP: SNTF 1026

Texas...

TEXAS CHAINSAW MASSACRE 2 (Film soundtrack) (Various artists).
Tracks: / Good to be bad: *Lords Of The New Church* / Mind warp: *Lords Of The New Church* / Goo goo muck: *Cramps*/ Haunted head: *Concrete Blonde* / Over your shoulders: *Concrete Blonde* / Life is hard: *Timbuk 3* / Shame on you: *Timbuk 3* / Torch song: *Timbuk 3* / White night: *Timbuk 3* / Strange things happen: *Copeland, Stewart* / No-one lives forever: *Oingo Boingo.*
LP: MIRF 1017
MC: MIRFC 1017

Texas Alexander

TEXAS ALEXANDER VOLS 1-4 (See under Alexander, Texas) ((Alexander, Texas)).

Texas (Group)

MOTHERS HEAVEN.
Tracks: / Mothers heaven / Why believe in you / Dream Hotel / This will all be mine / Beliefs / Alone with you / In my heart / Waiting / Wrapped in clothes of blue / Return / Walk the dust.
LP: 8485781
MC: 8485784

SOUTHSIDE.
Tracks: / I don't want a lover / Tell me why / Everyday now / Southside / Prayer for you / Thrill has gone / Fight the feeling / Fool for love / One choice / Future is promises.
LP: 838 171 1
MC: 838 171 4

Texas Guitar...

TEXAS GUITAR GREATS (Various artists).
LP: HCS 109
MC: HCS 109 TC

Texas Honky Tonk

STARS OF TEXAS HONKY TONK (Various artists).
LP: LTD 603

Texas In The Thirties

TEXAS IN THE THIRTIES (1935-38) (Various artists).
LP: DLP 540

Texas Instruments

TEXAS INSTRUMENTS.
LP: GWLP 29

Texas Lone Star

DESPERADOS WAITING FOR A TRAIN.
LP: BF 15011

Texas Mavericks

WHO ARE THESE MASKED MEN?.
LP: ROSE 112

Texas Tenors

TEXAS TENORS (Guerrero, Paul).
LP: JAZZ MARK 104

Texas Tornados

TEXAS TORNADOS.
LP: 7599262511
MC: 7599262514

Textones

BACK IN TIME.
Tracks: / Trying to hold on / Slip away / Redemption song / I second that emotion / Through the canyon / Love out of control / What do you want with me / Back in time / Gotta get that feelin' back / Something to believe in / Jokers are wild / If I could be / We don't get along / Standing in the line.
LP: FIEND 179

CEDAR CREEK.
LP: 3268 1

MIDNIGHT MISSION.
Tracks: / Standing in the line / Hands of the working man / No love in you / Running / Number one is to survive / Midnight mission / Upset me / Luck don't last forever / Clean cut kid / Light, The.
LP: VOLUME 012

Teyte, Dame Maggie

HER LIFE AND ART.
LP: REGL 369
MC: ZCF 369

Tezano, Johnny

SOUKOUS BOOGIE.
LP: AT 088

T-Ford

JUST KEEP IT UP.
Tracks: / Just keep it up / Let it rock / Love you like I do / Things you do / Goodtime baby / My special angel / Gonna send you back to Georgia / Mama don't you hit that boy / Mama's rock'n'roll / Good golly / Any old time / What'll become of me / Sixteen candles / Good rockin' tonight.
LP: SPLP 2001

Thackeray, Jake

JAKE THACKERAY AND SONGS.
LP: DIN 314

LAH-DI-DAH.
Tracks: / Lah-di-dah (With Roger Webb & His Orchestra) / On again. On again! / Country bus / Worried brown eyes / Cactus, The / Jolly captain / Caroline Diggeby-Pratte / Brother gorilla (Le Gorille) / Sophie / Personal column / Kiss, The (CD only.) / Castleford ladies magic circle (CD only.) / Jumble sale / Family tree / Isobel makes love upon national monuments / Ulysees (CD only.) / Bantam cock / Statues, The (With Roger Webb & His Orchestra.) / Sister Josephine / Grandad (CD only.) / Isobel / Last will and testament of Jake Thakray.
MC: TCIDL 115

LIVE PERFORMANCE.
LP: NTS 105

ON AGAIN, ON AGAIN.
Tracks: / On again, on again / To do with you / Ballad of Billy Kershaw / Rain on the mountainside / Isabella / I stayed off work today / Kiss / Poor sod / Hair of the widow of Bridlington / Over to Isobel / Brigadier / Joseph.
LP: UNKNOWN

VERY BEST OF JAKE THACKERAY.
LP: EMC 3103
MC: TCEMC 3103

Thackeray, William

MEMOIRS OF BARRY LYNDON VOL 1 (Boland, Arthur).
MCSET: COL 2006

VANITY FAIR (Bloom, Claire (nar)).
MC: 1669

Thailand

LAO MUSIC OF THE NORTH EAST (Various artists).
LP: LLST 7357

MUSIQUE DES TRIBUS DU TRIANGLE D'OR (refugiees en Thailande) (Various artists).
Tracks: / Les Yao: *Various artists* / Les Karen: *Various artists* / Les Meo: *Various artists* / Les Lahu: *Various artists* / Les Akha: *Various artists* / Les Lisu: *Various artists.*
LP: ARN 33535

THAILAND Various traditional Asian music (Various artists).
LP: PS 33522

THAILANDE ETERNELLE (Various artists).
Tracks: / Danse des montagnes: *Various artists* / Danse des recoltes: *Various artists* / Danse des sabres: *Various* artists / Danse villageoise du nord: *Various artists* / Danse de Palais: *Various artists* / Solo de percussions: *Various artists* / Danse des bambous: *Various artists* / Danse de fete: *Various artists* / Solo de pullu-i: *Various artists* / Danse des doigts: *Various artists* / Danse royale: *Various artists* / Danse paysanne: *Various artists* / Danse de combat: *Various artists.*
LP: ARN 33496

TRADITIONAL THAI MUSIC (Various artists).
MC: D58007

Thamat

SUMERIAN CRY.
LP: CMFT 6

Thamesdown Singers

SING.
LP: LPB 759

Thanatos

EMERGING FROM THE NETHERWORLDS.
LP: SHARK 015

Thandiwe

MADLALA BROTHERS, THE.
LP: TUS 8002
MC: ZCTUS 8002

Thanes

BETTER LOOK BEHIND YOU.
LP: DDTEP 004
LP: NISHI 211

HUBBLE BUBBLE.
LP: DDTEP 001

THANES OF CAWDOR.
Tracks: / Keep you out / You'll be blue / Days go slowly by / She was mine / Buzz buzz yeh yeh / Where have all the good times gone / All gone now / Kicks and chicks / Won't you c'mon girl / When I love you / Girls / Cold as ice / Before I go / Some kinda fun.
LP: DISPLP 11

Thanet Gospel Choir

20 BEST LOVED CAROLS.
LP: PC 319

Thank God It's Friday

THANK GOD IT'S FRIDAY (Film Soundtrack) (Various artists).
LP: K 66076

Thank You For...

THANK YOU FOR THE MUSIC (Various artists).
LP: SHM 3110

Thanks A Million

THANKS A MILLION/ON THE AVENUE (Film Soundtrack) (Various artists).
LP: SH 2083

Tharpe, Sister Rosetta

LEGEND IN GOSPEL MUSIC, A.
MC: DPC 727

LIVE IN PARIS 1964.
LP: FC 118

SWINGS AND ROCKS.
LP: RR 1317

That Night In Rio

THAT NIGHT IN RIO (see Weekend in Havana/That night in Rio) (Various artists).

That Petrol Emotion

BABBLE.
Tracks: / Swamp / Spin cycle / For what it's worth / Big decision / Static / Split! / Belly bugs / In the playpen / Inside / Chester Burnette / Creeping to the cross.
LP: TPELP 1
MC: TPEMC 1

CHEMICRAZY.
Tracks: / Hey venus / Blue to black / Mess of words / Sensitize / Another day / Gnaw mark / Scum surfin' / Compulsion / Tingle / Head staggered / Abandon / Sweet shiver burn.
LP: V 2618
MC: TCV 2618

END OF THE MILLENIUM PSYCHOSIS.
Tracks: / Sooner or later / Every little bit / Cellophane / Candy love satellite / Here it is...take it / Price of my soul, The / Groove check / Bottom line / Tension / Tired shattered man / Goggle box / Under the sky.
LP: V 2550
MC: TCV 2550

MANIC POP THRILL.
Tracks: / Fleshprint / Can't stop / Lifeblood / Natural kind of joy / It's a good thing / Circusville / Mouth crazy / Tight lipped / Million miles away, A / Lettuce / Cheapskate / Blindspot.
LP: FIEND 70
MC: FIENDCASS 70

That Summer

THAT SUMMER (Film Soundtrack) (Various artists).
Tracks: / I don't want to go to Chelsea: *Costello, Elvis* / Watching the detectives: *Costello, Elvis* / Sex and drugs and rock and roll: *Dury, Ian & The Blockheads* / What a waste: *Dury, Ian & The Blockheads* / She's so modern: *Boomtown Rats* / Kicks: *Boomtown Rats* / Spanish troll: *Deville, Mink* / Because the night: *Smith,* Patti Group / Rockaway beach: *Ramones* / Whole wide world: *Wreckless Eric* / I love the sound of breaking glass: *Lowe, Nick* / Another girl, another planet: *Only Ones* / Do anything you wanna do: *Eddie & The Hot Rods* / New life: *Zones* / Teenage kicks: *Undertones* / Blank generation: *Hell, Richard & The Voidoids.*
LP: SPART 1088
MC: TCART 1088

That Was The Swinging

THAT WAS THE SWINGING 60'S VOL.1 (See under 60's) (Various artists).

Thatcher on Acid

CURDLED.
Tracks: / Guess who's running the show / New thing / Taxi, The / Riff raff/ orthodox / Cage, The / Is it art? / Wind up, The / Thatcher on acid / Fly / Stop/ start.
LP: MAD 007
LP: MADLP 007

ILLUSION OF BEING TOGETHER.
LP: COX 025

That's Entertainment

THAT'S ENTERTAINMENT (Various artists).
LP: REC 638
MC: ZCM 638

THAT'S ENTERTAINMENT-PART II (Film soundtrack) (Various artists).
Tracks: / Rebound: *Various artists* / Lonely weekends: *Various artists* / Stairway to nowhere: *Barton, Ernie*/ She's gone away: *Various artists* / You don't care: *Felts, Narvel* / I wanna rock: *Holcolm, Patsy* / Memories of you: *Priesman, Magel* / Judy: *Grayzell, Rudy* / Overture: *Various artists* / Drive in: *Vickery,* Mack / That's entertainment: *Astaire, Fred, Kelly, Gene, Buchanan, Gene* / For me and my gal: *Garland, Judy & Fred Astaire* / I've got a feelin' you're foolin': *Taylor, Robert & Knight, June* / Hi lili hi lo: *Caron, Leslie*/ All of you: *Astaire, Fred* / Lady is a tramp, The: *Horne, Lena* / Smoke gets in your eyes: *Grayson, Kathryn*/ Rock baby rock it: *Various artists* / Temptation: *Crosby, Bing* / Tennessee zip: *Wheeler, Kenny* / Taking a chance on love: *Waters, Ethel* / Love crazy baby: *Various artists* / Treat me right: *Various artists*/ Inka dinka doo: *Durante, Jimmy* / Get it off your mind: *Various artists* / What's the reason: *Various artists*/ Easter parade: *Astaire, Fred & Garland, Judy* / You call everybody darlin': *Various artists* / Couple of swells, A: *Astaire, Fred & Garland, Judy* / Go ahead baby: *Luke McDaniel* / Huh babe: *Various artists* / High high high: *Various artists* / Good morning: *Reynolds, Debbie with Gene Kelly & Donald O'Connor* / My baby don't rock: *Various artists* / That's what I tell my heart: *Various artists* / Triplets: *Astaire, Fred & Fabray,Nanette* & Buchanan,Jack / Last time I saw Paris, The: *Shore, Dinah* / Born to sing the blues: *Jenkins, Harold* / I need your lovin' kiss: *Various artists* / I'll build a stairway to paradise: *Guetary, Georges* / Goin' crazy: *Self,* Mack / There's no business like show business: *Keel, Howard & Betty Hutton* / Mad at you: *Various artists*/ Have yourself a merry little Christmas: *Garland, Judy* / Good lookin' woman: *Williams, Jimmy* / Rockabye baby: *Various artists* / I got rhythm: *Kelly, Gene.*
MC: 40 70280
LP: CBS 70280

The The

COLD SPELL AHEAD.
Tracks: / Cold spell ahead / Hot ice.
LP: BZS4

INFECTED.
Tracks: / Infected / Out of the blue (into the fire) / Heartland / Sweet bird of truth / Slow train to dawn / Twilight of a champion / Mercy beat, The / Angels of deception / Disturbed.
LP: EPC 26770
MC: 40 26770

MIND BOMB.
Tracks: / Good morning beautiful / Armageddon days are here (again) / Violence of truth / Kingdom of rain / Beat(en) generation, The / August and September / Gravitate to me / Beyond love.
LP: 4633191
MC: 4633194

SOUL MINING.
Tracks: / I've been waiting for tomorrow (all of my life) / This is the day / Sinking feeling, The / Uncertain smile / Twilight hour, The / Soul mining / Giant / Perfect (Not on album.) / Three orange kisses from Kazan (Not on album.) / Nature of virtue (Not on album.) / Mental healing process (Not on album.) / Waitin' for the upturn (Not on album.) / Fruit of the heart (Not on album.).
LP: EPC 25525
MC: 40 25525
LP: 4663371
MC: 4663374

Theard, Sam

COMPLETE 1934-40 RECORDINGS.
LP: WJS 1008

LOVIN' SAM FROM DOWN IN 'BAM.
LP: BD 2044

Theatre...

CAVALCADE OF LONDON THEATRE (Various artists).
Tracks: / Oh what a lovely war (overture): *Various artists* / I'll make a man of you: *Various artists* / Heilige nacht: *Various artists* / Christmas day in the cookhouse: *Various artists* / Goodbye-ee: *Various artists*/ Pieces of eight: *Various artists* / Last to go: *Various artists* / Buy British: *Various artists* / Perchance to dream: *Various artists* / Love is my reason: *Various artists* / Pacific 1860: *Various artists* / Uncle Harry: *Various artists* / Strike a light: *Various artists* / Another love: *Various artists* / Stop the world, I want to get off: *Various artists* / What kind of fool am I: *Various artists* / Oliver: *Various artists*/ As long as he needs me: *Various artists* / Reviewing the situation: *Various*

artists / On the brighter side: *Various artists* / Lord Oxshott's dilemma: *Various artists* / One dam' thing after another: *Various artists*/ My heart stood still: *Various artists* / Wait a minim: *Various artists* / Ag pleez Daddy: *Various artists*/ This'll make you whistle: *Various artists* / World of Suzie Wong: *Various artists* / Ding dong song: *Various* artists / Nicol: *Various artists* / Mia Carlotta: *Various artists* / May I feel said he: *Various artists*/ Canterbury tales: *Various artists* / I have a noble cock: *Various artists* / If she has never loved before: *Various* artists / Little dog laughed: *Various artists* / Run rabbit run: *Various artists* / Flanagan and Allen: *Various* artists / Late joys: *Various artists* / Bird on Nellie's hat: *Various artists* / Ghost train: *Various* artists / Conclusion: *Various artists* / Anthing goes: *Various artists* / I get a kick out of you: *Various* artists / Wonder bar: *Various artists* / Hand in hand: *Various artists* / Two fools: *Various artists*/ Life: *Various artists* / Someday I'll find you: *Various artists* / Lock up your daughters: *Various artists*/ Kiss me again: *Various artists* / Ballad of the Liver bird: *Various artists* / Half a sixpence: *Various* artists / Flash bang wallop: *Various artists* / File on Dr Fink: *Various artists* / Look at me now: *Various* artists / Hush a bye: *Various* artists / Sir Walter Raleigh: *Various* artists / This can't be love: *Various* artists / Berinthia's recitation: *Various artists* / Fortune thou art a bitch: *Various artists* / Gumboot dance: *Various artists* / King Kong: *Various artists* / Other people's babies: *Various artists* / Dit dit song: *Various artists* / End of the news: *Various artists* / Jacob and sons: *Various artists* / Coat of many colours: *Various artists* / Any dream will do: *Various artists* / First weekend in June: *Various artists*/ Ordinary people: *Various artists* / No other love: *Various artists* / Have a try: *Various artists* / Vacancy: *Various artists* / Yonder blessed moon: *Various artists* / Fings: *Various artists* / Desert song: *Various artists* / Romance: *Various artists* / Alice blue gown: *Various artists* / Why do I love you: *Various artists* / Boadicea: *Various artists* / Let the people sing: *Various artists* / Dogs they had a party: *Various artists* / Late late show, The: *Various artists* / No strings: *Various artists*.
LPS: D 140 D 4

Theatre of Hate
ORIGINAL SIN (LIVE).
Tracks: / Original sin / Westworld / Klan, The / Conquistador / Poppies / Incinerator / Judgement hymn / 63 / Rebel without a brain / Legion.
LP: DOJOLP 19

REVOLUTION (SINGLES ALBUM).
Tracks: / Legion / Original sin / Rebel without a brain / My own invention / Nero / Do you believe in the west world / Propaganda / Hop / Incinerator / Eastworld / Americanos.
LP: TOH 2
MC: TOH 2C

WESTWORLD.
LP: TOH 1

Thee Amazing Colossal
TOTALE.
Tracks: / Lies / Take me higher / Blow this town (away) / Time allowed, The / Take the sheel / Come down again / First city upstart / Superlovexperience / Spring break / Head above water / Harbour town - midnight Tuesday.
LP: SRNLP 26
MC: SRNMC 26

Thee Eyes
THEE EYES.
LP: A 35

Thee Headcoats
HEADCOATITUDE.
Tracks: / Headcoatitude.
LP: YEAH-HUP 018

HEADCOATS DOWN.
LP: HANG 29 UP

KIDS ARE ALL SQUARE, THE.
LP: HANG 32 UP

Thee Hypnotics
COME DOWN HEAVY.
LP: SITU 028
MC: SITU 028 C

LIVER'N'GOD.
Tracks: / All night long / Let's get naked / Revolution stone / Rock me baby / Justice in freedom.
LP: SITUM 026

Thelin, Eje
PROJECT LIVE AT NEFERTITI.
LP: DRLP 128

Thelonius Monster
NEXT SATURDAY AFTERNOON.
LP: 88561-8174-1

Them
BELFAST GYPSIES.
Tracks: / Gloria's dream / Crazy world inside me, The / Midnight train / Aria of the fallen angels / Baby blue / People, let's freak out / Boom boom / Last will and testament, The / Portland town / Hey Gyp, dig the slowness / Suicide song / Secret police.
LP: SNTF 738

COLLECTION: THEM.
Tracks: / Baby please don't go / Bright lights, big city / I put a spell on you / Hello Josephine / Turn on your lovelight / Don't start crying now / Gloria / Story of Them, The / It's all over now, baby blue / I got a woman / My little baby / How long baby / Here comes the night / Stormy Monday / I like it like that / Go on home baby / Out of sight / Baby what you want me to do / Route 66 / Fridays child / Little girl / Hey girl / Call my name / Mystic eyes.
2LP: CCSLP 131
MC: CCSMC 131

NOW AND THEM.
LP: ZAP 6

ONE MORE TIME.
Tracks: / Here comes the night / I put a spell on you / Baby please don't go / All for myself / Don't look back / How long baby / Richard Cory / Philosophy / One more time / Don't start crying now / One two brown eyes / Half as much.
LP: 9286900

SINGLES, THE.
MC: SEEK 31

THEM.
Tracks: / Don't start crying now / Baby please don't go / Here comes the night / One more time / It won't hurt half as much / Mystic eyes / Call my name / Richard Cory / One two brown eyes / All for myself / If you and I could be as two / Don't you know / Friday's child / Story of Them, The (Part 1.) / Philosophy / How long baby / I'm gonna dress in black / Bring 'em on in / Little girl / I gave my love a diamond / Gloria / You just can't win / Go on home baby / Don't look back / I like it like that / Bright lights, big city / My little baby / Route 66.
LP: SEE 31
LP: LK 4700
LP: TAB 45

THEM AGAIN.
Tracks: / Could you would you / Something you got / Call my name / Turn on your love light / I put a spell on you / I can only give you everything / My lonely sad eyes / I got a woman / Out of sight / It's all over now, baby blue / Bad or good / How long baby / Hello Josephine / Don't you know / Hey girl / Bring 'em on in / One more time (US version).
LP: LK 4751

TIME OUT, TIME IN.
LP: ZAP 7

Them Howling Horrors
CHANGING TIDE.
LP: CRIMLP 133

LOOK OUT FOR THE CHANGING TIDE.
LP: CRIMLP 133

Them Indoors
THEM INDOORS (Various artists).
LP: IMP 2000
MC: IMPC 2000

Themis, John
ATMOSPHERIC CONDITIONS.
Tracks: / Emily / Trick, The / Post hypnotic suggestions / Cinderella's last waltz / Electric storm / Transition / Black mamba samba / Trouble.
LP: NAGE 1
MC: NAGEC 1

ENGLISH RENAISSANCE.
Tracks: / Over the dark cloud / James I / Open Arms / Catrina / Cross crusader / English renaissance / Steed for a king / Don't wake the dragon George.
LP: NAGE 11
MC: NAGEC 11

OTHER SIDE OF JOHN THEMIS, THE.
LP: CODA 25

SIRENS.
Tracks: / Goblins of Sherwood / Emily / Sirens / Trick, The / Post hypnotic suggestions / Trouble / Raid at the brothel / Electric storm / Transitions / Black mamba samba / Cinderella's last waltz.
LP: CODA 3
MC: COCA 3

ULYSSES AND THE CYCLOPS.
Tracks: / Atmospheric conditions / Final cruise / Free fall / Whales / Live at Camelot / Ulysses and the Cyclops / Run for miles / Lethal blow.
LP: CODA 10
MC: COCA 10

Then Jerico
BIG AREA.
Tracks: / Big area / What does it take (to win your love) / You ought to know / Song for the broken hearted / Darkest hour / Reeling / Where you lie / Sugar box / Helpless / Under fire.
LP: 828 122 1
MC: 828 122 4

FIRST (THE SOUND OF MUSIC).
Tracks: / Let her fall / Blessed days / Laughter party / Stable boy / Motive, The / Muscle deep / Quiet place, A (apathy and sympathy) / Play dead / Hitcher, The / Prairie rose / Blessed days (Tokyo mix) (Only available on cassette and compact disc.) / Fault (dub) (Only available on cassette and compact disc.).
LP: LONLP 26
MC: LONC 26

THEN JERICO - INTERVIEW PICTURE DISC.
LPPD: BAK 2144

Theobald, Jack
BLUEGRASS COUNTRY (See under Theobald, Mike) (Theobald, Jack & Mike).

Theodorakis, Mikis
BOUZOUKIS OF..., THE.
Tracks: / Sto parathiri stekoussoun / Myrtia / Tou mikou voria / Varka sto yalo / Marina / Yitonia ton anghelon / Balanda tou andrikou / To yelasto pedi / Apagoghi / To parathiro / Mana mou ke panayia.
LP: LPO 32532
MC: C 32532
MC: 111 694

SINGS THEODORAKIS.
Tracks: / Omorifi poli / Dioti den sinemorfothi / 18 noverbri / Gelasto paidi / Tin porta anigho / Chathika / Anigho to stoma / Imaste dio / Margrita margaro / Sto perigali / Mirtia / Afti pon tharfoun.
LP: INT 30591
MC: INT 30594

ZORBA THE GREEK (See Under Zorba the Greek (Film)) (Various artists).

There Was This Bloke
THERE WAS THIS BLOKE (Various artists).
Tracks: / John Blunt: *Various artists* / Only friend I own, The: *Various artists* / Crazy words: *Various* artists / Polly had a poodle: *Various artists* / Four letters: *Various artists* / Camp in the country: *Various* artists / Sir Quincy De Bas: *Various artists* / She loved a Portugese: *Various artists* / Irwell Delta blues: *Various artists* / My brudda Sylveste: *Various artists*.
LP: RUB 010

There's No Business..
THERE'S NO BUSINESS LIKE SHOW BUSINESS (Film soundtrack) (Various artists).
Tracks: / There's no business like show business: *Various artists* / When the midnight choo choo leaves for Alabama: *Various* artists / Play a simple melody: *Various artists* / After you get what you want, you don't want it if you believ: *Various* artists / Man chases a girl, A: *Various artists* / Lazy: *Various artists* / Heat way: *Various artists*/ Sailor's not a sailor ('til a sailor's been tattooed), A: *Various artists* / Alexander's ragtime band: *Various artists*.
LP: MCL 1727
MC: MCLC 1727

Theroux, Paul
GREAT RAILWAY BAZAAR BY TRAIN THROUGH ASIA.
MC: IAB 88071

These Immortal Souls
GET LOST (DON'T LIE).
Tracks: / Marry me (lie lie) / Hide / These immortal souls / Hey little child / I ate the knife / Blood and sand she said / One in shadow one in sun / Open up and bleed / Blood and sand she said (alternate) / I ate the knife (alternate) / These immortal souls (alternate).
LP: STUMM 48

Thessink, Hans
BABY WANTS TO BOOGIE.
LP: FF 455

Theta
THETA SAMPLER (Various artists).
LP: TETS 1
MC: TETSC 1

They All Laughed
THEY ALL LAUGHED (Various artists).
Tracks: / Best of Spike Milligan, The: *Various artists* / Me and my tune: *Various artists* / Girls like, The: *Various artists* / Airport routine: *Various artists* / Willy: *Various artists* / End of my old cigar: *Various artists* / Goldyloppers: *Various artists* / Happy go lucky: *Various artists* / Sheik of Araby, The: *Various artists*.
2LP: PYL 7006
MC: PYM 7006

They Call That...
THEY CALL THAT AN ACCIDENT (Film soundtrack) (Various artists).
LP: ISTA 2
MC: ICT 2

They Eat Their Own
THEY EAT THEIR OWN.
LP: 104171
MC: 104174

They Live (film)
THEY LIVE (Film soundtrack) (Various artists).
LP: 73367.1
MC: 73367.4

They Might Be Giants
DON'T LET'S START.
Tracks: / Don't let's start.
LP: TPLP 14
MC: TPC 14

FLOOD.
Tracks: / Theme from flood / Lucky ball and chain / Dead / Particle man / We want a rock / Birdhouse in your soul / Istanbul (not Constaninople) / Your racist friend / Twisting.
LP: EKT 68
MC: EKTC 68

LINCOLN.
LP: TPLP 12
LP: EKT 89
MC: EKT 89C

THEY MIGHT BE GIANTS.
Tracks: / Everything right is wrong again / Put your hand inside the puppet head / Number three / Don't lets start / Footsteps / Toddler hiway / Rabid child / Nothing's gonna change my clothes / (She was a) hotel detective / She's an angel / Youth culture killed / My dog / Boat of car / Absolutely Bill's mood chess piece face / I hope that I get old before I die / Alienation's for the rich / Day, The / Rhythm section want ad.
LP: ROUGH 115
MC: ROUGHC 115
LP: EKT 80
MC: EKT 80 C

They Must Be Russians
THEY MUST BE RUSSIANS.
LP: FF 2

They Sold A Million
THEY SOLD A MILLION VOL.2 (Various artists).
LP: 2354 041

They Wrote The Songs
THEY WROTE THE SONGS (Various artists).
LP: 3970651
MC: 3970654

They'll Never Keep
THEY'LL NEVER KEEP US DOWN... (Various artists).
LP: ROUNDER 4012
MC: ROUNDER 4012C

They're Playing ...
THEY'RE PLAYING OUR SONG (Original London Cast) (Various artists).
Tracks: / Overture: *Various artists* / Fallin': *Various artists* / If he really knew me: *Various artists*/ Workin' it out: *Various artists* / They're playing my song: *Various artists* / If she really knew me: *Various* artists / Right: *Various artists* / Entr'acte: *Various artists* / Just for tonight: *Various artists*/ When you're in my arms: *Various artists* / Fill in the words: *Various artists* / THey're playing our song (finale): *Various artists*.
LP: TER 1035
MC: ZCTER 1035
LP: CHOPE 6
MC: CHOPK 6

Thezanas, Moise
HONORE L'ANMOU.
LP: PV 9366

Thibeaud The Crusader
THIBEAUD THE CRUSADER (Original Soundtrack) (Various artists).
LP: PST 502

Thibodeaux, Ambrose
AMBROSE THIBODEAUX.
LP: 112

AUTHENTIC CAJUN FRENCH MUSIC AND FOLK SONGS.
LP: 143

MORE AUTHENTIC ACADIAN FRENCH MUSIC.
LP: 119

THAT FRENCH ACADIAN SOUND.
LP: 133
MC: 133 TC

Thibodeaux, Rufus

CAJUN COUNTRY FIDDLE OF RUFUS THIBODEAUX.
LP: 129
MC: 129 TC

CAJUN FIDDLE.
LP: 137

Thief

THIEF (see under Tangerine Dream) (Film soundtrack).

Thief Of Baghdad

THIEF OF BAGHDAD (Original Soundtrack) (Various artists).
LP: PHCAM 010

Thielemans, Toots

AUTUMN LEAVES.
Tracks: / I do it for your love / Dat mistige rooie beest / Lady be good / Old friends / Bye bye blackbird / Dirty old man / Tenor madness / Strange boogie man / Autumn leaves.
LP: 823 442-1
MC: 823 442-4

COLLAGE COLLECTION (Thielemans, Toots & Jan Akkerman).
LP: CBS 88557

HARMONICA JAZZ.
Tracks: / Scotch on the rocks / Sophisticated lady / Cocktails for two / Don't be that way / Stars fell on Alabama / I let a song go out of my heart / I'm putting all my eggs in one basket / Skylark / Diga diga doo / So rare / On the Alamo / Sonny boy.
LP: CBS 21108
MC: 40 21108

LIVE IN THE NETHERLANDS (Thielemans, Toots,Joe Pass,Niels Henning,Orsted Pedersen).
Tracks: / Blues in the closet / Mooche / Thriving from a riff / Autumn leaves / Someday my prince will come.
LP: 230 8233
MC: K08 233

LIVE: TOOTS THEILEMANS.
LP: 2489 175

MUSIC FOR THE MILLIONS.
Tracks: / What are you doing the rest of your life? / First time ever I saw your face, The / Open your window / Friendly persuasion / Glimmie's theme / Big bossa / Love remembered / You've got it bad, girl / Ben / This nearly was mine / Gentle rain, The / Old friends.
LP: 2426 039
MC: 3212 033

ONLY TRUST YOUR HEART.
LP: CJ 355
MC: CJ 355 C

SOUL OF TOOTS THIELEMANS, THE.
LP: FS 184

SUN GAMES.
Tracks: / Sun games / Palestina / Nancy's dance / Swimming pool / Broken circles / I love chick / Tarsican / Lush life / Monkey.
LP: SJP 167

TOOT AND SVEND (See Asmussen, Svend) (Thielemans, Toots/Svend Asmussen).

WORLD HITS (See Clark, Benny) (Thielemans, Toots/Benny Clark).

YESTERDAY AND TODAY (Thielemans, Toots/Svend Asmussen).
Tracks: / Sophisticated lady / Mr. Nashville / Who can sail without the wind / Yesterday and today / Spirit feel / Denise / Blues on blue.
LP: SNTF 822
LP: 805528

YOUR PRECIOUS LOVE.
LP: SNTF 939

Thieving Dreamer

HOT LOVE 2.
LP: IRDTD 2

Thigpen, Ed

ACTION-RE-ACTION.
LP: SNTF 689
LP: GNPS 2098

ERNIE WILKINS & THE ALMOST BIG BAND/KENNY DREW/ED THIGPEN (See Wilkins, Ernie) (Thigpen, Ed/Ernie Wilkins).

PRIZE WINNERS (See Under Drew, Kenny) (Thigpen, Ed/ Drew/ Henning/ Pedersen/ Asmussen).

Thilo, Jesper

FERSKEDRIVHUSMELONER (see under Hansen, Finn Otto).

FROG (Thilo, Jesper/Terry Clark Quintet).
LP: SLP 4072

JESPER THILO QUARTET AND HARRY EDISON (Thilo, Jesper Quartet).
LP: SLP 4120

SWINGIN' FRIENDS (Thilo, Jesper Quartet).
LP: SLP 4065

TRIBUTE TO FROG (see Terry, Clark Quintet/Jesper Thilo).

Thin Blue Line (film)

THIN BLUE LINE, A (Film Soundtrack) (Various artists).
Tracks: / Opening credits: *Glass, Philip* / Interrogation (part one): *Glass, Philip* / Turko (part one): *Glass*, Philip / Vidor: *Glass, Philip* / Adam's story: *Glass, Philip* / Defense attorney's: *Glass, Philip*/ Judge, The: *Glass, Philip* / Trial, The (part two): *Glass, Philip* / Mystery eyewitness (part two), The: *Glass*, Philip / Thin blue line, The: *Glass, Philip* / Defense attorney's (part two): *Glass, Philip* / Harris' crimes (part two): *Glass, Philip* / Hell on earth: *Glass, Philip* / Confession, The: *Glass, Philip* / Prologue: *Glass, Philip* / Interrogation (part two): *Glass, Philip* / Turko (part two): *Glass, Philip* / Harris' story: *Glass, Philip* / Comets and Vegas: *Glass, Philip* / Harris' crimes (part one): *Glass, Philip* / Trial, The (part one): *Glass, Philip* / Mystery eyewitness (part one), The: *Glass, Philip* / Mystery eyewitness (part three), The: *Glass, Philip* / Electric chair: *Glass, Philip* / Harris' testimony: *Glass, Philip*/ Mystery eyewitness (part five), The: *Glass, Philip* / Harris' childhood: *Glass, Philip* / End credits: *Glass, Philip*.
LP: K979 2091
MC: K979 2094

Thin Lizzy

ADVENTURES OF THIN LIZZY, THE.
LP: LIZTV 1

BAD REPUTATION.
Tracks: / Bad reputation / Dancing in the moonlight / Dear Lord / Downtown sundown / Killer without cause / Opium train / Soldier of fortune / Southbound / That woman's gonna break your heart.
LP: PRICE 12
MC: PRIMC 12
LP: 9102 016

BEST OF PHIL LYNOTT & THIN LIZZY.
Tracks: / Whisky in the jar / Waiting for an alibi / Sarah / Parisienne walkways / Do anything you want to / Yellow pearl / Chinatown / King's call / Boys are back in town / Rosalie (cowgirl's song) / Dancing in the moonlight / Don't believe a word / Jailbreak / Out in the fields / Killer on the loose / Still in love with you.
LP: STAR 2300
MC: STAC 2300

BLACK ROSE.
Tracks: / Do anything you want to / Toughest street in town / S & M / Waiting for an alibi / Sarah / Got to give it up / Get out of here / With love / Roisin dubh.
LP: PRICE 90
MC: PRIMC 90

BLACK ROSE: A ROCK LEGEND.
Tracks: / Black rose / Shenandoah / Danny boy / Mason's apron / Do anything you want to / Get out of here / Got to give it up / S & M / Sarah / Toughest street in town / Waiting for an alibi / With love.
LP: 9102 032
MC: 7231 032

BOYS ARE BACK IN TOWN.
Tracks: / Boys are back in town / Don't play around with love / Emerald / Half caste / Bad reputation / Me and the boys / Memory pain / Sha-la-la / Got to give it up / For those who love to live / Pressure will blow, The.
LP: CN 2066
MC: CN4 2066

CHINATOWN.
Tracks: / We will be strong / Chinatown / Sweetheart / Sugar blues / Killer on the loose / Havin' a good time / Genocide / Didn't I / Hey you.
LP: PRICE 95
MC: PRIMC 95
LP: 6359 030

COLLECTION: THIN LIZZY.
Tracks: / Black boys on the corner / Little girl in bloom / Randolph's tango / Return of the farmer's son / Remembering / Whisky in the jar / Rocker, The / Buffalo gal / Sitamoia / Song for while I'm away, A / Baby face / Ray gun and Sarah / Eire / Vagabond of the western world / Friendly ranger at Clontarf Castle / Mama Nature said / Here I go again / Hero and the madman / Little darlin'.
2LP: CCSLP 117
MC: CCSMC 117

CONTINUING SAGA OF THE AGEING ORPHANS.
Tracks: / Things ain't working out down at the farm / Buffalo gal / Sarah / Honesty is no excuse / Look what the wind blew in / Mama Nature said / Hero and the madman / Slow blues / Dublin / Brought down / Vagabond of the western world.
LP: SKL 5298

DEDICATION - THE BEST OF THIN LIZZY.
Tracks: / Whiskey in the jar / Boys are back in town / Dancin' in the moonlight / Parisienne walkways / Out in the fields / Sarah / Jailbreak / Rosalie / Cowgirl song (live) / Waiting for an alibi / Do anything you want to do / Killer on the loose / Rocker, The / Don't believe a word / Dedication / Bad reputation (Only on MC and CD.) / Still in love with you (live) (Only on MC and CD.) / Emerald (live) (Only on MC and CD.) / China Town (Only on MC and CD.).
LP: 848 192 1
MC: 848 192 4

FIGHTING.
Tracks: / Ballad of a hard man / Fighting my way back / For those who love to live / Freedom song / King's vengeance / Rosalie / Silver dollar / Spirit slips away / Suicide / Wild one.
LP: PRICE 32
MC: PRIMC 32
LP: 6360 121

JAILBREAK.
Tracks: / Angel from the coast / Boys are back in town / Cowboy song / Emerald / Fight or fall / Jailbreak / Romeo and the lonely girl / Running back / Warriors.
LP: PRICE 50
MC: PRIMC 50
LP: 9102 008

JOHNNY THE FOX.
Tracks: / Boogie woogie dance / Borderline / Don't believe a word / Fools' gold / Johnny / Johnny the fox meets Jimmy the weed / Massacre / Old flame / Rocky / Sweet Marie.
LP: PRICE 11
MC: PRIMC 11
LP: 9102 012

LIVE.
Tracks: / Thunder and lightning / Waiting for an alibi / Jailbreak / Baby please don't go / Holy war / Renegade / Hollywood / Got to give it up / Angel of death / Are you ready? / Boys are back in town / Cold sweat / Don't believe a word / Killer on the loose / Sun goes down, The / Emerald / Black rose / Still in love with you / Rocker.
2LP: VERD 6
MCSET: VERDC 6

LIVE AND DANGEROUS - IN CONCERT.
Tracks: / Boys are back in town / Dancing in the moonlight / Massacre / I'm still in love with you / Me and the boys (Full title: Me and the boys were wondering what you and the girls were) / Don't believe a word / Warriors / Are you ready? / Sha-la-la-la / Baby drives me crazy.
2LP: PRID 6
MCSET: PRIDC 6
2LP: 6641 807

LIZZY LIVES 1976-84.
LP: SLAM 4

NIGHT LIFE.
Tracks: / Banshee / Dear heart / Frankie Carroll / It's only money / Night life / Philomena / Sha-la-la / She knows / Showdown / Still in love with you.
LP: PRICE 31
MC: PRIMC 31

REMEMBERING.
LP: DT6 28377

REMEMBERING, PART 1.
Tracks: / Black boys on the corner / Song for while I'm away, A / Randolph tango / Little girl in bloom / Sitamoia / Little darlin' / Remembering / Gonna creep up on you / Whisky in the jar / Rocker.
LP: SKL 5249
MC: KSKC 5249

RENEGADE.
Tracks: / Angel of death / Renegade / Pressure will blow, The / Leave this town / Hollywood (down on your luck) / No one told him / Fats / Mexican blood / It's getting dangerous.
LP: 6359 083
MC: 7150 083

ROCKERS.
Tracks: / Whisky in the jar / Baby face / Mama Nature said / Song for while I'm away, A / Call the police / Rocker, The / Sarah / Slow blues / Little darlin' / Sitamoia / Gonna creep up on you.
LP: TAB 28
MC: KTBC 28

SHADES OF A BLUE ORPHANAGE.
Tracks: / Rise and dear demise of the funky nomadic tribes / Buffalo gal / I don't want to forget how to live / Sarah / Brought down / Baby face / Chatting today / Call the police / Shades of a blue orphanage.
LP: TXS 108

THUNDER AND LIGHTNING.
Tracks: / Thunder and lightning / This is the one / Sun goes down, The / Holy war / Cold sweat / Someday / She is going to hit back / Baby please don't go / Bad habits / Heart attack.
LP: VERL 3
MC: VERLC 3

TWO GREAT POP CLASSICS.
Tracks: / Boys are back in town / Emerald / Johnny / Fools gold / Massacre / Boogie woogie dance.
2LP: 830191 1

WHISKEY IN THE JAR (CONTOUR).
Tracks: / Whiskey in the jar / Rocker, The / Black boys on the corner / Little darlin' / Buffalo gal / Sitamoia / Honesty is no excuse / Things ain't working down on the farm / Song for while I'm away, A / Remembering / Sarah / Vagabond of the Western world.
LP: CN 2080
MC: CN4 2080

WHISKEY IN THE JAR (KARUSSELL).
Tracks: / Boys are back in town / Jailbreak / Don't believe a word / Sarah / Renegade / Thunder and lightning / Whiskey in the jar / Dancing in the moonlight / Waiting for an alibi / Chinatown / Do anything you want to / Killer on the loose.
LP: 822 694 1
MC: 822 694 4

Thin White Rope

BOTTOM FEEDERS.
Tracks: / Ain't that loving you baby / Macy's window / Waking up / Valley of the bones / Atomic imagery / Rocket USA.
LP: ZANE 005

EXPLORING THE AXIS.
Tracks: / Down in the desert / Disney girl / Soundtrack / Lithium / Dead grammas on a train / Three song / Eleven / Roger's tongue / Real West / Exploring the axis.
LP: ZONG 006
MC: ZONGCASS 006

IN THE SPANISH CAVE.
Tracks: / Mr. Limpet / Ring / Its OK / Ahr Skidar / Red Sun / Elsie crashed the party / Timing / Wand / July'.
LP: FIEND 114

MOONHEAD.
Tracks: / Not your fault / Wire animal / Take it home / Thing, The / Moonhead / Wet heart / Mother / Come around / If those tears / Crow piss freeze.
LP: ZONG 017

RED SUN.
Tracks: / Red sun / Town without pity / Man with the golden gun, The / They're hanging me tonight / Some velvet morning / Red sun (original).
LP: VEX 8

RUBY SEA.
LP: 346322
MC: 346324

SACK FULL OF SILVER.
Tracks: / Hidden lands / Sack full of silver / Yoo doo right / Napkin song, The / Americana / Ghost, The / Whirling dervish / Triangle song, The / Diesel man / On the floe.
LP: PL 90469
MC: PK 90469

SQUATTER'S RIGHTS.
LP: FLP 1035

Thing (1)

FROM ANOTHER WORLD.
Tracks: / Sturm und drang / Hitcher, The / Crawl / My fun / Salt / How I rose from / Don't / Creepy town / Unclean / Dissolve / Mistery X / From another.
LP: CONTE 134

Thing Called Love

THING CALLED LOVE, A (Various artists).
LP: SHM 3172
MC: HSC 3172

Thing (Film)

THING, THE (Film soundtrack) (Various artists).

LP: . . . . MCF 3148
LP: . . . . MCA 6111

Things

OUTSIDE MY WINDOW.
LP: . . . . LOLITA 5047

Things That Go

THINGS THAT GO (Various artists).
MC: . . . . ST 3633

Things to Come (film)

THINGS TO COME (Film soundtrack) (Royal Philharmonic Orchestra).
LP: . . . . ED 291053 1
MC: . . . . ED 291053 4

Thinking Plague

MOON SONGS.
Tracks: / Warhead / Etude for combo / Collarless fog that one day soon / Inside out / Moonsongs.
LP: . . . . DMC 007

Thirakwa, Ahmedjan

RHYTHMS OF INDIA.
LP: . . . . ECSD 1335
MC: . . . . TC 7140

Third Ear Band

AIR, EARTH, FIRE, WATER.
LP: . . . . SHVL 773

ALCHEMY.
Tracks: / Mosaic / Ghetto raga / Druid one / Stone circle / Egyptian book of the dead / Area three / Dragon lines / Lark rise.
LP: . . . . DO 1999
LP: . . . . SHVL 756

LIVE GHOSTS.
Tracks: / Hope mosaic / Druid three / Ghetto raga / Live ghosts.
LP: . . . . MASO 33047

MACBETH.
LP: . . . . BGOLP 61

THIRD EAR BAND.
LP: . . . . BGOLP 89

Third Fusiliers

REGIMENTAL BAND & CORPS OF DRUMS (Recorded on Location in Germany).
LP: . . . . MM 0555

Third Kind Of Blue

THIRD KIND OF BLUE (Various artists).
LP: . . . . MM 006

Third Man (bk)

THIRD MAN, THE (Graham Greene) (Mason, James (nar)).
MC: . . . . TC LFP 7103

THIRD MAN, THE (See Under Karas, Anton) (Karas, Anton).

Third Mind

THIRD MIND, THE (Various artists).
LP: . . . . TMLP 050

Third World

96 DEGREES IN THE SHADE.
LP: . . . . ILPS 9443
MC: . . . . ICT 9443
MC: . . . . RRCT 16

ALL THE WAY STRONG.
Tracks: / Love is out to get you / Swing low / Come on home / Seasons when / Lagos jump / All the way strong / Rock and rave / Once there's love.
LP: . . . . CBS 25473

FORBIDDEN LOVE.
Tracks: / Forbidden love / Forbidden love (no rap) (Only on 7" single.) / Forbidden love (12" remix) (Only on 12" and CD single.) / Forbidden love (dub) (Only on 12" and CD single.) / Forbidden love (version) / Theme from the underdog.
MCSET: . . . . MERMC 288

HOLD ON TO LOVE.
Tracks: / Spirit lives, The / Get outta town / Hold on to love / We could be Jammin' Reggae / Corruption / Reggae radio station / Pyramid / Simplicity / Manners / Peace Flags.
LP: 4501451
MC: 4501454

JOURNEY TO ADDIS.
Tracks: / One cold vibe (couldn't stop dis ya boogie) / Cold sweat / Cool meditation / African woman / Now that we've found love / Journey to Addis / Fret not thyself / Rejoice.
LP: . . . . ILPS 9554
MC: . . . . ICT 9554

PRISONER IN THE STREET.
Tracks: / Now that we've found love / Prisoner in the street / Third world man / Cold sweat / 96 degrees in the shade / African woman / Irie ites / Street fighting.
LP: . . . . ILPS 9616
MC: . . . . ZCI 9616

REGGAE GREATS.
Tracks: / Now that we've found love / Prisoner in the street / Always around / Talk to me / Cool meditation / Satta a masagana / Ninety-six degrees in the shade / African woman / Rhythm of life.
LP: . . . . IRG 9
MC: . . . . IRGC 9
MC: . . . . ICM 2050
MC: 842 573 4

ROCK THE WORLD.
Tracks: / Rock the world / Spiritual revolution / Who gave you? / Dub music / Shine like a blazing fire / Dancing on the floor / There's no need to question why / Peace and love / Standing in the rain / Hug it up.
LP: . . . . CBS 32686
MC: 40 32686
LP: . . . . CBS 85027

SENSE OF PURPOSE.
Tracks: / One to one / Sense of purpose / World of uncertainty / Rock me / One more time / Children of the world / Can't get you (outta my mind) / Girl from Hiroshima / Reggae jam boogie / How can you? / One song (Nyahbingi).
LP: . . . . CBS 26266
MC: 40 26266

SERIOUS BUSINESS.
Tracks: / Forbidden love / Keep your head to the sky / Never say never / Theme from the Underdog (version) / Reggae ambassador / Love will always be there / Theme from the Underdog.
LP: 836 952-1
MC: 836 952-4

STORY'S BEEN TOLD.
Tracks: / Talk to me / Irie ites / Always around / Tonight for me / Come together / Having a party / Story's been told.
LP: . . . . ILPS 9569

THIRD WORLD.
Tracks: / Sata amasa gana / Kumina / Slavery days / Brand new beggar / Cross reference / Got to get along / Sun don't shine / Freedom song.
LP: . . . . ILPS 9369

YOU'VE GOT THE POWER.
Tracks: / Try Jah love / Ride on / You're playing too close / Before you make the move (melt with everyone) / Jah Jah children moving up / You've got the power (to make a change) / Inna time like this / I wake up crying / Low key jammin'.
LP: 4503581
MC: 4503588
LP: . . . . CBS 85563

Thirteen

13 (Various artists).
LP: . . . . ARTY 13
MC: . . . . ARTY 13 C

Thirteen Moons

LITTLE DREAMING BOY.
LP: . . . . WRLP 003

ORIGINS.
Tracks: / Origins / Mowgli and baloo / T as in togetherness / Milkyway / Boundaries, blow away / Suddenly one summer / Undercurrent / As the dreams meet the soil / Good one's go first, The / La lumiere.
LP: . . . . WRLP 004

YOU WILL FIND MERCY ON YOUR ROAD.
LP: . . . . WRLP 012

Thirty...

30 MINUTES (Various artists).
MC: . . . . EBS 10

Thirty Six Hours

36 HOURS (Film soundtrack) (Various artists).
LP: . . . . STV 81071

Thirty Years Of ...

ALL RECORDINGS (See under 30 Years Of ...) (Various artists).

Thirty-Nine Steps

THIRTY-NINE STEPS (Film soundtrack) (Various artists).
LP: . . . . UAG 30208
MC: . . . . TCK 30208

Thirty-two Twenty

GUITAR GUITAR.
Tracks: / Guitar guitar / Pour me / Stooge, The / Light fantastic / Thunderbird / Holloway boys / Water & wine / I need a woman / Spaghetti western / Australian love song.
LP: . . . . HAI 110

Thirwell, Jim

STINKFIST (See under Lunch, Lydia) (Lunch, Lydia with Jim Thirwell).

This Earth Is Mine

THIS EARTH IS MINE (Film soundtrack) (Various artists).
LP: . . . . VC 81076
LP: . . . . STV 81076

This England

THIS ENGLAND (Special Double Compilation) (Various artists).
LP: . . . . DPA 302930
MC: . . . . KDPC 28051

This Heat

DECEIT.
LP: . . . . HEAT 2

THIS HEAT.
LP: . . . . HEAT 1

This House...

THIS HOUSE IS NOT A MOTEL (Various artists).
LP: . . . . EFA 4481

This Is Disco

THIS IS DISCO! (See under Disco ...) (Various artists).

This Is Doctor Beat

THIS IS DOCTOR BEAT (Various artists).
LP: . . . . DOBLP 1
MC: . . . . DOBMC 1

This Is Garage

THIS IS GARAGE (See under Garage) (Various artists).

This Is Hot

THIS IS HOT (Various artists).
LP: . . . . HOT ONE

THIS IS HOT TOO (Various artists).
LP: . . . . HOT TWO

This Is Music

THIS IS MUSIC VOL.3 (Various artists).
MC: . . . . CHV 310

THIS IS MUSIC VOL.4 (Various artists).
MC: . . . . CHV 326

THIS IS MUSIC VOL.5 (Various artists).
MC: . . . . CHV 335

This Is Ska

THIS IS SKA (See under Ska) (Various artists).

This Is The Army

THIS IS THE ARMY (Film soundtrack) (Various artists).
LP: . . . . SH 2035
LP: . . . . HS 408

This Is The Big One

THIS IS THE BIG ONE (Various artists).
LP: . . . . BIGA D2

This Is The Blues

THIS IS THE BLUES (See under Blues) (Various artists).

This Is War

THIS IS WAR (Various artists).
LP: . . . . RAPT 1
MC: . . . . ZCRAPT 1

This Mortal Coil

BLOOD.
2LP: . . . . DAD 1005
MC: . . . . DADC 1005

FILIGREE AND SHADOW.
2LP: . . . . DAD 609
MC: . . . . DADC 609

IT'LL END IN TEARS.
Tracks: / Kangaroo / Song to the siren / Holocaust / Fyt / Fond affections / Last ray, The / Waves become wings / Another day / Barramundi / Dreams made flesh / Not me / Single wish, A.
LP: . . . . CAD 411
MC: . . . . CADC 411

This Picture

VIOLENT IMPRESSION, A.
LP: . . . . DEDLP 002
MC: . . . . DEDMC 002

This Scarlet Train

FIMBRIA.
Tracks: / Picture frame / Autumn hood / Candice / Kistvaen / Still rain / Lilyhaze.
LP: . . . . NISHI 202

This Thing Called...

THIS THING CALLED LOVE (Various artists).
LP: . . . . CBD 2004

This Way Up

FEELIN' GOOD ABOUT IT.
Tracks: / If I can't have you / Let go the reins / Louise / Tell me why / Flying back South / Shake baby shake / Feeling good / Sweet rhapsody / Inside my love / I will / Move on up to heaven (CD only) / If I can't have you (12" remix) (CD only) / Tell me why (12" remix) (CD only) / I will (12" remix) (CD only).
LP: . . . . V 2453
MC: . . . . TCV 2453

Thomas, A.A.

HE SET ME FREE.
LP: . . . . AAT 4

Thomas, B.J.

AMAZING GRACE.
Tracks: / Amazing grace / His eye is on the sparrow / Unclouded day, The / In the garden / You'll never walk alone / Old rugged cross, The / Just a closer walk with thee / I believe / Just as I am / Beyond the sunset.
LP: . . . . WST 9611
MC: . . . . WC 9611

BEST OF B.J. THOMAS.
MC: 16-14

B.J.THOMAS.
MC: . . . . ZCGAS 723

CLOSE TO YOU.
MC: . . . . ORC 008

MIRACLE.
LP: . . . . MYR 1128
MC: . . . . MC 1128

NEW LOOKS.
Tracks: / New looks from an old lover / Wind beneath my wings / I'm saving all the good times for you / You keep the man in me happy (and the child in me alive) / Whatever happened to old-fashioned love? / Rock and roll you're beautiful / Memory machine / I love us / I just sing.
LP: . . . . EPC 25378
MC: 40 25378

YOU GAVE ME LOVE.
LP: . . . . WRD 3006
MC: . . . . TC WRD 3006

Thomas, Buddy

KITTY PUSS FIDDLER.
LP: . . . . ROUNDER 0032

Thomas, Carter

SONOMA.
LP: . . . . P 5001

Thomas, Caryl

HARP.
LP: . . . . SAIN 1414 D

Thomas, Cess

TOL AND TOL.
LP: . . . . ADD 15

Thomas, Charlie

GREATEST HITS LIVE: CHARLIE THOMAS (Thomas, Charlie & The Drifters).
Tracks: / Save the last dance for me / Up on the roof / On Broadway / Under the boardwalk.
MC: . . . . KTOP 143
LP: . . . . TOP 143

Thomas, Chris

BEGINNING, THE.
LP: . . . . ARHOOLIE 1096
MC: . . . . C 1096

CRY OF THE PROPHETS.
Tracks: / Angel lady / Wanna die with a smile on my face / Dance to the music till my savior comes / Alpha omega / Last real man / Cry of the prophets / Heart and soul / Help us, somebody / I'm gonna make it / All nite long / I need you.
LP: 7599261861
MC: 7599261864

Thomas, David

BLAME THE MESSENGER.
Tracks: / My town / Fact about trains, A / King Knut / When love is uneven / Storm breaks / Long rain, The / Having time / Velikovsky two-step, The.
LP: . . . . ROUGH 120

MONSTER WALKS ON WINTER LAKE, THE (Thomas, David & the Wooden Buds).
LP: . . . . ROUGH 100

MORE PLACES FOREVER (Thomas,David & The Pedestrians).
LP: . . . . ROUGH 80

SOUND OF THE SAND, THE (Thomas,David & The Pedestrians).
LP: . . . . ROUGH 30

VARIATIONS ON A THEME (Thomas,David & The Pedestrians).
LP: . . . . ROUGH 60

WINTER COMES HOME.
LP: . . . . UNKNOWN

Thomas, Dylan

ADVENTURES IN THE SKIN TRADE.
MCSET: 2078

AND DEATH SHALL HAVE NO DOMINATION.
MC: 1018

BOY GROWING UP, A (see under Boy Growing Up) (Williams, Emlyn (nar)).

CHILD'S CHRISTMAS IN WALES, A.
MC: 1002

DYLAN THOMAS READING HIS POETRY.
MC: 001042467

MC: 1342

DYLAN THOMAS READS A PERSONAL ANTHOLOGY.
MC: 1294

DYLAN THOMAS SOUNDBOOK.
LPS: SBR 102
MCSET: SBC 102

IN COUNTRY HEAVEN (the evolution of a poem).
MC: 1281

MAN BE MY METAPHOR.
MC: TTC/PS03

OVER SIR JOHN'S HILL.
MC: 1043

QUITE EARLY ONE MORNING.
MC: 1132

UNDER MILK WOOD (Various artists).
MCSET: 2005

UNDER MILK WOOD (Tracey, Stan/ Donald Houston).
LP: TAA 271

UNDER MILK WOOD (Featuring Richard Burton) (Various artists).
MCSET: SAY 13
MCSET: ARGO 1016

UNDER MILK WOOD - A PLAY FOR VOICES (Various artists).
Tracks: / Main theme: *Various artists* / Johnnie Crack and Flossie Snail: *Various artists* / I loved a man: *Various artists* / Love duet: *Various artists* / Evening prayer, An: *Various artists* / Come and sweep my chimney (Mr. Waldo): *Various artists*.
2LP: SCXD 6715
MCSET: TCSCXD 6715

VISIT TO AMERICA, A.
MC: 1061

Thomas, Evelyn

HIGH ENERGY.
LP: SOHOLP 4

STANDING AT THE CROSSROADS.
Tracks: / Standing at the crossroads / How many hearts? / Cold shoulder / Sorry wrong number / Reflections suite, The / Reflections (love tempo) / Number one lover / Reflections / Tightrope.
LP: SOHOLP 10
MC: SOHOTC 10

Thomas, Gary

SEVENTH QUADRANT.
Tracks: / Foresight / Tablet of destinies / Seven quadrant / Eternal present, The / Preparation and subterfuge / First sketches / Labyrinth.
LP: ENJA 5047

WHILE THE GATE IS OPEN.
Tracks: / Strode rode / Star eyes / You stepped out of a dream / Song is you, The / Invitation / Chelsea bridge / On the trail / Epistrophy.
LP: 8344391

Thomas, Henry

RAGTIME TEXAS.
2LP: HERWIN 409

Thomas, Irma

BREAKAWAY.
Tracks: / Without love / Take a look / Time is on my side / Wish someone would care / It's starting to get to me now / He's my guy / What are you trying to do / I'm gonna cry till my tears run dry / You don't miss a good thing (until it's gone) / Anyone who knows what love is (will understand) / It's raining / Please send me someone to love / Another woman's man / While the city sleeps / Straight from the heart / It's a man's woman's world / I've been there before / I need you so / Breakaway.
LP: SSL 6032
MC: TC-SSL 6032

DOWN AT MUSCLE SHOALS.
Tracks: / We got something good / Good to me / Here I am,take me / Security / Let's do it over / Somewhere crying / Woman will do wrong, A / Yours until tomorrow / I gave you everything / I've been loving you too long / Don't make me stop now / Cheater man.
LP: GCH 8104

HIP SHAKING MAMA.
LP: CRM 2019

IN BETWEEN TEARS.
LP: CRB 1020

IRMA THOMAS SINGS (Minit and Bandy Originals).
LP: BANDY LP 101

LIVE: IRMA THOMAS.
LP: HELP 29

NEW RULES, THE.
Tracks: / New rules, The / Gonna cry til my tears run dry / I needed somebody / Good things don't come easy / Love of my man, The / One more time / Thinking of you / Wind beneath my wings / I gave you everything / Yours until tomorrow.
LP: REU 1001
LP: ROUNDER 2046
MC: ROUNDER 2046C

RULER OF HEARTS.
Tracks: / I did my part / Cry on / For goodness sake / It's raining / Look up / It's too soon to know / Somebody told you / Your love is true / (You ain't) hittin' on nothing / Gone / Two winters long / I done got over it / That's all I ask / Ruler of my heart / Girl needs boy / It's too soon to know.
LP: CRB 1226
MC: TCCRB 1226

RULER OF HEARTS/SHOW ME THE WAY (Thomas, Irma/Aaron Neville).
MC: TCAD 24

SOUL QUEEN OF NEW ORLEANS.
LP: 1005
MC: 1005 TC

TIME IS ON MY SIDE.
Tracks: / Take a look / Time is on my side / Baby don't look down / Times have changed / I done got over it / It's raining / Somebody told you / Wait, wait, wait / Breakaway / I haven't got time to cry / Some things you never get used to / Ruler of my heart / I need your love so bad / Wish someone would care / I want a true true love.
MC: KENC 010
LP: KENT 010

WAY I FEEL, THE.
Tracks: / Old records / Baby I love you / Sorry wrong number / You can think twice / Sit down and cry / All I know is the way I feel / I'm gonna hold you to your promise / I'll take care of you / Dancing in the street / You don't know nothing about love.
LP: FIEND 112
LP: ROUNDER 2058
MC: ROUNDER 2058 C

WISH SOMEONE WOULD CARE.
LP: LAX 313

Thomas, Jah

DANCE HALL CONNECTION.
LP: SCLP 010

DANCE HALL STYLEE.
LP: SCLP 5

LOVERGIRL (See under Keating, Junior) (Keeting, Junior/Jah Thomas).

NAH FIGHT OVER WOMAN.
LP: STLP 1018

SING LITTLE BIRD (See under McKay, Freddie).

STOP YU LOAFIN'.
Tracks: / Stop yu loafin' / Black star liner / Love and happiness / Bicycle skank / Send me the pillow that you dream on / Uncle Lester / Mr. Nkruma / Landlord / My Jamaican girl / Sister Dawn.
LP: GREL 3

TRIBUTE TO REGGAE KING, BOB N. MARLEY.
LP: STLP 1955

Thomas, James Son

JAMES 'SON' THOMAS ALBUM, THE.
LP: LR 42048

PLAYS AND SINGS DELTA BLUES CLASSICS.
LP: 2102

Thomas, Joe

BLOWNIN' IN FROM K.C..
LP: UP 27 12

JUMPING WITH JOE.
LP: ST 1017

MAKE YOUR MOVE.
Tracks: / Make your move / Your love is so good to me / Caught you lying again / Plato's retreat / Let me be the one / Get on back / Sugar shack.
LP: TKR 83374

RAW MEAT.
LP: UP 27 01

Thomas, John

PETRISEN.
Tracks: / Boneddwr mawr or bala / Talidion minion menai / Hiraeth am feirion / Cyffes y meddwyn / Yr ysgol yn y wlad / Mari, rhowch morgan ar y tan / Castiau gwraig / Robin fy mrawsd / Can yr aderyn / Hen ffon fy nain / Gwenith Gwyn / O fy nghariad annwyl / Y tylwyth teg / Tatws llaeth / Jane ni sy'n un iawn / Limericks / Tren o bala i ffestiniog.
MC: 60-051

SOLIEL, A STEP BEYOND.
Tracks: / Our dreams come true / Dancing in the wind / Keep on smiling / Whisper to me / Be yourself / Con amor / Wind changes / Thinking of you again / One step at a time.
MC: OUTSTANDING 29

Thomas, Ken

BEAT THE LIGHT.
LP: FIESA 001

Thomas, Kid

LOST SESSIONS, THE 1957 VOL 1 (Thomas, Kid Dixieland Band).
Tracks: / Singing the blues / Cindy oh Cindy / It's all over now / St. Louis blues / Shake it and break it.
LP: LPS 30

WITH THE ALGIERS STOMPERS VOL. 3 (Thomas, Kid and the Algiers Stompers).
LP: JCE 13

Thomas, Leon

PIECE OF CAKE, A (Thomas, Leon & Freddy Hubbard).
LP: PAL 15006

Thomas, Leslie (aut)

ADVENTURES OF GOODNIGHT AND LOVING (See under Adventures of...) (Barron, Keith (nar)).

DANGEROUS DAVIES THE LAST DETECTIVE.
MC: CAB 344

VIRGIN SOLDIERS, THE (Bennett, Hywel).
MCSET: ZC SWD 360

Thomas, Lillo

ALL OF YOU.
Tracks: / Your love's got a hold on me / Holding on / Show me / Settle down / All of you / My girl / Never give you up / I like your style.
LP: EJ 2402171

LET ME BE YOURS.
Tracks: / I love it / Trust me / Who do you think you are / Just my imagination / Hot love / Good girl / Joy of your love / Let me be yours.
LP: EST 7122901
MC: TC-EST 7122904

LILLO.
Tracks: / I'm in love / Her love / Sweet surrender / That guy (could have been me) / Sexy girl / Wanna make love (all night long) / I've been loving you too long (to stop now) / Downtown / Put your foot down.
LP: EST 2031
MC: TCEST 2031

Thomas, Luther

LUTHER THOMAS'S CREATIVE ENSEMBLE & LESTER BOWIE.
LP: RK 15

Thomas, Mike

CIRCULAR MOTION.
Tracks: / Circular motion.
LP: POW 5501

Thomas, Nicky

DOING THE MOONWALK.
LP: TRLS 288
MC: ZCTRL 288

IMAGES OF YOU.
LP: HRLP 701

LOVE OF THE COMMON PEOPLE.
Tracks: / God bless the children / Rainy night in Georgia / If I had a hammer / Turn back the hands of time / Doing the moonwalk / Love of the common people / Mama's song / Have a little faith / Don't touch / Lonely feeling / I who have nothing / Let it be.
LP: TBL 143

LOVE OF THE COMMON PEOPLE (OLD GOLD) (See under Boothe, Ken/ Everything I own (Old G).

TELL IT LIKE IT IS.
Tracks: / Tell it like it is / Watch that little girl / Deep in the morning / Yesterday man / We people / Lay lady lay / In the midnight hour / Just because your love has gone / Soul power / I can't stand it / Isn't it a pity / BBC / Love peace and happiness.
LP: TRLS 25

Thomas, Pat

IN ACTION VOL.2.
LP: ERT 1001

IT'S A LONG LONG WAY.
LP: HEY 001

PAT THOMAS & EBO TAYLOR (Thomas, Pat & Ebo Taylor).
LP: DANNYTONE 002

Thomas, Philip Michael

LIVIN' THE BOOK OF LIFE.
Tracks: / Livin' the book of life / Just the way I planned it / You might be the lucky one / Fish and chips / Everything happens in it's own time / She's a liar / I'm in love with the love that you give me / Stay (in my loving arms tonight) / All my love / La Mirada.
LP: WX 34
MC: WX 34 C

SOMEBODY.
LP: 790 960-1
MC: 790 960-4

Thomas, Ray

FROM MIGHTY OAKS.
LP: THS 16

Thomas, Rene

MEETING MISTER THOMAS (Thomas, Rene Quintet).
LP: FS 214

Thomas, Robert

BLUES AND BOOGIE FROM ALABAMA (See under Macon, Albert) (Thomas, Robert & Albert Macon).

Thomas, Rockin' Tabby

BLUES TRAIN.
Tracks: / Blues train / Mojo / Welfare blues / I'll make the trip / Crawling king snake / I can't hold out / Candy / How many more years / Li'l red rooster / Please baby please / Leave it like it is.
LP: CH 209
LP: 1016
MC: 1016 TC

KING OF SWAMP BLUES.
LP: 1026
MC: 1026 TC

ROCKIN' TABBY THOMAS Rockin' with the blues.
LP: 1010
MC: 1010 TC

Thomas, R.S.(poet)

R.S. THOMAS READS HIS POEMS.
LP: OR 004

Thomas, Ruddy

DON'T WANT TO LOSE YOU.
LP: WENLP 3034

Thomas, Rufus

DO THE FUNKY CHICKEN (OLD GOLD) (See under Jean Knight - Mr. Big Stuff).

JUMP BACK.
Tracks: / Jump back / All night worker / Little Sally Water / Chicken scratch / World is round, The / Sister's got a boyfriend / Talkin' about true love / Sophisticated cissy / Memphis train / Greasy spoon / Dog, The / Walking the dog / Can your monkey do the dog / I want to be loved / I want to get married / Fine and mellow.
LP: ED 134

THAT WOMAN IS POISON.
Tracks: / That woman is poison / Big fine hunk of woman / Somebody's got to go / Walk, The / I just got to know / Blues in the basement / Breaking my back / All night worker.
LP: AL 4769

Thomas, Sam Fan

MAKASSI.
LP: TAM 004

MAKASSI PLUS.
LP: MS 5004

Thomas, Tabby

HOODOO PARTY.
Tracks: / Boogie woogie children / Playgirl / Keep on trying / Man, I don't care / So hard to bear / Roll on mule / Brother Brown / Whole world in his hands.
LP: FLY 621

Thomas, Tasha

MIDNIGHT RENDEZVOUS.
Tracks: / Midnight rendezvous / Street fever / Shoot me / Hot buttered boogie / You put the music in me / Wake up morning glory / You're the one I love / Drinking again.
LP: K 50572

Thomas & Taylor

TRUE LOVE (BOOK 1).
Tracks: / Lonely too long / True love / You can't blame love (remix) / You can't blame love / Freedom / My room / Love and affection (remix) / Call me / I love you.
LP: INRLP 1
MC: INRC 1

Thomas & the King

THOMAS & THE KING (Original London Cast) (Various artists).
LP: TERS 1009

Thomas the Tank Engine

EDWARD, GORDON AND HENRY (up to age 8) (Unknown narrator(s)).
MC: PLBE 159

PERCY AND HAROLD (up to age 8) (Unknown narrator(s)).
MC: PLBE 223

PERCY RUNS AWAY (up to age 8) (Unknown narrator(s)).

MC: PLBE 156

PERCY'S PREDICAMENT (up to age 8) (Unknown narrator(s)).
MC: PLBE 230

POP GOES THE DIESEL (up to age 8) (Unknown narrator(s)).
MC: PLBE 228

RAILWAY STORIES (See under Railway Stories) (Morris, Johnny (nar)).

THOMAS AND BERTIE (up to age 8) (Unknown narrator(s)).
MC: PLBE 155

THOMAS AND TERENCE (up to age 8) (Unknown narrator(s)).
MC: PLBE 158

THOMAS AND THE MISSING CHRISTMAS TREE (up to age 8) (Unknown narrator(s)).
MC: PLBE 234

THOMAS AND TREVOR (up to age 8) (Unknown narrator(s)).
MC: PLBE 190

THOMAS COMES TO BREAKFAST (up to age 8) (Unknown narrator(s)).
MC: PLBE 229

THOMAS GOES FISHING (up to age 8) (Unknown narrator(s)).
MC: PLBE 157

THOMAS, PERCY AND THE COAL (up to age 8) (Unknown narrator(s)).
MC: PLBE 189

THOMAS'S CHRISTMAS PARTY (up to age 8) (Unknown narrator(s)).
MC: PLBE 198

TOBY AND THE STOUT GENTLEMAN (up to age 8) (Unknown narrator(s)).
MC: PLBE 160

Thomas, Timmy

NEW YORK EYES (see under Nicole) (Nicole/Timmy Thomas).

WHY CAN'T WE LIVE TOGETHER (ALBUM).
Tracks: / Why can't we live together? / Rainbow power / Take care of home / First time ever I saw your face, The / Coldest day of my life / In the beginning / Cold cold people / Opportunity / Dizzy dizzy world / Funky me.
LP: 2486268
MC: 3186096

WHY CAN'T WE LIVE TOGETHER (OLD GOLD) (See under Dobie Gray - Drift Away).

Thomas, Walter

HOT JAZZ.
LP: HQ 2032

Thomas,Vaneese

VANEESE THOMAS.
Tracks: / (I wanna get) close to you / Let's talk it over / Keep it up / Heading in the right direction / Rockin' and lovin' / Ultimate love / I'm gonna love you.
MC: 9241414
LP: 9241411

Thompson, B

B.THOMPSON AND THE BLACK EAGLE JAZZ BAND (See under Black Eagle Jaz Band) (Thompson, B & The Black Eagle Jazz Band).

Thompson, Barbara

BARBARA THOMPSON AND ROD ARGENT (Thompson, Barbara & Rod Argent).
Tracks: / Ghosts / With you / Poltergeist.
LP: MCF 3125

BARBARA THOMPSON'S PARAPHERNALIA - WILDE TALES.
LP: MCF 3047

CRY FROM THE HEART, A (Live in London) (Thompson, Barbara Paraphernalia).
2LP: ZTM 12
MC: ZCTM 12

FANTASY.
LP: TM 5
MC: ZCTM 5

HEAVENLY BODIES.
LP: TM 10
MC: ZCTM 10

JUBIABA.
Tracks: / Funky flunky / Seega / Helena / Cuban thing / Black pearl / Touch of blue / Slum goddess.
LP: MCL 1700

JUST MUSIC (See under Rendell, Don) (Thompson, Barbara & Don Rendell).

MOTHER EARTH (Thompson, Barbara Paraphernalia).
LP: TM 1
MC: ZCTM 1

PARAPHERNALIA 'LIVE'.
LP: MCL 1605
2LP: MCSP 309

PURE FANTASY (Thompson, Barbara Paraphernalia).
Tracks: / Pure fantasy / Mother earth suite.
LP: TM 5
MC: ZCTM 5

SPECIAL EDITION.
Tracks: / Country dance / Fear of spiders / City lights / Little Annie ooh (live) / Fields of flowers / Dusk: nightwatch / Listen to the plants / Out to lunch (live) / Sleepwalker / Midday riser / Times past / Voices behind locked doors (live).
MC: ZCTM 11

WILDE TALES.
LP: MCL 1796

Thompson, Becky

AFTER ALL THIS TIME.
LP: ATR 1100

Thompson, Bob

WILDERNESS.
LP: ENVLP 545

Thompson, Bobby

7 IN 7 OUT.
Tracks: / 7 in 7 out / Where do we go from here / Caribbean feeling / Journey to my home / Street beat / All in love is fair / Listen to the wind song.
LP: RR 2010
MC: CRR 2010

BOBBY THOMPSON LAUGH-IN, THE.
Tracks: / Laugh-in / Dreamin' / You little waster.
LP: RUB 038
MC: RUBC 038

LITTLE WASTER, THE.
LP: RUB 032
MC: RUBC 032

WHAT FETTLE.
LP: MWM SP 5
MC: MWMC SP 5

Thompson, Butch

A' SOLAS.
LP: SOS 1037

BUTCH THOMPSON AND HAL SMITH (Thompson, Butch & Hal Smith).
LP: SOS 1075

BUTCH THOMPSON AND HIS BERKELEY GANG (Thompson, Butch & His Berkeley Gang).
LP: SOS 1127

IN CHICAGO (Thompson, Butch & His Boys & Frank Chase).
LP: J 146

MILENBERG JOYS (Thompson, Butch/ Hal Smith/Charlie Devore).
LP: SOS 1116

ONE IN A MILLION (Thompson, Butch & Chicago Rhythm).
LP: SOS 1059

PLAYS JELLY ROLL MORTON.
LP: CEN 4

PLAYS JELLY ROLL MORTON VOL.2.
LP: CEN 9

Thompson, Carroll

CARROLL THOMPSON.
LP: SG 21
MC: SGC 21

HOPELESSLY IN LOVE.
LP: CGLP 15
MC: CGCAS 15

Thompson, Charles

DAY I JOIN THE GOLF CLUB, THE.
MC: DHC 6

Thompson, Chris

HIGH COST OF LIVING, THE.
Tracks: / Love and loneliness / What a woman wants / It don't bother me / High cost of living / Empty house / It's not over / Living for the thrill / Missing / She's dangerous / This is not a world of our making.
LP: 381655 1
MC: 381655 4

PUSH AND SHOVE (see O'Connor, Hazel) (Thompson, Chris & Hazel O'Connor).

Thompson, Colin

THREE KNIGHTS.
Tracks: / Gypsy laddie, The / Brisk young lively lad (or the vailiant lady) / Bonnie lass among the heather / Three knights, The / Linden Lea / Lord Thomas and fair Eleanor / Oakham poachers / John of Hazelgreen / Banstead Downs (Georgie) / Parting glass, The.
LP: FE 021

Thompson, Danny

ELEMENTAL.
Tracks: / Beirut / Fair Isle friends / Musing Mingus / Searchin' / Women in war / Freedom/prayer/dance/ thanksgiving.
LP: AN 8753
MC: ANC 8753
MC: ICM 2057
LP: ILPM 2057

SONGHAI (Thompson, Danny/Toumani Diabate/Ketama).
LP: HNBL 1323
MC: HNBC 1323

WHATEVER.
Tracks: / Idle Monday / Till Minne av jan / Yucateca / Lovely Joan / Swedish dance / Lament for Alex / Crusader / Minor escapade.
LP: HNBL 1326
MC: HNBC 1326

WHATEVER NEXT.
Tracks: / Dargai / Hopdance (invitation to dance) / Beanpole / Wildfinger / Full English basket, A / Sandansko oro (Bulgarian dance) / Take it off the top / Major escapade.
MC: ANC 8743
LP: AN 8743
MC: ICM 2055

Thompson, Don

BEAUTIFUL FRIENDSHIP, A (Thompson, Don Quartet).
Tracks: / Even Steven / My one and only love / Blues for Jim-San / I've never been in love before / Beautiful friendship, A / For Scott La Faro / East it / Dreams.
LP: CJ 243

COAST TO COAST.
LP: AML 307

COUNTRY PLACE.
LP: PM 008

DANCE TO THE LADY (See under Bickert, Ed) (Thompson, Don & Ed Bickert).

IN CONCERT AT THE GARDEN PARTY (See under Bickert, Ed) (Thompson, Don & Ed Bickert).

LIVE AT THE CAFE CARLYLE (see Shearing, George) (Thompson, Don & George Shearing).

Thompson, Eddie

AIN'T SHE SWEET (Thompson, Eddie Trio/Spike Robinson).
LP: HEP 2002

AT CHESTERS (Thompson, Eddie Trio/ Spike Robinson).
LP: HEP 2028

AT CHESTERS VOL 2 (Thompson, Eddie Trio/Spike Robinson).
LP: HEP 2031

BY MYSELF.
LP: 77LUE 12 39

I HEAR MUSIC.
LP: DM 17

MEMORIES OF YOU (Thompson, Eddie Trio/Spike Robinson).
LP: HEP 2021

WHEN THE LIGHTS ARE LOW (Thompson, Eddie & Roy Williams).
LP: HEP 2007

Thompson, Eric

ADAM AND EVE HAD THE BLUES (Thompson, Eric & Suzy).
LP: ARHOOLIE 5041

BLUEGRASS GUITAR.
Tracks: / Paddy on the turnpike / Blackberry blossom / Crazy creek / Thompson's reel / Forked deer / Say old man / Ragtime Annie / Panhandle rag / Stoney creek / Beaumont rag / Dixie hoedown / Dill pickles rag / Cross-eyed fiddler.
LP: SNKF 151

MAGIC ROUNDABOUT STORIES.
LP: REC 243
MC: MRMC 047

TWO GUITARS (Thompson, Eric & Alan Senauke).
LP: FF 393

Thompson, Hank

20 GOLDEN PIECES: HANK THOMPSON.
Tracks: / Who left the door to Heaven open? / When my blue moon turns to gold again / Honky tonk angel / I recall a gypsy woman / Mama don't allow / Wait a little longer baby / Loving on a back street / Whatever's left / Fair weather love / Red necks, white socks and blue ribbon beer / Country bumpkin / I've come awful close / Oklahoma hills / Mark of a heel / Humpty Dumpty heart / Green light / Smokey the bear / Squaws along the Yukon / Wild side of life / Next time I fall in love.
LP: BDL 2042
MC: BDC 2042

AT THE GOLDEN NUGGETT.
LP: HAT 3076
MC: HATC 3076

BEST OF THE BEST OF HANK THOMPSON.
LP: GT 0060

CAPITOL COLLECTORS SERIES: HANK THOMPSON.
Tracks: / Humpty dumpty heart / Whoa, sailor / Wild side of life, The / Waiting in the lobby of your heart / Rub-a-dub-dub / Yesterday's girl / Wake up, Irene / Breakin' the rules / Honky tonk gal / We've gone too far / New green light, The / Breakin' in another heart / Don't take it out on me / Blackboard of my heart / Rockin' in the Congo / Squaws along the Yukon / Six pack to go, A / She's just a whole lot like you / Oklahoma hills / Hangover tavern.
LP: EMS 1349
LP: 792 124 1
MC: TCEMS 1349
MC: 792 124 4

DANCE RANCH.
LP: HAT 3027
MC: HATC 3027

HANK THOMPSON.
Tracks: / Six pack to go / Wild side of life / Oklahoma hills / Breakin' the rules / Blondes with no last name / Walkin' on new grass / Pick pocket / Honky tonk good ole Galls and Hillbilly / Let my heart do the talking for me / Swingin' side of them swingin' doors.
LP: IMCA 39089
MC: IMCAC 39089

HANK THOMPSON 1952.
Tracks: / Darling what more can I do / Square dab from the country / Brand in my heart / I'm lost without you / Judy / Be my life's companion / Shotgun boogie / Sixty.
LP: RFD 9003

HANK THOMPSON COLLECTION, THE.
Tracks: / Six pack to go, A / Wild side of life, The / Bubbles in my beer / John Henry / Swing wide your gate of love / San Antonio rose / Most of all / Rovin' gambler / Nine pound hammer / Cocaine blues / Lost John / Total strangers / Wabash cannonball / Shotgun boogie.
MC: KNMC 13059

IN THE STUDIO, ON THE ROAD.
Tracks: / John Henry / Crying in the deep blue sea / You'll be the one / Hang your head in shame / There's no you / Give a little, take a little / Summit ridge drive / Shot gun boogie / September in the rain / Warm red wine / Total stranger / Honky tonk town / Welcome to the fair introduction / Deep in the heart of Texas / My heart is a playground / Charmaine / How many teardrops / New wears off too fast / Rub-a-dub-dub / Beautiful Texas / We will start it all over / River road two step / Texas fight song / I cast a lonesome shadow / Simple Simon / There's a little bit of everything.
LP: SEE 263

SONGS FOR ROUNDERS.
Tracks: / Three times seven / I'll be a bachelor till I die / Drunkards blues / Teach 'em how to swim / Dry bread / Cocaine blues / Deep elm / Bummin' around / Little blossom / Roving gambler / Left my gal in the mountains / May I sleep in your barn tonight Mister.
LP: HAT 3052
MC: HATC 3052

Thompson, Hayden

BOONEVILLE MISSISSIPPI FLASH.
Tracks: / Ah poor little baby / Drivin' me out of my mind / Born to lose / Had a little talk / Don't say that you're sorry / I'm gonna sit right down and cry over you / Eeny meeny miney mo / Hands of time, The / Boy from Tupelo / I wanna get home / Girl named Betty, A / When my blue moon turns to gold again.
LP: CR 30245

EARLY DAYS.
Tracks: / Brown eyed handsome man / Call me Shorty / It won't be long till the summer / I guess I'd better be moving along / Kansas city / Going steady / Frankie and Johnny / I'll hold you in my heart / Pardon me / Pretending your not wearing my ring / I love country music / Funny how time slips away / I feel the blues coming on / Act like you love me / Pardon me (2) / Queen bee / Keys to my kingdom, The / How I wish / Pardon me / Old Kris Kringle / Mighty big wall.
LP: SJLP 569

FAIRLANE ROCK.
Tracks: / Love my baby / One broken heart / Blues blues blues / Fairlane rock /

One broken heart (take 2) / Love my baby (take 2) / Pretending / Your true love / Kansas city / Four seasons of life, The / This is country / I wanna get home / I guess I'd better be moving along / I need a break / 16.88 / Lonesome for my baby / This old windy city.
LP: . . . . BFX 15263

FUNNY HOW TIME SLIPS AWAY.
Tracks: / Frankie and Johnny / Guess I'd better be moving along / Pardon me / Funny how time slips away / How I wish / Keys to my Kingdom, The.
LP: . . . . MFLP 1051

HERE'S HAYDEN THOMPSON.
LP: . . . . KS 3507

ROCKABILLY GUY 1954-1962.
Tracks: / I feel the blues coming on / Act like you love me / Rockabilly gal / Love my baby / One broken heart / Blues blues blues / You are my sunshine / Mama, mama, mama / Call me Shorty / Brown eyed handsome man / I'll hold you in my heart / Kansas City / It won't be long till the summer / Old Kris Kringle / Pardon me / Queen bee / Going steady.
LP: . . . . CR 30262

ROCKIN' COUNTRY MAN, THE.
Tracks: / Ah poor little baby / Drivin' me out of my mind / Born to lose / Had a little talk / Don't say that you're sorry / I'm gonna sit right down and cry over you / Eenie meenie miny mo / Hands of time, The / Boy from Tupelo / I wanna get home / When my blue moon turns to gold again / Girl named Betty, A.
LP: . . . . SJLP 563

TIME IS NOW, THE.
LP: . . . . SJLP 589

Thompson, Iain

TO A WORKING COLLIE.
MC: . . . . MR 1011

Thompson, Keith

CAN'T TAKE IT (See under Black Havana for details) (Thompson, Keith/ Black Havana).

CAN'T TAKE IT (See under Black Havana).

Thompson, Lawrie

MUSIC FOR THE GOURMET.
LP: . . . . KPM 3
MC: . . . . TCKPM 3

Thompson, Lincoln

NATURAL WILD (Thompson, Lincoln & Rasses).
Tracks: / Mechanical devices / Natural wild / My generation / Spaceship / People's minds / People love music / Smiling faces.
LP: . . . . UAG 30309

Thompson, Linda

ONE CLEAR MOMENT.
Tracks: / Can't stop the girl / One clear moment / Telling me lies / In love with the flame / Les trois beaus oiseaux de paradis / Take me on the subway / Best of friends / Hell, high water, and heartache / Just enough to keep me hanging on / Lover won't you throw me a line? / Only a boy.
LP: 925164 1
MC: 925164 4

Thompson, Linval

BABY FATHER.
Tracks: / Love me forever / If you want my love / Shouldn't lift your hand / Yes I'm coming / Baby father / All night long / Run down vanity / Poor man / She gone / Tell me the right time.
LP: . . . . GREL 51
MC: . . . . GREEN 51

I LOVE MARIJUANA.
Tracks: / I love marijuana / Dread are the controller / Children of the ghetto / Don't push your brother / Begging for apology / Not follow fashion / Roots lady / Big big girl / Just another girl / Starlight / Jamaican calley.
LP: . . . . TRLS 151

LINVAL.
LP: . . . . STLP 1027

LOOK HOW ME SEXY.
Tracks: / Are you ready / You're young / Look how me sexy / Call me / Sure of the one you love / Baby mother / I spy / Things couldn't be the same / Holding on to my girlfriend / Lick up the chalice.
LP: . . . . GREL 33

LOVE IS THE QUESTION.
LP: . . . . BS 1014

NEGREA LOVE DUB (Thompson, Linval/Revolutionaries).
Tracks: / Rock me in dub / Channel one in dub / Thompson in dub / Negrea Africa dub / Jah Jah children / Lion dub / Natty dread dub / Roots dub / Jamaica calley dub / African love dub.
LP: . . . . TRLS 153

RESCUE LOVER.
LP: . . . . GGLP 002

STARLIGHT.
Tracks: / Mercy / Halla the A halla / Poor man / Starlight / Case up / Soon come / Looks like it gonna rain / Bragg and show off / Greedy / Huff and puff.
LP: . . . . ILPS 9907

Thompson, Lucky

IN PARIS 1956.
LP: . . . . SW 8404

LUCKY THOMPSON FEATURING OSCAR PETTIFORD.
Tracks: / Tom-kattin' / Old reliable / Lady's vanity / Translation / Tricrotism / Bo-bi my boy / Body and soul / O.P. meets L.T..
LP: . . . . JASM 1037

LUCKY THOMPSON WITH GERARD POCHONET (Thompson, Lucky/Gerard Pochonet Quartet).
LP: . . . . FS 246

TEST PILOT.
LP: . . . . ST 1005

Thompson, Malachi

SPIRIT.
LP: . . . . DS 442

Thompson, Mayo

CORKY'S DEBT TO HIS FATHER.
LP: . . . . GLALP 015

Thompson, Michael

HOW LONG (Thompson, Michael Band).
Tracks: / Secret information / 1000 nights / Can't miss / How long / Give love a chance / Gloria / Baby come back.
LP: . . . . WX 254
MC: . . . . WX 254 C

Thompson, Prince

HUMANITY.
LP: . . . . GSLP 200

NATURAL WILD.
LP: . . . . VSLP 400

PRINCE LINCOLN AND THE ROYAL RASSES.
LP: . . . . GSLP 100

RIDE WITH THE RASSES.
LP: . . . . GSLP 100

Thompson, Rev. Johnny

GLORIOUS FEELING (Thompson, Rev. Johnny & Gospel Singers).
LP: . . . . CLGLP 009

Thompson, Richard

ACROSS A CROWDED ROOM.
Tracks: / When the spell is broken / You don't say / I ain't going to drag my feet no more / Love is a faithless country / Fire in the engine room / Walking through a wasted land / Little blue number / She twists the knife again / Ghosts in the wind.
LP: . . . . POLD 5175
MC: . . . . POLDC 5175

AMNESIA.
Tracks: / Turning of the tide / Gypsy love songs / Reckless kind / Jerusalem on the jukebox / I still dream / Don't tempt me / Yankee, go home / Can't win / Waltzing's for dreamers / Pharaoh.
LP: . . . . EST 2075
MC: . . . . TCEST 2075
LP: . . . . ATAK 169
MC: . . . . TCAK 169

BRIGHT LIGHTS (Thompson, Richard & Linda).
LP: . . . . CGLP 4407
MC: . . . . CGC 4407

DARING ADVENTURES.
LP: . . . . POLD 5202

FIRST LIGHT (Thompson, Richard & Linda).
Tracks: / Restless highway / Sweet surrender / Don't let a thief steal into your heart / Choice wife, The / Died for love / Strange affair / Layla / Pavanne / House of cards / First light.
LP: . . . . CGLP 4412
LP: . . . . CHR 1177
MC: . . . . ZCHS 1177
MC: . . . . CGC 4412

GUITAR/VOCAL.
Tracks: / Heart needs a home, A / Free as a bird / Night comes in / Pitfall/ Excursion / Calvary cross, The / Time will show the wiser / Throw away street puzzle / Mr. Lacey / Ballad of easy rider / Poor Will' and the jolly hangman / Sweet little Rock 'n' roller / Heart needs a home, A / Dark end of the street / It'll be me.
LP: . . . . HNBL 4801
MC: . . . . HNBC 4801

HAND OF KINDNESS.
Tracks: / Poisoned heart and a twisted memory, A / Tear stained letter / How I wanted to / Both ends burning / Wrong heartbeat / Hand of kindness / Devonside / Two left feet.
LP: . . . . HNBL 1313
MC: . . . . HNBC 1313

HENRY THE HUMAN FLY.
Tracks: / Roll over Vaughan Williams / Nobody's wedding / Poor ditching boy, The / Shaky Nancy / Angels took my racehorse away, The / Wheely down / New St George, The / Painted ladies / Cold feet / Mary and Joseph / Old changing way, The / Twisted.
LP: . . . . HNBL 4405
MC: . . . . HNBC 4405

HOKEY POKEY (Thompson, Richard & Linda).
Tracks: / Heart needs a home, A / Hokey pokey / I'll regret it all in the morning / Smiffy's glass eye / Egypt / Never again / Georgie on a spree / Old man inside a young man / Sun never shines on the poor / Mole in a hole.
LP: . . . . HNBL 4408
MC: . . . . HNBC 4408

I WANT TO SEE THE BRIGHT LIGHTS TONIGHT (Thompson, Richard & Linda).
Tracks: / When I get to the border / Calvary cross, The / Withered and died / I want to see the bright lights tonight / Down where the drunkards roll / We sing hallelujah / Has he got a friend for me? / Little beggar girl, The / End of the rainbow, The / Great Valerio.
LP: . . . . ILPS 9266
MC: . . . . ZCI 9266

MARKSMAN, THE (TV Soundtrack).
Tracks: / My time / Gordon / Rude health / Night school / Corniche pastiche / Crossing the water / Marksman, The / Kyrie / On yer eyes / Gutters on the run / Don't ever change / Up there.
LP: . . . . REB 660
MC: . . . . ZCF 660

POUR DOWN LIKE SILVER (Thompson, Richard & Linda).
Tracks: / Streets of paradise / For shame of doing wrong / Poor boy is taken away / Night comes in / Jet plane is a rocking chair / Beat the retreat / Hard luck stories / Dimming of the day / Dargai.
LP: . . . . HNBL 4404
MC: . . . . HNBC 4404

RUMOR AND SIGH.
Tracks: / Read about love / Feel so good / I misunderstood / Behind grey walls / You dream too much / Why must I plead / Vincent / Backlash love affair / Mystery wind / Jimmy Shand / Keep your distance / Mother knows best / God loves a drunk / Psycho Street.
LP: . . . . EST 2142
MC: . . . . TCEST 2142

SHOOT OUT THE LIGHTS (Thompson, Richard & Linda).
Tracks: / Man in need / Walking on a wire / Don't renage on our love / Just the motion / Shoot out the lights / Backstreet slide / Did she jump or was she pushed? / Wall of death.
LP: . . . . HNBL 1303
MC: . . . . HNBC 1303

SMALL TOWN ROMANCE.
Tracks: / Heart needs a home, A / Time to ring some changes / Beat the retreat / Woman or man? / For shame of doing wrong / Honky tonk blues / Small town romance / I want to see the bright lights tonight / Down where the drunkards roll / Love is bad for business / Great Valerio / Don't let a thief steal into your heart / Never again.
LP: . . . . HNBL 1316
MC: . . . . HNBC 1316

STRICT TEMPO.
Tracks: / Banish misfortune / Dundee hornpipe / Do if for my sake / Rockin' in rhythm / Random jig, The / Grinder / Will ye no come back again? / Cam o'er the steam Charlie / Ye banks and braes / Rufty tufty / Nonsuch a la mode de France / Andalus / Radio Marrakesh / Knife edge, The.
LP: . . . . CGLP 4409
LP: . . . . LP 1
MC: . . . . CGC 4409

SUNNYVISTA (Thompson, Richard & Linda).
Tracks: / Civilization / Borrowed time / Saturday rolling around / You're going to need somebody / Why do you turn your back / Sunnyvista / Lonely heart / Sisters / Justice in the streets / Traces of my love.
LP: . . . . CHR 1247
LP: . . . . CGLP 4403
MC: . . . . CGC 4403

Thompson, Ron

RESISTER TWISTER (Thompson, Ron & The Resistors).
LP: BP-2487

Thompson, Seamus

LONGFORD'S OWN.
MC: . . . . GTDC 094

Thompson, Sir Charles

FOR THE EARS (Honda/Corea/Vitous/ Haynes).
Tracks: / For the ears / Oh Joe / Memories of you / Bop this / Honeysuckle Rose / Swingtime in the Rockies / These foolish things / Sweet Georgia Brown / It's the talk of the town / Fore / Dynaflow / Under the sweetheart tree / Ready for Freddie / Sonny Howar's blues / Best by test / Hey there / Love for sale / Stompin' at the Savoy / Mister Sandman.
2LP: . . . . VJD 559

PORTRAIT OF A PIANO.
LP: 3037

Thompson, Sonny

CAT ON THE KEYS.
LP: . . . . ST 1027
MC: . . . . SC 1027

SWINGS IN PARIS.
LP: 33051

Thompson, Sue

SWEET MEMORIES.
Tracks: / Stay another day / How I love them old songs / What a woman in love won't do / Candy and roses / Sweet memories / Sad movies / How do you start over / Norman / Find out / Just plain country / Have a good time.
LP: . . . . SDLP 024

Thompson, Sydney

10 DANCE CHAMPIONSHIP DANCING (Thompson, Sydney & His Orchestra).
Tracks: / Who Mr & Mrs / Isn't she lovely / Apple blossom time / Adoration waltz / Guitar tango / Love affair in Roma / Wonderful Copenhagen / If / Tea for two / Do the disc samba / Sangria / Pennies from Heaven.
LP: . . . . REH 509
MC: . . . . ZCR 509

20 ALL TIME PARTY FAVOURITES (Thompson, Sydney & His Orchestra).
Tracks: / MacNamara's band / Boomps a daisy / March of the mods / Yellow submarine / Lambeth walk / Palais glide / Twisting in the mood / Chestnut tree, The / Knees up Mother Brown / Rock around the clock / St. Bernard waltz / Charleston / Cokey cokey / Ballin' the Jack / Pied Piper / Gay Gordons / I came, I saw, I conga'd / Zorba's dance / Dashing white sergeant / Popcorn samba / Auld lang syne.
LP: . . . . YU 104
MC: . . . . CYU 104

...AT THE RADIO 2 BALLROOM.
LP: . . . . REH 341
MC: . . . . ZCR 341

BALLROOM AND LATIN REPRISE.
LP: . . . . VOC 315

BALLROOM DANCING GREATS.
LP: . . . . DST 30

BALLROOM IN TEMPO.
LP: . . . . VOC 312
MC: . . . . C-VOC 312

CHA CHA CHAS AND SAMBAS.
LP: . . . . STC 13
MC: . . . . C STC 13
LP: . . . . STC 17

DANCING GUITARS.
LP: . . . . VOC 309
MC: . . . . C-VOC 309

DANCING GUITARS IN THE BALLROOM.
LP: . . . . VOC 311
MC: . . . . C-VOC 311

DOWN AT THE OLD BULL AND BUSH (Thompson, Sydney & His Orchestra).
LP: . . . . PDR 6

EVENING WITH SYDNEY THOMPSON.
LP: . . . . DST 25
MC: . . . . C DST 25

EVENING WITH SYDNEY THOMPSON VOL. 2.
LP: . . . . DST 26
MC: . . . . CDST 26

FAVOURITES IN DANCE AND SONG.
LP: . . . . VOC 302
MC: . . . . C-VOC 302

FAVOURITES IN DANCE AND SONG - VOL.3 BALLROOM AND LATIN.
LP: . . . . VOC 318

FAVOURITES IN DANCE AND SONG - VOL.2.
LP: . . . . VOC 306
MC: . . . . C-VOC 306

FIFTH COLLECTION-QUICKSTEPS & FOXTROTS.
LP: . . . . STC 19

FIFTH COLLECTION-WALTZES & TANGOS.
LP: STC 20

HAWAIIAN SERENADE.
LP: VOC 310
MC: C-VOC 310

JOIN SYDNEY THOMPSON FOR LATIN AMERICAN DANCING.
LP: DST 23

JOIN SYDNEY THOMPSON IN THE BALLROOM.
LP: DST 24

LATIN DANCING GREATS.
LP: DST 29

LATIN IN TEMPO.
LP: VOC 313
MC: C-VOC 313

MEMORIES.
LP: VOC 316

MORE BALLROOM FAVOURITES (Thompson, Sydney & His Orchestra).
LP: DST 28

MORE LATIN FAVOURITES (Thompson, Sydney & His Orchestra).
LP: DST 27

OLD TIME AND SEQUENCE CHAMPIONSHIP DANCING.
LP: OTS 251

OLD TIME AND SEQUENCE DANCING.
LP: OTS 256

OLDE TIME & SEQUENCE DANCING (Thompson, Sydney & His Orchestra).
LP: OTS 252

OLDE TYME DANCING PARTY (Thompson, Sydney & His Orchestra).
Tracks: / Marine four step / Doris waltz / Dinkie one step / Broadway quickstep / Georgella blues / Tangos / Saunter / Military two step / Veleta / Over the top medley / Palais glide / Gay gordons / Barn dance / Happy wanderer, The / New century march / Premier two step / Boston two step / Rialto two step / Pavlova gavotte / One step / Eva three step / Waltz / St. Bernard waltz.
LP: NTS 182
MC: TCNTS 182

PAUL JONES WITH SYDNEY THOMPSON.
LP: PDR 5

PLAYS FOR STRICT TEMPO BALLROOM DANCING.
LP: VOC 304
MC: C-VOC 304

QUICKSTEPS AND FOXTROTS.
LP: STC 11
MC: C STC 11
LP: STC 15

QUICKSTEPS AND FOXTROTS VOL. 2 (Thompson, Sydney & His Orchestra).
LP: STC 21

RADIO 2 BALLROOM PRESENTS.
Tracks: / Sail the summer winds / Put your arms around me honey / Edelweiss / Cavatina / If I knew then / Too young / Rivers of Babylon / El Choclo / Sweet and gentle / Money, money, money / All my loving / Copacabana / Amor / Come closer to me / Come on over to my place / I want to hold your hand.
LP: REH 406
MC: ZCR 406

RUMBAS AND JIVES.
LP: STC 18

RUMBAS AND PASO DOBLES.
LP: STC 14
MC: CSTC 14

SYDNEY THOMPSON, AT THE RADIO 2.
Tracks: / Oh your beautiful doll / Kiss me honey / Feelings / Perfidia / Abanda / Popcorn samba / Seven little girls / Spanish gypsy dance / Chinatown / Alexander's ragtime band / Alley cat song / There's a kind of hush / All alone / Shanty in old Shanty town / Love story / No other love.
LP: REB 216

SYDNEY THOMPSON COLLECTION (QUICKSTEPS & FOXTROTS).
LP: STC 1
MC: C STC 1
MC: C STC 6
LP: STC 6

SYDNEY THOMPSON COLLECTION (RUMBAS & PASO DOBLES).
LP: STC 9
MC: C STC 9

SYDNEY THOMPSON COLLECTION (VIENNESE WALZES & JIVES).
LP: STC 5
MC: C STC 5

SYDNEY THOMPSON COLLECTION (WALTZES & TANGOS).
LP: STC 2
MC: C STC 2
LP: STC 7
MC: C STC 7

SYDNEY THOMPSON INVITES YOU TO TAKE YOUR PARTNERS.
LP: OTS 255

SYDNEY THOMPSON PLAYS A BALLROOM ENCORE.
LP: VOC 308
MC: C-VOC 308

SYDNEY THOMPSON PLAYS A LATIN ENCORE.
MC: C-VOC 307
LP: VOC 307

SYDNEY THOMPSON PLAYS FOR BALLROOM & LATIN DANCI.
MC: C-VOC 314
LP: VOC 314

SYDNEY THOMPSON PLAYS FOR LATIN DANCING.
MC: C-VOC 305
LP: VOC 305

SYDNEY THOMPSON PLAYS FOR OLD TIME AND SEQUENCE DANCING.
LP: OTS 254

SYDNEY THOMPSON PLAYS FOR SEQUENCE DANCING.
LP: OTS 253

SYDNEY THOMPSON PLAYS LATIN DANCING FAVOURITES.
MC: C-VOC 301
LP: VOC 301

SYNDEY THOMPSON COLLECTION (CHA CHA CHAS & SAMBAS).
LP: STC 8
MC: C STC 8

TWENTY ALL TIME PARTY DANCE FAVOURITES.
MC: C-VOC 303
LP: VOC 303

VIENNESE WALTZES AND JIVES.
LP: STC 10
MC: C STC 10

WALTZES AND TANGOS.
LP: STC 12
MC: C STC 12

Thompson Twins

BEST OF THE THOMPSON TWINS, THE.
Tracks: / In the name of love '88 / Lies / Love on your side / Lay your hands on me / Gap, The / Hold me now / Doctor doctor / You take me up / King for a day / Get that love.
MC: 411220

BIG TRASH.
LP: WX 284
MC: WX 284C

CLOSE TO THE BONE.
Tracks: / Follow your heart / Bush baby / Get that love / 20th Century / Long goodbye / Stillwaters / Savage Moon / Gold fever / Dancing in your shoes / Perfect day.
LP: 208143
MC: 408143

GREATEST HITS: THOMPSON TWINS.
Tracks: / Hold me now / Lay your hands on me / King for a day / We are detective / Sister of mercy / Lies / Long goodbye, The / Doctor, doctor / Don't mess with Doctor dream / Gap, The / You take me up / Love on your side / Get that love / Revolution.
LP: SMR 092
MC: SMC 092

GREATEST MIXES / BEST OF THE THOMPSON TWINS.
Tracks: / In the name of love '88 (version) / Lies (remix) / Love on your side (remix) / Lay your hands on me.
LP: AL 8542

HERE'S TO FUTURE DAYS.
Tracks: / Don't mess with Doctor Dream / Lay your hands on me / Future days / You killed the clown / Revolution / King for a day / Love is the law / Emperor's new clothes, The (part 1) / Tokyo / Breakaway.
LP: 208979
MC: 408979
LP: 207164
MC: 407164

INTO THE GAP.
Tracks: / Doctor Doctor / You take me up / Day after day / No peace for the wicked / Sister of mercy / Into the gap / Hold me now / Storm on the sea / Who can stop the rain.
LP: 205971
MC: 405971

PRODUCT OF.....
Tracks: / When I see you / Politics / Slave trade / Could be her could be you / Make believe / Don't go away / Price, The / Animal laugh / Anything is good enough / Product of, A / Perfect game / Vendredi saint / Another fantasy.
LP: FA 3074
MC: TCFA 3074
LP: TELP 1

PRODUCT OF.../SET.
Tracks: / When I see you / Politics / Slave trade / Could be her could be you / Make believe / Don't go away / Price oumma aularesso / Anything is good enough / Product of, A / Perfect game / Vendredi Saint / In the name of love / Living in Europe / Bouncing / Tok tok / Good gosh / Rowe, The / Runaway / Fool's gold / Crazy dog / Blind.
MC: XTWO 22

QUICKSTEP AND SIDE KICK.
Tracks: / Kamikaze / Love on your side / If you were here / Judy do / Tears / Watching / We are detective / Love lies bleeding / All fall out / Lies / Tears.
LP: 41 3129 1
MC: 41 3129 4
LP: FA 3129
MC: TCFA 3129
LP: 204924
MC: 404924

SET.
Tracks: / In the name of love / Living in Europe / Bouncing / Tok tok / Good gosh / Rowe, The / Runaway / Another fantasy / Fool's gold / Crazy dog / Blind.
LP: FA 41 3109 1
MC: FA 41 3109 4
LP: FA 3109
MC: TCFA 3109
LP: TELP 2
MC: TEMC 2

WHO WANTS TO BE A MILLIONAIRE? (See under Harry, Debbie - Well, did you evah).

Thomson, Ally

DECEPTION IS AN ART.
Tracks: / Safe and warm / Foolish child / Don't hold back / Art gallery / Shells lay scattered / One and only / Man of the earth / Simple song / Secrets hide inside / Someone in motion.
LP: AMLH 64846

FALLING FOR YOU.
MC: CWGR 080

TRUCK DRIVIN' MAN.
MC: BWB 001

Thor

KEEP THE DOGS AWAY.
LP: GULP 1042

LIVE IN DETROIT.
Tracks: / Thunder on the tundra / Let the blood run red / Knock 'm' down / Rock the city / Lightning strikes / Anger / Keep the dogs away / Hot flames / Now comes the storm / When gods collide.
LP: RAWLP 008
MC: RAWTC 008

ONLY THE STRONG.
LP: RR 9790

UNCHAINED.
LP: NOISE 102

Thorburn, Billy

LET'S BREAK THE GOOD NEWS.
Tracks: / Let's break the good news / With the wind and the rain in your hair / Wish me luck as you wave me goodbye / I'd never fall in love again / All over the place / All alone with my shadow / Memory of a rose, The / Love makes the world go round / It's foolish but it's fun / Faithful forever / If I could paint a memory / There'll come another day / I-spy / You're so sweet to remember / Too many irons in the fire / I'm happy for your sake.
LP: SH 504
MC: TCSH 504

ORGAN, THE DANCE BAND AND ME, THE (Thorburn, Billy & Robinson Cleaver).
Tracks: / Never took a lesson in my life / You made me care / It costs so little but means so much / I hear bluebirds / Riding on a rainbow / In a little rocky valley / Nearness of you, The / Scatterbrain / Arm in arm / I'll never make the same mistake again / What do you think these ruby lips were made for? / Safe in my heart / Don't ever walk in the shadows / Journey to a star / I'm all alone / There'll come another day / I've seen you before / It's always you.
LP: PLE 514
MC: TC-PLE 514

Thore, Francke

ART OF RUMANIAN PAN FLUTE, THE.
MC: SC 021

GOOD AS GOLD (See Quay, Judy) (Thore, Francke/Judy Quay).

PIPE DREAMS.
Tracks: / Mon amour / Greensleeves for pipes / Solvejg's song / Way he makes me feel, The / Entracte / Pipe dreams / Spain / Blue rondo a la turk / Tretemps nippon / Thais meditation / Carillon / Thorn birds.
LP: PRIM 6002
MC: ZPRIM 6002

Thore Jederby

MORNING JUMP (Thore Jederby Jazz Groups(1940-1948)).
LP: DRLP 51

Thoreau, Henry David

CIVIL DISOBEDIENCE (MacLeish, Archibald).
MC: 1263

THOREAU'S WORLD.
MCSET: 2052

WALDEN (MacLeish, Archibald).
MC: 1261

Thorn Birds...

THORN BIRDS (LOVE THEME) (See under Martin, Juan).

THORN BIRDS (THEME FROM) (See under Mancini, Henry).

Thorn, Tracey

DISTANT SHORE, A.
Tracks: / Small town girl / Simply couldn't care / Seascape / Femme fatale / Dreamy / Plain sailing / New opened eyes / Too happy.
LP: BRED 35
MC: CMRED 35

Thornberry, Russell

TEN DOLLAR SONGS.
LP: GES 5009

Thornborough, Julie

I'M YOUR COUNTRY GIRL.
Tracks: / Everybody's reachin' / I was raised on country sunshine / Family Bible / I saw the light / Loving him was easier / I'm your country girl / Crying steel guitar waltz / Let me be there / Send me the pillow that you dream on / Louisiana bayou drive / Take me to your world.
LP: FHR 065

Thornbury Band

SEVERNSHIRE UP.
LP: LKLP 7004

Thorne, Stephen

BLUE ICE, THE (See also Hammond Innes).

PERFECT GALLOWS (See also Peter Dickinson).

Thornhill, Claude

1941 AND 1947 (Thornhill, Claude & His Orchestra).
LP: CLP 19

CLAUDE THORNHILL AND HIS ORCHESTRA (1947) (Thornhill, Claude & His Orchestra).
Tracks: / Snowfall / Robbins' nest / Cabin in the sky / Deed I do / Happy stranger / Jealous / Breezing along with the breeze / Just about this time last night / Donna Lee / Poor little rich girl / Polka dots and moonbeams / I may be wrong / Adios / Sometimes I'm happy / Puttin' and takin' / Sunday drivin' / Anthropology / Swinging down the lane.
LP: HSR 108
LP: HMP 5040

SNOWFALL (Thornhill, Claude & His Orchestra).
LP: FS 212

SONG IS YOU, THE.
Tracks: / Anthropology / Baia / Arab dance / Royal Garden blues / Polka dots and moonbeams / Sometimes I'm happy / September song / Godchild / Robbins' nest / I don't know why / Song is you, The / April in Paris / La paloma / Lover man / Elevation.
LP: HEP 17

TAPESTRIES.
Tracks: / Snowfall / Stop, you're breaking my heart / Portrait of a Guinea farm / Autumn nocturne / I'm somebody nobody loves / Smiles / Night and day / Buster's last stand / There's a small hotel / I don't know why (I just do) / Under the willow tree / Arab dance / I get the blues when it rains / Sunday kind of love, A / Early Autumn / La paloma / La paloma / Warsaw concerto / Thrivin' on a riff (take 1) / Thrivin' on a riff (take 2) / Sorta kinda / Robbins' nest / Lover man / Polka dots and moonbeams / Donna Lee / How am I to know? / For Heaven's sake / Whip-poor-will / That old feeling / Coquette / Yardbird suite / Let's call it a day.
2LP: AFSD 1040

Thornhill, Mac

MAC THORNHILL.
LP: . . . . THORN 1
MC: . . . . ZCTHORN 1

Thornton, Clifford

PANTHER AND THE LASH.
LP: . . . . AM 6113

Thornton, Phil

CLOUD SCULPTING.
Tracks: / Solid air / Empty canvass over the sea / Rising thermal / Castles in the air / Cloud sculptures A & B / As above so below / Goldfish don't whistle.
LP: . . . . KNEWL 02
MC: . . . . KNEWMC 02

EDGE OF DREAMS.
MC: . . . . C 142

FOREVER DREAM.
LP: . . . . LPLTD 002
MC: . . . . MCLTD 002

Thornton, Willie Mae

BALL AND CHAIN.
LP: . . . . ARHOOLIE 1039

BIG MAMA THORNTON.
MC: . . . . C 204
LP: . . . . ARHOOLIE 1032

IN EUROPE.
LP: . . . . ARHOOLIE 1028

QUIT SNOOPIN' ROUND MY DOOR (Thornton, Willie Mae 'Big Mama').
Tracks: / Rockabye baby / Hard times / I ain't no fool either / You don't move me no more / No Jody for me / Let your tears fall baby / Every time I think of you / Mischievious boogie / How come / Just like a dog / I've searched the world over / Nightmare / Story of my blues / Stop a-hoppin on me / Laugh laugh laugh / Fish.
LP: . . . . CH 170

STRONGER THAN DIRT/THE WAY IT IS.
Tracks: / Born under a bad sign / Hound dog / Ball and chain / Summertime / Rollin' stone / Lets go get stoned / Funky Broadway / That lucky old sun / Ain't nothin' you can do / I shall be released / Little red rooster / One black rat / Rock me baby / Wade in the water / Sweet little angel / Baby please don't go / Got my mojo working / Watermelon man / Don't need no doctor.
2LP: . . . . CDX 24
MC: . . . . TCCDX 24

YOU OLE HOUN' DAWG.
Tracks: / Hound dog / Walking blues / My man called me / Cotton pickin' blues / Willie Mae's blues / Big change, The / Partnership blues / I'm all fed up / I smell a rat / I just can't help myself / Yes baby / Tarzan and the signified monkey / They call me Big Mama / Before day (Big Mama's blues) / Me and my chauffeur.
LP: . . . . CHAD 277

Thorogood, George

BAD TO THE BONE (Thorogood, George & The Destroyers).
Tracks: / Back to Wentsville / Blue highway / Nobody but me / It's a sin / New boogie chillen / Bad to the bone / Miss Luann / As the years go passing by / No particular place to go / Wanted man.
LP: . . . . AML 3024
LP: . . . . BGOLP 94
MC: . . . . BGOMC 94

BETTER THAN THE REST (Thorogood, George & The Destroyers).
Tracks: / In the night / I'm ready / Goodbye baby / Howlin' for my darlin' / My weakness / Nadine / My way / You're gonna miss me / Worried about my baby / Huckle up baby.
LP: . . . . MCL 1623
MC: . . . . MCLC 1623

BORN TO BE BAD.
Tracks: / Shake your moneymaker / You talk too much / Highway 49 / Born to be bad / You can't catch me / I'm ready / Treat her right / I really like girls / Smokestack lightning / I'm movin' on.
LP: . . . . AML 3124
MC: . . . . TCAML 3124

GEORGE THOROGOOD AND THE DESTROYERS (Thorogood, George & The Destroyers).
Tracks: / Who do you love / Bottom of the sea / Night time / I drink alone / One bourbon one scotch one beer / Alley oop / Madison blues / Bad to the bone / Sky is crying / Reelin' and rockin'.
LP: . . . . ROUNDER 3013
MC: . . . . ROUNDER 3013C
LP: . . . . AML 3108
MC: . . . . TCAML 3108

GEORGE THOROGOOD & THE DESTROYERS (Thorogood, George & The Destroyers).
Tracks: / You got to lose / Madison blues / One bourbon, one scotch, one beer / Kind hearted woman / Can't stop lovin' my baby / Ride on Josephine / Homesick boy / John Hardy / I'll change my style / Delaware slide.
LP: . . . . FIEND 55
MC: . . . . FIENDCASS 55
LP: . . . . SNTF 760

LIVE: GEORGE THOROGOOD (Thorogood, George & The Destroyers).
Tracks: / Who do you love? / Bottom of the sea / Night time / I drink alone / One bourbon, one scotch, one beer / Alley oop / Madison blues / Bad to the bone / Sky is crying, The / Reelin' and rockin'.
LP: . . . . FA 3211
MC: . . . . TCFA 3211

MAVERICK (Thorogood, George & The Destroyers).
Tracks: / Gear jammer / I drink alone / Willie and the hand jive / What a price / Long gone / Dixie fried / Crawling king snake / Memphis Marie / Woman with the blues / Go go go / Ballad of Maverick.
LP: . . . . EJ 2402821
MC: . . . . EJ 2402824

MORE GEORGE THOROGOOD & THE DESTROYERS (Thorogood, George & The Destroyers).
Tracks: / I'm wanted / Kids from Philly / One way ticket / Bottom of the sea / Night time / Tip on in / Goodbye baby / House of blue lights / Just can't make it / Restless.
LP: . . . . FIEND 61
LP: . . . . SNTF 850
LP: . . . . ROUNDER 3045
MC: . . . . ROUNDER 3045 C

MOVE IT ON OVER (Thorogood, George and The Destroyers).
Tracks: / Move it on over / Who do you love / Sky is crying, The / Cocaine blues / It wasn't me / That same thing / So much trouble / I'm just your good thing / Baby, please set a date / New Hawaiian boogie.
MC: . . . . FIENDCASS 58
LP: . . . . SNTF 781
LP: . . . . ROUNDER 3024
MC: . . . . ROUNDER 3024C

Thorpe, Billy

CHILDREN OF THE SUN.
Tracks: / Children of the sun / We're leaving / We welcome you / Solar anthem / Beginning / Wrapped in the chains of your love / Dream maker / Simple life / Goddess of the night.
LP: 2391 424

Thorpe, Bo

SWINGING WITH BO, 1982.
Tracks: / Swinging with Bo / Where is the love / New York, New York / Ridin' 1.95 / I won't last a day without you / Razzmajazz / Native New Yorker / Thorpe plays Gershwin / I feel the earth move / Primitive man.
LP: . . . . HSR 315

Thorpe, Kay

NOT WANTED ON VOYAGE.
MC: . . . . PMB 008

Those Golden No.1's

THOSE GOLDEN NO.1'S (Various artists).
MC: . . . . AM 16

Those Nervous Animals

HYPERSPACE.
LP: . . . . TA 2015

Thought Criminals

YOU ONLY THINK TWICE.
LP: . . . . LRF 082

THP Orchestra

THP2 - TENDER IS THE NIGHT.
Tracks: / Tender is the night / If paradise is half as nice / Music is all you need / Weekend two step.
LP: . . . . TRAIN 5

Thrash..

F* ME I'M RICH** (Various artists).
LP: . . . . DAMP 104

FAREWELL TO ARMS (Various artists).
LP: . . . . NB 9

FAREWELL TO ARMS, A (A Japanese Hardcore Compilation) (Various artists).
Tracks: / Kill ugly pop: *Various artists* / Cops: *Various artists* / June: *Various artists* / I like cola: *Various artists* / Eyes, The: *Various artists* / Distortion faith: *Various artists* / Pressing on: *Various artists* / Jerusalem: *Various artists* / Ghost candle: *Various artists.*
LP: . . . . NB 009

FAST FORWARD TO HELL (Various artists).
LP: . . . . VOVC 664
MC: . . . . VOVCC 664

GRINDCRUSHER (The Earache sampler) (Various artists).
Tracks: / Chapel of ghouls: *Morbid Angel* / Exhume to consume: *Carcass* / Missing link, The: *Napalm Death* / Through the eye of terror: *Bolt Thunder* / Party and fight: *Filthy Christians* / He nota home: *Spazztic* Blurr (Only on CD.) / Horrendify and kill: *Sore Throat* (Only on CD.) / Radiation sickness: *Repulsion* / Streetcleaner: *Godflesh* / Dead shall rise: *Terrorizer* / Straight jacket: *Intense Degree* / Colostomy grab bag: *Old Lady Drivers* (Only on CD.) / Heresy: *Dead (film)* (Only on CD.) / Divisions: *Unseen Terror* (Only on CD.).
LP: . . . . MOSH 12
MC: . . . . MOSH 12 MC

MELTING PLOT (Various artists).
LP: . . . . SST 249
MC: . . . . SSTC 249

NEW YORK THRASH (Various artists).
MC: . . . . A 113

NORTH AMERICAN THRASH ASSAULT (Various artists).
LP: . . . . BOXLP 1

NORTH AMERICAN THRASH ASSAULT VOL.2 (Various artists).
LP: . . . . BOXLP 2

PLEASURES IN LIFE (Various artists).
LP: 082929

PROGRAM ANIHILATOR 2 (Various artists).
LP: . . . . SST 213
MC: . . . . SSTC 213

SPEED METAL HELL, VOL.3 (Various artists).
LP: . . . . NRR 29

STARS ON THRASH (Various artists).
LP: . . . . RR 94981

THRASH METAL ATTACK (Various artists).
LP: . . . . NRR 27
MC: . . . . NRC 27
MC: . . . . NRC 29

THRASH METAL VOL. 1 (See under Rather Nasty Dream..) (Various artists).

THRASH THE WALL (Various artists).
LP: . . . . RR 93931
MC: . . . . RR 93934

THRASH TILL DEATH (Various artists).
LP: . . . . PUS 0012-17

UK THRASH ASSAULT (Various artists).
LP: . . . . CFMT 1

Thrasher

BURNING AT THE SPEED OF LIGHT.
LP: . . . . MFN 45

Thrashing Doves

BEDROCK VICE.
Tracks: / Beautiful imbalance / Matchstick flotilla / Ginding stone / Killer for you / Rochdale house / Biba's basement / Castroville street / Magdalena / Tinderbox man / Northern civil war party / Jesus on the payroll / Grinding stone.
LP: . . . . AMA 5149
MC: . . . . AMC 5149

THRASHING DOVES.
LP: . . . . UNKNOWN

TROUBLE IN THE HOME.
Tracks: / Reprobate's hymn / Angel visit / Sister deals / Lorelei / Trouble in the home / Another deadly sunset / Mary Mary / Like heartbreak / Late show, The / Candy woman / Domestic rainchild.
LP: . . . . AMA 5235
MC: . . . . AMC 5235

Threadgill, Henry

EASILY SLIP INTO ANOTHER WORLD.
Tracks: / I can't wait till I get home / Black hands bejewelled / Spotted Dick is pudding / Let me look down your throat or say ah / My rock / Hail / Award the squadtett.
LP: . . . . PL 83025

RAG BUSH AND ALL.
Tracks: / Off the rag / Devil is on the loose & dancing with a monkey / Gift / Sweet holy rag.
LP: . . . . PL 83052
MC: . . . . PK 83052

YOU KNOW THE NUMBER (Threadgill, Henry Sextet).
Tracks: / Bermuda blues / Silver and gold baby / Thomas Cole, Theme from / Good times / To be announced / Those who eat cookies.
LP: . . . . PL 83013
MC: . . . . PK 83013

Threads

OUT AND ABOUT (See Risk) (Threads and the Risk).

TOGETHER AGAIN (see under Risk) (Threads and the Risk).

Three Billy Goats (bk)

THREE BILLY GOATS GRUFF (well loved tales up to age 9) (Unknown narrator(s)).
MC: . . . . PLB 93

THREE BILLY GOATS GRUFF.
MC: . . . . STC 303 B

Three Bites Of ...

THREE BITES OF THE APPLE (Film Soundtrack) (Various artists).
LP: . . . . MCA 25010
MC: . . . . MCAC 25010

Three Choirs Festival

THREE CHOIRS FESTIVAL (250th. Anniversary) (Various artists).
LP: . . . . LPB 772

Three Colours

THIS IS NORWOOD.
Tracks: / Raise the roof / Run run run / Not what I heard / Sitting pretty / Eventually / White stripes / Hop-a-long / Burn bright.
LP: . . . . SELECT 3

Three Deuces

STOMPIN' AND STRIDIN'.
LP: . . . . SOS 1185

Three Dog Night

EVERY ONE A MASTERPIECE.
Tracks: / It's for you / Change is gonna come, A / Mama told me not to come / Woman / I can hear you calling / I'll be creepin' / It ain't easy / I've got enough heartache / Joy to the world / Murder in my heart for the judge / My impersonal life / Freedom for the stallion / My old Kentucky home / Shamballa / I'd be so happy / Till the world ends / Everybody's a masterpiece.
LP: . . . . SEE 93

GOLDEN GREATS: THREE DOG NIGHT.
Tracks: / Try a little tenderness / One / Easy to be hard / Eli's coming / Celebrate / Mama told me not to come / Out in the country / One man band / Joy of the world / Liar / Old fashioned love song, An / Never been to Spain / Family of man / Black and white / Play something sweet / Let me serenade you.
LP: . . . . MCM 5022
MC: . . . . MCMC 5022

GREATEST HITS: THREE DOG NIGHT.
LP: . . . . BRLP 57
MC: . . . . BRMC 57

JOY TO THE WORLD (OLD GOLD) (See Under Woodstock (Old Gold)).

Three Fat Women...

THREE FAT WOMEN OF ANTIBES (Somerset Maugham) (Burden, Hugh (nar)).
MC: . . . . TTC/WSM 6

Three For The Road

THREE FOR THE ROAD (Film Soundtrack) (Various artists).
LP: . . . . STV 81319

Three Fugitives (film)

THREE FUGITIVES (Original Soundtrack) (Various artists).
LP: . . . . VS 5219
MC: . . . . VSC 5219

Three Guys Naked..

THREE GUYS NAKED FROM THE WAIST DOWN (Off Broadway cast) (Various artists).
Tracks: / Overture: *Various artists* / Promise of greatness: *Various artists* / Angry guy/ Lovely day: *Various* artists / Don't wanna be no superstar: *Various artists* / Operator: *Various artists* / Screaming clocks (The dummies song): *Various artists* / History of stand-up comedy, The: *Various artists* / Dreams of heaven: *Various* artists / Kamikaze kaberaet: *Various artists* / American dream: *Various artists* / What a ride: *Various* artists / Hello fellas TV special world tour, The: *Various artists* / Father now, A: *Various artists* / Three guys naked from the waist down theme: *Various artists* / I don't believe in heroes anymore: *Various artists* / Finale: *Various artists.*
LP: . . . . TER 1100
MC: . . . . ZCTER 1100

Three Jacksons

36 ACCORDION SUCCESSEN VAN THE THREE JACKSONS.
LP: 022 58251
MC: 222 58251

Three Johns

ATOM DRUM BOP.
MC: . . . . ABTC 010

DEATH OF EVERYTHING.
Tracks: / King is dead, The / Moonlight on Vermont / Spin me round / Humbug / Never and always / Bullshit, Aco / Go

ahead bikini / Nonsense spews from my song machine / Downhearted blues.
LP: . . . . MOTLP 20

EAT YOUR SONS.
LP: . . . . TUPLP 018
MC: . . . . TUPMC 018

LIVE IN CHICAGO - THREE JOHNS.
LP: . . . . LAST 001

ROCK 'N' ROLL DEMOCRACY.
LP: . . . . ABT 015

WORLD BY STORM.
LP: . . . . ABT 012
MC: . . . . ABTC 012

Three Legged Dog

LOADED.
LP: . . . . BLP 4036

Three Little Girls

THREE LITTLE GIRLS IN BLUE (Film soundtrack) (Various artists).
LP: . . . . HS 410

Three Little Pigs (bk)

THREE LITTLE PIGS (well loved tales age up to age 9) (Unknown narrator(s)).
LP: . . . . ST 3963
MC: . . . . PLB 51
MC: . . . . STC 302C
MC: . . . . STK 004

THREE LITTLE PIGS.
Tracks: / Three little pigs.
MLP: . . . . D 303

Three Little Words

WORDS AND MUSIC/THREE LITTLE WORDS (see under Words & Music) (Various artists).

Three Men in a Boat

THREE MEN IN A BOAT (see Jerome, Jerome K.) (Heller, Martin (nar)).

THREE MEN IN A BOAT (see under Jerome, Jerome K.) (Nicholas, Jeremy (nar)).

Three Minute Symphony

THREE MINUTE SYMPHONY (Various artists).
LP: . . . . XX 002

Three Peppers

THAT'S ALRIGHT (See under Eddie Cole) (Cole, Eddie/Three Peppers).

Three Sounds

BABE'S BLUES.
Tracks: / Babe's blues / Wait a minute / Work song / Blue Daniel / Sweet and lovely / Shiny stockings / Walking the floor over you / Between the devil and the deep blue sea / Stairway to the stars / Lazy cat.
LP: . . . . BST 84434

Three Strangers (bk)

THREE STRANGERS, THE (Hardy, Thomas) (Morant, Richard).
MC: . . . . TTC/TH 01

Three Suns

THREE SUNS, THE (1949-1957).
LP: . . . . CLP 75

Three Teens Kill Four

NO MOTIVE.
LP: . . . . LD 3

Three Times Dope

LIVE FROM ACKNIKULOUS.
LP: . . . . CBLP 7

Three Wishes...

THREE WISHES FOR JAMIE (Original Broadway cast) (Various artists).
LP: . . . . DS 15012

Three Worlds...

THREE WORLDS OF GULLIVER (Film soundtrack) (Various artists).
LP: . . . . CN 4003

Threepenny Opera

THREEPENNY OPERA (New York Festival production) (Various artists).
LP: . . . . PS 34326

THREEPENNY OPERA (Original Broadway cast) (Various artists).
Tracks: / Overture: *Various artists* / Ballad of Mack the Knife: *Various artists* / Morning anthem: *Various* artists / Instead-of-song: *Various artists* / Wedding song: *Various artists* / Pirate Jenny: *Various* artists / Army song: *Various artists* / Love song: *Various artists* / Ballad of dependency: *Various artists*/ Mellodrama/ Polly's song: *Various artists* / Ballad of the easy life: *Various artists* / World is mean, The: *Various artists* / Barbara song: *Various artists* / Tango ballad: *Various artists* / Jealousy duet: *Various* artists / How to survive: *Various artists* / Useless song: *Various artists* / Solomon song: *Various artists*/ Call from the grave: *Various artists* / Death message: *Various artists* / Finale: *Various artists* / Mounted messenger: *Various artists.*
LP: . . . . TER 1101
MC: . . . . ZCTER 1101

Threeway Street

DRUNKARDS AND LOVERS.
Tracks: / Marvo the mighty magician / Carnival song (Tune of a Dutch carnival melody.) / Drunkards and lovers / I wish you'd squeeze me (like you squeeze your squeezebox) / Midnight / Al comes around again / Money come the hard way easy go / Derek's hotel / When the circus comes to town / Moving on out Pierre / Unknown soldier, The / Fragments of a world.
LP: . . . . FE 048
MC: . . . . FE 048 C

Three-Wheel

AT THE ELEVENTH HOUR.
LP: . . . . SFA 057

Threshing...

THRESHING AND CULTIVATING BY STEAM POWER.
LP: . . . . ABBEY 607

Thrill Kill Kult

CONFESSIONS OF A KNIFE.
LP: . . . . WAX 089 LP
MC: . . . . WAX 089 MC

NAIVE (REMIX) (See Under KMFDM) (Thrill Kill Kult & KMFDM).

Thriller

MAKING OF MICHAEL JACKSON'S THRILLER (See under Jackson, Michael) (Jackson, Michael).

Thriller U

ON AND ON.
LP: . . . . MLLP 002
MC: . . . . MLC 002

PEACE (See also under Flourgon) (Thriller U & Flourgon).

THIEF (SINGLE) (See Under Yellowman) (Thriller U & Yellowman).

TWO GOOD TO BE TRUE (U, Thriller & Admiral Tibett).
LP: . . . . VPRL 1062

WAITING FOR YOU.
LP: . . . . LALP 31

YOUNG SINGLE AND FRESH.
LP: . . . . DSR 1673

Throbbing Gristle

2ND ANNUAL REPORT.
LP: . . . . FR 2001

20 JAZZ FUNK GREATS.
LP: . . . . MIR 003

D.O.A..
LP: . . . . MIR 002

D.O.A. THE THIRD AND FINAL REPORT OF THROBBING GRISTLE.
LP: . . . . IR 0004

GREATEST HITS: THROBBING GRISTLE.
LP: . . . . ROUGHUS 23

HEATHEN EARTH.
LP: . . . . MIR 004

IN THE SHADOW OF THE SUN.
LP: . . . . JAMS 35

IT'S THE PSYCHICK SACRIFICE.
LP: . . . . KILL 1

MISSION IN DEAD SOULS.
LP: . . . . MIR 005

NOTHING SHORT OF TOTAL WAR.
MC: . . . . CFC 016
LP: . . . . CFC 001

ONCE UPON A TIME.
LP: . . . . CAS 001J
LP: . . . . Unknown

SACRIFICE.
Tracks: / Weapon training / Convincing people / Hamburger lady / Chat up / Day song / Persuasion.
LP: . . . . DOJOLP 29

SECOND ANNUAL REPORT.
LP: . . . . MIR 001

SPECIAL TREATMENT.
LP: . . . . MD 01-1

THROBBING GRISTLE.
LPS: . . . . FX 1

Throbs

LANGUAGE OF THIEVES AND VAGABONDS, THE.
LP: . . . . DGC 24316
MC: . . . . DGCC 24316

Through The Looking...

THROUGH THE LOOKING GLASS (see Carroll, Lewis) (Greenwood, Joan/ Stanley Holloway).

Thrower, Percy

GREENFINGER GUIDE (Thrower, Percy & June Whitfield).
LP: . . . . LEG 10
MC: . . . . LEGC 10

GUIDE TO GOOD GARDENING.
LP: . . . . RES 002

Throwing Muses

FAT SKIER, THE.
LP: . . . . CAD 706
MC: . . . . CADC 706

HOUSE TORNADO.
Tracks: / Colder / Mexican women / River, The / Juno / Marriage tree / Run letter / Saving grace / Drive / Downtown / Giant / Walking in the dark.
LP: . . . . CAD 802
MC: . . . . CADC 802

HUNK PAPA.
Tracks: / Devil's roof / Dizzy / Dragonhead / Fall down / Angel / Burrow, The / Bea / No parachutes / Say goodbye / I'm alive / Mania / Take.
LP: . . . . CAD 901
MC: . . . . CADC 901

REAL RAMONA, THE.
LP: . . . . CAD 1002
MC: . . . . CADC 1002

THROWING MUSES.
Tracks: / Call me / Green / Hate my way / Vicky's box / Rabbits dying / America (she can't say no) / Fear / Stand up / Soul soldier / Delicate cutters.
LP: . . . . CAD 607
MC: . . . . CADC 607

Thu, Mo Cheol

LE CIARCAN MAC MATHUNA.
LP: . . . . CEF 064

Thule

WHEEL.
LP: . . . . WIJ 7

Thumbelina (bk)

THUMBELINA (Well Loved Tales Age Up to 9).
MC: . . . . PLB 65

THUMBELINA (Asher, Jane (nar)).
MC: . . . . LPMC 211

THUMBELINA.
MC: . . . . STK 014

THUMBELINA (See under Anderson, Hans Christian).

THUMBELINA/THE LITTLE MATCH GIRL.
MC: . . . . LP 211

Thunder

BACKSTREET SYMPHONY.
Tracks: / She's so fine / Dirty love / Don't wait for me / Higher ground / Until my dying day / Backstreet symphony / Love walked in / Englishman on holiday, An / Girl's going out of her head / Gimme some lovin' / Distant thunder (Not on album.).
LP: . . . . EMC 3570
MC: . . . . TCEMC 3570
LPPD: . . . . EMCPD 3570

Thunder Mountain

THUNDER MOUNTAIN (See under Grey, Zane) (Grey, Zane).

Thunder, Sam

MANOEUVERS.
LPPD: . . . . BULP 5

Thunder, Shelley

BACKBONE OF THE NATION.
MC: . . . . MCT 1079
LP: . . . . PLPS 1079

FRESH OUT THE PACK.
MC: . . . . MCT 1016
LP: . . . . MLPS 1016

SMALL HORSE WOMAN.
LP: . . . . MMLP 006
MC: . . . . HLP 015

Thunderball

THUNDERBALL (James Bond Film Soundtrack) (Various artists).
Tracks: / Thunderball, Theme from: *Jones, Tom* / Chateau fight: *Various artists* / Electrocution - searching Lippe's room: *Various artists* / Switching the body: *Various artists* / Vulcan crash landing - loading bombs into disc: *Various artists* / Cape Martinique - Mr. Kiss Kiss Bang Bang: *Various artists* / Thunderball: *Various artists*/ Death of Fiona: *Various artists* / Bond below Disco Volante: *Various artists* / Search for vulcan: *Various artists* / 007: *Various artists* / Mr. Kiss Kiss Bang Bang: *Various artists.*
LP: . . . . EMS 1268
MC: . . . . TCEMS 1268
LP: . . . . IC 054 82923
MC: 90628.4

Thunderbirds Are Go

THUNDERBIRDS ARE GO (Film soundtrack) (Various artists).
Tracks: / Thunderbirds theme: *Various artists* / Alan's dream: *Various artists* / Joie de vivre: *Various* artists / Martian mystery: *Various artists* / Thunderbirds theme (reprise): *Various artists* / Astronauts in trouble: *Various artists* / Zero X theme: *Various artists* / That dangerous game: *Various artists*/ Swinging star: *Various artists* / San Marino: *Various artists* / Jeremiah: *Various artists* / Tracy Island: *Various artists.*
LP: . . . . FILM 018
MC: . . . . FILMC 018

Thundercats

THUNDERCATS.
MC: . . . . 0 00 102213 X

THUNDERCATS: HO - THE MOVIE.
MC: 0 00 102149 4

THUNDERCATS: QUEST FOR THE MAGIC CRYSTAL.
MC: 0 00 102148 6

Thunderhead

BEHIND THE EIGHT BALL.
Tracks: / Behind the eight ball / Ready to roll / Take it to the highway / You don't keep me satisfied / Fire's burning / Let go / Open all night / Life in the city / Just another lover / Straight shooter / Take me to the limit.
LP: . . . . LLP 127
MC: . . . . LLK 127

BUSTED AT THE BORDER.
LP: . . . . MFN 110
MC: . . . . TMFN 110

Thunders, Johnny

ALBUM COLLECTION.
LPS: . . . . JT BOX 1

BOOTLEGGING THE BOOTLEGGERS.
Tracks: / You can't put your arms around a memory / Personality crisis / Sad vacation / I can tell / Little queenie / Stepping stone / As tears go by.
LP: . . . . FREUD 30
MC: . . . . FREUDC 30

COPY CATS (Thunders, Johnny & Patti Palladin).
LP: . . . . FREUD 20
MC: . . . . FREUDC 20

DTK - LIVE '77 (Thunders, Johnny & The Heartbreakers).
LP: . . . . FREUD 01
LPPD: . . . . FREUD P01

GANG WAR.
LP: . . . . DM 003

HURT ME.
LP: . . . . ROSE 26

IN COLD BLOOD.
LP: . . . . ROSE 18

LAMF (Thunders, Johnny & The Heartbreakers).
LP: . . . . FREUD 04
LPPD: . . . . FREUD P04
MC: . . . . FREUDC 04
LP: 2409 218

LIVE AT LYCEUM BALLROOM, LONDON 1984.
LP: . . . . ABCLP 2

LIVE AT MAX'S, KANSAS CITY (Thunders, Johnny & The Heartbreakers).
Tracks: / Intro / Milk me / Chinese rocks / Get off the phone / London / Take a chance / One track mind / All by myself / Let's go / I love you / Can't keep my eyes on you / I wanna be loved / Do you love me.
LP: . . . . BEGA 9

LIVE AT THE LYCEUM (Thunders, Johnny & The Heartbreakers).
LP: . . . . RRLP 134
MC: . . . . RRLC 134

QUE SERA SERA.
LP: . . . . FREUD 09
MC: . . . . FREUDC 09
LPPD: . . . . FREUD P09

SO ALONE.
Tracks: / Pipe line / You can't put your arm around a memory / Great big kiss / Ask me no questions / Leave me alone / Daddy rollin' stone / London boys / Untouchable / Subway train / Downtown.
LP: . . . . RAL 1

STATIONS OF THE CROSS.
MC: . . . . A 146
LP: . . . . DANLP 043
MC: . . . . DANMC 043

TOO MUCH JUNKIE BUSINESS.
MC: . . . . A 118
LP: . . . . DANLP 044
MC: . . . . DANMC 044

Thunderstick

BEAUTY AND THE BEASTS.
Tracks: / Contact angel / Afraid of the dark / Another turnaround / Heartbeat (in the night) / Rich girls (don't cry) / In the name of the father / Long way to go.
LP: . . . . THBL 008
MC: . . . . THBC 008

Thurber, James (aut)

THIRTEEN CLOCKS, THE (Ustinov, Peter).
MCSET: 2089

UNICORN IN THE GARDEN, THE (Ustinov, Peter).
MC: 1398

Thurlow, Matthias

CORNUCOPIA.
LP: . . . . IRS 949 162

Thurrock Marching

THURROCK MARCHING BRASS.
LP: . . . . GRS 1096

Thursday's Children

THURSDAY CHILDREN: 1965-69.
LP: . . . . VOXX 200.052

Thurso & Donreal...

NORTH OF THE HIGHLANDS (Thurso & Dounreay Strathspey & Reel Society).
Tracks: / Cork Hill (Pipe jig.) / Curlew, The / Hymn to the saviour / Alistair McCallum of Cairndow / Pipe major Jim Christie of Wick / Miss Jean Milligan / Harry's reel / Waves of Tory, The / Donald B McTaggart / O Luaidh / Longueval / King George V's army / MV Norland / Helen Black of Inveran / Humours of California, The / Little beauty waltz / Rope waltz, The / Stronsay waltz, The / Norwegian waltz / Chris Duncan two step, The / Ballintore fishermen / Heroes of Longhope / Wick and thurso marches.
LP: . . . . LAP 112
MC: . . . . LAP 112C

Thurston, Bobby

MAIN ATTRACTION.
Tracks: / Is something wrong with you / Main attraction / Love makes it complete / Keep it going / I know you feel like I feel / Very last drop / I really don't mean it / Life is what you make it.
LP: . . . . EPC 85070

SWEETEST PIECE OF THE PIE.
LP: . . . . HH 1135

YOU GOT WHAT IT TAKES.
Tracks: / You got what it takes / I wanna do it with you / Check out the groove / I want your body / Sittin' in the park.
LP: . . . . EPC 84257

Ti Celeste

OU PE KARE.
LP: . . . . HDD 2423

Tiamat

SUMERIAN CITY.
LP: . . . . CMFT 006

Tibbett, Lawrence

LAWRENCE TIBBETT (Gerschwin, Rossini, Verdi, Bizet).
MC: . . . . GK 87808

Tibbetts, Steve

BIG MAP IDEA.
Tracks: / Black mountain side / Black year / Big idea / Wish / Station / Start / Mile 234 / 100 moons / Wait / 3 letters.
LP: . . . . ECM 1380

EXPLODED VIEW.
Tracks: / Name everything / Another year / Clear day, A / Your cat / Forget / Drawing down the moon / X festival, The / Metal summer / Assembly field.
LP: . . . . ECM 1335

NORTHERN SONG.
LP: . . . . ECM 1218

SAFE JOURNEY.
LP: . . . . ECM 1270

YR.
Tracks: / UR / Sphexes / Ten years / One day / Three primates / You and it / Alien lounge / Ten year dance.
LP: . . . . ECM 1355

Tibet

ASIAN TRADITIONAL MUSIC (Various artists).
LP: . . . . PS 33504

MUSIQUE SACREE DES MOINES TIBETAINS (Various artists).
Tracks: / Moine tibetain en priere: *Various artists* / Appel des conques: *Various artists* / Office du matin: *Various artists* / Tambours a deux peaux: *Various artists* / Office de l'apres-midi: *Various artists*/ Moines tibetains en priere a Dharamsala: *Various artists* / Trompes telescopiques: *Various artists* / Office du soir: *Various artists*.
LP: . . . . ARN 33335

RITUALS OF DRUKPA ORDER FROM THIMPHU Tibetan Buddhist rites vol. 1 (Various artists).
LP: . . . . LLST 7255
MC: . . . . LLCT 7255

SACRED DANCES AND RITUALS OF THE NYINGMAPA & DRUKPA ORDERS Tibetan Buddhist Rites vol. 2 (Various artists).
LP: . . . . LLST 7256

SACRED MUSIC (Various artists).
LP: . . . . OCR 71
MC: 4559 011

SONGS OF MILAREPA, THE (Various artists).
LP: . . . . LLST 7285

TEMPLE RITUALS AND PUBLIC CEREMONIES Tibetan Buddhist Rites vol. 3 (Various artists).
LP: . . . . LLST 7257

TIBETAN & BHUTANESE INSTRUMENTAL & FOLK MUSIC Tibetan Buddhist Rites vol. 4 (Various artists).
LP: . . . . LLST 7258

TIBETAN BUDDHIST RITE FROM NEPAL (Various artists).
LP: . . . . LLST 7270

TIBETAN FOLK & MINSTREL MUSIC (Various artists).
LP: . . . . LLST 7196

TIBETAN FOLK MUSIC FROM LHASA & AMDO (Various artists).
LP: . . . . LLST 7286

TIBETAN MYSTIC SONGS (Various artists).
LP: . . . . LLST 7290

TIBETAN RITUAL MUSIC (Various artists).
LP: . . . . LLST 7181
MC: . . . . LLCT 7181

TIBETAN SONGS OF GODS AND DEMONS (Various artists).
LP: . . . . LLST 7291
MC: . . . . LLCT 7291

Tickell, Kathryn

BORDERLANDS.
Tracks: / Mary the maid (Medley) / David's hornpipe (Medley) / Sidlaw hills (Medley) / Brafferton Village / Stellgreen (Medley) / Loch rannoch (Medley) / Gypsey's lullaby (Medley) / Flowers of the forest (Medley) / Alston flower show (Medley) / Claudio's Polka (Medley) / Tents hornpipe (Medley) / Walker (Medley) / Lord Gordon's reel (Medley) / Robson (Medley) / Roly gentle (Medley) / Troy's wedding (Medley) / Tartar frigate (Medley) / Wark football team (Medley).
LP: . . . . CRO 210
MC: . . . . CROC 210

COMMON GROUND.
Tracks: / Walsh's hornpipe / Dorrington lads / Richard Moscrop's waltzes / Another knight / Mrs. Bolowski's / Neil Gow's lament / Andrew Knight's favourite / Shining pool, The / Outclassed / Glen Aln / Bill Charlton's fancy / Fenham / Catch a penny fox / Bowmont water / Geoff Heslop's reel / New rigged ship, The / Remember me / Rafferty's reel / Wild hills of Wannies.
LP: . . . . CRO 220
MC: . . . . CROC 220

KATHRYN TICKELL BAND.
MC: . . . . CROC 227
LP: . . . . CRO 227

ON KIELDER SIDE.
Tracks: / Joan's jig / Cut the file / Sweet Hesleyside / Hesleyside reel / Skate, The / Beeswing / Ronell's reel / Bob Thompson's / Crooked bawbee / J.B. Milne / Carrick hornpipe / Peacock followed the hen, The / Da slockit light / Kielder Jock / Matt's / Stage, The / Jean's reel / Johnny Cope / Tipsy sailor, The / Border spirit / A.B. hornpipe / Billy Pigg's hornpipe.
LP: . . . . SDL 343
MC: . . . . CSDL 343

Tickle Tune Typhoon

CIRCLE AROUND.
Tracks: / Tickle tune typhoon, Theme from / Muscle music / Vega boogie / Monster song / Tree dancin' / Hug bug / Sneakers / Bear hunt / Dinosaurs / Clap your hands / Magic penny / We circle around.
LP: . . . . TTTLP 001

HUG THE EARTH.
Tracks: / Tickle train / Got the rhythm / Skin / Doin' the robot / Kye kye jule / Sea song / Place in the choir / Super kids / Knickerbocker / If you're happy and you know it / Garbage blues / Family song / Hug the earth / Oh cedar tree.
LP: . . . . TTTLP 002

Tief Drin'in

GOLDEN BOHEMIAN BRASS.
LP: . . . . ISST 153

GOLDEN BOHEMIAN BRASS VOL 2.
LP: . . . . ISST 164

Tierra Buena Jazzband

OUR MONDAY DATE.
Tracks: / Stevedore stomp / Blame it on the blues / Too busy / Saturday night function / Wolverine blues / September in the rain / Coffee grinder / Good morning blues / Snake rag / Black eye blues / Black cat on a fence / East coast trot / Shimme sha wabble / Monday date.
MC: . . . . LCA 1

Tietchens, Asmus

WATCHING THE BURNING BRIDE (Tietchens, Asmus & Terry Burrows).
LP: . . . . HAM 16

Tiffany

HOLD AN OLD FRIEND'S HAND.
Tracks: / All this time / Oh Jackie / Hold an old friends hand / Radio romance / We're both thinking of her / Walk away while you can / Drop that bomb / It's the lover / I'll be the girl / Overture.
LP: . . . . MCF 3437
MC: . . . . MCFC 3437

TIFFANY.
Tracks: / Should've been me / Danny / Spanish eyes / Feelings of forever / Kid on a corner / I saw him standing there / Johnny's got the inside moves / Promises made / I think we're alone now / Could've been.
LP: . . . . MCF 3415
MC: . . . . MCFC 3415

Tiger

BAM BAM.
LP: . . . . RAS 3042
MC: . . . . RASC 3042

COME BACK TO ME.
LP: . . . . WRLP 31

LIVE: TIGER MEETS GENERAL TREES (Tiger & General Trees).
Tracks: / Me name is Tiger / Don is Don / Puppy love / Mi lover / Bad boy style / Lyrics fi yu / Money / Hill and gully style / No wanga gut / Na lef ya so / Mind reader / No way home / Peanut man / So so so so / Toothache / Minibus / Negril / Check fi police (medley).
LP: . . . . CSLP 25
MC: . . . . ZCSLP 25

LOVE AFFAIR.
MC: . . . . RRTGC 7787

ME NAME TIGER.
LP: . . . . ILPS 9870
MC: . . . . ICT 9870
LP: . . . . RAS 3021

RAIN FROM THE SKY (See under Nalvo, Anthony) (Tiger & Anthony Nalvo).

RAM DANCEHALL.
LP: . . . . VPRL 1052
MC: . . . . VPRC 1052

TEMPO.
LP: . . . . DSR 8994

TIGER A TIGER.
LP: . . . . NNMLPTT 3

TOUCH IS A MOVE.
LP: . . . . MLPS 1056
MC: . . . . MCT 1056

Tiger Moth

HOWLING MOTH.
Tracks: / Sloe benga / Polka volta / Olympia / Conquer your glasses / First wife, The / La bastringue / Gone with the lind / Flor marchita / Mustaphas horne schottische / Moth to California / Sestrina.
LP: . . . . FMSL 2012
MC: . . . . FMSC 3012

TIGER MOTH.
LP: . . . . FMSL 2006

Tiger Warsaw

TIGER WARSAW (Film soundtrack) (Various artists).
LP: . . . . X 1001

Tigertailz

BEZERK.
Tracks: / Sick sex / Love bomb baby / I can fight dirty too / Noise level critical / Heaven / Love overload / Action city / Twist and shake / Squeeze it dry / Call of the wild.
LP: . . . . MFN 96
MC: . . . . TMFN 96

YOUNG AND CRAZY.
Tracks: / Star attraction / Hollywood killer / Living without you / Shameless / City kids / Shoot to kill / Turn me on / She's too hot / Young & crazy / Fall in love again.
LPPD: . . . . MFN 78P
LP: . . . . MFN 78
MC: . . . . TMFN 78

Tight Fit

BACK TO THE 60'S (40 Non Stop Dancing Hits).
Tracks: / Proud Mary / Mr. Tambourine man / Oh pretty woman / Needles and pins / Dancing in the street / Mony mony.
LP: . . . . MFP 5631
MC: . . . . TCMFP 5631

BACK TO THE 60'S (JIVE).
LP: . . . . HIP 1

BACK TO THE 60'S VOL. 2 (40 Non-Stop Dancing Hits).
Tracks: / Let's dance / I get around / I saw her standing there / You really got me / Da doo ron ron / Baby love / Lazy Sunday / Hi ho silver lining / Daydream believer / Young ones, The / Down town / Young girl / Everlasting love / Get back / Something / Hey Jude / My cherie amour / Walk on by / World without love / Wichita lineman / Fire / Jumping Jack Flash / Substitute / Keep on running / I only want to be with you / Locomotion, The / Pretty woman / Get off my cloud / I can see for miles / Pinball wizard / You've lost that lovin' feeling / Something in the air / Sun ain't gonna sine anymore, The / Concrete and clay / Do you know the way to San Jose / There's always something there to remind me / River deep mountain high / Clapping song, The / Boat that I row, The / Night has a thousand eyes, The.
LP: . . . . MFP 5872
MC: . . . . TCMFP 5872

LION SLEEPS TONIGHT.
LP: . . . . MFP 4156411
MC: . . . . TCMFP 4156414

TIGHT FIT.
LP: . . . . HIP 2

Tik & Tok

INTOLERANCE.
LP: . . . . SURLP 008
MC: . . . . ZCSUR 8
LPPD: . . . . SURPX 8

Tikaram, Tanita

ANCIENT HEART.
Tracks: / Good tradition / Cathedral song / Sighing Innocents / I love you / World outside your window / For all these years / Twist in my sobriety / Poor cow / He likes the sun / Valentine heart / Preyed upon.
LP: . . . . WX 210
MC: . . . . WX 210C

EVERYBODY'S ANGEL.
LP: . . . . WX 401
MC: . . . . WX 401 C

SWEET KEEPER.
Tracks: / Once and not speak / It all come back today / Sunset's arrived / I owe all to you / Harm in your hands / Thursday's child / We almost got it together / Little sister leaving town / Love story.
LP: . . . . WX 330
MC: . . . . WXC 330

'Til Tuesday

EVERYTHING'S DIFFERENT NOW.
Tracks: / Everything's different now / RIP in heaven / Why must I / J for Jules / (Believed you were) lucky / Limits to love / Long gone Buddy / Other end of the telescope, The / Crash and burn / How can you give up.
LP: 4607371
MC: 4607374

VOICES CARRY.
Tracks: / Love in a vacuum / Looking over my shoulder / I could get used to this / No more crying / Voices carry / Winning the war / You know the rest / Maybe Monday / Don't watch me bleed / Sleep.
LP: . . . . EPC 26434
MC: 40 26434

WELCOME HOME.
Tracks: / What about love / Coming up close / On sunday / Will she just fall down / David denies / Lover's day / Have mercy / Sleeping and walking / Angels never call / No one is watching you now.
LP: . . . . EPC 57094
MC: 40 57094

Tilbury, Quenna

PRISONER OF A PROMISE (Spouse, Isobel).
MCSET: . . . . CLT 1011

Till, Emmitt

HIT MAN.
Tracks: / Hit man / American police / Hit man / New York Jets / Crime wave / Turn it up / Messin' / Alligator man / Groovin' / Oh momma blues / Is there anyone out there / Latin / Hot revs.
LP: . . . . EMM 1

Till, Sonny

HOLD ME THRILL ME KISS ME (Till, Sonny & The Orioles).
Tracks: / Hold me thrill me kiss me / It seems so long / Please give my heart a break / It's a cold Summer / We're supposed to be through / I need you so / Would you still be the one in my heart / When you're a long long way from home / I love you mostly / It's over because we're through / When you're not around / Shrimp boats / Barfly / Drowning every hope I ever had.
LP: . . . . **H 800**

Till The Clouds ...

TILL THE CLOUDS ROLL BY - THE JEROME KERN STORY (Film soundtrack) (Various artists).
LP: . . . . **MCA 25000**
MC: . . . . **MCAC 25000**

TILL THE CLOUDS ROLL BY/ SUMMER STOCK/LOVELY TO LOOK AT (Various artists).
Tracks: / Till the clouds roll by: *Various artists* / Look for the silver lining: *Garland, Judy* / Can't help lovin' dat man: *Horne, Lena* / Leave it to Jane and Cleopatterer: *Allyson, June* / Life upon the wicked stage: *O'Brien, Virginia* / Who?: *Garland, Judy* / Ol' man river: *Peterson, Caleb* / Get happy: *Garland, Judy* / Howdy neighbour, happy harvest: *Garland, Judy* / You wonderful you: *Kelly, Gene* / Friendly star: *Garland, Judy* / Heavenly music: *Kelly, Gene/Phil Silvers* / If you feel like singing, sing: *Garland, Judy* / Mem'ry island: *De Haven, Gloria/Pete Roberts* / Dig-dig-dig-dig for your dinner: *Kelly, Gene/Phil Silvers* / Lafayette: *Skelton, Red/ Howard Keel* / Lovely to look at: *Keel, Howard* / Smoke gets in your eyes: *Grayson, Kathryn/* You're devasting: *Grayson, Kathryn/Howard Keel/Ann Miller/Tommy Rall* / Yesterdays: *Grayson, Kathryn* / I'll be hard to handle: *Miller, Ann* / Touch of your hand/Lovely to look at: *Grayson, Kathryn/Howard Keel/Ann Miller/Tommy Rall*.
LP: . . . . **LPMGM 24**
LP: **794 873 1**
MC: . . . . **TCMGM 24**
MC: **794 873 4**

Tillet, Louis

CAST OF ASPERASIONS, A.
LP: . . . . **CGAS 812**

EGO TRIPPING AT THE GATES OF HELL.
LP: . . . . **CITLP 509**
LP: . . . . **CGAS 802**

Tilling, Richard

MUSIC IN MINATURE.
LP: . . . . **AVM 1005**
MC: . . . . **AVMC 1005**

Tillis, Mel

AIN'T NO CALIFORNIA.
LP: . . . . **MCA 40946**

COUNTRY STORE: MEL TILLIS.
Tracks: / Ruby don't take your love to town / Heaven everyday / Brand new mister me / Neon rose / Sawmill / Memory maker / Woman in the back of my world / Commercial affection / Arms of a fool, The / I ain't never / I can't stop loving you / Midnight / Best way I know how / Welcome to my world.
LP: . . . . **CST 17**
MC: . . . . **CSTK 17**

GREAT MEL, THE.
LP: . . . . **GT 0049**

LONG WAY TO DAYTONA, A.
LP: . . . . **E 160016**

NEW PATCHES.
Tracks: / Midnight love / New patches / Slow nights / Almost like you never went away / Faded blue / Texas on a Saturday night / You're as far as I can see (when I close my eyes) / Small change / Bed of roses / He drove her out of his mind.
LP: . . . . **MCF 3224**
MC: . . . . **MCFC 3224**

VERY BEST OF MEL TILLIS, THE.
Tracks: / Coca cola cowboy / What did I promise her last night / Good woman blues / Ain't no California / I got the hots / Send me down to Tuscon / I believe in you / Heart healer / Charlie's angel / Burning memories.
LP: . . . . **IMCA 27070**

Tillotson, Johnny

ALL THE HITS.
LP: . . . . **LSP 1059**

FABULOUS JOHNNY TILLOTSON, THE.
Tracks: / Poetry in motion / It keeps right on a-hurtin' / Dreamy eyes / True true happiness / Why do I love you so / Jimmy's girl / Without you / Send me the pillow that you dream on / I can't help it (if I'm still in love with you) / Out of my mind / You can never stop me loving you / Funny how time slips away.
MC: . . . . **FABC 003**

POETRY IN MOTION.
Tracks: / I got a feeling / It keeps right on a-hurtin' / Lonely street / I'm so lonesome I could cry / Funny how time slips away / I fall to pieces / What'll I do / Poetry in motion / I can't help it (if I'm still in love with you) / Take good care of her / Lonesome town / Send me the pillow that you dream on / Hello walls / Fool No. 1.
LP: . . . . **CH 74**

POETRY IN MOTION (OLD GOLD) (See under Teddy Bears/To know him is to...).

SCRAPBOOK.
Tracks: / True true happiness / Love is blind / Why do I love you so / Never let me go / Well I'm your man / Dreamy eyes / Poetry in motion / Princess Princess / Jimmie's girl / Cutie pie / Out of my mind / Empty feelin' / You can never stop me loving you / Very good year for girls, A / I got a feeling / Judy, Judy, Judy / Without you / It keeps right on a-hurtin' / Oh eine tolle frau (worried guy) / Ch traume immer wieder nur von dir (Previously unissued.).
LP: . . . . **BFX 15141**

Tilson Thomas, Michael

GERSHWIN LIVE (see Vaughan, Sarah) (Tilson Thomas, Michael & Sarah Vaughan).

Tilston, Steve

IN FOR A PENNY, IN FOR A POUND.
Tracks: / Easy come, easy go / Stirring it up / Who is that girl? / Red skies / B movie / Don't look down / Say no again / New disguise / One of these days / Wounds of love.
LP: . . . . **PROP 4**

LIFE BY MISADVENTURE.
Tracks: / These days / Nowhere to hide / Here comes the night / I call your name / Lazy tango / Life by misadventure / Lovers and dreamers / Polonaise / Tsetse fly shuffle / Sometimes in this life.
LP: . . . . **RRA 001**

SONGS FROM THE DRESS REHEARSAL.
LP: . . . . **CR 1**

SWANS AT COOLE.
LP: . . . . **RRA 011**
MC: . . . . **RRAMC 011**

Tilt

RIDE THE TIGER.
Tracks: / Ride the tiger / Jumping the gun / Blood and sand / Six string T's / Bedlam rock / One night Wanda / Wayward child / Dark heart / Red handed / May day.
LP: . . . . **UEZLP 2001**

Tilt (Film)

TILT (Film Soundtrack) (Various artists).
LP: . . . . **AA 1114**

Timb

TIMB.
LP: **083151**

Timbuk 3

EDEN ALLEY.
LP: . . . . **MIRG 1034**
MC: . . . . **MIRGC 1034**

EDGE OF ALLEGIANCE.
Tracks: / National holiday / Waves of grain / Dirty dirty rice / Pass it on / Standard white Jesus / Grand old party / Count to ten / B-side of life / Acid rain / Daddy's down in the mine / Don't give up on me / Wheel of fortune.
LP: . . . . **EIRSA 1022**
MC: . . . . **EIRSAC 1022**

GREETINGS FROM.
Tracks: / Future's so bright I gotta wear shaded, The / Life is hard / Hairstyles and attitudes / Facts about cats / I need you / Just another movie / Friction / Cheap black and white / Shame on you / I love you in the strangest way / Black and white.
LP: . . . . **MIRF 1015**
MC: . . . . **MIRFC 1015**

Time

ICE CREAM CASTLE.
Tracks: / Ice cream castles / My drawers / Chilli sauce / Jungle love / If the kid can't make you come / Bird, The.
LP: **925109 1**

PANDEMONIUM.
Tracks: / Dreamland / Pandemonium / Sexy socialites / Yount / Donald Trump (black version) / Cooking class / It's your world / Data bank / Pretty little woman / Jerk out / Blondie / Chocolate / Skillet / Sometimes I get lonely / Summertime thang.
LP: . . . . **WX 336**
MC: . . . . **WX 336C**

TIME.
LP: . . . . **K 56947**
MC: **K4 56947**

TIME FOR MEMORIES (Various artists).
MC: . . . . **KMOR 28104**

WHAT TIME IS IT?.
LP: . . . . **K 57017**

Time After Time

TIME AFTER TIME (Film Soundtrack) (Various artists).
Tracks: / Fanfare and prelude: *Various artists* / Search for the ripper: *Various artists* / Time machine, The: *Various artists* / Time travel: *Various artists* / Bank montage: *Various artists* / Utopia: *Various* artists / Ripper pursuit, The: *Various artists* / Time machine waltz: *Various artists* / Man before his time: *Various artists* / Redwoods: *Various artists* / Murder: *Various artists* / Fifth victim, The: *Various artists*.
LP: . . . . **ERS 6517**

Time Bandits

CAN'T WAIT FOR ANOTHER WORLD.
Tracks: / Wildfire / We'll be dancing / Pasadena dreamworld / True love / Earthlings / Every heartbeat / Can't wait for another world / Sail / Wherever we go / You're not at home.
LP: **4508781**
MC: **4508784**

FICTION.
Tracks: / Dancing on a string / I want to live / I won't steal away / You are every world / Runaway / Only a fool / Back against the wall / Endless road / America / I'm only shooting love.
LP: . . . . **CBS 26937**
MC: **40 26937**

TIME BANDITS.
Tracks: / I'm only shooting love / Only love will survive / Listen to the man with the golden voice / Power / Man's heart / Crazy world / Live it up / I'm specialised in you / Right or wrong / Holiday heartbreaker / Lookin' out / How does it feel.
LP: . . . . **CBS 25943**

Time (bk)

TIME (THE BIRTHDAY CLOCK).
MC: . . . . **STK 017**

Time For Hits

TIME FOR HITS (Various artists).
LP: . . . . **SPMP 105**
MC: . . . . **SPMC 105**

Time Is Right

TIME IS RIGHT, THE (Various artists).
LP: . . . . **TIRLP 001**

Time Machine

SUMMER OF LOVE.
Tracks: / Summer of love / San Francisco / Paper sun / Flowers in the rain / Whiter shade of pale, A / California dreamin' / All you need is love / Summer of love.
MLP: . . . . **NRIC 056**

Time Machine (film)

TIME MACHINE, THE (Film Soundtrack) (Various artists).
Tracks: / London 1900: *Various artists* / Time machine model: *Various artists* / Time machine: *Various artists/* Quick trip into the future: *Various artists* / All the time in the world: *Various artists* / Beautiful forest: *Various artists* / Great hall, The: *Various artists* / Fear: *Various artists* / Weena: *Various artists/* Rescue: *Various artists*.
LP: . . . . **GNPS 8008**
MC: **GNP5 8008**

Time Of Destiny

TIME OF DESTINY, A (Film soundtrack) (Various artists).
LP: **790938.1**
MC: **790938.4**
LP: . . . . **V 2539**
MC: . . . . **TCV 2539**

Time (show)

TIME (Original broadway cast) (Various artists).
Tracks: / Born to rock 'n' roll: *Richard, Cliff* / Time talking: *Ashford & Simpson* / Time: *Mercury, Freddie/* Ascention (The music of the spheres): *Orchestral* / Law of the Universe: *Thompson, Chris/ Miriam Stockley/Michael* Mullens / Time lord theme: *Christie, John* / John Christie: *Charge* / One human family: *Sayer, Leo/* What on Earth: *Warwick, Dionne* / I know, I know: *Sayer, Leo* / Your brother in soul: *Helme, Jimmy/* Case for the prosecution: *Christie, John* / Starmaker: *Ashford & Simpson* / Time will teach us all: *Lennon,* Julian / Object: *Christie, John* / In my defence: *Mercury, Freddie* / Within my world: *Warwick, Dionne/* Because: *Lennon, Julian* / Move the judge: *Helme, Jimmy* / She's so beautiful: *Richard, Cliff* / Beauty, truth, love, freedom, peace: *Olivier, Laurence* / If only you knew: *Lennon, Julian* / We're the UFO: *Head,* Murray / Time, Theme from: *Olivier, Laurence* / Harmony: *Christie, John* / Return, The: *Orchestral/* Time (reprise): *Mercury, Freddie* / It's in every one of us: *Richard, Cliff*.
2LP: . . . . **AMPM 1**
MCSET: . . . . **TCAMPM 1**
2LP: . . . . **EQ 5003**
MCSET: . . . . **TCEQ 5003**

Time To Die

TIME TO DIE, A (see under Smith, Wilbur) (Valentine, Anthony).

TIME TO DIE, A (Film Soundtrack) (Various artists).
LP: . . . . **C'BUS 119**

Time Will Show The

TIME WILL SHOW THE WISER (Various artists).
LP: . . . . **TRI 001**

Time You Say Goodbye

TIME YOU SAY GOODBYE (Various artists).
2LP: **80003**
MC: **850031/2**

Timebomb

A.
Tracks: / Crossfire / Flyingdale flyer / Working John, working Joe / Black Sunday / Protect and survive / Batteries not included / Uniform / 4 WD (low ratio) / Pine martin's jig / And further on / Bod.
LP: . . . . **CHR 1301**
MC: . . . . **ZCHR 1301**
LP: . . . . **CDL 1301**

Timeless...

TIMELESS COMPILATION (Various artists).
LP: . . . . **PWM 1**
MC: . . . . **PWMC 1**

Timeless All Stars

IT'S TIMELESS (LIVE AT KEYSTONE KORNER) (Curtis Fuller, Harold Land).
LP: . . . . **SJP 178**

TIMELESS HEART.
Tracks: / Hindsight / Tayamisha / Hand in glove / Fiesta Espagnol / World peace / Christina.
LP: . . . . **SJP 182**

Times

BEAT TORTURE.
LP: . . . . **CRELP 038**

BLUE PERIOD.
LP: . . . . **ARTPOP 2**

E FOR EDWARD.
LP: . . . . **CRELP 53**

ENJOY.
LP: . . . . **ART 15**

ET DIEU CREA LA FEMME.
Tracks: / Septieme ciel / Chagrin d'amour / Baisers voles / Sucette / Extase / Aurore boreale / Volupte / Pour Kylie / 1990 Anee erotique.
LP: . . . . **CRELP 070**
MC: . . . . **CCRE 070**

HELLO EUROPE.
LP: . . . . **ART 17**

HERE COMES THE HOLIDAYS (see Dee, Joni) (Times, (The)/Joni Dee).

I HELPED PATRICK MCGOOHAN ESCAPE.
Tracks: / Big painting / Stranger than fiction / Danger man theme / I helped Patrick McGoohan escape / All systems are go / Up against it.
LP: . . . . **NO 1**

LUNACY IS LEGEND EP (See under Sudden, Nikki) (Times/Nikki Sudden/ Necessitarians).

PINK BALL, BROWN BALL, RED BALL.
LP: . . . . **CRELP 073**
MC: . . . . **CCRE 073**

POP GOES ART.
Tracks: / Picture gallery / New arrangement / I helped Patrick McGoohan escape / Pop goes art / Miss London / Sun never sets, The / This is tomorrow.
LP: . . . . **WHAAM LP 01**
LP: . . . . **ART 020**
MC: . . . . **ARTC 020**

THIS IS LONDON.
Tracks: / This is London / Goodbye Piccadilly / Whatever happened to Thamesbeat / Big painting / If only / Stranger than fiction.
LP: . . . . **ART 19**

UP AGAINST IT.
LP: . . . . **ART 16**

Times Of Harvey Milk
TIMES OF HARVEY MILK, THE (see Never cry wolf) (Isham, Mark).

Times Square
TIMES SQUARE (Film Soundtrack) (Various artists).
Tracks: / Rock hard: *Quatro, Suzi* / Talk of the town: *Pretenders* / Same old scene: *Roxy Music* / Down in the park: *Numan, Gary* / Help me: *Levy, Marcy & Robin Gibb* / Life during wartime: *Talking Heads* / I wanna be sedated: *Ramones* / Pretty boys: *Jackson, Joe* / Take this town: *XTC* / Damn dog: *Johnson, Robin* / Your daughter is one: *Johnson, Robin* / Babylon's burning: *Ruts* / You can't hurry love: *Byron, David* / Walk on the wild side: *Reed, Lou* / Night was not: *Child, Desmond & Rouge* / Innocent not guilty: *Jeffreys, Garland* / Grinding halt: *Cure* / Pissing in the river: *Smith, Patti Group* / Flowers in the city: *Johansen, David*.
2LP: 265 814 5
MCSET: 352 422 2

Timex Social Club
VICIOUS RUMORS.
Tracks: / Rumors / Thinkin' about ya / Just kickin' it / Only you / mixed up world / Cokelife / Go away little girl / 363 (Natty Prep) / Vicious rumors.
LP: . . . . CTLP 2
MC: . . . . ZCTLP 2

Timey
BEST OF TIMEY.
LP: . . . . RELIC 5071

Timmons, Bobby
BOBBY TIMMONS IN PERSON.
LP: . . . . RSLP 391

JENKINS, JORDAN & TIMMONS (See under Jenkins, John) (Timmons, Bobby/ Clifford Jordan/John Jenkins).

THIS HERE.
LP: . . . . OJC 104

Timms, Sally
SOMEONE'S ROCKING MY DREAMBOAT.
LP: . . . . MOTLP 021

Timmy T
TIME AFTER TIME.
LP: . . . . TIMLP 1
MC: . . . . TIMMC 1

Timon Of Athens
TIMON OF ATHENS (see under Shakespeare, William) (Various artists).

Timothy, Christopher
SHADOW THE SHEEPDOG (see under Blyton, Enid (aut)).

Tims, Alfonia
FUTURE FUNK - UNCUT (Tims, Alfonia and his Flying Tigers).
MC: . . . . A 112

Tin Drum (film)
TIN DRUM, THE (Film Soundtrack) (Various artists).
LP: . . . . CL 0006

Tin Machine
TIN MACHINE.
Tracks: / Heaven's in here / Tin machine / Prisoner of love / Crack city / I can't read / Under the God / Amazing / Working class hero / Bus stop / Pretty thing / Video crimes / Run (Not on album.) / Sacrifice yourself (Not on album.) / Baby can dance.
MC: . . . . TCMTLS 1044
MC: 791 990 4
LP: . . . . MTLS 1044

TIN MACHINE II.
Tracks: / Baby universal / One shot / You belong in rock 'n' roll / If there is something / Amlapura / Betty wrong / You can't talk / Stateside / Shopping for girls / Big hurt, A / Sorry / Goodbye Mr. Ed.
LP: 8282721
MC: 8282724

Tin Pan Alley
TIN PAN ALLEY (Film Soundtrack) (Various artists).
LP: . . . . STK 110

Tin Star
SOMEBODY'S DREAMS.
LP: . . . . SPD 1004
MC: . . . . SPDC 1004

Tin Tin (bk)
TIN TIN STORIES (see under Herge).

Tina B
TINA B.
Tracks: / Honey to a bee / Ooh baby / Why did you do it / Gotta make this love last / Queen beat / Nothing's gonna come easy / Perception / Fool and his money / I always wanted to be free.
LP: 9603641

Tinder Box (bk)
TINDER BOX, THE (Hans Christian Andersen) (Asher, Jane (nar)).
MC: . . . . LPMC 209

TINDER BOX, THE (Well Loved Tales Up to Age 9).
MC: . . . . PLB 205

Tinklers
CASSEROLE.
Tracks: / Turn the screw in the crank / Ghost dance song / Elenor bumpers / Simple song of simple faith / I love a sandwich / What kind of God / Little league / Hokey Pokey / My eyes look into your eyes / Tough guys are probably sad / Splash splash / Workin' together united we are one / Bear came around / Black dog friendly dog / Lust for life / Mutations / Juvenile delinquency / Norman Meyer / Don't put your finger in the fan / Magazine / Tree song / Home by the river / Luther league / Mom cooks inside, Dad cooks outside / Don't put your finger in the sex places / I'm proud to be a citizen of the ... / We're not alone / Burpin' fungus ped / Maybe / Joan of Arc / Water's rushin' / Thinking too much.
LP: . . . . SHIMMY 025

Tinniswood, Peter
MORE TALES FROM A LONG ROOM (Read by Robin Bailey).
MC: . . . . TCLFP 417117-5

TALES FROM A LONG ROOM (Bailey, Robin (nar)).
MCSET: . . . . ZBBC 1021

TALES FROM A LONG ROOM VOL.1 & 2 (Bailey, Robin (nar)).
MCSET: . . . . LISF 0001/0002

Tinsley, John
SUNRISE BLUES.
LP: 2104

Tintypes
TINTYPES (Original Broadway Cast) (Various artists).
2LP: S2L 5196

Tiny lifeboat
TINY LIFEBOAT, THE (Various artists).
Tracks: / Tiny lifeboat, The: *Various artists* / General's concern, A: *Various artists* / Orphan who became Queen, The: *Various artists* / Friends indeed: *Various artists* / Change of heart, A: *Various artists* / Rich man's faith in a poor man, A: *Various artists*.
MC: . . . . ANV 634

Tiny Lights
HOT CHOCOLATE MASSAGE.
LP: . . . . ILLUSION 011

PRAYER FOR THE HALCYON FEAR.
LP: . . . . TOPY 025
LP: . . . . AGO 1993
MC: . . . . AGO 1993MC

Tinytown
LITTLE TIN GOD.
LP: . . . . EM 004

Tip Of The Iceberg
TIP OF THE ICEBERG VOL II (Various artists).
Tracks: / History book: *Plainsmen* / Look at me: *Sex Talk* / White babies: *Hippo Neal*.
MC: . . . . BOMB 002

Tip On In
DEVIL'S MUSIC.
LP: . . . . STING 001

Tippett (composer)
CHILD OF OUR TIME & THE WEEPING BABE, A (Various artists).
MC: 4251584

Tippett, Keith
66 SHADES OF LIPSTICK (Tippett, Keith/Andy Sheppard).
LP: . . . . EGED 64
MC: . . . . EGEDC 64

COUPLE IN SPIRIT.
Tracks: / Daybreak / Marching (We shall remember them) / Brimstone spring lullaby / Key at dusk, The / Morning psalm / Evening psalm / Grey mist with yellow waterfall entwines evening turquoise / Choir and the sunset improvisors, The.
LP: . . . . EGED 52
MC: . . . . EGEDC 52

FRAMES.
2LP: . . . . OGD 003/004

LIVE: KEITH TIPPETT (Tippett's,Keith Septet).
2LP: . . . . OGD 008/009

LOOSE KITE N A GENTLE... (Tippett's,Keith Septet).
LP: . . . . OG 007-8

MERCY DASH.
LP: . . . . CP 2001

OVARY LODGE.
LP: . . . . OG 600

Tippetts, Julie
ENCORE (see Auger, Brian) (Tippetts, Julie & Brian Auger).

VOICE.
LP: . . . . OG 110

Tippin, Aaron
YOU'VE GOT TO STAND FOR SOMETHING.
Tracks: / In my wildest dreams / I've got a good memory / You've got to stand for something / I wonder how far it is over you / Ain't that a hell of a note / Man that came between us (was me) / She made a memory out of me / Up against you / Sky's got the blues / Many, many, many beers ago.
LP: . . . . PL 82374
MC: . . . . PK 82374

Tipton, Lester
THIS WON'T CHANGE (See under Masqueraders - "How".

Tirabasso, John
LIVE AT DINO'S (Tirabasso, John Quartet).
LP: . . . . DS 884

Tirez Tirez
ETUDES.
LP: . . . . AUL 714

SOCIAL RESPONSIBILITY.
Tracks: / Somebody tell me / In your own backyard / My mistake / Paper bag / Edgetown / Wake up / See my problem / Spin your wheels / Uptight.
LP: . . . . ROUGH 111

Tiselius, Lars
HAMMOND DANCE PARTY.
LP: . . . . JOYS 222

Titan Force
TITAN FORCE.
LP: . . . . US 017

Titiyo
TITIYO.
Tracks: / Flowers / Do my thing / Peace and quiet / I know you better / Waiting for you / After the rain / Body and mind / Break my heart / L.O.V.E. / Man in the moon, The / Doin' his thing.
LP: 210977
MC: 410977

Tittle, Jimmy
JIMMY TITTLE.
LP: . . . . DFG 8412

Titus Andronicus
TITUS ANDRONICUS (see under Shakespeare, William) (Various artists).

Titus Groan
TITUS GROAN PLUS.
Tracks: / It wasn't for you / Hall of bright carvings / Liverpool / I can't change / It's all up with us / Fuschia / Open the door homer / Woman of the world.
LP: . . . . SEE 260

T.J.
I COULD NEVER LOVE ANOTHER.
LP: . . . . UJLP 12

Tjader, Cal
A FUEGO VIVO.
LP: . . . . CJ 176
MC: . . . . CJ 176 C

BREATHE EASY.
LP: . . . . GXY 5107

CAL'S PALS.
Tracks: / Perdido / Tambu in 7/4 / Ran kan kan / Noa noa / Curtain call / Mambo show / Te cres que / Cubano chant / Ginza samba / Why do you do right (get me some money too!).
LP: . . . . BGP 1003
MC: . . . . BGPC 1003

GAZAME.
LP: . . . . CJ 133

GOOD VIBES.
Tracks: / Guarachi guaro / Doxy / Shoshana / Speak low / Broadway / Cuban fantasy / Good vibes.
LP: . . . . CJP 247

HEATWAVE (see McRae, Carmen) (Tjader, Cal/Carmen McRae).

HURACAN.
LP: . . . . CCS 8003

SHINING SEA, THE.
LP: . . . . CJ 159

SOLAR HEAT.
Tracks: / Ode to Billy Joe / Never my love / Felicidade / Mambo sangria / Here of fried bananas / Amazon / La Bamba / Eye of the devil / Solar heat.
LP: . . . . RHAP 13

TAMBU (See under Byrd, Charlie) (Tjader, Cal & Charlie Byrd).

T.K.O.
IN YOUR FACE.
LP: . . . . MFN 33

T.M.A.
BEACH PARTY 2000.
Tracks: / Only time / Don't waste your time / What happened to you / You can try / Joe / Toll free / Slack / Babysitter, The / Hipster / Miserable / Where were you / Ode to Clancy / Tomorrow.
LP: . . . . SAVE 055

WHATS FOR DINNER.
LP: . . . . HOLY 010

TNT
INTUITION.
Tracks: / Nation free, A / Tonight I'm falling / Learn to love / Take me down / Caught between the tigers / Forever shine on / Ordinary lover / Wisdom.
LP: 836 777-1
MC: 836 777-4

KNIGHTS OF THE NEW THUNDER.
Tracks: / Seven seas / Ready to leave / Klassik romance / Last summer's evil / Without your love / Tor with the hammer / Break the key / U.S.A. / Deadly metal / Knights of the thunder.
LP: 818 865 1
MC: 818 865 4

TELL NO TALES.
Tracks: / Everyone's a star / 10,000 lovers (in one) / Sapphire / Northern lights / Everyone's a star / As far as the eye can see / Child's play / Smooth syncopation / Listen to your heart / Desperate night / Incipits / Tell no tales.
LP: . . . . VERH 39
MC: . . . . VERHC 39
LP: 830 979-1

To Be
TO BE.
LP: 0060 053

To Be Or Not To Be
TO BE OR NOT TO BE (Film Soundtrack) (Various artists).
LP: . . . . ISTA 6
MC: . . . . ICT 6

To Damascus
SUCCUMB.
LP: . . . . SAVE 086

To Hell With Burgundy
EARTHBOUND.
LP: . . . . FACT 217
MC: . . . . FACTC 217

To Kill A Priest
TO KILL A PRIEST (Film Soundtrack) (Various artists).
LP: . . . . VGC 8
MC: . . . . TCVGC 8

To Live & Die In L.A.
TO LIVE AND DIE IN L.A. (See under Wang Chung) (Wang Chung).

Toad The Wet Sprocket
BREAD AND CIRCUS.
Tracks: / Way away / Scenes from a vinyl recliner / Unquiet / Know me / When we recovered / One wind blows / Pale blue / Always changing probably / One little girl / Covered in roses.
LP: 4658501
MC: 4658504

Toasters
POOL SHARK.
LP: . . . . PHZA 5

RECRIMINATIONS.
LP: . . . . PHZA 18

THRILL ME UP.
LP: . . . . MRE 021

Tobermory (bk)
TOBERMORY & OTHER STORIES (See under Saki) (Newth, Jonathan).

Tobias, Heather (nar)
SELECTED STORIES FOR UNDER 5'S (See under Selected Stories...) (Branch, Andrew & Heather Tobias).

Tobin, Jim
VERY BEST OF JIM TOBIN.
LP: . . . . CMCSX 2001

Tobruk
PLEASURE AND PAIN.
Tracks: / Rock 'n' roll casualty / Love is in motion / Alleyboy / No paradise in Heaven / Burning up / Two hearts on the run / Let me out of here / Cry out in the night / Set me on fire.
LP: . . . . WKFMLP 105

MC: WKFMMC 105

WILD ON THE RUN.
Tracks: / Wild on the run / Falling / Running from the night / Hotline / Rebound / Poor girl / She's nobody's angel / Breakdown / Going down for the third time / Show must go on.
LP: TK 1
MC: TCTK 1

Toczek, Nick

BRITANARCHIST DEMO, THE.
Tracks: / Stiff with a quiff / Hitlers birthday party / Things to do on a Saturday night.
MC: BLUURG 49

INTOCZEKATED.
Tracks: / Living on the breadline / Sheer funk / Stiff with a quiff / Things to do on a saturday night / Lifetimes / Sanjay Gandhi's plane / Records on a radio show / Road crash / You gotta shout / 555 survive / Another cover.
LP: FISH 19
LP: ACER 002

Today

NEW FORMULA, THE.
Tracks: / I got the feelin' / Every little thing about you / Self centred / Let me know / Why you get funky on me / Trying to get over you / I wanna come back home / Home is where you belong / Tennis anyone / Gonna make you mine / No need to worry (On CD only.) / My happiness (On CD only.).
LP: ZL 72727
MC: ZK 72727

TODAY.
Tracks: / Him or me / Girl I got my eyes on you / Take it off / Take your time / Style / You stood me up / Your love is not true / Lady sexy lady.
LP: ZL 72650
MC: ZK 72650
LP: MOT 6261

Todd, Art

I LOVE A BANJO.
LP: GNPS 2011
MC: GNP5 2011

Todd, Dick

BLUE ORCHIDS.
Tracks: / Deep purple / You've got me crying again / Why begin again / Blue evening / Home in the clouds, A / I guess I'll go back home / Table in the corner, A / Manhattan / Time on my hands / Blue orchids / One morning in May / Lazy river / It's a hundred to one I'm in love / It's the talk of the town / I can't get started / Last night's gardenias.
LP: NL 90067
MC: NK 90067

Todd, Gary

SUNDAY BEST (See Turner, Roger) (Todd,Gary & Roger Turner).

Todd, Jimmy

HAPPY HOURS.
Tracks: / Happy hours / Swampland.
LP: MOR 4012

SALMON TAILS UP THE WATER.
LP: MOR 4022

Todd, Richard (nar)

BULLDOG DRUMMOND (see under Bulldog Drummond).

GREAT ESCAPE, THE (see under Great Escape (bk)).

Toddy

STORYTIME TOP TEN VOL.6.
MC: VCA 060

Toetsenman

FREEDOM (see Thunderthumbs) (Toetsenman/Thunderthumbs).

Together

PLAYING GAMES.
LP: NE 1053
MC: CE 2053

TOGETHER WE ARE BEAUTIFUL (Various artists).
LP: MALP 002

Together Brothers

STRICTLY FOR FRAMING.
LP: BLUETBLP 1
MC: BLUETBZC 1

Togo

KABI YE MUSIC FROM.
LP: OCR 76

Toibin, Niall

ENCORE.
MC: LRCS 8
LP: LRLP 8

LIVE AND KICKING.
MC: LRCS 3

Token Entry

JAYBIRD.
LP: HR 9539 1

WEIGHT OF THE WORLD.
LP: EM 93941

Tokens

LION SLEEPS TONIGHT,THE (OLD GOLD) (See under Browns - Three Bells).

Tokio Jo

VENUE, MAJORCA.
Tracks: / Lookin' for a lover / Blown in on love / Bollox to Terry / How much? - not enough / Fly away / Islands / Cookin.
LP: TOKIO 1

Tokyo Blade

BLACK HEARTS AND JADED SPADES.
LP: TBR 1

NIGHT OF THE BLADE.
LP: AMP 4

TOKYO BLADE.
LP: AMP 1

WARRIOR OF THE RISING SUN.
Tracks: / Madam Guillotine / Fever / Night of the blade / Breakout / Unleash the beat / Attack attack / Lightning strikes (Extended version) / Warrior of the rising sun / Someone to love / Mean Streak / If heaven is hell (Extended Version) / Break the chains / Dead of the night / Power game, The / Highway passion / Midnight rendezvous / Sunrise in Tokyo / Killer City / Liar / Death on mainstreet (Previously unreleased.).
2LP: RAWLP 005
MCSET: RAWTC 005

Tol & Tol

TOL AND TOL.
Tracks: / Centennial / Song for soprano / Kentucky lament / Old Jefferson's tune / Dawn over the Desna / Eleni / Himalaya / Rounding the Cape / La femme dans L'ombre / Beyond borders.
MC: ZDD 15
LP: ADD 15

Tolbert, Skeets

SKEETS TOLBERT AND HIS GENTLEMEN OF SWING (Tolbert, Skeets & His Gentlemen of Swing).
LP: EV 3001

Tolkien, J.R.R. (aut)

HOBBIT, THE.
LP: TC 1477
MC: CP 1477
MC: 0600560570
MCSET: MCFR 105/7

HOBBIT & THE FELLOWSHIP OF THE RING, THE.
MC: 1477

J.R.R. TOLKIEN COLLECTION, THE.
MC: 0001042734

J.R.R. TOLKIEN SOUNDBOOK.
LP: SBR 101
MC: SBC 101

LORD OF THE RINGS.
LP: REH 415
MC: ZCR 415
LP: TC 1478
MC: CP 1478

LORD OF THE RINGS (BOX SET) (Various artists).
LPS: RINGS 1

LORD OF THE RINGS, THE (Two Towers & the Return of the King).
MC: 1478

POEMS AND SONGS OF MIDDLE EARTH.
LP: TC 1231
MC: CP 1231

SILMARILLION, THE (of Beren and Luthien).
LP: TC 1564
MC: CDL 51564

SILMARILLION ,THE (of the Darkening of Valinor etc.).
LP: TC 1579
MC: CDL 51579

TOLKIEN SOUNDBOOK (Various artists).
MCSET: 101

Toll

PRICE OF PROGRESSION, THE.
Tracks: / Jazz clone clown / Jonathan Toledo / Smoke another cigarette / Soldier's room / Word of honour / Anna-41-box / Tamara told me / Living in the valley of pain / Stand in winter.
LP: WX 226
MC: WX 226C
LP: K 9242011
MC: K 9242014

Tollefsen, Toralf

ACCORDION EVERGREENS.
Tracks: / Pietro's return / Carnival of Venice / Tailspin / Dora Mazurka / Lido Mazurka / Elvira waltz / Dark eyes / Jolly Caballero / Bel viso / Beautiful days / Love smiles / Hot fingers.
LP: ZAFA 861
MC: ZAFAC 861

REFLECTIONS OF A SUMMER HOLIDAY.
Tracks: / Telemark suite / Norwegian suite No.1 / I see you outside the window / Halling fra Setesdale / Summer day in Fredrikstad / Reflections...Wild mountains / Fish on the hook / Play up / Dutch tourist / Farm boy / Coffee party / Memories Eskingdale.
LP: ZAFA 881
MC: ZAFAC 881

Tolley, David

STOP/DON'T (see Allen, Daevid & David Tolley) (Tolley, David & Daevid Allen).

Tolley, Maria

UP TO HERE.
LP: RHR 055

Tolliver, Charles

CHARLES TOLLIVER & HIS ALL STARS (Tolliver, Charles & His All Stars).
Tracks: / Earl's world / Peace with myself / Right now / Household of Saud / Lil's paradise / Paper man.
LP: BLP 30117

IMPACT.
LP: ENJA 2016

Tolly, Maria

VOICES.
LP: SC 53

Tolman, Russ

DOWN IN EARTHQUAKE TOWN.
Tracks: / Vegas / Domino / Down in earthquake town / Palm tree land / Midnight / Planes, train, automobiles / Baby / Face you wear / Jump into the fire / You don't have to say goodbye.
LP: FIEND 125

TOTEM POLES AND GLORY HOLES.
Tracks: / Lookin' for an angel / Talking hoover dam blues / Four winds / Everything you need and everything you want / Galveston mud / Better than before / I am not afraid / Nothin' slowing me down / Play hard to forget / Waitin' for rain.
LP: ZONG 012

Tolonen, Jukka

BLUE RAIN (Tolonen, Jukka & Costa Apetrea).
LP: SNTF 925

CROSSECTION.
Tracks: / Northern lights / Hysterical / Tiger / Windermere Avenue / Silva the cat / Wedding song, The.
LP: SNTF 699

IN A THIS YEAR TIME.
Tracks: / Sun love / In a this year time / Jungle jam / Moonlight skankin' / Suffering nations / Dance with me / Cool runnings.
LP: SNTF 887

MONTREUX BOOGIE.
Tracks: / Montreux boogie / Lama / Carnival / This one's for William / Can I have a slice / Hanryckning.
LP: SNTF 789

MOUNTAIN STREAM.
LP: SNTF 818

PASSENGER TO PARAMARIBO, (A).
Tracks: / Passenger to Paramaribo, A / Punski / Phantastes / Air rock / Dimitri / What went wrong.
LP: SNTF 768

RADIO ROMANCE.
LP: SNTF 967

TOLONEN.
Tracks: / Elements / Earth, fire, water, air / Ramblin' mountains / Wonderland / Last night.
LP: SNTF 652

TOUCH WOOD.
Tracks: / Autobahn / A minor / Improvisation / Socoa / Down by the lake / I remember Rovaniemi / Caravan road / Touch wood / Bouzouki / Gypsy / Cinq preludes.
LP: SNTF 865

Tolpuddle Martyrs

SONGS OF REVOLUTION (see under Travis, Dave) (Travis, Dave & Tolpuddle Martyrs).

Tolstoy, Leo (aut)

ANNA KARENINA (Worth, Irene).
LP: TC 1571
MC: CDL 1571

Tolvan Big Band

MONTREAUX AND MORE.
LP: DRLP 61

SPLIT VISION.
LP: DRLP 44

Tom Brown's Schooldays

TOM BROWN'S SCHOOLDAYS (see Hughes, Thomas) (Derby, Brown).

Tom Fobbles Day (bk)

TOM FOBBLES DAY (Garner, Alan (nar)).
LP: ZDSW 727

Tom, Georgia

1921-31 (see under Tampa Red) (Tom, Georgia & Tampa Red).

GEORGIA TOM, 1928-32.
LP: DLP 563

Tom & Jerry

TOM & JERRY MEET TICO & THE TRIUMPHS.
LP: B 600

Tom Jones (film)

TOM JONES/IRMA LA DOUCE (Film soundtrack) (Various artists).
LP: MCA 39068
MC: MCAC 39068

Tom Sawyer (bk)

ADVENTURES OF TOM SAWYER (See under Adventures of...) (Crosby, Bing).

TOM SAWYER (see Twain, Mark) (Unknown narrator(s)).

TOM SAWYER Mark Twain (Sherman, Bob).
MC: P 90013

Tom Thumb (bk)

TOM THUMB (well loved tales age up to 9) (Unknown narrator(s)).
MC: PLB 59

TOM THUMB (Film soundtrack) (Various artists).
LP: MCA 25006
MC: MCAC 25006

TOM THUMB (Hampshire, Susan).
MC: 3602

TOM THUMB AND OTHER FAIRY TALES.
MC: 1062

Tom Tom Club

BOOM BOOM CHI BOOM BOOM.
Tracks: / Don't say no / Suboceana / Shock the world / Femme fatale.
LP: SFLP 8
MC: SFMC 8

CLOSE TO THE BONE.
LP: ILPS 9738
MC: ICT 9738

TOM TOM CLUB.
Tracks: / Wordy rappinghood / Genius of love / Tom Tom theme / L'elephant / As above so below / Lorelei / On on on on / Booming and zooming.
LP: ILPM 9686
MC: ICM 9686
MC: 842 818 4

Tombs, David (nar)

BRITISH WILD BIRDS IN STEREO (see under British Wild Birds...) (Burton, John & David Tombs).

Tombs Of Atuan

TOMBS OF ATUAN (see Le Guin, Ursula) (Hood, Morag).

Tombstones

PREACHIN', PRAYIN' GUITAR.
Tracks: / Tombstone tales / Likkered up squashed flat / Snake oil boogie / Nobody / Axeman of New Orleans / Jailhouse tattoo / Preachin' , prayin' guitar playin'.
LP: HOLY 011

Tomcats

TOMCATS, THE.
LP: RR 501

Tomelty, Peter

IRISH EMIGRANT, THE.
MC: CT 109

MOUNTAINS OF MOURNE, THE.
Tracks: / Mountains of Mourne / Love thee dearest.
LP: STOL 122
MC: CT 122

PETER TOMELTY.
Tracks: / Irish emigrant, The / Star of the County Down / My lagan love.
LP: STOL 109

Tomfoolery

TOMFOOLERY (Original London Cast) (Various artists).
LP: MMT LP 102
MC: MMT TC 102
LP: TER 1137

MC: . . . . ZCTER 1137

Tomi

TELLING YOU HOW IT IS.
LP: 9608141

Tomita

BERMUDA TRIANGLE.
LP: . . . . PL 82885
MC: . . . . PK 82885

BOLERO.
LP: . . . . RL 13412
MC: . . . . RK 13412

DAWN CHORUS.
Tracks: / Cannon of the three stars / Whistle train / Vocalise / Dawn chorus / Adagio of the sky / Pegasus / Cosmic chorale / Vela-x pulsar.
LP: . . . . PL 85184
MC: . . . . PK 85184

FIREBIRD (Television Soundtrack).
Tracks: / Firebird suite / Prelude a l'apres midi d'un faune / Night on the bare mountain.
LP: . . . . ARLI 1312
MC: . . . . RK 11718

GRAND CANYON SUITE.
LP: . . . . PL 84317

GROFE / GRAND CANYON SUITE.
LP: . . . . RS 9005
MC: . . . . RSK 9005

KOSMOS.
Tracks: / Space fantasy / Unanswered question / Solvejg's song / Hora staccato / Sea named Solaris.
LP: . . . . RL 42652
MC: . . . . RK 42652

LIVE AT LINZ.
LP: . . . . RL 85461

PICTURES AT AN EXHIBITION.
Tracks: / Gnome, The / Old castle ,The / Tuileries / Bydlo / Ballet of the chicks in their shells / Samuel Goldenberg and Schmuyle / Limoges / Catacombs / Cum mortuis in lingua mortua / Hut of Baba Yaga, The / Great gate of Kiev, The.
LP: . . . . RCALP 3010
MC: . . . . RCAK 3010
LP: . . . . ARL 1 0838
LP: . . . . PL 80838
MC: . . . . PK 80838

PLANETS, THE.
LP: . . . . RL 81919
MC: . . . . RK 81919

SNOWFLAKES ARE DANCING.
Tracks: / Snowflakes are dancing (children's corner suite no.4) / Reverie / Gardens in the rain (estampes no 3) / Clair de lune / Arabesque No.1 / Engulfed cathedral, The (preludes book no.8) / Golliwogg's cake-walk / Footprints in the snow(preludes book no.6).
LP: . . . . PL 84587
MC: . . . . PK 84587
LP: . . . . ARL 1 0488

SOUND CREATURE.
2LP: . . . . RVC 7564/5

SPACE FANTASY.
LP: . . . . PL 42652

SPACE WALK....IMPRESSIONS OF AN ASTRONAUT.
LP: . . . . PL 85037
MC: . . . . PK 85037

TOMITA.
Tracks: / Grand Canyon suite / Syncopated clock.
LP: . . . . RS 9005

TOMITA'S GREATEST HITS.
LP: . . . . RCALP 3037
MC: . . . . RCAK 3037
LP: . . . . RL 43076

Tomkins, Thomas

CATHEDRAL MUSIC.
Tracks: / O sing unto the Lord / Then David mourned / My beloved spake / Above the stars / Magnificat and nunc dimittis from... / Glory be to God on high / Almighty God, the fountain of all wisdom / When David heard / My shepherd is the living Lord / Sing unto God / Behold the hour cometh / O God, the proud are risen against me.
MC: . . . . KA 66345

Tomlinson, Jill (aut)

OWL WHO WAS AFRAID OF THE DARK, THE (Lipman, Maureen).
MCSET: CC/007

Tomlinson, Michael

FACE UP IN THE RAIN.
LP: . . . . YL 0127

RUN THIS WAY FOREVER.
LP: . . . . YL 0116

STILL BELIEVE.
LP: . . . . YL 0104

Tommaso, Bruno

RAI BIG BAND.
LP: . . . . IJC 001

Tommy

TOMMY VOL 1 (Various artists).
LP: 2486 161
MC: 3186 064

TOMMY VOL 2 (Various artists).
LP: 2486 162
MC: 3186 065

Tommy Armstrong...

TOMMY ARMSTRONG OF TYNESIDE (Various artists).
LP: 12T 122

Tomney, Ed

RADICAL SONGBIRDS OF ISLAM (See Borofsky, Johnathan) (Tomney, Ed/ Johnathan Borofsky).

Tomorrow

TOMORROW.
Tracks: / My white bicycle / Colonel Brown / Real life permanent dream / Shy boy / Claremount lake / Revolution / Incredible journey of Timothy Chase,The / Auntie Mary's dress shop / Strawberry fields forever / Three jolly little dwarfs / Now your time has come / Hallucinations.
LP: . . . . LIK 2

Tomos, Rhiannon

DWED Y GWIR.
LP: . . . . SAIN 1232M

Tone Loc

LOC'ED AFTER DARK.
Tracks: / On fire (remix) / Wild thing / Loc'ed after dark / I got it going on / Cutting rhythms / Funky cold medina / Cheeba cheeba / Don't get close / Loc'in on the shaw / Homies, The.
LP: . . . . BRLP 526
LP: . . . . DV 3000
MC: . . . . BRCA 526
MC: . . . . ICM 2071
LP: . . . . ILPM 2071

Tones On Tail

POP.
Tracks: / Lions / War / Happiness / Never never / Performance / Slender fungus / Movement of fear / Real life / Rain.
LP: . . . . BEGA 51
MC: . . . . BEGC 51
LP: . . . . BBL 51
MC: . . . . BBLC 51

TONES ON TAIL.
LP: . . . . SITU 12
MC: . . . . SITC 12
LP: . . . . SITL 12
MC: . . . . SITLC 12

Toney, Oscar Jr

PAPA DON'S PREACHER.
Tracks: / For your precious love / Dark end of the street / Turn on your lovelight / Mon river / Any day now / You can lead your woman to the altar / Unlucky guy / He will break your heart / Without love / Down in Texas / Love that never grows old, A / Ain't that true love / Do right woman, do right man / That's all I want from you / Never get enough of your love / No sad songs.
LP: . . . . CRB 1183
MC: . . . . TCCRB 1183

Tonga

FRIENDLY ISLANDS, THE (Music from Tonga) (Various artists).
LP: . . . . TGM 122
MC: . . . . TGSMC 122

Tongue Man

JOYS OF A MEAT MASTER, THE.
LP: . . . . DS 003LP

Tongue 'N' Cheek

THIS IS TONGUE 'N' CHEEK.
Tracks: / This is Tongue 'N' Cheek / Forget me nots / Nobody / So fine / Street thang / Tomorrow / Cushion of love / It's a crime / Don't stop the love / Why? / Encore / Nobody - blue mix (CD only.) / Tomorrow - warehouse mix (CD only.) / Encore - 12" version (CD only.).
LP: . . . . SYLP 6006
LP: 794 910 1
MC: . . . . TCSYLP 6006
MC: 794 910 4

Tong,Winston

LIKE THE OTHERS.
LP: . . . . TWI 0452

THEORETICALLY CHINESE.
LP: . . . . LPOPA 004

Tonics

TONICS, THE.
Tracks: / You are my sunshine / Lemon twist / Unsere liebe ist zu ende / Ein Bild von dir / Ich such' ein Madchen in der Stadt / Dein Zarter blich / Unserrggeheimnis / Hilfe / Dynamite woman / Nuevo laredo / Baby baby goodbye / Cherry / Ich such' ein Schickes baby / Wo ist Susi? / Tausend Rosarote Pfeile / Wenn ich gerade so in Stimmung bin.
LP: . . . . BFX 15361

YOU ARE MY SUNSHINE.
Tracks: / You are my sunshine / Lemon twist / Unsere liebe ist zu ende / Ein bild von dir / Ich such ein madchen in der stadt / Hilfe / Dynamite woman / Nuevo laredo / Baby, baby goodbye / Wo ist Susie.
LP: . . . . BFX 15361

Tonight At Noon

DOWN TO THE DEVILS.
Tracks: / John MacLean march, The / Hawks and eagles fly like doves / Travelling song, The / Wire the loom / People's will, The / Run run / Hell of a man / Down to the devils / Nae trust / Mission hall, The / Harry Wigwam's / Banks of marble, The / Jack the tanner / Rolling seas.
LP: . . . . LIFL 7016
MC: . . . . LIFC 7016

TONIGHT AT NOON.
LP: . . . . STR 12001

Tonight Let's All...

TONIGHT LET'S ALL MAKE LOVE IN LONDON (Various artists).
LP: . . . . SEEG 258
MC: . . . . SEEK 258

Tonio K

NOTES FROM THE LOST CIVILISATION.
Tracks: / Executioner's song / Children's crusade / What women want / Where is that place / Without love / Stay / City life / You were there / Can't stand it / I can't stop.
LP: . . . . AMA 0763
MC: . . . . AMC 0763
LP: . . . . MYR R 6868
MC: . . . . MYR C 6868

ROMEO UNCHAINED.
LP: . . . . MYR R 6842

Tonnaugwenn

TONNAUGWENN (Various artists).
LP: . . . . GVR 215

Tonto's Expanding ...

ZERO TIME (Tonto's Expanding Head Band).
Tracks: / Cybernaut / Jetsex / Timewhys / Aurora / Riversong / Tama.
LP: . . . . K 40251

Tony D

DROPPIN' FUNKY VERSES.
MC: . . . . BRCA 574
LP: . . . . BRLP 574

Tony Toni Tone!

REVIVAL, THE.
Tracks: / Feels good / Oakland stroke / Let's have a good time / Whatever you want / Sky's the limit / Don't talk about me / Jo-Jo / All the way / Blues, The / It never rains / I care / All my love / Skin tight / Those were the days.
LP: 841 902-1
MC: 841 902-4

WHO?.
LP: 835549

Tony & Tyrone

JUST KEEP ON LOVING ME.
LP: . . . . DEAR 71

Too Nice

COLD FACTS.
Tracks: / Cold facts / Rock the girl, gee (every inch) / Phantom of hip hop, The / I get minze / Everybody loves sex / Here I come / Keep doggin' em / Two can play the game / Cold wild strong isle / I'm sad.
LP: 209843
MC: 409843

Too Short

BORN TO MACK.
LP: . . . . DM 1534

LIFE IS TOO SHORT.
LP: . . . . HIP 81
MC: . . . . HIPC 81

SHORT DOG'S IN THE HOUSE.
LP: . . . . HIP 106
MC: . . . . HIPC 106

Tools You Can Trust

AGAIN AGAIN AGAIN.
LP: . . . . T 801

YET MORE PROOF.
LP: . . . . T 601

Toop, David

NEW AND REDISCOVERED INSTRUMENTS (see Eastley,Max/ David Toop) (Toop, David/Max Eastley).

Tootles the Taxi (bk)

TOOTLES THE TAXI (rhyming stories for the very young) (Unknown narrator(s)).
MC: . . . . PLB 233

Toots

CHIKO'S BAR (Toots & Sivuca).
LP: . . . . SNTF 944

TOOTS IN MEMPHIS.
MC: . . . . ICT 9906
LP: . . . . ILPS 9906
LP: . . . . MLPS 9818

Toots & The Maytals

BEST OF TOOTS & THE MAYTALS.
Tracks: / 54-46 (was my number) / Revival reggae / African Doctor / Take me home country roads / Funky Kingston / I can't believe / Revolution / Pressure drop / Monkey man / Gold and silver / Redemption song / Pomp and pride / Time tough / In the dark.
LP: . . . . TRLS 171
MC: . . . . ZCTRL 171

CLASSIC TRACKS (See under Marley, Bob) (Toots & The Maytals/Bob Marley).

FROM THE ROOTS.
Tracks: / Pee pee cluck cluck / Loving spirit / Doctor Lester / Gola silver / Koo Koo / Revival reggae / Thy Kingdom come / Our eye Enos / Time to love, A / 9 o'clock / Know me good / Feel so good / Give peace a chance.
LP: . . . . TRLS 65

FUNKY KINGSTON.
Tracks: / Sit right down / Pomp and pride / Louie Louie / I can't believe / Redemption song / Daddy's home / Funky Kingston / It was written down.
LP: . . . . TRLS 201
MC: . . . . RRCT 21

IN THE DARK.
Tracks: / Got to be there / In the dark / Having a party / Time tough / I see you / Take a look in the mirror / Take me home country roads / Fever / Love gonna walk out on me / Revolution / 54-46 was my number / Sailing on.
LP: . . . . TRLS 202

JUST LIKE THAT.
Tracks: / Let's get it together / Chatty chatty / Gee whiz / Just like that / Turn it over / Dilly dally / Gone with the wind / Turn it up / Israel children / Journeyman.
LP: . . . . ILPS 9590
MC: . . . . ZCI 9590

KNOCKOUT.
LP: . . . . ILPS 9780

LIVE AT REGGAE SUNSPLASH.
LP: . . . . VSLP 8901

PASS THE PIPE.
Tracks: / Famine / Inside, outside / Feel free / Get up, stand up / No difference here / Rhythm down low / My love is so strong / Take it from me.
LP: . . . . ILPS 9534
MC: . . . . ZCI 9534

REGGAE GOT SOUL.
LP: . . . . ILPS 9374
MC: . . . . ZCI 9374

REGGAE GREATS.
MC: . . . . ICM 2051
MC: . . . . IRGC 1
MC: 842 820 4

TOOTS LIVE.
Tracks: / Pressure drop / Sweet 'n' dandy / Monkey man / Get up, stand up / Hallelujah / Funky Kingston / 54-46 (was my number) / Time tough.
LP: . . . . ILPS 9647

Tootsie

TOOTSIE (Film soundtrack) (Various artists).
LP: . . . . WB 23781

T.O.P.

EMOTION LOTION.
LP: . . . . ILPSX 9978
MC: . . . . ICT 9978

Top 10

TOP 10 '89 COMPLIATION (Various).
LP: . . . . SPLP 11

Top Brain Anansi

TOP BRAIN ANANSI (Various artists).
Tracks: / Top brain Aninsi: *Various artists* / First web, The: *Various artists* / Fancy dress party, The: *Various artists* / Old witch, The: *Various artists* / Tortoise race, The: *Various artists* / How hare lost his tail: *Various artists* / Treasure hunt, The: *Various artists* / How Anansi got his waist: *Various artists* / Rainbow's end: *Various artists*.
MC: . . . . ANV 658

Top Country Sound

IN THE MIDDLE OF NOWHERE.
Tracks: / What goes on / Lyin' eyes / Tomorrow never comes / Hey good

lookin' / Shutters and boards / Long thin dawn / In the middle of nowhere / Lonesome fugitive / Streets of Baltimore / Louisiana man / Letter edged in black / Steel rail blues.
LP: . . . . **FHR 093**

RIDIN' EASY.
Tracks: / If you let me know / Easy loving / Evangeline / In the early morning rain / She thinks I still care / Detroit City / Okie from Muskogee / Got the all overs for you / Idol of the band / Spinning wheel / Waiting for a train / Gonna buy me a bluebird.
LP: . . . . **FHR 104**
MC: . . . . **CFHR 104**

Top Gear

TOP GEAR (See Allman Brothers and Elton John) (Allman Brothers).

Top Gun (film)

TAKE MY BREATH AWAY (See under Berlin).

TOP GUN (Film soundtrack) (Various artists).
Tracks: / Danger zone: *Loggins, Kenny* / Mighty wings: *Cheap Trick* / Playing with the boys: *Loggins, Kenny* / Lead me on: *Marie, Teena* / Take my breath away: *Berlin* (Love theme from 'Top Gun') / Hot summer nights: *Miami* Sound Machine / Heaven in your eyes: *Lover Boy* / Through the fire: *Greene, Larry* / Destination unknown: *Marietta* / Top Gun anthem: *Faltermeyer, Harold & Steve Stevens.*
LP: . . . . **CBS 70296**
MC: **40 70296**

Top Of The Bill

TOP OF THE BILL (Various artists).
Tracks: / I love a lassie: *Lauder, Sir Harry* / Gas inspector, The: *Little Tich* / Put on your slippers: *Lloyd, Marie* / I may be crazy but I love you: *Stratton, Eugene* / Has anybody here seen Kelly?: *Forde, Florrie* / My old dutch: *Various artists* / Same as his father did before him: *Lauder, Sir Harry* / Going to the races: *Leno, Dan* / Hold your hand out you naughty boy: *Forde, Florrie* / E can't take a roise out of oi: *Chevalier, Albert* / Every little movement: *Lloyd, Marie* / Lily of Laguna: *Stratton, Eugene.*
LP: . . . . **RHA 6002**

Top of the Pops

15 YEARS OF THE TOP OF THE POPS (Various artists).
LP: . . . . **BELP 014**
MC: . . . . **ZCF 014**

BEST OF TOP OF THE POPS (1984 Edition) (Various artists).
LP: . . . . **SHM 3160**
MC: . . . . **HSC 3160**

BEST OF TOP OF THE POPS (1975 Edition) (Various artists).
LP: . . . . **BELP 001**

TOP OF THE POPS (Various artists).
LP: . . . . **REP 018**
LP: . . . . **BELP 016**

TOP OF THE POPS '89 (Various artists).
LP: . . . . **STAR 2383**
MC: . . . . **STAC 2383**

Top Secret

ANOTHER CRAZY DAY.
Tracks: / Another crazy day / Let me take your photograph / I love my video / I wanna be your TV / Oi referee / She's so ugly / Let me take your number / Don't say no / Do you like my stereo / Talking heads / It won't be long now / Radio.
LP: . . . . **SKATE 2**
MC: . . . . **KAT 2**

Top Secret (Film)

TOP SECRET (Film Soundtrack) (Various artists).
LP: . . . . **TER 1090**
MC: . . . . **CTV 81219**

Topic (label)

MEN AT WORK Topic Sampler No.3 (Various artists).
LP: . . . . **TPS 166**

Topkapi

TOPKAPI (Film soundtrack) (Various artists).
LP: . . . . **MCA 25118**
MC: . . . . **MCAC 25118**

Topol

TOPOL'S ISRAEL (TV soundtrack).
Tracks: / Just one more song / Market song / Promise, The / Remembering / Sea shores / My son are you laughing or crying / Kinneret Kinneret / On and on / Bedouin chant / Jerusalem / Cheribi cheribom / Massada.
LP: . . . . **REH 529**
MC: . . . . **ZCR 529**

Topsy, Tiny

AW SHUCKS BABY!.
Tracks: / Aw shucks baby / Woman's intuition, A / Miss you so / Come on, come on, come on / Ring around my finger / You shocked me / Just a little bit / Everybody needs some loving / Waterproof eyes / Western rock 'n' roll / Cha cha Sue.
LP: . . . . **SING 1161**

Toquinho

TOQUINHO.
LP: **7701**

Tora Tora

SURPRISE ATTACK.
Tracks: / Love's a bitch / 28 days / Hard times / Guilty / Phantom rider / Walkin' shoes / Riverside drive / She's good she's bad / One for the road / Being there.
LP: . . . . **AMA 5261**
MC: . . . . **AMC 5261**

Torananga

BASTARD BALLADS.
Tracks: / Sentenced / Dealers in death / Bastard ballads / Soldiers be brave / Time to burn / Retribution.
LP: . . . . **VILE 005**

GOD'S GIFT.
LP: . . . . **CHR 1771**
MC: . . . . **ZCHR 1771**

Torcello, John

STATE OF THE ART ACCORDION.
Tracks: / Partita piccola / Introspection / Trillo / Scherzo brillante / Sonata musette.
LP: . . . . **JTC 001**

Torch

ELECTIKISS.
LP: . . . . **SWORDLP 004**

TORCH.
LP: . . . . **SWORDLP 001**

Torch Song

WISH THING.
Tracks: / Don't look now / Telepathy / Ode to Billy Joe / Another place / Prepare to energise / Tattered dress / Sweet thing / You said you were comming / Water clock secret.
LP: . . . . **IRSA 7046**
MC: . . . . **IRSC 7046**

Torch Song Trilogy

TORCH SONG TRILOGY (Film soundtrack) (Various artists).
LP: **837 785-1**
MC: **837 785-4**

Torch, Sydney

AT THE CINEMA ORGAN (The Regal cinema, Marble Arch).
Tracks: / There's something about a soldier / Butterflies in the rain / Dance of the blue marionettes / Hot dog / Bugle call rag / Twelfth Street rag / Orient express / Temptation rag / Bei mir bist du schon / Remember me / Flying Scotsman / Teddy bear's picnic / Torch song parade of 1937 / In the still of the night.
LP: . . . . **SH 305**
MC: . . . . **TC SH 305**

SIDNEY TORCH AT THE THEATRE ORGAN(1932-39).
LP: . . . . **DO 1211 2**

Torero Band

TIJUANA CHRISTMAS.
Tracks: / Holly and the ivy, The / Silent night / Hark the herald angels sing / While shepherds watched their flocks by night / O Little town of Bethlehem / Good King Wenceslas / God rest ye merry gentlemen / Away in a manger / First Noel, The / Christians awake / Once in royal David's city / O come all ye faithful / Jingle bells (CD only.) / Ding dong merrily on high (CD only.) / We three kings of orient are (CD only.) / See amid the winter snow (CD only.) / It came upon a midnight clear (CD only.) / Good Christian men rejoice (CD only.) / Angels in the realms of glory (CD only.) / White Christmas (CD only.).
LP: . . . . **MFP 41 5666 1**
MC: . . . . **MFP 41 5666 4**
MC: . . . . **TCMFP 5901**

TIJUANA STYLE.
Tracks: / Hey Jude / Taste of honey, A / Yellow submarine / Tijuana taxi / With a little help from my friends / Casino Royale / I want to hold your hand / Guantanamera / These boots are made for walking / Spanish flea / Walk in the Black Forest, A / From me to you / Up Cherry Street / Can't buy me love / Hello Dolly / Eleanor Rigby / Yesterday / Mame / Ob la di ob la da / I'll never fall in love again / Man and a woman, A (From the film Un Homme Et Une Femme.) / A Banda / Lonely bull, The / America / Spanish Harlem / All my loving / If I were a rich man / Please, please me / Our day will come / Acapulco 1922 / She loves you / Happening, The.
MC: . . . . **TCDL 1152**
2LP: . . . . **DL 1152**

Torff, Brian

IN CONCERT AT THE PAVILION (see Shearing, George) (Torff, Brian & George Shearing).

MANHATTAN HOE-DOWN.
LP: . . . . **AP 182**

Torino

CUSTOMIZED.
LP: . . . . **WKFMLP 104**
MC: . . . . **WKFMMC 104**

ROCK IT.
Tracks: / Rock it / Nights on fire / Seven mountains / Baby blue / It takes a man to cry / Showdown / Dance all night / One in a million / Shine / Turn it up.
LP: . . . . **WKFMLP 123**
MC: . . . . **WKFMMC 123**

Torkanowsky, David

STEPPIN' OUT.
LP: . . . . **ROUNDER 2090**
MC: . . . . **ROUNDER 2090C**

Torme

DIE PRETTY, DIE YOUNG.
Tracks: / Let it rock / Real thing, The / Ready / Sex action / Ways of the East, The / Killer / Memphis / Louise / Crimes of passion / Ghost train.
LP: . . . . **HMRLP 94**
MC: . . . . **HMRMC 94**

OFFICIAL LIVE BOOTLEG.
LP: . . . . **ONS 3**

Torme, Bernie

ARE WE THERE YET?.
LP: . . . . **HMRLP 168**
MC: . . . . **HMRMC 168**

BACK TO BABYLON.
Tracks: / All around the world / Star / Eyes of the world / Burning bridges / Hardcore / Here I go / Family at war / Front line / Arabia / Mystery train / T.V.O.D. (CD only.) / Kerrap (CD only.) / Love, guns and money (CD only.).
LP: . . . . **ZEB 6**

BACK WITH THE BOYS.
Tracks: / Come Tomorrow / My baby loves a vampire / No Easy Way / Try and stop me (Previously Unreleased) / Don't give up your day job (Previously unreleased) / Turn out the lights / Wild West / Whats next (Previously unreleased version) / Lies (Previously unreleased version) / Night Lights (Previously unreleased version) / All day and all of the night / Back with the boys (Previously unreleased).
LP: . . . . **RAWLP 010**
MC: . . . . **RAWTC 010**

ELECTRIC GYPSIES.
Tracks: / Wild west / 20th century / Lightning / Strikes / Too young / Call of the wild / D.I.S.E / Presences / I can't control myself / Go go.
LP: . . . . **ZEB 1**
MC: . . . . **CZEB 1**

LIVE: BERNIE TORME.
Tracks: / Intro-presences / Wild west / Turn on the lights / Lightning strikes / Getting there / Too young / No easy way.
LP: . . . . **MZEB 3**

TURN OUT THE LIGHTS.
Tracks: / Turn out the lights / Painter man / Lies / America / Getting there / Possession / No reply / Chelsea girls / India / Oh no.
LP: . . . . **KAMLP 2**
MC: . . . . **KAMC 2**

Torme, Mel

BACK IN TOWN (Torme, Mel & Mel-Tones).
Tracks: / Makin' whoopee / Baubles, bangles and beads / What is this thing called love? / Truckin' / Bunch of the blues, The / Some like it hot.
LP: **2304 384**

DUKE ELLINGTON AND COUNT BASIE SONGBOOK, THE.
Tracks: / I'm gonna go fishin / Don't get around much anymore / I like the sunrise / Take the 'A' train / Reminiscin' in tempo / Outskirts of town, the / Just a sittin' and a rockin' / Down for double / I'm gonna move to the outskirts of town / Blue and sentimental / Oh what a night for love / Sent for you yesterday / In the evening.
LP: . . . . **VRV 8**
MC: . . . . **VRVC 8**
LP: **823 248-1**

ELEGANT EVENING, AN (See under Shearing, George) (Torme, Mel & George Shearing).

EVENING AT CHARLIE'S, AN (See under Shearing, George) (Torme, Mel & George Shearing).

GONE WITH THE WIND.
Tracks: / Day you came along, The / Mimi / Magic town / I'll always be in love with you / It's easy to remember / How long has this been going on / Little kiss each morning a little kiss each night, A / When is sometime / Gone with the wind / What are you doing New Year's Eve.
LP: . . . . **MVS 2005**

GREAT SINGERS OF THE FIFTIES.
LP: . . . . **GP 705**

GREAT SONG STYLISTS VOL.2.
Tracks: / Limehouse blues / Nightingale sang in Berkeley Square, A / I've got a lovely bunch of coconuts / These foolish things / Geordie / My one and only Highland fling / White cliffs of Dover, The / Danny boy / Let there be love / Greensleeves / Try a little tenderness / London pride / Time was / You've got me goin' ev'ry which way.
LP: . . . . **AX 5**

I CAN'T GIVE YOU ANYTHING BUT LOVE.
Tracks: / I can't give you anything but love / I'm yours / Little white lies / Love, you funny thing / Cottage for sale / Love is the sweetest thing / You're driving me crazy / Who cares what people say / My baby just cares for me / If I had a girl like you.
LP: . . . . **MVS 2000**

I DIG DUKE AND COUNT.
LP: **2304 402**

IN CONCERT - TOKYO (Torme, Mel & Marty Paich Dektette).
Tracks: / It don't mean a thing / Cottontail / More than you know / Sweet Georgia Brown / Just in time / When the sun comes out / Carioca / Too close for comfort / City, The / Bossa nova pot pourri / On the street where you live.
LP: . . . . **CJ 382**
MC: . . . . **CJ 382 C**

IT HAPPENED IN MONTEREY (Torme, Mel & Mel-Tones).
Tracks: / Dream awhile / Try a little tenderness / Born to be blue / There's no business like show business / That's where I came in / Night and day / Fine and dandy / There's no-one but you / It happened in Monterey / Willow Road / South America take it away.
LP: . . . . **MVS 510**

IT'S A BLUE WORLD.
Tracks: / I got it bad and that ain't good / Till the clouds roll by / Isn't it romantic? / I know why / All this and Heaven too / How long has this been going on? / Polka dots and moonbeams / You leave me breathless / I found a million dollar baby / Wonderful one / It's a blue world / Stay as sweet as you are.
LP: . . . . **AFF 138**

LIVE AT THE CRESCENDO (AFFINITY).
Tracks: / It's only a paper moon / What is this thing called love / One for my baby / Love is just a bug / Nightingale sang in berkely square / Autumn leaves / Just one of those things / Girl next door / Lover come back to me / Looking at you / Tender trap / I wish i was in love again / It's de-lovely / It's alright with me / Manhattan / Taking a chance on love / Home by the sea / I got plenty o' nuttin' / Nobody's heart.
2LP: . . . . **AFFD 100**

LIVE AT THE CRESCENDO (MCA).
LP: . . . . **MCL 1683**

LULU'S BACK IN TOWN (Torme, Mel & Marty Paich Dektette).
Tracks: / Lulu's back in town / When the sun Comes out / I love to watch the moonlight / Fascinating rhythm / Blues, the / Carioca / Lady is a tramp, The / I like to recognise the tune / Keeping myself for you / Lullaby of birdland / When April comes again / Sing for your supper.
LP: . . . . **AFF 85**

MEL AND GEORGE 'DO' WORLD WAR II (Torme, Mel & George Shearing).
Tracks: / Lili Marlene / I've heard that song before / I know why and so do you / Love / Aren't you glad you're you / Ellington medley / Walk medley / I could write a book / Lovely way to spend an evening, A / On the swing shift/Five o'clock whistle / Ac-cent-tchu-ate the positive / This is the army Mister Jones / We mustn't say goodbye.
MC: . . . . **CJ 471C**

MEL TORME (Compact/Walkman jazz).
Tracks: / Too close for comfort / Stranger in town, A / Don't get around much anymore / Body and soul / Surrey with the fringe on top / Welcome to the club / Sent for you yesterday / Truckin'.
MC: **833 282-4**

MEL TORME.
MC: .... ZCGAS 740
LP: .... ENT LP 13009
MC: .... ENT MC 13009

MEL TORME (2).
Tracks: / That old feeling / Blues in the night / 'Round midnight / I don't want to cry anymore.
LP: .... IMS 2304 500

MEL TORME AND FRIENDS RECORDED LIVE AT MARTY'S NEW YORK (Torme, Mel & Friends).
Tracks: / Let's take a walk around the block / New York state of mind / When the world was young / Pick yourself up / Silly habits / Mountain greenery / Cottage for sale / Take a letter, Miss Jones / Real thing, The / Line for Lyons / Venus de Milo / Walking shoes / Watch what happens / Fly me to the moon / You and the night and the music / Shakin' the blues away / Isn't it romantic / Summertime / They pass by, singin' / I got plenty o' nuttin' / It takes a long pull to get there / It ain't necessarily so / Strawberry woman / Oh Bess, oh where's my Bess? / Bess, you is my woman now / Folks who live on the hill, The / Chase me Charlie / Best is yet to come, The / Isn't it a pity / Wave / I guess I'll have to change my plan / Love for sale.
LP: .... FIND 5661
MC: .... ZCFID 5661

MEL TORME COLLECTION (20 golden greats).
Tracks: / That old black magic / Blue moon / Get out of town / Jeepers creepers / From this moment on / Our love is here to stay / Mountain greenery / Bernie's tune / Old devil moon / Get happy / Don't you believe it / Along with me / Changing my tune / They can't convince me / Guilty / For you, for me, for evermore / You're driving me crazy / Goody goody / Christmas song, The / q believe.
LP: .... DVLP 2046
MC: .... DVMC 2046

MEL TORME (GLENDALE).
Tracks: / Easy to remember / My funny valentine / September song / April showers / Blues in the night.
LP: .... GL 6018

MEL TORME LIVE Vol. 2.
LP: .... SG 5012

MEL TORME LIVE.
Tracks: / You're driving me crazy / You're the top / When the red, red robin comes bob, bob, bobbin' along / Everything happens to me / It's a most unusual day / Pythagoras how you stagger us / French lesson, The / It's dark on observatory hill / I've got the sun in the morning and the moon at night / On a slow boat to China.
LP: .... JASM 2529
MC: .... JASMC 2529

MEL TORME SINGS.
Tracks: / I'm getting sentimental over you / I can't believe that you're in love with me / Prelude to a kiss / I've got the world on a string / Devil and the deep blue sea / I surrender dear / I let a song go out of my heart / Don't worry 'bout me / One morning in May / I can't give you anything but love.
LP: .... BDL 1017
LP: 20069
MC: 40069

MEL TORME SINGS ABOUT LOVE.
LP: .... AP 67

MEL TORME, VOL.1.
Tracks: / Foggy day, A / I cover the waterfront / But beautiful / Until the real thing comes along / Makin' whoopee / Three little words / It's dream time.
LP: .... MVS 508

MEL TORME WITH THE MELTONES - LIVE!.
LP: .... SG 5006

MEL TORME/ROB MCCONNELL AND BOSS BRASS (Torme, Mel/Rob McConnell/Boss Brass).
Tracks: / Just friends / September song / Don'cha go 'way mad / House is not a home, A / Song is you, The / Cow cow boogie / Handful of stars, A / Stars fell on Alabama / It don't mean a thing / Do nothing till you hear from me / Mood indigo / Take the 'A' train / Sophisticated lady / Satin doll.
LP: .... CJ 306
MC: .... CJC 306

MUSICAL SOUNDS ARE THE BEST SONGS.
Tracks: / Flat foot floogie / Hut sut song, The / All of you / Just one more chance / It don't mean a thing / Tutti frutti / Cement mixer / Hold tight / Blue skies / Rose O'Day / Spellbound / I's a muggin'.
LP: .... JASM 1004

NIGHT AT THE CONCORD PAVILION.
Tracks: / Sing for your supper / Sing sing sing / Sing (sing a song) / You make me feel so young / Early Autumn / Guys and dolls medley / I could have told you / Losing my mind / Deep in a dream / Goin' out of my head / Too darn hot / Day in - day out / Down for double / You're driving me crazy / Sent for you yesterday.
MC: .... CJ 433 C

PRIME TIME.
LP: .... GP 701

REUNION (Torme, Mel & Marty Paich Dektette).
Tracks: / Sweet Georgia Brown / I'm wishing / Blues, The / Trolley song, The / More than you know / For whom the bell tolls / When you wish upon a star / Walk between raindrops / Bossa nova pot porri / Get me to the church on time / Goodbye look, The / Spain (I can recall).
LP: .... CJ 360
MC: .... CJ 360 C

ROUND MIDNIGHT.
LP: .... ST 252

SINGS HIS CALIFORNIA SUITE (Torme, Mel Orchestra).
Tracks: / Mountain desert / We think the west coast is the best coast in the land / Coney Island / Miami waltz, The / They go to San Diego / Sunday night in San Fernando / Got the gate on the Golden Gate / Prelude to poor little extra girl / Poor little extra girl.
LP: .... DS 910

SMOOTH ONE, THE.
MC: .... SLC 61005

SWINGS SCHUBERT ALLEY.
Tracks: / Too close for comfort / Once in love with Amy / Sleeping bee / On the street where you live / Just in time / Whatever Lola wants (Lola gets) / Surrey with the fringe on top / Old devil moon / Too darn hot / Lonely town.
LP: 2304235

THAT'S ALL.
Tracks: / I've got you under my skin / That's all / What is there to say / Do I love you / Folks that live on the hill / Isn't it a pity / Ho ba la / PS I love you / Nearness of you / My romance / Second time around / Haven't we met.
LP: 32313

TORME.
Tracks: / All in love is fair / First time ever I saw your face, The / New York state of mind / Stars / Send in the clowns / Ordinary fool / When the world was young / Yesterday when I was young / Bye bye blackbird.
LP: .... RHAP 3
LP: 2304 500
LP: 823 010 4

TORME SINGS ASTAIRE (Torme, Mel & Marty Paich Dektette).
Tracks: / Nice work if you can get it / Something's gotta give / Foggy day, A / Fine romance, A / Let's call the whole thing off / Top hat, white tie and tails / Way you look tonight / Piccolino, The / They can't take that away from me / Cheek to cheek / Let's face the music and dance / They all laughed.
LP: .... AFF 107
MC: .... TCAFF 107

VINTAGE YEAR (Torme, Mel & George Shearing).
Tracks: / Whisper not / Love me or leave me / Out of this world / Some day I'll find you / Midnight sun / New York, New York / Since I fell for you / Way you look tonight / Anyone can whistle / Tune for humming, A / When Sunny gets blue / Little man you've had a busy day / Folks who live on the hill, The (Bonus track on CD only.) / Bittersweet (Bonus track on CD only.).
LP: .... CJ 341
MC: .... CJC 341

Torment

ALL AROUND THE WORLD.
LP: .... NERD 050

HYPNOSIS.
LP: .... NERD 057

PSYCLOPS CARNIVAL.
LP: .... NERD 025

THREE'S A CROWD.
Tracks: / Torment / These chains / You did nothing / Three's a crowd / Scared of myself / Out of my head / I'm a loser / Missing you / Funeral party / Rules for fools.
LP: .... NERD 032

Tormentors

GODDESS OF LOVE.
LP: .... SKULL 8344

HANGING AROUND.
LP: .... EVA 12055

Torn, David

BEST LAID PLANS.
Tracks: / Before the bitter wind / Best laid plans / Hum of its parts, the / Removable tongue / In the fifth direction / Two face flash / Angle of incidents.
LP: .... ECM 1284

CLOUD ABOUT MERCURY.
Tracks: / Suyafhu skin..snapping the hollow reed / Mercury grid, the / 3 minutes of pure entertainment / Previous man / Network of sparks.
LP: .... ECM 1322

Torn In Two

TORN IN TWO (Various artists).
LP: .... TOR 002

Tornados

REMEMBERING.
Tracks: / Telstar / Love and fury / Globetrotter / Ridin' the wind / Jugle fever / Robot / Ice cream man / Nightrider / Hymn for teenagers / Indian brave / Breeze and I / Exodus.
LP: .... REM 4
MC: .... KREMC 481

WE WANT BILLY! (see Fury, Billy & The Tornados) (Tornados & Billy Fury).

Torner, Gosta

LIVING LEGEND.
LP: .... NOST 7607

Toro, Yomo

FUNKY JIBARO.
Tracks: / Funky jibaro / El sapo / Cuatro pachanga / Tributo a los angelitos negros / Recuerdame siempre / Mambo oriental / A la verde gue / Minerva / Raging toro / Cuarto feeling.
LP: .... AN 8723
MC: .... ANC 8723

GRACIAS.
LP: .... MLPS 1034
MC: .... MCT 1034

Toronto

GIRLS NIGHT OUT.
LP: .... MCF 3195
MC: .... MCFC 3195

HEAD ON.
Tracks: / Head on / Silver screen / Still talkin' 'bout love / Someone will play the blues / It comes from you / Enough is enough / Master of disguise / Blackmail / Gone in a flash.
LP: .... AMLH 64872

LOOKIN' FOR TROUBLE.
Tracks: / Even the score / 5035 / Get your hands off me / You better run / Don't stop me / Lookin' for trouble / Do watcha: be watcha / Delicious / Shot down / Tie me down.
LP: .... AMLH 64821

Torrance, Bill

BILL TORRANCE SINGS.
Tracks: / Heart / To be your man / She thinks I still care / Beyond these walls / When I dream / Fool such as I / Reason to believe / Cotton Jenny / My happiness / Drinkin' them beers / Me and the elephant / I don't want to talk about it.
LP: .... KLP 28

INCHLAGGAN.
LP: .... TREE 001
MC: .... TREE 001C

REFLECTION.
LP: .... KLP 43
MC: .... ZCKLP 43

Torrance, Lionel

SAX MAN SUPREME.
Tracks: / Rooty tooty / Roll on mule / Hey mama / If you were only mine / Saka / I found an angel / Moscow twist / Flim flam / Comin' round the mountain / Port Arthur shuffle / Anytime / If you don't want me / Rockin' jolie blonde / Shoo shoo chicken.
LP: .... FLY 615

Torres, Jaime

MUSIC FROM THE INCAS.
LP: C347 251

Torres, Liz

CAN'T GET ENOUGH (Torres, Liz/ Master C & J).
LP: .... LIZT 1
MC: .... ZCLIZT 1

QUEEN IS IN THE HOUSE, THE.
LP: .... HIP 83
MC: .... HIPC 83

Torres, Roberto

HOMANAJE A BENY MORE.
LP: .... SLP 1050

Torshavn Choir

BLATT (Torshavn Choir/Torshavn Chamber Choir).
LP: .... FKT 1

Torture

STORM ALERT.
Tracks: / Igominous slaughter / Slay ride / Storm alert / Whips / Blood portraits / Terror kingdom / Enter the chamber / Deceiver.
LP: .... CORE 2

Torvill & Dean

MAGIC OF TORVILL & DEAN (Various artists).
LP: .... SMR 8502
MCSET: .... SMC 8502

Tosca

TOSCA (See under Puccini) (Various artists).

Toscano, Paul

GYPSY KINGS (See under Nemeth, Yoska) (Nemeth, Yoska & Paul Toscano).

Tosh, Andrew

MAKE PLACE FOR THE YOUTH.
LP: 269672-1
MC: 269672-4

ORIGINAL MAN, THE.
Tracks: / Same dog bite / Too much rat / Heathen rage / My enemies / Maga dog / I'm the youngest / Poverty is a crime / Original man, The / My enemies (dub version) / Poverty is a crime (dub version) / Original man, The (dub version).
LP: .... ATLP 102

Tosh, Peter

BUSH DOCTOR.
Tracks: / You gotta walk don't look back / Pick myself up / I'm the toughest / Soon come / Moses the prophet / Bush doctor / Stand firm / Dem ha fe get a beatin' / Creation.
LP: .... FA 41 3139 1
MC: .... FA 41 3139 4
LP: .... TRPT 100
MC: .... ZCTRP 100

CAPTURED LIVE.
Tracks: / Coming in hot / Bush doctor / African / Get up stand up / Johnny b. goode / Equal rights / Downpresser man / Rastafari is.
LP: .... EG 2401671
LP: .... PTOSH 1

EQUAL RIGHTS.
Tracks: / Get up stand up / Downpressor man / I am that I am / Stepping razor / Equal rights / African / Jah guide / Apartheid.
LP: .... OVED 109

LEGALIZE IT.
Tracks: / Legalize it / Burial / Whatcha gonna do / No sympathy / Why must I cry / Igziabeher (Let Jah be praised) / Ketchy shuby / Till your well runs dry / Brand new secondhand.
LP: .... OVED 108
LP: .... V 2061
MC: .... OVEDC 108

MAMA AFRICA.
Tracks: / Mama Africa / Glasshouse / Not gonna give it up / Stop that rain / Johnny B. Goode / Where you gonna run / Peace treaty / Feel no way / Maga dog.
LP: .... RDC 2005
MC: .... TC RDC 2005

MYSTIC MAN.
Tracks: / Mystic man / Recruiting soldiers / Can't you see / Jah deh no / Fight on / Buk-in-ham Palace / Day the dollar die / Crystal ball / Rumours of war.
LP: .... CUN 39110
LP: .... TRPT 101
MC: .... ZCTRP 101

NO NUCLEAR WAR.
Tracks: / No nuclear war / Nah Goa Jail / Fight apartheid / Vampire / In my song / Lesson in my life / Testify / Come together.
LP: .... PCS 7309
MC: .... TCPCS 7309

TOUGHEST, THE.
Tracks: / Coming in hot / Don't look back / Pick myself up / Crystal ball / Mystic man / Reggaemylitis / Bush doctor / Maga dog / Johnny B. Goode / Equal rights / In my song.
LP: .... PCS 7318
MC: .... TCPCS 7318

WANTED DREAD AND ALIVE.
Tracks: / Coming in hot / Nothing but love / Reggaemylitis / Rock with me / Oh bumbo klaat / Wanted dread and alive / Rastafari is / Guide me from my friend / Fools die.
LP: .... CUNS 39113
MC: .... TC-CUNS 39113

Toshiko/Mariano

TOSHIKO MARIANO QUARTET (Toshiko Mariano Quartet).
LP: .... CS 9012

Toss The Feathers

LIVE AT THE 32 COUNTIES CLUB.
MC: BIP 304

SKIDOO.
Tracks: / Skidoo.
MC: BIP 404

Total Body Workout

ARNOLD SCHWARZENEGGER'S TOTAL BODY WORKOUT (See under Schwarzenegger, Arnold) (Various artists).

Total Contrast

BEAT TO BEAT.
Tracks: / Jody / Painting by numbers / Found somebody / Help me / Just a little bit / Kiss / Hidden in a heartbeat / Same old story / Teach me to forget / Jody - the dance hall version (On CD only).
LP: LONLP 45
MC: LONC 45

TOTAL CONTRAST.
Tracks: / Hit and Run / River, the / Where is love / How many reasons / Takes a Little time / What you gonna do about it / Sunshine / Entangled.
LP: LONLP 15
MC: LONC 15

Total Recall

TOTAL RECALL (Film soundtrack) (Various artists).
Tracks: / Dream, The: *Various artists* / Hologram, The: *Various artists* / Big jump, The: *Various artists* / Mutant, The: *Various artists* / Cleaver girl: *Various artists* / First meeting: *Various artists* / Treatment, The: *Various artists* / Where am I?: *Various artists* / End of a dream: *Various artists* / New life, A: *Various artists*.
LP: VS 5267
MC: VSC 5267

Totally Wired

TOTALLY WIRED (Various artists).
LP: JAZIDLP 13

TOTALLY WIRED 4 (Various artists).
LP: JAZIDLP 28

TOTALLY WIRED VOL.2 (Various artists).
LP: JAZIDLP 16

TOTALLY WIRED VOL.3 (Various artists).
LP: JAZIDLP 022

Toto

FAHRENHEIT.
Tracks: / Till the end / We can make it tonight / Without your Love / Can't stand it any longer / I'll be over you / Fahrenheit / Somewhere tonight / Could this be Love / Lea / Don't stop me now.
LP: CBS 57091
MC: 40 57091

HOLD THE LINE.
LP: SHM 3152
MC: HSC 3152

HYDRA.
Tracks: / Hydra / St. George and the dragon / 99 / Lorraine / All us boys / Mama / White sister / Secret love, A.
LP: CBS 32222
MC: 40 32222
LP: 83900
LP: CBS 83900

ISOLATION.
Tracks: / Carmen / Lion / Stranger in town / Angel don't cry / How does it feel / Endless / Isolation / Mr. Friendly / Change of heart / Holyanna.
LP: CBS 86305

SEVENTH ONE, THE.
Tracks: / Pamela / You got me / Anna / Stop loving you / Mushanga / Stay away / Straight for the heart / Only the children / Thousand years, A / These chains / Home of the brave.
LP: 4606451
MC: 4606454

TOTO.
Tracks: / Child's anthem / I'll supply the love / Georgie Porgie / Manuella run / You are the flower / Girl goodbye / Takin' it back / Rockmaker / Hold the line / Angela.
LP: 32165
MC: 40 32165
LP: 83148

TOTO IV.
Tracks: / Rossana / Make believe / I won't hold you back / Good for you / It's a feeling / Afraid of love / Lovers in the night / We made it / Waiting for your love / Africa.
LP: 4500881
MC: 4500884
LP: 85529

TOTO PAST TO PRESENT (1977-1990).
Tracks: / Love has the power / Africa / Hold the line / Out of love / Georgie Porgie / I'll be over you / Can you hear what I'm saying / Rosanna / I won't hold you back / Stop loving you / 99 / Pamela / Animal.
LP: 4659881
MC: 4659884

TURN BACK.
Tracks: / Gift with a golden gun / English eyes / Live for today / Million miles away / Goodbye Elenor / I think I could stand you forever / Turn back / If it's the last night.
LP: CBS 84609

Toto Coelo

ANGLIA REMIX VOL.2. (see Astaire/ Angie Gold/Toto Coelo).

Totterdell, Dave

ROOM FOR THOUGHT.
Tracks: / Yankee lady / Lynmouth flood / Live in peace / Ladies you leave behind / Bruton town / Remember how it used to be / One night stand / Play at war / Matty Groves / Mary Britt.
LP: BURL 003

Tottie (bk)

TOTTIE.
MCSET: DTO 10564

Tottle, Jack

BACK ROAD.
LP: ROUNDER 0067

Touch

BACK ALLEY VICES.
LP: EBON 28

MERIDIANS 1.
MC: T 2

TOUCH 33.
MC: T 33

Touch Of Class (Film)

TOUCH OF CLASS, A (Film Soundtrack) (Various artists).
LP: 6612 040

Touch Of Evil

TOUCH OF EVIL, A (See under Mancini, Henry) (Mancini, Henry & His Orchestra).

Touched

DEATH ROW.
LP: EBON 33

DREAM GIRL.
Tracks: / Dream girl / We'll fight back.
LP: EBON 27

Touchet Brothers

TOUCHET BROTHERS CAJUN MUSIC BAND, THE.
LP: 6055
MC: 6055 TC

Touchstone

JEALOUSY.
LP: SIF 1050
MC: CSIF 1050

NEW LAND, THE.
LP: SIF 1040
MC: CSIF 1040

Touff, Cy

CY TOUFF, HIS OCTET & QUINTET (Touff, Cy Octet And Quintet).
LP: FS 51

TOUFF ASSIGNMENT.
LP: FS 62

Tough Guys Don't Dance

TOUGH GUYS DON'T DANCE (Film soundtrack) (Various artists).
LP: STV 81346

Tough Language

TOUGH LANGUAGE (Various artists).
LP: T 6

Tough Ted (bk)

TOUGH TED (Simon Bond) (Blake, Roger (nar)).
MC: 00 1034596

Tough Young Tenors

ALONE TOGETHER.
MC: ANC 8765

Tougher Than Leather

TOUGHER THAN LEATHER (See under Run D.M.C.) (Run D.M.C.).

Toulai

HOMAGE TO NAZIM HIKMET (Toulai & Francois Rabbath).
Tracks: / Meviana celaleddin rumi / Koroglu / Karacaoglan / Nazim Hikmet.
LP: ARN 33636

TOULAI AND FRANCOIS RABBATH (Toulai & Francois Rabbath).
Tracks: / Leylim ley / Bara seni gerek seni / Kirdilar / Mapusane / Gozumde daim / Abidin / Dere geliyor / Elif / Ne bilir.
LP: ARN 33557

Toups, Wayne

BLAST FROM THE BAYOU.
Tracks: / Sweet Jolene / Tupelo honey / Sugar bee / Going back to Big Mamou / Tell it like it is / Two step mamou / Secret love, A.
LP: 8365181
MC: 8365184

CAJUN PARADISE.
LP: SNTF 814

Toure, Ali Farka

LA DROGUE.
LP: ESP 165558

RIVER, THE.
Tracks: / Heygana / Toungere / Tangambara / Ai bine / Kenouna / Goydiotodam / Boyrei / Lobo / Instrumental.
LP: WCB 017
MC: WCC 017

Toure Kunda

AMADOU TILO.
LP: CEL 6646

CASAMANCE.
LP: CEL 6663

E'MMA AFRICA.
MC: CELC 4478

LIVE.
LP: CEL 6106

Tourists

LUMINOUS BASEMENT.
Tracks: / Walls and foundations / Don't say I told you so / Weekdays / So you want to go away now / One step nearer the edge / Angels and demons / Talk to me / Round round blues / Let's take a walk / Time drags so slow / I'm going to change my mind.
LP: RCALP 5001

REALITY EFFECT.
Tracks: / I only want to be with you.
LP: GO 1019

TOURISTS, THE.
Tracks: / Blind among the flowers / Save me / Fools paradise / Can't stop laughing / Don't get left behind / Another english day / Deadly kiss / Ain't no room / Loneliest man in the world / Useless duration of time / He who laughs last laughs longest / Just like you.
LP: INTS 5096
MC: INTK 5096
LP: GO 1018
LP: LOGO 1018

Toussaint, Allen

FROM A WHISPER TO A SCREAM (Retro 87-88).
Tracks: / From a whisper to a scream / Chokin' kind, The / Sweet touch of love / What is success / Working in the coalmine / Everything I do gonh be funky / Either / Louie / Cast your fate to the wind / Number nine / Pickles.
LP: KENT 036

SOUTHERN NIGHTS.
Tracks: / Last train / Worldwide / Back in baby's arms / Country John / Basic lady / Southern nights / You will not lose / What do you want the girl to do / When the party's over / Cruel way to go down.
LP: ED 155

WILD SOUNDS OF NEW ORLEANS.
Tracks: / Up the creek / Tim Tam / Me And You / Bono / Java / Happy Times / Nowhere to go / Nashua / Po' Boy Walk / Pelican parade.
LP: ED 275

WITH THE STOKES.
LP: BANDY 70014

Touzet, Rene

BEST OF RENE TOUZET.
LP: GNPS 2000

GREATEST LATIN HITS (Touzet, Rene Orchestra).
LP: GNPS 74

Tovey, Frank

CIVILIAN.
Tracks: / Civilian.
LP: STUMM 56

EASY LISTENING FOR THE HARD OF HEARING (see under Rice, Boyd) (Tovey, Frank & Boyd Rice).

FAD GADGET SINGLES.
Tracks: / Back to nature / Box, The / Ricky's hand / Fireside favourite / Insecticide / Lady shave / Saturday night special / King of the flies / Life on the line / 4M / For whom the bells toll / Love parasite / I discover love / Collapsing new people / One man's meat.
LP: STUMM 37
MC: CSTUMM 37

SNAKES AND LADDERS.
LP: STUMM 23
MC: CSTUMM 23

TYRANNY AND THE HIRED HAND.
Tracks: / 31 depression blues / Hard times in the cotton mill / John Henry/Let your hammer ring / Blantyre explosion / Money cravin' folks / All I got's gone / Midwife song / Sam hall / Dark as a dungeon / Men of good fortune / Sixteen tons / North country blues / Buffalo skinners / Black lung song / Pastures of plenty / Joe hill.
LP: STUMM 73
MC: CSTUMM 73

Towards 2000

SCOTLAND THE WHAT?.
LP: STW 88
MC: CSTW 88

Tower Of Power

POWER.
Tracks: / Baby's got the power / Some days were meant for rain / Ball and chain / Count on me / Up against yourself / Credit / Boys night out / Through lovers eyes / On the one.
LP: YL 0106

TOWER OF POWER.
LP: LAB 17

WHAT IS HIP.
Tracks: / Maybe it'll rub off / On the serious side / Just enough and too much / So very hard to go / Soul vaccination / Don't change horses in the middle of a stream / What is hip / Get yo' feet back on the ground / Both sorry over nothing / Clean slate / Treat me like your man / Give me the proof / (To say the least) you're the most.
LP: ED 206

Towering Inferno

TOWERING INFERNO, THE (Film soundtrack) (Various artists).
Tracks: / Main title: *Various artists* / Architect's dream: *Various artists* / Lisolette and Harlee: *Various artists* / Something for Susan: *Various artists* / Trapped lovers: *Various artists* / We may never love like this again: *Various artists* / Susan and Doug: *Various artists* / Helicopter explosion, The: *Various artists*/ Planting the charges: *Various artists* / Finale: *Various artists*.
LP: K 56102

Town Like Alice (bk)

TOWN LIKE ALICE, A (See also Nevil Shute).

Town Mouse (bk)

TOWN MOUSE AND THE COUNTRY MOUSE, THE (well loved tales age up to 9) (Unknown narrator(s)).
MC: PLB 66

Town South Of

TOWN SOUTH OF BAKERSFIELD (Various artists).
LP: ENIGMA 20591

Towner, Ralph

BATIK.
LP: ECM 1121

BLUE SUN.
LP: ECM 1250

CITY OF EYES.
LP: ECM 1388

DEPART (see Azymuth with Ralph Towner) (Towner, Ralph with Azimuth).

DIARY.
Tracks: / Dark spirit / Entry in a diary / Images unseen / Icarus / Mon enfant / Ogden road / Erg / Silence of a candle, The.
LP: ECM 1032

FIVE YEARS LATER (Towner, Ralph & John Abercrombie).
LP: ECM 1207

KOPUTAI (See Clayton, Jay) (Towner, Ralph/ Jay Clayton/ Julian Preister).

MATCHBOOK (Towner, Ralph & Gary Burton).
LP: ECM 1056

SARGASSO SEA (Towner, Ralph & John Abercrombie).
LP: ECM 1080

SLIDE SHOW (Towner, Ralph & Gary Burton).
Tracks: / Maelstrom / Vessel / Around the bend / Blue in green / Beneath an evening sky / Donkey jamboree / Continental breakfast / Charlotte's tangle / Innocenti.
LP: ECM 1306

SOLSTICE.
Tracks: / Oceanus / Visitation / Drifting petals / Nimbus / Winter solstice / Piscean dance / Red and black / Sand.
LP: ECM 1060

SOUNDS AND SHADOWS (Towner, Ralph 's Solstice).
LP: ECM 1095

TRIOS.
LP: . . . . ECM 1025

WORKS: RALPH TOWNER.
Tracks: / Oceanus / Blue sun / New moon / Beneath an evening sky / Prince and the sage, The / Nimbus.
LP: 8232681
MC: 3100 390

Townley, John

JOHN TOWNLEY.
Tracks: / Shine on / Tell me you love me / Dream / Woman of age / Take me or leave me / Throwing it all away / More fool you / Hard night / To love you / You bother me.
LP: . . . . EMC 3298

MORE THAN A DREAM.
Tracks: / Hold me / But I do / Take me in / Won't you please / Lover / Slipping away / Sail away / War zone / Give me some love / Pity me.
LP: . . . . EMC 3371

Towns, Colin

BLIND JUSTICE.
LP: . . . . REB 714
MC: . . . . ZCF 714

FULL CIRCLE (Film soundtrack).
LP: . . . . V 2093

Townsend, Dave

PORTRAIT OF A CONCERTINA (Townsend, Dave/Nick Hooper).
Tracks: / Lovesick Polly / Staines morris / Three rusty swords / Flat pavane and galliard, The / Down the waggon way / Come ashore / John come kiss me now / Cuckoo's nest, The / Maid of the mill / Gallant hussar, The / Csardas / Lute suite in E Minor (J.S. Bach) / Roslyn Castle / Golden cross / Ratcliff Cross / Peschatore che va cantando / Saltarello / Hole in the wall / Bashful swain, The / Windsor Terrace / Benetev a Trevito.
LP: . . . . SDL 351
MC: . . . . CSDL 351

Townsend, Graham

CANADIAN FIDDLER.
LP: . . . . ROUNDER 7002

CLASSICS OF IRISH SCOTTISH & FRENCH-CANADIAN FIDDLERS.
LP: . . . . ROUNDER 7007

Townsend, Henry

HENRY TOWNSEND AND HENRY SPAULDING (1929-37) (Townsend, Henry & Henry Spaulding).
LP: . . . . WSE 117

ST. LOUIS BLUES (Townsend, Henry & Vernell).
LP: . . . . WOLF 120.495

Townsend, John

ALL KINDS OF EVERYTHING VOLUME 2.
Tracks: / Lark in the morning, The / Farewell / Tarawaithie / Spanish ladies / Sun and the moon, The / Dark-eyed sailor / Urge for going / Tailor's breeches, The / Hee ree who row / Let no man steal your thyme / Punch and Judy man / Easy and free / Roll Alabama roll.
LP: . . . . SFA 082

Townsend, Kim

READ ALL ABOUT IT.
Tracks: / Dance away / Silver tears (Extra track on 12" version only) / Dreamin' on (Extra track on 12" version only).
MC: . . . . AIRC 100

Townsend, Sue (aut)

GROWING PAINS OF ADRIAN MOLE, THE (Shatzberger, Simon).
MCSET: . . . . LFP 7184
MCSET: . . . . LFP 4171845

SECRET DIARY OF ADRIAN MOLE, THE (See under Adrian Mole).

SECRET RECORD OF ADRIAN MOLE AGED 13 3/4 (Various artists).
LP: . . . . ADE 1
MC: . . . . TC ADE 1

Townsend Townsend ...

TOWNSEND TOWNSEND TOWNSEND & ROGERS (Townsend Townsend Townsend & Rogers).
Tracks: / Wondering / Rock me sock me / Bring it down to the real / True love / It's a pleasure to have loved you / Playground / You can / It's too late to be nice to her now / It's you.
LP: . . . . CAL 2057

Townshend, Pete

ALL THE BEST COWBOYS HAVE CHINESE EYES.
Tracks: / Sea refuses no river / Communication / Exquisitely bored / North country girl / Slit skirts / Uniforms / Prelude / Somebody saved me / Face dances part two / Stardom in action / Stop hurting people.
LP: . . . . K 50889

ANOTHER SCOOP.
Tracks: / You better you bet / Brooklyn kids / Football fugue / Substitute / Call me lightning / Begin the beguine / La la la lies / Prelude £ 556 / Praying the game / Christmas / Don't let go the coat / Prelude, the right to write / Ask yourself / Shout, The / Girl in a suitcase / Pinball wizard / Happy Jack / Long live rock / Hollys like ivy / Viscious interlude / Catsnatch / Baroque ippanese / Driftin' blues / Pictures of Lily / Kids are alright, The / Never ask me / Ferry, The.
2LP: 839 350 1
MCSET: 839 350 4

EMPTY GLASS.
Tracks: / Rough boys / I am an animal / And I moved / Let my love open the door / Jools and Jim / Keep on working / Cats in the cupboard / Little is enough, A / Empty glass / Gonna getcha.
LP: . . . . K 50699

IRON MAN.
Tracks: / I won't run any more / Over the top / Man machines / Friend is a friend, A / I eat heavy metal / All shall be well / Was there life / Fast food / Fool says, A / Fire / New life (reprise).
LP: . . . . V 2592
MC: . . . . TCV 2592
MC: . . . . OVEDC 355
LP: . . . . OVED 355

ROUGH MIX (Townshend, Pete & Ronnie Lane).
Tracks: / My baby gives it away / Nowhere to run / Rough mix / Annie / Keep me turning / Catmelody / Misunderstood / April fool / Street in the city / Heart to hang onto / Till the rivers all run dry.
LP: 2442 147
LP: . . . . SPELP 55

SCOOP.
Tracks: / So sad about us / Squeezebox / Zelda / Politician / Dirty water / Circles / Piano / Tipperary / Unused piano / Quadrophenia / Melanchlia / Bargain / Things have changed / Popular / Bahind blue eyes / Magic bus / Cache cache / Cookin' / You're so clever / Body language / Initial machine experiments / Mary / Recorders / Goin' fishin' / To Barney Kessel / You come back / Love reign o'er.
2LP: . . . . B 0063

WHITE CITY.
Tracks: / Secondhand love / Give blood / Brilliant blues / Crashing by design / Lonely words / White City fighting / Face the face / All shall be well / Hiding out / Closing sequence.
LP: 252 392-1
MC: 252 392-4

WHO CAME FIRST.
LP: 2408 201

Townshend, Simon

MOVING TARGET.
Tracks: / Meet you / Barriers / Cat's away / Sorry / Price to pay / Believe in you / Addiction / Moving target / Frustrated heart / Genuine.
LP: 825 872 1

SWEET SOUND.
Tracks: / Sweet sound / I'm the answer / On the scaffolding / Mr. Sunday / So real / Palace in the air / More with you / Freakers / Heart stops.
LP: . . . . POLD 5128

Township

TOWNSHIP.
LP: . . . . TWLP 004

Tox

PRINCE OF DARKNESS.
LP: . . . . SKULL 8393

Toxic Reasons

ANYTHING FOR MONEY.
Tracks: / Just another day / Screamin' / Bad Georgia / Committed / Swingin' the hammer / Shoot to kill / Shut you down / Take this city / Anything for money / Wildin'.
LP: 086 808 1

BULLETS FOR YOU.
LP: . . . . VIRUS 55

DEDICATION.
Tracks: / Payback mix / Killing game / Your perfect world / Us and them / Critical condition / I'm ready / Whole world's on fire.
LP: . . . . FH 12-005

INDEPENDENCE.
LP: . . . . EFA 1655

KILL BY REMOTE CONTROL.
LP: . . . . VIRUS 41

Toxic Shock

CHANGE FROM REALITY.
Tracks: / Breakout / Burning down your life / Forbidden lust / Mad sounds / State of madness / Overloaded / Raging speed / United forces.
LP: . . . . NB 1001 R
LP: . . . . MB 1001

WELCOME HOME..NEAR DARK.
LP: . . . . NB 027
LP: 082 927

Toxic Waste

WE WILL BE FREE (See under Asylum) (Toxic Waste/ Asylum/ Stalag 17).

Toxik

THINK THIS.
Tracks: / Think this / Creed / Spontaneous / There stood the fence / Black and white / WIR NJN 8 (In God) / Machine dream / Shotgun logic / Time after time / Technical arrogance (Only on CD.) / Out on the tiles (Only on CD.).
LP: . . . . RO 94601

WORLD CIRCUS.
Tracks: / Heart attack / Social overload / Pain & misery / Voices / Door to hell / World circus / 47 seconds of sanity / False prophets / Haunted earth / Victims.
LP: . . . . RR 9572

Toxodeth

MYSTERIES ABOUT LIFE AND DEATH.
LP: . . . . WRE 9031

Toy

BAD NIGHT.
Tracks: / Son of St. Mary / Night after night / One way affair / Dolce vita / You won't regret it / Crazy Monday / Coconut / I found out / Bad night / Imagination / Car 54 where are you.
LP: . . . . MOGO 4010

Toy Dolls

20 TUNES LIVE IN TOKYO.
Tracks: / Wakey wakey intro / Cloughy is a bootboy / I've got asthma / Deidre's a slag / Bless you my son / Spiders in the dressing room / She goes to Fino's / Harry Cross / Wakey wakey outro / Wipeout / Dig that groove baby / Lambrusco kid / Peter practises practise place / Ashbrooke launderette, The / My girlfriend's dad's a vicar / Popeye medley / Fisticuffs in Frederick Street / Glenda and the test tube baby / When the saints / Nellie the elephant.
LP: . . . . RRLP 129
MC: . . . . RRLC 129

BAREFACED CHEEK.
Tracks: / Bare faced cheek / Yul Bryner was a skinhead / How do you deal with Neal / Howza bouta kiss babe / Fisticuffs in Frederick Street / A.Diamond / Quick to quit the Quentin / Nowt can compare to Sunderland Fine-Fare / Ashbrooke launderette, The.
LP: . . . . NIT 001
MC: . . . . NITC 001

DIG THAT GROOVE BABY.
Tracks: / Theme tune / Dig that groove baby / Dougy Giro / Spiders in the dressing room / Glenda and the test tube baby / Up the garden path / Nellie the elephant / Poor Davey / Stay mellow / Queen Alexandra Road / Worse things happen at sea / Blue suede shoes / Firey Jack.
LP: . . . . VOLP 1
MC: . . . . VOMC 1

FAR OUT DISC, A.
MC: . . . . VOMC 002
LP: . . . . VOLP 2

IDLE GOSSIP.
Tracks: / Idle gossip / Do you wanna be like Dougy Bell / You won't be merry on a North Sea ferry / Silly Billy / Peter Practice / I tried to trust Tracey / I'll get even with Steven / Keith's a thief / Never trust Tracy / Geordies gone to jail / Fosters club / Harry cross / Lambrusco kid / P C Stoker / Medley / Dougy bell / North sea ferry / Peter Practice / Glenda and the test tube baby.
LP: . . . . VOLP 003
MC: . . . . VOMC 003

SINGLES 1983-84.
LP: . . . . VOLM 020

TEN YEARS OF TOYS.
LP: . . . . NIT 002
MC: . . . . NITC 002

TOY DOLLS, THE.
LP: . . . . WOW LP 1

WAKEY WAKEY.
MC: . . . . RRLC 119

Toy Matinee

TOY MATINEE.
LP: 7599262351
MC: 7599262354

Toyah

ANTHEM.
LP: . . . . VOOR 1
MC: . . . . VOORC 1

BLUE MEANING, THE.
Tracks: / Ieya / Spaced walking / Ghosts / Mummies / Blue meanings / Tiger tiger / Vision / Insects / Love me / She.
LP: . . . . IEYA 666
MC: . . . . CIEYA 666
LP: . . . . PIPLP 015
MC: . . . . PIPMC 015

CHANGELING, THE.
LP: . . . . VOOR 9
MC: . . . . VOORC 9

DESIRE.
Tracks: / Echo beach / Moonlight dancing / Revive the world / View, The / Moon migration / Love's unkind / Dear diary / Deadly as a woman / Goodbye baby / When a woman cries / Desire.
LP: . . . . EGLP 71
MC: . . . . EGMC 71

LADY OR THE TIGER, THE.
Tracks: / Lady or the tiger, The / Discourager of hesitancy, The.
LP: . . . . EGED 44
MC: . . . . EGEDC 44

LOVE IS THE LAW.
LP: . . . . VOOR 10
MC: . . . . VOORC 10

MAYHEM.
LP: . . . . VOOR 77
MC: . . . . VOORC 77

MINX.
Tracks: / Soldier of fortune / Terrorist of love / Don't fall in love (I said) / Soul passing through soul / Sympathy / I'll serve you well / All in a rage / Space between the sounds / School's out / World in action / America for beginners / Over 21 (Extra track on cassette only) / Vigillante (Extra track on cassette only).
LP: . . . . PRT 26415
MC: 40 26415

NINE TO FIVE (see under Ant, Adam) (Ant, Adam & Toyah).

OPHELIA'S SHADOW.
LP: . . . . EGLP 78
MC: . . . . EGMC 78

PROSTITUTE.
Tracks: / Hello / Prostitute / Wife / Show, The / Dream house / Homecraft / Ghosts in the universe / Obsession / Let the power bleed / Restless / Falling to earth / Jazz singers in the trees / Vale of Evesham.
LP: . . . . EGED 59
MC: . . . . EGEDC 59

SHEEP FARMING IN BARNET.
Tracks: / Neon womb / Indecision / Waiting / Computer / Victims of the riddle / Elusive stranger / Our movie / Danced / Last goodbye / Victims of the riddle (vivisection) / Race through space.
LP: . . . . IC 064
MC: . . . . IC 264
LP: . . . . PIPLP 014
MC: . . . . PIPMC 014

TONY BANKS (EP) (see Banks, Tony) (Toyah/Tony Banks/Jim Diamond).

TOYAH TOYAH TOYAH.
LP: . . . . LIVE 2
MC: . . . . CLIVE 2
LP: . . . . NE 1268
MC: C1 1268
LP: . . . . PIPLP 016
MC: . . . . PIPMC 016

WARRIOR ROCK (Toyah on Tour).
Tracks: / Good morning universe / It's a mystery / Thunder in the mountains / I want to be free / Dawn chorus / Danced / Warrior rock / Jungles of Jupiter / Castaways / Angel and me / Brave new world / Packt / We are.
2LP: . . . . TNT 1
MCSET: . . . . CTNT 1

Toyan

DJ CLASH - NICODEMUS V TOYAN (see under Nicodemus) (Toyan/ Nicodemus).

HOT BUBBLEGUM.
LP: . . . . unknown

HOW THE WEST WAS WON.
LP: . . . . GREL 20

MURDER (Toyan/Tipper Lee/Johnny Slaughter).
LP: . . . . STLP 1023

Toyin

LOVE 'N' LEATHER.
LP: . . . . TEEF 1

Toyota Pipes & Drums

AMAZING GRACE.
Tracks: / Balmoral Highlanders, The / Tulloch castle / Duke of Sutherland / Mac an' Irish / Brechin Castle / Highland

laddie / Highland reel / Ben Guillion / Molly Connell / Lady Carol / Brolum / Silver spear / Rory O'More / Kesh jig / Colin Thompson / Arniston castle / Loch Carron / Amazing grace / Mount Fuji / Mull of Kintyre / Wooden heart / Sailing / Sands of time / Magnificent seven, The / Send in the clowns / Halls of Montezuma.
LP: . . . . LILP 5133
MC: . . . . LICS 5133

Toys Went Berserk

SMILER WITH A KNIFE, THE.
LP: . . . . ABE 912

Tozzi, Umberto

AMORE.
Tracks: / Ti amo / Gloria / Notte rosa / Please per Angela / Dimmi di no / Stella stai / Eva / Mama / Tu.
LP: . . . . CAL 149
MC: . . . . CAC 149

HIS GREATEST HITS:UMBERTO TOZZI.
Tracks: / Tiamo / Notte rosa / Tu / Eva / Gente di mare / Si puo dare di piu / Per Angela / Gloria / Stella stai / Mama / Alleluia se / Se non avessi te (e la verita) / Mamma Maremma / Nell 'aria C'e.
LP: . . . . TOZZ 001
MC: . . . . TOZZC 001
LP: . . . . CBS 84763

HURRAH.
LP: 206.411

T'Pau

BRIDGE OF SPIES.
Tracks: / Heart and soul / I will be with you / China in your hand / Friends like these / Sex talk / Bridge of spies / Monkey house / Valentine / Thank you for goodbye / You give up / China in your hand (reprise).
LP: . . . . SRNLP 8
MC: . . . . SRNMC 8
MC: . . . . OVEC 367
LP: . . . . OVED 367

PROMISE, THE.
MC: . . . . SRNMC 32
LP: . . . . SRNLP 32

RAGE.
Tracks: / Arms of love / Only the lonely / Running away / Between the lines / Road to our dream / Island / Heaven / Taking time out / Secret garden / Time will tell / This girl (CD only).
LP: . . . . SRNLP 20
MC: . . . . SRNMC 20
LP: . . . . OVED 291
MC: . . . . OVEDC 291

T'PAU: INTERVIEW PICTURE DISC.
LPPD: . . . . BAK 2081

Trace, Natchez

BEST OF THE IMMORTAL NATCHEZ TRACE.
Tracks: / I'm willin' / Beaucoups of blues / One more night / Jasper and the miners / Lou Marsh / Feelings so low / Night they drove old Dixie down, The / Southbound / She moved through the fair / Bringing Mary home / Pinto pony / Truck driving man / Strutt's strut / You're still on my mind / Are you all alone.
LP: . . . . SFA 048

Tracey, Clark

STIPERSTONES (Tracey, Clark Quintet).
Tracks: / Nipstone rock / Scattered rock / Cranberry rock / Devil's chair / Shepherd's rock / Manstone rock / Nipstone rock (reprise).
LP: . . . . SJ 115

SUDDENLY LAST TUESDAY (Tracey, Clark Quintet).
LP: . . . . SGC 1013

Tracey, Ian

ORGAN RECITAL.
Tracks: / Alla danza from 'Water Music' / Andante and allegro (Fiocco) / Toccata and fugue in D minor BWV 565 (Bach) / Badinerie from 'Suite No. 2 in B minor' (Bach) / Two trumpet tunes and air (Purcell) / Scherzo in G minor (Bossi) / Coronation march (1953) / Tuba tune (Cocker) / Elegy (Thalben-Ball) / Introduction and passacaglia in D minor (Reger) / Noel and toccata from 'Ten Byzantine sketches' (Mulet) / Toccatina for the flutes from 'L'Organo primativo' (Yon) / Toccata in F from 'Organ Symphony' No. 5 (Widor).
LP: . . . . CFP 4558
MC: . . . . TCCFP 4558

Tracey, Stan

ALONE (AT WIGMORE HALL 1974).
LP: . . . . SGC 1003

BRACKNELL CONNECTION.
LP: . . . . SJ 103

CAPTAIN ADVENTURE.
LP: . . . . SJ 102

GENESIS AND MORE... (Tracey, Stan & His Orchestra).
Tracks: / Beginning, The / Light, The / Firmament, The / Gathering, The / Sun, moon & the stars, The / Feather, fin & limb / Sixth day, The.
LP: . . . . SJ 114
MC: . . . . SJCAS 114

HELLO, OLD ADVERSARY.
LP: . . . . SJ 107

LIVE AT RONNIE SCOTT'S (Tracey's, Stan Hexad).
LP: . . . . SJ 113

NOW.
LP: . . . . SJ 110

ORIGINAL (Tracey, Stan & Mike Osborne).
LP: . . . . SGC 1002

PLAYIN' IN THE YARD (See under Rouse, Charlie) (Rouse, Charlie & Stan Tracey).

PLAYS DUKE ELLINGTON.
Tracks: / I let a song go out of my heart / Prelude to a kiss / Satin doll / In a mellow tone / Day dream / Great times / Sophisticated lady / Black butterfly / Lotus blossom.
LP: . . . . MOLE 10

POET'S SUITE, THE (Tracey, Stan Quartet).
LP: . . . . SJ 111

SALISBURY SUITE.
LP: . . . . SJ 105

SONATINAS (see under Surman, John) (Tracey, Stan & John Surman).

SOUTH EAST ASSIGNMENT (Tracey, Stan Quartet).
LP: . . . . SJ 108

TANDEM (Tracey, Stan & Mike Osborne).
LP: . . . . OG 210

TNT (Tracey, Stan & Keith Tippett).
LP: . . . . SJ 104

WE STILL LOVE YOU MADLY (Tribute to Duke Ellington) (Tracey, Stan & His Orchestra).
Tracks: / I'm beginning to see the light / Mood indigo / Blue feeling / I let a song go out of my heart / Stomp look and listen / Festival junction / In a sentimental mood / Just squeeze me / Lay by.
LP: . . . . MOLE 13
MC: . . . . MOLEMC 13

Tracie

FAR FROM THE HURTING KIND.
Tracks: / I love you when you sleep / Souls on fire / Nothing happens here but you / I can't hold on till Summer / Dr love / Thankyou / Spring summer autumn / Moving together / What did i hear you say / Far from the hurting kind.
LP: . . . . RRL 502

RATHER YOU THAN ME (See under Young, Tracie).

Tracks West

TRACKS WEST-PLATFORM 1 (Various artists).
Tracks: / Doctor Zagar: *1 To 1* / Extremist song: *Opposite Man* / Carnival queen: *Crazy House* / Let's get movin': *Frontier* / Rhythm of the night: *Hi-Fi* / Bright city lights: *Willcox, Sil* / Titanic, The: *Morrokko* / Boats to paradise: *Band On The Moon* / Good taste tango: *Alice The Mongrel* / Sleep with me tonight: *Maxwell Street.*
LP: . . . . PLAT 1

Tractor

TRACTOR.
Tracks: / All ends up / Little girl in yellow / Watcher, The / Ravenscroft's 13 bar boogie / Shubunkin' / Hope in favour / Every time it happens / Make the journey.
LP: . . . . THBL 002

Tracy, Arthur

ALWAYS IN SONG.
LP: . . . . ECM 2050

EVERYTHING I HAVE IS YOURS.
Tracks: / Everything I have is yours / If I didn't care / Let's fall in love / How was I to know / Robins and roses / I'll have the last waltz with mother / My gypsy rhapsody / I want to go home / Home on the range / Boy and a girl were dancing, A / Auf wiedersehen my dear / And so to bed / On the beach at bali bali / Play fiddle play / Little Dutch mill / Somewhere in the west / Farewell to arms / When the wandering boy goes home.
LP: . . . . JOY'D 296

I BRING A SONG (Tracy, Arthur (The Street Singer)).
Tracks: / Love in bloom / Rollin' home / As you desire me / Kiss me goodnight / Dreaming / In old Vienna / Trouble in paradise / June in January / Just a year ago to-night / Love me forever / All of my life / Take me in your arms / Gypsy fiddles / Wandering / Lovely to look at / With every breath I take / I bring a song / Last round-up, The.
LP: . . . . HDL 113
MC: . . . . CHDL 113

SOUTH OF THE BORDER.
Tracks: / Marta / South of the border / Laugh clown laugh / Way you look tonight / Music maestro please / Old sailor / Greatest mistake of my life / September in the rain / Moonlight on the waterfuall / De Lawd loves His people to sing / East of the sun / Solitude / Broken hearted clown / When the harvest moon is shining / Serenade in the night / Hometown / I'll sing you a thousand love songs / Old pal of mine / Did your mother come from Ireland.
LP: . . . . RFL 5

STREET SINGER, THE (Give Me a Heart to Sing to).
Tracks: / Smoke gets in your eyes / I love you truly / Across the great divide / Danny boy / Goodnight my love / Whistling waltz / Ol' man river / You are my heart's delight / I'll see you again.
2LP: . . . . RECDL 5
MCSET: . . . . RECDC 5

STREET SINGER/STREET SERENADE.
Tracks: / Street serenade / Where are you / Somebody's thinking of you tonight / Let us be sweethearts over again / Sailboat in the moonlight / So do I / Sailing home / Shake hands with a millionaire / In the mission by the sea / My heaven in the pines / Moon at sea / When the organ played O promise me / Pennies from Heaven / Can I forget you / You needn't have kept it a secret / Little old lady / Harbour lights.
2LP: . . . . RFL 29

THOUSAND LOVE SONGS, A.
Tracks: / Dance, gipsy, dance / Can I forget you / September in the rain / Hometown / Sympathy / Solitude / Whistling gipsy, The / Way you look tonight, The / In an old cathedral town / De Lawd loves His people to sing / Stay awhile / When I'm with you / Harbour lights / So do I / Whistling waltz, The / Sailboat in the moonlight, A / In the mission by the sea / East of the sun (and west of the moon) / Sailing home / I'll sing you a thousand love songs.
LP: . . . . CHD 152
MC: . . . . MCHD 152

Tracy, Dennis

NO MAN'S LAND.
LP: . . . . LRF 038

Tracy, Dick

DICK TRACY IN B-FLAT (Various artists).
LP: . . . . CC 100/1

Tracy, Jeanie

ME AND YOU.
Tracks: / Sing your own song / Your old stand by / I feel like dancing / Me and you / I'm your jeanie / Come make love to me / I want you / Tears on my pillow.
LP: . . . . FASLP 3001

Traddodiad Ofnus

WELSH TOURIST BORED.
Tracks: / Welsh tourist bored / Beth yn y byd / Weithiau / Dilyn y cach / Hwy / Byth / Ymgartref / Tec 21.
LP: . . . . CON 00031

Trader Horne

MORNINGWAY...PLUS.
LP: . . . . SEE 308

Tradia

TRADE WINDS.
Tracks: / Never gonna go / Let's not turn love away / Without you / Look away / No pain, no gain / Stand your ground / Don't play your ace / Take the chance / You've got me crying again / Exiles.
LP: . . . . WKFMLP 108
MC: . . . . WKFMMC 108

Tradition

RUNAWAY LOVE.
Tracks: / Don't know / Mash down / I am so glad / La la la la / Time / Music / Runaway love / I am thinking / African queen / True what I man say.
LP: . . . . PL 25273

SPIRIT OF ECSTACY.
LP: . . . . SGL 104

Traditional

MUSIC FOR THE HAMMERED DULCIMER (Various artists).
Tracks: / Jenny Lind polka: *Various artists* / Johnny get your hair cut: *Various artists* / Intrada and Minuet: *Various artists* / Londonderry Air: *Various artists* / Maid at the spinning, The: *Various artists* / Nola: *Various artists* / High cauled cap, The: *Various artists* / As I roved out: *Various artists* / Miss Hamilton: *Various artists* / Christine's Waltz: *Various artists* / Bells of St Mary's, The: *Various artists* / Devil's dream: *Various artists* / Enchanted valley, The: *Various artists* / La belle Katherine: *Various artists* / Fisher's hornpipe: *Various artists* / Swinging on a gate: *Various artists* / Norwegian wood: *Various artists* / Flower of England: *Various artists* / Snowflake, The: *Various artists* / Los ejes de mi carretta: *Various artists* / Perfect cure me, The: *Various artists* / Starry night to ramble: *Various artists* / Peel the carrot: *Various artists* / Take five: *Various artists.*
MC: . . . . CS-DL 335

MUSIQUE TRADITIONNELLE DE BRETAGNE vol.2 (Various artists).
Tracks: / Laride gavotte de Pontivy: *Various artists* / Pourlet: *Various artists* / Kaz ha barh: *Various* artists / Melodie vannetaise: *Various artists* / Rond de Loudeac: *Various artists* / Le marchand de velours: *Various artists* / Polka Plinn: *Various artists* / Pas de quatre: *Various artists* / Ronde des pecheurs du Conquet: *Various artists* / Hanter dro: *Various artists* / Suite des conscrits: *Various artists* / Cueillons, cueillons bien: *Various artists.*
LP: . . . . ARN 33692

MUSIQUE TRADITIONNELLE DE BRETAGNE vol.1 (Various artists).
Tracks: / Hanter dro: *Various artists* / Marches vannetaises: *Various artists* / Tamm Kerh: *Various artists* / Melodie vannetaise: *Various artists* / Piller-Lann: *Various artists* / Kost er Hoed: *Various artists* / Suite de polkas: *Various artists* / Marches de Pluherlin: *Various artists* / Laride: *Various artists* / Melodie du Scorff: *Various artists* / La sabotee: *Various artists* / Round pagan: *Various artists.*
LP: . . . . ARN 33580

TRADITIONAL ARABIC MUSIC (See under Arabia) (Various artists).

Traditional Fairy...

TRADITIONAL FAIRY STORIES (Reid, Beryl (nar)).
MC: . . . . P 90002

Traditional Music Of

TRADITIONAL MUSIC OF ALENTEJO (See under Portugal) (Various artists).

TRADITIONAL MUSIC OF BURUNDI (See under Burundi) (Various artists).

Traffic

BEST OF TRAFFIC.
Tracks: / Paper sun / Heaven is in your mind / No face, no name, no number / Coloured rain / Smiling phases / Hole in my shoe / Medicated goo / Forty thousand headmen / Feeling alright / Shanghai noodle factory / Dear Mr.Fantasy.
LP: . . . . ILPS 9112
MC: . . . . ZCI 9112

JOHN BARLEYCORN MUST DIE.
Tracks: / Glad / Freedom rider / Empty page / Stranger to himself / John Barleycorn / Every mother's son.
LP: . . . . ILPM 9116
MC: . . . . ICM 9116
MC: 842 780 4

LAST EXIT.
Tracks: / Just for you / Shanghai noodle factory / Something's got a hold of my toe / Withering tree / Medicated goo / Feeling good / Blind man.
LP: . . . . ILPS 9097

LOW SPARK OF HIGH-HEELED BOYS, THE.
Tracks: / Hidden treasure / Low spark of high heeled boys, The / Light up or leave me alone / Rock n roll stew / Many a mile to freedom / Rainmaker.
LP: . . . . ILPM 9180
MC: . . . . ICM 9180
MC: 842 779 4

MR. FANTASY.
Tracks: / Heaven is in your mind / Berkshire poppies / House for everyone / No face, no name, no number / Dear Mr.Fantasy / Dealer / Utterly simple / Coloured rain / Hope I never find me there / Giving to you.
LP: . . . . ILPM 9061
MC: . . . . ICM 9061
LP: . . . . ILPS 9061
MC: 842 783 4

SHOOT OUT AT THE FANTASY FACTORY.
Tracks: / Shoot out at the fantasy factory / Roll right stones / Evening blue / Tragic magic / Sometimes I feel so uninspired.
LP: . . . . ILPS 9224
MC: . . . . ZCI 9224

MC: ICM 9224
MC: 842 781 4

TRAFFIC.
Tracks: / You can all join in / Pearly queen / Don't be sad / Who knows what tomorrow may bring / Feeling alright / Vagabond virgin / Forty thousand headmen / Cryin' to be heard / No time to live / Means to an end.
LP: ILP 9081
MC: ICM 9081
LP: ILPM 9081
MC: 842 590 4

TRAFFIC ON THE ROAD.
Tracks: / Glad / Freedom rider / Tragic magic / Sometimes I feel so uninspired / Shoot out at the fantasy factory / Light up or leave me alone / Low spark of high heeled boys, The.
2LP: ISLD 2
MCSET: ZCID 102

TRAFFIC / YOU CAN ALL JOIN IN.
Tracks: / You can all join in / Pearly queen / Don't be sad / Who knows what tomorrow may bring / Feeling alright / Vagabond virgin / Forty thousand headmen / Cryin' to be heard / No time to live / Means to an end.
LP: ILPS 9081

WELCOME TO THE CANTEEN (Recorded Live).
Tracks: / Medicated goo / Sad and deep / As you / Forty thousand headmen / Shouldn't have took more than you gave / Dear Mr.Fantasy / Gimme some lovin'.
LP: ILPS 9166
MC: ZCI 9166

WHEN THE EAGLE FLIES.
LP: ILPS 9273
MC: ZCI 9273
MC: ICM 9273

Traffic Control

TRAFFIC CONTROL (See under UNESCO reports).

Tragic Error

KLATCH IN HANDEN.
LP: WHOS 22

Tragic Mulatto

CHARTREUSE TOULOUSE.
LP: VIRUS 080

JUDO FOR THE BLIND.
LP: VIRUS 37

Tragically Hip

ROAD APPLES.
LP: MCA 10173
MC: MCAC 10173

Trains...

AGAINST THE GRADE (Various).
MC: AC 160

ALL IN A DIESEL DAY (Various).
MC: AC 154
LP: ADL 154

BIG FOUR, THE (Various).
MC: AC 125

BLACK FIVES (Various).
MC: AC 101

BRITISH RAILWAYS STANDARD LOCOMOTIVES (Various).
MC: AC 105

BUILT SWINDON (Various).
MC: AC 102

CASTLES AND KINGS (Various).
LP: ATR 7015
MC: ZC ATR 7015

CHANGING TRAINS (Various).
LP: ATR 7018
MC: ZC ATR 7018

COPPER CAPPED ENGINES (Various).
LP: ATR 7008
MC: ZC ATR 7008

DELTIC DUTIES (Various).
MC: AC 131

DIESELS ON DAINTON (Various).
MC: AC 138

DIESELS ON THE LICKEY INCLINE (Various).
MC: AC 142

DOUBLE HEAD OF STEAM (Various).
LP: ATR 7024
MC: ZC ATR 7024

DYNAMIC DIESELS (Various).
MC: AC 130

EARLY 60'S STEAM (Are You Going to Get the Sound of it Coming In) (Various).
MC: GLTK 1

ECHOES OF ENGINES (Various).
LP: ATR 7034
MC: ZC ATR 7034

ENGINES FROM DERBY AND CREWE (Various).
LP: ATR 7032
MC: ZC ATR 7032

ENGINES WITH ACCENTS (Various).
LP: ATR 7036
MC: ZC ATR 7036

FAREWELL TO STEAM (Various).
LP: RMPL 1007
MC: AC 193

FAREWELL TO THE DELTICS (Various).
MC: AC 135
LP: ADL 135

FAREWELL TO THE FORTIES (Various).
MC: AC 155

FLYING SCOTSMAN AND OTHER LOCOMOTIVES (Various).
LP: PSP 8

FOOTPLATE DAYS (Various).
MC: AC 151

FROM THE FOOTPLATE (Various).
MC: AC 124

GONE WITH REGRET (Various).
LP: RMPL 1006
MC: AC 191

GREAT LITTLE TRAINS OF ENGLAND (Various).
MC: AC 120

GREAT NORTHERN FOR THE NORTH (Various).
MC: AC 139

GREAT TRAIN RECORD, THE (Various).
MC: AFP 142

GREAT WESTERN IN GLOUCESTERSHIRE (Various).
LP: SDLB 220
MC: CSDLB 220

GREAT WESTERN, THE (Various).
LP: ATR 7031
MC: ZC ATR 7031

GRESLEY BEAT, THE (Various).
MC: AC 192
LP: RMPL 1008

G.W.R. (Various).
LP: ATR 7011
MC: ZC ATR 7011

HST 125 & DMU (Various).
MC: AC 141

IRON-ORE STEAMERS (Various).
LP: SDLB 311
MC: CSDLB 311

LAST TRAIN TO RYDE (Various).
LP: RMPL 1004
MC: AC 194

LITTLE TRAINS OF WALES, THE (Various).
MC: AC 116

L.M.S. (Various).
LP: ATR 7004
MC: ZC ATR 7004

L.N.E.R. (Various).
LP: ATR 7010
MC: ZC ATR 7010

LOCOMOTIVES FROM LEEDS (Various).
MC: AC 137

MAGNIFICENT SEVERN, THE (Various).
MC: AC 133

MAIN LINE STEAM SPECIALS (Various).
LP: SSLP 804

MIDLAND AND NORTH WESTERN (Various).
LP: ATR 7021
MC: ZC ATR 7021

MOTIVE POWER VOL.1 (English Electric) (Various).
MC: AC 153

MOTIVE POWER VOL.2 (Sulzers and Shunters) (Various).
MC: AC 128

MOTIVE POWER VOL.4 (Diesels in Ireland) (Various).
MC: AC 159

MOTIVE POWER VOL. 3 (American Diesels) (Various).
MC: AC 158

NOCTURNAL STEAM (Various).
LP: SDLB 306
MC: CSDLB 306

NORTH OF KINGS CROSS (Various).
LP: ATR 7029
MC: ZC ATR 7029

PACIFIC POWER (Various).
LP: ATR 7022
MC: ZC ATR 7022
LP: SPA 563

PASSENGERS NO MORE (Various).
MC: AC 106

POWER OF STEAM, THE (Various).
LP: ATR 7028
MC: ZC ATR 7028

RAILWAY GUARD, A (Various).
MC: AC 148

RAILWAY RHYTHMS (Various).
LP: ATR 7002
MC: ZC ATR 7002

RAILWAY TO RICCARTON (Various).
LP: ATR 7013
MC: ZC ATR 7013

RAILWAYS RECALLED (Various).
LP: ATR 7017
MC: ZC ATR 7017

RAILWAYS ROUND THE CLOCK (Various).
LP: ATR 7005
MC: ZC ATR 7005

RAINHILL REMEMBERED (Various).
MC: AC 134

REAL DAYS OF STEAM (Various).
LP: PSP 2

REGIONAL ROUND NO. 1 EASTERN (Various).
MC: AC 104

REGIONAL ROUND NO. 2 SOUTHERN (Various).
MC: AC 118

REGIONAL ROUND NO. 3 MIDLAND (Various).
MC: AC 119

REGIONAL ROUND NO. 4 SCOTTISH (Various).
MC: AC 122

RETURN TO STEAM VOL. 1 (Various).
LP: SDLB 313
MC: CSDLB 313

RETURN TO STEAM VOL. 2 (Various).
LP: SDLB 319
MC: CSDLB 319

RHYTHMS OF STEAM (Various).
LP: ATR 7033
MC: ZC ATR 7033

SEVERN VALLEY STEAM (Various).
LP: SSLP 802

SHAP (Various).
LP: ATR 7035
MC: ZC ATR 7035

SHUNTING THE YARD (Various).
MC: AC 136

SOMERSET AND DORSET, THE (Various).
LP: ATR 7030
MC: ZC ATR 7030

SOMERSET & DORSET (Various).
MC: AC 103

SOUNDS OF SEVERN VALLEY RAILWAY (Various).
LP: RESM 020

SOUTHERN STEAM (Various).
LP: ATR 7006
MC: ZC ATR 7006

SPECIALS IN STEAM (Various).
MC: AC 121

STEAM FROM A TO V (Various).
LP: ATR 7038
MC: ZC ATR 7038

STEAM HAULED BY A STANIER BLACK 5 (Various).
LP: PSP 9

STEAM IN ALL DIRECTIONS (Various).
LP: ATR 7012
MC: ZC ATR 7012

STEAM IN SCOTLAND (Various).
LP: ATR 7003
MC: ZC ATR 7003

STEAM IN THE FIFTIES (Various).
LP: ATR 7001
MC: ZC ATR 7001

STEAM IN THE SEVENTIES (Various).
MC: AC 126

STEAM IN TWILIGHT (Various).
LP: SSLP 803

STEAM LOCOMOTIVES ON THE GRADIENT (Various).
LP: PSP 6

STEAM ON THE LICKEY INCLINE (Various).
LP: ATR 7026
MC: ZC ATR 7026

STEAM OVER THE PENNINES (Various).
MC: AC 152

STEAM RAILWAY MISCELLANY, A (Various).
LP: PSP 4

STEAM SPECIALS OF THE 70S (Various).
LP: SSLP 801

STEAM THROUGH ALL SEASONS (Various).
LP: ATR 7007
MC: ZC ATR 7007

STEAM WEEKEND, A (Various).
LP: PSP 5

STEAM'S FINAL HOURS (Various).
LP: SDLB 305
MC: CSDLB 305

STOREFIELD IN THE RAIN (Various).
LP: PSP 3

STOREFIELD STORY (Steam locomotives of the Storefield line) (Various).
LP: PSP 1

SUNSET OF STEAM (Various).
MC: AC 127

THIS IS YORK (Various).
LP: ATR 7014
MC: ZC ATR 7014

TRAINS IN THE HILLS (Various).
LP: ATR 7019
MC: ZC ATR 7019

TRAINS IN THE NIGHT (Various).
LP: ATR 7020
MC: ZC ATR 7020

TRAINS IN TROUBLE (Various).
LP: ATR 7016
MC: ZC ATR 7016

TRAINS TO REMEMBER (Various).
LP: ATR 7025
MC: ZC ATR 7025

TRIUMPH OF AN A4 PACIFIC, THE (Various).
LP: ATR 7009
MC: ZC ATR 7009

WEST OF EXETER (Various).
LP: ATR 7027
MC: ZC ATR 7027

WEST SOMERSET RAILWAY (sounds of) (Various).
LP: RESM 018

WESTERN STEAM IN THE MIDLANDS (Various).
MC: AC 117

WESTERN WAYS (Various).
MC: AC 143

WORKING ON THE FOOTPLATE (Various).
LP: ATR 7023
MC: ZC ATR 7023

WORLD OF RAILWAYS (Various).
LP: SPA 557

WORLD OF STEAM VOL 1 (Various).
MC: AC 144

WORLD OF STEAM VOL 2 (American Steam) (Various).
MC: AC 156

YORK COLLECTION, THE (Various).
MC: AC 123

Trammell, Bobby Lee

ARKANSAS TWIST.
Tracks: / Arkansas twist / Carolyn / Come on baby / It's all your fault / Sally twist (parts 1 & 2) / I tried not to cry / Watch me do the twist / Arkansas stomp / I like it / Bobby Lee needs love / Give me that good lovin' / If you ever get it once / New dance in France.
LP: BB 2036

BOBBY LEE TRAMMELL.
LP: BB 2039

TOOLIE FROOLIE.
Tracks: / Toolie froolie / Betty Jean / I can't sit still / Skimmy Lou / You make me feel so fine / Come on and love me / Am I satisfying you / Twenty four hours / Whole lotta shakin' goin' on / Little bit of soap, A / Chantilly lace / Love isn't love.
LP: BBLP 2040
LP: BB 2040

Trammps

BEST OF THE TRAMMPS.
Tracks: / Disco inferno / Night the lights went out / That's where the happy people go / Hooked for life / Disco party / Soul searchin' time / Body contact contract / I feel like I been livin' / Seasons for girls.
LP: K 50511

LEGENDARY ZING ALBUM, THE.
Tracks: / Penguin at the big apple / Zing went the strings of my heart / Pray all you sinners / Sixty minute man / Scruboard / Tom's song / Rubber band man / Hold back the night.
LP: KENT 088

MIXIN' IT UP.
Tracks: / Hard rock and disco / You can make it / Music freek / Let me dance real close / Dance contest / Everybody boogie / V.I.P. / Wake up from yesterday.
LP: K 50704

SLIPPING OUT.
Tracks: / Loveland / Trained - eye / Mellow out / Groove all mighty / Looking for you / Our thought (slipping away) / I don't want to ever lose your love / Is there any room for me / Breathtaking view.
LP: . . . . K 50769

WHOLE WORLD'S DANCING, THE.
Tracks: / Love insurance policy / Teaser / Whole world's dancing / My love, it's never been better / Soul bones / Love magnet / More good times to remember.
LP: . . . . K 50599

Trampolin

ILLUSIONS.
Tracks: / Illusions / Stars / Gonna make it alright / What does it take / Hooked on love / Nighthawk / Machines / Strange news / Living on sensation / My way.
LP: . . . . CBS 85152

Tran Quang Hai

MUSIC OF VIETNAM (Tran Quang Hai/ Hoang Mong Thuy).
LP: . . . . LLST 7337

Trance Mission

BACK IN A TRANCE.
LP: . . . . POW 5503

Tranquility

TRANQUILITY.
LP: . . . . GRAPEVINE 113
MC: . . . . PC 113

Transatlantic Jazz

FIRST CROSSING.
LP: . . . . FS 239

Transformers (bk)

AUTOBOT HOSTAGE (Unknown artist(s)).
MC: . . . . PLBT 251

AUTOBOTS' FIGHT BACK (for ages 5-10) (Unknown artist(s)).
MC: . . . . PLBT 165

AUTOBOTS' LIGHTING STRIKE (for ages 5-10) (Unknown artist(s)).
MC: . . . . PLBT 154

AUTOBOTS STRIKE OIL (Unknown artist(s)).
MC: . . . . PLBT 236

BATTLE FOR PLANET EARTH (Unknown artist(s)).
MCSET: . . . . DTO 10537

DECEPTICONS AT THE POLE (Unknown artist(s)).
MC: . . . . PLBT 235

DECEPTICON'S UNDERGROUND.
MC: . . . . PLBT 252

DECEPTION HIDE OUT (for ages 5-10) (Unknown artist(s)).
MC: . . . . PLBT 186

GALVATRON'S AIR ATTACK (for ages 5-10) (Unknown artist(s)).
MC: . . . . PLBT 185

LASERBEAK'S FURY (for ages 5-10) (Unknown artist(s)).
MC: . . . . PLBT 174

MEGATRON'S FIGHT FOR POWER (for ages 5-10) (Unknown artist(s)).
MC: . . . . PLBT 164

TRANSFORMERS-THE MOVIE (Film soundtrack) (Various artists).
Tracks: / Touch: *Bush, Stan* / Instruments of destruction: *NRG* / Death of Optimus prime: *Dicola, Vince*/ Dare: *Bush, Stan* / Nothin's gonna stand in our way: *Spectre General* / Tranformers (theme): *Lion* / Escape: *Dicola, Vince* / Hunger: *Spectre General* / Autobot: *Dicola, Vince* / Decepticon battle: *Dicola, Vince* / Dare to be stupid: *Yankovic, Weird Al*.
LP: . . . . EPC 70302
MC: 40 70302

TRANSFORMERS-THE MOVIE (for ages 5-10) (Unknown artist(s)).
MC: . . . . PLBT 201

Transgression

COLD WORLD.
Tracks: / Think for yourself / Prejudice kills / Pressures of society / It's here to stay / Go to hell / Won't bend my knees / Cold world / Regroup / Killing you / Senseless game / We've got to fight / Head in the smoke / Death to all / Final conflict, The.
LP: . . . . ACHE 16

Transit Of Earth (bk)

TRANSIT OF EARTH AND OTHER STORIES (Arthur C Clarke).
MC: 1566

Translator

HEARTBEATS AND TRIGGERS.
Tracks: / Everywhere that I'm not / Necessary spinning / Everything you see / When I am with you / Nothing is saving me / Sleeping snakes / Favourite drug / Everywhere / Dark region / My heart / Your heart.
LP: . . . . CBS 85953

NO TIME LIKE NOW.
Tracks: / Beyond today / I hear you follow / Break down barriers / L.A. I love you / No time like now / Everything is falling / Simple things / End of their love, The / About the truth / Circumstance laughing.
LP: . . . . CBS 25674
MC: 40 25674

TRANSLATOR.
Tracks: / Gravity / Fall forever / Come with me / Friends of the future / New song / Another American night / O Lazarus / Inside my mind / Heaven by a string / Breathless agony.
LP: . . . . CBS 26460
MC: 40 26460

Transmitters

AND WE CALL THAT LEISURE TIME.
Tracks: / Lovers not corpses / Equation / Purges / Paul is dead / Venus dread / Bite the bullet / Beat goes on / Money and sus / Time and motion / Background noises / Dachau.
LP: . . . . HB 4

Transvision Vamp

LITTLE MAGNETS VERSUS THE BUBBLE OF BABBLE, THE.
LP: . . . . MCA 10331
MC: . . . . MCAC 10331

POP ART.
Tracks: / Trash city / I want your love / Sister moon / Psychosonic Cindy / Revolution baby / Tell that girl to shut up / Wild star / Hanging out with Halo Jones / Andy Warhol's dead / Sex kick.
LP: . . . . MCF 3421
MC: . . . . MCFC 3421
LPPD: . . . . MCFP 3421

VELVETEEN.
Tracks: / Baby I don't care / Only one, The / Landslide of love / Falling for a goldmine / Down on you / Song to the stars / Kiss their sons / Born to be sold / Pay the ghosts / Bad valentine / Velveteen.
LP: . . . . MCG 6050
MC: . . . . MCGC 6050
LPPD: . . . . MCGP 6050

Transylvania

TRANSYLVANIA 6-5000 (Film Soundtrack) (Various artists).
LP: . . . . STV 81267

Trapeze

HOLD ON.
Tracks: / Don't ask me how I know / Take good care / When you get to heaven / Livin' on love / Hold on / Don't break my heart / Running / You are / Time will heal.
LP: . . . . AUL 708
MC: . . . . AUC 708

LIVE IN TEXAS - DEAD ARMADILLOS.
Tracks: / Black cloud / You are the music, we're just the band / Way back to the bone.
LP: . . . . AUL 717

WAY BACK TO THE BONE.
Tracks: / Coast to coast / Loser / Your love is alright / Touch my life / Way back to the bone / Seafull / Black cloud / You are the music / Medusa.
LP: . . . . BRF 2001

Trapezoid

ANOTHER COUNTRY.
LP: . . . . FF 287

COOL OF THE DAY.
LP: . . . . SH 1132

NOW AND THEN.
LP: . . . . FF 239

THREE FOLKS OF CHEAT.
LP: . . . . ROUNDER 0113
MC: . . . . ROUNDER 0113C

Trash

BURNING ROCK.
Tracks: / Boogie woogie man / Burnin' rock / Rock me rock you / Bad reputation / I can't get the one / Night after night / Hot legs black stockings / Take my flight / Rock n roll riot.
LP: 781 249-1

WATCH OUT.
Tracks: / Watch out / Bombay mail / Name of the game / Vicious / Drop and die / We gonna get foxes / High speed / Born to be on the top / No more rock tonight.
LP: . . . . RCALP 3112

Trash Can Sinatras

CAKE.
LP: 8282011
MC: 8282014

Trash County

TRASH COUNTY DOMINATORS, THE.
Tracks: / 99th floor / Wishing well / Sympathy / Action woman / Don't lose your mind / Out of our tree / Have love will travel / Come see me / Sympathy, Theme from / Strychnine / Night-time.
LP: . . . . SORC 3

Trash Museum

I'D RATHER DIE YOUNG.
LP: . . . . UNKNOWN

Trashmen

20 BIGGEST HITS.
LP: . . . . GARRETT 300

SURFIN' BIRD.
LP: . . . . LPGA 200

Traum, Artie

CAYENNE.
LP: . . . . ROUNDER 3084
MC: . . . . ROUNDER 3084C

FROM THE HEART (Traum, Artie/Pat Alger).
LP: . . . . ROUNDER 3039

LIFE ON EARTH.
LP: . . . . ROUNDER 3014

Traum, Happy

AMERICAN STRANGER.
LP: . . . . SNKF 142

BRIGHT MORNING STARS.
LP: . . . . WF 005

FRIENDS AND NEIGHBOURS.
LP: . . . . FF 4015

HARD TIMES IN THE COUNTRY (Traum, Happy & Art).
LP: . . . . ROUNDER 3007

RELAX YOUR MIND.
Tracks: / Relax your mind / Gypsy Davey / Worried blues / John Henry / Peggy Gordon / When first unto this country / Poor Howard / Fair and tender ladies / Boat up the river / Willie Moore / Weave room blues / Eighth of January / When I was a cowboy.
LP: . . . . SNKF 111

Trauma

TRAUMA (Various artists).
LP: . . . . SHM 3122
MC: . . . . HSC 3122

Travaganza

TRAVAGANZA.
LP: . . . . AUL 727

Travanti, David J.

THIN MAN, THE (See also Dashiell Hammett) (Travanti, David J. & Lyne Lipton).

Traveling Wilburys

TRAVELING WILBURYS.
Tracks: / Handle with care / Dirty world / Rattled / Last night / Not alone anymore / Congratulations / Heading for the light / Margarita / Tweeter and the monkey man / End of the line.
LP: . . . . WX 224
MC: . . . . WX 224C

TRAVELING WILBURYS VOLUME 3.
LP: . . . . WX 384
MC: . . . . WX 384C

Travellers

TRAVELLERS (Songs, Tunes & Tales of English Gypsies).
LP: 12TS 395

Traveller's Joy (bk)

TRAVELLER'S JOY (Allen, Maudie).
MCSET: . . . . MRC 1045

Travelling Man

TRAVELLING MAN (See under Browne, Duncan) (Browne, Duncan).

Travers, Pat

BLACK PEARL.
Tracks: / I la la la love you / I'd rather see you dead / Stand up / Who'll take the fall / Fifth / Misty morning / Can't stop the heartaches / Amgwanna kick booty / Rockin'.
LP: 2391553

BOOM BOOM.
Tracks: / Snorting whiskey, drinking cocaine / Life in London / I la la la love you / Getting better / Watcha gonna do without me / Daddy long legs / Heat in the street / School of hard knocks / Help me / Stevie / Ready or not / Boom boom / Born under a bad sign / Guitars from hell.
LP: . . . . ESDLP 140
MC: . . . . ESDMC 140

GO FOR WHAT YOU KNOW (Travers, Pat Band).
Tracks: / Hooked on music / Gettin' better / Go all night / Boom boom / Stevie / Making magic / Heat in the street / Makes no difference.
LP: . . . . POLS 1011

HEAT IN THE STREET.
Tracks: / Heat in the street / Killer's instinct / I tried to believe / Hammerhead / Go all night / Evie / One for me and one for you.
LP: . . . . POLD 5005

LIVE.
LP: . . . . ESDLP 140
MC: . . . . ESDMC 140

MAKING MAGIC.
Tracks: / Making magic / Rock 'n' roll Susie / You don't love me / Stevie / Statesboro blues / Need love / Hooked on music / What you mean to me.
LP: 2485 238
LP: 2383 436
LP: 2384 122

RADIO ACTIVE.
LP: 2391 499

SCHOOL OF HARD KNOCKS.
LP: . . . . LUSLP 4
MC: . . . . LUSMC 4

TURNING POINT (Travers, Pat Band).
LP: . . . . POLS 1017

Travers, P.L. (aut)

MARY POPPINS (Smith, Maggie).
MC: 1246

MARY POPPINS AND THE BANKS FAMILY (Smith, Maggie).
MC: 1270

MARY POPPINS COMES BACK (Smith, Maggie).
MC: 1269

MARY POPPINS OPENS THE DOOR (Smith, Maggie).
MC: 1271

Travers, Waldorf

NIGHT BLINDNESS.
Tracks: / Night blindness / Phoney / Thought I'd never see the day / Big time American girl / Avenger / Fairweather friend / Another crazy night / Turn out the night / Sad state of affairs.
LP: . . . . UAG 30234

Travis, Dave

BANKS OF THE OHIO.
MC: . . . . VCA 050

COUNTRY FEVER.
MC: . . . . SDC 5059

COUNTRY MUSIC MAN.
MC: . . . . SDC 5172

DAVE TRAVIS.
MC: . . . . VCA 037

HIGH ON LIFE (ALBUM).
Tracks: / Big river / Mental revenge / High on life / Tomorrow is a long time / Cycle of life / Go on home / Blue moon of Kentucky / Six days on the road / Swinging doors / I started world war one / Half breed / Your woman may have been here / Tonight I'll be coming back to you / Johnny B. Goode.
LP: . . . . SRLM 104
MC: . . . . SLB 104

LET'S FLAT GET IT.
Tracks: / Jukebox cadillac / Tweedle dee dee / Rock it right / Gonna be a fire / Boy meets girl / Shakin' and stompin' / Teen town hop / Hanging on for the blues / Don't that road look rough and rocky / Bip bop boom.
LP: . . . . MFLP 061

PICKIN' ON THE COUNTRY STRINGS.
LP: 236 557

ROCKABILLY FEVER.
Tracks: / Night train to Memphis / I'm gonna set my foot down / Help me find my baby / Dixiefried / Leroy / Your woman may have been here / Red hot / Put me down / Ooby dooby / I'm changing all those changes / Too much rock 'n' roll music / Since I met you baby / I ain't never / White lightnin' / Buddy's song / I'm on fire.
LP: . . . . SRLM 508
MC: . . . . VCA 048

ROCKABILLY KILLER.
Tracks: / Sugaree / Jitterbop baby / My baby's gone / Sugartime / Oklahoma baby / Good rockin' tonight / Everybody's movin' / Bop a Lena / My bucket's got a hole in it / Lightnin' cross the sky / Sarah Lee / All change / Blue levi jeans / Feel like I'm catching / Blues, The / Old country boy.
LP: . . . . MFLP 013
LP: . . . . SDLA 4003
MC: . . . . BBR 5010

SONGS OF REVOLUTION (Travis, Dave & Tolpuddle Martyrs).
LP: . . . . CHM 628

SOUNDS LIKE BUDDY HOLLY.
MC: . . . . VCA 040

Travis, Dave Lee

GUIDE TO CB RADIO (Travis, Dave Lee & Richard Hudson Evans).
MC: . . . . CB CASSETTE 1

Travis, Lane

I'M MOVIN' ON.
LP: . . . . BSS 182

Travis, Merle

BACK HOME.
Tracks: / Nine pound hammer / That's all / John Bolin / Muskrat / Dark as a dungeon / John Henry / Sixteen tons / Possum up a Simmon tree / I am a pilgrim / Over by number nine / Barbara Allen / Lost John.
LP: . . . . HAT 3044
MC: . . . . HATC 3044

CLAYTON MCMICHAN STORY, THE.
2LP: . . . . CMH 9028
MC: . . . . CMHC 9028

COUNTRY GUITAR GIANTS (Travis, Merle & Joe Maphis).
Tracks: / Free little bird / Mose Rager blues / Alabama jubilee / Hear dem bells / Eight more miles to Louisville / Little rosewood casket, The / John Henry / Cannonball rag / Beer barrel rag / My adobe hacienda / Lover / Snow deer / Ike Everly's rag / Sweet bunch of daisies / Somebody stole my gal / San Antonio rose / Li'l Liza Jane / Bury me beneath the willow / High noon / Down among the budded roses / Freight train / I wonder where you are tonight / Wildwood flower / Back in the saddle again / Memphis blues / Black mountain rag / Say 'si si' / Columbus stockade blues / Right or wrong smiles / I saw the light.
2LP: . . . . CMH 9017

GREAT SONGS OF THE DELMORE BROTHERS (Travis, Merle & Johnny Bond).
LP: . . . . HAT 3107
MC: . . . . HATC 3107

MERLE TRAVIS 1944-1946.
Tracks: / Nine pound hammer / Cannonball rag / Porky's boogie / Divorce me C.O.D. / Freight train blues / Dapper Dan / Ida / When you and I were young, Maggie / Osage stomp / Kansas City blues.
LP: . . . . RFD 9001

MERLE TRAVIS GUITAR, THE.
LP: . . . . HAT 3132
MC: . . . . HATC 3132

ROUGH, ROWDY AND BLUE.
LP: . . . . CMH 6262

TRAVIS.
LP: . . . . HAT 3080
MC: . . . . HATC 3080

TRAVIS PICKIN'.
Tracks: / Rose time / There'll be some changes made / Born to lose / Too tight rag / You're nobody 'til somebody loves you / Night sounds / Sugar moon / White heat / Midnight special / World is waiting for the sunrise, The / Sleep / Love letters in the sand / Drifting and dreaming / Sing baby sing.
LP: . . . . CMH 6255
MC: . . . . CMH 6255C

WALKIN' THE STRINGS.
LP: . . . . PM 1550801

Travis, Randy

ALWAYS AND FOREVER.
Tracks: / Too gone too long / My house / Good intentions / What'll you do about me? / I won't need you anymore / Forever and ever, Amen / I told you so / Anything / Truth is lyin' next to you, The / Tonight we're gonna tear down the walls.
LP: . . . . WX 107
MC: . . . . WX 107 C
LP: . . . . K 925568 1
MC: . . . . K 925568 4

HEROES AND FRIENDS.
LP: 7599263101
MC: 7599263104

NO HOLDING BACK.
LP: . . . . WX 292
MC: . . . . WX 292 C

OLD 8 BY 10.
Tracks: / Forever & ever, amen / Honky tonk moon / Deeper than a holler / It's out of my hands / Is it still over? / Written in stone / Blues in black and white / Here in my heart / We ain't out of love yet / Promises.
LP: . . . . WX 162
MC: . . . . WX 162C

STORMS OF LIFE.
Tracks: / On the other hand / Storms of life, The / My heart cracked / Diggin up bones / No place like home / 1982 / Send my body / Messin with my mind / Reasons I cheat / There'll always be a honky tonk somewhere.
LP: 925435 1
MC: 925435 4

Travolta, Joey

JOEY TRAVOLTA.
Tracks: / You matter to me / If this is love / Listen to your heart / Magic is you / I'd rather leave while I'm in love / I don't wanna go / Let's pretend / Steal away again / I don't want to be lonely / Something's up / This time you're really mine.
LP: . . . . XL 13057

Travolta, John

20 GOLDEN PIECES: JOHN TRAVOLTA.
Tracks: / Let her in / Never gonna fall in love again / Rainbows / Razzamatazz / I don't know what I like about you baby / Big trouble / Goodnight Mr. Moon / Sandy / Baby I could be so good at lovin' you / It had to be you / Slow dancing / Can't let you go / Easy evil / Back doors crying / What would they say / Right time of the night / Moonlight lady / Greased lightning / Settle down / You set my dreams to music.
LP: . . . . BDL 2021
MC: . . . . AJKL 2021

SANDY (ALBUM).
Tracks: / Snady / Slow dancing / You set my dreams to music / Whenever I'm away from you / Settle down / Back doors crying / Greased lightning / Moonlight lady / All strung out / Can't let you go / Easy evil / What would they say.
LP: . . . . POLD 5014

TWO OF A KIND (Film Soundtrack).
LP: . . . . EMC 1654611
MC: . . . . TCEMC 1654611

Treacherous Jaywalkers

GOOD MACHINE.
LP: . . . . SST 207

LA ISLA BONITA.
LP: . . . . SST 217

Treading The Boards

TREADING THE BOARDS (Stars of Music Hall & Variety) (Various artists).
Tracks: / Photo of the girl I left behind me, The: *Merson, Billy* / Golden dustman, The: *Elen, Gus* / Misery farm: *Handley, Tommy* / Bird in a gilded cage: *Forde, Florrie* / It's the first time I've ever done that: *Robey*, George / Little Dolly Daydream: *Elliott, G.H.* / Coster's wedding, The: *Lloyd, Marie Junior* / Call of the Yukon, The: *Bennett, Billy* / She's only been with us a week: *Whelan, Albert* / Whistling: *Jolly Brothers*/ What can you give a nudist on her birthday?: *Sarony, Leslie* / Little idea of my own: *Robey, George* / Fill 'em up: *King, Hetty* / 'E dunno where 'e are: *Elen, Gus* / You can't understand the ladies: *Whelan, Albert*/ Whistling: *Siziletta* / Spaniard that blighted my life, The: *Merson, Billy* / Lost policeman, The: *Powell, Sandy* / Sunny skies: *Elliott, G.H.* / Goodbye, Dolly Gray: *Forde, Florrie*.
LP: . . . . CHD 154
MC: . . . . MCHD 154

Treasure Girl (show)

TREASURE GIRL/CHEE CHEE (Original Show Scores) (Various artists).
Tracks: / I've got a crush on you: *Lewine, Richard - Betty Comden* / I don't think I'll fall in love today: *Lewine*, Richard - Betty Comden / Where's the boy? here's the girl: *Lewine, Richard - Betty Comden* / I must love you: *Lewine*, Richard - Betty Comden / Better be good to me: *Lewine, Richard - Betty Comden* / Dear oh dear: *Lewine, Richard* - Betty Comden / Moon of my delight: *Lewine, Richard - Betty Comden* / Singing a love song: *Lewine, Richard -Betty Comden*.
LP: . . . . TER 1039

Treasure Island

TREASURE ISLAND (Daneman, Paul (nar)).
MC: . . . . BKK 414

TREASURE ISLAND (Original London cast) (Various artists).
Tracks: / Overture: *Various artists* / Admiral Benbow Inn, The: *Various artists* / 15 men: *Various artists*/ Find that boy: *Various artists* / Shipmates: *Various artists* / Partn'rs and pals: *Various artists*/ Heave-oh-haul: *Various artists* / Billow the sails: *Various artists* / Land ho: *Various artists* / Deepwater sailors: *Various artists* / Cheese: *Various artists* / Cap'n Silver: *Various artists* / Far away from England: *Various artists* / Never get caught: *Various artists* / Treasure Island: *Various artists*.
LP: . . . . TER 1008

TREASURE ISLAND (see Stevenson, Robert Louis) (Unknown narrator(s)).

TREASURE ISLAND (Pertwee, Jon).
MC: . . . . P 90008

TREASURE ISLAND (see Stevenson, Robert Louis) (Buck, David).
MC: . . . . LFP 41 7170-5

Treasures Of The

TREASURES OF THE EXPLORER SERIES (Various artists).
LP: . . . . H 711

Treasury Of...

TREASURY OF FIELD RECORDINGS - VOL.1 (Treasury Of Field Recordings).
LP: 77LA 12 2

TREASURY OF FIELD RECORDINGS - VOL.2 (Treasury Of Field Recordings).
LP: 77LA 12 3

Treat

ORGANISED CRIME.
Tracks: / Ready for the taking / Party all over / Keep your hands to yourself / Stay away / Conspiracy / Mr Heartache / Gimme one more night / Get you on the run / Home is where your heart is / Fatal smile.
LP: 838 929 1
MC: 838 929 4

SCRATCH AND BITE.
Tracks: / Changes / Scratch and bite / Get you on the run / Hiding / Too wild / We are one / No room for strangers / You got me / Run with the fire.
LP: 824 353 1
MC: 824 353 4

TREAT.
Tracks: / Winner, The / Rev it up / Sole survivor / Strike without a warning / Outlaw / Fallen angel / Ride me high / World of promises / Save yourself / Best of me, The.
LP: 836 727-1
MC: 836 727-4
LP: 838 929-1
MC: 838 929-4

Treat Her Right

TREAT HER RIGHT.
Tracks: / I think she likes me / I got a gun / Everglades, The / Square / Trail of tears / Jesus everday / You don't need money / Don't look back / Honest job, An / Bringin' it all back home / Where did all the girls come from.
LP: . . . . FIEND 97

Tredegar...

BOUND IN BRASS (Tredegar Town Band).
LP: . . . . BM 6

SONGS FOR EVERYONE (Tredegar Orpheus Male Voice Choir).
Tracks: / Bandit's chorus (From 'Ernani') / Go down Moses / Nidaros / Evening's pastorale, An / Fantasia on famous Welsh airs / Myfanwy / Plantation songs / Ave Verum Corpus / Peacocks, The / Anvil chorus / Night song.
LP: . . . . NSPM 5001
MC: . . . . ZCMN 5001

TREDEGAR.
LP: . . . . CDPLP 1

VOICES AND BRASS OF WALES (Tredegar Orpheus Male Voice Choir).
Tracks: / March of the Peers / Air from Suite in D / Prisoners chorus from 'Fidelio' / Salamanca / Cymru fach / Dance of the Tumblers / Battle hymn of the Republic / Castell Caerfilli / Spanish eyes / Lord's prayer / Close thine eyes / Dance of the Russian sailors / Joy of the hunger / Llanfair.
LP: . . . . TB 3024

Tree Grows In Brooklyn

TREE GROWS IN BROOKLYN (Broadway Cast) (Various artists).
LP: . . . . AML 4405

Treece, H

SPLINTERED SWORD (Sheddon, John).
MCSET: . . . . COL 3004

WAR DOG (Steuart, David).
MCSET: . . . . COL 3005

Trees

GARDEN OF JANE DELAWNEY.
Tracks: / Nothing special / Great silkie, The / Garden of Jane Delawney, The / Lady Margaret / Glasgerion / She moved through the fair / Road / Epitaph / Snail's lament.
LP: . . . . LIK 15

ON THE SHORE.
Tracks: / Soldiers three / Murdoch / Streets of Derry / Sally free & easy / Fool / Adams toon / Geordie / While the iron is hot / Little Sadie / Polly on the shore.
LP: . . . . LIK 12

Trelawny

TRELAWNY (Original London cast) (Various artists).
Tracks: / Pull yourse lf together: *Various artists* / Walking on: *Various artists* / Ever of thee: *Various* artists / Trelawny of the Wells: *Various artists* / Tom Wrench's letter: *Various artists* / On approval: *Various* artists / Rules: *Various artists* / Back to the Wells: *Various artists* / Old friends: *Various artists*/ One who isn't there, The: *Various artists* / We can't keep 'em waiting: *Various artists* / Turn of Avonia Bunn, The: *Various artists* / Arthur's letter: *Various artists* / Two fools: *Various artists* / Life: *Various artists* / Finale: *Various artists*.
LP: . . . . TER 1081
MC: . . . . ZCTER 1081

Trelford, Donald (aut)

SNOOKERED (Powell, Robert (nar)).
MCSET: . . . . LFP 7270

Tremblers

TWICE NIGHTLY.
Tracks: / You can't do that / Steady Eddy / She was something else / I'll be taking her out tonight / Little lover / I screamed Anne / Wouldn't I / Dad said / Maybe I'll stay / Green shirt / Don't say it.
LP: . . . . EPC 84448

Tremeloes

6 TRACK HITS.
Tracks: / Here comes my baby / Me and my life / Silence is golden / Even the bad times are good / Call me / Number one / Words.
MC: 7SC 5034

16 GREATEST HITS.
LP: . . . . BRLP 03
MC: . . . . BRMC 03

AS IT HAPPENED.
Tracks: / Here come's my baby / Helule, helule / Silence is golden / Suddenly you love me / Hello world / Twist and shout / Even the bad times are good / Call me number one / Words / My little lady / Me and my life / Do you love me.
LP: . . . . CBS 25360
MC: 40 25360

GREATEST HITS: TREMELOES.
LP: . . . . SHM 3097
MC: . . . . HSC 3097
LP: . . . . TREMS 3002

HERE COME THE TREMELOES.
LP: . . . . SBPG 63017

SILENCE IS GOLDEN.
Tracks: / Even the bad times are good / Call me number one / Helule, helule / Candy man / Yellow river / Silence is golden / Suddenly you love me / Me and my life / Here come's my baby / Last word, The / Someone / Mu little lady (non Il girti mi) / words.
LP: . . . . MTLP 002

ULTIMATE COLLECTION.
2LP: . . . . CTVLP 002
MC: . . . . CTVMC 002

Trenet, Charles

CHANSONS.
LPS: . . . . PM 1129373

CHARLES TRENET.
Tracks: / Je chante / Boum / Il pleut dans ma chambre / L'a d' la joie / Menilmontant / La romance de Paris / Bonsoir jolie madame / Que feste-tal de hos amours / Debit de l'eau, debit de lait / Chacun son reve / N'y pensez pas trop / Douce France / Mes jeunes annees / L'ame des poetes / Une noix / La jolie sardane / Coin de rue / Source bleue / Route nationale No. 7 / La java du diable / Moi j'aime le music hall / Lorelei / Le jardin / Le piano de la plage / Narbonne mon amie / La famille musicienne / Dudrtier lalin / La mer.
2LP: 1568363
2LP: 2C 156 72602/3
MCSET: TC-2C 450 72604

DISQUE D'OR.
LP: 2C 070 72009

EXTRAORDINARY GARDEN, THE (Very best of Charles Trenet).
Tracks: / Boum (Orchestra Wal-Berg.) / L'ame de poetes (Orchestra dir. Trenet and quartet.) / Moi j'aime le music hall (Orchestra Guy Luypaerts.) / Vous qui passez sans me voir (Orchestra Hubert Rostaing.) / La jolie sardane (Orchestra Jo Boyer.) / En Avril a Paris (Orchestra Jo Boyer.) / Le jardin extraordinaire (Orchestra Wal-Berg.) / Coin de rue (Orchestra Jacques Helian.) / Mes jeunes annes (Orchestra Albert Lasry with the Raymond St. Paul Chorus.) / A la porte du garage (Orchestra Guy Luypaerts.) / France Dimanche (Orchestra Albert Lasry.) / Que reste-t-il de nos amours (Orchestra Leo Chauliac.) / Y'a d'la joie (Charles Trenet & His Orchestra.) / Douce France (Orchestra Albert Lasry.) / La polka du roi (Orchestra Trenet.) / Revoir Paris (Orchestra Albert Lasry.) / La folle complainte (Orchestra Jo Boyer.) / Le grand cafe (Orchestra Charles Trenet.) / La mer (Orchestra Albert Lasry.) / Menilmontant (Orchestra Wal-Berg. CD

only.) / Vous oubliez votre cheval (Orchestra Wal-Berg. CD only.) / La maison du poete (CD only.) / La famille musicienne (Orchestra Guy Luypaerts. CD only.) / Le chante (Orchestra Wal-Berg. CD only.).
LP: EMS 1361
MC: TCEMS 1361

FLORILEGE 86.
LP: 26793

J'AI TA MAIN.
2LP: 2C 150 15943/44

LA ROMANCE DE PARIS.
MC: 2526134

TOP SIXTEEN.
MC: PM 1562504

Trenhaile, John

MAN CALLED KYRIL, THE (See also Christian Rodska).
MC: CAB 326

Treniers

ROCKIN' IS OUR BUSINESS.
Tracks: / Rockin' is our business / Rock-a-beatin' boogie / Get out of the car / Hi-yo silver / It rocks, it rolls it swings / Plenty of money / Hadacol that's all / Rockin' on Sunday night / Go go go / Trapped in a web of love / Long distance blues / Hey little girl / Bald head / Poon Tang / Moon dog, The / Taxi blues.
LP: ED 117

YOU'RE KILLIN' ME.
Tracks: / Buzz buzz buzz / No baby no / Everybody get together / Sure had a wonderful time / Last night / Ain't she mean / You're killin' me / I'd do nothin' but grieve / Lover come back to me.
LP: DH 803
LP: H 803

Trent, Jackie

GOLDEN HOUR OF JACKIE TRENT.
MC: KGHMC 120

NIGHT, THE MUSIC AND..., THE.
MC: ZCP 11048

OUR WORLD OF MUSIC (Trent, Jackie/ Tony Hatch).
Tracks: / Bluer than blue / Love me to sleep / All the king's horses / It's the same old song / Early mornings / Sometimes when we touch / You light up my life / Longer, love / I just wanna stop / Where do we go from here / September morn.
LP: ACLP 004

Treorchy Male Choir

CALON LAN.
Tracks: / Calon lan / Kwmbayath / Ave Maria / O gymru / Arglwydd, mae yn nosi / Bridge over troubled water / Heavens are telling / Men of Harlech / Exekiel saw the wheel / Llan baglan / Seeds of love / Cytgan yr helwyr / There are many babies born.
LP: SCX 6619

CWM RHONDDA.
Tracks: / Huntsmens chorus / Calon lan / Arouse ye / Non nobis, Domine / Battle hymn of the republic / Roman war song / Llanfair / Jacob's ladder / Pirate's chorus / March of the Holy Grail / Cwm Rhondda.
LP: NTS 202
MC: TCNTS 202

DAVID OF THE WHITE ROCK.
Tracks: / Cwm Rhondda / Dear Lord and Father of mankind / Little innocent lamb / Finnish forest, The / I believe / Psalm 150 / David of the White Rock / Dashenka / Cytgan y pererinion / Takin' names / Annie's song / En route.
LP: SCX 6635
MC: TC SCX 6635

GREATEST HITS: TREORCHY MALE CHOIR.
Tracks: / Counting the goats / Myfanwy / Sanctus / Comrades in arms / Sara / Battle hymn of the Republic / Sospan fach / Morte Christe / Old woman, The / Laudamus / O mor ber yn y man (in the sweet bye and bye) / O Mary don't you weep / Cavalleria rusticana / Eater hymn (O rejoice that the Lord has risen).
LP: SCX 6685
MC: TC-SCX 6685

INSPIRATIONAL BEST OF THE..., THE.
Tracks: / Come let us sing to the Lord our God / O God of Bethel / Lord of our life / All in the April evening / Guide me o thou great Jehovah / Were you there? / By cool Siloam's shady rill / Close thine eyes / Love divine / Jesus shall reign / Psalm 23 (the Lord is my shepherd) / Praise the Lord, His glory show / What a friend we have in Jesus / Come let us join our cheerful song / Fight the good fight / Hail to the Lords anointed / Bells are ringing / O mighty Lord / Give Thou thy hand / Onward Christian soldiers.
LP: TWE 6003
MC: TC TWE 6003

LAND OF MY FATHERS.
MC: TCIDL 9

MAGIC SOUNDS OF..., THE.
LP: MFP 5617

MARCH OF THE MEN OF HARLECH.
Tracks: / March of the men of Harlech / Isle of Mull / Pueri hebraeurum / Kumbaya / Were you there / Hyfrydol / Y ddwy wydd dew / Matona / Holy City, The / Y fedwen arian 'The silver birch' / Calon lan / Dana Dana / Adoramus Te / Cwm Rhondda / Muss I denn / Deryn y bwn / Rockin' all night, A / Ezekiel saw de wheel / Lost chord, The.
LP: REC 319
MC: ZCM 319

MY WAY.
Tracks: / How lovely are thy dwellings / March of the men of Harlech / Cymru fach / With a voice of singing / All through the night / Wachet auf (sleepers wake from Bach's cantata) / Llef (deus salutis) / Wondrous love / Click go the shears / Bugeilio'r gwenth gwyn / Arwelfa / My way / Rachie (I Bob un syd ffyddlon).
LP: MFP 5794
MC: TCMFP 5794

ON GREAT LONE HILLS....
Tracks: / Aberystwyth / Lest we forget / Entrance and march of the peers / Sound of silence, The / Cantique de Jean Racine / Garland of Welsh folk songs, A / Memory / Unwaith eto'n nghymru annwyl / Diolch I ti yr hollalluog dduw / Hymn from 'Finlandia'.
LP: GRALP 2
MC: GRTC 2

SHOWSTOPPERS.
Tracks: / Another opening another show / Just one of those things / You do something to me / So in love / Who wants to be a millionaire / Love changes everything / Bring him home / Anthem (from Chess) / Climb every mountain / Somewhere / Do you hear the people sing / How to handle a woman / Impossible dream, The / Send in the clowns / On the street where you live / Another opening another show.
MC: TCMFP 5906

SOUND OF TREORCHY (Treorchy Male Choir/John Cynan Jones).
MC: TC2MOM 125

TOGETHER (SECOMBE/TREORCHY) (see under Secombe, Harry) (Treorchy Male Choir/Harry Secombe).

TREORCHY MALE CHOIR SINGS YOUR FAVOURITE HYMNS.
Tracks: / Crown Him with many crowns / In Heavenly love abiding / For all the saints / Rock of ages / Praise, my soul, the King of Heaven / Old rugged cross, The / Now thank we all our God / God's wonderful world / Love divine / To God be the glory / There is a green hill far away / Day thou gavest, Lord is ended, The.
LP: WRD R 3030
MC: WRD C 3030

VALLEY CALLED RHONDDA, A.
Tracks: / Valley called Rhondda, A / Where shall I be / Impossible dream, The / Kalinka / With you on my mind / We'll keep a welcome / Bandit's chorus (From 'Ernani') / Mae d'eisau di Bob Awr / What have they done to the rain / Christus redemptor (hyfrydol) / Hava nagila / Maria wanders through the thorn / God bless the Prince of Wales.
LP: EMS 1064111
MC: TCEMS 1064114

WEEKEND SOUNDS.
MC: ZCM 319

WE'LL KEEP A WELCOME - VOL.1.
LP: SM 391

WE'LL KEEP A WELCOME - VOL.2.
LP: SM 392

Treponem Pal

AGGRAVATION.
LP: RO 93321
MC: RO 93324

TREPONEM PAL.
Tracks: / Silico / Embodiment of frustration / Prettiest star, The / In out / Low man / Soft mouth vagina.
LP: RO 9456 1
MC: RO 9456 4

Tresize, Artie

BALCANQUHAL (see Fisher, Cilla) (Tresize, Artie & Cilla Fisher).

CILLA & ARTIE (see Fisher, Cilla) (Tresize, Artie & Cilla Fisher).

FOR FOUL DAY AND FAIR (see Fisher, Cilla) (Tresize, Artie & Cilla Fisher).

Trespassers W

DUMMY.
Tracks: / Whistle down the wind / Bite you in the head / Jealousy / Pine in the wood / Melancholy man / Nostalgia / No New York / Brel / Mr. Verdoux / Dentures for a godess / School days / Youth culture / T.V. world / Headshrinker / Neverland / It's Christmas time again / What's my life really worth / England swings / Paris in between the wars / Boundaries.
2LP: DUMMY 001

PRETTY LIPS.
Tracks: / Contras / Melancholy man / Echoes of Rhodesia / Spit and sawdust / Mascara cara / Another country / Neanderthal woman replica / Tentative lovesong / Living in the Hague / Chickenfarm / B-sides / Coventry / Picking flowers in Afghanistan / Faraway fathers.
LP: DMC 022

Tresvant, Ralph

RALPH TRESVANT.
LP: MCG 6120
MC: MCGC 6120

Trettine, Caroline

BE A DEVIL.
LP: UTIL 008

Treves, Katherine

FOURTH FOLLY (McBain, Rose).
MCSET: CLT 1004

Trial By Jury

TRIAL BY JURY (see under Gilbert & Sullivan).

Tri-Axle

MIGHTY 142, THE.
MC: MCLP 1002

Triban

TRIBAN.
LP: BM 7

Tribble, T.N.T.

T.N.T JUMP VOL 2 (Red hot boogie).
Tracks: / Groove / Good mama / Cadillac blues / T.N.T jump / Movin' man / Little house party / Red hot boogie / She walked right in / Long gone / Rockin' mama / That's alright / Alamo, The / Hey everybody.
LP: KK 828

T.N.T. TRIBBLE.
Tracks: / Cadillac blues / Twin h jump / Rockin' in rhythm / Long gone / Oh gone / oh babe / Hurricane lover / Annie's mambo / Red hot boogie / Little house party / Half pint of whiskey / Muddy water / Hot heat / Cookie.
LP: KK 809

Tribe Called Quest

PEOPLES INSTINCTIVE TRAVELS.
LP: HIP 96
MC: HIPC 96

Tribe, Tony

TONY TRIBE/UPSETTERS (See under Upsetters) (Tribe, Tony/Upsetters).

Tribute

NEW VIEWS.
LP: EULP 1042
MC: EUMC 1042

Tribute To...

TRIBUTE TO CARL ALAN AWARD WINNERS (Various artists).
LP: DS 051

TRIBUTE TO JAMES DEAN (Various artists).
LPPD: AR 30039

TRIBUTE TO JOHN FAHEY (Various artists).
LP: SNKF 155

TRIBUTE TO KENNY ROGERS (Various artists).
MC: AIM 42

TRIBUTE TO PAUL WHITEMAN (Various artists).
LP: SG 8015

TRIBUTE TO ROKY ERICKSON (WHERE THE PYRAMID) (See under Erickson, Roky) (Various artists).

TRIBUTE TO STEVE GOODMAN (See under Goodman, Steve) (Various artists).

TRIBUTE TO TRICKY RICKY, A (Various artists).
LP: RUSK 3

TRIBUTE TO WOODY GUTHRIE (See under Guthrie, Woody) (Various artists).

Trichot, Andre

26 SUCCESSES.
Tracks: / Soleil et corrida / Musettorama / Oui au tango.
2LP: 42022/34

COMME AU BAL.
Tracks: / Nous, les routiers sympas / Melodie pour Ysoline / Eternel tango / Coucou Tyrolien / Souvenir de bolero / Sambatina / La valse des tondeuses / Retour de tango / Tournette en la / Java des saucissons / Le patriarche / Elmira.
LP: 42009

VIENS DANSER.
Tracks: / C'est comme au bal / Indulgente / Echo Suisse / Tango des accordeonistes / El campionissimo / Moi / Je travaille / Adios Sevilla / Itogo / Porte close / Momo musette / Le denicheur / Maria-marinette / Tico tico / Paso d'hydra.
LP: 42017

Tricia & The Boogies

BREAKAWAY.
Tracks: / Everybody's gonna be happy / Your love is mine / Woman child (You can't know what I know) / We fit together / Make it easy / It's my turn / Mistaken identity / Nowhere to run / Breakaway / I don't mind.
LP: PTLS 1099
MC: PTLC 1099

Trick Or Treat (film)

TRICK OR TREAT (Film Soundtrack) (Fastway).
Tracks: / Trick or treat / After midnight / Don't stop the fight / Stand up / Tear down the wall / Get tough / Hold on to the nights / Heft / If you could see.
LP: 4504441
MC: 4504444

TRICK OR TREAT (Film score) (Brand, Oscar).
LP: TC 1624

Trick Switch

AN EXCHANGE OF CLIENTS.
MC: COCKPIT 2

T.S.T.S.
MC: COCKPIT 4

WHERE'S THE RAFT.
MC: COCKPIT 1

WHERE'S THE RAFT/AN EXCHANGE OF CLIENTS.
MCSET: COCKPIT 1/2

Trickster

BACK TO ZERO.
LP: JETLP 221

Triffids

BLACK SWAN.
Tracks: / Too hot to move, too hot to think / Falling over you / Bottle of love / Butterflies into worms / Good fortune rose / One mechanic town / Fairytale love / American sailors / Goodbye little boy / Spinning top song, The / Clown prince, The / New year's greetings / Black eyed Susan Brown.
MC: ICT 9928
LP: ILPS 9928

BORN SANDY DEVOTIONAL.
LP: HOT 1023

CALENTURE.
Tracks: / Trick of the night, A / Bury me deep in love / Kelly's blues / Home town farewell kiss / Unmade love / open for you / Holy water / Blinder by the hour / Vagabond holes / Jerdacuttup man / Calenture / Save what you can.
LP: ILPS 9885
MC: ICT 9885
MC: ICM 2027
MC: 842 718 4

IN THE PINES.
LP: HOT 1028

RAINING PLEASURE.
LP: MINIHOT 1

STOCKHOLM.
LP: MNWX 9
MC: MWNMCX 9

TREELESS PLAIN.
LP: HOT 1003

Triglia, B

D. WHITE/ B. TRIGLIA (See under White, D).

Triligy

NEXT IN LINE.
LP: AXE 7026

Trilobites

AMERICAN TV.
LP: CGAS 808

TURN IT AROUND.
LP: DAMP 069

Trimble, Gerald

CROSS CURRENTS.
LP: SIF 1065
MC: CSIF 1065

FIRST FLIGHT.
LP: SIF 1043
MC: CSIF 1043

HEARTLAND MESSENGER.
LP: SIF 1054
MC: CSIF 1054

Trimmer & Jenkins
LIVE FROM LONDON'S FABULOUS COMIC STRIP.
Tracks: / Jazz and poetry / And we love it / Muffa licki / You're the girl I wanna be with / Winsome losesome / World is fantastic, The / Happy hearts / Wipe out / We like bananas.
LP: CLASS 10

Trinder, Tommy
BAND WAGGON (See Under Askey, Arthur) (Trinder, Tommy & Arthur Askey & Richard Murdoch).

Trinidad Steel Band
MAGIE CARAIBE.
Tracks: / Somebody whisper to me / Liza / Coming home / Summertime / Brown skin gal / Carnivals bells / Mary-Ann / Yellow bird / Improvisation / Calypso jazz improvisation.
LP: ARN 33167
MC: ARN 433167

TRINIDAD STEEL BAND, (THE).
LP: H 72016

Trinidad Tropicana
ORIGINAL TRINIDAD TROPICANA STEEL BAND.
Tracks: / Archie / Barcarolle / Cachita / Guantanamera / Jamaica farewell / Love for sale / Moon over Naples / Paris / Peanut vendor / Silence is golden / Syncopation in C / Yellow bird.
LP: 2489 077
MC: SPEMC 38
LP: SPELP 38

Trinity
BAD CARD.
Tracks: / Ride on Sandra / Come on and groove me / Love you from the start / Rockers delight / Blues night / Time so wrought / I love mama / Bad card / Got to be wise / Need some loving.
LP: BMLP 042

BEST OF TRINITY.
Tracks: / I live a dream / Case eye thing / Simmer down / Kendal crash / Sam's / Bib bib man / Eastwood married.
LP: VSLP 5017

LOSE RESPECT (See under Levy, Barrington For Details) (Trinity/ Barrington Levy/Roman Stewart).

NATTY TIRED TO CARRY LOAD.
LP: BS 011

ONE MORE CHANCE (See under Thompson, Linval for details) (Trinity & Linval Thompson).

ROCK IN THE GHETTO.
Tracks: / Easy does it / Life is not easy / Tell it to me, mother / Have a little faith / Dangerous rockers / Don't lose me / Every trick in the book / Rock in the ghetto / Pope Paul dead and gone / Freedom style / Follow my heart.
LP: TRLS 170

SIDE KICKS.
LP: VSLP 4009

TEEN JAM.
Tracks: / Boom it up now / Little bit of soap, A / Pan-Coote / One night of loving / Teen jam / She get me mad / Mini skirt / Boll weevil / Come give me your love.
LP: KVL 9013

Trinity Boys Choir
CHRISTMAS COLLECTION, A.
Tracks: / Jingle bell rock / Sleigh ride / Have yourself a merry little Christmas / Sailing / Winter wonderland / Christmas song, The / Let it be / Amazing Grace / Christmas waltz / When a child is born / I'll be home for Christmas / White Christmas / Windmills of your mind / Away in a manger / Bridge over troubled water / Eleanor Rigby / Over the rainbow / Jerusalem.
MC: PWKMC 4032

Trio
BY CONTACT.
LP: UNKNOWN

DA DA DA (OLD GOLD) (See under Opus/Live is life).

TRIO.
Tracks: / To know him is to love him / Farther along / Wildflowers / Hobo's meditation / Rosewood casket.
LP: 6435 163
MC: 7106 163
LP: 9254911

Trio Bulgarka
BULGARIAN FOLK MUSIC.
LP: BHA 12490
MC: BHMC 7351

FOREST IS CRYING.
LP: HNBL 1342
MC: HNBC 1342

Trio Con Tromba
ABSOLUTE.
LP: DRLP 136

WHO'S SORRY NOW.
LP: DRLP 126

Trio Fontenay
PIANO TRIOS.
Tracks: / Piano trio no.2 (Brahms) / Piano trio no.1 (Dvorak).
LP: 244 177-1
MC: 244 177-4

Trio San Antonio
VIVA EL WEST SIDE.
LP: ARHOOLIE 3004

Trio UGB
TRIO UGB.
LP: AM 69

Trip (film)
TRIP, THE (See under Electric flag) (Electric Flag).

Trip Shakespeare
ACROSS THE UNIVERSE.
Tracks: / Turtledove / Snow days / Gone gone gone / Unlucky lady / Crane, The / Today you move / Pearle / Drummer like me / Slacks, The / Nail, The / Late.
LP: 395 2941
MC: 395 2944

Trip To The Dentist
TRIP TO THE DENTIST (Various artists).
Tracks: / Doctor: *Geisha Girls* / I'm not fightin': *Afraid Of Mice* / No way out: *Attempted Moustache*/ Don't hurry, don't worry: *Walking Boots* / Muscle + my heroes: *Luminous Beings* / One more record: *Relations*/ Just for you & me: *Stopouts* / And the dance goes on: *Hussey, Wayne* / T.V. can kill: *Luminous Beings*/ Transparent: *Afraid Of Mice* / Leave you alone: *Walking Boys* / Little Arthur: *Two Orkie Twins* / I don't know why: *Upsets* / Shadows of giants: *Luminous Beings* / When the music's over: *Windows*.
LP: SKULP 1

Triplet Trouble
BEST OF TRIPLET TROUBLE.
Tracks: / I'll never regret loving you / Sweet soul music / Gentle rain, The / Indoor games / True love.
LP: PM 2071
MC: PMC 2071

Triplets
THICKER THAN WATER.
MC: 8482904
LP: 8482901

Trippel, Fritz
BLUE HARMONICA.
LP: CA 107LP

Trireach, Aghan
BARDIC MOODS OF MUSIC, THE.
LP: CEF 059

Trischka, Tony
BANJOLAND.
LP: ROUNDER 0087
MC: ROUNDER 0087C

BLUEGRASS LIGHT (BANJO).
LP: ROUNDER 0048

HEARTLANDS.
LP: ROUNDER 0062
MC: ROUNDER 0062C

HILL COUNTRY.
LP: ROUNDER 0203
MC: ROUNDER 0203C

ROBOT PLANE FLIES OVER ARKANSAS, A.
LP: ROUNDER 0171
MC: ROUNDER 0171C

SKYLINE DRIVE.
LP: FF 388
MC: FF 388C

STRANDED IN THE MOONLIGHT (Trischka, Tony & Skyline).
LP: FF 304

Trisomie 21
CHAPTER IV.
LP: FACE 16

CHAPTER IV (REMIX).
LP: FACE 016R
MC: FACE 016R MC

LE REPOS DES ENFANTS HEUREUX & PASSIONS DIVISEES.
Tracks: / Il se noie / There's something / Strange tonight / Logical animals / Coming from darkness / Breaking down.
LP: LD 8714
LP: LD 8814

MILLION LIGHTS.
LP: BIAS 076

PASSIONS DIVISEES.
Tracks: / See the devil in me / Relapse / Djakarta / Moving by you / Is anybody home / No way / Love for a life / Fear and desire / Everything is on fire / Lost in violence / Sorrow and pain / 35 poems / One the third day / My sister called silence / Pain came, the.
LP: ST 006
LP: LD 8813
MC: LD 8813C

PLAYS THE PICTURES.
Tracks: / Brewsters millions / At this time of writing / Right to reply / Into the light / Cinema hall / Friday report / Take the shock away / One last play / Moonlight / Remember me / W.S.W. / Bambou / Ceremony.
LP: BIAS 182

RAW MATERIAL.
LP: BIAS 181
MC: BIAS 181MC

T21 PLAYS THE PICTURES.
LP: BIAS 152
MC: BIASMC 152

WORKS.
LP: BIAS 122
MC: BIASMC 122

Tristan De Cunha
TRISTAN DE CUNHA (Songs Dances and Customs).
MC: 90-609

Tristano, Lennie
BLUES OF A KIND.
LP: BB 01

COOL IN JAM.
LP: BLJ 8033

CROSS CURRENTS (Tristano, Lennie & Tadd Dameron).
Tracks: / Wow / Crosscurrent / Yesterdays / Marionette / Sax of a King / Intuition / Digression / Sid's delight / Casbah / John's delight / What's new / Heaven's doors are open wide / Focus.
LP: AFF 149

IN EUROPE (Tristano, Lennie/Lee Konitz).
LP: UJ 21

LENNIE TRISTANO.
Tracks: / Line up / Requiem / Turkish mambo / East thirty-second / These foolish things / You go to my head / If I had you / Ghost of a change / All the things you are.
LP: K 50245

LOST SESSION, THE (See under Swope, Earl) (Tristano, Lennie & Earl Swope Sextet).

MANHATTAN STUDIO.
LP: 9602641

NEW SOUNDS IN THE FORTIES (Tristano, Lennie/Boyd Raeburn).
LP: BLJ 8007

Tristram, Geoffrey
ORGAN MUSIC FROM LAKELAND.
LP: GRS 1004

Triton
WILDERNESS OF GLASS.
LP: GCM 782

Tritonz
EDGE OF HELL, THE.
LP: GWLP 13

Tritten, Charles (aut)
HEIDI GROWS UP (Francis, Jan (nar)).
MCSET: LFP 7268

Triumph
ALLIED FORCES.
Tracks: / Fool for your love / Magic power / Air raid / Allied forces / Hot time (In this city tonight) / Fight the good fight / Ordinary man / Petite etude / Say goodbye.
LP: RCALP 6002
MC: RCAK 6002

JUST A GAME.
Tracks: / Movin'on / Lay it on the line / Young enough to try / American girls / Just a game / Fantasy serenade / Hold on / Suitcase blues.
LP: INTS 5154
MC: INTK 5154
LP: PL 13224

NEVER SURRENDER.
Tracks: / Too much thinking / World of fantasy, A / Minor prelude, A / All the way / Battle cry / Overture (processional) / Never surrender / When the lights go down / Writing on the wall / Epilogue (resolution).
LP: RCALP 6067
MC: RCAK 6067

PROGRESSIONS OF POWER.
Tracks: / I live for the weekend / I can survive / In the night / Nature's child / Woman in love / Take my heart / Tear the roof off / Fingertalkin' / Hard road.
LP: MCL 1852
MC: MCLC 1852
LP: RCALP 3039
MC: RCAK 3039
LP: PL 13524

ROCK 'N' ROLL MACHINE.
Tracks: / Takes time / Bringing it on home / Rocky mountain way / Street fighter / Street fighter (reprise) / 24 hours a day / Blinding light show/ Moonchild / Rock 'n' roll machine.
LP: MCL 1856
MC: MCLC 1856

SPORT OF KINGS, THE.
LP: MCF 3331
MC: MCFC 3331

STAGES.
Tracks: / When the lights go down / Never surrender / Hold on / Magic power / Rock and roll machine / Lay it on the line / World of fantasy, A / Midsummer's daydream / Spellbound / Follow your heart / Fight the good fight / Mind games / Empty inside / Allied forces / Druh mer selbo.
2LP: MCMD 7002
MCSET: MCMDC 7002

THUNDER SEVEN.
Tracks: / Spellbound / Midsummer's daydream / Killing time / Little boy blues / Follow your heart / Rock out, roll on / Time goes by / Time canon / Stranger in a strange land / Cool down.
LP: MCF 3246
MC: MCFC 3246

TRIUMPH.
Tracks: / Takes time / Bringing it on home / Rocky Mountain way / Street fighter / 24 hours a day / Blinding light show / Moonchild / Rock'n'roll machine.
LP: INTS 5153
MC: INTK 5153
LP: LAT 1012
LP: PL 12982

Triumph Of The..(film)
TRIUMPH OF THE SPIRIT (see under Eidelman, Cliff) (Eidelman, Cliff).

Triumph Street Pipe
DRAM BEFORE YA GO, A.
LP: LILP 5156
MC: LICS 5156

Triumphant
GIVE PRAISES.
LP: TRIU 1

Triumvirat
RUSSIAN ROULETTE.
LP: IC 064 45834

Trixter
TRIXTER.
Tracks: / Line of fire / Heart of steel / One in a million / Surrender / Give it to me good / Only young once / Bad / Always a victim / Play rough / You'll never see me cryin' / Ride the whip / On and on.
LP: MCA 6389
MC: MCAC 6389
LP: MCG 6114
MC: MCGC 6114

Troccolli, Kathy
HEART AND SOUL.
LP: RRA 0005
MC: RRA C 0005

IMAGES: KATHY TROCCOLLI.
LP: RRA R 0014
MC: RRA C 0014

PORTFOLIO.
LP: RRA R 0025
MC: RRA C 0025

Trockener Kecks
BETAALDE LIEFDE.
Tracks: / Betaalde liefde / Dood van een held / Souvenir / De split go to the mosk / Naar de top / Betaalde liefde / Los Zand / Mijn Laatse beer.
LP: TK 11

IN DE KROCKTEN VAN DE GEETS.
Tracks: / Afrodisiac / In de krockten van de geets / Asfalt / Iemand anders / Huurmoordenaar de man in de lucht / Koud en donker / Pumps nooit meer honger / Levend vlees / Speelkwartier.
LP: TK 5

SCHLIESSBAUM.
Tracks: / Schliessbaum / Het meisje van de donutshop / De gifbekker mokerslagen / Trottoirterreur / Slagboom, (Zig was een) / Bouquet / Gienlijn zeuws meisje / 22.22 / Samen met Jose / Lidmaatschap / Ik slik de zever niet / Femme fatale.
LP: TK 2

Troggs
AU.
LP: ROSE 186

BEST OF THE TROGGS.
LP: 2215265
MC: 2115265
LP: FOR 001
LP: RNLP 118
MC: RNC 118

BLACK BOTTOM.
LP: ROSE 4
LP: PL 30084

DOUBLE HITS COLLECTION (Troggs/ Dave Dee, Dozy, Beaky, Mick & Tich).
LP: PLAT 3908
MC: PLAC 3908

FROM NOWHERE - THE TROGGS.
LP: TL 5355

GOLDEN HITS: TROGGS.
LP: 20046
MC: 40046

GREATEST HITS: TROGGS (IMPORT).
LP: BRLP 28
MC: BRMC 28
LP: MA 28487
MC: MAMC 928487

HOT DAYS.
MC: ASK 779

LIVE AT MAX'S, KANSAS CITY.
Tracks: / Got love if you want it / Satisfaction / Love is all around / Feels like a woman / Strange movie / Summertime / Walking the dog / Memphis / No particular place to go / Wild thing / Gonna make you.
LP: MKC 100

ROCK IT BABY.
LP: ARLP 103

TROGGLODYNAMITE.
LP: POL 001

TROGGS-VOLUME 1 AND VOLUME 2.
MCSET: TWO 410

WILD THINGS.
Tracks: / I got lovin' if you want it / Good vibrations / No particular place to go / Summertime / Satisfaction / Full blooded band / Memphis Tennessee / Peggy Sue / Wild thing / Get you tonight / Different me, A / Down South in Georgia / After the rain / Rock 'n' roll lady / Walking the dog / We rode through the night / Gonna make you / Supergirl / I'll buy you an island / Rolling stone.
LP: KOMA 788021
LP: SEE 256

Troika

UKRAINIAN FOLK MUSIC.
Tracks: / Hopak / Verhovyno / Gritsyu / Kolomeiki / Arkan / Ribbon dance / Hata bila / Polonez / Lisorubi / Krakowac / Snow on the mountain / Moldyavinushka.
MC: SAM 1

Troilus & Cressida

TROILUS & CRESSIDA (see under Shakespeare, William) (Various artists).

TROILUS & CRESSIDA (see under Chaucer, Geoffrey) (Various artists).

Trois Places Pour ...

TROIS PLACES POUR LE 26 (Film soundtrack) (Various artists).
LP: 836 733 1
MC: 836 733 4

Trojan...

TROJAN HITS (Various artists).
2LP: CR 127
MCSET: CRT 127

TROJAN STORY, VOL 2 (Various artists).
LPS: TALL 200
MCSET: ZTALL 200

TROJAN'S GREATEST HITS (Various artists).
Tracks: / At the discotheque: *Pioneers* / Further you look, The: *Holt, John* / Come back Liza: *Livingstone*, Dandy / Private number: *Bob & Marcia* / Time hard: *Agard, George* / Struggling man: *Cimarons* / New morning: *Thomas, Nicky* / Star trek: *Vulcans* / Then he kissed me: *Marvels* / Lord pity us all: *Riley*, Martin / Oh what a feeling: *Simon, Tito* / Everybody plays the fool: *Chosen Few* / Blue moon: *Platonics*/ Big 1: *Judge Dread*.
LP: TBL 208

Trojan (Group)

CHASING THE STORM.
LP: RR 9756

MARCH IS ON, THE.
LP: GILP 444
MC: GIMC 444

Trojans

A LA SKA.
LP: GAZLP 002

SAVE THE WORLD.
Tracks: / Save the world / Don't slip and fall / Last rhino, The / Travelin' light / Stop breaking my heart / I don't want to see you cry / Leaps and bounds / Crazy mixed up world / One Earth (war on Earth) / Everybody loves a lover / You were mean't for me / Feeling stronger.
LP: GAZLP 005

SPIRIT.
LP: GAZLP 003

TROJANS LIVE.
MC: GAZ 200

Troll Turned To Stone

BURNING TROLL.
LP: ISST 141

TROLL TURNED TO STONE.
LP: ISST 125

Trollope, Anthony

BARCHESTER TOWERS (See under Barchester Towers).

DOCTOR THORNE (West, Timothy (nar)).
MCSET: CC/051

WARDEN, THE (See under Warden for details) (Sutcliffe, Irene (nar)).

Tron

TRON (Film soundtrack) (Various artists).
MC: D 34DC
LP: CBS 70223
MC: 40 73665

Troop

TROOP.
LP: 818511

Trooper

FLYING COLOURS.
LP: MCF 3030

Tropea, John

TO TOUCH YOU AGAIN.
Tracks: / Livin' in the jungle / In this time / Look what they've done to my song / You're my every need / To touch you again / Lady blue / Yours next to mine / Do you wanna be loved.
LP: TKR 83355

Tropic Tonic

TROPIC TONIC (Various artists).
LP: CEL 6761

Tropical Fish

HOLIDAY IN (see Deane, Geoff) (Tropical Fish & Geoff Deane).

Tropiques

ILES DES TROPIQUES (Chants, rythmes & danses).
LP: ARN 33764
MC: ARN 433764

Trostel, Rolf

DER PROPHET.
LP: U 008

Trotman, Trinidad Bill

MR. SOCA.
LP: GS 2301

Trotsky Icepick

BABY.
LP: SST 197
MC: SSTC 197

DANNY AND THE DOORKNOBS.
LP: SST 254
MC: SSTC 254

EL KABONG.
LP: SST 246
MC: SSTC 246

POISON SUMMER.
Tracks: / Gaslight, The / Nightingale drive / Just the end of the world / Clowns on fire / Ivory tour / Commissioner, The / Big dreams / Drawing fire / Hit parade / You look like something Goya drew.
LP: SST 239
MC: SSTC 239

Trotter, John Scott

MUSIC HALL HIGHLIGHTS (See under Crosby, Bing) (Trotter, John Scott/ Bing Crosby Orchestra).

Trotto

TROTTO Music and Song from Middle Ages to Present Day.
LP: FRR 005

Troubadors

NED O' THE HILL.
LP: PSH 104

Troubadours ...

MISSA LUBA (Troubadours Du Roi Baudouin).
LP: SBL 7952

Trouble

RUN TO THE LIGHT.
Tracks: / Misery show, The / Thinking of the past / Peace of mind / Born in a prison / Tuesdays child / Beginning, The.
LP: RR 9606

SKULL.
LP: RR 9791

TROUBLE.
Tracks: / At the end of my daze / Wolf, The / Psychotic reaction / Sinner's fame, A / Misery shows (act II), The / Rip / Black shapes of doom / Heaven on my mind / END / All is forgiven.
LP: 8424211
MC: 8424214

Trouble Done ...

TROUBLE DONE BORE ME ME DOWN (Various artists).
LP: AB 2011

Trouble Funk

BOMB HAS DROPPED, THE.
Tracks: / Pump me up / Hey fellas / Let's get hot / Drop the bomb / Get on up / Don't try to use me.
LP: BLAT 5
MC: BLATMC 5

DROP THE BOMB.
Tracks: / Hey fellas / Get on up / Let's get hot / Drop the bomb / Pump me up / Don't try to use me / My love (burning love) / Caravan to midnight / I'm out to get you / Lost in love / Fool / It's for you / Birthday boy / King of the dances / Sail on.
LP: SHLP 5554
LP: SHLP 1006

SAY WHAT.
LP: DCLP 101
MC: DCCA 101

TROUBLE OVER HERE TROUBLE OVER THERE.
Tracks: / Break it up / Sexy / New money / Stroke / All over the world / Hey tee bone / Woman of principle / Trouble.
LP: BRLP 513
MC: BRCA 513
MC: ICM 2052
MC: 842 711 4

Trouble In Mind

TROUBLE IN MIND (Film soundtrack) (Various artists).
LP: 90501.1

Trouble In Tahiti

TROUBLE IN TAHITI (1952 TV Musical) (Various artists).
LP: 827845.1
MC: 827845.4

Trouble Man (film)

TROUBLE MAN (See under Gaye, Marvin) (Gaye, Marvin).

Trouble Tribe

SOMETHING SWEET.
Tracks: / Tattoo / Here comes trouble / Gimme something sweet / In the end / Back to the well / Boys nite out / Tribal beast / Red light zone / Angel with a devil's kiss / Dear Prudence / One by one / Cold heart / F's nightmare.
LP: CHR 1740
MC: ZCHR 1740

Troubles Troubles

TROUBLES TROUBLES (Various artists).
LP: ZS 58

TROUBLES TROUBLES & NEW ORLEANS LADIES (Various artists).
LP: ZS 60

Troup, Bobby

BOBBY TROUP PLAYS JOHNNY MERCER.
Tracks: / Jamboree ones / Midnight sun / Come rain or come shine / Laura / That old black magic / One for my baby / Cuckoo in the clock / Day in, day out / Jeepers, creepers / Loves got me in a lazy mood / Skylark / I'm with you.
LP: AFF 174

DISTINCTIVE STYLE OF BOBBY TROUP, THE.
LP: FS 234

IN A CLASS BEYOND COMPARE.
LP: AP 98

Trout, Walter

LIFE IN THE JUNGLE (Trout, Walter Band).
Tracks: / Good enough to eat / Mountain song, The / Life in the jungle / Spacefosh / Red house / She's out there somewhere / Frederica (I don't need you) / In my mind / Cold cold feeling / Serve me right to suffer.
LP: PRL 70201
MC: PRL 70204

Trowbridge, Douglas

SECOND STORY.
LP: ML R 7016
MC: ML C 7016

SONGS UNSPOKEN.
LP: ML R 7007
MC: ML C 7007

Trower, Robin

BACK IT UP.
Tracks: / Back it up / River / Black to red / Benny dancer / Time is short / Islands / None but the brave / Captain Midnight / Settling the score.
LP: CHR 1420
MC: ZCHR 1420

BEYOND THE MIST.
LP: MFN 51
MC: TMFN 51

B.L.T..
Tracks: / Into money / What it is / Won't let you down / No island lost / It's too late / Life on earth / Once the bird has flown / Carmen / Feel the heat / End game.
LP: CHR 1324
MC: ZCHR 1324

BRIDGE OF SIGHS.
Tracks: / Day of the eagle / Bridge of sighs / In this place / Fool and me, The / Too rolling stoned / About to begin / Lady love / Little bit of sympathy.
LP: CHR 1057
MC: ZCHR 1057

CARAVAN TO MIDNIGHT.
Tracks: / My love (burning love) / I'm out to get you / Lost in love / Fool / It's for you / Birthday boy / King of the dance / Sail on.
LP: CHR 1189
MC: ZCHR 1189

COLLECTION: ROBIN TROWER.
MC: CCSMC 291

FOR EARTH BELOW.
Tracks: / Shame the Devil / It's only money / Confessin' / Midnight / Fine day / Althea / Tale untold, A / Gonna be more suspicious / For earth below.
LP: CHR 1073
MC: ZCHR 1073

IN CITY DREAMS.
Tracks: / Somebody calling / Sweet wine of love / Bluebird / Falling star / Farther on up the road / Pride / Sailing / S.M.O. / I can't live without you / Messin' the blues.
LP: CHR 1148
MC: ZCHR 1148

LIVE: ROBIN TROWER.
Tracks: / Too rolling stoned / Daydream / Rock me baby / Lady love / I can't wait much longer / Alethea / Little bit of sympathy.
LP: CHR 1089
MC: ZCHR 1089

LONG MISTY DAYS.
Tracks: / Same rain falls / Long misty days / Hold me / Caledonia / Pride / Sailing / S.M.O. / I can't live without you / Messin' the blues.
LP: CHR 1107
MC: ZCHR 1107

PASSION.
Tracks: / Caroline / Secret doors / If forever / Won't even think about you / Passion / No time / Night / Bad time / One more word.
LP: PRT N6563
MC: ZCN 6563

PORTFOLIO (The Classic Collection).
Tracks: / Bridge of sighs / Too rolling stoned / For earth below / Caravan to midnight / Day of the eagle / Shame the devil / Fine day / Daydream (live) / Lady love (live) / Alethea (live) / Caledonia live / Messin' the blues / Bluebird / Victims of fury / Mad house / Into money / Gonna shut you down / Thin ice / Benny dance.
LP: CNW 3
MC: ZCNW 3

TAKE WHAT YOU NEED.
Tracks: / Tear it up / Take what you need / Love attack / I want you home / Shattered / Over you / Careless / Second time, The / Love won't wait forever.
LP: K 781 838 1
MC: K 781 838 4

TRUCE (see Bruce, Jack & Robin Trower) (Trower, Robin/Jack Bruce).

TWICE REMOVED FROM YESTERDAY.
Tracks: / I can't wait much longer / Daydream / Hannah / Man of the world / I can't stand it / Rock me baby / Twice removed from yesterday / Sinner's song / Ballerina.
LP: CHR 1039
MC: ZCHR 1039

VICTIMS OF THE FURY.
Tracks: / Jack and Jill / Roads to freedom / Victims of the fury / Ring, The / Only time / Into the flame / Shout, The / Mad house / Ready for the taking / Fly low.
LP: CHR 1215
MC: ZCHR 1215

Troy, Doris

WHATCHA GONNA DO ABOUT IT (See under Tandy,Sharon "Hold on").

Trucking

14 GREAT TRUCK HITS (Various artists).
Tracks: / Movin' on: *Haggard, Merle* / From a jack to a king: *Miller, Ned* / Six days on the road: *Dudley*, Dave / Born to be a trucker: *Simpson, Red* / Trucker's paradise: *Reeves, Del* / Tombstone every mile: *Curless, Dick*.
LP: 022-58173
MC: 222-58173

40 MILES OF BAD ROAD (Various artists).
LP: GT 0057

COUNTRY TRUCK FESTIVAL VOL.1 (Various artists).
MC: SUCCESS 2030

COUNTRY TRUCK FESTIVAL VOL.2 (Various artists).
MC: SUCCESS 2031

GREAT SONGS OF THE AMERICAN TRUCK DRIVERS (Various artists).
Tracks: / Six days on the road: *Dudley, Dave* / Truck drivin' son of a gun: *Dudley, Dave* / Highways: *Various* artists / Truck driver's prayer: *Dudley, Dave* / Going to Memphis: *Perkins, Carl* / Truck driver's waltz: *Dudley, Dave* / Sunday morning coming down: *Kennedy, Jerry* / Convoy: *McCall, C.W.* / Truck drivin' man: *Dudley, Dave* / King of the road: *Miller, Roger* / Just a few miles more: *Dudley, Dave* / Sugerland USA: *Dudley, Dave* / I'm movin' on: *Dudley, Dave* / Take me home country roads: *Statler Brothers*.
LP: 6498 214
MC: 7133 214

KEEP ON TRUCKING (Various artists).
Tracks: / Let's truck together: *Price, Kenny* / Roll on truckers: *Newton, Juice & Silver Spur* / Truck driving man: *Fell, Terry* / Little diesel driving devil: *Bowman, Dan* / Caffeine, nicotine and benzedrine: *Stucky*, Nat / White line fever: *Brewer, Bud* / Peterbilt: *Knight, Carl* / I'm a truck: *Russel, Johnny* / Somebody stole my rig: *Silverstein, Shel* / Six days on the road: *Snow, Hank* / Long thin dawn: *Hamilton*, George IV / Roll big wheels roll: *Oxford, Vernon* / Truckers paradise: *Nicholls, Nev* / Truck driving woman: *Jean, Norma* / Truck driver truck driver: *Bare, Bobby* / Mama was a truck driver queen: *Brewer, Bud* / Diesel cowboy: *McAuley, Ray And Wild Country* / Ten miles from home: *McKenna, Fred* / One more dusty road: *Hawkes, Chip*.
LP: NL 89023
MC: NK 89023
LP: INTS 5076

ME & OL' C.B. TRUK 3 (Various artists).
MC: VCA 621

ROAD MUSIC (Various artists).
2LP: GTV 107

ROADRUNNER (Various artists).
LP: GT 0053

SUPER SLAB HITS (Various artists).
LP: GT 0052

TRUCK DRIVER SONGS (Various artists).
LP: KLP 866
MC: GT 5866

TRUCKIN' ON (Various artists).
LP: GT 0054

TRUCKING U.S.A. (Various artists).
MC: AIM 61

TRUCKING USA VOL.2 (Various artists).
MC: AM 65

TRUCKING VOL. 2 (Various artists).
MC: AM 111

Trucks...

TRUCKS TRAINS & AIRPLANES (Various artists).
LP: GT 0081

Trudy

TUNE-IN TO THE TRUDY LOVE-RAY.
LP: TDY 054

True Believers

TIME AIN'T LONG.
Tracks: / He's just a prayer away / If it ain't one thing / Don't let nothing shake your faith / He's alright / What can I give? / I love Him / He's keeping me alive / Learning to lean on Jesus / Time ain't long.
LP: MIR 5021
MC: MIR 5021MC

TRUE BELIEVERS.
Tracks: / Tell her / Ring the bell / So blue about you / Rebel kind / Train round the bend / Lucky moon / We're wrong / I get excited / Sleep enough to dream / Rain won't help you when it's over.
LP: AML 3107
MC: TC-AML 3107

True Confessions

TRUE CONFESSIONS (Film soundtrack) (Various artists).
LP: TER 1013

True Grit

BLACK COUNTRY, THE.
LP: KB 001
MC: KB 001 C

GET EDUCATED.
Tracks: / Get educated / I decorated your house / You've got something on your mind / Give me your love / Just good friends / Fool on love / Everyday blues / Fatman sings rock'n'roll / Living in the real world.
LP: SPAC 001

True Grit (film)

TRUE GRIT/THE COMMANCHEROS (See under Commancheros, The) (Various artists).

True Mathematics

TRUE MATHEMATICS GREATEST HITS.
Tracks: / For The Money / K A O S S / After Dark / For the lover in you / Get funky everybody / I don't love you anymore / Be my girl / Portrait of a rap star / Greeks in the house / True mathematics.
MC: CHAMPK 1014
LP: CHAMP 1014

True Saints

FROM THE HEART (True Saints with Mama).
Tracks: / God will take care of you / Like Him / It's in my heart / Shine the light / Pieces back / May I / Jesus / I can't even walk / He's coming back / In time like this / Come unto Jesus.
LP: MIR 5011
MC: ZCMIR 5011

True Stories

TRUE STORIES (Film soundtrack) (Various artists).
Tracks: / Road song: *Byrne, David* / Freeway son: *Byrne, David* / Brownie's theme: *Byrne, David* / Mall musak: *Finch, Carl* (Consists of : part i) Building a highway; ii) Puppy polka; iii) Party gi) / Dinner music: *Kronos* Quartet / Disco hits!: *Byrne, David* / City of steel: *Byrne, David* / Love theme from true stories: *Byrne*, David / Festa para um rei negro: *Banda Eclipse* / Buster's theme: *Finch, Carl* / Soy de tejas: *Jordan, Steve* / I love metal buildings: *Byrne, David* / Glass operator: *Byrne, David*.
LP: EMC 3520
MC: TCEMC 3520

True Voices

TRUE VOICES (Various artists).
Tracks: / Changes: *Various artists* / Devil eyes: *Various artists* / Lady came from Baltimore, The: *Various* artists / Thank you for being there: *Various artists* / Simple song of freedom: *Various artists* / Which will: *Various artists* / To love someone: *Various artists* / At the end of the day: *Various artists* / Loving arms: *Various artists* / Across the great divide: *Various artists* / Dreamer, The: *Various artists*.
LP: FIEND 165

True West

DRIFTERS.
Tracks: / Look around / At night they speak / Speak easy / Shoot you down / What about you / Hold on / And then the rain / Blackroad bridge song / Ain't no hangman / Morning light.
LP: ZONG 004
LP: ROSE 45
MC: ROSE 45C

HOLLYWOOD HOLIDAY/ DRIFTERS.
LP: ROSE 23

Truesdale, Tommy

C'MON EVERYBODY.
Tracks: / Roll over Beethoven / Be bop a lula / Somethin' else / Sunflower / Baby I don't care / I'm ready / C'mon everybody / Lonely blue boy / My kinda life / Sea cruise / Whole lotta woman / Cut across Shorty.
LP: NA 116

DON'T BE CRUEL.
LP: BGC 294

TOMMY TRUESDALE, SINGS COUNTRY.
LP: BGC 401
MC: KBGC 401

TREE IN THE MEADOW, A.
MC: KITV 529

Truetones

BELIEVE AND RECEIVE.
Tracks: / Believe and recieve / When this life is over / Victory shall be mine / Move satan / Talk it over with Jesus / He's the one / Healing / Yesterday is gone.
LP: MIR 5005
MC: ZCMIR 5005

Truffaut, Francois

MUSIC FROM THE FILMS OF FRANCOIS TRUFFAUT VOL 1 (See under Film Music) (Various artists).

Truffauts

BILLY ZE KICK.
LP: PUT 7

FANNY.
LP: PUT 3

Trull, Teresa

STEP AWAY, A.
LP: RR 412

Truly Unforgettable

TRULY UNFORGETTABLE (32 Truly Unforgettable Songs) (Various artists).
Tracks: / When I fall in love: *Cole, Nat King* / Be my love: *Lanza, Mario* / Only you: *Platters* / It's all in the game: *Edwards, Tommy* / Spanish eyes: *Martino, Al* / On the street where you live: *Damone, Vic*/ He'll have to go: *Reeves, Jim* / Misty: *Mathis, Johnny* / Can't get used to losing you: *Williams, Andy*/ Dream lover: *Darin, Bobby* / Move over darling: *Day, Doris* / Never be anyone else but you: *Nelson, Rick(y)*/ It's only make believe: *Twitty, Conway* / End of the world: *Davis, Skeeter* / More than I can say: *Vee*, Bobby / It's over: *Orbison, Roy* / Cry me a river: *London, Julie* / Love letters: *Lester, Ketty*/ I left my heart in San Francisco: *Bennett, Tony* / Make it easy on yourself: *Walker Brothers* / Joanna: *Walker*, Scott / You don't have to say you love me: *Springfield, Dusty* / Look homeward angel: *Ray, Johnnie* / Every time we say goodbye: *Fitzgerald, Ella* / God bless the child: *Holiday, Billie* / Passing strangers: *Eckstine*, Billy & Sarah Vaughan / What a wonderful world: *Armstrong, Louis* / Folks who live on the hill, The: *Lee, Peggy*/ Stand by me: *King, Ben E.* / Save the last dance for me: *Drifters* / Unforgettable: *Cole, Nat King*.
2LP: EMTVD 55
MCSET: TCEMTVD 55

Truman, Freddie

UMPIRE STRIKES BACK, THE.
LP: VJRB 111

Truman, Harry S.

TRUMAN TAPES, THE.
LP: TC 2085
MC: CDL 52085

Trumbauer, Frankie

BIX AND TRAM (See Under Beiderbecke, Bix) (Trumbauer, Frankie/ Bix Beiderbecke).

BIX BEIDERBECKE WITH FRANKIE TRUMBAUER (See Under Beiderbecke, Bix) (Trumbauer, Frankie/Bix Beiderbecke).

FIRST TIME VOL. 2 (Trumbauer, Frankie/Paul Whiteman/Louis).
LP: IAJRC 21

FRANKIE TRUMBAUER 1937-38.
LP: IAJRC 13

JACK TEAGARDEN AND FRANKIE TRUMBAUER TNT (Trumbauer, Frankie / Jack Teagarden).
Tracks: / Dixie Lee / Clambake / Fare thee well to Harlem / I'm so in love with you / Basin street blues / Christmas night in Harlem / Beale street blues / Prohibition / Wildcat / Bouncing ball / F blues / Nobody's sweetheart / Wabash blues / Flight of the haybag / Old man of the mountain, The / I'm the mayor of Alabam' / China boy.
LP: AIRCHECK 9

Trummer Jazz

JAZZ AND HOT DANCE AFTER THE NAZIS 1946-49.
LP: HQ 2052

Trump Jack All Stars

TRUMP JACK EXPLOSION (Various artists).
LP: TJPLP 002

Trumpet Battle

TRUMPET BATTLE 1952 (Various artists).
Tracks: / Jam session: *Various artists* / I can't get started: *Various artists* / Summertime: *Various artists*/ Sweet Lorraine: *Various artists* / It's the talk of the town: *Various artists* / Cocktails for two: *Various artists* / Trumpet battle.
LP: VRV 2

Trumpet Call

TRUMPET CALL, THE (See under Barinov, Valeri) (Various artists).

Trumpet Music

MAN THE MEASURE OF ALL THINGS (See under Wallace, John for full details) (Wallace, John).

TRUMPET AND HORN CONCERTOS (See under Haydn) (Philharmonia Orchestra).

Trumpeteers

MILKY WHITE WAY.
LP: RF 1401

Trunkles

TRADITIONAL.
Tracks: / Trunkles delight / John Barleycorn / Innocent hare, The / Joseph the baker / Rise up Jack / Benjamin bowmaneer / Pretty Maggie Morrisey / Winster galop / Bobby Shaftoe / Boscastle breakdown / Australia / Furze field / Foxhunter's jig, The / Broom besoms / Balance the straw / Lollipop man / Black Joe.
LP: SFA 088

Truss & Bucket Band

TRUSS & BUCKET BAND.
LP: TB LP 1

Trust

BEST OF TRUST.
Tracks: / Antisocial / L'elite / Bosser huit heures / M comedie / Le mitard / Serre les poings / Police milice / Saumur / Ideal / Ton dernier acte.
LP: 4505941
MC: 4505944

MARCHE OUR CREVE.
LP: CBS 32740

REPRESSION.
Tracks: / Antisocial / Mr. Comedy / In the name of the race / Death instinct / Walk alone / Paris is still burning / Pick me up, put me down / Get out your claws / Sects / Le mitard.
MC: 40 84958
LP: CBS 84958

SAVAGE.
Tracks: / Big illusion / Savage / Repression / Junta / Mindless / Loneliness / Work or die / Crusades / Your final gig.
LP: CBS 85546

Truth

PLAYGROUND.
LP: MIRF 1001
MC: MIRC 1001

Truthettes

FLOWING.
LP: MALP 4434

GOD WILL MAKE THINGS ALRIGHT.
LP: MAL 04410

Truths Of Dune

TRUTHS OF DUNE (Herbert, Frank (aut)).
LP: TC 1616
MC: CDL 51616

TSA

HEAVY HEAVY METAL.
LP: AKP 10

SPUNK.
LP: MEGATONLP 2

Tsai-Ping, Liang

CHINESE CHENG-ANCIENT & MODERN.
LP: LLST 7302

Tse-Tung, Mao

QUOTATIONS FROM THE CHAIRMAN (See Under Mao, Tse-Tung).

Tshala Muana

M'POKOLA.
LP: SAS 057

T.S.O.L.

BENEATH THE SHADOWS.
LP: GWLP 52

CHANGE TODAY.
LP: 1076 1

DANCE WITH ME.
Tracks: / Sounds of laughter / Core blue / Triangle / 80 times / I'm tired of life / Love storm / Silent scream / Funeral march / Die for me / Peace thru power / Dance with me.
LP: WS 033

HIT AND RUN.
LP: ENIG 32621
LP: ENIG 32631

REVENGE.
LP: 3211 1

STRANGE LOVE.
LP: LS 9391

Tsuchiya, Masami

RICE MUSIC.
Tracks: / Rice music / Se! Se! Se! / Haina-Haila / Tao-tao / Neo-rice music / Kafka / Rice dog jam / Secret party / Silent object / Night in the park.
LP: EPC 85935

Tsunami

TSUNAMI.
LP: MFN 9

TT Highlights

TT HIGHLIGHTS 1965/8 VOL 2 (Various).
LP: BLP 703

TT HIGHLIGHTS 1957/64 VOL 1 (TT Highlights 1957/64 vol 1).
LP: BLP 702

Tubal Cain

LOOK OUT.
LP: MYR 1197
MC: MC 1197

Tubb, Ernest

BLUE CHRISTMAS (Tubb, Ernest And His Texas Troubadours).
LP: HAT 3020
MC: HATC 3020

COUNTRY MUSIC HALL OF FAME.
Tracks: / Walking the floor over you / Mean mama blues / Soldier's last letter / Let's say goodbye like we said hello / I'm bitin' my fingernails & thinking of you / Too old to cut the mustard / Hank, it will never be the same without you / Jimmie Rodgers' last thoughts / Thirty days / Hey, Mr. Bluebird / Thoughts of a fool / Thanks a lot / Mr. and Mrs. Used To Be / Pass the booze / Another story, another time, another place / Texas troubadour.
LP: CDLM 8078

DADDY OF EM ALL, THE.
LP: HAT 3015
MC: HATC 3015

ERNEST TUBB STORY, THE.
Tracks: / I'll get along somehow / Slippin' around / Filipino baby / When the world has turned you down / Have you ever been lonely / There's a little bit of everything in Texas / Walking the floor over you / Driftwood on the river / There's nothing more to say / Rainbow at midnight / I'll be glad to take you back / Let's say goodbye like we said hello / Careless darling / I wonder why you said goodbye / Last night I dreamed / Letters have no arms / Though the days were only seven / I love you because / You nearly lose your mind / I'll miss you when you go / It's been so long darling / Tomorrow never comes / Blue christmas.
2LP: IMCA2 4040

FAMILY BIBLE, THE.
LP: HAT 3120

FAVOURITES: ERNEST TUBB.
LP: HAT 3011
MC: HATC 3011

GOLDEN FAVOURITES.
Tracks: / I'll get along somehow / Slipping around / Filipino baby / Have you ever been lonely / There's a little bit of everything in Texas / Walking the floor over you / Driftwood on the river / There's nothing more to say / Rainbow at midnight / I'll always be glad to take you back / Let's say goodbye like we said hello / When the world has turned you down.
LP: IMCA 84

GREATEST HITS: ERNEST TUBB.
Tracks: / Walking the floor over you / Rainbow at midnight / Let's say goodbye like we said hello / Another story, another time, another place / Thanks a lot / Half a mind / I'll get along somehow / Waltz across Texas / It's been so long darling / Mr. Juke Box / I wonder why you said goodbye.
LP: IMCA 16

HIGH LIVIN'.
Tracks: / How long will she keep loving me / Just like the night before / You know how to keep me satisfied / Honey please change your mind / You don't love me yet / Only for me / Who's gonna love me / If it takes forever / She's the greatest kind of woman / Someone to be with me / I'll be back to love you tonight / What about you.
LP: MAN 5010

HONKY TONK CLASSICS.
Tracks: / Blue eyed Elaine / I ain't going honky tonkin' anymore / Try one more time / You nearly lose your mind / Answer to walking the floor over you / There's gonna be some changes made around here / Filipino baby / That wild and wicked look in your eye / Letters have no arms / You don't have to be a baby to cry / I need attention bad / Jealous loving heart.
LP: SS 14
MC: SSC 14

IMPORTANCE OF BEING ERNEST, THE.
Tracks: / I'm a long gone daddy / All those yesterdays / San Antonio rose / That, my darlin', is me / Educated mama / I wonder why I worry over you / Your cheatin' heart / It makes no difference now / Ships that never come in / Don't change your old fashioned sweetheart / It's the age that makes the difference.
LP: HAT 3006
MC: HATC 3006

MIDNIGHT JAMBOREE.
Tracks: / Walking the floor over you / Same thing as me, The / I only meant to borrow / Boy with a future / I hate to see you go / Hands you're holding now, The / Rose city chimes / I'm sorry now / Pass me by / Sweet lips / I want you to know I love you / Shoes / It is no secret.
LP: HAT 3032
MC: HATC 3032

Tubb, Justin

JUSTIN TUBB.
Tracks: / There's a little bit of everything / Blue eyed Elaine / Walking the floor over you / Just you and me, Daddy / Coronation day / Waltz across Texas / Sing 'blue eyed Elaine' again / I will miss you when you go / Be better to your baby / Thanks, troubadour, thanks.
LP: IMCA 39032
MC: IMCAC 39032

STAR OF THE GRAND OLE OPRY.
Tracks: / One for you, one for me / Looking back to see / I'd know you anywhere / Women / How the other half lives / That's alright / Five minutes of the latest blues / How's it feel / One eyed Red / Your side of the story / I've gotta get my baby / If you don't want me.
LP: OFF 9004

Tube Album

TUBE ALBUM (Various artists).
LP: TUBE 1
MC: TUBEK 1

Tube, Shem

ABANA BA NASERY (Tube, Shem/ Justo Osala/Enos Okola).
Tracks: / Atisa wangu / Khwatsia ebunangwe / Servanus andai / Nilimwacha muke risavu / Mapenzi kama karata / Noah libuko / Omukhana meri / Abasiratsi muhulire / Ndakhomela / Ebijana bie bubayi / Mushalo ebutula / Rosey wangu / Willison oluhambo.
LP: ORB 052

Tubes

COMPLETION BACKWARD PRINCIPLE,THE.
Tracks: / Talk to ya later / Let's make some noise / Matter of pride / Mr. Hate / Attack of the fifty foot woman / Think about me / Sushi girl / Don't want to wait anymore / Power tools / Amnesia / When I see you / Politics / Slave trade / Could be her ... could be you / Make believe / Don't go away / Price, The / Animal laugh / Anything is good enough / Product of..., A / Perfect game / Vendredi saint.
LP: EST 26285
LP: BGOLP 100
MC: BGOMC 100

OUTSIDE/INSIDE.
Tracks: / She's a beauty / No not again / Out of the business / Monkey time / Glass house / Wild women of wongo / Tip of my tongue / Fantastic delusion / Drums / Theme park / Outside looking in.
LP: EST 12260
MC: TCEST 12260

PRIME TIME.
LP: PLASLP 006

PRIME TIME (OLD GOLD) (See under Styx/Babe).

REMOTE CONTROL.
Tracks: / Turn me on / T.V. is king / Prime time / I want it all now / No way out / Get overture / No mercy / Only the strong survive / Be mine tonight / Love is a mystery / Telecide.
LP: AMLH 64751
MC: CAM 64751

TRASH.
Tracks: / Drivin all night / What do you want from life / Turn me on / Slipped my disco / Mondo bondage / Love will keep us together / I'm just a mess / Only the strong survive / Don't touch me there / White punks on dope / Prime time.
LP: AMLH 64870
MC: CAM 64870

TUBES, THE.
Tracks: / Haloes / Up from the deep / Space baby / Malaguena / Mondo bondage / What do you want from life / Boy crazy / White punks on dope.
LP: FA 3066
MC: TCFA 3066

WHAT DO YOU WANT FROM LIFE?.
Tracks: / Overture / Got yourself a deal / Show me a reason / What do you want from life / God-bird-change / Special ballet / Don't touch me there / Mondo bondage / Smoke (La vie en fumer) / Crime medley (Themes from "The Untouchables", "Peter Gunn" & "Perry") / I was a punk before you were a punk / I saw her standing there / Drum solo / Boy crazy / You're no fun / Stand up and shout / White punks on dope.
2LP: AMLM 68460
MCSET: CLM 68460
2LP: 396 003-1

Tubeway Army

REPLICAS.
Tracks: / Me, I disconnect from you / Are friends electric / Machman / Praying to the aliens / Sown in the park / You are in my vision / Replicas / It must have been years / I nearly married a human.
LP: BEGA 7
LP: BBL 7
MC: BBLC 7
MC: BEGC 7

TUBEWAY ARMY.
Tracks: / Listen to the sirens / My shadow in vain / Life machine, The / Friends / Something's in the house / Everyday I die / Steel and you / My love is a liquid / Are you real / Dreams police, The / Jo the waiter / Zero bars.
LP: FA 3060
MC: TCFA 3060
LP: BBL 4
MC: BBLC 4
LP: BEGA 4

Tubridy, Michael

EAGLE'S WHISTLE, THE.
LP: CC 27
MC: 4CC 27

Tuck & Patti

DREAM.
Tracks: / Dream / One hand, one heart / Togetherness / Friends in high places / Voodoo music, The / From now on we're one / I wish / Sitting in limbo / High heel blues / All the love / As time goes by.
MC: WT 0130

LOVE WARRIORS.
Tracks: / Love warriors / Honey pie / They can't take that away from me / Hold out hold up and hold on / Cantador (like a lover) / On a clear day / Europa / Castles made of sand / Little wing / Glory glory / If it's magic.
LP: 37 01161
MC: 37 01164
MC: WT 0116

TEARS OF JOY.
Tracks: / Tears of joy / Takes my breath away / I've got just about everything / Time after time / Everything's gonna be alright / Better than anything / My romance / Up and at it / Mad mad me / Love is the key.
LP: 37-0111-1
MC: 37-0111-4
MC: WT 0111

Tucker, Adrian

LONDON BLUES.
Tracks: / Done it all wrong / Can't get her off my mind / Off to the country / Take me to an island / Uncle Bodger / Motoring rag / You pays your money / Junk stall Joanna / Computer date blues / Skyports dream / Rag and blues.
MC: 60-037

Tucker, Bessie

1928 RECORDINGS also see Ida Mae Mack (Tucker, Bessie & Ida Mae Mack).
LP: PY 1815

QUEEN OF TEXAS BLUES 1928-29.
LP: DLP 556

RARE BLUES (1927 - 1935).
LP: HLP 4

Tucker, Colin Lloyd

MIND BOX.
LP: UNKNOWN

TOY BOX.
LP: PLASLP 001

Tucker (Film)

TUCKER (See Under Jackson, Joe) (Jackson, Joe).

Tucker, George

DEATH OF FLOYD COLLINS.
LP: ROUNDER 0064

Tucker, Junior

DON'T TEST (LP).
LP: DIX 93
MC: CDIX 93

Tucker, Mickey

CRAWL, THE.
LP: MR 5223

MYSTER MYSTERIOUS.
LP: MR 5174

SWEET LOTUS LIPS.
Tracks: / Gettin' there / Return ticket / All of you / Sweet lotus lips / Portrait of a peaceful scene / There for a woogie boogie / Kap'n'kryptonito / Tribute to Bean, A / Japanese soundscope / Bogue ballad bossa.
LP: YX 7535

WOOGIE BOOGIE, THEME FROM.
LP: YX 7804

Tucker, Moe

LIFE IN EXILE AFTER ABDICATION.
LP: MOE 7 1
MC: MOE 7 4

MOE, JAD, KATE AND BARRY.
LP: KSLP 010

Tucker, Sophie

ALL OF ME.
LP: LKLP 6046

FOLLOW A STAR.
Tracks: / Follow a star / That's where the south begins / Oh you have no idea / Washing the blues from my soul / Makin' wickey wackey down in Waikiki / There's something Spanish in my eyes / I'm the last of the red hot mamas / If your kisses can't hold the man you love / 'Cause I fell lowdown / I can never think of the words / That man of my dreams / What good am I without you? / Aren't women wonderful? / Some of these days.
LP: AJA 5046
MC: ZC AJA 5046

GOLDEN AGE OF SOPHIE TUCKER THE.
LP: GX 41 2533 1
MC: GX 41 2533 4

LAST OF THE RED HOT MAMA'S.
Tracks: / Aggravatin' Papa / Hule Lou / Some of these days / Red hot Mama / You've got to see Mama every night / After you've gone / I ain't nobody / 50,000,000 Frenchmen can't be wrong / My yiddishe momma / What'll you do / One sweet letter from you / There'll be some changes made / I ain't taking orders from no one.
LP: 32318

SOME OF THESE DAYS.
LP: SH 234
MC: TC SH 234

SOPHIE TUCKER COLLECTION (20 golden greats).
Tracks: / Red hot mama / My Yiddishe momma / Hula Lou / Stay at home, papa / Man I love, The / Louisville lady / What'll you do? / I've got a cross-eyed papa / When a lady meets a gentleman down South / Oh, you have no idea / Some of these days / No one man is ever going to worry me / Aggravatin' papa / I ain't taking orders from no one / Life begins at forty / He hadn't up 'til yesterday.
LP: DVLP 2099
MC: DVMC 2099

Tucker, Tanya

BEST OF TANYA TUCKER, THE.
MCSET: GTV 15770

CHANGES.
Tracks: / Cry / Shame on the moon / Until you're mine / Baby I'm yours / I don't want you to go / Heartache and a half / Changes / Feel right / Thing called love, A / Too long.
LP: 204756

COUNTRY STORE: TANYA TUCKER.
Tracks: / Delta dawn / Bed of roses / Why me Lord / You are so beautiful / Best of my love / Loving arms / Almost persuaded / I'll be your lady / Blood red and going down / Pass by me / How can I tell him / Let me be there / Jamestown Ferry / Guess I'll have to love him more / Chokin' kind, The (Only on CD) / South is gonna rise again, The (Only on CD) / What if we were running out of love (Only on CD) / I'm so lonesome I could cry (Only on CD).
LP: CST 35
MC: CSTK 35

DREAM LOVERS.
LP: MCF 3109

GIRLS LIKE ME.
Tracks: / One love at a time / I'll come back as another woman / Fool fool heart / Just another love / Girls like me / Somebody to care / It's only over for you / Daddy long legs / You could change my mind / Still hold on.
LP: EST 2007
MC: TCEST 2007

GREATEST HITS: TANYA TUCKER.

Tracks: / Daddy and home / Strong enough to bend / Love me like you used to / Just another love / I'll come back as another woman / My arms stay open all night / If it don't come easy / I won't take less than your love / One love at a time / It's only over for you.
LP: C1 91814
MC: C4 91814
LP: 791 814 1
MC: 791 814 4

LOVE ME LIKE YOU USED TO.
Tracks: / If it don't come easy / Love me like you used to / I won't take less than your love / I wonder what he's doing tonight / I'll Tennessee you in / Alien / Temporarily blue / If I didn't love you / Heartbreaker / Hope you find what you're loving for.
MC: TCEST 2036
LP: EST 2036

STRONG ENOUGH TO BEND.
Tracks: / You're not alone / Strong enough to bend / As long as I'm dreaming / Lonesome town / Daddy and home / Highway robbery / Lonely at the right time / Playing for keeps / Call on me / Back on my feet.
LP: EST 2069
MC: TCEST 2069

TENNESSEE WOMAN.
Tracks: / Take another run / Shotgun / Your old magic / Don't go out with him / There's a Tennessee woman/Ben's song / Goodbye baby / It won't be me / As long as there's a heartbeat / Walking shoes / Oh what it did to me.
MC: C4 91821

TNT.
Tracks: / Lover goodbye / I'm the singer, you're the song / Not fade away / Angel from Montgomery / Heartbreak Hotel / Brown eyed handsome man / River and the wind / If you feel it / It's nice to be with you.
LP: MCF 3530

WHY DON'T WE JUST SLEEP ON IT TONIGHT (See under Campbell, Glen) (Tucker, Tanya & Glen Campbell).

Tucker, Tommy

1933: TOMMY TUCKER (Tucker, Tommy & His Californians).
LP: CLP 124

1942: TOMMY TUCKER (Tucker, Tommy & His Orchestra).
LP: CLP 15

MEMPHIS BADBOY.
Tracks: / Miller's cave / Man in love, The / Lovin' Lil / You learn something now everyday / Ghost of Mary Lou, The / You don't love me / Miller's cave (2) / Will the circle be unbroken / I couldn't believe it was true / Joe Bodine / I ain't had enough / You hitched your wagon to a loser / Bridge of life, The / Glory train / Will the circle be unbroken (part 2).
LP: Z 2001

MOTHER TUCKER.
LP: RL 022

ROCKS IS MY PILLOW, COLD GROUND IS MY BED.
Tracks: / Alimony / Made your move too soon / J.R.'s blues / Isn't she sweet / Five long years / I just want to make love to you / Watch out / You're the one.
LP: RL 0037

TITANS OF R&B (See under Turner, Titus) (Turner, Titus and Tommy Tucker).

Tuckwell, Barry

PLAY THE MUSIC OF COLE PORTER (See under Shearing, George) (Tuckwell, Barry / George Shearing).

Tudor, Johnny

RATTLE MY BONES.
Tracks: / Rattle my bones / I'm sorry / Lately / Daydream / All in love is fair / I need a girl / Somewhere in the night / Reno / She / Clarabella.
LP: PRX 22
MC: TCPRX 22

Tudor Lodge

TUDOR LODGE.
LP: ZAP 4

Tudor, Stanley

CINEMA ORGAN ENCORES.
LP: DEROY 871

WURLITZER ORGAN ENCORES.
LP: DEROY 885

Tuff City Squad

BREAKMANIA.
LP: TUFLP 0561

Tuff Crew

DANGER ZONE.
LP: WAR 2705

Tuff Luck

TUFF LUCK.
LP: NRR 18
MC: NRC 18

Tuff, Ricky

YOUR LOVE (See under Prophet, Michael) (Tuff, Ricky & Michael Prophet).

Tuff, Tony

BEST OF TONY TUFF.
LP: VSLP 2004

CATCH A FIRE.
LP: Unknown

RENDER YOUR HEART.
Tracks: / Trying man / Sticky wicket / Render your heart / Turn me on / Separation / Feel like dancing / Good lovin' / It's happening / Give me / Sweet Mary Ann.
LP: CSLP 11

SAILING.
Tracks: / Love you baby / Up chin chaere / Come again / Sailing / No steady lover / Don't mind them / Follow fashion / Hard to get / You don't know.
LP: PHLP 0014

TONY TUFF.
Tracks: / Don't follow bad company / Jah almighty / Rumours of war / Lovers rocking and skanking / We want no war / I'm so glad / Gimme wha' me want / Sweet Maureen / Now I know.
LP: ILPS 9619

TUFF SELECTION.
Tracks: / Show on the road / No more.
LP: ILPS 9714

WHA WE A GO DO.
LP: Unknown

Tuff Turf

TUFF TURF (Film soundtrack) (Various artists).
2LP: RNDF 308

Tukano & Cuna

MUSIC OF THE TUKANO AND CUNA PEOPLES OF MADNESS (Various artists).
LP: FTS NSA 002

Tulla Ceili Band

40TH ANNIVERSARY.
MC: GTDC 014

CLADDAGH RING.
LP: STAL 1002

IRELAND GREEN.
LP: STAL 1029

SWEETHEARTS IN THE SPRING.
LP: ISLE 3004

Tullo, Pappa

HUNDRED POUNDS OF COLLIE (see Campbell, Cornell) (Tullo, Pappa & Cornell Campbell).

LEND ME A CHOPPER (see Osbourne, Johnny) (Tullo, Pappa & Johnny Osbourne).

ROCK AND COME ON YA (see Osbourne, Johnny) (Tullo, Pappa & Johnny Osbourne).

Tulpa

MOSAIC FISH.
LP: CHIME 10

Tumatoe, Duke

DUKES UP.
LP: BP-1584

Tumba Cuarta & Ka'l

TUMBA CUARTA & KA'L (Various artists).
LP: OMA 202

Tummings, Chris

FREEDOM (see Connolly, Billy) (Tummings, Chris & Billy Connolly).

Tundra

KENTISH GARLAND.
LP: SFA 078

KENTISH SONGSTER THE.
Tracks: / Jolly Jack of Dover / Herne Bay dance, The / Dutchman, The / Sweet orange pippin / Yeoman of Kent, The / Cells / Lullingstone hunt, The / Pretty maids of Greenwich / Kentish frolick, The / Hops / Old man and his wife, The / Hop supper, The.
LP: GVR 208

SONGS FROM GREENWICH.
Tracks: / Greenwich Park / Pretty maids of Greenwich / Rambling sailor / Rebellion of Watt Tyler / Admiral Benbow / Greenwich lovers / Garland, The / Homeward bound / Blackheath burglar / Lady of Greenwich / So handy / Jack at Greenwich / Shallow brown.
LP: GVR 218

Tune Weavers

HAPPY, HAPPY BIRTHDAY, BABY.
Tracks: / Happy, happy birthday baby / Ol' man river / I remember dear / Pamela Jean / There stands my love / I'm cold / Little boy / Lonesome road, The / My congratulations / This can't be love / I hear the mission bells.
LP: OFF 6015

Tune Wranglers

WESTERN SWING VOL.4 (From the 1950's).
LP: OT 119

Tunisia

TUNISIAN MUSIC (Various artists).
LP: RIKS CAP 1090

TUNISIE ETERNELLE Chants En Danses (Various artists).
Tracks: / Introduction au Malouf: *Various artists* / Chant d'amour I: *Various artists* / Chant d'amour II: *Various* artists / Danse des gargoulettes: *Various artists* / Danse des anciens esclaves noirs: *Various artists* / Danse nuptiale: *Various artists* / Danse bedouine: *Various artists.*
LP: ARN 33693
MC: ARN 433693

Tunisie

SOULAMIA DE TUNISIE (Ensemble du Cheikh Abdelaziz Ben Mahmoud).
Tracks: / Amis, je ne supporte plus votre eloignement / Chant de la Confrerie El Kadria / Improvisation au 'oud / Extrait des chants de la Confrerie Soulamia / Nouba de ma louf / Improvisation au nay / Extrait des chants de la Confrerie El Issaouia.
LP: ARN 33537

Tunnel Frenzies

KNEE DEEP AND WASTED.
LP: PROBE M25

Tunney, Paddy

FLOWERY VALE, THE.
LP: 12TS 289

IRELAND HER OWN (Tunney, Paddy & Arthur Kearney).
LP: 12T 153

IRISH EDGE, THE.
Tracks: / Craigie Hill / Lark in the morning, The / Johnny, lovely Johnny / Cow that drank the poteen, The / Blackwater side / Out of the window / Month of January / Rambling boys of pleasure, The / Lowlands of Holland, The / Wearing of the britches, The / Old man rocking the cradle, The / She's a gay old hag / St. Peter's day was dawning.
LP: 12T 165

LOUGH ERNE SHORE.
LP: LUNA 334

MOUNTAIN STREAMS WHERE THE MOORCOCKS GROW, THE.
Tracks: / Mountain streams where the moorcocks crow, (The) / Wee weaver, The / Boys of Mullabawn / Old petticoat, The / Coinleach glas an fhomair / Donall og / Reaping of the rushes green, The / One morning in June / Lady Margaret / Inis dhun ramha / Old oak tree, The / Drinking good whiskey / Sweet Omagh town / Green fields of Canada.
LP: 12TS 264

WILD BEES' NEST, A.
LP: 12T 139

Tunnoch Brae Ceildn

SCOTTISH NATIONAL DANCES VOL.1.
LP: SK 2007

Tupac-Amaru

SNOW MUSIC (Flutes of Andes).
Tracks: / Virgenes del sol / Anatas / Nancahuazu / Tres bailectos / Baile de San Benito / Huayno / Sikuriadas / Vasija de barro / Pastora, (La) / Estidio para Charango / Cholita Linda.
LP: SNTF 650

Tupou, Manu

RAVEN.
LP: TC 1422
MC: CDL 51422

Turandot

TURANDOT (See under Puccini) (Various artists).

Turbans

PRESENTING THE TURBANS.
LP: HERALD 5009

Turbines

LAST DANCE BEFORE THE HIGHWAY.
LP: BTA 007

MAGIC FINGERS AND HOURLY RATES.
LP: ROSE 118

Turbinton, Earl

BROTHERS FOR LIFE.
LP: ROUNDER 2064
MC: ROUNDER 2064C

Turbo

DEAD END.
LP: FLAG 47
MC: TFLAG 47

LAST WARRIOR, THE.
Tracks: / Last warrior, The / Berud's sword / Trojan horse / Seance with vampire / Tempest's son / Goddess of confusion / Angel from hell.
LP: N 0113
MC: N 0113-2
LP: NUK 113
MC: ZCNUK 113

Turbo Charge

TURBO CHARGE (See Under Niney The Observer) (Various artists).

Turkey

CHANT DES DERVICHES DE TURQUIE (Musique soufi vol.1) (Various artists).
Tracks: / La ceremonie du Zikr: *Various artists.*
LP: ARN 33446

DERVICHES TOURNEURS DE TURQUIE (See under Derviches Tourneurs...) (Various artists).

FOLK MUSIC OF TURKEY (Various artists).
LP: 12TS 333

MUSICAL JOURNEY, A (Various artists).
LP: H 72067

TRADITIONAL SONGS AND MUSIC (See under Folk).

TURKISH FOLK MUSIC (Various artists).
LP: LLST 7289

TURKISH VILLAGE MUSIC (Various artists).
LP: H 72050

Turkey Bones

NO WAY BEFORE THE WEEKEND (Turkey Bones & The Wild Dogs).
Tracks: / Feel the purple hills / Plane crash / Snake / Indian reservation / Shake / Motorbike.
LP: NED 13

Turkish

TURKISH (see Language Courses).

Turn Blue

EMOTIONAL ORGASM.
MC: DHC 19

SCANDAL ANGLE.
MC: DHC 29

TOURNIQUET BLUE (Turn Blue/Dave Arnold/Paul Mitten).
MC: DHC 17

Turn Of The Screw

TURN OF THE SCREW, THE (see under James, Henry) (Various artists).

Turn On The Heat

TURN ON THE HEAT.
LP: BDLP 002

Turner, Big Joe

BEST OF JOE TURNER.
LP: 231 0848
MC: K10 848

BIG JOE RIDES AGAIN.
LP: 90668

BIG JOE TURNER (Turner, Big Joe/ Knocky Parker & Houserockers).
LP: SLP 13

BIG JOE TURNER MEMORIAL ALBUM.
Tracks: / Miss Bump Suzie / Chill is on, The / I'll never stop loving you / Don't you cry / Poor lover's blues / Still in love / Baby I still want you / T.V. mama / Married woman / You know I love you / Midnight cannonball / In the evening / Morning noon and night / Ti-Ri-Lee / Lipstick, powder and paint / Rock a while / After a while / Trouble in mind / World of trouble / Love rollercoaster / I need a girl / Teenage letter / Wee baby blues / (We're gonna) Jump for joy / Sweet Sue / My reasons for living / Love oh careless love / Got you on my mind / Chains of love / My little honeydripper / Tomorrow night / Honey, hush.
2LP: 781 663-1
MCSET: 781 663-4

BLUES TRAIN (Turner, Big Joe & Roomful of Blues).
Tracks: / Crawdad hole / Red sails in the sunset / Cock-a-doodle-doo / Jumpin' for Joe / I want a little girl / I know you love me / Last night / I love the way (my baby sings the blues) / Blues train.

LP: MR 5293
MC: MRC 5293

BOSS OF THE BLUES (That's jazz Vol.14).
Tracks: / Cherry red / Roll 'em Pete / I want a little girl / Low down dog / Wee baby blues / You're driving me crazy / How long blues / Morning glories / St. Louis blues / Piney Brown blues.
LP: K 50244

BOSS OF THE BLUES SESSIONS 1956.
Tracks: / Roll em' Pete / Cherry red / Testing the blues / Morning glories / Low down dog / St. Louis blues / You're driving me crazy.
LP: KC 108

BOSSES, THE (See Basie, Count) (Turner, Big Joe/Count Basie).

EVERY DAY I HAVE THE BLUES (see under Crayton, Pee Wee) (Turner, Joe, Pee Wee Crayton & Sonny Stitt).

GREAT RHYTHM AND BLUES OLDIES.
LP: BRP 2024

GREAT RHYTHM & BLUES - VOL.4.
Tracks: / Honey hush / Chains of love / Roll 'em Pete / Piney Brown blues / Cherry red / Nothin' from nothin' blues / Shake, rattle and roll / Corina Corina / T.V. mama / Wee baby blues / Squeeze me, baby.
LP: BDL 1003

GREATEST HITS: BIG JOE TURNER.
LP: 817521
LP: 817521

HAVE NO FEAR, BIG JOE IS HERE.
Tracks: / S.K. Blues / Watch that jive / Howling wind / Low down dog / Mad blues / Playboy blues / My gal's a jockey / Sally Zu-Zazz / Oowee baby blues / Lucille Lucille / Careless love / Hollywood bed / Johnson & Turner blues / I got love for sale.
2LP: WL 70822
MCSET: WK 70822
2LP: SJL 2223
LP: 231 0863
MC: K10 863

HONEY HUSH.
Tracks: / Shake, rattle and roll / Chains of love / Roll 'em hawk / Piney Brown blues / Cherry red / Nothin' from nothin' blues / Honey hush / Corina Corina / T.V. mama / Wee baby blues / Squeeze me baby.
LP: MFLP 064

I DON'T DIG IT.
Tracks: / Goin' to Chicago blues / I can't give you anything but love / Blues in the night / Rocks in my bed / Sun risin' blues / Mardi gras boogie / Cry baby blues / Rainy weather blues / I don't dig it / Boogie woogie baby / My heart belongs to you / Born to gamble / I love you, I love you / Oo-ouch-stop / Wish I had a dollar / Fuzzy wuzzy honey.
LP: JB 618

IN THE EVENING.
LP: 231 0776
MC: K10 776

JUMPIN' THE BLUES (Turner,Joe/Pete Johnson).
LP: ARHOOLIE 2004

JUMPIN' TONIGHT.
LP: PM 1561431

JUMPIN' WITH JOE.
Tracks: / Bump Miss Susie / Honey bush / Ti-ri-lee / Oke-she-moke-she-pop / T.V. mama / Shake, rattle and roll / In the evening / Well all right / Morning, noon and night / Hide and seek / Flip flop and fly / Chicken and the hawk / Boogie woogie country girl / Lipstick, powder and paint / Teenage letter / We're gonna jump for joy.
LP: CRB 1070
MC: TCCRB 1070

KANSAS CITY, HERE I COME.
Tracks: / Down home blues / Call the plumber / Since I fell for you / Kansas City here I come / Big legged woman / Sweet sixteen / Time after time.
LP: 231 0904

KANSAS CITY SHOUT (See under Vinson, Eddie for details) (Turner, Joe, Count Basie & Eddie Vinson).

MIDNIGHT SPECIAL, THE.
LP: 231 0844
MC: K10 844

NOBODY IN MIND (Turner, Joe & Jimmy Witherspoon).
LP: 231 0760

PATCHA PATCHA (Turner, Joe & Jimmy Witherspoon).
Tracks: / Patcha patcha / Blues lament / You got me runnin' / Kansas City on my mind / JT's blues / I want a little girl.
LP: 231 0913
MC: K10 913

ROCK THIS JOINT.
Tracks: / Roll me baby / Low down dog / Stormy Monday blues / Roll 'em Pete / Shake, rattle and roll / When the sun goes down / Morning noon and night / Hide and seek / How long blues.
LP: MFM 022
LP: CL 19983
MC: CLMC 919983

STEPPIN' OUT.
Tracks: / Adam bit the apple / Still In The Dark / Just a travellin' man / Life is like a card game / Feeling Happy / After 'While You'll Be Sorry / When the rooster crows / Dawn Is breaking through / Roll 'em Pete / Kansas City Blues / Jockey blues / Playful Baby / Yancey Special / Pete's boogie special / Swanee River boogie.
LP: CHD 243

THINGS THAT I USED TO DO.
LP: 231 0800
MC: K10 800

TRUMPET KINGS MEET JOE TURNER, THE.
LP: 231 0717
MC: K10 717

Turner, Bruce

DIRTY BOPPER, THE (Turner, Bruce Quartet).
Tracks: / Sandpiper / Turner Minor / April / Toddington toddle / Have you met Miss Jones / Dirty bopper, The / Laura / Alto chop suey / Body and soul / Sinner, The.
LP: CLGLP 003
MC: ZCLG 003

JAZZ MASTERS (see Barnes, Johnny & Bruce Turner) (Turner, Bruce & Johnny Barnes).

MELODY MAKER TRIBUTE TO LOUIS ARMSTRONG.
LP: 2460 123

NEW ORLEANS.
LP: MEP 1091

SALUTE TO SATCHMO (see Welsh, Alex) (Turner, Bruce/Alex Welsh/ Humphrey Lyttleton/George Chisholm).

SHIEK OF ARABY.
Tracks: / Shiekd of Araby / Fishmouth / Summertime / Oh baby / Exactly like you / My Monday date.
LP: LF 1214

Turner, Chuck

ONE THE HARD WAY.
Tracks: / Forever girl / Who say / What is the feeling / It's a long time / Come rock with me / Tears / One the hard way / Runaround girl / I need you / We rule.
LP: LALP 21

PRESENTING CHUCK TURNER.
LP: TJPLP 005

Turner, Geraldine

OLD FRIENDS.
LP: LRF 169

STEPHEN SONDHEIM SONGBOOK.
Tracks: / Like it was / Old friends / Losing my mind / Not while I'm around / Could I leave you / With so much to be sure of / Miller's son, The / Buddy's blues / I remember / Parade in town, A / There won't be trumpets / Being alive / Anyone can whistle / Another hundred people / Goodbye for now.
LP: SONG 001
MC: SONG C 001

Turner, Ike

IKE TURNER AND HIS KINGS OF RHYTHM.
LP: CH 22

IKE TURNER AND HIS KINGS OF RHYTHM VOL.2.
LP: CHD 146

IKE TURNER AND THE KINGS OF RHYTHM.
LP: FLY 578

Turner, Ike & Tina

BLACK ANGEL.
LP: CV 1342

BLACK BEAUTY.
LP: CV 1323
MC: C 20195

COLLECTION: IKE AND TINA TURNER.
Tracks: / Mississippi rolling stone / Living for the city / Golden empire / I'm looking for my mind / Shake a hand / Bootsie Whitelaw / Too much man for one woman / I know (you don't want me no more) / Rockin' and rollin' / Never been to spain / Sugar sugar / Push / Raise your hand / Tinas prayer / Chicken / If you want it / Let's get it on / You're up to something / You're still my baby / Jesus.
MC: CCSMC 170
2LP: CCSLP 170

CRAZY 'BOUT YOU.
LP: PLP 30
MC: PMC 30

CUSSIN', CRYIN' AND CARRYIN' ON.
Tracks: / Black angel / Getting nasty / It sho' ain't me / Fool in love, A / Nothing you can do boy / I better get ta steppin' / Shake a tail feather / We need an understanding / You're so fine / Too hot to hold / I'm fed up / You got what you wanted / Betcha can't kiss me (just one time) / Cussin, cryin, and carryin, on / Ain't nobody's business / Funky mule / Thinking black / Black beauty / Ghetto funk / Black's alley.
LP: SMT 014

DYNAMIC DUO, THE.
Tracks: / If I can't be first / Goodbye so long / I don't need / Flee flee flee / It's crazy baby / Hard times / Don't you blame it on me / Gonna have fun / I wish my dream would come true / Am I a fool in love / Something came over me / Hurt is all you gave me.
LP: GEM 004
MC: GEMC 004

FANTASTIC IKE & TINA.
LP: SLS 50205
MC: TCS 50205

FINGERPOPPIN' - THE WARNER BROS YEARS.
Tracks: / Finger poppin' / Tell her I'm not home / (Please) leave me alone / Just so I can be with you / Too many tears / No tears to cry / Merry christmas baby / Somebody (somewhere) needs you / All I could do was cry / You must believe (in) me / It's all over / Fool for you, A.
LP: ED 243

GOLDEN EMPIRE.
Tracks: / Mississippi rolling stone / Living for the city / Golden empire / I'm looking for my mind / Shake a hand / Bootsie Whitelaw / Too much man for one woman / I know (you don't want me no more) / Rockin' and rollin' / Never been to Spain.
LP: 6 26297
MC: 4 26297

GOLDEN EMPIRE 1 & 2.
Tracks: / Mississippi rolling stone / Living in the city / Golden empire / I'm looking for my mind / Shake a much hand / Bootsie Whitelaw / Too much man for one woman / I know (you don't want me no more) / Rockin' and rollin' / Never been to Spain.
LP: SPDP 2

GREAT ALBUM, THE.
2LP: ALB 148

HER MAN...HIS WOMAN.
Tracks: / Get it - get it / I believe / I can't believe (what you say) / My babe / Strange / You weren't ready / That's right / Rooster / Five long years / Things that I used to do.
LP: EG 2607331
MC: EG 2607334
MC: ZCGAS 716

HEY HEY.
Tracks: / Hey hey / Why should I / Jack Rabbit / Ho ho / In your eyes baby / Star above / Prancing / Angel of love / I do love you / You're the only one / Look at that chick / Gotta have you for myself / Shirley can't you see / I don't want to lose your love / Bag pipe special / Moving slow / Evening train / East St. Louis rock / Dear lovin' man / Leaving Kansas city.
LP: RL 0047

IKE AND TINA SESSIONS.
Tracks: / Lose my cool / Goodbye, so long / You can't miss nothing / My baby now / Flee flee flee / Makin' plans together / It's crazy baby / I wish my dreams would come true / Something came over me / If I can't be first / Hurt is all you gave me / Gonna have fun / I don't need / Give me your love / I can't believe what you say / I need a man / Baby don't do it / Over you / He's the one / Don't you blame it on me.
MC: KENC 065
LP: KENT 065

IKE AND TINA TURNER.
LP: SM 3913

IKE & TINA TURNER SHOW LIVE, THE.
Tracks: / Finger poppin' / Down in the valley / Good times / You are my sunshine / Havin' a good time / Twist and shout / I know (you don't want me no more) / Tight pants / My man, he's a lovin' man / I can't stop loving you / To tell the truth.
LP: ED 152

I'M TORE UP.
Tracks: / Sad as a man can be / If I never had known you / I'm tore up / Let's call it a day / Take your fine frame home / Do right, baby / No coming back / Just one more time / Gonna wait for my chance / What can it be? / Big question, (The) / She made my blood run cold / Do you mean it? / Hoo doo say / I'm tired of beggin' / You don't love me (I know) / Rock a bucket.
LP: RL 016

JUKE BOX GIANTS.
Tracks: / Betcha can't kiss me (just one time) / Ghetto funk / Black angel / Poor fool (fool to long) / It sho ain't me / We need an understanding / Blacks alley / Too hot to hold / I'm fed up / Make 'em wait / Black beauty / Poor little fool / Nothing you can do boy / Nuttin up / Scotty souling / So blue over you / Sad Sam / Thinking black / I better get ta steppin' / Getting nasty.
LP: AFEMP 1021

NICE 'N' ROUGH.
Tracks: / Funky street / I heard it through the grapevine / Honky tonk women / Baby get it on / Working together / I've been loving you too long / Proud Mary / Nutbush city limits / Acid Queen / Come together / Get back / Sweet Rhode Island red / I want to take you higher / River deep, mountain high (Live.) / Goodbye, so long.
LP: LBR 2600211
MC: TCLBR 2600214

NUTBUSH CITY LIMITS.
Tracks: / Nutbush city limits.
LP: 1A 022 58164
MC: 1A 222 58164

PROUD MARY (The best of Ike & Tina Turner).
Tracks: / Fool in love, A / I idolize you / I'm jealous / It's gonna work out fine / Poor fool / Tra la la la la / You shoulda reated me right / Come together / Honky tonk woman / I want to take you higher / Workin' together / Proud Mary / Funkier than a mosquita's tweeter / Ooh poo pah doo / I'm yours (use me any way you wanna) / Up in heah / River deep, mountain high / Nutbush city limits / Sweet Rhode island red / Sexy Ida (part one) / Sexy Ida (part two) / Baby-get it on / Acid queen.
MC: TCEMS 1431

PROUD MARY AND OTHER HITS.
MC: 4XLL 9191

RIVER DEEP, MOUNTAIN HIGH.
Tracks: / River deep, mountain high / I idolize you / Love like yours, A / Fool in love, A / Make 'em wait / Hold on baby / Save the last dance for me / Oh baby / Everyday I have to cry / Such a fool for you / It's gonna work out fine / I'll never need you more than this.
LP: MFP 50443
LP: SPR 8548
MC: SPC 8548
MC: AMC 3179
LP: AMA 3179
LP: HAU 8396

ROCK ME BABY.
Tracks: / Crazy 'bout you baby / Too hot to hold / Please love me / I smell trouble / It sho' ain't me / We need an understanding / Beauty is just skin deep / Shake a tail feather / Rock me baby / So fine / My babe / Ain't nobody's business / I better get ta steppin' / Betcha can't kiss me (just one time) / Fool in love, A / You're so fine.
LP: BDL 1045
LP: 20015
MC: 40015
LP: TOP 111
MC: KTOP 111
MC: BDC 1045

ROCKIN' BLUES.
Tracks: / Prancing / Things I used to do / Gully / Think / You're still my baby / Katanga / Tacks in my shoes / Right on / Rockin' blues / That's alright / Broken hearted / If you love me like you say / Bootie lip / City, The / Neckin' / These dreams / Soppin' molasses.
LP: SSL 6008
MC: TC-SSL 6008

SO FINE.
Tracks: / My babe / I better get ta steppin' / Shake a tail feather / We need an understanding / You're so fine / Here's your heart / Please love me / Freedom sound / Crazy 'bout you baby.
LP: B 80054
MC: MB 980054
LP: LILP 400158

SOUL OF IKE & TINA, THE.
Tracks: / Goodbye, so long / It can't be first / Chicken shack / I don't ned / I wish my dreams would come true / Hard times / It's crazy, baby / Gonna have fun / Am I a fool in love? / Something came over me / Hurt is all you gave me / Don't blame it on me / I can't believe what you say.
LP: KENT 014

SOUL SELLERS.
LP: LBR 1002
MC: TCR 1002

SUPERGOLD.
Tracks: / Nutbush city limits / River deep mountain high / Living for the city / Proud Mary / Honky tonk women / Baby get it on.
2LP: 1C 13482758/9

TALENT SCOUT BLUES.
Tracks: / Take the world by storm / Back stabbing / Make some noise / Woman just won't do, A / I'm tired of being / Nobody seems to want me / I miss you / Nobody wants me / Why did you leave me / Everybody's talkin' / Love is a gamble / Feeling good / I smell trouble / Five long years / Mother in law blues / Dust my blues / That's alright / Twistin' the night away.
LP: CHD 244

TOO HOT TO HANDLE.
MC: ORC 001

TOUGH ENOUGH.
Tracks: / Stagger Lee and Billy / This man's crazy / Foolish / Two is a couple / Prancing (instrumental) / Worried and hurtin' inside / Dear John / You should've treated me right / Too many ties (you've got) / Gonna find me a substitute / Sleepless / Groove (instrumental) / Fool in love, A / It's gonna work out fine / I'm gonna do all I can to do right by my man / Can't chance a break up.
LP: EG 2602511
MC: EG 2602514

WHAT YOU SEE (IS WHAT YOU GET).
Tracks: / What you see / Down in the valley / Proud Mary / Shake / Locomotion, The / I know.
LP: STMDL 18
MC: STMDC 18

Turner, Jean

STAN KENTON/JEAN TURNER, 1963 (See under Kenton, Stan) (Turner, Jean & Stan Kenton).

Turner, Jesse Lee

SHAKE BABY SHAKE.
LP: TURNER 8011

Turner, Joe

ANOTHER EPOCH STRIDE PIANO.
LP: 231 0763
MC: K10 763

BOOGIE WOOGIE AND MORE.
Tracks: / Goin' away blues / Roll 'em, Pete / Cherry red / Baby, look at you / Lovin' mama blues / Cafe society rag / How long, how long blues / Shake it and break it / Low down dirty shame blues / Joe Turner blues / Beale street blues / I got a gal / It's the same old story / Around the clock (part 1) / Around the clock (part 2) / Married woman blues.
LP: OFF 6028

BOSSES OF THE BLUES (Turner, Joe & T Bone Walker).
Tracks: / Lonesome train / Corina, Corina / How long, how long blues / Careless love / Two loves have I / Every day I have the blues / Vietnam / Shake it baby / Cold, cold feeling / Sail on.
LP: NL 88311
MC: NK 88311

FEEL SO FINE (See under Clayton, Buck) (Turner, Joe & Buck Clayton).

KANSAS CITY SHOUT (See under Basie, Count) (Basie, Count, Joe Turner, Eddie Vinson).

KANSAS CITY SOUL (See under Basie, Count) (Turner, Joe, Count Basie & Eddie Vinson).

MIDNIGHT SPECIAL.
Tracks: / I left my heart in San Francisco / I'm gonna sit right down / I can't give you anything but love / You're driving me crazy / So long / After my laughter came tears / Midnight special / Stoop down baby.
LP: 201 084 4

STEPPIN' OUT.
LP: CH 243

STRIDDIN' IN PARIS.
LP: 500101

Turner, Joe Lynn

RESCUE YOU.
Tracks: / Losing you / Young hearts / Prelude - endlessly / Rescue you / Feel the fire / Get tough / Eyes of love / On the run / Soul searcher / Race is on, The.
LP: EKT 20
MC: EKT 20C

Turner, John

JEWEL.
Tracks: / Jewel / Bring in the pink / When I find my freedom / Trying on new youth / Golf balls / Tantalas / Yellow and blue / Snow / Every little thing / Snooker / Alpha to omega / Adios amigo / All we want is to live.
LP: JEWEL 1

Turner, Ken

BLACKPOOL SALUTES THE CHAMPION (Turner, Ken & His Orchestra).
LP: DS 031
MC: TDS 031

COLLECTION: KEN TURNER.
LP: DS 023
MC: TDS 023

FOUR FESTIVAL REQUESTS IN STRICT TEMPO (Turner, Ken & His Orchestra).
LP: DS 014
MC: TDS 014

Turner, Mary Lou

BILLY BOY AND MARY LOU (See Anderson, Bill) (Turner, Mary Lou and Bill Anderson).

Turner, Nik

SPHYNX-XITINTODAY.
Tracks: / Awakening, The / Pyramid spell / Hall of double truth, The / Anubis Thoth / Horos, Isis & Nepthys.
LP: CHC 51

Turner, Pierce

HE'S ONLY A LONG WAY ACROSS.
LP: BEGA 77
MC: BEGC 77
LP: BBL 77
MC: BBLC 77

NOW IS HEAVEN.
LP: BEGA 120
MC: BEGAC 120

SKY AND THE GROUND, THE.
Tracks: / Sky and the ground, The / Mayhem / Answer, The / Time flies / You can never know Jem / Surface in heaven / His reason / Have you looked at the sun (lately) / I set you up to shake / You can never know Jem (instrumental).
LP: BEGA 97
MC: BEGC 97

Turner, Roger

AMMO (see Minton,Phil & Roger Turner) (Turner, Roger & Phil Minton).

SUNDAY BEST (Turner, Roger & Gary Todd).
LP: INCUS 32

Turner, Ruby

MOTOWN SONGBOOK, THE.
LP: HIP 58
MC: HIPC 58

OTHER SIDE, THE.
LP: HIP 111
MC: HIPC 111

PARADISE.
Tracks: / Paradise / It's gonna be alright / It's a crying shame / Leaves in the wind / There's no better love / Everytime I breathe / Sexy / See me / Surrender / It's you my heart beats for.
LP: HIP 89
MC: HIPC 89

WOMEN HOLD UP HALF THE SKY.
LP: HIP 36
MC: HIPC 36

Turner, Ruth

LIVING IN THE LOVE (Turner, Ruth & Cheryl Mead).
Tracks: / You can't part me from my God / I have called you / Who is this man / I call to the Lord / Lord you'll always be there / I'm living in the love / My spirit / Get up and go.
MC: PCN 120

Turner, Simon

SIMON TURNER.
LP: CRELP 64
MC: CREC 64

Turner, Simon Fisher

BONE OF DESIRE.
LP: PULP 33

CARAVAGGIO 1610 (Film soundtrack).
Tracks: / Hills of Abruzzi, The / Dog star / All paths lead to Rome / Fantasia, childhood memories / How blue sky was / Light and dark (From Missa Lux Et Orrigo) / Umber wastes / Cafe of the moors / Timeout and mind / In the still of the night / Michele of the shadows / Waters of forgetfullness, The / Running, running / Frescobaldi, the greatest organist of our time / Hourglass / I love you more than my eyes.
LP: ACME 6

Turner, Steve

BRAIDING.
Tracks: / Glendy Burke / Swanee river hornpipe / Lorry ride, The / Nelly was a lady / Joe Liddy's reels / Emily Jane / Hard times / 1812 (medley).
LP: FE 058
MC: FE 058C

ECLOGUE.
Tracks: / Wounded whale, The / White copper alley / Prospect providence / Old Manchester hornpipe, The / Boomer's story / Girls of Glossop Road / Diamantina drover, The / Napoleons farewell to Paris / Bunch of rushes, The / Lord Thomas of Winesbury / Me and my uncle / Tamlin / Carlisle / Francis T Robertson.
LP: FE 042

JIGGING ONE NOW.
Tracks: / Squid jigging ground, The / Salt creek / Hare-lipped Susie / Growling old man and the cackling old woman, The / Johnny laddie / Bonnie Annie / Few days / Make and break harbour / Bracelet, The / Jack's getting a wife / Skipper's wedding song, The / All hands upon deck / Morpeth lasses / North Sea tug, The / Down by the greenwood side / Keepers and the drivers, The.
LP: FE 030

OUT STACK.
Tracks: / Plains of Waterloo / Barratt's privateers / Red joak, The / Isle of St Helena / Spailpin a run / Flowers of Bermuda, The / Valentine O'Hara / Farewell dearest Nancy / Sax word / Da saandie burn reel / Cruel sister, The / Is your love in vain.
LP: FE 018
MC: FE 018 C

Turner, Tina

ACID QUEEN.
Tracks: / Under my thumb / Let's spend the night together / Acid queen / I can see for miles / Whole lotta love / Baby git it on / Bootsie Whitelaw / Pick me tonight / Rockin' and rollin'.
LP: FA 41 3141 1
MC: FA 41 3141 4
LP: FA 3141
MC: TCFA 3141

BEST RARITIES.
LP: MA 1211184
MC: MAMC 9121184

BREAK EVERY RULE.
Tracks: / What you get is what you see / Change is gonna come, A / Addicted to love / In the midnight hour / 634-5789 / Land of a thousand dances / Typical male / Two people / Till the right man comes along / Afterglow / Girls / Back where you started / Break every rule / Overnight sensation / Paradise is here / I'll be thunder.
LP: EST 2018
MC: TCEST 2018

FOREIGN AFFAIR.
Tracks: / Steamy windows / Best, The / You know who (is doing you know what) / Undercover agent for the blues / Look me in the heart / Be tender with me baby / You can't stop me loving you / Ask me how I feel / Falling like rain / I don't wanna lose you / Not enough romance / Foreign affair.
LP: ESTU 2103
MC: TCESTU 2103

IT TAKES TWO (See under Stewart, Rod) (Turner, Tina & Rod Stewart).

IT'S ONLY LOVE (See under Adams, Bryan) (Turner, Tina & Bryan Adams).

LIVE IN EUROPE: TINA TURNER.
Tracks: / What you get is what you see / Break every rule / I can't stand the rain / Two people / Typical male / Better be good to me / Addicted to love / Private dancer / We don't need another hero / What's love got to do with it. / Let's stay together / Show some respect / Land of a thousand dances / In the midnight hour / 634-5789 / Change is gonna come, A / Tearing us apart / Proud Mary / Help / Tonight / It's only love / Nutbush City limits / Paradise is here / Let's dance / Girls (Extra track on cassette & CD only) / Back where you started (Extra track on cassette & CD only) / River deep, mountain high (Extra track on casette & CD only) / Overnight sensation (Extra track on cassette & CD only.).
2LP: ESTD 1
MCSET: TCESTD 1

LOVE EXPLOSION.
Tracks: / Love explosion / Fool for your love / Sunset on sunset / Music keeps me dancin' / I see home / Backstabbers / Just a little lovin' (early in the morning) / You got what I'm gonna get / On the radio.
LP: UAG 30267
LP: ATAK 155
LP: PRG 795 212 1
MC: TCATAK 155
MC: TCPRG 795 2124

PRIVATE DANCER.
Tracks: / I might have been queen / Whats love got to do with it / Show some respect / I can't stand the rain / Private dancer / Lets stay together / Better be good to me / Steel claw / Help.
LP: TINA 1
MC: TCTINA 1
LPPD: TINAP 1
LP: EJ 2401521
MC: EJ 2401524

ROUGH.
Tracks: / Fruits of the night / Bitch is back, The / Woman I'm supposed to be / Viva la money / Funny how time slips away / Earthquake hurricane / Root, toot undisputable rock 'n' roller / Fire down below / Sometimes when we touch / Woman in a man's world / Night time is the right time.
LP: UAG 30211
LP: ATAK 154
LP: PRG 795 213 1
MC: TCATAK 154
MC: TCPRG 795 2134

SIMPLY THE BEST.
Tracks: / Best, The / What's love got to do with it / I don't wanna lose you / Nutbush city limits 90's / Let's stay together / Private dancer / We don't need another hero / Better be good to me / River deep - mountain high / Steamy window / Typical male / It takes two / Addicted to love / Be tender with me baby / I want you near me / Love thing.
2LP: ESTV 1
MC: TCESTV 1

TEARING US APART (See under Clapton, Eric) (Turner, Tina & Eric Clapton).

TINA TURNER.
LP: ENT LP 13004
MC: ENT MC 13004

TINA TURNER BOX SET.
LPS: TTGIFT 1
LPS: 795 246 1
MCSET: TCTTGIFT 1
MCSET: 795 246 4

TINA TURNER GOES COUNTRY.
LP: NSPLP 501
MC: NSPMC 501

TINA TURNER: INTERVIEW PICTURE DISC.
LPPD: BAK 2076

TOO HOT TO HANDLE.
Tracks: / Please love me / I better get ta steppin' / Crazy 'bout you baby / My babe / Shake a tail feather / We need an understanding / You're so fine / Here's your heart.
LP: UNKNOWN
MC: UNKNOWN
LP: UNKNOWN

VOICES IN THE WIND (see under Hendrix, Jimi) (Turner, Tina/Jimi Hendrix).

WAY OF THE WORLD.
Tracks: / Way of the world / I don't wanna lose you / Foreign affair (Only on 12" and CD single).
MC: TCCL 637

Turner, Troy

TEENAGE BLUES IN BATON ROUGE.
Tracks: / Teenage blues in baton rouge / She's burning / Your Daddy wants you back / House without a home / Express train / Hold me close / Life is a gamble / My little woman / Lady at the bottom of the sea / Try to satisfy.
LP: KIN 4038
MC: KIN 4038 MC

Turner, Uncle John

UNCLE JOHN TURNER AND JOHNNY WINTER LIVE (Turner, Uncle John & Johnny Winter).
LP: FC 059

Turner, Zeb

JERSEY ROCK.
Tracks: / Jersey rock / Travellin' boogie / You're my cutie pie / Gone gone gone / Back, back to Baltimore / Tennessee boogie / Chew tobacco rag / Huckleberry boogie / Boogie woogie Lou / Dolly Dimple dance / I got a load / Crazy heart / No more nothing (but getting off your mind) / I'm tying up the blues with a big blue ribbon / I got a lot of things for a lot of nothing / Hard hearted you and chicken hearted you / You're gonna be lonesome someday (Downhearted and blue) / All dressed up / Never been so lonesome / I could lose the blues (if my baby were back).
LP: BFX 15166

Turner's

TURNERS MERRY-GO-ROUND VOL.2
Bursens and Verbek organ (Bursens & Verbek Organ).
Tracks: / Valencia / Leaning on a lamp post / Viva Espana / In the chapel in the moonlight / Tulips from Amsterdam / Moonlight and roses / Red roses for a blue lady / Clair / You won't find another

fool like me / Buona sera / Carousel / Horsey horsey / Bill Bailey (won't you please come home) / Underneath the arches / Burlington Bertie / Knees up Mother Brown / Let's all go down the Strand / Maybe it's because I'm a Londoner / Down at the old Bull and Bush / Alexander's ragtime band / Dinah / Back home in Tennessee / Oh you beautiful doll / My home in Dixieland / Chris's ragtime / Sheik of Araby, The / Everybody's doing it now / That mysterious rag / Whistling Rufus / Yes sir, that's my baby / Bye bye blackbird / You're driving me crazy / Red red robin / My blue Heaven / Ukulele lady / See you in my dreams / Coal black Mammy of mine / Ragtime violin / I wonder does my baby do the Charleston? / Blue skies.
LP: . . . . GRS 1133
MC: . . . . KGRS 1133

Turning Curious

SOUL LIGHT SEASON.
LP: . . . . CL 0062

Turning Point

CREATURES OF THE NIGHT.
Tracks: / My lady C / Journey, The / Vanishing dream / Creatures of the night / Princess Aura / Rain dance / Better days.
LP: . . . . GULP 1022

SILENT PROMISE.
Tracks: / Silent promise / Awakening / May day morn / Beginning again / Queen of the white E / Mirror mirror mirror / Green tranquility.
LP: . . . . GULP 1027

Turning Shrines

CINNABAR AND PORCELAIN.
Tracks: / Are You Experienced / Wonderful gift / Mystification / 23 Stillings St. / Iron nights / Process / Cinnabar and porcelain.
LP: . . . . TOMPY 33

Turnpike Cruisers

AMSTERDAMAGED.
Tracks: / Rockin' possesed / Love you for lunch / What's the matter with you Frank / Getting wasted / No dog / Eddie's ghost.
MC: . . . . TPC 1

DRIVE DRIVE DRIVE.
Tracks: / Weird and crazy guys / Assault and battery / Soaked hell / Sleaze attack at the Edge City drive-in / Eddie's ghost / Can't judge a book / Do it / I wish someone would come and take my baby awa / War / Drive drive drive / Nice and slow.
LP: . . . . LINKLP 091

SLEAZE ATTACK AT THE EDGE CITY DRIVE IN.
Tracks: / Getting wasted / No dog / Louie Louie / Unlucky in love / Doin' shit and writing songs / Palookaville express / Don't wanna be your man / Spirit head.
LP: . . . . ABCLP 13

Turow, Scott

PRESUMED INNCOENT.
MC: 0600560538

Turre, Steve

FIRE AND ICE.
LP: . . . . ST 275

VIEWPOINT AND VIBRATIONS.
LP: . . . . ST 270

Turrentine, Stanley

BEST OF STANLEY TURRENTINE.
Tracks: / Little Sheri / Since I fell for you / River's invitation / In memory of (CD only.) / Smile Stacy / God bless the child / Feeling good (CD only. From The Roar Of The Greasepaint, The Smell Of The Crowd.) / Lonesome lover (CD only.) / Plum.
LP: B1 93201
LP: 793 201 1

BLUE FLAMES (See under Scott, Shirley) (Scott, Shirley/Stanley Turrentine).

BLUE HOUR.
Tracks: / I want a little girl / Gee baby ain't I good to you / Blue riff / Since I fell for you / Willow weep for me.
LP: . . . . BST 84057

COMIN' YOUR WAY.
Tracks: / My girl is just enough woman for me / Then I'll be tired of you / Fine I'll lass / Thomasville / Someone to watch over me / Stolen sweets / Fin I'll lass (alt. take) (CD only.) / Just in time (CD only.).
LP: . . . . BLJ 84065

HOME AGAIN.
Tracks: / Paradise / You can't take my love / I'll be there / I knew it couldn't happen / Blow / At the club / Gemini / Holy one.
LP: 9602011
LP: . . . . E 0201

JOYRIDE.
Tracks: / River's invitation / I wonder where our love has gone / Little Sheri / Mattie / Bayou / Taste of honey, A.
LP: . . . . BST 84201

JUBILEE SHOUT.
Tracks: / Jubilee shout / My ship / You said it / Brother Tom / Cotton walk / You better go now.
LP: . . . . BST 84122

LA PLACE.
Tracks: / Terrible T / Cruisin' / Night breeze / Take 4 / Touching / La place street / Sparkle.
LP: B1 90261
LP: 790 261 1

NEW TIME SHUFFLE.
LP: . . . . LBR 1026

STANLEY TURRENTINE.
2LP: . . . . BND 4006

STRAIGHT AHEAD.
Tracks: / Plum / Child is born, A / Other side of time / Straight ahead / Longer you wait, The / Ah Rio.
LP: . . . . BT 85105

TENDER TOGETHERNESS.
Tracks: / Hermanos / I'll give you my love / Tamarac / After the love is gone / Cherubim / Only you and me / World chimes / Pure love / Havin' fun with Mr. T.
LP: . . . . K 52313

THAT'S WHERE IT'S AT.
Tracks: / Smile Stacey / Soft pedal blues / Pia / We'll se yaw'll after while, ya heah / Dorene don't cry / Light blue.
LP: . . . . BST 84096

USE THE STAIRS.
Tracks: / Tomorrow / Sometimes bread / Georgia on my mind / Lamp is low, The / Till the very end / On a misty night / Jordu / Pay the price.
LP: . . . . F 9604

WHAT ABOUT YOU.
Tracks: / Heritage / Feel the fire / Disco dancing / Manhattan skyline / My wish for you / Wind and sea.
LP: . . . . FT 551

WONDERLAND (The Music of Stevie Wonder).
Tracks: / Bird of beauty / Creepin' / Living for the city / Boogie on reggae woman / Rocket love / Don't you worry 'bout a thing / Sir Duke / You and I.
LP: . . . . BT 85140

Z.T.'S BLUES.
Tracks: / Z.T.'s blues / More than you know / Lamp is low, The / Way you look tonight / For heaven's sake / I wish I knew / Be my love.
LP: . . . . BST 84424
MC: 4BN 84424
LP: 784 424 1

Turriff & District...

PIPING FROM THE NORTH (Turriff & District Pipe Band).
LP: . . . . TPB 001
MC: . . . . CTPB 001

Turriff Schoolchildren

SCHOOLDAYS.
MC: . . . . CWGR 003

Turtle, Henry

EVERLASTING LOVE (See also Hightower, Rosetta) (Turtle, Henry & Rosetta Hightower).

Turtles

20 GOLDEN CLASSICS: TURTLES.
MC: 260 421 4

COLLECTION: TURTLES.
LP: . . . . MA 12186
MC: . . . . MAMC 12186

HAPPY TOGETHER (The Very Best of...).
MC: . . . . MCTC 046

HAPPY TOGETHER (ALBUM).
LP: . . . . HAU 8330

IT AIN'T ME, BABE.
LP: 6 25262

PRESENT THE BATTLE OF THE BANDS.
LP: . . . . RNLP 70156

TURTLE SOUP.
LP: . . . . RNLP 70157

WOODEN HEAD.
LP: . . . . RNLP 154

Tusa, Frank

FATHER TIME.
LP: . . . . ENJA 2056

Tutone, Tommy

TUTONE 2.
Tracks: / 867 5309 / Jenny / Baby it's alright / Shadow on the road ahead / Bernadiah / Why baby why / Which man are you / No way to cry / Steal away / Tonight / Only one, The / Not say goodbye.
LP: . . . . CBS 85222

Tutt, Ron

SHEFFIELD DRUM RECORD (See under Keltner, Jim) (Keltner, Jim & Ron Tutt).

Tutti Frutti (TV)

TUTTI FRUTTI (See under The Majestics (TV)) (Majestics (tv)).

Tutu

SAFULA (Tutu & Pablo).
LP: . . . . BR 013

Tutu, Bishop Desmond

BISHOP DESMOND TUTU - TRIBUTE ALBUM.
2LP: . . . . SHAN 43057/8

Tuxedo Moon

DESIRE.
Tracks: / East jinx / Incubus / Blue suit / Desire again / In the name of talent / Holiday for plywood.
LP: . . . . PREX 4
MC: . . . . PRICS 4
LP: . . . . CBOY 3030
LP: . . . . CHC 66

HALF-MUTE.
LP: . . . . CBOY 1010

HOLY WARS.
LP: . . . . CBOY 2020

PINHEADS ON THE MOVE.
2LP: . . . . CBOY 5050

SCREAM WITH A VIEW.
LP: . . . . CBOY 4040

SHIP OF FOOLS.
LP: . . . . CBOY 6060

THOUSAND LIVES BY PICTURES, A.
LP: . . . . TX 8354

YOU.
Tracks: / You.
LP: . . . . CBOY 9090

TV 21

THIN RED LINE, A.
Tracks: / Waiting for the drop / Ideal way of life / This is zero / Ticking away / It feels like it's starting to rain / Snakes and ladders / What's going on / Something's wrong / When I scream / Tomorrow / Attention span.
LP: . . . . SML 1123
MC: . . . . KSCMML 1123

TV & Film Themes

FAMOUS THEMES: REMEMBER THESE? (Various artists).
Tracks: / Portrait of a flirt: *Various artists* (Link pieces for 'In Town Tonight') / Journey into melody: *Various* artists / Sapphires and sables: *Various artists* / Invitation waltz (ring round the moon): *Various artists*/ By the sleepy lagoon: *Various artists* / Puffin Billy: *Various artists* / Coronation Scot: *Various artists*/ Rhythm on rails (Morning music): *Various artists* / Music everywhere (Rediffusion's call sign): *Various artists*/ Horse guards, Whitehall (Down Your Way): *Various artists* / Devil's gallop (Dick Barton Special Agent): *Various artists*/ Destruction by fire (Pathe News): *Various artists* / On a spring note: *Various artists* / All sports march: *Various* artists / Cavalcade of youth: *Various artists* / Drum majorette: *Various artists* / Girls in grey (BBC TV news): *Erstwhile* / Elizabethan serenade: *Various artists* / Melody on the move: *Various artists* / Alpine pastures (My Word): *Various artists* / Young ballerina (Potters Wheel interlude): *Various artists* / Horse feathers (Meet the Huggets): *Various artists* / Willo the wisp: *Various artists* / Jumping bean: *Various artists.*
LP: . . . . GRALP 10
MC: . . . . GRTC 10

JONATHAN KING PRESENTS ENTERTAINMENT USA 2 (Various artists).
LP: . . . . PTVR 1
MC: . . . . PTVT 1

MINSTREL STARS, THE (Stars From The Black & White Minstrel TV Show) (Various artists).
MC: . . . . URMC 105

MORE FAMOUS THEMES (Various artists).
Tracks: / Voice of London: *Queen's Hall Light Orchestra* (Queen's Hall Light Orchestra signature tune.) / Calling all workers: *Various artists* (Music while you work.) / Champagne march: *Various artists* (Current Release / Movietime.) / Out of tune march: *Various artists* (Hello Mum.) / Miss world: *Various artists* / Skippy: *Various artists*(Seeing sport.) / Westminster waltz: *Various artists* (In town tonight.) / Star is born, A: *Various artists* (In town tonight.) / Holiday spirit: *Various artists* (In town tonight.) / High adventure: *Various artists* (Friday night is music night.) / Quiet stroll, A: *Various artists* (Farming.) / Looking around: *Various artists* (The Appleyards.) / Country canter: *Various artists* (Horseman riding by, A.) / Moomin: *Various artists* / Shooting star: *Various* artists (Kaleidoscope.) / Muse in Mayfair: *Various artists* (Music goes round.) / Old clockmaker, The: *Various* artists (Jennings at school.) / Melody fair: *Various artists* / Sporting occasion: *Various artists* (Wimbledon closing theme.).
LP: . . . . GRALP 20
MC: . . . . GRTC 20

MUSIC FROM CHRISTABEL (Various artists).
Tracks: / I'm following you: *Various artists* / Christabel, Theme from: *Various artists* / Missouri scrambler: *Various artists* / Night and day: *Various artists* / Deep in a dream: *Various artists* / Lambeth walk: *Various artists.*
LP: . . . . 12 RX 229

TV Personalities

AND DON'T THE KIDS JUST LOVE IT.
LP: . . . . ROUGH 24
LP: . . . . REFIRELP 7
MC: . . . . REFIREMC 7

MUMMY, YOU'RE NOT WATCHING ME.
LP: . . . . BIG 4
LP: . . . . REFIRELP 8
MC: . . . . REFIREMC 8

PAINTED WORD THE.
LP: . . . . BIG 7
LP: . . . . JAMS 37
LP: . . . . REFIRELP 10
MC: . . . . REFIREMC 10

PRIVILEGE.
Tracks: / Paradise is for the blessed / Conscience tells me no / All my dreams are dead / Man who paints the rainbows, The / Sad Mona Lisa / Sometimes I think you know me / Privilege / Good and faithful servant / My hedonistic tendencies / Salvador Dali's garden party / What if it's raining? / Engine driver song, The / Better than I know myself.
LP: . . . . BIG 6
LP: . . . . FIRELP 21
MC: . . . . FIREMC 21

THEY COULD HAVE BEEN BIGGER THAN THE BEATLES.
Tracks: / Psychedelic holiday / David Hockney's diary / Boy in the paisley shirt / When Emily cries.
LP: . . . . BIG 2
LP: . . . . WHAAM LP 05
LP: . . . . REFIRELP 9
MC: . . . . REFIREMC 9

TV Slim

TV SLIM AND FLAT FOOT SAM (TV Slim & Flat Foot Sam).
LP: . . . . BLP 101

Twa Toots

PLEASE DON'T PLAY A RAINY DAY IN GEORGIA.
LP: . . . . CC 103

Twain, Mark (aut)

ADVENTURES OF TOM SAWYER (See under Adventures of) (Crosby, Bing).

HUCKLEBERRY FINN (Shale, Kerry).
MC: . . . . LFP 41 7206 5

HUCKLEBERRY FINN (Begley, Ed).
MC: 2038

PRINCE AND THE PAUPER, THE (Unknown narrator(s)).
MCSET: . . . . DTO 10580

PRINCE AND THE PAUPER THE.
LP: . . . . TC 1542
MC: . . . . CDL 51542

TOM SAWYER (children's classics) (Unknown narrator(s)).
MC: . . . . PLBC 214

TOM SAWYER (Adventures with Injun Joe) (Begley, Ed).
MC: 1165

TOM SAWYER (Glorious whitewasher, The) (Begley, Ed).
MC: 1205

Twain Soundbook

TWAIN SOUNDBOOK (Various artists).
MC: . . . . SBC 119

Twang

TWANG! (London Cast) (Various artists).
Tracks: / Welcome to Sherwood: *Various artists* / What makes a star: *Various artists* / Make an honest woman of me: *Various artists* / To the woods: *Various artists* / Roger the ugly: *Various artists* / Dreamchild: *Various artists* / With bells on: *Various artists* / Twang!: *Various artists* / Unseen hands: *Various*

artists / Sighs: *Various artists* / You can't catch me: *Various artists* / Follow your leader: *Various* artists / Wander: *Various artists* / Whose little girl are you: *Various artists* / I'll be hanged: *Various artists*.
LP: TER 1055
MC: ZCTER 1055

Twardzik, Richard

CHET IN PARIS - VOL. 1 (See under Baker, Chet) (Baker, Chet & Richard Twardzik).

TRIO (see under Freeman, Russ) (Freeman, Russ Trio/Richard Twardzik Trio).

Twelve 88 Cartel

EVIDENCE.
LP: BB 019

MAXIM.
LP: BB 015

Twelve Dancing... (bk)

TWELVE DANCING PRINCESSES, THE (Unknown narrator(s)).
MC: PLB 239

Twelve Labours (bk)

TWELVE LABOURS OF HERACLES, THE (Padraic Colum) (Quayle, Anthony (nar)).
MC: 1256

Twenty 4 Seven

STREET MOVES.
LP: BCM 33247
MC: BCM 50247

Twenty Of Another Kind

TWENTY OF ANOTHER KIND (Various artists).
LP: POLS 1006

Twice A Man

WALK ON YELLOW.
LP: DMC 003

Twiggy

PLEASE GET MY NAME RIGHT.
LP: 9102 601

TWIGGY.
LP: 9102 600

Twilight

MODERN FOLK ARRANGEMENTS.
Tracks: / Skewball / Greenan Castle / Mermaid's song, The / Golden keyboards / Hunter's purse, The / Silkie / Alchemist, The / Astrologer / Fine flowers in the valley / Peter's tune / Leaving Lismore / Major Kord's jig / Captain Ward / Trip to Sligo, The.
LP: LIFL 7014
MC: LIFC 7014

ONCE UPON A TIME (Twilight, featuring Joel Katz).
LP: 8001

Twilly, Dwight

SCUBA DIVERS.
Tracks: / I'm back again / Somebody to love / 10,000 American scuba divers dancin' / Touchin the wind / Later that night / I think it's that girl / Dion baby / Cryin' over me / I found the magic / Falling in love again.
LP: AML 3021

Twin Hype

TWIN HYPE.
Tracks: / Do it to the crowd / For those who like to groove / My metaphors / Tales of the twins / Smooth / Suckers never change / Twin hype / Lori / Fanatics / Serious attitude.
LP: FILER 270
MC: FILERCT 270
LP: PRO 1281

Twin Peaks (tv)

MUSIC FROM TWIN PEAKS (See under Badalmenti, Angelo) (Badalmenti, Angelo).

TWIN PEAKS (THEME FROM) (See under Cruise, Julee 'Falling') (Cruise, Julee).

Twink

MAGIC EYE (Twink & Bevis Frond).
LP: WOO 13

MR. RAINBOW.
LP: TWKLP 1

Twinkle Brothers

ALL IS WELL.
LP: NG 520

ALL THE HITS FROM 1970-88.
LP: NG 513

ANTI-APARTHEID.
LP: NG 506
MC: NG 506C

BREAKING DOWN THE BARRIERS.
Tracks: / Breaking down the barriers / Urban Babylon / Truth and rights / You nice / Just like that / Don't let it happen to you / Me nah stop burn Ganja / Secure your love / So many things to do.
LP: NG 511
MC: NG 511C

BURDEN BEARER.
LP: NG 501
MC: NG 501C

COUNTRYMAN.
Tracks: / I don't want to be lonely anymore / Pattoo / Never get burnt / Free us now / Free us now / Kingdom come / Since I threw the comb away / One head / Bite me.
LP: NG 510
MC: NG 510C

CRUCIAL CUTS.
Tracks: / One head / Free Africa / Dread in the ghetto / Since I threw the comb away / Solid as a rock / Jahovah / Never get burnt / Africa / Love / Babylon falling.
LP: VX 1012

DUB MASSACRE PART 2 (REMIX).
LP: NG 502

DUB MASSACRE PART 3.
LP: NG 505

DUB MASSACRE PART 4 (The killing zone).
LP: NG 515

DUB MASSACRE PART 5.
LP: NG 519

DUB MASSACRE VOL. 1.
Tracks: / Jehoviah / Dub assasinator / Magnetic enforcer / Nation liquidation / Escape from hell / Dub examiner / Kingdom dub / Give rasta dub / One royal dub / War zone.
LP: NG 741

ENTER ZION.
LP: NG 503
MC: NG 503C

FREE AFRICA.
Tracks: / I don't want to be lonely anymore / Free Africa / Love / I love you so / Gone already / Solid as a rock / Come home / Shu be dub (you can do it too) / Patoo / Never get burn / Dread in the ghetto / Watch the hypocrites / Jahovah / Since I threw the comb away / One head / Free us.
MC: FLC 9008

KILIMANJARO.
LP: NG 753
MC: NG 753C

LIVE FROM REGGAE SUNSPLASH.
LP: VSLP 8907

LIVE IN WARSAW.
LP: NG 517

LOVE.
Tracks: / free africa / Watch the hypocrites / Love / Distant drums / Solid as a rock / Jahovah / I love you so / In this time.
LP: NG 512

ME NO YOU.
LP: NG 632
MC: NG 632C

NEW SONGS FOR JAH.
LP: NG 518

PRAISE JAH.
LP: FL 1041

RASTA PON TOP.
LP: VSLP 4043

RASTAFARI CHANT.
LP: NG 516

RESPECT AND HONOUR.
Tracks: / Respect and honour / Reveal in revelation / mob fury / Me no care / I give blessings / It's just a mirage / You make my day / Say you will / Forever and a day / River Jordan.
LP: NG 508
MC: NG 508C

SINCE I THROW THE COMB AWAY.
LP: TRLS 8907

TWINKLE IN POLAND.
Tracks: / Move onto Zion / What are we doing / Vanity / Retribution / Dub / Psalm 23 (the Lord is my shepherd) / One & one / All over the world / Last train to Zion.
LP: NG 514

TWINKLE LOVE SONGS.
Tracks: / Bite me / Don't want to be lonely anymore / Love / It was a vision I had / Baby I've been missing you / Down came the rain / Shame shame shame / Don't let it end / Too late / Then came you.
LP: NG 507
MC: NG 507C

UNDERGROUND.
LP: NG 500
MC: NG 500C

UNIFICATION.
LP: NG 521

WIND OF CHANGE.
LP: NG 522

Twins (Film)

TWINS (Film soundtrack) (Various artists).
Tracks: / Twins: *Little Richard & Phil Bailey* / Brother to brother: *Spinners* / It's too late: *Nayobe*/ I only have eyes for you: *Scott, Marilyn* / Yakety yak: *2 Live Crew* / No way of knowin': *Summer, Henry* Lee / Train kept a rollin': *Beck, Jeff* / I'd die for this dance: *Larson, Nicolette* / Going to Santa Fe: *McFerrin, Bobby/Herbie Hancock* / Main title: *Various artists*.
LP: SP 45036
MC: SPT 45036
LP: 4632661
MC: 4632664

Twist

THIS IS YOUR LIFE.
Tracks: / Silly people / Planners / Clown court / Ads / Monday morning / Doreen / This is your life / Rebound / House of the rising sun / Karen / Can I get a witness / Life on earth.
LP: 2383552

Twist in the Tale (bk)

TWIST IN THE TALE, A (see under Archer, Jeffrey).

Twisted Nerve

SEANCE.
Tracks: / Seance / Yes man / Twisted nervosis / Scaramouche / Freak of nature / It's all in the mind.
LP: NERVE 1

Twisted Sister

COME OUT AND PLAY.
Tracks: / Come out and play / Leader of the pack / You want what we got / I believe in rock'n'roll / Fire still burns, The / Be chrool to your scuel / I believe in you / Out in the street / Looking after no. 1 / Kill or be killed.
LP: 781 275-1
LPPD: 781275 1P

LOVE IS FOR SUCKERS.
Tracks: / Wake up (the sleeping guitar) / Hot love / Love is for suckers (like me and you) / I'm so hot for you / Tonight / Me and the boys / One bad habit / I want this night (to last forever) / You are all that I need / Yeah right.
LP: 871 772 1
MC: 871 772 4
LP: WX 120
MC: WX 120 C

STAY HUNGRY.
Tracks: / Stay hungry / We're not gonna take it / Burn in hell / Horrorteria / I wanna rock / Price, The / Don't let me down / Beast, The / S.M.F..
LP: 780 156-1
MC: 780 156-4

TWISTED SISTER: INTERVIEW PICTURE DISC.
LPPD: BAK 2088

UNDER THE BLADE.
Tracks: / What you don't know / Bad boys (of rock'n'roll) / Run for your life / Sin after sin / Shoot 'em down / Destroyer / Under the blade / Tear it loose / Day of the rocker.
LP: SECX 9
MC: TSECX 9
LP: RR 9946

YOU CAN'T STOP ROCK 'N' ROLL.
Tracks: / Kids are back, The / Like a knife in the back / Ride to live, live to ride / I am (I'm me) / Power and the glory / We're gonna make it / I've had enough / I'll take you alive / You're not alone (Suzette's song) / You can't stop rock 'n' roll.
LP: A 0074
MC: A 0074 4

Twits (bk)

TWITS, THE Roald Dahl (Kinnear, Roy (nar)).
MC: PTB 618

Twitty, Conway

20 CONWAY CLASSICS.
LP: MCF 3276
MC: MCFC 3276

BEAT GOES ON.
LP: CR 30242

BEST OF CONWAY AND LORETTA (Twitty, Conway and Loretta Lynn).
Tracks: / Louisiana woman, Mississippi man / Lead me on / As soon as I hang up the phone / Let me be there / It's only make believe / From seven till ten / Let your love flow / Letter, The / Back home again / Lovin' what your lovin' does to me / Release me / It's true love / Feelings / I can't love you enough / Hey good lookin' / After the fire is gone.
LP: MCL 1823
MC: MCLC 1823

BIG TOWN.
Tracks: / Ever since you went away / Big town / Blue is the way I feel / Treat me mean, treat me cruel / Road that I walk, The / Don't go too far / Broken heart / Angel's wings / Turn the other cheek / Wonder if you told her / Midnight / You made me what I am / Big train / Sitting in a dim cafe / Let me be the judge / Diggin' / Have I been away too long / Where I stand / Riskin' one.
LP: SHLP 142
MC: SHTC 142

BIG TRAIN.
LP: 20114
MC: 40114

BOOGIE BRASS BAND.
Tracks: / Boogie brass band / I've just got to know / She's a woman all the way / Julie / One night honeymoon / Your love had taken me that high / I've been around enough to know / My woman knows / That's all she wrote / You were named the co-respondent.
LP: MCF 2878

BORDERLINE.
Tracks: / Julia / Lonely town / I want to know you before we make love / Borderline / Not enough love to go 'round / Snake boots / I'm for awhile / Fifteen to forty-three / Everybody needs a hero / That's my job.
LP: IMCA 5659
MC: IMCAC 5659

CLASSIC CONWAY.
Tracks: / Tight fittin' jeans / I can't believe she gives it all to me / Play guitar play / Grandest lady of them all, The / We had it all / Georgia keeps pulling on my ring / Your love has taken me that high / Over thirty(not over the hill) / I am the dreamer (you are the dream) / Red neckin' love makin' night.
LP: IMCA 1574

CONWAY TWITTY SINGS.
LP: HAT 3127

COUNTRY PARTNERS (see Lynn,Loretta & Conway Twitty) (Twitty, Conway and Loretta Lynn).

CROSSWINDS.
LP: MCF 3038

DYNAMIC DUO (see under Lynn, Loretta) (Twitty, Conway and Loretta Lynn).

GREAT CONWAY TWITTY, THE.
LP: DEMAND 0020

GREAT COUNTRY HITS.
LP: MCF 3268
MC: MCFC 3268
LP: WW 5102
MC: WW 4 5102

GREATEST HITS: CONWAY TWITTY VOL.1.
Tracks: / Hello darlin' / I wonder what she'll think about me leaving / Fifteen years ago / Darling, you know I wouldn't lie to you / That's when she started to stop loving you / To see my angel cry / I can't be without you / Next in line / How much more can she stand / Image of me, The / I love you more today.
LP: IMCA 1473

HOUSE ON OLD LONESOME ROAD.
Tracks: / She's got a single thing in mind / Play Ruby play / Nobody can fill your shoes / Child with child / Pieces of you / Who's gonna know / House on old lonesome road / Private part of my heart / Take me home to Mama / Too white to sing the blues.
LP: MCA 42297
MC: MCAC 42297

IT'S ONLY MAKE-BELIEVE (LP).
LP: WW 2044

LIVE AT CASTAWAY LOUNGE 1963.
LP: DEMAND 0030

MGM YEARS, THE.
Tracks: / I need your lovin' kiss / Crazy dreams / Give me some love / Just in time / Born to sing the blues / Maybe baby / Shake it up / I need your lovin' / Golly gosh oh gee / Double talk baby / Why can't I get through to you / It's only make believe / I'll try / When (will you love me then, as you love me now) / I vibrate (from my head to my feet) / (I get so lonely) when I'm not with you / Don't you know / Story of my love / My one and only you / Going home / Make me know you're mine / Judge of hearts / First romance / I need you so / Mona Lisa / Sentimental journey / Hallelujah, I love her so / You'll never walk alone / Hey little Lucy / Teasin' / Heavenly / Halfway to heaven / Just because / Cry Janie cry / Blueberry Hill / Heartbreak hotel / You win again / Danny boy / Hey Miss Ruby / Restless / She's mine / Beach comber / Easy to fall in love / Rosaleena / My adobe hacienda / Star spangled heaven / Huggin' and a kissin', A' / Can't we go steady / Lonely blue boy / Sorry / Blue

moon / Eternal tears / Foggy river / Platinum high school / Trouble in mind / Pretty eyed baby / Rebound / Hurt in my heart, The / Maybe tomorrow we'll know / Tell me one more time / What am I living for / Fallen star, A / I'd still play the fool / Betty Lou / Knock three times / What a dream / Is a bluebird blue / Whole lotta shakin' goin' on / My heart cries / Sweet Georgia Brown / That's where my lovin' goes / Don't you dare let me down / Send her to me / Flame / C'est si bon / Long black train / Blue suede shoes / Great balls of fire / Jailhouse rock / Treat me nice / Handy man / Girl can't help it, The / Shake, rattle and roll / Diana / Splish splash / Reelin' and rockin' / Million teardrops, A / Tree in the meadow, A / Love fast, love hard, die young (I wanna) / I'm in a blue mood / Above and beyond / Man alone, A / Donna's dream / Tower of tears / I can hear my heart break / Prisoner of love / Unchained melody / Sweet sorrow / It's driving me wild / Turn around / Walk on by / Portrait of a fool / There is something on your mind / Mister Jones / Hang up the phone / Little piece of my heart, A / She knows me like a book / Comfy 'n cozy / Looking back / Pledging my love / It's too late / I almost lost my mind / I got a woman / My babe / Let the good times roll / Fever / Boss man / Don't cry no more / City lights / Faded love / Don't let the stars get in your eyes / Ages and ages ago / I hope, I think, I wish / Pick up / Hound dog / She ain't no angel / Got my Mojo working / Little piece of my heart, A / Sweet sorrow / It's driving me wild.
LPS: . . . . BFX 15174/9

NEVER ENDING SONG OF LOVE (See under Lynn, Loretta for details) (Twitty, Conway & Loretta Lynn).

REFLECTIONS.
Tracks: / It's only make believe / Walk on by / I'm in a blue mood / Fever / Beach comber / Pledging my love / Sentimental journey / Danny boy / My babe / Unchained melody / I almost lost my mind / Going home / You'll never walk alone.
MC: CN4 2091
LP: . . . . CN 2091

REPLAY ON CONWAY TWITTY.
LP: . . . . FEDB 5014
MC: . . . . FEDC 5014

SHAKE IT UP BABY.
Tracks: / Born to sing the blues / Golly gosh oh gee / Crazy dreams / Shake it up baby / Maybe baby / Why can't I get through to you / Double-talk baby / I need your lovin' / This road that I walk / I wonder if you told her about me / Midnight / You made me what I am today.
LP: . . . . BDL 1044
LP: 20071
MC: 40071

SONGWRITER.
Tracks: / Hello darlin' / (Lost her love) on the first date / Baby's gone / You've never been this far before / I'm not through loving you / Linda on my mind / After all the good is gone / Games that daddies play, the / I can't believe she gives it all to me / I've already loved you in my mind.
LP: . . . . IMCA 5700

YOU MADE ME WHAT I AM.
Tracks: / Treat me mean, treat me cruel / Have I been away too long / You made me what I am / Blue is the way I feel / Where I stand / Ever since you went away / Turn the other cheek / Let me be the judge / This road that I walk / Sitting in a dim cafe.
LP: . . . . ALEB 2306
MC: . . . . ZCALB 2306

Two

DREAMING SPIRES.
LP: . . . . FL 3

Two Bit Thief

ANOTHER SAD STORY IN THE BIG CITY.
LP: 086129

Two Brothers

TWO BROTHERS, THE (Various artists).
Tracks: / Two brothers, The: *Various artists* / Fox and the geese, The: *Various artists* / Farmer's daughter, The: *Various artists* / Iron man: *Various artists* / Cock, the hen and the brindled cow, The: *Various artists*.
MC: . . . . ANV 622

Two For The Road

TWO FOR THE ROAD (Film Soundtrack) (Various artists).
LP: . . . . NL 45119

Two For The Seesaw

TWO FOR THE SEESAW (Film Soundtrack) (Various artists).
LP: . . . . MCA 25016
MC: . . . . MCAC 25016

Two Hearts

TWO HEARTS ONE LOVER.
Tracks: / Two hearts, one lover / Midnight girl,sunset town / I'll be faithfull to you / Going gone / Mon ami, mon amour / He was onto something / If I could win your love / Friendship / Sister / Turn me loose.
LP: . . . . PTLP 005
MC: . . . . PTLC 005

Two Moon Junction

TWO MOON JUNCTION (Film soundtrack) (Various artists).
LP: 704.520

Two Of A Kind

TWO OF A KIND (See under Travolta, John) (Travolta, John).

Two Of Us

TWO OF US (Various artists).
LP: . . . . NE 1222
MC: . . . . CE 2222

Two Points To Tonka

TWO POINTS TO TONKA (Various artists).
MC: . . . . SOINEV CASS 01

Two Ronnies

BEST OF THE TWO RONNIES.
Tracks: / Moira McKellar and Kenneth Anderson / Brass band, The / Plumpstead Ladies male voice choir, The / Gilbert and Sullivan / Scouts jamboree show / Russian choir, The / Boys in the ballet / Short and fat minstrels, The.
LP: . . . . SPR 8518
MC: . . . . SPC 8518
LP: . . . . TRS 116

VERY BEST OF ME AND THE VERY BEST OF HIM, THE.
Tracks: / But first the news / Plain speaking / Mark my words / Train of events / British Rail / Night night / Limerick writers / Complete book, The / Restaurant, The / Castaway, The / Language barrier, The / Cheers / Late news, The.
LP: . . . . REC 514
MC: . . . . ZCM 514

Two Timer

ROCK TO ROCK.
LP: . . . . HMASP 61

Two to Tango

TWO TO TANGO (Various artists).
LP: . . . . SJLP 2

Two's Company

GOLDEN MEMORIES.
LP: . . . . KLP 240

LET'S START ALL OVER AGAIN.
LP: . . . . HPE 642

MADE FOR EACH OTHER.
LP: . . . . BRL 4048

TWO'S COMPANY.
LP: . . . . TVLP 12
MC: . . . . ZCTV 12

WHEN THE ROSES BLOOM AGAIN.
MC: . . . . FACS 018

YOU'RE MY BEST FRIEND.
LP: . . . . BRL 4074

Tygers Of Pan Tang

BEST OF TYGERS OF PAN TANG.
LP: . . . . MCF 3191

BURNING IN THE SHADE.
LP: . . . . ZEB 10

CAGE, THE.
Tracks: / Rendezvous / Lonely at the top / Letter from L.A. / Paris by air / Tides / Making tracks / Actor, The / Cage, The / Love potion No.9 / You always see what you want to see / Danger in paradise.
LP: . . . . MCL 1797
MC: . . . . MCLC 1797
LP: . . . . MCF 3150

CRAZY NIGHTS.
LP: . . . . MCF 3123
LP: . . . . MCL 1780

FIRST KILL.
LP: . . . . NEAT 1037

SPELLBOUND.
Tracks: / Gangland / Take it / Minotaur / Hellbound / Mirror / Silver and gold / Tyger Bay / Story so far, The / Black Jack / Don't stop by.
LP: . . . . MCL 1747
MC: . . . . MCLC 1747
LP: . . . . MCF 3104

WILD CAT.
Tracks: / Euthanasia / Slave to freedom / Don't touch me there / Money / Killers / Fireclown / Wild cat / Suzie smiled / Badger badger / Insanity.
LP: . . . . FA 3063
MC: . . . . TCFA 3063
LP: . . . . MCL 1610
MC: . . . . MCLC 1610
LP: . . . . MCF 3075

WRECK-AGE, THE.
LP: . . . . MFN 50
MC: . . . . TMFN 50

Tyketto

DON'T COME EASY.
LP: . . . . DGC 24317
MC: . . . . DGCC 24317

Tyla Gang

MOONPROOF.
Tracks: / Tropical love / Oakland red / It's gonna rain / Did you hear it on the radio / Rodeo / Spanish streets / No roses / American mother / Suicide jockey / Flashing in the subway.
LP: . . . . BSERK 16

YACHTLESS.
Tracks: / Hurricane / Dust on the needle / On the street / New York sun / Speedball morning / Don't shift a gear / Lost angels / Young lords / Whizz kids / Don't turn your radio on.
LP: . . . . BSERK 11

Tyla, Sean

SEAN TYLA'S JUST POPPED OUT.
LP: . . . . RIEN 1
MC: . . . . RIENK 1

Tyler, Alvin 'Red'

GRACIOUSLY.
LP: . . . . ROUNDER 2061
MC: . . . . ROUNDER 2061C

HERITAGE.
LP: . . . . ROUNDER 2047
MC: . . . . ROUNDER 2047C
LP: . . . . REU 1002

ROCKIN' AND ROLLIN' (Tyler, Alvin & The Gyros).
LP: . . . . CH 182

Tyler, Bonnie

DIAMOND CUT.
Tracks: / If you ever need me again / Too good to last / What a way to treat my geart / Eyes of a fool / Words can change your life / My guns are loaded / I'm a fool / Louisiana rain.
LP: . . . . PL 25194

FASTER THAN THE SPEED OF NIGHT.
Tracks: / Have you ever seen the rain? / Faster than the speed of night / Getting so excited / Total eclipse of the heart / It's a jungle out there / Going through the motions / Tears / Take me back / Straight from the heart.
LP: . . . . CBS 25304
MC: 40 25304
LP: . . . . CBS 32747
MC: 40 32747

GOODBYE TO THE ISLAND.
Tracks: / I'm just a woman / We danced on the ceiling / Wild love / Closer you get / Sometimes when we touch / Goodbye to the island / Wild side of life / Whiter shade of pale / Sitting on the edge of the ocean / I believe in your sweet love.
LP: . . . . RCALP 5002

GREATEST HITS: BONNIE TYLER.
MC: . . . . STAC 2291
LP: . . . . STAR 2291

HEAVEN AND HELL (Tyler, Bonnie/ Meatloaf).
LP: . . . . STAR 2361
MC: . . . . STAC 2361

HIDE YOUR HEART (ALBUM).
Tracks: / Notes from America / Hide your heart / Don't turn around / Save up all your tears / To love somebody / Take another look at your heart / Best, The / Shy with you / Streets of little Italy / Turtle blues.
LP: 4601251
MC: 4601254

HOLDING OUT FOR A HERO (OLD GOLD) (See under Williams, Deniece 'Let's hear it..').

NATURAL FORCE.
Tracks: / It's a heartache / Blame me / Living for the city / If I sing you a love song / Heaven / Yesterday dreams / Hey love / (You make me feel like) a natural woman / Here I am / Baby goodnight.
MC: . . . . CLAMC 232

NIGHTRIDING: BONNIE TYLER.
Tracks: / It's a heartache / To love somebody / Best, The / Closer you get / Before the night is through / Getting so excited / Natural woman, A / Band of gold / Straight from the heart / Louisiana rain / Living for the city / Under suspicion / Sometimes when we touch / Whiter shade of pale, A.
MC: . . . . KNMC 10020

SECRET DREAMS AND FORBIDDEN FIRE.
Tracks: / Ravishing / If you were a woman / Loving you's a dirty job / No way to treat a lady / Band of gold / Rebel without a clue / Lovers again / Holding out for a hero.
LP: . . . . CBS 86319
MC: 40 86319

VERY BEST OF BONNIE TYLER,THE.
Tracks: / Lost in France / More than a lover / Heaven / Hey love / It's a heartache / If I sing you a love song / Here I am / Louisana rain / What a way to treat my heart / My guns are loaded / World is full of married men, The / Goodbye to the Island / Sitting on the egde of the ocean / I believe in your sweet love / I'm just a woman / We danced on the ceiling.
LP: . . . . NL 70126
MC: . . . . NK 70126
LP: . . . . RCALP 5046

WORLD STARTS TONIGHT, THE.
Tracks: / Got so used to loving you / Love of a rolling stone / Lost in France / Piece of my heart / More than a lover / Give me your love / World starts tonight, The / Here's Monday / Love tangle / Let the show begin.
LP: . . . . NL 70029
MC: . . . . NK 70029
MC: . . . . CLAMC 231

Tyler, Charles

60 MINUTE MAN.
LP: . . . . AD 5011

DEFINITE 2 (Tyler, Charles Quartet).
LP: . . . . SLP 4099

DEFINITES VOL 1 (Tyler, Charles Quartet).
LP: . . . . SLP 4098

FOLK AND MYSTERY STORIES (Tyler, Charles Ensemble).
Tracks: / Uptown Manhattan / Puerto Rico / Folk like / Friday thirteenth / Warlock mystery drama, The.
LP: . . . . SNTF 849

SAGA OF THE OUTLAWS.
LP: . . . . N 16

Tyler, T Texas

NBC 1950 (see under Tubb, Ernest - Nashville 1946).

T. TEXAS TYLER.
Tracks: / Remember me / In my little red book / Filipino baby / Who's to blame / You turned a good man down / Careless love / Texas Tyler / Oklahoma hills / It's been so long darling / T. Texas blues / You nearly lose your mind / I hung my head and cried / Gals don't mean a thing.
LP: . . . . SING 721

Tymes

MS. GRACE / YOU LITTLE TRUST MAKER (OLD GOLD) (See under Hues Corporation/Rock the boat).

SOUL GEMS.
LP: . . . . PRST 506
MC: . . . . ZPRST 506

Tymon Dogg

BATTLE OF WILLS.
LP: . . . . Y 29LP

Tympany Five

1944/5 (see Jordan, Louis) (Tympany Five/Louis Jordan).

LOOK OUT (see Jordan, Louis) (Tympany Five/Louis Jordan).

Tynator

LIVING IN PAIN.
LP: . . . . CCG 003

Tyndall, Nik

EINKLANG.
LP: . . . . SKY 106

ENTSPANNUNG.
LP: . . . . SKY 096

Tyner, McCoy

4 X 4 (Tyner, McCoy Quartets).
Tracks: / Inner glimpse / Manha de carnaval / Paradox / Backward glace / Forbidden land / Pannonica / I wanna stand over there / Seeker / Blues in the minor / Stay as sweet as you are / It's you or no one.
LP: . . . . M 55007

BON VOYAGE.
Tracks: / Bon voyage / Don't blame me / Summertime / You stepped out of a dream / Jazz walk / How deep is the ocean / Blues for Max / Yesterdays (On CD only).
LP: . . . . SJP 260

DIMENSIONS.

Tracks: / One for Dea / Prelude to a kiss / Precious one / Just in time / Understanding / Uncle Bubba.
LP: **9603501**

DOUBLE TRIOS.
Tracks: / Latino suite / Li'l darlin' / Dreamer / Satin doll / Down home / Sudan lover / Lover man / Rhythm a ning.
MC: . . . . **CC 12**

EXPANSIONS.
Tracks: / Vision / Song of happiness / Smitty's place / Peresina / I thought I'd let you know.
LP: . . . . **BST 84338**

FOCAL POINT.
Tracks: / Mes trois fils / Parody / Indo-serenade / Mode for dulcimer / Departure / Theme from Nana.
LP: . . . . **M 9072**

GREETING.
Tracks: / Hand in hand / Fly with the wind / Pictures / Naima / Greeting.
LP: . . . . **M 9085**

HORIZON.
Tracks: / Horizon / Woman of tomorrow / Motherland / One for honour / Just feelin'.
LP: . . . . **M 9094**

IT'S ABOUT TIME (Tyner, McCoy & Jackie McLean).
Tracks: / Spur of the moment / You taught my heart to sing / It's about time / Hip toe / No flowers please / Travellin'.
LP: . . . . **BT 85102**
MC: . . . . **TCBT 85102**

LA LEYENDA DE LA HORA.
Tracks: / La vida feliz / Ja'cara / La habana sol / Walk spirit, talk spirit / La busca.
LP: . . . . **CBS 85143**

LIVE AT MUSICIANS EXCHANGE.
Tracks: / Senor Carlos / Lover man / You taught my heart to sing / Port au blues / Island birdie / What's new? / Hip toe (CD only.).
LP: . . . . **GATE 7021**
MC: . . . . **CGATE 7021**

LOOKING OUT.
Tracks: / Love surrounds us everywhere / Hannibal / I'll be around / Senor Carlos / In search of my heart / Island birdie.
LP: . . . . **CBS 85895**

NIGHTS OF BALLADS AND BLUES.
Tracks: / Satin doll / We'll be together again / Round midnight.
LP: . . . . **JAS 35**
MC: . . . . **JAS C35**

PASSION DANCE.
Tracks: / Moment's notice / Passion dance / Search for peace / Promise / Song of the New World.
LP: . . . . **M 9091**

PLAYS ELLINGTON.
Tracks: / Duke's place / Caravan / Solitude / Searchin' / Mr. Gentle and Mr. Cool / Satin doll / Gypsy without a song / It don't mean a thing / I got it bad and that ain't good / Gypsy without a song (Alternate take).
LP: . . . . **JAS 56**
MC: . . . . **JAS C56**

REAL MCCOY, THE.
Tracks: / Passion dance / Contemplation / Four by five / Search for peace / Blues on the corner.
LP: . . . . **BST 84264**

REFLECTIONS.
Tracks: / Ebony queen / Native song / Above the rainbow / Rebirth / Naima / Impressions / Ruby, my dear / Offering / Nebula / My one and only love / Desert cry / Afro blue / Song of the new world.
2LP: . . . . **M 47062**

REVELATIONS.
Tracks: / Yesterdays / You taught my heart to sing / In a mellow tone / View from the hill / Lazy bird / Don't blame me / Rio / How deep is the ocean / Someone to watch over me / Contemplation / Autumn leaves (CD only.) / Peresina (CD only.) / When I fall in love (CD only.).
LP: **B1 91651**

TENDER MOMENTS.
Tracks: / Mode to John / Man from Tanganyika / High priest, The / Utopia / All my yesterdays / Lee plus three.
LP: . . . . **BST 84275**

TIME FOR TYNER.
Tracks: / African village / Little Madimba / May street / I didn't know what time it was / Surrey with the fringe on top / I've grown accustomed to your face.
LP: . . . . **BST 84307**

TOGETHER.
Tracks: / Nubia / Shades of light / Bayou fever / One of another kind / Ballad for Aisha / Highway one.
LP: . . . . **M 9087**

Type O Negative

SLOW DEEP AND HARD.
LP: . . . . **RO 93131**
MC: . . . . **RO 93134**

Tyran' Pace

LONG LIVE METAL.
LP: . . . . **N 0027**

WATCHING YOU.
LP: . . . . **N 0055**

Tyrant

FIGHT FOR YOUR LIFE.
LP: **934308**

LEGIONS OF THE DEAD.
LP: . . . . **RR 9765**

MEAN MACHINE.
LP: . . . . **SKULL 8366**

RUNNING HOT.
Tracks: / Rock your bottom / Breakout / Taste of paradise / When the raven flies again / Running hot / Fire at sea / Take the most dangerous way / Get ready / She's a killer / Starlight.
LP: **805 072**

TOO LATE TO PRAY.
Tracks: / Tyrants revelation II / Too late to pray / Beyond the grave / Valley of death / Nazarene, The / Bells of Hades / Into the flames / Babylon / Verdalack / Beginning of the end / Eve of destruction.
LP: . . . . **RR 9658**

Tyree

NATION OF HIP HOUSE.
Tracks: / Let the music take control / Hip house is a style / Tonight / Nation of hip house, The / Move your body / This is how it should be done / On the smooth tip / Night time / Ruthless (Only on cassette and CD.).
LP: **466 147 1**
MC: **466 147 4**

TYREE'S GOT A BRAND NEW HOUSE.
Tracks: / Acid over / Turn up the bass / Acid is my life / Acid overture / Life / Let's get together / I'll never let you go / House line / T's revenge / T.J.G.P..
LP: **828 141 1**
MC: **828 141 4**

Tyrrall, Gordon

FAREWELL TO FOGGY HILLS.
LP: . . . . **HD 002**

HOW CAN I LIVE AT THE TOP OF A MOUNTAIN.
LP: . . . . **CM 016**

Tyson Dog

BEWARE OF THE DOG.
Tracks: / Hammerhead / Dog soldiers / Demon / Inquisitor / Dead meat / Painted heroes / Voice from the grave / Day of the butcher / In the end.
LP: . . . . **NEAT 1017**
MC: . . . . **NEATC 1017**

CRIMES OF INSANITY.
LP: . . . . **NEAT 1031**

Tyson, Ian

COWBOYOGRAPHY.
Tracks: / Springtime / Navajo rug / Summer wages / Fifty years ago / Rockies turn rose / Claude Dallas / Own heart's delight / Cowboy pride / Old Cheyenne / Coyote and the cowboy, The.
LP: . . . . **SH 1021**
MC: . . . . **ZCSH 1021**

FOUR STRONG WINDS (Tyson, Ian & Sylvia).
Tracks: / Jesus met the woman at the well / Tomorrow is a long time / Katy dear / Poor Lazarus / Four strong winds / Ella Speed / Long lonesome road / V' la l'bon vent / Royal canal / Lady Carlisle / Spanish is a loving tongue / Greenwood side / Every night when the sun goes down / Every time I feel the spirit.
LP: . . . . **VMLP 2149**
MC: . . . . **VMMC 2149**

Tytan

ROUGH JUSTICE.
Tracks: / Blind men and fools / Money for love / Women on thr frontline / Cold bitch / Ballad of Edward Case / Rude awakening / Watcher, The / Far cry / Sadman / Forever gone / Don't play their way / Far side of destiny.
LP: . . . . **METALP 105**

Tyzik, Jeff

JAMMIN' IN MANHATTAN.
Tracks: / New York woman / When I look in your eyes / You're my woman, you're my lady / Killer Joe / Jammin' in Manhattan / Better and better / Melange / Echoes.
LP: **8216051**

SMILE.
Tracks: / Smile / Sweet surrender / Face / Prized possession / Love won't wait / Hip hop / My heart's desire / I'm in love again / Rare moments.
LP: **827 272-1**
MC: **827 272-4**

Tzachi & Yael

JEWISH SONGS.
LP: **63 972**

Tziganka Ensemble

ACROSS THE RUSSIAN STEPPES.
LP: . . . . **BCLP 6**

BEYOND THE VOLGA.
Tracks: / Heart / Stenka razin / Andriusha / Linden tree / Wicker gate / Bublichki / Willow tree / Long road / When the poplar trees blossom / I want to love / No songs are heard on deck / How good / Tambourine is playing / Beautiful night / Vaniusha / Hava nagila.
LP: . . . . **MORR 521**

SONGS OF RUSSIA'S GYPSIES.
Tracks: / Ekh, Tziganka / Alyoshka / Lyotsa Pesynya / Katyusha / Druzhba / Kolyeso / Sing, gypsies / Dunya, I love your pancakes / Do not be angry / Yablochko / Solokov's guitar / Kalinka.
LP: . . . . **SFA 039**

Tzuke, Judie

BEST OF JUDIE TZUKE.
Tracks: / New friends again / Black furs / Sukarita / Sports car / For you / These are the laws / Welcome to the cruise / Come hell or waters high / Higher and higher / Chinatown / Stay with me till dawn / Bring the rain.
LP: . . . . **HISPD 23**
MC: . . . . **REWND 23**

CAT IS OUT, THE.
LP: . . . . **LLP 102**
MC: . . . . **LLK 102**
LP: . . . . **LLM 3008**
MC: . . . . **LLMK 3008**

I AM THE PHOENIX.
Tracks: / Black furs / Higher and higher / Fat wheels / Come hell or waters high / You were the place / City of swimming pools / You are the phoenix / Flesh is weak, The / I never know where my heart is.
LP: . . . . **PRICE 30**
MC: . . . . **PRIMC 30**
LP: . . . . **TRAIN 15**

LEFT HAND TALKING.
Tracks: / One day I will live in France / I could feel you / Liam / Left hand talking / Jesus was a crossmaker / Stay with me 'til dawn / God only knows / Bailey's song / Calling me back / Outlaws.
LP: **4674831**
MC: **4674834**

PORTFOLIO.
2LP: . . . . **CHR 1640**
MC: . . . . **ZCHR 1640**

RITMO.
Tracks: / Face to face / Nighthawks / How do I feel / Another country / Jeannie no / She don't live here anymore / Shoot from the heart / Walk don't walk / Push push / Chinatown / City of swimming pools.
LP: . . . . **CDL 1442**
MC: . . . . **ZCDL 1442**

ROAD NOISE-THE OFFICIAL BOOTLEG.
Tracks: / Heaven can wait / Chinatown / I'm not a loser / Information / Flesh is weak, The / Sports car / For you / Come hell or waters high / Southern smiles / Kateria Island / Love on the border / Black furs / City of swimming pools / Bring the rain / Sukarita / Stay with me till dawn / Hunter, The.
MC: . . . . **ZCTY 1405**
2LP: . . . . **CTY 1405**

SHOOT THE MOON.
Tracks: / Heaven can wait / Love on the border / Information / Beacon Hill / Don't let me sleep / I'm not a loser / Now there is no love at all / Late again / Liggers at your funeral / Water in motion / Shoot the moon.
MC: . . . . **ZCDL 1382**
LP: . . . . **CDL 1382**

SPORTS CAR.
Tracks: / Chinatown / Choices you've made / Living on the coast / Molly nightline / Rain on the hills / Rise of heart, The / Sports car / Understanding.
LP: . . . . **PRICE 29**
MC: . . . . **PRIMC 29**
LP: . . . . **TRAIN 9**

TURNING STONES.
Tracks: / We'll go dreaming / Dominique / Sound of my sister's tears / Don't go / Modern killers / Let me be the pearl / Take it all / Run to win / Everything will come / Turning stones.
LP: **839 087-1**
MC: **839 087-4**

WELCOME TO THE CRUISE.
Tracks: / Bring the rain / For you / Kateria Island / Ladies night / New friends again / Southern smiles / Stay with me till dawn / Sukarita / These are the laws / Welcome to the cruise.
LP: . . . . **PRICE 76**
MC: . . . . **PRIMC 76**
LP: . . . . **TRAIN 7**

U

U2

ACHTUNG, BABY!.
MC: . . . . UC 28
LP: . . . . U 28

BOY.
Tracks: / Twilight / An cat dubh / Out of control / Stories for the boys / Ocean, The / Day without me, A / Another time another place / Electric Co., The / Shadows and tall trees.
LP: . . . . ILPS 9646
MC: . . . . ICT 9646
LP: . . . . ISL 9646

JOSHUA TREE.
Tracks: / Where the streets have no name / I still haven't found what I'm looking for / With or without you / Bullet / Running the standstill / Redhill mining town / In God's country / Trip through your wires / One tree will / Exit / Mothers' of the disappeared.
LP: U2 6
MC: . . . . UC 26

LOVE'S HIGHWAY.
LPPD: . . . . I'MLOOKING 4

MUSIC AND MEDIA INTERVIEW PICTURE DISC.
LPPD: . . . . MM 1212

MUSIC AND MEDIA INTERVIEW PICTURE DISC.
LPPD: U2 21

OCTOBER.
LP: . . . . ILPS 9680
MC: . . . . ICT 9680

OUTSIDE IT'S AMERICA.
LP: . . . . JOSHUA THREE

PHILADELPHIA INTERVIEWS VOL.1, THE.
LPPD: . . . . BAK 6008

PHILADELPHIA INTERVIEWS VOL.2, THE.
LPPD: . . . . BAK 6010

RATTLE AND HUM.
Tracks: / Helter skelter / Hawkmoon 269 / Van Diemen's land / Desire / Angel of Harlem / I still haven't found what I'm looking for / When love comes to town / God part III / Bullet the blue sky / Silver and gold / Love and rescue / Love rescue me / Heartland / Star spangled banner, The / All I want is you.
MC: . . . . UC 27
2LP: . . . . U 27

U2: INTERVIEW PICTURE DISC (U2 (Bono)).
LPPD: . . . . BAK 2060

U2: INTERVIEW PICTURE DISC.
LPPD: . . . . BAK 2004

U2 - THE EDGE - INTERVIEW PICTURE DISC.
LPPD: . . . . BAK 2142

UNDER A BLOOD RED SKY (Live).
Tracks: / 11 o'clock tick tock / I will follow / Party girl / Gloria / Sunday Bloody Sunday / Electric Co., The / New year's day / '40'.
LP: . . . . IMA 3
MC: . . . . IMC 3
MC: . . . . ICM 2053
MC: 818 008 4

UNFORGETTABLE FIRE, THE.
Tracks: / Sort of homecoming / Pride (in the name of love) / 4th of July / Wire / Unforgettable fire, The / Promenade / Indian Summer sky / MLK / Elvis Presley and America.
LP: U2 5
MC: U2C 5
LP: . . . . ISM 1026
MC: . . . . ISMC 1026

WAR.
Tracks: / Sunday bloody Sunday / Seconds / Like a song / New Years day / Two hearts beat as one / Refugee / Drowning man / Red light / 409 / Surrender.
LP: . . . . ILPS 9733
MC: . . . . ICT 9733
MC: . . . . ICM 9733

WIDE AWAKE IN AMERICA.
Tracks: / Bad / Sort of homecoming / Three sunrises / Love comes tumbling.
MLP: . . . . ISSP 22
MLP: 902 791A
MC: . . . . 902 794 A

U Thant

BUGEILIO.
LP: . . . . THANT 002

UB40

BAGGARIDDIM.
Tracks: / King step (mark 1), The / Buzz feeling, The / Lyric officer Mk.2 / Demonstrate / Two in a one mk.1 / Hold your position Mk3 / Hip hop lyrical robot / Style Mk.4 / V's version / Don't break my heart / I got you babe / Mi spliff / Fight fe come in Mk.2.
LP: . . . . LPDEP 10
MC: . . . . CADEP 10
LP: . . . . OVED 288
MC: . . . . OVEDC 288

BEST OF UB40, THE (VOL. 1).
Tracks: / Red red wine / I got you babe / One in ten / Food for thought / Rat in mi kitchen / Don't break my heart / Cherry oh baby / Many rivers to cross / Please don't make me cry / If it happens again / Sing our own song / Maybe tomorrow / My way of thinking / King.
LP: . . . . UBTV 1
MC: . . . . UBTVC 1

GEFFREY MORGAN.
Tracks: / Riddle me / As always you were wrong again / If it happens again / D.U.B. / Pillow, The / Nkomo a go-go / Seasons / You're not an army / I'm not fooled so easily / You're eyes were open.
LP: . . . . LPDEP 6
MC: . . . . CADEP 6

I'LL BE YOUR BABY TONIGHT (see under Palmer, Robert) (Palmer, Robert/ UB 40).

LABOUR OF LOVE.
Tracks: / Johnny too bad / Guilty / Sweet sensation / Many rivers to cross / Red red wine / Please don't make me cry / She caught the train / Keep on moving / Cherry oh baby / Version girl.
MC: . . . . CADEP 5
LP: . . . . LPDEP 5

LABOUR OF LOVE VOL. II.
Tracks: / Here I am (come and take me) / Tears from my eyes / Groovin' / Way you do the things you do, The / Wear you to the ball / Singer man / Kingston town / Baby / Wedding day / Sweet cherrie / Stick by me / Just another girl / Homely girl / Impossible love.
LP: . . . . LPDEP 14
MC: . . . . CADEP 14

PRESENT ARMS.
Tracks: / Present arms / Sardonicus / Don't let it pass you by / Wild cat / One in ten / Don't slow down / Silent witness / Lambs bread / Don't walk on the grass / Doctor X.
MC: . . . . CADEP 1
LP: . . . . LPDEP 1

PRESENT ARMS IN DUB.
Tracks: / Present arms in dub / Smoke it / B line / King's row / Return of Dr. X / Walk out / One in ten / Neon haze.
LP: . . . . LPDEP 2
MC: . . . . CADEP 2

RAT IN MI KITCHEN.
Tracks: / All I want to do / You could meet somebody / Tell it like this / Elevator, The / Watchdogs / Rat in mi kitchen / Looking down at my reflection / Don't blame me / Sing our own song.
LP: . . . . LPDEP 11
MC: . . . . CADEP 11

RECKLESS (See under Bambaataa, Afrika) (Bambaataa, Afrika & Family).

SIGNING OFF.
LP: . . . . GRADLP 2
MC: . . . . GRADC 2

SINGLES ALBUM: UB40.
Tracks: / Food for thought / King / My way of thinking / I think its going to rain today / Dream a lie / Tyler / Adella / Little by little / Earth dies screaming.
LP: . . . . GRADLP 3
MC: . . . . GRADC 3

UB40 FILE, THE.
Tracks: / Tyler / King / 12 bar / Burden of shame / Adella / I think it 's going to rain today / 25% / Food for thought / Little by little / Signing off / Madame Medusa / Strange fruit / Reefer madness / My way of thinking / Earth dies screaming / Dream a lie.
2LP: . . . . VGD 3511
MC: . . . . VGDC 3511

UB40 LIVE.
Tracks: / Food for thought / Sardonicus / Don't slow down / Folitician / Tyler / Present arms / Piper calls the tune, The / Love is all is alright / Burden of shame / One in ten.
LP: . . . . LPDEP 4
MC: . . . . CADEP 4

UB44.
Tracks: / So here I am / I won't close my eyes (remix) / Forget the cost / Love is all is alright (remix) / Piper calls the tune, The / Key, The / Don't do the crime / Folitician (remix) / Prisoner, The.
LP: . . . . LPDEP 3
MC: . . . . CADEP 3

UB 40.
Tracks: / Dance with the devil / Come out to play (On 7" & CD only) / Breakfast in bed / You're always pulling me down / I would do for you / 'Cause it isn't true / Where did I go wrong / Contaminated minds / Matter of time / Music so nice / Dance with the devil (reprise).
LP: . . . . LPDEP 13
MC: . . . . CADEP 13

U-Brown

MISTER BROWN SOMETHING.
LP: . . . . FL 1003

SUPERSTAR.
LP: . . . . VSLP 5005

YOU CAN'T KEEP A GOOD MAN DOWN.
LP: . . . . FL 1030

Ubu, Pere

SONG OF THE BAILING MAN.
LP: . . . . ROUGH 33

UC

IBIZA MI AMOR.
LP: . . . . LR 42.002

UDO

ANIMAL HOUSE.
Tracks: / Animal house / Go back to Hell / They want war / Black widow / In the darkness / Lay down the law / We want it loud / Warrior / Coming home / Run for cover.
LP: . . . . PL 71552
MC: . . . . PK 71552

FACELESS WORLD.
Tracks: / Heart of gold / Blitz of lightning / System of life / Faceless world / Stranger / Restricted area / Living on a frontline / Trip to nowhere / Born to run / Can't get enough / Unspoken words / Future land.
LP: . . . . PL 74510
MC: . . . . PK 74510

MEAN MACHINE.
Tracks: / Don't look back / Break the rules / We're history / Painted love / Mean machine / Dirty boys / Streets on fire / Lost passion / Sweet little child / Catch my fall / Still in love with you.
LP: . . . . PL 72994
MC: . . . . PK 71994

TIMEBOMB.
Tracks: / Gutter, The (instrumental) / Metal eater / Thunderforce / Overloaded (instrumental) / Burning heat / Back in pain / Timebomb / Powersquad / Kick in the face / Soldiers of darkness / Metal maniac master mind.
LP: . . . . PL 74953
MC: . . . . PK 74953

UFO

AIN'T MISBEHAVIN'.
Tracks: / (Between a) rock and a hard place / Another Saturday night / At war with the world / Hunger in the night / Easy money / Rock boyz, rock / Lonely cities (of the heart) (Extra track on CD.).
LP: . . . . WKFMLP 107
MC: . . . . WKFMMC 107

ANTHOLOGY - UFO.
Tracks: / Rock bottom / Built for comfort / Highway lady / Can you roll her / Fool for love / Shoot shoot / Too hot to handle / Gettin' ready / Only you can rock me / Looking for number one / Hot 'n' ready / Mystery train / No place to run / Profession and violence / Chains chains / Something else / Doing it for all of you / When it's time to rock / Diesel in the dust.
LP: . . . . RAWLP 029
MC: . . . . RAWTC 029

C'MON EVERYBODY.
LP: 6.24836

COLLECTION: UFO.
Tracks: / Flying / Silver bird / Starstorm / Unidentified flying object / Shake it about / Timothy / Evil / (Come away) Melinda / Follow you home / Treacle people / C'mon everybody (live) / Who do you love (live) / Prince Kajuku (coming of Prince Kajuku).
2LP: . . . . CCSLP 101
MC: . . . . CCSMC 101

FORCE IT.
Tracks: / Let it roll / Shoot shoot / High flyer / Love lost love / Out in the street / Mother Mary / Too much of nothing / Dance your life away / This kid's.
LP: 41 3104 1
MC: 41 3104 4
LP: . . . . CHR 1074
MC: . . . . ZCHR 1074

HEADSTONE - THE BEST OF UFO.
Tracks: / Doctor doctor / Rock bottom / Fool for your loving / Shoot shoot / Too hot to handle / Only you can rock me / Love drive / She said she said / Lights out / Armed and ready / Young blood / Criminal tendencies / Lonely heart / We belong to the night / Let it rain / Couldn't get it right / Electric phase / Doing it all for you.
2LP: . . . . CTY 1437
MC: . . . . ZCTY 1437

LIGHTS OUT.
Tracks: / Too hot to handle / Just another suicide / Try me / Lights out / Gettin' ready / Alone again or / Electric phase / Love to love.
LP: . . . . CHR 1127
MC: . . . . ZCHR 1127

MAKING CONTACT.
Tracks: / Blinded by a lie / Diesel in the dust / Fool for love / You and me / When it's time to rock / Way the wild wind blows / Call my name / All over you / No getaway / Push / It's love.
LP: . . . . CHR 1402
MC: . . . . ZCHR 1402

MECHANIX.
Tracks: / Writer, The / Something else / Back into my life / You'll get love / Doing it all for you / We belong to the night / Let it rain / Terri / Feel it / Dreaming.
LP: . . . . CHR 1360
MC: . . . . ZCHR 1360

MECHANIX / LIGHTS OUT.
MCSET: . . . . ZCDP 107

MISDEMEANOR.
Tracks: / This time / One heart / Meanstreets / Name of love / Blue / Dream the dream / Heaven's gate / Wreckless.
LP: . . . . CHR 1518
MC: . . . . ZCHR 1518

NO HEAVY PETTING.
Tracks: / Natural thing / I'm a loser / Can you roll her / Belladonna / Reasons love / Highway / On with the action / Fool in love, A / Martian landscape.
LP: . . . . CHR 1103
MC: . . . . ZCHR 1103

NO PLACE TO RUN.
Tracks: / Alp-ha Centauri / Letting go / Mystery train / This fire burns tonight / Gone in the night / Young blood / No place to run / Take it or leave it / Money money / Anyday.
LP: . . . . CHR 1239
MC: . . . . ZCHR 1239

OBSESSIONS.
Tracks: / Only you can rock me / Pack it up (and go) / Arbory Hill / Ain't no baby / Looking after no. 1 / Hot 'n' ready / Cherry / You don't fool me / One more for the rodeo / Born to lose.
LP: . . . . CDL 1182
MC: . . . . ZCDL 1182

PHENOMENON.
Tracks: / Oh my / Crystal light / Doctor doctor / Space child / Rock bottom / Too young to know / Time on my hands / Built for comfort / Lipstick traces (on a cigarette) / Queen of the deep.
LP: . . . . CHR 1059
MC: . . . . ZCHR 1059

SPACE METAL.
LP: 6 28363

STRANGERS IN THE NIGHT.

Tracks: / Natural thing / Out in the street / Only you can rock me / Doctor doctor / Mother Mary / This kid's / Love to love / Lights out / Rock bottom / Too hot to handle / I'm a loser / Let it roll / Shoot shoot.
2LP: CJT 5
MCSET: ZCJT 5

WILD, THE WILLING AND THE INNOCENT, THE.
Tracks: / Chains chains / Long gone / Wild, the willing and the innocent, The / It's killing me / Makin' moves / Lonely heart / Couldn't get it right / Profession of violence.
LP: CHR 1307
MC: ZCHR 1307

Ug & the Cavemen

UG & THE CAVEMAN.
LP: MB 16

Ugarte, Enrique 'Kike'

ENRIQUE UGARTE, ACCORDION CHAMPION.
Tracks: / Bolero / Sabre dance / Czardas.
LP: EULP 1151
MC: EUMC 1151

FOLKLORE VASCO.
LP: EULP 1157
MC: EUMC 1157

Ugly Americans

WHO'S SLEEPING IN MY BED.
LP: AR 001

Ugly As Sin

GOOD, THE BAD AND THE UGLY, THE.
MC: 841 922 4
LP: 841 922 1

Ugly Duckling

UGLY DUCKLING Story told by Susan Hampshire (Hampshire, Susan).
MC: 3603

UGLY DUCKLING (Various artists).
MC: STC 019

UGLY DUCKLING, THE (Various artists).
MC: STC 019

UGLY DUCKLING, THE (Unknown narrator(s)).
MC: STK 005

UGLY DUCKLING, THE (well loved tales age up to 9) (Unknown narrator(s)).
MC: TS 309
MC: PLB 52
MC: STC 305B

Ugly Noise Inc

DANCE LIKE A BASTARD.
LP: CHAPLP 50

Ugulongo

PIERROT MOUYENGA.
LP: WIRE 001
MC: WIRE 001 C

UK

DANGER MONEY.
Tracks: / Danger money / Rendezvous 602 / Only thing she needs / Caesar's palace blues / Nothing to lose / Carrying no cross.
LP: POLD 5019

NIGHT AFTER NIGHT.
Tracks: / Night after night / Rendezvous 6.02 / Nothing to lose / As long as you want me here / Alaska / Time to kill / Presto vivace / In the dead of the night / Caesar's palace blues.
LP: POLD 5026
LP: EGLP 42

UK.
Tracks: / In the dead of the night / By the light of day / Presto vivace and reprise / Thirty years / Alaska / Time to kill / Nevermore / Mental medication.
LP: CRE 102
LP: 2302 080
LP: EGLP 35

UK Decay

FOR MADMEN ONLY.
LP: FRESH LP 5

UK Ladies

UK LADIES (Various artists).
LP: ANG 006LP

UK Players

NO WAY OUT.
Tracks: / Dancing in the street / So good to be alive / No way out / Missbehavin' / Saving up your love / Can't shake your love / First time love / Star of my show / Killing time.
LP: AMLH 68544

UK Subs

ANOTHER KIND OF BLUES.
Tracks: / C.I.D. / I couldn't be you / I love in a car / Tomorrow's girls / Killer / World war / Rockers / I.O.D. / TV blues / Blues / Lady esquire / All I wanna know / Crash course / Young criminals / B.I.C. / Disease / Stranglehold.
LP: GEMLP 100
MC: AABTC 801

BRAND NEW AGE.
Tracks: / You can't take it anymore / Brand new age / Public servant / Warhead / Barbie's dead / Organised crime / Rat race / Emotional blackmail / Kicks / Teenage / Dirty girls / 500 c.c. / Bomb factory.
LP: GEMLP 106
MC: AABTC 802

CRASH COURSE, LIVE.
Tracks: / C.I.D. / I couldn't be you / I live in a car / Tomorrows girls / Left for dead / Kicks / Rat race / New York State police / Warhead / Public servant / Telephone numbers / Organised crime / Rockers / Brand new age / Dirty girls / Same thing / Crash course / Teenage / Killer / Emotional blackmail.
LP: GEMLP 111
MC: GEMK 111
MC: AABTC 803

DEMONSTRATION TAPES.
MC: AMOK 778005
LP: KOMA 788005

DIMINISHED RESPONSIBILITY.
Tracks: / You don't belong / So what / Confrontation / Fatal / Time and matter / Violent city / Too tired / Party in Paris / Gangster / Face the machine / New order / Just another jungle / Collision cult.
LP: GEMLP 112
MC: AABTC 804

FLOOD OF LIES.
Tracks: / Another typical city / In the wild / Seas / Dress code / Still life / Tampa boy / After the war / In the red / Revenge of the jelly devils.
LP: FALL LP 018
MC: FALL CLP 018

GROSS OUT USA.
LP: FALL LP 031

HUNTINGTON BEACH.
LP: RFB LP 1
MC: RFB CA 1
LP: REVLP 150
MC: REVMC 150

IN ACTION.
LP: RFB LP 2
MC: RFB CA 2

IN ACTION (10 YEARS).
LP: REVLP 142
MC: REVMC 142

JAPAN TODAY.
LP: FALL LP 045

KILLING TIME.
LP: FALL LP 047
MC: FALL C 047

LEFT FOR DEAD.
MC: A 142

RAW MATERIAL.
Tracks: / Organised crime / Bomb factory / Dirty girls / Waiting for the man / Rat race / Teenager / Warhead / Sensitive boys / CID / Tomorrows girls / Left for dead / She's not there / Kicks / I don't need your love / Limo love / Cocaine.
LP: KILP 2001

RECORDED 1979-81.
Tracks: / Stranglehold / Tomorrow's girls / Teenage / Warhead / C.I.D. / Party in Paris / Keep on running.
LP: AABT 300

SUBS STANDARDS.
Tracks: / C.I.D. / Tomorrows girls / Telephone numbers / You don't belong / Rockers / T.V. blues / Crash course / New York State police / New order / Violent city / Emotional blackmail / Warhead / Brand new age.
LP: DOJOLP 28

U.K. Symphony

GREEN AND PLEASANT LAND (U K Symphony Orchestra).
LP: STAR 2270
MC: STAC 2270

UK To JA

UK TO JA (Various artists).
LP: SGL 101

Ukamau Amerindia

FOLKLORE DE BOLIVIA.
LP: EULP 1013
MC: EUMC 1013

Ukraine National ...

MEMORIES OF THE UKRAINE.
Tracks: / Advance Ukraine / Friends rejoice / Kolomyikas / Star of Bethlehem / Christmas bells / Dear carpathians / Freedom fighters.
LP: VP 459

Ukrainians

UKRAINIANS, THE.
LP: COOK 044
MC: COOKC 044

Ukulele Orchestra

UKULELE VARIATION, THE.
Tracks: / Nobody's child / Red cross / Before the conifers / Labours of Heracles, The / On suicide / Trout, the / Still life with ukulele / Midnight in Moscow / Presto tango / Hymn / Satisfaction / Candy says / Four men in big hats / Tosto che l'alba.
LP: EFNILP 2
MC: EFNIZZZ 2

Ullman, Tracey

FOREVER.
Tracks: / Breakaway / They don't know / Helpless / Terry / I don't want our lovin' to die / Move over darling / You broke my heart in 17 places / Sunglasses / My guy / Alone / Falling in and out of love / Shattered / You caught me out / Bobby's girl.
LP: SEEZ 59
MC: ZSEEZ 59

YOU BROKE MY HEART IN 17 PLACES.
Tracks: / Breakaway / Long live love / Shattered / Oh what a night / Life is a rock but the radio rolled me / Move over darling / Bobby's girl / They don't know / I'm always touched by your presence dear / You broke my heart in 17 places / I close my eyes and count to ten.
LP: SEEZ 51
MC: ZSEEZ 51

YOU CAUGHT ME OUT.
Tracks: / You caught me out / Little by little / Bad motorcycle / Loving you is easy / Sunglasses / Helpless / If I had you / Where the boys are / I know what boys like / Give him a great big kiss / Baby I lied.
LP: SEEZ 56
MC: ZSEEZ 56

Ulloa, Francisco

MERENGUE!.
Tracks: / La tijera / Agua de tu fuente / La situacion / El beso robao / Tongoneate / Ramonita / Manana por la manana / Los caballos / Linda Mujer / Lucas y radhames / La lengua / San Francisco / Homenaje a bolo.
LP: ORB 020

Ullulators

FLAMING KHAOS.
LP: DMLP 1021

Ulmer, James "Blood"

AMERICA: DO YOU REMEMBER THE LOVE?.
Tracks: / I belong in the USA / Lady blue / After dark / Show me your love / Black sheep / Wings.
LP: BT 85136

ARE YOU GLAD TO BE IN AMERICA.
Tracks: / Are you glad to be in America / TV blues.
LP: ROUGH 16

BLACK ROCK.
Tracks: / Open house / Black rock / Moon beam / Family affair / More blood / Love has two faces / Overnight / Fun house / We bop.
LP: CBS 25064

BLUES ALL-NIGHT (Ulmer, James "Blood" Blues Experience).
Tracks: / Blues all night / Calling Mary / Peace and happiness / She ain't so cold / Changing times / Baby snatcher / Boss machine / I don't know why.
LP: 70051

FREELANCING.
Tracks: / Timeless / Pleasure control / Night lover / Where did all the girls come from / High time / Hi Jack / Freelancing / Stand up to yourself / Rush hour / Happy time.
LP: CBS 85224

LIVE AT THE CARAVAN.
LP: CDP 85004

ODYSSEY.
Tracks: / Church / Little red house / Love dance / Are you glad to be in America / Election / Odyssey / Please tell her / Swing and things.
LP: CBS 25602

PART TIME.
LP: ROUGH 65

REVEALING.
Tracks: / Revealing / D.H. / M.O. / Little tree.
LP: 70071

Ulster Outcry

ULSTER OUTCRY.
LP: SOLP 1019

Ultima Thule

MIND THE GAP (See under I Refuse It) (Ultima Thule/I Refuse It).

Ultimate

ULTIMATE.
Tracks: / Love is the ultimate / Dancing in the night / Touch me baby / Ritmo de Brazil / Music in my heart / Take me to Chinatown.
LP: CAL 2048

Ultimate 60's

ULTIMATE 60'S COLLECTION (See under Sixties...) (Various artists).

Ultimate Blues ...

ULTIMATE BLUES COLLECTION, THE (See under Blues...) (Various artists).

Ultimatum

CROSS SECTION.
MC: LDC 5008

KNOCKOUT BEATS.
LP: ULT 001

Ultra Magnetic MC's

CRITICAL BEATDOWN.
Tracks: / Watch me now / Ease back / Ego trippin' (MC's ultra remix) / Moe luv's theme / Kool Keith housing things / Travelling at the speed of thought (remix) / Feeling it / One minute less / Ain't it good / Funky (remix) / Give the drummer some / Break North / Critical beatdown / When I burn / Ced-gee (Delta force one).
LP: 828 137 1
MC: 828 137 4

Ultra Vivid Scene

JOY 1967-1990.
Tracks: / It happens every time / Three stars / Grey turns white / Guilty pleasure / Beauty No. 2 / Praise the low / Staring at the sun / Special one / Poison / Extraordinary / Kindest cut / Lightning.
LP: CAD 0005
MC: CAD C 0005

ULTRA VIVID SCENE.
Tracks: / She screamed / Crash / You didn't say please / Lynne-Marie 2 / Nausea / Mercy seat / Dream of love / Lynne-Marie / This isn't real / Whore of God, The / Bloodline / How did it feel / Hail Mary.
LP: CAD 809
MC: CADC 809

Ultramarine

DE.
Tracks: / Djanea / U song / Dub it / Ivory coast / De / Bod kan'nal / Modakofa.
LP: 500 051
MC: 500 052

Ultras

COMPLETE HANDBOOK OF SONGWRITING.
LP: TX 92791

Ultraviolets

CHANGING TIMES.
LP: MMLP 030

Ultravox

3 INTO 1.
Tracks: / Young savage / Rockwork / Dangerous rhythm / Man who dies everyday / Wild, the beautiful and the damned, The / Slow motion / Just for a moment / My sex / Quiet man / Hiroshima mon amour.
LP: ILPM 9614
MC: ICM 9614
MC: 842 999 4

COLLECTION: ULTRAVOX.
Tracks: / Dancing with tears in my eyes / Hymn / Thin wall / Voice, The / Vienna / Passing strangers / Sleepwalk / Reap the wild wind / All stood still / Visions in blue / We came to dance / One small day / Love's great adventure / Lament.
LP: UTV 1
MC: ZUTV 1

HA HA HA.
Tracks: / Rockwork / Frozen ones / Fear in the western world / Distant smile / Man who dies everyday / Artificial life / While I'm still alive / Hiroshima mon amour.
LP: ILPS 9505
LP: 25499

LAMENT.
Tracks: / White China / One small day / Dancing with tears in my eyes / Lament / Man of two worlds / Heart of the country / When the time comes I'll cry / Friend I call desire.
MC: ZCDL 1459
LP: CDL 1459

MONUMENT.
Tracks: / Monument / Reap the wild wind / Voice, The / Vienna / Mine for life / Hymn.
MC: ZCUX 1452

LP: . . . . CUX 1452

QUARTET.
Tracks: / Reap the wild wind / Serenade / Mine for life / Hymn / Visions in blue / When the scream subsides / We came to dance / Cut and run / Song (we go), The.
LP: . . . . CDL 1394
MC: . . . . ZCDL 1394

RAGE IN EDEN.
Tracks: / Voice / We stand alone / I remember death in the afternoon / Thin wall / Stranger within / Accent on youth / Ascent / Rage in Eden / Your name has slipped my mind again.
LP: . . . . CDL 1338
MC: . . . . ZCDL 1338

SYSTEMS OF ROMANCE.
Tracks: / Systems of romance / Slow motion / Quiet man / Just for a moment / Dislocation.
LP: . . . . ILPS 9555
MC: . . . . ICT 9555
LP: 26453

THREE INTO ONE.
Tracks: / Young savage / Rockwrok / Dangerous rhythm / Man who dies everyday / Wild, the beautiful and the damned / Slow motion / Just for a moment / Quiet men / My sex / Hiroshima mon amour.
LP: . . . . ILPS 9614

ULTRAVOX.
Tracks: / Ultravox / Saturday night in the city of the dead / Life at rainbow end / Slip away / I want to be a machine / Wide boy / Dangerous rhythm / Lonely hunter / Wild, the beautiful and the damned, The / My sex.
LP: . . . . ILPS 9449
LP: 28193

U-VOX.
Tracks: / Same old story / Sweet surrender / Dream on / Prize, The / All fall down / Time to kill / Moon madness / Follow your heart / All in one day.
LP: . . . . CDL 1545
MC: . . . . ZCDL 1545

VIENNA.
Tracks: / Astradyne / New Europeans / Private lives / Passing strangers / Mr. X / Sleepwalk / Western promise / Vienna / All stood still.
LP: . . . . CHR 1296
MC: . . . . ZCHR 1296

VIENNA/RAGE IN EDEN.
Tracks: / Astradyne / New Europeans / Vienna / Sleepwalk / All stood still / Private lives / Mr.X / Passing strangers / Western promise / Thin wall / Voice, The / We stand alone / I remember / Death in the afternoon / Stranger within / Accent on youth / Ascent / Rage in Eden / Your name has slipped my mind again.
MCSET: . . . . ZCDP 109

Ulysses

ULYSSES (Various artists).
MCSET: 0328

Ulysses (film)

ULYSSES (Film Soundtrack) (Various artists).
LP: . . . . IM 007

Umbrellas Of Cherbourg

UMBRELLAS OF CHERBOURG (Original Soundtrack) (Various artists).
2LP: 822 457-1

UMBRELLAS OF CHERBOURG/GO-BETWEEN, THE (See under Legrand, Michel) (Legrand, Michel).

U-Men

STEP ON A BUG.
Tracks: / Whistlin' Pete / Three year old could do that, A / Flea circus / Willie Dong hurts dogs / Pay the bubba / 2x4 / Juice party / Too good to be food / Papa doesn't love his children anymore.
LP: . . . . TUPLP 012

STOP SPINNING.
LP: . . . . HMS 024

Umps & Dumps

MOON'S IN A FIT, THE.
Tracks: / Marmalade polka / Watercress girl / Darktown strutters' ball / Maybe she'll write me / Cajun two step / Underneath her apron / Up sides / After you've got / Woodland voices / Rogue's march / Dashing white sergeant / Here it comes again / Lichfield tattoo / Willow tree / Donkey, Jack donkey.
LP: 12TS 416

Unapproachable

STILL ON TOP.
Tracks: / Easier / Today / She died / Walk talk / Personal crime / Kick out the youth / Baby in my mind / She's too real / Voodoo chile / Dead man's land / Cherry bomb / Bad news.
LP: . . . . WB 8820

Unbearable Lightness

UNBEARABLE LIGHTNESS OF BEING, THE (Film Soundtrack) (Various artists).
Tracks: / Fairytale III: *Various artists* / Holy Virgin of Frydek: *Various artists* / In the mist: *Various* artists / Hey Jude: *Various artists* / Joy, joy, joy: *Various artists* / String quartet No. 2 'intimate pages': *Various artists* / Sonata for violin & piano: *Various artists* / Bird of ill omen lingers on: *Various artists*/ On the overgrown path, set 2: *Various artists* / String quartet No. 1, III: *Various artists* / Blow-away leaf, A: *Various artists* / Goodnight: *Various artists* / Idyll for string orchestra, II: *Various artists.*
LP: 835 918 1

Unclaimed

UNCLAIMED, THE.
LP: . . . . R 33/8707

Uncle Festive

YOUNG PEOPLE WITH FACES.
Tracks: / El tio / King Kent / Northern night / Monks / Young people with faces / All those with wings / Soup of the day / Uncle Sandwich / To you.
MC: . . . . CC 25

Uncle Mac

UNCLE MAC'S NURSERY RHYMES.
LP: . . . . MRS 5133

Uncle Meat

UNCLE MEAT (See under Zappa, Frank) (Zappa, Frank).

Uncle Sam (2)

HEAVEN OR HOLLYWOOD.
Tracks: / Live for the day / Don't be shy / Alice D / No reason why / Candy man / Don't you ever / All alone / Peace of mind, piece of body / Under sedation / Heaven or Hollywood / Steppin stone / Train kept a rollin'.
LP: . . . . RAZ 40

Uncle Slam

SAY UNCLE.
Tracks: / Wierdo man / Ugly dude, The / Judgement day / Micro logic / Contaminated / Up from beneath / Come alive / Executioner, The / Prophecy / Say uncle / Immolation / Eye of the end.
LP: . . . . CARLP 1
MC: . . . . CARC 1

Unconquerables

PING PONG POPPIN'.
Tracks: / Ping pong poppin' / Cowboy flix / Doctor Beat / Breakhoven / Hong Kong maiden / Storm warning / Nineteen 68 / Jungle voodoo / Head spin / Morning chorus / Scorpion sting / Rain dance / Reaction man / Mexico / Jester / Helicopter / Dark, The / Off the hook / Webb, The / Six point star rap / Take off.
LP: . . . . CRX 11

Undead

KILLING OF REALITY, THE.
LP: . . . . CITY 006

Under African Skies

UNDER AFRICAN SKIES (TV Soundtrack) (Various artists).
2LP: . . . . REQ 745
MCSET: . . . . ZCQ 745

Under Fire

UNDER FIRE (Film Soundtrack).
LP: 9239651

Under Freedom's Flag

UNDER FREEDOM'S FLAG (Various artists).
MCSET: . . . . WW 6041
MCSET: . . . . M 10304

Under Milk Wood

UNDER MILK WOOD (see under Thomas, Dylan) (Various artists).

Under The Coconut Tree

UNDER THE COCONUT TREE (Various artists).
MC: . . . . OMA 201C

Under The Covers

UNDER THE COVERS (Various artists).
LP: . . . . K 242268-1
MC: . . . . K 242268-4
MC: . . . . WX 146C
LP: . . . . WX 146

Undercover

3-28-87.
MC: . . . . BRKC 0500
LP: . . . . BRKR 0500

BOYS AND GIRLS.
LP: . . . . ASRR 0919
MC: . . . . ASRC 0919

Underdog

RABIES IN TOWN.
LP: . . . . SKULL 8331

UNDERDOG.
Tracks: / Lightnin' fever / Night shock / Shut up you dudes / No way to lose / Burnin' eyes / Damned man alive / Red alert / Speed attack / Hammer my nail into you / Underdog / Shout it out together.
LP: . . . . THBL 005

Underground...

UNDERGROUND ROCKERS (Various artists).
LP: . . . . LINK LP 053

Underground Zero

NEVER REACH THE STARS.
LP: . . . . SHARP 023

THROUGH THE LOOKING GLASS.
Tracks: / Atom child / Genocide (live) / Robert / Between worlds / Elite, The.
LP: . . . . BLUNT 038

Underlings

FATAL PURPOSE.
LP: . . . . CHIME 0020

Undernation

SOMETHING ON THE TV.
LP: . . . . OUTLP 106

Underneath

LUNATIC DAWN OF THE DISMANTLER.
Tracks: / Positive force for good and evil / Thick black angular / Black England/ White bomb / No / Tragedy boys and girls / Zophia / Bayonet / Smear / Another death in the family / Parenticide / Partyclens plus / This lady devoid / Hanging / Letter from an institution.
LP: . . . . ACME 9

Underneath The Arches

UNDERNEATH THE ARCHES (Original Cast) (Various artists).
Tracks: / Old bull and bush, The: *Various artists* / Just for laughs: *Various artists* / Underneath the arches: *Various artists* / Maybe it's because I'm a Londoner: *Various artists* / Home town: *Various artists* / Umbrella man: *Various artists* / Strollin': *Various artists* / Siegfried line: *Various artists.*
LP: . . . . TER 1015
MC: . . . . ZCTER 1015

Underneath What?

WHAT IS IT?.
LP: . . . . WX 302
MC: . . . . WX 302 C

Underscore

UNDERSCORE (Original Soundtrack) (Various artists).
LP: . . . . ENIG 32661

Understanding....

UNDERSTANDING & COPING WITH ANXIETY May, Rollo.
MC: . . . . PT 38

UNDERSTANDING & MANAGING JEALOUSY Clanton, Gordon.
MC: . . . . PT 40

UNDERSTANDING & OVERCOMING LONELINESS Peplau, L. A..
MC: . . . . PT 39

Undertones

ALL WRAPPED UP.
Tracks: / Teenage kicks / Get over you / Jimmy Jimmy / Here comes the summer / You got my number (why don't you use it) / My perfect cousin / Wednesday week / It's going to happen / Julie Ocean / Beautiful friend / Love parade / Got to have you back / Chain of love / True confessions / Smarter than you / Emergency cases / Really really / She can only say no / Mars bars / One way love / Top twenty / Let's talk about girls / I don't wanna see you again / I told you so / Fairly in the money now / Kiss in the dark / Life's too easy / Like that / Turning blue / Shopping for new clothes.
2LP: . . . . ARD 1654283
MCSET: TC2-ARD 1654289
LP: . . . . ARDM 1654281
MC: . . . . ARDM 1654284

CHER O'BOWLIES (Pick of the Undertones).
Tracks: / Teenage kicks / True confessions / Get over you / Family entertainment / Jimmy Jimmy / Here comes the summer / You got my number (why don't you use it) / My perfect cousin / See that girl / Tearproof / Wednesday week / It's going to happen / Julie Ocean / You're welcome / Forever paradise / Beautiful friend / Save me / Love parade / Valentine's treatment / Love before romance.
LP: . . . . EMS 1172
MC: . . . . TCEMS 1172
LP: . . . . ATAK 77
MC: . . . . TCATAK 77
LP: . . . . FA 3226
MC: . . . . TCFA 3226

HYPNOTISED.
Tracks: / More songs about chocolate and girls / There goes Norman / See that girl / Whizz kids / Under the boardwalk / Way girls talk / Hard luck / My perfect cousin / Boys will be boys / Tearproof / Wednesday week / Nine times out of ten / Girls that don't talk / What's with Terry.
LP: . . . . FA 3145
MC: . . . . TCFA 3145
LP: . . . . SRK 6088
LP: . . . . ARDM 1647421

PEEL SESSIONS: UNDERTONES.
Tracks: / Listening in / Family entertainment / Billy's third / Here comes the summer / Girls that don't talk / Tear proof / What's with Terry / Rock 'n' roll / Untouchable / Love parade, The / Luxury / Sin of pride, The.
LP: . . . . SFRLP 103
MC: . . . . SFRMC 103

POSITIVE TOUCH.
Tracks: / Fascination / Julie Ocean / Life's too easy / Crises of mine / You're welcome / His good looking girlfriend / Positive touch, The / When Saturday comes / It's going to happen / Sign and explode / I don't know / Hannah Doot / Boy wonder / Forever paradise.
LP: . . . . ATAK 46
MC: . . . . TCATAK 46
LP: . . . . ARD 103
MC: . . . . TCARD 103

SIN OF PRIDE, THE.
Tracks: / Got to have you back / Untouchable / Valentine's treatment / Love before romance / Luxury / Bye bye baby blue / Love parade / Soul seven / Conscious / Chain of love / Save me / Sin of pride.
LP: . . . . ATAK 47
MC: . . . . TCATAK 47
LP: . . . . ARD 104

UNDERTONES.
Tracks: / Family entertainment / Girls don't like it / Male model / I gotta getta / Teenage kicks / Wrong way / Jump boys / Here comes the summer / Get over you / Billy's third / Jimmy Jimmy / True confessions / She's a runaround / I know a girl / Listening in / Casbah rock.
LP: . . . . FA 3188
MC: . . . . TCFA 3188
LP: . . . . ATAK 71
MC: . . . . TCATAK 71
LP: . . . . SRK 6071
LP: . . . . ARDM 1647391

Underworld

CHANGE THE WEATHER.
LP: . . . . WX 289
MC: . . . . WX 289 C

UNDERNEATH THE RADAR.
Tracks: / Glory glory / Call me number one / Rubber ball / Show some emotion / I need a doctor / Bright white flame / God song, The.
MC: 925627 4
LP: 925627 1

Undisputed Truth

METHOD TO THE MADNESS.
Tracks: / Cosmic contact / Method to the madness / Sunshine / You + me = love / Hole in the wall / Loose life ain't so easy / Take a vacation / From life (and visit your dreams) / Let's go down to the disco.
LP: . . . . K 56289

SMOKIN'.
Tracks: / Show time / Talkin' to the wind / Atomic funk / I can't get enough of your love / Misunderstood / Sandman / Tazmanian monster / Space machine.
LP: . . . . K 56497

Undivided

ORIGINAL UNDIVIDED.
LP: . . . . MKLP 001

ORIGINAL UNDIVIDED, THE.
LP: . . . . ILPS 9873

Undivided Roots

ULTIMATE EXPERIENCE.
Tracks: / Party nite / Stranger to my eyes / Duke of Earl / Someone to love / Never get away / Rock dis ya music / To love again / Mad about you / Nature of love.
LP: . . . . ENLP 1001

UNDIVIDED ROOTS.
Tracks: / Party Nite / Duke of Earl / Never get away / Mystic man / Mad about you / Stranger to my eyes / Someone to love / Rock dis ya music / To love again / Nature of love.
LP: . . . . MLPS 1042
MC: . . . . MCT 1042
LP: 842 014 1
MC: 842 014 4

UNESCO Reports

BURDEN OF POPULATION (Peking, Tokyo, Unesco).
MC: . . . . IR 113

BUSINESS TRADING ETHICS.

MC: IR 104

FOOD FOR MILLIONS (China, USA, Third World, UK).
MC: IR 120

INDUSTRIAL ESPIONAGE (New York, Tokyo, Bonn, London).
MC: IR 111

JOB SATISFACTION (Stockholm, Tokyo, New York, London).
MC: IR 103

MORALITY OF STRIKES.
MC: IR 108

OIL A WORLD CRISIS (Beirut, Washington, London).
MC: IR 101

PETROL AND POLLUTION (Coventry, Brussels, New York).
MC: IR 105

POLLUTION AND INDUSTRY.
MC: IR 102

ROOTS OF INFLATION (Bonn, New York, London, Buenos Aires).
MC: IR 106

SILICON CHIPS - THEIR IMPACT.
MC: IR 119

SILICON CHIPS - THEIR USES.
MC: IR 118

SOURCES OF ENERGY (England, New York, Tel Aviv).
MC: IR 109

SPORT AND POLITICS (Controversies in World Sport).
MC: IR 107

TRAFFIC CONTROL (Bonn, Tokyo, London).
MC: IR 115

UNWILLING TO SCHOOL (Los Angeles, Paris, Moscow, London).
MC: IR 112

WHY OVERTIME? (Moscow, New York, London).
MC: IR 110

Unexpected Guest (bk)

UNEXPECTED GUEST (Agatha Christie).
MC: ZCF 533

Unfinished Boogie

UNFINISHED BOOGIE (Various artists).
LP: MUSKADINE 104

Unforgettable...

UNFORGETTABLE VOICES VOL.1.
LP: VDL 1003

UNFORGETTABLE VOICES VOL.2.
LP: VDL 1004

UNFORGETTABLE VOICES, VOL.3 (Various artists).
LP: VDL 1015

Unforgiven

UNFORGIVEN.
Tracks: / All is quiet on the western front / Hang 'em high / I hear the call / Roverpack / Cheyenne / Gauntlet, The / With my boots on / Ghost dance / Loner, The / Preacher, The / Grace.
LP: 9604611
MC: 9604614

Ungar, Jay

CATSKILL MOUNTAIN GOOSE CHASE.
LP: PHILO 1040

SONGS, BALLADS & FIDDLE TUNES.
LP: PHILO 1023

Union

ON STRIKE.
Tracks: / Mainstreet USA / Next stop London / Stay away from the honky tonks / Care of me / Keep the summer alive / On strike / Texas cannonball / Pacific Northwest blues / Invitation / All night long.
LP: PRT 85121

Union Carbide

IN THE AIR TONIGHT.
LP: CALCLP 056

Unique 3

JUS' UNIQUE.
LP: DIX 98
MC: DIXC 98
LP: DIXG 98

Uniques

SHOWCASE VOLUME 1.
LP: TWS 935

Unit 5

SCARED OF THE DARK.
LP: CLO 14

United Jazz & Rock

LIVE OPUS 6.
LP: TM6 28642

United Nations

FIRST MOVE, THE.
Tracks: / Sound of the eighties / Night that lasts forever, The / First move, The / You cheated / Common denominator / Violation of a nation (freedom for the network) / We will live forever / Blackheart / Speak after the tone / Paying the price for love.
LP: MAGL 5067

United States...

UNITED STATES OF AMERICA (United States Of America).
Tracks: / American metaphysical, The / Circus / Hard coming love / Cloud song / Garden of earthly delights / I won't leave my wooden wife for you / Sugar / Where is yesterday / Coming down / Love song for the dead, The / Stranded in time / American way of love, The.
LP: ED 233

UNITED STATES OF EXISTENCE (United States of Existence).
LP: KIRI 048

Unity

CHANGES.
LP: PC 123

Unity Creates...

UNITY CREATES STRENGTH (Various artists).
LP: NEVLP 007

Unity Rockers

EVERYTHING TO ME (see Black Harmony & Unity Rockers) (Unity Rockers/Black Harmony).

Universal Congress

MECOLODICS.
LP: SST 204
MC: SST 204C

Universals

ACAPELLA SHOWCASE.
LP: RELIC 5006

University Of Keele

COME LIVING GOD (University of Keele Chapel Choir).
LP: GRS 1039

University Six

UNIVERSITY SIX-VOLUME 1 1925-26.
Tracks: / Desdemona / Camel walk / She was just a sailor's sweetheart / Fallin' down / Smile a little bit / Then I'll be happy / In your green hat / Dustin' the donkey / I love my baby / Georgianna / What a man / Sittin' around / Tiger rag / San / Ace in the hole.
LP: HQ 2036

UNIVERSITY SIX-VOLUME 2 1926-27.
Tracks: / Tiger Rag / San / Ace in the hole / St. Louis hop / Oh, if only I had you / I ain't got nobody / Give me a ukulele / Wait'll you see my brand new mama / My baby knows how / It takes a good woman / Lonely eyes / I wish I could shimmy like my sister... / Beale street blues / Nobody but (my baby is getting my love) / Oh Lizzie.
LP: HQ 2056

Unjust

HAMMERHEAD.
LP: BCR 11

Unknown Mix

MIX 3.
LP: REC 018
LP: RECREC 18

Unknowns

DREAM SEQUENCE.
Tracks: / Dream Sequence / Gun fighting man / Action reactions / Suzanne / Not my memory / Tax-Deductible.
MLP: MINI 3626

Unlimited Touch

YES WE'RE READY.
Tracks: / Yes I'm ready / Your love is serious / Love explosion / No one can love me / Good living.
LP: PRL 25294

Unmarried Woman

UNMARRIED WOMAN, AN (Film Soundtrack) (Various artists).
LP: BT 557

Unrest

THINK OF....
LP: HR 015

Unseen Terror

HUMAN ERROR.
LP: MOSH 4

Unsere Schonsten Jahre

UNSERE SCHONSTEN JAHRE (Various artists).
Tracks: / Das ist der alte refrain: *Gregor, Harald* / Sieben einsame tage: *Ulbertson, Chris* / Behalt mich lieb cheri: *Sorensen, Margit* / Lieber sandmann: *Sorensen, Margit* / Frauen sind wie rosen: *Augustin, Liane*/ Wenn dein haar erst langsam grau wird: *Bieler, Ernie* / Ich furcht mich so: *Von Schmedes, Maria* / Weil mir so fad ist: *Qualtinger, Helmut* / Du kannst mir so den kopf verdrehen: *Eckhardt, Fritz* / Lasst der Herrgott einmal die welt untergehn: *Lang, Hans & Maria Andergast* / Du bist die rose vom Worthersee: *Lang, Hans & Maria Andergast*/ Die sennerin von St Kathrein: *Gutwell, Anita* / Ich mocht gern dein herz klopfen horn: *Lechner Trio* / Junger wer'n ma nimmer: *Horbiger, Paul* / Weisse chrysanthemen schenk' ich dir zur hochzeitsnacht: *Gregor, Harald* / Ich bin a stiller zecher: *Leopoldi, Hermann* / Bleib ma no a wengerl sitzen: *Sanguiniker, Die* / Weil mir mondscheinbruder san: *Subert, Frank* / Alle wasser der erde: *Bennett, Robert* / Ein zigeuner ist mein herz: *Low, Bruce*/ Gib mir den Wodka, Anuschka: *Muliar, Fritz* / Lieserl, komm hier: *Rank, Charlotte* / In der nacht ist der mensch nicht gern alleine: *Rokk, Marika.*
LP: V 130 002

UNSERE SCHONSTEN JAHRE, FOLGE 2 (Various artists).
Tracks: / C'est si bon: *Morell, Gert* / Nachte in dalmatia: *Morell, Gert* / Das machen nur die beine von Dolores: *Christ, Rudolf* / Lass die welt daruber reden: *Gregor, Harald* / Im rosengarten von sansoussi: *Gregor, Harald*/ Ein kleines stuck vom grossen gluck: *Gregor, Harald* / Deine, liebe: *Gregor, Harald* / Addio donna gracia: *Kreuzberger*, Rudi / In Hamburg sind die nachte lang: *Sorensen, Margit* / Uber's jahr wen die kornblumen bluhen: *Kreuzberger*, Rudi / Vaya con dios: *Maya, Easy* / Der student von Paris: *Gutwell, Anita* / Forsterliesl: *Gutwell, Anita*/ Es gibt nur ein Paris: *Gutwell, Anita* / Wenn der Herrgott will: *Low, Bruce* / Mehr will ich nicht von dir: *Ulbertson*, Chris / Moulin Rouge: *Augustin, Liane* / Sonntag nacht auf der Reeperbahn: *Augustin, Liane* / Tango max: *Augustin*, Liane / Cindy Oh Cindy: *Kent, Evi* / Harry Lime theme: *Lechner Trio* / Jim, Jonny und Jonas: *Ulbertson*, Chris & Teddy Windholz / Love in Portofino: *Roxy Sisters* / Hernando's cabaret: *Schmidt, Bobby* / Istanbul - Konstantinopel: *Trio Teddy Windholz.*
LP: V 130 006

Unsinkable Molly Brown

UNSINKABLE MOLLY BROWN, THE (Film Soundtrack) (Various artists).
LP: MCA 25011
MC: MCAC 25011

Unsung Heroes

UNSUNG HEROES, THE (Various artists).
LP: PHZA 17

Untamed Youth

SOME KINDA FUN.
LP: 207

Untermeyer, Louis

DISCOVERING RHYTHM & RHYME IN POETRY (Harris, Julie).
MC: 1156

Until September

UNTIL SEPTEMBER (Original soundtrack) (Various artists).
LP: STV 81226

Untouchables

AGENT DOUBLE O SOUL.
Tracks: / Agent double o soul / Stripped to the bone / World gone crazy / Cold city / Education / Let's get together / Airplay / Under the boardwalk / Sudden attack / Shama lama ding dong.
LP: ENVLP 524
MC: TCENV 524

WILD CHILD.
LP: SEEZ 57
MC: ZSEEZ 57

Untouchables (film)

UNTOUCHABLES, THE (See under Morricone, Ennio) (Morricone, Ennio).

Unwanted

SECRET PAST.
LP: NUMBER ONE

Unwilling to School

UNWILLING TO SCHOOL (See under UNESCO reports).

Unwin, Stanley

ROTATEY DISKEYS WITH UNWIN.
Tracks: / Pidey pipeload of Hamling / Goldyloppers and the three bearloaders / Olympicold B.C. / Hi de fido / Arty-craft / Professor Unwin meetit the press and chettery on / Populode of the musicolly / Classicold musee / Professor Unwin answery most questions on manifold subjy.
LP: FBLP 8101
MC: ZCFBL 8101

Unyque

MAKES ME HIGHER.
Tracks: / Keep on making me high / Party down / It's hot / Disco lullaby / Grand slam.
LP: DJF 20562

Up...

UP THE TOWN (Various artists).
LP: RUB 039
MC: RUBC 039

Up In Arms

UP IN ARMS (Original Soundtrack) (Various artists).
LP: STK 113

U.P. Wilson

ON MY WAY Texas guitar tornado.
Tracks: / Seven comes eleven / Reconsider baby / U.P. Express / Bluebird boog-a-loo / Hold on baby / Mean old world / Como station / I'll be coming home / Cross cut saw / On my way.
LP: RL 0078

Upchurch, Phil

COMPANIONS.
Tracks: / Companions / Song for Lenny / Mr. T.B.A's song / Show your love / Tell me I'm not dreaming / Blues in the middle / Rosanna / See See rider.
LP: PAL 4
MC: PADC 4

Updike, John

COUPLES / PIGEON FEATHERS.
MC: 1276

Upfront (group)

SPIRIT.
LP: DM 002

Upper Astral

CRYSTAL CAVE.
MC: C 309

ENTRANCE TO THE SECRET LAGOON (music of higher consciousness).
MC: C 313

HIGHER-SELF RENDEZVOUS (music of higher consciousness).
MC: C 323

SKYBIRDS - MUSIC OF HIGHER CONSCIOUSNESS.
MC: C 311

UPPER ASTRAL SUITE-MUSIC OF HIGHER CONSCIOUSNESS.
MC: C 301

Upper Norwood Band...

ALL THINGS BRIGHT & BEAUTIFUL (Upper Norwood Band Of The Salvation Army).
LP: BAB 3513
MC: TC BAB 3513

Upright Citizens

MAKE THE FUTURE...BOMBS OF PEACE.
LP: RUDELP 003

Uproar

LORD SAID LET THERE BE.
LP: BTSLP 1

Ups And Downs

SLEEPLESS.
LP: GOES ON 04

Upset Noise

NOTHING MORE TO BE SAID.
Tracks: / Weekend massacre / Upset noise / Gott mit uns / No one's concerned / One minute drama / Walking on my brain / Who said / Sex's a crime / Non voglio.
LP: HH 006

Upsetters

AFRICA'S BLOOD.
LP: TBL 166

BLACKBOARD JUNGLE DUB.
LP: LPCT 0115
MC: LPCTC 0115

DJANGO (OLD GOLD) (See under Collins, Dave/Double barrel) (Collins, Dave & Ansel).

NEW ORLEANS CONNECTION, (THE) (Upsetters/Larry Birdsong/Leonard Carbo).
Tracks: / Hatti Malatti / Strip, The / Girl in every city, A / Wake up / Bald head baby / Upsetter / Mama Loochie / Upsetter rock / Pigtails and blue jeans / So tired / I'm pleading just for you / If you don't want me no more / Time / My darling / Baby, baby / I don't want to lose her.
LP: CRB 1084

SCRATCH AND COMPANY.
LP: LPCT 0114

MC: LPCTC 0114

UPSETTER COLLECTION.
Tracks: / Cold sweat / Return of Django / Check him out / Django shoots first / Kill them all / Vampire / Drugs & poison / Sipreano / Black I.P.A. / Bucky skank / Words of my mouth / Tipper special / Cow thief skank / French connection / Better days / Freak out skank.
LP: TRLS 195
MC: ZCTRL 195

Upshall, Helen (aut)

CANDLES FOR THE SURGEON (see under Candles for the...(bk)) (Boyd, Carole (nar)).

Upshaw, Dawn

KNOXVILLE.
LP: 9791871
MC: 9791874

Upton, Harry

WHY CAN'T IT ALWAYS BE SATURDAY?.
Tracks: / Buttercup Joe / Ship that never returned, The / Life of a man, The / Dockyard gate / Female drummer / Bonnie blue handkerchief / Good old Jeff / Royal Albion, The / Little cabin boy, The / Why can't it always be Saturday ? / I'm a man that's done wrong / Seaweed / In the cottage by the sea / In wayward town / Trashing machine, The / I come from the country.
LP: SP 104

Uptown Jazzband

IN COLONIAL YORK PA.
LP: SOS 1030

Urban Acid

URBAN ACID.
LP: URBLP 15
MC: URBMC 15

Urban Africa

URBAN AFRICA (Various artists).
LP: 847 470 1

Urban Cowboy

URBAN COWBOY (Film Soundtrack) (Various artists).
Tracks: / Hi lo Texas: *Buffett, Jimmy* / All night long: *Walsh, Joe* / Times like these: *Fogelberg, Dan* / Nine tonight: *Seger, Bob & The Silver Bullet Band* / Stand by me: *Gilley, Mickey* / Here comes the hurt again: *Gilley, Mickey* / Orange blossom special: *Gilley, Mickey* / Hoedown: *Gilley, Mickey* / Could I have this dance: *Murray, Anne* / Cherokee fiddle: *Lee, Johnny* / Lookin' for love: *Lee, Johnny* / Lyin' eyes: *Eagles* / Look what you've done to me: *Scaggs, Boz* / Don't it make you want to dance: *Raitt, Bonnie* / Darlin': *Raitt, Bonnie* / Hearts against the wind: *Ronstadt, Linda* / Devil went down to Georgia: *Daniels, Charlie Band* / Love the world away: *Rogers, Kenny* / Falling in love for the night: *Daniels, Charlie Band*.
LP: K 99101
MC: K4 99101

Urban Dance Squad

MENTAL FLOSS FOR THE GLOBE.
Tracks: / Fast lane / No kid / Deeper shade of soul / Brainstorm on the U.D.S. / Big apple / Piece of rock / Prayer for my demo / Devil, The / Famous when you're dead / Mental floss of the globe / Hitchhike HD / God blasts the Queen.
LP: 210325
MC: 410325

Urban De Luxe

DE LUXE BLUES BAND.
LP: AP 040

Urban Dogs

NO PEDIGREE.
LP: SHARP 032

URBAN DOGS.
LP: FALL LP 012
MC: FALL CLP 012

Urban Sax

URBAN SAX.
LP: COB 37004

URBAN SAX PART 3 & 4.
LP: COB 37017

Urban Verbs

EARLY DAMAGE.
Tracks: / When the dance is over / Jar my blood / Acceleration / Early damage / Promise / For your eyes only / Business and the rational mind / In the heat / Terminal bar.
LP: K 56896

URBAN VERBS.
Tracks: / Subways / Angry young men / Next question / Frenzy / Ring ring / Only one of you / Luca Brasi / Tina Grey / Good life.
LP: K 56810

Urbaniak, Michal

CINEMODE.
LP: SNTF 1009

FRIDAY NIGHT AT THE VILLAGE VANGUARD.
LP: SLP 4093

RECITAL (Urbaniak, Michel/Vladislav Sendecki).
LP: FLC 5073

SONGS FOR POLAND.
LP: SNTF 1025

TAKE GOOD CARE OF MY HEART.
LP: SCS 1195

Urbaniax

URBANIAX.
LP: SNTF 917

Ure, Midge

ANSWERS TO NOTHING.
Tracks: / Answers to nothing / Take me home / Sister and brother / Dear God / Leaving, The / Just For You / Hell To Heaven / Lied / Homeland.
LP: CDL 1649
MC: ZCHR 1649

GIFT, THE.
Tracks: / If I was / When the winds blow / Living in the past / That certain smile / Gift, The / Antilles / Wastelands / Edo / Chieftain, The / She cried.
LP: CHR 1508
MC: ZCHR 1508

PURE.
LP: 211922
MC: 411922

Urge

LISTEN CAREFULLY.
LP: 084550

Urge Overkill

AMERICRUISER.
LP: TGLP 52

JESUS URGE SUPERSTAR.
LP: TGLP 37

Urgh, A Music War

URGH, A MUSIC WAR (Film soundtrack) (Various artists).
Tracks: / Driven to tears: *Police* / Back in flesh: *Wall Of Voodoo* / Dance: *Toyah* / Enola Gay: *O.M.D.* / Ain't this the life: *Oingo Boingo* / Respectable street: *XTC* / Offshore banking business: *Members* / We got the beat: *Go-Go's* / Total eclipse: *Nomi, Klaus* / Where's Captain Kirk: *Athletico Spizz 80* / Nothing means nothing any more: *Alley Cats* / Foolish I know: *Holland, Jools* / Ku klux klan: *Steel Pulse* / Uncontrollable urge: *Devo* / Come again: *Au Pairs* / Puppet: *Echo & the Bunnymen* / Tear it up: *Cramps* / Bad reputation: *Jett, Joan & The Blackhearts* / Birdies: *Ubu, Pere* / Down in the park: *Numan, Gary* / Shadow line: *Fleshtones* / He'd send in the army: *Gang Of Four* / Cheryl's goin' home: *Otway, John* / Homicide: *Various artists* / Beyond and back: *X* / Model worker: *Magazine* / Sign of the cross: *Skafish*.
LP: AMLX 64692
MC: CXM 64692

Uriah Heep

ABOMINOG.
Tracks: / Too scared to run / Chasing shadows / On the rebound / Hot night in a cold town / That's the way it is / Prisoner sell your soul / Hot persuasion / Think it over / Running all night (with the lion).
LP: CLALP 110
MC: CLAMC 110
LP: BRON 538

ANTHOLOGY - URIAH HEEP.
Tracks: / Gypsy / Bird of prey / Lady in black / Look at yourself / Salisbury / Love machine / Easy livin' / Wizard, The / Sweet Lorraine / Magician's birthday / Come back to me / Free me / Fools / Too scared to run / Think it over.
2LP: RAWLP 012
MC: RAWTC 012

BEST OF URIAH HEEP.
Tracks: / Gypsy / Bird of prey / July morning / Look at yourself / Easy livin / Wizard, The / Sweet Lorraine / Stealin / Suicidal man / Return to fantasy.
LP: BRON 375

COLLECTION: URIAH HEEP.
Tracks: / Love machine / Look at yourself / Firefly / Return to fantasy / Rainbow demon / That's the way it is / Love is blind / On the rebound / Easy livin' / July morning / Running all night (with the lion) / Been away too long / Gypsy / Wake up (set your sights) / Can't keep a good band down / All of my life.
2LP: CCSLP 177
MC: CCSMC 177
LP: LLM 3019
2LP: CCSLP 226
MC: CCSMC 226

CONQUEST.
Tracks: / Carry on / Feelings / Fools / Imagination / It ain't easy / No return / Out on the street / Won't have to wait too long.
LP: BRON 524

DEMONS AND WIZARDS.
Tracks: / Wizard, The / Traveller in time / Easy loving / Poet's justice / Circle of hands / Rainbow demon / All my life / Paradise / Spell, The.
LP: CLALP 108
MC: CLAMC 108
LP: ILPS 9193
LP: BRNA 193

DIFFERENT WORLD.
LP: LLP 137
MC: LK 137

EQUATOR.
Tracks: / Rockarama / Bad blood / Lost one love / Angel / Holding on / Party time / Poor little rich girl / Skool's burning / Heartache city / Night of the wolf.
LP: PRT 26414

FALLEN ANGEL.
Tracks: / Woman of the night / Falling in love / One more night / Last farewell, The / Put your lovin' on me / Come back to me / Whad'ya say / Save it / Love or nothing / I'm alive / Fallen angel.
LP: BRNA 512
LP: CLALP 176
MC: CLAMC 176

FIREFLY.
Tracks: / Hanging tree, The / Been away too long / Who needs me / Wise man / Do you know / Rollin on / Sympathy.
LP: BRNA 483
LP: CLALP 190

HEAD FIRST.
Tracks: / Other side of midnight, The / Stay on top / Lonely nights / Sweet talk / Love is blind / Rool-overture / Red light / Rollin' the rock / String through the heart / Weekend warriors.
LP: BRON 545
MC: BRONC 545
LP: CLALP 208

HIGH AND MIGHTY.
Tracks: / One way or another / Weep in silence / Misty eyes / Midnight / Can't keep a good band down / Woman of the world / Footprints in the snow / Can't stop singing / Make a little love / Confession.
LP: BRNA 384
LP: CLALP 191
LP: ILPS 9384

INNOCENT VICTIM.
Tracks: / Keep on ridind / Flyin' high / Roller / Free 'n' easy / Illusion / Free me / Cheat and lie / Dance, The / Choice.
LP: BRON 504
LP: CLALP 210

LIVE AT SHEPPERTON '74.
Tracks: / Easy loving / So tired / I won't mind / Something or nothing / Stealin' / Love machine / Easy road, The / Rock'n'roll medley.
LP: HEEPLP 1
MC: HEEPTC 1
LP: CLALP 192

LIVE IN EUROPE,1979.
Tracks: / Easy livin' / Look at yourself / Lady in black / Free me / Stealin' / Wizard / July morning / Falling in love / Woman of the night / I'm alive / Who needs me / Sweet Lorraine / Free'n'easy / Gypsy.
LP: RAWLP 030
MC: RAWTC 030

LIVE IN MOSCOW (Cam B Mockbe).
LP: LLP 118
MC: LLK 118

LIVE: URIAH HEEP.
Tracks: / Sunrise / Sweet Lorraine / Traveller in time / Easy livin / July morning / Tears in my eyes / Gypsy / Circle of hands / Look at yourself / Magician's birthday / Love machine / Rock and roll medley / Roll over Beethoven / Blue suede shoes / Mean woman blues / Hound dog / At the hop / Whole lotta shakin' goin' on.
2LP: BRSP 1

LOOK AT YOURSELF.
Tracks: / Look at yourself / I wanna be free / July morning / Tears in my eyes / Shadows of grief / What should be done / Love machine.
LP: CLALP 107
MC: CLAMC 107
LP: ILPS 9169

LOOK AT YOURSELF/VERY 'EAVY, VERY 'UMBLE.
Tracks: / Look at yourself / I wanna be free / July morning / Tears in my eyes / Shadows of grief / What should be done / Love machine / Gypsy / Walking in your shadow / Come away Melinda / Lucy blues / Dreammare / Real turned on / I'll keep on trying / Wake up (set your sights).
MC: TFOMC 7
2LP: TFOLP 7

MAGICIAN'S BIRTHDAY, THE.
Tracks: / Sunrise / Spider woman / Blind woman / Echoes in the dark / Rain / Sweet Lorraine / Tales / Magician's birthday.
LP: CLALP 109
MC: CLAMC 109
LP: BRNA 213
LP: ILPS 9213

RAGING SILENCE.
LP: LLP 120
MC: LLK 120
LPPD: LLPPD 120

RETURN TO FANTASY.
Tracks: / Return to fantasy / Shady lady / Devil's daughter / Beautiful dream / Prima donna / Your turn to remember / Showdown / Why did you go / Year or a day, A.
LP: BRNA 335
LP: ILPS 9335
LP: CLALP 175
MC: CLAMC 175

SALISBURY.
Tracks: / Bird of prey / Park, The / Time to live / Lady in black / High priestess / Salisbury.
LP: CLALP 106
LP: BRNA 152
MC: CLAMC 106

STILL 'EAVY, STILL PROUD.
LP: LLP 133
MC: LLK 133

SWEET FREEDOM.
Tracks: / Dreamin / Stealin' / One day / Sweet freedom / If I had the time / Seven stars / Circus / Pilgrim.
LP: BRNA 245
LP: ILPS 9245
LP: CLALP 183

TWO DECADES IN ROCK.
Tracks: / July morning / Sweet Lorraine / Gypsy / Look at yourself / Easy livin'.
LPS: ESBLP 022

URIAH HEEP LIVE.
2LP: ISLD 1

URIAH HEEP LIVE JAN '73.
LP: RAWLP 041

URIAH HEEP STORY, THE.
LPPD: ROHALP 2
MC: ROHAMC 2

VERY 'EAVY ...VERY 'UMBLE.
Tracks: / Gypsy / Walking in your shadow / Come away Melinda / Lucy blues / Dreammare / Real turned on / I'll keep on trying / Wake up (set your sights).
LP: CLALP 105
MC: CLAMC 105

WONDERWORLD.
LP: ILPS 9280
LP: CLALP 184

Urlich, Margaret

SAFETY IN NUMBERS.
Tracks: / Escaping / Number one (remember when we danced all night) / Only my heart calling / Give me some credit / Guilty people / Tide keeps rolling in, The / Your love / Open up / Slip on by / Deep down / God bless the child.
LP: 4656521
MC: 4656524

U-Roy

BEST OF U-ROY.
LP: LALP 08
MC: SSRC 003

CRUCIAL CUTS.
Tracks: / Control tower / Rivers of Babylon / Peace and love in the ghetto / Wear you to the ball / Small axe / Ain't that lovin' you / Drive her home / Evil doers / Tide is high, The / Love in the arena.
LP: VX 1013

DJ MASTERPIECES (U-Roy & Friends).
LP: VSLP 4057

DREAD IN A BABYLON.
Tracks: / Runaway girl / Chalice in the palace / I can't love another / Dreadlocks dread / Great psalms, The / Natty don't fear / African message / Silver bird / Listen to the teacher / Trench Town rock.
LP: VX 1007
MC: FLC 9007
LP: FL 9007

DREAD IN A BABYLON (THREE FROM THE FRONTLINE) (See under Three From The ...).

MUSIC ADDICT.
Tracks: / I originate / Come fe warn them / King Tubby's skank / Reggae party / I feel good / Music addict / Ja Jah call you / Haul and pull / Waterboat.

LP: . . . . RAS 3024

NATTY REBEL.
Tracks: / Babylon burning / Natty rebel / So Jah Jah say / Natty kung fu / If you should leave me / Do you remember / Travelling man / Have mercy / Badie boo / Go there natty / Fire in a Trench Town.
LP: . . . . VX 1008

SEVEN GOALS.
LP: . . . . RMN 367

TRUE BORN AFRICAN.
LP: . . . . AIRLP 071

VERSION GALORE.
LP: . . . . Unknown

VERSION OF WISDOM.
MC: . . . . FLC 9003

WAKE THE TOWN AND TELL THE PEOPLE.
LP: . . . . TRLD 410

WITH A FLICK OF MY MUSICAL WRIST (U-Roy & Friends).
LP: . . . . TRLS 268
MC: . . . . ZCTRL 268

WITH WORDS OF WISDOM.
Tracks: / Honey come foreward / Treasure Isle skank / Rule the nation / Everybody bawling / Drive her home / Tom Drunk / Words of wisdom / Merry go round / Wake the town / What is catty / Ain't that lovin' you / Behold.
LP: . . . . FLX 4004

Urquart, Robert

TALES OF PARA HANDY, THE.
Tracks: / Master mariner / Piper O'Dumbarton / Para Handy's piper / Trump selection / Duelling canaries / Wee teeny / My baby O / Painting the maids / Mairi Bhan / Wet man o' Muscadale / Western isles.
MC: . . . . CBNC 009

Urry, Mick

COCKNEY CAPERS (Urry, Mick With His Showband & Singers).
LP: . . . . BSS 378

I'M IN THE MOOD FOR DANCING (Urry, Mick & his Orchestra).
LP: . . . . MTS 9

IN A DANCING MOOD (Urry, Mick & his Orchestra).
LP: . . . . MTS 5

IN A PARTY MOOD (Urry, Mick His Orchestra & Singers).
LP: . . . . MTS 8
MC: . . . . CMTS 8

INVITATION TO THE BALL (Urry, Mick & Orchestra/Brenda Blackman/Mick Urry Strings).
LP: . . . . MTS 21

U.S.A.

U.S.A..
Tracks: / I love you / Hard life / One who really loved you / Come back baby / Alone in the world / Teenage rock 'n' roller / Last song, The / Ya think this is love / Can't get you out of my mind / She said no.
LP: . . . . PWLP 1002

USA For Africa

WE ARE THE WORLD.
Tracks: / We are the world.
LP: . . . . USAIDF 1
MC: . . . . USAIDC 1

Usher, Claire

SUPER CLAIRE.
Tracks: / Superman / I'm into something good / Shadows / My guy / Rainbow / My boy lollipop / It's 'orrible being in love when you're eight and a half / Raining in my heart / Big sister / Rubber ball / Born too late.
LP: . . . . REB 606
MC: . . . . ZCF 606

Usry, Johnny

HEALING.
Tracks: / Healing / Forgotten heroes / Johnny's rap (give peace a chance) / Chu-lai Charlie / Healing (reprise) / Girl of the night / When love is gone / Mom / Homeless / Girl of the night (instrumental).
LP: . . . . USC 4006
MC: . . . . ZCUSC 4006

U.S.Scooters

YOUNG GIRLS.
Tracks: / Young girls / Big brother / Stuck on you / Over and over / Someone tonight / Falling / Drive away / Take me home / Let me in / On my way / Set and ready.
LP: . . . . AML 3011

USSR Academic Choir

RUSSIAN FOLK SONGS.
MC: . . . . SM 00217
LP: . . . . COS 2004

USSR Defence Ministry

FAMOUS RUSSIAN MARCHES (USSR Defence Ministry Band).
LP: . . . . CSD 3782

Ustinov, Peter

GRAND PRIX OF GIBRALTAR.
MC: . . . . RLPC 833

HOWARD BLAKE: GRANPA (See under Brightman, Sarah) (Ustinov, Peter & Sarah Brightman).

MANY VOICES OF..., THE.
LP: . . . . REC 248
MC: . . . . MRMC 014

MOUSE AND HIS CHILD.
LP: . . . . TC 1550
MC: . . . . CDL 51550

UT

CONVICTION.
LP: . . . . OUTRO 3

EARLY LIFE LIVE.
LP: . . . . BFFP 12

GRILLER.
Tracks: / Safe burning / Canker / Possee necks / Wailhouse / Spore / Doctor No / How it goes / Rummy / Fuel / Scrape / Griller.
LP: . . . . BFFP 36

IN GUT'S HOUSE.
LP: . . . . BFFP 17

Utah Symphony

ADVENTURES OF ROBIN HOOD (See under Adventures of Robin Hood).

AMERICAN IN PARIS (see under Gershwin).

HOMAGE TO ERIK SATIE, VOL.1 (see under Satie, Erik).

U.T.F.O

DOIN' IT.
LP: . . . . SEL 21629

SKEEZER PLEEZER.
Tracks: / Just watch / Where did you go / We work hard / Kangol and Doc / House will rock, The / Split personality / Pick up the pace / Bad luck Barry.
LP: . . . . CHR 1551
MC: . . . . ZCHR 1551

Utley, Michael

UTLEY JUBILEE (See Under Greenidge, Robert) (Utley, Michael & Robert Greenidge).

Utopia

ADVENTURES IN UTOPIA.
Tracks: / Road to Utopia / You make me crazy / Second nature / Set me free / Caravan / Last of the new wave riders / Shot in the dark / Very last time / Love alone / Rock love.
LP: . . . . ILPS 9602

COLLECTION: UTOPIA.
Tracks: / Where does the world go to hide / Freedom fighters / All smiles / Lysistrata / Always late / Love in action / Rock love / Set me free / Seven rays, The / Trapped / Swing to the right / One world / Heavy metal kids / Very last time, The / Crazy lady blue / Feel too good / Love alone / Love is the answer.
2LP: . . . . CCSLP 181
MC: . . . . CCSMC 181

DEFACE THE MUSIC.
Tracks: / I just want to touch you / Crystal ball / Where does the world go to hide / Silly boy / Alone / That's not right / Take it home / Hoi poloi / Life goes on / Feel too good / Always late / All smiles / Everybody else is wrong.
LP: . . . . ILPS 9642

OBLIVION.
Tracks: / Maybe I could change / Cry baby / Welcome to my revolution / Winston Smith takes it on the jaw / I will wait / Itch in my brain / Love with a thinker / Bring me my longbow / If I didn't try / Too much water.
LP: . . . . WX 4
MC: . . . . WX 4C

OOPS WRONG PLANET / ADVENTURES IN UTOPIA.
Tracks: / Trapped / Windows / Love in action / Crazy lady blue / Back on the street / Marriage of heaven and hell / Martyr, The / Abandon city / Gangrene / My angel / Rape of the young / Love is the answer / Road to Utopia, The / You make me crazy / Second nature / Set me free / Caravan / Last of the new wave riders / Shot in the dark / Very last time, The / Love alone / Rock love.
MC: . . . . TFOMC 9
2LP: . . . . TFOLP 9

SWING TO THE RIGHT (See under Rundgren, Todd for details).

TRIVIA (12 Track Compilation).
Tracks: /
LP: . . . . PB 6053
MC: . . . . PBC 6053

UTOPIA.
Tracks: / Libertine / Bad little actress / Feet don't fail me now / Neck on up / Say yeah / Call it what you will / I'm looking at you but I'm talking to myself / Hammer in my heart / Burn three times / There goes my inspiration.
LP: . . . . EPC 25207

Uttley, Alison

BROWN MOUSE & THE LITTLE RED FOX, THE.
MC: . . . . TC LFP 7071

LITTLE GREY RABBIT: FUZZYPEG GOES TO SCHOOL.
MC: 00 102150 8

LITTLE GREY RABBIT, THE.
MC: 00 102218 0

LITTLE RED FOX BOOK & BROWN MOUSE BOOK (Scales, Prunella (nar)).
MCSET: . . . . LFP 7373

Utu

UTU (Original soundtrack) (Various artists).
LP: . . . . SCRS 1008

UV

UNIQUE VISION, THE.
LP: . . . . SR 824882

UV Pop

BENDY BABY MAN.
LP: . . . . EXTRALP 001

NO SONGS TOMORROW.
LP: . . . . FM 004

U.V.'S

CRAYON JUNGLE.
LP: . . . . ZINLP 3

Uwandile

APARTHEID.
LP: . . . . MALP 01

UZI

SLEEP ASYLUM.
LP: . . . . HMS 055

V

V2

V2.
LP: N 0114
MC: N 0114-2
LP: NUK 114
MC: ZCNUK 114

V. Spy V. Spy

A.O. MOD. T.V. VERS..
Tracks: / Don't tear it down / Credit cards / Mission man / Pockets of pride / Go to work / Sallie-Anne / Snowblind / Use your heard / Peace and quiet / Take me away.
LP: 254458 1
MC: 254458 4

TRASH THE PLANET.
LP: 2292569201
MC: 2292569204

V, Stevie

DIRTY CASH (MONEY TALKS) (See under Stevie V).

Vache, Allan

CLARINET CLIMAX (see Hedges, Chuck) (Vache, Allan & Chuck Hedges).

HIGH SPEED SWING.
LP: AP 192

JAZZ MOODS.
LP: AP 176

Vache, Warren

BLUES WALK (Vache, Warren With Scott Hamilton & John Bunch.).
LP: DR 101

EASY GOING (Vache, Warren Sextet).
Tracks: / Little girl / Easy going bounce / Warm valley / You'd be so nice to come home to / Michelle / It's been so long / Was I to blame for falling in love with you? / London by night / Mandy make up your mind / Moon song (That wasn't meant for me).
LP: CJ 323
MC: CJC 323

FIRST TIME OUT.
LP: AP 196
LP: MES 7081

IRIDESCENCE.
LP: CJ 153

MIDTOWN JAZZ.
Tracks: / I'm old fashioned / Rhythm-a-ning / Tempus fugit / Two for the road / We'll be together again / Time for love, A / I let a song go out of my heart / Out of nowhere / Love in the spring / I remember April.
LP: CJ 203

SCOTT HAMILTON & WARREN VACHE (See under Hamilton, Scott) (Vache, Warren & Scott Hamilton).

Vagabond Joy

BABY'S NOT A GURU.
Tracks: / Walking with Pandora (On the psychic trail) / If you remember my name / Who left me down by the river / Not a friend in the world / Oh my little pretty thing / End of creation / We're going home / Killing fields, The / Over my head / They might be giants / For the life of me / Dogs of Cairo (Not on album.) / Sleep in Monastir.
LP: SBKLP 7
MC: SBKTC 7

Vagina Dentata

MUSIC FOR HASHASINS.
LP: TOPY 012

Vai, Steve

FLEX-ABLE.
Tracks: / Little green men / Viv women / Lovers are crazy / Salamanders in the sun / Boy, The / Girl song / Attitude song / Call it sleep / Junkie / Bill's private parts / Next stop earth / There's something dead in here.
LP: GRUB 3
MC: TGRUB 3

PASSION AND WARFARE.
Tracks: / Liberty / Erotic nightmares / Animal, The / Answers / Riddle, The / Ballerina 12/24 / For the love of God / Audience is listening, The / I would love to / Blue powder / Greasy kids stuff / Alien water kiss / Sisters / Love secrets.
MC: TGRUB 17
LP: GRUB 17

Vain

NO RESPECT.
Tracks: / Secrets / Beat the bullet / Who's watching you / 1000 degrees / Aces / Smoke and shadows / No respect / Laws against love / Down for the 3rd time / Icy / Without you.
MC: ICT 9938
LP: ILPS 9938

Vakarelis, Janis

GERSHWIN (Vakarelis, Janis/RPO/ Henry Lewis).
Tracks: / Piano concerto / American in Paris, An.
MC: ZC RPO 8009
LP: RPO 8009

Val, Joe

BOUND TO RIDE (Val, Joe & New England Bluegrass Boys).
LP: ROUNDER 0109

COLD WIND (Val, Joe & New England Bluegrass Boys).
Tracks: / Cold wind / Wrong road again / You're running wild / Sea of regret / 'Neath a cold grey tomb of stone / Never again / When the cactus is in bloom / Mother's prayer / Stormy waters / I've been all around this world / Rocking alone in an old rocking chair.
LP: ROUNDER 0182
MC: ROUNDER 0182C

JOE VAL & THE NEW ENGLAND BLUEGRASS BOYS Vol. 2 (Val, Joe & New England Bluegrass Boys).
LP: ROUNDER 0025

NOT A WORD FROM HOME (Val, Joe & New England Bluegrass Boys).
LP: ROUNDER 0082

ONE MORNING IN MAY (Val, Joe & New England Bluegrass Boys).
LP: ROUNDER 0003

SPARKLING BROWN EYES (Val, Joe & New England Bluegrass Boys).
LP: ROUNDER 0152
MC: ROUNDER 0152C

Valdes, Chucho

LUCUMI.
LP: 15975

Valdor, Frank

SHALL WE DANCE....IN STRICT TEMPO RHYTHM.
LP: NR 1006

Vale, Jerry

GREATEST HITS: JERRY VALE.
Tracks: / Pretend you don't see her / Go chase a moonbeam / Prima donna / Go / Innamorata / And this is my beloved / Two purple shadows / You don't know me / If / Enchanted / And no one knows / Solitaire.
LP: CBS 32414

REQUESTS THE BIG BALLADS.
Tracks: / Don't tell my heart to stop loving you / She gives me love / Can't take my eyes off you / Love letters / This guy's in love with you / Look of love / By the time I get to Phoenix / You don't have to say you love me / What a wonderful world / I'll walk alone / Till there was you / It's easy to remember.
LP: 32314

SAME OLD MOON.
LP: CBS 32411

Valence, Ricky

RAINBOW.
Tracks: / Pure love / Rainbows / Try a little kindness / By the time I get to Phoenix / For the good times / Change the dial / Hello Mary Lou / Making excuses / Walking in the sunshine / Melba from Melbourne / Tell Laura I love her / Everything a man could ever need.
LP: BSS 324

Valens, Ritchie

GRAFFITI COLLECTION.
MC: GRMC 01

GREATEST HITS: RITCHIE VALENS.
Tracks: / La Bamba / Bluebirds over the mountain / In a Turkish town / Ooh my head / Paddiwack song / Stay beside me / Malaguena / Come on let's go / Donna / Fast freight / We belong together / That's my little Suzie / Hurry up / Little God.
LP: PL 90058
MC: PK 90058

HISTORY OF..., A.
LP: RNBC 2798

I REMEMBER RITCHIE VALENS His greatest hits.
LP: PTLS 1001

LA BAMBA.
LP: 2237724
MC: 2136724

RITCHIE VALENS.
Tracks: / La Bamba / Bluebirds over the mountain / Stay beside me / Big baby blues / Cry, cry, cry / Ritchie blues / Now you're gone / Hurry up / Paddy wack song.
LP: HAR 8535

ROCK L'IL DARLIN'.
LP: JOYS 254

Valente, Caterina

CATERINA VALENTE'S GREATEST HITS.
Tracks: / Malaguena / Poinciana / La Paloma / Peanut vendor / What a difference a day made / Breeze and I / La golondrina / Amapola / Estrellita / Besame mucho / My shawl.
LP: JASM 2206

CATERINA'S GREATEST HITS.
LP: SKL 4737

C'EST SI BON.
Tracks: / Musik musik musik / Kuss mich bitte, bitte, kuss mich (Kiss me honey, honey, kiss me) / Quando, quando / El condor pasa / As time goes by / Girl from Ipanema, The / Blueberry Hill / Volare / etc.
MC: 4.26652

EDITION 1 1954/55 Schwarze engel.
Tracks: / Ganz Paris traunt von der liebe / Schwarze engel / Bambino / Wenn es nacht wird in Paris / Ja in Madrid und Barcelona / O mama, O mamajo / Die damen welt in Chile / Malaguena / Baiao Bongo / Bablou / Breeze and I (Sung in English) / Jalousie / Just for you, just me / Istanbul / El mosouito / Malaguena.
LP: BFX 15291

EDITION 2 1955 Chanson d'amour.
Tracks: / Coco Polka / Casanova / Fiesta Cubana / Chanson d'amour / Oho aha / Es ist so schon bei dir nach den sternen / Chanson d'amour / Fiesta Cubana / Begin the beguine / Siboney / Fiesta Cubana / This must be wrong / Donne ta main et viens.
LP: BFX 15292

EDITION 3 (1955-56) - SING BABY SING.
Tracks: / Sing, baby, sing / Bim-bam-bim-bam-bina / Eventual / Andalucia / Pietro, zeeg mir dein herz / Mackie messer / Wir kamen in die strasse / My lonely lover / If hearts could talk / Temptation / This ecstasy / Way you love me, The / Bouquet des reves / Det ar nog fel / Chanson d'amour.
LP: BFX 15293

EDITION 4 (1955-56) - KOMM EIN BISSCHEN MIT NACH.
Tracks: / Bonjour Kathrin / Es geht besser, besser, besser / Eine frau aus Paris / Komm ein bisschen mit nach Italien / Wie war's / Steig in das traumboot der liebe / Gaucho / Gespenster blues / Bitte nach ihnen / Granada / Similau / There but for the grace of God / Look into my eyes / Bim-bam-bim-bam-bina / Sunny day / Oho aha / Una donna di parigi.
LP: BFX 15294

EDITION 5 1956 - O BILLY BOY.
Tracks: / Du bist musik / Das hab ich gleich gewusst / Daisy, crazy Daisy / Tschi-bam, tschi-bam-bo-bam-billa / Goldenen spangen, Die / O Billy boy / Ukulele, du musst weinen / Ja das sind die kleinen geschichten (hat sie gesagt) / Bonjour Catherine / Une femme dans Paris / Si tout etait fini / Les filles de Paris / L'amour defendu / Dans ma vie / La vie me pousse / Granada.
LP: BFX 15295

EDITION 6 1956 GRANADA.
Tracks: / El cumbanchero / Tres Clavelas / No te importa Saberaquarello do Brasil / Quiereme mucho / El Negro Zumbon (Anna) / Por un capricho / Quien sera / Mucho, mucho, mucho / Maria Christina / Ah si, ah si / Babalu / Granada / Piel canela.
LP: BFX 15296

EDITION 7 (1956/57) FLAMINGO.
Tracks: / Someday, sweetheart / Out of nowhere / Moonlight in Vermont / Flamingo / Where or when / Alone together / Poinciana / Nocturne for the blues / I'm in the market for you / Take me in your arms / When you walked out / In the still of the night / I remember April / Every time we say goodbye.
LP: BFX 15297

EDITION 8 1956/57 - MELODIA D'AMORE.
Tracks: / Das ist die Hafenmelodie / Du wirst alles vergessen / Ich war so gern bei dir / Adieu, adieu, du mein schones Samoa / Papa Piccolino / Melodia d'amore / Ou est tu ma joie-rendezvous / Moi, j'aime t'aimer / Complainte de Mackie / Si tout etait fini / Lorsque l'amour vient / La chanson de Piccolino / Bravo Caterina / Cos'e la nostalgia / Mai mai mai.
LP: BFX 15298

EDITION 9 1957 - BRAVO CATERINA.
Tracks: / Dich werd ich nie vergessen / Wenn in zwei herzen die liebe fallt / Frag mich nie,was Heimweh ist / Amadeo, ich will warten / Melodia d'amore / Tipitipitipso / Baia / Take me to your heart / Sait on jamais / Bravo Caterina / Ma valle descend du ciel / Amadeo, mon boheme / Tschi co calypso.
LP: BFX 15299

EDITION 10 1957/58 - MUSIK LIEGHT IN DER LUFT.
Tracks: / Musik liegt in der Luft / Spiel noch einmal furf mich, Habanero (einstimmig) / Eine nacht am Rio Grande / Bei dir ist alles anders / Ich lass dich niemals mehr allein / Spiel noch einmal fur mich Habanero / Du du du dei / Davon mochte ich mal traumen / Rot war der Mohn / Calypso haba-nero / Una notte al rio grande / Il sole mia fa cante / Tutto e diverso / Amedeo / E sempre bello / Pupa piccolina / Volevo un tango.
LP: BFX 15300

EDITION 11 1957/58 - WO MEIN SONNE SCHEINT.
Tracks: / Wo meine sonne scheint / Romeo / Roter wein und musik in toskanein / So war's im alten Mexico / Tambourin / Auf ja ma maika / Am golf von Mexico / Ich kann so lang nicht warten / Haiti cherie / Sognami, Pensami, Amami / Forsok med mej / Jeremi, voici l'heure / Une nuit a Rio Grande / Tschi bam / Toi, ma musique / Daisy, sacree Daisy.
LP: BFX 15301

EDITION 12 1958 - C'EST SI BON.
Tracks: / Side by side / Secret love / Stairway to the stars / All my love / Them there eyes / Tenderly / Yes my darling daughter / C'est si bon / You better go now / Kiss of fire / Over the rainbow / Golden earrings / Mine, mine, mine / Be mine tonight.
LP: BFX 15302

EDITION 13 1958 - ARRIBA.
Tracks: / Somebody bad stole de wedding bell(Englisch) / Casa dda lolouna aventura mas / Dos cruces / Noche de ronda / Cha cha cha flamenco / La mucura / El manicero / Copacabana / Aquellos ojos verdes / Quizas, quizas / Un poquito de tu amor.
LP: BFX 15303

GOLDEN HOUR OF CATERINA VALENTE.
Tracks: / Malaguena / Breeze and I / I won't last a day without you / We've only just begun / You got me, I got yoiu / My little friend / Day alone with you / I'm going back / Canto de Ossanha / True love / Laughter in the rain / September is a long time / Love music / What I did for love / Falling in love with the wind / Be my love / 59th Street Bridge song / Put a little love away / Love said goodbye / Love will come again.
LP: GH 677

HIER BIN ICH- HIER BLEIB ICH... UND ABENDS IN DI Original filmmusik (Valente, Caterina/Bill Haley).
Tracks: / Immer wieder neu / Mal sehn, Kapitan / Der gondoliere sang nie mehr so schon / Pardon Madame / Ein bisschen pompadour (mademoiselle) / Spiel noch einmal fur mich, habanero / Bei dir ist alles Anders / Ich lass dich niemals mehr allein / Ich lass dich niemals mehr allein (instrumental) / Eine

nacht am Rio Grande / Djiko / Musik liegt in der luft / Kleine revue.
LP: BFX 15304

Valenti, Joe

WITH A SONG IN MY HEART (Valenti, Joe & Bill Baker).
Tracks: / With a song in my heart / Love for sale / Here's that rainy day / Hanalei / There will never be another you / Sabor a mi' (be true to me) / It might as well be Spring / L.A. has happened to me / Private eyefull / Pick yourself up.
MC: OUTSTANDING 26

Valentin, Dave

FLUTE JUICE.
Tracks: / Crotona Park / Loquita (crazy lady) / Flute juice / Latin jazz dance / Times long gone / Footprints / Merle the pearl / Crotona Park (reprise).
LP: GRPA 1004
MC: GRPC 1004

JUNGLE GARDEN.
Tracks: / Awakening / Oasis / Bones / Love light in flight / Jungle garden / Very nice indeed / I loves you Porgy / Eighty-one / Tabasco.
LP: GRP 91016
MC: GRPC 1016

KALAHARI.
LP: GRP 91009
MC: C 1009

LIGHT STRUCK.
Tracks: / Miss V. / One thing I can't change is my heart, The / Grand slam / Village, The / AM-FM / Chris-cross / Prince of wands / Prelude to a kiss.
LP: GRP 91028
MC: GRPM 91028

LIVE AT THE BLUE NOTE.
LP: GR 9568
MC: GRC 9568

MIND TIME.
LP: GRP 91043
MC: GRPM 91043

TWO AMIGOS (Valentin, Dave & Herbie Mann).
Tracks: / Bronx bad boys / Moonlight walk / Jesse's samba / First date / Rambo the cat / Two amigos / Old hill (morro velho) / Savana / Obsession.
LP: GRP 96061
MC: GRP 96064

Valentine Brothers

PICTURE THIS.
Tracks: / Somebody took my love / No better love / She loves me / In my time / Cut backs / Used to be lovers / What you gonna do with love? / Ladies' delight / Funk attack / Starship.
LP: AML 3123
MC: TCAML 3123

Valentine, Dickie

VERY BEST OF DICKIE VALENTINE, THE (Greatest Hits).
Tracks: / All the time and ev'rywhere / That lovely weekend / Finger of suspicion / King of Dixieland / I could have told you / Blossom fell, A / In a golden coach / Mother Nature and Father Time / Where are you tonight / I wonder / Birth of the blues / Mister Sandman / Chapel of the roses / No such luck / Christmas alphabet / You belong to me / Christmas Island / Clown who cried, The / I see you again every night (CD only.) / Snowbound for Christmas (CD only.) / One I love (belongs to somebody else) (CD only.) / Old pi-anna rag (CD only.) / Mister Sandman (CD only.) / Star you wished upon last night (CD only.) / Kiss to build a dream on, A (CD only.).
LP: RFL 40

VOICE, THE.
Tracks: / Just in time / Puttin' on the style / Song of the trees / Blossom fell, A / I could have told you / Get well soon / All the time and ev'rywhere / Broken wings / Ma'moiselle / In a golden coach / Voice, The / It all started with your kiss / Chapel of the roses / Hello Mrs Jones (is Mary there) / No such luck / Star you wished upon last night, The / That lovely weekend / You too can be a dreamer / Hand of friendship, The / Convicted.
LP: PLE 528
MC: TC-PLE 528

WORLD OF....
Tracks: / All the time and ev'rywhere / Blossom fell, A / East of the sun / Endless / King of Dixieland / Finger of suspicion / Song of the trees / Birth of the blues / Mister sandman / Kiss to build a dream on, A / Clown who cried, The.
LP: SPA 171

Valentine, Kid Thomas

ALGIERS STOMPERS.
LP: GHB 80

AT KOHLMAN'S TAVERN.
LP: NOR 7201

AT MOULIN ROUGE.
LP: CEN 14

AT THE OLD GRIST MILL (Valentine, Kid Thomas & His New Orleans Joymakers).
LP: GHB 73

CITY OF A MILLION DREAMS (see Lewis, George) (Valentine, Kid Thomas/ George Lewis).

ECHOES OF NEW ORLEANS VOL.2.
LP: SLP 212

HIS NEW ORLEANS JAZZ BAND.
LP: F 1016

IN DENMARK VOL.1 (Valentine, Kid Thomas & Louis Nelson).
LP: SLP 241

IN SCANDINAVIA.
LP: RARITIES 16

JAZZOLOGY POLL WINNERS 1964 (Thomas,Kid/George Lewis/Don Ewell).
LP: GHB 200

KID THOMAS AND LOUIS NELSON IN DENMARK 2 (Valentine, Kid Thomas & Louis Nelson).
LP: SLP 246

KID THOMAS' DIXIELAND BAND (Recorded New Orleans 1968) (Valentine, Kid Thomas & His Dixieland Band).
LP: NOLA LP 14
MC: TC 014

KID THOMAS, EMANUEL PAUL AND BARRY MARTYN.
LP: 77LA12/26

KID THOMAS & THE NEW BLACK EAGLE JAZZ BAND (Valentine, Kid Thomas & The New Black Eagle Jazz Band).
LP: GHB 145

KID THOMAS VALENTINE (With Louis Nelson/New Iberia Stompers) (Valentine, Kid Thomas/Louis Nelson/ New Iberia Stompers).
MC: TCS 7

KID THOMAS VALENTINE'S CREOLE JAZZ BAND.
LP: 77LA 12/9

KID THOMAS/RAYMOND BURKE AND THE ORIGINAL ALGIER (Valentine, Kid Thomas & Raymond Burke).
LP: JCE 30

LOVE SONGS OF THE NILE.
LP: GHB 183

NEW ORLEANS JAZZ.
LP: ARHOOLIE 1016

NIGHT AT THE 100 CLUB, A (Valentine, Kid Thomas/Louis Nelson/New Iberia Stompers).
LP: LPS 7

ON STAGE (Valentine, Kid Thomas & The Algiers Stompers).
LP: GHB 53

PORTRAIT OF KID THOMAS VALENTINE.
LP: SLP 233

RAGTIME STOMPERS (Valentine, Kid Thomas & George Lewis).
LP: GHB 5

ROCKIN' THIS JOINT TONITE (Valentine, Kid Thomas, Floyd Dixon & Ace Holder).
Tracks: / Rockin' this joint tonite / You are an angel / Wail baby wail / Lookie there / Cozy lounge blues / Five long years / Don't leave me baby / Late freight twist / Me quieres / Tell me tell me / Leave me woman alone / Happy anniversary / Wabba Suzy Q.
LP: JSP 1002

WITH SAMMY RIMINGTON 1981 (Valentine, Kid Thomas & Sammy Rimington).
LP: DTS 033
LP: GHB 291

Valentine Music Group

ONCE UPON A FAIRY TALE.
Tracks: / Jack and the beanstalk / Tom Thumb / Dick Whittington / Rumplestiltskin / Goldilocks and the three bears / Beauty and the beast.
MC: TCEME 6507
LP: EME 6507

Valentino

ANNIVERSARY.
Tracks: / More / And I love you so / Side by side medley / Love / Anniversary Waltz / Always / Let me call you sweetheart / Only girl in the world,The(You belong to me) / Can't help falling in love / Man and woman / Made me love you / Evergreen / True love.
LP: JPR 1058

AROUND THE WORLD.
Tracks: / Around the world / Sideways / Charmaine / Under the bridges of Paris / Yesterday once more / Irish reels / She / I do like to be beside the seaside / All the nice girls love a sailor / Lily of Laguna / Mother Kelly's doorstep / Aloha-oe / Piccadilly dawn / Penalty / Dambusters march / Viva Espana.
LP: JPR 1056

BEST OF VALENTINO.
Tracks: / Telstar / Warsaw concerto / More / Never on a Sunday / Arrivederci Roma / Love is like a violin / Intermezzo / Lara's theme / Rodrigo's guitar concerto de aranjuez / Love story theme / Days of Pearly Spencer / Harry Lime theme / Hungarian goulash / Cobblers / Exodus / Lawrence of Arabia.
LP: JPR 1055

INCREDIBLE SOUNDS, THE.
Tracks: / El bimbo / Good, the bad and the ugly, The / Morning has broken / Toccata / Hawaiian wedding song / Zorba's dance / Star wars / Load of old Cobras / Zither medley / Barrel organ medley / Czardas / If I never sang another song / It's now or never.
LP: JPR 1070

MON ETOILE.
LP: ROSE 101

TO THE ONE I LOVE.
Tracks: / There's a kind of hush/Till there was you / Change your mind / Killing me softly with her song / Don't you forget it / You don't have to say / All my love (with all of your heart) / Love me tender / My honeysuckle / Love is / When I'm sixty four / Feelings.
LP: JPR 1059
MC: Unknown

VALENTINO.
LP: ROSE 53

VALENTINO SHOW, THE.
Tracks: / One two three / Sting, The / Sheba / Alley cat / Colonel Bogey / Scottish medley / Spanish eyes / Smoke, The / Danny boy / Lyne / Last night at the proms (medley) / Old piano roll blues, The / Strollin' / Finale.
LP: JPR 1054

Valeri, Michele

DINOSAUR ROCK (Valeri, Michele & Michael Stein).
MC: 1739

Valez, Marth

ESCAPE FROM BABYLON.
Tracks: / Money man / There you are / Wild bird / Disco night / Bend down low / Happiness / Come on in / Get up stand up.
LP: SRK 6019
LP: 910 3256

Valiant Sailor

SONGS & BALLADS OF NELSON'S NAVY.
LP: 12TS 232

Valida

HIGH HAT TRUMPET & RHYTHM With Billy Mason & His Orchestra.
Tracks: / I wish I were twins / I can't dance / It had to be you / Savage in me / Imagination / Sing you sinners / Whisper sweet / Sing / Singin' in the rain / Until the real thing comes along / High hat trumpet and rhythm / I want a lot of love / Take care of you for me / Lovable and sweet / I must have that man / You're not the kind.
LP: SH 309

SWING IS THE THING.
LP: SH 354

Vallee, Rudy

HEIGH-HO EVERYBODY, THIS IS RUDY VALLEE.
Tracks: / Heigh ho everybody, heigh ho / Betty co-ed / If I had a girl like you / Let's do it / I still remember / Salaaming the rajah / My heart belongs to the girl who belongs to somebody else / One in the world, The / I'll be reminded of you / You'll do it someday, so why not now? / Kitty from Kansas City / That's when I learned to love you / Outside / Dream sweetheart / Love made a gypsy out of me / Perhaps / Little kiss each morning a little kiss each night, A / Verdict is life with you, The / Lover come back to me / Stein song, The.
LP: AJA 5009
MC: ZC AJA 5009

RUDY VALLEE AND HIS CONNECTICUT YANKEES (Vallee, Rudy/his Connecticut Yankees).
Tracks: / Deep night / Little kiss each morning a little kiss each night, A / I love the moon / M-a-r-y I love you / Stein song, The / St. Louis blues / Kitty from Kansas city / How come you do me like you do / Betsy co-ed / Would you like to take a walk? / Ninety-nine out of a hundred wanna be loved / When Yuba plays the rumba on the tuba / This is the missus / Life is just a bowl of cherries.
LP: HDL 105
MC: CHDL 105

RUDY VALLEE: ON THE AIR.
Tracks: / We did it before and we can do it again / I don't want to walk without you.
LP: TOTEM 1027

SING FOR YOUR SUPPER.
Tracks: / Naturally / Flying down to Rio / Sing for your supper / Stranger in Paree, A / Vieni vieni / Whiffenpoof song, The / Nasty man / You and me that used to be, The / Drunkard song, The (There is a Tavern in the town) / I'm just a vagabond lover / Me minus you / Latin Quarter, The / Orchids in the moonlight / Life is a song / This can't be love / Ha-cha-cha / I wanna go back to Bali / Goodnight, my love.
LP: CMS 005
MC: CMSC 005

Vallelly, Brian

SONG OF CHANTER (see Davis, Paul) (Vallelly, Brian & Paul Davis).

Vallely, Finton

FINTAN VALLELY.
LP: SHAN 29019

Valley Folk

ALL BELLS IN PARADISE.
LP: 12T 192

Valley Girl

VALLEY GIRL (Original soundtrack) (Various artists).
LP: AVAL 5

Valley Girls

NAVY LARK (see Deane, Geoff) (Valley Girls & Geoff Deane).

Valli, Frankie

20 GREATEST HITS: FRANKIE VALLI & FOUR SEASONS (Valli, Frankie & Four Seasons).
Tracks: / Sherry / Big girls don't cry / Walk like a man / Dawn (go away) / Rag doll / Stay / Let's hang on / Working my way back to you / Opus 17 (Don't you worry about me) / I've got you under my skin / C'mon Marianne / You're ready now / Who loves you / Dec '63 (oh what a night) / Silver star / My eyes adored you / Swearing to God / Fallen angel / Grease / Can't take my eyes off you.
LP: PLAT 4902
MC: PLAC 4902

COLLECTION: FOUR SEASONS (Valli, Frankie & Four Seasons).
Tracks: / Who loves you / Let's hang on / Working my way back to you / Dawn / Walk like a man / My eyes adored you / You're ready now / Swearin' to God / Opus 17 / Can't take my eyes off you / Rag doll / Sherry / Big girls don't cry / Dec' 63 / I've got you under my skin / Silver star / Grease / Beggin'.
LP: STAR 2320
MC: STAC 2320

FRANKIE VALLI & THE FOUR SEASONS (Valli, Frankie & Four Seasons).
2LP: NE 1177 AB
MCSET: CE 2177 AB

HEAVEN ABOVE ME.
LP: MCF 3081

REUNITED LOVE (Valli, Frankie & Four Seasons).
Tracks: / Who loves you / Our day will come / Save it for me / Rag doll / Dawn / Let's hang on / Can't take my eyes off you / Fallen angel / Silver star / Slip away / December 1963 / Swearin' to God / My eyes adored you / Workin' my way back to you / Will you still love me / Opus 17 / Spend the night in love / Heaven must have sent you / Grease / Sherry / Walk like a man / Big girls don't cry / Bye bye baby.
2LP: K 66098
MC: K4 66098

STREETFIGHTER.
LP: MCF 3316
MC: MCFC 3316

VERY BEST OF FRANKIE VALLI.
Tracks: / Grease / Can't take my eyes off you / My eyes adored you / Swearing to God.
LP: MCL 1606
LP: MCF 3053

Valmouth

VALMOUTH (Original cast) (Various artists).
LP: TER 1019
MC: ZCTER 1019
LP: FBLP 8102

Valotti, Willi

AKKORDEON ZAUBER.
Tracks: / Tanzended finger / Jurafahrt / D'Gass Ab / Czardas / Avec plaisir /

Flurina / Frieda's traum / Retour des hirondelles / Dizzy fingers / Ole guapa / Brijou / Schlitzaugli / Zeughauskeller - Marsch.
LP: 099/098 9

Vamp

RICH DON'T ROCK, THE.
MC: 781974 4
LP: 781974 1

Van Beethoven, Eugene

SIN FUNNY.
LP: SAVE 088

Van Clark, Walter

OX-BOW INCIDENT (see under Ox-Bow Incident (bk)) (Fonda, Henry (nar)).

Van Dam, Jose

MUSIC TEACHER, THE (Van Dam, Jose & Others).
MC: PTLC 1109

Van Damme, Art

ART VAN DAMME AND FRIENDS.
Tracks: / Let yourself down / Satin doll / I didn't know what time it was / Cheek to cheek / Rosetta.
LP: NLP 107

Van Den Broeck, Rob

FREE FAIR (Van Denbroeck, R/D. Vennick/E. Ineke/H. Emmery/R. Burnet).
LP: SJP 122

HEAVY DUTY.
LP: SJP 220

Van Der Graaf

GODBLUFF.
Tracks: / Undercover man, The / Scorched earth / Arrow / Sleepwalkers, The.
LP: CHC 13
MC: CHCMC 13

H TO HE, WHO AM THE ONLY ONE.
Tracks: / Killer / With no door / Emperor in his war room / Lost / Pioneers over C.
LP: 6321 126

LEAST WE CAN DO IS WAVE TO EACH OTHER, THE.
Tracks: / Darkness / Refugees / White hammer / Whatever would Robert have said? / Out of my book / After the flood.
LP: CHC 5
MC: CHCMC 5
LP: CAS 1007

NOW AND THEN.
Tracks: / Liquidator / Gentlemen prefer blondes / Main slide, The / Spooks / Saigon roulette / Tropic of conversation / Tarzan the epilogue.
LP: THBL 042

PAWN HEARTS.
Tracks: / Lemmings (including Cog) / Man erg / Pictures/Lighthouse / Eyewitness / S.H.M. / Kosmos tours / Clot thickens, The / Land's end / We go now / Presence of the night / (Custards) last stand.
LP: CHC 54

PAWN HEARTS/STILL LIFE.
Tracks: / Lemmings (including Cog) / Man-erg / Eyewitness (Part 1 of Plague of Lighthouse Keepers) / Pictures/ Lighthouse (Part 2 of Plague of Lighthouse Keepers) / S.H.M. (Part 4 of Plague of Lighthouse Keepers) / Presence of the night (Part 5 of Plague of lighthouse Keepers) / Kosmos tours (Part 6 of Plague of Lighthouse Keepers) / (Custards) last stand (Part 7 of Plague of Lighthouse Keepers) / Clot thickens, The (Part 8 of Plague of Lighthouse Keepers) / Land's end (Part 9 of Plague of Lighthouse Keepers) / We go now (Part 10 of Plague of Lighthouse Keepers) / Pilgrims / Still life / La Rossa / My room (waiting for wonderland) / Childlike faith in childhood's end.
MCSET: CASMC 106

QUIET ZONE PLEASURE DOME.
Tracks: / Lizard play / Habit of the broken heart, The / Siren song / Last frame / Wave, The / Cat's eye, yellow fever (running) / Sphinx in the face, The / Chemical world / Sphinx returns, The.
LP: CHC 32
MC: CHCMC 32

REPEAT PERFORMANCE.
Tracks: / Afterwards / Refugees / Boat of millions of years / W / White hammer / Necromancer / Emperor in his war room / Man-erg.
LP: BG 003

STILL LIFE.
Tracks: / Pilgrims / Still life / La Rossa / My room (waiting for wonderland) / Childlike faith in childhood's end.
LP: CHC 55

TIME VAULTS.
Tracks: / Liquidator / Rift valley / Tarzan / Coil night / Time vaults / Drift / Roncevaux / It all went red / Faint and forsaken / Black room.
LP: DM 003

WORLD RECORD.
Tracks: / When she comes / Place to survive, A / Masks / Meurglys 111 (The songwriters guild) / Wondering.
LP: CAS 1120
LP: CHC 62

Van der Zee, Karen

SECRET SORROW, A (Seaward, Lesley).
MC: PMB 016

Van Dusen, George

IT'S PARTY TIME AGAIN (LP).
Tracks: / It's party time again / Izzy izzy izzy / Yodelling sailor, The / Poloski's Russian party / It's holiday time again / Come along Lisa / Let's have a knees up / It's party time again (reprise) / Murphy's wedding day / Holiday time is jollity time / Wee drop of scotch, A / Jigging with George / Yiddisher yodeller, The / Yodelling working man, The / Day O Reilly got wed, The.
LP: BTLP 123
MC: BTLC 123

Van Duser, Guy

FINGER-STYLE GUITAR SOLOS.
LP: ROUNDER 3021
MC: ROUNDER 3021C

GET YOURSELF A NEW BROOM (Van Duser, Guy/Novick, Billy).
LP: ROUNDER 3027

GOT THE WORLD ON A STRING.
LP: ROUNDER 3081
MC: ROUNDER 3081C

RAISIN' THE RENT (Van Duser, Guy/ Novick, Billy).
LP: ROUNDER 3071
MC: ROUNDER 3071C

STRIDE GUITAR.
LP: ROUNDER 3059
MC: ROUNDER 3059C

THESE 'N THAT 'N THOSE (Van Duser, Guy/Novick, Billy).
LP: ROUNDER 3091

Van Dyke, Jost

CARNIVAL IN ST. THOMAS.
LP: ROUNDER 5002

Van Dyke, Leroy

AUCTIONEER, THE.
Tracks: / Auctioneer, The / Pocketbook song / My good mind went bad on me / Honky tonk song / Leather jacket / I fell in love with a pony tail / One heart / Heartbreak cannonball / I'm movin' on / Chicken shack.
LP: CH 99

ORIGINAL AUCTIONEER, THE.
Tracks: / Auctioneer, The / I fell in love with a pony tail / Leather jacket / I'm movin' on / My good mind (went bad on me) / Heartbreak cannonball / Chicken shack / Poor boy / What this old work needs / Every time I ask my heart / Pocketbook song / Down at the south end of town / Honky tonk song / One heart.
LP: BFX 15270

Van Enkhuizen, Joe

BACK ON THE SCENE (Enkhuizen, Joe Van Quartet).
LP: CRISS 1013

Van Eps, George

13 STRINGS (See Under Alden, Howard) (Van Eps, George & Howard Alden).

MELLOW GUITAR "Classic performances by the master of the five-.
Tracks: / I'll remember April / What is this thing called love? / Let's do it / Yesterdays / They can't take that away from me / 'S wonderful / Have you met Miss Jones? / Tango el bongo / Dancing on the ceiling / Lost canyon / Boy next door, The / I never knew.
LP: COR 121

Van Halen

1984.
Tracks: / 1984 / Jump / Panama / Top Jimmy / Drop dead legs / Hot for teacher / I'll wait / Girl gone bad / House of pain.
LP: 923985 1
MC: 923985 4

5150.
Tracks: / Good enough / Why can't this be love / Get up / Dreams / Summer nights / Best of both worlds / Love walks in / "5150" / Inside.
LP: W 5150
MC: W 5150C

DIVER DOWN.
Tracks: / Where have all the good times gone / Hang 'em high / Cathedral / Secrets / Intruder / Oh pretty woman / Dancing in the street / Little guitar (intro) / Little guitars / Big bad Bill is sweet William now / Bull bug, The / Happy trails.
LP: K 57003
MC: K4 57003

FAIR WARNING.
Tracks: / Mean street / Dirty movies / Sinners swing / Hear about it later / Unchained / Push comes to shove / So this is love / Sunday afternoon in the park / One foot out of the door.
LP: K 56899
MC: K4 56899

OU812.
Tracks: / Mine all mine / When it's love / A.F.U. (naturally wired) / Cabo wabo / Source of infection / Feels so good / Come back and finish what you started / Black and blue / Sucker in a 3 piece.
LP: WX 177
MC: WX 177C

VAN HALEN.
Tracks: / You really got me / Jamie's cryin' / On fire / Runnin' with the Devil / I'm the one / Ain't talkin' bout love / Little dreamer / Feel your love tonight / Atomic punk / Eruption / Ice cream man.
LP: K 56470
MC: K4 56470
LP: WX 420
MC: WX 420C

VAN HALEN I & II (Double play cassette).
Tracks: / Runnin' with the devil / Eruption / You really got me / Ain't talkin' 'bout love / I'm the one / Jamie's cryin' / Atomic punk / Feel your love tonight / Little dreamer / Ice cream man / On fire / You're no good / Dance the night away / Somebody get me a doctor / Bottom's up / Outta love again / Light up the sky / Spanish fly / D.O.A. / Women in love / Beautiful girls.
MC: K4 66104

VAN HALEN II.
Tracks: / You're no good / Dance the night away / Somebody get me a doctor / Bottoms up / Outta love again / Light up the sky / D.O.A. / Women in love / Spanish fly / Beautiful girls.
LP: K 56616
MC: K4 56616

WOMEN AND CHILDREN FIRST.
Tracks: / Tora tora / Cradle will rock / Romeo delight / Fools / In a simply rhyme / Could this be magic? / Loss of control / Take your whiskey home / Every body wants some.
LP: K 56793
MC: K4 56793

Van Hove, Fred

KKWTT.
Tracks: / Kkwtt: 1re partie / 2e partie / 3e partie (marche finale).
LP: NATO 355

Van Riper, Earl

DETROITS GRAND PIANO MAN w. Dave Young (Van Riper, Earl & Marcus Belgrave).
LP: PARKWOOD 109

Van Ronk, Dave

HESITATION BLUES.
Tracks: / Samson and Delilah / Fixin' to die / Long John / Motherless children / I buyed me a little dog / Poor Lazarus / Cruel ship's captain, The / Kansas City blues / House carpenter / Fair and tender ladies / Hesitation blues / Hang me, oh hang me / Come back baby / Sprig of thyme / Silver dagger / Death letter blues.
LP: WIK 84

SUNDAY STREET.
LP: PHILO 1036

YOUR BASIC DAVE VAN RONK.
LP: SNTF 885

Van Schaik, Oattes

LIMIT, THE.
LP: PRT 26076
MC: 40 26076

Van Senger, Dominik

FIRST, THE.
LP: VBR 20071

Van Shelton, Ricky

RVS III.
LP: 4663481
MC: 4663484

WILD-EYED DREAM.
Tracks: / Ultimately fine / Crime of passion / Life turned her that way / I don't care / Don't we all have the right / Wild-eyed dream / Baby I'm ready / Somebody lied / Crazy over you / Working man blues.
LP: 4611201
MC: 4611204

Van Tieghem, David

STRANGE CARGO.
Tracks: / Strange cargo / Volcano diving / Hell or high water / Eye of the beholder / Flying hearts / They drive by night / Ghost writer theme, The / Particle ballet / Yesterday island / Carnival of souls / She's gone.
LP: 210.073
MC: 410.073

Van Veen, Herman

FOURTEEN SONGS.
Tracks: / Stay with me / Be my lonesome / Security / Home and dry / To the dogs / That tender kind of feeling / Afternoon departure / All at sea / Power of habit / Splitting up / Heroes / Girls of days gone by / Asylum / Waterlogged clowns.
LP: EPC 84256

Van Zandt, Johnny

NO MORE DIRTY DEALS.
Tracks: / No more dirty deals / Coming home / 634-5789 / Put my trust in you / Only the strong survive / Hard luck story / Stand your ground / Never too late / Keep on rolling / Standing in the darkness.
LP: 2391472

ROUND TWO (Van Zandt, Johnny Band).
Tracks: / Right or wrong / Standing in the falling rain / Yesterday's gone / Let there be music / Keep our love alive / Night time lady / Drive my car / Shotdown / Cold hearted woman / Play my music.
LP: 2391 515

Van Zandt, Townes

AT MY WINDOW.
Tracks: / Snowin' on Raton / Blue wind blew / At my window / For the sake of the song / Ain't leaving your love / Buckskin stallion blues / Little sundance / Still lookin' for you / Gone gone blues / Catfish song, The.
LP: HLD 003
LP: SH 1020

DELTA MOMMA BLUES.
Tracks: / FFV / Delta momma blues / Only him or me / Turnstyled, junkpiled / Tower song / Come tomorrow / Brand new companion / Rake / Nothin'.
LP: TOM 7013
LP: LIK 25
MC: TCLIK 25

FLYIN' SHOES.
Tracks: / Loretta / No place to fall / Flyin' shoes / Who do you love / When she don't need me / Dollar bill blues / Rex's blues / Pueblo waltz / Brother flower / Snake song.
MC: TCLIK 59
LP: LIK 59

FOR THE SAKE OF THE SONG.
LP: PYS 40001

HIGH LOW AND IN BETWEEN.
Tracks: / Two hands / You are not needed now / Greensboro woman / Highway kind / Standin' / No deal / To live is to fly / When he offers his hand / Mr. Gold and Mr. Mud / Blue Ridge mountains / High low and in between.
LP: LIK 50
MC: TCLIK 50
LP: TOM 7012

LATE, GREAT TOWNES VAN ZANDT, THE.
Tracks: / No lonesome tune / Sad Cinderella / German mustard / Don't let the sunshine fool ya' / Honky tonkin' / Snow don't fall / Fraulein / Pancho and Lefty / If I needed you / Silver ships of Andilar / Heavenly houseboat blues.
LP: TOM 7001
LP: ED 293
MC: TCLIK 49
LP: LIK 49

LIVE AND OBSCURE.
Tracks: / Dollar bill blues / Many a fine lady / Pueblo waltz / Talking Thunderbird blues / Loretta / Snake Mountain blues / Waitin' around to die / Tecumseh Valley / Pancho and Lefty / You are not needed now.
LP: HLD 004

LIVE AT THE OLD QUARTER, HOUSTON, TEXAS.
Tracks: / Announcement / Pancho and Lefty / Mr Mudd and Mr Gold / Don't you take it too bad / Tow girls / Fraternity blue / If I needed you / Brand new companion / White freightliner blues / To live is to fly / She came and she touched me / Talking thunderbird blues / Rex's blues / Nine pound hammer / For the sake of the song / No place to fall / Loretta / Kathleen / Tower song / Waiting 'round to die / Tecumseh valley / Lungs / Only him or me.
2LP: LIKD 57
MCSET: TCLIKD 57

OUR MOTHER THE MOUNTAIN.
Tracks: / Be here to love me / Kathleen / She came and she touched me / Like a summer Thursday / Our mother the mountain / Second lovers song / St. John the gambler / Tecumseh valley / Snake mountain blues / My proud mountains / Why she's acting this way.
LP: . . . . **LIK 17**
MC: . . . . **TCLIK 17**

TOWNES VAN ZANDT.
Tracks: / For the sake of the song / Columbine / Waiting around to die / Don't take it too bad / Colorado girl / Lungs / I'll be here in the morning / Fare thee well, Miss Carousel / (Quick silver day dreams of) Maria / None but the rain.
LP: . . . . **LIK 32**
MC: . . . . **TCLIK 32**

TOWNES/LIVE IN THE LATIN QUARTER.
MC: . . . . **TCAD 21**

Vandals

SLIPPERY WHEN ILL.
LP: . . . . **GWLP 39**

WHEN IN ROME DO AS THE VANDALS.
LP: . . . . **HYBLP 3**
LP: . . . . **NT 884**

Vandenbos, Conny

HET BESTE VAN CONNY VANDENBOS.
LP: **022-58078**
MC: **222-58078**

Vandenburg

ALIBI.
Tracks: / All the way / Pedal to the metal / Once in a lifetime / Voodoo / Dressed to kill / Fighting against the world / How long / Prelude mortale / Alibi / Kamikaze.
LP: **790 295-1**
MC: **790 295-4**

BEST OF VANDENBURG.
Tracks: / Your love is in vain / Nothing to lose / Rock on / Burning heart / Wait / Welcome to the club / Prelude mortale / Alibi / Different worlds / Pedal to the metal / Fighting against the world.
LP: . . . . **K 790 928 1**
MC: . . . . **K 790 928 4**

HEADING FOR A STORM.
Tracks: / Friday night / Welcome to the club / Time will tell / Different worlds / This is war / I'm on fire / Heading for a storm / Rock on / Waiting for the night.
LP: **790121 1**

VANDENBURG.
Tracks: / Your love is in vain / Back on my feet / Wait / Burning heart / Ready for you / Too late / Nothing to lose / Lost in a city / Out in the streets.
LP: . . . . **K 50904**

Vander, Christian

TRISTAN ET ISEULT.
LP: **90171**

Vandross, Luther

ANY LOVE (ALBUM).
Tracks: / I wonder / She won't talk to me / I know you want to / Come back / Any love / Love won't let me wait / Are you gonna love me / For you to love / Second time around.
LP: **4629081**
MC: **4629084**

BEST OF LUTHER VANDROSS, THE (Best Of Love, The).
Tracks: / Searching / Glow of love, The / Never too much / If this world were mine / Bad boy / Having a party / Since I lost my baby / Promise me / Til my baby comes home / In only for one night / Creepin' superstar / Until you come back to me / Stop to love / So amazing / There's nothing better than love / Give me the reason / Any love / I really didn't mean it / Love won't let me wait / Treat you right / Here and now.
LP: **4658011**
MC: **4658014**

BUSY BODY.
Tracks: / I wanted your love / Busy body / I'll let you slide / Make me a believer / For the sweetness of your love / How many times can we say goodbye / Superstar / Until you come back to me.
LP: . . . . **EPC 25608**
MC: **40 25608**

BUSY BODY.
LP: **460183 1**
MC: **460183 4**

FOREVER, FOR ALWAYS, FOR LOVE.
Tracks: / Bad boy/Having a party / You're the sweetest one / Since I lost my baby / Forever, for always, for love / Better love / Promise me / She loves me back / Once you know how.
LP: **4630011**
MC: **4630014**
LP: . . . . **EPC 25013**

GIVE ME THE REASON.
Tracks: / Stop to love / See me / I gave it up (when I fell in love) / So amazing / Give me the reason / There's nothing better than love / I really didn't mean it / Because it's really love / Anyone who had a heart.
LP: **4501341**
MC: **4501344**

LUTHER VANDROSS.
Tracks: / Bad boy / Having a party / Since I lost my baby / She loves me back / House is not a home, A / Never too much / She's a super lady / Sugar and spice (I found me a girl) / Better love / You're the sweetest one.
LP: . . . . **EPC 25220**
MC: **40 25520**
LP: **4606971**
MC: **4606974**

LUTHER VANDROSS - THE 12" TAPE.
Tracks: / Never too much / I gave it up (when I fell in love) / Stop to love / It's over now / Never too much.
MC: **4689864**

NEVER TOO MUCH.
Tracks: / Never too much / Sugar and spice (I found me a girl) / Don't you know that? / I've been working / She's a super lady / You stopped loving me / House is not a home, A.
LP: . . . . **EPC 32807**
MC: **40 32807**
LP: . . . . **EPC 85275**

NIGHT I FELL IN LOVE, THE.
Tracks: / Till my baby comes home / Night I fell in love, The / If only for one night / Creepin' / It's over now / Wait for love / My sensitivity (Gets in the way) / Other side of the world.
LP: . . . . **EPC 26387**
MC: **40 26387**
LP: **4624891**
MC: **4624894**

POWER OF LOVE.
Tracks: / She doesn't mind / Power of love/ Love power / I'm gonna start today / Rush, The / I want the night to stay / Don't want to be a fool / I can tell you that / Sometimes it's only love / Emotional love / I who have nothing.
LP: **4680121**
MC: **4680124**

Vaness, Theo

BAD BAD BOY.
Tracks: / As long as it's love / Sentimentally it's you / Love me now / No romance / Keep on dancing / I'm a bad bad boy.
LP: . . . . **EPC 83678**

Vangelis

ALBEDO 0.39.
Tracks: / Pulstar / Freefall / Mare tranquilitatis / Main sequence / Sword of Orion, The / Alpha / Nucleogenesis (part 2) / Albedo 0.39.
LP: . . . . **PL 70088**
MC: . . . . **PK 70088**
LP: . . . . **RS 1080**
LP: . . . . **NL 74208**
MC: . . . . **NK 74208**

ANTARCTICA (Original Soundtrack).
Tracks: / Antarctica, Theme from / Antarctica echoes / Kinematic song of white / Life of Antarctica / Memory of Antarctica / Other side of Antarctica / Deliverance.
LP: **815 732-1**
MC: **815 732-4**

BEAUBOURG.
Tracks: / Beaubourg (Part 1) / Beaubourg (Part 2).
LP: . . . . **FA 3168**
MC: . . . . **TCFA 3168**
MC: . . . . **NK 70010**
MC: . . . . **NK 74516**

BEST OF VANGELIS.
Tracks: / Pulstar / Spiral / To the unknown man / Albedo 0.39 / Bacchanale / Aries / Beaubourg excerpt / So long long ago so clear.
LP: . . . . **PL 70011**
MC: . . . . **PK 70011**

CHARIOTS OF FIRE (Film Soundtrack).
Tracks: / Titles / Five circles / Abraham's theme / Eric's theme / 100 metres / Jerusalem / Chariots of fire.
LP: . . . . **POLS 1026**
MC: . . . . **POLDC 5160**
LP: . . . . **POLD 5160**

CHARIOTS OF FIRE (BOX SET).
Tracks: / Five circles / Abraham's theme / Eric's theme / 100 metres / Jerusalem / Chariots of fire / Chung kuo (the long march) / Dragon Himalaya / Little fete / Long march / Plum blossom / Summit / Tao of love / Yin and Yang / Chromatique / L'enfant / Flamant roses / Hymne / Irlande / Mouettes / Reve.
LPS: . . . . **BOX 1**

CHINA.
Tracks: / Chung kuo (the long march) / Dragon / Himalaya / Little fete / Long march / Plum blossom / Summit / Tao of love / Yin and Yang.
LP: . . . . **SPELP 19**
MC: . . . . **SPEMC 19**
LP: . . . . **POLD 5018**

CHINA (BOX SET) (See Under Chariots Of Fire Box Set).

CITY.
LP: . . . . **WX 398**
MC: . . . . **WX 398C**

DIRECT.
Tracks: / Motion of stars, The / Will of the wind, The / Metallic rain / Elsewhere / Glorianna (hymn a la femme) / Rotations logic / Oracle of Apollo, The / Message / Ave / First approach / Dial out / Intergalactic radio station.
LP: **209149**
MC: **409149**

DISPLAY PACK.
LP: . . . . **VGPK 1**

DRAGON, THE.
Tracks: / Dragon / Stuffed aubergine / Stuffed tomato.
LP: . . . . **CRL 5013**

EARTH.
LP: **6499 693**

GREATEST HITS: VANGELIS.
LP: . . . . **NL 70078**

HEAVEN AND HELL.
Tracks: / Heaven and hell (part 1) / So long long ago so clear / Heaven and hell (part 2).
LP: . . . . **NL 71148**
MC: . . . . **NK 71148**
LP: . . . . **PL 70009**
MC: . . . . **PK 70009**
LP: . . . . **RS 1025**

HYPOTHESIS.
LP: . . . . **AFF 11**

INVISIBLE CONNECTIONS.
Tracks: / Invisible connections / Atom blaster / Thermo vision.
LP: **4151961**
LP: **4151964**

L'APOCALYPSE DES ANIMAUX.
MCSET: **3574 140**
LP: . . . . **SPELP 72**
MC: . . . . **SPEMC 72**

MAGIC MOMENTS.
Tracks: / Pulstar / Aries / A way / Albedo 0.39 / To the unknown man / So long ago so clear / Sword of Orion / Bacchanale / Intestinal bat / Alpha / Main sequence / Spiral / Beauborg / Dervish D / Freefall / Mare tranquilitatis.
MC: . . . . **NK 70345**

MASK.
Tracks: / Movement 1 / Movement 2 / Movement 3 / Movement 4 / Movement 5 / Movement 6.
LP: . . . . **POLH 19**
MC: . . . . **POLHC 19**

OPERA SAUVAGE.
Tracks: / Hymne / Reve / L'enfant / Mouettes / Chromatique / Irlande / Flamant roses.
LP: . . . . **SPELP 81**
MC: . . . . **SPEMC 81**

OPERA SAUVAGE (BOX SET) (See Under Chariots Of Fire (Box Set).

SAVAGE BEAST, THE.
LP: . . . . **PL 30036**

SEE YOU LATER.
Tracks: / See you later / I can't take it anymore / Multitrack suggestion / Memories of green / Not a bit all of it / Suffocation.
LP: **230 210 1**

SOIL FESTIVITIES.
Tracks: / Movement 1 / Movement 2 / Movement 3 / Movement 4 / Movement 5.
LP: . . . . **POLH 11**
MC: . . . . **POLHC 11**
LP: . . . . **SPELP 106**
MC: . . . . **SPEMC 106**

SPIRAL.
Tracks: / Spiral / Ballad / Dervish D / To the unknown man / 3 plus 3.
LP: . . . . **NL 70568**
MC: . . . . **NK 70568**

THEMES.
Tracks: / Bladerunner (end titles) / Main theme (Missing) / L'Enfant / Chung kuo (the long march) / Hymn / Tao of love / Antarctica, Theme from / Blade Runner love theme / Opening titles from Mutiny on the bounty / Mutiny on the Bounty (closing titles) / Memories of green / La petite fille de la mer / Chariots of fire / Five circles.
LP: . . . . **LPVGTV 1**
MC: . . . . **MCVGTV 1**

TO THE UNKNOWN MAN VOLS 1 & 2.
Tracks: / Pulstar / Aries / Way, A / Albedo 0.39 / To the unknown man / Main sequence / Sword of Orion, The / Bacchanale / Intestinal bat / Alpha / So long ago / So clear / Spiral / Beaubourg excerpt / Dervish D.
2LP: . . . . **RCALP 1002/3**
MCSET: . . . . **RCAK 1002/3**

VANGELIS BOX SET.
MCSET: . . . . **NK 74378**

Vanilla Chainsaws

WINE DARK SEA.
LP: . . . . **PHMLP 3**

Vanilla Fudge

MYSTERY.
Tracks: / Golden age dreams / Jealousy / Mystery / Under suspicion / It gets stronger / Walk on by / My world is empty / Don't stop now / Hot blood / Stranger.
LP: **790 149-1**
MC: **790 149-4**

VANILLA FUDGE.
LP: **588 086**

Vanilla Ice

EXTREMELY LIVE.
Tracks: / Intro/Ice is working out / Hooked / Stop that train / Rollin' in my 5.0 / Ice ice baby (Miami drop mix) / Havin' a roni / Satisfaction / V.I.P. possee one by one / Life is a fantasy / Road to my riches / I love you / Move / I like it / Play that funky music / Satisfaction (studio version) (Not on album).
LP: . . . . **SBKLP 12**
MC: . . . . **SBKTC 12**

HOOKED.
Tracks: / Ice ice baby / Play that funky music / Hooked / Satisfaction / I love you / Dancin' / Go ill / It's a party / Ice cold / Rosta man.
LP: . . . . **ULT 4019**
MC: . . . . **ULTMC 4019**

TO THE EXTREME.
Tracks: / Ice ice baby / Yo Vanilla / Stop that train / Hooked / Ice is workin' it / Life is a fantasy / Play that funky music / Dancin' / Go ill / It's a party / Juice to get loose boy / Ice cold / Rosta man / I love you / Havin' a roni.
MC: . . . . **SBKTC 9**
LP: . . . . **SBKLP 9**

Vanishing Indians

VANISHING INDIANS - THE MAYANS OF GUATEMALA AND BELIZE.
LP: . . . . **LLST 7371**

Vanishing Point

VANISHING POINT (Original Soundtrack) (Various artists).
LP: . . . . **SHU 8420**

Vanishment of

VANISHMENT OF THOMAS TULL, THE (Janet Ahlberg) (Carrington, Nigel (nar)).
MC: . . . . **TS 356**

Vanity

SKIN ON SKIN.
Tracks: / Under the influence / Manhunt / Romantic voyage / Confidential / Animals / Skin on skin / Gun shy / Ouch / In the jungle.
LP: . . . . **ZL 72399**
MC: . . . . **ZK 72399**

WILD ANIMAL.
Tracks: / Flippin' out / Pretty mess / Samuelle / Strap on Robbie baby / Wild animal / Crazy maybe / Mechanical emotion.
LP: . . . . **ZL 72283**
MC: . . . . **ZK 72283**

Vanity 6

VANITY 6.
Tracks: / Nasty girl / Wet dream / Drive me wild / He's so dull / If a girl answers (don't hang up) / Make up / Bite the beat / 3X2=6.
LP: . . . . **K 57023**

Vannelli, Gino

BLACK CARS.
Tracks: / Black cars / Other man, The / It's over / Here she comes / Hurts to be in love / Total stranger / Just a motion away / Imagination / How much.
LP: **825 108-1**
MC: **825 108-4**

BROTHER TO BROTHER.
Tracks: / Appaloosa / River must flow, The / I just wanna stop / Love and emotion / Feel like flying / Brother to brother / Wheels of fire / Evil eye / People I belong to, The.
LP: . . . . **AMLH 64722**

INCONSOLABLE MAN.
Tracks: / Rhythm of romance / If I should lose this love / Shame / Sunset on L.A. / Moment to moment / Cry of love

/ Time of day, The / Bound to cry / Joker's wild, The / Inconsolable man.
MC: 843 639 4

NIGHTWALKER.
Tracks: / Nightwalker / Seek and you shall find / Put the weight on my shoulders / I believe / Santa Rosa / Living inside myself / Stay with me / Sally, she says the sweetest things.
LP: . . . . SPART 1148

PAUPER IN PARADISE.
Tracks: / Mardi gras / Valleys of Valhalla / Surest things can change, The / One night with you / Song and dance, A / Black and blue / Pauper in paradise, A.
LP: . . . . AMLH 68443

POWERFUL PEOPLE.
Tracks: / People gotta move / Lady / Son of a New York gun / Jack miraculous / Jo Jo / Powerful people / Felicia / Work verse, The / Poor happy Jimmy.
LP: . . . . AMLS 63630

Van't Hoff, Ernst

HERE WE ARE (Hoff, Ernst Van't & Dick Wille Brandts).
LP: . . . . HEP 10

Vanwarmer, Randy

EVERY NOW AND THEN.
Tracks: / Stories, trophies and memories / Ain't nothin' coming / Every now and then / You were the one / Tomorrow would be better / She's the reason / Appaloosa night / Beautiful rose / Just when I needed you most / Love is a cross you bear / Safe harbour / I never got over you.
MC: . . . . ETCAS 190

TERRAFORM.
Tracks: / Whatever you decide / I discovered love / All we have is tonight / I'm gonna prove it / Doesn't matter anymore / Down like a rock / Terraform / Falling free / I've got a ticket / 21st century / Farther along.
LP: . . . . ILPS 9618

WARMER.
Tracks: / Losing out on love / Just when I needed you most / Your light / Gotta get out of here / Convincing lies / Call me / Forever loving you / I could sing / Deeper and deeper / One who loves you.
LP: . . . . ILPS 9586

Vapirov, Anatoly

DE PROFUNDIS.
LP: . . . . LR 159

INVOCATIONS (Vapirov, Anatoly Quintet).
LP: . . . . LR 121

MACBETH (Vapirov, Anatoly with Chamber Orchestra).
LP: . . . . LR 130

SENTENCED TO SILENCE (see also Sergey Kuryokhin) (Vapirov, Anatoly & Sergey Kuryokhin).
LP: . . . . LR 110

Vapors

MAGNETS.
Tracks: / Jimmie Jones / Spiders / Isolated case / Civic Hall / Live at the Marquee / Daylight titans / Johnny's in love again / Can't talk anymore / Silver machine / Magnets.
LP: . . . . LBG 30324
MC: . . . . TC LBG 30324

NEW CLEAR DAYS.
LP: . . . . UAG 30300

Varda, James

HUNGER.
Tracks: / Just a beginning / From the Bellevue Hotel / Sunday before the war / I can't stand it / Strange weather / This train is lost / Crawl in the pen / Trust the rain / In my house / Black on black.
LP: . . . . MUR 1001

Vardis

100 M.P.H..
Tracks: / Out of the way / Move along / Lion's share / Situation negative / Destiny / Loser / Living out of touch / Let's go / 100 m.p.h. / If I were king / Dirty money.
LP: . . . . METALPS 115
LP: . . . . MOGO 4012

LIONS SHARE, THE.
LP: . . . . RAZ 3

ONE HUNDRED MPH (see under "100 M.P.H.").

QUO VARDIS.
Tracks: / Do I stand accused / Where there's mods there's rockers / Please do / Dream with me / Gary Glitter (Part 1) / Walkin' / To be with you / Together tonight / Boogie blitz / Plot to rock the world, The.
LP: . . . . UNKNOWN
MC: . . . . UNKNOWN

VIGILANTE.
Tracks: / Don't mess with the best / Radio rockers / Learn how to shoot straight / All the world's eyes / I wanna be a guitar hero (just for you) / Bad company (the contract) / I must be mad / Wild sound / Radio-active / Running.
LP: . . . . RAWLP 022
MC: . . . . RAWTC 022

WORLD'S INSANE, THE.
Tracks: / Powder under foot / Money grabber / World's insane, The / Blue rock (I miss you) / Silver machine / Police patrol / All you'll ever need / Curse the gods / Love is dead / Steamin' along.
LP: . . . . LOGO 1026
MC: . . . . KLOGO 1026

Vards, Miljo Verket

NOW'S THE "FRIPPE" TIME.
LP: . . . . DRLP 82

Varekamp, Victoria

HOT DOGS & VICTORIA VAREKAMP (Varekamp, Victoria & the Hot Dogs).
LP: . . . . SOS 1033

Varicose Veins

BEIRUT EVERYWHERE.
LP: . . . . CROM 303

Various Traditions

VARIOUS TRADITIONS (Various artists).
MC: . . . . TCS 01/CS

Varney, Reg

VARIETY OF VARNEY.
Tracks: / Vienna time medley / Abi my boy / Night and day / Mistakes / Rag medley / Smoke gets in your eyes / Waltz medley / Jingling rag / Jeanne / Rose in a garden of weeds / Cornish rhapsody / Anniversary.
LP: . . . . FBLP 8100
MC: . . . . ZCFBL 8100

Varsity Eight

VARSITY EIGHT VOL.1.
LP: . . . . HQ 2055

Varsity Rag

VARSITY RAG (see under Betjeman, Sir John) (Betjeman, Sir John).

Vartan, Sylvie

AT THE PALAIS DU CONGRES.
2LP: . . . . NL 70106
MCSET: . . . . NK 70106

GOLDEN ALBUM.
LP: . . . . PL 70363
MC: . . . . PK 70363

I DON'T WANT THE NIGHT TO END.
Tracks: / I don't want the night to end / Please stay / Easy love / Rest of my life / Don't you worry / Pure love / Distant shores / Keep on rockin' / Dance to the rhythm of your love / Hot time tonight.
LP: . . . . PL 13015

TWENTY YEARS OF HITS VOL 1.
LP: . . . . NL 70619
MC: . . . . NK 70619

TWENTY YEARS OF HITS VOL 2.
LP: . . . . NL 70623
MC: . . . . NK 70623

Varukers

ANOTHER RELIGION ANOTHER WAR.
LP: . . . . 12 RIOT 31

BLOOD SUCKERS.
LP: . . . . CITY 005

LIVE IN HOLLAND.
LP: . . . . DUTCH 001

ONE STRUGGLE, ONE FIGHT.
LP: . . . . LIB 1

PREPARE FOR THE ATTACK.
LP: . . . . ATLP 001

Vasconcelos, Nana

BUSH DANCE.
Tracks: / Mamae cade baleia / Bush dance / Xingo xango / Paleto / Eyes and smiles / Calmaria / Aquela do milton / Estrella brilhante / Futebol.
MC: . . . . ANC 8701
LP: . . . . AN 8701

DUAS VOZES (see Gismonti, Elberto & Nana Vasconcelos) (Vasconcelos, Nana & Elberto Gismonti).

RAIN DANCE.
MC: . . . . ANC 8741
LP: . . . . AN 8741

Vaselines

DUM DUM.
LP: . . . . AGAS 7

Vasey, Al

GEORGE KELLY & AL VASEY / FESSORS SESSION BOYS (See under Kelly, George) (Vasey, Al & Fessors Session Boys & George Kelly).

Vassili Lackluck

VASSILI LACKLUCK (Various artists).
Tracks: / Vassili Lackluck: *Various artists* / Semyon the speedy: *Various artists* / Frog princess, The: *Various artists* / Miller's son, The: *Various artists*.
MC: . . . . ANV 667

Vatten

PLAIN WATER.
LP: . . . . GUTS 003

SMALT VATTEN.
LP: . . . . GUTS 004

VATTENDRAG.
LP: . . . . GUTS 007

Vaughan Brothers

FAMILY STYLE, THE.
Tracks: / Hard to be / White boots / D/FW / Good Texan / Hillbillies from outerspace / Long way from home / Tick tock / Telephone song / Baboom/Mama said / Brothers.
LP: 4670141
MC: 4670144

Vaughan, Frankie

100 GOLDEN GREATS.
LP: . . . . RTDX 2021

EMI YEARS, THE: FRANKIE VAUGHAN.
Tracks: / There must be a way / Mame / You're nobody 'til somebody loves you / So tired / My son my son / Girl talk / Nevertheless / One I love belongs to somebody else, The / Istanbul (not Constantinople) / I'll never smile again / Jilted / Games that lovers play / Happy days and lonely nights / Unchained melody / From the vine came the grape / If I didn't care.
LP: . . . . EMS 1360
MC: . . . . TCEMS 1360

FRANKIE VAUGHAN AT THE LONDON PALLADIUM.
LP: . . . . BDL 7330

FRANKIE VAUGHAN (DOUBLE CASSETTE).
MCSET: . . . . DTO 10208

FRANKIE VAUGHAN'S SONGBOOK.
LP: . . . . DBL 001

GOLDEN HOUR OF FRANKIE VAUGHAN.
MC: . . . . KGHMC 113

GREATEST HITS: FRANKIE VAUGHAN.
Tracks: / Give me the moonlight / Garden of Eden / Tower of strength / Milord / Hello Dolly / Green door / Long time no see / Loop de loop / Bei mir bist du schon / Kisses sweeter than wine / Pennies from Heaven / Cabaret.
LP: . . . . SPR 8535
MC: . . . . SPC 8535

LOVE HITS & HIGH KICKS.
Tracks: / When I fall in love / I just called to say I love you / Woman in love / Sometimes when we touch / It's all in the game / Stella by starlight / Way we were, The / Hello / Begin the beguine / Ring-a-ring-a-roses / Smoke gets in your eyes / I'm a fool to want you / I can't fake it anymore / Can't smile without you / Lullaby of Broadway / Hello Dolly / Cabaret / Singin' in the rain / Some enchanted evening / Mame / 42nd Street / There's no business like show business / Give my regards to Broadway / If I were a rich man / Thank Heaven for little girls / I get a kick out of you / If you were the only girl in the world / Party's over, The.
2LP: . . . . FVLP 3
MCSET: . . . . CFV 3

MANY MOODS OF....
LP: . . . . SPIN 210

MOONLIGHT & LOVE SONGS.
LP: . . . . SRT 79421

MR. MOONLIGHT.
Tracks: / There must be a way / I can't begin to tell you / Call me irresponsible / I don't know why / That old feeling / There, I've said it again / Maybe you'll be there / Serenata / If I had a dozen hearts / Time after time / One I love belongs to somebody else, The / I'll never smile again / Mame / Red roses for a blue lady / Happy days and lonely nights / Nevertheless (I'm in love with you) / If I had my way / More I see you, The / Games that lovers play / My sweetie went away / My son, my son / You're nobody till somebody loves you / So tired.
2LP: . . . . MFP 1030
MCSET: . . . . TCMFP 1030

MUSIC MAESTRO PLEASE.
Tracks: / One / Mr. Sandman / You're nobody / I'll never smile again / Music Maestro please / Sonny boy / Hava nagila / Feelings / Red sails in the sunset / Ragtime piano Joe / With these hands / Who's sorry now.
LP: . . . . FBLP 8095
MC: . . . . ZCFBL 8095

THERE MUST BE A WAY.
Tracks: / There must be a way / I can't begin to tell you / Call me irresponsible' / I don't know why / That old feeling / There, I've said it again / Maybe you'll be there / Serenata / If I had a dozen hearts / Time after time / One I love belongs to someone else, The / I'll never smile again.
LP: C5-514
MC: C5K-514
LP: . . . . ASCX 6200

TIME AFTER TIME.
Tracks: / There must be a way / I can't begin to tell you / Call me irresponsible / I don't know why (I just do) / That old feeling / There, I've said it again / Games that lovers play / My sweetie went away / My son, my son / You're nobody till somebody loves you / So tired / Maybe you'll be there / Serenata / If I had a dozen hearts / Time after time / One I love belongs to somebody else, The / I'll never smile again / Mame / Red roses for a blue lady / Nevertheless (I'm in love with you) / If i had my way / More i see you, The / Love, more love / Funk factory / It makes you feel like dancin'.
MC: . . . . HR 8118
MC: . . . . HR 4181184

Vaughan, Malcolm

EMI YEARS, THE: MALCOLM VAUGHAN.
Tracks: / My special angel / Mama / With your love / Love me as though there were no tomorrow / Lady of Spain / More than ever / Wait for me / You'll never walk alone / St Therese of the roses / To be loved / Heart of a child, The / Chapel of the roses / Wedding, The / Everyday of my life / World is mine, The / Holy city, The.
LP: . . . . EMS 1358
MC: . . . . TCEMS 1358

VERY BEST OF MALCOLM VAUGHAN - 16 FAVOURITES OF.
Tracks: / My special angel / Wait for me / Only you / With your love / Oh my papa / More than ever / Miss you / Willingly / Chapel of the roses / To be loved / You'll never walk alone.
LP: . . . . MFP 415647 1
MC: . . . . TCMFP 415647 4

Vaughan, Sarah

16 ORIGINAL HITS: SARAH VAUGHAN.
MC: . . . . MC 1632

18 PHONOGRAPHIC MEMORIES.
MC: . . . . DVREMC 56

AFTER HOURS.
Tracks: / My favourite things (From The Sound of Music.) / Every time we say goodbye / Wonder why / Easy to love / Sophisticated lady / Great day / Ill wind / If love is good to me / In a sentimental mood / Vanity.
LP: . . . . ROU 1003
LP: 793 271 1

BEST OF SARAH VAUGHAN (Compact/Walkman jazz).
Tracks: / How high the moon / Misty / Take the 'A' train / Summertime / Sweetest sounds, the / Poor butterfly / Shulie a bop / Embraceable you.
MC: 830 699-4

BRAZILIAN ROMANCE.
Tracks: / Make this city ours tonight / Romance / Love and passion / So many stars / Photography / Nothing will be as it was / It's simple / Obsession / Wanting more / Your smile.
LP: 4601561
MC: 4601564

CBS YEARS, THE.
LP: 4655971
MC: 4655974

COMPACT JAZZ: SARAH VAUGHAN.
Tracks: / Lullaby of Birdland / Summertime / Embraceable you.
MC: 831 699-4

COPACABANA.
Tracks: / Copacabana / Smiling hour / To say goodbye / Dreamer / Gentle rain, The / Tete / Dindi / Double rainbow / Bonita.
LP: 2312 125
MC: . . . . K 12 125

DIVINE.
LP: . . . . ENT LP 13036
MC: . . . . ENT MC 13036

DIVINE (2).
2LP: 400009

DIVINE SARAH, VOL.1, THE.
Tracks: / If you could see me now / My kinda love / I've got a crush on you / I'm through with love / Everything I have is

yours / Body and soul / I cover the waterfront / Tenderly / Don't blame me / Motherless child / I don't stand a ghost of a chance with you.
LP: MVS 504

DIZZY GILLESPIE/SARAH VAUGHAN/CHARLIE PARKER (See under Gillespie, Dizzy) (Vaughan, Sarah/ Charlie Parker/Dizzy Gillespie).

DUKE ELLINGTON SONG BOOK, VOL. 2.
Tracks: / I ain't got nothin' but the blues / Black butterfly / Chelsea Bridge / What am I here for? / Tonight I shall sleep / Rocks in my bed / I got it bad and that ain't good / Everything but you / Mood indigo / It don't mean a thing / Prelude to a kiss.
LP: 2312 116
MC: K 12 116

DUKE ELLINGTON SONG BOOK, VOL. 1.
Tracks: / In a sentimental mood / I'm just a lucky so and so / Solitude / I let a song go out of my heart / I didn't know about you / All too soon / Lush life / In a mellow tone / Sophisticated lady / Daydream.
LP: 2312 111
MC: K 12 111

ESSENTIAL, THE.
MC: 4671524

FOGGY DAY, A.
LP: 20117
MC: 40117

GERSHWIN LIVE (Vaughan, Sarah/ Michael Tilson Thomas).
Tracks: / Porgy and Bess medley / But not for me / Do it again / Embraceable you / Someone to watch over me / Man I love, The / Sweet and lowdown / Fascinating rhythm / My man's gone now / Nice work if you can get it / They can't take that away from me / 'S wonderful / Swanee / Strike up the band / Foggy day / I've got a crush on you.
LP: CBS 73650
MC: 40 73650

GOLDEN HITS: SARAH VAUGHAN.
Tracks: / Moonlight in Vermont / Poor butterfly / Misty / Broken hearted melody / Autumn in New York / Smooth operator / Yesterday / Close to you / Eternally / Whatever Lola wants (Lola gets) / Lullaby of Birdland / How important can it be? / Make yourself comfortable / Tea for two.
LP: 9279 149
MC: 7259 149

HOW LONG HAS THIS BEEN GOING ON.
Tracks: / I've got the world on a string / Midnight sun / How long has this been going on? / You're blase / Easy living / More than you know / My old flame / Teach me tonight / Body and soul / When your lover has gone.
LP: 2312 821
MC: K 12 821

IRVING BERLIN SONGBOOK (Vaughan, Sarah/Billy Eckstein).
Tracks: / Alexander's ragtime band / Isn't this a lovely day / I've got my love to keep me warm / All of my life / Cheek to cheek / You're just in love / Remember / Always / Easter parade / Girl that I marry, The / Now it can be told / Thanks for the memory / Start believing me now / My funny valentine / Foggy day, A / Send in the clowns / Like someone in love / Detour ahead / Three little words / You may not be an angel / If you could see me now.
LP: TOP 135
MC: KTOP 135
LP: 8255261
MC: 8255264

LIVE IN JAPAN.
MC: 557302

LOVER MAN, VOL.3.
Tracks: / Love me or leave me / Button up your overcoat / I'm through with love / What a difference a day made / Nature boy / It's magic / Ghost of a chance / Lover man / Gentleman friend / I feel so smoochie.
LP: MVS 2006

LULLABY OF BIRDLAND.
LP: 6336 709

MAGIC OF SARAH VAUGHAN, THE.
Tracks: / That old black magic / Separate ways / Mary Contrary / I've got the world on a string / What's so bad about it / Misty / Careless / Are you certain / Broken hearted melody / Friendly enemies / Sweet affection.
MC: VENUMC 1

MAN I LOVE, THE.
MC: 771504

MAN I LOVE, THE.
Tracks: / Trouble is a man / I'm gonna sit right down and write myself a l. / I can't get started / Man I love, The / One i love / It's you or no one / Once in a while / I get a kick out of you / I'll wait & pray / I'm glad there is you / Time and again.
LP: MVS 2002

MY FIRST 15 SIDES.
Tracks: / I'll wait and pray / Signing off / Interlude / No smokes blues / East of the sun / Lover man oh, where can you be / What more can a woman do? / I'd rather have a memory than a dream / Mean to me / All too soon / I'm scared / You go to my head / I could make you love me / It might as well be spring / We're through.
LP: OFF 3003
MC: OFF 43003

NO COUNT SARAH.
Tracks: / Smoke gets in your eyes / Doodlin' / Darn that dream / Just one of those things / Moonlight in Vermont / No 'count blues / Cheek to cheek / Stardust / Missing you.
LP: MMC 14021

O, SOME BRASILEIRO DE.
LP: 110 0018
MC: 710 0315

PASSING STRANGERS (Vaughan, Sarah/Billy Eckstein).
Tracks: / Passing strangers / Alexander's ragtime band / Isn't this a lovely day / I've got my love to keep me warm / All of my life / Cheek to cheek / You're just in love / Remember / Always / Easter parade / Girl that I marry, The / Now it can be told.
LP: TIME 02
MC: TIMEC 02
LP: 6463 041

PASSING STRANGERS (2).
2LP: 6641 866
MCSET: 7599 366

PERDIDO (See Basie, Count) (Vaughan, Sarah/Count Basie).

PORTRAIT OF A SONG STYLIST.
Tracks: / That old black magic / Separate ways / Mary Contrary / I've got the world on a string / What's so bad about it / Misty / Careless / Are you certain? / Broken hearted melody / Friendly enemies / Sweet affection.
MC: HARMC 117

RODGERS AND HART SONGBOOK, THE.
Tracks: / My funny valentine / Little girl blue / Tree in the park, A / It's got to be love / Ship without a sail, A / Bewitched / Thou swell / It never entered my mind / It's easy to remember / Why can't I / My romance / My heart stood still.
LP: 824 864-1
MC: 824 864-4

ROULETTE YEARS (VOL.1 & VOL.2).
Tracks: / Every time we say goodbye / Great day / Just in time / You stepped out of a dream / Have you met Miss Jones / Jump for joy / Perdido / I cried for you / Mean to me / Lover man / Honeysuckle rose / I can't give you anything but love / When lights are low / All or nothing at all / 'Round midnight / Solitude / I'll never be the same / Man I love, The / I'll be seeing you / Maria / I fall in love too easily / Glad to be unhappy / I remember you / Spring can really hang you up.
MCSET: TC2ROU 1020
MC: 794 983 4

ROULETTE YEARS - VOL. 1.
Tracks: / Every time we say goodbye / Great day / Just in time / You stepped out of a dream / Have you met Miss Jones / Jump for joy / Perdido / I cried for you / Mean to me / Lover man / Honeysuckle rose / I can't give you anything but love.
LP: ROU 1020
LP: 794 984 1

ROULETTE YEARS - VOL. 2.
Tracks: / When lights are low / All or nothing at all / 'Round midnight / Solitude / I'll never be the same / Man I love, The / I'll be seeing you / Maria / I fall in love too easily / Glad to be unhappy / I remember you / Spring can really hang you up the most.
LP: ROU 1021

ROUND MIDNIGHT.
LP: ZET 701

SARAH + 2.
LP: FS 298

SARAH VAUGHAN.
Tracks: / Lullaby of birdland / April in Paris / He's my guy / Jim / You're not the kind / Embraceable you / I'm glad there is you / September song / It's crazy.
MC: ZCGAS 728
LP: ENT LP 13006
MC: ENT MC 13006

SARAH VAUGHAN COLLECTION (20 golden greats).
Tracks: / Scat blues / I feel pretty / Won't you come home, Bill Bailey / Polka dots and moonbeams / Embraceable you / What is this thing called love? / East of the sun / Gentleman friend / Motherless child / Signing off / What a difference a day made / Tenderly / Lord's Prayer, The / Time after time / You or no one / September song / One I love belongs to somebody else, The / Hundred years from today / I cried for you / Sometimes I'm happy.
LP: DVLP 2023
MC: DVMC 2023

SARAH VAUGHAN LIVE (Compact/ Walkman Jazz).
MC: 832572-4

SARAH VAUGHAN, VOL 1.
Tracks: / Just in time / When Sunny gets blue / All I do is dream of you / I understand / Goodnight sweetheart / Baby won't you please come home / When lights are low / Key largo / Just squeeze me / All or nothing at all / Very thought of you, The.
LP: JR 109

SARAH VAUGHAN, VOL 2.
Tracks: / I believe in you / Honeysuckle rose / Moonlight on the Ganges / Lady's in love with you, The / After you've gone / Garden in the rain / I can't give you anything but love / Trolley song / I'm gonna live till I die / Falling in love with love / Great day / Nobody else but me.
LP: N 103
MC: ZCN 103
LP: JR 128

SEND IN THE CLOWNS (Vaughan, Sarah/Count Basie).
Tracks: / I gotta right to sing the blues / Just friends / Ill wind / If you could see me now / I hadn't anyone till you / Send in the clowns / All the things you are / Indian Summer / When your lover has gone / From this moment on.
LP: 2312 130
MC: K 12 130

SINGLES SESSIONS, THE.
Tracks: / Serenata / My dear little sweetheart / Green leaves of summer / Them there eyes / Don't go to strangers / Love / What's the use / Wallflower waltz / True believer / April / If not for you / Oh, lover / One mint julet / Mama, he treats your daughter mean.
LP: ROU 1022
LP: 795 331 1

SINGS GREAT SONGS FROM HIT SHOWS.
LP: MOIR 127
MC: CMOIR 127

SPOTLIGHT ON SARAH VAUGHAN.
Tracks: / You're mine now / Best is yet to come, The / Witchcraft / So long / Second time around / I could write a book / Marie / Baubles, bangles and beads / Fly me to the moon / Moonglow / Invitation / On Green Dolphin Street / Dreamy / Hands across the table / More I see you, The / I'll be seeing you / Star eyes / You've changed / Trees / Why was I born? / My ideal / Crazy he calls me / Stormy weather / Moon over Miami.
2LP: SPOT 6804
MCSET: ZCSPT 6804

SUMMERTIME.
LP: CBS 21114
MC: 40 21114

TENDERLY.
Tracks: / It's you or no one / Tenderly / Lord's Prayer, The / What a difference a day made / Gentleman friend / East of the sun / Motherless child / One I love belongs to somebody else, The / September song / Time after time / Hundred years from today / Signing off.
LP: BDL 1009
LP: 20070
MC: 40070

TIME AFTER TIME (Vaughan, Sarah/ Teddy Wilson).
Tracks: / September song / Just one of those things / When we're alone / I want to be happy / Moon faced and starry eyed / Sheik of Araby / Whispering / Time after time / Moonlight on the Ganges / Don't worry about me / Chinatown my Chinatown / Bess, you is my woman now.
LP: MVS 2001

TWO SOUNDS OF SARAH VAUGHAN.
Tracks: / I believe in you / Honeysuckle rose / When Sunny gets blue / Just in time / All I do is dream of you / Lady's in love with you, The / Just squeeze me / Very thought of you, The / After you've gone / Key Largo / Garden in the rain / Baby won't you please come home? / When lights are low / I can't give you anything but love / Trolley song, The / All or nothing at all / Moonlight in the Ganges / I'm gonna live 'til I die / Great days / I understand / Falling in love with love / Nobody else but me / Goodnight sweetheart.
MC: ZCVJD 543

VAUGHAN AND VIOLINS.
Tracks: / Gone with the wind / Day by day / Please be kind / Live for love / I'll close my eyes / Misty / Midnight sun will never set, The / That's all / I'm lost / Love me / Thrill is gone, The.
LP: MOIR 113
MC: CMOIR 113

YOU'RE MINE YOU (With Quincy Jones) (Vaughan, Sarah & Quincy Jones).
LP: FS 318

Vaughan, Stevie Ray

COULDN'T STAND THE WEATHER (Vaughan, Stevie Ray & Double Trouble).
Tracks: / Scuttle buttin' / Couldn't stand the weather / Things that I used to do / Voodoo chile / Cold shot / Tin Pan Alley / Honey bee / Stang's swang.
LP: EPC 25940
MC: 40 25940
MC: 4655714

IN STEP.
Tracks: / House is rockin', The / Tightrope / Leave my girl alone / Wall of denial / Love me darlin' / Crossfire / Let me love you baby / Travis walk / Scratch 'n' sniff / Riviera paradise.
LP: 4633951
MC: 4633954

LIVE ALIVE.
Tracks: / Say what / Ain't gonna give up on love / Pride and joy / Mary had a little lamb / Superstition / I'm leaving you (commit a crime) / Cold shot / Willie the wimp / Look at little sister / Texas flood / Voodoo chile / Lovestruck baby / Change it / Life without you.
LP: 4502381
MC: 4502384

SOUL TO SOUL.
Tracks: / Say what / Looking out the window / Look at little sister / Ain't gonna give up on love / Gone home / Change it / You'll be mine / Empty arms / Come on / Life without you.
LP: EPC 26441
MC: 40 26441
MC: 4663304

TEXAS FLOOD (Vaughan, Stevie Ray & Double Trouble).
Tracks: / Lovestruck baby / Pride and joy / Texas flood / Tell me / Testify / Rude mood / Mary had a little lamb / Dirty pool / I'm cryin' / Lenny.
LP: EPC 25534
MC: 40 25534
LP: 4609511
MC: 4609514

Vaughan Williams

FANTASIA (Abravanel, Maurice).
MC: VETC 6520

LONDON SYMPHONY, A (London Philharmonic Orchestra).
LP: EL 749 394 1
MC: EL 749 394 4

LONDON SYMPHONY NO.2, A Concerto Grosso (London Symphony Orchestra).
LP: ABRD 1318
MC: ABTD 1318

SINFONIA ANTARTICA - SYMPHONY NO. 8 (London Philharmonic Orchestra & Choir).
MC: 4251574

SYMPHONY NO.2 (VAUGHAN WILLIAMS) (See under Philharmonia Orchestra) (Philharmonia/ Hughes).

SYMPHONY NO.6 (VAUGHAN WILLIAMS) In E minor (London Symphony Orchestra).
LP: ABRD 1379
MC: ABTD 1379

WIND MUSIC OF HOLST AND VAUGHAN WILLIAMS (see under London Wind) (London Wind Orchestra).

WORLD OF VAUGHAN WILLIAMS (Various artists).
Tracks: / Fantasia on Greensleeves: *Various artists* / Linden lea: *Various artists* / Silent noon: *Various* artists / Vagabond, The: *Various artists* / Lark ascending, The: *Various artists* / Three Shakespeare songs: *Various artists* / English folk song suite: *Various artists* / O clap your hands: *Various artists* / O taste and see: *Various artists* / Fantasia on Christmas carols: *Various artists.*
MC: 4300934

Vaughn, Ben

BEAUTIFUL THINGS (Vaughn, Ben Combo).
LP: 2216 1

BLOWS YOUR MIND.
Tracks: / Daddy's gone for good / Darlene / Trashpickin' / True love / Tantalize / Hey man hey / She's your

problem now / Carved in stone / Charlene / You're so young / El rambler dorado / This property is condemned.
LP: . . . . ENVLP 513
MC: . . . . TCENV 513

DRESSED IN BLACK.
Tracks: / Big drum sound / Man who has everything, The / Dressed in black / Doormat / Long black hair / New wave dancing / Cashier girl / Words can't say what I want to say / Hey Romeo / Too sensitive for this world / Growin' a beard / Don't say you don't wanna / Poor Jimmy Gordon.
LP: . . . . FIEND 166

Vaughn, Billy

CHRISTMAS SONGS.
LP: . . . . HDY 1906
MC: . . . . ZCHDY 1906

MOONLIGHT SERENADE (Vaughn, Billy Orchestra).
LP: . . . . WH 5010
MC: . . . . WH 6010

NIGHT AND DAY (Vaughn, Billy Orchestra).
Tracks: / Magic moments / Love story / My sweet Lord / Greensleeves / Hotel California / Bridge over troubled water / Windmills of your mind / Strangers in the night / Green green grass of home / Love is blue / Spanish eyes / Amazing grace / When I need you / Fernando / Somewhere my love / Sloop John B / Red roses for a blue lady / Paloma blanca / Ciao ciao bambina / Santa Lucia / O sole mio / Come prima / Quando, quando, quando / Capri fischer / Marina / El condor pasa / Soli (Italian suite) / Santa Maria / Now and forever / Buona sera / Non ho l'eta / Evening in Rome, An / Mama Leone.
MCSET: . . . . CRT 024

Vaughn, Maurice John

GENETIC BLUES.
LP: . . . . STING 002

Vaughn, Nark

NARK VAUGHN QUINTET.
LP: . . . . PRO 7073

Vaya Con Dios

NIGHT OWLS.
Tracks: / What's a woman / Far gone now / Something's got a hold on me / Pack your memories / Sunny days / I don't want to know / Just a friend of mine / Night owls / Sally / Nah neh nah / Travelling light / With you / Quand elle rit aux eclats.
LP: . . . . PL 74688
MC: . . . . PK 74688

VAYA CON DIOS.
Tracks: / Don't cry for Louie / Moonshiner, The / Lord help me please / Lay your hands (off my man) / Lulu's song / Just a friend of mine / Sold my soul / One silver dollar / Philadelphia / Remember / Puerto Rico / Johnny, tu n'es pas un ange.
LP: 210.141
MC: 410.141

Vayne, Stevie

GUARANA.
Tracks: / Violent dreams / Room of tears / Love to hate / Helterskelter times / Street crazy / Fatal charm / Graham said / What's going on.
LP: . . . . NTVLP 051

Vaynes

GTF.
LP: . . . . USS 103

VAYNE GLORIOUS.
LP: . . . . CALCLP 060
LP: . . . . NTVLP 45

Vazz

WHISPER NOT.
MC: . . . . CRV 7404

YOUR LUNGS AND YOUR TONGUES.
LP: . . . . CRV 6402

VDO

MUSIC FOR THE ASSASSINS, IN MEMORY OF HASAN SABBAH.
LP: . . . . VDO 1

Veal, Charles

ONLY THE BEST.
Tracks: / Happy is the man / We can / It's alright / Prelude / What good is a song / How does it feel / Live your life and let live / If you ever need somebody / I believe in you / This must be magic / Someday we'll all be free / Thankful.
LP: . . . . EST 12095

Vectom

RULES OF MYSTERY.
Tracks: / Der Anfang / Prisoner's back / Dipsomania / Metallic war / Why am I alive / Outlaw / Feelings of freedom / Caught by insanity / Evil run / This/is/the/end.
LP: 805 034

SPEED REVOLUTION.
LP: 934317

Vedishceva, A

FOLK SONGS.
MC: . . . . M 00161

Vee, Bobby

BEST OF BOBBY VEE.
Tracks: / Rubber ball / Run to him / Night has a thousand eyes, The / More than I can say / Suzie baby / Devil or angel / Stayin' in / How many tears / Walkin' with my angel / Letter from Betty, A / Sharing you / Buddy's song / Charms / Take good care of my baby / Please don't ask about Barbara / Punish her / Someday / Come back when you grow up / Beautiful people / Maybe just today.
LP: 1A 022 58257
MC: 1A 222 58257
LP: . . . . EG 2607611
MC: . . . . EG 2607614

BOBBY VEE MEETS THE CRICKETS.
LP: 2C 068 83094
LP: . . . . LBY 1086

BOBBY VEE MEETS THE VENTURES.
LP: 2C 068 83093

BOBBY VEE RECORDING SESSION, A.
LP: . . . . LBY 1084

BOBBY VEE SINGLES ALBUM.
Tracks: / Take good care of my baby / Night has a thousand eyes, The / Rubber ball / Run to him / Sharing you / Suzie baby / Devil or angel / Stayin' in / More than I can say / How many tears / Everyday / Walkin' with my angel / Please don't ask about Barabara / Someday / Charms / Letter from Betty, A / Come back when you grow up / Forever kind of love / Punish her / Bobby tomorrow.
LP: . . . . FA 3021
MC: . . . . TCFA 3021
LP: . . . . UAG 30253

BOBBY VEE SINGS RARE ROCK 'N' ROLL TRACKS.
LP: . . . . FLS 7001

BOBBY VEE'S GREATEST HITS.
MC: 4XLL 9540

EP COLLECTION, THE: BOBBY VEE.
LP: . . . . SEE 297
MC: . . . . SEEK 297

GOLDEN GREATS: BOBBY VEE.
LP: . . . . LBY 112

HITS OF THE ROCKIN' 50'S.
LP: . . . . HAG 2406

I REMEMBER BUDDY HOLLY.
LP: . . . . PM 1550811

NIGHT HAS A THOUSAND EYES, THE (ALBUM).
LP: . . . . LIB 1139

TAKE GOOD CARE OF MY BABY (ALBUM).
LP: . . . . HAG 2428

TWENTY ROCK'N'ROLL HITS: BOBBY VEE.
LP: . . . . IC 064 82757

Vee Jays

HARBOUR BLUES.
LP: . . . . CCR 1017

Vee VV

LIFE, LIBERTY & THE PURSUIT OF HAPPINESS.
Tracks: / Red Shelley / Fish on a Friday / Betto the devil / Shoot the moon / Romance is over, The / Love canal.
LP: . . . . PAYLP 001

Veeda, Rig

BANANA FISH ON THE MOON (Veeda, Rig & the Twins).
MC: . . . . BI-JOOP 010

Vega, Alan

COLLISION DRIVE.
LP: . . . . ILPS 9692

DEUCE AVENUE.
LP: . . . . CHAPLP 45
LP: 105581
MC: 105584

JUST A MILLION DREAMS.
Tracks: / On the run / Shooting for you / Hot fox / Too late / Wild heart / Creation / Cry fire / Ra ra baby.
LP: . . . . EKT 15
MC: . . . . EKT 15C

POWER ON TO THE ZERO HOUR.
LP: 108121
MC: 108124

SATURN STRIP.
Tracks: / Saturn drive / Video babe / American dreamer / Kid congo / Goodbye darling / Wipeout beat / Je t'adore / Angel / Every 1's a winner.
LP: . . . . K 960259-1

Vega Brothers

INTO SOMETHING GOOD.
LP: . . . . IMCA 5686

Vega, Suzanne

DAYS OF OPEN HAND.
LP: . . . . AMA 5293
MC: . . . . AMC 5293

SOLITUDE STANDING.
Tracks: / Tom's diner / Luka / Ironbound / Fancy poultry / In the eye / Night vision / Solitude standing / Calypso / Language / Gypsy / Wooden horse.
LP: . . . . SUZLP 2
MC: . . . . SUZMC 2
MC: . . . . AMC 24102

SUZANNE VEGA.
Tracks: / Cracking / Freeze tag / Marlene on the wall / Small blue thing / Straight lines / Undertow / Some journey / Queen and the soldier, The / Night movies / Neighbourhood girls.
LP: . . . . AMA 5072
MC: . . . . AMC 5072

TOM'S ALBUM.
LP: 395363 1
MC: 395363 4

TOM'S DINER (1990) (See under DNA) (DNA and Suzanne Vega).

Vega, Tata

GIVING ALL MY LOVE.
Tracks: / Giving all my love / You keep me hangin' on / Abandoned / Reachin' all around my love / There's love in the world / You better watch out / Love your neighbour / Second wind / I get so used to you being around.
LP: . . . . STML 12138

TIME'S SO RIGHT.
LP: . . . . RMLP 037
MC: . . . . RMC 037

TRY MY LOVE.
Tracks: / Come on and try my love / I need you now / Get it up, for love / If love must go / Magic feeling / Gonna do my best to love you / I just keep thinking about you baby / Whoppre bopper show stopper / In the morning.
LP: . . . . STML 12103

Veil

BEST DAYS OF OUR LIVES, THE.
Tracks: / Best days of our lives, The / Double up / Pistol boys / Last voice, The / Only the lonely / Run with the wild / Zinc alloy / December skies / View inside, The / Kiss your body blue / Hearts on fire / Free from the gun.
LP: . . . . EAR 006

SURRENDER.
LP: . . . . CLAYLP 14

Veitch, Doug

ORIGINAL, THE.
LP: . . . . CDVLP 001
MC: . . . . CDVMC 001

Vela, Rosie

ZAZU.
Tracks: / Fool's paradise / Magic smile / Interlude / Tonto / Sunday / Taxi / 2nd emotion / Boxes / Zazu.
MC: . . . . AMC 5016
LP: . . . . AMA 5016

Velons

MOONLIGHT & MUSIC.
LP: . . . . SS 5981

Veloso, Caetano

ESTRANGEIRO.
Tracks: / Estrangeiro / Branquinha / Jasper / Outro retrato / Etc / Rai das cores / Os outros romaticos / Este amor / Meia lua inteira / Genipapo / Absoluto.
MC: . . . . MCT 1028
LP: . . . . MLPS 1028

Velvet Angels

VELVET ANGELS, THE.
LP: . . . . RELIC 5004

Velvet Elvis

VELVET ELVIS.
Tracks: / When it comes / I got everything / Privilege / This could be / Something better / Something happened today / Ambition / Take it if you want it / What in the world / Second best / Don't tell me stories / Over and out.
LP: . . . . ENVLP 510
MC: . . . . TCENV 510

Velvet Monkeys

RAKE.
LP: . . . . ROUGH 159

ROTTING CORPSE AUGOGO.
LP: . . . . SHIMMY 018

Velvet Underground

1969 VOL. 1.
MC: 834823-4

1969 VOL. 2.
MC: 834824-4

AND SO ON.
Tracks: / It's alright (the way that you live) / I'm not too sorry / Stephanie says.
LP: . . . . SECOND 1

ANDY WARHOLS VELVET UNDERGROUND.
2LP: 2683 006

ANOTHER VIEW.
Tracks: / We're gonna have a real good time together / I'm gonna move right in / Hey Mister Rain (version 1) / Ride into the sun / Coney Island steeplechase / Guess I'm falling in love (inst) / Hey Mister Rain (version 2) / Ferryboat Bill / Rock and roll (original version).
LP: 829 405-1
MC: 829 405-4
LP: . . . . POLD 5208

BEST OF THE VELVET UNDERGROUND.
Tracks: / I'm waiting for the man / Femme fatale / Run run run / Heroin / All tomorrow's parties / I'll be your mirror / White light/White heat / Stephanie says / What goes on / Beginning to see the light / Pale blue eyes / I can't stand it / Lisa says / Sweet Jane / Rock and roll.
LP: 841 164 1
MC: 841 164 4

ETC.
Tracks: / Ostrich, The / Cycle Annie / Sneeky Pete / Noise.
LP: . . . . FIRST 1

GREATEST HITS: VELVET UNDERGROUND.
2LP: 2664 438
MCSET: 3578 485

LIVE 1969 WITH LOU REED.
Tracks: / Beginning to see the light / Femme fatale / Heroin / I'll be your mirror / I'm waiting for the man / Lisa says / New age / Ocean / Over you / Pale blue eyes / Rock and roll / Some kinda love / Sweet Bonnie Brown / It's just too much / Sweet Jane / We're gonna have a real good time together / What goes on / White light / White heat.
2LP: . . . . PRID 7
LP: 927 914 1
2LP: 834 823 1

LIVE AT MAX'S KANSAS CITY.
Tracks: / I'm waiting for the man / Sweet Jane / Lonesome Cowboy Bill / Beginning to see the light / I'll be your mirror / Pale blue eyes / Sunday morning / New age / Femme fatale / After hours.
LP: . . . . K 30022

LOADED.
Tracks: / Who loves the sun / Sweet Jane / Rock and roll / Cool it down / New age / Head held high / Lonesome Cowboy Bill / I found a reason / Train round the bend / Oh sweet nuthin'.
LP: . . . . K 40113

VELVET UNDERGROUND.
Tracks: / Candy says / What goes on / Some kinda love / Pale blue eyes / Jesus / Beginning to see the light / I'm set free / Murder mystery / After hours / Story of my life.
LP: . . . . VUBOX 1

VELVET UNDERGROUND.
Tracks: / White light / White heat / What goes on / Venus in furs / That's the story of my life / Here she comes now / Beginning to see the light / Jesus / Run run run / Some kinda love / Gift, The / I'm set free / I heard her call my name.
LP: . . . . SPELP 39
MC: . . . . SPEMC 39

VELVET UNDERGROUND AND NICO (Velvet Underground and Nico).
Tracks: / Sunday morning / I'm waiting for the man / Femme fatale / Venus in furs / Run run run / All tomorrows parties / Heroin / There she goes again / I'll be your mirror / Black angels death song / European son.
LP: . . . . SPELP 20
MC: . . . . SPEMC 20

V.U..
Tracks: / I can't stand it / Stephanie says / She's my best friend / Lisa says / Ocean / Foggy notion / Temptation inside your heart / One of these days / Andy's chest / I'm sticking with you.
LP: . . . . POLD 5167
MC: . . . . POLDC 5167

WHITE LIGHT, WHITE HEAT.
Tracks: / White light / White heat / Gift, The / Lady Godiva's operation / Here she comes now / I heard her call my name / Sister Ray.
LP: . . . . SPELP 73
MC: . . . . SPEMC 73

Velveteen Rabbit

VELVETEEN RABBIT, THE.
MC: 00 102219 9

Velvets

LET THE GOOD TIMES ROLL.
2LP: . . . . 22 AAP 2241

Velvett Fogg

VELVETT FOGG PLUS.
Tracks: / Yellow cave woman / New York mining disaster 1941 / Wizard of Gobsolod / Once among the trees / Lady Caroline / Come away Melinda / Owed to the dip / Within the night / Plastic man / Telstar '69.
LP: . . . . SEE 259

Vendetta

BRAIN DAMAGE.
LP: . . . . NUK 121
MC: . . . . ZCNUK 121
LP: . . . . N 0121 1
MC: . . . . N 0121 2

GO AND LIVE, STAY AND DIE.
LP: . . . . N 0102
LP: . . . . NUK 102
MC: . . . . ZCNUK 102
MC: . . . . N 0102 2

Venetian Twins

VENETIAN TWINS, THE (Various artists).
LP: . . . . LRF 086

Vengeance

ARABIA.
Tracks: / Arabia / Broadway-Hollywood-Beverly hills / Cry of the sirens / Wallbanger / Best gunfighter in town, The / Castles in the air / If lovin' you is wrong / Children of the streets / Just what the doctor ordered / That's the way the story goes / Bad boy for love / How about tonight.
LP: 4634371
MC: 4634374

TAKE IT OR LEAVE IT.
Tracks: / Take it or leave it / Code of honour / Rock 'n' roll shower / Take me to the limit / Engines / Hear me out / Women in the world / Looks of a winner / Ain't gonna take you home.
LP: 4600701
MC: 4600704

WE HAVE WAYS.
LP: . . . . CBS 26898
MC: 40-26898

Venom

AT WAR WITH SATAN.
Tracks: / At war with Satan / Rip pride / Genocide / Cry wolf / Stand up (and be counted) / Women, leather and hell / Aaaaarrghh.
LP: . . . . NEAT 1015
MC: . . . . NEATC 1015

BLACK METAL.
Tracks: / Side black / Black metal / To hell and back / Buried alive / Raise the dead / Teacher's pet / Leave me in hell / Sacrifice / Heaven's on fire / Countess Bathory / Don't burn the witch / At war with Satan (intro).
LP: . . . . NEAT 1005
LP: . . . . RR 9708

CALM BEFORE THE STORM.
Tracks: / Black Xmas / Chanting of the priest, The / Metal punk / Under a spell / Calm before the storm / Fire / Beauty and the Beast / Deadline / Gypsy / Muscle.
LP: . . . . MOMENT 115
MC: . . . . MOMENTC 115

EINE KLEINE NACHTMUSIK.
Tracks: / Too loud (for the crowd) / Seven gates of hell / Leave me in hell / Nightmare / Countess Bathory / Die hard / Schizo / Guitar solo by Mantas / Inomine Satanas / Witching hour / Black metal / Chanting of the priest, The / Satanchrist / Fly trap / Warhead / Buried alive / Love amongst / Bass solo Cronos / Welcome to hell / Bloodlust.
2LP: . . . . NEAT 1032
MCSET: . . . . NEATC 1032
LP: . . . . RR 9639

FROM HELL TO THE UNKNOWN.....
Tracks: / Sons of Satan / Welcome to hell / Schizo / Mayhem with mercy / Poison / Live like an angel / Witching hour / 1000 days in sodom / Angel dust / In league with Satan / Red light fever / Bursting out / At war with satan (intro) / Die hard (live version) / Senile decay / Black metal / Possessed / Seven gates of hell (live version) / Buried alive / Too loud for the crowd / Radio interview (metro radio with Alan Robson).
2LP: . . . . RAWLP 001
MC: . . . . RAWTC 001

GERMAN ASSAULT.
LP: . . . . RR 9659

LIVE 84/85.
LP: . . . . APK 12

OBSCENE MIRACLE.
LPPD: . . . . APKPD 12

POSSESSED.
Tracks: / Powerdrive / Flytrap / Satanchrist / Burn this place (to the ground) / Harmony dies / Possessed / Hellchild / Moonshine / Wing and a prayer / Suffer not the children / Voyeur / Mystique / Too loud (for the crowd).
LP: . . . . NEAT 1024
MC: . . . . NEATC 1024
LPPD: . . . . NEATP 1024
LP: . . . . RR 9794

PRIME EVIL.
LP: . . . . FLAG 36
MC: . . . . TFLAG 36

SINGLES '80-'86.
Tracks: / In league with Satan / Live like an angel / Blood lust / In nomine satanus / Die hard / Acid queen / Busting out / Warhead / Lady lust / Seven gates of hell / Manitou / Dead of the nite.
MC: . . . . RAWTC 024
LP: . . . . RAWLP 024

SPEED REVOLATION.
LP: 941317

TEAR YOUR SOUL APART.
LP: . . . . FLAG 50

TEMPLES OF ICE.
Tracks: / Temples of ice.
LP: . . . . FLAG 56
MC: . . . . TFALG 56

WELCOME TO HELL.
Tracks: / Sons of Satan / Welcome to hell / Schizo / Mayhem with mercy / Poison / Live like an angel / Witching hour / One thousand days in Sodom / Angel dust / In league with Satan / Red light fever.
LP: . . . . NEAT 1002
LPPD: . . . . NEATP 1002
LP: . . . . RR 9707

WELCOME TO HELL/BLACK METAL.
MCSET: . . . . RR 49653

Vent De Panique

VENT DE PANIQUE (Film Soundtrack) (Various artists).
LP: . . . . A 349

Ventura, Anthony

DREAM LOVER (Ventura, Anthony Orchestra).
LP: . . . . WH 5007

Ventura, Charlie

ACES AT THE DEUCES (see Harris, Bill) (Ventura, Charlie & Bill Harris).

BIRDLAND.
LP: . . . . FS 177

BOP FOR THE PEOPLE (Ventura, Charlie Featuring Jackie Cain/Roy Kral).
Tracks: / Yesterdays / Peanut vendor / Euphoria / Fine and dandy / East of Suez / Great lie, The / Turnpike / If I had you / I'm forever blowing bubbles / Pennies from Heaven / How high the moon / They can't take that away from me / Honey jump, The.
LP: . . . . AFF 104

CHARLIE BOY (1946).
LP: . . . . LP 6

CHARLIE VENTURA & HIS BAND.
Tracks: / Birdland / Flamingo / Body and soul / Lullaby in rhythm / Boptura / Over the rainbow / Dark eyes / High on an open mike.
LP: . . . . JR 103

CHARLIE VENTURA IN CONCERT.
LP: . . . . GNPS 1

CHARLIE VENTURA QUINTET IN HI-FI(1956) (Ventura Quintet,Charlie).
Tracks: / High on an open mike / Charlie's ant / Cry me a river / Love and the weather / Euphoria / Parlay 2 / Jazz roost / Sleep till noon / East of suez / Bernies tune.
LP: . . . . HQ 2009

EUPHORIA.
LP: . . . . SJL 2243

IN CHICAGO-1947 (Ventura Quintet,Charlie).
LP: . . . . ZM 1004

LIVE AT THE THREE DEUCES (see Harris, Bill) (Ventura, Charlie & Bill Harris).

TOWN HALL CONCERT VOL.2.
LP: . . . . HMC 5002

Ventures

BEST OF THE VENTURES.
Tracks: / Apache '65 / Ram-bunk-shush / Telstar / Wipe out / Cruel sea / Perfidia / Rebel rouser / Walk don't run / Penetration / Pipeline / Diamond head / Hawaii five-O / Out of limits / Slaughter on Tenth Avenue(live) / Journey to the stars(live).
LP: 1A 022 58200
MC: 1A 222 58200

COLLECTION: VENTURES.
Tracks: / Telstar / Hawaii five-O / Tequila / Wheels / Bumble bee rock / Slaughter on Tenth Avenue / Ghost riders in the sky / Perfidia / Walk don't run / Memphis / Rebel rouser / Apache / Pipeline.
2LP: . . . . CCSLP 156
MC: . . . . CCSMC 156

EP COLLECTION, THE: VENTURES.
Tracks: / No trespassing / Night train / Ram bunk shush / Lonely heart / Ups 'n' downs / Torquay / Bulldog / Meet Mr Callaghan / Trambone / Josie / Yellow jacket / Bluer than blue / Gringo / Moon dawg / Sunny river / Guitar twist / Telstar / Percolator / Silver city / Wildwood flower / Wabash cannonball / Secret agent man / Man from uncle, The / Hot line.
LP: . . . . SEE 292
MC: . . . . SEEK 292

GREATEST HITS: VENTURES.
MC: 2636044

LEGENDARY MASTERS.
LP: . . . . UAD 60051

NOW PLAYING.
LP: . . . . IC 064 96851

TWENTY ROCK'N'ROLL HITS: VENTURES.
Tracks: / Walk, don't run / Raunchy / Ram-bunk-shush / Perfidia / Bulldog / Blue moon / Let's twist again / Wipe out / Green onions / Tequila / Slaughter on Tenth Avenue / Let's go / Sukiyaki / Night train / Action / Secret agent man / Last night / Rebel rouser / Memphis / Last date.
LP: . . . . IC 064 82754

VENTURES TODAY,THE.
LP: . . . . VAL 8054
MC: . . . . VAL 68054

Venus Beads

BLACK ASPIRIN.
LP: . . . . EM 9264 1

Venus Fly Trap

MARS.
LP: . . . . DANMLP 011

TOTEM.
LP: . . . . DANLP 024
MC: . . . . DANC 024

Venus In Furs

MEGALOMANIA.
LP: . . . . NCHLP 16

PLATONIC LOVE.
LP: . . . . MOVEMENT 1

REAL MORAL FIBRE.
LP: . . . . NCHLP 12

SPEED OF A PUN, THE.
LP: . . . . NCHLP 17

STRIP.
LP: . . . . NCHMLP 6

Venus & Razorblades

SONGS FROM SUNSHINE JUNGLE.
LP: . . . . SRLP 125

Venuti, Joe

BIG BANDS OF JOE VENUTI 1928-30 VOL.1 (Venuti, Joe Big Band).
LP: . . . . JSP 1111

DOIN' THINGS.
Tracks: / Man from the south / Ragging the scale / Sensation / Jig saw puzzle blues / Put & take / To to blues / Wild dog / Runnin' ragged / Doin' things / Beale street blues / After you've gone / Wild cat / Farewell blues / Someday sweetheart / I've found a new baby / I'll never be the same again.
LP: . . . . RAL 502

ELECTRIC JOE.
LP: . . . . JUMP 0143

INCREDIBLE JOE VENUTI, THE.
LP: . . . . AP 118

JANUARY 28TH & 30TH,1957 (Venuti, Joe & His Blue Four).
Tracks: / Howdown lowdown / Hot 'n' trot / Bohemian bounce / Concerto for new sounds / Blue five swing / Black rhythm / Nobody loves me / Fickle fiddle / Fleur-de-lis / Gee it's great / Desert flower / Distant lake.
LP: . . . . JV 109

JAZZ CLASSICS IN DIGITAL STEREO (Joe Venuti & Eddie Lang 1926-1933) (Venuti, Joe & Eddie Lang).
Tracks: / Stringing the blues / Bugle call rag / Four string Joe / Krazy kat / Sensation / My baby came home / Wild dog / Church Street sobbin' blues / Shivery stomp / Running ragged / Hot heels / Put and take / Oh Peter / Beale Street blues / Vibraphonia / Eddie's twister.
MC: . . . . ZCF 644
LP: . . . . REB 644

JAZZ ME BLUES.
LP: . . . . J 0124

JOE IN CHICAGO.
LP: . . . . FF 077

JOE VENUTI AND EDDIE LANG, VOL.1 (Venuti, Joe & Eddie Lang).
LP: . . . . S 1266
LP: . . . . S 817

JOE VENUTI AND HIS BAND-1945 (Venuti, Joe & His Band).
LP: . . . . GELP 15061

JOE VENUTI & HIS ORCHESTRA.
LP: . . . . HMG 5023

JOE VENUTI JAZZ GROUP (Venuti, Joe Jazz Group & Gil Cuppini Big Band).
LP: . . . . JUMP 0118

JOE VENUTI QUARTET (Venuti,Joe Quartet).
LP: . . . . J 0110

JOE VENUTI VOL.2.
LP: . . . . JSP 1112

JOE VENUTI'S JAZZ GROUP.
LP: . . . . J 0118

JOE & ZOOT (See under Sims, Zoot) (Venuti, Joe & Zoot Sims).

MAD FIDDLER FROM PHILLY, THE.
LP: . . . . SS 111

PLAYS GEORGE GERSHWIN AND JEROME KERN.
LP: . . . . J 0121

'S WONDERFUL GIANTS OF SWING.
LP: . . . . FLY 0006

SLIDING BY (Venuti, Joe & Bucky Pizzarelli).
Tracks: / Sliding by / Red velvet / That's a plenty / But not for me / Clarinet marmalade / Lover / Black satin / Rhapsodic / Sophisticated lady / Sweet Georgia Brown.
LP: . . . . SNTF 734
MC: . . . . ZCSN 734

VENUPELLI BLUES (see Grappelli, Stephane) (Venuti, Joe/Stephane Grappelli).

VENUTIANA.
LP: . . . . JUMP 0132

VIOLIN JAZZ.
LP: . . . . L 1062

VeraBra

VERABRA RETROSPECTIVE '80/'90 (Various artists).
Tracks: / Bob the bob: *Lounge Lizards* / Minha rua: *Xiame* / Sundown: *Cerletti, Marco* / Pipeland: *Schaffer, Janne* / Bagus: *Toshiyuki Honda* / Act natural: *Grolnick, Don* / D.U.V.: *De Winkel/Hattler* / Yellow fellow: *Mynta* / No name: *Von Senger, Dominik* / Algodoal: *Herting, Mike* / Flamencos en nueva York: *Nunez, Gerardo* / Lilo and Max: *De Winkel, Torsten* / Azure treasure: *Shlomo Bat-Ain* / Cousin butterfly: *Never Been There* / Joyride: *Thompson, Barbara Paraphernalia* / At the top of the hill: *Marsh, Hug* / De sabado pra dominguinhes: *Pascoal, Hermeto.*
MC: . . . . VBR 20404

Verbal Abuse

JUST AN AMERICAN BAND.
LP: . . . . EFA 1651

ROCKS YOUR LIVER.
LP: . . . . BR 07
LP: 081 228

Verbal Assault

TINY GIANTS.
Tracks: / Tiny giants.
LP: . . . . K 001/115

TRIAL.
LP: . . . . K 001/114

Verbeke, Harry

SHIRT STOP (Verbeke, Harry Quartet).
LP: . . . . SJP 136

Verden, Jake

DOIN' WHAT I LIKE DOIN.
LP: . . . . BSS 330

Verdi (composer)

AIDA AND DON CARLOS HIGHLIGHTS (Various artists).
MC: 4277154

AIDA/DON CARLOS-HIGHLIGHTS (Various artists).
MC: . . . . MC 4277154 GW

LA TRAVIATA (Film soundtrack) (Various artists).
2LP: 2500721
MCSET: 2500724

OTELLO Scenes and arias (Various artists).
LP: 4213242

RIGOLETTO & TROVATORE HIGHLIGHTS (Various artists).
MC: 4277164

RIGOLETTO/TROVATORE-HIGHLIGHTS (Various artists).
MC: MC 4277164 GW

Vereen, Ben

SIGNED, SEALED & DELIVERED.
LP: P 18018
MC: BT 18018

Verelli,Andre

MASTER PERFORMANCE VOLUME 5.
MC: AIM 99

Vergari, Madeline

THIS IS MY LUCKY DAY.
Tracks: / Lucky day / Since I fell for you / I'm beginning to see the light / More than you know / Take the 'A' train / Don't get around much anymore / Duke's place / Perdido / It don't mean a thing / More today than yesterday / Come in from the rain / Too close for comfort / Time for love, A / Alright okay you win / Embraceable you.
MC: OUTSTANDING 33

Vergat, Vic

DOWN TO THE BONE.
Tracks: / Down to the bone / Breakaway / I don't wanna lose you / Walk / Hot love / You never tell me you love me / I believe in love music / Mean mean cat / Hey love.
LP: SHSP 4117

Veritas

MO SMO SOKEI.
LP: EULP 1078
MC: EUMC 1078

Verity

INTERRUPTED JOURNEY.
Tracks: / Rescue me / Just another day (in the life of a fool) / Stay with me baby / Love is blind / Are you ready for this / You're the loser / It's comin' right / Chippin' away at the stone / In the arms of someone else / Falling.
LP: LBP 100
MC: ZCLB 100

Verity, John

INTERRUPTED JOURNEY.
Tracks: / Rescue me / Just another day (in the life of a fool) / Stay with me baby / Love is blind / Are you ready for this / You're the loser / It's comin' right / Chippin' away at the stone / In the arms of someone else / Falling.
LP: LBP 100
MC: ZCLB 100

TRUTH OF THE MATTER.
Tracks: / Roll the dice / Looking for love / Hold on / Keep a little love in your heart / Who do you think you're foolin' / Honesty and emotion / Only in a dream / Ride the wind / Stompin' ground / No pretending.
LP: LBP 7971
MC: ZLBP 7971

DREAMTIME.
Tracks: / There's a reason / Penetration / Always / Blue robe / Without a word / Mr. Blur / Fragile / Future in noise / Down on the farm / Mary Marie.
LP: K 56919

FLASH LIGHT.
Tracks: / Cry mercy Judge / Say a prayer / Town called Walker, A / Song / Scientist / Bomb / 4 a.m. / Funniest thing, The / Annie's telling me / Sundown.
LP: SFLP 1
MC: SFMC 1

TOM VERLAINE.
Tracks: / Grip of love / Souvenir from a dream / Kingdom come / Mr. Bingo / Yonki time / Flash lightning / Red leaves / Last night / Breakin' in my heart.
LP: K 52156

WONDER, THE.
LP: 8424201
MC: 8424204

WORDS FROM THE FRONT.
Tracks: / Present arrived / Postcard from Waterloo / True story / Clear it away / Words from the front / Coming apart / Days on the mountain.
LP: OVED 87
LP: V 2227

Verlaines

BIRD DOG.
LP: FNE 21

HALLELUJAH ALL THE WAY HOME.
LP: FN 40

JUVENILIA.
LP: FNUK 10

Vermuelen, Bram

RODE WUN.
LP: EM 9570 1
MC: EM 9570 4

Verne, Jules (author)

20,000 LEAGUES UNDER THE SEA see also under film title (Mason, James (nar)).
MC: 1472

AROUND THE WORLD IN 80 DAYS (See under Around the World in 80 Days).

AROUND THE WORLD IN 80 DAYS (children's classics) (Unknown narrator(s)).
MC: PLBC 84

JOURNEY TO THE CENTRE OF THE EARTH (unknown narrators) (Unknown narrator(s)).
MC: PLBC 77

JOURNEY TO THE CENTRE OF THE EARTH (Narrated by James Mason).
MC: 1581

JOURNEY TO THE CENTRE OF THE EARTH (Baker, Tom).
MCSET: ARGO 1241

JOURNEY TO THE CENTRE OF THE EARTH.
MCSET: SAY 53

JOURNEY TO THE CENTRE OF THE EARTH (Jon Pertwee (nar)).
MC: P 90028

JOURNEY TO THE CENTRE OF THE EARTH.
MC: CDL 51581

Vernon, Dave

CHILD OF 1945.
LP: LM 103 GF

Vernon & GI's

GI BOP.
LP: GOAT 002

Vernon, Lucy

JACKDAW & OTHER STORIES,THE.
LP: RESM 015

Vernon, Millie

OLD SHOES.
LP: AP 178

Vernons

SLIGHT RUN IN WITH THE DEVIL, THE.
LP: PROBE 24

VERNONS.
LP: PROBE 24

Veronika Voss

VERONIKA VOSS (Original soundtrack) (Various artists).
LP: SL 9508
MC: SLC 9508

VerPlanck, Marlene

I LIKE TO SING.
LP: AP 186

I THINK OF YOU WITH EVERY.
LP: AP 62

LOVES JOHNNY MERCER.
LP: AP 138

NEW YORK SINGER, A.
LP: AP 160

PURE AND NATURAL.
LP: AP 235

SINGS ALEC WILDER.
LP: AP 218

WARMER PLACE, A.
LP: AP 169

YOU'D BETTER LOVE ME.
LP: AP 121

Vertigo

VERTIGO (Original Soundtrack) (Various artists).
LP: SRI 75117

Vertinsky, Alexander

FOLK MUSIC.
MC: M 00191

Verve (label)

GREAT VERVE SONGBOOK (Various artists).
LP: 2615 061

Very Best Of....

VERY BEST OF: MILITARY BANDS (Various military bands).
LP: TWOX 1070

VERY BEST OF NEVILLE KING, THE (Various artists).
LP: NKRLP 004

VERY BEST OF TRASH HORROR VOL.2 (Various artists).
LP: JOCK LP 10

Very Good Eddie

VERY GOOD EDDIE (Original Broadway cast) (Various artists).
LP: DRG 6100

Very Merry Disco

VERY MERRY DISCO,A Various Artists (Various artists).
LP: WW 5136
MC: WW 4 5136

Very Things

BUSHES SCREAM WHILE MY DADDY PRUNES,THE.
LP: LEX 3

MOTORTOWN.
LP: UNKNOWN

Very Warm For May

VERY WARM FOR MAY Original cast recording (Various artists).
LP: AEI 1156

Veryovka Ukranian

VERYOVKA UKRANIAN FOLK CHOIR.
LP: CM 02735-6

Vesala, Edward

LUMI.
Tracks: / Wind, The / Frozen melody / Calypso bulbosa / Third moon / Lumi / Camel walk / Fingo / Early messenger / Together.
LP: ECM 1339

ODE TO THE DEATH OF JAZZ.
Tracks: / Sylvan swizzle / Infinite express / Time to think / Winds of Sahara / Watching for the signal / Glimmer of sepal, A / Mop mop / What? Where? Hum hum.
LP: ECM 1413

Vesey, John

JOHN VESEY.
LP: SHAN 29006

Vesta

SPECIAL.
LP: 3953471
MC: 3953474

Veterans Of Variety

VETERANS OF VARIETY Various Artists (Various artists).
LP: SH 357

Veto

VETO.
LP: 941309

Vex

VEX.
LP: 081152

Vhutemus/Archtypi

VHUTEMUS/ARCHTYPI Various artists (Various artists).
LP: SER 05

Vibes

WHAT'S INSIDE.
LP: ATEX 6

Vibrators

ALASKA 127.
LP: RAMLP 01
LP: CAL 205

BATTERIES INCLUDED.
Tracks: / Yeah, yeah, yeah / Petrol / Automatic lover / No heart / 24 hour people / London girls / Judy says / You broke my heart / Baby, baby / War zone / Whips and furs / Sulphate / Wrecked on you / Pushing too hard / Fall in love.
LP: CBS 31840

FIFTH AMENDMENT.
LP: CHIP LP 002
MC: ZCCHP 002

GUILTY.
Tracks: / Wolfman howl / Rocket to the moon / Fighter pilot / Day they caught the killer / Kick it / Baby baby / Jumpin Jack Flash / Parties / Do a runner.
LP: GRAM 02

MELTDOWN.
Tracks: / Office girls / Don't cha lean on me / So young / Speedtrap / Other side of midnight, The / Cruel to you / (Na na na) U 238 / Dynamite / Letting you go / Danger Street / Let's go / Baby / Sally gardens / Don't trust anyone (CD only.) / Wasted life (CD & cassette only.).
LP: REVLP 121
MC: REVMC 121

RECHARGED.
Tracks: / String him along / Hey little doll / I don't trust you / Go go go / Hey nonny no (instrumental) / Picture of you / Everyday I die a little / Too dumb / Rip it up, tear it up / Someone stole my heart / Electricity / Tight black jeans / Reach for that star.
LP: REV LP 101
MC: REV MC 101

V2.
Tracks: / Pure mania / Automatic lover / Flying duck theory / Public enemy no.1 / Destroy / Nazi baby / Wake up / Sulphate / 24 hour people / Fall in love / Feel alright / War zone / Troops of tomorrow.
LP: EPC 82495

VIBRATORS LIVE.
LP: REV LP 85

VIBRATORS, THE.
LP: EPC 82907

VICIOUS CIRCLE.
LP: REVLP 135
MC: REVMC 135

VOLUME 10.
LP: REVLP 159
MC: REVMC 159

Vicar Of Wakefield

VICAR OF WAKEFIELD, THE (see under Goldsmith, Oliver) (Jacobi, Derek (nar)).

Vice Squad

LAST ROCKERS (Singles).
MC: AABTC 805

NO CAUSE FOR CONCERN.
Tracks: / Young blood / Coward / Nothing / Summer fashion / 1981 / Saturday night special / Offering / Times they are a changing / Evil / Angry youth / It's a sell-out / Still dying / Last rockers.
LP: ZEM 103

STAND STRONG STAND PROUD (ALBUM).
Tracks: / Stand strong stand proud / Humane / Cheap / Gutterchild / Rock 'n' roll massacre / Fist full of dollars / Freedom begins at home / Out of reach / Saviour machine / No right of reply / Death wish / Propaganda.
LP: ZEM 104

Viceroys

BRETHREN AND SISTREN.
Tracks: / Girl it's over / Brethren and sistren / Ain't nobody love nobody / Please stop them / There is hopes / United nations / You can hear all / Over hills and valleys / My love / Ya ho.
LP: CSLP 5
MC: ZCSLC 5

CHANCERY LANE.
Tracks: / Take care of the youths / Crime don't pay / Push push / Tears are falling / New clothes / Voice like thunder / Life is not an easy game / Chancery Lane / Return.
LP: GREL 67

NEW CLOTHES (see under Larry & Alvin's "Throw me").

WE MUST UNITE.
Tracks: / Come closer my love / Show me your company / We must unite / Intelligence of her mind / They can't stop us now / Love is a key / My mission is impossible / Time is important to me / I'm trying on / Rising the strength of jah.
LP: TRLS 208

YA HO.
Tracks: / Send us / Consider yourself / Detour / Jah ho jah / My mission is impossible / Get to know / Do we have to fight / Ya ho / Sing a good song / Girl it's over.
LP: BS 1063

Vicious Barreka

OUTRAGE, INSANITY, PROFANITY.
LP: KILLER 7022

Vicious Circle

BARBED WIRE SLIDE.
MC: SBZLP 002

PRICE OF PROGRESS.
LP: GURT 5

RHYME WITH REASON.
Tracks: / Rule 17 / Pseudo genocide / Broadcast of terror / Turn to stone / Hope and wait / Inside operation / Personality crisis / Doubtful season / Nightmare so quick / Under the surface / Police brutality / One more step.
LP: ACHE 12

Vicious Rumours

ANYTIME DAY OR NIGHT.
LP: OIR 005

DIGITAL DICTATOR.
Tracks: / Replicant / Digital dictator / Minute to kill / Lady took a chance / Towns on fire / Out of sounds / Worlds and machines / Crest, The / Condemned / R L H / Out of the shadows.
LP: RR 9571

SICKEST MAN IN TOWN.
LP: LINK LP 022

SOLDIERS OF THE NIGHT.
LP: RR 9734

VICIOUS RUMOURS.

Tracks: / Don't wait for me / World church / On the edge / Ship of fools / Can you hear it? / Down to the temple / Hellraiser / Electric twilight / Thrill of the hunt / Axe and smash.
LP: 7567820751
MC: 7567820754

Vicious, Sid

LIVE AT THE ELECTRIC BALLROOM.
LP: . . . . JOCK LP 2

LOVE KILLS N.Y.C..
LP: . . . . KOMA 788020

REAL SID AND NANCY, THE.
LP: . . . . JOCK LP 4

SID SINGS.
Tracks: / Born to lose / I wanna be your dog / Take a chance on me / Stepping stone / My way / Belsen was a gas / Something else / Chatterbox / Search and destroy / Chinese rocks / I killed the cat.
LP: . . . . OVED 85
MC: . . . . OVEDC 85
LP: . . . . V 2144

SID VERSUS EDDIE (Vicious, Sid & Eddie Cochran).
LP: . . . . JOCK LP 6

SID VICIOUS LIVE.
LP: . . . . RITCHIE 1

Vick, Shakey

ON THE BALL (Shakey Vick Blues Band).
LP: . . . . AP 022

Vickers Barrow Works

SUPERB BRASS.
LP: . . . . LKLP 7040

Vickers, Mike

CAPTAIN KREMMEN (RETRIBUTION) (See under ' Everett, Kenny' for details).

Vicky D.

THIS BEAT IS MINE (OLD GOLD) (See under Browne, Sharon/I specialise in love).

Victims Family

THINGS I HATE TO ADMIT (Various artists).
LP: . . . . K 001 119

VOLTAGE AND VIOLETS.
LP: . . . . K 103

Victor & Barry

HEAR VICTOR & BARRY AND FAINT.
Tracks: / Kelvinside men / Marks & Spencers / Recipe of life / Smile costs nothing, A / Glasgow / Proclaimers song, The / It's hard being a celebrity / Why isn't things the way they used to be / Dreams can come true.
MC: . . . . JRCP 881

Victor Victoria

VICTOR VICTORIA (Film soundtrack) (Various artists).
Tracks: / You and me: *Victor Victoria* / Shady dame from Seville, The: *Victor Victoria* / Alone in Paris: *Victor* Victoria / King's can can: *Victor Victoria* / Le jazz hot: *Victor Victoria* / Crazy world: *Victor Victoria*/ Chicago Illinois: *Victor Victoria* / Cat and mouse: *Victor Victoria* / Gay Paree: *Victor Victoria* / Finale: *Victor Victoria.*
LP: . . . . MG 15407
MC: . . . . CT 15407
LP: 2315 437
MC: 3110 393

Victoria Plum

ANGELA RIPPON READS VICTORIA PLUM STORIES (Rippon, Angela (nar)).
LP: 6381 043

VICTORIA PLUM (See Hyks, Veronika) (Various artists).

Victorian

VINTAGE MELODIES (Songs of the Victorian era) (Various artists).
Tracks: / Come into the garden Maud: *Various artists* / Won't you buy my pretty flowers ?: *Various artists* / Mistletoe bough, The: *Various artists* / End of a perfect day, A: *Various artists* / My pretty Jane: *Various artists* / Drinking: *Various artists* / I'll be your sweetheart: *Various artists* / Silent worship: *Various* artists / In the gloaming: *Various artists* / Road to Mandalay, The: *Various artists* / Mother take the wheel away: *Various artists* / Excelsior: *Various artists.*
LP: . . . . NA 109

Victorian musical

VICTORIAN MUSICAL EVENING, A (Aba Daba) (Various artists).
Tracks: / Home sweet home: *Various artists* / Londonderry air: *Various artists* / Moon has raised her lamp above, The: *Various artists* / Come into the garden, Maud: *Various artists* / Amorous goldfish, The: *Various artists*/ Baby on the shore, The: *Various artists* / Sam Hall: *Various artists* / Polly Perkins of Paddington Green: *Various* artists / She was poor, but she was honest: *Various artists* / Lost chord, The: *Various artists* / Soldiers of the Queen: *Various artists* / Ring the bell softly: *Various artists* / Come home, father: *Various artists*/ Love's old sweet song: *Various artists* / My old dutch: *Various artists* / Champagne Charlie: *Various artists*/ Daisy Bell: *Various artists* / Two lovely black eyes: *Various artists* / Night before Christmas, The: *Various artists.*
MC: . . . . TT 001
LP: . . . . SHE 501

Victorian Parents

SILENCE FOLLOWS.
LP: . . . . POLS 1049
MC: . . . . POLSC 1049

Victory

CULTURE KILLED THE NATIVE.
Tracks: / More and more / Never satisfied / Don't tell no lies / Always the same / Power strikes the earth / Lost in the night / On the loose / Let it rock on / So they run / Standing on the edge / Warning, The / Into the darkness (Only on CD).
LP: 837 781-1
MC: 837 781-4

HUNGRY HEARTS.
Tracks: / One track mind / Bigger they are, The / I'm a survivor / Never leave you again / Tough on love / You run away / Look in a mirror / Look in the mirror / Feel the fire / Hi honey.
LP: . . . . METALLP 120

Victory in Europe

VICTORY IN EUROPE (Archive Sound Recordings) (Various artists).
LP: . . . . REC 562
MC: . . . . ZCM 562

Victory Mansions

LOVE, LIFE & DRINK.
LP: . . . . SETLP 001
LP: . . . . SEJLP 001

Video Kids

NEVER TOO YOUNG TO DANCE.
LP: . . . . VK 001
MC: . . . . 2C VK 001

Videodrome

VIDEODROME (Film soundtrack) (Various artists).
LP: . . . . STV 81173

Vienna Boys Choir

FOLKSONGS AND SONGS FOR CHILDREN.
LP: 651 418 8

WALTZES & POLKAS BY JOHANN STRAUSS.
LP: . . . . RL 12754
MC: . . . . RK 12754

Vienna Conservatory

SING CHILDREN SING (Vienna Conservatory Childrens' Choir).
LP: . . . . TC 1578
MC: . . . . CDL 51578

Vienna gold

VIENNA GOLD (Various artists).
LPS: . . . . EGS 45007
LPS: . . . . EC EGS 45007

Vienna Philharmonic..

PETRUSHKA (See under Stravinsky (composer)) (Vienna Philharmonic Orchestra).

Vienna Philharmonic

SYMPHONY NO.9/ CARNIVAL OVERTURE (See under Dvorak (Composer)).

Vienna State Opera

HUNGARIAN AND RUMANIAN RHAPSODIES (see under Liszt).

PIANO CONCERTOS NOS. 24 & 20 (see under Mozart).

SYMPHONY 'FANTASTIQUE' (see under Berlioz).

SYMPHONY NO.4 (MIDSUMMER NIGHT'S DREAM) (see under Mendelssohn).

SYMPHONY NO.9 (See under Dvorak (Composer)).

SYMPHONY NOS. 103 (DRUMROLL) AND 104 (LONDON) (see under Haydn).

Vienna Symphony

ORCHESTRAL ROCK.
LP: . . . . DINTV 3
MC: . . . . DINMC 3

SYMPHONIC ROCK.
Tracks: / Rock me Amadeus / Kyrie / Brothers in arms / St. Elmo's Fire / Private dancer / Welcome to the pleasure dome / Hearts on fire (Theme from Rocky IV) / Power of love, The / View to a kill, A / Night in Vienna, A / Classic touch, The.
2LP: . . . . SMR 730
MCSET: . . . . SMC 730

Viennese

VIENNESE ENCHANTMENT (Various artists).
MC: TC2MOM 121

Vierra, Christina

CHRISTINA VIERRA.
Tracks: / You can float in my boat / I can't hold out anymore / Your personal possession / L word, The / Those eyes / Use up all my love / Doctor, could you please / Break these chains.
LP: . . . . WX 206
MC: . . . . WX 206 C

Vierra E Sev Conjunto

LAMBAGA.
Tracks: / Lambada do ru / Ela voltou / Bicharada No 2 / Mariazinha / O Seresteiro / Duas linguas / Lambada do mapinguan / Soia / Voce Se Afastou / Lambada do sino / Melo do Bode / Sambista Brasileiro.
LP: . . . . STERNS 2001

Vietnam

TRADITIONAL VIETNAMESE ENSEMBLES (Various artists).
Tracks: / Vong co: *Various artists* / Nam xuan, nam ai, trong ai: *Various artists* / Piece xang xe: *Various* artists / Dep dam giao dau: *Various artists* / Trong phu thuy: *Various artists* / Chau van: *Various artists*/ Tam tau tuong: *Various artists* / Solo de six tambours: *Various artists.*
LP: . . . . ARN 33783
MC: . . . . ARN 433783

Vietnam Chain

SUSMOALA BEAT.
Tracks: / Hoodoo / Lumberjack blues / Before I go / Grandmother / Before I go (version) / Sunny Sunday / I walked with Doro Pesch (instrumental) / Banana split / Beast in me / Cold turkey.
LP: . . . . MMLP 021

Vietnam Veterans

CATFISH EYES.
LP: . . . . MMLP 008

DAYS OF PEARLY SPENCER, THE.
LP: . . . . MMLP 014

GREEN PEAS.
2LP: . . . . MMLP 001/2

IN ANCIENT TIMES.
LP: . . . . MMLP 003

ON THE RIGHT TRACK NOW.
LP: . . . . MMLP 66004

View From Here

VIEW FROM HERE, THE (Various artists).
LP: . . . . MR 2707

View From The Hill

IN TIME.
Tracks: / No conversation / I'm no rebel / Stay and let me love you / Desperately / Boys in blue / Lover's confession / On the corner / Turn out the light.
LP: . . . . EMC 3523
MC: . . . . TCEMC 3523

View to a Kill

VIEW TO A KILL, A (Film Soundtrack) (Various artists).
LP: . . . . BOND 1
MC: . . . . TCBOND 1

Vig, Tommy

ENCOUNTER WITH TIME (Vig, Tommy & His Orchestra).
LP: . . . . DS 780

Vigard, Kristen

KRISTEN VIGARD.
Tracks: / Gnossiennes / Waiting for you / Announcement / Stone city / 12 bar blues / Paint my head / Out in the woods / Slave to my emotions / Use me / Me so far / My old ways / Steel morning.
LP: 210709
MC: 410709

Vigil

VIGIL.
Tracks: / Until the seasons / White magic spell / I am waiting / Gargoyles / I love you equinox / Whistle in the yard / Celiba sea, The / Garden, the / Born again / Benefit of the doubt, The.
LP: . . . . CHR 1568

Vigilants

RUN FOR COVER.
LP: . . . . HMASP 45

Vignoles, Roger

BLAH BLAH BLAH AND OTHER TRIFLES (see under Walker, Sarah) (Vignoles, Roger & Sarah Walker).

CABARET SONGS (see Walker, Sarah) (Vignoles, Roger & Sarah Walker).

CAROLE FARLEY SINGS PROKOFIEV (see under Prokofiev) (Vignoles, Roger/ Carole Farley).

Viking

DO OR DIE.
Tracks: / Warlord / Hellbound / Militia of death / Prelude - scavenger / Valhalla / Burning from within / Berserker / Killer unleashed / Do or die.
LP: . . . . RR 9569

Vikings (film)

VIKINGS, THE (Film soundtrack) (Various artists).
LP: . . . . LD 4

Villa De Ville

FOR THE TIME BEING.
Tracks: / Subculture 22 / Everything counts / Crocodile tears / Nothing to gain / Porcelain piece / Life is only real / C.V. set / Villa de ville / Confidence tricksters / Rack and Rouen.
LP: . . . . RCALP 5045
MC: . . . . RCAK 5045

Villa Rides

VILLA RIDES (Film Soundtrack) (Various artists).
LP: 254140.1

Village People

CRUISIN'.
LP: 9109 614

GO WEST (ALBUM).
Tracks: / In the navy / Go West / Citizens of the world / I wanna shake your hand / Get away holiday / Manhattan woman / Y.M.C.A..
LP: 9109 621

GREATEST HITS: VILLAGE PEOPLE (REMIX).
Tracks: / Y.M.C.A. / Macho man / San Francisco / Can't stop the music / In the navy / In Hollywood / Fire island.
LP: . . . . GMLP 1003
MC: . . . . GMMC 1003

HITS, THE.
LP: . . . . QUALP 1

LIVE AND SLEAZY.
Tracks: / Fire island / Hot cop / San Francisco / In Hollywood / Macho man / In the navy / Y.M.C.A / Sleazy / Rock and roll is back again / Ready for the '80's / Save me.
2LP: 6641980

NEW YORK CITY.
Tracks: / New York City (vocal) / New York City (Instrumental).
LP: . . . . SOHOLP 5
MC: . . . . SOHOTC 5

RENAISSANCE.
Tracks: / Do you wanna spend the night / 5 o'clock in the morning / Fireman / Jungle city / Action man / Diet / Food fight.
LP: 6399 204
MC: 7199 204

VILLAGE PEOPLE: THE HITS.
Tracks: / YMCA / Macho man / San Francisco (you've got me) / Can't stop the music / Megamix / In the navy / In Hollywood / Fire island / Go West / Village people / Ready for the 80's / Do you wanna spend the night.
MC: . . . . MCTC 004

Village School

VILLAGE SCHOOL By Miss Read (Watford, Gwen (nar)).
MC: . . . . CAB 009

Villard, Michel

MUSIC FROM THE CHARLIE CHAPLIN FILMS.
Tracks: / Les temps modernes / Une vie de chien / Le dictateur / Le pelerin / Charlot soldat / Les lumieres de la ville / Un roi a New York / Limelight les feux de la rampe / La comtesse de Hong Kong / La ruee vers l'or.
MC: 771 057

MUSIC FROM THE FILMS OF CHARLIE CHAPLIN.
Tracks: / Titina / Le violeter / Green lantern snag / Smile / Mandolin serenade / Marche militaire / Evening star / Hungarian dance no. 5 / Limelight / Pilgrim, The (medley) / This is my song / Shoulder arms (medley) / Spring song / Goldrush (medley).
LP: . . . . GNPS 2064
MC: GNP5 2064

Villiers, George

DAWN (Villiers, George Ensemble).
MC: . . . . GVEMC 2

PLAYS GUITAR.
LP: . . . . IPLP 1
MC: . . . . IPMC 1

Villiers, James (nar)

WAVING ALL EXCUSES (see under Waving All Excuses).

Vincent, Carrie

HOLDING OUT FOR A HERO.
MC: . . . . CHV 312

Vincent, Gene

2 ORIGINALS OF GENE VINCENT.
2LP: 2C 134 82076/7

20 ROCK'N'ROLL HITS: GENE VINCENT.
LP: . . . . IC 064 85997

ABC OF ROCK.
LPPD: . . . . AR 30076

AIN'T THAT TOO MUCH.
Tracks: / Ain't that too much / Bird doggin' / Love is a bird / Lonely street / Hurtin' for you baby / Poor man's prison / Born to be a rolling stone / Hi lili hi lo / I'm a lonesome fugitive / I've got my eyes on you.
LP: . . . . CBR 1006
MC: . . . . KCBR 1006

BABY BLUE.
Tracks: / Story of the rockers / Pickin poppies / Be bop a lula / Pistol packin mama / Say mama / Rocky road blues / Baby blue / Whole lotta shakin' goin' on / Day the world turned blue, The / Story of the rockers (instrumental).
LP: . . . . SHLP 122
MC: . . . . SHTC 122

BEST OF GENE VINCENT AND HIS BLUE CAPS, THE.
Tracks: / Race with the devil / Be bop a lula / Woman love / I sure miss you / Crazy legs / Gonna back up baby / Who slapped John / Important words / Rollin' Danny / In my dreams / Baby blue / Git it / Somebody help me / Summertime / Beautiful brown eyes / Say Mama.
LP: . . . . EG 2607601
MC: . . . . EG 2607604
LP: . . . . ATAK 151
MC: . . . . TCATAK 151

BIRD DOGGIN'.
Tracks: / I've got my eyes on you / Ain't that too much / Bird doggin' / Love is a bird / Lonely street / Hurtin' for you baby / Poor man's prison / Born to be a rolling stone / Hi lili hi lo / I'm a lonesome fugitive.
LP: . . . . BDL 3001
MC: . . . . AJLK 3001

BLUE JEAN BOP.
LP: 2C 064 82077

BOP THEY COULDN'T STOP, THE.
Tracks: / Rockin robin / In the pines / Be bop a lula / Rainbow at midnight / Black letter / White lightning / Sexy ways / Ruby baby / Lotta lovin / Circle never broken / No.9 (Lonesome whistle) / Scarlet ribbons.
LP: . . . . MFLP 007
MC: . . . . MFC 007

BORN TO BE A ROLLING STONE.
Tracks: / Born to be a rolling stone / Hi lili hi lo / Bird doggin' / Love is a bird / Ain't that too much / Am I that easy to forget / Hurtin' for you baby / I'm a lonesome fugitive / Poor man's prison / Words and music / I've got my eyes on you / Lonely street.
LP: . . . . TOP 122
MC: . . . . KTOP 122
LP: . . . . MA 11101183
MC: . . . . MAMC 01183

CAPITOL YEARS, THE (BOX SET).
LPS: . . . . BOX 108

CRAZY BEAT.
LP: 2C 064 85037

CRAZY TIMES.
LP: 1432
LP: . . . . T 1342

CRUISIN' WITH GENE VINCENT (Vincent, Gene & The Bluecaps).
LP: . . . . RSRLP 1007

DRESSED IN BLACK.
Tracks: / Be bop a lula / Say mama / Pistol packin' mama / Whole lotta shakin' goin' on / Good golly Miss Molly / Rocky road blues / Last word in lonesome, The / Pretty girls / Blue jean bop / Baby blue / I'm movin' on.
LP: . . . . MFLP 016

EDDIE COCHRANE & GENE VINCENT (Vincent, Gene & Eddie Cochran).
LPPD: . . . . PM 2600440

EP COLLECTION, THE: GENE VINCENT.
Tracks: / Race with the devil / Crazy legs / Hold me, hug me, rock me / Wayward wind / Somebody help me / Five feet of lovin' / Peace of mind / Look what you gone and done to me / Summertime / Keep it a secret / Rocky road blues / Dance to the bop / Baby blue / Dance in the street / Lovely Loretta / Important words / Gone gone gone / She she little Sheila / Weeping willow / Crazy beat / I'm gonna catch me a rat / If you want my lovin'.
LP: . . . . SEE 253
MC: . . . . SEEK 253

FOR THE COLLECTORS ONLY.
Tracks: / Why don't we get ourselves together? / No. 9 (lonesome whistle) / Pistol packin' mama / Good golly Miss Molly / Be bop a lula / Speech message from Gene to English fans 1967 / Say mama / Rocky road blues / Baby blue / Maybellene / Whole lotta shakin' goin' on / Dance to the bop.
LP: . . . . MFM 020

FROM L.A. TO 'FRISCO.
Tracks: / Interviews / Sunshine / Lonesome whistle / Maybellene / Whole lotta shakin' goin' on / Woman love / Be bop a lula / Rainday sunshine / Green grass / Mister love / Roll over Beethoven.
LP: . . . . MFLP 1023

GENE SINGS VINCENT, '56.
Tracks: / Race with the devil / Be bop a lula / Jezebel / Who slapped John? / Jumps giggles and shouts / Blue jean bop / You told a fib / Teenage partner / Catman / Hold me, hug me, rock me / Cruisin' / Important words.
LP: 2C 068 86309

GENE SINGS VINCENT, '57-'59.
Tracks: / Time will bring you everything / True to you / Baby blue / Yes, I love you, baby / Teenage partner / Night is so lonely, The / In love again / Be bop boogie boy / Important words / My baby don't know / Vincent blues / Pretty pearly / Darlene / Greenback dollar.
LP: 2C 068 86310

GENE VINCENT.
Tracks: / Say mama / Blue jean bop / Wild cat / Right here on earth / Who slapped John / Walkin home from school / Five feet of lovin / She-she little Sheila / Be bop a lula / Jump back / Dance in the street / Pistol packin mama / Crazy beat / High blood pressure / Five days, five days / Bi bickey bi bo bo boo.
LP: . . . . MFP 41 5749 1
MC: . . . . MFP 41 5749 4
MC: . . . . TC MFP 5749

GENE VINCENT AND THE BLUE CAPS.
LP: 2C 064 82076

GENE VINCENT RECORD DATE, A.
LP: 2C 066 80038

GENE VINCENT ROCKS AND THE BLUE CAPS ROLL.
LP: 2C 064 82075

GENE VINCENT SINGLES ALBUM, THE.
Tracks: / Blue jean bop / Lotta lovin' / Race with the devil / Pistol packin' Mama / Baby blue / Wild cat / I'm goin' home / Woman love / Rocky road blues / Dance to the bop / Say mama / Crazy legs / My heart / Well I knocked him (bim bam) / She little Sheila / Rollin' Danny / Over the rainbow / Git it / Bi bickey bi bo bo boo / Be bop a lula.
LP: . . . . EST 26223
MC: . . . . TCEST 26223

GENE VINCENT'S GREATEST.
Tracks: / Be bop a lula / Race with the devil / Gonna back up baby / Who slapped John / Blue jean bop / Bop street / Jump back / Honey / Bi bickey bi bo bo boo / Lotta lovin' / Dance to the bop / Dance in the street / Rocky road blues / Say mama / Anna Annabelle / She she little Sheila / Wild cat.
LP: . . . . FA 3017
MC: . . . . TCFA 3017
LP: . . . . CAPTS 1001

GENE VINCENT'S TOP SIXTEEN.
LP: . . . . PM 1562474

GREATEST HITS VOL 2: GENE VINCENT.
Tracks: / Cruisin' / Baby blue / Crazy legs / Git it / Jumps, giggles and shouts / Hold me, hug me, rock me / Night is so lonely / Right here on earth / Pistol packin' mama / Brand new beat / Red blue jeans and a pony tail / Five feet of lovin' / I got a baby / Blues stay away from me / Woman love / Unchained melody.
LP: . . . . CAPS 1028

IMPORTANT WORKS (Previously unissued recordings & studio chatter).
Tracks: / Maybelline / You're the one for me / High blood pressure / Lonesome boy / Rip it up / I might have known / Beautiful brown eyes / Important words / Crazy beat / I'm gonna catch me a rat / It's been nice / That's the trouble with love / Good lovin' / Mr. Loneliness / Teardrops / If you want my lovin' / Spaceship to Mars.
LP: . . . . RSRLP 1020

INTO THE SEVENTIES.
Tracks: / Sunshine / I need woman's love / 500 miles from home / Slow time's coming / Listen to the music / If only you could see me today / Million shades of blue, The / Tush hog / How I love them old songs / High on life / North Carolina line / There is something on your mind / Day the world turned blue, The / Boppin' the blues / Looking back / Oh lonesome me / Woman in black, The / Danse colinda (Available on CD only) / Geese (Available on CD only) / You can make it if you try (Available on CD only) / Our souls (Available on CD only).
LP: . . . . SEE 233

LONESOME FUGITIVE.
Tracks: / Ain't that too much / Bird doggin / Love is a bird / Lonely street / Hurtin' for you baby / Poor man's prison / Born to be a rolling stone / Hi lili hi lo / I'm a lonesome fugitive / I've got my eyes on you / Words and music / Am I that easy to forget.
LP: . . . . MFM 027

MEMORIAL ALBUM.
Tracks: / Be bop a lula / Race with the devil / Say mama / Frankie and Johnnie / Ready Teddy / Double talkin' baby / Dance in the street / Catman / Bop street / Flea brain / Maybellene / I got a baby / Somebody help me / I love you / Blue jean bop / Jump back / True to you / Woman love / Rollin' Danny / It's no lie / My baby don't know / Baby blue / Red blue jeans & a pony tail / I can't help it / Lovely Loretta / Over the rainbow / Lotta lovin' / 5 feet of lovin'.
2LP: 2C 156 81001/2

ON TOUR (See under Cochran, Eddie) (Vincent, Gene & Eddie Cochran).

ROCK 'N' ROLL LEGENDS.
LPS: 2C 154 85071/4

ROCK ON WITH GENE VINCENT.
Tracks: / Say Mama / Be bop a lula / Rip it up / Flea brain / Ready Teddy / Maybellene.
LP: . . . . MFP 50463
MC: . . . . TCMFP 50463

SHAKIN' UP A STORM (Vincent, Gene & The Shouts).
Tracks: / Hey hey hey / Lavender blue / Private detective / Shimmy shammy shingle / Someday you'll want me to want you / Another Saturday night / Slippin' and slidin' / Long tall Sally / Send me some lovin' / Love love love / Good golly Miss Molly / Baby blue / Suzie Q / You are my sunshine.
LP: . . . . EMS 1050491
MC: . . . . TCEMS 1050491
LP: . . . . PM 1550821
LP: 3C 054 82021

SINGS SONGS FROM HOT ROD GANG.
LP: . . . . DEMAND 0045

SOUNDS LIKE GENE VINCENT.
LP: 2C 066 82074

STAR - '56-'58.
LPS: . . . . PM 1551953

THEIR FINEST YEARS 1956 & 1958 (See under Cochran, Eddie) (Vincent, Gene & Eddie Cochran).

TWIST CRAZY TIMES.
LP: 2C 064 82073

Vincent, Holly Beth

HOLLY & THE ITALIANS.
Tracks: / Honalu / For what it's worth / Only boy / Revenge / Samurai and courtesan / Cool love (is spreading around) / Uptown / We danced / Unoriginal sin / Just like me.
LP: . . . . V 2234
MC: . . . . TCV 2234

Vincent, James

ENTER IN.
Tracks: / You'll be right there / Don't trust your feelings / In you I'm free / Take my life / Spiritual Israel / Make a joyful noise / Hearken my love / Come follow me / Enter in / What's going on / Walking in the light.
LP: . . . . BIRD 123
MC: . . . . TC BIRD 123

Vincent, Kathy

HOTTER THAN FIRE.
Tracks: / Tonight's the night / Sweet dynamite / Running through the night / One too many heartaches / Seal the deed / Shakin' all over / 17 electric / Hold tight don't fight / baby don't like / Close to the edge.
LP: . . . . BUBELP 1

Vincent, Lynne

LOVE BLONDE.
MC: . . . . CHV 330

Vincent, Rhonda

DREAM COME TRUE, A.
LP: . . . . REBEL 1682
MC: . . . . REBELMC 1682

NEW DREAMS AND SUNSHINE.
LP: . . . . REBEL 1665
MC: . . . . REBELMC 1665

Vincent, Vinnie

ALL SYSTEMS GO.
Tracks: / Let freedom rock / Naughty naughty / Ecstasy / That time of year / Breakout / Burn / Love kills / Dirty rhythm / Deeper and deeper / Heavy pettin' / Ashes to ashes.
LP: . . . . CHR 1626
MC: . . . . ZCHR 1626

VINNIE VINCENT INVASION.
Tracks: / Boys are gonna rock / Shoot you full of love / No substitute / Animal / Twisted / Do you wanna make love / Back on the streets / I wanna be your victim / Baby o / Invasion.
LP: . . . . CHR 1529
MC: . . . . ZCHR 1529

Vincson, Walter

1928-36 (See Under McCoy, Charlie) (Vincson, Walter & Charlie McCoy).

Vinding, Mads

PLAYTIME (See also under Kenny Drew).
LP: . . . . MLP 15695

Vines

WALK THE FLOOR.
LP: . . . . SANE 2

Vinnegar, Leroy

LEROY WALKS.
Tracks: / Walk on / Would you like to take a walk / On the sunny side of the street / Walkin / Walkin my baby back home / I'll walk alone / Walkin by the river.
LP: . . . . COP 011

LEROY WALKS.
LP: 1007 542

LEROY WALKS AGAIN (Vinnegar, Leroy Quintet).
Tracks: / Hard to find / For Carl / Down under / Restin' in jail.
LP: 1007 608

MY FAIR LADY (see Manne,Shelly) (Vinnegar,Leroy/Shelly Manne/Andre Previn).

NIGHT FLIGHT TO DAKAR (see Cohn,Al/Billy Mitchell/Dolo Coker etc.).

Vinson, Eddie

BACK IN TOWN.
Tracks: / Cleanhead's back in town / That's the way to treat your woman / Trouble in mind / Kidney stew / Sweet lovin' baby / Caldonia / It ain't necessarily so / Cherry red / Is you is or is you ain't my baby / I just can't keep the tears from tumblin down / Your baby ain't sweet like mine / Hold it right there.
LP: . . . . CRB 1046

BACK IN TOWN (Live at Sandys).
LP: . . . . MR 5208

BATTLE OF THE BLUES VOL. 4 (Vinson, Eddie, Roy Brown & Wynomie Harris).
Tracks: / Big mouth gal / Bring it back / If you don't think I'm sinking / Trouble at midnight / Peas and rice / Rock Mr. Blues / Lonesome train / Old age boogie / Ball headed blues / Grandma plays the numbers / Good bread alley / Queen of diamonds.
LP: . . . . SING 668

CHERRY RED BLUES.
LP: . . . . BID 8023

CHERRY RED BLUES.
MCSET: . . . . GD 5035

CLEAN MACHINE, THE.
LP: . . . . MR 5116

CLEANHEAD AND A ROOMFUL OF BLUES.
Tracks: / House of joy / Friend of mine, A / Movin with Lester / No bones / That's the groovy thing / Past sixty blues / Street light / Farmer's daughter blues.
LP: . . . . MR 5282

CLEANHEAD AND CANNONBALL (Vinson, Eddie & Cannonball Adderley).
LP: . . . . LLP 1309

FUN IN LONDON.
LP: . . . . JSP 1012

I WANT A LITTLE GIRL.
Tracks: / I want a little girl / Somebody got to go / Blues in the closet / No good for me / Stormy Monday / Straight, no chaser / Worried mind blues.
LP: 231 0866
MC: K10 866

JAMMIN' THE BLUES.
Tracks: / Just a dream / Laura / Person to person / Now's the time / Hold it right there / Home boy / C jam blues.
LP: . . . . BLP 30168

KANSAS CITY SHOUT (See under Basie, Count) (Vinson, Eddie, Count Basie & Joe Turner).

KANSAS CITY SOUL (See under Basie, Count) (Vinson, Eddie, Count Basie & Joe Turner).

MIDNIGHT CREEPER.
LP: BMLP 1063

MR. CLEANHEAD STEPS OUT.
LP: BP 507

MR. CLEANHEAD'S BACK IN TOWN.
Tracks: / Home boy / Meats too high / Somebody's got to go / Somebody else is taking my place / Investigation blues / If you were my buddy / Old maid boogie / That's all / Travelling.
LP: JSP 1046

REAL "MR. CLEANHEAD", THE.
Tracks: / Suffer fool / Big chief / Tomorrow may never come / Anxious heart / Old man boogie / You can't have my love no more / Juice head baby / Cherry red / Somebody's got to go / Too many women blues / Just a dream / Cleanhead blues / When a woman loves / King for a day blues / Railroad porter's blues.
LP: OFF 6041

Vinson, Eddie

BOSSES OF THE BLUES VOL 2 (See under Spann, Otis) (Spann, Otis & Eddie 'Cleanhead' Vinson).

Vinson, Walter

RATS BEEN ON MY CHEESE.
LP: AB 2003

Vintage

MIGHTY BOTTLE, THE.
LP: GS 2293

Vintage Irving Berlin

VINTAGE IRVING BERLIN (Various artists).
Tracks: / Oh how I hate to get up in the morning: *Berlin, Irving* / Mandy: *Van & Schenck* / Pretty girl is like a melody ,A: *Steele, John* / Rockabye baby: *Moore, Grace* / Shakin' the blues away: *Etting, Ruth* / It all belongs to me: *Etting, Ruth* / Where is the song of songs for me: *Velez,Lupe* / Let me sing and I'm happy: *Jolson, Al* / Puttin on the ritz: *Richman, Harry* / Not for all the tea in China: *Webb, Clifton* / How's chances: *Webb, Clifton* / Heatwave: *Waters, Ethel* / How deep is the ocean: *Merman, Ethel* / Cheek to cheek: *Rogers, Ginger* / Louisiana purchas: *Bruce, Carol*.
LP: NW 238

Vintage Opera

VINTAGE COLLECTION (Various artists).
LP: REH 715
MC: ZCR 715

Vinton, Bobby

BLUE VELVET (ALBUM).
Tracks: / Blue velvet / Blue on blue / Let's kiss and make up / There I've said it again / I love the way you are / Trouble is my middle name / Halfway to paradise / Roses are red (my love) / Mr. Lonely / My heart belongs to only you / Rain rain go away / Over the mountain (across the sea) / Tell me why.
LP: 4675701
MC: 4675704

ROSES ARE RED.
MC: MC 62087

Vinx

ROOM IN MY FATHA'S HOUSE.
Tracks: / Tell my feet / I should have told her / My TV / While the city sleeps / I'll give my all to you / Captain's song / Somehow did you know / Little queen / Temporary love / Porch light / Don't got to be that way / Little bit more, A.
MC: EIRSAC 1059

Vinyl Frontier

VINYL FRONTIER (Various artists).
LP: BBPLP 02

Violence

ETERNAL NIGHTMARE.
Tracks: / Eternal nightmare / Serial killer / Phobophobia / Calling in the coroner / T.D.S. take it as you will / Bodies on bodies / Kill on command.
LP: MCF 3423
MC: MCFC 3423

Violent Blue

YOU'VE GOT TO STAY YOUNG.
Tracks: / Given you up / I won't give in loving you / Stick together / Autumn / Faces stare / Losing you / Happy for you / Everything's gonna be alright / Tension / Give me love / Heart beats fast / Big wheel.
LP: MAGL 5064

Violent Femmes

'3'.
Tracks: / Nightmares / Just like my father / Dating days / Fat / Fool in the full moon / Nothing worth living for / World we're living in / Outside the palace / Telephone book / Mother of a girl / See my ships.
LP: 828 130-1
MC: 828 130-4

BLIND LEADING THE NAKED, THE.
Tracks: / Old Mother Reagan / No killing / Love and make me three / Faith / Breakin hearts / Special / I held her in my arms / Children of the revolution / Good friends / Heartaches / Cold canyon / Two people / Candlelight song / Country death song / Black girls / World without mercy.
LP: SLAP 10
MC: SMAC 10

HALLOWED GROUND.
Tracks: / Country death song / I hear the rain / Never tell / Jesus walking on the water / I know it's true but I'm sorry to say / Hallowed ground / Sweet misery blues / Black girls / It's gonna rain.
LP: SLAP 1
MC: SMAC 1

VIOLENT FEMMES.
Tracks: / Gone daddy gone / Add it up / To the hill / Kiss off / Good feeling / Confessions / Promises.
LP: SLMP15

WHY DO BIRDS SING ?.
Tracks: / American music / Out the window / Do you really want to hurt me? / Hey nonny nonny / Used to be / Girl trouble / He likes me / Life is a scream / Flamingo baby / Lack of knowledge / More money tonight / I'm free.
LP: 8282391
MC: 8282394

Violent Force

MALEVOLENT ASSAULT.
LP: RR 9612

Violet Hour

FIRE SERMON, THE.
Tracks: / Dream of me / Spell, The / By a river / Could have been / Offertory song / Falling / Hold me / Wind blowin' / House, The / Better be good / For mercy.
LP: 468420 1
MC: 468420 4

Violet White

SWEET DISEASE.
LP: JERK 1

Violets Are Blue...

VIOLETS ARE BLUE 16 more timeless love songs (Various artists).
MC: IHMC 06

Violin...

VIOLIN FAVOURITES (Various artists).
MC: TC2MOM 118

Violin Summit

VIOLIN SUMMIT (Various artists).
Tracks: / Summit soul: *Various artists* / Pentup house: *Various artists* / Timme's blues: *Various artists*/ It don't mean a thing: *Various artists* / Pennies from Heaven: *Various artists* / Only time will tell: *Various artists* / Hot toddy: *Various artists*.
LP: 8213031

Violinsky

NO CAUSE FOR ALARM.
LP: JETLP 219

Viorst, Judith

ALEXANDER & THE TERRIBLE, HORRIBLE, NO GOOD (very bad day) (Danner, Blythe).
MC: 1722

HOW DID I GET TO BE 40 & OTHER ATROCITIES.
MC: 1586

Viper Mad Blues

VIPER MAD BLUES (16 songs of dope and depravity) (Various artists).
LP: JASS 4

Vipers Skiffle Group

VIPERS SKIFFLE GROUP (Coffee bar session).
Tracks: / Gloryland / John B. sails / Wanderin / I saw the light / Precious memories / I know the Lord laid his hands on me / This land is your land / If I had a hammer / Easy rider / Cumberland gap / Hey Liley Liley o / Don't you rock me daddy-o / It takes a worried man / Maggie Mae / 10,000 years ago / Streamline train / Pick a bale of cotton / Ain't you glad / Darlin'.
LP: ROLL 2011

V.I.P.s (Film)

V.I.P.S, THE (Film soundtrack) (Various artists).
LP: MCA 25001
MC: MCAC 25001

Virgin Prunes

HIDDEN LIE (Live in Paris).
Tracks: / Sweethome (under white clouds) / Lady Day / God bless the child / Never ending story / Pagan love song / Love is danger / Moon looked down and laughed, The / Caucasian walk / Blues song, The.
LP: BABY 008
MC: BABYC 008

IF I DIE I DIE.
LP: ROUGH 49

MOON LOOKED DOWN AND LAUGHED, THE.
LP: BABY 005
MC: BABY 005C

OVER THE RAINBOW.
LP: BABY 002
MC: BABYT 2

Virgin soldiers

VIRGIN SOLDIERS, THE (See under Thomas, Leslie (author)).

Virgin Steele

AGE OF CONSENT.
LP: 084 604

Virgin Steele II

GUARDIANS OF THE FLAME.
LP: MFN 5

Virgin & The Gypsy

VIRGIN & THE GYPSY, THE (See also D.H. Lawrence).

Virginia Wolf

PUSH.
Tracks: / Don't break away / One night / Standing on the edge of time / Open door / Man in the moon, The / Let it go / You don't know what you've got / Can you feel the fire / Tables have turned / Strangest thing, The.
LP: K 781 756 1
MC: K 781 756 4

VIRGINIA WOLF.
Tracks: / Are we playing with fire? / Make it tonight / Only love / It's in your eyes / Waiting for your love / Living on a knife edge / For all we know / Don't run away / Take a chance / Goodbye don't mean forever.
LP: 781 274-1
MC: 781 274-4

Virginians

BALLADS & BLUEGRASS (see Harrell, Bill) (Virginians/Bill Harrell).

Virgo

VIRGO.
Tracks: / Do you know who you are / Going thru life / Ride / Never want to lose you / In a vision / Take me higher / School hall / All the time.
LP: VIRGO 1
MC: ZCVIRGO 1

Virtue, Frank

GUITAR BOOGIE SHUFFLE (Virtue, Frank & The Virtues).
Tracks: / Guitar boogie shuffle / Mambo rock / Jimmy's shuffle / Rollin' and rockin' / Ooh ya gotta / Let's have a party / My constant love / Toodle-oo Kangaroo / Hop skip jump mambo / Go Joe go / I think you're lying / I ain't gonna do it no more / Goodbye mambo.
LP: PRX 16

Virtue In Danger

VIRTUE IN DANGER (Original London cast) (Various artists).
LP: TER 1079
MC: ZCTER 1079

Virtuous Lady (bk)

VIRTUOUS LADY (Madeleine Ker) (Boyd, Carole (nar)).
MC: PMB 007

Virunga, Orc

MALAKO.
LP: ERT 1006

Virus

FORCE RECON.
LP: VOV 669
MC: VOVC 669

LUNACY.
LP: VOV 677
MC: VOVMC 677

PRAY FOR WAR.
LP: VOV 665

SYSTEMATIC DEATH, MAD CONFLUX ETC..
LP: JHL 108

Visage

ANVIL, THE.
Tracks: / Anvil / Damned don't cry / Move up / Night train / Horseman / Look what they've done / Again we love / Wild life / Whispers.
LP: POLD 5050

BEAT BOY.
Tracks: / Beat boy / Casualty / Questions / Only the good die young / Can you hear me / Promise / Love glove / Yesterday's shadow.
LP: POLH 12

FADE TO GREY - THE SINGLES COLLECTION.
Tracks: / Fade to grey / Mind of a toy / Visage / We move / Tar / In the year 2525 / Anvil (night club school) / Night train / Pleasure boys / Damned don't cry.
LP: POLD 5117
MC: POLDC 5117

VISAGE.
LP: 2490 157

VISAGE / THE ANVIL.
Tracks: / Visage / Blocks on blocks / Dancer / Tar / Fade to grey / Malpaso man / Mind of a toy / Moon over Moscow / Steps / Damned don't cry / Anvil (night club school) / Move up / Night train / Horseman / Look what they've done / Again we love / Wild life / Whispers.
MCSET: 3577 379

Viseur, Gus

SOUVENIRS MUSETTE.
Tracks: / Soir de dispute / Josseline / Bourrasque / Belle touche / Gracieuzette / Adios Pepita / Bolajo.
LP: 509160

Vision

DUBVISION.
Tracks: / Dub start / Lingo dub / Forward dub / Reality dub / Whirl dub / Dub vision / Radionic / Dub cool-out part II.
LP: EFA 4530

EXPOSED.
Tracks: / Exposed / Victim, The / Can't let her go / Do it tonight / Kisses don't lie / Seduction, The / Private passion / Where did our love go / Lust 4 U.
LP: DOM LP 1
LP: WIL 3002

INTRODUCING VISION.
LP: BSS 312

VISION, THE.
LP: EFA 4525

Vision Quest

VISION QUEST (Film Soundtrack) (Various artists).
LP: GEF 70263

Visionaries

AGE OF MAGIC BEGINS, THE.
MC: 00 102163 X

DARK HAND OF TREACHERY, THE.
MC: 00 102164 8

Visions

VISIONS - 28 SCREEN SMASHES (Various artists).
2LP: CR 5145
MCSET: CRT 5145

Visions (Group)

VISIONS.
Tracks: / Visions / You're gonna be mine / Perfect love affair / Hypnotized / Missing you / It's a choice / First time / Love calls / Special one.
LP: URBLP 12
MC: URBMC 12

Visions Of Change

VISIONS OF CHANGE.
LP: FLYP 1

Visitors

MOTHERLAND.
LP: MR 5094

VISITORS.
Tracks: / V-I-S-I-T-O-R-S '81 / Everybody now / A-E-I-E-O / Reveille toi-svegliati-get up / Mental slavery / Joyo can you hear (Part 1) / Joyo can you hear (Part 2) / Don't squeeze / Try.
LP: RCALP 6010
MC: RCAK 6010

Vita (label)

BEST OF VITA, THE (Various artists).
LP: VITA 5007

Vital Dub

WELL CHARGED.
Tracks: / Roof top dub / Ital step / Fence (dub) / Ishens dub / Total dub / Merciful dub / Cell block 11 / Killer dub / Black a black dub.
LP: V 2055

Vital Excursions

GIVE.
LP: Z1

Vitale, Joe

PLANTATION HARBOUR.
Tracks: / Plantation harbour / Never gonna leave you alone / Laugh laugh / Man gonna love you / Cabin weirdos,

Theme from / Lady of the rock / Bamboo jungle / Sailor man / I'm flyin'.
LP: K 52293

Vitale, Lito

CUARTETO.
LP: 15994

Vitamin Z

RITES OF PASSAGE.
Tracks: / Hi hi friend / Casablanca / Circus ring (we scream about) / Something we can do / Burning flame / Angela / Everytime that I see you / Anybody out there.
LP: MERH 73
MC: MERHC 73

SHARP STONE RAIN.
Tracks: / Can't live without you / Wipe your tears / Save me / Burn for you / Heal the pain / Run for our lives / Don't wait for me / How far to Queensland / Burning flame / Everchanging heart / Run for you.
LP: 838 847 1
MC: 838 847 4

Vitesse

VITESSE.
Tracks: / Out in the country / Running and hiding / Rollin' through the midnight rain / Do you love me / Last boat / Goin' down / Only rebels / We'll do the music tonight / Come on Camaro / I'll be fine / Take off / You can't beat me / Fly on / Spirit.
LP: IAG 30250

Vitous, Miroslav

DREAM (see Honda, Toshiyuki) (Vitous, Miroslav/Toshiyuki Honda/Chick Corea/ Roy Haynes).

EMERGENCE.
Tracks: / Epilogue / Transformation / Atlantis suite: / Atlantis suite-Emergence of the spirit / Atlantis suite-Matter and spirit / Atlantis suite-choice, The / Atlantis suite-Destruction into energy / Wheel of fortune (when the face gets pale) / Regards to Gershwin's honeyman / Alice in Wonderland / Morning lake for ever / Variations on Spanish themes.
LP: EMC 1312

JOURNEY'S END.
Tracks: / U dunaje u prespurka / Tess / Carry on No. 1 / Paragraph Jay / Only one / Windfall.
LP: ECM 1242

MIROSLAV VITOUS GROUP (Vitous/ Surman/Kirkland/Christensen).
LP: ECM 1185

MOUNTAIN IN THE CLOUDS (THAT'S JAZZ SERIES).
Tracks: / Freedom jazz dance / Mountain in the clouds / Epilogue / Cerecka / Indinate search / I will tell him on you / When face gets pale.
LP: K 50406

Viva

DEALERS OF THE NIGHT.
Tracks: / Falling in love / Ten years later / I didn't see it coming / Dealer of the night / Some kind of wonderful / Take me to the doors / Spend the night / Looking for an answer.
LP: 1060 557

Viva La Revolution

VIVA LA REVOLUTION (Various artists).
2LP: CR 5157
MCSET: CRT 5157

Viva Saturn

VIVA SATURN.
LP: SERVS 003

Viva Um Khomto

VIVA UM KHOMTO (Various artists).
LP: K 031 104
MC: KO 104

Viva Vivaldi

BESSES O' TH' BARN BAND.
LP: GRS 1042

Vivaldi (composer)

CONCERTOS FOR RECORDER, LUTE, 2 MANDOLINS ETC (Various artists).
MC: 4278244

FOUR SEASONS (Kennedy, Nigel & English Chamber Orchestra).
LP: EL 7495571
MC: EL 7495574

FOUR SEASONS, THE (Kennedy, Nigel & English Chamber Orchestra).
LP: NIGE 2
MC: TCNIGE 2

FOUR SEASONS, THE (Various artists).
MC: VETC 6514

GUITAR CONCERTOS NOS 93, 82, 580, 532 & 425 (San Antonio Symphony Orchestra).
MC: 426 076-4

JESU, JOY OF MANS DESIRING (see under Bach, J.S.) (Various artists).

TRUMPET MUSIC FROM THE ITALIAN BAROQUE (See under Trumpet Music for details) (Various artists).

VIVALDI: THE FOUR SEASONS (Handel: Water music)(see under English Chamber Orchestra) (English Chamber Orchestra).

VIVALDI VOL.1 (Various artists).
MC: DLCMC 201

Vivat Regina

VIVAT REGINA (A ROYAL PORTRAIT IN SOUND) (Various artists).
2LP: REL 273
MC: ZCD 273

Vivo

VIVO (Various artists).
LP: MASO 33040LP
MC: MASO 33040C

Vixen

REV IT UP.
Tracks: / Rev it up / How much love / Love is a killer / Not a minute too soon / Streets in paradise / Hard 16 / Bad reputation / Fallen hero / Only a heartbeat away / It wouldn't be love / Wrecking ball.
LP: MTL 1054
LP: 792 923 1
MC: TCMTL 1054
MC: 792 923 4

VIXEN.
Tracks: / Edge of a broken heart / I want you to rock me / Crying / American dream / Desperate / One night alone / Hellraisers / Love made me / Waiting / Cruisin' / Charmed life (CD only.).
LP: MTL 1028
MC: TCMTL 1028
LP: FA 3256
MC: TCFA 3256

VIXEN: INTERVIEW PICTURE DISC.
LPPD: BAK 2159

Vocal Groups

VOCAL GROUPS OF THE 40'S & 50'S (Vocal Groups Of The 40's & 50's).
Tracks: / Paper doll / Glow worm / Gypsy, The / To each his own / Three coins in the fountain / Stranger in paradise / Rag mop / Undecided / On top of old smokey / Kisses sweeter than wine / Only you / I'll be with you in... / Don't fence me in / Moonglow / It's almost tomorrow / Jingle jangle / Coming on in.
LP: MCL 1863
MC: MCLC 1863

VOCAL GROUPS, THE (Various artists).
MC: PLAC 343

V'Od, Klezmer

ENCOUNTERS OF THE YIDDISH KIND.
MC: GVMMC 113

Vogel, Karsten

EVERGREENS (Vogel, Karsten Quartet).
LP: SLP 4143

Voi Vod

DIMENSION HATROSS.
LP: N 0106
MC: N 01062
LP: NUK 106
MC: ZCNUK 106

KILLING TECHNOLOGY.
LP: NUK 058
MC: ZCNUK 058
LP: N 0058
MC: N 0068

NOTHING FACE.
Tracks: / Unknown knows, The / Astronomy knows, The / X-ray mirror / Pre-ignition / Sub-effect / Nothingface / Missing sequences / Inner combustion / Into my hypercube.
LP: MCG 6070
MC: MCGC 6070

RRROOOAAARRR.
LP: N 0040
LP: NUK 040

WAR AND PAIN.
Tracks: / Voi void / Suck your bone / War and pain / Live for violence / Nuclear war / Warriors of ice / Iron gang / Blower / Black city.
LP: RR 9825

Voice of America

I WILL TELL.
LP: TAB 24

Voice Of Authority

VERY BIG IN AMERICA RIGHT NOW.
LP: BRED 62

Voice of Cricket

VOICE OF CRICKET, THE (Arlott, John (nar)).
MCSET: ZBBC 1108

Voice Of God

SOUNDS LIKE BROMLEY (see under Jenkins, Billy) (Voice Of God Collective & Billy Jenkins).

Voice Of Music

VOICE OF MUSIC (Various).
LP: 80082
LP: 80083

Voice Of Progress

SHADOW AFTER DARK.
Tracks: / Working on a site / Shadow after dark / Lost in space / Mini bus driver / Rich man / Can't take the gun / Give thanks / Tell your friend.
LP: BMLP 059

Voice Of The Beehive

HONEY LINGERS.
LP: 8282591
MC: 8282594

Voices (Film)

VOICES (Film soundtrack) (Various artists).
Tracks: / I will always wait for you: *Various artists* / Rosemarie's theme: *Various artists* / Disco if you want to: *Various artists* / Children's song: *Various artists* / Family theme: *Various artists* / Anything that's rock 'n' roll: *Various artists* / I will always wait for you (instrumental): *Various artists* / On a stage: *Various* artists / Across the river: *Various artists* / Bubbles in my beer: *Various artists* / Rosemarie and drew: *Various artists* / Drunk as a punk: *Various artists* / Children's song (instrumental): *Various artists*/ Rosemarie's dance: *Various artists.*
LP: K 52158

Voices Of Our Fantasy

VOICES OF OUR FANTASY (Various artists).
LP: SNTF 1022

Voices Of Progress

MINI-BUS DRIVER.
LP: NERLP 003

Void

SPLIT (Void/Faith).
LP: DISCHORD 8

Voiz

BOANERGES.
LP: PC 110

Volcano

RAT RACE.
LP: CORE 7

Volcano Suns

ALL NIGHT LOTUS PARTY.
LP: HMS 070

BRIGHT ORANGE.
LP: HMS 020

FARCED.
LP: SST 210
MC: SSTC 210

THINGS OF BEAUTY.
LP: SST 257
MC: SSTC 257

Volcanoes

INTO THE PSYCHE.
LP: HYBLP 8

Vollenweider, Andreas

BEHIND THE GARDENS, BEHIND THE WALL, UNDER THE T.
Tracks: / Behind the gardens, behind the wall, under the tree / Pyramid-in the wood-in the bright light / Micro macro / Skin and skin / Moonlight wrapped around us / Lion and sheep / Sunday / Hands and clouds / Afternoon.
LP: CBS 85545

DANCING WITH THE LION.
Tracks: / Unto the burning circle / Dancing with the lion / Hippolyte / Dance of the masks / Pearls and tears / Garden of my childhood / Still life / And the long shadows / See, my love .... silver dew / Golden grass / Ascent from the circle.
LP: 4633311
MC: 4633314

DOWN TO THE MOON.
Tracks: / Down to the moon / Moon dance / Steam forest / Water moon / Might fire dance / Quiet observer / Silver wheel / Drown in pale light / Secret, the candle and love, The / Hush patience at bamboo forest / Three silver ladies dance / La lune at l'enfant.
LP: CBS 57001
MC: 40 57001

TRILOGY, THE.
MCSET: 4676294

WHITE WINDS.
Tracks: / White winds the white boat, The (First view) / Hall of the mosaics (meeting you) / Glass hall (choose the crystal), The / Play of the five balls/The five planets/Canopy / Woman and the stone, The / Stone (close up), The / Phases of the three moons / Flight feet and root hands / Brothership / Sisterseed / Trilogy (at the white magic gardens) / White winds.
LP: FM 26195
MC: 40 26195

Volt Face

HAUTE TENSION.
LP: ZLP 7232

Volume Unit

TERRA INCOGNITA.
LP: ST 7548

Volz, Greg

COME OUT FIGHTING.
LP: MYR R 6865
MC: MYR C 6865

RIVER IS RISING, THE.
LP: MYR R 1220
MC: MYR C 1220

Vomit Launch

MR SPENCH.
LP: MR 1901
MC: MR 1901MC

Vomito Negro

DARE.
LP: KK 009

HUMAN.
LP: KK 050

SHOCK.
LP: KK 023

Von Deyen, Adelbert

IMPRESSIONS.
LP: SKY 097

Von Karajan, Herbert

HOLST: THE PLANETS.
MC: 4352894
LP: 4352891

Von Magnet

EL DON IMAN.
LP: INNR 002

EL SEXO SURREALISTA.
LP: INNR 004

Von Schmedes, Maria

IHRE SCHONSTEN LIEDER.
Tracks: / Von lech bis St Anton / I hab rote haar / Ich furcht mich so / Wenn ich geburtstag hab / Ich zahl mir's an den knopfen ab / Es ist ein abschied nur fur heut / I kann net bugeln / Oh Susannah / Verliebt / Mein kaffeehaferl / Zwischen simmering und favoriten / Die rosdarote kuh / Zum abschied reich' ich dir die hande.
LP: V 130 003

Von Schmidt, Eric

ERIC VON SCHMIDT AND THE CRUEL FAMILY (Von Schmidt, Eric & The Cruel Family).
LP: PH 1052

Vonk, Henny

REROOTIN' HENNY VONK.
Tracks: / Fran dance / Circle / Dolphin dance / Blessing, The / Tribute to someone, A / Cloud of knowledge / Pompel.
LP: SJP 164

Vonnegut, Kurt

BREAKFAST OF CHAMPIONS.
MC: CDL 51602

CAT'S CRADLE.
MC: 1346

SLAUGHTERHOUSE FIVE.
MC: 1376

VONNEGUT SOUNDBOOK (Various artists).
MC: SBC 120

Vono

MODEL LEBEN.
LP: SKY 86

Voodoo Child

ACID TAILS AND MERMAIDS.
LP: AFT 2

Voodoo Dolls

PROBLEMS WITH GIRLS.
LP: JAY 861

VOODOO DOLLS.
LP: RD 3002

Voodoo Gang

RETURN OF THE TURTLE.
LP: ENJA 4064

Vorhaus, David

WHITE NOISE.
LP: . . . . V 2032
MC: . . . . TCV 2032

WHITE NOISE 2.
Tracks: / Movements 1-3.
LP: . . . . OVED 204

Voronezh Vocal Group

VORONEZH GIRLS VOCAL GROUP (TRADITIONAL SONGS).
LP: . . . . CM 04391-2

Vortex

LE CLAN DES CHAOTIQUES.
Tracks: / Le seigneur dul mal / Stop that / Sortle nocturne / L'horreur / Continental nightmare / Le clan des chaotiques / La salope / La terreur du troquet / Jack the ripper / Revolution saiglante / Lost in the underdark / Buvez du le.
LP: . . . . STK 2001B

Voss, Jane

ALBUM OF SONGS, AN.
LP: . . . . BAY 207

Vow Wow

CYCLONE.
LP: . . . . ERLP 50
MC: . . . . ERMC 50

HELTER SKELTER (ALBUM).
Tracks: / I feel the power / Talking 'bout you / Spellbound / Helter skelter / Boy, The / Rock me now / Turn on the light / Never let you go / Night by night / You're the one for me / Sign of the times.
LP: 209691
MC: 409691

LIVE: VOW WOW.
Tracks: / Introduction - beat of metal motion / Doncha wanna come (hangar 15) / Too late to turn back / Mask of flesh (Masquerade) / Pains of love / Love walks / Premonition / Hurricane / Shot in the dark / Nightless city.
LP: . . . . PBL 102
MC: . . . . PBLT 102

VOW WOW.
Tracks: / Don't tell me lies / Somewhere in the night / Girl in red / Breakout / Cry no more / Same town / Born to die / Waited for a lifetime / Don't leave me now / War man / Don't leave me now (extended version) (Extra track on cassette and CD only.).
2LP: . . . . HMILP 109
MCSET: . . . . HMIMC 109

VOW WOW: INTERVIEW PICTURE DISC.
LPPD: . . . . CT 1022

VOW WOW V.
Tracks: / You're mine / Jets / Clean machine / Can't get back to you / Heels of the wind / Poor man's Eden / 20th century child / Abnormal weather / Welcome to the monster city / Breakout the trick / Warning from stardust / Getting back on the road / Don't cry baby / Devil woman / Vow wow, Theme from.
LP: 208678
MC: 408678

WARNING FROM STARDUST.
Tracks: / You're mine / Jets / Clean machine / Can't get back to you / Heels of the wind / Poor man's Eden / 20th century child / Abnormal weather / Welcome to the monster city / Breakout the trick / Warning from stardust.
LP: . . . . HMILP 5

Vox nouveau

VOX NOUVEAU (Various artists).
LP: . . . . SELP 001

Voyage

VOYAGE.
LP: . . . . GTLP 030

Voyager (Group)

ACT OF LOVE.
Tracks: / Sing out, love is easy / Keeping the music alive / Whatever happened to Cherry? / You're always the last to know / Clever girl / Leadhead / At the lido / Grass / Cling to me.
LP: . . . . TOPS 127

HALFWAY HOTEL.
Tracks: / Judas / E.S.P / Standing still / 4-2-4 or 4-4-2 / Straight actors / Total amnesia / Halfway hotel / Captain Remus / I love it.
LP: . . . . TOPS 124

VOYAGER.
Tracks: / King of Siam / Charlie's band / Out on loan / Lucky / When it gets too much / Rosie / Cue for you / When I need a friend / Quelles impasse / Two hearts.
LP: . . . . RCALP 5020
MC: . . . . RCAK 5020

Voyager (various)

VOYAGER (Various artists).
LP: . . . . STL 4
MC: . . . . STC 4

Voyages Of Sinbad

VOYAGES OF SINBAD (See under Sinbad the Sailor) (Jones, Terry (nar)).

Vrethammar, Sylvia

IN GOODMAN'S LAND (see Fame, Georgie & Sylvia Vrethammer) (Vrethammar, Sylvia & Georgie Fame).

RIO DE JANEIRO.
LP: . . . . SNTF 943

Y VIVA ESPANA.
LP: . . . . SNTF 664

Vrtacek, Charles

MONKEY ON A HARD ROLL.
LP: . . . . LT 003

V.S.O.P. The Quintet

FIVE STARS.
LP: . . . . 30 AP 1036

LIVE UNDER THE SKY.
2LP: . . . . 40 AP 1037/8

Vuchovich, Larry

BLUES FOR RED (Vuckovich, Larry Trio).
LP: . . . . HH 1001

CITY SOUNDS, VILLAGE VOICES.
LP: . . . . PA 8030

TRES PALABRAS.
Tracks: / Serbo afro / Historia de un amor / You go to my head / Ah, se eu pudesse / I know why (Only on CD.) / Serenade in blue (Only on CD.) / Blues in the night / Dreamy (Only on CD.) / Cast your fate to the wind / Tres palabras / Blues for Alexi (Only on CD.) / Rio.
MC: . . . . CJ 416 C

Vujicsics

VUJICSICS.
LP: . . . . HNBL 1310
MC: . . . . HNBC 1310

Vulcano

BLOODY VENGEANCE.
Tracks: / Dominions of death / Spirits of evil / Ready to explode / Holocaust / Incubus / Death metal / Voices from hell / Bloody vengeance.
LP: . . . . VOV 676

Vuti, Emma

BILLY LE KID.
LP: . . . . MA 4037

V.V.S.I.

NO ACE AT HAND.
LP: . . . . NRR 21
MC: . . . . NRC 21

Vyllies

LILLITH.
Tracks: / Whispers in the shadows / Seventh heaven / Bad trip / Food prayer, The / La, nuit des Vyllies / Give me a name / Beautiful diseases / Black raven, The / Desire (repetition desperation).
LP: . . . . AFTER 2

SACRED GAMES.
LP: . . . . AFTER 4

W

Wa Wa Nee

WA WA NEE.
Tracks: / One and one (ain't I good enough) / Teacher / Stimulation / Jelly baby / Gone / Sugar free / When the world is a home / Manchild / Love reaction / I could make you love me.
LP: **4503461**
MC: **4503464**

Wachsmann

IMPROVISATIONS ARE FOREVER NOW (see under Riley) (Wachsmann/Riley/Guy).

Wackie's Rhythm Force

AFRICAN ROOTS ACT IV.
LP: . . . . **W 2453**

AFRICAN ROOTS ACT V.
LP: . . . . **W 2456**

Wade In The Water

WADE IN THE WATER (Various artists).
LP: . . . . **JR 157**

Wade, Norman

REAL COUNTRY.
LP: . . . . **JIN 9021**

Wade, Paul

SHAKESPEARE SONGS OF THE TWENTIETH CENTURY.
Tracks: / Songs of the clown / Music for love's labours lost / Songs for moth / Come unto these yellow sands / Tell me where is fancy bred / Three Shakespeare songs / Five Shakespeare songs / Four Shakespeare songs.
LP: . . . . **LK/LP 6125**

Wade, Wayne

LOOKING FOR LOVE.
LP: . . . . **DUBLP 004**

RESPECT DUE ALWAYS.
LP: . . . . **FJ 3302**

Wadham, John

DRUMS AND FRIENDS (Wadham, John & Louis Stewart).
Tracks: / Clarence's place / Floatin' / Winter song / Pompeiian.
LP: . . . . **LRLP 2**

Wadling, Freddie

DICE MAN, THE.
LP: . . . . **RAO 78**

Waggoner, Jean

PATTERN OF SHADOWS, A.
MCSET: . . . . **MRC 1029**

Wagner (composer)

DER FLIEGENDE HOLLANDER/DIE MEISTERSINGER VON NU (Various artists).
MC: . . . . **MC 4277214 GW**

DUTCHMAN & MEISTERSINGER HIGHLIGHTS (Various artists).
MC: **4277214**

EXCERPTS FROM TRISTAN UND ISOLDE AND OTHERS (Orchestre De Paris).
MC: **4278254**

FLYING DUTCHMAN, THE - OVERTURE (See under Solti, Sir George) (Chicago Symphony Orchestra).

LOHENGRIN & TANNHAUSER HIGHLIGHTS (Various artists).
MC: **4277204**

LOHENGRIN/TANNHAUSER-HIGHLIGHTS (Various artists).
MC: . . . . **MC 4277204 GW**

SIEGFRIED IDYLL (See under Mahler (composer) Symphony No. 9) (Various artists).

WAGNER'S GREATEST HITS (Various artists).
MC: **40 79022**

Wagner, Jack

DON'T GIVE UP YOUR DAY JOB.
Tracks: / Weatherman says / Island fever / Love...find it / It's what we don't say / Easy way out / Common man / Lovers in the night / Sneakin' suspicions / It's been a long time / Back home again.
LP: **925562 1**
MC: **925562 4**

Wagner, Roger

BEST OF THE ROGER WAGNER CHORALE CHRISTMAS CAROL (Wagner, Roger Chorale).
LP: . . . . **MFP 5588**
MC: . . . . **TCMFP 5588**

Wagoneers

STOUT AND HIGH.
Tracks: / I confess / Help me to get over you / So many mistakes / Please don't think I'm guilty / Stout and high / I wanna know her again / It'll take some time / Lie and say you love me / Every step of the way / Hell town / All nite.
LP: . . . . **AMA 5200**
MC: . . . . **AMC 5200**

Wagoner, Porter

20 OF THE BEST: PORTER WAGONER.
Tracks: / Satisfied mind, A / Your old love letters / Carroll County accident / Eat drink and be merry / I'll go down swinging / Company's coming / Big wind / Cold dark winter / Skid Row Joe / What would you do if Jesus came to your house / Green green grass of home / Everything I've always wanted / I just came to smell the flowers / Misery loves company / Old slew foot / What ain't to be just might happen / I've enjoyed as much of this as I can stand / When Lea Jane sang / Sorrow on the rocks / Cold hard facts of life, The.
LP: . . . . **NL 89094**
MC: . . . . **NK 89094**
LP: . . . . **INTS 5197**

BEST OF PORTER WAGONER.
Tracks: / Cold hard facts of life / Big wind / Little boy's prayer / I couldn't wait forever / Men with broken hearts / Ol' slew foot / Carroll County accident, The / You gotta have a licence / When you're hot you're hot / Banks of the Ohio / Pastor's absent on vacation.
LP: . . . . **LSA 3006**

BEST OF PORTER WAGONER AND DOLLY PARTON, THE (See under Dolly Parton) (Wagoner, Porter/Dolly Parton).

BLUEGRASS STORY, THE.
LP: . . . . **HAT 3113**
MC: . . . . **HATC 3113**

COUNTRY MEMORIES.
MC: . . . . **GM 0215**

HITS OF DOLLY PARTON & PORTER WAGONER (Wagoner, Porter/Dolly Parton).
Tracks: / Better move it on home / Just someone I used to know / If teardrops were pennies / Tomorrow is forever / We found it / Yours, love / Burning the midnight oil / Please don't stop loving me / Daddy was an old time preacher man / Say forever you'll be mine / Right combination, The / Lost forever in your kiss / Together always / How can I (help you forgive me).
LP: . . . . **PL 42193**
MC: . . . . **PK 42193**

HITS OF PORTER WAGONER.
LP: . . . . **PL 42182**
MC: . . . . **PK 42182**

LOVE SHINE.
LP: **20115**
MC: **40115**

MAKING PLANS (See under Parton, Dolly for details) (Wagoner, Porter/Dolly Parton).

PORTER WAGONER.
Tracks: / One more time / Love paid it all / Sugar foot rag / For a good time call Naomi / Louisiana Saturday night / Same way you came in, The / Sorrow on the rocks / What a memory we'd make / Satan wore satin / Uncle Pen.
LP: . . . . **IMCA 39053**
MC: . . . . **ZCGAS 710**

PORTER WAGONER COLLECTION.
Tracks: / Green, green grass of home / Ole slew foot / Skid Row Joe / I thought I heard you call my name / Katy did / Carroll County accident / I've enjoyed as much of this as I can stand / Pick me up on your way down / Trouble in amen corner / I'm so lonesome I could cry / He stopped loving her today / If you're gonna do me wrong (do it right) / Cold hard facts of life, The / Old love letters / Satisfied mind, A / Rose, The / Crying my heart out over you / Have I told you lately that I love you? / Misery loves company / Is anybody going to San Antone?.
2LP: . . . . **PPD 2005**
MC: . . . . **PPK 2005**

SATISFIED MIND.
Tracks: / Satisfied mind, A / I like girls / Company's coming / Midnight / I guess I'm crazy / Living in the past / My bonfire / Ivory tower / Born to lose / That's it / I'm stepping out tonight / Tricks of the trade.
LP: . . . . **HAT 3064**
MC: . . . . **HATC 3064**

THIN MAN FROM WEST PLAINS.
LP: . . . . **HAT 3099**
MC: . . . . **HATC 3099**

TODAY.
Tracks: / I'm gonna feed you now / Ole slewfoot / I'm gonna act right / Tennessee Saturday night / High country / Banks of the Ohio / I couldn't care less / I guess I'm crazy / Old love letters / All I need.
LP: . . . . **PL 13210**

Wah!

NAH POO THE ART OF BLUFF.
LP: . . . . **CLASSIC 1**

WAY WE WAH, THE.
Tracks: / Other boys / Somesay / Seven thousand names of Wah, The / Seven minutes to midnight / Death of Wah, The / Story of the blues part 1 & 2, The / Sleep (a lullaby for Josie) / You can't put your arms around a memory / Hope (remix) / Remember.
LP: . . . . **WX 11**
MC: . . . . **WX 11C**

Wahl, Jan (nar)

RUNAWAY JONAH & OTHER BIBLICAL ADVENTURES.
MC: **1779**

Wahlberg, Donnie

RIGHT COMBINATION, THE (See under Seiko for details) (Seiko and Donnie Wahlberg).

Wahnfried, Richard

MEGATONE.
Tracks: / Angry young boys / Agamemory / Rich meets Max.
LP: . . . . **THBL 031**

PLAYS MEGATONE.
LP: . . . . **ID 20006**

TIME ACTOR.
Tracks: / Time actor / Time factory / Charming the wind / Grandma's clockwork / Distorted emission / Silent sound of the ground, The / Time echoes.
LP: . . . . **RRK 15027**

Waihirere Maori Club

MUSIC OF AOTEAROA.
Tracks: / Pawa poi / Naumai / He puti puti poi / Waiata poi / Nga kaihau / Kura tiwaka / Kua tutuki ra / Karangatia ra / Tapapa poi / Koraki / Takitmu poi / Tena I poua / Combination finale.
LP: . . . . **SLC 117**
MC: . . . . **TC SLC 117**

Waikiki Islanders

MAGIC OF HAWAII.
Tracks: / Blue moon / You are my lucky star / Dream / Last waltz, The / Can't take my eyes off you / Yesterday / Quiet nights of quiet stars / This guy's in love with you / Breeze and I / Sukiyaki / Strangers in the night / Moon river / More / Three coins in the fountain / All my love / Shadow of your smile / Somewhere my love / Stranger on the shore / Blue bayou / What a wonderful world.
LP: . . . . **NTS 223**

Waikikis

HAWAII TATTOO (The best of the Waikikis).
Tracks: / Hawaii tattoo / Hawaii fair / Laguna punch / Hawaiian lollipops / E mama e / Lollipops rag / Le cinema / Hawaiian fever / Pacific punch / Hawaiian march / Waikikis on parade / Third man, Theme from.
LP: . . . . **GES 1186**
MC: . . . . **KGEC 1186**

HAWAIIAN FAVOURITES (Waikiki Beach Boys).
Tracks: / Hawaiian wedding song / Hawaiian march / Analani E / Ports of paradise / Shimmering sands / My little grass shack in Kealakua Hawaii / Kono knoi / Mamoola moon / Kahola march / Hawaiia calls / Hawaii tattoo / Sweet Leilani / Flower of the islands / Honi kaua / Garlands for your hair / Song of the islands / Tiny bubbles / Beautiful Moorea / Hawaiian honeymoon / March to Diamond Head.
MC: . . . . **HR 8113**
MC: . . . . **HR 4181134**

PLAY YOUR 40 ALL-TIME HAWAIIAN FAVOURITES (Waikiki Beach Boys).
Tracks: / Hawaiian wedding song / Hawaiian march / Analanie / Ports of paradise / Shimmering sands / My little grass shack in Kealakekua Hawaii / Hawaii tattoo / Flower of the Islands / Honi kaua / Song of the islands / Honolulu / My tane / Poinciana / Hawaiian dreamboat / Hilo kiss / Menehune march / Ka lu a / Breeze of Hawaii / Moonlight Hawaii / Hawaiian war chant / On the beach at Waikiki / Blue Hawaii / Harbour lights / Pagan love song / South sea island magic / I'll remember sweet Hawaii / Lovely hula hands / Coral reef / Moon of Manakoora / Goodbye Hawaii / Hawaiian hotel march / Beyond the reef / Tiny bubbles / Hawaiian honeymoon / March to diamond head / Tamoure / My island paradise / Koni koni / Mamoola moon / Hawaii calls.
2LP: . . . . **MFP 1005**
MCSET: . . . . **TCMFP 1005**

WAIKIKI WELCOME.
LP: . . . . **GES 1194**
MC: . . . . **KGEC 1194**

Wailer, Bunny

BLACKHEART MAN.
Tracks: / Blackheart man / Fighting against conviction / Oppressed song, The / Fig tree, The / Dream land / Rastaman / Reincarnated soul / Amagideon / Bide up / This train.
LP: . . . . **ILPS 9415**
MC: . . . . **RRCT 6**
MC: **846266 4**

BUNNY WAILER SINGS THE WAILERS.
Tracks: / Dancing shoes / Mellow mood / Dreamland / Keep on moving / Hypocrite / I'm the toughest / Rule this land / Burial / I stand predominate / Walk the proud land.
LP: . . . . **ILPS 9629**
MC: . . . . **ICT 9629**

LIBERATION.
LP: . . . . **SHAN 43059**
MC: . . . . **SHANC 43059**

LIVE: BUNNY WAILER.
LP: . . . . **SM 009**

MARKETPLACE.
LP: . . . . **SMLP 010**
MC: . . . . **SHMC 43071**

PROTEST.
Tracks: / Moses children / Get up, stand up / Scheme of things / Quit trying, follow fashion monkey / Wanted children / Who feels it / Johnny too bad.
LP: . . . . **ILPS 9512**
MC: . . . . **RRCT 7**
MC: **846267 4**

ROCK 'N' ROLL GROOVE.
LP: . . . . **DSR 3029**
LP: . . . . **DSR 2798**

ROOTS MAN SKANKING.
LP: . . . . **SHAN 43043**
MC: . . . . **SHANC 43043**

ROOTS RADICS ROCKERS REGGAE.
LP: . . . . **SHAN 43013**
MC: . . . . **SHANC 43013**

RULE DANCE HALL.
LP: . . . . **DSR 3111**
LP: . . . . **SHAN 43050**
MC: . . . . **SHANC 43050**

SINGS THE WAILERS.
Tracks: / Dancing shoes / Mellow mood / Dreamland / Keep on moving / Hypocrite / I'm the toughest / Rule this land / Burial / I stand predominate / Walk the proud land.
LP: . . . . **ILPS 9629**
MC: . . . . **RRCT 8**
MC: **846268 4**

TRIBUTE TO THE LATE ROBERT NESTER MARLEY.
Tracks: / Soul rebel / I shot the sheriff / Crazy bald head / Time will tell / War /

Slave driver / Redemption song / No woman no cry.
LP: .... VW 1001
LP: .... SM 007
LP: .... SMP 007

Wailers

BEAUTIFUL GARDEN (See under Donald & Lulu) (Wailers with Donald & Lulu).

BURNING.
LP: .... TGLLP 2

EARTH MUST BE HELL.
Tracks: / True born african / Unity strength & love / Can't you see it's time / Country woman / Earth must be hell / Let the music play / Wake up Suzy / I stand before you / How do you think I feel / Isn't it wrong / Writing on the wall.
LP: .... ATRA 1001

I.D..
Tracks: / Solution / Reggae love / Love is forever / Rice and peas / Life goes on / P's and Q's / Children of the world / Irie / Changing tomorrow / Love one another / One one coco.
LP: .... WX 256
MC: .... WX 256 C

MAJESTIC WARRIORS.
LP: 364002 1
MC: 364002 4

OUT OF OUR TREE.
LP: .... FC 043

TRIBUTE TO CARLY BARRETT.
LP: .... ATRA 1008

Wailing Souls

BEST OF THE WAILING SOULS.
LP: .... JJ 167

FIRE HOUSE ROCK.
Tracks: / Firehouse rock / Run dem down / Oh what a feeling / Kingdom rise, kingdom fall / Act of affection / Busnah / Fool will fall, A / Bandits taking over / Who lives it / See Baba Joe.
LP: .... GREL 21
MC: .... GREEN 21

INCHPINCHERS.
Tracks: / Inchpinchers / Things and time / Baby come rock / Mass charley ground / Oh what a lie / Ghetto of Kingston Town / Tom sprang / Don't get lost / Modern slavery / Infidels.
LP: .... GREL 47
MC: .... GREEN 47

KINGSTON 14.
Tracks: / Kingston 14 / Dem coming / Front door / Ring my bell / Don't run / Full moon / Yet the world waits / Pity the poor / Real rock.
LP: .... LLLP 28

ON THE ROCKS.
Tracks: / Down on the rocks / Sticky stay / Stop red eye / Gun / Jah is watching you / Riddim of life / What is your meaning / Ishen tree / Don't burn baby.
LP: .... GREL 59
MC: .... GREEN 59

SOUL AND POWER.
LP: .... SOLP 1002

STRANDED.
Tracks: / Stranded in L. A. / File for your machete / Thinking / Peace and love shall reign / Helmet of salvation / War deh round a John shop / Eyes of love / Divided and rule / Sunrise till sunset / Best is yet to come, The.
LP: .... GREL 73

VERY BEST OF THE WAILING SOULS.
Tracks: / War / Jah give us life / Bredda / Old broom / Kingdom rise kingdom fall / Firehouse rock / Who no waan come / Things and time / Stop red eye / Sticky stay / They don't know Jah / War deh round a John shop.
LP: .... GREL 99
MC: .... GREEN 99

WILD SUSPENSE.
Tracks: / Row fisherman / Slow coach / We got to be together / Feel the spirit / Bredda / Wild suspense / They never knew / Black rose / Something funny / Very well.
LP: .... ILPS 9523

Wailing Ultimate

WAILING ULTIMATE (Various artists).
LP: .... HMS 079
MC: .... HMS 79C

Wain, John

...READING THEIR POETRY (Wain, John & Ted Hughes).
MC: .... OC27 SC

Waine, Raney

FOURMOST GUITARS WITH RANEY WAINE.
Tracks: / Two dreams of soma / I'm old fashioned / You stepped out of a dream / Time was / Scholars mate / Easy mate / Easy living / Ain't misbehavin' / Gone with the wind / If I love again / Li'l basses / Yesterdays.
LP: .... JASM 1041

Wainwright, Loudon III

ALBUM II.
Tracks: / Me and my friend the cat / Motel blues / Nice jewish girls / Be careful / There's a baby in the house / Say your name in the paper / Samson and the warden / Plane, too / Cook that dinner, Dora / Old friend / Old paint / Winter song.
LP: .... ED 310
LP: .... K 40272

ALBUM III.
Tracks: / Dead skunk / Red guitar / East Indian princess / Muse blues / Hometeam crown / B side / Needless to say / Smokey Joe's cafe / New paint / Trilogy (circa 1967) / Drinking song / Say that you love me.
LP: .... ED 168
MC: .... CED 168
LP: 65238

ATTEMPTED MOUSTACHE.
Tracks: / Swimming song, The / A.M. world / Bell bottom pants / Liza / I am the way / Clockwork chartreuse / Down drinking at the bar / Man who couldn't cry, The / Come a long way / Nocturnal stumblebutt / Dilated to meet you / Lullaby / Clockwork Chartreuse / Man who couldn't cry, The.
LP: .... ED 269

FAME AND WEALTH.
Tracks: / Reader and advisor / Grammy song, The / Dump the dog / Five years old / Westchester county / Saturday morning fever / April fools day morn / Fame and wealth / Thick and thin / Revenge / Ingenue, The / IDTTYWLM.
LP: .... FIEND 5
LP: .... ROUNDER 3076
MC: .... ROUNDER 3076C

I'M ALRIGHT.
Tracks: / One man guy / Lost love / I'm alright / Not John / Cardboard boxes / Screaming issue / How old are you? / Animal song / Out of this world / Daddy take a nap / Ready or not (so ripe) / Career moves.
LP: .... FIEND 54
MC: .... FIENDCASS 54
LP: .... ROUNDER 3096
MC: .... ROUNDER 3096C

LIVE ONE, A.
Tracks: / Motel blues / Hollywood hopeful / Whatever happened to us / Natural disaster / Suicide song / School days / Kings and queens / Down drinking at the bar / B-side / Nocturnal stumblebutt / Red guitar / Clockwork chartreuse / Lullaby.
LP: .... ED 223
MC: .... CED 223
LP: .... ROUNDER 3050
MC: .... ROUNDER 3050C
LP: .... RAD 24

LOUDON WAINWRIGHT III.
Tracks: / School days / Ode to a Pittsburgh / Uptown / Four is a magic number / Central Square song / Bruno's place / Hospital lady / Glad to see you've got religion / Black Uncle Remus / I don't care / Movies are a mother.
LP: .... ED 308

MORE LOVE SONGS.
Tracks: / Hard day on the planet / Synchronicity / Your mother and I / I eat out / No / Home stretch, The / Unhappy anniversary / Mans world / Vampire blues / Overseas calls / Expatriot / Back nine, The.
LP: .... FIEND 79
MC: .... FIENDCASS 79
LP: .... ROUNDER 3106
MC: .... ROUNDER 3106C

THERAPY.
Tracks: / Therapy / T.S.D.H.A.V. / Aphrodisiac / Nice guys / Your father's car / You don't want to know / This year / Bill of goods / Harry's wall / Fly paper / Thanksgiving / Me and all the other mothers / Mind read (it belonged to you).
LP: .... ORELP 500
MC: .... OREC 500

UNREQUITED.
Tracks: / Sweet nothin's / Lowly trust, The / Kings and queens / Kick in the head / Whatever happened to us / Crime of passion / Absence makes the heart grow fonder / On the rocks / Mr. Guilty / Guru / Hardy Boys at the Y, The / Unrequited to the ninth degree / Rufus is a tit man.
LP: 80 696
LP: .... ED 273

Waite, John

IGNITION.
Tracks: / White heat / Change / Mr. Wonderful / Going to the top / Desperate love / Temptation / By my baby tonight / Make it happen / Still in love with you / Wild life.
LP: .... CHR 1376
MC: .... ZCHR 1376

MASK OF SMILES.
Tracks: / Every step of the way / Lay down / Welcome to paradise / Lust for life / Ain't that peculiar / Just like lovers / Choice, The / You're the one / No brakes.
LP: .... WAITE 1
MC: .... TC WAITE 1

NO BRAKES.
Tracks: / Saturday night / Missing you / Dark side of the sun / Restless heart / Tears / Euroshima / Dreamtime - shake it up / For your love / Love collision.
LP: .... WAIT 1
MC: .... TC WAIT 1

ROVER'S RETURN.
Tracks: / These times are hard / Act of love / Encircled / Woman's touch, A / Wild one / Don't lose any sleep / Sometimes / She's the one / Big time for love.
LP: .... AML 3121
MC: .... TCAML 3121

Waiting for Willa (bk)

WAITING FOR WILLA By D. Eden (Bloom, Claire (nar)).
MC: .... CAB 023

Waitresses

BRUISEOLOGY.
Tracks: / Girl's gotta do, A / Make the weather / Everything's wrong / Luxury / Open City / Thinking about sex again / Bruiseology / Pleasure / Spin / They're all out of liquor, let's find another party.
LP: .... POLD 5080
MC: .... POLDC 5080

WASN'T TOMORROW WONDERFUL.
Tracks: / No guilt / Wise up / Quit / It's my car / Wasn't tomorrow wonderful / I know what boys like / Heat night / Redland / Pussy strut / Go on / Jimmy tomorrow.
LP: .... POLS 1063

Waits, Tom

ASYLUM YEARS.
Tracks: / Diamonds on my windshield / Looking for the heart of Saturday night / Martha / Ghosts of Saturday night, The / Grapefruit moon / Small change / Burma shave / I never talk to strangers / Tom Traubert's blues / Blue valentines / Potter's field / Kentucky Avenue / Somewhere / Ruby's arms.
2LP: 960 321-1
MC: 960 321-4

BIG TIME.
MC: .... ITWC 4
LP: .... ITW 4

BLUE VALENTINE.
Tracks: / Red shoes by the drugstore / Christmas card from a hooker in Minneapolis / Romeo is bleeding / $29 / Wrong side of the road / Whistlin' past the graveyard / Kentucky Avenue / Sweet litle bullet from a pretty blue gun, The / Title track.
LP: .... K 53088

BOUNCED CHECKS.
Tracks: / Heart attack and vine / Jersey girl / Eggs and sausages / I never talk to strangers / Piano has been drinking / Whistlin' past the graveyard / Mr. Henry / Diamonds on my windshield / Burma shave / Tom Traubert's blues.
LP: .... K 52316

CLOSING TIME.
Tracks: / Ol' 55 / Hope that I don't fall in love with you / Virginia Avenue / Old shoes / Midnight lullaby / Martha / Rosie / Ice cream man / Little trip to heaven / Grapefruit moon / Closing time.
LP: .... K 53030

EARLY YEARS, VOL. 1.
LP: .... ED 332
MC: .... CED 332

FOREIGN AFFAIRS.
Tracks: / Cinny's waltz / Muriel / I never talk to strangers / Sight for sore eyes / Potters field / Burma shave / Barber shop / Foreign affair.
LP: .... K 53068

FRANKS WILD YEARS.
Tracks: / Hang on St. Christopher / Straight to the top (Rhumba) / Blow wind blow / Temptation / I'll be gone / Yesterday is here / Please wake me up / Franks theme / More than rain / Way down in the hole / Straight to the top / I'll take New York / Telephone call from Istanbul / Cold cold ground / Train song / Innocent when you dream.
LP: .... ITW 3
MC: .... ITWC 3
LP: .... ILPS 9863
MC: .... ICM 2024

HEART ATTACK AND VINE.
Tracks: / In shades / Saving all my love for you / Downtown / Jersey girl / Til the money runs out / On the nickel / Mr. Seigal / Ruby's arms.
LP: .... K 52252
MC: K4 52252

HEART OF SATURDAY NIGHT, THE.
Tracks: / New coat of paint / San Diego serenade / Semi suite / Shiver me timbers / Diamonds on my windshield / Looking for the heart of Saturday night / Fumblin' with the blues / Please call me, baby / Depot depot / Drunk on the moon / Ghosts of Saturday night, The.
LP: .... K 53035
MC: K4 53035

NIGHTHAWKS AT THE DINER.
Tracks: / Emotional weather report / On a foggy night / Eggs and sausages / Better off without a wife / Nighthawk postcards / Warm beer and cold women / Putnam county / Spare parts 1 / Nobody / Big Joe and Phantom 309.
2LP: .... K 63002

RAIN DOGS.
Tracks: / Singapore / Clap hands / Cemetery polka / Jockey full of Bourbon / Tango till they're sore / Big black Maria / Diamonds and gold / Hang down your head / Time / Rain dogs / Midtown / 9th and headpin / Gun Street girl / Union Square / Blind love / Walking Spanish / Downtown train / Bride of raindog / Anywhere I lay my head.
LP: .... ILPS 9803
MC: .... ICT 9803
MC: .... ICM 9803
LP: .... ILPM 9803

SMALL CHANGE.
Tracks: / Tom Traubert's blues / Step right up / Jitterbug boy / I wish I was in New Orleans / Piano has been drinking / Invitation to the blues / Pasties and a G string / Bad liver and a broken heart / One that got away, The / Small change / I can't wait to get off work.
LP: .... K 53050

SWORDFISHTROMBONES.
Tracks: / Underground / Shore leave / Dave the butcher / Johnsburg, Illinois / 16 shells from A 30.6 / Town with no cheer / In the neighbourhood / Just another sucker on the vine / Frank's wild years / Swordfish trombones / Down, down, down / Soldier's things / Gin soaked boy / Trouble's braids / Rainbirds.
LP: .... ILPM 9762
MC: .... ICM 9762
MC: 842 496 4

TOM WAITS - INTERVIEW PICTURE DISC.
LPPD: .... BAK 2141

Wake

HARMONY.
Tracks: / Favour / Heartburn / Immaculate conception rag / Transmission / Glittering prize.
LP: .... FACT 60

HERE COMES EVERYBODY.
LP: .... FACT 130

MAKE IT LOUD.
LP: .... SARAH 602
MC: .... SARAHRE 2

Wake RSV

PRAYERS TO A BROKEN STONE.
LP: .... PLASLP 025

Wake Up & Live

WAKE UP AND LIVE (Film soundtrack) (Various artists).
LP: .... HS 403

Wakefield, Frank

FRANK WAKEFIELD & GOOD OL' BOYS (Wakefield, Frank & Good Ol' Boys).
Tracks: / Bluegrass band No. 1 / Blue and lonesome / T for Texas / Cattle in the cane / Musician's waltz / Hobo song, The / Sally Ann / I though I heard you calling my name / Train I ride, The / David, David / New musician's waltz / Greek, The.
LP: .... FF 049

FRANK WAKEFIELD WITH COUNTRY COOKING.
LP: .... ROUNDER 0007

Wakeford, Alan

ALAN WAKEFORD PLAYS FOR YOU.
LP: .... PC 863

Wakelin, Johnny

GOLDEN HOUR OF JOHNNY WAKELIN.
Tracks: / In Zaire / Reggae, soul and rock 'n' roll / Doctor Frankenstein's disco party / Out of time / It's building up / 28 days in Deutschland / I am Capricorn / Sleep on baby / Me and my woman / America (you've been good to me) / Black superman / American man /

Fly away to the sun / No jive talking / Gotta keep on going / She can boogie / Cream puff / You got the bug / Never let it fade away / Tennessee hero.
LP: . . . . **GH 680**

REGGAE, SOUL & ROCK 'N' ROLL.
Tracks: / Reggae, soul and rock 'n' roll / Cream puff / In Zaire / Me, I'm a capricorn / Sleep on baby / Out of time / Black superman / Gotta keep on going / You got the bug / Never let it fade away / America.
LP: . . . . **NSPL 18487**
MC: . . . . **ZCP 18487**

Wakely, Jimmy

SANTA FE TRAIL.
Tracks: / Along the Santa Fe trail / Take me back to my boots and saddle / There's a goldmine in the sky / Red river valley / Blue shadows on the trail / Call of the canyon, The / We'll rest at the end of the trail / Sierra Nevada / It's a lonely trail tonight / Carry me back to the lone prairie / True love (is a sacred thing).
LP: . . . . **HAT 3012**
MC: . . . . **HATC 3012**

Wakeman, Rick

1984.
Tracks: / 1984 Overture / Wargames / Julie's song / Hymn / Brainwash / Robot man / No name / Sorry / Forgotten memories / Proles / 1984.
MC: . . . . **CHCMC 41**
LP: . . . . **CHC 41**

1984/THE BURNING (Film Soundtracks).
Tracks: / 1984 Overture part one / 1984 Overture part two / Wargames / Julia / Hymn / Room (brainwash) / Robot man / Sorry / No name / Forgotten memories / Proles, The / 1984 / Burning, The / Chase continues, The / Variations on the fire / Shear terror and more / Burning (end title theme), The / Campfire story / Fire / Doin' it / Devil's creek breakdown / Chase, The / Shear terror and more.
LP: . . . . **CDS 4022**
MC: **7144 136**
MCSET: . . . . **CASMC 111**

BLACK KNIGHT AT THE COURT OF FERDINAND.
MC: **A10MC 1**

BURNING, THE (1980 soundtrack music).
LP: . . . . **CLASS 12**
LP: . . . . **STV 81162**

COST OF LIVING, THE.
Tracks: / Twij / Pandamonia / Gone but not forgotten / One for the road / Bedtime stories / Happening man / Shakespeare run / Monkey nuts / Elegy written in a country churchyard.
LP: . . . . **CHC 63**
MC: . . . . **CHCMC 63**

COUNTRY AIRS.
LP: . . . . **NAGE 10**
MC: . . . . **NAGEC 10**

CRIMES OF PASSION (1985 film soundtrack).
LP: . . . . **RW 3**
MC: . . . . **RWK 3**

CRIMINAL RECORD.
Tracks: / Statute of justice / Crime of passion / Chambers of horrors / Birdman of Alcatraz / Breathalyser, The / Judas Iscariot.
LP: . . . . **AMID 125**
MC: . . . . **CMID 125**
LP: . . . . **AMLK 64660**

FAMILY ALBUM, THE.
Tracks: / Adam (Rick's second son) / Black beauty (black rabbit) / Jemma (Rick & Nina's daughter) / Benjamin (Rick's third son) / Oscar (Rick & Nina's son) / Oliver (Rick's eldest son) / Nina (Rick's wife) / Wiggles (black & white rabbit) (Only on cassette and CD.) / Chloe / Kookie (cat) / Tilly / Mum / Dad / Day after the fair, The / MacKintosh.
LP: . . . . **RW 4**
MC: . . . . **RWK 4**

G'OLE (Film soundtrack).
Tracks: / International flag / Dove, The (opening ceremony) / Wayward spirit / Latin reel (theme from G'Ole) / Red island / Spanish holiday / No possibla / Shadows / Black pearls / Frustration / Spanish montage / G'ole.
LP: . . . . **CAS 1162**
MC: . . . . **CASMC 1162**

GOSPELS, THE.
2LP: . . . . **SMR 729**
MCSET: . . . . **SMC 729**
2LP: . . . . **SMR 626**
MCSET: . . . . **SMC 626**

JOURNEY TO THE CENTRE OF THE EARTH.
LP: . . . . **SHM 3164**
MC: . . . . **HSC 3164**
LP: . . . . **AMLH 63621**

LIVE AT HAMMERSMITH.
Tracks: / Arthur / Three wives / Journey / Merlin.
LP: . . . . **RW 2**

MYTHS AND LEGENDS OF KING ARTHUR, THE.
Tracks: / Arthur / Lady of the lake / Guinevere / Sir Lancelot and the black knight / Merlin the magician / Sir Galahad / Last battle, The.
LP: . . . . **AMLH 64515**
MC: . . . . **CAM 64515**
LP: . . . . **RW 2**
MC: . . . . **RWK 2**

NIGHT AIRS.
LP: . . . . **RW 9**
MC: . . . . **RWK 9**

NO EARTHLY CONNECTION.
LP: . . . . **AMLK 64583**

PHANTOM POWER.
MC: **A10MC 2**

RHAPSODIES.
Tracks: / Pedra de Gavea / Front line / Bombay duck / Animal showdown / Big Ben / Rhapsody in blue / Wooly willy tango / Pulse / Swan lager / March of the gladiators / Flacons de Neige / Flasher / Palais / Stand by / Sea horses / Half holiday / Summertime.
2LP: . . . . **AMLX 68508**

ROCK 'N' ROLL PROPHET.
LP: . . . . **LUNLP 1**
MC: . . . . **ZCLUN 1**

SEA AIRS.
Tracks: / Harbour lights / Pirate, The / Storm clouds / Lost at sea / Mermaid, The / Waves / Fisherman, The / Flying fish / Marie Celeste, The / Time and tide / Lone sailor, The / Sailor's lament, The.
LP: . . . . **RW 8**
MC: . . . . **RWK 8**

SILENT NIGHTS.
Tracks: / Tell 'em all you know / Opening line, The / Opera, The / Man's best friend / Glory boys / Silent nights / Ghost of a rock 'n'roll star / Dancer / Elgin mansions / That's who I am.
LP: . . . . **RW 1**
MC: . . . . **RWK 1**

SIX WIVES OF HENRY VIII, THE.
Tracks: / Catherine of Aragon / Ann of Cleves / Catherine Howard / Jane Seymour / Anne Boleyn / Katherine Parr.
MC: . . . . **CAM CR 8**
LP: . . . . **AMLH 64361**
MC: . . . . **CAM 64361**

SUITE OF GODS (Wakeman, Rick & Ramon Ramedios).
LP: . . . . **RW 5**
MC: . . . . **RWK 5**

ZODIAQUE (Wakeman, Rick & Tony Fernandez).
LP: . . . . **RW 6**
MC: . . . . **RWK 6**

Wakenins, Ulf

AQUARELA DO BRAZIL.
LP: . . . . **SNTF 938**

Waking Dream

WAKING DREAM, THE (Various artists).
LP: . . . . **PYSCHO 35**

Walcott, Collin

CLOUD DANCE.
LP: . . . . **ECM 1062**

GRAZING DREAMS.
Tracks: / Song of the morrow / Gold sun / Swarm, The / Mountain morning / Jewel ornament / Grazing dreams / Samba tala / Moon lake.
LP: . . . . **ECM 1096**

WORKS: COLLIN WALCOTT.
Tracks: / Scimitar / Song of the morrow / Like that of sky / Travel by night / Godumada / Hey da boom lullaby / Prancing / Cadona / Awakening / Padma / Travel by day.
LP: **8372761**

Wald, Jerry

CALL OF THE WILD, THE.
LP: . . . . **GELP 15005**

Walden, Narada Michael

AWAKENING.
Tracks: / Love me only / I don't want nobody else / Give your love a chance / They want the feeling / Awakening suite (part 1) / Awakening, The / Listen to me / Full and satisfied / Will you ever know.
LP: . . . . **K 50570**

CONFIDENCE.
Tracks: / You're my number 1 / Summer lady / I'm ready / Safe in my arms / Confidence / Holiday / You ought to love me / Blue side of midnight.
LP: . . . . **K 50883**

GARDEN OF LOVE LIGHT.
Tracks: / White night / Garden of love light / Delightful / First love / Meditation / Sun is dancing, The / You got the soul / Saint and the rascal / You are love.
LP: . . . . **K 50329**

I CRY, I SMILE.
Tracks: / I need your love / Better man, A / Soul bird / I remember / Oneness-cry / Mango bop / Rainbow sky / I cry, I smile / Heaven's just a step ahead / So long.
LP: . . . . **K 50417**

NATURE OF THINGS.
Tracks: / That's the way it is / High above the clouds / Gimme gimme gimme / Live it up / Nature of things / Suspicion / Dancin' on main street / Wear your love.
LP: **925176 1**
MC: **925176 4**

VICTORY.
Tracks: / Real thing, The / Take it to the bossman / Alone without you / Get up / Lucky fella / You will find your way / Victory suite / Theme / Battle (hero soldiers battle the hostile forces) / Victory for the hero soldiers.
LP: . . . . **K 50743**
MC: **K4 50743**

Walden, Wanda

SEARCHIN' FOR LOVE.
Tracks: / Searchin' for love / Take your heart / Don't you want my love / Lost and found / Wanna love you tonight / Holdin' on / Just to love you / It's gone now.
LP: . . . . **K 52286**

Walder, Russel

ELEMENTS (Walder, Russel/Ira Stein).
LP: . . . . **C 1020**

Waldman, Wendy

LETTERS HOME.
LP: . . . . **YL 0102**

Waldo, Elisabeth

REALM OF THE INCAS.
LP: . . . . **GNPS 603**
MC: **GNP5 603**

RITES OF THE PAGAN.
LP: . . . . **GNPS 601**
MC: **GNP5 601**

Waldo, Terry

TERRY WALDO AND THE GOTHAM CITY BAND (Waldo, Terry & The Gotham City Band).
LP: . . . . **SOS 1120**

Waldos Gutbucket

SUSAN LAMARCHE & WALDOS GUTBUCKET SYNCOPATORS (see under Lamarche, Susan).

WALDOS GUTBUCKET SYNCOPATORS PRESENTS....
LP: . . . . **SOS 1036**

Waldo's Ragtime...

WALDO'S RAGTIME ORCHESTRA VOL.2 (Waldo's Ragtime Orchestra).
LP: . . . . **SOS 1069**

Waldron, Mal

BLACK GLORY.
LP: . . . . **ENJA 2004**

BLUES FOR LADY DAY (Personal Tribute to Billie Holiday).
Tracks: / Blues for Lady Day / Just friends / Don't blame me / You don't know what love is / Man I love, The / You're my thrill / Strange fruit / Easy living / Mean to me.
LP: . . . . **BLP 30142**

CALL, THE.
LP: . . . . **JAPO 60001**

ENCOUNTERS (Waldron, Mal/Dave Friesen).
LP: . . . . **MR 5305**

FREE AT LAST (Waldron, Mal Trio).
Tracks: / Rat now / 1-3-234 / Willow weep for me / Balladina / Rock my soul / Boo.
LP: . . . . **ECM 1001**

HARD TALK (Waldron, Mal Quintet).
LP: . . . . **ENJA 2050**

HOT HOUSE (See Under Lacy, Steve) (Waldron, Mal & Steve Lacy).

LEFT ALONE '86 (Waldron, Mal & Jackie McLean).
LP: . . . . **K 28P 6453**

MINGUS LIVES.
LP: . . . . **ENJA 3075**

MOODS.
LP: . . . . **ENJA 3021**

ONE ENTRANCE MANY EXITS.
LP: . . . . **PA 8014**
MC: . . . . **PAC 8014**

ONE UPMANSHIP (Waldron, Mal Quintet/Steve Lacy).
LP: . . . . **ENJA 2092**

QUEST, THE (Waldron, Mal/Eric Dolphy).
Tracks: / Status seeking / Duquility / Thirteen / We did it / Warm canto / Warp and woof / Fire waltz.
LP: . . . . **OJC 082**

SET ME FREE.
Tracks: / Set me free / You were always there / Yeah / Jamaica libre / Desillusion / Atilla the hun.
LP: . . . . **AFF 116**

SIGNALS.
LP: . . . . **FLP 41042**

SUPER QUARTET - LIVE AT SWEET BASIL, THE.
LP: . . . . **K 28P 6471**

TOUCH OF BLUES, A.
LP: . . . . **ENJA 2062**

UP POPPED THE DEVIL.
LP: . . . . **ENJA 2034**

WHAT IT IS (Waldron, Mal Quartet).
LP: . . . . **ENJA 4010**

YOU AND THE NIGHT AND THE MUSIC.
Tracks: / Way you look tonight / Bag's groove / Round midnight / You and the night and the music / Georgia on my mind / Billie's bounce / Waltz for my mother.
LP: . . . . **K 28P 6272**

Wales...

20 WELSH MALE CHOIR FAVOURITES (Various artists).
LP: . . . . **NTS 191**
MC: . . . . **TCNTS 191**

COMRADES IN SONG (Various artists).
MC: . . . . **ZCR 630**

CYMANSA GANN (Various artists).
LP: . . . . **REC 53 M**

FESTIVAL OF WELSH MALE VOICE CHOIRS, A (Various artists).
Tracks: / Myfanwy: *Various artists* / Cwm Rhondda: *Various artists* / Speed your journey: *Various artists*/ Steal away: *Various artists* / March of the men of Harlech: *Various artists* / Kumbaya: *Various artists*/ Sospan fach: *Various artists* / Bless this house: *Various artists* / Jacobs ladder: *Various artists*/ O Mary, don't you weep: *Various artists* / Comrades in arms: *Various artists* / Counting the goats: *Various* artists / All through the night: *Various artists* / Soldiers chorus: *Various artists* / Lord's prayer (The): *Various artists* / Jerusalem: *Various artists* / Immortal, invisible, God only wise: *Various artists*/ Ave Maria: *Various artists* / We'll keep a welcome: *Various artists* / Michael, row the boat ashore: *Various* artists / God bless the Prince of Wales: *Various artists* / A-rockin' all night: *Various artists* / Lily of the valley: *Various artists* / Mae hen wlad fy nhadau: *Various artists.*
2LP: . . . . **DL 41 1080 3**
MC: . . . . **DL 41 1080 9**
2LP: . . . . **DL 1080**
MC: . . . . **TCDL 1080**

FIRST FESTIVAL OF WELSH LADIES CHOIRS (Various artists).
LP: . . . . **BM 39**

GOLDEN HOUR OF WELSH CHOIRS, A (Various artists).
MC: . . . . **KGHMC 142**

GORAU GWERIN Best of Welsh folk vol 2 (Various artists).
LP: . . . . **SAIN 1333 H**

GREAT WELSH CHOIRS (Various artists).
Tracks: / How great thou art: *Various artists* / Soldiers chorus: *Various artists* / Credo: *Various artists*/ Rose, The: *Various artists* / Das morgenrot: *Various artists* / Maja moja: *Various artists* / You'll never walk alone: *Various artists* / Let it be me: *Various artists* / Sanctus from Requiem: *Various artists*/ Calm is the sea: *Various artists* / Kalinka: *Various artists* / Jesu who didst ever guide me: *Various artists*/ Finnish forest, The: *Various artists* / What shall we do with the drunken sailor: *Various artists* / We'll keep a welcome: *Various artists* / Rock-a-my-soul: *Various artists* / Cydganed pawb (let all the world in every corner sing): *Various artists* / Sound of silence, The: *Various artists* / Down among the dead men: *Various artists*/ Duet from the Pearl Fishers: *Various artists* / Comrades in arms: *Various artists* / Memory: *Various artists*/ Roman war song from Rienzi: *Various artists* / Bywyd y bugail: *Various artists* / My bonny lass she smileth: *Various artists* / I'm gonna walk: *Various artists* / Tydi a roddaist: *Various artists* / Chorus and Lauras song from Casanova: *Various artists.*
MCSET: . . . . **DTO 10295**

IDEAL WELSH CHOIRS (Various artists).
Tracks: / All through the night: Various artists / Myfanwy: Various artists / We'll keep a welcome: Various artists / March of the men of Harlech: Various artists / Tydi a roddaist: Various artists / Gwahoddiad: Various artists / Laudamus: Various artists / David of the white rock: Various artists / Valley called Rhondda, A: Various artists.
MC: . . . . **EE 260 091-4**

MINER'S PITTANCES (Various artists).
Tracks: / Sospan fach: Various artists / Yr eneth gadd ei gwrthod: Various artists / Golden ring: Various artists / Daisy: Various artists / Guide me o thou great Jehovah: Various artists / Best little door-boy: Various artists / Hogyn amaethwr (The farmer's boy): Various artists / Ton-y-botl: Various artists/ Treorchy stories: Various artists.
MC: **60-055**

NEVER FORGET YOUR WELSH VOL.1 (Various artists).
LP: . . . . **BM 55**

SECOND FESTIVAL OF WELSH MIXED VOICES (Various artists).
Tracks: / God save the queen: Various artists / Praise, o praise God: Various artists / Were you there: Various artists / Dynaoned a wraig: Various artists / All in the April evening: Various artists / Worthy is the lamb: Various artists / Amen chorus: Various artists / Yr utgorn: Various artists / Prince Igor choral dance: Various artists / Pantyfedwen: Various artists / Dance a Cachucha: Various artists / Diadem: Various artists / Hen wlad fy Nhadau: Various artists.
LP: . . . . **NTS 194**

SONGS AND TUNES FROM WALES (see under Calennig) (Calennig).

SONGS FROM THE VALLEYS From the 3rd Festival of 1,000 Welsh Male Voices (Various artists).
Tracks: / God save Queen: Various artists / Go down Moses: Various artists / This ol' hammer: Various artists/ My Lord what a mornin': Various artists / Dies irae: Various artists / Kumbaya: Various artists / Sailor's chorus: Various artists / Soldier's chorus: Various artists / Roman war song: Various artists/ Requiem in D minor: Various artists / By Babylon's wave: Various artists / Myfanwy: Various artists/ Cwm Rhondda: Various artists / Land of my fathers: Various artists.
LP: . . . . **NTS 171**

SONGS FROM THE VALLEYS (double cassette) (Various artists).
MCSET: . . . . **DTO 10274**

SOUNDS OF WALES, THE (Various artists).
Tracks: / We'll keep a welcome: Morriston Orpheus Choir / Myfanwy: Monmouthshire Massed Choir (Recorded at Ebbw Vale Leisure Centre, October 1973.) / Speed your journey: Second Festival Of One Thousand Welsh Male Voices (Recorded at the Royal Albert Hall, London, October 1970.) / March of the men of Harlech: Morriston Orpheus Choir / Soldiers' chorus: Monmouthshire Massed Choir (Recorded at Ebbw Vale Leisure Centre, October 1973.) / Land of song, The: Morriston Orpheus Choir / All through the night: Various artists / Men of Wales: Band of the 1st Bat The Welsh Regiment / Steal away: Morriston Orpheus Choir / Battle hymn of the Republic: Various artists / Thou gavest: Monmouthshire Massed Choir (Recorded at the Ebbw Vale Leisure Centre, October 1973.) / Tros y garreg: Morriston Orpheus Choir / Counting the goats: Various artists / Cartref: Morriston Orpheus Choir / Sanctus: Various artists / Hiraeth: Morriston Orpheus Choir / Laudamus: Festival of Massed Welsh Choirs (Recorded at the Royal Albert Hall, London, October 1969.) / When I survey the wondrous cross: Various artists / Elizabethan serenade: Morristons Orpheus Choir & Band of the Welsh Guards / Comrades in arms: Various artists / Llef (Deus salutis): Monmouthshire Massed Choir (Recorded at the Ebbw Vale Leisure Centre, October 1973.) / Unwaith eto'n nghymru annwyl: Morriston Orpheus Choir/ Silver birch, The: Second Festival Of One Thousand Welsh Male Voices (Recorded at the Royal Albert Hall, London, October 1970.) / Guide me o thou great Redeemer: Third Festival Of One Thousand Welsh Male Voices / Land of my fathers: Third Festival Of One Thousand Welsh Male Voices.
2LP: . . . . **DL 1128**
MC: . . . . **TCDL 1128**

STOUTHEARTED MEN One thousand Welsh male voices (Various artists).
Tracks: / Stouthearted men: Various artists / Annie's song: Various artists / Yellow bird: Various artists/ My lord what a morning: Various artists / Bryn myrddin: Various artists / Troyte's chant: Various artists/ Morte christe: Various artists / Gwahoddiad: Various artists / Speed your journey: Various artists/ Joy of the hunter: Various artists / Cyfir geifr: Various artists / Crossing the plain: Various artists/ Moab: Various artists / Deep harmony: Various artists.
LP: . . . . **REC 463**
MC: . . . . **ZCM 463**

THIRD FESTIVAL WELSH MIXED VOICES (Various artists).
LP: . . . . **BM 53**

THIS IS WALES (Various artists).
Tracks: / Men of Harlech: Various artists / Swansea Town: Various artists / Bugeilio'r gwenth gwyn: Various artists / Gwenith Gwyn: Various artists / War song of Dinas Fawr: Various artists / Angelsey prayer: Various artists / Old druids: Various artists / All through the night: Various artists / We'll keep a welcome: Various artists / Counting the goats: Various artists / Calon lan: Various artists / Twm sion cati: Various artists / Llanfair: Various artists / Myfanwy: Various artists / Cwm Rhondda: Various artists.
LP: . . . . **THIS 6**
MC: . . . . **TCTHIS 6**

VALLEY LIGHTS Folk songs of Wales today (Various artists).
LP: . . . . **SAIN 1342**

VERY BEST OF WELSH CHOIRS (Various artists).
LP: . . . . **EMC 3099**
MC: . . . . **TCEMC 3099**

WALES-LAND OF SONG (Various artists).
MCSET: . . . . **DTO 10228**

WE'LL KEEP A WELCOME (Various artists).
Tracks: / We'll keep a welcome: Welsh Male Voice Choir / Bryan Myrddin: Welsh Male Voice Choir / How great thou art: Welsh Male Voice Choir / Memory: Welsh Male Voice Choir / Aberystwyth: Welsh Male Voice Choir/ Sound of silence, The: Welsh Male Voice Choir / Hymn (from 'Finlandia'): Welsh Male Voice Choir / Christus redemptor (hyfrydol): Welsh Male Voice Choir / Softly as I leave you: Welsh Male Voice Choir / Comrades in arms: Welsh Male Voice Choir / Let it be me: Welsh Male Voice Choir / Creation's hymn: Welsh Male Voice Choir/ You'll never walk alone (from 'Carousel'): Welsh Male Voice Choir / Martyrs of the arena: Welsh Male Voice Choir.
LP: . . . . **CFRC 504**
MC: . . . . **MCFRC 504**

WELSH CHOIRS (Various artists).
MC: . . . . **ED 2600914**
MC: . . . . **EE 2600914**

WELSH CHORAL FAVOURITES (See under Welsh Choirs) (Various artists).

WELSH CHORAL FAVOURITES (Various artists).
Tracks: / My little Welsh home: Dunvant Male Choir / Soldier's farewell: Dunvant Male Choir / Close thing eyes: Dunvant Male Choir / Stodole pumpa: Gwalia Male Choir / Heimat: Gwalia Male Choir / Marching song: Gwalia Male Choir / Steal away: Gwalia Male Choir / Hiraeth: Morriston Orpheus Choir / Hyder: Morriston Orpheus Choir / American trilogy, An: Morriston Orpheus Choir / My dearest dear: Morriston Orpheus Choir/ Martyrs of the arena: Morriston Orpheus Choir / My hero: Morriston Orpheus Choir / Ride the chariot: Pontarddulais Male Choir / Windmills of your mind, The: Pontarddulais Male Choir / Mil harddach wyt na'r rhosyn Gwyn: Pontarddulais Male Choir / Memory: Canoldir Male Choir / Eli Jenkins prayer: Canoldir Male Choir / My love is like a red red rose: Canoldir Male Choir.
MC: . . . . **HR 8197**

WELSH MALE CHOIRS (Various artists).
Tracks: / Hymn from Finlandia: Treorchy Male Choir / Unwaith eto'n nghymru annwyl: Treorchy Male Choir / Lest we forget: Treorchy Male Choir / Shepherd, shepherd: Candoldir Male Choir / Lord's prayer, The: Candoldir Male Choir / Finnish forest, The: Candoldir Male Choir / Joanna, Crugybar, Ebenezer: Morriston Orpheus Choir/ Cymru fach: Morriston Orpheus Choir / Dies Irae: Morriston Orpheus Choir / Bryn Myrddin: Pontarddulais male choir / Memory: Pontarddulais male choir (From "Cats") / Diolch I'r Ior: Pontarddulais male choir / Soldiers chorus: Dunvant Male Choir / Lily of the valley: Dunvant Male Choir / Bandit's chorus: Dunvant Male Choir (From 'Ernani') / Deus salutis: Dunvant Male Choir / Silver birch, The: Gwalia Male Choir / Nant y mynydd: Gwalia Male Choir / Hava nagila: Welsh Male Choirs.
MC: . . . . **HR 8146**

WELSH TRADITIONS The Mari Lwyd (Various artists).
MC: **60-050**

WORLD OF GREAT WELSH CHOIRS (Various artists).
Tracks: / God bless the Prince Of Wales: Various artists / Steal away: Various artists / Little ole you: Various artists / Brahm's lullaby: Various artists / Holy City, The: Various artists / Jacob's ladder: Various artists / Myfanwy: Various artists / Nos da: Various artists / Aberystwyth: Various artists / Leaf: Various artists / Linden lea: Various artists / Tydi a roddaist: Various artists / Poor old Joe: Various artists / Ar hyd y nos: Various artists / Shepherd's lullaby: Various artists / Smiling through: Various artists / We'll keep a welcome: Various artists.
LP: . . . . **SPA 591**

Wales, Josey

CODE OF CONDUCT.
LP: . . . . **DSR 3906**

HAVE TO SAY SO.
LP: . . . . **DSR 8013**

JOSEY WALES MEETS EARLY B (Wales, Josey & Early B).
LP: . . . . **Unknown**

NA LEF JAMAICA.
Tracks: / One time / Don't run away from yard / Solomon style / Better nuh deh / Na lef Jamaica / Bad bwoy / Move up / Water come a me eye / Josie medley / Give me love up.
LP: . . . . **ILPS 9894**
MC: . . . . **ICT 9894**

NO WAY BETTER THAN YARD.
Tracks: / It have fe sail / World is like a mirror, The / Yu too greedy / Eden a try / No way no better than yard / Drug abusing / Ja Jah move / Maxine / Yu wrong fe send come call me / Zion home.
LP: . . . . **GREL 76**

OUTLAW JOSEY WALES, THE.
Tracks: / In a fi burn / Love I want / Can't put it on / Beg you come home / Jam it again / Let go mi hand / No bother tax me / Stalk of Sensimilia / Music diseases / Asking for love.
LP: . . . . **GREL 55**

RULIN'.
LP: . . . . **DSR 6796**

TWO GIANTS CLASH (See under Yellowman) (Wales, Josey & Yellowman).

Walk on Fire

BLIND FAITH.
Tracks: / Blind faith / Crime of loving you / Caledonia / Hands of time, The / Miracle of life / Wastelands / Tell it like it is / Hearts of gold / Hungry for heaven / Close my eyes.
LP: . . . . **MCG 6063**
MC: . . . . **MCGC 6063**

Walk The West

WALK THE WEST.
Tracks: / Living at night / Backside / Too much of a good thing / Precious time / Lonely boy / Sheriff of love / Think it over / Solitary man / Calvary Hill / Do you wanna dance.
LP: . . . . **EST 2021**
MC: . . . . **TCEST 2021**

Walkabouts

SEE BEAUTIFUL RATTLESNAKE GARDENS.
LP: **089204**

Walker

WALKER (Film Soundtrack) (Strummer, Joe).
Tracks: / Filibustero / Omotepe / Sandstorm / Machete / Viperland / Nica Libre / Latin romance / Brooding side of madness, The / Tennessee rain / Smash everything / Tropic of no return / Unknown immortal, The / Musket waltz.
MC: . . . . **TCV 2497**
LP: . . . . **V 2497**

Walker, Albertina

SPIRIT.
MC: . . . . **REJ C 5006**
LP: . . . . **REJ R 5006**

Walker, Billy

ANSWER GAME, THE (See under Fairchild, Barbara) (Walker, Billy & Barbara Fairchild).

BEST OF THE BEST OF BILLY WALKER.
LP: . . . . **GT 0040**

BILLY WALKER.
Tracks: / Charlie's shoes / Funny how time slips away / Cross the Brazos at Waco / Singing those lovesick blues again / Coffee brown eyes / I won't ever let you down / Stop hiding your heart / Am I blue / I'm gonna love you / Someone left the light on.
LP: . . . . **IMCA 39090**
MC: . . . . **IMCAC 39090**

FOR MY FRIENDS.
Tracks: / Singing those lovesick blues again / Jesse / He sang the songs about El Paso / Charlie's shoes / Touch of my woman / Don't ever leave me in Texas / Instead of giving up (I'm giving in) / Love boat / Cross the Brazos at Waco / Anything your heart desires / Cool in the daylight (fire in the dark) / Funny how time slips away.
LP: . . . . **BDL 3004**

PRECIOUS MEMORIES.
LP: . . . . **WST 9664**
MC: . . . . **WC 9664**

Walker, Billy Jo Jr.

HOUSE, THE.
Tracks: / Midnight romance / Flower song / Creation / Peace and harmony / Defeated creek / Lost in Mexico / Raindrops on the roof / Moonlight on the water / Enchanted forest / Children play, The.
LP: . . . . **IMCA 42041**
MC: . . . . **IMCAC 42041**

WALK, THE.
Tracks: / Walk, The / Hourglass / Dream on / Mystery man / Street dancing / Illusions / Free flight / Fields of stone / Crystal speak to me / Breezes.
MC: . . . . **GEFC 24315**

Walker Brothers

AFTER ALL THE LIGHT GOES OUT.
LP: **8428311**
MC: **8428314**

GREATEST HITS: WALKER BROTHERS.
Tracks: / Baby make it the last time / Sun ain't gonna shine, The / You're all around me.
LP: **6430 152**
MC: **7240 044**

HITS.
Tracks: / Make it easy on yourself / Love her / My ship is coming in / Dancing in the street / Sun ain't gonna shine anymore, The / Land of a thousand dances / Baby you don't have to tell me / Another tear falls / Deadlier than the male / Stay with me baby / Walking in the rain / Stand by me.
LP: . . . . **PRICE 37**
MC: . . . . **PRIMC 37**
LP: **6463 139**

IMAGES: WALKER BROTHERS.
LP: . . . . **SBL 7770**

LINES.
LP: . . . . **GTLP 014**

LIVE IN JAPAN.
2LP: . . . . **AIDA 076**
MC: . . . . **CAIDA 076**

MOTIVE SERIES.
Tracks: / Love her / My ship is coming in / Another tear falls / Sun ain't gonna shine anymore, The / Make it easy on yourself / Their goes my baby / Land of a thousand dances / Here comes the night / In my room / Living above your head / I need you / No sad songs for me / Stay with me baby / Summertime.
LP: **643 088**
MC: **7145 088**

MUSIC FOR THE MILLIONS.
Tracks: / Sun ain't gonna shine any more / Make it easy on yourself / There goes my baby / My ship is coming in / Land of a thousand dances / Here comes the night / In my room / Living above your head / I need you / No sad songs for me / Stay with me baby / Summertime.
LP: **812345 1**
MC: **812345 4**

NO REGRETS.
LP: . . . . **GTLP 007**

SUN AIN'T GONNA SHINE ANYMORE, THE.
Tracks: / Sun ain't gonna shine anymore, The / Baby you don't have to tell me / Stay with me / Annabella / Joanna / Love her / Make it easy on yourself / Walking in the rain / Another tear falls / Deadlier than the male / Jackie / My ship is coming in / Sun ain't gonna shine anymore, The.
LP: **824 674 1**
MC: **824 674 4**

TAKE IT EASY.
LP: . . . . **BL 7691**

WALKER BROTHERS.
LP: **8322561**

MC: 8322564

WALKER BROTHERS STORY.
2LP: DBL 002

Walker, Bryon

DON'T LOOK ANY FURTHER (Walker, Bryon/Sandra Edwards).
Tracks: / Don't look any further.
LP: SGLP 026

Walker, Charlie

CHARLIE WALKER.
Tracks: / Pick me up on your way down / Mean woman with green eyes / One step away / If I were you I'd fall in love with me / I was doin' her wrong / Don't squeeze my sharmon / Right or wrong / I'm gonna get together with your... / That ol' Texas two step / Does Fort Worth ever cross your mind.
LP: IMCA 39078
MC: IMCAC 39078

WHO WILL BUY THE WINE (See also Reeves, Jack) (Walker, Charlie & Jack Reeves).

Walker, Corporal

PIPE BANDS OF DISTINCTION.
MC: ZCMON 804

Walker, David T.

SWING STREET CAFE (See Sample, Joe) (Walker, David T./Joe Sample).

Walker, Dean

OVER NOW.
LP: SUM 1
MC: SUMC 1

Walker, Dee

DIAL L FOR LOVE.
LP: DEE 1

Walker, Eddie

PICKING MY WAY.
LP: RAGR 003

RED SHOES ON MY FEET.
LP: RAGR 001

Walker, Ian

FLYING HIGH.
Tracks: / Roses in December / Sing me a song Mr Bloom / Beats of the heart / Too far from she / Don't turn the key / Some Hae meat / Hawks and eagles / Child on the green / Do you see my face / Greatest thrill, The / Amazing satellite picture show / Catch a rainbow.
LP: FE 060
MC: FE 060C

SHADOWS IN TIME.
Tracks: / Shadows in time / Ladder of life / Portrait of a woman / Sun / Let me hear you smile / Ghost train / Dancing on the sun / When the bough breaks / Mountain boy / Blodwen's dream / Rising of the green / Million city lights.
LP: FE 073
MC: FE 073C

Walker, Jerry Jeff

JERRY JEFF WALKER.
Tracks: / Eastern Avenue river / Railway blues / Lone wolf / Bad news / Boogie mama / I'm not strange / Her good lovin' grace / Comfort and crazy / Follow / Banks of old Bandera.
LP: K 52106

NAVAJO RUG.
Tracks: / Navajo rug / Just to celebrate / Blue mood / Lucky man / Detour / I'm all through throwing good love after bad / Rockin' on the river / Nolan Ryan (a hero to us all) / Flowers in the snow / If I'd loved you then.
MC: TTCS 9175

Walker, Jimmy

ORIGINAL SOUTHSIDE BLUES PIANO.
LP: WOLF 120 712

Walker, Joe Louis

BLUE SOUL.
Tracks: / Prove your love / Ain't nothin' goin' on / T.L.C. / Personal baby / Since you've been gone / Alligator / Dead sea / City of angels / I'll get to Heaven on my own.
LP: FIEND 159

COLD IS THE NIGHT.
Tracks: / Why do you run / Madness of it all (was once and still is) / Cold is the night / Ten more shows to play / Moanin' news / One woman / I need someone / Brother go ahead and take her / Fuss and fight / Gettin' even / Ridin' high / Don't play games.
LP: CH 208

GIFT, THE.
Tracks: / One time around / Thin line / 747 / Gift, The / What about you? / Shade tree mechanic / 1/4 to 3 / Mama didn't raise no fools / Everybody's had the blues / Main goal.
LP: CH 241
MC: CHC 241

LIVE AT SLIM'S.
LP: FIEND 212
MC: FIENDMC 212

Walker, John

MY FAVOURITE LENNON/ MCCARTNEY (Walker, John & The Digital Sunset).
MC: C5MK 565

PLAY MY FAVOURITE SINATRA - A TRIBUTE (Walker, John & The Digital Sunset).
Tracks: / New York, New York / Something stupid / Strangers in the night / It's been a long long time / Five minutes more / Saturday night is the loneliest night of the / Love and marriage / Three coins in the fountain / It's nice to go travellin' / I'll be seeing you / Nancy (with the laughing face) / I'm a fool to want you / Come fly with me / Witchcraft / Nice 'n' easy / London by night / Tender trap, The / Begin the beguine / I've got you under my skin / Night and day / All the way / High hopes / If you never come to me / Hey jealous lover / Lady is a tramp, The / My kind of town / Young at heart / My way.
MC: C5K-530
LP: C5-530

Walker, Junior

ANTHOLOGY - JUNIOR WALKER (Walker, Junior & The All Stars).
Tracks: / Shotgun / Do the boomerang / Shake and fingerpop / Cleo's back / Cleo's mood / I'm a roadrunner / How sweet it is to be loved by you / Money (that's what I want) / Pucker up buttercup / Shoot your shot / Come see about me / Hip city (part 1) / Home cookin' / What does it take to win your love / These eyes / I've got to find a way to win Maria back / Gotta hold on to this feeling / Do you see my love (for you growing) / Holy holy / Take me girl I'm ready / Right on brothers and sisters / Don't blame the children / Moody junior / Way back home / Walk in the night.
2LP: TMSP 1129

BACK STREET BOOGIE.
Tracks: / Backstreet boogie / Girl I wanna marry you / Wishing on a star / Hole in the wall / Don't let me go astray / Tiger in my tank / Sax attack.
LP: K 56668

BLOW THE HOUSE DOWN.
Tracks: / Sex pot / Rise and shine / Closer than close / Ball baby / T-oo (t double oo) / Urgent / In and out / Blow the house down.
LP: STML 12194
MC: CSTML 12194

JUNIOR WALKER'S GREATEST HITS.
Tracks: / Shotgun / How sweet it is to be loved by you / Road runner / Hip city part 1 / Cleo's mood / Money (that's what I want) / Shoot your shot / Picker up buttercup / Come see about me / What does it take to win your love / Shake and fingerpop / Home cookin' / Baby you know you ain't right / Anyway you wanna.
LP: STMS 5054
MC: CSTMS 5054
LP: WL 72097
MC: WK 72097

SHAKE AND FINGERPOP.
Tracks: / Shotgun / How sweet it is to be loved by you / Home cookin' / Money / Pucker up buttercup / What does it take (to win your love) / Come see about me / Hip city / Cleo's mood / Shake and fingerpop / Shoot your shot.
LP: BMLP 072

WHOPPER BOPPER SHOW STOPPER.
Tracks: / Whopper bopper show stopper / You are the sunshine of my life / You're on fire / Leap and peep / Don't make no plans / I could never love another (after loving you) / I want you / Love ain't enough / My love.
LP: STML 12048

Walker, Lawrence

LEGEND AT LAST, A.
LP: 6051

TRIBUTE TO THE LATE, GREAT LAWRENCE WALKER.
LP: 126
MC: 126 TC

Walker, Paulette

IS THERE A PLACE IN YOUR HEART ME?.
LP: BFMLP 102

Walker, Philip

BLUES.
Tracks: / How many more years / 90 proof / What'd you hope to gain / Don't be afraid of the dark / Big rear window / Her own keys / Talk to that man / Sometime girl / I had a dream.
LP: FIEND 128

BOTTOM OF THE TOP, THE.
Tracks: / I can't lose (with the stuff I use) / Tin Pan Alley / Hello central / Hello my darling / Laughin' and clownin' / Crazy girl / It's all in your mind / Bottom of the top, The / Hey, hey, baby's gone / Crying time.
LP: FIEND 158

SOMEDAY YOU'LL HAVE THE BLUES.
Tracks: / Someday you'll have these blues / Beaumont blues / Breakin' up somebody's home / Mama's gone / When it needs gettin' done / Sure is cold / Part time love / El Paso blues / Don't tell me / If we can find it.
LP: SNTF 831

TOUGH AS I WANT TO BE.
LP: ROUNDER 2038
MC: ROUNDER 2038C
LP: 33588

Walker, Sarah

BLAH BLAH BLAH AND OTHER TRIFLES (Walker, Sarah/Roger Vignoles).
Tracks: / Blah, blah, blah / They all laughed / Three times a day / Boy, what love has done to me / Tale of the oyster / Where, oh where? / Who am I? / Place settings / Usherettes blues / Song of a nightclub proprietress / Lime jello marshmallow cottage cheese surprise / Word on my ear, A / There are fairies at the bottom of our garden / Transatlantic lullaby / Someone is sending me flowers.
MC: KA 66289

CABARET SONGS (Walker, Sarah/ Roger Vignoles).
Tracks: / Someone to watch over me / I love to rhyme / Lorelei.
LP: E 77056

Walker, Scott

BEST OF SCOTT WALKER.
Tracks: / Joanna / Lights of Cincinnati / Will you still be mine / I will wait for you / Montague terrace (in blue) / When Joanna loved me / Jackie / Lady came from Baltimore, The / If she walked into my life / Me I never knew, The / If you go away / Impossible dream, The.
LP: PRICE 43
MC: PRIMC 43
LP: 6381 073

BOY CHILD.
Tracks: / Plague, The / Such a small love / Plastic palace people / Big Louis / Seventh seal, The / Old man's back again, The / Little things (that keep us together) / Girls from the streets, The / Copenhagen / War is over, The / Montague Terrace (in blue) / Amorous Humphrey Plugg, The / Bridge, The / We came through / Boy child / Prologue / Time operator / It's raining today / On your own again / Rope and the colt, The.
LP: 8428321
MC: 8428324

CLIMATE OF HUNTER, THE.
Tracks: / Rawhide / Dealer / Sleepwalkers woman / Blanket roll blues.
LP: V 2303
MC: TCV 2303
LP: OVED 149
MC: OVEDC 149

FIRE ESCAPE IN THE SKY (The Godlike genius of Scott Walker).
LP: ZOO 2

SCOTT.
LP: SBL 7816

SCOTT 2.
LP: SBL 7840

SCOTT 3.
LP: SBL 7900

SCOTT WALKER SINGS JACQUES BREL.
Tracks: / Jackie / Next / Girls and the dogs, The / If you go away / Funeral tango / Mathilde / Amsterdam / Sons of / My death / Little things (that keep us together).
LP: 6359 090

SONGS FROM HIS TV SERIES.
LP: SBL 7900

Walker, Sheila (nar)

BERTHA (see under Bertha (bk)) (Kinnear, Roy & Sheila Walker).

Walker, Sylford

LAMB'S BREAD.
LP: GREL 119

Walker, T-Bone

BLUESWAY SESSIONS.
Tracks: / Goin to funky town / Party girl / Why my baby (keep on bothering me) / Jealous woman / Going to build me a playhouse / Long skirt baby blues / Struggling blues / I'm in an awful mood / I wish my baby (would come home at night) / I'm gonna stop this nite life / Little girl don't you know / Every night I have to cry / I'm still in love with you / Cold hearted woman / Treat me so low down / Stormy Monday / Confusion blues / I gotta break away / Flower blues.
2LP: CDX 31
MC: TCCDX 31

BOSSES OF THE BLUES (See under Turner, Joe) (Turner, Joe & T Bone Walker).

COLLECTION: T-BONE WALKER.
Tracks: / T-Bone jumps again / Sun went down, The / Call it stormy Monday / I got the blues / Railroad station blues / Hypin' woman blues / Hustle, The / I'm still in love with you / Blues is a woman / Born to be no good / T-Bone shuffle / Baby you broke my heart / Bye bye, baby / I'm about to lose my mind / First love blues / I wish you were mine / Travellin' blues / Evil-hearted woman / Bobby sox blues / Blues for my baby.
LP: DVLP 2047
MC: DVMC 2047

FUNKY TOWN.
LP: BGOLP 116

GOOD FEELIN'.
LP: 2393 007

HIS ORIGINAL 45-50 PERFORMANCES.
LP: 2C 068 86523

HOT LEFTOVERS.
LP: PM 1561451

I DON'T BE JIVIN'.
Tracks: / T-Bone's back on the scene / I used to be a good boy / I ain't your fool no more / Baby she's a hit / Reconsider baby (hate to see you go) / Don't let your heartache catch you / Sometimes I wonder / I don't be jivin' / T-Bone's jam / I ain't your fool no more / I wonder why / Further up the road / All night long / How long blues (that evening train) / Louisiana bayou drive.
LP: BFX 15277

I GET SO WEARY.
LP: PM 156 144 1

I WANT A LITTLE GIRL.
LP: DL 633

INVENTOR OF THE ELECTRIC GUITAR BLUES, THE.
Tracks: / Wichita falls blues / Sail on boogie / I'm still in love with you / T-Bone boogie / Mean old world blues / That's better for me / Hard pain blues / Hustle is on, The / Baby broke my heart / I walked away / No reason / My baby is now on my mind / Pony tail / When the sun goes down.
LP: BB 304

NATURAL BLUES, THE (18 tracks recorded 1946-48).
Tracks: / Lone some woman blues / Vacation blues / She had to let me down / Don't give me the runaround / Hard pain blues / So blue blues / I'm waiting for your call / Natural blues, The / That's better for me / Inspiration blues / Description blues / I want a little girl / Time seems so long, The / Home town blues / Misfortune blues / I'm still in love with you / She's the no sleepiest woman / I'm gonna move you out and let somebody else.
LP: CRB 1057

PLAIN OLE BLUES.
Tracks: / I'm gonna find my baby / Don't leave me baby / No worry blues / It's a lowdown dirty deal / I'm in a awful mod / Long skirt baby blues / Goodbye blues / Plain old down home blues / That old feeling is gone.
LP: CRB 1037

STORMY MONDAY.
Tracks: / Stormy Monday blues / All night long / My patience keeps running out / Glamour girl / T-Bones's way / That evening train / Louisiana bayou drive / When we were schoolmates / Don't go back to New Orleans / Got to cross the deep blue sea / You'll never find anyone to be a slave like me / Left home / When I was a kid.
LP: CR 30144
LP: INS 5022
MC: TCINS 5022

T-BONE BLUES.
LP: SD8258

T-BONE JUMPS AGAIN.
Tracks: / Hypin' woman blues / Too much trouble blues / I got a break baby / Mean old woman / Bobby sox blues / I know your wig has gone / T-Bone jumps again / Call it stormy monday / You're my best poker hand / First love blues / She's my old time used to be / On your way blues / I wish you were mine / Wise man blues / Born to be no good / T-Bone shuffle.
LP: CRB 1019
MC: TCCRB 1019

Walker, Tim

CLASSICAL FOLK GUITAR.
MC: KH 88027

Walkie Talkies

SURVEILLANCE.
Tracks: / Whose world is this / We tell no lies / Spin it out / Photosynthesis / Cover up / Man on Cobo Bay / Surveillance / Dangerous dancing.
LP: ALTO 101
MC: ZCALT 101

Walking on the Moon

WALKING ON THE MOON (Various artists).
LP: CREST 001
MC: CRESTMC 001

Walking Seeds

BAD ORB...WHIRLING BALL.
LP: PAPLP 001
MC: PAPMC 001

SKULL F*CK.
Tracks: / Iron man / Doom patrol / 666 squadron / When girls ruled the world / Life vs filth / Blue cheer / Kill kill kill for inner peace / Obeying the law / St. Albans / Blathering out.
LP: PROBE 13

UPWIND OF DISASTER, DOWNWIND OF ATONEMENT.
Tracks: / 281F / We rise / Sexorcist / Wreck of the white star / Imperious vain selfish and wilful / Louie Louie Louie / Help me, mummy's gone.
LP: GLALP 034

Walks, Dennis

MEET DENNIS WALKS.
Tracks: / Misty / Sad sweet dreamer / Down the avenue / Bless you for being an angel / Heart don't leap / Margaret / Parent eyes / Drifter / Only time will tell / Party down.
LP: HM 107

Wall

DIRGES AND ANTHEMS.
Tracks: / Who are you / Nice to see you / Wunderkind / Epitaph / Money whores / Barriers / Pete's song / Tyburn / Walpurgis night / Only dreaming / Foot steps / Chinese whispers / Everybody's ugly / English history / Anthem.
LP: POLS 1048

PERSONAL TROUBLES AND PUBLIC ISSUES.
LP: FRESH LP 2

Wall, Alwyn

FRIENDS ON TOUR (see Norman, Larry) (Wall, Alwyn/Larry Norman/ Barratt Band).

Wall, Dan

SONG FOR THE NIGHT.
LP: LD 1002

TRIO, THE (Wall, Dan Trio).
LP: AP 143

Wall Of Voodoo

7 DAYS IN SAMMYSTOWN.
MC: MIRFC 1005

CALL OF THE WEST.
LP: ILP 010

DARK CONTINENT.
Tracks: / Back in flesh / Me and my dad / Call box / Two minutes till lunch / Red light / Animal day / This way out / Good times / Tsetse fly / Full of tension / Crack the bell.
LP: SP 70022

GRANDMA'S HOUSE.
Tracks: / Ring of fire / Long arm / Passenger, The / Can't make love / On interstate 15 / Lost weekend / Mexican radio / Call box / Red light / Tomorrow / Crack the bell / Call of the West / Granma's house.
LP: IRSA 7048

HAPPY PLANET.
Tracks: / Do it again / Hollywood the second time / Empty rooms / Chains of luck / When the lights go out / Joanne / Elvis bought Dora a cadillac / Grass is greener / Ain't my day.
LP: MIRF 1022
MC: MIRFC 1022

UGLY AMERICANS IN AUSTRALIA.
LP: ILP 022

Wall Street

WALL STREET/SALVADOR (Film Soundtrack) (Various artists).
Tracks: / Bud's scam: *Copeland, Stewart* / Are you with me: *Copeland, Stewart* / Trading begins: *Copeland, Stewart* / Tall weeds, The: *Copeland, Stewart* / Break up: *Copeland, Stewart* / Anacott steel: *Copeland*, Stewart / El playon: *Vancouver Symphony Orchestra* / Siege at Santa Fe: *Vancouver Symphony Orchestra* / Goodby Maria: *Vancouver Symphony Orchestra* / At the border: *Vancouver Symphony Orchestra* / Road block: *Vancouver Symphony Orchestra* / Love theme: Finale: *Vancouver Symphony Orchestra*.
LP: TER 1154
MC: ZCTER 1154

WALL STREET/TALK RADIO (See under Talk Radio) (Copeland, Stewart).

Wall Street Crash

EUROPEAN AFFAIR.
Tracks: / European affair / Soft target / Catch a falling star / Carousel / You're my world / La banda / Susie's bar / Taking it to the streets / Only a step away / Madison Square.
MC: ZCMAG 5056
LP: MAGL 5056

WALL STREET CRASH.
Tracks: / Down in Hollywood / Mountains of Mourne / Life on Mars / Swing swing swing / Sweet Georgia Brown / Ain't she sweet / It's alright by me / I could do that / I could have danced all night / There ain't nobody here but us chickens / Class / I'm so glad I'm standing here today walking on air.
MC: ZCMAG 5045

Wallace, Bennie

ART OF THE SAXOPHONE, THE.
Tracks: / Edith Head / You go to my head / Rhythm head / Monroe County moon / Thangs / All too soon / Chester leaps in / Prelude to a kiss / Prince Charles.
MC: CC 16

BENNIE WALLACE PLAYS MONK.
LP: ENJA 3091

BORDER TOWN.
Tracks: / Skanctified / Stormy weather / East 9 / Bordertown / Bon-a-rue / Seven sisters / Carolina moon / Dance with a dolly (with a hole in her stocking) / It's only a paper moon.
LP: B1 48014
LP: 748 014 1

BRILLIANT CORNERS (Wallace, Bennie with Yosuke Yamashita).
Tracks: / It don't mean a thing / Light blue / P.S. I love you / Night in Tunisia / Brilliant corners / Blues Yamashita / My ideal / Rhythn-a-ning / Another beauty.
MC: CC 26

FOURTEEN BAR BLUES.
LP: ENJA 3029

FREE WILL.
LP: ENJA 3063

LIVE AT THE PUBLIC THEATRE.
LP: ENJA 3045

SWEEPING THROUGH THE CITY.
LP: ENJA 4078

TWILIGHT TIME.
Tracks: / All night dance / Is it true what they say about Dixie? / Sainte fragile / Tennessee waltz / Fresh out / Willie Mae / Trouble in mind / Saint expedito / Twilight time.
LP: BT 85107

Wallace, Edgar (aut)

MIND OF MR. J.G.REEDER, THE (West, Timothy (nar)).
Tracks: / Poetical policeman, The / Treasure hunt, The / Troupe, The / Stealer of marble, The.
MCSET: SAY 116

MIND OF MR. J.G.REEDER VOL.2 (see Sheer melodrama & other etc) (West, Timothy (nar)).

SHEER MELODRAMA AND OTHER STORIES (West, Timothy (nar)).
Tracks: / Sheer melodrama / Green mamba, The / Strange case, The / Investors, The.
MCSET: SAY 117

Wallace, Frankie

FRANKIE AND CLARA 1929-30 (Wallace, Frankie & Clara Burston).
LP: DLP 584

Wallace, George

HEROES LIKE YOU AND ME.
Tracks: / Back at seventeen / Talk to me / Gotta get outta here / She give away / American dream / Stand up / Give me your money / Romeo's home at last / Larger than life.
LP: PRT 84923

Wallace, Hugh & Tillie

WARINGSFORD RISING STAR.
Tracks: / Old orange tree / Kimallen hare hunt / Murder of the McBriars / Waringsford rising star / Factory girl / Carrickmannon lake / Dolly's brae / Auld orange flute / Farmers boy / South Down militia / Marksman / Shepherds boy / Aghalee heroes / Sash my father wore.
MC: COAS 3029
LP: OAS 3029

Wallace, Ian

CELEBRATION.
Tracks: / Rose of Tralee, The / Lazin' / Roses of Picardy / Long ago in Alcala / I'll walk beside you / For you alone / Moon river / This is my lovely day / Smoke gets in your eyes / Tit willow / Very thought of you, The / Spanish lady / September song / Reverie.
2LP: CR 5166
MCSET: CRT 5166

CHRISTMAS COLLECTION (Wallace, Ian/St.Joseph's School Choir).
Tracks: / Storke carol, The / I wonder as I wander / Virgin Mary had a baby boy, The / Little road to Bethlehem, The / Monkey's carol, The / First mercy / Now we go to Bethlehem.
LP: WRD R 3023
MC: WRD C 3023

MY KIND OF MUSIC.
Tracks: / Leanin' / Youth of the heart, The / My ain folk / Simon the cellarer / She moved through the fair / On the road to Mandalay / Through the eyes of a child / Annie Laurie / Mud (the hippopotamus song) / Shenandoah / Old house / Perfect day.
LP: MFP 50563
MC: TCMFP 50563

MY MUSIC.
Tracks: / Roses of Picardy / Limehouse reach / O mistress mine / Long ago in Alcala / Rose of Tralee, The / Elephant song, The / Welcome home / Margate / When a woman smiles / Laird of Cockpen, The / Silent worship / Sweethearts and wives / Love is a very light thing / Lazin' / Moon river / Armadillo / Very thought of you, The / Tit willow / For you alone / Ill wind / Who is Sylvia / I'll walk beside you / Mud (the hippopotamus song) / Bonnie Mary of Argyle / Cobbler's song, The / September song / Spanish lady / This is my lovely day / Reverie.
MCSET: DTO 10291

Wallace, Joe

LAKELAND AND BORDER SONGS.
MC: MWMC 102

Wallace, Robert

CHANCE WAS A FINE THING.
LP: CC 38
MC: 4CC 38

Wallace, Sippie

SINGS THE BLUES.
LP: SLP 4017

SIPPIE WALLACE.
Tracks: / Women be wise / Up the country blues / I'm a mighty tight woman / Won't you come to my house / You've been a good old wagon / Man that don't want me / You got to know how / Suitcase blues / Say it isn't so / Everybody loves my baby / Mama's gone, goodbye.
LP: SD 19350

Wallace, Valerie

LOVE IS A SONG.
MC: SENC 1084

Wallacestone...

ECOSSE (Wallacestone & District Pipeband).
LP: SB 387

Wallenstein

FRAULEINS.
LP: IC 064 45932

Waller, Fats

20 GOLDEN PIECES: FATS WALLER.
Tracks: / Ain't misbehavin' / Your feets too big / Honeysuckle Rose / I'm gonna sit right down and write myself a letter / I've got my fingers crossed / Joint is jumpin', The / Sweet Sue / Nagasaki / Lonesome me / Hallelujah / Handful of keys / Christopher Columbus / It's a sin to tell a lie / Until the real thing comes along / Crazy 'bout my baby / Things look rosy now / Thousand dreams of you, A / Old Grandad / Dark eyes / Jingle bells.
LP: BDL 2004
MC: BDC 2004

20 GREATEST HITS.
LP: U 50040

1939: FATS WALLER.
LP: SM 3086

1943.
LP: BLJ 8031

1927-29 (Waller, Fats & Morris' Hot Babies).
Tracks: / Fats Waller Stomp / Savannah blues / Won't you take me home / I ain't got nobody / Digah's stomp, The / Red hot Dan / Geechee / Please take me out of jail / Minor drag, The / Harlem fuss / Lookin' good but feelin bad / I someone like you / Lookin' for another sweetie / Ridin' but walkin' / Won't you get off it, please ? / When I'm alone.
LP: S 850

AFRICAN RIPPLES.
Tracks: / You look good to me / Something tells me / African ripples / In the gloaming / If I were you / Shame shame (everybody knows your game) / My fate is in your hands / Every day's holiday / Patty cake baker man / Hold my hand / Fair and square / I love to whistle / Tell me with your kisses / Let's break the good news / Baby oh where can you be / Yacht club swing.
LP: NL 89008
MC: NK 89008
LP: INTS 5095

AIN'T MISBEHAVIN' (Waller, Fats & His Rhythm).
Tracks: / Honeysuckle rose / Ain't misbehavin' / I can't give you anything but love / Two sleepy people / I'm gonna sit right down and write myself a letter / It's a sin to tell a lie / Minor drag, The / Joint is jumpin', The / Hold tight / Your feet's too big / Tea for two.
LP: NL 89087
MC: NK 89087
LP: INTS 5009

ARMFUL O' SWEETNESS (Waller, Fats & His Rhythm).
Tracks: / Porter's love song to a chambermaid, A / I wish I were twins / Armful o' sweetness / Do me a favour / Georgia May / Then I'll be tired of you / Don't let it bother you / Have a little dream on me / Serenade for a wealthy widow / How can you face me / Sweetie pie / Mandy / Lets pretend there's a moon / You're not the only oyster in the stew / I'm growing fonder of you / If it isn't love / Breakin' the ice.
MC: CSVL 182
LP: SVL 182

BEST OF FATS WALLER.
Tracks: / Sweet Sue / Nagasaki / Crazy 'bout my baby / It's a sin to tell a lie / Lonesome me / Handful of keys / Honeysuckle rose / Ain't misbehavin / I've got my fingers crossed / Solitude / Hallelujah / Sometimes I feel like a motherless child / Two sleepy people.
LP: SM 3110

BOUNCIN' ON A V DISC.
LP: S 1227

CHRONOLOGICAL VOL.1 (Waller, Fats & His Rhythm).
LP: JSP 1106

CLASSIC YEARS IN DIGITAL STEREO (Fats Waller 1934-1936).
Tracks: / Lulu's back in town / Whose honey are you / It's a sin to tell a lie / Somebody stole my gal / Christopher Columbus / If it isn't love / Pianna / To pay / Swingin' them jingle bells / Curse of an aching heart, The / Bye bye baby / Dream man / Oh Susannah / There's going to be the devil / Take it easy / Big chief De Sota / Have a little dream on me.
LP: REB 684
MC: ZCF 684

COMMODORE CLASSICS (see under Condon, Eddie) (Condon, Eddie & Fats Waller).

COMPLETE EARLY BAND WORKS (1927-9).
Tracks: / Fats Waller stomp / Savannah blues / Won't you take me home / He's gone away / Red hot Dan / Geechee / Please take me out of jail / Minor drag / Harlem fuss / Lookin' good but feelin' bad / I need someone like you / Lookin' for another sweetie / Ridin' but walkin' / Won't you get off it / When I'm alone.
LP: HDL 115
MC: CHDL 115

DUST OFF THAT OLD PIANO (Waller, Fats & His Rhythm).
Tracks: / I'm a hundred per cent for you / Baby Brown / Night wind / Because of once upon a time / I believe in miracles / You fit into the picture / Louisiana fairy tale / I ain't got nobody / Whose honey are you? / Rosetta / Pardon my love / What's the reason (I'm not pleasin' you)? / Cinders / (Oh Suzanna) dust off that old pianna / Lulu's back in town / Sweet and slow / You've been taking lessons in love (from somebody new) / You're the cutest one / I'm gonna sit right down and write myself a letter / Hate to talk about myself.
LP: SVL 189
MC: CSVL 189

FATS AT THE ORGAN.
Tracks: / Eighteenth Street strut / I'm coming, Virginia / If I could be with you one hour tonight / Laughin' cryin' blues / Midnight blues / Papa better watch your step / T'aint nobody's business if I do / Your time now will be mine after a while / Nobody but my baby is getting my love / Do it, mister so-and-so / Clearing house

blues / You can't do what my last man did / Don't try to take my loving man away / Squeeze me.
LP: . . . . **AJA 5007**
MC: . . . . **ZC AJA 5007**

FATS WALLER.
Tracks: / My very good friend the milkman / Don't let it bother you / You're not the only oyster in the stew / Dinah / It's a sin to tell a lie / Hold tight / Honeysuckle rose / I'm gonna sit right down & write myself a / When somebody thinks you're wonderful / You're not the kind / Joint is jumpin', The / Two sleepy people / Your feet's too big / Sheik of Araby, The / Until the real thing comes along / Ain't misbehavin'.
LP: . . . . **SM 4022**
LP: . . . . **LSA 3112**
LP: . . . . **SM 4022**
LP: . . . . **LPJT 2**

FATS WALLER 1935 & 43.
LP: . . . . **CC 19**

FATS WALLER AND MORRIS' HOT BABIES.
LP: . . . . **SM 3080**

FATS WALLER COLLECTION (20 golden greats).
Tracks: / Dinah / Blue black bottom / Numb fumblin' / Twelfth St. rag / Whose honey are you? / I ain't got nobody / Mandy / Don't let it bother you / Ain't misbehavin' / Sometimes I feel like a motherless child / If it isn't love / Serenade for a wealthy widow / You've been taking lessons in love / Somebody stole my gal / Goin' about / Breakin' the ice / Fat and greasy / Stay / Oh Susannah, dust off that old pianna / Blue because of you.
LP: . . . . **DVLP 2059**
MC: . . . . **DVMC 2059**

FATS WALLER IN LONDON.
Tracks: / London suite / Don't try your jive on me / Ain't misbehavin' / Flat foot boogie / Pent up in a penthouse / Music maestro please / Tisket a tasket, A / That old feeling / I can't give you anything but love / Smoke dreams of you / You can't have your cake and eat it.
LP: . . . . **EG 2604421**
MC: . . . . **EG 2604424**
LP: . . . . **SW 8442/3**

FINE ARABIAN STUFF.
LP: . . . . **DE 601**

FRIENDS OF FATS VOL. 2.
LP: . . . . **CI 017**

FROM THE BEGINNING, VOL. 2.
LP: . . . . **JSP 1108**

FROM THE BEGINNING VOL. 3 (Waller, Fats & His Rhythm).
LP: . . . . **JSP 1113**

HALLELUJAH, I'M A BUM.
MC: . . . . **SLC 61011**

HANDFUL OF KEYS.
Tracks: / Handful of keys / You're not the only oyster in the stew / Valentino stomp / Honeysuckle rose / St. Louis blues / I'm crazy 'bout my baby / Alligator crawl / Blue turning grey over you / Viper's drag / Your feet's too big / Carolina shout / Ain't misbehavin'.
LP: . . . . **CL 89805**
MC: . . . . **CK 89805**

HIS PIANO AND HIS RHYTHM VOL. 3.
LP: **502011**

HONEY ON THE MOON.
Tracks: / Dinah / Alligator crawl / Honey hush / There's honey on the moon tonight / You look good to me / Old grand dad / Swinging them jingle bells / You're not the only oyster in the stew / Pantin' in the panther room / What a pretty miss / Last night a miracle happened / You've been reading my mail.
LP: . . . . **MTM 009**

HONEYSUCKLE ROSE.
Tracks: / Let's pretend there's a moon / Honeysuckle rose / Serenade for a wealthy widow / How can you face me / Don't let it bother you / Have a little dream on me / My feelings are hurt / Sweetie pie / African ripples / Mandy / Handful of keys / Do me a favour / You're not the only oyster in the stew / Ridin' but walking / Alligator crawl / Viper's drag / Dream man / Smashin' thirds.
LP: . . . . **RAL 509**

INDISPENSABLE FATS WALLER VOLS.5 & 6.
Tracks: / S'posin' / Hallelujah / Cryin' mood / Boo hoo / Honeysuckle rose / Smarty / Bat it out / How ya baby / Neglected / Florida Flo / Skrontch / Sheik of Araby, The / T'ain't good.
2LP: . . . . **NL 89745**
MCSET: . . . . **NK 89745**

INDISPENSABLE FATS WALLER VOLS.9 & 10.
Tracks: / My mommie sent me to the store / Fats Waller's original E-flat blues / Hey stop kissing my sister / Everybody loves my baby / T'aint nobody's business if I do / Abercrombie had a zombie / Scram / My melancholy baby / Mamacita / Pantin' in the panther room / Shortnin' bread / Pan-pan / I wanna hear swing songs / All that meat and no potatoes / Carolina shout / Twenty four robbers / Sad sap sucker am I / Chant off the groove / Come and get it / Rump steak serenade / Buck jumpin' / Winter weather / Cash for your trash / Don't give me that jive / Your socks don't match / Really fine / Jitterbug waltz / By the light of the silvery moon / Swing out to victory / Moppin' and boppin' / Ain't misbehavin'.
2LP: . . . . **NL 89971**
MC: . . . . **NK 89971**

INDISPENSABLE FATS WALLER VOLS.3 & 4 1935-1936.
Tracks: / Big Chief De Sota / Rosetta / Whats the reason / Lulu's back in town / Dinah / Blue because of you / 12th Street rag / Sweet sue / Truckin' / Got a bran' new suit / Fat and greasy / Functionizin' / I got rhythm / Paswonkly.
2LP: . . . . **PM 43696**
2LP: . . . . **NL 89819**

INDISPENSABLE FATS WALLER VOLS.1 & 2 1926-1935.
2LP: . . . . **PM 43686**
2LP: . . . . **NL 89742**

INDISPENSABLE FATS WALLER VOLS.7 & 8.
Tracks: / Hold my hand / If I were you / Two sleepy people / Good man is hard to find, A / Hold tight / 'Taint what you do / Your feet's too big / Darktown strutters ball / I can't give you anything but love / Cheatin' on me / Dry bones.
MC: . . . . **NK 89273**
2LP: . . . . **NL 89273**

JAZZ CLASSICS IN DIGITAL STEREO (Fats Waller 1927-1934).
LP: . . . . **REB 598**
MC: . . . . **ZCF 598**

JAZZ TIME VOL.17.
LP: **502717**

JOINT IS JUMPIN'.
Tracks: / Ain't misbehavin' / Crazy 'bout my baby / Handful of keys / Nagasaki / Joint is jumpin' / Sweet Sue / Just you / Honeysuckle rose / I'm gonna sit right down & write myself a letter / It's a sin to tell a lie / Until the real thing comes along / Christopher Columbus / Your feet's too big.
LP: . . . . **TOP 139**
MC: . . . . **KTOP 139**

JUGGLING JIVE OF FATS WALLER (LIVE).
LP: . . . . **GOJ 1041**
MC: . . . . **GOJC 1041**

L'ART VOCAL VOLUME 4: LA SELECTION 1934-1939 (See Under L'Art Vocal).

LAST YEARS, THE (1940-1943).
Tracks: / Old grand dad / Fat and greasy / Little curly hair in a high chair / (You're a) square from Delaware / You run your mouth, I'll run my business / Too tired / Send me Jackson / Epe, ipe, wanna piece of pie / Stop pretending / I'll never smile again / My mommie sent me to the store / Dry bones / Fats Waller's original E-flat blues / Stayin' at home / Hey - stop kissing my sister / Everybody loves my baby / I'm gonna salt away some sugar / T'ain't nobody's business if I do / Abercrombie had a zombie / Blue eyes / Scram / My melancholy baby / Mamacita / Liver lip Jones / Buckin' the dice / Pantin' in the Panther room / Come down to earth, my angel / Shortnin' break / I repent / Do you have to got pan-pan / I wanna hear swing songs / You're gonna be sorry / All that meat and no potatoes / Let's get away from it all / Twenty four robbers / I understand / Sad sap sucker am I / Headlines in the news / Chant of the groove / Come and get it / Rump steak serenade / Ain't nothin' to it / Oh baby, sweet baby / Buck jumpin' / That gets it Mr. Joe / Bells of San Raquel, The / Bessie, Bessie, Bessie / Clarinet marmalade / Winter weather / Cash for your trash / Don't give me that jive / Your socks don't match / We need a little love / You must be losing your mind / Really fine / Jitterbug waltz / By the light of the silvery moon / Swing out to victory / Up jumped you with love / Romance a la mode / Moppin' and boppin' / Ain't misbehavin'.
LPS: . . . . **NL 90411**
MCSET: . . . . **NK 90411**

LEGENDARY PERFORMER.
Tracks: / Ain't misbehavin' / I'm gonna sit right down / Handful of keys / Jitterbug waltz / How ya baby? / Joint is jumpin' / Honeysuckle rose / Viper's drag / Your feet's too big / I've got a feeling I'm falling / Yacht club swing / Keepin' out of mischief now / Lounging at the Waldorf.
LP: . . . . **PL 12904**

LIVE AT THE YACHT CLUB VOL.1.
Tracks: / Yacht Club swing / Hold my hand / Pent-up in a penthouse / Honeysuckle rose / You look good to me / Hallelujah / St. Louis blues / Flat foot floogie / After you've gone / You can't be mine (and someone else's too) / Monday mornin' / What do you know about love? / I had to do it.
LP: . . . . **GOJ 1029**
MC: . . . . **GOJC 1029**

LIVE AT THE YACHT CLUB VOL.2.
Tracks: / Lila Lou / Frenesi / So you're the one / Dark eyes / Perfidia / When you and I were young, Maggie / Hold my hand / Stop beatin' around the mulberry bush / What's the matter with you? / Hallelujah / What's your name? / Whatcha know, Joe? / I give my word.
LP: . . . . **GOJ 1035**
MC: . . . . **GOJC 1035**

MAGIC MOMENTS.
Tracks: / Ain't misbehavin' / Smashing thirds / You've got me under your thumb / Honeysuckle rose / Spring cleaning / She's tall, she's tan, she's terrific / You're my dish / Blue, turning grey over you / I'm on a seesaw / Have a little dream on me / You meet the nicest people in your dreams / Lulu's back in town / My very good friend the milkman / Do me a favour / Us on a bus / Porter's love song to a chambermaid / When stars are tired of gleaming I'll be tired / There's honey on the moon tonight / Georgia on my mind / I'm crazy 'bout my baby / Lost and found / Meanest thing you ever did was to kiss me, The / I'm gonna put you in your place.
MC: . . . . **NK 89897**

MASTERS OF JAZZ.
LP: . . . . **CL 42343**

MOST IMPORTANT RECORDINGS OF FATS WALLER, THE.
Tracks: / Birmingham blues / Henderson stomp / St Louis blues / Thou swell / Handful of keys / Minor drag, The / Numb fumbling / Valentine stomp / Lookin' good but feelin' bad / I'm crazy about my baby / You're not the only oyster in the stew / Alligator crawl / Viper's drag / Baby brown / Lulu's back in town / I'm gonna sit down and write myself a letter / Sweet Sue / I got rhythm / It's a sin to tell a lie / Swingin' them jingle bells / Meanest thing you ever did was kiss me, The / Honeysuckle rose / Keepin' out of mischief now / Joint is jumpin', The / Two sleepy people / Hold tight / Spider and the fly, The / You feet's too big / Darktown strutter's ball / Carolina shout / Ain't misbehavin' / Waller jive / Hallelujah.
LPS: . . . . **OFF 3030-2**

MY VERY GOOD FRIEND THE MILKMAN (Waller, Fats & His Rhythm).
Tracks: / I'm gonna sit right down and write myself a letter / Dinah / My very good friend the milkman / Baby brown / Whose honey are you / Blue because of you / 12th Street rag / You've been taking lessons in love / Somebody stole my gal / Breakin' the ice / I ain't got nobody / Just as long as the world goes round and round / I'm on a see-saw / I got rhythm / Sweet Sue / Rhythm and romance / Sweet thing / Serenade for a wealthy widow.
LP: . . . . **PLE 525**

OH MERCY, LOOKA HERE.
LP: . . . . **HR 5000-3**

ON THE AIR.
LP: . . . . **CC 10**

ONE AND ONLY, THE.
MC: . . . . **CMOIR 306**

OUR VERY GOOD FRIEND, FATS.
LP: . . . . **DBD 16**
MC: . . . . **DBDC 16**

PIANO SOLOS (1929-1941).
Tracks: / Blue black bottom / Handful of keys / Numb fumblin' / Ain't misbehavin' / Sweet savannah Sue / I've got a feeling I'm falling / Love me or leave me / Gladyse / Valentine stomp / Waiting at the end of the road / Baby, oh where can you be / Goin' about / My feelin's are hurt / Smashing thirds / My fate is in your hands / Turn on the heat / St. Louis blues / After you've gone / African ripples / Clothes-line ballet / Alligator crawl / Viper's drag / Down home blues / E flat blues / Zonky / Keepin' out of mischief now / Stardust / Basin Street blues / Tea for two / I ain't got nobody / Georgia on my mind / Rockin' chair / Carolina shout / Honeysuckle rose / Ring dem bells.
2LP: . . . . **NL 89741**
MCSET: . . . . **NK 89741**
2LP: . . . . **PM 43270**

RARE FATS WALLER (1927-42).
LP: . . . . **S 1243**

RARE PIANO BOOGIE.
LP: . . . . **PM 1648671**
MC: . . . . **PM 1648674**

RHYTHM 1934 VOL 1.
Tracks: / A porters love song / I wish you were twins / Armful o' sweetness / Sweetie pie / You're not the only oyster in the stew / Honeysuckle rose / I'm growing fonder of you / If it isn't love.
MC: . . . . **NEO 851**

SPREADIN' RHYTHM AROUND (Waller, Fats & His Rhythm).
Tracks: / Sweet beginning like this, A / Got a bran' new suit / I'm on a see-saw / Thief in the night / When somebody thinks you're wonderful / I've got my fingers crossed / Spreadin' rhythm around / Little bit independent, A / You stayed away too long / Sweet thing / Panic is on, The / Sugar rose / Oooh look-a there / Ain't she pretty / Moon rose / West wind / That never-to-be-forgotten night / Sing an old fashioned song / Garbo green / All my life / Christopher Columbus.
LP: . . . . **SVL 204**
MC: . . . . **CSVL 204**

TAKE IT EASY (Waller, Fats & His Rhythm).
Tracks: / Dinah / Take it easy / You're the picture (I'm the frame) / My very good friend the milkman / Blue because of you / There's going to be the devil to pay / 12th Street rag / There'll be some changes made / Somebody stole my gal / Sweet Sue - just you / Truckin' / Sugar blues / As long as the world goes 'round and 'round / Georgia rockin' chair / Brother, see and ye shall find / Girl I left behind me, The / You're so darn charming / Woe is me / Rhythm and romance / Loafin' time.
LP: . . . . **SVL 194**
MC: . . . . **CSVL 194**

THAT OLD FEELING.
LP: . . . . **S 1246**

THOMAS 'FATS' WALLER VOL.1.
LP: **502003**

THOMAS 'FATS' WALLER VOL.2.
LP: **502006**

TURN ON THE HEAT (The Fats Waller Piano Solos).
2LP: . . . . **NL 82482**
MCSET: . . . . **NK 82482**

VOCAL FATS, THE.
Tracks: / My very good friend the milkman / Don't let it bother you / You're not the only oyster in the stew / Dinah / It's a sin to tell a lie / Hold tight / Honey suckle rose / I'm gonna sit right down and write myself a letter / When somebody thinks you're wonderful / You're not the kind / Joint is jumpin', The / Two sleepy people / Your feet's too big / Sheik of Araby, The / Until the real thing comes along / Ain't misbehavin'.
LP: . . . . **NL 89574**
MC: . . . . **NK 89574**

YOU RASCAL, YOU.
Tracks: / Georgia May / I'm crazy 'bout my baby / Breakin' the ice / Baby, oh where can you be? / If it isn't love / Won't you get off it, please? / I wish I were twins / Numb fumblin' / You rascal, you / Ain't misbehavin' / Porter's love song to a chambermaid, A / Draggin' my heart around / Minor drag, The / My fate is in your hands / That's what I like about you / Harlem fuss / Believe it, beloved / Honeysuckle rose.
LP: . . . . **AJA 5040**
MC: . . . . **ZC AJA 5040**

YOUNG FATS WALLER.
LP: . . . . **SM 3093**

Wallgren, Jan Edvard

LAVORO INCORSO (Wallgren, Jan Edvard/Swedish Radio Jazz Group).
LP: . . . . **DRLP 89**

PIANO BLUEPRINTS.
LP: . . . . **DRLP 147**

TRIPLE PLAY JAZZ PIANO (see Werner, Lasse) (Wallgren, Jan/Lasse Werner).

Wallin, Bengt A

LIVE AT MONTREUX: BENGT A WALLLIN (see under Hudik Big Band) (Wallin, Bengt A/Hudik Big Band/ Georgie Fame).

Wallin, Per Henrik

BLUES WORK.
LP: . . . . **DRLP 35**

MOON OVER CALCUTTA.
LP: . . . . **DRLP 143**

Wallington, George

AT THE CAFE BOHEMIA (Wallington, George Quintet).

LP: PRO 7001

BE-BOP KEYBOARD MASTERS (See Be bop Keyboard Masters).

Wallington, Mark

FIVE HUNDRED MILE WALKIES (Oddie, Bill).
MCSET: LFP 7324

Wallis, Bob

DOCTOR JAZZ.
LP: SLP 256

EVERYBODY LOVES SATURDAY NIGHT (Wallis, Bob & His Storyville Jazz Men).
LP: BUY 023

LIVE: BOB WALLIS (Wallis, Bob & His Storyville Jazz Men).
LP: SLP 247

Wallis, Ruth

20 X RATED SONGS OF THE 50'S.
Tracks: / Boobs / Great to be a broad / Marriage Jewish style / Pizza / My first Englishman / Johnny's got a yo-yo / Freddie the fisherman's song / Mama always told us / First lei in Hawaii / How to stay sexy though married / He called me comrade / Red lights and bells / Changing partners / Give me what you promised / Admirals daughter / Ubangi / Pistol song, The / Davy's dinghy / Gay young blade from Trinidad / Battle of the sexes.
MC: CYU 109

Wallis, Shani

BEST OF SHANI WALLIS.
LP: MCL 1811

Wallochmore Ceilidh Band

FULL THROTTLE.
LP LAP 106
MC LAP 106 C

HIGHLANDERS COMPANION, THE (Dr Walloch's Fifth Prescription).
Tracks: / Paddy's potion / Canadian barn dance / St. Bernards waltz / Broon's reel / Eva three step / Jacky tar two step / Gay Gordons / Corn rigs / Welcome Christmas morning / Wee Todd / Polka / Retreat marches / Pride of Erin waltz / Hornpipe and reel / Final dose.
LP LAP 111
MC LAP 111 C

LOOKING FOR A PARTNER.
LP LAP 101
MC LAP 101 C

SECOND CHANCE.
LP LAP 104
MC LAP 104 C

SLIGHTLY CASUAL.
LP LAP 108
MC LAP 108 C

Walls, Van

THEY CALL ME PIANO MAN.
Tracks: / Open the door / Air mail boogie / Big leg mama / Idaho boogie / Easter parade / They call me piano man / Unlock my chain of love / Felicia blues.
LP: KM 711

Wally Dugs

ROAD TO DUNDEE, THE.
LP: ITV 435
MC: KITV 435
LP: EULP 1038

Walpurgis Volta

WALPURGIS VOLTA.
Tracks: / Le quot idien / Le telephone / Roule la rolls / Suicide, suicide / Cowboy solitaire / Vietnam blues / La bombe / Le crepuscule des loups / Regard glace / Dossier 55 / L'ethylique / La tete qui voyage.
LP: FRACTION 1

Walrath, Jack

JACK WALRATH AND SPIRIT LEVEL (Walrath, Jack & Spirit Level).
LP: SPJ LP 25

MASTER OF SUSPENSE.
Tracks: / Meat / Children / No mystery / Study in porcine / Bouquet of roses / Lord's calypso, The / I'm so lonesome I could cry / Monk on the moon / Hymn for the discontented, A.
LP: BLJ 46905
LP: BT 85120

NEOHIPPUS.
Tracks: / Village of the darned / Watch your head / Fright night / Annie Lee / England / Beer / Future reference (CD only.) / Smell of the blues, The (CD only.).
LP: B1 91101

PLEA FOR SANITY, A.
Tracks: / Jinx / Ballad for old time's sake / Li'l stinker / Free fall / Mucene the genie / Plea for sanity, A / St. Home in Rome.
LP: ST 223

REVENGE OF THE FAT PEOPLE (Walrath, Jack Group).
LP: ST 221

Walsh, Aidan

LIFE STORY OF MY LIFE.
Tracks: / Hucklebuck, The / Have you ever given money away / Community games, The / I am Aiden / Hokey cokey / Kissin' and eatin' with women / I may be bad but I'm not that bad / Laughing my way out of the army / Mummy mummy the eagles have landed / I'm the world's greatest bank robber / Masterplan, The.
LP: KSLP 002
MC: KSC 002

Walsh, Brose

GOLDEN MEMORIES.
MC: GTDC 082

Walsh, Joe

BEST OF JOE WALSH.
Tracks: / Turn to stone / Mother says / Help me thru the night / Rocky mountain way / Meadows / Country fair / Funk no.49 / Time out / Walk away.
LP: MCL 1751
MC: MCLC 1751

BUT SERIOUSLY FOLKS.
Tracks: / Over and over / Second hand store / Indian Summer / At the station / Tomorrow / Inner tube / Boat Weirdos, Theme from / Life's been good.
LP: K 53081
MC: K4 53081

CONFESSOR.
Tracks: / Problems / I broke my leg / Bubbles / Slow dancing / 15 years / Confessor / Rosewood bitters / Good man down / Dear John.
LP: 925281 1
MC: 925281 4

GOT ANY GUM.
Tracks: / Radio song, The / Fun / In my car / Malibu / Half of the time / Got any gum ? / Up to me / No peace in the jungle / Memory lane / Time.
LP: 925606 1
MC: 925606 4

JOE WALSH LIVE (You can't argue with a sick mind).
Tracks: / Walk away / Meadows / Rocky mountain way / Time out.
LP: MCL 1613
MC: MCLC 1613

NIGHTRIDING: WALSH ICE.
MC: KNMC 10023

ORDINARY AVERAGE GUY.
Tracks: / Two sides to every story / Ordinary average guy / Gamma goochee, The / All of a sudden / Alphabetical order / Look at us now / I'm actin' different / Up all night / You might need somebody / Where I grew up / School days.
LP: 4681281
MC: 4681284

THERE GOES THE NEIGHBORHOOD.
Tracks: / Things / Made your mind up / Down on the farm / Rivers / Life of illusion / Bones / Rockets / You never know.
LP: K 52285

WELCOME TO THE CLUB.
Tracks: / Turn to stone / Coming down / Welcome to the club / Rocky mountain way / Time out / Happy ways / Bookends / Here we go / Country fair / Days gone by.
LP: RAWLP 036
MC: RAWTC 036

YOU BOUGHT IT YOU NAME IT.
Tracks: / I can play that rock 'n' roll / Told you so / Here we are now / Worry song / ILBTs / Space age whizz kids / Love letters / Class of 65 / Shadows / Theme from island weirdos.
LP: 923884 1

YOU CAN'T ARGUE WITH A SICK MIND.
Tracks: / Walk away / Meadows / Rocky mountain way / Time out / Help me thru the night / Turn to stone.
LP: FA 3051
MC: TCFA 3051
LP: ABCL 5156

Walsh, John G

GALWAY RAMBLER, THE.
MC: GTDC 100

Walsh, Maurice

GREEN RUSHES - THE QUIET MAN (Adair, Peter).
MCSET: COL 2004

Walsh, Paddy

MAINSAIL HAUL.
MC: 60-206

Walsh, Seamus

TRADITIONAL MUSIC OF IRELAND.
MC: GTDC 005

Walsh, Sean

COUNTRY AND IRISH.
MC: GTDC 103

HAYMAKER, THE.
MC: HAYC 001

WILL THE CIRCLE BE UNBROKEN.
MC: GTDC 008

Walsh, Sheila

DON'T HIDE YOUR HEART.
Tracks: / Don't hide your heart / Under the gun / Jesus call your lambs / Alpha omega / You'll never be the same / Light across the world / We are all one / It's for you / Not guilty / Thief in the night.
LP: BIRD 165
MC: TC BIRD 165

DRIFTING.
Tracks: / Drifting (Duet with Cliff Richard) / Turn turn turn / Mystery / Sunset skies / Private Life / Yes, He lives / Fooled by a feeling / Sleepwalking / It's lonely when the lights go on / Fighter.
LP: MYR R 1215
MC: MYR C 1215
LP: DJF 20581
MC: DJH 40581

DRIFTING (EP) (see Richard, Cliff) (Walsh, Sheila & Cliff Richard).

DRIFTING (SINGLE) (See under Richard, Cliff) (Walsh, Sheila & Cliff Richard).

FUTURE EYES.
Tracks: / Here with me / He weeps for our tears / Love in my life / Future eyes / Back to the old routine / Burn on / You're so important to me / Eyes of a different kind / Fear of silence / Breaking the ice / Mona Lisa.
LP: WRD 3013
MC: TC WRD 3013

PORTRAIT: SHEILA WALSH.
LP: BIRD R 187
MC: BIRD C 187

SAY SO.
Tracks: / Wind of change / Surrender / Love is the answer / Trapeze / Dorai sani / Empty / Boxes / Angels with dirty faces / Jesus loves the Church / Human cry / Hope for the hopeless.
LP: MYR R 1242
MC: MYR C 1242

SHADOWLANDS.
LP: MYRR 1216
MC: MYRC 1216

TRIUMPH IN THE AIR.
LP: BIRD 152
MC: TC BIRD 152

Walt Disney

DISNEY SPECTACULAR, A (See under Cincinnati Pops Orch) (Cincinnati Pops Orchestra).

WALT DISNEY SUPER SOUNDTRACK ORIGINALS (see under Disney) (Various artists).

Walter, Harriet

THUNDER ON THE RIGHT (See also Stewart, Mary).

Walters, Dave

COMES SAILING IN (Folk Guitarist).
LP: FE 004

INNOCENCE AND EXPERIENCE.
LP: GVR 204

KITES.
LP: SHY 7017

Walters, Hank

PROGRESS.
LP: ROXLP 003

Walters, Rosemary

JUST ROSE.
LP: NERLP 002

Walters, Trevor

WALTERS GOLD WITH LOVE.
LP: DELP 001

Walther, Gisela

ACCORDION CONCERTO (Solo Acc).
LP: LP 8021

Walton, Cedar

ANIMATION.
Tracks: / Animation / Jacob's ladder / Charmed circle / Another star / Precious mountain / March of the fisherman / If it could happen / Ala Eduardo.
LP: CBS 83504

BLUESVILLE TIME (Walton, Cedar Quartet).
LP: CRISS 1017

BREAKTHROUGH (Walton, Cedar & Hank Mobley).
LP: MR 5132

CEDAR BLUES (Live) (Walton, Cedar Quintet).
LP: VPA 179

CEDAR WALTON (Walton, Cedar, David Williams, Billy Higgins).
LP: SJP 223

EASTERN REBELLION (Walton, Cedar Quartet).
Tracks: / Bolivia / 5/4 thing / Mode for Joe / Naima / Bittersweet.
LP: SJP 101
MC: SJP 1101

EASTERN REBELLION VOL.2 (Walton, Cedar, Bob Berg, Sam Jones & Billy Higgins).
LP: SJP 106

EASTERN REBELLION VOL.3 (With Curtis Fuller,Bob Berg,Sam jones & Billy Higgins).
LP: SJP 143

FIRM ROOTS.
LP: MR 5059

FIRST SET.
LP: SCS 1085

LOVE....
LP: VPA 189

MAESTRO, THE.
LP: MR 5244

NIGHT AT BOOMERS, A (see Jordan, Clifford) (Walton, C./Clifford Jordan).

NIGHT AT BOOMERS, A (VOL.1) (See Under Jordan, Clifford) (Walton, Cedar & Cliff Jordan).

NIGHT AT BOOMERS, A (VOL.2).
LP: MR 5022

SECOND SET (Walton, Cedar Quartet).
LP: SCS 1113

TRIO, THE (Walton, Cedar, David Williams, Billy Higgins).
LP: VPA 192

Walton (composer)

CORONATION TE DEUM/ BELSHAZZAR'S FEAST (Various artists).
MC: 4251544

Walton, Jake

GLOAMING GREY, THE.
Tracks: / Beggarman, The / Cork march, The / Black nag, The / Tristan's song / Varsuviana puppet waltz / Lamachree and Megrum / Toutouig / Gloaming grey, The / Innisfree / Wind that shakes the barley, The / Durham rangers, The / Bonnie labouring boy, The / Echoes.
LP: PLR 021
LP: FF 4001

SUNLIGHT AND SHADE.
LP: FF 4012

Walton, Mercy Dee

MERCY DEE WALTON AND HIS PIANO.
LP: ARHOOLIE 1007

Waltones

DEEPEST.
Tracks: / Deepest, The / Everything's just fine / Don't understand / She's everywhere but here / Million different ways, A / Going wrong / When it all turns sour / Smile / Rainfall / I've got nothing.
LP: MC 018 LP

Waltons

THANK GOD FOR THE WALTONS.
LP: 081 466

Waltz of Hearts (bk)

WALTZ OF HEARTS, THE (Barbara Cartland) (Sinden, Jeremy (nar)).
MC: IAB 88093

Wammack, Travis

SCR-SCR-SCRATCHY.
Tracks: / Scratchy / Firefly / Up set / Flip flop and bop / Technically speaking / Find another man / Distortion part 2 / Louie louie / Hallelujah, I love her so / Hideaway / You are my sunshine / Memphis / Night train.
LP: ZK 2013

Wampas

CHAUDS SALES ET HUMIDES.
LP: ROSE 161
MC: ROSE 161C

Wanderers

ONLY LOVERS LEFT ALIVE, THE.
Tracks: / Fanfare for 1984 / No dreams / Doctor Beter / Little bit frightening / Take them and break them / It's all the same / Times they are a-changin' / Ready to snap / Can't take you anymore / Sold your soul for fame / Circles of time / There'll be no tomorrow.
LP: POLS 1028

Wanderers (film)

WANDERERS, THE (Film Soundtrack) (Various artists).
Tracks: / You really got a hold on me: *Miracles* / Shout: *Isley Brothers* / Big girls don't cry: *Four Seasons*/ Ya ya: *Dorsey, Lee* / My boyfriend's back: *Angels* / Soldier boy: *Shirelles* / Pipeline: *Chantays*/ Do you love me: *Contours* / Wipe out: *Surfaris* / Wanderer, The: *Dion* / Stand by me: *King, Ben E.* / Tequila: *Champs*.
LP: SHM 3069
LP: GEMLP 103
MC: GEMK 103

Wanderley, Walter

BRAZIL'S GREATEST HITS.
Tracks: / A felicidade / Wave / Tristeza / Meditation / Recado / Feelings / Baia / Carnaval / Mas que nade / Girl from Ipanema / Canta de Ossanha / Triste / One note Samba / Quiet nights / Berimbau / Desfinado / Summer samba / How insensitive / Samba de Orpheu / Brazil.
LP: NI 8001
LP: GNPS 2137
MC: GNP5 2137

PERPETUAL MOTION LOVE.
LP: GNPS 2142

Wang Chung

MOSAIC.
Tracks: / Fun tonite / Hypnotize me / Flat horizon / Betrayal / Let's go / Eyes of the girl / Fool and his money / World in which we live.
LP: WX74

POINTS OF A CURVE.
Tracks: / Don't let go / Dance hall days / Devoted friend, The / Talk it out / Even if you dream / Don't be my enemy / Waves / Look at me now / Wait.
LP: 904004 1
MC: 904004 4

TO LIVE AND DIE IN L.A (Film soundtrack).
Tracks: / To live and die in L.A / Lullaby / Wake up, stop dreaming / Wait / City of the angels / Red stare, The / Black-blue-white / Every big city / Dance hall days.
LP: GEF 70271
MC: 4070271
MC: GEFC 24081

WARMER SIDE OF, THE.
LP: WX 251
MC: WX 251C

Wangford, Hank

HANK WANGFORD.
LP: COW 1

HANK WANGFORD BUMPER PACK, THE.
MC: CCP 1

LIVE: HANK WANGFORD.
LP: COW 2

RODEO RADIO.
LP: SITU 16
MC: SITC 16

STORMY WEATHER.
LP: RUE 004
MC: RUEMC 004

Wansel, Dexter

CAPTURED.
Tracks: / Captured / Do what you wanna do / Year of living dangerously, The / Heart on the line / Each moment / Conversations / Turn me on / Nam (I can't sleep at night) / In the wind / East meets west.
LP: DIX 36
MC: CDIX 36

VOYAGER.
Tracks: / All night long / Solutions / Voyager / I just want to love you / Time is the teacher / Latin love / I'm in love.
LP: PIR 82786
MC: 40 82786

Wappat, Frank

BOTH SIDES OF FRANK WAPPAT.
Tracks: / Sugartime / Heart and soul / Something to remember you by / Your heart and my heart / Deep in a dream of you / Little drummer boy / Just a little walk with Jesus / I wonder / Higher ground / Dear brother / I found a friend / I saw the light.
LP: RUB 035

FAITH OF OUR FATHERS SONGS FOR SINGING.
Tracks: / Songs for singing / Showers of blessing / Oh for a 1000 tongues / Yes God is good / Miracle song, The / Flowers of the rarest / Rockin all night / Thou shepherd of Israel / Faith of our fathers / Love divine / When I survey the wondrous cross / Hark the gospel news is sounding / Happy / In the sweet bye and bye / Oh thou who cameth from above / Ave Maria.
LP: MWM 1013

PRAISE YE THE LORD-SONGS FOR SINGING VOL.2.
Tracks: / Songs for singing / Glory halleluja / Onward Christian soldiers / Shepherd of love / Cabin in the corner / I am so glad that Jesus loves me / I've got the joy / What a friend we have in Jesus / Grumblers / Noah found grace / Goodbye goodbye / Sinking sands / Praise ye the lord / We'll be there / In the garden / When the roll is called up yonder / In the sweet bye and bye.
LP: MWM 1015

War

LIFE.
Tracks: / Happiness / W.W.III / Dawning of night / Waiting at the church / When the nightmare comes / Shaking it down / Summerdreams / U-2 medley.
LP: RCALP 3113

LOVE IS ALL AROUND (War featuring Eric Burdon).
Tracks: / Love is all around / Tobacco Road / Day in the life, A / Magic mountain / Home dream / Paint it black.
LP: ABCL 5207

ON FIRE.
Tracks: / On fire / Roses are blue / Ripe bananas / Exodus / Churchin' / Nothing you can do / Cup of soul, A / Afro cuban opus No. 1 / God is love / Glorissa superba.
LP: THBL 1.041

OUTLAW.
Tracks: / You got the power / Outlaw / Jungle (medley) / Beware it's a jungle out there / Street of walls, The / Street of lights, The / Street of now, The / Just because / Baby it's cold outside / I'm about somebody / Cinco de Mayo.
LP: RCALP 3069

WAR GIVE YOU...THE FREEDOM TO ROCK.
LP: WARLP 8621
MC: ZCWARLP 8621

War Dog

WAR DOG (see Treece, H) (Steuart, David).

War & Friends

BLACK CAUCUS CONCERT (War/ Curtis Mayfield/Kool & The Gang).
Tracks: / Wild and peaceful / Give me your love / On and on / Gypsy man / Going down slow.
LP: GCH 8033
MC: GCHK 78033

War Games

WAR GAMES (Film soundtrack) (Various artists).
LP: POLD 5124
LP: 815 005-1
MC: 815 005-4

War In Korea

WAR IN KOREA 1950-1953 (Original TV soundtrack) (Various artists).
LP: REC 639
MC: ZCM 639

War Machine

UNKNOWN SOLDIER.
LP: NEAT 1036

War of the Worlds

HIGHLIGHTS FROM WAR OF THE WORLDS (See under Wayne, Jeff) (Various artists).

WAR OF THE WORLDS (Various artists).
LP: WOW 100

WAR OF THE WORLDS (Various artists).
Tracks: / Coming of the Martians, The: *Various artists* / Eve of the war, The: *Various artists* / Horsell Common and the heat ray: *Various artists* / Artilleryman and the fighting machine, The: *Various artists* / Forever Autumn: *Various artists* / Thunder child: *Various artists* / Earth under the Martians, The: *Various artists* / Red weed, The (part 1): *Various artists* / Red weed, The (part 2): *Various artists* / Spirit of man, The: *Various artists* / Brave new world: *Various artists* / Dead London: *Various artists* / Epilogue (part 1): *Various artists* / Epilogue (part 2): *Various artists*.
2LP: CBS 96000
MCSET: 40 96000

WAR OF THE WORLDS (Wells) (Hardy, Robert (nar)).
MC: TC-LFP 7020

WAR OF THE WORLDS (see under H.G. Wells).

WAR OF THE WORLDS (Highlights from) (Various artists).
Tracks: / Eve of the war, The: *Wayne, Jeff* / Horsell Common and the heat ray: *Wayne, Jeff* / Forever autumn: *Wayne, Jeff* / Fighting machine, The: *Wayne, Jeff* / Thunderchild: *Wayne, Jeff* / Red weed, The: *Wayne, Jeff* / Spirit of man, The: *Wayne, Jeff* / Dead London: *Wayne, Jeff* / Brave new world: *Wayne, Jeff*.
LP: CBS 32356
MC: 40 32356
LP: CBS 85337

War & Peace (film)

WAR AND PEACE (Film Soundtrack) (Ovchinnikov, Vyacheslav).
LP: TER 1020

Warburton, Paul

WAR DELIGHT (Warburton, Paul & Dale Bruning).
LP: 7986-1
MC: 7986-4

Ward, Anita

ANITA WARD.
Tracks: / I'm ready for your love / Curtains up / This must be love / Ring my bell / Sweet splendour / There's no doubt about it / You lied / Make believe lovers / If I could feel that old feeling again / Spoiled by your love / I won't stop loving you.
LP: TRPL 115

SONGS OF LOVE.
Tracks: / Make believe lovers / If I could feel that old feeling again / Spoiled by your love / I won't stop loving you / Ring my bell / Sweet splendor / There's no doubt about it / You lied.
LP: TKR 83371

Ward, Billy

14 ORIGINAL GREATEST HITS:BILLY WARD (Ward, Billy & His Dominoes).
LP: K 5005

21 ORIGINAL GREATEST HITS (Ward, Billy & His Dominoes).
LP: K 5008

BILLY WARD AND HIS DOMINOES (Bellaphone label) (Ward, Billy & The Dominoes).
LP: BID 8005

BILLY WARD AND HIS DOMINOES, VOL. 2 (Bellaphon Label).
LP: BID 8008

BILLY WARD & HIS DOMINOES (Ward, Billy & His Dominoes).
Tracks: / Sixty minute man / Do something for me / That's what you're doing to me / Deep sea blues / Pedal pushin' papa / Don't leave me this way / Have mercy baby / I am with you / Chicken blues / Weeping willow blues / Love, love, love / Bells, The.
LP: SING 559

FEAT (Ward, Billy & His Dominoes).
Tracks: / Tenderly / Over the rainbow / Learnin' the blues / When the swallows come back to Capistano / Harbour lights / These foolish things / Three coins in the fountain / Little things mean a lot / Rags to riches / May I never love again / Lonesome road / Until the real thing comes along.
LP: SING 733

Ward Brothers

MADNESS OF IT ALL, THE.
Tracks: / Why do you run / Easy prey / I trusted you / Over the border / Shadows of you / Don't talk to strangers / Limbo / Cross that bridge / Madness of it all, The.
LP: SIRENLP 5
MC: SIRENC 5

Ward, Carlos

LIVE AT NORTH SEA FESTIVAL 1988 (Ward, Carlos Quartet).
LP: LR 166

LIVE AT SWEET BASIL (see Dollar Brand/Carlos Ward) (Ward, Carlos/ Dollar Brand).
Tracks: / Dream / Find me shelter in the storm / Mummy / For coltrane / New york city / Anthem for the new nation / Gwangwa / King kong / Black lightning / Gwidza / Stride / Soweto.
LP: EKAPA 004

Ward Clarke, Jennifer

BRAHMS CLARINET TRIO AND SONATAS (see under Brahms (Composer)) (Ward Clarke, Jennifer/ Alan Hacker/Richard Burnett).

Ward, Clifford T.

BOTH OF US.
Tracks: / Still not free / Messenger / Watchin' the TV news / Leaving / Both of us / Where do angels really come from? / Contrary / Before the world was round / Waiting for the garda / Change of heart / Twenty minutes / Best is yet to come, The.
LP: 814 777 1
MC: 814 777 4

ESCALATOR.
Tracks: / Way of love, The / Jigsaw girl / Escalator / Trespass / We could be talking / Day to myself, A / Miner / Mr. Bilbo Baggins / Cellophane / Sad affair.
LP: CHC 57

HOME THOUGHTS FROM ABROAD.
Tracks: / Gaye / Wherewithal / Dubious circus company, The / Where would that leave me / Traveller, The / Home thoughts from abroad / Where's it going to end / Time the magician / Give me one more chance / Cold wind blowing / Open university, The / Crisis / Nightingale.
LP: CHC 56
LP: CAS 1066
MC: CHCMC 56

HOME THOUGHTS FROM ABROAD/ MANTLEPIECES.
Tracks: / Gaye / Wherewithal / Dubious circus company, The / Nightingale / Where would that leave me / Traveller, The / Home thoughts from abroad / Where's it going to end / Time the magician / Give me one more chance / Cold wind blowing / Open university, The / Crisis / Scullery / Not waving - drowning / Are you really interested? / Sad cliche, A / To an air hostess / All modern conveniences / Wayward / Screen test / For Debbie and her friends / Tea cosy.
MCSET: CASMC 107

MANTLEPIECES.
Tracks: / Scullery / Not waving - drowning / Are you really interested? / Sad cliche, A / To an air hostess / All modern conveniences / Wayward / Screen test / For Debbie and her friends / Tea cosy.
LP: CHC 37
MC: CHCMC 37
LP: CAS 1077

SOMETIME NEXT YEAR.
Tracks: / Prams / Who cares / Another radio station / Quiz show / They must think me a fool / Sometime next year / Losin' after all (nothin' new) / Stains / Turbo / Like an old song / Today in parliament / Lost in the flow of your love.
LP: TMB 111
MC: TMBC 111

Ward Drive

GIMME GIMME.
Tracks: / Bang the drum / I 4 U / Words / Take take me now / Stay on stay on / Moments away / Crying girl / Eyes on you / Rock 'n' the boat / Making time stand still.
LP: MFN 99
MC: TMFN 99

Ward, Fields

BURY ME NOT ON THE PRAIRIE.
LP: ROUNDER 0036

Ward, Jack

MORE SANKEYS FAVOURITES.
LP: PC 731

ORGAN SELECTION VOL.1, AN.
MC: WC 5032

ORGAN SELECTION VOL.2, AN.
MC: WC 9514

SANKEY MEDLEY.
LP: PC 821

SANKEYS FAVOURITES.
LP: PC 724

Ward, John

SHRINKING WORLD, THE.
Tracks: / Man of destiny, A / How many ships / Shrinking world, The / Dallastry Brookenders St. Blues / My love lies a thousand miles away / Dog on the rocks / When will the circle be broken / Blood of the world / Eve / Fields of youth, The / I won't be blinded to the beauty.
LP: FSLP 4

Ward, Matthew

ARMED AND DANGEROUS.
LP: OAK R 3004
MC: OAK C 3004

TOWARD ETERNITY.
Tracks: / It's all right / Soft spot / Noah's song / Walls fall down, The / Gotta do better than this / Your love came over me / Hold on / Angels unaware / Summer snow / Vineyard, The.
LP: BIRD 121
MC: TC BIRD 121
MC: OAK C 0014

Ward, Michael

INTRODUCING MICHAEL WARD.
LP: 6308 189

Ward, Pete

BETWEEN THE EYES.
Tracks: / Between the eyes / That I can't ignore / Foot in the door / Off my guard / Figure in grey.
MC: PCN 105

DISTANCE GROWS.
Tracks: / Shameful secret / My time is yours / Can't bear this pain / Distance grows / Shameful lovers.

MC: PCN 118

RON GOES TO TOWN.
Tracks: / Watching you / What's inside? / Message from outside / Waiting on the hill / Figure in grey / Changing one by one.
MC: PCN 103

UNUSUAL SHADE.
Tracks: / Eating me / Say what it's worth / Unusual shade / Blue sky.
MC: PCN 111

Ward, Rachel

VIRTUOSO HARP, THE.
Tracks: / Faur / Parry / Salzedo / Francisque / Britten / Handel.
LP: REG 102

Ward Singers

BEST OF THE FAMOUS.
LP: DBL 7015

Wardells, Steve

CREOLE BELLS - FRISCO COMES TO MLBRN.
LP: SOS 1173

Warden (bk)

WARDEN, THE (Sutcliffe, Irene (nar)).
MCSET: CC/015
MCSET: ZBBC 1213

Ware, David S.

PASSAGE TO MUSIC (Ware, David S. Trio).
LP: SHLP 113

Ware, Gillian

KING OF INSTRUMENTS.
Tracks: / Toccata and fugue in D minor / Noel vi in D minor / Naiades from pieces de fantaisie / Chorale No. 3 in A minor / Concerto for organ in F Op. 4. No. 4 / Prelude and fugue on Bach.
LP: REN 678
MC: ZCF 678

Ware, Leon

LEON WARE.
LP: E 160050

MUSICAL MESSAGE.
Tracks: / Learning to love you / Instant love / Body heat / Share your love / Holiday / Phantom lover / Journey into you / Musical message / French waltz / Turn out the light.
LP: STML 12050

ROCKING YOU ETERNALLY.
Tracks: / Little boogie / Baby don't stop me / Sure do what you now / Our time / Rocking you eternally / Got to be loved / Don't stay away / In our garden.
LP: K 52282

UNDERCOVER LOVER.
LP: LP 80017

Ware, Tim

SHELTER FROM THE NORM (Ware, Tim Group).
LP: VR 014
MC: VR 014C

TIM WARE GROUP, THE.
LP: F 13

Ware, Tom

FOURTH CIRCLE, THE.
LP: SKY 098

Warfare

CONFLICT OF HATRED.
Tracks: / Waxworks / Revolution / Dancing in the flames of insanity / Evolution / Fatal vision / Deathcharge / Order of the dragons / Elite forces / Rejoice the feast of quarantine / Noise filth and fury.
LP: NEAT 1044
MC: NEATC 1044

HAMMER HORROR.
Tracks: / Hammer horror / Plague of the zombies / Ballad of the dead / Phantom of the opera / Baron Frankenstein / Velvet rhapsody / Sold of shadows / Prince of darkness / Tales of the gothic genre / Scream of the vampire.
LP: REVLP 147
MC: REVMC 147

MAYHEM F*IN MAYHEM** Hardcore 88.
Tracks: / Abortion sequence / Hungry dogs / Generator / You've really got me / Ebony dreams / Extremely finance / Projectile vomit / M.F.M. / Atomic slut / Machine gun breath / Muder on Melrose.
LP: NEAT 1040
MC: NEATC 1040

METAL ANARCHY.
Tracks: / Electric mayhem / Death vigilance / Wrecked society / Living for the last days / Disgrace / Military shadow / Metal anarchy / Psycho / Rape / Burning up / Destroy.
LP: NEAT 1029

PURE FILTH.
Tracks: / Warning / Total Armageddon (full scale attack) / This machine kills / Let the show go on / Breakout / Burn the Kings Road / New age of total warfare / Collision / Dance of the dead / Limit Crescendo / Rose petals fall from her face / Warfare and venom.
LP: NEAT 1021

Warhawk

WARHAWK, THE (See under Batman bk).

Warhead

SPEEDWAY.
LP: FIST 8357

Warhorse

BEST OF WARHORSE.
Tracks: / St. Louis / Ritual / Woman of the devil / Red sea / Back in time / Sybilla / I who have nothing.
LP: THBL 030

RED SEA.
Tracks: / Red sea / Back in time / Confident but wrong / Feeling better / Sybilla / Mouth piece / I who have nothing.
LP: THBL 010
MC: THBC 010

VULTURE BLOOD.
Tracks: / Vulture blood / No chance / Burning / St. Louis / Ritual / Solitude / Woman of the devil.
LP: THBL 004

Warhust, Roy

NORTHWEST REBELLION (See under Damron, Dick) (Warhust, Roy/ Dick Damron).

Wariner, Steve

I GOT DREAMS.
LP: MCA 42272
MC: MCAC 42272

IT'S A CRAZY WORLD.
Tracks: / Small town girl / Lynda / If I could make a livin' (out of lovin' you) / There's always a first time / Why do heroes die so young / When it rains / It's a crazy world / Hey alarm clock / Weekend, The / Fast break.
LP: MCF 3363
MC: MCFC 3363

Warleigh, Ray

ONE WAY (See under Chase, Tommy) (Warleigh, Ray & Tommy Chase).

Warlock

BURNING THE WITCHES.
Tracks: / Signs of satan / After the bomb / Dark fade / Homicide rocker / Without you / Metal racer / Burning the witches / Hateful guy / Holding me.
LP: VERH 42
MC: VERHC 42
MC: SKULL 78323
LP: SKULL 8325

FORCE MAJEURE (See under Doro & Warlock) (Doro & Warlock).

HELLBOUND.
Tracks: / Hellbound / All night / Earth shaker rock / Wrathchild / Down and out / Out of control / Time to die / Shout it out / Catch my heart.
LP: 824 660-1
MC: 824 660-4

MUSIC AND MEDIA INTERVIEW PICTURE DISCS.
LPPD: MM 1246

TRIUMPH AND AGONY.
Tracks: / All we are / 3 minute warning / I rule the ruins / Kiss of death / Make time for love / East meets west / Touch of evil / Metal tango / Cold cold world / Fur immer.
LP: VERH 50

TRUE AS STEEL.
Tracks: / Mr. Gold / Fight for rock / Love in the danger zone / Speed of sound / Midnight in China / Vorwarts.all right! / True as steel / Lady in a rock'n'roll hell / Love song / Igloo on the moon (reckless) / T.O.L.
LP: HERH 41
MC: VERHC 41

Warlock (Film)

WARLOCK (Film Soundtrack) (Various artists).
Tracks: / Sentence, The: *Various artists* / Ill wind: *Various artists* / Ring, The: *Various artists*/ Trance, The: *Various artists* / Old age: *Various artists* / Growing pains: *Various artists* / Weather vane, The: *Various artists* / Nails: *Various artists* / Uninvited, The: *Various artists* / Salt water attack: *Various artists* / Salt flats: *Various artists.*
LP: FILM 038

Warlord

THY KINGDOM COME.
Tracks: / Mrs. Victoria / Aliens / Child of the damned / Beginning/Lucifer's hammer / Black mass / Lost and lonely days / Soliloquy / Deliver us from evil / Hands and feet.
LP: RR 9637

Warm

NOVA VAGA.
LP: PFLP 201

Warman, Johnny

FROM THE JUNGLE TO THE NEW HORIZON.
Tracks: / From the jungle to the new horizon / Spirit in the sky / Looking back / China's moving west / I love my planet / State of America / Flying out of windows / Dream dream dream.
LP: TRAIN 22

WALKING INTO MIRRORS.
Tracks: / Walking into mirrors / Radio active / Searchlights / Martian summer / Screaming jets / Three minutes / Will you dance with me / Sending out signals / Dancing dolls / Fantastic light.
LP: TRAIN 17

Warner Brothers (film)

GREAT WARNER BROTHERS ACTION MOVIES (Warner Brothers Studio Orchestra).
Tracks: / Enter the dragon / Bullitt / John Paul Jones / Adventures of Robin Hood / Wild bunch, The / Bonnie and Clyde.
LP: K 26120
MC: K4 26120

Warner, Florence

ANOTHER HOT NIGHT.
Tracks: / You can't win em' all / All in one night / Easy / Love on a shoestring / Hold me once / I miss your heartbeat / Drawing pictures / Love gone by / Take good care of my baby / Staying with it / Why do you pick the people you pick.
LP: 6359033

Warner, Frank

STORY OF A FOLKSONG U.S.A..
MC: 90-901

Warner, Jack

ORDINARY COPPER, AN.
Tracks: / Ordinary copper, An / My bruvver in the life guards / Walking hup and dahn the rawlway laines / You can't help laughing / Sea lions and seals / Bunger up o' rat 'oles / Fumper and a flattener of fevvers / Caster up of alalbaster plaster / Claude and his sword / Turkish bath attendant / If I'd only put an X instead / Thank you my lady / Frank and his tank / I didn't orter a'ett it.
LP: OU 2237

Warner, Jeff

WILDER JOY (Warner, Jeff/Davis, Jeff).
LP: FF 431

Warner, Kai

MOTIVE SERIES.
LP: 6449 070
MC: 7143 070

VERY BEST OF KAI WARNER.
LP: 2371 052

Warner's Seven Aces

1923-1927 (White Jazz And Hot Dance From Atlanta) (Various artists).
Tracks: / Lovesome lovesick blues: *Warner's Seven Aces* / Mean eyes: *Warner's Seven Aces* / Ace of spades: *Warner's* Seven Aces / Bessie couldn't help it: *Warner's Seven Aces* / When my sugar walks down the street: *Warner's Seven* Aces / Blues have got me, The: *Warner's Seven Aces* / Go get 'em Caroline: *Warner's Seven Aces* / Breakin' the leg: *Warner's Seven Aces* / Hangin' around: *Warner's Seven Aces* / Who'd be blue: *Warner's Seven Aces*/ You've got those 'wanna go back again' blues: *Warner's Seven Aces* / So is your old lady: *Warner's Seven Aces*/ That's my hap-hap-happiness: *Warner's Seven Aces* / There's everything nice about you: *Warner's Seven Aces* / When Jennie does her low down dance: *Warner's Seven Aces.*
LP: HQ 2030

Warnes, Jennifer

BEST OF JENNIFER WARNES.
Tracks: / Right time of the night / It goes like it goes / I know a heartache when I see one / When the feeling comes around / I'm restless / Could it be love? / Run to her / I'm dreaming / Shot through the heart / Come to me.
LP: 204427

FAMOUS BLUE RAINCOAT.
Tracks: / First we take Manhattan / Bird on the wire / Famous blue raincoat / Joan of Arc / Ain't no cure for love / Coming back to you / Song of Bernadette / Singer must die, A / Came so far for beauty.
LP: PL 90048
MC: PK 90048

I'VE HAD THE TIME OF MY LIFE (see Medley, Bill) (Warnes, Jennifer & Bill Medley).

JENNIFER WARNES.
Tracks: / Love hurts / Round and round / Shine a light / You're the one I love / I'm dreaming / Mama / Right time of the night / Bring ol' Maggie back home / Don't lead me on / Daddy don't go / O God of loveliness (O bello dio del paradiso).
LP: SPART 1006

RIGHT TIME OF THE NIGHT (OLD GOLD) (See under Mary McGregor - Torn Between Two).

SHOT THROUGH THE HEART.
Tracks: / Shot through the heart / I know a heartache when I see one / Don't make me over / You remember me / Sign on the window / I'm restless / Tell me just one more time / When the feeling comes around / Frankie in the rain / Hard times / Come again no more.
LP: SPART 1097
MC: TCART 1097

Warning Sign

WARNING SIGN (Film Soundtrack) (Various artists).
LP: SCRS 1012

Warp 9

FADE IN FADE OUT.
Tracks: / Skips a beat / Dirty looks / Big fun / Reach for your star / Cutting edge, The / You'll get over it / To the last drop.
LP: ZL 72414
MC: ZK 72414

Warrant

CHERRY PIE (ALBUM).
Tracks: / Cherry pie / Uncle Tom's cabin / I saw red / Bed of roses / Sure feels good to me / Love in stereo / Blind faith / Song and dance man / Only hell your mama ever raised, The / Mr. Rainmaker / Train, train.
LP: 4671901
MC: 4671904

DIRTY ROTTEN FILTHY STINKING RICH.
Tracks: / 32 pennies in a ragu jar / Down boys / Big talk / Sometimes she cries / So damn pretty (against the law) / D.R.F.S.R. / In the sticks / Heaven / Ridin' high / Cold sweat.
LP: 4650521
MC: 4650524

ENFORCER, THE.
LP: N 0023

Warren, Annette

BEING A WOMAN.
Tracks: / Getting away / This house / Don't bother / Me now little girl / Questionnaire, the / Eyes / Hold lightly / Song for my child to be / Lullabye / Glamourous waltz.
LP: OUTSTANDING 15

Warren, Day

DAY WARREN.
LP: R&C 1002

Warren, Harry

GREAT BRITISH DANCE BANDS PLAY THE MUSIC OF HARRY WARREN (See under Dance Bands...) (Various artists).

SONGS OF HARRY WARREN.
LP: CT 6030

WHO'S HARRY WARREN? Vol 2, 42nd Street (Various artists).
Tracks: / 42nd street: *Who's Harry Warren* / You'll never know: *Who's Harry Warren* / You must have been a beautiful baby: *Who's Harry Warren* / Rose of the Rio Grande: *Who's Harry Warren* / I'll string along with you: *Who's* Harry Warren / We're in the money: *Who's Harry Warren* / You're getting to be habit with me: *Who's Harry Warren*/ About a quarter to nine: *Who's Harry Warren* / Dames: *Who's Harry Warren* / Shuffle off to Buffalo: *Who's Harry Warren* / I found a million dollar baby: *Who's Harry Warren* / Lullaby of Broadway: *Who's Harry Warren.*
LP: PHONT 7413
MC: PHONT 8413

WHO'S HARRY WARREN? Vol 1: Jeepers creepers (Various artists).
Tracks: / Lulu's back in town: *Various artists* / I had the craziest dream: *Various artists* / Summer night: *Various* artists / You're my everything: *Various artists* / Cheerful little earful: *Various artists* / Jeepers creepers: *Various artists* / I only have eyes for you: *Various artists* / There will never be another you: *Various artists*/ This heart of mine: *Various artists* / I wish I knew: *Various artists* / Serenade in blue: *Various artists*/ Nagasaki: *Various artists.*
LP: PHONT 7412
MC: PHONT 8412

Warren, James

BURNING QUESTIONS (Warren, James (Korgis)).
Tracks: / Burning questions / Climate of treason / They don't believe in magic / Possessed / I know something / True life confessions / It won't be the same old place / Loneliness / Can you bear the spirit dying / I want to remember.
LP: SNTF 956

Warren, Johnny

JUST PLAYIN' IN THE RAIN.
Tracks: / Indian creek / Tom and Jerry / 50 year ago waltz / Limerock / Tea kettle hornpipe / Saint Anne's reel / Just playin' in the rain / Frank Ryan's hornpipe / Hiram's hornpipe / What a friend we have in Jesus / Daley's reel / Black eyed Susan Brown.
LP: REBEL 1614
MC: REBELMC 1614

Warren, Paul

AMERICA'S GREATEST BREAKDOWN FIDDLER (Warren, Paul & Lester Flatt & Nashville Grass).
Tracks: / Durham's reel / Indian creek / Katy Hill / 8th of January / Twinkle little star / Pretty Polly Ann / Denver belle / Listen to the mockingbird / Stony fork / Liberty / Leather britches / Sally Johnson / Dusty Miller / Hop light ladies / New five cents / Grey eagle / Sally Goodin' / Tennessee wagoner / Hoedown in Hickman county / Black eyed Susan Brown.
LP: CMH 6237
MC: CMHC 6237

Warren, Peter

SOLIDARITY.
LP: JAPO 60034

Warren, Robert Penn

ROBERT PENN WARREN READS.
MC: 1654

SELECTED POEMS (Read by Robert Penn Warren).
MC: UNKNOWN

Warren, Rusty

BOTTOMS UP.
LP: GNPS 2103

KNOCKERS UP.
2LP: GNPS 2079
MCSET: GNP5 2079

KNOCKERS UP '76.
LP: GNPS 2088
MC: GNP5 2088

RUSTY WARREN BOUNCES BACK.
2LP: GNPS 2080
MCSET: GNP5 2080

RUSTY WARREN LAYS IT ON THE LINE.
LP: GNPS 2081
MC: GNP5 2081

SEXPLOSION.
LP: GNPS 2114

Warrior

FIGHTING FOR THE EARTH.
Tracks: / Fighting for the earth / Only the strong survive / Ruler / Mind over matter / Defenders of creation / Day of evil (beware) / Cold fire / PTM 1 / Welcome aboard.
MC: CDIX 6
LP: XID 6

Warrior Soul

DRUGS, GOD AND THE NEW REPUBLIC.
LP: DGC 24389
MC: DGCC 24389

LAST DECADE, DEAD CENTURY.
Tracks: / I see the ruins / We cry out / Losers, The / Down town / Trippin' on ecstasy / One minute years / Super power dreamland / Charlie's out of prison / Blown away / Lullaby / In conclusion / Four more years.
LP: WX 344
MC: WX 344C
MC: DGCC 24285

Warriors

BEHIND THE MASK.
Tracks: / Hot apple / Warrior / Midnight oil / Bustin loose / Warrior's dream / Destination / Je ne sais quoi / Drive / Unsung heroes.
LP: ENVY 6001
MC: ENCAS 6001

WARRIORS.
LP: A 42

Warriors (film)

WARRIORS (Film Soundtrack) (Various artists).
Tracks: / In the city: *Various artists* / Warriors theme: *Various artists* / Baseball furies chase: *Various artists* / Fight: *Various artists* / Echoes in my mind: *Various artists*.

LP: AMLH 64761
LP: SP 3151
MC: CS 3151
LP: SP 4761

Warsaw Concerto

WARSAW CONCERTO (Original Soundtrack) (Various artists).
Tracks: / Warsaw concerto: *Various artists* / Dangerous moonlight: *Various artists* / Rhapsody on a theme of Paganini: *Various artists* / Story of three loves, The: *Various artists* / Dream of Olwen: *Various artists* / While I live: *Various artists* / Cornish rhapsody: *Various artists* / Love story: *Various artists* / Escape me never: *Various artists* / Invaders, The: *Various artists* / 49th parallel: *Various artists* / Things to come: *Various artists*.
LP: VIV 5
MC: 4212614

Warsaw Philharmonic...

BEATLES SYMPHONY.
LP: JOBLP 1
MC: JOBMC 1

Wartime

FAST FOOD FOR THOUGHT.
Tracks: / Mindfield / Wartime / Right to life / Whole truth, The / Franklin's tower.
LP: CHR 1753
MC: ZCHR 1753

Warum Joe

ALLAH MODE.
LP: ROSE 142
MC: ROSE 142C

LA METHODE DU DISCOURS.
LP: ROSE 105

LE TRAIN SIFFLERA, CROIS-MOI.
Tracks: / Peste noire / Ralph Und Karl / Effluves / Music Box / Les rives de cayenne / Tchang / Bogota / Les colline des potences / Eliane III / Electrolyse / El condor pasa / Stupid Joe / Datcha / Casablanca / Idi Amin / T bird / Jivago / Western.
LP: FC 024

TOCARE LA VERITA.
LP: ROSE 32

Warwick, Dionne

6 TRACK HITS: DIONNE WARWICK.
Tracks: / Walk on by / Reach out for me / Do you know the way to San Jose? / You'll never get to Heaven / Valley of the dolls / Anyone who had a heart.
MC: 7SC 5001

20 GOLDEN PIECES: DIONNE WARWICK.
Tracks: / I'll never fall in love again / Anyone who had a heart / I say a little prayer / Do you know the way to San Jose? / Raindrops keep falling on my head / Don't make me over / Alfie / I just don't know what to do with myself / Make it easy on yourself / This girl's in love with you / Walk on by / Trains and boats and planes / You'll never get to Heaven / Wives and lovers / As long as he needs me / Message to Michael / Didn't we? / Games people play / My way / Promises, promises.
LP: BDL 2029
MC: BDC 2029

25TH ANNIVERSARY COLLECTION.
Tracks: / Walk On By / Close To You / There's always something there to remind me / Wishin' and hopin' / Look of love, The / Message To Michael / I Just Don't Know What To Do With Myself / Wives and lovers / Reach Out For Me / Are you there (with another girl) / Do you know the way to San Jose / I say a little prayer.
LP: SHM 3243
MC: HSC 3243

ANTHOLOGY - DIONNE WARWICK 1962-1971.
2LP: RNDA 1100

ANYONE WHO HAD A HEART.
MC: 2636234

BEST OF DIONNE WARWICK.
Tracks: / Then came you / One less bell to answer / Love in the afternoon / Ronnie Lee / Close to you / I think you need love / If we only have to love / You're gonna need me / Do you believe in love at first sight / Track of the cat / We'll burn our bridges behind us / Just being myself.
MC: 16-10
LP: NPL 28079
LP: W 3814

DIONNE.
Tracks: / Who, what, when, where and why / After you / Letter, The / I'll never love this way again / Deja vu / Feeling old feelings / In your eyes / My everlasting love / Out of my hands / All the time.
LP: SPART 1096
MC: TCART 1096

DIONNE WARWICK.
Tracks: / Walk on by / Anyone who had a heart / Reach out for me / I just don't know what to do with myself / Don't make me over / Always something there to remind me / Do you know the way to San Jose? / Trains and boats and planes / Wishin' and hopin' / Valley of the dolls / House is not a home, A / I'll never fall in love again.
LP: COUNT 6
MC: ZC CNT 6

DIONNE WARWICK COLLECTION, THE.
Tracks: / Heartbreaker / I'll never love this way again / Friends in love / Deja vu / No night so long / Take the short way home / All the love in the world / Love so right / Letter, The / Betcha by golly wow / Easy love / Our day will come / Yours / Who, what, when, where and why / It's the falling in love / With a touch / All the time / What is this? / Walk on by / Anyone who had a heart / You'll never get to heaven / House is not a home, A / Message to Michael / Trains and boats and planes / Look of love, The / Close to you / Do you know the way to San Jose? / Valley of the dolls / There's always something there to remind me / Make it easy on yourself / Promises, promises / What the world needs now is love.
MCSET: PDC 001
2LP: DIONE 1
MCSET: ZCDIO 1
2LP: PDA 001

DIONNE WARWICK SINGS BACHARACH.
LP: ENT LP 13050
MC: ENT MC 13050

DIONNE WARWICK SINGS COLE PORTER.
Tracks: / Night and day / I love Paris / I get a kick out of you / What is thing called love? / So in love (medley) / You're the top / I've got you under my skin / Begin the beguine / It's alright with me / Anything goes / You'd be so nice to come home to / All of you / I concentrate on you / Night and day (jazz version) (Only on CD and Cassette.) / Just one of those things.
LP: 210918
MC: 410918

DIONNE WARWICK VOL 1.
MC: ZCGAS 715

DIONNE WARWICK VOL 3.
MC: ZCGAS 735

DIONNE WARWICK VOL 4.
MC: ZCGAS 744

FRIENDS.
Tracks: / That's what friends are for / Whisper in the dark / Remember your heart / Love at second sight / Moments are moments / Stronger than before / Stay devoted / No one there to sing me a love song / How long / Extravagent gestures.
LP: 207438
MC: 407438
LP: 209652
MC: 409652

FRIENDS IN LOVE.
Tracks: / For you / Friends in love / Never gonna let you go / Can't hide love / Betcha by golly wow / More than fascination / Got you where I want you / With a touch / What is this? / Love so right.
LP: SPART 1192
MC: TCART 1192

GOLDEN HITS: DIONNE WARWICK, VOL 2.
Tracks: / Do you know the way to San Jose? / I just don't know what to do with myself / Message to Michael / Trains and boats and planes / Are you there (with another girl)? / I say a little prayer / What the world needs now is love / Windows of the world / Who can I turn to?.
LP: PHX 1023

GOLDEN HITS: DIONNE WARWICK, VOL 1.
Tracks: / Don't make me over / Wishin' and hopin' / You'll never get to Heaven / Make it easy on yourself / Any old time of day / Walk on by / Reach out for me / Anyone who had a heart / Always something there to remind me.
LP: PHX 1015

GREATEST HITS: DIONNE WARWICK.
LP: WNS 1

GREATEST HITS: DIONNE WARWICK.
Tracks: / I say a little prayer / Do you know the way to San Jose? / You'll never get to Heaven / Alfie / Hurt so bad / Somewhere / Who can I turn to? / In between the heartaches / Anyone who had a heart / I just don't know what to do with myself.
LP: 1A 022 1582721
MC: 1A 022 1582724

MCSET: DTO 10002

GREATEST HITS: DIONNE WARWICK.
LP: 2236235
MC: 2136235

GREATEST HITS: DIONNE WARWICK (IMPORT).
LP: FUN 9037
MC: FUNC 9037

GREATEST HITS VOL 2: DIONNE WARWICK.
LP: WNS 2

HEARTBREAKER.
Tracks: / All the love in the world / I can't see anything but you / You are my love / Just one more night / Our day will come / Heartbreaker / Yours / Take the short way home / It makes no difference / Misunderstood.
LP: 208719
MC: 408719
LP: 204974

HERE WHERE THERE IS LOVE.
LP: NPL 28096

HOT, LIVE AND OTHERWISE.
Tracks: / What you won't do for love / Don't make me over / Alfie / One-in-a-million you / Walk on by / Anyone who had a heart / You'll never get to Heaven / House is not a home, A / Message to Michael / Trains and boats and planes / Look of love, The / Close to you / Do you know the way to San Jose? / Valley of the dolls / There's always something there to remind me / Make it easy on yourself / Promises, promises / What the world needs now is love / Then came you / Deja vu / Easy love / No night so long / We never said goodbye / I'll never love this way again / There's a long road ahead of us / Dedicate this heart / Some changes are for good / Even a fool would let go / Now we're starting over again.
2LP: DARTY 10
MCSET: TCDAR 10

JUST DIONNE WARWICK.
LP: SM 4046

LOVE SONGS COLLECTION.
Tracks: / I'll never fall in love again / Let it be me / Here where there is love / I love Paris / Hurt so bad / As long as he needs me / Blowing in the wind / One hand, one heart / You can have him / People / This girl's in love with you / You're all I need to get by / Baubles, bangles and beads / Getting ready for the heartbreak / Who can I turn to / People got to be free / It's the good life / Somewhere / Unchained melody / Valley of the dolls.
LP: SHM 3258
MC: HSC 3258

LOVE SONGS, THE.
Tracks: / Heartbreaker / I'll never love this way again / Walk on by / Deja vu / No one in this world / Run to me / How many times can we say goodbye / Take good care of you and me / All the love in the world / Love power / Do you know the way to San Jose? / Reservations for two / Yours / You'll never get to heaven / So amazing / That's what friends are for.
LP: 210441
MC: 410441

NO NIGHT SO LONG.
Tracks: / Easy love / No night so long / It's the falling in love / When the world runs out of love / We never said goodbye / How you once loved me / Reaching for the sky / Sweetie pie / Somebody's angel / We had this time.
LP: SPART 1132
MC: TCART 1132

ORIGINAL SOUL OF DIONNE WARWICK, THE.
Tracks: / Don't make me over / I smiled yesterday / This empty place / Wishin' and hopin' / Make the music play / Please make him love me / Love of a boy, The / It's love that really counts / Make it easy on yourself / Anyone who had a heart / Walk on by / Any old time of day / Getting ready for the heartbreak / Oh Lord what are you doing to me? / You'll never get to Heaven / Reach out for me / You can have her / Looking with my eyes / Are you there (with another girl)? / Message to Michael / I just don't know what to do with myself / Windows of the world / I say a little prayer / Do you know the way to San Jose? / Who is gonna love me? / Lonely in my heart / Yesterday I heard the rain / Do right woman, do right man / I've been loving you too long / I'm your puppet / Walk the way you talk / Love of my man, The.
2LP: CDX 18
MC: TCCDX 18

PRESENTING DIONNE WARWICK.
LP: NPL 28037

RESERVATIONS.
Tracks: / Reservations for two / For everything you are / Love power / You're my hero / Close enough / In a world such

as this / Another chance to love / Cry on me / Heartbreak of love / No one in the world.
LP: 208213
MC: 408213

SO AMAZING.
Tracks: / How many times can we say goodbye / I do it 'cause I like it / Will you love me tomorrow / Got a date / I can let go now / So amazing / What can a miracle do / Two ships passing in the night.
LP: 205755
MC: 405755

THIS GIRL'S IN LOVE.
Tracks: / Do you know the way to San Jose? / Who can I turn to / Reach out for me / Loneliness remembers / Make it easy on yourself / Wives and lovers / Goin' out of my head / Trains and boats and planes / I say a little prayer / This girl's in love with you / Look of love, The / Valley of the dolls, Theme from / House is not a home, A / What the world needs now is love / You'll never get to heaven / I'll never fall in love again / Message to Michael / Let me be lonely / Windows of the world / Promises, promises / There's always something there to remind me / Raindrops keep falling on my head / Walk on by / Alfie / Don't make me over / I just don't know what to do with myself.
2LP: CR 031
MCSET: CRT 031

UNFORGETTABLE: DIONNE WARWICK (16 Golden Classics).
Tracks: / Games people play / Hey Jude / Look of love, The / If I ruled the world / Goin' out of my head / Only love can break a heart / Summertime / Unchained melody / Yesterday / You'll never walk alone / Alfie / Trains and boats and planes / You've lost that lovin' feeling / Anyone who had a heart / Walk on by / Always something there to remind me.
LP: UNLP 005
MC: UNMC 005

VALLEY OF THE DOLLS.
LP: NSPL 28114

VERY BEST OF DIONNE WARWICK, THE.
Tracks: / Walk on by / Don't make me over / One hand, one heart / With these hands / Baubles, bangles and beads / Trains and boats and planes / Getting ready for the heartbreak / Make the music play / Unchained melody / Here where there is love / You can have him / House is not a home, A / Close to you / What'd I say? / Make it easy on yourself / Always something there to remind me / Wishin' and hopin' / Another night / If I ever make you cry / Blowing in the wind / Look of love, The / People / Wives and lovers / Message to Michael / Are you there (with another girl)?.
MCSET: DTO 10059

WITHOUT YOUR LOVE.
Tracks: / No one in the world / Without your love / Run to me / Finder of lost loves / Love don't live here anymore / It's you / It's love / Bedroom eyes / Weakness / You made me want to love again.
LP: 206571
MC: 406571
LP: 208553
MC: 408553

Was Not Was

ARE YOU OKAY?.
Tracks: / Are you okay? / I feel better than James Brown / Papa was a rollin' stone / How the heart behaves / Maria Novarro / In K Mart wardrobe / Dressed to be killed / You, you, you / I blew up the United States / Elvis' Rolls Royce / Just another couple broken hearts / Look what's back.
LP: 8463511
MC: 8463514

BORN TO LAUGH AT TORNADOS.
Tracks: / Out come the freaks / Professor night / Party broke up / Smile / Zaz turned blue / Knocked down / Made small / Bow wow wow wow / Betrayal / Shake your head / Man vs the empire brain building.
LP: GEF 25922

OUT COME THE FREAKS.
LP: IMA 10
MC: IMC 10

WAS (NOT WAS).
LP: ILPS 7015
MC: ICT 7015
MC: 842 683 4
LP: 842 683 1

WHAT UP, DOG.
Tracks: / Spy In The House of Love / Boy's gone crazy, The / Anything Can Happen / Somewhere in America / Out Come The Freaks / What up dog? / Love can be bad luck / 11 Miles An Hour.
LP: SFLP 4
MC: SFMC 4

Wasa Express

CHECKMATE.
Tracks: / Borderline / 1-2-3 / Midnight to six man / Question of temperature / Teenage were-wolf / Slow down / Devil's danceland / Work with me Annie / Cocovoodoobana song.
LP: SNTF 810

Wasch

METAL GOES MOUNTAIN.
LP: SBR 18LP

Wash House Stompers

THERE'LL BE SOME CHANGES MADE.
Tracks: / There'll be some changes made / I want a little girl / As long as I live / Lazy river / Swinging the blues / Some of these days / Original Dixieland one-step / Special one / Since you first came my way / Someday you'll be sorry / New Orleans / Shine.
LP: BLM 51110

Washboard Doc

EARLY MORNING BLUES (Washboard Doc & Lucky & Flash).
LP: LR 42.010

Washboard Rhythm Boys

1933.
LP: WRB 4014

Washboard Sam

1935-47, VOLUME 1.
LP: DLP 507

BIG BILL BROONZY AND WASHBOARD SAM (See Broonzy, Big Bill) (Washboard Sam/Big Bill Broonzy).

I'M NOT THE LAD.
LP: BT 2012

WASHBOARD SAM 1936-42.
LP: BOB 1

WASHBOARD SAM 1935-1941.
LP: BC 10

Washboard Willie

MOTOR TOWN BOOGIE.
Tracks: / C.C. Rider / Move after hours / Summit ridge drive / Dupree blues / Struttin' that stuff / 10.20 special / Calvin's blues / Shake your money maker / No name blues / Fool on a mule.
LP: JSP 1036

Washburn, Lalomie

MY MUSIC IS HOT.
LP: RRL 2002

Washington Behind (tv)

WASHINGTON BEHIND CLOSED DOORS (Original TV Soundtrack) (Various artists).
LP: REB 327
MC: ZCF 327

Washington Dead Cats

MONSTER TALES.
MC: WDC 1C

Washington, Deborah

LOVE AWAITS.
Tracks: / Boogie baby / Back in love again / Can't be a fool for love / Rock it / Loving you / World of pain / For the love of him / Lonelines.
LP: ARL 5042

Washington, Dinah

ARNETT COBB AND HIS MOB (See under Cobb, Arnett) (Washington, Dinah & Arnett Cobb).

BACK TO THE BLUES.
LP: FS 295

BESSIE SMITH SONGBOOK.
Tracks: / After you've gone / Send me to the 'lectric chair / Jailhouse blues / Trombone butter / You've been a good old wagon / Careless love / Back water blues / If I could be with you one hour tonight / Me and my gin / Fine fat daddy.
LP: 826 631-1
MC: 826 663-4

BEST OF DINAH WASHINGTON (Compact/Walkman jazz).
Tracks: / No hard feelings / Your nobody till somebody loves you / He's my guy / Good life / Do nothing till you hear from me / I wanna be around / Destination moon / If it's the last thing I do / Call me irresponsible / Don't say nothing at all / What kind of fool am I / For all we know / Unforgettable / Easy living / Backwater blues / If I were a bell / Teach me tonight / Keepin' out of mischief now / All of me / This bitter earth / What a difference a day made / If I could write a book / Make me a present of you / Smoke gets in your eyes / I wanna be loved / Manhattan / I've got you under my skin / I remember Clifford.
MC: 830 700-4

COMPLETE DINAH VOL.1 (1943-1945).
Tracks: / Evil gal blues / I know how to do it / Salty papa blues / Homeward bound / Blow top blues / Wise woman blues / Walking blues / No voot no boot / Chewin' mama blues / My lovin' papa / Rich man's blues / All or nothing at all / Beggin' mama blues / Mellow mama blues / My voot is really vout / Blues for a day / Pacific coast blues.
LP: OFF 3004
MC: OFF 43004

COMPLETE DINAH VOL.2.
Tracks: / Embraceable you / I can't get started with you / When a woman loves a man / Joy juice / Oo-wee walkie talkie / Man I love, The / You didn't want me then / Slick chick, A / Postman blues / That's why a woman loves a heel / Mean and evil blues / Stairway to the stars / I want to be loved / You satisfy / Fool that I am / There's got to be a change.
LP: OFF 3005
MC: OFF 43005

COMPLETE DINAH VOL.3.
Tracks: / Mean and evil blues / Since I fell for you / West side baby / You can depend on me / Early in the morning / I'm afraid of you / I love you, yes I do / Don't come knocking at my door / I wish I knew the name of the boy / No more lonely gal blues / Walkin' and talkin' / Ain't misbehavin' / What can I say after I say I'm sorry / Tell me so / I can't face the music / Pete.
LP: OFF 3007
MC: OFF 43007

COMPLETE DINAH VOL.4.
Tracks: / Am I asking too much? / I'm getting old before my time / Record ban blues / Resolution blues / I want to cry / Long John blues / In the rain / I sold my heart to the junkman / I'll wait / It's too soon to know / Why can't you behave? / It's funny / Laughing boy / Am I really sorry? / How deep is the ocean? / New York, Chicago and Los Angeles.
LP: OFF 3008
MC: OFF 43008

COMPLETE DINAH VOL.5.
Tracks: / Give me back my tears / Good daddy blues / Baby get lost / I only know / Drummer man / I challenge your kiss / Fast movin' mama / Juice head man of mine / Shuckin' and jivin' / Richest guy in the graveyard / Journey's end / It isn't fair / My kind of man / If I loved you / Why don't you think things over / Big deal.
LP: OFF 3012
MC: OFF 43012

COMPLETE DINAH VOL.6.
Tracks: / I'll never be free / I wanna be loved / Love (me) with misery / Harbour lights / I cross my fingers / Time out for tears / Only a moment ago / Fine fine daddy / Please send me someone to love / Ain't nobody's business / I'm so lonely I could cry / My heart cries for you / I apologize / I won't cry anymore / Don't say you're sorry again / Mixed emotions.
LP: OFF 3013
MC: OFF 43013

COMPLETE DINAH VOL.7 (1951-52).
Tracks: / Cold, cold heart / Baby, did you hear / New blowtop blues / What's the matter with you baby / Don't hold it against me / Be fair to me / Just one more chance / Saturday night / If you don't think I'm leavin' / I'm a fool to want you / I'm crying / Out in the cold again / Hey good lookin' / Wheel of fortune / Tell me why / Trouble in mind.
LP: OFF 3018
MC: OFF 43018

COMPLETE DINAH VOL.8.
Tracks: / When the sun goes down / I thought about you / Mad about the boy / I can't face the music / Stormy weather / My devotion / Make believe dreams / Pillow blues / No caviar / Double dealing daddy / My song / Half as much / I cried for you / Gambler's blues / You let my love grow cold / Surprise party.
LP: OFF 3021
MC: OFF 43021

COMPLETE DINAH VOL.9 (1953).
Tracks: / Don't get around much anymore / Ain't nothing good / Fat daddy / Go pretty daddy / TV is the thing / Feel like I wanna cry / Lean baby / Never, never / I ain't gonna cry no more / Am I blue / Pennies from Heaven / Set me free / Since my man has gone and went / Silent night / Lord's prayer / My man's an undertaker.
LP: OFF 3025
MC: OFF 43025

COMPLETE DINAH VOL.10.
Tracks: / Mean and evil / Short John / Old man's darlin' / Love for sale / Our love is here to stay / Such a night / Until sunrise / One Arabian night / I let a song go out of my heart / Foggy day, A / Bye bye blues.
LP: OFF 3028
MC: OFF 43028

COMPLETE DINAH VOL.11.
Tracks: / Blues skies / You can't love two / What a great sensation / Raindrops / Big long slidin' thing / Dream / I don't hurt anymore / Soft winds / If it's the last thing I do / Introduction / I've got you under my skin / No more / Darn that dream.
LP: OFF 3036
MC: OFF 43036

COMPLETE DINAH VOL.12 (1954).
Tracks: / You go to my head / Lover come back to me / Come rain or come shine / Crazy he calls me / There is no greater love / I'll remember April.
LP: OFF 3040
MC: OFF 43040

COMPLETE DINAH VOL.13.
LP: OFF 3051
MC: OFF 43051

COMPLETE DINAH VOL.14.
LP: OFF 83057

DINAH '63.
Tracks: / Make someone happy / Rags to riches / Take me in your arms / Drown in my own tears / Why was I born / In San Francisco / Show must go on, The / I'm glad for your sake / There must be a way / What kind of fool am I / Bill / I wanna be around.
LP: ROU 1014
LP: 794 576 1

DINAH WASHINGTON (Compact/Walkman Jazz).
MC: 832 573 4

DINAH WASHINGTON: HER TOP TEN HITS.
MC: MC 827

DINAH WASHINGTON SINGS VOL.2.
Tracks: / Coquette / Love is the sweetest thing / I didn't know about you / Our love / These foolish things / Make someone happy / I'll close my eyes / Miss you / I left my heart in San Francisco / What kind of fool am I / Handful of stars, A / Good life / What's new / That Sunday that summer / Red sails in the sunset.
LP: JR 135

DINAH WASHINGTON SINGS VOL 1.
Tracks: / After you've gone / Send me to the 'lectric chair / Jailhouse blues / Trombone butter / You've been a good ole wagon / Careless love / Back water blues / If I could be with you one hour tonight / Me and my girl / Fine fat daddy.
LP: JR 117

DINAH WASHINGTON/BROOK BENTON (Washington, Dinah & Brook Benton).
Tracks: / There goes my heart / Call me / Baby (you've got what it takes) / Love walked in / Not one step behind / Rockin' good way, A / Someone to believe in / This I promise you / I do / Because of everything / Again / I believe.
LP: 6463 181
MC: 7145 181

DRINKING AGAIN.
Tracks: / Drinking again / Just friends / I'm gonna laugh you out of my life / I'll be around / Lament (love, I found you gone) / I don't know you anymore / Baby won't you please come home / Lover man (oh, where can you be) / Man that got away, The / For all we know / Say it isn't so / On the street of regret.
LP: ROU 1002
LP: 793 270 1

FATS WALLER SONGBOOK, THE.
Tracks: / Christopher Columbus / T'aint nobody's business if I do / Jitterbug waltz / Someone's rocking my dreamboat / Ain't cha glad / Squeeze me / Ain't misbehavin' / Black and blue / Everybody loves my baby / I've got a feeling I'm falling / Honeysuckle rose / Keeping out of mischief.
LP: 8189301
MC: 8189304

IF YOU DON'T BELIEVE I'M LEAVING.
LP: JB 1102

IMMORTAL.
Tracks: / My devotion / Me & the one I love / That (that summer) / Something's got to give / I'm glad for your sake / I'll never stop loving you / To forget about you / Somebody else is taking my place / Don't say nothing at all / Love is the sweetest thing.
LP: JLP 1056

JAZZ SIDES THE.
Tracks: / I could write a book / Make the man love me / Blue gardenia / You don't know what love is / My old flame / Blue skies / Lover come back to me / Crazy love / Backwater blues / All of me / Easy living / I get a kick out of you / This can't be love / If I had you / I let a song go out of my heart / Soggy day, A / Bye bye blues.
LP: 6641573

QUEEN OF THE BLUES (Original Soul Sister).
Tracks: / Look to the rainbow / Ill wind / Cottage for sale / All of me / More than you know / There'll be some changes made / Goodbye / Willow weep for me / Make me a present of you / Smoke gets in your eyes / I could have told you / Accent on youth.
LP: . . . . **MOIR 131**
MC: . . . . **CMOIR 131**

STRANGER ON EARTH, A.
LP: . . . . **FS 319**

TWO OF US, THE (Washington, Dinah & Brook Benton).
Tracks: / Two of us, The / Again / Baby / Because of everything / Call me / I believe / I do / Love walked in / Not one step behind / Rockin' good way, A / Someone to believe in / There goes my heart / This I promise you / Passing strangers / Alexander's ragtime band / All of my life / Always / Cheek to cheek / Easter parade / Girl that I marry, The / Isn't this a lovely day / I've got my love to keep me warm / Now it can be told / Remember / You're just in love.
2LP: **6641 868**
MCSET: **7599 368**

VERY BEST, THE.
Tracks: / September in the rain / This better Earth / It isn't fair / What a difference a day made / I wanna be loved / I don't hurt anymore / Unforgettable / Dream / Teach me tonight / Baby get lost / Trouble in mind / Make me a present of you / I'll never be free / There is no greater love / Salty papa blues / Tell love hello.
LP: . . . . **TIME 05**
MC: . . . . **TIMEC 05**

Washington, Ella

NOBODY BUT ME.
Tracks: / All the time / Stop giving your man away / I'm losing the feeling / Doin' the best I can / Starving for love / He'll be back / Too weak to fight / Nobody but me / Sweet talking candy man / Cry cry cry (You're gonna) / Sit down and cry / He called me baby / Grass is always greener, The / I want to walk through this life with you.
LP: . . . . **CRB 1144**

Washington, Ernestine

GOSPEL SINGING IN WASHINGTON.
LP: . . . . **C 5529**

Washington, Geno

HAND CLAPPIN'-FOOT STOMPIN'-FUNKY BUTT-LIVE (Washington, Geno & The Ram Jam Stars).
Tracks: / Philly dog / Ride your pony / Up tight / Road runner / Hold on / Don't fight it / Land of a thousand dances / Respect / Willy nilly / Get down with it / Michael / Que sera sera / You don't know.
LP: . . . . **NSPL 18618**
LP: . . . . **NPL 38026**

HIP-SHAKIN' SOUL-BREAKIN' EARTH-QUAKIN' LIVE! (Washington, Geno & The Ram Jam Band).
LP: . . . . **PYL 4018**
MC: . . . . **PYM 4018**

HIPSTERS, FLIPSTERS AND FINGER POPPIN' DADDIES.
LP: . . . . **NSPL 38032**

LIVE SIDEWAYS (Washington, Geno & The Ram Jam Stars).
LP: . . . . **GENOLP 1**

PUT OUT THE CAT.
LP: **6.24665**

TAKE THAT JOB AND STUFF IT.
LP: . . . . **KOMO 788027**

THAT'S WHY HOLLYWOOD LOVES ME.
Tracks: / That's why Hollywood loves me / Get some bad tonight / Thanks for loving me / Baby come back / Caught in the middle / My money, your money.
LP: . . . . **DJF 20561**

Washington, Grover Jr

ALL THE KING'S HORSES.
Tracks: / No tears / In the end / All the king's horses / Where is the love? / Body and soul / Lean on me / Lover man / Interlude No. 2 / Love song 1700.
LP: . . . . **STMS 5056**
MC: . . . . **CSTMS 5056**

ANTHOLOGY (ELEKTRA): GROVER WASHINGTON JR..
Tracks: / Best is yet to come, The / East River drive / Be mine tonight / Can you dig it? / In the name of love / Just the two of us / Jamming / Little black samba / Jet stream / Let it flow.
LP: . . . . **EKT 17**
MC: . . . . **EKT 17C**

ANTHOLOGY (MOTOWN): GROVER WASHINGTON JR.
Tracks: / Inner city blues / Mercy mercy me / Where is the love? / Mr. Magic / It feels so good / Secret place / Masterpiece / Trouble man / Summer song / Santa Cruzin' / Snake eyes.
2LP: . . . . **TMSP 6015**
MCSET: . . . . **CTMSP 6015**
2LP: . . . . **ZL 72168**

BADDEST.
Tracks: / Black frost / Do dat / Summer song / Secret place / Ain't no sunshine / Mercy mercy me / It feels so good / Mr. Magic / No tears in the end / Inner city blues / Lean on me / Masterpiece.
2LP: . . . . **TMSP 6011**
MC: . . . . **CTSMP 6011**

BEST IS YET TO COME.
Tracks: / Can you dig it? / Best is yet to come, The / More than meets the eye / Things are getting better / Mixed emotions / Brazilian memories / I'll be with you / Cassie's theme.
LP: . . . . **E 0215**
MC: . . . . **E 02154**

COME MORNING.
Tracks: / East River drive / Come morning / Be mine (tonight) / Reaching out / Jamming / Little black samba / Making love to you / I'm all yours.
LP: . . . . **K 52337**
MC: . . . . **K 452337**

FEELS SO GOOD.
Tracks: / Sea lion / Knucklehead / Moonstreams / Feels so good / Hydra.
LP: . . . . **STMS 5028**
MC: . . . . **CSTMS 5028**
LP: . . . . **WL 72080**

GREATEST PERFORMANCES.
Tracks: / Mr. Magic / It feels so good / Secret place / Do dat / Lean on me.
MC: . . . . **CSTMS 5099**
LP: . . . . **STMS 5099**
LP: . . . . **WL 72125**
MC: . . . . **WK 72125**

INNER CITY BLUES.
Tracks: / Inner city blues / Georgia on my mind / Mercy mercy me / Ain't no sunshine / Better days / Until it's time for you to go / I loves you, Porgy.
LP: . . . . **STMS 5055**
MC: . . . . **CSTMS 5055**
LP: . . . . **WL 72098**
MC: . . . . **WK 72098**

INSIDE MOVES.
Tracks: / Inside moves / Dawn song / Watching you watching me / Secret sounds / Jet stream / When I look at you / Sassy stew.
LP: **9603181**
MC: **9603184**

LIVE AT THE BIJOU.
Tracks: / On the cusp / You make me dance / Lock it in the pocket / Sausalito / Funkfoot / Summer song / Juffure / Days in our lives / Mr. Magic.
2LP: . . . . **WL 72267**
MCSET: . . . . **WK 72267**

MISTER MAGIC.
Tracks: / Earth tones / Passion flower / Mister magic / Black frost.
LP: . . . . **STMS 5027**
MC: . . . . **CSTMS 5027**

PARADISE.
Tracks: / Paradise / Icey / Answer in your eyes, The / Asia's theme / Shana / Tell me about it / Feel it comin'.
LP: . . . . **K 52130**

PLAYBOY JAZZ FESTIVAL (Washington Grover, Jr & Weather Report).
LP: **9602981**

REED SEED.
Tracks: / Do dat / Step 'n' thru / Reed seed / Maracas beach / Santa Cruzin' / Just the way you are / Loran's dance.
LP: . . . . **STMS 5072**
MC: . . . . **CSTMS 5072**
LP: . . . . **WL 72106**
MC: . . . . **WK 72106**

SECRET PLACE, A.
Tracks: / Secret place / Dolphine dance / Not yet / Love makes it better.
LP: . . . . **STMS 5029**
MC: . . . . **CSTMS 5029**
LP: . . . . **WL 70281**

SKYLARKIN'.
Tracks: / Easy loving you / Bright moments / Snake eyes / I can't help it / Love / Open up your mind.
LP: . . . . **WL 72107**
MC: . . . . **WK 72107**
LP: . . . . **STML 12131**

STRAWBERRY MOON.
Tracks: / Strawberry moon / Look of love, The / Shivaree Ride / Caught a touch of your love / Maddie's Blues / I will be here for you / Keep in touch / Summer nights.
LP: **4504641**
MC: **4504644**

THEN AND NOW.
Tracks: / Blues for D.P. / Just enough / French connections / Something borrowed, something blue / Lullaby for Shana Bly / In a sentimental mood / Stella by starlight.
LP: . . . . **OC 44256**
LP: **4625161**
MC: **4625164**

TIME OUT OF MIND.
LP: **4655261**
MC: **4655264**

WINELIGHT.
Tracks: / Winelight / Let it flow / In the name of love / Take me there / Just the two of us / Make me a memory.
LP: . . . . **K 52262**

WINELIGHT/PARADISE.
MC: . . . . **K 462039**

Washington, Leroy

WILD CHERRY.
LP: . . . . **FLY 574**

Washington Philips

DENOMINATION BLUES.
LP: . . . . **AB 2006**

Washington Squares

FAIR AND SQUARE.
Tracks: / Everybody knows / Charcoal / Neal Cassady / Greenback dollar / My true love and I / Fourth day of man / Pride of man, The / La roue de fortune / Join together / Other side of sin, The / Fourth day of July.
LP: . . . . **VGC 10**
MC: . . . . **TCVGC 10**

WASHINGTON SQUARES, THE.
Tracks: / New generation / Can't stop the rain / You are not alone / D train / You can't kill me / Daylight / He was a friend of mine / Lay down your arms / Samson and Delilah / Walls (Polish union songs).
LP: . . . . **VGC 4**
MC: . . . . **TCVGC 4**

Washington, Tuts

NEW ORLEANS PIANO PROFESSOR.
LP: . . . . **ROUNDER 2041**
MC: . . . . **ROUNDER 2041C**

Washington, Walter

GOOD AND JUICY (Washington, Walter "Wolfman").
Tracks: / It's rainin' in my life / Good and juicy / Girl don't ever leave me / Nobody's fault but mine / Honky tonk / Get on up (the wolfman's song) / You got me worried / Sure enough it's you / Lovely day.
LP: . . . . **LIM 100**

OUT OF THE DARK (Washington, Walter "Wolfman").
LP: . . . . **ROUNDER 2068**
MC: . . . . **ROUNDER 2068C**

RAININ' MY LIFE (Washington, Walter "Wolfman").
LP: **1022**
MC: . . . . **1022 TC**

WOLF MAN.
LP: . . . . **REU 1011**

WOLF TRACKS (Washington, Walter "Wolfman").
LP: . . . . **ROUNDER 2048**
MC: . . . . **ROUNDER 2048C**

Waso

GYPSY SWING VOL.4.
LP: . . . . **BM 150227**

GYPSY SWING VOL.5.
LP: . . . . **BM 150246**

LIVE IN LAREN.
Tracks: / Douce ambiance / Georgia on my mind / Sugar / Si tu savais / You took advantage of me / Summertime / Blues en mineur / Clair de lune / It had to be you / Nuages / La danseur de Charleston.
MC: **2925 111**

WASO PLAY GIPSY SWING.
LP: . . . . **AP 243**

W.A.S.P.

HEADLESS CHILDREN, THE.
Tracks: / Heretic (the lost child) / Real me, The / Headless children, The / Thunderhead / Mean man / Neutron bomber, The / Mephisto waltz / Forever free / Maneater / Rebel in the F.D.G..
LP: . . . . **EST 2087**
MC: . . . . **TCEST 2087**
LPPD: . . . . **ESTPD 2087**

INSIDE THE ELECTRIC CIRCUS.
Tracks: / Big welcome, The / I don't need no doctor / Nasty restless gypsy / Shoot from the hip / I'm alive / Easy living / Sweet cheetah / Mantronic / King of Sodom and Gomorrah / Rock rolls on, The.
LP: . . . . **EST 2025**
MC: . . . . **TCEST 2025**
LP: . . . . **ATAK 133**
MC: . . . . **TCATAK 133**
LP: . . . . **FA 3238**
MC: . . . . **TCFA 3238**

LAST COMMAND, THE.
Tracks: / Wild child / Ballcrusher / Fistful of diamonds / Cries in the night / Blind in Texas / Widowmaker / Running wild in the streets / Sex drive / Last command, The / Jack action.
LP: . . . . **WASP 2**
MC: . . . . **TCWASP 2**
LP: . . . . **FA 3218**
MC: . . . . **TCFA 3218**
LP: . . . . **EJ 2404291**
MC: . . . . **EJ 2404294**

LIVE IN THE RAW.
Tracks: / Inside the electric circus / I don't need no doctor / L.O.V.E. machine / Wild child / 9.5 nasty / Sleeping (in the fire) / Manimal / I wanna be somebody / Harder faster / Blind in Texas / Scream until you like it.
LP: . . . . **EST 2040**
MC: . . . . **TCEST 2040**
LP: . . . . **FA 3249**
MC: . . . . **TCFA 3249**

MUSIC AND MEDIA INTERVIEW PICTURE DISC.
LPPD: . . . . **MM 1240**

W.A.S.P.
Tracks: / I wanna be somebody / L.O.V.E. machine / Flame / B.A.D. / School daze / Hellion / Sleeping (in the fire) / On your knees / Tormentor / Torture never stops, The.
LP: . . . . **EJ 2401951**
MC: . . . . **EJ 2401954**
LP: . . . . **FA 3201**
MC: . . . . **TCFA 3201**

W.A.S.P. INTERVIEW PICTURE DISC.
LPPD: . . . . **BAK 2025**

Wasp Factory

PRETTY QUICKLY, UGLY SLOWLY.
LP: . . . . **CHIME 106**

Wassailers

WASSAILERS.
Tracks: / Harvest song / Phil's favourite / My love's in Germany / My donal / Whitby whaler / She touched you / Bold dragoon, The / Over the hills and far away / Bonnie briar, The / Three jolly sportsmen / Read Hall foxhunt / Roll the woodpile down / Demon lover, The / Gay fusiliers, The.
LP: . . . . **FE 012**

Wasserman, Rob

SOLO.
LP: . . . . **ROUNDER 0179**
MC: . . . . **ROUNDER 0179C**

Waste Land

WASTE LAND (see under Eliot, T.S.) (Guinness, Alec).

Wasted Youth

BEGINNING OF THE END.
LP: . . . . **BHLP 007**
MC: . . . . **BHLP 007C**

BLACK DAZE.
LP: . . . . **GWLP 44**

FROM THE INNER DEPTHS.
LP: . . . . **VCLP 1**

WILD AND WONDERFUL CRIES.
LP: . . . . **BHLP 006**

Wat, Angor

GENERAL STRIKE.
LP: . . . . **GURT 8**

Watanabe, Kazumi

BEST PERFORMANCE, THE.
Tracks: / Unicorn / Village in bubbles / Kylyn / Talk you all night / Olive's step / Lonesome cat / To Chi Ka / Please don't bundle me.
MC: . . . . **CC 19**

KILOWATT.
Tracks: / 100 mega / Capri / No one / Jive / Papyrus / Sunspin / Pretty soon / Bernard / Dolphin dance / Good night machines.
LP: **794 151**
MC: **794 154**

LONESOME CAT.
Tracks: / Somebody, somebody / Mirrors / Aqua beauty / Blackstone / Moving nozzle / Lonesome cat.
LP: . . . . **YX 7525**

MOBO 1.
Tracks: / Walk, don't run / Half blood / Yenshu tsubame gaeshi / American shorthair / Mobo 2.
LP: . . . . **GR 8404**
MC: . . . . **GRC 8404**

MOBO 2.
Tracks: / Voyage / Yatokesa / Alicia / Shang hi / All beets are coming.
LP: . . . . **GR 8406**

MOBO CLUB.
LP: **1885061**
MC: **1885064**

MOBO SPLASH.
LP: **1886021**
MC: **1886024**

SPICE OF LIFE TOO.
Tracks: / Andre / Fu bu ki / Small wonder / Kaimon / We planet / Rain / Concrete cows / Men and angels.
LP: **1888101**
MC: **1888104**

SUGARLOAF EXPRESS (See under Ritenour, Lee) (Watanabe, Kazumi & Lee Ritenour).

Watanabe, Sadao

CALIFORNIA SHOWER.
LP: . . . . **MLP 3005**

FILL UP THE NIGHT.
LP: **2501611**

GOOD TIME FOR LOVE.
Tracks: / Good time for love / Love birds whisper in my ear / When we make a home / Step out on the street / I love to say your name / Pogo / All the way / Loving you is easy.
LP: **253037 1**
MC: **253037 4**

IBERIAN WALTZ (see under Mariano, Charlie).

LIVE AT THE BUDOKAN.
Tracks: / Up country / Mzuri / Tsumagoi / All about love / Nice shot / Seeing you / No problem / Boa noite / Sun dance / M and M Studio / My dear life.
2LP: . . . . **CBS 22081**

MAISHA.
Tracks: / What's now? / Men and women / Road song / Times we shared / Good news / Desert ride / Tip away / Stray birds / Maisha / Paysages.
LP: **252194 1**

ORANGE EXPRESS.
Tracks: / Orange express / Ride on / Call me / Good for all night / Bagamoyo / Zanzibar / Straight to the top / Mbla I Africa.
LP: . . . . **CBS 85304**

RENDEZVOUS.
LP: **250804 1**

Watch

WATCH (Music & songs from the schools TV series) (Various artists).
LP: . . . . **REC 314**
MC: . . . . **ZCM 314**

WATCH AGAIN (Music from the BBC TV schools series) (Various artists).
LP: . . . . **REC 375**
MC: . . . . **ZCM 375**

WATCH - THE THIRD WATCH (Various artists).
Tracks: / Prima ballerina: *Various artists* / Body song, The: *Various artists* / Down the trail: *Various* artists / I am a mole: *Various artists* / Brown girl in the ring: *Various artists* / Hold high the eagles: *Various artists* / This old house: *Various artists* / Indian chants: *Various artists* / Heigh ho: *Various* artists / House is a house: *Various artists* / Parcel song, The: *Various artists* / Catch a germ: *Various artists* / Captain Cook suite: *Various artists.*
LP: . . . . **REC 477**
MC: . . . . **ZCM 477**

Watch Your Step

WATCH YOUR STEP (The Beat Era Vol 1) (Various artists).
Tracks: / She ain't no good: *Clique* / Magic potion: *Searchers* / It ain't fear: *Boys* / Shades of blue: *Revolution* / Take a heart: *Sorrows* / Leave my kitten alone: *First Gear* / He's in town: *Rockin' Berries* / Now the sun has gone: *Beatmen* / Have I the right: *Honeycombs* / Watch your step: *Jackson*, Tony / I stand accused: *Colton,Tony* / Zulu stomp: *Brand* / Jump and dance: *Carnaby* / I'll follow the sun: *Johns,Glynn* / She was tall: *Lancastrians* / Something better beginning: *Kinks* / Put yourself in my place: *Episode Six* (CD bonus track.) / Somewhere in the night: *Koobas* (CD bonus track.) / It's all over now baby blue: *Cops & Robbers (bk)* (CD bonus track.) / Now: *Wolves* (CD bonus track.) / Baja: *Jones, John Paul* (CD bonus track.).
LP: . . . . **NEXLP 107**

Watchman

WATCHMAN, THE.
Tracks: / Laundry days / Summer at the empty playground II / Captain's tune, The / Freddy's race / Considering the lowlands of Holland / Lowland tune / Darling angel / I wanna be with you / Wiener cowboy / After the night shift / Letter to your wedding / Farewell baby.
LP: . . . . **HNBL 1362**
MC: . . . . **HNBC 1362**

Watchtower

CONTROL AND RESISTANCE.
Tracks: / Instruments of random murder / Eldritch, The / Mayday in Kiev / Fall of reason, The / Control and resistance / Hidden instincts / Life cycles / Dangerous toy.
LP: . . . . **NUK 140**
MC: . . . . **ZCNUK 140**
LP: . . . . **N 0140 1**
MC: . . . . **N 0140 4**

Water

WATER (Original soundtrack) (Various artists).
LP: . . . . **YEAR 2**
LP: . . . . **YEAMC 2**

Water Babies

WATER BABIES (Film soundtrack) (Various artists).
LP: . . . . **ARLB 5030**
MC: . . . . **ZCARL 5030**

WATER BABIES, THE (Charles Kingsley (aut)).
MC: . . . . **CDL 51728**

WATER BABIES, THE (see under Kingsley, Charles) (Greene, Sarah (nar)).

Water Margin

WATER MARGIN (THEME FROM) (See under Godiego) (Godiego).

Water Pumping Top Ten

WATER PUMPING TOP TEN (Various artists).
LP: . . . . **TRDLP 12183**

Water Walk

WATER WALK.
LP: . . . . **NTL 30013**

Waterboys

BEST OF THE WATERBOYS, THE (1981 - 1990).
Tracks: / Girl called Johnny / Big music, The / All the things she gave me / Whole of the moon, The / Spirit / Don't bang the drum / Fisherman's blues / Killing my heart / Strange boat / And a bang on the ear / Old England / Man is in love, A.
LP: . . . . **CHEN 19**
MC: . . . . **ZCHEN 19**

FISHERMAN'S BLUES.
Tracks: / Fisherman's blues / Strange boat / Sweet thing / Has anybody seen Hank? / When ye go away / We will not be lovers / World party / And a bang on the ear / When will we be married / Stolen child, The.
LP: . . . . **CHEN 5**
MC: . . . . **ZCHEN 5**
LP: . . . . **CHR 1589**
MC: . . . . **ZCHR 1589**

PAGAN PLACE, A.
Tracks: / Church not made with hands / All the things she gave me / Thrill is gone, The / Rags / Somebody might wave back / Big music, The / Red army blues / Pagan place.
LP: . . . . **CHEN 2**
MC: . . . . **ZCHEN 2**
LP: . . . . **ENCL 3**

ROOM TO ROAM.
Tracks: / In search of a rose / Song from the end of the world / Man is in love, A / Kaliope House / Bigger picture / Natural bridge blues / Something that is gone / Star and the sea, The / Life of Sundays, A / Island man / Raggle taggle gypsy, The / How long will I love you / Upon the wind and waves / Spring comes to Spiddal / Trip to Broadford, The / Further up, further in / Room to roam.
LP: . . . . **CHEN 16**
MC: . . . . **ZCHEN 16**

THIS IS THE SEA.
Tracks: / Don't bang the drum / Whole of the moon, The / Pan within, The / Medicine bow / Old England / Be my enemy / Trumpets / This is the sea.
LP: . . . . **CHEN 3**
MC: . . . . **ZCHEN 3**
LP: . . . . **ENCL 5**

WATERBOYS: INTERVIEW PICTURE DISC.
LPPD: . . . . **BAK 2154**

WATERBOYS, THE.
Tracks: / December / Girl called Johnny / Three day man / Gala / I will not follow / It should have been you / Girl in the swing / Savage earth heart.
LP: . . . . **ENCL 1**
MC: . . . . **ENCC 1**
LP: . . . . **CHEN 1**
MC: . . . . **ZCHEN 1**

Waterfall

BENEATH THE STARS.
LP: . . . . **GUN 003**

THREE BIRDS.
Tracks: / But I love you / Soon / Woodland glade / Three birds / Smiler / Thanks / Stranger / Friends / Swansong.
LP: . . . . **AVA 104**

Waterfall, Linda

BODY ENGLISH.
LP: . . . . **FF 439**

Waterford, Crown

SHOUTIN' THE BLUES.
LP: . . . . **OL 8011**

Waterfront

WATERFRONT.
LP: **837 970-1**
MC: **837 970-4**

Watergate Seven Plus

ALLIGATOR CRAWL.
LP: . . . . **SOS 1165**

Waterman, Dennis

I COULD BE SO GOOD FOR YOU.
Tracks: / Jamaica woman / Wasn't love strong enough? / Holding on to love / What you see is what you get / Gone wrong song / Love's left me bleeding / Nothing at all / Love is like a rainbow / I could be so good for you / Lady's up to no good, The.
LP: . . . . **MFP 4156371**
MC: . . . . **TC MFP 5637**

SO GOOD FOR YOU.
Tracks: / Jamaica woman / Wasn't love strong enough / Holding on to love / What you see is what you get / Gone wrong song / Love's left me bleeding / Nothing at all / Love is like a rainbow / I could be so good for you / Lady's up to no good, The.
LP: . . . . **EMC 3349**

WHAT ARE WE GONNA GET 'ER INDOORS? (see Cole, George & Dennis Waterman) (Waterman, Dennis & George Cole).

Watermelon Men

PAST PRESENT AND FUTURE.
LP: . . . . **GOES ON 02**

Waters, Benny

ON THE SUNNY SIDE OF THE STREET.
LP: . . . . **JSP 1027**

TRUE SIDE OF BENNY WATERS.
LP: . . . . **KS 2041**

WHEN YOU'RE SMILING (See under Williams, Roy) (Waters, Benny & Roy Williams).

Waters, Crystal

SURPRISE.
LP: **3471511**

Waters, Ethel

1938-39 (The Complete Bluebird Sessions).
LP: . . . . **RR 1314**

ETHEL WATERS.
LP: . . . . **MES 6812**

ETHEL WATERS 1924-8 (Inc. Coleman Hawkins, etc.).
LP: . . . . **WJS 1009**

ETHEL WATERS (GLENDALE).
Tracks: / Cabin in the sky / Dinah / Summertime blues / Am I blue?.
LP: . . . . **GL 9011**

ETHEL WATERS: ON THE AIR.
Tracks: / Taking your time / Darkies never dream / Them green pastures / There'll be some changes made / Stormy weather / Woman without a man, A / Dinah / St Louis blues / Smoke gets in your eyes / Summertime / Can't help lovin' dat man / Sometimes I feel like a motherless child / Happiness is a thing called Joe.
LP: . . . . **TOTEM 1041**

FOREMOTHERS (Volume 6).
MC: . . . . **RC 1314**

NO-ONE CAN LOVE ME.
MC: **041**

STAGE AND SCREEN 1925-1940.
LP: . . . . **CCL 2792**

WHO SAID BLACKBIRDS ARE BLUE ?.
LP: . . . . **SH 2060**

Waters, Freddie

JUST ENOUGH TO GET ME COD.
LP: . . . . **MVLP 22**

Waters, John L

MUSIC OF THE STARS - ARIES.
LP: . . . . **BIRTHLP 6**
MC: . . . . **BIRTHMC 6**

Waters, Muddy

20 BLUES CLASSICS.
Tracks: / Mannish boy / They call me Muddy Waters / She's all right / I'm your hoochie coochie man / Still a fool / Mopper's blues / Just a dream / I'm ready / Forty days and forty nights / My life is ruined / Crawling king snake / Standing around crying / I want you to love me / She moves me / Lonesome road blues / Southbound train / I feel so good / Walking through the park / I just want to make love to you / Just to be with you.
LP: **265 233 1**
MC: **265 233 4**

AT NEWPORT 1960.
LP: . . . . **BRP 2026**

BACK IN THE EARLY DAYS VOL.1 AND 2.
Tracks: / I feel like going home / Mean red spider / You're gonna miss me / Muddy jumps one / Streamline women / Evan shuffle / Country boy / All night long / Baby please don't go / My fault / Gone to main street / Please have mercy / She's all / Who's gonna be your sweet man / Sad sad day / Lovin' man / I'm a natural born lover / Blow wind blow / Oh yeah / She's so pretty / I don't know why / Ooh wee / Young fashioned ways / Clouds in my heart / I want to be loved / My eyes keep me in trouble / I got to find my baby / Sugar sweet.
2LP: . . . . **SC 001/2**

BEST OF MUDDY WATERS.
Tracks: / I just want to make love to you / Long distance call / Louisiana blues / Honey bee / Rollin' stone / I'm ready / Hoochie coochie man / She moves me / I want you to love me / Standing around crying / Still a fool / I can't be satisfied.
LP: . . . . **GCH 8044**
MC: . . . . **GCHK 78044**

BEST OF MUDDY WATERS (VOGUE).
LP: **515038**

CAN'T GET NO GRINDIN'.
Tracks: / Can't get no grindin' / Mothers bad luck / Funky butt / Sad letter / Someday I'm gonna ketch you / Love weapon / Garbage man / After hours / Whiskey ain't no good / Muddy Waters' shuffle.
LP: . . . . **LPM 7002**
LP: . . . . **CH 9319**

CHESS BOX SET.
LPS: . . . . **CH 680002**

CHESS MASTERS:MUDDY WATERS.
Tracks: / I just wanna make love to you / Rollin' stone / I'm ready / Hoochie coochie man / Just to be with you / Gypsy woman / Louisiana blues / Mannish boy / Long distance call / Same thing / Rollin' and a tumblin' / She loves me / 40 days and 40 nights / Canary bird.
LP: . . . . **SMR 850**
MC: . . . . **SMC 850**

CHESS MASTERS-MUDDY WATERS 1.
Tracks: / Sad letter / Gonna need my help / Whiskey blues / Down South blues / Train fare blues / Kind hearted woman / Hello little girl / Too young to know / Early morning blues / She's alright / Landlady / Baby please don't go / I feel like going home / You're gonna miss me / Mean red spider / Burying ground / Where's my woman been? / Stuff you gotta watch / Lonesome day / Who's gonna be your sweet man? / Gone to Main Street / Iodine in my coffee / Flood / Last time I fool around with you.
2LP: . . . . **CXMD 4000**

CHESS MASTERS-MUDDY WATERS 2.
Tracks: / Sad letter / Gonna need my help / Whiskey blues / Down South blues / Train fare blues / Kind hearted woman / Hello little girl / Early morning blues / Too young to know / She's all right / Landlady / Baby please don't go / I feel like going home / You're gonna miss me / Mean red spider / Burying around / Stuff you gotta watch / Where's my woman been / Lonesome day / Who's gonna be your sweet man / Gone to main street / Iodine in my coffee / Flood / Last time I fool around with you.
2LP: . . . . **CXMD 4006**

CHESS MASTERS-MUDDY WATERS 3.
Tracks: / My fault / They call me Muddy Waters / All night long / Please have mercy / Sad sad day / Blow wind blow / She's so pretty / Oh yeah / I don't know why / I'm a natural born lover / Ooh wee / Young fashioned ways / I want to be loved / All aboard / Don't go no further / I love the life I live / Got my mojo working / Nineteen years old / Close to you / I wanna put a tiger in your tank / Meanest woman / You shook me / You need love / Five long years.
2LP: . . . . **CXMD 4015**

CHICAGO BLUES.
Tracks: / Rollin' stone / Louisiana blues / Long distance call / Honey bee / I want you to love me / I just want to make love to you / I'm your hoochie coochie man / Mannish boy / I'm ready / Forty days and forty nights / She's alright / Walkin' blues / She moves me / Still a fool.
MC: . . . . **TCINS 5003**

LP: INS 5003

CHICAGO GOLDEN YEARS VOL.1.
2LP: 427005

CHICAGO GOLDEN YEARS VOL.2.
2LP: 427015

CHICKEN SHACK (See under Johnson, Luther) (Waters, Muddy & Luther Johnson).

COLLECTION: MUDDY WATERS (20 Blues Greats).
Tracks: / Baby please don't go / Got my mojo working / Rollin' stone / Mean mistreater / Rock me / Mean red spider / Forty days and forty nights / Stuff you gotta watch / All aboard / Lonesome room blues / Please have mercy / She's alright / Iodine in my coffee / Rollin' and tumblin' / I'm ready / You gonna miss me / Sad sad day / Oh yeah / I can't call her Sugar / I feel so good.
LP: DVLP 2034
MC: DVMC 2034

DOWN ON STOVALL'S PLANTATION.
LP: T 2210

FATHERS AND SONS (Waters, Muddy & Michael Bloomfield).
Tracks: / All aboard / Mean disposition / Blow wind blow / Can't lose what you ain't never had / Walkin' through the park / Forty days and forty nights / Standin' round crying / I'm ready / Twenty four hours / Sugar sweet / Long distance call / Baby please don't go / Honey bee / Same thing, The / Got my mojo working (part 1) / Got my mojo working (part 2).
2LP: 6 28593

FOLK SINGERS.
Tracks: / My home is in the delta / Long distance / My captain / Good morning little schoolgirl / Your gonna need my help / Cold weather blues / Beg leg woman / Country boy / Feel like going home.
LP: GCH 8040
MC: GCHK 78040
LP: 515016

GOOD NEWS VOL.3.
Tracks: / Trouble no more / Don't go no further / Diamonds at your feet / Evil / All aboard / I love the life I live / Mean mistreater / Recipe for love / Good news / Come home baby / I won't go / She's got it / Close to you.
LP: SC 002

HARD AGAIN.
Tracks: / Mannish boy / Bus driver / I want to be loved / Jealous hearted man / I can't be satisfied / Blues had a baby and they named it rock 'n' roll / Deep down in Florida / Cross-eyed cat / Little girl.
LP: SKY 32357
MC: 40 32357

HOOCHIE COOCHIE MAN.
Tracks: / Mannish boy / I'm ready / Champagne and reefer / Baby please don't go / I want to be loved / Sad sad day / I'm a king bee / Blues had a baby and they named it rock 'n' roll / She's 19 years old / I can't be satisfied / Screamin' and cryin' / I'm your hoochie coochie man.
LP: SKY 25565
MC: 40 25565
LP: 4611861
MC: 4611864
LP: CL 30683
MC: CLMS 930683

I CAN'T BE SATISFIED.
Tracks: / I can't call her sugar / You can't lose what you ain't never had / Sad letter / I can't be satisfied / Baby please don't go / Walkin' thru the park / Trainfare blues / Sittin' here drinkin' / I got a rich man's woman / Mean mistreater.
MC: SHTC 141
LP: SHLP 141

I'M READY.
MC: BGOMC 108
LP: BGOLP 108

IN MEMORIAM.
2LP: 6 28622

KING BEE.
Tracks: / I'm a king bee / Too young to know / Mean old Frisco blues / Forever lonely / I feel like going home / Champagne and reefer / Sad sad day / Keep me in trouble / Deep down in Florida 2 / No escape from the blues.
LP: SKY 84918

LIVE 65-68.
Tracks: / Blow wind blow / Hoochie coochie man / Sunrise blues / Honey Bee / Baby please don't go / All night long / Goodbye baby.
LP: CFPC 401

LIVE AT MR KELL'S.
LP: 515037

LIVE AT NEWPORT 1960.
LP: 515039

LIVE IN ANTIBES 1974.
Tracks: / Honky tonk women / Blow wind blow / Off the wall / Can't get no grindin' / Trouble no more / Garbage man / I'm your hoochie coochie man / Baby, please don't go / Mannish boy / Everything gonna be alright / Got my mojo working.
LP: FC 116

LIVE IN PARIS 1968.
LP: FC 121

LONDON MUDDY WATERS SESSIONS, THE.
Tracks: / Blind man blues / Key to the highway / Young fashioned ways / I'm gonna move to the outskirts of town / Who's gonna be your sweet man when I'm gone / Walkin' blues / I'm ready / Sad sad day / I don't know why.
LP: CXMP 2005
LP: CH 9298

MISSISSIPPI.
LP: CL 914983
MC: CLMC 914983

MISSISSIPPI ROLLIN' STONE.
Tracks: / I can't call her sugar / You can't lose what you ain't never had / Sad letter / I can't be satisfied / Baby please don't go / Walkin' thru the park / Train fare blues / Sittin' here drinkin' / I got a rich man's woman / Mean mistreater.
LP: BMLP 1014

MORE REAL FOLK BLUES.
LP: 515020

MUD IN YOUR EAR.
Tracks: / Diggin' my potatoes / Watchdog / Sting it / Why d'you do me? / Natural wig / Mud in your ear / Excuse me baby / Sad day uptown / Top of the boogaloo / Long distance call / Mini dress / Remember me / Snake / Comin' home baby / Blues for hippies / Chicken shack / Love 'u' trouble / I'm so glad / Love without jealousy / Evil.
LP: MR 5008
LP: B 90077

MUDDY AT NEWPORT/WHOSE MUDDY SHOES (Feat. Elmore James & John Brim).
MC: TCAD 27

MUDDY MISSISSIPPI WATERS LIVE.
Tracks: / Mannish boy / She's nineteen years old / Nine below zero / Streamline woman / Howling wolf / Baby please don't go / Deep down in Florida.
LP: SKY 83422

MUDDY WATERS ANTHOLOGY.
MC: PLAC 3911

MUDDY WATERS AT NEWPORT.
Tracks: / I got my brand on you / Baby, please don't go / Soon forgotten / Tiger in your tank / I feel so good / I got my Mojo working / I got my Mojo working / Goodbye Newport blues.
LP: GCH 8022
MC: GCHK 78022

MUDDY WATERS BOX SET.
LPS: BOX 259
MCSET: TCBOX 259

MUDDY WATERS LIVE.
LP: BGOLP 109
MC: BGOMC 109

MUDDY WATERS LIVE 1958.
LP: KK 7405

MUDDY WATERS LIVE 65-68 (With Pinetop Perkins and Pee Wee Madison).
LP: CPFC 401

MUDDY WATERS-VOLUME 2.
LP: 6 24801

ORIGINAL HOOCHIE COOCHIE.
LP: 20028
MC: 40028

ORIGINAL HOOCHIE COOCHIE MAN.
Tracks: / Stuff you gotta watch / Iodine in my coffee / Close to you / You gonna miss me / Mean red spider / Diamonds at your feet / You gonna need my help / She's alright / So glad I'm living / One more mile.
LP: BMLP 1023

PROFILE: MUDDY WATERS.
LP: 6.24474

RARE AND UNISSUED.
Tracks: / Little Annie May / Mean disposition / Feel like going home / You're gonna miss me / Stand here trembling / Last time I fool around with you / Where's my woman been / Gal you gotta watch / Lonesome day / Iodine in my coffee / Smokestack lightning / Let me hang around / Born lover / Down in my heart.
LP: GCH 8010
MC: GCHK 78010
LP: CXMP 2057
LP: 515040

REAL FOLK BLUES.
LP: 515008

ROCK ME.
LP: CL 915983
MC: CLMC 915983

ROLLIN' STONE.
Tracks: / 40 days and 40 nights / Rollin' and tumblin' / All aboard / Rock me / Rollin' stone / I'm ready / Standing around cryin' / She moves me / I feel so good / Going home.
LP: BMLP 1006

SINGS BIG BILL BROONZY.
Tracks: / Tell me baby / Southbound train / When I get to thinking / Just a dream (on my mind) / Double trouble / I feel so good / I done got wise / Moppers blues / Lonesome road blues / Hey hey.
LP: GCH 8029
MC: GCHK 78029
LP: 515029

SWEET HOME CHICAGO.
LP: 20027
MC: 40027

THEY CALL ME MUDDY WATERS.
Tracks: / When the eagle flies / Crawling king snake / County jail / It's all over / Bird nest on the ground / They call me Muddy Waters / Find yourself another fool / Kinfolk's blues / Making friends / Blind man / Howling wolf / Two steps forward.
LP: 515036
LP: GCH 8109
MC: GCHK 78109

TROUBLE NO MORE.
Tracks: / Sugar sweet / Trouble no more / All aboard / Don't go further / I love the life I live, I live... / Rock me / Got my mojo working / She's got it / Close to you / Mean mistreater.
LP: CH 9291

'UNK' IN FUNK.
Tracks: / Rollin' and tumblin' / Just to be with you / Electric man / Trouble no more / 'unk' in funk / Drive my blues away / Katy / Waterboy waterboy / Everything gonna be alright.
LP: GCH 8115
MC: GCHK 78115

UNK IN FUNK/SINGS BIG BILL BROONZY.
MC: TCAD 26

WARSAW SESSIONS, 1976, VOL 1 (Waters, Muddy Blues Band).
LP: PSJ 79

WARSAW SESSIONS, 1976, VOL 2 (Waters, Muddy Blues Band).
LP: PSJ 80

WE THREE KINGS (see under Howlin Wolf) (Howlin' Wolf, Little Walter & Muddy Waters).

Waters Of The World

WATERS OF THE WORLD (Heyerdahl, Dr.T./ Dr. D. George).
MC: SS 110

Waters, Patty

PATTY WATERS SINGS.
LP: ESP 1025

Waters, Roger

BODY, THE (Film Soundtrack) (Waters, Roger & Ron Geesin).
Tracks: / Our song / Seashell and soft stone / Red stuff writhe / Gentle breeze through life / Lick your partners / Bridge passage for three plastic teeth / Chain of life / Womb bit / Embryo thought / March past of the embryos / More than seven dwarfs in Penis-land / Dance of the red corpuscles / Body transport / Hand dance - full evening dress / Breathe / Old folks ascension / Bedtime climb / Piddle in perspex / Embryonic womb walk / Mrs. Throat goes walking / Give birth to a smile.
LP: ATAK 56
MC: TCATAK 56
LP: SHSP 4008
MC: TCSHSP 4008

PROS AND CONS OF HITCH HIKING, THE.
Tracks: / Apparently they were travelling abroad / Running shoes / Arabs with knives and West German skies / For the first time today (part 2) / Sexual revolution / Remains of our love, The / Go fishing / For the first time today - part 1 / Dunroamin duncarin dunlivin' / Pros and cons of hitch hiking / Every stranger's eyes.
LP: SHVL 2401051
MC: TCSHVL 2401054

RADIO K.A.O.S..
Tracks: / Radio waves / Who needs information / Me or him / Powers that be, The / Sunset strip / Home / Four minutes / Tide is turning, The.
LP: KAOS 1
MC: TCKAOS 1

WALL, THE (CONCERT) (See under 'Wall (concert)) (Various artists).

Waters, Ron

MYSTERIOUS PEOPLE.
Tracks: / Only make believe / Walk on by / I will never pass this way again / There I've said it again / Take my hand / Mysterious people / Lady is a woman / If the whole world stopped loving / Memories are made of this / Little things mean a lot / Answer me / Dear hearts and gentle people.
LP: SRTX CUS055

Watership Down

WATERSHIP DOWN (Richard Adams) (Various artists).
LPS: ZSW 574/7
MCSET: K 30K 44

WATERSHIP DOWN (Original soundtrack) (Various artists).
LP: CBS 70161
MC: 40 70161

Watership Down (book)

WATERSHIP DOWN (Dotrice, Roy (nar)).
MC: MCFR 117
MCSET: MCFR 110/2

WATERSHIP DOWN (Richard Adams) (Dotrice, Roy (nar)).
MC: 0600560589

Waterson, Jack

WHOSE DOG.
LP: SERV 005
LP: HEY 005 1
MC: HEY 005 4

Waterson, Lal & Norma

TRUE HEARTED GIRL A.
Tracks: / Young Billy Brown / Betsy Belle / Beggarman, The / Welcome sailor, The / Meeting is a pleasure / I wish I had never / Wealthy squire, The / Jenny Storm / Bonnie light horseman, The / Unfortunate lass, The / Flowers of the forest / Grace Darling.
LP: 12TS 331

Waterson, Mike

MIKE WATERSON.
Tracks: / Wensleydale lad, The / Brisk lad, The / Two brothers, The / Man o'war / Charlady's son, The / Light dragoon, The / Cruel ship's carpenter, The / Bye bye, skipper / Tamlin / Lord Rothschild / Swansea town / Seven yellow gypsies.
LP: 12TS 332

Watersons

BRIGHT PHOEBUS (Waterson, Lal & Mike).
Tracks: / Rubber band / Scarecrow / Fine horseman / Winifer odd / Danny Rose / Child among the weeds / Magical man / Never the same / To make you stay / Shady lady / Red wine promises / Bright phoebus.
LP: LES 2076

FOUR PENCE AND SPICY ALE.
Tracks: / Country life / Swarthfell rocks / Barney / Swinton May song / Bellman / Adieu, adieu / Apple tree / Wassailing song, The / Sheep shearing / Three day millionaire / King Pharin / T stands for Thomas / Malpas wassail song / Chickens in the garden / Good old way, The.
LP: 12TS 265

FROST AND FIRE.
Tracks: / Here we come a wassailing / Derby ram, The / Jolly old hawk / Pace egging song / Seven virgins or the leaves of life / Hal-an-tow / Earsdon sword dance song / John Barleycorn / We gets up in the morn / Souling song / Christmas is now drawing near at hand / Herod and the cock / Wassailing song, The / Holly bears a berry, The.
LP: 12T 136
MC: KTSC 136

GREENFIELDS.
Tracks: / Stormy winds / Rosebuds in June / We'll all go a-hunting today / Brave ploughboy, The / Sedgefield Fair / Fare thee well, cold winter / Young banker / While gamekeepers lie sleeping / Prickle-holly bush / Hares in the old plantation / Furze field / I went to market / Three pretty maidens / Lincolnshire shepherd.
LP: 12TS 415

SOUND, SOUND YOUR INSTRUMENTS OF JOY.
Tracks: / God bless the master / While shepherds watched their flocks by night / Windham / Heavenly aeroplane / Christian's hope / Bitter withy / Emmanuelle (Above listed musicians are Gabriel's Horns.) / Idumea / Sound, sound your instruments of joy / Come all ye faithful Christians / Green fields / David's lamentation / Morning trumpet / Joy, health, love and peace..
LP: 12TS 346

WATERSONS, THE.
Tracks: / Dibo, bendigo / North country maid, The / Brave wolfe / Jolly Waggoners / I'm a rover / Fathom the bowl / Thirty foot trailer / Holmfirth anthem, The / Twanky dillo / White hare of Howden, The / Plains of Mexico, The / All for me grog.
LP: **12T 142**

YORKSHIRE GARLAND A.
Tracks: / Poacher's fate, The / Morning looks charming, The / Pretty drummer boy, The / Tour of the dales, The / Willy went to Westerdale / L'anson's racehorse / Ploughboy, The / White cockade, The / Sorry the day I was married / Ye noble spectators / Stow brow / Wanton wife of Castlegate, The / Yorkshire tup, The / Whitby lad, The.
LP: **12T 167**

Waterston, Sam (nar)

THIRTY-NINE STEPS, THE (see under Thirty Nine Steps (bk).

Watford, Gwen (nar)

SECRET GARDEN, THE (see under Secret Garden).

Watkins, Bill

RETURN OF BIG GUITAR.
LP: . . . . **ROCK 8904**

Watkins, Geraint

GERAINT WATKINS AND DOMINATORS (Watkins, Geraint & Dominators).
Tracks: / Blue moon of Kentucky / Cakewalk into town / Casting my spell / Deep in the heart of Texas / Don't you just know it / Grow, too old / I got to find my baby / If walls could talk / In the night / Man smart, woman smarter / My baby left me / Nobody / Paralysed.
LP: **9102033**

Watkins, Kit

LABYRINTH.
LP: . . . . **SRLP 105**

Watkins, Mary

WINDS OF CHANGE.
LP: . . . . **UNKNOWN**

Watkiss, Cleveland

BLESSING IN DISGUISE.
LP: **8490751**
MC: **8490754**

GREEN CHIMNEYS.
Tracks: / Green chimneys II / Iswahdis / Sea the sky, The / Song for you / Incandescent dreams / Newborn / To a songstress / Puss in boots / Seeds of sin II.
LP: **839 722-1**
MC: **839 722-4**

Watkiss, Gerald

PURGATORY AND PARADISE.
Tracks: / City life / Picture days / Come back to me / Remember me / Globetrotter / I like it that way / Hold on / If the line broke on my world / Purgatory & paradise.
LP: . . . . **NSPL 18553**

Watley, Jody

JODY WATLEY.
Tracks: / Looking for a new love / Still a thrill / Some kind of lover / For the girls / Love injection / Don't you want me / Do it to the beat / Most of all / Learn to say no / Looking for a new love (extended club version) (Extra track available on cassette and compact disc only.).
LP: . . . . **MCG 6024**
MC: . . . . **MCGC 6024**

LARGER THAN LIFE.
Tracks: / Real love / Everything / L.O.V.E.R. / Lifestyle / Something new / Come into my life / Friends / What'cha gonna do for me / For love's sake / Precious love / Once you leave / Only you.
LP: . . . . **MCG 6044**
MC: . . . . **MCGC 6044**

Watrous, Bill

LIVE AT THE PIZZA EXPRESS 1982.
Tracks: / Straight, no chaser / When your lover has gone / Diane / Falling in love with love / There is no greater love / Dearly beloved / I should care.
LP: . . . . **MOLE 7**

Watson, Bobby

INVENTOR, THE.
Tracks: / Heckle and jeckle / Inventor, The / P.D. on Great Jones Street / Sun, The / For children of all ages / Dreams so real / Shaw of Newark, The / Homemade blues (CD only.) / Long way home.
LP: **B1 91915**
LP: **791 915 1**

NO QUESTION ABOUT IT.
Tracks: / Country corn flakes / Forty acres and a mule / What can I do for you / Blood count / No question about it / Moonrise / And then again.
LP: **B1 90262**
LP: **790 262 1**

Watson, Diz

RHUMBALERO.
Tracks: / Junco partner / Dominos medley / Hadacol bounce / Tico tico / So well when you're well / Rhumbalero medley / Can't believe you wanna leave / Big chief / Her mind is gone / Blues for Alexis.
LP: . . . . **CH 124**

Watson, Doc

BALLADS FROM DEEP (Watson, Doc & Merle).
Tracks: / Roll in my sweet baby's arms / Wreck, The / Cuckoo, The / My rough and rowdy ways / Gambler's yodel.
MC: . . . . **VMMC 6576**

DOWN SOUTH.
LP: . . . . **SH 3742**
MC: . . . . **ZCSH 3742**

ESSENTIAL DOC WATSON, THE.
Tracks: / Tom Dooley / Alberta / Froggie went a courtin' / Beaumont rag / St. James hospital / Down in the valley to pray / Blue railroad train / Rising sun blues / Shady grove / My rough and rowdy ways / Train that carried my girl from town, The / Black mountain rag / I was a stranger / Blue Ridge Mountain blues / Country blues / Ground hog / Little orphan girl / Blackberry blossom / Goin' down the road feeling bad / Rambling hobo / Little Omie Wise / Handsome Molly / White house blues / I want to love him more / Way downtown.
2LP: . . . . **VSD 45/46**

ESSENTIAL DOC WATSON VOL.1.
Tracks: / Tom Dooley / Alberta / Froggie went a courtin' / Beaumont rag / St. James hospital / Muskrat / Down in the valley to pray / Blue railroad train / Rising sun blues / Shady grove / My rough and rowdy ways / Train that carried my girl from town, The.
LP: . . . . **VMLP 7308**
MC: . . . . **VMMC 7308**

FOLK AND COUNTRY LEGEND,A (Watson, Doc & Merle).
LP: . . . . **LR 44.008**

GUITAR ALBUM, THE (Watson, Doc & Merle).
Tracks: / Sheeps in the meadow / Stoney fork / Talking to Casey / Liza / Lady be good / Black pine waltz / Guitar polka / Going to Chicago blues / Black mountain rag / Cotton row / John Henry / Worried blues / Twinkle twinkle / Take me out to the ballgame / Gonna lay down my old guitar.
LP: . . . . **FF 301**

IN THE PINES.
Tracks: / Doc's guitar / In the pines / Mama blues / Sally Goodin / Am I born to die / What would you give in exchange for your soul / Tom Dooley / Little stream of whiskey / Worried blues / Doc's talking blues / Liza Jane / Midnight on the stormy deep.
LP: . . . . **SDLP 1012**
MC: . . . . **SDC 1012**

ON PRAYING GROUND.
Tracks: / You must come in at the door / Precious Lord / On praying ground / I'll live on / Gathering buds / Beautiful golden somewhere / We'll work 'till Jesus comes / Ninety and nine, The / Farther along / Christmas lullaby / Did Christ o'er sinners weep / Uncloudy day.
LP: . . . . **SH 3779**
MC: . . . . **ZCSH 3779**

OUT IN THE COUNTRY.
LP: . . . . **MA 24983**

PICKIN' THE BLUES (Watson, Doc/ Merle Watson).
Tracks: / Mississipppi heavy water blues / Sittin' hear pickin' the blues / Stormy weather / Windy and warm / St. Louis blues / Jailhouse blues / Freight train blues / Hobo Bill's last ride / Carroll county blues / Blue ridge mountain blues / I'm a stranger here / Honey babe blues.
LP: . . . . **FF 352**

PORTRAIT: DOC WATSON.
Tracks: / I'm worried now / Nobody knows but me / Leaving London / Stay in the middle of the road / Risin' sun blues / George Gudger's overalls / Tucker's barn / Storms on the ocean / Prayer bells of Heaven / Tough luck man / My blue eyed Jane.
LP: . . . . **SH 3759**
MC: . . . . **ZCSH 3759**

RED ROCKING CHAIR (Watson, Doc & Merle).
Tracks: / Sadie / Fisher's hornpipe / Devil's dream / Along the road / Smoke, smoke, smoke / Below freezing / California blues / John Hurt / Mole in the ground / Any old time / Red rocking chair / How long blues / Down yonder.
LP: . . . . **FF 252**

RIDIN' THE MIDNIGHT TRAIN.
LP: . . . . **SH 3752**
MC: . . . . **ZCSH 3752**

SONGS FOR LITTLE PICKERS.
Tracks: / Talkin' guitar / Mole in the ground / Mama blues / Foggy went a courtin' / Shady grove / Riddle song, The / Sing song kitty / John Henry / Sally Goodin / Crawdad song / Grass grew all around, The / Liza Jane / Tennessee stud, The.
LP: . . . . **SH 3786**
MC: . . . . **ZCSH 3786**

Watson, Donald

VIRTUOSO CLARINETTIST, THE (see under Bradbury, Colin) (Watson, Donald/ Colin Bradbury/Oliver Davies).

Watson Family

TRADITION.
LP: . . . . **ROUNDER 0129**

WATSON FAMILY TRADITION THE.
Tracks: / Georgie / Fish in the mill pond / Children's songs / I heard my mother weeping / Reuben's train / Biscuits / Tucker's barn / Give the fiddler a dram / Am I born to die / Marthy, won't you have some good old cider / Roving on a winter's night, A / Arnold's tune / Pretty saro / Early early in the spring / Little Maggie / Bill Banks / Rambling hobo / One morning in may / Faithful soldier, The / Omie wise / Jimmy Sutton.
LP: **12TS 336**

Watson, Gene

GREATEST HITS: GENE WATSON.
Tracks: / Between this time and next time / Maybe I should have been listening / Fourteen carat mind / Speak softly (you're talking to my heart) / This dream's on me / What she don't know won't hurt her / You're out doing what I'm here doing without / Sometimes I get lucky and forget / Drinkin' my way back home / Forever again.
LP: . . . . **IMCA 5572**

HEARTACHES LOVE AND STUFF.
LP: . . . . **MCF 3256**

LITTLE BY LITTLE.
Tracks: / Little by little / My memories of you / Chesapeake bay, The / Leavin's been comin' for a long, long time / Ballad of Richard Lindsey, The / Forever again / With any luck at all / Growing apart / She has no memory of me / Drinkin' my way back home.
LP: . . . . **MCF 3213**
MC: . . . . **MCFC 3213**

LOVE IN THE HOT AFTERNOON.
MC: **4XL 9048**

OLD LOVE NEVER DIES.
Tracks: / Old love never dies / Girl I used to run around with, The / Roads and other reasons / Till Melinda comes round / Speak softly (you're talking to my heart) / Nothing about her reminds me of you / Fourteen carat mind / Lonely me / Sun never comes up again, The / Missing you just started hittin' home.
LP: . . . . **IMCA 27066**

REFLECTIONS.
Tracks: / One sided conversations / Take off them shoes / Farewell party / Let's give it up or get it on / For the memories / I wonder how it is in Colorado / Pick the wildwood flower / I know what it's like in her arms / Mama sold roses / I don't know how to tell her.
LP: . . . . **EST 11805**

SOMETIMES I GET LUCKY.
Tracks: / Speak well of me / Sometimes I get lucky and forget / She sure makes leaving look easy / You waltzed yourself right into my life / You put out an old flame last night / You're just another beer drinkin' song / Thinkin' 'bout leaving / If I were you I'd fall in love with me.
LP: . . . . **IMCA 5384**

TEXAS SATURDAY NIGHT.
Tracks: / Texas Saturday night / Got no reason now for going home / You waltzed yourself right into my life / My memories of you / If I were you I'd fall in love with me / You're just another beer drinkin' song / One hell of a heartache / You sure make cheatin' seem easy / I'm tellin' me a lie / Drinkin' my way back home.
LP: . . . . **IMCA 5670**

THIS DREAM'S ON ME.
Tracks: / This dream's on me / Fighting fire with fire / Baby me baby / Full time fool / This torch that I carry for you / What she don't know won't hurt her / From cotton to satin / You sure make cheatin' seem easy / Last thing I planned to do today was cheat, The / Somethin' 'bout bein' gone.
LP: . . . . **IMCA 885**

Watson, George

INTRODUCING BIG GEORGE.
LP: . . . . **GES 1160**

Watson, Gwen (nar)

BEST LOVED VERSE (see under Best Loved Verse (bk)) (Watson, Gwen (nar) & Richard Pasco (nar)).

Watson, Helen

BLUE SLIPPER.
Tracks: / You're not the rule (you're the exception) / Boys own world / When you love me I get lazy / New island rock line / Blue slipper / Don't stop now / I'm jealous dear / Sway / Chrome soldier / Don't forget to say your prayers / Rock myself to sleep.
LP: . . . . **SCX 6710**
MC: . . . . **TCSCX 6710**

SONGBIRD (see Adams, Suzie) (Watson, Helen and Suzie Adams).

WEATHER INSIDE, THE.
Tracks: / I wish that love was simple / You're so hard to get hold of / Road that ends in tears / Weather inside, The / Your face / Hanging out the washing (in a small back yard) / Thrill enough to know, A / Dangerous daybreak / Now we'll move the river / Ready to fly / Letters of introduction.
LP: . . . . **SCX 6717**
MC: . . . . **TCSCX 6717**

Watson, Jim

MEETING IN THE AIR (Watson, Jim/ Craver/Thompson).
Tracks: / Anchored in love / While the band is playing Dixie / Stern old bachelor / Winding stream, The / School house on the hill, The / Wayworn traveller / Meeting in the air / I ain't gonna work tomorrow / One little word / Dixie darling / Lulu walls / Are you tired of me my darling / Give me the roses / When the roses bloom in Dixieland.
LP: . . . . **FF 219**

Watson, Johnny

AIN'T THAT A BITCH.
Tracks: / I need it / I want to ta ta you baby / Superman lover / Ain't that a bitch / Since I met you baby / We're no exception / Won't you forgive me baby.
LP: . . . . **DJM 22100**
MC: . . . . **DJM 42100**

...AND THE FAMILY CLONE.
Tracks: / Clone information / Family clone / Forget the Joneses / Ain't movin' / Come and dance with me / Rio dreamin' / What is love / Voodoo what you do.
LP: . . . . **DJF 20574**
MC: . . . . **DJH 40574**

FUNK BEYOND THE CALL OF DUTY.
Tracks: / Funk beyond the call of duty / It's all about the dollar bill / Give me my love / It's a damn shame / I'm gonna get you baby / Barn door / Love that will not die.
LP: . . . . **DJM 22101**
MC: . . . . **DJM 42101**

GANGSTER IS BACK, THE.
Tracks: / Too tired / Hot little mama / Blues side, The / I love to love you / Oh baby / Someone cares for me / She moves me / Love me baby / Gangster of love / One room country shack / Acoustic instrumental / One more kiss / Johnny guitar / Looking back / Eagle is back, The.
LP: . . . . **RL 013**

GANGSTER OF LOVE.
LP: . . . . **BID 8013**

GETTIN' DOWN WITH....
Tracks: / Witchcraft / I cried for you / I'll remember April / Polka dots and moonbeams / Exactly like you / When did you leave heaven / Reconsider baby / Misty.
LP: . . . . **GCH 8017**
MC: . . . . **GCHK 78017**

GIANT.
Tracks: / Miss Frisco (Queen of the disco) / Tu jours amour / Gangster of love / Guitar disco / Wrapped in black mink / You can stay but the noise must go / Baby face.
LP: . . . . **DJM 22102**
MC: . . . . **DJM 42102**

HIT THE HIGHWAY.
Tracks: / Hot little mama / Those lonely lonely nights / Oh baby / I'm gonna hit that highway / I love to love you / Someone cares for me / Too tired / Ain't gonna hush / Lonely girl / Ruben / She moves me / Give me a little / Love me baby / Three hours past midnight.
LP: . . . . **CH 70**

I HEARD THAT.
Tracks: / Highway 60 / Motor head baby / No I can't / What's going on / Walking to my baby / Thinking / I got eyes / Space

guitar / Half pint of whiskey / Gettin' drunk / You can't take it with you / Cuttin' in / Sweet lovin mama / In the evening / Those lonely, lonely feelings / Gangster of love.
LP: . . . . **CRB 1101**
MC: . . . . **TCCRB 1101**

LOVE JONES.
Tracks: / Booty ooty / Love Jones / Going up in smoke / Close encounters / Asante sana / Telephone bill / Lone Ranger, The / Jet plane / Children of the universe.
LP: . . . . **DJM 22104**
MC: . . . . **DJM 42104**

REAL MOTHER, A.
LP: . . . . **DJM 22105**
MC: . . . . **DJM 42105**

STRIKE ON COMPUTERS.
Tracks: / You do me bad so good / Boogie down party down / Scratching "85" / Let's get together / Strike on computers / Byrd ball train / Statue of Liberty / Please send me someone to love.
LP: . . . . **SOS 2001**
MC: . . . . **SOSMC 2001**

THAT'S WHAT TIME IT IS.
LP: . . . . **AMLH 64880**

VERY BEST OF JOHNNY 'GUITAR' WATSON.
LP: . . . . **DJF 20576**
MC: . . . . **DJH 40576**

VERY BEST OF..., THE / MR GUITAR.
MCSET: . . . . **TWO 417**

WHAT THE HELL IS THIS.
Tracks: / Real mother for ya, A / Ain't that a bitch / Booty ooty / Mother-in-law / Miss Frisco / I want to ta ta you baby / Your love is my love / It's all about the dollar bill / Lover Jones / What the hell is this / I need it / I don't want to be president / Wrapped in black mink / Strung out.
LP: . . . . **DJM 22103**
MC: . . . . **DJM 42103**
LP: . . . . **DJF 20557**

Watson, Jonathan

ONLY A WORLD CUP EXCUSE (Watson, Jonathan & Tony Roper).
Tracks: / 1974 / 1978 / 1982 / 1986 / 1990.
MC: . . . . **ZCF 779**

ONLY AN EXCUSE (Real history of Scottish football) (Watson, Jonathan & Tony Roper).
MC: . . . . **ZCM 722**

ONLY ANOTHER EXCUSE (Watson, Jonathan & Tony Roper).
MC: . . . . **ZCR 752**

Watson, Leo

SCAT MAN 1937-1946, THE (Watson, Leo & His Orchestra).
LP: . . . . **SC 1026**

Watson, Merle

GUITAR ALBUM, THE (See under Watson, Doc) (Watson, Doc & Merle).

PICKIN' THE BLUES (see Watson, Doc) (Watson, Merle/Doc Watson).

RED ROCKING CHAIR (See under Watson, Doc) (Watson, Doc & Merle).

Watson, Robert

ALL BECAUSE OF YOU.
Tracks: / In Maya's apartment / All because of you / Fuller love / Pamela / Second party / Days of wine and roses.
LP: . . . . **NSPL 28276**

BEATITUDES (Watson, Robert & Curtis Lundy).
LP: . . . . **HEP 2024**

ESTIMATED TIME OF ARRIVAL.
LP: . . . . **NSPL 28250**

JEWEL (Watson, Robert Sextet).
LP: . . . . **AMLP 846**

MIXED TRAFFIC.
Tracks: / Venezuela / Planxty Irwin / Three jovial miners / Stow brow / Princess Royal / Nottingham miners / Where oh where / Berkeley Square / Brother, can you spare a dime / Derbyshire colliers / Iniskillen dragoon / Jeanette Jeannot / Broadway.
LP: . . . . **GVR 210**
MC: . . . . **GVR 210**

Watson, Roger

CHEQUERED ROOTS.
LP: . . . . **PLR 078**
MC: . . . . **PLC 078**

RADIOLAND (Watson, Roger/Debby McClatchy).
LP: . . . . **PLR 079**
MC: . . . . **PLC 079**

Watson, Wayne

GIANTS IN THE LAND.
LP: . . . . **DAY R 4135**
MC: . . . . **DAY C 4135**

Watsonian Institute

MASTER FUNK.
LP: . . . . **DJF 20529**
MC: . . . . **DJH 40529**

Watt, Ben

NORTH MARINE DRIVE.
Tracks: / On Box Hill / Some things don't matter / Lucky one / Empty bottles / North Marine Drive / Waiting like mad / Thirst for knowledge / Long time no sea / You're gonna make me lonesome when you go / Walter and John / Aquamarine / Slipping slowly / Another conversation with myself / Girl in winter, A.
LP: . . . . **BRED 40**

Watt, John

14 SONGS.
Tracks: / Wild colonial boy / Give an Irish girl to me.
MC: . . . . **CHRL 198**

BEST OF IRELAND'S SINGING FARMER.
Tracks: / Unicorn / Delaney's donkey / Where the three counties meet / Where my Eileen is waiting for me / Give an Irish girl to me / Wild colonial boy / Those brown eyes / Leprechaun / Oul Lammas fair / Old Dungannon road / Rathfriland on the hill / Granny's old armchair / Singing farmer / Hometown on the Foyle.
LP: . . . . **HRL 198**

IRELAND'S SINGING FARMER VOL 1.
Tracks: / Rathfriland on the hill / Pretty little girl from Omagh / There's a bridle hanging on the wall / Newcastle by the sea / Bonnie Kellswater / Those brown eyes / I'll settle for Old Ireland / Long before your time / Mother the queen of my heart / Delaney's donkey / My Swatragh home / Any dream will do / Aul Lammas fair / Green glens of Antrim / Granny's old armchair.
LP: . . . . **PHL 414**
MC: . . . . **CPHL 414**
LP: . . . . **HRL 128**
MC: . . . . **CHRL 128**

IRELAND'S SINGING FARMER VOL 2.
LP: . . . . **HRL 141**
MC: . . . . **CHRL 141**

IRELAND'S SINGING FARMER VOL 3.
Tracks: / Stone outside Dan Murphy's door, The / Where my Eileen is waiting / Fishermen of Co. Down.
LP: . . . . **HRL 161**
MC: . . . . **CHRL 161**

SHORES OF THE NORTH (Watt, John/ Davey Stewart).
Tracks: / Fife's got everything including Blue Skies / Farewell tae the Ferries / Poacher, The / New Toon Hall, The / Bobby Muldoon / Schooldays over / Eany Meany / Kelty clippie / Eyemouth disaster / Annabelle Rosabelle / Boatie rows, The / My wee dog / Pittenweem Jo / Dunfermline linen / Fisher's hornpipe / Shores of the Forth, The / Lochaber gathering - Tam Bain's Lum.
LP: . . . . **SPR 1002**
MC: . . . . **SPRC 1002**

SINGING FARMER.
Tracks: / My handle's farmer John / Four country roads / Stock car crazy / Old turf fire / Ploughman Hugh Barr / Three cheers for Billy Bingham & his boys / Shoreland of Lough Foyle / Joey Dunlop / My Aunt Jane / Master McGrath / Northwest 200 Hall of Fame / As others look at you.
LP: . . . . **PHL 448**
MC: . . . . **CPHL 448**

SONG OF HOME.
Tracks: / Song of home / When the hammer strikes the anvil (the blacksmith) / Barry McGuigan / Portstewart by the sea / Country boy / Island / Rathlin Island / Catch me if you can / Poet of the roe / Old bushmills / Do you want yer oul lobby washed down / Pat Jennings.
LP: . . . . **PHL 475**
MC: . . . . **CPHL 475**

Watt, Sandy

BENEATH STILL WATERS.
MC: . . . . **CSW 101**

I'M JUST ME.
MC: . . . . **CWGR 084**

LIFE'S RAILWAY TO HEAVEN.
MC: . . . . **CWGR 069**

SINGING FISHERMAN, THE.
Tracks: / Last two days, The / For the good times / For rockall we are bound / Old loves never die / We both hide tears / No one will ever know / You don't need to understand / I saw a man / Jesus / Old Account, The / We'll talk it over / Old country church / Sheltered in the arms of gold.
MC: . . . . **CSW 100**

Watters, Lu

50'S RECORDINGS VOL 1 (Watters, Lu & the Yerba Buena Jazz Band).
LP: . . . . **DC 12010**

50'S RECORDINGS VOL 2 (Watters, Lu & the Yerba Buena Jazz Band).
LP: . . . . **DC 12011**

AIR SHOTS FROM THE DAWN CLUB 1941 (Yerba Buena Jazz Band).
LP: . . . . **H 107**

BUNK JOHNSON & LU WATTERS (See under Johnson, Bunk) (Watters, Lu & Bunk Johnson).

LU WATTERS & BUNK JOHNSON (See Johnson, Bunk) (Watters, Lu & Bunk Johnson).

YERBA BUENA JAZZ BAND VOL 1
Voc. Clancy Hayes.
LP: . . . . **H 101**

YERBA BUENA JAZZ BAND VOL 2
Voc. Clancy Hayes.
LP: . . . . **H 102**

YERBA BUENA JAZZBAND VOL.4 (Watters, Lu & the Yerba Buena Jazz Band).
LP: . . . . **H 104**

Watts, Alan

ZEN-THE ETERNAL NOW.
MC: . . . . **SS 121**

Watts, Andre

GERSHWIN SOLO PIANO MUSIC.
LP: . . . . **CBS 60311**
MC: **40 60311**

Watts, Charlie

FROM ONE CHARLIE (Watts, Charlie Quintet).
LP: . . . . **UFO 002**

LIVE AT FULHAM TOWN HALL (Watts, Charlie and his Orchestra).
Tracks: / Stompin' at the Savoy / Lester leaps in / Moonglow / Robbins nest / Scrapple from the apple / Flying home.
LP: **4502531**
MC: **4502534**

Watts, Ernie

CHARIOTS OF FIRE.
Tracks: / Chariots of fire / Hold on / Lady / Gigolo / Valdez in the country / Abraham's theme / Five circles.
LP: . . . . **K 56982**

ERNIE WATTS QUARTET (Watts, Ernie Quartet).
MC: . . . . **JC 3309**
LP: . . . . **JLP 3309**

LOOK IN YOUR HEART.
Tracks: / Look in your heart / Just holdin' on / Dance music, makin' music / Let's sail away / Beyond the cosmic void suite (starship outness) / Love in transit / Marching to Cretonia.
LP: . . . . **E 6285**

MUSICIAN.
Tracks: / Music prayer for peace / Where the spirit lives / Rock camping / One love / Red dress / Looking glass / Don't you know / Urban renewal / Keepin' on.
LP: **925283 1**

Watts, John

ICEBERG MODEL.
Tracks: / Iceberg model / Interference / Man in someone else's skin / I smelt roses in the underground / I was in love with you / Money and power / Mayday mayday / Prisoner's dilemma / Menagerie makers / Face to remember.
LP: . . . . **EMC 3427**

ONE MORE TWIST.
Tracks: / One voice / Lagonda lifestyle / Watching you / Carousel / That's not enough for me / I know it now / Victims of fashion / Speaking a different language / Involuntary movement / Relax.
LP: . . . . **EMC 3402**

Watts, Noble Thin Man

BLAST OFF.
LP: . . . . **FLY 547**

NOBLE AND NAT (Watts, Noble 'Thin Man' & Nat Adderley).
Tracks: / Yo yo / Rheumatism / My grannie doobie / Night time is the right time, The / Creep, The / Camp meeting / Help is on the way / Into the sun / Keep it.
LP: . . . . **KIN 4041**
MC: . . . . **KIN 4041MC**

RETURN OF THE THIN MAN.
LP: . . . . **BEDLP 3**

Watts, Phil

DO IT WITH LOVE.
LP: . . . . **WATLP 1**
MC: . . . . **WATC 1**

Watts, Trevor

APPLICATION, INTERACTION AND... (see Stevens, John) (Watts, Trevor & John Stevens & Barry Guy & Howard Riley).

CLOSER TO YOU.
Tracks: / Ye Dublin ting / South of nowhere / Keep right / Dear Roland.
LP: . . . . **OG 528**

CYNOSURE.
LP: . . . . **OG 526**

ENDGAME (see Guy, Barry) (Watts, Trevor & John Stevens & Barry Guy & Howard Riley).

MOIRE MUSIC (Watts, Trevor Moire Music).
LP: . . . . **ARC 02**

MOIRE MUSIC SEXTET.
Tracks: / Saalfelden encore / Don't stop now.
LP: . . . . **SGC 1015**

NO FEAR (see Stevens, John) (Watts, Trevor/John Stevens/Barry Guy).

STELLA MALU (See under Krimsky, Katrina) (Watts, Trevor & Katrina Krimsky).

Waugh, Evelyn

BRIDESHEAD REVISITED (see under Brideshead Revisited (bk)) (Gielgud, Sir John (nar)).

Waut, Elisa

ELISA WAUT.
LP: . . . . **STAB 3**

Wavelength

HURRY HOME.
LP: **204.652**
MC: **404.652**

WAVELENGTH.
Tracks: / After hours / Rio / Man in the moon, The / Win some lose some / Hurry home / Don't make me do it / Thank you for the party / Crying over you / I don't want you hanging around / Do I still figure in your life.
LP: . . . . **ARL 5069**

Wavelength (film)

WAVELENGTH (Film Soundtrack) (Tangerine Dream).
LP: . . . . **STV 81207**
MC: . . . . **CTV 81207**

Wavestar

MOONWIND.
LP: . . . . **SYN 309**
MC: . . . . **SYNC 309**

Waving All Excuses

WAVING ALL EXCUSES (Patrick Campbell) (Villiers, James (nar)).
MCSET: . . . . **LISF 0007/0008**

Wavy Gravy

FOUR HAIRY POLICEMEN.
LP: . . . . **BEWARE 999**

WAVY GRAVY For adult enthusiasts (Various artists).
LP: . . . . **BEWARE 001**

Wax

AMERICAN ENGLISH.
Tracks: / American English / Marie Claire / Hear no evil / In some other world / Ready or not / Call it destiny / Bridge to your heart / Share the glory / Alright tonight / Promise, The / Heaven in her bed / Bug in the machine.
LP: . . . . **PL 71430**
MC: . . . . **PK 71430**

HUNDRED THOUSAND IN FRESH NOTES, A.
Tracks: / Anchors aweigh / Wherever you are / Railroad to heaven / He said she said / Spell on you / Don't play that song / Pictures of Paris / Maybe / Madelaine / Credit where credit's due.
LP: . . . . **PL 74182**
MC: . . . . **PK 74182**

MAGNETIC HEAVEN.
Tracks: / Right between the eyes / Hear no evil / Shadows of love / Marie Claire / Ball and chain / Systematic / Breakout / Only a visitor / Rise up / Magnetic heaven.
LP: . . . . **PL 70937**
MC: . . . . **PK 70937**

Waxing Poetics

BED TIME STORY.
Tracks: / Frankenstein's daughter / Shake / Semaphore signals / Sugar daddy / East of Jesus / Manakin moon / Fear no evil / Little things in little boxes / Attic of the underground, The / Jet black plastic pistol / Roll that stone (over me) / Under a fake blue sky.
LP: . . . . **EM 9371-1**
MC: . . . . **EMC 9371**

HERMITAGE.
LP: . . . . **EM 9610**

MANAKIN MOON.
Tracks: / Where your name is / Baby Jane / Ghost writer / Downstairs /

Needles in the camel's eye / Father son and ghost / Blue eyed soul / Side by side sometime / don't tread on me.
LP: . . . . EM 95571

Waxing The Winners

WAXING THE WINNERS VOL.1 Melody Maker all star poll winners (Various artists).
Tracks: / Brand's essence: *Various artists* / Marshall's plan: *Various artists* / Ballot box: *Various artists*/ Ballot box (take 2): *Various artists* / Coronation jump: *Various artists* / Coronation jump (take 2): *Various* artists / Anidina: *Various artists* / Up the poll (take 2): *Various artists* / Up the poll (take 4): *Various* artists / Leap year (take 2): *Various artists* / Leap year (take 4): *Various artists* / M.M. special: *Various artists.*
LP: . . . . ESQ 321

WAXING THE WINNERS VOL.2 Melody Maker all star poll winners (Various artists).
LP: . . . . ESQ 325

Waxman, Franz

ADVENTURES OF A YOUNG MAN (See under Hemingways Adventures).

CLASSIC FILM SCORES BY FRANZ WAXMAN (see under Films) (Various artists).

LEGENDS OF HOLLYWOOD VOL. 1.
LP: . . . . VS 5242
MC: . . . . VSC 5242

Way, Darryl

HUMAN CONDITION, THE (Way,Daryl/ Opus20).
Tracks: / Pursuit of pleasure / Flirtation, infatuation / Eternal struggle, The / Age of innocence / Thirst for power / Chase, The / Corridor of uncertainty / Spirit.
LP: . . . . VE 8
MC: . . . . TCVE 8

Way Down South

WAY DOWN SOUTH IN DIXIE (Various artists).
LP: . . . . MS 45005

Way It Used To Be

WAY IT USED TO BE, THE (Great Love Songs) (Various artists).
Tracks: / Way it used to be, The: *Humperdinck, Engelbert* / You're a lady: *Skellern, Peter* / Without love: *Jones,* Tom / Laughter in the rain: *Sedaka, Neil* / Little green apples: *Miller, Roger* / Lights of Cincinnati: *Walker,* Scott / Last farewell, The: *Whittaker, Roger* / Music: *Miles, John* / It looks like I'll never fall in love again: *Jones, Tom* / I don't believe in 'IF' anymore: *Whittaker, Roger* / Winter world of love: *Humperdinck, Engelbert* / Way you look tonight, The: *Woodward, Edward* / Our last song together: *Sedaka, Neil.*
MC: CN4 2101

Way of the World

WAY OF THE WORLD, THE (William Congreve) (Various artists).
MCSET: 339

Way Out West

WAY OUT WEST (Songs of the singing cowboys) (Various artists).
LP: . . . . MOIR 506
MC: . . . . CMOIR 506

Way Out West (Group)

ATOMIC COCKTAIL.
Tracks: / Atom bomb / Rollercoaster / Right man / Don't say that you won't / Run and hide / Big gun / Little sister / You can't catch me / 98 miles / Five devils stings / Folsom Prison blues / Way out west.
MC: . . . . TPC 2

Way We Were

WAY WE WERE (Original Soundtrack) (Various artists).
MC: . . . . JCT 32801

WAY WE WERE, THE (Film Soundtrack) (Various artists).
LP: . . . . JS 32830
MC: . . . . JST 32830

Way West

WAY WEST, THE (Film Soundtrack) (Various artists).
LP: . . . . MCA 25045
MC: . . . . MCAC 25045

Wayfarers

WAYFARERS, THE.
Tracks: / Lancashire lad / Banks of the sweet primroses / Four poster bed, The / Geordie black / Calico printers clerk / Poverty knock / Byker hill / Lish young buy a broom / Baby lie easy / Three score and ten / Reels in 'A' / Apprentice song / Greenland whale / Jovial collier.
LP: . . . . FHR 010
LP: . . . . LOLITA 10009

WORLD FARE.
LP: . . . . LOLITA 5050

Waylon & Company

WAYLON AND COMPANY (See under Jennings, Waylon) (Jennings, Waylon & Friends).

Waymon, Sam

MAGIC MAN.
Tracks: / Circus / Chico / Magic Man / If all the words are right / Galaxy / They'll never know you / It's a long way down / Down on me.
LP: . . . . PIR 0687

Wayne, Chris

PROGRESS.
LP: . . . . HB 51

Wayne, Chuck

CHARLIE PRIDE SONGBOOK VOL 1.
MC: . . . . AIM 115

STRING FEVER.
LP: . . . . FS 302

TASTY PUDDING (Wayne, Chuck,Brew Moore,Zoot Sims).
LP: . . . . WL 70525

TRAVELLING.
LP: . . . . PRO 7008

Wayne, Frances

SONGS FOR MY MAN.
LP: . . . . FS 175

Wayne, Jeff

WAR OF THE WORLDS (See under War Of The Worlds) (Various artists).

Wayne, John

JOHN WAYNE WITH SLY & ROBBIE AND THE AGGROVATORS.
LP: . . . . VSLP 4025

MONEY AND WOMEN (See under Carlos, Don) (Wayne,John & Don Carlos).

MUSIC FROM JOHN WAYNE WESTERNS VOL 2 (Various artists).
Tracks: / Shootist, The (main title): *Various artists* / Ride: *Various artists* / In the fire: *Various artists*/ Necktie party: *Various artists* / Nocturne: *Various artists* / Riders: *Various artists* / Reunion: *Various artists* / All Jake: *Various artists* / Buzzards: *Various artists* / Going home (finale): *Various artists.*
LP: 704.350
MC: . . . . C 704.350

Wayne, Jon

TEXAS FUNERAL.
LP: . . . . TEX 1

Wayne, Kid

BRIGHT LIGHTS AND COUNTRY MUSIC (Wayne, Kid & The Islanders).
Tracks: / That's what makes the jukebox play / Stoney mountain, West Virginia / I wonder where I'll find you at tonight / Bright lights and country music / So much for me, so much for you / Overlookin' underthinkin' / Down through the years / Daydreams about night things / Tennessee sunshine / Not until the next time / Linda on my mind / Workin' woman / Until my dreams come true / She didn't come here for the money.
LP: . . . . PHL 415
MC: . . . . CPHL 415

Wayne, Wee Willie

TRAVELLIN' FROM TEXAS TO NEW ORLEANS.
LP: . . . . CG 709-02
LP: 2C 068 83294
LP: . . . . SG 709-02

Wayra, Pukaj

MUSIC FROM BOLIVIA (See under Bolivia for details).

Waysted

COMPLETELY WAYSTED.
Tracks: / Women in chains / Hang 'em high / Won't get out alive / Sleazy / Hot love / Dead on your legs / Hurt so good / Somebody to love / Around and around / Rock steady / Love loaded / Hi ho my baby / Toy with passion.
LP: . . . . RAWLP 019
MC: . . . . RAWTC 019

GOOD THE BAD AND THE WAYSTED, THE.
LP: . . . . MFN 43
MC: . . . . TMFN 43

SAVE YOUR PRAYERS.
Tracks: / Walls fall down, The / Black and blue / Singing to the night / Hell comes home / Heroes die young / Heaven tonight / How the west was won / Wild night / Out of control / So long.
LP: . . . . PCS 7307
MC: . . . . TCPCS 7307

VICES.
Tracks: / Love loaded / Sleazy / Night of the wolf / Toy with the passion / Can't take that love away / Hot love / All belongs to you / Somebody to love.
LP: . . . . CHR 1438
MC: . . . . ZCHR 1438

WAYSTED.
LP: . . . . MFN 31
MC: . . . . TMFN 31

Wayward Souls

PAINTED DREAMS.
LP: . . . . HYBLP 5

Wazmo Nariz

THINGS AREN'T RIGHT.
Tracks: / Mind is willing, but the flesh is weak / Who does it hurt? / Luncheonette lovers / Stubbies / Plunger, The / Deeply / Checking out the checkout girl / This is your elbow / Oven / Lips / Germ proof cleaners / Al's radiator.
LP: . . . . ILP 003

Wazobias

ONYE BINI ONU.
LP: . . . . MLP 012

We.....

WE ARE MOST AMUSED (The very best of British comedy) (Various artists).
2LP: . . . . RTD 2067 A/B
MCSET: . . . . 4CRTD 2067 A/B

WE HAVE A DREAM (Various artists).
Tracks: / Building bridges: *Oneworld Peacesongs Singers* / Stand up: *Oneworld Peacesongs Singers* / Opposition, The: *Random, Margo* / Four minutes to midnight: *Johnson, Rebecca* / Carry Greenham home: *Seeger, Peggy*/ Like a mountain (you can't kill the spirit): *Morena, Naomi Littlebear/ Oneworld Peacesongs Singers* / Tierra sol: *Guest* Stars / Speech to apollo: *Armstrong, Frankie* / Out of the darkness: *Armstrong, Frankie* / Women make your choice: *Oneworld Peacesongs Band* / Woman in front of the bus, The: *Oneworld Peacesongs Trio* / Tomorrow: *Seeger,* Peggy / No more genocide: *Near Holly* / Silos song, The: *Johnson, Rebecca* / Oneworld world: *Oneworld Peacesongs Band.*
LP: 1WPS 1
MC: 1WPS 1C

We Are Going To Eat

EVERYWHEN.
Tracks: / If I could / Heart in hand / This conspiracy / Each life a mystery / Glory / Ride upon the tide / Eye to eye / On a day like this / Just another one / Here always / If you believe / Her dreamworld.
LP: . . . . ABB 014
MC: . . . . ABB 014 C

We Are Still Married

WE ARE STILL MARRIED (Keillor, Garrison (author)).
MCSET: . . . . ZBBC 1156

We Dig Cole

WE DIG COLE (Various artists).
LP: . . . . JASS 13

We Free Kings

HELL ON EARTH AND ROSY CROSS.
Tracks: / Motorcycle rain / Long train / Scarecrow / Flowers / Jesus wept / Still standing / Rosy cross / Wipeout gang / Brilliant.
LP: . . . . DISPLP 10
MC: . . . . DISPC 10

We Heel

BY DANNY AND DAD.
Tracks: / Annie get your Martini / Dan-dan and Michael / Two little rascals / You need a sole on these / Pubic side boards / Jabba jabba / Mad Uncle Fred - Kerfang, kerfang / Me best mate Sherriff / Paul the pooper / Big bad Rori's gone / Poon Tang / I'll get this, Mick / Stevie's in Spain / Up the Spurs / Crib on Mondays / Hole in one / Anyone seen Richie? / Feel like I've done it wrong / Hello Pat.
LP: . . . . COBB 1

We Love Norway

WE LOVE NORWAY (Vi Alskar Norge) (Various artists).
Tracks: / Three little words: *We Love Norway* / If you were mine: *We Love Norway* / Smo-o-oth one, A: *We Love* Norway / I'll get by: *We Love Norway* / Blue Lou: *We Love Norway* / What is this thing called love?: *We Love Norway* / I cried for you: *We Love Norway* / Pennies from Heaven: *We Love Norway* / Blue and sentimental: *We Love Norway* / Pick yourself up: *We Love Norway.*
LP: . . . . PHONT 7513

We Three Kings

WE THREE KINGS (Various artists).
LP: . . . . GHB 45

Weapon Of Peace

WEAPON OF PEACE.
LP: . . . . SWOP 1
MC: . . . . SWOPC 1

Weapons

CAPTIVE AUDIENCE.
LP: . . . . SAMR 044
MC: . . . . TCSAMR 044

Weather Girls

BIG GIRLS DON'T CRY.
Tracks: / Lock me up / Big girls don't cry / Well-a-wiggy / No-one can love you more than me / Down on the corner / March / Laughter in the rain / You can do it.
LP: . . . . CBS 26474
MC: 40 26474

SUCCESS.
LP: . . . . CBS 25719

WEATHER GIRLS.
Tracks: / Land of the believer / Love's on the way / Why can't we show our love / Opposite directions / Love you like a train / Worth my weight in love / Burn me / Something for nothing.
LP: 4604701
MC: 4604704

Weather, Kid Stormy

DEEP SOUTH BLUES PIANO 1935-37.
LP: . . . . DLP 576

Weather Prophets

JUDGES, JURIES AND HORSEMEN.
LP: . . . . CRELP 033

MAYFLOWER.
Tracks: / Why does the rain / Key to my love is green,The / Can't keep my mind off you / Mayflower / Head over heels / She comes from the rain / Almost prayed / Faithful / Swimming pool blues / Walking under a spell / Naked as the day you were born / Sleep.
LP: . . . . ELV 1
MC: . . . . ELV 1 C

TEMPERANCE HOTEL.
LP: . . . . CRELP 50

Weather Report

8.30.
Tracks: / Black market / Scarlet woman / Teen town / Remark you made / Slang / In a silent way / Birdland / Thanks for the memory / Badia / Boogie woogie waltz medley / 8.30 / Brown Street / Orphan / Sightseeing.
2LP: 22134
2LP: . . . . CBS 88455

BIRDLAND (OLD GOLD) (see under Franklin, Rodney - The Groove).

BLACK MARKET.
LP: . . . . CBS 32226

COLLECTION: WEATHER REPORT.
2LP: . . . . CCSLP 244
MC: . . . . CCSMC 244

DOMINO THEORY.
Tracks: / Can it be done / D flat waltz / Peasant, The / Predator / Blue sound-note / Swamp cabbage / Domino theory.
LP: . . . . CBS 25839
MC: 40 25839

GREATEST HITS: WEATHER REPORT.
LP: 4669961
MC: 4669964

HEAVY WEATHER.
Tracks: / Birdland / Remark you made, A / Teen town / Harlequin / Rumba mama / Palladium / Juggler, The / Havona.
LP: . . . . CBS 32358
MC: 40 32358
LP: . . . . CBS 81775

I SING THE BODY ELECTRIC.
LP: . . . . CBS 32062

MR GONE.
Tracks: / Pursuit of the woman in the feathered hat / River people / Young and fine / Elders, The / Mr. Gone / Punk jazz / Pinocchio / And then.
LP: 32790
MC: 40 32790
LP: . . . . CBS 82775

NIGHT PASSAGE.
Tracks: / Dream clock / Port of entry / Forlorn / Rockin' in rhythm / Fast city / Night passage / Three views of a secret / Madagascar.
LP: . . . . CBS 84597

PROCESSION.
Tracks: / Procession / Plaza real / Two lines / Where the moon goes / Well, The / Molasses run.
LP: . . . . CBS 25241
MC: 40 25241

SPORTIN' LIFE.
Tracks: / Corner pocket / Indiscretions / Hot cargo / Confians / Pearl on the half-shell / What's going on? / Face on the bar room floor, The / Icepick Willy.
LP: . . . . CBS 26367
MC: 40 26367

THIS IS THIS.
Tracks: / This is this / Face the fire / I'll never forget you / Jungle stuff (part 1) / Man with the copper fingers / Consequently / Update / China blues.
LP: CBS 57052
MC: 40 57052

WEATHER REPORT.
Tracks: / Volcano for hire / Current affairs / N.Y.C. / Dara factor one / When it was now / Speechless.
LP: CBS 32024
LP: CBS 85326

Weatherbird Jazzband

FIREWORKS.
LP: SOS 1034

Weatherburn, Robert

DUETS ALBUM, THE (Weatherburn, Robert & Rhondda Gillespie).
LP: AVM 1022
MC: AVMC 1022

Weatherburn, Ron

AFTER THE BALL.
LP: SOS 1107

Weatherley, Roy

PIANO PARTY (Weatherley, Roy & Dennis Hayward).
LP: SAV 136

Weathermen

BLACK ALBUM ACCORDING TO THE WEATHERMEN, THE.
Tracks: / Timebomb Benny / Barbie and Ken / Twisting doorknob / Tar pit / Tuff times / Mud (I would) / Punishment park / 1000 women / Poison / Rubber gods.
LP: BIAS 089

TEN DEADLY KISSES.
LP: BIAS 042

Weathers, Barbara

BARBARA WEATHERS.
Tracks: / Barbi doll / My only love / Master key, The / All I know / Our love runs deep / Our love will last forever / Where can you run / Where did our love go / Anywhere.
LP: 7599261661
MC: 7599261664

Weaver, Curley

GEORGIA GUITAR WIZARD 1928-36.
LP: BD 2004

Weaver, Patty

PATTY WEAVER.
Tracks: / One love too late / Somebody's gonna get hurt / Shot in the dark / I wanted it all / Part time man / It's your move / Don't want a heartache / Line of fire / Best is yet to come, The.
LP: K 57001

Weaver, Sylvester

ACCOMPANIST, THE.
LP: BD 2026

REMAINING TITLES OF....
LP: BD 615

SMOKETOWN STRUT.
LP: AB 2010

Weavers

BEST OF THE WEAVERS.
LP: MCL 1803
MC: MCLC 1803

WEAVERS AT CARNEGIE HALL.
LP: VMLP 5302
MC: VMTC 6302

Webb, Bill Boogie

DRINKIN' AND STINKIN'.
LP: FF 506

Webb, Cassell

CASSELL WEBB.
LP: STAT LP 29

CONVERSATIONS AT DAWN.
LP: VE 901
MC: VECC 901

LLANO.
Tracks: / Llano / Voices to rivers / In Arcadia / Everytime I get around to you / Total recall / Gypsy solitaire / Wandering ones / When the rain stops falling.
LP: VE 22
MC: TCVE 22
LP: ROSE 85

SONGS OF A STRANGER.
Tracks: / P F Sloan / Warmth / Slip away / I had to tell you / Tomb of the unknown love / Time has told me / If I needed you / Jim Dean of Indiana.
LP: VE 45
MC: TCVE 45

Webb, Chick

AT THE SOUTHLAND OF BOSTON (See Fitzgerald, Ella) (Webb, Chick/Ella Fitzgerald).

CHICK WEBB VOL.1.
LP: KLJ 20017

ELLA FITZGERALD & THE CHICK WEBB ORCHESTRA (see Fitzgerald, Ella) (Webb, Chick Orchestra/Ella Fitzgerald).

ELLA WITH (see under Fitzgerald, Ella) (Webb, Chick/his orch/Ella Fitzgerald/MillsBros/Benny Goodman).

IN THE GROOVE (Big band bounce & boogie).
Tracks: / Don't be that way / What a shuffle / Blue Lou / Go Harlem / You'll have to swing it / Strictly jive / Rock it for me / Squeeze me / If dreams come true / Tisket a tasket, A / Azure / Spinnin' the web / Liza / Undecided / T'aint what you do (it's the way that you do it) / In the groove at the Groove.
LP: AFS 1007

RHYTHM MAN.
LP: HEP 1023

SOUTHLAND CAFE (see Basie, Count) (Webb, Chick/his orchestra/Count Basie).

STOMPIN' AT THE SAVOY (Webb, Chick Orchestra/Ella Fitzgerald).
LP: CC 17

STOMPIN' AT THE SAVOY 1936 (Webb, Chick/his orchestra).
LP: CLP 81

Webb, George

GEORGE WEBB'S DIXIELANDERS (Webb, George & His Dixielanders).
LP: J 122

Webb Ivory Newhall

FROM BANDSTAND TO CONCERT HALL.
Tracks: / Concert prelude / Springtime / Wellington march / Scherzo / Highlander / Early one morning / Camptown races / Dumbo's dance / Funiculi funicula / Appreciation / My love is like a red, red rose / Clair de lune / Honest toil.
LP: GRS 1075

Webb, Jimmy

ANGEL HEART.
Tracks: / Angel heart / God's gift / One of the few / Scissors cut / Work for a dollar / His world / Our movie / Nasty love / In cars / Old wing mouth.
LP: CBS 85757

SONGWRITERS FOR THE STARS 1 (Webb, Jimmy & Rupert Holmes).
Tracks: / By the time I get to Phoenix / Scissors cut / Christian no / Moon is a harsh mistress, The / Up, up and away / Wichita lineman / MacArthur Park / Galveston / Studio musician / Escape / Lullaby for myself / Black Jack / Queen bee.
LP: 6327 078

Webb, John

RED HOT GUITARS (Webb, John & R.Warner).
LP: LC 15S

Webb, Marti

ALWAYS THERE.
Tracks: / Always there (Howard's Way theme) / Onedin line / Reilly, ace of spies - theme / Moonlighting / To have and to hold / I could be so good for you (Theme from Minder) / To serve them all my days / EastEnders.
LP: REB 619
MC: ZCF 619

ENCORE.
Tracks: / Fantasy / If you love me now / Life on Mars / It had to be you / Wind beneath my wings / Ben / Love of my life / My foolish heart / Part-time love / When love was all we had / All by myself.
LP: BLEND 1
MC: ZCEND 1

I'M NOT THAT KIND OF GIRL.
Tracks: / Seven outside Mr. Chows / Didn't mean to fall in love / Shampoo and miracle please / I'm not that kind of girl / I'll see you when I see you / Dear Janet Reger / What would Jane Fonda do? / No problem / Getting it right / Traffic jam.
LP: POLD 5071

MARTI WEBB SINGS GERSHWIN.
Tracks: / Fascinating rhythm / I got rhythm / Rhapsody in blue / Porgy I's your woman now / Love walked in / Love is here to stay / Somebody loves me / How long has this been going on? / Someone to watch over me / Do it again / Summertime / But not for me / Man I love, The / Embraceable you / He loves and she loves.
MC: HSC 657

STAGES.
LP: STAR 2391
MC: STAC 2391

TELL ME ON A SUNDAY (TV soundtrack).
Tracks: / Capped teeth and Caesar salad / Come back with the same look in your eyes / I'm very you, you're very me / It's not the end of the world / If he's married -if he's younger - if I lose him / Let me finish / Let's talk about you / Letter home to England / Nothing like you've ever known / Second letter home / Sheldon bloom / Take that look off your face / Tell me on a Sunday / You made me think you were in love.
LP: POLD 5031
MC: POLDC 5031

WON'T CHANGE PLACES.
Tracks: / Won't change places / All I am / Your ears should be burning now / Angry and sore / Don't cry for me Argentina / I've been in love too long / What you gonna do with your freedom / Don't / Masquerade / I guess I'll miss the man.
LP: 2442 186

Webb, Peta

I HAVE WANDERED IN EXILE.
Tracks: / I have wandered in exile (Farr, Lucy - fiddle.) / Oxford City / Moorlough shore, The / Blackbird of sweet Avondale (Lucy Farr - fiddle, Reg. Hall - melodeon) / Blackwater side / Pride of Glencoe, The (Michael Plunkett - fiddle.) / I am a poor girl / Moorlough Mary / Lovely banks of Lea, The (Lucy Farr - fiddle.).
LP: 12TS 223

PETA WEBB AND PETE COOPER (Webb, Peta & Pete Cooper).
LP: HR 1

Webb, Roger

GENTLE TOUCH, THE.
Tracks: / Gentle touch / Cavatina / Song for Guy / Just the way you are / Bright eyes / Pavane / Julia / Memory / Best that you can do / Gymnopedie no.1 / Maggie / Yesterday's love.
LP: LBR 007
MC: LBT 007
LP: ABRD 1050

MAGIC OF COLE PORTER/MIDNIGHT MAGIC.
Tracks: / Love for sale / Night and day / In the still of the night / I've got you under my skin / True love / You'd be so nice to come home to / I love Paris / Let's do it / I get a kick out of you / Just one of those things / Begin the beguine / Every time we say goodbye / Fool if you think it's over / Ebony and ivory / Chariots of fire / One day in your life / Hill Street blues / Blue eyes / Evergreen / Misty / Lately / Cavatina / M.A.S.H. / Way we were, The / Just the way you are / Lady / As time goes by / Memory / Arthur's theme / Send in the clowns / Imagine / One day I'll fly away.
2LP: WW 5133/4
MCSET: WW 4 5133/4

PARADISE POSTPONED (TV soundtrack) (See under Paradise Postponed) (Webb, Roger Orchestra (The)).

ROMANTIC PIANO, THE (Webb, Roger Orchestra (The)).
Tracks: / One day in your life / Blue eyes / Evergreen / One day I'll fly away / Lately / Cavatina / Fool if you think it's over / Misty / Ebony and ivory / Chariots of fire / MASH / Way we were, The / Just the way you are / Lady / As time goes by / Memory / Arthur's theme / Send in the clowns / Hill Street blues / Imagine.
LP: WW 2011
MC: WW 20114

Webb, Stan 'Chicken

ROADIES CONCERTO.
Tracks: / Tell me / Why I sing the blues / Back door man / Black night / So far back / End, The - prisoner / Poor boy / Shake your moneymaker / Hideaway.
LP: RCALP 5013
MC: RCAK 5013

SIMPLY LIVE.
LP: 088823

Webber, A.J.

OF THIS LAND.
LP: GUN 002 LP

Webber, Geoffrey

ENGLISH ANTHEM, THE (c. 1900-1930) (see under Magdalen College) (Webber, Geoffrey/Magdalen College Oxford Choir/Paul Brough).

Webcore

WEBCORE.
Tracks: / Elephant / Running for the President / Nothing can stop us now / Flight 23 over Bolivia / Now / Domesday has been cancelled / Telwaz / Feather mask, The / Pocket full of poses, A / My shoes.
LP: FREUD 16

WEBCORE, WEBCORE.
LP: FREUD 22

Weber (composer)

TRUMPET CONCERTOS AND FANFARES (See under Trumpet Music - Classical) (Philharmonia Orchestra).

Weber, Eberhard

COLOURS OF CHLOE, THE.
LP: ECM 1042

FOLLOWING MORNING, THE.
Tracks: / T on a white horse / Moana I / Following morning, The / Moana II.
LP: ECM 1084

LATER THAT EVENING.
LP: ECM 1231

ORCHESTRA SOLO BASS (Weber, Eberhard Orchestra).
LP: ECM 1374

PASSENGERS (See under Burton, Gary) (Weber, Eberhard & G.Burton).

SILENT FEET (Weber, Eberhard Colours).
LP: ECM 1107

WORKS: EBERHARD WEBER.
Tracks: / Sand / Dark spell, A / More colours / Touch / Eyes that can see in the dark / Moana II.
LP: 8254291

YELLOW FIELDS.
Tracks: / Touch / Sand-Glass / Yellow fields / Left lane.
LP: ECM 1066

Weber, Hajo

WINTEREISE (A winter journey) (Weber, Hajo & Ulrich Ingenbold).
LP: ECM 1235

Weber, Janice

WIEN, WEBER UND STRAUSS.
Tracks: / Fantasia on Johann Strauss / Wien, weib nd Gesang / Fruhlingsstimmen / Kunstlerleben / Die fledermaus waltz / O schoner mai.
MC: MCC 12

Webster, Ben

ALUMNI MASTERS, THE (see Gray, Wardell) (Webster, Ben & Wardell Gray).

AT THE NUWAY CLUB.
Tracks: / Dancing on the ceiling / Indiana / Ow / I remember you / Exactly like you / Man I love, The / Ad lib blues.
LP: NOST 7630

AT THE RENAISSANCE.
Tracks: / Georgia on my mind / Caravan / Ole Miss blues / Stardust.
LP: COP 026

ATMOSPHERE FOR LOVERS AND THIEVES.
Tracks: / Blue light / Stardust / What's new? / Autumn leaves / Easy to love / My romance / Yesterdays / Days of wine and roses.
LP: BLP 30105

BALLADS.
2LP: 2683 049

BEAN AND BEN (See Hawkins, Coleman) (Webster, Ben & Coleman Hawkins).

BEN AND SWEETS (Webster, Ben & Harry Sweets Edison).
Tracks: / Better go / How long has this been going on / Kitty / My Romance / Did you call her today / Embraceable you.
LP: 4606131

BEN AT THE NUWAY CLUB (Webster, Ben Quartet).
LP: 1011

BEN WEBSTER.
Tracks: / Round horn / Moonglow / Satin doll / For Max / But not for me / For all we know / Sunday.
LP: AG6 24058
LP: BLP 60141

BEN WEBSTER (2).
Tracks: / Perdido / Yesterday / I'm gonna sit right down / Set call / That's all / Gone with the wind / Over the rainbow / Indiana / Misty.
LP: BLP 60125

BEN WEBSTER AND ASSOCIATES.
LP: 2304 221

BEN WEBSTER AND FRIENDS.
LP: 2332 086

BEN WEBSTER AND JIMMY WITHERSPOON (See under Witherspoon, Jimmy for details) (Webster, Ben & Jimmy Witherspoon).

BEN WEBSTER AND JOE ZAWINUL (Webster, Ben & Joe Zawinul).
Tracks: / Travellin' light / Like someone in love / Too late now / Come Sunday / Frog legs / Soulmate / Governor / Evol deklaw ni / Where are you now / In a mellow tone / I surrender dear / Crazy rhythm.
2LP: M 47056

BEN WEBSTER & COLEMAN HAWKINS Compact/Walkman jazz (see under Webster,Ben) (Webster, Ben & Coleman Hawkins).

BEN WEBSTER IN EUROPE VOL.2.
Tracks: / Ben's bounce / Sunday / I got it bad and that ain't good / Cottontail / For all we know / That's all / You'd be so nice to come home to / I got rhythm.
LP: . . . . **RARITIES 55**

BEN WEBSTER MEETS OSCAR PETERSON.
Tracks: / Touch of your lips / When your lover has gone / Bye bye blackbird / How deep is the ocean / In the wee small hours of the morning / Sunday / This can't be love.
LP: **2304 455**
LP: . . . . **VRV 1**

BEN WEBSTER PLAYS DUKE ELLINGTON.
LP: . . . . **SLP 4133**

BEN WEBSTER (SMALL GROUPS).
LP: . . . . **JA 35**

BLUE LIGHT.
Tracks: / Autumn leaves / Blue light / Stardust / What's new / Easy to love / My romance / Yesterdays / Days of wine and roses.
LP: **2340 004**

COLEMAN HAWKINS AND BEN WEBSTER (see Hawkins, Coleman) (Hawkins, Coleman & Ben Webster).

DAYS OF WINE AND ROSES.
LP: **2273512**
MC: **2173512**

DID YOU CALL.
LP: . . . . **N 8**

DUKE'S IN BED.
Tracks: / What's I'm gotchere / Close your eyes / There is no greater love / Brother John's blues / Stompy Jones / Nancy with the laughing face / I got it bad and that ain't good / Duke's in bed.
LP: . . . . **BLP 30137**

FOR THE GUV'NOR.
Tracks: / I got it bad and that ain't good / Drop me off in Harlem / One for the guv'nor / Prelude to a kiss / In a sentimental mood / John Brown's body / Work song / Preacher, The / Straight no chaser / Rockin' in rhythm.
2LP: . . . . **AFFD 40**

GERRY MULLIGAN MEETS BEN WEBSTER (See under Mulligan, Jerry) (Webster, Ben & Gerry Mulligan).

HE PLAYED IT THAT WAY.
LP: . . . . **IAJRC 30**

HORN 1944, THE (Webster, Ben and His Orchestra).
LP: . . . . **CLP 41**

HORN AND HIS ORCHESTRA, THE.
LP: . . . . **CLP 42**

KING OF THE TENORS.
Tracks: / Tenderly / Jive at six / Don't get around much any more / That's all / Bounce blues / Pennies from Heaven / Cottontail / Danny boy.
LP: **837 431 1**

LIVE AT PIO'S.
LP: . . . . **ENJA 2038**

LIVE IN AMSTERDAM.
Tracks: / Johnny come lately / Indiana / Blues in F / Perdido / Sunday / Come Sunday / How long has this been going on? / Old folks / For all we know.
LP: . . . . **AFF 202**
MC: . . . . **TCAFF 202**

LIVE IN PARIS, 1972.
LP: . . . . **FC 131**

MAKIN WHOOPEE (Webster, Ben Quartet).
Tracks: / Prelude to a kiss / Johnny come lately / Autumn leaves / I want a little girl / Makin' whoopee / You better go now / Ash's cap / Hal's blues.
LP: . . . . **SPJ LP 9**

MASTERS OF JAZZ VOL 5.
LP: . . . . **SLP 4105**

MIDNIGHT AT THE MONTMARTRE.
Tracks: / Friskin' the frog / Stormy weather / Teach me tonight / Perdido / Yesterdays / I'm gonna sit right down and write myself a letter / Set call.
LP: . . . . **BLP 30173**

MPS JAZZ TIME VOL..9.
Tracks: / Blues for Dottie Mae / Lullaby to Dottie Mae / Sundae / Perdido / When Ash meets Henry / Caravan.
LP: **5C 064 60412**

NO FOOL, NO FUN.
Tracks: / Did you call her today / Cottontail / Old folks / Please don't talk about me when I'm gone / Impromptu / Song is ended, The / Baby, it's cold outside.
LP: . . . . **SPJ 142**

ONE O'CLOCK JUMP 1953 (see under Brown,Ray) (Webster, Ben/Brown, Ray).

PLAYS BALLADS.
LP: . . . . **SLP 4118**

SATURDAY NIGHT AT THE MONTMARTRE.
Tracks: / Our love is here to stay / My romance / Blues for Herluf / Londonderry air / Mck the knife / I can't get started / Theme.
LP: . . . . **BLP 30155**

SCANDINAVIAN DAYS.
LP: . . . . **RARITIES 45**

SEE YOU AT THE FAIR.
Tracks: / See you at the fair / Over the rainbow / Our love is here to stay / In a mellow tone.
LP: . . . . **JAS 33**
MC: . . . . **JAS C33**

SOULMATES.
LP: . . . . **OJC 109**

SOULVILLE.
LP: **2304 314**

STORMY WEATHER.
LP: . . . . **BLP 60108**

SUNDAY MORNING AT THE MONTMARTRE.
Tracks: / Sunday / That's all / Gone with the wind / Over the rainbow / Indiana / Misty / Set call.
LP: . . . . **BLP 30182**

TATUM GROUP MASTERPIECES (SEPTEMBER 1956) (see under Tatum, Art) (Webster, Ben/ Art Tatum).

TWO KINGS OF THE TENOR SAX 44-45 (See under Byas, Don) (Webster, Ben/Don Byas).

WARM MOODS, THE (Webster, Ben With Strings).
Tracks: / Stella by starlight / But beautiful / There's no you / I'm beginning to see the light / Time after time / Nancy.
LP: . . . . **DS 818**
MC: . . . . **DSC 818**

WEBSTER'S DICTIONARY.
Tracks: / Love is here to stay / Where are you / Willow weep for me / For all we know / That's all / Someone to watch over me / Shadow of your smile / Come Sunday / For heaven's sake / Old folks.
LP: . . . . **N 112**

Webster, E.T.

MUSICAL EXPLOSION.
LP: . . . . **WB 28**

Webster, John

DUCHESS OF MALFI, THE (Various artists).
MCSET: **0334**

Webster, Katie

CLOSE TO MY HEART.
Tracks: / Baby baby / Sunny side of love / I feel so low / Close to my heart / Hey Mr. Love / Cry cry darlin' / God is so wonderful / Sea of love / Your cheatin' heart / I keep a-calling you / Goodbye baby / Sunny side of love / Lonely for you / If I ask you.
LP: . . . . **FLY 613**

MANY FACES OF KATIE WEBSTER, THE.
LP: . . . . **SCH 103**

POUNDS OF BLUES.
Tracks: / Going crazy about you / Things that I used to do / Pounds of blues / Half of everything / Katie's blues / Little one / Worry my life no more / Never too old / What in the world have I done wrong / Dilly wally, dilly woe / Trouble blues / My baby's got bad feet.
LP: . . . . **CRB 1087**

SWAMP BOOGIE QUEEN.
LP: . . . . **AL 4766**

TWO FISTED MAMA.
LP: . . . . **AL 4777**

YOU KNOW THAT'S RIGHT (Webster, Katie (with Hot Links)).
LP: . . . . **ARHOOLIE 1094**
MC: . . . . **C 1094**

Webster, Max

MAGNETIC AIR (Webster, Max Band).
Tracks: / Paradise skies / Night fights / Lip service / Charmonium / Waterline / High class in borrowed shoes / Diamonds, diamonds / Gravity / Coming off the moon / Hangover.
LP: . . . . **EST 25392**
MC: . . . . **TC EST 25392**

MILLION VACATIONS.
Tracks: / Paradise skies / Night flights / Charmonium / Sun voices / Moon voices / Million vacations / Lookout / Let go the line / Rascal Houdi / Research.
LP: . . . . **EST 11937**

MUTINY UP MY SLEEVE.
LP: . . . . **EST 11776**

UNIVERSAL JUVENILES.
Tracks: / In the world of giants / Check / Battle scar / April in Toledo / Juveniles don't stop / Chalkers / Drive and desire / What do you do with the urge / Blue river liquor shine / Cry out for your life.
LP: **633 714 4**

Webster, Tom

TOM WEBSTER AND THE LOMOND CORNKISTERS (Webster, Tom & The Lomond Cornkisters).
MC: . . . . **CWGRTV 7**

Wechselberger, Petra

FROLICH RUNDE (Und die Krimmler Saitenmusi).
LP: . . . . **ISST 189**

Wechter, Julius

NATURALLY (Wechter, Julius & The Baja Marimba Band).
Tracks: / Morning train / Alone again naturally / El abondonado / Deep throat, Theme from / Alley cat / Shout / Elegant rag, The / Las flores / Spanish flea / Fowl play / Coney Island / Up Cherry Street.
LP: . . . . **PRCV 127**

Weckl, Dave

LAYIN BACK WITH BEN.
LP: . . . . **HD 6606**

MASTER PLAN.
Tracks: / Tower of inspiration / Here and there / Festival de Ritmo / In common / Garden wall / Auratune / Softly, as in a morning sunrise / Master plan / Island magic.
LP: . . . . **GRP 96191**
MC: . . . . **GRP 96194**

Wedding Anniversary

WEDDING ANNIVERSARY, THE.
LP: . . . . **DANLP 010**
MC: . . . . **DANC 010**

Wedding Present

BIZARRO.
Tracks: / Brassneck / Crushed / No / Thanks / Kennedy / What have I said now / Granadaland / Bewitched / Take me / Be honest.
LP: . . . . **PL 74302**
MC: . . . . **PK 74302**

GEORGE BEST.
Tracks: / Everyone thinks he looks daft / What did your last servant die of / Don't be so hard / Million miles, A / All this and more / My favourite dress / Something and nothing / It's what you want that matters / Give my love to Kevin / Anyone can make a mistake / You can't moan can you.
LP: . . . . **LEEDS 001**
MC: . . . . **LEEDS 001C**

SEAMONSTERS.
Tracks: / Dalliance / Dare / Suck / Blonde / Rotterdam / Lovenest / Corduroy / Carolyn / Heather / Octopussy.
LP: . . . . **PL 75012**
MC: . . . . **PK 75012**

TOMMY.
Tracks: / Go out and get 'em boy / Everything's spoiled again / Once more / At the edge of the sea / Living and learning / This boy can wait / You should always keep in touch with your friend / Felicity / What becomes of the broken hearted? / Never said / Every mothers son / My favourite dress.
LP: . . . . **LEEDS 002**
MC: . . . . **LEEDS 002C**
LP: . . . . **CHIME 0037 M**

UKRAINSKI VISTUPI V JOHNA PEELA.
Tracks: / Davni chasy / Yikhav khozak za dunai / Tiutiunyk / Zadumay didochok / Svitit misyats / Katrusya / Vasya vasyl'ok / Hude dnipro hude / Verhovyno.
LP: . . . . **REC 010**
MC: . . . . **REC 010C**
LP: . . . . **PL 74104**
MC: . . . . **PK 74104**

Weddings, Parties...

NO SHOW WITHOUT PUNCH (Weddings, Parties & Anything).
LP: . . . . **UTIL 004**

ROARING DAYS (Weddings, Parties & Anything).
Tracks: / Industrial town / Under the clocks / Gun / Brunswick / Tilting at windmills / Sergeant Small / Sisters of mercy / Roaring days / Say the word / Missing in action / Laughing boy / Big river / Summons in the morning, A / Morton (Song for Tex).
LP: . . . . **COOK 026**
MC: . . . . **COOKC 026**

Wedlock, Fred

FOLKER,THE.
Tracks: / Folker, The / British bobby / Moreton bay / Thee's got'n where thee cassn't back'n hassn't / Spencer the rover / Skinheads / Bristol buses / Bruton town / Lurn theeself fawk.
LP: . . . . **VTS 7**

FRED WEDLOCK LIVE.
Tracks: / Let's walk round the harbour again / Old Somerset weather poem / Filton first air fellowship / Folk alphabet / Giving up giving up / Kung fu woman / Vet / Village production of Hamlet / Hereford scrotum / Sheep at half the price / Just kidding.
LP: . . . . **TRAIN 19**

FROLLICKS.
Tracks: / Vicar & the frog / Robin Hood / Handier household help / Salvation army lassie / Examinations rag / Oh sha la la / Vatican rag / Robin head / Wild rover / Lovely like me / Superman / Talking folk club blues.
LP: . . . . **VTS 20**

OLDEST SWINGER IN TOWN.
Tracks: / Oldest swinger in town / Do it yourself / Vicar & the frog / Examinations rag / Lady recruit / Punk one / American trilogy / Jogger's song / Ballad of the Clevedon kid / Union psalm / Nuages / I got rhythm / Widow & the fairy / Hippies and the hairies.
LP: . . . . **TRAIN 13**

THIS IS (OUT OF WEDLOCK).
Tracks: / I couldn't spell **** / English urban garden / Gnome, The / Three drunken nights / Riddle song / Threshing machine / Clevedon cowboy / Plumber / Great fish finger disaster, The / Early one evening / Intercity / British railway pies / 10 inch steel / Mini-Cooper.
LP: . . . . **THIS 32**

Wednesday Week

WHAT WE HAD.
LP: **3215 1**

Wee MacGreegor (bk)

WEE MACGREEGOR (J.S. Bell) (Copeland, James (nar)).
MCSET: . . . . **COL 2013**

Wee Papa Girl Rappers

BE AWARE.
Tracks: / Power and the glory, The / Best of my love / Westside / Bump, The / Hardcore (here's the plan) / Group of MC's, A / Get in the groove / We got the roots / Be aware / Funky stuff / On a roll / Jealous people.
LP: . . . . **HIP 103**
MC: . . . . **HIPC 103**

BEAT, THE RHYME, THE REASON, THE.
Tracks: / Beat, the rhyme, the noise, The / We need you / Soulmate / Faith / Blow house down.
LP: . . . . **HIP 67**
MC: . . . . **HIPC 67**

WEE PAPA GIRL RAPPERS: INTERVIEW PICTURE DISC.
LPPD: . . . . **BAK 2123**

Weed, Buddy

FEBRUARY 4TH AND 6TH, 1958 (Weed, Buddy Septet).
Tracks: / Five o'clock rush / I'm gonna flag that train / Mr. Imagination / Honky-tonk mama / Blue boy / Rajah's spree / Sweet reminiscence / Jackpot rag / Brazilian serenade / Minor swing.
LP: . . . . **JV 115**

Weedon, Bert

16 COUNTRY GUITAR GREATS.
LP: **2384 102**

20 GOLDEN GUITAR GREATS.
LP: . . . . **WW 5019**

40 GUITAR GREATS.
Tracks: / Guitar boogie shuffle / Apache / Bert's boogie / If / Tomorrow / Summer knows / Vincent / Fascination / Love is / Help me make it through the night / Love story / Romance / Didn't we / Song for Anna / Killing me softly with her song.
2LP: . . . . **PLD 8012**
MCSET: . . . . **PLDC 8012**

BERT WEEDON & HIS DANCING GUITARS.
Tracks: / Yesterday / Sailing / Dancing guitars / Spanish eyes / Moon river / Soap / Once in a while.
LP: . . . . **DS 053**

BEST OF THE EMI YEARS: BERT WEEDON.
Tracks: / Jolly gigolo / Pretty baby / Rippling tango / Guitar boogie shuffle / Twelfth Street rag / Nashville boogie / Apache / Sorry Robbie / Ginchy / Ghost train / Red guitar / Poinciana / Twist a Napoli / South of the border / Charlie boy / Can't help falling in love / Dark eyes / It

happened in Monterey / Stranger than fiction / McGregor's leap.
MC: . . . . TCEMS 1411

BLUE ECHOES.
LP: 2384 095

ENCORE.
Tracks: / First man you remember, The / I dreamed a dream / Bali Ha'i / Losing my mind / Can't help lovin' dat man / 42nd street / True love / Song on the sand / I've grown accustomed to her face / True love ways / Last night of the world, The / Bewitched / I won't send roses / Anything goes / Heather on the hill / What I did for love / How to handle a woman / All I ask of you.
MC: . . . . PWKMC 4025

GUITAR FAVOURITES.
MCSET: . . . . DTO 10072

GUITAR GOLD - 20 GREATEST HITS.
LP: . . . . PLE 7011
MC: . . . . PLC 7011

HEART STRINGS.
Tracks: / Love letters / Way we were / Do that to me one more time / Treasures / Les bicyclettes de Belsize / Bright eyes / Plasir d'amour / Annie's song / Just the way you are / New World theme.
LP: . . . . ACLP 002

HONKY TONK GUITAR PARTY.
LP: . . . . SRS 5198
MC: . . . . TC SRS 5198

HOUR OF BERT WEEDON, AN.
Tracks: / China boogie / Flannel foot / Guitar boogie shuffle / Bert's boogie / Blue guitar / Stardust / Nashville boogie / King size guitar / Big beat boogie / Summer place, A (theme from) / Twelfth St. rag / Apache / Lonely guitar / Sorry Robbie / Easy beat / Ginchy / Mr. Guitar / Ghost train / China doll / Night cry / Lonely nights / Gin mill guitar / Tokyo melody / Limelight / Twelve-string shuffle / High steppin' / Malaguena.
MC: . . . . HR 8151

KING SIZE GUITAR.
LP: . . . . BUY 026

LOVE LETTERS.
Tracks: / Love letters / Way we were / Do that to me one more time / Treasures / Les bicyclettes de Belsize / Bright eyes / Plasir d'amour / Annie's song / Just the way you are / New world theme / Kisses in spring / Heart strings.
LP: . . . . CBR 1015
MC: . . . . KCBR 1015

MR GUITAR.
Tracks: / China boogie / Boy with the magic guitar / Flannel foot / Soho fair / Red guitar / South of the border / Night cry / It happened in Monterey / Lonely night / Gin Mill guitar / Can't help falling in love / Tokyo melody / High steppin' / Malaguena.
2LP: . . . . DL 41 10521
MC: . . . . TCDL 41 1052

ONCE MORE WITH FEELING (16 Great love songs).
Tracks: / Love letters / Three times a lady / Music of the night / Always on my mind / I just called to say I love you.
MC: . . . . HSC 3249

Weeds (film)

WEEDS (Original soundtrack) (Various artists).
LP: . . . . STV 81350
MC: . . . . CTV 81350

Weekend

LA VARIETE.
LP: . . . . ROUGH 39

LIVE AT RONNIE SCOTT'S.
Tracks: / Where flamingo fly / Winter moon / Nostalgia / Weekend off / Day in the life, A.
MLP: . . . . RTM 139

Weekend In Havana

WEEKEND IN HAVANA/THAT NIGHT IN RIO (Original soundtracks) (Various artists).
LP: . . . . CC 100-14

Weekers, Peter

RHAPSODIES.
MC: . . . . PK 74752

Weeks, Anson

ANSON WEEKS, 1932.
Tracks: / Let's fly away / You do something to me / I can't give you anything but love / With a song in my heart / Who's your little who's zis / Dancing on the ceiling / You're my everything / When it's sleepy time down South / Was that the human thing to do / Fine and dandy / You're blase / Rain, rain, go away / Say it isn't so / Sweet and lowdown / I guess I'll have to change my plans / Georgia on my mind / On the Alamo / My ideal / I'll get by / Egyptian shimmy.
LP: . . . . HSR 146

ANSON WEEKS & HIS ORCHESTRA, 1932.
Tracks: / Let's fly away / You do something to me / I can't give you anything but love / With a song in my heart / Who's your little whozis / Dancing on the ceiling / You're my everything / When it's sleepy time down South / Was that the human thing to do / Fine and dandy / You're blase / Rain rain go away / Say it isn't so / Sweet and low down / I guess I'll have to change my plan / Georgia on my mind / On the Alamo / My ideal / I'll get by / Egyptian shimmy.
LP: . . . . HMA 5070

Weems, Ted

HEARTACHES 1933 - 51 (Weems, Ted & His Orchestra).
LP: . . . . BS 7141
MC: . . . . BS 7141C

MARVELLOUS (Weems, Ted & His Orchestra).
Tracks: / Marvellous / Oh, if I only had you / From Saturday night to Sunday morning / She'll never find a fellow like me / Chick, chick, chick, chick, chicken / Cobblestones / You're the cream in my coffee / My troubles are over / Piccolo Pete / Man from the south / Come on baby / Harmonica Harry / Mysterious Mose / Slappin' the bass / Washing dishes with my sweetie / Egyptian Ella / Jig time / Play that hot guitar / Oh Mo'nah / My favourite band.
LP: . . . . AJA 5029
MC: . . . . ZC AJA 5029

TED WEEMS BAND 1940/1 BEAT THE BAND SHOWS.
LP: . . . . FANFARE 31 131

Ween

GOD WEEN SATAN.
LP: . . . . TTR 891861
MC: . . . . TTR 891864

Weersma, Melle

SWING FROM NETHERLANDS (Weersma, Melle/Red Debroy).
LP: . . . . H 2009

Wehrmacht

BIERMACHT.
Tracks: / You broke my heart / Gore fix / Beer is here, The / Drink beer be free / Everb / Micro E / Balance of opinion / Suck / Drink Jack / Radical dissection / Beermacht / Outro.
LP: . . . . SHARK 009

SHARK ATTACK.
LP: . . . . NRR 23
LP: . . . . SHARK 2

Weider, John

INTERVALS IN SUNLIGHT.
Tracks: / Intervals in sunlight / Ravenscourt / Galopp / Solitude / Echo in angel city / Lines and shadows / Prelude / Poca favilla / Adagio / Different you, A.
LP: . . . . VGC 3
MC: . . . . TCVGC 3

JOHN WEIDER.
Tracks: / Promises / Distance / Don't give up on me / Say do / Prelude 2 / Ambush Alice / What you want / I found love / Never give up on love / Poor boy.
LP: . . . . ANCL 2018

Weight Loss

WEIGHT LOSS (see under 'Sutphen, Dick') (Sutphen, Dick).

Weil, Cynthia

SONGWRITERS FOR THE STARS 2 (see Foster, David) (Weil, Cynthia/David Foster/Barry Mann).

Weill, Kurt

GOOD VIBES FOR KURT WEILL (See under Chiasson, Warren).

Weiner, Lawrence

DEUTSCHE ANGST (see Gordon, Peter) (Weiner, Lawrence & Peter Gordon).

Weiner

SWAN LAKE (VIDEO) (see under Tchaikovsky (composer)).

Weins, Edith

SYMPHONY NO.2 (MENDELSSOHN) (see under Mendelssohn (Composer)) (Weins, Edith/Leipzig Gewandhaus Orch/Leipzig Radio Chorus/).

Weir, Bob

ACE.
Tracks: / Greatest story ever told / Walk in the sunshine / Looks like rain / One more saturday night / Black throated wind / Playing in the band / Mexicali blues / Cassidy.
LP: . . . . GDV 4004
MC: . . . . GDTC 4004

KINGFISH.
Tracks: / Lazy lightnin' / Supplication / Wild northland / Asia minor / Home to Dixie / Jump for joy / Goodbye yer honer / Big iron / This time / Hypnotize / Bye and bye.
LP: . . . . GDV 4012
MC: . . . . GDTC 4012

Weird Science

WEIRD SCIENCE (Film soundtrack) (Various artists).
LP: . . . . MCF 3295
MC: . . . . MCFC 3295

Weirdstone of...

WEIRDSTONE OF BRISINGAMEN (Layton, George).
MC: . . . . P 90005

Weisberg, Steve

I CAN'T STAND ANOTHER NIGHT ALONE (IN BED WITH YOU).
Tracks: / Table for one / Walking home alone / Waking up alone / Trapped in true love / You can't have anything.
LP: . . . . XW 01

Weisberg, Tim

HIGH RISK.
LP: . . . . YL 0101

OUTRAGEUS TEMPTATIONS.
LP: . . . . YL 0123

Weiss, Harold

DRUM WHISPERS.
LP: . . . . ECM 1249

TROMMELGEFLUSTER.
Tracks: / Trommelgefluster (1) / Trommelgefluster (2).
LP: . . . . ECM 1249

Weiss, Klaus

KLAUS WEISS.
LP: . . . . CAL 30 623

Weiss, Michael

MICHAEL WEISS QUINTET FEATURING... (Tom Kirkpatrick/R. Lalama/R. Drummond).
LP: . . . . CRISS 1022

Weissberg, Eric

DELIVERANCE (1972 film soundtrack) (Weissberg, Eric/Steve Mandell).
Tracks: / Duelling banjos / Little Maggie / Shuckin' the corn / Pony Express / Old Joe Clark / Eight more miles to Louisville / Farewell blues / Earl's breakdown / End of a dream / Buffalo gals / Reuben's train / Riding the waves / Fire on the mountain / Eighth of January / Bugle call rag / Hard ain't it hard / Mountain dew / Rawhide.
LP: . . . . K 46214
MC: K4 46214

Weisser, Michael

BEAM SCAPE (See under Mergener, Peter) (Weisser, Michael & Peter Mergener).

Welch, Bob

BOB WELCH.
Tracks: / Two to do / Remember / Bend me shape me / That's what we said / If you think you know how to love me / It's what ya don't say / You can't do that / Secrets / Imaginary fool / To my heart again / Drive.
LP: . . . . RCALP 6019
MC: . . . . RCAK 6019

COLLECTION: BOB WELCH.
LP: . . . . IC 038 85266

FRENCH KISS.
LP: . . . . EST 11663

OTHER ONE.
Tracks: / Rebel rouser / Love came 2X / Watch the animals / Straight up / Hideaway / Future games / Oneonone / Don't let me fall / Spanish dancers / Old man of 17.
LP: . . . . EST 12017

THREE HEARTS.
Tracks: / Three hearts / Oh Jenny / I saw her standing there / Here comes the night / China / Ghost of flight 401 / Precious love / Church / Come softly to me / Devil wind / Don't wait too long / Little star.
LP: . . . . EAST 11907

Welch, Ed

ED WELSH ORCHESTRA PLAYS POPULAR CLASSICS (Welch, Ed & His Orchestra).
Tracks: / Piano concerto no. 1 in B flat minor / Concierto de Aranjuez / Guitar concerto / Liebestraum / Sheep may safely graze / Symphony 'The New World' / Rondo Alla Turca / Cradle song / Swan, The / Peter and the wolf / Greensleeves / Silent night.
LP: . . . . SLS 50427

IF YOU TAKE THE TIME (see Carter,Diane) (Welch, Ed & Diane Carter).

MOONSHOT.
Tracks: / Dawn at Cape Kennedy / Blast off / In orbit / T.L.I. / Behind the moon / Eagle has wings / Lunar descent / Sea of tranquility / One giant step / Moon rock / White House to the moon / Lunar blast off / Splashdown / President Kennedy remembered.
LP: . . . . UAK 30248

SPIKE MILLIGAN & ED WELCH SING SONGS FROM Q8.
Tracks: / Q8 theme / Woe is me / Love to make music by / Baboon / I don't have a song about Jesus / Living again / Taken you for granted / One sunny day / Lady / I couldn't wait to tell you / Carpet's always greener / I've got that photograph.
LP: . . . . UAG 30223

Welch, Elisabeth

ELISABETH WELCH LIVE IN NEW YORK.
MC: . . . . ZCVIR 8313

ELISABETH WELCH SINGS IRVING BERLIN SONGBOOK.
LP: . . . . VIR 8305
MC: . . . . ZCVIR 8305

ELISABETH WELCH SINGS JEROME KERN SONGBOOK.
LP: . . . . VIR 8310
MC: . . . . ZCVIR 8310

ELIZABETH WELCH IN CONCERT.
LP: . . . . SCENE 4
MC: . . . . SCENEC 4

MISS ELISABETH WELCH (1933-1940).
Tracks: / Solomon / Soft lights and sweet music medley / Far away in a shanty town / Girl I knew / Man I love, The / It still suits me / Sleepy river / Harlem in my heart / One kiss / Much more lovely / And so do I / These foolish things / Nightingale sang in Berkeley Square / Nearness of you.
LP: . . . . SH 328

THIS THING CALLED LOVE.
Tracks: / What is this thing called love / Hello my lover goodbye / Porgy / When your lover has gone / Yesterday / Boy what love has done to me / If I ever fall in love again / Long before I knew you / I love you truly / True love / How do you do it / I'll follow my secret heart / Losing my mind / One life to live / Moon river / Give me something to remember you by.
LP: . . . . VIR 8309
MC: . . . . ZCVIR 8309

WHERE HAVE YOU BEEN.
Tracks: / It was worth it / I got it bad and that ain't good / My love is a wanderer / I always say hello (to a flower) / How littlw we know / Where have you been / Manhattan madness / He was too good to me / Little girl blue / You were there / Dancing in the dark / Mean to me / As long as I live / Come rain or come shine / Remember.
LP: . . . . SL 5202
MC: . . . . SLC 5202

Welch, Jay

DO YOU HEAR WHAT I HEAR (Welch, Jay Chorale & Utah Symphony Orchestra).
Tracks: / Do you hear what I hear / White Christmas / Twelve days of Christmas / We three kings of Orient are / First Noel.
LP: . . . . VCDM 1000: 70

Welcome Home...

WELCOME HOME ROXY CARMICHAEL (See under Newman, Thomas) (Newman, Thomas).

Welcome To L.A.

WELCOME TO L.A. (Original Soundtrack) (Various artists).
LP: . . . . MCA 25040
MC: . . . . MCAC 25040

Welcome To The Club

WELCOME TO THE CLUB (Various artists).
LP: . . . . JSLP 1001

Weldon, Casey Bill

1935-37.
LP: . . . . DLP 565
LP: . . . . OT 1206

KOKOMO ARNOLD AND CASEY BILL WELDON (see under Arnold, Kokoma) (Weldon, Casey Bill & Kokoma, Arnold).

Weldon, Fay

WATCHING YOU, WATCHING ME.
MCSET: 060055972X

Weldon, Liam

DARK HORSE ON THE WIND.
LP: . . . . LUN 006

We'll Meet Again (tv)

WE'LL MEET AGAIN (See under King, Denis) (King, Denis).

Well Red

MOTION.
Tracks: / Yes we can / Love gone crazy (LP only) / Come back / System / Get lucky / Mixed up / Turn me on / Honey (12" version) / Saturday (garage mix) (CD only) / Limit of your loving (12" version) (CD only) / Let me out (CD only) / Love gone crazy (12" version) (CD & MC only) / Saturday (MC only).
LP: V 2418
MC: TCV 2418
LP: OVED 264
MC: OVEDC 264

RESPECT DUE.
Tracks: / Rocketship of love / Baby / Use me / Keep those wheels turning / Jungle life / More (CD & MC only) / Minute of your time / Hard / Sugar Kane / M.F.S.B. / Love gone crazy (CD & MC only).
LP: V 2548
MC: TCV 2548

Well Up...And Bubble

WELL UP...AND BUBBLE (Various artists).
LP: BALANCE 2

Well Well Well

DANGEROUS DREAMS.
Tracks: / Revolution / Back To You / Murderous people / Someone you need / One in a million / Dangerous dreams / Possession / Empty eyes / I will / Freedom.
LP: 208966
MC: 408966
LP: 209014
MC: 409014

Weller, Don

COMMIT NO NUISANCE (Weller, Don Spring Quartet).
LP: AFF 44

DON WELLER.
LP: AFF 43

Weller, Freddy

BACK ON THE STREET.
Tracks: / Midnight driver / Right in the prime of her love / Shootin' from the heart / Trying to get around to 'em all / If you knew how much I wanted you / Back on the street / Time machine / Intensive care / You believed in a dreamer / Midlife crisis / One dream at a time / Atlanta.
LP: BDL 3003

Welling, George

WURLITZER STARS VOL. 2 (Welling, George/Jackie Brown).
Tracks: / March of the Bowmen / Song of Alassio / Spread a little happiness / Birth of the blues / Let's do it / Man I love, (The) / 'S wonderful / What a wonderful world / From this moment on / Mer, (La) / As long as he needs me / Party's over, (The) / March of the organs.
MC: AC 177

Wellington Citadel...

MARCHES.
Tracks: / Red shield / Youthful warriors / Jamaica citadel / Tremont / Southern Australia / Rousseau / Wellingtonian / Liberator / On the king's highway / Indomitable / Christmas joy / St. Ethelwald.
LP: XPS 5072
MC: CXP 55072

Wellington, Sheena

KERELAW.
Tracks: / Derwentwaters's farewell / Newport braes / Death of Queen Jane, The / Irish boy, The / Last Leviathian, The / Bunch of Thyme / Nicky tams / Aileen Aroon / Eh'll bide a wiver o / Sheath and knife.
MC: DUNC 005
LP: DUN 005

Wellington, Valerie

MILLION DOLLAR SECRET.
LP: R 2619

Wellins, Bobby

BIRDS OF BRAZIL.
LP: BW 11

PRIMROSE PATH (See under Knepper, Jimmy) (Wellins, Bobby & Jimmy Knepper).

Wells, Brandi

WATCH OUT.
Tracks: / Watch out.
LP: V 2224
MC: TCV 2224

Wells Cathedral Choir

CHRISTMAS CAROLS (Beautiful music v8).
Tracks: / Once in Royal David's city / There is no rose / Holly and the ivy, The / Good King Wenceslas / Coventry carol / God rest ye merry gentlemen / Hark the herald angels sing / Great and mighty wonder, A / Ding dong merrily on high / Babe is born, A / First Noel, The.
LP: ABM 757
MC: ZC ABM 757

WELLS CATHEDRAL CHOIR & SCHOOL CHAMBER ORCHESTRA (Wells Cathedral Choir & School Chamber Orchestra).
LP: APS 329
MC: CAPS 329

Wells, Dicky

BONES FOR THE KING.
Tracks: / Bones for the king (Dedicated to the late Tommy Dorsey.) / Sweet daddy spo-de-o / You took my heart / Hello, smack (Dedicated to the late Fletcher Henderson) / Come and get it / Stan's dance.
LP: AFF 164

LONESOME ROAD.
LP: UP 27 07

TROMBONE FOUR IN HAND.
Tracks: / Blue moon / Airlift / It's all over now / Wine O junction / Heavy duty / Short, tall, fat and small / Girl hunt.
LP: AFF 168

Wells, H.G. (author)

HISTORY OF MR. POLLY, THE (Jeffrey, Peter (nar)).
MCSET: 418 159-4
MCSET: ARGO 1085

MAGIC SHOP AND THE RED ROOM, THE (Bartlett, Peter).
MC: TS 352

MAN WHO COULD WORK MIRACLES, THE.
MC: TS 357

TIME MACHINE, THE (Hardy, Robert (nar)).
MC: TC LFP 7044

TIME MACHINE, THE (Mason, James (nar)).
MC: 1678

WAR OF THE WORLDS (Hardy, Robert (nar)).
MCSET: LFP 7502

Wells, Junior

BLUES HIT BIG TOWN.
LP: DL 640

CHIEFLY WELLS (Wells, Junior/Magic Sam).
Tracks: / Two headed woman / Cha cha cha in blues / Lovey dovey lovey one / I'm a stranger / Things i'd do for you / I need me a car / I'll get you too / One day / Calling all blues / Love me / Galloping horses a lazy mule / Magic sam, you don't have to work / Mr. Charlie / My love is your love / She belongs to me / Shakey jake:respect me baby / Hard road.
LP: FLY 605

DRINKIN' TNT 'N' SMOKIN' DYNAMITE (see Guy, Buddy) (Wells, Junior & Buddy Guy).

HOODOO MAN BLUES.
LP: DL 612

IN MY YOUNGER DAYS.
LP: RL 007

IT'S MY LIFE BABY.
Tracks: / It's my life baby / Country girl / Stormy Monday blues / Checking on my baby / I got a stomach ache / Slow, slow / It's so sad to be lonely / You lied to me / Shake it baby / Early in the morning / Look how baby / Everything's going to be alright.
LP: VMLP 5311
MC: VMTC 6311

MESSIN' WITH THE BLUES (VIDEO) (See under Waters, Muddy) (Waters, Muddy, Buddy Guy & Junior Wells).

MESSIN' WITH THE KID.
Tracks: / Messin' with the kid / I'm a stranger / Come on in this house / Little by little / Cha cha cha in blues / Prison bars all round me / Love me / It hurts me too / Things I'd do for you / I could cry / So tired / Lovey dovey lovely one / I need me a car / You sure look good to me / You don't care / Two headed woman.
LP: CRB 1133

ON TAP.
LP: DS 635
LP: DL 635

ORIGINAL BLUES BROTHERS - LIVE (see Guy, Buddy).

SOUTHSIDE BLUES JAM.
LP: DS 628
LP: DL 628

UNIVERSAL ROCK.
LP: FLY 588

Wells, Kitty

COUNTRY HIT PARADE.
LP: HAT 3037
MC: HATC 3037

COUNTRY MUSIC HALL OF FAME.
LP: CDL 8504

GOLDEN YEARS 1949-57, THE.
Tracks: / Death at the bar / Love or hate / Gathering flowers for the master's bouquet / Don't wait until the last minute to pray / How far is heaven / My mother / Make up your mind / I'll be all smiles tonight / It wasn't God who made honky tonk angels / I don't want your money, I want your time / Searching for a soldier's grave / I'm too lonely to smile / Things I might have been, The / I heard the jukebox playing / Wedding ring ago, A / Divided by two / Crying steel guitar waltz / Paying for that back street affair / Icicles hanging from your heart / I don't claim to be an angel / Honky tonk waltz / Life they live in songs, The / You said you could do without me / Whose shoulder will you cry on / Hey Joe / My cold cold heart is melted now / I'll love you til the day I die / I've kissed you my last time / You're not easy to forget / Satisfied, so satisfied / One by one / I'm a stranger in my home / I gave my wedding dress away / Cheatin's a sin / Release me / After dark / (Don't hang around) he's married to me / Thou shalt not steal / Lonely side of town / I hope my divorce is never granted / I'm in love with you / As long as you live / No one but you / Make believe / I'd rather stay home / I was wrong / There's poison in your heart / Goodbye Mr. Brown / Searching / How far is heaven / Dust on the bible / Beside you / I'm counting on you / They can't take your love / I'm tired of pretending / Oh so many years / One week later / When I'm with you / Can you find it in your heart / Repenting / I guess I'll go on dreaming / Each day / Pace that kiss, The / Change of heart, A / Stubborn heart / Standing room only / Mansion on the hill / Your wild life's gonna get you down / Right or wrong / Winner of your heart, The / Dancing with a stranger / Three ways (to love you) / She's no angel / Broken marriage vows / What about you / Sweeter than the flowers / You can't conceal a broken heart / Just when I needed you most / Lonely street / That's me without you / Cheated out of love / Waltz of the angels, The / May you never be alone / If teardrops were pennies / Touch and go heart / My used to be darling / I'll always be your fraulein / Love me to pieces / What I believe dear (is all up to you) / I can't stop loving you / Slowly dying.
LPS: BFX 15239/6

GOLDEN YEARS, THE.
LP: SS 13
MC: SSC 13

GREATEST HITS: KITTY WELLS.
MC: GM 0211

GREATEST HITS:KITTY WELLS.
Tracks: / It wasn't God who made honky tonk angels / This white circle / Mommy for a day / Release me / I gave my wedding dress away / Amigo's guitar / Heartbreak USA / I'll repossess my heart / Password / Searching (for someone like you) / Making believe.
LP: IMCA 121

KITTY WELLS STORY, THE.
Tracks: / It wasn't God who made honky tonk angels / I heard the jukebox playing / Wedding ring ago, A / Paying for that back street affair / I don't claim to be an angel / Whose shoulder will you cry on / I gave my wedding dress away / Release me / After dark / Lonely side of town / Making believe / Searching (for someone like you) / Repenting / Your wild life's gonna get you down / Three ways to love you / She's no angel / Touch and go heart / Jealousy / I can't help wondering / Mommy for a day / Amigo's guitar / All the time / Other cheek The / Left to right.
2LP: IMCA2 4031

KITTY'S CHOICE.
LP: HAT 3018
MC: HATC 3018

MAKIN' BELIEVE.
LP: N 23006
MC: 43006

ORIGINAL QUEEN OF COUNTRY MUSIC, THE.
Tracks: / Thou shalt not steal / I don't claim to be an angel / After dark / One by one / Making believe / Poison in your heart / I've kissed you my last time / On the lonely side of town / You and me.
LP: BDL 1025
MC: BDC 1025

SONGS MADE FAMOUS BY JIM REEVES.
Tracks: / Four walls / Billy Bayou / Is it really over? / I'm gonna change everything / I won't forget you / She'll have to go / Welcome to my world / Bimbo / Am I losing you? / According to my heart / Guilty / This is it.
LP: HAT 3009
MC: HATC 3009

Wells, Mary

GREATEST HITS: MARY WELLS.
Tracks: / My guy / What's easy for two is so hard for one / One who really loves you / You lost the sweetest boy / You beat me to the punch / Operator / Two lovers / Laughing boy / I don't want to take a chance / My baby just cares for me / Your old stand by / Strabge love / What love has joined us together / Oh little boy / Old love / Bye bye baby.
LP: STMS 5093
MC: CSTMS 5093
LP: SPR 90008

KEEPING MY MIND ON LOVE.
LP: MOTCLP 40

MARY WELLS SINGS MY GUY.
Tracks: / He's the one I love / Whisper you love me boy / My guy / Does he love me / How / When my heart belongs to you / He holds his own / My baby just cares for me / I only have eyes for you / You do something to me / It had to be you / If you love me / At last.
LP: STMS 5057
MC: CSTMS 5057

MY GUY.
Tracks: / He's the one I love / Whisper you love me boy / My guy / Does he love me? / How? / When my heart belongs to you / He holds his own / My baby just cares for me / I only have eyes for you / You do something to me / It had to be you / If you love me, really love me / At last.
MC: WK 72730

OLD, NEW AND BEST OF MARY WELLS.
Tracks: / My guy / One who really loves you / Two lovers / You beat me to the punch / Oh little boy what did you do to me / Bye bye baby / Whats easy for two is hard for one / What love has joined together / You lost the sweetest boy / Old love, let's try again.
LP: ALE 5601
MC: ZCALE 5601

Wells, Phil

CRYSTAL DANCER.
MC: C 102

CRYSTAL PIANO, THE.
MC: C 101

DREAMS OF AVALON.
MC: C 138

LAST SURVIVORS, THE.
LP: SGRLP 101

Wells, Terri

JUST LIKE DREAMIN'.
Tracks: / I'm givin' all my love / Just like dreamin' Falling leaves / Can't stop / I already know / I'll be around / Who's that stranger / Don't make me wait in line.
LP: LONLP 4
MC: LONC 4

Wells, Tracy

BEST OF TRACY WELLS.
LP: HRL 145

BEST OF TRACY WELLS VOL 2.
Tracks: / Honey / Dear John, a letter / Delta Dawn / One day at a time / I fall to pieces / Letter to heaven / Country sunshine / Cry, cry again / No charge / Come my little son / I love you Jesus / Making believe / Little boy soldier / Family bible.
LP: HRL 165
MC: CHRL 165

COUNTRY ROADS.
LP: STOL 125
LP: CTV 125

COUNTRY SUNSHINE.
LP: HRL 124
MC: CHRL 124

GIVE DADDY BACK TO ME.
LP: HRL 108

JUST BECAUSE I'M A WOMAN.
Tracks: / Back home again / Queen of the silver dollar / Burning bridges / Rodeo cowboy / All for the love of sunshine / Further along / Harper Valley P.T.A. / To know him is to love him / Rollin' in the sunshine / Just because I'm a woman / Ribbon of darkness / Wedding.
LP: PHL 421
MC: CPHL 421

MAY THE GOOD LORD BLESS AND KEEP YOU.
LP: HRL 157

OTHER SIDE OF THE MORNING.

MC: . . . . CWGR 037

THROUGH THE EYES OF A CHILD.
LP: . . . . HRL 139
MC: . . . . CHRL 139

Wells, William

CONSTANT BILLY.
Tracks: / Talk/Morris poem, cake (Spoken word) / Highland Mary / Leafield (field town) (Spoken word) / Maid of the mill / Bobbing around / Two princesses, six music instrumentals (Spoken word) / Dumb maid, the / Own song / Flowers of Edinburgh / Dancing booths (Spoken word) / Country dance (Spoken word) / Every dog has his day (Spoken word) / Quaker / Brighton camp / Glorishears / Banbury hill / Green garters / Interviews (Spoken word) / Shepherd's hey.
MC: 90-084

Wellstood, Dick

ALONE.
LP: . . . . JCE 73

CAFE DES COPAINS - AFTER YOU'VE GONE.
LP: . . . . DDA 1008

DICK WELLSTOOD AND MARTY GROSZ (see Grosz, Marty/Dick Wellstood) (Wellstood, Dick/Marty Grosz).

DUET (See Wilber, Bob) (Wellstood, Dick & Bob Wilber).

IN A MELLO ROLL (Wellstood, Dick/ Kenny Davern Quartet).
LP: . . . . BE 1

JAZZ BANJO (see also under Sayer, Cynthia) (Wellstood, Dick / Cynthia Sayer).

LIVE AT THE CAFE DES COPAINS.
LP: . . . . DDA 1003

LIVE HOT JAZZ (See under Davern, Kenny) (Wellstood, Dick/Kenny Davern Quartet).

PIANO SOLOS.
LP: . . . . 88 UR 005

RAPPORT (See under Butterfield, Billy) (Wellstood, Dick/Billy Butterfield).

SOME HEFTY CATS.
Tracks: / China boy / Save it pretty mama / Carolina shout / Gone with the wind / Snowy morning blues / Monday date / Red rides again / Sweet Lorraine / Don't get around much anymore / 'S wonderful / Blues at the Copely / Bounce it.
LP: . . . . HJ 100

THIS IS THE ONE.
LP: . . . . AP 120

THREE IS COMPANY (see Galloway, Jim) (Wellstood, Dick/Jim Galloway/Pete Magadini).

Welsh, Alex

ALEX WELSH SHOWCASE VOLUME 2.
Tracks: / You were meant for me / This is all I ask / Fascinating rhythm / Minor lament / Critics choice / What is this thing called love / You are the sunshine of my life / Recado / Limehouse blues.
LP: . . . . BLP 12121

AT HOME: ALEX WELSH.
LP: . . . . DM 16

CHINESE TAKE AWAY BLUES (See under Alan Randall) (Welsh, Alex & Alan Randall).

DIXIELAND TO DUKE.
LP: . . . . DM 7

EVENING WITH ALEX WELSH, PART 1.
LP: 2460 179

IN A PARTY MOOD (Welsh, Alex Band).
LP: . . . . OU 2196

LIVE AT ROYAL FESTIVAL HALL VOL.1 1954-5 (Welsh, Alex/George Melley).
Tracks: / Panama rag / Memphis blues / Clarinet marmalade / Clark and Randolph blues / New Orleans function / Maryland my Maryland / Wild man blues / New Orleans stomp / Maple leaf rag / Mississippi mud / Mama don't allow/ When the saints.
LP: . . . . LA 5008
MC: . . . . LA 5008C

SALUTE TO SATCHMO (Welsh, Alex/ Humphrey Lyttleton/Bruce Turner/ George Chisholm).
Tracks: / Hear me talkin' to ya / Georgia on my mind / Basin street blues / Muskrat ramble / Ory's creole trombone / Rockin' chair / Wild man blues / I double dare you / That's my home / Ain't misbehavin' / Way down yonder in New Orleans / Royal Garden blues / St. James infirmary / When you're smiling / When it's sleepy time down South.

2LP: . . . . BLPX 12161/2

Welsh Choirs

WORLD OF WALES (Various artists).
LP: . . . . SPA 214
MC: . . . . KCSP 214

Welsh Folk

FOLKSONGS IN WELSH (See under Cleaver, Emrys) (Cleaver, Emrys).

Welsh Fusiliers

RED DRAGON, THE.
Tracks: / Men of Glamorgan / Royal Welsh Fusiliers / Great big David / Red dragon, The / Glorious victory / Impressions on a Welsh air / Jaguar / Great little army / God bless the Prince of Wales / British grenadiers, The / Men of Harlech / Land of my fathers / Strike up the band / Themes from 007 / Misty / Brass fever / Echoes of an era (Beatles medley).
MC: . . . . ZC BND 1028
LP: . . . . BND 1028

Welsh Guards Band

AT HICKSTEAD.
LP: . . . . DR 1

CHRISTMAS WITH THE WELSH GUARDS.
LP: . . . . DR 107

CLASSICAL SPECTACULAR (live at the Royal Albert Hall)(see under Royal Philharmonic (Scots Guards/Welsh Guards bands/Royal Philharmonic Orchestra).

CYMRU AM BYTH.
Tracks: / Men of Harlech / We'll keep a welcome / Great and glorious / Guardsman, The / Hodie, Christus natus est / Welsh patrol / Rising of the lark, (The) / David of the white rock / Royal review / Dychwelyd / Leek, The / Cwm Rhondda.
LP: . . . . DAFFODIL 221

FAMOUS MARCHES.
MC: . . . . VCA 017

GILBERT AND SULLIVAN.
Tracks: / Overture- The yeoman of the guard / Take a pair of sparkling eyes / Regular royal queen, A / When a wooer goes a wooing / Cheerily carols the lark / I am a courtier grave and serious / When the night wind howls / Hornpipe from Ruddigore / Man who would woo a fair maid, A / Refrain audacious tar / I hear the soft note / Long years ago / If you're anxious for to shine / Minerva / When the buds are blossoming / Strange adventure / Once more gondolieri.
MC: . . . . ZC BND 1024
LP: . . . . BND 1024

GOD BLESS THE PRINCE OF WALES.
Tracks: / Triple crown / Men of Harlech / Rising of the lark, The / Trumpet tune / Processional interlude / Cwm Rhondda / Staffordshire knot, The / Princess of Wales, The / Watermill, The / Royal Windsor / Watching the wheat / Dove, The / Entry of the Queen of Sheba / God bless the Prince of Wales.
LP: . . . . RCD 1
MC: . . . . ZC RCD 1

HOUR OF THE GUARDS, AN (Welsh Guards/Grenadier Guards).
Tracks: / Nimrod / Children's patrol / Norwegian carnival / Hoch heidecksburg / I hope I get better / At the ballet / I can do that / Nothing / One / What I did for love / Entry of The Boyards / Cardiff arms / Bilitis / Abide with me / In the Dolomites / In storm and sunshine / Kennebec / True comrades in arms / Washingon Grays / Bridge too far, A / Robinson's grand entree / Birdcage walk / Army and Marine / Children of the regiment / Piper in the meadow / Man o'brass / Always Vienna (CD only.) / Raiders of the lost ark (CD only.).
MC: . . . . HR 8176

MUSIC FROM THE SHOWS.
Tracks: / White Horse Inn (medley) / Arcadians, The (medley) / King's rhapsody (medley) / Sound of music (medley) / My fair lady (medley) / West side story (medley).
LP: . . . . LSA 3273

NIMROD.
Tracks: / Nimrod / Always Vienna / Trumpet trio (nine busy fingers) / Hoch heidecksburg! (March) / Children's patrol (March) / Bilitis (Oboe solo) / Norwegian carnival / Cardiff arms (March) / Sailing by (March) / Sutherland's law theme (March) / Entry of the boyards (Truimphal march) / I hope I get better (A chorus line spectacular) / At the ballet (A chorus line spectacular) / I can do that (A chorus line spectacular) / Nothing (A chorus line spectacular) / One (A chorus line spectacular) / What I did for love (A chorus line spectacular) / Abide with me.
LP: . . . . GRALP 13

MC: . . . . GRTC 13

RISING OF THE LARK.
Tracks: / Men of Harlech / Arms park / Semper fidelis / Ridgewood / Chi mai / Last starfighter, The / Hooked on classics / Comedians gallop / Oxen minuet / Two little finches / Gypsy trumpeter / Bavarda / Ulster division, The / Sarafand / My congratulations / Fool on the hill / Rising of the lark.
LP: . . . . BND 1019
MC: . . . . ZC BND 1019

SING THE SONGS OF OUR HOMELAND (Welsh Guards/London Welsh Male Voice Choir).
LP: . . . . EMS 1170
MC: . . . . TCEMS 1170
2LP: . . . . SCX 6700

THEIR MOST POPULAR RECORDINGS.
Tracks: / Colonel Bogey / Changing of the guard / Flotsam and jetsam / Elizabethan serenade / Radetzky march / Bell a'peal / Casatchok / War and peace theme / British Isles medley / Liberty bell / Eye level / Sentry song Iolanthe / Rozenstraten / Colditz march / Amazing grace / Jerusalem / Allthrough the night / God bless the Prince of Wales / Land of my fathers / Evening hymn and last post / Last post.
LP: . . . . REC 361
MC: . . . . ZCM 361

TROOPING OF THE COLOUR 1981, THE.
LP: . . . . QBP 4

TROOPING THE COLOUR.
MC: . . . . BBM 143

WELSH GUARDS SHOWCASE NO. 1.
Tracks: / Welsh rhapsody / Michelle / Ida and Dot / Goose fair / Hands across the sea / Can Can for band / God bless the Prince of Wales / Space City USA / Gold and silver / Facilita / Night flight to Madrid / Rondo / Land of my fathers.
LP: . . . . DR 56
MC: . . . . CDR 56

Welsh, Lillie

LET ME HAVE THE CHANCE (See under Campbell, Bill) (Welsh, Lillie/Bill Campbell).

Welsh Male Choirs

SOUND AN ALARM (Various artists).
LP: . . . . REC 267
MC: . . . . ZCM 267

Welsh Rugby...

OTHER SIDE OF THE DRAGON, THE (Welsh Rugby All Stars).
Tracks: / Sloop John B / All I have to do is dream / Green green grass of home / Mighty Quinn / Calon lan / Last thing on my mind / Sospan Bach / I am a little collier / Country roads / Were you there / Welsh moon.
LP: . . . . EVLP 3

Wemba, Papa

LE VIE EST BELLE.
LP: . . . . TUG 001
MC: . . . . TUGC 001

PAPA WEMBA.
LP: . . . . STERNS 1026
MC: . . . . STC 1026

Wench

TIDY SIZE CHUNK OF SOMETHING, A.
LP: . . . . CORE 5

Wenders, Wim

WIM WENDERS ROADSHOW VOL 1 (Wim Wenders/Jurgen Knieper).
LP: A372
MC: C372

WIM WENDERS ROADSHOW (VOL 2) (Wenders, Wim/Jurgen Knieper).
LP: A519
MC: C519

Wendy & Lisa

EROICA.
Tracks: / Rainbow lake / Strung out / Mother of pearl / Don't try to tell me / Crack in the pavement / Porch swing / Why wait for heaven / Turn me inside out / Skeleton key / Valley vista / Staring at the sun.
LP: . . . . V 2633
MC: . . . . TCV 2633

FRUIT AT THE BOTTOM.
Tracks: / Lolly lolly / Satisfaction / Everyday / Tears of joy / Fruit at the bottom / Are you my baby / Always in my dreams / From now on / I think it was December / Someday.
LP: . . . . V 2580
MC: . . . . TCV 2580
LP: . . . . VWL 2580
MC: . . . . TCVWL 2580

WENDY AND LISA.
Tracks: / Honeymoon express / Sideshow / Waterfall / Stay / White Blues away / Song about / Chance to grow / Life, The / Everything but you / Light.
LP: . . . . V 2444
MC: . . . . TCV 2444
LP: . . . . OVED 343
MC: . . . . OVEDC 343

WENDY AND LISA: INTERVIEW PIC DISC.
LPPD: . . . . BAK 2136

Wendy & The Rockets

DAZED FOR DAYS.
Tracks: / No control / Security / Play the game / Have you been telling me lies / Over yonder / I can't tell you / How come you're still haning 'round / Magic bullet / Nightflier.
LP: . . . . AMLX 64947

Wenzani

WENZANI (Original Cast) (Various artists).
MC: . . . . PCN 109

Werewolves

WEREWOLVES.
Tracks: / Flesh express, The / Hollywood millionaire / Too hard / City by the sea / Never been to Hades / Lisa / Two fools, The / Heaven help me / Deux voix / One night / Silence.
LP: . . . . PL 12746
MC: . . . . PK 12746

Werner, David

DAVID WERNER.
Tracks: / Can't imagine / What's right / What do you need to love / Melanie cries / Eye to eye / Hold on tight / Every new romance / Too late to try / High class blues / She sent me away.
LP: . . . . EPC 83862

Werner, Ken

BEYOND THE FOREST OF MIRKWOOD.
LP: . . . . ENJA 3061

Werner, Lasse

TRIPLE PLAY JAZZ PIANO (Werner, Lasse/Jan Wallgren/Bobo Stenson).
LP: . . . . DRLP 12

Werner, Margot

DREAMFLIGHTS (Margot Werner sings Robert Stolz).
Tracks: / Dreamflights / Don't ask me why / Tee-ka, tee-ka, tah / Our finest hour / Come to me / Men, men, men / Romeo (Salome) / I love you so / I'm no longer Juliet / Breath of scandal, A / You too / Thank you for the music.
LP: 6.26708

Wernherr, Otto Van

WILD DANCING (See under Madonna) (Wernherr, Otto Van & Madonna).

Wernick, Pete

DOCTOR BANJO STEPS OUT.
LP: . . . . FF 046

Werth, Howard

SIX OF ONE AND HALF A DOZEN OF THE OTHER.
LP: . . . . SIXOF 1

Wesco, Ade

NA SO YOU BE.
LP: . . . . ORLPS 010

Wesker, Arnold (aut)

DRAMATIST SPEAKS, THE (See under Dramatist Speaks) (Arden, John (nar)).

Wesley, Fred

TO SOMEONE.
LP: . . . . HNL 2002

WHAT GOES AROUND COMES AROUND (see also under: Byrd, Bobby & Parker, Maceo) (Byrd, Bobby/Maceo Parker/Fred Wesley).

Wesley, Mary

CAMOMILE LAWN, THE (Phillips, Sian).
MCSET: . . . . ZBBC 1090

Wess, Frank

2 FRANKS PLEASE (see Foster, Frank) (Wess, Frank/Frank Foster).

DEAR MR. BASIE (Wess, Frank & Harry Edison Orchestra).
Tracks: / Jumpin' at the woodside / Very thought of you, The / Blue on blue / All riled up / This is all I ask / I wish I knew / Whirly bird / Li'l darlin' / Dejection blues / Battle royal / One o clock jump.
MC: . . . . CJ 420 C

ENTRE NOUS (Wess, Frank Orchestra).
Tracks: / Order in the court / Entre nous / Blues in the 2% / St. James Infirmary / Shiny stockings / But beautiful (Only on CD) / Imus the blues / Rink rat / Pit pat blues (Only on CD).
MC: . . . . CJ 456 C

FLUTE JUICE.
Tracks: / Lover come back to me / Spring is here / Riled up / There is no greater love / Nada Mas / Battle royal.
LP: PRO 7057

FRANKLY SPEAKING (see Foster, Frank) (Wess, Frank/Frank Foster).

I HEAR YA TALKIN'.
LP: WL 70503

LIVE AT THE 1990 CONCORD JAZZ FESTIVAL (Second Set) (Wess, Frank & Marshal Royal & Rick Wilkins).
Tracks: / Blues walk / Lush life / Don't get around much anymore / Easy living / Just squeeze me (but don't tease me) / Broadway.
MC: CJ 452C

TWO AT THE TOP (See under Coles, Johnny) (Wess, Frank/Johnny Coles).
LP: UP 27 14

TWO FOR THE BLUES (see Foster, Frank) (Wess, Frank/Frank Foster).

WESS OF THE MOON.
LP: 6.25897

West Bam

CABINET.
Tracks: / Cabinet of Dr Weststein / Hold me back / Voices of excess / Roof is on fire, The / Wall, The / Monkey town / Go East bam / Bring that beat back / Sentimental scratching.
LP: SYR LP 2
MC: SYR MC 2

West, Bruce & Laing

WHY DON'TCHA.
LP: 2479 111

West, Clint

CLINT WEST.
LP: JIN 9005

CLINT WEST AND THE BOOGIE KINGS (West, Clint/Boogie Kings).
LP: JIN 4003
MC: JIN 4003 TC

FABULOUS KINGS.
LP: JIN 4004

West Coast All Stars

TV JAZZ THEMES.
LP: FS 164

West Coast Pop Art..

TRANSPARENT DAY (West Coast Pop Art Experimental Band).
Tracks: / Shifting sands / I won't hurt you / 1906 / Will you walk with me / Transparent day / Leiyla / Here's where you belong / High coin / Suppose they give a war and no-one comes / Buddah / Smell of incense / Overture - WCAPAEB part II / Carte blanche / If you want this love / Help I'm a rock.
LP: ED 180
MC: CED 180

West, Dottie

20 OF THE BEST: DOTTIE WEST.
Tracks: / Let me off at the corner / Love is no excuse / Gettin' married has made us strangers / Would you hold it against me / Mommy, can I still call him daddy ? / There's a story (goin' round) / Paper mansions / Forever yours / Rings of gold / Last time I saw him / Here come's my baby / Before the ring on your finger turns green / What's come over my baby ? / Like a fool / Sweet memories / Country girl / Reno / Slowly / House of love / Country sunshine.
LP: NL 89851
MC: NK 89851

BEST OF DOTTIE WEST, THE.
Tracks: / Here comes my baby / Careless hands / Once you were mine / Country girl / Six weeks every summer / Forever yours / Paper mansions / If you go away / Would you hold it against me / Reno.
LP: LSA 3152

CLASSICS (see Rogers, Kenny) (West, Dottie/Kenny Rogers).

EVERY TIME TWO FOOLS COLLIDE (see under Kenny Rogers) (West, Dottie/ Kenny Rogers).

EVERY TIME TWO FOOLS COLLIDE (SINGLE) (See under Rogers, Kenny) (Rogers, Kenny & Dottie West).

I FALL TO PIECES.
LP: GT 0085

SPECIAL DELIVERY.
LP: UAG 30290

West End

WEST END NIGHT OUT (Various artists).
MC: AIM 10

West End Jazz Band

RED HOT CHICAGO.
LP: SOS 1042

WEST END JAZZ BAND-VOLUME 2.
LP: SOS 1085

West End Stompers

AIN'T YOU GLAD?.
Tracks: / Stevedore stomp / Louisiana / Shout 'em Aunt Tillie / Texas moaner / Ace in the hole / Tuxedo rag / Working man blues / Stockyards strut / Ain't you glad? / Marchand de poissons / Bei mir bist du schon.
LP: SFA 113

TOO BUSY.
Tracks: / Wa, wa, wa / Nothing blues / Thriller rag / Mood indigo / Wild cat blues / Gatemouth / Grandpa's spells / Too busy / Come back, sweet Papa / Storyville blues / Carry me back to old Virginny / Preacher, The.
LP: SFA 083

West, Gordie

ALBERTA BOUND.
Tracks: / Alberta bound / Strawberry roan, The / Sweet music man / Blue Canadian Rockies / Canadian Pacific / That's my pa / Alberta skyline / Loser making good, A / Boot rockies / Rose of San Antone.
LP: WRS 138

GORDIE WEST.
LP: CBS 32343

West, Hedy

BALLADS.
Tracks: / Love Henry / Beaulampkin / Down in Adairsville / Unquiet grave, The / Lucy Wan / Sheffield apprentice, The / Foggy dew, The / George Collins / Texas rangers / Cruel mother / Little Sadie / Girl I left in Danville.
LP: 12T 163

GETTING FOLK OUT OF THE COUNTRY (West, Hedy/Bill Clifton).
Tracks: / Free little bird / Maid on the shore / Little Sadie / Pity me all day / Whitehouse blues / Mary of the wild moor / Blow ye gentle winds / Curly headed baby / S.A.V.E.D. / Picture's from life's other side / Angel band / Instrumental / Mississippi sawyer.
LP: BF 15008

LOVE, HELL AND BISCUITS.
Tracks: / Shady grove / Erin's green shore / Molly Bawn / Single girl / Whores lament, The / Devil perceived / When I lay my burden down / Pans of biscuits / How can a poor man stand such times and live / Little lump of coal / Green rolling hills of West Virginia / Come all ye Lewiston factory girls / Babies in the mill / Red river valley / Rio Jarama / Roll on weary river, roll on.
LP: BF 15003

OLD TIMES AND HARD TIMES.
Tracks: / Wife wrapt in weather's skin, The / Fair Rosamund / Barbara Allen / Old Joe Clark / Coal miner's child, The / Gamblin' man / Brother Euphus / Polly / Davison wilder blues, The / Rich Irish lady, The / Shut up in the mines at coal creek / Wife of Usher's well, The / Lament for Barney Graham.
LP: 12T 117

PRETTY SARO.
Tracks: / House carpenter / Pretty Saro / Old smokey / Blow ye gentle winds / My soul's full of glory / Promised land / Over there / Little matty groves / Rake and the rambling boy / Joe Bowers / Whistle daughter whistle / I'm an old bachelor / Johnny sands / My good old man / Frankie silvers / Lee Tharin's bar room.
LP: 12T 146

West India Company

NEW DEMONS.
Tracks: / Shankara / My shooting star / Lion sleeps tonight, The / Jungle tumble / O je suis seul / Night country / Bengalis from outer space / Pandi / Driver / Bengalis re-enter / Juggernaut.
LP: EGED 61
MC: EGEDC 61

West Indies

POETS OF THE WEST INDIES (ed. Figueroa, John) (Various artists).
MC: 1379

West Java

FLUTE AND GAMELAN.
LP: TGS 137

West, Jesse

NO PRISONERS.
Tracks: / No prisoners / Renegade / I'm a warrior / State of your mind / Prelude to madness / This is madness / Do you wanna party / I saw you / Master, The / For James / Concrete jungle / Black bomb.
LP: ZL 72695
MC: ZK 72695

West, John

BEYOND THE SUNSET (West, John & Family).
MC: CJR 003

West, Keith

FOR THOSE WHO CARE.
LP: BSS 318

West, Mae

ON THE AIR (Radio Broadcasts 1934-60).
MC: CSH 2098
LP: SH 2098

ON THE RADIO.
LP: MR 1126

West Side Blues...

CHICAGO BLUES SESSION 7 (West Side Blues Singers).
LP: WOLF 120 853

West Side Story

WEST SIDE STORY (Original Broadway cast) (Various artists).
Tracks: / West side story: Prologue: *Various artists* / Jet song: *Various artists* / Something's coming: *Various* artists / Dance at the gym (blues promenade jump): *Various artists* / Maria: *Various artists* / Tonight: *Various* artists / America: *Various artists* / Cool: *Various artists* / One hand, one heart: *Various artists*/ Tonight: *Various artists* / Rumble, The: *Various artists* / I feel pretty: *Various artists* / Somewhere: *Various artists* / Gee Officer Krupke: *Various artists* / Boy like that, A: *Various artists* / I have a love: *Various artists* / West side story: Finale: *Various artists.*
LP: CBS 32193
MC: 40 32193
MC: PST 32603

WEST SIDE STORY (Various artists).
LPPD: AR 30045

WEST SIDE STORY (FILM) (Various artists).
Tracks: / Jet song: *Various artists* / Something's coming: *Various artists* / Dance at the gym (blues promenade jump): *Various artists* / America: *Various artists* / Maria: *Various artists* / Tonight: *Various* artists / Gee officer Krupke: *Various artists* / I feel pretty: *Various artists* / One hand one heart: *Various* artists / Quintet: *Various artists* / Rumble: *Various artists* / Cool: *Various artists* / Boy like that, A: *Various artists* / I have a love: *Various artists* / Somewhere: *Various artists.*
LP: CBS 70006
MC: 407 000 6
LP: BPG 62058
LP: 4676061
MC: 4676064

WEST SIDE STORY (FILM 2) (Various artists).
Tracks: / Jet song: *Various artists* / Something's coming: *Various artists* / Maria: *Various artists*/ Tonight: *Various artists* / America: *Various artists* / Cool: *Various artists* / One hand, one heart: *Various artists* / I feel pretty: *Various artists* / Somewhere: *Various artists* / Gee Officer Krupke: *Various artists* / Boy like that, A: *Various artists* / I have a love: *Various artists* / Taunting scene: *Various artists* / Finale: *Various artists.*
LP: 415 963 1
MC: 415 963 4

WEST SIDE STORY (ORIGINAL) (Film soundtrack) (Various artists).
LP: BBL 7530

WEST SIDE STORY (SHOW) (Various artists).
LP: BBL 7277
LP: SBBL 504

WEST SIDE STORY (STUDIO) (Various artists).
Tracks: / Prologue and jet song: *Various artists* / Something's coming: *Various artists* / Dance at the gym (blues promenade jump): *Various artists* / Maria: *Various artists* / Tonight: *Various artists* / Rumble: *Various* artists / I feel pretty: *Various artists* / Somewhere: *Various artists* / Gee officer Krupke: *Various artists* / Boy like that, A: *Various artists* / I have a love: *Various artists* / Finale: *Various artists.*
2LP: 4152531
MCSET: 4152534

WEST SIDE STORY (STUDIO 2) (Various artists).
LP: 45963

WEST SIDE STORY/ON THE WATERFRONT (Film soundtracks) (New York Philharmonic Orchestra).
LP: CBS 61096
MC: 40 61096

West, Speedy

GUITAR SPECTACULAR.
LP: HAT 3093
MC: HATC 3093

STEEL GUITAR.
Tracks: / Speedin' west / Railroadin' / West of Samoa / Caffeine patrol / Our paradise / Flippin' the lid / This ain't the blues / Stainless steel / Steelin' moonlight / Truck driver's ride / Sunset / Steel strike.
LP: HAT 3045
MC: HATC 3045

TWO GUITARS COUNTRY STYLE (see Bryant,Jimmy/Speedy West) (West, Speedy/Jimmy Bryant).

West Street Mob

WEST STREET MOB.
Tracks: / Let's dance / Get up and dance / Natural living / Never alone / You're killing me / Gotta give it up / Sometimes late at night.
LP: SHLP 1004
MC: ZCSH 1004

West, Timothy (nar)

BARCHESTER TOWERS (See under Barchester Towers).

Westbrook, Forrest

THIS IS THEIR TIME, OH YES.
LP: REV 11

Westbrook, Mike

CITADEL/ROOM 315.
Tracks: / Overture / Construction / Pistache / View from the drawbridge / Love and understanding / Tender love / Bebop de rigeur / Pastorale / Sleepwalker awaking in sunlight / Outgoing song / Finale.
MC: NK 74987

CORTEGE.
2LP: ORA 309

GOOSE SAUCE.
LP: ORA 001

LITTLE WESTBROOK MUSIC, A (Westbrook, Kate & Mike/Chris Biscoe).
LP: LWM 1
MC: ZCLWM 1

LONDON BRIDGE IS BROKEN DOWN.
Tracks: / London bridge is broken down / Wenceslas Square / Nahe des geliebten (Part 1 of Berlin Wall) / B.V.B.W. (Belle-vue Berlin Wall) (Part 2 of Berlin Wall) / Traurig aber falsch (Part 3 of Berlin Wall) / Ein vogel / Viennese waltz / Fur sie / Blighters / Les morts / Picardie three / Picardie four / Une fenetre / Picardie six / Aucassin et Nicolette.
LPS: VEB 13
MCSET: TCVEB 13

MAMA CHICAGO.
Tracks: / Mama / Train boogie / Virgins of Illinois / Jackie-ing / Corkscrew / Prohibition / Slaughterhouse / Voyage / Seascape / Prisoners' hymn / Prelude / Preconceived ideas / Heart in heart, hand in hand / Goin' to Chicago / Apple pie / Mama Chicago (part 4) / Mama Chicago (part 5) / Windy City / Titanic song / Concrete / Shipwrecked sailor.
2LP: PL 25252

PARIS ALBUM, THE.
2LP: 2655 008

PIANO.
LP: ORA 002

PIER RIDES.
LP: WMLP 1

WESTBROOK BLAKE BRIGHT AS A FIRE, THE (setting of William Blake).
Tracks: / Fields, The / I see thy form / London songs / Poison tree, A / Holy Thursday / Let the slave / Price of experience, The.
LP: ORA 203

Westbrook, Roger

I'N'T 'EE A GRAND LAD.
Tracks: / Sister Josephine / All along the Rossendale / Cockfight, (The) / Old Pendle / Gypsy Davey / Brother Sylveste / Rawtenstall annual fair / Bantam cock / Jimmy Spoons / Introduction by Bernard Wrigley.
LP: SFA 069

STILL HE SINGS.
LP: SFA 119

WESTBROOK/WRIGLEY (Westbrook, Roger/Bernard Wrigley).
LP: SFA 089

Westcliff High School

CAROLS (Westcliff High School Junior Girls Choir).
LP: AJP 1006

Western, Billy's Brass

WESTERN RAILROAD.
LP: ISST 104

Western, Johnny

GUNFIGHTER.
Tracks: / Ballad of Paladin / Guns of Rio Muerto, The / Lonely man / Rollin' dust / Hannah Lee / Long tall shadow, The / Nineteen men / Searchers, The / Gunfighter, The / Geronimo / Echo of your voice, The / Ten years / Uh huh (Previously unissued.) / Stranger drive away (Previously unissued.) / All by my lonesome (Previously unissued.) / Time has run out on me (Previously unissued.).
LP: BFX 15081

JOHNNY WESTERN.
LP: BFX 15070

Western Promise

SHOWDOWN WITH FATE.
Tracks: / Day the president died / Red skies / Hot rain / If you tell me you love me / Waiting / Justice / Still in love with you / All the king's horses / Kingdom come / Katyn wood / Steelyard.
LP: CHIME 58

Western Themes

WESTERN MOVIE THEMES (See Under Nashville Sound...) (Nashville Sound Orchestra).

Western Vacation

WESTERN VACATION.
LP: W 69 DY1

Westhall, Robert

MACHINE GUNNERS, THE (Bolam, James (nar)).
MCSET: CC/034

Westlake, David

WESTLAKE.
LP: CRELP 019

Westminster Abbey

PALESTRINA.
MC: KA 66316

STORY OF (WESTMINSTER) ABBEY (Westminster Abbey Choir/Various Artists).
MC: WHC 003

WESTMINSTER ABBEY CHOIR.
LP: LPB 791
MC: LPBC 791

Westminster Cathedral

20 FAVOURITE HYMNS (see 20 favourite Hymns of Charles Wesley) (Westminster Central Hall Choir).

FESTIVAL OF CAROLS, A.
LP: SHM 3150
MC: HSC 3150

IN HONOUR OF OUR LADY.
MC: CACA 501

PORTUGUESE POLYPHONY.
LP: A 66218

WESTMINSTER CATHEDRAL CHOIR.
MC: AIM 59

Westminster Symphony

TCHAIKOVSKY BALLET (Westminster Symphony Orchestra).
MCSET: DTO 10032

Weston, Calvin

DANCE ROMANCE.
Tracks: / Chocolate rock / I can tell / Planetarian citizen / Preview / Dance romance / House blues.
LP: IORLP 002

Weston, Kim

IT TAKES TWO (see Gaye, Marvin) (Weston, Kim & Marvin Gaye).

IT TAKES TWO (See under Gaye, Frankie) (Weston, Kim & Frankie Gaye).

Weston, Paul

CINEMA CAMEOS (Weston, Paul & His Orchestra).
Tracks: / Gone with the wind / Wuthering heights / Dark victory / Lost horizons / Spellbound / Since you went away / King's Row / Now voyager / Laura / For whom the bell tolls.
LP: COR 107

CRESCENT CITY ("A musical portrait of New Orleans") (Weston, Paul & His Orchestra).
Tracks: / Crescent City / Vieux carre / Riverfront blues / Storyville / Bayou St. John / High society / Creole songs and dances / Miss Lucy / Ferryboat to Algiers / Esplanade at sunset / Nobody knows the trouble I've seen / Mardi gras.
LP: COR 116

EASY JAZZ (Weston, Paul & His Orchestra).
Tracks: / Body and soul / Georgia on my mind / My funny valentine / You are too beautiful / I'm confessin' / Foggy day, A / When it's sleepy time down South / Sweet Lorraine / Hundred years from today / Autumn in New York / Talk of the town / Nice work if you can get it.
LP: COR 109

Weston, Randy

BERKSHIRE BLUES.
Tracks: / Three blind mice / Perdido / Purple gazelle / Berkshire blues / Lagos / Sweet meat / Ifran.
LP: FLP 41026

BLUES TO AFRICA.
Tracks: / African village / Bedford stuyvesant / Tangier Bay / Blues to Africa / Kasbah kids / Uhuru Kwanza / Call, The / Kucheza blues / Sahel.
LP: FLP 41014

CARNIVAL.
Tracks: / Carnival / Tribute to Duke Ellington / Mystery of love.
LP: FLP 41004

HEALERS, THE (see under Murray, David) (Weston, Randy/ David Murray).

HIGHLIFE.
Tracks: / Caban bamboo highlife / Niger mambo / Zulu / In memory of / Congolese children / Blues to Africa / Mystery of love.
LP: ROU 1019
LP: 794 509 1

HOW HIGH THE MOON.
Tracks: / Loose wig / Run Joe / Theme for Teddy, A / In a little Spanish town / Don't blame me / JK blues / Well you needn't / How high the moon.
LP: MTLP 018

MODERN ART OF JAZZ, THE.
LP: FS 284

NUIT AFRICAINE.
LP: ENJA 2086

PORTAITS OF DUKE ELLINGTON.
LP: 8413121
MC: 8413124

UHURU, AFRICA.
LP: VG DRY21006

UHURU, AFRICA (2).
Tracks: / Uhuru kwanza (part one): Introduction / Uhuru kwanza (part two): 1st movement / African lady: 2nd movement / Bantu: 3rd movement / Kucheza blues.
LP: ROU 1018
LP: 794 508 1

Weston, Tom Four

BRANDED.
LP: BSS 204

Westworld

WHERE THE ACTION IS.
Tracks: / Where the action is / Fly westworld / King Creole / Johnny Blue.
LP: PL 71429
MC: PK 71429

Westworld (film)

WESTWORLD (Various artists).
LP: MCA 25004
MC: MCAC 25004

Wet 'n' Wild

DON'T STOP THE BOP.
Tracks: / Wet'n'wild / Teenage boogie / Pink and black / Just for rock'n'roll / Wanderer / Don't push / Just go wild over rock 'n' roll / Dance the bop / Honey don't / Bop a Lena / Hot dog buddy buddy / Flip flop and fly / Rockabilly son of a gun / Sixteen chicks.
LP: MFLP 022

Wet Wet Wet

HOLDING BACK THE RIVER.
Tracks: / Sweet surrender / Can't stand the night / Blue for you / Brokeaway / You've had it / I wish / Keys to your heart / Maggie May / Hold back the river.
LP: 842 011 1
MC: 842 011 4

MEMPHIS SESSIONS, THE.
Tracks: / I don't believe / Sweet little mystery (Memphis version) / East of the river / This time / Temptation / I remember / For you are / Heaven help us all.
LP: JWWWL 2
MC: JWWWM 2

POPPED IN SOULED OUT.
Tracks: / Wishing I was lucky / East of the river / I remember / Angel eyes / Sweet little mystery / Temptation / I can give you everything / Moment you left me, The.
LP: JWWWL 1
MC: JWWWM 1

Wetherby

WETHERBY (Original Soundtrack) (Various artists).
LP: TER 12 010

Wettling, George

BARRELHOUSE PIANO (See under Zack, George) (Wettling,George/George Zack).

COMMODORE STYLE (See under Freeman, Bud) (Wettling,George/Bud Freeman).

GEORGE WETTLING JAZZ BAND (Wettling, George Jazz Band).
LP: JSP 1103

WETTLING, GEORGE.
MC: HM 03

Wetton, John

CAUGHT IN THE CROSSFIRE.
LP: EGLP 47

KING'S ROAD 1972-1980.
Tracks: / Nothing to lose / In the dead of night / Baby come back / Caught in the crossfire / Night after night / Turn on the radio / Rendezvous 602 / Book of Saturday / Paper talk / As long as you want me here / Cold is the night / Eyesight to the blind (CD only) / Starless (CD only).
LP: EGLP 70
MC: EGMC 70

Wetton/Manzanera

WETTON/MANZANERA.
Tracks: / It's just love / Keep on loving yourself / You don't have to leave my life / Suzanne / Round in circles / Do it again / Every trick in the book / One world / I can't let you go / Have you seen her tonight.
LP: 9241471
MC: 9241474

We've Got A Fuzzbox...

BOSTIN STEVE AUSTIN (We've Got A Fuzzbox And We're Gonna Use It).
Tracks: / Love is the slug / Wait and see / Jackie / Spirit in the sky / XX sex / Alive / Whats the point / You got me / Hollow girl / Console me / Rules and regulations / Preconceptions.
LP: FBOX 1
MC: FBOXC 1

We've Suffered...

WE'VE SUFFERED, NOW IT'S YOUR TURN (Various artists).
LP: LA 03

Wexler, Sarah

HELIX.
MC: C 158

Whales

WHALE NOISES (See under Deep Voices - Sound Of Whales) (Various artists).

Whales Of August

WHALES OF AUGUST, THE (Film soundtrack) (Various artists).
LP: STV 81347
MC: CTV 81347

Wham

12" TAPE: WHAM.
Tracks: / Wham rap (enjoy what you do) / Careless whisper / Freedom / Everything she wants / I'm your man.
MC: 4501254

FANTASTIC.
Tracks: / Bad boys / Ray of sunshine, A / Love machine / Wham rap (enjoy what you do?) / Club Tropicana / Nothing looks the same in the light / Come on / Young guns (go for it).
LP: IVL 25328
MC: 40 25 328
LP: 4500901
MC: 4500904

FINAL, THE.
Tracks: / Wham rap (enjoy what you do) / Young guns go for it / Bad boys / Club tropicana / Wake me up before you go go / Careless whisper / Freedom / Last Christmas / Everything she wants / I'm your man / Blue (armed with love) / Different corner, A / Battlestations / Where did your heart go / Edge of heaven.
LP: EPC 88681
MC: 40 88681

MAKE IT BIG.
Tracks: / Wake me up before you go go / Everything she wants / Heartbeat / Like a baby / Freedom / If you were there / Credit card baby / Careless whisper.
LP: EPC 86311
MC: 40 86311
LP: 4655761
MC: 4655764

WHAM.
Tracks: / Where did your heart go / Edge of heaven / Different corner, A / Wham rap (enjoy what you do) / Young guns (go for it) / Bad boys / Club Tropicana / Wake me up before you go go / Careless whisper / Freedom / Last Christmas (pudding mix) / Everything she wants (remix) / I'm your man (Extended simulation) / Blue (armed with love) / Battlestations.
LP: WHAM 2

WHAM: INTERVIEW PICTURE DISC.
LPPD: BAK 2038

Wharton, Edith

HOUSE OF MIRTH, THE (Bron, Eleanor (nar)).
MCSET: CC/053

What A Mess

WHAT A MESS (Muir, Frank).
MC: TS 324

What A Nice Way...

WHAT A NICE WAY TO TURN 17 LP (Various artists).
LP: RATHER 13

What About Luv ?

WHAT ABOUT LUV ? (Various artists).
MC: ZCTER 1171

What Can I Do?

WHAT CAN I DO? (Various artists).
MC: MRMC 023

What Else Do You Do?

WHAT ELSE DO YOU DO? (Various artists).
LP: SDE 9021

What If

IT BE WHAT IT BE.
LP: 400 244

What Noise

FAT.
LP: BND 8 LP

What One Dance Can Do

WHAT ONE DANCE CAN DO (Various artists).
LP: DGLP 187

What One Rhythm Can Do

WHAT ONE RHYTHM CAN DO (Various artists).
LP: DGLP 186

What Surf

WHAT SURF 2 (Various artists).
LP: KIX4U 3342
LP: ROCK 3342

What's What

OPEN CHANNEL D.
LP: JAZIDLP 021

Wheater, Paul

TWENTY GOOD YEARS.
MC: CLMC 01

Wheater, Tim

AWAKENINGS.
MC: C 109

BEFORE THE RAINS.
Tracks: / Woman at the well / Where all the waters meet - yeah / White lake / Under moon under moor / Quest, The / Thousand heartbeats, A / Bidi's Song / Beyond time / That distant star / Ring Around The Moon / Stella Maris / Unseen shadows.
LP: TET 4
MC: CTET 4

CALMER PANORAMA, A.
MC: C 506

ENCHANTER, THE.
MC: C 118

NAKED FLAME, THE.
MC: C 146

Wheatley, Dennis

DEVIL RIDES OUT, THE (Rodgers, Anton).
MC: TC-LFP 7111

Wheatstraw, Peetie

DEVILS SON IN LAW, THE (1937-41).
LP: OT 1200
LP: BOB 10

PEETIE WHEATSTRAW 1930-41.
LP: BD 2011

PEETIE WHEATSTRAW AND KOKOMO ARNOLD.
LP: BC 4

Wheel, Catherine

PAINFUL THING EP (See under Catherine Wheel).

Wheel Of Danger

WHEEL OF DANGER, THE (See under Leeson, Robert (Leeson, Robert).

Wheel To Reel

WHEEL TO REEL (Various artists).
MC: ICT 4005

Wheeler, Audrey

LET IT BE ME.
Tracks: / Irresistible / Love on the inside / Forget about her / Somewhere in your life / Time for passion / I miss you, love / Don't lose your touch / Let it be me.
LP: EST 2050
MC: TC EST 2050

Wheeler, Billy Edd

WILD MOUNTAIN FLOWERS.
Tracks: / Coal tattoo / Gypsies drink whisky / Flowers / Lullaby to dad / Coming of the roads, The / Rev. Mr Black, The / High flyin' bird / All American boy / Whistling in the rain / Picker's prayer, A.
LP: . . . . FF 085

Wheeler, Caron

UK BLAK.
Tracks: / UK blak / Livin' in the light (remix) / Blue (is the colour of pain) / No regrets / This is mine / Don't quit (Only on CD) / Jamaica / Never lonely / Song for you / Somewhere / Enchanted / Proud / Kama yo (Only on CD) / Livin' in the light (original story).
LP: . . . . PL 74751
MC: . . . . PK 74751

Wheeler, Ian

REED ALL ABOUT IT (See under Rimington, Sammy) (Wheeler, Ian/ Sammy Rimington).

Wheeler, Kenny

AZIMUTH (see under Taylor, John) (Wheeler, Kenny/John Taylor).

DEER WAN.
LP: . . . . ECM 1102

DOUBLE DOUBLE YOU.
Tracks: / Foxy trot / Ma bel / W. W. / Three for D'reen / Blue for Lou / Mark time.
LP: . . . . ECM 1262

GNU HIGH.
LP: . . . . ECM 1069

LYSIS PLUS KENNY WHEELER (see under Lysis, Roger Dean's) (Wheeler, Kenny & Roger Dean's Lysis).

MUSIC FOR LARGE AND SMALL ENSEMBLES.
Tracks: / Part I (opening) / Part II (For H) / Part III (for Jan) / Part IV (for P.A.) / Part V (know where you are) / Part VI (consolation) / Part VII (Freddy C) / Part VIII (closing) / Sophie / Sea lady / Gentle piece / Trio / Duet I / Duet II / Duet III / Trio / By myself.
2LP: . . . . ECM 1415/16

SONG FOR SOMEONE.
LP: . . . . INCUS 10

WALK SOFTLY (Wheeler, Kenny & Guildhall Jazz Band).
LP: . . . . WAVE LP 32
MC: . . . . WAVE C 32

WIDOW IN THE WINDOW (Wheeler, Kenny Trio).
Tracks: / Aspire / Ma balle Helene / Widow in the window, The / Ana / Hotel le hot / Now, and now again.
LP: . . . . ECM 1417

Wheeler, Onie

JOHN'S BEEN SHUCKIN' MY CORN.
Tracks: / John's been shuckin' my corn / Shuckin' my way to the hall of fame / Run em off / Onie's bop / Might as well hang my britches up / Mother prays loud in her sleep / I saw Mother with God last night / Mother rang the dinner bell / There's heaven to gain, hell to lose / Go home.
LP: . . . . IB 1001

Wheeler, Peter (nar)

BLESS ME FATHER (see under Bless Me Father (bk)).

HIGH COMMISSIONER, THE (see under High Commissioner (bk)).

Wheels Of The World

WHEELS OF THE WORLD (Various artists).
LP: . . . . SHAN 33001

Whelen, Cliff

COUNTRY BOY.
Tracks: / Country boy / Where in this world / When your love was mine / Bridle hanging on the wall / My special angel / My cathedral / Fools rush in / How important can it be? / I'll bet you my heart I love you / Rainbow in my daddy's eyes / Billy Bayou / What God made mothers for.
LP: . . . . SFA 101

HEAVEN TOGETHER.
Tracks: / Unchained melody / They'll never know / Danny boy / Old spinning wheel / Bless you / She wears my ring / I love you more / Trees / Wishful thinking / Heaven together / Railroad bum / It is no secret.
LP: . . . . SFA 081

WELCOME TO MY WORLD.
Tracks: / When you are gone / Welcome to my world / Rose Marie / Virginia / He'll have to go / Legend in my time, A / Yo ho valley / Be nobody's darling but mine / Worthless without you / You're the only good thing / Cup of joy / Kathleen.
LP: . . . . SFA 061

Whelen, John

PRIDE OF WEXFORD.
LP: . . . . SOLP 1024
MC: . . . . COX 1024

Whellans, Mike

DIRT WATER FOX.
LP: . . . . MPA 016

MIKE WHELLANS AND ALY BAIN (Whellans, Mike & Aly Bain).
LP: . . . . LER 2022

SWING TIME JOHNNY RED.
LP: . . . . TP 036
MC: . . . . CTP 036

When A Man Loves A

WHEN A MAN LOVES A WOMAN (Various artists).
LP: . . . . PER 33 8607
MC: . . . . PER 733 8607

When Dinosaurs

WHEN DINOSAURS RULED THE EARTH (Various artists).
2LP: . . . . DLD 3

When Father's Away...

WHEN FATHER'S AWAY ON A BUSINESS TRIP (Original soundtrack) (Various artists).
LP: . . . . A 279

When Greek Meets Greek

WHEN GREEK MEETS GREEK Greene, Graham (Burden, Hugh (nar)).
MC: . . . . TTC/GG 01

When I Was A Cowboy

WHEN I WAS A COWBOY: SONGS OF COWBOY LIFE (Various artists).
LP: 45008

When In Rome

WHEN IN ROME.
Tracks: / Promise, The / Heaven knows / Something going on / I can't stop / If only / Sight of your tears / Wide wide sea / Child's play / Total devotion / Everything / Big city (CD only) / Whatever the weather (CD only).
LP: . . . . DIX 73
MC: . . . . CDIX 73

When Jenny Lost (bk)

WHEN JENNY LOST HER SCARF/ JENNY'S ADOPTED BROTHER (Esther Averill) (Grimes, Tammy (nar)).
MC: . . . . CDL 51608

When Lights Are Low

WHEN LIGHTS ARE LOW (Various artists).
2LP: 6612 103

When Man Is The Prey

WHEN MAN IS THE PREY (Film Soundtrack) (Various artists).
LP: . . . . C'BUS 0118

When People Were

BOBBY.
Tracks: / Muddy Mississippi line / Broomstick cowboy / Watching Scotty crow / Straight life, The / If you've got a heart / See the funny little clown / Can you feel it / Honey / Little things / Autumn of my life / Voodoo woman / With pen in hand / It's too late / My Japanese boy / I'm a drifter.
LP: . . . . SDE 8913
LP: . . . . SHIMMY 024

When The Boys Meet ...

WHEN THE BOYS MEET THE GIRLS (Film Soundtrack) (Various artists).
LP: . . . . MCA 25013
MC: . . . . MCAC 25013

When The Lights Are

WHEN THE LIGHTS ARE LOW (Various artists).
MC: 8429054

When The Whales..

WHEN THE WHALES CAME (Film soundtrack) (Various artists).
Tracks: / Bryher and the curse of Samson: *Various artists* / Gracie plays truant: *Various artists* / Birdman's gift, The: *Various artists* / Islanders, The: *Various artists* / Tempest: *Various artists* / Crown investigators, The: *Various artists* / Daniel's gift for the Birdman: *Various artists* / War and Jack's dilemma: *Various* artists / Birdman's warning: *Various artists* / Lured to Samson: *Various artists* / Clemmie's lament: *Various artists* / Whale beached: *Various artists.*
LP: . . . . FILM 049
MC: . . . . FILMC 049

When the Wind Blows

WHEN THE WIND BLOWS (Film soundtrack) (Various artists).
Tracks: / When the wind blows: *Bowie, David* / Facts and figures: *Cornwell, Hugh* / Brazilian: *Genesis*/ What have they done: *Squeeze* / Shuffle, The: *Hardcastle, Paul* / Towers of faith: *Waters, Roger with the* Bleeding Heart Band / Russian missile, The: *Waters, Roger with the Bleeding Heart Band* / Hilda's dream: *Waters,* Roger with the Bleeding Heart Band / American bomber, The: *Waters, Roger with the Bleeding Heart Band* / Anderson shelter, The: *Waters, Roger with the Bleeding Heart Band* / British submarine, The: *Waters, Roger with the Bleeding Heart Band*/ Attack, The: *Waters, Roger with the Bleeding Heart Band* / Fallout: *Waters, Roger with the Bleeding Heart Band*/ Hilda's hair: *Waters, Roger with the Bleeding Heart Band* / Folded flags: *Waters, Roger with the Bleeding Heart Band.*
LP: . . . . V 2406
MC: . . . . TCV 2406
LP: . . . . OVED 259
MC: . . . . OVEDC 259

WHEN THE WIND BLOWS (SINGLE) (See under Bowie, David).

When We Were...(bk)

WHEN WE WERE VERY YOUNG.
MCSET: . . . . DTO 10560

WHEN WE WERE VERY YOUNG (see under Milne, A.A.) (Shelley, Norman).

When You're in Love...

WHEN YOU'RE IN LOVE THE WHOLE WORLD IS JEWISH (See under Booker, Bob).

Where Eagles Dare (bk)

WERE EAGLES DARE (Film soundtrack) (Various artists).
LP: . . . . MCA 25082
MC: . . . . MCAC 25082

WHERE EAGLES DARE (read by Martin Jarvis).
MC: . . . . TC LFP 7084

WHERE EAGLES DARE/633 SQUADRON (Film Soundtracks) (Various artists).
Tracks: / Where eagles dare (main title): *Various artists* (Where Eagles Dare.) / Ascent on the cable car: *Various* artists (Where Eagles Dare.) / Pursued by the enemy: *Various artists* (Where Eagles Dare.) / Booby trap, The: *Various* artists (Where Eagles Dare.) / Encounter in the castle: *Various artists* (Where Eagles Dare.) / On enemy territory: *Various artists* (Where Eagles Dare.) / Descent and fight on the cable car: *Various artists* (Where Eagles Dare.) / Chase to the airfield: *Various artists* (Where Eagles Dare.) / Six three three squadron (main title): *Various artists*(633 Squadron.) / Memories of Norway: *Various artists* (633 Squadron.) / Love theme: *Various artists* (633 Squadron.) / Attack begins, The: *Various artists* (633 Squadron.) / Murder mission: *Various artists* (633 Squadron.) / Crash flight: *Various artists* (633 Squadron.) / Love theme: *Various artists* (633 Squadron.) / Escape from Norway: *Various* artists (633 Squadron.) / Peace and war: *Various artists* (633 Squadron.) / Apprehension: *Various artists*(633 Squadron.) / Love theme (End title): *Various artists* (633 Squadron.).
LP: . . . . LPMGM 13
LP: 794 094 1
MC: . . . . TCMGM 13
MC: 794 094 4

Where Eagles Fly

WHERE EAGLES FLY (Various artists).
MC: . . . . ZCF 771

Where Have We Met

WHERE HAVE WE MET BEFORE (Various artists).
Tracks: / We'll be the same: *Various artists* / You forgot your gloves: *Various artists* / And so to bed: *Various* artists / Where have we met before: *Various artists* / Let's call it a day: *Various artists* / Are you making any money: *Various artists* / Coffee in the morning: *Various artists* / What can you say in a love song: *Various* artists / That lucky fellow: *Various artists* / Boys and girls like you and me: *Various artists* / Only another boy and girl: *Various artists* / Nobody else but me: *Various artists* / Can you just see yourself: *Various artists.*
LP: . . . . NW 240

Where The River ...

WHERE THE RIVER RUNS BLACK (Film soundtrack) (Various artists).
LP: . . . . STV 81290
MC: . . . . CTV 81290

Where The Wild Things

WHERE THE WILD THINGS ARE AND OTHER STORIES (Sendak, Maurice) (Grimes, Tammy (nar)).
LP: . . . . TC 1531
MC: . . . . CDL 51531

Whidden, Jay

MORE WE ARE TOGETHER (Whidden, Jay & His New Midnight Follies Band).
Tracks: / You've got those wanna-go-back-again blues / Hello, baby / Let's all go to Mary's house / For my sweetheart / Hangin' around / Me and my shadow / Up and at 'em / I don't want nobody / More we are together / Always some new baby / Shepherd of the hills / Since Tommy Atkins taught the Chinese / At sundown.
LP: . . . . SH 426

While The Billy Boils

WHILE THE BILLY BOILS (Various artists).
2LP: . . . . LRD 901/2

Whiplash

INSULT TO INJURY.
Tracks: / Voice of sanity / Hiroshima / Insult to injury / Dementia B / Essence of evil / Witness to the terror / Battle scars / Rape to the mind / Ticket to mayhem / 4.E.S. / Pistolwhipped.
LP: . . . . RO 9482-1

POWER AND PAIN.
LP: . . . . RR 9718

TICKET TO MAYHEM.
LP: . . . . RR 9596

Whippersnapper

PROMISES (Whippersnapper Featuring Dave Swarbrick).
Tracks: / Whenever / Banks of the sweet primroses / A Sean bhean bhocht / John Gaudie / One way donkey ride / Hard times of old England / Downtown rodeo / Carolanning / Loving Hannah / Lizzie Wan / An Sean bhean bhocht / Gipsys rest, The / John broke the prison door.
LP: . . . . WPS 001

THESE FOOLISH STRINGS.
MC: . . . . WPSC 003

TSUBO.
Tracks: / Farewell my lovely Nancy / Pride of Kildare, The / Rouge and the red shoes / I wandered by a Brookside / Seven keys, The / Romanitza / Deneze sous doue (on the wall) / Frank Dempsey's lament and joy / My little fiddle / There's a river.
LP: . . . . WPS 002

WHIPPERSNAPPER.
Tracks: / Farewell my lovely Nancy / Pride of kildare, The / Rouge and the red shoes / I wandered by a brookside / Seven keys, The / Romanitza / Deneze sous doue (on the wall) / Frank Dempsey's lament and joy / My little fiddle / There's a river.
LP: . . . . WPS 001

Whirlpool Guest House

PICTURES ON THE PAVEMENT.
LP: . . . . SUML 004

Whirlwind

BLOWING UP A STORM.
Tracks: / Boppin' high school baby / My bucket's got a hole in it / My advice / Thousand stars, A / One more chance / Don't be crazy / Rockin daddy / Slow down / Blue moon of Kentucky / Together for ever / Who's that knocking tore apart.
LP: . . . . CWK 3007

MIDNIGHT BLUE.
Tracks: / Midnight blue / Teenage cutie / You got class / Honey hush / Cruisin' around / Stay cool / Running wild / Okie's in the polie / Heaven knows / Big Sandy / Such a fool / Nightmares / If it's all the same to you / Stayin' out all night.
LP: . . . . CWK 3012
MC: . . . . TC CWK 3012

Whiskey, Nancy

FREIGHT TRAIN (See under McDevitt, Chas) (Whiskey, Nancy & Chas McDevitt).

Whisnant, Johnnie

JOHNNIE WHISNANT.
LP: . . . . ROUNDER 0038

Whisperers

WHISPERERS, THE (Film Soundtrack) (Various artists).
LP: . . . . MCA 25041
MC: . . . . MCAC 25041

Whispering Wind Band

WHISPERING WIND BAND.
LP: . . . . HAR 811
MC: . . . . HAC 811

Whispers

BEST OF THE WHISPERS.
Tracks: / Beat goes on / Make it with you / Lost & turned out / Loving together / One for the money / I can make it better / It's a love thing.
LP: . . . . SOLA 12
MC: . . . . SOLC 12

HEADLIGHTS.
Tracks: / Headlights / (Olivia) Lost and turned out / (Let's go) All the way / (You're a) Special part of my life / Planets of life, The / Try and make it better / Disco melody / Children of tomorrow.
LP: . . . . FL 12774
MC: . . . . FK 12774

IMAGINATION.
Tracks: / It's a love thing / Say you would love for me too / Continental shuffle / I can make it better / Imagination / Girl I need you / Up on soul train / Fantasy.
LP: . . . . SOLA 7

JUST GETS BETTER WITH TIME.
Tracks: / I want you / Special FX / Rock steady / No pain, no gain / In the mood / Just gets better with time / Love's calling / Give it to me.
LP: . . . . MCF 3381
MC: . . . . MCFC 3381
LP: . . . . MIRF 1021
MC: . . . . MIRFC 1021

LOVE FOR LOVE.
Tracks: / Tonight / Keep on lovin' me / Love for love / This time / Had it not been for you / Try it again / Do they turn you on / Keep your love around / Lay it on me.
LP: E0216

LOVE IS WHERE YOU FIND IT.
Tracks: / In the raw / Turn me out / Cruisin' in / Emergency / Say yes / Love is where you find it / Only you / Small talkin'.
LP: . . . . K 52344

MORE OF THE NIGHT.
Tracks: / Innocent / Girl don't make me wait / Misunderstanding / Forever lover / Babes / More of the night / My heart your heart / Mind blowing / Is it good to you / Don't be late for love (Cassette & CD only.) / You are the one (Cassette & CD only.) / I want 2B the 14U (Cassette & CD only.) / Help them see the light (Cassette & CD only.).
LP: . . . . EST 2130
LP: 792 957 1
MC: . . . . TCEST 2130
MC: 792 957 4

OPEN UP YOUR LOVE.
Tracks: / Make it with you / Chocolate girl / Love is a dream / Open up your love / I fell in love last night (at the disco) / You are Number One / You never miss your water / I'm gonna make you my wife.
LP: . . . . FL 12270

SO GOOD.
Tracks: / Some kinda lover / Contagious / Sweet sensation / Impact / Romancin'III / Suddenly / Don't keep me waiting / Are you going my way / Never too late / So good.
LP: . . . . MCL 1845
MC: . . . . MCLC 1845
LP: . . . . MCF 3252
MC: . . . . MCFC 3252
LP: 603 561

THIS KIND OF LOVIN.
Tracks: / This kind of lovin' / World of a thousand dreams / I'm the one for you / Got to get away / I'm gonna love you more / Can't stop loving you baby / What will I do / Bright lights and you girl, The.
LP: . . . . SOLA 9
MC: . . . . SOLC 9

WHISPER IN YOUR EAR.
Tracks: / Homemade livin' / If I don't get your love / Whisper in your ear / Love at its best / Can't do without love / Pretty lady / You'll never get away.
LP: . . . . FL 13105

WHISPERS.
Tracks: / Song for Donny / My girl / Lady can you do the boogie / Beat goes on / I love you / Out the box / Welcome into my dream.
LP: . . . . SOLA 1

Whistle

WHISTLE.
LP: . . . . CHAMP 1002
MC: . . . . CHAMPK 1002

Whistle Away Your

WHISTLE AWAY YOUR BLUES (Various artists).
Tracks: / Whistle away your blues: *Whidden, Jay Band* / Mon Paris: *Whidden, Jay Band* / Why Robinson Crusoe got the blues: *Savoy Havana Band* / When it's night time in Italy: *Casino Dance Orchestra* / Sunny Havana: *New Prince Toronto Band* / To know you is to love you: *Hylton, Jack* / Dreamy Honolulu: *Hylton, Jack* / Today's a sunny day for me: *Shakespeare, Lloyd Band* / Laughing marionette: *Shakespeare, Lloyd Band* / Here I am broken hearted: *Gold, Lou Band* / Little old church in the valley: *Layton & Johnstone* / Carolina moon: *Blair, Norman* / Just plain folk: *Blair, Norman* / Gonna get a girl: *Admirals* / White wings: *Oakland, Will* / Side by side: *Lanin, Sam* / I love a lassie: *Lauder, Harry* / Wedding of Lauchie McGraw, The: *Lauder, Harry* / Wee Deoch an' Doris: *Lauder, Harry.*
MC: . . . . CSDL 370

Whistlebinkies

WHISTLEBINKIES, VOL 1.
LP: . . . . CC 22
MC: 4CC 22

WHISTLEBINKIES, VOL 2.
LP: . . . . CC 31
MC: 4CC 31

WHISTLEBINKIES, VOL 3.
LP: . . . . CC 34
MC: 4CC 34

WHISTLEBINKIES, VOL. 4.
LP: . . . . CC 43
MC: 4CC 43

Whistleblower

WHISTLEBLOWER, THE (Film soundtrack) (Royal Philharmonic Orchestra).
Tracks: / Whistleblowers, The / Quiet times with Cynthia / Whistle power, Theme from / Hidden world, The / Frank and Bob (Their secret world) / Back in the cell / Dodgesongs defection / Death of Bob / Tidy room, The / Who is big mole / They have put out the lights / Why was my son killed / Penetrating the hidden world / Meeting big mole / Whistleblowers, The: Epilogue.
LP: . . . . TER 1139

Whitburn Burgh Band

CHRISTMAS WITH BRASS.
Tracks: / God rest ye merry gentlemen / Deck the hall / Infant holy / Angel Gabriel, The / See, amid the winter's snow / Beside thy cradle / Good King Wenceslas / Smiling morn / Pastoral symphony / O come all ye faithful / Away in a manger / Angels from the realms of glory / Little road to Bethlehem, The / Ding dong merrily on high / Little church bell / Silent night / In the bleak mid winter / Rocking carol, The / We wish you a merry Christmas / Guid new year, A.
LP: . . . . NTS 139

WITHBURN BRASS.
Tracks: / Lenzburg / Lazy trumpeter / Falcons / Belmont variations / Barber of Seville overture / I need thee / Phil the fluter's ball / Send in the clown / Royal border bridge.
LP: . . . . NA 112

Whitchurch Male Choir

ABIDE WITH ME (Whitchurch Male Voice Choir).
LP: . . . . BBX 501

Whitcomb, Ian

ALL THE HITS PLUS MORE.
LP: . . . . PRST 005
MC: . . . . ZPRST 005

AT THE RAGTIME BALL (Whitcomb, Ian and His Melody Makers).
LP: . . . . AP 147

BOOGIE WOOGIE JUNGLE SNAKE.
Tracks: / Rough trade / Eat you up / Don't trust your heart / Sally in the garage / Whole lotta woman / Pure sorrow / Boogie woogie jungle snake / Roses in the rain / Approaching youths / Yellow bird / Yomping / Changes.
LP: . . . . ITW 1

DON'T SAY GOODBYE (Whitcomb, Ian & Dick Zimmerman).
LP: . . . . SOS 1017

MY WIFE IS DANCING MAD (See under Zimmerman, Dick) (Whitcomb, Ian & Dick Zimmerman).

OCEANS OF LOVE.
LP: . . . . ITW 4

ON THE STREETS OF DREAMS.
LP: . . . . ITW 3

PIANOMELT.
LP: . . . . SRS 8708

RAG ODYSSEY.
Tracks: / Every now and then / Cocaine Lil / Blue jeans / At the vicarage party / Night childs / Roots / Lotusland-a rag of southern California / Till you come home / When the folks high up do the mean low down / Emma Louise (in old Los Angeles) / Lazy / Marzipan a ragtime confection / Someday, somebody's gonna get you / Storybook farm / Brown eyes why are you blue?.
LP: . . . . MTM 006

STEPPIN' OUT (Whitcomb, Ian & Dick Zimmerman).
LP: . . . . AP 225

TREASURES OF TIN PAN ALLEY.
LP: . . . . AP 115

White, Alan

RAMSHACKLED.
LP: . . . . K 50217

RUN WITH THE FOX (See under Squire, Chris) (White, Alan & Chris Squire).

White, Andy

HIMSELF.
Tracks: / In a groovy kinda way / 1,000,000 miles / Six string street / Freeze out / Just jumped out of a tree / 20 years / Guildford four, The / Pale moonlight, The / Bird of passage / St.Patrick's good luck / Coup I / Whole love story, The / Six string street (30 mph) (Only on CD.) / Travelling circus (Only on CD.).
LP: . . . . COOK 029
MC: . . . . COOKC 029

KISS THE BIG STONE.
Tracks: / Come down to the sea / Daisy / Broken hearted / Tower of Babel time / You and your blue skies / Here come the girls / Go tell Susanne / Hanging around with you / West wind blues.
LP: . . . . FLP 101
MC: . . . . FMC 101

RAVE ON ANDY WHITE.
Tracks: / Soldier's sash / Vision of you / Reality row / I will wait / Things start to unwind / Religious persuasion / Tuesday apocalypse 13 / Rembrandt hat / Walking wounded / Big rain.
LP: . . . . FLP 100
MC: . . . . FMC 100

White, Anthony

WALK AWAY FROM LOVE (See under Simpson, Paul for details) (White, Anthony/Paul Simpson).

White, Artie

DARK END OF THE STREET.
Tracks: / Tore up / Clock don't tick / Nite before pay day / Not in the begging business / Somebody changed my sweet baby's mind / Dark end of the street / Hit the nail on the head / I intend to take your place / Darlin' you know I love you / I'm mean.
LP: . . . . ICH 1117
MC: . . . . ICH 1117MC

NOTHING TAKES THE PLACE OF YOU.
Tracks: / Wondering how you keep your man / How could you do it to me / Lies I want to hear / All you got / Funny how time slips away / Nothing takes the place of you / Ever loving man / I found a woman / I need someone.
LP: . . . . ICH 1008
MC: . . . . ZCICH 1008

THINGS GOT TO CHANGE.
Tracks: / Things got to change / Rainy day / I ain't taking no prisoners / You upset me baby / Thank you pretty baby / Hattie Mae / I wonder why / Reconsider baby / Somebody's on my case.
LP: . . . . ICH 1044
MC: . . . . ZCICH 1044

TIRED OF SNEAKIN' AROUND.
Tracks: / Today I started loving you / Thinking about making a change / Jodie / Peeping Tom / Tired of sneaking around / Don't pet my dog / Can't get you off my mind / I can't seem to please you / Turn about is fair play / Nose to the grindstone.
LP: . . . . ICH 1061
MC: . . . . ICH 1061MC

WHERE IT'S AT.
LP: . . . . ICH 1026
MC: . . . . ZCICH 1026

White, Barry

BARRY AND GLODEAN (White, Barry & Glodean).
Tracks: / Our theme / I want you / You're the only one for me / This love / Better love is / You / We can't let go of love / You make my life easy livin' / Didn't we make it happen baby.
LP: . . . . ULG 84870
MC: 40 84870

BARRY WHITE-HEART AND SOUL.
Tracks: / You're the first, the last, my everything / I'm gonna love you just a little bit more baby / Standing in the shadows of love / What am I gonna do about you? / Never never gonna give you up / I love to sing the songs I sing / Don't make me wait too long / You see the trouble with me / Love serenade / It's ecstasy when you lay down next to me / I can't get enough of you're love / I'm qualified to satisfy you / Sha la la means I love you / Honey please can't you see / I've found someone / Let me live my life loving you babe / Let the music play / Baby we better try and get it together / Playing your game baby / I've got so much to give / September when I first met you / Love's theme.
LP: . . . . NE 1314
MC: . . . . CE 2314

BARRY WHITE'S SHEET MUSIC.
Tracks: / Sheet music / Lady / Sweet lady / I believe in love / Ghetto letto / Rum and coke / She's everything to me / Love makin' music.
LP: . . . . ULG 83927
MC: 40 83927

BEST OF BARRY WHITE.
Tracks: / I've got so much to give / Midnight and you / Bring back my yesterdays / Love's theme / I've found someone / Under the influence of love / You're the first, the last, my everything / Together brothers (From the film.) / I'll do for you anything you want me to / I belong to you.
LP: 9279 576
MC: 7259 576

BEST OF BARRY WHITE AND LOVE UNLIMITED ORCHESTRA.
Tracks: / Let the music play / Midnight and you / Don't make me wait too long / I'm qualified to satisfy you / Under the influence of love / Love's theme / Your sweetness is my weakness / I'll do for you anything you want me / I belong to you.
LP: 8129431
MC: 8129434

BEST OF OUR LOVE.
Tracks: / I love to sing the songs I sing / Let me live my life loving you babe / It's ecstasy when you lay down next to me / I'm gonna love you just a little bit more / Can't get enough of your love babe / You're the first the last my everything / You see the trouble with me / Playing your game baby / September when I first met you / Just the way you are / Oh love well we finally made it / I'm under the influence of love / I belong to you / Walkin' in the rain with the one I love / I guess I'm just (another girl in love) / My sweet summer suite / Midnight and you / Satin soul / Baby blues / Love's theme.
LP: . . . . ULG 88520

CAN'T GET ENOUGH.
LP: . . . . BT 444

CHANGE.
Tracks: / Change / Turnin' on, tunin' in / Let's make tonight an evening to remember / Don't tell me about heartaches / Passion / I've got that love fever / I like you, you like me / It's all about love.
LP: . . . . ULG 85788

COLLECTION: BARRY WHITE.
Tracks: / You're the first, the last, my everything / You see the trouble with me / Can't get enough of your love babe / I'll do for you anything you want me to / Just the way you are / Walking in the rain (with the one I love) / It may be Winter outside / Love's theme / Sho' you right / What am I gonna do with you? / Never never gonna give you up / Baby we better try and get it together / Let the music play / Don't make me wait too long / I'm gonna love you just a little more babe / Right night, The.
LP: . . . . BWTV 1
MC: . . . . BWTVC 1

DEDICATED.
Tracks: / America / Free / Don't forget... remember / Life / Love song / All in the run of a day / Don't let 'em blow your mind / Dreams.
LP: . . . . ULG 25474
MC: 40 25474

GREATEST HITS: BARRY WHITE, VOL.1.
Tracks: / What am I gonna do with you / You're the first, the last, my everything / Can't get enough of your love, babe / Honey please can't you see / Love serenade / Never never gonna give ya up / I'm gonna love you just a little more baby / I've found someone / I've too much to give / Standing in the shadows of love.
LP: . . . . PRICE 13
MC: . . . . PRIMC 13
LP: . . . . BTH 8000
LP: . . . . T 493

GREATEST HITS: BARRY WHITE, VOL. 2.
LP: . . . . BTH 8001

HEART AND SOUL.
LP: . . . . NE 1316

I LOVE TO SING THE SONGS I SING.
Tracks: / I love to sing the songs I sing / Girl, what's your name / Once upon a time / Oh me oh my / I can't leave you alone / Call me baby / How did you know it was me.
LP: . . . . T 590

JUST ANOTHER WAY TO SAY I LOVE YOU.
LP: . . . . BT 466

LET THE MUSIC PLAY.
LP: . . . . BT 502

MAN IS BACK, THE.

Tracks: / Responsible / Super lover / L.A. my kinda place / Follow that and see (where it leads y'all) / When will I see you again / I wanna do it good to ya / It's getting harder all the time / Don't let go / Loves interlude / Goodnight my love.
LP: . . . . AMA 5256
MC: . . . . AMC 5256

MAN, THE.
Tracks: / Look at her / Your sweetness is my weakness / Sha la la means I love you / September when I first met you / It's only love doing it's thing / Just the way you are / Early years.
LP: . . . . BT 571

MESSAGE IS LOVE,THE.
Tracks: / It ain't love baby / Hung up in your love / You're the one I need / Any fool could see / Love ain't easy / I'm on fire / I found love.
LP: . . . . ULG 83475
MC: 40 83475

PUT ME IN YOUR MIX.
LP: 395377 1
MC: 395377 4

RHAPSODY IN WHITE.
LP: . . . . NSPL 28191

RIGHT NIGHT AND BARRY WHITE, THE.
Tracks: / Sho' you right / For your love / There is a place / Love is in your eyes / Right night, The / I'm ready for love / Share / Who's the fool.
LP: . . . . AMA 5154
MC: . . . . AMC 5154

SATIN AND SOUL.
Tracks: / You're the first, the last, my everything / Can't get enough of your love babe / It may be Winter outside / I'll do for you anything you want me to / Honey please can't you see / Satin soul / Never gonna give ya up / I love to sing the songs I sing / You see the trouble with me / Playing your game / I needed your love, you were there / Hard to believe that I found you / Standing in the shadows of love / I can't let him down / Only you can make me blue / Heavenly that's what you are to me / Oh love we finally made it / Love serenade / Just the way you are / Bring back my yesterdays / Baby blues / Midnight and you / September when I first met you / Love's theme.
LP: . . . . VSOPLP 101
MC: . . . . VSOPMC 101

STONE GON'.
LP: . . . . NSPL 28186

WITH LOVE UNLIMITED.
Tracks: / Walking in the rain with the one I love / Don't make me wait too long / Don't tell me about heartaches / I won't settle for less than the best / Didn't we make it happen baby / Let me in, let's begin with love / Let the music play / Lady sweet lady / I like you, you like me / Change / Gotta be where you are / What am I gonna do with you / You're the one I need / Life / Any fool could see / I found love / Our theme (part 2) / Baby we better try and get it together / She's everything to me / Let's make tonight an evening to remember / I can't let him down / You're the only one for me.
2LP: . . . . VSOPLP 154
MCSET: . . . . VSOPMC 154

White Brothers

LIVE IN SWEDEN (White Brothers & The New Kentucky Colonels).
LP: . . . . ROUNDER 0073

White, Buck

BUCK WHITE/DOWNHOME FOLKS.
LP: . . . . SAVE 033

DARKNESS ON THE DELTA (See under Baker, Kenny) (Baker, Kenny & Bob Hicks).

MORE PRETTY GIRLS THAN ONE.
LP: . . . . SH 3710

White, Bukka

ABERDEEN MISSISSIPPI BLUES 1937-40.
Tracks: / Pine bluff arkansas / Shake 'em on down / Black train blues / Strange places blues / Where I change my clothes / Sleepy man blues / Parchman farm blues / Good gin blues / High fever blues / District attorney blues / Fixin' to die / Aberdeen Mississippi Blues / Bukka's jitterbug swing / Special streamline.
LP: . . . . TM 806

BIG DADDY.
Tracks: / Black cat bone blues / 1936 triggertoe / Cryin' Holy unto the Lord / Shake my hand blues / Sic 'Em Dogs On / Gibson Hill / Mama Don' Low / Hot springs Arkansas / Jelly Roll working / Black crepe blues / Glory bound train / Aberdeen Mississippi blues.
LP: . . . . BMLP 1039

FURRY AND BUKKA 1968 (White, Bukka/Furry Lewis).
LP: . . . . C 5524

LEGACY OF THE BLUES VOL. 1 (See under Legacy of the Blues).

SKY SONGS VOL.1.
LP: . . . . ARHOOLIE 1019

SKY SONGS VOL.2.
LP: . . . . ARHOOLIE 1020

White, Carla

ANDRULINE (White, Carla & Manny Duran Band).
LP: . . . . ST 237

White, Chris

SHADOWDANCE.
Tracks: / Control / Mr. Fats / New day, A / Shadowdance / Don't take no / Jericho walls / Eve's song / You will / Dreamtime / Brillant silence / Way of life, A.
LP: 26007162
MC: 46007162
LP: . . . . LELP 11

White, Christine

PURE LOVE.
LP: . . . . BJLP 001

White, Clarence

MULESKINNER.
LP: . . . . RRR 016

White, Clifford

ASCENSION.
MC: . . . . C 113

LIFESPRING, THE.
Tracks: / Last snows of winter, The / Voyage, voyage / In the beginning / Lost at shore / Rain trek / Hym-Malaya / Water garden / Lifestream / Plateau / Shimmering gold / First to love.
LP: . . . . STL 21
MC: . . . . STC 21

White Cross

BRIDE, THE.
LP: . . . . CSH 1205

White, D

D. WHITE/ B. TRIGLIA (White, D & B. Triglia).
LP: . . . . SPJ LP 26

White Door

WINDOWS.
LP: . . . . CLAYLP 7

White, Dr. Michael

CRESCENT CITY SERENDADE.
MC: . . . . ANC 8763

White Flag/ Necros

GEIGER COUNTER.
LP: JC9D 12

SGT. PEPPER.
LP: . . . . WETLP 001

White, Frank

ONE MORE LONELY NIGHT.
Tracks: / One more lonely night / Louisiana 1927 / Love sweet love / Doctor Rhythm / I took a chance / Takin' the easy way / You made a promise / Don't walk away / Preacher, The.
LP: . . . . PYL 16
MC: . . . . PYM 16

White, Freddie

DO YOU DO.
LP: . . . . LUN 044

LIVE TOUR 1978.
LP: . . . . LUN 032

LONG DISTANCE RUNNER.
Tracks: / Werewolf / Wedding in Cherokee county / Frozen heart / Long distance runner / It's you / Voices / Love like blood / Down without a fight / Christmas in Capetown / Goodbye this time.
LP: . . . . TA 3013
MC: 4TA 3013

White, Georgia

GEORGIA WHITE.
LP: . . . . BD 2080

SINGS AND PLAYS THE BLUES.
LP: . . . . RR 1307

White Glove Test

LEAP.
Tracks: / Leap / Worshipping boys / Lisa / Pandora's song / Moment / Between the oars / Poignant / Bicycle / All and everything / Everyday.
LP: . . . . SAVE 81

LOOK.
Tracks: / Look / Gasping for air / Break song / Blue is my colour / At The Village Gates.
LP: . . . . WEEAT 003

White Hart

IN SEARCH OF REWARD.
LP: . . . . TSR 033

White Heart

DON'T WAIT FOR THE MOVIE.
LP: . . . . BIRD R 179
MC: . . . . BIRD C 179

FREEDOM.
Tracks: / Bye bye Babylon / Sing your freedom / Kingdom come / Over me / Eighth wonder / Power tools (Warning of dangerous leaders; Khomeini, or is the target nearer home?) / Invitation / Let it go / I'll meet you there.
LP: . . . . SP R 1194
MC: . . . . SP C 1194

White Heat

IN THE ZERO HOUR.
Tracks: / City beat / Nervous breakdown / Bad jokes / Living in the UK / Twenty one and wasted / Funny suits / In the zero hour / Marilyn Monroe / Still hungry / Streets after dark.
LP: . . . . VALP 101

White Heather Show

WHITE HEATHER SHOW (Various artists).
MCSET: . . . . DTO 10095

White Horse Inn

WHITE HORSE INN (Stage play) (Various artists).
Tracks: / White Horse Inn: *Various artists* / Goodbye: *Various artists* / My song of love: *Various artists*/ Your eyes: *Various artists* / Sigismund: *Various artists.*
2LP: . . . . SLS 5184
MC: . . . . TCSLS 5184

White, James

JAMES WHITE AND THE BLACKS (White, James & The Blacks).
Tracks: / Off white / Contort yourself / Stained sheets / Heatwave / Almost black / White savages / Off black / White devil / Bleached black.
LP: . . . . ILPS 7008

SAX MANIAC (White, James & The Blacks).
Tracks: / Irresistible impulse / That old black magic / Disco jaded / Money to burn / Sax maniac / Sax machine / Twitch.
LP: . . . . CHR 1401

White, John

COUNTRY AND IRISH FAVOURITES.
MC: . . . . GTDC 085

MACHINE MUSIC (White, John/Gavin Bryars).
LP: . . . . EGED 28

NIGHT PEOPLE.
Tracks: / I need your love / Can't get you out of my system / Night people / Forbidden love / Victim / Don't let it be too late / Fooled around / Mood for love / I wanna get close to you / Let's talk it over / Keep it up / Heading in the right direction / Rockin' & lovin' / New love / Ultimate love / I'm gonna love you.
LP: 9241251
MC: 9241254

SONGS OF HOME AND FAR AWAY.
MC: . . . . HSMC 046

White, Josh

BLUES ANS SPIRITUALS (White, Josh & The Ronnie Sisters).
LP: . . . . SM 3512

JOSH WHITE JUNIOR.
LP: . . . . VSD 79406

JOSH WHITE, VOL.2 1929-35.
LP: . . . . BD 619

JOSHUA WHITE 1936-41 (White, Josh & his Carolinians).
LP: . . . . BOB 11

JOSHUA WHITE = PINEWOOD TOM 1932-33.
LP: . . . . BD 606

LEGEND OF LEADBELLY (White, Josh/ Sonny Terry).
LP: . . . . SM 3964

WORLD OF JOSH WHITE, THE.
LP: . . . . SPA 44

White, Karyn

KARYN WHITE.
Tracks: / Way you love me, The / Secret rendezvous / Slow down / Super woman / Family man / Love saw it / Don't mess with me / Tell me tomorrow / One wish.
LP: . . . . WX 235
MC: . . . . WX 235 C

RITUAL OF LOVE.
MC: . . . . WX 411C
LP: . . . . WX 411

White, Kitty

SUITE TALK.
LP: . . . . FS 219

White, Lenny

STREAMLINE.
Tracks: / Struttin' / Lady Madonna / 12 bars from Mars / Earthlings / Spazmo strikes again / Time / Pooh bear / Lockie's inspiration / I'll see you soon / Night games / Cosmic indigo.
LP: . . . . K 52108

TWENNYNINE WITH LENNY WHITE.
Tracks: / Just right for me / It's music, it's magic / My melody / Kid stuff / Fancy dancer / Love & be loved / Back to you / Slip away / We had to break away / 11th fanfare.
LP: . . . . K 52257

White Lightning

AS MIDNIGHT APPROACHES.
Tracks: / Lesson one / Danger man / Blue horizon / Hypocrite / London nightlife / Right between the eyes / This poison fountain / Losing streak / Frightened children.
LP: . . . . PP 2000
LP: . . . . JOBLP 2
MC: . . . . JOBMC 2

White Line Fever

WHITE LINE FEVER (Various artists).
LP: . . . . LBR 1045
MC: . . . . TCR 1045

White Lion

BIG GAME.
LP: . . . . WX 277
MC: . . . . WX 277C

FIGHT TO SURVIVE.
LP: . . . . SLAM 1

MANE ATTRACTION.
LP: . . . . WX 415

PRIDE.
Tracks: / Hungry / Lonely nights / Don't give up / Sweet little loving / Lady of the valley / Wait / All you need is rock 'n' roll / Tell me / All join our hands / When the children cry.
LP: 781 768-1
MC: 781 768-4

White, Lynn

LOVE AND HAPPINESS.
Tracks: / See you later bye / Eight men, four women / Your woman is home tonight / If you think you're lonely now / Steal away / Love me like you do / I'm gonna find me a lover tonight / Love and happiness / Fool don't live here anymore / Don't quit.
LP: . . . . TRPL 123

SUCCESS.
Tracks: / Don't let success / I made a mistake / Anyway the wind blows / Baby for you / Giving it all I got / I can't give you what you want / Sorry / Gonna be some changes made / Caught you with your love down / All because of your love.
LP: . . . . TRLP 105

YES I'M READY.
LP: . . . . WAY 2695051
MC: . . . . WAY 2695054

White Mansions

WHITE MANSIONS (A tale from the American Civil War 1861-65) (Various artists).
Tracks: / Story to tell: *Various artists* / Dixie, hold on: *Various artists* / Join around the flag: *Various* artists / White trash: *Various artists* / Last dance and the Kentucky racehorse, The: *Various artists* / Southern boys: *Various artists* / Union mare and confederate grey: *Various artists* / No one would believe a summer could be so cold: *Various artists* / Southland's bleeding, The: *Various artists* / Bring up the twelve pounders: *Various* artists / They laid waste to our land: *Various artists* / Praise the lord: *Various artists* / King has called me home, The: *Various artists* / Bad man: *Various artists* / Dixie now your done: *Various artists.*
2LP: . . . . AMLX 64691
MC: . . . . CXM 64691

White, Maurice

MAURICE WHITE.
Tracks: / Switch on your radio / Jamboree / Stand by me / Sea of glass / I need you / Believe in magic / Lady is love / Invitation / Sleeping flame / Alpha dance / Children of Africa.
LP: . . . . CBS 26637
MC: 40 26637

White, Michael

CHESTER ZARDIS & HIS HOT FIVE/ MICHAEL WHITE & HIS LIBERTY... (see Zardis,Chester) (White, Michael/ Chester Zardis).

MICHAEL WHITE.
Tracks: / Fantasy / I know you need someone / Bring on the night / Matriach / One good turn / Psychometry / Deja vu / Jumpin' the fence / Radio.

LP: 781 753-1
MC: 781 753-4

MICHAEL WHITE'S NEW ORLEANS MUSIC.
Tracks: / Shake it and break it / Am I blue / Please don't talk about me when I'm gone / In the upper garden / Mama Inez / It's a sin to tell a lie / Apex blues / Girl of my dreams / Baby won't you please come home / Exactly like you.
LP: . . . . NOLA LP 22

SHAKE IT BREAK IT.
LP: . . . . LPS 6

WENDELL EUGENE AND FRIENDS (See Under Eugene, Wendell) (White, Michael, Wendell Eugene, Teddy Riley, Kid Sheik Cola).

X FACTOR, THE.
LP: . . . . K 52095

White Mischief

WHITE MISCHIEF (Film soundtrack) (Various artists).
MC: . . . . ZCTER 1153
LP: . . . . TER 1153

White Monkey (bk)

WHITE MONKEY, THE (see under Galsworthy, James) (Jarvis, Martin (nar)).

White Nights

WHITE NIGHTS (Film soundtrack) (Various artists).
Tracks: / Separate lives: *Collins, Phil & Marilyn Martin* / People on a string: *Flack, Roberta* / Snake charmer: *Hiatt, John* / Prove me wrong: *Pack, David* / People have to move: *Burton, Jenny* / Other side of the world, The: *Khan, Chaka* / My love is chemical: *Reed, Lou* / Far Post: *Plant, Robert* / Raymond's tune: *Rogers,Nile* / This is your day: *Rogers, Nile & Sandy Stewart.*
LP: 781 273-1
MC: 781 273-4

White Noise

ELECTRIC STORM, AN.
LP: . . . . ILPS 9099

White Palace

WHITE PALACE (Original Soundtrack) (Various artists).
LP: . . . . VS 5289
MC: . . . . VSC 5289

White, Robert

BEAUTIFUL DREAMER Robert White sings Stephen Foster.
Tracks: / Beautiful dreamer / I dream of Jeannie with the light brown hair / Come with thy sweet voice again / Ah may the red rose live always / My old Kentucky home / Old folks at home / Sweetly she sleeps my Alice fair / Some folks / Gentle Annie / Linger in blissful repose / Slumber my darling / Old black Joe.
LP: . . . . PL 70306
MC: . . . . PK 70306
LP: . . . . RCALP 6035

BY THE LIGHT OF THE SILVERY MOON.
Tracks: / My blue Heaven / Poor butterfly / Bye bye blackbird / When I grow too old to dream / Shine on harvest moon / By the light of the silvery moon / Look for the silver lining / Charmaine / Get out and get under the moon / All alone by the telephone / Remember / Me and my shadow / At sundown love's old sweet song.
LP: . . . . PL 89136
MC: . . . . PK 89136
LP: . . . . RCALP 6012

DANNY BOY AND OTHER IRISH BALLADS.
Tracks: / Old house / Trottin' to the fair / Harp that once through Tara's hall, The / She moved through the fair / Bard of Armagh, The / Fairy tree / Ireland, mother Ireland / Danny boy / Next market day / Believe me if all those endearing young / My Lagan love / Killarney / Irish emigrant, The / Come back to Erin.
LP: . . . . RL 83442
MC: . . . . RK 83442

FAVOURITE IRISH SONGS OF PRINCESS GRACE.
Tracks: / Danny boy / I'll take you home again Kathleen / Mother Machree / MacNamara's band / Molly Malone / Rose of Tralee, The / Macushla / Last rose of summer / Pretty Kitty Kelly / Galway bay / Oft in the stilly night / Foggy dew, The / I hear you calling me / My wild Irish rose / Sally gardens / She is far from the land / Star of the County Down / Mistress Biddy was a giddy little widdy / Off to Philadelphia.
LP: . . . . VC 7907051
MC: . . . . VC 7907054

GALLANT TROUBADOUR, THE.
Tracks: / Again, my lyre / Bonnie laddie, highland laddie / Parting kiss, The / Helpless woman / Sweetest lad waw Jamie, The / Judy, lovely matchless creature / Deserter, The / Oh who, my dear Dermont / Merch megan or, Peggy's daughter / Soldier am I, A / Robin is my joy / Where ha'e ye been the day / My love is like the red, red rose / John Anderson, my Jo' / Soothing shades of gloaming, The / Yes, thou mays't walk / True hearted was he / O poor tith cauld and restless love.
LP: . . . . EL 270 323 1
MC: . . . . EL 270 323 4

MEMORIES OF JOHN MCCORMACK.
Tracks: / Little grey home in the west / Whispering hope / Trumpeter trees / I'll sing thee songs of Araby / I dream of Jeannie with the light brown hair / Come into the garden Maud / Just a-wearing' for you / Two blue eyes / Thora / Plaisir d'amour / I'll walk beside you / Christopher Robin is saying his prayers.
LP: . . . . GL 70734
MC: . . . . GK 70734

SINGS THE AMERICAN SONG BOOK.
Tracks: / Once is not enough / How are things in Glocca Morra / Look to the rainbow / All the things you are / Long ago and far away / Love walked in / He loves and she loves / Foggy night and day, A / Certain smile, A / I'll be seeing you.
LP: . . . . PL 70305
MC: . . . . PK 70305
LP: . . . . RCALP 6073

WHEN YOU AND I WERE YOUNG, MAGGIE.
Tracks: / Butterfield / When you and I were young, Maggie / Beautiful dreamer / Irish folk song / Mother of mine / May day carol / Sylvia / Little boy blue / Smilin' through / Vacant chair / Rosary, The / I love you truly Duna / By the bend of the river / Silver threads among the gold / I'll take you home again Kathleen / Perfect day.
LP: . . . . PL 89326
MC: . . . . PK 89326

White Rock

WHITE ROCK (Original Soundtrack) (Various artists).
LP: . . . . AMLH 64614
MC: . . . . CAM 64614

White, Roland

KENTUCKY COLONELS 1965-1967 (White, Roland & Clarence).
LP: . . . . ROUNDER 0070
MC: . . . . ROUNDER 0070C

White Rose

IT'S A LONG TIME.
LP: . . . . LKLP 6021

White, Roy

SHANTY.
Tracks: / Stand in line / Don't stop tomorrow / Sophie's choice / Criminal mind / Shanty / Strange to be with you / Shoot myself / Nothing to remind me / Angel loves Joe / Ice on the sun / Reputation / Lest we forget.
LP: . . . . CBS 26581
MC: 40 26581

White, Scott

SUCCESS NEVER ENDS.
Tracks: / Hypnotized / Never ends / Love emergency / Success / I don't understand it / Friends / Time has hold on love / Let me be.
LP: . . . . PL 90246
MC: . . . . PK 90246

White Sister

FASHION BY PASSION.
Tracks: / Place in the heart, A / Fashion by passion / Dancin' on midnight / Save me tonight / Ticket to ride / April / Until it hurts / Troubleshooters / Lonely teardrops / Place in my heart, A.
LP: . . . . WKFMLP 76
MC: . . . . WKFMMC 76
LP: . . . . WKFMLWP 726
LPPD: . . . . WKFMPD 76

WHITE SISTER.
Tracks: / Don't say that you're mine / Straight from the heart / Love don't make it right / Breakin' all the rules / Whips / Can't say no / Promises / Walk away / One more night / Just for you.
LP: . . . . HMUSA 7
LP: . . . . HMUSA 7 W

White, Snowy

SNOWY WHITE.
Tracks: / Land of freedom / Long summer days / Peace on earth / Fortune / So breathless / Waters edge / Stepping stones / Chinese burn / When I arise.
LP: . . . . TOWLP 8
MC: . . . . ZCTOW 8

THAT CERTAIN THING.
Tracks: / Muddy fingers / For you / That certain thing / Lonely heart / This heart of mine / I can't believe it / Walking away / I'll be holding on / Voices in the rain.
LP: . . . . LMA 2
MC: . . . . LMT 2

WHITE FLAMES.
LP: . . . . TOWLP 3
MC: . . . . ZCTOW 3

White, Tam

DREAM ON (See under Anderson, Lynn) (White, Tam & Lynn Anderson).

LET THE GOOD TIMES ROLL (White, Tam & The Dexters).
LP: . . . . DEX 2

White, T.H.

BOOK OF MERLYN, THE (Plummer, Christopher).
LP: . . . . TC 1852
MC: . . . . CDL 51852

KING ARTHUR AND MERLYN'S ANIMAL COUNCIL (Plummer, Christopher).
MC: 1630

MERLYN'S ANIMAL COUNCIL.
MC: . . . . CDL 51630

White Tiger

YEAR OF THE TIGER.
LP: . . . . EMC 3653

White, Tony Joe

BEST OF TONY JOE WHITE.
Tracks: / Polk salad Annie / Willie and Laura Mae Jones / Soul Francisco / Don't steal my love / Roosevelt and Ira Lee / For Le Ann / Elements and things / Rainy night in Georgia / High sheriff of Calhoun Parrish / Widow Wimberly / Stud spider / Old man willis / Groupie girl / Save your sugar for me.
LP: . . . . K 56149

ROOSEVELT AND IRA LEE.
LP: 20095
MC: 40095

White Witch

WHITE WITCH, THE (see Goudge, Elizabeth) (Guthrie, Gwyneth).

White Wolf

STANDING ALONE.
Tracks: / Standing alone / Headlines / Shadows in the night / What the war will bring / Night rider / Homeward bound / Metal thunder / Trust me.
LP: . . . . PL 70559
MC: . . . . PK 70559

White Zombie

MAKE THEM DIE SLOWLY.
Tracks: / Demonspeed / Disaster blaster / Murderworld / Revenge / Acid flesh / Power hungry / Godslayer.
LP: . . . . CARLP 3
MC: . . . . CARC 3

SOUL CRUSHER.
LP: . . . . SILENT 002

Whitehall Flute Band

MARCHING WITH WHITEHALL FLUTE BAND.
MC: C2LP 1698

PRIDE OF WHITEHILL FLUTE BAND.
Tracks: / Le reve passe / Imperial echoes / True and trusty / Two maids / Officer of the day / British Grenadiers, The / Girl I left behind me, The / Waveney / Ramblin' Ulsterman / White gates / Anchors a-weigh / Murder of McBriars / Dinah's delight / Londonderry / Liberty bell / Springtime / Our director / Moore Street.
LP: . . . . ZLP 1698

Whitehead, Annie

MIX UP.
Tracks: / Alien style (12") / Pigeon post / Mozambique / Freedom marching / Time change / Badger, The / Rainy daze / Mambo III / Alien style.
LP: . . . . PAL 6
MC: . . . . PALC 6

Whitehead, Tim

DECISION (Whitehead, Tim Band).
Tracks: / Verao / Out / Early days / You and I / Checkpoint Charlie (CD & Cassette only) / Jiggery pokery (CD & Cassette only) / When I fall in love (CD & Cassette only) / Decision.
LP: . . . . EGED 58
MC: . . . . EGEDC 58

ENGLISH PEOPLE (Whitehead's, Tim Borderline).
Tracks: / Little flower / Yellow hill / Rip rap / I want to talk about you / Diggin' the parch / English people / Impossible question, The.
LP: . . . . SPJ 523

Whitelaw Brothers

WHITELAW BROTHERS - VOL.1.
LP: . . . . ART 301

Whiteley, John Scott

GREAT ROMANTIC ORGAN MUSIC.
Tracks: / Improvisation of the Te Deum / Menuet-scherzo Op. 53 / Tues petra / Trois preludes et fugues / Hochzeitspraludium (Wedding prelude) / Three pastels / Eleven chorale preludes / Prelude and fugue on Bach.
MC: . . . . YORK MC 101

Whiteman, Paul

1938 (Whiteman, Paul & His Orchestra).
LP: . . . . SOL 516

BIRTH OF RHAPSODY IN BLUE, THE.
LPS: . . . . MMD 20113X/14T
MCSET: . . . . MMD 40113W/14M

BIX 'N' BING (see under Beiderbecke, Bix) (Whiteman, Paul orchestra/Bix Beiderbecke/Bing Crosby).

FOREVER POPS (Whiteman, Paul & His Orchestra).
LP: SR5001

JAZZ A LA KING 1920-1936.
Tracks: / Wang wang blues / Whispering / Everybody step / Hot lips / Way down yonder in New Orleans / Nuthin' but / Charleston / Footloose / Red hot Henry Brown / Milenberg joys / Charlestonette / Bell hoppin' blues / St. Louis blues / Wistful and blue / Muddy waters / I'm coming Virginia / Side by side / Magnolia / Sensation stomp / Five step / Lonely melody / Mississippi mud / From Monday on / Stop the Sun, stop the Moon / Rockin' chair / G. blues / Itchola / Serenade for a wealthy widow / Nobody's sweetheart / Farewell blues / Announcer's blues / Saddle your blues to a wild mustang.
2LP: . . . . PM 42413

LEGENDARY, THE.
MC: . . . . MRT 40032

MUSIC OF THE ROARING 20'S (Whiteman, Paul & His Orchestra).
LP: . . . . WAVE LP 27

NEW PAUL WHITEMAN ORCHESTRA, THE (Whiteman, Paul & His Orchestra).
LP: . . . . MES 7078

PAUL WHITEMAN COLLECTION (20 golden greats).
Tracks: / Song of India / Japanese sandman / What'll I do? / Whispering / Hot lips / Coquette / When / Lovable / Is it gonna be long? / Oh, have you no idea? / Anytime, anyday, anywhere / My man / Love nest, The / I'll build a stairway to Paradise / Three o'clock in the morning / Felix the cat / Tain't so, honey, tain't so / I'd rather cry over you / Georgie Porgie / Out-of-town girl.
LP: . . . . DVLP 2110
MC: . . . . DVMC 2110

SHAKING THE BLUES AWAY 1920-1927 (Whiteman, Paul & His Orchestra).
Tracks: / Wang wang blues / On the gin gin ginny shore / Stumbling / Hot lips / I'll build a stairway to paradise / Everything is K.O. in K.Y. / If I can't have the sweetie I want / Shake your feet / Steppin' out / Lazy / Charleston / Ukelele lady / Steppin' in society / Footloose / Got no time / No foolin' Manhattan / Sweet and low down / Birth of the blues / Shakin' the blues away.
LP: . . . . HAL 21

WANG WANG BLUES.
MC: 40184

WHITEMAN STOMP 1923-36.
LP: . . . . HDL 116
MC: . . . . CHDL 116

Whites

FOREVER YOU.
Tracks: / Forever you / Pins and needles / Mama don't you know your little girl / (Our own) Jole' Blon / Ring of clover / Move it on over / Blue baby now / I didn't come here to cry / I just started living today / Living in the name of love.
LP: . . . . IMCA 5490

GREATEST HITS: WHITES.
Tracks: / You put the blue in me / Hangin' around / Give me back that old familiar feeling / It ain't love (let's leave it alone) / I wonder who's holding my baby tonight / Love won't wait / Pins and needles / Forever you / When the new wears off our love / Home town gossip.
LP: . . . . IMCA 5717
MC: . . . . IMCAC 5717

POOR FOLKS PLEASURE.
Tracks: / Cowboy lives forever, The / Home / Jealous heart / Virginia's real / Southland / Poor folks pleasure / Another lonesome morning / By the fireside with baby / House of gold / Mexican holiday.
LP: . . . . SDLP 052
MC: . . . . SDC 052

Whitesnake

BEST OF WHITESNAKE.
Tracks: / Still of the night / Don't break my heart again / Fool for your loving / Here I go again.
LP: 0627485481

CHRIS TETLEY INTERVIEWS WHITESNAKE.
LPPD: CT 1006

COME AN' GET IT.
Tracks: / Come an' get it / Hot stuff / Don't break my heart again / Lonely days, lonely nights / Wine, women and song / Child of Babylon / Would I lie to you / Girl / Hit and run / Till the day I die.
LP: LBG 30327
MC: TC LBG 30327
LP: FA 3219
MC: TCFA 3219
LP: ATAK 94
MC: TCATAK 94

LIVE IN THE HEART OF THE CITY.
Tracks: / Come on / Sweet talker / Walking in the shadow of the blues / Love hunter / Fool for your loving / Ain't gonna cry no more / Ready an' willing / Take me with you / Might just take your life / Lie down / Ain't no love in the heart of the city / Trouble / Mistreated.
2LP: SNAKE 1
MCSET: TC2SNAKE 1
2LP: ATAK 124
MCSET: TCATAK 124

LOVEHUNTER.
Tracks: / Long way from home / Walking in the shadow of the blues / Help me thro' the day / Medicine man / You'n'me / Mean business / Love hunter / Outlaw / Rock'n'roll women / We wish you well.
LP: FA 4130951
MC: FA 4130954
LP: GHS 24176
LP: FA 3095
MC: TCFA 3095
LP: UAG 30264

NORTHWINDS (See under Coverdale, David).

READY AN' WILLING.
Tracks: / Fool for your loving / Sweet talker / Ready an' willing / Carry your load / Blindman / Ain't gonna cry no more / Love man / Black and blue / She's a woman.
LP: FA 41 3134 1
LP: FA 3134
MC: FA 41 3134 4
MC: TCFA 3134
LP: UAG 30302

SAINTS 'N' SINNERS.
Tracks: / Young blood / Rough and ready / Bloody luxury / Victim of love / Crying in the rain / Here I go again / Love and affection / Rock and roll angels / Dancing girls / Saints and sinners.
LP: FA 3177
MC: TCFA 3177
LP: LBG 30354
LP: ATAK 10
MC: TCATAK 10

SLIDE IT IN.
Tracks: / Gambler, The / Slide it in / Standing in the shadow / Give me more time / Love ain't no stranger / Slow an' easy / Spit it out / All or nothing / Hungry for love / Guilty of love / Need your love so bad (Tape only.).
LP: LBG 2400001
MC: LBG 2400008
LP: ATAK 120
LP: WHITE 1
MC: TCATAK 120
MC: TCWHITE 1

SLIP OF THE TONGUE.
Tracks: / Slip of the tongue / Cheap an' nasty / Fool for your loving / Now you're gone / Kittens got claws / Wings of the storm / Deeper the love, The / Judgment day / Slow poke music / Sailing ships.
LP: EMD 1013
MC: TCEMD 1013

SNAKEBITE.
Tracks: / Keep on giving me love / Queen of hearts / Breakdown.
LP: 5C 062 61290
LP: GHS 24174
MC: XGHS 24174

TROUBLE.
Tracks: / Take me with you / Love to keep you warm / Lie down / Day tripper / Nighthawk (vampire blues) / Time is right for love, The / Trouble / Belgian Tom's hat trick / Free flight / Don't mess with me.
LP: EMS 1257
MC: TCEMS 1257
LP: FA 3002
MC: TCFA 3002
LP: INS 3022
LP: ATAK 106
MC: TCATAK 106
LP: UAG 30305
LP: FA 3234
MC: TCFA 3234

WHITESNAKE (See under Coverdale, David).

WHITESNAKE 1987.
Tracks: / Still of the night / Bad boys / Give me all your love / Looking for love / Crying in the rain / Is this love / Straight for the heart / Don't turn away / Children of the night / Here I go again (1987) / You're gonna break my heart again (CD only.).
LPPD: EMCP 3528
LP: EMC 3528
MC: TCEMC 3528
LP: EMCX 3528
MC: TCEMCX 3528

WHITESNAKE: INTERVIEW PICTURE DISC.
LPPD: BAK 2049

WHITESNAKE/NORTHWINDS (See under Coverdale, David).

Whitfield, Barrence

CALL OF THE WILD (Whitfield, Barrence & The Savages).
LP: REU 1029

DIG YOURSELF (Whitfield, Barrence & The Savages).
LP: REU 1006
LP: ROUNDER 9007
MC: ROUNDER 9007C

LET'S LOSE IT.
LP: ROSE 240
MC: ROSK 240

LIVE EMULSIFIED (Whitfield, Barrence & The Savages).
LP: ROSE 189

OW! OW! OW! (Whitfield, Barrence & The Savages).
LP: ROUNDER 9011
MC: ROUNDER 9011C
LP: ROSE 139

Whitfield, David

DAVID WHITFIELD SINGS STAGE & SCREEN FAVOURITES.
MCSET: DTO 10303

GREATEST HITS: DAVID WHITFIELD.
Tracks: / Cara mia / Santo natale / Book, The / Mama / Ev'rywhere / Rags to riches / When you lose the one you love / My son John / Bridge of sighs / My September love / Answer me / Beyond the stars / Adoration waltz / On the Street where you live / Willingly / I'll find you / Right to love, The / Cry my heart / My unfinished symphony / I believe.
LP: TAB 52
MC: KTAC 52
MC: KTBC 52

MAGIC OF DAVID WHITFIELD, THE.
MC: KTBC 93
LP: TAB 93

SINGS THE GREAT SONGS.
MCSET: DTO 10251

WORLD OF DAVID WHITFIELD, THE.
Tracks: / My September love / I believe / Maria / You're my hearts delight / You'll never walk alone / Mama / I will know / Answer me / My son John / On the street where you live / Goodbye / Cara mia.
LP: SPA 40
MC: KCSP 40

WORLD OF DAVID WHITFIELD - VOL.2.
Tracks: / My heart and I / Willingly / Adoration waltz / Tear, a kiss, a smile, A / Afraid / Book, The / Ramona / Bridge of sighs / Beyond the stars / When you lose the one you love / How, when or where / It's never too late to pray.
LP: SPA 388

Whitfield, June

TREASURY OF FAIRY TALES CHAPTERS 3 AND 4 (Whitfield, June/ Jenny Hanley).
2LP: 2668 023

Whitfield, Weslia

LUCKY TO BE ME.
Tracks: / Lucky to be me / Something to remember you by / Do I love you? / Glad to be unhappy / Moments like this / My buddy / This funny world / He was too good to me / By myself / Be careful, it's my heart / For all we know / Face like yours, A / Rhode Island is famous for you / Don't you know I care / Two for the road.
LP: LLP 1524

Whithead, John

I NEED MONEY BAD.
LP: 834 310-1

Whiting, Margaret

COME A LITTLE CLOSER.
LP: AP 173

GOIN' PLACES.
Tracks: / Gypsy in my soul / Sentimental journey / Any place I hang my hat is home / I'm gonna move to the outskirts of town / Gone with the wind / Runnin' wild / Between the devil and the deep blue sea / Over the rainbow / Hit the road to dreamland / East of the sun / Song of the wanderer / Home.
LP: JASM 1514

JEROME KERN SONGBOOK, THE.
Tracks: / Fine romance, a / Song is you, The / I'm old fashioned / Yesterday / Look for the silver lining / I won't dance / Long ago and far away / Smoke gets in your eyes / You couldn't be cuter / Way you look tonight / Dearly beloved / Bill / She didn't say yes / All the things you are.
LP: MOIR 125
MC: CMOIR 125

LADY'S IN LOVE WITH YOU, THE.
LP: AP 207

LOVE SONGS BY MARGARET WHITING.
Tracks: / My ideal / Moonlight in Vermont / Bill / You're an old smoothie / Younger than Springtime / I've never been in love before / It might as well be spring / Tree in the meadow, A / He's funny that way / Wonderful guy / Come rain or come shine / If I had you.
LP: ED 2604221
MC: ED 2604224

TOO MARVELOUS FOR WORDS.
LP: AP 152

Whitley, Chris

LIVING WITH THE LAW.
Tracks: / Excerpt / Living with the law / Big sky country / Kick the stones / Make the dirt stick / Poison girl / Dust radio / Phone call from Leavenworth / I forget you every day / Long way around / Look what love has done / Bordertown.
LP: 4685681
MC: 4685684

Whitley, Keith

DON'T CLOSE YOUR EYES.
Tracks: / Flying colours / It's all coming back to me now / Lucky dog / Don't close your eyes / Birmingham turnaround / Some old side road / Would these arms be in your way / I'm no stranger to the rain / I never go around mirrors / When you say nothing at all / Day in the life of a fool, A / Honky tonk heart.
LP: PL 90313
MC: PK 90313

SUNDOWN (see under Skaggs, Ricky) (Whitley, Keith & Ricky Skaggs).

Whitman, Jim

CUTTIN' LOOSE (Whitman, Jim & Texas).
LP: LLR 5

GREEN FIELDS OF IRELAND.
Tracks: / Green fields of Ireland / My lovely Lagan River / Up in the Paltry Mountains / Just a blind Irish boy / My heart is in Connemara / Today you say you are leaving / Kiss the Blarney Stone / In Annalee / River Bann flows on forever / Girl from Carlow Town / Pride of County Down / Take me back to Ireland.
LP: PFL 3015
MC: PFT 3015

Whitman, Slim

20 GREATEST LOVE SONGS.
Tracks: / I love you because / It's all in the game / Love letters in the sand / Fool such as I / Please help me I'm falling / Tammy / I'll never find another you / Unchained melody / Very precious love / Don't let the stars get in your eyes / Only you / Together / More than yesterday / Just lovin' you / Loveliest night of the year / My heart cries for you / Guess who / My happiness / Silver threads among the gold / Stranger on the shore.
LP: MFP 50516

ALL KINDS OF EVERYTHING.
MC: TCIDL 20

ANGELINE.
Tracks: / Cry baby heart / But she loves me / Tryin' to outrun the wind / Angeline / Blue memories / Dreamin' / Scarlet ribbons / Blue bayou / Place in the sun / Four walls.
LP: EPC 25901

BEST OF SLIM WHITMAN.
LP: 1A 022 58098
MC: 1A 222 58098

BIRMINGHAM JAIL AND OTHER COUNTRY ARTISTS.
Tracks: / Birmingham jail / Wabash waltz / Let's go to church / I'm casting my lasso towards the sky / Tears can never drown the flame (that's in my heart) / I'll never pass this way again.
LP: CDM 1018
MC: CAM 433

CHRISTMAS ALBUM, THE.
LP: ED 2607341
MC: ED 2607344

COLLECTION: SLIM WHITMAN.
MC: KNMC 13053

COLLECTION: SLIM WHITMAN.
Tracks: / Rose Marie / My blue Heaven / Bouquet of roses / Lorena / How could I not love you / Take me in your arms and hold me / When my dreamboat comes home / I'd trade all of my tomorrows (for just one yesterday) / White silver sands / Nobody's darlin' but mine / Indian love call / I'm walking behind you / I'd climb the highest mountain / Tell me / Ride away (with a song in my heart) / Little green valley / Born to lose / At mail call today / In the valley of the moon / Blue eyes crying in the rain / Marie Elena / Home (when shadows fall) / Song of the waterwheel, The / Ages and ages ago / Each night at nine / Smoke signals / Brahms' lullaby / I'll never stop loving you / Never / Forty shades of green / Among my souvenirs / Careless love / I dreamed of an old love affair / Travellin' man / From heaven to heartache / Forever / I really don't want to know / I'll hold you in my heart / Silver threads among the gold / Happy anniversary.
2LP: EM 1326
MCSET: TCEM 1326

COUNTRY CLASSICS.
Tracks: / Most beautiful girl in the world, The / Send me the pillow that you dream on / My elusive dreams / Don't be angry / Candy kisses / Lovesick blues / I love you a thousand ways / Blue eyes crying in the rain / Just call me lonesome / I forgot more than you'll ever know / There goes my everything / Satisfied mind, A / Faded love / From a jack to a king / Little bitty tear, A / I'll sail my ship alone / Think I'll go somewhere and cry myself to sleep / Walk through this world with me / She thinks I still care / I fall to pieces.
LP: ED 2606821
MC: ED 2606824

COUNTRY CLASSICS BY SLIM.
MC: 4XLL 8315

COUNTRY STYLE.
Tracks: / Rhinestone cowboy / Red river valley / Tumbling tumbleweeds / Kentucky waltz / Home on the range / I can't stop loving you / Cattle call / Rose Marie / Riders in the sky / From a jack to a king / Broken wings / Paper roses / It keeps right on a-hurtin' / Wayward wind / Top of the world / Cool water.
LP: MFP 41 5688 1
MC: MFP 41 5688 4
MC: TCMFP 5688

FAVOURITES.
Tracks: / Beautiful dreamer / I went to your wedding / Marjie / I remember you / Carolina moon / Oh my darling (I love you) / Just an echo in the valley / If I had my life to live over / Silver haired daddy of mine / Ghost riders in the sky / Edelweiss / Take good care of her / Secret love / Can't help falling in love / When you wore a tulip / You are my sunshine / Rose Marie / Mr. Songman / Goodbye little darlin' goodbye / Where did yesterday go?.
LP: EMS 1281
MC: TCEMS 1281
LP: HAT 3135
MC: HATC 3135

GHOST RIDERS IN THE SKY.
Tracks: / Ghost riders in the sky / Carolina moon / All kinds of everything / Girl of my dreams / Margie / Perfect day / Calypso / You are my sunshine / Puff, the magic dragon / Tears stained my pillow / When it's harvest time sweet Angeline / Goodbye little darlin' goodbye.
LP: UATV 30202

GOLDEN COUNTRY HITS.
MC: 4XLL 8348

GREATEST HITS: SLIM WHITMAN.
Tracks: / Indian love call / Keep it a secret / Northwind / Secret love / Rose Marie / Cattle call / I'm a fool / China doll / Tumbling tumbleweeds / I'll take you home again Kathleen / More than yesterday / Twelfth of never / Rainbows are back in style / Shutters and boards / Guess who / Something beautiful / Happy anniversary.
LP: LBR 2600531
MC: TCLBR 2600534

HAPPY ANNIVERSARY.
LP: UAS 29670

HOME ON THE RANGE.
LP: UATV 30102

I'LL TAKE YOU HOME AGAIN, KATHLEEN.
LP: SHM 959
MC: HSC 334

IRISH SONGS, THE SLIM WHITMAN WAY.
LP: LBS 83019

LOVE SONGS OF THE WATERFALL.
LP: SLS 50153
MC: TCS 50153

MR SONGMAN.
Tracks: / Destiny / Can't help falling in love / Open up your heart / Flowers / My melody of love / Mr. Songman / I went to your wedding / Tonight is the night (we fell in love) / Oh my darling (I love you).
LP: LBG 30343
MC: TCLBG 30343

RED RIVER VALLEY.
Tracks: / Rhinestone cowboy / Mr.Ting-a-ling / Too young / Let me call you sweetheart / Small world / Somewhere my love / Una paloma blanca / Red river valley / My elusive dreams / Cara mia / When the moon comes over the mountain / Now is the hour.
LP: UAS 29993

SLIM WHITMAN.
Tracks: / Rose Marie / I wanna go to heaven / Where did yesterday go / Aura Lee / I remember you / Lavender blue / Girl of my dreams / Secret love / You are my sunshine / Margie / Nearer my love to you / When you wore a tulip / Till we meet again / Sands of time / Since you went away / All kinds of everything / Ghost riders in the sky / Take good care of her / Edelweiss / Just an echo in the valley / Goodbye little darlin' goodbye / When it's harvest time sweet Angeline / Calypso / Carolina moon / My buddy / When / Tears stained my pillow / Puff the magic dragon / Where do I go from here / That silver haired daddy of mine.
MCSET: CRT 019

SLIM WHITMAN (2).
Tracks: / Rose Marie / Virginia / When I'm gone you'll soon forget / Valley of tears / Careless hands / Gonna find me a bluebird / Mockingbird hill / My blue heaven / From a jack to a queen / Tears on my pillow / Roses are red my love / I can't stop loving you / Love song of the waterfall / Please help me I'm falling / Silver threads among the gold / Ramblin' rose.
LP: SHM 3089
MC: HSC 3089

SLIM WHITMAN SONG BOOK.
MC: AM 51
MC: AM 116

SLIM WHITMAN STORY, THE.
LPS: ALBUM 24
MCSET: CASSETTE 24

SLIM WHITMAN'S 20 GREATEST LOVE SONGS.
Tracks: / Please help me, I'm falling / Loveliest night of the year / Fool such as I, A.
LP: UAG 30270

SONG I LOVE TO SING.
Tracks: / When / Secret love / Since you went away / I could only dream / Last farewell, The / I remember you / Rose Marie / Where do i go from here / Silver haired daddy of mine, The / Beautiful dreamer.
LP: CBS 32774
MC: 40 32774
LP: EPC 32774
LP: UAG 30322

TILL WE MEET AGAIN.
Tracks: / I wanna go to heaven / Just an echo in the valley / White cliffs of Dover, The / Lavender blue / When you wore a tulip / Where did yesterday go / Edelweiss / My buddy / Nights of splendour / Nearer my love to you / Aura Lee / Take good care of her / Sands of time / Till we meet again.
LP: UAG 30297
MC: TCK 30297

VERY BEST OF SLIM WHITMAN, THE.
Tracks: / Rose Marie / Cool water / I'll take you home again, Kathleen / I remember you / Secret love / Snowbird / Ramblin' rose / Love song of the waterfall / Old spinning wheel / It's a sin to tell a lie / Happy anniversary / Twelfth of never / Serenade / Roses are red / China doll / Walking in the sunshine / When you were sweet sixteen / Honeymoon feelin' / Have I told you lately that I love you / Indian love call.
LP: UAS 29898
MC: TCK 29898

YODELLING.
MC: 4XLL 9278

Whitman, Walt

CROSSING BROOKLYN FERRY (Begley, Ed).
MC: 1233

I HEAR AMERICA SINGING (Leaves of grass) (Begley, Ed).
MC: 1037

SONG OF THE OPEN ROAD (Leaves of grass) (Begley, Ed).
MC: 1154

Whitren, Jackie

INTERNATIONAL TIMES (Whitren, Jackie & John Cartwright).
LP: LR 1
MC: LRC 1

Whitstein Brothers

OLD TIME DUETS.
Tracks: / Mansion on the hill / We parted by the riverside / There's an open door waiting / Sinner you'd better get ready / We met in the saddle / I'm troubled / That silver haired daddy / Seven year blues / Weary lonesome blues / Somewhere in Tennessee / Maple on the hill / If I could hear my mother pray again / Pitfall / Beautiful lost river valley.
LP: ROUNDER 0264
MC: ROUNDERC 0264

ROSE OF MY HEART.
Tracks: / Rose of my heart / Highway headin' South / Kentucky / My curly headed baby / Weary days / Weary blues from waiting / Arkansas / Bridge over troubled water / Eighth wonder of the world / Scared of the blues / Where the old river flows / Smokey mountain memories.
LP: ROUNDER 0206
MC: ROUNDER 0206C

TROUBLE AIN'T NOTHING BUT THE BLUES.
Tracks: / Showboat gambler / What about you / Freight train boogie / When I found you / High cost of living / Everglades, The / Looks like rain today / Trouble in mind / I don't believe you've met my baby / Ozark Mountain lullaby / My baby came back / My Texas girl.
LP: ROUNDER 0229
MC: ROUNDER 0229C

Whittaker, Heather

TAKE HER WITH HEART.
LP: DIN 331

Whittaker, Roger

20 ALL-TIME GREATS.
Tracks: / Dirty old town / Durham town / From both sides now / He ain't heavy, he's my brother / I believe / I don't believe in if anymore / If I was a rich man / Impossible dream, The / Last farewell, The / Mamy blue / Mexican whistler / Moon shadow / Morning, please don't come / New world in the morning / Special kind of man, A / Streets of London / Sunrise, sunset / What a wonderful world / Why... / Faster than the speed of light / Bring the hammer down / Fire power / Read all about it / To the limit / To the top / Battle zone / Live at the inferno / Star war / UXB / 20/21 / Hold back the fire / Chain saw.
LP: POLTV 8
MC: POLVM 8

22 FAVOURITES.
LP: 2648041
MC: 2648044

45 FAVOURITES.
MC: 264 824 4
LP: 264 824 1

BUTTERFLY.
Tracks: / Butterfly / Settle down / After the laughter came tears / Santa Anna / Steel men / Mud puddle / You've got a friend / Handful of dreams / Sinner, The / Sunrise, sunset / Acre of wheat / Impossible dream, The / Time is tough / Jenny's gone (And I don't care).
LP: CN 2003
MC: CN4 2003

CHANGES.
Tracks: / When I dream / Changes / Honolulu city lights / Smooth sailing / River runs still / I can hear Kentucky calling me / Rocky top / Moonshine / How does it feel / So good to so bad / River lady / Bar room country singer.
LP: EMC 3398

COLLECTION: ROGER WHITTAKER.
Tracks: / Durham Town / All of my love / Before she breaks my heart / My world / Why / I was born / My son / Time / Summer days / Man without love, A / Last prayer / For I could love you / Come into my dream / New England in the rain / Forever with you / Candle in the night / Take me to the stars / Sleep to be kind / Best days of my life / Sing out good people.
2LP: CCSLP 155
MC: CCSMC 155

COMPACT MOMENTS (see under Warwick, Dionne) (Warwick, Dionne/ Roger Whittaker/Gilbert O'Sullivan/Cleo Lain).

COUNTRY FEEL OF ROGER WHITTAKER.
Tracks: / Changes / Honolulu city lights / Ride a country road / River runs still / I can hear Kentucky calling me / When I dream / Good old ear and H / First hello, the last goodbye, The / I can't help it (if I'm still in love with you) / Smooth sailing / Rocky top / Moonshine / How does it feel / So good to so bad / Everything is going to be the last time / River lady / Don't let them change / Blue eyes crying in the rain / Bar room country singer / Red river valley.
2LP: TMB 104
MCSET: TMBC 104

DURHAM TOWN.
Tracks: / Durham town, (The leaving of) / Morning has broken / Dirty old town / Impossible dream, The / San Miguel / I don't believe in 'if' anymore / Mamy blue / Taste of honey, A / Why / Those were the days / Scarborough fair / By the time I get to Phoenix.
LP: CN 2061
MC: CN4 2061

EASYRIDING: ROGER WHITTAKER.
Tracks: / Last farewell, The / From both sides now / Paradise / Streets of London / He starts below / My kind / Mamy blue / I don't believe in if anymore / New world in the morning / Morning please don't come / Candy cloud / Special kind of man, A / No blade of grass / Moonshine / If I were a rich man / Mexican whistler / Durham town.
MC: KNMC 11001
LP: KNLP 11001

GENIUS OF LOVE, THE.
Tracks: / Genius of love / Miss Lapotaire / Your voice / Railway hotel / Destiny / Jerusalem goodbye / Candle, The / Yur fool / One more chance / Too emotional / Everybody's got a lonely heart / Only the lonely.
LP: TMB 108
MC: TMBC 108
LP: 2646031
MC: 2646034

HEART-TOUCHING FAVOURITES.
Tracks: / Red roses for a blue lady / Somewhere my love / Unchained melody / Sentimental journey / Scarlet ribbons / Red sails in the sunset / Eternally / Tenderly / Stranger on the shore / I love you because / Making believe / It's now or never / Have I told you lately that I love you / I can't help it (if I'm still in love with you) / Blue eyes crying in the rain / Red river valley / There goes my everything / Vaya con dios.
LP: TMB 103
MC: TMBC 103

HIS FINEST COLLECTION.
MCSET: CRT 017
2LP: RWTV 1

HOME LOVIN' MAN.
Tracks: / Home lovin' man / Love changes everything / Wind beneath my wings / Love me tender / Most beautiful girl, The / I love you because / True love / He ain't heavy he's my brother / Welcome home / Something's gotten hold of my heart / When I need you / It's so easy / There goes my everything / Where good love goes / Unchained melody / I love you.
LP: RWTV 2
MC: RWTVC 2

I DON'T BELIEVE IN IF ANY MORE.
LP: SCX 6404

IN CONCERT: ROGER WHITTAKER.
Tracks: / Hello good morning happy day / New world in the morning / Dirty old town / Mamy blue / Boa constrictor / Got to head on down the road / Lonesome traveller / Calypso medley / I don't believe in if anymore / Durham town / I believe / Show me your mountain / Watu hatari / Cincinnati kid / Fox / Yellow bird / Lemon tree / Mexican whistler / Boil them cabbage down / Jailer bring me water / Early one morning / Michael row the boat / African whistler / Wimoweh / Leaving of Liverpool / Green green.
LP: SL 807
MC: SLC 807
LP: 2681012

IT'S CHRISTMAS.
LP: 2648011
MC: 2648014

LIVE IN VIENNA.
Tracks: / Here I come / Scarlet ribbons / Impossible dream, The / River lady / Yarmouth Quay / From the people to the people / Indian lady / Proud Mary / Hound dog / Long tall Sally / You've lost that lovin' feelin' / By the time I get to Phoenix / Demon run / Special kind of man / Last song, The / Last farewell, The.
LP: NTS 188

LIVING AND LOVING.
Tracks: / I love you / So far so good / It's so easy / Where good love goes / Mist across the water / Always have a dream / Living and loving / Thank you love / One night with you / Gravy boat / Other side, The / Welcome home.
LP: TMB 119
MC: TMBC 119
MC: NK 74912

LOVE ALBUM, THE.
LP: ADAH 440
MC: ADAHC 440

LOVE C'EST UNE MUSIQUE.
LP: 2648021
MC: 2648024

LOVE LASTS FOREVER.
Tracks: / Love lasts forever / Angels of love / Marriage / Yarmouth Quay / Everybody is looking for an answer / If I knew just what to say / America / Mother mine, sleep on / Time went on / They loved their lives away / Seagull.
LP: SCX 6592

LOVE WILL BE OUR HOME.
Tracks: / Morning has broken / What a wonderful world / Love's a many-splendoured thing / Somewhere (from West Side Story) / One day at a time / Kumbaya / Love will be our home.
LP: WST R 9701
MC: WST C 9701

MUSIC FOR THE MILLIONS.
Tracks: / Mamy blue / Scarborough fair / Fire and rain / By the time I get to phoenix / Tatse of honey / My song / Why / I believe / What I left behind / You've lost that loving feeling / Fairytale / Sing hallelujah.
LP: 6321 151
MC: 7152 151

MY FAVOURITE LOVE SONGS.
Tracks: / I love you because / Making believe / It's now or never / Have I told you lately that I love you / I can't help it / Blue eyes crying in the rain / Red river valley / There goes my everything / Vaya con dios / Red roses for a blue lady / Somewhere my love / Unchained melody / Sentimental journey / Scarlet ribbons / Red sails in the sunset / Eternally / Tenderly / Stranger on the shore.
LP: EMC 3431
MC: TCEMC 3431

NEW WORLD IN THE MORNING.
Tracks: / New world in the morning / Streets of London / Early one morning / Lemon tree / Morning please don't come / Last farewell, The / From both sides now / Water boy / Special kind of man, A / Leaving of Liverpool / Mexican whistler.
LP: 814 086 1
MC: 814 086 4
LP: SCX 6456

ROGER WHITTAKER ALBUM, THE.
Tracks: / Streets of London / Early one morning / Lemon tree / Morning don't come / Wimoweh / From both sides now / Water boy / Special kind of man / Leaving of Liverpool / Mexican whistler / Last farewell, The.
LP: NE 1105
MC: CE 2105
MC: CN4 2048
LP: CN 2048

ROGER WHITTAKER COLLECTION VOL.2.
Tracks: / I don't believe in if anymore / mistral / Emily / Flap flap / Finnish whistler / Book / Berceuse pour mon amour / I should have taken my time / Festival / Sugar my tea / Swaggy / Halfway up the mountain.
LP: 238 412 4

ROGER WHITTAKER COLLECTION VOL.1.
Tracks: / Durham town / Petite fleur / This moment / Storm / Sunrise, sunset / Water boy / Dirty old town / Those were the days / Impossible dream, The / San Miguel / Where's Jack / Good morning starshine.
LP: 2384 113

ROGER WHITTAKER IN CONCERT (Live From The Tivoli).
Tracks: / New world in the morning / I love you / My land in Kenya / What a wonderful world / Mexican whistler / Wimoweh (The lion sleeps tonight) / I'll tell me ma / Skye boat song, The / I don't believe in if anymore / Russellin' along / Rocky top / Wilkommen / Cabaret / Oh mein papa / Send in the clowns / If I were a rich man / Thank you love / Make the world go away / Durham town / Last farewell, The / Kilgarry mountain.
MC: PK 74854

ROGER WHITTAKER IN KENYA (TV soundtrack).
LP: 8129491
MC: 8129494

ROGER WHITTAKER - LIVE.
MCSET: M 10204

ROGER WHITTAKER SINGS THE HITS.
LP: SCX 6601

ROMANTIC SIDE OF ROGER WHITTAKER (MFP).
Tracks: / Its your love / One another / Love will / New love / Man without love, A / I would if I could / See you shine / Tall dark stranger / Goodbye / My world / Don't fight / Before she breaks my heart / Time / Summer days / Pretty bird of love / Let me be your sun / Indian lady (CD only.) / Here we stand (CD only.) / Newport Belle (CD only.) / For I loved you (CD only.).
MC: TCMFP 5882

ROMANTIC SIDE OF ROGER WHITTAKER.
Tracks: / It's your love / Before she breaks my heart / Indian lady / Time / My world / Say my goodbyes to the rain / Here we stand / Summer days / Pretty bird of love / All the way to Richmond / Let me be your sun / New love / Love will / Don't fight / My son / One another / For I loved you / I am but a small voice / Tall dark stranger / Newport belle / I would if I could / See you shine / Man without love, A / Goodbye.
2LP: TMB 105
MCSET: TMBC 105

SECOND ALBUM OF THE VERY BEST OF ROGER WHITTAKER.
LP: EMC 3117

SINCERELY YOURS.
Tracks: / New world in the morning / Before she breaks my heart / Say my goodbyes to the rain / I can't help it (if I'm still in love with you) / All the way to Richmond / Summer days / Imagine / Love will / My son / Feelings / I would if I could / Man without love, A / It's your love / Time / Weekend in New England / Pretty bird of love / Let me be your sun / New love / Here we stand / Don't fight / One another / For I loved you / Shoe you shine / What a wonderful world.
LP: VSOPLP 129
MC: VSOPMC 129

SINGING THE HITS.
Tracks: / Sailing / Imagine / Evergreen / What a wonderful world / Bright eyes / Wind beneath my wings / Miss you nights / Weekend in New England / Time in a bottle / Feeling / Calypso / Please come to Boston / Your song / I can see clearly now / Home loving man / She / Send in the clowns / When I need you / Too beautiful to cry / Annie's song.
2LP: TMB 106
MCSET: TMBC 106

SKYE BOAT SONG AND OTHER GREAT SONGS.
LP: TMB 113
MC: TMBC 113

SONGS OF LOVE AND LIFE.
Tracks: / Flip flap / Sugar in my tea / Halfway up the mountain / Berceuse pour mon amour / Book, The / I believe / Finnish whistler / Emily / I should have taken my time / Festival / Swaggy / Mistral.
LP: CN 2072
MC: CN4 2072

SONGWRITER, THE.
Tracks: / New world in the morning / I'm back / You are my miracle / All of my life / Call my name / Last farewell, The / Durham town / Surf / And still the sea / Why / Mexican whistler / High / Image to my mind / Hold on tight / Oh, no not me / I was born / Seasons (come and go), The / Smiler / Albany / So long / I don't believe in if anymore.
LP: TMB 107
MC: TMBC 107

TAKE A LITTLE, GIVE A LITTLE.
Tracks: / Bitter and sweet / Brave and strong / Dover to Calais / Old mother nature's garden / Happy everything / Boogaloo bossanova and rock 'n' roll / Take a little give a little / Mary / So far (safari) / Charlie Mahon / My silver eagle.
LP: TMB 101
MC: TMBC 101

TIDINGS OF COMFORT AND JOY.
Tracks: / Ding dong merrily on high / God rest ye merry gentlemen / O come all ye faithful / Twelve days of Christmas, The / In the bleak mid winter / Christmas song, The / Angels from the realms of glory / Mary's boy child / Away in a manger / Have yourself a merry little Christmas / Holly and the ivy, The / White Christmas / First Noel, The / Little drummer boy / Sussex carol / Hark the herald angels sing / Infant holy / Rockin' / Winter wonderland / Past three o'clock / Merry Christmas / Silent night.
2LP: TMB 102
MCSET: TMBC 102

UNFORGETTABLE: ROGER WHITTAKER (16 Golden Classics).
Tracks: / Stranger on the shore / It's now or never / Home loving man / Show me the way / Yarmouth quay / Mother of mine sleep on / Angels of love / Kids ain't bad / Imagine / What a wonderful world / Bright eyes / Child within me, The / Smiler / Idle dreamer / Thorn trees of Africa / Everybody's looking for an answer.
LP: UNLP 012
MC: UNMC 012

VERY BEST OF ROGER WHITTAKER.
LP: SCX 6560

VOYAGER.
Tracks: / I was born / Paper bird / I see you in the sunrise / Here I am / Lighthouse / Sail away / Yele / I'll be there / Love is a cold wind / All of my life / Song for the captain / On my own again.
LP: SCX 6632

WISHES.
Tracks: / Call my name / Goodnight Ruby / Please come to Boston / Family / Carry me / You are my miracle / Wishes / Kentucky song bird / I know you sunset / Blow gentle breeze / It takes a lot.
LP: SCX 6626
MC: TCSCX 6626

WITH LOVE.
Tracks: / Love will / Don't fight / My son / One another / For i loved you / I am but a small voice / Tall dark stranger / Newport belle / I would if i could / See you shine / Man without love, A / Goodbye.
LP: SCX 6634

YOU DESERVE THE BEST.
Tracks: / Good old love / You deserve the best / Just across the Rio Grande / Early morning memories / Take away my pain / One song / Keep on chasing rainbows / I have you / But she loves me / Little love can go a long, long way, A / Only real hero, The / I'd fall in love tonight.
MC: PK 74817
LP: PL 74817

Whittle, Tommy

JIG SAW (Whittle, Tommy Quartet).
LP: AJ 4501

MORE WAXING WITH WHITTLE.
Tracks: / Archer's treat / Pyramid / Willow weep for me / Crazy rhythm / Ten-bar gait / Finisher, The / Someone to watch over me / Harry's blues / Flamingo / (I don't stand) a ghost of a chance(with you) / I'll remember April / You've done something to my heart / Stars fell on Alabama.
LP: ESQ 334

STRAIGHT EIGHT (Whittle, Tommy & Alan Barnes).
Tracks: / Stgraight eight / Con Alma / Joking / Pelppercorn / Note 8.7 / Goodbye / That's all / Early / Stablemates.
LP: MM 001

WAXING WITH WHITTLE.
LP: ESQ 305

WHY NOT (Whittle, Tommy Quartet).
LP: JAM 648

Who

BEST OF THE SIXTIES.
Tracks: / Substitute / I'm a boy / Pictures of Lily / Won't get fooled again / Long live rock / Happy Jack / Kids are alright, The / I can see for miles / Seeker, The / 5:15 / Magic bus.
LP: 825 746-1
MC: 825 746-4

BEST, THE (MUSIC FOR THE MILLIONS).
Tracks: / Bucket 'T' / I'm a boy / Pictures of Lily / Doctor, doctor / I can see for miles / Substitute / Happy Jack / Last time, The / In the city / Call me lightning / Mary Anne with the shaky hand / Dogs.
LP: 2485 206
MC: 3201 280

COLLECTION: WHO.
2LP: SMR 570
MCSET: SMC 570

FACE DANCES.
Tracks: / You better you bet / Don't let go the coat / Cache cache / Quiet one, The / Did you steal my money / How can you do it alone / Daily records / You / Another tricky day.
LP: WHOD 5037
MC: WHODC 5037
LP: SPELP 112
MC: SPEMC 112

GREATEST HITS: WHO.
LP: ADAH 427
MC: ADAHC 427

HOOLIGANS.
LP: MCA 212001
MC: MCAC 212001

IT'S HARD.
Tracks: / Athena / It's your turn / Cooks county / Dangerous / Eminence front / I've known no war / One life's enough / It's hard / One at a time / Why did I fall for that? / Man is a man, A / Cry if you want.
LP: WHOD 5066

JOIN TOGETHER.
Tracks: / Overture / 1921 / Amazing journey / Sparks / Hawker, The (eyesight to the blind) / Christmas / Cousin Kevin / Acid queen, The / Pinball wizard / Do you think it's alright / Fiddle about / There's a doctor / Go to the mirror / Smash the mirror / Tommy can you hear me? / I'm free / Miracle cure / Sally Simpson / Sensation / Tommy's holiday camp / We're not gonna take it / Eminence front / Face the face / Dig / I can see for miles / Little is enough, A / 5.15 / Love, reign o'er me / Trick of the light / Rough boys / Join together / You better you bet / Behind blue eyes / Won't get fooled again.
LPS: VDT 102
MCSET: TCVDT 102

KIDS ARE ALRIGHT, THE (Film soundtrack).
Tracks: / My generation / I can't explain / Happy Jack / I can see for miles / Magic bus / Long live rock / Anyway anyhow anywhere / Young man blue / Baba O'Riley / My wife / Quick one / Tommy can you hear me / Sparks / Pinball wizard / See me, feel me / Join together / Road runner / My generation blues / Won't get fooled again.
2LP: 2675 179
MC: 3577 343

LIVE AT LEEDS.
Tracks: / Magic bus / My generation / Shakin' all over / Substitute / Summer time blues / Young man blues.
LP: SPELP 50
MC: SPEMC 50
LP: 2406 001

MEATY, BEATY BIG AND BOUNCY.
Tracks: / I can't explain / Kids are alright, The / Happy Jack / I can see for miles / Pictures of Lily / My generation / Seeker, The / Anyway, anyhow, anywhere / Pinball wizard / Legal matter, A / Boris the spider / Magic bus / Substitute / I'm a boy.
LP: 2406 006
MC: 3191 006

MY GENERATION (BRUNSWICK).
LP: LAT 8616

MY GENERATION (KARUSSELL).
Tracks: / My generation / Substitute / I'm a boy / Pictures of Lily / Long live rock / Won't get fooled again / Happy Jack / Kids are alright, The / Seeker, The / I can see for miles / 5:15 / Magic bus.
LP: 2872 120
MC: 3472 120

MY GENERATION (POLYDOR).
Tracks: / My generation / Substitute / Seeker, The / Magic bus / Happy jack / I'm free / Pictures of Lily / Let's see action / I'm a boy / Kids are alright, The / Pinball wizard / I can see for miles.
LP: 2486 140
MC: 3195 235

MY GENERATION (VIRGIN).
Tracks: / Out in the street / I don't mind / Good's gone, The / La la la lies / Much too much / My generation / Kid's are alright, The / Please please please / It's not true / I'm a man / Legal matter, A / Ox, The.
LP: V 2179
MC: TCV 2179

ODDS AND SODS.
LP: 2406 116
MC: 3191 116

ONCE UPON A TIME.
Tracks: / My generation / Heatwave / Smash the mirror / Doctor Jekyll and Mr. Hyde / Overture from Tommy / Doctor Doctor / In the city / Mary Anne with the shaky hand / I can see for miles / Sally Simpson / Magic bus / You see my way / Acid queen, The / We're not gonna take it / Summertime blues / Bucket 'T' / Our love was / Christmas / Don't look away / Call me lightning.
LP: 2664 435
MC: 3578 482

QUADROPHENIA.
Tracks: / I am the sea / Real me, The / Cut my hair / Punk and the godfather, The / I'm one / Dirty jobs, The / Helpless dancer / Is it in my head / I've had enough / 5:15 / Sea and sand / Drowned / Bell boy / Doctor Jimmy / Rock, The / Love reign o'er me.
2LP: 265 701 3
MCSET: 352 600 1

QUADROPHENIA (Film soundtrack) (Various artists).
Tracks: / I am the sea: *Who* / Real me: *Who* / I'm one: *Who* / 5.15: *Who* / I've had enough: *Who* / Love reign o'er me: *Who* / Bell boy: *Who* / Helpless dancer: *Who* / Doctor Jimmy: *Who*/ 4 faces: *Who* / Get out and stay out: *Who* / Joker James: *Who* / Punk and the Godfather: *Who*/ Louie Louie: *Kingsmen* / Zoot suit: *High Numbers* / Hi heel sneakers: *Cross Section* / Night train: *Brown, James* / Green onions: *Booker T & The MGs* / He's so fine: *Chiffons* / Rhythm of the rain: *Cascades*/ Be my baby: *Ronettes* / Da doo ron ron: *Crystals*.
2LP: 262 503 7
MCSET: 357 735 2

QUICK ONE, A.
Tracks: / Run run run / Boris the spider / I need you / Whiskey man / Heatwave / Cobwebs and strange / Don't look away / See my way / So sad / About us / Quick one, A / While he's away.
LP: SPELP 114
MC: SPEMC 114
LP: 593 002
LP: 2683 038
MC: 3533 022

RARITIES.
Tracks: / Join together / I don't know myself / Heaven and hell / When I was a boy / Let's see action / Relay / Wasp man / Here for more / Water / Baby don't do it.
LP: 2311 132
MC: 3100 630

RARITIES VOLUME 1 (1966-68).
LP: SPELP 9
MC: SPEMC 9

RARITIES VOLUME 2 (1970-1973).
LP: SPELP 10
MC: SPEMC 10

RARITIES VOLUMES 1 AND 2.
MC: 8476704

SINGLES, THE.
Tracks: / Substitute / I'm a boy / Happy Jack / Pictures of lily / I can see for miles / Magic bus / Pinball wizard / My generation / Summertime blues / Won't get fooled again / Let's see action / Join together / Squeeze box / Who are you / You better you bet.
LP: WHOH 17
MC: WHOHC 17

STORY OF THE WHO, THE.
Tracks: / Magic bus / Substitute / Boris the spider / Run run run / I'm a boy / Heatwave / My generation / Pictures of Lily / Happy Jack / Seeker, The / I can see for miles / Bargain / Squeeze box / Amazing journey / Acid queen, The / Do you think it's alright / Fiddle about / Pinball wizard / I'm free / Tommy's holiday camp / We're not gonna take it / See me feel me / Summertime blues / Baba O'Riley / Behind blue eyes / Slip kid / Won't get fooled again.
2LP: 2683 069
MCSET: 3519 020

TOMMY (Film soundtrack).
LP: 2657 002
MC: 3526 002

TOMMY.
Tracks: / Overture / It's a boy / 1921 / Amazing journey / Sparks / Eyesight to the blind / Miracle cure / Sally Simpson / I'm free / Welcome / Tommy's holiday camp / We're not gonna take it / Christmas / Cousin Kevin / Acid queen, The / Underture / Do you think it's alright / Fiddle about / Pinball wizard / There's a doctor / Go to the mirror / Tommy can you hear me / Smash the mirror / Sensation.
2LP: 613 0123/4
2LP: 2486 161/2

TOMMY (Who/London Symphony Orchestra).
2LP: ESSLP 029
MC: ESSMC 029

TOMMY - PART 2.
Tracks: / Do you think it's alright / Fiddle about / Pinball wizard / There's a doctor / Go to the mirror / Tommy, can you hear me / Smash the mirror / Sensation / Miracle cure / Sally Simpson / I'm free / Welcome / Tommy's holiday camp / We're not gonna take it.
LP: 2406 008
MC: 914 625

TWO'S MISSING.
LP: SPELP 117
MC: SPEMC 117
LP: 837 558-1
MC: 837 558-4

WHO ARE YOU.
Tracks: / New song / Had enough / 905 / Music must change / Trick of the light / Guitar and pen / Love is coming down / Who are you.
LP: SPELP 77
MC: SPEMC 77
LP: WHOD 5004
MC: 831 557 4

WHO BY NUMBERS, THE.
Tracks: / Slip kid / However much I booze / Squeeze box / Dreaming from the waist / Imagine a man / Success

story / They are all in love / Blue, red and grey / How many friends / In a hand or a face.
LP: SPELP 68
MC: SPEMC 68
LP: 2490 129
MC: 3194 129
MC: 831 552 4

WHO COLLECTION VOLUME 1, THE.
Tracks: / I can't explain / Anyway, anyhow, anywhere / My generation / Substitute / Legal matter, A / Kids are alright, The / I'm a boy / Happy Jack / Boris the spider / Pictures of Lily / I can see for miles / Won't get fooled again / Seeker, The / Let's see action / Join together / Relay / Love reign o'er me / Squeeze box / Who are you / Long live rock / 5:15 / You better, you bet / Magic bus / Summertime blues / Shakin' all over / Pinball wizard / Acid queen, The / I'm free / We're not gonna take it / Baba O'Riley / Behind blue eyes / Bargain.
2LP: IMDP 4
MCSET: IMDK 4

WHO: INTERVIEW PICTURE DISC.
LPPD: BAK 2040

WHO SELL OUT, THE.
Tracks: / Armenia City in the sky / Heinz baked beans / Mary Anne with the shaky hand / Odorono / Tattoo / Our love was / I can see for miles / Can't reach you / Medac / Silas Stingy / Sunrise / Rael (1 and 2).
MC: TWOMC 8
LP: SPELP 115
MC: SPEMC 115
LP: 613 002

WHO'S BETTER WHO'S BEST (Very best of The Who).
Tracks: / My generation / Anyway, anyhow, anywhere / Kids are alright, The / Substitute / I'm a boy / Happy Jack / Pictures of Lily / I can see for miles / Who are you / Won't get fooled again / Magic bus / I can't explain / Pinball wizard / I'm free / See me feel me / Squeeze box / Join together / You better you bet / Baba O'Riley (Extra track on CD.).
LP: WTV 1
MC: WTVC 1

WHO'S LAST.
Tracks: / My generation / I can't explain / Substitute / Boris the spider / Magic bus / Twist and shout.
LP: WHO 1
MC: WHOC 1

WHO'S MISSING.
LP: SPELP 116
MC: SPEMC 116
LP: 837 557-1
MC: 837 557-4

WHO'S NEXT.
Tracks: / Baba O'Riley / Getting in tune / Love ain't for keeping / My wife / Song is over / Bargain / Going mobile / Behind blue eyes / Won't get fooled again.
LP: SPELP 49
MC: SPEMC 49
MC: 3577 378
LP: 2408 102

Who Framed... (film)

WHO FRAMED ROGER RABBIT (Film soundtrack) (London Symphony Orchestra).
Tracks: / Maroon logo / Maroon cartoon / Valiant and valiant / Weasels, The / Hungarian rhapsody / Judge doom / Why don't you do right / No justice for toons / Merry go round broke down (Roger's song) / Jessica's theme / Toontown / Eddie's theme / Gag factory, The / Will, The / Smile darn ya smile / That's all folks / End title.
LP: 4630591
MC: 4630594

Who Framed...(bk)

WHO FRAMED ROGER RABBIT? (Unknown narrator(s)).
MC: DIS 009

Who Owns The Game

WHO OWNS THE GAME (Various artists).
LP: LP 302

Who Pays The Ferryman

WHO PAYS THE FERRYMAN (See under Markopoulos, Yannis) (Markopoulos, Yannis).

Who? What? Why?...

WHO? WHAT? WHY? WHERE? WHEN? (Various artists).
LP: MORT 4

Whodini

COLLECTION: WHODINI.
LP: HIP 99
MC: HIPC 99

OPEN SESAME.
LP: JL 8494
MC: HIPC 50
LP: HIP 50

WHODINI.
Tracks: / Haunted house of rock / Nasty lady / Underground / It's all in Mr. Magic's wand / Magic's wand / Yours for a night / Rap machine / Haunted house of rock (vocoder version).
LP: HIP 10
MC: HIPC 10
LP: HIP 16
MC: HIPC 16

Whole Lotta Drinkin'

WHOLE LOTTA DRINKIN' ON THE BLOCK (Various artists).
Tracks: / Won't be me: *King, Charles* / Bop cat stomp (inst.): *King, Charles* / Honey bee: *Left Hand Charlie* / Whole lotta drinkin' on the block: *Left Hand Charlie* / Miss my lagnion: *Left Hand Charlie* / But you thrill me: *King Charles/ Left Hand Charlie* / Ooh wee baby ohh wee: *Sheffield, Charles 'Mad Dog'* / Isabella: *Sheffield,* Charles 'Mad Dog' / No no baby: *Garlow, Clarence* / Nothing to talk about: *Garlow, Clarence* / Train came down the track: *Garlow, Clarence.*
LP: GFCL 104

Whole Lotta Shakin'...

WHOLE LOTTA SHAKIN' GOIN' ON (Various artists).
LP: GT 0103

Whoopee, John

40 GREATEST HITS.
LP: PC 380

40 POLKA'S AND WALTZES.
LP: PC 383

Whooping Cranes

THATS WHAT I NEED.
LP: MD 7915

Who's In The Kitchen

STRUCTURE RUPTURE.
LP: BB 018

Who's Sleeping...

WHO'S SLEEPING... (Various artists).
LP: BRAIN 001

Who's That Compilation

WHO'S THAT COMPILATION (Various artists).
LP: WHOS 025

Who's That Girl

WHO'S THAT GIRL (Film soundtrack) (Various artists).
Tracks: / Who's that girl: *Various artists* / Causing a commotion: *Various artists* / Look of love, The: *Various* artists / 24 hours: *Various artist* / Turn it up: *Various artists* / Best thing ever: *Various artists/* Can't stop: *Various artists* / El loco loco: *Various artists.*
LP: WX 102
MC: WX 102 C

Why Mosquitos Buzz

WHY MOSQUITOS BUZZ IN PEOPLES' EARS... Aardema, Verna (Davis, Ossie & Ruby Dee).
MC: 1592

Why Overtime

WHY OVERTIME? (See under UNESCO reports).

Whycliffe

ROUGHSIDE.
LP: MCA 10282
MC: MCAC 10282

Whyos

WHYOS, THE.
LP: LPL 8410

Whyte, Ronny

AT THE CONSERVATORY.
LP: AP 151

I LOVE A PIANO.
LP: AP 127

SOFT WHYTE.
LP: AP 204

Whyton, Wally

50 ALL TIME CHILDREN'S FAVOURITES.
LP: HMA 218

50 CHILDREN'S FAVOURITES VOL.1.
Tracks: / See-saw, Margery Daw / Ring a ring a roses / Hickory dickory dock / Three blind mice / Three mice went into a hole / Pussy cat, where have you been / Goosey gander / Froggie went a courtin' / Mary had a little lamb / One man went to Moe / One two three four five once I caught a fish alive / Oranges and lemons / Ole King Cole / Grand old Duke of York, The / Sing a song of sixpence / Polly put the kettle on / Lucky Lockett / What are little boys made of / Wee Willie Winkie / Billy boy / Little boy blue / Little Bo Peep / Little Miss Muffet / Hush little baby / Bye'n'bye / Bye baby Bunting / Diddle dumpling / Hey diddle diddle / Cat went fiddle I fee, The / Three little kitchens / Baa baa, black sheep / Cock-a-doodle-doo / If I had a donkey / Ten in a bed / Ten little indians / London Bridge is falling down / Pop goes the weasel / Queen of hearts / Humpty Dumpty / What are little girls made of? / Curley locks, curley locks / Mary, Mary / This is the house that Jack built / Simple Simon / Bobby Shaftoe / Little Jack Horner / Little nut tree / Twinkle, twinkle little star / Dance to your daddy / Hush-a-bye baby.
MC: KIDM 8003

CHILDREN'S FAVOURITE NURSERY RHYMES.
LP: DAX 101
MC: ZCDAX 101

CHILDREN'S PARTY TIME.
LP: DAX 102
MC: ZCDAX 102

CHILDREN'S SING-A-LONG.
LP: DAX 103
MC: ZCDAX 103

WALLY WHYTON'S GOLDEN HOUR OF NURSERY RHYMES (see Nursery Rhymes).

Wiata, Iniate

WIATA MAORI (Te Wiata, Inia).
Tracks: / Haere mai / Hokihoki tonu mai / Pokarekare ana / Te arava e / E noho e koroki / Toia mai te waka ect / E te iwi e akia kia rite / Karu karu / He puru tai tama ect / E tango ana kow / Tahi nei taru kino / Aue te iwi e / E pari ra / Haere ra e hoa ma ect.
MC: TS SLA 122
LP: SLC 004

Wibbley Brothers

GO WEIRD.
LP: ABOUT 11

Wibbly Wobbly Walk

WIBBLY WOBBLY WALK, THE (Various artists).
Tracks: / Wibbly wobbly walk, (The): *Various artists* / Oh by jingo, oh by gee: *Various artists* / I miss my Swiss: *Various artists* / Everything's at home except your wife: *Various artists* / Spaniard that blighted my life, (The): *Various artists* / Tickle me Timothy: *Various artists* / Little ford rambled right along, The: *Various artists/* Wallaperoo: *Various artists* / I love me: *Various artists* / Come back to Georgia: *Various artists/* All by yourself in the moonlight: *Sarony, Leslie* / Little wooden whistle wouldn't whistle, The: *Various artists/* Why did I kiss that girl?: *Various artists* / Felix kept on walking: *Various artists* / I parted my hair in the middle: *Formby, George* / There's a rickety rackety shack: *Various artists* / Down south: *Various artists/* Parade of the wooden soldiers: *Various artists.*
LP: SDL 350
MC: CSDL 350

Wice, Malcolm

FAMILY FAVOURITES NO. 2 (Wice, Malcolm Duo).
Tracks: / Oh Johnny oh Johnny oh / Bill Bailey won't you please come home / Yankee doodle dandy / Kiss me goodnight / Sargeant major / Quartermasters stores / Roll out the barrel / Neighbours / Friends and neighbours / Bobbin' up and down / All by yourself in the moonlight / In a shanty in old shantytown / Home on the range / Cockles and mussels / When Irish eyes are smiling / Locomotion / Albatross / Love changes everything / I know him so well / Eye level / Patricia (cha cha) / Softly as in a morning sunrise / New fangled tango / Pickin' a chicken / I yi yi yi yi.
LP: MTS 25

Wick Scottish Dance

BY PEAT FIRE (Wick Scottish Dance Band).
LP: SK 2003

Wick Scottish Dance

HEATHER AND SHAMROCK.
LP: SK 2001

Wicked Everywhere

WICKED EVERYWHERE (Various artists).
LP: SPL 105

Wicked Prince...(bk)

WICKED PRINCE AND THE WONDERFUL MUSICIAN (Dotrice, Roy (nar)).
MC: LP 102

Wicked Willy

RECORD SIZE WILLY.
LP: WILLY 1
MC: WILLY C1

Wicker, Mike

MOVING FORCE, THE.
LP: PC 338

Wickman, Putte

BUNDAS DO BRASIL.
Tracks: / No more blues / Lovers / Velas icadus / My autumn leaves / Bundas do Brasil / Once I loved / Metlancia / Wave / Samba do bra / Watch what happens.
LP: SNTF 997

DESIRE.
LP: FLC 5076

MEMORIES OF YOU (See Omnibus Big Band) (Wickman, Putte/Omnibus Big Band).

MISS OEDIPUS.
Tracks: / Miss oidipus / I thought about you / Up with lark / Dear one / But not for me / After the storm / I'll remember April.
LP: DRLP 132

MISTER CLARINET.
LP: FLC 5083

PUTTE WICKMAN AND TRIO (Wickman, Putte & Trio).
LP: BELL 148

SIVUCA.
LP: FLC 6002

Wicks, Johnny

JOCKEY JACK BLUES (Wicks, Johnny swingin' Ozarks).
LP: PL 13

Wide Open

WIDE OPEN (Various artists).
LP: CRAK 001

Widespread

BOOGIE IN THE BARNYARD (Widespread Depression Orchestra).
LP: ST 206

DOWNTOWN UPROAR (Widespread Depression Orchestra).
LP: ST 203

ROCKIN' IN RHYTHM (Widespread Depression Orchestra).
Tracks: / Early morning rock / Do nothing till you hear from me / Alabamy home / Dream blues / VIP boogie / Rabbit jumps, The / What am I here for / I got it bad and that ain't good / Rockin' in rhythm / Don't get around much anymore / Just squeeze me / Morning glory.
LP: PHONT 7527

Widespread Depression

TIME TO JUMP AND SHOUT.
LP: ST 212

Widespread Jazz

PARIS BLUES.
LP: 26561
MC: 40 26561

SWING IS THE THING.
LP: ECJ 403

Widor (composer)

CHARLES-MARIE WIDOR: ORGAN SYMPHONIES NO.5/6 (Kaunzinger, Gunther.).
Tracks: / Organ Symphony no.5 (Widor) (Opus 42: including the toccata.) / Organ Symphony no.6 (Widor) (Opus 42.).
LP: 150 015-1
MC: 150 015-4

CHARLES-MARIE WIDOR: ORGAN SYMPHONIES NO.9/10 (Kaunzinger, Gunther.).
Tracks: / Organ symphony no.9 (Widor) ('Gothic') / Organ symphony no.10 (Widor) ('Roman').
LP: 150 038-1
MC: 150 038-4

Wiedlin, Jane

FUR.
Tracks: / Inside a dream / Rush hour / One heart one way / Home boy / End of love / Lover's night / Fur / Give / Song of the factory / Whatever it takes.
LP: MTL 1029
MC: TCMTL 1029

JANE WIEDLIN.
Tracks: / Blue kiss / Goodbye cruel world / Sometimes you really get on my nerves / East meets west / Somebody's going to get into this house / Forever / Modern romance / I will wait for you / One hundred years of solitude / Where we can go / My travelling heart.
LP: MIRF 1005
MC: MIRC 1005

TANGLED.
Tracks: / Rain on me / At the end of the day / Guardian angel / Flowers on the battlefield / Tangled / World on fire / Paper heart / Big rock candy mountain / 99 ways / Euphoria.
LP: MTL 1053
MC: TCMTL 1053

Wiedorje

WIEDORJE.
LP: . . . . COB 37014

Wier, Rusty

KUMBAK BAR & GRILL.
Tracks: / Kum-bak bar & grill / Cheryl Doreen / Daytime drinkin' / Wonderful tonight / I kept thinkin' about you / Other side of the hill / Close your eyes / Alibi lies / All my give a damn is gone / Lone star lady.
LP: . . . . SDLP 057
MC: . . . . SDC 057

Wife of Bath...(bk)

WIFE OF BATH'S TALE (see under Chaucer, Geoffrey) (Scales, Prunella (nar) & Richard Bebb (nar)).

Wigan Metro Schools..

WIGAN METRO SCHOOLS BRASS BAND.
Tracks: / National emblems / Morning, noon and night / Count your blessings / Playbox / Men of Harlech / Strand on the green / Two guitars / William Tell / March overture / Ceramic City festival.
LP: . . . . CAS LP 005

Wiggins, Gerald

KING AND I, THE (Wiggins, Gerald Trio).
LP: . . . . FS 56

WIGGIN' OUT.
LP: . . . . FS 194

Wiggins, Phil Hea

SWEET BITTER BLUES (see under Bowling Green John) (Wiggins, Phil Hea & Bowling Green John Cephas).

Wiggs, Johnny

CONGO SQUARE (Wiggs, Johnny & Maxine Sullivan).
LP: . . . . NOR 7206

Wigwam

RUMOURS ON THE REBOUND.
2LP: . . . . VGD 3503

Wijnkamp, Leo Jr

RAGS TO RICHES.
LP: . . . . SNKF 108

RETURN OF DR HACKENBUSH.
Tracks: / Return of Dr. Hackenbush / Alabama song / Hilarity rag / Pavane for the sleeping beauty / Golliwogg's cake-walk / St. Louis blues / When I'm sixty four / Jimbo's lullaby / Man ya beserka / Valse du spleen pour Philip / Anda Jerico / Little military march.
LP: . . . . SNKF 156
LP: . . . . KM 160

Wilber, Bob

BOB WILBER (Various artists).
LP: . . . . PHON 50-14

BOB WILBER AND HIS FAMOUS JAZZ BAND (Wilber, Bob & His Famous Jazz Band).
LP: . . . . J 44

BOB WILBER AND THE BECHET LEGACY.
Tracks: / Down in Honky Tonk Town / Si tu vois ma mere / Stop shimmying sister / Lazy blues / If I let you get away with it / Roses of Picardy / Petite fleur / Rue des Champes Elysees / Chant in the night / I'm a little blackbird / Kansas City man blues / China boy.
LP: . . . . BW 103

CLOSE AS PAGES IN A BOOK (See under Sullivan, Maxine) (Wilber, Bob & Maxine Sullivan).

DIZZY FINGERS (Wilber, Bob Sextet).
Tracks: / Dizzy fingers / Poor butterfly / Airmail special / Foolin' myself / Soft winds / Jumpin' at the Woodside / Clarinade / Rose room / Royal Garden blues / What a little moonlight can do / Memories of you / World is waiting for the sunrise, The.
LP: . . . . BW 101
LP: . . . . AP 187

DUET (Wilber, Bob & Dick Wellstood).
LP: . . . . PARKWOOD 103

GROOVIN' AT THE GRUNEWALD.
Tracks: / My blue Heaven / Did I remember? / Love, your magic spell is everywhere / Please be kind / End of a beautiful friendship / Everywhere you go / Groovin' at the Grunewald / June night / Someone to watch over me / I'm beginning to see the light / Lotus blossom / Best thing for you, The.
LP: . . . . PHONT 7414

IN THE MOOD FOR SWING.
Tracks: / I'm in the mood for swing / Talk of the town / Dinah / I'm confessin' / When lights are low / Ring dem bells / Memories of you / Bei mir bist du schon / Yours and mine / Chinatown.
LP: . . . . PHONT 7526

MOZART K581, K498.
LP: . . . . ARTE 7109

MUSIC OF HOAGY CARMICHAEL (Wilber, Bob & Kenny Davern).
LP: . . . . MES 6917

MUSIC OF KING OLIVER'S CREOLE (Wilber, Bob Ensemble).
LP: . . . . GHB 201

MUSIC OF KING OLIVER-VOL 1, THE (Wilber, Bob Jazz Repertory Orch).
LP: . . . . BW 107

NEW ORLEANS STYLE OLD AND NEW (See Bechet, Sidney) (Wilber, Bob & Sidney Bechet).

ODE TO BECHET (Wilber, Bob & The Bechet Legacy).
Tracks: / Margie / Blues in the air / I can't believe that you're in love with me / I get the blues when it rains / Mooche, The / I ain't gonna give nobody none of my jelly-roll / When my dreamboat comes home / Ode to Bechet / Quincy Street stomp / Sailboat in the moonlight / High society / Bechet's fantasy / Shake it and break it.
LP: . . . . BW 104
MC: . . . . BWC 104

ON THE ROAD (Wilber, Bob & The Bechet Legacy).
Tracks: / Lady be good / Georgia cabin / What a dream / I keep calling your name / Polka dot stomp / Egyptian fantasy / Ghost of the blues / Summertime / Love for sale / Santa Claus blues / Indian Summer / Dans la rue d'antibes.
LP: . . . . BW 105
MC: . . . . BWC 105

ORIGINAL WILBER.
Tracks: / Movin' 'n' groovin' / BG / Treasure / Land of the midnight sun / Don't go away / Windsong / Wequaset Wall / I've loved you all my life / Hymn: In memory of Joe Oliver / I can't forget you now / Crawfish shuffle.
LP: . . . . PHONT 7519

RAPTUROUS REEDS.
Tracks: / Jumping at the Woodside / Chloe / Sherman shuffle / Sultry summer day / Stompin' at the Savoy / You are my lucky star / I've loved you all my life / I double dare you / Alone together / Linger awhile / Yours is my heart alone.
LP: . . . . PHONT 7517

REFLECTIONS (Wilber, Bob & The Bodeswell Strings).
LP: . . . . CLP 98
LP: . . . . BW 106

SHERMAN SHUFFLE (see under Tate, Buddy) (Wilber, Bob/Buddy Tate).

SOPRANO SUMMIT (Wilber, Bob & Kenny Davern).
Tracks: / Swing parade / Song of songs / Meet me tonight in dreamland / Penny rag / Mooche, The / Oh sister ain't that hot / Steal away / Egyptian fantasy / Fish vendor, The / Johnny was there / Please clarify / Where are we.
LP: . . . . WJLPS 5

SOPRANO SUMMIT 2 (Wilber, Bob & Kenny Davern).
Tracks: / Frog-I-more rag / Solace 1 / Tango a la Caprice / If you went away / Lincoln garden stomp / Solace 2 / Sidewalk blues / Creole nights / Rialto ripples / Sunflower slow drag.
LP: . . . . WJLPS 13

SOPRANO SUMMIT CONCERTO (Wilber, Bob & Kenny Davern).
LP: . . . . CJ 129

SWINGIN' FOR THE KING.
Tracks: / Let's dance / It's been so long / Changes / Goodnight my love / Best things in life are free, The / I had to do it / Bach goes to town / By myself / Silhouetted in the moonlight / Jubilee / Why do I love you? / Seven come eleven / Jersey bounce / Deep night / All the things you are / We'll meet again / Keep your sunny side up / Rachel's dream / Lullaby in rhythm / Miss my lovin' time / Someone else is taking my place / Lovely to look at / Stealin' apples / Goodbye.
2LP: . . . . PHONT 7406/07

VITAL WILBER.
Tracks: / I'm gonna sit right down and write myself a letter / Nice work if you can get it / Clarion song / After you've gone / Sunday / Limehouse blues / Treasure / How long has this been going on? / Good Friday bounce / Don't get around much anymore / Sugar.
LP: . . . . PHON 7

Wilbrandt, Thomas

ELECTRIC V, THE.
Tracks: / Crescendo of Spring, The / Electric bird, The / Sketches of spring / Idyll / Twilight / Heat, The / Hot stuff / Meditation, The / Thunder and lightning / Leaves and chutes / Hi celebration / Wide white horizon / Electric harpsichord, The / Radio music / Dancing / Breaking the ice / Beating the cold / Farewell, The / Winter song.
LP: 818 147 1
MC: 818 147 4

Wilbur, Jay

HI GANG! (Jay Wilbur & His Band).
Tracks: / Easy come, easy go / Straight from the shoulder / It's the talk of the town / Sailboat in the moonlight / It's all forgotten now / Mist on the river / Same old story / In a little rocky valley / Why doesn't somebody tell me these things.
LP: . . . . RFL 21

MELODY OUT OF THE SKY 1933-8.
Tracks: / Here come's cookie / On a steamer coming over / I've got you under my skin / Whispers in the dark / Stay as sweet as you are / Let's call the whole thing off / Way you look tonight, The.
LP: . . . . RD 6

Wilbur, Richard

RICHARD WILBUR READING HIS POETRY.
MC: 1248

Wilburn Brothers

CITY LIMITS.
LP: . . . . HAT 3061
MC: . . . . HATC 3061

COUNTRY GOLD.
Tracks: / I don't care / When I stop dreaming / I don't love you anymore / Crazy arms / I dreamed of an old love affair / Wonder why you said goodbye / I wonder where you are tonight / Before I'm over you / I can stand it / World of forgotten people / I guess I'm crazy / Don't let me cross over.
LP: . . . . HAT 3007
MC: . . . . HATC 3007

TEDDY AND DOYLE.
LP: . . . . HAT 3035
MC: . . . . HATC 3035

WILBURN BROTHERS SHOW, THE.
LP: . . . . HAT 3017
MC: . . . . HATC 3017

Wilce, Malcolm

FAMILY FAVOURITES - DANCE (Wilce, Malcolm Duo).
LP: . . . . MTS 17

GOING PLACES (Wilce, Malcolm Duo).
LP: . . . . MTS 12

LET IT SWING (Wilce, Malcolm Duo).
LP: . . . . MTS 7

SINCERELY YOURS (Wilce, Malcolm Duo).
LP: . . . . MTS 22

THERE GOES THAT SONG AGAIN (Wilce, Malcolm Duo,The/Tommy Sanderson).
LP: . . . . MTS 13

Wild And Frantic

WILD AND FRANTIC (Various artists).
LP: 21667

Wild At Heart

WILD AT HEART (Film soundtrack) (Various artists).
Tracks: / Im abendrot: *Various artists* / Slaughterhouse: *Various artists* / Cool cat walk: *Various artists*/ Love me: *Various artists* / Baby please don't go: *Various artists* / Up in flames: *Various artists*/ Wicked game: *Various artists* / Be bop a lula: *Various artists* / Smoke rings: *Various artists* / Perdita: *Various artists* / Blue Spanish sky: *Various artists* / Dark Spanish symphony (50's version): *Various artists*/ Dark Lolita: *Various artists* / Love me tender: *Various artists.*
LP: 845 128 1
MC: 845 128 4

Wild Bill

BABY YUM YUM (Lala blues from Louisiana's Bayous 1969) (Wild Bill's Blue Washboard Band).
LP: . . . . FLY 543

Wild Blue

NO MORE JINX.
Tracks: / Only You / Fire with fire / Nowhere left to run / When I think about you / Blue daze / Give me a reason / Leather blues / Taboo / International language of dance.
LP: . . . . CHR 1531
MC: . . . . ZCHR 1531

Wild Bunch

PLEASE BE WITH ME.
LP: . . . . SFA 055

WILD BUNCH, THE.
LP: . . . . ARILP 015
MC: . . . . A 139

Wild Canyon

LIKE A POKER GAME.
Tracks: / Where are you / I dreamed I was a cowboy / It's just like a poker game / Everything I do / Things we say are true / I'll be here with you / Step up / Blue steel blues / Come on with me / Okie from Muskogee / Mexican lady.
LP: . . . . BFX 15290

NEW WRAPPING.
Tracks: / Teen scene / Entertainer, The / Canyon hop / Dobro / My memories / New wrapping medley / Enchanted canyon 86 / Skip along / Flamingo shuffle / What is happiness / Country gentleman / Sail place.
LP: . . . . BFX 15251

THIS WORLD OF OURS.
Tracks: / Cinder track, The / Great adventure / This world of ours / Imprisoned, but wasn't guilty / Why must we wait so long? / Nur wur / Walking in the sunshine / Good-hearted woman / Laura / Mamas don't let your babies grow up to be cowboys / What about you? / She thinks I still care.
LP: . . . . BFX 15197

'TWAS A LONG TIME AGO.
Tracks: / 'Twas a long time ago / Rodeo rider, The / Good old days will not return, The / Poor boy jamboree / You shouldn't do it / Golden ages (are they gone) / Buffalo skip / Blanket on the ground / Vacation time / Bob Wills is still the king / Jim Bridger / Door is always open, The / Taker, The / Folsom Prison blues.
LP: . . . . BFX 15131

Wild Cherry

PLAY THAT FUNKY MUSIC (OLD GOLD) (See under Joe Tex - Ain't Gonna Bump).

Wild Connections

WILD CONNECTIONS (Various artists).
LP: . . . . BRMLP 001
MC: . . . . BRMMC 001

Wild & Crazy Noise ...

WILD AND CRAZY NOISE MERCHANTS (Various artists).
LP: 12009
MC: 12010

Wild Dogs

REIGN OF TERROR.
Tracks: / Metal fuel (in the blood) / Man against machine / Call of the dark / Siberian vacation / Psychoradio / Streets of Berlin / Spellshock / Reign of terror / We rule the night.
LP: . . . . MFN 80

Wild Fantasy

JUNGLE DRUMS.
Tracks: / Jungle drums / Gypsy lady / Get it on / Africa / Funky people / Smile / Very thought of you / Boogie boogie boogie.
LP: . . . . MAGL 5027
MC: . . . . TCMAGL 5027

Wild Flowers

DUST.
LP: . . . . CHAPLP 15

JOY OF IT ALL, THE.
LP: . . . . LEX 2

SOMETIME SOON.
LP: . . . . CHAPLP 25

TALES LIKE THESE.
Tracks: / Shakedown / This feeling's gone / Put the blame on me / No holy spirits / Tales like these / Green hotel / Someone's stolen (my dreams) / Love like fire / Fever tree / Hopes crash down.
LP: 828 192 1
MC: 828 192 4

Wild Geese

FLIGHT 2.
LP: . . . . JLP 207

IN FULL FLIGHT.
LP: . . . . JLP 215
LP: . . . . JLT 215
MC: . . . . JLPC 215

Wild Geese (film)

WILD GEESE, THE (Original soundtrack) (Various artists).
LP: . . . . AMLH 64730

Wild Hills O'Wannie

WILD HILLS O'WANNIE (The small pipes of Northumbria).
LP: 12TS 227

Wild Honey

SWEET COUNTRY.
Tracks: / Rockabilly rebel / Just back from No Man's Land / Angel Judy / Tennessee whisky and Texas women / Mary of Dunloe / Swimming hole / Hickory holler's tramp / Riding my thumb to Mexico / Diane / Guitar boogie shuffle / Standing at the station / You made it right.
LP: . . . . BGC 313
MC: . . . . KBGC 313

Wild Horses

STAND YOUR GROUND.
Tracks: / I'll give you love / In the city / Another lover / Back in the USA / Stand your ground / Axe / Miami justice / Precious / New York City / Stake out.
LP: EMC 3368

WILD HORSES.
Tracks: / Reservation / Face down / Blackmail / Fly away / Dealer / Street girl / No strings attached / Criminal tendencies / Nights on the town / Woman.
LP: EMC 3326
MC: TCEMC 3326
LP: EMC 3324

Wild Oats

AGINCOURT.
LP: SFA 015

Wild Ones

SOUNDS LIKE GENE VINCENT.
LP: LP 8804

WRITING ON THE WALL.
LP: HMRLP 171
MC: HMRMC 171

Wild Orchid

WILD ORCHID (Original soundtrack) (Various artists).
Tracks: / Wild orchid (main title): *Paradise* / Elejibo: *Menezes, Margereth* / Dark secret: *Rudder, David* & Margareth Menezes / Shake the Sheikh: *Dissidenten* / I want to fly: *Haza, Ofra* / Slave dream: *Haza, Ofra* / Bird boy: *Vasconcelos, Nana & Bushdances* / Twistin' with Annie: *Ballard, Hank* / Magic jewelled limousine: *Nasa* / Oxossi: *Geronimo* / Children of fire: *Rudder, David* / Promised land: *Underworld* / Flor cubana: *Moreno, Simone* / Wheeler's howl: *Rhythm Methodists* / Just a carnival: *Rudder, David.*
LP: 7599261271
MC: 7599261274

Wild Rovers

WILD ROVERS (Film soundtrack) (Various artists).
LP: MCA 25141
MC: MCAC 25141

Wild Seeds

BRAVE, CLEAN AND REVERENT.
Tracks: / Sharlene / Big mimosa sky / Girl can tell, A / Hurricane girls / When the fever breaks / Pure heart / I work hard / Heaven bound / Love will make you weak / Big moon / Shake this world.
LP: ZONG 019

Wild Spirit

DO THAT THING.
LP: HMRLP 164
MC: HMRMC 164

Wild Strawberries

WILD STRAWBERRIES.
LP: METALP 116

Wild Style

ORIGINAL WILD STYLE BREAKBEATS ALBUM, THE.
LP: STEAL 1

Wild Style (film)

WILD STYLE (Film soundtrack) (Wild Style).
Tracks: / Wild style theme rap 1 / MC battle / Basketball throwdown / Fantastic freaks at the Dixie / Military cut scratch mix / Cold Crush Brothers at the Dixie / Stoop rap / Double trouble at the ampitheatre / Wild style subway rap 2 / Gangbusters scratch mix / Rammellzee and shock Dell at the ampitheatre.
LP: CHR 1453
MC: ZCHR 1453

Wild Swans

BRINGING HOME THE ASHES.
Tracks: / Young manhood / Bible dreams / Bitterness / Archangels / Northern England / Whirlpool heart / Bringing home the ashes / Mythical beast / Now and forever / Worst year of my life, The.
LP: 9256971
MC: 9256974

Wild Tchoupitoulas

WILD TCHOUPITOULAS, THE.
Tracks: / Brother John / Meet de boys on de battlefront / Here dey come / Hey pocky a-way / Indian red / Big chief got a golden crown / Hey mama / Hey hey.
LP: ILPS 9360
MC: ICT 9360
MC: ICM 2067
MC: 842 549 4

Wild Thyme

WILD THYME PLAYS FALLIBROOME.
Tracks: / Merry companion, The / Zephyrs & Flora / Monk's march with the wanders / Topaz, The / Bouzar castle / Shropshire lass / Easter Thursday / Happy pair, The / Miss Sayer's Allemande / Huntington's maggot / Cream pot / Draper's gardens / In the fields of frost and snow / Woodlark.
LP: SDL 339
MC: CSDL 339

Wildcat

LOVE ATTACK.
LP: RR 9736

UNOFFICIAL ACTION.
LP: WC 1

Wildcats

WILDCATS (See under Bomphray, Clint - Late Special) (Various artists).

Wilde, Danny

ANY MAN'S HUNGER.
Tracks: / Time runs wild / Ain't I good enough / This old town / In a bordertown / Set me free / Every goodbye / Any man's hunger / Contradiction / Too many years gone by.
LP: 924179 1
MC: 924179 4

Wilde, Dee Dee

NO WAY OUT.
LP: BRLP 527
MC: BRCA 527
MC: ICM 2066
MC: 846 605 4

RUNAWAY (STRAIGHT UP MIX) (See under Urban High) (Urban High feat. Dee Dee Wilde).

Wilde, Eugene

EUGENE WILDE.
LP: BRLP 502
MC: BRCA 502

GO WILDE.
LP: MCA 42282

I CHOOSE YOU TONIGHT.
MC: MCAC 42282

SERENADE.
LP: MCF 3321
MC: MCFC 3321

Wilde, Kim

ANOTHER STEP (CLOSER TO YOU).
Tracks: / Say you really want me (on CD only) / You keep me hangin' on (on CD only) / Hit him / Another step (closer to you) / Thrill of it, The / I've got so much love / She hasn't got time for you / Brothers / Don't say nothing's changed / Schoolgirl / Missing / How do you want my love / Victim (on CD only).
MC: KIMLC 1
MC: MCFC 3339
LP: MCF 3339
LP: KIML 1

CATCH AS CATCH CAN.
Tracks: / House of Salome / Backstreet Joe / Stay awhile / Love blonde / Dream sequence / Dancing in the dark / Shoot to disable / Can you hear it / Sparks / Sing it out for love.
LP: SRAK 165408

CLOSE.
Tracks: / Hey Mr. Heartache / You came / Four letter word / Love in the natural way / Love's a no / Never trust a stranger / You' be the one who'll lose / European soul / Stone / Lucky.
LP: MCG 6030
MC: MCGC 6030

KIM WILDE.
Tracks: / Water on glass / Our town / Everything we know / Young heroes / Kids in America / Chequered love / 2-6-5-8-0 / You'll never be so wrong / Falling out / Tuning in, turning on.
LP: ATAK 49
MC: TCATAK 49
LP: FA 3214
MC: TCFA 3214
LP: SRAK 544

KIM WILDE: INTERVIEW PICTURE DISC.
LPPD: BAK 2102

LOVE MOVES.
Tracks: / It's here / Storm in our hearts / Someday / Who's to blame / In Hollywood / Love (send him back to me) / World in perfect harmony / Time / Can't get enough (of you) / I can't say goodbye.
LP: MCG 6088
MC: MCGC 6088

ROCKIN' AROUND THE CHRISTMAS TREE (See Smith, Mel) (Mel & Kim (Smith & Wilde)).

SELECT.
Tracks: / Ego / Words fell down / Action city / View from a bridge / Just a feeling / Chaos at the airport / Take me tonight / Can you come over / Wendy sadd / Cambodia reprise.
LP: 41 3130 1
MC: 41 3130 4
LP: SRAK 548

TEASES AND DARES.
Tracks: / Touch, The / Is it over / Suburbs of Moscow / Fit in / Rage to love / Second time, The / Bladerunner / Janine / Shangri-la / Thought it was goodbye.
LP: MCF 3250
MC: MCFC 3250

TOP SIXTEEN.
MC: PM 1562594

VERY BEST OF KIM WILDE, THE.
Tracks: / Kids in America / Chequered love / Water on glass / 2-6-5-8-0 / Boys / Our town / Everything we know / You'll never be so wrong / Cambodia / View from a bridge / Love blonde / House of Salome / Dancing in the dark / Child come away / Take me tonight / Stay awhile.
LP: ATAK 63
MC: EJ 2601084
MC: TCWILDE 1
MC: TCATAK 63
LP: EJ 260 108 1
LP: WILDE 1

Wilde, Marty

BAD BOY.
LP: 6831 048
MC: 7215 048

GOOD ROCKIN' - THEN AND NOW.
LP: 6382 102

HITS OF MARTY WILDE, THE.
Tracks: / Endless sleep / Teenager in love / Donna / Bad boy / Sea of love.
LP: TIME 08
MC: TIMEC 08

WILDCAT ROCKER.
LP: 33.8007

Wilde, Oscar (author)

BALLAD OF READING GAOL (NARRATIVE) (see under Ballad of Reading Gaol) (Mason, James (nar)).

CANTERVILLE GHOST, THE (see under Canterville Ghost (bk) (Quayle, Anthony (nar)).

FAIRY STORIES VOL.1 READ BY ROBERT RIETTY.
MC: BKK 406

FAIRY STORIES VOL.2 READ BY ROBERT RIETTY.
MC: BKK 407

HAPPY PRINCE AND OTHER FAIRY TALES (Rathbone, Basil (nar)).
MC: 1044

HAPPY PRINCE, THE (see also under Happy prince).
MC: PLBC 113
MC: TTC/OWO 3

IMPORTANCE OF BEING EARNEST, THE (See also under Importance of being earnest) (Gielgud, Sir John & Dame Edna Evans).
MCSET: LFP 7242
MCSET: LFP 4172425

IMPORTANCE OF BEING EARNEST, THE (Various artists).
MCSET: 0329

LORD ARTHUR SAVILE'S CRIME.
MC: TCC/OW 01

PICTURE OF DORIAN GRAY, THE (See also under Picture of Dorian Gray) (Hatfield, Hurd).
MC: 1095

STORIES FOR CHILDREN (Morley, Robert).
Tracks: / Happy prince, The / Star child, The / Selfish giant, The / Nightingale & the rose, The / Young king, The.
MCSET: SAY 72

Wilder, Alex

MUSIC OF ALEX WILDER.
Tracks: / Theme and varioations / Air for flute / Air for English horn / Slow dance / Air for oboe / Seldom the sun / Her old man was suspicious / His first long pants / It's silk feel it / Pieces of eight / Such a tender night / She'll be seven in May.
LP: CBS 61989

Wilder, Joe

HANGIN' OUT (see under Newman, Joe) (Wilder, Joe & Joe Newman).

Wilder, Matthew

BOUNCIN' OFF THE WALLS.
Tracks: / Mad for you / Bouncin' off the walls / Hey little girl / Scandal / Naked truth / Open up / Cry just a little / Love of an amazon / Fortune cookie.
LP: EPC 26202

Wilder, Webb

HYBRID VIGOR.
Tracks: / Hittin' where it hurts / Cold front / Wild honey / Skeleton crew / Do you know something / Safeside / What's got wrong with you / Louisiana Hannah.
LP: ILPS 9946
MC: ICT 9946

IT CAME FROM NASHVILLE (Wilder, Webb & The Beatnicks).
Tracks: / How long can she last / Horror hayride / I'm burning / Is this all there is / Devil's right hand / Move on down the line / One taste of the bait / I'm wise to you / It gets in your blood / Poolside / Ruff rider / Keep it on your mind.
LP: SPD 1011
MC: SPDC 1011

Wilderness Family

CROSSING LAKE RILEY.
LP: BUENLP 1

Wildfire

BRUTE FORCE AND IGNORANCE.
MC: TAPE 78307

SUMMER LIGHTNING.
LP: SKULL 8338

Wildflower Roots

WILDFLOWER ROOTS (Various artists).
LP: PL 1001

Wildflower (show)

WILDFLOWER (Original London Cast).
LP: SH 279

Wilding, Griselda

PARISIAN ROMANCE.
MC: 85 1003

Wildlife

BURNING.
Tracks: / Burning / Playing it too close to the heart / Alena / Misplaced love / If the night / Incredible shrinking love / I'm winning / That diamond / Too late / Only a fool.
LP: CHR 1288

WILDLIFE.
Tracks: / Rat race / Mr. Wonderful / Who do you love / Hey, don't let me down / Let's go / Lament for the lost / Land of the lost / Million to one shot blues / Life's end / So long / Danced my life away / Wildlife.
LP: 4673611
MC: 4673614

WILDLIFE (SWANSONG).
Tracks: / Somewhere in the night / Just a friend / Surrender / Charity / One last chance / Haven't you heard the news / Midnight stranger / Rock and roll dreams / Downtown heartbreak.
LP: B 0078

Wildlife (natural)

GLOUCESTERSHIRE WILDLIFE TAPESTRY (Various).
LP: SDL 304
MC: CSDL 304

SOUTH ATLANTIC ISLANDS (Various).
LP: SDL 299
MC: CSDL 299

Wildroot Orchestra

WILDROOT ORCHESTRA, THE.
LP: LAT 1115

Wildwood

GOOD HEARTED FRIENDS.
LP: WRS 111

WILDWOOD.
LP: WRS 095

Wildwood, John

GOOD OLD COUNTRY MUSIC.
LP: BSS 208

Wiley, Fletch

ART OF PRAISE, THE.
LP: SR R 2058

ART OF PRAISE, THE VOL.2.
MC: SSC 8075

NIGHTWATCH.
Tracks: / Fiesta / I am what I am / People get ready / Started right / Are you ready / Nightwatch / Joy dance.
LP: PRIM 6000
MC: ZPRIM 6000

PERFECT PRAISE.
MC: WST C 9090

Wiley, Ken

VISAGE.
LP: PJ 88020
MC: PJC 88020

Wiley, Lee

BACK HOME AGAIN.
LP: MES 7041

DUOLOGUE 1954 (Wiley, Lee & Ellis Larkins).
LP: BLP 60911

I GOT A RIGHT TO SING THE BLUES.
LP: JASS 19

LEE WILEY AND BUNNY BERIGAN (1940) (Wiley, Lee & Bunny Berigan).
LP: T 1013

LEE WILEY: ON THE AIR VOLUME 1.
Tracks: / You came to my rescue / Three little words / You turned the tables on me / Here's love in your eyes / South in my soul, The / I'm coming Virginia / Thousand goodnights, A / Funny little world / Sometimes I feel like a motherless child / If I love again / Little things you used to do, The / Robins and roses / When I'm with you / Crosspatch.
LP: . . . . TOTEM 1021

LEE WILEY: ON THE AIR VOLUME 2.
Tracks: / I've got a crush on you / Sweet and low down / You're lucky to me / On the sunny side of the street / Sugar / Don't blame me / When your lover has gone / How long has this been going on? / Ghost of a chance / I can't get started / Someone to watch over me / Any old time / Man I love, The / Down with love.
LP: . . . . TOTEM 1033

LEE WILEY SINGS GERSHWIN AND COLE PORTER.
LP: . . . . MES 7034

LEE WILEY SINGS RODGERS AND HART AND HAROLD ARLE.
LP: . . . . MES 6807
LP: . . . . AP 10

LEGENDARY-COLLECTORS ITEMS..
LP: TJ6004

SINGS THE SONGS OF GEORGE & IRA GERSHWIN & COLE PORTER.
LP: . . . . AP 1

SWEET AND LOWDOWN.
Tracks: / 'S wonderful / But not for me / Easy to love / Let's do it.
LP: . . . . HAL 6

TOUCH OF THE BLUES, A.
Tracks: / Memphis blues, The / From the land of the sky blue water / Ace in the hole, The / Someday you'll be sorry / My melancholy baby / Hundred years from today / Blues in my heart / Maybe you'll be there / Between the devil and the deep blue sea / I don't want to walk without you / Make believe / Touch of the blues, A.
LP: . . . . NL 90041
MC: . . . . NK 90041

YOU LEAVE ME BREATHLESS.
LP: . . . . JASS 15

Wilhelm, Michael

MEAN OLE FRISCO.
LP: . . . . ROSE 70

MICHAEL WILHELM.
LP: . . . . FC 003

Wilhoit, Sam

MY OLD FLAMES (Wilhoit, Sam Quintet).
LP: . . . . PRO 7068

Wilken, Arden

BRAIN TAPE, THE.
MC: . . . . C 404

DREAM TIME - MUSIC FOR SLEEP.
MC: . . . . C 406

INNER FOCUS - MUSIC FOR MEDITATION.
MC: . . . . C 405

INNER HARMONY.
MC: . . . . C 403

MUSIC FOR CHILDREN - DAY PLAY AND NIGHT REST.
MC: . . . . C 407

MUSIC FOR HEALING.
MC: . . . . C 401

Wilkerson, Don

PREACH BROTHER.
LP: . . . . BST 84107

TEXAS TWISTER, THE.
LP: . . . . RSLP 332

Wilkin, Marijohn

ONE DAY AT A TIME.
Tracks: / One day at a time / So much to thank you for / Behold the man / Let your light so shine / God is love / Here I am / Living sermon for thee, A / Back in the fold / Living tree, The / Where I'm going / Give it away / Speak louder / Our little old home town / Let the spirit work in silence / Scars in the hands of Jesus, The / Reach up and touch God's hand / You still the troubled waters / Follow the Jesus sign / It's a brand new world / I have returned.
LP: . . . . TWE 6005
MC: . . . . TC TWE 6005

Wilkins, Ernie

BIG NEW BAND OF THE 60'S, THE (Wilkins, Ernie Orchestra).
LP: . . . . FS 199

ERNIE WILKINS ALMOST BIG BAND LEVEL.
LP: MTX-29203

ERNIE WILKINS & THE ALMOST BIG BAND/KENNY DREW/ED THIGPEN (Wilkins, Ernie and the Almost Big Band/ Kenny Drew/Ed Thigpen).
LP: . . . . SLP 4051

Wilkins, Rick

LIVE A THE 1990 CONCORD JAZZ FESTIVAL (See Under Wess, Frank) (Wilkins, Rick & Frank Wess & Marshal Royal).

Wilkins, Robert

BEFORE THE REVERENCE.
LP: . . . . PY 1800

ORIGINAL ROLLING STONE.
LP: . . . . HER 215

ROBERT WILKINS 1928-35.
LP: . . . . WSE 111

Wilkinson, Colm

STAGE HEROES.
Tracks: / Man from Mancha / Impossible dream, The / Pity the child / Anthem (Chess) / Maria / Somewhere / Phantom of the opera / Music of the night / Bring him home / Empty chairs at empty tables / Some enchanted evening / This nearly was mine / How to handle a woman / If ever I would leave you / Summertime / It ain't necessarily so.
LP: . . . . BL 74105
MC: . . . . BK 74105

Wilkinson, Sue

LOOKING FOR COVER.
Tracks: / Now possessed / Extra marital affair / Never gonna let you forget me / You're still there / I can't stand a night without you / Let's pretend / No one's making love anymore / You've gotta be a hustler if you wanna get on / Toy boys / Women only / Double dealin' pay / Bad loser / Yesterday's Alice / Moment of glory / Time n' tide / Mr. Polski's theme.
LP: . . . . SUW 001

Will, Ray

LAST VISIT (See under Ferguson, Max - Where do we go).

Will to Power

JOURNEY HOME.
Tracks: / Journey home / Don't like it / Fly bird / Best friend's girl / Clock on the wall / Koyaanisqatsi / Boogie nights / I'm not in love / It's my life / Fly bird (reprise).
LP: 4670991
MC: 4670994

WILL TO POWER.
LP: 4631341
MC: 4631344

Willard, Kelly

BLAME IT ON THE ONE I LOVE.
Tracks: / Friend so true, A / You're welcome here / Dear Jesus / Similes / Cares chorus / Me myself in Christ / Oh gentle love / Blame it on the one I love / Walk with me / Pass the salt / Dad song / Rest / Heart's prayer.
LP: . . . . MM 0047
MC: . . . . TC MM 0047

WILLING HEART.
Tracks: / Willing heart / To obey Him / Comfortable with you / Faithful love / Million ways, A / Hold on / Jesus / Only you / Yesterday's gone / Narrow way, The.
LP: . . . . MM 0079
MC: . . . . TC MM 0079

Willberg, Bob

DJANGO'S MUSIC (See Peters, Mike) (Willberg,Bob/Birelli lagrene/Mike Peters).

Willcocks, David (Sir)

CAROLS FOR CHRISTMAS (see under Jones, Aled) (Willcocks, David/Aled Jones/Royal College.Music ChamberChoir).

Willebrandts, Dick

DICK WILLEBRANDTS EN ZIJN ORKEST (1943-4).
LP: . . . . H 2012

Willesden Dodgers

FIRST BASE.
Tracks: / Not this president / Act of terrorism / Reckless / Mean street / Breakin' out / Gunsmoke breakout / Venetian encounter.
LP: . . . . HIP 34
MC: . . . . HIPC 34

Willett Family

ROVING JOURNEYMEN.
LP: 12T 84

Willetts, Dave

ON AND OFF STAGE.
Tracks: / Phantom of the opera / Les miserables / La cage aux folles / Nine / Guys and dolls / Rose, The / Music of the night.
LP: . . . . SONG 902
MC: . . . . SONGC 902

Willetts, Trevor

DOUBLE TOUCH (see under Smitton, Charles) (Trevor Willetts & Smitton Charles).
LP: . . . . CF 210

William Tell

WILLIAM TELL (Daneman, Paul (nar)).
MC: . . . . BKK 402

WILLIAM TELL (TV soundtrack) (Various artists).
Tracks: / Straight through the apple: *Various artists* / Waxing moon, The: *Various artists* / To live and die: *Various artists* / Ballad of William, The: *Various artists* / Ballad: *Various artists* / Shadows: *Various* artists / Fruits of the forest: *Various artists* / Enchantment: *Various artists* / Dance, The: *Various* artists / Interlude: *Various artists* / Just pursuits: *Various artists* / Point of no return: *Various artists* / Ride, The: *Various artists* / Song of the crossbow: *Various artists.*
LP: . . . . V 2585
MC: . . . . TCV 2585

Williams, Alan

COUNTRY SIDE OF ME.
LP: . . . . BSS 128

LONESOME LEAVIN' BLUES.
LP: . . . . BSS 382

MIXED FEELIN'.
LP: . . . . BSS 228

Williams, Alyson

COOKED - THE REMIX ALBUM (Remixed tracks from the 'Raw' album).
LP: 4667991
MC: 4667994

RAW.
Tracks: / Just call my name / We're gonna make it / I looked into your eyes / Not on the outside / Masquerade / I'm so glad / My love is so raw / On the rocks / Still my No.1 / I need your lovin' / Sleep talk.
LP: 4632931
MC: 4632934

Williams, Andre

DIRECTLY FROM THE STREETS.
Tracks: / Chicago / Sygnifying monkey / Dark gable (song of cadillac Jim) / Sinderella / Slick bitch (left hand right hand) / Night before Xmas / What would you do.
LP: . . . . SDE 4020
MC: . . . . SDEMC 4020

Williams, Andy

6 TRACK HITS: ANDY WILLIAMS.
Tracks: / By the time I get to Phoenix.
MC: 7SC 5050

ALMOST THERE.
LP: . . . . BPG 62533

ANDY WILLIAMS CHRISTMAS ALBUM, THE.
MC: . . . . HSC 888
LP: . . . . SHM 888
MC: . . . . HSC 242

ANDY WILLIAMS COLLECTION.
2LP: . . . . PDA 050
MCSET: . . . . PDC 050

ANDY WILLIAMS COLLECTION (CASTLE).
Tracks: / Can't take my eyes off you / Alfie / Killing me softly with her song / Danny boy / Feelings / Unchained melody / Softly as I leave you / Long and winding road, The / On the street where you live / Good morning starshine / Kisses sweeter than wine / Strangers in the night / For once in my life / People / Spanish harlem / Love's a cold wind / What now my love / More I see you, The / Secret love / Summertime / Misty / 'll be there / Never can say goodbye / Village of St. Bernadette.
MC: . . . . CCSMC 169
2LP: . . . . CCSLP 169

ANDY WILLIAMS' GREATEST HITS.
LP: 63920
MC: 40 63920

ANDY WILLIAMS' GREATEST HITS VOL.2.
LP: . . . . CBS 32013
LP: . . . . CBS 65151

ANDY WILLIAMS SHOW.
LP: . . . . CBS 64127

ANDY WILLIAMS SOUND OF MUSIC.
LP: . . . . CBS 63920

BORN FREE.
LP: . . . . SBPG 63027

CAN'T GET USED TO LOSING YOU.
LP: . . . . BPG 62146

CAN'T HELP FALLING IN LOVE.
LP: . . . . CBS 64067

CAN'T TAKE MY EYES OFF YOU.
LP: . . . . SHM 893
MC: . . . . HSC 248

CLOSE ENOUGH FOR LOVE.
Tracks: / How do you keep the music playing / Moon river / Change partners / Lucky to be me / My funny Valentine / Days of wine and roses / Through the eyes of love / Close enough for love / Music of goodbye / Round midnight.
LP: . . . . WX 82
MC: . . . . WX 82 C

DANNY BOY.
Tracks: / Danny boy / Tammy / Twelfth of never / I'm old fashioned / Come to me bend to me / Secret love / Heather on the hill / Can I forget you / It could happen to you / I want to be wanted / Summertime / Misty.
LP: . . . . CBS 32419

FROM ANDY WITH LOVE.
Tracks: / Love story (where do I begin) / Godfather love theme / Days of wine and roses.
LP: . . . . SHM 3167
MC: . . . . HSC 3167

GET TOGETHER WITH ANDY WILLIAMS.
LP: . . . . CBS 63800

GREAT SONGS FROM MY FAIR LADY.
LP: . . . . BPG 62430

GREAT SONGS OF THE 60'S.
Tracks: / Up, up and away / By the time I get to Phoenix / My co,louring book / Can't help falling in love / Walk right back / Alfie / Here, there and everywhere / Raindrops keep falling on my head / Sweet Caroline / Somewhere my love / Man and a woman, A / Scarborough fair / Wichita lineman / Born free / For once in my life / Groovin' / Sunny / Little green apples / Love is blue / Both sides now / My cherie amour / Gentle on my mind / Something stupid / Windy / Days of wine and roses / Can't get used to losing you / Spanish eyes / MacArthur Park.
2LP: . . . . CBS 22111

GREAT SONGS OF THE SEVENTIES.
Tracks: / Hungry years / Imagine / Solitaire / Feelings / Way we were / My sweet Lord / Mandy / Song sung blue / Killing me softly with her song / Most beautiful girl / Bridge over troubled water.
2LP: . . . . CBS 88473
MC: 40 88473

GREATEST LOVE CLASSICS (Williams, Andy & the Royal Philharmonic Orchestra.).
Tracks: / Romeo and Juliet / Love made me a fool / Vino de amor / Different light, A / Another winters day / Vision, The / Journey's end / Twist of fate, A / Home / Brave new world / She'll never know / In my world of illusion / Words.
LP: . . . . ANDY 1
MC: . . . . TC ANDY 1
LP: . . . . MFP 5761
MC: . . . . TCMFP 5761

HAPPY HEART.
LP: . . . . CBS 63614

HOME LOVING MAN.
LP: . . . . CBS 64286

HONEY.
LP: . . . . CBS 63311

IF WE ONLY HAD THE TIME (see Children of the world) (Children Of The World/Andy Williams).

I'M OLD FASHIONED.
LP: . . . . SHM 3198
MC: . . . . HSC 3198

IMPOSSIBLE DREAM, THE.
LP: . . . . CBS 67236

LET'S LOVE WHILE WE CAN.
LP: . . . . CBS 84136
MC: 40 84136

LOVE ANDY.
LP: . . . . CBS 63167

LOVE STORY.
LP: . . . . CBS 64467

LOVE THEME FROM THE GODFATHER.
LP: . . . . CBS 64869

MAY EACH DAY.
LP: . . . . BPG 62658

MERRY CHRISTMAS.
Tracks: / Sleigh ride / Have yourself a merry little christmas / Winter wonderland / My favourite things / Let it snow, let it snow, let it snow / Christmas holiday / Some children see him / Do you hear what I hear? / Little altar boy / Silver bells / Mary's boy child / Bells of St. Mary's.
LP: 4604601
MC: 4604604

PORTRAIT OF A SONG STYLIST.

Tracks: / Somewhere / Days of wine and roses / What kind of fool am I / Misty / Summertime / Blue Hawaii / Impossible dream, The / Falling in love with you / Spanish eyes / Twelfth of never / Love is a many splendoured thing / I want to be wanted / Moon river / Mona Lisa / More I see you, The / Kisses sweeter than wine / Taste of honey, A.
LP: HARLP 104
MC: HARMC 104

REFLECTIONS.
Tracks: / Moon river / Both sides now / Home loving man / Seasons in the sun / Days of wine and roses / Happy heart / Born free / Love story / Almost there / Can't help falling in love / Can't get used to losing you / God only knows / Solitaire / Your song / Way we were, The / Can't take my eyes off you / My way / May each day of the year be a good one.
LP: 10006
MC: 40 10006
MC: 4687814

SHADOW OF YOUR SMILE.
LP: CBS 62633

SOLITAIRE.
LP: CBS 65638

UNCHAINED MELODY.
LP: SHM 932
MC: HSC 303

VERY BEST OF ANDY WILLIAMS, THE.
Tracks: / Moon river / Way we were, The / Home loving man / Can't take my eyes off you / God only knows / Can't get used to losing you / It's so easy / Last tango in Paris / Almost there / In the Summertime / Born free / Can't help falling in love / Watch what happens / More / Solitaire / Danny boy.
LP: SHM 3135
MC: HSC 3135

WAY WE WERE, THE.
Tracks: / You're the best thing that ever happened to me / I won't last a day without you / Killing me softly with her song / Touch me in the morning / Play our love's theme / Sunshine on my shoulders / Way we were / Most beautiful girl / Seasons in the sun / If I could ever go back again.
LP: CBS 32482
MC: 40 32482
LP: CBS 80152

WEDDING AND ANNIVERSARY ALBUM.
Tracks: / Hawaiian wedding song / Very thought of you / When I look in your eyes / They long to be close to you / I'll never stop loving you / Embraceable you / Touch me in the morning / Anniversary song / Where do I begin / We've only just begun / Man and a woman, A / Touch of your lips / You are the sunshine of my life / Moon river / Since I fell for you / I wish you love / What are you doing the rest of your life.
LP: CBS 32051

Williams, Anthony

LIFETIME.
Tracks: / Red / Green / Tomorrow afternoon / Memory / Barb's song to the wizard.
LP: BST 84180

Williams, Audrey

RAMBLIN' GAL.
Tracks: / What put the pep in Grandma / I like that kind / My tight wad daddy / Model "T" love / Don't be too quick to judge / How can you refuse him now / Honky tonkin' / I forgot more than you'll ever know / Slowly you taught me / Help me understand / Ramblin' gal / To my pal - Bosephus.
LP: BFX 15346

Williams, Big Joe

BABY PLEASE DON'T GO.
LP: BT 2007

BIG JOE & SONNY BOY WILLIAMSON (Williams, Big Joe & Sonny Boy Williamson).
LP: BC 21

BIG JOE WILLIAMS.
LP: SLP 224
LP: F 1053

BIG JOE WILLIAMS (Williams, Big Joe/ Little Brother Montgomery/Memphis Slim).
LP: FLY 577

BIG JOE WILLIAMS LIVE.
LP: WOLF 120.918

FIELD RECORDINGS. 1973-80.
LP: LR 42.047

LEGACY OF THE BLUES VOL. 6 (See under Legacy of the Blues).

MALVING MY SWEET WOMAN.
LP: OL 2804

MISSISSIPPI BLUES (see Blues roots vol.1).

NINE STRING GUITAR BLUES.
LP: DS 627

PINEY WOOD BLUES.
LP: DL 602

RAMBLIN' AND WANDERIN'BLUES (see Blue Roots Vol.5).

THINKING OF WHAT THEY DID.
LP: ARHOOLIE 1053

THROW A BOOGIE WOOGIE (See under Williamson, Sonny Boy) (Williams, Big Joe & Sonny Boy Williamson).

TOUGH TIMES.
LP: ARHOOLIE 1002

Williams Brothers

BLESSED.
LP: MAL 04400

HAND IN HAND.
LP: MAL 04409

TWO STORIES.
Tracks: / Some become strangers / Inch by inch / How long / Keeping me alive / Spark of life / You like me / Straight A's in love / State of mind / All pumped up / Rain came down.
LP: K 925547 1
MC: K 925547 4

Williams, Buster

CRYSTAL REFLECTIONS (See under Ayers, Roy) (Williams, Buster & Roy Ayers).

HEARTBEAT.
LP: MR 5171

PINNACLE.
LP: MR 5080

SOMETHING MORE.
Tracks: / Air dancing / Christina / Fortunes dance / Ballade / Deception / Sophisticated lady / I didn't know what time it was.
LP: 70041

TOKUDO.
Tracks: / Tokudo / This time the dreams on me / Guego / This is the end of a beautiful friendship / Some day my prince will come.
LP: YX 7531

Williams, Christopher

ADVENTURES IN PARADISE.
LP: K 9242201
MC: K 9242204

Williams, Clarence

1929-1931 (Williams, Clarence Jazz Kings).
Tracks: / Breeze / Mountain city blues / In our cottage of love / Them things got me / Whoop it up / I'm not worrying / Pane in the glass / Freeze out / Nervous breakdown / Railroad rhythm / Zonky / You've got to be modernistic / High society blues / Lazy levee loungers / Shout sister shout / Papa de da da / Baby won't you please come home.
LP: VLP 47

1933-1935 VOL. 1 (WITH HIS WASHBOARD BAND).
Tracks: / Mississippi basin / I like to go back in the evening / Black eyed Susan Brown / Mama stayed out all night long / Beer garden blues / Right key but the wrong keyhole / Dispossin me / She's just got a little bit left / After tonight / Bimbo / Chocolate Avenue / Harlem rhythm dance.
LP: S 811
LP: CJM 14

CLARENCE WILLIAMS AND HIS ORCHESTRA.
LP: 22025
MC: 42025

CLARENCE WILLIAMS & HIS WASHBOARD BAND VOL. 4 (Williams, Clarence & His Washboard Band).
LP: CJM 17

CLARENCE WILLIAMS JAZZ KINGS 1927/9.
LP: VLP 37

CLARENCE WILLIAMS JUG BANDS 1929-34.
LP: S 827

CLARENCE WILLIAMS JUG & WASHBOARD BANDS.
LP: RK 2001

CLARENCE WILLIAMS & THE WASHBOARD BAND 33-5 Volume 5 (Williams, Clarence & the Washboard Band).
LP: S 815

CLARENCE WILLIAMS & THE WASHBOARD BAND 33-5 Volume 2 (Williams, Clarence & the Washboard Band).
Tracks: / Way down home / For sale (Hanna Johnson's big jack ass) / Swaller-tail coat / Looka there, ain't she pretty / St. Louis blues / How can I get it ? / How can I get it ? (take 2) / On the sunny side of the street / On the sunny side of the street (unissued) / Won't you come over and say "hello" / Old street sweeper / I'm gonna wash my sins away / Jimmy had a nickel / He's a Colonel from Kentucky / Pretty baby, is it yes or no ? / Mister, will you serenade ?.
LP: S 812

CLARENCE WILLIAMS & THE WASHBOARD BAND 33-5 Volume 4 (Williams, Clarence & the Washboard Band).
LP: S 814

CLARENCE WILLIAMS & THE WASHBOARD BAND 33-5 Volume 3 (Williams, Clarence & the Washboard Band).
LP: S 813

CLARENCE WILLIAMS, VOL. 2 1924-30.
LP: S 854

CLARENCE WILLIAMS/EVA TAYLOR 1925-26 (Williams, Clarence & Eva Taylor).
LP: S 835

JAZZ CLASSICS IN DIGITAL STEREO (Clarence Williams 1927-1934).
Tracks: / Candy lips / I can't beat you doin' what you're doin' to me / Chizzlin' Sam / Log cabin blues / You're bound to look like a monkey / Pain in the glass, A / Walk that broad / Trouble / You ain't too old / Close fit blues / Lazy mama / He wouldn't stop doin' it / Worn out blues / Chocolate Avenue / Have you ever felt that way / Organ grinder blues.
LP: REB 721
MC: ZCF 721

PIANO ALBUM.
LP: MERITT 4

RARE SELECTION, VOL.1 1927-30.
LP: S 853

WILD CAT BLUES (Williams, Clarence Blue Five (1923-1935)).
LP: RHA 6031

WNYC JAZZ FESTIVAL (Williams, Clarence Jazz Kings).
LP: JU 3

Williams, Claude

KANSAS CITY GIANTS.
Tracks: / One for the Count / Kansas City / Fiddler, The / Teach me tonight / Little bit of country / 51st and swope / Them there eyes / That certain someone / Texicana / Hundred years from today.
LP: BEAR 25

Williams, Cootie

ART FORD'S JAZZ PARTY August 1958.
LP: AFJP 4

BOYS FROM HARLEM 1937-40.
LP: S 1333

BOYS FROM HARLEM VOL.2 1937-39.
LP: S 1359

COOTIE WILLIAMS AND BOYS FROM HARLEM.
LP: M 8005

COOTIE WILLIAMS & HIS ORCHESTRA.
LP: SLP 803

COOTIE WILLIAMS & HIS RUG CUTTERS (Williams, Cootie & His Rug Cutters).
LP: TAX 8011

COOTIE WILLIAMS & HIS SAVOY BALLROOM ORCHESTRA.
LP: FS 210

COOTIE WILLIAMS & THE BOYS FROM HARLEM (Williams, Cootie & The Boys From Harlem).
LP: TAX 8005

ECHOES OF HARLEM (Williams, Cootie and His Orchestra).
Tracks: / Echoes of Harlem / Things ain't what they used to be / Tess' torch song / You talk a little trash / Sweet Lorraine / Cherry red / Round midnight / Is you is or is you ain't my baby / Blue garden blues / Floogie boo / I don't know / Gotta do some work / My old flame / Now I know / Somebody's got to go / Honeysuckle rose.
LP: AFS 1031

FROM FILMS 1944-46 (Williams, Cootie & Billy Eckstine).
Tracks: / Wild fire / Things ain't what they used to be / Go 'long mule / Keep on jumping / Second balcony jump / Rhythm in a riff / You call it madness / Lonesome lover blues / Taps Miller / I cried for you / I want to talk about you / Our delight / Prisoner of love.
LP: HQ 2068

MEMORIAL.
LP: NL 89811
MC: NK 89811

RHYTHM AND JAZZ IN THE MID FORTIES.
Tracks: / Blue Gordon blues / Is you is, or is you ain't my baby / Somebody's gotta go / Juice head baby / Salt Lake City bounce / House of joy / When my baby left me / Everything but you / Stingy blues / Echoes of harlem / That's the lick / Wrong neighbourhood / I may be easy, but I ain't no fool / Let's do the whole thing or nothing at all / Ain't got no blues today / Bring 'em down front.
LP: OFF 3014

ROLL 'EM.
MC: 40182

SEXTET AND ORCHESTRA.
LP: LP 1

THINGS AIN'T WHAT THEY USED TO BE (Williams, Cootie and His Orchestra).
Tracks: / Echoes of Harlem / 'Gator lady / Lady be good / Across the alley from the Alamo / I shoulda been thinkin' instead of drinkin' / Let 'em roll / Wrong neighbourhood / Soft winds.
LP: JB 623

TYPHOON.
LP: ST 1003

Williams, Danny

BEST OF DANNY WILLIAMS, THE.
MC: CASSGP 006

MOON RIVER AND OTHER GREAT SONGS.
Tracks: / Our day will come / Until it's time for you to go / Here's that rainy day / Didn't we / To be loved by you / Moon river / Close to you / What are you doing for the rest of your life / More / It's impossible / Can't help falling in love.
LP: 2482 331

Williams, David

CEDAR WALTON (See under Walton, Cedar) (Williams, David/Cedar Walton/ Billy Higgins).

I ATE UP THE APPLE TREE.
LP: NOR 7204

SOMETHING SPECIAL.
LP: PTLS 1115
MC: PTLC 115

Williams, Delroy

I STAND BLACK.
LP: MESS 1006

Williams, Deniece

AS GOOD AS IT GETS.
Tracks: / I can't wait / This is as good as it gets / We are here to change the world / All I need / Memories / There's no other / I am sure / It's you I'm after / Don't stop the love / Hold me tight.
LP: 4629201
MC: 4629204

FROM THE BEGINNING.
LP: SPR 1256
MC: SPC 1256

HOT ON THE TRAIL.
Tracks: / Wiser and weaker / Hot on the trail / He loves me, he loves me not / Video / I feel the night / We're together / Straight from the heart / Healing.
LP: CBS 26690
MC: 40 26690

I'M SO PROUD.
Tracks: / Do what you feel / I'm so proud / So deep in love / I'm glad it's you / Heaven in your eyes / They say / Love / Peace and unity / It's OK.
LP: CBS 25352
MC: 40 25352

LET'S HEAR IT FOR THE BOY.
Tracks: / Let's hear it for the boy / I want you / Picking up the pieces / Black butterfly / Next love / Haunting me / Don't tell me we have nothing / Blind dating / Wrapped up / Whiter than snow.
LP: CBS 26010

LOVE WON'T LET ME WAIT (see Mathis, Johnny) (Williams, Deniece & Johnny Mathis).

MY MELODY.
Tracks: / My melody / It's your conscience / Silly / Strangers / What two can do / You're all that matters / Suspicious / Sweet surrender.
LP: CBS 84874

NIECY.
Tracks: / Waiting by the hot line / It's gonna take a miracle / Love notes / I believe in miracles / How does it feel / Waiting / Now it's time for love / Part of love.
LP: CBS 85602

SO DEEP IN LOVE (see Mathis, Johnny) (Williams, Deniece & Johnny Mathis).

SO GLAD I KNOW.

Tracks: / Just in time / Wings of an eagle / My soul desire / They say / Straight ahead / So glad I know / I surrender all / If we are the light / What you do for me.
LP: . . . . BIRD R 177
MC: . . . . BIRD C 177

SPECIAL LOVE.
LP: . . . . SP R 1174
MC: . . . . SP C 1174

THAT'S WHAT FRIENDS ARE FOR (see under Mathis, Johnny) (Williams, Deniece & Johnny Mathis).

THIS IS NIECY.
Tracks: / It's important to me / That's what friends are for / How'd I know that love would slip away? / 'Cause you love me, baby / Free / Watching over / If you don't believe.
LP: . . . . CBS 32530
MC: 40 32530
LP: . . . . CBS 81869

UNTIL YOU COME BACK TO ME (See under Mathis, Johnny) (Mathis, Johnny & Deniece Williams).

WATER UNDER THE BRIDGE.
Tracks: / I confess / Never say never / Water under the bridge / Love finds you / Not by chance / One less lonely heart / I believe in you / Someone for someone / Baby this is love / Don't blame it on my heart.
LP: 4505981
MC: 4505984

WHEN LOVE COMES CALLING.
Tracks: / When love comes calling / Why can't we fall in love / God knows / Like magic / I found love / Turn around / I've got the next dance / Are you thinking / Touch me again / My prayer.
LP: . . . . CBS 83202

Williams, Dicky

I WANT YOU FOR BREAKFAST.
Tracks: / Weekend playboy / You hurt the wrong man / I've been loving you too long / Letter from a soldier / Need your love / Lost my woman to a woman / Good used man / I'm in love with two women / I want you for breakfast / Let me love you before we make love / Don't give your love to anyone but me / Little closer, A.
LP: . . . . ICH 1115
MC: . . . . ICH 1115MC

IN YOUR FACE.
Tracks: / Same motel, The / I didn't do nothin' / Come back pussy / Laughin' and grinnin' / I wanna know why / Ugly men / Fat girls / Do you know (where your woman is tonight) / Bad luck and hard times.
LP: . . . . CMC 4012
MC: . . . . CMCMC 4012

Williams, Don

6 TRACK HITS: DON WILLIAMS.
Tracks: / Ruby Tuesday / There's always something there to remind me.
MC: 7SC 5055

AS LONG AS I HAVE YOU.
Tracks: / Learn to let it go / One good well / Cryin' eyes / I've been loved by the best / Broken heartland / Just as long as I have you / Why get up / Maybe that's all it takes / We're all the way / Flowers won't grow (in the gardens of stone) / If you love me, won't you love me like you love me.
LP: . . . . PL 90393
MC: . . . . PK 90393

BROKEN HEART NEVER MENDS, A.
Tracks: / I recall a gypsy woman / Fairweather friends / It must be love / Falling again / Such a lovely lady / Especially you / Some broken hearts never mend / Oh misery / You're the only one / Standin' in a sea of teardrops / Nobody but you / You've got a hold on me / You're my best friend / Years from now / (Turn out the lights) and love me tonight / Loving you for so long now / I'll need someone to hold me when I cry / Now and then / Slowly but surely / Fly away / Down the road I go / If I needed you / I'll take your love anytime / Don't stop loving me now.
2LP: . . . . VSOPLP 115
MC: . . . . VSOPMC 115

CAFE CAROLINA.
Tracks: / Only game in town, The / Walkin' a broken heart / Maggie's dream / That's the thing about love / Leaving / Beautiful woman / True blue hearts / I'll never need another you / It's time for love / I'll be faithful to you.
LP: . . . . MCF 3225

COUNTRY BOY.
LP: . . . . ABCL 5233

COUNTRY COLLECTION.
Tracks: / I believe in you / Listen to the radio / (Turn out the light and) love me tonight / I'm just a country boy / Amanda / Say it again / If Hollywood don't need you / Love me over again / You're my best friend / Some broken hearts never mend / Only love / Down the road I go / Don't you believe / Miracles / Fairweather friends / I recall a gypsy woman.
LP: . . . . ADEH 403
MC: . . . . ADEHC 403

COUNTRY GREATS.
Tracks: / You're my best friend / We should be together / I believe in you / Miracles / It must be love / That's the thing about love / If I needed you / Fairweather friends / Tulsa time / Lay down beside me / Story of my life / Steal my heart away / Come early morning / Down the road I go.
LP: . . . . MFP 5805
MC: . . . . TCMFP 5805

COUNTRY SUPERSTARS (See under Bare, Bobby) (Williams, Don & Bobby Bare).

DON WILLIAMS VOL.1.
Tracks: / Gypsy woman / Amanda / Shelter of my arms.
LP: . . . . MCL 1628
MC: . . . . MCLC 1628

DON WILLIAMS VOL.2.
Tracks: / I wish I was in Nashville / Your sweet love / She's in love with a rodeo man / Atta way to go / We should be together / Loving you so long now / Miller's cave / Oh misery / I don't think about her no more / Down the road I go.
LP: . . . . MCL 1541

ESPECIALLY FOR YOU.
Tracks: / Fairweather friends / I don't want to love you / Years from now / Lord, I hope this day is good / Especially you / If I need you / Now and then / Smooth talking baby / I've got you to thank for that / Miracles.
LP: . . . . MCF 3114

EXPRESSIONS.
LP: . . . . ABCL 5253
MC: . . . . CAB 5253

EXPRESSIONS/PORTRAIT.
Tracks: / I would like to see you again / You've got a hold on me / Tears of the lonely / All I'm missing is you / Tulsa time / Lay down beside me / Give it to me / Not a chance / It must be love / When I'm with you / It only rains on me / We've never tried it with each other / We're all the way / Circle driveway / You get to me / Steal my heart away / Love's endless war / Woman you should be in movies / Love me over again / Good ole boys like me.
MCSET: . . . . MCA 2 104

GOLDEN GREATS: DON WILLIAMS.
Tracks: / Amanda / Come early morning / We should be together / I wouldn't want to live if you didn't love me / I'm just a country boy / Tulsa time / Turn out the lights (love me tonight) / Till the rivers all run dry / I recall a gypsy woman / You're my best friend / I believe in you / Years from now / Story of my life / Stay young / Love is on a roll / Listen to the radio.
LP: . . . . MCM 5016
MC: . . . . MCMC 5016

GREATEST HITS: DON WILLIAMS, VOL.1.
Tracks: / Amanda / Come early morning / Shelter of your eyes, The / What a way to go / She's in love with a rodeo man / Down the road I go / I wouldn't want to live if you didn't love me / We should be together / Ties that bind, The / Ghost story / Don't you believe? / I recall a gypsy woman.
LP: . . . . SHM 3193
MC: . . . . HSC 3193
LP: . . . . ABCL 5147
LP: . . . . MCL 1761
MC: . . . . MCLC 1761

HARMONY.
Tracks: / Till the rivers all run dry / You keep coming 'round / Don't you think it's time / I don't want the money / Where the Arkansas river leaves Oklahoma / Say it again / Maybe I just don't know / Magic carpet / Time / Ramblin' (instrumental) / She never knew me.
LP: . . . . MCL 1801
MC: . . . . MCLC 1801

HARMONY/VISIONS.
Tracks: / Till the rivers all run dry / You keep coming round / Don't you think it's time? / I don't want the money / Where the Arkansas river leaves Oklahoma / Say it again / Maybe I just don't know / Magic carpet / Time / Ramblin' / She never knew me / Time on my hands / I'll forgive but I'll not forget / I'm getting good at missing you / Some broken hearts never mend / Falling in love again / We can sing / I'll need someone to hold me (when I cry) / Expert at everything / Cup of tea, A / In the morning / Missing you, missing me.
MCSET: . . . . MCA 2 112

I BELIEVE IN YOU.
Tracks: / Falling again / Good to see you / I want you back again / Simple song / I believe in you / Ain't it amazing? / Just enough love (for one woman) / I keep putting off getting over you / Rainy nights and memories / Slowly but surely.
LP: . . . . MCF 3077
MC: . . . . MCFC 3077

I BELIEVE IN YOU/ESPECIALLY FOR YOU.
Tracks: / Falling again / I want you back again / I believe in you / Just enough love (for one woman) / Rainy nights and memories / Fairweather friends / Years from now / Especially for you / Now and then / I've got to thank you for that / It's good to see you / Simple song / Ain't it amazing / I keep putting off getting over you / Slowly but surely / I don't want to love you / Lord, I hope this day if good / If I needed you / Smooth talking baby / Miracles.
MC: . . . . MCAC 26941

IMAGES: DON WILLIAMS.
LP: . . . . NE 1033

IN MY LIFE.
Tracks: / Where do we go from here / Strawberry fields forever / Something / Apartment No.9 / Ruby Tuesday / Always something there / Follow me back to Louisville / On her way to be a woman / Take my hand for a while / Long walk from childhood / In my life.
LP: . . . . SHLP 120
MC: . . . . SHTC 120
LP: 20016
MC: 40016

IT'S GOTTA BE MAGIC.
Tracks: / It's gotta be magic / I would like to see you again / Lay down beside me / Tears of the lonely / You've got a hold on me / Fallin' in love again / I need someone to hold me (when I cry) / Turn out the light and love me tonight / Lovin' understandin' man / Fly away / Your sweet love / Tempted / No use running / Oh misery / Sweet fever / Missing you, missing me.
MC: . . . . HSC 3283

LISTEN TO THE RADIO.
LP: . . . . MCF 3135

LOVE STORIES.
Tracks: / I believe in you / Listen to the radio / Good to see you / Love's endless war / Yellow moon / Fool, fool heart / Falling again / Years from now / I'm still looking for you / Story of my life / You get to me / Stay young / Now and then / Love is on a roll / Miracles / Ain't it amazing / Especially you / Only love.
LP: . . . . NE 1252
MC: . . . . CE 2252

LOVERS AND BEST FRIENDS.
Tracks: / You're my best friend / Story of my life / Pressure makes diamonds / Love me tonight / You get to me / Love me over again / I would't want to live if you didn't love me / Ain't it amazing / Love is on a roll / I'll need someone to hold me when I cry / We're all the way / I'll be faithful to you.
LP: . . . . MCF 3357
MC: . . . . MCFC 3357

NEW HORIZONS.
LP: . . . . NE 1048

NEW MOVES.
Tracks: / Heartbeat in the darkness / I'll never love this way again / Shot full of love / We got love / Send her roses / Senorita / Light in your eyes / It's about time / Then it's love / We've got a good fire goin'.
LP: . . . . EST 2004
MC: . . . . TCEST 2004

SOME BROKEN HEARTS.
Tracks: / Stay young / You're my best friend / I'm just a country boy / Listen to the radio / All I'm missing is you / Some broken hearts never mend / I believe in you / Turn out the lights (love me tonight) / Tulsa time / Years from now / Say it again / 'Till the rivers all run dry / Amanda / I wouldn't want to live if you didn't love me / We should be together / Come early morning.
LP: . . . . PLAT 301
MC: . . . . PLAC 301

TRACES.
Tracks: / Desperately / Easy touch / Come from the heart / Running out of reasons to run / I wouldn't be a man / Looking back / Till I can't take it anymore / Another place, another time / Old Coyote town / You love me through it all.
LP: . . . . EST 2048
MC: . . . . TCEST 2048

TRUE LOVE.
Tracks: / True love / Lord have mercy on a country boy / Darlin' that's what your love does to me / Come a little closer / Just 'cause I'm in love with you / Back in my younger days / Donald and June / Diamonds to dust / Jamaica farewell / Lovin' you is like comin' home.
LP: . . . . PL 90538
MC: . . . . PK 90538

VERY BEST OF DON WILLIAMS.
Tracks: / You're my best friend / Lay down beside me / Till the rivers all run dry / Ghost story / Good ole boys like me / Love me over again / It must be love / Amanda / Tulsa time / Shelter of your eyes, The / She's in love with a Rodeo man / I believe in you / Time on my hands / Turn down the lights / Some broken hearts never mend / I recall a gypsy woman.
LP: . . . . MCG 4014
MC: . . . . MCGC 4014

VERY BEST OF DON WILLIAMS, VOL 2.
Tracks: / Listen to the radio / Miracles / I wouldn't want to live without your love / She never knew me / Story of my life / I'm just a country boy / I've got a winner in you / Falling again / Love is on a roll / I hope this day is good / Rake and ramblin' man / Mistakes / Say it again / Nobody but you / If Hollywood don't need you.
LP: . . . . MCF 3203
MC: . . . . MCFC 3203

VISIONS.
LP: . . . . ABCL 5200

WHERE DO WE GO FROM HERE.
Tracks: / Where do we go from here? / Just an ordinary day / Apartment No.9 / Ruby Tuesday / Always something there / Follow me back to Louisville / On her way to be a woman / Take my hand for a while / Long walk from childhood / In my life.
LP: . . . . SDLP 1004

YELLOW MOON.
LP: . . . . MCF 3159

YOU'RE MY BEST FRIEND.
Tracks: / You're my best friend / Help yourselves to each other / I don't wanna let go / Sweet fever / Someone like you / Love me tonight / Where are you? / You're the only one / Reason to be / Tempted / Tempted.
LP: . . . . MCL 1768
MC: . . . . MCLC 1768
LP: . . . . SHM 3222
MC: . . . . HSC 3222
LP: . . . . ABCD 5127

YOU'RE MY BEST FRIEND, VOLS I & 2.
Tracks: / You're my best friend / Help yourselves to each other / I don't wanna let go / Sweet fever / Someone like you? / Love me tonight / Where are you? / You're the only one / Reason to be / I wish I was in Nashville / Your sweet dream / She's in love with a rodeo man / What a way to go / We should be together / Loving you so long now / Oh misery / Miller's cave / I don't think about her no more / Down the road I go.
MCSET: . . . . MCA 2 116

Williams, Donnett

CAN'T STAND THE PRESSURE (see under White,Christine Joy "Get ready").

Williams, E.A.

JESUS FOR THE PEOPLE.
LP: . . . . EAW 1

Williams, Emlyn (nar)

BOY GROWING UP, A (see under Boy Growing Up).

Williams, Eric

WOODEN HORSE (see Hancock,Sheila) (Hancock,Sheila/Eric Williams).

Williams, Esther

INSIDE OF ME.
Tracks: / I'll be your pleasure / Inside of me / Make it with you / You are the spice of my life / You can use it / Ready for love / Who said it was wrong / You can have it all.
LP: . . . . RCALP 5039
MC: . . . . RCAK 5039

Williams Family

I GAVE MY LIFE TO JESUS.
LP: . . . . MAL 04374

Williams, Fat Man

LIVE AT FEMO.
LP: . . . . ML 110

Williams, Fess

FESS WILLIAMS & HIS ROYLE FLUSH ORCHESTRA (Williams, Fess & His Royle Flush Orchestra).
LP: . . . . FJ 116

FESS WILLIAMS VOL.3 (Rare masters).
LP: . . . . HQ 2062

FESS WILLIAMS VOLUME ONE 1929.
Tracks: / Here 'tis / Few riffs / Hot town / Friction / Kentucky blues / Do shuffle /

Snag nasty / Big shot / Sell it / Betsy Brown / Sweet Savannah Sue / Ain't misbehavin' / Buttons / Musical camp meeting / Goin' to getcha / Slide, Mr. Jelly.
LP: HQ 2039

FESS WILLIAMS-VOLUME 2 (Complete sessions 1929-30).
Tracks: / Do shuffle (2 takes) / Betsy Brown / She's still dizzy / Hot mama / 11.30 Saturday night / I'm feelin devilish / Al for grits and gravy / Playing my saxophone (2 takes) / You can't go wrong / Ida, sweet as apple cider / Everything's OK with me / Dinah / Just to be with you.
LP: HQ 2040

Williams, Gari

GALW GARI.
LP: CC 101
MC: CHCH 101C

Williams, Geoffrey

PRISONER OF LOVE.
LP: WX 298
MC: WX 298C

Williams, George

RHYTHM WAS HIS BUSINESS (Williams, George Orchestra).
LP: FS 80

Williams, G.O.

BACK TO BOOGIE WOOGIE (Williams, G.O. & Dave Collett).
Tracks: / Boogie elbow oogie / Lingerin' boogie / If I can help somebody / Cut and run boogie / Night train / Steam shovel boogie / Goofy stuff / Casablanca / Blue room / Freight train / Song of India / Mainline boogie.
LP: BLM 51012

Williams, Griff

GRIFF WILLIAMS, 1946-51.
Tracks: / Romantic guy I, A / I could write a book / What a deal / I know that you know / When spring is in the air / Let's fly away / 'Swonderful / Dream music / Of Thee I sing / You're wonderful / Hot canary, The / Laura / Saturday night in Central Park / Use your imagination.
LP: HSR 175

Williams, Hank

16 ORIGINAL HITS: HANK WILLIAMS.
MC: MC 1625

BEYOND THE SUNSET.
LP: 831 574-1

COLLECTORS NO. 4.
Tracks: / I'm a long gone daddy / Message to my mother / Beyond the sunset / Jesus remembered me / With tears in my eyes / If you'll be a baby to me / Teardrops on a rose / No not now / I don't care / Fool about you / When God comes and gathers His jewels / Please don't let me love you / Help me understand / I ain't got nothin' but time / Home in heaven / Wearin' out your walkin' shoes.
LP: 2391 519

COUNTRY STORE: HANK WILLIAMS.
Tracks: / Lovesick blues / You're gonna change / I just don't like this kind of livin' / Moanin' the blues / Howlin' at the moon / I'll never get out of this world alive / Lost highway / Mind your own business / My bucket's got a hole in it / Why don't you leave me / Cold cold heart / I can't help it / Baby we're really in love / Jambalaya.
LP: CST 50
MC: CSTK 50

GRAFFITI COLLECTION.
MC: GRMC 14

GREAT HITS OF HANK WILLIAMS SNR.
Tracks: / Hey good lookin' / Lovesick blues / My son calls another man daddy / You win again / Take these chains from my heart / Your cheatin' heart / Jambalaya / I'm so lonesome I could cry / Settin' the woods on fire / Kaw-liga / My bucket's got a hole in it / Cold, cold heart.
MC: CN4 2076
LP: CN 2076

GREATEST HITS 1.
LP: 35001
MC: 65001

GREATEST HITS 2.
LP: 35002
MC: 65002

HANK WILLIAMS 40 GREATEST HITS.
Tracks: / Baby, we're really in love / Cold cold heart / Crazy heart / Dear John / Half as much / Hey, good lookin' / Honky tonk blues / Howlin' at the moon / I can't help it / I just don't like this kind of living / I saw the light / I won't be home no more / I'll never get out of this world alive / I'm so lonesome I could cry / I'm sorry for you my friend / Jambalaya / Kaw-liga / Lonesome whistle / Long gone lonesome blues / Lost highway / Lovesick blues / Mansion on the hill / Mind your own business / Moanin' the blues / Move it on over / My bucket's got a hole in it / My son calls another man daddy / Nobody's lonesome for me / Ramblin' man / Settin' the woods on fire / Take these chains from my heart / They'll never take her love from me / Weary blues / Wedding bells / Why don't you love me / Why should we try anymore / Window shopping / You win again / Your cheatin' heart / You're gonna change.
2LP: 2683 071
MCSET: 3271 302

HANK WILLIAMS COLLECTION (20 Golden Greats).
Tracks: / I'm so lonesome I could cry / Honky tonk blues / Your cheatin' heart / Lovesick blues / Half as much / Hey good lookin' / Lost highway / Move it on over / Kaw-liga / Jambalaya / Take these chains from my heart / I'll never get out of this world alive / I'm sorry for you my friend / Cold cold heart / My bucket's got a hole in it / Long gone lonesome blues / Ramblin' man / I heard that lonesome whistle blow / Howlin' at the moon / My son calls another man daddy.
LP: DVLP 2081
MC: DVMC 2081

HANK WILLIAMS GREATEST HITS VOL.3.
Tracks: / I can't get you off my mind / My love for you / Ready to go home / No one will ever know / Let's turn back the years / I've been down that road before / House of gold / I'm satisfied with you / Rootie tootie / Be careful of stones that you throw / Angel of death / My heart would know / I wish I had a nickel / Just waitin' / I can't escape from you / Let's turn back the years.
LP: 419

HANK WILLIAMS GREATEST HITS VOL.2.
LP: 2482506

HANK WILLIAMS GREATEST HITS VOL.1.
Tracks: / Your cheatin' heart / Move it on over / I'm so lonesome, I could cry / Honky tonk blues / Ramblin' man / Honky tonky / There'll be no teardrops tonight / Mind your own business / My bucket's got a hole in it / Long gone lonesome blues.
LP: 2482 505
MC: 3192 631

HANK WILLIAMS & THE DRIFTING COWBOYS (Williams, Hank & The Drifting Cowboys).
Tracks: / Jambalaya / Hey porter / Half as much / If I were a carpenter / Cold cold heart / Howlin' at the moon / Then you can tell me goodbye / Dear John / Your cheatin' heart / Raining in my heart / Window shopping / After you / Ain't that a shame / Endless sleep / Mule skinner blues / I'm so lonesome I could cry.
LP: CW 202
MC: JAM 202

HEY GOOD LOOKIN' (Dec 1950-July 1951).
2LP: 831 634-1

I AIN'T GOT NOTHIN' BUT TIME.
Tracks: / You're gonna change / My son calls another man daddy / First year blues / Are you building a temple in heaven / No one will ever know / I'm so lonesome I could cry / House without love / When the book of life is read / You better keep it in your mind / Fool about you / Wedding bells / I've just told mama goodbye / If you'll be a baby to me / House of gold / We're getting close to the grave each day / Thy burdens are greater than mine / I just don't like this kind of living / My bucket's got a hole in it / Waltz of the wind / How can you refuse him now / Fool about you.
2LP: 825 557-1
MC: 825 557-4
2LP: 825 548-1

I WON'T BE HOME NO MORE (Vol. 8 June 1952 - Sept. 1952).
2LP: 833 752-1

I'M SO LONESOME I COULD CRY.
LP: 2-POL-825557 1

LET'S TURN BACK THE YEARS VOL. 7 (July 1951 - June 1952).
2LP: 833 749-1

LIVE AT THE GRAND OLE OPRY.
LP: MG 15019

LONG GONE LONESOME BLUES (August 1949 - December 1950).
2LP: 831 633-1

LOST HIGHWAY (DECEMBER '48-MARCH '49).
Tracks: / There'll be no teardrops tonight / Lost on the river / I heard my mother praying for me / California zephyr / Teardrop on a rose, A / Honky tonk blues / Mind your own business / I'm free at last / Wait for the light to shine / No, not now / Lost highway / May you never be alone / Dixie cannonball / Blue love in my heart / Angel of death / Jesus remembered me / Dear brother / Singing waterfall / I'm going home / Sundown and sorrow / Alabama waltz.
2LP: 825 554-1
MC: 825 554-4

LOVESICK BLUES.
LP: 2 POL 825551 1
2LP: 825 551-1

MORE RARE RADIO PROGRAMMES VOL.1.
MC: JAM 201

ON THE AIR.
LP: POL 825531 1
LP: 827 531-1

RADIO SHOWS.
LP: ATOM 6
MC: CATOM 6

RARE RADIO BROADCASTS 1949.
LP: CW 201

RARE TAKES AND RADIO CUTS.
LP: 823 695-1

SINGLES COLLECTION, THE.
MCSET: 847 194 4

VERY BEST OF HANK WILLIAMS.
LP: ADAH 446
MC: ADAHC 446

VERY BEST OF HANK WILLIAMS VOL.1, THE.
Tracks: / Lovesick blues / Crazy heart / I'm sorry for you my friend / Wedding bells / Window shopping / Honky tonk blues / I heard that lonesome whistle blow / Half as much / Jambalaya / Dear John / Prodigal son / I saw the light / I won't be home no more / There's room in my heart (for the blues) / We live in two different worlds / Long gone lonesome blues.
LP: CN 2084
MC: CN4 2084

Williams, Hank Jr.

ARE YOU SURE HANK DONE IT THIS WAY.
Tracks: / Family tradition / Kaw-liga / Whisky bent and hell bound / Are you sure Hank done it this way / Women I've never had / Old habits / Dixie on my mind / If you don't like Hank Williams / Move it on over / Texas women / All my rowdy friends are coming over tonight / Heaven ain't a lot like Dixie / Country boy can survive, A / Honky tonkin' / Leave them boys alone / Man of steel.
MC: 2405184
LP: 2405181

BEST OF HANK WILLIAMS JR. VOL 3.
LP: K925 834 1
MC: K925 834 4

COUNTRY STORE: HANK WILLIAMS JR..
Tracks: / Long gone lonesome blues / Standing in the shadows / Cajun baby / Rainin' in my heart / Send me the pillow that you dream on / Ain't that a shame / Losing you / Wolverton Mountain / Walk on by / Ring of fire / It's all over but the crying / I'd rather be gone / All for the love of sunshine / I walk the line.
LP: CST 20
MC: CSTK 20

FIVE-O.
Tracks: / I'm for love / I really like girls / Nashville scene, The / Ain't misbehavin' / Something to believe in / Lawyers, guns and money / This ain't Dallas / I've been around / New Orleans / Outlaws reward.
LP: 925267 1
MC: 925267 4

HANK WILLIAMS JUNIOR FEATURING HANK WILLIAMS SENIOR.
Tracks: / Jambalaya / Your cheatin' heart / Ain't that a shame.
MC: CN4 2092
LP: CN 2092

HIGH NOTES.
Tracks: / Heaven ain't a lot like Dixie / Whisky on ice / High and pressurized / I can't change my tune / South's gonna rattle again, The / Ain't makin' no headlines (here without you) / I've been down / If you wanna get to heaven / Norwegian wood / Honky tonkin'.
LP: K 52384

WILD STREAK.
LP: 925725 1
MC: 925725 4

Williams, Heathcote

FALLING FOR A DOLPHIN.
MC: WAIL C2

WHALE NATION.
MC: WAIL C1

Williams, Huw

SUCH IS LIFE (Williams, Huw & Tony).
LP: SPR 1002

Williams, Iris

BEAUTIFUL.
Tracks: / He was beautiful / Love me good / Send in the clowns / He's out of my life / Now while I still remember how / My prayer / I have loved me a man / Dearest friend / We don't make each other laugh anymore / Run like the wind / Let the music begin / No regrets / Above the tears / Hi there / Men in my life, The / I'll never love this way again.
LP: MFP 41 5743 1
MC: MFP 41 5743 4
MC: TC MFP 5743

GENTLE TOUCH.
Tracks: / Gentle touch, The / Summer wind / Old man & the sea / I have the right to be wrong / Memory / Stay the night / So sad the song / Bluer than blue / Someone that I used to love / What'll I do / All by myself / You are my story.
LP: POLD 5118

HE WAS BEAUTIFUL.
Tracks: / Niagara / Love me good / Now while I still remember how / I have loved me a man / Let the music begin / Above the tears / We don't make each other laugh anymore / Run like the wind / Men in my life, The / I can't hold on / I never said I love you / He was beautiful.
LP: SCX 6627
MC: TC SCX 6627

JUST FOR YOU.
Tracks: / Just for you / You are my life / Stay, stay / Don't cry my love / Love comes and love goes / My prayer / Loving you the first time / Shoes and rice / If I was a bird / You blew it / Magic in your eyes.
LP: EMC 3376

MANY MOODS OF IRIS WILLIAMS.
LP: MWSL5 506

PEACE MUST COME AGAIN.
LP: PTLS 1081
MC: PTLC 1081

PICTURE ME LOVE.
Tracks: / Picture me love / Love is falling in love again / Waterfalls / Using things and loving people / Got to get you into my life / He's out of my life / You make me high / Beautiful / Show me your love / What am I supposed to do / No walls no ceilings no floors / If you'd really cared.
LP: SCX 6633

YOU BELONG TO ME.
Tracks: / You belong to me / As time goes by / I'm in the mood for love / Folks who live on the hill / Let there be love / What is this thing called love / La vie en rose / Man I love, The / When I grow too old to dream / Danny boy / September in the rain / Send in the clowns / Bewitched / How high the moon / No regrets / Summertime.
LP: EMC 3418
MC: TCEMC 3418

Williams, James

ALTER EGO.
Tracks: / Black scholars / Alter ego / Havana days / Fourplay / Touching affair, A / Waltz and monk / Beauty within.
LP: SSC 1007

ARIOSO TOUCH, THE (Williams, James Trio).
LP: CJ 192

FLYING COLOURS (Williams, James/ Slide Hampton).
LP: ZMS 2005

IMAGES OF THINGS TO COME.
LP: CJ 140

PROGRESS REPORT (Williams, James Sextet).
Tracks: / Progress report / Episode from a village dance / Affaire d'amour / Mr. Day's dream / Unconscious behaviour / Renaissance lovers.
LP: SSC 1012

Williams, James 'D

IN YOUR EYES.
Tracks: / In your eyes / Order in the house / With all my heart / If you knew what I know / Shadow of another love / Runner / Curious / Child of love / Diamond in the night / My friend / Smile.
LP: 4610461
MC: 4610464

MIRACLES OF THE HEART.
Tracks: / You are everything / Oh how I love you (girl) / Miracle of the heart /

Misunderstandings / Let me love you / Ice melts into rain / I got your number / Stand up and fight.
LP: 4500661
MC: 4500664

Williams, Jane Kelly

UNEXPECTED WEATHER.
Tracks: / There's a curtain going down / Reachin' down in Mississippi / Boy, I'm just getting over you / Graceful man / I measure your love / 'Cept you / Gina / Nothing but the wind / Ones we do not know / Carry him.
LP: TWI 893

Williams, Jerry 'Swamp

DANCIN' WITH SOUL (Williams, Jerry 'Swamp Dogg'/Michelle Williams).
Tracks: / Some kind of wonderful / Hold on I'm coming / Funktastic / Galacticklerock / This is it / All she wants is reggae music / Foxy foxy rapp / Loverise / Don't stop the boogie / Mad love / Make me yours.
LP: RARE LP 1

TOO FAST TO LIVE, TOO FAST TO DIE.
Tracks: / No money down / Git it / Guitar Nelly / Serving time / Rock on / Look out heart / Slow down / That'll be the day / Willie and the hand jive / Burn out / Little honda.
LP: SNTF 791

Williams, Jessica (2)

NOTHIN' BUT THE BLUES.
LP: BKH 51301

Williams, J.J.

PLATH'S RETURN (Williams, J.J. & Ensemble).
LP: ECJ 402

Williams, Jodie

LEADING BRAND, THE (see Hooker,Earl) (Williams, Jodie/Earl Hooker).

Williams, Joe

CHAINS OF LOVE.
LP: JASS 6

COUNT BASIE AND JOE WILLIAMS (see under Basie, Count) (Williams,Joe/ Count Basie).

COUNT BASIE PLAYS, JOE WILLIAMS SINGS (See under Basie, Count) (Williams,Joe/Count Basie).

EVERY NIGHT.
LP: 833 236 1

EVERYDAY I HAVE THE BLUES.
LP: SJL 1140

HAVING THE BLUES....
Tracks: / Don't get around much anymore / Satin doll / Experiment / Gee baby ain't I good to you / Early in the morning / Nobody know the way I feel this morning / What a difference a day made / Goin' to Chicago blues / Everyday I have the blues / Alright, okay, you win / Evenin' / Roll 'em Pete / One o'clock jump.
MC: MC 7684

HAVING THE BLUES UNDER EUROPEAN SKY.
MC: MC 7684

IN GOOD COMPANY.
Tracks: / Just friends / Baby you got what it takes / How deep is the ocean / Ain't got nothing but the blues / Love without money / Between the... / Is you is or is you ain't (my baby) / Too good to be true / Embraceable you / Please don't talk about me.
LP: 837 932 1
MC: 837 932 4

JOE WILLIAMS.
MC: MC 9005

JOE WILLIAMS & COUNT BASIE (See under Basie, Count) (Williams,Joe/ Count Basie).

JUST THE BLUES (See Basie, Count) (Williams,Joe/Count Basie).

LIVE AT BIRDLAND.
Tracks: / September in the rain / Come back baby / 5 o'clock in the morning / By the river Sainte Marie / This can't be love / Teach me tonight / I was telling her about you / Have you met Miss Jones? / Well oh well.
LP: FS 297

MAN AIN'T SUPPOSED TO CRY, A.
Tracks: / What's new / It's the talk of the town / I'll never smile again / I'm thru' with love / Where are you / I've only myself to blame / Say it isn't so / What will I tell my heart / You've got me crying again / Can't we talk it over / I laugh to keep from cryin' / Man ain't supposed to cry, A.
LP: ROU 1001

NOTHIN' BUT THE BLUES.
Tracks: / Who she do / Just a dream / Please send me someone to love / Alright, OK, you win / Hold it right there / In the evening / Rocks in my bed / Sent for you yesterday / Goin' to Chicago blues / Ray Brown's in town.
LP: DMS 4001

OVERWHELMING JOE WILLIAMS, THE.
Tracks: / Everyday / Come back baby / All God's chillun got rhythm / Do you wanna jump children / April in Paris / In the evening / Just a sittin' and a rockin' / Wrap your troubles in dreams / Jump for joy / Every night / Rocks in my bed / Early in the morning / Kansas city / Prelude to a kiss / On the sunny side of the street.
LP: NL 86464
MC: NK 86464

SWINGIN' NIGHT AT BIRDLAND, A.
Tracks: / September in the rain / Come back baby / 5 o'clock in the morning / By the river Sainte Marie / This can't be love / Teach me tonight / Well alright OK you win / I was telling her about you / Have you met Miss Jones? / Roll 'em Pete / You're everything but mine (CD only.) / Falling in love with love (CD only.) / Goin' to Chicago blues (CD only.) / Very thought of you, The (CD only.).
LP: ROU 1026
LP: 795 335 1

TOGETHER (Williams, Joe & Harry Edison).
LP: FS 296

Williams, John

RIDE ON DOWN THIS ROAD.
LP: LRF 141

RIVER, THE.
MC: VSC 5298

SPANISH GUITAR CONCERTOS.
LP: 447911

Williams, John

FESSOR'S NIGHTHAWKS (see under Cheatham, Doc) (Cheatham, Doc/John Williams/Herb Hall).

HERE'S WHAT I'M HERE FOR (Williams, John & Company).
Tracks: / Let's fall in love / Stormy weather / My shining hour.
LP: DS 891
MC: DSC 891

Williams, John

AISLE SEAT (Williams, John & Boston Pops).
Tracks: / E.T., Theme from / Chariots of fire / Raiders of the lost ark / Yes, Giorgio / New York, New York / Gone with the wind / Wizard of Oz, The / Singin' in the rain / Friendly persuasion / Meet me in St. Louis.
LP: 6514 328
MC: 7337 328

BY REQUEST (Williams, John & The Boston Pops Orchestra).
Tracks: / Olympic fanfare and theme / Close Encounters of the Third Kind (excerpts) / March from Midway / Luke and Leia / Return of the Jedi (theme from) / Flying from E.T. / Liberty fanfare / Superman march / Yoda's / Empire strikes back, The / March from 1941 / Jaws / Imperial march (Empire Strikes Back) / Mission / Star wars (theme from).
LP: 420178-1
MC: 420178-4

EMPIRE STRIKES BACK, THE.
LP: SDG 313

E.T. - THE EXTRA TERRESTRIAL.
LP: MCF 3160

FIDDLER ON THE ROOF (See under Fiddler on the roof) (Williams, John/ Isaac Stern).

OUT OF THIS WORLD (Williams, John & Boston Pops).
Tracks: / Return of the Jedi / Battlestar Galactica / Twilight zone / Star trek / E.T., The / Alien / 2001.
LP: 411 185-1
MC: 411 185-4

POPS ON BROADWAY (Williams, John (Composer) & Boston Pops Orch).
LP: 6302 124

STOMPIN' AT THE SAVOY (Williams, John & Boston Pops).
Tracks: / Opus one / Begin the beguine / Sunrise serenade / Stompin' at the Savoy / Tuxedo Junction / Satin doll / In the mood / Sing, sing, sing / Moonlight serenade / String of pearls / Sleepy lagoon / Song of India / Snowfall / Swing swing swing.
LP: 412 626-1
MC: 412 626-4

SYMPHONIC SUITES.
LP: MFP 5594
MC: TCMFP 5594

Williams, John

BEST FRIENDS (see under Laine, Cleo) (Williams, John & Cleo Laine).

BEST OF JOHN WILLIAMS, THE.
Tracks: / Cavatina / Horizon / Raga vilaskhani todo / Sarabande / Deer may safely graze / River God, The / Z, Theme from / All at sea minor / Bach changes / Dance of the emperor's clouds / Dance of the living / El tuno / Good morning freedom / J.S.B. / Lisa Larne / Lorelei / Spanish trip.
MC: MCTC 007

BRIDGES.
LP: WH 5015

CAVATINA.
Tracks: / Z (theme from) / Bach changes / Spanish trip / Because / Raga vilasakhani todi / Woodstock / Good morning freedom / Cavatina / Nuages / Sarabande / New sun rising.
LP: HIFLY 32

CHANGES.
Tracks: / Bach changes / Z, Theme from / Cavatina / Spanish trip (canarios) / Because / Raga vilasakhani todi / Woodstock / Good morning freedom / Nuages / Sarabande new sun rising.
LP: FEDB 5009
MC: CFEDB 5009

COLLECTION: JOHN WILLIAMS.
Tracks: / Air on a G string / Good morning freedom / Woodstock / House of the rising sun / Height below, The / Sambalaya / Cavatina / Bach changes / J.S.B. / All at sea minor / Spanish trip / Dance of the emperor's clouds / Dance of the living Lorelie / El tuno / Rasa vilaskhani todi / Nuages / Nadias theme / Lisa Larne / Lorelei / Sans souci.
2LP: CCSLP 190
MC: CCSMC 190

CONCERTO FOR GUITAR AND JAZZ ORCHESTRA-PAUL HART.
Tracks: / Rondo la ronde / Song without words in D / Duet for two.
LP: FM 42332
MC: FMT 42332

EASYRIDING: JOHN WILLIAMS.
Tracks: / Cavatina / House of the rising sun / Lorelei / Sheep may safely graze / Z, Theme from / Good morning freedom / Because / Sarabande / Woodstock / Horizon / Sambalaya / Air on a G string.
MC: KNMC 11010
LP: KNLP 11010

GUITAR IS THE SONG, THE.
Tracks: / Shenandoah / Skye boat song / Waly waly / Wraggle-taggle gypsies / So we'll go no more a-roving / Hajra kati / Csak egy Kislany van a vilagon / Queen of hearts / Catari catari / Petronella / St Patricks day / Buacallan buidhe / Scarborough fair / Carnaval / Seis por derecho / Mashilae / Music box tune / Tu ca' nun chiagne.
LP: CBS 73679
MC: 40 73679

IMAGES: JOHN WILLIAMS.
Tracks: / Cavatina / Height below, The / El tuno / House of the rising sun / Portrait / Good morning freedom / Air on a G string.
MC: KNMC 16006

JOHN WILLIAMS/PACO PENA/INTI-ILLIMANI (Williams, John/Paco Pena/ Inti-Illimani).
Tracks: / Danza di cala luna / El corazon a contraluz / Cristalino / La preguntona / El carnaval / Fragmentos de un sueno / La cuidad / El mercado / La calahorra en libertad (sevillanas) / Danza.
LP: M 44574
MC: MT 44574

LET THE MUSIC TAKE YOU (Williams, John & Cleo Laine).
Tracks: / Baby don't cry no more / One / Imagine / Colours of my life / I never went away / Let the music take you / First time i ever saw your face / Dreams of castilla without words / It's not easy / So quiet the night / So many stars.
LP: CBS 25751
MC: 40 25751

MAGIC GUITAR OF JOHN WILLIAMS, THE.
LP: SHM 3186
MC: HSC 3186

OFF THE RECORD WITH JOHN WILLIAMS.
2LP: FEDD 1001
MCSET: CFEDD 1001

PAUL HART: SUITE FOR GUITAR.
LP: CBS 42332

PLATINUM COLLECTION.
Tracks: / Cavatina / River God / Portrait / Spanish trip / Sambalaya / J.S.B. / From the top / Eleanor Rigby / Killing me softly / Air on a G string / Sarabande / Sheep may safely graze.
2LP: PLAT 1006
MCSET: ZCPLT 1006

PLAYS SPANISH MUSIC.
LP: CBS 72860

PORTRAIT OF JOHN WILLIAMS.
LP: D 37791
MC: 40 37791
LP: 45538
MC: 40 45538

PORTRAIT OF JOHN WILLIAMS (MCA) (Williams, John).
LP: MCF 3045

RECOLLECTIONS.
LP: CBS 10016
MC: 40 10016

REPLAY ON (THE HEIGHT BELOW).
Tracks: / Emperor Nero / Duet for guitar & lute / Lisa Larne / Dance of the emperor's clouds / Dance of the dead / A dherrin dhu / Sans souci / Height below, The / Sambalaya / El tuno / Horizon.
LP: FEDB 5036
MC: CFEDB 5036

RODRIGO: CONCERTO DE ARANUEZ (Williams, John & English Chamber Orchestra).
LP: CBS 79369

SPOTLIGHT ON JOHN WILLIAMS.
Tracks: / Cavatina / Portrait / River god, The / Sarabande / Nuages / Romanza / Bach changes / JSB / From the top / Swagman, The / House of the rising sun / All at sea minor / Z, Theme from / Spanish trip / Good morning freedom / Woodstock / Height below, The / Air on a G string / Because / Horizon / Raga vilasakhani todi / El tuno / Sheep may safely graze.
2LP: SPOT 1001
MCSET: ZCSPT 1001

THIS IS THE YEAR OF THE BUFFALO (Williams, John Octet).
Tracks: / F.F.R.B. / Year of the buffalo / Snow palace / Ricardos overture.
LP: SPJ 532

TRAVELLING.
LP: HIFLY 27
LP: FEDB 5020

UNFORGETTABLE: JOHN WILLIAMS (16 Golden Classics).
Tracks: / Cavatina (With Cleo Laine. A lyric version of musical composition Cavatina .).
LP: UNLP 003
MC: UNMC 003

WERELD SUCCESSEN (Williams, John & Cleo Laine).
Tracks: / He was beautiful / If / Killing me softly with his song / Feelings / Eleanor Rigby.
2LP: 2646 105

WHEN WE ALL GET TO HEAVEN.
LP: MIR 5003
MC: ZCMIR 5003

WORLD OF JOHN WILLIAMS, THE.
Tracks: / Travelling / Lorelei / Spanish trip / Nuages / All at sea minor / Duet for guitar and koto / Sarabande / River god, The / Horizon / Z, Theme from / Raga vilasakhani todi / Good morning freedom.
LP: NE 1364
MC: CE 2364

Williams, John Jr.

I'VE GOT A CRUSH ON YOU.
Tracks: / All too soon / Sometimes I'm happy / Memphis in June / Back in your own back yard / It's only a paper moon / Then who would I sing my songs to / Satin doll / Shine on your shoes.
LP: J 004

Williams, John Towner

JOHN TOWNER WILLIAMS.
LP: FS 252

Williams, Kenneth

BONA ALBUM OF JULIAN AND SANDY (Williams, Kenneth & Hugh Paddick).
LP: DJM 22084

JUST WILLIAMS.
Tracks: / Episodes 1-3 / Episodes 4-6 / Episodes 6-8 / Episodes 8-10.
MCSET: ZBBC 1046

MORE WILLO THE WISP STORIES.
LP: REC 473
MC: ZCM 473

PARLOUR POETRY.
Tracks: / Jabberwocky / Green eye of the yellow god / Dong with the luminous nose, The / Billy's rose / Wreck of the Hesperus / Walrus and the carpenter, The / Pobble who has no toes, The.
LP: SDL 294
MC: CSDL 294

STORYTIME TOP TEN VOL 9.
MC: VCA 063

WIND IN THE WILLOWS, THE (See under Kenneth Grahame).

Williams, Kymm

KYMM.
LP: .... NEVLP 116

Williams, Larry

ALACAZAM.
Tracks: / Hey now / Aby's crazy / I was a fool / Zing zing / Hoochie coo / Make a little love / Short fat fannie / Jockomo / Hocus pocus / Took a trip / Jelly belly Nellie / Love charms / Heebie jeebies / Rockin' pneumonia and the boogie woogie flu / Dummy, the / Oh babe.
LP: .... CH 203

BALL AND CHAIN (See Thornton, Big Mama) (Williams, Larry/Willie Mae Thornton).

DIZZY MISS LIZZY.
Tracks: / Dizzy Miss Lizzy / Lawdy Miss Clawdy / You bug me baby / She said yeah / Teardrops / Let me tell you baby / Dummy, The / Bad boy / Bony Moronie / Slow down / Just because / Peaches and cream / Hoochie coo / Little school girl / Make a little love / Short fat Fannie.
LP: .... CH 129
MC: .... CHC 129

LARRY WILLIAMS ON STAGE.
LP: .... LIVE 1

LARRY WILLIAMS SHOW, THE (Willliams, Larry).
Tracks: / Slow down / Louisiana Hannah / Two hours past midnight / Baby / Out of tears / For your love / Whole lotta shakin' goin' on / Hoochie coo / Sweet little baby / Looking back / Stormsville groove / Trust in me.
LP: .... ED 119

SLOW DOWN.
LP: .... SPS 2225

Williams, Lawton

LIGHTNING JONES.
Tracks: / Blue grass skirt / Foreign love / I'll still love you / Casino on the hill / Train of thought / If you're waiting on me / Don't burn the bridge behind you / Rhinelander waltz / Moon Joe / Lightning Jones / Carpetbaggers / Squawlein / Stay on the ball / Mama pinch a penny / Everything's OK on the L.B.J.(parts 1 & 2).
LP: .... BFX 15178

Williams, Lenny

LOVE CURRENT.
LP: .... MCF 3014

Williams, Leon

CELEBRATION.
LP: .... TRLS 285

Williams, Leona

HEART TO HEART (See under Haggard, Merle) (Williams, Leona, Merle Haggard).

LEONA WILLIAMS AND HER DIXIE BAND (Williams, Leona & Her Dixie Band).
LP: .... FB 303

Williams, Lester

DOWLING STREET HOP.
Tracks: / Wintertime blues / I'm so glad / Dowling street hop / I know that chick / Don't treat me so low down / Texas town / Hey jack / Folk's round the corner / My home ain't here / Brand new baby / Let's do it / Crazy 'bout you baby / Don't take your love / Good loving baby.
LP: .... KK 7412

TEXAS TROUBADOUR.
Tracks: / I can't lose with the stuff I use / Disgusted blues / Going away baby / Crawling blues / Lost gal / Lonely heart blues / Let me tell you a thing or two / Don't leave me baby / When I miss her the most / My home ain't here / Sweet lovin' daddy / If you knew how much I love you / Trying to forget / Brand new baby.
LP: .... CHD 202

Williams, Lucinda

LUCINDA WILLIAMS.
Tracks: / I just wanted to see you so bad / Big red sun blues / Night's too long, The / Like a rose / Changed the locks / Passionate kisses / Crescent city / Price to pay / Abandoned / Am I too blue / Side of the road / I asked for water.
LP: .... ROUGH 130
MC: .... ROUGHC 130

Williams, Marc

FRESH FISH.
LP: .... FF 059

Williams, Marion

I'VE COME SO FAR.
LP: .... SF 1002

STRONG AGAIN.
Tracks: / Strong again.
MC: .... SFMC 1013

Williams, Mary Lou

BEST OF MARY LOU WILLIAMS.
LP: 2310 856
MC: K10 856

DON BYAS.
LP: .... GNPS 9030
MC: GNP5 9030

EMBRACED (Williams, Mary Lou/Cecil Taylor).
2LP: 2620 108
MC: K20 108

FIRST LADY OF PIANO.
LP: .... LPJT 20
LP: 500078

FREE SPIRITS.
LP: .... SCS 1043

I LOVE A PIANO (see Wilson, Teddy Trio) (Williams, Mary Lou/Teddy Wilson Trio).

MARY LOU WILLIAMS IN LONDON.
LP: .... GNPS 9029

MY MAMA PINNED A ROSE ON ME.
Tracks: / Blues / N.G. blues / Dirge blues / Baby bear boogie / Turtle speed blues / Blues for Peter / My mama pinned a rose on me / Prelude to prism / What's your story morning glory / Prelude to love roots / Rhythmic pattern / J.B's waltz / No title blues.
LP: 231 0819
MC: K10 819

ROLL EM' 1944 (Hitherto unknown titles) (Williams, Mary Lou/Teddy Wilson Trio).
LP: .... AP 8

SOLO RECITAL MONTREUX JAZZ FESTIVAL 1978.
Tracks: / Over the rainbow / Offertory meditation / Tea for two / Concerto alone at Montreux / Little Joe from Chicago / Man I love, The / What's your story morning glory / Honeysuckle rose.
LP: 2308 218
MC: .... K 08 218

WALKIN' AND SWINGIN'.
LP: .... LPJT 20
MC: .... MCJT 20

Williams, Mason

CLASSICAL GAS (Williams, Mason & Mannheim Steamroller).
LP: .... AG 800
MC: .... AGC 800

Williams, Maurice

MAURICE WILLIAMS & THE ZODIACS (Williams, Maurice & The Zodiacs).
LP: .... HERALD 5017

Williams, Michelle

DANCIN' WITH SOUL (see Williams,Jerry'Swamp Dogg') (Williams, Michelle/Jerry'Swamp Dogg'Williams).

Williams, Otis

16 ORIGINAL GREATEST HITS:OTIS WILLIAMS (Williams, Otis & The Charms).
LP: .... K 5015

OTIS WILLIAMS & HIS CHARMS (Williams, Otis & The Charms).
LP: .... BID 8040

SING THEIR ALL-TIME HITS (Williams, Otis & His Charms).
Tracks: / Hearts of stone / Bazoom (I need your loving) / Ivory tower / Ko-ko-mo / Friends call me a fool / Gum drop / Ling ting tong / Walking after midnight / Creation of love / That's your mistake / Pardon me / Two hearts.
LP: .... SING 570

Williams, Paul

CLASSICS.
MC: .... SPC 8575

HUCKLEBUCK (Williams, Paul & His Orchestra).
LP: .... BP 500

IN MEMORY OF ROBERT JOHNSON.
LP: .... SNTF 654
LP: 6.24212

JUST AN OLD FASHIONED LOVE SONG.
LP: .... AMLH 64327
MC: .... CAM 64327

LITTLE ON THE WINDY SIDE.
Tracks: / Moonlight becomes you / Little on the windy side / Save me a dream / For goodness sake / Brand new song / Little more like you / This strange new feeling / Here's another fine mess / My fair share / For the life of me / Gift.
LP: .... PRT 83197

SPIDER SENT ME (Williams, Paul & The Hucklebuckers).
LP: .... BP 510

Williams, Richard

NEW HORN IN TOWN.
LP: .... CS 79003

REJOICE (Williams, Richard, Junior Singers).
LP: .... BM 13

RICHARD WILLIAMS COLLECTION,THE.
LP: .... BM 4

Williams, Robert

NOSFERATU (See also Cornwell, Hugh) (Williams, Robert & Hugh Cornwell).

Williams, Robert Pete

LEGACY OF THE BLUES VOL. 9 (See under Legacy of the Blues).

ROBERT PETE WILLIAMS & ROOSEVELT SYKES (Williams, Robert Pete & Roosevelt Sykes).
LP: .... 77 LEU 12/50

ROBERT PETE WILLIAMS WITH BIG JOE WILLIAMS.
LP: .... SLP 225

ROBERT P.WILLIAMS LIVE.
LP: .... WOLF 120 919

THOSE PRISON BLUES.
LP: .... ARHOOLIE 2015

Williams, Robin

ALL BROKEN HEARTS ARE THE SAME (Williams, Robin & Linda).
Tracks: / Rollin' & ramblin' (the death of Hank Williams / All broken hearts are the same / Baby rocked her dolly / Leaving this land / Annie / Riding on the Santa Fe / Pan handle wind / Pine country / Stone wall country / Across the blue mountains / After the flood.
LP: .... SH 1022

CLOSE AS WE CAN GET (Williams, Robin & Linda).
LP: .... FF 327

NINE 'TIL MIDNIGHT (Williams, Robin & Linda).
LP: .... FF 359

PECOS BILL (See under Pecos Bill) (Williams, Robin & Ry Cooder).

RHYTHM OF LOVE, THE (Williams, Robin & Linda).
Tracks: / Rhythm of love, The / When I hear that whistle blow / House of gold / I'll remember your love in my prayers / Gone to the West / Hired gun / They all faded away / Six o'clock news / Hill county song / Devil is a mighty wind, The / Poor wayfaring stranger / You done me wrong.
LP: .... SH 1027
MC: .... ZCSH 1027

Williams, Robin

REALITY....WHAT A CONCEPT.
Tracks: / Nicky Lenin / Pop goes the weasel / Touch of Fairfax / Kindergarten of the stars / Reverend Earnest Angry / Shakespeare / Thank you Boyce / Roots people / Hollywood casting session / Come inside my mind / Grandpa Funk.
LP: .... NBLP 7162
LP: .... CALH 2053

Williams, Roger

GOLDEN CHRISTMAS.
LP: .... HDY 1927
MC: .... ZCHDY 1927

Williams, Roy

ROY WILLIAMS IN SWEDEN AGAIN (Williams, Roy & Friends).
LP: .... PHONT 7579

ROYAL TROMBO.
LP: .... PHONT 7556

SOMETHING WONDERFUL.
LP: .... HEP 2015

WHEN YOU'RE SMILING (Williams, Roy & Benny Waters).
LP: .... HEP 2010

Williams, Sharon

NAKED CITY (See under Turbolenz) (Turbolenz Featuring Sharon Williams).

Williams, Simon

WASHINGTONS OF ENGLAND, THE.
LP: .... LSE LP 1

Williams, Tennessee

GLASS MENAGERIE, THE (Various artists).
MCSET: 301

ROSE TATTOO, THE (Various artists).
MCSET: 0324

STREETCAR NAMED DESIRE, A (Various artists).
MCSET: 0357

Williams, Tex

IN LAS VEGAS, LIVE.
Tracks: / My window faces the south / Tomorrow's just another day to cry / Wild card / Dusty skies / Time changes everything / You can't break my heart / Downtown poker club / With men who know tobacco death / Ten years / Cowboy's prayer / Nine pound hammer / I'd trade all of my tomorrows / Little Dollie.
LP: .... SLS 50429

SMOKE, SMOKE, SMOKE.
Tracks: / Smoke, smoke, smoke / Start even / One-eyed Sam / Leaf of love, The / Shame on you / That's what I like about the west / Shot gun boogie / Castle of my dreams / Reno / Who me / He'll have to go / Ballad of thunder road, The.
LP: .... HAT 3047
MC: .... HATC 3047

TEX WILLIAMS IN LAS VEGAS.
LP: .... HAT 3105
MC: .... HATC 3105

Williams, Texas T.

14 ALL TIME COUNTRY HITS.
Tracks: / Wild side of life / Blackboard of my heart / 500 miles.
LP: .... HRL 115
MC: .... CHRL 115

Williams, Tim

CREOLE NIGHTINGALE.
LP: 11022
MC: .... 11022 TC

Williams, Tommy

SPRINGTIME IN BATTERSEA.
LP: .... FRR 008

Williams, Tony

ANGEL STREET.
Tracks: / Angel Street / Touch me / Red mask / Kiss me / Dreamland / Only with you / Pee wee / Thrill me / Obsession.
LP: B1 48494
MC: TCB1 48494

CIVILIZATION.
Tracks: / Geo rose / Warrior / Ancient eyes / Soweto nights / Slump, The / Civilization / Mutants on the beach / Citadel.
LP: .... BT 85138

FOREIGN INTRIGUE.
Tracks: / Foreign intrigue / My Michelle / Life of the party / Takin' my time / Clearways / Sister Cheryl / Aboretum.
LP: .... BT 85119

JOY OF FLYING.
Tracks: / Going far / Hip skip / Hittin' on 6 / Open fire / Tony / Eris / Coming back home / Morgan's motion.
LP: .... CBS 83338

NATIVE HEART.
Tracks: / Native heart / Extreme measures / Two worlds / Liberty / City of lights / Juicy fruit / Crystal Palace.
LP: B1 93170

NEW WORLD (see Lockwood, Didier etc.) (Williams, Tony/Niels Pedersen/Didier Lockwood/Gordon Beck).

SPRING.
Tracks: / Extras / Echo / From before / Love song / Tee.
LP: .... BST 84216

THIRD PLANE (see under Hancock, Herbie) (Williams, Tony/Herbie Hancock/Ron Carter).

Williams, Ursula Moray

JEFFY, THE BURGLAR'S CAT.
MC: 3CCA 3066

Williams, Vanessa

RIGHT STUFF, THE.
LP: .... WNGLP 1
MC: .... WNGMC 1

Williams, Vaughan

HODIE (A CHRISTMAS CANTATA) (Fantasia On Christmas Carols) (London Symphony Orchestra & Chorus).
MC: .... EL 754 128 4

Williams, Vern

BEAUTIFUL BOUQUET, A (see Maddox, Rose) (Williams, Vern/Rose Maddox Band).

BLUEGRASS FROM GOLD COUNTRY (Vern Williams Band).
LP: .... ROUNDER 0131
MC: .... ROUNDER 0131C

ROSE MADDOX & VERN WILLIAMS BAND (see under Maddox, Rose).

Williams, Vesta

VESTA.
Tracks: / Something about you / Sweet thang / Don't blow a good thing / Get out of my life / I can make your dreams come true / My heart is yours / You make me want to (love again) / It's you / Don't let me down / Once bitten twice shy.
LP: .... AMA 5118
MC: .... AMC 5118

VESTA 4 U.

Tracks: / Hearsay / Sweet sweet love / How u feel / Hunger / All on u / 4 U / Best I ever had / Congratulations.
LP: . . . . **AMA 5223**
MC: . . . . **AMC 5223**

Williams, Victoria

HAPPY, COME HOME.
Tracks: / Shoes / Frying pan / Merry-go-round / Happy / TC / I'll do his will / Big fish / Main road / Lights / Opalousas / Statue of a bum / Poetry / Animal world.
LP: . . . . **BYN 10**
MC: . . . . **BYNC 10**

SWING THE STATUE.
LP: . . . . **ROUGH 140**
MC: . . . . **ROUGHC 140**

Williams, Wayne

ROCKABILLY MEETING (Williams, Wayne & Royce Porter).
LP: . . . . **REDITA 117**

Williams, Wendy O.

DEFFEST AND BADDEST (Williams, Wendy O./Ultrafly & The Hometown Girls).
Tracks: / Rulers of rock / 10 million dollars winner / Super jock / Early days / Know w'am sayin' / I.R.T. (out in space) / Lies intro : 41 / La la land / Laffin' and scratchin'.
LP: . . . . **GRAM 35**

Williams, Willie

ROOTS AND CULTURE (see under Brown, Barry) (Williams,Willie/Barry Brown).

UNITY.
LP: . . . . **STAR 1**

Williams-Fairey...

FREEDOM (Williams-Fairey Engineering Band).
Tracks: / Silkstream / Scheherazade / Laughter in the rain / Brassmens holiday / Disney fantasy / Swiss air / Lass of Richmond Hill / Thoughts of love / Freedom.
LP: . . . . **PRL 038D**
MC: . . . . **CPRL 038D**

GOLDEN JUBILEE (Williams-Fairey Engineering Band).
Tracks: / Tritsch Tratsch Polka / Swing low sweet chariot / Kim / Piper in the meadow / Pie Jesu / Marching with Sousa / Carnival for brass / Scarecrow and Mrs. King / Serenade / Bohemian rhapsody / Folk festival.
LP: . . . . **GRALP 17**
MC: . . . . **GRTC 17**

PROCESSION TO THE MINSTER (Williams-Fairey Engineering Band).
MC: . . . . **GRTC 42**

TOURNAMENT FOR BRASS (Williams-Fairey Engineering Band).
Tracks: / President, The / Over the rainbow / Tournament for brass / Trouble with the tuba is.... The / Blenheim flourishes / Fest musik der stadt wien / Military overture / Ballycastle bay / Twin peaks / Neapolitan scenes.
LP: . . . . **GRALP 35**
MC: . . . . **GRTC 35**

Williamson, Ann

BLUE BABY BLUE.
Tracks: / Don't it make my brown eyes blue / I fall to pieces / Like strangers / Seeing is believing / Four in the morning / She's got you / Blue baby blue / I'll get over you / (Why me) why me Lord / Cold, cold heart / Forsaking all the rest / Heaven's just a sin away.
LP: . . . . **JULEP 22**
MC: . . . . **KJULEP 22**

COUNT YOUR BLESSINGS.
Tracks: / Morning has broken / By cool Siloam's shady rill / O love that wilt not let me go / Safe in the arms of Jesus / Mine eyes have seen the glory / How sweet the name of Jesus sounds / All things bright and beautiful / Whispering hope / When I survey the wondrous cross / O perfect love / All people that on Earth do dwell / Count your blessings / I need thee every hour / In the sweet bye and bye.
LP: . . . . **ERTV 2**
MC: . . . . **ERTVC 2**

COUNTRY EVERGREENS.
Tracks: / I can't stop loving you / Send me the pillow that you dream on / How great thou art / Invisible tears / Bonaparte's retreat / Bargain store / Tennessee waltz / When you and I were young Maggie / Your cheatin' heart / I can't help / Dear John a letter.
LP: . . . . **GES 5016**
MC: . . . . **KGEC 5016**

LIKE STRANGERS (see under Daniels, Roly) (Williamson, Ann & Roly Daniels).

MORE EVERGREENS.
Tracks: / Ramblin' rose / Release me / Amazing Grace / Answers on a postcard please / True love / Heartaches by the number / Blueberry Hill / I'm not that lonely yet / Blue eyes crying in the rain / Old rugged cross, The / Tie a yellow ribbon / Always / You'll never walk alone / Married by the Bible.
LP: . . . . **GES 1235**
MC: . . . . **KGEC 1235**

PRECIOUS MEMORIES.
Tracks: / Precious memories / In the garden / Abide with me / Rock of ages / Just a closer walk with thee / What a friend we have in Jesus / When the roll is called up yonder / It is no secret / Tell me the old, old story / Nearer my God to thee / One day at a time / Lord's my shepherd, The / Old time religion / Shall we gather at the river?.
LP: . . . . **ERTV 1**
MC: . . . . **ERTVC 1**

TINY BUBBLES.
Tracks: / Just out of reach / Heart of my heart / You don't have to tell me / Tiny bubbles / Nightingale sang in Berkley Square / Rose coloured glasses / Among my souvenirs / Crying time / Softly softly / Baby blue / Let bygones be bygones / Behind the footlights.
LP: . . . . **GES 1225**
MC: . . . . **KGEC 1225**

Williamson, Bob

SUPER TURN.
Tracks: / Joe's commercials / Where do you go to my ugly / Good greenall's beer / All sides now / Aeroplane song, The / Uncle Tony's protest song / Jose Cantina / Saga of Jonathan and Gertrude, The / Talking mushroom blues / Perils of hot toast, The / Kid's programmes.
LP: . . . . **SFA 031**

Williamson, Claude

FABULOUS C. WILLIAMSON TRIO, THE (Williamson, Claude Trio).
LP: . . . . **FS 192**

HOLOGRAPHY.
LP: . . . . **IP 7708**

KEYS WEST (Williamson, Claude Trio).
LP: . . . . **AFF 62**

LA FIESTA (Williamson, Claude Trio).
Tracks: / Nica's dream / In your quiet place / La fiesta / Love of a child / First trip / Black forest.
LP: . . . . **DS 862**
LP: . . . . **IP 7727**
MC: . . . . **TUMIC 012**

MULLS THE MULLIGAN SCENE.
LP: . . . . **FS 191**

NEW DEPARTURE.
LP: . . . . **IP 7717**

SALUTE TO BUD (Williamson, Claude Trio).
Tracks: / Salute to Bud / Bouncing with Bud / Penny / Thou swell / Woody 'n' you / Obsession / Indiana / Over the rainbow / Curtistan / Claudehopper / All God's chillun got rhythm.
LP: . . . . **AFF 72**

SERMON, THE.
LP: . . . . **FS 299**

THEATRE PARTY.
LP: . . . . **FS 220**

Williamson, Harry

ANTHEM FROM TARKA (See under Phillips, Anthony) (Williamson, Harry/ Antony Philips).

TARKA (Williamson, Harry/Antony Philips).
Tracks: / Movement 1 / Movement 2 / Movement 3 / Anthem, The.
LP: . . . . **PYL 18**
MC: . . . . **PYM 18**

TARKA THE OTTER (Attenborough, David).
MCSET: . . . . **LFP 7034**
MCSET: . . . . **LFP 4170345**
MCSET: . . . . **TCLFP 7034**

Williamson, James

KILL CITY (See under Iggy Pop for details) (Williamson, James/Iggy Pop).

Williamson, Malcolm

IN RECITAL (see Michelow, Sybil) (Williamson, Malcolm & Sybil Michelow).

PROCESSION OF PALMS.
LP: . . . . **LPB 805**

Williamson, Mark

GET THE DRIFT (Williamson, Mark Band).
Tracks: / Midnight diamond / All very well / Junior / Somebody told me / So far so good / Dance / Don't turn your back / Feeling alright / Rising / I would have listened.
LP: **CLS8003**

MARK WILLIAMSON.
LP: . . . . **PC 118**

MISSING IN ACTION (Williamson, Mark Band).
LP: . . . . **MYR 1154**
MC: . . . . **MC 1154**

Williamson, Nicol

HOBBIT, THE (See under J.R.R. Tolkien).

HOUND OF THE BASKERVILLES, THE (see under Sherlock Holmes (bk)).

Williamson, Robin

AMERICAN STONEHENGE (Williamson, Robin & His Merry Band).
LP: . . . . **FF 062**

DRAGON HAS TWO TONGUES, THE.
LP: . . . . **TER 1133**
MC: . . . . **ZCTER 1133**
LP: . . . . **TVLP 1**
MC: . . . . **ZCTV 1**

GLINT OF THE KINDLING, A (Williamson, Robin & His Merry Band).
LP: . . . . **AWL 1006**
MC: . . . . **AWT 1006**
LP: . . . . **FF 096**

JOURNEYS EDGE (Williamson, Robin & His Merry Band).
LP: . . . . **FF 033**

LEGACY OF SCOTTISH HARPERS.
LP: . . . . **CCF 12**
MC: **4CCF 12**

LEGACY OF THE SCOTTISH HARPERS, VOL.2.
LP: . . . . **CCF 16**
LP: . . . . **FF 390**
MC: **4CCF 16**

MUSIC FOR THE MABINOGI.
LP: . . . . **CCF 10**

SONGS AND MUSIC 1977 (Williamson, Robin & His Merry Band).
Tracks: / Tune I hear so well, The / Mythic times / When evening shadows fall / Bells, the.
LP: . . . . **AWL 1005**
MC: . . . . **AWT 1005**

SONGS FOR CHILDREN.
LP: . . . . **CCF 19**
MC: **4CCF 19**

SONGS FROM THE MABINOGI.
LP: . . . . **FF 340**

SONGS OF LOVE AND PARTING.
LP: . . . . **CCF 5**
LP: . . . . **FF 257**

TEN OF SONGS, THE.
LP: . . . . **PLR 081**
MC: . . . . **PLC 081**

WINTER'S TURNING.
LP: . . . . **PLR 075**
MC: . . . . **PLC 075**
LP: . . . . **FF 407**

Williamson, Sonny Boy

ANIMALS WITH SONNY BOY WILLIAMSON (See under Animals) (Williamson, Sonny Boy/Animals).

BLUEBIRD BLUES (Williamson, John Lee 'Sonny Boy').
LP: . . . . **BT 2006**

BLUES OF SONNY BOY WILLIAMSON, THE.
LP: . . . . **SLP 4062**

CHESS MASTERS-SONNY BOY WILLIAMSON 2.
Tracks: / Born blind / Work with me / You killing me / Keep it to yourself / Don't lose your eye / Good evening everybody / Too close together / Let your conscience be your guide / I wonder why / This is my apartment / Like wolf / One way out / Have you ever been in love / Cool disposition / I know what love is all about / Your imagination / Hurts me so / 99 / Goat, The / I never do wrong / Nine below zero / Bye bye bird / Help me.
2LP: . . . . **CXMD 4012**

CHESS MASTERS-SONNY BOY WILLIAMSON 1.
2LP: . . . . **CXMD 4001**

CHESS YEARS, THE.
Tracks: / Good evening everybody / All my love in vain / Don't start me to talkin' / You killin' me (on my feet) / Work with me / Let me explain / I know what love is all about / Your imagination / I wonder why / Don't lose your eye / Keep it to yourself / Key (to your door), The / Have you ever been in love / Please forgive / Fattening frogs for snakes / Hurts me so much / I don't know / This is my apartment / Like wolf / Cross my heart / Unseen eye / Ninety nine / Dissatisfied / Born blind / Little village / Wake up baby / She got next to me / Your funeral my trial / Let your conscience be your guide / Unseeing eye / Keep your hand out of my pocket / Cool diposition / Goat, The / I never do wrong / Santa Claus / It's sad to be alone / I can't do without you / Open road / Checkin' up on my baby / Peach tree / Lonesome cabin / Temperature 110 / Down child / Trust my baby / Somebody help me / This old life / Too young to die / She's my baby / Stop right now / That's all I want / Too close together / Hunt,The / Too old to think / Nine below zero / One way out / Bye bye bird / Got to move / Help me / One way out / Bring it on home / My younger days / Stop cryin' / Trying to get back on my feet / Understand my life / Decoration day / One way out / Close to me (I want you) / Don't make a mistake / Find another woman / I can't be alone / My name is Sonny Boy / Key (to your door), The / Hurts me so much / Cool disposition / Dissatisfied / Cross my heart / She got next to me / Fattening frogs for snakes / Your funeral my trial / Cool disposition / Goat, The / Ninetynine.
LPS: . . . . **BOX 1**

CHICAGO GOLDEN YEARS.
2LP: **427004**

COLLECTION: SONNY BOY WILLIAMSON (20 blues greats).
Tracks: / Mister Downchild / I don't care no more / Out on the water coast / Baby don't you worry / Nine below zero / Eyesight to the blind / I cross my heart / West Memphis blues / Do it if you wanna / Crazy about you baby / Pontiac blues / My babe / I'm gonna put you down / Night time is the right time / Cool cool blues / Come on back home / Mighty long time / Sonny Boy's Christmas blues / Stop now, baby / She brought life back to the dead.
LP: . . . . **DVLP 2074**
MC: . . . . **DVMC 2074**

DOWN AND OUT BLUES.
Tracks: / Don't start me talkin' / I don't know / All my love in vain / Key, The / Keep it to yourself / Dissatisfied / Fattening frogs for snakes / Wake up baby / Your funeral and my trail / 99 / Cross my heart / Let me explain.
LP: . . . . **NPL 28036**
LP: . . . . **CH 9257**

HARMONICA ACE, 1937-45.
LP: . . . . **OT 1205**

JAM SESSION (see under Page, Jimmy) (Williamson, Sonny Boy/Brian Auger/ Jimmy Page).

KING BISCUIT TIME (Williamson, John Lee 'Sonny Boy').
LP: . . . . **ARHOOLIE 2020**

MORE REAL FOLK BLUES.
LP: **515018**

NEWCASTLE DECEMBER 1963 (see under Animals/Sonny Boy Williamson) (Williamson, Sonny Boy/Animals).

ONE WAY OUT.
Tracks: / Born blind / Work with me / You killing me / Keep it to yourself / Don't lose your eye / Good evening everybody / Too close together / Let you consience be your guide / I wonder why / This is my apartment / One way out / Like wolf / Have you ever been in love / Cool disposition / I know what love is all about.
LP: . . . . **GCH 8006**
MC: . . . . **GCHK 78006**
LP: . . . . **BRP 2015**
LP: **515015**
MC: . . . . **CH 9116**

PORTRAIT IN BLUES, A.
LP: . . . . **SLP 4016**

RARE SONNY BOY.
Tracks: / Sugar mama blues / Skinny woman / Worried me blues / Black gal blues / Frigidaire blues / Suzanna blues / Early in the morning / My little Cornelius / Decoration blues / You can lead me baby / Miss Louisa blues / Sunnyland / I'm tired trucking my blues away / Beauty parlour / My baby I've been your slave / Doggin' my love around / Little low woman blues / Sugar mama blues No.2 / Good gravy / Good gal blues / I'm not pleasing you / Tell me, baby / Honey bee blues / I'm gonna catch you soon / Blues that made me drunk / Elevator woman / Mellow chick swing / Lacey belle / Apple tree swing / Sugar gal / No friend blues / I love you for myself / Bring another half a pint / Southern dream / Better cut that out.
LP: . . . . **NL 90027**

REAL FOLK BLUES.
LP: **515010**

SOLO HARP (1963-65).
LP: . . . . **DLP 575**

SONNY BOY WILLIAMSON.
MC: . . . . **C 216**

SONNY BOY WILLIAMSON 1940-42.
LP: . . . . **WSE 135**

SONNY BOY WILLIAMSON 1937-1941.
LP: BC 3

SONNY BOY WILLIAMSON (CHESS).
MC: CHXT 108

SONNY BOY WILLIAMSON & MEMPHIS SLIM IN PARIS (Williamson, Sonny Boy & Memphis Slim).
LP: GNPS 10003

SONNY BOY WILLIAMSON STORY, THE.
Tracks: / Crazy about you baby / Mr. Downchild / Stop crying / Eyesight to the blind / Sonny Boy's Christmas blues / Cool cool blues / Take it easy baby / Bye bye bird / Pontiac blues / She brought life back to the dead / Do it if you wanna / I cross my heart / Come on back home / Out on the water coast / Nine below zero / Western Arizona / West Memphis blues / Stop now baby / Hours too long / I don't care no more / Lost care, A / Mighty long time.
MCSET: DVREMC 25

SONNY BOY WILLIAMSON VOL.3.
LP: BC 24

SONNY BOY WILLIAMSON VOL. 2 1937-1946.
LP: BC 20

SONNY BOY WILLIAMSON & YARDBIRDS 1963 (with Eric Clapton) (Williamson, Sonny Boy & The Yardbirds).
LP: LR 42.020

THROW A BOOGIE WOOGIE (Williamson, Sonny Boy/Big Joe Williams).
Tracks: / Good morning little schoolgirl / Sugar mama blues / Got the bottle up and gone / Early in the morning / Black gal blues / Moonshine / Whiskey headed blues / You give an account / Rootin' ground hog / Brother James / Peach orchard mama / Crawling king snake / Highway 49 / Please don't go / North wind blues / Throw a boogie woogie.
LP: NL 90320
MC: NK 90320

UNISSUED 1963 BLUES FESTIVAL, THE (see under Slim, Memphis).

Williamson, Steve

WALTZ FOR GRACE, THE.
Tracks: / Soon come / Mandela / Synthesis / Ornithology / Lauren / Visions / Mandy's mood / Straight ahead / Groove thang / Hummingbird / Words within words / Awakening / Waltz for grace.
MC: 843 088 4
LP: 843 088 1

Williamson, Stu

STU WILLIAMSON.
LP: FS 150

STU WILLIAMSON PLAYS.
LP: FS 201

Willing, Foy

FOY WILLING & THE RIDERS OF THE PURPLE SAGE.
Tracks: / Holiday for the blues / Little white house (with you inside) / Twilight on the trail / Ragtime Cowboy blues / Blue shadows on the trail / Across the valley from the Alamo / Prairie echoes / Nobody's lost on the lonesome trail / Hang your head in shame / Trail to Mexico / Cool water / When the white roses bloom down in red river valley.
MC: CSR 4C

Willis Brothers

BEST OF THE WILLIS BROTHERS.
LP: SLP 960
MC: GT 5960

Willis, Bruce

IF IT DON'T KILL YOU IT JUST MAKES YOU STRONGER.
Tracks: / Pep talk / Crazy mixed up world / Turn it up a little louder / Soul shake / Here comes trouble again / Save the last dance for me / Blues for Mr.D / Tenth Avenue tango / Can't leave her alone / Barnyard boogie (On CD only.) / Love makes the world go round / I'll go crazy (On CD only.).
LP: ZL 72680
MC: ZK 72680

RETURN OF BRUNO, THE.
Tracks: / Comin' right up / Respect yourself / Down in Hollywood / Young blood / Under the boardwalk / Secret agent man (James Bond is back) / Jackpot / Fun time / Lose myself / Flirting with disaster.
LP: ZL 72571
MC: ZK 72571

Willis, Chick

BACK TO THE BLUES.
Tracks: / Don't let success (turn our love around) / Goin' to the dogs / Bow legged woman / I ain't superstitious / Tell papa / Story of my life / My adorable one / I ain't jivin' baby / Strange things happenin'.
LP: ICH 1106
MC: ICH 1106 MC

CHICK SINGS CHUCK.
Tracks: / C.C. rider / Don't deceive me / Betty and Dupree / Charged with cheating / C & B New Albany jam / Whatcha gonna do when your baby leaves / My story / That train is gone / What am I living for, one more chance.
LP: ICH 1012
MC: ZCICH 1012

FOOTPRINTS ON MY BED.
Tracks: / Love crazy / Use what you got / What's to become of the world / Roll the dice / Footprints in my bed / Big red caboose / Hello central / Jack you up / Voodoo woman / Nuts for sale.
LP: ICH 1054
MC: ICH 1054 MC

NOW.
Tracks: / I want a big fat woman / What have you got on me / I want to play with your poodle / I can't stop loving you / For your precious love / Stoop down '88 / It's all over / Garbage man.
LP: ICH 1029
MC: ZCICH 1029

Willis, Chuck

BE GOOD OR BE GONE.
LP: ED 159
MC: CED 159

KEEP A DRIVIN'.
Tracks: / There's got to be a way / It's too late / My life / Kansas City woman / Rider / Juanita / Watcha gonna do when your baby leaves you / Ease the panic / My baby / Betty and Dupree / Thunder and lightning / From the bottom of my heart / Sugar sugar / Hang up my rock 'n' roll shoes / What am I living for / Keep-a drivin.
LP: CRB 1074
MC: TCCRB 1074

MY STORY.
Tracks: / Can't you see / Be good or be gone / It ain't right to treat me wrong / Let's jump tonight / It's too late / I rule my house / Baby on my mind / I tried / Here I come / Caldonia / Loud mouth Lucy / Salty tears / I've been treated wrong too long / Take it like a man / Wrong lake to catch a fish / My story / Don't deceive me / My baby's coming home / You know you don't love me / When my day is over / Going to the river / My baby have left me again / You're still my baby / What's your name? / I feel so bad / I need one more chance / Keep a knockin' / Change my mind / My heart's been broken again / I don't mind if I do / Welcome home dear / Give and take / I've been away way too long / Love struck / It were you / Lawdy Miss Mary / Come on home / Search my heart / One more break / I can tell / Ring-ring-doo / Two spoons of tears / Charged with cheating / Bless her heart / Night of misery / There's got to be a way / It's too late / My life / Kansas City woman / Juanita / Whatcha gonna do when your baby leaves you / Ease the pain / C.C. rider / Just one kiss / Train has gone, The / My baby / Love me Cherry / Betty and Dupree / My cryin' eyes / Thunder and lightning / From the bottom of my heart / You'll be my love / What am I living for? / Hang up my rock 'n' roll shoes / Keep a drivin' / Big drops of rain / Stop and think / Sugar sugar / I'll be so glad when your heart is mine / Love of loves.
LPS: OFF 6030-5

Willis, Ike

SHOULD' A GONE BEFORE I LEFT.
LP: ST 73292
LP: 3292 1

Willis, Jack

ORLEANS STREET SHUFFLE (Willis, Jack & His New Orleans Band).
LP: LPS 5
MC: TCS 5

Willis, Ralph

CAROLINA BLUES.
LP: BC 22

FADED PIC BLUES (See under Howard, Paul) (Willis, Ralph & Paul Howard).

Willo The Wisp (tv)

BEANSTALK, THE (Various artists).
MC: LL 41 8006 4

CHRYSALIS, THE (Various artists).
MC: LL 41 8002 4

GAMES WITH EDNA (Various artists).
MC: LL 41 8001 4

JOYS OF SPRING, THE (Various artists).
MC: LL 41 8005 4

MAGIC GOLF (Various artists).
MC: LL 41 8004 4

WILLO THE WISP (Williams, Kenneth (nar)).
Tracks: / Bridegroom, The / Food for thought / You know what, The / Chrysalis, The / Flight of Mavis, The / Holidays / Hot hot day, The / Gnome, The / Beauty contents, The / Midas touch, The / Beanstalk, The / Christmas box.
LP: REC 427
MC: ZCM 427

WISHBONE, THE (Various artists).
MC: LL 41 8003 4

Willoughby, Larry

BUILDING BRIDGES.
Tracks: / Lorraine / Held in love / Careless love / Stone cold / Sweet little lisa / Heart on the line / Building bridges / Hurricane rose / Angel eyes / Devil's on the loose.
LP: WEA 790112-1

Willow

UNDERGROUND MAN.
MC: FTM 5447

YOUNG GIRL FROM THE MOUNTAINS.
Tracks: / Here I stand.
MC: FTM 5449

Willow (film)

WILLOW (Film Soundtrack) (Horner, James/L.S.O. & King's College Choir).
Tracks: / Elora Danan / Escape from the tavern / Canyon of mazes / Tir asleen / Willow's theme / Willow's journey begins / Bavmorda's spell is cast / Willow the sorcerer.
LP: V 2538
MC: TCV 2538
LP: 790939.1
MC: 790939.4

Wills, Billy Jack

BILLY JACK WILLS & HIS WESTERN SWING BAND (Wills, Billy Jack & His Western Swing Band).
LP: WESTERN 2002

CRAZY MAN CRAZY (Wills, Billy Jack & His Western Swing Band).
LP: WESTERN 2004

Wills, Bob

BEST OF BOB WILLS.
Tracks: / San Antonio rose / Eight'r from decatur / Deep in the heart of Texas / Silver bells / Across the valley from the Alamo / Cimarron / South of the border / Milk cow blues / My adobe hacienda / Southwestern waltz / Big ball in cowtown, A.
LP: IMCA 153

BEST OF BOB WILLS VOL. 1 & 2.
Tracks: / San Antonio rose / Eight'r from decatur / Deep in the heart of Texas / Silver bells / Across the valley from the Alamo / South of the border (down Mexico way) / Milk cow blues / My adobe hacienda / South-western waltz / Four or five times / Time changes everything / Texas double eagle / You're the only star in my blue heaven / Song of the wanderer / Pan handle rag / My Mary / Beaumont rag / Whose heart are you breaking now / Brown skin gal / Cimarron.
2LP: IMCA2 4092

BEST OF THE TIFFANYS (Wills, Bob & His Texas Playboys).
Tracks: / Roly poly / Bring it down to my house / Faded love / Stay a little longer / Take me back to Tulsa / Steel guitar rag / Maiden's prayer / Cotton eyed Joe / Corina, Corina / San Antonio rose / Time changes everything / Right or wrong / Cherokee maiden / Ida red.
LP: ED 322
MC: EDC 322

BOB WILLS ANTHOLOGY (Wills, Bob & His Texas Playboys).
LP: CBS 31611

BOB WILLS & HIS TEXAS PLAYBOYS (Wills, Bob & His Texas Playboys).
Tracks: / Talking 'bout you / Panhandle rag / Across the alley from the Alamo / Running bear / Milk cow blues / Slow poke / San Antonio rose / Faded love / Four or five times / Brown skin gal / Kansas city / Wills breakdown / Riders in the sky / Lone star rag / Orange blossom special / Big beaver.
LP: CR 30223

FROM THE HEART OF TEXAS (Wills, Bob & His Texas Playboys).
Tracks: / Deep in the heart of Texas / You're the only star in my blue heaven / What's Fort Worth / Big ball in Cowtown, A / Pinto beans / Where do I go from here / My Adobe hacienda / Kansas City / Gone Indian (instrumental) / Guess I'll move on down the line / If no news is good news / I just can't take it anymore.
LP: HAT 3058
MC: HATC 3058

GOLDEN ERA, THE (Wills, Bob & His Texas Playboys).
2LP: C 240149

GREATEST HITS OF TEXAS,THE (Wills, Bob & His Texas Playboys).
LP: RNDF 284

MORE RARE PRESTO TRANSCRIPTIONS.
Tracks: / Bob Wills talks to Allen Franklyn / In the mood / Sugar moon / Elmer's tune / My life's been a pleasure / Texas home / Dipsy doodle / Just a little lovin' / Sunrise serenade / Cherokee maiden / Osage stomp / You're the sweetest rose in Texas / Don't let your deal go down / Molly darling / Yearning (just for you) / Those gone and left me blues / Little star of heaven.
MC: CSR 2C

PAPA'S JUMPIN'.
Tracks: / Silver lake blues / Little cowboy lullaby / Closed for repairs / Dog house blues / Bubbles in my beer / 'Neath Hawaiin palms / Papa's jumpin' / Don't be ashamed of your age / Blackout blues / Spanish fandango / I want to be near you / Sally Goodin / She's gone / I had a little mule / Go home with the girls in the mornin' / Still the water runs deepest / Cotton pitch blues / Nothin' but the best for my baby / Blues for Dixie / Cross my heart I love you / Keeper of my heart / I have somebody else / Thorn in my heart / Playboy charms / Hop, skip and jump over Texas / Texas drummer boy / I married the rose of San Antone / Ida Red likes the boogie / Warm red wine / I ain't got nobody / Boot Hill rag / Nothing but trouble / Anything / Bob Wills square dance (Parts 1-4) / King without a queen / Hold your tears / When it's Christmas on the range / Santa's on his way / Mean woman with green eyes / My little rock candy baby / Jolie Blonde likes the boogie / Pastime blues / Faded love / Awake but dreamin' / I betcha my heart I love you / I laugh when I think how I cried over you / I'll be lucky someday / I didn't realise / Rock a bye baby blues / I'm dotting each "i" with a teardrop / End of the line / 'Tater pie / Little girl, little girl / I'm tired of living this lie / Pitney Jane / Twinkle star / Brown skin gal / Sitting on top of the world / Silver bells / Last goodbye / Just to be loved / Send me a red rose / Hubbin' it / I can't stand this loneliness / You always keep me in hot water / 'Cause I'm in love / Three miles south of cash in Arkansas / I'm all alone / Three little kittens / Won't be back tonight / Charlie changed his mind / I'm only a friend / Steamboat stomp / I want to be wanted / Snatchin' and grabbin' / Real hot needle, A / Trouble, trouble blues (take 1) / Trouble, trouble blues / Broken heart for a souvenir, A / As I sit broken hearted / Bottle baby boogie / I want to go to Mexico / I'm human same as you / I hit the jackpot (when I won you) / Maiden's prayer / Fallen angel / She's a quarter house type of gal / B. Bowman hop / Doin' the bunny hop / St. Louis blues / So long, I'll see you later / Cadillac in model "A" / Waltzing in old San Antone / I've got a new road under my wheels / Texas blues / Live for you.
LPS: BFX 15179/6

RARE PRESTO TRANSCRIPTION, THE.
Tracks: / Tennessee Saturday night / Draggin' the bow twin guitar special / Will you miss me when I'm gone / Bob Wills boogie / No wonder / Tierney's boogie / Sitting on top of the world / C jam blues / San Antonio rose / There'll be some changes made / C Schottische / Judy / Tumbling tumbleweeds / Sally Johnson / Blues for Dixie / Blue flame.
MC: CSR 1C

SAN ANTONIO ROSE AND OTHER HITS (Wills, Bob & His Texas Playboys).
MC: 4XLL 9193

TIFFANY TRANSCRIPTIONS VOL.1 (Wills, Bob & His Texas Playboys).
Tracks: / Nancy Jane / Mission to Moscow / Dinah / Lone star rag / Cotton patch blues / Sweet Jennie Lee / I hear you talking / Girl I left behind me, The / Straighten up and fly right / Little Betty Brown / Nobody's sweetheart now / Blackout blues / What's the matter with the mill / Jumpin' at the woodside.
LP: ED 321
LP: F 16
MC: C 16

TIFFANY TRANSCRIPTIONS VOL.2 (Wills, Bob & His Texas Playboys).
LP: F 19
MC: C 19

TIFFANY TRANSCRIPTIONS VOL.3 (Basin street blues) (Wills, Bob & His Texas Playboys).
Tracks: / Basin Street blues / I'm a ding dong daddy / Crazy rhythm / Milk cow

blues / Please don't talk about me when I'm gone / Four or five times / Frankie Jean / It's your red wagon / Good man is hard to find, A / You just take her / Barnard blues / Baby won't you come home / Take the A train.
LP: F 20
MC: C 20
LP: ED 323
MC: EDC 323

TIFFANY TRANSCRIPTIONS VOL.4 (Wills, Bob & His Texas Playboys).
Tracks: / Texas Playboy theme / You're from Texas / Beaumont rag / Lum and Abner special / Texarkana baby / Little Joe the wrangler / New Spanish two-step / Texas plains / Home in San Antone / Blue Bonnet Lane / Across the alley from the Alamo / Along the Navajo trail / Spanish fandango / My brown eyed Texas rose / Red river valley / Texas Playboy theme (closing).
LP: ED 324
MC: EDC 324
LP: F 21
MC: C 21

TIFFANY TRANSCRIPTIONS VOL.5 (Wills, Bob & His Texas Playboys).
Tracks: / My window faces South / Swing blues / I had someone else before I had you / Smooth one, A / Don't cry baby / Three guitar special / China town / Fat boy rag / Lazy river / Sweet Georgia Brown / At the woodchoppers ball / Sweet kind of love / If it's wrong to love you.
LP: F 25
MC: C 25
LP: ED 325
MC: EDC 325

TIFFANY TRANSCRIPTIONS VOL.6 (Sally Goodin') (Wills, Bob & His Texas Playboys).
Tracks: / Oklahoma hills / Sally Goodin / I had a little mule / Playboy chimes / Never no more hard time blues / I'll get mine bye and bye / Jesse polka / Oh Monah / Smith's reel / I'm putting all my eggs in one basket / Oklahoma rag / Dev'lish Mary / It's my lazy day / Sally Goodin (inst).
LP: F 27
MC: C 27
LP: ED 326

TIFFANY TRANSCRIPTIONS VOL.7 (Wills, Bob & His Texas Playboys).
Tracks: / Keep knockin' (but you can't come in) / Honeysuckle Rose / Worried mind / Okie boogie / C-Jam blues / I can't go on this way / Sweet moments / My gal Sal / I'm gonna be boss from now on / Lonesome hearted blues / Joe's place / Sugar blues / Too long / Tea for two.
LP: F 29
MC: C 29
LP: ED 327

TIFFANY TRANSCRIPTIONS VOL.8 (More Of The Best) (Wills, Bob & His Texas Playboys).
Tracks: / Miss Molly / Ten years / Blues for Dixie / Twinkle twinkle little star / Sun bonnet Sue / Sitting on top of the world / Big beaver / There's gonna be a party for the old folks / South / Trouble in mind / Little Liza Jane / Sioux City Sue / My confessions / Get along home Cindy.
LP: F 32
MC: C 32
LP: ED 328

TIME CHANGES EVERYTHING.
LP: HAT 3024
MC: HATC 3024

VERY BEST OF BOB WILLS & THE TEXAS PLAYBOYS,THE.
Tracks: / San Antonio rose / Bubbles in my beer / Stay a little longer / Keeper of my heart / Deep water / Hang your head in shame / Roly poly / Trouble in mind / Heart to heart talk / Time changes everything / Right or wrong / Blue for Dixie / Cindy / Image of me, The / Mississippi river blues / Convict and the rose / Ida Red likes the boogie / Take me back to Tulsa.
LP: SLS 2600 431
MC: TC SLS 2600434

Wills, Charlie

CHARLIE WILLS.
LP: LEA 4041

UP TO THE RIGS.
Tracks: / Talk about himself (Spoken word) / Flag of old England, the / Germany clockmaker / Spotted cow / Lord Thomas / Whisker's on a baby's face / Female cabin boy, The / Little ball of yarn, the / Game of cards, the / Foggy dew, The / Turn over another leaf / Home boys home / Ram song, The / Suit of corderoy / Barbara Allen / Tis a wonder I'm alive to tell the tale / Ruth Butcher (local murder ballad) / Brennan on the moor / Go and leave me, if you wish it / Sailor cut down in his prime, The.
MC: 60-097

Wills, Johnny Lee

OPERATORS' SPECIALS.
Tracks: / Swing me / Milk cow blues / She's sweet / Blue man / Rockin' rollin' mama / Ramblers stomp / Nickel in the kitty / Panhandle shuffle / Big ball's in cowtown, A / Too long / Jive and smile / Mean old sixty-five blues / Woodchip blues / Sometimes / It's a long way to Tipperary.
LP: STR 807

REUNION.
LP: FF 069

ROMPIN', STOMPIN', SINGIN', SWINGIN' (Wills, Johnny Lee & His Boys).
Tracks: / She took / Hat check baby / There are just two I's in Dixie / Thingamajig / Let me be / Two timin' / Bees in my bonnet / Oo oooh daddy / Ten little bluebirds in my lapel / Blackberry boogie / Honey in the horn / A-l-b-u-q-u-e-r-q-u-e / Sold out doc / Two step side step.
LP: BFX 15103

TULSA SWING.
LP: ROUNDER 1027

Wills, Luke

HIGH VOLTAGE GAL.
Tracks: / Shut up and drink your beer / Never turn your back to a woman / Louisiana blues / Bob Wills two-step / Corn fed Arkanasas gal / Is it true what they say / Gotta get to Oklahoma city / Long train blues / I'm a married man / Uncle Tom Wills Schottische / High voltage gal / Texas special, The / Oklahoma blues / Si si senorita / Cain's stomp / Honky tonkin' Sal / Nickel in the jukebox, A / Woman was the cause of it all, A / Fly in the ointment / High voltage gal (2).
LP: BFX 15333

Wills, Mick

FERN HILL.
LP: W 009

Wilmer X

NOT GLAMOUROUS.
LP: MNWP 164

Wilson, Ada

WHAT THE WORLD WANTS.
Tracks: / Jimmy Bishop / Former beauty queen / Left behind / What the girl wants / Need your love so bad / One horse gangster town / Money like water / Just the job / Second hand dreams.
LP: NTVLP 9

Wilson, Al

COUNT THE BOYS.
Tracks: / Earthquake / You got it / Count the boys / Save a dance / Is this the end / Since I'm without you / You really turn me on / Tomorrow's sun.
LP: FL 13215

DANCING HAMMOND.
Tracks: / Mr. Sandman / Mack the knife / Un-sentimental / I'll be seeing you / Come fly with me / Yeh, yeh / When the red, red robin comes bob, bob, bobbin' along / Bye bye blackbird / Nikita / This is all I ask / Once in a while / If love is good to me / You always hurt the one you love / I know I'll never love this way again / I'll get a kick out of you.
LP: SUS 513
MC: CSUS 513

SNAKE, THE (OLD GOLD) (See under Main Ingredient 'Just don't want..').

Wilson, Art

SIX A SIDE (Wilson, Art & Rhythmaires).
LP: SUS 531

SIX A SIDE VOL.2 (Wilson, Art & Rhythmaires).
Tracks: / Ampola / They can't black out the moon / Zigeuner, you have stolen my heart / You didn't have to tell me / Fascinating little lady / Be mine tonight / Don't sleep in the subway darling / Green eyes / Magic in the moonlight / Please don't be scared / You belong to my heart / Take my heart / Here in my heart / At my time of life / Don't worry 'bout me / I dreamed / Just an old fashioned girl.
LP: SUS 532

TEA DANCE.
Tracks: / Would you / For you / Sweetest sounds, The / Golden days / Spread a little happiness / Dancing with my shadow / Everything stops for tea / I'll do anything / Neighbours / Nice cup of tea, A / Nice people / I'm ready willing & able / I enjoy being a girl / Sons and daughters / One day in your life / You are the sunshine of my life / Embraceable you / Just good friends / Storm in a teacup / Love is here to stay / That old feeling / Living doll / Aunty Vi's / Some of these days / Play to me gypsy / Golden tango.
LP: SUS 523

Wilson, Bob

SOMEBODY LOVES YOU (Wilson, Bob & Pauline).
Tracks: / I'll keep my eyes on Jesus / With love in your eyes / Joyful melody / Vision: power and glory / You can't hide / Somebody loves you / Lullaby of love / In the spirit / Jesus is my Lord.
LP: MYR 1102
MC: MC 1102

STANLEY BAGSHAW.
MC: 881654

Wilson, Brian

BRIAN WILSON.
Tracks: / Love and mercy / Walkin' the line / Melt away / Baby let your hair grow long / Little children / One for the boys / There's so many / Night time / Let it shine / Rio Grande / Meet me in my dreams tonight.
LP: WX 157
MC: WX 157 C

Wilson Brothers

ANOTHER NIGHT.
Tracks: / Feeling like we're strangers again / Another night / Thanking heaven / Shadows / Just like a lover knows / Lost and a long way from home / Can we still be friends? / Ticket to my heart / Take me to your heaven / Like yesterday.
LP: K 50643

Wilson, Calum

CALUM WILSON AND HIS SCOTTISH COUNTRY DANCE BAND.
Tracks: / College hornpipe, The / Two step medley / Scottish waltzes / Accordion duet / Pipe marches / Gay Gordons / Jigs medley / Grand march / Gaelic waltz medley / Fiddle solo / Eva three step / Trip to Bavaria.
LP: LILP 5109
MC: LICS 5109

Wilson, Carl

CARL WILSON.
Tracks: / Hold me / Bright lights / What you gonna do about me / Right lane / Hurry love / Heaven / Grammy / Seems so long ago.
LP: CRB 84840

YOUNGBLOOD.
Tracks: / What more can I say? / She's mine / Givin' you up / One more night alone / Rockin' all over the world / What you do to me / Youngblood / Of the times / Too early to tell / If I could talk to love / Time.
LP: CRB 25225
MC: 40 25225

Wilson, Cassandra

BLUE SKIES.
LP: 834419-1

DAYS AWEIGH.
Tracks: / Electromagnolia / Let's face the music and dance / Days aweigh / Subatomic blues / Apricots on their wings / If you only know how / You belong to you / Some other time / Black and yellow.
LP: JMT 870012

JUMPWORLD.
Tracks: / Woman on the edge / Lies / Whirlwind / Rock this calling / Domination switch / Phase jump / Dancing in dream time / Warm spot.
LP: 834 431 1
MC: 834 431 4

SHE WHO WEEPS.
Tracks: / Iconic Memories / Chelsea bridge / Out loud (jeris' blues) / She who weeps / Angel / Body and soul / New African blues.
LP: 8344431
MC: 8344434

Wilson, Charles

BLUES IN THE KEY OF C.
Tracks: / Who it's going to be / Is it over / Leaning tree / You cut off my love supply / Let's have a good time / Selfish lover / It's a crying shame / I've got a good woman.
LP: ICH 1120
MC: ICH 1120MC

Wilson, Chris

MUSIC FOR TWO LUTES (Wilson,Chris & Tom Finucane).
LP: PLR 058

Wilson, Clive

ORIGINAL CAMELIA JAZZBAND OF NEW ORLEANS (Wilson, Clive & Trevor Richards).
LP: GHB 244

PLAYS NEW ORLEANS JAZZ.
LP: NOR 7210

Wilson, Colin

OUTSIDER - 20 YEARS ON.
MC: SS 125

Wilson, Delroy

20 GOLDEN HITS: DELROY WILSON.
2LP: TWD 001

22 SUPER HITS.
LP: BLP 17

BEST OF DELROY WILSON.
LP: JJ 166

COOL OPERATOR.
LP: VSLP 4010

DEAN OF REGGAE, THE.
LP: Unknown

ISLANDS IN THE STREAM (see under Jennifer Lara) (Wilson, Delroy & Jennifer Lara).

LOOKIN' FOR LOVE.
LP: PHILLP 1008

NICE TIMES.
Tracks: / Never never / Odessey of love / Play play girl.
LP: VSLP 4032

OLDIES BUT GOODIES (see Gray, Owen) (Wilson, Delroy & Owen Gray).

PLACE IN THE SUN (see under Isaacs, David).

REGGAE CLASSICS.
Tracks: / Islands in the stream / Wish you were here / Hard to say I'm sorry / There's always something there to... / New york city / You've lost that lovin' feeling / Letter to mummy and daddy / Suspicion.
LP: LDLP 004
LP: LDR LP 004

SARGE.
LP: TRLS 233

SUPER MIX HITS.
Tracks: / Oh Donna / Shirley my love / Darlin' / Must I go out / Never never / Love is a treasure / People get ready / Live good / Red red wine / Move out a Baylon / Train to Africa / Cherry baby / Sincerely / For your love / Lonely street.
LP: STLP 1006

WHICH WAY IS UP.
Tracks: / Can't tell which way is up / Homely girl / Turn to stone / Reason / Woman needs love, a / Doing me wrong / You don't love me / Hey girl.
LP: BMLP 015

WHO DONE IT.
LP: TDWD 8

WORTH YOUR WEIGHT IN GOLD.
LP: BS 1060

Wilson, Dennis

PACIFIC OCEAN BLUE.
Tracks: / River song / What's wrong / Moonshine / Friday night / Dreamer / Thoughts of you / Time / You and I / Pacific ocean blue / Farewell my friend / Rainbows / End of the show.
LP: CRB 32438
MC: 4683514

Wilson, Eddie

DANKESCHON, BITTESCHON, WIEDERSEHEN.
Tracks: / Wabash cannonball / Strictly nothin' / Streets of Laredo / Mid the green fields of Virginia / It's OK / I wish I could / Johnny Reb / I found my girl in the USA / Show her lots of gold / Long time to forget.
LP: BFX 15028

Wilson, Edith

EDITH WILSON WITH JOHNNY DUNN'S JAZZ HOUNDS.
LP: FB 302

Wilson, Ernest

JUDITH CAN'T RESIST.
LP: WRT 32

Wilson, Garland

PIANO SOLOS. (1930 ONWARDS).
Tracks: / Dear old Southland / Limehouse blues / Memories of you / Rockin' chair / Blues in B flat / Mood indigo / China boy / Just a mood / You made me love you / Montmartre moan.
MC: NEO 855

WAY I FEEL, THE.
LP: CI 016

Wilson, Gerald

GOLDEN SWORD, THE (Wilson, Gerald and His Orchestra).
LP: DS 901
MC: DSC 901

GROOVIN' HIGH (Wilson, Gerald/ Wilbert Baranco/Jimmy Mundy).
LP: HEP 15

JESSICA (Wilson, Gerald and His Orchestra).

Tracks: / Jessica / Love you madly / Blues, bones and Bobby / Getaway / Sophisticated lady / Don't get around much more.
LP: TR 531
MC: TRC 531

LOMELIN (Wilson, Gerald Orchestra Of The Eighties).
LP: DS 833
MC: DSC 833

Wilson, Harold

PRIME MINISTER ON PM'S, A.
MCSET: Unknown

Wilson, Herman

AT THE WOODWINDS BALL (Wilson, Herman Chamber Group).
LP: SPJ 512

Wilson, Hop

STEEL GUITAR FLASH (Wilson, Hop & His Two Buddies).
Tracks: / My woman has a black cat bone / I'm a stranger / I ain't got a woman / Merry christmas darling / Rockin' in the coconuts / Why do you twist / You don't move me anymore / You don't love me anymore / Feel so glad / Be careful with the blues / My woman done quit me / Dance to it / Fuss too much.
LP: CHD 240

Wilson, Jack

CORCOVADO (Wilson, Jack Quartet).
Tracks: / Corcovado / Jackley / Blues we use / Harbour freeway / De critifeux / Nirvana and Dana.
LP: DS 872

GUILTY (see under Daley, Tracey) (Wilson, Jack & Tracey Daley).

INNOVATIONS.
Tracks: / Autumn sunset / Waltz for Ahmad / Invitation / Our waltz.
LP: DS 777

MARGO'S THEME (Wilson, Jack Trio).
LP: DS 805

RONI (See also Pure Silk) (Wilson, Jack & Pure Silk).

Wilson, Jackie

14 ORIGINAL GREATEST HITS:JACKIE WILSON/BILLY WARD (Wilson, Jackie/Billy Ward).
LP: K 5007

20 GREATEST HITS: JACKIE WILSON.
Tracks: / Your love keeps lifting me / Lonely teardrops / Reet petite / That's why I love you so / To be loved / Tear of the year, The / No pity (in the naked city) / Am I the man / I'm comin' on back to me / Whispers / Night / Baby workout / You were made for all / Please tell me why / You better know it / I just can't help it / I get the sweetest feeling / Doggin' around / Woman, a lover, a friend, A.
MC: 2662544
LP: 2662541
LP: BRLP 48
MC: BRMC 48

CLASSIC JACKIE WILSON.
Tracks: / Reet petite / To be loved / Lonely teardrops / That's why (I love you so) / I'll be satisfied / You better know it / Talk that talk / Night / Doggin' around / Passing through / Woman, a lover, a friend, A / Am I the man? / Please tell me why / I'm coming on back to you / You don't know what it means / I just can't help it / Baby workout / Danny boy / I get the sweetest feeling / No pity (in the naked city) / She's alright / Whispers / Your love keeps lifting me higher and higher / You got me walking.
LP: JAK 101
MC: ZCJAK 101

FIFTEEN CLASSIC TRACKS.
Tracks: / Reet petite / Tear of the year / Your one and only love / Alone at last / Greatest hurt / Years from now / Baby work out / Shake, shake, shake / Higher and higher / For your precious love / Think twice / Chain gang / To change my love / Uptight / Doggin' around.
LP: 4504551
MC: 4504554

GREATEST HITS: JACKIE WILSON.
LP: MA 18287
MC: MAMC 918287
LP: 211854
MC: 411854

I DON'T WANT TO LOSE YOU (See under Adam's Apples).

I'M GONNA GET YOU (see under Baker, Laverne) (Wilson, Jackie/Laverne Baker).

JACKIE WILSON.
LP: BID 8007

REET PETITE.
Tracks: / Shake, shake, shake / Why can't you be mine? / I'm wanderin' / Lonely teardrops / Yeah yeah / It's so fine / Come back to me / Shake a hand / Reet petite / If I can't have you / All my love / So much / I know I'll always be in love with you / Danny boy / Doggin' around / Do Lord.
LP: CH 125
MC: CHC 125

SOUL YEARS, THE.
Tracks: / Soul galore / I've lost you / Who who song, The / I don't want to lose you / Just be sincere / I'm the one to do it / I get the sweetest feeling / Nothing but blue skies / I can feel those vibrations (this love is real) / Because of you / Try it again / What 'cha gonna do about love / You left the fire burning / You got me walking / You brought about a change in me / Open the door to your heart.
LP: KENT 027
MC: KENC 027

SOUL YEARS VOL.2, THE.
Tracks: / Whispers / Since you showed me how to be happy / Uptight / You can count on me / Somebody up there likes you / My heart is calling / Hard to get a thing called love / Those heartaches / Don't you know I love you / I've learned about life / It's all over / Do it the right way / You keep me hangin' on / To change my love / Love is funny that way / Nobody but you.
LP: KENT 054

THRU THE YEARS.
Tracks: / Right now / I'm wanderin' / We have love / So much / Way I am, The / You only live twice / Do lord / Silent one / Think twice / Since you showed me how to be happy / I still love you / Didn't I / Love is funny that way / You left the fire burning.
LP: RNLP 70230
MC: RNC 70230

Wilson, Jimmy

TROUBLE IN MY HOUSE.
LP: DD 4305

Wilson, Joe Lee

SECRETS FROM THE SUN.
LP: IC 1042

WITHOUT A SONG.
LP: IC 1064

Wilson, John

DOVE SINGALONG (Wilson, John Singers).
LP: PC 795

Wilson, Julie

SINGS THE KURT WEILL SONGBOOK.
Tracks: / One touch of Venus / That's him / Foolish heart / Ballad of Mack the Knife.
MC: SLC 5207
LP: SL 5207

SINGS THE STEPHEN SONDHEIM SONGBOOK.
Tracks: / Good thing going / Not a day goes by / Send in the clowns.
MC: SLC 5206
LP: SL 5206

Wilson, Junior

WILLOW.
LP: MMLP 0012

Wilson, Justin

CAJUN CHRISTMAS, A.
Tracks: / Santa Claus done brought himself to town / When Christmas angels sing / All I want for Christmas is my two front teeth / Randolph the rouge nosed reindeer.
LP: 5010
MC: 5010 TC

C'EST SI BON.
LP: 11017
MC: 11017 TC

CHRISTMAS STORIES.
Tracks: / Night before Christmas, The / Santa Claus and the mouse / Year without a Santa Claus, The / Little engine that could, The.
LP: 5014
MC: 5014 TC

FOR TRUE.
LP: 5015
MC: 5015 TC

GOIN' FISHIN'.
LP: 11015
MC: 11015 TC

HUNT DEM DUCK AND SHOOT.
LP: 11014
MC: 11014 TC

HUNTING.
LP: 5007
MC: 5007 TC

IN ORBIT.
LP: 5013
MC: 5013 TC

INTOXICATED TALES.
LP: 5009
MC: 5009 TC

KEEP IT CLEAN.
LP: 5011
MC: 5011 TC

LET THE GOOD TIMES ROLL.
LP: 11016
MC: 11016 TC

OLD FAVORITES.
LP: 11013
MC: 11013 TC

OLD MASTER STORY TELLER, THE.
LP: 5008
MC: 5008 TC

PASS A GOOD TIME.
LP: 5006
MC: 5006 TC

SPORT, THE.
LP: 5012
MC: 5012 TC

Wilson, Kevin

KEV'S BACK (RETURN OF THE YOBBO).
Tracks: / Last wager waltz / That's what he really said / Kev's courtin' song / Breathe through my ears / Mick the master farter / Pubic hair song / It was over (Kev's lament) / Dick ta'phone / Hey Santa Claus.
LP: 4503271
MC: 4503274

X RATED.
MC: BANNEDWK 01

Wilson, Kid Wesley

LEOLA B WILSON & KID WESLEY WILSON 1928-33 (See under Wilson, Leola B) (Wilson, Kid Wesley & Leola B Wilson).

Wilson, Leola B

LEOLA B WILSON & KID WESLEY WILSON 1928-33 (Wilson, Leola B & Wilson, Kid Welsey).
LP: DLP 549

Wilson, Mari

I THOUGHT ABOUT YOU.
LP: ST 250
LP: LRF 145

MARI WILSON.
Tracks: / Red hot / I've got what you need / You make me feel so good / Warm summer night, A / Pick up the pieces / You're the light that guides my way / Midnight dancer.
LP: STML 12124

RHYTHM ROMANCE, THE.
LP: DINTV 31
MC: DINMC 31

SHOW PEOPLE.
LP: COMP 2
MC: KCOMP 2

Wilson, Marty

RHYME.
LP: RACS 0114

Wilson, Meri

FIRST TAKE.
LP: NSPL 28242
MC: ZCP 28242

Wilson, Mike 'Hitman'

MIKE 'HITMAN' WILSON.
Tracks: / Ordinary pain (Featuring Reggie Hall) / Are you free tonight? (Featuring Shawn Christopher.) / Feel it (Featuring Mercury T) / You can't tell us (how to play our music) (Featuring Tommy Brown) / I'll do ya right / Feel my groove (Featuring Kim Ross) / Another sleepless night (Featuring Shaw Christopher) / Revelations / Make it funky (Featuring Tommy Brown).
LP: 210976
MC: 410976

Wilson, Nancy

LADY WITH A SONG, A.
Tracks: / Do you still dream about me / Now I know / Time out for love / Don't ask my neighbours / Lady with a song, A / That's what I remember / This love is what I need / Other side of the storm / Melody is you / Heavens hands.
LP: 4664331
MC: 4664334

LIFE, LOVE AND HARMONY.
Tracks: / Life, love and harmony / Here's to us / This is our song / Sunshine / You're the one / Open up your heart / Wrapped up in the comfort of your love / Best of the woman in me / Heaven.
LP: EST 11943

LUSH LIFE.
Tracks: / Free again / Midnight sun / Only the young / When the world was young / Right to love / Lush life / Over the weekend / You've changed / River shallow / Sunny / I stayed too long at the fair.
LP: CAPS 2600061
MC: TCCAPS 2600064

NANCY WILSON'S GREATEST HITS.
Tracks: / How glad I am / Face it girl it's over / Can't take my eyes off you / Uptight / Peace of mind / Now I'm a woman / Tell me the truth / I want to be with you / Don't come running back to me.
MC: 4XL 9449

TWO OF US, THE.
Tracks: / Ram / Midnight rendezvous / Breaker beat / Slippin' away / Two of us / Quiet storm / Never wanna say goodnight / Closer than close / Song without words.
LP: CBS 25976
MC: 40 25976

Wilson, Natasha

INTRODUCING NATASHA WILSON.
LP: NCR 1576

Wilson, Paul

ONE-EYED FIDDLER, THE (Wilson, Paul & Ben Van Weede).
Tracks: / Jacob / Haul away the hauser / Johnny Sands / Reele / Ragged beggarman / Blue eyed stranger / Turnpike gate / Labouring man / Hunt the squirrel / Rakish young fellow / Joan's ale / Breast knot / Butcher and the parson / Favourite / Tippy / Jig / Long a-growing / Dribbles of brandy / Bampton Fair / One eyed fiddler, The / Cliff / Southern English labourer / Miss Richard's hornpipe.
LP: SDL 115

Wilson Phillips

WILSON PHILLIPS.
Tracks: / Hold on / Release me / Impulsive / Next to you (someday I'll be) / You're in love / Over and over / Reason to believe, A / Ooh you're gold / Eyes like twins / Dream is still alive.
LP: SBKLP 5
LP: 793 745 1
MC: SBKTC 5
MC: 793 745 4

Wilson, Precious

KENDRICK COLLECTION, THE (see under All Souls, Langham Place) (Wilson, Precious/All Souls' Orchestra/Choir).

ON THE RACE TRACK (Wilson, Precious & Sky Train).
Tracks: / We are on the race track / Cry to me / Stop running / Stay by my side / You ain't got love / Together forever / Mr. Pilot man / Funky dancer / Killing me softly.
LP: EPC 84895

PRECIOUS WILSON.
Tracks: / I'll be your friend / Love can't wait / She don't really wanna know / Letter, the / Nice girls don't last / State of relations / Jewel of the nile, the / New moon in the summer / Don't take it away.
LP: HIP 37
MC: HIPC 37

RED LIGHT.
Tracks: / Red light / I don't know why / Why don't I run away from you / Kisuraheli / You haven't heard the last of me / Raising my family / Night the music died / All coloured in love / Every day will be like a holiday / Your face stays on my mind / I need you.
LP: EPC 25058

Wilson, Reuben

CISCO KID, THE.
LP: PLEO 1

Wilson, Robert

BEST OF ROBERT WILSON, THE.
MC: CWGR 115

Wilson, Robert Anton

SECRETS OF POWER, THE.
LP: AMA 23
MC: AMA 23C

Wilson, Roger

PALM OF YOUR HAND, THE.
LP: HAR 002
MC: HARC 002

Wilson, Sandy

DIVORCE ME, DARLING.
LP: SH 15009

Wilson, Shanice

DISCOVERY.
Tracks: / I think I love you / No half steppin' / Baby tell me can you dance / Spend some time with me / He's so cute / I bet she's got a boyfriend / Do I know you / Just a game / Way you love me, The.
LP: AMA 5128
MC: AMC 5128

Wilson, Smokey

88TH STREET BLUES.
LP: MB 1003

Wilson, Teddy

2ND TIME AROUND.
LP: 2273222
MC: 2173222

AIR MAIL SPECIAL.
LP: BLP 60115

AMERICAN DANCES BROADCASTS-1939.
LP: JASM 2519
MC: JASMC 2519

AS TIME GOES BY (Wilson, Teddy & Kay Penton).
Tracks: / After you've gone / How high the moon / Isn't it romantic / These foolish things / It's the talk of the town / Rose room.
LP: MVS 2007

BLUES FOR THOMAS WALLER.
Tracks: / Honeysuckle rose / My fate is in your hands / Ain't cha glad / I've got a feeling I'm falling / Stealin' apples / Blues for Thomas Waller / Handful of keys / Striding after Fats / Squeeze me / Zonky / Blue turning grey over you / Ain't misbehavin' / Black and blue.
LP: GNPS 9014
LP: BLP 60131

BODY AND SOUL.
2LP: VJD 535

COLE PORTER CLASSICS.
Tracks: / Get out of town / Just one of those things / I get a kick out of you / It's alright with me / Why shouldn't I? / Love for sale.
LP: BLM 51505

DEAR TEDDY (With Red Norvo & Charlie Shavers) (Wilson, Teddy Sextet).
Tracks: / China boy / (I'm) confessin' / Rose room / After you've gone / How high the moon / I surrender dear / Whispering / Stompin' at the Savoy / I know that you know / Sheik of Araby, The / Body and soul / Dinah / Flying home / Sweet Georgia Brown / It's the talk of the town / Undecided / Speculation / Central Avenue blues.
LP: ESQ 335

D.S.C.B. MEETS TEDDY WILSON (Wilson, Teddy/Dutch Swing College Band).
LP: TTD 525

ELEGANT PIANO (Wilson, Teddy/ Marion McPartland).
LP: S 1330

GENE KRUPA, LIONEL HAMPTON & TEDDY WILSON (see Krupa, Gene) (Wilson, Teddy/Gene Krupa/Lionel Hampton).

GENTLEMEN OF KEYBOARD.
Tracks: / Somebody loves me / Sailin' / I've found a new baby / Just a mood / I got rhythm / Wham / Liza / 71 / China boy / Indiana / I want to be happy / Rose room / Just like a butterfly / Fine and dandy / Under a blanket of blue / Airmail special.
LP: LPJT 91

HOW HIGH THE MOON.
LP: KLJ 20011

I GOT RHYTHM.
2LP: VJD 544

I LOVE A PIANO (Wilson, Teddy Trio/ Mary Lou Williams Quartet).
LP: ESQ 304

IMPECCABLE MR WILSON, THE.
LP: 2304 513

IN TOKYO.
LP: 2005

JUMPIN' FOR JOY (Wilson, Teddy/his orchestra/Billie Holiday).
Tracks: / Somebody loves me / Blues in C sharp minor / Why do I lie to myself about you? / Way you look tonight / Sailin' / Why was I born? / I've found a new baby / You can't stop me from dreaming / Just a mood / Don't blame me / More than you know / Jumpin' for joy / Jumpin' on the blacks and whites / Wham (re-bop-boom-bam) / 711 / China boy / Fine and dandy.
LP: AFS 1044

LIVE AT SANTA TECLA.
LP: CLE 21032

MASTERS OF JAZZ VOL.11 (Wilson, Teddy Sextet).
LP: SLP 4111

MOONGLOW.
Tracks: / Moonglow / Flying home / As time goes by / Ain't misbehavin' / I'm through with love / Airmail special.
LP: BLP 30133

MR WILSON & MR GERSHWIN.
LP: 21125
MC: 40-21125

NOBLE ART OF..., THE.
Tracks: / My silent love / You brought a new kind of love to me / Paradise / My heart stood still / Serenata / Indiana / April in Paris / 'Deed I do / Autumn in New York / Ain't misbehavin' / Serenade in blue / It's alright with me.
LP: SLP 4086

OF THEE I SWING (Wilson, Teddy Trio).
Tracks: / You turned the tables on me / Sing, baby, sing / Easy to love / With thee I swing / Way you look tonight, The / Who loves you? / Pennies from Heaven / That's life / Sailin' / I can't give you anything but love / I'm with you (right or wrong) / Where the lazy river goes by / Tea for two / I'll see you in my dreams / He ain't got rhythm / This year's kisses.
LP: HEP 1020

PRESS AND TEDDY (Wilson, Teddy/ Lester Young).
Tracks: / All of me / Prisoner of love / Louise / Pres returns / Love me or leave me / Taking a chance on love / Love is here to stay.
LP: 2304 213

PREZ AND TEDDY (See under Young, Lester) (Young, Lester & Teddy Wilson).

RAREST..., THE.
LP: E 1003

REVISITS THE GOODMAN YEARS (1980 - Copenhagen) (Wilson, Teddy Trio).
LP: SLP 4046

RUNNIN' WILD.
Tracks: / One o'clock jump / Mood indigo / Take the 'A' train / Satin doll / Smoke gets in your eyes / Runnin' wild / St. James' Infirmary blues / After you've gone.
LP: BLP 30149

SCHOOL FOR PIANIST.
LP: MERITT 23

STOMPING AT THE SAVOY.
Tracks: / I can't get started / Sometimes I'm happy / Body and soul / I'll never be the same / Easy living.
LP: BLP 30114

STRIDING AFTER FATS.
Tracks: / Striding after Fats / Blue turning grey over you / I've got a feeling I'm falling / Handful of keys.
LP: 65108
LP: BLP 30156
MC: BLP 30156C

SUNDAY MORNING.
Tracks: / I've got the world on a string / Fine and dandy / Why shouldn't I? / All of me / Long ago and far away / Cheek to cheek / Ain't misbehavin' / You're my favourite memory / I'm yours / Living in dreams / You took advantage of me.
LP: MVS 2008

SWEDISH JAZZ MY WAY.
Tracks: / Swing in F / Jam session cupol / Too late / Nobody is like you / Fantasy in B / Melody in B / Almost bald / My love is yours / Inspired by you / You can't be in love with a dream / Nice to have them around.
LP: SNTF 618

TEDDY WILSON (2).
MC: MC 9003

TEDDY WILSON 1936/37.
Tracks: / Breaking in a pair of shoes / Remember me / Hour of parting / All my life / Mary had a little lamb / Coquette / Ain't misbehavin' / Blues in C sharp minor / Just a mood / Honeysuckle rose / Between the devil and the deep blue sea / I'm comin', Virginia.
MC: NEO 848

TEDDY WILSON AND BILLIE HOLIDAY 1936/37 (Wilson, Teddy & Billie Holiday).
Tracks: / You turned the tables on me / Sing baby sing / Easy to love / With thee I swing / Way you look tonight, The / Who loves you / Pennies from Heaven / That's life / Sailin' / I can't give you anything but love / I'm with you / Where the lazy river goes by / Tea for two / I'll see you in my dreams / He ain't got rhythm / This years kisses.
LP: HEP 1020

TEDDY WILSON, BENNY GOODMAN, HARRY JAMES (Wilson, Teddy/Benny Goodman/Harry James).
LP: MERITT 3

TEDDY WILSON & BIG BAND 1939-40 (Wilson, Teddy & Big Band).
LP: TAX 8018

TEDDY WILSON & BILLIE HOLIDAY VOL. 2 (Wilson, Teddy & Billie Holiday).
LP: HEP 1014

TEDDY WILSON COLLECTION (20 Golden Greats).
Tracks: / Sweet Lorraine / Sugar plum / What a little moonlight can do / Sunbonnet blue / Yankee Doodle never went to town / Miss Brown to you / I wished on the moon / What a night, what a moon / Eeny meeny miney mo / After you've gone / Who? / China boy / Lady be good / Nobody's sweetheart / Dinah / Moonglow / Stompin' at the Savoy / Sweet Sue / Whispering.
LP: DVLP 2111
MC: DVMC 2111

TEDDY WILSON & HIS ALL STARS, VOL 1.
LP: MVS 502

TEDDY WILSON, VOL 1.
Tracks: / I got rhythm / When your lover has gone / Sweet Georgia Brown / Too late / Limehouse blues / On the sunny side of the street / Smiles / My love is yours / As time goes by.
LP: JR 108

TEDDY WILSON, VOL 2.
Tracks: / Rose room / Just one of those things / Shiny stockings / Body and soul / Sweet Lorraine / Moonglow / But not for me / Nice work if you can get it / It had to be you / Someone to watch over me.
LP: JR 127
LP: JA 36

TEDDY WILSON WITH BILLIE HOLIDAY (Wilson, Teddy & Billie Holiday).
Tracks: / Nice work if you can get it / Where the lazy river goes by / If you were mine / My last love affair / Why do I lie to myself about you? / Mood that I'm in, The / I'm coming, Virginia / Easy living / How am I to know? / Hour of parting / Coquette / You let me down / I've found a new baby / All my life / Mary had a little lamb / Miss Brown to you / What a little moonlight can do / I wished on the moon.
LP: AJA 5053
MC: ZC AJA 5053

TEDDY'S CHOICE.
LP: JCE 86

TIME AFTER TIME (see Vaughan, Sarah) (Wilson, Teddy/Sarah Vaughan).

TOO HOT FOR WORDS (Wilson, Teddy/ his orchestra/Billie Holiday).
Tracks: / I wished on the moon / What a little moonlight can do / Miss Brown to you / Sunbonnet blue, A / It never dawned on me / Spreadin' rhythm round the world / You let me down / Sugar plum / Rosetta / Liza / Sweet Lorraine.
LP: HEP 1012

TOWN HALL CONCERT 1945 (See Coleman, Bob) (Wilson, Teddy/Bob Coleman).

TWO GOOD MEN (Wilson, Teddy/Jess Stacy).
LP: ESQ 314

Wilson, Tony

CATCH ONE.
Tracks: / Give your lady what she wants / Lay next to you / Fool around / Just when I needed you most / Africa / Try love / New Orleans music / Love, I thought I would never find love / I really love you / Forever young.
LP: K 55526

Wilson, Tug

COUNTRY MUSIC LOVIN' KINDA GUY.
LP: WGR 024
MC: CWGR 024

NASHVILLE HALL OF FAME.
MC: KBGC 221

Wilson-James, Victoria

PERSEVERANCE.
Tracks: / Through / Bright lights / One world / 2nd nature / Angel calling / Through (classic club mix) / Women of colours / Perseverance works / Rest of your life / Future world / Works (instrumental).
LP: 4674731
MC: 4674734

Wilsons

WILSONS, THE.
Tracks: / That's not the kind of love I need / Every road leads back to you / Face in the crowd / Not a day goes by / Falling in love again / You did / Playing with a tender heart / Reason to live / Show must go on, The / Star in momma's eyes, A / I'm on my way / Like strangers.
LP: PRST 505
MC: ZPRST 505

Wilton, Len

TRIBUTE TO BING CROSBY (Wilton, Len & The New Rhythm Boys).
Tracks: / Sweet Sue / Gonna love you till the cows come home / I surrender dear / Brother can you spare a dime / Please / Someone stole Gabriel's horn / Moonburn / St. Louis blues / Lazybones / Just a gigalo / She reminds me of you / Sweet Georgia Brown.
LP: SRTX 79

Wiltshire Moonrakers

DIALECT STORIES, SONGS, DANCES & CUSTOMS.
MC: 45-406

Wimpole Village

FIRE ON THE FARM.
MC: 39570

Win

FREAKY TRIGGER.
Tracks: / What'll you do till Sunday baby / Taboo / What's love if you can kill for chocolate / Love units / Mind the gravy / Rainbow / Dusty heartfelt / Truckee river / We could cover up the 'C' / Love units (12" mix) (CD only) / What's love if you can kill for chocolate (12" mix) (CD only) / How do you do.
LP: V 2571
MC: TCV 2571

TENDER TRIGGER.
LP: UNKNOWN

UH, TEARS BABY.
Tracks: / Super popoid groove / Shampoo tears / Binding love spell / Unamerican broadcasting / Hollywood baby too / Empty holsters / You've got the power / Charms of powerful trouble / It may be a beautiful sky tonight / Charms / Baby cutting / Shampoo tears (remix) (Only available on cassette and compact disc.) / You've got the power (remix) (Only available on cassette and compact disc.).
LP: LONLP 31
MC: LONC 31

Winans, Bebe & Cece

BEBE & CECE WINANS.
Tracks: / I O U Me / No hiding place / Call me / In return / I don't know why / For always / Change your nature / He's coming soon.
LP: BIRD R 193
MC: BIRD C 193

DECISIONS.
Tracks: / Ain't no need to worry / Millions / Breaking of day / What can I say / Right, left in a wrong world / Don't let the sun go down on me / Love has no colour / Give me you / How can you live without Christ?.
LP: K 925510 1
MC: K 925510 4

HEAVEN.
Tracks: / Heaven / Celebrate new life / Lost without you / You / Wanna be more / Hold up the light (With Whitney Houston.) / Meantime / Don't cry / Trust him / Bridge over troubled water.
LP: EST 2081
MC: TCEST 2081

Winans, Daniel

DANIEL WINANS AND THE SECOND HALF (Winans, Daniel And The Second Half).
LP: REJ R 5020
MC: REJ C 5020

Winans (group)

LET MY PEOPLE GO.
Tracks: / Choose ye / Redeemed / Perfect love / Straighten my life out / Let my people go / I'll follow where you lead / Special lady / Very real way.
LP: 925344 1

RETURN.
LP: 7599261611
MC: 7599261614

TOMORROW.
LP: LS 7073
MC: LC 7073

WINANS.
LP: LS 7063
MC: LC 7063

WINANS, THE (live at Carnegie Hall).
Tracks: / Ain't no need to worry / Tomorrow / What a friend we have in Jesus.
2LP: SL R 7501
MCSET: SL C 7501

Winbush, Angela

REAL THING, THE.
LP: 838 866 1
MC: 838 866 4

SHARP.
LP: 8327331

Winchester Cathedral

CAROLS FOR CHRISTMAS.
Tracks: / O come all ye faithful / Unto us a boy is born / Rocking / God rest ye merry gentlemen / Away in a manger / First Noel, The / Once in Royal David's city / Silent night / In dulci jubilo / While shepherds watched their flocks / Coventry carol / O little town of Bethlehem / In the bleak mid winter / Hark the herald angels sing.
MC: 411279

CAROLS FROM WINCHESTER CATHEDRAL.
Tracks: / Holly and the ivy, The / First Noel, The / In dulci jubilo / O come, all ye faithful / I saw three ships / Spotless rose, A / Jesus Christ the apple tree / God rest ye merry gentlemen / Noel etranger / Once in Royal David's city / Three kings, The / Il est ne, le divin enfant / Zither carol / O little town of Bethlehem / Noel.
LP: ACM 2036
MC: ZC ACM 2036
MC: ZC QS 6011

CHORAL SHOWCASE, A (Winchester Cathedral Choir/James Lancelot).
Tracks: / Coelos ascendit hodie / I waited for the Lord (Mendelssohn) / Faire is the Heaven (Harris) / Antiphon (Britten) / I love the Lord (Harvey) / Wilderness, The (Wesley) / Lord is my shepherd, The (Berkeley) / Nunc dimittis (Howells) / Organ solos (Howells) / Toccata (Dubois) / Cantabile (Franck).
MC: ZC QS 6025

CHRISTMAS CAROLS (See under Christmas Carols).

EVENSONG FOR ASH WEDNESDAY.
LP: ALH 915
MC: ZC ALH 915

GOLDEN AGE OF ENGLISH CATHEDRAL MUSIC, THE.
Tracks: / Laudibus in sanctus / Salvator Mundi / See, see the Word is incarnate / Hosanna to the Son of David / This is the record of John / O Lord, arise / Out of the deep / Fantasie in three parts / Dum transisset Sabbatum.
LP: ALH 943
MC: ZC ALH 943

HEAR MY PRAYER.
2LP: COMP 3
MCSET: ZCCOM 3

MESSIAH HIGHLIGHTS (see under Handel) (Winchester Cathedral Choir/ London Handel Orchestra).

Winchester College

LEAD ME, LORD (see under Quiristers).

Winchester, Jesse

BEST OF JESSE WINCHESTER.
Tracks: / Payday / Biloxi / Snow / Brand new Tennessee waltz, The / Yankee lady / Midnight bus / Do it / All your own stories / Mississippi, you're on my mind / Third rate romance / End is not in sight, The / Defying gravity / Let the rough side drag / Blow on, chilly wind / Nothing but a breeze / Seems like only yesterday / Touch on the rainy side, A / I'm looking for a miracle / Say what / Talk Memphis.
LP: SEE 231

HUMOUR ME.
LP: SH 1023

Winchester, Kay

STADDLECOMBE (Thomson, Hilary).
MCSET: CLT 1010

Wind In The Willows

WIND IN THE WILLOWS (River bank/ wild wood).
MC: ST 407

WIND IN THE WILLOWS.
MC: STK 028

WIND IN THE WILLOWS.. (Braddeley, John (nar)).
MC: TTS 9833

WIND IN THE WILLOWS (Open road/ Adventures of Mr Toad).
MC: ST 408

WIND IN THE WILLOWS (Further adventures of Mr Toad).
MC: ST 409

WIND IN THE WILLOWS (see under Grahame, Kenneth) (Various artists).

WIND IN THE WILLOWS: THE OPEN ROAD (Braddeley, John (nar)).
MC: TTS 9834

WIND IN THE WILLOWS VOL I (TV soundtrack) (Various artists).
Tracks: / Wind in the willows, The: *Various artists* / On the river: *Various artists* / Ducks ditty: *Various* artists / Open road: *Various artists* / Mr Toad the motorist: *Various artists* / Wild wood: *Various artists*/ Mr Badger: *Various artists* / Dolce Domum: *Various artists* / Further adventures of Mr Toad, The: *Various* artists / Hero's song, A: *Various artists* / Battle: *Various artists* / When Toad came home: *Various artists*.
LP: RD BLP 1150
MC: ZCRDB 1150

WIND IN THE WILLOWS VOL II (TV soundtrack) (Various artists).
2LP: RDBLP 1151
MCSET: ZCRDB 1151

Wind In The Willows

WIND IN THE WILLOWS.
Tracks: / Moments spent / Uptown girl / So sad to watch good love go bad / My uncle used to love me but she died / There is but one truth / Daddy / Friendly lion / Park Avenue blues / Djini Judy / Little people / She's fantastic and she's yours / Wheel of changes.
LP: CAPS 1030

Windbreakers

DIFFERENT SORT, A.
Tracks: / Knowing me / Fit in / You closed your eyes / Better left unsaid / So far away / Different sort, A / So much / We never understand / Forget again / Any longer.
LP: ZONG 022

RUN.
Tracks: / I don't wanna know / This time - she said / Visa cards and antique mirrors / run / You don't know / Ghost town / I'll be back / Voices in my head / Braver on the telephone / Don't say no / Nation of two.
LP: ZONG 015

TERMINAL.
LP: HMS 005

Winding, Kai

GIANT BONES 80.
Tracks: / Love 4 rent / Sweetness / I fall in love too easy / Scrapple from the apple / Corriente / Nu groove / Never never land / Hola.
LP: SNTF 834
MC: ZCSN 834

GREAT KAI AND J.J. (see Johnson, J.J.) (Winding, Kai & J.J. Johnson).

JANUARY 31ST AND FEBRUARY 15TH,1963 (Winding, Kai,Trombones).
Tracks: / Don't panic / Waltz on the wild side / Paul finks out / Thirteenth instant / Samba dis / Rotten blues / Raven / Blues for Indian Jim / Rum and bossa nova / Button up your lip / I knew Dana / That's where it is.
LP: JV 107

KAI AND JAY (Winding, Kai & Jay Jay Johnson).
Tracks: / Out of this world / Thous sweet / Lover / Lope city / Stolen bass / It's alright with me / Mad about the boy / Yes sir, that's my baby / That's how I feel about you / Gong rock.
LP: AFF 161
MC: TCAFF 161

TROMBONE BY THREE (See Johnson, J.J) (Winding, Kai/Bennie Green/ J.J.Johnson).

Windjammer

WINDJAMMER II.
Tracks: / Live without your love / Tossing and turning / Anxiously waiting / Am I right / Call me up / You're out the box / Sneak attack / Stay, part II / I'll always love you / Dive inside my love.
LP: MCF 3231
MC: MCFC 3231

WINDJAMMER III.
LP: MCF 3290
MC: MCFC 3290

Windows

FRENCH LAUNDRY, THE.
LP: YL 0124

UPPERS ON DOWNERS.
Tracks: / Immortal / Toolbox guitars / Electric cowboys / Creation dub / Prime-evil scream / Tenement girl / When the music's over.
LP: SKULP 2

Windross, Rose

FAIR PLAY (see under Soul II Soul).

Winds Of Change

ILLUSIONS.
Tracks: / Fantasia / Illusions / Scherzo / Midsummer night's dream / Sneakin' up behind you / Girl with the flaxen hair, The / Birdland / Bouquet of barbed wire / Noble savage / Uncle Remus / Canon in D.
LP: EMA 791

Windsor Parish Church

CAROLS FROM WINDSOR PARISH CHURCH.
Tracks: / Joy to the world / Hark the herald angels sing / First Noel, The / See, amid the winter's snow / Silent night / Good King Wenceslas / It came upon a midnight clear / O come all ye faithful / While shepherds watched their flocks by night / As with gladness men of old / Holly and the ivy, The / Christians awake / Once in Royal David's city / Air on a G string.
LP: JOYS 182

Windwalker

WINDWALKER (Film Soundtrack) (Various artists).
LP: C'BUS 0202

Windy City

WINDY CITY (Various artists).
LP: EMC 3420

Wine And Candlelight

WINE AND CANDLELIGHT (Various artists).
MC: AM 33

Winesburg, Ohio (play)

WINESBURG, OHIO: THE CONSCIENCE OF WINESBURG (Anderson, Sherwood) (Various artists).
MC: SBRC 504

Wingates Temperance

FIREWORKS AND SPARKLERS.
LP: GRS 1045

SOUNDS OF BRASS SERIES VOL. 38.
Tracks: / Peace and war / St. Louis blues march / Little brown jug / In the mood / Moonlight serenade / Pennsylvania 6-5000 / Chattanooga choo choo / Shadow of your smile / Symphony No. 4 / Finale / Soldier's chorus / Trumpeter's holiday / Elegy / Jesus Christ Superstar.
LP: SB 338

Winger

IN THE HEART OF THE YOUNG.
Tracks: / Can't get enuff / Miles away / Rainbow in the rose / Under one condition / Baptized by fire / In the heart of the young / Loosen up / Easy come easy go / In the day we'll never see / Little dirty blonde / You are the Saint, I am the sinner.
LP: 7567821031
MC: 7567821034

WINGER.
Tracks: / Madalaine / Hungry / Seventeen / Without the night / Purple haze / State of emergency / Time to surrender / Poison angel / Hangin' on / Headed for a heartbreak.
LP: K 781 867 1
MC: K 781 867 4

Wings

BACK TO THE EGG (SUNNY SIDE UP).
Tracks: / Reception / Getting closer / We're open tonight / Spin it on / Again and again and again / Old Siam sir / Arrow through me / Rockestra theme / To you / After the ball / Million miles / Winter rose / Love awake / Broadcast, The / So glad to see you here / Baby's request / Daytime nightime suffering (CD only.) / Wonderful Christmas time (CD only.) / Rudolph the red nosed reggae (CD only.).
LP: PCTC 257
MC: TCPCTC 257

BAND ON THE RUN.
Tracks: / Band on the run / Jet / Bluebird / Mrs. Vanderbilt / Let me roll it / Marmunia / No words / Picasso's last words / 1985.
LP: ATAK 19
MC: TCATAK 19
LP: PAS 10007
MC: TCPAS 10007

GREATEST HITS: WINGS.
Tracks: / Another day / Silly love songs / Live and let die / Junior's farm / With a little luck / Band on the run / Uncle Albert / Admiral Halsey / Hi hi hi / Let'em in / My love / Mull of Kintyre.
LP: ATAK 15
MC: TCATAK 15
LP: PCTC 256
MC: TCPCTC 256

LONDON TOWN.
Tracks: / London town / Gate on the left bank / I'm carrying / Backwards traveller / Cuff link / Chicken children / I've had enough / With a little luck / Famous groupies / Deliver your children / Name and address / Don't let it bring you down / Morse moose and the grey goose / Girlfriend / Girls school.
LP: ATAK 18
MC: TCATAK 18
LP: PAS 10012
MC: TCPAS 10012
LP: FA 3223
MC: TCFA 3223

RED ROSE SPEEDWAY (See under McCartney, Paul) (McCartney, Paul & Wings).

VENUS AND MARS.
Tracks: / Venus and Mars / Rock show / Love in song / You gave me the answer / Magneto and Titanium man / Letting go / Venus and Mars reprise / Spirits of ancient egypt / Medicine jar / Call me back again / Listen to what the man said / Treat her gently - lonely old people / Crossroads.
LP: ATAK 14
MC: TCATAK 14
LP: FA 3213
MC: TCFA 3213
LP: PCTC 254

WILD LIFE.
Tracks: / Mumbo / Bip bop / Love is strange / Wild life / Some people never know / I am your singer / Bip bop link (CD only.) / Tomorrow / Dear friend / Mumbo link (CD only.) / Oh woman, oh why? (CD only.) / Mary had a little lamb (CD only.) / Little woman love (CD only.).
LP: FA 413101 1
MC: FA 413101 4
LP: FA 3101
MC: TCFA 3101

WINGS AT THE SPEED OF SOUND.
Tracks: / Let 'em in / Note you never wrote, The / She's my baby / Beware my love / Wino junko / Silly love songs / Cook of the house / Time to hide / Must do something about it / San Ferry Anne / Warm and beautiful.
LP: ATAK 13
MC: TCATAK 13
LP: PAS 10010
MC: TCPAS 10010
LP: FA 3229
MC: TCFA 3229

WINGS OVER AMERICA.
Tracks: / Venus and Mars / Rock show / Jet / Let me roll it / Spirits of ancient Egypt / Medicine jar / Maybe I'm amazed / Call me back again / Lady Madonna / Long and winding road, The / Live and let die / Picasso's last words / Richard Cory / Bluebird / I've just seen a face / Blackbird / Yesterday / You gave me the answer / Magneto and titanium man / Go now / My love / Listen to what the man said / Let 'em in / Silly love songs.
LPS: ATAK 17
MCSET: TCATAK 17
2LP: PCSP 720
MCSET: TCPCSP 720

Wings, Johnny

NEW ORLEANS JAZZ.
LP: GHB 102

Wings Of Desire

WINGS OF DESIRE (Film soundtrack) (Various artists).
LP: A 316
MC: C 316

WINGS OF DESIRE (Film soundtrack) (Various artists).
LP: IONIC 2

Wings Of History

WINGS OF HISTORY VOL.1 Sounds at Shuttleworth 1909-42 (Various artists).
LP: AFP 01
MC: AFP 01T

WINGS OF HISTORY VOL.2 Return to Shuttleworth (Various artists).
LP: AFP 02
MC: AFP 02T

WINGS OF HISTORY VOL.3 Rendezvous - Shuttleworth (Various artists).
LP: AFP 03
MC: AFP 03T

WINGS OF HISTORY VOL.4 Power in the sky (Various artists).
MC: AFP 04T

Winkler, Harry

PLASTIC ZOO.
LP: ISST 163

Winland, Leo

SONATAS FOR CELLO AND PIANO (Winland, Leo/Janos Solyom).
LP: PHONT 7110
LP: ARTE 7110

Winner, Jim

THAT OLD SONG AND DANCE (see under Lipari, Bo) (Winner, Jim & Bo Lipari).

Winners

WINNERS.
LP: GOJ 1018

Winnick, Maurice

SO MANY MEMORIES.
Tracks: / Sweetest music this side of heaven / Leave it to love / Every single little tingle of my heart / There won't be any Spring / Bei mir bist du schon / I wished on the moor / There's a goldmine in the sky / Roses in December / Linger longer island / Star fell out of heaven, A / So many memories / Sunset trail, The / First time I saw you, The / You started me dreaming / Did I remember / Alone / Kiss me goodnight / It's time to say goodnight.
LP: BUR 020
MC: 4 BUR 020

SWEETEST MUSIC THIS SIDE OF HEAVEN, THE (Winnick, Maurice and his Orchestra).
LP: . . . . WRCSH 225

Winnie

WINNIE (Original cast recording) (Various artists).
Tracks: / Army, the Navy and the Air-Force, The: *London stage cast* / Who's taking you home tonight?: *London stage* cast / Run rabbit run: *London stage cast* / Bless 'em all: *London stage cast* / All over the place: *London* stage cast / What more can I say?: *London stage cast* / That lovely weekend: *London stage cast* / There's something about a soldier: *London stage cast* / London pride: *London stage cast* / There'll always be an England: *London stage cast* / Kiss me goodnight, Sergeant Major: *London stage cast* / Colonel's complaint, The: *London* stage cast / I would say to the House...(speech): *London stage cast* / Winnie: *London stage cast* / Did you call, darling?: *London stage cast* / Wish me luck as you wave me goodbye: *London stage cast* / We'll meet again: *London stage cast* / Yours: *London stage cast* / Nightingale sang in Berkeley Square, A: *London stage cast*/ Don't cry, darling: *London stage cast* / You'll never know: *London stage cast* / I'm going to get lit up when the lights gop up in London: *London stage cast* / Harrow song, The: *London stage cast* / Song speaks of giants... (speech): *London stage cast* / VE Day: *London stage cast* / My dear friends... (speech): *London stage cast*/ Winnie (reprise): *London stage cast* / In distant tomorrows: *London stage cast*.
LP: . . . . SCX 6713
MC: . . . . TCSCX 6713

Winnie The Pooh

HOUSE AT POOH CORNER PART 1. (see Milne, A.A.).

HOUSE AT POOH CORNER PART 2. (see Milne, A.A.).

THREE CHEERS FOR POOH (See under Milne, A.A.) (Tear, Robert & Phillip Ledger).

WINNIE THE POOH (See under Milne, A.A.) (Bennett, Alan (nar)).

WINNIE THE POOH (see under Milne, A.A.) (Shelley, Norman).

WINNIE THE POOH AND KANGA AND ROO (See under Milne, A.A.) (Channing, Carol).

WINNIE THE POOH AND THE BLUSTERY DAY.
MC: . . . . DIS 007

WINNIE THE POOH AND THE HOUSE AT POOH CORNER (See under Milne, A.A.) (Bennett, Alan (nar)).

WINNIE THE POOH PART 1 (see Milne, A.A.).

WINNIE THE POOH PART 2. (see Milne, A.A.).

WINNIE THE POOH & THE HONEY TREE (See under Milne, A.A.) (Various artists).

WINNIE THE POOH & TIGGER TOO (See under Milne, A.A.) (Various artists).

Winski, Colin

ROCK THERAPY.
Tracks: / Rock therapy / Bop a Lena / Love me / Jitterbop baby / Burnin' desire / Rockaround / Rock 'n' roll baby / Tennessee rock 'n' roll / Red Cadillac / That's right / City dump rock / Whispering pines.
LP: . . . . CHR 1318

Winston

WAITING ROOM.
LP: . . . . C - 1012
LP: C-1025

Winston, George

AUTUMN.
Tracks: / Colors/dance / Woods / Longing/love / Road / Moon / Sea / Stars.
LP: 371012-1
MC: 371012-4
LP: . . . . WHA 1012
LP: . . . . WH 1012
MC: . . . . WT 1012

DECEMBER.
Tracks: / Thanksgiving / Jesus, Jesus, rest your head / Joy / Prelude / Carol of the bells / Night: / Midnight (part 2) / Minstrels (part 3) / Variations on the kannon, by Johann Pachelbel / Holly and the ivy, The / Some children see Him / Peace / Snow (part 1).
LP: 371025-1
MC: 371025-4
LP: . . . . WHA 1025
LP: . . . . WH 1025
MC: . . . . WT 1025

HELLO CENTRAL- GIVE ME DR. JAZZ (see Brozman,Bob with George Winston) (Winston, George/Bob Brozman).

WINTER INTO SPRING.
Tracks: / January stars / February sea / Ocean waves (o mar) / Reflection / Rain/ dance / Blossom meadow / Venice dreamer, The / Introduction (part 1) / Part 2.
LP: 371019-1
MC: 371019-4
LP: . . . . WHA 1019
LP: . . . . WH 1019
MC: . . . . WT 1019

Winston, Jarrett

EARTH MUST BE HELL (See Andy, Horace) (Wailers, The).

Winston & The ...

BREWING SINCE 1983 (Winston & The Churchills).
LP: . . . . OIR 016

WINSTON & THE CHURCHILLS (Winston & The Churchills).
Tracks: / Why do you / I feel so glad / I don't hear her / Come off it / Watching on the line / Girlfriend's friend / Studio wrestling / Maggie / Giant mushroom.
LP: . . . . COLDLP 5

Winstone, Eric

AFTER MIDNIGHT.
MC: . . . . AM 7

Winstone, N

AZIMUTH (see under Taylor, John) (Winstone, N/John Taylor/K. Wheeler).

Winstone, Norma

SOMEWHERE CALLED HOME.
Tracks: / Cafe / Somewhere called home / Sea lady / Some time ago / Prologue / Celeste / Hi lili hi lo / Out of this world / Tea for two.
LP: . . . . ECM 1337

Winter, Cathy

BREATH ON MY FIRE.
LP: . . . . FF 342

TRAVELLING HOME.
LP: . . . . FF 449

Winter, Edgar

ALBUM.
Tracks: / It's your life to live / Above and beyond / Take it the way it is / Dying to live / Please don't stop / Make it last / Do what / It took your love to bring me out / Forever in love.
LP: . . . . SKY 83648

BEST OF EDGAR WINTER, THE.
LP: 4675071
MC: 4675074

THEY COME OUT AT NIGHT.
Tracks: / Hangin' around / When it comes / Alta mira / Free ride / Frankenstein / Round and round / Rock 'n' roll boogie woogie / Autumn / We all had a real good time / Undercover man.
LP: . . . . EPC 32518

Winter, Johnny

1ST LP.
Tracks: / I'm yours and I'm hers / Be careful with a fool / Dallas / Mean mistreater / Leland Mississippi / When you got a good friend / I'll drown my tears / Back door friend.
LP: . . . . ED 163
MC: . . . . CED 163

AND.
LP: . . . . BGOLP 105

BACK IN BEAUMONT (Winter, Johnny & Uncle John Turner).
Tracks: / Made in the shade / They call my lazy / Family rules / Ooh pooh pah do / Drivin' wheel / Allons dancez / Struggle in Houston / You're humbuggin' me / Just a little bit / Rainin' breakdown.
LP: . . . . THBL 077

BROTHERS IN ROCK 'N' ROLL (Winter, Johnny & Edgar).
Tracks: / Frankenstein / Johnny B Goode / Let it bleed / Tobacco Road / I can't turn you loose / Jumpin' Jack Flash / Back in the USA / Good morning little schoolgirl / Like a rolling stone / Bony Moronie / Highway 61 revisited / It's all over now.
MC: . . . . ELITE 012MC

COLLECTION: JOHNNY WINTER.
Tracks: / Rock and roll hoochie coo / Cheap tequila / On the limb / Slippin' and slidin' / Johnny B. Goode / Rock me baby / Let it bleed / Stray cat blues / Riot in cell block 9 / Bony Moronie / Highway 61 revisited / Raised on rock / Pick up on my mojo / Thirty days / Good morning little schoolgirl / Jumpin' Jack Flash / It's my own fault / Rock and roll medley.
2LP: . . . . CCSLP 167
MC: . . . . CCSMC 167

EARLY WINTER.
Tracks: / Ease my pain / That's what love does / Crying in my heart / Guy you left behind / Shed so many tears / Creepy / Gangster of love / Road runner / Leave my woman alone / I can't believe you want to leave / Broke and lonely / Oh my darling / By the light of the silvery moon / Five after four A.M..
LP: . . . . PRCV 116

FIVE AFTER FOUR AM.
Tracks: / Oh my darling / Five after four am / That's what love does / Shed so many tears / Road runner / Guy you left behind / gangster of love / By the light of the silvery moon / Leave my woman alone / I can't believe you want to leave.
LP: . . . . THBL 073

GUITAR SLINGER.
Tracks: / It's my life baby / Iodine in my coffee / Trick bag / Mad dog / Boot Hill / I smell trouble / Lights out / Kiss tomorrow goodbye / My soul / Don't take advantage of me.
LP: . . . . SNTF 914

JOHNNY WINTER AND ....
LP: . . . . CBS 64117

JOHNNY WINTER AND LIVE.
LP: . . . . BGOLP 29
LP: . . . . CBS 64289

JOHNNY WINTER LIVE.
LP: 4663321
MC: 4663324

LET ME IN.
MC: . . . . VPBTC 5
LP: . . . . VPBLP 5

LIVE IN HOUSTON.
MC: . . . . THBC 100

LIVIN' IN THE BLUES.
Tracks: / Low down gal of mine / Going down slow / Avocado green / Parchman farm / Livin' in the blues / Leaving blues / 48-32-20 / Bad news / Kind hearted woman / Mojo boogie (Lenoir) / Love, life and money (Dixon/Glover) / Evil on my mind (Winter) / See see baby (King/ Thompson) / Tin pan alley (Jones) / I'm good (Collins/Lee) / Third degree (Boyd/ Dixon) / Shake your moneymaker (James) / Bad girl blues / Broke and lonely (Watson).
LP: . . . . SHLP 132
MC: . . . . SHTC 132

NOTHING BUT THE BLUES.
LP: . . . . BGOLP 104

OUT OF SIGHT.
Tracks: / Road runner / Leave my woman alone / I can't believe you want to leave / Five after four AM / Out of sight / Leaving blues / Kind hearted woman / Livin' in the blues / Bad news / Oh my darling / Guy you left behind / Gangster of love / That's what love does / Parchman farm / Low down gal of mine / Going down slow.
LP: . . . . TOP 168
MC: . . . . KTOP 168

PROGRESSIVE BLUES EXPERIMENT.
LP: . . . . MACH 7
LP: . . . . LBR 1001

RAISED ON ROCK.
Tracks: / Good morning little schoolgirl / Mean mistreater / Memory pain / Rock and roll / Hoochie coo / Jumpin' Jack flash / Johnny B. Goode / Silver train / Sill alive and well / Let it bleed / Blinded by love / Bad luck situation / Rock and roll people / Raised on rock / Mind over matter / Sweet papa John / Roll with me / Mercy mercy / Everybody's blues / Good morning little schoolgirl / Divin' duck / It's all over now.
LP: . . . . SKY 22112
MC: 40 22112

RAISIN' CAIN.
Tracks: / Crawl / Sitting in the jailhouse / Like a rolling stone / New York, New York / Bon ton roulet / Rollin' and tumblin' / Talk is cheap / Wolf in sheeps clothing / Don't hide your love / Mother-in-law blues / Walkin' slowly.
LP: . . . . SKY 84103

SECOND WINTER.
Tracks: / Memory pain / Good love, The / Miss Ann / Highway 61 revisited / Hustled down in Texas / Fast life rider / I'm not sure / Slippin' and slidin' / Johnny B. Goode / I love everybody.
LP: . . . . CBS 66321
LP: . . . . ED 312

SERIOUS BUSINESS.
Tracks: / Master mechanic / Sound the bell / Murdering the blues / It ain't your business / Good time woman / Unseen eye / My time after awhile / Serious as a heart attack / Give it back / Route 90.
LP: . . . . SNTF 948
MC: . . . . ZCSN 948

THIRD DEGREE.
Tracks: / Mojo boogie / Love life and money / Evil on my mind / See see baby / Tin Pan Alley / I'm good / Third degree / Shake your moneymaker / Bad girl blues / Broke and lonely.
MC: . . . . ZCSN 965
LP: . . . . SNTF 965

UNCLE JOHN TURNER AND JOHNNY WINTER LIVE (See under Turner, Uncle John) (Winter, Johnny & Uncle John Turner).

WINTER OF '88.
Tracks: / Close to me / Stranger blues / Lightning / Anything for your love / Rain / Ain't that just like a woman / Looking for trouble / Look away.
LP: . . . . MCF 3436
MC: . . . . MCFC 3436

Winter, Paul

EARTHBEAT.
LP: . . . . LM 0015
MC: . . . . LC 0015

Winter Wonderland

WINTER WONDERLAND (Various artists).
LP: 4677041
MC: 4677044

Winters, Bernie

WORLD I'D LIKE TO SEE (See under Crowther, Leslie) (Winters, Bernie/Leslie Crowther).

Winters, George

GEORGE WINTERS & DUSKO GOYKOVICH (Winters, George & Orchestra).
LP: . . . . ISST 124

LIGHTS ON (Winters, George & Orchestra).
LP: . . . . ISST 111

Winters, Jerrie

SOMEBODY LOVE ME.
LP: . . . . FS 289

Winters, Mike

FOR MUMS AND DADS OF ALL AGES (Winters, Mike & Bernie).
Tracks: / Mums and dads / Happy birthday sweet sixteen / How lucky you are / So do I / Ballin' the Jack / Darktown strutters ball / Five foot two eyes of blue / Baby face / Mister Sandman / What a crazy world (we're living in) / Music maestro please / Puttin' on the style / Somebody stole my gal / Yes sir that's my baby / Ain't she sweet / Together.
LP: . . . . SPK 6000

Winters Reign

IN THE BEGINNING.
LP: . . . . LOPL 501
MC: . . . . LOPC 501

WINTERS REIGN.
LP: . . . . GWLP 100
MC: . . . . GWTC 100

Winters, Robert

MAGIC MAN (Winters, Robert & Fall).
Tracks: / Face the music / Into my world / Touched by you / She beleives in me / Magic man / When will my love be right / Watchin' you / How can love be wrong / Happiness.
LP: . . . . BDLP 4068

Winters, Ruby

I WILL.
Tracks: / For the good times / If this is our last time / I can't fake it anymore / I won't mention it again / Come to me / Treat me right / Neither one of us / Love me now / Lonely heartaches.
LP: . . . . CRLP 512

SONGBIRD.
LP: . . . . NE 1045
MC: . . . . CE 2045

Winters, Smiley

SMILEY WINTERS.
2LP: . . . . ARHOOLIE 8004/

Winter's Tale

WINTER'S TALE, THE (see under Shakespeare, William) (Various artists).

Winters, Tiny

CAFE SOCIETY ORCHESTRA (Winters, Tiny, Cafe Society Orchestra).
Tracks: / Zing went the strings / You brought a new kind of love / Easy to love / I don't know why / It's de-lovely / Don't blame me / Who / Apple for teacher, An / Sleepy time gal / Dancing in the dark / Peg o' my heart / One, two, button your shoe / Once in a while / Three little words.
LP: . . . . ZR 1018

Winther, Jens

LOOKING THROUGH (Winther, Jens Quintet).
LP: . . . . SLP 4127

Winwood, Steve

ARC OF A DIVER.
Tracks: / While you see a chance / Second hand woman / Slowdown

sundown / Spanish dancer / Night train / Dust / Arc of a diver.
LP: ILPS 9576
MC: ICT 9576

BACK IN THE HIGH LIFE.
Tracks: / Higher love / Take it as it comes / Freedom overspill / Back in the high life / Finer things / Wake me up on judgement day / Split decision / My love's leavin'.
LP: ILPS 9844
MC: ICT 9844

CHRONICLES.
Tracks: / Wake me up on judgement day / While you see a chance / Vacant chair / Help me angel / My loves leavin' / Valerie / Arc of a diver / Higher love / Spanish dancer / Talking back to the night.
LP: SSW 1
MC: SSWC 1

KEEP ON RUNNING.
MC: ICT 9975
LP: ILPS 9975

REFUGEES OF THE HEART.
Tracks: / You'll keep on searching / Every day (oh Lord) / One and only man / I will be here / Another deal goes down / Running on / Come out and dance / In the light of day.
LP: V 2650
MC: TCV 2650

ROLL WITH IT.
Tracks: / Roll with it / Holding on / Morning side, The / Put on your dancing shoes / Don't you know what the night can do? / Hearts on fire / One more morning / Shining song.
LP: V 2532
MC: TCV 2532
LP: OVED 334
MC: OVEDC 334

STEVE WINWOOD.
LP: ILPS 9494

TALKING BACK TO THE NIGHT.
LP: ILPS 9777
MC: ICT 9777

Wipers

CIRCLE, THE.
LP: ENVLP 516
MC: TCENV 516

IS THIS REAL.
LP: WS 024
LP: PSYCHO 22

LAND OF THE LOST.
LP: 2094 1

LIVE: WIPERS.
LP: ENIGMA 20261

OVER THE EDGE.
LP: 2187 1
LP: EATER 2

YOUTH OF AMERICA.
LP: PSYCHO 23

Wir

FIRST LETTER, THE.
LP: STUMM 87
MC: CSTUMM 87

Wiradiredja, Yus

SOUND OF SUNDA, THE (See under Komariah, Euis) (Komariah, Euis & Yus Wiradiredja).

Wire

154.
Tracks: / I should have known better / Two people in a room / 15th, The / Other window / Single K.O. / Touching display / On returning / Mutual friend / Blessed state / Once is enough / Map ref 41 degrees N.95 degrees S.W / Indirect enquiries / 40 versions.
LP: SHSP 4105
LP: SHVL 819

BELL IS A CUP UNTIL IT IS STRUCK, A.
Tracks: / Silk skin paws / Finest drops / Queens of Ur and The King of Um, The / Free falling divisions / It's a Bob / Boiling boy / Kidney bongos / Come back in two halves / Follow the locust / Public place, The.
LP: STUMM 54
MC: CSTUMM 54

CHAIRS MISSING.
Tracks: / Practice makes perfect / French film blurred / Another the letter / Men 2nd / Marooned / Sand in my joints / Being sucked in again / Heartbeat / Mercy / Outdoor miner / I am the fly / I feel mysterious today / From the nursery / Used to / Too late.
LP: SHSP 4093
MC: TCSHSP 4093

DOCUMENT AND EYEWITNESS.
LP: ROUGH 29
MC: ROUGHC 29

IDEAL COPY, THE.
Tracks: / Point of collapse, The / Ahead / Madman's honey / Feed me / Ambitious / Cheeking tongues / Still shows / Over theirs / Ahead (II) (CD only.) / Serious of snakes, A (CD only.) / Drill (CD only.) / Advantage in height, An (CD only.) / Up to the sun (CD only.) / Ambulance chasers (CD only.) / Feed me (II) (CD only.) / Vivid riot of red (CD only.).
LP: STUMM 42
MC: CSTUMM 42

IN THE PINK.
Tracks: / Pink flag / 12XU / Map ref 41 degrees N.95 degrees S.W / Reuters / Brazil / Different to me / Practice makes perfect / Outdoor miner / I am the fly / I should have known better / Other window, The / Single K.O. / Mutual friend.
LP: DOJOLP 36

IT'S BEGINNING TO AND BACK AGAIN.
Tracks: / Finest drops / Eardrum buzz / German shepherds / Public place / It's a boy / Illuminated / Boiling boy / Over theirs / Eardrum buzz (12" version) / Offer, The / In vivo.
LP: STUMM 66
MC: CSTUMM 66

MANSCAPE.
LP: STUMM 80
MC: CSTUMM 80

ON RETURNING.
Tracks: / 1.2.X.U. / It's so obvious / Mr. Suit / Three girl rhumba / Ex lion tamer / Lowdown / Strange / Reuters / Feeling called love / I am the fly / Practice makes perfect / French film blurred / I feel mysterious today / Marooned / Sand in my joints / Outdoor miner / Question of degree, A / I should have known better / Other window, The / 40 versions / Touching display, A / On returning / Another the letter (CD only.) / Straight line (CD only.) / 106 beats that (CD only.) / Field day for the Sundays (CD only.) / Dot dash (CD only.) / Men 2nd (CD only.) / Two people in room (CD only.) / Blessed state (CD only.).
LP: SHSP 4127
MC: TCSHSP 4127

PEEL SESSIONS: WIRE VOL.2.
LP: SFRLP 108
MC: SFRMC 108

PINK FLAG.
LP: SHSP 4076
MC: TCSHSP 4076

WIRE PLAY POP.
LP: PINKY 7

Wire Train

BETWEEN TWO WORDS.
Tracks: / Last perfect thing / Skills of summer / When she was a girl / With God on our side / Love, love, love / I will / No pretties / Ocean, The / Two persons / Home.
LP: CBS 26670
MC: 40 26670

IN A CHAMBER.
Tracks: / I'll do you / Everything's turning up down again / Never / Like / I forget it all when I see you / Chamber of hellos / Slow down / She's on fire / I gotta go / Love against me.
LP: CBS 25762
MC: 40 25762

TEN WOMEN.
Tracks: / She comes on / Take me back / Diving / She's a very pretty thing / Breakwater days / She's got you / Mercy mercy / Certainly no one / Too long alone / Compassion.
LP: 4506151
MC: 4506154

WIRE TRAIN.
Tracks: / Spin / Should she cry / She / If you see her go / Dakota / Moonlight dream / Simply racing / Precious time / Oh me, oh my / Tin Jesus / All night livin'.
LP: MCG 6101
MC: MCGC 6101

Wired

WIRED (Film soundtrack) (Various artists).
Tracks: / I'm a king bee: *Various artists* / Soul man: *Various artists* / Raven's theme: *Various artists*/ Two thousand pounds: *Various artists* / Still looking for a way: *Various artists* / You are so beautiful: *Various* artists / I can't turn you loose: *Various artists* / You don't know like I know: *Various artists* / Choice, The: *Various artists* / Bee: *Various artists* / Angel of death: *Various artists.*
LP: VS 5237
MC: VSC 5237

Wired For Clubs

WIRED FOR CLUBS (Various artists).
Tracks: / Wired for games: *Various artists* / She talks to me with her body: *Various artists* / Feels so good: *Various artists* / Is this the future?: *Various artists* / Ms. got the body: *Various artists* / You can't run from my love: *Various artists* / Touching in the dark: *Various artists.*
LP: CLUB 1

Wisdom (Film)

WISDOM (Film soundtrack) (Various artists).
LP: VS 5209
MC: VSC 5209

Wise Blood

DIRTDISH.
Tracks: / Prime gonzola / Zero zero / Stumbo / Someone drowned in my pool / Godbrain / Fudge punch, The / Stumbo (12" remix) (Available on cassette only.) / Someone drowned (12" remix) (on cassette only) / Motoroslug death Race 2,000 (Only on cassette.).
LP: WISE 003
MC: WISE C003

Wise, Skipper

CLOCK AND THE MOON, THE.
LP: YL 0129

Wiseman, Mac

BLUEGRASS FAVOURITES.
LP: HAT 3039
MC: HATC 3039

CLAYTON MCMICHAN STORY, THE (See under Travis, Merle) (Wiseman, Mac & Merle Travis).

CONCERT FAVOURITES.
LP: HAT 3100
MC: HATC 3100

COUNTRY MUSIC MEMORIES.
Tracks: / They'll never take her love from me / I'll sail my ship alone / Don't be angry / Green light / All for the love of a girl / My baby's gone / I wonder where you are tonight / I love you a thousand ways / Flesh and blood / Me and Bobby McGee / Mother, the queen of my heart.
LP: CMLF 1022
LP: CMH 6202
MC: CMHC 6202

EARLY DOT RECORDINGS VOL 1.
Tracks: / Love letters in the sand / I'm a stranger / Dreams of mother and home / Going to see my baby / When the roses bloom again / Little white church, The / I wonder how the old folks are at home / Little home in Tennessee / Dreaming of a little cabin / Let me borrow your heart / Rainbow in the valley / By the side of the road.
LP: CCS 108
MC: CCS 108MC

EARLY DOT RECORDINGS VOL 2.
LP: CCS 109
MC: CCS 109MC

ESSENTIAL BLUEGRASS ALBUM, THE (See under Osbourne Brothers) (Wiseman, Mac/Osbourne Brothers).

GOLDEN CLASSICS: MAC WISEMAN.
LP: GT 0047

MAC WISEMAN STORY, THE.
Tracks: / Love letters in the sand / Little blossom / I've got no use for women / Dark hollow / Wreck of old 97, The / Ballad of the Lawson family, The / May I sleep in your barn tonight, Mister / Bringing Mary home / Girl in the blue velvet band / I'll be all smiles tonight / I wonder how the old folks are at home / Jimmie Brown, the newsboy / Little box of pine in the 7:29, The / These hands / Baggage coach ahead, The / I still write your name in the sand / Six more miles / 'Tis sweet to be remembered / Dreaming of a little cabin.
2LP: CMH 9001
MC: CMHC 9001

SHENANDOAH VALLEY MEMORIES.
LP: CGS 8510

SINGS GORDON LIGHTFOOT.
Tracks: / Did she mention my name? / Cotton Jenny / Rainy day people / Summertime dream / For lovin' me / Steel rail blues / Ribbon of darkness / House you live in, The / Early morning rain / Old Dan's records / Sundown.
LP: CMH 6211
MC: CMHC 6211

SONGS THAT MADE THE JUKEBOX PLAY.
2LP: CMH 9021
MC: CMHC 9021

Wish I Had...

WISH I HAD MY TIME AGAIN, VOL 2 (Various artists).
LP: MS 45004

Wish You...

MY BEAUTIFUL LAUNDERETTE/ SAMMY & ROSY GET LAID/W (See under My Beautiful Laundrette) (Various artists).

WISH YOU WERE HERE (Original London cast) (Various artists).
Tracks: / Wish you were here: *Various artists* / Where did the night go?: *Various artists* / Relax: *Various* artists / Summer afternoon: *Various artists* / Mix and mingle: *Various artists* / Don Jose of Far Rockaway: *Various artists* / Camp Karefree song: *Various artists* / Ballad of a social director: *Various artists*/ Shop around: *Various artists.*
LP: DS 15015
MC: DSC 15015

Wishbone Ash

ARGUS.
Tracks: / Time was / Sometime world / Blowin' free / King will come, The / Leaf and stream / Warrior / Throw down the sword.
LP: MCL 1787
MC: MCLC 1787
LP: CLALP 140
MC: CLAMC 140
LP: MDKS 8006
LP: DMCL 1787

BEST OF WISHBONE ASH.
Tracks: / Blind eye / Blowin' free / King will come, The / Persephone.
LP: MCF 3134

BOTH BARRELS BURNING.
LP: ASH 1

CLASSIC ASH.
Tracks: / Blind eye / Phoenix / Pilgrim, The / Blowin' free / King will come, The / Rock 'n' roll widow / Persephone / Outward bound / Throw down the sword (live).
LP: MCL 1621
MC: MCLC 1621
LP: FA 3053
MC: TCFA 3053

FRONT PAGE NEWS.
Tracks: / Surface to air / Front page news / Midnight dancer / Goodbye baby, hello friend / Come in from the rain / Right or wrong / Heart beat / Day I found your love / Diamond Jack / 714.
LP: MCL 1655
MC: MCLC 1655
LP: MCG 3524

HERE TO HEAR.
Tracks: / Cosmic jazz / Keeper of the light / Mental radio / Walk on water / Witness on wonder / Lost cause in paradise / Why don't we / In the case / Hole in my heart (part one) / Hole in my heart (part two).
LP: EIRSA 1006
MC: EIRSAC 1006

JUST TESTING.
LP: MCF 3052

LIVE DATES.
Tracks: / King will come, The / Warrior / Throw down the sword / Lady whiskey / Phoenix / Rock 'n' roll widow / Ballad of the beacon / Baby what you want me to do / Pilgrim, The / Blowin' free / Jailbait.
2LP: MCSP 254
MCSET: MCSPC 254

LIVE DATES II.
LP: MCG 4012
LP: MCL 1799

LOCKED IN.
LP: MCF 2750

NEW ENGLAND.
Tracks: / Mother of pearl / You rescue me / Runaway / Lorelei / Outward bound / Prelude / When you know love / Lonely island / Candlelight.
LP: MCL 1699
MC: MCLC 1699
LP: MCG 3523

NO SMOKE WITHOUT FIRE.
LP: MCG 3528

NOUVEAU CALLS.
Tracks: / Tangible evidence / Clousseau / Flags of concenience / From Soho to Sunset / Arabesque / In the skin / Something's happening in room 602 / Johnny left home without it / Spirit flies free, the / Rose is a rose, A / Real guitars have wings.
LP: MCF 1028
MC: MCFC 1028
LP: MIRF 1028

NUMBER THE BRAVE.
LP: MCF 3103

PILGRIMAGE.
Tracks: / Vas dis / Pilgrim / Jailbait / Alone / Lullaby / Valediction / Where were you tomorrow.
LP: MCL 1762
MC: MCLC 1762
LP: MDKS 8004

PILGRIMAGE/ARGUS.
Tracks: / Pilgrim / Time was / Vas dis / Throw down the sword / Warrior / Leaf and stream / King will come, The / Blowin' free / Sometime world / Jailbait / Alone / Valediction / Where were you tomorrow / Lullaby.
MCSET: MCA 2 103

RAW TO THE BONE.
Tracks: / Cell of fame / People in motion / Don't cry / Love is blue / Long live the night / Rocket in my pocket / It's only love / Don't you mess / Dreams / Perfect timing.
LP: **NEAT 1027**
MC: **NEATC 1027**
LPPD: **NEATP 1027**

STRANGE AFFAIR.
Tracks: / Strange affair / Wings of desire / Dream train / You / Hard times / Standing in the rain / Renegade / Say you will / Rollin' / Some conversation.
LP: **EIRSA 1045**
MC: **EIRSAC 1045**

THERE'S THE RUB.
LP: **MCF 2585**

TWIN BARRELS BURNING.
LP: **ASH 1**

WISHBONE ASH.
LP: **MKPS 2014**

WISHBONE ASH IN CONCERT.
MC: **WINCMC 4**

WISHBONE FOUR.
LP: **MDKS 8011**

Wiss

MR SUNSHINE.
LP: **JLLP 018**

Wistreich, Richard

MUSICAL LIFE OF SAMUEL PEPYS.
MC: **CSDL 385**

Witch

HEX IS ON, THE.
Tracks: / Damnation / Bewitched / Cinderella / Nervous wreck / Wet and wild.
LP: **HMUSA 37**

Witcham Toll

WITCHAM TOLL.
Tracks: / Overgate, The / Barbara Allan / Jog on / King's delight / Beggin', A / Hiring, The / Blantyre explosion / Grey mare / Go ho dobbini poor Rosy / Derrydown fair / Good ale.
MC: **BH 8802 C**

Witcher, Wolfie

GUMMIN' THE GOB IRON (Witcher, Wolfie & His Brew).
LP: **ET 2003 C**

INDOOR BUSKIN' - A LIVE ALBUM.
LP: **ET 2001**

Witches Of Eastwick

WITCHES OF EASTWICK (Film soundtrack) (Various artists).
LP: **925607 1**
MC: **925607 4**

Witchfinder General

DEATH PENALTY.
Tracks: / Invisible hate / Free country / Death penalty / No stayer / Witchfinder general / Burning a sinner / R.I.P..
LP: **HMRLP 8**

FRIENDS OF HELL.
LP: **HMRLP 13**

Witchfynde

CLOAK AND DAGGER.
LP: **EXIT 5**

GIVE 'EM HELL.
Tracks: / Ready to roll / Divine victim, The / Leaving Nadir / Getting heavy / Give 'em hell / Unto the ages of the ages / Pay now love later.
LP: **ABOUT 1**
MC: **CARB 1**

LORDS OF SIN.
LP: **SKULL 8352**
MC: **TAPE 78352**

STAGE FRIGHT.
Tracks: / Stage fright / Doing the right thing / Would not be seen dead in heaven / Wake up screaming / Big deal / Moon magic / In the stars / Trick or treat / Madeleine.
LP: **ABOUT 2**
MC: **CARB 2**

Witchkiller

DAY OF THE SAXONS.
LP: **601826**

Witch's Revenge (bk)

WITCH'S REVENGE, THE.
MCSET: **DTO 10567**

Withered Arm (bk)

WITHERED ARM, THE (see Hardy, Thomas) (Redgrave, Corin).

WITHERED ARM, THE (See under Hardy, Thomas) (Morant, Richard).

Withers, Benny

UP JUMPED THE BLUES (See under Smith, Keith) (Withers, Benny & Keith Smith's Chosen 5).

Withers, Bill

BILL WITHERS.
Tracks: / Lovely day / Use me / Ain't no sunshine / Harlem / Kissing my love / Lean on me / Steppin' right along / Grandma's hands / Lonely town, lonely street / Who is he what is he to you.
LP: **4668241**
MC: **4668244**
LP: **4668240**

'BOUT LOVE.
Tracks: / All because of you / Dedicated to you my love / Don't it make it better / You got the stuff / Look to each other for love / Love / Love is / Memories are the way.
LP: **CBS 83176**

GREATEST HITS: BILL WITHERS.
Tracks: / Just the two of us / Use me / Ain't no sunshine / Lovely day / I want to spend the night / Soul shadows / Lean on me / Grandma's hands / Hello like before / Who is he, what is he to you?.
LP: **32343**
MC: **40 32343**
LP: **CBS 85049**
LP: **CBS 84710**

MENAGERIE.
Tracks: / Lovely day / I want to spend the night / Lovely night for dancing / Then you smile at me / She wants to (get on down) / It ain't because of me baby / Tender things / Winter time / Let me be the one you need.
LP: **CBS 32694**
MC: **40 32694**
LP: **CBS 82265**

SOUND OF SOUL, THE.
LP: **BLATLP 13**
MC: **BLATMC 13**

WATCHING YOU, WATCHING ME.
Tracks: / Oh yeah / Something that turns you on / Don't make me wait / Heart in your life / Watching you watching me / We could be sweet lovers / You just can't smile it away / Steppin' right along / Whatever happens / You try to find a love.
LP: **CBS 26200**
MC: **40 26200**

Withers, Tex

BLUE RIBBON COUNTRY.
Tracks: / Wreck of the old '97 / I can't stop loving you / Billy bayou / Jambalaya / For the good times / They don't understand / Heartaches by the number / Help me make it through the night / Okie from Muskogee / Crazy arms / Burn some bridges / Me and Bobby Magee.
MC: **CHRL 206**

TRUCK DRIVING MAN.
MC: **VCA 005**

Witherspoon, Jimmy

AIN'T NOBODY'S BUSINESS.
Tracks: / Ain't nobody's business / In the evening / Frog-I-more rag / McShann bounce / How long blues / Money's getting cheaper / Skid Row blues / Spoon calls Hootie / Backwater blues / Jumpin' with Louis / Destruction blues.
LP: **BLP 30147**

AT THE MONTEREY JAZZ FESTIVAL.
Tracks: / No rollin blues / Good rockin' tonight / Big fine girl / Ain't nobody's business / When I been drinking / Times gettin' tougher than tough / How long / Corina, Corina / See see rider / Roll em Pete / Everyday / (I'm gonna move to the) outskirts of town / Kansas City / Trouble in mind / St. Louis blues.
LP: **AFF 182**

BEN WEBSTER & JIMMY WITHERSPOON (That's Jazz Series) (Witherspoon, Jimmy & Ben Webster).
LP: **K 56295**

BIG BLUES.
LP: **JSP 1032**

BLOWIN' IN FROM KANSAS CITY.
LP: **CHD 279**

COLLECTION: JIMMY WITHERSPOON (20 blues greats).
Tracks: / Ain't nobody's business / How long blues / In the evening / Going to Kansas City / Skid Row blues / Money's getting cheaper / Frog-I-more rag / Backwater blues / Corina Corina / Blowin' the blues away / I make a lot of money / Spoon calls Hootie / Good rockin' tonight / Time's gettin' tougher than tough / St. Louis blues / Everyday / Outskirts of town / Destruction blues / Trouble in mind / Gee baby ain't I good to you.
LP: **DVLP 2113**
MC: **DVMC 2113**

CRY THE BLUES (Witherspoon, Jimmy & Groove Holmes).
Tracks: / Tell him I was flyin' (part 1) / In blues / Loser's blues / Please send me someone to love / Life's highway / Cry the blues / Out blues / Since I fell for you / Everything / Tell him I was flyin' (part 2).
LP: **BDL 1012**

EVENIN' BLUES.
LP: **OBC 511**

FEDERAL SESSIONS, THE.
Tracks: / Lucille / Two little girls / One fine gal / Corn whiskey / Day is dawning, The / Jay's blues (part 1) / Jay's blues (part 2) / Miss Miss Mistreater / Back home / It / Back door blues / Fast woman - slow gin / Just for you / Move my baby / 'Cause I love you / Oh boy.
LP: **SING 1162**

GERRY MULLIGAN AND JIMMY WITHERSPOON (see under Mulligan, Gerry) (Witherspoon, Jimmy & Gerry Mulligan).

HEY, MR. LANDLORD.
LP: **KIX 31**

LIVE AT CONDON'S, NEW YORK.
Tracks: / Goin' to Chicago / Gee, baby, ain't I good to you / You got me runnin' / Big boss man / Sweet lotus blossom / I'm gonna move to the outskirts of town (On CD only.) / If I didn't get well no more / Money's getting cheaper (On CD only.) / In the dark / I'm knocking out your teeth tonite / Ain't nobody's business (On CD only.) / Trouble in mind (On CD only.) / Don't you miss your baby.
MC: **CGATE 7023**
LP: **GATE 7023**

LIVE IN PARIS (see Clayton, Buck) (Witherspoon, Jimmy & Buck Clayton).

MEAN OLD FRISCO.
Tracks: / Mean old Frisco blues / Bad bad whiskey / One scotch one bourbon one beer / Blues and trouble / I'll go on living / It's a lonesome old world / Rocks in my bed / Baby baby baby / Lonely boy blues / Endless sleep / I can't hardly see.
LP: **PR 7855**

MIDNIGHT LADY CALLED THE BLUES.
Tracks: / New York City blues / Barber / Blinded by love / Happy hard times / Something rotten in East St Louis / Midnight lady called the blues / Blues hall of fame.
MC: **MRC 5327**

NEVER KNEW THIS KIND OF HURT BEFORE (The bluesway sessions).
Tracks: / Never knew hurt like this before / I made a lot of mistakes / Pillar to post / You can't do a thing when you're drunk / Parcel post blues / Bags under my eyes / Bug to put 'n' you' ear / Thoughts of home / I don't know / Evenin' / No rolling blues / Pay the consequences / Going down slow / Testifying / Nobody wants to hear nobody's troubles / Blow wind blow / Look at granny run run / Just a dream / Handbags and gladrags / Night they drove old Dixie down, The.
2LP: **CDX 32**

NEW ORLEANS BLUES (Witherspoon, Jimmy & Wilbur De Paris).
Tracks: / Lotus blossom / Trouble in mind / Big fine girl / How long blues / Good rollin' blues / Careless love / Tain't nobody's business If I do / St Louis blues / When the sun goes down / See see rider.
LP: **OFF 6046**

OLYMPIA CONCERT.
LP: **500091**

ON CONSTELLATION, 1961-62 (Witherspoon, Jimmy & Groove Holmes).
LP: **FS 314**

SINGS THE BLUES WITH PANAMA FRANĆIS AND THE SAVOY SULTANS.
Tracks: / Sent for you yesterday / I want a little girl / Don't you miss your baby / Goodmorning blues / Goin' to Chicago / Sometimes I feel like a motherless child / Boogie woogie (I may be wrong) / Rain keeps falling down / Gee baby ain't I good to you.
LP: **MR 5288**

SPIRITUALS.
LP: **FS 313**

SPOON SO EASY.
LP: **CH 93003**

WHO'S BEEN JIVIN' YOU.
Tracks: / Jump children / Connie Lee / Take me back baby / Big fine girl / Same old blues / Your red wagon / Who's been jivin' with you / I'll be right on down / Oh mother, dear mother / Don't ever move a woman in to your house / Real ugly woman / Baby baby / Slow your speed / Doctor blues.
LP: **CH 92**

Withnail & I

WITHNAIL AND I (Original soundtrack) (Various artists).
Tracks: / While my guitar gently weeps: *Beatles* / Voodoo chile: *Hendrix, Jimi Experience* / Marwood returns: *Various artists* / Whiter shade of pale, A: *Curtis, King* / Mother black cap: *Various artists* / Crow crag: *Various artists* / All along the watchtower: *Various artists* / Chevel blanc: *Various artists* / La fite: *Various artists* / Wolf, The: *Various artists* / Margeaux: *Various artists* / To the crow: *Various* artists / Monty remembers: *Various artists* / Marwood leaves: *Various artists* / Withnail's theme: *Various artists.*
LP: **MOMENT 110**
MC: **MOMENTC 110**

Witness

HOUSE CALLED LOVE.
LP: **3971241**
MC: **3971244**

RAW PATCH (See under Meatmouth for details).

SACRED COW HEART.
LP: **COMM 003**
MC: **COMM 003C**

Witness (Film)

WITNESS (Film soundtrack) (Various artists).
LP: **TER 1098**
MC: **ZCTER 1098**

Witness (Musical)

WITNESS, THE (Various artists).
Tracks: / Witness, The: *Witness (Musical)* / Nothin' ever happens: *Witness (Musical)* / When you find the truth: *Witness (Musical)* / Wedding at Cana: *Witness (Musical)* / Mary's song (whatever he says): *Witness (Musical)*/ Born again: *Witness (Musical)* / Life giver: *Witness (Musical)* / You are the Christ: *Witness (Musical)*/ My boys: *Witness (Musical)* / Make me like you: *Witness (Musical)* / Hosanna (triumphal entry): *Witness* (Musical) / In love for me: *Witness (Musical)* / Silver and gold: *Witness (Musical)* / Crucifixion dirge: *Witness (Musical)* / He came in love: *Witness (Musical)* / They took him down: *Witness (Musical)* / Victor, The: *Witness (Musical)* / I love you, Lord: *Witness (Musical)* / Lambs alone: *Witness (Musical)* / Room upstairs, The: *Witness (Musical)* / Get ready: *Witness (Musical)* / Life giver (Reprise): *Witness (Musical)*/ Born again (reprise): *Witness (Musical)* / You are the Christ: *Witness (Musical).*
LP: **LSA 7047**
MC: **LCA 7047**

Witticombe Fair

WITTICOMBE FAIR HAPPY DAYS.
LP: **SRTZ 76370**

Wittstatt, Hans "Pepe"

LOVE IS THE KEY.
Tracks: / Caligari / Las Canteras / Terminal symbol / Love is the key / Dream of Westerland / Nautical march / Sir Edward-George / A.B.A.D..
LP: **PRCV 131**

Wiz

WIZ, THE (Original soundtrack) (Various artists).
Tracks: / Wiz, The (main title and overture): *Various artists* / Feeling that we have: *Various artists* / Can I go on?: *Various artists* / Glinda's theme: *Various artists* / He's the wizard: *Various artists* / Soon as I get home: *Various artists* / Home: *Various artists* / You can't win: *Various artists* / Ease on down the road: *Various artists* / What would I do if I could feel: *Various artists* / Slide some oil to me: *Various* artists / I'm a mean ole lion: *Various artists* / Poppy girls: *Various artists* / Be a lion: *Various* artists / End of the yellow brick road: *Various artists* / Emerald city: *Various artists* / So you wanted to see the wizard: *Various artists* / Is this what the feeling gets: *Various artists* / Don't nobdoy bring me no bad news: *Various artists* / Liberation agitato: *Various artists* / Brand new day: *Various artists* / Believe in yourself: *Various artists* / Liberation ballet: *Various artists* / Good witch: *Various artists*/ Glinda: *Various artists.*
2LP: **MCA 21430**
2LP: **MCSP 287**
MCSET: **MCSPC 287**

Wizard Of Earthsea

WIZARD OF EARTHSEA (see Le Guin, Ursula) (Hood, Morag).

Wizard Of Oz

BEHIND THE SCENES AT WIZARD OF OZ (Complete NBC Maxwell House Good News Broadcast) (Various artists).
LP: **JASS 17**

LAND OF OZ, THE (abridged) (Baum, L. Frank).
MC: **1618**

WIZARD OF OZ.

MC: . . . . STK 027

WIZARD OF OZ, THE (abridged) (Baum, L. Frank).
MC: 1512

WIZARD OF OZ, THE (Various artists).
LP: . . . . D 347
MC: . . . . D 13DC

WIZARD OF OZ, THE (Moore, Stephen (nar)).
MCSET: . . . . TC LFP 417142 5

WIZARD OF OZ, THE (Film soundtrack) (Various artists).
Tracks: / Over the rainbow: *Various artists* / Munchkinland: *Various artists* / If only I had a brain: *Various* artists / If only I had a heart: *Various artists* / If only I had the nerve: *Various artists* / If I were king of the forest: *Various artists* / Courage: *Various artists* / Ding dong the witch is dead: *Various artists*/ There's no place like home: *Various artists*.
LP: . . . . CBS 70289
MC: 40 70289

WIZARD OF OZ, THE (Moore, Stephen (nar)).
MCSET: . . . . LFP 7448

WIZARD OF OZ, THE (well loved tales up to age 9).
MC: . . . . PLB 179

WIZARD OF OZ, THE (see Baum, L. Frank) (Bolger, Ray).

WIZARD OF OZ, THE (DIGITAL RECORDING) (Original cast) (Various artists).
LP: . . . . TER 1165
MC: . . . . ZCTER 1165

Wizzard

INTRODUCING EDDY AND THE FALCONS.
LP: . . . . K 52029

WIZZARD BREW.
LP: . . . . SHSP 4025

WIZZARD/SLADE (See under Slade) (Wizzard/Slade).

WNUA

WNUA.
MC: . . . . C 8801

WNUA SAMPLER.
MC: . . . . C 8803

Wobble, Jah

BETRAYAL.
Tracks: / Betrayal / Beat the drum for me / Blueberry hill / Not another / Tales from outer space / Today is the first day of the....? / Dan McCarther / Pineapple.
MLP: . . . . OVED 205
MLP: . . . . V 2158

BLUEBERRY HILL.
MLP: . . . . VS 361-12

NEON MOON (Wobble, Jah & Ollie Marland).
LP: . . . . IPS 9828
MC: . . . . ICT 9828

PSALMS.
LP: . . . . WOB 7

SNAKE CHARMER (Wobble, Jah/The Edge/Holger Czukay).
LP: . . . . IMA 1
MC: . . . . IMC 1

TRADEWINDS (Wobble, Jah & Ollie Marland).
LP: . . . . LAGO 7

Wodehouse, P.G.

ANSELM GETS HIS CHANCE.
MC: . . . . TTC/PGW 5

CLICKING OF CUTHBERT.
MC: . . . . TTC/PGW 6

GOLF OMNIBUS (See under Golf Omnibus).

JEEVES (Various artists).
MC: 1137

JEEVES AND THE FEUDAL SPIRIT.
MCSET: . . . . ZBBC 1116

JEEVES AND THE YULETIDE SPIRIT.
MC: . . . . TTC/PGW 2

LORD EMSWORTH & THE GIRLFRIEND.
MC: . . . . TTC/PGW 1

MULLINER'S BUCK U UPPO.
MC: . . . . TTC/PGW 4

SUMMER LIGHTNING (Carmichael, Ian).
MCSET: . . . . ZBBC 1044

UKRIDGE'S ACCIDENT SYNDICATE.
MC: . . . . TTC/PGW 3

VERY GOOD JEEVES.
MCSET: 0600560767

Wofford, Mike

AFTERTHOUGHTS.
Tracks: / Oblivion / I'll see you again / Our waltz / Monk's mood / Off minor / Naked city theme / I've got a crush on you / Afterthoughts / Cabin in the sky / Nina never knew / What are you doing the rest of your life? / Struttin' with some barbecue / What is there to say?.
LP: . . . . DS 784
MC: . . . . DSC 784

BIRD OF PARADISE (Wofford, Mike Trio).
LP: . . . . DS 778

PLAYS JEROME KERN, VOL.2 (Wofford, Mike Quartet).
Tracks: / Smoke gets in your eyes / All the things you are / Dearly beloved / Why was I born / Sure thing / All through the day / You are love.
LP: . . . . DS 816

PLAYS JEROME KERN, VOL.3 (Wofford, Mike Trio).
Tracks: / Long ago and far away / I dream too much / I won't dance / Folks who live on the hill, The / Waltz in swing time, The / All in fun / Pick yourself up / Lovely to look at / Go little boat.
LP: . . . . DS 827

Wogan, Terry

TWO HEADS ARE BETTER THAN ONE (see under Young, Jimmy) (Wogan, Terry & Jimmy Young).

Wolf

CANIS LUPUS.
Tracks: / Void, The / Isolation waltz / Go down / Wolf / Cadenza / Chanson sans paroles / McDonald's lament.
LP: . . . . SDL 14

EDGE OF THE WORLD.
LP: . . . . SKULL 8323
MC: . . . . TAPE 78323

LOVE TO SHARE (Wolf and his soft rock guitar).
LP: . . . . ISST 169

NIGHT MUSIC.
LP: . . . . SML 1116

STILL ON MY WAY.
LP: . . . . ISST 134

Wolf (composer)

MORIKE-LIEDER GOETHE-LEIDER (Lott, Felicity & Geoffrey Parsons).
LP: . . . . ABRD 1366
MC: . . . . ABTD 1366

Wolf, Kate

BACKROADS (Wolf, Kate & Wildwood Flower).
Tracks: / Lately / Emma Rose / Sitting on the porch / Redtail hawk, The / Telluride / Goodbye babe / It ain't in the wine / Tequila and me / Legend in his time / Riding in the country / Oklahoma going home / Back roads.
LP: . . . . F 6
MC: . . . . C 6

CLOSE TO YOU.
Tracks: / Across the great divide / Legget serenade / Like a river / Unfinished life / Friend of mine / Love still remains / Eyes of a painter / Here in California / Stone in the water / Close to you.
LP: . . . . F 15
MC: . . . . C 15

EVENING IN AUSTIN, AN.
Tracks: / Eyes of a painter / Green eyes / Carolina pines / Give yourself to love / Let's get together / Friend of mine.
MC: . . . . C 36

GIVE YOURSELF TO LOVE.
Tracks: / Give yourself to love / Desert wind / Peaceful easy feeling / Ballad of Weaverville, The / Green eyes / You're not standing like you used to / Hobo, The / Hurry home / Some kind of love / Who knows were time goes / Cornflower blue / Picture puzzle / Far off shore / Agent orange / These times we're living in / Sweet companion / Medicine trail / Pacheco / Redtail hawk / Friend of mine.
LP: . . . . F 3000
MC: . . . . C 3000

GOLD IN CALIFORNIA.
Tracks: / Full time woman / She rises like a dolphin / Like a river / Telluride / Muddy roads / Across the great divide / Lilac and the apple, The / Unfinished life / Early morning melody / Safe at anchor / Redtail hawk, The / Sun is burning, The / Brother warrior / Two way waltz / Eyes of a painter / Emma Rose / Here in California / Poet's heart / Carolina pines / Trumpet vines, The.
LP: . . . . F 3001
MC: . . . . C 3001

LINES ON THE PAPER (Wolf, Kate & Wildwood Flower).
Tracks: / I don't know why / Lines on paper / You're not standing like you used to / Picture puzzle / Heart, The / Trumpet vine, The / I never knew my father / Amazed to find / Everybody's looking for the same thing / Lilac and the apple, The / Midnight on the water / Lay me down easy.
LP: . . . . F 7
MC: . . . . C 7

POET'S HEART.
Tracks: / Poet's heart / In China or a woman's heart / Slender thread / Brother warrior / Crying shame / Muddy roads / Carolina pines / All he ever saw was you / See here, she said.
LP: . . . . F 24
MC: . . . . C 24

SAFE AT ANCHOR.
Tracks: / Safe at anchor / Early morning melody / Sweet love / She rises like a dolphin / Great love of my life / Shining / September song / Seashore mountain lady / Looking back at you / Two way waltz.
LP: . . . . F 11
MC: . . . . C 11

WIND BLOWS WILD.
Tracks: / Old Jerome / Statues made of clay / Monday in the mountains / Streets of Calgary / Give yourself to love / Wind blows wild, The / Clearing in the forest.
LP: . . . . F 30
MC: . . . . C 30

Wolf, Peter

COME AS YOU ARE.
Tracks: / Can't get started / Run silent run deep / Magic moon / 2 lane / Mama said / Flame of love / Come as you are / Wind me up / Blue Avenue / Thick as thieves / Love on ice.
LP: . . . . AML 3119
MC: . . . . TCAML 3119

LIGHTS OUT.
Tracks: / Lights out / I need you tonight / Oo ee diddley bob / Gloomy Sunday / Baby please don't let me go / Crazy / Poor girl's heart / Here comes that hurt / Pretty lady / Mars need women / Billy bigtime.
LP: . . . . EJ 2401851
MC: . . . . EJ 2401854

Wolf Spider

DRIFTEN IN THE SULLEN SEA.
LP: . . . . FLAG 63

KINGDOM OF PARANOIA.
Tracks: / Manifestants / Pain / Black'n'white / Foxes / Waiting for sense / Desert / Sickened nation / Nasty-ment / Survive / Weakness.
LP: . . . . FLAG 49
MC: . . . . TFLAG 49

Wolf & The......

WOLF & THE 7 LITTLE KIDS (well loved tales up to age 9) (Unknown narrator(s)).
MC: . . . . PLB 67

Wolf & Wolf

WOLF AND WOLF.
LP: . . . . ZL 72177
MC: . . . . ZK 72177

Wolfer, Bill

WOLF.
Tracks: / Call me / So shy / Window on a dream / Papa was a rollin' stone / Nobody knows / Why do you do me / Wake up / Soaring / Camouflage / Pop quiz.
LP: . . . . E 0187

Wolfetones

20 GOLDEN IRISH BALLADS VOL. 1.
Tracks: / Deportees / Rights of man, The / Raynard the fox / Teddy bears head / Long black veil / Peeler and the goat, The / Goodbye Mrs. Durkin / Ode to Biddy McGee / Foggy dew, The / Man from Mullingar, The / Up the border / Boys of Wexford / Four strong winds / Follow me up to Carlow / Banks of the Sweet Smirla Side / Merry Ploughboy / Old maid, The / Blow ye winds in the morning / Black ribbon band / Gay Galtree mountains, The.
MC: . . . . DOCX 9007

20 GOLDEN IRISH BALLADS VOL. 2.
Tracks: / I'm a rover / Down by the Liffey side / Banks of the Ohio / Enniskillen Fusilier / Come all ye drunken sailors / I still miss someone / Come to the bower / Dying rebel / Limerick rake / Finding of Moses, The / Glenswilly / Tri coloured ribbon / Banna strand / Song of the backwoods / Blow ye winds in the morning / Rosin dubh / Wrap the green flag 'round me / Lagan love / Valley of the Knockanure / Treat me daughter kindly.
MC: . . . . DOCX 9008

25TH ANNIVERSARY : WOLFETONES.
LP: . . . . HM 050

25TH ANNIVERSARY : WOLFETONES (2).
MCSET: . . . . SHMC 52024/5

ACROSS THE BROAD ATLANTIC.
LP: . . . . TRL 1002
MC: . . . . TRC 1002

ALIVE-OH.
LP: . . . . TRL 1005
MC: . . . . TRC 1005

AS GAEILGE.
LP: . . . . TRL 1008
MC: . . . . TRC 1008

BELT OF THE CELTS.
LP: . . . . TRL 1003
MC: . . . . TRC 1003

GREATEST HITS: WOLFE TONES.
Tracks: / My heart is in Ireland / Streets of New York / Dreams of home / Only our rivers / Quare things in Dublin / Padraic pearse / On the one road / God save Ireland / Irish eyes / Song of liberty / Uncle Nobby's steamboat / Let the people sing / Nation once again, A / Spancil hill / Paddle your own canoe / Some say the devil is dead / Let the people sing / Nation once again, A.
LP: . . . . NE 1326
MC: . . . . CE 2326
LP: . . . . ONCE 1326

IRISH TO THE CORE.
LP: . . . . TRL 1001
MC: . . . . TRC 1001

LET THE PEOPLE SING.
LP: . . . . DOL 1004
LP: . . . . TRL 1007
MC: . . . . TRC 1007

RIFLES OF THE I.R.A..
LP: . . . . DOL 1002

SENSE OF FREEDOM, A.
LP: . . . . TRL 1012
MC: . . . . TRC 1012

SING OUT FOR IRELAND.
LP: . . . . TRL 1015

SPIRIT OF THE NATION.
LP: . . . . TRL 1006
MC: . . . . TRC 1006

TEDDY BEAR'S HEAD (Wolff, Francis).
Tracks: / Teddy bear's head / Up the border / Wrap the green flag 'round me / Rights of Man, The / Foggy dew, The / Gay Galtree mountains, The / Lagan love / Peeler and the goat, The / Banks of the sweet Smirla Side / Glenswilly / Ode to Billy McGee / Four strong winds / Come to the bower.
LP: . . . . DOLM 5005
MC: . . . . DOCM 5005

TILL IRELAND'S A NATION.
LP: . . . . DOL 1006
LP: . . . . TRL 1011
MC: . . . . TRC 1011

UP THE REBELS.
Tracks: / Man from Mullingar, The / Tri coloured ribbon / Dying rebel / Finding of Moses, The / Banna strand / Banks of the Ohio / Down by the Liffey side / Valley of Knockanure / Blow ye winds in the morning / Black ribbon band / Old maid, The / Goodbye Mrs. Durkin / Song of the backwoods.
LP: . . . . DOLM 5003
MC: . . . . DOCM 5003

WOLFE TONES, THE.
Tracks: / My heart is in Ireland / Wearing of the green, The / Mullinger fleadh / Plastic bullets / Masushla Mavoureen / Song of liberty / Women of Ireland / Butcher's apron / Little Jimmy Murphy / Sailor of St Brendan / Too-ra-loo-ra-loo-ra / Far away in Australia.
LP: . . . . MCF 3292
MC: . . . . MCFC 3292
LP: . . . . WTLP 1
MC: . . . . WTC 1
LP: . . . . TRL 1014

Wolff, Henry

TIBETAN BELLS II (Wolff, Henry & Nancy Hennings).
LP: . . . . LPCEL 005
MC: . . . . MCCEL 005

TIBETAN BELLS III.
LP: . . . . LPCEL 027
MC: . . . . MCCEL 027

Wolfgamme, Bill

HAWAIIAN SUNSET.
Tracks: / Pearly shells / Ricardo / Wabash blues / Cherokee / La Rosita / Steel guitar rag / Amigo's guitars / Say si si / Hawaiian war chant / Siboney / Maui chimes.
LP: . . . . SPVP 121

Wolfgamme, Nani

HAWAII CALLS (Wolfgamme, Nani & His Islanders).
LP: . . . . SPVP 152
MC: . . . . SPVP 152 C

HAWAIIAN COCKTAIL (Wolfgamme, Nani & South Pacific Strings).

Tracks: / Hiki mai / Pania of the reef / Te arawa E / He puti puti pai / Awhi mai hine / Paki O matariki / Blue smoke.
LP: . . . . . SPVP 168

POLYNESIAN LOVE SONG (Wolfgamme, Nani & His Islanders).
LP: . . . . . SPVP 148
MC: . . . . . SPVP 148 C

Wolfgang Press

BIRD WOOD CAGE.
Tracks: / King of soul / Raintime / Bottom drawer / Kansas / Swing like a baby / See my wife / Holy man, The / Hang on me / Shut that door.
LP: . . . . . CAD 810
MC: . . . . . CADC 810

BURDEN OF MULES, THE.
LP: . . . . . CAD 308

LEGENDARY WOLFGANG PRESS AND OTHER TALL STORIES.
LP: . . . . . CAD 514

QUEER.
LP: . . . . . CAD 1011
MC: . . . . . CADC 1011

STANDING UP STRAIGHT.
Tracks: / Dig a hole / My life / Hammer the halo / Bless my brother / Fire-fly / Rotten fodder / Forty days, thirty nights / I am the crime.
MC: . . . . . CADC 606
LP: . . . . . CAD 606

Wolfhounds

ATTITUDE.
LP: . . . . . CHIME 1.07
MC: . . . . . CHIME 1.07 CC

BLOODSTAINED BANDAGE, THE.
LP: . . . . . CSDBL 511

BLOWN AWAY.
LP: . . . . . CHIME 057F
MC: . . . . . CHIME 057C

BRIGHT AND GUILTY.
LP: . . . . . CHIME 048
MC: . . . . . CHIME 048 C

ESSENTIAL, THE.
LP: . . . . . CHIME 0032S

ESSENTIAL WOLFHOUNDS, THE.
LP: . . . . . CHIME 0038 S

IRELAND BOY'S HURRAGH.
LP: . . . . . SDBL 509

IRELAND BOYS HURRAH.
LP: . . . . . CSDBL 509

IRELAND'S REBEL SONGS.
LP: . . . . . CSDBL 501

IRISH BALLADS.
LP: . . . . . CSDBL 506

RIGHT OF MAN TO BE FREE, THE.
LP: . . . . . CSDBL 513

Wolfpack

TOTAL HEAD REMOVAL.
LP: . . . . . CRE 101

Wolfram, William

MUSIC FOR VIOLIN & PIANO VOL. 4 (see under Schumski, Oscar) (Wolfram, William/Oscar Schumski).

Wolfsbane

ALL HELL'S BREAKING LOOSE (Down at little Kathy Wilson's place).
Tracks: / Steel / Paint the town red / Loco / Hey babe / Totally nude / Kathy Wilson.
MLP: 8469671
MC: 8469674

LIVE FAST DIE FAST.
Tracks: / Man hunt / Shakin' killing machine / Fell out of heaven / Money to burn / Greasy / I like it hot / All or nothing / Tears from a fool / Pretty baby.
LP: 8384861
MC: 8384864

Wolowic, Stan

ALL-TIME FAVOURITE POLKAS.
Tracks: / Beer barrel polka / Pennsylvania polka / Just because / There is a tavern in the town / Blue skirt waltz / Hoop dee doo / You can't be true dear / Liechtensteiner polka / Too fat polka.
MC: 4XL 9283

Wolstenholme, Woolly

MAESTOSO.
Tracks: / Sail away / Quiet islands / Prospect of Whitby / Lives on the line / Patriots / Gates of heaven / American excess / Maestoso / Hymn in the roof of the world / Waveform.
LP: 2374165

Wolverines Orchestra

WOLVERINES ORCHESTRA 1924.
LP: . . . . . FJ 114

Wolverton Brothers

SUCKING HIND TIT.
LP: . . . . . OK 33012
MC: . . . . . OK 33012MC

Wolves Of Willoughby

WOLVES OF... (NARRATION) (Hordern, Sir Michael).
MC: . . . . . ZCTER 8311

WOLVES OF WILLOUGHBY CHASE, THE (Original soundtrack) (Various artists).
MC: . . . . . ZCTER 1162

Womack, Bobby

AIN'T NOTHING LIKE THE LOVIN' WE GOT (See under Brown, Shirley for details) (Womack, Bobby/Shirley Brown).

BOBBY WOMACK AND THE VALENTINOS (Womack, Bobby & The Valentinos).
Tracks: / I found a true love / What about me / Do it right / I'm gonna forget about you / Let's get together / I've come a long way / See me through / Darling darling darling / Sweeter than the day before / Baby girl / Lonesome man,A.
LP: . . . . . GCH 8031
MC: . . . . . GCHK 78031

CHECK IT OUT.
Tracks: / Interlude / I don't know / Holdin' on to my baby's love / That's heaven to me / Got to get you back / Tarnished rings / Preacher, The / More than I can stand / Check it out / Woman's gotta have it / Point of no return / It's all over now / Daylight / Yes, Jesus loves me.
LP: . . . . . SSL 6013
MC: . . . . . TCSSL 6013

CHESS MASTERS (Womack, Bobby & The Valentinos).
Tracks: / I found a true love / What about me / Do it right / I'm gonna forget about you / Let's get together / I've come a long way / See me through / Darling darling darling / Sweeter than the day before / Baby girl / Lonesome man.
LP: . . . . . CXMB 7202

FACTS OF LIFE.
Tracks: / Nobody wants you when you're down and out / I'm through trying to prove my love to you / If you can't give her love, give her up / That's heaven to me / Holdin' on to my baby's love / Nobody / Fact of life / He'll be there when the sun goes down / Can't stop a man in love / Look of love, The / Natural man / All along the watchtower / Interlude no.1 (I don't know) / Superstar / If you want my love, put something down on it / Git it / What's your world / Check it out / Interlude No. 2 / Jealous love / It's all over now / Yes Jesus loves me.
MC: . . . . . TCCDX 39
2LP: . . . . . CDX 39

HOME IS WHERE THE HEART IS.
Tracks: / Home is where the heart is / Little bit salty, A / Standing in the safety zone / How long (has this been going on) / I could never be satisfied / Something for my head / Change is gonna come, A / We've only just begun.
LP: . . . . . ED 172
MC: . . . . . CED 172
LP: . . . . . CBS 81693

LAST SOUL MAN.
Tracks: / Living in a box / When the weekend comes / I still love you / Gina / World where no one cries / Woman likes to hear that, A / Real love please stand up / Things we do (when we're lonely), The / Falling in love again / Outside myself.
LP: . . . . . MCF 3408
MC: . . . . . MCFC 3408

LOOKIN' FOR A LOVE AGAIN.
Tracks: / Lookin' for a love / I don't wanna be hurt by your love again / Doing it my way / Let it hang out / Point of no return / You're welcome, stop on by / You're messing up a good thing / Don't let me down / Copper kettle / There's one thing that beats failing.
LP: . . . . . CRB 1193
MC: . . . . . TCRB 1193
LP: . . . . . ED 291

MIDNIGHT MOVER, THE.
Tracks: / I can understand it / Looking for a love / It's all over now / I'm a midnight mover / I'm in love / Arkansas state prison / That's heaven to me / Harry hippie / Tried and convicted / Don't look back / Fly me to the moon / California dreamin' / Woman's gotta have it / Behind closed doors.
LP: . . . . . INS 5000
MC: . . . . . TCINS 5000

POET II, THE.
Tracks: / Love has finally come at last / It takes a lot of strength to say goodbye / Through the eyes of a child / Surprise surprise / Tryin' to get over you / Tell me why / Who's foolin' who / I wish I had someone to go home to / American dream.
MC: . . . . . ZK 72205
LP: . . . . . ZL 72205

POET, THE.
Tracks: / So many sides of you / Lay your lovin' on me / Secrets / Just my imagination / Stand up / Games / If you think you're lonely now / Where do we go from here.
LP: . . . . . STML 12168
MC: . . . . . CSTML 12168
MC: . . . . . BGCX 10000
LP: . . . . . BG 10000

PORTRAIT OF BOBBY WOMACK.
Tracks: / I can understand it / I don't know / Love ain't somethin' you can get for free / Daylight / Sweet Caroline / Woman's gotta have it / All along the watchtower / Feel a groove comin' on / Preacher / More than I can stand / That's the way I feel about cha / Lookin' for a love / It's all over now / Harry Hippie.
LP: . . . . . UAG 30245

SAFETY ZONE/B.W. GOES C & W.
Tracks: / Everything's gonna be alright / I wish it would rain / Trust me / Where there's a will there's a way / Love ain't something you can get for free / Something you got / Daylight / I feel a groove comin' on / Don't make this the last date for you and me / Behind closed doors / Bouquet of roses / Tired of living in the country / Tarnished rings / Big bayou / Song of the mockingbird / I'd be ahead if I could quit while I'm behind / You / I take it on home.
2LP: . . . . . CDX 47
MC: . . . . . TCCDX 47

SO MANY RIVERS.
Tracks: / I wish he didn't trust me so much / So baby don't leave home without it / So many rivers / Got to be with you tonight / What ever happened to those times / Let me kiss it where it hurts / Only survivor / That's where it's at / Check it out / Gypsy woman.
LP: . . . . . MCF 3282

SOMEBODY SPECIAL.
Tracks: / Broadway walk / What is this / I'm in love / Trust me / I'm a midnight mover / Somebody special / What you gonna do (when your love is gone) / More than I can stand / I can understand it / That's the way I feel about cha / You're welcome, stop on by / Harry Hippie / If you want my love, put something down on it / If you don't want my love, give it back / Lookin' for a love.
LP: . . . . . EG 2602501
MC: . . . . . EG 2602504

SUPER SOUL SEDUCTION.
LP: . . . . . ESDLP 141
MC: . . . . . ESDMC 141

UNDERSTANDING - COMMUNICATION.
Tracks: / I can understand it / Woman's gotta have it / And I love her / Got to get you back / Simple man / Ruby Dean / Thing called love, A / Sweet Caroline (good times never seemed so goo / Harry hippie / Communication / Come l'amore / Fire and rain / If you don't want my love, give it back / (They long to be) close to you / Everything is beautiful / That's the way I feel about cha / Yield not to temptation.
MC: . . . . . TCCDX 36
LP: . . . . . CDX 36

WOMACK IN MEMPHIS.
Tracks: / Fly me to the moon (in other words) / Baby you oughta think it over / I'm a midnight mover / What is this / Somebody special / Take me / Moonlight in Vermont / Love, the time is now / I'm in love / California dreamin' / No money in my pocket / Little Mae / How I miss you baby / More than I can stand / It's gonna rain / Everyone's gone to the moon / I can't take it like a man / I left my heart in San Francisco / Arkansas State Prison / I'm gonna forget about you / Don't look back / Tried and convicted / Thank you.
LP: . . . . . CDX 46
MC: . . . . . TCCDX 46

WOMACK LIVE.
Tracks: / Let it out / Intro / Oh how I miss you baby / California dreamin' / Something / Everybody's talkin' / Laughin' and clownin' / To live the past / I'm a midnight mover / More than I can stand.
LP: . . . . . CRB 1201
MC: . . . . . TCCRB 1201

WOMACK WINNERS.
Tracks: / Broadway walk / Somebody special / I'm a midnight mover / What is this / How I miss you baby / More than I can stand / Communication / That's the way I feel about cha / If you don't want my love, give it back / I can understand it / Woman's gotta have it / Harry Hippie / Across 110th street / Nobody wants you when you're down and out / I'm through trying to prove my love to you / Lookin' for a love / You're welcome, stop on by / I don't know (what the world is coming to) / If you want my love, put something down on it / Check it out / It's all over now / Where there's a will / Daylight.
MC: . . . . . TCCDX 37
LP: . . . . . CDX 37

WOMAGIC.
Tracks: / I wanna make love to you / When the weekend comes / All the things you do / I can't stay mad too long / Hear the music / Outside myself / I ain't got to love nobody else / More than love / It ain't me.
LP: . . . . . MCG 6020
MC: . . . . . MCGC 6020

Womack, Steve

NORTHERN COMFORT.
LP: . . . . . PLR 044

Womack & Womack

CONSCIENCE.
Tracks: / Conscious of my conscience / MPD / Friends / Slave / Teardrops / Good man monologue / Life's just a ballgame / I am love / Celebrate the world.
MC: . . . . . BRCA 519
LP: . . . . . BRLP 519

FAMILY SPIRIT.
Tracks: / Family spirit / Uptown / Refusal / Living in a different world / United (in paradise) / My dear (the letter) / Blue Jean baby / Danceworld / Keep on climbing / Lonely island.
LP: 211 356
MC: 411 356

LOVE WARS.
LP: 960293

RADIO M.U.S.I.C. MAN.
Tracks: / No release / Maze / Night rider / Eyes / Radio M.U.S.I.C. man / Love's calling / Strange and funny / Romeo and Juliet / Here comes the sun.
LP: . . . . . EKT 6
MC: . . . . . EKT 6 C

STARBRIGHT.
Tracks: / Soul love, soul man / It's my party / Starbright / New York city / Find yourself another girl / Reason (must be love), The / Take me / Rejoice.
LP: . . . . . MTL 1005
MC: . . . . . TCMTL 1005

WOMACK AND WOMACK.
Tracks: / Love wars / Express myself / Baby I'm scared of you / T.K.O. / A.P.B. / Catch and don't look back / Woman / Angie / Good times.
LP: 9602931
MC: 9602934

Woman In Love

WOMAN IN LOVE (Various artists).
LP: . . . . . SLTD 14
MC: . . . . . SLTK 14

Woman In Red (film)

WOMAN IN RED (Film soundtrack) (See under Wonder, Stevie) (Wonder, Stevie).

Woman In White (bk)

WOMAN IN WHITE, THE (William Wilkie Collins) (Holm, Ian (nar)).
MCSET: CC/018

Woman Next Door

WOMAN NEXT DOOR, THE (Original soundtrack) (Various artists).
LP: . . . . . SL 9507
MC: . . . . . SLC 9507

Woman of No ...(bk)

FORTY YEARS ON/A WOMAN OF NO IMPORTANCE (see under Forty Years On (bk) (Gielgud, Sir John/Patricia Routledge (nars)).

Wombats

MUD PUDDLES.
LP: . . . . . HMS 034

Wombles

20 WOMBLING GREATS.
LP: . . . . . PR 5022

KEEP ON WOMBLING.
LP: . . . . . CBS 80526

REMEMBER YOU'RE A WOMBLE.
LP: . . . . . CBS 80191

WOMBLING HITS.
Tracks: / Wombling song / Remember you're a womble / Wombling white tie & tails / Hall of the mountain womble / Minuetto allegretto / Let's womble to the party tonight / Wombling merry Christmas / Orinoco kid, The / Superwomble.
LP: 4661181
MC: 4661184

WOMBLING SONGS.
LP: . . . . . CBS 65803

Women

WOMEN (Various artists).
LP: . . . . **NL 86755**
MC: . . . . **NK 86755**

Women In Love

WOMEN IN LOVE (double cassette) (Various artists).
MCSET: . . . . **DTO 10279**

WOMEN IN LOVE VOL.3 (Various artists).
2LP: . . . . **ADEH 100**

Women Talk

CARIBBEAN DUB POETRY.
LP: . . . . **HB 25**

Wonder Band

STAIRWAY TO LOVE.
Tracks: / Stairway to love / Whole lotta love / Finale / Wonderful medley / Wonder, The / Stairway to heaven.
LP: . . . . **K 50573**

Wonder Bar

WONDER BAR (Original soundtrack) (Various artists).
LP: . . . . **HS 402**

Wonder, Stevie

12-YEAR-OLD GENIUS - LIVE.
Tracks: / Fingertips / Soul bongo la la la la / (I'm afraid) / Masquerade is over, The / Hallelujah / I love her so / Drown in my own tears / Don't you know.
LP: . . . . **STMR 9003**
MC: . . . . **CSTMR 9003**

ANTHOLOGY - STEVIE WONDER.
LPS: **M9 804**

CHARACTERS.
Tracks: / You will know / Dark 'n' lovely / In your corner / With each beat of my heart / One of a kind / Skeletons / Get it / Galaxy paradise / Cryin' through the night / Free / Come let me make your love come down (Track on cassette/CD only.) / My eyes don't cry (on cassette and compact disc only).
LP: . . . . **ZL 72001**
MC: . . . . **ZK 72001**

DOWN TO EARTH.
Tracks: / Place in the sun, A / Bang bang (my baby shot me down) / Down to earth / Thank you love / Be cool be calm (and keep yourself together) / Sylvia / My world is empty without you / Lonesome road / Angel baby / Mr. Tambourine man / Sixteen tons / Hey love.
LP: . . . . **STMS 5022**
MC: . . . . **CSTMS 5022**

EBONY AND IVORY (see McCartney, Paul) (Wonder, Stevie & Paul McCartney).

ESSENTIAL STEVIE WONDER.
Tracks: / Yester-me, yester-you, yesterday / My cherie amour / If you really love me / We can work it out / Signed, sealed, delivered (I'm yours) / Never had a dream come true / Something out of the blue / Heaven help us all / Do yourself a favour / I was made to love her / Thank you love / Until you come back to me / I'm wondering / Shoo-be-doo-be-doo-da-day / Angie girl / More than a dream / For once in my life / You met your match / Don't know why I love you / Uptight / Music talk / Ain't that asking for trouble / Love a-go-go / Nothing's too good for my baby / Be cool be calm (and keep yourself together) / I'd cry / Travellin' man / Place in the sun, A / Blowin' in the wind / Fingertips / Workout Stevie,workout / Hey harmonica man / Kiss me baby / High heel sneakers / Happy Street / Don't you feel it / Castles in the sand / Contract on love / I call it pretty music, but the old folks call it the blues.
2LP: . . . . **WL 72585**
MCSET: . . . . **WK 72585**

FOR ONCE IN MY LIFE.
Tracks: / For once in my life / Shoo-be-doo-be-doo-da-day / You met your match / I wanna make her love me / I'm more than happy (I'm satisfied) / Don't know why I love you / Sunny / I'd be a fool right now / Ain't no lovin' / God bless the child / Do I love her / House on the hill.
LP: . . . . **STMS 5074**
MC: . . . . **CSTMS 5074**
LP: . . . . **WL 72183**
MC: . . . . **WK 72183**

FULFILLINGNESS FIRST FINALE.
Tracks: / Smile please / Heaven is ten zillion light years away / Too shy to say / Boogie on reggae woman / Creepin' / You haven't done nothin' / It ain't no use / They won't go when I go / Bird of beauty / Please don't go.
LP: . . . . **STMA 8019**
MC: . . . . **CSTMA 8019**
MC: . . . . **WK 72607**
LP: . . . . **WL 72607**

GREATEST HITS: STEVIE WONDER.
Tracks: / Shoo-be-doo-be-doo-da-day / Place in the sun, A / Uptight / Travellin' man / High heel sneakers / Sad boy / Kiss me, baby / Workout Stevie, workout / Fingertips (part 2) / Hey, harmonica man / Contract on love / Castles in the sand / Nothing's too good for my baby / I was made to love her / Blowin' in the wind / I'm wondering.
LP: . . . . **STML 11075**
MC: . . . . **CSTML 11075**
LP: . . . . **ZL 72023**
MC: . . . . **ZK 72023**

GREATEST HITS: STEVIE WONDER, VOL.2.
Tracks: / Signed, sealed, delivered (I'm yours) / We can work it out / For once in my life / If you really love me / Shoo-be-doo-be-doo-da-day / You met your match / My Cherie amour / Yester-me, yester-you, yesterday / Never had a dream come true / Heaven help us all / Don't know why I love you / Never dreamed you'd leave in summer.
LP: . . . . **STML 11196**
MC: . . . . **CSTML 11196**
LP: . . . . **ZL 72026**
MC: . . . . **ZK 72026**

HOTTER THAN JULY.
Tracks: / Did I hear you say you love me? / All I do / Rocket love / I ain't gonna stand for it / As if you read my mind / Master blaster / Do like you / Cash in your face / Lately / Happy birthday.
LP: . . . . **STMA 8035**
MC: . . . . **CSTMA 8035**
LP: . . . . **ZL 72015**
MC: . . . . **ZK 72015**

I WAS MADE TO LOVE HER.
Tracks: / I was made to love her / Send me some lovin' / I'd cry / Everybody needs somebody (I need you) / Respect / My girl / Baby don't you do it / Fool for you, A / Can I get a witness / I pity the fool / Please, please, please / Every time I see you I go wild.
LP: . . . . **STMS 5094**
MC: . . . . **CSTMS 5094**

IN SQUARE CIRCLE.
Tracks: / Part time lover / I love you too much / Whereabouts / Stranger on the shore of love / Never in your sun / Spiritual walkers / Land of la la / Go home / Overjoyed / It's wrong (la la) / I wish he didn't trust me so much / Baby don't leave home without it / So many rivers / Got to be with you tonight / What ever happened to those times / Let me kiss it where it hurts / Only survivor / That's where it's at / Check it out.
LP: . . . . **ZL 72005**
MC: . . . . **ZK 72005**

INNERVISIONS.
Tracks: / Too high / Visions / Living for the city / Golden lady / Higher ground / Jesus children of America / All in love is fair / Don't you worry about a thing / He's misstra know it all.
LP: . . . . **STMA 8011**
MC: . . . . **CSTMA 8011**
LP: . . . . **ZL 72012**
MC: . . . . **ZK 72012**

JAZZ SOUL OF LITTLE STEVIE, THE.
Tracks: / Fingertips / Square / Soul bongo / Manhattan at six / Paulsby / Some other time / Wondering / Session number 112 / Barn.
LP: . . . . **STMS 5058**
MC: . . . . **CSTMS 5058**

JUNGLE FEVER (Film Soundtrack).
Tracks: / Fun day / Queen in the black / These three words / Each other's throat / If she breaks your hearts / Gotta have you / Make sure you're sure / Jungle fever / I go sailing / Chemical love / Lighting up the candles.
LP: . . . . **ZL 72750**
MC: . . . . **ZK 72750**

LIGHT MY FIRE.
LP: . . . . **MFP 50420**

LIVE AT THE TALK OF THE TOWN.
Tracks: / Pretty world / Never had a dream come true / Shoo-be-doo-be-doo-da-day / My cherie amour / Alfie / Bridge over troubled water / For once in my life / Yester-me, yester-you, yesterday / I was made to love her / Signed, sealed, delivered (I'm yours).
LP: . . . . **WL 72369**
MC: . . . . **WK 72369**

LOVE SONGS: STEVIE WONDER (TELSTAR).
Tracks: / My cherie amour / Yester-me, yester-you, yesterday / Never had a dream come true / If you really love me / Heaven help us all / Never dreamed you'd leave in Summer / Place in the sun, A / Alfie / For once in my life / We can work it out / I was made to love her / Don't know why I love you / Blowin' in the wind / I'm wondering / Shoo-be-doo-be-doo-da-day / Signed, sealed, delivered I'm yours.
LP: . . . . **STAR 2251**
MC: . . . . **STAC 2251**

MUSIC OF MY MIND.
Tracks: / Love having you around / Superwoman / I love every little thing about you / Sweet little girl / Happier than the morning sun / Girl blue / Seems so long / Keep on running / Evil.
LP: . . . . **STMA 8002**
MC: . . . . **CSTMA 8002**
LP: . . . . **ZL 72146**

MY CHERIE AMOUR.
Tracks: / My cherie amour / Hello young lovers / At last / Light / Light my fire / Shadow of your smile / You and me / Pearl / Somebody knows somebody cares / Yester you yester me yesterday / Angie girl / Give you love / I've got you.
LP: . . . . **WL 72077**
MC: . . . . **WK 72077**
LP: . . . . **STML 11128**
LP: . . . . **STMS 5024**

ORIGINAL MUSIQUARIUM.
Tracks: / Isn't she lovely / You are the sunshine of my life / Higher ground / Superwoman / Send me your love / Do I do / Superstition / Living for the city / Front line / You haven't done nothin' / Sir Duke / Ribbon in the sky / Masterblaster / That girl / I wish / Boogie on reggae woman.
2LP: . . . . **TMSP 6012**

PEOPLE MOVE HUMAN PLAY.
LP: . . . . **STMA 8040**
MC: . . . . **CSTMA 8040**

POPS, WE LOVE YOU (see under Ross, Diana) (Ross, Diana/Stevie Wonder/ Marvin Gaye/Smokey Robinson).

SECRET LIFE OF PLANTS.
LP: . . . . **ZL 72145**
MC: . . . . **ZK 72145**

SECRET LIFE OF PLANTS.
Tracks: / Earth's creation / First garden, The / Voyage to India / Same old story / Venus flytrap and the bug / Ai no sono / Seed's a star and tree medley, A / Power flower / Secret life of plants, The / Tree / Finale / Send one your love / Race babbling (instrumental) / Send one your love / Outside my window / Black orchid / Ecclesiastes / Kesse ye lolo de ye / Come back as a flower.
2LP: . . . . **TMSP 6009**
MCSET: . . . . **CTMSP 6009**

SIGNED, SEALED, DELIVERED, I'M YOURS.
Tracks: / Never had a dream come true / We can work it out / Signed, sealed, delivered, I'm yours / Heaven help us all / You can't judge a book by the cover / Sugar / Don't wonder why / Anything you want me to do / I can't let my heaven walk away / Joy (takes over me) / I gotta have a song / Something to say.
LP: . . . . **STMS 5025**
MC: . . . . **CSTMS 5025**
LP: . . . . **WL 72186**
MC: . . . . **WK 72186**

SOME DAY AT CHRISTMAS.
Tracks: / Some day at Christmas / Silver bells / Ave Maria / Little drummer boy / One little Christmas tree / Day that love began, The / Christmas song, The / Bedtime for toys / Christmastime / Twinkle twinkle little me / Warm little home a hill, A / What Christmas means to me.
LP: . . . . **STMS 5086**
MC: . . . . **CSTMS 5086**
LP: . . . . **WL 72357**
MC: . . . . **WK 72357**

SONGS IN THE KEY OF LIFE.
Tracks: / Love's in need of love today / Have a talk with God / Village ghetto land / Confusion / I am singing / If it's magic / As / Another star / I wish / Knocks me off my feet / Pastime paradise / Summer soft / Ordinary pain / Isn't she lovely / Joy inside my tears / Black man / Sir Duke / Ngiculela es una historia.
2LP: . . . . **TMSP 6002**
MCSET: . . . . **CTMSP 6002**
2LP: . . . . **ZL 72131**
MCSET: . . . . **ZK 72131**

STEVIE WONDER'S ORIGINAL MUSIQUARIUM.
LP: . . . . **ZL 72133**
MC: . . . . **CTSMP 6012**

TALKING BOOK.
Tracks: / You are the sunshine of my life / Maybe your baby / You and I / Tuesday heartbreak / You've got it bad, girl / Superstition / Big Brother / Blame it on the sun / Lookin' for another true love / I believe.
LP: . . . . **STMA 8007**
MC: . . . . **CSTMA 8007**
LP: . . . . **ZL 72011**
MC: . . . . **ZK 72011**

TRIBUTE TO UNCLE RAY.
Tracks: / Hallelujah, I love her so / Ain't that love? / Don't you know? / Masquerade, The / Frankie and Johnny / Drown in my own tears / Come back, baby / Mary Ann / Sunset / My baby's gone.
LP: . . . . **STMS 5059**
MC: . . . . **CSTMS 5059**

UPTIGHT.
Tracks: / Love a go go / Hold me / Blowing in the wind / Nothing's too good for my baby / Teach me tonight / Uptight / Ain't that asking for trouble / I want my baby back / Pretty little angel / Music talk / Contract on love / With a child's heart.
LP: . . . . **STMS 5023**
MC: . . . . **CSTMS 5023**
LP: . . . . **TMS 3504**
MC: . . . . **TMC 3504**
LP: . . . . **WL 72185**

WHERE I'M COMING FROM.
Tracks: / Look around / Do yourself a favour / Think of me as your soldier / Something out of the blue / If you really love me / I wanna talk to you / Take up a course in happiness / Never dreamed you'd leave in summer / Sunshine in their eyes.
LP: . . . . **STMS 5075**
MC: . . . . **CSTMS 5075**
LP: . . . . **WL 72108**
MC: . . . . **WK 72108**

WITH A SONG IN MY HEART.
Tracks: / With a song in my heart / When you wish upon a star / Smile / Make someone happy / Dream / Put on a happy face / On the sunny side of the street / Get happy / Give your heart a chance / Without a song.
LP: . . . . **STMS 5060**
MC: . . . . **CSTMS 5060**

WOMAN IN RED (Film soundtrack).
Tracks: / Woman in red / It's you / It's more than you / I just called to say I love you / Love light in flight / Moments aren't moments / Weakness / Don't drive drunk.
LP: . . . . **ZL 72285**
MC: . . . . **ZK 72285**

Wonder Stuff

EIGHT LEGGED GROOVE MACHINE, THE.
Tracks: / Red berry joy town / No for the 13th time / It's yer money I'm after baby / Rue the day / Give give give me more more more / Merry go round / Animals and me, The / Wish away, A / Grin / Mother and I / Sad sad someone / Ruby horse / Unbearable / Poison.
LP: . . . . **GONLP 1**
MC: . . . . **GONMC 1**

HUP.
Tracks: / 30 years in the bathroom / Piece of sky / Golden green / Don't let me down gently / Cartoon boyfriend / Good night though / Them big oak trees / Room 410 / Let's be other people / Unfaithful / Can't shape up / Radio ass kiss.
LP: **841 187-1**
MC: **841 187-4**

NEVER LOVED ELVIS.
Tracks: / Never loved Elvis.
LP: **847 252-1**

Wonder, Wayne

WAYNE WONDER.
LP: . . . . **DGLP 20**

WAYNE WONDER AND SANCHEZ PT. 2 (Wonder, Wayne & Sanchez).
LP: . . . . **DGLP 21**

Wonder Woman...

WONDER WOMAN IN TORMENT IN PARADISE (Various artists).
MC: **41 5718 4**

Wonderama

CHAOSTROPHY.
Tracks: / Chaostrophy.
MC: . . . . **RES 339134**

Wonderful... (bk)

WONDERFUL WHAT A MESS (See under Muir, Frank).

Wonderful Town

WONDERFUL TOWN (Original London Cast) (Various artists).
Tracks: / Wonderful town (overture): *Various artists* / Christopher Street: *Various artists* / Ohio: *Various artists* / One hundred ways to lose a man: *Various artists* / What a waste: *Various artists* / Little bit in love, A: *Various artists* / Pass the football: *Various artists* / Conversation piece: *Various artists*/ Quiet girl: *Various artists* / Conga: *Various artists* / Darling Eileen: *Various artists* / Swing: *Various artists* / It's love: *Various artists* / Vortex ballet: *Various artists* / Wrong note rag: *Various artists*/ Finale: *Various artists.*
LP: . . . . **CAST 6**
MC: . . . . **CASTC 6**

WONDERFUL TOWN (Original Broadway Cast) (Various artists).

LP: MCA 1528
MC: MCAC 1528

Wonderful Wizard Of Oz

WONDERFUL WIZARD OF OZ (Percival, Lance (nar)).
MC: P 90017

Wonderful World

WONDERFUL WORLD (Various artists).
LP: KM 006
MC: KMCAS 006

Wonderland

MOSCOW.
Tracks: / Moscow / Poochy / Boomerang / Peeping and hiding / Jump Anna trampolene / Count down / Teachers and preachers / On my way / Rock and roll people / King of America / Gas balloon / Try to be what you are / Do you remember / Burdon / Mama.
LP: BTS 943400

NO. 1.
Tracks: / Heya Donan Laya / Liberal, The / John F Baverstock / Heavy rider / I make music / Country clown / Unfaithful / Hill, The.
LP: BTS 943402

Wonderwall

BLUEPRINT.
LP: BYO 21

Woo Woo Kid

WOO WOO KID, THE (Original soundtrack) (Various artists).
LP: K 781 781 1
MC: K 781 781 4

Wood Children

GODS MUST BE CRAZY.
LP: ABB 11X

SHOPAHOLIC.
Tracks: / Fine by me / Talk about yourself again / Vat of tea / Mannipple / Can't stand the sound of my own voice / Pollute my heart / Epitaph for Miss World / Worlds apart / Heroin(e) / Golden mine / You cheated me / Heart of the matter / Sell my soul (Available on CD only) / Tribe (Available on CD only) / Aeroplane (Available on CD only) / Maybe mood (Available on CD only).
LP: FIEND 155
MC: FIENDCASS 155

Wood, John (nar)

SHERLOCK HOLMES' ADVENTURES (see under Sherlock Holmes (bk).

Wood, Mark

LA MEZCLA.
Tracks: / La mezcla / Fourplay / Rainmaker / Dream J.D. / Be yourself / Big squeeze / Soft loft, The / User friendly / Made in Japan / Chorale.
LP: LPMMC 1015
MC: TCMMC 1015

Wood, Robert

TAROT.
LP: ED 00 61020

Wood, Ronnie

1, 2, 3, 4.
Tracks: / 1, 2, 3, 4 / Fountain of love / Outlaws / Redeyes / Wind howlin' through / Priceless / She was out there / Down to the ground / She never told me.
LP: CBS 85227

1 2 3 4 / GIMME SOME NECK.
2LP: TFOLP 25
MC: TFOMC 25

CANCEL EVERYTHING.
Tracks: / I can feel the fire / Far east man / Mystifies me / Take a look at the guy / Act together / Am I groovin' you / Shirley / Cancel everything / Sure the one you need / If you gotta make a fool of somebody / Crotch music.
LP: THBL 2.034
MC: THBC 2.034
LPPD: THBL 2.034P

GIMME SOME NECK.
Tracks: / Worry no more / Breaking my heart / Delia / Buried alive / Come to realise / Infekshun / Seven days / We all get old / F.U.C. her / Lost and lonely / Don't worry.
LP: CBS 83337

MAHONEY'S LAST STAND (Wood, Ronnie & Ronnie Lane).
Tracks: / Tonights number / From the late to the early / Chicken wired / Chicken wired / I'll fly away / Title one / Just for a moment / Mona the blues / Car radio / Hay tumble / Woody's thing / Rooster funeral.
LP: THBL 067
LPPD: THBL 067P

NOW LOOK.
Tracks: / I got lost when I found you / Big bayou / Breathe on me / If you don't want my love for you / I can say she's alright / Caribbean boogie / Now look / Sweet baby of mine / I can stand the rain / It's unholy / I got a feeling.
LP: THBL 046
MC: THBC 046
LPPD: THBL 046P

Wood, Roy

BEST OF AND THE REST OF, THE (Wood, Roy & Wizzard).
Tracks: / Indiana rainbow / Any old time will do / Look thru the eyes of a fool / Rattlesnake roll / Rain came down on everything, The / I can't help my feelings / Marathon man / Thing is this, The / Are you ready to rock / Mustard / You sure got it now / Why does such a pretty girl sing / Those sad songs / Song,The / Get on down home / Strider / Dream on Unwin / Bengal jig / Rock and roll winter.
MC: ARLC 1009

BEST OF ROY WOOD (1970-1974).
Tracks: / Ball park incident / Tonight / Brontosaurus / Until your mamas gone / Angel fingers / When grandma plays the piano / California man / See my baby jive / Chinatown / Dear elaine / When alice comes back to the farm / Forever / I wish it could be christmas every day / Goin' down the road.
LP: MFP 41 5697 1
MC: MFP 41 5697 4

BOULDERS.
LP: SHVL 803

MANCUNIAN WAY, THE (see under Perry, Roy).

SINGLES, THE.
Tracks: / See my baby jive / Are you ready to rock / Oh what a shame / Fire brigade / Forever / I can hear the grass grow / OTT / Blackberry way / Angel fingers / We're on the road again / Flowers in the rain / Green glass windows / Keep your hands on the wheel / Rock & roll winter / This is the story of my love (baby).
LP: SPEED 1000

STARTING UP.
Tracks: / Red cars are after me / Raining in the city / Under fire / Turn your body to the light / Hot cars / Starting up / Keep it steady / On top of the world / Ships in the night.
LP: LLP 106
MC: LLK 106

YOU CAN DANCE THE ROCK 'N' ROLL (Roy Wood Years '71-'73).
Tracks: / Ball park incident / Until your moma's gone / Dear Elaine / Ella James / First movement / California man / Whisper in the night / Chinatown / You can dance your rock 'n' roll / Forever / Angel fingers / Look at me now / Tonight / See my baby jive / Wake up (CD only.) / It wasn't my idea to dance (CD only.) / Nancy, sing me a song (CD only.) / Songs of praise (CD only.).
LP: SHSM 2030
MC: TCSHSM 2030

Wood, Scott

SCOTT WOOD & HIS SIX SWINGERS (1935-1936).
LP: SH 249

Wood, Smokey

HOUSTON HIPSTER,THE.
LP: RAMBLER 107

Wood, Tim

GETTING YOUR OWN BACK.
LP: CM 008

WHISPER, THE.
LP: DWM 001

Wood, Victoria

LUCKY BAG (Victoria Wood as seen on TV).
LP: VCLP 001
MC: 2CVCL 1

SMILE SONG, THE (See Under Hale & Pace - "The Stonk').

VICTORIA WOOD LIVE.
Tracks: / It would never have worked / Barry and Freda / Happy to be here / Holidays / Sex / Hospital.
LP: SCX 6716
MC: TCSCX 6716

Wood, Windy

WEST TEXAS SWING.
Tracks: / Let's be sure we know / Somewhere in San Antone / Sugar moon / Texas bluebonnet swing / Don't keep it a secret / Ten years / Right or wrong / Rosetta / If no news is good news / Heart to heart talk / When my dreamboat comes home / Orange blossom special.
LP: SDLP 036
MC: SDC 036

Woodbine, Lizzie

NIGHT OUT WITH WOODBINE LIZZIE, A.
Tracks: / Whiskey in the jar / Whistling gypsy / D-day dodgers / My brother Sylveste / Take me on to t'fair / Brewer's droop / Ballad of Jed Clampett / Foggy moutain breakdown / Putting on the style / Folker, The / Honky tonk music.
LP: FE 025

WOODBINE LIZZIE BY NUMBERS.
Tracks: / They don't write 'em like that any more / Dirty photographs / And the band played Waltzing Matilda / Three score and ten / Folker, The / Wild mountain thyme / Jolly Waggoners / Olga from the Volga / Soldier, The / Twa recruiting sergeants / Windy Sue / Icy acres.
LP: FE 019

Woodcocks

WOODCOCKS.
Tracks: / Raul / Lester's lament / This old man / Wagoneer / Everclear / Keep me sane / Young country / Instrumental / Tisons.
LP: 089211

Wooden Buds

MONSTER WALKS ON WINTER LAKE, THE (see Thomas, David & The Wooden Buds).

Wooden Horse

WOODEN HORSE (Eric Williams) (Hancock,Sheila).
MC: TCLFP 417 122 5

Woodentops

GIANT.
LP: ROUGH 87
MC: ROUGHC 87

HYPNOBEAT LIVE.
Tracks: / Well well well / Love train / Travelling man / Get it on / Plenty / Why / Everyday living / Good thing / Everything breaks / Move me.
LP: ROUGH 117
MC: ROUGHC 117

WOODEN FOOT COPS ON THE HIGHWAY.
LP: ROUGH 127
MC: ROUGHC 127

Woodhouse, Barbara

TRAINING DOGS THE WOODHOUSE WAY.
LP: REC 455
MC: ZCM 455

Woodland & Garden

WOODLAND AND GARDEN BIRDS (Various).
2LP: REF 235
MC: HRMC 235

Woodland, Jim

MIRACLES.
MC: HARC 008

Woodleiff, Norman

LONNIE AUSTIN AND NORMAN WOODLEIFF (Woodleiff, Norman & Lonnie Austin).
LP: LEA 4045

Woodman, Britt

IN L.A..
LP: FJP 100

Woodroffe, Jezz

JEZZ WOODROFFE.
LP: GRADLP 1

Woods

IT'S LIKE THIS.
Tracks: / Sign of the times / Next rain / Girlfriends / Chain my heart / Some other world / I don't want her (anymore) / Battleship chains / Sand / What about me / Close as you get / Why / Come off with your lies.
LP: FIEND 93

Woods Band

WOODS BAND, THE.
LP: LUN 015

Woods, Gay

TENDER HOOKS (Woods, Gay & Terry).
LP: MUL 020

Woods, Ian

HOOKS AND NETS (Woods, Ian/ Charley Yarwood).
LP: TSR 044

Woods, Jimmy

CONFLICT (Woods, Jimmy Sextet).
Tracks: / Apart together / Look to your heart / Pazmuerte / Aim / Conflict / Coming home.
LP: COP 005

Woods, Mick

TRIBUTE TO JOHN MCKENNA.
LP: INC 7420

Woods, Mitch

MR. BOOGIE'S BACK IN TOWN (Woods, Mitch & His Rocket 88s).
LP: BP-2888

STEADY DATE (Woods, Mitch & His Rocket 88s).
LP: BP-1784

Woods, Oscar 'Buddy'

COMPLETE RECORDINGS 1930-38.
LP: DLP 517

Woods, Pat

CONCERT REQUESTS.
Tracks: / Fields of Athenry / Nancy Spain / Molly darlin' / Rathlin Island / Gentle Annie / Whistling gypsy / Little sweetheart in the spring / Leaving Nancy / Silver in the stubble / When you & I were young Maggie / Abbeyshrule / My own native land / Red is the rose / Rose of Allandale.
LP: PHL 467
MC: CPHL 467

IN THE CORNER OF MY PRISON CELL.
Tracks: / In the corner of my prison cell (Side 1 track 1. 3.45 minutes.) / When it's moonlight in Mayo (Side 1 track 2) / May morning dew,The (Side 1 track 3) / Moonshiner (Side 1 track 4) / Village of Astee, The (Side 1 track 5) / Donegal Rose (Side 1 track 6) / Kitty Wells (Side 1 track 7) / Croce di oro (Cross of gold) (Side 2 track 1) / Rose of Clare (Side 2 track 2) / My Kathleen (Side 2 track 3) / Slievenamon (Side 2 track 4) / Shamrock on mother's grave (Side 2 track 5) / Blarney stone, The (Side 2 track 6) / In a little pub in London (Side 2 track 7).
MC: CPHL 492

PAT WOODS FROM COUNTY ARMAGH.
LP: HRL 191

RARE OULD TIMES.
Tracks: / Come back Paddy Reilly to Ballyjamesduff / Master McGrath / Green willow / Cruel war / My home in County Down / And the band played Waltzing Matilda / Rare ould times / Guinness song / When you were sweet sixteen / My Lagan flows softly / Hills of Kerry / Galway Bay.
LP: PHL 454
MC: UNKNOWN

WILD COLONIAL BOY, THE.
Tracks: / Astoreen Bawn / Treat my daughter kindly / Wind in the willows / Rambles of spring / Give an Irish girl to me / Mary from Dungloe / Isle of Innisfree / Any Tipperary town / Curragh of Kildare, The / Ferryman, The / Wild colonial boy / Old rustic bridge.
LP: PHL 481
MC: CPHL 481

Woods, Phil

ALL BIRD'S CHILDREN (Woods, Phil Quintet).
Tracks: / All bird's children / Gotham serenade / Ixtlan / My man Benny / From this moment on / Best is yet to come, The / Just a mood / Ole dude / With a song in my heart.
MC: CJ 441 C

BOP STEW (Woods, Phil Quintet).
Tracks: / Dreamsville / Bop stew / Poor Butterfly / Yes there is a Coya.
LP: CJ 345
MC: CJ 345 C

BOUQUET (Live at the Fujitsu Concord Jazz Festival) (Woods, Phil Quintet).
LP: CJ 377
MC: CJ 377 C

CHROMATIC BANANA.
Tracks: / Chromatic banana / Ultimate choice / Sans melodie / Look back / Day when the world comes alive.
LP: AFF 84

CRAZY HORSE (Woods, Phil & Chris Swansen).
LP: SB 2008

DIZZY GILLESPIE MEETS PHIL WOODS QUINTET (see under Gillespie, Dizzy) (Woods, Phil Quintet).

EUROPEAN TOUR, LIVE.
LP: VPA 163

EVOLUTION (Woods Phil, Little Big Band).
Tracks: / Alvin G / Black flag / Hal mallet / Miles ahead (Only on CD.) / Rain go away (Only on CD.) / Song for Sisyphus / Thaddeus / Which way is uptown.
LP: CJ 361
MC: CJ 361 C

FLASH (Woods, Phil Quintet Plus One).
Tracks: / Journey to the center / Autumn nocturne / Dr Dunk / Flash / Misirlou / Ebullition / Weaver (Available on CD only) / Rado (Available on CD only) / Bradley's revenge (Available on CD only).
MC: CJ 408C

GRATITUDE (Woods, Phil Quartet).
Tracks: / 111-444 / Another Jones / Gratitude / My azure / Serenade in blue /

Tenor of the times / Times mirror / Ya know.
MC: . . . . CC 14

HEAVEN (Woods, Phil Quintet).
Tracks: / I'm getting sentimental over you / Heaven / Duke, The / Azure / 222 / Occurrence.
LP: . . . . BKH 50401
MC: . . . . BKHMC 50401

INTEGRITY (Woods, Phil Quintet).
2LP: . . . . VPA 177

LIVE AT ARMADILLO (Woods, Phil Quartet).
LP: . . . . ECJ 401

MUSIQUE DU BOIS.
LP: . . . . MR 5037

MY MAN BENNY, MY MAN PHIL (See under Carter, Benny) (Woods, Phil & Benny Carter).

PAIRING OFF.
LP: . . . . OJC 092

PHIL & QUILL WITH PRESTIGE (Woods, Phil/Gene Quill quintet).
LP: . . . . OJC 215

PHIL WOODS LIVE.
Tracks: / Sleepin' bee, A / Rain danse / Bye bye baby / Django's castle (all mine almost) / Cheek to cheek / I'm late / Superwoman (where were you when I needed you) / High clouds / How's your mama (Phil's theme).
MC: . . . . NK 83104

PHIL WOODS SIX, THE.
Tracks: / Sleepin' bee, A / Rain danse / Bye bye baby / Django's castle / I'm late / Superwoman (where were you when I needed you) / High clouds / How's your mama (Phil's theme) / Cheek to cheek / Lady J / Little Niles / Little peace, A / Brazilian affair / Prelude (preludio) / Love song (Cancao de amor) / Wedding dance / Joy (alegria).
LP: . . . . PL 02202

PIPER AT THE GATES OF DAWN (Woods, Phil & Chris Swansen).
LP: . . . . SB 2019

RIGHTS OF SWING.
Tracks: / Prelude and part 1 / Part 2 (ballad) / Part 2 (waltz) / Part 4 (scherzo) / Part 5 (presto).
LP: . . . . CS 9016

SONG FOR SISYPHUS (Woods, Phil Quintet).
Tracks: / Song for Sisyphus / Last night when we were young / Nuages / Change partners / Monking business / Summer afternoon / When my dreams come true / Shaw 'nuff.
LP: . . . . PL 25179

THREE FOR ALL (Woods, Phil/Tommy Flanagan/Red Mitchell).
LP: . . . . ENJA 3081

WOODS NOTES (Woods, Phil & European Rhythm Machine).
LP: . . . . LOP 14 083

Woods, Rev. Maceo

BRINGING IN THE SHEAVES.
LP: . . . . DBL 7074

Woods, Rosemary

IRISH BALLADS.
LP: . . . . HRL 221

Woodstock Mountains

BACK TO MUD ACRES.
LP: . . . . ROUNDER 3065
MC: . . . . ROUNDER 3065C

PRETTY LUCKY.
LP: . . . . ROUNDER 3025

Woodstock Workshop

NEW MOON.
LP: . . . . PAL 15007

Woodvale Quintet

GUIDE ME LORD.
LP: . . . . PC 36

Woodvine, John

JOE LIVES.
Tracks: / Keep your feet still Geordie Hinny / Geordie haud the bairn / No work, O dear what mun I de / Row upon the stairs, The / Landlord's daughter, The / Strike, The / Charity / Snooks' Dinah / Teetotal doo / Drunken dolly / Sally Wheatley / Fightin' Dan / Neighbour Nell / Me mother's warnin.
LP: . . . . MWM 1003

Woodward, Edward

AFRICAN QUEEN, THE (C.S. Forester).
MC: . . . . TC LFP 7072

DON'T GET AROUND MUCH ANYMORE.
Tracks: / Whiffenpoof song, The / My foolish heart / I'll remember April / I couldn't sleep a wink last night / I've heard that song before / Lazy river / Nightingale sang in Berkeley Square, A / Me and my girl / As time goes by / Lili Marlene.
LP: . . . . DJM 22099
MC: . . . . DJM 42099
LP: . . . . DJF 20559

EDWARDIAN WOODWARD.
Tracks: / Champagne Charlie / I'll be your sweetheart / Comrades / Silver threads / Broken doll / In the twi twilight / I'm shy Mary Ellen / They didn't believe me / Goodbye Dolly Gray / I'll take you home again Kathleen / I wonder who's kissing her now / Who were you with last night.
LP: . . . . DJM 22096
MC: . . . . DJM 42096

LOVE IS THE KEY.
Tracks: / Love song / Way we were, The / Play me / Last thing on my mind / What I did for love / Send in the clowns / If you go away / Feelings / Our love / My love / Someday / Happy days, The / I need you to turn to.
LP: . . . . DJM 22097
MC: . . . . DJM 42097

ROMANTIC HOUR.
MCSET: . . . . TWO 416

THIS EDWARD WOODWARD ALBUM.
LP: . . . . JAM 103

THIS MAN ALONE.
LP: . . . . DJLPS 405

THOUGHT OF YOU, THE.
Tracks: / Can't smile without you / Time in a bottle / You are beautiful / Folks who live on the hill, The / Smile / Party's over, The / I'm old fashioned / Growing older / Feeling younger / I've told every little star / Love look at us now / Very thought of you, The / Evergreen.
LP: . . . . DJM 22098
MC: . . . . DJM 42098

WOODWARD AGAIN.
Tracks: / Lights of Cincinnati / If ever I would leave you / And I love you so / Carry on London / Leon / Have you seen the most beautiful girl in the world / Love of my life / If / How good it is to know you / Try to remember / Somewhere in the world.
LP: . . . . DJM 22095
MC: . . . . DJM 42095

Woofe, Vicki

SHAPE UP FOR SEX.
Tracks: / Wherever I lay my hat / Red red wine / Do you really want to hurt me / Tahiti / It's late.
LP: . . . . LEG 24
MC: . . . . LEGC 24

Wooley, Sheb

BLUE GUITAR.
Tracks: / Whatcha gonna do? / It takes a heap of livin' / Humdinger / Boogie woogie waltz / Don't stop kissing me tonight / Hillbilly mambo / Texas tango / Panama Pete / Blue guitar / Changing your name (Now you're) / Fool about you / Listening to your footsteps / Knew I had lost / I'll return the letters / Love at first sight / Aircastle.
LP: . . . . BFX 15175

COUNTRY BOOGIE, WILD & WOOLEY (1948-1955).
Tracks: / Love is a fever / Tom / Boogie woogie Tom Cat, The / Mule boogie / Country kisses / Hoot owl boogie / I go outa my mind / I flipped / Back room boogie / Over the barrel / White lightning / Down in the toolies / 38 25 35 / You're the cat's meow / Love is just another merry go round / Wha' happen to my baby / Rover scoot over.
LP: . . . . BFX 15099

Woolf, Virginia (aut)

MRS. DALLOWAY / TO THE LIGHTHOUSE (Johnson, Celia (nar)).
MC: 1105

ROOM OF ONE'S OWN, A (Bloom, Claire (nar)).
MC: 1718

Woolley, Bruce

ENGLISH GARDEN (Woolley, Bruce & Camera Club).
Tracks: / English garden / Video killed the radio star / Dancing with the sporting boys / Johnny / No surrender / Flying man / You got class / W.W.9. instrumental / Clean clean / Get away William / Goodbye to yesterday / You're the circus.
LP: . . . . EPC 83893

Woolley, Robert

CARLOS SEIXAS HARPSICHORD SONATAS (see under Seixas (composer)).

Woolley, Shep

GOODBYE SAILOR.
Tracks: / Messing around in the dockyard / Nobby Hall / Regulating school Olympic games, The / Fishing for Octopus / Jenny Wren bride / Manuel the Maltese dockyard law enforcement officer / Wrens on Waterloo station / Bernards suit, The / Battle of Trafalgar / Montague whale / Night in the North Sea, A / Royal Naval rules for snake bites / Roll on me time / Southsea love song / Loneliest day in the navy, The.
2LP: . . . . SFAX 068

PIPE DOWN.
Tracks: / Wayward boy, The / Girl with the cauliflower ears, The / Irish bank robber, The / Nellie Higginbottom / Ram it I'm R.D.P. / Working on the buses in Brum / Little Aggie / Casey's last ride / Desert Island risque / Best of society, The.
LP: . . . . SFA 008

SONGS OF OARS AND SCRUBBERS & OTHER DIRTY HABITS.
Tracks: / Introduction / Handy household help / Rubber fetishist, The / Side by side / Sam's medal / Moonbeams / Does your hair hang low? / Skinheads / Antiseptic C and W song / Gnome, The / Draft dodger's rag.
LP: . . . . SFA 028

Woolly Rhino

WOOLLY RHINO, THE (Shelley, Norman).
LP: . . . . ZDSW 729

Woosh, Jah

DJ LEGEND.
LP: . . . . OMLP 9

DREADLOCKS AFFAIR.
Tracks: / Omega dollar / Midnight version / Albert Classau / Shimi skank / Riding melody / Falling in love / Dreadlocks affair / Natty ball head / Don't do that / Rocking blues / Black freedom / In deh.
LP: . . . . TRLS 133

MARIJUANA WORLD TOUR.
LP: . . . . OMLP 017

REBELLION (Woosh, Jah & Sis Bee).
LP: . . . . BM 1003

RELIGIOUS DREAD.
Tracks: / Religious dread / Going to the hill / More love / Racialism / Chant freedom / Pagan men / Reggae music / Four aces skank / Marcus say / Take heed / Justice for I / Straight to pagan heart.
LP: . . . . TRLS 157

SENSIMELIA SONG.
LP: . . . . OMLP 020

WE CHAT YOU ROC (Woosh, Jah & I. Roy).
LP: . . . . TRLS 296
MC: . . . . ZCTRL 296

Wooten Brothers

TRY MY LOVE.
LP: 3953311

Wootton, Brenda

BOY JAN... CORNISHMAN.
Tracks: / Boy Jan / Humphrey Davy / Mermaid, The / Abel George / Tishomingo blues / Kerra kernow / Five threes / Allan apple / Loving eyes / James Ruse / Charlie Bate / I wish that I were crossing now / Pensevyk byghan.
LP: . . . . BURL 005

CARILLON.
Tracks: / Cornwall the land I love / Rape of the mackerel shoal / I love again / Kenavo dew genough why / Paris / Silver net / Reed beds of Erygh / Love's old sweet refrain / Eles (she angel) / Country style.
LP: . . . . TRA 360

GWAVAS LAKE (with the Four Lanes Male Choir).
Tracks: / Ma chere cornouaille / Le chouchenn / Tamar / An duren / Plougastel / Little eyes / Les mademoiselles de guilvinec / Hello how do you do / Can yffarn / Chere Patrie / Kernow he breizh / Mon dieu / La belle histoire d'amour.
LP: . . . . BURL 008

LA GRANDE CORNOUALLAISE.
Tracks: / Ma chere Cornouaille / Le chouchenn / Tamar / An duren / Plougastel / Little eyes / Les mademoiselles de guilvinec / Canyffarn / Chere patrie / Kernow he breizh / Mon dieu / La belle histoire d'amour.
LP: . . . . BURL 007

MY LAND.
LP: . . . . PL 70234
MC: . . . . PK 70234

SEAGULL.
LP: 506223
MC: 706223

Wop Bop Torledo

WOP BOP TORLEDO.
LP: . . . . DIX 87
MC: . . . . CDIX 87

Worcester Cathedral

CHRISTMAS CAROLS (Worcester Cathedral Choir).
Tracks: / Past three o' clock / Holly and the ivy, The / On Christmas night 'Sussex carol' / Silent night / God rest ye merry gentlemen / Away in a manger / Twelve days of Christmas / I saw three ships / Bethlehem down / Come all you worthy gentlemen / Come all ye faithful Christians / In the bleak mid winter / Fantasia on Christmas Carols / Noel noel / O little town of Bethlehem / Whild shepherds watched their flocks / Once in Royal David's City / Hark the herald angels sing.
LP: . . . . ETMP 9

MUSIC FOR CHRISTMAS (Worcester Cathedral Choir).
LP: . . . . LPB 787

WORCESTER CATHEDRAL CHOIR (Worcester Cathedral Choir).
Tracks: / I was glad / How lovely are Thy dwellings / Locus iste / Ave verum corpus / God so loved the world / Blessed be the God and Father.
LP: . . . . XPS 105
LP: . . . . LPB 764

Worcestershire...

MARCH 'N' SWING AND THE WOOFERS (Worcestershire & Sherwood Foresters Regiment).
LP: . . . . MM 0561

WOOFERS IN CONCERT (Worcestershire & Sherwood Foresters Regiment).
LP: . . . . MM 0603

WOOFERS ON TOUR (Worcestershire & Sherwood Foresters Regiment).
LP: . . . . MM 0524

Word Soun' 'Ave Power

WORD SOUN' 'AVE POWER (Various artists).
LP: . . . . HB 15
MC: . . . . HBC 15

Words & Music

WORDS AND MUSIC/THREE LITTLE WORDS (Film Soundtracks) (Various artists).
Tracks: / Manhattan: *Rooney, Mickey* (Words & Music.) / Johnny one note: *Garland, Judy* (Words & Music.) / There's a small hotel: *Garrett, Betty* (Words & Music.) / Lady is a tramp, The: *Horne, Lena* (Words & Music.) / Where's that rainbow?: *Sothern Ann* (Words & Music.) / I wish I were in love again: *Rooney, Mickey/Judy Garland* (Words & Music.) / Where or when: *Horne, Lena* (Words & Music.) / Thou swell: *Allyson, June* (Words & Music.) / Slaughter on Tenth Avenue (Ballet): *Various artists* (Words & Music.) / All alone Monday: *Robbins, Gale* (Three Little Words.) / Who's sorry now?: *De Haven, Gloria* (Three Little Words.) / I wanna be loved by you: *Kane, Helen* (Three Little Words.) / Nevertheless (I'm in love with you): *Astaire, Fred/Red Skelton/Anita Ellis* (Three Little Words.) / I love you so much: *Dahl, Arlene* (Three Little Words.) / Where did you get that girl: *Astaire, Fred/Anita Ellis* (Three Little Words.) / Thinking of you: *Ellis, Anita* (Three Little Words.) / Three little words: *Astaire, Fred* (Three Little Words.).
LP: . . . . LPMGM 14
LP: 794 159 1
MC: . . . . TCMGM 14
MC: 794 159 4

Wordsworth, William

POETRY OF WORDSWORTH, THE (Hardwicke, Sir Cedric).
MC: 1026

Worell, Rev. S.J.

BLACK BILLY SUNDAY (Worell, Rev. S.J. "Steamboat Bill").
LP: . . . . WSE 136

Work Don't...

WORK DON'T BOTHER ME Old time comic songs (Various artists).
LP: . . . . ROUNDER 1035

Work For The Future

WORK FOR THE FUTURE (PART 1) (Various artists).
LP: . . . . JLLP 020

Work, Jimmy

CRAZY MOON.
Tracks: / Don't play with my heart / If I should lose you / Crazy moon / I'm lonesome for someone / Little popcorn man / How can I love you / Puttin' on the dog / Out of my mind / Smokey mountain moon / Bluegrass ticklin' my feet / Please don't let me love you / Surrounded by water and bars / Who's been here since I've been gone / I would send roses (but they cost too much).
LP: . . . . BFX 15267

MAKING BELIEVE.
Tracks: / That's the way it's gonna be / Rock Island Line / Puttin' on the dog / When she said you all / Digging my own grave / Don't give me a reason to wonder why / Blind heart(1) / You've got a heart like a merry-go-round / That cold, cold look in your eyes / Hands away from my heart / That's the way the juke box plays / There's only one you / Making believe / Blind heart(2) / Let 'em talk / Just like downtown / My old stomping ground / Don't knock just come on in.
LP: BFX 15177

Working Girl

WORKING GIRL (Film soundtrack) (Various artists).
Tracks: / Let the river run: *Simon, Carly* / In love (instrumental): *Simon, Carly* / Man that got away, The (instrumental): *Various artists* / Scar, The (instrumental): *Simon, Carly* / Let the river run: *St. Thomas Choir Of Men & Boys* / Lady in red: *De Burgh, Chris* / Carlotta's heart: *Simon, Carly* / Looking through Katherine's house: *Simon, Carly* / Poor butterfly: *Rollins, Sonny* / I'm so excited: *Pointer Sisters.*
LP: 209767
MC: 409767

Working Week

BLACK AND GOLD.
LP: DIX 95
MC: CDIX 95

COMPANEROS.
Tracks: / Too much time / Dancing in motion / Friend (Touche pas mon pote) / South Africa / Shot in the dark / Soul train / King of the night / Touching Heaven / Southern Cross.
LP: V 2397
MC: TCV 2397

FIRE IN THE MOUNTAIN.
Tracks: / Eldorado / This time / Waters of the moon / Fire from the mountain / Eldorado (ortega mix) (Only on CD.) / Waiting in vain / Flamingo / Blade / Lost weekend.
LP: DIX 86
MC: CDIX 86

PAYDAY (Highlights collection).
Tracks: / Soul train / Venceremos / South Africa / King of the night / Touching heaven / Doctor, The / Friend, A / Largo / Knocking on your door / Strut / Apocalypse / I thought I'd never see you again / Storm of light / Sweet nothing / Who's foolin' who / We will win (jazz dance 12").
2LP: VEGD 19
MC: TCVGD 19

SURRENDER.
Tracks: / Surrender / Strut / Largo / Justine / Come to me / Doctor, The / Ain't that peculiar / Knocking on your door / Are you on your own tonight / Work work work (CD & MC only).
MC: TCV 2468
LP: V 2468
LP: OVED 300
MC: OVEDC 300

WORKING NIGHTS.
Tracks: / Inner city blues / Sweet nothing / Who's foolin' who / I thought I'd never see you again / Autumn buy / Solo / Venceremos / No cure no pay / Stella marina (CD only).
LP: OVED 216
MC: OVEDC 216
LP: V 2343

Workman, Nimrod

MOTHER JONES' WILL.
LP: ROUNDER 0076

Workman, Reggie

SUCH GREAT FRIENDS (See Under Cowell, Stanley) (Cowell, Stanley, Billy Harper, Reggie Workman & Billy Hart).

SUPER JAZZ TRIO, THE (see under Flanagan, Tommy) (Workman, Reggie and Tommy Flanagan and Joe Chambers).

SYNTHESIS (Workman, Reggie Ensemble).
LP: LR 131

WORKS OF WORKMAN, THE.
LP: YX 7539

Works Many Voices

WORK'S MANY VOICES (Various artists).
MC: C 224

WORKS MANY VOICES VOL.1 (Various artists).
LP: JEMF 110

WORKS MANY VOICES VOL.2 (Various artists).
LP: JEMF 111

Workshy

GOLDEN MILE, THE.
LP: WX 300
MC: WX 300C

World Apart (film)

WORLD APART, A (Film soundtrack) (Various artists).
LP: A 302
MC: C 302

World At War

WORLD AT WAR (TV SOUNDTRACK) (Various artists).
LP: DVL 6

World Ballroom...

DANCE, DANCE, DANCE (World Ballroom Orchestra).
Tracks: / Can't buy me love / Walk in the Black Forest / Lorraine / Edelweiss / Jeanie with the light brown hair / Moonlight serenade / Woodchopper's ball / Little Pepito / Chiquita cha cha / Quando quando quando / Wedding samba / El bandolero / Rio tango / Tango 65.
LP: SLS 50424

World Beat

WORLD BEAT EXPLOSION (Various artists).
LP: SH 64008

World Class Music

JVC WORLD CLASS MUSIC (Various artists).
MC: JC 3307

JVC WORLD CLASS MUSIC 2 (Various artists).
Tracks: / Maracuja: *Castro-Neves, Oscar* / Donna: *Guitar Workshop In LA* / Face to face: *Okoshi, Tiger* / Cool shadow: *Okoshi, Tiger* / Front runner: *Holman, Bill Band* / Beverly Hills: *Guitar Workshop In LA* / Over the rainbow: *Okoshi, Tiger* / Yamato dawn: *Neptune, John Kaizan* / New face, A: *Watts, Ernie Quartet.*
MC: JC 3317

World Domination...

HOT FROM HIT CITY (World Domination Enterprises).
LP: 33 PROD 24

LET'S PLAY DOMINATION (World Domination Enterprises).
LP: 33PROD 18
MC: 33CPROD 18

LOVE FROM LEAD CITY (World Domination Enterprises).
LP: PROD 24
MC: PRODC 24

World Famous

(HEY YOU) ROCKSTEADY CREW (OLD GOLD) (See under Rocksteady crew/Hey D.J) (World Famous Supreme Team).

RAPPIN' (World Famous Supreme Team).
Tracks: / Hey DJ / Rappin' / Radio man / Misery / Planet E / City life / Seven / Crazy cuts / Mother.
LP: CHC 70
MC: CHCMC 70
LP: CAS 1169

ROUND THE OUTSIDE, ROUND THE OUTSIDE (World Famous Supreme Team).
LP: V 2646
MC: TCV 2646

World (Group)

BREAK THE SILENCE.
LP: K 9602911

World Is Full Of..

WORLD IS FULL OF MARRIED MEN, THE (Film Soundtrack) (Various artists).
2LP: RTD 2038

World Music

AROUND THE WORLD Near East, Egypt, Iran & Morocco (Various artists).
LP: LLST 7287

AROUND THE WORLD (FOR A SONG) (Various artists).
LP: RACS 0217

BEST OF MUSIC AND RHYTHM (Womad) (Various artists).
LP: PVC 6902
MC: PVCC 6902

CUMBIA CUMBIA (Various artists).
LP: WCB 016
MC: WCC 016

DISAPPEARING WORLD, THE (Various artists).
MC: CSDL 376

FESTIVALS OF THE HIMALAYAS, VOL II (Various artists).
Tracks: / Bhounra: *Various artists* / Dance of Mahasu: *Various artists* / Loka: *Various artists* / Humbey, humbey: *Various artists* / Jug jeeya dhara deo guijiro: *Various artists* / Dance from Saraj Valley: *Various artists* / Bahmana ra chhoru: *Various artists* / Bhiagrha: *Various artists* / Mahan: *Various artists*/ Jhuri lagi mahari naunchi: *Various artists* / Lahul Nati: *Various artists.*
LP: H 72079

GLOBESTYLE WORLDWIDE -- YOUR GUIDE (Various artists).
Tracks: / Saludando: *Various artists* / Yachilvi veyachail: *Various artists* / Kesetse Mahiomolenu: *Various artists* / Chorepste: *Various artists* / Raha manina: *Various artists* / Sirvientas: *Various artists*/ El anillo: *Various artists* / Le Brijano: *Various artists* / Iyole: *Various artists* / El Beso: *Various artists* / Ah laa jarah: *Various artists* / Knowale: *Various artists* / Chedh Hime Dh'Loumayere: *Various artists* / Fuego Lento, A: *Various artists* / Les Dorlanes: *Various artists* / Feam Baliha: *Various artists.*
MC: ORBC 018
LP: ORBM 018

GO SOUTH (Various artists).
LP: CERT 4001

IN THE BLOOD (Various artists).
LP: RACS 0174

LUO ROOTS (Various artists).
LP: ORBD 061

MUSIC AND RHYTHM (Various artists).
Tracks: / Burundi: *Drums of Makebuko* / Across the river: *Gabriel, Peter* / Kpan logo: *Ekome* / It's nearly Africa: *XTC* / Zuu waa: *Dagbamba Cultural Group* / Mirror in the bathroom: *Beat* / Sweet mother: *Mbarga, Prince Nico* / Music and rhythm: *Mighty Sparrow* / What you talkin' about?: *Rico* / Marrakesh: *Pert, Morris* / Ascension two: *Townshend, Pete* / Pengosekan: *Coppersmith-Heaven, Vic* / Ba benzele: *Hassell, Jon* / Balinese ketjak: *Khan, Nusrat Fateh Ali* / Noor azli chamkia: *Khan, Nusrat Fateh Ali* / Ritual mask: *Gabriel, Peter* / His wife refused: *Byrne, David* / Sudurum kumosora: *Konte, Alhaji Bai & Malamini Jobate*/ Mkazi wa mulomo: *Chewane, Lonesi & Joni Hetara* / Himalaya: *Shankar, Ravi & Bill Lovelady* / Persian love: *Czukay, Holger.*
LP: K 68045
MC: K4 68045

MUSIC OF THE SANDINISTA GUERRILLAS (Various artists).
MC: ROUNDER 4022C
LP: ROUNDER 4022

OLD COUNTRY MUSIC IN A NEW LAND (Various artists).
Tracks: / Sedliacky Zabavny Czardas (The farmer's diversion Czardas): *Mike Lapeak Slovensky Hudba* / Malenky Barabanshtchik (The little drummer-boy): *Krestyanskyj* / Kassaka Polka: *Aili and Lyyli Wainikainen* (Full Title: Kassaka Polka (Cossack Polka)(Polka 'Tchornyj Ostrov'-"Black) / Zalim te Momce (I saw you, lad): *Braca Kapugi Tamburica Orchestra* / Stack o barley: *Patrick Killoran and His Pride of Erin Orchestra* / Tailor's thimble, The: *Morrison, James & John McKenna*/ El coco-cancion (The Coconut Song): *Lydia Mendoza y Familia* / La piedrera: *Santiago Jimenez y Sus Valedores*/ I tickled 'em: *New Arkansas Travelers* / Jeuns gens campagnard (Young men from the country): *McGee, Dennis* / La valse de bon baurche (valse du bambocheur): *Deshotel, Elsie & His Louisiana Rhythmaires* / Pastorale: *Unidentified* Players / Yar Ounenal (I love you): *Sarkisian, Reuben* / Sayf Lahziq (Your sword has pierced me): *Simon, Nahem*/ Siteiako (Dance of Siteia): *Piperakis, Harilaos* / Kuomet Sokis (When you dance): *Mahanojaus Leitviska Maineriu Orkestra*/ Red haired lass, The: *Morrison, James & John McKenna.*
LP: NW 264

OYE LISTEN (Compacto Caliente) (Various artists).
Tracks: / Defiendeme Santa Barbara: *Leida, Linda* / Arroz con manteca: *Leida, Linda* / Olvidame: *Rodriguez*, Bobby / La mulata cubana: *Valdes, Alfredo* / Con carino a Panama: *Monguito 'el unico'* / Festival in Guarare: *La Sonora De Baru* / Ay, se paso la serie: *Rolando la serie* / Ocana sordi: *Los guaracheros de oriente*/ Como se baila el son: *La india del oriente* / Bancon-tim: *Super All Star* / Prende la vela: *Calzado, Rudy*(on CD and cassette only.) / Saludando a los rumberos (CD & MC only): *Marti, Virgilio.*
LP: ORB 014
MC: ORBC 014

PASSION SOURCES (Various artists).
Tracks: / Shamus ud doja: *Various artists* / Call to prayer: *Various artists* / Sankarabaranam pancha nadai pallavi: *Various artists* / Ulvi: *Various artists* / Fallahi: *Various artists* / Sabahiva: *Various artists*/ Atejbeit: *Various artists* / Prelude in tchahargah: *Various artists* / Wedding song: *Various artists*/ Magdelene's house: *Various artists* / Yoky: *Various artists* / Nass el ghiwane: *Various artists* / Song of complaint: *Various artists.*
LP: RWLP 2
MC: RWMC 2

POCKET WOMAD, THE (Various artists).
Tracks: / Nalilia: *Orchestre Super Matimila* / Yuhn na thi: *Bhosle* / Gamelam gomg kebyar: *Mulyo, Sasono*/ Vakaringa vombo: *Bhundu Boys* / Daye ez xezalim: *Perwer, Sivan* / Meend koyi: *Najma* / Entrada: *Cabral*, Pedro Caldiera / Les veuves de Basile: *Piage, Vermenton* / Crum solo: *Musicians Of The Nile* / Tsi tsi wangu: *Real Sounds* / Diata: *Diabate, Toumani* / Kami Yalivyoni papa: *Toorab Orchestra* / Mother and child: *Mwenda, Jean* / Mateso: *Bagomayo Group* / Ya Mohammid: *Khan, Nusrat Fateh Ali* / Raindrops pattering on: *Jin, Tion* / Ivan and Donka are: *Karadjova, Nadka* / Cielito lindo: *Jimenez, Flaco* / Chunni ud ud jae: *Alaap*/ Ekipe: *Kanda Bongo Man.*
MC: WOMBIPC 001

PROVENCE ETERNELLE (Various artists).
Tracks: / La respelido: *Various artists* / Li jardiniero: *Various artists* / Parpaioun, marido-til: *Various artists* / La targo: *Various artists* / Ai rescountra ma mio: *Various artists* / Magali: *Various artists*/ Li metamourfosi: *Various artists* / Danso di courdello: *Various artists* / Farandole: *Various artists*/ Rodo que roudaras: *Various artists* / Lou rossignou sauvage: *Various artists* / La mazurka souto li pin: *Various artists* / L'autre jour mi passejavi: *Various artists* / Lou porto-aigo: *Various artists* / Air de troubadour: *Various artists.*
LP: ARN 33244

RAI REBELS (Various artists).
Tracks: / N'sel fik: *Fadela, Chaba & Cheb Sahraoui* / Khadidja: *Hamid, Cheb* / Ya loualid: *Zahouania, Chaba* & Cheb Khaled / Foug-e-ramla: *Benchenet, Houari* / Deblet gualbi: *Sahraoui, Cheb* / Sahr liyali: *Zahouania, Chaba* / Sidi boumedienne: *Khaled, Cheb* / Mali galbi: *Benchenet, Houari.*
LP: EWV 7
MC: TCEWV 7

RAINDROPS ON BANANA LEAVES (Various artists).
LP: WOMAD 001

SABROSO! (Various artists).
Tracks: / A los rumberos de belen: *Sierra Maestra* / El son de Nicaragua: *Orquesta Chepin* / Chilindron de Chivo: *Conjunto Casino* / Anda ven y muevete: *Orquesta Los Van Van* / Se que tu sabes que yo se: *Orquestra Reve*/ Camina y ven: *Gonzalez, Celina* / Rucu rucu a Santa Clara: *Grupo, Irakere* / De kabinde a kunene: *Los Karachi*/ Vuela la paloma: *Conjunto Rumbavana* / Frutas del caney: *Grupo Monumental.*
LP: EWV 11
MC: TCEWV 11

SPIRIT OF THE EAGLE (Various artists).
Tracks: / Masvingo netara: *Various artists* / Ngoma yekwedu: *Various artists* / Yambozha vauya: *Various artists*/ Dzinomwa muna save: *Various artists* / Mombe yeumai: *Various artists* / Nyamutamba ne mombe: *Various artists*/ Tsiga mureza: *Various artists* / Ndiana apisa moto: *Various artists* / Wenhamo ndewe nhamo: *Various artists.*
LP: EWV 18
MC: TCEWV 18

SUPER ALL STAR (Various artists).
Tracks: / Francisco guayabal: *Various artists* / El platanal de bartolo: *Various artists* / Tres linda cubanas: *Various artists* / Ban-con-tim: *Various artists* / Alto songo: *Various artists* / Malanga: *Various artists* / El sopon: *Various artists* / La cascara: *Various artists.*
LP: ORB 017
MC: ORBC 017

TAKE COVER VOL.2 (Various artists).
MC: AFRIC 005

TAKE COVER - ZIMBABWE HITS (Various artists).
LP: SHAN 43045

THIS IS WOMAD (Various artists).
LP: WOMAD 007

TRANSKIE SPECIAL ACCORDIAN MBAQANGA EARLY 70'S (Various artists).
LP: TWLP 003

VENT D'QUEST - LE CHANT D'UN MONDE (songs of the world) (Various artists).
LP: . . . . ARN 34776

VIVA EL RITMO:CUBAN-BAILA (Various artists).
LP: . . . . EMW 5501

WOMAD TALKING BOOK VOL.1 Introduction to world music (Various artists).
LP: . . . . WOMAD 002
MC: . . . . WOMCAS 002

WOMAD TALKING BOOK VOL.2 Introduction to Africa (Various artists).
LP: . . . . WOMAD 003
MC: . . . . WOMCAS 003

WOMAD TALKING BOOK VOL.3 Introduction to Europe (Various artists).
LP: . . . . WOMAD 005
MC: . . . . WOMCAS 005

WOMAD TALKING BOOK VOL.4 Introduction to Asia (Various artists).
LP: . . . . WOMAD 006
MC: . . . . WOMCAS 006

WORLD MUSIC ALBUM (Various artists).
Tracks: / Finale: *Piazzolla, Astor* / Neend koyi: *Najma* / Bolingo: *Doudongo, M Poto* / Puente de Los Alunados: *Nunez, Gerardo* / Milagre dos peixes: *Nascimento, Milton* / Humpty dumpty: *Palmieri, Eddie* / Alvorada: *Mariano* / Souareba: *Keita, Salif* / Flash of the spirit (laughter): *Hassell, Jon/Farafina* / Chebba: *Khaled, Cheb* / Galapagos: *Nuemann And Zapf*.
LP: . . . . TUIT 1000
LP: 791 310 1
MC: . . . . TCTUIT 1000
MC: 791 310 4

WORLD WIDER YOUR GUIDER (Various artists).
LP: . . . . ORBM 050
MC: . . . . ORBC 050

ZOUKOLLECTION (Various artists).
Tracks: / Malavoi: *Moin, Carresse* / Mwen malad aw: *Kassav* / Kole sere: *Beroard, Jocelyne* / Pa ni passe lan win: *Jurad, Simon* / Gade leta zouk la mate moin: *Jurad, Simon* / Danse soleil: *Chasseur, Tony* / Yaka danse: *Raft*.
LP: 87004
MC: . . . . C 87004

World Party

GOODBYE JUMBO.
LP: . . . . CHEN 10
MC: . . . . ZCHEN 10

PRIVATE REVOLUTION.
Tracks: / Private revolution / Making love (to the world) / Ship of fools / All come true / Dance of the happy lads / It can be beautiful (sometimes) / Ballad of the little man / Hawaiian island world / All I really want to do / World Party / It's all mine.
LP: . . . . CHEN 4
MC: . . . . ZCHEN 4

World Pipe Band

WORLD PIPE BAND CHAMPIONSHIPS (See under Pipe Bands for details).

World Rhythm Band

IBEX (World Rhythm Band & Jeff Pressing Quintet).
Tracks: / Less trocanter / Huseybi saz demaisi / Ibex / Flight / Home and mind / Stumbling along.
LP: . . . . DS 865

World Saxophone...

DANCES AND BALLADS (World Saxophone Quartet).
MC: 979164 4
LP: 979164 1

PLAYS DUKE ELLINGTON (World Saxophone Quartet).
LP: . . . . K 979137 1
MC: . . . . K 979137 4

World Trade

WORLD TRADE.
MC: 839 626 4
LP: 839 626 1

World War III

WORLD WAR III.
LP: . . . . HWDLP 3

World's Greatest...

SONGS THAT LOST THE WAR (Worlds Greatest Dixie Band).
MC: . . . . JAZZ CASS 002

WORLD'S GREATEST LOVER, THE (Film Soundtrack) (Various artists).
Tracks: / Fox trademark: *Various artists* / Adolph Zitz, movie mogul: *Various artists* / Rudy's tango: *Various artists* / Valentino movie: *Various artists* / World's greatest lover tango: *Various artists* / Going crazy in Milwaukee: *Various artists* / Los Angeles train: *Various artists* / You oughta be in pictures: *Various artists* / That's my weakness now: *Various artists* / Hollywood - garden music: *Various artists* / Reaching for someone: *Various artists* / Sex by the numbers: *Various artists* / Ain't it kinda wonderful: *Various artists* / Enter Uncle Harry: *Various artists* / Red rose Uncle Harry: *Various artists* / I'm bringing a red, red rose: *Various artists* / Love just in your left eye: *Various artists* / Shuffle off to Buffalo: *Various artists* / Rudy meets Valentino: *Various artists* / Gene Valentino montage: *Various artists* / Annie meets Valentino: *Various artists* / Tent scene: *Various artists* / Fascination: *Various artists* / Ain't it kinda wonderful: *Various artists* / Tent scene (gypsy presto): *Various artists* / Annie and the gangsters: *Various artists* / Getting ready for the finals: *Various artists* / Gangster's walk: *Various artists* / Valentino tango (noche de amor): *Various artists* / Girls kicking: *Various artists* / Final audition, The: *Various artists* / Finale: *Various artists*.
LP: . . . . BL 12709
MC: . . . . BK 12709

World's Greatest Jazz

HARK THE HERALD ANGELS SWING (Featuring Yank Lawson and Bob Haggart).
LP: . . . . WJLPS 2

IN CONCERT AT CARNEGIE HALL.
Tracks: / At the jazz band ball / Just a closer walk with thee / Walk with thee / I've found a new baby / Hundred years from today / Lady is a tramp, The / Sweet Georgia Brown / Muskrat ramble / When your lover has gone / I gotta right to sing the blues / Keeping out of mischief / Chicago / Swing that music.
LP: . . . . WJLPS 4

IN CONCERT AT MASSEY HALL, VOL 1 (Featuring Yank Lawson and Bob Haggart).
Tracks: / Original dixieland one-step / Crawfish shuffle / I want to be happy / Do you know what it means (to Miss New Orleans) / California here I come / Fidgety feet / South / Lover come back to me / If you knew Susie / St. Louis Blues.
LP: . . . . WJLPS 3

ON TOUR (Featuring Yank Lawson and Bob Haggart).
Tracks: / Sheik of Araby, The / Basin street blues / Wrap your troubles in dreams / Just one of those things / Do you know what it means to Miss New Orleans / St. Louis blues / Mandy make up your mind / Stardust / Limehouse blues / Dear old Southland / When the saints go marching in / Stumbling / Poor butterfly / Caravan / Running wild / Big butter and egg man / I've got the world on a string / Too marvellous / Squeeze me / Hindustan.
2LP: . . . . WJLPS 8/10

PLAYS COLE PORTER (Featuring Yank Lawson and Bob Haggart).
Tracks: / Love for sale / All of you / It's alright with me / Let's do it / I concentrate on you / Just one of those thing / Anything goes / It's de-lovely / Rosalie / So in love / You'd be so nice to come home to / From this moment on.
LP: . . . . WJLPS 6

PLAYS DUKE ELLINGTON (Featuring Yank Lawson and Bob Haggart).
Tracks: / Take the 'A' train / Mood indigo / Just squeeze me / I got it bad and that ain't good / Perdido / Satin doll / Prelude to a kiss / In a mellow tone / Do nothing till you hear from me / Rockin' in rhythm.
LP: . . . . WJLPS 9

PLAYS GEORGE GERSHWIN (Featuring Yank Lawson and Bob Haggart).
Tracks: / Liza / I've got a crush on you / But not for me / How long has this been going on / Embraceable you / Strike up the band / Who cares / Maybe / Fascinating rhythm / Soon / 'S wonderful.
LP: . . . . WJLPS 11

PLAYS RODGERS & HART (Featuring Yank Lawson and Bob Haggart).
Tracks: / Mountain greenery / Have you met Miss Jones / Isn't it romantic / My funny Valentine / Blue room / You took advantage of me / Lady is a tramp, The / Dancing on the ceiling / Where or when / Bewitched / Thou swell / Lover.
LP: . . . . WJLPS 7

Worlock, Monty

LIVE JAZZ FROM THE SOLENT AREA (Worlock, Monty and Ray D'Inverno Trios).
MC: . . . . VOL 5

Worries & Problems..

WORRIES AND PROBLEMS DUB '86 (Various artists).
LP: . . . . PM 001

Worst Witch (bk)

WORST WITCH, THE (Jill Murphy) (Margolyes, Miriam (nar)).
MCSET: CC/012

Worth, Billie

CALL ME MADAM (Worth, Billie & Anton Walbrook).
LP: . . . . MES 7013

Worzel Gummidge (bk)

ADVENTURES OF WORZEL GUMMIDGE, THE (See under Adventures of... (Spoken Word)) (Pertwee, Jon).

FAIR OLD PULLOVER - A LITTLE LEARNING.
MC: . . . . KC 004

NEW FRIENDS FOR WORZEL - VILLAGE FETE.
MC: . . . . KC 001

SAUCY NANCY - WORZEL'S 'ANSOM 'EAD.
MC: . . . . KC 003

SCARECROW HOP - THE TEA PARTY.
MC: . . . . KC 002

WORZEL GIVES A LECTURE - WORZEL'S WEDDING.
MC: . . . . KC 006

WORZEL GUMMIDGE Waterhouse, Keith and Willis Hall (Pertwee, Jon).
Tracks: / New friends for Worzel / Village fete.
MCSET: . . . . KC 001

WORZEL GUMMIDGE (Unknown narrator(s)).
MCSET: . . . . DTO 10520

WORZEL GUMMIDGE AND HIS NEPHEW (Pertwee, Jon).
MC: . . . . TTS 9839

WORZEL GUMMIDGE AND MUVVERS DAY (Pertwee, Jon).
MC: . . . . TTS 9837

WORZEL GUMMIDGE - FIRE DRILL (Pertwee, Jon).
MC: . . . . TTS 9838

WORZEL GUMMIDGE - THE TRIAL... (Pertwee, Jon).
MC: . . . . TTS 9840

Wot Cheor Geordie

WOT CHEOR GEORDIE (Various artists).
LP: . . . . MWM SP 4
MC: . . . . MWM CSP 4

Wot Zat

WOT ZAT.
LP: . . . . ZAT 1

Would-Be-Goods

CAMERA LOVES ME.
Tracks: / Camera loves me, The / Velazquez and I / Cecil Beaton's scrapbook / Pinstriped rebel / Rose du Barry / Marvellous boy / Young man from Caracas / Amaretto / Motor bike girl / Death a la carte / Perfect dear.
LP: . . . . ACME 14

Wow What A Party

WOW WHAT A PARTY (Various artists).
LP: . . . . NE 1388
MC: . . . . CE 2388

Woya

KACOU ANANZE.
LP: . . . . T 425004

Wrabit

WRABIT.
LP: . . . . MCF 3126

W.R.A.C.

RESOLUTE (WRAC Staff Band).
Tracks: / A.T.S. march past / Greensleeves / Girls in green / Resolute / Drum majorette / Sons of the brave / Swing march / HRH The Duke of Cambridge / Festive overture / Rockford Files theme / Trombones trocadero / Waltz in blue / Trumpets wild / Post horn galop / Take five / Dixie in F / Cole Porter- A symphonic portrait / WRAC march.
LP: . . . . BND 1036
MC: . . . . ZC BND 1036

Wraith

WRAITH (Film soundtrack) (Various artists).
Tracks: / Where's the fire?: *Feehan, Tim* (Tim Feehan.) / Those were the days: *Honeymoon Suite* (Honeymoon Suite) / Hearts versus heads: *Bush, Stan* (Stan Bush) / Hold on, blue eyes: *Lamarca* (Lamarca) / Young love, hot love: *Michaels, Jill* (Hill Michaels) / Secret loser: *Osbourne, Ozzy* (Ozzy Osbourne) / Never surrender: *Lion*(Lion) / Bad mistake: *House, James* (James House) / Wake up call: *Hunter, Ian* (Ian Hunter) / Matter of the heart: *Tyler, Bonnie* (Bonnie Tyler).
LP: 4503731
MC: 450 373-4

Wraith (Group)

NAKED AGGRESION.
LP: . . . . AZTY 001

Wrath

FIT OF ANGER.
LP: . . . . MEGATON 0015

WRATH.
LP: . . . . MID 94011

Wrathchild

BIZ SUXX (BUT WE DON'T CARE), THE.
Tracks: / Biz suxx, The / Millionaire / Hooked / (Na na) nukklear rokket / Wild wild honey / Ring my bell / Hooligunz / She'z no angel / O.K. U.K. / Noo sensation / Stikky fingerz.
LP: . . . . WKFMLP 116
MC: . . . . WKFMMC 116
LP: . . . . HMR LP 116
MC: . . . . HMR MC 116
LPPD: . . . . HMR PD 116

DELIRIUM.
Tracks: / Delirium / Watch me shake it / That's what U get / My girlz / Long way 2 go / Good girlz / Do what you wanna / Kid pusher / She's high on luv / Rock me over / Only 4 the fun / Drive me krazy.
LP: . . . . WKFMLP 137
MC: . . . . WKFMMC 137

STAKK ATTAKK.
Tracks: / Stakk attakk / Too wild to tame / Trash queen / Sweet surrender / Kick down the walls / Tonight / Law abuzer / Shokker / Alrite with the boyz / Wreckless.
LP: . . . . HMR LP 18
MC: . . . . HMRMC 18
LPPD: . . . . HMRPD 18

TRASH QUEENS.
Tracks: / Do you want my love? / Rock the city down / Lipstik killers / Trash queen / Teenage revolution / Twist of the knife / Cock rock shock / It's a party.
LP: . . . . DOJOLP 6

Wrathchild (US)

CLIMBING THE WALLS.
LP: . . . . PR 2572-4

Wray, Jimmy

ROCKIN' IN LOUISIANA (see under Harris, Johnny Ray).

ROCKIN' IN LOUISIANA VOL.2 (See under Harris, Johnny Ray) (Wray, Jimmy & Johnny Ray Harris).

Wray, Link

APACHE.
Tracks: / Wild one, The / Big boss man / Joker, The / Beautiful brown eyes / Green hornet / Dallas blues / Shawnee / Apache / Stars and stripes forever / Dick Tracy, private eye.
LP: . . . . CH 286

BULLSHOT.
Tracks: / Good good lovin' / Fever / Snag / Just that kind / Switchblade / It's all over now / Baby blue / Rawhide / Wild party / Sky is falling, The / Don't.
LP: . . . . CAS 1143

EARLY RECORDINGS.
Tracks: / Batman / Ace of spades / Cross ties / Jack the ripper / Hidden charms / I'm branded / Shadow knows, (The) / Fat back / Run, chicken, run / Black widow / Scatter / Turnpike U.S.A. / Mr. Guitar / Rumble.
LP: . . . . CH 6

GOOD ROCKIN' TONIGHT.
Tracks: / Good rockin' tonight / Deuces wild / Mustang / Heartbreak hotel / Law of the jungle, The / Blueberry Hill / Swag, The / Rumble / Run boy run / Honky tonk / Sweeper, The / Hound dog / That'll be the day / Zip code / Scatter.
LP: . . . . CH 69
LP: . . . . UP 002

GROWLING GUITAR.
Tracks: / Climbing a high wall / Genocide / Earth is crying, The / Growlin' guts / Hungry / Ace of spades / Ruby baby / Hang on / Summer dreams / Sorrento / Peggy Sue / Alone / Girl from the north country / You hurt me so / Fuzz, The.
LP: . . . . WIK 65

JACK THE RIPPER.
Tracks: / Mr. Guitar / Deacon Jones / Cross ties / Ace of spades / Fat back / Dinosaur / Mash potato party / Rendezvous / My Beth / Steel trap / Jack the ripper / Hidden charms / Run chicken run / Big Ben / I'll do anything for you / Slinky.

LP: . . . . HANG 33 UP

LINK WRAY AND THE RAYMEN (Wray, Link & His Raymen).
Tracks: / Dixie-doodle / Ramble / Caroline / Rawhide / Right turn / Golden strings / Comanche / Hambone / Mary Ann / Rumble mambo / Ain't that loving you baby / Slinky / Hand clapper / Lillian / Radar / Studio blues.
LP: . . . . ED 149

LINK WRAY / GOOD ROCKIN' TONIGHT.
Tracks: / Batman / Ace of spades / Cross ties / Jack the Ripper / Hidden charms / I'm branded / Shadow knows, The / Fat back / Run, chicken, run / Black widow / Scatter / Turnpike U.S.A. / U.S.A. / Mr. Guitar / Rumble / Good rockin' tonight / Deuces wild / Mustang / Heartbreak hotel / Law of the jungle, The / Blueberry Hill / Swag, The / Run boy run / Honky tonk / Sweeper, The / Hound dog / That'll be the day / Zip code.
MCSET: . . . . CHC 802

LIVE AT THE PARADISO.
Tracks: / Blue suede shoes / Ace of spades / Walk away from love / I saw her standing there / Run, chicken, run / She's no good / Rumble / Rawhide / Subway blues / Money / Shake, rattle and roll / Be bop a lula.
LP: . . . . MFLP 008
LP: . . . . MFM 012

LIVE IN 85.
Tracks: / Rumble / It's only words / Fire / Mystery train / I got a woman / Baby let's play house / Jack the ripper / Love me / King Creole / I'm counting on you / Rawhide / Born to be wild.
LP: . . . . WIKM 42

ROCK 'N' ROLL RUMBLE (Wray, Link/ Waymen).
Tracks: / Rumble / Swag, The / El toro / Tijuana / Rumble mambo / Jack the ripper / Black widow / Weekend / Turnpike U.S.A. / Sweeper, The / Good rockin' / Tonight / I'm branded / Hang on / Batman / Alone / Ace of spades / Hidden charms.
LP: . . . . CR 30171

RUMBLE MAN.
Tracks: / Draggin' / Aces wild / Bull dawg / I'm gonna sit right down and cry over you / I will be home again / Street beat / Honest, I swear somebody lied / Rumple man, The / Big city walk / Copenhagen boogie / Thrill of your love, The.
LP: . . . . CH 266

STUCK IN GEAR.
LP: . . . . V 2050

SWAN DEMOS '64.
LP: . . . . HANG 31 UP

WAY I WALK (See under Gordon, Robert) (Wray, Link/Robert Gordon).

WILD SIDE OF THE CITY LIGHTS.
Tracks: / Hotel loneliness / Flying wedge, The / American sunset / Love me tender / Viva zapata / Raunchy / Don't leave me / Little Sister / Wild side of the city lights / As long as I have you.
LP: . . . . CH 296

Wreck

SOUL TRAIN.
LP: . . . . BIAS 173

Wreckery

LAYING DOWN THE LAW.
LP: . . . . CGAS 809

Wrecking Crew

BALANCE OF TERROR.
LP: . . . . HR 9493 1

Wreckless Eric

AT THE SHOP.
Tracks: / Big old world / Waiting for the shit (to hit the fan) / Bony Moronie / Our neck of the woods / If it makes you happy / Depression (version Francaise) / Semaphore signals / You're the girl for me.
LP: . . . . NR 312

BIG SMASH.
Tracks: / Popsong / Tonight / Too busy / Broken doll / Can I be your hero? / Back in my hometown / Whole wide world / Take the cash / Let's go to the pictures / Walking on the surface of the moon / Hit and miss Judy / I wish it would rain / It'll soon be the weekend / Strange towns / Excuse me / Break my mind / Good conversation / Out of the blue / Reconnez cherie / Veronica / Brain thieves / Semaphore signals / I need a situation / Final taxi / There isn't anything else.
2LP: . . . . SEEZ 21
MCSET: . . . . ZSEEZ 21

LE BEAT GROUP ELECTRIQUE.
Tracks: / Tell me I'm the only one / Wishing my life away / Depression / It's a sick sick world / Just for you / Sarah / Sun is pouring down, The / I'm not going to cry / You sweet big thing / Fu** by fu** / Parallel beds / True happiness.
LP: . . . . ROSE 179

WONDERFUL WORLD OF WRECKLESS ERIC.
2LP: . . . . SEEZ 9

WRECKLESS ERIC.
Tracks: / Reconnez cherie / Rags 'n' tatters / Waxworks / Grown ups / Telephone home / Whole wide world / Rough kids / Personal hygiene / Brain thieves / There isn't anything.
LP: . . . . SEEZ 6

Wrecks 'N' Effect

WRECKS 'N' EFFECT.
Tracks: / Go for what you know / We be Mafia / I need money / Let's do it again / Wrecks 'n' effect.
LP: . . . . K 781 860 1
MC: . . . . K 781 860 4

WRECKS 'N' EFFECT (2).
Tracks: / New Jack swing / Leave the mike smokin' / Juicy / Club head / Soul man / Deep / Wipe your sweat / V-man / Peanut butter / Friends to the end / Rock steady.
LP: . . . . ZL 72679
MC: . . . . ZK 72679

Wren, Jenny

EDWARD AND MRS. SIMPSON.
Tracks: / I've danced with a man / Very thought of you, The / Room with a view / If I had you / Of cabbages and kings / Bring down the curtain / One more dance / Dance little lady / Tango / When love grows cold / Murmurs in the wind.
LP: . . . . RKLP 5003

Wrencher, Big John

BIG JOHN'S BOOGIE.
Tracks: / Honeydripper / Third degree / Now darling / Where did you stay last night / Trouble makin' woman / Lonesome in my cabin / How many more years / Come on over / Telephone blues / Runnin' wild.
LP: . . . . BEAR 4

Wretched

LA TUA MORTE NON ASPETTA.
LP: . . . . CP 8.9/86

Wright, Andrew

PIPERS OF DISTINCTION.
MC: . . . . ZCMON 802

Wright, Bernard

I CAN TELL.
Tracks: / Happy 2 be with u / Got to give it up / Music lover / I can tell / We'll keep striving / Don't take your love from me / Tonight / Change for the better / Crack.
LP: . . . . MTL 1011
MC: . . . . TCMTL 1011

MR. WRIGHT.
Tracks: / After you / Who do you love / Love you so / Yo nard / Too darn hot / Killin' me / Just when I thought you were mine / Brown shoes.
LP: . . . . MTL 1000

NARD.
Tracks: / Haboglabotribin / Firebolt hustle / Music is the key / Spinnin' / Just chillin' out / Bread sandwiches / Master rocker / We're just the band / Solar.
LP: . . . . GRP 5011

Wright, Betty

4U2 NJOY.
Tracks: / 4U2NJOY / It's been real / Quiet storm / Keep love new / From pain to joy / Valley of lonely / Lightning / We "down" / Won't be long now.
LP: . . . . MSB 3308
MC: . . . . MSBC 3308
LP: . . . . SDLP 2
MC: . . . . SDLC 2

BETTY WRIGHT.
Tracks: / What are you going to do with it / I like your loving / Indivisible / Body slang / Dancin' on the one / Give a smile / I come to you / Make me love the rain / One bad habit.
LP: . . . . EPC 84882

BETTY WRIGHT LIVE.
LP: . . . . GMLP 1001

GOLDEN CLASSICS.
LP: . . . . COL 5118

MOTHER WIT.
MC: . . . . MSBC 3301
LP: . . . . MSB 3301

SEVENS.
LP: . . . . F 9644

TRAVELIN' IN THE WRIGHT CIRCLE.
Tracks: / I'm telling you now / Child of the man / You're just what I need / My love is / Open the door to your heart / Love train / I believe it's love / Thank you for the many things you've done / Listen to the music.
LP: . . . . TKR 83352

WRIGHT BACK AT YOU.
Tracks: / Burning desire / She's older now / Be your friend / I promise you / Live, love, rejoice / Special love / Show me / Reggae the night away / Gimme just another try.
LP: . . . . EPC 25358
MC: 40 25358

Wright, Billy

HEY BABY DON'T YOU WANT A MAN LIKE ME (Wright, Billy & Little Richard).
Tracks: / Little Richard / Directly from my heart / I love my baby / Maybe I'm right / Ain't that good news / Fool at the wheel / Rice, red beans and turnip greens / Don't want a man like me / Let's be friends / Question, The / Bad luck, heartaches... / Always.
LP: . . . . CHA 193

STACKED DECK.
Tracks: / After dark blues / Thinkin' blues / Fore day blues / Billy's boogie blues / Mercy mercy / Married woman's boogie / Keep your hands on your heart / Stacked deck / Turn your lamps down low / Every evening / Four cold cold walls / Live the life / I remember / Do something.
LP: . . . . KIX 13

Wright Brothers

WRIGHT BROTHERS BIOGRAPHY.
MC: . . . . ZCHM 00022

Wright, Frank

ONE FOR JOHN.
LP: . . . . AFF 33

Wright, Gary

DREAM WEAVER, THE.
Tracks: / Love is alive / Let it out / Can't find the judge / Made to love you / Power of love / Dream weaver / Blind feeling / Murch higher / Feel for me.
LP: . . . . K 56141

HEADIN' HOME.
Tracks: / Keep love in your soul / Love awake inside / You don't own me / Moonbeams / Stand / I'm the one who'll be by your side / Follow next to you / I can feel you cryin' / Let me feel your love again / Love is why.
LP: . . . . K 56585

LIGHT OF SMILES.
Tracks: / Water sign / Time machine / I am the sky / Who am I / Silent fury / Phantom writer / Light of smiles, The / I'm alright / Empty inside / Are you weeping / Child of light.
LP: . . . . K 56278

RIGHT PLACE, THE.
LP: . . . . K 56877

WHO AM I.
LP: . . . . YL 0111

Wright, George

ENCORES - VOL.2 (Wurlitzer Pipe Organ).
LP: . . . . DO 1420

I'S ALL WRIGHT.
LP: . . . . DO 1213

ROARING 20'S - WURLITZER THEATRE ORGAN.
LP: . . . . DO 1418

SHOWTIME AT THE MIGHTY THEATRE ORGAN.
LP: . . . . DO 1417

Wright, Ginny

WHIRLWIND THE FABOR RECORDINGS VOLUME 1.
Tracks: / Lonesome seagull / I'm in heaven / Wonderful world / I love you / My chihuahua dog / Indian moon / Your eyes feasted upon her / Where were you / I want you yes / I saw Esau (kissing Mary Lou) / Whirlwind / I could still tell you more / Turn around my darling / I've got somebody new / Please leave my darlin' alone / How to get married.
LP: . . . . BFX 15188

Wright, Graeme

I HEAR MUSIC (Farfisa Coronet Organ).
Tracks: / Pavanne / What is this thing called love / Ring ding / Delicado / It's only a paper moon / Dream of Olwen / I hear music / Air on a G string / Stardust / Eleanora / Moonlight in Vermont / Stars fell on Alabama / Half a mo.
LP: . . . . GRS 1062

SOMETHING SPECIAL.
Tracks: / Port au prince / Pavanne / Dream / Cinnamon and cloves / September in the rain / Siciliano / Jazz pizzicato / Jazz legato / Syncopated clock / Yesterday / Yesterdays / Tambourin / Bach goes to town / Aria (From cantata 156).
LP: . . . . GRS 1131
MC: . . . . KGRS 1131

Wright, Jim

SHANRON' ROSE.
LP: . . . . POL 804

SHEPHERD OF LOVE.
LP: . . . . PC 860

Wright, Jimmy

LET'S GO CRAZY, BABY.
LP: . . . . BP 1301

Wright, John

LAUGHTER THROUGH TEARS.
Tracks: / Laughter through the tears / Going to the steamy / Fair on Glasgow green / Park rendezvous / City slaves / Angel / Up or close / Wee Willie Wellie / Simon's shelter / High rise cowboy / Time tells no lies.
LP: . . . . na 111

UNACCOMPANIED.
LP: 12T 348

Wright, Katrina

SUSANNAH'S SECRET.
MC: . . . . SOUND 19

Wright, Michelle

DO RIGHT BY ME.
LP: . . . . SVLP 9206
MC: . . . . SVMC 9406

Wright, Oscar

OSCAR AND EUGENE WRIGHT (Wright, Oscar & Eugene).
LP: . . . . ROUNDER 0089

Wright, O.V.

GONE FOR GOOD.
Tracks: / You're gonna make me cry / Can't find true love / Poor boy / Bachelor's blues / I could write a book / Eight men, four women / Gone for good / Ace of spades / What about you / This hurt is real / Nickel and a nail, A / I'll take care of you / I'd rather be blind, crippled and crazy / Drowning on dry land.
LP: . . . . CRB 1050

HERE'S ANOTHER THING.
Tracks: / I've been searching / What more can I do / I was born all over / Only thing that saved me, The / Nobody but you / Slow and easy / Henpecked man / Don't let my baby ride / Lost in the shuffle / When you took your love from me / Heartaches - heartaches / He's my son (just the same) / Ghetto child / I'm gonna forget about you / Memory blues / I'm going home (to live with God).
LP: . . . . CRB 1204

O.V. WRIGHT LIVE.
Tracks: / I'd rather be blind, crippled & and crazy / Eight men, four women / Love and happiness / When a man loves a woman / You're gonna make me cry / Ace of spades / Precious precious / God blessed of our love / That's how strong my love is / Into something (can't shake loose).
LP: . . . . HIUKLP 426

WRIGHT STUFF - LIVE IN JAPAN.
Tracks: / Into something (can't shake loose) / I feel love growin' / Precious, precious / Trying to live my life without you / Your good thing is about to end / Bottom line / I don't do windows / I don't know why / Time we have, The / You gotta have love / Rhymes / Without you / I'd rather be blind, crippled and crazy / Ace of spades / Eight men, four women / Love and happiness / God blessed of our love / When a man loves a woman / That's how strong my love is / You're gonna make me cry.
LP: . . . . HIUKLP 414

Wright, Peggy Sue

DYNAMITE COUNTRY.
LP: . . . . SKYL 7004

Wright, Richard

BLACK BOY (Peters, Brock).
MCSET: 2030

NATIVE SON (Jones, James Earl).
MC: 2068

Wright, Sandra

WOUNDED WOMAN.
Tracks: / Wounded woman / Sha-la bandit, The / I'm not strong enough to love you again / I come running back / Lovin' you, lovin' me / Man can't be a man (without a woman), A / Midnight affair / I'll see you through / Please don't say goodbye.
LP: . . . . FIEND 138

Wright, Stephen

I HAVE A PONY.
Tracks: / Seven and museums / Water / Jiggs Casey / Cross country / Book store / Winny / Apt. / Babies and skiing / Introduction / Hitchhiking / Ice / Dog stay / Achel.
LP: 925335 1
MC: 925335 4

Wright, Steve

ALL SHOOK UP (KARAOKE) (Various artists).
Tracks: / All shook up: *Various artists* / Jailhouse rock: *Various artists* / It's now or never: *Various artists* / Return to sender: *Various artists* / Hound dog: *Various artists*.
MC: KRMC 109

BROKEN HEARTED, THE (KARAOKE) (Various artists).
Tracks: / What becomes of the broken hearted: *Various artists* / Walk on by: *Various artists* / You've lost that lovin' feeling: *Various artists* / You keep me hanging on: *Various artists* / Sun ain't gonna shine anymore, The: *Various artists*.
MC: KRMC 106

CALIFORNIA DREAMIN' (KARAOKE) (Various artists).
Tracks: / California dreamin': *Various artists* / Mr Tambourine man: *Various artists* / Good vibrations: *Various artists* / All you need is love: *Various artists* / San Francisco: *Various artists*.
MC: KRMC 110

DO IT AGAIN (KARAOKE) (Various artists).
Tracks: / Do it again: *Various artists* / Barbara Ann: *Various artists* / I get around: *Various artists*/ Help me Rhonda: *Various artists* / California girls: *Various artists*.
MC: KRMC 111

EVERLASTING LOVE (KARAOKE) (Various artists).
Tracks: / Everlasting love: *Various artists* / Love letters: *Various artists* / When a man loves a woman: *Various artists* / Then he kissed me: *Various artists* / God only knows: *Various artists*.
MC: KRMC 105

HELLO, GOODBYE (KARAOKE) (Various artists).
Tracks: / Hello, goodbye: *Various artists* / Yesterday: *Various artists* / Michelle: *Various artists*/ With a little help from my friends: *Various artists* / Hey Jude: *Various artists*.
MC: KRMC 103

HITSVILLE USA VOL. 1 (KARAOKE) (Various artists).
Tracks: / My guy: *Various artists* / I heard it through the grapevine: *Various artists* / Be my baby: *Various artists* / It's the same old song: *Various artists* / Where did our love go?: *Various artists*.
MC: KRMC 102

HITSVILLE USA VOL. 2 (KARAOKE) (Various artists).
Tracks: / Baby love: *Various artists* / Reach out, I'll be there: *Various artists* / Da doo ron ron: *Various artists* / My girl: *Various artists* / Dancing in the street: *Various artists*.
MC: KRMC 104

IT'S NOT UNUSUAL (KARAOKE) (Various artists).
Tracks: / It's not unusual: *Various artists* / Green green grass of home: *Various artists* / Delilah: *Various artists* / Kiss: *Various artists* / Detroit city: *Various artists*.
MC: KRMC 108

THAT'LL BE THE DAY (KARAOKE) (Various artists).
Tracks: / That'll be the day: *Various artists* / Oh boy: *Various artists*/ Rave on: *Various artists*/ Think it over: *Various artists* / Peggy Sue: *Various artists*.
MC: KRMC 107

YEAH YEAH YEAH (KARAOKE) (Various artists).
Tracks: / From me to you: *Various artists* / She loves you: *Various artists* / Can't buy me love: *Various artists* / Hard day's night, A: *Various artists* / Help: *Various artists*.
MC: KRMC 101

Wright, Wayne

ACOUSTIC GUITAR DUETS (see under Grosz, Marty).

MARTY GROSZ AND WAYNE WRIGHT (See Grosz, Marty) (Wright, Wayne and Marty Grosz).

Wrigley, Bernard

BOLTON BULLFROG, THE.
MC: LOO 7

INSTRUMENTAL ALBUM, THE.
MC: LOO 9

PHENOMENAL BERNARD WRIGLEY, THE (Folk Songs, Tunes and Drolleries).
LP: 12TS 211

PHENOMENAL BERNARD WRIGLEY/ ROUGH AND WRIGLEY.
MCSET: LOO 3/4

ROUGH AND WRIGLEY.
Tracks: / Manchester recruits, The / Plastic pies / Parson in the peas / Campanero / Strike the bell / Drop of good beer, A / Saucy sailor / Free and easy / Bertie's fancy / Collier brig, The / First day at t'mill / Hand loom v power loom / Along the rossendale / Old bill / Constant Billy / Holes in the road / Old man and his wife, The / Ten thousand miles away / Rigs of London town, The.
LP: 12TS 241

RUDE BITS.
MC: LOO 8

SONGS, STORIES AND ELEPHANTS.
MC: LOO 5

TENTON SPECIAL.
MC: LOO 6

WESTBROOK/WRIGLEY (see under Westbrook, Roger) (Wrigley, Bernard/ Roger Westbrook).

Wrigley, Yolande

RACHMANINOV AND CHOPIN CELLO SONATAS (see under Gregor-Smith, Bernard) (Wrigley, Yolande/Bernard Gregor-Smith).

Written In The Wind

WRITTEN IN THE WIND (Film Soundtrack) (Various artists).
LP: VC 81074

Writz

WRITZ.
Tracks: / Night nurse / Luxury / Swinging with the reptiles / Drive away / Movies / TV times / Robberoni / Private lives / Super heroes / Muscle culture.
LP: TRIX 12

Wu & The Dragon

WU & THE DRAGON (Various artists).
Tracks: / Wu & the dragon: *Various artists* / Ambassador from Tibet, The: *Various artists* / Eels and gold: *Various* artists / Wonderful tapestry, The: *Various artists* / Priest and the pear tree, The: *Various artists* / Heavenly bowman, The: *Various artists*.
MC: ANV 665

Wunderlich, Fritz

GLORIOUS VOICE OF FRITZ WUNDERLICH, THE.
LP: MOIR 116
MC: CMOIR 116
LP: 2489 519

GRANADA.
Tracks: / Du bist die welt fur mich / Ich kusse ihre hand, madame / Schlaf ein, mein blond - engelein / Caro mio ben / Eine kleine fruhlingsweise / Annchen von tharau / Granada / Be my love / Plaisir d'amour / Serenade / Weine nicht bricht eine schone frau dir das herz / Still wie die nacht.
LP: 2489 044
LP: MOIR 104
MC: CMOIR 104

SINGS EVERGREENS.
LP: DG 410 965-1

Wunderlich, Klaus

28 TOP HITS.
LP: 1-205.674
MC: 1-405.674

AROUND THE WORLD WITH KLAUS WUNDERLICH.
2LP: DP6 28001
MCSET: CT4 28001

BRAZIL.
Tracks: / Amor amor amor / Summer samba / Besame mucho / One note samba / Brazil / Amorada.
LP: 6.25213
MC: CF4 25213

BROADWAY MELODIES.
Tracks: / Ol' man river / People will say we're in love / Aquarius / One / Bali Ha'i / Up, up and away / Welcome / Maria / If I were a rich man / Sound of music, The / I'll never fall in love again.
MC: 4.26636

CELEBRATION.
Tracks: / What you're proposing / All over the world / This ole house / Somethings gotten hold of my heart / Lies / Celebration / Ich steig aus, ich will frei sein / Woman in love / Matador / Wennich dich nicht hatte / Angel of mine / Strings of paradise / Der teufel unde der junge mann / Some broken hearts never mend / Johnny and Mary / Dance little bird / Making your mind up / Lay all your love on me / Geh nicht / Wann siehst du mich schon weinen / Hands up / Loreley / You drive me crazy / Johnny blue / Leib mich ein letztes mal / Seven tears / Liebe ist nicht ein wort / Woman / Smoke gets in your eyes / On the street where you live / Felicidad (Margherita) (CD only.) / Willi, willi (CD only.) / Ich weib, was ich will (CD only.) / Life is for living (CD only.) / Es gibt ein leben nach dem tod (CD only.) / Mamutschka (CD only.) / La provence (CD only.) / Waltz of happiness (CD only.) / Villa's song (CD only.) / You are my hearts delight (CD only.) / Girls were made to love and kiss (CD only.).
LP: MFP 5874
MC: TCMFP 5874

CLASSIC KLAUS.
Tracks: / Adagio cantabile / Wedding day at Troldhaugen / To the spring / Entry of the gladiators / Prince Igor, Theme from / Prelude in C flat minor / Humoresque / Liebestraum / Flight of the bumble bee / Waltz of the flowers / Merry wives of Windsor overture / Hunting chorus from Der Freischutz / Sabre dance.
LP: TAB 77
MC: KTBC 77

CLUB DANCING.
LP: 6.22637
MC: CH4 22637

COLLECTION: KLAUS WUNDERLICH.
Tracks: / Fly robin fly / Nights on Broadway / Also sprach Zarathustra / Waterloo / Teenage rampage / Devil gate drive / Chirpy chirpy cheep cheep / Sunny / Rose garden / Cracklin' rosie / Never can say goodbye / Jenny gotta dance / Shame shame shame / Let me be the one / Oh boy / Only you can / Honey honey / Kissin' in the back row of the movies / Sugar baby love / This will be / Mississippi / There goes my first love / Guantanamera / Rhinestone cowboy / What am I gonna do with you / I write the songs / Concierto de Aranjuez / Little love and understanding, A / Nostalgia / Are you lonesome tonight / Look at me / Delta queen / Clair / Get down / Downtown / Sunshine lover / Amazing Grace / Mother of mine / Sugar me / Standing in the road / Till I kissed you / Do you wanna dance / Kailaki Kailako / Una paloma blanca / Fox on the run / Only yesterday / Bye bye baby / Amore grande amore libero / Breaking up is hard to do / Mandy / Entertainer, The / Si / I'm leaving it all up to you / Tweedle dee tweedle dum / How do you do / Never ending song of love / Poppa Joe / You never listen to a reason / Let's twist again / Mamma mia / Jackson / Charly Brown / Love to love you baby / Last farewell, The / My prayer.
2LP: CCSLP 128
MCSET: CCSMC 128

COLLECTION: KLAUS WUNDERLICH VOL.2.
Tracks: / Rain, rain, rain / Love and rainy weather / It never rains in Southern California / Most beautiful girl in the world / Seasons in the sun / Cabaret / Song for joy / Julie do ya love me / Teneriffa melody / Rosetta / Jack in the box / Cast your fate to the wind / Funny funny / Las Vegas / My sweet Lord / Knock three times / She's a lady / Silver moon / Put your hand in the hand / Lady Rose / Scarborough fair / Spinning wheel / Superstar / Soley soley / Beautiful sunday / I've found my freedom / Lion sleeps tonight, The / I'd like to teach the world to sing / Son of my father / Beg steal or borrow / Popcorn / Apache / Corn flakes / Molina / Crocodile rock / Mama mia / I will follow him / Diana / Wig wam bam.
MCSET: CCSMC 171
2LP: CCSLP 171

DREAM CONCERTO.
LP: DKLR 1001/2
MC: KDKC 28072

EL CUMBANCHERO (16 South American Favourites).
Tracks: / El cumbanchero / Rumba tambah / Amor, amor, amor / La felicidad / Ave Maria / Besame mucho / Ole guapa / La cumparsita / Maria Delores / Brazil / Cu-cu-rru-cu-cu-paloma / etc.
LP: 6.25660
MC: 425660

ENTERTAINER, THE.
Tracks: / Spanish flea / Mame / Taste of honey, A / Last waltz, The / Zwei Augen, wie deine / Massachusetts / Spanish eyes / Green green grass of home / Strangers in the night / Something stupid / Yesterday / Sun ain't gonna shine anymore, The / Fancy pants / I can do it / Una paloma blanca / Fox on the run / Desafinado / Quando caliente el sol / Kiss of fire / Honey honey / Kissin' in the back row of the movies / Sugar baby love / Hustle, The / Puzzle, The / Love story theme / Didn't we? / My way / Money, money, money / Sunny / Tante Emma / Wand'rin' star / Wonder of you, The / It's impossible / Si / I'm leaving it all up to you / Lion sleeps tonight, The / I'd like to teach the world to sing / Son of my father / Beg, steal or borrow / Two hearts in waltz time / Amor amor / Besame mucho / Maria Elena / Feelings / I can't stop loving you / Are you lonesome tonight?.
MCSET: KDBC2 13
2LP: DBC 13

FANTASTIC SOUND OF KLAUS WUNDERLICH.
LP: WH 5013

FAVOURITES.
LP: 6.22278
MC: CH4 22278

FROM NEW YORK TO YOKOHAMA.
Tracks: / New York, New York / Carnival in Rio / San Francisco / Das hab'ich in Paris gerlent / An einem Sonntag in Avignon (On a Sunday in Avignon) / White rose of Athens, The / In Hamburg sind die nachte lang / Londonderry air / Berliner luft / Foggy day in London town, A / Carnival of Venice / Heut' kommen d'Engerin auf urlaub nach Wien / Tulpen aus Amsterdam (Tulips from Amsterdam) / Lisbon Antigua / Moskau (Moscow) / Yokohama melody.
LP: 6.26378
MC: 4.26378

GOLDEN HAMMOND POPS.
2LP: DP6 28075
MC: CT4 28075

GOLDEN SOUND OF HAMMOND, VOL 2.
LP: 6.23079
MC: CH4 23079

HIT WORLD OF KLAUS WUNDERLICH, THE.
LP: SPA 434
MC: KCSP 434

ILLUSION.
LP: 1-205.675
MC: 1-405.675

IMAGES: KLAUS WUNDERLICH.
Tracks: / Memory / Laura / Swingin' safari, A / Dawn / Song for guy / Misty / Begin the beguine.
MC: KNMC 16003

IN A ROMANTIC MOOD (28 romantic melodies).
Tracks: / Limelight / Breeze and I / More / I could have danced all night / Love story (where do I begin?) / Feelings / Don't cry for me Argentina / Un homme et une femme / I love Paris / Our love is here to stay / La vie en rose / Over the rainbow / Lara's theme / This is my song / Twilight time / They can't take that away from me / C'est si bon / I kiss your hand Madame / If you could read my mind / Massachusetts / Something stupid / Greensleeves / Parlez-moi d'amour / Song of the Indian guest / Killing me softly with his song / Ave Maria / Deine spuren im sand / Strangers in the night / This guy's in love with you.
LP: MFP 5781
MC: TCMFP 5781

IN THE GLENN MILLER MOOD (Klaus Wunderlich spielt Glenn Miller).
Tracks: / In the mood / Moonlight serenade / Little brown jug / Tuxedo junction / Chattanooga choo choo / Pennsylvania 6-5000 / American patrol / String of pearls / St. Louis blues march / I know why / Johnson rag / Flying home.
LP: 6.23026
MC: CT4 23026

IN THE WUNDERLICH MOOD.
Tracks: / In the mood / Angela / In Hamburg sind die nachte lang / Mit 66 jahren / Eine hand ist keine faust / Moonlight serenade / Jenseits von Eden / Fur alle / American patrol / Ballade pour Adeline / Rivers of Babylon / I just called to say I love you(flieg mit mir zu den sterne) / Londonderry air / I've grown accustomed to her face / Disco 'Beethoven', The (Medley includes: The disco "Beethoven", Take a chance on me and You are) / Live is life / Adagio cantabile / Einsamer hirte / Oxygene (part IV) / Magic fly / I feel love.
MC: 4.26476

JINGLE BELLS.
Tracks: / Holy advent / Jingle bells / Es wird schon bald dunkel / Leise rieselt der schnee / Little drummer boy / Winter wonderland / Ihr kinderlein kommet / Largo / Ave Maria / O du frohliche, o du selige / Joy to the world / White Christmas / O little town of Bethlehem / O Tannenbaum / Am Weihnachtsbaum di Lichter brennen / Petit papa Noel / Mary's boy child / First Noel, The / Heidsche bumbeidschi / God rest ye merry gentlemen / O come all ye faithful / Vom himmel hoch / Stille nacht / Susser die glocken nie klingen.
LP: 6.26682
MC: 4.26682

KLAUS WUNDERLICH.
Tracks: / All of me / You're driving me crazy / Undecided / On the street where you live / I left my heart in San Francisco / Tea for two / Millionaire, The / Patricia / Rock your baby / Kung fu fighting / Get

down / Downtown / Sunshine lover / Chicago / Lion sleeps tonight, The / I'd like to teach the world to sing / Son of my father / Moon river / Blueberry Hill / Moonglow / Sentimental journey / Most beautiful girl, The / Seasons in the sun / Cabaret / Maria Elena / Feelings / I can't stop loving you / Slow boat to China.
LP: CN 2060
MC: CN4 2060

KLAUS WUNDERLICH IN CONCERT
Classical hits.
Tracks: / Themes from Symphony No. 5 / Piano concerto in B minor / Nocturne in E flat / Eine kleine nachtmusik / In the hall of the mountain king / Rhapsody No. 2 / Prince Igor / Triumphal march from 'Aida' / Pilgrims chorus from Tannhauser / Dance of the hours / Vilia's song / You are my hearts delight / Girls were made to love and kiss.
LP: ODN 1003

KLAUS WUNDERLICH PLAYS ROBERT STOLZ MELODIES.
LP: 6.21183
MC: CT4 21183

LATIN COLLECTION.
Tracks: / La felicidad / Limbo rock / El cumbanchero / La cumparsita / Canari-cha-cha / Mambo jambo / Breeze and I / Girl from Ipanema / Frenesi / Anna / Tico Latin hustle / La paloma / Bossa-nova rhapsodie / Amor / Eso es el amor / Summer samba / Amapola / Un rayo de sol / Manha de carnaval.
LP: DBC 17
MC: KDBC2 17

MAGIC OF KLAUS WUNDERLICH, THE.
Tracks: / Up, up and away / St. Louis blues march / My lady of Spain / Shalom / Dreams are ten a penny / Desafinado / Cherokee / April in Portugal / Summertime / Impossible dream, The / Spanish flea / Mame / Taste of honey, A / We are goin' down Jordan / Freedom come, freedom go / Gypsies, tramps and thieves / Young new Mexican puppeteer, The / Wand'rin' star / It's impossible / Wonder of you, The / Guantanamera / Rhinestone cowboy / What am I gonna do with you? / Massachusetts / Spanish eyes / Green green grass of home / Dancing queen / I love to love.
LP: CN 2068
MC: CN4 2068

MR HAMMOND.
2LP: DP6 28006

MULTI ORCHESTRAL ORGAN SOUND.
Tracks: / Opus one / I'm always chasing rainbows / Trumpet blues and cantabile / Red roses for a blue lady / Skyliner / Li'l darlin' / Sleigh ride / Mr. Anthony's boogie / I've got my love to keep me warm / Baby elephant walk / Take the 'A' train / Charmaine / Intermission riff / Patricia.
LP: 6.26513
MC: 4.26513

MUSIC IS FOREVER.
Tracks: / Clair / What the world needs now is love / Raindrops keep falling on my head / Lara's theme / Petite fleur / St. Louis blues march / Tuxedo Junction / Can't take my eyes off you / Born free / Mull of Kintyre / Liebestraum / Moonlight in Vermont / Brazil / Strangers in the night / Coppelia waltz / Java melody in F / Summer samba / I've got my love to keep me warm / Moonlight serenade.
LP: CN 2050
MC: CN4 2050

MUSICAL.
Tracks: / There's no business like show business (Annie get your gun) / Ol' man river (Showboat) / People will say we're in love (Oklahoma) / Aquarius (From 'Hair') / I've grown accustomed to her face (My fair lady) / One (A chorus line) / Bali Ha'i / Welcome / Maria (West side story) / Hello, Dolly / If I were a rich man / Sound of music, The / I'll never fall in love again / Superstar.
LP: 6.26229
MC: 4.26229

MY WAY.
Tracks: / Everybody loves somebody / Summerwind / Hallelujah / Love me tender / Solveig's song / La Montanara / I left my heart in San Francisco / Something stupid / Der schleier fiel / Yesterday / Tenderly / Clair / Till / Tango Italiano / Spiel mir das Lied vom Tod / My way.
LP: 6.26893
MC: 4.26893

NEW WUNDERLICH POPS.
Tracks: / Comment ca va / Biscaya / Jambo jambo / Wunderbar / Die sonne und du / Santa Lucia by night / Reach out / I just called to say I love you / Life is life / Jenseits von Eden / Fur alle / Angela / Also lebe ich / Am strand von Griechenland / Manner brauchen liebe / Lab es mich ganz leise sagen / Hurra, wir leben noch / Aufrecht geh'n / Goodbye my love / Frankreich, frankreich / Flieg mit mir zu den sternen / Blue night shadow / Mein tuut tuut / Katrin / I war am liabsten mit dir ganz alloa / Extension / Abends / Lieb ohne leiden.
LP: 6.26326
MC: 4.26326

OLDIES AND NEWIES IN HAMMOND SOUND.
Tracks: / Lass'die sonne in dien herz / Cheek to cheek / La la la / Herz aus glas (Heart of glass) / Air, Theme from / Please release me / Mit musik geht alles besser / Poem / Ich hor so gern musik / Give me peace on earth / Pretend / Fata morgana / Schenk deiner frau doch hin und wieder rote rosen / Heisse nachte (in Palermo) / Hallo kleines fraulein (Hello, little girl) / An einem tag im Fruhling / Heimet deine sterne / Hallo, leiber Gott (Hello, dear God) / Uber die brucke geh'n / Resi i hol di mit mei'm traktor ab / Uberall bluhen rosen (L'important c'est la rose) / Es war auf Capri (Isle of Capri) / In Japan geht die sonne auf / Perfidia / Viva la Mexico / Sonata in C (Mozart). Theme from / New York-Rio-Tokyo.
LP: 6.26610
MC: 4.26610

ON THE SUNNY SIDE OF THE STREET.
Tracks: / Honeysuckle rose / Exactly like you / Star wars / Flashdance... what a feeling / On the sunny side of the street / Falling in love again / When is your birthday Johnny / You came along / When day is done / Blue eyes / Song for Guy / Puttin' on the Ritz / Blue skies / Alexander's ragtime band / When I take my sugar to tea / Ain't she sweet / Too soon.
LP: SPELP 101
MC: SPEMC 101
LP: POLD 5133

ORGAN POWER.
Tracks: / Tico tico / Mas que nada / Quando caliente el sol / La felicidad / Brazil / Amorado / String of pearls / Strangers in the night / Delicado / Lara's theme / Love is blue / Amboss polka.
MC: 4.26627

PHASE 4 WORLD OF KLAUS WUNDERLICH.
LP: SPA 532
MC: KCSP 532

POLKA POPS.
Tracks: / Puppet on a string / Die perle tirols / Klitsch-klatsch / Polka / Rosamunde / Anneliese / Schone maid.
LP: 6.25212

POLKA POPS, VOL 2.
LP: 6 2114
MC: CT4 2114

POP EVERGREENS.
Tracks: / Ein ehrenwertes haus / Tanze mit mir in den morgen (Dance with me in the morning) / Aber bitte mit sahne (But with cream, please) / Wunder gisst es immer weider / Whiter shade of pale, A / Way to happiness, The / A banda (not to be changed to Banda, A) / Apache / La bostella / Capri-fischer / O my darling Caroline / Das machen nur die beine von Dolores / Desafinado / Girl from Ipanema, The / Ich bin verliebt in die liebe / Du kannst nicht immer siebzehn sein / Y viva Espana / What a wonderful world / Sunrise call / Die kleine kneipe / Anna Baiao / Komm' ein bisschen mit nach Italien / Liebeskummer lohnt sich nicht.
LP: 246 238-1
MC: 246 238-4

POP ORGAN HIT PARTY 2.
Tracks: / Lay all your love on me / Geh nicht / Wann siehst du mich schon weinen / Shaddup you face / Malaika / Oh no no / Ich sah nur sie / Samstag Abend / Dance little bird / This ole house / Making your mind up / Seven tears / Liebe ist nicht ein Wort / Woman / Life is for living / Es gibt ein Leben nach dem Tod / Mamutschka / La provence / Waltz of happiness / Hands up / Loreley / You drive me crazy / Johnny Blue / Something's gotten hold of my heart / Leib'mich ein letzes mal / Gaby wartet im park / Ai no corrida / Agadou.
LP: ODN 1005

POP ORGAN PARTY.
LP: PM 1552833
MC: PM 1552839
LP: 623802
MC: CT4 23802

PORTRAIT.
LP: BRLP 30
MC: BRMC 30

PORTRAIT IN GOLD.
LP: DX6 30101

PORTRAIT: KLAUS WUNDERLICH.
Tracks: / Tico tico / Mas que nada / Brazil / All of me / On the street where you live / Blueberry Hill / Sag mir, wo die blumen sind / Perfidia / Tea for two / Patricia / Strangers in the night / Lara's theme / Liechtensteiner polka / Delicado / La paloma / Amboss polka / Canari-cha-cha / Raindrops keep fallin' on my head / etc.
LP: 6.28507
MC: 4.28507

PROFILE: KLAUS WUNDERLICH.
LP: 6.24287
MC: CL4 24287

RENDEZVOUS.
Tracks: / Breeze and I / More / I could have danced all night / Love story theme / Feelings / Don't cry for me Argentina / Un homme et une femme / I love Paris / Love is here to stay / La vie en rose / Over the rainbow / Lara's theme / Limelight / Twilight time / They can't take that away from me / C'est si bon / I kiss your hand, Madame / If you could read my mind / Massachusetts / Something stupid / Greensleeves / Parlez-moi d'amour / Song of the Indian guest / Killing me softly with his song / Ave Maria / Deine spuren im sand / Strangers in the night / This guy's in love with you.
LP: ODN 1006
MC: TCODN 1006

ROMANTIC MELODIES.
Tracks: / You make my world so beautiful / Memory / Swingin' safari, A / Laura / Dawn / Summer place, A (Theme from) / You taught my heart a song of love / Intermezzo of Notre Dame / Begin the beguine / Linger awhile / Misty / Dreams are free / Le premier rendezvous / Goodnight.
LP: POLD 5162
MC: POLDC 5162

SAMBA SOUTH AMERICA (Samba Sudamerika).
Tracks: / Amor, amor, amor / Cu-cu-rru-cu-cu-paloma / Summer samba / Besame mucho / Mas que nada / One note samba / La felicidad / Desafinado / Brazil / Amorada / Amapola / El cumbanchero.
MC: 4.27419

SENSATIONAL ORGAN SOUND OF KLAUS WUNDERLICH.
MC: CT4 28463

SOUND VARIATION.
LP: 6.23994
MC: CT4 23994

SOUTH AMERICAN HAMMOND ORGAN 3.
LP: 6.22594
MC: CT4 22594

SOUTH AMERICAN HAMMOND ORGAN 1.
LP: 6.21027
MC: CT4 21027

SOUTH AMERICAN HAMMOND ORGAN 2.
LP: 6.21083
MC: CT4 21083

STRICTLY FOR DANCING.
LP: POLD 5180
MC: POLDC 5180

SWING AND HAPPY (Wunderlich, Klaus & H. Deuringer).
2LP: DP6 28045

THIS IS KLAUS WUNDERLICH.
Tracks: / Shaddup you face / Malaika / Oh no no / Dance little bird / This ole house / Making your mind up / Johnny Blue / Something's gotten hold of my heart / Lieb' mich ein letztes mal / Super trouper / My old piano / Feels like I'm in love / What you're proposing / Lies / Celebration / All over the world / Ich steig'aus, ich will frei sein / Gaby wartet im park / Ai no corrida / Agadou / Symphony No. 5, Theme from / Piano concerto in B minor / Nocturne in E flat / Eine kleine nachtmusik / In the hall of the mountain king / Rhapsody No 2 / Prince Igor, Theme from / Triumphal march from Aida / Pilgrims' chorus (from 'Tannhauser') / Dance of the hours / American in Paris, An / I got rhythm / Lady be good / Fascinating rhythm / American in Paris, An / Man I love, The / 'S wonderful / Embraceable you / Rhapsody in blue, Theme from / Summertime / Concerto in F, Theme from / American in Paris, An.
MC: TCEMS 1293

TIME FOR ROMANCE.
Tracks: / Lover / Love to love you, baby / Last farewell, The / My prayer / Strangers in the night / Something stupid / Yesterday / Sun ain't gonna shine anymore, The / Amore grande, amore libero / Breaking up is hard to do / Mandy / Speak softly love / L.O.V.E. / Amor amor / I'm not in love / Godfather, The II / Nostalgia / Are you lonesome tonight? / Love is blue / Love story theme / Didn't we? / My way / Till.
LP: CN 2064
MC: CN4 2064

TOUR OF BRITAIN.
Tracks: / Amazing grace / Ash grove, The / Auld lang syne / Down at the old Bull and Bush / Elizabethan serenade / Fings ain't wot they used t'be / Lambeth walk / Land of hope and glory / Mull of Kintyre / Nightingale sang in Berkeley Square, A / Scarborough fair / Scotland the brave / There'll always be an England / White cliffs of Dover, The.
LP: 6.26948
MC: 4.26948

TRAVELLIN' ON.
Tracks: / Cherokee / Moon river / Amarillo / Sacramento / Tuxedo junction / Java / Moscow nights / American in Paris, An / Paloma blanca / Fox on the run / In San Francisco / Moonlight serenade / Chicago / Y viva Espana / Shalom / Lover / Waterloo / Wonderful Copenhagen.
2LP: DBC 15
MCSET: KDBC2 15

TRIBUTE TO FRANK SINATRA, A.
MC: NSPMC 502

UNFORGETTABLE: KLAUS WUNDERLICH (16 Golden Classics).
Tracks: / Feelings (Cleo Laine.) / Wave (With Cleo Laine) / Portrait / From the top / Air on a G string / Bach changes / Woodstock / If (With Cleo Laine) / Dance of the living / Lorelei / Duet for guitar and koto / Lisa Larne / Dance of the emperor's clouds / Dance of the dead / A dherrin dhu / Magic fly / I feel love / Derrin dhu, A / Night fever / Disco (Beethoven symphony no 5) / Take a chance on me / You're the one that I want / Verde / Le reve / Grease / Oxygene / More more more / I'm a train / Hustle puzzle / Amarillo / Power to all our friends / Letter to Lucille / Money money money / A fair l'amore / Take me high / Free electric band / Get up and boogie.
LP: UNLP 017
MC: UNMC 017

UNIQUE KLAUS WUNDERLICH SOUND, THE.
2LP: DBC 5/6
MCSET: KDBC2 8094

WONDERLAND BY NIGHT.
LP: SHM 3178
MC: HSC 3178

WUNDERLICH POPS 5.
LP: 6.22588
MC: CT4 22588

WUNDERLICH POPS 6.
LP: 6.23068
MC: CT4 23068

WUNDERLICH POPS 7.
LP: 6.23434
MC: CT4 23434

Wurges, Paul

ROCKING ALL STARS (Der Deutsche Bill Haley).
Tracks: / Mary / Mary Lou / Let's go baby / Way down yonder in New Orleans / So high so low / Li'l Liza Jane / Dum dum / Night ride / Red river rock / Pepe / Geisha baby / Three bells, The / Perfidia.
LP: BFX 15059

Wurzels

ADGE CUTLER AND THE WURZELS (See under Cutler, Adge) (Wurzels & Adge Cutler).

COMBINE HARVESTER.
LP: OU 2138

GIVE ME ENGLAND.
Tracks: / Give me England / Willie Friese Greene / Sally Army teacher / Tremble on the mixerman's lament / Speedy Gonzales / Farmer Jonesie's travellin' disco show / Sousaphone Sam / Jubilee day, The / Hey come with me / Nellie the bionic cow / Haggis farewell / Farmer Bill's cowman.
LP: NTS 138

GOLDEN DELICIOUS.
LP: NTS 122

GREATEST HITS: WURZELS.
Tracks: / I am a cider drinker / Morning glory / Rock around the A38 / Schooldays, young days / Speedy Gonzalez / Give me England / One for the Bristol City / Farmer Bill's cowman / Drink up thy zider / Don't tell I, tell 'ee / Funky farmyard / Tractor song / Our village band / I got my beady little eye on thee / Blackbird / I'll never get a scrumpy here / Combine harvester.
LP: NTS 190
MC: TCNTS 190

I AM A CIDER DRINKER.
Tracks: / I am a cider drinker / Down our street / Springtime / Back of my old car / I keep smilin' / Cabot song / Sousaphone Sam / Sally-Army teacher / Nellie the bionic cow / Farmer Jonesies' travellin' disco show / Shepton Mallet matador / Who needs summer? / Gotta have tenderness / My Somerset crumpet horn / Crabapple Hill / Mevagissey / Drunk on a Saturday night.
LP: . . . . **ONCR 523**

WURZELS.
MC: . . . . **TC IDL 22**

Wuthering Heights

WUTHERING HEIGHTS (Various artists).
MC: **SAG/CAS/2**
LP: **SAG/LPR/2**

Wuthering Heights (bk)

WUTHERING HEIGHTS (Emily Bronte) (Routledge, Patricia (nar)).
MCSET: **CC/002**

WUTHERING HEIGHTS (Emily Bronte) (Massey, Daniel (nar)).
MCSET: . . . . **LFP 7168**
MCSET: . . . . **LFP 4171685**

WUTHERING HEIGHTS (Emily Bronte) (McEnery, Peter (nar)).
MC: **0600560465**

WUTHERING HEIGHTS (Emily Bronte) (Bloom, Claire (nar)).
MCSET: **2086**

Wuzzles

WUZZLES, THE.
LP: . . . . **PIPLP 718**
MC: . . . . **ZCPIP 718**

Wyands, Richard

THEN, HERE AND NOW.
LP: . . . . **SLP 4083**

Wyatt, Gene

ROCKS AGAIN.
Tracks: / Campus queen / Little girl / One, two, three little kisses / Lona Lige / Rhythm / Like last night / Contest, The / Go go Merle / Gene's bop / Grandpa's teaching the limbo rock / Twistin' bones / Waiting / Guitar led / Too big for tears.
LP: . . . . **WLP 8887**

TOMMY BLAKE & GENE WYATT (See under Blake, Tommy) (Wyatt, Gene & Tommy Blake).

Wyatt, Robert

1982-1984.
LP: . . . . **RTSP 25**

ANIMALS.
LP: . . . . **ROUGH 40**

DOUDESTAN.
LP: . . . . **R 2741**
MC: . . . . **R 2744**

END OF AN EAR.
Tracks: / Las Vegas tango / To mark everywhere / To saintly Bridget / To Oz alien Daevyd and Gilly / To Nick everyone / To caravan and brother Jim / To the old orld / To Carla, Marsha and Caroline.
LP: . . . . **CBS 31846**

NOTHING CAN STOP US.
LP: . . . . **ROUGH 35**
MC: . . . . **ROUGHC 35**

OLD ROTTEN HAT.
LP: . . . . **ROUGH 69**
MC: . . . . **ROUGHC 69**

ROCK BOTTOM.
Tracks: / Sea song / Last straw, The / Little Red Riding Hood hit the road / Alifib / Little Red Robin Hood hit the road.
LP: . . . . **V 2017**
MC: . . . . **TCV 2017**

ROCK BOTTOM/RUTH IS STRANGER THAN RICHARD.
Tracks: / Sea song / Last straw, The / Little Red Riding Hood hit the road / Alifib / Little Red Robin Hood hit the road / Soup song / Sonia / Team spirit / Song for Che / Muddy mouse (A) / Solar flares / Muddy mouse (B) / Five black notes and one white note / Muddy mouse (C) / Muddy mouth.
2LP: . . . . **VGD 3505**
MC: . . . . **VGDC 3505**

RUTH IS STRANGER THAN RICHARD.
Tracks: / Soup song / Sonia / Team spirit / Song for Che / Muddy mouse (A) / Solar flares / Muddy mouse (B) / Five black notes and one white note / Muddy mouse (C) / Muddy mouth.
LP: . . . . **V 2034**
MC: . . . . **TCV 2034**

Wycoff, Michael

COME TO MY WORLD.
Tracks: / Come to my world / Feel my love / Someone standing by / One alone / Do ya think / Just as long / Love makes me sing.
LP: . . . . **RCALP 5008**

LOOKING UP TO YOU (See under Thornton, Fonzi/Beverley).

LOOKING UP TO YOU (OLD GOLD) (See under Thorton, Fonzi/Beverley).

ON THE LINE.
Tracks: / On the line / There's no easy way / You've got it coming / So close / Tell me love / I'll do anything for you / Do it to me baby / You are everything.
LP: . . . . **BSLP 5002**
MC: . . . . **BSK 5002**

Wygals

HONEYOCKS IN THE WHITHERSOEVER.
LP: . . . . **ROUGH 134**
MC: . . . . **ROUGHC 134**

Wylde Mammoths

GO BABY GO.
LP: . . . . **CRYPT 011**

THINGS THAT MATTER.
LP: . . . . **CRYPT 012**

Wylie, Pete

SINFUL.
Tracks: / Sinful / Shoulder to shoulder / Breakout the banners / Fourelevenfortyfour / If I love you / Train to Piranhaville / We can rule the world / All the love.
MC: . . . . **SRNMC 10**
LP: . . . . **SRNLP 10**
LP: . . . . **OVED 290**
MC: . . . . **OVEDC 290**

SINFUL (See under Eurythmics - Sexcrime (1984).

Wyman, Bill

BILL WYMAN.
Tracks: / Ride on, baby / New fashion / Nuclear reactions / Visions / Jump up / Come back, Suzanne / Rio de Janeiro / Girls / Seventeen / Si si, je suis un rock star.
LP: . . . . **AMLH 68540**
MC: . . . . **CAM 68540**

MONKEY GRIP.
LP: . . . . **COC 59102**

WILLIE AND THE POOR BOYS (Wyman, Bill & Friends).
Tracks: / Baby please don't go / Can you hear me / These arms of mine / Revenue man / You never can tell / Slippin' and slidin' / Saturday night / Let's talk it over / All night long / Chicken-shack boogie / Sugar bee / Poor boy boogie.
LP: . . . . **BILL 1**
MC: . . . . **KBILL 1**

Wyman, Jane

ZING A LITTLE ZONG (see under Crosby, Bing) (Wyman, Jane & Bing Crosby).

Wyndham, John (aut)

DAY OF THE TRIFFIDS, THE (Powell, Robert (nar)).
MCSET: . . . . **LFP 7298**

Wyndham-Read, Martyn

ACROSS THE LINE.
LP: . . . . **GVR 232**

ANDY'S GONE.
Tracks: / Bodmon town / Andy's gone with cattle / Grimsby lads / Soldier's dream of home, The / In the hills of Shiloh / Ploughboy, The / Lemonay / Mower, The / Faithful Emma / Harry Dale the drover / Forlorn lover, The / Seasons of the year.
LP: . . . . **BRO 134**
MC: . . . . **KBRO 134**

BALLAD SWINGER.
LP: . . . . **ALLP 218**

EMU PLAINS.
Tracks: / Stockman's last bed, The / Ile-de-France, The / Reedy river / Declaration / Water lily / Flash Jack from Gundagai / Gentle Annie / Wandering Aengus / Do you think I do not know? / Ae waukin O / Shearing in a bar / Where the brumbies come to water / Exile of Erin, The / Bush lullaby, A.
LP: . . . . **FE 027**

GREAT AUSTRALIAN LEGEND (Wyndham-Read, Martyn & Trevor Lucas).
Tracks: / Waltzing Matilda / Jim Jones / Wild colonial boy / Streets of Forbes / Hold up at Eugowra Rocks / Flash stockman, The / Five miles from Gundagai / Click go the shears / Flash jack from Gundagai / Road to Gundagai / Hard track / On the road with Liddy.
LP: **12TS 203**

MARTIN WYNDHAM-READ.
LP: . . . . **LER 2028**

NED KELLY AND THAT GANG.
LP: . . . . **LER 2009**

OLD SONGS, THE.
LP: . . . . **GVR 225**

Wynette, Tammy

20 COUNTRY CLASSICS.
LP: . . . . **PR 5040**

ANNIVERSARY: 20 YEARS OF HITS.
Tracks: / I don't wanna play house / D.I.V.O.R.C.E. / Stand by your man / Singing my song / Run, woman, run / We sure can love each other / Good loving (makes it right) / Bedtime story / Till I get it right / Kids say the darndest things / Another lonely song / We're gonna hold on (with George Jones.) / Woman to woman / Till I can make it on my own / Golden ring (with George Jones.) / You and me / One of a kind / Two storey house (with George Jones.) / Alive and well / Apartment No.9 / Your good girl's gonna go bad.
LP: **4503931**
MC: **4503934**

BEST OF TAMMY WYNETTE.
Tracks: / Stand by your man / Lonely street / D.I.V.O.R.C.E. / Gentle on my mind / Take me to your world / Almost persuaded / Your good girl's gonna go bad / Apartment No.9 / Hey good lookin' / I don't wanna play house / My arms stay open late / There goes my everything.
LP: . . . . **CBS 32015**
MC: **40 32015**
LP: . . . . **EPC 63578**

BEST OF TAMMY WYNETTE VOL 2.
Tracks: / You and me / Let's get together (one last time) / Womanhood / I still believe in fairytales / One of a kind / Till I can make it on my own / This time I almost made it / Southern California / I'd like to see Jesus / Dear daughters.
LP: . . . . **EPC 83214**

BIGGEST HITS.
Tracks: / I don't wanna play house / Take me to your world / D.I.V.O.R.C.E. / Stand by your man / Ways to love a man, The / When he loves me (he loves me all the way) / Run woman run / Bedtime story / My man / Till I get it right / Kids say the darndest things / Till I can make it on my own / You and me / Starting over / Cowboys don't shoot straight / Crying in the rain.
LP: . . . . **EPC 32302**

CHRISTMAS WITH TAMMY.
Tracks: / Silent night, holy night / O little town of Bethlehem / It came upon a midnight clear / Joy to the world / Away in a manger / Gentle shepherd / Blue Christmas / Merry Christmas (We must be having one) / White Christmas / One happy Christmas / Lonely Christmas call / Let's put Christ back into Christmas.
LP: **4604631**
MC: **4604634**

CLASSIC COLLECTION.
Tracks: / Stand by your man / You and me / I don't wanna play house / Golden ring / No charge / Apartment No.9 / Gentle on my mind / Womanhood / Your good girl's gonna go bad / Almost persuaded / Ode to Billy Joe / Southern California / Let's get together (one last time) / Crying in the chapel / Yesterday / Help me make it through the night / D.I.V.O.R.C.E. / There goes my everything / Cheatin' is / My elusive dreams / One of a kind / Sweet music man / Bedtime story / Roll in my sweet baby's arms / Till I can make it on my own / Honey (I miss you) / Woman to woman / Near you / Please come to Boston / I'd like to see Jesus on the midnight special / Kids say the darndest things / My man (understands).
2LP: . . . . **EPC 22136**
MCSET: **40 22136**

COUNTRY GIRL MEETS COUNTRY BOY.
LP: . . . . **PR 5039**

COUNTRY STARS (Wynette, Tammy & George Jones).
MC: . . . . **PLAC 351**

COUNTRY STORE COLLECTION (See under Jones, George) (Wynette, Tammy & George Jones).

COUNTRY STORE: TAMMY WYNETTE.
Tracks: / Heaven's just a sin away / You needed me / Only the strong survive / Yesterday / Take me to your world / My elusive dreams / I don't wanna play house / Stand by your man / Starting over / Crying in the rain / Help me make it through the night / There goes my everything / Gentle on my mind / It's just a matter of time / Unwed fathers (Only on CD.) / If I could only win your love (Only on CD.) / Bottle, The (Only on CD.) / Cowboys don't shoot straight (Only on CD.).
LP: . . . . **CST 1**
MC: . . . . **CSTK 1**

COUNTRY STORE: TAMMY WYNETTE AND GEORGE JONES (See under Jones, George) (Jones, George & Tammy Wynette).

COUNTRY SUPERSTAR - TAMMY WYNETTE.
MCSET: . . . . **DTO 10306**

COUNTRY WORLD OF TAMMY WYNETTE.
Tracks: / Ode to Billy Joe / There goes my everything / Cry / Hey good lookin' / Gentle on my mind / This time I almost made it / Old reliable / (When he loves me) he loves me all the way / Dear daughter / Bring my baby back to me / Take me to your world / Honey / He was there (when I needed you) / Slighly used woman, A / Let's get together (one last time) / Starting over / Easy come, easy go / Only the strong survive / Yesterday / Crying in the rain.
MCSET: . . . . **DTO 10083**
MCSET: . . . . **DTOL 10083**

D.I.V.O.R.C.E..
Tracks: / D.I.V.O.R.C.E. / Send me no roses / Please come to Boston / Just as soon as I get over loving you / Don't touch me / Almost persuaded / Your good girl's gonna go bad / I wound easy / I'm not mine to give / Walk through this world with me / Jackson ain't a very big town / Apartment No.9.
LP: . . . . **CBS 31676**

EVEN THE STRONG GET LONELY.
Tracks: / Unwed fathers / I'm so afaid that I'd live through it / Slightly used woman / Only the strong survive / With a friend like you / Still in the ring / Midnight love / Overdue / Darlin' take care of yourself / Even the strong get lonely.
LP: . . . . **EPC 25585**

FIRST LADY OF COUNTRY.
Tracks: / You and me / Every now and then / You hurt the love right out of me / Hawaiian wedding song / Little things / Jesus send a song / One of these days / When love was all we had / Dixieland / Funny face.
LP: . . . . **SPR 8509**
MC: . . . . **SPC 8509**
LP: . . . . **SHM 3182**
MC: . . . . **HSC 3182**

GREATEST HITS: TAMMY WYNETTE AND GEORGE JONES (See under Jones, George) (Jones, George & Tammy Wynette).

HEART OVER MIND.
Tracks: / Let's call it a day today / I'm turning you loose / Suddenly single / What goes with blue / Just for a minute there / Half the way home / I'm falling heart over mind / Where's the fire / If you were the friend / One stone at a time.
LP: **4673551**
MC: **4673554**

HIGHER GROUND.
Tracks: / Your love / Tempted / Some things will never change / Beneath a painted sky / I wasn't meant to live my life alone / Higher ground / Talkin' to myself again / Slow burning fire, A / There's no heart so strong / All through throwing good love after bad.
LP: **4511481**
MC: **4511484**

I LOVE COUNTRY.
Tracks: / Womanhood / Two storey house / Crying in the rain / Bring my baby back to me / He was there when I needed you / Cheatin' is / Heaven's just a sin away / Cowboys don't shoot straight / Sometimes when we touch (With Mark Gray) / Funny face / You need me / Sweet music man / Pair of old sneakers, A / Dear daughters / Easy come, easy go / I'd like to see Jesus (on the midnight special).
LP: . . . . **EPC 54943**
MC: **40 54943**

IN LOVE.
Tracks: / Just in case / Easy come easy go / You can be replaced / If I could only win your love / World's most broken heart / Where some good love has been / Till I can make it on my own / Love is something good for everybody / He's just an old love turned memory.
LP: . . . . **SHM 3026**
MC: . . . . **HSC 3026**

IT SURE IS GOOD (Wynette, Tammy and George Jones).
Tracks: / Ceremony, The / Up and at 'em / We're gonna hold on / Back home again in Indiana / Too marvellous for words / (We're not) the jet set / We loved it away / Mean to me / God's gonna getcha (for that) / Sweet Georgia Brown / I'm confessin' / Golden ring / Neenah / Near you / Southern California / I cover the waterfront / Pair of old sneakers, A / Two storey house / We could / Crying time / Did you ever / When I stop

dreaming / After the fire is gone / It sure was good.
LP: . . . . **PMP 1006**
MC: . . . . **PMPK 1006**

JUST TAMMY.
Tracks: / They call it making love / We'll talk about it later / Somewhere / Mania / Your little girl fell / I'm not ready yet / No one else in the world / You don't know the half of it / I L-O-V-E Y-O-U / You never cross my mind / Let me be me.
LP: . . . . **EPC 83695**
MC: **40 83695**

KING AND QUEEN OF COUNTRY MUSIC (Wynette, Tammy & George Jones).
Tracks: / I'll be there / If you don't somebody else will / Even the bad times are good / I've seen better days / Keep the change / Tattle tale eyes / Did you ever / Golden ring / Cryin' time / Near you.
LP: . . . . **SHM 3024**

NEXT TO YOU.
Tracks: / Next to you / I'm so afraid of losing you again / You left memories layin' (all over the place) / When a girl becomes a wife / If you let him drive you crazy (he will) / Note, The / Thank the cowboy for the ride / I almost forgot / We called it everything but quits / Liar's roses.
LP: **4650281**
MC: **4650284**

ONLY LONELY SOMETIMES.
Tracks: / He was there (when I needed you) / I'll be thinking of you / Never knew / Come with me / You needed me / Starting over / Out of the spotlight / Only the names have been changed / When you love me / Ozark Mountain lullaby.
MC: . . . . **SPC 8578**
LP: . . . . **EPC 84343**

QUEEN OF COUNTRY.
Tracks: / D.I.V.O.R.C.E. / Don't touch me / Almost persuaded / (You make me want to be) a mother / Another lonely song / Kid's say the darndest things / Love's the answer / Send me no roses / Apartment No.9 / Woman to woman / Bedtime story / Stand by your man / Your good girl's gonna go bad / Wound easy (but I heal fast) / I'm not mine to give / Walk through this world with me / Jackson ain't a very big town / Just as soon as I get over you / Good lovin' (makes it right) / Reach out your hand / My man understands / Please come to me / 'Til I get it right / There goes that old steel guitar / Help me make it through the night.
LP: . . . . **SSP 3073**
MC: . . . . **SSC 3073**
MCSET: . . . . **DTOL 10043**

SOFT TOUCH.
Tracks: / Old reliable / She can't take my love off the bed / Being gone / What's it like to be a woman / I'll still be loving you this much / Another chance / If I didn't have a heart / You still get to me in my dreams / Sometimes I'm a little girl / Dancing your memory away.
LP: . . . . **EPC 85727**

SOMETIMES WHEN WE TOUCH.
Tracks: / Sometimes when we touch / You can lead a heart to love (but you can't make it fall) / Breaking away / Everytime you touch her / Between twenty-nine and danger / It's only over for you / Party of the first part, The / It's hard to be the dreamer (When I used to be the dream) / If it ain't love / He talks to me.
LP: . . . . **EPC 26403**
MC: **40 26403**

STAND BY YOUR MAN.
Tracks: / You make me want to be a mother / Another lonely song / Kids say the darndest things / Love's the answer / Woman to woman / Bedside story / Stand by your man / Good lovin' / Reach out your hand / Please come to Boston / Till I get it right / My man (understands) / There goes that old steel guitar / Help me make it through the night.
LP: . . . . **CBS 32772**
MC: **40 32772**
LP: . . . . **EPC 69141**

TOGETHER AGAIN (See under Jones, George) (Jones, George & Tammy Wynette).

WOMAN TO WOMAN.
Tracks: / Your good girl's gonna go bad / Singing my song / Ways to love a man, The / I'll see him through / He loves me all the way / Run woman run / We sure love each other / Good lovin' / Bedtime story / My man / Till I get it right / Kids say the darndest things / Another lonely song / Woman to woman / Till I can make it on my own / You and me.
LP: . . . . **PMP 1001**
MC: . . . . **PMPK 1001**

YOU BROUGHT ME BACK.
Tracks: / Cowboys don't shoot straight / Crying in the rain / Bring back my baby to me / You brought me back / Goodnight cowboy goodnight / Easy street / I don't think I see me in your eyes anymore / Best there is / Easy come easy go / He's rolling over and over.
LP: . . . . **EPC 84987**

Wynn, Big Jim

BLOW WYNN, BLOW.
Tracks: / Ee-bobaliba / Buzz buzz buzz / I want a little girl / Cherry red / Rock woogie / Shipyard woman / J W bop / Rhapsody in A minor / Blow Wynn blow / Jelly jelly blues / Fat meat / Farewell baby / Put me down blues / I'm the boss / Goofin' off / Down to the ocean.
LP: . . . . **KM 703**

Wynn, Steve

KEROSENE MAN.
LP: . . . . **SERV 011**
MC: . . . . **SERV 011MC**

Wynne-Jones, Tim

THINKING ROOM, THE/THE JOGGER (Various artists).
MC: . . . . **NF 14**

Wyoming

WYOMING.
LP: **4502601**
MC: **4502604**

Wyss, Johann (aut)

SWISS FAMILY ROBINSON (Quayle, Anthony (nar)).
MC: **1485**

SWISS FAMILY ROBINSON (children's classics) (Unknown narrator(s)).
MC: . . . . **PLBC 75**

X

AIN'T LOVE GRANDE.
Tracks: / Burning house of love / Love shack / My soul cries your name / My goodness / Around my heart / What's wrong with me / All or nothing / Watch the sun go down / I'll stand up for you / Little honey / Supercharged.
LP: . . . . **EKT 12**

LIVE AT THE WHISKEY A GO-GO.
Tracks: / Los Angeles / House I call home / New world / Around my heart / Surprise surprise / Because I do / Burning house of love / My goodness / Blue spark / Once over twice, The / In the time it takes / Devil doll / Hungry wolf / Just another perfect day / Unheard music / Riding with Mary / World's a mess, The / True love / White girl / Skin deep town / So long / Call of the wreckin' ball / Year 1 / Johnny hit and run Pauline.
LP: . . . . **K 9607881**
MC: . . . . **K 9607884**

MORE FUN IN THE NEW WORLD.
Tracks: / New world / We're having much more fun / Poor girl / Make the music go bang / Painting the town blue / breathless / I must not think bad thoughts / Devil doll / True love / Hot house / Drunk in my past / I see red.
LP: **9602831**
MC: **9602834**

SEE HOW WE ARE.
Tracks: / I'm lost / You / 4th of July / In the time it takes / Anyone can fill your shoes / See how we are / Left and right / When it rains / Holiday story / Surprise surprise / Cyrano de Bergerec's back.
LP: . . . . **K 960 492-1**
MC: . . . . **K 960 492-4**

UNDER THE BIG BLACK SUN.
Tracks: / Hungry wolf / Motel room in my bed / Riding with mary / Come back to me / Under the big black sun / Because I do / Blue spark / Dancing with tears in my eyes / Real child of hell / How I learned my lesson / Have nots.
LP: . . . . **K 52401**

X Calibur

EVERYTHING I OWN (See under D Moet) (X Calibur & D Moet).

X Dreamysts

XDREAMYSTS.
LP: **2442 181**

X, Francis

SOUL-INCEST (X. Francis and The Bushmen).
Tracks: / Mirror church / Come with me / Harlequin / Bits and pieces / Wicked love / Power of zero.
LP: . . . . **REVSP 84**

Xalam

XALAM.
LP: . . . . **CEL 6656**

Xanadu

XANADU (Film soundtrack) (Various artists).
Tracks: / I'm alive: *E.L.O.* / Fall, The: *E.L.O.* / Don't walk away: *E.L.O.* / All over the world: *E.L.O.* / Xanadu: *Newton-John, Olivia & ELO* / Magic: *Newton-John, Olivia* / Suddenly: *Newton-John, Olivia & Cliff* Richard / Dancin': *Newton-John, Olivia* / Suspended in time: *Newton-John, Olivia* / Whenever you're away from me: *Newton-John, Olivia & Gene Kelly*.
LP: . . . . **JETLX 526**
MC: . . . . **JETCX 526**

Xanadu In Africa

XANADU IN AFRICA.
LP: . . . . **XAN 180**

Xanten, Peter

DON'T DISTURB MY CROCODILE (Xanten, Peter Ragtime Band).
LP: . . . . **ISST 107**

Xarmakos, Stavros

DARK SIDE OF THE SUN, THE (T.V. soundtrack).
Tracks: / Dark side of the sun / Anne's theme / Mendraki harbour / Relentless pursuit / Don's theme / Chasapikol / Road to Lindos, The / Walk on the shore, A / Anne's theme / Carnival / Sadness / Aspri mera / Gathering storm, The / Cafe Nikos / Dark side of the sun (closing music).
LP: . . . . **REB 487**
MC: . . . . **ZCF 487**

Xavier

POINT OF PLEASURE.
Tracks: / Work that sucker to death / Rock me, sock me / Dial the love man / Do it to the max / What goes around / Truly devoted / Love is on the one.
LP: . . . . **LBG 30347**

Xaviera

XAVIERA.
LP: . . . . **BUSR 246**

X-Clan

FROM THE EAST BACKWARDS.
MC: . . . . **ICM 2065**
LP: . . . . **ILPM 2065**

Xentrix

DILUTE TO TASTE.
LP: . . . . **RO 93201**
MC: . . . . **RO 93204**

FOR WHOSE ADVANTAGE?.
Tracks: / Questions / Human condition, The / Bitter end, The / Desperate remedies / Black embrace / For those advantage? / False ideals / New beginnings / Kept in the dark / Running white faced city boy.
LP: . . . . **RO 9366-1**
MC: . . . . **RO 9366-4**

SHATTERED EXISTENCE.
Tracks: / No compromise / Balance of power / Crimes back in the real world / Dark enemy / Bad blood / Reasons for destruction / Position of security / Heaven cent.
LP: . . . . **RO 9444 1**
MC: . . . . **RO 9444 4**

Xiame

XIAME (OUR EARTH).
Tracks: / Xiame / Nosso destino / Minha rua / Guaratiba / Rio De Janeiro / Um brasileiro em Berlin / Mutio swer / Gone but still here / 'Round midnight / Choro de crainza / I can't stand the pain / Flor da terra / Xiame.
LP: . . . . **VBR 20361**
MC: . . . . **VRB 20364**

XL Recordings

XL RECORDINGS - THE FIRST CHAPTER (Various artists).
LP: . . . . **XLLP 105**
MC: . . . . **XLMC 105**

X-Mal Deutschland

FETISCH.
Tracks: / Qual / Geheimnis / Young man / In der nacht / Orient / Hand in hand / Kaempfen / Danghem / Boomerang / Stummes kind / Qual (remix) (CD only) / Sehnsucht (CD only) / Zeit (CD only).
LP: . . . . **CAD 302**

TOCSIN.
Tracks: / Mondicht / Eiland / Reigen / Tag fur tag (day by day) / Augen blich / Begrab / Mein herz / Nacht schatten / Xmas in Australia / Der wisch / Incubus succubus II (CD only) / ViFo (CD only).
MC: . . . . **CAD 407**

VIVA.
Tracks: / Matador / Eisengrau / Sickle moon / If only / Feuerwerk / Morning (will there really be) / Manchmal / Polarlicht / Ozean / Dogma 1 / Illusion (CD & MC only) / Four (CD & MC only).
LP: . . . . **XMALP 1**
MC: . . . . **XMAMC 1**

X-mas Project

X-MAS PROJECT (Various artists).
LP: . . . . **SHARK 005**

X-Men

LILLIES FOR MY PUSSY.
LP: . . . . **MB 11**

Xoduz

NICE GIRL FROM THE CAKE SHOP.
MC: . . . . **XOD 1**

Xolton, Blake

COOL ON MY SKIN.
LP: . . . . **ROSE 166**

X-Posse

PROJECT X.
Tracks: / X-Posse theme / Kickin' it live / X and the V, The / X army / Ain't got the time / Return of the breaks / Project X / I got talent / Suckers / X-Posse (reprisal).
LP: . . . . **ILPS 9931**
MC: . . . . **ICT 9931**

X-Rated

X-RATED VOLUME 1 (Various artists).
LP: . . . . **VPRL 2017**

X-Ray Spex

GERM FREE ADOLESCENTS.
LP: . . . . **INS 3023**
MC: . . . . **TC INS 3023**

OBSESSED WITH YOU.
LP: . . . . **RRLP 145**

XTC

BEESWAX.
Tracks: / She's so square / Dance band / Hang on to the night / Heatwave / Instant tunes / Pulsing, pulsing / Don't lose your temper / Smokeless zone / Somnambulist, The / Blame the weather / Tissue tigers / Punch and Judy / Heaven is paved with broken glass.
LP: . . . . **OVED 9**
MC: . . . . **OVEDC 9**

BIG EXPRESS, THE.
Tracks: / Wake up / All you pretty girls / Shake you donkey up / Seagulls screaming kiss her kiss her / This world over / Everyday story of smalltown, The / I bought myself a liarbird / Reign of blows / You're the wish you are I had / I remember the sun / Train running low on soul coal / Red brick dream (CD & MC only) / Washaway (CD & MC only) / Blue overall (CD & MC only).
LP: . . . . **V 2325**
MC: . . . . **TCV 2325**
LP: . . . . **OVED 181**
MC: . . . . **OVEDC 181**

BLACK SEA.
Tracks: / Respectable street / Generals and majors / Living through another Cuba / Love at first sight / Rocket from a bottle / No language in our lungs / Towers of London / Paper & iron (notes & coins) / Burning with optimism's flame / Sgt. Rock (is going to help me) / Travels in nihilon / Smokeless zone (CD only) / Don't lose your temper (CD only) / Somnambulist, The (CD only).
LP: . . . . **OVED 83**
MC: . . . . **OVEDC 83**
LP: . . . . **V 2173**

DRUMS AND WIRES.
Tracks: / Making plans for Nigel / Helicopter / Day in, day out / When you're near me I have difficulty / Ten feet tall / Roads girdle the globe / Real by reel / Millions / That is the way / Outside world / Scissor man / Complicated game.
LP: . . . . **OVED 113**
MC: . . . . **OVEDC 113**
LP: . . . . **V 2129**

ENGLISH SETTLEMENT.
Tracks: / Runaways / Ball and chain / Senses working overtime / Jason and the Argonauts / No thugs in our house / Yacht dance / All of a sudden (it's too late) / Melt the guns / Leisure (LP & MC only) / It's nearly Africa / Knuckle down / Fly on the wall / Down in the cockpit (LP & MC only) / English roundabout / Snowman.
MC: . . . . **TCV 2223**
LP: . . . . **V 2223**

EXPLODE TOGETHER (Dub Experiments '70-'80).
MC: . . . . **OVEDC 308**

GO 2.
Tracks: / Meccanik dancing / Crowded room / Battery brides (Andy paints Brian) / Buzzcity talking / Rhythm, The / Beattown / Life is good in the greenhouse / I am the audience / Ted / My weapon / Jumping in Gomorrah / Super-tuff / Are you receiving me? (CD only).
LP: . . . . **OVED 61**
MC: . . . . **OVEDC 61**
LP: . . . . **V 2108**

MUMMER.
Tracks: / Beating of hearts / Wonderland / Love on a farmboy's wages / Great fire / Deliver us from the elements / Human alchemy / Ladybird / In loving memory of a name / Me and the wind / Funk pop a roll.
LP: . . . . **OVED 142**
MC: . . . . **OVEDC 142**
LP: . . . . **V 2264**

ORANGES AND LEMONS.
Tracks: / Garden of earthly delights / King for a day / Loving, The / Across the antheap / Pink thing / Chalkhills and children / Mayor of Simpleton / Here comes President kill again / Poor skeleton steps out / Hold me daddy / Minature sun / One of the millions / Scarecrow people / Merely a man / Cynical days.
2LP: . . . . **V 2581**
MC: . . . . **TCV 2581**

RAG 'N' BONE BUFFET.
MC: . . . . **OVEDC 311**

SKYLARKING.
Tracks: / Summer's cauldron / Grass / Meeting place, The / That's really super, supergirl / Ballet for a rainy day / 1000 umbrellas / Season cycle / Earn enough for us / Big day / Another satellite / Mermaid smiled / Man who sailed around his soul, The / Dying / Sacrificial bonfire.
LP: . . . . **V 2399**
MC: . . . . **TCV 2399**
MC: . . . . **OVEDC 352**
LP: . . . . **OVED 352**

WAXWORKS.
Tracks: / Science friction / Statue of liberty / This is pop? / Are you receiving me / Life begins at the hop / Making plans for Nigel / Wait till your boat goes down / Generals and majors / Towers of London / Sgt. Rock (is going to help me) / Senses working overtime / Ball and chain.
LP: . . . . **V 2251**
MC: . . . . **TCV 2251**

WHITE MUSIC.
Tracks: / Radios in motion / Cross wires / This is pop? / Do what you do / Statue of Liberty / All along the watchtower / Into the atom age / I'll set myself on fire / I'm bugged / Spinning top / Neon shuffle / New town animal in a furnished cage / Science friction (CD only) / She's so square (CD only) / Dance band (CD only) / Hang on to the night (CD only) / Heatwave (CD only) / Traffic light rock (CD only) / Instant tunes (CD only).
LP: . . . . **OVED 60**
MC: . . . . **OVEDC 60**
LP: . . . . **V 2095**

Xtro

XTRO (Film soundtrack) (Various artists).
LP: . . . . **TER 1052**

Xtron

XTRON NO.S 1-13.
MC: . . . . **MMATT 27**

Xymox

CLAN OF XYMOX.
LP: . . . . **CAD 503**

MEDUSA.
LP: . . . . **CAD 613**

PHOENIX.
LP: **8492931**
MC: **8492934**

TWIST OF SHADOWS.
Tracks: / Evelyn / Craving / River, The / Tonight / In a city / Obsession / Blind hearts / Million things, A / Imagination / Clementina.
LP: **839 233-1**
MC: **839 233-4**

Xyster

BLACK BIBLE.
LP: . . . . **CCG 002**

IN GOOD FAITH.
Tracks: / Subnormal / Sentenced by Pilate / Genetic deformity / Die on the cross / Inquisition, The / Frozen mind / Black bible / Suicide / Massacre of the priests.
LP: . . . . **CMFT 1**
MC: . . . . **CMFT 1C**

XYZ

HUNGRY.
Tracks: / Face down in the gutter / Don't say no / Fire and water / When the night comes down / Off to the sun / Feels good / Shake down the walls / When I find love / H. H. boogie / Sun also rises in hell, The / Roll of the dice, A / Whiskey on a heartache.
LP: . . . . **EST 2150**
MC: . . . . **TCEST 2150**

XYZ.

Tracks: / Maggy / Inside out / What keeps me loving you / Take what you can / Follow the night / Come on 'N' love me / Souvenirs / Tied up / Nice day to die / After the rain.

LP: . . . . ENVLP 1002 MC: . . . . TCENV 1002

Y

Y & D Showcase

Y AND D SHOWCASE (Various artists).
LP: YYD LP 002

Y & T

ANTHOLOGY: Y & T.
Tracks: / Rescue me / I believe in you / Squeeze / Hungry for rock / Don't wanna lose / Hell or high water / Winds of change / Bar room boogie / Black tiger / In the name of rock / Summertime girls / All american boy / Hands of time, The / Mean streak / Take you to the limit / Down and dirty / Hang 'em high / Open fire (live) / Go for the throat (live) / Forever (live).
LP: RAWLP 040
MC: RAWTC 040

BLACK TIGER.
Tracks: / From the moon / Open fire / Don't wanna lose / Hell or high water / Forever / Black tiger / Bar room boogie / My way or the highway / Winds of change.
LP: AMLH 64910
MC: CAM 64910

CONTAGIOUS.
Tracks: / Contagious / L.A. rocks / Temptation / Kid goes crazy, The / Fight for your life / Armed and dangerous / Rhythm or not / Bodily harm / Eyes of a stranger / I'll cry for you.
LP: 9241421
MC: 9241424

DOWN FOR THE COUNT.
Tracks: / In the name of rock / All American boy / Anytime at all / Anything for money / Face like an angel / Summertime girls / Looks like trouble / Your mama don't dance / Don't tell me what to wear / Hands of time, The.
LP: AMA 5101
MC: AMC 5101

EARTHSHAKER.
Tracks: / Hungry for rock / Dirty girl / Shake it loose / Squeeze / Rescue me / Young and tough / Hurricane / Let me go / Knock you out / I believe in you.
LP: AMLH 64867
MC: CAM 64867

IN ROCK WE TRUST.
Tracks: / Rock and roll's gonna save the world / Life, life, life / Masters and slaves / I'll keep on believin' (do you know) / Breakout tonight / Lipstick and leather / Don't stop runnin' / Your love is driving me crazy / She's a liar / This time.
LP: AMLX 65007
MC: CXM 65007

MEAN STREAK.
Tracks: / Mean streak / Straight thru the heart / Lonely side of town / Midnight in Tokyo / Breaking away / Hang 'em high / Take you to the limit / Sentimental fool / Down and dirty.
LP: AMLX 64960
MC: CXM 64960

OPEN FIRE (LIVE).
Tracks: / Open fire / Go for the throat / 25 hours a day / Rescue me / Summer time girls / Forever / Bar room boogie / I believe in you.
LP: AMA 5076
MC: AMC 5076

TEN.
LP: 7599242831
MC: 7599242834

TEN (The best of).
MC: GEFC 24283

YESTERDAY AND TODAY LIVE.
LP: ZORRO 21
MC: TZORRO 21

Ya Ya

ALBUM, THE.
Tracks: / Caught in a lie / When the world cried / Love in vain / Fear of flying / Toughest race, The / Julia / First time / All through the night / Set me free.
LP: WX 148
MC: WX 148C

SCARRED.
Tracks: / Don't talk / She don't wanna know / We've only tonight / Those eyes / Dead lovers / Stop, breaking me up / Just go / Talk to me / Cut me up / Are you ready.
LP: CBS 26082

Yabby You

FLEEING FROM THE CITY.
LP: SHAN 43026
MC: SHANC 43026

JAH JAH WAY.
Tracks: / Jah Jah way / Stop your quarrellig / Free Africa / Jah vengeance / Jah bible / Lady lady / I feel lonely / Ballistic dread / Chalice specialist / Dread locks man.
LP: ILPS 9615

YABBY YOU COLLECTION.
Tracks: / Deliver me from my enemies / Anti Christ / Run come rally / Babylon gone down / Chant down Babylon / Judgement time / Carnal mind / Fire fire / Conquering lion / One love, one heart.
LP: GREL 68

Yacht Club Jazz Band

YACHT CLUB JAZZ BAND, THE.
LP: S 1375

Yachts

WITHOUT RADAR.
Tracks: / Consequences / On the bridge / Trust you / Out of luck / This thing that thing / March of the moderates / There's a ghost in my house / Life saving's easy / Now I'm spoken for / Lush / Don't call us / Spimosa.
LP: RAD 27

YACHTS, THE.
Tracks: / Box 202 / In a second / Love you love you / Tantamount to bribery / Easy to please / Mantovani's hits / Then and now / Semaphore love / I can't stay long / Heads will turn / I'll be leaving you / Yachting type.
LP: RAD 19

Yacoub, Gabriel

ELEMENTARY LEVEL OF FAITH.
LP: SHAN 29003

GABRIEL YACOUB.
LP: SIF 3038
MC: CSIF 3038

Yakity Yak

YAKITY YAK.
LP: SRTZ 76356

Yalla

YALLA- HITLIST EGYPT (Various artists).
LP: MLPS 1040
MC: MCT 1040

Yamaha Quartet

T'DA-A-A-A-A (see Fischer, Clare) (Yamaha Quartet & Clare Fischer).

Yamamoto, Tsuyoshi

ZEPHYR.
Tracks: / Just in time / Moonlight in Vermont / I got rhythm / Waters of March / You go to my head / Satin doll / Shade of love, A / Smokehouse blues / Solitude.
LP: CJ 218

Yamashita, Yosuke

BANSLIKANA.
LP: ENJA 2080

CLAY (Yamashita, Yosuke trio).
LP: ENJA 2052

INNER SPACE.
LP: ENJA 3001

TRIBUTE TO MAL WALDRON.
LP: ENJA 3057

Yamashta, Stomu

GO (Yamashta, Stomu & Steve Winwood).
LP: ILPS 9387
MC: ZCI 9387

SEA AND SKY.
Tracks: / Photon, A / Appeared / And / Touched / Ah... / Time / To see / To know.
LP: LPKUCK 072
MC: MCKUCK 072

STOMU YAMASHTA.
LP: DSLO 1

Yanagisawa, Rie

KUROKAMI - THE MUSIC OF JAPAN (Yanagisawa, Rie/Clive Bell).
Tracks: / Hari no umi (Sea in spring) / Kurokami (Black hair) / Disguised as a silverer of mirrors / Midare rinzetsu (Forest snow) / Yugao (The moon-flower) / Esashi Oiwake / Aki no shirabe (Tune of Autumn).
MC: CSDL 367

Yancey, Jimmy

IMMORTAL JIMMY YANCEY, THE.
LP: OL 2813

IN THE BEGINNING.
LP: JCE 51

JIMMY YANCEY VOL.1 Immortal, The.
LP: OL 2802

PIANO BLUES OF 1939-40.
LP: S 824

PIANO SOLOS 1939.
Tracks: / Jimmy's stuff / Rolling the stone / Steady rock blues / P.I.K. special / South side stuff / Yancey's gateway / La salle street breakdown / Two o'clock blues / Janie's joys / Lean bacon / Big bear train / Lucile's lament.
LP: SM 3101

PITCHIN' BOOGIE.
LP: S 1235

YANCEY - LOFTON SESSION VOL.2 (Yancey, Jimmy & Cripple Clarence Lofton).
LP: SLP 239

YANCEY - LOFTON SESSION. VOL. 1 (Yancey, Jimmy & Cripple Clarence Lofton).
LP: SLP 238

Yancy Family

FROM ONE CHRISTIAN FAMILY TO ANOTHER.
Tracks: / Victory / Free indeed / Care taker / What about you / Lifted me higher / Bright hopes / Just tell Jesus / Higher.
LP: MIR 4016
MC: MIR 4016MC
LP: GCR 4016
MC: GCR 4016MC

Yankee Brass Band

YANKEE BRASS BAND, THE.
Tracks: / Arizona quickstep / Bond's serenade / No one to love / Blondinette polka / Mabel waltz / Helene Schottisch / American hymn, An / Red stocking quickstep / Mockingbird quickstep / Memories of home-waltz / Schottische / Moon is above us / Brin d'amour polka / Goodnight my angel / Firemen's polka.
LP: NW 312

Yankee Doodle Dandy

YANKEE DOODLE DANDY (Original soundtrack) (Various artists).
LP: CC 100.13

Yankee Rhythm Kings

CLASSIC JAZZ OF THE TWENTIES.
LP: GHB 83

Yankees

HALBSTARK.
Tracks: / Halbstark la la la la la la / I was born to love you / Play gypsy / So ein luder / Liehelei / In der roten Strassenbahn / Mein Schlaraffenland.
LP: BF 15018

HIGH 'N' INSIDE.
Tracks: / Take it like a man / Everyday I have to cry / Bad boy / Lovesick / Talking 'bout my baby / Boys night out / Believe / Something about you / Give it up / Take me home and make me like it / Somebody like you / Wait your turn.
LP: SHY 8531

Yankovic, Frank

AMERICAS FAVOURITE.
LP: 830 407-1
MC: 830 407-4

Yankovic, Frankie

FORTY GREATEST POLKAS AND WALTZES.
LP: PC 381

Yankovic, Weird Al

EVEN WORSE.
Tracks: / F.A.T. / Eat it / This song's just six words long / I think I'm a clone now / Lasanga / Alimony / Stuck in a closet with you / You make me / Melanie / Velvet Elvis / Twister / Good old days.
LP: POLD 5229
MC: POLDC 5229

IN 3D.
Tracks: / Eat it / Midnight star / Brady bunch / Buy me a condo / I lost on jeopardy / Polkas on 45 / Mr. Popeil / King of suede / That boy could dance / Theme from Roxy XIII / Nature trail to hell.
LP: SCT 25916

Yanks

YANKS (Film soundtrack) (Various artists).
Tracks: / I'll be seeing you: *Various artists* / String of pearls: *Various artists* / Elmer's tune: *Various artists* / Don't sit under the apple tree: *Various artists* / Two o clock jump: *Various artists*.
LP: MCA 3181
LP: UAG 30282

Yanni

CHAMELEON DAYS.
Tracks: / Swept away / Marching season / Chasing shadows / Rain must fall, The / Days of summer / Reflections of passion / Walkabout / Everglade run / Word in private.
LP: 209644
MC: 409644

KEYS TO IMAGINATION.
Tracks: / North shore of Matsushima / Looking glass / Nostalgia / Santorini / Port of mystery / Keys to imagination / Forgotten yesterdays / Forbidden dreams.
LP: 209.960
MC: 409.960

NIKI NANA.
Tracks: / Niki nana (We're one) / Dance with a stranger / Running time / Soemday / Human condition / First touch / Nightbird / Quiet man.
LP: 210208
MC: 410208

OUT OF SILENCE.
LP: 20 9965
MC: 40 9965

REFLECTIONS OF PASSION.
Tracks: / After the sunrise / Mermaid, The / Quiet man / Nostalgia / Almost a whisper / Acrorali / Rain must fall, The / Swept away / Farewell / Secret vow / Flight of fantasy / Word in private, A / First touch / Reflections.
LP: 210652
MC: 410652

Yarbrough & Peoples

BE A WINNER.
Tracks: / Don't waste your time / I'm ready to jam / I'll be there / I only love you / Be a winner / Who said that / Let me have it / I gave my all.
LP: FL 89384
MC: FK 89384

GUILTY.
Tracks: / Wrapped around your finger / I'll give anything to have you back / Let the music play on / Anytime / Who is she / Everything / Closer love affar, A / Guilty / Guilty (inst).
LP: FL 85715
MC: FK 85715

HEARTBEATS.
Tracks: / Heartbeats / Innermost feelings / Feels so good / You love me you love me not / As one / What's that you slipped into my wine / Party night / What about me.
LP: TEL 1
MC: TELC 1

TWO OF US.
Tracks: / Don't stop the music / Crazy / Third degree / Easy tonight / Want you back again / Come to me / You're my song / Two of us / I believe I'm falling in love.
LP: 9110 162

Yard Trauma

NO CONCLUSIONS.
LP: LOLITA 5049

Yardbirds

6 TRACK HITS.
MC: 7SC 5036

20 GREATEST HITS: YARDBIRDS.
LP: U 80050
MC: MU 980050

COLLECTION:YARDBIRDS.
Tracks: / I wish you would / Good morning little schoolgirl / I ain't got you / Boom boom / Good morning little schoolgirl (instrumental) / Got to hurry / For your love / Too much monkey business / Got love if you want it / Here 'tis / Pontiac blues / 23 hours too long /

Let it rock / Smokestack lightning / Honey in your hips / Heart full of soul / Evil hearted you / Still I'm sad / I'm a man / Jeff's blues / You're a better man than I / Shapes of things / Stroll on.
2LP: . . . . **CCSLP 141**
MC: . . . . **CCSMC 141**

COMPLETE SESSIONS/FIRST SESSION.
MC: . . . . **TCAD 22**

FIRST RECORDINGS-LONDON 1963.
Tracks: / Smokestack lightnin' (live) / Honey in your hips (live) / You can't judge a book by it's cover / Talkin' about you / Honey in your hips / Let it rock (live) / I wish you would (live) / Who do you love (live) / Boom boom.
LP: . . . . **LR 44.001**
LP: . . . . **LIK 58**
MC: . . . . **TCLIK 58**

FIVE LIVE YARDBIRDS.
Tracks: / Too much monkey business / I got love if you want it / Smokestack lightning / Good morning little schoolgirl / Respectable / Five long years / Pretty girl / Louise / I'm a man / Here 'tis.
LP: . . . . **CR 30173**
MC: . . . . **CFK 1017**
LP: . . . . **LIK 55**
MC: . . . . **TCLIK 55**

FOR YOUR LOVE.
Tracks: / For your love / Good morning little schoolgirl / I'm a man / I wish you would / Certain girl, A / Got to hurry / Heartful of soul / Shapes of things / Steeled blues / You're a better man than I / Someone to love (Parts 1 & 2).
LP: . . . . **TOP 103**
MC: . . . . **KTOP 103**

GOT LOVE IF YOU WANT IT (See under Clapton, Eric) (Clapton, Eric & The Yardbirds).

GREATEST HITS: YARDBIRDS VOL.1.
Tracks: / For your love / Heartful of soul / I'm a man / Evil hearted you / Shapes of things.
LP: . . . . **RNLP 70128**
LP: . . . . **FUN 9008**
MC: . . . . **FUNC 9008**

HITS AND MORE.
Tracks: / For your love / Shapes of things / Still I'm sad / Evil hearted you / I wish you would / Good morning little schoolgirl / Got to hurry / Heartful of soul / Certain girl, A / Smokestack lightning / I ain't got you / My girl sloopy / I ain't done wrong / I'm a man.
LP: . . . . **INS 5012**
MC: . . . . **TCINS 5012**

LEGEND OF THE YARDBIRDS VOL 1.
Tracks: / Evil hearted you / Train kept a rolling / I ain't got you / What you want / Got to hurry / Too much monkey business / Steeled blues.
LP: . . . . **F 80017**
MC: . . . . **MF 80017**

LEGEND OF THE YARDBIRDS VOL 2.
Tracks: / Shape of things / Still I'm sad / New York city blues / For your love / I'm a man / Heart full of soul / I'm not talking / You're a better man than I.
LP: . . . . **F 80018**
MC: . . . . **MF 80018**

LEGEND OF THE YARDBIRDS VOL 3.
Tracks: / Jeff's blues / I wish you would / Certain girl, A / Sweet music / Good morning little schoolgirl / My girl sloopy / She's so respectable / I'm a man / Certain girl, A / Smokestack lightning / Here 'tis.
LP: . . . . **F 80019**
MC: . . . . **MF 80019**

LITTLE GAMES.
Tracks: / Little games / Puzzles / Smile on me / White Summer / Tinker tailor / Glimpses / Ten little indians / Ha ha said the clown / Drinking muddy water / No excess baggage / Stealing stealing / Only the black rose / Little soldier boy / Think about it / I remember the night / Goodnight sweet Josephine / Together now (1991 release only).
LP: . . . . **FA 41 3124 1**
MC: . . . . **FA 41 3124 4**
LP: . . . . **EMS 1389**
MC: . . . . **TCEMS 1389**

ON AIR.
LP: . . . . **BOJLP 20**
MC: . . . . **BOJMC 20**

OUR OWN SOUND.
Tracks: / Still I'm sad / I'm a man / Evil hearted you / Steeled blues / Certain girl, A / I wish you would / For your love / Heart full of soul / I'm not talking / My girl sloopy / Got to hurry.
LP: . . . . **CFF 7001**

OVER UNDER SIDEWAYS DOWN (ALBUM).
LP: . . . . **RVLP 12**

ROGER THE ENGINEER.
Tracks: / Happenings ten years time ago / Psycho daisies / Over under sideways down / Nazz are blue, The / Rack my mind / Lost women / I can't make your way / Farewell / Jeff's boogie / Hot house of Omagarashid / He's always there / Turn into earth / What do you want / Ever since the world began.
LP: . . . . **ED 116M**
LP: . . . . **ED 116S**
MC: . . . . **CED 116**

SHAPES OF THINGS A collection of classic Yardbirds recordings 1964-66.
Tracks: / Shapes of things / Too much monkey business / I wish you would / Good morning little schoolgirl / For your love / Certain girl, A / Got to hurry / Smokestack lightning / Evil hearted you / Still i'm sad / Steeled blues / Train kept a rollin' / Here 'tis / What do you want / New York city blues / For R.S.G. / You're a better man than I / Jeff's blues / I ain't got you / I ain't done wrong / Someone to love (Parts 1 & 2) / Boom boom / My girl sloopy.
MC: . . . . **TCCDX 1**
2LP: . . . . **CDX 1**

SHAPES OF THINGS (BOX SET).
LPS: . . . . **BOX 104**

SONNY BOY WILLIAMSON & YARDBIRDS 1963 (see under Williamson, Sonny Boy) (Yardbirds & Sonny Boy Williamson).

STUDIO SESSIONS, THE.
Tracks: / I wish you would / Certain girl, A / Good morning little schoolgirl / I ain't got you / Putty in your hands / Sweet music / Got to hurry / For your love / Heartful of soul (master version) / Heartful of soul (sitar version) / Steeled blues / Still I'm sad / I'm not talking / I ain't done wrong / My girl sloopy / Evil hearted you / You're a better man than I / Train kept a rolling / Shapes of things / New York city / I'm a man / Stroll on.
2LP: . . . . **LIKD 56**
MC: . . . . **TCLIK 56**

YARDBIRDS (LP).
LP: . . . . **SX 6063**

YARDBIRDS, THE Featuring Eric Clapton.
Tracks: / For your love / I'm a man / I wish you would / Good morning little schoolgirl / Certain girl, A / Got to hurry / Too much monkey business / Got love if you want it / Smokestack lightning.
LP: . . . . **CR 30194**

YARDBIRDS, THE Featuring Jeff Beck.
Tracks: / Shapes of things / What do you want / New York City blues / Someone to love / For R.S.G. / Mister you're a better man than I / Jeff's blues / I ain't done wrong / I ain't got you.
LP: . . . . **CR 30195**

YARDBIRDS, THE (CAMBRA).
Tracks: / Smokestack lightning / Good morning little schoolgirl / Got to hurry / Someone to love / Certain girl, A / You're a better man than I / Heartful of soul / Jeff's blues / Too much monkey business / Train kept a-rolling / Still I'm sad / I got love if you want it / I'm a man / For your love / For R.S.G. / I wish you would / Shapes of things / Evil-hearted you / Five long years.
2LP: . . . . **CR 107**
MCSET: . . . . **CRT 107**

Yared, Gabriel

SHAMROCK.
LP: . . . . **TWI 854**

Yargo

BODYBEAT.
Tracks: / Carrying mine / Bodybeat blues / Lately / Get there / Help / Cocaine / Another Moss Side night / Bedtime for Rio.
LP: . . . . **BODY 002**
MC: . . . . **BODY 002C**
LP: . . . . **LONLP 64**
MC: . . . . **LONC 64**

COMMUNICATE.
Tracks: / Other side of midnight, The / Communicate / Round and round / Believe / Time / Free / One step / Missing you / Strange fruit / Rock the house.
LP: **828 171 1**
MC: **828 171 4**

YARGO LIVE.
LP: . . . . **BODYLP 007**
MC: . . . . **BODYMC 007**

Yarra Yarra Jazzband

ON TOUR VOL 1.
LP: . . . . **GHB 78**

Yasmin

YASMIN.
Tracks: / Yasmin.
LP: . . . . **GEF 24411**
MC: . . . . **GEFC 14411**

Yates, Chris

DAY IN BED, A.
LP: . . . . **TWI 757**

Yates, John

FORECAST (see MacRae, Dave) (Yates, John & Dave MacRae).

Yates, Lori

CAN'T STOP THE GIRL.
Tracks: / Promises promises / Scene of the crime / Time after time / Heaven's waiting / How much does it take / Can't stop the girl / Blue side of town / Lonesome desire / Lover's jamboree / Heart in a suitcase.
LP: **4632881**
MC: **4632884**

Yates, Tom

SONG OF THE SHIMMERING WAY.
LP: . . . . **SATL 4007**

Yaz Kaz

EGG OF PURANA.
LP: . . . . **GR 7015**

Yazoo

UPSTAIRS AT ERIC'S.
LP: . . . . **STUMM 7**
MC: . . . . **CSTUMM 7**

YOU AND ME BOTH.
LP: . . . . **STUMM 12**

Yazz

WANTED.
Tracks: / Where has all the love gone / Got to share / Fine time / Stand up for your love rights / Wanted / Something special / Systematic people / Turn it up.
LP: . . . . **YAZZLP 1**
MC: . . . . **YAZZMC 1**
LPPD: . . . . **YAZZLP 1 P**

WANTED REMIXES, THE.
LP: . . . . **BLBXLP 1**
MC: . . . . **BLBXMC 1**

Yeah God

NOISEGASM.
LP: . . . . **CHAPLP 41**
LP: . . . . **CHAPLP 22**

Yeah Jazz

SIX LANE ENDS.
Tracks: / Sharon / Stones / Lee Marvin / All of my days / Freeland / Step into the light / Heaven / Girl the years were kind to, The / Dirty windows / Make a fist / Stranger than fiction / All the stars.
LP: . . . . **BRED 82**

Yeah Yeah Noh

CUTTING THE HEAVENLY LAWN OF GREATNESS.
LP: . . . . **IT 021**

FUN ON THE LAWN LAWN LAWN.
LP: . . . . **BAAD 2**

Year Of Living

YEAR OF LIVING DANGEROUSLY (Film Soundtrack) (Jarre, Maurice).
LP: . . . . **TER 1065**
MC: . . . . **CTV 81182**

Year Of The Dragon

YEAR OF THE DRAGON (Original soundtrack) (Various artists).
LP: . . . . **STV 81266**
MC: . . . . **CTV 81266**

Yeats, W.B.

FIVE ONE-ACT PLAYS (Various artists).
MCSET: **0315**

POETRY OF WILLIAM BUTLER YEATS, THE (Various artists).
MC: **1081**

Yello

1980-1985 THE NEW MIX IN ONE GO.
Tracks: / Daily disco / Swing / Evening's young, The / Pinball cha cha / I love you / Sometimes (Dr. Hirsch) / Base for Alec / Oh yeah / Lost again / Tub dub / Angel no / Desire / Bananas to the beat / Koladi-ola / Domingo / Bostich / Live at the Roxy.
LP: . . . . **MERD 95**
MC: . . . . **MERDC 95**

BABY.
Tracks: / Intro / Rubberbandman / Sticky jungle / Ocean club / Who's groove / Capri calling / Lazy / On the run / Blender / Sweet thunder.
MC: **8487914**
LP: **8487911**

CLARO QUE SI.
Tracks: / Daily disco / No more Roger / Take it all / Evening's young, The / She's got a gun / Ballet mechanique / Quad el habib / Lorry, The / Homer hossa / Pinball cha cha.
LP: . . . . **PRICE 114**
MC: . . . . **PRIMC 114**

FLAG.
Tracks: / Tied up / Of course I'm lying / 3rd of June / Blazing saddles / Race, The / Alhambra / Otto di catania / Tied up in red / Tied up in gear.
LP: **836 778 1**
MC: **836 778 4**

FLAG.
Tracks: / Tied up / Of course I'm lying / 3rd of June / Blazing saddles / Race, The / Alhambra / Tied up in gear.
LP: **836 426 1**
MC: **836 426 4**

ONE SECOND.
Tracks: / Habanera / Moon on ice / Call it love / Le secret farida / Hawaiian chance / Rhythm divine, The / Santiago / Goldrush / Doctor Van Steiner / Si senor and the hairy grill.
LP: . . . . **MERH 100**
MC: . . . . **MERHC 100**

SOLID PLEASURE.
Tracks: / Bimbo / Night flanger / Reverse lion / Downdown samba / Magneto / Massage / Assistant's cry / Bostich / Rock stop / Coast to polka / Blue green / Eternal legs / Stanztrigge / Bananas to the beat.
LP: . . . . **PRICE 113**
MC: . . . . **PRIMC 113**

STELLA.
Tracks: / Desire / Vicious games / Oh yeah / Desert inn / Stalakdrama / Koladiola / Domingo / Sometimes (Dr. Hirsch) / Let me cry / Ciel ouvert / Angel no.
LP: . . . . **PRICE 116**
MC: . . . . **PRIMC 116**
LP: . . . . **EKT 1**

YELLO: INTERVIEW PICTURE DISC.
LPPD: . . . . **BAK 2132**

YOU GOTTA SAY YES TO ANOTHER EXCESS.
Tracks: / I love you / Look again / No more words / Crash dance / Great mission / You gotta say yes to another excess / Swing / Heavy whispers / Smile on you / Pumping velvet / Salut mayoumba.
LP: . . . . **PRICE 115**
MC: . . . . **PRIMC 115**
LP: . . . . **SEEZ 48**

Yellow Jackets

FOUR CORNERS.
Tracks: / Out of town / Wildlife / Sightseeing / Open road, The / Mile high / Past ports / Postcard / Room with a view / Geneva.
LP: . . . . **IMCA 5994**
MC: . . . . **IMCAC 5994**

GREENHOUSE.
Tracks: / Freedomland / Greenhouse / Seven stars / Indian Summer / Spirits / Brown zone / Liam/Rain dance / Invisible people / Freda / Peace.
MC: . . . . **GRC 9630**

MIRAGE A TROIS.
LP: **923813 1**

POLITICS.
LP: . . . . **MCA 6236**

SAMURAI SAMBA.
Tracks: / Homecoming / Dead beat / Daddy's gonna miss you / Sylvania / Silverlake / Lonely weekend / Los mambos / Samurai samba.
LP: **925204 1**

SHADES.
Tracks: / And you know that / New shoes / One family / Revelation / Oasis / Regular folks / Back tie / Sonja's Sanfona.
LP: . . . . **IMCA 5752**
MC: . . . . **IMCAC 5752**
LP: . . . . **MCA 5752**

SPIN, THE.
LP: . . . . **MCA 6304**
MC: . . . . **MCAC 6304**

YELLOW JACKETS.
Tracks: / Matinee idol / Imperial strut / Sittin' in it / Rush hour / Hornet / Priscilla / It's almost gone.
LP: . . . . **K 56920**

Yellow Magic Orchestra

AFTER SERVICE.
LP: . . . . **LPU 004**

BGM.
Tracks: / Ballet / Music plans / Rap phenomena / Happy end / 1000 knives / Cue / U.T. / Camouflage / Mass / Loom.
LP: . . . . **AMLH 64853**

MULTIPLIES.
Tracks: / Technopolis / Absolute ego dance / Behind the mask / Computer game (theme from Invaders) / Firecracker / Snakeman show / Nice age / Multiplies / Snakeman show / Citizens of science / Tighten up.
LP: . . . . **AMLH 68516**

SOLID STATE SURVIVOR (ALFA/CBS VERSION).

Tracks: / Technopolis / Absolute ego dance / Rydeen / Castalia / Behind the mask / Day tripper / Insomnia / Solid state survivor.
LP: . . . . **ALF 85664**
MC: **40 85664**

YELLOW MAGIC ORCHESTRA.
Tracks: / Computer game (theme from Invaders) / Fire cracker / Simoon / Cosmic surfin' / Yellow magic / La femme Chinoise / Bridge over troubled music / Mad Pierrot.
LP: . . . . **AMLH 68506**

Yellow Submarine

YELLOW SUBMARINE (See under Beatles) (Various artists).

Yellow Thread Street

YELLOW THREAD STREET (Original Soundtrack) (Various artists).
LP: . . . . **V 2609**
MC: . . . . **TCV 2609**

Yellowman

BAD BOY SKANKING (Yellowman & Fathead).
Tracks: / Bad boy skanking / Pon-wee-line / King ina the jungle / I can't stand it / Give Jah thanks / Bam Bam / Love fat thing / Come when Jah call you / Natty dread something / Crying for love.
LP: . . . . **GREL 44**

BADNESS.
LP: . . . . **LALP 005**

BLUEBERRY HILL.
Tracks: / Blueberry Hill / Letter to Rosey / Jean a miss follow fashion / Who say yellow don't go hotel / Nah pay no tax / Anything me say / Young girl be wise / Another Saturday night.
LP: . . . . **GREL 107**
MC: . . . . **GREEN 107**

DIVORCED (Yellowman & Fathead).
LP: . . . . **BS 1055**

DON'T BURN IT DOWN.
LP: . . . . **GREL 110**
MC: . . . . **GREEN 110**

GALONG GALONG GALONG.
Tracks: / Galong galong galong / Beat it / Under mi fat thing / Cus cus / Reggae get the grammy / Throw me corn / Skank quadrille / Blow saxophone / Money make friend / Bubble with mi ting.
LP: . . . . **GREL 87**
MC: . . . . **GREEN 87**

KING OF THE DANCE HALL.
LP: . . . . **RRTG 7717**

KING Y. MEETS THE MIGHTY J.W. (Yellowman & Josey Wales).
LP: . . . . **ALP 009**

KING YELLOWMAN (Yellowman & Charlie Chaplin).
Tracks: / Jamaica nice / Take me home country roads / Strong me strong / Mi believe / Summer holiday / Bloodstain / Moving on / Disco reggae / Girls can't do what the guys do / Reggae calypso / Sea cruise / If you should lose me / You'll lose a good thing.
LP: . . . . **CBS 25922**
MC: **40 25922**

LIVE AT REGGAE SUNSPLASH.
LP: . . . . **VSLP 8903**

MISTER YELLOWMAN.
Tracks: / Natty sat upon the rock / Lost mi love / Mr. Chin / Two to six super mix / Morning ride / How you keep a dance / Jamaica a little Miami / Yellowman get's married / Duppy or gunman / Cocky did a hurt me.
LP: . . . . **GREL 35**
MC: . . . . **GREEN 35**

NEGRIL CHILL (Yellowman & Charlie Chaplin).
Tracks: / Arrival, The / Feeling sexy / Don't sell yourself / Nuff punany / Naw breed again / Undergal frock / Blueberry Hill / Reason with entertainers / Gone a South Africa / Jah mi fear / Trouble Rosie / Old lady / Listen Charlie / Same way it taste / Calypso jam / Don't drop yu pants / Rent a dread.
MC: . . . . **A 155**
LP: . . . . **DANLP 037**

NOBODY MOVE - NOBODY GET HURT.
Tracks: / Nobody move nobody get hurt / Strictly mi belly / Bedroom mazuka / Body move / Good lovin' / Wreck a pum pum / Hill and gully rider / Yellowman a lover boy / Watch your words / Why you bad so.
LP: . . . . **GREL 71**
MC: . . . . **GREEN 71**

ONE IN A MILLION.
LP: . . . . **SHAN 44003**

REGGAE CALYPSO ENCOUNTER.
LP: . . . . **RMJL 0101**
MC: . . . . **RMJLC 0101**

THIEF.
LP: . . . . **MLLP 004**
MC: . . . . **MLC 004**

TWO GIANTS CLASH (Yellowman & Josey Wales).
Tracks: / Society party / Strictly bubbling / Mr. Big shot / King of the crop / Wrong girl to play with / Bobo dread / Mi have Fi get you / Cure for the fever / Jah a mi guiding star / Sorry to say.
LP: . . . . **GREL 63**
MC: . . . . **GREEN 63**

WALKING JEWEL STONE.
LP: . . . . **Unknown**

YELLOW LIKE CHEESE.
Tracks: / Budget / Easy me ting / Gaze / Want a woman / To touch ya so / Yellow like cheese / No get nuthin' / Ain't no meaning / Na no lyrics / Mi mother love, my father love.
LP: . . . . **RAS 3019**
MC: . . . . **RASC 3019**

YELLOW, THE PURPLE & THE NANCY (Yellowman/Purpleman/Sister Nancy).
Tracks: / Feeling Irie / Mr. Wong / Any man can test Nancy / Get ready / Baby father / Dance upon the corner / Out of hand / Mash it up now / Bang belly / Westmorland skank.
LP: . . . . **GREL 49**

YELLOWMAN GOING TO THE CHAPEL.
Tracks: / Look in a me eye / Rub-a-dub / Going to the chapel / Hunnu fi move / Come back to Jamaica / No lucky in gambling / Ready fe them / Amen / To the bump.
LP: . . . . **GREL 97**

YELLOWMAN MEETS CHARLIE CHAPLIN (Yellowman & Charlie Chaplin).
LP: . . . . **Unknown**

YELLOWMAN RIDES AGAIN.
LP: . . . . **RAS 3034**
MC: . . . . **RASC 3034**

ZUNGGUZUNGGUGUZUNGGUZENG.
Tracks: / Zungguzungguguzungguzeng / Good, the bad and the ugly, The / Rub-a-dub a play / Dem sight the boss / Can't hide from Jah / Who can make the dance ram / Yellowman wise / Take me to Jamaica / Friday night jamboree / Jah Jah are we guiding star.
LP: . . . . **GREL 57**
MC: . . . . **GREEN 57**

Yelvington, Malcolm

GONNA HAVE MYSELF A BALL.
Tracks: / Drinkin' wine spo-dee-o-dee / Just rolling along / Yakety yak / Blues in the bottom of my shoes / Gal named Jo, A / It's me baby / Rockin' with my baby / Gonna have myself a ball / Goodbye Marie / First and last love / Mr. Blues / Did I ask you to stay / Trumpet / Ocean / Let the moon say goodnight.
LP: . . . . **SUN 1010**

Yemen Arabia

MUSIC FROM YEMEN ARABIA Sanaani, Laheji, Adeni (Various artists).
LP: . . . . **LLST 7283**

MUSIC OF YEMEN ARABIA VOL. 2 Samar (Various artists).
LP: . . . . **LLST 7284**

Yemm, Bryn

BRYN YEMM CHRISTMAS COLLECTION.
Tracks: / Winter wonderland / Little donkey / Away in a manger / Rudolph the red nosed reindeer / White Christmas / Evensong / Fall softly snow / Jingle bells / Scarlet ribbons / Sleigh ride / Mary's boy child / Holy night.
LP: . . . . **BAY 104**
MC: . . . . **BAYK 104**

GATEWAY TO SONG (Yemm, Bryn Meets The Morriston Orpheus Choir).
Tracks: / Old rugged cross, The / I believe / Myfanwy / Cwm Rhondda / Aberfan / Lord you gave me a mountain / All through the night / Men of Harlech / Haffron / Green green grass of home / Holy city, The / Anna Marie / You'll never walk alone / Land of my fathers.
LP: . . . . **DMT 3001**

HOW DO I LOVE THEE.
Tracks: / How do I love thee / Valley that time forgot, The / Child's prayer, A / In the rain / I have a dream / I've got faith in you / When a child is born / Candlelight / Swing low sweet chariot / Why me Lord.
LP: . . . . **LEG 17**
MC: . . . . **LEGC 17**

HOW GREAT THOU ART.
LP: . . . . **LEG 15**

INSPIRATIONS.
Tracks: / Green green grass of home / One day at a time / Anna Marie / There goes my everything / If I only had time / Old rugged cross, The / You'll never walk alone / Why me lord / How great thou art / You light up my life / Please help me, I'm falling / It is no secret / I believe / Little things mean a lot / Scarlet ribbons / At the end of the day.
LP: . . . . **MODEM 1019**
MC: . . . . **MODEMC 1019**

LET THERE BE PEACE.
Tracks: / Lord's prayer (The) / Nearer my God to thee / Turn,turn,turn / Jesu, joy of man's desiring.
LP: . . . . **WST R 9676**
MC: . . . . **WST C 9676**

MY TRIBUTE (Bryn Yemm inspirational album).
LP: . . . . **WST R 9665**
MC: . . . . **WST C 9665**

THAT LOVING FEELING.
Tracks: / You've lost that lovin' feeling / Sound of silence, The / Who's sorry now / Please don't go / Everything is beautiful / Daydream believer / Anniversary song / Wind beneath my wings / World without love / This guy's in love with you / Without you / Young girl / Can't take my eyes off you / True love.
LP: . . . . **MODEM 1027**
MC: . . . . **MODEMC 1027**

WILL YOU STILL LOVE ME TOMORROW (Yemm, Bryn & Ann).
LP: . . . . **UNKNOWN**

Yen

AIR.
LP: . . . . **EIRSA 1035**
MC: . . . . **EIRSAC 1035**

Yendall, Penny

TAKING THE STRAIN.
LP: . . . . **REC 407**
MC: . . . . **ZCM 407**

Yeomen Of The Guard

YEOMEN OF THE GUARD, THE (see under Gilbert & Sullivan).

Yepes, Narciso

GUITAR.
LP: **4138691**

WORLD OF SPANISH GUITAR.
LP: . . . . **SPA 179**
MC: . . . . **KCSP 179**

Yes

9012 LIVE-THE SOLOS.
Tracks: / Hold on / Si / Solly's beard / Soon / Changes / Amazing grace / Whitefish.
LP: **790 474-1**
MC: **790 474-4**

90125.
Tracks: / Owner of a lonely heart / Hold on / It can happen / Changes / Cinema / Leave it / Our song / City of love / Hearts.
LP: **790 125-1**
MC: **790 125-4**

BIG GENERATOR.
Tracks: / Rhythm of love / Big generator / Shoot high aim low / Almost like love / Love will find a way / Final eyes / I'm running / Holy lamb.
LP: . . . . **WX 70**
MC: . . . . **WX 70 C**

CLASSIC YES.
Tracks: / Heart of the sunrise / Wondrous stories / Yours is no disgrace / Starship trooper / Long distance runaround / Fish / And you and I.
LP: . . . . **K 50842**
MC: **K4 50842**

CLOSE TO THE EDGE.
Tracks: / Solid time of change / Total mass retain / I get up, I get down / Seasons of man / And you and I / Cord of life / Eclipse / Preacher, The / Teacher / Siberian Khatru.
LP: . . . . **K 50012**
MC: **K4 50012**

DRAMA.
Tracks: / Machine messiah / White car / Does it really happen / Into the lens / Run through the light / Tempus fugit.
LP: . . . . **K 50736**

FRAGILE.
Tracks: / Roundabout / Cans and Brahms / We have heaven / South side of the sky / Five per cent for nothing / Long distance runaround / Fish / Mood for a day / Heart of the sunrise.
LP: . . . . **K 50009**
MC: **K4 50009**
LP: **2409 019**

FRAGILE / CLOSE TO THE EDGE.
MC: **K4 60166**

GOING FOR THE ONE.
Tracks: / Going for the one / Turn of the century / Parallels / Wondrous stories / Awaken.
LP: . . . . **K 50379**
MC: **K4 50379**

RELAYER.
Tracks: / Gates of delirium, The / Sound chaser / To be over.
LP: . . . . **K 50096**
MC: **K4 50096**

TALES FROM TOPOGRAPHIC OCEANS.
Tracks: / Revealing science of God, The / Remembering, The / Ancient, The / Ritual.
2LP: . . . . **K 80001**
MCSET: **K4 80001**

TIME AND A WORD.
Tracks: / No opportunity necessary / No experience needed / Then / Everdays / Sweet dreams / Prophet, The / Clear days / Astral traveller / Time and a word.
LP: . . . . **K 40085**
MC: **K4 40085**
LP: **2400 006**

TORMATO.
Tracks: / Future times / Rejoice / Don't kill the whale / Madrigal / Release release / Arriving UFO / Circus of heaven / Onward / On the silent wings of freedom.
LP: . . . . **K 50518**

UNION.
Tracks: / I would have waited forever / Shock to the system / Masquerade / Lift me up / Without hope you cannot start the day / Saving my heart / Miracle of life / Silent talking / More we live-let go, The / Angkor Wat (Only on cassette and CD.) / Dangerous / Holding on / Evensong / Take the water to the mountain / Give and take (Only on cassette and CD.).
LP: **211558**
MC: **411558**

YES.
Tracks: / Beyond and before / I see you / Yesterday and today / Looking around / Harold land / Every little thing / Sweetness / Survival.
LP: . . . . **K 40034**
MC: **K4 40034**

YES ALBUM, THE.
Tracks: / Yours is no disgrace / Clap, The / Starship trooper / Life seeker / Disillusion / Wurm / I've seen all the good people / Your move / All good people / Venture, A / Perpetual change.
LP: . . . . **K 40106**
MC: **K4 40106**
LP: **2400 101**

YESSHOWS.
Tracks: / Parallels / Time and a word / Going for the one / Gates of Delirium, The.
2LP: . . . . **K 60142**

YESSONGS.
Tracks: / Opening: Excerpt from the firebird suite / Siberian Khatru / Heart of the sunrise / Perpetual change / And you and I / Cord of life / Eclipse / Preacher and the teacher, The / Apocalypse, The / Mood for a day / Excerpts from the six wives of Henry VIII / Roundabout / Your move / I've seen all the good people / Long distance runaround / Fish, The / Close to the edge / Solid time of change, The / Total mass retain / I get up, I get down / Seasons of man / Yours is no disgrace / Starship trooper / Life seeker / Disillusion / Wurm.
LP: . . . . **K 60045**

YESTERDAYS.
Tracks: / America / Looking around / Time and a word / Sweet dreams / Then / Survival / Astral traveller / Dear father.
LP: . . . . **K 50048**

Yes Giorgio

YES GIORGIO (Original soundtrack) (Various artists).
Tracks: / If we were in love: *Various artists* / Santa lucia: *Various artists* / Mattinata: *Various artists*/ O sole mio: *Various artists* / Ave Maria: *Various artists* / I left my heart in San Francisco: *Various artists*/ Cielo e mar: *Various artists*.
LP: . . . . **SXDL 7589**

Yes Minister

YES MINISTER (TV soundtrack) (Various artists).
LP: . . . . **REB 432**
MC: . . . . **ZCF 432**

YES MINISTER 1 (Various artists).
MCSET: . . . . **ZBBC 1147**

YES MINISTER 2 (Various artists).
MCSET: . . . . **ZBBC 1177**

Yes Sir, That's My...

YES SIR, THAT'S MY BABY Various artists (Various artists).
Tracks: / Whispering: *Whiteman, Paul & His Orchestra* / April showers: *Jolson, Al* / Collegiate: *Waring's Pennsylvanians* / Dinah: *Waters, Ethel* / Good man is hard to find, A: *Lewis, Ted/his orchestra* / Gimme a little kiss,will ya huh?: *Smith, Jack* / Deed I do: *Etting, Ruth* / There'll be some changes made: *Tucker, Sophie* / Sunday: *Edwards, Cliff* / Yes sir, that's my baby: *Seeley, Blossom* / Mississippi Mud: *Rhythm* Boys, Paul Whiteman &

His Orchestra / My blue Heaven: *Austin, Gene* / Deep night: *Vallee, Rudy* / Ain't misbehavin: *Armstrong, Louis & His Orchestra*.
LP: . . . . NW 279

Yesterday

YESTERDAY Various artists (Various artists).
LP: . . . . MRL 5007

YESTERDAY WHEN WE WERE YOUNG Various artists (Various artists).
LP: . . . . WW 1002
MC: . . . . WW 10024

Yetties

FIDDLER KNOWS, THE.
MC: . . . . ZC ALA 3010

LITTLE BIT OF DORSET, A.
Tracks: / Poor poor farmer / Bell ringing, The / Beggar's song, The / Windmills / Back 'n' back yer you / Gypsy woman / Life of a man, The / Last rose of summer / Bloody fields of Flanders, The / Nellie the elephant / My grandfather's clock / Levi Jackson's rag / Grey hawk, The / Curate and the vicar, The / Ruined maid, The / Needle cases / Us poor fellows / D'ye ken John Peel? / Thomas Hardy medley (The rigged ship/The soldier's joy/The fairy dance).
LP: . . . . ALA 3001
MC: . . . . ZC ALA 3001

MUSICAL HERITAGE OF THOMAS HARDY.
MCSET: . . . . ZC ALD 4010
2LP: . . . . ALD 4010

OUR FRIENDS THE YETTIES.
Tracks: / Aunt Hessie's white horse / Villa fiord / Out in the green fields / Lamorna / Flop eared mule / Hen and chickens / Sheehan's reel / Colonel Rodney / Towersey fair / Rolling hills of the borders / Rodney's glory / Sweet thyme / Santa Ana / Derry hornpipe / Bottom of the punchbowl / Lark in the morning, The / Kelly's joy / Bells / Father Kelly's jig / Swallow's nest / Teetotaller, The / Dreadnought, The / King of the fairies, The / Dancers of Stanton Drew, The / Thrashing machine, The.
MC: . . . . KZFC 32

PROPER JOB, A.
Tracks: / Singing all the way / Beaumont rag / Jolly ploughboys, The / Ball of yarn / Romance / John Barleycorn / Primrose polka, The / Linden Lea / Scarlet and the blue, The / Astley's ride / Balquhidder lasses / Wanderer / Rose in June / Bluebell polka / Ee weren't all bad / Lilliburlero / Dorsetshire hornpipe / Early one evening / Farewell she / Frost is all over, The / High level reel.
LP: . . . . ALA 3003
MC: . . . . ZC ALA 3003

UP MARKET.
LP: . . . . SKL 5282

WORLD OF THE YETTIES, THE.
Tracks: / Out in the green fields / Nightingale, The / McCann's jig / Lilting fisherman, The / Drowsy Maggie / Lark in the morning, The / Spanish ladies / Dancing on the green (rigs o' Marlow) / Cuckoo's nest, The / Can't you dance the polka / Lamorna / King of the fairies, The / South Australia / Mallard, The / Banks of Newfoundland / Dorset fourhand reel / Landlord fill the flowing bowl.
LP: . . . . SPA 436
MC: . . . . KCSP 436

YETTIES IN CONCERT.
Tracks: / Razzamatazz / Roll, Alabama roll / Farmer, won't you marry me / Scarecrow / Suzannah's a funny old sow / Lark in the clear air / Dorset forearm smash / Dad's medals / Lucky knickers / Village pump / My little Liza / Five drunken nights / Sailor cut down in his prime / Sailin' on the briny sea / My brudda Sylvest / Dancing days / Alabama jubilee.
LP: . . . . SKL 5311

YETTIES, THE.
Tracks: / Over the hills and far away / Rabbit winter / John Barleycorn / Polka medley / I live not where I love / We've got oil / Sally the salvage Queen / Man at the nore, The / Carolina moon / Beautiful dreamer / Bread and cheese and kisses / Wave over wave / Long pond / Praise o'Dorset.
LP: . . . . ALA 3007
MC: . . . . ZC ALA 3007

Yggdrasil

ANTIFONALE.
LP: . . . . HJF 20

CONCERTO GROTTO.
LP: . . . . HJF 18

HEYGAR OG DREYGAR.
LP: . . . . HJF 15

Yglesia, Francisco

SHIMMERING HARP.
Tracks: / Ballade pour Adeline / M.A.S.H / Bell bird / Yesterday / Alborada / Vamos amigos / Speak softly love / Never on Sunday / Cascada / Shimmering harp / Sonata in G / Chariots of fire.
LP: . . . . MFP 50547
MC: . . . . TCMFP 50547

Yip Yip Coyote

YIP YIP COYOTE.
LP: . . . . ILP 014

Yo La Tengo

NEWWAVE HOTDOGS.
LP: . . . . GOES ON 13

PRESIDENT YO LA TENGO.
LP: . . . . GOESON 28

RIDE THE TIGER.
Tracks: / Cone of silence, The / Big sky / Evil that men do, The / Forest green, The / Pain of pain, The / Way some people die, The / Empty pool, The / Alrok's bells / Five years / Screaming dead balloons / Living in the country.
LP: . . . . SHIGLP 2

Yoakam, Dwight

BUENOS NOCHES FROM A LONELY ROOM.
Tracks: / I got you / One more name / What I don't know / Home of the blues / Buenos noches from a lonely room / She wore red dresses / I hear you knocking / I sang Dixie / Streets of Bakersfield / Floyd county / Send me the pillow that you dream on / Hold onto God.
LP: . . . . WX 193
MC: . . . . WX 193C

GUITARS, CADILLACS ETC.ETC..
Tracks: / Honky tonk man / It won't hurt / I'll be gone / South of Cincinnati / Bury me / Guitars, cadillacs / 20 years / Ring of fire / Miner's prayer / Heartaches by the number.
LP: 925372 1
MC: 925372 4

HILLBILLY DELUXE.
Tracks: / Little ways / Smoke along the track / Johnson's love / Please, please baby / Readin', rightin', RT.23 / Always late with your kisses / 1,000 miles / Throughout all times / Little sister / This drinking will kill me.
LP: . . . . WX 106
MC: . . . . WX 106 C
LP: . . . . K 925567 1
MC: . . . . K 925567 4

IF THERE WAS A WAY.
Tracks: / Distance between you and me, The / Heart that you own, The / Takes a lot to rock you / Nothing's changed here / Sad, sad music / Since I started drinkin' again / If there was a way / Turn it on, turn it up, turn me loose / It only hurts when I cry / Send a message to my heart / I don't need it done / You're the one.
LP: . . . . WX 392
MC: . . . . WX 392C

JUST LOOKIN' FOR A HIT.
LP: . . . . WX 310
MC: . . . . WX 310 C

Yobs

YOBS CHRISTMAS ALBUM.
LP: . . . . RUDE 1
LP: . . . . PIPLP 006

Yoga For All

YOGA FOR ALL (Bullard, Marie).
MC: . . . . GB 008

Yogo, Dindo

LA VIE EST HEUREUSE.
LP: 085771

Yokels

YER WE BE.
LP: . . . . SFA 063

Yolanda & The Thief

YOLANDA & THE THIEF/YOU'LL NEVER GET RICH (Original soundtrack) (Various artists).
LP: . . . . HS 5001

Yolocamba I Ta

CARA O CRUZ (HEADS OR TAILS).
LP: . . . . FF 503

Yonco, Frank

OLD GREYHOUND (Yonco, Frank And The Everglades).
LP: . . . . SFA 091

Yondo Syster

BAZO (Yondo Syster & Soukous Stars).
LP: . . . . KBK 900

Yoneya, Iwao

SHAKUHACHI - ANOTHER WORLD.
Tracks: / Way we were, The / Close to you / Till there was you / Sound of silence / This masquerade / Danny boy / Moon / If / Superstar / Killing me softly with his song / Girl / Eleanor Rigby / Stone / Goodbye.
LP: . . . . LR 2002

Yor - Hunter From ...

YOR - HUNTER FROM THE FUTURE (Original soundtrack) (Various artists).
LP: . . . . SCRS 1005

York, Michael (nar)

BIGGLES (see under Biggles (bk)).

York Minster

CAROLS BY CANDLELIGHT (Chapter House Choir).
Tracks: / O come, O come Emmanuel / Es ist ein' ros' entsprungen / Adam lay ybounden / I sing of a maiden / Virgin most pure, A / I wonder as I wander / O'er the hill and o'er the vale / Past three a clock / Maiden most gentle, A / Ding dong merrily on high / Little road to Bethlehem, The / Austrian yodel carol / Stille nacht (Silent night) / Twelve days of Christmas / O little town of Bethlehem / Good King Wenceslas / Jingle bells / Von himmel hoch BWV 738 - J.S. Bach.
MC: . . . . HAC 792

CHRISTMAS AT YORK MINSTER (York Minster Choir).
Tracks: / O come, O come, Emmanuel / Great and mighty wonder, A / I sing the birth / Benedicamus domino / I sing of a maiden / O little town of Bethlehem / Babe is born, A / Tomorrow shall be my dancing day / Away in a manger / See amid the winter snow / Child is born in Bethlehem, A / We've been awhile a-wandering / I saw three ships / Three kings, The / Unto us a child is born.
MC: . . . . HAC 846

NOCTURNE (Sequence of Music for the Night) (Chapter House Choir).
Tracks: / O Lord the maker of all thing / Tu pauperum refugium / Lustorum animae / O care, thou wilt despatch me / Hence care, thou art too cruel / Sweet Suffolk owl / Draw on, sweet night / Hear my prayer / An die sterne / Calme des nuits / Ye spotted snakes / Long day closes, The.
MC: . . . . YORK MC 104

ORGAN AT YORK MINSTER 1 (Jackson, Francis/John Scott Whiteley).
Tracks: / Postlude in D (Smart) / Scherzo in A flat (Bairstow) / Prelude and fugue in B (Dupre) / Concert overture in C minor (Hollins) / Rhosymedre (Vaughan Williams) / Scherzetto (Jongen) / Carillon de Westminster (Vierne).
MC: . . . . HAC 791

ORGAN AT YORK MINSTER 2 (Music By Lefebure-Wely) (Whitely, John Scott).
Tracks: / Sortie in E flat / Prelude in A major / Pastorale in C major / Elevation in E major / Offertoire in F major / Sortie in B flat / Elevation in A minor / Sortie in G minor / Prelude in F major / Offertoire in C minor.
MC: . . . . HAC 831

ORGAN AT YORK MINSTER 3 (Jackson, Francis).
Tracks: / Paean and sortie (Whitlock) / Sonata in E flat (Bairstow) / Fantasia in E minor (Silas) / Suite Modale (Peeters).
MC: . . . . HAC 833

York Minster Choir

CHRISTMAS AT YORK MINSTER.
LP: 2384 089
MC: 3192 369

MUSIC FOR EASTER.
LP: . . . . LPB 793

York Railway Institute

BRASS ON TRACK.
LP: . . . . LKLP 6467

York, Rusty

ROCK 'N' ROLL MEMORIES.
LP: . . . . JEWEL 917

York Waits

MUSIC FROM THE TIME OF RICHARD III.
MC: . . . . CSDL 364

MUSIC FROM THE TIME OF THE SPANISH ARMADA.
Tracks: / Queene's visiting of the campe at Tilsburie / Spanish pavan / Galliard (la gamba) / Crimson velvet / La doune cella / La shy myze / La bounette / Obtaining of the great galleazzo / Browninge my dere / Browninge fantasy / Les bransles gays / Delight pavan / Galliard to delight pavan / Staines morris / Quarter brawles / Pavana / Galiarda / Coranto / Watkin's ale / Robin is to the greenwood gone / Wilson's fantasie / Spanish lady / Cushion dance / Dulcina / All you that love good fellowes / Eighty-eight or Sir Francis Drake / Les bransles de Champagne / Carman's whistle / Under and over / Pepper is black / Millfield / Roowe well ye marynors.
MC: . . . . CSDL 373

Yorke, Margaret

NO MEDALS FOR THE MAJOR.
MCSET: . . . . CAT 4030

Yorke, Peter

MOOD FOR LOVE.
Tracks: / Im in the mood for love / I only have eyes for you / These foolish things / Roses of Picardy / Valse of vanite / Body and soul / Smoke gets in your eyes / Stardust / Bells of St. Mary's / By the sleepy lagoon / Hearts and flowers / Somewhere a voice is calling / Love, there is my heart / To a wild rose / Moonlight and roses / Just a-wearyin' for you.
LP: . . . . SH 334
MC: . . . . TC SH 334

Yorkshire Dialect

FIRST O T'SORT.
LP: . . . . LTRA 505

Yorkshire Garland

TROTTING TO LANE.
Tracks: / Sports of Multifarnham / This is no my ain lassie / Thou bonnie wood o'Craigielie / Johnny Cope / Girl of Bruree / Rights of man, The / Kathleen Asthore / O'Hara's cup / Tree polka's from Gneevgullia / Dark island / Abercairney Highlanders / Earl of Crawford's reel, The / Jackson's favourite / Donnybrook fair / Knights of St. Patrick / Fairies hornpipe / Ferrie reel / Meg Merilees / High road to Linton / Fairy's love song, A / Trotting to Larne.
LP: . . . . RUB 042

Yorkshire Imperial

CONCERTO.
Tracks: / North east fantasy / Cornet concerto / Barnard castle / Mattheson's air / Go for gold / Autumn leaves / Swing low / Double top.
LP: . . . . PRL 015
MC: . . . . CPRL 015

MR.SMITH'S PERENNIAL FAVOURITES.
Tracks: / Waltz of the flowers / Summertime / Hunting the hare / Piper in the meadow / Shepherd's song / Country gardens / My love is like a red, red rose / Dear Lord and Father of Mankind / Gardner's 'tap' / Autumn leaves / Lass of Richmond Hill / Shepherd's hymn / Scarborough fair / Prizewinner, The.
LP: . . . . PRL 006
MC: . . . . CPRL 006

MUSIC OF NOEL GAY, THE.
LP: . . . . MFP 41 5675 1
MC: . . . . MFP 41 5675 4

Yorkshire Jazz Band

KING TUBA.
LP: . . . . ESQ 338

Yorkshire Relish

AN OLD FAMILY BUSINESS.
LP: . . . . TSR 034

You Ain't Seen Nothin'

YOU AIN'T SEEN NOTHIN YET (See under Rediscover Series) (Various artists).

You Be

YOU BE (Various artists).
LP: . . . . MM 007

You Can Tell The World

YOU CAN TELL THE WORLD ABOUT THIS Classic ethnic recordings from the 1920's (Various artists).
LP: . . . . MS 45006

You Only Live Twice

YOU ONLY LIVE TWICE (Film Soundtrack) (Various artists).
Tracks: / You only live twice: *Sinatra, Nancy* / Capsule in space: *Various artists* / Fight at Kobe Dock: *Various* artists / Halga: *Various artists* / Tanaka's world: *Various artists* / Drop in the ocean, A: *Various* artists / Death of Aki, The: *Various artists* / Mountains and sunsets: *Various artists* / Wedding, The: *Various* artists / James Bond astronout: *Various artists* / Countdown for Blofeld: *Various artists* / Bond averts World War III: *Various artists* / Twice is the only way to live: *Various artists.*
LP: . . . . IC 054 82920
MC: . . . . E 41 E 90626

Youlou

1 X 2 = MABE.
LP: . . . . AP 050

Youmans, Vincent

THROUGH THE YEARS WITH VINCENT YOUMANS.
2LP: . . . . MES 7086/87

Young Black Teenagers

YOUNG BLACK TEENAGERS.
LP: . . . . MCA 10031

MC: MCAC 10031

Young Blood

YOUNG BLOOD (Original soundtrack) (Various artists).
Tracks: / Opening score: *Orbit, William* / Stand in the fire: *Thomas, Mickey* / Talk me into it: *Jones, Glenn*/ Something real: *Mr. Mister* / I'm a real man: *Hiatt, John* / Cut you down to size: *Starship* / Footsteps: *Gilder, Nick* / Soldier of fortune: *Jordan, Marc* / Winning is everything: *Autograph*.
LP: BL 87172
MC: BK 87172

YOUNGBLOOD (War - Film soundtrack) (Various artists).
Tracks: / Youngblood (livin' in the streets): *Various artists* / Sing a happy song: *Various artists* / Keep on doin': *Various artists* / Kingsmen sign: *Various artists* / Walking to war: *Various artists* / This funky music makes you feel good: *Various artists* / Junk yard: *Various artists* / Superdude: *Various artists*/ Youngblood and Sybil: *Various artists* / Flying machine: *Various artists* / Searching for Youngblood and Rommel: *Various artists*.
LP: MCF 2864
MC: MCFC 2864

Young, Bob

IN QUO COUNTRY.
Tracks: / Down down / Caroline / Living on a island / Mean girl.
LP: SPRAY 104
MC: CSPRAY 104

Young Disciples

ROAD TO FREEDOM.
Tracks: / Get yourself together / Apparently nothin' (soul river) / Funky yeh funki (mek it) / Talkin' what I feel / All I have / Move on / As we come (to be) / Step right on / Freedom / Wanting / To be free.
LP: 5100971
MC: 5100974

Young, Edwin

CHIEF CRAZY.
LP: CR 004

Young, Eldridge,

LAUGHIN'.
LP: 2304 487

Young, Faron

CAPITOL COUNTRY CLASSICS.
Tracks: / Live fast, love hard / Going steady / If you ain't lovin' / All right / It's a great life / I've got five dollars and it's Saturday night / Sweet dreams / I miss you already / Alone with you / Country girl / Riverboat / Your 'old used to be / Hello walls / Backtrack / Three days / Comeback.
LP: CAPS 1036

FOUR IN THE MORNING.
Tracks: / It's four in the morning / If you ain't lovin' (you ain't livin') / All right / Three days / Sweet dreams / Going steady / Hello walls / Backtrack / Wine me up / Your times comin' / I miss you already / This little girl of mine.
LP: TOP 144
MC: KTOP 144

IT'S FOUR IN THE MORNING.
LP: 6338 095

SHERIFF, THE.
Tracks: / Hello walls / I'll be there / I fall to pieces / Once a day / Your cheatin' heart / I can't help it / Life is a picture / Is she all you thought she would be / Hey Mr. Bluebird.
LP: ALEB 2305
MC: ZCALB 2305

SWEETHEARTS OR STRANGERS.
LP: HAT 3026
MC: HATC 3026

TALK ABOUT HITS.
Tracks: / Don't let the stars get in your eyes / I'll go on alone / Almost / Mom and Dad's waltz / I don't hurt anymore / Chattanooga shoeshine boy / Hey good lookin' / Bouquet of roses / Slowly / Tennessee waltz / Making believe / Bimbo.
LP: HAT 3046
MC: HATC 3046

THIS IS FARON YOUNG.
LP: HAT 3092
MC: HATC 3092

TOP COUNTRY FRIEND.
Tracks: / Hello walls / You're still mine / Three days / Alone with you / Country girl / Riverboat / Congratulations / Back track / Face to the wall / If you ain't lovin' (you ain't livin').
LP: BDL 1030

Young Fresh Fellows

INCLUDES A HELMET.
LP: UTIL 010

MEN WHO LOVED MUSIC.
LP: FLP 1021
MC: 461114

TOTALLY LOST.
MC: 461614
LP: 461611

Young, Garth

PIANO FAVOURITES.
Tracks: / Robins' return / Norwegian cradle song / Narcissus / Fur elise / Tango in D / Rememberence / Humoresque / Elizabethan serenade / Souvenir / In a Persian market.
LP: SPVP 5015

Young Generation

DISNEY TODAY (Young Generation/ Mike Curb Congregation).
Tracks: / Zip a dee doo dah / Bare necessities / Winnie the pooh / Snow White medley / Little April shower / Dream is a wish your heart makes, A / I've got no strings / Once upon a dream / Siamese cat song / When I see an elephant fly / Mary Poppins medley.
LP: GH 860

Young, George

CHANT.
Tracks: / Chant / Reggie / Leetah / Chinos y criollas / Snake, The / Ode to a friend.
LP: K 28P 6366

OLEO.
LP: K 28P 6481

Young Gifted...

YOUNG GIFTED & BOP-A-COMPILATION (Various artists).
MC: BIP 206

Young Gods

RED WATER, THE.
LP: BIAS 130

YOUNG GODS.
Tracks: / Nous de la lune / Jusqu'au bout / Ciel ouvert / Jimmy / Fai la mouette / Percussions / Feu / Did you miss me / Si tu gardes.
LP: 33PROD 10
LP: LD 8821

YOUNG GODS PLAY KURT WEILL, THE.
LP: BIAS 188

Young, Gordon

ACCORDION TODAY.
Tracks: / Cutting bracken / Criogal cree / High road to Linton / Masons apron / Timour the Tartar / Alpine slopes / Dark Lochnagar / Bel flore / Barren rocks of Aden / Scotch on the rocks / Campbeltown Loch / Gillan's reel / Janice's reel / Karen McDonald's reel / Cradel song / Music of the Spey / Highland wedding / He ho ho rum / Sleepy Maggie / Hindu waltz / My love is like a red, red rose / Teviot Brig / Bugle call, The / Kenmore's up and awa' / Laird of Drumblair, The / Miss Susan Cooper / Tuskar, (The).
LP: LOCLP 1011
MC: ZCLOC 1011

DANCING FINGERS.
Tracks: / Sailing / Dashing white sergeant / Uist tramping song / Rake of Mallow / When you and I were young, Maggie / Banks of the Ohio / Sailor / What time? / Paddy's leather breeches / Sorrento / Shoals of herring / Castle dangerous / Battle of the Somme / Island spinning song / Banjo breakdown / Czardas / Harvest home hornpipe / Harvest home reel / Rolling in rye grass / Bel viso / Dark island / Drunken piper / Welcome to Tay / Princess accordian / Westering home / Rothesay bay / Loch Lomond / Will ye no come back again?.
LP: LOCLP 1002
MC: ZCLOC 1002

Young Holt Unlimited

WACK WACK.
Tracks: / Wack wack / Give it up / Gotta find me a lover / Just ain't no love / Straight ahead / Who's making love / Soulful strut / In crowd, The / Wade in the water / Ain't there something money can't buy / You know that I love you / You gimmie thum / What now my love / Dig her walk / Baby your light is out / How insensitive / Mellow yellow.
LP: KENT 062

Young, James

BALLYMENA COWBOY, THE.
Tracks: / Ballymena cowboy, The / Hairy tale, A / There's a lounge in the town / Oh Derry's walls / Stormont pudding / Bingo crazy / Boom / I'm a private detective / Cherryvalley debutramp, The / U.L.S.T.E.R. / Sixty years from now / Party political broadcast, A.
LP: BER 017

BEHIND THE BARRICADES.
Tracks: / Behind the barricades / Latest news,The / I'm a Belfast beauty / Ireland in the sun / Ugliest woman in Ireland, The / Why some people go to church / Holidays in Bangor / Belfast chambermaid, A / Glentoran supporter,The / Gas meter man,The / We emigrated / I eat all I can.
LP: GES 1033
MC: KGEC 1033
LP: BER 003
MC: KBER 003

CITY SLICKER (Young,James/Jan Hammer).
Tracks: / City slicker / Something to remember you by / Waiting / Still feel your love / Chain me down / No mistake / Prisoner of war / Wild dogs in the night / Empty promises.
LP: WKFMLP 69
MC: WKFMMC 69

FOREVER YOUNG.
Tracks: / James 'Foo' Young / Lord Mayor speaks, The / Crabbed old woman, The / Ulster's spaceman / Our wee boy / James joins up / Hilda / O come ye to Ulster / What's on tonight / Wife, The (Big Aggie) / American view of Ulster, An / School days / My old slum clearance home / PM speaks, The.
LP: ERTV 3
MC: ERTVC 3

JAMES YOUNG SINGS ULSTER PARTY PIECES.
Tracks: / Clyde valley / Gerry's walls / Me da / Non sectarian football team / I'm the only catholic (on the Linfield team) / Changed times / We're all ecumenical now / I protest / Civil rioteers / Jimmie the Belfast folk singer / Wrong fut, The / Bg Aggie's man.
MC: KBER 015

MEET JAMES YOUNG.
Tracks: / Meet James Young / Smithfield Market / Orange Lily / Behind the barricades / Presentation, The / Gerry's walls / Boy finds out the facts, A / Ballymena cowboy, The / T.V. commercial / I believe in Ulster / I married a papist / Carpenter Crimmond / Stranger, The / Ould black man, The / Wee Davy / Slum clearance / Feud, The.
2LP: GES 1136/7
MCSET: KGEC 1136/7
MCSET: KGEC 28040

VERY MUCH LIVE IN CANADA.
Tracks: / Hello Toronto / Meet James Young / Wee Davy / Letter, The / Matrimonial agency, The / Drama critic, The / Ecumenical ball / Belfast working man, The / Engagement ring, The / School boy, The / Wee Sammy / Farewell to Canada.
MC: KBER 016

YOUNG AT HEART.
Tracks: / Meets James Young / T.V.commercial / Year 2000, The / I loved a parish / Boy finds out the facts, A / Slum clearance / On the hunt / Why am I here.
LP: BER 010
MC: KBER 010

YOUNG ULSTERMAN,THE.
Tracks: / Me mammy / Mr. Thompson goes to Dublin / Young Ulsterman looks for a job,The / St. Patrick / Orange Lily / History lesson / Romeo and Juliet / Man from Ballymena,The / We're here for such a little time.
LP: BER 009
MC: KBER 009

Young, Jesse Colin

AMERICAN DREAMS.
Tracks: / Rave on / Slow and easy / Maui sunrise / Reveal your dreams / Knock on wood / American dream suite / City boy / Music in the streets / Can we carry on the dream / Sanctuary / What if we stay.
LP: K 52105

HIGHWAY IS FOR HEROES, THE.
LP: YL 0103

Young Jessie

HIT GIT AND SPLIT.
Tracks: / Git git and split / Don't happen no more / Don't think I will / Do you love me / Down at Haydens / Nothing seems right / Mary Lou / I smell a rat / Lonesome desert / Oochie coochie / Here comes Henry / Hot dog / Well baby / Rabbit on a log.
LP: CH 58

SHUFFLE IN THE GRAVEL.
LP: RB 1004

SHUFFLIN' & JIVIN'.
Tracks: / Pretty soon / Oochie coochie / It don't happen no more / Mary lou / Don't think I will / Why do I love you / Hot dog / Lonesome desert / Do you love me / Here comes Henry / Well baby / Nothing seems right / Hit git and split.
LP: CHD 225

Young, Jimmy

THIS IS JIMMY YOUNG.
Tracks: / Unchained melody / Too young / All I do is dream of you / You'd be so nice to come home to / No one but you / Nearness of you / Volare / There, I've said it again / Miss you / I get along without you very well / Her hair was yellow / You're wonderful and you're mine / Angel on my shoulder / Music / Only you / Moonlight becomes you / Love me again.
LP: THIS 20

TOO YOUNG.
Tracks: / Too young / Story of my life / If you were the only girl in the world / It was you / I'll see you in my dreams / When I fall in love / Together / Love is here to stay / You'll never know / Red roses for a blue lady / Unchained melody / Why did I choose you / Que sera sera / If / Dream / I'll remember April / You belong to me / All alone / Mean to me / What a wonderful world.
LP: JY 1
MC: VCJY 1

WHAT A WONDERFUL WORLD.
Tracks: / Too young / If you were the only girl in the world / Que sera sera / All alone / Red roses for a blue lady / I'll see you in my dreams / Unchained melody / You'll never know / You belong to me / When I fall in love / Together / What a wonderful world.
LP: FBLP 8083
MC: ZCFBL 8083

Young, John Paul

JOHN PAUL YOUNG.
Tracks: / Heaven sent / Don't you walk that way / I don't wanna lose you / Love you so bad it hurts / Hot for you baby / Can't get you out of my system / I ain't ready / Bad side of the city.
LP: ARL 5037

Young, Johnny

CHICAGO BLUES BAND.
LP: ARHOOLIE 1029

JOHNNY YOUNG AND BIG WALTER (Young, Johnny/Big Walter).
LP: ARHOOLIE 1037

Young, Karen

HOT SHOT (ALBUM).
Tracks: / Bring on the boys / Where is he / Baby you ain't nothin' without me / Hot shot / God knows I'm just a woman / Beau.
LP: K 50551

NOBODY'S CHILD (OLD GOLD) (See under White Plains - When You Are A King).

Young, La Monte

THEATRE OF ETERNAL MUSIC.
LP: SHAN 83510

WELL TUNED PIANO, THE.
LPS: 1887011

Young, Larry

UNITY.
Tracks: / Zolitah / Monk's dream / If / Moontrane, The / Softly as a morning sunsrise / Beyond all limits.
LP: BST 84221

Young, Lester

1939-40 (Young, Lester & Charlie Christian).
LP: JA 42

ALTERNATIVE LESTER, THE.
LP: M 8000

BIRD AND PRES CARNEGIE HALL 1949 (See under Parker, Charlie) (Young, Lester & Charlie Parker).

CLASSIC TENORS (see Hawkins, Coleman) (Young, Lester & Coleman Hawkins).

COMPLETE SAVOY SESSIONS.
2LP: WL 70505
MC: WK 70505

GENIUS OF LESTER YOUNG, THE.
2LP: 2683 058

HISTORICAL PREZ LESTER YOUNG 1940-44.
LP: EV 3002

IN PARIS.
LP: 2034 489

IN WASHINGTON D.C. 1956.
Tracks: / Foggy day / Whin you're smiling / I can't get started / Fast Bob blues / D.B. blues / Tea for two / Jeepers creepers.
LP: 230 8219
MC: K 08 219

IN WASHINGTON D.C. - VOL.2.
LP: 230 8225
MC: K 08 225

IN WASHINGTON D.C. - VOL.3.

Tracks: / Just you, just me / Sometimes I'm happy / Up 'n Adam / Indiana / G's if you please / There'll never be another you.
LP: 230 8228
MC: K 08 228

IN WASHINGTON D.C. - VOL.4.
Tracks: / Talk of the town / I cover the waterfront / Pennies from Heaven / G's, if you please / Almost like being in love / D.B. blues / I'm confessin'.
LP: 230 8230
MC: K 08 230

LESTER LEAPS.
Tracks: / Saxy blues / I cover the waterfront / These foolish things / Lester leaps in / Lovers leap / Leap frog.
LP: SJAZZ 10
MC: SJAZZC 10

LESTER LEAPS AGAIN.
Tracks: / Up 'n' at 'em / Indiana / Too marvellous for words / Mean to me / Sweet Georgia Brown / I'm confessin' / Neenah / I cover the waterfront / Lester leaps in / I don't stand a ghost of a chance / How high the moon / Bebop boogie / D.B. blues / Lavender blues / These foolish things / Just you, just me / Lester leaps again.
2LP: AFFD 80

LESTER LEAPS IN.
LP: BLJ 8021

LESTER YOUNG.
LP: LPJT 9

LESTER YOUNG AND THE PIANO GIANTS (Compact/Walkman jazz) (Young, Lester & The Piano Giants).
Tracks: / This year's kisses / September in the rain / Red boy blues / I want to be happy / Up 'n Adam / Press returns / Just you, just me / Too marvellous for words / Three little words / I guess I'll have to change my plans / Man I love, The.
MC: 835 316-4

LESTER YOUNG COLLECTION (Retrospective).
Tracks: / Blue Lester / Jump, Lester, jump / Back home again in Indiana / Improvisation / Too marvellous for words / Pennies from Heaven / These foolish things / Polka dots and moonbeams / Three little words / Jumpin' with Symphony Sid / Up 'n' at 'em / Neenah / Ghost of a chance.
LP: DVLP 2126
MC: DVMC 2126

LESTER YOUNG STORY - VOL.5.
Tracks: / Louisiana / Easy does it / Let me see / Blow top / I'm pulling through / Laughing at life / Time on my hands / Evenin' / World is mad / What's your number? / Five o'clock whistle / Broadway / All of me.
LP: CBS 88493

LESTER YOUNG - VOL.1.
Tracks: / Pennies from Heaven / Stardust / Mean to me / On the sunny side of the street / Three little words.
LP: JR 111

LESTER YOUNG - VOL.2.
Tracks: / Bebop boogie / These foolish things / DB blues / Just you just me / I cover the waterfront / How high the moon / Sunday.
LP: JR 130
LP: JA 5174

LESTER YOUNG - VOL.3.
Tracks: / Blues tree / I cover the waterfront / These foolish things / Lester leaps in / Sunday / Destination moon.
LP: JR 143

LESTER YOUNG/COLEMAN HAWKINS (see Hawkins, Coleman) (Young, Lester & Coleman Hawkins).

LESTER-AMADEUS (with Count Basie).
Tracks: / Moten swing / Shout and feel it / You and me that used to be, The / Count steps in, The / They can't take that away from me / I'll always be in love with you / Swing, brother, swing / Bugle blues / I got rhythm / Allez oop / Blues with Helen / I ain't got nobody / Don't be that way / Song of the wanderer / Mortgage stomp.
LP: NOST 7639

MASTERS OF JAZZ VOL.7.
LP: SLP 4107

MOST IMPORTANT RECORDINGS OF LESTER YOUNG, THE.
Tracks: / Shoe shine boy / Shoe shine boy 2 / Oh, lady be good / This year's kisses / Sailboat in the moonlight, A / Every tub / Doggin' around / Jumpin' at the woodside / I can't get started / Shorty George / Taxi war dance / Dickie's dream / Lester leaps in / Tickle toe / I never knew / All of me / Body and soul / Hello babe / Just you, just me / Lester leaps again / I got rhythm / Exercise in swing / Blue Lester / Midnight symphony / D.B. blues / These foolish things / Lover come back to me / She's funny that way / Jumpin' with symphony Sid / Something to remember you by / St Louis blues II / Fine and mellow.
LPS: OFF 3035-2

ON THE AIR.
LP: QU 001

PREZ AND COMPLETE SAVOY RECORDS.
Tracks: / Circus in rhythm / Poor little plaything / Tush / These foolish things / Exercise in swing / Salute to fats / Basie english / Blue Lester / I don't stand a ghost of a chance / Indiana / Jump Lester jump / Crazy over J-Z / Ding dong / Blues'n'bells / June bug.
LP: SJL 2202

PREZ AND FRIENDS (Young, Lester & The Kansas City Six).
LP: 6.24292

PREZ AT HIS VERY BEST.
Tracks: / Just you just me / I never knew / Afternoon of a basie-ite / Sometimes i'm happy / Ater theatre jump / Six cats and a prince / Lester leaps again / Destination k.c..
LP: 6336 346

PREZ CONFERENCE.
LP: GNPS 2122
MC: GNP5 2122

PREZ LIVES.
LP: WL 70528

PREZ, THE.
LP: CP 504

PREZ, THE.
LP: LPJT 67

PREZ'S HAT, VOL 1.
LP: 214W 6

PREZ'S HAT, VOL 2.
LP: 214W 7

PREZ'S HAT, VOL 3.
LP: 214W 8

PREZ'S HAT, VOL 4.
LP: 214W 9

SWEET GEORGIA BROWN.
LP: 2600221

SWINGIN' SAX.
Tracks: / Saxy blues / I cover the waterfront / These foolish things / Lester leaps in / Younger than sax time / Prophet / Lovers leap / Leap frog.
LP: MAN 5035

TENOR TRIUMVERATE (see Hawkins, Coleman) (Young, Lester/Coleman Hawkins/Chu Berry).

TOGETHER (see Hawkins, Coleman) (Young, Lester & Coleman Hawkins).

TOO MARVELLOUS FOR WORDS.
LP: JAZ 2004
MC: ZCJAZ 2004

Young Lions

YOUNG LIONS, THE (Original soundtrack) (Various artists).
LP: STV 81115

Young Man With A Horn

YOUNG MAN WITH A HORN (Original Soundtrack) (Various artists).
LP: ACL 582
MC: BT 582

Young Marble Giants

COLOSSAL YOUTH.
LP: ROUGH 8

Young MC

BRAINSTORM.
Tracks: / That's the way love goes / Keep your eyes on the prize / Do you feel like I do / After school / Um dee dun song, The / Album filler / Keep it in your pants / Use your head / Inside my head / Life in the fast lane.
LP: EST 2148
MC: TCEST 2148

STONE COLD.
Tracks: / Come off / Bust a move / Name is Young, The / Roll with the punches / Stone cold buggin' / Principal's office / Fastest rhyme, The / Know how / I let 'em know / Just say no.
LP: BRLP 540

STONE COLD RHYMIN'.
LP: BRLP 543
MC: BRCA 543
MC: ICM 2068
LP: ILPM 2068

Young, Mighty Joe

BLUES WITH A TOUCH OF SOUL.
LP: DL 629

LEGACY OF THE BLUES VOL. 4 (See under Legacy of the Blues).

Young, Mike

SUPERTED: SUPERTED & BULK'S STORY (See under Superted) (Hawkins, Peter).

SUPERTED: SUPERTED IN SUPERTED'S DREAM (See under Superted) (Hawkins, Peter).

SUPERTED: SUPERTED & THE LUMBERJACKS (See under Superted) (Hawkins, Peter).

SUPERTED: SUPERTED & THE POTHOLE RESCUE (See under Superted) (Hawkins, Peter).

Young, Neil

AFTER THE GOLDRUSH.
Tracks: / Tell me why / After the goldrush / Only love can break a heart / Southern man / Till the morning comes / Oh, lonesome me / Don't let it bring you down / Birds / When you dance I can really love / I believe in you / Cripple Creek ferry.
LP: RSLP 6383
MC: K 444088
LP: K 44088

AFTER THE GOLDRUSH/ HARVEST.
MC: K4 64044

AMERICAN STARS AND BARS.
Tracks: / Old country waltz / Saddle up the palomino / Hey babe / Hold back the tears / Bite the bullitt / Star of Bethlehem / Will to live / Like a hurricane / Homegrown.
LP: K 54088
MC: K4 54088

COMES A TIME.
Tracks: / Goin' back / Comes a time / Look out for my love / Peace of mind / Lotta love / Human highway / Already one / Field of opportunity / Motorcycle mama / Four strong winds.
LP: K 54099
MC: K4 54099

CRAZY HORSE (Young, Neil & Crazy Horse).
Tracks: / Gone dead train / Dance, dance, dance / Look at all the things / Beggars day / I don't want to talk about it / Carolay / Dirty, dirty / Nobody / I'll get by / Crow Lady Jane.
LP: ED 175
LP: K 44114
MC: K4 44114

CRAZY MOON (Young, Neil & Crazy Horse).
LP: PL 13054

DECADE.
Tracks: / Down to the wire / Burned / Mr. Soul / Broken arrow / Expecting to fly / Sugar mountain / I am a child / Loner, The / Old laughing lady, The / Cinnamon girl / Down by the river / Cowgirl in the sand / I believe in you / After the goldrush / Southern man / Helpless / Ohio / Soldier / Old man / Man needs a maid / Heart of gold / Star of Bethlehem / Needles and the damage done, The / Tonight's the night (part 1) / Turnstiles / Winterlong / Deep forbidden lake / Like a hurricane / Love is a rose / Cortez the killer / Campaigner / Long may you run / Harvest.
LPS: K 64037
MCSET: K4 64037

EVERYBODY KNOWS THIS IS NOWHERE.
Tracks: / Cinnamon girl / Everybody knows this is nowhere / Round and round / Down by the river / Losing end, The / Running dry (Requiem for the rockets) / Cowgirl in the sand.
LP: K 44073

EVERYBODY'S ROCKIN'.
Tracks: / Betty Lou's got a new pair of shoes / Rainin' in my heart / Payole blues / Wonderin' / Kinda fonda Wanda / Jolly roll men / Bright lights / Big city / Cry cry cry / Mystery train / Everybody's rockin'.
LP: 9040131
MC: 9040134
LP: GEF 25590

FREEDOM (Young, Neil & The Restless).
LP: WX 257
MC: WX 257 C

HARVEST.
Tracks: / Out on the weekend / Harvest / Man needs a maid / Heart of gold / Are you ready for the country? / Old man / There's a world / Alabama / Needle and the damage done / Words between the lines of age.
LP: K 54005
MC: K4 54005

HAWKS & DOVES.
LP: K 54109

LANDING ON WATER.
Tracks: / Weight of the world / Violent side / Hippie dream / Bad news beat / Touch the night / People on the street / Hard luck stories / I got a problem / Pressure / Drifter.
LP: 9241091
MC: 9241094
MC: GEFC 24109

LIFE (Young, Neil & Crazy Horse).
Tracks: / Mideast vacation / Long walk home / Around the world / Inca Queen / Too lonely / Prisoners of rock'n' roll / Crying eyes / When your lonely heart breaks / We never danced.
LP: WX 109
MC: WX 109C

LIVE RUST (Young, Neil & Crazy Horse).
Tracks: / Sugar mountain / I am a child / Comes a time / After the goldrush / My, my, hey, hey (out of the blue) / When you dance I can really love / Loner, The / Needle and the damage done / Lotta love / Sedan delivery / Powder finger / Cortez the killer / Cinnamon girl / Like a hurricane / Hey hey, my my (into the black) / Tonight's the night.
2LP: K 64041
MC: K4 64041

NEIL YOUNG.
Tracks: / Emperor of Wyoming, The / Loner, The / If I could have her tonight / I've been waiting for you / Old laughing lady, The / String quartet from whiskey boot hill / Here we are in the years / What did you do to my life / I've loved her so long / Last trip to Tulsa, The.
LP: K 44059
MC: 923956 4

OLD WAYS.
Tracks: / Wayward wind / Get back to the country / Are there any more real cowboys / Once an angel / Misfits / California sunset / Old ways / My boy / Bound for glory / Where is the highway tonight?.
LP: GEF 26377
MC: 4026377

ON THE BEACH.
Tracks: / Walk on / See the sky about to rain / Revolution blues / For the turnstiles / Vampire blues / On the beach / Motion pictures / Ambulance blues.
LP: K 54014

RAGGED GLORY (Young, Neil & Crazy Horse).
LP: WX 374
MC: WX 374C

RE-AC-TOR.
Tracks: / Opera star / Surfer Joe and Moe the sleaze / T-Bone / Get back on it / Southern Pacific / Motor city / Rapid transit / Shots.
LP: K 54116

RUST NEVER SLEEPS (Young, Neil & Crazy Horse).
Tracks: / My my, hey hey (out of the blue) / Thrasher / Ride my llama / Pocohontas / Sail away / Powder finger / Welfare mothers / Sedan delivery / Hey hey, my my (into the black).
LP: K 54105
MC: K4 54105

THIS NOTE IS FOR YOU (Young, Neil & The Blue Notes).
Tracks: / Ten men workin' / This note's for you / Coupe de ville / Life in the city / Twilight / Married man / Sunny inside / Can't believe your lyin' / Hey hey / One thing.
LP: WX 168
MC: WX 168C
LP: K 925719 1
MC: K 925719 4

TIME FADES AWAY.
LP: K 54010
MC: K4 54010

TONIGHT'S THE NIGHT.
Tracks: / Tonight's the night / Speakin' out / World on a string / Borrowed tune / Come on baby / Let's go down-town / Mellow my mind / Roll another number (for the road) / Albuquerque / New mama / Look out, Joe / Tired eyes / Tonight's the night (part 2).
LP: K 54040

TRANS.
LP: 9020181
MC: 9020184
LP: GEF 25019

ZUMA.
Tracks: / Don't cry no tears / Danger bird / Pardon my heart / Lookin' for a love / Barstool blues / Stupid girl / Drive back / Cortez the killer / Through my salis.
LP: K 54057

Young, Paul

12" TAPE: PAUL YOUNG.
Tracks: / Wherever I lay my hat / Come back and stay / Love of the common people / I'm gonna tear your playhouse down / Everytime you go away.
MC: 4501244

BETWEEN TWO FIRES.
Tracks: / Some people / Wonderland / War games / In the long run / Wasting my time / Prisoner of conscience / Why does a man have to be strong / Certain passion, A / Between two fires / Wedding day.
LP: **4501501**
MC: **4501504**

BOTH SIDES NOW (See under Clannad) (Clannad/ Paul Young).

EARLY YEARS, THE.
MC: . . . . **VSOPMC 160**

FROM TIME TO TIME (The Singles Collection).
Tracks: / Every time you go away / Come back and stay / I'm only foolin' myself / Senza una Donna (without a woman) / I'm gonna tear your playhouse down / Broken man / Everything must change / Wonderland / Don't dream it's over / Love of the common people / Wherever I lay my hat (that's my home) / Both sides now / Oh Girl / Softly whispering I love you / Some people (Only on cassette and CD.).
LP: **4688251**
MC: **4688254**

LIVE: PAUL YOUNG & THE Q-TIPS (Young, Paul & The Q-Tips).
LP: . . . . **SHM 3175**
MC: . . . . **HSC 3175**

NO PARLEZ.
Tracks: / Come back and stay / Love will tear us apart / Wherever I lay my hat / Ku-ku kurama / No parlez / Love of the common people / Oh women / Iron out the rough spots / Broken man / Tender trap, The / Sex.
LP: . . . . **CBS 25521**
MC: **40 25521**
LP: **4609091**
MC: **4609094**

OTHER VOICES.
Tracks: / Heaven can wait / Little bit of love, A / Softly whispering I love you / Together / Stop on by / Our time has come / Oh girl / Right about now / It's what she didn't say / Calling you.
MC: **4669174**
LP: **4669171**

SECRET OF ASSOCIATION, THE.
Tracks: / Bite the hand that feeds / Everytime you go away / I'm gonna tear your playhouse down / Standing on the edge / Soldier's things / Everything must change / Tomb of memories / One step forward / Hot fun / This means anything / I was in chains.
LP: . . . . **CBS 26234**
MC: **40 26234**
LP: **4655771**
MC: **4655774**

SENZA UNA DONNA (WITHOUT A WOMAN) (See under Zucchero for details) (Young, Paul & Zucchero).

STREETBAND (see under Streetband).

Young, Robert

EMERALD VEIN.
Tracks: / Worship / Messiah, The / Out of my head / Completely nothing / Promise, The / In his world.
LP: . . . . **SUB 33013-18**

Young, Rose

SECRET OF ABBEY PLACE.
MCSET: . . . . **MRC 1048**

Young Savages

YOUNG SAVAGES, THE (Original Soundtrack) (Various artists).
LP: . . . . **LAALP 1011**

Young Sherlock Holmes

YOUNG SHERLOCK HOLMES (Original soundtrack) (Sinfonia Of London).
Tracks: / Main title / Solving the crime / Library love (Waxflatter's first flight) / Pastries and crypts / Waxing Elizabeth / Holmes and Elizabeth (love theme) / Ehtar's escape / Final duel / Final farewell / Riddles solved - end credits.
LP: . . . . **MCF 3311**
MC: . . . . **MCFC 3311**

Young, Sterling

STERLING YOUNG, 1939-49.
Tracks: / Blue is the night / It all comes back to me now / Three little words / At least you could say hello / So you're the one / I'm fit to be tied / Pinch me / It's a blue world / Answer is love, The / Goody goodbye / All the things you are / Make with the kisses / Stay in my arms Cinderella / It had to be you / Careless / Cherokee.
LP: . . . . **HSR 113**

Young, Steve

HONKY TONK MAN.
LP: . . . . **ROUNDER 3087**
MC: . . . . **ROUNDER 3087C**

LONG TIME RIDER.
LP: . . . . **VD 105**

LOOK HOMEWARD ANGEL.
LP: . . . . **MILL 5031**

NO PLACE TO FALL.
Tracks: / No place to fall / Montgomery in the rain / Dreamer / Always loving you / Drift away / Seven Bridges road / I closed my heart's door / Don't think twice, it's alright / I can't sleep / I got the same old blues.
MC: . . . . **PK 12510**
LP: . . . . **PL 12510**

OLD MEMORIES.
Tracks: / Renegade picker / Lonesome on'ry & mean / Old memories / Always loving you / Don't think twice, it's all right / Seven Bridges Road / Light of my life / Dreamer / All her lovers want to be the hero / Montgomery in the rain.
LP: . . . . **CRLP 1002**

RENEGADE PICKER.
Tracks: / Renegade picker / I can't be myself / Old memories / It's not supposed to be that way / Tobacco road / Light of my life / Lonesome, on'ry and mean / All her lovers want to be the hero / Broken hearted people / Sweet thing / Home sweet home.
LP: . . . . **PL 11759**

ROCK SALT AND NAILS.
Tracks: / That's how strong my love is / Rock salt and nails / I'm a one woman man / Coyote / Gonna find me a bluebird / Love in my time / Seven bridges road / Kenny's song / Holler in the swamp / Hoboin' / My sweet love ain't around.
LP: . . . . **ED 193**

SEVEN BRIDGES ROAD.
Tracks: / Seven bridges road / Montgomery in the rain / Ragtime blue guitar / Long way to Hollywood / Down in the flood / Ballad of William Sycamore / My Oklahoma / Wild goose / Days of 49 / Lonesome, on'ry and mean.
LP: . . . . **SNTF 870**
LP: . . . . **ROUNDER 3058**
MC: . . . . **ROUNDER 3058C**

TO SATISFY YOU.
Tracks: / Think it over / To satisfy you / Top of the world / No expectations / Contender, The / Corina, Corina / All your stories / Wild world / They call it love / River and the swan, The.
LP: . . . . **ROUNDER 3057**
MC: . . . . **ROUNDER 3057C**

Young, Tommie

WOMAN CALLED MOSES (Sings themes).
LP: . . . . **MCF 2869**
MC: . . . . **MCFC 2869**

Young Tradition

YOUNG TRADITION, THE.
Tracks: / Pembroke unique ensemble / Whitsuntide carol / Banks of Claudy, The / Upon the bough / John Barleycorn / Daddy Fox / Banks of the Nile / Bitter Withy / Lyke wyke dirge / Chicken on a raft / Byker Hill / Idumea / Innocent hare, The / Ratcliffe highway / Loyal lover / Randy dandy-O / Agincourt carol / Brisk young widow / Wondrous love.
LP: . . . . **TRANDEM 5**

Young, Trummy

STRUTTIN' WITH SOME BARBECUE (Young, Trummy & Barney Bigard).
LP: . . . . **ZR 1017**

Young Tuxedo Brass

NEW ORLEANS.
LP: . . . . **LPS 10**
MC: . . . . **TCS 10**

SOUNDS OF NEW ORLEANS STREET FUNERAL & PARADE.
Tracks: / Lead me saviour / Eternal peace / Medley of hymns / Just a closer walk with thee / Bourbon Street parade / Lord Lord Lord / Just a little while to stay here / Panama / It feels so good / Joe Avery's piece / John Cashmir's whoopin' blues.
LP: . . . . **K 50404**

Young, Val

SEDUCTION.
Tracks: / Mind games / If you should ever be lonely / Let's fall in love / Telling me lies / Come hang out / Seduction, The / Piece of my heart / Waiting for you / Make up your mind.
LP: . . . . **ZL 72387**
MC: . . . . **ZK 72387**

Young, Victor

QUIET MAN, THE.
LP: . . . . **VS 81073**

Young Warriors

YOUNG WARRIORS, THE (Original soundtrack) (Various artists).
LP: . . . . **STV 81186**

Young, Webster

WEBSTER YOUNG PLAYS THE MILES DAVIS SONGBOOK, VOL 3.
LP: . . . . **VGM 0006**

WEBSTER YOUNG PLAYS THE MILES DAVIS SONGBOOK, VOL 2.
LP: . . . . **VGM 0005**

WEBSTER YOUNG PLAYS THE MILES DAVIS SONGBOOK, VOL 1.
LP: . . . . **VGM 0004**

Young, Zora

STUMBLING BLOCKS & STEPPING STONES.
LP: . . . . **STING 007**

Youngblood, Sydney

FEELING FREE.
Tracks: / Feeling free / If only I could / I'd rather go blind / Sit and wait / Kiss and say goodbye / Ain't no sunshine / I'm your lover / Not just a lover but a friend / Congratulations / Could it me (I'm in love) / That was yesterday / Good times bad times.
LP: . . . . **CIRCA 9**
MC: . . . . **CIRC 9**

Youngbloods

EARTH MUSIC.
Tracks: / Euphoria / All my dreams blue / Monkey Business / Dreamer's dream / Sugar Babe / Long and tall / I Can Tell / Don't Play Games / Wine song / Fool me / Reason to believe.
LP: . . . . **ED 274**

ELEPHANT MOUNTAIN.
Tracks: / Darkness, darkness / Smug / On Sir Frances Drake / Sunlight / Double sunlight / Beautiful / Turn it over / Rain song (don't let the rain..) / Trillium / Quicksand / Black mountain breakdown / Sham / Ride the wind.
LP: . . . . **ED 276**

FROM THE GASLIGHT TO THE AVALON.
Tracks: / Grizzly bear / All over the world / Get together / Other side of life, The / Merry go round / Euphoria / I can tell / Sugar babe / Wine song / Darkness darkness / Sunlight / Double sunlight / Sham / Ride the wind.
LP: . . . . **LIK 38**
MC: . . . . **TCLIK 38**

POINT REYES STATION.
Tracks: / It's a lovely day / She caught the Katy / Dreamboat / Running bear / Light shine / That's how strong my love is / Will the circle be unbroken / La bamba / Circus face / Fiddler a dram / Faster all the time / Get together / Sugar babe.
LP: . . . . **ED 244**

YOUNGBLOODS.
Tracks: / Grizzly bear / All Over The World / Statesboro Blues / Get Together / One note man / Other side of this life / Tears Are Falling / Four In The Morning / Foolin' Around / Ain't that lovin' you / C.C. rider.
LP: . . . . **EDLP 271**

Young,Christopher

HAUNTED SUMMER (Film soundtrack) (See under Haunted Summer).

Younger Generation

YOUNGER GENERATION Various artists (Various artists).
LP: . . . . **DYCBLP 002**

Your Cheatin' Heart

YOUR CHEATIN' HEART (BBC TV Series) (Various artists).
MC: . . . . **ZCF 791**

Your Fantasies

ROLLER BOOGIE.
Tracks: / Is disco dead? / Getcha wheels rollin' / Roll over / Rollin' / I thought I could fake it with you.
LP: . . . . **SEL 2**

Your Kind Of Music...

YOUR KIND OF MUSIC (Various artists).
MCSET: . . . . **DTO 10070**

You're driving me

YOU'RE DRIVING ME CRAZY (Various artists).
Tracks: / Ring dem bells: *Various artists* / Confessin': *Various artists* / Rockin' chair: *Various artists*/ Happy feet: *Various artists* / Somebody loves me: *Various artists* / You're driving me crazy: *Various artists*/ New Orleans hop scop blues: *Various artists* / Sheik of Araby, The: *Various artists* / Mood indigo: *Various* artists / I got rhythm: *Various artists* / Here comes Emily Brown: *Various artists* / If I could be with you: *Various artists* / When I'm alone: *Various artists* / Heebie jeebies: *Various artists* / I can't believe that you're in love with me: *Various artists* / Okay baby: *Various artists.*
LP: . . . . **NOST 7618**
MC: . . . . **NOST 8618**

Yours, Anne

YOURS, ANNE (Original New York Cast) (Various artists).
Tracks: / Dear kitty, I'm 13 years old: *Various artists* / She doesn't understand me: *Various artists* / Schlaf: *Various artists* / In the night: *Various artists* / You don't have to: *Various artists* / Hollywood: *Various* artists / Dear kitty I have a nicer side: *Various artists* / We live with fear (Parts 1 & 2): *Various artists*/ Writer, A: *Various artists* / I am not a Jew: *Various artists* / First chanukah night: *Various artists*/ Dear Kitty it's a new year: *Various artists* / We're here: *Various artists* / My life: *Various artists*/ Dear Kitty I am longing: *Various artists* / I remember: *Various artists* / I think myself out: *Various artists*/ Mightmare: *Various artists* / For the children: *Various artists* / Something to get up for: *Various artists*/ When we are free: *Various artists* / Much too young: *Various artists* / I am only 15: *Various artists*/ Something is new: *Various artists.*
LP: . . . . **TER 1118**
MC: . . . . **ZCTER 1118**

Yours Mine & Our

YOURS MINE & OUR (Original Soundtrack) (Various artists).
LP: . . . . **MCAL 1434**
MC: . . . . **MCAC 1434**

Yours Truly

TRULY YOURS.
Tracks: / I really love you / I wanna make love to you / Hold me / I'm sorry / I don't wanna lose your love / Gonna miss the one / I'll give you everything / I've got to show you / Come and get it / All of me / I'll be watching you / I've got to show you / Back to yesterday.
LP: . . . . **ZL 72754**
MC: . . . . **ZK 72754**

Youth

EMPTY QUARTER, THE.
LP: . . . . **JAMS 36**

Youth Brigade

SOUND AND FURY.
LP: . . . . **BYO 2**

WHAT PRICE HAPPINESS.
LP: . . . . **BYO 6**

Youth Of Today

BREAK DOWN THE WALLS.
LP: . . . . **PF 11**

CAN'T CLOSE MY EYES.
Tracks: / Expectations / Crucial times / I have faith / Youth of today / Take a stand / Positive out / Can't close my eyes / We just... / Youth crew.
LP: **601299**

WE'RE NOT IN THIS ALONE.
LP: . . . . **FH 12014**

Youth With A Mission

WINDOWS I I exalt Thee.
LP: . . . . **WST R 8982**
MC: . . . . **WST C 8982**

WINDOWS II Giving glory.
LP: . . . . **WST R 8998**
MC: . . . . **WST C 8998**

WINDOWS ON THE WORLD (1).
Tracks: / Victor's crown / Jesus we enthrone You / All that you are we want / We bow down / When I survey / Let us adore the Lord / Crown Him / We will glorify / Robed in majesty / Thou art my God, o Lord / Glory that is due his name, The / Sing unto the Lord / Great is the Lord.
LP: . . . . **SOP R 2015**
MC: . . . . **SOP C 2015**

You've Got To Laugh

YOU'VE GOT TO LAUGH (Various artists).
LP: . . . . **TVLP 15**
MC: . . . . **ZCTV 15**

Yr Hwntws

YR HWNTWS.
LP: . . . . **LOCO 1001**

Ysgol Morgan Llwyd

FFATRI BREUDDYDION.
LP: . . . . **LOCO 1009**

Ythan Fiddlers

YTHAN FAVOURITES.
MC: . . . . **LC 002**

Yucca, Terence

FANTASY GAMES.
LP: . . . . **ISST 175**

Yugoslavia

FOLK MUSIC OF YUGOSLAVIA (Various artists).
LP: **12TS 224**

FOLK SONGS & DANCES FROM YUGOSLAVIA (Various artists).
LP: . . . . IC 058-99707

YUGLOSLAVIA: 3. CROATIA (Yugoslav Music).
MC: 45 603

YUGOSALVIA:1.BOSNIA & HERCEGORINA (Yugoslav Music).
MC: 45 601

YUGOSLAV FOLK MUSIC (Various artists).
LP: . . . . LLST 7189

YUGOSLAVIA: 2. MONTENEGRO & SLOVENIA (Yugoslav Music).
MC: 45 602

YUGOSLAVIA: 4. MACEDONIA (Yugoslav Music).
MC: 45 604

YUGOSLAVIA: 5. SERBIA (Yugoslav Music).
MC: 45 605

Yuletracks

YULETRACKS (Various artists).
LP: . . . . GVR 235

Yung Wu

SHORE LEAVE.
LP: . . . . TTC 87119
LP: . . . . ROUGH 118

Yung, Yukio

EXCREMENT.
LP: . . . . LOGICAL FISH 3

Yuro, Timi

18 UNFORGETTABLE BALLADS.
MC: 260 403 4

COLLECTION: TIMI YURO.
LP: . . . . MA 2686
MC: . . . . MAMC 92686

HURT.
Tracks: / Hurt / Make the world go away / What's the matter baby / Only love can break a heart / Little things mean a lot / Thank you for calling / It must be him / Smoke gets in your eyes / I'm sorry / Let me go lover / Its only make believe / All alone am I / It hurts to be in love / You've lost that lovin' feeling / Tears on my pillow / Cry / I can't stop loving you / Only you.
LP: . . . . CR 30259
MC: . . . . TCCR 30259

HURT.
LP: 1A 022 58068
MC: 1A 222 58068

HURT (OLD GOLD) (see under Carr, Vikki (It must be him) (Carr, Vikki/Timi Yuro).

SENSATIONAL VOICE OF, (THE).
Tracks: / Hurt (a chil) / I'm afraid the masquerade is over / All I need is you / I love my man / I didn't know what time it was / I got it bad (and that ain't good) / If / Maybe you'll be there / I can dream, can't I / Johnny / There must be a way / My foolish heart / I'm still around / Cuttin ' in.
LP: 8125 841
MC: 8125 844
LP: . . . . IMS 8125841

VERY BEST OF TIMI YURO.
Tracks: / Hurt / I apologise / Let me call you sweetheart / You'll never know / Make the world go away / There goes my heart / Once in a while / I'm confessin' / My prayer / It's too soon to know / What's the matter baby / Don't blame me / Fever / Smile / Just say I love him / Cry / Stardust / Love of a boy, The / Insult to injury / Should I ever love again.
LP: . . . . LBR 1034
MC: . . . . TCLBR 1034

VERY ORIGINAL AND GREATEST HITS.
LP: 5C 054 83193

WHAT'S A MATTER BABY?.
Tracks: / What's a matter baby? / I ain't gonna cry no more / Insult to injury / Confessin' (that I love you) / There goes my heart / Fever / Should I ever love again / If you gotta make a fool of somebody / I'd fight the world / That's right, walk on by / Stardust / Leavin' on your mind.
LP: . . . . SLS 50399

Yusuf, Mohammed

ROOTICAL TIES.
MC: . . . . BIP 603

Yutaka

YUTAKA.
Tracks: / Colors of the wind / Warm and sunny Sunday morning / Peach blossom spring / Dreamland / Aka tombo / Red dragonfly / Night wave / Living inside your love / Shadows, The / Outdoor live / Reflections / Aurora (Extra track on CD.).
LP: . . . . GRP 91046
MC: . . . . GRPM 91046

YUTAKA.
Tracks: / Brazasia / East by South / Morena / Chuva / Lambada nova (you're good for me) / Urban jungle / Wayward wind / (If I only have) one chance / Sao jorge / Say you do.
LP: . . . . GRP 96161
MC: . . . . GRP 96164

Yves Choir

BY PRESCRIPTION ONLY.
Tracks: / Rush hour / After the rain / Rocky Road / D B / By prescription only / Mad about town / Far side, The / Follow me to the edge / Bianca / Morocco junction.
LP: 103 251
MC: 103 252

Z

Z Cars

Z CARS (THEME FROM) (See under Keating, Johnny) (Keating, Johnny).

Z (film)

Z (Original soundtrack) (Various artists).
LP: CBS 63639
LP: 40-63639

Zabel, Jennifer (aut)

ADVENTURES OF CREAMCAKE AND COMPANY (See under Adventures of ... (Stubbs, Una (nar)).

MORE ADVENTURES OF MY LITTLE PONY See also Antonia Swinson.
MC: 00 103460X

MY LITTLE PONY: BABY QUACKERS & THE SAD QUOLLY.
MC: 0 00 102124 9

MY LITTLE PONY: DANCING & BAD TEMPERED BUTTERFLIES.
MC: 0 00 102123 0

MY LITTLE PONY: GUSTY AND GENIE.
MC: 00 102119 2

MY LITTLE PONY: LITTLE PONIES & THE PIXIE SEA PIRATE.
MC: 0 00 102121 4

MY LITTLE PONY: THE GRAND PONY PARADE.
MC: 00 102120 6

MY LITTLE PONY: THE LITTLE MAGIC NUT TREE.
MC: 0 00 102122 2

Zachariah

ZACHARIAH (Original soundtrack) (Various artists).
Tracks: / Lonely rider: *Various artists* / Camino/Used horse salesman: *Various artists* / Zachariah (main title): *Various artists* / Laguna salada: *James Gang* / We're the crackers: *Country Joe & The Fish* / William Tell: *Haskell, Jimmie* / All I need: *Country Joe & The Fish* / Ballad of Job Cain: *Kershaw, Doug* / Country fever: *James Gang* / Camino waltz: *Haskell, Jimmie* / Gravedigger: *New York Rock Ensemble* / Shy Ann: *White Lightning* / Matthew: *Haskell, Jimmie* / Zachariah (end title): *Haskell, Jimmie*.
LP: SEE 91

Zack, George

BARRELHOUSE PIANO (Zack,George/ George Wettling).
LP: 6.25895

Zadig, Man of Destiny

ZADIG, MAN OF DESTINY (Various artists).
MC: ANV 631

Zadora, Pia

I AM WHAT I AM.
Tracks: / I am what I am / All of me / I got it bad and that ain't good / Foggy day in London town, A / Day by day / I'm beginning to see the light / If he walked into my life / For once in my life / How about you / I had the craziest dream / One I love belongs to somebody else, The / Time after time / Pennies from Heaven / It's been a long, long time / Lady is a tramp, The.
LP: 4501421
MC: 4501424

PIA.
Tracks: / I'm in love again / Never gonna do you wrong / Say yes / You can't keep a good love down / Baby it's you / Love who you love / Somebody somewhere / Those eyes / It's wrong for me to love you / How'd you get me this way.
LP: K 52397

PIA AND PHIL (Zadora, Pia/London Philharmonic Orchestra).
Tracks: / Maybe this time / Embraceable you / It had to be you / All my tomorrows / Smile (though your heart is breaking) / Come rain or come shine (end s1) / When the sun comes out / East of the sun (and west of the moon) / But not for me / I thought about you / Boy next door, The / Man that got away, The.
LP: EPC 26769
MC: 40 26769
LP: PZP 1000
MC: PZPK 1000
LP: MCF 3267

WHEN THE LIGHTS GO OUT.
Tracks: / I don't wanna love / Still remembered / Dance out of my head / Laughing at you / When the lights go out / Pia's interlude / I really like you (not him) / Silence / Since I've been loving you / Pia's theme / It's always the same.
LP: 4609831
MC: 4609834

WHEN THE RAIN BEGINS TO FALL (see Jackson, Jermaine) (Zadora, Pia/ Jermaine Jackson).

Zager, Michael

LIFE'S A PARTY (Zager, Michael Band).
Tracks: / Life's a party / You don't know a good thing / I wish you could make up your mind / Love, love, love / Still not over / On and on / Using you.
LP: PVLP 1045

ZAGER (Zager, Michael Band).
Tracks: / Don't sneak on me / Time heals every wound / Your love / Zorba the Greek / Call me / Bring me love / I'd love to make up with you / Rasputin / I'm afraid to let you know.
LP: EMC 3328

Zahcurim

MORAL REARMAMENT.
LP: ST 3005

Zahouania, Shaba

NIGHTS WITHOUT SLEEPING.
MC: ICT 9914
LP: ILPS 9914

Zaiko Langa L

AMOUR THYTHY'NA.
LP: MA 4003

NKOLO MBOKA.
LP: KBK 901

Zaire

ANGOLAN BORDER, THE (MUSICIANS OF THE TSHOKWE..) (see under Angola) (Various artists).

SANZA AND GUITAR (MUSIC OF THE BENA LULUWA) (see under Angola) (Various artists).

Zak, Peter

SONGS FROM TWO STATES.
LP: 100 ZLP

Zakatek, Lenny

LENNY ZAKATEK.
LP: AMLH 64777

Zambia

VOIX DES MASQUES DE ZAMBIE, LA (Various artists).
Tracks: / Chants d'initiation: *Various artists* / Rituels Nyau: *Various artists* / Rituels Makashi: *Various artists*.
LP: ARN 33605

ZAMBIA: AN INTRODUCTION (Various artists).
Tracks: / Chingolongolo: *Shalawambe* / Kuchibombo: *Amayenge* / Mwilalila: *Chilambe, Teddy* / Bonse niba wiso: *Kalusha, Alfred Chisala (Jnr)* / Apongozi amasiku ano: *Kazembe, Nashil Pichen* / Makubi: *Masasu Band*/ Sunge ilyashi: *Chisala, P.K.* / Mama ye sungwe: *Julizya* / Chisale: *Fire Family* / Kapele: *Lima Jazz Band*.
LP: MON 001S

Zambiance

ZAMBIANCE (Various artists).
Tracks: / Kambowa: *Shalawambe* / Mao: *Amayenge* / Nyina kataila: *Kalambo hit parade* / By air: *Various artists* / Tai yaka: *Julizya* / Icupo cha kuala pa mpapa: *Shalawambe* / Itumba: *Kalusha, Alfred Chisala (Jnr)* / Ni Maggie: *Kalusha, Alfred Chisala (Jnr)*.
LP: ORB 037

Zamfir, Gheorghe

ATLANTIS.
Tracks: / Andrew's theme (film theme from 'Misunderstood') / Wonderland / I'll give you the sun / Gymnopedie no.1 / Top of the world / Stranger on the shore / Message from Atlantis / Seagulls / Elodie / Hi George / If you go away / Ladie's waltz / Amapola.
LP: 824 048 1
MC: 824 048 4

BEAUTIFUL DREAMS.
Tracks: / Shadow of your smile / Annie's song / Memories / Danny boy / Birds of winter / What now my love / All I ask of you / Midnight blue / Beautiful dreams / Plaisir D'amour / Somewhere my love / Amazing grace.
LP: PHH 7
MC: PHHC 7

BEST OF GHEORGHE ZAMFIR.
Tracks: / Lonely sheperd / She / Your song / Solitude / Summer of 42 / Alouette / Don't cry for me argentina / Yesterday / Romance no. 2 / Till / Cockeyes song / Ave maria.
LP: WEF 3
MC: ZCWEF 3
LP: PHH1

CHRISTMAS ALBUM, A.
Tracks: / O, du frohliche / Jingle bells / O tannenbaum / Six colours / Hark the herald angels sing / Noel roumains (medley) / White Christmas / Little drummer boy / Ave Maria / Petit Papa Noel / Pour toi Jesus / Silent night / Notre pere / Angels we have heard on high.
LP: 822 571 1
MC: 822 571 4

EASYRIDING: GHEORGHE ZAMFIR.
Tracks: / Blue Navajo / Lonely shepherd / Your song / Just the way you are / Yesterday / Floral dance, The / Summer of 42, Theme from / Rose, The / Limelight / Run to me / She / Bilitis / L'arte del violino / Traumerei.
MC: KNMC 11005
LP: KNLP 11005

EXTRAORDINARY PAN PIPE VOL.1.
LP: CBS DDLX 18

EXTRAORDINARY PAN PIPE VOL.2.
LP: CBS DDLX 19

EXTRAORDINARY PAN PIPE VOL.3.
LP: CBS DDLX 37

GOLDEN PAN FLUTE.
LP: 2627021
MC: 2627024

GREAT SUCCESSES OF....
LP: CBS DDLX 98

HARMONY.
Tracks: / Cent mille chansons / I know him so well / Serenade / Another you, another me / To my son Teo / Sleepy shores / Recuerdos / Concerto for clarinet in A / Wild theme / Cavalleria rusticana / Only love / Elvira madigan / Themanual.
LP: PHH 5
MC: PHHC 5

HOMMAGE A GHEORGHE ZAMFIR.
LP: 6313 094

IMAGES: GHEORGHE ZAMFIR.
Tracks: / Chariots of fire / Yesterday / Top of the world / Rose, The / Your song / If you go away / Run to me.
MC: KNMC 16004

IMPRESSIONS.
LP: EPC 82904
MC: 40 82904

IN PARIS.
2LP: CBS DDLX 27/8

IN PARIS 1.
LP: CBS DDLX 34

IN PARIS 2.
LP: CBS DDLX 35

KING OF PAN FLUTE.
MC: 817
LP: 2627011
MC: 2627014

L'ALOUETTE.
LP: 6325 143
MC: 7102 584

LONELY SHEPHERD, THE.
Tracks: / Lonely shepherd / Jasmine / Ete d'amour / Inima / Serenissime / Nadjenka / Floral dance, The / Rose, The / Deguello / L'alouette / Mourir a Madrid / Gloria.
LP: PRICE 64
MC: PRIMC 64
LP: 6395197

MASTER OF THE PAN-FLUTE.
Tracks: / Blue Navajo / Lonely shepherd / Your song / Just the way you are / Yesterday / Floral dance, The / Summer of 42, Theme from / Rose, (The) / Limelight / Run to me / She / Bilitis / L'arte del violino / Traumerei.
LP: 818 404 1
MC: 818 404 4

MOTIVE SERIES.
LP: 6395 091
MC: 7206 091

MUSIC BY CANDLELIGHT.
Tracks: / Adagio 8 / Bilitis / Black rose / Don't cry for me Argentina / Elsha / Floral dance / Laryssa / Limelight / Run to me / She / Summer of '42 / Meditation.
LP: 910 1194
LP: ADAH 432
MC: ADAHC 432

MUSIC FOR THE MILLIONS.
Tracks: / Ete d'amour / Mourir a Madrid / Inima / Pluie d'ete / Je joue a l'abube / Vitrail de lune / Derilium / Deguello / Derenissime / L'alouette.
LP: 6395 215
MC: 7206 215

PICNIC AT HANGING ROCK, THEME FROM.
LP: EPC 81780
MC: 40 81780

ROCKING CHAIR.
Tracks: / Sylvania / Rocking chair / Nausicaa / Blue blue nite / Reflexion X / Sprina / Pipe-line / Sweet France / Odyssee 81 / Why not / Sunrise / Colours of Spring.
LP: 1313169

ROMANCE.
Tracks: / Blue Navajo / Missing / Yesterday / Aranjuez mon amour / Just the way you are / Till / Chariots of fire / Midnight horses / Danny's night / Your song / Agata / Un amour de Tchaikovsky.
LP: 6313 438
MC: 7200 438

ROUMANIAN FLUTES VOL.2.
LP: ARN 30T095
MC: K7 ARN 40 30095

ROUMANIAN FLUTES VOL. 1.
Tracks: / Craitele / Rustemul ca la listeava / Doina oltului si ora / Cintecul jianvlui / Briul / Bocet / Hora lautareasca / Geamparalele de la costesti si sirba munteneas / Hora ca din caval / Sirba din dolj / Au plecat olten la coasa / Hora de la Bascov / Cintecul lui oleac / Jocul dianca / Pe marginea Dunarii / Suita de melodii din Maramures.
LP: ARN 30073
MC: ARN 430073

ROUMANIAN FOLKLORE INSTRUMENTS.
LP: CBS DDLX 22

SECRET WORLD OF....
LP: CBS DDLX 75

THEME LIGHT OF EXPERIENCE.
MC: 40 81638

WERELDSUCCESSEN.
Tracks: / Lonely shepherd / She / Limelight / Run to me / Don't cry for me Argentina.
2LP: 6878 127
MCSET: 7413 127

ZAMFIR.
LP: CBS DDLX901

Zanman'n

COULEURS.
LP: 51523

Zantees

OUT FOR KICKS.
LP: CR 30214

RHYTHM BOUND.
LP: LP 8401

Zant,Van

MIDNIGHT SENSATION.
LP: CBS 26483

Zanzibar

TAARAB 3 - THE MUSIC OF ZANZIBAR (See under Taarab) (Various artists).

TARAAB 3 (Various artists).
LP: ORB 040

Zap Pow

REVOLUTION.
LP: TRLS 130

Zapp

NEW ZAPP 1V U, THE.
Tracks: / It doesn't really matter / Computer love / Itchin' for your twitchin' / Radio people / I only have eyes for you / Rock and roll / Cas-ta-spellome / Make me feel good / Ja ready to rock.

LP: 925327 1

V.
LP: WX 315
MC: WX 315C

ZAPP 5.
LP: 925 807-1
MC: 925 807-4

Zappa, Dweezil

CONFESSIONS.
2LP: GRUB 19
MC: TGRUB 19

HAVIN' A BAD DAY.
LP: CDL 1581

MY GUITAR WANTS TO KILL YOUR MAMA.
LP: CHR 1633
MC: ZCHR 1633

Zappa, Frank

200 MOTELS (Original soundtrack).
LP: 2C UAS 29218/9
2LP: MCA 2 4183
MC: MCAC 2 4183

200 MOTELS.
MC: 3C 254 92854

200 MOTELS 2.
MC: 3C 254 92855

APOSTROPHE.
Tracks: / Don't eat the yellow snow / Nanook rubs it / Sy. Alfonzo's pancake breakfast / Father O'Blivion / Cosmik / Debris / Excentrifugal forz / Apostrophe / Uncle Remus / Stink-foot.
LP: K 59201

BEST BAND YOU NEVER HEARD IN YOUR LIFE.
MCSET: TZAPPA 38

BROADWAY THE HARD WAY.
LP: ZAPPA 14
MC: TZAPPA 14

BURNT WEENY SANDWICH (Mothers of Invention).
Tracks: / WPLJ / Igor's boogie, phase one / Overture to a holiday in Berlin / Burnt Weeny sandwich, Theme from / Igor's boogie, phase two holiday in Berlin / Full blown / Aybe sea / Little house I used to live in / Valerie.
LP: K 44083
LP: RSLP 6370
LP: ZAPPA 335
MC: TZAPPA 35

CHUNGA'S REVENGE.
Tracks: / Transylvania boogie / Road ladies / Twenty small cigars / Nancy and Mary music, The (parts 1-3) / Tell me you love me / Would you go all the way? / Chunga's revenge / Clap, The / Rudy wants to buy yez drink / Sharleena.
LP: K 44020
LP: RSLP 2030

FRANK ZAPPA AND BARKING PUMPKIN DIGITAL GRATIFIC.
Tracks: / Opus 1-4.
LP: EJ270256 1

FRANK ZAPPA: INTERVIEW PICTURE DISC.
LPPD: BAK 2019

FRANK ZAPPA MEETS THE MOTHERS OF PREVENTION.
Tracks: / We're turning again / Alien orifice / Yo cats / What's new in Baltimore? / I don't even care / One man, one vote / H.R. 2911 / Little beige sambo / Aerobics in bondage.
LP: EMC 3507
MC: TCEMC 3507

GRAND WAZOO (Zappa, Frank/ Mothers of Invention).
Tracks: / For Calvin (and his next two hitch-hikers) / Grand wazoo / Gletus awreetus-awrightus / Eat that question / Blessed relief.
LP: K 44209

GUITAR.
Tracks: / Sexual harrassment in the workplace / Republicans / That's not really reggae / When no one was no one / Once again, without the net / Outside Now / Jim and Tammy's upper room / Were we ever really safe / That ol' G minor thing again / Move it or park it / Sunrise redeemer / But who was Fulcanneli? / Republicans / Winos do not match / Systems of edges / Things that look like meat / Watermelon in Easter hay.
2LP: ZAPPA 6
MC: TZAPPA 6

HOT RATS.
Tracks: / Peaches en regalia / Willie the pimp / Son of Mr. Green Genes / Little umbrellas / Gumbo variations, The / It must be a camel.
LP: K 44078
LP: RSLP 6356

JAZZ FROM HELL.
Tracks: / Night school / Beltway bandits, The / While you were art / Jazz from hell / G-spot tornado / Damp ankles / St. Etienne / Massaggio galore.
LP: EMC 3521
MC: TCEMC 3521

JOE'S GARAGE ACT 1.
Tracks: / Central scrutinizer / Joe's garage / Catholic girls / Crew slut / Wet t-shirt nite / Toad-O-Line / Why does it hurt when I pee? / Lucille has messed my mind up.
LP: CBS 86101
MC: 40 86101

JOE'S GARAGE ACTS 2 & 3.
Tracks: / Token of his extreme, A / Stick it out / Syborg / Doing work for yuda / Keep it greasy / Outside now / He used to cut the grass / Packard goose / Watermelon in Easter hay / Little green Rosetta, A.
2LP: CBS 88475
MCSET: 40 88475

JOE'S GARAGE ACTS I, II & III.
Tracks: / Central Scrutinizer / Joe's Garage / Catholic Girls / Crew Slut / Wet T-Shirt Nite / Toad-O-Line / Why Does It Hurt When I Pee? / Lucille Has Messed My Mind Up / Token of his exteem, A / Stick it out / Sy Borg / Doing Work For yuda / Keep It Greasy / Outside Now / He Used To Cut The Grass / Packard goose / Watermelon In Easter Hay / Little Green Rosetta, A.
2LP: FZAP 1
2LP: ZAPPA 20
MCSET: TZAPPA 20

LIVE IN NEW YORK.
LP: ZAPPA 37
MC: TZAPPA 37

LONDON SYMPHONY ORCHESTRA VOL.2.
Tracks: / Bogus pomp / Bob in Dacron / Strictly genteel.
LP: ZAPPA 5
MC: TZAPPA 5

MAKE A JAZZ NOISE HERE.
Tracks: / Make a jazz noise here.
MCSET: TZAPPA 41

MAN FROM UTOPIA.
Tracks: / Cocaine decisions / Dangerous kitchen, The / Tink walks amok / Radio is broken, The / Moggio / Man from Utopia meets Mary Lou / Stick together / Sex / Jazz discharge party hats, The / We are not alone.
LP: EMC 3500
MC: TCEMC 3500
LP: FA 3203
MC: TCFA 3203
LP: CBS 25251

OLD MASTERS - BOX 1, THE.
LPS: BPR 7777

OLD MASTERS - BOX 2, THE.
LPS: BPR 8888

OLD MASTERS - BOX 3, THE.
LPS: BPR 9999

ONE SIZE FITS ALL.
Tracks: / Inca roads / Can't afford no shoes / Sofa No. 1 / Po-jama people / Florentine / Pogen / Evelyn, a modified dog / San ber'dino / Andy / Sofa No. 2.
LP: K 59207

ORCHESTRAL FAVOURITES.
Tracks: / Strictly genteel / Pedro's dowry / Naval aviation in art / Duke of prunes / Bogus pomp.
LP: K 59212
MC: K4D 59212
MC: TZAPPA 45

SHEIK YERBOUTI.
Tracks: / I have been in you / Flakes / Broken hearts are for assholes / I'm so cute / Jones crusher / Whatever happened to all the fun in the world / Rat tango / We gotta get into something real / Bobby Brown / Rubber shirt / Sheik Yerbouti tango, The / Baby snakes / Tryin' to grow a chin / City of tiny lites / Dancin' fool / Jewish princess / Wild love / Yo mama.
2LP: EN 5001
MCSET: TCEN 5001
2LP: CBS 88339
MCSET: 4088339
2LP: ZAPPA 28
MCSET: TZAPPA 28

SHIP ARRIVING TOO LATE TO SAVE A DROWNING WITCH.
Tracks: / No not now / Valley girl / I come from nowhere / Drowning witch / Envelopes / Teenage prostitutes.
LP: FA 3180
MC: TCFA 3180
LP: EMC 3501
MC: TCEMC 3501
LP: CBS 85804
MC: 40 85804
LP: ZAPPA 42
MC: TZAPPA 42

SHUT UP 'N PLAY YER GUITAR.
Tracks: / Five, five, five / Hog Heaven / Shut up 'n' play yer guitar / While you were out / Treacherous cretins / Heavy duty Judy / Soup 'n old clothes / Variations on the Carlos Santana / Gee, I like your pants / Canarsie / Ship ahoy / Deathless horsie, The / Pink napkins / Beat it with your fist / Return of the son of shut up 'n play / Pinocchio's furniture / Why Johnny can't read / Stucco Homes / Canard du Jour.
2LP: FZAP 2
LP: CBS 66368

SLEEP DIRT.
Tracks: / Filthy habits / Flambay / Spider of destiny / Regyption strut / Time is money / Sleep dirt / Ocean is the ultimate solution.
LP: K 59211
MC: TZAPPA 43

STUDIO TAN.
Tracks: / Greggery Peccary / Let me take you to the beach.
LP: K 59210
MC: TZAPPA 44

THEM OR US.
Tracks: / Closer you are, The / In France / Ya hozna / Sharleena / Sinister footwear II / Truck driver divorce / Stevie's spanking / Baby take your teeth out / Marque - son's chicken / Planet of my dreams / Be in my video / Them or us / Frogs with dirty little lips / Whipping post.
2LP: FZD 1
MCSET: FZDTC 1
2LP: EN 2402343
MCSET: EN 2402345

THING FISH.
Tracks: / Prologue / Mammy nuns, The / Harry and Rhonda / Galoot up-date / Torchum never stops, The / That evil prince / You are what you are / Mud club, The / Meek shall inherit nothing, The / Clowns on velvet / Harry as a boy / He's so gay / Massive improve'lence, The / Artificial Rhonda / Crabbgrass baby, The / White boy troubles, The / No not now / Brief case boogie / Brown Moses / Wistful wit a fist-full / Drop dead.
LP: EX 2402943
MC: EX 2402949

TINSEL TOWN REBELLION.
Tracks: / Fine girl / Easy meat / For the young sophisticate / Love of my life / I ain't got no heart / Party rap / Tell me you love me / Now you see it now you don't / Dance contest / Blue light,The / Tinsel Town rebellion / Pick me, I'm clean / Bamboozled by love / Brown shoes don't make it / Peaches 111.
2LP: EN 5002
MCSET: TCEN 5002
LP: CBS 88516

WAKA/JAWAKA HOT RATS.
Tracks: / Big Swifty / Your mouth / It might just be a one-shot deal / Waka / Jawaka.
LP: K 44203

WEASELS RIPPED MY FLESH (Zappa, Frank And The Mothers Of Invention).
Tracks: / Didja get any onya / Directly from my heart to you / Prelude to the afternoon of a sexually aroused / Toads of the short forest / Get a little / Eric Dolphy memorial barbecue / Dwarf Nebula processional march / Oh no / Orange county lumber truck, The / Weasels ripped my flesh.
LP: K 44019
LP: RSLP 2028

YOU ARE WHAT YOU IS.
Tracks: / Teenage wind / Harder than your husband / Doreen / Goblin girl / Third movement of sinister footwear, Theme from / Society pages / I'm a beautiful guy / Beauty knows no pain / Charlie's enormous mouth / Any downers? / Conehead / You are what you is / Mudd club / Meek shall inherit nothing, The / Dumb all over / Heavenly bank account / Suicide chump / Jumbo go away / If only she woulda / Drafter again.
2LP: EN 5000
MCSET: TCEN 5000
LP: CBS 88560

YOU CAN'T DO THAT ON STAGE ANYMORE SAMPLER.
LP: ZAPPA 7

ZAPPA.
Tracks: / Perfect stranger / Naval aviation in art / Girl in the magnesium dress / Outside now / Love story / Dupree's paradise / Jonestown.
LP: CEC 747 125 2

ZAPPA IN NEW YORK.
Tracks: / Titties and beer / I promise not to come in your mouth / Punky's whips / Manx needs women / Black page drum solo, The / Black page 1 / Big leg Emma / Black page 2 / Honey don't you want a man like me / Illinois enema bandit, The / Purple lagoon, The.
2LP: K 69204

ZOOT ALLURES.
Tracks: / Wind up workin' in a gas station / Torture never stops, The / Ms. Pinky / Find her finer / Friendly little finger / Wonderful wind / Zoot allures / Disco boy.
LP: K 56298
MC: K4 56298

Zardis, Chester

CHESTER ZARDIS & HIS HOT FIVE/ MICHAEL WHITE & HIS LIBERTY... (Zardis,Chester & his hot five/Michael White & his liberty...).
LP: LPS 11
MC: TCS 11

Zavaroni, Lena

HOLD TIGHT, ITS LENA.
Tracks: / Hold tight / I'll see you in my dreams / Ain't she sweet / Very though of you / T'aint what you do / Meet me in St. Louis / Sing, sing, sing / C.C. Rider / Penny lane / You needed me / It's a miracle / Certain smile, A / Bridge over troubled water.
LP: REH 443
MC: ZCF 443

LENA ZAVARONI & HER MUSIC.
Tracks: / I am / You keep me dancing / Until the night / Back in time / Then again you're gonna wake up / Somebody should have told me / Dancing free / Dancing all night / I don't need a doctor / Spotlight.
LP: GAL 6022
MC: GAL4 6022

MA.
LP: 6308 201

PRESENTING LENA ZAVARONI.
Tracks: / Whole world in His hands / Won't somebody dance with me? / Napony / As usual / Rose, Rose / Mama Tembu's wedding / Speak to me pretty / If it wasn't for you, dear / Air love / Can't we make it go away? / Say, has anybody seen my sweet Gypsy Rose? / Pinch me, am I dreaming?.
LP: GAL 6012
MC: GALC 6012

SONGS ARE SUCH GOOD THINGS.
LP: GAL 6020

Zawinul, Joe

DIALECTS.
Tracks: / Harvest, The / Waiting for the rain / Zeebop / Great empire,The / Carnavalito / 6 a.m. / Walking on the Nile / Peace.
LP: CBS 26813
MC: 40 26813

ZAWINUL.
Tracks: / Doctor Honoris Causa / In a silent way / His last journey / Double image / Arrival in New York.
LP: K 40349

Zawinul Syndicate

BLACK WATER.
Tracks: / Carnavalito / Familial / In the same boat / Little rootie tootie / Black water / Medicine man / Monk's mood / They had a dream.
LP: 4653441
MC: 4653444

IMMIGRANTS, THE.
Tracks: / March of the lost children / Criollo / Shadow and light / No mercy for me (mercy, mercy, mercy) / Devil never sleeps, The / You understand / From Venice to Vienna.
LP: 4607801
MC: 4607804

Zawose, Hukwe

MATESO.
LP: TERRA 104
MC: TERRAC 104

TANZANIA YETU.
LP: TERRA 101
MC: TERRAC 101

Zazou

NOIR ET BLANC (Zazou/Bikaye).
LP: CRAM 025

Zazou,Hector

GEOGRAPHIES.
LP: MTM 5

Ze Noiz

THY WILL BE DONE.
Tracks: / Prisonland / Shooting on Downtown trains / Secret hits the eye / Didn't wanna shoot / Johnny / I hate Andy / Tattoo chile / She's alright / Hanging down / G.G.Y.Y. / All soul's day.
LP: GRP 001

Ze, Tom

BRAZIL CLASSICS 4.
LP: 7599263961
MC: 7599263964

Zebra

NO TELLIN' LIES.
Tracks: / Wait until the summer's gone / I don't like it / Bears / I don't care / Lullaby / No tellin' lies / Takin' a stance / But no more / Little things / Drive me crazy.
LP: 780 159-1

ZEBRA.
Tracks: / Tell me what you want / One more chance / Slow down / Blue suede shoes / As I said before / Who's behind the door / When you get there / Take your fingers from my hair / Don't walk away / La la song.
LP: 780 054-1

Zebra Stripes

ZEBRA IS HER NAME.
LP: . . . . ID 123313

Zebra, Tony

SCHOOL GIRL (see under Melody, Delroy) (Zebra, Tony/Delroy Melody).

Zed

VISIONS OF DUNE.
LP: . . . . IRC 003

Zed & Two Noughts

ZED AND TWO NOUGHTS (Original Soundtrack) (Nyman, Michael).
Tracks: / Angelfish decay / Car crash / Lapse, The / Prawn watching / Bisocosis populi / Swan rot / Delft waltz / Up for crabs / Vermer's wife / Venus de Milo / Lady in the red hat / L'escargot.
LP: . . . . TER 1106
MC: . . . . ZCTER 1106
LP: . . . . VE 54
MC: . . . . TCVE 54

Zed Yago

PILGRIMAGE.
Tracks: / Pilgrim choir / Fear of death, The / Black bone song / Man who stole the holy fire / Pale man, The / Fallen angel / Pilgrimage / Pioneer of the storm / Rose of martyrdom / Achilles heel / Omega child.
LP: . . . . PL 719 49
MC: . . . . PK 719 49

Zee

IDENTIFY.
Tracks: / Confusion / Voices / Private person / Strange rhythm / Cuts like a diamond / By touching / How do you do it / Seems we were dreaming.
LP: . . . . SHSP 2401011

Zehetmair, Thomas

DUOS FOR VIOLIN AND VIOLA (see under Mozart (composer)) (Zehetmair, Thomas/Tabea Zimmermann).

Zeitgeist

TRANSLATE SLOWLY.
LP: . . . . DBAT 75

Zeitlin, Denny

TIDAL WAVE.
LP: . . . . PA 8044

TIME REMEMBERS ONE TIME ONCE (Zeitlin, Denny & Charlie Haden).
LP: . . . . ECM 1239

Zelaia, Enrike

LAPURDI.
LP: . . . . ELKAR 115

Zelly & Me

ZELLY AND ME (Original Soundtrack) (Various artists).
LP: 704.420
MC: . . . . C 704.420

Zen Attack

ZEN ATTACK.
LP: . . . . STLP 006

Zenamon

PROMENADE.
LP: . . . . TET 2
MC: . . . . CTET 2

Zeni Geva

MAXIMUM MONEY MONSTER.
MC: . . . . PATH 5C

Zenith Hot Stompers

25TH ANNIVERSAY ALBUM.
LP: SOS1191

Zeno

ZENO.
Tracks: / Eastern sun / Little more love, A / Love will live / Signs on the sky / Far away / Don't tell the wind / Heart on the wing / Circles of dawn / Sent by heaven / Sunset.
LP: . . . . PCSD 102
MC: . . . . TCPCSD 102

Zenter, Si

GREAT BAND WITH GREAT VOICES SWING The great voices of the great bands (Zenter, Si & His Orchestra/ Johnny Mann Singers).
Tracks: / Mississippi mud / Marie / Chattanooga choo choo / At last / On the sunny side of the street / Undecided / Paper doll / If I didn't care / Hut sut song, The / It happened in Monterey / I'll never smile again / Rum and coca cola.
LP: . . . . EMS 1164
MC: . . . . TC EMS 1164

Zepf, Manfred

PAINTINGS Manfred Zepf meets Andrew Cyrille (Zepf, Manfred & Andrew Cyrille).
LP: . . . . WW 003

Zephaniah, Benjamin

DUB RANTING.
LP: . . . . UP LP 2

RASTA.
LP: . . . . UPLP 2

US AND DEM.
LP: . . . . MLPS 1043
MC: . . . . MCT 1043
LP: 846 271 1
MC: 846 271 4

Zephyr

ZEPHYR.
LP: . . . . BGOLP 41

Zero

HERE GOES NOTHIN'.
LP: . . . . RRLP 2030

Zero 9

WHITE LIES.
LP: . . . . HMILP 57

Zero Boys

VICIOUS CIRCLE.
Tracks: / Vicious circle / Amphetamine addiction / New generation / Dirty alleys, dirty minds / Civilizations dying / Livin' in the 80's / Drug free youth / High places / Human body / Mom's wallet / Down the drain / Outta style / You can touch me / Forced entry / High time / Charlie's place / Trying harder / Johny better get / 'Nergy / Dingy bars suck.
LP: . . . . SAVE 053

Zero Kama

SECRET EYE OF LAYLAH, THE.
LP: . . . . PER 009

Zeroheroes

FREEDOM FIGHTERS.
MC: 70071

RADIO FREE EUROPE.
LP: . . . . JUNGLE 70070

Zerouki, Charef

GHOZALI - MY GAZELLE (Cerouki, Zerouki).
Tracks: / Ma andaklah tgoulili kalma / Al wa'ad arrmani / Al 'achaq / Ghozali / Al 'adra / Yamra.
LP: . . . . ORB 047

Zerra One

DOMINO EFFECT (ALBUM).
Tracks: / Rescue me / Domino effect / I know I feel I stand / Hands up / Forever and ever / Cry for you / All forgiven / Guardian angel / Heaven.
LP: . . . . MERH 93
MC: . . . . MERHC 93

ZERRA 1.
Tracks: / Mountains & water / Tumblin' down / Diaries / I feel it / Other side, The / Rain / I know / Nothing / Young love / Children.
LP: . . . . MERL 53

Zetrospective

ZETROSPECTIVE:- HOPE SPRINGS ETERNAL (Various artists).
MC: . . . . ICT 9969
MC: 846 225 4

Zetterlund, Monica

SPRING IS HERE.
LP: . . . . DRLP 171

Zev

50 GATES.
MC: . . . . TAPE 001

BUST THIS.
LP: . . . . ST 7544

INVISIBLE MAN, THE.
LP: . . . . COERCIONLP 001

SCHONSTE MUSIEK.
LP: . . . . ST 7510

Zevon, Warren

ENVOY, THE.
Tracks: / Envoy, The / Overdraft, The / Hula hula boys, The / Jesus mentioned / Let nothing come between you / Ain't pretty at all / Charlie's medicine / Looking for the next best thing / Never too late for love.
LP: . . . . K 52354
MC: K4 52354

EXCITABLE BOY.
Tracks: / Johnny strikes up the road / Roland the headless thompson gunner / Excitable boy / Werewolves of London / Accidentally like a martyr / Nightime in the switching yard / Veracruz / Tenderness on the block / Lawyers guns and money.
LP: . . . . K 53073
MC: K4 53073

QUIET NORMAL LIFE, A (The best of Warren Zevon).
Tracks: / Werewolves of London / Play it all night long / Roland the headless Thompson gunner / Envoy, The / Mohammed's radio / Desperados under the eaves / I'll sleep when I'm dead / Lawyers guns and money / Ain't that pretty at all / Poor poor pitiful me / Accidentally like a martyr / Looking for the next best thing.
LP: . . . . WX 81
MC: . . . . WX 81C

SENTIMENTAL HYGIENE.
Tracks: / Sentimental hygiene / Boom boom Mancini / Factory / Trouble waiting to happen / Reconsider me / Detox mansion / Bad karma / Even a dog can shake hands / Heartache, The / Leave my monkey alone.
LP: . . . . V 2433
MC: . . . . TCV 2433

STAND IN THE FIRE.
Tracks: / Stand in the fire / Jeannie needs a shooter / Excitable boy / Mohammed's radio / Werewolves of London / Lawyers guns and money / Sin, The / Poor, poor, pitiful me / I'll sleep when I'm dead / Bo Diddley's a gunslinger/Bo Diddley.
LP: . . . . K 52265
MC: K4 52265

TRANSVERSE CITY.
Tracks: / Transverse city / Run straight down / Long arm of the law, The / Turbulence / They moved the moon / Splendid isolation / Networking / Gridlock / Down in the mall / Nobody's in love this year.
LP: . . . . VUSLP 9
MC: . . . . VUSMC 9

WARREN ZEVON.
Tracks: / Frank and Jesse James / Mama couldn't be persuaded / Backs turned looking down the path / Hasten down the wind / Poor poor pitiful me / French inhaler, The / Mohammed's radio / I'll sleep when I'm dead / Carmelita / Join me in L.A. / Desperados under the eaves.
LP: . . . . K 53039

Ziegfeld Follies

ZIEGFELD FOLLIES OF 1946 (Original soundtrack) (Various artists).
2LP: . . . . CC 100-15/16

Ziegfeld Girl

ZIEGFELD GIRL (Original soundtrack) (Various artists).
LP: . . . . CIF 3006

Ziegler, Anne

GOLDEN AGE OF ANNE ZIEGLER AND WEBSTER BOOTH (Ziegler, Anne & Webster Booth).
Tracks: / If you were the only girl in the world / Paradise for two, A / Wanting you / I'll see you again / Lover, come back to me / Ah, sweet mystery of life / Fold your wings / Deep in the heart, dear / Only the rose / You, just you / Love's old sweet song / Will you remember / When we are married / So deep is the night / Barcarolle / Indian love call / Love steals your heart / We'll gather lilacs / Hear my song, Violetta / Love's last word is spoken.
LP: . . . . GX 2510
MC: . . . . TCGX 2510

MUSIC FOR ROMANCE (Ziegler, Anne & Webster Booth).
Tracks: / Flower / Golden song / Love me tonight / Tomorrow / What is done you never can undo / Without your love / Dearest love / Liebestraum / Nocturne / Music for romance / Lehar medley / Life and love / Dream duet / Throw open wide your window dear / Swing high swing low / Now is the hour.
LP: . . . . ONCM 530

SWEETHEARTS IN SONG (Ziegler, Anne & Webster Booth).
Tracks: / If you were the only girl in the world / Paradise for two / Wanting you / I'll see you again / Lover, come back to me / Ah, sweet mystery of life / Fold your wings / Deep in my heart, dear / Only a rose / You, just you / Love's old sweet song / Will you remember? / When we are married / So deep is the night / Barcarolle / Indian love call / Love steals your heart / We'll gather lilacs / Hear my song, Violetta / Love's last word is spoken.
LP: . . . . ONCM 519

Zig It Up

ZIG IT UP (Various artists).
LP: . . . . PICKLP 010

Zig Zawya

ZIG ZAWYA (Various artists).
LP: . . . . UMLP 001

Ziggurat Folk Group

MUSICAL PRIEST.
Tracks: / Rabbit hill / Moorland ride / Egloshayle ringers / In the night / Sweet Georgia Brown / Wish hounds of Dartmoor / Jigged hare / Bright morning stars / Space oddity / 'S wonderful / Wild swan, the / Wear a smile for me / Seagulls cry / Spring seasons.
MC: 60-090

Ziggy Stardust

WHITE LIGHT, WHITE HEAT (See under Bowie, David).

ZIGGY STARDUST (SINGLE) (See under Bowie, David).

ZIGGY STARDUST - THE MOTION PICTURE (Film soundtrack) (see under Bowie, David) (Bowie, David).

Zil

ZIL.
MC: 841 929 4

Zimbabwe...

VIVA ZIMBABWE (Various artists).
LP: . . . . ELP 2001
LP: . . . . CGLP 4411
MC: . . . . CGC 4411

ZIMBABWE FRONTLINE (Various artists).
Tracks: / Pidigori: *Mapfumo, Thomas* / Rudo imoto: *Four Brothers* / Ndatambura newe: *Moyo, Johah & Devera* Ngwena / Muti usina zita: *Manatsa, Zexie & The Green Arrows* / Ndanga ndabaiwa: *Mutukudzi, Oliver* / Emeriya usanyengedzwe: *Mkwamba, Patrick & The Four Brothers* / Ozvoko: *Mapfumo, Susan & The Black Salutarys* / Nyimbo yakwasu: *Banda, Robson & The New Black Eagles* / Taxi driver: *Moyo, Johah & Devera Ngwena* / Kuleliyanizwe: *Majaivana, Lovemore* (CD only) / Non-aligned movement: *Real Sounds* (CD only) / Vapanduki: *Master Chivero* (CD only).
LP: . . . . EWV 9
MC: . . . . TCEWV 9

ZIMBABWE HITS (Various artists).
LP: . . . . AFRILP 01

Zimbabwe Dread

EARTHMAN CONNECTION.
Tracks: / How long Jah / Earthman connection / Fire burning / Sounds of reality / National music / Ladder of progress / Dread so attractive / Ethiopians going home / Testing of faith / Shipsail / Sail fast.
LP: . . . . KVL 9009

Zimmer, Hans

CAR BUILDING (See under McKee, Maria 'Show me heaven').

DIAMOND SKULLS (SOUNDTRACK) (See under Burning Secret).

DRIVING MISS DAISY (See under Zimmer, Hans).

FRUIT MACHINE (See under Burning Secret).

Zimmerman, Dick

MY WIFE IS DANCING MAD! (Zimmerman, Dick & Ian Whitcomb).
LP: . . . . SOS 1049

Zimmermann, Tabea

DUOS FOR VIOLIN AND VIOLA (see under Mozart (composer)) (Zimmermann, Tabea/Thomas Zehetmair).

Zinja

ZINJA (Original soundtrack) (Various artists).
LP: . . . . MOMENT 103
MC: . . . . MOMENTC 103

Zinker, H.P.

AND THEN THERE WAS LIGHT.
LP: . . . . NECKLP 004

HOVERING.
LP: . . . . NECKLP 006

Zinova, Faina

RUSSIAN SONGS (Zinova, Faina and her Russian Gypsy Ensemble 'Tziganka').
Tracks: / Ekh byla - nie byla / Chrysanthemum / Coachman, spare the horses / Vyso chto bylo / If I could express in sound / Enough / Moon is shining, The / Tatyana / Gossip / Kalinka / Chto mnie gorye / Troika bells.
LP: . . . . SFA 059

Zion Harmonizers
YOU DONT HAVE TO GET IN TROUBLE.
LP: FF 002

Zion Pentecostal...
HOLD TO HIS HAND (Zion Pentecostal Ensemble).
Tracks: / Hold to his hand / He'll be there / I will make the darkness light / God is able / Come thou fount / Use me / Lord, I lift my spirit to you.
LP: MIR 5026
MC: MIR 5026MC

Zior
ZIOR...PLUS.
Tracks: / I really do / Za za za Zilda / Love's desire / New land / Now I'm sad / Give me love / Quabala / Oh Mariya / Your life will burn / I was fooling / Before my eyes go blind / Rolling thunder / Dudi Judy / Evolution / Cat's eyes / Strange kind of magic / Ride me baby / Entrance of the devil (the Chicago spine) (Available on CD only) / Every inch a man (Available on CD only) / Angel of the highway (Available on CD only).
LP: SEE 276

Zipcodes
SOLD - SIGHT UNSEEN.
MC: PCN 124

Ziz
ALBANIAN SUMMER.
LP: UNKNOWN

Z'Looke
TAKE YOU BACK TO MY PLACE.
LP: DI 75600

Zmiros
CHOLENT WITH HUCKLEBERRY.
MC: GVMMC 129

ECLECTIC KLEZZ.
MC: GVMMC 110

Znowhite
ACT OF GOD.
Tracks: / Last breath, The / Baptised by fire / Pure blood / Thunderdome / War machine / Disease bigotry / Something wicked / Rest in peace / Soldiers greed, A.
LP: RR 95871

ALL HAIL TO THEE.
Tracks: / Sledgehammer / Saturday night / Something for nothing / Bringing the hammer down / Do or die / Never felt like this / Rock city destruction.
LP: THBM 002

Zodiac Mindwarp
HIGH PRIEST OF LOVE (Zodiac Mindwarp & The Love Reaction).
LP: WARP 1

TATOOED BEAT MESSIAH.
Tracks: / Prime mover / Sull spark joker / Backseat education / Let's break the law / Kid's stuff / Planet girl / Bad city girl / Tatooed beat messiah / Driving on holy gasoline / Spasm gang / Messianic reprise.
LP: ZODLP 1
MC: ZODMC 1

ZODIAC MINDWARP: INTERVIEW PICTURE DISC.
LPPD: CT 1014
LPPD: BAK 2095

Zoetrope
LIFE OF CRIME, A.
LP: MFN 76

Zola, Emile
NANA (See Under Nana) (Worth, Irene).

Zoller, Attila
COMMON CAUSE.
LP: ENJA 3043

CONJUNCTION.
LP: ENJA 3051

DREAM BELLS.
LP: ENJA 2078

Zoltan
L'AME TZIGANE (Zoltan Et Son Ensemble Gypsy).
Tracks: / Chant et danse de Moldavie / Hora staccato / Chant et danse gypsy / Deux guitares / Chant du Caucase / Les yeux noirs / Gypsy tango / Chant et danse de Hongrie / Tzigane / Chant et danse de Roumanie.
LP: ARN 33694
MC: ARN 433694

Zombies
BEGIN HERE.
Tracks: / Road runner / Summertime / I can't make up my mind / Way I feel inside, The / Work 'n' play / You've really got a hold on me / She's not there / Sticks and stones / Can't nobody love you / Woman / I don't want to know / I remember when I loved her / What more can I do / I got my mojo working.
LP: DOA 4

BEST OF THE ZOMBIES.
Tracks: / She's not there / Time of the season / I must move / I got my mojo working / I remember how I loved her / Summertime / What more can I do / Can't nobody love you / Can't make up my mind / Tell her no / I don't want to know / I love you / You really got a hold on me / Whenever you're ready / You make me feel good / Roadrunner.
MC: MCTC 002

COLLECTION: ZOMBIES.
Tracks: / Goin' out of my head / Leave me be / Gotta get a hold on myself / I can't make up my mind / Kind of girl / Sticks and stones / Summertime / Woman / I got my mojo working / Road runner / You really got a hold on me / Nothing's changed / You make me feel good / She's not there / Don't go away / How we were before / Tell her no / Whenever you're ready / Just out of reach / Remember you / Indication / She does everything for me / Time of the season / I love you.
2LP: CCSLP 196
MC: CCSMC 196

FIVE LIVE ZOMBIES.
LP: RAZM 41

LIVE ON THE BBC 1965-67.
LP: RNLP 120

NEW WORLD.
Tracks: / New world (my America) / Love breaks down / I can't be wrong / Lula Lula / Heaven's gate / Time of the season / Moonday morning dance / Blue nights on fire / Losing you / Alone in paradise / Knowing you / Love conquers all.
MC: ESSMC 131
LP: ESSLP 131

NIGHT RIDING: ZOMBIES.
MC: KNMC 10015

ODYSSEY & ORACLE.
Tracks: / Care of cell / Rose for Emily, A / Maybe after he's gone / Beechwood Park / Brief candles / Hung up on a dream / Changes / I want her she wants me / This will be our year / Butchers tale (Western front 1914) / Friends of mine / Time of the season.
LP: MACH 6

SHE'S NOT THERE.
Tracks: / She's not there / How we were before / Indication / Way I feel inside, The / Whenever you're ready / Leave me be / Tell her no / Goin' out of my head / You make me feel good / Woman / I remember when I loved her / Gotta get a hold on myself / Remember you / What more can I do.
LP: TAB 34
MC: KTBC 34

SINGLES A'S & B'S.
Tracks: / She's not there / Leave me be / Tell her no / She's coming home / I want her back / Whenever you're ready / Is this the dream / Remember you / Indication / Gotta get a hold on myself / Goin' out of my head / You make me feel good / Woman / What more can I do / I must move / I remember when I loved her / I love you / Don't go away / Just out of reach / How we were before / Way I feel inside, The / She does everything for me.
MC: SEEK 30
LP: SEE 30

WORLD OF THE ZOMBIES.
LP: SPA 85

Zone Troopers
ZONE TROOPERS (Original soundtrack) (Various artists).
LP: STV 81262
MC: CTV 81262

Zones
UNDER INFLUENCE.
LP: SPART 1095

Zonjic, Alexander
ROMANCE WITH YOU.
LP: OP 3207

Zoo (label)
SHORES OF LAKE PLACID (Various artists).
LP: ZOO 4

Zoogz Rift
EPECAC.
LP: A 8401

MURDERING HELL'S HAPPY CRETINS.
LP: SST 211
MC: SST 211 C

WATER : AT A SAFE DISTANCE.
LP: SST 137

Zoom Tunes
ZOOM TUNES (Various artists).
LP: ROUNDER 8005

Zoot & The Roots
GUARDIAN OF THE GROOVE.
LP: BEE 002

THIS HEART.
Tracks: / This heart.
MC: NTV 025C

ZOOT & THE ROOTS.
LP: BEELP 001

Zoots
BAD DAYS ARE GONE.
LP: STING 003

Zorba
ZORBA - THE MUSICAL (Original Broadway Cast) (Various artists).
LP: ABL 1 4732
MC: ABK 1 4732

Zorba The Greek (film)
ZORBA THE GREEK (Original soundtrack) (Various artists).
Tracks: / Zorba the greek: *Various artists* / Full catastrophe, The: *Various artists* / Life goes on: *Various* artists / One unforgiveable sin, The: *Various artists* / Questions without answers: *Various artists* / Zorba's dance: *Various artists* / Fire inside, The: *Various artists* / Clever people and grocers: *Various artists*/ Always look for trouble: *Various artists* / Free: *Various artists* / That's me - Zorba: *Various artists.*
LP: 6463 165
MC: 7145 165
LP: 826245.1
MC: 825245.4
LP: T 903
MC: C 903

Zorn, Bill
WAKE UP & DRESS FUNNY (Zorn, Bill & Jon Benns).
LP: GO 41T

Zorn, John
BIG GUNDOWN.
LP: 9791391
MC: 9791394

SPILLANE.
LP: K 979172 1
MC: K 979172 4

SPY VS SPY - THE MUSIC OF ORNETTE COLEMAN.
LP: K 960 844 1
MC: K 960 844 4

TORTURE GARDEN (Zorn, John & Naked City).
LP: MOSH 28
MC: MOSH 28 MC

Zot
ZOT.
Tracks: / Uranium / Someone / I believe in miracles / Little bit longer / Insanity / Something in my heart / I told you from the start / Run for cover / Bright nights / We're on your side / Try.
LP: EKT 2

Zottola, Glenn
CHRISTMAS IN JAZZTIME.
LP: DR 110

Zouk Machine
AN PA TE SAV.
LP: HDD 2431

Zoukan's
TENDRESS.
LP: 2446

Zounds
CURSE OF ZOUNDS.
LP: ROUGH 31

Zsaratnock Ensemble
FOLK MUSIC FROM THE BALKANS.
LP: SLPX 18105

Zu Zu
CALYPSO CALYPSO (see Metro, Peter) (Zu Zu & Peter Metro).

Zubiria, Amaia
EGUN ARGI HARTAN.
LP: ELKAR 97

Zucchero
ZUCCHERO.
Tracks: / Diamante / Wonderful world / Il mare / Mama / Dunes of mercy / Senza una Donna / You're losing me / Solo una sana / You've chosen me / Diavolo in me (Only on CD and cassette) / Overdose (d'amore) (Only on CD and cassette) / Nice (nietzsche) che dice (Only on CD and cassette).
LP: 828 209 1
MC: 828 209 4
MC: 849 063 4
LP: 849 063 1

Zuice
I'M A SURVIVOR.
LP: MERH 115
MC: MERHC 115

Zukie, Tappa
RAGAMUFFIN.
LP: TZLP 0

Zulema
Z-LICIOUS.
Tracks: / Prologue / Higher plane / Change / I'm not dreaming / See / Hanging on to a memory / You've got something for me / Praying for a miracle / What do I do now / Gotta find a way / Epilogue.
LP: SH 8532

Zulu
ISCATHAMIYA 1982-85 (Zulu Worker's Choir).
LP: HT 313

ZULU & OTHER AFRICAN FOLKTALES... Aardema, Verna (Davis, Ossie & Ruby Dee).
MC: 1474

Zulu Dawn
ZULU DAWN (Original Soundtrack) (Various artists).
LP: C'BUS 201

Zulu (film)
ZULU (Original Soundtrack) (Various artists).
Tracks: / Istanchiwania: *Various artists* / News of the massacre: *Various artists* / First Zulu: *Various* artists / Wagons over: *Various artists* / Durnford's horses arrive and depart: *Various artists* / Zulu's final appearance and salute: *Various artists* / V.C. roll and men of Harlech, The: *Various artists* / Elizabeth theme: *Various artists* / From Russia with love: *Various artists* / Four in the morning: *Various artists.*
LP: FILM 022
MC: FILMC 022

Zulu, Philomon
HOW LONG.
LP: SHAN 43048

Zulu Records
ZULU COMPILATION (Various artists).
LP: ZULU 6

Zulu Warriors
WARRIOR DUB.
LP: MOWLP 004

Zuma II
ZUMA.
LP: BFZ 40519

Zumzeaux
WOLF AT YOUR DOOR.
LP: PUG 1

Zurke, Bob
BOB ZURKE & DELTA RHYTHM BAND (Zurke, Bob & Delta Rhythm Band).
LP: MERITT 16

Zushii
THERE CAN BE ONLY ONE.
LP: U 77022

Zvuki Mu
ZVUKI MU (See under Mu, Zvuki).
LP: UNKNOWN

Zwerin, Mike
NOT MUCH NOISE.
LP: SPJ LP 19

Zwingerberger, Axel
BOOGIE WOOGIE LIVE.
LP: CLGLP 011

Zwol, Walter
EFFECTIVE IMMEDIATELY.
LP: AML 3009

Zydeco
ZYDECO (Various artists).
LP: ARHOOLIE 1009

ZYDECO BIRTH (Various artists).
Tracks: / Calcasieu zydeco blues (inst): *Chavis, Boozoo* / Paper in my shoe: *Chavis, Boozoo* / Za belle: *Garlow, Clarence* / Make me cry: *Garlow, Clarence* / Gonna boogie: *Chavis, Boozoo* / Forty one days: *Chavis, Boozoo*/ Long black curly hair: *Chavis, Boozoo* / Oh babe: *Chavis, Boozoo* / Bye bye catin: *Chavis, Boozoo* / Catch that morning train: *Declouet, Thaddus* / Shake it up all night long: *Declouet, Thaddus* / Lake Charles do-do-dia (inst): *Declouet, Thaddus* / Trouble trouble baby: *Declouet, Thaddus.*
LP: GFCL 103

ZYDECO BLUES (Various artists).
LP: FLY 539

ZYDECO BLUES AND BOOGIE (Various artists).

Tracks: / I'm coming home to stay: *Carriere, Roy* / Don't put your hand on that: *Bad Weather* / Strange things: *Reed, Dalton* / Right on girl: *Semien, Nolton* / Love repair man: *Jacob, Donald* / Restless night: *Matte*, Bill / What you gonna do: *Carriere, Roy* / Giving on into love: *Reed, Dalton* / I'm gonna move: *Thomas*, Leo / She kept chewing gum: *Jacob, Donald* / Jacqueline: *Prudhomme, Willis* / That Zydeco stuff: *Bad Weather* / I found my woman: *Carriere, Roy*.
LP: . . . . **GUMBO 001**
MC: . . . . **GUMBOC 001**

ZYDECO BLUES VOL.2 (Various artists).
Tracks: / Snap beans aren't salty: *Bob, Joseph* / Hey la la: *Fernest & Thunders* / It happened so fast: *Chenier*, Clifton / Goodbye baby: *Chenier, Clifton* / Worried life blues: *Chenier, Clifton* / Hey mama: *Chenier*, Clifton / You told me: *Dopsee, Rockin'* / Run here to my baby: *Dopsee, Rockin'* / Sweetest thing: *Dopsee*, Rockin' / You don't have to go: *Dugas, Marcel* / You got me running: *Dugas, Marcel* / Bald headed woman: *Dugas, Marcel*.
LP: . . . . **FLY 600**

ZYDECO FESTIVAL (Various artists).
LP: **1024**
MC: . . . . **1024 TC**

ZYDECO: LOUISIANA CREOLE MUSIC (Various artists).
LP: . . . . **ROUNDER 6009**
MC: . . . . **ROUNDER 6009C**

Zydeco Ceilidh Band

ZYDECO CEILIOH BAND.
Tracks: / Dancing feet / Just like I treat you / Ragin' cajun / Great western road / Suidh, The / Rivonia / Oh Willie we have missed you / Cajun rammy / Marchons / Kelvingrove / Blues with a feeling / Home town / Two step / Cornbread rough / Zydeco cha cha.
LP: . . . . **FE 062**
MC: . . . . **FE 062C**

Zykina, Ludmila

FOLK SONGS.
MC: . . . . **SM 00202**

POPULAR FOLK SONGS.
MC: . . . . **SM 00425**

Zyklome A

MADE IN BELGIUM.
LP: . . . . **TORPO 001**

Zyman, Samuel

BASHE.
Tracks: / "Bashe" trio for violin, cello, and piano 19.16 / Sonata concertante for violin and piano 17/18.
MC: . . . . **ANC 8703**
LP: . . . . **AN 8703**

ZZ Top

AFTERBURNER.
Tracks: / Sleeping bag / Stages / Woke up with wood / Rough boy / Can't stop rockin' / Planet of women / I got the message / Velcro fly / Dipping low / Delirious.
LP: . . . . **WX 27**
MC: . . . . **WX 27C**

BEST OF ZZ TOP.
Tracks: / Tush / Waitin' for the bus / Jesus just left Chicago / Francine / Just got paid / La grange / Blue jean blues / Backdoor love affair / Beer drinkers and hell raisers / Heard it on the X.
LP: . . . . **K 56598**
MC: **K4 56598**

CHRIS TETLEY INTERVIEWS ZZ TOP.
LPPD: . . . . **CT 1005**

DEGUELLO.
Tracks: / I thank you / She loves my automobile / I'm bad I'm nationwide / Fool for your stockings, A / Manic mechanic / Dust my broom / Lowdown in the street / Hi-fi mama / Cheap sunglasses / Esther be the one.
LP: . . . . **K 56701**
MC: **K4 56701**

EL LOCO.
Tracks: / Tube snake boogie / I wanna drive you home / Ten foot pole / Leila / Don't tease me / It's so hard / Pearl necklace / Groove little hippie pad / Heaven, Hell or Houston / Party on the patio.
LP: . . . . **K 56929**
MC: **K4 56929**

ELIMINATOR.
Tracks: / Gimme all your lovin' / Got me under pressure / Sharp-dressed man / I need you tonight / I got the six / Legs / Thug / T.V. dinners / Dirty dog / If I could only flag her down / Bad girl.
LPPD: . . . . **W 3774 P**
LP: . . . . **W 3774**
MC: . . . . **W 3774 4**

FANDANGO.
Tracks: / Thunderbird / Jailhouse rock / Backdoor medley / Backdoor love affair / Mellow down easy / Backdoor love affair no.2 / Long distance boogie / Nasty dogs and funky kings / Blue jean blues / Balinese / Mexican blackbird / Heard it on the X / Tush.
LP: . . . . **K 56604**
MC: **K4 56604**
LP: . . . . **SHU 8482**

MUSIC AND MEDIA INTERVIEW PICTURE DISC.
LPPD: . . . . **ZZ 1016**

RECYCLER.
LP: . . . . **WX 390**
MC: . . . . **WX 390C**

RIO GRANDE MUD.
Tracks: / Francine / Just got paid / Mushmouth shoutin' / Ko ko blue / Chevrolet / Apologies to pearly / Bar-b-q / Sure got cold after the rain fell / Whisky 'n' mama / Down brownie.
LP: . . . . **K 56602**
MC: **K4 56602**

TEJAS.
Tracks: / It's only love / Arrested for driving while blind / El diablo / Snappy kakkie / Enjoy and get it on / Ten dollar man / Pan Am highway blues / Avalon hideaway / She's a heartbreaker / Asleep in the desert.
LP: . . . . **K 56605**
MC: **K4 56605**

TRES HOMBRES.
Tracks: / Waitin' for the bus / Jesus just left Chicago / Beer drinkers and hell raisers / Master of sparks / Hot blues and righteous / Move me on down the line / Precious and grace / La grange / Sheik / Have you heard.
LP: . . . . **K 56603**
MC: **K4 56603**

TRES HOMBRES / FANDANGO.
MC: **K4 66121**

ZZ TOP'S FIRST ALBUM.
Tracks: / Somebody else been shaking your tree / Brown sugar / Squank / Goin' down to Mexico / Old man / Neighbour, neighbour / Certified blues / Bedroom thang / Just got back from my baby's / Backdoor love affair.
LP: . . . . **K 5660 1**
MC: **K4 56601**

RECORD LABEL PREFIX INDEX

PREFIX	LABEL
33SX	Columbia/EMI
396	A & M
397	A & M
40	CBS
40	Epic
4BN	Blue Note
781	Atlantic
790	Atlantic
795	Capitol
795	SBK One
795	Parlophone
795	Capitol
795	Roulette (EMI)
795	Ideal
795	MGM (EMI)
846	4th & Broadway
846	Island
846	Mercury
846	Vertigo
846	Philips
846	Fontana
846	Mango
ABCL	ABC
AC	Alligator
AC	Audiocord
AFF	Affinity
AFFD	Affinity
AIM	Aim Budget Cassettes
AL	Alligator
ALCD	Alligator
AM	A & M
AMA	A & M
AMC	A & M
AMCD	A & M
AMID	A & M
AML	EMI America
AMLH	A & M
AMLX	A & M
ARL	Ariola

PREFIX	LABEL
BAK	Baktabak
BBCCD	BBC
BCD	Bear Family
BEGA	Beggars Banquet
BEGC	Beggars Banquet
BFX	Bear Family
BLCD	Black Lion
BLM	Black Lion
BLP	Black Lion
BLP	Blue Note
BNS	Blue Note
BNZ	Blue Note
BRCA	4th & Broadway
BRCD	4th & Broadway
BRLP	4th & Broadway
BRON	Bronze
BRONC	Bronze
BST	Blue Note
BT	Blue Note
BTC	20th Century
CAD	4 AD
CADC	4 AD
CADCD	4 AD
CAM	A & M
CAS	Charisma
CBAK	Baktabak
CBS	CBS
CCD	Chrysalis
CCD	Concord Jazz
CCSCD	Castle Collector
CCSLP	Castle Collector
CCSMC	Castle Collector
CDA	A & M
CDAFF	Affinity
CDB	MFP
CDCH	Ace
CDCHARLY	Charly
CDEST	Capitol
CDL	Chrysalis

CDMFP ... MFP
CDP ... Blue Note
CDP ... Capitol
CDP ... Columbia
CDP ... EMI
CDP ... Liberty
CDP ... Parlophone
CDPCS ... Parlophone
BT ... Black Top (USA)
CAM ... RCA Camden
CDSTUMM ... Mute
CDX ... Charly
CE ... KTel
CH ... Ace
CHC ... Ace
CHC ... Charisma
CHCMC ... Charisma
CHD ... Ace
CHIP ... Jive
CHR ... Chrysalis
CID ... Island
CJ ... Concord Jazz
CJC ... Concord Jazz
CL ... Capitol
CLACD ... Castle Classics
CLALP ... Castle Classics
CLAMC ... Castle Classics
CMCAD ... MCA
CN ... Contour
CN4 ... Contour
CR ... Cambra
CR ... Charly
CRB ... Charly R & B
CRE ... Creation
CRECD ... Creation
CRELP ... Creation
CRT ... Cambra
CSTML ... Motown
CSTMS ... Motown
CSTUMM ... Mute
CZ ... Capitol
CZ ... EMI
DJF ... DJM
DJH ... DJM
DMCF ... MCA
DMCG ... MCA
DMCL ... MCA
DTO ... Ditto
DTOL ... Ditto
EA ... EMI America
ED ... Capitol
ED ... Edsel
EGCD ... EG
EGLP ... EG
EGMC ... EG
EJ ... Capitol
EMS ... Capitol
EMS ... EMI
EMTV ... EMI
EPC ... Epic
EST ... Capitol
FA ... Fame
FACT ... Factory
FIEND ... Demon
FIENDCASS ... Demon
FIENDCD ... Demon
FILM ... Silva Screen
GD ... RCA
GEF ... Geffen
GK ... RCA
GNP5 ... GNP Crescendo
GNPS ... GNP Crescendo
GREL ... Greensleeves
HA ... London American
HIP ... Jive
HIPC ... Jive
HSC ... Hallmark
HSC ... Pickwick
ICM ... Island
ICT ... Island
ILPM ... Island
ILPS ... Island
IMCA ... MCA
IMCAC ... MCA
IMCD ... Island
INTS ... RCA International

Prefix	Label
K	Various WEA labels
LBG	Liberty
LBR	Liberty
LFP	Listen For Pleasure
LILP	Lismor
LK	Decca
LSA	RCA
MCA	MCA
MCAC	MCA
MCAD	MCA
MCF	MCA
MCFC	MCA
MCG	MCA
MCL	MCA
MCLC	MCA
MERH	Mercury
MERHC	Mercury
MERL	Mercury
MERLC	Mercury
MFP	MFP
NCD	KTel
ND	Bluebird (BMG)
ND	RCA
NE	KTel
NK	Bluebird (BMG)
NK	RCA
NL	Bluebird (BMG)
NL	RCA
OG	Old Gold
OVED	Virgin
OVEDC	Virgin
PCD	Pickwick
PCS	Parlophone
POLD	Polydor
POLDC	Polydor
POLH	Polydor
POLHC	Polydor
POLSC	Polydor
PWK	Pickwick
PWKMC	Pickwick
PWKS	Pickwick
RCALP	RCA
REB	BBC
REC	BBC
REH	BBC
RFL	Decca
ROUGH	Rough Trade
RR	Roadrunner
SAY	Argo (Polygram)
SCX	Columbia
SEE	See For Miles
SEEZ	Stiff
SHM	Hallmark
SHM	Pickwick
SKL	Decca
SLP	Storyville
SNTCD	Alligator
SNTCD	Sonet
SNTF	Alligator
SNTF	Sonet
SPA	Decca
SPART	Arista
SPELP	Polydor
SPEMC	Polydor
STAC	Telstar
STAR	Telstar
STMA	Motown
STML	Motown
STMS	Motown
STUMM	Mute
T	20th Century
TAB	Decca
TBL	Trojan
TCAFS	Affinity
TCART	Arista
TCCDX	Charly
TCCRB	Charly R & B
TCD	Telstar
TCDL	MFP
TCEMS	Capitol
TCEST	Capitol
TCFA	Fame
TCMFP	MFP
TCPCS	Parlophone
TCSCX	Columbia
TCV	Virgin

Prefix	Label
TRLS	Trojan
UAG	United Artists
UAS	United Artists
V	Virgin
VERH	Vertigo
VIRUS	Alternative Tentacles
VSOPCD	Connoisseur Collection
VSOPLP	Connoisseur Collection
VSOPMC	Connoisseur Collection
WD	Motown
WIK	Big Beat
WK	Motown
WL	Motown
ZBBC	BBC
ZCDL	Chrysalis
ZCF	BBC
ZCHR	Chrysalis
ZCM	BBC
ZCTRL	Trojan

NOTES

NOTES

NOTES

NOTES

NOTES

NOTES